GB Rail Timetable

Sunday 08 Dec 2013 to Saturday 17

Britain's national railway network and stations are owned by Network Ra
included in this Timetable, who work together closely to provide a co
opportunities. Details and identification codes are shown on the Train O

This Timetable contains rail services operated over the National Rail
Ireland, the Isle of Man, the Isle of Wight and the Channel Islands. Netw
are operated on their behalf by the Train Operating Companies. Details a...
shows the number of the individual table for each route.
http://www.nationalrail.co.uk/passenger_services/maps/Network_Rail_national_map.pdf

C000157081

Contents

YOUR FEEDBACK IS VALUABLE TO US

If you have any comments on the content of this book or feedback on how you feel it could be improved then please contact the Publications Manager by writing to;

Victoria Fox, Network Rail, The Quadrant : MK
Elder Gate, Milton Keynes, Buckinghamshire, MK9 1EN
Or E-mail: Victoria.Fox@Networkrail.co.uk

A BIG THANK YOU AGAIN TO ALL VOLUNTEERS

We would again like to thank our numerous volunteers for your continuous help and support throughout the timetable process. Thank you for giving your own valuable time to better the timetable. We greatly appreciate your continued support and look forward to working with you in the future.

Services on Public Holidays

An amended service will operate on many parts of the rail network during Public Holidays and you are strongly advised to confirm your journey details if travelling around a holiday period. For more information visit www.nationalrail.co.uk/holidays

Engineering Work

It is sometimes necessary to carry out essential Engineering Work which means that services may be changed, particularly late at night or at weekends to allow this work to be carried out. Engineering Work is usually planned many weeks in advance and details of changes to train times can be obtained from the National Rail Enquiries website – www.nationalrail.co.uk/engineering

National Rail Conditions of Carriage

Details of the conditions against which all National Rail tickets are issued, including the conditions which apply to the carriage of luggage and cycles can be obtained from the National Rail Enquiries website – www.nationalrail.co.uk/nrcc

'What's New?

Arriva Train Wales - AW
A new bus service (Service T9) will operate between Cardiff bay & Cardiff international Airport. The service will call at (Stand D1) at Cardiff bus station and will operate every 20mins from 04.25 & 23.25 (Mon- Sat) and 05.25 to 23.25 (Sun). Through ticketing is also available from most stations. Full details of the timetables and further information on both services can be obtained from Traveline on 0871 200 22 33 or visit www.traveline.info.

East Midlands Train - EM
Services to and from London St Pancras have been revamped following extensive line speed improvement infrastructure works on the Midland Mainline route. This has allowed journey times to be considerably reduced, with new 'headline' fastest journey times of 2 hours for Sheffield to London and 91 minutes for Nottingham to London. Average journey times for all services have also been reduced considerably. As result of these changes the clockface timetable has been altered to fit in with the new timings leading to new departure times for many services.
The 09.00 weekday service from London St Pancras to Kettering is extended to run through to Corby and the 10.26 Kettering to London St Pancras return service will start back from Corby at 10.16.

East Coast - GR
Mondays to Fridays: A new early morning departure from Newark Northgate to London Kings Cross will be introduced at 05.35. This is an extension of the previous 05.44 service from Grantham. Saturdays: The 07.00 service from London Kings Cross to Edinburgh will call additionally at Stevenage at 07.20.

Grand Central – GC
A new 4th service between Bradford Interchange and London Kings Cross will be introduced on 8 December. This service will leave Bradford Interchange at 07.52 and will call at Halifax, Brighouse, Mirfield, Wakefield Kirkgate, Pontefract Monkhill and Doncaster. There will be an additional service from London Kings Cross to Bradford Interchange at 16.03. This service will call at Doncaster, Wakefield Kirkgate, Mirfield, Brighouse and Halifax.

Preston – Leeds
Blackpool/Preston-Leeds/York services will be suspended between Burnley Manchester Road and Hebden Bridge between 9/11/13-30/3/14. This is to allow repairs to Holme Tunnel. Buses will replace trains between Burnley and Hebden Bridge, with extended journey times.

Scotrail - SR
Timetables includes additional calls at Monifieth and on Sundays an improved hourly service on the Fife Circle. Free Wi-Fi is being rolled out across our Class 170 and 380 fleets and fitted to selected stations. See also new Shipping Table 227D.

Station News
The following stations are expected to open at the start of the December 2013 timetable:

Station	Location
Energlyn & Churchill Park	Between Aber and Llanbradach on Cardiff-Rhymney route
James Cook University Hospital	Between Middlesbrough and Marton on the Whitby route

Cranbrook, which was mentioned in the May 2013, is now expected to open until at least May 2014.

Southern - SN
Following completion of infrastructure work by Network Rail and the introduction of new trains, many peak trains between South London and London Victoria via Balham are lengthened to a maximum of 10 carriages. More London Bridge via Sydenham trains will run at the maximum 10 car length and London Bridge via Peckham Rye trains at the maximum 8 car length, and some additional carriages for some East Grinstead London trains.

London Bridge: As part of the Thameslink upgrade at the station no Southern services will call at London Bridge between 23/08/14-31/08/14-.Some Thameslink route services will be retimed and some Southeastern services may be altered.

London Overground: An additional train will run from Barking to South Tottenham on weekdays at 0652.

West Coast Main Line: The West Coast Main Line will be closed at Watford Junction between these dates: 03/05/14-05/05/14, 09/08/14-25/08/14, 25/12/14-29/12/14, 14/02/15-22/02/15 and 03/04/15-06/04/15. The alternative travel arrangements have yet to be published. Further details can be found on the Network Rail website: www.networkrail.co.uk/improvements/west-coast-main-line/.

How to use this Timetable

Some tables are self-contained (such as Table 1 London–Shoeburyness) showing every train
two stations on the route. Train journey lengths vary from the under ¾ mile Stourbridge Town tc
shuttle to the 773 mile Aberdeen to Penzance service. To show details of longer-distance ser
short-distance services are omitted, these appearing in separate 'composite' tables.

WHICH TABLE?

General Layout of the Timetable

There are several ways of finding the correct table(s) for a journey. Tables start with the north bank of the Thames and radiate anti-clockwise around London as far as the south bank (Table 212, London-Faversham-Margate) with non-London tables (like the Cardiff Valleys) placed close to the appropriate London route. Internal Scottish routes follow from Table 216. Tables numbered 400-406 cover domestic Sleeper services. Once familiar with to this geographic layout, required tables can usually be found with relative ease, but there are more precise methods:

Using the Index

Look up your destination. If it appears in up to five tables, those tables are listed (for example Hilsea appears in Tables 156, 157, 158, 165 and 188). If it appears in six or more then there may be sub-divisions. If your destination is sub-divided in this way and your origin is NOT shown (for example Shipley is not shown under Lancaster) then look up the origin instead as it probably has fewer tables. Alongside the station name is shown a two character code indicating which operator is responsible for operating the facilities at that station (see also Train Operator pages).

Using the Timetable Network Map

If your journey is more complicated and involves several changes between tables, the Timetable Network Map will be very useful. For example, to plan a journey from North Berwick to Pontypridd one would not expect to find both in the same table. The map makes it clear that one has to change at Edinburgh and Cardiff and, as there is no through service between North Berwick and Pontypridd, allows one to look up possible routes, for example, via Crewe and Shrewsbury (Tables 65 and 131), Crewe and Birmingham (Tables 57 and 65) or York and Birmingham (Tables 51 and 57). http://www.nationalrail.co.uk/passenger_services/maps/Network_Rail_national_map.pdf

Using Route/Network Diagrams

For many tables a Route or Network Diagram is also provided. Route Diagrams are generally used for longer distance tables (for example Table 26) and show the route and stations served in diagrammatic form as well as the principal connecting links. Network Diagrams (for example Tables 152–154) are generally used where there is a dense network of shorter distance routes and show *all* stations and routes in the area concerned in diagrammatic form.

Using the Table

Having found the table you require make sure you look at the correct set of pages: Mondays to Fridays, Mondays to Saturdays, Saturdays, Sundays plus any relevant dates. Look for the station from which you will leave, read across until you find a suitable train, then read down to see when you will arrive at your destination.

↪ indicates the train is continued **in** a later column.

↩ indicates the train is continued **from** an earlier column.

Bold times denote through trains whilst light, *italic,* times are connections (Please read carefully the section on the "Connections" page). Check if there is a column-heading and if there is, refer to the foot of the table for an explanation.

Because of the large number of services that 'cross' Midnight, a Railway Timetable needs to be precise in the meaning of 'a day'. Trains starting their journeys before Midnight are shown towards the end of a table – but if you are looking for the 'last' train do not stop there, as there may be later ones at the start of the table!

A train crossing Midnight will be shown in full at the END of a table and any column heading denoting the day of the week applies to the day the train STARTS. For example a 2350 train headed 'SO' (see the general notes on inside front cover) commences 2350 Saturday and runs into Sunday. The train will also be shown at the front of the Sunday table with the times prior to Midnight shown with note 'p', e.g. 23p50, to indicate that they refer to the previous night.

Do not worry about the ambiguity as to which day Midnight itself belongs, for, to avoid this problem, all times skip from 2359 to 0001 and neither 0000 nor 2400 is ever used!

A two character code is shown at the head of each train column indicating which operator is providing the train service (see also Train Operator pages).

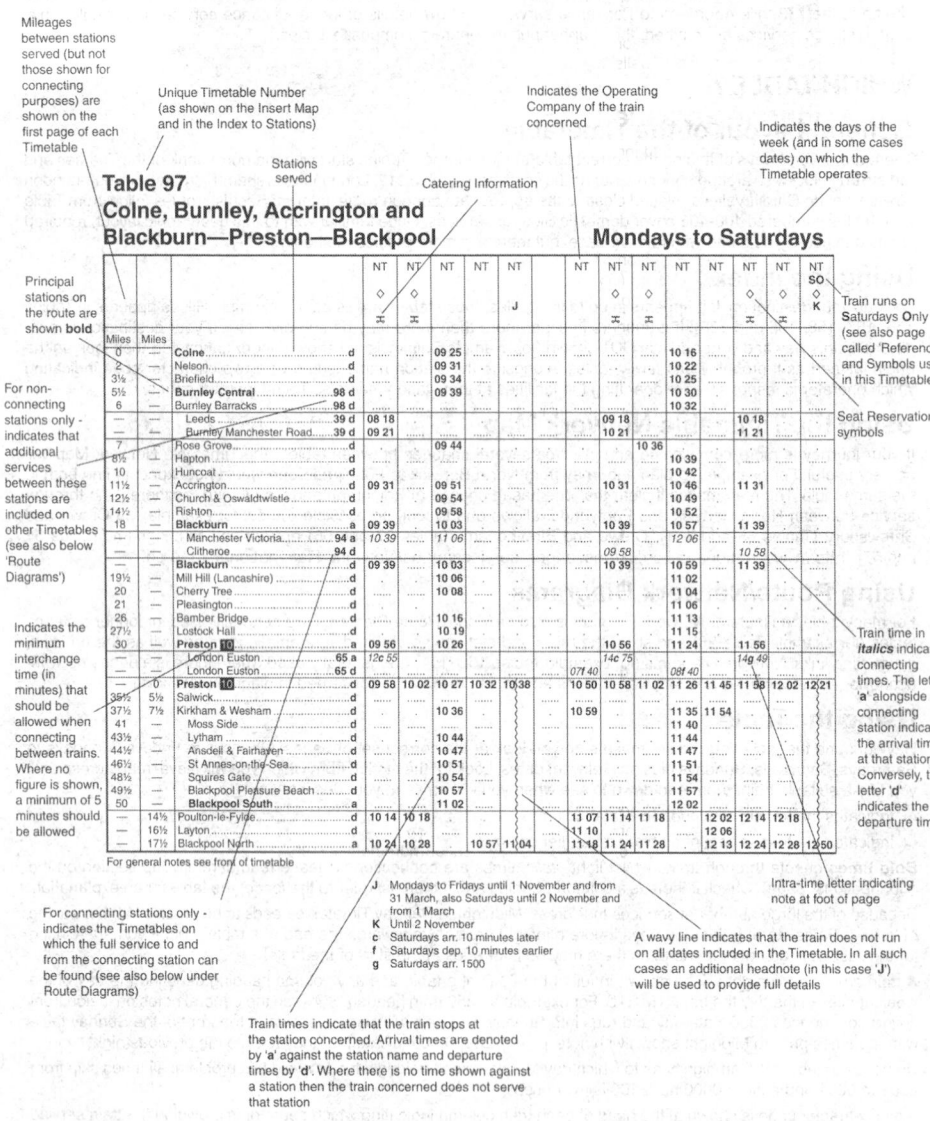

Mileages between stations served (but not those shown for connecting purposes) are shown on the first page of each Timetable

Unique Timetable Number (as shown on the Insert Map and in the Index to Stations)

Indicates the Operating Company of the train concerned

Indicates the days of the week (and in some cases dates) on which the Timetable operates

Stations served

Catering Information

Table 97
Colne, Burnley, Accrington and Blackburn—Preston—Blackpool

Mondays to Saturdays

Miles	Miles		NT	NT	NT	NT	NT		NT	NT	NT	NT	NT	NT	NT	NT SO
			◇ ⌶	◇ ⌶			J			◇ ⌶	◇ ⌶			◇ ⌶	◇ ⌶	◇ K
0	—	**Colne** d			09 25							10 16				
2	—	Nelson d			09 31							10 22				
3½	—	Briefield d			09 34							10 25				
5½	—	**Burnley Central** 98 d			09 39							10 30				
6	—	Burnley Barracks 98 d										10 32				
—	—	Leeds 39 d	08 18							09 18				10 18		
—	—	Burnley Manchester Road 39 d	09 21							10 21				11 21		
7	—	Rose Grove d			09 44						10 36					
8½	—	Hapton d										10 39				
10	—	Huncoat d										10 42				
11½	—	Accrington d	09 31		09 51					10 31		10 46		11 31		
12½	—	Church & Oswaldtwistle d			09 54							10 49				
14½	—	Rishton d			09 58							10 52				
18	—	**Blackburn** a	09 39		10 03					10 39		10 57		11 39		
—	—	Manchester Victoria 94 a	*10 39*		*11 06*							*12 06*				
—	—	Clitheroe 94 d								*09 58*				*10 58*		
—	—	**Blackburn** d	09 39		10 03					10 39		10 59		11 39		
19½	—	Mill Hill (Lancashire) d			10 06							11 02				
20	—	Cherry Tree d			10 08							11 04				
21	—	Pleasington d										11 06				
26	—	Bamber Bridge d			10 16							11 13				
27½	—	Lostock Hall d			10 19							11 15				
30	—	**Preston 10** a	09 56		10 26					10 56		11 24		11 56		
—	—	London Euston 65 a	*12c 55*							*14c 75*				*14g 49*		
—	—	London Euston 65 d							*07f 40*			*08f 40*				
—	0	**Preston 10** d	09 58	10 02	10 27	10 32	10 38		10 50	10 58	11 02	11 26	11 45	11 58	12 02	12 21
35½	5½	Salwick d														
37½	7½	Kirkham & Wesham d			10 36				10 59			11 35	11 54			
41	—	Moss Side d										11 40				
43½	—	Lytham d			10 44							11 44				
44½	—	Ansdell & Fairhaven d			10 47							11 47				
46½	—	St Annes-on-the-Sea d			10 51							11 51				
48½	—	Squires Gate d			10 54							11 54				
49½	—	Blackpool Pleasure Beach d			10 57							11 57				
50	—	**Blackpool South** a			11 02							12 02				
—	14½	Poulton-le-Fylde d	10 14	10 18					11 07	11 14	11 18		12 02	12 14	12 18	
—	16½	Layton d							11 10				12 06			
—	17½	Blackpool North a	10 24	10 28		10 57	11 04		11 18	11 24	11 28		12 13	12 24	12 28	12 50

For general notes see front of timetable

J Mondays to Fridays until 1 November and from 31 March, also Saturdays until 2 November and from 1 March
K Until 2 November
c Saturdays arr. 10 minutes later
f Saturdays dep. 10 minutes earlier
g Saturdays arr. 1500

Principal stations on the route are shown **bold**

For non-connecting stations only - indicates that additional services between these stations are included on other Timetables (see also below 'Route Diagrams')

Indicates the minimum interchange time (in minutes) that should be allowed when connecting between trains. Where no figure is shown, a minimum of 5 minutes should be allowed

Train runs on **S**aturdays **O**nly (see also page called 'References and Symbols used in this Timetable')

Seat Reservations symbols

Train time in ***italics*** indicate connecting times. The letter **'a'** alongside a connecting station indicates the arrival time at that station. Conversely, the letter **'d'** indicates the departure time

Intra-time letter indicating note at foot of page

For connecting stations only - indicates the Timetables on which the full service to and from the connecting station can be found (see also below under Route Diagrams)

A wavy line indicates that the train does not run on all dates included in the Timetable. In all such cases an additional headnote (in this case **'J'**) will be used to provide full details

Train times indicate that the train stops at the station concerned. Arrival times are denoted by **'a'** against the station name and departure times by **'d'**. Where there is no time shown against a station then the train concerned does not serve that station

Route/Network Diagrams (see previous page): For many tables a Route/Network Diagram is also provided to show the routes and stations served in diagrammatic form. Where this is the case, a reference to the Route/Network Diagram will be provided at the top of each page of the Timetable concerned. Timetable numbers for connecting or alternative services will not be included within the Table itself; instead this will be indicated on the accompanying Route/Network Diagram

For South London tables 170, 171, 172, 173, 177, 178, 179, 181, 182 stations in bold indicate where the full train service is shown to and from the other stations on the table

General Information

Smoking Policy

Smoking is not permitted on any National Rail service or in any station. In England and Wales, this includes all covered and uncovered concourses, ticket halls, platforms, footbridges and subways at station premises.

Left Luggage Facilities

Details of Left Luggage Facilities at individual stations are available at www.nationalrail.co.uk/stations

Penalty Fares

Penalty Fares are charged by Train Companies at some stations and on some trains. Where this is the case, warning notices will be displayed. Those stations at which Penalty Fares are in operation are indicated in the Station Index and the individual Table numbers section (see also Train Operator pages). Please be aware that at some stations where Penalty Fare Schemes are in place not all Train Operator services calling at that station are included in the scheme.

If you cannot produce a valid ticket for your entire journey when asked to do so, you may be charged a Penalty Fare. This will be either twice the full single fare to the next station at which the train is due to stop, or £20 (£80 on Transport for London services and stations, reducing to £40 if paid within 21 days), whichever is the greater. Any travel beyond the next station will be charged at the full single fare.

To avoid paying a Penalty Fare, you must purchase a valid ticket to your destination, before starting your journey. If the ticket office is closed and you cannot buy the ticket you need from a self service ticket machine, you must buy a Permit to Travel paying as much of your fare as possible. This permit must be exchanged for a valid ticket at the first opportunity.

More information is available at nationalrail.co.uk/penaltyfares.

Timetable Accuracy, Contents, Presentation

Every effort is made to ensure that the information contained in this Timetable is correct, however errors can still occur. We welcome feedback about accuracy, contents and presentation; please contact us on the address given on page 1.

If you have any questions or queries about the train services shown in this Timetable, please contact the appropriate operator shown in the Directory of Train Operators.

Other GB Rail Timetables

Regional and route specific Timetables are available from individual train companies. Please contact the relevant train company to request the latest version of the Timetable you require.

National Rail Enquiries offers an online 'Pocket Timetable' service which gives you the flexibility to create a customised Timetable based around your origin and destination, your own time requirements and the days of the week that you intend to travel. Visit www.nationalrail.co.uk/pockettimetables for more details.

Connections

Bold type times in vertical columns in the timetable show direct trains. In a few cases, where one train overtakes another, the times appear in more than one column and arrow symbols indicate where the train continues in the Timetable.

Many more journey opportunities are possible by changing trains. To help plan such journeys, times in light italic type are shown in some of the Timetables for departures (if the time is earlier than the bold type times for the station below in the column at which you should change trains) or arrivals (if they are later than the bold type times for the station above in the column at which you should change trains).

Where light type italic times are not shown you may have to refer to other tables in the book to work out your connecting services. In order to find the right table to reference, first look at the Route/Network Diagram that covers the table you are working from. This will show the principal connecting links and their table references, which may include the destination you are searching for. If your journey is not covered, follow the advice given on 'How to use this Timetable' under the headings 'Using the Timetable Network Map' and 'Using the Index'.

Connections between trains cannot be guaranteed. The nature of the integrated operation of railway passenger services means that to delay one train to await customers from a late running train arriving at a station may cause significant disruption to many other customers when they make connections at other stations along the route. Every endeavour is made to minimise the total disruption and particular attention is given to services operating infrequently and the last train services each day.

The aim of all Train Operating Companies is to run punctually; inevitably some disruption occurs from time to time. When planning a journey you may wish to consider the effects which any disruption could have and to allow some contingency margin when planning connections.

Minimum Interchange Times at Stations

Unless a connection is shown by times printed in light type, you should generally allow a minimum of five minutes between arrival and departure.

The exceptions to this rule are indicated by minimum interchange times (e.g. **15**) alongside the station name in the tables. In certain cases the minimum interchange time is different according to the Train Operators involved.

These are detailed below:-

STATION AND 'STANDARD' MINIMUM CONNECTIONAL ALLOWANCE (Minutes)		***EXCEPTIONS Showing the Train Operator(s) and minimum connectional allowance applicable***	
Barnham	5	*SN*	2
Bournemouth	5	*SW*	3
Brighton	10	*SN*	4
Cardiff Central	7	*AW*	3*
Clapham Junction	10	*SN*	5
Gatwick Airport	10	*SN*	5
Guildford	5	*GW*	4
Leatherhead	5	*SN*	3
London Blackfriars	3	SE	5
London Victoria	15	*SE, SN*	10
Luton	10	*FC*	4
Luton Airport Parkway	7	*FC*	4
Redhill	5	*SN*	3
St. Denys	5	*SW*	3
Southampton Central	5	*SN, SW*	4
Tulse Hill	3	FC	4
Wimbledon	6	*SN, FC*	5

Example

At Barnham a different minimum connectional allowance applies for Train Operator SN. This means that if your journey involves changing between two trains *both of which* are operated by SN, you need only allow 2 minutes. If, however, one or both trains are provided by any other Operator then the minimum of 5 minutes (as shown after the station name) applies.

* Applicable to Valley Lines services only (table 130).

Train Information

National Rail Enquiries

Timetable and Fares are available 24 hours a day at www.nationalrail.co.uk or, if you are on the move, at www.mobile.nationalrail.co.uk

National Rail Enquiries provides up-to-the-minute advice on all aspects of journey planning, fares and buying tickets, live train running updates and other useful information.

08457 48 49 50 **24 Hours Daily**

(calls may be recorded for training purposes)

0845 60 40 500 **Welsh Language**

0845 60 50 600 **Textphone – 0600 - 2100 Daily**

(for customers with hearing impairments)

TrainTracker

For live train times for today and train Timetables for the next three months call TrainTracker™ on:

0871 200 49 50

Average calls to TrainTracker cost 10p a minute from a BT Landline. Charges from other operators and mobiles may vary. Calls may be recorded for training purposes.

TrainTracker Text

For live departure and arrival times direct to your mobile text station name to TrainTracker™ Text on:

8 49 50

TrainTracker texts cost 25p for each successful response (plus usual text costs)

Train company numbers for disabled passengers requiring assistance:–

Company	Telephone	Textphone
Arriva Trains Wales	08453 003 005	08457 585 469
c2c	01702 357640	08457 125 988
Chiltern Railways	08456 005 165	08457 078051
CrossCountry	0844 811 0125	0844 811 0126
East Coast	08457 225 225	18001 08457 225 225
East Midlands Trains	08457 125 678	18001 08457 125 678
Eurostar	08432 186 186	Not available
First Capital Connect	0800 058 2844	0800 975 1052
First Great Western	0800 197 1329/0845 600 5604	0800 294 9209
First Hull Trains	08450 710 222	08456 786 967
First TransPennine Express	0800 107 2149	0800 107 2061
Gatwick Express	0800 138 1016	0800 138 1018
Grand Central	0844 811 0072	0845 305 6815
Greater Anglia	0800 028 28 78	0845 606 7245
Heathrow Connect	0845 678 6975	0800 294 9209
Heathrow Express	0845 600 1515	Not available
Island Line	0800 528 2100	0800 692 0792
London Midland	0800 0924260	0844 811 0134
London Overground	0845 601 4867	020 3031 9331
Merseyrail	0151 702 2071	0870 0552 681
Northern	0808 1561606	08456 045 608
ScotRail	0800 912 2 901	18001 0800 912 2 901
South West Trains	0800 52 82 100	0800 692 0792
Southeastern	0800 783 4524	0800 783 4548
Southern	0800 138 1016	0800 138 1018
Virgin Trains	08457 443366	08457 443367

Train Information (continued)

London Travel Information

0843 222 1234	24 hours (Daily)	www.tfl.gov.uk

Services to Europe on Eurostar via the Channel Tunnel

08432 186 186	0800-1900 (Daily) 0900-1700 (S+S)	www.eurostar.com

Ireland

NI Railways 028 90 66 6630	0700-2000 (M-F) 0800-1800 (S+S)	www.translink.co.uk
Iarnrod Eireann (IE) (Irish Rail)	00 353 183 66 222	www.irishrail.ie

Transport Direct

Plan journeys by car, bus, train, tube, coach, plane at www.transportdirect.info. Transport Direct is the first door-to-door on-line journey planner for Great Britain.

It's free to use; simply enter your departure point, destination and time of travel and Transport Direct will offer a number of options by different modes of transport - both public and private. Journey plans are presented as step-by-step instructions supported by detailed maps including bus stops and other points of interest to travellers. Tickets for rail and coach journeys can be booked via retail web sites without the need to re-enter journey details. Transport Direct includes live travel news for rail and car users. The car journey planner gives route information that takes account of historical traffic level data, offering the user the choice to travel at a different time, or choose public transport. When travelling by public transport, users can adjust their expected walking speed to plan rail, coach and bus connections more efficiently. You can also access Transport Direct via mobile phone and PDA to find out when your next train is due or to check road conditions.

Bus Information in Great Britain

For details of buses within Greater London ring the Transport for London line: 0843 222 1234 (24-hours).

Bus information for the rest of Great Britain is available nationally from 'Traveline' which is run by local authorities and bus operators. There are regional call centres all of which share the same telephone number and any centre will switch calls pertaining to another part of the country through to the relevant centre. Alternatively codes for reaching the appropriate centre direct can be obtained from www.traveline.info/powercodes.html

The number is 0871 200 22 33 (calls from landlines cost 10p per minute) and centres are open at least between the hours of 0800 and 2000 daily (except Christmas Day and Boxing Day). Website: www.traveline.info

PlusBus

PlusBus is an easy-to-use add-on to your train ticket which gives unlimited bus travel on most bus services around the whole urban area of your origin or destination town or city. ***PlusBus*** is available to many towns and cities across Great Britain with season tickets also available for most ***PlusBus*** destinations. For more information visit www.plusbus.info

Traintaxi

Taxi symbols on the Station index pages

Where TAXI appears against any station that has sub-entries, there will be a taxi rank outside the station from which taxis should usually be available. This also applies to Basingstoke, Bournemouth, Chelmsford, Cheltenham, Colchester, Lincoln, Middlesbrough, Milton Keynes, Northampton, Sunderland and Swindon.

Where TAXI appears against any other station, there will be a taxi rank or a cab office within 100 metres of the station. However, you are advised to check availability before travelling, and to pre-book if necessary. Indication of a rank or office is no guarantee of cabs being available.

Visit **www.traintaxi.co.uk** for information on taxi firms serving **all** train, tram, metro and underground stations in Great Britain, and all bus and ferry destinations listed in this *GB Rail Timetable*.

Rail Travel for Disabled Passengers

All train operators are able to carry disabled passengers and can provide additional assistance for boarding and alighting and information during train journeys.

If using a wheelchair, it is recommended that passengers book assistance in advance as space on trains for wheelchair users is limited.

National Rail produce a booklet called 'Rail Travel Made Easy' which details the provisions Train Companies make for disabled people. The booklet is available from major stations or can be obtained by writing to: Rail Travel Made Easy, PO Box 11631, Laurencekirk AB30 9AA. Alternatively, you can download a copy by visiting www.nationalrail.co.uk/passenger_services/disabled_passengers/

You can also see what facilities and services are available at stations throughout the UK, including step-free routes by visiting www.nationalrail.co.uk

Seat Reservations, Luggage, Cycles and Animals

Seat Reservations

You can reserve seats on any train marked Ⓡ, 🅁, ◇ or ✂ at the top of the column in the timetable pages. Further detailed information is shown in the Directory of Train Operators.

Reservations can normally be made from about 12 weeks in advance of the day of travel, up to about 2 hours before the train departs from its start point, or, for early morning trains, up to 1600 hours the previous evening.

Where and How to Reserve

You can reserve either by visiting a station identified in the Index pages by ◇, or a rail appointed travel agent or by calling one of the telephone booking facilities listed on each Train Operator's page. Telephone reservations are only available when made in conjunction with purchasing a ticket. When reserving you will need to tell your station or agent:

1. Starting and finishing point of your journey.
2. Date of travel (Take care if your departure is soon after Midnight – see "How to use this Timetable").
3. Departure time of train.
4. Number of seats required.
5. You may be able to specify other preferences such as facing or back to direction of travel*, window seat, seat in Restaurant Car where available, seats round a table or airline style with fold down table where available.
   *Customers should note that some trains reverse their direction of travel during the journey.
6. First Class or Standard Accommodation (if you do not specify class of travel it will be assumed that you require Standard Accommodation).

Names on Seats

Your name can be included in your seat reservation label or on the electronic display above your seat, if you wish, when travelling First Class on some East Coast, East Midlands Trains and Greater Anglia services or First and Standard Class on CrossCountry, First Great Western, First TransPennine Express, ScotRail and Virgin Trains services.

Connecting Reservations

If your journey involves changing between trains on which seats are reservable (including journeys crossing London or other major cities), through reservations on both services are available.

Children

Seats may be reserved for children, however, for a child under 5 years of age a seat may be reserved only if an appropriate child rail ticket is held.

Reservations Recommended

Trains shown 🅁 at the head of a column in the Timetable pages are expected to be very busy. Seat Reservations are therefore recommended for a comfortable journey and will consequently be provided free of charge to holders of valid travel tickets.

Seat Reservations, Luggage, Cycles and Animals (continued)

Reservations Compulsory

On trains shown Ⓡ at the head of a column, Reservations are compulsory.Passengers may not be able to board the train if they do not have a reservation.

Trains For Weekends Away

Most long distance services after 1400 on Fridays and on Saturday mornings, also trains arriving in London on Sunday evenings and Monday mornings can be extremely busy.

Customers are advised to reserve seats in advance if planning to travel at these times.

Travelling at Peak Holiday Periods

Trains are usually extremely busy immediately before and after Bank Holidays and in some cases access to trains is only by reservation and/or boarding pass. Customers are advised to reserve seats as early as possible.

Cycles by Train

You can take your cycle on many National Rail services, however reservations may be required and restrictions may apply for peak services. Folded cycles can be carried on most train services. More information is shown in the Directory of Train Operators, the National Rail 'Cycling by Train' leaflet and online at www.nationalrail.co.uk/cycling. Cycle storage is also available at many stations.

Weekend First

Weekend First is available on many CrossCountry, East Coast*, East Midlands Trains, First Great Western*, First TransPennine Express*, Grand Central*, Greater Anglia, ScotRail*, South West Trains* and Virgin Trains services on Saturdays, Sundays and Bank Holidays. If you hold a ticket for travel in Standard Class, you may be able to upgrade to the added comfort of First Class Accommodation on payment of an additional fare. On some services a 'Weekend First' ticket allows you to upgrade to First Class at weekends and Bank Holidays. Holders of Annual Gold Cards may also be able to upgrade on off-peak services for a small amount. Costs vary depending on the journey you are making.

*(subject to availability) may only be purchased on trains at time of travel

More information can be found at www.nationalrail.co.uk/firstclass

Customers' Luggage and Animals

Customers may take up to 3 items of personal luggage free of charge; this includes 2 large items (such as suitcases or rucksacks) and 1 item of smaller hand luggage (such as a briefcase). Folded prams, non-folding prams and carrycots are also able to be carried. Full details of the free allowances are available at stations. Excess luggage and certain more bulky items (such as skis) may be carried, subject to available space, at an extra charge.

Passengers may take dogs, cats and other small animals (maximum two per passenger), free of charge and subject to certain conditions, provided they do not endanger or inconvenience other passengers or staff.

ScotRail allows dogs to accompany able-bodied passengers in Sleeper Services subject to a charge for cleaning of the compartment. The booking must be First Class, Standard Class with two people travelling together, or a Solo supplement is payable for exclusive use of a twin-berth cabin. First Great Western do **not** allow animals (except Guide Dogs) to travel in Sleeper Accommodation. There is no charge for Guide Dogs.

More information can be found at www.nationalrail.co.uk/luggageandanimals

Directory of Train Operators

The following pages contain details of the Train Operating Companies who operate trains included in this Timetable and indicate the services they provide.

Each operator is identified by a two character code listed below. The codes are displayed in the index alongside the station name indicating which operator is responsible for operating the facilities at that station. The code is also shown at the head of each train column in the timetable pages indicating which operator is providing the train service.

17 stations are the operating responsibility of Network Rail and are shown in the index by the code NR and information about Network Rail is shown at the end of the Train Operating Company pages.

Page No	Train Company Name	Code
12	Arriva Trains Wales	AW
13	c2c	CC
14	CrossCountry	XC
15	Chiltern Railways	CH
16	Devon & Cornwall Railway	DC
17	East Coast	GR
18	East Midlands Trains	EM
19	First Capital Connect	FC
20	First Great Western	GW
21	First Hull Trains	HT
22	First TransPennine Express	TP
23	Gatwick Express	GX
24	Grand Central	GC
25	Greater Anglia	LE
26	Heathrow Connect	HC
27	Heathrow Express	HX
28	Island Line	IL
29	London Midland	LM
30	London Overground	LO
31	Merseyrail	ME
32	North Yorkshire Moors Railway	NY
33	Northern	NT
34	ScotRail	SR
35	South West Trains	SW
36	Southeastern	SE
37	Southern	SN
38	Virgin Trains	VT
39	West Coast Railway Co.	WR

Arriva Trains Wales

AW

ADDRESS	St Mary's House 47 Penarth Road Cardiff CF10 5DJ Telephone: 0845 6061 660 Website: www.arrivatrainswales.co.uk Email: customer.relations@arrivatrainswales.co.uk
MANAGING DIRECTOR	Ian Bullock
RESERVATIONS AND TICKETS BY TELEPHONE AND ONLINE	Tickets may be booked in advance and seats reserved, by telephone, from the following numbers (0800–2000 daily): 0870 9000 773 for Great Britain, tickets and reservations. 0870 9000 767 for Group and 0845 300 3005 for Disabled travel arrangements. Textphone 0845 758 5469 Please allow 5 days for delivery.
RESERVATION DETAILS	All seat reservations are free to ticket holders.
CATERING ON TRAINS	At-seat catering service of cold snacks, sandwiches and hot and cold drinks on all services marked ⚲, for all or part of the journey. Complimentary meal service for first class and a counter service of hot and cold snacks for standard class on trains with ☒. Train catering on Arriva Trains Wales services is provided by: At Seat Catering (2003) Ltd St Mary's House 47 Penarth Road Cardiff CF10 5DJ
CYCLES	See Cycling by Train leaflet, a guide to Arriva Trains Wales services for full details.
LOST PROPERTY	Contact Arriva Trains Wales Customer Relations on 0845 6061 660.
TRAIN SERVICE UPDATE	Please consult our website at www.arrivatrainswales.co.uk for real time service updates.
PENALTY FARES	Penalty Fares do not apply on Arriva Trains Wales services. Customers are reminded that they must have a valid ticket when boarding at a staffed station, if not it will be necessary to charge you the full single/return fare for the journey.
DISABLED PEOPLE'S PROTECTION POLICY	Address as above.
CODE OF PRACTICE FOR COMMENTS, COMPLAINTS AND SUGGESTIONS	Address as above.

ALCOHOL POLICY

Arriva Trains Wales have prohibited the consumption of alcohol on all services and stations between Caerphilly - Rhymney, and Pontypridd - Treherbert/Merthr Tydfil/Aberdare

c2c

CC

A member of the National Express Group plc

ADDRESS	2nd Floor Cutlers Court 115 Houndsditch London EC3A 7BR Telephone: 0845 601 4873 Website: www.c2c-online.co.uk
MANAGING DIRECTOR	Julian Drury
RESERVATIONS AND TICKETS BY TELEPHONE AND ONLINE	Online through c2c-online.co.uk or Tel: 08457 44 44 22 open Monday to Saturday 08.00 - 20.00; Sunday 10.00 - 20.00 **c2c Group Travel:** Call our Ticket sales hotline on 08457 44 44 22 selecting 'Group Travel' to find out more. **c2c Assisted Travel:** Tel: 01702 357 640 open 05.30 - 22.00 Monday to Friday; Saturday 06.00 - 21.00; Sunday 07.00 - 17.00
RESERVATION DETAILS	Reservations are not available.
CATERING ON TRAINS	Not available.
CYCLES	• Cycles are not permitted on weekday services arriving in London Fenchurch Street between 07.15 and 09.45, or leaving London Fenchurch Street between 16.30 and 18.42. • If you plan to travel with 3 or more cyclists please contact the cycle helpline on 01702 357640 where we can advise you further. • Tandems and tricycles are not permitted. • During engineering work, cycles cannot be accommodated on c2c replacement bus services. • Motorcycles cannot be carried on any service. • Cycles are carried at owners risk (see National Rail Conditions of Carriage) or for further information visit www.nationalrail.co.uk/cycling • Cycles must be carried in the designated area on the train and must not obstruct doors and aisles. • Reservations are not required. • Please do not lock your cycle to any part of the train. You are also reminded not to leave your cycle unattended at any time during your journey. You can view which stations have cycle bays by visiting c2c-online.co.uk
LOST PROPERTY	c2c Rail Ltd, Westcliff Station, Station Road, Westcliff-on-Sea, SS0 7SB Telephone: 01702 357 699
TRAIN SERVICE UPDATE	Real time up to date train running information is available on the c2c website www.c2c-online.co.uk, the National Rail Enquiries website at nationalrail.co.uk
PENALTY FARES	If you travel without a valid ticket you may be charged a penalty fare of £20 or twice the full single fare, whichever is the greater.
DISABLED PEOPLE'S PROTECTION POLICY	Available from:- Customer Relations c2c Rail Ltd, FREEPOST ADM3968, Southend, SS1 1ZS. Telephone: 0845 601 4873 Open Monday to Friday 08.00 - 18.00 Textphone: 0845 606 7245 Available Monday to Friday 08.30 - 17.00
CODE OF PRACTICE FOR COMMENTS, COMPLAINTS AND SUGGESTION	Available from Customer Relations at the above address

XC CrossCountry XC

ADDRESS	CrossCountry 5th Floor, Cannon House, 18 Priory Queensway, Birmingham B4 6BS Telephone: 08447 369 123 Textphone: 0121 200 6420 Fax: 0121 200 6005 Website: www.crosscountrytrains.co.uk Email: customer.relations@crosscountrytrains.co.uk
MANAGING DIRECTOR	Andy Cooper
RESERVATIONS AND TICKETS BY TELEPHONE AND ONLINE	Online at crosscountrytrains.co.uk is the easiest way to purchase your tickets. If you prefer, you can also make telephone bookings on 0844 811 0124 between 0800 and 2200 daily. Parties of 10 or more should contact Group Travel on 0871 244 2388 between 0800 and 1800 weekdays
RESERVATION DETAILS	You are strongly advised to make a seat reservation in advance; especially when travelling on trains shown with the ■ symbol in timetables. Seat reservations are free of charge.
CATERING ON TRAINS	Catering is available on most CrossCountry trains. In First Class, on weekdays between 0630 and 1830 customers can enjoy complimentary light refreshments including hot and soft drinks, served at seat. In Standard Class we offer a range of quality snacks, sandwiches and hot drinks plus soft and alcoholic beverages between 0600 and 2000. For more information on the Nottingham - Cardiff and Birmingham - Stansted Airport routes please refer to our timetables.
CYCLES	We do not charge to carry your cycle. However, as space is very limited you will need to reserve in advance on nearly all our services. Please enquire before travelling. We are unable to accept powered cycles, tricycles, tandems or trailers on any of our services.
LOST PROPERTY	Contact Customer Relations on 08447 369 123 between 0800 and 2000 Monday to Saturday; or email lost.property@crosscountrytrains.co.uk
TRAIN SERVICE UPDATE	Details of major disruption to services and weekend engineering work are summarised on BBC and BBCi on digital TV. Live travel updates are available online at crosscountrytrains.co.uk and details of all service disruptions can be found at nationalrail.co.uk/disruption/
PENALTY FARES	A Penalty Fares scheme is not currently in operation on CrossCountry trains. Visit crosscountrytrains.co.uk for the most up to date information. Should you board one of our trains without a valid ticket you will be charged the full Single or Return fare for your journey unless the ticket office is closed and a self-service ticket machine is not available.
DISABLED PEOPLE'S PROTECTION POLICY	We provide a Journey Care service for the disabled, elderly and infirm. By phoning our team on 0844 811 0125, textphone 0844 811 0126, beforehand we will, where possible, arrange help for your journey. Our Disabled People's Protection Policy is available on-line at crosscountrytrains.co.uk
CODE OF PRACTICE FOR COMMENTS, COMPLAINTS AND SUGGESTIONS	Copies of our Complaints Handling Procedure and Passenger's Charter are available on-line at crosscountrytrains.co.uk

Chiltern Railways

CH

ADDRESS

Customer Services
Banbury ICC
Merton Street
Banbury
Oxfordshire OX16 4RN
Telephone: 08456 005 165 (Mondays to Fridays 0830-1730)
Fax: 01926 729 914
Website: www.chilternrailways.co.uk

MANAGING DIRECTOR

Rob Brighouse

RESERVATIONS AND TICKETS BY TELEPHONE AND ONLINE

Telephone 08456 005 165 (0700-2000, 7 days a week)

RESERVATION DETAILS

Reservations can be made for travel in the Business Zone of our Mainline Silver trains. Reservations are not available on any other services.

CATERING ON TRAINS

Our Mainline Silver trains offer an on-board kitchen serving drinks and freshly cooked bacon-rolls and pastries on morning trains, Mondays to Fridays. An at-seat catering service is available on Mondays to Fridays on most other Mainline trains arriving in London before 1345 and leaving London between 0700 and 1445. If your train does not offer catering do not forget that our main stations offer excellent catering facilities. For more details check our website. Please allow enough time to purchase your refreshments before boarding your train.

CYCLES

Subject to space being available, and at the discretion of our staff, you can take your bike (except tandems) on any Chiltern Railways train on Saturdays, Sundays or Public Holidays. On Mondays to Fridays you can also use most of our trains. The only exceptions are our busiest peak hour services. For the safety and comfort of all our passengers bikes are not allowed at any point during the journey on any train:

• Arriving London Marylebone or Birmingham Moor Street from 0745 to 1000

• Leaving London Marylebone or Birmingham Moor Street from 1630 to 1930

On our Mainline Silver trains you must put your bike in the special storage area at one end of the train. We are sorry, but bikes cannot be taken on rail replacement buses at any time. There are no restrictions on folding bikes at any time, provided they are fully folded. For information about cycle storage facilities at our stations see our website. Cycles can be hired from just outside London Marylebone station. For information visit www.tfl.gov.uk/barclayscyclehire.

LOST PROPERTY

If we find any item of lost property, we will always do our best to contact the owner if they can be identified. Items can be collected from London Marylebone up to 3 months after they have been handed in - we charge a collection fee to cover our administration costs.

If you lose something on one of our trains or stations you can report it by:

* Using the online form on our website

* Using a Lost Property Form available at any Chiltern Railways ticket office, and returning it to a member of Chiltern Railways Staff.

* By phone, fax or post using the contact details below:

Phone: 08456 005 165
Fax: 020 7333 3002
Write to: Chiltern Railways Lost Property
Marylebone Station
London NW1 6JJ.

Lost Property Office Operating Hours: Mondays to Fridays 1200 to 2000. Please allow up to 2 weeks for processing lost items. If you do not hear from us in that period, you should assume the item has not been found.

TRAIN SERVICE UPDATE

Visit our website www.chilternrailways.co.uk for current train running information and details of changes to train times because of engineering work or other special events.

PENALTY FARES

If you do not have a valid rail ticket for the journey you are making, you will have to pay a Penalty Fare of £20 or twice the single fare, whichever is the greater, for the journey you are making on Chiltern Railways services. For full details write to the above address, or see our website.

DISABLED PEOPLE'S PROTECTION POLICY

Copies of the Disabled People's Protection Policy can be obtained from the above address, or from our website.

CODE OF PRACTICE FOR COMMENTS, COMPLAINTS AND SUGGESTIONS

If you have any comments, complaints or suggestions regarding Chiltern Railways services, please write to the address shown above or telephone 08456 005 165 (0830-1730 Mondays to Fridays), Fax 01926 729 914. Alternatively you can use the 'Contact Us' option on our website.

DC Devon & Cornwall Railway DC

ADDRESS

MANAGING DIRECTOR

RESERVATIONS AND TICKETS BY TELEPHONE AND ONLINE

New operator – Commencement to be confirmed

RESERVATION DETAILS

CATERING ON TRAINS

CYCLES

LOST PROPERTY

TRAIN SERVICE UPDATE

PENALTY FARES

DISABLED PEOPLE'S PROTECTION POLICY

CODE OF PRACTICE FOR COMMENTS, COMPLAINTS AND SUGGESTIONS

East Coast

ADDRESS	Freepost RSRJ-LJCX-GHST Plymouth PL4 6AB Telephone: 08457 225 333 Open 0700-2200 Monday to Sunday Fax: 01752 828482 Website: www.eastcoast.co.uk Email: customers@eastcoast.co.uk
MANAGING DIRECTOR	Karen Boswell
RESERVATIONS AND TICKETS BY TELEPHONE AND ONLINE	Internet Purchase tickets via the internet 24 hours a day at www.eastcoast.co.uk Self service ticket machines are available at all East Coast stations. Purchase tickets for today or collect pre-booked tickets. Travel enquiries and Telesales 08457 225 225 Open 0800-2000 Monday-Saturday, 1000-2000 Sunday Group Travel Open 0800-2000 Monday-Friday Discounts may be available for groups of 10 or more people. Assisted Travel Open 0800-2000 Monday-Saturday, 1000-2000 Sunday Web support 0800-2000 Monday to Saturday, 1000-2000 Sunday Tickets can be printed at home on the same day as purchased or please allow at least 5 working days prior to travel for tickets to reach you through the post.
RESERVATION DETAILS	Seat Reservations can usually be made on any East Coast train up to twelve weeks in advance. They are available to any ticket holder upon request and are compulsory with some ticket types. Only one reservation can be made per single journey.
CATERING ON TRAINS	Passengers travelling in First Class will receive complimentary food and drink on board. For shorter journeys, you will be offered drinks and snacks, while on longer trips you can look forward to something a little more substantial. Passengers in Standard Class can enjoy a wide range of refreshments from our caféBAR. An at-seat trolley service will also be available on selected services.
CYCLES	Bicycles are welcome on East Coast trains. A reservation must be made and bookings are subject to space being available.Reservations can be made by calling 08457 225 225 or any East Coast ticket office.
LOST PROPERTY	If you lose something on a East Coast train or at a station please speak to a member of staff or contact us on 08457 225 333. Please note that charges are normally made for returning items of lost property and that we are unable to forward items of lost property on train services.
TRAIN SERVICE UPDATE	Visit www.eastcoast.co.uk/travel information or call National Rail Enquiries on 08457 48 49 50 (calls may be recorded for training purposes).
PENALTY FARES	East Coast does not operate a Penalty Fares scheme. However, you should always purchase a ticket valid for travel before you board any East Coast service as only full fare tickets are sold on our trains. The only exception being Disabled Railcard holders who will be sold appropriate discounted tickets on-board.
DISABLED PEOPLE'S PROTECTION POLICY	A copy of our Making Rail Accessible can be obtained free of charge from the address at the top of this page. Our Assisted Travel Team can help you plan your journey and organise tickets, assistance and Seat Reservations. To ensure the best possible levels of assistance we recommend that you contact us no later than 1800 the day before you intend to travel. Telephone 08457 225 225 or textphone 18001. 08457 225 225* (open 0800-2000 Monday-Saturday, 1000-2000 Sunday). * Please note that this number should only be used to contact the Assisted Travel Team. For all other enquiries please telephone 08457 225 225.
CODE OF PRACTICE FOR COMMENTS, COMPLAINTS AND SUGGESTIONS	Our Passenger's Charter is available from all East Coast stations or from our website www.eastcoast.co.uk. All correspondence should be sent using the address at the top of this page.

East Midlands Trains

EM

ADDRESS	East Midlands Trains Prospect Place Millennium Way Pride Park Derby DE24 8HG Telephone: 08457 125 678 Website: www.eastmidlandstrains.co.uk Email: getintouch@eastmidlandstrains.co.uk
MANAGING DIRECTOR	David Horne
RESERVATIONS AND TICKETS BY TELEPHONE AND ONLINE	Buy your tickets online at eastmidlandstrains.co.uk. You can buy tickets for all rail journeys (within Great Britain) with us. Alternatively call 08457 125 678 between 0800-2000 (7 days a week).
RESERVATION DETAILS	Seat Reservations on East Midlands Trains services are free. Just book in advance when you buy your ticket. We advise that you always make a reservation, as seats cannot be guaranteed without one. On our Local Services reservations are available on the Liverpool to Norwich services.
CATERING ON TRAINS	On our East Midlands London Services (to/from St Pancras International), we offer a range of delicious food options, plus snacks and hot and cold drinks. A trolley service is available on selected East Midlands Local Services (denoted by a symbol within the Timetable).
CYCLES	Two bicycles per train are accepted for free on all East Midlands Trains services; however reservations must be made in advance on reservable services subject to availability.
LOST PROPERTY	Please allow a minimum of 24 hours for the items to be received at a lost property office. If your item is located you may be charged for the return of it and will be advised of this cost. To enquire about lost property, please call our Lost Property office, ideally between the hours of 0800 and 1800 Monday to Friday on 08457 125 678.
TRAIN SERVICE UPDATE	Details of services and real time running information, including travel alerts by email are available through our website. Visit www.eastmidlandstrains.co.uk. Alternatively, call National Rail Enquiries on 08457 48 49 50 (calls may be recorded for training purposes).
PENALTY FARES	You should always buy a ticket in advance of boarding your train. Penalty Fares may be in operation on your service.
DISABLED PEOPLE'S PROTECTION POLICY	We aim to make travelling with us accessible to all our customers. If you require assistance in travelling, have special needs or mobility problems please call our team on 08457 125 678 option 3 to arrange help for your journey. A text direct service is also available on 18001 08457 125 678 (for people with hearing problems) or complete a form at eastmidlandstrains.co.uk.
CODE OF PRACTICE FOR COMMENTS, COMPLAINTS AND SUGGESTIONS	Our Customer Relations team is available to receive your comments, complaints or suggestions. Please write to Customer Relations at the above address, or email getintouch@eastmidlandstrains.co.uk or call us on 08457 125 678 (option 5, 3 and 2)

FC

First Capital Connect

FC

A member of the First Rail Division

ADDRESS

Freepost, RRBR-REEJ-KTKY
First Capital Connect
Customer Relations Department
PO Box 443
Plymouth PL4 6WP
Telephone: 0845 026 4700 (open 7 days a week 0700-2200 with the exception of Christmas Day)
Fax: 0845 676 9904
Website: www.firstcapitalconnect.co.uk
Email: customer.relations.fcc@firstgroup.com

MANAGING DIRECTOR

David Statham

RESERVATIONS AND TICKETS BY TELEPHONE AND ONLINE

First Capital Connect does not offer telesales, however tickets can be booked at www.firstcapitalconnect.co.uk

RESERVATION DETAILS

Reservations are not available.

CATERING ON TRAINS

None.

CYCLES

We welcome passengers with bicycles on services where they can be safely accommodated. Folding bicycles can be carried at any time. However we are unable to carry non-folding bicycles:

- At any time between Drayton Park and Moorgate.
- On Great Northern route trains south of Stevenage and Hertford North timed to arrive in London between 0700 and 0930 or depart from London between 1600 and 1900 Monday to Friday. (Restrictions do not apply on Saturdays, Sundays and Public Holidays.)
- On Great Northern route trains between Cambridge and Ely that are timed to arrive at or depart from Cambridge between 0745 and 0845 with the exception of the 0715 and 0745 departures from London King's Cross Monday to Friday. (Restrictions do not apply on Saturdays, Sundays and Public Holidays)
- On the Great Northern route between Royston and Cambridge on the 0706 train from London King's Cross which departs Royston at 0806 and is due to arrive at Cambridge at 0829.
- On Thameslink route trains travelling towards London that are timed to arrive at or pass through any central London station between 0700 and 1000, or travelling away from London and timed to depart from or pass through any central London station between 1600 and 1900 Monday to Friday. (Restrictions do not apply on Saturdays, Sundays and Public Holidays.)
- On replacement bus services unless otherwise stated in associated publicity.
- On any train where your bicycle may cause an obstruction to other customers (i.e. where a number of people are standing) or when a member of staff asks you to remove your bicycle.
- On many London Underground lines – see tfl.gov.uk for details.

LOST PROPERTY

If you have lost something please visit firstcapitalconnect.co.uk/lostproperty and complete our online lost property form.

TRAIN SERVICE UPDATE

For current train information call National Rail enquiries on 08457 48 49 50 (calls may be recorded for training purposes) or check our website at: www.firstcapitalconnect.co.uk/live-info

PENALTY FARES

First Capital Connect operates a Penalty Fares System. If you do not have a valid ticket or permit to travel, you will be liable to pay a penalty fare. This is £20 or twice the appropriate single fare to the next station stop, whichever is greater. This does not apply for travel from Crews Hill. If you do not buy a ticket, you could also be prosecuted and this can lead to a Criminal Conviction.

DISABLED PEOPLE'S PROTECTION POLICY

Our Disabled People's Protection Policy is available from Customer Relations, and is also available on our website and available at all staffed stations. First Capital Connect operates a dedicated telephone and textphone service for disabled or mobility impaired customers, the contact details are: Telephone: 0800 058 2844, 0800 975 1052

These are available 0700 - 2200, every day, with the exception of Christmas Day.

CODE OF PRACTICE FOR COMMENTS, COMPLAINTS AND SUGGESTIONS

Our Passenger's Charter details our code of practice and is available from all staffed stations and from our Customer Relations Department. The Customer Relations Department will be happy to assist with any comments, complaints or suggestions and can be contacted using the contact details above.

First Great Western

GW

A member of the First Rail Division

ADDRESS	Milford House 1 Milford Street Swindon SN1 1HL Telephone: 01793 499400 Fax: 01793 499460 Website: www.firstgreatwestern.co.uk. On our website you can create and print your own personalised timetables, download complete timetable booklets, find departure and arrival times for specific journeys, buy tickets, obtain live timetable updates specific to individual stations, check any late alterations to our services, view promotions and contact us with your comments.
MANAGING DIRECTOR	Mark Hopwood
RESERVATIONS AND TICKETS BY TELEPHONE AND ONLINE	Tickets may be booked in advance using credit and debit cards and seats reserved by ringing **08457 000 125** (open 0700-2200 daily). Allow at least 5 working days for postal delivery. A next day delivery can be arranged at £5 per transaction. Arrangements can be made for tickets to be collected from Fast Ticket machines (the credit or debit card used for purchase will be needed at many stations). For Group Travel call **08457 000 125**.
RESERVATION DETAILS	A seat reservation, free of charge, can be made at the time of purchasing your ticket. Additional reservations, including those made by season ticket holders, are subject to a £5 fee.
CATERING ON TRAINS	Most First Great Western high speed services offer an Express Café service with freshly brewed coffee, hot baguettes and paninis and a wide range of drinks and snacks. A Travelling Chef is available on many weekday services, preparing meals and snacks to order for both First and Standard Class customers. On a small number of weekday services, a Pullman restaurant provides à la carte dining to First and Standard Class customers, subject to availability. First Class customers also enjoy additional complimentary services: • An at-seat trolley service offering light refreshments (available on most Monday to Friday services between 0700-1900), including hot and cold drinks and light snacks appropriate to the time of day. The trolley also offers a range of items for sale from our Express Café. • At the weekend and on weekdays after 1900, complimentary refreshments are available from the Express Cafe on production of valid travel tickets.
CYCLES	First Great Western welcomes customers with bicycles on services where they can be safely accommodated. However it is not possible to carry bicycles on some services, particularly during peak periods. For full details of when bicycles cannot be carried or when reservations are required please visit our website or pick up a leaflet at any of our staffed stations.
LOST PROPERTY	Customers who have left property on First Great Western services should contact our Customer Services team on **08457 000 125**.
TRAIN SERVICE UPDATE	For current train information including details of engineering work please visit our website: www.firstgreatwestern.co.uk
PENALTY FARES	These operate on most of our services. A penalty fare of £20 or twice the appropriate single fare to the next station stop (whichever is the greater) will be charged to anybody who is unable to produce a valid ticket or other authority when required to do so. For further information, pick up a leaflet about Penalty Fares from any staffed station.
DISABLED PEOPLE'S PROTECTION POLICY	Available from Customer Services Team First Great Western PO Box 313 Plymouth PL4 6YD Tel: 08457 000 125 Email: fgwfeedback@firstgroup.com Opening hours 0700-2200 daily Customers requiring assistance should contact 0800 197 1329 (18001 0800 197 1329 textphone service), if possible giving 24 hours notice of travel plans.
CODE OF PRACTICE FOR COMMENTS, COMPLAINTS AND SUGGESTIONS	Your views leaflets and copies of the Passenger's Charter are available to download from our website www.firstgreatwestern.co.uk, at all staffed First Great Western stations or alternatively from the Customer Services Team at the address above.

First Hull Trains

HT

ADDRESS	First Hull Trains Customer Services Freepost RLYY-XSTG-YXCK 4th Floor Europa House 184 Ferensway Hull HU1 3UT Telephone: 08456 76 99 05 Website: www.hulltrains.co.uk Email: customer.services@hulltrains.co.uk
MANAGING DIRECTOR	Cath Bellamy
RESERVATIONS AND TICKETS BY TELEPHONE AND ONLINE	First Hull Trains tickets can be booked in advance and seats reserved by ringing 08450 710 222 (0700 to 2200 Monday to Friday and 0800 to 1900 Saturday and Sunday). Please allow five working days for delivery. Tickets on departure are available.
RESERVATION DETAILS	Seat Reservations are free for First and Standard Class ticket holders. Season Ticket holders may reserve seats at a cost of £2 for First Class and £1 for Standard Class.
CATERING ON TRAINS	First Hull Trains provides a buffet on all services, and a comprehensive catering package for First Class passengers. Catering is subject to availability and may be limited when services are disrupted by engineering works or Bank Holidays.
CYCLES	Cycles and tandems are carried free of charge, however, a reservation is compulsory. Please telephone 08450 710 222
LOST PROPERTY	Please contact Customer Services.
TRAIN SERVICE UPDATE	Available at www.hulltrains.co.uk, or by telephone on 08450 710222.
PENALTY FARES	Penalty Fares do not apply on Hull Trains.
DISABLED PEOPLE'S PROTECTION POLICY	Available at: www.hulltrains.co.uk. Alternatively, a copy can be requested from Customer Services.
CODE OF PRACTICE FOR COMMENTS, COMPLAINTS AND SUGGESTIONS	First Hull Trains' Passenger's Charter is available at www.hulltrains.co.uk. Alternatively, any comments, complaints or suggestions can be sent to Customer Services

TP

First TransPennine Express

TP

A joint venture between First and Keolis

ADDRESS	7th Floor Bridgewater House 60 Whitworth Street Manchester M1 6LT Telephone: 08700 005151 Website: www.tpexpress.co.uk
MANAGING DIRECTOR	Nick Donovan
RESERVATIONS AND TICKETS BY TELEPHONE AND ONLINE	Reservations and tickets are available at www.tpexpress.co.uk and from all local staffed stations.
RESERVATION DETAILS	Seat Reservations are available at staffed stations. Seat Reservations for travel on First TransPennine Express services can be booked up until the day before travel. There is no charge for making a Seat Reservation if you have a rail ticket, or buy one at the same time.
CATERING ON TRAINS	Catering trolley services are available between 0700 and 1900 Monday to Friday on First TransPennine Express trains between Manchester Piccadilly and York, Manchester Piccadilly and Doncaster and Manchester Piccadilly and Preston. In addition to the above, all services between Manchester Airport, Manchester Piccadilly, Carlisle, Glasgow Central and Edinburgh convey a trolley service for the whole journey. This facility is also provided at weekends.
CYCLES	Customers may take their bicycle with them on First TransPennine Express trains at no extra cost. As space is limited to two bicycles per train, reservations for cycle space should be made at least 24 hours before the journey.
LOST PROPERTY	Customers who have left their property on First TransPennine Express trains or stations should contact 0845 600 1672.
TRAIN SERVICE UPDATE	For current train information call National Rail Enquiries on 0845 48 49 50 (calls may be recorded for monitoring purposes) or check our website at: www.tpexpress.co.uk/travelupdates
PENALTY FARES	Penalty Fares are not applicable on First TransPennine Express services. Customers are reminded that they must have a valid ticket when they travel. If not it will be necessary to charge the full Open Single or Return Fare for the journey.
DISABLED PEOPLE'S PROTECTION POLICY	Available online at www.tpexpress.co.uk and also from: Customer Relations First TransPennine Express ADMAIL 3878 Freepost Manchester M1 9YB Customers who have special needs and require customer assistance should contact us on 0800 107 2149. A textphone service is available on 0800 107 2061.
CODE OF PRACTICE FOR COMMENTS, COMPLAINTS AND SUGGESTIONS	Feedback leaflets and copies of the Passenger's Charter are available from all stations served by First TransPennine Express services or alternatively contact: Customer Relations, First TransPennine Express, ADMAIL 3878, Freepost, Manchester M1 9YB. Telephone: 0845 600 1671 Email: tpecustomer.relations@firstgroup.com

GX Gatwick Express GX

ADDRESS

Gatwick Express Customer Services
PO Box 3021
Bristol BS2 2BS
Telephone: 0845 850 1530
Fax: 020 8929 8687 (Overseas: +44 208 9298687)
Website: www.gatwickexpress.com
Email: customerservices@gatwickexpress.com

MANAGING DIRECTOR

Chris Burchell

RESERVATIONS ARE NOT NECESSARY ON GATWICK EXPRESS SERVICES

Reservations are not necessary on Gatwick Express services. For information please call 0845 850 1530. Tickets can also be purchased through our website at www.gatwickexpress.com

RESERVATION DETAILS

Reservations are not available.

CATERING ON TRAINS

An at-seat trolley service of drinks and light refreshments is available on most services.

CYCLES

Fully folded cycles are welcome on Gatwick Express services at anytime and should be fully folded and carried before going through the gateline. However, restrictions do apply to the carriage of regular (non-folding cycles) and these cannot be conveyed on services scheduled to arrive into London Victoria between 0700 and 1000 or depart from London Victoria between 1600 and 1900 Monday to Friday (excluding bank holidays).

LOST PROPERTY

Please call our Lost Property Office on 0845 850 1530, select option 2.

TRAIN SERVICE

Normal journey time is 30 minutes in both directions. First Class and Standard Class accommodation is available.

From London Victoria trains normally depart every 15 minutes between 0500 and midnight with additional trains at 0030, 0330 ,0430.
From Gatwick Airport trains normally depart every 15 minutes between 0550 and 0050 with additional trains at 0135, 0435, 0520.

For current train information call 0845 850 1530, select option 2.
Some early morning, late evening,overnight and peak trains have longer journey times or longer intervals between trains.

PENALTY FARES

Gatwick Express operates a Penalty Fare Scheme on all trains. You must buy a valid ticket (or permit to travel) for your journey before boarding a train. If you do not have a valid ticket or permit to travel, you may have to pay a Penalty Fare of £20.00 or twice the single fare, whichever is the greater. Please pick up a Penalty Fare leaflet from a staffed station for your information.

DISABLED PEOPLE'S PROTECTION POLICY

Customers requiring assistance can book this prior to travel. Arrangements can be made by calling 0845 138 1016, textphone available 0800 138 1018. It is advisable to give 24 hours notice of travel plans, although customers will be given assistance if they arrive at the stations without notice but please allow a little extra time.

CODE OF PRACTICE FOR COMMENTS, COMPLAINTS AND SUGGESTIONS

A copy of our passengers charter is available from our website or by contacting our customer service team.if you wish to contact us for information,to make a Comment,suggestion or complaint you can call,email or write to us(details above) or pick up a comments form from any of our staffed stations.

Grand Central

GC

ADDRESS

Grand Central Railway Company Ltd
River House
17 Museum Street
York YO1 7DJ
Telephone: 0845 603 4852
Fax: 01904 466066
Website: www.grandcentralrail.com
Email: customer.services@grandcentralrail.com

MANAGING DIRECTOR

Richard McClean

RESERVATIONS AND TICKETS BY TELEPHONE AND ONLINE

Reservations are strongly advised on Friday afternoons, at weekends and Bank Holidays. Tickets and seat Reservations are available in advance on our website www.grandcentralrail.com or over the phone by calling 0844 811 0071 (Mon - Fri 9 - 5pm).

Tickets can be purchased via grandcentralrail.com and through manned rail stations. Tickets booked in advance can be printed at home if purchased through our telesales, sent by post (allow 5 working days), collected from self-service ticket machines at certain stations or sent electronically by email for print at home.

Tickets can also be purchased from the staff on the train without paying a penalty for last-minute travel.

For group bookings, business travel and Carnet tickets please call 0845 603 4852.

RESERVATION DETAILS

Complimentary Seat Reservations are available; these must be booked at least 24 hours in advance. To guarantee a seat we advise that you always make a reservation. Reservations are strongly advised on Friday afternoons, at weekends and Bank Holidays.

CATERING ON TRAINS

A buffet service is available on all services. In First Class customers enjoy complimentary light refreshments including hot and cold drinks, served at-seat. Daily newspapers are provided. In Standard class a buffet is available offering a selection of fair trade and locally sourced products, including hot, soft and alcoholic drinks, sandwiches, crisps and a large selection of other sweet and savoury snacks.

CYCLES

Normal sized cycles are conveyed free of charge subject to room being available, cycle reservations can be made by calling 0845 603 4852 or at any station ticket office. Cycle reservations are not normally required, but if a group of cyclists are travelling, you should call 0845 603 4852 to reserve cycle space.
During engineering work cycles cannot be accommodated on replacement bus services.

LOST PROPERTY

For trains travelling towards Sunderland or Bradford, please contact Northern Rail's Lost Property office on 0845 00 00 125. For trains travelling towards London, please contact King's Cross Lost Property Office on 0207 278 3310.

TRAIN SERVICE UPDATE

Visit grandcentralrail.com for live arrivals and departures information. Alternatively visit the Twitter feed @NRE_Grand_Centr, call National Rail Enquiries on 08457 48 49 50, visit nationalrail.co.uk or call Train Tracker on 0871 200 4950.

Details of engineering work will be available on our website www.grandcentralrail.com or by calling 0845 603 4852.

DISABLED PEOPLE'S PROTECTION POLICY

Assisted travel can be booked by calling 0844 811 0072 (0800-2200 7 days a week) or using our text phone service on 0845 305 6815 please call at least 48 hours in advance. Our Disabled People's Protection Policy is available on-line at grandcentralrail.com, by calling 0845 603 4852 or by writing to us at the address above. Copies are available at staffed stations on our route.

CODE OF PRACTICE FOR COMMENTS, COMPLAINTS AND SUGGESTIONS

Our Passenger Charter is available on-line at grandcentralrail.com.

Greater Anglia

LE

ADDRESS	Contact Centre Greater Anglia Norwich Railway Station Station Approach Norwich NR1 1EF Telephone: 0845 600 7245 Fax: 01603 214567 Website: www.greateranglia.com Email: contactcentre@greateranglia.co.uk
MANAGING DIRECTOR	Ruud Haket
RESERVATIONS AND TICKETS BY TELEPHONE AND ONLINE	Tickets may be booked in advance by telephoning 0845 600 7245 between 0800 and 2200 (Mondays to Fridays) and 0900 and 1800 (weekends and Bank Holidays). For Business Travel, please telephone 0845 850 9080
RESERVATION DETAILS	Greater Anglia offers Seat Reservations on services between London Liverpool Street and Norwich at a charge of £2.50 per seat (£1 for season ticket holders).
CATERING ON TRAINS	Hot and cold drinks, sandwiches and light snacks are generally available on main line services between Norwich and London Liverpool Street and on Stansted Express services. Complimentary light refreshments will be available to First Class customers on these services.
CYCLES	Accompanied bicycles are conveyed free of charge on most GA services, but are not permitted on Stansted Express services at any time or on weekday peak services to and from London. A similar restriction also applies at Cambridge. On main line and rural services, the number of bicycles per train is limited, so a free reservation is recommended. For further details, please call Greater Anglia customer services on 0845 600 7245.
LOST PROPERTY	If you have lost an item of property on one of our trains or stations, please contact Greater Anglia customer services on 0845 600 7245 or email us at lostproperty@greateranglia.co.uk
TRAIN SERVICE UPDATE	For current train service information, please contact GA customer services on 0845 600 7245.
PENALTY FARES	Greater Anglia operates a Penalty Fares System on most of its network, except on designated 'paytrain' routes and from certain specified stations without ticket issuing facilities. Stations within the Penalty Fares area are identified by warning notices at each entrance. When travelling from these stations, you must have a valid ticket for your journey. For journeys where Oyster Pay as you Go (PAYG) is accepted, you must hold a valid Oyster card which has been touched in at the start of your journey. Oyster PAYG is not valid for travel outside the area where PAYG is accepted. If you cannot present a valid ticket for the journey you are making, you may be liable for a Penalty Fare (minimum £20).
DISABLED PEOPLE'S PROTECTION POLICY	Available from: Contact Centre, Greater Anglia, Norwich Station, Station Approach, Norwich NR1 1EF. Customers who require assistance are recommended to book at least 24 hours in advance on 0800 028 2878 or Textphone 0845 606 7245.
CODE OF PRACTICE FOR COMMENTS, COMPLAINTS AND SUGGESTIONS	Available from: Contact Centre, Greater Anglia, Norwich Station, Station Approach, Norwich NR1 1EF. The Greater Anglia Passenger's Charter is also available from the same address.

Heathrow Connect

HC

A joint venture between First Rail Division and BAA (Heathrow Express)

ADDRESS	Freepost RLRZ-TZXE-BYKY Heathrow Connect 6th Floor, 50 Eastbourne Terrace London W2 6LX Telephone: 0845 678 6975 Fax: 020 8750 6615 Website: www.heathrowconnect.com Email: web_customer_correspondence@baa.com
MANAGING DIRECTORS	*Heathrow Connect is a joint venture between First Great Western and BAA (Heathrow Express).* Mark Hopwood (First Great Western) Keith Greenfield (Heathrow Express)
RESERVATIONS AND TICKETS BY TELEPHONE AND ONLINE	Reservations are not necessary. Tickets can be booked by telephone on 0845 700 0125. Open 0700-2200 (0800-1900 Saturdays and Sundays). Allow 3 working days for delivery. A next day delivery can be arranged at £5 per transaction. Tickets may also be purchased through our website www.heathrowconnect.com
RESERVATION DETAILS	Reservations are not available.
CATERING ON TRAINS	Catering on trains is not available.
CYCLES	Cycles are carried free of charge, but are not allowed on trains timed to arrive at London Paddington between 0745-0945, or depart London Paddington between 1630-1830 Mondays to Fridays. In the interest of safety and customer comfort, we reserve the right to limit the number of cycles at other times.
LOST PROPERTY	Property lost at Paddington Station is collected by Network Rail, who can be contacted on 020 7313 1514. For items lost at Heathrow Airport call 020 8745 7727. For items lost on Heathrow Express trains, please ask our Customer Service Representatives, or alternatively email Heathrow Airport Lost Property at lrh.lostproperty@bagport.co.uk
TRAIN SERVICE UPDATE	For current train information call 0845 678 6975. Website: www.heathrowconnect.com
PENALTY FARES	Penalty Fares apply at stations between Hayes & Harlington and Paddington (incl). Customers are liable to a Penalty Fare of £20 to the next station stop.
DISABLED PEOPLE'S PROTECTION POLICY	This is available from Customer Relations at the above address and telephone number.
CODE OF PRACTICE FOR COMMENTS, COMPLAINTS AND SUGGESTIONS	It is our aim to try and resolve any issues or grievances on the spot. All our Customer Services Representative have a supply of comment forms and our Customer Care Line on 0845 604 15 15 can deal with any issues over the telephone or submit any comments to web_customer_correspondance@baa.com. If you wish to write with a suggestion or complain, please write to Customer Relations at the address at the top of this page, or through our website www.heathrowexpress.com

Heathrow Express

HX

ADDRESS	Heathrow Express Customer Relations FREEPOST London W2 6LG Telephone: 0845 604 1515 (call centre) Fax: 020 8750 6615 Website: www.heathrowexpress.com Email: web_customer_correspondence@baa.com
MANAGING DIRECTOR	Keith Greenfield
RESERVATIONS AND TICKETS BY TELEPHONE AND ONLINE	Reservations are not necessary on Heathrow Express services. Tickets may be purchased online and from www.heathrowexpress.com as well as our ticket offices at Heathrow Airport, Paddington station and other appointed outlets. For details call our Customer Services team on 0845 600 1515 (24 hour service - local rate call) or visit www.heathrowexpress.com
RESERVATION DETAILS	Reservations are not available.
CATERING ON TRAINS	As the overall journey time is only 15 minutes, or 21 minutes to Terminal 5, there is currently no catering on Heathrow Express services.
CYCLES	Limited accommodation is available for cycles on Heathrow Express services, for passengers flying with their cycles from the airport. Heathrow Express reserve the right to limit the number of cycles conveyed on each train to no more than three at busy times. Cyclists not travelling onwards by air may use the service to and from Heathrow Terminals, subject to space being available for airline passengers.
LOST PROPERTY	Property lost at Paddington station is collected by Network Rail, who can be contacted on 020 7313 1514. For items lost at Heathrow Airport call 020 8745 7727. For items lost on Heathrow Express trains, please ask our Customer Service Representatives, or alternatively write to: Excess Baggage Co., Heathrow Airport, Middlesex UB3 5AP or email to heathrow.lostproperty@excess-baggage.com
TRAIN SERVICE UPDATE	For current information on train services please contact our customer care line on 0845 604 15 15, or through our website www.heathrowexpress.com
PENALTY FARES	Penalty Fares do not apply on Heathrow Express services, therefore customers may join the train without having first purchased a ticket or authority to travel. Customer Service Representatives on every train will accept cash, debit and credit cards, for ticket purchase. Please note however for tickets purchased on board there is a £5.00 premium to pay. Only full fare tickets are available to purchase on board the train. (However Disabled Railcard is accepted on board).
DISABLED PEOPLE'S PROTECTION POLICY	Heathrow Express trains have been specially designed with the needs of the disabled in mind. Platforms at all our stations give level access into the trains and there is space for wheelchairs on all trains. For further information on facilities for the disabled, call the Customer Care Line on 0845 604 15 15, or write to the Managing Director at the address at the top of this page.
CODE OF PRACTICE FOR COMMENTS, COMPLAINTS AND SUGGESTIONS	It is our aim to try and resolve any issues or grievances on the spot. All our Customer Service Representatives have a supply of comment forms and our Customer Care Line on 0845 604 15 15 can deal with any issues over the telephone or submit any comments at web_customer_correspondence@baa.com. If you wish to write with a suggestion or complaint, please write to the Managing Director at the address at the top of this page, or through our website www.heathrowexpress.com

Island Line Trains

IL

ADDRESS	Friars Bridge Court 41–45 Blackfriars Road London SE1 8NZ Telephone: 08700 005151 Fax: 020 7620 5177 Website: www.southwesttrains.co.uk,www.islandlinetrains.co.uk Email: customerrelations@swtrains.co.uk
MANAGING DIRECTOR	Tim Shoveller
RESERVATIONS AND TICKETS BY TELEPHONE AND ONLINE	Reservations are not required on Island Line Trains services. Group travel information can be obtained by calling 023 8072 8162.
RESERVATION DETAILS	Reservations are not available.
CATERING ON TRAINS	There are no catering facilities on trains.
CYCLES	A maximum of 4 cycles may be carried in the Shanklin end of all trains at no extra charge. For the safety and comfort of our passengers, the guard may refuse to carry any further cycles on the train.
LOST PROPERTY	All items of lost property are retained at Ryde Esplanade Ticket Office. If you have lost an item please telephone the Ticket Office on 01983 562492 (0900-1700 Daily). A charge may be applicable on collection.
TRAIN SERVICE UPDATE	For current train information, please call our helpline on 0845 6000 650 or visit www.islandlinetrains.co.uk
PENALTY FARES	Penalty Fares are not in force on any Island Line Trains services.
DISABLED PEOPLE'S PROTECTION POLICY	Island Line Trains is committed to making travel easier for customers with disabilities including wheelchair users. For travel on the mainland, please call our Assisted Travel line on 0800 5282 100 (textphone 0800 692 0792), giving 24 hours notice before travelling. Please note that mobility scooters cannot be conveyed on any Island Line Trains Service. For journeys wholly within Island Line Trains, please telephone 01983 812591 giving 24 hours notice if assistance is required.
CODE OF PRACTICE FOR COMMENTS, COMPLAINTS AND SUGGESTIONS	Feedback leaflets are available at Ryde Esplanade or Shanklin Ticket Offices. Copies of Island Line Trains' and South West Trains' Passenger's Charters are available from any staffed station or by writing to: Customer Service Centre South West Trains Overline House Southampton SO15 1GW Telephone 0845 6000 650 Fax 023 8072 8187 Email: customerrelations@swtrains.co.uk The Passenger's Charter is also featured on the website www.islandlinetrains.co.uk and www.southwesttrains.co.uk

London Midland

LM

ADDRESS	PO Box 4323 Birmingham B2 4JB Telephone: 0844 811 0133 Website: www.londonmidland.com Email: comments@londonmidland.com
MANAGING DIRECTOR	Patrick Verwer
RESERVATIONS AND TICKETS BY TELEPHONE AND ONLINE	Tickets can be booked in advance online at www.londonmidland.com or by ringing 0844 811 0133, 0800-2000 Monday to Sunday, please allow 5 days for delivery.
RESERVATION DETAILS	Seat reservations are not available. Group travel enquiries and bookings can be made on 0844 811 0133.
CATERING ON TRAINS	Catering is not available.
CYCLES	Cycles are carried free of charge on most off-peak services, however advance reservations are required for our Birmingham–Liverpool, Birmingham-London and Crewe–London services. Cycles cannot be conveyed on trains arriving into London Euston between 0700 and 0959 and departing London Euston between 1600 and 1859 on Mondays to Fridays (excluding Bank Holidays). Folding cycles, completely folded down, are regarded as accompanied luggage and carried free.
LOST PROPERTY	Enquiries can be made at your nearest staffed station or by ringing Customer Relations on 0844 811 0133.
TRAIN SERVICE UPDATE	Available from National Rail Enquiries on 08457 48 49 50 (calls may be recorded for training purposes).
PENALTY FARES	A Penalty Fares System is in place across most of the London Midland network. If you board a service from a staffed station without a valid ticket or permit to travel, you will be liable to a £20 penalty fare or twice the standard single fare to the next station whichever is the greater. You can only purchase a ticket on-train when travelling from an unstaffed station. Details of the scheme are available at www.londonmidland.com or by writing to Customer Relations at the address below.
DISABLED PEOPLE'S PROTECTION POLICY	Available from Customer Relations London Midland PO Box 4323 Birmingham B2 4JB Telephone: 0844 811 0133
CODE OF PRACTICE FOR COMMENTS, COMPLAINTS AND SUGGESTIONS	Available from Customer Relations at the above address.

London Overground

LO

Operated by London Overground Rail Operations Ltd. (LOROL)
on behalf of Rail for London Ltd., a subsidiary of TfL

ADDRESS
125 Finchley Road
London NW3 6HY
Telephone: 0845 601 4867
Textphone 020 3031 9331
Website: www.tfl.gov.uk/overground
Email: overgroundinfo@tfl.gov.uk

MANAGING DIRECTOR
Peter Austin

RESERVATIONS AND TICKETS BY TELEPHONE AND ONLINE
Tickets may be booked in advance and seats reserved on many long distance national rail services from most London Overground ticket offices. Oyster tickets may be purchased online from https://oyster.tfl.gov.uk

RESERVATION DETAILS
Reservations are not available.

CATERING ON TRAINS
Catering is not provided on London Overground services.

CYCLES
London Overground allows folding bicycles free of charge on all trains at all times, provided it is safe to do so. Non-folding bicycles are also accepted free of charge but due to space constraints they are not permitted on the following routes between the times shown:

- Willesden Junction (High Level) and Gospel Oak in both directions Mondays to Fridays (except Public Holidays) 0700-1000 and 1600-1900
- Gospel Oak and Blackhorse Road in both directions Mondays to Fridays (except Public Holidays) 0700-1000 and 1600-1900
- Watford Junction and Euston Mondays to Fridays (except Public Holidays) on services timed to arrive at Euston 0700-1000 or depart from Euston 1600-1900
- Highbury & Islington and Clapham Jn / Crystal Palace in both directions Mondays to Fridays (except Public Holidays) 0700-1000 and 1600-1900.
- Dalston Jn and New Cross / West Croydon in both directions Mondays to Fridays (except Public Holidays) 0700-1000 and 1600-1900.

Only one bicycle is allowed per customer within a limit of one bicycle per vestibule area. Tandems and three-wheeled vehicles cannot be accomodated on any London Overground train. Only folding bicycles can be carried on buses that replace trains due to engineering work.

LOST PROPERTY
Please contact the TfL Lost Property Office at Baker Street on 0845 330 9882 or our Customer Services Team on 0845 601 4867.

TRAIN SERVICE UPDATE
Information about London Overground services and fares can be obtained by telephoning either:

- London Travel Information on 0843 222 1234
- National Rail Enquiries 08457 48 49 50 (calls may be recorded for training purposes). (Textphone 08456 050 600, 0800-2000 daily)

A wide range of information about London Overground is also available from our website: www.tfl.gov.uk/overground

PENALTY FARES
London Overground operates a Penalty Fares Scheme. If you cannot produce, on request, a valid ticket for your entire journey or, when using Oyster to pay as you go, your Oyster card containing a record of the start of your Pay as you go journey, you will be liable to pay a Penalty Fare.

DISABLED PEOPLE'S PROTECTION POLICY
This can be obtained at any London Overground station or from our Customer Services Team at the above address.

CODE OF PRACTICE FOR COMMENTS, COMPLAINTS AND SUGGESTIONS
For a copy of the London Overground Customer Charter leaflet please ask at any London Overground station or contact our Customer Services Team at the above address.

Merseyrail

ME

A Serco/Abellio company

ADDRESS	Rail House Lord Nelson Street Liverpool L1 1JF Telephone: 0151 702 2071 Website: www.merseyrail.org
MANAGING DIRECTOR	Maarten Spaargaren
RESERVATIONS AND TICKETS BY TELEPHONE AND ONLINE	Tickets may be booked in advance and seats reserved from most Merseyrail stations for National Rail Services.
RESERVATION DETAILS	Reservations are not available.
CATERING ON TRAINS	Catering is not available.
CYCLES	Cycles carried free of charge at any time, subject to sufficient space being available.
LOST PROPERTY	Please contact:- Lost Property Office James Street Station James Street Liverpool L2 7PQ Phone: 0151 702 2951
TRAIN SERVICE UPDATE	For current train information please call 08457 48 49 50 (calls may be recorded for training purposes).
PENALTY FARES	Please refer to notices displayed at stations for details of the Penalty Fare Scheme in operation or visit www.merseyrail.org/tickets/penalty-fares.html
DISABLED PEOPLE'S PROTECTION POLICY	Available from:– Customer Relations Merseyrail Rail House Lord Nelson Street Liverpool L1 1JF Phone : 0151 702 2071 (Textphone 0870 0552 681) Fax : 0151 702 2413 or email: comment@merseyrail.org
CODE OF PRACTICE FOR COMMENTS, COMPLAINTS AND SUGGESTIONS	Available from above address

North Yorkshire Moors Railway

NY

(Operators of steam and heritage services between Whitby, Grosmont, Goathland and Pickering)

ADDRESS	Pickering Station Pickering North Yorkshire YO18 7AJ Telephone: 01751-472508 (Customer Services and Information) Fax: 01751-476048 Website: www.nymr.co.uk Email: info@nymr.co.uk
GENERAL MANAGER	Philip Benham
RESERVATIONS AND TICKETS BY TELEPHONE AND ONLINE	Telephone: 01751-472508 Hours of operation: 27 December to 05 January;18 to 25 February;05 April to 02 November. 0930-1630 (Monday - Friday), 1000-1430 (Saturday and Sunday); All other times: 1000-1430 (Monday - Friday). At least 5 days should be allowed for receipt of tickets purchased online or by telephone. National Rail tickets can be booked in advance from our office in Whitby – telephone 01947 605872.
RESERVATION DETAILS	Reservations are not available on normal services. They can be made for groups of 20 or more passengers and are required on North Yorkshire Moors Railways dining train services (between Pickering and Grosmont).
CATERING ON TRAINS	An at-seat trolley service of drinks and snacks is provided on most trains.
CYCLES	Cycles and dogs are carried for a charge of £2 (subject to space being available).
LOST PROPERTY	Enquiries about lost property should be made to Pickering Station at the above, or by telephone 01751-472508.
TRAIN SERVICE UPDATE	Updated train service information on all North Yorkshire Moors Railway is available on the website (see address above). A 'talking timetable' is also available giving current details of all North Yorkshire Moors Railway services by telephoning 01751-473535.
PENALTY FARES	Penalty Fares do not apply on North Yorkshire Moors Railway.
DISABLED PEOPLE'S PROTECTION POLICY	Available from the address above, or Pickering and Grosmont Stations.
CODE OF PRACTICE FOR COMMENTS, COMPLAINTS AND SUGGESTIONS	North Yorkshire Moors Railway welcomes comments from passengers. Comments/suggestion cards are available from stations and on-board staff, or alternatively please write to the General Manager. Details of the company's policy are available from the above address, or Pickering and Grosmont Stations.

NT Northern NT

A joint venture between Serco and Abellio

ADDRESS	Northern Rail Ltd Northern House 9 Rougier Street York YO1 6HZ Telephone: 0845 00 00 125 Website: www.northernrail.org
MANAGING DIRECTOR	Alex Hynes (Managing Director)
RESERVATIONS AND TICKETS BY TELEPHONE AND ONLINE	You cannot reserve seats on Northern services.
RESERVATION DETAILS	Tickets can be purchased in advance online at www.northernrail.org. Reservations and tickets are also available from all local staffed stations. For groups of 10 or more travelling on the Leeds-Settle-Carlisle line telephone 0800 9800 766, between 0900 and 1700 on Mondays to Fridays to make a booking. All accommodation on Northern trains is Standard Class.
CATERING ON TRAINS	On most Leeds-Settle-Carlisle services, food and drink can be purchased from the trolley which will pass through the train.
CYCLES	Up to two cycles can be carried on each service. This is subject to space being available, however, and cannot be booked in advance. For further details telephone 0845 000 0125.
LOST PROPERTY	Call 0845 000 0125, contact your nearest staffed station or write to Northern at the address below.
TRAIN SERVICE UPDATE	Information about Northern services and fares can be obtained by telephoning: **08457 48 49 50** (calls may be recorded for training purposes) or access the website on www.nationalrail.co.uk For more information on our services, please visit our website on www.northernrail.org The latest information on train running is available by phoning TrainTracker™ from National Rail Enquiries on 0871 200 4915 or by texting TrainTracker™. Text to 84950.
PENALTY FARES	Penalty Fares are not in force on any Northern service.
DISABLED PERSON'S PROTECTION POLICY **Making Rail Accessible**	If you would like a copy of Northern's guide for older and disabled passengers or wish to arrange assistance for your journey, please phone: 0808 561 606. (Textphone 0845 604 5608) or by writing to Customer Relations, Northern, FREEPOST (RLSL-ABEC-BGUU), Leeds LS1 4DY or email: assistance@northernrail.org
CODE OF PRACTICE FOR COMMENTS, COMPLAINTS AND SUGGESTIONS	Please contact our Customer Helpline on 0845 000 0125, a textphone is available on 0845 604 5608. Alternatively you can write to us at: Customer Relations, Northern, FREEPOST (RLSL-ABEC-BGUU), Leeds LS1 4DY. If you would like a copy of the Northern Passenger's Charter, or Northern's guide 'Making Rail Accessible - Helping older and disabled passengers' please contact our Customer Relations team.

ScotRail

A member of the First Rail Division

ADDRESS	1st Floor Atrium Court 50 Waterloo Street Glasgow G2 6HQ Telephone: 08700 00 51 51 Fax: 0141 335 4592 Website: www.scotrail.co.uk Email: scotrailcustomer.relations@firstgroup.com
MANAGING DIRECTOR	Steve Montgomery
RESERVATIONS AND TICKETS BY TELEPHONE AND ONLINE	Tickets may be purchased in advance and Sleepers or seats reserved, by telephone, using a debit/credit card from the following number: 08457 550033 (opening hours 0700-2200) Please allow 5 days for tickets by post, tickets on departure arrangements available at selected stations. Tickets can also be purchased through the website - www.scotrail.co.uk ScotRail customers can buy selected Caledonian Sleeper tickets online - and have the ticket confirmation sent to their mobile phone. Passengers simply turn up for their train, show the text message to train staff and hop on board. A confirmatory email is sent as a back-up. This free SMS service is only available for 'Bargain Berth' tickets on the Caledonian Sleeper, which connects Scottish cities to Central London. Tickets can be booked up to 12 weeks in advance of travel - and right up until Midday on the day of travel, subject to availability. The berths start from just £19, one way.
RESERVATION DETAILS	Seat Reservations are free and can be made from 12 weeks in advance up to approximately two hours prior to the departure of the train. Reservations are mandatory on Caledonian Sleeper services and are advised on longer distance routes.
CATERING ON TRAINS	A Lounge Car is provided on all Caledonian Sleeper services offering a wide range of drinks, snacks and hot meals. A trolley service is available on many longer-distance daytime services as indicated in the timetable. To ensure a safe and enjoyable journey for all our passengers, we successfully introduced a ban on the consumption and visible carrying of alcohol between 2100 and 1000 on our daytime services - the Caledonian Sleepers are excluded.
CYCLES	Cycles are carried free on all ScotRail services subject to availability. Reservations are required on Caledonian Sleeper services and on longer distance routes. Tandems, tricycles, cycle trailers, motorcycles, mopeds or motorised cycles are not carried on any ScotRail service but folding bikes are carried on all services, provided they are folded.
LOST PROPERTY	Please phone 0141 335 3276 (0700-1900 Mon-Sat)
TRAIN SERVICE UPDATE	Register with JourneyAlert on our website: www.scotrail.co.uk/disruption Alternatively, download our mobile app by texting ScotRail to 86688.
PENALTY FARES	Penalty Fares are not in force on any ScotRail services.
DISABLED PEOPLE'S PROTECTION POLICY	Available from ScotRail Customer, PO Box 7031, Fort William PH33 6WW. Tel: 0800 912 2 901 or 18001 0800 912 2 901 Fax: 0141 335 4611 Travel arrangements may be made for disabled people by calling 0800 912 2 901*. A light travel scooter, length 104cm, width 56cm with a turning radius of 99cm and combined weight of 300kg can be conveyed. Details of station facilities and information on accessibility are available at www.nationalrail.co.uk or www.scotrail.co.uk. *For assisted travel, an advance notice is appreciated (48 hours for accessible Sleeper berth).
CODE OF PRACTICE FOR COMMENTS, COMPLAINTS AND SUGGESTIONS	ScotRail welcomes comments on the services we provide. A leaflet is available at all staffed ScotRail stations and also from the Customer Relations Manager at the address above. Tel: 0845 601 5929. Feedback can also be provided via our website. Click on the Contact Us link on our homepage.

South West Trains

SW

ADDRESS

Friars Bridge Court
41–45 Blackfriars Road
London SE1 8NZ
Telephone: 08700 005151 Fax: 020 7620 5177
Website: www.southwesttrains.co.uk
Email: customerrelations@swtrains.co.uk

MANAGING DIRECTOR

Tim Shoveller

RESERVATIONS AND TICKETS BY TELEPHONE AND ONLINE

Tickets may be booked in advance by telephone, on the following number: 0845 6000 650.

Tickets may also be purchased via the South West Trains website (see above). When ordering, please allow 5 working days for ticket delivery.

RESERVATION DETAILS

Reservations are not available.

CATERING ON TRAINS

Catering on South West Trains is provided on those services marked with the symbol for all or part of the journey. Catering may be provided from a buffet area, at seat trolley service or a combination of both according to the route and time of day. Comments on the service should be sent to the Customer Service Centre at the address below.

CYCLES

A limited number of cycles can be carried on most of our services except during the Monday to Friday peak periods. Restrictions apply on certain routes into and out of London Waterloo between 0715 and 1000 and between 1645 and 1900. At all times some services require advance reservations, as space is limited.

To obtain full details of South West Trains Cycling Policy and full details of routes and times when cycles are not carried visit www.southwesttrains.co.uk, pick up a leaflet from stations served by South West Trains or contact our Customer Service Centre at the address shown.

Cycles that can be folded to a size which allows them to be carried safely in the luggage racks on our services may be carried folded at all times.

For reasons of safety and comfort of our passengers, if the available identified cycle spaces on the train are already taken, the guard has the right to refuse to carry any further cycles on that train.

LOST PROPERTY

A lost property helpline is available between 0730-1900 Mondays to Fridays by calling 020 7401 7861

TRAIN SERVICE UPDATE

For current train information, please call our helpline on 0845 6000 650 or visit www.southwesttrains.co.uk

PENALTY FARES

South West Trains has a duty to its fare paying passengers to ensure no-one travels for free. To this end South West Trains operates a Penalty Fares Scheme across its network, with the only exceptions being Dean, Mottisfont & Dunbridge and Romsey.

Passengers travelling to and from stations within the penalty fares area without a valid ticket may be liable to a penalty of £20 or twice the single fare to the next station at which their train stops (whichever is the greater).

DISABLED PEOPLE'S PROTECTION POLICY

For a copy of this publication, please contact the Customer Service Centre at the address below.

Assistance for mobility impaired passengers can be arranged by telephoning 0800 5282 100 between 0600 - 2200 daily. Please give at least 24 hours notice.

A textphone facility is available on 0800 6920 792 (calls are charged at local rates).

CODE OF PRACTICE FOR COMMENTS, COMPLAINTS AND SUGGESTIONS

Copies of South West Trains Passenger's Charter are available from any staffed station or by writing to:
Customer Service Centre, South West Trains, Overline House, Blechynden Terrace, Southampton SO15 1GW
Telephone 0845 6000 650. Fax 023 8072 8187
Email: customerrelations@swtrains.co.uk
The Passenger's Charter is also available on our website www.southwesttrains.co.uk

Southeastern

SE

ADDRESS

Southeastern Customer Services
PO Box 63428
London SE1P 5FD
Telephone: 0845 000 2222
Assisted Travel: 0800 783 4524 (Textphone 0800 783 4548)
Fax: 0845 678 6976
Textphone: 0800 783 4548
Website: southeasternrailway.co.uk

Southeastern Customer Services is staffed 24 hours a day, seven days a week (closed Christmas Day). Comments and complaints are dealt with here by post, fax, and website as well as on the telephone.

MANAGING DIRECTOR

Charles Horton

RESERVATIONS AND TICKETS BY TELEPHONE AND ONLINE

Group travel (parties of 10 persons or more) on Southeastern services must be booked at least seven days in advance so that space can be allocated. To order, go to southeasternrailway.co.uk, select tickets, then group, then complete the online form.

Customers can buy or renew their Season Tickets for one month or longer online at southeasternrailway.co.uk or by completing the Season Ticket application form at their local ticket office.

RESERVATIONS

Reservations are not available. Reservations are only needed on Southeastern services for Group Travel and mobility impaired customers who require assistance.

CATERING ON TRAINS

Catering is available on some services.

CYCLES

Cycles are not permitted on peak time services, which are those timed to arrive in London terminals between 0700 and 0959, and those timed to leave between 1600 and 1859. Folding cycles are permitted provided they are folded.

LOST PROPERTY

Customers who have lost property on a train or at a station should contact Southeastern Customer Services on 0845 000 2222.

TRAIN SERVICE UPDATE

For current train running information contact Southeastern Customer Services on 0845 000 2222

Information is also available from national and local radio station travel updates and from our website: southeasternrailway.co.uk, select journey.

PENALTY FARES

Southeastern operate a Penalty Fares Scheme on all routes. You must buy a valid ticket (or permit to travel) for your journey before boarding a train. If you do not have a valid ticket or permit to travel, you may have to pay a Penalty Fare of £20.00 or twice the single fare, whichever is the greater. Please pick up a Penalty Fare leaflet from a staffed station for your information.

DISABLED PEOPLE'S PROTECTION POLICY

Copies of 'Making Rail Accessible' are available from any Southeastern sales point and Southeastern Customer Services.

If you have any special needs and would like help with planning your journey anywhere in Great Britain please call 0800 783 4524 or use the Textphone 0800 783 4548 - open 24 hours a day.

The Southeastern Assisted Travel team will offer advice and make any special arrangements you need. If at least 24 hours' notice can be given, this will be very much appreciated.

CODE OF PRACTICE FOR COMMENTS, COMPLAINTS AND SUGGESTIONS

Southeastern Passengers' Charter leaflets are available at any Southeastern sales point or Southeastern Customer Services at the address shown above.

Southern

SN

ADDRESS	Southern Customer Services PO Box 3021 Bristol BS2 2BS Telephone: 08451 27 29 20 (Customer Services) Fax: 08451 27 29 30 (Customer Services) Website: www.southernrailway.com Email: comments@southernrailway.com
MANAGING DIRECTOR	Chris Burchell
RESERVATIONS AND TICKETS BY TELEPHONE AND ONLINE	Advance Tickets are available from the Southern website.
RESERVATION DETAILS	Reservations are only required for Advance tickets. These reservations authorise the holder to travel on the specified train but do not identify individual seats.
CATERING ON TRAINS	A light refreshment of food and drinks is available on trains marked with ⊤ in the timetable.
CYCLES	Fully folded cycles are welcome on Southern services at anytime and should be fully folded and carried before going through the gateline. Non folding cycles cannot be conveyed on Southern weekday trains scheduled to arrive into London/Brighton or Kensington Olympia between 0700 and 1000 or depart from London/Brighton or Kensington Olympia between 1600 and 1900 Monday to Friday. See www.southernrailway.com/cyclepolicy for full details including a map identifying where cycles can be carried at any time subject to space being available.
LOST PROPERTY	Please call our lost property office on 08451 27 29 20 "and select option 6"
TRAIN SERVICE UPDATE	For train running information and timetable enquires contact National Rail Enquiries on 08457 48 49 50
PENALTY FARES	Southern operates a Penalty Fares Scheme on all routes. You must buy a valid ticket (or permit to travel) for your journey before boarding a train. If you do not have a valid ticket or permit to travel, you may have to pay a Penalty Fare of £20.00 or twice the single fare, whichever is the greater. Please pick up a Penalty Fare leaflet from a staffed station for your information.
DISABLED PEOPLE'S PROTECTION POLICY	Available from Southern Customer Services at PO Box 3021 Bristol BS2 2BS. "or online at www.southernrailway.com/accessibility" To get advice about accessible travel or to book assistance please call 0800 136 1016; Minicom/textphone – 0800 138 1018, Fax – 0800 138 1017
CODE OF PRACTICE FOR COMMENTS, COMPLAINTS AND SUGGESTIONS	A copy of our Passengers Charter is available from our website or by contacting our customer service team. If you wish to contact us for information, to make a comment, suggestion or complaint you can call, email or write to us (details above) or pick up a comments form from any of our staffed stations.

VT	Virgin Trains	VT

VT Virgin Trains VT

The trading name of West Coast Trains Ltd

ADDRESS	Virgin Trains 85 Smallbrook Queensway Birmingham B5 4HA Telephone: 0845 000 8000 Textphone: 0121 654 7528 Website: www.virgintrains.com Email: customer.relations@virgintrains.co.uk
CHIEF EXECUTIVE	Tony Collins
RESERVATIONS AND TICKETS BY TELEPHONE AND ONLINE	Buy tickets for Virgin Trains and any other train company in Great Britain on the internet at www.virgintrains.com or by calling 0871 977 4222 (calls to this number cost 10p a minute from a BT landline; calls from other operators may vary and cost more) - between 0800 and 2200 7 days a week. If you have a disability or have specific needs and wish to arrange assistance on your journey call the Virgin Trains JourneyCare service on 08457 44 33 66 (Textphone 08457 44 33 67) between 0800 and 2200 every day except Christmas Day or Boxing Day.
RESERVATION DETAILS	You are strongly advised to make a Seat Reservation in advance. Reservations can be made for the Quiet Zone carriage, where customers should refrain from using mobile phones or creating unnecessary noise. On routes to and from London, Standard Class Quiet Zone is in coach A and in coach H for First Class. On other routes, Quiet Zone is located in Standard Class, coach F. Seat reservations are free of charge.
CATERING ON TRAINS	In First Class on a Pendolino from Monday to Friday customers can enjoy a selection of snacks throughout the day, including a cooked breakfast on many morning peak services. In addition, Fairtrade tea, Fairtrade coffee, soft drinks and alcoholic drinks (alcohol is not offered with breakfast services) are served at seat throughout the day. A complimentary newspaper is also available. In First Class on Super Voyager from Monday to Friday customers can enjoy complimentary light refreshments, including Fairtrade tea, Fairtrade coffee, soft drinks and a newspaper with an at-seat service available, on most services. In Standard, we have a wide range of snacks and sandwiches, Fairtrade teas, fresh ground Fairtrade coffee, soft and alcoholic drinks and a selection of non-food items available at our onboard shop. The shop is generally open throughout. Pendolinos offer an at-seat trolley service to standard customers on Mondays to Fridays. For more information about our onboard service pick up a copy of Travelling with Virgin Trains.
CYCLES	Subject to availability of space cycles can be carried on all trains. Most trains can carry 3 cycles, and on journeys to and from London Euston, Pendolinos can carry tandems (however, tandems are not carried on Voyager services). An advance reservation is required for all journeys.
LOST PROPERTY	Call Customer Relations on 0845 000 8000 – 0830 to 1800 Mondays to Fridays, 0900 to 1600 Saturdays, answerphone available at all other times.
TRAIN SERVICE UPDATE	Details of any disruption to services or weekend engineering work are summarised on BBCi on digital TV. Details of Engineering work can also be found at www.virgintrains.com.
PENALTY FARES	Penalty Fares are not applicable on any Virgin Trains service.
DISABLED PEOPLE'S PROTECTION POLICY	Our Customer Relations Manager (at the address above) will be pleased to supply a free copy of the Disabled People's Protection Policy. It can also be downloaded at www.virgintrains.com. For information on station accessibility and to arrange special help please contact Virgin Trains JourneyCare (details above).
CODE OF PRACTICE FOR COMMENTS, COMPLAINTS AND SUGGESTIONS	We want you to tell us what you think of our service, good or bad. A copy of our Code of Practice for handling comments, complaints and suggestions together with Virgin Trains Passenger's Charter is available free on request from our Customer Relations Manager at the above address.

West Coast Railway Company

WR

(Operators of the 'Jacobite' and 'Cambrian' Steam Services)

ADDRESS	Jesson Way Carnforth Lancashire LA5 9UR Telephone: 01524 737751/737753 Fax: 01524 735518 Website: www.westcoastrailways.co.uk Email: jacobite@wcrc.co.uk
GENERAL MANAGER	Mrs Pat Marshall
COMMERCIAL MANAGER	James Shuttleworth
RESERVATIONS AND TICKETS BY TELEPHONE AND ONLINE	Advance bookings are recommended and can be made on line, at www.westcoastrailways.co.uk, by post (enclose SAE) to the Carnforth Office (address above) or by telephone, on 01524 737751/737753, during normal office hours. Credit cards accepted. Tickets can also be purchased from the WCR Guard/Train Manager, on the train, on the day of travel (subject to availablility).
RESERVATION DETAILS	Phone 01524 737751/737753
CATERING ON TRAINS	A buffet service, serving hot and cold drinks and cold snacks, is available on all trains.
CYCLES	Cycles carried free of charge, subject to space.
LOST PROPERTY	Telephone: 01524 737751/737753
PENALTY FARES	Penalty Fares do not apply on West Coast Railway Services.
TRAIN SERVICE UPDATE	For current train information please phone 08457 48 49 50 (calls may be recorded for training purposes).
DISABLED PEOPLE'S PROTECTION POLICY	Available from the above address.
CODE OF PRACTICE FOR COMMENTS, COMPLAINTS AND SUGGESTIONS	West Coast Railway Company welcomes comments on services provided. Write to Carnforth office (address above).

NR Network Rail NR

ADDRESS	King's Place York Way London N1 9AG Telephone: 020 7557 8000 Fax: 020 7557 9000 Website: www.networkrail.co.uk
CHIEF EXECUTIVE	David Higgins

Network Rail is responsible for operating 17 managed stations, indicated in the index by the code **NR**. Details of facilities provided, including the Disabled Peoples Protection Policy, are obtainable from the Network Rail Station Manager at the following station addresses:–

London Bridge	Network Rail Offices, Platform 14, London Bridge Station, Station Approach, London SE1 9SP
London Cannon Street	Cannon Street Station, Cannon Street, London EC4N 6AP
London Charing Cross	Network Rail Offices, Charing Cross Station, The Strand, London WC2 5HS
London Euston	Room 430, Stephenson Room, East Colonnade, Euston, London NW1 2RT
London Fenchurch Street	Network Rail Office, Fenchurch Place, London EC3M 4AJ
London King's Cross	Room 304, West Side Offices, King's Cross Station, London N1 9AP
London Liverpool Street	Network Rail Station Reception, Platform 10, Liverpool Street Station, London EC2M 7PY
London Paddington	Room B115, Tournament House, Paddington Station, London W2 1FT
London Victoria	3rd Floor, Kent Side Offices, Victoria Station, London SW1V 1JU
London Waterloo	CP2-4-G General Offices, Waterloo Station, London SE1 8SW
Birmingham New Street	Reception, Network Rail Offices, Station Forecourt, Birmingham New Street Station, Birmingham B2 4ND
Edinburgh	Room 255, North Block, Waverley Station, Edinburgh EH1 1BB
Glasgow Central	Glasgow Central Station, Gordon Street, Glasgow G1 3SL
Leeds	Room 405, Administration Block, Leeds City Station, Leeds LS1 4DY
Manchester Piccadilly	9th Floor, Piccadilly Tower, Piccadilly Station, Manchester M60 7RA
Liverpool Lime Street	Station Manager, The Barrier Line Building, Liverpool Lime Street Station, Liverpool L1 1JF
London St Pancras International	Station Reception, St Pancras International Station, Pancras Road, London NW1 2QP

Staffed Left Luggage facilities, offering maximum security, are available at all Network Rail Stations.

If you wish to raise any issue concerning the rail infrastructure or the 17 managed stations operated by Network Rail (excluding matters concerning the running of trains or ticket purchase) please call the national 24 hour Helpline:- **08457 11 41 41**

Other Addresses

Department for Transport

Great Minster House, 33 Horseferry Road, London SW1P 4DR

Telephone: 0300 330 3000

Email: rail@dft.gsi.gov.uk

Office of Rail Regulation

One Kemble Street, London WC2B 4AN

Telephone: 020 7282 2000

Fax: 020 7282 2040

Chair of the Board: Anna Walker
Chief Executive: Richard Price

The main areas of the Regulator's statutory functions are:

- the issue, modification and enforcement of licences to operate trains, networks, stations and light maintenance depots;
- the approval of agreements for access by operators of railway assets to track, stations and light maintenance depots;
- the enforcement of domestic competition law; and consumer protection including a duty under the Railways Act 1993 in relation to the protection of the interests of users of railway services, including the disabled.

Publications are available from:

Sue MacSwan, The Library, ORR, 1 Waterhouse Square, 138–142 Holborn, London EC1N 2TQ

Telephone: 020 7282 2001

Email: rail.library@orr.gsi.gov.uk

Association of Train Operating Companies (ATOC)

2nd Floor, 200 Aldersgate Street,London,EC1A 4HD.

Telephone: 020 7841 8000

Chief Executive: Michael Roberts

ATOC represents the interests of most of the national and international passenger Train Operating Companies whose services are shown in this timetable. It manages a range of network services, products and responsibilities on behalf of these train operators including:

- the National Rail Conditions of Carriage (the passenger's contract with the train operators)
- the National Rail Enquiries Service
- the licensing of rail appointed travel agents
- National Railcards, the London Travelcard and Network Railcard.

London Underground Limited

Head Office

55 Broadway, London SW1H 0BD

Telephone: 020 7222 5600

Responsible for the operation of stations indicated in the Stations Index by the code **LT**

How to Cross London

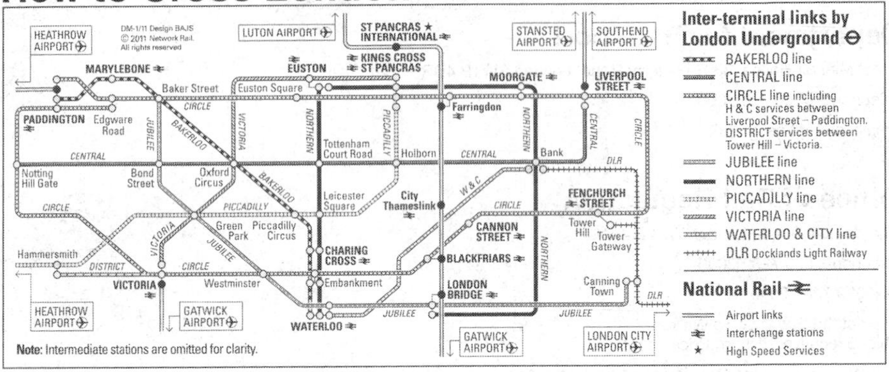

Introduction

The time taken to travel between London's stations will vary from journey to journey dependent on distance, mode of transport, time of day and the need to change en route. The quickest way to cross London is usually by the Underground network with frequent services operating between the following hours*:

- 0530 to 0015 on Monday to Friday
- 0630 to 0115 on Saturday
- 0700 to 0001 on Sunday

(* Times shown are approximate)

Buses also link many of London's main terminal stations including an extensive network of Night Bus services.

Ticket & Fares

Rail tickets for journeys routed via London are valid for transfer by London Underground or First Capital Connect services between London terminal stations, and other designated interchange stations* appropriate to the route of the through journey being made, at no extra cost. For example a Brighton to Leeds ticket is valid on London Underground services from Victoria to Kings Cross (Victoria Line), or alternatively on First Capital Connect services to St Pancras International. A Chelmsford to Southampton ticket is valid on London Underground services to Waterloo via either Liverpool Street (Circle Line) or Stratford (Jubilee Line).

(*NB. check on which cross London routes your ticket is valid before you travel. A break of journey is permitted at an intermediate Underground station, but a further ticket must be purchased in order to continue the journey)

London's Fare Zones – National Rail, Underground and Docklands Light Railway (DLR) stations within the Greater London area are in one of nine Fare Zones. Single and return tickets are available for through journeys to and from all Underground and DLR stations with prices determined by the number of zones crossed or travelled through.

A range of day and longer period Travelcards are also available and provide unlimited travel on National Rail, London Underground, London Overground, Docklands Light Railway and Tramlink services within the Fare Zones for which they are valid. All Travelcards, irrespective of the zones for which they are issued, can also be used on any London bus displaying this sign ⊖.

For information on ticket prices and availability contact your local staffed station, call National Rail Enquiries anytime on **08457 48 49 50*** (Textphone **0845 60 50 600**), or visit www.nationalrail.co.uk. * Calls may be recorded for training purposes.

More detailed information about London's Underground and Bus services, also Docklands Light Railway and London Tramlink is available anytime from London Travel Information on **0843 222 1234** (textphone **020 7918 3015**) or visit **www.tfl.gov.uk**.

First Capital Connect and Southeastern

First Capital Connect operates fast, direct services from Bedford, Luton and St Albans via Central London to East Croydon, Gatwick Airport and Brighton and stopping trains between Luton, St Albans, North London, the City, Streatham, Wimbledon and Sutton. There are nine Central London First Capital Connect stations with Underground connections. First Capital Connect connects with East Midlands Trains at Luton, Luton Airport Parkway, London St Pancras and Bedford – see Tables 52 and 53.

Southeastern, in partnership with First Capital Connect also operate trains between Kentish Town, the City and Sevenoaks and at peak times between Bedford, Luton, the City and various destinations in Kent.

London Overground

Direct trains run between:

- Richmond and Stratford
- Clapham Junction and Willesden Jn/ Stratford
- Watford Junction and Euston
- Gospel Oak and Barking
- Highbury & Islington and Clapham Jn/ Crystal Palace
- Dalston Junction and New Cross/ West Croydon

Southern Services

Direct trains are provided between South Croydon,South London, Clapham Junction and stations to Watford Junction and Milton Keynes Central. These trains also stop at Imperial Wharf, West Brompton, Kensington (Olympia) and Shepherd's Bush. See table 176.

These trains provide connections to most of the Southern network at Clapham Junction.

Passengers requiring step free interchange for Southern main line trains to Gatwick Airport and the Sussex Coast should change at East Croydon, and step free interchange for Southern Metro trains is usually available at Balham.

Interchange for the West Midlands and North West is available at either Watford Junction or Milton Keynes Central.

Cross London Transfer Times (in minutes)

	Blackfriars	Cannon Street	Charing Cross	Euston	Farringdon	Fenchurch Street*	Kings Cross	Liverpool Street	London Bridge	Marylebone	Paddington	St Pancras International †	Victoria	Waterloo
Blackfriars	–	23	23	49	(b)	27	(b)	40	(b)	45	49	(b)	44	40
Cannon Street	23	–	34	60	44	30	55	43	(a)	56	60	58	55	51
Charing Cross	23	34	–	44	n/a	38	50	51	(a)	38	43	52	47	(a)
Euston	49	60	44	–	n/a	57	35	43	52	51	43	38	54	53
Farringdon	(b)	44	n/a	n/a	–	40	n/a	29	(b)	45	39	n/a	n/a	n/a
Fenchurch Street*	27	30	38	57	40	–	52	26	47	68	60	52	68	56
Kings Cross	(b)	55	50	35	n/a	52	–	41	50	50	45	30	56	55
Liverpool Street	40	43	51	43	29	26	41	–	49	56	55	41	63	62
London Bridge	(b)	(a)	(a)	52	(b)	47	50	49	–	58	62	60	n/a	(a)
Marylebone	45	56	38	51	45	68	50	56	58	–	32	53	58	47
Paddington	49	60	43	43	39	60	45	55	62	32	–	45	62	51
St Pancras International †	(b)	58	52	38	(b)	52	30	41	60	53	45	–	56	61
Victoria	44	55	47	54	n/a	68	56	63	n/a	58	62	56	–	62
Waterloo	40	51	(a)	53	n/a	56	55	62	(a)	47	51	61	62	–

All times are based on use of London Underground services and are shown as a guide only – extra time should be allowed during the early morning/late evening and on Sundays.

* Tower Hill Underground Station
† An additional 35 minutes should be allowed for Eurostar Connections
(a) Direct train services available (operated by Southeastern)
(b) Direct train services available (operated by First Capital Connect)
n/a Transfer not likely to be required as part of a through rail journey

Some other useful transfers

If your journey requires a transfer between any of the following pairs of stations, you should allow a margin of at least the number of minutes shown when planning connections. All transfers are assumed to be by foot unless otherwise stated.

Ash Vale – North Camp	19
Bicester North – Town	30
Burnley Central – Manchester Rd	25
Burscough Bridge – Junction	20
Canterbury East – West	25
Catford – Bridge	10
Clock House – Kent House	15
Dorchester South – West	15
Dorking – Dorking Deepdene	9
East Croydon – West Croydon	25
Edenbridge – Edenbridge Town	20
Enfield Chase – Town	29
Falkirk High – Grahamston	44
Farnborough Main – North	24
Forest Gate – Wanstead Park	13
Gainsborough Central – Lea Rd	33
Hackney Central – Downs	14
Harringay – Green Lanes	14
Heath High Level – Low Level	10
Hertford North – East	34
Maidstone Barracks – East	16
New Mills Central – Newtown	25
Penge East – West	19
Purley Oaks – Sanderstead	10
Seven Sisters – South Tottenham	14
Southend Central – Victoria	17
Upper Warlingham – Whyteleafe	10
Walthamstow Central – Queen's Rd	14
West Hampstead – Thameslink	11
Windsor & Eton Central – Riverside	14
Yeovil Junction – Yeovil Pen Mill	15*
Glasgow Central-Glasgow Queen Street	15

* This is a bus service which runs every 30 mins between 0700 and 1900 Mondays to Saturdays.

For table numbers of trains to and from London please see the end of the Station Index section

Airport Links

Aberdeen Airport

Aberdeen Airport is close to Dyce station, from where trains operate to Aberdeen, Elgin and Inverness. There are also some direct trains to Glasgow and Edinburgh. A shuttle bus runs between Dyce station and the airport, connecting with most trains during the day.

For full bus timetable information, call **0871 200 22 33**, or visit **www.travelinescotland.com**

Birmingham International Airport

Birmingham Airport is alongside Birmingham International station. The free Air-Rail Link transit system operates to the passenger terminals about every 2 minutes with a journey time of less than 2 minutes. Birmingham International station is served by direct trains from London Euston and Manchester Piccadilly. In addition a frequent service operates between Birmingham New Street and Birmingham International providing connections at Birmingham New Street to and from all parts of the country. (See Tables 65, 66, 68, 71, 74 and 116). Regular buses operated by National Express West Midlands (966) also run from Solihull station (see Tables 71 and 115) and through fares are available by purchasing a PlusBus ticket. The journey time is approximately 20 minutes and through ticketing is available. Solihull is served by Chiltern Railways services from London Marylebone, Gerrards Cross, Beaconsfield, High Wycombe, Princes Risborough, Haddenham & Thame Parkway, Bicester North, Banbury, Leamington Spa and Warwick and by London Midland local services.

Bournemouth (Hurn) International Airport

Bournemouth (Hurn) International Airport now has an hourly bus service to and from Bournemouth station. See www.bournemouth-airport-shuttle.co.uk or phone 01202 557007 for details.

Bristol International Airport

The Bristol Airport Flyer is the only express link between Bristol Temple Meads station, Bristol Bus Station, Clifton and Bristol Airport. The journey time to the city centre is approximately 30 minutes with services operating (every 10 minutes at Peak times) daily between 0230 and 0045.

Cardiff International Airport

The airport is served by a bus link from Rhoose Cardiff International Rail Station to/from the airport is operated by New Adventure Travel. Full details of the timetable and further information can be obtained from Traveline on **0871 200 22 33** or visit **www.traveline.info.**

Bus Service T9 also operates from Cardiff Central Bus Station (Stand D1) directly to the airport. Journey time is approximately 30 minutes and buses operate every 20 minutes durring the daytime everyday.Through ticketing is available.

Durham Tees Valley Airport

Durham Tees Valley Airport is located 7 miles east of Darlington Rail station. For information about Durham Tees Valley Airport visit www.durhamteesvalleyairport.com.

From Darlington - Arriva service 12 operates half-hourly throughout the day Mondays to Saturdays and hourly early mornings, evenings and Sundays, from Parkgate outside Darlington Station direct to the airport site. Journey time is approximately 25 minutes.

Please note that when the service is operating two buses an hour that one bus an hour serves the airport terminal directly whilst the other terminates at the hotel on the airport site. The hotel is a 10-minute walk from the terminal building.

For more information please telephone Traveline on **0871 200 22 33** or visit **www.traveline.info**

East Midlands Airport

East Midlands Airport is located close to East Midlands Parkway Station, served by East Midlands Trains.
A taxi transfer service operates between East Midlands Parkway and the Airport.

From Nottingham - a Skylink bus operates with a journey time of approximately 55 minutes; and from Long

From Derby – a Kinch bus service operates with a journey time of approximately 20 minutes.

Eaton with a journey time of approximately 20mins.
A bus add-on ticket is available. For more information, please telephone Traveline on 0871 200 2233 or visit traveline.info

Edinburgh Airport

There are two ways to get to Edinburgh Airport by rail and bus:

- If you are travelling from Fife, Dundee and other areas north, you should catch a train to Inverkeithing – from here a frequent bus service operates to Edinburgh Airport
- If you are travelling from other parts of Scotland, including the Glasgow area, you should catch a train to Haymarket or Edinburgh Waverley – a frequent bus service operates to Edinburgh Airport from both these stations

For full bus timetable information, call **0871 200 22 33**, or visit **www.travelinescotland.com**

Exeter International Airport

Stagecoach operates an hourly daytime service (Service Number 56) from Exeter St. Davids station forecourt direct to Exeter Airport. For more information call Traveline on **0871 200 22 33** or visit **www.traveline.info.**

Airport Links (continued)

Glasgow Airport

There are three ways to get to Glasgow Airport by rail and bus:

- If you are travelling from Ayrshire or Inverclyde, you should catch a train to Paisley Gilmour Street – a frequent bus service operates from here to Glasgow Airport
- If you are travelling from north west Glasgow, Milngavie, Dumbarton, Helensburgh and the West Highlands, you should catch a train to Partick – from here a frequent bus service operates to Glasgow Airport
- If you are travelling from other parts of Scotland, including Edinburgh and the central belt, you should catch a train to Glasgow Central or Glasgow Queen Street – a frequent bus service operates to Glasgow Airport from both these stations

For full bus timetable information, call **0871 200 22 33**, or visit **www.travelinescotland.com**

Leeds Bradford International Airport

Leeds Bradford International Airport is located to the north of the cities of Bradford and Leeds, to the south of Harrogate and to the west of York. For more information on Leeds Bradford International Airport visit **www.leedsbradfordairport.co.uk**

From Leeds - Centrebus Airport Direct 757, operates half hourly throughout the day Mondays to Saturdays (hourly early mornings, evenings and Sundays) every day from Stand S7 from outside Leeds Rail Station (Leeds Station Interchange). The journey time is approximately 40 minutes. Through ticketing is available.

From Bradford - a half hourly combined service, provided by Centrebus Airport Direct services 737 and 747, operates throughout the day from Bradford Interchange rail station. Airport Direct 747 also operates close to Bradford Forster Square rail station (hourly). The journey time from Bradford is approximately 40 minutes. Through ticketing is available with a PlusBus ticket.

From Harrogate - Airport Direct 737, operates hourly, every day from Harrogate Bus Station to the airport. The journey time from Harrogate is approximately 35 minutes.

From York - There is no bus service between York and the airport. If you are travelling from the North East, please travel via Leeds, purchasing a combined rail and bus travel ticket.

Centrebus Airport Direct services 737, 747 and 757 run alongside other local bus services which link to Leeds Bradford International Airport.

For more information please telephone Traveline on **0871 200 22 33** or visit **www.traveline.info**

Liverpool John Lennon Airport

Regular bus services operate between Liverpool John Lennon Airport and the Liverpool South Parkway station; journey time is 10 minutes. Liverpool South Parkway is served by direct services from North, South and East Liverpool, Leeds, York, Sheffield, Nottingham, Manchester, Warrington, Southport, Crewe, Stafford, Wolverhampton and Birmingham.

The airport is located to the south of the city centre. A direct bus service operates between Lime Street, Moorfields and James Street stations to the airport seven days a week. Buses run every 30 minutes between 0600 & 0100 hours from the Liverpool City Centre Stations to the Airport, and between 0515 and 0015 from the Airport to the Liverpool City Centre Stations. Journey time is approximately 45 minutes.

For further information please contact **0871 200 22 33**, or visit **www.traveline.info**.

London City Airport

London City Airport is located in London's Docklands, to the east of the capital. There are no National Rail services direct to the airport.

Access to the airport is available via the Docklands Light Railway to and from London City Airport Station which is located next to the terminal building. Between Central London and the airport, passengers can travel on the London Underground Jubilee Line and change at Canning Town for the Docklands Light Railway. Connections between National Rail and the Docklands Light Railway are available at Greenwich, Lewisham, Limehouse, Stratford and Woolwich Arsenal.

For further information on London City Airport telephone **020 7646 0088** or visit **www.londoncityairport.com**.

London Gatwick Airport

Gatwick has its own railway station underneath the South Terminal. Access to the North Terminal is via a free transit.

Airport to/from London

Gatwick Express operate a dedicated non-stop service every 15 minutes throughout most of the day between London Victoria and Gatwick Airport (See Table 186).

Southern provides frequent trains throughout the day and hourly throughout the night between London Victoria and Gatwick Airport (See Table 186).

First Capital Connect operate direct services throughout the day between London St Pancras International, Farringdon, City Thameslink, London Blackfriars, London Bridge and Gatwick Airport (generally every 15 mins, See Table 52), a reduced frequency operates throughout the night.

Airport to/from Reading

First Great Western operate a direct rail service between Reading and Gatwick – (See Table 148). Customers using this route should allow at least 7 minutes at Reading to make a connection.

Other direct services to/from Airport

Southern also operates direct services to/from Hastings, Southampton, Portsmouth and intermediate stations on the South Coast (See Tables 186, 188, 189) Clapham Jn and East Croydon (SeeTable 186).

First Great Western operate services from Wokingham, North Camp and Guildford (See Table 148).

Airport Links (continued)

First Capital Connect provide regular direct services from Gatwick Airport to St. Albans, Luton, Bedford, East Croydon, Haywards Heath and Brighton (See Table 52). At Luton Airport Parkway, Luton and Bedford, they also offer convenient connections with East Midlands Trains to Leicester, Derby, Nottingham and Sheffield (See Table 53).

London Heathrow Airport

Airport to/from Central London

Heathrow Express operates a direct high-speed rail service from the Airport to London Paddington. Stations are located in all Heathrow terminals - Heathrow Central (Terminals 1, 2 & 3), Terminal 4 and Terminal 5. Journey time is 15 minutes between Paddington and Terminals 1, 2 and 3, with a further 6 minutes to Terminal 5. Trains run every 15 minutes. A free transfer service operates to Terminal 4 from Heathrow Central, departing every 15 minutes and arriving in 4 minutes.

- 0510 to 2325 from Paddington
- 0507 to 2342 from Heathrow Terminal 5 (0503 to 2348 on Sundays)
- 0512 to 2348 from Heathrow Terminal 1, 2 and 3 (0508 to 2353 on Sundays)

For further details see Table 118.

Through tickets can be purchased from any National Rail or London Underground Station to the airport via Heathrow Express.

For further information visit **www.heathrowexpress.com**.

Heathrow Connect operates a local rail service every 30 minutes between Heathrow Central and London Paddington, calling at Hayes & Harlington, Southall, Hanwell, West Ealing and Ealing Broadway. For details see Table 117.

Through tickets are available from most stations.

The London Underground Piccadilly Line connects central London with all five terminals (Terminal 1/2/3, Terminal 4 and Terminal 5).

Through single and return tickets can be issued to customers travelling via a Rail terminus in Zone 1. Sample journey time from Piccadilly Circus to the Airport is approximately one hour.

Airport to/from Reading

RailAir coaches leave from Reading railway station every 20 minutes during the daytime on Mondays to Fridays (every 30 minutes early weekday mornings and evenings, on weekends and public holidays). The luxury, air-conditioned coaches run non-stop to Terminals 1, 2 and 3 in 40-50 minutes. On the return journey from Heathrow Airport they only pick up passengers at Heathrow Central Bus Station (stands one and two) and not the terminals. Customers travelling to/from Terminal 4 should use Heathrow Connect from Terminal 1.

Follow the RailAir signs from your platform at Reading station. You can buy your ticket in the RailAir lounge, or combined rail and coach tickets are also available from many stations. You should allow 15 minutes at Reading to transfer between train and coach.

For further information telephone **0118 957 9425** or visit **www.RailAir.com.**

Airport to/from Woking

Coaches leave at half-hourly intervals throughout most of the day to/from Terminal 5 and Heathrow Central Bus Station (for Terminals 1, 2 and 3) (see Table 158A).

Customers travelling to Heathrow should exit on platform 5 and the coach leaves from outside the station.

On arrival at Woking customers should allow at least 10 minutes to transfer to your train after the arrival of the coach at the station. Combined rail and coach tickets are available from most National Rail stations and from the Railair sales points at the airport. Tickets may also be booked at **www.nationalexpress.com** or by calling **08717 818 181**. For through trains and coach times, telephone **08457 48 49 50.** (calls may be recorded for training purposes)

Airport to/from Feltham

London Buses operates frequent bus services from Feltham Station to Heathrow Airport. Route 285 operates to Hatton Cross and Heathrow Central Bus Station for Terminals 1, 2 and 3. Buses operate every 10 minutes during the day, 15 minutes in the evenings and on Sundays and 30 minutes throughout the night.

Route 490 operates to Hatton Cross and Terminals 4 and 5. Buses operate every 12 minutes during the day, 20 minutes in the evenings and on Sundays.

Customers should allow 10 minutes at Feltham to transfer between train and bus from the station forecourt adjoining platform 1.

Other direct services to/from Airport

A coach service, Green Line 724, runs throughout the day between Heathrow, West Drayton, Uxbridge, Rickmansworth, Watford, St. Albans, Hatfield, Welwyn Garden City, Hertford and Harlow. Tickets can only be purchased on the coach. A frequent bus service (route 140) runs 24 hours between Hayes & Harlington and Heathrow Airport (Central Bus Station).

For further information telephone **0870 608 7261** (Green Line Travel Information)

London Luton Airport

A frequent dedicated shuttle bus links Luton Airport with Luton Airport Parkway station - journey time 10 minutes. Luton Airport Parkway is served by frequent First Capital Connect services direct to Bedford, Central London, South London, Gatwick Airport and Brighton – see Table 52 for details. East Midlands Trains services link Luton Airport Parkway with St Pancras International and Leicester, Derby, Nottingham and Sheffield – see Table 53 for details.

In addition a coach link operates between the Airport, Luton railway station and town centre and Milton Keynes Central railway station and town centre.

Airport Links (continued)

London Stansted Airport

Stansted Airport has its own railway station right in the heart of the airport terminal building.

The Stansted Express is a dedicated rail service operating between London Liverpool Street and Stansted Airport station (See Table 22). Trains run every 15 minutes throughout the day, seven days per week.

CrossCountry operates an hourly express service seven days a week between Birmingham and Stansted Airport calling at Leicester, Peterborough and Cambridge – see Table 49 – offering connections with services to Yorkshire and the North East. Customers should be advised to arrive at the airport 1 hour 45 minutes prior to their latest check-in time.

London Southend Airport

Southend Airport is served by its own brand new station adjacent to the airport, operated by Stobart Group. The station is served by trains on the London Liverpool Street to Southend Victoria line, generally every 20 minutes (every 10 minutes at peak times). Journey times to and from London are 52-54 minutes off-peak (55-56 minutes at peak times) and 62 minutes on Sundays.

Manchester Airport

The airport railway station is right in the heart of the airport complex, linked by covered travellators. The station is served by up to 8 trains per hour from Manchester Piccadilly and direct services operate between Middlesbrough, Newcastle, York, Leeds, Huddersfield, Cleethorpes, Doncaster, Sheffield, Edinburgh, Glasgow, Carlisle, Barrow-in-Furness, Windermere, Lancaster, Preston, Liverpool and the Airport. Additional regular services operate during the day, to/from many stations which can be found under the entry for Manchester Airport in the index in this timetable.

Newcastle Airport

Tyne & Wear Metro trains operate every 12 - 15 minutes most of the day between Newcastle Central Station and Newcastle Airport providing links with Northern, East Coast, First TransPennine Express and CrossCountry services. The journey time is about 25 minutes.

Tyne & Wear Metro services also run to Sunderland Rail station, a journey time of about an hour providing connections with Northern and Grand Central services.

Through ticketing is available to Newcastle Airport via the Tyne & Wear Metro.

For information please telephone Traveline on **0871 200 22 33** or visit **www.traveline.info**

Prestwick International Airport

Prestwick International Airport has its own rail station, served by fast and frequent trains from Glasgow, Paisley, Ayr and intermediate stations.

See Table 221 for details.

Robin Hood Airport

Doncaster Airport or Doncaster Sheffield

Robin Hood Airport is situated 7 miles south of Doncaster. For more information on Robin Hood Airport visit **www.robinhoodairport.com**

From Doncaster - First service 91 runs half hourly throughout the day Mondays to Saturdays, hourly early mornings, evenings and Sundays from Doncaster Frenchgate Interchange, which is adjacent to Doncaster Rail station, direct to the airport. Journey time is approximately 25 minutes.

Through ticketing is available to Robin Hood Airport via service 91.

Service 91 runs alongside other local bus services which link to Robin Hood Airport, including service X19 from Barnsley.

For more information please telephone Traveline on **0871 200 22 33** or visit **www.traveline.info**

Southampton Airport

Southampton Airport (Parkway) station is adjacent to Southampton Airport.

South West Trains operate up to 3 trains per hour between London Waterloo, Winchester and Southampton Airport (Parkway) with up to 2 direct services to Bournemouth, Poole, Wareham and Weymouth and most intermediate stations (See Table 158).

CrossCountry services link Southampton Airport Parkway with Bournemouth, Reading, Oxford, Newcastle and Manchester (see Table 51).

On Saturdays Southern operate trains every two hours between Brighton, Worthing, Chichester, Havant, Cosham, Fareham and Southampton Airport, at other times use Southern's regular trains to Southampton Central and connecting train to Southampton Airport.

Station index and table numbers

■10 Connection time
Ⓟ Station Car Park
🚲 Bicycle storage facility
◇ Seat reservations can be made at this station
⚠ Penalty Fare Schemes in operation on some or all services from this station
🚕 Taxi rank or cab office at station, or signposted and within 100 metres
Ⓤ Unstaffed station
[ ] Station Operator Code

A

Abbey Wood [SE] Ⓟ 🚲 ◇ ⚠ 🚕 200
Aber [AW] Ⓟ 130
Abercynon [AW] Ⓤ 130
Aberdare [AW] ❸ Ⓟ ◇ 130
Aberdeen [SR] Ⓟ 🚲 ◇ 🚕
- Birmingham 51, 65
- Blackpool 65
- Bournemouth 51
- Bristol 51
- Cambridge 26
- Cardiff 51
- Carlisle 65
- Crewe 65, *Sleepers* 402
- Darlington 26
- Derby 51
- Doncaster 26
- Dundee 229
- Dyce 240
- Edinburgh 229
- Elgin 240
- Exeter 51
- Glasgow 229
- Grantham 26
- Inverkeithing 229
- Inverness 240
- Inverurie 240
- Kirkcaldy 229
- Kyle of Lochalsh 239
- Leeds 26
- Liverpool 65
- London 26, *Sleepers* 402
- Manchester 65
- Newcastle 26
- Newport (South Wales) 51
- Norwich 26
- Oxenholme Lake District 65
- Oxford 51
- Paignton 51
- Penzance 51
- Perth 229
- Peterborough 26
- Plymouth 51
- Preston 65, *Sleepers* 402
- Reading 51
- Sheffield 26
- Southampton 51
- Stirling 229
- Thurso 239
- Torquay 51
- Watford 65
- Wick 239
- York 26

Aberdour [SR] Ⓟ 🚲 242
Aberdovey [AW] 🚲 Ⓤ 76
Abererch [AW] Ⓤ 76
Abergavenny [AW] Ⓟ 🚲 ◇ 🚕 131
Abergele & Pensarn [AW] Ⓟ Ⓤ 81
Aberystwyth [AW] Ⓟ ◇ 🚕 76
Accrington [NT] Ⓟ ◇ 🚕 41, 97
Achanalt [SR] Ⓟ 🚲 Ⓤ 239
Achnasheen [SR] Ⓟ 🚲 Ⓤ 239
Achnashellach [SR] Ⓟ 🚲 Ⓤ 239
Acklington [NT] Ⓟ 🚲 Ⓤ 48
Acle [LE] Ⓟ 🚲 Ⓤ 15
Acocks Green [LM] Ⓟ ⚠ 71
Acton Bridge [LM] Ⓟ Ⓤ 91
Acton Central [LO] 🚲 ⚠ 59
Acton Main Line [GW] ⚠ 117
Acton, South [LO] (see South Acton)
Adderley Park [LM] ◇ ⚠ 68
Addiewell [SR] Ⓟ 🚲 Ⓤ 225
Addlestone [SW] ⚠ 🚕 149
Adisham [SE] Ⓟ ⚠ Ⓤ 212
Adlington (Cheshire) [NT] Ⓟ Ⓤ 84
Adlington (Lancashire) [NT] Ⓟ 82
Adwick [NT] Ⓟ 🚲 Ⓤ 29, 31
Agbrigg [NT] (See Sandal & Agbrigg)
Aigburth [ME] Ⓟ ⚠ 103
Ainsdale [ME] Ⓟ ⚠ 103
Aintree [ME] Ⓟ ⚠ 105
Airbles [SR] Ⓟ 🚲 Ⓤ 226
Airdrie [SR] Ⓟ 🚲 ◇ 🚕 226
Albany Park [SE] ◇ ⚠ 200
Albrighton [LM] Ⓟ Ⓤ 74
Alderley Edge [NT] Ⓟ 🚲 84
Aldermaston [GW] Ⓟ Ⓤ 116
Aldershot [SW] Ⓟ 🚲 ◇ ⚠ 🚕 149, 155
Aldrington [SN] ⚠ Ⓤ 188
Alexandra Palace [FC] 🚲 ⚠ 🚕 24
Alexandra Parade [SR] 🚲 Ⓤ 226
Alexandria [SR] Ⓟ 🚲 226
Alfreton [EM] Ⓟ ◇ ⚠ 🚕 34, 49, 53
Allens West [NT] 🚲 Ⓤ 44
Alloa [SR] Ⓟ 🚲 Ⓤ 🚕 230
Alness [SR] Ⓟ 🚲 Ⓤ 239
Alnmouth for Alnwick [NT] Ⓟ 🚲 ◇ 26, 48, 51
Alresford [LE] 🚲 ⚠ 11
Alsager [EM] Ⓤ 50, 67
Althorne [LE] Ⓟ 🚲 Ⓤ 5
Althorpe [NT] Ⓤ 29
Altnabreac [SR] 🚲 Ⓤ 239
Alton [SW] Ⓟ 🚲 ◇ ⚠ 🚕 155
Altrincham [NT] Ⓟ 🚲 ◇ 🚕 88
Alvechurch [LM] Ⓟ ⚠ Ⓤ 69
Ambergate [EM] Ⓟ Ⓤ 56
Amberley [SN] 🚲 ⚠ Ⓤ 188
Amersham [LT] Ⓟ 🚲 ⚠ 🚕 114
Ammanford [AW] Ⓤ 129
Ancaster [EM] Ⓟ Ⓤ 19
Anderston [SR] 🚲 226
Andover [SW] Ⓟ 🚲 ⚠ ◇ 🚕 160
Anerley [LO] 🚲 ⚠ 177, 178
Angel Road [LE] ⚠ Ⓤ 22
Angmering [SN] ❸ Ⓟ 🚲 ◇ ⚠ 🚕 188
Annan [SR] Ⓟ 🚲 Ⓤ 216
Anniesland [SR] 🚲 🚕 226, 232
Ansdell & Fairhaven [NT] Ⓤ 97
Appleby [NT] Ⓟ ◇ 36
Appledore (Kent) [SN] Ⓤ 189
Appleford [GW] Ⓤ 116
Appley Bridge [NT] Ⓟ Ⓤ 82
Apsley [LM] Ⓟ 66
Arbroath [SR] Ⓟ 🚲 ◇ 🚕 26, 51, 229, *Sleepers* 402
Ardgay [SR] Ⓟ 🚲 Ⓤ 239
Ardlui [SR] 🚲 Ⓤ 227, *Sleepers* 404
Ardrossan Harbour [SR] Ⓟ 🚲 Ⓤ 221, *Ship* 221A
Ardrossan South Beach [SR] Ⓟ 🚲 221
Ardrossan Town [SR] 🚲 Ⓤ 221
Ardwick [NT] Ⓤ 78, 79
Argyle Street [SR] 226
Arisaig [SR] Ⓟ 🚲 Ⓤ 227
Arlesey [FC] Ⓟ 🚲 ⚠ 25
Armadale [SR] Ⓟ 🚲 Ⓤ 226
Armadale (Skye) *Ship* 227A
Armathwaite [NT] Ⓟ Ⓤ 36
Arnside [TP] Ⓤ 82
Arram [NT] Ⓤ 43
Arrochar & Tarbet [SR] Ⓟ 🚲 Ⓤ 227, *Sleepers* 404
Arundel [SN] Ⓟ 🚲 ◇ ⚠ 🚕 188
Ascot [SW] ❸ Ⓟ 🚲 ◇ ⚠ 🚕 149
Ascott-under-Wychwood [GW] Ⓤ 126
Ash [SW] Ⓟ 🚲 ◇ ⚠ 148, 149
Ash Vale [SW] 🚲 ◇ ⚠ 149, 155
Ashburys [NT] Ⓤ 78, 79
Ashchurch for Tewkesbury [GW] Ⓟ 🚲 Ⓤ 57, 103
Ashfield [SR] 🚲 Ⓤ 232
Ashford International [SE] Ⓟ 🚲 ◇ ⚠ 🚕 189, 194, 196, 207
Ashford (Surrey) [SW] Ⓟ 🚲 ◇ ⚠ 149
Ashley [NT] Ⓟ Ⓤ 88
Ashtead [SN] Ⓟ 🚲 ◇ ⚠ 152, 182
Ashton-under-Lyne [NT] Ⓟ 🚲 39
Ashurst [SN] Ⓟ ⚠ Ⓤ 184
Ashurst New Forest [SW] Ⓟ 🚲 ⚠ Ⓤ 158
Ashwell & Morden [FC] Ⓟ 🚲 ⚠ 25
Askam [NT] Ⓟ Ⓤ 100
Aslockton [EM] Ⓟ Ⓤ 19
Aspatria [NT] Ⓟ Ⓤ 100
Aspley Guise [LM] Ⓤ 64
Aston [LM] ⚠ 69, 70
Atherstone [LM] Ⓟ Ⓤ 67
Atherton [NT] Ⓟ 🚲 82
Attadale [SR] 🚲 Ⓤ 239
Attenborough [EM] ⚠ Ⓤ 56, 57

Station index and table numbers

10 Connection time
Ⓟ Station Car Park
🚲 Bicycle storage facility
◇ Seat reservations can be made at this station
⚠ Penalty Fare Schemes in operation on some or all services from this station
🚕 Taxi rank or cab office at station, or signposted and within 100 metres
Ⓤ Unstaffed station
[ ] Station Operator Code

Attleborough [LE] Ⓟ Ⓤ 17
Auchinleck [SR] Ⓟ 🚲 Ⓤ 216
Audley End [LE] Ⓟ 🚲 ⚠ 🚕 22, 49
Aughton Park [ME] ⚠ 105
Aviemore [SR] Ⓟ 🚲 ◇ 🚕 229, *Sleepers* 403
Avoncliff [GW] Ⓤ 123
Avonmouth [GW] **2** Ⓟ 🚲 Ⓤ 133
Axminster [SW] Ⓟ 🚲 ◇ 🚕 160
Aylesbury [CH] Ⓟ 🚲 ◇ ⚠ 🚕 114, 115
Aylesbury Vale Parkway [CH] Ⓟ 🚲 ◇ ⚠ 114
Aylesford [SE] ⚠ Ⓤ 208
Aylesham [SE] Ⓟ ◇ ⚠ 212
Ayr [SR] Ⓟ 🚲 ◇ 🚕 218, 221,221B

B

Bache [ME] Ⓤ107
Backwell [GW] (see Nailsea)
Baglan [AW] Ⓟ 🚲 Ⓤ 128
Bagshot [SW] Ⓟ 🚲 ◇ ⚠ 149
Baildon [NT] Ⓟ Ⓤ 38
Baillieston [SR] 🚲 Ⓤ 220
Balcombe [SN] ◇ ⚠ 52, 186
Baldock [FC] Ⓟ ⚠ 25
Balham [SN] **4** ◇ ⚠ 🚕 170, 171, 172, 176, 182
Balloch [SR] 🚲 🚕 226
Balmossie [SR] 🚲 Ⓤ 229
Bamber Bridge [NT] Ⓟ Ⓤ 97
Bamford [NT] Ⓟ Ⓤ 78
Banavie [SR] Ⓟ 🚲 Ⓤ 227
Banbury [CH] Ⓟ 🚲 ◇ ⚠ 🚕 51, 71, 75, 115, 116
Bangor (Gwynedd) [AW] Ⓟ ◇ 🚕 65, 75, 81, 131
Bank Hall [ME] ⚠ 103
Banstead [SN] ⚠ Ⓤ 182
Barassie [SR] Ⓟ 🚲 Ⓤ 221
Bardon Mill [NT] Ⓟ Ⓤ 48
Bare Lane [NT] Ⓟ Ⓤ 36, 98
Bargeddie [SR] Ⓟ 🚲 Ⓤ 220
Bargoed [AW] 🚕 130
Barking [CC] **5** ◇ ⚠ 🚕 1, 62
Barlaston Orchard Place *Bus* 67
Barming [SE] Ⓟ ◇ ⚠ 196
Barmouth [AW] 🚲 76
Barnehurst [SE] **4** Ⓟ ◇ ⚠ 🚕 200
Barnes [SW] 🚲 ◇ ⚠ 149
Barnes Bridge [SW] 🚲 ◇ ⚠ Ⓤ 149
Barnetby [TP] Ⓟ Ⓤ 27, 28, 29, 30
Barnham [SN] Ⓟ 🚲 ◇ ⚠ 🚕 123, 188
Barnhill [SR] 🚲 Ⓤ 226
Barnsbury [LO] (see Caledonian Road)
Barnsley [NT] Ⓟ 🚲 ◇ 🚕 30, 34
Barnstaple [GW] Ⓟ 🚲 ◇ 🚕 136
Barnt Green [LM] Ⓟ ⚠ Ⓤ 69, 71
Barrhead [SR] Ⓟ 🚲 🚕 222
Barrhill [SR] Ⓟ 🚲 218
Barrow Haven [NT] Ⓤ 28
Barrow-in-Furness [TP] Ⓟ ◇ 🚕 65, 82, 100
Barrow Upon Soar [EM] ⚠ Ⓤ 53
Barry [AW] **3** Ⓟ ◇ 🚕 130
Barry Docks [AW] Ⓤ 130
Barry Island [AW] Ⓤ 130
Barry Links [SR] 🚲 Ⓤ 229
Barton-on-Humber [NT] Ⓟ Ⓤ 28
Basildon [CC] 🚲 ◇ ⚠ 🚕 1
Basingstoke [SW] Ⓟ 🚲 ◇ ⚠ 🚕
Aberdeen 51
Bath 160
Birmingham 51
Bournemouth 158
Bristol 160
Brockenhurst 158
Clapham Junction 155
Coventry 51
Crewe 51
Derby 51
Dorchester 158
Dundee 51
Eastleigh 158
Edinburgh 51
Exeter 160
Fareham 158
Farnborough 158
Glasgow 51
Leeds 51
London 155
Lymington 158
Manchester 51
Newcastle 51
Oxford 51
Poole 158
Portsmouth 158
Preston 51
Reading 122
Salisbury 160
Sheffield 51
Southampton 158
Southampton Airport 158
Stoke-on-Trent 51
Surbiton 155
Weymouth 158
Weybridge 155
Wimbledon 155
Winchester 158
Woking 155
Wolverhampton 51
Yeovil 160
York 51
Bat & Ball [SE] Ⓟ ⚠ Ⓤ 52, 195
Bath Spa [GW] **7** Ⓟ 🚲 ◇ ⚠ 🚕 123, 125, 132, 135, 160
Bathgate [SR] Ⓟ 🚲 ◇ 🚕 226
Batley [NT] Ⓟ 🚲 Ⓤ 39
Battersby [NT] Ⓤ 45
Battersea Park [SN] **4** ◇ ⚠ 170, 171
Battle [SE] Ⓟ ◇ ⚠ 🚕 206
Battlesbridge [LE] Ⓟ 🚲 Ⓤ 5
Bayford [FC] Ⓟ ⚠ Ⓤ 24
Beaconsfield [CH] Ⓟ 🚲 ◇ ⚠ 🚕 115
Bearley [LM] Ⓟ ⚠ Ⓤ 115
Bearsden [SR] Ⓟ 🚲 🚕 226
Bearsted [SE] Ⓟ 🚲 ◇ ⚠ 196
Beasdale [SR] 🚲 Ⓤ 227
Beaulieu Road [SW] 🚲 ⚠ Ⓤ 158
Beauly [SR] Ⓟ 🚲 Ⓤ 239
Bebington [ME] Ⓟ ⚠ 🚕 107
Beccles [LE] Ⓟ 🚲 Ⓤ 13
Beckenham Hill [SE] 🚲 ◇ ⚠ 52, 195
Beckenham Junction [SE] **4** Ⓟ 🚲 ◇ ⚠ 🚕 173, 195
Bedford [FC] **7** Ⓟ 🚲 ◇ ⚠ 🚕
Barnsley 53
Bletchley 64
Brighton 52, 186
Chesterfield 53
Derby 53
Doncaster 53
East Croydon 52
Gatwick Airport 52, 186
Haywards Heath 52, 186
Herne Hill 52
Hove 186
Kettering 53
Leeds 53
Leicester 53
London 52
Luton 52
Luton Airport Parkway 52
Meadowhall 53
Nottingham 53
Redhill 52, 186
St Albans 52
Sheffield 53
Sutton (Surrey) 52
Wakefield 53
Wellingborough 53
Wimbledon 52
York 53
Bedford St Johns [LM] Ⓤ 64
Bedhampton [SW] 🚲 ◇ ⚠ 156, 157, 188
Bedminster [GW] Ⓤ 134
Bedworth [LM] Ⓟ Ⓤ 67
Bedwyn [GW] Ⓟ 🚲 Ⓤ 116
Beeston [EM] Ⓟ 🚲 ◇ ⚠ 53, 56, 57
Bekesbourne [SE] Ⓟ ⚠ Ⓤ 212
Belfast
Port of *Ship* (via Ayr/Cairnryan) 221B
Belle Vue [NT] Ⓤ 78

Station index and table numbers

[10] Connection time
℗ Station Car Park
🚲 Bicycle storage facility
◇ Seat reservations can be made at this station
⚠ Penalty Fare Schemes in operation on some or all services from this station
🚕 Taxi rank or cab office at station, or signposted and within 100 metres
Ⓤ Unstaffed station
[ ] Station Operator Code

Bellgrove [SR] 🚲 Ⓤ 226
Bellingham [SE] 🚲 ◇ ⚠ 52, 195
Bellshill [SR] ℗ 🚲 225, 226
Belmont [SN] ⚠ Ⓤ 182
Belper [EM] ⚠ Ⓤ 56
Beltring [SE] ⚠ Ⓤ 208
Belvedere [SE] ◇ ⚠ 200
Bempton [NT] Ⓤ 43
Ben Rhydding [NT] ℗ Ⓤ 38
Benfleet [CC] ℗ 🚲 ◇ ⚠ 🚕 1
Bentham [NT] ℗ Ⓤ 36
Bentley [SW] ℗ 🚲 ◇ ⚠ 155
Bentley (S. Yorks.) [NT] ℗ 🚲 Ⓤ 29, 31
Bere Alston [GW] ℗ Ⓤ 139
Bere Ferrers [GW] ℗ 🚲 Ⓤ 139
Berkhamsted [LM] ℗ 🚲 ◇ ⚠ 🚕 66, 176
Berkswell [LM] ℗ 🚲 ⚠ 68
Berney Arms [LE] 🚲 Ⓤ 15
Berry Brow [NT] Ⓤ 34
Berrylands [SW] ℗ 🚲 ◇ ⚠ 152
Berwick [SN] ℗ 🚲 ◇ ⚠ 189
Berwick-upon-Tweed [GR] ℗ 🚲 ◇ 🚕 26, 26K, 51
Bescar Lane [NT] Ⓤ 82
Bescot Stadium [LM] ℗ ◇ ⚠ 70
Betchworth [GW] Ⓤ 148
Bethnal Green [LE] 🚲 ⚠ Ⓤ 20, 21, 22
Betws-y-Coed [AW] Ⓤ 102
Beverley [NT] ℗ ◇ 🚕 43
Bexhill [SN] **[4]** ◇ ⚠ 🚕 189
Bexley [SE] ℗ ◇ ⚠ 🚕 200
Bexleyheath [SE] ℗ 🚲 ◇ ⚠ 🚕 200
Bicester North [CH] **[3]** ℗ 🚲 ◇ ⚠ 🚕 115
Bicester Town [CH] ℗ 🚲 Ⓤ 116
Bickley [SE] **[4]** ℗ ◇ ⚠ 52, 195
Bidston [ME] ℗ ⚠ 101, 106
Biggleswade [FC] ℗ 🚲 ⚠ 25
Bilbrook [LM] Ⓤ 75
Billericay [LE] ℗ 🚲 ⚠ 🚕 5
Billingham [NT] 🚲 🚕 Ⓤ 44
Billingshurst [SN] ℗ 🚲 ◇ ⚠ 🚕 188
Bingham [EM] ℗ Ⓤ 19
Bingley [NT] ℗ 🚲 ◇ 36
Birchgrove [AW] Ⓤ 130
Birchington-on-Sea [SE] ℗ 🚲 ◇ ⚠ 🚕 194, 212
Birchwood [TP] ℗ 🚲 🚕 39, 89
Birkbeck [SN] ⚠ Ⓤ 173
Birkdale [ME] ℗ ⚠ 103
Birkenhead Central [ME] ⚠ 107
Birkenhead North [ME] ⚠ 106
Birkenhead Park [ME] ⚠ 106
Birmingham International [VT] (for National Exhibition Centre and Airport) ℗ 🚲 ◇ ⚠ 🚕
Aberdeen 65
Aberystwyth 76
Banbury 71
Bangor (Gwynedd) 65, 81
Basingstoke 51
Birmingham 68
Blackpool 65
Bournemouth 51
Carlisle 65
Chester 65, 75, 81
Clapham Junction 66
Coventry 68
Crewe 65, 81
Derby 51
Dundee 65
East Croydon 66
Edinburgh 51, 65
Glasgow 51, 65
Holyhead 65, 75, 81
Inverness 65
Leamington Spa 71
Leeds 51
Liverpool 65
London 66, 116
Manchester 65
Manchester Airport 65
Milton Keynes Central 66
Newcastle 51
Northampton 66
Nottingham 51
Oxenholme Lake District 65
Oxford 51
Preston 65
Pwllheli 76
Reading 51
Rugby 66
Sheffield 51
Shrewsbury 74,75, 76
Southampton 51
Stafford 68
Stoke-on-Trent 65
Watford 66
Wolverhampton 68
Wrexham 75
York 51

Birmingham
Moor Street [CH] ◇ ⚠ 🚕
New Street [NR] **[12]** 🚲 ◇ ⚠ 🚕
Snow Hill [LM] ℗ ◇ ⚠
Aberdeen 51, 65
Aberystwyth 76
Banbury 71
Bangor (Gwynedd) 65, 81
Barmouth 75
Barrow-in-Furness 65
Basingstoke 51
Birmingham International 68
Blackpool 65
Bournemouth 51
Bristol 57
Bromsgrove 71
Burton-on-Trent 57
Cambridge 49
Cardiff 57
Carlisle 65
Cheltenham Spa 57
Chester 75, 81
Clapham Junction 66
Coventry 68
Crewe 65
Darlington 51
Derby 57
Douglas (IOM) 98A
Dundee 51, 65
East Croydon 66
Edinburgh 51, 65
Ely 49
Exeter 51
Glasgow 51, 65
Gloucester 57
Hereford 71
Holyhead 65, 75, 81
Inverness 65
Kidderminster 71
Leamington Spa 71
Leeds 51
Leicester 57
Lichfield 69
Liverpool 65, 91
Llandudno 81
London 66, 115, 116
Longbridge 69
Manchester 65, 84
Manchester Airport 65, 84
Milton Keynes Central 66
Newcastle 51
Newport (South Wales) 57
Northampton 66
Norwich 49
Nottingham 57
Nuneaton 57
Oxenholme Lake District 65
Oxford 116
Paignton 135
Penzance 135
Peterborough 49
Plymouth 135
Preston 65
Reading 116
Redditch 69
Rugby 66
Rugeley 70
Sheffield 51
Shrewsbury 74,75,76
Solihull 71
Southampton 51
Stafford 68
Stansted Airport 49
Stockport 65
Stoke-on-Trent 65
Stourbridge 71
Stratford-upon-Avon 71
Telford 74, 75, 76
Torquay 135
Walsall 70
Warrington 65
Warwick 71
Watford 66
Wigan 65
Wolverhampton 68,74,75,76
Worcester 71
Wrexham 75

[10] Connection time
Ⓟ Station Car Park
🚲 Bicycle storage facility
◇ Seat reservations can be made at this station
⚠ Penalty Fare Schemes in operation on some or all services from this station
🚕 Taxi rank or cab office at station, or signposted and within 100 metres
Ⓤ Unstaffed station
[ ] Station Operator Code

Station index and table numbers

York 51
Birnam [SR] (see Dunkeld)
Bishop Auckland [NT] Ⓟ 🚕 Ⓤ 44
Bishopbriggs [SR] 🚲 228, 230
Bishops Lydeard Hithermead *Bus* 135E
Bishops Stortford [LE] Ⓟ 🚲 ◇ ⚠ 🚕 22
Bishopstone [SN] Ⓤ 189
Bishopton [SR] Ⓟ 🚲 219
Bitterne [SW] Ⓟ 🚲 ⚠ Ⓤ 165
Blackburn [NT] Ⓟ ◇ 🚕 41, 94, 97
Blackfriars [FC] (see London)
Blackheath [SE] [4] ◇ ⚠ 🚕 200
Blackhorse Road [LT] ⚠ 62
Blackpool
North [NT] Ⓟ ◇ 🚕
Pleasure Beach [NT] Ⓤ
South [NT] 🚕 Ⓤ
Birmingham 65
Birmingham International 65
Blackburn 97
Bolton 82
Bradford 41
Burnley 97
Colne 97
Coventry 65
Crewe 65
Lancaster 65
Leeds 41
Liverpool 65, 90
London 65
Manchester 82
Manchester Airport 82
Milton Keynes Central 65
Preston 97
Rugby 65
St Helens 90
Stafford 65
Stockport 82
Warrington 65
Watford 65
Wigan 65
Wolverhampton 65
York 41
Blackridge [SR] Ⓟ 🚲 Ⓤ 226
Blackrod [NT] Ⓤ 82
Blackwater [GW] Ⓟ Ⓤ 148
Blaenau Ffestiniog [AW] Ⓤ 102
Blair Atholl [SR] Ⓟ 🚲 229, *Sleepers* 403
Blairhill [SR] Ⓟ 🚲 🚕 226
Blake Street [LM] Ⓟ ⚠ 69
Blakedown [LM] Ⓟ ⚠ Ⓤ 71
Blantyre [SR] Ⓟ 🚲 226
Blaydon [NT] Ⓤ 48
Bleasby [EM] Ⓤ 27
Bledlow, Village Hall *Bus* 115A
Bletchley [LM] Ⓟ 🚲 ◇ ⚠ 🚕 64, 66, 176
Bloxwich [LM] ⚠ Ⓤ 70
Bloxwich North [LM] ⚠ Ⓤ 70
Bluewater [SE] (see Greenhithe for Bluewater)
Blundellsands & Crosby [ME] Ⓟ ⚠ 103
Blythe Bridge [EM] Ⓟ Ⓤ 50
Bodmin Mount Folly *Bus* 135C
Bodmin Parkway [GW] Ⓟ 🚲 ◇ 🚕 51, 135, *Bus* 135C, *Sleepers* 406
Bodorgan [AW] Ⓟ Ⓤ 81
Bognor Regis [SN] Ⓟ 🚲 ◇ ⚠ 🚕 188
Bogston [SR] 🚲 Ⓤ 219
Bolton [NT] 🚲 ◇ 🚕 65, 82, 94
Bolton-upon-Dearne [NT] Ⓟ Ⓤ 31
Bookham [SW] Ⓟ 🚲 ◇ ⚠ 🚕 152, 182
Bootle [NT] Ⓤ 100
Bootle New Strand [ME] ⚠ 🚕 103
Bootle Oriel Road [ME] Ⓟ ⚠ 103
Bordesley [LM] ⚠ Ⓤ 71
Borehamwood [FC] (see Elstree)
Borough Green & Wrotham [SE] Ⓟ ◇ ⚠ 🚕 196
Borth [AW] Ⓟ Ⓤ 76
Bosham [SN] 🚲 ⚠ 188
Boston [EM] Ⓟ 🚲 ◇ 🚕 19
Botley [SW] Ⓟ 🚲 ⚠ Ⓤ 158
Bottesford [EM] Ⓟ Ⓤ 19
Bourne End [GW] [3] Ⓟ 🚲 ⚠ 120
Bournemouth [SW] Ⓟ 🚲 ◇ ⚠ 🚕 51, 158
Bournville [LM] ⚠ 69
Bow Brickhill [LM] Ⓤ 64
Bowes Park [FC] ⚠ 24
Bowling [SR] Ⓟ 🚲 Ⓤ 226
Box Hill & Westhumble [SN] Ⓟ ⚠ Ⓤ 🚲 152, 182
Bracknell [SW] Ⓟ 🚲 ◇ ⚠ 🚕 149
Bradford
Forster Square [NT] Ⓟ 🚲 ◇ 🚕
Interchange [NT] 🚲 ◇ 🚕
Blackpool 41
Blackburn 41
Brighouse 41
Cambridge 26
Carlisle 36
Grantham 26
Halifax 41
Huddersfield 41
Ilkley 38
Lancaster 36
Leeds 37
London 26
Manchester 41
Morecambe 36
Newark 26
Norwich 26
Peterborough 26
Preston 41
Retford 26
Rochdale 41
Selby 40
Settle 36
Shipley 37
Skipton 36
York 40
Bradford-on-Avon [GW] Ⓟ 🚲 ◇ 🚕 123, 160
Brading [IL] Ⓟ Ⓤ 167
Braintree [LE] Ⓟ 🚲 ⚠ 🚕 11
Braintree Freeport [LE] 🚲 ⚠ Ⓤ 11
Bramhall [NT] 84
Bramley (Hants) [GW] ⚠ 122
Bramley [NT] Ⓟ Ⓤ 37, 41
Brampton (Cumbria) [NT] Ⓟ Ⓤ 48
Brampton (Suffolk) [LE] Ⓤ 13
Branchton [SR] Ⓟ 🚲 Ⓤ 219
Brandon [LE] Ⓟ Ⓤ 17
Branksome [SW] Ⓟ 🚲 ◇ ⚠ 158
Braystones [NT] Ⓤ 100
Bredbury [NT] Ⓟ 🚲 78
Breich [SR] 🚲 Ⓤ 225
Brentford [SW] Ⓟ 🚲 ◇ 🚕 149
Brentwood [LE] Ⓟ 🚲 ⚠ 🚕 5
Bricket Wood [LM] Ⓤ 61
Bridge of Allan [SR] Ⓟ 🚲 Ⓤ 229,230
Bridge of Orchy [SR] Ⓟ 🚲 Ⓤ 227, *Sleepers* 404
Bridgend [AW] Ⓟ 🚲 ◇ 🚕 125, 128, 130
Bridgeton [SR] 🚲 🚕 226
Bridgwater [GW] Ⓟ ◇ 134, 135
Bridlington [NT] Ⓟ 🚲 ◇ 🚕 43
Brierfield [NT] Ⓟ Ⓤ 97
Brigg [NT] Ⓟ Ⓤ 30
Brighouse [NT] Ⓟ Ⓤ 26, 32, 41
Brighton [SN] [10] Ⓟ 🚲 ◇ ⚠ 🚕
Ashford International 189
Bath Spa 123
Bedford 52
Bognor Regis 188
Bristol 123
Cardiff 123
Chichester 188
Eastbourne 189
East Croydon 176, 186
Elstree & Borehamwood 52
Gatwick Airport 186
Hastings 189
Haywards Heath 186
Hove 188
Isle of Wight 167
Kensington (Olympia) 176
Lewes 189
Littlehampton 188
London 186
Luton 52
Luton Airport Parkway 52
Mill Hill Broadway 52
Milton Keynes Central 176
Portsmouth 188

Station index and table numbers

[10] Connection time
Ⓟ Station Car Park
🚲 Bicycle storage facility
◇ Seat reservations can be made at this station
⚠ Penalty Fare Schemes in operation on some or all services from this station
🚕 Taxi rank or cab office at station, or signposted and within 100 metres
Ⓤ Unstaffed station
[ ] Station Operator Code

Radlett 52
Redhill 186
St Albans 52
Salisbury 123
Seaford 189
Southampton Central 188
Watford Junction 176
West Hampstead Thameslink 52
Worthing 188
Brimsdown [LE] ⚠ 22
Brinnington [NT] 78
Bristol International Airport *Bus* 🚕 125B
Bristol
Parkway [GW] [7] Ⓟ 🚲 ◇ ⚠ 🚕
Temple Meads [GW] [10] Ⓟ 🚲 ◇ ⚠ 🚕
Aberdeen 51
Bath Spa 132
Birmingham 57
Brighton 123
Bristol International Airport *Bus* 125B
Cardiff 132
Carlisle 51
Cheltenham Spa 57
Crewe 51
Darlington 51
Derby 57
Dundee 51
Edinburgh 51
Exeter 135
Glasgow 51
Gloucester 134
Great Malvern 123
Leeds 51
London 125, 160
Manchester 51
Newcastle 51
Newport (South Wales) 132
Nottingham 57
Paignton 135
Penzance 135
Plymouth 135
Portsmouth 123
Preston 51
Reading 125
Salisbury 123
Severn Beach 133
Sheffield 51
Slough 125
Southampton Central 123
Stoke-on-Trent 51
Swindon 125
Taunton 134
Temple Meads/Parkway 134
Torquay 135
Westbury 123
Weston-super-Mare 134
Weymouth 123
Wolverhampton 51
Worcester 57
York 51

Brithdir [AW] Ⓤ 130
British Steel Redcar [NT] Ⓤ 44
Briton Ferry [AW] Ⓟ Ⓤ 128
Brixton [SE] ◇ ⚠ 195
Broad Green [NT] 90
Broadbottom [NT] Ⓟ 79
Broadstairs [SE] Ⓟ 🚲 ◇ 🚕 194, 207, 212
Brockenhurst [SW] [3] Ⓟ 🚲 ◇ ⚠ 🚕 51, 158
Brockholes [NT] Ⓤ 34
Brockley [LO] 🚲 ⚠ 171, 177, 178
Brodick *Ship* 221A
Bromborough [ME] Ⓟ 🚲 ⚠ 107
Bromborough Rake [ME] ⚠ 107
Bromley Cross [NT] Ⓟ 🚲 94
Bromley North [SE] Ⓟ ◇ ⚠ 🚕 204
Bromley South [SE] [4] ◇ ⚠ 🚕 52, 195, 196, 212
Bromsgrove [LM] Ⓟ Ⓤ 69, 71
Brondesbury [LO] 🚲 ⚠ 59
Brondesbury Park [LO] 🚲 ⚠ 59
Brookmans Park [FC] Ⓟ 🚲 ⚠ 24
Brookwood [SW] [3] Ⓟ 🚲 ◇ ⚠ 🚕 155
Broome [AW] Ⓤ 129
Broomfleet [NT] Ⓟ Ⓤ 29
Brora [SR] Ⓟ 🚲 Ⓤ 239
Brough [TP] Ⓟ 🚲 ◇ 🚕 29, 39
Broughty Ferry [SR] 🚲 Ⓤ 229
Broxbourne [LE] [3] Ⓟ 🚲 ⚠ 🚕 22
Bruce Grove [LE] ⚠ 21
Brundall [LE] Ⓟ 🚲 15
Brundall Gardens [LE] 🚲 Ⓤ 15
Brunstane [SR] 🚲 Ⓤ 242
Brunswick [ME] Ⓟ 🚲 103
Bruton [GW] Ⓟ Ⓤ 123
Bryn [NT] Ⓤ 90
Buckenham [LE] 🚲 Ⓤ 15
Buckingham (Tesco) *Bus* 65A
Buckley [AW] Ⓟ Ⓤ 101
Bucknell [AW] Ⓤ 129
Buckshaw Parkway [NT] Ⓟ 82
Bude Strand *Bus* 135D
Bugle [GW] 🚲 Ⓤ 142
Builth Road [AW] Ⓤ 129
Bulwell [EM] Ⓟ Ⓤ 55
Bures [LE] 🚲 Ⓤ 10
Burgess Hill [SN] [4] Ⓟ 🚲 ◇ ⚠ 🚕 52, 186, 188
Burley Park [NT] Ⓟ Ⓤ 35
Burley-in-Wharfedale [NT] Ⓟ 🚲 Ⓤ 38
Burnage [NT] 85
Burneside [TP] Ⓤ 83
Burnham [GW] Ⓟ 🚲 ⚠ 🚕 117
Burnham-on-Crouch [LE] Ⓟ 🚲 5
Burnham-on-Sea [GW] (see Highbridge)
Burnley Barracks [NT] Ⓤ 97
Burnley Central [NT] Ⓟ ◇ 97

Burnley Manchester Road [NT] Ⓟ Ⓤ 41, 97
Burnside [SR] 🚲 223
Burntisland [SR] Ⓟ 🚲 242
Burry Port [AW] (see Pembrey)
Burscough Bridge [NT] Ⓟ 82
Burscough Junction [NT] Ⓟ Ⓤ 99
Bursledon [SW] Ⓟ 🚲 ⚠ Ⓤ 165
Burton Joyce [EM] Ⓤ 27
Burton-on-Trent [EM] Ⓟ ◇ 🚕 51, 57
Bury St Edmunds [LE] Ⓟ 🚲 ◇ 🚕 14
Busby [SR] Ⓟ 🚲 Ⓤ 222
Bushey [LO] Ⓟ 🚲 ⚠ 🚕 60, 66
Bush Hill Park [LE] Ⓟ ⚠ 🚕 21
Butlers Lane [LM] ⚠ 69
Buxted [SN] Ⓟ 🚲 ⚠ 184
Buxton [NT] Ⓟ ◇ 82, 86
Byfleet & New Haw [SW] 🚲 ◇ ⚠ 🚕 149, 155
Bynea [AW] Ⓤ 129

C

Cadoxton [AW] Ⓟ ◇ 130
Caergwrle [AW] Ⓤ 101
Caerphilly [AW] [3] Ⓟ 🚲 ◇ 🚕 130
Caersws [AW] Ⓟ Ⓤ 76
Cairnryan (Loch Ryan Port) *Ship* 221B
Caldercruix [SR] Ⓟ 🚲 Ⓤ 226
Caldicot [AW] Ⓤ 132
Caledonian Rd & Barnsbury [LO] ⚠ 🚲 59
Calstock [GW] Ⓟ 🚲 Ⓤ 139
Cam & Dursley [GW] Ⓟ 🚲 Ⓤ 134
Camberley [SW] Ⓟ 🚲 ◇ ⚠ 🚕 149
Camborne [GW] Ⓟ 🚲 ◇ 🚕 51, 135, *Sleepers* 406
Cambridge [LE] Ⓟ 🚲 ◇ ⚠ 🚕
Birmingham 49
Bishops Stortford 22
Broxbourne 22
Doncaster 26
Edinburgh 26
Ely 17
Finsbury Park 25
Grantham 26
Harlow 22
Harwich International 14
Hitchin 25
Ipswich 14
Kings Lynn 17
Leeds 26
Leicester 49

Station index and table numbers

■10 Connection time
℗ Station Car Park
🚲 Bicycle storage facility
◇ Seat reservations can be made at this station
⚠ Penalty Fare Schemes in operation on some or all services from this station
🚕 Taxi rank or cab office at station, or signposted and within 100 metres
Ⓤ Unstaffed station
[ ] Station Operator Code

Station index and table numbers

[10] Connection time
Ⓟ Station Car Park
🚲 Bicycle storage facility
◇ Seat reservations can be made at this station
⚠ Penalty Fare Schemes in operation on some or all services from this station
🚕 Taxi rank or cab office at station, or signposted and within 100 metres
🚶 Unstaffed station
[ ] Station Operator Code

Causeland [GW] 🚶 140
Cefn-y-Bedd [AW] Ⓟ 101
Chadwell Heath [LE] 🚲 ⚠ 5
Chafford Hundred Lakeside [CC] Ⓟ 🚲 ◇ ⚠ 1
Chalfont & Latimer [LT] Ⓟ 🚲 ⚠ 🚕 114
Chalkwell [CC] 🚲 ◇ ⚠ 🚕 1
Chandlers Ford [SW] Ⓟ 🚲 ◇ ⚠ 158
Chapel-en-le-Frith [NT] Ⓟ 🚶 86
Chapelton [GW] Ⓟ 🚶 136
Chapeltown [NT] 🚶 34
Chappel & Wakes Colne [LE] 🚲 🚶 10
Charing [SE] Ⓟ ◇ ⚠ 196
Charing Cross (Glasgow) **[SR]** 🚲 226
Charing Cross [NR] (see London)
Charlbury [GW] Ⓟ 🚲 126
Charlton [SE] [4] ◇ ⚠ 200
Chartham [SE] ⚠ 🚶 207
Chassen Road [NT] 89
Chatelherault [SR] 🚲 🚶 226
Chatham [SE] [4] Ⓟ ◇ ⚠ 🚕 194, 200, 212
Chathill [NT] Ⓟ 🚶 48
Cheadle Hulme [NT] Ⓟ 🚲 84
Cheam [SN] Ⓟ 🚲 ◇ ⚠ 🚕 182
Cheddington [LM] Ⓟ 66
Chelford [NT] Ⓟ 🚲 🚶 84
Chelmsford [LE] [3] Ⓟ 🚲 ◇ ⚠ 🚕 11
Chelsfield [SE] [3] Ⓟ ◇ ⚠ 🚕 204
Cheltenham Spa [GW] Ⓟ 🚲 ◇ 🚕 51, 57, 125
Chepstow [AW] Ⓟ 132
Cherry Tree [NT] Ⓟ 🚶 97
Chertsey [SW] Ⓟ 🚲 ◇ ⚠ 🚕 149
Cheshunt [LE] Ⓟ 🚲 ⚠ 🚕 21, 22
Chessington North [SW] Ⓟ 🚲 ◇ ⚠ 🚕 152
Chessington South [SW] Ⓟ 🚲 ◇ ⚠ 152
Chester [AW] Ⓟ ◇ 🚕
Altrincham 88
Bangor (Gwynedd) 75, 81
Birmingham 75, 81
Cardiff 75, 81, 131
Crewe 81
Hereford 75, 131
Holyhead 75, 81
Liverpool 107
Llandudno 75, 81
Llandudno Junction 75, 81
London 65
Manchester 81, 88
Newport (South Wales) 75, 131
Northwich 88
Rhyl 75, 81
Runcorn East 81
Shrewsbury 75, 131
Stafford 65
Stockport 88
Warrington 81
Wolverhampton 65, 75
Wrexham 75
Chester Road [LM] Ⓟ ⚠ 69
Chesterfield [EM] Ⓟ 🚲 ◇ ⚠ 🚕 34, 49, 51, 53
Chester-le-Street [NT] Ⓟ 🚲 ◇ 🚕 🚶 26, 39, 44, 51
Chestfield & Swalecliffe [SE] ◇ ⚠ 212
Chetnole [GW] 🚶 123
Chichester [SN] [4] Ⓟ 🚲 ◇ ⚠ 🚕 123, 165, 188
Chilham [SE] Ⓟ ⚠ 🚶 207
Chilworth [GW] 🚶 148
Chingford [LE] Ⓟ 🚲 ⚠ 🚕 20
Chinley [NT] Ⓟ 🚶 78
Chinnor, Estover Way *Bus* 115A
Chinnor, Lower Road *Bus* 115A
Chinnor, The Red Lion *Bus* 115A
Chinnor, The Wheatsheaf *Bus* 115A
Chippenham [GW] Ⓟ 🚲 ◇ ⚠ 🚕 123, 125
Chipping Norton West Street *Bus* 126A
Chipstead [SN] Ⓟ ⚠ 181
Chirk [AW] Ⓟ 🚶 75
Chislehurst [SE] Ⓟ ◇ ⚠ 🚕 204
Chiswick [SW] Ⓟ 🚲 🚶 149
Cholsey [GW] Ⓟ 🚲 116
Chorley [NT] Ⓟ ◇ 82
Chorleywood [LT] Ⓟ 🚲 ⚠ 🚕 114
Christchurch [SW] Ⓟ 🚲 ◇ ⚠ 🚕 158
Christs Hospital [SN] Ⓟ 🚲 ◇ ⚠ 188
Church Fenton [NT] Ⓟ 🚲 🚶 33, 40
Church & Oswaldtwistle [NT] 🚶 97
Church Stretton [AW] Ⓟ 🚶 129, 131
Cilmeri [AW] 🚶 129
City Thameslink [FC] (see London)
Clacton-on-Sea [LE] Ⓟ 🚲 ◇ ⚠ 🚕 11
Clandon [SW] Ⓟ 🚲 ◇ ⚠ 152
Clapham High Street [LO] 🚲 ⚠ 178
Clapham Junction [SW] [10] ◇ ⚠ 🚕
Alton 155
Andover 160
Ascot 149
Basingstoke 155, 158
Bexhill 189
Birmingham 66
Birmingham International 66
Bognor Regis 188
Bournemouth 158
Brighton 186
Bristol 160
Chertsey 149
Chessington 152
Chichester 188
Coventry 66
Crystal Palace 171
Dorking 152, 182
Eastbourne 189
East Croydon 175,
East Grinstead 184
Effingham Junction 152
Epsom 152, 182
Epsom Downs 182
Exeter 160
Gatwick Airport 186
Guildford 152, 156
Hampton Court 152
Hastings 189
Haywards Heath 186
Highbury & Islington 178
Horsham 186
Hounslow 149
Hove 186
Kensington (Olympia) 176
Kingston 149, 152
Lewes 189
London
Victoria 170, 175
Waterloo 149, 152, 182
Milton Keynes Central 66, 176
Northampton 66
Oxted 184
Portsmouth 156, 158, 188
Purley 181
Reading 149
Redhill 186
Rugby 66
Salisbury 160
Shepperton 152
Southampton 158, 188
Staines 149
Surbiton 152
Sutton (Surrey) 182
Tattenham Corner 181
Twickenham 149
Uckfield 184
Watford Junction 66, 176, 186
West Croydon 170, 171, 172
Weybridge 155
Whitechapel 178
Willesden Junction 176
Wimbledon 152
Windsor 149
Woking 155
Worthing 188
Yeovil Junction 160
Clapham (Nth Yorkshire) [NT] Ⓟ 🚶 36
Clapton [LE] ⚠ 20, 22
Clarbeston Road [AW] 🚶 128
Clarkston [SR] 🚲 222
Claverdon [LM] ⚠ 🚶 115
Claygate [SW] Ⓟ 🚲 ◇ ⚠ 🚕 152
Cleethorpes [TP] Ⓟ 🚲 ◇ 🚕 27, 28, 29, 30
Cleland [SR] Ⓟ 🚲 🚶 225

Station index and table numbers

[10] Connection time
℗ Station Car Park
🚲 Bicycle storage facility
◇ Seat reservations can be made at this station
⚠ Penalty Fare Schemes in operation on some or all services from this station
🚕 Taxi rank or cab office at station, or signposted and within 100 metres
🚶 Unstaffed station
[ ] Station Operator Code

Clifton [NT] 🚶 82
Clifton Down [GW] ℗ 🚶 133
Clitheroe [NT] ℗ 94
Clock House [SE] 🚲 ◇ ⚠ 🚕 203
Clunderwen [AW] ℗ 🚶 128
Clydebank [SR] 🚲 🚕 226
Coatbridge Central [SR] ℗ 🚲 🚕 🚶 224, 226
Coatbridge Sunnyside [SR] ℗ 🚲 226
Coatdyke [SR] ℗ 🚲 🚶 226
Cobham & Stoke d'Abernon [SW] ℗ 🚲 ◇ ⚠ 🚕 152
Codsall [LM] ℗ 🚶 75
Cogan [AW] ℗ 🚶 130
Colchester [LE] **[4]** ℗ 🚲 ◇ ⚠ 🚕 10, 11, 14
Colchester Town [LE] ℗ 🚲 ⚠ 11
Coleshill Parkway [LM] ℗ 🚲 ◇ 🚕 49, 57
Coll *Ship* 227B
Collingham [EM] 🚶 27
Collington [SN] ⚠ 🚶 189
Colne [NT] ℗ 🚶 97
Colonsay *Ship* 227B
Colwall [LM] ℗ ⚠ 🚶 71,126
Colwyn Bay [AW] ℗ ◇ 🚕 75, 81
Combe [GW] 🚶 126
Commondale [NT] 🚶 45
Congleton [NT] ℗ ◇ 51, 65, 84
Conisbrough [NT] ℗ 🚶 29
Connel Ferry [SR] ℗ 🚲 🚶 227
Conon Bridge [SR] ℗ 🚲 🚶 239
Cononley [NT] ℗ 🚶 36
Conway Park [ME] 106
Conwy [AW] 🚶 81
Cooden Beach [SN] 🚲 ◇ ⚠ 189
Cookham [GW] ℗ 120
Cooksbridge [SN] ℗ ⚠ 🚶 189
Coombe Junction Halt [GW] 🚶 140
Copplestone [GW] ℗ 🚶 136
Corbridge [NT] ℗ 🚶 48
Corby [EM] ⚠ 🚕 53
Corby George Street *Bus* 26B
Corkerhill [SR] 🚲 🚶 217
Corkickle [NT] 🚶 100
Corpach [SR] ℗ 🚲 🚶 227
Corrour [SR] 🚲 🚶 227, *Sleepers* 404
Coryton [AW] 🚶 130
Coseley [LM] ℗ ⚠ 68
Cosford [LM] ℗ 🚶 74
Cosham [SW] ℗ 🚲 ◇ ⚠ 🚕 123, 158, 165, 188
Cottingham [NT] ℗ 🚕 🚶 43
Cottingley [NT] 🚶 39
Coulsdon South [SN] ℗ ⚠ 🚕 186
Coulsdon Town [SN] ℗ ◇ 181
Coventry [VT] ℗ 🚲 ◇ ⚠ 🚕
Aberdeen 65
Barrow-in-Furness 65
Banbury 71
Basingstoke 51
Birmingham 68
Birmingham International 68
Blackpool 65
Bournemouth 51
Brighton 66
Carlisle 65
Clapham Junction 66
Crewe 65
Derby 51
Dundee 65
East Croydon 66
Edinburgh 51, 65
Gatwick Airport 66
Glasgow 51, 65
Holyhead 65
Inverness 65
Leamington Spa 71
Leeds 51
Liverpool 65
London 66
Manchester 65
Manchester Airport 65
Milton Keynes Central 66
Newcastle 51
Northampton 66
Nuneaton 67
Oxenholme Lake District 65
Oxford 51
Preston 65
Reading 51
Rugby 66
Sheffield 51
Southampton 51
Stafford 67, 68
Stoke-on-Trent 65
Watford 66
Wolverhampton 68
York 51
Cowden [SN] ℗ ⚠ 🚶 184
Cowdenbeath [SR] 🚲 ◇ 242
Cradley Heath [LM] ℗ 🚲 ◇ ⚠ 71, 115
Craigendoran [SR] ℗ 🚲 🚶 226
Craignure *Ship* 227B
Cramlington [NT] ℗ 🚲 🚶 48
Craven Arms [AW] ℗ 🚶 129, 131
Crawley [SN] ℗ 🚲 ◇ ⚠ 🚕 186, 188
Crayford [SE] ℗ ◇ ⚠ 200
Crediton [GW] ℗ 🚲 🚶 136
Cressing [LE] 🚲 ⚠ 🚶 11
Cressington [ME] ℗ ⚠ 103
Creswell [EM] 🚶 55
Crewe [VT] **[10]** ℗ 🚲 ◇ 🚕
Aberdeen 65, *Sleepers* 402
Bangor (Gwynedd) 81
Barrow-in-Furness 65
Birmingham 65
Birmingham International 65
Blackpool 65
Bournemouth 51
Bristol 51
Cardiff 131
Carlisle 65
Cheltenham Spa 51
Chester 81
Coventry 65, 67
Derby 50
Douglas (IOM) 98A
Dundee 65, *Sleepers* 402
Edinburgh 65
Exeter 51
Fort William *Sleepers* 404
Glasgow 65
Hartford 91
Hereford 131
Holyhead 81
Inverkeithing *Sleepers* 402
Inverness 65, *Sleepers* 403
Kirkcaldy *Sleepers* 402
Lancaster 65
Liverpool 91
Liverpool South Parkway 91
Llandudno 81
London 65, 67
Manchester 84
Manchester Airport 84
Milton Keynes Central 65, 67
Newport (South Wales) 131
Northampton 67
Oxenholme Lake District 65
Oxford 51
Paignton 51
Penzance 51
Perth 65, *Sleepers* 403
Plymouth 51
Preston 65
Reading 51
Rugby 65, 67
Runcorn 91
Shrewsbury 131
Southampton 51
Stafford 65, 67
Stirling *Sleepers* 403
Stockport 84
Stoke-on-Trent 50
Torquay 51
Watford 65
Wilmslow 84
Wolverhampton 65
Crewkerne [SW] ℗ 🚲 ◇ ⚠ 160
Crews Hill [FC] ⚠ 🚶 24
Crianlarich [SR] ℗ 🚲 🚶 227, *Sleepers* 404
Criccieth [AW] ℗ 🚲 🚶 76
Cricklewood [FC] 🚲 ◇ ⚠ 52
Croftfoot [SR] 🚲 223
Crofton Park [SE] ◇ ⚠ 52,195
Cromer [LE] ℗ 🚲 🚶 16
Cromford [EM] ℗ 🚶 54, 56
Crompton [NT] (see Shaw)
Crookston [SR] 🚲 🚶 217
Crosby [ME] (see Blundellsands)
Crossflatts [NT] ℗ 🚲 🚶 36
Cross Gates [NT] ℗ 40

Station index and table numbers

❿ Connection time
Ⓟ Station Car Park
🚲 Bicycle storage facility
◇ Seat reservations can be made at this station
⚠ Penalty Fare Schemes in operation on some or all services from this station
🚕 Taxi rank or cab office at station, or signposted and within 100 metres
Ⓤ Unstaffed station
[ ] Station Operator Code

Cross Keys [AW] Ⓤ 127
Crosshill [SR] 223
Crossmyloof [SR] 🚲 Ⓤ 222
Croston [NT] Ⓟ Ⓤ 99
Crouch Hill [LO] ⚠ 🚲 62
Crowborough [SN] Ⓟ 🚲 ◇ ⚠ 184
Crowhurst [SE] Ⓟ ⚠ 206
Crowle [NT] Ⓤ 29
Crowthorne [GW] Ⓟ 🚲 148
Croy [SR] ❸ Ⓟ 🚲 228, 230
Croydon
see East Croydon
see South Croydon
see West Croydon
Crystal Palace [LO] ❹ Ⓟ ⚠ 🚕 🚲 171, 173, 177, 178
Cuddington [NT] Ⓟ Ⓤ 88
Cuffley [FC] Ⓟ 🚲 ⚠ 🚕 24
Culham [GW] Ⓟ 🚲 Ⓤ 116
Culrain [SR] 🚲 Ⓤ 239
Cumbernauld [SR] Ⓟ 🚲 🚕 224
Cupar [SR] Ⓟ 🚲 ◇ 51, 229
Curriehill [SR] Ⓟ 🚲 Ⓤ 225
Cuxton [SE] Ⓟ ⚠ Ⓤ 208
Cwmbach [AW] Ⓟ Ⓤ 130
Cwmbran [AW] Ⓟ 🚲 ◇ 🚕 131
Cynghordy [AW] Ⓤ 129

D

Dagenham Dock [CC] Ⓟ 🚲 ◇ ⚠ 1
Daisy Hill [NT] Ⓟ 🚲 82
Dalgety Bay [SR] Ⓟ 🚲 🚕 Ⓤ 242
Dalmally [SR] Ⓟ 🚲 Ⓤ 227
Dalmarnock [SR] 226
Dalmeny [SR] Ⓟ 🚲 242
Dalmuir [SR] Ⓟ 🚲 226, 227, *Sleepers* 404
Dalreoch [SR] Ⓟ 🚲 226
Dalry [SR] Ⓟ 🚲 Ⓤ 221
Dalston [NT] Ⓟ Ⓤ 100
Dalston Junction [LO] 🚲 ⚠ 177, 178
Dalston Kingsland [LO] ⚠ 59
Dalton [NT] Ⓟ Ⓤ 82
Dalwhinnie [SR] Ⓟ 🚲 Ⓤ 229, *Sleepers* 403
Danby [NT] Ⓟ Ⓤ 45
Danescourt [AW] Ⓤ 130
Danzey [LM] Ⓟ ⚠ Ⓤ 71
Darlington [GR] ❼ Ⓟ 🚲 ◇ 🚕
Aberdeen 26
Birmingham 51
Bishop Auckland 44
Bournemouth 51
Bristol 51
Cambridge 26
Cardiff 51
Catterick Garrison *Bus* 26H
Derby 51
Doncaster 26
Durham 26
Dundee 26
Edinburgh 26
Exeter 51
Glasgow 26
Grantham 26
Huddersfield 39
Leeds 26
Liverpool 39
London 26
Manchester 39
Manchester Airport 39
Middlesbrough 44
Newark 26
Newcastle 26
Newport (South Wales) 51
Norwich 26
Northallerton 26
Oxford 51
Paignton 51
Penzance 51
Peterborough 26
Plymouth 51
Reading 51
Redcar 44
Retford 26
Richmond *Bus* 26H
Saltburn 44
Sheffield 26
Southampton 51
Stansted Airport 26
Sunderland 26, 44
Torquay 51
Whitby 45
York 26
Darnall [NT] Ⓤ 30
Darnley [SR] (see Priesthill)
Darsham [LE] Ⓟ 🚲 Ⓤ 13
Dartford [SE] ❹ Ⓟ ◇ ⚠ 🚕 200, 212
Darton [NT] Ⓟ Ⓤ 34
Darwen [NT] Ⓤ 94
Datchet [SW] 🚲 ◇ ⚠ 149
Davenport [NT] Ⓟ 86
Dawlish [GW] Ⓟ ◇ 🚕 51, 135
Dawlish Warren [GW] Ⓟ 🚲 Ⓤ 135
Deal [SE] Ⓟ 🚲 ◇ ⚠ 🚕 194, 207
Dean [GW] 🚲 Ⓤ 158
Deansgate [NT] 82, 84, 85, 86, 89
Deganwy [AW] Ⓤ 81, 102
Deighton [NT] Ⓤ 39
Delamere [NT] Ⓟ Ⓤ 88
Denby Dale [NT] Ⓟ Ⓤ 34
Denham [CH] Ⓟ 🚲 ◇ ⚠ 115
Denham Golf Club [CH] ⚠ Ⓤ 115
Denmark Hill [SE] ❹ ◇ ⚠ 52, 178, 195, 200
Dent [NT] Ⓟ Ⓤ 36
Denton [NT] Ⓤ 78
Deptford [SE] ◇ ⚠ 200
Derby [EM] ❻ Ⓟ 🚲 ◇ ⚠ 🚕
Barnsley 53
Bedford 53
Belper 53, 56
Birmingham 57
Birmingham International 51
Bournemouth 51
Bristol 57
Burton-on-Trent 57
Cardiff 57
Chesterfield 53
Coventry 51
Crewe 50
Doncaster 53
Edinburgh 51
Exeter 51
Gloucester 57
Kettering 53
Leeds 53
Leicester 53
London 53
Long Eaton 56
Loughborough 53
Luton 53
Market Harborough 53
Matlock 56
Meadowhall 53
Newcastle 51
Newport (South Wales) 57
Nottingham 56
Oxford 51
Paignton 51
Penzance 51
Plymouth 51
Reading 51
Sheffield 53
Southampton 51
Stoke-on-Trent 50
Wakefield 53
Wellingborough 53
York 53
Derby Road [LE] 🚲 Ⓤ 13
Dereham 🚕 *Bus* 26A
Devonport [GW] Ⓟ 🚲 Ⓤ 135, 139
Dewsbury [TP] Ⓟ 🚲 ◇ 🚕 39, 41
Didcot Parkway [GW] Ⓟ 🚲 ◇ ⚠ 🚕 116, 125
Digby & Sowton [GW] Ⓟ Ⓤ 136
Dilton Marsh [GW] Ⓤ 123
Dinas Powys [AW] Ⓤ 130
Dinas Rhondda [AW] Ⓟ Ⓤ 130
Dingle Road [AW] Ⓤ 130
Dingwall [SR] Ⓟ 🚲 ◇ 🚕 239
Dinsdale [NT] Ⓤ 44
Dinting [NT] ❸ Ⓟ 🚲 79
Disley [NT] Ⓟ 86
Diss [LE] Ⓟ 🚲 ◇ 🚕 11
Dockyard [GW] Ⓤ 135, 139
Dodworth [NT] Ⓟ Ⓤ 34
Dolau [AW] 🚲 Ⓤ 129
Doleham [SN] Ⓤ 189
Dolgarrog [AW] Ⓤ 102
Dolwyddelan [AW] Ⓟ Ⓤ 102

10 Connection time
℗ Station Car Park
🚲 Bicycle storage facility
◇ Seat reservations can be made at this station
⚠ Penalty Fare Schemes in operation on some or all services from this station
🚕 Taxi rank or cab office at station, or signposted and within 100 metres
Ⓤ Unstaffed station
[ ] Station Operator Code

Station index and table numbers

E

Station index and table numbers

10 Connection time
Ⓟ Station Car Park
🚲 Bicycle storage facility
◇ Seat reservations can be made at this station
⚠ Penalty Fare Schemes in operation on some or all services from this station
🚕 Taxi rank or cab office at station, or signposted and within 100 metres
Ⓤ Unstaffed station
[ ] Station Operator Code

[10] Connection time
Ⓟ Station Car Park
🚲 Bicycle storage facility
◇ Seat reservations can be made at this station
⚠ Penalty Fare Schemes in operation on some or all services from this station
🚕 Taxi rank or cab office at station, or signposted and within 100 metres
👤 Unstaffed station
[ ] Station Operator Code

Station index and table numbers

Station index and table numbers

❿ Connection time
Ⓟ Station Car Park
🚲 Bicycle storage facility
◇ Seat reservations can be made at this station
⚠ Penalty Fare Schemes in operation on some or all services from this station
🚕 Taxi rank or cab office at station, or signposted and within 100 metres
Ⓤ Unstaffed station
[ ] Station Operator Code

Milton Keynes Central 176
Portsmouth 188
Radlett 52
Reading 148
St Albans 52
St Pancras International 52
Southampton Central 188
Watford Junction 176
West Hampstead Thameslink 52
Worthing 188
York 53
Georgemas Junction [SR] ❶ Ⓟ 🚲 Ⓤ 239
Gerrards Cross [CH] ❶ Ⓟ 🚲 ◇ ⚠ 🚕 115
Gidea Park [LE] ❷ Ⓟ 🚲 ⚠ 🚕 5
Giffnock [SR] Ⓟ 🚲 Ⓤ 222
Giggleswick [NT] Ⓟ Ⓤ 36
Gilberdyke [NT] Ⓟ Ⓤ 29
Gilfach Fargoed [AW] Ⓤ 130
Gillingham (Dorset) [SW] Ⓟ 🚲 ◇ 🚕 160
Gillingham (Kent) [SE] ❹ Ⓟ ◇ ⚠ 🚕 194, 200, 212
Gilshochill [SR] 🚲 Ⓤ 232
Gipsy Hill [SN] ◇ ⚠ 🚲 171, 173
Girvan [SR] Ⓟ 🚲 218
Glaisdale [NT] Ⓟ Ⓤ 45
Glan Conwy [AW] Ⓤ 102
Glasgow
Central [NR] ⓯ Ⓟ 🚲 ◇ 🚕
Queen Street [SR] ❿ Ⓟ 🚲 ◇ 🚕
Aberdeen 229
Airdrie 226
Alloa 230
Anniesland 226, 232
Ardrossan 221
Ayr 221
Balloch 226
Barrhead 222
Bathgate 226
Belfast *Ship* 221B
Birmingham New Street 51, 65
Birmingham International 51, 65
Blackpool 65
Bournemouth 51
Bristol 51
Cambridge 26
Carlisle 65
Carstairs 225
Cathcart 223
Clyde Coast *Ship* 219A, 219B, 221A
Crewe 65
Croy 230
Cumbernauld 224
Dalmuir 226
Darlington 26
Doncaster 26
Dumfries 216
Dunblane 230
Dundee 229
Dyce 229
East Kilbride 222
Edinburgh 225, 226, 228
Edinburgh Park 226
Exeter 51
Falkirk 224, 228
Fort William 227
Girvan 218
Gourock 219
Greenock 219
Hamilton 226
Helensburgh 226, 227
Inverness 229
Inverurie 229
Kilmarnock 222
Kyle of Lochalsh 239
Lanark 226
Lancaster 65
Largs 221
Larkhall 226
Leeds 26
Lenzie 230
Liverpool 65
Livingston South 225
London 26, 65, *Sleepers* 401
Mallaig 227
Manchester 65
Manchester Airport 65
Maryhill 232
Milngavie 226
Milton Keynes Central 65
Motherwell 225, 226
Neilston 223
Newcastle 26, 216
Newton 223, 226
Norwich 26
Oban 227
Oxenholme Lake District 65
Oxford 51
Paignton 51
Paisley 217, 219, 221
Penzance 51
Perth 229
Peterborough 26
Plymouth 51
Preston 65
Prestwick International Airport 221
Reading 51
Sheffield 26
Shotts 225
Southampton 51
Springburn 224, 226
Stafford 65
Stirling 230
Stranraer 218
Thurso 239
Torquay 51
Warrington 65
Watford 65, *Sleepers* 401
Wemyss Bay 219
Western Isles *Ship*
via Inverness 239B
via Mallaig 227A
via Oban 227B, 227C
Whifflet 220
Wick 239
Wigan 65
York 26
Glasshoughton [NT] Ⓟ 🚲 Ⓤ 32
Glazebrook [NT] Ⓟ 89
Gleneagles [SR] Ⓟ 🚲 Ⓤ 229, *Sleepers* 403
Glenfinnan [SR] Ⓟ 🚲 Ⓤ 227
Glengarnock [SR] Ⓟ 🚲 221
Glenrothes With Thornton [SR] Ⓟ 🚲 Ⓤ 242
Glossop [NT] Ⓟ 🚲 79
Gloucester [GW] ❼ Ⓟ 🚲 ◇ 🚕
Birmingham 57
Bristol 134
Cardiff 132
Carmarthen 128
Cheltenham 57
Chepstow 132
Derby 57
Didcot 125
Kemble 125
London 125
Lydney 132
Maesteg 128
Newcastle 51
Newport (South Wales) 132
Nottingham 57
Reading 125
Sheffield 51
Stroud 125
Swansea 128
Swindon 125
Taunton 134
Weston-super-Mare 134
Worcester 57
York 51
Glynde [SN] Ⓟ ⚠ Ⓤ 189
Goathland [NY] Ⓟ 45
Gobowen [AW] Ⓟ 75
Godalming [SW] Ⓟ 🚲 ◇ ⚠ 🚕 156
Godley [NT] Ⓤ 79
Godstone [SN] ⚠ Ⓤ 186
Goldthorpe [NT] Ⓟ Ⓤ 31
Golf Street [SR] Ⓤ 229
Golspie [SR] Ⓟ 🚲 Ⓤ 239
Gomshall [GW] Ⓟ Ⓤ 148
Goodmayes [LE] 🚲 ⚠ 5
Goole [NT] Ⓟ 🚲 ◇ 🚕 29, 32
Goostrey [NT] Ⓟ Ⓤ 84
Gordon Hill [FC] Ⓟ 🚲 ⚠ 24
Goring & Streatley [GW] Ⓟ 🚲 116
Goring-by-Sea [SN] Ⓟ 🚲 ◇ ⚠ 188
Gorton [NT] 78, 79
Gospel Oak [LO] 🚲 ⚠ 59, 62, 176
Gourock [SR] Ⓟ 🚲 ◇ 🚕 219, *Ship* 219A
Gowerton [AW] Ⓟ Ⓤ 128, 129
Goxhill [NT] Ⓤ 28
Grange Park [FC] Ⓟ ⚠ 24
Grange-over-Sands [TP] ◇ 82
Grangetown [AW] Ⓤ 130

❿ Connection time
Ⓟ Station Car Park
🚲 Bicycle storage facility
◇ Seat reservations can be made at this station
⚠ Penalty Fare Schemes in operation on some or all services from this station
🚕 Taxi rank or cab office at station, or signposted and within 100 metres
Ⓤ Unstaffed station
[ ] Station Operator Code

Station index and table numbers

H

Station index and table numbers

- **10** Connection time
- Ⓟ Station Car Park
- 🚲 Bicycle storage facility
- ◇ Seat reservations can be made at this station
- ⚠ Penalty Fare Schemes in operation on some or all services from this station
- 🚕 Taxi rank or cab office at station, or signposted and within 100 metres
- Ⓤ Unstaffed station
- [ ] Station Operator Code

Cowdenbeath 242
Crewe 65
Croy 228
Darlington 26
Derby 51
Doncaster 26
Dunbar 238
Dunblane 230
Dundee 229
Dunfermline 242
Edinburgh Park 226
Exeter 51
Glasgow 225, 226, 228
Inverness 229
Lancaster 65
Larbert 230
Leeds 26
Liverpool 65
Livingston 225, 226
London 26, 65
Manchester 65
Manchester Airport 65
Motherwell 225
Newcastle 26
Newcraighall 242
North Berwick 238
Oxenholme Lake District 65
Oxford 51
Paignton 51
Penzance 51
Perth 229
Peterborough 26
Plymouth 51
Preston 65
Reading 51
Sheffield 26
Southampton 51
Stirling 230
Torquay 51
York 26

Haywards Heath [SN] **3** Ⓟ 🚲 ◇ ⚠ 🚕
Bedford 52
Brighton 186
Clapham Junction 186
Eastbourne 189
East Croydon 186
Gatwick Airport 186
Hastings 189
Hove 188
Lewes 189
London 186
Littlehampton 188
Luton 52, 186
Portsmouth 188
St Albans 52
Seaford 189
Southampton Central 188
West Hampstead Thameslink 52
Worthing 188

Hazel Grove [NT] Ⓟ 🚲 78, 82, 86
Headcorn [SE] Ⓟ ◇ ⚠ 🚕 207
Headingley [NT] Ⓟ Ⓤ 35
Headstone Lane [LO] ⚠ 60
Heald Green [NT] Ⓟ 🚲 82, 85
Healing [NT] Ⓤ 28
Heath High Level [AW] Ⓤ 130
Heath Low Level [AW] Ⓤ 130
Heathrow London Airport [HX] ◇ 🚕 117, 118, *Bus* 125A, *Bus* 158A
Heaton Chapel [NT] 🚲 84, 86
Hebden Bridge [NT] Ⓟ 🚲 ◇ 41
Heckington [EM] Ⓟ 🚲 Ⓤ 19
Hedge End [SW] Ⓟ 🚲 ◇ ⚠ 158
Hednesford [LM] Ⓟ ⚠ Ⓤ 70
Heighington [NT] Ⓟ Ⓤ 44
Helensburgh Central [SR] Ⓟ 🚲 ◇ 🚕 226
Helensburgh Pier *Ship* 219A
Helensburgh Upper [SR] 🚲 Ⓤ 227, *Sleepers* 404
Hellifield [NT] Ⓟ Ⓤ 36
Helmsdale [SR] Ⓟ 🚲 Ⓤ 239
Helsby [AW] Ⓟ Ⓤ 81, 109
Helston Coinagehall Street *Bus* 135A
Hemel Hempstead [LM] Ⓟ ◇ ⚠ 🚕 66, 176
Hendon [FC] Ⓟ 🚲 ◇ ⚠ 52
Hengoed [AW] Ⓟ Ⓤ 130
Henley-in-Arden [LM] Ⓟ ⚠ Ⓤ 71
Henley-on-Thames [GW] Ⓟ 🚲 🚕 121
Hensall [NT] Ⓤ 32
Hereford [AW] **7** Ⓟ 🚲 ◇ 🚕 71, 75, 126, 131
Herne Bay [SE] Ⓟ 🚲 ◇ ⚠ 194, 212
Herne Hill [SE] **4** 🚲 ◇ ⚠ 52, 173, 179, 182, 195
Hersham [SW] 🚲 ◇ ⚠ 155
Hertford East [LE] Ⓟ 🚲 ⚠ 🚕 22
Hertford North [FC] Ⓟ 🚲 ⚠ 🚕 24, 25
Hessle [NT] Ⓤ 29
Heswall [AW] Ⓟ Ⓤ 101
Hever [SN] Ⓟ 🚲 ⚠ Ⓤ 184
Heworth [NT] Ⓟ 🚲 🚕 Ⓤ 44
Hexham [NT] Ⓟ 🚲 ◇ 🚕 44, 48
Heyford [GW] Ⓟ Ⓤ 116
Heysham Port [NT] Ⓤ 36 98, 98A
High Brooms [SE] Ⓟ ◇ ⚠ 🚕 207
High Street (Glasgow) **[SR]** 226
High Wycombe [CH] **1** Ⓟ 🚲 ◇ ⚠ 🚕 115
Higham [SE] Ⓟ ◇ ⚠ 200
Highams Park [LE] Ⓟ 🚲 ⚠ 20
Highbridge & Burnham [GW] Ⓟ 🚲 Ⓤ 134
Highbury & Islington [LT] ⚠ 24, 59, 176, 177, 178
Hightown [ME] 🚲 ⚠ 103
Hildenborough [SE] Ⓟ 🚲 ◇ ⚠ 204
Hillfoot [SR] Ⓟ 🚲 🚕 Ⓤ 226
Hillington East [SR] 🚲 219
Hillington West [SR] 🚲 219
Hillside [ME] ⚠ 103
Hilsea [SW] ⚠ 156, 157, 158, 165, 188
Hinchley Wood [SW] 🚲 ◇ ⚠ 152
Hinckley [EM] Ⓟ ◇ 🚕 57
Hindley [NT] Ⓟ 82
Hinton Admiral [SW] Ⓟ 🚲 ◇ ⚠ 158
Hitchin [FC] **4** Ⓟ 🚲 ◇ ⚠ 🚕 24, 25
Hither Green [SE] **4** ◇ ⚠ 199, 200, 204
Hockley [LE] Ⓟ 🚲 ⚠ 🚕 5
Hollingbourne [SE] Ⓟ ⚠ Ⓤ 196
Holmes Chapel [NT] Ⓟ 🚲 84
Holmwood [SN] 🚲 ⚠ Ⓤ 182
Holsworthy *Bus* 135D
Holton Heath [SW] Ⓟ 🚲 ⚠ Ⓤ 158
Holyhead [AW] ◇ 🚕 65, 75, 81, 81A, 131
Holytown [SR] Ⓟ 🚲 Ⓤ 225, 226
Homerton [LO] 🚲 ⚠ 59
Honeybourne [GW] Ⓟ Ⓤ 126
Honiton [SW] Ⓟ 🚲 ◇ ⚠ 🚕 160
Honley [NT] Ⓤ 34
Honor Oak Park [LO] 🚲 ⚠ 171, 177, 178
Hook [SW] Ⓟ 🚲 🚕 155
Hooton [ME] Ⓟ 🚲 ⚠ 107
Hope (Derbyshire) [NT] Ⓟ Ⓤ 78
Hope (Flintshire) [AW] Ⓤ 101
Hopton Heath [AW] Ⓤ 129
Horley [SN] **4** 🚲 ◇ ⚠ 186, 188
Hornbeam Park [NT] Ⓟ Ⓤ 35
Hornsey [FC] 🚲 ⚠ 24
Horsforth [NT] Ⓟ 🚲 ◇ 35
Horsham [SN] **4** Ⓟ 🚲 ◇ ⚠ 🚕 182, 186, 188
Horsley [SW] Ⓟ 🚲 ◇ ⚠ 🚕 152
Horton-in-Ribblesdale [NT] Ⓟ Ⓤ 36
Horwich Parkway [NT] Ⓟ 🚲 82
Hoscar [NT] Ⓤ 82
Hough Green [NT] Ⓟ 89
Hounslow [SW] Ⓟ 🚲 ◇ ⚠ 🚕 149
Hove [SN] **2** Ⓟ 🚲 ◇ ⚠ 🚕 123, 186, 188
Hoveton & Wroxham [LE] Ⓟ 🚲 🚕 Ⓤ 16
Howden [NT] Ⓟ 🚲 Ⓤ 29, 39
How Wood (Herts) **[LM]** Ⓤ 61
Howwood (Renfrewshire) **[SR]** Ⓟ 🚲 Ⓤ 221
Hoxton [LO] 🚲 ⚠ 177, 178
Hoylake [ME] Ⓟ 🚲 ⚠ 106
Hubberts Bridge [EM] Ⓤ 19
Hucknall [EM] Ⓟ Ⓤ 55
Huddersfield [TP] Ⓟ 🚲 ◇ 🚕
Barnsley 34
Bradford 41
Brighouse 41
Darlington 39
Durham 39
Halifax 41

Station index and table numbers

[10] Connection time
Ⓟ Station Car Park
🚲 Bicycle storage facility
◇ Seat reservations can be made at this station
⚠ Penalty Fare Schemes in operation on some or all services from this station
🚕 Taxi rank or cab office at station, or signposted and within 100 metres
Ⓤ Unstaffed station
[ ] Station Operator Code

Hull 39
Leeds 39
Liverpool 39
London 26
Manchester 39
Manchester Airport 39
Meadowhall 34
Middlesbrough 39
Newcastle 39
Peterborough 26
Scarborough 39
Selby 39, 41
Sheffield 34
Wakefield 39
York 39
Hull [TP] Ⓟ 🚲 ◇ 🚕
Aberdeen 26
Beverley 43
Bridlington 43
Cambridge 26
Darlington 26
Doncaster 29
Durham 26
Edinburgh 26
Filey 43
Glasgow 26
Goole 29
Grantham 26
Huddersfield 39
Leeds 39
Liverpool 39
London 26, 29
Manchester 29, 39
Manchester Airport 29, 39
Newark 26
Newcastle 26
Norwich 26
Peterborough 26
Retford 26
Scarborough 43
Selby 29
Sheffield 29
Stockport 29
York 33
Hull Paragon Interchange 🚕 *Bus* 28
Humphrey Park [NT] Ⓤ 89
Huncoat [NT] Ⓤ 97
Hungerford [GW] Ⓟ 🚲 🚕 Ⓤ 116, 135
Hunmanby [NT] Ⓤ 43
Hunstanton Bus Station *Bus* 17A
Hunts Cross [ME] ⚠ 89, 103
Huntingdon [FC] Ⓟ 🚲 ◇ ⚠ 🚕 25
Huntly [SR] Ⓟ 🚲 ◇ 240
Hurst Green [SN] [3] Ⓟ 🚲 ◇ ⚠ 184
Hutton Cranswick [NT] Ⓟ Ⓤ 43
Huyton [NT] Ⓟ 90
Hyde [NT] (see Newton for Hyde)
Hyde Central [NT] Ⓟ Ⓤ 78
Hyde North [NT] Ⓟ Ⓤ 78
Hykeham [EM] Ⓟ Ⓤ 27
Hyndland [SR] 🚲 226
Hythe (Essex) **[LE]** 🚲 ⚠ Ⓤ 11

I

IBM [SR] 🚲 Ⓤ 219
Ifield [SN] 🚲 ◇ ⚠ 186
Ilford [LE] [2] 🚲 ◇ ⚠ 5
Ilkley [NT] Ⓟ 🚲 ◇ 38
Imperial Wharf [LO] 🚲 ⚠ 66, 170, 176
Ince [NT] Ⓤ 82
Ince & Elton [NT] Ⓟ Ⓤ 109
Ingatestone [LE] Ⓟ 🚲 ⚠ 11
Insch [SR] Ⓟ 🚲 Ⓤ 240
Invergordon [SR] Ⓟ 🚲 Ⓤ 239
Invergowrie [SR] 🚲 Ⓤ 229
Inverkeithing [SR] Ⓟ 🚲 ◇ 🚕
Aberdeen 229
Birmingham 51
Bournemouth 51
Bristol 51
Carlisle 51
Crewe *Sleepers* 402
Derby 51
Dundee 229
Edinburgh 242
Inverness 229
London 26, *Sleepers* 402
Newcastle 26
Oxford 51
Penzance 51
Perth 229
Plymouth 51
Preston 51, *Sleepers* 402
Reading 51
Sheffield 51
Southampton 51
York 26
Inverkip [SR] Ⓟ 🚲 Ⓤ 219
Inverness [SR] Ⓟ 🚲 ◇ 🚕
Aberdeen 240
Birmingham 65
Cambridge 26
Carlisle 65
Crewe 65, *Sleepers* 403
Dingwall 239
Edinburgh 229
Elgin 240
Glasgow 229
Inverkeithing 229
Kingussie 229
Kirkcaldy 229
Kyle of Lochalsh 239
Leeds 26
Liverpool 65
London 26, 65, *Sleepers* 403
Manchester 65
Newcastle 26
Norwich 26
Orkney Isles *Ship* 239A
Perth 229
Preston 65, *Sleepers* 403
Stirling 229
Thurso 239
Western Isles *Ship* 239B
Wick 239
York 26
Inverness Bus Station 🚕 *Bus* 239B
Invershin [SR] Ⓟ 🚲 Ⓤ 239
Inverurie [SR] Ⓟ 🚲 ◇ 🚕 229, 240
Ipswich [LE] Ⓟ 🚲 ◇ 🚕 11, 13, 14, 17
Irlam [NT] Ⓟ Ⓤ 89
Irvine [SR] Ⓟ 🚲 🚕 221
Isle of Man *Ship* 98A
Isle of Wight [IL] 158, 167
Isleworth [SW] Ⓟ 🚲 ⚠ 🚕 Ⓤ 149
Islington (see Highbury & Islington)
Islip [CH] Ⓟ 🚲 Ⓤ 116
Iver [GW] 🚲 ⚠ 117
Ivybridge [GW] Ⓟ 🚲 Ⓤ 135

J

James Street [ME] (see Liverpool)
James Cook University Hospital [NT] 45
Jewellery Quarter [LM] ⚠ 71
Johnston [AW] Ⓤ 128
Johnstone [SR] Ⓟ 🚲 🚕 221
Jordanhill [SR] 🚲 Ⓤ 226

K

Kearsley [NT] Ⓤ 82
Kearsney [SE] Ⓟ ⚠ 212
Keighley [NT] Ⓟ 🚲 ◇ 🚕 26, 36
Keith [SR] Ⓟ 🚲 ◇ 240
Kelvedon [LE] Ⓟ 🚲 ⚠ 11
Kelvindale [SR] Ⓟ 🚲 Ⓤ 232
Kemble [GW] Ⓟ ◇ 🚕 125
Kempston Hardwick [LM] Ⓤ 64
Kempton Park [SW] ⚠ 152
Kemsing [SE] Ⓟ ⚠ Ⓤ 196
Kemsley [SE] ⚠ Ⓤ 212
Kendal [TP] Ⓟ 🚕 Ⓤ 83
Kenley [SN] Ⓟ ◇ ⚠ 181
Kennett [LE] Ⓟ 🚲 Ⓤ 14
Kennishead [SR] 🚲 Ⓤ 222
Kensal Green [LT] 60
Kensal Rise [LO] 🚲 ⚠ 59
Kensington (Olympia) [LO] 🚲 ◇ ⚠ 59, 66, 170, 176
Kent House [SE] [4] 🚲 ◇ ⚠ 195
Kentish Town [LT] ⚠ 🚕 52, 195
Kentish Town West [LO] 🚲 ⚠ 59
Kenton [LT] 60
Kenton (South) [LT] (see South Kenton)

Station index and table numbers

[10] Connection time
Ⓟ Station Car Park
🚲 Bicycle storage facility
◇ Seat reservations can be made at this station
⚠ Penalty Fare Schemes in operation on some or all services from this station
🚕 Taxi rank or cab office at station, or signposted and within 100 metres
Ⓤ Unstaffed station
[ ] Station Operator Code

■10 Connection time
Ⓟ Station Car Park
🚲 Bicycle storage facility
◇ Seat reservations can be made at this station
⚠ Penalty Fare Schemes in operation on some or all services from this station
🚕 Taxi rank or cab office at station, or signposted and within 100 metres
Ⓤ Unstaffed station
[ ] Station Operator Code

Station index and table numbers

Brighouse 41
Bristol 51
Burnley 41
Cambridge 26
Cardiff 51
Carlisle 36
Carnforth 36
Chesterfield 53
Darlington 26
Derby 53
Dewsbury 39
Doncaster 31
Edinburgh 26
Exeter 51
Glasgow 26
Goole 32
Grantham 26
Halifax 41
Harrogate 35
Huddersfield 39, 41
Hull 39
Ilkley 38
Keighley 36
Knaresborough 35
Lancaster 36
Leicester 53
Liverpool 39, 41
London 26, 53
Luton 53
Manchester 39, 41
Manchester Airport 39
Meadowhall 31
Morecambe 36
Newark 26
Newcastle 26
Newport (South Wales) 51
Norwich 26
Nottingham 53
Oxford 51
Paignton 51
Penzance 51
Peterborough 26
Plymouth 51
Preston 41
Reading 51
Retford 26
Rochdale 41
Scarborough 39
Selby 40
Settle 36
Sheffield 31
Shipley 37
Skipton 36
Stansted Airport 26
Southampton 51
Torquay 51
Wakefield 31
Warrington 39
York 35, 40

Leicester [EM] Ⓟ 🚲 ◇ ⚠ 🚕 49, 53, 57
Leigh (Kent) [SN] ⚠ Ⓤ 186
Leigh-on-Sea [CC] Ⓟ 🚲 ◇ ⚠ 🚕 1
Leighton Buzzard [LM] Ⓟ 🚲 ◇ ⚠ 🚕 66, 176
Lelant [GW] Ⓟ Ⓤ 144
Lelant Saltings [GW] Ⓟ Ⓤ 144
Lenham [SE] Ⓟ ◇ ⚠ 196
Lenzie [SR] ■3 Ⓟ 🚲 🚕 228, 230
Leominster [AW] Ⓟ 131
Letchworth Garden City [FC] 🚲 ⚠ 🚕 24, 25
Leuchars [SR] ■3 Ⓟ 🚲 ◇ 🚕 26, 51, 229, 229A, *Sleepers* 402
Levenshulme [NT] 84, 86
Levisham [NY] 🚲 45
Lewes [SN] ■4 Ⓟ 🚲 ◇ ⚠ 🚕 186, 189
Lewisham [SE] ■4 Ⓟ 🚲 ◇ ⚠ 🚕
Bexleyheath 200
Dartford 200
Gillingham (Kent) 200
Gravesend 200
Hayes (Kent) 203
London 195, 199
Orpington 199, 204
Sidcup 200
Woolwich Arsenal 200
Leyland [NT] Ⓟ ◇ 🚕 82, 90
Leyton Midland Road [LO] 🚲 ⚠ 62
Leytonstone High Road [LO] 🚲 ⚠ 62
Lichfield City [LM] Ⓟ ◇ ⚠ 🚕 69
Lichfield Trent Valley [LM] Ⓟ ◇ ⚠ 65, 67, 69
Lidlington [LM] Ⓤ 64
Limehouse [CC] ⚠ 1
Lincoln [EM] Ⓟ 🚲 ◇ 🚕 18, 27, 30, 53
Lincoln [GR] 🚲 🚕
Lingfield [SN] Ⓟ 🚲 ◇ ⚠ 🚕 184
Lingwood [LE] Ⓟ 🚲 Ⓤ 15
Linlithgow [SR] Ⓟ 🚲 ◇ 228, 230
Liphook [SW] Ⓟ 🚲 ◇ ⚠ 🚕 156
Liskeard [GW] ■6 Ⓟ 🚲 ◇ 51, 135, 140, *Sleepers* 406
Lismore *Ship* 227B
Liss [SW] Ⓟ 🚲 ◇ ⚠ 156
Lisvane & Thornhill [AW] Ⓟ Ⓤ 130
Litherland [ME] (see Seaforth & Litherland)
Little Kimble [CH] ⚠ Ⓤ 115
Little Sutton [ME] Ⓤ 107
Littleborough [NT] Ⓟ 41
Littlehampton [SN] ■4 Ⓟ 🚲 ◇ ⚠ 🚕 188
Littlehaven [SN] ◇ ⚠ 186
Littleport [FC] 🚲 ⚠ Ⓤ 17
Liverpool
Central [ME] ■10 ⚠ 🚕
James Street [ME] ◇ ⚠
Lime Street (Main Line) **[NR]** ■10 Ⓟ 🚲 ◇ 🚕
Lime Street (Low Level) **[ME]** ■10 ◇ ⚠ 🚕
Moorfields [ME] ■10 ⚠

Aberdeen 65
Barrow-in-Furness 65
Birkenhead 106,107
Birmingham 65
Birmingham International 65
Blackpool 65, 90
Bolton 82
Cambridge 49
Carlisle 65
Chester 107
Coventry 65
Crewe 91
Darlington 39
Douglas (IOM) 98A
Dundee 65
Durham 39
Edinburgh 65
Ellesmere Port 107
Ely 49
Gatwick Airport 65
Glasgow 65
Hartford 91
Hooton 106
Huddersfield 39
Hull 39
Hunts Cross 89, 103
Inverness 65
Kirkby 104
Lancaster 65
Leeds 39
Liverpool South Parkway 91,103
London 65
Manchester 89, 90
Manchester Airport 89
Middlesbrough 39
Milton Keynes Central 65
Mossley Hill 91
Motherwell 65
New Brighton 106
Newcastle 39
Norwich 49
Nottingham 49
Nuneaton 65
Ormskirk 105
Oxenholme Lake District 65
Peterborough 49
Preston 90
Rhyl 81
Rochdale 95
Rock Ferry 107
Rugby 65
Runcorn 91
St Helens 90
Scarborough 39
Sheffield 89
Southport 103
Stafford 65
Stansted Airport 49
Stockport 89
Wakefield 39
Warrington 89, 90
Watford 65
West Kirby 106
Wigan 82, 90
Windermere 65

Station index and table numbers

[10] Connection time
Ⓟ Station Car Park
🚲 Bicycle storage facility
◇ Seat reservations can be made at this station
⚠ Penalty Fare Schemes in operation on some or all services from this station
🚕 Taxi rank or cab office at station, or signposted and within 100 metres
ⓤ Unstaffed station
[ ] Station Operator Code

Wolverhampton 65
York 39
Liverpool Landing Stage *Ship* 98A
Liverpool South Parkway [ME] **[7]** Ⓟ 🚲 ⚠ 🚕 39,49, 65, 89, 91, 103
Liverpool Street [NR] (see London)
Livingston North [SR] Ⓟ 🚲 ⓤ 226
Livingston South [SR] Ⓟ 🚲 ⓤ 225
Llanaber [AW] ⓤ 76
Llanbedr [AW] ⓤ 76
Llanbister Road [AW] ⓤ 129
Llanbradach [AW] Ⓟ ⓤ 130
Llandaf [AW] Ⓟ 130
Llandanwg [AW] ⓤ 76
Llandecwyn [AW] ⓤ 76
Llandeilo [AW] Ⓟ ⓤ 129
Llandovery [AW] Ⓟ ⓤ 129
Llandrindod [AW] Ⓟ ◇ 129
Llandudno [AW] ◇ 🚕 75, 81, 102
Llandudno Junction [AW] Ⓟ ◇ 🚕 65,75, 81, 102, 131
Llandybie [AW] Ⓟ ⓤ 129
Llanelli [AW] ◇ 🚕 128, 129
Llanfairfechan [AW] Ⓟ ⓤ 81
Llanfairpwll [AW] Ⓟ ⓤ 81
Llangadog [AW] ⓤ 129
Llangammarch [AW] ⓤ 129
Llangennech [AW] ⓤ 129
Llangynllo [AW] ⓤ 129
Llanharan [AW] Ⓟ ⓤ 128
Llanhilleth [AW] Ⓟ ⓤ 127
Llanishen [AW] Ⓟ ⓤ 130
Llanrwst [AW] ⓤ 102
Llansamlet [AW] Ⓟ ⓤ 128
Llantwit Major [AW] Ⓟ 🚲 ⓤ 130
Llanwrda [AW] ⓤ 129
Llanwrtyd [AW] Ⓟ ⓤ 129
Llwyngwril [AW] ⓤ 75
Llwynypia [AW] Ⓟ ⓤ 130
Loch Awe [SR] Ⓟ 🚲 ⓤ 227
Loch Eil Outward Bound [SR] 🚲 ⓤ 227
Lochailort [SR] Ⓟ 🚲 ⓤ 227
Lochboisdale *Ship* 227C
Locheilside [SR] Ⓟ 🚲 ⓤ 227
Lochgelly [SR] Ⓟ 🚲 ⓤ 242
Lochluichart [SR] Ⓟ ⓤ 239
Lochmaddy *Ship* 239B
Lochwinnoch [SR] Ⓟ 🚲 ⓤ 221
Lockerbie [SR] Ⓟ 🚲 ◇ 🚕 51, 65
Lockwood [NT] Ⓟ ⓤ 34
London
- **Blackfriars [FC]** **[3]** ◇ ⚠ 🚕
- **Cannon Street [NR]** **[4]** ◇ ⚠ 🚕
- **Charing Cross [NR]** **[4]** ◇ ⚠ 🚕
- **City Thameslink [FC]** **[3]** ◇ ⚠ 🚕
- **Euston [NR]** **[15]** Ⓟ 🚲 ◇ ⚠ 🚕
- **Farringdon [LT]** **[3]** ⚠
- **Fenchurch Street [NR]** **[7]** ◇ ⚠ 🚕
- **Kings Cross [NR]** **[15]** Ⓟ 🚲 ◇ ⚠ 🚕
- **Liverpool Street [NR]** **[15]** 🚲 ◇ ⚠ 🚕
- **London Bridge [NR]** **[4]** 🚲 ◇ ⚠ 🚕
- **Marylebone [CH]** **[10]** 🚲 ◇ ⚠ 🚕
- **Moorgate [LT]** ⚠
- **Paddington [NR]** **[15]** Ⓟ 🚲 ◇ ⚠ 🚕
- **St Pancras International [NR]** **[15]** Ⓟ ◇ ⚠ 🚕
- **Victoria [NR]** **[15]** Ⓟ 🚲 ◇ ⚠ 🚕
- **Waterloo [NR]** **[15]** Ⓟ 🚲 ◇ ⚠ 🚕
- **Waterloo East [SE]** **[4]** ⚠

Aberdeen 26, *Sleepers* 402
Aldershot 149, 155
Alexandra Palace 24
Alnmouth 26
Alton 155
Amersham 114
Arbroath 26, *Sleepers* 402
Ascot 149
Ashford International 196, 207
Aviemore *Sleepers* 403
Aylesbury 114, 115
Balham 170, 171, 172
Banbury 115, 116
Bangor (Gwynedd) 65
Barking 1
Barnsley 53
Barrow-in-Furness 65
Basingstoke 155, 158
Bath Spa 125, 160
Beckenham Junction 173, 195
Bedford 52
Belper 53
Berwick-upon-Tweed 26
Bexhill 189
Bicester 115, 116
Birmingham 66, 115, 116
Birmingham International 66
Bishops Stortford 22
Blackburn 97
Blackpool 65
Bletchley 66
Bodmin Parkway 135, *Sleepers* 406
Bognor Regis 188
Bourne End 120
Bournemouth 158
Bradford 26
Braintree 11
Brighton 186
Bristol 125, 160
Bromley North 204
Bromley South 195
Broxbourne 22
Camborne 135, *Sleepers* 406
Cambridge 22, 25
Canterbury 207, 212
Cardiff 125
Carlisle 65, *Sleepers* 400, 401
Carstairs 65, *Sleepers* 401
Carmarthen 128
Caterham 181
Chatham 200, 212
Chelmsford 11
Cheltenham Spa 125
Chertsey 149
Chessington 152
Chester 65
Chesterfield 53
Chichester 188
Chingford 20
Clacton-on-Sea 11
Clapton 20, 22
Cleethorpes 29
Colchester 11
Coulsdon Town 181
Coventry 66
Crewe 65
Cromer 16
Crystal Palace 171, 177, 178
Darlington 26
Dartford 200
Derby 53
Didcot 116
Doncaster 26, 53
Dorking 152, 182
Douglas (IOM) 98A
Dover 207, 212
Dundee 26, *Sleepers* 402
Durham 26
Eaglescliffe 26
Eastbourne 189
East Croydon 175
East Grinstead 184
Edinburgh 26, *Sleepers* 400
Effingham Junction 152
Ely 17
Enfield Town 21
Epsom 152, 182
Epsom Downs 182
Exeter 135, 160, *Sleepers* 406
Fareham 158, 188
Felixstowe 13
Finsbury Park 24, 25
Folkestone 207
Fort William *Sleepers* 404
Gatwick Airport 186
Gillingham (Kent) 200, 212
Glasgow 26, 65, *Sleepers* 401
Gloucester 125
Grantham 26
Gravesend 200
Grays 1
Great Yarmouth 15
Greenford 117
Grove Park 204
Guildford 152, 155, 156
Halifax 26
Hampton Court 152

10 Connection time
℗ Station Car Park
Bicycle storage facility
◇ Seat reservations can be made at this station
Penalty Fare Schemes in operation on some or all services from this station
Taxi rank or cab office at station, or signposted and within 100 metres
Unstaffed station
[ ] Station Operator Code

Station index and table numbers

Station index and table numbers

■10 Connection time
Ⓟ Station Car Park
🚲 Bicycle storage facility
◇ Seat reservations can be made at this station
⚠ Penalty Fare Schemes in operation on some or all services from this station
🚕 Taxi rank or cab office at station, or signposted and within 100 metres
Ⓤ Unstaffed station
[ ] Station Operator Code

M

Station index and table numbers

[10] Connection time
Ⓟ Station Car Park
🚲 Bicycle storage facility
◇ Seat reservations can be made at this station
⚠ Penalty Fare Schemes in operation on some or all services from this station
🚕 Taxi rank or cab office at station, or signposted and within 100 metres
Ⓤ Unstaffed station
[ ] Station Operator Code

  - Wolverhampton 65
  - York 39
- **Manchester Airport [TP]** ◇
  - Bangor (Gwynedd) 81
  - Barrow-in-Furness 82
  - Birmingham 65
  - Birmingham International 65
  - Blackburn 94
  - Blackpool 82
  - Bolton 82
  - Carlisle 65
  - Coventry 65
  - Crewe 84
  - Darlington 39
  - Doncaster 29
  - Durham 39
  - Edinburgh 65
  - Glasgow 65
  - Huddersfield 39
  - Hull 29, 39
  - Holyhead 81
  - Lancaster 82
  - Leeds 39
  - Liverpool 89
  - London 65
  - Manchester 85
  - Middlesbrough 39
  - Motherwell 65
  - Newcastle 39
  - Oxenholme Lake District 82
  - Penrith North Lakes 65
  - Preston 82
  - St Helens 90
  - Salford 82
  - Scarborough 39
  - Sheffield 78
  - Southport 82
  - Stafford 65, 84
  - Wakefield 39
  - Warrington 89
  - Watford 65
  - Wigan 82
  - Wilmslow 84
  - Windermere 82
  - Wolverhampton 65
  - York 39
- **Manea [LE]** Ⓤ 14, 17
- **Manningtree [LE]** [2] Ⓟ 🚲 ⚠ 🚕 11, 14
- **Manor Park [LE]** 🚲 ⚠ 5
- **Manor Road [ME]** 🚲 ⚠ 106
- **Manorbier [AW]** Ⓤ 128
- **Manors [NT]** Ⓤ 48
- **Mansfield [EM]** Ⓟ 🚲 🚕 55
- **Mansfield Woodhouse [EM]** Ⓟ Ⓤ 55
- **March [LE]** Ⓟ ◇ 🚕 14, 17, 49
- **Marden [SE]** Ⓟ ◇ ⚠ 207
- **Margate [SE]** [4] Ⓟ 🚲 ◇ ⚠ 🚕 194, 207, 212
- **Market Harborough [EM]** Ⓟ 🚲 ◇ ⚠ 🚕 53
- **Market Rasen [EM]** Ⓟ 🚲 Ⓤ 27
- **Markinch [SR]** Ⓟ 🚲 🚕 51, 229
- **Marks Tey [LE]** [2] Ⓟ 🚲 ⚠ 10, 11
- **Marlow [GW]** 🚲 Ⓤ 120
- **Marple [NT]** Ⓟ 🚲 78
- **Marsden [NT]** Ⓟ Ⓤ 39
- **Marske [NT]** 🚲 Ⓤ 44
- **Marston Green [LM]** Ⓟ ◇ ⚠ 68
- **Martin Mill [SE]** Ⓟ ⚠ 207
- **Martins Heron [SW]** Ⓟ 🚲 ◇ ⚠ 149
- **Marton [NT]** Ⓟ 🚲 Ⓤ 45
- **Maryhill [SR]** 🚲 Ⓤ 232
- **Maryland [LE]** 🚲 ⚠ 🚕 5
- **Marylebone [CH]** (see London)
- **Maryport [NT]** Ⓟ Ⓤ 100
- **Matlock [EM]** Ⓟ Ⓤ 56
- **Matlock Bath [EM]** Ⓟ Ⓤ 56
- **Mauldeth Road [NT]** 85
- **Maxwell Park [SR]** 🚲 Ⓤ 223
- **Maybole [SR]** Ⓟ 🚲 Ⓤ 218
- **Maze Hill [SE]** ◇ ⚠ 200
- **Meadowhall [NT]** Ⓟ 🚲 ◇
  - Barnsley 34
  - Castleford 34
  - Cleethorpes 29
  - Doncaster 29
  - Gainsborough 30
  - Grimsby 29
  - Huddersfield 34
  - Hull 29
  - Leeds 31
  - Lincoln 30
  - Manchester 29
  - Manchester Airport 29
  - Penistone 34
  - Pontefract 33
  - Retford 30
  - Rotherham 29
  - Scunthorpe 29
  - Sheffield 29
  - Wakefield 31
  - Worksop 30
  - York 29, 33
- **Meldreth [FC]** Ⓟ 🚲 ⚠ 25
- **Melksham [GW]** Ⓟ Ⓤ 123
- **Melrose** *Bus* 26K
- **Melton [LE]** Ⓟ 🚲 🚕 Ⓤ 13
- **Melton Mowbray [EM]** Ⓟ 🚲 ◇ 🚕 49, 53
- **Menheniot [GW]** Ⓟ Ⓤ 135
- **Menston [NT]** Ⓟ 🚲 ◇ 38
- **Meols [ME]** Ⓟ 🚲 ⚠ 🚕 106
- **Meols Cop [NT]** Ⓤ 82
- **Meopham [SE]** Ⓟ ◇ ⚠ 🚕 212
- **Merryton [SR]** 🚲 Ⓤ 226
- **Merstham [SN]** Ⓟ 🚲 ◇ ⚠ 🚕 186
- **Merthyr Tydfil [AW]** Ⓟ ◇ 130
- **Merthyr Vale [AW]** Ⓤ 130
- **Metheringham [EM]** Ⓟ 🚲 Ⓤ 18
- **Metrocentre [NT]** Ⓤ 44, 48
- **Mexborough [NT]** Ⓟ 🚲 ◇ 29
- **Micheldever [SW]** Ⓟ 🚲 ◇ ⚠ 158
- **Micklefield [NT]** Ⓟ 🚲 Ⓤ 40
- **Middlesbrough [TP]** Ⓟ 🚲 ◇ 🚕 26, 39, 44, 45
- **Middlewood [NT]** Ⓤ 86
- **Midgham [GW]** Ⓟ Ⓤ 116
- **Milford Haven [AW]** Ⓟ 🚕 Ⓤ 128
- **Milford (Surrey) [SW]** Ⓟ 🚲 ⚠ 156
- **Millbrook (Bedfordshire) [LM]** Ⓤ 64
- **Millbrook (Hants.) [SW]** 🚲 ⚠ Ⓤ 158
- **Mill Hill Broadway [FC]** Ⓟ 🚲 ◇ ⚠ 🚕 52
- **Mill Hill (Lancashire) [NT]** Ⓤ 97
- **Milliken Park [SR]** 🚲 Ⓤ 221
- **Millom [NT]** Ⓟ Ⓤ 100
- **Mills Hill [NT]** Ⓟ Ⓤ 41
- **Milngavie [SR]** Ⓟ 🚲 226
- **Milton Keynes Central [LM]** Ⓟ 🚲 ◇ ⚠ 🚕
  - Birmingham International 66
  - Birmingham New Street 66
  - Blackpool 65
  - Bletchley 66
  - Brighton 66
  - Coventry 66, 67
  - Crewe 65, 67
  - Edinburgh 65
  - Gatwick Airport 66
  - Glasgow 65
  - Lancaster 65
  - Liverpool 65
  - London 67
  - Manchester 65
  - Northampton 66, 67
  - Oxenholme Lake District 65
  - Preston 65
  - Rugby 66, 67
  - Stafford 65, 67
  - Stockport 65
  - Stoke-on-Trent 65, 67
  - Tring 66
  - Warrington 65
  - Watford Junction 66, 176, 177
  - Wembley Central 66, 176, 177
  - Wigan 65
  - Wolverhampton 66
- **Minehead Bancks Street** *Bus* 135E
- **Minehead Butlins** *Bus* 135E
- **Minehead Parade** *Bus* 135E
- **Minffordd [AW]** Ⓤ 75
- **Minster [SE]** [4] Ⓟ ⚠ Ⓤ 207
- **Mirfield [NT]** Ⓟ 🚲 Ⓤ 39, 41
- **Mistley [LE]** 🚲 Ⓤ 11
- **Mitcham Eastfields [SN]** ◇ ⚠ 52, 173,179,182
- **Mitcham Junction [SN]** Ⓟ 🚲 ◇ ⚠ 52, 173, 179, 182

Station index and table numbers

[10] Connection time
Ⓟ Station Car Park
🚲 Bicycle storage facility
◇ Seat reservations can be made at this station
⚠ Penalty Fare Schemes in operation on some or all services from this station
🚕 Taxi rank or cab office at station, or signposted and within 100 metres
Ⓤ Unstaffed station
[ ] Station Operator Code

N

Station index and table numbers

[10] Connection time
Ⓟ Station Car Park
🚲 Bicycle storage facility
◇ Seat reservations can be made at this station
⚠ Penalty Fare Schemes in operation on some or all services from this station
🚕 Taxi rank or cab office at station, or signposted and within 100 metres
🚷 Unstaffed station
[ ] Station Operator Code

Newhaven Town [SN] 🚲 ⚠ 189
Newington [SE] Ⓟ ⚠ 212
Newmarket [LE] Ⓟ 🚲 🚷 14
Newport (Essex) [LE] Ⓟ 🚲 ⚠ 22
Newport (S. Wales) [AW] Ⓟ 🚲 ◇ 🚕 75,123
- Aberdeen 51
- Bangor (Gwynedd) 131
- Bath Spa 132
- Birmingham 57
- Bristol 132
- Cardiff 132
- Cheltenham Spa 57
- Chester 131
- Crewe 131
- Darlington 51
- Derby 57
- Dundee 51
- Durham 51
- Edinburgh 51
- Exeter 135
- Gloucester 132
- Hereford 131
- Holyhead 131
- Leeds 51
- Llandudno Junction 131
- London 125
- Maesteg 128
- Manchester 131
- Milford Haven 128
- Newcastle 51
- Nottingham 57
- Paignton 135
- Penzance 135
- Plymouth 135
- Portsmouth 123
- Reading 125
- Sheffield 51
- Shrewsbury 131
- Slough 125
- Swansea 128
- Swindon 125
- Torquay 135
- Weymouth 123
- Worcester 57
- York 51

Newquay [GW] Ⓟ 🚲 🚕 🚷 51, 135, 142
Newstead [EM] Ⓟ 🚷 55
Newton (Lanarks.) **[SR]** 🚲 223, 226
Newton Abbot [GW] Ⓟ 🚲 ◇ ⚠ 🚕 51, 135, *Sleepers* 406
Newton Aycliffe [NT] Ⓟ 🚷 44
Newton for Hyde [NT] Ⓟ ◇ 79
Newton St Cyres [GW] 🚷 136
Newton-le-Willows [NT] Ⓟ 81, 90
Newtonmore [SR] Ⓟ 🚲 🚷 229, *Sleepers* 403
Newton-on-Ayr [SR] 🚲 🚷 221
Newtown (Powys) [AW] 🚕 75
Ninian Park [AW] 🚷 130
Nitshill [SR] 🚲 🚷 222
Norbiton [SW] Ⓟ 🚲 ◇ ⚠ 152
Norbury [SN] Ⓟ 🚲 ◇ ⚠ 170, 173, 176
Normans Bay [SN] 🚷 189
Normanton [NT] Ⓟ 🚷 34
North Berwick [SR] Ⓟ 🚲 🚷 238
North Camp [GW] Ⓟ 🚲 148
North Dulwich [SN] 🚲 ⚠ 173
North Fambridge [LE] Ⓟ 🚲 🚷 6
North Llanrwst [AW] Ⓟ 🚷 102
North Queensferry [SR] Ⓟ 🚲 🚷 242
North Road [NT] 🚲 🚷 44
North Sheen [SW] ◇ ⚠ 149
North Walsham [LE] Ⓟ 🚲 🚕 16
North Wembley [LT] 60
Northallerton [TP] Ⓟ 🚲 ◇ 🚕 26, 39
Northampton [LM] Ⓟ 🚲 ◇ 🚕 65, 66, 67, 68
Northfield [LM] Ⓟ ◇ ⚠ 69
Northfleet [SE] ◇ ⚠ 200
Northolt Park [CH] ⚠ 115
Northumberland Park [LE] ⚠ 22
Northwich [NT] Ⓟ ◇ 88
Norton Bridge Station Drive *Bus* 67A
Norwich [LE] Ⓟ 🚲 ◇ 🚕
- Birmingham 49
- Cambridge 17
- Colchester 11
- Cromer 16
- Darlington 26
- Doncaster 26
- Edinburgh 26
- Ely 17
- Great Yarmouth 15
- Harwich 11
- Ipswich 11
- Leeds 26
- Leicester 49
- Liverpool 49
- London 11
- Lowestoft 15
- Manchester 49
- Newcastle 26
- Nottingham 49
- Peterborough 17
- Retford 26
- Sheffield 49
- Sheringham 16
- Stockport 49
- Stratford 11
- York 26

Norwood Junction [LO] **[2]** Ⓟ 🚲 ⚠ 🚕
- Balham 171
- Brighton 186
- Caterham 181
- Clapham Junction 171
- Crystal Palace 177
- East Croydon 175,177
- East Grinstead 184
- Gatwick Airport 186
- Haywards Heath 186
- Horsham 186
- London 175
- New Cross Gate 175,177
- Oxted 184
- Purley 181
- Redhill 186
- Sutton (Surrey) 172
- Tattenham Corner 181
- Tonbridge 186
- Uckfield 184
- Wandsworth Common 171
- West Croydon 171, 177

Nottingham [EM] **[8]** Ⓟ 🚲 ◇ ⚠ 🚕
- Barnsley 34
- Bedford 53
- Birmingham 57
- Birmingham International 51
- Bournemouth 51
- Bristol 57
- Cambridge 49
- Cardiff 57
- Cheltenham Spa 57
- Cleethorpes 27
- Coventry 51
- Derby 56
- Doncaster 53
- Exeter 51
- Gloucester 57
- Grantham 19
- Grimsby Town 27
- Kettering 53
- Leeds 34, 53
- Leicester 53
- Lincoln 27
- Liverpool 49
- London 53
- Loughborough 53
- Luton 53
- Manchester 49
- Mansfield 55
- Market Harborough 53
- Matlock 56
- Meadowhall 34, 53
- Newark 27
- Newport (South Wales) 57
- Nuneaton 57
- Oxford 51
- Paignton 51
- Penzance 51
- Peterborough 49
- Plymouth 51
- Reading 51
- Sheffield 34, 53
- Skegness 19
- Southampton 51
- Stockport 49
- Wakefield 34, 53

Station index and table numbers

10 Connection time
Ⓟ Station Car Park
🚲 Bicycle storage facility
◇ Seat reservations can be made at this station
⚠ Penalty Fare Schemes in operation on some or all services from this station
🚕 Taxi rank or cab office at station, or signposted and within 100 metres
Ⓤ Unstaffed station
[ ] Station Operator Code

■10 Connection time
℗ Station Car Park
🚲 Bicycle storage facility
◇ Seat reservations can be made at this station
⚠ Penalty Fare Schemes in operation on some or all services from this station
🚕 Taxi rank or cab office at station, or signposted and within 100 metres
🚶 Unstaffed station
[ ] Station Operator Code

Station index and table numbers

Pickering Eastgate *Bus* 26G
Pilning [GW] ℗ 🚶 132
Pinhoe [SW] ⚠ 🚶 160
Pitlochry [SR] ℗ 🚲 🚕 229, *Sleepers* 403
Pitsea [CC] ℗ 🚲 ◇ ⚠ 🚕 1
Pleasington [NT] ℗ 🚶 97
Pleasure Beach [NT] (see Blackpool)
Plockton [SR] ℗ 🚲 🚶 239
Pluckley [SE] ℗ 🚲 ◇ ⚠ 207
Plumley [NT] ℗ 🚶 88
Plumpton [SN] ℗ ◇ ⚠ 189
Plumstead [SE] ◇ ⚠ 200
Plymouth [GW] ℗ 🚲 ◇ ⚠ 🚕
Aberdeen 51
Birmingham 51, 135
Bristol 135
Cardiff 135
Carlisle 51
Crewe 51
Derby 51
Dundee 51
Edinburgh 51
Exeter 135
Glasgow 51
Gunnislake 139
Leeds 51
London 135, *Sleepers* 406
Manchester 51
Newcastle 51
Newton Abbot 135
Nottingham 51
Paignton 135
Penzance 135
Preston 51
Reading 135, *Sleepers* 406
Sheffield 51
Taunton 135
Torquay 135
Wolverhampton 51
York 51
Pokesdown [SW] 🚲 ◇ ⚠ 158
Polegate [SN] ℗ 🚲 ◇ ⚠ 🚕 189
Polesworth [LM] ℗ 🚶 67
Pollokshaws East [SR] 🚲 🚶 223
Pollokshaws West [SR] 🚲 🚶 222
Pollokshields East [SR] 🚲 223
Pollokshields West [SR] 🚲 🚶 223
Polmont [SR] ■3 ℗ 🚲 ◇ 🚕 228, 230
Polsloe Bridge [GW] 🚶 136
Ponders End [LE] ⚠ 22
Pontarddulais [AW] ℗ 🚶 129
Pontefract Baghill [NT] ℗ 🚶 33
Pontefract Monkhill [NT] ℗ 🚶 26, 31, 32
Pontefract Tanshelf [NT] ℗ 🚶 32
Pontlottyn [AW] ℗ 🚶 130
Pont-y-Pant [AW] 🚶 102
Pontyclun [AW] ℗ 🚶 128
Pontypool & New Inn [AW] ℗ 🚶 131
Pontypridd [AW] ■3 🚲 ◇ 🚕 130
Poole [SW] ■4 ℗ 🚲 ◇ ⚠ 🚕 158
Poppleton [NT] ℗ 🚲 🚶 35
Portchester [SW] 🚲 ⚠ 158, 165, 188
Port Glasgow [SR] 🚲 🚕 219
Porth [AW] ℗ ◇ 130
Porthmadog [AW] 🚶 75
Portlethen [SR] ℗ 🚲 🚶 229
Portslade [SN] ℗ 🚲 ◇ ⚠ 188
Portsmouth Arms [GW] ℗ 🚶 136
Portsmouth 123
Harbour [SW] 🚲 ◇ ⚠ 🚕
& Southsea [SW] ℗ 🚲 ◇ ⚠ 🚕
Bognor Regis 188
Brighton 188
Bristol 123
Cardiff 123
Chichester 188
Crawley 188
East Croydon 188
Exeter 160
Fareham 165
Gatwick Airport 188
Guildford 156
Haslemere 156
Havant 157
Horsham 188
Littlehampton 188
London 156, 158, 188
Reading
via Eastleigh 158
via Guildford 156
Redhill 188
Ryde 167
Salisbury 123
Sandown 167
Shanklin 167
Southampton Central 165
Winchester 158
Worthing 188
Port Sunlight [ME] 🚲 ⚠ 107
Port Talbot Parkway [AW] ℗ 🚲 ◇ 🚕 125, 128
Possilpark & Parkhouse [SR] 🚲 🚶 232
Potters Bar [FC] ℗ ◇ ⚠ 🚕 24, 25
Poulton-le-Fylde [NT] ℗ ◇ 🚕 41, 82, 97
Poynton [NT] ℗ 84
Prees [AW] 🚶 131
Prescot [NT] ℗ 90
Prestatyn [AW] ◇ 🚕 🚶 75, 81
Prestbury [NT] ℗ 🚶 84
Preston [VT] ■8 ℗ 🚲 ◇ 🚕
Aberdeen 65, *Sleepers* 402
Barrow-in-Furness 82
Birmingham 65
Birmingham International 65
Blackburn 97
Blackpool 97
Bolton 82
Bournemouth 51
Bradford 41
Bristol 51
Burnley 97
Carlisle 65
Chorley 82
Clitheroe 94, 97
Colne 97
Coventry 65
Crewe 65
Douglas (IOM) 98A
Dundee 65, *Sleepers* 402
Edinburgh 65
Exeter 51
Fort William *Sleepers* 404
Glasgow 65
Inverkeithing *Sleepers* 402
Inverness 65, *Sleepers* 403
Kirkcaldy *Sleepers* 402
Lancaster 65
Leeds 41
Liverpool 90
London 65
Manchester 82
Manchester Airport 82
Milton Keynes Central 65
Ormskirk 99
Oxenholme Lake District 65
Oxford 51
Paignton 51
Penzance 51
Perth 65, *Sleepers* 403
Plymouth 51
Reading 51
Rugby 65
Southampton 51
Stafford 65
Stirling *Sleepers* 403
Stockport 82
Torquay 51
Warrington 65
Watford 65
Wigan 65
Windermere 65
Wolverhampton 65
York 41
Preston Park [SN] ◇ ⚠ 52, 186, 188
Prestonpans [SR] ℗ 🚲 🚶 238
Prestwick International Airport 🚕 🚶 218, 221
Prestwick Town [SR] ℗ 🚲 🚕 218, 221
Priesthill & Darnley [SR] 🚲 🚶 222
Princes Risborough [CH] ■2 ℗ 🚲 ◇ ⚠ 🚕 115, 115A
Prittlewell [LE] ℗ 🚲 ⚠ 6
Prudhoe [NT] ℗ 🚲 🚶 48
Pulborough [SN] ℗ 🚲 ◇ ⚠ 🚕 188
Purfleet [CC] ℗ 🚲 ◇ ⚠ 1

Station index and table numbers

[10] Connection time
Ⓟ Station Car Park
🚲 Bicycle storage facility
◇ Seat reservations can be made at this station
⚠ Penalty Fare Schemes in operation on some or all services from this station
🚕 Taxi rank or cab office at station, or signposted and within 100 metres
Ⓤ Unstaffed station
[ ] Station Operator Code

Purley [SN] [4] Ⓟ ◇ ⚠ 🚕 170, 177, 181, 186
Purley Oaks [SN] Ⓟ ⚠ 181
Putney [SW] 🚲 ◇ ⚠ 149
Pwllheli [AW] 🚲 🚕 76
Pyle [AW] Ⓟ 🚲 Ⓤ 128

Q

Quakers Yard [AW] Ⓤ 130
Queenborough [SE] Ⓟ ◇ ⚠ 212
Queens Park (Glasgow) **[SR]** 🚲 223
Queen's Park (London) **[LT]** 60
Queen's Road, Peckham [SN] 🚲 ◇ ⚠ 173, 178
Queen's Road, Walthamstow [LO] (see Walthamstow Queen s Road)
Queenstown Road (Battersea) [SW] ⚠ Ⓤ 149
Quintrell Downs [GW] Ⓤ 142

R

Radcliffe (Notts.) **[EM]** Ⓟ Ⓤ 19
Radlett [FC] Ⓟ 🚲 ◇ ⚠ 🚕 52
Radley [GW] Ⓟ Ⓤ 116
Radyr [AW] [3] Ⓟ 🚲 ◇ 130
Rainford [NT] Ⓟ Ⓤ 82
Rainham (Essex) **[CC]** Ⓟ 🚲 ◇ ⚠ 1
Rainham (Kent) [SE] Ⓟ ◇ ⚠ 🚕 194, 212
Rainhill [NT] 90
Ramsgate [SE] [4] Ⓟ 🚲 ◇ ⚠ 🚕 194, 207, 212
Ramsgreave & Wilpshire [NT] Ⓟ Ⓤ 94
Rannoch [SR] Ⓟ 🚲 Ⓤ 227, *Sleepers* 404
Rauceby [EM] Ⓤ 19
Ravenglass for Eskdale [NT] Ⓤ 100
Ravensbourne [SE] ◇ ⚠ 52, 195
Ravensthorpe [NT] Ⓤ 39
Rawcliffe [NT] Ⓤ 32
Rayleigh [LE] Ⓟ 🚲 ⚠ 🚕 6
Raynes Park [SW] [6] 🚲 ◇ ⚠ 🚕 152
Reading [GW] [7] Ⓟ 🚲 ◇ ⚠ 🚕
Aberdeen 51
Ascot 149
Banbury 116
Basingstoke 122
Bath Spa 125
Birmingham 116
Bodmin Parkway 135, *Sleepers* 406
Bournemouth 158
Bristol 125
Camborne 135, *Sleepers* 406
Cardiff 125
Carlisle 51
Cheltenham Spa 125
Clapham Junction 149
Coventry 51
Crewe 51
Derby 51
Didcot 116
Dundee 51
Edinburgh 51
Exeter 135, *Sleepers* 406
Gatwick Airport 148
Glasgow 51
Gloucester 125
Guildford 148
Hayle 135, *Sleepers* 406
Heathrow Airport *Bus* 125A
Henley-on-Thames 121
Hereford 126
Leamington Spa 116
Leeds 51
Liskeard 135, *Sleepers* 406
London 116, 117, 149
Lostwithiel 135, *Sleepers* 406
Manchester 51
Milford Haven 128
Moreton-in-Marsh 126
Newbury 116
Newcastle 51
Newport (South Wales) 125
Newton Abbot 135, *Sleepers* 406
Oxford 116
Paignton 135
Par 135, *Sleepers* 406
Penzance 135, *Sleepers* 406
Plymouth 135, *Sleepers* 406
Poole 158
Portsmouth
via Basingstoke 158
via Guildford 156
Preston 51
Redhill 148
Redruth 135, *Sleepers* 406
Rosslare Harbour 128
Sheffield 51
Slough 117
Southampton 158
St Austell 135, *Sleepers* 406
St Erth 135, *Sleepers* 406
Staines 149
Swansea 125
Swindon 125
Taunton 135
Torquay 135
Truro 135, *Sleepers* 406
Weston-super-Mare 125
Weymouth 158
Winchester 158
Wolverhampton 51
Worcester 126
York 51
Reading West [GW] [3] 116, 122
Rectory Road [LE] ⚠ 21
Redbridge [SW] Ⓟ ⚠ Ⓤ 158
Redcar British Steel [NT] Ⓤ 44
Redcar Central [NT] Ⓟ 🚲 ◇ 🚕 44
Redcar East [NT] 🚲 Ⓤ 44
Reddish North [NT] Ⓟ 🚲 78
Reddish South [NT] Ⓤ 78
Redditch [LM] Ⓟ ◇ ⚠ 69
Redhill [SN] Ⓟ 🚲 ◇ ⚠ 🚕 148, 186, 188
Redland [GW] 🚲 Ⓤ 133
Redruth [GW] Ⓟ 🚲 ◇ 🚕 51, 135, *Sleepers* 406
Reedham (Norfolk) [LE] Ⓟ 🚲 Ⓤ 15
Reedham (Surrey) **[SN]** ⚠ 181
Reigate [SN] Ⓟ 🚲 ◇ ⚠ 148, 186
Renton [SR] 🚲 Ⓤ 226
Retford [GR] [10] Ⓟ 🚲 ◇ 🚕 26, 30
Rhiwbina [AW] Ⓤ 130
Rhoose Cardiff Int. Airport [AW] Ⓟ 🚲 Ⓤ 130
Rhosneigr [AW] Ⓤ 81
Rhyl [AW] ◇ 🚕 75, 81
Rhymney [AW] [3] Ⓟ 🚕 Ⓤ 130
Ribblehead [NT] Ⓟ Ⓤ 36
Rice Lane [ME] ⚠ 104
Richmond (Greater London) **[SW]** Ⓟ 🚲 ◇ ⚠ 🚕 59, 149
Richmond (Market) 🚕 *Bus* 26H
Rickmansworth [LT] Ⓟ 🚲 ⚠ 114
Riddlesdown [SN] 🚲 ◇ ⚠ 184
Ridgmont [LM] Ⓤ 64
Riding Mill [NT] Ⓟ 🚲 Ⓤ 48
Risca & Pontymister [AW] Ⓟ Ⓤ 127
Rishton [NT] Ⓟ 🚲 Ⓤ 97
Robin Hood Airport 🚕 *Bus* 26F
Robertsbridge [SE] Ⓟ ◇ ⚠ 206
Roby [NT] 90
Rochdale [NT] Ⓟ ◇ 🚕 41, 82
Roche [GW] Ⓤ 142
Rochester [SE] [4] Ⓟ ◇ ⚠ 🚕 194, 200, 212
Rochford [LE] Ⓟ 🚲 ⚠ 🚕 6
Rock Ferry [ME] Ⓟ 🚲 ◇ ⚠ 🚕 107,
Rogart [SR] Ⓟ 🚲 Ⓤ 239
Rogerstone [AW] Ⓟ Ⓤ 127
Rolleston [EM] Ⓤ 27
Roman Bridge [AW] Ⓤ 102
Romford [LE] 🚲 ◇ ⚠ 🚕 4, 5, 6, 11
Romiley [NT] Ⓟ 🚲 78
Romsey [GW] Ⓟ 🚲 123, 158
Roose [NT] Ⓟ Ⓤ 82
Rose Grove [NT] Ⓤ 97
Rose Hill Marple [NT] Ⓟ 🚲 ◇ 78
Rosslare Harbour *Ship* 128
Rosyth [SR] Ⓟ Ⓤ 242
Rotherham Central [NT] Ⓟ ◇ 🚕 29, 31, 33

■10 Connection time
Ⓟ Station Car Park
🚲 Bicycle storage facility
◇ Seat reservations can be made at this station
⚠ Penalty Fare Schemes in operation on some or all services from this station
🚕 Taxi rank or cab office at station, or signposted and within 100 metres
Ⓤ Unstaffed station
[ ] Station Operator Code

Station index and table numbers

Station index and table numbers

■10 Connection time
Ⓟ Station Car Park
🚲 Bicycle storage facility
◇ Seat reservations can be made at this station
⚠ Penalty Fare Schemes in operation on some or all services from this station
🚕 Taxi rank or cab office at station, or signposted and within 100 metres
Ⓤ Unstaffed station
[ ] Station Operator Code

Station index and table numbers

10 Connection time
Ⓟ Station Car Park
🚲 Bicycle storage facility
◇ Seat reservations can be made at this station
⚠ Penalty Fare Schemes in operation on some or all services from this station
🚕 Taxi rank or cab office at station, or signposted and within 100 metres
ⓤ Unstaffed station
[ ] Station Operator Code

Woking 158
Wolverhampton 51
Worthing 188
Yarmouth (IOW) 158
Yeovil 160
York 51
Southbourne [SN] ◇ ⚠ 188
Southbury [LE] ⚠ 21
Southease [SN] ⓤ 189
Southend Airport [LE] ⚠ 🚕 6
Southend Central [CC] Ⓟ 🚲 ◇ ⚠ 🚕 1
Southend East [CC] Ⓟ 🚲 ◇ ⚠ 1
Southend Victoria [LE] 🚲 ◇ ⚠ 🚕 6
Southminster [LE] Ⓟ 🚲 ⓤ 6
Southport [ME] 🚲 ◇ ⚠ 🚕 82, 103
Southsea [SW] (see Portsmouth & Southsea)
Southwick [SN] 🚲 ◇ ⚠ 188
Sowerby Bridge [NT] Ⓟ 🚲 ⓤ 41
Sowton [GW] (see Digby & Sowton)
Spalding [EM] Ⓟ 🚲 🚕 18
Spean Bridge [SR] Ⓟ 🚲 ⓤ 227, *Sleepers* 404
Spital [ME] 🚲 ⚠ 107
Spondon [EM] ⚠ ⓤ 56
Spooner Row [LE] ⓤ 17
Spring Road [LM] ⚠ 71
Springburn [SR] 🚲 224, 226
Springfield [SR] 🚲 ⓤ 229
Squires Gate [NT] ⓤ 97
Stafford [VT] Ⓟ 🚲 ◇ 🚕
Bangor (Gwynedd) 65
Birmingham 68
Blackpool 65
Bournemouth 51
Bristol 51
Carlisle 65
Chester 65
Coventry 67, 68
Crewe 65
Edinburgh 65
Exeter 51
Glasgow 65
Holyhead 65
Lichfield 67
Liverpool 65
London 65
Manchester 84
Manchester Airport 84
Nuneaton 67
Oxenholme Lake District 65
Oxford 51
Paignton 51
Penzance 51
Plymouth 51
Preston 65
Reading 51
Rugby 65
Southampton 51
Stockport 84
Stoke-on-Trent 65, 68A
Tamworth 67
Torquay 51
Watford 65
Wolverhampton 68
Staines [SW] Ⓟ 🚲 ◇ ⚠ 🚕 149
Stainforth [NT] (see Hatfield & Stainforth)
Stallingborough [NT] ⓤ 28
Stalybridge [TP] Ⓟ 🚲 ◇ 39
Stamford [EM] Ⓟ ◇ 49
Stamford Hill [LE] ⚠ 21
Stanford-le-Hope [CC] Ⓟ 🚲 ◇ ⚠ 1
Stanlow & Thornton [NT] ⓤ 109
Stansted Airport [LE] 🚲 ◇ ⚠ 🚕 17, 22, 26, 49
Stansted Mountfitchet [LE] Ⓟ 🚲 ⚠ 🚕 22
Staplehurst [SE] Ⓟ 🚲 ◇ ⚠ 🚕 207
Stapleton Road [GW] 🚲 ⓤ 133, 134
Starbeck [NT] 🚲 ⓤ 35
Starcross [GW] 🚲 ⓤ 135
Staveley [TP] ⓤ 83
Stechford [LM] ⚠ 68
Steeton & Silsden [NT] Ⓟ 🚲 ⓤ 36
Stepps [SR] Ⓟ 🚲 ⓤ 224
Stevenage [FC] **4** Ⓟ 🚲 ◇ ⚠ 🚕 24, 25, 26
Stevenston [SR] 🚲 ⓤ 221
Stewartby [LM] ⓤ 64
Stewarton [SR] Ⓟ 🚲 ⓤ 222
Stirling [SR] Ⓟ 🚲 ◇ 🚕 26, 229, 230, *Sleepers* 403
Stockport [VT] Ⓟ 🚲 ◇ 🚕
Altrincham 88
Birmingham 65
Birmingham International 65
Blackpool 82
Bolton 82
Bournemouth 51
Bristol 51
Buxton 86
Cambridge 49
Cardiff 131
Chester 88
Coventry 65
Crewe 84
Doncaster 29
Ely 49
Exeter 51
Hazel Grove 86
Hull 29
Liverpool 89
London 65
Macclesfield 84
Manchester 84
Newport (South Wales) 131
Northwich 88
Norwich 49
Nottingham 49
Oxford 51
Paignton 51
Penzance 51
Peterborough 49
Plymouth 51
Preston 82
Reading 51
Rugby 65
Salford Crescent 82
Sheffield 78
Southampton 51
Stafford 84
Stoke-on-Trent 84
Torquay 51
Watford 65
Wigan 82
Wolverhampton 65
Stocksfield [NT] Ⓟ 🚲 ⓤ 48
Stocksmoor [NT] Ⓟ 🚲 ⓤ 34
Stockton [NT] 🚲 🚕 ⓤ 44
Stoke d'Abernon [SW] (see Cobham)
Stoke Mandeville [CH] Ⓟ 🚲 ⚠ 114
Stoke Newington [LE] ⚠ 21
Stoke-on-Trent [VT] Ⓟ 🚲 ◇ 🚕 50, 51, 65, 67, 84
Stone [LM] 67
Stone Crown Street *Bus* 67
Stone Granville Square *Bus* 67
Stone Crossing [SE] ◇ ⚠ 200
Stonebridge Park [LT] 60
Stonegate [SE] Ⓟ 🚲 ◇ ⚠ 206
Stonehaven [SR] Ⓟ 🚲 ◇ 26, 51, 229, *Sleepers* 402
Stonehouse [GW] Ⓟ 125
Stoneleigh [SW] 🚲 ◇ ⚠ 152
Stornoway *Ship* 239B
Stourbridge Junction [LM] **2** Ⓟ ◇ ⚠ 71, 72, 115
Stourbridge Town [LM] ⚠ 72
Stowmarket [LE] Ⓟ 🚲 ◇ 🚕 11, 14
Stranraer [SR] 🚲 ◇ 218
Stratford (London) **[LE]** **7** ⚠ 🚕
Barking 1
Basildon 1
Bishops Stortford 22
Braintree 11
Broxbourne 22
Bury St. Edmunds 14
Cambridge 14
Chelsmford 11
Cheshunt 22
Clacton-on-Sea 11
Colchester 11
Ely 14
Gospel Oak 59, 176
Hackney 59
Harlow 22
Harwich 11
Hertford East 22
Highbury & Islington 59, 176
Ilford 5
Ipswich 11
London 5, 6
Manningtree 11

Station index and table numbers

■10 Connection time
Ⓟ Station Car Park
🚲 Bicycle storage facility
◇ Seat reservations can be made at this station
⚠ Penalty Fare Schemes in operation on some or all services from this station
🚕 Taxi rank or cab office at station, or signposted and within 100 metres
Ⓤ Unstaffed station
[ ] Station Operator Code

Norwich 11
Peterborough 14
Richmond 59
Romford 5,6
Shenfield 5
Shoeburyness 1
Southend 1,6
Southminster 6
Stansted Airport 22
Stowmarket 11
Tottenham Hale 22
Upminster 1
Walton-on-the-Naze 11
West Hampstead 59, 176
Wickford
Willesden Junction 59
Witham 11

Stratford International [SE] ⚠ 194, 200, 207, 208, 212
Stratford-upon-Avon [LM] Ⓟ 🚲 ◇ ⚠ 🚕 71, 115
Stratford-upon-Avon Parkway [LM] 71, 115
Strathcarron [SR] Ⓟ 🚲 Ⓤ 239
Strawberry Hill [SW] 🚲 ◇ ⚠ 149, 152
Streatham [SN] ■4 ◇ ⚠ 52,173, 179 182
Streatham Common [SN] ■4 Ⓟ 🚲 ◇ ⚠ 170,173,176
Streatham Hill [SN] ◇ ⚠ 🚕 🚲 171
Streatley [GW] (see Goring & Streatley)
Streethouse [NT] Ⓟ Ⓤ 32
Strines [NT] Ⓟ Ⓤ 78
Stromeferry [SR] Ⓟ 🚲 Ⓤ 239
Stromness 🚕 *Ship* 239A
Strood [SE] ■4 Ⓟ 🚲 ◇ ⚠ 🚕 194, 200, 208, 212
Stroud [GW] Ⓟ 🚲 ◇ 🚕 125
Sturry [SE] ⚠ 207
Styal [NT] Ⓟ Ⓤ 84
Sudbury (Suffolk) **[LE]** 🚲 Ⓤ 10
Sudbury & Harrow Road [CH] ⚠ Ⓤ 115
Sudbury Hill Harrow [CH] ⚠ Ⓤ 115
Sugar Loaf [AW] Ⓤ 129
Summerston [SR] Ⓤ 232
Sunbury [SW] Ⓟ 🚲 ◇ ⚠ 152
Sunderland [NT] ◇ 🚕 26, 44, 48
Sundridge Park [SE] Ⓟ ◇ ⚠ 204
Sunningdale [SW] Ⓟ 🚲 ◇ ⚠ 🚕 149
Sunnymeads [SW] ⚠ Ⓤ 149
Surbiton [SW] ■6 Ⓟ 🚲 ◇ ⚠ 🚕 152, 155
Surrey Quays [LO] 🚲 ⚠ 178
Sutton Coldfield [LM] Ⓟ 🚲 ◇ ⚠ 69
Sutton Common [FC] ⚠ Ⓤ 52, 179
Sutton Parkway [EM] Ⓟ Ⓤ 55
Sutton (Surrey) [SN] ■4 Ⓟ 🚲 ◇ ⚠ 170,171,172,173,179,182

Swaffham *Bus* 26A
Swale [SE] ⚠ Ⓤ 212
Swalecliffe [SE] (see Chestfield & Swalecliffe)
Swanley [SE] ■4 Ⓟ ◇ ⚠ 🚕 52, 195, 196, 212
Swanscombe [SE] ◇ ⚠ 200
Swansea [AW] Ⓟ 🚲 ◇ 🚕
Bristol 128
Cardiff 128
Camarthen 128
Crewe 131
Derby 57
Fishguard Harbour 128
Gloucester 57
Hereford 131
Llandrindod 129
London 125, 128
Manchester 128, 131
Pembroke Dock 128
Portsmouth 128
Reading 125, 128
Rosslare Harbour 128
Shrewsbury 129
Slough 125
Tenby 128

Swanwick [SW] Ⓟ 🚲 ◇ ⚠ 🚕 165, 188
Sway [SW] Ⓟ 🚲 ◇ ⚠ 158
Swaythling [SW] Ⓟ 🚲 ◇ ⚠ 158
Swinderby [EM] Ⓤ 27
Swindon [GW] Ⓟ 🚲 ◇ ⚠ 🚕 123, 125
Swineshead [EM] Ⓤ 19
Swinton (Gtr. Manchester) **[NT]** 82
Swinton (S. Yorks.) [NT] Ⓟ 🚲 ◇ 29, 31, 33
Sydenham [LO] 🚲 ⚠ 🚕 171, 177,178
Sydenham Hill [SE] Ⓟ ⚠ 195
Syon Lane [SW] 🚲 ⚠ Ⓤ 149
Syston [EM] Ⓟ ⚠ Ⓤ 53

T

Tackley [GW] Ⓤ 116
Tadworth [SN] ◇ ⚠ 181
Taffs Well [AW] Ⓟ Ⓤ 130
Tain [SR] Ⓟ Ⓤ 239
Talsarnau [AW] Ⓤ 75
Talybont [AW] Ⓤ 75
Tal-y-Cafn [AW] Ⓤ 102
Tame Bridge Parkway [LM] Ⓟ 🚲 ◇ ⚠ 70, 75
Tamworth [LM] Ⓟ ◇ 🚕 51, 57, 65, 67
Taplow [GW] Ⓟ 🚲 ⚠ 🚕 117
Tarbert *Ship* 239B
Tattenham Corner [SN] Ⓟ ◇ ⚠ 181
Taunton [GW] Ⓟ 🚲 ◇ ⚠ 🚕 51, 134, 135, *Bus* 135E
Taynuilt [SR] Ⓟ 🚲 Ⓤ 227

Teddington [SW] 🚲 ◇ ⚠ 149, 152
Tees-side Airport [NT] Ⓤ 44
Teignmouth [GW] Ⓟ 🚲 ◇ 🚕 51, 135
Telford Central [LM] Ⓟ ◇ 🚕 74, 75
Templecombe [SW] Ⓟ 🚲 ◇ ⚠ 160
Tenby [AW] Ⓟ Ⓤ 128
Tewkesbury [GW] (see Ashchurch)
Teynham [SE] Ⓟ ◇ ⚠ 212
Thame [CH] (see Haddenham & Thame Parkway)
Thames Ditton [SW] 🚲 ⚠ 152
Thatcham [GW] Ⓟ 🚲 116, 135
Thatto Heath [NT] Ⓟ 90
The Hawthorns [LM] Ⓟ ⚠ 71
The Lakes (Warwickshire) **[LM]** ⚠ Ⓤ 71
Theale [GW] Ⓟ 🚲 116, 135
Theobalds Grove [LE] ⚠ 21
Thetford [LE] Ⓟ ◇ 🚕 17, 49
Thirsk [TP] Ⓟ ◇ 26, 39
Thornaby [TP] Ⓟ 🚲 ◇ 🚕 39, 44
Thorne North [NT] Ⓟ 🚲 29
Thorne South [NT] Ⓟ Ⓤ 29
Thornford [GW] Ⓤ 123
Thornhill [AW] (see Lisvane)
Thornliebank [SR] 🚲 Ⓤ 222
Thornton (Ches.) **[NT]** (see Stanlow & Thornton)
Thornton (Fife) **[SR]** (see Glenrothes With Thornton)
Thornton Abbey [NT] Ⓤ 28
Thorntonhall [SR] 🚲 Ⓤ 222
Thornton Heath [SN] 🚲 ◇ ⚠ 🚕 170, 173 176,
Thorpe Bay [CC] Ⓟ 🚲 ◇ ⚠ 🚕 1
Thorpe Culvert [EM] Ⓟ Ⓤ 19
Thorpe-le-Soken [LE] ■1 Ⓟ 🚲 ⚠ 11
Three Bridges [SN] ■4 Ⓟ 🚲 ◇ ⚠ 🚕 52, 186, 188
Three Oaks [SN] Ⓤ 189
Thurgarton [EM] Ⓤ 27
Thurnscoe [NT] Ⓟ Ⓤ 31
Thurso [SR] Ⓟ 🚲 ◇ 🚕 239, *Ship* 239A
Thurston [LE] Ⓟ 🚲 Ⓤ 14
Tilbury Riverside [CC] Ⓤ *Bus* 1A
Tilbury Town [CC] ■3 🚲 ◇ ⚠ 1, *Bus* 1A
Tile Hill [LM] Ⓟ ⚠ 68
Tilehurst [GW] Ⓟ 🚲 116
Tipton [LM] Ⓟ ⚠ 68
Tiree *Ship* 227B
Tir-phil [AW] Ⓟ Ⓤ 130
Tisbury [SW] Ⓟ 🚲 ◇ ⚠ 160
Tiverton Parkway [GW] Ⓟ 🚲 ◇ ⚠ 🚕 51, 135
Todmorden [NT] Ⓟ 🚲 🚕 41

[10] Connection time
Ⓟ Station Car Park
🚲 Bicycle storage facility
◇ Seat reservations can be made at this station
⚠ Penalty Fare Schemes in operation on some or all services from this station
🚕 Taxi rank or cab office at station, or signposted and within 100 metres
Ⓤ Unstaffed station
[ ] Station Operator Code

Station index and table numbers

U

V

W

Station index and table numbers

[10] Connection time
Ⓟ Station Car Park
🚲 Bicycle storage facility
◇ Seat reservations can be made at this station
⚠ Penalty Fare Schemes in operation on some or all services from this station
🚕 Taxi rank or cab office at station, or signposted and within 100 metres
ⓤ Unstaffed station
[ ] Station Operator Code

Station index and table numbers

[10] Connection time
℗ Station Car Park
🚲 Bicycle storage facility
◇ Seat reservations can be made at this station
⚠ Penalty Fare Schemes in operation on some or all services from this station
🚕 Taxi rank or cab office at station, or signposted and within 100 metres
Ⓤ Unstaffed station
[ ] Station Operator Code

Station index and table numbers

[10]	Connection time
Ⓟ	Station Car Park
🚲	Bicycle storage facility
◇	Seat reservations can be made at this station
⚠	Penalty Fare Schemes in operation on some or all services from this station
🚕	Taxi rank or cab office at station, or signposted and within 100 metres
🚶	Unstaffed station
[ ]	Station Operator Code

Worcester Foregate Street [LM] [7] ◇ ⚠ 🚕 71, 126
Worcester Shrub Hill [LM] [7] Ⓟ ◇ ⚠ 🚕 57, 71, 125, 126
Worcester Park [SW] Ⓟ 🚲 ◇ ⚠ 🚕 152
Workington [NT] Ⓟ ◇ 100
Worksop [NT] Ⓟ ◇ 30, 55
Worle [GW] Ⓟ 🚲 🚶 134
Worplesdon [SW] Ⓟ 🚲 ◇ ⚠ 155, 156
Worstead [LE] Ⓟ 🚲 🚶 16
Worthing [SN] [4] Ⓟ 🚲 ◇ ⚠ 🚕 123, 188
Wrabness [LE] Ⓟ 🚲 🚶 11
Wraysbury [SW] Ⓟ ⚠ 🚶 149
Wrenbury [AW] Ⓟ 🚶 131
Wressle [NT] 🚶 29
Wrexham Central [AW] 🚶 101
Wrexham General [AW] Ⓟ ◇ 🚕 65, 75, 101
Wrotham [SE] (see Borough Green & Wrotham)
Wroxham [LE] (see Hoveton & Wroxham)
Wye [SE] Ⓟ ◇ ⚠ 207
Wylam [NT] Ⓟ 🚲 🚶 48
Wylde Green [LM] Ⓟ ⚠ 69
Wymondham [LE] Ⓟ 🚕 17
Wythall [LM] ⚠ 71

Y

Yalding [SE] Ⓟ ⚠ 🚶 208
Yardley Wood [LM] Ⓟ ⚠ 71
Yarm [TP] Ⓟ 🚶 39
Yarmouth (IOW) *Ship* 🚕 158
Yate [GW] Ⓟ 🚲 134
Yatton [GW] Ⓟ 🚲 134
Yeoford [GW] 🚶 136
Yeovil Bus Station *Bus* [SW] Ⓟ 🚲 123A
Yeovil Junction [SW] Ⓟ 🚲 ◇ ⚠ 🚕 123A,160
Yeovil Pen Mill [GW] Ⓟ ◇ 123, 123A
Yetminster [GW] Ⓟ 🚶 123
Ynyswen [AW] 🚶 130
Yoker [SR] 🚲 🚶 226
York [GR] [8] Ⓟ 🚲 ◇ 🚕
Aberdeen 26
Bedford 53
Birmingham 51
Birmingham International 51
Blackpool 41
Bournemouth 51
Bradford 40
Bristol 51
Cambridge 26
Cardiff 51
Darlington 26
Derby 53
Doncaster 26
Dundee 26
Eden Camp *Bus* 26G
Edinburgh 26
Exeter 51
Flamingo Land *Bus* 26G
Glasgow 26
Grantham 26
Halifax 41
Harrogate 35
Hartlepool 26
Huddersfield 39
Hull 33
Knaresborough 35
Leeds 35, 40
Leicester 53
Liverpool 39
London 26
Luton 53
Manchester 39
Manchester Airport 39
Middlesbrough 26
Newark 26
Newcastle 26
Newport (South Wales) 51
Newton Abbot 51
Norwich 26
Nottingham 53
Oxford 51
Paignton 51
Penzance 51
Peterborough 26
Pickering Eastgate *Bus* 26G
Plymouth 51
Preston 41
Reading 51
Retford 26
Scarborough 39
Selby 33
Sheffield 29
Stansted Airport 26
Southampton 51
Sunderland 26
Torquay 51
Whitby *Bus* 26G
Yorton [AW] Ⓟ 🚶 131
Ystrad Mynach [AW] [3] Ⓟ ◇ 130
Ystrad Rhondda [AW] Ⓟ 🚶 130

Travelling from/to London

The below London stations can be found in the following tables:

Blackfriars: 52, 173, 175, 179, 182, 186, 195, 196, 199, 212

Cannon Street: 199, 200, 203, 204, 206, 207, 212

Charing Cross: 199, 200, 203, 204, 206, 207, 212

City Thameslink: 52, 173, 175, 179, 182, 186, 195, 196, 212

Euston: 60, 65, 66, 67, 68, 81, 84, 91, 402, 403

Farringdon: 52, 173, 175, 179, 182, 186, 195, 196, 212

Fenchurch Street: 1

King's Cross: 17, 24, 25, 26, 29, 32, 36, 41, 44

Liverpool Street: 1, 5, 6, 11, 15, 20, 21, 22

London Bridge: 52, 170, 171, 172, 173, 175, 177, 179, 181, 182, 184, 186, 189, 199, 200, 203, 204, 206, 207, 212

Marylebone: 71, 114, 115

Moorgate: 24

Paddington: 116, 117, 118, 120, 121, 123, 125, 126, 128, 135

St Pancras International: 52, 53, 173, 175, 179, 182, 186, 194, 195, 196, 200, 207, 208, 212

Victoria: 170, 171, 172, 175, 181, 182, 184, 186, 188, 189, 195, 196, 199, 200, 212

Waterloo: 149, 152, 155, 156, 158, 160, 170, 182

Waterloo East: 199, 200, 203, 204, 206, 207, 212

Network Diagram for Tables 1, 4

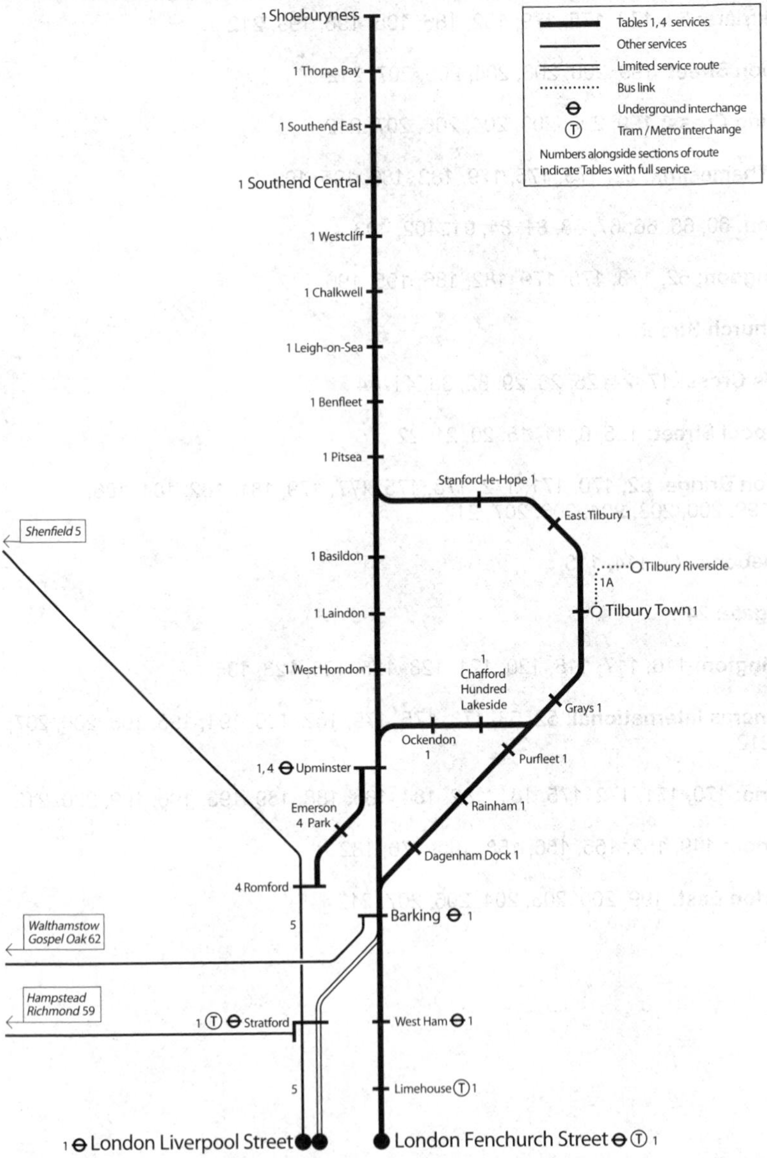

TOCs operating on this network - C2C (CC), Greater Anglia (LE)

Table 1

Mondays to Fridays

9 December to 16 May

London - Southend Central and Shoeburyness

Network Diagram - see first page of Table 1

Miles	Miles	Miles	Miles			CC MO	CC MX	CC MO	CC MX	CC MX	CC MX	CC MO	CC MX	CC MX		CC MX	CC MX	CC MO	CC MX	CC MX	CC	CC	CC	CC
0	0	—	—	**London Fenchurch St** 7 ⊖	d											00 01		00 10	00 15	00 25		05 10		05 40
1¾	1¾	—	—	Limehouse DLR	d													00 14	00 19	00 29		05 14		05 44
4¾	4¾	—	—	West Ham ⊖	d											00 09		00 19	00 24	00 34		05 19		05 49
—	—	—	0	**London Liverpool St** 15 ⊖	d																			
—	—	—	4	Stratford 7 ⊖	d																			
7½	7½	—	7¾	Barking ⊖	d											00 15	00 05	00 24	00 30	00 40		05 25	05 39	05 55
15¼	—	0	—	Upminster ⊖	d							00 02		00 05		00 24	00 14	00 32		00 49	05 28	05 34	05 48	06 04
—	—	3	—	Ockendon	d												00 19				05 33		05 56	
—	—	5	—	Chafford Hundred Lakeside	d												00 23				05 37		06 00	
19¼	—	—	—	West Horndon	d							00 07		00 10				00 37		00 54		05 39		06 09
22¾	—	—	—	Laindon	d							00 12		00 16		00 32		00 42		00 59		05 44		06 14
24½	—	—	—	Basildon	d							00 15		00 19		00 35		00 45		01 02		05 47		06 17
—	10½	—	—	Dagenham Dock	d														00 35					
—	12¾	—	—	Rainham	d														00 39					
—	16	—	—	Purfleet	d								00 04						00 44					
—	19¾	7½	—	Grays	d								00a10				00 27		00a50		05a41		06a05	
—	21½	—	—	**Tilbury Town** 3	d						00 01						00 30							
—	25¼	—	—	East Tilbury	d						00 06						00 36							
—	27¼	—	—	Stanford-le-Hope	d						00 10						00 40							
26½	32¼	—	—	Pitsea	d					00 03	00 18	00 19		00 22			00 48	00 49		01 06		05 51		06 21
29¼	35	—	—	Benfleet	d					00 07	00 22	00 22		00 27		00 42	00 52	00 52		01 10		05 55		06 25
32½	38¼	—	—	Leigh-on-Sea	d					00 11	00 27	00 27		00 31		00 46	00 56	00 57		01 14		06 00		06 30
34	39¾	—	—	Chalkwell	d				00 03	00 14	00 30	00 29		00 34		00 49	00 59	00 59		01 17		06 03		06 33
34¾	40½	—	—	Westcliff	d		00 02	00 02	00 06	00 17	00 32	00 32		00 37		00 52	01 02	01 02		01 20		06 05		06 35
35¾	41½	—	—	**Southend Central**	a		00 04	00 04	00 08	00 19	00 35	00 34		00 39		00 54	01 04	01 04		01 22		06 08		06 38
—	—	—	—		d	00 01	00 04	00 05	00 08	00 19	00 35	00 35		00 39		00 54	01 04	01 05		01 22		06 08		06 38
36½	42¼	—	—	Southend East	d	00 03	00 06	00 07	00 10	00 21	00 37	00 37		00 41		00 56	01 06	01 07		01 24		06 10		06 40
38	43¾	—	—	Thorpe Bay	d	00 05	00 10	00 09	00 14	00 25	00 40	00 39		00 45		01 00	01 10	01 09		01 28		06 14		06 44
39½	45¼	—	—	**Shoeburyness**	a	00 13	00 16	00 17	00 20	00 31	00 47	00 47		00 51		01 06	01 16	01 17		01 34		06 18		06 48

		CC	CC	CC	CC	CC	CC	CC	CC	CC		CC	CC	CC	CC	CC	CC	CC	CC	CC		CC	CC	CC	CC
London Fenchurch St 7 ⊖	d				06 10	06 20	06 40		06 44	06 48		07 00	07 09	07 13	07 15	07 30	07 40	07 43	07 48	07 50		08 00		08 03	08 09
Limehouse DLR	d				06 14	06 24	06 44		06 48	06 52			07 13				07 44			07 54				08 07	08 13
West Ham ⊖	d				06 19	06 29	06 49		06 53	06 57		07 08	07 18		07 23	07 38	07 49	07 53		07 59		08 08		08 12	08 18
London Liverpool St 15 ⊖	d																								
Stratford 7 ⊖	d																								
Barking ⊖	d	05 45	06 05		06 25	06 35	06 55	06 50	07 00	07 03		07 14	07 25	07 26	07 29	07 44	07 55	07 58		08 05		08 14		08 18	08 24
Upminster ⊖	d			06 31	06 34		07 04		07 10			07 23	07 34		07 38	07 53	08 04		08 09	08 15		08 23			08 33
Ockendon	d			06 36					07 15						07 45				08 16						
Chafford Hundred Lakeside	d			06 40					07 19						07 49				08 20						
West Horndon	d				06 39		07 09						07 39				08 09			08 20					08 38
Laindon	d				06 45		07 14						07 44				08 14			08a26		08 31			08 44
Basildon	d				06 48		07 17					07 33	07 47			08 03	08 17					08 34			08 47
Dagenham Dock	d	05 50	06 10			06 40		06 55		07 08				07 31				08 03						08 23	
Rainham	d	05 54	06 14			06 44		06 59		07 12				07 35				08 07						08 27	
Purfleet	d	05 59	06 19			06 50		07 04		07 17				07 40				08 13						08 33	
Grays	d	06 05	06 25	06a44		06 55		07 10	07a23	07 25				07 46	07 54			08 18	08 25					08 38	
Tilbury Town 3	d	06 08	06 28			06 59		07 13		07 28					07 58			08 22						08 42	
East Tilbury	d	06 14	06 34			07 05		07 19		07 34					08 04			08 28						08 48	
Stanford-le-Hope	d	06 18	06 38			07 09		07 23		07 38				07 56	08 08			08 32	08 35				←	08 52	
Pitsea	d	06 26	06a46		06 51	07 18	07 22	07a31		07a46			07 51	08a03	08a15		08 21	08 41	08a44			08 38	08 41	08a59	08 51
Benfleet	d	06 31			06 55	07 22	07 26					07 39	07 55			08 09	08 25	→				08 42	08 45		08 55
Leigh-on-Sea	d	06 35			07 00	07 27	07 30					07 44	07 59			08 14	08 30					08 46	08 50		08 59
Chalkwell	d	06 38			07 03	07 30	07 33					07 47	08 02			08 17	08 33					08 49	08 53		09 02
Westcliff	d	06 41			07 05	07 32	07 36					07 49	08 05			08 19	08 35					08 52	08 55		09 05
Southend Central	a	06 43			07 08	07 35	07 38					07 52	08 07			08 22	08 38					08 54	08 58		09 08
	d	06 43			07 08	07 35	07 38					07 52	08 07			08 22	08 38					08 55			09 08
Southend East	d	06 45			07 10	07 37	07 40					07 54	08 09			08 24	08 40					08 57			09 10
Thorpe Bay	d	06 49			07 14	07 40	07 44					07 58	08 13			08 28	08 44					09 00			09 14
Shoeburyness	a	06 53			07 20	07 45	07 48					08 02	08 17			08 32	08 48					09 05			09 18

For services between London Liverpool Street and Southend Victoria refer to Table 6

Table 1

Mondays to Fridays

9 December to 16 May

London - Southend Central and Shoeburyness

Network Diagram - see first page of Table 1

		CC		CC	CC	CC	CC	CC	CC	CC	CC	CC		CC	CC	CC	CC	CC	CC	CC	CC	CC		CC	CC
London Fenchurch St 7 ⊖	d	08 14		08 20	08 30		08 40	08 50	08 54	09 00		09 10		09 16	09 20	09 30		09 35	09 40		09 50	10 00			10 05
Limehouse DLR	d			08 24			08 44	08 54				09 14		09 20	09 24			09 39	09 44		09 54				10 09
West Ham ⊖	d	08 23		08 29	08 38		08 49	08 59		09 08		09 19		09 25	09 29	09 38		09 44	09 49		09 59	10 08			10 14
London Liverpool St 15 ⊖	d																								
Stratford 7 ⊖	d																								
Barking ⊖	d	08 30		08 37	08 45		08 55	09 07	09 09	09 16		09 25		09 31	09 35	09 44		09 50	09 55		10 05	10 14			10 20
Upminster ⊖	d	08 41			08 54		09 04		09 18	09 25		09 34			09 45	09 53			10 04		10 14	10 23			
Ockendon	d	08 46							09 23						09 50						10 19				
Chafford Hundred Lakeside	d	08 50							09 27						09 54						10 23				
West Horndon	d						09 09					09 39							10 09						
Laindon	d				09 03		09 14			09 34		09 44				10 01			10 14			10 31			
Basildon	d				09 06		09 17			09 37		09 47				10 04			10 17			10 34			
Dagenham Dock	d			08 42				09 12						09 36				09 55							10 25
Rainham	d			08 46				09 16						09 40				09 59							10 29
Purfleet	d			08 51				09 21						09 45				10 04							10 34
Grays	d	08a54		08 57				09 27	09a31					09 51	09 58			10a10			10 27				10a40
Tilbury Town 3	d			09 00				09 30						09 54	10 02						10 30				
East Tilbury	d			09 06				09 36						10 00	10 08						10 36				
Stanford-le-Hope	d			09 10		←		09 40						10 04	10 12					←	10 40				
Pitsea	d			09 18	09 09	09 18	09 21	09 48			←	09 51		10 12	10 25		←		10 21	10 25	10 48			←	
Benfleet	d			→	09 13	09 22	09 26	09 52		09 43	09 52	09 55		10 16	→	10 11	10 16		10 25	10 29	10 52	10 41		10 52	
Leigh-on-Sea	d				09 18	09 27	09 30	→		09 48	09 57	10 00		→		10 15	10 20		10 30	10 34	→	10 45		10 56	
Chalkwell	d				09 21	09 30	09 33			09 51	10 00	10 03				10 18	10 23		10 33	10 37		10 48		10 59	
Westcliff	d				09 23	09 32	09 36			09 53	10 02	10 05				10 21	10 26		10 35	10 39		10 51		11 02	
Southend Central	a				09 26	09 35	09 38			09 56	10 05	10 08				10 23	10 28		10 38	10 42		10 53		11 05	
	d				09 26	09 35	09 38			09 56		10 08				10 23	10 28		10 38	10 42		10 53			
Southend East	d				09 28	09 37	09 40			09 58		10 10				10 25	10 30		10 40	10 44		10 55			
Thorpe Bay	d				09 32	09 40	09 44			10 02		10 14				10 29	10 34		10 44	10 48		10 59			
Shoeburyness	a				09 36	09 45	09 48			10 06		10 18				10 33	10 38		10 48	10 53		11 03			

		CC	CC	CC	CC	CC	CC	CC		CC	CC	CC	CC	CC	CC	CC	CC	CC		CC	CC	CC	CC	CC	CC
London Fenchurch St 7 ⊖	d	10 10	10 20	10 30		10 35	10 40	10 50		11 00		11 05	11 10	11 20	11 30		11 35	11 40		11 50	12 00		12 05	12 10	12 20
Limehouse DLR	d	10 14	10 24			10 39	10 44	10 54				11 09	11 14	11 24			11 39	11 44		11 54			12 09	12 14	12 24
West Ham ⊖	d	10 19	10 29	10 38		10 44	10 49	10 59		11 08		11 14	11 19	11 29	11 38		11 44	11 49		11 59	12 08		12 14	12 19	12 29
London Liverpool St 15 ⊖	d																								
Stratford 7 ⊖	d																								
Barking ⊖	d	10 25	10 35	10 44		10 50	10 55	11 05		11 14		11 20	11 25	11 35	11 44		11 50	11 55		12 05	12 14		12 20	12 25	12 35
Upminster ⊖	d	10 34	10 44	10 53			11 04	11 14		11 23			11 34	11 44	11 53			12 04		12 14	12 23			12 34	12 44
Ockendon	d		10 49					11 19						11 49						12 19					12 49
Chafford Hundred Lakeside	d		10 53					11 23						11 53						12 23					12 53
West Horndon	d	10 39					11 09						11 39					12 09						12 39	
Laindon	d	10 44		11 01			11 14			11 31			11 44		12 01			12 14			12 31			12 44	
Basildon	d	10 47		11 04			11 17			11 34			11 47		12 04			12 17			12 34			12 47	
Dagenham Dock	d					10 55						11 25					11 55						12 25		
Rainham	d					10 59						11 29					11 59						12 29		
Purfleet	d					11 04						11 34					12 04						12 34		
Grays	d		10 57			11a10		11 27				11a40		11 57			12a10			12 27			12a40		12 57
Tilbury Town 3	d		11 00					11 30						12 00						12 30					13 00
East Tilbury	d		11 06					11 36						12 06						12 36					13 06
Stanford-le-Hope	d		11 10					11 40						12 10						12 40					13 10
Pitsea	d	10 51	11 18		←		11 21	11 48			←		11 51	12 18		←		12 21		12 48		←		12 51	13 18
Benfleet	d	10 55	11 22	11 11	11 22		11 25	11 52		11 41	11 52		11 55	12 22	12 11	12 22		12 25		12 52	12 41	12 52		12 55	13 22
Leigh-on-Sea	d	11 00	→	11 15	11 26		11 30	→		11 45	11 57		12 00	→	12 15	12 26		12 30		→	12 45	12 57		13 00	→
Chalkwell	d	11 03		11 18	11 29		11 33			11 48	12 00		12 03		12 18	12 29		12 33			12 48	13 00		13 03	
Westcliff	d	11 05		11 21	11 32		11 35			11 51	12 02		12 05		12 21	12 32		12 35			12 51	13 02		13 05	
Southend Central	a	11 08		11 23	11 35		11 38			11 53	12 05		12 08		12 23	12 35		12 38			12 53	13 05		13 08	
	d	11 08		11 23			11 38			11 53			12 08		12 23			12 38			12 53			13 08	
Southend East	d	11 10		11 25			11 40			11 55			12 10		12 25			12 40			12 55			13 10	
Thorpe Bay	d	11 14		11 29			11 44			11 59			12 14		12 29			12 44			12 59			13 14	
Shoeburyness	a	11 18		11 33			11 48			12 03			12 18		12 33			12 48			13 03			13 18	

		CC	CC	CC		CC	CC	CC	CC	CC	CC	CC	CC	CC		CC	CC	CC	CC	CC	CC	CC	CC	CC	
London Fenchurch St 7 ⊖	d	12 30		12 35		12 40	12 50	13 00		13 05	13 10	13 20	13 30			13 35	13 40	13 50	14 00		14 05	14 10	14 20	14 30	
Limehouse DLR	d			12 39		12 44	12 54			13 09	13 14	13 24				13 39	13 44	13 54			14 09	14 14	14 24		
West Ham ⊖	d	12 38		12 44		12 49	12 59	13 08		13 14	13 19	13 29	13 38			13 44	13 49	13 59	14 08		14 14	14 19	14 29	14 38	
London Liverpool St 15 ⊖	d																								
Stratford 7 ⊖	d																								
Barking ⊖	d	12 44		12 50		12 55	13 05	13 14		13 20	13 25	13 35	13 44			13 50	13 55	14 05	14 14		14 20	14 25	14 35	14 44	
Upminster ⊖	d	12 53				13 04	13 14	13 23			13 34	13 44	13 53				14 04	14 14	14 23			14 34	14 44	14 53	
Ockendon	d						13 19					13 49						14 19					14 49		
Chafford Hundred Lakeside	d						13 23					13 53						14 23					14 53		
West Horndon	d					13 09					13 39						14 09					14 39			
Laindon	d	13 01				13 14		13 31			13 44		14 01				14 14		14 31			14 44		15 01	
Basildon	d	13 04				13 17		13 34			13 47		14 04				14 17		14 34			14 47		15 04	
Dagenham Dock	d			12 55						13 25						13 55					14 25				
Rainham	d			12 59						13 29						13 59					14 29				
Purfleet	d			13 04						13 34						14 04					14 34				
Grays	d			13a10			13 27			13a40		13 57				14a10		14 27			14a40		14 57		
Tilbury Town 3	d						13 30					14 00						14 30					15 00		
East Tilbury	d						13 36					14 06						14 36					15 06		
Stanford-le-Hope	d						13 40					14 10						14 40					15 10		
Pitsea	d		←			13 21	13 48		←		13 51	14 18		←			14 21	14 48		←		14 51	15 18		
Benfleet	d	13 11	13 22			13 25	13 52	13 41	13 52		13 55	14 22	14 11	14 22			14 25	14 52	14 41	14 52		14 55	15 22	15 11	
Leigh-on-Sea	d	13 15	13 27			13 30	→	13 45	13 57		14 00	→	14 15	14 26			14 30	→	14 45	14 56		15 00	→	15 15	
Chalkwell	d	13 18	13 30			13 33		13 48	14 00		14 03		14 18	14 29			14 33		14 48	14 59		15 03		15 18	
Westcliff	d	13 21	13 32			13 35		13 51	14 02		14 05		14 21	14 32			14 35		14 51	15 02		15 05		15 21	
Southend Central	a	13 23	13 35			13 38		13 53	14 05		14 08		14 23	14 35			14 38		14 53	15 05		15 08		15 23	
	d	13 23				13 38		13 53			14 08		14 23				14 38		14 53			15 08		15 23	
Southend East	d	13 25				13 40		13 55			14 10		14 25				14 40		14 55			15 10		15 25	
Thorpe Bay	d	13 29				13 44		13 59			14 14		14 29				14 44		14 59			15 14		15 29	
Shoeburyness	a	13 33				13 48		14 03			14 18		14 33				14 48		15 03			15 18		15 33	

For services between London Liverpool Street and Southend Victoria refer to Table 6

Table 1

London - Southend Central and Shoeburyness

Mondays to Fridays

9 December to 16 May

Network Diagram - see first page of Table 1

Station		CC	CC	CC	CC	CC	CC	CC	CC	CC		CC	CC	CC	CC	CC	CC	CC	CC	CC		CC	CC	CC	CC
London Fenchurch St 7 ⊖	d		14 35	14 40	14 50	15 00		15 05	15 10	15 20		15 25	15 30	15 35	15 40		15 50	15 55	16 00	16 10		16 13	16 20	16 28	16 30
Limehouse DLR	d		14 39	14 44	14 54			15 09	15 14	15 24				15 39	15 44		15 54	15 59		16 14		16 17	16 24		16 34
West Ham ⊖	d		14 44	14 49	14 59	15 08		15 14	15 19	15 29		15 33	15 38	15 44	15 49		15 59	16 04	16 08	16 19		16 22	16 29	16 36	16 39
London Liverpool St 15 ⊖	d																								
Stratford 7 ⊖	d																								
Barking ⊖	d		14 50	14 55	15 05	15 14		15 20	15 25	15 35		15 39	15 44	15 50	15 54		16 05	16 10	16 14	16 25		16 28	16 35		16 45
Upminster ⊖	d			15 04	15 14	15 23			15 34	15 44		15 48	15 53		16 02		16 14		16 23	16 34			16 45		16 55
Ockendon	d				15 19					15 49							16 19						16 50		
Chafford Hundred Lakeside	d				15 23					15 53							16 23						16 54		
West Horndon	d			15 09					15 39						16 07					16 39					17 00
Laindon	d			15 14		15 31			15 44			15 56	16 01		16 12					16 44				16 56	17a08
Basildon	d			15 17		15 34			15 47			15 59	16 04		16 15				16 33	16 47				16 59	
Dagenham Dock	d		14 55					15 25						15 55				16 15				16 33			
Rainham	d		14 59					15 29						15 59				16 19				16 37			
Purfleet	d		15 04					15 34						16 04				16 25				16 43			
Grays	d		15a10		15 27			15a40		15 57				16a10			16 27	16a33				16 49	16 59		
Tilbury Town 3	d				15 30					16 00							16 30					16 52	17 02		
East Tilbury	d				15 36					16 06							16 36					16 58	17 08		
Stanford-le-Hope	d				15 40					16 10						←	16 40					17 02	17a15		
Pitsea	d	←		15 21	15 48		←		15 51	16 22		16 03			16 19	16 22	16a48			16 51		17a12			
Benfleet	d	15 22		15 25	15 52	15 41	15 52		15 55	→		16 07	16 11		16 22	16 26			16 40	16 55				17 06	
Leigh-on-Sea	d	15 26		15 30	→	15 45	15 56		16 00			16a12	16 15		16 27	16 30			16 45	17 00				17 11	
Chalkwell	d	15 29		15 33		15 48	15 59		16 03				16 18		16 29	16 33			16 48	17 03				17 14	
Westcliff	d	15 32		15 35		15 51	16 02		16 05				16 21		16 32	16 36			16 50	17 05				17 16	
Southend Central	a	15 35		15 38		15 53	16 05		16 08				16 23		16 34	16 41			16 53	17 08				17 19	
	d			15 38		15 53			16 08				16 23		16 35				16 53	17 08				17 19	
Southend East	d			15 40		15 55			16 10				16 25		16 37				16 55	17 10				17 21	
Thorpe Bay	d			15 44		15 59			16 14				16 29		16 39				16 59	17 14				17 24	
Shoeburyness	a			15 48		16 03			16 20				16 33		16 44				17 05	17 20				17 31	

Station		CC	CC	CC	CC	CC		CC	CC	CC	CC	CC	CC	CC	CC	CC		CC	CC	CC	CC	CC	CC	CC	CC
London Fenchurch St 7 ⊖	d	16 34	16 37	16 45	16 48	16 55		17 00	17 02	17 05	17 07	17 10	17 15	17 18	17 20	17 23		17 26	17 30	17 32	17 35	17 37	17 41	17 45	17 47
Limehouse DLR	d	16 38	16 41	16 49	16 52	16 59				17 09	17 12	17 15	17 19		17 24	17 28		17 30			17 39	17 42	17 45	17 49	17 52
West Ham ⊖	d	16 43	16 46		16 57	17 04					17 17	17 20		17 26	17 29	17 33		17 35		17 40	17 44	17 47	17 50		17 57
London Liverpool St 15 ⊖	d																								
Stratford 7 ⊖	d																								
Barking ⊖	d	16 49	16 52	16 59	17 03	17 10			17 15	17 19	17 22	17 26			17 35	17 39		17 42		17 46	17 50	17 53	17 56		
Upminster ⊖	d		17 02	17 07	17 13				17 24		17 31		17 36	17 40		17 47				17 56		18 03			18 10
Ockendon	d		17 08						17 29											18 02					18 15
Chafford Hundred Lakeside	d		17 12						17 34											18 06					18 20
West Horndon	d				17 18						17 36					17 52						18 08			
Laindon	d			17 16	17a26					17 35	17a43				17 51	17a59					18 07	18a15			
Basildon	d			17 19						17 39				17 50	17 55						18 10				
Dagenham Dock	d	16 54				17 15						17 31						17 47					18 01		
Rainham	d	16 58				17 19						17 35						17 51					18 05		
Purfleet	d	17 04				17 25						17 40						17 56					18 11		
Grays	d	17 10	17a18			17 31			17a40			17 46						18 02		18a13			18 17		18a26
Tilbury Town 3	d	17 13				17 34						17 50						18 06					18 20		
East Tilbury	d	17 19				17 40						17 56						18 12					18 26		
Stanford-le-Hope	d	17 23				17 44						18 00						18 16					18 30		
Pitsea	d	17a33		17 23		17a54				17 42		18a09		17 54	17 58			18a25			18 14		18a40		
Benfleet	d			17 27				17 33		17 46			17 52	17 58	18 03				18 08		18 18			18 24	
Leigh-on-Sea	d			17 32				17 38		17 51			17 56	18 02	18 07				18 12		18 23			18 28	
Chalkwell	d			17 34				17 41		17 53			17 59	18 05	18 10				18 15		18 26			18 31	
Westcliff	d			17 37				17 43		17 56			18 02	18 08	18 13				18 18		18 28			18 34	
Southend Central	a			17 39				17 46		17 58			18 04	18 13	18 15				18 20		18 31			18 36	
	d			17 39				17 46		17 58			18 04		18 15				18 20		18 31			18 36	
Southend East	d			17 41				17 48		18 00			18 06		18 17				18 22		18 33			18 38	
Thorpe Bay	d			17 44				17 50		18 03			18 10		18 21				18 26		18 36			18 42	
Shoeburyness	a			17 51				17 57		18 11			18 16		18 28				18 32		18 43			18 48	

Station		CC		CC	CC	CC	CC	CC	CC	CC	CC	CC		CC	CC	CC	CC	CC	CC	CC	CC	CC		CC	CC
London Fenchurch St 7 ⊖	d	17 51		17 53	17 56	18 00	18 02	18 06	18 09			18 12		18 21			18 23	18 27		18 31	18 35	18 42			18 46
Limehouse DLR	d			17 57	18 00		18 06	18 10	18 13			18 16					18 27	18 31		18 35	18 39				18 51
West Ham ⊖	d	17 59			18 05	18 08	18 11		18 18			18 21					18 32	18 36		18 40		18 50			18 56
London Liverpool St 15 ⊖	d																								
Stratford 7 ⊖	d																								
Barking ⊖	d			18 08	18 11		18 17	18 20	18 24			18 28						18 42		18 46	18 49				19 01
Upminster ⊖	d	18 14					18 27		18 34								18 46	18 51			18 58				19 10
Ockendon	d						18 33										18 51				19 06				
Chafford Hundred Lakeside	d						18 38										18 55				19 11				
West Horndon	d			18 21					18 39									18 56							19 15
Laindon	d			18 27				18 37	18 43					18 47				19 01							19 20
Basildon	d	18 24		18 31		18 35		18 41	18 47					18 51				19 04				19 12			19 23
Dagenham Dock	d				18 16							18 33								18 51					
Rainham	d				18 20							18 37								18 55					
Purfleet	d				18 25							18 42								19 01					
Grays	d				18 31		18 42					18 48					19 00			19 07	19a17				
Tilbury Town 3	d				18 35		18 46					18 52					19 03			19 10					
East Tilbury	d				18 41		18 52					18 58					19 09			19 16					
Stanford-le-Hope	d				18 45		18 56			←	←	19 02					19 13		←	19 20					
Pitsea	d	18 28		18 34	18 57	18 38	19 03	18 44	18 50	18 57	19 03	19a11			←	←	19 21	19 08	19 21	19a30				←	19 26
Benfleet	d	18 32		18 39	→	18 43	→	18 49	18 54	19 03	19 07			18 58	19 03	19 07	→	19 12	19 25			19 19		19 25	19 30
Leigh-on-Sea	d	18 37		18 43		18 47		18 53	18 59	→	→			19 03	19 07	19a14		19 16	→			19 24		19a32	19 35
Chalkwell	d	18 40		18 46		18 50		18 56	19 01					19 06	19 10			19 19				19 27			19 37
Westcliff	d	18 42		18 49		18 53		18 59	19 04					19 08	19 13			19 21				19 29			19 40
Southend Central	a	18 45		18 51		18 55		19 01	19 09					19 11	19 15			19 24				19 32			19 42
	d	18 45		18 51		18 55		19 01						19 11	19 15			19 24				19 32			19 42
Southend East	d	18 47		18 53		18 57		19 03						19 13	19 17			19 26				19 34			19 44
Thorpe Bay	d	18 50		18 57		19 01		19 07						19 16	19 21			19 28				19 37			19 47
Shoeburyness	a	18 58		19 03		19 07		19 13						19 23	19 28			19 35				19 44			19 53

For services between London Liverpool Street and Southend Victoria refer to Table 6

Table 1

Mondays to Fridays

9 December to 16 May

London - Southend Central and Shoeburyness

Network Diagram - see first page of Table 1

		CC	CC	CC	CC	CC	CC	CC		CC	CC	CC	CC	CC	CC	CC	CC	CC		CC	CC	CC	CC	CC	CC
London Fenchurch St 7 ⊖	d	18 51	19 00	19 02	19 05		19 08	19 11		19 20	19 30		19 32	19 35	19 40	19 50	20 00			20 05	20 10	20 20	20 30		
Limehouse DLR	d	18 55			19 09		19 12	19 15		19 24			19 36	19 39	19 44	19 54				20 09	20 14	20 24	20 34		
West Ham ⊖	d	19 00		19 10			19 17	19 20		19 29			19 41	19 44	19 49	19 59	20 08			20 14	20 19	20 29	20 39		
London Liverpool St 15 ⊖	d																								20 35
Stratford 7 ⊖	d																								20 43
Barking ⊖	d	19 06		19 16	19 19		19 23	19 26		19 35			19 47	19 50	19 55	20 05	20 14			20 20	20 25	20 35	20 45		20 50
Upminster ⊖	d			19 26	19 30			19 35		19 44	19 50		19 56		20 04	20 14	20 23				20 34	20 44	20 54		
Ockendon	d			19 33						19 49						20 19						20 49			
Chafford Hundred Lakeside	d			19 39						19 53						20 23						20 53			
West Horndon	d							19 40					20 01		20 09						20 39				
Laindon	d		19 26					19 45					20a07		20 14		20 31				20 44		21 02		
Basildon	d				19 40			19 48			20 00				20 17		20 34				20 47		21 05		
Dagenham Dock	d	19 11					19 28							19 55						20 25					20 55
Rainham	d	19 15					19 32							19 59						20 29					20 59
Purfleet	d	19 21					19 37							20 04						20 34					21 04
Grays	d	19 27		19 46			19a43			19 57				20a10		20 27				20a40		20 57			21a12
Tilbury Town 3	d	19 30		19 50						20 00						20 30						21 00			
East Tilbury	d	19 36		19 56						20 06						20 36						21 06			
Stanford-le-Hope	d	19 40		20 00		←				20 10						20 40						21 10			
Pitsea	d	19 48		20a07	19 44	19 48		19 52		20 18		←			20 21	20 48		←			20 51	21 18		←	
Benfleet	d	→	19 33		19 48	19 52		19 56		20 22	20 06	20 22			20 26	20 52	20 41	20 52			20 55	21 22	21 12	21 22	
Leigh-on-Sea	d		19 38		19 52	19 56		20 00		→	20 11	20 27			20 30	→	20 45	20 56			21 00	→	21 16	21 26	
Chalkwell	d		19 41		19 55	19 59		20 03			20 14	20 30			20 33		20 48	20 59			21 03		21 19	21 29	
Westcliff	d		19 43		19 58	20 02		20 06			20 16	20 32			20 36		20 51	21 02			21 05		21 22	21 32	
Southend Central	a		19 46		20 00	20 07		20 08			20 19	20 35			20 38		20 53	21 05			21 08		21 24	21 35	
	d		19 46		20 00			20 08			20 19				20 38		20 53				21 08		21 24		
Southend East	d		19 48		20 02			20 10			20 21				20 40		20 55				21 10		21 26		
Thorpe Bay	d		19 50		20 06			20 14			20 25				20 44		20 59				21 14		21 30		
Shoeburyness	a		19 57		20 10			20 18			20 29				20 48		21 03				21 18		21 34		

		CC	CC	CC		CC	CC	CC	CC	CC	CC	CC	CC	CC		CC	CC	CC	CC	CC	CC	CC	CC	CC	
London Fenchurch St 7 ⊖	d	20 40	20 50	21 00			21 05	21 10	21 20	21 30			21 40	21 50		22 00		22 05	22 10	22 20	22 35	22 40	22 50	23 00	
Limehouse DLR	d	20 44	20 54				21 09	21 14	21 24	21 34			21 44	21 54				22 09	22 14	22 24	22 39	22 44	22 54		
West Ham ⊖	d	20 49	20 59	21 08			21 14	21 19	21 29	21 39			21 49	21 59		22 08		22 14	22 19	22 29	22 44	22 49	22 59	23 08	
London Liverpool St 15 ⊖	d											21 35													
Stratford 7 ⊖	d											21 43													
Barking ⊖	d	20 55	21 05	21 14			21 20	21 25	21 35	21 45		21 50	21 55	22 05		22 14		22 20	22 25	22 35	22 50	22 55	23 05	23 14	
Upminster ⊖	d	21 04	21 14	21 23				21 34	21 44	21 54			22 04	22 14		22 23			22 34	22 44		23 04	23 14	23 23	
Ockendon	d		21 19						21 49					22 19						22 49			23 19		
Chafford Hundred Lakeside	d		21 23						21 53					22 23						22 53			23 23		
West Horndon	d	21 09						21 39					22 09						22 39			23 09			
Laindon	d	21 14		21 31				21 44		22 02			22 14			22 31			22 44			23 14		23 31	
Basildon	d	21 17		21 34				21 47		22 05			22 17			22 34			22 47			23 17		23 34	
Dagenham Dock	d						21 25					21 55						22 25			22 55				
Rainham	d						21 29					21 59						22 29			22 59				
Purfleet	d						21 34					22 04						22 34			23 04				
Grays	d		21 27				21a40		21 57			22a12		22 27				22a40		22 57	23a10		23 27		
Tilbury Town 3	d		21 30						22 00					22 30						23 00			23 30		
East Tilbury	d		21 36						22 06					22 36						23 06			23 36		
Stanford-le-Hope	d		21 40						22 10					22 40						23 10			23 40		
Pitsea	d	21 21	21 48			←		21 51	22 18		←		22 21	22 48			←		22 51	23 18		23 22	23 48		
Benfleet	d	21 25	21 52	21 41		21 52		21 55	22 22	22 12	22 22		22 25	22 52		22 41	22 52		22 55	23 22		23 26	23 52	23 41	
Leigh-on-Sea	d	21 30	→	21 45		21 56		22 00	→	22 16	22 26		22 30	→		22 45	22 56		23 00	23 26		23 30	→	23 45	
Chalkwell	d	21 33		21 48		21 59		22 03		22 19	22 29		22 33			22 48	22 59		23 03	23 29		23 33		23 48	
Westcliff	d	21 35		21 51		22 02		22 05		22 22	22 32		22 35			22 51	23 02		23 06	23 32		23 36		23 51	
Southend Central	a	21 38		21 53		22 05		22 08		22 24	22 35		22 38			22 53	23 05		23 08	23 34		23 38		23 53	
	d	21 38		21 53				22 08		22 24			22 38			22 53	23 05		23 08	23 34		23 38		23 53	
Southend East	d	21 40		21 55				22 10		22 26			22 40			22 55	23 07		23 10	23 36		23 40		23 55	
Thorpe Bay	d	21 44		21 59				22 14		22 30			22 44			22 59	23 10		23 14	23 40		23 44		23 59	
Shoeburyness	a	21 48		22 03				22 18		22 34			22 48			23 03	23 15		23 18	23 46		23 50		00 05	

		CC	CC	CC	CC	CC	CC	CC	CC
London Fenchurch St 7 ⊖	d		23 05	23 10		23 20	23 35	23 40	23 50
Limehouse DLR	d		23 09	23 14		23 24	23 39	23 44	23 54
West Ham ⊖	d		23 14	23 19		23 29	23 44	23 49	23 59
London Liverpool St 15 ⊖	d								
Stratford 7 ⊖	d								
Barking ⊖	d		23 20	23 25		23 35	23 50	23 55	00 05
Upminster ⊖	d			23 34		23 44		00 05	00 14
Ockendon	d					23 49			00 19
Chafford Hundred Lakeside	d					23 53			00 23
West Horndon	d			23 39				00 10	
Laindon	d			23 44				00 16	
Basildon	d			23 47				00 19	
Dagenham Dock	d		23 25				23 55		
Rainham	d		23 29				23 59		
Purfleet	d		23 34				00 04		
Grays	d		23 42			23 57	00a10		00 27
Tilbury Town 3	d		23 45			00 01			00 30
East Tilbury	d		23 51			00 06			00 36
Stanford-le-Hope	d		23 55		←	00 10			00 40
Pitsea	d	←	00 03	23 52	00 03	00 18		00 22	00 48
Benfleet	d	23 52	→	23 56	00 07	00 22		00 27	00 52
Leigh-on-Sea	d	23 56		23 59	00 11	00 27		00 31	00 56
Chalkwell	d	23 59		00 03	00 14	00 30		00 34	00 59
Westcliff	d	00 02		00 06	00 17	00 32		00 37	01 02
Southend Central	a	00 04		00 08	00 19	00 35		00 39	01 04
	d	00 04		00 08	00 19	00 35		00 39	01 04
Southend East	d	00 06		00 10	00 21	00 37		00 41	01 06
Thorpe Bay	d	00 10		00 14	00 25	00 40		00 45	01 10
Shoeburyness	a	00 16		00 20	00 31	00 47		00 51	01 16

For services between London Liverpool Street and Southend Victoria refer to Table 6

Table 1

Saturdays

London - Southend Central and Shoeburyness

14 December to 17 May

Network Diagram - see first page of Table 1

		CC	CC	CC	CC	CC	CC	CC	CC	CC		CC	CC	CC	CC	CC	CC	CC	CC	CC		CC	CC	CC	CC
London Fenchurch St 7 ⊖	d							00 01		00 15		00 25		05 10	05 35	05 50	06 05	06 10	06 20	06 35		06 40	06 50	07 05	07 10
Limehouse DLR	d									00 19		00 29		05 14	05 39	05 54	06 09	06 14	06 24	06 39		06 44	06 54	07 09	07 14
West Ham ⊖	d							00 09		00 24		00 34		05 19	05 44	05 59	06 14	06 19	06 29	06 44		06 49	06 59	07 14	07 19
London Liverpool St 15 ⊖	d																								
Stratford 7 ⊖	d																								
Barking ⊖	d							00 15	00 05	00 30		00 40		05 24	05 49	06 04	06 19	06 24	06 34	06 49		06 54	07 04	07 19	07 24
Upminster ⊖	d						00 05	00 24	00 14			00 49	05 27	05 32		06 12		06 32	06 42			07 02	07 12		07 32
Ockendon	d								00 19				05 32			06 18			06 48				07 18		
Chafford Hundred Lakeside	d								00 23				05 36			06 21			06 51				07 21		
West Horndon	d						00 10					00 54		05 37				06 37				07 07			07 37
Laindon	d						00 16	00 32				00 59		05 42				06 42				07 12			07 42
Basildon	d						00 19	00 35				01 02		05 45				06 45				07 15			07 45
Dagenham Dock	d									00 35					05 54		06 24			06 54				07 24	
Rainham	d									00 39					05 57		06 27			06 57				07 27	
Purfleet	d					00 04				00 44					06 03		06 33			07 03				07 33	
Grays	d					00a10			00 27	00a50			05a42		06a12	06 25	06a42		06 55	07a12			07 25	07a42	
Tilbury Town 3	d				00 01				00 30							06 28			06 58				07 28		
East Tilbury	d				00 06				00 36							06 34			07 04				07 34		
Stanford-le-Hope	d				00 10				00 40							06 37			07 07				07 37		
Pitsea	d			00 03	00 18		00 22		00 48			01 06		05 50		06 45		06 49	07 15			07 19	07 45		07 49
Benfleet	d			00 07	00 22		00 27	00 42	00 52			01 10		05 54		06 49		06 52	07 19			07 22	07 49		07 52
Leigh-on-Sea	d			00 11	00 27		00 31	00 46	00 56			01 14		05 58		06 53		06 57	07 23			07 27	07 53		07 57
Chalkwell	d		00 03	00 14	00 30		00 34	00 49	00 59			01 17		06 01		06 56		06 59	07 26			07 29	07 56		07 59
Westcliff	d	00 02	00 06	00 17	00 32		00 37	00 52	01 02			01 20		06 03		06 58		07 02	07 28			07 32	07 58		08 02
Southend Central	a	00 04	00 08	00 19	00 35		00 39	00 54	01 04			01 22		06 06		07 04		07 05	07 34			07 35	08 04		08 05
	d	00 04	00 08	00 19	00 35		00 39	00 54	01 04			01 22		06 07				07 06				07 36			08 06
Southend East	d	00 06	00 10	00 21	00 37		00 41	00 56	01 06			01 24		06 09				07 08				07 38			08 08
Thorpe Bay	d	00 10	00 14	00 25	00 40		00 45	01 00	01 10			01 28		06 12				07 10				07 40			08 10
Shoeburyness	a	00 16	00 20	00 31	00 47		00 51	01 06	01 16			01 34		06 19				07 18				07 48			08 18

		CC	CC	CC	CC	CC		CC	CC	CC	CC	CC	CC	CC	CC	CC		CC	CC	CC	CC	CC	CC	CC	CC
London Fenchurch St 7 ⊖	d	07 20	07 35	07 40	07 50	08 05		08 10	08 20	08 35	08 40	08 50	09 00		09 05	09 10		09 20	09 30		09 35	09 40	09 50	10 00	
Limehouse DLR	d	07 24	07 39	07 44	07 54	08 09		08 14	08 24	08 39	08 44	08 54			09 09	09 14		09 24			09 39	09 44	09 54		
West Ham ⊖	d	07 29	07 44	07 49	07 59	08 14		08 19	08 29	08 44	08 49	08 59	09 08		09 14	09 19		09 29	09 38		09 44	09 49	09 59	10 08	
London Liverpool St 15 ⊖	d																								
Stratford 7 ⊖	d																								
Barking ⊖	d	07 34	07 49	07 54	08 04	08 19		08 24	08 34	08 49	08 54	09 04	09 13		09 19	09 24		09 34	09 43		09 49	09 54	10 04	10 13	
Upminster ⊖	d	07 42		08 02	08 12			08 32	08 42		09 02	09 12	09 21			09 32		09 42	09 51			10 02	10 12	10 21	
Ockendon	d	07 48			08 18				08 48			09 18						09 48					10 18		
Chafford Hundred Lakeside	d	07 51			08 21				08 51			09 21						09 51					10 21		
West Horndon	d			08 07				08 37			09 07					09 37						10 07			
Laindon	d			08 12				08 42			09 12		09 29			09 42			09 59			10 12		10 29	
Basildon	d			08 15				08 45			09 15		09 32			09 45			10 02			10 15		10 32	
Dagenham Dock	d		07 54			08 24				08 54					09 24						09 54				
Rainham	d		07 57			08 27				08 57					09 27						09 57				
Purfleet	d		08 03			08 33				09 03					09 33						10 03				
Grays	d	07 55	08a12		08 25	08a42			08 55	09a12		09 25			09a42			09 55			10a12		10 25		
Tilbury Town 3	d	07 58			08 28				08 58			09 28						09 58					10 28		
East Tilbury	d	08 04			08 34				09 04			09 34						10 04					10 34		
Stanford-le-Hope	d	08 07			08 37				09 07			09 37						10 07					10 37		
Pitsea	d	08 15		08 19	08 45			08 49	09 15		09 19	09 45		←		09 49		10 15		←		10 19	10 45		←
Benfleet	d	08 19		08 22	08 49			08 52	09 19		09 22	09 49	09 38	09 49		09 52		10 19	10 08	10 19		10 22	10 49	10 38	10 49
Leigh-on-Sea	d	08 23		08 27	08 53			08 57	09 23		09 27	→	09 42	09 53		09 57		→	10 12	10 23		10 27	→	10 42	10 53
Chalkwell	d	08 26		08 29	08 56			08 59	09 26		09 29		09 45	09 56		09 59			10 15	10 26		10 29		10 45	10 56
Westcliff	d	08 28		08 32	08 58			09 02	09 28		09 32		09 47	09 58		10 02			10 17	10 28		10 32		10 47	10 58
Southend Central	a	08 34		08 35	09 04			09 05	09 34		09 35		09 50	10 04		10 05			10 20	10 34		10 35		10 50	11 04
	d			08 36				09 06			09 36		09 50			10 06			10 20			10 36		10 50	
Southend East	d			08 38				09 08			09 38		09 52			10 08			10 22			10 38		10 52	
Thorpe Bay	d			08 40				09 10			09 40		09 55			10 10			10 25			10 40		10 55	
Shoeburyness	a			08 48				09 18			09 48		10 02			10 18			10 32			10 48		11 02	

		CC		CC	CC	CC	CC	CC	CC	CC	CC	CC		CC	CC	CC	CC	CC	CC	CC	CC	CC	CC	CC	CC
London Fenchurch St 7 ⊖	d	10 05		10 10	10 20	10 30		10 35	10 40	10 50	11 00			11 05	11 10	11 20	11 30		11 35	11 40	11 50	12 00		12 05	12 10
Limehouse DLR	d	10 09		10 14	10 24			10 39	10 44	10 54				11 09	11 14	11 24			11 39	11 44	11 54			12 09	12 14
West Ham ⊖	d	10 14		10 19	10 29	10 38		10 44	10 49	10 59	11 08			11 14	11 19	11 29	11 38		11 44	11 49	11 59	12 08		12 14	12 19
London Liverpool St 15 ⊖	d																								
Stratford 7 ⊖	d																								
Barking ⊖	d	10 19		10 24	10 34	10 43		10 49	10 54	11 04	11 13			11 19	11 24	11 34	11 43		11 49	11 54	12 04	12 13		12 19	12 24
Upminster ⊖	d			10 32	10 42	10 51			11 02	11 12	11 21				11 32	11 42	11 51			12 02	12 12	12 21			12 32
Ockendon	d				10 48					11 18						11 48					12 18				
Chafford Hundred Lakeside	d				10 51					11 21						11 51					12 21				
West Horndon	d			10 37					11 07						11 37					12 07					12 37
Laindon	d			10 42		10 59			11 12		11 29				11 42		11 59			12 12		12 29			12 42
Basildon	d			10 45		11 02			11 15		11 32				11 45		12 02			12 15		12 32			12 45
Dagenham Dock	d	10 24						10 54						11 24					11 54					12 24	
Rainham	d	10 27						10 57						11 27					11 57					12 27	
Purfleet	d	10 33						11 03						11 33					12 03					12 33	
Grays	d	10a42			10 55			11a12		11 25				11a42		11 55			12a12		12 25			12a42	
Tilbury Town 3	d				10 58					11 28						11 58					12 28				
East Tilbury	d				11 04					11 34						12 04					12 34				
Stanford-le-Hope	d				11 07					11 37						12 07					12 37				
Pitsea	d			10 49	11 15		←		11 19	11 45		←			11 49	12 15		←		12 19	12 45		←		12 49
Benfleet	d			10 52	11 19	11 08	11 19		11 22	11 49	11 38	11 49			11 52	12 19	12 08	12 19		12 22	12 49	12 38	12 49		12 52
Leigh-on-Sea	d			10 57	→	11 12	11 23		11 27	→	11 42	11 53			11 57	→	12 12	12 24		12 27	→	12 42	12 53		12 57
Chalkwell	d			10 59		11 15	11 26		11 29		11 45	11 56			11 59		12 15	12 26		12 29		12 45	12 56		12 59
Westcliff	d			11 02		11 17	11 28		11 32		11 47	11 58			12 02		12 17	12 29		12 32		12 47	12 58		13 02
Southend Central	a			11 05		11 20	11 34		11 35		11 50	12 04			12 05		12 20	12 34		12 35		12 50	13 04		13 05
	d			11 06		11 20			11 36		11 50				12 06		12 20			12 36		12 50			13 06
Southend East	d			11 08		11 22			11 38		11 52				12 08		12 22			12 38		12 52			13 08
Thorpe Bay	d			11 10		11 25			11 40		11 55				12 10		12 25			12 40		12 55			13 10
Shoeburyness	a			11 18		11 32			11 48		12 02				12 18		12 32			12 48		13 02			13 18

For services between London Liverpool Street and Southend Victoria refer to Table 6

Table 1

Saturdays

14 December to 17 May

London - Southend Central and Shoeburyness

Network Diagram - see first page of Table 1

		CC	CC	CC	and at the same minutes past each hour until	CC	CC	CC	CC	CC	CC	CC	CC	CC	CC		CC	CC	CC	CC	CC	CC	CC	CC
London Fenchurch St 7 ⊖	d	12 20	12 30			18 35	18 40	18 50	19 00		19 05	19 10	19 20	19 30			19 35	19 40	19 50	20 00		20 05	20 10	20 20
Limehouse DLR	d	12 24				18 39	18 44	18 54			19 09	19 14	19 24				19 39	19 44	19 54			20 09	20 14	20 24
West Ham ⊖	d	12 29	12 38			18 44	18 49	18 59	19 08		19 14	19 19	19 29	19 38			19 44	19 49	19 59	20 08		20 14	20 19	20 29
London Liverpool St 15 ⊖	d																							
Stratford 7 ⊖	d																							
Barking ⊖	d	12 34	12 43			18 49	18 54	19 04	19 13		19 19	19 24	19 34	19 43			19 49	19 54	20 04	20 13		20 19	20 24	20 34
Upminster ⊖	d	12 42	12 51				19 02	19 12	19 21			19 32	19 42	19 51				20 02	20 12	20 21			20 32	20 42
Ockendon	d	12 48						19 18					19 48						20 18					20 48
Chafford Hundred Lakeside	d	12 51						19 21					19 51						20 21					20 51
West Horndon	d						19 07					19 37						20 07					20 37	
Laindon	d		12 59				19 12		19 29			19 42		19 59				20 12		20 29			20 42	
Basildon	d		13 02				19 15		19 32			19 45		20 02				20 15		20 32			20 45	
Dagenham Dock	d					18 54					19 24						19 54					20 24		
Rainham	d					18 57					19 27						19 57					20 27		
Purfleet	d					19 03					19 33						20 03					20 33		
Grays	d	12 55				19a12		19 25			19a42		19 55				20a12		20 25			20a42		20 55
Tilbury Town 3	d	12 58						19 28					19 58						20 28					20 58
East Tilbury	d	13 04						19 34					20 04						20 34					21 04
Stanford-le-Hope	d	13 07						19 37					20 07						20 37					21 07
Pitsea	d	13 15		←			19 19	19 45		←		19 49	20 15		←			20 19	20 45		←		20 49	21 15
Benfleet	d	13 19	13 08	13 19			19 22	19 49	19 38	19 49		19 52	20 19	20 08	20 19			20 22	20 49	20 38	20 49		20 52	21 19
Leigh-on-Sea	d	→	13 12	13 23			19 27	→	19 42	19 53		19 57	→	20 12	20 23			20 27	→	20 42	20 53		20 57	21 23
Chalkwell	d		13 15	13 26			19 29		19 45	19 56		19 59		20 15	20 26			20 29		20 45	20 56		20 59	21 26
Westcliff	d		13 17	13 28			19 32		19 47	19 58		20 02		20 17	20 28			20 32		20 47	20 58		21 02	21 28
Southend Central	a		13 20	13 34			19 35		19 50	20 04		20 05		20 20	20 34			20 35		20 50	21 04		21 05	21 34
	d		13 20				19 36		19 50			20 06		20 20				20 36		20 50			21 06	
Southend East	d		13 22				19 38		19 52			20 08		20 22				20 38		20 52			21 08	
Thorpe Bay	d		13 25				19 40		19 55			20 10		20 25				20 40		20 55			21 10	
Shoeburyness	a		13 32				19 48		20 02			20 18		20 32				20 48		21 02			21 18	

		CC		CC	CC	CC	CC	CC	CC	CC	CC	CC		CC	CC	CC	CC	CC	CC	CC	CC	CC		CC	CC
London Fenchurch St 7 ⊖	d	20 35		20 40	20 50	21 00		21 05	21 10	21 20	21 35	21 40		21 50	22 00		22 05	22 10	22 20	22 35	22 40	22 50		23 05	23 10
Limehouse DLR	d	20 39		20 44	20 54			21 09	21 14	21 24	21 39	21 44		21 54			22 09	22 14	22 24	22 39	22 44	22 54		23 09	23 14
West Ham ⊖	d	20 44		20 49	20 59	21 08		21 14	21 19	21 29	21 44	21 49		21 59	22 08		22 14	22 19	22 29	22 44	22 49	22 59		23 14	23 19
London Liverpool St 15 ⊖	d																								
Stratford 7 ⊖	d																								
Barking ⊖	d	20 49		20 54	21 04	21 13		21 19	21 24	21 34	21 49	21 54		22 04	22 13		22 19	22 24	22 34	22 49	22 55	23 04		23 19	23 25
Upminster ⊖	d			21 02	21 12	21 21			21 32	21 42		22 02		22 12	22 21			22 32	22 42		23 03	23 12			23 33
Ockendon	d				21 18					21 48				22 18					22 48			23 18			
Chafford Hundred Lakeside	d				21 21					21 51				22 21					22 51			23 21			
West Horndon	d			21 07					21 37			22 07						22 37			23 08				23 38
Laindon	d			21 12		21 29			21 42			22 12			22 29			22 42			23 13				23 43
Basildon	d			21 15		21 32			21 45			22 15			22 32			22 45			23 16				23 46
Dagenham Dock	d	20 54						21 24			21 54						22 24			22 54				23 24	
Rainham	d	20 57						21 27			21 57						22 27			22 57				23 27	
Purfleet	d	21 03						21 33			22 03						22 33			23 03				23 33	
Grays	d	21a12			21 25			21a42		21 55	22a12			22 25			22a42		22 55	23a12		23 25		23 38	
Tilbury Town 3	d				21 28					21 58				22 28					22 58			23 28		23 41	
East Tilbury	d				21 34					22 04				22 34					23 04			23 34		23 47	
Stanford-le-Hope	d				21 37					22 07				22 37					23 07			23 37		23 50	
Pitsea	d			21 19	21 45		←		21 49	22 15		22 19		22 45		←		22 49	23 15		23 19	23 45		23 58	23 49
Benfleet	d			21 22	21 49	21 38	21 49		21 52	22 19		22 22		22 49	22 38	22 49		22 52	23 19		23 23	23 49		→	23 53
Leigh-on-Sea	d			21 27	→	21 42	21 53		21 57	22 23		22 27		→	22 42	22 53		22 57	23 23		23 28	23 53			23 58
Chalkwell	d			21 29		21 45	21 56		21 59	22 26		22 29			22 45	22 56		22 59	23 26		23 30	23 56			00 01
Westcliff	d			21 32		21 47	21 58		22 02	22 28		22 32			22 47	22 58		23 02	23 28		23 33	23 58			00 03
Southend Central	a			21 35		21 50	22 04		22 05	22 34		22 35			22 50	23 04		23 05	23 31		23 35	00 01			00 05
	d			21 36		21 50			22 06			22 36			22 50			23 06	23 31		23 35	00 01			00 05
Southend East	d			21 38		21 52			22 08			22 38			22 52			23 08	23 33		23 37	00 03			00 07
Thorpe Bay	d			21 40		21 55			22 10			22 40			22 55			23 10	23 35		23 40	00 05			00 10
Shoeburyness	a			21 48		22 02			22 18			22 48			23 02			23 18	23 42		23 47	00 12			00 17

		CC	CC	CC	CC	CC	CC
London Fenchurch St 7 ⊖	d		23 20	23 35	23 40		23 50
Limehouse DLR	d		23 24	23 39	23 44		23 54
West Ham ⊖	d		23 29	23 44	23 49		23 59
London Liverpool St 15 ⊖	d						
Stratford 7 ⊖	d						
Barking ⊖	d		23 34	23 49	23 55		00 04
Upminster ⊖	d		23 42		00 03		00 12
Ockendon	d		23 48				00 18
Chafford Hundred Lakeside	d		23 51				00 21
West Horndon	d				00 08		
Laindon	d				00 13		
Basildon	d				00 16		
Dagenham Dock	d			23 54			
Rainham	d			23 57			
Purfleet	d			00 03			
Grays	d		23 55	00 08			00 25
Tilbury Town 3	d		23 58	00 11			00 28
East Tilbury	d		00 04	00 17			00 34
Stanford-le-Hope	d	←	00 07	00 20		←	00 37
Pitsea	d	23 58	00 15	00 28	00 19	00 28	00 45
Benfleet	d	00 01	00 19	→	00 23	00 31	00 49
Leigh-on-Sea	d	00 06	00 23		00 28	00 36	00 53
Chalkwell	d	00 08	00 26		00 30	00 38	00 56
Westcliff	d	00 11	00 28		00 33	00 41	00 58
Southend Central	a	00 13	00 31		00 35	00 43	01 01
	d	00 13	00 31		00 35	00 43	01 01
Southend East	d	00 15	00 33		00 37	00 45	01 03
Thorpe Bay	d	00 18	00 35		00 40	00 48	01 05
Shoeburyness	a	00 25	00 42		00 47	00 55	01 12

For services between London Liverpool Street and Southend Victoria refer to Table 6

Table 1

Sundays

8 December to 11 May

London - Southend Central and Shoeburyness

Network Diagram - see first page of Table 1

		CC A	CC A	CC A	CC A	CC A	CC A	CC A	CC	CC	CC	CC	CC	CC	CC	CC	CC	CC	CC	CC	CC	CC	CC
London Fenchurch St [7] ⊖	d								00 10	00 40	06 40		07 10	07 40	07 50	08 10			08 40	08 50	09 10		
Limehouse DLR	d								00 14	00 44	06 44		07 14	07 44	07 54	08 14			08 44	08 54	09 14		
West Ham ⊖	d								00 19	00 49	06 49		07 19	07 49	07 59	08 19			08 49	08 59	09 19		
London Liverpool St [15] ⊖	d																						
Stratford [7] ⊖	d																						
Barking ⊖	d							00 04	00 25	00 55	06 54	07 04	07 24	07 54	08 04	08 24	08 29	08 34	08 54	09 04	09 24	09 29	09 34
Upminster ⊖	d					00 03		00 12	00 33	01 03	07 02	07 12	07 32	08 02	08 12	08 32		08 42	09 02	09 12	09 32		09 42
Ockendon	d							00 18				07 18			08 18			08 48		09 18			09 48
Chafford Hundred Lakeside	d							00 21				07 21			08 21			08 51		09 21			09 51
West Horndon	d					00 08			00 38	01 08	07 07		07 37	08 07		08 37			09 07		09 37		
Laindon	d					00 13			00 43	01 13	07 12		07 42	08 12		08 42			09 12		09 42		
Basildon	d					00 16			00 46	01 16	07 15		07 45	08 15		08 45			09 15		09 45		
Dagenham Dock	d																08 33					09 33	
Rainham	d																08 37					09 37	
Purfleet	d						00 03										08 42					09 42	
Grays	d						00 08	00 25				07 25			08 25		08a50	08 55		09 25		09a50	09 55
Tilbury Town [3]	d						00 11	00 28				07 28			08 28			08 58		09 28			09 58
East Tilbury	d				00 04		00 17	00 34				07 34			08 34			09 04		09 34			10 04
Stanford-le-Hope	d				00 07		00 20	00 37				07 37			08 37			09 07		09 37			10 07
Pitsea	d				00 15	00 19	00 28	00 45	00 49	01 19	07 19	07 45	07 49	08 19	08 45	08 49		09 15	09 19	09 45	09 49		10 15
Benfleet	d			00 01	00 19	00 23	00 31	00 49	00 53	01 23	07 22	07 49	07 52	08 22	08 49	08 52		09 19	09 22	09 49	09 52		10 19
Leigh-on-Sea	d			00 06	00 23	00 28	00 36	00 53	00 58	01 28	07 27	07 53	07 57	08 27	08 53	08 57		09 23	09 27	09 53	09 57		10 23
Chalkwell	d		00 01	00 08	00 26	00 30	00 38	00 56	01 00	01 30	07 29	07 56	07 59	08 29	08 56	08 59		09 26	09 29	09 56	09 59		10 26
Westcliff	d		00 03	00 11	00 28	00 33	00 41	00 58	01 03	01 33	07 32	07 58	08 02	08 32	08 58	09 02		09 28	09 32	09 58	10 02		10 28
Southend Central	a		00 05	00 13	00 31	00 35	00 43	01 01	01 05	01 35	07 34	08 04	08 05	08 34	09 04	09 05		09 34	09 35	10 04	10 05		10 34
	d	00 01	00 05	00 13	00 31	00 35	00 43	01 01	01 05	01 35	07 36		08 06	08 36		09 06			09 36		10 06		
Southend East	d	00 03	00 07	00 15	00 33	00 37	00 45	01 03	01 07	01 37	07 38		08 08	08 38		09 08			09 38		10 08		
Thorpe Bay	d	00 05	00 10	00 18	00 35	00 40	00 48	01 05	01 10	01 40	07 40		08 10	08 40		09 10			09 40		10 10		
Shoeburyness	a	00 12	00 17	00 25	00 42	00 47	00 55	01 12	01 17	01 47	07 48		08 18	08 48		09 18			09 48		10 18		

		CC	CC	CC	CC	CC		CC	CC	CC	CC	CC	CC	CC	CC	CC	CC	CC	CC	CC	CC	CC
London Fenchurch St [7] ⊖	d	09 40	09 50	10 10		10 20		18 40	18 50	19 10		19 20	19 40	19 50	20 10		20 20	20 40	20 50	21 10		21 20
Limehouse DLR	d	09 44	09 54	10 14		10 24		18 44	18 54	19 14		19 24	19 44	19 54	20 14		20 24	20 44	20 54	21 14		21 24
West Ham ⊖	d	09 49	09 59	10 19		10 29		18 49	18 59	19 19		19 29	19 49	19 59	20 19		20 29	20 49	20 59	21 19		21 29
London Liverpool St [15] ⊖	d																					
Stratford [7] ⊖	d																					
Barking ⊖	d	09 54	10 04	10 24	10 29	10 34		18 54	19 04	19 24	19 29	19 34	19 54	20 04	20 24	20 29	20 34	20 54	21 04	21 24	21 29	21 34
Upminster ⊖	d	10 02	10 12	10 32		10 42		19 02	19 12	19 32		19 42	20 02	20 12	20 32		20 42	21 02	21 12	21 32		21 42
Ockendon	d		10 18			10 48			19 18			19 48		20 18			20 48		21 18			21 48
Chafford Hundred Lakeside	d		10 21			10 51			19 21			19 51		20 21			20 51		21 21			21 51
West Horndon	d	10 07		10 37				19 07		19 37			20 07		20 37			21 07		21 37		
Laindon	d	10 12		10 42			and at the same minutes past each hour until	19 12		19 42			20 12		20 42			21 12		21 42		
Basildon	d	10 15		10 45				19 15		19 45			20 15		20 45			21 15		21 45		
Dagenham Dock	d				10 33						19 33					20 33					21 33	
Rainham	d				10 37						19 37					20 37					21 37	
Purfleet	d				10 42						19 42					20 42					21 42	
Grays	d		10 25		10a50	10 55			19 25		19a50	19 55		20 25		20a50	20 55		21 25		21a50	21 55
Tilbury Town [3]	d		10 28			10 58			19 28			19 58		20 28			20 58		21 28			21 58
East Tilbury	d		10 34			11 04			19 34			20 04		20 34			21 04		21 34			22 04
Stanford-le-Hope	d		10 37			11 07			19 37			20 07		20 37			21 07		21 37			22 07
Pitsea	d	10 19	10 45	10 49		11 15		19 19	19 45	19 49		20 15	20 19	20 45	20 49		21 15	21 19	21 45	21 49		22 15
Benfleet	d	10 22	10 49	10 52		11 19		19 22	19 49	19 52		20 19	20 22	20 49	20 52		21 19	21 22	21 49	21 52		22 19
Leigh-on-Sea	d	10 27	10 53	10 57		11 23		19 27	19 53	19 57		20 23	20 27	20 53	20 57		21 23	21 27	21 53	21 57		22 23
Chalkwell	d	10 29	10 56	10 59		11 26		19 29	19 56	19 59		20 26	20 29	20 56	20 59		21 26	21 29	21 56	21 59		22 26
Westcliff	d	10 32	10 58	11 02		11 28		19 32	19 58	20 02		20 28	20 32	20 58	21 02		21 28	21 32	21 58	22 02		22 28
Southend Central	a	10 35	11 04	11 05		11 34		19 35	20 04	20 05		20 34	20 35	21 04	21 05		21 32	21 35	22 04	22 05		22 31
	d	10 36		11 06				19 36		20 06			20 36		21 06		21 32	21 36		22 06		22 31
Southend East	d	10 38		11 08				19 38		20 08			20 38		21 08		21 34	21 38		22 08		22 33
Thorpe Bay	d	10 40		11 10				19 40		20 10			20 40		21 10		21 36	21 40		22 10		22 36
Shoeburyness	a	10 48		11 18				19 48		20 18			20 48		21 18		21 44	21 48		22 18		22 43

A not 8 December

For services between London Liverpool Street and Southend Victoria refer to Table 6

Table 1

Sundays

8 December to 11 May

London - Southend Central and Shoeburyness

Network Diagram - see first page of Table 1

			CC		CC	CC	CC	CC	CC	CC
London Fenchurch St 7	⊖	d	21 40		21 50	22 10	22 40	22 50	23 10	23 40
Limehouse	DLR	d	21 44		21 54	22 14	22 44	22 54	23 14	23 44
West Ham	⊖	d	21 49		21 59	22 19	22 49	22 59	23 19	23 49
London Liverpool St 15	⊖	d								
Stratford 7	⊖	d								
Barking	⊖	d	21 54		22 04	22 24	22 54	23 04	23 24	23 54
Upminster	⊖	d	22 02		22 12	22 32	23 02	23 12	23 32	00 02
Ockendon		d			22 18			23 18		
Chafford Hundred Lakeside		d			22 21			23 21		
West Horndon		d	22 07			22 37	23 07		23 37	00 07
Laindon		d	22 12			22 42	23 12		23 42	00 12
Basildon		d	22 15			22 45	23 15		23 45	00 15
Dagenham Dock		d								
Rainham		d								
Purfleet		d								
Grays		d			22 25			23 25		
Tilbury Town 3		d			22 28			23 28		
East Tilbury		d			22 34			23 34		
Stanford-le-Hope		d			22 37			23 37		
Pitsea		d	22 19		22 45	22 49	23 19	23 45	23 49	00 19
Benfleet		d	22 22		22 49	22 52	23 22	23 49	23 52	00 22
Leigh-on-Sea		d	22 27		22 53	22 57	23 27	23 53	23 57	00 27
Chalkwell		d	22 29		22 56	22 59	23 29	23 56	23 59	00 29
Westcliff		d	22 32		22 58	23 02	23 32	23 58	00 02	00 32
Southend Central		a	22 35		23 01	23 04	23 34	00 01	00 04	00 34
		d	22 36		23 01	23 05	23 35	00 01	00 05	00 35
Southend East		d	22 38		23 03	23 07	23 37	00 03	00 07	00 37
Thorpe Bay		d	22 40		23 05	23 09	23 39	00 05	00 09	00 39
Shoeburyness		a	22 48		23 13	23 17	23 47	00 13	00 17	00 47

For services between London Liverpool Street and Southend Victoria refer to Table 6

Table 1R

Mondays to Fridays

Shoeburyness and Southend Central - London

9 December to 16 May

Network Diagram - see first page of Table 1

Miles	Miles	Miles	Miles			CC MX	CC MX	CC	CC	CC	CC	CC	CC	CC		CC	CC	CC	CC	CC	CC	CC	CC	CC
0	0	—	—	**Shoeburyness**	d				04 20		04 40	05 00		05 13		05 23			05 27		05 45			05 56
1½	1½	—	—	Thorpe Bay	d				04 24		04 44	05 04		05 17		05 27			05 31		05 49		05 56	06 00
3	3	—	—	Southend East	d				04 27		04 47	05 07		05 20		05 30			05 34		05 52		05 59	06 03
3¾	3¾	—	—	**Southend Central**	a				04 29		04 49	05 09		05 22		05 32			05 36		05 54		06 01	06 05
—	—	—	—		d				04 29		04 50	05 09		05 23		05 32			05 36	05 47	05 54		06 02	06 06
4¾	4¾	—	—	Westcliff	d				04 31		04 52	05 11		05 25		05 34			05 38	05 49	05 56		06 04	06 08
5½	5½	—	—	Chalkwell	d				04 34		04 54	05 14		05 27		05 37			05 41	05 51	05 59		06 06	06 10
7	7	—	—	Leigh-on-Sea	d				04 37		04 57	05 17		05 30		05 40			05 44	05 54	06 02		06 09	06 13
10¼	10¼	—	—	Benfleet	d				04 41		05 02	05 21		05 35		05 44			05 48	05 59	06 07		06 14	06 18
13	13	—	—	Pitsea	d				04 45		05 06	05 25		05 39		05 48			05 52	06 04	06 11		06 24	
—	18	—	—	Stanford-le-Hope	d			04 29			05 13			05 46					05 59	06 11			06 31	
—	20	—	—	East Tilbury	d			04 33			05 17			05 50					06 03	06 15			06 35	
—	23¾	—	—	**Tilbury Town 3**	d			04 39			05 23			05 56					06 09	06 21			06 41	
—	25½	0	—	Grays	d			04 42		05 09	05 26		05 48	06 00				06 11	06 13	06 25		06 29	06 45	
—	29¼	—	—	Purfleet	d						05 32			06 05					06 19			06 34	06 51	
—	32½	—	—	Rainham	d						05 37			06 10					06 24			06 40	06 56	
—	34¾	—	—	Dagenham Dock	d						05 40			06 14					06 27			06 43	07 00	
15	—	—	—	Basildon	d				04 49			05 29				05 52					06 15			06 25
16¾	—	—	—	Laindon	d				04 52			05 32				05 55					06 18			06 29
20¼	—	—	—	West Horndon	d				04 57			05 37				06 00					06 23			
—	—	2½	—	Chafford Hundred Lakeside	d			04 46		05 13			05 52					06 15		06 30				
—	—	4½	—	Ockendon	d			04 50		05 17			05 56					06 19		06 37				
24¼	—	7½	—	Upminster ⊖	d			04 57	05 03	05a22		05 43	06 02			06 06	←	06a25		06 44	06 29			06 38
32	37¾	—	0	Barking ⊖	d			05 06	05 11		05 46	05 51	06 11	06 20		06 15	06 20		06 34	→	06 38	06 50	07 06	
—	—	—	4	Stratford 7 ⊖	a			05 15						↪									↪	
—	—	—	7¾	**London Liverpool St 15** ⊖	a			05 29																
35	40¾	—	—	West Ham ⊖	d		00 04		05 17		05 52	05 57	06 16			06 21	06 26		06 40		06 44	06 55		
37¾	43½	—	—	Limehouse DLR	d	00 01	00 09		05 22		05 57	06 02	06 21			06 26	06 31		06 45		06 49	07 00		06 55
39½	45¼	—	—	**London Fenchurch St 7** ⊖	a	00 05	00 13		05 28		06 03	06 08	06 27			06 30	06 37		06 50		06 53	→		07 01

		CC	CC	CC	CC	CC	CC	CC	CC	CC		CC	CC	CC	CC	CC	CC	CC	CC	CC		CC	CC	CC	CC
Shoeburyness	d			06 04			06 13		06 17			06 28			06 33	06 46								06 51	
Thorpe Bay	d			06 08		06 13	06 17		06 21			06 32			06 37	06 50								06 55	
Southend East	d			06 11		06 16	06 20		06 24			06 35			06 40	06 53								06 58	
Southend Central	a			06 13		06 18	06 22		06 26			06 37			06 42	06 55								07 00	
	d			06 13		06 18	06 23		06 26			06 38			06 42	06 55								07 00	
Westcliff	d			06 15		06 20	06 25		06 28			06 40			06 44	06 57								07 02	
Chalkwell	d			06 18		06 23	06 27		06 31			06 42			06 47	07 00								07 05	
Leigh-on-Sea	d			06 21		06 26	06 30		06 34			06 45			06 50	07 03								07 08	
Benfleet	d			06 26		06 31	06 35		06 39			06 50			06 55	07 08								07 13	
Pitsea	d			06 30		06 39			06 43					06 52	06 59				07 00				07 16	07 17	
Stanford-le-Hope	d					06 46								06 59					07 07				07 23		
East Tilbury	d					06 50								07 03					07 11				07 27		
Tilbury Town 3	d					06 56								07 09					07 18				07 33		
Grays	d				06 50	07 00								07 13					07 22	07 30			07 37		
Purfleet	d					07 05								07 18						07 35					
Rainham	d					07 11								07 24						07 41					
Dagenham Dock	d					07 14								07 27						07 44					
Basildon	d			06 34			06 42		06 47			06 57			07 03	07 15								07 21	
Laindon	d			06 37					06 50						07 07			07 20				07 37		07 25	
West Horndon	d			06 42					06 55						07 12			07 25				07 42			
Chafford Hundred Lakeside	d				06 54														07 26				07 41		
Ockendon	d		←		06 58					←									07 30				07 46		
Upminster ⊖	d		06 44	06 48	07 05			←	07 01	07 05		07 10	←		07 18		←	07 30	07 37			07 47	07 54		←
Barking ⊖	d			06 57	→	07 21	07 01	07 06	07 10	07 14			07 21	07 34	07 27		07 34	07 39	07 46	07 51		07 56		07 42	07 46
Stratford 7 ⊖	a					↪								↪					↪	↪		↪			
London Liverpool St 15 ⊖	a																								
West Ham ⊖	d	←	06 58	07 03			07 07	07 12	07 16	07 20		07 23	07 26				07 39	07 44						07 47	07 52
Limehouse DLR	d	07 00	07 03					07 17	07 21	07 25			07 32		07 36		07 44	07 49						07 52	
London Fenchurch St 7 ⊖	a	07 07	07 09	07 13			07 17	07 23	07 27	07 31		07 34	07 38		07 42	07 45	07 51	07 56					08 17	07 59	08 02

		CC	CC	CC	CC	CC		CC	CC	CC	CC	CC	CC	CC	CC	CC		CC	CC	CC	CC	CC	CC	CC	CC
Shoeburyness	d		07 03					07 17					07 22		07 34								07 49		
Thorpe Bay	d		07 07			07 12		07 21					07 26		07 38						07 42		07 53		
Southend East	d		07 10			07 15		07 24					07 29		07 41						07 45		07 56		
Southend Central	a		07 12			07 17		07 26					07 31		07 43						07 47		07 58		
	d	07 08	07 13			07 18		07 27					07 32		07 43						07 48		07 59		
Westcliff	d	07 10	07 15			07 20		07 29					07 34		07 45						07 50		08 01		
Chalkwell	d	07 12	07 17			07 22		07 31					07 36		07 48						07 52		08 03		
Leigh-on-Sea	d	07 16	07 20			07 25		07 34					07 39		07 51						07 55		08 06		
Benfleet	d	07 20	07 25			07 30		07 39					07 44		07 56						08 00		08 11		
Pitsea	d	07 25				07 34						07 41	07 48						07 48	07 52	08 04				
Stanford-le-Hope	d	07 32									07 42	07 48							07 55	08 00					08 11
East Tilbury	d	07 36										07 52								08 04					08 15
Tilbury Town 3	d	07 42										07 58								08 10					08 21
Grays	d	07 46									07 52	08 02							08 06	08 14					08 25
Purfleet	d	07 51										08 07								08 19					
Rainham	d	07 57										08 13								08 25					
Dagenham Dock	d	08 00										08 16								08 28					
Basildon	d		07 32			07 39							07 53								08 09				
Laindon	d					07 42				07 50			07 56					08 07			08 12			08 22	
West Horndon	d									07 55								08 12						08 27	
Chafford Hundred Lakeside	d										07 57								08 10						08 29
Ockendon	d										08 01								08 17						08 33
Upminster ⊖	d			←	←				←	08 02	08 09			←	08 13	←		08 17	08 24			←	08 28	08 32	08 40
Barking ⊖	d	08 07		07 51	07 56	07 59			08 07	08 10	08 18	08 23	08 13	08 18		08 23		08 26		08 35	08 29	08 35		08 42	08 50
Stratford 7 ⊖	a	↪									↪	↪								↪					→
London Liverpool St 15 ⊖	a																								
West Ham ⊖	d			07 57	08 01				08 12	08 16			08 19	08 23		08 28		08 32	08 38		08 35			08 47	
Limehouse DLR	d		07 59	08 02	08 06	08 08		08 13	08 17	08 21			08 24		08 30	08 33		08 37			08 40	08 45	08 48	08 52	
London Fenchurch St 7 ⊖	a		08 05	08 08	08 12	08 15		08 19	08 24	08 27			08 31	08 34	08 37	08 40		08 43	08 48		08 46	08 51	08 55	08 58	

Table 1R

Mondays to Fridays

9 December to 16 May

Shoeburyness and Southend Central - London

Network Diagram - see first page of Table 1

		CC	CC	CC	CC	CC	CC	CC	CC	CC	CC	CC	CC	CC	CC	CC	CC	CC	CC	CC	CC
Shoeburyness	d		07 54		08 05					08 11		08 25					08 40				
Thorpe Bay	d		07 58		08 09					08 15		08 29					08 44				
Southend East	d		08 01		08 12					08 18		08 32					08 47				
Southend Central	a		08 03		08 14					08 20		08 34					08 49				
	d		08 03		08 15					08 20		08 34					08 50			09 06	
Westcliff	d		08 05		08 17					08 22		08 36					08 52			09 08	
Chalkwell	d		08 08		08 19					08 25		08 39					08 54			09 10	
Leigh-on-Sea	d		08 11		08 22					08 28		08 42					08 57			09 13	
Benfleet	d		08 16		08 27					08 33		08 47					09 02			09 18	
Pitsea	d	08 12	08 20					08 24	08 35	08 37		08 51				08 54	09 06				09 08
Stanford-le-Hope	d	08 19						08 33	08 42							09 01					09 16
East Tilbury	d	08 23						08 37	08 46							09 05					09 20
Tilbury Town [3]	d	08 29						08 43	08 52							09 11					09 26
Grays	d	08 33						08 47	08 56					09 03		09 15					09 29
Purfleet	d	08 39						08 52						09 08		09 20					
Rainham	d	08 44						08 58						09 13		09 26					
Dagenham Dock	d	08 48						09 01						09 17		09 29					
Basildon	d		08 24							08 41		08 55					09 11			09 25	
Laindon	d		08 28				08 38			08 45					09 04		09 14		09 17	09 28	
West Horndon	d						08 43								09 10				09 22		
Chafford Hundred Lakeside	d								09 01												09 34
Ockendon	d								09 05				←								09 38
Upminster	⊖ d			←		←	08 49		09 12	08 54	←	09 06	09 12		09 16			←	09 28	09 38	09 45
Barking	⊖ d	08 54	08 45	08 50		08 54	08 58	09 08	→	09 03	09 08		09 21	09 23	09 25	09 35	09 30	09 35	09 37	09 46	09 53
Stratford [7]	⊖ a	→						→								→					
London Liverpool St [15]	⊖ a																				
West Ham	⊖ d		08 51	08 55		09 00	09 04			09 09			09 26	09 29	09 31				09 43	09 52	09 59
Limehouse	DLR d		08 56			09 05	09 09			09 14	09 17	09 23	09 31	09 34	09 36			09 44	09 48	09 57	10 04
London Fenchurch St [7]	⊖ a		09 02	09 06	09 08	09 11	09 15			09 20	09 23	09 29	09 38	09 40	09 43		09 45	09 51	09 54	10 03	10 08

		CC	CC	CC	CC	CC	CC	CC	CC	CC	CC		CC	CC	CC	CC	CC	CC	CC	CC	CC	CC	CC
Shoeburyness	d	09 05			09 20		09 35			09 50			14 05			14 20		14 35			14 50		15 05
Thorpe Bay	d	09 09			09 24		09 39			09 54			14 09			14 24		14 39			14 54		15 09
Southend East	d	09 12			09 27		09 42			09 57			14 12			14 27		14 42			14 57		15 12
Southend Central	a	09 14			09 29		09 44			09 59			14 14			14 29		14 44			14 59		15 14
	d	09 15		09 20	09 30		09 45		09 50	10 00			14 15		14 20	14 30		14 45		14 50	15 00		15 15
Westcliff	d	09 17		09 23	09 32		09 47		09 53	10 02			14 17		14 23	14 32		14 47		14 53	15 02		15 17
Chalkwell	d	09 19		09 25	09 34		09 49		09 55	10 04			14 19		14 25	14 34		14 49		14 55	15 04		15 19
Leigh-on-Sea	d	09 22		09 28	09 37		09 52		09 58	10 07			14 22		14 28	14 37		14 52		14 58	15 07		15 22
Benfleet	d	09 27		09 33	09 42		09 57		10 03	10 12			14 27		14 33	14 42		14 57		15 03	15 12		15 27
Pitsea	d	09 32		09 37			10 02		10 07				14 32		14 37			15 02		15 07			15 32
Stanford-le-Hope	d			09 44					10 14			and at the same minutes past each hour until			14 44					15 14			
East Tilbury	d			09 48					10 18						14 48					15 18			
Tilbury Town [3]	d			09 54					10 24						14 54					15 24			
Grays	d		09 46	09 57				10 16	10 27					14 46	14 57				15 16	15 27			
Purfleet	d		09 51					10 21						14 51					15 21				
Rainham	d		09 56					10 26						14 56					15 26				
Dagenham Dock	d		10 00					10 30						15 00					15 30				
Basildon	d	09 36			09 49		10 06			10 19			14 36			14 49		15 06			15 19		15 36
Laindon	d	09 39			09 52		10 09			10 22			14 39			14 52		15 09			15 22		15 39
West Horndon	d	09 44					10 14						14 44					15 14					15 44
Chafford Hundred Lakeside	d			10 01					10 31						15 01					15 31			
Ockendon	d			10 05		←			10 35		←				15 05		←			15 35		←	
Upminster	⊖ d	09 50		10 12	10 02	10 12	10 20		10 42	10 32	10 42		14 50		15 12	15 02	15 12	15 20		15 42	15 32	15 42	15 50
Barking	⊖ d	09 58	10 06	→	10 10	10 20	10 28	10 36	→	10 40	10 50		14 58	15 06	→	15 10	15 20	15 28	15 36	→	15 40	15 50	15 58
Stratford [7]	⊖ a																						
London Liverpool St [15]	⊖ a																						
West Ham	⊖ d	10 04	10 11		10 16	10 26	10 34	10 41		10 46	10 56		15 04	15 11		15 16	15 26	15 34	15 41		15 46	15 56	16 04
Limehouse	DLR d	10 09	10 16			10 31	10 39	10 46			11 01		15 09	15 16			15 31	15 39	15 46			16 01	16 09
London Fenchurch St [7]	⊖ a	10 13	10 21		10 24	10 35	10 43	10 51		10 54	11 05		15 13	15 21		15 24	15 35	15 43	15 51		15 54	16 05	16 13

		CC	CC	CC	CC	CC	CC	CC	CC	CC	CC	CC	CC	CC	CC	CC	CC	CC	CC	CC	CC	CC	CC
Shoeburyness	d			15 20		15 35			15 50		16 05				16 15			16 28					16 50
Thorpe Bay	d			15 24		15 39			15 54		16 09				16 19			16 32					16 54
Southend East	d			15 27		15 42			15 57		16 12				16 22			16 35					16 57
Southend Central	a			15 29		15 44			15 59		16 14				16 24			16 37					16 59
	d		15 20	15 30		15 45		15 48	16 00		16 15			16 19	16 25	16 31		16 38				16 53	17 00
Westcliff	d		15 23	15 32		15 47		15 50	16 02		16 17			16 21	16 27	16 33		16 40				16 55	17 02
Chalkwell	d		15 25	15 34		15 49		15 53	16 04		16 19			16 23	16 29	16 35		16 42				16 58	17 04
Leigh-on-Sea	d		15 28	15 37		15 52		15 56	16 07		16 22			16 26	16 32	16 38		16 45				17 01	17 07
Benfleet	d		15 33	15 42		15 57		16 00	16 12		16 27			16 31	16 37	16 43		16 50				17 05	17 12
Pitsea	d		15 37			16 02		16 04			16 31			16 35		16 47		16 54			16 57	17 09	17 16
Stanford-le-Hope	d		15 44					16 11						16 42							17 04		
East Tilbury	d		15 48					16 15						16 46							17 08		
Tilbury Town [3]	d		15 54					16 21						16 52							17 14		
Grays	d	15 46	15 57				16 16	16 26				16 39	16 52	16 57							17 18		
Purfleet	d	15 51					16 21					16 44	16 57										
Rainham	d	15 56					16 26					16 49	17 02										
Dagenham Dock	d	16 00					16 30					16 53	17 06										
Basildon	d			15 49		16 06			16 19		16 35				16 43	16 51		16 58				17 13	17 20
Laindon	d			15 52		16 09			16 22		16 38							17 01		17 13		17 17	
West Horndon	d					16 14					16 43							17 06				17 22	
Chafford Hundred Lakeside	d		16 01					16 30						17 01							17 23		
Ockendon	d		16 05		←			16 34		←				17 08					←		17 32		
Upminster	⊖ d		16 12	16 02	16 12	16 20		16 41	16 30	16 41	16 48			17 15	16 54		←	17 11	17 15	17 23	17 39	17 28	17 31
Barking	⊖ d	16 06	→	16 10	16 20	16 28	16 36	→	16 38	16 49	16 57	17 00	17 16	→	17 03	17 09	17 16	17 20	17 25	17 32	→	17 36	17 40
Stratford [7]	⊖ a												→										
London Liverpool St [15]	⊖ a																						
West Ham	⊖ d	16 11		16 17	16 26	16 34			16 44		17 02				17 09		17 22		17 31				
Limehouse	DLR d	16 16			16 31	16 39					17 08	17 10			17 14			17 29		17 42			
London Fenchurch St [7]	⊖ a	16 21		16 26	16 36	16 43	16 48		16 52	17 03	17 12	17 15			17 18	17 24	17 30	17 33	17 39	17 46		17 49	17 52

Table 1R

Mondays to Fridays

9 December to 16 May

Shoeburyness and Southend Central - London

Network Diagram - see first page of Table 1

Station		CC	CC	CC	CC		CC	CC	CC	CC	CC	CC	CC	CC	CC		CC	CC	CC	CC	CC	CC	CC	CC	CC
Shoeburyness	d		16 56							17 10			17 30		17 46				18 05				18 20		
Thorpe Bay	d		17 00							17 14			17 34		17 50				18 09				18 24		
Southend East	d		17 03							17 17			17 37		17 53				18 12				18 27		
Southend Central	a		17 05							17 19			17 39		17 55				18 14				18 29		
	d		17 06							17 19			17 40		17 56				18 15		18 20		18 30		
Westcliff	d		17 08							17 21			17 42		17 58				18 17		18 23		18 32		
Chalkwell	d		17 10							17 24			17 44		18 00				18 19		18 25		18 34		
Leigh-on-Sea	d		17 13							17 27			17 47		18 03				18 22		18 28		18 37		
Benfleet	d		17 18							17 32			17 52		18 08				18 27		18 33		18 42		
Pitsea	d		17 22						17 28	17 36		17 45	17 56	18 01	18 12			18 14	18 32		18 37				
Stanford-le-Hope	d				17 19				17 35			17 52		18 08				18 21			18 44				
East Tilbury	d				17 23				17 39			17 56		18 12				18 25			18 48				
Tilbury Town 3	d				17 29				17 46			18 02		18 18				18 31			18 54				
Grays	d	17 22			17 32		17 46		17 51			18 06		18 22				18 35		18 54	18 57	19 22			
Purfleet	d	17 27			17 38		17 51					18 11						18 40		18 59		19 27			
Rainham	d	17 32			17 43		17 56					18 16						18 45		19 04		19 32			
Dagenham Dock	d	17 36			17 46		18 00					18 20						18 49		19 08		19 36			
Basildon	d		17 26							17 40			18 00		18 16				18 36				18 49		
Laindon	d							17 49		17 44	18 06		18 03		18 19				18 39				18 52		
West Horndon	d							17 54			18 11				18 24				18 44						
Chafford Hundred Lakeside	d								17 55					18 27							19 02				
Ockendon	d			←					18 01					18 33			←				19 07				←
Upminster ⊖	d			17 39				18 00	18 08		18 17			18 39	18 31		18 39		18 50		19 13		19 02	←	19 13
Barking ⊖	d	17 42	17 44	17 47	17 52		18 06	18 08	18 16		18 25	18 27		→	18 39			18 55	18 58	19 14	→	19 42	19 10	19 14	19 22
Stratford 7 ⊖	a																			→		→			
London Liverpool St 15 ⊖	a																								
West Ham ⊖	d		17 49		17 58		18 11	18 14			18 30	18 33	18 26		18 45			19 00	19 04				19 16	19 20	19 27
Limehouse DLR	d				18 03			18 19			18 35	18 38			18 50			19 05	19 09						19 32
London Fenchurch St 7 ⊖	a	17 54	17 58	18 00	18 08		18 20	18 23	18 29	18 11	18 39	18 42	18 34		18 54		18 59	19 10	19 13				19 24	19 28	19 37

Station			CC	CC	CC	CC	CC	CC	CC	CC	CC		CC	CC	CC	CC	CC	CC	CC	CC	CC		CC	CC	CC
Shoeburyness	d		18 35			18 50			19 05		19 20				19 35			19 50			20 05				20 20
Thorpe Bay	d		18 39			18 54			19 09		19 24				19 39			19 54			20 09				20 24
Southend East	d		18 42			18 57			19 12		19 27				19 42			19 57			20 12				20 27
Southend Central	a		18 44			18 59			19 15		19 29				19 44			19 59			20 14				20 29
	d		18 45	18 48		19 00			19 15	19 20	19 30				19 45		19 50	20 00			20 15			20 20	20 30
Westcliff	d		18 47	18 51		19 02			19 17	19 23	19 32				19 47		19 53	20 02			20 17			20 23	20 32
Chalkwell	d		18 49	18 53		19 04			19 19	19 25	19 34				19 49		19 55	20 04			20 19			20 25	20 34
Leigh-on-Sea	d		18 52	18 56		19 07			19 22	19 28	19 37				19 52		19 58	20 07			20 22			20 28	20 37
Benfleet	d		18 57	19 01		19 12			19 27	19 33	19 42				19 57		20 03	20 12			20 27			20 33	20 42
Pitsea	d		19 02	19 05					19 32	19 37					20 02		20 07				20 32			20 37	
Stanford-le-Hope	d			19 12						19 44							20 14							20 44	
East Tilbury	d			19 16						19 48							20 18							20 48	
Tilbury Town 3	d			19 22						19 54							20 24							20 54	
Grays	d			19 25	19 48					19 57						20 16	20 27						20 46	20 57	
Purfleet	d				19 53											20 21							20 51		
Rainham	d				19 58											20 26							20 56		
Dagenham Dock	d				20 02											20 30							21 00		
Basildon	d		19 06			19 19			19 36		19 49				20 06			20 19			20 36				20 49
Laindon	d		19 09			19 22			19 39		19 52				20 09			20 22			20 39				20 52
West Horndon	d		19 14						19 44						20 14						20 44				
Chafford Hundred Lakeside	d			19 29						20 01							20 31							21 01	
Ockendon	d			19 34				←		20 05				←			20 35		←					21 05	
Upminster ⊖	d		19 20	19 40		19 32	←	19 40	19 50	20 12	20 02		←	20 12	20 20		20 42	20 32	20 42		20 50			21 12	21 02
Barking ⊖	d		19 28	→	20 12	19 40	19 42	19 50	19 58	→	20 10		20 12	20 20	20 28	20 36	→	20 40	20 50	20 51	20 58		21 06	→	21 10
Stratford 7 ⊖	a				→								20 21							21 00			21 15		
London Liverpool St 15 ⊖	a												20 33							21 12			21 26		
West Ham ⊖	d		19 34			19 46	19 48	19 56	20 04		20 16			20 26	20 34	20 41		20 46	20 56		21 04				21 16
Limehouse DLR	d		19 39				19 53	20 01	20 09					20 31	20 39	20 46			21 01		21 09				
London Fenchurch St 7 ⊖	a		19 43			19 54	19 58	20 05	20 13		20 25			20 35	20 43	20 51		20 54	21 05		21 13				21 24

Station		CC	CC	CC	CC	CC	CC		CC	CC	CC	CC	CC	CC	CC	CC	CC		CC	CC	CC	CC			
Shoeburyness	d		20 35			21 05				21 20		21 35			22 05				22 35			23 05			
Thorpe Bay	d		20 39			21 09				21 24		21 39			22 09				22 39			23 09			
Southend East	d		20 42			21 12				21 27		21 42			22 12				22 42			23 12			
Southend Central	a		20 44			21 14				21 29		21 45			22 14				22 44			23 14			
	d		20 45		20 50	21 15			21 20	21 30		21 45		21 50	22 15		22 20		22 45	22 50		23 15			
Westcliff	d		20 47		20 53	21 17			21 23	21 32		21 47		21 53	22 17		22 23		22 47	22 53		23 17			
Chalkwell	d		20 49		20 55	21 19			21 25	21 34		21 49		21 55	22 19		22 25		22 49	22 55		23 19			
Leigh-on-Sea	d		20 52		20 58	21 22			21 28	21 37		21 52		21 58	22 22		22 28		22 52	22 58		23 22			
Benfleet	d		20 57		21 03	21 27			21 33	21 42		21 57		22 03	22 27		22 33		22 57	23 03		23 27			
Pitsea	d		21 02		21 07	21 32			21 37			22 02		22 07	22 32		22 37		23 02	23 07		23 32			
Stanford-le-Hope	d				21 14				21 44					22 14			22 44			23 14					
East Tilbury	d				21 18				21 48					22 18			22 48			23 18					
Tilbury Town 3	d				21 24				21 54					22 24			22 54			23 24					
Grays	d			21 16	21 27		21 46		21 57				22 16	22 27		22 46	22 57			23 27	23 33				
Purfleet	d			21 21			21 51						22 21			22 51					23 38				
Rainham	d			21 26			21 56						22 26			22 56					23 43				
Dagenham Dock	d			21 30			22 00						22 30			23 00					23 47				
Basildon	d		21 06			21 36				21 49		22 06			22 36				23 06			23 36			
Laindon	d		21 09			21 39				21 52		22 09			22 39				23 09			23 39			
West Horndon	d		21 14			21 44						22 14			22 44				23 14			23 44			
Chafford Hundred Lakeside	d				21 31				22 01					22 31			23 01			23 31					
Ockendon	d	←			21 35				22 05		←			22 35			23 05			23 35					
Upminster ⊖	d	21 12	21 20		21 42	21 50			22 12	22 02	22 12	22 20		22 42	22 50		23 12		23 20	23 42		23 50			
Barking ⊖	d	21 20	21 28	21 36	21 50	21 58	22 07		→	22 10	22 20	22 28	22 36	22 50	22 58	23 06	23 20		23 28	23 50	23 55	23 58			
Stratford 7 ⊖	a																				00 09				
London Liverpool St 15 ⊖	a																				00 21				
West Ham ⊖	d	21 26	21 34	21 41	21 56	22 04	22 12			22 16	22 26	22 34	22 41	22 56	23 04	23 11	23 26		23 34	23 56		00 04			
Limehouse DLR	d	21 31	21 39	21 46	22 01	22 09	22 17				22 31	22 39	22 46	23 01	23 09	23 16	23 31		23 39	00 01		00 09			
London Fenchurch St 7 ⊖	a	21 35	21 43	21 52	22 05	22 13	22 22			22 24	22 35	22 43	22 52	23 05	23 13	23 21	23 35		23 43	00 05		00 13			

Table 1R

Saturdays

14 December to 17 May

Shoeburyness and Southend Central - London

Network Diagram - see first page of Table 1

		CC	CC	CC	CC	CC	CC	CC	CC	CC		CC	CC	CC	CC	CC	CC	CC	CC	CC		CC	CC	CC	CC
Shoeburyness	d				04 20		05 05			05 35				06 05			06 35			07 05					07 35
Thorpe Bay	d				04 23		05 08			05 38				06 08			06 38			07 08					07 38
Southend East	d				04 26		05 11			05 41				06 11			06 41			07 11					07 41
Southend Central	a				04 28		05 13			05 43				06 13			06 43			07 13					07 43
	d				04 29		05 14		05 20	05 44			05 50	06 14		06 20	06 44		06 50	07 14			07 20		07 44
Westcliff	d				04 31		05 16		05 23	05 46			05 53	06 16		06 23	06 46		06 53	07 16			07 23		07 46
Chalkwell	d				04 33		05 18		05 25	05 48			05 55	06 18		06 25	06 48		06 55	07 18			07 25		07 48
Leigh-on-Sea	d				04 36		05 21		05 28	05 51			05 58	06 21		06 28	06 51		06 58	07 21			07 28		07 51
Benfleet	d				04 40		05 25		05 32	05 55			06 02	06 25		06 32	06 55		07 02	07 25			07 32		07 55
Pitsea	d				04 44		05 29		05 36	05 59			06 06	06 29		06 36	06 59		07 06	07 29			07 36		07 59
Stanford-le-Hope	d			04 29					05 42				06 12			06 42			07 12				07 42		
East Tilbury	d			04 32					05 45				06 15			06 45			07 15				07 45		
Tilbury Town 8	d			04 38					05 51				06 21			06 51			07 21				07 51		
Grays	d			04 41				05 48	05 54			06 18	06 24		06 48	06 54		07 18	07 24			07 48	07 54	08 18	
Purfleet	d							05 53				06 23			06 53			07 23				07 53		08 23	
Rainham	d							05 58				06 28			06 58			07 28				07 58		08 28	
Dagenham Dock	d							06 02				06 32			07 02			07 32				08 02		08 32	
Basildon	d				04 47		05 32			06 02				06 32			07 02			07 32					08 02
Laindon	d				04 50		05 35			06 05				06 35			07 05			07 35					08 05
West Horndon	d				04 55		05 40			06 10				06 40			07 10			07 40					08 10
Chafford Hundred Lakeside	d			04 45					05 59				06 29			06 59			07 29				07 59		
Ockendon	d			04 49		05 16			06 02				06 32			07 02			07 32				08 02		
Upminster ⊖	d			04a57	05 02	05a23	05 46		06 09	06 16			06 39	06 46		07 09	07 16		07 39	07 46			08 09		08 16
Barking ⊖	d				05 10		05 54	06 08	06 17	06 24		06 38	06 47	06 54	07 08	07 17	07 24	07 38	07 47	07 54		08 08	08 17	08 38	08 24
Stratford 7 ⊖	a																							→	
London Liverpool St 15 ⊖	a																								
West Ham ⊖	d		00 04		05 16		06 00	06 14	06 23	06 30		06 44	06 53	07 00	07 14	07 23	07 30	07 44	07 53	08 00		08 14	08 23		08 30
Limehouse DLR	d	00 01	00 09		05 21		06 05	06 19	06 28	06 35		06 49	06 58	07 05	07 19	07 28	07 35	07 49	07 58	08 05		08 19	08 28		08 35
London Fenchurch St 7 ⊖	a	00 05	00 13		05 27		06 12	06 26	06 34	06 42		06 56	07 04	07 12	07 26	07 34	07 42	07 56	08 04	08 12		08 26	08 34		08 42

		CC	CC	CC	CC	CC		CC	CC	CC	CC	CC	CC	CC	CC	CC		CC	CC	CC	CC	CC	CC	CC	CC
Shoeburyness	d			07 50				08 05			08 20			08 35				08 50			09 05			09 20	
Thorpe Bay	d			07 53				08 08			08 23			08 38				08 53			09 08			09 23	
Southend East	d			07 56				08 11			08 26			08 41				08 56			09 11			09 26	
Southend Central	a			07 58				08 13			08 28			08 43				08 58			09 13			09 28	
	d	07 50		07 59				08 14	08 20		08 29			08 44	08 50			08 59			09 14	09 20		09 29	
Westcliff	d	07 53		08 01				08 16	08 23		08 31			08 46	08 53			09 01			09 16	09 23		09 31	
Chalkwell	d	07 55		08 03				08 18	08 25		08 33			08 48	08 55			09 03			09 18	09 25		09 33	
Leigh-on-Sea	d	07 58		08 06				08 21	08 28		08 36			08 51	08 58			09 06			09 21	09 28		09 36	
Benfleet	d	08 02		08 10				08 25	08 32		08 40			08 55	09 02			09 10			09 25	09 32		09 40	
Pitsea	d	08 06						08 29	08 36					08 59	09 06						09 29	09 36			
Stanford-le-Hope	d	08 12							08 42						09 12							09 42			
East Tilbury	d	08 15							08 45						09 15							09 45			
Tilbury Town 8	d	08 21							08 51						09 21							09 51			
Grays	d	08 24	08 48						08 54	09 18					09 24	09 48						09 54	10 18		
Purfleet	d		08 53							09 23						09 53							10 23		
Rainham	d		08 58							09 28						09 58							10 28		
Dagenham Dock	d		09 02							09 32						10 02							10 32		
Basildon	d			08 16				08 32			08 46			09 02				09 16			09 32			09 46	
Laindon	d			08 19				08 35			08 49			09 05				09 19			09 35			09 49	
West Horndon	d							08 40						09 10							09 40				
Chafford Hundred Lakeside	d	08 29							08 59						09 29							09 59			
Ockendon	d	08 32				←			09 02				←		09 32					←		10 02			
Upminster ⊖	d	08 39		08 28	←	08 39		08 46	09 09		08 58	←	09 09	09 16	09 39			09 28	←	09 39	09 46	10 09		09 58	←
Barking ⊖	d	→	09 08	08 36	08 38	08 47		08 54	→	09 38	09 06	09 08	09 17	09 24	→	10 08		09 36	09 38	09 47	09 54	→	10 38	10 06	10 08
Stratford 7 ⊖	a		→							→						→							→		
London Liverpool St 15 ⊖	a																								
West Ham ⊖	d			08 42	08 44	08 53		09 00			09 12	09 14	09 23	09 30				09 42	09 44	09 53	10 00			10 12	10 14
Limehouse DLR	d				08 49	08 58		09 05				09 19	09 28	09 35					09 49	09 58	10 05				10 19
London Fenchurch St 7 ⊖	a			08 53	08 56	09 04		09 12			09 23	09 26	09 34	09 42				09 53	09 56	10 04	10 12			10 23	10 26

		CC		CC	CC	CC	CC	CC	CC	CC	CC	CC		CC	CC	CC	CC	CC	CC	CC	CC	CC		CC	CC
Shoeburyness	d			09 35			09 50			10 05				10 20			10 35			10 50				11 05	
Thorpe Bay	d			09 38			09 53			10 08				10 23			10 38			10 53				11 08	
Southend East	d			09 41			09 56			10 11				10 26			10 41			10 56				11 11	
Southend Central	a			09 43			09 58			10 13				10 28			10 43			10 58				11 13	
	d			09 44	09 50		09 59			10 14	10 20			10 29			10 44	10 50		10 59				11 14	11 20
Westcliff	d			09 46	09 53		10 01			10 16	10 23			10 31			10 46	10 53		11 01				11 16	11 23
Chalkwell	d			09 48	09 55		10 03			10 18	10 25			10 33			10 48	10 55		11 03				11 18	11 25
Leigh-on-Sea	d			09 51	09 58		10 06			10 21	10 28			10 36			10 51	10 58		11 06				11 21	11 28
Benfleet	d			09 55	10 02		10 10			10 25	10 32			10 40			10 55	11 02		11 10				11 25	11 32
Pitsea	d			09 59	10 06					10 29	10 36						10 59	11 06						11 29	11 36
Stanford-le-Hope	d				10 12						10 42							11 12							11 42
East Tilbury	d				10 15						10 45							11 15							11 45
Tilbury Town 8	d				10 21						10 51							11 21							11 51
Grays	d				10 24	10 48					10 54	11 18						11 24	11 48						11 54
Purfleet	d					10 53						11 23							11 53						
Rainham	d					10 58						11 28							11 58						
Dagenham Dock	d					11 02						11 32							12 02						
Basildon	d			10 02			10 16			10 32				10 46			11 02			11 16				11 32	
Laindon	d			10 05			10 19			10 35				10 49			11 05			11 19				11 35	
West Horndon	d			10 10						10 40							11 10							11 40	
Chafford Hundred Lakeside	d				10 29						10 59							11 29							11 59
Ockendon	d	←			10 32				←		11 02					←		11 32				←			12 01
Upminster ⊖	d	10 09		10 16	10 39		10 28	←	10 39	10 46	11 09			10 58	←	11 09	11 16	11 39		11 28	←	11 39		11 46	12 09
Barking ⊖	d	10 17		10 24	→	11 08	10 36	10 38	10 47	10 54	→	11 38		11 06	11 08	11 17	11 24	→	12 08	11 36	11 38	11 47		11 54	→
Stratford 7 ⊖	a					→						→							→						
London Liverpool St 15 ⊖	a																								
West Ham ⊖	d	10 23		10 30			10 42	10 44	10 53	11 00				11 12	11 14	11 23	11 30			11 42	11 44	11 53		12 00	
Limehouse DLR	d	10 28		10 35				10 49	10 58	11 05					11 19	11 28	11 35				11 49	11 58		12 05	
London Fenchurch St 7 ⊖	a	10 34		10 42			10 53	10 56	11 04	11 12				11 23	11 26	11 34	11 42			11 53	11 56	12 04		12 12	

Table 1R

Saturdays

14 December to 17 May

Shoeburyness and Southend Central - London

Network Diagram - see first page of Table 1

		CC	CC	CC	CC	CC	CC	CC		CC	CC	CC	CC	CC	CC	CC	CC	CC		CC	CC	CC	CC	CC	CC
Shoeburyness	d		11 20			11 35				11 50			12 05			12 20				12 35			12 50		
Thorpe Bay	d		11 23			11 38				11 53			12 08			12 23				12 38			12 53		
Southend East	d		11 26			11 41				11 56			12 11			12 26				12 41			12 56		
Southend Central	a		11 28			11 43				11 58			12 13			12 28				12 43			12 58		
	d		11 29			11 44	11 50			11 59			12 14	12 20		12 29				12 44	12 50		12 59		
Westcliff	d		11 31			11 46	11 53			12 01			12 16	12 23		12 31				12 46	12 53		13 01		
Chalkwell	d		11 33			11 48	11 55			12 03			12 18	12 25		12 33				12 48	12 55		13 03		
Leigh-on-Sea	d		11 36			11 51	11 58			12 06			12 21	12 28		12 36				12 51	12 58		13 06		
Benfleet	d		11 40			11 55	12 02			12 10			12 25	12 32		12 40				12 55	13 02		13 10		
Pitsea	d					11 59	12 06						12 29	12 36						12 59	13 06				
Stanford-le-Hope	d						12 12							12 42							13 12				
East Tilbury	d						12 15							12 45							13 15				
Tilbury Town 3	d						12 21							12 51							13 21				
Grays	d	12 18					12 24	12 48						12 54	13 18						13 24	13 48			
Purfleet	d	12 23						12 53							13 23							13 53			
Rainham	d	12 28						12 58							13 28							13 58			
Dagenham Dock	d	12 32						13 02							13 32							14 02			
Basildon	d		11 46			12 02				12 16			12 32			12 46				13 02			13 16		
Laindon	d		11 49			12 05				12 19			12 35			12 49				13 05			13 19		
West Horndon	d					12 10							12 40							13 10					
Chafford Hundred Lakeside	d						12 29							12 59							13 29				
Ockendon	d				←		12 32					←		13 02				←			13 32				←
Upminster ⊖	d		11 58	←	12 09	12 16	12 39			12 28	←	12 39	12 46	13 09		12 58	←	13 09		13 16	13 39		13 28	←	13 39
Barking ⊖	d	12 38	12 06	12 08	12 17	12 24	→	13 08		12 36	12 38	12 47	12 54	→	13 38	13 06	13 08	13 17		13 24	→	14 08	13 36	13 38	13 47
Stratford 7 ⊖	a	↪						↪							↪							↪			
London Liverpool St 15 ⊖	a																								
West Ham ⊖	d		12 12	12 14	12 23	12 30				12 42	12 44	12 53	13 00			13 12	13 14	13 23		13 30			13 42	13 44	13 53
Limehouse	DLR d			12 19	12 28	12 35					12 49	12 58	13 05				13 19	13 28		13 35				13 49	13 58
London Fenchurch St 7 ⊖	a		12 23	12 26	12 34	12 42				12 53	12 56	13 04	13 12			13 23	13 26	13 34		13 42			13 53	13 56	14 04

		CC	CC	CC		CC	CC	CC	CC	CC	CC	CC	CC	CC		CC	CC	CC	CC	CC	CC	CC	CC	CC	
Shoeburyness	d	13 05				13 20			13 35			13 50				14 05			14 20			14 35			
Thorpe Bay	d	13 08				13 23			13 38			13 53				14 08			14 23			14 38			
Southend East	d	13 11				13 26			13 41			13 56				14 11			14 26			14 41			
Southend Central	a	13 13				13 28			13 43			13 58				14 13			14 28			14 43			
	d	13 14	13 20			13 29			13 44	13 50		13 59				14 14	14 20		14 29			14 44	14 50		
Westcliff	d	13 16	13 23			13 31			13 46	13 53		14 01				14 16	14 23		14 31			14 46	14 53		
Chalkwell	d	13 18	13 25			13 33			13 48	13 55		14 03				14 18	14 25		14 33			14 48	14 55		
Leigh-on-Sea	d	13 21	13 28			13 36			13 51	13 58		14 06				14 21	14 28		14 36			14 51	14 58		
Benfleet	d	13 25	13 32			13 40			13 55	14 02		14 10				14 25	14 32		14 40			14 55	15 02		
Pitsea	d	13 29	13 36						13 59	14 06						14 29	14 36					14 59	15 06		
Stanford-le-Hope	d		13 42							14 12							14 42						15 12		
East Tilbury	d		13 45							14 15							14 45						15 15		
Tilbury Town 3	d		13 51							14 21							14 51						15 21		
Grays	d		13 54	14 18						14 24	14 48						14 54	15 18					15 24	15 48	
Purfleet	d			14 23							14 53							15 23						15 53	
Rainham	d			14 28							14 58							15 28						15 58	
Dagenham Dock	d			14 32							15 02							15 32						16 02	
Basildon	d	13 32				13 46			14 02			14 16				14 32			14 46			15 02			
Laindon	d	13 35				13 49			14 05			14 19				14 35			14 49			15 05			
West Horndon	d	13 40							14 10							14 40						15 10			
Chafford Hundred Lakeside	d		13 59							14 29							14 59						15 29		
Ockendon	d		14 02					←		14 32				←			15 02				←		15 32		
Upminster ⊖	d	13 46	14 09			13 58	←	14 09	14 16	14 39		14 28	←	14 39		14 46	15 09		14 58	←	15 09	15 16	15 39		
Barking ⊖	d	13 54	→	14 38		14 06	14 08	14 17	14 24	→	15 08	14 36	14 38	14 47		14 54	→	15 38	15 06	15 08	15 17	15 24	→	16 08	
Stratford 7 ⊖	a			↪							↪							↪						↪	
London Liverpool St 15 ⊖	a																								
West Ham ⊖	d	14 00				14 12	14 14	14 23	14 30			14 42	14 44	14 53		15 00			15 12	15 14	15 23	15 30			
Limehouse	DLR d	14 05					14 19	14 28	14 35				14 49	14 58		15 05				15 19	15 28	15 35			
London Fenchurch St 7 ⊖	a	14 12				14 23	14 26	14 34	14 42			14 53	14 56	15 04		15 12			15 23	15 26	15 34	15 42			

		CC	CC	CC	CC	CC	CC	CC	CC	CC		CC	CC	CC	CC	CC	CC	CC	CC	CC		CC	CC	CC	CC
Shoeburyness	d	14 50			15 05			15 20				15 35			15 50			16 05				16 20			16 35
Thorpe Bay	d	14 53			15 08			15 23				15 38			15 53			16 08				16 23			16 38
Southend East	d	14 56			15 11			15 26				15 41			15 56			16 11				16 26			16 41
Southend Central	a	14 58			15 13			15 28				15 43			15 58			16 13				16 28			16 43
	d	14 59			15 14	15 20		15 29				15 44	15 50		15 59			16 14	16 20			16 29			16 44
Westcliff	d	15 01			15 16	15 23		15 31				15 46	15 53		16 01			16 16	16 23			16 31			16 46
Chalkwell	d	15 03			15 18	15 25		15 33				15 48	15 55		16 03			16 18	16 25			16 33			16 48
Leigh-on-Sea	d	15 06			15 21	15 28		15 36				15 51	15 58		16 06			16 21	16 28			16 36			16 51
Benfleet	d	15 10			15 25	15 32		15 40				15 55	16 02		16 10			16 25	16 32			16 40			16 55
Pitsea	d				15 29	15 36						15 59	16 06					16 29	16 36						16 59
Stanford-le-Hope	d					15 42							16 12						16 42						
East Tilbury	d					15 45							16 15						16 45						
Tilbury Town 3	d					15 51							16 21						16 51						
Grays	d					15 54	16 18						16 24	16 48					16 54	17 18					
Purfleet	d						16 23							16 53						17 23					
Rainham	d						16 28							16 58						17 28					
Dagenham Dock	d						16 32							17 02						17 32					
Basildon	d	15 16			15 32			15 46				16 02			16 16			16 32				16 46			17 02
Laindon	d	15 19			15 35			15 49				16 05			16 19			16 35				16 49			17 05
West Horndon	d				15 40							16 10						16 40							17 10
Chafford Hundred Lakeside	d					15 59							16 29						16 59						
Ockendon	d			←		16 02				←			16 32				←		17 02					←	
Upminster ⊖	d	15 28	←	15 39	15 46	16 09		15 58	←	16 09		16 16	16 39		16 28	←	16 39	16 46	17 09			16 58	←	17 09	17 16
Barking ⊖	d	15 36	15 38	15 47	15 54	→	16 38	16 06	16 08	16 17		16 24	→	17 08	16 36	16 38	16 47	16 54	→	17 38		17 06	17 08	17 17	17 24
Stratford 7 ⊖	a						↪							↪						↪					
London Liverpool St 15 ⊖	a																								
West Ham ⊖	d	15 42	15 44	15 53	16 00			16 12	16 14	16 23		16 30			16 42	16 44	16 53	17 00				17 12	17 14	17 23	17 30
Limehouse	DLR d		15 49	15 58	16 05				16 19	16 28		16 35				16 49	16 58	17 05					17 19	17 28	17 35
London Fenchurch St 7 ⊖	a	15 53	15 56	16 04	16 12			16 23	16 26	16 34		16 42			16 53	16 56	17 04	17 12				17 23	17 26	17 34	17 42

Table 1R

Saturdays

14 December to 17 May

Shoeburyness and Southend Central - London

Network Diagram - see first page of Table 1

		CC	CC	CC	CC	CC		CC	CC	CC	CC	CC	CC	CC	CC	CC		CC	CC	CC	CC	CC	CC	CC	CC
Shoeburyness	d			16 50				17 05			17 20			17 35				17 50			18 05			18 20	
Thorpe Bay	d			16 53				17 08			17 23			17 38				17 53			18 08			18 23	
Southend East	d			16 56				17 11			17 26			17 41				17 56			18 11			18 26	
Southend Central	a			16 58				17 13			17 28			17 43				17 58			18 13			18 28	
	d	16 50		16 59				17 14	17 20		17 29			17 44	17 50			17 59			18 14	18 20		18 29	
Westcliff	d	16 53		17 01				17 16	17 23		17 31			17 46	17 53			18 01			18 16	18 23		18 31	
Chalkwell	d	16 55		17 03				17 18	17 25		17 33			17 48	17 55			18 03			18 18	18 25		18 33	
Leigh-on-Sea	d	16 58		17 06				17 21	17 28		17 36			17 51	17 58			18 06			18 21	18 28		18 36	
Benfleet	d	17 02		17 10				17 25	17 32		17 40			17 55	18 02			18 10			18 25	18 32		18 40	
Pitsea	d	17 06						17 29	17 36					17 59	18 06						18 29	18 36			
Stanford-le-Hope	d	17 12							17 42						18 12							18 42			
East Tilbury	d	17 15							17 45						18 15							18 45			
Tilbury Town 3	d	17 21							17 51						18 21							18 51			
Grays	d	17 24	17 48						17 54	18 18					18 24	18 48						18 54	19 18		
Purfleet	d		17 53							18 23						18 53							19 23		
Rainham	d		17 58							18 28						18 58							19 28		
Dagenham Dock	d		18 02							18 32						19 02							19 32		
Basildon	d			17 16				17 32			17 46			18 02				18 16			18 32			18 46	
Laindon	d			17 19				17 35			17 49			18 05				18 19			18 35			18 49	
West Horndon	d							17 40						18 10							18 40				
Chafford Hundred Lakeside	d	17 29							17 59						18 29							18 59			
Ockendon	d	17 32				←			18 02				←		18 32					←		19 02			
Upminster ⊖	d	17 39		17 28	←	17 39		17 46	18 09		17 58	←	18 09	18 16	18 39			18 28	←	18 39	18 46	19 09		18 58	←
Barking ⊖	d	→	18 08	17 36	17 38	17 47		17 54	→	18 38	18 06	18 08	18 17	18 24	→	19 08		18 36	18 38	18 47	18 54	→	19 38	19 06	19 08
Stratford 7 ⊖	a		→							→						→							→		
London Liverpool St 15 ⊖	a																								
West Ham ⊖	d			17 42	17 44	17 53		18 00			18 12	18 14	18 23	18 30				18 42	18 44	18 53	19 00			19 12	19 14
Limehouse DLR	d				17 49	17 58		18 05				18 19	18 28	18 35					18 49	18 58	19 05				19 19
London Fenchurch St 7 ⊖	a			17 53	17 56	18 04		18 12			18 23	18 26	18 34	18 42				18 53	18 56	19 04	19 12			19 23	19 26

		CC		CC	CC	CC	CC	CC	CC	CC	CC	CC		CC	CC	CC	CC	CC	CC	CC	CC	CC		CC	CC
Shoeburyness	d			18 35			18 50			19 05				19 20			19 35		19 50			20 05			
Thorpe Bay	d			18 38			18 53			19 08				19 23			19 38		19 53			20 08			
Southend East	d			18 41			18 56			19 11				19 26			19 41		19 56			20 11			
Southend Central	a			18 43			18 58			19 13				19 28			19 43		19 58			20 13			
	d			18 44	18 50		18 59			19 14	19 20			19 29			19 44	19 50	19 59			20 14			20 20
Westcliff	d			18 46	18 53		19 01			19 16	19 23			19 31			19 46	19 53	20 01			20 16			20 23
Chalkwell	d			18 48	18 55		19 03			19 18	19 25			19 33			19 48	19 55	20 03			20 18			20 25
Leigh-on-Sea	d			18 51	18 58		19 06			19 21	19 28			19 36			19 51	19 58	20 06			20 21			20 28
Benfleet	d			18 55	19 02		19 10			19 25	19 32			19 40			19 55	20 02	20 10			20 25			20 32
Pitsea	d			18 59	19 06					19 29	19 36						19 59	20 06				20 29			20 36
Stanford-le-Hope	d				19 12						19 42							20 12							20 42
East Tilbury	d				19 15						19 45							20 15							20 45
Tilbury Town 3	d				19 21						19 51							20 21							20 51
Grays	d				19 24	19 48					19 54	20 18						20 24						20 48	20 54
Purfleet	d					19 53						20 23												20 53	
Rainham	d					19 58						20 28												20 58	
Dagenham Dock	d					20 02						20 32												21 02	
Basildon	d			19 02			19 16			19 32				19 46			20 02		20 16			20 32			
Laindon	d			19 05			19 19			19 35				19 49			20 05		20 19			20 35			
West Horndon	d			19 10						19 40							20 10					20 40			
Chafford Hundred Lakeside	d				19 29						19 59							20 29							20 59
Ockendon	d	←			19 32				←		20 02					←		20 32			←				21 02
Upminster ⊖	d	19 09		19 16	19 39		19 28	←	19 39	19 46	20 09			19 58	←	20 09	20 16	20 39	20 28	←	20 39	20 46			21 09
Barking ⊖	d	19 17		19 24	→	20 08	19 36	19 38	19 47	19 54	→	20 38		20 06	20 08	20 17	20 24	→	20 36	20 38	20 47	20 54		21 08	21 17
Stratford 7 ⊖	a					→						→													
London Liverpool St 15 ⊖	a																								
West Ham ⊖	d	19 23		19 30			19 42	19 44	19 53	20 00				20 12	20 14	20 23	20 30		20 42	20 44	20 53	21 00		21 14	21 23
Limehouse DLR	d	19 28		19 35				19 49	19 58	20 05					20 19	20 28	20 35			20 49	20 58	21 05		21 19	21 28
London Fenchurch St 7 ⊖	a	19 34		19 42			19 53	19 56	20 04	20 12				20 23	20 26	20 34	20 42		20 53	20 56	21 04	21 12		21 26	21 34

		CC	CC	CC	CC	CC	CC	CC		CC	CC	CC	CC	CC	CC	CC	CC	CC		CC	CC	CC	CC		
Shoeburyness	d		20 35		20 50			21 05				21 35			22 05			22 35				23 05			
Thorpe Bay	d		20 38		20 53			21 08				21 38			22 08			22 38				23 08			
Southend East	d		20 41		20 56			21 11				21 41			22 11			22 41				23 11			
Southend Central	a		20 43		20 58			21 13				21 43			22 13			22 43				23 13			
	d		20 44	20 50	20 59			21 14			21 20	21 44		21 50	22 14		22 20	22 44			22 50	23 14	23 20		
Westcliff	d		20 46	20 53	21 01			21 16			21 23	21 46		21 53	22 16		22 23	22 46			22 53	23 16	23 23		
Chalkwell	d		20 48	20 55	21 03			21 18			21 25	21 48		21 55	22 18		22 25	22 48			22 55	23 18	23 25		
Leigh-on-Sea	d		20 51	20 58	21 06			21 21			21 28	21 51		21 58	22 21		22 28	22 51			22 58	23 21	23 28		
Benfleet	d		20 55	21 02	21 10			21 25			21 32	21 55		22 02	22 25		22 32	22 55			23 02	23 25	23 32		
Pitsea	d		20 59	21 06				21 29			21 36	21 59		22 06	22 29		22 36	22 59			23 06	23 29	23 36		
Stanford-le-Hope	d			21 12							21 42			22 12			22 42				23 12		23 42		
East Tilbury	d			21 15							21 45			22 15			22 45				23 15		23 45		
Tilbury Town 3	d			21 21							21 51			22 21			22 51				23 21		23 51		
Grays	d	21 18		21 24						21 48	21 54		22 18	22 24		22 48	22 54			23 18	23 24		23 54		
Purfleet	d	21 23								21 53			22 23			22 53				23 23					
Rainham	d	21 28								21 58			22 28			22 58				23 28					
Dagenham Dock	d	21 32								22 02			22 32			23 02				23 32					
Basildon	d		21 02		21 16			21 32				22 02			22 32			23 02				23 32			
Laindon	d		21 05		21 19			21 35				22 05			22 35			23 05				23 35			
West Horndon	d		21 10					21 40				22 10			22 40			23 10				23 40			
Chafford Hundred Lakeside	d			21 29							21 59			22 29			22 59				23 29		23 59		
Ockendon	d			21 32			←				22 02			22 32			23 02				23 32		00 02		
Upminster ⊖	d		21 16	21 39	21 28	←	21 39	21 46			22 09	22 16		22 39	22 46		23 09	23 16			23 39	23 46	00 08		
Barking ⊖	d	21 38	21 24	→	21 36	21 38	21 47	21 54		22 08	22 17	22 24	22 38	22 47	22 54	23 08	23 17	23 24		23a39	23 47	23 55	00a18		
Stratford 7 ⊖	a	→																							
London Liverpool St 15 ⊖	a																								
West Ham ⊖	d		21 30		21 42	21 44	21 53	22 00		22 14	22 23	22 30	22 44	22 53	23 00	23 14	23 23	23 30			23 53	00 01			
Limehouse DLR	d		21 35			21 49	21 58	22 05		22 19	22 28	22 35	22 49	22 58	23 05	23 19	23 28	23 35			23 58	00 06			
London Fenchurch St 7 ⊖	a		21 42		21 53	21 56	22 04	22 12		22 26	22 34	22 42	22 56	23 04	23 12	23 26	23 34	23 42			00 04	00 12			

Table 1R

Sundays

8 December to 11 May

Shoeburyness and Southend Central - London

Network Diagram - see first page of Table 1

		CC A	CC A	CC	CC	CC	CC	CC	CC	CC	CC	CC	CC	CC	CC		CC	CC	CC	CC	CC		CC	CC
Shoeburyness	d			05 35	06 05	06 11	06 35	07 05	07 11	07 35	08 05			08 35			20 05			20 35			21 05	
Thorpe Bay	d			05 38	06 08	06 14	06 38	07 08	07 14	07 38	08 08			08 38			20 08			20 38			21 08	
Southend East	d			05 41	06 11	06 17	06 41	07 11	07 17	07 41	08 11			08 41			20 11			20 41			21 11	
Southend Central	a			05 43	06 13	06 19	06 43	07 13	07 19	07 43	08 13			08 43			20 13			20 43			21 13	
	d			05 44	06 14	06 20	06 44	07 14	07 20	07 44	08 14	08 20		08 44	08 50		20 14	20 20		20 44	20 50		21 14	21 20
Westcliff	d			05 46	06 16	06 23	06 46	07 16	07 23	07 46	08 16	08 23		08 46	08 53		20 16	20 23		20 46	20 53		21 16	21 23
Chalkwell	d			05 48	06 18	06 25	06 48	07 18	07 25	07 48	08 18	08 25		08 48	08 55		20 18	20 25		20 48	20 55		21 18	21 25
Leigh-on-Sea	d			05 51	06 21	06 28	06 51	07 21	07 28	07 51	08 21	08 28		08 51	08 58		20 21	20 28		20 51	20 58		21 21	21 28
Benfleet	d			05 55	06 25	06 32	06 55	07 25	07 32	07 55	08 25	08 32		08 55	09 02		20 25	20 32		20 55	21 02		21 25	21 32
Pitsea	d			05 59	06 29	06 36	06 59	07 29	07 36	07 59	08 29	08 36		08 59	09 06		20 29	20 36		20 59	21 06		21 29	21 36
Stanford-le-Hope	d					06 42			07 42			08 42			09 12	and at		20 42			21 12			21 42
East Tilbury	d					06 45			07 45			08 45			09 15	the same		20 45			21 15			21 45
Tilbury Town 3	d					06 51			07 51			08 51			09 21	minutes		20 51			21 21			21 51
Grays	d					06 54			07 54			08 54	08 59		09 24	past		20 54	20 59		21 24			21 54
Purfleet	d												09 04			each			21 04					
Rainham	d												09 09			hour until			21 09					
Dagenham Dock	d												09 13						21 13					
Basildon	d			06 02	06 32		07 02	07 32		08 02	08 32			09 02			20 32			21 02			21 32	
Laindon	d			06 05	06 35		07 05	07 35		08 05	08 35			09 05			20 35			21 05			21 35	
West Horndon	d			06 10	06 40		07 10	07 40		08 10	08 40			09 10			20 40			21 10			21 40	
Chafford Hundred Lakeside	d					06 59			07 59			08 59			09 29			20 59			21 29			21 59
Ockendon	d		00 02			07 02			08 02			09 02			09 32			21 02			21 32			22 02
Upminster ⊖	d		00 08	06 16	06 46	07 09	07 16	07 46	08 09	08 16	08 46	09 09		09 16	09 39		20 46	21 09		21 16	21 39		21 46	22 09
Barking ⊖	d		00a18	06 25	06 55	07 17	07 25	07 55	08 17	08 25	08 55	09 17	09a20	09 25	09 47		20 55	21 17	21a20	21 25	21 47		21 55	22 17
Stratford 7 ⊖	a																							
London Liverpool St 15 ⊖	a																							
West Ham ⊖	d	00 01		06 31	07 01	07 23	07 31	08 01	08 23	08 31	09 01	09 23		09 31	09 53		21 01	21 23		21 31	21 53		22 01	22 23
Limehouse DLR	d	00 06		06 36	07 06	07 28	07 36	08 06	08 28	08 36	09 06	09 28		09 36	09 58		21 06	21 28		21 36	21 58		22 06	22 28
London Fenchurch St 7 ⊖	a	00 12		06 42	07 12	07 34	07 42	08 12	08 34	08 42	09 12	09 34		09 42	10 04		21 12	21 34		21 42	22 04		22 12	22 34

		CC	CC	CC	CC	CC
Shoeburyness	d		21 35	22 05		22 35
Thorpe Bay	d		21 38	22 08		22 38
Southend East	d		21 41	22 11		22 41
Southend Central	a		21 43	22 13		22 43
	d		21 44	22 14	22 20	22 44
Westcliff	d		21 46	22 16	22 23	22 46
Chalkwell	d		21 48	22 18	22 25	22 48
Leigh-on-Sea	d		21 51	22 21	22 28	22 51
Benfleet	d		21 55	22 25	22 32	22 55
Pitsea	d		21 59	22 29	22 36	22 59
Stanford-le-Hope	d				22 42	
East Tilbury	d				22 45	
Tilbury Town 3	d				22 51	
Grays	d	21 59			22 54	
Purfleet	d	22 04				
Rainham	d	22 09				
Dagenham Dock	d	22 13				
Basildon	d		22 02	22 32		23 02
Laindon	d		22 05	22 35		23 05
West Horndon	d		22 10	22 40		23 10
Chafford Hundred Lakeside	d				22 59	
Ockendon	d				23 02	
Upminster ⊖	d		22 16	22 46	23 09	23 16
Barking ⊖	d	22a20	22 25	22 55	23 17	23 25
Stratford 7 ⊖	a					
London Liverpool St 15 ⊖	a					
West Ham ⊖	d		22 31	23 01	23 23	23 31
Limehouse DLR	d		22 36	23 06	23 28	23 36
London Fenchurch St 7 ⊖	a		22 42	23 12	23 34	23 42

A not 8 December

Table 1A

Mondays to Fridays

9 December to 16 May

Tilbury Town - Tilbury Riverside

Bus Service

Network Diagram - see first page of Table 1

		CC	CC	CC	CC	CC	CC	CC	CC	CC		CC	CC	CC	CC	CC	CC	CC	CC	CC		CC	CC	CC	CC
Tilbury Town [3]	d	05 31	06 14	06 46	07 14	07 40	08 15	08 41	09 05	10 03		10 35	11 05	11 35	12 05	12 35	13 05	13 35	14 05	15 05		15 35	16 05	16 35	17 05
Tilbury Riverside	a	05 33	06 16	06 48	07 16	07 42	08 17	08 43	09 07	10 05		10 37	11 07	11 37	12 07	12 37	13 07	13 37	14 07	15 07		15 37	16 07	16 37	17 07

		CC	CC	CC	CC
Tilbury Town [3]	d	17 34	17 56	18 33	18 59
Tilbury Riverside	a	17 36	17 58	18 35	19 01

Saturdays

14 December to 17 May

		CC	CC	CC	CC	CC	CC	CC	CC	CC		CC	CC	CC	CC	CC	CC	CC	CC	CC		CC	CC	CC	CC
Tilbury Town [3]	d	05 43	06 07	07 03	07 33	08 03	08 33	09 03	10 03	10 33		11 03	11 33	12 03	12 33	13 03	13 33	14 03	15 03	15 33		16 03	16 33	17 03	17 33
Tilbury Riverside	a	05 45	06 09	07 05	07 35	08 05	08 35	09 05	10 05	10 35		11 05	11 35	12 05	12 35	13 05	13 35	14 05	15 05	15 35		16 05	16 35	17 05	17 35

		CC	CC	CC
Tilbury Town [3]	d	18 03	18 33	19 03
Tilbury Riverside	a	18 05	18 35	19 05

No Sunday Service

Table 1A-R

Mondays to Fridays

9 December to 16 May

Tilbury Riverside - Tilbury Town

Bus Service

Network Diagram - see first page of Table 1

		CC	CC	CC	CC	CC		CC	CC	CC	CC	CC	CC	CC	CC	CC		CC	CC	CC	CC	CC	CC	CC	CC
Tilbury Riverside	d	05 50	06 25	06 55	07 20	07 50		08 20	08 50	09 10	10 13	10 40	11 10	11 40	12 10	12 40		13 10	13 40	14 10	15 13	15 40	16 10	16 40	17 15
Tilbury Town [3]	a	05 58	06 33	07 03	07 28	07 58		08 28	08 58	09 18	10 21	10 48	11 18	11 48	12 18	12 48		13 18	13 48	14 18	15 21	15 48	16 18	16 48	17 23

		CC		CC	CC	CC
Tilbury Riverside	d	17 40		18 10	18 39	19 08
Tilbury Town [3]	a	17 48		18 18	18 47	19 16

Saturdays

14 December to 17 May

		CC	CC	CC	CC	CC	CC	CC	CC	CC		CC	CC	CC	CC	CC	CC	CC	CC	CC		CC	CC	CC	CC
Tilbury Riverside	d	05 50	06 18	07 18	07 48	08 18	08 48	09 08	10 13	10 38		11 08	11 38	12 08	12 38	13 08	13 38	14 08	15 13	15 38		16 08	16 38	17 08	17 38
Tilbury Town [3]	a	05 58	06 26	07 26	07 56	08 26	08 56	09 16	10 21	10 46		11 16	11 46	12 16	12 46	13 16	13 46	14 16	15 21	15 46		16 16	16 46	17 16	17 46

		CC	CC	CC
Tilbury Riverside	d	18 08	18 38	19 08
Tilbury Town [3]	a	18 16	18 46	19 16

No Sunday Service

Table 4

Romford - Upminster

Mondays to Saturdays

9 December to 17 May

Network Diagram - see first page of Table 1

Miles			LE	LE	LE	LE	LE	LE	LE	LE	LE		LE	LE	LE	LE	LE	LE	LE	LE	LE		LE	LE	LE
0	Romford	d	06 11	06 41	07 11	07 41	08 11	08 41	09 11	09 41	10 11		10 41	11 11	11 41	12 11	12 41	13 11	13 41	14 11	14 41		15 11	15 41	16 11
2	Emerson Park	d	06 15	06 45	07 15	07 45	08 15	08 45	09 15	09 45	10 15		10 45	11 15	11 45	12 15	12 45	13 15	13 45	14 15	14 45		15 15	15 45	16 15
3½	Upminster ⊖	a	06 20	06 50	07 20	07 50	08 20	08 50	09 20	09 50	10 20		10 50	11 20	11 50	12 20	12 50	13 20	13 50	14 20	14 50		15 20	15 50	16 20

		LE	LE	LE	LE	LE	LE		LE
Romford	d	16 41	17 11	17 41	18 11	18 41	19 11		19 41
Emerson Park	d	16 45	17 15	17 45	18 15	18 45	19 15		19 45
Upminster ⊖	a	16 50	17 20	17 50	18 20	18 50	19 20		19 50

No Sunday Service

Table 4R

Upminster - Romford

Mondays to Saturdays

9 December to 17 May

Network Diagram - see first page of Table 1

Miles			LE	LE	LE	LE	LE	LE		LE	LE	LE	LE	LE	LE	LE	LE	LE		LE	LE	LE	LE	LE	LE
0	Upminster ⊖	d	06 24	06 54	07 24	07 54	08 24	08 54		09 24	09 54	10 24	10 54	11 24	11 54	12 24	12 54	13 24		13 54	14 24	14 54	15 24	15 54	16 24
1½	Emerson Park	d	06 28	06 58	07 28	07 58	08 28	08 58		09 28	09 58	10 28	10 58	11 28	11 58	12 28	12 58	13 28		13 58	14 28	14 58	15 28	15 58	16 28
3½	Romford	a	06 33	07 03	07 33	08 03	08 33	09 03		09 33	10 03	10 33	11 03	11 33	12 03	12 33	13 03	13 33		14 03	14 33	15 03	15 33	16 03	16 33

		LE	LE	LE		LE	LE	LE	LE
Upminster ⊖	d	16 54	17 24	17 54		18 24	18 54	19 24	19 54
Emerson Park	d	16 58	17 28	17 58		18 28	18 58	19 28	19 58
Romford	a	17 03	17 33	18 03		18 33	19 03	19 33	20 03

No Sunday Service

Network Diagram for Tables 5, 6, 10, 11

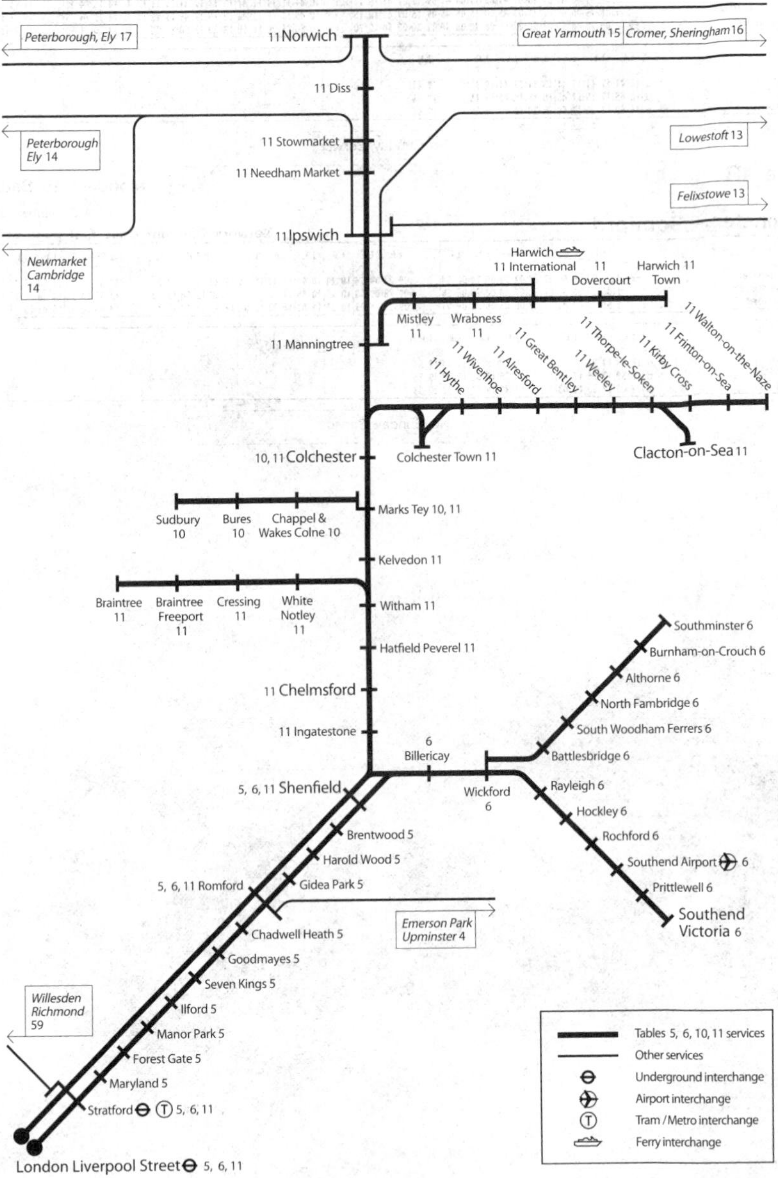

Peterborough, Ely 17
11 Norwich
Great Yarmouth 15
Cromer, Sheringham 16
11 Diss
Peterborough
Ely 14
11 Stowmarket
Lowestoft 13
11 Needham Market
Felixstowe 13
11 Ipswich
Newmarket
Cambridge
14
Harwich
11 International
11
Dovercourt
Harwich 11
Town
Mistley
11
Wrabness
11
11 Manningtree
11 Walton-on-the-Naze
11 Frinton-on-Sea
11 Kirby Cross
11 Thorpe-le-Soken
11 Weeley
11 Great Bentley
11 Alresford
11 Wivenhoe
11 Hythe
10, 11 Colchester
Colchester Town 11
Clacton-on-Sea 11
Sudbury
10
Bures
10
Chappel &
Wakes Colne 10
Marks Tey 10, 11
Kelvedon 11
Braintree
11
Braintree
Freeport
11
Cressing
11
White
Notley
11
Witham 11
Hatfield Peverel 11
Southminster 6
Burnham-on-Crouch 6
Althorne 6
North Fambridge 6
South Woodham Ferrers 6
11 Chelmsford
11 Ingatestone
6
Billericay
Battlesbridge 6
5, 6, 11 Shenfield
Wickford
6
Rayleigh 6
Hockley 6
Brentwood 5
Rochford 6
Harold Wood 5
Southend Airport 6
5, 6, 11 Romford
Gidea Park 5
Prittlewell 6
Southend
Victoria 6
Chadwell Heath 5
Emerson Park
Upminster 4
Goodmayes 5
Seven Kings 5
Willesden
Richmond
59
Ilford 5
Manor Park 5
Forest Gate 5
Maryland 5
Stratford 5, 6, 11
London Liverpool Street 5, 6, 11
Tables 5, 6, 10, 11 services
Other services
Underground interchange
Airport interchange
Tram / Metro interchange
Ferry interchange

TOCs operating on this network - Greater Anglia (LE)

Table 5

Mondays to Fridays

9 December to 16 May

London Liverpool Street - Ilford - Shenfield

Network Diagram - refer to first Page of Table 5

Miles	Miles			LE MX	LE MO	LE MO 1 A	LE MX 1 A	LE MX	LE MX	LE MO	LE MO 1 A	LE MX 1 B		LE MX 1 A	LE	LE ◇1 C	LE A	LE	LE	LE	LE	LE		LE	LE
0	0	**London Liverpool Street 15 ⊖**	d	00 01	00 05	00 14	00 15	00 20	00 32	00 35	00 44	00 46		00 50	00 55	05 23	05 28	05 37	06 00	06 10	06 20	06 30		06 40	06 50
4	4	Stratford 7 ⊖	d	00 08	00 12	00 21	00 22	00 27	00 39	00 42	00 51	00 53		00 57	01 02	05 30	05 35	05 44	06 07	06 17	06 27	06 37		06 47	06 57
4½	4½	Maryland	d	00 10	00 14			00 29	00 41	00 44					01 04			05 46	06 09	06 19	06 29	06 39		06 49	06 59
5¼	5¼	Forest Gate	d	00 12	00 16			00 31	00 43	00 46					01 06			05 48	06 11	06 21	06 31	06 41		06 51	07 01
6¼	6¼	Manor Park	d	00 14	00 18			00 33	00 45	00 48					01 08			05 50	06 13	06 23	06 33	06 43		06 53	07 03
7¼	7¼	Ilford 2	d	00 17	00 21			00 36	00 48	00 51					01 11		05 40	05 53	06 16	06 26	06 36	06 46		06 56	07 06
8½	—	Seven Kings	d	00 19	00 23			00 38	00 50	00 53					01 13		05 42	05 55	06 18	06 28	06 38	06 48		06 58	07 08
9¼	—	Goodmayes	d	00 21	00 25			00 40	00 52	00 55					01 15			05 57	06 20	06 30	06 40	06 50		07 00	07 10
10	—	Chadwell Heath	d	00 23	00 27			00 42	00 54	00 57					01 17			05 59	06 22	06 32	06 42	06 52		07 02	07 12
12½	—	Romford	d	00 27	00 31	00 34	00 32	00 46	00 58	01 01	01 04			01 08	01 21	05 38	05 48	06 03	06 26	06 36	06 46	06 56		07 06	07 16
13½	—	Gidea Park 2	a	00 31	00 36	00 38		00 50	01 02	01 06	01 08	01 07			01 25		05 51	06 07	06 30	06 40	06 50	07 00		07 10	07 20
—	—		d			00 38		00 50			01 08	01 07			01 25		05 51	06 07	06 30	06 40	06 50	07 00		07 10	07 20
15	—	Harold Wood	d			00 41		00 53			01 11				01 28		05 54	06 10	06 33	06 43	06 53	07 03		07 13	07 23
18¼	—	Brentwood	d			00 46		00 57			01 16				01 32		05 59	06 14	06 37	06 47	06 57	07 07		07 17	07 27
20¼	—	**Shenfield 3**	a			00 51	00 44	01 03			01 21	01 17		01 20	01 38	05 47	06 04	06 20	06 43	06 53	07 03	07 13		07 23	07 33

		LE	LE	LE 1 A	LE	LE	LE	LE		LE	LE	LE	LE	LE	LE	LE	LE	LE	LE	LE 1 D	LE	LE	LE	LE	
London Liverpool Street 15 ⊖	d	07 00	07 10	07 13	07 20	07 30	07 40	07 50		08 00	08 10	08 20	08 30	08 40	08 50	09 00	09 10	09 20	09 30	09 38	09 40	09 50	10 00	10 10	
Stratford 7 ⊖	d	07 07	07 17	07 20	07 27	07 37	07 47	07 57		08 07	08 17	08 27	08 37	08 47	08 57	09 07	09 17	09 27	09 37	09 45	09 47	09 57	10 07	10 17	
Maryland	d	07 09	07 19		07 29	07 39	07 49	07 59		08 09	08 19	08 29	08 39	08 49	08 59	09 09	09 19	09 29	09 39		09 49	09 59	10 09	10 19	
Forest Gate	d	07 11	07 21		07 31	07 41	07 51	08 01		08 11	08 21	08 31	08 41	08 51	09 01	09 11	09 21	09 31	09 41		09 51	10 01	10 11	10 21	
Manor Park	d	07 13	07 23		07 33	07 43	07 53	08 03		08 13	08 23	08 33	08 43	08 53	09 03	09 13	09 23	09 33	09 43		09 53	10 03	10 13	10 23	
Ilford 2	d	07 16	07 26		07 36	07 46	07 56	08 06		08 16	08 26	08 36	08 46	08 56	09 06	09 16	09 26	09 36	09 46		09 56	10 06	10 16	10 26	
Seven Kings	d	07 18	07 28		07 38	07 48	07 58	08 08		08 18	08 28	08 38	08 48	08 58	09 08	09 18	09 28	09 38	09 48		09 58	10 08	10 18	10 28	
Goodmayes	d	07 20	07 30		07 40	07 50	08 00	08 10		08 20	08 30	08 40	08 50	09 00	09 10	09 20	09 30	09 40	09 50		10 00	10 10	10 20	10 30	
Chadwell Heath	d	07 22	07 32		07 42	07 52	08 02	08 12		08 22	08 32	08 42	08 52	09 02	09 12	09 22	09 32	09 42	09 52		10 02	10 12	10 22	10 32	
Romford	d	07 26	07 36	07 28	07 46	07 56	08 06	08 16		08 26	08 36	08 46	08 56	09 06	09 16	09 26	09 36	09 46	09 56	09 53	10 06	10 16	10 26	10 36	
Gidea Park 2	a	07 30	07 40		07 50	08 00	08 10	08 20		08 30	08 40	08 50	09 00	09 10	09 20	09 30	09 40	09 50	10 00		10 10	10 20	10 30	10 40	
	d	07 30	07 40		07 50	08 00	08 10	08 20		08 30	08 40	08 50	09 00	09 10	09 20	09 30	09 40	09 50	10 00		10 10	10 20	10 30	10 40	
Harold Wood	d	07 33	07 43		07 53	08 03	08 13	08 23		08 33	08 43	08 53	09 03	09 13	09 23	09 33	09 43	09 53	10 03		10 13	10 23	10 33	10 43	
Brentwood	d	07 37	07 47		07 57	08 07	08 17	08 27		08 37	08 47	08 57	09 07	09 17	09 27	09 37	09 47	09 57	10 07		10 17	10 27	10 37	10 47	
Shenfield 3	a	07 43	07 53	07 38	08 03	08 13	08 25	08 35		08 43	08 53	09 03	09 13	09 23	09 33	09 43	09 53	10 03	10 13	10 02	10 23	10 33	10 43	10 53	

		LE 1 A		LE	LE	LE 1 D	LE	LE	LE	LE	LE 1 A		LE	LE	LE 1 D	LE	LE	LE	LE	LE	LE		LE	LE
London Liverpool Street 15 ⊖	d	10 13		14 20	14 30	14 38	14 40	14 50	15 00	15 10	15 13		15 20	15 30	15 38	15 40	15 50	16 00	16 10	16 20	16 28		16 36	16 40
Stratford 7 ⊖	d	10 20		14 27	14 37	14 45	14 47	14 57	15 07	15 17	15 20		15 27	15 37	15 45	15 47	15 57	16 07	16 17	16 27	16 35		16 43	16 47
Maryland	d		and at	14 29	14 39		14 49	14 59	15 09	15 19			15 29	15 39		15 49	15 59	16 09	16 19	16 29	16 37			16 49
Forest Gate	d		the same	14 31	14 41		14 51	15 01	15 11	15 21			15 31	15 41		15 51	16 01	16 11	16 21	16 31	16 39			16 51
Manor Park	d		minutes	14 33	14 43		14 53	15 03	15 13	15 23			15 33	15 43		15 53	16 03	16 13	16 23	16 33	16 41			16 53
Ilford 2	d		past	14 36	14 46		14 56	15 06	15 16	15 26			15 36	15 46		15 56	16 06	16 16	16 26	16 36	16 44		16 50	16 56
Seven Kings	d		each	14 38	14 48		14 58	15 08	15 18	15 28			15 38	15 48		15 58	16 08	16 18	16 28	16 38	16 47		16 52	
Goodmayes	d		hour until	14 40	14 50		15 00	15 10	15 20	15 30			15 40	15 50		16 00	16 10	16 20	16 30	16 40	16 49		16 54	
Chadwell Heath	d			14 42	14 52		15 02	15 12	15 22	15 32			15 42	15 52		16 02	16 12	16 22	16 32	16 42	16 51		16 56	17 00
Romford	d	10 28		14 46	14 56	14 53	15 06	15 16	15 26	15 36	15 28		15 46	15 56	15 53	16 06	16 16	16 26	16 36	16 46	16 55		17 00	17 04
Gidea Park 2	a			14 50	15 00		15 10	15 20	15 30	15 40			15 50	16 00		16 10	16 20	16 30	16 40	16 50	17 00		17 04	17 10
	d			14 50	15 00		15 10	15 20	15 30	15 40			15 50	16 00		16 10	16 20	16 30	16 40	16 50			17 04	
Harold Wood	d			14 53	15 03		15 13	15 23	15 33	15 43			15 53	16 03		16 13	16 23	16 33	16 43	16 53			17 07	
Brentwood	d			14 57	15 07		15 17	15 27	15 37	15 47			15 57	16 07		16 17	16 27	16 37	16 47	16 57			17 11	
Shenfield 3	a	10 38		15 03	15 13	15 02	15 23	15 33	15 43	15 53	15 38		16 03	16 13	16 02	16 23	16 33	16 43	16 53	17 03			17 19	

		LE	LE	LE	LE	LE	LE	LE		LE	LE	LE	LE	LE	LE	LE	LE A	LE		LE	LE	LE	LE	LE	LE
London Liverpool Street 15 ⊖	d	16 47	16 50	16 57	17 00	17 07	17 10	17 17		17 20	17 27	17 30	17 36	17 39	17 42	17 46	17 49	17 52		17 56	17 59	18 02	18 07	18 10	18 17
Stratford 7 ⊖	d	16 54	16 57	17 04	17 07	17 14	17 17	17 24		17 27	17 34	17 37	17 43	17 46	17 49	17 53	17 56	17 59		18 03	18 06	18 09	18 14	18 17	18 24
Maryland	d		16 59		17 09		17 19			17 29		17 39	17 45			17 55				18 05				18 19	
Forest Gate	d		17 01		17 11		17 21			17 31		17 41			17 52			18 02				18 12		18 21	
Manor Park	d		17 03		17 13		17 23			17 33		17 43		17 50			18 00				18 10			18 23	
Ilford 2	d	17 00	17 06	17 10	17 16	17 20	17 26	17 30		17 36	17 40	17 46	17 50	17 53	17 56	18 00	18 03	18 06		18 10	18 13	18 16	18 20	18 26	18 30
Seven Kings	d	17 02		17 12		17 22		17 32			17 42		17 52	17 56	17 59	18 02	18 06	18 09		18 12	18 16	18 19	18 22		18 32
Goodmayes	d	17 04		17 14		17 24		17 34			17 44		17 54	17 58	18 01	18 04	18 08	18 11		18 14	18 18	18 21	18 24		18 34
Chadwell Heath	d	17 06	17 10	17 16	17 20	17 26	17 30	17 36		17 40	17 46	17 50	17 56	18 00	18 03	18 06	18 10	18 13		18 16	18 20	18 23	18 26	18 30	18 36
Romford	d	17 10	17 14	17 20	17 24	17 30	17 34	17 40		17 44	17 50	17 54	18 00	18 04	18 07	18 10	18 14	18 17		18 20	18 24	18 27	18 30	18 34	18 40
Gidea Park 2	a	17 14	17 20	17 24	17 30	17 34	17 40	17 44		17 50	17 54	18 00	18 04	18 09	18 12	18 14	18 18	18 22		18 24	18 29	18 32	18 34	18 40	18 44
	d	17 14		17 24		17 34		17 44			17 54		18 04			18 14	18 18			18 24			18 34		18 44
Harold Wood	d	17 17		17 27		17 37		17 47			17 57		18 07			18 17	18 21			18 27			18 37		18 47
Brentwood	d	17 21		17 31		17 41		17 51			18 01		18 11			18 21	18 25			18 31			18 41		18 51
Shenfield 3	a	17 29		17 39		17 49		17 59			18 09		18 19			18 29	18 33			18 39			18 49		18 59

A To Southend Victoria
B To Colchester
C To Clacton-on-Sea
D To Colchester Town

Table 5

Mondays to Fridays

9 December to 16 May

London Liverpool Street - Ilford - Shenfield

Network Diagram - refer to first Page of Table 5

		LE	LE	LE	LE	LE	LE	LE	LE	LE	LE	LE	LE	LE	LE	LE	LE	LE	LE	LE	LE	LE	LE
																		1 A			1 B		
London Liverpool Street 15 ⊖	d	18 20	18 27	18 30	18 37	18 40	18 47	18 50	18 57	19 00	19 10	19 20	19 30	19 40	19 50	20 00	20 10	20 13	20 20	20 30	20 38	20 40	20 50
Stratford 7 ⊖	d	18 27	18 34	18 37	18 44	18 47	18 54	18 57	19 04	19 07	19 17	19 27	19 37	19 47	19 57	20 07	20 17	20 20	20 27	20 37	20 45	20 47	20 57
Maryland	d	18 29		18 39		18 49		18 59		19 09	19 19	19 29	19 39	19 49	19 59	20 09	20 19		20 29	20 39		20 49	20 59
Forest Gate	d	18 31		18 41		18 51		19 01		19 11	19 21	19 31	19 41	19 51	20 01	20 11	20 21		20 31	20 41		20 51	21 01
Manor Park	d	18 33		18 43		18 53		19 03		19 13	19 23	19 33	19 43	19 53	20 03	20 13	20 23		20 33	20 43		20 53	21 03
Ilford 2	d	18 36	18 40	18 46	18 50	18 56	19 00	19 06	19 10	19 16	19 26	19 36	19 46	19 56	20 06	20 16	20 26		20 36	20 46		20 56	21 06
Seven Kings	d		18 42		18 52		19 02		19 12	19 18	19 28	19 38	19 48	19 58	20 08	20 18	20 28		20 38	20 48		20 58	21 08
Goodmayes	d		18 44		18 54		19 04		19 14	19 20	19 30	19 40	19 50	20 00	20 10	20 20	20 30		20 40	20 50		21 00	21 10
Chadwell Heath	d	18 40	18 46	18 50	18 56	19 00	19 06	19 10	19 16	19 22	19 32	19 42	19 52	20 02	20 12	20 22	20 32		20 42	20 52		21 02	21 12
Romford	d	18 44	18 50	18 54	19 00	19 04	19 10	19 14	19 20	19 26	19 36	19 46	19 56	20 06	20 16	20 26	20 36	20 28	20 46	20 56	20 53	21 06	21 16
Gidea Park 2	a	18 50	18 54	19 00	19 04	19 08	19 14	19 20	19 24	19 30	19 40	19 50	20 00	20 10	20 20	20 30	20 40		20 50	21 00		21 10	21 20
	d		18 54		19 04	19 08	19 14		19 24	19 30	19 40	19 50	20 00	20 10	20 20	20 30	20 40		20 50	21 00		21 10	21 20
Harold Wood	d		18 57		19 07	19 11	19 17		19 27	19 33	19 43	19 53	20 03	20 13	20 23	20 33	20 43		20 53	21 03		21 13	21 23
Brentwood	d		19 01		19 11	19 15	19 21		19 31	19 37	19 47	19 57	20 07	20 17	20 27	20 37	20 47		20 57	21 07		21 17	21 27
Shenfield 3	a		19 09		19 19	19 23	19 29		19 39	19 43	19 53	20 03	20 13	20 23	20 33	20 43	20 53	20 38	21 03	21 13	21 02	21 23	21 33

		LE	LE	LE	LE	LE	LE	LE	LE	LE	LE	LE		LE
				1 A			1 B				1 A			
London Liverpool Street 15 ⊖	d	21 00	21 10	21 13	21 20	21 30	21 38	21 40	21 50	22 05	22 13	22 20		23 50
Stratford 7 ⊖	d	21 07	21 17	21 20	21 27	21 37	21 45	21 47	21 57	22 12	22 20	22 27		23 57
Maryland	d	21 09	21 19		21 29	21 39		21 49	21 59	22 14		22 29		23 59
Forest Gate	d	21 11	21 21		21 31	21 41		21 51	22 01	22 16		22 31	and	00 01
Manor Park	d	21 13	21 23		21 33	21 43		21 53	22 03	22 18		22 33	every 15	00 03
Ilford 2	d	21 16	21 26		21 36	21 46		21 56	22 06	22 21		22 36	minutes	00 06
Seven Kings	d	21 18	21 28		21 38	21 48		21 58	22 08	22 23		22 38	until	00 08
Goodmayes	d	21 20	21 30		21 40	21 50		22 00	22 10	22 25		22 40		00 10
Chadwell Heath	d	21 22	21 32		21 42	21 52		22 02	22 12	22 27		22 42		00 12
Romford	d	21 26	21 36	21 28	21 46	21 56	21 53	22 06	22 16	22 31	22 28	22 46		00 16
Gidea Park 2	a	21 30	21 40		21 50	22 00		22 10	22 20	22 35		22 50		00 20
	d	21 30	21 40		21 50	22 00		22 10	22 20	22 35		22 50		00 20
Harold Wood	d	21 33	21 43		21 53	22 03		22 13	22 23	22 38		22 53		00 23
Brentwood	d	21 37	21 47		21 57	22 07		22 17	22 27	22 42		22 57		00 27
Shenfield 3	a	21 43	21 53	21 38	22 03	22 13	22 02	22 23	22 33	22 48	22 38	23 03		00 33

Saturdays

14 December to 17 May

		LE	LE	LE	LE	LE	LE	LE	LE	LE	LE	LE	LE	LE	LE	LE	LE	LE	LE	LE	LE	LE	
			1 A			1 C	1 A		A	1 D			1 E				1 A			1 B			
London Liverpool Street 15 ⊖	d	00 01	00 15	00 20	00 32	00 46	00 50	00 55	05 28	05 34	05 40	06 10	06 38	06 40	07 00	07 10	07 13	07 20	07 30	07 38	07 40	07 50	
Stratford 7 ⊖	d	00 08	00 22	00 27	00 39	00 53	00 57	01 02	05 35	05 41	05 47	06 17	06 45	06 47	07 07	07 17	07 20	07 27	07 37	07 45	07 47	07 57	
Maryland	d	00 10		00 29	00 41			01 04			05 49	06 19		06 49	07 09	07 19		07 29	07 39		07 49	07 59	and at
Forest Gate	d	00 12		00 31	00 43			01 06			05 51	06 21		06 51	07 11	07 21		07 31	07 41		07 51	08 01	the same
Manor Park	d	00 14		00 33	00 45			01 08			05 53	06 23		06 53	07 13	07 23		07 33	07 43		07 53	08 03	minutes
Ilford 2	d	00 17		00 36	00 48			01 11	05 40		05 56	06 26		06 56	07 16	07 26		07 36	07 46		07 56	08 06	past
Seven Kings	d	00 19		00 38	00 50			01 13	05 42		05 58	06 28		06 58	07 18	07 28		07 38	07 48		07 58	08 08	each
Goodmayes	d	00 21		00 40	00 52			01 15			06 00	06 30		07 00	07 20	07 30		07 40	07 50		08 00	08 10	hour until
Chadwell Heath	d	00 23		00 42	00 54			01 17			06 02	06 32		07 02	07 22	07 32		07 42	07 52		08 02	08 12	
Romford	d	00 27	00 32	00 46	00 58		01 08	01 21	05 48	05 49	06 06	06 36	06 53	07 06	07 26	07 36	07 28	07 46	07 56	07 53	08 06	08 16	
Gidea Park 2	a	00 31		00 50	01 02	01 07		01 25	05 51		06 10	06 40		07 10	07 30	07 40		07 50	08 00		08 10	08 20	
	d			00 50		01 07		01 25	05 51		06 10	06 40		07 10	07 30	07 40		07 50	08 00		08 10	08 20	
Harold Wood	d			00 53				01 28	05 54		06 13	06 43		07 13	07 33	07 43		07 53	08 03		08 13	08 23	
Brentwood	d			00 57				01 32	05 59		06 17	06 47		07 17	07 37	07 47		07 57	08 07		08 17	08 27	
Shenfield 3	a		00 44	01 03		01 17	01 20	01 38	06 04	05 58	06 23	06 53	07 02	07 23	07 43	07 53	07 38	08 03	08 13	08 02	08 23	08 33	

		LE	LE	LE	LE	LE	LE	LE	LE	LE	LE	LE	LE	LE	LE	LE	LE	LE	LE	LE	LE	LE	LE
				1 A			1 B					1 A			1 B					1 A			1 B
London Liverpool Street 15 ⊖	d	18 00	18 10	18 13	18 20	18 30	18 38	18 40	18 50	19 00	19 10	19 13	19 20	19 30	19 38	19 40	19 50	20 00	20 10	20 13	20 20	20 30	20 38
Stratford 7 ⊖	d	18 07	18 17	18 20	18 27	18 37	18 45	18 47	18 57	19 07	19 17	19 20	19 27	19 37	19 46	19 47	19 57	20 07	20 17	20 20	20 27	20 37	20 45
Maryland	d	18 09	18 19		18 29	18 39		18 49	18 59	19 09	19 19		19 29	19 39		19 49	19 59	20 09	20 19		20 29	20 39	
Forest Gate	d	18 11	18 21		18 31	18 41		18 51	19 01	19 11	19 21		19 31	19 41		19 51	20 01	20 11	20 21		20 31	20 41	
Manor Park	d	18 13	18 23		18 33	18 43		18 53	19 03	19 13	19 23		19 33	19 43		19 53	20 03	20 13	20 23		20 33	20 43	
Ilford 2	d	18 16	18 26		18 36	18 46		18 56	19 06	19 16	19 26		19 36	19 46		19 56	20 06	20 16	20 26		20 36	20 46	
Seven Kings	d	18 18	18 28		18 38	18 48		18 58	19 08	19 18	19 28		19 38	19 48		19 58	20 08	20 18	20 28		20 38	20 48	
Goodmayes	d	18 20	18 30		18 40	18 50		19 00	19 10	19 20	19 30		19 40	19 50		20 00	20 10	20 20	20 30		20 40	20 50	
Chadwell Heath	d	18 22	18 32		18 42	18 52		19 02	19 12	19 22	19 32		19 42	19 52		20 02	20 12	20 22	20 32		20 42	20 52	
Romford	d	18 26	18 36	18 28	18 46	18 56	18 53	19 06	19 16	19 26	19 36	19 28	19 46	19 56	19 54	20 06	20 16	20 26	20 36	20 28	20 46	20 56	20 53
Gidea Park 2	a	18 30	18 40		18 50	19 00		19 10	19 20	19 30	19 40		19 50	20 00		20 10	20 20	20 30	20 40		20 50	21 00	
	d	18 30	18 40		18 50	19 00		19 10	19 20	19 30	19 40		19 50	20 00		20 10	20 20	20 30	20 40		20 50	21 00	
Harold Wood	d	18 33	18 43		18 53	19 03		19 13	19 23	19 33	19 43		19 53	20 03		20 13	20 23	20 33	20 43		20 53	21 03	
Brentwood	d	18 37	18 47		18 57	19 07		19 17	19 27	19 37	19 47		19 57	20 07		20 17	20 27	20 37	20 47		20 57	21 07	
Shenfield 3	a	18 43	18 53	18 38	19 03	19 13	19 02	19 23	19 33	19 43	19 53	19 38	20 03	20 13	20 03	20 23	20 33	20 43	20 53	20 38	21 03	21 13	21 02

A To Southend Victoria
B To Colchester Town
C To Colchester
D To Ipswich
E To Harwich International

Table 5

Saturdays

14 December to 17 May

London Liverpool Street - Ilford - Shenfield

Network Diagram - refer to first Page of Table 5

		LE	LE	LE	LE 1 A	LE	LE	LE 1 B	LE	LE	LE 1 A	LE	LE 1 C	LE	LE 1 A	LE	LE	LE 1 A	LE	LE	LE 1 A	LE
London Liverpool Street 15 ⊖	d	20 40	20 50	21 05	21 13	21 20	21 35	21 38	21 50	22 05	22 13	22 20	22 32	22 35	22 44	22 47	23 05	23 14	23 17	23 35	23 44	23 47
Stratford 7 ⊖	d	20 47	20 57	21 12	21 20	21 27	21 42	21 45	21 57	22 12	22 20	22 27	22 41	22 42	22 51	22 54	23 12	23 21	23 24	23 42	23 51	23 54
Maryland	d	20 49	20 59	21 14		21 29	21 44		21 59	22 14		22 29		22 44			23 14			23 44		
Forest Gate	d	20 51	21 01	21 16		21 31	21 46		22 01	22 16		22 31		22 46		22 57	23 16		23 27	23 46		23 57
Manor Park	d	20 53	21 03	21 18		21 33	21 48		22 03	22 18		22 33		22 48		22 59	23 18		23 29	23 48		23 59
Ilford 2	d	20 56	21 06	21 21		21 36	21 51		22 06	22 21		22 36		22 51		23 02	23 21		23 32	23 51		00 02
Seven Kings	d	20 58	21 08	21 23		21 38	21 53		22 08	22 23		22 38		22 53		23 04	23 23		23 34	23 53		00 04
Goodmayes	d	21 00	21 10	21 25		21 40	21 55		22 10	22 25		22 40		22 55		23 06	23 25		23 36	23 55		00 06
Chadwell Heath	d	21 02	21 12	21 27		21 42	21 57		22 12	22 27		22 42		22 57		23 08	23 27		23 38	23 57		00 08
Romford	d	21 06	21 16	21 31	21 28	21 46	22 01	21 53	22 16	22 31	22 28	22 46	22 49	23 01	23 04	23 12	23 31	23 34	23 42	00 01	00 04	00 12
Gidea Park 2	a	21 10	21 20	21 35		21 50	22 05		22 20	22 35		22 50		23 05	23 08	23 17	23 35	23 38	23 47	00 05	00 08	00 17
	d	21 10	21 20	21 35		21 50	22 05		22 20	22 35		22 50		23 05	23 08		23 35	23 38		00 05	00 08	
Harold Wood	d	21 13	21 23	21 38		21 53	22 08		22 23	22 38		22 53		23 08	23 11		23 38	23 41		00 08	00 11	
Brentwood	d	21 17	21 27	21 42		21 57	22 12		22 27	22 42		22 57		23 12	23 16		23 42	23 46		00 12	00 16	
Shenfield 3	a	21 23	21 33	21 48	21 38	22 03	22 18	22 02	22 33	22 48	22 38	23 03	22 58	23 18	23 21		23 48	23 51		00 18	00 21	

Sundays

8 December to 11 May

		LE	LE 1 A	LE	LE	LE 1 A	LE	LE (bus)	LE (bus)	LE	LE (bus)	LE	LE (bus)	LE	LE	LE 1 A	LE	LE 1 A	LE	LE 1 A	LE	LE	LE 1 A
London Liverpool Street 15 ⊖	d	00 01	00 15	00 20	00 32	00 50	00 55			06 35		07 05		07 35	08 05	08 14	08 35	08 44	09 05	09 14	09 17	09 35	09 44
Stratford 7 ⊖	d	00 08	00 22	00 27	00 39	00 57	01 02			06 42		07 12		07 42	08 12	08 21	08 42	08 51	09 12	09 21	09 24	09 42	09 51
Maryland	d	00 10		00 29	00 41		01 04			06 44		07 14		07 44	08 14		08 44		09 14			09 44	
Forest Gate	d	00 12		00 31	00 43		01 06			06 46		07 16		07 46	08 16		08 46		09 16		09 27	09 46	
Manor Park	d	00 14		00 33	00 45		01 08			06 48		07 18		07 48	08 18		08 48		09 18		09 29	09 48	
Ilford 2	d	00 17		00 36	00 48		01 11	06 00	06 30	06a52	07 00	07a22	07 30	07a52	08 21		08 51		09 21		09 32	09 51	
Seven Kings	d	00 19		00 38	00 50		01 13								08 23		08 53		09 23		09 34	09 53	
Goodmayes	d	00 21		00 40	00 52		01 15								08 25		08 55		09 25		09 36	09 55	
Chadwell Heath	d	00 23		00 42	00 54		01 17								08 27		08 57		09 27		09 38	09 57	
Romford	d	00 27	00 32	00 46	00 58	01 08	01 21	06 20	06 50		07 20		07 50		08 31	08 34	09 01	09 04	09 31	09 34	09 42	10 01	10 04
Gidea Park 2	a	00 31		00 50	01 02		01 25	06 27	06 57		07 27		07 57		08 35	08 38	09 05	09 08	09 35	09 38	09 47	10 05	10 08
	d			00 50			01 25	06 27	06 57		07 27		07 57		08 35	08 38	09 05	09 08	09 35	09 38		10 05	10 08
Harold Wood	d			00 53			01 28	06 34	07 04		07 34		08 04		08 38	08 41	09 08	09 11	09 38	09 41		10 08	10 11
Brentwood	d			00 57			01 32	06 49	07 19		07 49		08 19		08 42	08 46	09 12	09 16	09 42	09 46		10 12	10 16
Shenfield 3	a		00 44	01 03		01 20	01 38	06 59	07 29		07 59		08 29		08 48	08 51	09 18	09 21	09 48	09 51		10 18	10 21

		LE		LE	LE 1 A	LE	LE	LE 1 A	LE	LE	LE 1 A	LE	LE	LE 1 A	LE	LE 1 A	LE	LE 1 A
London Liverpool Street 15 ⊖	d	09 47		21 05	21 14	21 17	21 35	21 44	21 47	22 05	22 14	22 17	22 35	22 44	23 05	23 14	23 35	23 44
Stratford 7 ⊖	d	09 54		21 12	21 21	21 24	21 42	21 51	21 54	22 12	22 21	22 24	22 42	22 51	23 12	23 21	23 42	23 51
Maryland	d		and at	21 14			21 44			22 14			22 44		23 14		23 44	
Forest Gate	d	09 57	the same	21 16		21 27	21 46		21 57	22 16		22 27	22 46		23 16		23 46	
Manor Park	d	09 59	minutes	21 18		21 29	21 48		21 59	22 18		22 29	22 48		23 18		23 48	
Ilford 2	d	10 02	past	21 21		21 32	21 51		22 02	22 21		22 32	22 51		23 21		23 51	
Seven Kings	d	10 04	each	21 23		21 34	21 53		22 04	22 23		22 34	22 53		23 23		23 53	
Goodmayes	d	10 06	hour until	21 25		21 36	21 55		22 06	22 25		22 36	22 55		23 25		23 55	
Chadwell Heath	d	10 08		21 27		21 38	21 57		22 08	22 27		22 38	22 57		23 27		23 57	
Romford	d	10 12		21 31	21 34	21 42	22 01	22 04	22 12	22 31	22 34	22 42	23 01	23 04	23 31	23 34	00 01	00 04
Gidea Park 2	a	10 17		21 35	21 38	21 47	22 05	22 08	22 17	22 35	22 38	22 47	23 05	23 08	23 35	23 38	00 05	00 08
	d			21 35	21 38		22 05	22 08		22 35	22 38		23 05	23 08	23 35	23 38	00 05	00 08
Harold Wood	d			21 38	21 41		22 08	22 11		22 38	22 41		23 08	23 11	23 38	23 41	00 08	00 11
Brentwood	d			21 42	21 46		22 12	22 16		22 42	22 46		23 12	23 16	23 42	23 46	00 12	00 16
Shenfield 3	a			21 48	21 51		22 18	22 21		22 48	22 51		23 18	23 21	23 48	23 51	00 18	00 21

A To Southend Victoria

B To Colchester Town

C To Colchester

Table 5R

Mondays to Fridays

9 December to 16 May

Shenfield - Ilford - London Liverpool Street

Network Diagram - refer to first Page of Table 5

Miles	Miles			LE FO A	LE MO A	LE FO A	LE TW ThO A	LE B	LE	LE B	LE [1] C	LE	LE	LE	LE	LE	LE	LE	LE	LE	LE	LE	LE
0	—	**Shenfield [3]**	d					04 39		05 09	05 24		05 29	05 44		06 04	06 14	06 24	06 34		06 44		06 54
2	—	Brentwood	d					04 42		05 12			05 32	05 47		06 07	06 17	06 27	06 37		06 47		06 57
5¼	—	Harold Wood	d					04 47		05 17			05 37	05 52		06 12	06 22	06 32	06 42		06 52		07 02
6¾	0	Gidea Park [2]	d				00 03	04 51		05 21	05 31		05 41	05 56	06 06	06 16	06 26	06 36	06 45	06 49	06 55	06 59	07 05
7¾	1¼	Romford	d				00 05	04 53		05 23			05 43	05 58	06 08	06 18	06 28	06 38	06 48	06 51	06 58	07 01	07 08
10¼	3½	Chadwell Heath	d		00 01	00 02	00 09	04 57		05 27			05 47	06 02	06 12	06 22	06 32	06 42	06 52	06 55	07 02	07 05	07 12
11	4¼	Goodmayes	d		00 03	00 04	00 11	04 59		05 29			05 49	06 04	06 14	06 24	06 34	06 44		06 57		07 07	
11¾	5	Seven Kings	d		00 05	00 06	00 13	05 01		05 31	05 36		05 51	06 06	06 16	06 26	06 36	06 46		06 59		07 09	
12¾	6¼	Ilford [2]	d		00 08	00 09	00 16	05 04	05 09	05 34		05 39	05 54	06 09	06 19	06 29	06 39	06 49	06 57	07 02	07 07	07 12	07 17
14	7¼	Manor Park	d		00 10	00 12	00 18		05 11			05 41	05 57	06 12	06 22	06 32	06 42	06 52		07 05		07 15	
15	8¼	Forest Gate	d		00 13	00 14	00 21		05 14			05 44	05 59	06 14	06 24	06 34	06 44	06 54		07 07		07 17	
15¾	9	Maryland	d	00 01	00 15	00 16	00 23		05 16			05 46	06 01	06 16	06 26	06 36	06 46	06 56		07 09		07 19	
16¼	9½	Stratford [7] ⊖	d	00 04	00 17	00 19	00 25	05 10	05 18	05 40	05 42	05 48	06 04	06 19	06 29	06 39	06 49	06 59	07 03	07 12	07 15	07 22	07 25
20¼	13½	**London Liverpool Street [15] ⊖**	a	00 12	00 26	00 27	00 34	05 18	05 26	05 48	05 55	05 56	06 12	06 27	06 37	06 47	06 57	07 07	07 13	07 22	07 25	07 32	07 35

		LE	LE	LE	LE	LE	LE	LE	LE	LE	LE	LE	LE	LE	LE B	LE	LE	LE	LE	LE	LE	LE	LE
Shenfield [3]	d		07 04		07 14		07 24		07 34		07 44		07 50		07 54	08 00			08 10			08 22	
Brentwood	d		07 07		07 17		07 27		07 37		07 47		07 53		07 57	08 03			08 13			08 25	
Harold Wood	d		07 12		07 22		07 32		07 42		07 52		07 58		08 02	08 08			08 18			08 30	
Gidea Park [2]	d	07 09	07 15	07 19	07 25	07 29	07 35	07 39	07 45	07 49	07 55	07 59	08 02	08 05	08 09	08 12	08 15	08 19	08 22		08 29	08 34	
Romford	d	07 11	07 18	07 21	07 28	07 31	07 38	07 41	07 48	07 51	07 58	08 01	08 04	08 07	08 11	08 14	08 17	08 21	08 24		08 31	08 36	
Chadwell Heath	d	07 15	07 22	07 25	07 32	07 35	07 42	07 45	07 52	07 55	08 02	08 05	08 08	08 11	08 15	08 18	08 21	08 25	08 28		08 35	08 40	
Goodmayes	d	07 17		07 27	07 34	07 37	07 44	07 47	07 54	07 57	08 04	08 07	08 10	08 13	08 17	08 20	08 23	08 27	08 30		08 37	08 42	
Seven Kings	d	07 19		07 29	07 36	07 39	07 46	07 49	07 56	07 59	08 06	08 09	08 12	08 15	08 19	08 22	08 25	08 29	08 32		08 39	08 44	
Ilford [2]	d	07 22	07 27	07 32	07 39	07 42	07 49	07 52	07 59	08 02	08 09	08 12	08 15	08 18	08 22	08 25	08 28	08 32	08 35	08 38	08 42	08 47	08 50
Manor Park	d	07 25		07 35		07 45		07 55		08 05				08 21			08 31			08 41			08 53
Forest Gate	d	07 27		07 37		07 47		07 57		08 07				08 23			08 33			08 43			08 55
Maryland	d	07 29		07 39		07 49		07 59		08 09				08 25			08 35			08 45			08 57
Stratford [7] ⊖	d	07 32	07 35	07 42	07 45	07 52	07 55	08 02	08 05	08 12	08 15	08 18	08 21	08 28	08 31	08 34	08 38	08 41	08 44	08 48	08 51	08 54	09 00
London Liverpool Street [15] ⊖	a	07 42	07 45	07 52	07 55	08 02	08 05	08 12	08 15	08 22	08 25	08 28	08 31	08 38	08 41	08 43	08 48	08 51	08 53	08 58	09 01	09 03	09 10

		LE	LE	LE	LE	LE	LE [1] B	LE	LE	LE	LE	LE	LE	LE [1] B	LE	LE	LE	LE [1] D	LE	LE	LE	LE [1] B	LE
Shenfield [3]	d		08 32			08 44	08 46	08 54	09 04	09 14	09 24	09 34	09 44	09 45	09 54	10 04	10 14	10 18	10 24	10 34	10 44	10 45	10 54
Brentwood	d		08 35			08 47		08 57	09 07	09 17	09 27	09 37	09 47		09 57	10 07	10 17		10 27	10 37	10 47		10 57
Harold Wood	d		08 40			08 52		09 02	09 12	09 22	09 32	09 42	09 52		10 02	10 12	10 22		10 32	10 42	10 52		11 02
Gidea Park [2]	d	08 41	08 44		08 51	08 56		09 06	09 16	09 26	09 36	09 46	09 56		10 06	10 16	10 26		10 36	10 46	10 56		11 06
Romford	d	08 43	08 46		08 53	08 58	08 55	09 08	09 18	09 28	09 38	09 48	09 58	09 53	10 08	10 18	10 28	10 26	10 38	10 48	10 58	10 53	11 08
Chadwell Heath	d	08 47	08 50		08 57	09 02		09 12	09 22	09 32	09 42	09 52	10 02		10 12	10 22	10 32		10 42	10 52	11 02		11 12
Goodmayes	d	08 49	08 52		08 59	09 04		09 14	09 24	09 34	09 44	09 54	10 04		10 14	10 24	10 34		10 44	10 54	11 04		11 14
Seven Kings	d	08 51	08 54		09 01	09 06		09 16	09 26	09 36	09 46	09 56	10 06		10 16	10 26	10 36		10 46	10 56	11 06		11 16
Ilford [2]	d	08 54	08 57	09 00	09 04	09 09		09 19	09 29	09 39	09 49	09 59	10 09		10 19	10 29	10 39		10 49	10 59	11 09		11 19
Manor Park	d			09 03		09 12		09 22	09 32	09 42	09 52	10 02	10 12		10 22	10 32	10 42		10 52	11 02	11 12		11 22
Forest Gate	d			09 05		09 14		09 24	09 34	09 44	09 54	10 04	10 14		10 24	10 34	10 44		10 54	11 04	11 14		11 24
Maryland	d			09 07		09 16		09 26	09 36	09 46	09 56	10 06	10 16		10 26	10 36	10 46		10 56	11 06	11 16		11 26
Stratford [7] ⊖	d	09 03	09 06	09 10	09 13	09 19	09s05	09 29	09 39	09 49	09 59	10 09	10 19	10 01	10 29	10 39	10 49	10 34	10 59	11 09	11 19	11 01	11 29
London Liverpool Street [15] ⊖	a	09 13	09 14	09 20	09 23	09 27	09 16	09 37	09 47	09 58	10 07	10 17	10 27	10 10	10 37	10 47	10 57	10 43	11 07	11 17	11 27	11 10	11 37

		LE	LE	LE [1] D		LE	LE	LE	LE [1] B	LE	LE	LE	LE [1] D	LE	LE	LE	LE [1] B	LE	LE	LE	LE	LE
Shenfield [3]	d	11 04	11 14	11 20	and at the same minutes past each hour until	14 24	14 34	14 44	14 45	14 54	15 04	15 14	15 20	15 24	15 34	15 44	15 45	15 54	16 04	16 14	16 24	16 34
Brentwood	d	11 07	11 17			14 27	14 37	14 47		14 57	15 07	15 17		15 27	15 37	15 47		15 57	16 07	16 17	16 27	16 37
Harold Wood	d	11 12	11 22			14 32	14 42	14 52		15 02	15 12	15 22		15 32	15 42	15 52		16 02	16 12	16 22	16 32	16 42
Gidea Park [2]	d	11 16	11 26			14 36	14 46	14 56		15 06	15 16	15 26		15 36	15 46	15 56		16 06	16 16	16 26	16 36	16 46
Romford	d	11 18	11 28	11 28		14 38	14 48	14 58	14 53	15 08	15 18	15 28	15 28	15 38	15 48	15 58	15 53	16 08	16 18	16 28	16 38	16 48
Chadwell Heath	d	11 22	11 32			14 42	14 52	15 02		15 12	15 22	15 32		15 42	15 52	16 02		16 12	16 22	16 32	16 42	16 52
Goodmayes	d	11 24	11 34			14 44	14 54	15 04		15 14	15 24	15 34		15 44	15 54	16 04		16 14	16 24	16 34	16 44	16 54
Seven Kings	d	11 26	11 36			14 46	14 56	15 06		15 16	15 26	15 36		15 46	15 56	16 06		16 16	16 26	16 36	16 46	16 56
Ilford [2]	d	11 29	11 39			14 49	14 59	15 09		15 19	15 29	15 39		15 49	15 59	16 09		16 19	16 29	16 39	16 49	16 59
Manor Park	d	11 32	11 42			14 52	15 02	15 12		15 22	15 32	15 42		15 52	16 02	16 12		16 22	16 32	16 42	16 52	17 02
Forest Gate	d	11 34	11 44			14 54	15 04	15 14		15 24	15 34	15 44		15 54	16 04	16 14		16 24	16 34	16 44	16 54	17 04
Maryland	d	11 36	11 46			14 56	15 06	15 16		15 26	15 36	15 46		15 56	16 06	16 16		16 26	16 36	16 46	16 56	17 06
Stratford [7] ⊖	d	11 39	11 49	11 36		14 59	15 09	15 19	15 01	15 29	15 39	15 49	15 36	15 59	16 09	16 19	16 01	16 29	16 39	16 49	16 59	17 09
London Liverpool Street [15] ⊖	a	11 47	11 57	11 45		15 07	15 17	15 27	15 10	15 37	15 47	15 57	15 45	16 07	16 17	16 27	16 11	16 37	16 47	16 57	17 07	17 17

		LE	LE	LE	LE	LE	LE	LE	LE	LE	LE	LE	LE	LE	LE	LE	LE	LE [1] E	LE	LE	LE	LE	LE
Shenfield [3]	d	16 44	16 54	17 04	17 14		17 24		17 34		17 44		17 54		18 04		18 14	18 20		18 24	18 34	18 44	18 54
Brentwood	d	16 47	16 57	17 07	17 17		17 27		17 37		17 47		17 57		18 07		18 17			18 27	18 37	18 47	18 57
Harold Wood	d	16 52	17 02	17 12	17 22		17 32		17 42		17 52		18 02		18 12		18 22			18 32	18 42	18 52	19 02
Gidea Park [2]	d	16 56	17 06	17 16	17 26	17 32	17 36	17 42	17 46	17 52	17 56	18 02	18 06	18 12	18 16	18 22	18 26		18 32	18 36	18 46	18 56	19 06
Romford	d	16 58	17 08	17 18	17 28	17 34	17 38	17 44	17 48	17 54	17 58	18 04	18 08	18 14	18 18	18 24	18 28	18 28	18 34	18 38	18 48	18 58	19 08
Chadwell Heath	d	17 02	17 12	17 22	17 32		17 42		17 52		18 02		18 12		18 22		18 32			18 42	18 52	19 02	19 12
Goodmayes	d	17 04	17 14	17 24	17 34		17 44		17 54		18 04		18 14		18 24		18 34			18 44	18 54	19 04	19 14
Seven Kings	d	17 06	17 16	17 26	17 36		17 46		17 56		18 06		18 16		18 26		18 36			18 46	18 56	19 06	19 16
Ilford [2]	d	17 09	17 19	17 29	17 39	17 42	17 49	17 52	17 59	18 02	18 09	18 12	18 19	18 22	18 29	18 32	18 39		18 42	18 49	18 59	19 09	19 19
Manor Park	d	17 12	17 22	17 32		17 45		17 55		18 05		18 15		18 25		18 35			18 45	18 52	19 02	19 12	19 22
Forest Gate	d	17 14	17 24	17 34		17 47		17 57		18 07		18 17		18 27		18 37			18 47	18 54	19 04	19 14	19 24
Maryland	d	17 16	17 26	17 36		17 49		17 59		18 09		18 19		18 29		18 39			18 49	18 56	19 06	19 16	19 26
Stratford [7] ⊖	d	17 19	17 29	17 39	17 45	17 52	17 55	18 02	18 05	18 12	18 15	18 22	18 25	18 32	18 35	18 42	18 45	18 36	18 52	18 59	19 09	19 19	19 29
London Liverpool Street [15] ⊖	a	17 27	17 37	17 47	17 53	18 00	18 03	18 10	18 13	18 20	18 23	18 30	18 33	18 40	18 43	18 50	18 53	18 45	19 00	19 07	19 17	19 27	19 37

A From Shenfield
B From Southend Victoria
C From Colchester
D From Colchester Town
E From Braintree

Table 5R

Shenfield - Ilford - London Liverpool Street

Mondays to Fridays

9 December to 16 May

Network Diagram - refer to first Page of Table 5

	LE	LE	LE	LE	LE	LE	LE	LE	LE	LE	LE	LE	LE	LE	LE	LE	LE	LE	LE	LE	LE
			1 A				1 B				1 C				1 B						
Shenfield 3 d	19 04	19 14	19 20	19 24	19 34	19 44	19 45	19 54	20 04	20 14	20 20	20 24	20 34	20 44	20 45	20 54	21 04	21 14	21 24	21 34	21 44
Brentwood d	19 07	19 17		19 27	19 37	19 47		19 57	20 07	20 17		20 27	20 37	20 47		20 57	21 07	21 17	21 27	21 37	21 47
Harold Wood d	19 12	19 22		19 32	19 42	19 52		20 02	20 12	20 22		20 32	20 42	20 52		21 02	21 12	21 22	21 32	21 42	21 52
Gidea Park 2 d	19 16	19 26		19 36	19 46	19 56		20 06	20 16	20 26		20 36	20 46	20 56		21 06	21 16	21 26	21 36	21 46	21 56
Romford d	19 18	19 28	19 28	19 38	19 48	19 58	19 53	20 08	20 18	20 28	20 28	20 38	20 48	20 58	20 53	21 08	21 18	21 28	21 38	21 48	21 58
Chadwell Heath d	19 22	19 32		19 42	19 52	20 02		20 12	20 22	20 32		20 42	20 52	21 02		21 12	21 22	21 32	21 42	21 52	22 02
Goodmayes d	19 24	19 34		19 44	19 54	20 04		20 14	20 24	20 34		20 44	20 54	21 04		21 14	21 24	21 34	21 44	21 54	22 04
Seven Kings d	19 26	19 36		19 46	19 56	20 06		20 16	20 26	20 36		20 46	20 56	21 06		21 16	21 26	21 36	21 46	21 56	22 06
Ilford 2 d	19 29	19 39		19 49	19 59	20 09		20 19	20 29	20 39		20 49	20 59	21 09		21 19	21 29	21 39	21 49	21 59	22 09
Manor Park d	19 32	19 42		19 52	20 02	20 12		20 22	20 32	20 42		20 52	21 02	21 12		21 22	21 32	21 42	21 52	22 02	22 12
Forest Gate d	19 34	19 44		19 54	20 04	20 14		20 24	20 34	20 44		20 54	21 04	21 14		21 24	21 34	21 44	21 54	22 04	22 14
Maryland d	19 36	19 46		19 56	20 06	20 16		20 26	20 36	20 46		20 56	21 06	21 16		21 26	21 36	21 46	21 56	22 06	22 16
Stratford 7 ⊖ d	19 39	19 49	19 36	19 59	20 09	20 19	20 01	20 29	20 39	20 49	20 36	20 59	21 09	21 19	21 01	21 29	21 39	21 49	21 59	22 09	22 19
London Liverpool Street 15 ⊖ a	19 47	19 57	19 45	20 07	20 17	20 27	20 10	20 37	20 47	20 57	20 45	21 07	21 17	21 27	21 10	21 37	21 47	21 57	22 07	22 17	22 27

	LE	LE	LE	LE	LE	LE	LE	LE	LE	LE	LE	LE	LE	LE	LE	LE	LE	LE	LE	LE
					MT WO	ThFO	MT WO	ThFO	MT WO	ThFO	MT WO	ThFO	ThFO	MT WO	MT WO	ThFO	ThFO	MT WO	ThFO	MT WO
	1 B			1 C									1 A	1 A			1 D	1 D		
Shenfield 3 d	21 45	21 59	22 14	22 20	22 26	22 29	22 41	22 44	22 56	22 59	23 11	23 14	23 20	23 20	23 26	23 29	23 39	23 39	23 44	23 51
Brentwood d		22 02	22 17		22 29	22 32	22 44	22 47	22 59	23 02	23 14	23 17			23 29	23 32			23 47	23 54
Harold Wood d		22 07	22 22		22 34	22 37	22 49	22 52	23 04	23 07	23 19	23 22			23 34	23 37			23 52	23 59
Gidea Park 2 d		22 11	22 26		22 38	22 41	22 53	22 56	23 08	23 11	23 23	23 26			23 38	23 41			23 56	00 03
Romford d	21 53	22 13	22 28	22 28	22 40	22 43	22 55	22 58	23 10	23 13	23 25	23 28	23 28	23 28	23 40	23 43	23 47	23 47	23 58	00 05
Chadwell Heath d		22 17	22 32		22 44	22 47	22 59	23 02	23 14	23 17	23 29	23 32			23 44	23 47			00 02	00 09
Goodmayes d		22 19	22 34		22 46	22 49	23 01	23 04	23 16	23 19	23 31	23 34			23 46	23 49			00 04	00 11
Seven Kings d		22 21	22 36		22 48	22 51	23 03	23 06	23 18	23 21	23 33	23 36			23 48	23 51			00 06	00 13
Ilford 2 d		22 24	22 39		22 51	22 54	23 06	23 09	23 21	23 24	23 36	23 39			23 51	23 54			00 09	00 16
Manor Park d		22 27	22 42		22 53	22 57	23 08	23 12	23 23	23 27	23 38	23 42			23 53	23 57			00 12	00 18
Forest Gate d		22 29	22 44		22 56	22 59	23 11	23 14	23 26	23 29	23 41	23 44			23 56	23 59			00 14	00 21
Maryland d		22 31	22 46		22 58	23 01	23 13	23 16	23 28	23 31	23 43	23 46			23 58	00 01			00 16	00 23
Stratford 7 ⊖ d	22 01	22 34	22 49	22 36	23 00	23 04	23 15	23 19	23 30	23 34	23 45	23 49	23 36	23s42	23 59	00 04	23 56	00s03	00 19	00 25
London Liverpool Street 15 ⊖ a	22 10	22 42	22 57	22 45	23 09	23 12	23 24	23 27	23 39	23 42	23 54	23 57	23 45	23 51	00 09	00 12	00 05	00 12	00 27	00 34

Saturdays

14 December to 17 May

	LE	LE	LE	LE	LE	LE	LE	LE	LE	LE	LE	LE	LE	LE	LE	LE	LE	LE	LE	LE	LE	LE	LE
	E	E	B		B	1 F		1 B					1 B						1 C				1 B
Shenfield 3 d			04 39		05 09	05 24		05 35	05 44		06 14		06 35		06 44		07 04	07 14	07 20	07 24	07 34	07 44	07 45
Brentwood d			04 42		05 12				05 47		06 17				06 47		07 07	07 17		07 27	07 37	07 47	
Harold Wood d			04 47		05 17				05 52		06 22				06 52		07 12	07 22		07 32	07 42	07 52	
Gidea Park 2 d			04 51		05 21	05 31			05 56	06 16	06 26	06 36		06 46	06 56	07 06	07 16	07 26		07 36	07 46	07 56	
Romford d			04 53		05 23			05 43	05 58	06 18	06 28	06 38	06 43	06 48	06 58	07 08	07 18	07 28	07 28	07 38	07 48	07 58	07 53
Chadwell Heath d		00 02	04 57		05 27				06 02	06 22	06 32	06 42		06 52	07 02	07 12	07 22	07 32		07 42	07 52	08 02	
Goodmayes d		00 04	04 59		05 29				06 04	06 24	06 34	06 44		06 54	07 04	07 14	07 24	07 34		07 44	07 54	08 04	
Seven Kings d		00 06	05 01		05 31	05 36			06 06	06 26	06 36	06 46		06 56	07 06	07 16	07 26	07 36		07 46	07 56	08 06	
Ilford 2 d		00 09	05 04	05 09	05 34		05 39		06 09	06 29	06 39	06 49		06 59	07 09	07 19	07 29	07 39		07 49	07 59	08 09	
Manor Park d		00 12		05 11			05 41		06 12	06 32	06 42	06 52		07 02	07 12	07 22	07 32	07 42		07 52	08 02	08 12	
Forest Gate d		00 14		05 14			05 44		06 14	06 34	06 44	06 54		07 04	07 14	07 24	07 34	07 44		07 54	08 04	08 14	
Maryland d	00 01	00 16		05 16			05 46		06 16	06 36	06 46	06 56		07 06	07 16	07 26	07 36	07 46		07 56	08 06	08 16	
Stratford 7 ⊖ d	00 04	00 19	05 10	05 18	05 40	05 42	05 48	05 51	06 19	06 39	06 49	06 59	06 51	07 09	07 19	07 29	07 39	07 49	07 36	07 59	08 09	08 19	08 01
London Liverpool Street 15 ⊖ a	00 12	00 27	05 18	05 26	05 48	05 55	05 56	06 00	06 27	06 47	06 57	07 07	07 00	07 17	07 27	07 37	07 47	07 57	07 45	08 07	08 17	08 27	08 10

	LE		LE	LE	LE	LE	LE	LE	LE	LE	LE	LE	LE	LE	LE	LE	LE	LE	LE	LE	LE
					1 C				1 B				1 C				1 B			1 C	
Shenfield 3 d	07 54	and at the same minutes past each hour until	19 04	19 14	19 20	19 24	19 34	19 44	19 45	19 54	20 04	20 14	20 20	20 24	20 34	20 44	20 45	20 59	21 14	21 20	21 29
Brentwood d	07 57		19 07	19 17		19 27	19 37	19 47		19 57	20 07	20 17		20 27	20 37	20 47		21 02	21 17		21 32
Harold Wood d	08 02		19 12	19 22		19 32	19 42	19 52		20 02	20 12	20 22		20 32	20 42	20 52		21 07	21 22		21 37
Gidea Park 2 d	08 06		19 16	19 26		19 36	19 46	19 56		20 06	20 16	20 26		20 36	20 46	20 56		21 11	21 26		21 41
Romford d	08 08		19 18	19 28	19 28	19 38	19 48	19 58	19 53	20 08	20 18	20 28	20 28	20 38	20 48	20 58	20 53	21 13	21 28	21 28	21 43
Chadwell Heath d	08 12		19 22	19 32		19 42	19 52	20 02		20 12	20 22	20 32		20 42	20 52	21 02		21 17	21 32		21 47
Goodmayes d	08 14		19 24	19 34		19 44	19 54	20 04		20 14	20 24	20 34		20 44	20 54	21 04		21 19	21 34		21 49
Seven Kings d	08 16		19 26	19 36		19 46	19 56	20 06		20 16	20 26	20 36		20 46	20 56	21 06		21 21	21 36		21 51
Ilford 2 d	08 19		19 29	19 39		19 49	19 59	20 09		20 19	20 29	20 39		20 49	20 59	21 09		21 24	21 39		21 54
Manor Park d	08 22		19 32	19 42		19 52	20 02	20 12		20 22	20 32	20 42		20 52	21 02	21 12		21 27	21 42		21 57
Forest Gate d	08 24		19 34	19 44		19 54	20 04	20 14		20 24	20 34	20 44		20 54	21 04	21 14		21 29	21 44		21 59
Maryland d	08 26		19 36	19 46		19 56	20 06	20 16		20 26	20 36	20 46		20 56	21 06	21 16		21 31	21 46		22 01
Stratford 7 ⊖ d	08 29		19 39	19 49	19 36	19 59	20 09	20 19	20 01	20 29	20 39	20 49	20 36	20 59	21 09	21 19	21 01	21 34	21 49	21 36	22 04
London Liverpool Street 15 ⊖ a	08 37		19 47	19 57	19 45	20 07	20 17	20 27	20 10	20 37	20 47	20 57	20 45	21 07	21 17	21 27	21 10	21 42	21 57	21 45	22 12

A From Ipswich
B From Southend Victoria
C From Colchester Town
D From Southminster
E From Shenfield
F From Colchester

Table 5R

Saturdays

14 December to 17 May

Shenfield - Ilford - London Liverpool Street

Network Diagram - refer to first Page of Table 5

		LE	LE	LE	LE	LE	LE	LE	LE	LE	LE	LE	LE	LE
			1			1					1		1	
			A			B					C		D	
Shenfield 3	d	21 44	21 45	21 59	22 14	22 20	22 29	22 41	22 56	23 11	23 20	23 26	23 41	23 44
Brentwood	d	21 47		22 02	22 17		22 32	22 44	22 59	23 14		23 29		23 47
Harold Wood	d	21 52		22 07	22 22		22 37	22 49	23 04	23 19		23 34		23 52
Gidea Park 2	d	21 56		22 11	22 26		22 41	22 53	23 08	23 23		23 38		23 56
Romford	d	21 58	21 53	22 13	22 28	22 28	22 43	22 55	23 10	23 25	23 28	23 40	23 49	23 58
Chadwell Heath	d	22 02		22 17	22 32		22 47	22 59	23 14	23 29		23 44		00 02
Goodmayes	d	22 04		22 19	22 34		22 49	23 01	23 16	23 31		23 46		00 04
Seven Kings	d	22 06		22 21	22 36		22 51	23 03	23 18	23 33		23 48		00 06
Ilford 2	d	22 09		22 24	22 39		22 54	23 06	23 21	23 36		23 51		00 09
Manor Park	d	22 12		22 27	22 42		22 57	23 08	23 23	23 38		23 53		00 12
Forest Gate	d	22 14		22 29	22 44		22 59	23 11	23 26	23 41		23 56		00 14
Maryland	d	22 16		22 31	22 46		23 01	23 13	23 28	23 43		23 58		00 16
Stratford 7 ⊖	d	22 19	22 01	22 34	22 49	22 36	23 04	23 15	23 30	23 45	23s42	23 59	00s03	00 19
London Liverpool Street 15 ⊖	a	22 27	22 10	22 42	22 57	22 46	23 12	23 24	23 39	23 54	23 51	00 09	00 12	00 27

Sundays

8 December to 11 May

		LE	LE	LE	LE	LE	LE	LE	LE	LE	LE	LE	LE	LE	LE	LE	LE	LE	LE	LE	LE	LE	LE
																1		1			1		
		E														F		A			A		
			bus		bus		bus			bus			bus		bus								
Shenfield 3	d						05 58			06 28			06 58		07 28	08 11	08 13	08 23		08 43	08 53		09 13
Brentwood	d						06 08			06 38			07 08		07 38		08 16	08 26		08 46	08 56		09 16
Harold Wood	d						06 23			06 53			07 23		07 53		08 21	08 31		08 51	09 01		09 21
Gidea Park 2	d		05 30		06 00		06 30			07 00			07 30		08 00		08 25	08 35	08 41	08 55	09 05	09 11	09 25
Romford	d		05 37		06 07		06 37			07 07			07 37		08 07	08 21	08 27	08 37	08 43	08 57	09 07	09 13	09 27
Chadwell Heath	d	00 02															08 31		08 47	09 01		09 17	09 31
Goodmayes	d	00 04															08 33		08 49	09 03		09 19	09 33
Seven Kings	d	00 06															08 35		08 51	09 05		09 21	09 35
Ilford 2	d	00 09	05a58	06 08	06a28	06 38	06a58	07 08	07 24	07a28	07 38	07 54	07a58	08 08	08a28	08 28	08 38		08 54	09 08		09 24	09 38
Manor Park	d	00 12		06 10		06 40		07 10			07 40			08 10			08 40		08 56	09 10		09 26	09 40
Forest Gate	d	00 14		06 13		06 43		07 13			07 43			08 13			08 43		08 59	09 13		09 29	09 43
Maryland	d	00 16		06 15		06 45		07 15			07 45			08 15			08 45			09 15			09 45
Stratford 7 ⊖	d	00 19		06 17		06 47		07 17	07 29		07 47	07 59		08 17		08 33	08 47	08 50	09 02	09 17	09 20	09 32	09 47
London Liverpool Street 15 ⊖	a	00 27		06 26		06 56		07 26	07 38		07 56	08 08		08 26		08 42	08 56	09 02	09 11	09 26	09 29	09 41	09 56

		LE		LE	LE	LE	LE	LE	LE	LE	LE	LE	LE	LE	LE	LE	LE	LE	LE	LE	LE	LE
		1				1			1			1			1			1			1	
		A				A			A			A			A			A			A	
Shenfield 3	d	09 23	and at the same minutes past each hour until		16 43	16 53		17 13	17 23		17 43	17 53		18 13	18 23		18 43	18 53		19 13	19 23	
Brentwood	d	09 26			16 46	16 56		17 16	17 26		17 46	17 56		18 16	18 26		18 46	18 56		19 16	19 26	
Harold Wood	d	09 31			16 51	17 01		17 21	17 31		17 51	18 01		18 21	18 31		18 51	19 01		19 21	19 31	
Gidea Park 2	d	09 35		16 41	16 55	17 05	17 11	17 25	17 35	17 41	17 55	18 05	18 11	18 25	18 35	18 41	18 55	19 05	19 11	19 25	19 35	19 41
Romford	d	09 37		16 43	16 57	17 07	17 13	17 27	17 37	17 43	17 57	18 07	18 13	18 27	18 37	18 43	18 57	19 07	19 13	19 27	19 37	19 43
Chadwell Heath	d			16 47	17 01		17 17	17 31		17 47	18 01		18 17	18 31		18 47	19 01		19 17	19 31		19 47
Goodmayes	d			16 49	17 03		17 19	17 33		17 49	18 03		18 19	18 33		18 49	19 03		19 19	19 33		19 49
Seven Kings	d			16 51	17 05		17 21	17 35		17 51	18 05		18 21	18 35		18 51	19 05		19 21	19 35		19 51
Ilford 2	d			16 54	17 08		17 24	17 38		17 54	18 08		18 24	18 38		18 54	19 08		19 24	19 38		19 54
Manor Park	d			16 56	17 10		17 26	17 40		17 56	18 10		18 26	18 40		18 56	19 10		19 26	19 40		19 56
Forest Gate	d			16 59	17 13		17 29	17 43		17 59	18 13		18 29	18 43		18 59	19 13		19 29	19 43		19 59
Maryland	d				17 15			17 45			18 15			18 45			19 15			19 45		
Stratford 7 ⊖	d	09 50		17 02	17 17	17 20	17 32	17 47	17 50	18 02	18 17	18 20	18 32	18 47	18 50	19 02	19 17	19 20	19 32	19 47	19 50	20 02
London Liverpool Street 15 ⊖	a	09 59		17 11	17 26	17 29	17 41	17 56	17 59	18 11	18 26	18 31	18 41	18 56	18 59	19 11	19 26	19 29	19 41	19 56	19 59	20 11

		LE	LE	LE	LE	LE	LE	LE	LE	LE	LE	LE	LE	LE	LE	LE	LE	LE	LE	LE	LE
			1			1			1			1		1		1		1		1	
			A			A			A			A		A		A		A		A	
Shenfield 3	d	19 43	19 53		20 13	20 23		20 43	20 53		21 13	21 23	21 43	21 53	22 13	22 23	22 43	22 53	23 13	23 23	23 43
Brentwood	d	19 46	19 56		20 16	20 26		20 46	20 56		21 16	21 26	21 46	21 56	22 16	22 26	22 46	22 56	23 16	23 26	23 46
Harold Wood	d	19 51	20 01		20 21	20 31		20 51	21 01		21 21	21 31	21 51	22 01	22 21	22 31	22 51	23 01	23 21	23 31	23 51
Gidea Park 2	d	19 55	20 05	20 11	20 25	20 35	20 41	20 55	21 05	21 11	21 25	21 35	21 55	22 05	22 25	22 35	22 55	23 05	23 25	23 35	23 55
Romford	d	19 57	20 07	20 13	20 27	20 37	20 43	20 57	21 07	21 13	21 27	21 37	21 57	22 07	22 27	22 37	22 57	23 07	23 27	23 37	23 57
Chadwell Heath	d	20 01		20 17	20 31		20 47	21 01		21 17	21 31		22 01		22 31		23 01		23 31		00 01
Goodmayes	d	20 03		20 19	20 33		20 49	21 03		21 19	21 33		22 03		22 33		23 03		23 33		00 03
Seven Kings	d	20 05		20 21	20 35		20 51	21 05		21 21	21 35		22 05		22 35		23 05		23 35		00 05
Ilford 2	d	20 08		20 24	20 38		20 54	21 08		21 24	21 38		22 08		22 38		23 08		23 38		00 08
Manor Park	d	20 10		20 26	20 40		20 56	21 10		21 26	21 40		22 10		22 40		23 10		23 40		00 10
Forest Gate	d	20 13		20 29	20 43		20 59	21 13		21 29	21 43		22 13		22 43		23 13		23 43		00 13
Maryland	d	20 15			20 45			21 15			21 45		22 15		22 45		23 15		23 45		00 15
Stratford 7 ⊖	d	20 17	20 20	20 32	20 47	20 50	21 02	21 17	21 20	21 32	21 47	21 50	22 17	22 20	22 47	22 50	23 17	23 20	23 47	23 50	00 17
London Liverpool Street 15 ⊖	a	20 26	20 29	20 41	20 56	20 59	21 11	21 26	21 29	21 41	21 56	21 59	22 26	22 29	22 56	22 59	23 26	23 31	23 56	23 59	00 26

A From Southend Victoria
B From Colchester Town
C From Ipswich
D From Southminster
E not 8 December. From Shenfield
F From Colchester

Table 6

Mondays to Fridays

9 December to 16 May

London Liverpool Street - Shenfield - Wickford - Southminster - Southend

Network Diagram - refer to first Page of Table 5

Miles	Miles	Station																							
				LE	LE	LE	LE	LE	LE	LE	LE	LE		LE	LE	LE	LE	LE	LE	LE	LE	LE		LE	LE
				MO	TW ThO	MO	MX	MX	MO	MX	MO	MX		MX	MO										
				1	1	1	1	1	1		1	1		1	1	1		◇1	1			1			◇1
0	0	**London Liverpool Street** 15 ⊖	d	00 02		00 14	00 15	00 18		00 20	00 44	00 46		00 50			00 55	05 23		05 28	05 37	05 55		06 00	06 02
4	4	Stratford 7 ⊖	d	00 09		00 21	00 22	00 25		00 27	00 51	00 53		00 57			01 02	05 30		05 35	05 44	06 02		06 07	06 09
12½	—	Romford	d			00 34	00 32		←	00 46	01 04			01 08	←		01 21	05 38		05 48	06 03			06 26	
20¼	—	**Shenfield** 3	a	00 31		00 51	00 44	00 47	00 51	01 03	01 21	01 17		01 20	01 21		01 38	05 47		06 04	06 20	06 18		06 43	06 24
—	—	**Shenfield**	d			00 51	00 45		00 51		01 21			01 20	01 21				05 55	06 04		06 19			
24¼	—	Billericay	d			→	00 51		00 57		→			01 26	01 27				06 01	06 10		06 25			
29	29	**Wickford** 2	d				00 56		01 03					01 31	01 33	05 16			06 09	06 16		06 31			
—	31½	Battlesbridge	d													05 20			06 13						
—	34	South Woodham Ferrers	d													05 24			06 17						
—	37¼	North Fambridge	d													05 41			06 24						
—	40¼	Althorne	d													05 46			06 29						
—	43¼	Burnham-on-Crouch	d													05 51			06 34						
—	45½	**Southminster**	a													05 57			06 40						
33	—	Rayleigh	d		00 04		01 01		01 08					01 36	01 38					06 21		06 36			
36	—	Hockley	d		00 09		01 06		01 12					01 41	01 42					06 26		06 41			
38¾	—	Rochford	d		00 12		01 09		01 16					01 44	01 46					06 29		06 44			
39¾	—	Southend Airport ✈	d		00 15		01 12		01 18					01 47	01 48					06 33		06 47			
41	—	Prittlewell	d		00 18		01 15							01 50						06 35		06 50			
41½	—	**Southend Victoria**	a		00 26		01 23		01 29					01 58	01 59					06 39		06 54			

Station																									
		LE	LE	LE	LE	LE	LE	LE		LE	LE	LE	LE	LE	LE	LE	LE	LE		LE	LE	LE	LE	LE	LE
		1		1	1			1		1		1		1	1		1	1			1	◇1			1
London Liverpool Street 15 ⊖	d		06 10	06 12	06 15	06 20	06 30	06 35		06 38	06 40	06 48	06 50	06 55		07 00	07 02	07 08		07 10	07 13	07 18	07 20	07 30	07 33
Stratford 7 ⊖	d		06 17	06 19	06 22	06 27	06 37	06 42		06 45	06 47	06 55	06 57	07 02		07 07	07 09	07 15		07 17	07 20	07 25	07 27	07 37	07 42
Romford	d		06 36			06 46	06 56				07 06		07 16			07 26				07 36	07 28		07 46	07 56	
Shenfield 3	a		06 53	06 35	06 38	07 03	07 13	06 58		07 00	07 23	07 11	07 33	07 18		07 43	07 24	07 30		07 53	07 38	07 40	08 03	08 13	07 59
Shenfield	d	06 32			06 39			06 59						07 19							07 39				07 59
Billericay	d	06 38			06 45			07 05						07 25							07 45				08 05
Wickford 2	d	06 46			06 51			07 11						07 31	07 36						07 51				08 11
Battlesbridge	d	06 50													07 40										
South Woodham Ferrers	d	06 54													07 44										
North Fambridge	d	07 03													07 53										
Althorne	d	07 08													07 58										
Burnham-on-Crouch	d	07 13													08 03										
Southminster	a	07 19													08 09										
Rayleigh	d				06 56			07 16						07 36							07 56				08 16
Hockley	d				07 01			07 21						07 41							08 01				08 21
Rochford	d				07 04			07 24						07 44							08 04				08 24
Southend Airport ✈	d				07 07			07 27						07 47							08 07				08 27
Prittlewell	d				07 10			07 30						07 50							08 10				08 30
Southend Victoria	a				07 14			07 34						07 54							08 16				08 34

Station																									
		LE	LE	LE		LE	LE	LE	LE	LE	LE	LE	LE	LE		LE	LE	LE	LE	LE	LE	LE	LE	LE	
		1	1			1		1		1	1		1	1		◇1			1	1		1		1	
London Liverpool Street 15 ⊖	d		07 36	07 40		07 46	07 50	07 57	08 00	08 00	08 06	08 10	08 13			08 17	08 20	08 30	08 32	08 36	08 40	08 48	08 50	08 55	
Stratford 7 ⊖	d		07 45	07 47		07 54	07 57	08 05	08 07	08 08	08 14	08 17	08 21			08 25	08 27	08 37	08 42	08 45	08 47	08 55	08 57	09 02	
Romford	d			08 06			08 16		08 26			08 36					08 46	08 56			09 06		09 16		
Shenfield 3	a		08 01	08 25		08 10	08 35	08 22	08 43	08 25	08 30	08 53	08 38			08 41	09 03	09 13	08 59	09 01	09 23	09 11	09 33	09 18	
Shenfield	d							08 22					08 39						08 59					09 19	
Billericay	d							08 28					08 45						09 05					09 25	
Wickford 2	d	08 16						08 34					08 51	08 56					09 11					09 31	
Battlesbridge	d	08 20												09 00											
South Woodham Ferrers	d	08 24												09 04											
North Fambridge	d	08 31												09 11											
Althorne	d	08 36												09 16											
Burnham-on-Crouch	d	08 41												09 21											
Southminster	a	08 47												09 27											
Rayleigh	d							08 39					08 56						09 16					09 36	
Hockley	d							08 44					09 01						09 21					09 41	
Rochford	d							08 47					09 04						09 24					09 44	
Southend Airport ✈	d							08 50					09 07						09 27					09 47	
Prittlewell	d							08 53					09 10						09 30					09 50	
Southend Victoria	a							08 57					09 14						09 34					09 54	

Station																									
		LE	LE	LE	LE	LE	LE	LE	LE	LE		LE	LE	LE	LE	LE	LE	LE	LE	LE		LE	LE	LE	LE
		1		1		1	◇1			1		1	1		1		1		1			1	1	◇1	
London Liverpool Street 15 ⊖	d		09 00	09 02	09 10	09 13	09 18	09 20	09 30	09 34			09 38	09 40	09 48	09 50	09 55	10 00	10 02	10 10		10 13		10 18	10 20
Stratford 7 ⊖	d		09 07	09 09	09 17	09 21	09 25	09 27	09 37	09 42			09 45	09 47	09 55	09 57	10 02	10 07	10 09	10 17		10 20		10 25	10 27
Romford	d		09 26		09 36			09 46	09 56				09 53	10 06		10 16		10 26		10 36		10 28			10 46
Shenfield 3	a		09 43	09 24	09 53	09 38	09 40	10 03	10 13	09 58			10 02	10 23	10 11	10 33	10 19	10 43	10 24	10 53		10 38		10 40	11 03
Shenfield	d					09 39				09 59							10 19					10 39			
Billericay	d					09 45				10 05							10 25					10 45			
Wickford 2	d	09 36				09 51				10 11		10 16					10 31					10 51	10 56		
Battlesbridge	d	09 40										10 20											11 00		
South Woodham Ferrers	d	09 44										10 24											11 04		
North Fambridge	d	09 51										10 31											11 11		
Althorne	d	09 56										10 36											11 16		
Burnham-on-Crouch	d	10 01										10 41											11 21		
Southminster	a	10 07										10 47											11 27		
Rayleigh	d					09 56				10 16							10 36					10 56			
Hockley	d					10 01				10 21							10 41					11 01			
Rochford	d					10 04				10 24							10 44					11 04			
Southend Airport ✈	d					10 07				10 27							10 47					11 07			
Prittlewell	d					10 10				10 30							10 50					11 10			
Southend Victoria	a					10 14				10 34							10 54					11 14			

Table 6

Mondays to Fridays

9 December to 16 May

London Liverpool Street - Shenfield - Wickford - Southminster - Southend

Network Diagram - refer to first Page of Table 5

	LE	LE 1	LE 1	LE	LE 1		LE	LE 1	LE 1	LE	LE 1	LE	LE 1	LE ◇1	LE		LE	LE 1	LE 1	LE 1	LE	LE 1	LE	LE 1
London Liverpool Street 15 ⊖ d	10 30	10 35	10 38	10 40	10 48		10 50	10 55		11 00	11 02	11 10	11 13	11 18	11 20		11 30	11 35		11 38	11 40	11 48	11 50	11 55
Stratford 7 ⊖ d	10 37	10 42	10 45	10 47	10 55		10 57	11 02		11 07	11 09	11 17	11 20	11 25	11 27		11 37	11 42		11 45	11 47	11 55	11 57	12 02
Romford d	10 56		10 53	11 06			11 16			11 26		11 36	11 28		11 46		11 56			11 53	12 06		12 16	
Shenfield 3 a	11 13	10 58	11 02	11 23	11 11		11 33	11 18		11 43	11 24	11 53	11 38	11 40	12 03		12 13	11 58		12 02	12 23	12 11	12 33	12 18
Shenfield d		10 59						11 19					11 39					11 59						12 19
Billericay d		11 05						11 25					11 45					12 05						12 25
Wickford 2 d		11 11						11 31	11 36				11 51					12 11	12 16					12 31
Battlesbridge d									11 40										12 20					
South Woodham Ferrers d									11 44										12 24					
North Fambridge d									11 51										12 31					
Althorne d									11 56										12 36					
Burnham-on-Crouch d									12 01										12 41					
Southminster a									12 07										12 47					
Rayleigh d		11 16						11 36					11 56					12 16						12 36
Hockley d		11 21						11 41					12 01					12 21						12 41
Rochford d		11 24						11 44					12 04					12 24						12 44
Southend Airport ✈ d		11 27						11 47					12 07					12 27						12 47
Prittlewell d		11 30						11 50					12 10					12 30						12 50
Southend Victoria a		11 34						11 54					12 14					12 34						12 54

	LE		LE 1	LE	LE 1	LE 1	LE ◇1	LE	LE	LE 1	LE 1		LE	LE 1	LE	LE 1	LE 1	LE	LE 1	LE	LE 1		LE ◇1	LE
London Liverpool Street 15 ⊖ d	12 00		12 02	12 10	12 13		12 18	12 20	12 30	12 35	12 38		12 40	12 48	12 50	12 55		13 00	13 02	13 10	13 13		13 18	13 20
Stratford 7 ⊖ d	12 07		12 09	12 17	12 20		12 25	12 27	12 37	12 42	12 45		12 47	12 55	12 57	13 02		13 07	13 09	13 17	13 20		13 25	13 27
Romford d	12 26			12 36	12 28			12 46	12 56		12 53		13 06		13 16			13 26		13 36	13 28			13 46
Shenfield 3 a	12 43		12 24	12 53	12 38		12 40	13 03	13 13	12 58	13 02		13 23	13 11	13 33	13 19		13 43	13 24	13 53	13 38		13 40	14 03
Shenfield d					12 39					12 59						13 19					13 39			
Billericay d					12 45					13 05						13 25					13 45			
Wickford 2 d					12 51	12 56				13 11						13 31	13 36				13 51			
Battlesbridge d						13 00											13 40							
South Woodham Ferrers d						13 04											13 44							
North Fambridge d						13 11											13 51							
Althorne d						13 16											13 56							
Burnham-on-Crouch d						13 21											14 01							
Southminster a						13 27											14 07							
Rayleigh d					12 56					13 16						13 36					13 56			
Hockley d					13 01					13 21						13 41					14 01			
Rochford d					13 04					13 24						13 44					14 04			
Southend Airport ✈ d					13 07					13 27						13 47					14 07			
Prittlewell d					13 10					13 30						13 50					14 10			
Southend Victoria a					13 14					13 34						13 54					14 14			

	LE	LE 1	LE 1	LE 1	LE	LE 1	LE		LE 1	LE	LE 1	LE	LE 1	LE 1	LE ◇1	LE	LE		LE 1	LE 1	LE	LE 1	LE	LE 1
London Liverpool Street 15 ⊖ d	13 30	13 35		13 38	13 40	13 48	13 50		13 55	14 00	14 02	14 10	14 13		14 18	14 20	14 30		14 35	14 38	14 40	14 48	14 50	14 55
Stratford 7 ⊖ d	13 37	13 42		13 45	13 47	13 55	13 57		14 02	14 07	14 09	14 17	14 20		14 25	14 27	14 37		14 42	14 45	14 47	14 55	14 57	15 02
Romford d	13 56			13 53	14 06		14 16			14 26		14 36	14 28			14 46	14 56			14 53	15 06		15 16	
Shenfield 3 a	14 13	13 58		14 02	14 23	14 11	14 33		14 18	14 43	14 24	14 53	14 38		14 40	15 03	15 13		14 58	15 02	15 23	15 11	15 33	15 18
Shenfield d		13 59							14 19				14 39						14 59					15 19
Billericay d		14 05							14 25				14 45						15 05					15 25
Wickford 2 d		14 11	14 16						14 31				14 51	14 56					15 11					15 31
Battlesbridge d			14 20											15 00										
South Woodham Ferrers d			14 24											15 04										
North Fambridge d			14 31											15 11										
Althorne d			14 36											15 16										
Burnham-on-Crouch d			14 41											15 21										
Southminster a			14 47											15 27										
Rayleigh d		14 16							14 36				14 56						15 16					15 36
Hockley d		14 21							14 41				15 01						15 21					15 41
Rochford d		14 24							14 44				15 04						15 24					15 44
Southend Airport ✈ d		14 27							14 47				15 07						15 27					15 47
Prittlewell d		14 30							14 50				15 10						15 30					15 50
Southend Victoria a		14 34							14 54				15 14						15 34					15 54

	LE 1	LE	LE 1		LE	LE 1	LE ◇1	LE	LE	LE 1	LE 1	LE 1	LE		LE 1	LE	LE 1	LE	LE 1	LE	LE 1	LE ◇1	LE 1	
London Liverpool Street 15 ⊖ d		15 00	15 02		15 10	15 13	15 18	15 20	15 30	15 35		15 38	15 40		15 48	15 50	15 55	16 00	16 02	16 10	16 10	16 14	16 17	
Stratford 7 ⊖ d		15 07	15 09		15 17	15 20	15 25	15 27	15 37	15 42		15 45	15 47		15 55	15 57	16 02	16 07	16 09	16 17	16 18	16 22	16 25	
Romford d		15 26			15 36	15 28		15 46	15 56			15 53	16 06			16 16		16 26		16 36				
Shenfield 3 a		15 43	15 24		15 53	15 38	15 40	16 03	16 13	15 58		16 02	16 23		16 11	16 33	16 18	16 43	16 24	16 53	16 34	16 38	16 41	
Shenfield d						15 39				15 59							16 19				16 34			
Billericay d						15 45				16 05							16 25				16 41			
Wickford 2 d	15 36					15 51				16 11	16 14						16 31				16 48			
Battlesbridge d	15 40										16 18													
South Woodham Ferrers d	15 44										16 22													
North Fambridge d	15 51										16 29													
Althorne d	15 56										16 34													
Burnham-on-Crouch d	16 01										16 39													
Southminster a	16 07										16 45													
Rayleigh d						15 56				16 16							16 36				16 53			
Hockley d						16 01				16 21							16 41				16 57			
Rochford d						16 04				16 24							16 44				17 01			
Southend Airport ✈ d						16 07				16 27							16 47				17 03			
Prittlewell d						16 10				16 31							16 50				17 06			
Southend Victoria a						16 14				16 34							16 54				17 15			

Table 6

Mondays to Fridays

9 December to 16 May

London Liverpool Street - Shenfield - Wickford - Southminster - Southend

Network Diagram - refer to first Page of Table 5

		LE	LE 1	LE 1	LE 1	LE 1	LE	LE 1	LE	LE 1		LE 1	LE	LE ◇1	LE 1	LE	LE 1	LE	LE 1	LE 1		LE 1	LE	LE 1	LE
London Liverpool Street [15] ⊖	d	16 20	16 24		16 32	16 34	16 36	16 40	16 47	16 47		16 54	16 57	17 02	17 04	17 07	17 15	17 17	17 20	17 22		17 25	17 27	17 34	17 36
Stratford [7] ⊖	d	16 27	16 31			16 42	16 43	16 48	16 54	16 55		17 02	17 04	17 10	17 13	17 14	17 23	17 24	17 29	17 32		17 34	17 34	17 43	17 43
Romford	d	16 46					17 00		17 10				17 20			17 30		17 40					17 50		18 00
Shenfield [3]	a	17 03	16 49		16 54	16 58	17 19	17 04	17 29	17 11		17 19	17 39	17 26	17 30	17 49	17 39	17 59	17 45			17 51	18 09	17 59	18 19
Shenfield	d		16 49					17 04				17 19			17 30		17 39					17 52		18 00	
Billericay	d		16 56					17 11				17 26			17 37		17 46					17 58		18 06	
Wickford [2]	d		17 03	17 06				17 18				17 33			17 44		17 53			18 00		18 05		18 13	
Battlesbridge	d			17 10																18 04					
South Woodham Ferrers	d			17 14																18 08					
North Fambridge	d			17 21																18 14					
Althorne	d			17 26																18 19					
Burnham-on-Crouch	d			17 31																18 24					
Southminster	a			17 37																18 32					
Rayleigh	d		17 08					17 23				17 38			17 49		17 58					18 10		18 18	
Hockley	d		17 12					17 27				17 42			17 53		18 02					18 15		18 23	
Rochford	d		17 16					17 31				17 46			17 57		18 06					18 18		18 26	
Southend Airport ✈	d		17 18					17 33				17 48			17 59		18 08					18 21		18 29	
Prittlewell	d		17 21					17 36				17 51			18 02		18 11					18 24		18 32	
Southend Victoria	a		17 27					17 42				17 57			18 08		18 17					18 30		18 38	

		LE 1	LE 1	LE	LE	LE 1		LE	LE 1	LE 1	LE 1	LE	LE	LE 1	LE	LE 1		LE 1	LE	LE 1	LE	LE ◇1	LE	LE 1	LE 1
London Liverpool Street [15] ⊖	d	17 40	17 45	17 46	17 49	17 54		17 56	18 00	18 02	18 05		18 07	18 14	18 17	18 20		18 25	18 27	18 35	18 37	18 38	18 40	18 41	18 45
Stratford [7] ⊖	d		17 53	17 53	17 56	18 03		18 03	18 09	18 12	18 14		18 14	18 23	18 24	18 29		18 33	18 34	18 43	18 44	18 46	18 47	18 49	18 53
Romford	d			18 10	18 14			18 20				←	18 30		18 40				18 50		19 00		19 04		
Shenfield [3]	a	18 05	18 09	18 29	18 33	18 19		18 39	18 25		18 31	18 33	18 49	18 40	18 59	18 45		18 50	19 09	18 59	19 19	19 02	19 23		19 10
Shenfield	d		18 09		18 36	18 20					18 31	18 36		18 41				18 50		18 59					19 10
Billericay	d		18 16		→	18 26					18 38	18 42		18 47				18 57		19 06					19 17
Wickford [2]	d		18 23			18 33				18 41	18 45	18 49		18 54				19 04		19 13				19 19	19 24
Battlesbridge	d									18 45														19 23	
South Woodham Ferrers	d									18 49														19 27	
North Fambridge	d									18 55														19 34	
Althorne	d									19 00														19 39	
Burnham-on-Crouch	d									19 05														19 44	
Southminster	a									19 13														19 52	
Rayleigh	d		18 28			18 38					18 50	18 54		18 59				19 09		19 18					19 29
Hockley	d		18 32			18 43					18 55	18 59		19 04				19 13		19 22					19 33
Rochford	d		18 36			18 46					18 58	19 02		19 07				19 17		19 26					19 37
Southend Airport ✈	d		18 38			18 49					19 01	19 06		19 10				19 19		19 28					19 39
Prittlewell	d		18 41			18 52					19 04	19 08		19 13				19 22		19 31					19 42
Southend Victoria	a		18 47			18 58					19 10	19 14		19 19				19 28		19 37					19 47

		LE		LE 1	LE	LE	LE 1	LE	LE 1	LE ◇1	LE	LE		LE 1	LE 1	LE 1	LE	LE 1	LE	LE 1	LE	LE ◇1		LE	LE 1
London Liverpool Street [15] ⊖	d	18 47		18 55	18 57	19 00	19 02	19 10	19 15	19 18	19 20	19 30		19 35		19 38	19 40	19 48	19 50	19 55	20 00	20 02		20 10	20 13
Stratford [7] ⊖	d	18 54		19 03	19 04	19 07	19 09	19 17	19 22	19 25	19 27	19 37		19 42		19 45	19 47	19 55	19 57	20 02	20 07	20 09		20 17	20 20
Romford	d	19 10			19 20	19 26		19 36			19 46	19 56					20 06		20 16		20 26			20 36	20 28
Shenfield [3]	a	19 29		19 20	19 39	19 43	19 24	19 53	19 38	19 40	20 03	20 13		19 58		20 00	20 23	20 11	20 33	20 18	20 43	20 24		20 53	20 38
Shenfield	d			19 20					19 39					19 59						20 19					20 39
Billericay	d			19 27					19 45					20 05						20 25					20 45
Wickford [2]	d			19 34					19 51					20 11	20 16					20 31					20 51
Battlesbridge	d														20 20										
South Woodham Ferrers	d														20 24										
North Fambridge	d														20 31										
Althorne	d														20 36										
Burnham-on-Crouch	d														20 41										
Southminster	a														20 47										
Rayleigh	d			19 39					19 56					20 16						20 36					20 56
Hockley	d			19 43					20 01					20 21						20 41					21 01
Rochford	d			19 47					20 04					20 24						20 44					21 04
Southend Airport ✈	d			19 49					20 07					20 27						20 47					21 07
Prittlewell	d			19 52					20 10					20 30						20 50					21 10
Southend Victoria	a			19 58					20 14					20 34						20 54					21 14

		LE 1	LE ◇1	LE	LE	LE 1	LE 1	LE		LE 1	LE	LE 1	LE 1	LE	LE 1	LE	LE 1	LE ◇1		LE	LE	LE 1	LE 1	LE 1	LE
London Liverpool Street [15] ⊖	d		20 18	20 20	20 30	20 35	20 38	20 40		20 48	20 50	20 55		21 00	21 02	21 10	21 13	21 18		21 20	21 30	21 35		21 38	21 40
Stratford [7] ⊖	d		20 25	20 27	20 37	20 42	20 45	20 47		20 55	20 57	21 02		21 07	21 09	21 17	21 20	21 25		21 27	21 37	21 42		21 45	21 47
Romford	d			20 46	20 56		20 53	21 06			21 16			21 26		21 36	21 28			21 46	21 56			21 53	22 06
Shenfield [3]	a		20 40	21 03	21 13	20 58	21 02	21 23		21 11	21 33	21 18		21 43	21 24	21 53	21 38	21 40		22 03	22 13	21 58		22 02	22 23
Shenfield	d					20 59						21 19					21 39					21 59			
Billericay	d					21 05						21 25					21 45					22 05			
Wickford [2]	d	20 56				21 11						21 31	21 36				21 51					22 11	22 16		
Battlesbridge	d	21 00											21 40										22 20		
South Woodham Ferrers	d	21 04											21 44										22 24		
North Fambridge	d	21 11											21 51										22 31		
Althorne	d	21 16											21 56										22 36		
Burnham-on-Crouch	d	21 21											22 01										22 41		
Southminster	a	21 27											22 07										22 47		
Rayleigh	d					21 16						21 36					21 56					22 16			
Hockley	d					21 21						21 41					22 01					22 21			
Rochford	d					21 24						21 44					22 04					22 24			
Southend Airport ✈	d					21 27						21 47					22 07					22 27			
Prittlewell	d					21 30						21 50					22 10					22 30			
Southend Victoria	a					21 34						21 54					22 14					22 34			

Table 6

Mondays to Fridays

9 December to 16 May

London Liverpool Street - Shenfield - Wickford - Southminster - Southend

Network Diagram - refer to first Page of Table 5

		LE	LE	LE	LE	LE	LE	LE	LE	LE	LE	LE	LE	LE	LE	LE	LE	LE	LE	LE	LE	LE
													ThFO	MT WO		ThFO	MT WO		ThFO	MT WO	ThFO	MT WO
		1		1	1		1	1	◇1			1	1	1		1	1		1	1	◇1	◇1
London Liverpool Street 15 ⊖	d	21 48	21 50	21 55	22 02	22 05	22 13		22 18	22 20	22 35	22 38	22 45	22 45	22 50	23 02	23 02	23 05	23 15	23 15	23 18	23 18
Stratford 7 ⊖	d	21 55	21 57	22 02	22 09	22 12	22 20		22 25	22 27	22 42	22 45	22 52	22 52	22 57	23 09	23 09	23 12	23 22	23 22	23 25	23 25
Romford	d		22 16			22 31	22 28			22 46	23 01				23 16			23 31				
Shenfield 3	a	22 11	22 33	22 18	22 24	22 48	22 38		22 40	23 03	23 18	23 00	23 08	23 16	23 33	23 24	23 31	23 48	23 38	23 46	23 40	23 49
Shenfield	d			22 19			22 39						23 09	23 17					23 39	23 47		
Billericay	d			22 25			22 45						23 15	23 23					23 45	23 53		
Wickford 2	d			22 31			22 51	22 56					23 21	23 29					23 51	23 59		
Battlesbridge	d							23 00														
South Woodham Ferrers	d							23 04														
North Fambridge	d							23 11														
Althorne	d							23 16														
Burnham-on-Crouch	d							23 21														
Southminster	a							23 27														
Rayleigh	d			22 36			22 56						23 26	23 34					23 56	00 04		
Hockley	d			22 41			23 01						23 31	23 39					00 01	00 09		
Rochford	d			22 44			23 04						23 34	23 42					00 04	00 12		
Southend Airport ✈	d			22 47			23 07						23 37	23 45					00 07	00 15		
Prittlewell	d			22 50			23 10						23 40	23 48					00 10	00 18		
Southend Victoria	a			22 54			23 14						23 48	23 56					00 18	00 26		

		LE	LE	LE	LE	LE	LE	LE
				ThFO	MT WO	ThFO	MT WO	
				1	1	1	1	
London Liverpool Street 15 ⊖	d	23 20	23 35	23 45	23 45	23 48	23 48	23 50
Stratford 7 ⊖	d	23 27	23 42	23 52	23 52	23 55	23 55	23 57
Romford	d	23 46	00 01					00 16
Shenfield 3	a	00 03	00 18	00 08	00 16	00 10	00 19	00 33
Shenfield	d			00 09	00 17			
Billericay	d			00 15	00 23			
Wickford 2	d			00 21	00 29			
Battlesbridge	d							
South Woodham Ferrers	d							
North Fambridge	d							
Althorne	d							
Burnham-on-Crouch	d							
Southminster	a							
Rayleigh	d			00 26	00 34			
Hockley	d			00 31	00 39			
Rochford	d			00 34	00 42			
Southend Airport ✈	d			00 37	00 45			
Prittlewell	d			00 40	00 48			
Southend Victoria	a			00 48	00 56			

Saturdays

14 December to 17 May

		LE	LE	LE	LE	LE	LE	LE	LE	LE	LE	LE	LE	LE	LE	LE	LE	LE	LE	LE	LE	LE	LE
		1	1		1	1	1		1		1		1		1		◇1	1	1		1	1	1
London Liverpool Street 15 ⊖	d	00 15	00 18	00 20	00 46	00 50		00 55		05 28	05 34	05 40	06 02	06 05		06 10	06 18	06 35	06 38	06 40	06 48	06 55	
Stratford 7 ⊖	d	00 22	00 25	00 27	00 53	00 57		01 02		05 35	05 41	05 47	06 09	06 12		06 17	06 25	06 42	06 45	06 47	06 55	07 02	
Romford	d	00 32		00 46		01 08		01 21		05 48	05 49	06 06				06 36			06 53	07 06			
Shenfield 3	a	00 44	00 47	01 03	01 17	01 20		01 38		06 04	05 58	06 23	06 24	06 30		06 53	06 40	06 58	07 02	07 23	07 11	07 18	
Shenfield	d	00 45				01 20				06 04				06 30				06 59				07 19	
Billericay	d	00 51				01 26				06 10				06 36				07 05				07 25	
Wickford 2	d	00 56				01 31	05 36		06 12	06 16				06 43	06 56			07 11				07 31	07 36
Battlesbridge	d						05 40		06 16						07 00								07 40
South Woodham Ferrers	d						05 44		06 20						07 04								07 44
North Fambridge	d						05 51		06 31						07 11								07 51
Althorne	d						05 56		06 36						07 16								07 56
Burnham-on-Crouch	d						06 01		06 41						07 21								08 01
Southminster	a						06 07		06 47						07 27								08 07
Rayleigh	d	01 01				01 36				06 22				06 48				07 16				07 36	
Hockley	d	01 06				01 41				06 26				06 53				07 21				07 41	
Rochford	d	01 09				01 44				06 30				06 56				07 24				07 44	
Southend Airport ✈	d	01 12				01 47				06 33				06 59				07 27				07 47	
Prittlewell	d	01 15				01 50				06 35				07 02				07 30				07 50	
Southend Victoria	a	01 23				01 58				06 39				07 05				07 34				07 54	

Table 6

Saturdays

14 December to 17 May

London Liverpool Street - Shenfield - Wickford - Southminster - Southend

Network Diagram - refer to first Page of Table 5

	LE		LE 1	LE	LE 1	LE ◇1	LE	LE	LE 1	LE 1	LE 1		LE	LE 1	LE	LE 1	LE	LE 1	LE	LE 1	LE 1		LE ◇1	LE
London Liverpool Street 15 ⊖ d	07 00		07 02	07 10	07 13	07 18	07 20	07 30	07 35		07 38		07 40	07 48	07 50	07 55	08 00	08 02	08 10	08 13			08 18	08 20
Stratford 7 ⊖ d	07 07		07 09	07 17	07 20	07 25	07 27	07 37	07 42		07 45		07 47	07 55	07 57	08 02	08 07	08 09	08 17	08 20			08 25	08 27
Romford d	07 26			07 36	07 28		07 46	07 56			07 53		08 06		08 16		08 26		08 36	08 28				08 46
Shenfield 3 a	07 43		07 24	07 53	07 38	07 40	08 03	08 13	07 58		08 02		08 23	08 11	08 33	08 18	08 43	08 24	08 53	08 38			08 40	09 03
Shenfield d					07 39				07 59							08 19				08 39				
Billericay d					07 45				08 05							08 25				08 45				
Wickford 2 d					07 51				08 11	08 16						08 31				08 51	08 56			
Battlesbridge d										08 20											09 00			
South Woodham Ferrers d										08 24											09 04			
North Fambridge d										08 31											09 11			
Althorne d										08 36											09 16			
Burnham-on-Crouch d										08 41											09 21			
Southminster a										08 47											09 27			
Rayleigh d					07 56				08 16							08 36				08 56				
Hockley d					08 01				08 21							08 41				09 01				
Rochford d					08 04				08 24							08 44				09 04				
Southend Airport ✈ d					08 07				08 27							08 47				09 07				
Prittlewell d					08 10				08 30							08 50				09 10				
Southend Victoria a					08 14				08 34							08 54				09 14				

	LE	LE 1	LE 1	LE	LE 1	LE	LE 1		LE 1	LE	LE 1	LE	LE 1	LE ◇1	LE	LE	LE 1		LE 1	LE 1	LE	LE 1	LE	LE 1
London Liverpool Street 15 ⊖ d	08 30	08 35	08 38	08 40	08 48	08 50	08 55			09 00	09 02	09 10	09 13	09 18	09 20	09 30	09 35			09 38	09 40	09 48	09 50	09 55
Stratford 7 ⊖ d	08 37	08 42	08 45	08 47	08 55	08 57	09 02			09 07	09 09	09 17	09 20	09 25	09 27	09 37	09 42			09 45	09 47	09 55	09 57	10 02
Romford d	08 56		08 53	09 06		09 16				09 26		09 36	09 28		09 46	09 56				09 53	10 06		10 16	
Shenfield 3 a	09 13	08 58	09 02	09 23	09 11	09 33	09 18			09 43	09 24	09 53	09 38	09 40	10 03	10 13	09 58			10 02	10 23	10 11	10 33	10 18
Shenfield d		08 59					09 19						09 39				09 59							10 19
Billericay d		09 05					09 25						09 45				10 05							10 25
Wickford 2 d		09 11					09 31		09 36				09 51				10 11		10 16					10 31
Battlesbridge d									09 40										10 20					
South Woodham Ferrers d									09 44										10 24					
North Fambridge d									09 51										10 31					
Althorne d									09 56										10 36					
Burnham-on-Crouch d									10 01										10 41					
Southminster a									10 07										10 47					
Rayleigh d		09 16					09 36						09 56				10 16							10 36
Hockley d		09 21					09 41						10 01				10 21							10 41
Rochford d		09 24					09 44						10 04				10 24							10 44
Southend Airport ✈ d		09 27					09 47						10 07				10 27							10 47
Prittlewell d		09 30					09 50						10 10				10 30							10 50
Southend Victoria a		09 34					09 54						10 14				10 34							10 54

	LE	LE 1	LE		LE 1	LE 1	LE ◇1	LE	LE	LE 1	LE 1	LE	LE 1		LE	LE 1	LE 1	LE	LE 1	LE	LE 1	LE ◇1	LE	
London Liverpool Street 15 ⊖ d	10 00	10 02	10 10		10 13		10 18	10 20	10 30	10 35	10 38	10 40	10 48		10 50	10 55		11 00	11 02	11 10	11 13	11 18	11 20	
Stratford 7 ⊖ d	10 07	10 09	10 17		10 20		10 25	10 27	10 37	10 42	10 45	10 47	10 55		10 57	11 02		11 07	11 09	11 17	11 20	11 25	11 27	
Romford d	10 26		10 36		10 28			10 46	10 56		10 53	11 06			11 16			11 26		11 36	11 28		11 46	
Shenfield 3 a	10 43	10 24	10 53		10 38		10 40	11 03	11 13	10 58	11 02	11 23	11 11		11 33	11 18		11 43	11 24	11 53	11 38	11 40	12 03	
Shenfield d					10 39					10 59						11 19					11 39			
Billericay d					10 45					11 05						11 25					11 45			
Wickford 2 d					10 51	10 56				11 11						11 31	11 36				11 51			
Battlesbridge d						11 00											11 40							
South Woodham Ferrers d						11 04											11 44							
North Fambridge d						11 11											11 51							
Althorne d						11 16											11 56							
Burnham-on-Crouch d						11 21											12 01							
Southminster a						11 27											12 07							
Rayleigh d					10 56					11 16						11 36					11 56			
Hockley d					11 01					11 21						11 41					12 01			
Rochford d					11 04					11 24						11 44					12 04			
Southend Airport ✈ d					11 07					11 27						11 47					12 07			
Prittlewell d					11 10					11 30						11 50					12 10			
Southend Victoria a					11 14					11 34						11 54					12 14			

	LE	LE 1	LE 1	LE 1	LE	LE 1	LE	LE 1	LE		LE 1	LE	LE 1	LE 1	LE ◇1	LE	LE	LE 1	LE 1		LE	LE 1	LE	LE 1
London Liverpool Street 15 ⊖ d	11 30	11 35		11 38	11 40	11 48	11 50	11 55	12 00		12 02	12 10	12 13		12 18	12 20	12 30	12 35	12 38		12 40	12 48	12 50	12 55
Stratford 7 ⊖ d	11 37	11 42		11 45	11 47	11 55	11 57	12 02	12 07		12 09	12 17	12 20		12 25	12 27	12 37	12 42	12 45		12 47	12 55	12 57	13 02
Romford d	11 56			11 53	12 06		12 16		12 26			12 36	12 28			12 46	12 56		12 53		13 06		13 16	
Shenfield 3 a	12 13	11 58		12 02	12 23	12 11	12 33	12 18	12 43		12 24	12 53	12 38		12 40	13 03	13 13	12 58	13 02		13 23	13 11	13 33	13 18
Shenfield d		11 59						12 19					12 39					12 59						13 19
Billericay d		12 05						12 25					12 45					13 05						13 25
Wickford 2 d		12 11	12 16					12 31					12 51	12 56				13 11						13 31
Battlesbridge d			12 20											13 00										
South Woodham Ferrers d			12 24											13 04										
North Fambridge d			12 31											13 11										
Althorne d			12 36											13 16										
Burnham-on-Crouch d			12 41											13 21										
Southminster a			12 47											13 27										
Rayleigh d		12 16						12 36					12 56					13 16						13 36
Hockley d		12 21						12 41					13 01					13 21						13 41
Rochford d		12 24						12 44					13 04					13 24						13 44
Southend Airport ✈ d		12 27						12 47					13 07					13 27						13 47
Prittlewell d		12 30						12 50					13 10					13 30						13 50
Southend Victoria a		12 34						12 54					13 14					13 34						13 54

Table 6

Saturdays

14 December to 17 May

London Liverpool Street - Shenfield - Wickford - Southminster - Southend

Network Diagram - refer to first Page of Table 5

		LE 1	LE	LE 1	LE	LE 1		LE ◇1	LE	LE	LE 1	LE 1	LE 1	LE	LE 1	LE		LE 1	LE	LE 1	LE	LE 1	LE 1	LE ◇1	LE
London Liverpool Street 15 ⊖	d		13 00	13 02	13 10	13 13		13 18	13 20	13 30	13 35		13 38	13 40	13 48	13 50		13 55	14 00	14 02	14 10	14 13		14 18	14 20
Stratford 7 ⊖	d		13 07	13 09	13 17	13 20		13 25	13 27	13 37	13 42		13 45	13 47	13 55	13 57		14 02	14 07	14 09	14 17	14 20		14 25	14 27
Romford	d		13 26		13 36	13 28			13 46	13 56			13 53	14 06		14 16			14 26		14 36	14 28			14 46
Shenfield 3	a		13 43	13 24	13 53	13 38		13 40	14 03	14 13	13 58		14 02	14 23	14 11	14 33		14 18	14 43	14 24	14 53	14 38		14 40	15 03
Shenfield	d					13 39					13 59							14 19				14 39			
Billericay	d					13 45					14 05							14 25				14 45			
Wickford 2	d	13 36				13 51					14 11	14 16						14 31				14 51	14 56		
Battlesbridge	d	13 40										14 20											15 00		
South Woodham Ferrers	d	13 44										14 24											15 04		
North Fambridge	d	13 51										14 31											15 11		
Althorne	d	13 56										14 36											15 16		
Burnham-on-Crouch	d	14 01										14 41											15 21		
Southminster	a	14 07										14 47											15 27		
Rayleigh	d					13 56					14 16							14 36				14 56			
Hockley	d					14 01					14 21							14 41				15 01			
Rochford	d					14 04					14 24							14 44				15 04			
Southend Airport ✈	d					14 07					14 27							14 47				15 07			
Prittlewell	d					14 10					14 30							14 50				15 10			
Southend Victoria	a					14 14					14 34							14 54				15 14			

		LE		LE 1	LE 1	LE	LE 1	LE	LE 1	LE 1	LE	LE 1		LE	LE 1	LE ◇1	LE	LE	LE 1	LE 1	LE 1	LE		LE 1	LE
London Liverpool Street 15 ⊖	d	14 30		14 35	14 38	14 40	14 48	14 50	14 55		15 00	15 02		15 10	15 13	15 18	15 20	15 30	15 35		15 38	15 40		15 48	15 50
Stratford 7 ⊖	d	14 37		14 42	14 45	14 47	14 55	14 57	15 02		15 07	15 09		15 17	15 20	15 25	15 27	15 37	15 42		15 45	15 47		15 55	15 57
Romford	d	14 56			14 53	15 06		15 16			15 26			15 36	15 28		15 46	15 56			15 53	16 06			16 16
Shenfield 3	a	15 13		14 58	15 02	15 23	15 11	15 33	15 18		15 43	15 24		15 53	15 38	15 40	16 03	16 13	15 58		16 02	16 23		16 11	16 33
Shenfield	d			14 59					15 19						15 39				15 59						
Billericay	d			15 05					15 25						15 45				16 05						
Wickford 2	d			15 11					15 31	15 36					15 51				16 11	16 16					
Battlesbridge	d									15 40										16 20					
South Woodham Ferrers	d									15 44										16 24					
North Fambridge	d									15 51										16 31					
Althorne	d									15 56										16 36					
Burnham-on-Crouch	d									16 01										16 41					
Southminster	a									16 07										16 47					
Rayleigh	d			15 16					15 36						15 56				16 16						
Hockley	d			15 21					15 41						16 01				16 21						
Rochford	d			15 24					15 44						16 04				16 24						
Southend Airport ✈	d			15 27					15 47						16 07				16 27						
Prittlewell	d			15 30					15 50						16 10				16 30						
Southend Victoria	a			15 34					15 54						16 14				16 34						

		LE 1	LE	LE 1	LE	LE 1	LE 1	LE ◇1		LE	LE	LE 1	LE 1	LE	LE 1	LE	LE 1	LE 1		LE	LE 1	LE	LE 1	LE ◇1	LE
London Liverpool Street 15 ⊖	d	15 55	16 00	16 02	16 10	16 13		16 18		16 20	16 30	16 35	16 38	16 40	16 48	16 50	16 55			17 00	17 02	17 10	17 13	17 18	17 20
Stratford 7 ⊖	d	16 02	16 07	16 09	16 17	16 20		16 25		16 27	16 37	16 42	16 45	16 47	16 55	16 57	17 02			17 07	17 09	17 17	17 20	17 25	17 27
Romford	d		16 26		16 36	16 28				16 46	16 56		16 53	17 06		17 16				17 26		17 36	17 28		17 46
Shenfield 3	a	16 18	16 43	16 24	16 53	16 38		16 40		17 03	17 13	16 58	17 02	17 23	17 11	17 33	17 18			17 43	17 24	17 53	17 38	17 40	18 03
Shenfield	d	16 19				16 39						16 59					17 19						17 39		
Billericay	d	16 25				16 45						17 05					17 25						17 45		
Wickford 2	d	16 31				16 51	16 56					17 11					17 31	17 36					17 51		
Battlesbridge	d						17 00											17 40							
South Woodham Ferrers	d						17 04											17 44							
North Fambridge	d						17 11											17 51							
Althorne	d						17 16											17 56							
Burnham-on-Crouch	d						17 21											18 01							
Southminster	a						17 27											18 07							
Rayleigh	d	16 36				16 56						17 16					17 36						17 56		
Hockley	d	16 41				17 01						17 21					17 41						18 01		
Rochford	d	16 44				17 04						17 24					17 44						18 04		
Southend Airport ✈	d	16 47				17 07						17 27					17 47						18 07		
Prittlewell	d	16 50				17 10						17 30					17 50						18 10		
Southend Victoria	a	16 54				17 14						17 34					17 54						18 14		

		LE	LE 1	LE 1		LE 1	LE	LE 1	LE	LE 1	LE	LE 1	LE	LE 1		LE 1	LE ◇1	LE	LE	LE 1	LE 1	LE	LE 1	LE	
London Liverpool Street 15 ⊖	d	17 30	17 35			17 38	17 40	17 48	17 50	17 55	18 00	18 02	18 10	18 13			18 18	18 20	18 30	18 35	18 38	18 40	18 48	18 50	
Stratford 7 ⊖	d	17 37	17 42			17 45	17 47	17 55	17 57	18 02	18 07	18 09	18 17	18 20			18 25	18 27	18 37	18 42	18 45	18 47	18 55	18 57	
Romford	d	17 56				17 53	18 06		18 16		18 26		18 36	18 28				18 46	18 56		18 53	19 06		19 16	
Shenfield 3	a	18 13	17 58			18 02	18 23	18 11	18 33	18 18	18 43	18 24	18 53	18 38			18 40	19 03	19 13	18 58	19 02	19 23	19 11	19 33	
Shenfield	d		17 59							18 19				18 39						18 59					
Billericay	d		18 05							18 25				18 45						19 05					
Wickford 2	d		18 11	18 16						18 31				18 51		18 56				19 11					
Battlesbridge	d			18 20												19 00									
South Woodham Ferrers	d			18 24												19 04									
North Fambridge	d			18 31												19 11									
Althorne	d			18 36												19 16									
Burnham-on-Crouch	d			18 41												19 21									
Southminster	a			18 47												19 27									
Rayleigh	d		18 16							18 36				18 56						19 16					
Hockley	d		18 21							18 41				19 01						19 21					
Rochford	d		18 24							18 44				19 04						19 24					
Southend Airport ✈	d		18 27							18 47				19 07						19 27					
Prittlewell	d		18 30							18 50				19 10						19 30					
Southend Victoria	a		18 34							18 54				19 14						19 34					

Table 6

Saturdays

14 December to 17 May

London Liverpool Street - Shenfield - Wickford - Southminster - Southend

Network Diagram - refer to first Page of Table 5

		LE ■1	LE ■1	LE	LE ■1	LE	LE ■1	LE ◇■1	LE	LE		LE ■1	LE ■1	LE ■1	LE ■1	LE	LE ■1	LE	LE ■1	LE		LE ■1	LE	LE ■1	LE ■1
London Liverpool Street [15] ⊖	d	18 55		19 00	19 02	19 10	19 13	19 18	19 20	19 30		19 32	19 35		19 38	19 40	19 48	19 50	19 55	20 00		20 02	20 10	20 13	
Stratford [7] ⊖	d	19 02		19 07	19 09	19 17	19 20	19 25	19 27	19 37		19 39	19 43		19 46	19 47	19 55	19 57	20 02	20 07		20 09	20 17	20 20	
Romford	d			19 26		19 36	19 28		19 46	19 56					19 54	20 06		20 16		20 26			20 36	20 28	
Shenfield [3]	a	19 18		19 43	19 24	19 53	19 38	19 40	20 03	20 13		19 56	19 59		20 03	20 23	20 11	20 33	20 18	20 43		20 24	20 53	20 38	
Shenfield	d	19 19					19 39						20 00						20 19					20 39	
Billericay	d	19 25					19 45						20 06						20 25					20 45	
Wickford [2]	d	19 31	19 36				19 51						20 12	20 16					20 31					20 51	20 56
Battlesbridge	d		19 40											20 20											21 00
South Woodham Ferrers	d		19 44											20 24											21 04
North Fambridge	d		19 51											20 31											21 11
Althorne	d		19 56											20 36											21 16
Burnham-on-Crouch	d		20 01											20 41											21 21
Southminster	a		20 07											20 47											21 27
Rayleigh	d	19 36					19 56						20 17						20 36					20 56	
Hockley	d	19 41					20 01						20 22						20 41					21 01	
Rochford	d	19 44					20 04						20 25						20 44					21 04	
Southend Airport ✈	d	19 47					20 07						20 28						20 47					21 07	
Prittlewell	d	19 50					20 10						20 31						20 50					21 10	
Southend Victoria	a	19 54					20 14						20 35						20 54					21 14	

		LE ◇■1	LE	LE	LE ■1	LE ■1		LE	LE ■1	LE	LE ■1	LE ■1	LE ■1	LE	LE ■1	LE ◇■1		LE	LE ■1	LE ■1	LE	LE ■1	LE ■1	LE	LE ■1
London Liverpool Street [15] ⊖	d	20 18	20 20	20 30	20 35	20 38		20 40	20 48	20 50	20 55		21 02	21 05	21 13	21 18		21 20	21 35		21 35	21 38	21 48	21 50	21 55
Stratford [7] ⊖	d	20 25	20 27	20 37	20 42	20 45		20 47	20 55	20 57	21 02		21 09	21 12	21 20	21 25		21 27	21 42		21 42	21 45	21 55	21 57	22 02
Romford	d		20 46	20 56		20 53		21 06		21 16				21 31	21 28			21 46			22 01	21 53		22 16	
Shenfield [3]	a	20 40	21 03	21 13	20 58	21 02		21 23	21 11	21 33	21 18		21 24	21 48	21 38	21 40		22 03	21 57		22 18	22 02	22 11	22 33	22 18
Shenfield	d				20 59						21 19				21 39				21 59						22 19
Billericay	d				21 05						21 25				21 45				22 05						22 25
Wickford [2]	d				21 11						21 31	21 36			21 51				22 11	22 16					22 31
Battlesbridge	d											21 40								22 20					
South Woodham Ferrers	d											21 44								22 24					
North Fambridge	d											21 51								22 31					
Althorne	d											21 56								22 36					
Burnham-on-Crouch	d											22 01								22 41					
Southminster	a											22 07								22 47					
Rayleigh	d				21 16						21 36				21 56				22 16						22 36
Hockley	d				21 21						21 41				22 01				22 21						22 41
Rochford	d				21 24						21 44				22 04				22 24						22 44
Southend Airport ✈	d				21 27						21 47				22 07				22 27						22 47
Prittlewell	d				21 30						21 50				22 10				22 30						22 50
Southend Victoria	a				21 34						21 54				22 14				22 34						22 54

		LE ■1		LE	LE ■1	LE ■1	LE ◇■1	LE	LE ■1	LE	LE ■1	LE ■1		LE	LE ■1	LE ■1	LE	LE ■1	LE ■1						
London Liverpool Street [15] ⊖	d	22 02		22 05	22 13		22 18	22 20	22 32	22 35	22 44	23 02		23 05	23 14	23 32	23 35	23 44	23 58						
Stratford [7] ⊖	d	22 09		22 12	22 20		22 25	22 27	22 41	22 42	22 51	23 09		23 12	23 21	23 41	23 42	23 51	00 05						
Romford	d			22 31	22 28			22 46	22 49	23 01	23 04			23 31	23 34		00 01	00 04							
Shenfield [3]	a	22 24		22 48	22 38		22 40	23 03	22 58	23 18	23 21	23 32		23 48	23 51	00 03	00 18	00 21	00 29						
Shenfield	d				22 39						23 21				23 51			00 21							
Billericay	d				22 45						23 27				23 57			00 27							
Wickford [2]	d				22 51	22 56					23 33				00 03			00 33							
Battlesbridge	d					23 00																			
South Woodham Ferrers	d					23 04																			
North Fambridge	d					23 11																			
Althorne	d					23 16																			
Burnham-on-Crouch	d					23 21																			
Southminster	a					23 27																			
Rayleigh	d				22 56						23 38				00 08			00 38							
Hockley	d				23 01						23 42				00 12			00 42							
Rochford	d				23 04						23 46				00 16			00 46							
Southend Airport ✈	d				23 07						23 48				00 18			00 48							
Prittlewell	d				23 10						23 51				00 21			00 51							
Southend Victoria	a				23 14						23 59				00 29			00 59							

Sundays

8 December to 11 May

		LE ■1	LE ■1	LE	LE ■1	LE ■1	LE	LE ■1	LE	LE ■1		LE ■1	LE ■1	LE ◇■1	LE	LE ■1	LE ■1	LE	LE ■1	LE ■1	LE ◇■1			
London Liverpool Street [15] ⊖	d	00 15	00 18	00 20	00 50		00 55	07 55	08 05			08 14		08 30	08 35	08 44	09 02	09 05	09 14		09 32	and at the same minutes past each hour until		
Stratford [7] ⊖	d	00 22	00 25	00 27	00 57		01 02	08 02	08 12			08 21			08 42	08 51	09 09	09 12	09 21		09 39			
Romford	d	00 32		00 46	01 08		01 21		08 31			08 34			09 01	09 04		09 31	09 34					
Shenfield [3]	a	00 44	00 47	01 03	01 20		01 38	08 24	08 48			08 51		08 58	09 18	09 21	09 31	09 48	09 51		10 01			
Shenfield	d	00 45			01 20							08 51				09 21			09 51					
Billericay	d	00 51			01 26							08 57				09 27			09 57					
Wickford [2]	d	00 56			01 31	07 30				08 06		09 03	09 06			09 33			10 03	10 06				
Battlesbridge	d					07 34				08 10			09 10							10 10				
South Woodham Ferrers	d					07 38				08 14			09 14							10 14				
North Fambridge	d					07 44				08 21			09 21							10 21				
Althorne	d					07 49				08 26			09 26							10 26				
Burnham-on-Crouch	d					07 54				08 31			09 31							10 31				
Southminster	a					08 00				08 37			09 37							10 37				
Rayleigh	d	01 01			01 36							09 08				09 38			10 08					
Hockley	d	01 06			01 41							09 12				09 42			10 12					
Rochford	d	01 09			01 44							09 16				09 46			10 16					
Southend Airport ✈	d	01 12			01 47							09 18				09 48			10 18					
Prittlewell	d	01 15			01 50																			
Southend Victoria	a	01 23			01 58							09 25				09 55			10 25					

Table 6

Sundays

8 December to 11 May

London Liverpool Street - Shenfield - Wickford - Southminster - Southend

Network Diagram - refer to first Page of Table 5

		LE	LE 1	LE 1	LE	LE 1	LE 1	LE ◇1	LE	LE 1	LE 1	LE	LE 1	LE ◇1	LE	LE 1	LE 1	LE	LE 1	LE 1	LE	LE 1
London Liverpool Street 15 ⊖	d	20 35	20 44	21 02	21 05	21 14		21 32	21 35	21 44	22 02	22 05	22 14	22 32	22 35	22 44	23 02	23 05	23 14	23 32	23 35	23 44
Stratford 7 ⊖	d	20 42	20 51	21 09	21 12	21 21		21 39	21 42	21 51	22 09	22 12	22 21	22 39	22 42	22 51	23 09	23 12	23 21	23 39	23 42	23 51
Romford	d	21 01	21 04		21 31	21 34			22 01	22 04		22 31	22 34		23 01	23 04		23 31	23 34		00 01	00 04
Shenfield 3	a	21 18	21 21	21 31	21 48	21 51		22 01	22 18	22 21	22 31	22 48	22 51	23 01	23 18	23 21	23 31	23 48	23 51	00 01	00 18	00 21
Shenfield	d		21 21			21 51				22 21			22 51			23 21			23 51			00 21
Billericay	d		21 27			21 57				22 27			22 57			23 27			23 57			00 27
Wickford 2	d		21 33			22 03	22 06			22 33			23 03			23 33			00 03			00 33
Battlesbridge	d						22 10															
South Woodham Ferrers	d						22 14															
North Fambridge	d						22 21															
Althorne	d						22 26															
Burnham-on-Crouch	d						22 31															
Southminster	a						22 37															
Rayleigh	d		21 38			22 08				22 38			23 08			23 38			00 08			00 38
Hockley	d		21 42			22 12				22 42			23 12			23 42			00 12			00 42
Rochford	d		21 46			22 16				22 46			23 16			23 46			00 16			00 46
Southend Airport ✈	d		21 48			22 18				22 48			23 18			23 48			00 18			00 48
Prittlewell	d																					
Southend Victoria	a		21 55			22 25				22 55			23 28			23 58			00 28			00 58

Table 6R

Mondays to Fridays

9 December to 16 May

Southend - Southminster - Wickford - Shenfield - London Liverpool Street

Network Diagram - refer to first Page of Table 5

Miles	Miles		LE	LE	LE [1]	LE [1]	LE [1]	LE [1]	LE [1]		LE [1]	LE [1]	LE	LE [1]	LE [1]	LE [1]	LE [1]	LE [1]	LE		LE [1]	LE [1]	LE [1]	LE [1]
0	—	**Southend Victoria** d	04 00	04 30	05 00	05 20		05 40	06 00		06 11		06 26	06 40	06 50		07 03	07 13	07 18		07 23	07 32	07 42	
0½	—	Prittlewell d	04 02	04 32	05 02	05 22		05 42	06 02		06 13		06 28	06 42	06 52		07 05	07 15	07 20		07 25	07 34	07 44	
1¾	—	Southend Airport ✈ d	04 05	04 35	05 05	05 25		05 45	06 05		06 16		06 31	06 45	06 55		07 08	07 18	07 23		07 28	07 37	07 47	
2¾	—	Rochford d	04 08	04 38	05 08	05 28		05 48	06 08		06 19		06 34	06 48	06 58		07 11	07 21	07 26		07 31	07 40	07 50	
5½	—	Hockley d	04 12	04 42	05 12	05 32		05 52	06 12		06 23		06 38	06 52	07 02		07 15	07 25	07 30		07 35	07 44	07 54	
8¼	—	Rayleigh d	04 16	04 46	05 16	05 36		05 56	06 16		06 27		06 42	06 56	07 06		07 19	07 29	07 34		07 39	07 48	07 58	
—	0	**Southminster** d					05 26					06 09				06 48								07 37
—	2¼	Burnham-on-Crouch d					05 30					06 13				06 52								07 41
—	5¼	Althorne d					05 35					06 18				06 57								07 46
—	8¼	North Fambridge d					05 41					06 24				07 03								07 52
—	11½	South Woodham Ferrers d					05 46					06 30				07 10								07 59
—	14	Battlesbridge d					05 50					06 34				07 14								
12½	16½	**Wickford [2]** d	04 21	04 51	05 21	05 41	05a56	06 01	06 21		06 32	06 40	06 47	07 01	07 11	07 19	07 24	07 34	07 39		07 44	07 53	08 03	08 07
17¼	21¼	Billericay d	04 28	04 58	05 27	05 47		06 07	06 27		06 39	06 46	06 54	07 08	07 18	07 26	07 31	07 41	07 46		07 51	08 00	08 10	08 14
—	—	**Shenfield** a	04 39	05 09	05 35	05 55		06 15	06 35		06 45	06 53	07 01	07 14	07 24	07 32		07 47	07 53		07 57	08 06	08 16	
21¼	25¼	**Shenfield [3]** d	04 39	05 09	05 35	05 55		06 15	06 35		06 45	06 53	07 01	07 14	07 24	07 32		07 47	07 54		07 57	08 06	08 16	
29	—	Romford d	04 53	05 23															08 11					
37½	41½	Stratford [7] ⊖ d	05 10	05 40	05 49	06 10		06 31	06 49		07s02	07s09	07s19	07s31	07s41	07s49	07s52	08s04	08 31		08s15	08s23	08s33	08s35
41½	45½	**London Liverpool Street [15]** ⊖ a	05 18	05 48	05 58	06 19		06 40	06 58		07 13	07 21	07 30	07 42	07 52	08 01	08 03	08 15	08 41		08 26	08 36	08 46	08 48

	LE [1]	LE [1]	LE [1]	LE [1]	LE [1]		LE [1]	LE [1]	LE [1]	LE [1]	LE [1]	LE [1]	LE [1]	LE [1]	LE [1]		LE [1]	LE [1]	LE [1]	LE [1]	LE [1]	LE [1]	LE [1]	LE [1]
Southend Victoria d	07 52	08 03	08 12		08 30		08 52		09 10	09 30		09 50	10 10		10 30		10 50		11 10	11 30		11 50	12 10	
Prittlewell d	07 54	08 05	08 14		08 32		08 54		09 12	09 32		09 52	10 12		10 32		10 52		11 12	11 32		11 52	12 12	
Southend Airport ✈ d	07 57	08 08	08 17		08 35		08 57		09 15	09 35		09 55	10 15		10 35		10 55		11 15	11 35		11 55	12 15	
Rochford d	08 00	08 11	08 20		08 38		09 00		09 18	09 38		09 58	10 18		10 38		10 58		11 18	11 38		11 58	12 18	
Hockley d	08 04	08 15	08 24		08 42		09 04		09 22	09 42		10 02	10 22		10 42		11 02		11 22	11 42		12 02	12 22	
Rayleigh d	08 08	08 19	08 28		08 46		09 08		09 26	09 46		10 06	10 26		10 46		11 06		11 26	11 46		12 06	12 26	
Southminster d				08 16				08 56			09 36			10 16				10 56			11 36			12 16
Burnham-on-Crouch d				08 20				09 00			09 40			10 20				11 00			11 40			12 20
Althorne d				08 25				09 05			09 45			10 25				11 05			11 45			12 25
North Fambridge d				08 31				09 11			09 51			10 31				11 11			11 51			12 31
South Woodham Ferrers d				08 37				09 16			09 56			10 36				11 16			11 56			12 36
Battlesbridge d				08 41				09 20			10 00			10 40				11 20			12 00			12 40
Wickford [2] d	08 13	08 24	08 33	08 46	08 51		09 13	09a26	09 31	09 51	10a06	10 11	10 31	10a46	10 51		11 11	11a26	11 31	11 51	12a06	12 11	12 31	12a46
Billericay d	08 20	08 31	08 40	08 53	08 58		09 20		09 37	09 57		10 17	10 37		10 57		11 17		11 37	11 57		12 17	12 37	
Shenfield a	08 26	08 37	08 46	08 59	09 04		09 27		09 45	10 05		10 25	10 45		11 05		11 25		11 45	12 05		12 25	12 45	
Shenfield [3] d	08 26	08 37	08 46	08 59	09 04		09 27		09 45	10 05		10 25	10 45		11 05		11 25		11 45	12 05		12 25	12 45	
Romford d			08 55						09 53				10 53						11 53				12 53	
Stratford [7] ⊖ d	08s43	08s56	09s05	09s16	09s22		09s43		10 01	10 19		10 39	11 01		11 19		11 39		12 01	12 19		12 39	13 01	
London Liverpool Street [15] ⊖ a	08 56	09 08	09 16	09 29	09 33		09 55		10 10	10 28		10 48	11 10		11 28		11 48		12 10	12 28		12 48	13 10	

	LE [1]		LE [1]	LE [1]	LE [1]	LE [1]	LE [1]	LE [1]	LE [1]	LE [1]	LE [1]		LE [1]	LE [1]	LE [1]	LE [1]	LE [1]	LE [1]	LE [1]	LE [1]	LE [1]		LE [1]	LE [1]
Southend Victoria d	12 30		12 50		13 10	13 30		13 50	14 10		14 30		14 50		15 10	15 30		15 50	16 10		16 30		16 50	17 10
Prittlewell d	12 32		12 52		13 12	13 32		13 52	14 12		14 32		14 52		15 12	15 32		15 52	16 12		16 32		16 52	17 12
Southend Airport ✈ d	12 35		12 55		13 15	13 35		13 55	14 15		14 35		14 55		15 15	15 35		15 55	16 15		16 35		16 55	17 15
Rochford d	12 38		12 58		13 18	13 38		13 58	14 18		14 38		14 58		15 18	15 38		15 58	16 18		16 38		16 58	17 18
Hockley d	12 42		13 02		13 22	13 42		14 02	14 22		14 42		15 02		15 22	15 42		16 02	16 22		16 42		17 02	17 22
Rayleigh d	12 46		13 06		13 26	13 46		14 06	14 26		14 46		15 06		15 26	15 46		16 06	16 26		16 46		17 06	17 26
Southminster d				12 56			13 36			14 16				14 56			15 36			16 14				
Burnham-on-Crouch d				13 00			13 40			14 20				15 00			15 40			16 18				
Althorne d				13 05			13 45			14 25				15 05			15 45			16 23				
North Fambridge d				13 11			13 51			14 31				15 11			15 51			16 29				
South Woodham Ferrers d				13 16			13 56			14 36				15 16			15 56			16 34				
Battlesbridge d				13 20			14 00			14 40				15 20			16 00			16 38				
Wickford [2] d	12 51		13 11	13a26	13 31	13 51	14a06	14 11	14 31	14a46	14 51		15 11	15a26	15 31	15 51	16a06	16 11	16 31	16a44	16 51		17 11	17 31
Billericay d	12 57		13 17		13 37	13 57		14 17	14 37		14 57		15 17		15 37	15 57		16 17	16 37		16 57		17 17	17 37
Shenfield a	13 05		13 25		13 45	14 05		14 25	14 45		15 05		15 25		15 45	16 05		16 25	16 45		17 05		17 25	17 45
Shenfield [3] d	13 05		13 25		13 45	14 05		14 25	14 45		15 05		15 25		15 45	16 05		16 25	16 45		17 05		17 25	17 45
Romford d					13 53				14 53						15 53									
Stratford [7] ⊖ d	13 19		13 39		14 01	14 19		14 39	15 01		15 19		15 39		16 01	16 19		16 39	16 59		17 19		17 39	17 59
London Liverpool Street [15] ⊖ a	13 28		13 48		14 10	14 28		14 48	15 10		15 28		15 48		16 11	16 28		16 48	17 13		17 29		17 49	18 11

	LE [1]	LE [1]	LE [1]	LE [1]	LE [1]	LE [1]	LE [1]		LE [1]	LE [1]	LE [1]	LE [1]	LE [1]	LE [1]	LE [1]	LE [1]	LE [1]		LE [1]	LE [1]	LE [1]	LE [1]	LE [1]	LE [1]
Southend Victoria d		17 25	17 35	17 50	18 05		18 20		18 30	18 50		19 10	19 30		19 50	20 10			20 30	20 50		21 10	21 30	
Prittlewell d		17 27	17 37	17 52	18 07		18 22		18 32	18 52		19 12	19 32		19 52	20 12			20 32	20 52		21 12	21 32	
Southend Airport ✈ d		17 30	17 40	17 55	18 10		18 25		18 35	18 55		19 15	19 35		19 55	20 15			20 35	20 55		21 15	21 35	
Rochford d		17 33	17 43	17 58	18 13		18 28		18 38	18 58		19 18	19 38		19 58	20 18			20 38	20 58		21 18	21 38	
Hockley d		17 37	17 47	18 02	18 17		18 32		18 42	19 02		19 22	19 42		20 02	20 22			20 42	21 02		21 22	21 42	
Rayleigh d		17 41	17 51	18 06	18 21		18 36		18 46	19 06		19 26	19 46		20 06	20 26			20 46	21 06		21 26	21 46	
Southminster d	17 06					17 56					18 36			19 19			20 16				20 56			21 36
Burnham-on-Crouch d	17 10					18 00					18 40			19 23			20 20				21 00			21 40
Althorne d	17 15					18 05					18 45			19 28			20 25				21 05			21 45
North Fambridge d	17 21					18 14					19 01			19 39			20 31				21 11			21 51
South Woodham Ferrers d	17 26					18 19					19 06			19 44			20 36				21 16			21 56
Battlesbridge d	17 30					18 23					19 10			19 48			20 40				21 20			22 00
Wickford [2] d	17 37	17 46	17 56	18 11	18 26	18a29	18 41		18 51	19 11	19 17	19 31	19 51	19 55	20 11	20 31	20a46		20 51	21 11	21a26	21 31	21 51	22a07
Billericay d		17 52	18 02	18 17	18 32		18 47		18 57	19 17	19 23	19 37	19 57		20 17	20 37			20 57	21 17		21 37	21 57	
Shenfield a	17 48	18 00	18 10	18 25	18 40		18 55		19 05	19 25	19 33	19 45	20 05	20 08	20 25	20 45			21 05	21 25		21 45	22 05	
Shenfield [3] d	17 49	18 00	18 10	18 25	18 40		18 57		19 05	19 25		19 45	20 05		20 25	20 45			21 05	21 25		21 45	22 05	
Romford d												19 53				20 53						21 53		
Stratford [7] ⊖ d	18 08	18 14	18 25	18 39	18 55		19 11		19 19	19 39		20 01	20 19		20 39	21 01			21 19	21 39		22 01	22 19	
London Liverpool Street [15] ⊖ a	18 17	18 24	18 35	18 48	19 04		19 20		19 28	19 48		20 10	20 28		20 48	21 10			21 28	21 48		22 10	22 28	

Table 6R

Southend - Southminster - Wickford - Shenfield - London Liverpool Street

Mondays to Fridays

9 December to 16 May

Network Diagram - refer to first Page of Table 5

		LE	LE	LE ThFO		LE MT WO	LE ThFO	LE MT WO	LE ThFO	LE MT WO
		1	1	1		1	1	1	1	1
Southend Victoria	d	22 00		22 30		22 30	23 00	23 00		
Prittlewell	d	22 02		22 32		22 32	23 02	23 02		
Southend Airport ✈	d	22 05		22 35		22 35	23 05	23 05		
Rochford	d	22 08		22 38		22 38	23 08	23 08		
Hockley	d	22 12		22 42		22 42	23 12	23 12		
Rayleigh	d	22 16		22 46		22 46	23 16	23 16		
Southminster	d		22 16						22 56	22 56
Burnham-on-Crouch	d		22 20						23 00	23 00
Althorne	d		22 25						23 05	23 05
North Fambridge	d		22 31						23 11	23 11
South Woodham Ferrers	d		22 36						23 16	23 16
Battlesbridge	d		22 40						23 20	23 20
Wickford 2	d	22 21	22a46	22 51		22 51	23 21	23 21	23 26	23 26
Billericay	d	22 27		22 57		22 57	23 27	23 27	23 32	23 32
Shenfield	a	22 35		23 05		23 05	23 35	23 35	23 39	23 39
Shenfield 3	d	22 35		23 05		23 05	23 35	23 35	23 39	23 39
Romford	d								23 47	23 47
Stratford 7 ⊖	d	22 49		23 19		23s26	23 49	23s57	23 56	00s03
London Liverpool Street 15 ⊖	a	22 58		23 28		23 35	23 58	00 05	00 05	00 12

Saturdays

14 December to 17 May

		LE	LE	LE	LE	LE	LE	LE	LE	LE		LE	LE	LE	LE	LE	LE	LE	LE	LE		LE	LE	LE	LE
				1	1	1	1	1	1	1		1	1	1	1	1	1	1	1	1		1	1	1	1
Southend Victoria	d	04 00	04 30	05 00	05 30	06 00		06 30	06 50			07 10	07 30		07 50	08 10		08 30	08 50			09 10	09 30		09 50
Prittlewell	d	04 02	04 32	05 02	05 32	06 02		06 32	06 52			07 12	07 32		07 52	08 12		08 32	08 52			09 12	09 32		09 52
Southend Airport ✈	d	04 05	04 35	05 05	05 35	06 05		06 35	06 55			07 15	07 35		07 55	08 15		08 35	08 55			09 15	09 35		09 55
Rochford	d	04 08	04 38	05 08	05 38	06 08		06 38	06 58			07 18	07 38		07 58	08 18		08 38	08 58			09 18	09 38		09 58
Hockley	d	04 12	04 42	05 12	05 42	06 12		06 42	07 02			07 22	07 42		08 02	08 22		08 42	09 02			09 22	09 42		10 02
Rayleigh	d	04 16	04 46	05 16	05 46	06 16		06 46	07 06			07 26	07 46		08 06	08 26		08 46	09 06			09 26	09 46		10 06
Southminster	d						06 16			06 56				07 36			08 16			08 56				09 36	
Burnham-on-Crouch	d						06 20			07 00				07 40			08 20			09 00				09 40	
Althorne	d						06 25			07 05				07 45			08 25			09 05				09 45	
North Fambridge	d						06 31			07 11				07 51			08 31			09 11				09 51	
South Woodham Ferrers	d						06 36			07 16				07 56			08 36			09 16				09 56	
Battlesbridge	d						06 40			07 20				08 00			08 40			09 20				10 00	
Wickford 2	d	04 21	04 51	05 21	05 51	06 21	06a46	06 51	07 11	07a26		07 31	07 51	08a06	08 11	08 31	08a46	08 51	09 11	09a26		09 31	09 51	10a06	10 11
Billericay	d	04 28	04 58	05 27	05 57	06 27		06 57	07 17			07 37	07 57		08 17	08 37		08 57	09 17			09 37	09 57		10 17
Shenfield	a	04 39	05 09	05 35	06 05	06 35		07 05	07 25			07 45	08 05		08 25	08 45		09 05	09 25			09 45	10 05		10 25
Shenfield 3	d	04 39	05 09	05 35	06 05	06 35		07 05	07 25			07 45	08 05		08 25	08 45		09 05	09 25			09 45	10 05		10 25
Romford	d	04 53	05 23	05 43		06 43						07 53				08 53						09 53			
Stratford 7 ⊖	d	05 10	05 40	05 51	06 19	06 51		07 19	07 39			08 01	08 19		08 39	09 01		09 19	09 39			10 01	10 19		10 39
London Liverpool Street 15 ⊖	a	05 18	05 48	06 00	06 28	07 00		07 28	07 48			08 10	08 28		08 48	09 10		09 28	09 48			10 10	10 28		10 48

		LE	LE	LE	LE	LE		LE	LE	LE	LE	LE	LE	LE	LE	LE		LE	LE	LE	LE	LE	LE	LE	LE
		1	1	1	1	1		1	1	1	1	1	1	1	1	1		1	1	1	1	1	1	1	1
Southend Victoria	d	10 10		10 30	10 50			11 10	11 30		11 50	12 10		12 30	12 50			13 10	13 30		13 50	14 10		14 30	14 50
Prittlewell	d	10 12		10 32	10 52			11 12	11 32		11 52	12 12		12 32	12 52			13 12	13 32		13 52	14 12		14 32	14 52
Southend Airport ✈	d	10 15		10 35	10 55			11 15	11 35		11 55	12 15		12 35	12 55			13 15	13 35		13 55	14 15		14 35	14 55
Rochford	d	10 18		10 38	10 58			11 18	11 38		11 58	12 18		12 38	12 58			13 18	13 38		13 58	14 18		14 38	14 58
Hockley	d	10 22		10 42	11 02			11 22	11 42		12 02	12 22		12 42	13 02			13 22	13 42		14 02	14 22		14 42	15 02
Rayleigh	d	10 26		10 46	11 06			11 26	11 46		12 06	12 26		12 46	13 06			13 26	13 46		14 06	14 26		14 46	15 06
Southminster	d		10 16			10 56				11 36			12 16			12 56				13 36			14 16		
Burnham-on-Crouch	d		10 20			11 00				11 40			12 20			13 00				13 40			14 20		
Althorne	d		10 25			11 05				11 45			12 25			13 05				13 45			14 25		
North Fambridge	d		10 31			11 11				11 51			12 31			13 11				13 51			14 31		
South Woodham Ferrers	d		10 36			11 16				11 56			12 36			13 16				13 56			14 36		
Battlesbridge	d		10 40			11 20				12 00			12 40			13 20				14 00			14 40		
Wickford 2	d	10 31	10a46	10 51	11 11	11a26		11 31	11 51	12a06	12 11	12 31	12a46	12 51	13 11	13a26		13 31	13 51	14a06	14 11	14 31	14a46	14 51	15 11
Billericay	d	10 37		10 57	11 17			11 37	11 57		12 17	12 37		12 57	13 17			13 37	13 57		14 17	14 37		14 57	15 17
Shenfield	a	10 45		11 05	11 25			11 45	12 05		12 25	12 45		13 05	13 25			13 45	14 05		14 25	14 45		15 05	15 25
Shenfield 3	d	10 45		11 05	11 25			11 45	12 05		12 25	12 45		13 05	13 25			13 45	14 05		14 25	14 45		15 05	15 25
Romford	d	10 53						11 53				12 53						13 53				14 53			
Stratford 7 ⊖	d	11 01		11 19	11 39			12 01	12 19		12 39	13 01		13 19	13 39			14 01	14 19		14 39	15 01		15 19	15 39
London Liverpool Street 15 ⊖	a	11 10		11 28	11 48			12 10	12 28		12 48	13 10		13 28	13 48			14 10	14 28		14 48	15 10		15 28	15 48

		LE		LE	LE	LE	LE	LE	LE	LE	LE	LE		LE	LE	LE	LE	LE	LE	LE	LE	LE		LE	LE
		1		1	1	1	1	1	1	1	1	1		1	1	1	1	1	1	1	1	1		1	1
Southend Victoria	d			15 10	15 30		15 50	16 10		16 30	16 50			17 10	17 30		17 50	18 10		18 30	18 50			19 10	19 30
Prittlewell	d			15 12	15 32		15 52	16 12		16 32	16 52			17 12	17 32		17 52	18 12		18 32	18 52			19 12	19 32
Southend Airport ✈	d			15 15	15 35		15 55	16 15		16 35	16 55			17 15	17 35		17 55	18 15		18 35	18 55			19 15	19 35
Rochford	d			15 18	15 38		15 58	16 18		16 38	16 58			17 18	17 38		17 58	18 18		18 38	18 58			19 18	19 38
Hockley	d			15 22	15 42		16 02	16 22		16 42	17 02			17 22	17 42		18 02	18 22		18 42	19 02			19 22	19 42
Rayleigh	d			15 26	15 46		16 06	16 26		16 46	17 06			17 26	17 46		18 06	18 26		18 46	19 06			19 26	19 46
Southminster	d	14 56				15 36			16 16			16 56				17 36			18 16			18 56			
Burnham-on-Crouch	d	15 00				15 40			16 20			17 00				17 40			18 20			19 00			
Althorne	d	15 05				15 45			16 25			17 05				17 45			18 25			19 05			
North Fambridge	d	15 11				15 51			16 31			17 11				17 51			18 31			19 11			
South Woodham Ferrers	d	15 16				15 56			16 36			17 16				17 56			18 36			19 16			
Battlesbridge	d	15 20				16 00			16 40			17 20				18 00			18 40			19 20			
Wickford 2	d	15a26		15 31	15 51	16a06	16 11	16 31	16a46	16 51	17 11	17a26		17 31	17 51	18a06	18 11	18 31	18a46	18 51	19 11	19a26		19 31	19 51
Billericay	d			15 37	15 57		16 17	16 37		16 57	17 17			17 37	17 57		18 17	18 37		18 57	19 17			19 37	19 57
Shenfield	a			15 45	16 05		16 25	16 45		17 05	17 25			17 44	18 05		18 25	18 45		19 05	19 25			19 45	20 05
Shenfield 3	d			15 45	16 05		16 25	16 45		17 05	17 25			17 45	18 05		18 25	18 45		19 05	19 25			19 45	20 05
Romford	d			15 53				16 53						17 53				18 53						19 53	
Stratford 7 ⊖	d			16 01	16 19		16 39	17 01		17 19	17 39			18 01	18 19		18 39	19 01		19 19	19 39			20 01	
London Liverpool Street 15 ⊖	a			16 10	16 28		16 48	17 10		17 28	17 48			18 10	18 28		18 48	19 10		19 28	19 48			20 10	20 28

Table 6R

Saturdays

14 December to 17 May

Southend - Southminster - Wickford - Shenfield - London Liverpool Street

Network Diagram - refer to first Page of Table 5

		LE 1	LE 1	LE 1	LE 1	LE 1	LE 1	LE 1	LE 1	LE 1	LE 1	LE 1	LE 1	LE 1	LE 1	LE 1
Southend Victoria	d		19 50	20 10		20 30	20 50		21 10	21 30		22 00		22 30	23 00	
Prittlewell	d		19 52	20 12		20 32	20 52		21 12	21 32		22 02		22 32	23 02	
Southend Airport ✈	d		19 55	20 15		20 35	20 55		21 15	21 35		22 05		22 35	23 05	
Rochford	d		19 58	20 18		20 38	20 58		21 18	21 38		22 08		22 38	23 08	
Hockley	d		20 02	20 22		20 42	21 02		21 22	21 42		22 12		22 42	23 12	
Rayleigh	d		20 06	20 26		20 46	21 06		21 26	21 46		22 16		22 46	23 16	
Southminster	d	19 36			20 16			20 56			21 36		22 16			22 56
Burnham-on-Crouch	d	19 40			20 20			21 00			21 40		22 20			23 00
Althorne	d	19 45			20 25			21 05			21 45		22 25			23 05
North Fambridge	d	19 51			20 31			21 11			21 51		22 31			23 11
South Woodham Ferrers	d	19 56			20 36			21 16			21 56		22 36			23 16
Battlesbridge	d	20 00			20 40			21 20			22 00		22 40			23 20
Wickford 2	d	20a06	20 11	20 31	20a46	20 51	21 11	21a26	21 31	21 51	22a06	22 21	22a46	22 51	23 21	23 26
Billericay	d		20 17	20 37		20 57	21 17		21 37	21 57		22 27		22 57	23 27	23 32
Shenfield	a		20 25	20 45		21 05	21 25		21 45	22 05		22 35		23 05	23 35	23 40
Shenfield 3	d		20 25	20 45		21 05	21 25		21 45	22 05		22 35		23 05	23 35	23 41
Romford	d			20 53					21 53							23 49
Stratford 7 ⊖	d		20 39	21 01		21 19	21 39		22 01	22 19		22 49		23s26	23s56	00s03
London Liverpool Street 15 ⊖	a		20 48	21 10		21 28	21 48		22 10	22 28		23 04		23 35	00 05	00 12

Sundays

8 December to 11 May

		LE (bus)	LE 1	LE (bus)	LE 1	LE (bus)	LE (bus)	LE 1	LE 1	LE 1	LE 1	LE 1		LE 1	LE 1	LE 1	LE 1	LE 1	LE 1	LE 1	LE 1	
Southend Victoria	d		06 15		06 45			07 30	07 49		08 19	08 49			16 19	16 49		17 19	17 49		18 19	
Prittlewell	d																					
Southend Airport ✈	d		06 19		06 49			07 34	07 53		08 23	08 53			16 23	16 53		17 23	17 53		18 23	
Rochford	d		06 22		06 52			07 37	07 56		08 26	08 56			16 26	16 56		17 26	17 56		18 26	
Hockley	d		06 26		06 56			07 41	08 00		08 30	09 00	and at		16 30	17 00		17 30	18 00		18 30	and at
Rayleigh	d		06 30		07 00			07 45	08 04		08 34	09 04	the same		16 34	17 04		17 34	18 04		18 34	the same
Southminster	d									08 06			minutes	16 06			17 06			18 06		minutes
Burnham-on-Crouch	d									08 10			past	16 10			17 10			18 10		past
Althorne	d									08 15			each	16 15			17 15			18 15		each
North Fambridge	d									08 21			hour until	16 21			17 21			18 21		hour until
South Woodham Ferrers	d									08 26				16 26			17 26			18 26		
Battlesbridge	d									08 30				16 30			17 30			18 30		
Wickford 2	d		06 35		07 05			07 50	08 10	08a37	08 40	09 10		16a37	16 40	17 10	17a37	17 40	18 10	18a37	18 40	
Billericay	d		06 41		07 11			07 56	08 16		08 46	09 16			16 46	17 16		17 46	18 16		18 46	
Shenfield	a		06 52		07 22			08 03	08 23		08 53	09 23			16 53	17 23		17 53	18 23		18 53	
Shenfield 3	d	05 58		06 28		06 58	07 28		08 23		08 53	09 23			16 53	17 23		17 53	18 23		18 53	
Romford	d	06a37		07a07		07a37	08a07		08 37		09 07	09 37			17 07	17 37		18 07	18 37		19 07	
Stratford 7 ⊖	d								08 50		09 20	09 50			17 20	17 50		18 20	18 50		19 20	
London Liverpool Street 15 ⊖	a								09 02		09 29	09 59			17 29	17 59		18 31	18 59		19 29	

		LE 1	LE 1	LE 1	LE 1	LE 1	LE 1	LE 1	LE 1
Southend Victoria	d	20 49		21 19	21 49		22 19	22 49	
Prittlewell	d								
Southend Airport ✈	d	20 53		21 23	21 53		22 23	22 53	
Rochford	d	20 56		21 26	21 56		22 26	22 56	
Hockley	d	21 00		21 30	22 00		22 30	23 00	
Rayleigh	d	21 04		21 34	22 04		22 34	23 04	
Southminster	d		21 06			22 06			22 45
Burnham-on-Crouch	d		21 10			22 10			22 49
Althorne	d		21 15			22 15			22 54
North Fambridge	d		21 21			22 21			23 00
South Woodham Ferrers	d		21 26			22 26			23 05
Battlesbridge	d		21 30			22 30			23 09
Wickford 2	d	21 10	21a37	21 40	22 10	22 36	22 40	23 10	23 15
Billericay	d	21 16		21 46	22 16		22 46	23 16	
Shenfield	a	21 23		21 53	22 23	22 47	22 53	23 23	23 26
Shenfield 3	d	21 23		21 53	22 23		22 53	23 23	
Romford	d	21 37		22 07	22 37		23 07	23 37	
Stratford 7 ⊖	d	21 50		22 20	22 50		23 20	23 50	
London Liverpool Street 15 ⊖	a	21 59		22 29	22 59		23 31	23 59	

Table 10

Mondays to Fridays

9 December to 16 May

Marks Tey - Sudbury

Network Diagram - refer to first Page of Table 5

Miles			LE	LE	LE	LE	LE	LE	LE	LE	LE	LE	LE	LE	LE	LE	LE	LE	LE	LE	LE
0	**Colchester** [4]	d																			
5	Marks Tey [2]	d	06 01	06 52	07 39	08 22	09 09	10 01	11 01	12 01	13 01	14 01	15 01	16 01	17 08	18 05	19 14	20 05	21 01	22 01	23 01
8½	Chappel & Wakes Colne	d	06 07	06 58		08 28	09 15	10 07	11 07	12 07	13 07	14 07	15 07	16 07	17 14	18 11	19 20	20 11	21 07	22 07	23 07
11¾	Bures	d	06 13	07 04		08 34	09 21	10 13	11 13	12 13	13 13	14 13	15 13	16 13	17 20	18 17	19 26	20 17	21 13	22 13	23 13
16¾	**Sudbury**	a	06 21	07 12	07 55	08 42	09 29	10 21	11 21	12 21	13 21	14 21	15 21	16 21	17 28	18 25	19 34	20 25	21 21	22 21	23 21

Saturdays

14 December to 17 May

		LE	LE	LE	LE	LE	LE	LE	LE	LE	LE	LE	LE	LE	LE	LE	LE	LE	LE
Colchester [4]	d	05 50																	
Marks Tey [2]	d	06 01	07 01	08 01	09 01	10 01	11 01	12 01	13 01	14 01	15 01	16 01	17 01	18 01	19 01	20 01	21 01	22 01	23 01
Chappel & Wakes Colne	d	06 07	07 07	08 07	09 07	10 07	11 07	12 07	13 07	14 07	15 07	16 07	17 07	18 07	19 07	20 07	21 07	22 07	23 07
Bures	d	06 13	07 13	08 13	09 13	10 13	11 13	12 13	13 13	14 13	15 13	16 13	17 13	18 13	19 13	20 13	21 13	22 13	23 13
Sudbury	a	06 21	07 21	08 21	09 21	10 21	11 21	12 21	13 21	14 21	15 21	16 21	17 21	18 21	19 21	20 21	21 21	22 21	23 21

Sundays

8 December to 11 May

		LE	LE	LE	LE	LE	LE	LE	LE	LE	LE	LE	LE	LE	LE	LE
Colchester [4]	d	07 01														
Marks Tey [2]	d	07 15	08 15	09 15	10 15	11 15	12 15	13 15	14 15	15 15	16 15	17 15	18 15	19 15	20 15	21 15
Chappel & Wakes Colne	d	07 21	08 21	09 21	10 21	11 21	12 21	13 21	14 21	15 21	16 21	17 21	18 21	19 21	20 21	21 21
Bures	d	07 27	08 27	09 27	10 27	11 27	12 27	13 27	14 27	15 27	16 27	17 27	18 27	19 27	20 27	21 27
Sudbury	a	07 35	08 35	09 35	10 35	11 35	12 35	13 35	14 35	15 35	16 35	17 35	18 35	19 35	20 35	21 35

Table 10R

Mondays to Fridays

9 December to 16 May

Sudbury - Marks Tey

Network Diagram - refer to first Page of Table 5

Miles			LE	LE	LE	LE	LE	LE	LE	LE	LE	LE	LE	LE	LE	LE	LE	LE	LE	LE	LE	LE
0	**Sudbury**	d	05 30	06 29	07 16	07 59	08 46	09 33	10 26	11 26	12 26	13 26	14 26	15 26	16 32	17 32	18 37	19 38	20 32	21 26	22 26	23 26
5	Bures	d	05 37	06 36	07 23	08 06	08 53	09 40	10 33	11 33	12 33	13 33	14 33	15 33	16 39	17 39	18 44	19 45	20 39	21 33	22 33	23 33
8¼	Chappel & Wakes Colne	d	05 43	06 42	07 29	08 12	08 59	09 46	10 39	11 39	12 39	13 39	14 39	15 39	16 45	17 45	18 50	19 51	20 45	21 39	22 39	23 39
11¾	Marks Tey [2]	a	05 49	06 48	07 35	08 18	09 05	09 52	10 45	11 45	12 45	13 45	14 45	15 45	16 51	17 51	18 56	19 57	20 51	21 45	22 45	23 45
16¾	**Colchester** [4]	a																				00 01

Saturdays

14 December to 17 May

		LE	LE	LE	LE	LE	LE	LE	LE	LE	LE	LE	LE	LE	LE	LE	LE	LE	LE
Sudbury	d	06 26	07 26	08 26	09 26	10 26	11 26	12 26	13 26	14 26	15 26	16 26	17 26	18 26	19 26	20 26	21 26	22 26	23 26
Bures	d	06 33	07 33	08 33	09 33	10 33	11 33	12 33	13 33	14 33	15 33	16 33	17 33	18 33	19 33	20 33	21 33	22 33	23 33
Chappel & Wakes Colne	d	06 39	07 39	08 39	09 39	10 39	11 39	12 39	13 39	14 39	15 39	16 39	17 39	18 39	19 39	20 39	21 39	22 39	23 39
Marks Tey [2]	a	06 45	07 45	08 45	09 45	10 45	11 45	12 45	13 45	14 45	15 45	16 45	17 45	18 45	19 45	20 45	21 45	22 45	23 45
Colchester [4]	a																		00 01

Sundays

8 December to 11 May

		LE	LE	LE	LE	LE	LE	LE	LE	LE	LE	LE	LE	LE	LE	LE
Sudbury	d	07 42	08 42	09 42	10 42	11 42	12 42	13 42	14 42	15 42	16 42	17 42	18 42	19 42	20 42	21 42
Bures	d	07 49	08 49	09 49	10 49	11 49	12 49	13 49	14 49	15 49	16 49	17 49	18 49	19 49	20 49	21 49
Chappel & Wakes Colne	d	07 55	08 55	09 55	10 55	11 55	12 55	13 55	14 55	15 55	16 55	17 55	18 55	19 55	20 55	21 55
Marks Tey [2]	a	08 01	09 01	10 01	11 01	12 01	13 01	14 01	15 01	16 01	17 01	18 01	19 01	20 01	21 01	22 01
Colchester [4]	a															22 10

Table 11

Mondays to Fridays

9 December to 16 May

London - Chelmsford, Colchester, Walton-on-Naze, Clacton, Harwich, Ipswich and Norwich

Network Diagram - refer to first Page of Table 5

Miles	Miles	Miles	Miles	Miles			LE	LE FO [1]	LE TW ThO ◇[1]	LE TW ThO [1]	LE MO [1]	LE FO [1]	LE TW ThO [1]	LE MO [1]	LE		LE MX [1]		LE	LE MX [1]	LE [1]	LE	LE [1]	LE [1]	LE [1]
0	—	—	—	—	**London Liverpool Street** [15] ⊖	d								00 02			00 18			00 46					
4	—	—	—	—	Stratford [7] ⊖	d								00 09			00 25			00 53					
12¼	—	—	—	—	Romford	d																			
20¼	—	—	—	—	Shenfield [3]	d					00 02	00 11	00 20	00 32			00 47			01 17					
23½	—	—	—	—	Ingatestone	d						00 15	00 24	00 36			00 52			01 21					
29¾	—	—	—	—	**Chelmsford** [3]	d			00 01		00 11	00 22	00 31	00 43			00 59			01 28					
36	—	—	—	—	Hatfield Peverel	d						00 28	00 37	00 49			01 05								
38½	0	—	—	—	**Witham** [2]	d		00 05	00 12	00 14	00 22	00 35	00 44	00 56			01 11			01 39	05 21				
—	3	—	—	—	White Notley	d		00 12		00 21											05 28				
—	4¼	—	—	—	Cressing	d		00 14		00 23											05 30				
—	5½	—	—	—	Braintree Freeport	d		00 17		00 26											05 33				
—	6¼	—	—	—	**Braintree**	a		00 21		00 30											05 37				
42¼	—	—	—	—	Kelvedon	d						00 39	00 48	01 00			01 16								
46¾	—	—	—	—	Marks Tey [2]	d					00 29	00 45	00 54	01 06			01 21								
51¾	—	—	—	—	**Colchester** [4]	a			00 24		00 43	00 59	01 08	01 20			01 35			01 58					
—	0	0	—	—	**Colchester** [4]	d			00 25														05 40		
—	—	2¼	—	—	Colchester Town	a																			
—	—	—	—	—		d																			
—	2¾	3¼	—	—	Hythe	d																			
—	—	5¾	—	—	Wivenhoe [3]	d			00 32																
—	—	7½	—	—	Alresford (Essex)	d			00 36																
—	—	9¾	—	—	Great Bentley	d			00 40																
—	—	12½	—	—	Weeley	d																			
—	—	14¾	0	—	Thorpe-le-Soken [1]	a			00 47																
—	—	—	—	—		d			00 47																
—	—	—	4¾	—	**Clacton-on-Sea**	a			01 02																
—	—	17¼	—	—	Kirby Cross	d																			
—	—	18½	—	—	Frinton-on-Sea	d																			
—	—	19¾	—	—	**Walton-on-the-Naze**	a																			
59½	—	—	—	0	Manningtree [2]	d																	05 49		05 56
—	—	—	—	1¾	Mistley	d																			06 00
—	—	—	—	5¾	Wrabness	d																			06 05
—	—	—	—	9½	Harwich International	d																			06 13
—	—	—	—	10¾	Dovercourt	d																			06 16
—	—	—	—	11¼	**Harwich Town**	a																			06 20
68¾	—	—	—	—	**Ipswich**	a																	05 59		
—	—	—	—	—		d																05 10	06 00	06 16	
77	—	—	—	—	Needham Market	d																05 20		06 25	
80¾	—	—	—	—	Stowmarket	d																05a26	06a11	06a30	
95	—	—	—	—	Diss	d																			
115	—	—	—	—	**Norwich**	a																			

			LE [1]	LE [1]	LE [1]	LE [1]	LE ◇[1]	LE [1]	LE [1]	LE [1]	LE ◇[1]		LE [1]	LE [1]	LE ◇[1]	LE [1]	LE ◇[1]	LE [1]	LE [1]	LE [1]	LE [1]		LE [1]	LE ◇[1]	LE [1]
London Liverpool Street [15] ⊖	d						05 23				06 00				06 02	06 12	06 25			06 38	06 48			07 00	
Stratford [7] ⊖	d						05 30								06 09	06 19	06u33			06 45	06 55				
Romford	d						05 38																		
Shenfield [3]	d						05 48								06 25	06 36				07 01	07 11			07u22	
Ingatestone	d						05 52									06 40					07 15				
Chelmsford [3]	d						05 59				06 30				06 34	06 47	06 58			07 10	07 22				
Hatfield Peverel	d						06 05									06 53									
Witham [2]	d						06 12	06 16							06 45	07 03	07 09			07 21	07 33				
White Notley	d							06 23								07 10									
Cressing	d							06 25								07 12									
Braintree Freeport	d							06 28								07 15									
Braintree	a							06 32								07 19									
Kelvedon	d						06 16								06 49					07 25					
Marks Tey [2]	d						06 22								06 55					07 31	07 40				
Colchester [4]	a						06 29				06 49				07 02		07 22			07 38	07 47			07 50	
Colchester [4]	d			06 10	06 20		06 30				06 50				07 02		07 23		07 26	07 43	07 48			07 51	07 56
Colchester Town	a				06 27														07 34		07 56				08 03
	d																		07 38						08 07
Hythe	d														07 07				07 42						08 11
Wivenhoe [3]	d						06 37								07 11				07 46						08 15
Alresford (Essex)	d														07 14										08 19
Great Bentley	d														07 18										08 23
Weeley	d														07 22										08 26
Thorpe-le-Soken [1]	a						06 50								07 28				07 57						08 31
	d		06 02			06 30	06 50							06 57	07 28			07 37	07 57						08 40
Clacton-on-Sea	a						06 59								07 37				08 06						↪
Kirby Cross	d		06 10			06 38								07 05				07 45							
Frinton-on-Sea	d		06 13			06 41								07 08				07 48							
Walton-on-the-Naze	a		06 17			06 45								07 12				07 52							
Manningtree [2]	d			06 18							06 58		07 24				07 31			07 51				07 59	
Mistley	d			06 22									07 28							07 55					
Wrabness	d			06 27									07 33							08 01					
Harwich International	d			06 35									07 41							08 10					
Dovercourt	d			06 38									07 44							08 13					
Harwich Town	a			06 40									07 46							08 15					
Ipswich	a										07 10						07 42							08 11	
	d								06 39	06 54	07 11						07 44						08 03	08 12	
Needham Market	d									07 03															
Stowmarket	d								06 51	07a08	07 22						07 55						08a15	08 23	
Diss	d								07 04		07 35						08 08							08 36	
Norwich	a								07 24		07 54						08 27							08 55	

Table 11

Mondays to Fridays

9 December to 16 May

London - Chelmsford, Colchester, Walton-on-Naze, Clacton, Harwich, Ipswich and Norwich

Network Diagram - refer to first Page of Table 5

		LE 1	LE 1	LE 1	LE ◇1	LE 1	LE ◇1 ☕		LE 1	LE 1		LE ◇1 ☕	LE 1	LE 1	LE 1	LE 1	LE 1		LE ◇1	LE 1	LE ◇1 ☕	LE 1	LE 1	LE 1	LE ◇1 ☕
London Liverpool Street 15 ⊖	d	07 02		07 08	07 18		07 30		07 36	07 46		07 55		08 00		08 06			08 17		08 30	08 36	08 48		09 00
Stratford 7 ⊖	d	07 09		07 15	07 25		07u38		07 45	07 54				08 08		08 14			08 25		08u38	08 45	08 55		
Romford	d																								
Shenfield 3	d	07 25		07 31	07 41				08 01	08 11				08 25		08 30			08 41			09 03	09 11		
Ingatestone	d				07 45				08 05							08 34			08 45				09 15		
Chelmsford 3	d	07 34		07 40	07 52		08 03		08 12	08 20				08 34		08 41			08 52		09 03	09 12	09 22		
Hatfield Peverel	d	07 40														08 47									
Witham 2	d	07 48		07 51	08 03				08 23	08 35	08 38			08 45		08 54			09 03			09 23	09 35		
White Notley	d	07 55								08 42													09 42		
Cressing	d	07 57								08 44													09 44		
Braintree Freeport	d	08 00								08 47													09 47		
Braintree	a	08 04								08 51													09 51		
Kelvedon	d			07 55					08 27					08 49								09 27			
Marks Tey 2	d			08 01	08 11				08 33					08 55					09 10			09 33			
Colchester 4	a			08 08	08 18		08 22		08 40		08 53	08 45		09 02		09 06			09 17		09 22	09 40			09 46
Colchester 4	d			08 08	08 19		08 23		08 41		08 56	08 47		09 02		09 06	09 14		09 18		09 23	09 41			09 47
Colchester Town	a								08 49		09 03						09 21					09 49			
	d										09 07														
Hythe	d				08 23						09 11														
Wivenhoe 3	d				08 27						09 15								09 25						
Alresford (Essex)	d										09 19														
Great Bentley	d										09 23														
Weeley	d					←					09 26									←					
Thorpe-le-Soken 1	a				08 38	08 31					09 31								09 36	09 31					
	d				08 38	08 40					09 38								09 36	09 38					
Clacton-on-Sea	a				08 47						→								09 45						
Kirby Cross	d					08 45														09 43					
Frinton-on-Sea	d					08 48														09 46					
Walton-on-the-Naze	a					08 52														09 50					
Manningtree 2	d			08 16			08 31					08 55			09 00	09 14					09 31				09 55
Mistley	d		08 02												09 04										
Wrabness	d														09 09										
Harwich International	d														09 17										
Dovercourt	d														09 20										
Harwich Town	a														09 22										
Ipswich	a		08 17	08 29			08 43					09 07		09 21		09 26					09 43				10 07
	d		08 20				08 44					09 08	09 20								09 44			10 00	10 08
Needham Market	d		08 29										09 29												
Stowmarket	d		08a34				08 55						09a34								09 55			10a11	
Diss	d						09 08					09 29									10 08				10 29
Norwich	a						09 27					09 48									10 27				10 50

		LE 1	LE 1		LE 1	LE 1	LE ◇1	LE 1	LE 1	LE ◇1 ☕	LE 1	LE 1	LE ◇1 ☕		LE 1	LE 1	LE 1	LE 1	LE ◇1	LE 1	LE 1	LE ◇1 ☕	LE 1		LE 1
London Liverpool Street 15 ⊖	d					09 02	09 18			09 30	09 38	09 48	10 00					10 02	10 18			10 30	10 38		10 48
Stratford 7 ⊖	d					09 09	09 25			09u38	09 45	09 55						10 09	10 25			10u38	10 45		10 55
Romford	d										09 53												10 53		
Shenfield 3	d					09 25	09 41				10 03	10 11						10 25	10 41				11 03		11 11
Ingatestone	d						09 45					10 15							10 45						11 15
Chelmsford 3	d					09 34	09 52			10 03	10 12	10 22						10 34	10 52			11 03	11 12		11 22
Hatfield Peverel	d					09 40												10 40							
Witham 2	d					09 47	10 03				10 23	10 34						10 47	11 03				11 23		11 34
White Notley	d											10 41													11 41
Cressing	d											10 43													11 43
Braintree Freeport	d											10 46													11 46
Braintree	a											10 50													11 50
Kelvedon	d					09 51					10 27							10 51					11 27		
Marks Tey 2	d					09 57					10 33							10 57					11 33		
Colchester 4	a					10 04	10 15			10 22	10 40		10 46					11 04	11 15			11 22	11 40		
Colchester 4	d				09 56	10 04	10 16		10 20	10 23	10 41		10 47				10 56	11 04	11 16		11 20	11 23	11 41		
Colchester Town	a				10 03				10 27		10 49						11 03				11 27		11 49		
	d				10 07												11 07								
Hythe	d				10 11												11 11								
Wivenhoe 3	d				10 15		10 23										11 15		11 23						
Alresford (Essex)	d				10 19												11 19								
Great Bentley	d				10 23												11 23								
Weeley	d				10 26			←									11 26			←					
Thorpe-le-Soken 1	a				10 31		10 35	10 31									11 31		11 35	11 31					
	d				10 37		10 35	10 37									11 37		11 35	11 37					
Clacton-on-Sea	a				→		10 44										→		11 44						
Kirby Cross	d							10 42												11 42					
Frinton-on-Sea	d							10 45												11 45					
Walton-on-the-Naze	a							10 49												11 49					
Manningtree 2	d		10 00			10 12				10 31			10 55			11 00		11 12				11 31			
Mistley	d		10 04													11 04									
Wrabness	d		10 09													11 09									
Harwich International	d		10 17													11 17									
Dovercourt	d		10 20													11 20									
Harwich Town	a		10 22													11 22									
Ipswich	a					10 25				10 43			11 07					11 25				11 43			
	d	10 20								10 44			11 08		11 20							11 44			
Needham Market	d	10 29													11 29										
Stowmarket	d	10a34								10 55					11a34							11 55			
Diss	d									11 08			11 29									12 08			
Norwich	a									11 27			11 50									12 27			

Table 11

Mondays to Fridays

9 December to 16 May

London - Chelmsford, Colchester, Walton-on-Naze, Clacton, Harwich, Ipswich and Norwich

Network Diagram - refer to first Page of Table 5

		LE 1	LE ◇1 ⊏P	LE 1	LE 1	LE 1	LE 1	LE ◇1	LE 1		LE 1	LE ◇1 ⊏P	LE 1	LE 1	LE ◇1 ⊏P	LE 1	LE 1	LE 1	LE 1		LE ◇1	LE 1	LE 1	LE ◇1 ⊏P	LE 1
London Liverpool Street 15 ⊖	d		11 00				11 02	11 18				11 30	11 38	11 48	12 00				12 02		12 18			12 30	12 38
Stratford 7 ⊖	d						11 09	11 25				11u38	11 45	11 55					12 09		12 25			12u38	12 45
Romford	d												11 53												12 53
Shenfield 3	d						11 25	11 41					12 03	12 11					12 25		12 41				13 03
Ingatestone	d							11 45						12 15							12 45				
Chelmsford 3	d						11 34	11 52				12 03	12 12	12 22					12 34		12 52			13 03	13 12
Hatfield Peverel	d						11 40												12 40						
Witham 2	d						11 47	12 03					12 23	12 34					12 47		13 03				13 23
White Notley	d													12 41											
Cressing	d													12 43											
Braintree Freeport	d													12 46											
Braintree	a													12 50											
Kelvedon	d						11 51						12 27						12 51						13 27
Marks Tey 2	d						11 57						12 33						12 57						13 33
Colchester 4	a		11 46				12 04	12 15				12 22	12 40		12 46				13 04		13 15			13 22	13 40
Colchester 4	d		11 47			11 56	12 04	12 16			12 20	12 23	12 41		12 47			12 56	13 04		13 16		13 20	13 23	13 41
Colchester Town	a					12 03					12 27		12 49					13 03					13 27		13 49
	d					12 07												13 07							
Hythe	d					12 11												13 11							
Wivenhoe 3	d					12 15		12 23										13 15			13 23				
Alresford (Essex)	d					12 19												13 19							
Great Bentley	d					12 23												13 23							
Weeley	d					12 26			←									13 26				←			
Thorpe-le-Soken 1	a					12 31		12 35	12 31									13 31			13 35	13 31			
	d					12 37		12 35	12 37									13 37			13 35	13 37			
Clacton-on-Sea	a					→		12 44										→			13 44				
Kirby Cross	d								12 42													13 42			
Frinton-on-Sea	d								12 45													13 45			
Walton-on-the-Naze	a								12 49													13 49			
Manningtree 2	d		11 55		12 00		12 12					12 31			12 55		13 00		13 12					13 31	
Mistley	d				12 04												13 04								
Wrabness	d				12 09												13 09								
Harwich International	d				12 17												13 17								
Dovercourt	d				12 20												13 20								
Harwich Town	a				12 22												13 22								
Ipswich	a		12 07				12 25					12 43			13 07				13 25					13 43	
	d	11 58	12 08	12 20								12 44			13 08	13 20								13 44	
Needham Market	d			12 29												13 29									
Stowmarket	d	12a09		12a34								12 55				13a34								13 55	
Diss	d		12 29									13 08			13 29									14 08	
Norwich	a		12 50									13 27			13 50									14 27	

		LE 1	LE 1	LE ◇1 ⊏P	LE 1		LE 1	LE 1	LE 1	LE ◇1	LE 1	LE 1	LE ◇1 ⊏P	LE 1	LE 1		LE ◇1 ⊏P	LE 1	LE 1	LE 1	LE 1	LE ◇1	LE 1	LE 1	LE ◇1 ⊏P
London Liverpool Street 15 ⊖	d	12 48		13 00					13 02	13 18			13 30	13 38	13 48		14 00				14 02	14 18			14 30
Stratford 7 ⊖	d	12 55							13 09	13 25			13u38	13 45	13 55						14 09	14 25			14u38
Romford	d													13 53											
Shenfield 3	d	13 11							13 25	13 41				14 03	14 11						14 25	14 41			
Ingatestone	d	13 15								13 45					14 15							14 45			
Chelmsford 3	d	13 22							13 34	13 52			14 03	14 12	14 22						14 34	14 52			15 03
Hatfield Peverel	d								13 40												14 40				
Witham 2	d	13 34							13 47	14 03				14 23	14 34						14 47	15 03			
White Notley	d	13 41													14 41										
Cressing	d	13 43													14 43										
Braintree Freeport	d	13 46													14 46										
Braintree	a	13 50													14 50										
Kelvedon	d								13 51					14 27							14 51				
Marks Tey 2	d								13 57					14 33							14 57				
Colchester 4	a			13 46					14 04	14 15			14 22	14 40			14 46				15 04	15 15			15 22
Colchester 4	d			13 47				13 56	14 04	14 16		14 20	14 23	14 41			14 47			14 56	15 04	15 16		15 20	15 23
Colchester Town	a							14 03				14 27		14 49						15 03				15 27	
	d							14 07												15 07					
Hythe	d							14 11												15 11					
Wivenhoe 3	d							14 15		14 23										15 15		15 23			
Alresford (Essex)	d							14 19												15 19					
Great Bentley	d							14 23												15 23					
Weeley	d							14 26			←									15 26			←		
Thorpe-le-Soken 1	a							14 31		14 35	14 31									15 31		15 35	15 31		
	d							14 37		14 35	14 37									15 37		15 35	15 37		
Clacton-on-Sea	a							→		14 44										→		15 44			
Kirby Cross	d										14 42												15 42		
Frinton-on-Sea	d										14 45												15 45		
Walton-on-the-Naze	a										14 49												15 49		
Manningtree 2	d			13 55			14 00		14 12				14 31				14 55		15 00		15 12				15 31
Mistley	d						14 04												15 04						
Wrabness	d						14 09												15 09						
Harwich International	d						14 17												15 17						
Dovercourt	d						14 20												15 20						
Harwich Town	a						14 22												15 22						
Ipswich	a			14 07					14 25				14 43				15 07				15 25				15 43
	d		13 58	14 08	14 20								14 44				15 08	15 20							15 44
Needham Market	d				14 29													15 29							
Stowmarket	d		14a09		14a34								14 55					15a34							15 55
Diss	d			14 29									15 08				15 29								16 08
Norwich	a			14 50									15 27				15 48								16 27

Table 11

Mondays to Fridays

9 December to 16 May

London - Chelmsford, Colchester, Walton-on-Naze, Clacton, Harwich, Ipswich and Norwich

Network Diagram - refer to first Page of Table 5

		LE	LE	LE	LE	LE	LE	LE	LE	LE	LE	LE	LE	LE	LE	LE	LE	LE	LE	LE	LE	LE
														■				■				
		1	1	1	◇1	1	1	1	1	1	◇1	1	1	1	1	1	1	1	1	1	1	1
					☕									☕				☕				
London Liverpool Street 15 ⊖	d	14 38	14 48		15 00				15 02		15 18			15 30		15 38	15 48	16 00				16 02
Stratford 7 ⊖	d	14 45	14 55						15 09		15 25					15 45	15 55					16 09
Romford	d	14 53														15 53						
Shenfield 3	d	15 03	15 11						15 25		15 41					16 03	16 11					16 25
Ingatestone	d		15 15								15 45				15 58		16 15					
Chelmsford 3	d	15 12	15 22						15 34		15 52			16 00	16 05	16 12	16 22					16 34
Hatfield Peverel	d								15 40						16 11							16 40
Witham 2	d	15 23	15 35						15 47		16 03				16 18	16 23	16 35					16 47
White Notley	d		15 42														16 42					
Cressing	d		15 44														16 44					
Braintree Freeport	d		15 47														16 47					
Braintree	a		15 51														16 51					
Kelvedon	d	15 27							15 51						16 22	16 27						16 51
Marks Tey 2	d	15 33							15 57						16 28	16 33						16 57
Colchester 4	a	15 40			15 46				16 04		16 15			16 21	16 36	16 40		16 46				17 04
Colchester 4	d	15 41			15 47			15 56	16 04	16 14	16 16		16 20	16 21		16 41		16 47			16 56	17 04
Colchester Town	a	15 49						16 03					16 27			16 49					17 03	
	d							16 07													17 07	
Hythe	d							16 11													17 11	
Wivenhoe 3	d							16 15			16 23										17 15	
Alresford (Essex)	d							16 19													17 19	
Great Bentley	d							16 23													17 23	
Weeley	d							16 26				←									17 26	
Thorpe-le-Soken 1	a							16 31			16 35	16 31									17 31	
	d							16 37			16 35	16 37									17 37	
Clacton-on-Sea	a							↪			16 44										↪	
Kirby Cross	d											16 42										
Frinton-on-Sea	d											16 45										
Walton-on-the-Naze	a											16 49										
Manningtree 2	d				15 55		16 00		16 12	16 23				16 29				16 55		17 00		17 12
Mistley	d						16 04			16 27										17 04		
Wrabness	d						16 09			16 32										17 09		
Harwich International	d						16 17			16 41										17 17		
Dovercourt	d						16 20			16 44										17 20		
Harwich Town	a						16 22			16 46										17 22		
Ipswich	a				16 07				16 25					16 40				17 07				17 27
	d			16 00	16 08	16 20								16 41				17 08	17 20			
Needham Market	d					16 29													17 29			
Stowmarket	d			16a12		16a34								16 52				17 19	17a34			
Diss	d				16 29									17 05				17 32				
Norwich	a				16 50									17 24				17 53				

Table 11

Mondays to Fridays

9 December to 16 May

London - Chelmsford, Colchester, Walton-on-Naze, Clacton, Harwich, Ipswich and Norwich

Network Diagram - refer to first Page of Table 5

		LE	LE	LE	LE	LE	LE	LE	LE	LE	LE	LE	LE		LE	LE	LE	LE
		1	1	◇1	1	1	R 1 ☕	1	1	1	1	1	◇1		1	1	R 1 A ☕	1
London Liverpool Street [15] ⊖	d			16 14		16 17	16 30			16 32	16 34		16 44			16 47	17 00	
Stratford [7] ⊖	d			16 22		16 25					16 42		16 52			16 55		
Romford	d																	
Shenfield [3]	d			16 38		16 41				16 54	16 58					17 11		
Ingatestone	d					16 46										17 16		
Chelmsford [3]	d			16 48		16 53				17 04	17 08		17 15			17 23		
Hatfield Peverel	d										17 14							
Witham [2]	d					17a06				17 14	17 21					17a36		
White Notley	d										17 28							
Cressing	d										17 30							
Braintree Freeport	d										17 33							
Braintree	a										17 39							
Kelvedon	d			16 59									17 27					
Marks Tey [2]	d			17 05									17 32					
Colchester [4]	a			17 12			17 16			17 26			17 40					
Colchester [4]	d		17 09	17 16			17 17		17 24	17 27			17 44	17 47	17 56			
Colchester Town	a		17 16						17 33						18 03			
	d								17 37						18 07			
Hythe	d			17 20					17 41						18 11			
Wivenhoe [3]	d			17 24					17 45				17 51		18 15			
Alresford (Essex)	d								17 49				17 55		18 19			
Great Bentley	d								17 53				17 59		18 23			
Weeley	d				←				17 56			←			18 26			
Thorpe-le-Soken [1]	a			17 35	17 31				18 01			18 01	18 06		18 31			
	d			17 35	17 37				18 10			18 10	18 06		18 38			
Clacton-on-Sea	a			17 46					↪				18 17		↪			
Kirby Cross	d				17 42							18 15						
Frinton-on-Sea	d				17 45							18 18						
Walton-on-the-Naze	a				17 49							18 22						
Manningtree [2]	d	17 24								17 35				17 57				
Mistley	d	17 28												18 01				
Wrabness	d	17 33												18 06				
Harwich International	d	17 41												18 15				
Dovercourt	d	17 44												18 18				
Harwich Town	a	17 46												18 22				
Ipswich	a						17 34			17 50							17 59	
	d						17 36	17 49									18 00	18 17
Needham Market	d							17 58										18 26
Stowmarket	d						17 47	18a03										18a31
Diss	d						18 00										18 21	
Norwich	a						18 22										18 42	

A The East Anglian

Table 11

Mondays to Fridays

9 December to 16 May

London - Chelmsford, Colchester, Walton-on-Naze, Clacton, Harwich, Ipswich and Norwich

Network Diagram - refer to first Page of Table 5

		LE ◇1	LE 1	LE ◇1				LE 1	LE 1		LE 1		LE R 1 ☕	LE 1	LE ◇1		LE 1		LE 1	LE 1	LE 1		LE R 1 ☕	LE 1	
London Liverpool Street 15 ⊖	d	17 02		17 08				17 12	17 18		17 20		17 30		17 32		17 38				17 40		17 50		
Stratford 7 ⊖	d	17 10		17 16				17 20	17 26		17 29				17 40		17 46								
Romford	d																								
Shenfield 3	d	17 26									17 45										18 05				
Ingatestone	d										17 49										18 09				
Chelmsford 3	d	17 36		17 40				17 44	17 50		17 57				18 05		18 12				18 17				
Hatfield Peverel	d							17 50							18 11										
Witham 2	d	17 46		17 50				17a59			18 10				18 17						18 31				
White Notley	d										18 17														
Cressing	d										18 19														
Braintree Freeport	d										18 22														
Braintree	a										18 28														
Kelvedon	d			17 55					18 02								18 25				18 37				
Marks Tey 2	d	17 54		18 00											18 25										
Colchester 4	a	18 01		18 08					18 12						18 32		18 36				18 48		18 42		
Colchester 4	d	18 01		18 12	18 16				18 12						18 32		18 36			18 41	18 49		18 43		
Colchester Town	a				18 26																18 59				
	d																								
Hythe	d			18 16																18 45					
Wivenhoe 3	d			18 20											18 40					18 49					
Alresford (Essex)	d			18 24																18 53					
Great Bentley	d			18 28																18 57					
Weeley	d		←																	19 00					
Thorpe-le-Soken 1	a		18 31	18 35											18 51					19 05					
	d		18 38	18 35											18 51				18 56	19 05					
Clacton-on-Sea	a			18 46											19 02					19 14					
Kirby Cross	d		18 43																19 04						
Frinton-on-Sea	d		18 46																19 07						
Walton-on-the-Naze	a		18 50																19 11						
Manningtree 2	d	18 09							18 20				18 27	18 35			18 44						18 52		
Mistley	d													18 39											
Wrabness	d													18 44											
Harwich International	d													18 52											
Dovercourt	d													18 55											
Harwich Town	a													18 57											
Ipswich	a	18 20							18 35				18 37				18 59						19 03		
	d	18 25											18 39										19 04	19 13	
Needham Market	d																							19 22	
Stowmarket	d	18 36											18 50										19 16	19a27	
Diss	d	18 48											19 03										19 29		
Norwich	a	19 09											19 25										19 50		

			LE ◇1	LE 1	LE 1		LE 1			LE R 1 ☕	LE 1		LE ◇1	LE 1	LE 1	LE 1		LE 1		LE R 1 ☕	LE 1		LE 1	LE 1	LE 1
London Liverpool Street 15 ⊖	d		17 52		17 58		18 00			18 10			18 12		18 18			18 20		18 30					
Stratford 7 ⊖	d		18 00		18 06		18 09						18 20		18 26			18 29							
Romford	d																								
Shenfield 3	d						18 25											18 45							
Ingatestone	d						18 29											18 49							
Chelmsford 3	d		18 25				18 37						18 47		18 52			18 57							
Hatfield Peverel	d				18 35								18 53	←											
Witham 2	d		18 36		18 41		19 02						18 59	19 02				19 11							
White Notley	d						↪							19 09											
Cressing	d													19 11											
Braintree Freeport	d													19 14											
Braintree	a													19 20											
Kelvedon	d				18 46										19 07			19 17							
Marks Tey 2	d		18 46										19 07					19 23							
Colchester 4	a		18 53		18 56					19 00			19 14		19 17			19 30		19 21					
Colchester 4	d		18 54		18 57					19 02	19 06		19 15		19 18	19 20		19 30		19 23					
Colchester Town	a										19 13					19 27								←	
	d										19 19														
Hythe	d		18 58								19 24		19 19											19 24	
Wivenhoe 3	d		19 02								↪		19 23											19 28	
Alresford (Essex)	d																							19 31	
Great Bentley	d																							19 35	
Weeley	d																							19 39	
Thorpe-le-Soken 1	a		19 13										19 34											19 44	
	d		19 13										19 34										19 39	19 44	
Clacton-on-Sea	a		19 24										19 45											19 53	
Kirby Cross	d																						19 44		
Frinton-on-Sea	d																						19 47		
Walton-on-the-Naze	a																						19 51		
Manningtree 2	d			19 00	19 05					19 11					19 26			19 40		19 32	19 38				
Mistley	d			19 04																	19 42				
Wrabness	d			19 09																	19 47				
Harwich International	d			19 17														20a01			19 55				
Dovercourt	d			19 20																	19 58				
Harwich Town	a			19 22																	20 00				
Ipswich	a				19 19					19 21					19 41					19 42					
	d									19 23										19 44					20 00
Needham Market	d																								
Stowmarket	d									19 34										19 55					20a11
Diss	d									19 47										20 08					
Norwich	a									20 09										20 30					

Table 11

Mondays to Fridays

9 December to 16 May

London - Chelmsford, Colchester, Walton-on-Naze, Clacton, Harwich, Ipswich and Norwich

Network Diagram - refer to first Page of Table 5

		LE		LE	LE	LE			LE	LE	LE	LE	LE	LE	LE	LE	LE		LE	LE	LE	LE	LE	LE	LE
		1		◇1	◇1	1			R 1 ☕	1	1	1	1	◇1	◇1	1	R 1 ☕		1	1	1	1	1	◇1 ☕	
London Liverpool Street 15 ⊖	d	18 32		18 38	18 48				19 00		19 02			19 08	19 18		19 30			19 32		19 38	19 48	20 00	
Stratford 7 ⊖	d	18 40		18 46	18 56						19 09			19 15	19 25					19 39		19 45	19 55		
Romford	d																								
Shenfield 3	d			19 02							19 25				19 41							20 01	20 11		
Ingatestone	d			19 07											19 45								20 15		
Chelmsford 3	d	19 05		19 14	19 20						19 34			19 38	19 52					20 02		20 10	20 22		
Hatfield Peverel	d	19 11									19 40											20 16			
Witham 2	d	19 17		19 24	19 30						19 49			19 50	20 03					20 13		20 23	20 34		
White Notley	d										19 56												20 41		
Cressing	d										19 58												20 43		
Braintree Freeport	d										20 01												20 46		
Braintree	a										20 05												20 50		
Kelvedon	d	19 22												19 55								20 27			
Marks Tey 2	d			19 32										20 00								20 33			
Colchester 4	a	19 33		19 39	19 43				19 47					20 07	20 15		20 19			20 25		20 40		20 46	
Colchester 4	d	19 37	19 39	19 39	19 44				19 47				19 56	20 08	20 16		20 20		20 20	20 25		20 41		20 47	
Colchester Town	a		19 50										20 03						20 27			20 49			
	d												20 07												
Hythe	d				19 48								20 11												
Wivenhoe 3	d	19 44			19 52								20 15		20 23										
Alresford (Essex)	d	19 48											20 19												
Great Bentley	d	19 52											20 23												
Weeley	d	19 55				←							20 26			←									
Thorpe-le-Soken 1	a	20 00			20 04	20 00							20 31		20 35	20 31									
	d	20 09			20 04	20 09							20 37		20 35	20 37									
Clacton-on-Sea	a	→			20 15								→		20 44										
Kirby Cross	d					20 14										20 42									
Frinton-on-Sea	d					20 17										20 45									
Walton-on-the-Naze	a					20 23										20 49									
Manningtree 2	d			19 47					19 55			20 00		20 16			20 28			20 34	20 38			20 55	
Mistley	d											20 04									20 42				
Wrabness	d											20 09									20 47				
Harwich International	d											20 17								20a54	20 55				
Dovercourt	d											20 20									20 58				
Harwich Town	a											20 22									21 00				
Ipswich	a			20 03					20 07					20 30			20 40							21 07	
	d								20 08	20 20							20 41							21 08	21 17
Needham Market	d									20 29															21 27
Stowmarket	d								20 19	20a34							20 52							21 19	21a33
Diss	d								20 32								21 05							21 32	
Norwich	a								20 51								21 24							21 51	

		LE	LE		LE	LE	LE	LE	LE	LE	LE	LE	LE		LE	LE	LE	LE	LE	LE	LE	LE	LE		LE
		1	1		1	◇1	◇1	1	1	◇1 ☕	1	1	1		◇1 ☕		1	1	1	◇1	1	◇1 ☕	1		1
London Liverpool Street 15 ⊖	d					20 02	20 18			20 30	20 38	20 48			21 00				21 02	21 18		21 30	21 38		21 48
Stratford 7 ⊖	d					20 09	20 25			20u38	20 45	20 55							21 09	21 25		21u38	21 45		21 55
Romford	d										20 53												21 53		
Shenfield 3	d					20 25	20 41				21 03	21 11							21 25	21 41			22 03		22 11
Ingatestone	d						20 45					21 15								21 45					22 15
Chelmsford 3	d					20 34	20 52			21 03	21 12	21 22							21 34	21 52		22 03	22 12		22 22
Hatfield Peverel	d					20 40													21 40						
Witham 2	d					20 47	21 03				21 23	21 34							21 47	22 03			22 23		22 34
White Notley	d											21 41													22 41
Cressing	d											21 43													22 43
Braintree Freeport	d											21 46													22 46
Braintree	a											21 50													22 50
Kelvedon	d					20 51					21 27								21 51				22 27		
Marks Tey 2	d					20 57					21 33								21 57				22 33		
Colchester 4	a					21 04	21 15			21 22	21 40				21 46				22 04	22 15		22 22	22 40		
Colchester 4	d				20 56	21 04	21 16		21 20	21 23	21 41				21 47			21 56	22 04	22 16		22 23	22 41		
Colchester Town	a				21 03				21 27		21 49							22 03					22 49		
	d				21 07													22 07							
Hythe	d				21 11													22 11							
Wivenhoe 3	d				21 15		21 23											22 15		22 23					
Alresford (Essex)	d				21 19													22 19							
Great Bentley	d				21 23													22 23							
Weeley	d				21 26			←										22 26			←				
Thorpe-le-Soken 1	a				21 31		21 35	21 31										22 31		22 35	22 31				
	d	20 54			21 37		21 35	21 37										22 37		22 35	22 37				
Clacton-on-Sea	a	21 03			→		21 44											→		22 44					
Kirby Cross	d							21 42													22 42				
Frinton-on-Sea	d							21 45													22 45				
Walton-on-the-Naze	a							21 49													22 49				
Manningtree 2	d		21 00			21 12				21 32					21 56		22 00		22 12			22 32			
Mistley	d		21 04														22 04								
Wrabness	d		21 09														22 09								
Harwich International	d		21 17										21 38				22 17		22a28						
Dovercourt	d		21 20														22 20								
Harwich Town	a		21 22														22 22								
Ipswich	a					21 25				21 43			22 04		22 07							22 43			
	d									21 45					22 09	22 19						22 45			
Needham Market	d															22 29									
Stowmarket	d									21 56					22 20	22a35						22 56			
Diss	d									22 09					22 33							23 09			
Norwich	a									22 29					22 53							23 29			

Table 11

Mondays to Fridays

9 December to 16 May

London - Chelmsford, Colchester, Walton-on-Naze, Clacton, Harwich, Ipswich and Norwich

Network Diagram - refer to first Page of Table 5

		LE	LE	LE	LE	LE	LE	LE	LE		LE	LE	LE	LE	LE	LE	LE	LE	LE		LE	LE	LE		
															ThFO	MT WO	ThFO	MT WO	ThFO		MT WO	ThFO	MT WO		
		■1	■1	■1	■1	■1	◇■1	■1	◇■1		■1	■1	■1		■1	■1	◇■1	◇■1	◇■1		◇■1	■1	■1		
									☕										☕		☕				
London Liverpool Street ■15 ⊖	d	22 00		22 02			22 18		22 30			22 38			23 02	23 02	23 18	23 18	23 30		23 30	23 48	23 48		
Stratford ■7 ⊖	d			22 09			22 25		22u38			22 45			23 09	23 09	23 25	23 25	23u38		23u39	23 55	23 55		
Romford	d																								
Shenfield ■3	d			22 25			22 41					23 01			23 25	23 32	23 41	23 50				00 11	00 20		
Ingatestone	d						22 45					23 05					23 45	23 54				00 15	00 24		
Chelmsford ■3	d	22 28		22 34			22 52		23 03			23 12			23 34	23 41	23 52	00 01	00 03		00 11	00 22	00 31		
Hatfield Peverel	d			22 40											23 40	23 47						00 28	00 37		
Witham ■2	d			22 47			23 03					23 23	23 25		23 47	23 54	00 03	00 12				00 35	00 44		
White Notley	d												23 32												
Cressing	d												23 34												
Braintree Freeport	d												23 37												
Braintree	a												23 41												
Kelvedon	d			22 51								23 27			23 51	23 58						00 39	00 48		
Marks Tey ■2	d			22 57								23 33		23 46	23 57	00 04						00 45	00 54		
Colchester ■4	a	22 47		23 05			23 15		23 22			23 47		00 01	00 04	00 11	00 15	00 24	00 22		00 30	00 59	01 08		
Colchester ■4	d	22 47			22 56		23 16		23 23						00 04	00 11	00 16	00 25	00 23		00 31				
Colchester Town	a				23 03																				
	d				23 07																				
Hythe	d				23 11																				
Wivenhoe ■3	d				23 15		23 23										00 23	00 32							
Alresford (Essex)	d				23 19												00 27	00 36							
Great Bentley	d				23 23												00 31	00 40							
Weeley	d				23 26			←																	
Thorpe-le-Soken ■1	a				23 31		23 35	23 31									00 38	00 47							
	d				23 37	23 16	23 35	23 37									00 38	00 47							
Clacton-on-Sea	a				→	23 25	23 44										00 53	01 02							
Kirby Cross	d							23 42																	
Frinton-on-Sea	d							23 45																	
Walton-on-the-Naze	a							23 49																	
Manningtree ■2	d	22 55	23 00						23 32		23 36				00 12	00 19			00 32		00 40				
Mistley	d		23 04								23 40														
Wrabness	d		23 09								23 45														
Harwich International	d		23 17								23 53														
Dovercourt	d		23 20								23 56														
Harwich Town	a		23 22								23 58														
Ipswich	a	23 08							23 43						00 30	00 37			00 43		00 51				
	d								23 45										00 45		00 53				
Needham Market	d																								
Stowmarket	d								23 56										00 56		01 04				
Diss	d								00 09										01 09		01 17				
Norwich	a								00 29										01 35		01 43				

Table 11

Saturdays

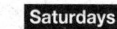

14 December to 17 May

London - Chelmsford, Colchester, Walton-on-Naze, Clacton, Harwich, Ipswich and Norwich

Network Diagram - refer to first Page of Table 5

		LE 1	LE 1	LE 1	LE 1	LE 1	LE	LE 1	LE 1	LE 1	LE 1	LE 1	LE ◇1 ⊡	LE 1	LE 1	LE 1	LE 1	LE 1	LE 1	LE ◇1	LE 1
London Liverpool Street 15 ⊖	d			00 18	00 46							05 34							06 02	06 18	
Stratford 7 ⊖	d			00 25	00 53							05 41							06 09	06 25	
Romford	d											05 49									
Shenfield 3	d		00 11	00 47	01 17							05 59							06 25	06 41	
Ingatestone	d		00 15	00 52	01 21							06 03								06 45	
Chelmsford 3	d		00 22	00 59	01 28							06 10							06 34	06 52	
Hatfield Peverel	d		00 28	01 05								06 16							06 40		
Witham 2	d	00 05	00 35	01 11	01 39	05 34						06 23		06 34					06 47	07 03	
White Notley	d	00 12				05 41								06 41							
Cressing	d	00 14				05 43								06 43							
Braintree Freeport	d	00 17				05 46								06 46							
Braintree	a	00 21				05 50								06 50							
Kelvedon	d		00 39	01 16								06 27							06 51		
Marks Tey 2	d		00 45	01 21								06 33							06 57		
Colchester 4	a		00 59	01 35	01 58							06 40							07 04	07 15	
Colchester 4	d							05 40		05 52	06 20	06 40						06 56	07 04	07 16	
Colchester Town	a										06 27							07 03			
	d																	07 07			
Hythe	d																	07 11			
Wivenhoe 3	d																	07 15		07 23	
Alresford (Essex)	d																	07 19			
Great Bentley	d																	07 23			
Weeley	d																	07 26			←
Thorpe-le-Soken 1	a																	07 31		07 35	07 31
	d														06 37			07 37		07 35	07 37
Clacton-on-Sea	a																	→		07 44	
Kirby Cross	d														06 42						07 42
Frinton-on-Sea	d														06 45						07 45
Walton-on-the-Naze	a														06 49						07 49
Manningtree 2	d							05 49		06 00		06 48				07 00			07 12		
Mistley	d									06 04						07 04					
Wrabness	d									06 09						07 09					
Harwich International	d									06 17						07 17					
Dovercourt	d									06 20						07 20					
Harwich Town	a									06 22						07 22					
Ipswich	a							05 59				07 00							07 25		
	d						05 10	06 00	06 16				07 10				07 20				
Needham Market	d						05 20		06 25								07 29				
Stowmarket	d						05a26	06a11	06a30				07 21				07a34				
Diss	d												07 34								
Norwich	a												07 53								

		LE ◇1 ⊡	LE 1	LE 1	LE 1	LE 1	LE ◇1 ⊡	LE 1	LE 1	LE 1	LE 1	LE ◇1	LE 1	LE 1	LE ◇1 ⊡	LE 1	LE 1	LE ◇1 ⊡	LE 1	LE 1	LE 1	LE 1
London Liverpool Street 15 ⊖	d	06 30	06 38		06 48		07 00				07 02	07 18			07 30	07 38	07 48	08 00				08 02
Stratford 7 ⊖	d	06u38	06 45		06 55						07 09	07 25			07u38	07 45	07 55					08 09
Romford	d		06 53													07 53						
Shenfield 3	d		07 03		07 11						07 25	07 41				08 03	08 11					08 25
Ingatestone	d				07 15							07 45					08 15					
Chelmsford 3	d	07 03	07 12		07 22						07 34	07 52			08 03	08 12	08 22					08 34
Hatfield Peverel	d										07 40											08 40
Witham 2	d		07 23		07 34						07 47	08 03				08 23	08 34					08 47
White Notley	d				07 41												08 41					
Cressing	d				07 43												08 43					
Braintree Freeport	d				07 46												08 46					
Braintree	a				07 50												08 50					
Kelvedon	d		07 27								07 51					08 27						08 51
Marks Tey 2	d		07 33								07 57					08 33						08 57
Colchester 4	a	07 22	07 40				07 46				08 04	08 15			08 22	08 40		08 46				09 04
Colchester 4	d	07 23	07 40	07 44			07 47	07 56			08 04	08 16		08 20	08 23	08 41		08 47			08 56	09 04
Colchester Town	a			07 51				08 03						08 27		08 49					09 03	
	d							08 07													09 07	
Hythe	d							08 11													09 11	
Wivenhoe 3	d							08 15				08 23									09 15	
Alresford (Essex)	d							08 19													09 19	
Great Bentley	d							08 23													09 23	
Weeley	d							08 26					←								09 26	
Thorpe-le-Soken 1	a							08 31				08 35	08 31								09 31	
	d							08 37				08 35	08 37								09 37	
Clacton-on-Sea	a							→				08 44									→	
Kirby Cross	d												08 42									
Frinton-on-Sea	d												08 45									
Walton-on-the-Naze	a												08 49									
Manningtree 2	d	07 31	07 48				07 55			08 00	08 12				08 31			08 55		09 00		09 12
Mistley	d								08 02	08 04										09 04		
Wrabness	d									08 09										09 09		
Harwich International	d		08a09							08 17										09 17		
Dovercourt	d									08 20										09 20		
Harwich Town	a									08 22										09 22		
Ipswich	a	07 43					08 07		08 17		08 25				08 43			09 07				09 25
	d	07 44				08 00	08 08		08 20						08 44			09 08	09 20			
Needham Market	d								08 29										09 29			
Stowmarket	d	07 55				08a11			08a34						08 55				09a34			
Diss	d	08 08					08 29								09 08			09 29				
Norwich	a	08 27					08 50								09 27			09 50				

Table 11

Saturdays

14 December to 17 May

London - Chelmsford, Colchester, Walton-on-Naze, Clacton, Harwich, Ipswich and Norwich

Network Diagram - refer to first Page of Table 5

		LE ◇1	LE 1	LE 1	LE ◇1 ⊏P	LE 1	LE 1	LE 1		LE ◇1 ⊏P	LE 1	LE 1	LE 1	LE 1	LE ◇1	LE 1	LE 1	LE ◇1 ⊏P		LE 1	LE 1	LE ◇1 ⊏P	LE 1	LE 1	LE 1
London Liverpool Street 15 ⊖	d	08 18			08 30	08 38	08 48			09 00				09 02	09 18			09 30		09 38	09 48	10 00			
Stratford 7 ⊖	d	08 25			08u38	08 45	08 55							09 09	09 25			09u38		09 45	09 55				
Romford	d					08 53														09 53					
Shenfield 3	d	08 41				09 03	09 11							09 25	09 41					10 03	10 11				
Ingatestone	d	08 45					09 15								09 45						10 15				
Chelmsford 3	d	08 52			09 03	09 12	09 22							09 34	09 52			10 03		10 12	10 22				
Hatfield Peverel	d													09 40											
Witham 2	d	09 03				09 23	09 34							09 47	10 03					10 23	10 34				
White Notley	d						09 41														10 41				
Cressing	d						09 43														10 43				
Braintree Freeport	d						09 46														10 46				
Braintree	a						09 50														10 50				
Kelvedon	d					09 27								09 51						10 27					
Marks Tey 2	d					09 33								09 57						10 33					
Colchester 4	a	09 15			09 22	09 40				09 46				10 04	10 15			10 22		10 40		10 46			
Colchester 4	d	09 16		09 20	09 23	09 41				09 47			09 56	10 04	10 16		10 20	10 23		10 41		10 47			10 56
Colchester Town	a			09 27		09 49							10 03				10 27			10 49					11 03
	d												10 07												11 07
Hythe	d												10 11												11 11
Wivenhoe 3	d	09 23											10 15		10 23										11 15
Alresford (Essex)	d												10 19												11 19
Great Bentley	d												10 23												11 23
Weeley	d		←										10 26			←									11 26
Thorpe-le-Soken 1	a	09 35	09 31										10 31		10 35	10 31									11 31
	d	09 35	09 37										10 37		10 35	10 37									11 37
Clacton-on-Sea	a	09 44											→		10 44										→
Kirby Cross	d		09 42													10 42									
Frinton-on-Sea	d		09 45													10 45									
Walton-on-the-Naze	a		09 49													10 49									
Manningtree 2	d				09 31					09 55		10 00		10 12				10 31				10 55		11 00	
Mistley	d											10 04												11 04	
Wrabness	d											10 09												11 09	
Harwich International	d											10 17												11 17	
Dovercourt	d											10 20												11 20	
Harwich Town	a											10 22												11 22	
Ipswich	a				09 43					10 07				10 25				10 43				11 07			
	d				09 44			09 58		10 08	10 20							10 44				11 08	11 20		
Needham Market	d										10 29												11 29		
Stowmarket	d				09 55			10a09			10a34							10 55					11a34		
Diss	d				10 08					10 29								11 08				11 29			
Norwich	a				10 27					10 50								11 27				11 50			

		LE 1	LE ◇1	LE 1		LE 1	LE ◇1 ⊏P	LE 1	LE 1	LE 1	LE ◇1 ⊏P	LE 1	LE 1	LE 1		LE 1	LE ◇1	LE 1	LE 1	LE ◇1 ⊏P	LE 1	LE 1	LE ◇1 ⊏P	LE 1	
London Liverpool Street 15 ⊖	d	10 02	10 18				10 30	10 38	10 48		11 00					11 02	11 18			11 30	11 38	11 48	12 00		
Stratford 7 ⊖	d	10 09	10 25				10u38	10 45	10 55							11 09	11 25			11u38	11 45	11 55			
Romford	d							10 53													11 53				
Shenfield 3	d	10 25	10 41					11 03	11 11							11 25	11 41				12 03	12 11			
Ingatestone	d		10 45						11 15								11 45					12 15			
Chelmsford 3	d	10 34	10 52				11 03	11 12	11 22							11 34	11 52			12 03	12 12	12 22			
Hatfield Peverel	d	10 40														11 40									
Witham 2	d	10 47	11 03					11 23	11 34							11 47	12 03				12 23	12 34			
White Notley	d								11 41													12 41			
Cressing	d								11 43													12 43			
Braintree Freeport	d								11 46													12 46			
Braintree	a								11 50													12 50			
Kelvedon	d	10 51						11 27								11 51					12 27				
Marks Tey 2	d	10 57						11 33								11 57					12 33				
Colchester 4	a	11 04	11 15				11 22	11 40			11 46					12 04	12 15			12 22	12 40		12 46		
Colchester 4	d	11 04	11 16			11 20	11 23	11 41			11 47			11 56		12 04	12 16		12 20	12 23	12 41		12 47		
Colchester Town	a					11 27		11 49						12 03					12 27		12 49				
	d													12 07											
Hythe	d													12 11											
Wivenhoe 3	d		11 23											12 15			12 23								
Alresford (Essex)	d													12 19											
Great Bentley	d													12 23											
Weeley	d			←										12 26				←							
Thorpe-le-Soken 1	a		11 35	11 31										12 31			12 35	12 31							
	d		11 35	11 37										12 37			12 35	12 37							
Clacton-on-Sea	a		11 44											→			12 44								
Kirby Cross	d			11 42														12 42							
Frinton-on-Sea	d			11 45														12 45							
Walton-on-the-Naze	a			11 49														12 49							
Manningtree 2	d	11 12					11 31				11 55		12 00			12 12				12 31			12 55		
Mistley	d												12 04												
Wrabness	d												12 09												
Harwich International	d												12 17												
Dovercourt	d												12 20												
Harwich Town	a												12 22												
Ipswich	a	11 25					11 43				12 07					12 25				12 43			13 07		
	d						11 44			11 58	12 08	12 20								12 44			13 08	13 20	
Needham Market	d											12 29												13 29	
Stowmarket	d						11 55			12a09		12a34								12 55				13a34	
Diss	d						12 08				12 29									13 08			13 29		
Norwich	a						12 27				12 50									13 27			13 50		

Table 11

Saturdays

14 December to 17 May

London - Chelmsford, Colchester, Walton-on-Naze, Clacton, Harwich, Ipswich and Norwich

Network Diagram - refer to first Page of Table 5

		LE 1	LE 1	LE 1	LE ◇1	LE 1	LE 1	LE ◇1 ☕	LE 1	LE 1	LE 1	LE ◇1 ☕	LE 1	LE 1	LE 1	LE 1	LE ◇1	LE 1	LE 1	LE ◇1 ☕	LE 1	LE 1	LE ◇1 ☕
London Liverpool Street 15 ⊖	d			12 02	12 18			12 30	12 38	12 48		13 00				13 02	13 18			13 30	13 38	13 48	14 00
Stratford 7 ⊖	d			12 09	12 25			12u38	12 45	12 55						13 09	13 25			13u38	13 45	13 55	
Romford	d								12 53												13 53		
Shenfield 3	d			12 25	12 41				13 03	13 11						13 25	13 41				14 03	14 11	
Ingatestone	d				12 45					13 15							13 45					14 15	
Chelmsford 3	d			12 34	12 52			13 03	13 12	13 22						13 34	13 52			14 03	14 12	14 22	
Hatfield Peverel	d			12 40												13 40							
Witham 2	d			12 47	13 03				13 23	13 34						13 47	14 03				14 23	14 34	
White Notley	d									13 41												14 41	
Cressing	d									13 43												14 43	
Braintree Freeport	d									13 46												14 46	
Braintree	a									13 50												14 50	
Kelvedon	d			12 51					13 27							13 51					14 27		
Marks Tey 2	d			12 57					13 33							13 57					14 33		
Colchester 4	a			13 04	13 15			13 22	13 40			13 46				14 04	14 15			14 22	14 40		14 46
Colchester 4	d		12 56	13 04	13 16		13 20	13 23	13 41			13 47			13 56	14 04	14 16		14 20	14 23	14 41		14 47
Colchester Town	a		13 03				13 27		13 49						14 03				14 27		14 49		
	d		13 07												14 07								
Hythe	d		13 11												14 11								
Wivenhoe 3	d		13 15		13 23										14 15		14 23						
Alresford (Essex)	d		13 19												14 19								
Great Bentley	d		13 23												14 23								
Weeley	d		13 26			←									14 26			←					
Thorpe-le-Soken 1	a		13 31		13 35	13 31									14 31		14 35	14 31					
	d		13 37		13 35	13 37									14 37		14 35	14 37					
Clacton-on-Sea	a		→		13 44										→		14 44						
Kirby Cross	d					13 42												14 42					
Frinton-on-Sea	d					13 45												14 45					
Walton-on-the-Naze	a					13 49												14 49					
Manningtree 2	d	13 00		13 12				13 31				13 55		14 00		14 12				14 31			14 55
Mistley	d	13 04												14 04									
Wrabness	d	13 09												14 09									
Harwich International	d	13 17												14 17									
Dovercourt	d	13 20												14 20									
Harwich Town	a	13 22												14 22									
Ipswich	a			13 25				13 43				14 07				14 25				14 43			15 07
	d							13 44			13 58	14 08	14 20							14 44			15 08
Needham Market	d												14 29										
Stowmarket	d							13 55			14a09		14a34							14 55			
Diss	d							14 08				14 29								15 08			15 29
Norwich	a							14 27				14 50								15 27			15 48

		LE 1	LE 1	LE 1	LE 1	LE ◇1	LE 1	LE 1	LE ◇1 ☕	LE 1	LE 1	LE 1	LE ◇1 ☕	LE 1	LE 1	LE 1	LE 1	LE ◇1	LE 1	LE 1	LE ◇1 ☕	LE 1	LE 1
London Liverpool Street 15 ⊖	d				14 02	14 18			14 30	14 38	14 48		15 00				15 02	15 18			15 30	15 38	15 48
Stratford 7 ⊖	d				14 09	14 25			14u38	14 45	14 55						15 09	15 25			15u38	15 45	15 55
Romford	d									14 53												15 53	
Shenfield 3	d				14 25	14 41				15 03	15 11						15 25	15 41				16 03	16 11
Ingatestone	d					14 45					15 15							15 45					16 15
Chelmsford 3	d				14 34	14 52			15 03	15 12	15 22						15 34	15 52			16 03	16 12	16 22
Hatfield Peverel	d				14 40												15 40						
Witham 2	d				14 47	15 03				15 23	15 34						15 47	16 03				16 23	16 34
White Notley	d										15 41												16 41
Cressing	d										15 43												16 43
Braintree Freeport	d										15 46												16 46
Braintree	a										15 50												16 50
Kelvedon	d				14 51					15 27							15 51					16 27	
Marks Tey 2	d				14 57					15 33							15 57					16 33	
Colchester 4	a				15 04	15 15			15 22	15 40			15 46				16 04	16 15			16 22	16 40	
Colchester 4	d			14 56	15 04	15 16		15 20	15 23	15 41			15 47			15 56	16 04	16 16		16 20	16 23	16 41	
Colchester Town	a			15 03				15 27		15 49						16 03				16 27		16 49	
	d			15 07												16 07							
Hythe	d			15 11												16 11							
Wivenhoe 3	d			15 15		15 23										16 15		16 23					
Alresford (Essex)	d			15 19												16 19							
Great Bentley	d			15 23												16 23							
Weeley	d			15 26			←									16 26			←				
Thorpe-le-Soken 1	a			15 31		15 35	15 31									16 31		16 35	16 31				
	d			15 37		15 35	15 37									16 37		16 35	16 37				
Clacton-on-Sea	a			→		15 44										→		16 44					
Kirby Cross	d						15 42												16 42				
Frinton-on-Sea	d						15 45												16 45				
Walton-on-the-Naze	a						15 49												16 49				
Manningtree 2	d		15 00		15 12				15 31				15 55		16 00		16 12				16 31		
Mistley	d		15 04												16 04								
Wrabness	d		15 09												16 09								
Harwich International	d		15 17												16 17								
Dovercourt	d		15 20												16 20								
Harwich Town	a		15 22												16 22								
Ipswich	a				15 25				15 43				16 07				16 25				16 43		
	d	15 20							15 44			15 58	16 08	16 20							16 44		
Needham Market	d	15 29												16 29									
Stowmarket	d	15a34							15 55			16a09		16a34							16 55		
Diss	d								16 08				16 29								17 08		
Norwich	a								16 27				16 50								17 27		

Table 11

Saturdays

14 December to 17 May

London - Chelmsford, Colchester, Walton-on-Naze, Clacton, Harwich, Ipswich and Norwich

Network Diagram - refer to first Page of Table 5

		LE ◇1 ⊡		LE 1	LE 1	LE 1	LE 1	LE ◇1	LE 1	LE 1	LE ◇1 ⊡	LE 1		LE 1	LE 1	LE ◇1 ⊡	LE 1	LE 1	LE 1	LE 1	LE ◇1	LE 1		LE 1	LE ◇1 ⊡
London Liverpool Street 15 ⊖	d	16 00					16 02	16 18			16 30	16 38		16 48		17 00				17 02	17 18				17 30
Stratford 7 ⊖	d						16 09	16 25			16u38	16 45		16 55						17 09	17 25				17u38
Romford	d											16 53													
Shenfield 3	d						16 25	16 41				17 03		17 11						17 25	17 41				
Ingatestone	d							16 45						17 15							17 45				
Chelmsford 3	d						16 34	16 52			17 03	17 12		17 22						17 34	17 52				18 03
Hatfield Peverel	d						16 40													17 40					
Witham 2	d						16 47	17 03				17 23		17 34						17 47	18 03				
White Notley	d													17 41											
Cressing	d													17 43											
Braintree Freeport	d													17 46											
Braintree	a													17 50											
Kelvedon	d						16 51					17 27								17 51					
Marks Tey 2	d						16 57					17 33								17 57					
Colchester 4	a	16 46					17 04	17 15			17 22	17 40				17 46				18 04	18 15				18 22
Colchester 4	d	16 47				16 56	17 04	17 16		17 20	17 23	17 41				17 47			17 56	18 04	18 16			18 20	18 23
Colchester Town	a					17 03				17 27		17 49							18 03					18 27	
	d					17 07													18 07						
Hythe	d					17 11													18 11						
Wivenhoe 3	d					17 15		17 23											18 15		18 23				
Alresford (Essex)	d					17 19													18 19						
Great Bentley	d					17 23													18 23						
Weeley	d					17 26			←										18 26			←			
Thorpe-le-Soken 1	a					17 31		17 35	17 31										18 31		18 35	18 31			
	d					17 37		17 35	17 37										18 37		18 35	18 37			
Clacton-on-Sea	a					→		17 44											→		18 44				
Kirby Cross	d								17 42													18 42			
Frinton-on-Sea	d								17 45													18 45			
Walton-on-the-Naze	a								17 49													18 49			
Manningtree 2	d	16 55			17 00		17 12				17 31					17 55		18 00		18 12					18 31
Mistley	d				17 04													18 04							
Wrabness	d				17 09													18 09							
Harwich International	d				17 17													18 17							
Dovercourt	d				17 20													18 20							
Harwich Town	a				17 22													18 22							
Ipswich	a	17 07					17 25				17 43					18 07				18 25					18 43
	d	17 08		17 20							17 44				17 58	18 08	18 20								18 44
Needham Market	d			17 29													18 29								
Stowmarket	d	17 19		17a34							17 55				18a09		18a34								18 55
Diss	d	17 32									18 08					18 29									19 08
Norwich	a	17 51									18 27					18 50									19 27

		LE 1	LE 1	LE ◇1 ⊡	LE 1	LE 1	LE 1	LE 1		LE ◇1	LE 1	LE 1	LE ◇1 ⊡	LE 1	LE 1	LE 1	LE ◇1 ⊡	LE 1		LE 1	LE 1	LE 1	LE ◇1	LE 1	LE 1
London Liverpool Street 15 ⊖	d	17 38	17 48	18 00				18 02		18 18			18 30	18 38	18 48		19 00					19 02	19 18		
Stratford 7 ⊖	d	17 45	17 55					18 09		18 25			18u38	18 45	18 55							19 09	19 25		
Romford	d	17 53												18 53											
Shenfield 3	d	18 03	18 11					18 25		18 41				19 03	19 11							19 25	19 41		
Ingatestone	d		18 15							18 45					19 15								19 45		
Chelmsford 3	d	18 12	18 22					18 34		18 52			19 03	19 12	19 22							19 34	19 52		
Hatfield Peverel	d							18 40														19 40			
Witham 2	d	18 23	18 34					18 47		19 03				19 23	19 34							19 47	20 03		
White Notley	d		18 41												19 41										
Cressing	d		18 43												19 43										
Braintree Freeport	d		18 46												19 46										
Braintree	a		18 50												19 50										
Kelvedon	d	18 27						18 51						19 27								19 51			
Marks Tey 2	d	18 33						18 57						19 33								19 57			
Colchester 4	a	18 40		18 46				19 04		19 15			19 22	19 40			19 46					20 04	20 15		
Colchester 4	d	18 41		18 47			18 56	19 04		19 16		19 20	19 23	19 41			19 47				19 56	20 04	20 16		20 20
Colchester Town	a	18 49					19 03					19 27		19 49							20 03				20 27
	d						19 07														20 07				
Hythe	d						19 11														20 11				
Wivenhoe 3	d						19 15			19 23											20 15		20 23		
Alresford (Essex)	d						19 19														20 19				
Great Bentley	d						19 23														20 23				
Weeley	d						19 26				←										20 26			←	
Thorpe-le-Soken 1	a						19 31			19 35	19 31										20 31		20 35	20 31	
	d						19 37			19 35	19 37										20 37		20 35	20 37	
Clacton-on-Sea	a						→			19 44											→		20 44		
Kirby Cross	d										19 42													20 42	
Frinton-on-Sea	d										19 45													20 45	
Walton-on-the-Naze	a										19 49													20 49	
Manningtree 2	d			18 55		19 00		19 12					19 31				19 55			20 00		20 12			
Mistley	d					19 04														20 04					
Wrabness	d					19 09														20 09					
Harwich International	d					19 17														20 17					
Dovercourt	d					19 20														20 20					
Harwich Town	a					19 22														20 22					
Ipswich	a			19 07				19 25					19 43				20 07					20 25			
	d			19 08	19 20								19 44			19 58	20 08	20 20							
Needham Market	d				19 29													20 29							
Stowmarket	d				19a34								19 55			20a09		20a34							
Diss	d			19 29									20 08				20 29								
Norwich	a			19 50									20 27				20 50								

Table 11

Saturdays

14 December to 17 May

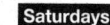

London - Chelmsford, Colchester, Walton-on-Naze, Clacton, Harwich, Ipswich and Norwich

Network Diagram - refer to first Page of Table 5

		LE ◇1 ☕	LE 1	LE 1		LE 1	LE ◇1 ☕	LE	LE 1	LE 1	LE 1	LE ◇1	LE 1	LE 1		LE ◇1 ☕	LE 1	LE 1	LE 1	LE 1	LE	LE 1	LE 1	LE 1	
London Liverpool Street 15 ⊖	d	19 30	19 32	19 38		19 48	20 00				20 02	20 18				20 30	20 38	20 48		21 00				21 02	
Stratford 7 ⊖	d	19u38	19 39	19 46		19 55					20 09	20 25				20u38	20 45	20 55						21 09	
Romford	d			19 54													20 53								
Shenfield 3	d		19 57	20 04		20 11					20 25	20 41					21 03	21 11						21 25	
Ingatestone	d					20 15						20 45						21 15							
Chelmsford 3	d	20 03	20 07	20 13		20 22					20 34	20 52				21 03	21 12	21 22						21 34	
Hatfield Peverel	d										20 40													21 40	
Witham 2	d		20 20	20 24		20 34					20 47	21 03					21 23	21 34						21 47	
White Notley	d					20 41												21 41							
Cressing	d					20 43												21 43							
Braintree Freeport	d					20 46												21 46							
Braintree	a					20 50												21 50							
Kelvedon	d			20 28							20 51						21 27							21 51	
Marks Tey 2	d			20 34							20 57						21 33							21 57	
Colchester 4	a	20 22	20 32	20 41			20 46				21 04	21 15				21 22	21 40			21 46				22 04	
Colchester 4	d	20 23	20 32	20 42			20 47			20 56	21 04	21 16		21 20		21 23	21 41			21 47			21 56	22 04	
Colchester Town	a			20 50						21 03				21 27			21 49						22 03		
	d									21 07													22 07		
Hythe	d									21 11													22 11		
Wivenhoe 3	d									21 15		21 23											22 15		
Alresford (Essex)	d									21 19													22 19		
Great Bentley	d									21 23													22 23		
Weeley	d									21 26			←										22 26		
Thorpe-le-Soken 1	a									21 31		21 35	21 31										22 31		
	d									21 37		21 35	21 37										22 37		
Clacton-on-Sea	a									→		21 44											→		
Kirby Cross	d												21 42												
Frinton-on-Sea	d												21 45												
Walton-on-the-Naze	a												21 49												
Manningtree 2	d	20 31	20 40				20 55		21 00		21 12					21 32				21 55		22 00		22 12	
Mistley	d								21 04													22 04			
Wrabness	d								21 09													22 09			
Harwich International	d		20a56						21 17										21 38			22 17		22a28	
Dovercourt	d								21 20													22 20			
Harwich Town	a								21 22													22 22			
Ipswich	a	20 43					21 07				21 25					21 43			22 03	22 08					
	d	20 44					21 08	21 17								21 45					22 19				
Needham Market	d							21 27													22 29				
Stowmarket	d	20 55						21a33								21 56					22a35				
Diss	d	21 08					21 29									22 09									
Norwich	a	21 27					21 50									22 29									

		LE ◇1	LE 1	LE ◇1 ☕	LE 1	LE 1	LE 1	LE 1	LE 1	LE 1		LE 1	LE ◇1	LE 1	LE ◇1 ☕	LE 1	LE 1	LE 1	LE	LE		LE 1	LE	LE ◇1 ☕	LE 1
London Liverpool Street 15 ⊖	d	21 18		21 30	21 38	21 48	22 00		22 02				22 18		22 30		22 32					23 02		23 30	23 32
Stratford 7 ⊖	d	21 25		21u38	21 45	21 55			22 09				22 25		22u38		22 41					23 09		23u38	23 41
Romford	d				21 53												22 49								
Shenfield 3	d	21 41			22 03	22 11			22 25				22 41				22 59					23 33			00 04
Ingatestone	d	21 45				22 15							22 45				23 03								00 08
Chelmsford 3	d	21 52		22 03	22 12	22 22	22 28		22 34				22 52		23 03		23 10					23 42			00 15
Hatfield Peverel	d								22 40								23 16								00 21
Witham 2	d	22 03			22 23	22 34			22 47				23 03				23 23	23 25				23 53			00 28
White Notley	d					22 41												23 32							
Cressing	d					22 43												23 34							
Braintree Freeport	d					22 46												23 37							
Braintree	a					22 50												23 41							
Kelvedon	d				22 27				22 51								23 27					23 57			00 32
Marks Tey 2	d				22 33				22 57								23 33			23 46		00 03			00 38
Colchester 4	a	22 15		22 22	22 40		22 47		23 05				23 15		23 22		23 47			00 01		00 10		00 26	00 52
Colchester 4	d	22 16		22 23	22 41		22 48			22 56			23 16		23 23							00 10		00 26	
Colchester Town	a				22 49					23 03															
	d									23 07															
Hythe	d									23 11															
Wivenhoe 3	d	22 23								23 15			23 23												
Alresford (Essex)	d									23 19															
Great Bentley	d									23 23															
Weeley	d		←							23 26				←											
Thorpe-le-Soken 1	a	22 35	22 31							23 31			23 35	23 31											
	d	22 35	22 37							23 37		23 16	23 35	23 37											
Clacton-on-Sea	a	22 44								→		23 25	23 44												
Kirby Cross	d		22 42											23 42											
Frinton-on-Sea	d		22 45											23 45											
Walton-on-the-Naze	a		22 49											23 49											
Manningtree 2	d			22 32			22 56	23 00							23 32	23 36						00 18		00 35	
Mistley	d							23 04								23 40									
Wrabness	d							23 09								23 45									
Harwich International	d							23 17								23 53									
Dovercourt	d							23 20								23 56									
Harwich Town	a							23 22								23 58									
Ipswich	a			22 43			23 08								23 43							00 36		00 47	
	d			22 45											23 45									00 48	
Needham Market	d																								
Stowmarket	d			22 56											23 56									01 00	
Diss	d			23 09											00 09									01 13	
Norwich	a			23 29											00 35									01 38	

Table 11

Saturdays

14 December to 17 May

London - Chelmsford, Colchester, Walton-on-Naze, Clacton, Harwich, Ipswich and Norwich

Network Diagram - refer to first Page of Table 5

		LE 1
London Liverpool Street 15 ⊖	d	23 58
Stratford 7 ⊖	d	00 05
Romford	d	
Shenfield 3	d	00 30
Ingatestone	d	
Chelmsford 3	d	00 39
Hatfield Peverel	d	
Witham 2	d	00 50
White Notley	d	
Cressing	d	
Braintree Freeport	d	
Braintree	a	
Kelvedon	d	
Marks Tey 2	d	
Colchester 4	a	01 09
Colchester 4	d	
Colchester Town	a	
	d	
Hythe	d	
Wivenhoe 3	d	
Alresford (Essex)	d	
Great Bentley	d	
Weeley	d	
Thorpe-le-Soken 1	a	
	d	
Clacton-on-Sea	a	
Kirby Cross	d	
Frinton-on-Sea	d	
Walton-on-the-Naze	a	
Manningtree 2	d	
Mistley	d	
Wrabness	d	
Harwich International	d	
Dovercourt	d	
Harwich Town	a	
Ipswich	a	
	d	
Needham Market	d	
Stowmarket	d	
Diss	d	
Norwich	a	

Sundays

8 December to 11 May

		LE 1	LE 1 A	LE 1	LE 1 A	LE	LE 1	LE 1	LE	LE		LE 1	LE 1	LE 1	LE 1	LE 1	LE 1	LE 1	LE ◇1	LE 1		LE 1	LE 1	LE 1	LE 1
London Liverpool Street 15 ⊖	d						00 18									07 55			08 30						09 02
Stratford 7 ⊖	d				00 05		00 25									08 02									09 09
Romford	d																								
Shenfield 3	d		00 04		00 30		00 47									08 25	08 28		08 58				09 02		09 32
Ingatestone	d		00 08				00 51										08 33								09 36
Chelmsford 3	d		00 15		00 39		00 58									08 34	08 40						09 11		09 43
Hatfield Peverel	d		00 21				01 04										08 46								09 49
Witham 2	d	00 05	00 28		00 50		01 11	07 35				08 25				08 45	08 52						09 22	09 25	09 56
White Notley	d	00 12						07 42				08 32												09 32	
Cressing	d	00 14						07 44				08 34												09 34	
Braintree Freeport	d	00 17						07 47				08 37												09 37	
Braintree	a	00 21						07 51				08 41												09 41	
Kelvedon	d		00 32				01 15										08 57								10 00
Marks Tey 2	d		00 38				01 21										09 03						09 29		10 06
Colchester 4	a		00 52		01 09		01 35									08 57	09 10		09 25				09 37		10 13
Colchester 4	d			00 30										08 18	08 37	08 57	09 14		09 25			09 32	09 37		10 13
Colchester Town	a																								
	d																								
Hythe	d																								
Wivenhoe 3	d			00 37											08 45								09 45		
Alresford (Essex)	d			00 41											08 48								09 48		
Great Bentley	d			00 45											08 52								09 52		
Weeley	d																								
Thorpe-le-Soken 1	a			00 52											08 59								09 59		
	d			00 52											08 59					09 01			09 59		
Clacton-on-Sea	a			01 01											09 08								10 08		
Kirby Cross	d																			09 06					
Frinton-on-Sea	d																			09 09					
Walton-on-the-Naze	a																			09 13					
Manningtree 2	d													08 26		09 05	09 22	09 26	09 33			09 40			10 21
Mistley	d													08 30				09 30							
Wrabness	d													08 35				09 35							
Harwich International	d												08 30	08 43		09a25		09 43							
Dovercourt	d													08 46				09 46							
Harwich Town	a													08 48				09 48							
Ipswich	a												08 53				09 34		09 45			09 51			10 33
	d									07 32			09 02						09 46			09 55			
Needham Market	d									07 42			09 12												
Stowmarket	d									07a48			09a17						09 57			10a06			
Diss	d																		10 10						
Norwich	a																		10 31						

A not 8 December

Table 11

Sundays

8 December to 11 May

London - Chelmsford, Colchester, Walton-on-Naze, Clacton, Harwich, Ipswich and Norwich

Network Diagram - refer to first Page of Table 5

Station		LE [1]	LE	LE ◇[1] ☕	LE [1]	LE [1]		LE ◇[1]	LE [1]	LE	LE [1]	LE [1]	LE	LE ◇[1] ☕	LE [1]	LE ◇[1]		LE [1]	LE	LE [1]	LE [1]	LE [1]	LE	LE ◇[1] ☕	LE [1]
London Liverpool Street [15] ⊖	d			09 30				09 32			10 02			10 30		10 32					11 02			11 30	
Stratford [7] ⊖	d							09 39			10 09					10 39					11 09				
Romford	d																								
Shenfield [3]	d							10 02			10 32					11 02					11 32				
Ingatestone	d										10 36										11 36				
Chelmsford [3]	d							10 11			10 43					11 11					11 43				
Hatfield Peverel	d										10 49										11 49				
Witham [2]	d							10 22	10 25		10 56					11 22		11 25			11 56				
White Notley	d								10 32									11 32							
Cressing	d								10 34									11 34							
Braintree Freeport	d								10 37									11 37							
Braintree	a								10 41									11 41							
Kelvedon	d										11 00										12 00				
Marks Tey [2]	d							10 29			11 06					11 29					12 06				
Colchester [4]	a			10 25				10 37			11 13			11 25		11 37					12 13			12 25	
Colchester [4]	d			10 25				10 37			11 13			11 25		11 37					12 13			12 25	
Colchester Town	a																								
	d																								
Hythe	d																								
Wivenhoe [3]	d							10 45								11 45									
Alresford (Essex)	d							10 48								11 48									
Great Bentley	d							10 52								11 52									
Weeley	d																								
Thorpe-le-Soken [1]	a							10 59								11 59									
	d					10 01		10 59							11 01	11 59									
Clacton-on-Sea	a							11 08								12 08									
Kirby Cross	d					10 06									11 06										
Frinton-on-Sea	d					10 09									11 09										
Walton-on-the-Naze	a					10 13									11 13										
Manningtree [2]	d	10 26		10 33							11 21	11 26		11 33							12 21	12 26		12 33	
Mistley	d	10 30										11 30										12 30			
Wrabness	d	10 35										11 35										12 35			
Harwich International	d	10 43										11 43										12 43			
Dovercourt	d	10 46										11 46										12 46			
Harwich Town	a	10 48										11 48										12 48			
Ipswich	a			10 45							11 33			11 45							12 33			12 45	
	d			10 46	11 02									11 46						11 55				12 46	13 02
Needham Market	d				11 12																				13 12
Stowmarket	d			10 57	11a18									11 57						12a06				12 57	13a18
Diss	d			11 10										12 10										13 10	
Norwich	a			11 31										12 31										13 31	

Station		LE [1]		LE ◇[1]	LE [1]	LE	LE [1]	LE [1]	LE	LE ◇[1] ☕	LE [1]	LE ◇[1]		LE [1]	LE	LE [1]	LE [1]	LE [1]	LE	LE ◇[1] ☕	LE [1]	LE [1]		LE ◇[1]	LE [1]
London Liverpool Street [15] ⊖	d			11 32			12 02			12 30		12 32					13 02			13 30				13 32	
Stratford [7] ⊖	d			11 39			12 09					12 39					13 09							13 39	
Romford	d																								
Shenfield [3]	d			12 02			12 32					13 02					13 32							14 02	
Ingatestone	d						12 36										13 36								
Chelmsford [3]	d			12 11			12 43					13 11					13 43							14 11	
Hatfield Peverel	d						12 49										13 49								
Witham [2]	d			12 22	12 25		12 56					13 22		13 25			13 56							14 22	14 25
White Notley	d				12 32									13 32											14 32
Cressing	d				12 34									13 34											14 34
Braintree Freeport	d				12 37									13 37											14 37
Braintree	a				12 41									13 41											14 41
Kelvedon	d						13 00										14 00								
Marks Tey [2]	d			12 29			13 06					13 29					14 06							14 29	
Colchester [4]	a			12 37			13 13			13 25		13 37					14 13			14 25				14 37	
Colchester [4]	d			12 37			13 13			13 25		13 37					14 13			14 25				14 37	
Colchester Town	a																								
	d																								
Hythe	d																								
Wivenhoe [3]	d			12 45								13 45												14 45	
Alresford (Essex)	d			12 48								13 48												14 48	
Great Bentley	d			12 52								13 52												14 52	
Weeley	d																								
Thorpe-le-Soken [1]	a			12 59								13 59												14 59	
	d	12 01		12 59							13 01	13 59										14 01		14 59	
Clacton-on-Sea	a			13 08								14 08												15 08	
Kirby Cross	d	12 06									13 06											14 06			
Frinton-on-Sea	d	12 09									13 09											14 09			
Walton-on-the-Naze	a	12 13									13 13											14 13			
Manningtree [2]	d						13 21	13 26		13 33							14 21	14 26		14 33					
Mistley	d							13 30										14 30							
Wrabness	d							13 35										14 35							
Harwich International	d							13 43										14 43							
Dovercourt	d							13 46										14 46							
Harwich Town	a							13 48										14 48							
Ipswich	a						13 33			13 45							14 33			14 45					
	d									13 46						13 55				14 46	15 02				
Needham Market	d																				15 12				
Stowmarket	d									13 57						14a06				14 57	15a18				
Diss	d									14 10										15 10					
Norwich	a									14 31										15 31					

Table 11

Sundays

8 December to 11 May

London - Chelmsford, Colchester, Walton-on-Naze, Clacton, Harwich, Ipswich and Norwich

Network Diagram - refer to first Page of Table 5

		LE	LE 1	LE 1	LE	LE ◇1 ⊏P	LE 1	LE ◇1		LE 1	LE	LE 1	LE 1	LE 1	LE	LE ◇1 ⊏P	LE 1	LE 1		LE ◇1	LE 1	LE	LE 1	LE 1	LE
London Liverpool Street 15 ⊖	d		14 02			14 30		14 32					15 02			15 30				15 32			16 02		
Stratford 7 ⊖	d		14 09					14 39					15 09							15 39			16 09		
Romford	d																								
Shenfield 3	d		14 32					15 02					15 32							16 02			16 32		
Ingatestone	d		14 36										15 36										16 36		
Chelmsford 3	d		14 43					15 11					15 43							16 11			16 43		
Hatfield Peverel	d		14 49										15 49										16 49		
Witham 2	d		14 56					15 22		15 25			15 56							16 22	16 25		16 56		
White Notley	d									15 32											16 32				
Cressing	d									15 34											16 34				
Braintree Freeport	d									15 37											16 37				
Braintree	a									15 41											16 41				
Kelvedon	d		15 00										16 00										17 00		
Marks Tey 2	d		15 06					15 29					16 06							16 29			17 06		
Colchester 4	a		15 13			15 25		15 37					16 13			16 25				16 37			17 13		
Colchester 4	d		15 13			15 25		15 37					16 13			16 25				16 37			17 13		
Colchester Town	a																								
	d																								
Hythe	d																								
Wivenhoe 3	d							15 45												16 45					
Alresford (Essex)	d							15 48												16 48					
Great Bentley	d							15 52												16 52					
Weeley	d																								
Thorpe-le-Soken 1	a							15 59												16 59					
	d						15 01	15 59										16 01		16 59					
Clacton-on-Sea	a							16 08												17 08					
Kirby Cross	d						15 06											16 06							
Frinton-on-Sea	d						15 09											16 09							
Walton-on-the-Naze	a						15 13											16 13							
Manningtree 2	d		15 21	15 26		15 33							16 21	16 26		16 33							17 21	17 26	
Mistley	d			15 30										16 30										17 30	
Wrabness	d			15 35										16 35										17 35	
Harwich International	d			15 43										16 43										17 43	
Dovercourt	d			15 46										16 46										17 46	
Harwich Town	a			15 48										16 48										17 48	
Ipswich	a		15 33			15 45							16 33			16 45							17 33		
	d					15 46						15 55				16 46	17 02								
Needham Market	d																17 12								
Stowmarket	d					15 57						16a06				16 57	17a18								
Diss	d					16 10										17 10									
Norwich	a					16 31										17 31									

		LE ◇1 ⊏P	LE 1	LE ◇1		LE 1	LE	LE 1	LE 1	LE 1	LE	LE ◇1 ⊏P	LE 1	LE 1		LE ◇1	LE 1	LE	LE 1	LE 1	LE	LE ◇1 ⊏P	LE 1	LE ◇1	
London Liverpool Street 15 ⊖	d	16 30		16 32					17 02			17 30				17 32			18 02			18 30		18 32	
Stratford 7 ⊖	d			16 39					17 09							17 39			18 09					18 39	
Romford	d																								
Shenfield 3	d			17 02					17 32							18 02			18 32					19 02	
Ingatestone	d								17 36										18 36						
Chelmsford 3	d			17 11					17 43							18 11			18 43					19 11	
Hatfield Peverel	d								17 49										18 49						
Witham 2	d			17 22		17 25			17 56							18 22	18 25		18 56					19 22	
White Notley	d					17 32											18 32								
Cressing	d					17 34											18 34								
Braintree Freeport	d					17 37											18 37								
Braintree	a					17 41											18 41								
Kelvedon	d								18 00										19 00						
Marks Tey 2	d			17 29					18 06							18 29			19 06					19 29	
Colchester 4	a	17 25		17 37					18 13			18 25				18 37			19 13			19 25		19 37	
Colchester 4	d	17 25		17 37					18 13			18 25				18 37			19 13			19 25		19 37	
Colchester Town	a																								
	d																								
Hythe	d																								
Wivenhoe 3	d			17 45												18 45								19 45	
Alresford (Essex)	d			17 48												18 48								19 48	
Great Bentley	d			17 52												18 52								19 52	
Weeley	d																								
Thorpe-le-Soken 1	a			17 59												18 59								19 59	
	d		17 01	17 59										18 01		18 59							19 01	19 59	
Clacton-on-Sea	a			18 08												19 08								20 08	
Kirby Cross	d		17 06											18 06									19 06		
Frinton-on-Sea	d		17 09											18 09									19 09		
Walton-on-the-Naze	a		17 13											18 13									19 13		
Manningtree 2	d	17 33							18 21	18 26		18 33							19 21	19 26		19 33			
Mistley	d									18 30										19 30					
Wrabness	d									18 35										19 35					
Harwich International	d									18 43										19 43					
Dovercourt	d									18 46										19 46					
Harwich Town	a									18 48										19 48					
Ipswich	a	17 45							18 33			18 45							19 33			19 45			
	d	17 46						17 55				18 46	19 02									19 46			
Needham Market	d												19 12												
Stowmarket	d	17 57						18a06				18 57	19a18									19 57			
Diss	d	18 10										19 10										20 10			
Norwich	a	18 31										19 31										20 31			

Table 11

Sundays

8 December to 11 May

London - Chelmsford, Colchester, Walton-on-Naze, Clacton, Harwich, Ipswich and Norwich

Network Diagram - refer to first Page of Table 5

Station		LE [1]	LE	LE ◇[1] ⊏P	LE [1]	LE [1]	LE	LE ◇[1] ⊏P	LE	LE [1]		LE ◇[1]		LE	LE [1]	LE [1]	LE	LE [1]	LE [1]	LE [1]		LE ◇[1] ⊏P	LE ◇[1]	LE [1]	LE
London Liverpool Street [15] ⊖	d			19 00	19 02			19 30				19 32				20 02						20 30	20 32		
Stratford [7] ⊖	d				19 09							19 39				20 09							20 39		
Romford	d																								
Shenfield [3]	d				19 32							20 02				20 32							21 02		
Ingatestone	d				19 36											20 36									
Chelmsford [3]	d				19 43							20 11				20 43							21 11		
Hatfield Peverel	d				19 49											20 49									
Witham [2]	d	19 25			19 56							20 22			20 25	20 56							21 22	21 25	
White Notley	d	19 32													20 32									21 32	
Cressing	d	19 34													20 34									21 34	
Braintree Freeport	d	19 37													20 37									21 37	
Braintree	a	19 41													20 41									21 41	
Kelvedon	d				20 00											21 00									
Marks Tey [2]	d				20 06							20 29				21 06							21 29		
Colchester [4]	a			19 55	20 13			20 25				20 37				21 13						21 25	21 37		
Colchester [4]	d			19 55	20 13			20 25				20 40	20 46			21 13						21 25	21 37		
Colchester Town	a																								
	d																								
Hythe	d																								
Wivenhoe [3]	d											20 48											21 45		
Alresford (Essex)	d											20 51											21 48		
Great Bentley	d											20 55											21 52		
Weeley	d																								
Thorpe-le-Soken [1]	a											21 02											21 59		
	d									20 01		21 02						21 04					21 59		
Clacton-on-Sea	a											21 11											22 08		
Kirby Cross	d									20 06								21 09							
Frinton-on-Sea	d									20 09								21 12							
Walton-on-the-Naze	a									20 13								21 16							
Manningtree [2]	d			20 03	20 21	20 26		20 33					20 55			21 21				21 26		21 34			
Mistley	d					20 30														21 30					
Wrabness	d					20 35														21 35					
Harwich International	d					20 43							21a14						21 10	21 43					
Dovercourt	d					20 46														21 46					
Harwich Town	a					20 48														21 48					
Ipswich	a			20 15	20 33			20 45								21 33			21 37			21 45			
	d			20 16				20 46	21 02													21 47			
Needham Market	d								21 12																
Stowmarket	d			20 27				20 57	21a18													21 58			
Diss	d			20 40				21 10														22 11			
Norwich	a			21 01				21 31														22 31			

Station		LE [1]	LE	LE [1]	LE [1]	LE		LE ◇[1] ⊏P	LE ◇[1]	LE [1]	LE	LE [1]	LE	LE ◇[1] ⊏P	LE [1]	LE ◇[1]		LE [1]	LE [1]	LE ◇[1]	LE [1]				
London Liverpool Street [15] ⊖	d			21 02				21 30	21 32			22 02		22 30		22 32			23 02	23 30	23 32				
Stratford [7] ⊖	d			21 09					21 39			22 09				22 39			23 09		23 39				
Romford	d																								
Shenfield [3]	d			21 32					22 02			22 32				23 02			23 32		00 02				
Ingatestone	d			21 36								22 36							23 36						
Chelmsford [3]	d			21 43					22 11			22 43				23 11			23 43		00 11				
Hatfield Peverel	d			21 49								22 49							23 49						
Witham [2]	d			21 56					22 22	22 25		22 56				23 22		23 25	23 56		00 22				
White Notley	d									22 32								23 32							
Cressing	d									22 34								23 34							
Braintree Freeport	d									22 37								23 37							
Braintree	a									22 41								23 41							
Kelvedon	d			22 00								23 00							23 59						
Marks Tey [2]	d		22 02	22 06					22 29			23 06				23 29			00 06		00 29				
Colchester [4]	a		22 10	22 13				22 25	22 37			23 13		23 25		23 37			00 13	00 25	00 43				
Colchester [4]	d			22 13				22 25	22 37			23 13		23 25		23 37			00 13	00 25					
Colchester Town	a																								
	d																								
Hythe	d																								
Wivenhoe [3]	d								22 45							23 45									
Alresford (Essex)	d								22 48							23 48									
Great Bentley	d								22 52							23 52									
Weeley	d																								
Thorpe-le-Soken [1]	a								22 59							23 59									
	d	22 01							22 59						23 01	23 59									
Clacton-on-Sea	a								23 08							00 14									
Kirby Cross	d	22 06													23 06										
Frinton-on-Sea	d	22 09													23 09										
Walton-on-the-Naze	a	22 13													23 13										
Manningtree [2]	d			22 21	22 26			22 34				23 21		23 34					00 21	00 34					
Mistley	d				22 30																				
Wrabness	d				22 35																				
Harwich International	d				22 43																				
Dovercourt	d				22 46																				
Harwich Town	a				22 48																				
Ipswich	a			22 33				22 45				23 33		23 45					00 39	00 45					
	d							22 47						23 47						00 47					
Needham Market	d																								
Stowmarket	d							22 58						23 58						00 58					
Diss	d							23 11						00 11						01 11					
Norwich	a							23 31						00 31						01 36					

Table 11R

Mondays to Fridays

9 December to 16 May

Norwich, Ipswich, Harwich, Clacton, Walton-on-Naze, Colchester and Chelmsford - London

Network Diagram - refer to first Page of Table 5

Miles	Miles	Miles	Miles	Miles			LE FO	LE TW ThO	LE	LE	LE	LE	LE	LE	LE	LE	LE	LE	LE	LE	LE	LE	LE	LE
							1	1	1	1	◇1	1	1	◇1	◇1	1	1	◇1	1	1	1	1	R 1	◇1
0	—	—	—	—	**Norwich**	d									05 00								05 30	
20	—	—	—	—	Diss	d									05 18								05 48	
34¼	—	—	—	—	Stowmarket	d									05 30					05 52			06 00	
38	—	—	—	—	Needham Market	d														05 57				
46¼	—	—	—	—	**Ipswich**	a									05 42					06 07			06 12	
—	—	—	—	—		d					05 14				05 44				06 00				06 14	
—	0	—	—	—	**Harwich Town**	d						05 24												
—	0½	—	—	—	Dovercourt	d						05 26												
—	1¾	—	—	—	Harwich International	d						05 29												
—	5½	—	—	—	Wrabness	d						05 35												
—	9½	—	—	—	Mistley	d						05 41												
55½	11¼	—	—	—	Manningtree 2	d					05 25	05a46			05 54				06 11				06 24	
—	—	0	—	—	**Walton-on-the-Naze**	d										05 33					06 03			
—	—	1¼	—	—	Frinton-on-Sea	d										05 36					06 06			
—	—	2½	—	—	Kirby Cross	d										05 39					06 09			
—	—	—	0	—	**Clacton-on-Sea**	d								05 20				05 40						06 10
—	—	5	4¾	—	Thorpe-le-Soken 1	a								05 28		05 45		05 48			06 15			06 18
—	—	—	—	—		d								05 28				05 48						06 18
—	—	7¼	—	—	Weeley	d												05 52						
—	—	10	—	—	Great Bentley	d												05 56						
—	—	12¼	—	—	Alresford (Essex)	d												06 00						
—	—	14	—	—	Wivenhoe 3	d								05 38				06 04						06 29
—	—	16½	—	—	Hythe	d												06 08						06 33
—	—	18	—	—	Colchester Town	a																		
—	—	—	—	—		d																06 19		
63¼	—	—	—	—	**Colchester 4**	a					05 34			05 46	06 03			06 14	06 20			06 26	06 33	06 39
—	—	19¾	—	—	**Colchester 4**	d			04 43	05 12	05 35			05 47	06 05			06 15	06 20			06 27	06 35	06 40
68¼	—	—	—	—	Marks Tey 2	d			04 49	05 18				05 53					06 26			06 33		
72¾	—	—	—	—	Kelvedon	d			04 54	05 23				05 59				06 25	06 32					06 50
—	—	—	—	0	**Braintree**	d	00 25	00 34					05 45											
—	—	—	—	0¾	Braintree Freeport	d	00 27	00 36					05 47											
—	—	—	—	2	Cressing	d	00 30	00 39					05 50											
—	—	—	—	3¼	White Notley	d	00 33	00 42					05 53											
76½	—	—	—	6¼	**Witham 2**	d	00a41	00a50	05 00	05 29	05 48		06a02	06 05			06 18	06 31	06 38			06 47		
79	—	—	—	—	Hatfield Peverel	d			05 04	05 33							06 22							
85¼	—	—	—	—	**Chelmsford 3**	d			05 11	05 40	05 58			06 14			06 29	06 40	06 47			06 56		07 03
91½	—	—	—	—	Ingatestone	d			05 18	05 47							06 36					07 03		
94¾	—	—	—	—	Shenfield 3	a			05 23	05 52				06 24			06 41	06 50				07 08		
102¾	—	—	—	—	Romford	a																		
111¾	—	—	—	—	Stratford 7 ⊖	a			05 42	06 07	06s22			06 39	06s44		06s57	07s06				07s23	07s15	07s27
115	—	—	—	—	**London Liverpool Street 15** ⊖	a			05 55	06 16	06 34			06 48	06 54		07 09	07 18	07 24			07 35	07 27	07 38

Table 11R

Mondays to Fridays

9 December to 16 May

Norwich, Ipswich, Harwich, Clacton, Walton-on-Naze, Colchester and Chelmsford - London

Network Diagram - refer to first Page of Table 5

		LE	LE	LE	LE	LE	LE	LE	LE	LE	LE	LE	LE	LE	LE	LE	LE	LE	LE	LE	LE	LE	LE
		1	1	1	1	R 1 ☕	1	1	1	◇1	1	1	1		1	◇1	R 1 ☕	1	1	1	1	◇1	◇1
Norwich	d					06 00											06 24						
Diss	d					06 18											06 42						
Stowmarket	d					06 30								06 42			06 54						07 03
Needham Market	d													06 47									
Ipswich	a					06 42								07 00			07 06						07 16
	d		06 29			06 44					06 52		06 59				07 08						07 17
Harwich Town	d			06 24								06 52											
Dovercourt	d			06 26								06 54											
Harwich International	d			06 29								06 57	07a28										
Wrabness	d			06 35								07 03											
Mistley	d			06 41								07 09											
Manningtree 2	d		06 39	06a46		06 54					07 02	07a14					07 18						07 27
Walton-on-the-Naze	d							06 31											06 58				
Frinton-on-Sea	d							06 34											07 01				
Kirby Cross	d							06 37											07 04				
Clacton-on-Sea	d						06 28			06 38						06 47		06 51				07 05	
Thorpe-le-Soken 1	a						06 36	06 43		06 46						06 55		06 59	07 10			07 13	
	d						06 36			06 46						06 55		06 59				07 13	
Weeley	d						06 40											07 03					
Great Bentley	d						06 43											07 06					
Alresford (Essex)	d						06 47											07 10					
Wivenhoe 3	d						06 51			06 57						07 06		07 14				07 24	
Hythe	d						06 55			07 01						07 10		07 18					
Colchester Town	a						06 59											07 22					
	d				06 47		07 03											07 27					
Colchester 4	a		06 48		06 54	07 03	07 13			07 07	07 12					07 16	07 27	07 36				07 32	07 37
Colchester 4	d		06 49		06 55	07 05				07 08	07 13					07 17	07 30					07 33	07 38
Marks Tey 2	d		06 55		07 01						07 19					07 23							07 44
Kelvedon	d		07 00							07 18						07 29						07 43	07 49
Braintree	d	06 40																			07 26		
Braintree Freeport	d	06 42																			07 28		
Cressing	d	06 45																			07 31		
White Notley	d	06 48																			07 34		
Witham 2	d	06 57	07 06		07 10				07 17						07 29	07 35					07 43	07 50	07 55
Hatfield Peverel	d	07 02													07 33						07 48		
Chelmsford 3	d	07 09			07 19				07 27	07 31	07 35				07 40					07 49	07 55	07 59	
Ingatestone	d								07 33		07 42									07 56			
Shenfield 3	a	07 19							07 39	07 41					07 50					08 01		08 09	
Romford	a																						
Stratford 7 ⊖	a	07s35	07s38		07s44				07s55	07s58	08s01				08s07	08s09				08s18	08s20	08s25	08s28
London Liverpool Street 15 ⊖	a	07 46	07 50		07 56	07 58			08 07	08 09	08 13				08 19	08 21	08 23			08 30	08 32	08 38	08 40

Table 11R

Mondays to Fridays

9 December to 16 May

Norwich, Ipswich, Harwich, Clacton, Walton-on-Naze, Colchester and Chelmsford - London

Network Diagram - refer to first Page of Table 5

		LE	LE	LE	LE	LE	LE	LE	LE	LE	LE	LE	LE	LE	LE	LE	LE	LE	LE	LE	LE	LE
				R				R							R							
		1	1	1	1	1	◇1	1		1	1	1	1	1	1	1	1	1	◇1	◇1	1	1
															A							
				☕				☕							☕							
Norwich	d			06 48				07 05							07 40							
Diss	d			07 06				07 23							07 58							
Stowmarket	d			07 18				07 35	07 45											08 11		
Needham Market	d								07 50													
Ipswich	a			07 30				07 47	08 02						08 18					08 24		
	d			07 32			07 38	07 49							08 20					08 26		
Harwich Town	d				07 16												07 58				08 28	
Dovercourt	d				07 18												08 00				08 30	
Harwich International	d		07 15		07 21												08 03				08 33	
Wrabness	d				07 27												08 09				08 39	
Mistley	d				07 33												08 15				08 45	
Manningtree 2	d		07 31	07 43	07 38		07 49	07 59									08 20			08 36	08a50	
Walton-on-the-Naze	d											07 38						08 00				
Frinton-on-Sea	d											07 41						08 03				
Kirby Cross	d											07 44						08 06				
Clacton-on-Sea	d					07 16								07 45		←						
Thorpe-le-Soken 1	a					07 24						07 50		07 53		07 50		08 11				
	d					07 24						07 58		07 53		07 58		08 12				
Weeley	d					07 28						→				08 02						
Great Bentley	d					07 31										08 05						
Alresford (Essex)	d					07 35										08 09						
Wivenhoe 3	d					07 39								08 03		08 13		08 22				
Hythe	d					07 43										08 17		08 26				
Colchester Town	a															08 21			←			
	d												08 00			08 32						
Colchester 4	a		07 41		07 47	07 50	07 58	08 08					08 09	08 16		08 40	08 29	08 35	08 40	08 45		
Colchester 4	d		07 42		07 54		07 59	08 10					08 18			08 48	08 37		08 48	08 45		
Marks Tey 2	d		07 48				08 05						08 24			→			→			
Kelvedon	d				08 04		08 10						08 30									
Braintree	d										08 12											
Braintree Freeport	d										08 14											
Cressing	d										08 17											
White Notley	d										08 20											
Witham 2	d		08 03		08 10		08 16				08 28		08 36				08 50					08 58
Hatfield Peverel	d		08 07								08 32											09 02
Chelmsford 3	d	08 09	08 14		08 19					08 30	08 39		08 45				08 59			09 04		09 09
Ingatestone	d	08 16								08 37	08 46											09 16
Shenfield 3	a	08 21	08 24		08 29					08 42	08 51		08 55									09 21
Romford	a																					
Stratford 7 ⊖	a	08s38	08s40		08s45		08s48	08s52		08s59	09s08						09s23			09s28		09s37
London Liverpool Street 15 ⊖	a	08 50	08 54	08 42	08 58		09 01	09 04		09 11	09 19		09 21		09 24		09 36			09 40		09 49

A The East Anglian

Table 11R

Mondays to Fridays

9 December to 16 May

Norwich, Ipswich, Harwich, Clacton, Walton-on-Naze, Colchester and Chelmsford - London

Network Diagram - refer to first Page of Table 5

		LE	LE	LE	LE	LE	LE	LE	LE	LE	LE	LE	LE	LE	LE	LE	LE	LE	LE	LE	LE	LE
		◇1	◇1	R 1 ☕	1	1	1	1	R 1 ☕	1	1	◇1	1	1	1	1	R 1 ☕	1	1	1	1	◇1 ☕
Norwich	d			08 00					08 30								09 00					09 30
Diss	d			08 17					08 47								09 17					09 47
Stowmarket	d			08 29				08 45		09 14							09 29				09 45	
Needham Market	d							08 50													09 50	
Ipswich	a			08 41				09 02	09 08	09 28							09 41				10 02	10 08
	d			08 43			08 48		09 09					09 30			09 43			09 52		10 09
Harwich Town	d															09 28						
Dovercourt	d															09 30						
Harwich International	d															09 33						
Wrabness	d															09 39						
Mistley	d															09 45						
Manningtree 2	d			08 53			08 58		09 19					09 40		09a50	09 53			10 02		10 19
Walton-on-the-Naze	d										09 00											
Frinton-on-Sea	d										09 03											
Kirby Cross	d										09 06											
Clacton-on-Sea	d		08 11									09 05			←							
Thorpe-le-Soken 1	a		08 19								09 12	09 13			09 12							
	d		08 19								09 17	09 13			09 17							
Weeley	d		08 23								→				09 21							
Great Bentley	d		08 26												09 24							
Alresford (Essex)	d		08 30												09 28							
Wivenhoe 3	d		08 34									09 23			09 32							
Hythe	d		08 38												09 36							
Colchester Town	a	←													09 40							
	d					08 58							09 35		09 44			10 00				
Colchester 4	a	08 40	08 46	09 02		09 05	09 08		09 28			09 31	09 42	09 49	09 52		10 02	10 07		10 11		10 28
Colchester 4	d	08 48		09 03		09 12			09 30			09 33	09 43	09 50			10 03			10 12		10 30
Marks Tey 2	d	08 54				09 18								09 56						10 18		
Kelvedon	d	09 00				09 23							09 52							10 23		
Braintree	d				09 00														10 00			
Braintree Freeport	d				09 02														10 02			
Cressing	d				09 05														10 05			
White Notley	d				09 08														10 08			
Witham 2	d	09 06			09 16	09 29						09 46	09 58	10 05					10 16	10 29		
Hatfield Peverel	d					09 33														10 33		
Chelmsford 3	d	09 15		09 21	09 26	09 40						09 56	10 07	10 14			10 21		10 26	10 40		
Ingatestone	d				09 32							10 02							10 32			
Shenfield 3	a	09 25			09 38	09 50						10 08	10 17						10 38	10 50		
Romford	a												10 26									
Stratford 7 ⊖	a	09s41			09 52	10 05						10 22	10 34				10s45		10 52	11 05		
London Liverpool Street 15 ⊖	a	09 53		09 56	10 01	10 14			10 19			10 31	10 43	10 44			10 55		11 01	11 14		11 19

		LE	LE	LE	LE	LE	LE	LE	LE	LE	LE	LE	LE	LE	LE	LE	LE	LE	LE	LE	LE	LE	LE
		1	1	◇1	1	1	◇1 ☕	1	1	1	1	◇1 ☕	1	1	1	◇1	1	1	◇1 ☕	1	1	1	1
Norwich	d						10 00					10 30							11 00				
Diss	d						10 17					10 47							11 17				
Stowmarket	d						10 29				10 45		11 14						11 29				11 45
Needham Market	d										10 50												11 50
Ipswich	a						10 41				11 02	11 08	11 28						11 41				12 02
	d						10 43			10 52		11 09							11 43			11 52	
Harwich Town	d	10 28												11 28									
Dovercourt	d	10 30												11 30									
Harwich International	d	10 33												11 33									
Wrabness	d	10 39												11 39									
Mistley	d	10 45												11 45									
Manningtree 2	d	10a50					10 53			11 02		11 19		11a50					11 53			12 02	
Walton-on-the-Naze	d		10 00												11 00								
Frinton-on-Sea	d		10 03												11 03								
Kirby Cross	d		10 06												11 06								
Clacton-on-Sea	d			10 05		←										11 05		←					
Thorpe-le-Soken 1	a		10 12	10 13		10 12									11 12	11 13		11 12					
	d		10 17	10 13		10 17									11 17	11 13		11 17					
Weeley	d		→			10 21									→			11 21					
Great Bentley	d					10 24												11 24					
Alresford (Essex)	d					10 28												11 28					
Wivenhoe 3	d			10 23		10 32										11 23		11 32					
Hythe	d					10 36												11 36					
Colchester Town	a					10 40												11 40					
	d				10 35	10 44		11 00									11 35	11 44		12 00			
Colchester 4	a			10 31	10 42	10 52	11 02	11 07		11 11		11 28				11 31	11 42	11 52	12 02	12 07		12 11	
Colchester 4	d			10 33	10 43		11 03			11 12		11 30				11 33	11 43		12 03			12 12	
Marks Tey 2	d				10 49					11 18							11 49					12 18	
Kelvedon	d				10 54					11 23							11 54					12 23	
Braintree	d								11 00												12 00		
Braintree Freeport	d								11 02												12 02		
Cressing	d								11 05												12 05		
White Notley	d								11 08												12 08		
Witham 2	d			10 46	11 00				11 16	11 29						11 46	12 00				12 16	12 29	
Hatfield Peverel	d									11 33												12 33	
Chelmsford 3	d			10 56	11 09		11 21		11 26	11 40						11 56	12 09		12 21		12 26	12 40	
Ingatestone	d			11 02					11 32							12 02					12 32		
Shenfield 3	a			11 08	11 19				11 38	11 50						12 08	12 19				12 38	12 50	
Romford	a				11 28												12 28						
Stratford 7 ⊖	a			11 22	11 36		11s45		11 52	12 05						12 22	12 36		12s45		12 52	13 05	
London Liverpool Street 15 ⊖	a			11 31	11 45		11 55		12 01	12 14		12 19				12 31	12 45		12 55		13 01	13 14	

Table 11R

Mondays to Fridays

9 December to 16 May

Norwich, Ipswich, Harwich, Clacton, Walton-on-Naze, Colchester and Chelmsford - London

Network Diagram - refer to first Page of Table 5

		LE ◇1 ☕	LE 1	LE 1	LE ◇1		LE 1	LE 1	LE ◇1 ☕	LE 1	LE 1	LE 1	LE 1	LE ◇1 ☕	LE 1		LE 1	LE 1	LE ◇1	LE 1	LE 1	LE ◇1 ☕	LE 1	LE 1	LE 1
Norwich	d	11 30							12 00					12 30								13 00			
Diss	d	11 47							12 17					12 47								13 17			
Stowmarket	d								12 29				12 45		13 14							13 29			
Needham Market	d												12 50												
Ipswich	a	12 08							12 41				13 02	13 08	13 28							13 41			
	d	12 09							12 43			12 52		13 09								13 43			13 52
Harwich Town	d		12 28														13 28								
Dovercourt	d		12 30														13 30								
Harwich International	d		12 33														13 33								
Wrabness	d		12 39														13 39								
Mistley	d		12 45														13 45								
Manningtree 2	d	12 19	12a50						12 53			13 02		13 19			13a50					13 53			14 02
Walton-on-the-Naze	d			12 00														13 00							
Frinton-on-Sea	d			12 03														13 03							
Kirby Cross	d			12 06														13 06							
Clacton-on-Sea	d				12 05			←											13 05		←				
Thorpe-le-Soken 1	a			12 12	12 13			12 12										13 12	13 13		13 12				
	d			12 17	12 13			12 17										13 17	13 13		13 17				
Weeley	d			→				12 21										→			13 21				
Great Bentley	d							12 24													13 24				
Alresford (Essex)	d							12 28													13 28				
Wivenhoe 3	d				12 23			12 32											13 23		13 32				
Hythe	d							12 36													13 36				
Colchester Town	a							12 40													13 40				
	d						12 35	12 44		13 00										13 35	13 44		14 00		
Colchester 4	a	12 28			12 31		12 42	12 52	13 02	13 07		13 11		13 28					13 31	13 42	13 52	14 02	14 07		14 11
Colchester 4	d	12 30			12 33		12 43		13 03			13 12		13 30					13 33	13 43		14 03			14 12
Marks Tey 2	d						12 49					13 18								13 49					14 18
Kelvedon	d						12 54					13 23								13 54					14 23
Braintree	d										13 00													14 00	
Braintree Freeport	d										13 02													14 02	
Cressing	d										13 05													14 05	
White Notley	d										13 08													14 08	
Witham 2	d				12 46		13 00				13 16	13 29							13 46	14 00				14 16	14 29
Hatfield Peverel	d											13 33													14 33
Chelmsford 3	d				12 56		13 09		13 21		13 26	13 40							13 56	14 09		14 21		14 26	14 40
Ingatestone	d				13 02						13 32								14 02					14 32	
Shenfield 3	a				13 08		13 19				13 38	13 50							14 08	14 19				14 38	14 50
Romford	a						13 28													14 28					
Stratford 7 ⊖	a				13 22		13 36		13s45		13 52	14 05							14 22	14 36		14s45		14 52	15 05
London Liverpool Street 15 ⊖	a	13 19			13 31		13 45		13 55		14 01	14 14		14 19					14 31	14 45		14 55		15 01	15 15

			LE 1	LE ◇1 ☕	LE 1	LE 1	LE ◇1	LE 1	LE 1	LE ◇1 ☕	LE 1		LE 1	LE 1	LE 1	LE ◇1 ☕	LE 1	LE 1	LE 1	LE ◇1	LE 1		LE 1	LE ◇1 ☕	LE 1
Norwich	d			13 30						14 00						14 30								15 00	
Diss	d			13 47						14 17						14 47								15 17	
Stowmarket	d		13 45							14 29					14 45		15 14							15 29	
Needham Market	d		13 50												14 50										
Ipswich	a		14 02	14 08						14 41					15 02	15 08	15 28							15 41	
	d			14 09						14 43				14 52		15 09								15 43	
Harwich Town	d				14 28													15 28							
Dovercourt	d				14 30													15 30							
Harwich International	d				14 33													15 33							
Wrabness	d				14 39													15 39							
Mistley	d				14 45													15 45							
Manningtree 2	d			14 19	14a50					14 53				15 02		15 19		15a50						15 53	
Walton-on-the-Naze	d					14 00													15 00						
Frinton-on-Sea	d					14 03													15 03						
Kirby Cross	d					14 06													15 06						
Clacton-on-Sea	d						14 05		←											15 05			←		
Thorpe-le-Soken 1	a					14 12	14 13		14 12										15 12	15 13			15 12		
	d					14 17	14 13		14 17										15 17	15 13			15 17		
Weeley	d					→			14 21										→				15 21		
Great Bentley	d								14 24														15 24		
Alresford (Essex)	d								14 28														15 28		
Wivenhoe 3	d						14 23		14 32											15 23			15 32		
Hythe	d								14 36														15 36		
Colchester Town	a								14 40														15 40		
	d							14 35	14 44		15 00										15 35		15 44		16 00
Colchester 4	a			14 28			14 31	14 42	14 52	15 02	15 07			15 11		15 28				15 31	15 42		15 52	16 02	16 07
Colchester 4	d			14 30			14 33	14 43		15 03				15 12		15 30				15 33	15 43			16 03	
Marks Tey 2	d							14 49						15 18							15 49				
Kelvedon	d							14 54						15 23							15 54				
Braintree	d												15 00												
Braintree Freeport	d												15 02												
Cressing	d												15 05												
White Notley	d												15 08												
Witham 2	d						14 46	15 00					15 16	15 29						15 46	16 00				
Hatfield Peverel	d													15 33											
Chelmsford 3	d						14 56	15 09		15 21			15 26	15 40						15 55	16 09			16 21	
Ingatestone	d						15 02						15 32							16 02					
Shenfield 3	a						15 08	15 19					15 38	15 50						16 07	16 19				
Romford	a							15 28																	
Stratford 7 ⊖	a						15 22	15 36		15s45			15 52	16 05						16 22	16 35			16s45	
London Liverpool Street 15 ⊖	a			15 19			15 33	15 45		15 55			16 01	16 14		16 17				16 31	16 44			16 55	

Table 11R

Mondays to Fridays

9 December to 16 May

Norwich, Ipswich, Harwich, Clacton, Walton-on-Naze, Colchester and Chelmsford - London

Network Diagram - refer to first Page of Table 5

		LE 1	LE 1	LE 1	LE ◇1 ☕	LE 1	LE 1		LE ◇1	LE 1	LE 1	LE 1	LE ◇1 ☕	LE 1	LE 1	LE 1	LE 1		LE 1	LE ◇1 ☕	LE 1	LE 1	LE ◇1	LE 1	LE 1
Norwich	d				15 30								16 00							16 30					
Diss	d				15 47								16 17							16 47					
Stowmarket	d			15 45									16 29				16 45				17 14				
Needham Market	d			15 50													16 50								
Ipswich	a			16 02	16 08								16 41				17 02			17 08	17 28				
	d		15 52		16 09								16 43			16 52				17 09					
Harwich Town	d					16 28													16 53						
Dovercourt	d					16 30													16 55						
Harwich International	d					16 33													16 58						
Wrabness	d					16 39													17 04						
Mistley	d					16 45													17 10						
Manningtree 2	d		16 02		16 19	16a50							16 53			17 02			17a15	17 19					
Walton-on-the-Naze	d						16 00															17 00			
Frinton-on-Sea	d						16 03															17 03			
Kirby Cross	d						16 06															17 06			
Clacton-on-Sea	d								16 05			←											17 05		
Thorpe-le-Soken 1	a						16 12		16 13			16 12										17 12	17 13		
	d						16 17		16 13			16 17										17 17	17 13		
Weeley	d						→					16 21										→			
Great Bentley	d											16 24													
Alresford (Essex)	d											16 28													
Wivenhoe 3	d								16 23			16 32											17 23		
Hythe	d											16 36													
Colchester Town	a											16 40													
	d									16 35		16 44		16 56											17 30
Colchester 4	a		16 11		16 28				16 31	16 42		16 54	17 02	17 05		17 11				17 28			17 31		17 37
Colchester 4	d		16 12		16 30				16 33	16 43	16 53		17 03			17 12				17 30			17 33		17 48
Marks Tey 2	d		16 18								16 59					17 18									17 55
Kelvedon	d		16 23							16 52						17 23									18 00
Braintree	d	16 00													17 00									17 44	
Braintree Freeport	d	16 02													17 02									17 46	
Cressing	d	16 05													17 05									17 49	
White Notley	d	16 08													17 08									17 52	
Witham 2	d	16 17	16 29						16 46	16 58	17 08				17 16	17 29							17 46	18 00	18 06
Hatfield Peverel	d		16 33							17 02						17 33									18 10
Chelmsford 3	d	16 27	16 40						16 56	17 09	17 17		17 21		17 26	17 40							17 56	18 09	18 17
Ingatestone	d	16 34							17 02						17 32								18 02		
Shenfield 3	a	16 39	16 50						17 08	17 19	17 27				17 38	17 50							18 08	18 19	18 27
Romford	a																							18 28	
Stratford 7 ⊖	a	16 54	17 05						17 22	17 36	17 42		17s45		17 52	18 06							18 22	18 36	18 42
London Liverpool Street 15 ⊖	a	17 03	17 16		17 19				17 34	17 46	17 53		17 58		18 01	18 15				18 19			18 31	18 45	18 51

		LE 1	LE 1		LE 1	LE ◇1 ☕	LE 1	LE 1	LE 1	LE 1	LE ◇1 ☕	LE 1	LE ◇1		LE 1	LE 1	LE 1	LE 1	LE 1	LE 1	LE ◇1 ☕	LE 1	LE 1		LE 1
Norwich	d					17 00					17 30										18 00				
Diss	d					17 17					17 47										18 17				
Stowmarket	d					17 29	17 45				17 59										18 29				
Needham Market	d						17 50																		
Ipswich	a					17 41	18 04				18 11										18 41				
	d		17 33			17 43					18 13						18 22				18 43				18 47
Harwich Town	d				17 28			18 00												18 26					
Dovercourt	d				17 30			18 02												18 28					
Harwich International	d				17 33			18 05												18 31					
Wrabness	d				17 39			18 11												18 37					
Mistley	d				17 45			18 17												18 43					
Manningtree 2	d		17 43		17a50	17 53		18a22									18 33			18a48	18 53				18 57
Walton-on-the-Naze	d											17 57											18 34		
Frinton-on-Sea	d											18 00											18 37		
Kirby Cross	d											18 03											18 43		
Clacton-on-Sea	d	←											18 05					←							
Thorpe-le-Soken 1	a	17 12										18 09	18 13					18 09					18 49		
	d	17 17										18 17	18 13					18 17							
Weeley	d	17 21										→						18 21							
Great Bentley	d	17 24																18 24							
Alresford (Essex)	d	17 28																18 28							
Wivenhoe 3	d	17 32											18 23					18 32							
Hythe	d	17 36																18 36							
Colchester Town	a	17 40																18 40							
	d	17 44													18 32			18 44							
Colchester 4	a	17 52	17 52			18 02					18 28		18 33		18 39		18 42	18 52			19 02				19 06
Colchester 4	d					18 03				18 12	18 30		18 33				18 43		18 55		19 03				19 12
Marks Tey 2	d									18 18							18 49		19 01						19 18
Kelvedon	d									18 23							18 54								19 23
Braintree	d															18 33									
Braintree Freeport	d															18 36									
Cressing	d															18 39									
White Notley	d															18 42									
Witham 2	d								18 16	18 29			18 46			18 51	19 00		19 16						19 29
Hatfield Peverel	d									18 33						18 56						←			19 33
Chelmsford 3	d					18 21			18 26	18 40			18 56			19 03	19 09		19 26		19 21	19 26			19 40
Ingatestone	d								18 32				19 02						→			19 32			
Shenfield 3	a								18 38	18 50			19 08			19 13	19 19					19 38			19 50
Romford	a																19 28								
Stratford 7 ⊖	a					18s45			18 52	19 05			19 22			19 27	19 36				19s45	19 52			20 05
London Liverpool Street 15 ⊖	a					18 55			19 01	19 14	19 17		19 31			19 36	19 45				19 55	20 01			20 14

Table 11R

Mondays to Fridays

9 December to 16 May

Norwich, Ipswich, Harwich, Clacton, Walton-on-Naze, Colchester and Chelmsford - London

Network Diagram - refer to first Page of Table 5

		LE 1	LE 1	LE ◇1 ☕	LE 1	LE 1	LE 1	LE ◇1	LE 1		LE 1	LE 1	LE 1	LE 1	LE 1	LE 1	LE ◇1 ☕	LE 1	LE 1		LE 1	LE 1	LE 1	LE ◇1	LE 1
Norwich	d			18 30													19 00							19 30	
Diss	d			18 47													19 17							19 47	
Stowmarket	d	18 45												19 14			19 29						19 45		
Needham Market	d	18 50																					19 50		
Ipswich	a	19 02		19 08										19 28			19 41						20 04	20 09	
	d			19 09								19 23			19 35		19 43					19 52		20 09	
Harwich Town	d				19 05											19 28									20 05
Dovercourt	d				19 07											19 30									20 07
Harwich International	d				19 10											19 33									20 10
Wrabness	d				19 16											19 39									20 16
Mistley	d				19 22											19 45									20 22
Manningtree 2	d			19 19	19a27							19 36			19 45	19a50	19 53					20 02		20 19	20a27
Walton-on-the-Naze	d						18 57		19 18																
Frinton-on-Sea	d						19 00		19 21																
Kirby Cross	d						19 03		19 24																
Clacton-on-Sea	d							19 02					←												
Thorpe-le-Soken 1	a						19 09	19 10	19 30				19 09												
	d						19 17	19 10					19 17												
Weeley	d						↪						19 21												
Great Bentley	d												19 24												
Alresford (Essex)	d												19 28												
Wivenhoe 3	d							19 23					19 32												
Hythe	d												19 36												
Colchester Town	a												19 40												
	d		19 08								19 35		19 44						20 00						
Colchester 4	a		19 15	19 28				19 31			19 42	19 46	19 52		19 54		20 02		20 07			20 11		20 29	
Colchester 4	d			19 30				19 33			19 43				19 55		20 03					20 12		20 30	
Marks Tey 2	d										19 49				20 01							20 18			
Kelvedon	d										19 54											20 23			
Braintree	d					19 25															20 11				
Braintree Freeport	d					19 27															20 13				
Cressing	d					19 30															20 16				
White Notley	d					19 33															20 19				
Witham 2	d					19 42		19 46			20 00				20 16						20 27	20 31			
Hatfield Peverel	d																	←				20 35			
Chelmsford 3	d					19 51		19 56			20 09				20 26		20 21	20 26			20 36	20 42			
Ingatestone	d							20 02							↪			20 32							
Shenfield 3	a							20 08			20 19							20 38			20 46	20 52			
Romford	a										20 28														
Stratford 7 ⊖	a					20 14		20 22			20 36						20s45	20 52				21 07			
London Liverpool Street 15 ⊖	a			20 19		20 23		20 31			20 45						20 55	21 01			21 12	21 16		21 19	

		LE 1	LE ◇1	LE 1	LE 1		LE 1	LE 1	LE 1	LE ◇1 ☕	LE 1	LE 1	LE 1	LE 1	LE ◇1		LE 1	LE ◇1	LE 1	LE 1	LE 1	LE 1	LE 1	LE ◇1 ☕	LE 1
Norwich	d									20 00					20 30									21 00	
Diss	d									20 17					20 47									21 17	
Stowmarket	d									20 29				20 45							21 14			21 29	21 45
Needham Market	d													20 50											21 50
Ipswich	a									20 41				21 00	21 08						21 28			21 41	22 02
	d						20 22			20 43				21 01	21 09						21 28			21 43	
Harwich Town	d								20 28										21 04				21 28		
Dovercourt	d								20 30										21 06				21 30		
Harwich International	d								20 33				20 45	21a30					21 09				21 33		
Wrabness	d								20 39										21 15				21 39		
Mistley	d								20 45										21 21				21 45		
Manningtree 2	d						20 32		20a50	20 53			20 58		21 19				21 26		21 38		21a50	21 53	
Walton-on-the-Naze	d	19 56		20 33													21 00								
Frinton-on-Sea	d	19 59		20 36													21 03								
Kirby Cross	d	20 02		20 42													21 06								
Clacton-on-Sea	d		20 05					←										21 05				←			
Thorpe-le-Soken 1	a	20 08	20 13	20 48				20 08									21 12	21 13				21 12			
	d	20 17	20 13					20 17									21 17	21 13				21 17			
Weeley	d	↪						20 21									↪					21 21			
Great Bentley	d							20 24														21 24			
Alresford (Essex)	d							20 28														21 28			
Wivenhoe 3	d		20 23					20 32										21 23				21 32			
Hythe	d							20 36														21 36			
Colchester Town	a							20 40														21 40			
	d				20 35			20 44			21 00									21 35		21 44			
Colchester 4	a		20 31		20 42		20 45	20 52		21 02	21 07		21 07		21 28			21 31	21 35	21 42	21 51	21 52		22 02	
Colchester 4	d		20 33		20 50					21 03			21 12		21 30			21 33		21 43				22 03	
Marks Tey 2	d				20 56								21 18							21 49					
Kelvedon	d				21 01								21 23							21 54					
Braintree	d											21 00													
Braintree Freeport	d											21 02													
Cressing	d											21 05													
White Notley	d											21 08													
Witham 2	d		20 46		21 07							21 16	21 29					21 46		22 00					
Hatfield Peverel	d												21 33												
Chelmsford 3	d		20 56		21 16					21 21		21 26	21 40					21 56		22 09				22 21	
Ingatestone	d		21 02									21 32						22 02							
Shenfield 3	a		21 08		21 26							21 38	21 50					22 08		22 19					
Romford	a																			22 28					
Stratford 7 ⊖	a		21 22		21 42					21s45		21 52	22 05					22 22		22 36				22s45	
London Liverpool Street 15 ⊖	a		21 31		21 51					21 55		22 01	22 14		22 19			22 31		22 45				22 55	

Table 11R

Mondays to Fridays

9 December to 16 May

Norwich, Ipswich, Harwich, Clacton, Walton-on-Naze, Colchester and Chelmsford - London

Network Diagram - refer to first Page of Table 5

		LE 1	LE ThFO 1	LE MT WO 1	LE 1	LE ThFO ◇1	LE MT WO ◇1	LE ThFO 1	LE MT WO 1	LE 1
Norwich	d									
Diss	d									
Stowmarket	d									
Needham Market	d									
Ipswich	a									
	d							22 23	22 23	
Harwich Town	d									
Dovercourt	d									
Harwich International	d									
Wrabness	d									
Mistley	d									
Manningtree 2	d							22 33	22 33	
Walton-on-the-Naze	d				22 00					
Frinton-on-Sea	d				22 03					
Kirby Cross	d				22 06					
Clacton-on-Sea	d					22 05	22 05			←
Thorpe-le-Soken 1	a				22 12	22 13	22 13			22 12
	d				22 17	22 13	22 13			22 17
Weeley	d				→					22 21
Great Bentley	d									22 24
Alresford (Essex)	d									22 28
Wivenhoe 3	d					22 23	22 23			22 32
Hythe	d									22 36
Colchester Town	a									22 40
	d		22 00	22 00						22 44
Colchester 4	a		22 07	22 07		22 31	22 31	22 42	22 42	22 52
Colchester 4	d		22 12	22 12		22 33	22 33	22 43	22 43	
Marks Tey 2	d		22 18	22 18				22 49	22 49	
Kelvedon	d		22 23	22 23				22 54	22 54	
Braintree	d	22 00								
Braintree Freeport	d	22 02								
Cressing	d	22 05								
White Notley	d	22 08								
Witham 2	d	22 16	22 29	22 29		22 46	22 46	23 00	23 00	
Hatfield Peverel	d		22 33	22 33						
Chelmsford 3	d	22 26	22 40	22 40		22 56	22 56	23 09	23 09	
Ingatestone	d	22 32				23 02	23 02			
Shenfield 3	a	22 38	22 50	22 50		23 08	23 08	23 19	23 19	
Romford	a							23 28	23 28	
Stratford 7 ⊖	a	22 52	23 05	23s12		23 22	23s29	23 36	23s42	
London Liverpool Street 15 ⊖	a	23 01	23 15	23 21		23 31	23 38	23 45	23 51	

		LE 1	LE 1	LE ThFO ◇1	LE MT WO ◇1	LE 1	LE 1	LE 1	LE 1	LE 1 A	LE 1 B	LE 1	LE
Norwich	d			22 00	22 00							23 05	
Diss	d			22 17	22 17							23 22	
Stowmarket	d			22 29	22 29	22 45				23 08	23 08	23 34	23 48
Needham Market	d					22 50							23 53
Ipswich	a			22 41	22 41	23 02				23 21	23 22	23 48	00 05
	d			22 43	22 43					23 22	23 22		
Harwich Town	d	22 28											
Dovercourt	d	22 30											
Harwich International	d	22 33											
Wrabness	d	22 39											
Mistley	d	22 45											
Manningtree 2	d	22a50		22 53	22 53					23 32	23 32		
Walton-on-the-Naze	d							23 00					
Frinton-on-Sea	d							23 03					
Kirby Cross	d							23 06					
Clacton-on-Sea	d								23 05				
Thorpe-le-Soken 1	a							23 12	23 13				
	d								23 13				
Weeley	d								23 17				
Great Bentley	d								23 20				
Alresford (Essex)	d								23 24				
Wivenhoe 3	d								23 28				
Hythe	d								23 32				
Colchester Town	a												
	d					23 00							
Colchester 4	a			23 02	23 02	23 07			23 38	23 43	23 43		
Colchester 4	d			23 03	23 03								
Marks Tey 2	d												
Kelvedon	d												
Braintree	d		22 56										
Braintree Freeport	d		22 58										
Cressing	d		23 01										
White Notley	d		23 04										
Witham 2	d		23a12	23 16	23 16								
Hatfield Peverel	d												
Chelmsford 3	d			23 25	23 25								
Ingatestone	d												
Shenfield 3	a			23s36	23s36								
Romford	a												
Stratford 7 ⊖	a			23s52	00s01								
London Liverpool Street 15 ⊖	a			00 02	00 10								

		LE 1	LE 1
Norwich	d		
Diss	d		
Stowmarket	d		
Needham Market	d		
Ipswich	a		
	d		
Harwich Town	d	23 28	
Dovercourt	d	23 30	
Harwich International	d	23 33	
Wrabness	d	23 39	
Mistley	d	23 45	
Manningtree 2	d	23 50	
Walton-on-the-Naze	d		
Frinton-on-Sea	d		
Kirby Cross	d		
Clacton-on-Sea	d		
Thorpe-le-Soken 1	a		
	d		
Weeley	d		
Great Bentley	d		
Alresford (Essex)	d		
Wivenhoe 3	d		
Hythe	d		
Colchester Town	a		
	d		
Colchester 4	a	23 59	
Colchester 4	d		
Marks Tey 2	d		
Kelvedon	d		
Braintree	d		23 45
Braintree Freeport	d		23 47
Cressing	d		23 50
White Notley	d		23 53
Witham 2	d		00a01
Hatfield Peverel	d		
Chelmsford 3	d		
Ingatestone	d		
Shenfield 3	a		
Romford	a		
Stratford 7 ⊖	a		
London Liverpool Street 15 ⊖	a		

A from 30 December B until 27 December

Table 11R

Saturdays

14 December to 17 May

Norwich, Ipswich, Harwich, Clacton, Walton-on-Naze, Colchester and Chelmsford - London

Network Diagram - refer to first Page of Table 5

		LE 1	LE 1	LE 1	LE 1	LE	LE 1	LE ◇1 ☕	LE 1	LE 1		LE ◇1 ☕	LE 1	LE 1	LE ◇1	LE 1	LE 1	LE 1	LE ◇1 ☕	LE 1		LE 1	LE 1	LE	LE ◇1 ☕
Norwich	d							05 00				05 30							06 00						06 30
Diss	d							05 17				05 47							06 17						06 47
Stowmarket	d							05 29											06 29					06 44	
Needham Market	d																							06 49	
Ipswich	a							05 41				06 08							06 41					07 02	07 08
	d							05 43				06 09							06 43			06 52	06 59		07 09
Harwich Town	d												06 28												
Dovercourt	d												06 30												
Harwich International	d												06 33										07a28		
Wrabness	d												06 39												
Mistley	d												06 45												
Manningtree 2	d							05 53				06 19	06a50						06 53			07 02			07 19
Walton-on-the-Naze	d													06 00											
Frinton-on-Sea	d													06 03											
Kirby Cross	d													06 06											
Clacton-on-Sea	d						05 30								06 05	06 24		←							
Thorpe-le-Soken 1	a						05 38							06 12	06 13	06 32		06 12							
	d						05 38							06 17	06 13			06 17							
Weeley	d													→				06 21							
Great Bentley	d																	06 24							
Alresford (Essex)	d																	06 28							
Wivenhoe 3	d						05 48								06 23			06 32							
Hythe	d																	06 36							
Colchester Town	a																	06 40							
	d																06 35	06 44							
Colchester 4	a						05 57	06 02				06 28			06 31		06 42	06 52	07 02			07 11			07 28
Colchester 4	d		04 43	05 12	05 43	05 50		06 03		06 12		06 30			06 33		06 43		07 03			07 12			07 30
Marks Tey 2	d		04 49	05 18	05 49	05a57				06 18							06 49					07 18			
Kelvedon	d		04 54	05 23	05 54					06 23							06 54					07 23			
Braintree	d	00 25							06 00											07 00					
Braintree Freeport	d	00 27							06 02											07 02					
Cressing	d	00 30							06 05											07 05					
White Notley	d	00 33							06 08											07 08					
Witham 2	d	00a41	05 00	05 29	06 00				06a16	06 29					06 46		07 00			07 16		07 29			
Hatfield Peverel	d		05 04	05 33	06 04					06 33												07 33			
Chelmsford 3	d		05 11	05 40	06 11			06 21		06 40					06 56		07 09		07 21	07 26		07 40			
Ingatestone	d		05 18	05 47	06 18										07 02					07 32					
Shenfield 3	a		05 23	05 52	06 23					06 50					07 08		07 19			07 38		07 50			
Romford	a																07 28								
Stratford 7 ⊖	a		05 42	06 07	06 38			06s45		07 05					07 22		07 36		07s45	07 52		08 05			
London Liverpool Street 15 ⊖	a		05 55	06 16	06 47			06 55		07 14		07 19			07 31		07 45		07 55	08 01		08 14			08 19

		LE 1	LE ◇1	LE 1	LE 1	LE 1		LE ◇1 ☕	LE 1	LE 1	LE 1	LE	LE ◇1 ☕	LE 1	LE 1	LE ◇1		LE 1	LE 1	LE ◇1 ☕	LE 1	LE 1	LE 1	LE 1	LE ◇1 ☕
Norwich	d							07 00					07 30							08 00					08 30
Diss	d							07 17					07 47							08 17					08 47
Stowmarket	d							07 29				07 45								08 29				08 45	
Needham Market	d											07 50												08 50	
Ipswich	a							07 41				08 02	08 08							08 41				09 02	09 08
	d							07 43			07 52		08 09							08 43			08 52		09 09
Harwich Town	d					07 28								08 28											
Dovercourt	d					07 30								08 30											
Harwich International	d			07 20		07 33								08 33											
Wrabness	d					07 39								08 39											
Mistley	d					07 45								08 45											
Manningtree 2	d			07 33		07a50		07 53			08 02		08 19	08a50						08 53			09 02		09 19
Walton-on-the-Naze	d	07 00													08 00										
Frinton-on-Sea	d	07 03													08 03										
Kirby Cross	d	07 06													08 06										
Clacton-on-Sea	d		07 05		←											08 05			←						
Thorpe-le-Soken 1	a	07 12	07 13		07 12										08 12	08 13			08 12						
	d	07 17	07 13		07 17										08 17	08 13			08 17						
Weeley	d	→			07 21										→				08 21						
Great Bentley	d				07 24														08 24						
Alresford (Essex)	d				07 28														08 28						
Wivenhoe 3	d		07 23		07 32											08 23			08 32						
Hythe	d				07 36														08 36						
Colchester Town	a				07 40														08 40						
	d				07 44				08 00									08 35	08 44		09 00				
Colchester 4	a		07 31	07 42	07 52			08 02	08 07		08 11		08 28			08 31		08 42	08 52	09 02	09 07		09 11		09 28
Colchester 4	d		07 33	07 43				08 03			08 12		08 30			08 33		08 43		09 03			09 12		09 30
Marks Tey 2	d			07 49							08 18							08 49					09 18		
Kelvedon	d			07 54							08 23							08 54					09 23		
Braintree	d									08 00												09 00			
Braintree Freeport	d									08 02												09 02			
Cressing	d									08 05												09 05			
White Notley	d									08 08												09 08			
Witham 2	d		07 46	08 00						08 16	08 29					08 46		09 00				09 16	09 29		
Hatfield Peverel	d										08 33												09 33		
Chelmsford 3	d		07 56	08 09				08 21		08 26	08 40					08 56		09 09		09 21		09 26	09 40		
Ingatestone	d		08 02							08 32						09 02						09 32			
Shenfield 3	a		08 08	08 19						08 38	08 50					09 08		09 19				09 38	09 50		
Romford	a			08 28														09 28							
Stratford 7 ⊖	a		08 22	08 36				08s45		08 52	09 05					09 22		09 36		09s45		09 52	10 05		
London Liverpool Street 15 ⊖	a		08 31	08 45				08 55		09 01	09 14		09 19			09 31		09 45		09 55		10 01	10 14		10 19

Table 11R

Saturdays

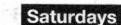

14 December to 17 May

Norwich, Ipswich, Harwich, Clacton, Walton-on-Naze, Colchester and Chelmsford - London

Network Diagram - refer to first Page of Table 5

		LE 1		LE 1	LE 1	LE ◇1	LE 1	LE 1	LE ◇1 ☕	LE 1	LE 1	LE 1		LE 1	LE ◇1 ☕	LE 1	LE 1	LE ◇1	LE 1	LE 1	LE ◇1 ☕	LE 1		LE 1	LE 1
Norwich	d								09 00						09 30						10 00				
Diss	d								09 17						09 47						10 17				
Stowmarket	d	09 14							09 29					09 45							10 29				
Needham Market	d													09 50											
Ipswich	a	09 28							09 41					10 02	10 08						10 41				
	d								09 43			09 52			10 09						10 43				10 52
Harwich Town	d			09 28												10 28									
Dovercourt	d			09 30												10 30									
Harwich International	d			09 33												10 33									
Wrabness	d			09 39												10 39									
Mistley	d			09 45												10 45									
Manningtree 2	d			09a50					09 53			10 02			10 19	10a50					10 53				11 02
Walton-on-the-Naze	d				09 00												10 00								
Frinton-on-Sea	d				09 03												10 03								
Kirby Cross	d				09 06												10 06								
Clacton-on-Sea	d					09 05		←										10 05		←					
Thorpe-le-Soken 1	a				09 12	09 13		09 12									10 12	10 13		10 12					
	d				09 17	09 13		09 17									10 17	10 13		10 17					
Weeley	d				→			09 21									→			10 21					
Great Bentley	d							09 24												10 24					
Alresford (Essex)	d							09 28												10 28					
Wivenhoe 3	d					09 23		09 32										10 23		10 32					
Hythe	d							09 36												10 36					
Colchester Town	a							09 40												10 40					
	d						09 35	09 44		10 00									10 35	10 44		11 00			
Colchester 4	a					09 31	09 42	09 52	10 02	10 07		10 11			10 28			10 31	10 42	10 52	11 02	11 07			11 11
Colchester 4	d					09 33	09 43		10 03			10 12			10 30			10 33	10 43		11 03				11 12
Marks Tey 2	d						09 49					10 18							10 49						11 18
Kelvedon	d						09 54					10 23							10 54						11 23
Braintree	d										10 00													11 00	
Braintree Freeport	d										10 02													11 02	
Cressing	d										10 05													11 05	
White Notley	d										10 08													11 08	
Witham 2	d					09 46	10 00				10 16	10 29						10 46	11 00					11 16	11 29
Hatfield Peverel	d											10 33													11 33
Chelmsford 3	d					09 56	10 09		10 21		10 26	10 40						10 56	11 09		11 21			11 26	11 40
Ingatestone	d					10 02					10 32							11 02						11 32	
Shenfield 3	a					10 08	10 19				10 38	10 50						11 08	11 19					11 38	11 50
Romford	a						10 28												11 28						
Stratford 7 ⊖	a					10 22	10 36		10s45		10 52	11 05						11 22	11 36		11s45			11 52	12 05
London Liverpool Street 15 ⊖	a					10 31	10 45		10 55		11 01	11 14			11 19			11 31	11 45		11 55			12 01	12 14

		LE 1	LE ◇1 ☕	LE 1	LE 1	LE 1	LE ◇1	LE 1		LE 1	LE ◇1 ☕	LE 1	LE 1	LE 1	LE 1	LE ◇1 ☕	LE 1	LE 1		LE ◇1	LE 1	LE 1	LE ◇1 ☕	LE 1	LE 1
Norwich	d		10 30								11 00					11 30							12 00		
Diss	d		10 47								11 17					11 47							12 17		
Stowmarket	d	10 45		11 14							11 29				11 45								12 29		
Needham Market	d	10 50													11 50										
Ipswich	a	11 02	11 08	11 28							11 41				12 02	12 08							12 41		
	d		11 09								11 43			11 52		12 09							12 43		
Harwich Town	d				11 28												12 28								
Dovercourt	d				11 30												12 30								
Harwich International	d				11 33												12 33								
Wrabness	d				11 39												12 39								
Mistley	d				11 45												12 45								
Manningtree 2	d		11 19		11a50						11 53			12 02		12 19	12a50						12 53		
Walton-on-the-Naze	d					11 00												12 00							
Frinton-on-Sea	d					11 03												12 03							
Kirby Cross	d					11 06												12 06							
Clacton-on-Sea	d						11 05			←										12 05		←			
Thorpe-le-Soken 1	a					11 12	11 13			11 12								12 12		12 13		12 12			
	d					11 17	11 13			11 17								12 17		12 13		12 17			
Weeley	d					→				11 21								→				12 21			
Great Bentley	d									11 24												12 24			
Alresford (Essex)	d									11 28												12 28			
Wivenhoe 3	d						11 23			11 32										12 23		12 32			
Hythe	d									11 36												12 36			
Colchester Town	a									11 40												12 40			
	d							11 35		11 44		12 00									12 35	12 44		13 00	
Colchester 4	a		11 28				11 31	11 42		11 52	12 02	12 07		12 11		12 28				12 31	12 42	12 52	13 02	13 07	
Colchester 4	d		11 30				11 33	11 43			12 03			12 12		12 30				12 33	12 43		13 03		
Marks Tey 2	d							11 49						12 18							12 49				
Kelvedon	d							11 54						12 23							12 54				
Braintree	d												12 00												13 00
Braintree Freeport	d												12 02												13 02
Cressing	d												12 05												13 05
White Notley	d												12 08												13 08
Witham 2	d						11 46	12 00					12 16	12 29						12 46	13 00				13 16
Hatfield Peverel	d													12 33											
Chelmsford 3	d						11 56	12 09			12 21		12 26	12 40						12 56	13 09		13 21		13 26
Ingatestone	d						12 02						12 32							13 02					13 32
Shenfield 3	a						12 08	12 19					12 38	12 50						13 08	13 19				13 38
Romford	a							12 28													13 28				
Stratford 7 ⊖	a						12 22	12 36			12s45		12 52	13 05						13 22	13 36		13s45		13 52
London Liverpool Street 15 ⊖	a		12 19				12 31	12 45			12 55		13 01	13 14		13 19				13 31	13 45		13 55		14 01

Table 11R

Saturdays

14 December to 17 May

Norwich, Ipswich, Harwich, Clacton, Walton-on-Naze, Colchester and Chelmsford - London

Network Diagram - refer to first Page of Table 5

		LE 1	LE 1	LE ◇1 ☕	LE 1	LE 1	LE 1	LE ◇1	LE 1	LE 1	LE ◇1 ☕	LE 1	LE 1	LE 1	LE 1	LE ◇1 ☕	LE 1	LE 1	LE ◇1	LE 1	LE 1	LE ◇1 ☕
Norwich	d			12 30							13 00					13 30						14 00
Diss	d			12 47							13 17					13 47						14 17
Stowmarket	d		12 45		13 14						13 29				13 45							14 29
Needham Market	d		12 50												13 50							
Ipswich	a		13 02	13 08	13 28						13 41				14 02	14 08						14 41
	d	12 52		13 09							13 43			13 52		14 09						14 43
Harwich Town	d					13 28											14 28					
Dovercourt	d					13 30											14 30					
Harwich International	d					13 33											14 33					
Wrabness	d					13 39											14 39					
Mistley	d					13 45											14 45					
Manningtree 2	d	13 02		13 19		13a50					13 53			14 02		14 19	14a50					14 53
Walton-on-the-Naze	d						13 00											14 00				
Frinton-on-Sea	d						13 03											14 03				
Kirby Cross	d						13 06											14 06				
Clacton-on-Sea	d							13 05		←									14 05		←	
Thorpe-le-Soken 1	a						13 12	13 13		13 12								14 12	14 13		14 12	
	d						13 17	13 13		13 17								14 17	14 13		14 17	
Weeley	d						→			13 21								→			14 21	
Great Bentley	d									13 24											14 24	
Alresford (Essex)	d									13 28											14 28	
Wivenhoe 3	d							13 23		13 32									14 23		14 32	
Hythe	d									13 36											14 36	
Colchester Town	a									13 40											14 40	
	d								13 35	13 44		14 00								14 35	14 44	
Colchester 4	a	13 11		13 28				13 31	13 42	13 52	14 02	14 07		14 11		14 28			14 31	14 42	14 52	15 02
Colchester 4	d	13 12		13 30				13 33	13 43		14 03			14 12		14 30			14 33	14 43		15 03
Marks Tey 2	d	13 18							13 49					14 18						14 49		
Kelvedon	d	13 23							13 54					14 23						14 54		
Braintree	d												14 00									
Braintree Freeport	d												14 02									
Cressing	d												14 05									
White Notley	d												14 08									
Witham 2	d	13 29						13 46	14 00				14 16	14 29					14 46	15 00		
Hatfield Peverel	d	13 33												14 33								
Chelmsford 3	d	13 40						13 56	14 09		14 21		14 26	14 40					14 56	15 09		15 21
Ingatestone	d							14 02					14 32						15 02			
Shenfield 3	a	13 50						14 08	14 19				14 38	14 50					15 08	15 19		
Romford	a								14 28											15 28		
Stratford 7 ⊖	a	14 05						14 22	14 36		14s45		14 52	15 05					15 22	15 36		15s45
London Liverpool Street 15 ⊖	a	14 14		14 19				14 31	14 45		14 55		15 01	15 14		15 19			15 31	15 45		15 55

		LE 1	LE 1	LE 1	LE 1	LE ◇1 ☕	LE 1	LE 1	LE 1	LE ◇1	LE 1	LE 1	LE ◇1 ☕	LE 1	LE 1	LE 1	LE 1	LE ◇1 ☕	LE 1	LE 1	LE ◇1	LE 1	LE 1
Norwich	d					14 30							15 00					15 30					
Diss	d					14 47							15 17					15 47					
Stowmarket	d				14 45		15 14						15 29				15 45						
Needham Market	d				14 50												15 50						
Ipswich	a				15 02	15 08	15 28						15 41				16 02	16 08					
	d			14 52		15 09							15 43			15 52		16 09					
Harwich Town	d							15 28											16 28				
Dovercourt	d							15 30											16 30				
Harwich International	d							15 33											16 33				
Wrabness	d							15 39											16 39				
Mistley	d							15 45											16 45				
Manningtree 2	d			15 02		15 19		15a50					15 53			16 02		16 19	16a50				
Walton-on-the-Naze	d								15 00											16 00			
Frinton-on-Sea	d								15 03											16 03			
Kirby Cross	d								15 06											16 06			
Clacton-on-Sea	d									15 05		←									16 05		←
Thorpe-le-Soken 1	a								15 12	15 13		15 12								16 12	16 13		16 12
	d								15 17	15 13		15 17								16 17	16 13		16 17
Weeley	d								→			15 21								→			16 21
Great Bentley	d											15 24											16 24
Alresford (Essex)	d											15 28											16 28
Wivenhoe 3	d									15 23		15 32									16 23		16 32
Hythe	d											15 36											16 36
Colchester Town	a											15 40											16 40
	d	15 00									15 35	15 44		16 00								16 35	16 44
Colchester 4	a	15 07		15 11		15 28				15 31	15 42	15 52	16 02	16 07		16 11		16 28			16 31	16 42	16 52
Colchester 4	d			15 12		15 30				15 33	15 43		16 03			16 12		16 30			16 33	16 43	
Marks Tey 2	d			15 18							15 49					16 18						16 49	
Kelvedon	d			15 23							15 54					16 23						16 54	
Braintree	d		15 00												16 00								
Braintree Freeport	d		15 02												16 02								
Cressing	d		15 05												16 05								
White Notley	d		15 08												16 08								
Witham 2	d		15 16	15 29						15 46	16 00				16 16	16 29					16 46	17 00	
Hatfield Peverel	d			15 33												16 33							
Chelmsford 3	d		15 26	15 40						15 56	16 09		16 21		16 26	16 40					16 56	17 09	
Ingatestone	d		15 32							16 02					16 32						17 02		
Shenfield 3	a		15 38	15 50						16 08	16 19				16 38	16 50					17 08	17 19	
Romford	a										16 28											17 28	
Stratford 7 ⊖	a		15 52	16 05						16 22	16 36		16s45		16 52	17 05					17 22	17 36	
London Liverpool Street 15 ⊖	a		16 01	16 14		16 19				16 31	16 45		16 55		17 01	17 14		17 19			17 31	17 45	

Table 11R

Saturdays

14 December to 17 May

Norwich, Ipswich, Harwich, Clacton, Walton-on-Naze, Colchester and Chelmsford - London

Network Diagram - refer to first Page of Table 5

	LE ◇1 ☕	LE 1	LE 1	LE 1	LE 1		LE ◇1 ☕	LE 1	LE 1	LE 1	LE ◇1	LE 1	LE 1	LE ◇1 ☕	LE 1		LE 1	LE 1	LE 1	LE ◇1 ☕	LE 1	LE 1	LE ◇1	LE 1
Norwich d	16 00						16 30							17 00						17 30				
Diss d	16 17						16 47							17 17						17 47				
Stowmarket d	16 29				16 45			17 14						17 29					17 45	17 59				
Needham Market d					16 50														17 50					
Ipswich a	16 41				17 02		17 08	17 28						17 41					18 02	18 11				
Ipswich d	16 43			16 52			17 09							17 43				17 52		18 13				
Harwich Town d									17 28												18 28			
Dovercourt d									17 30												18 30			
Harwich International d									17 33												18 33			
Wrabness d									17 39												18 39			
Mistley d									17 45												18 45			
Manningtree 2 d	16 53			17 02			17 19		17a50					17 53				18 02			18a50			
Walton-on-the-Naze d										17 00												18 00		
Frinton-on-Sea d										17 03												18 03		
Kirby Cross d										17 06												18 06		
Clacton-on-Sea d											17 05		←										18 05	
Thorpe-le-Soken 1 a										17 12	17 13		17 12									18 12	18 13	
Thorpe-le-Soken 1 d										17 17	17 13		17 17									18 17	18 13	
Weeley d										→			17 21									→		
Great Bentley d													17 24											
Alresford (Essex) d													17 28											
Wivenhoe 3 d											17 23		17 32										18 23	
Hythe d													17 36											
Colchester Town a													17 40											
Colchester Town d		17 00										17 35	17 44		18 00									18 35
Colchester 4 a	17 02	17 07		17 11			17 28				17 31	17 42	17 52	18 02	18 07			18 11		18 28			18 31	18 42
Colchester 4 d	17 03			17 12			17 30				17 33	17 43		18 03				18 12		18 30			18 33	18 43
Marks Tey 2 d				17 18								17 49						18 18						18 49
Kelvedon d				17 23								17 54						18 23						18 54
Braintree d			17 00														18 00							
Braintree Freeport d			17 02														18 02							
Cressing d			17 05														18 05							
White Notley d			17 08														18 08							
Witham 2 d			17 16	17 29							17 46	18 00					18 16	18 29					18 46	19 00
Hatfield Peverel d				17 33														18 33						
Chelmsford 3 d	17 21		17 26	17 40							17 56	18 09		18 21			18 26	18 40					18 56	19 09
Ingatestone d			17 32								18 02						18 32						19 02	
Shenfield 3 a			17 38	17 50							18 08	18 19					18 38	18 50					19 08	19 19
Romford a												18 28												19 28
Stratford 7 ⊖ a	17s45		17 52	18 05							18 22	18 36		18s45			18 52	19 05					19 22	19 36
London Liverpool Street 15 ⊖ a	17 55		18 01	18 14			18 19				18 31	18 45		18 55			19 01	19 14		19 19			19 31	19 45

	LE 1		LE ◇1 ☕	LE 1	LE 1	LE 1	LE 1	LE ◇1 ☕	LE 1	LE 1	LE 1		LE ◇1	LE 1	LE 1	LE ◇1 ☕	LE 1	LE 1	LE 1	LE 1	LE 1		LE 1	LE 1
Norwich d			18 00					18 30								19 00								
Diss d			18 17					18 47								19 17								
Stowmarket d			18 29				18 45		19 14							19 29				19 45				
Needham Market d							18 50													19 50				
Ipswich a			18 41				19 02	19 08	19 28							19 41				20 02				
Ipswich d			18 43			18 52		19 09								19 43			19 52		20 09			
Harwich Town d										19 28													20 28	
Dovercourt d										19 30													20 30	
Harwich International d										19 33													20 33	
Wrabness d										19 39													20 39	
Mistley d										19 45													20 45	
Manningtree 2 d			18 53			19 02		19 19		19a50						19 53			20 02		20 19		20a50	
Walton-on-the-Naze d											19 00													20 00
Frinton-on-Sea d											19 03													20 03
Kirby Cross d											19 06													20 06
Clacton-on-Sea d	←												19 05		←									
Thorpe-le-Soken 1 a	18 12										19 12		19 13		19 12									20 12
Thorpe-le-Soken 1 d	18 17										19 17		19 13		19 17									20 17
Weeley d	18 21										→				19 21									→
Great Bentley d	18 24														19 24									
Alresford (Essex) d	18 28														19 28									
Wivenhoe 3 d	18 32												19 23		19 32									
Hythe d	18 36														19 36									
Colchester Town a	18 40														19 40									
Colchester Town d	18 44			19 00										19 35	19 44		20 00							
Colchester 4 a	18 52		19 02	19 07		19 11		19 28					19 31	19 42	19 52	20 02	20 07		20 11		20 28			
Colchester 4 d			19 03			19 12		19 30					19 33	19 43		20 03			20 12		20 30			
Marks Tey 2 d						19 18								19 49					20 18					
Kelvedon d						19 23								19 54					20 23					
Braintree d					19 00													20 00						
Braintree Freeport d					19 02													20 02						
Cressing d					19 05													20 05						
White Notley d					19 08													20 08						
Witham 2 d					19 16	19 29							19 46	20 00				20 16	20 29					
Hatfield Peverel d						19 33													20 33					
Chelmsford 3 d			19 21		19 26	19 40							19 56	20 09		20 21		20 26	20 40					
Ingatestone d					19 32								20 02					20 32						
Shenfield 3 a					19 38	19 50							20 08	20 19				20 38	20 50					
Romford a														20 28										
Stratford 7 ⊖ a			19s45		19 52	20 05							20 22	20 36		20s45		20 52	21 05					
London Liverpool Street 15 ⊖ a			19 55		20 01	20 14		20 19					20 31	20 45		20 55		21 01	21 14		21 17			

Table 11R

Saturdays

14 December to 17 May

Norwich, Ipswich, Harwich, Clacton, Walton-on-Naze, Colchester and Chelmsford - London

Network Diagram - refer to first Page of Table 5

		LE	LE	LE	LE	LE	LE	LE		LE	LE	LE	LE	LE	LE	LE	LE	LE		LE	LE	LE	LE	LE	LE
		◇1	1	1	◇1 ☕	1	1	1		1	1	1	◇1	1	1	1	1	◇1 ☕		1	1	1	1	1	◇1
Norwich	d				20 00													21 00							
Diss	d				20 17													21 17							
Stowmarket	d				20 29					20 45					21 14			21 29					21 45		
Needham Market	d									20 50													21 50		
Ipswich	a				20 41					21 00					21 28			21 41					22 02		
	d				20 43					21 01	21 09				21 28			21 43				21 52			
Harwich Town	d																21 28								
Dovercourt	d																21 30								
Harwich International	d							20 45		21a30							21 33								
Wrabness	d																21 39								
Mistley	d																21 45								
Manningtree 2	d				20 53			20 58			21 19				21 38		21a50	21 53				22 02			
Walton-on-the-Naze	d											21 00												22 00	
Frinton-on-Sea	d											21 03												22 03	
Kirby Cross	d											21 06												22 06	
Clacton-on-Sea	d	20 05		←									21 05			←									22 05
Thorpe-le-Soken 1	a	20 13		20 12								21 12	21 13			21 12								22 12	22 13
	d	20 13		20 17								21 17	21 13			21 17								22 17	22 13
Weeley	d			20 21								→				21 21								→	
Great Bentley	d			20 24												21 24									
Alresford (Essex)	d			20 28												21 28									
Wivenhoe 3	d	20 23		20 32									21 23			21 32									22 23
Hythe	d			20 36												21 36									
Colchester Town	a			20 40												21 40									
	d		20 35	20 44		21 00								21 35		21 44				22 00					
Colchester 4	a	20 31	20 42	20 52	21 02	21 07		21 07			21 28		21 31	21 42	21 49	21 52		22 02		22 07		22 11			22 31
Colchester 4	d	20 33	20 43		21 03			21 12			21 30		21 33	21 43				22 03				22 12			22 33
Marks Tey 2	d		20 49					21 18						21 49								22 18			
Kelvedon	d		20 54					21 23						21 54								22 23			
Braintree	d						21 00														22 00				
Braintree Freeport	d						21 02														22 02				
Cressing	d						21 05														22 05				
White Notley	d						21 08														22 08				
Witham 2	d	20 46	21 00				21 16	21 29					21 46	22 00							22 16	22 29			22 46
Hatfield Peverel	d							21 33														22 33			
Chelmsford 3	d	20 56	21 09		21 21		21 26	21 40					21 56	22 09				22 21			22 26	22 40			22 56
Ingatestone	d	21 02					21 32						22 02								22 32				23 02
Shenfield 3	a	21 08	21 19				21 38	21 50					22 08	22 19							22 38	22 50			23 08
Romford	a		21 28											22 28											
Stratford 7 ⊖	a	21 22	21 36		21s45		21 52	22 05					22 22	22 36				22s45			22 52	23s12			23s29
London Liverpool Street 15 ⊖	a	21 31	21 45		21 55		22 01	22 14			22 17		22 31	22 46				23 01			23 07	23 22			23 38

		LE	LE	LE		LE	LE	LE	LE	LE	LE	LE	LE	LE		LE	LE	LE
		1	1	1		1	◇1	1	1	1	1	1	1	1			1	1
Norwich	d						22 00							23 05				
Diss	d						22 17							23 22				
Stowmarket	d						22 29	22 45					23 08	23 36		23 48		
Needham Market	d							22 50								23 53		
Ipswich	a						22 41	23 02					23 22	23 50		00 05		
	d	22 23					22 43				23 15		23 22					
Harwich Town	d			22 28													23 28	
Dovercourt	d			22 30													23 30	
Harwich International	d			22 33													23 33	
Wrabness	d			22 39													23 39	
Mistley	d			22 45													23 45	
Manningtree 2	d	22 33		22a50			22 53				23 25		23 32				23 50	
Walton-on-the-Naze	d									23 00								
Frinton-on-Sea	d									23 03								
Kirby Cross	d									23 06								
Clacton-on-Sea	d		←									23 05						
Thorpe-le-Soken 1	a		22 12							23 12		23 13						
	d		22 17									23 13						
Weeley	d		22 21									23 17						
Great Bentley	d		22 24									23 20						
Alresford (Essex)	d		22 28									23 24						
Wivenhoe 3	d		22 32									23 28						
Hythe	d		22 36									23 32						
Colchester Town	a		22 40															
	d		22 44						23 00									
Colchester 4	a	22 42	22 52				23 02		23 07		23 35	23 38	23 43				23 59	
Colchester 4	d	22 43					23 03											
Marks Tey 2	d	22 49																
Kelvedon	d	22 54																
Braintree	d					22 56												23 45
Braintree Freeport	d					22 58												23 47
Cressing	d					23 01												23 50
White Notley	d					23 04												23 53
Witham 2	d	23 00				23a12	23 16											00a01
Hatfield Peverel	d																	
Chelmsford 3	d	23 09					23 25											
Ingatestone	d																	
Shenfield 3	a	23 19					23s37											
Romford	a	23 28																
Stratford 7 ⊖	a	23s42					23s59											
London Liverpool Street 15 ⊖	a	23 51					00 10											

Table 11R

Sundays

8 December to 11 May

Norwich, Ipswich, Harwich, Clacton, Walton-on-Naze, Colchester and Chelmsford - London

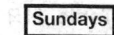

Network Diagram - refer to first Page of Table 5

		LE	LE	LE	LE	LE	LE	LE	LE	LE		LE	LE	LE	LE	LE	LE	LE	LE	LE		LE	LE	LE	LE
		1				1		1	1	◇1		1	1	◇1	1	◇1	1	1	1	◇1		1	◇1	1	1
			🚌	🚌	🚌					☕						☕							☕		
Norwich	d									07 00						08 00							09 00		
Diss	d									07 17						08 17							09 17		
Stowmarket	d									07 29						08 29							09 29		
Needham Market	d																								
Ipswich	a									07 41						08 41							09 41		
	d									07 43		07 51			08 09	08 43						09 09	09 43		
Harwich Town	d																	08 53							09 53
Dovercourt	d																	08 55							09 55
Harwich International	d								07 20			08a19						08 58							09 58
Wrabness	d																	09 04							10 04
Mistley	d																	09 10							10 10
Manningtree 2	d								07 33	07 53					08 19	08 53		09a15				09 19	09 53		10a15
Walton-on-the-Naze	d																08 30							09 30	
Frinton-on-Sea	d																08 33							09 33	
Kirby Cross	d																08 36							09 36	
Clacton-on-Sea	d													07 36						08 36					
Thorpe-le-Soken 1	a													07 44			08 42			08 44				09 42	
	d													07 44						08 44					
Weeley	d																								
Great Bentley	d													07 49						08 49					
Alresford (Essex)	d													07 53						08 53					
Wivenhoe 3	d													07 57						08 57					
Hythe	d																								
Colchester Town	a																								
	d																								
Colchester 4	a								07 42	08 02				08 05	08 29	09 02				09 05		09 29	10 02		
Colchester 4	d			05 40	06 10	06 54	07 01	07 24	07 42	08 03				08 06	08 30	09 03				09 06		09 30	10 03		
Marks Tey 2	d					07 00	07a14	07 30						08 12	08 36					09 12		09 36			
Kelvedon	d					07 05		07 35							08 41							09 41			
Braintree	d	00 25											08 00						09 00						
Braintree Freeport	d	00 27											08 02						09 02						
Cressing	d	00 30											08 05						09 05						
White Notley	d	00 33											08 08						09 08						
Witham 2	d	00a41		06 05	06 35	07 11		07 41	07 55				08a16	08 21	08 47				09a16	09 21		09 47			
Hatfield Peverel	d					07 15		07 45							08 51							09 51			
Chelmsford 3	d		05 53	06 30	07 00	07 22		07 52	08 04					08 30	08 58					09 30		09 58			
Ingatestone	d		06 13			07 29		07 59							09 05							10 05			
Shenfield 3	a		06 25	06 55	07 25	07 40		08 10	08 20					08 40	09 10					09 40		10 10			
Romford	a							08 21																	
Stratford 7 ⊖	a		07s13	07s43	08s13			08 33	08s50					09s05	09s35					10s05		10s35			
London Liverpool Street 15 ⊖	a		07 33	08 03	08 33			08 42	08 59	09 04				09 14	09 44	10 03				10 14		10 44	11 03		

		LE	LE	LE	LE	LE		LE	LE	LE	LE	LE	LE	LE	LE	LE		LE	LE	LE	LE	LE	LE	LE	LE
		1	◇1	1		◇1		1	1	1	◇1	1	◇1	1	1	1		◇1	1	1	◇1	1	1	1	◇1
						☕							☕								☕				
Norwich	d					10 00							11 00								12 00				
Diss	d					10 17							11 17								12 17				
Stowmarket	d				10 18	10 29							11 29							12 18	12 29				
Needham Market	d				10 23															12 23					
Ipswich	a				10 36	10 41							11 41							12 36	12 41				
	d			10 09		10 43						11 09	11 43						12 09		12 43				
Harwich Town	d								10 53						11 53								12 53		
Dovercourt	d								10 55						11 55								12 55		
Harwich International	d								10 58						11 58								12 58		
Wrabness	d								11 04						12 04								13 04		
Mistley	d								11 10						12 10								13 10		
Manningtree 2	d			10 19		10 53			11a15			11 19	11 53		12a15				12 19		12 53		13a15		
Walton-on-the-Naze	d							10 30						11 30								12 30			
Frinton-on-Sea	d							10 33						11 33								12 33			
Kirby Cross	d							10 36						11 36								12 36			
Clacton-on-Sea	d		09 36								10 36							11 36							12 36
Thorpe-le-Soken 1	a		09 44					10 42			10 44			11 42				11 44				12 42			12 44
	d		09 44								10 44							11 44							12 44
Weeley	d																								
Great Bentley	d		09 49								10 49							11 49							12 49
Alresford (Essex)	d		09 53								10 53							11 53							12 53
Wivenhoe 3	d		09 57								10 57							11 57							12 57
Hythe	d																								
Colchester Town	a																								
	d																								
Colchester 4	a		10 05	10 29		11 02					11 05	11 29	12 02					12 05	12 29		13 02				13 05
Colchester 4	d		10 06	10 30		11 03					11 06	11 30	12 03					12 06	12 30		13 03				13 06
Marks Tey 2	d		10 12	10 36							11 12	11 36						12 12	12 36						13 12
Kelvedon	d			10 41								11 41							12 41						
Braintree	d	10 00								11 00						12 00								13 00	
Braintree Freeport	d	10 02								11 02						12 02								13 02	
Cressing	d	10 05								11 05						12 05								13 05	
White Notley	d	10 08								11 08						12 08								13 08	
Witham 2	d	10a16	10 21	10 47						11a16	11 21	11 47				12a16		12 21	12 47					13a16	13 21
Hatfield Peverel	d			10 51								11 51							12 51						
Chelmsford 3	d		10 30	10 58							11 30	11 58						12 30	12 58						13 30
Ingatestone	d			11 05								12 05							13 05						
Shenfield 3	a		10 40	11 10							11 40	12 10						12 40	13 10						13 40
Romford	a																								
Stratford 7 ⊖	a		11s05	11s35							12s05	12s35						13s05	13s35						14s05
London Liverpool Street 15 ⊖	a		11 14	11 44		12 03					12 14	12 44	13 03					13 14	13 44		14 03				14 14

Table 11R

Sundays

8 December to 11 May

Norwich, Ipswich, Harwich, Clacton, Walton-on-Naze, Colchester and Chelmsford - London

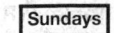

Network Diagram - refer to first Page of Table 5

		LE		LE	LE	LE	LE	LE	LE	LE	LE	LE		LE	LE	LE	LE	LE	LE	LE	LE	LE		LE	LE
		■1		■1	◇■1	■1	■1	■1	◇■1	■1	■1	◇■1		■1	■1	■1	◇■1	■1	■1	◇■1	■1	■1		■1	◇■1
					CP							CP								CP					
Norwich	d				13 00							14 00								15 00					
Diss	d				13 17							14 17								15 17					
Stowmarket	d			13 14	13 29						14 18	14 29							15 14	15 29					
Needham Market	d										14 23														
Ipswich	a			13 28	13 41						14 36	14 41							15 28	15 41					
	d	13 09			13 43					14 09		14 43						15 09		15 43					
Harwich Town	d						13 53								14 53							15 53			
Dovercourt	d						13 55								14 55							15 55			
Harwich International	d						13 58								14 58							15 58			
Wrabness	d						14 04								15 04							16 04			
Mistley	d						14 10								15 10							16 10			
Manningtree ■2	d	13 19			13 53		14a15			14 19		14 53			15a15			15 19		15 53		16a15			
Walton-on-the-Naze	d					13 30								14 30							15 30				
Frinton-on-Sea	d					13 33								14 33							15 33				
Kirby Cross	d					13 36								14 36							15 36				
Clacton-on-Sea	d								13 36								14 36								15 36
Thorpe-le-Soken ■1	a					13 42			13 44					14 42			14 44				15 42				15 44
	d								13 44								14 44								15 44
Weeley	d																								
Great Bentley	d								13 49								14 49								15 49
Alresford (Essex)	d								13 53								14 53								15 53
Wivenhoe ■3	d								13 57								14 57								15 57
Hythe	d																								
Colchester Town	a																								
	d																								
Colchester ■4	a	13 29			14 02				14 05	14 29		15 02					15 05	15 29		16 02					16 05
Colchester ■4	d	13 30			14 03				14 06	14 30		15 03					15 06	15 30		16 03					16 06
Marks Tey ■2	d	13 36							14 12	14 36							15 12	15 36							16 12
Kelvedon	d	13 41								14 41								15 41							
Braintree	d							14 00								15 00								16 00	
Braintree Freeport	d							14 02								15 02								16 02	
Cressing	d							14 05								15 05								16 05	
White Notley	d							14 08								15 08								16 08	
Witham ■2	d	13 47						14a16	14 21	14 47						15a16	15 21	15 47						16a16	16 21
Hatfield Peverel	d	13 51								14 51								15 51							
Chelmsford ■3	d	13 58							14 30	14 58							15 30	15 58							16 30
Ingatestone	d	14 05								15 05								16 05							
Shenfield ■3	a	14 10							14 40	15 10							15 40	16 10							16 40
Romford	a																								
Stratford ■7 ⊖	a	14s35							15s05	15s35							16s05	16s35							17s05
London Liverpool Street ■15 ⊖	a	14 44			15 03				15 14	15 44		16 03					16 14	16 44		17 03					17 14

		LE	LE	LE	LE	LE	LE	LE		LE	LE	LE	LE	LE	LE	LE	LE	LE		LE	LE	LE	LE	LE	LE
		■1	■1	■ ■1	■1	■1	■1	◇■1		◇■1	■1	■1	◇■1	■1	■1	■1	◇■1	■1		■1	◇■1	■1	■1	■1	◇■1
				CP						CP			CP								CP				
Norwich	d			16 00						16 20			17 00								18 00				
Diss	d			16 17						16 38			17 17								18 17				
Stowmarket	d		16 18	16 29						16 50		17 11	17 29							18 18	18 29				
Needham Market	d		16 23																	18 23					
Ipswich	a		16 36	16 41						17 02		17 25	17 41							18 36	18 41				
	d	16 09		16 43						17 05	17 09		17 43					18 09			18 43				
Harwich Town	d					16 53									17 53								18 53		
Dovercourt	d					16 55									17 55								18 55		
Harwich International	d					16 58									17 58								18 58		
Wrabness	d					17 04									18 04								19 04		
Mistley	d					17 10									18 10								19 10		
Manningtree ■2	d	16 19		16 53		17a15					17 19		17 53		18a15			18 19			18 53		19a15		
Walton-on-the-Naze	d				16 30									17 30								18 30			
Frinton-on-Sea	d				16 33									17 33								18 33			
Kirby Cross	d				16 36									17 36								18 36			
Clacton-on-Sea	d							16 36									17 36								18 36
Thorpe-le-Soken ■1	a				16 42			16 44						17 42			17 44					18 42			18 44
	d							16 44									17 44								18 44
Weeley	d																								
Great Bentley	d							16 49									17 49								18 49
Alresford (Essex)	d							16 53									17 53								18 53
Wivenhoe ■3	d							16 57									17 57								18 57
Hythe	d																								
Colchester Town	a																								
	d																								
Colchester ■4	a	16 29		17 02				17 05		17 20	17 29		18 02				18 05	18 29			19 02				19 05
Colchester ■4	d	16 30		17 03				17 06		17 23	17 30		18 03				18 06	18 30			19 03				19 06
Marks Tey ■2	d	16 36						17 12			17 36						18 12	18 36							19 12
Kelvedon	d	16 41									17 41							18 41							
Braintree	d						17 00									18 00								19 00	
Braintree Freeport	d						17 02									18 02								19 02	
Cressing	d						17 05									18 05								19 05	
White Notley	d						17 08									18 08								19 08	
Witham ■2	d	16 47					17a16	17 21			17 47					18a16	18 21	18 47						19a16	19 21
Hatfield Peverel	d	16 51									17 51							18 51							
Chelmsford ■3	d	16 58						17 30			17 58						18 30	18 58							19 30
Ingatestone	d	17 05									18 05							19 05							
Shenfield ■3	a	17 10						17 40			18 10						18 40	19 10							19 40
Romford	a																								
Stratford ■7 ⊖	a	17s35						18s05			18s35						19s05	19s35							20s05
London Liverpool Street ■15 ⊖	a	17 44		18 03				18 14		18 30	18 44		19 03				19 14	19 44			20 03				20 14

Table 11R

Sundays

8 December to 11 May

Norwich, Ipswich, Harwich, Clacton, Walton-on-Naze, Colchester and Chelmsford - London

Network Diagram - refer to first Page of Table 5

		LE 1	LE 1	LE ◇1 🛒	LE 1	LE 1	LE 1	LE ◇1	LE 1	LE 1	LE 1	LE 1	LE ◇1 🛒	LE 1	LE 1	LE ◇1	LE 1	LE 1	LE ◇1	LE 1	LE 1	LE 1
Norwich	d			19 00									20 00						21 00			
Diss	d			19 17									20 17						21 17			
Stowmarket	d		19 11	19 29								20 18	20 29					21 11	21 29			
Needham Market	d											20 23										
Ipswich	a		19 25	19 41								20 36	20 41					21 25	21 41			
	d	19 09	19 25	19 43					20 09			20 36	20 43				21 09	21 25	21 43			
Harwich Town	d					19 53								20 53							21 53	
Dovercourt	d					19 55								20 55							21 55	
Harwich International	d					19 58					20 35	21a05		20 58							21 58	
Wrabness	d					20 04								21 04							22 04	
Mistley	d					20 10								21 10							22 10	
Manningtree 2	d	19 19	19 35	19 53		20a15			20 19		20 48		20 53	21a15			21 19	21 35	21 53		22a15	
Walton-on-the-Naze	d				19 30					20 30										21 30		
Frinton-on-Sea	d				19 33					20 33										21 33		
Kirby Cross	d				19 36					20 36										21 36		
Clacton-on-Sea	d							19 36								20 36						
Thorpe-le-Soken 1	a				19 42			19 44		20 42						20 44				21 42		
	d							19 44								20 44						
Weeley	d																					
Great Bentley	d							19 49								20 49						
Alresford (Essex)	d							19 53								20 53						
Wivenhoe 3	d							19 57								20 57						
Hythe	d																					
Colchester Town	a																					
	d																					
Colchester 4	a	19 29	19 46	20 02				20 05	20 29		20 57		21 02			21 05	21 29	21 46	22 02			
Colchester 4	d	19 30		20 03				20 06	20 30		20 57		21 03			21 06	21 30		22 03			
Marks Tey 2	d	19 36						20 12	20 36							21 12	21 36					
Kelvedon	d	19 41							20 41								21 41					
Braintree	d						20 00								21 00							22 00
Braintree Freeport	d						20 02								21 02							22 02
Cressing	d						20 05								21 05							22 05
White Notley	d						20 08								21 08							22 08
Witham 2	d	19 47					20a16	20 21	20 47						21a16	21 21	21 47					22a16
Hatfield Peverel	d	19 51							20 51								21 51					
Chelmsford 3	d	19 58						20 30	20 58		21 15					21 30	21 58					
Ingatestone	d	20 05							21 05								22 05					
Shenfield 3	a	20 10						20 40	21 10		21 25					21 40	22 10					
Romford	a																					
Stratford 7 ⊖	a	20s35						21s05	21s35		21s53					22s00	22s30					
London Liverpool Street 15 ⊖	a	20 44		21 03				21 14	21 44		22 02		22 04			22 10	22 40		23 03			

		LE ◇1	LE 1	LE 1	LE 1	LE 1	LE 1	LE ◇1	LE 1	LE 1	LE
Norwich	d							22 00		23 05	
Diss	d							22 17		23 22	
Stowmarket	d				22 18			22 29		23 34	23 55
Needham Market	d				22 23						23 59
Ipswich	a				22 36			22 41		23 50	00 11
	d		22 09					22 43			
Harwich Town	d								22 53		
Dovercourt	d								22 55		
Harwich International	d								22 58		
Wrabness	d								23 04		
Mistley	d								23 10		
Manningtree 2	d		22 19					22 53	23 15		
Walton-on-the-Naze	d			22 17							
Frinton-on-Sea	d			22 20							
Kirby Cross	d			22 23							
Clacton-on-Sea	d	21 36				22 22					
Thorpe-le-Soken 1	a	21 44		22 29		22 30					
	d	21 44				22 30					
Weeley	d										
Great Bentley	d	21 49									
Alresford (Essex)	d	21 53									
Wivenhoe 3	d	21 57				22 40					
Hythe	d										
Colchester Town	a										
	d										
Colchester 4	a	22 05	22 29			22 48		23 02	23 24		
Colchester 4	d	22 06	22 30					23 03			
Marks Tey 2	d	22 12	22 36								
Kelvedon	d		22 41								
Braintree	d						22 56				
Braintree Freeport	d						22 58				
Cressing	d						23 01				
White Notley	d						23 04				
Witham 2	d	22 21	22 47				23a12	23 16			
Hatfield Peverel	d		22 51								
Chelmsford 3	d	22 30	22 58					23 25			
Ingatestone	d		23 05								
Shenfield 3	a	22 40	23 10					23s36			
Romford	a										
Stratford 7 ⊖	a	23s00	23s30					23s57			
London Liverpool Street 15 ⊖	a	23 10	23 40					00 07			

Network Diagram for Tables 13, 14, 15, 16, 17

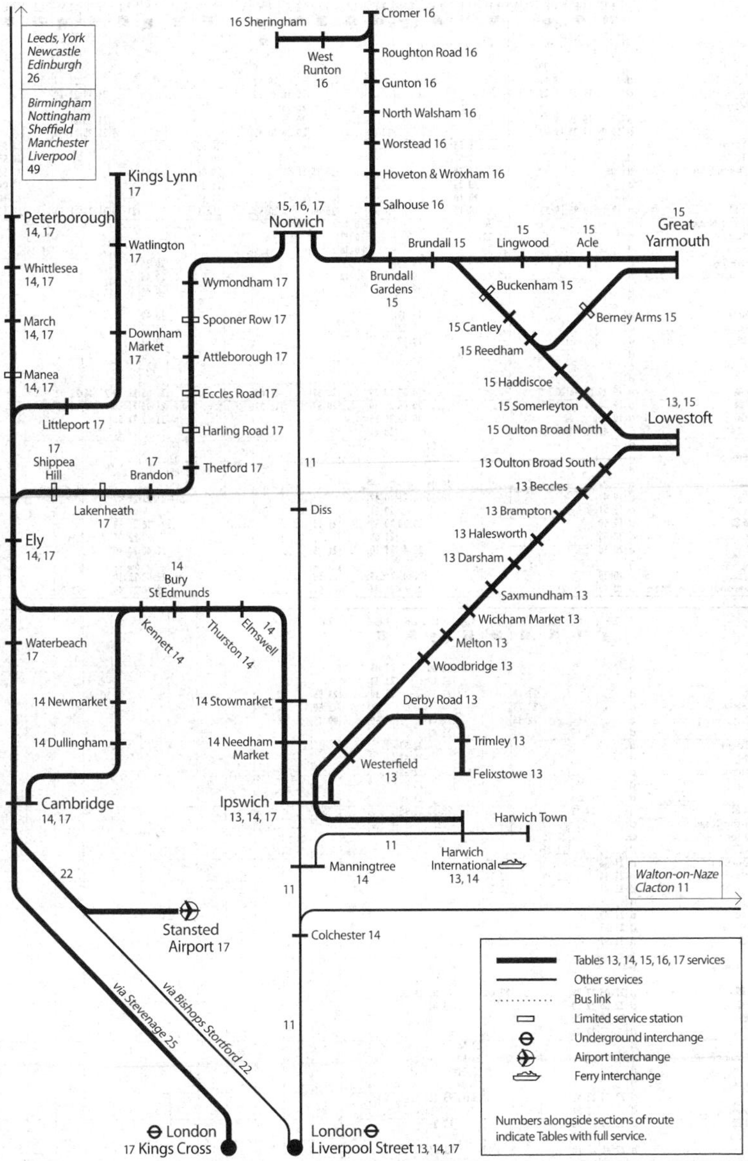

Leeds, York Newcastle Edinburgh 26
Birmingham Nottingham Sheffield Manchester Liverpool 49
16 Sheringham
West Runton 16
Cromer 16
Roughton Road 16
Gunton 16
North Walsham 16
Worstead 16
Hoveton & Wroxham 16
Salhouse 16
Kings Lynn 17
Peterborough 14, 17
Watlington 17
15, 16, 17 Norwich
Brundall 15
15 Lingwood
15 Acle
15 Great Yarmouth
Whittlesea 14, 17
Wymondham 17
Brundall Gardens 15
Buckenham 15
March 14, 17
Downham Market 17
Spooner Row 17
15 Cantley
Berney Arms 15
Attleborough 17
15 Reedham
Manea 14, 17
Eccles Road 17
15 Haddiscoe
15 Somerleyton
13, 15 Lowestoft
Littleport 17
Harling Road 17
15 Oulton Broad North
17 Shippea Hill
17 Brandon
Thetford 17
11
13 Oulton Broad South
13 Beccles
Lakenheath 17
Diss
13 Brampton
13 Halesworth
Ely 14, 17
13 Darsham
14 Bury St Edmunds
Saxmundham 13
Wickham Market 13
Kennett 14
Thurston 14
14 Elmswell
Waterbeach 17
Melton 13
Woodbridge 13
14 Newmarket
14 Stowmarket
Derby Road 13
14 Dullingham
14 Needham Market
Trimley 13
Westerfield 13
Felixstowe 13
Cambridge 14, 17
Ipswich 13, 14, 17
Harwich Town
11
Harwich International 13, 14
22
Manningtree 14
11
Walton-on-Naze Clacton 11
Stansted Airport 17
Colchester 14
via Stevenage 25
via Bishops Stortford 22
11
London Kings Cross 17
London Liverpool Street 13, 14, 17
Tables 13, 14, 15, 16, 17 services
Other services
Bus link
Limited service station
Underground interchange
Airport interchange
Ferry interchange
Numbers alongside sections of route indicate Tables with full service.

TOCs operating on this network - Greater Anglia (LE), Cross Country (XC), First Capital Connect (FC), East Midlands Trains (EM)

Table 13

Mondays to Fridays

9 December to 16 May

Ipswich - Felixstowe and Lowestoft

Network Diagram - see first Page of Table 13

Miles	Miles			LE	LE	LE	LE	LE	LE	LE	LE	LE 1		LE	LE	LE	LE 1	LE	LE	LE	LE 1	LE		LE	LE
—	—	London Liverpool Street 15 ⊖	d																						
—	—	Harwich International	d																						
0	—	**Ipswich**	d	05 04	06 04	06 20		07 14	07 35	08 25	08 57	09 17		09 58	10 17	10 58	11 17	11 58	12 17	12 58	13 17	13 58		14 17	14 58
3½	0	Westerfield	d	05 10	06 10	06 26		07 20	07 41	08 31	09 03			10 04		11 04		12 04		13 04		14 04			15 04
—	2½	Derby Road	d	05 15	06 15			07 25		08 36	09 08			10 09		11 09		12 09		13 09		14 09			15 09
—	10½	Trimley	d	05 24	06 24			07 34		08 45	09 17			10 18		11 18		12 18		13 18		14 18			15 18
—	12¼	**Felixstowe**	a	05 30	06 30			07 40		08 51	09 23			10 24		11 24		12 24		13 24		14 24			15 24
10¼	—	Woodbridge	d			06 37			07 53			09 32			10 32		11 32		12 32		13 32			14 32	
11½	—	Melton	d			06 41			07 57			09 36			10 36		11 36		12 36		13 36			14 36	
15¾	—	Wickham Market	d			06 48			08 04			09 43			10 43		11 43		12 43		13 43			14 43	
22½	—	Saxmundham	d			06a58	07 44		08 15			09 54			10 54		11 54		12 54		13 54			14 54	
26¾	—	Darsham	d				07 51		08 21			10 00			11 00		12 00		13 00		14 00			15 00	
32	—	Halesworth	d				08 00		08 31			10 10			11 10		12 10		13 10		14 10			15 10	
36	—	Brampton (Suffolk)	d				08x07		08x37			10x16			11x16		12x16		13x16		14x16			15x16	
40¼	—	Beccles	d				08 16		08 46			10 25			11 25		12 25		13 25		14 25			15 25	
46¾	—	Oulton Broad South	d				08 25		08 56			10 35			11 35		12 35		13 35		14 35			15 35	
49	—	**Lowestoft**	a				08 33		09 06			10 43			11 43		12 43		13 43		14 43			15 43	

		LE 1	LE	LE	LE	LE 1	LE	LE		LE	LE 1	LE	LE	LE	LE 1	LE 1	LE
London Liverpool Street 15 ⊖	d																
Harwich International	d															21 38	
Ipswich	d	15 17	15 54	15 58	16 58	17 17	17 58	18 13		18 58	19 17	19 58	20 17	20 58	21 17	22 17	22 28
Westerfield	d		16 00	16 04	17 04		18 04	18 19		19 04		20 04		21 04			22 34
Derby Road	d			16 09	17 09		18 09			19 09		20 09		21 09			22 39
Trimley	d			16 18	17 18		18 18			19 18		20 18		21 18			22 48
Felixstowe	a			16 24	17 24		18 24			19 24		20 24		21 24			22 57
Woodbridge	d	15 32	16 18			17 32		18 30			19 32		20 32		21 32	22 32	
Melton	d	15 36	16 22			17 36		18 34			19 36		20 36		21 36	22 36	
Wickham Market	d	15 43	16 29			17 43		18 40			19 43		20 43		21 43	22 43	
Saxmundham	d	15 54	16 40			17 54		18 51			19 54		20 54		21 54	22 54	
Darsham	d	16 00	16 47			18 00		18 58			20 00		21 00		22 00	23 00	
Halesworth	d	16 10	16 56			18 10		19 07			20 10		21 10		22 10	23 10	
Brampton (Suffolk)	d	16x16	17x03			18x16		19x14			20x16		21x16		22x16	23x16	
Beccles	d	16 25	17 19			18 25		19 25			20 25		21 25		22 25	23 25	
Oulton Broad South	d	16 35	17 28			18 35		19 35			20 35		21 35		22 35	23 35	
Lowestoft	a	16 43	17 36			18 43		19 43			20 43		21 43		22 43	23 43	

Saturdays

14 December to 17 May

		LE	LE	LE	LE	LE	LE	LE 1	LE	LE		LE	LE 1	LE	LE	LE	LE 1	LE	LE	LE		LE 1	LE	LE	LE
London Liverpool Street 15 ⊖	d																								
Harwich International	d																								
Ipswich	d	05 58	06 58	07 17	07 58	08 17	08 58	09 17	09 58	10 17		10 58	11 17	11 58	12 17	12 58	13 17	13 58	14 17	14 58		15 17	15 58	16 17	16 58
Westerfield	d	06 04	07 04		08 04		09 04		10 04			11 04		12 04		13 04		14 04		15 04			16 04		17 04
Derby Road	d	06 09	07 09		08 09		09 09		10 09			11 09		12 09		13 09		14 09		15 09			16 09		17 09
Trimley	d	06 18	07 18		08 18		09 18		10 18			11 18		12 18		13 18		14 18		15 18			16 18		17 18
Felixstowe	a	06 24	07 24		08 24		09 24		10 24			11 24		12 24		13 24		14 24		15 24			16 24		17 24
Woodbridge	d			07 32		08 32		09 32		10 32			11 32		12 32		13 32		14 32			15 32		16 32	
Melton	d			07 36		08 36		09 36		10 36			11 36		12 36		13 36		14 36			15 36		16 36	
Wickham Market	d			07 43		08 43		09 43		10 43			11 43		12 43		13 43		14 43			15 43		16 43	
Saxmundham	d			07 54		08 54		09 54		10 54			11 54		12 54		13 54		14 54			15 54		16 54	
Darsham	d			08 00		09 00		10 00		11 00			12 00		13 00		14 00		15 00			16 00		17 00	
Halesworth	d			08 10		09 10		10 10		11 10			12 10		13 10		14 10		15 10			16 10		17 10	
Brampton (Suffolk)	d			08x16		09x16		10x16		11x16			12x16		13x16		14x16		15x16			16x16		17x16	
Beccles	d			08 25		09 25		10 25		11 25			12 25		13 25		14 25		15 25			16 25		17 25	
Oulton Broad South	d			08 35		09 35		10 35		11 35			12 35		13 35		14 35		15 35			16 35		17 41	
Lowestoft	a			08 43		09 43		10 43		11 43			12 43		13 43		14 43		15 43			16 43		17 51	

		LE 1	LE	LE	LE	LE 1		LE	LE	LE	LE 1	LE 1	LE
London Liverpool Street 15 ⊖	d												
Harwich International	d											21 38	
Ipswich	d	17 17	17 58	18 17	18 58	19 17		19 58	20 17	20 58	21 17	22 17	22 28
Westerfield	d		18 04		19 04			20 04		21 04			22 34
Derby Road	d		18 09		19 09			20 09		21 09			22 39
Trimley	d		18 18		19 18			20 18		21 18			22 48
Felixstowe	a		18 24		19 24			20 24		21 24			22 54
Woodbridge	d	17 32		18 32		19 32			20 32		21 32	22 32	
Melton	d	17 36		18 36		19 36			20 36		21 36	22 36	
Wickham Market	d	17 43		18 43		19 43			20 43		21 43	22 43	
Saxmundham	d	17 54		18 54		19 54			20 54		21 54	22 54	
Darsham	d	18 00		19 00		20 00			21 00		22 00	23 00	
Halesworth	d	18 10		19 10		20 10			21 10		22 10	23 10	
Brampton (Suffolk)	d	18x16		19x16		20x16			21x16		22x16	23x16	
Beccles	d	18 25		19 25		20 25			21 25		22 25	23 25	
Oulton Broad South	d	18 35		19 35		20 35			21 35		22 35	23 35	
Lowestoft	a	18 43		19 43		20 43			21 43		22 43	23 43	

Table 13

Sundays

8 December to 11 May

Ipswich - Felixstowe and Lowestoft

Network Diagram - see first Page of Table 13

		LE 1		LE	LE	LE 1	LE	LE	LE	LE	LE	LE 1		LE	LE	LE 1	LE	LE	LE	LE 1					
London Liverpool Street 15 ⊖	d																								
Harwich International	d																								
Ipswich	d	10 02		10 55	11 55	12 02	12 55	13 55	14 02	14 55	15 55	16 02		16 55	17 55	18 02	18 55	19 55	20 02	22 02					
Westerfield	d	10 08		11 01	12 01	12 08	13 01	14 01	14 08	15 01	16 01	16 08		17 01	18 01	18 08	19 01	20 01	20 08	22 08					
Derby Road	d			11 06	12 06		13 06	14 06		15 06	16 06			17 06	18 06		19 06	20 06							
Trimley	d			11 15	12 15		13 15	14 15		15 15	16 15			17 15	18 15		19 15	20 15							
Felixstowe	a			11 21	12 21		13 21	14 21		15 21	16 21			17 21	18 21		19 21	20 21							
Woodbridge	d	10 19				12 19			14 19			16 19				18 19			20 19	22 19					
Melton	d	10 23				12 23			14 23			16 23				18 23			20 23	22 23					
Wickham Market	d	10 29				12 29			14 29			16 29				18 29			20 29	22 29					
Saxmundham	d	10 40				12 40			14 40			16 40				18 40			20 40	22 40					
Darsham	d	10 47				12 47			14 47			16 47				18 47			20 47	22 47					
Halesworth	d	10 56				12 56			14 56			16 56				18 56			20 56	22 56					
Brampton (Suffolk)	d	11x03				13x03			15x03			17x03				19x03			21x03	23x03					
Beccles	d	11 12				13 12			15 12			17 12				19 12			21 12	23 12					
Oulton Broad South	d	11 21				13 21			15 21			17 21				19 21			21 21	23 21					
Lowestoft	a	11 30				13 30			15 30			17 30				19 30			21 30	23 30					

Table 13R

Lowestoft and Felixstowe - Ipswich

Mondays to Fridays

9 December to 16 May

Network Diagram - see first Page of Table 13

Miles	Miles			LE	LE [1]	LE	LE [1]	LE [1]	LE	LE		LE	LE	LE [1]	LE	LE	LE	LE [1]	LE	LE		LE	LE [1]	LE	LE
0	—	**Lowestoft**	d		05 25		06 16	06 41		07 27				09 07		10 07		11 07		12 07			13 07		14 07
2¼	—	Oulton Broad South	d		05 31		06 22	06 47		07 33				09 13		10 13		11 13		12 13			13 13		14 13
8½	—	Beccles	d		05 41		06 32	06 57		07 43				09 25		10 25		11 25		12 25			13 25		14 25
13	—	Brampton (Suffolk)	d		05x49		06x40	07x05		07x51				09x33		10x33		11x33		12x33			13x33		14x33
17	—	Halesworth	d		05 56		06 47	07 12		07 58				09 41		10 41		11 41		12 41			13 41		14 41
22¼	—	Darsham	d		06 05		06 56	07 21		08 07				09 49		10 49		11 49		12 49			13 49		14 49
26½	—	Saxmundham	d		06 13		07 04	07 29		08 17				09 57		10 57		11 57		12 57			13 57		14 57
33¼	—	Wickham Market	d		06 23		07 14	07 39		08 27				10 07		11 07		12 07		13 07			14 07		15 07
37¼	—	Melton	d		06 30		07 21	07 46		08 34				10 13		11 13		12 13		13 13			14 13		15 13
38¾	—	Woodbridge	d		06 35		07 26	07 51		08 39				10 18		11 18		12 18		13 18			14 18		15 18
—	0	**Felixstowe**	d	05 34		06 36			07 47			08 54	09 28		10 28		11 28		12 28			13 28		14 28	
—	1¾	Trimley	d	05 37		06 39			07 50			08 57	09 31		10 31		11 31		12 31			13 31		14 31	
—	9¾	Derby Road	d	05 47		06 49			08 00			09 09	09 41		10 41		11 41		12 41			13 41		14 41	
45½	12¼	Westerfield	d	05 52		06 54	07 37	08 02	08 06			09 14	09 46		10 46		11 46		12 46			13 46		14 46	
49	—	**Ipswich**	a	06 01	06 53	07 02	07 44	08 09	08 14	08 57		09 24	09 54	10 36	10 54	11 36	11 54	12 36	12 54	13 36		13 54	14 36	14 54	15 36
—	—		d		06 59																				
—	—	Harwich International	a		07 28																				
—	—	London Liverpool Street [15] ⊖	a																						

		LE	LE [1]	LE	LE	LE		LE [1]	LE	LE	LE	LE [1]	LE	LE	LE	LE		LE
Lowestoft	d		15 07		16 07			17 02		18 07		19 07		20 07		21 07		
Oulton Broad South	d		15 13		16 13			17 08		18 13		19 13		20 13		21 13		
Beccles	d		15 25		16 25			17 25		18 25		19 25		20 25		21 25		
Brampton (Suffolk)	d		15x33		16x33			17x33		18x33		19x33		20x33		21x33		
Halesworth	d		15 41		16 41			17 41		18 41		19 41		20 41		21 41		
Darsham	d		15 49		16 49			17 49		18 49		19 49		20 49		21 49		
Saxmundham	d		15 57		17 07			17 57		18 57		19 57		20 57		21 57		
Wickham Market	d		16 07		17 17			18 07		19 07		20 07		21 07		22 07		
Melton	d		16 13		17 23			18 13		19 13		20 13		21 13		22 13		
Woodbridge	d		16 18		17 28			18 18		19 18		20 18		21 18		22 18		
Felixstowe	d	15 28		16 28		17 28			18 28		19 28		20 28		21 28			23 01
Trimley	d	15 31		16 31		17 31			18 31		19 31		20 31		21 31			23 04
Derby Road	d	15 41		16 41		17 41			18 41		19 41		20 41		21 41			23 14
Westerfield	d	15 46		16 46		17 46			18 46		19 46		20 46		21 46	22 29		23 19
Ipswich	a	15 54	16 36	16 54	17 46	17 54		18 36	18 54	19 36	19 54	20 37	20 54	21 36	21 54	22 36		23 27
	d																	
Harwich International	a																	
London Liverpool Street [15] ⊖	a																	

Saturdays

14 December to 17 May

		LE	LE [1]	LE	LE [1]	LE	LE	LE	LE [1]	LE		LE	LE	LE [1]	LE	LE	LE	LE [1]	LE	LE		LE	LE [1]	LE	LE
Lowestoft	d		06 07		07 07		08 07		09 07			10 07		11 07		12 07		13 07		14 07			15 07		16 07
Oulton Broad South	d		06 13		07 13		08 13		09 13			10 13		11 13		12 13		13 13		14 13			15 13		16 13
Beccles	d		06 25		07 25		08 25		09 25			10 25		11 25		12 25		13 25		14 25			15 25		16 25
Brampton (Suffolk)	d		06x33		07x33		08x33		09x33			10x33		11x33		12x33		13x33		14x33			15x33		16x33
Halesworth	d		06 41		07 41		08 41		09 41			10 41		11 41		12 41		13 41		14 41			15 41		16 41
Darsham	d		06 49		07 49		08 49		09 49			10 49		11 49		12 49		13 49		14 49			15 49		16 49
Saxmundham	d		06 57		07 57		08 57		09 57			10 57		11 57		12 57		13 57		14 57			15 57		16 57
Wickham Market	d		07 07		08 07		09 07		10 07			11 07		12 07		13 07		14 07		15 07			16 07		17 07
Melton	d		07 13		08 13		09 13		10 13			11 13		12 13		13 13		14 13		15 13			16 13		17 13
Woodbridge	d		07 18		08 18		09 18		10 18			11 18		12 18		13 18		14 18		15 18			16 18		17 18
Felixstowe	d	06 28		07 28		08 28		09 28		10 28			11 28		12 28		13 28		14 28			15 28		16 28	
Trimley	d	06 31		07 31		08 31		09 31		10 31			11 31		12 31		13 31		14 31			15 31		16 31	
Derby Road	d	06 41		07 41		08 41		09 41		10 41			11 41		12 41		13 41		14 41			15 41		16 41	
Westerfield	d	06 46		07 46		08 46		09 46		10 46			11 46		12 46		13 46		14 46			15 46		16 46	
Ipswich	a	06 54	07 36	07 54	08 36	08 54	09 36	09 54	10 36	10 54		11 36	11 54	12 36	12 54	13 36	13 54	14 36	14 54	15 36		15 54	16 36	16 54	17 36
	d																								
Harwich International	a																								
London Liverpool Street [15] ⊖	a																								

		LE	LE [1]	LE	LE	LE		LE [1]	LE	LE	LE	LE	LE
Lowestoft	d		17 07		18 07			19 07		20 07		21 07	
Oulton Broad South	d		17 13		18 13			19 13		20 13		21 13	
Beccles	d		17 25		18 25			19 25		20 25		21 25	
Brampton (Suffolk)	d		17x33		18x33			19x33		20x33		21x33	
Halesworth	d		17 41		18 41			19 41		20 41		21 41	
Darsham	d		17 49		18 49			19 49		20 49		21 49	
Saxmundham	d		17 57		18 57			19 57		20 57		21 57	
Wickham Market	d		18 07		19 07			20 07		21 07		22 07	
Melton	d		18 13		19 13			20 13		21 13		22 13	
Woodbridge	d		18 18		19 18			20 18		21 18		22 18	
Felixstowe	d	17 28		18 28		19 28			20 28		21 28		22 58
Trimley	d	17 31		18 31		19 31			20 31		21 31		23 01
Derby Road	d	17 41		18 41		19 41			20 41		21 41		23 11
Westerfield	d	17 46		18 46		19 46			20 46		21 46	22 29	23 16
Ipswich	a	17 54	18 36	18 54	19 36	19 54		20 36	20 54	21 36	21 54	22 36	23 24
	d												
Harwich International	a												
London Liverpool Street [15] ⊖	a												

Table 13R

Sundays

8 December to 11 May

Lowestoft and Felixstowe - Ipswich

Network Diagram - see first Page of Table 13

		LE 1		LE 1	LE	LE	LE	LE	LE	LE 1	LE	LE		LE 1	LE	LE	LE	LE	LE	LE 1
Lowestoft	d	08 05		10 05			12 05			14 05				16 05			18 05			20 05
Oulton Broad South	d	08 11		10 11			12 11			14 11				16 11			18 11			20 11
Beccles	d	08 21		10 21			12 21			14 21				16 21			18 21			20 21
Brampton (Suffolk)	d	08x29		10x29			12x29			14x29				16x29			18x29			20x29
Halesworth	d	08 36		10 36			12 36			14 36				16 36			18 36			20 36
Darsham	d	08 44		10 44			12 44			14 44				16 44			18 44			20 44
Saxmundham	d	08 53		10 53			12 53			14 53				16 53			18 53			20 53
Wickham Market	d	09 02		11 02			13 02			15 02				17 02			19 02			21 02
Melton	d	09 09		11 09			13 09			15 09				17 09			19 09			21 09
Woodbridge	d	09 14		11 14			13 14			15 14				17 14			19 14			21 14
Felixstowe	d				11 25	12 25		13 25	14 25		15 25	16 25			17 25	18 25		19 25	20 25	
Trimley	d				11 28	12 28		13 28	14 28		15 28	16 28			17 28	18 28		19 28	20 28	
Derby Road	d				11 38	12 38		13 38	14 38		15 38	16 38			17 38	18 38		19 38	20 38	
Westerfield	d	09 24		11 24	11 43	12 43	13 24	13 43	14 43	15 24	15 43	16 43		17 24	17 43	18 43	19 24	19 43	20 43	21 24
Ipswich	a	09 32		11 32	11 50	12 50	13 32	13 50	14 50	15 32	15 50	16 50		17 32	17 50	18 50	19 32	19 50	20 50	21 32
	d																			
Harwich International	a																			
London Liverpool Street 15 ⊖	a																			

Table 14

Mondays to Fridays

9 December to 27 December

Ipswich - Bury St. Edmunds, Cambridge, Ely and Peterborough

Network Diagram - see first Page of Table 13

Miles	Miles	Miles			LE	LE 1	LE 1	LE 1	LE 1	LE 1	LE 1	LE 1	LE 1		LE 1	LE 1	LE 1	LE 1	LE 1	LE 1	LE 1	LE 1	LE 1		LE 1
—	—	—	Colchester	d		05 40																			
—	—	—	Manningtree	d		05 49																			
—	—	0	Harwich International	d						07 50															
0	0	18	**Ipswich**	d	05 10	06 00	06 16	06 54	08 03	08 20	09 20	10 00	10 20		11 20	11 58	12 20	13 20	13 58	14 20	15 20	16 00	16 20		17 20
8¼	—	—	Needham Market	d	05 20		06 25	07 03		08 29	09 29		10 29		11 29		12 29	13 29		14 29	15 29		16 29		17 29
11¾	11¾	—	Stowmarket	d	05 26	06 12	06 31	07 09	08 15	08 35	09 35	10 12	10 35		11 35	12 11	12 35	13 35	14 11	14 35	15 35	16 12	16 35		17 35
17¾	—	—	Elmswell	d	05 35		06 39	07 17		08 44	09 43		10 43		11 43		12 43	13 43		14 43	15 43		16 43		17 43
22¼	—	—	Thurston	d	05 41		06 45	07 23		08 50	09 49		10 49		11 49		12 49	13 49		14 49	15 49		16 49		17 49
—	—	—	**Bury St Edmunds**	a	05 48	06 28	06 51	07 29	08 31	08 56	09 55	10 28	10 55		11 55	12 27	12 55	13 55	14 27	14 55	15 55	16 29	16 55		17 55
26¼	26¼	—	**Bury St Edmunds**	d	05 49	06 29	06 54	07 33	08 31	08 57	09 57	10 29	10 57		11 57	12 29	12 57	13 57	14 29	14 57	15 57	16 29	16 57		17 57
36	—	—	Kennett	d	06 00		07 04	07 43			10 07				12 07			14 07			16 07		17 07		18 07
41	—	—	Newmarket	d	06 09		07 14	07 52		09 16	10 17		11 16		12 17		13 16	14 17		15 16	16 17		17 17		18 17
44¼	—	—	Dullingham	d	06 14		07 19	08 00		09 21			11 21				13 21			15 21					
55½	—	—	**Cambridge**	a	06 33		07 39	08 19		09 39	10 39		11 39		12 39		13 39	14 39		15 39	16 39		17 39		18 39
—	50¾	—	**Ely 6**	a		06 56			08 58			10 58				12 58			14 58			16 58			
—	—	—		d		06 56			08 58			10 58				12 58			14 58			16 58			
—	—	—	Manea	a																					
—	66¼	—	March	a		07 12			09 15			11 14				13 14			15 14			17 14			
—	74	—	Whittlesea	a		07 24			09 26			11 26				13 26			15 26			17 26			
—	81¼	—	**Peterborough 8**	a		07 35			09 37			11 37				13 37			15 37			17 37			

		LE 1	LE 1	LE 1	LE 1	LE 1	LE	LE
Colchester	d							
Manningtree	d							
Harwich International	d							
Ipswich	d	17 49	18 17	19 13	20 00	20 20	21 17	22 19
Needham Market	d	17 58	18 26	19 22		20 29	21 27	22 29
Stowmarket	d	18 04	18 32	19 28	20 12	20 35	21 33	22 35
Elmswell	d	18 12	18 40	19 36		20 43	21 42	22 44
Thurston	d	18 18	18 46	19 42		20 49	21 48	22 50
Bury St Edmunds	a	18 24	18 52	19 48	20 28	20 55	21 55	22 57
Bury St Edmunds	d	18 25	18 57	19 57	20 29	20 57	21 56	
Kennett	d			20 07			22 07	
Newmarket	d		19 16	20 17		21 16	22 17	
Dullingham	d		19 21			21 21	22 23	
Cambridge	a		19 39	20 39		21 39	22 40	
Ely 6	a	18 52			20 59			
	d	18 58			20 59			
Manea	a							
March	a	19 15			21 15			
Whittlesea	a	19 26			21 26			
Peterborough 8	a	19 37			21 37			

Mondays to Fridays

30 December to 16 May

		LE	LE 1	LE 1	LE 1	LE 1	LE 1	LE 1	LE 1	LE 1		LE 1	LE 1	LE 1	LE 1	LE 1	LE 1	LE 1	LE 1	LE 1		LE 1	LE 1	LE 1	LE 1
Colchester	d		05 40																						
Manningtree	d		05 49																						
Harwich International	d						07 50																		
Ipswich	d	05 10	06 00	06 16	06 54	08 03	08 20	09 20	10 00	10 20		11 20	11 58	12 20	13 20	13 58	14 20	15 20	16 00	16 20		17 20	17 49	18 17	19 13
Needham Market	d	05 20		06 25	07 03		08 29	09 29		10 29		11 29		12 29	13 29		14 29	15 29		16 29		17 29	17 58	18 26	19 22
Stowmarket	d	05 26	06 12	06 31	07 09	08 15	08 35	09 35	10 12	10 35		11 35	12 11	12 35	13 35	14 11	14 35	15 35	16 12	16 35		17 35	18 04	18 32	19 28
Elmswell	d	05 35		06 39	07 17		08 44	09 43		10 43		11 43		12 43	13 43		14 43	15 43		16 43		17 43	18 12	18 40	19 36
Thurston	d	05 41		06 45	07 23		08 50	09 49		10 49		11 49		12 49	13 49		14 49	15 49		16 49		17 49	18 18	18 46	19 42
Bury St Edmunds	a	05 48	06 28	06 51	07 29	08 31	08 56	09 55	10 28	10 55		11 55	12 27	12 55	13 55	14 27	14 55	15 55	16 29	16 55		17 55	18 24	18 52	19 48
Bury St Edmunds	d	05 49	06 29	06 54	07 33	08 31	08 57	09 57	10 29	10 57		11 57	12 29	12 57	13 57	14 29	14 57	15 57	16 29	16 57		17 57	18 25	18 57	19 57
Kennett	d	06 00		07 04	07 43			10 07				12 07			14 07			16 07		17 07		18 07			20 07
Newmarket	d	06 09		07 14	07 52		09 16	10 17		11 16		12 17		13 16	14 17		15 16	16 17		17 17		18 17		19 16	20 17
Dullingham	d	06 14		07 19	08 00		09 21			11 21				13 21			15 21							19 21	
Cambridge	a	06 33		07 39	08 19		09 39	10 39		11 39		12 39		13 39	14 39		15 39	16 39		17 39		18 39		19 39	20 39
Ely 6	a		06 56			08 58			10 58				12 58			14 58			16 58				18 52		
	d		06 56			08 58			10 58				12 58			14 58			16 58				18 58		
Manea	a		07x07			09x09			11x09				13x09			15x09			17x09				19x09		
March	a		07 14			09 16			11 16				13 16			15 16			17 16				19 16		
Whittlesea	a		07 26			09 28			11 28				13 28			15 28			17 28				19 28		
Peterborough 8	a		07 37			09 39			11 39				13 39			15 39			17 39				19 39		

Please see table 17 for complete service between Ely and Peterborough

Table 14

Ipswich - Bury St. Edmunds, Cambridge, Ely and Peterborough

Mondays to Fridays

30 December to 16 May

Network Diagram - see first Page of Table 13

		LE 1	LE 1	LE	LE
Colchester	d				
Manningtree	d				
Harwich International	d				
Ipswich	d	20 00	20 20	21 17	22 19
Needham Market	d		20 29	21 27	22 29
Stowmarket	d	20 12	20 35	21 33	22 35
Elmswell	d		20 43	21 42	22 44
Thurston	d		20 49	21 48	22 50
Bury St Edmunds	a	20 28	20 55	21 55	22 57
Bury St Edmunds	d	20 29	20 57	21 56	
Kennett	d			22 07	
Newmarket	d		21 16	22 17	
Dullingham	d		21 21	22 23	
Cambridge	a		21 39	22 40	
Ely 6	a	20 59			
	d	20 59			
Manea	a	21x09			
March	a	21 17			
Whittlesea	a	21 28			
Peterborough 8	a	21 39			

Saturdays

14 December to 21 December

		LE	LE 1	LE 1	LE 1	LE 1	LE 1	LE 1	LE 1	LE 1
Colchester	d		05 40							
Manningtree	d		05 49							
Harwich International	d						07 50			
Ipswich	d	05 10	06 00	06 16	07 20	08 00	08 20	09 20	09 58	10 20
Needham Market	d	05 20		06 25	07 29		08 29	09 29		10 29
Stowmarket	d	05 26	06 12	06 31	07 35	08 12	08 35	09 35	10 11	10 35
Elmswell	d	05 35		06 39	07 43		08 44	09 43		10 43
Thurston	d	05 41		06 45	07 49		08 50	09 49		10 49
Bury St Edmunds	a	05 48	06 28	06 51	07 55	08 28	08 56	09 55	10 27	10 55
Bury St Edmunds	d	05 49	06 29	06 54	07 57	08 29	08 57	09 57	10 29	10 57
Kennett	d	06 00		07 04	08 07			10 07		
Newmarket	d	06 09		07 14	08 17		09 16	10 17		11 16
Dullingham	d	06 14		07 19	08 22		09 21			11 21
Cambridge	a	06 32		07 39	08 39		09 39	10 39		11 39
Ely 6	a		06 56			08 58			10 58	
	d		06 56			08 58			10 58	
Manea	a									
March	a		07 12			09 14			11 14	
Whittlesea	a		07 24			09 26			11 26	
Peterborough 8	a		07 35			09 37			11 37	

		LE 1	LE 1	LE 1	LE 1	LE 1	LE 1	LE 1	LE 1	LE 1	LE 1	LE 1	LE 1	LE 1
Colchester	d													
Manningtree	d													
Harwich International	d													
Ipswich	d	11 20	11 58	12 20	13 20	13 58	14 20	15 20	15 58	16 20	17 20	17 58	18 20	19 20
Needham Market	d	11 29		12 29	13 29		14 29	15 29		16 29	17 29		18 29	19 29
Stowmarket	d	11 35	12 11	12 35	13 35	14 11	14 35	15 35	16 11	16 35	17 35	18 11	18 35	19 35
Elmswell	d	11 43		12 43	13 43		14 43	15 43		16 43	17 43		18 43	19 43
Thurston	d	11 49		12 49	13 49		14 49	15 49		16 49	17 49		18 49	19 49
Bury St Edmunds	a	11 55	12 27	12 55	13 55	14 27	14 55	15 55	16 27	16 55	17 55	18 27	18 55	19 55
Bury St Edmunds	d	11 57	12 29	12 57	13 57	14 29	14 57	15 57	16 29	16 57	17 57	18 29	18 57	19 57
Kennett	d	12 07			14 07			16 07		17 07	18 07			20 07
Newmarket	d	12 17		13 16	14 17		15 16	16 17		17 17	18 17		19 16	20 17
Dullingham	d			13 21			15 21						19 21	
Cambridge	a	12 39		13 39	14 39		15 39	16 39		17 39	18 39		19 39	20 39
Ely 6	a		12 58			14 58			16 58			18 58		
	d		12 58			14 58			16 58			18 58		
Manea	a													
March	a		13 14			15 14			17 14			19 14		
Whittlesea	a		13 26			15 26			17 26			19 26		
Peterborough 8	a		13 37			15 37			17 37			19 37		

		LE 1	LE 1	LE	LE
Colchester	d				
Manningtree	d				
Harwich International	d				
Ipswich	d	19 58	20 20	21 17	22 19
Needham Market	d		20 29	21 27	22 29
Stowmarket	d	20 11	20 35	21 33	22 35
Elmswell	d		20 43	21 42	22 44
Thurston	d		20 49	21 48	22 50
Bury St Edmunds	a	20 27	20 55	21 55	22 57
Bury St Edmunds	d	20 29	20 57	21 56	
Kennett	d			22 07	
Newmarket	d		21 16	22 17	
Dullingham	d		21 21	22 23	
Cambridge	a		21 39	22 40	
Ely 6	a	20 58			
	d	20 58			
Manea	a				
March	a	21 14			
Whittlesea	a	21 26			
Peterborough 8	a	21 37			

Please see table 17 for complete service between Ely and Peterborough

Table 14

Saturdays

28 December to 17 May

Ipswich - Bury St. Edmunds, Cambridge, Ely and Peterborough

Network Diagram - see first Page of Table 13

		LE	LE 1	LE 1	LE 1	LE 1		LE 1	LE 1	LE 1	LE 1	LE 1	LE 1	LE 1	LE 1	LE 1		LE 1	LE 1	LE 1	LE 1	LE 1	LE 1	LE 1	LE 1
Colchester	d		05 40																						
Manningtree	d		05 49																						
Harwich International	d							07 50																	
Ipswich	d	05 10	06 00	06 16	07 20	08 00		08 20	09 20	09 58	10 20	11 20	11 58	12 20	13 20	13 58		14 20	15 20	15 58	16 20	17 20	17 58	18 20	19 20
Needham Market	d	05 20		06 25	07 29			08 29	09 29		10 29	11 29		12 29	13 29			14 29	15 29		16 29	17 29		18 29	19 29
Stowmarket	d	05 26	06 12	06 31	07 35	08 12		08 35	09 35	10 11	10 35	11 35	12 11	12 35	13 35	14 11		14 35	15 35	16 11	16 35	17 35	18 11	18 35	19 35
Elmswell	d	05 35		06 39	07 43			08 44	09 43		10 43	11 43		12 43	13 43			14 43	15 43		16 43	17 43		18 43	19 43
Thurston	d	05 41		06 45	07 49			08 50	09 49		10 49	11 49		12 49	13 49			14 49	15 49		16 49	17 49		18 49	19 49
Bury St Edmunds	a	05 48	06 28	06 51	07 55	08 28		08 56	09 55	10 27	10 55	11 55	12 27	12 55	13 55	14 27		14 55	15 55	16 27	16 55	17 55	18 27	18 55	19 55
Bury St Edmunds	d	05 49	06 29	06 54	07 57	08 29		08 57	09 57	10 29	10 57	11 57	12 29	12 57	13 57	14 29		14 57	15 57	16 29	16 57	17 57	18 29	18 57	19 57
Kennett	d	06 00		07 04	08 07				10 07			12 07			14 07				16 07		17 07	18 07			20 07
Newmarket	d	06 09		07 14	08 17			09 16	10 17		11 16	12 17		13 16	14 17			15 16	16 17		17 17	18 17		19 16	20 17
Dullingham	d	06 14		07 19	08 22			09 21			11 21			13 21				15 21						19 21	
Cambridge	a	06 32		07 39	08 39			09 39	10 39		11 39	12 39		13 39	14 39			15 39	16 39		17 39	18 39		19 39	20 39
Ely 6	a		06 56			08 58				10 58			12 58			14 58				16 58			18 58		
	d		06 56			08 58				10 58			12 58			14 58				16 58			18 58		
Manea	a		07x07			09x09				11x09			13x09			15x09				17x09			19x09		
March	a		07 14			09 16				11 16			13 16			15 16				17 16			19 16		
Whittlesea	a		07 26			09 28				11 28			13 28			15 28				17 28			19 28		
Peterborough 8	a		07 37			09 39				11 39			13 39			15 39				17 39			19 39		

		LE 1		LE 1	LE	LE
Colchester	d					
Manningtree	d					
Harwich International	d					
Ipswich	d	19 58		20 20	21 17	22 19
Needham Market	d			20 29	21 27	22 29
Stowmarket	d	20 11		20 35	21 33	22 35
Elmswell	d			20 43	21 42	22 44
Thurston	d			20 49	21 48	22 50
Bury St Edmunds	a	20 27		20 55	21 55	22 57
Bury St Edmunds	d	20 29		20 57	21 56	
Kennett	d				22 07	
Newmarket	d			21 16	22 17	
Dullingham	d			21 21	22 23	
Cambridge	a			21 39	22 40	
Ely 6	a	20 58				
	d	20 58				
Manea	a	21x09				
March	a	21 16				
Whittlesea	a	21 28				
Peterborough 8	a	21 39				

Sundays

8 December to 11 May

		LE	LE 1	LE 1	LE 1	LE 1	LE 1	LE 1	LE 1	LE 1		LE 1	LE 1	LE 1	LE
Colchester	d			09 32											
Manningtree	d			09 40											
Harwich International	d		08 30												
Ipswich	d	07 32	09 02	09 55	11 02	11 55	13 02	13 55	15 02	15 55		17 02	17 55	19 02	21 02
Needham Market	d	07 42	09 12		11 12		13 12		15 12			17 12		19 12	21 12
Stowmarket	d	07 48	09 18	10 07	11 18	12 07	13 18	14 07	15 18	16 07		17 18	18 07	19 18	21 18
Elmswell	d	07 57	09 27		11 27		13 27		15 27			17 27		19 27	21 27
Thurston	d	08 03	09 33		11 33		13 33		15 33			17 33		19 33	21 33
Bury St Edmunds	a	08 10	09 40	10 23	11 40	12 23	13 40	14 23	15 40	16 23		17 40	18 23	19 40	21 40
Bury St Edmunds	d	08 11	09 41	10 24	11 41	12 24	13 41	14 24	15 41	16 24		17 41	18 24	19 41	21 41
Kennett	d	08 22	09 52		11 52		13 52		15 52			17 52		19 52	21 52
Newmarket	d	08 31	10 01		12 01		14 01		16 01			18 01		20 01	22 01
Dullingham	d	08 36	10 06		12 06		14 06		16 06			18 06		20 06	22 06
Cambridge	a	08 57	10 24		12 24		14 25		16 25			18 25		20 24	22 24
Ely 6	a			10 51		12 51		14 51		16 51			18 51		
	d			10 52		12 52		14 52		16 52			18 52		
Manea	a														
March	a			11 08		13 08		15 08		17 08			19 08		
Whittlesea	a			11 20		13 20		15 20		17 20			19 20		
Peterborough 8	a			11 36		13 31		15 31		17 31			19 31		

Please see table 17 for complete service between Ely and Peterborough

Table 14

Peterborough, Ely, Cambridge and Bury St. Edmunds - Ipswich

Mondays to Fridays

9 December to 27 December

Network Diagram - see first Page of Table 13

Miles	Miles	Miles			LE 1	LE	LE 1	LE	LE 1	LE 1	LE 1	LE 1		LE 1	LE 1	LE 1	LE 1	LE 1	LE 1	LE 1	LE 1	LE 1		LE 1	LE 1
0	—	—	**Peterborough 8**	d						07 45				09 45			11 45			13 45				15 45	
7	—	—	Whittlesea	d						07 53				09 53			11 53			13 53				15 53	
14¾	—	—	March	d						08 04				10 04			12 04			14 04				16 04	
—	—	—	Manea	d																					
30¼	—	—	**Ely 6**	a						08 31				10 31			12 31			14 31				16 31	
—	—	—		d						08 32				10 32			12 32			14 32				16 32	
—	0	—	**Cambridge**	d				06 42	07 44		08 44	09 44			10 44	11 44		12 44	13 44		14 44	15 44			16 44
—	11¼	—	Dullingham	d					08 00			10 00				12 00			14 00			16 00			17 00
—	14½	—	Newmarket	d				07 02	08 05		09 04	10 05			11 04	12 05		13 04	14 05		15 04	16 05			17 05
—	19½	—	Kennett	d				07 10			09 12				11 12			13 12			15 12				17 13
—	—	—	**Bury St Edmunds**	a				07 23	08 23	08 58	09 23	10 23		10 58	11 23	12 23	12 58	13 23	14 23	14 58	15 23	16 23		16 58	17 24
54½	29¼	—	**Bury St Edmunds**	d	05 31	06 21		07 23	08 24	08 58	09 24	10 24		10 58	11 24	12 24	12 58	13 24	14 24	14 58	15 24	16 24		16 58	17 25
—	33¼	—	Thurston	d	05 37	06 27		07 30	08 30		09 30	10 30			11 30	12 30		13 30	14 30		15 30	16 30			17 31
—	37¾	—	Elmswell	d	05 43	06 34		07 36	08 36		09 36	10 36			11 36	12 36		13 36	14 36		15 36	16 36			17 37
69	43¾	—	Stowmarket	d	05 52	06 42	07 03	07 45	08 45	09 14	09 45	10 45		11 14	11 45	12 45	13 14	13 45	14 45	15 14	15 45	16 45		17 14	17 45
—	47¼	—	Needham Market	d	05 57	06 47		07 50	08 50		09 50	10 50			11 50	12 50		13 50	14 50		15 50	16 50			17 50
81¼	55½	0	**Ipswich**	a	06 07	07 00	07 16	08 02	09 02	09 28	10 02	11 02		11 28	12 02	13 02	13 28	14 02	15 02	15 28	16 02	17 02		17 28	18 04
—	—	—		d			07 17																		
—	—	18	Harwich International	a																					
—	—	—	Manningtree	a			07 27																		
—	—	—	Colchester	a			07 37																		

		LE 1	LE 1	LE 1	LE 1	LE 1	LE 1	LE 1		LE 1	LE
Peterborough 8	d		17 45			19 45				21 45	
Whittlesea	d		17 53			19 53				21 53	
March	d		18 04			20 04				22 04	
Manea	d										
Ely 6	a		18 31			20 31				22 25	
	d		18 32			20 32				22 26	
Cambridge	d	17 44		18 44	19 44		20 44	21 44			22 44
Dullingham	d	18 00			20 00			22 00			23 00
Newmarket	d	18 05		19 04	20 05		21 04	22 05			23 06
Kennett	d	18 13		19 12			21 12				23 14
Bury St Edmunds	a	18 24	18 58	19 23	20 23	20 58	21 23	22 23		22 52	23 26
Bury St Edmunds	d	18 25	18 58	19 24	20 24	20 58	21 24	22 24		22 52	23 27
Thurston	d	18 31		19 30	20 30		21 30	22 30			23 33
Elmswell	d	18 37		19 36	20 36		21 36	22 36			23 39
Stowmarket	d	18 45	19 14	19 45	20 45	21 14	21 45	22 45		23 08	23 48
Needham Market	d	18 50		19 50	20 50		21 50	22 50			23 53
Ipswich	a	19 02	19 28	20 04	21 00	21 28	22 02	23 02		23 22	00 05
	d				21 01	21 28				23 22	
Harwich International	a				21 30						
Manningtree	a					21 38				23 32	
Colchester	a					21 51				23 43	

Mondays to Fridays

30 December to 16 May

		LE 1	LE	LE 1	LE	LE 1	LE 1	LE 1	LE 1	LE 1		LE 1	LE 1	LE 1	LE 1	LE 1	LE 1	LE 1	LE 1	LE 1		LE 1	LE 1	LE 1	LE 1
Peterborough 8	d						07 50			09 50				11 50			13 50			15 50				17 50	
Whittlesea	d						07 58			09 58				11 58			13 58			15 58				17 58	
March	d						08 09			10 09				12 09			14 09			16 09				18 09	
Manea	d						08x17			10x17				12x17			14x17			16x17				18x17	
Ely 6	a						08 31			10 31				12 31			14 31			16 31				18 31	
	d						08 32			10 32				12 32			14 32			16 32				18 32	
Cambridge	d				06 42	07 44		08 44	09 44			10 44	11 44		12 44	13 44		14 44	15 44			16 44	17 44		18 44
Dullingham	d					08 00			10 00				12 00			14 00			16 00			17 00	18 00		
Newmarket	d				07 02	08 05		09 04	10 05			11 04	12 05		13 04	14 05		15 04	16 05			17 05	18 05		19 04
Kennett	d				07 10			09 12				11 12			13 12			15 12				17 13	18 13		19 12
Bury St Edmunds	a				07 23	08 23	08 58	09 23	10 23	10 58		11 23	12 23	12 58	13 23	14 23	14 58	15 23	16 23	16 58		17 24	18 24	18 58	19 23
Bury St Edmunds	d	05 31	06 21		07 23	08 24	08 58	09 24	10 24	10 58		11 24	12 24	12 58	13 24	14 24	14 58	15 24	16 24	16 58		17 25	18 25	18 58	19 24
Thurston	d	05 37	06 27		07 30	08 30		09 30	10 30			11 30	12 30		13 30	14 30		15 30	16 30			17 31	18 31		19 30
Elmswell	d	05 43	06 34		07 36	08 36		09 36	10 36			11 36	12 36		13 36	14 36		15 36	16 36			17 37	18 37		19 36
Stowmarket	d	05 52	06 42		07 45	08 45	09 14	09 45	10 45	11 14		11 45	12 45	13 14	13 45	14 45	15 14	15 45	16 45	17 14		17 45	18 45	19 14	19 45
Needham Market	d	05 57	06 47		07 50	08 50		09 50	10 50			11 50	12 50		13 50	14 50		15 50	16 50			17 50	18 50		19 50
Ipswich	a	06 07	07 00		08 02	09 02	09 28	10 02	11 02	11 28		12 02	13 02	13 28	14 02	15 02	15 28	16 02	17 02	17 28		18 04	19 02	19 28	20 04
	d																								
Harwich International	a																								
Manningtree	a																								
Colchester	a																								

Please refer to Table 17 for complete service between Ely and Peterborough

Table 14

Peterborough, Ely, Cambridge and Bury St. Edmunds - Ipswich

Mondays to Fridays

30 December to 16 May

Network Diagram - see first Page of Table 13

		LE [1]	LE [1]	LE [1]	LE [1]	LE [1]	LE
Peterborough [8]	d		19 50			21 45	
Whittlesea	d		19 58			21 53	
March	d		20 09			22 04	
Manea	d		20x17			22x12	
Ely [6]	a		20 31			22 25	
	d		20 32			22 26	
Cambridge	d	19 44		20 44	21 44		22 44
Dullingham	d	20 00			22 00		23 00
Newmarket	d	20 05		21 04	22 05		23 06
Kennett	d			21 12			23 14
Bury St Edmunds	a	20 23	20 58	21 23	22 23	22 52	23 26
Bury St Edmunds	d	20 24	20 58	21 24	22 24	22 52	23 27
Thurston	d	20 30		21 30	22 30		23 33
Elmswell	d	20 36		21 36	22 36		23 39
Stowmarket	d	20 45	21 14	21 45	22 45	23 08	23 48
Needham Market	d	20 50		21 50	22 50		23 53
Ipswich	a	21 00	21 28	22 02	23 02	23 21	00 05
	d	21 01	21 28			23 22	
Harwich International	a	21 30					
Manningtree	a		21 38			23 32	
Colchester	a		21 51			23 43	

Saturdays

14 December to 21 December

		LE	LE	LE [1]	LE [1]	LE [1]	LE [1]	LE [1]	LE [1]	LE [1]	LE [1]	LE [1]
Peterborough [8]	d				07 45			09 47			11 45	
Whittlesea	d				07 53			09 55			11 53	
March	d				08 04			10 06			12 04	
Manea	d											
Ely [6]	a				08 31			10 31			12 31	
	d				08 32			10 32			12 32	
Cambridge	d		06 42	07 44		08 44	09 44		10 44	11 44		12 44
Dullingham	d			08 00			10 00			12 00		
Newmarket	d		07 02	08 05		09 04	10 05		11 04	12 05		13 04
Kennett	d		07 10			09 12			11 12			13 12
Bury St Edmunds	a		07 23	08 23	08 58	09 23	10 23	10 58	11 23	12 23	12 58	13 23
Bury St Edmunds	d	06 23	07 23	08 24	08 58	09 24	10 24	10 58	11 24	12 24	12 58	13 24
Thurston	d	06 29	07 30	08 30		09 30	10 30		11 30	12 30		13 30
Elmswell	d	06 36	07 36	08 36		09 36	10 36		11 36	12 36		13 36
Stowmarket	d	06 44	07 45	08 45	09 14	09 45	10 45	11 14	11 45	12 45	13 14	13 45
Needham Market	d	06 49	07 50	08 50		09 50	10 50		11 50	12 50		13 50
Ipswich	a	07 02	08 02	09 02	09 28	10 02	11 02	11 28	12 02	13 02	13 28	14 02
	d											
Harwich International	a											
Manningtree	a											
Colchester	a											

		LE [1]	LE [1]	LE [1]	LE [1]	LE [1]	LE [1]	LE [1]	LE [1]	LE [1]	LE [1]	LE [1]
Peterborough [8]	d		13 45			15 45			17 45			19 45
Whittlesea	d		13 53			15 53			17 53			19 53
March	d		14 04			16 04			18 04			20 04
Manea	d											
Ely [6]	a		14 31			16 31			18 31			20 31
	d		14 32			16 32			18 32			20 32
Cambridge	d	13 44		14 44	15 44		16 44	17 44		18 44	19 44	
Dullingham	d	14 00			16 00		17 00	18 00			20 00	
Newmarket	d	14 05		15 04	16 05		17 05	18 05		19 04	20 05	
Kennett	d			15 12			17 13	18 13		19 12		
Bury St Edmunds	a	14 23	14 58	15 23	16 23	16 58	17 24	18 24	18 58	19 23	20 23	20 58
Bury St Edmunds	d	14 24	14 58	15 24	16 24	16 58	17 25	18 25	18 58	19 24	20 24	20 58
Thurston	d	14 30		15 30	16 30		17 31	18 31		19 30	20 30	
Elmswell	d	14 36		15 36	16 36		17 37	18 37		19 36	20 36	
Stowmarket	d	14 45	15 14	15 45	16 45	17 14	17 45	18 45	19 14	19 45	20 45	21 14
Needham Market	d	14 50		15 50	16 50		17 50	18 50		19 50	20 50	
Ipswich	a	15 02	15 28	16 02	17 02	17 28	18 02	19 02	19 28	20 02	21 00	21 28
	d										21 01	21 28
Harwich International	a										21 30	
Manningtree	a											21 38
Colchester	a											21 49

		LE [1]	LE [1]	LE [1]	LE
Peterborough [8]	d			21 45	
Whittlesea	d			21 53	
March	d			22 04	
Manea	d				
Ely [6]	a			22 25	
	d			22 26	
Cambridge	d	20 44	21 44		22 44
Dullingham	d		22 00		23 00
Newmarket	d	21 04	22 05		23 06
Kennett	d	21 12			23 14
Bury St Edmunds	a	21 23	22 23	22 52	23 26
Bury St Edmunds	d	21 24	22 24	22 52	23 27
Thurston	d	21 30	22 30		23 33
Elmswell	d	21 36	22 36		23 39
Stowmarket	d	21 45	22 45	23 08	23 48
Needham Market	d	21 50	22 50		23 53
Ipswich	a	22 02	23 02	23 22	00 05
	d			23 22	
Harwich International	a				
Manningtree	a			23 32	
Colchester	a			23 43	

Please refer to Table 17 for complete service between Ely and Peterborough

Table 14

Saturdays

28 December to 17 May

Peterborough, Ely, Cambridge and Bury St. Edmunds - Ipswich

Network Diagram - see first Page of Table 13

		LE	LE	LE 1	LE 1	LE 1		LE 1	LE 1	LE 1	LE 1	LE 1	LE 1	LE 1	LE 1	LE 1		LE 1	LE 1	LE 1	LE 1	LE 1	LE 1	LE 1	LE 1
Peterborough 8	d				07 50				09 50			11 50			13 50				15 50			17 50			19 50
Whittlesea	d				07 58				09 58			11 58			13 58				15 58			17 58			19 58
March	d				08 09				10 09			12 09			14 09				16 09			18 09			20 09
Manea	d				08x17				10x17			12x17			14x17				16x17			18x17			20x17
Ely 6	a				08 31				10 31			12 31			14 31				16 31			18 31			20 31
	d				08 32				10 32			12 32			14 32				16 32			18 32			20 32
Cambridge	d		06 42	07 44		08 44		09 44		10 44	11 44		12 44	13 44		14 44		15 44		16 44	17 44		18 44	19 44	
Dullingham	d			08 00				10 00			12 00			14 00				16 00		17 00	18 00			20 00	
Newmarket	d		07 02	08 05		09 04		10 05		11 04	12 05		13 04	14 05		15 04		16 05		17 05	18 05		19 04	20 05	
Kennett	d		07 10			09 12				11 12			13 12			15 12				17 13	18 13		19 12		
Bury St Edmunds	a		07 23	08 23	08 58	09 23		10 23	10 58	11 23	12 23	12 58	13 23	14 23	14 58	15 23		16 23	16 58	17 24	18 24	18 58	19 23	20 23	20 58
Bury St Edmunds	d	06 23	07 23	08 24	08 58	09 24		10 24	10 58	11 24	12 24	12 58	13 24	14 24	14 58	15 24		16 24	16 58	17 25	18 25	18 58	19 24	20 24	20 58
Thurston	d	06 29	07 30	08 30		09 30		10 30		11 30	12 30		13 30	14 30		15 30		16 30		17 31	18 31		19 30	20 30	
Elmswell	d	06 36	07 36	08 36		09 36		10 36		11 36	12 36		13 36	14 36		15 36		16 36		17 37	18 37		19 36	20 36	
Stowmarket	d	06 44	07 45	08 45	09 14	09 45		10 45	11 14	11 45	12 45	13 14	13 45	14 45	15 14	15 45		16 45	17 14	17 45	18 45	19 14	19 45	20 45	21 14
Needham Market	d	06 49	07 50	08 50		09 50		10 50		11 50	12 50		13 50	14 50		15 50		16 50		17 50	18 50		19 50	20 50	
Ipswich	a	07 02	08 02	09 02	09 28	10 02		11 02	11 28	12 02	13 02	13 28	14 02	15 02	15 28	16 02		17 02	17 28	18 02	19 02	19 28	20 02	21 00	21 28
	d																							21 01	21 28
Harwich International	a																							21 30	
Manningtree	a																								21 38
Colchester	a																								21 49

		LE 1		LE 1	LE 1	LE
Peterborough 8	d				21 45	
Whittlesea	d				21 53	
March	d				22 04	
Manea	d				22x12	
Ely 6	a				22 25	
	d				22 26	
Cambridge	d	20 44		21 44		22 44
Dullingham	d			22 00		23 00
Newmarket	d	21 04		22 05		23 06
Kennett	d	21 12				23 14
Bury St Edmunds	a	21 23		22 23	22 52	23 26
Bury St Edmunds	d	21 24		22 24	22 52	23 27
Thurston	d	21 30		22 30		23 33
Elmswell	d	21 36		22 36		23 39
Stowmarket	d	21 45		22 45	23 08	23 48
Needham Market	d	21 50		22 50		23 53
Ipswich	a	22 02		23 02	23 22	00 05
	d				23 22	
Harwich International	a					
Manningtree	a				23 32	
Colchester	a				23 43	

Sundays

8 December to 11 May

		LE	LE 1	LE 1	LE 1	LE 1	LE 1	LE 1	LE 1	LE 1		LE 1	LE 1	LE 1	LE
Peterborough 8	d			11 45		13 46		15 45		17 45			19 45		
Whittlesea	d			11 53		13 54		15 53		17 53			19 53		
March	d			12 04		14 05		16 04		18 04			20 04		
Manea	d														
Ely 6	a			12 31		14 31		16 23		18 23			20 23		
	d			12 32		14 32		16 29		18 29			20 29		
Cambridge	d	09 12	11 12		13 12		15 12		17 12			19 12		21 12	22 50
Dullingham	d	09 28	11 28		13 28		15 28		17 28			19 28		21 28	23 06
Newmarket	d	09 34	11 34		13 34		15 34		17 34			19 34		21 34	23 12
Kennett	d	09 42	11 42		13 42		15 42		17 42			19 42		21 42	23 20
Bury St Edmunds	a	09 54	11 54	12 58	13 54	14 58	15 54	16 55	17 54	18 55		19 54	20 55	21 54	23 32
Bury St Edmunds	d	09 55	11 55	12 58	13 55	14 58	15 55	16 55	17 55	18 55		19 55	20 55	21 55	23 33
Thurston	d	10 01	12 01		14 01		16 01		18 01			20 01		22 01	23 39
Elmswell	d	10 07	12 07		14 07		16 07		18 07			20 07		22 07	23 45
Stowmarket	d	10 18	12 18	13 14	14 18	15 14	16 18	17 11	18 18	19 11		20 18	21 11	22 18	23 55
Needham Market	d	10 23	12 23		14 23		16 23		18 23			20 23		22 23	23 59
Ipswich	a	10 36	12 36	13 28	14 36	15 28	16 36	17 25	18 36	19 25		20 36	21 25	22 36	00 11
	d									19 25		20 36	21 25		
Harwich International	a											21 05			
Manningtree	a									19 35			21 35		
Colchester	a									19 46			21 46		

Please refer to Table 17 for complete service between Ely and Peterborough

Table 15

Norwich - Great Yarmouth and Lowestoft

Mondays to Fridays

9 December to 16 May

Network Diagram - see first Page of Table 13

Miles	Miles	Miles			LE	LE	LE 1	LE	LE	LE	LE	LE 1	LE		LE	LE	LE	LE 1	LE	LE	LE	LE	LE		LE
—	—	—	London Liverpool Street 15 ⊖	d																					
0	0	0	**Norwich**	d	05 06	05 36	06 11	06 27	06 50	07 00	07 36	07 50	08 09		08 36	08 55	09 36	10 05	10 36	10 58	11 36	12 05	12 36		12 58
4¾	4¾	4¾	Brundall Gardens	d		05 43	06 18		06 57			07 57			08 43		09 43		10 43		11 43		12 43		
5¾	5¾	5¾	Brundall	d	05 15	05 46	06 21	06 36	07 00	07 09	07 45	08 00			08 46		09 46	10 14	10 46		11 46	12 14	12 46		
8	—	—	Lingwood	d			06 26		07 05				08 21		08 51		09 51		10 51				12 51		
10½	—	—	Acle	d			06 35		07 10				08 28		08 58		09 56		10 56				12 56		
—	7¾	7¾	Buckenham	d																					
—	10	10	Cantley	d		05 52				07 15	07 51	08 06						10 20			11 52	12 20			
—	12¼	12¼	Reedham (Norfolk)	d		05 56		06 44		07 19	07 55	08 11						10 24			11 57	12 24			
—	16	—	Berney Arms	d							08x01										12x03				
18¼	20½	—	**Great Yarmouth**	a	05 40		06 49		07 23		08 12		08 41		09 11		10 09		11 09		12 13		13 09		
—	—	16¼	Haddiscoe	d		06 05				07 28		08 19						10 33				12 33			
—	—	18	Somerleyton	d		06 09				07 32		08 23						10 37				12 37			
—	—	22	Oulton Broad North	d		06 15		06 59		07 38		08 33				09 25		10 43		11 28		12 43			13 28
—	—	23½	**Lowestoft**	a		06 22		07 06		07 45		08 40				09 32		10 50		11 35		12 50			13 35

		LE	LE	LE	LE	LE	LE	LE	LE		LE	LE 1	LE	LE	LE	LE	LE	LE	LE		LE	LE	LE	LE	LE
London Liverpool Street 15 ⊖	d																								
Norwich	d	13 36	14 05	14 36	14 58	15 36	15 50	16 40	16 58		17 06	17 36	17 50	18 06	18 40	19 05	19 33	20 05	20 40		21 05	21 40	22 05	22 40	23 00
Brundall Gardens	d	13 43		14 43		15 43		16 47			17 13	17 43		18 13	18 47		19 40		20 47			21 47			
Brundall	d	13 46	14 14	14 46		15 46	15 59	16 50	17 07		17 16	17 46	17 59	18 16	18 50	19 14	19 43	20 14	20 50		21 14	21 50	22 14	22 49	23 09
Lingwood	d	13 51		14 51		15 51		16 55			17 21	17 51		18 21	18 55		19 48		20 55			21 55			23 14
Acle	d	13 56		14 56		15 56		17 00			17 28	17 56		18 28	19 00		19 53		21 00			22 00			23 18
Buckenham	d																								
Cantley	d		14 20		15 10		16 05		17 13				18 05			19 20		20 20			21 20		22 20	22 55	
Reedham (Norfolk)	d		14 24		15 15		16 09		17 17				18 09			19 24		20 24			21 24		22 24	22 59	
Berney Arms	d																								
Great Yarmouth	a	14 09		15 09		16 09		17 13			17 41	18 09		18 41	19 13		20 06		21 13			22 13			23 31
Haddiscoe	d		14 33				16 18		17 26				18 18			19 33		20 33			21 33		22 33	23 08	
Somerleyton	d		14 37				16 22		17 30				18 22			19 37		20 37			21 37		22 37	23 12	
Oulton Broad North	d		14 43		15 30		16 28		17 36				18 28			19 43		20 43			21 43		22 43	23 18	
Lowestoft	a		14 50		15 36		16 35		17 43				18 35			19 50		20 50			21 50		22 50	23 25	

Saturdays

14 December to 17 May

		LE	LE	LE	LE	LE 1	LE	LE 1	LE	LE		LE	LE	LE	LE	LE	LE	LE	LE	LE		LE	LE	LE	LE
London Liverpool Street 15 ⊖	d																								
Norwich	d	05 30	05 40	06 36	06 50	07 06	07 36	07 50	08 09	08 36		08 55	09 36	10 05	10 36	10 58	11 36	12 05	12 36	12 58		13 36	14 05	14 36	14 58
Brundall Gardens	d		05 47	06 43		07 13		07 57		08 43			09 43		10 43		11 43		12 43			13 43		14 43	
Brundall	d	05 39	05 50	06 46	06 59	07 16	07 45	08 00		08 46			09 46	10 14	10 46		11 46	12 14	12 46			13 46	14 14	14 46	
Lingwood	d			06 51		07 21			08 21	08 51			09 51		10 51				12 51			13 51		14 51	
Acle	d			06 56		07 28			08 28	08 58			09 56		10 56				12 56			13 56		14 56	
Buckenham	d													10x18											
Cantley	d		05 56		07 05		07 51	08 06						10 22			11 52	12 20					14 20		15 10
Reedham (Norfolk)	d	05 47	06 01		07 09		07 55	08 11						10 26			11 57	12 24					14 24		15 15
Berney Arms	d						08x01										12x03								
Great Yarmouth	a	06 02		07 09		07 41	08 12		08 41	09 11			10 09		11 09		12 13		13 09			14 09		15 09	
Haddiscoe	d		06 09		07 18			08 19						10 35				12 33					14 33		
Somerleyton	d		06 13		07 22			08 23						10 39				12 37					14 37		
Oulton Broad North	d		06 20		07 28			08 30				09 25		10 45		11 28		12 43		13 28			14 43		15 30
Lowestoft	a		06 26		07 35			08 36				09 32		10 52		11 35		12 50		13 35			14 50		15 36

		LE	LE	LE	LE	LE		LE 1	LE	LE	LE	LE	LE	LE	LE	LE		LE	LE 1	LE	LE
London Liverpool Street 15 ⊖	d																				
Norwich	d	15 36	15 50	16 40	16 58	17 06		17 36	17 50	18 06	18 40	19 05	19 33	20 05	20 40	21 05		21 40	22 05	22 40	23 00
Brundall Gardens	d	15 43		16 47		17 13		17 43		18 13	18 47		19 40		20 47			21 47			
Brundall	d	15 46	15 59	16 50	17 07	17 16		17 46	17 59	18 16	18 50	19 14	19 43	20 14	20 50	21 14		21 50	22 14	22 49	23 09
Lingwood	d	15 51		16 55		17 21		17 51		18 21	18 55		19 48		20 55			21 55			23 14
Acle	d	15 56		17 00		17 28		17 56		18 28	19 00		19 53		21 00			22 00			23 18
Buckenham	d																				
Cantley	d		16 05		17 13				18 05			19 20		20 20		21 20			22 20	22 55	
Reedham (Norfolk)	d		16 09		17 17				18 09			19 24		20 24		21 24			22 24	22 59	
Berney Arms	d																				
Great Yarmouth	a	16 09		17 13		17 41		18 09		18 41	19 13		20 06		21 13			22 13			23 31
Haddiscoe	d		16 18		17 26				18 18			19 33		20 33		21 33			22 33	23 08	
Somerleyton	d		16 22		17 30				18 22			19 37		20 37		21 37			22 37	23 12	
Oulton Broad North	d		16 28		17 36				18 28			19 43		20 43		21 43			22 43	23 18	
Lowestoft	a		16 35		17 43				18 35			19 50		20 50		21 50			22 50	23 25	

Table 15

Sundays

8 December to 11 May

Norwich - Great Yarmouth and Lowestoft

Network Diagram - see first Page of Table 13

		LE [1]	LE	LE	LE	LE	LE	LE	LE	LE	LE [1]	LE	LE	LE [1]	LE A	LE B	LE	LE A	LE B	LE	LE	LE [1]	LE
London Liverpool Street [15] ⊖	d																						
Norwich	d	07 25	07 36	08 45	08 57	09 36	10 45	10 57	11 36	12 45	12 57	13 36	14 45	14 57	15 36	15 36	16 45	16 57	16 57	17 36	18 45	18 57	19 36
Brundall Gardens	d			08 52			10 52			12 52			14 52				16 52				18 52		
Brundall	d		07 45	08 55	09 06	09 45	10 55	11 06	11 45	12 55	13 06	13 45	14 55	15 06	15 45	15 45	16 55	17 06	17 06	17 45	18 55	19 06	19 45
Lingwood	d			09 00			11 00			13 00			15 00				17 00				19 00		
Acle	d			09 05			11 05			13 05			15 05				17 05				19 05		
Buckenham	d					09x49			11x49						15x49	15x49		17x10					
Cantley	d		07 51		09 12	09 53		11 12	11 53		13 12	13 51		15 12	15 53	15 53		17 14	17 14	17 51		19 12	19 51
Reedham (Norfolk)	d		07 55		09 16	09 57		11 16	11 57		13 16	13 55		15 16	15 57	15 57		17 18	17 18	17 55		19 16	19 55
Berney Arms	d		08x01			10x03			12x03			14x01			16x03								
Great Yarmouth	a		08 12	09 18		10 14	11 18		12 14	13 18		14 12	15 18		16 14	16 14	17 18			18 10	19 18		20 10
Haddiscoe	d				09 25			11 25			13 25			15 25				17 27	17 27			19 25	
Somerleyton	d				09 29			11 29			13 29			15 29				17 31	17 31			19 29	
Oulton Broad North	d	07 53			09 35			11 35			13 35			15 35				17 37	17 37			19 35	
Lowestoft	a	08 00			09 42			11 42			13 42			15 42				17 44	17 44			19 42	

		LE		LE [1]	LE	LE
London Liverpool Street [15] ⊖	d					
Norwich	d	20 45		20 57	21 36	22 36
Brundall Gardens	d	20 52				22 43
Brundall	d	20 55		21 06	21 45	22 46
Lingwood	d	21 00				22 51
Acle	d	21 05				22 56
Buckenham	d					
Cantley	d			21 12	21 51	
Reedham (Norfolk)	d			21 16	21 55	
Berney Arms	d					
Great Yarmouth	a	21 18			22 10	23 09
Haddiscoe	d			21 25		
Somerleyton	d			21 29		
Oulton Broad North	d			21 35		
Lowestoft	a			21 42		

A from 30 March

B until 23 March

Table 15R

Lowestoft and Great Yarmouth - Norwich

Mondays to Fridays

9 December to 16 May

Network Diagram - see first Page of Table 13

Miles	Miles	Miles			LE	LE [1]	LE	LE	LE [1]	LE	LE [1]	LE	LE	LE	LE [1]	LE	LE	LE	LE [1]	LE	LE	LE	LE
0	—	—	**Lowestoft**	d		05 42		06 35			07 35	07 52			08 50		09 48		10 57		11 48		12 57
1½	—	—	Oulton Broad North	d		05 46		06 39			07 39	07 56			08 54		09 52		11 01		11 52		13 01
5½	—	—	Somerleyton	d		05 52		06 45			07 45				09 00		09 58				11 58		
7¼	—	—	Haddiscoe	d		05 56		06 49			07 49				09 04		10 02				12 02		
—	0	0	**Great Yarmouth**	d	05 45		06 24		06 56	07 32			08 17	08 47		09 17		10 17		11 17		12 17	
—	—	4½	Berney Arms	d																			
11¼	—	8¼	Reedham (Norfolk)	d		06 05		06 58			07 58	08 11			09 13		10 11				12 11		
13½	—	10½	Cantley	d		06 09		07 02			08 02	08 16			09 17		10 15				12 15		
15¾	—	12¾	Buckenham	d																			
—	8	—	Acle	d	05 56		06 35		07 10	07 43			08 28	08 58		09 28		10 28		11 28		12 28	
—	10½	—	Lingwood	d	06 01		06 40		07 14	07 48			08 33	09 03		09 33		10 33		11 33		12 33	
17¾	12¾	14¾	Brundall	d	06 05	06 16	06 44	07 09	07 19	07 52	08 09		08 37		09 24	09 37	10 22	10 37		11 37	12 22	12 37	
18¾	13¾	15¾	Brundall Gardens	d	06 08		06 47		07 21	07 55			08 40			09 40		10 40		11 40		12 40	
23½	18½	20½	**Norwich**	a	06 18	06 27	06 57	07 20	07 34	08 05	08 20	08 31	08 50	09 17	09 40	09 50	10 33	10 50	11 33	11 50	12 33	12 50	13 33
—	—	—	London Liverpool Street [15] ⊖	a																			

		LE	LE	LE	LE	LE	LE	LE	LE	LE	LE A	LE B	LE	LE [1]	LE	LE	LE	LE	LE	LE [1]	LE	LE	LE
Lowestoft	d		13 48		14 57		15 48		16 48				17 48			18 48		19 55		20 57		21 48	
Oulton Broad North	d		13 52		15 01		15 52		16 52				17 52			18 52		19 59		21 01		21 52	
Somerleyton	d		13 58				15 58		16 58				17 58			18 58		20 05				21 58	
Haddiscoe	d		14 02				16 02		17 02				18 02			19 02		20 09				22 02	
Great Yarmouth	d	13 17		14 17		15 12		16 17		17 17	17 47	17 47		18 17	18 47		19 17		20 17		21 17		22 17
Berney Arms	d					15x19					17x54												
Reedham (Norfolk)	d		14 11			15 27	16 11		17 11		18 01	18 01	18 11		19 01	19 11		20 18				22 11	
Cantley	d		14 15			15 31	16 15		17 15		18 05	18 05	18 15		19 05	19 15		20 22				22 15	
Buckenham	d																						
Acle	d	13 28		14 28				16 28		17 28				18 28			19 28		20 28		21 28		22 28
Lingwood	d	13 33		14 33				16 33		17 33				18 33			19 33		20 33		21 33		22 33
Brundall	d	13 37	14 22	14 37		15 37	16 22	16 37	17 22	17 37	18 12	18 12	18 22	18 37	19 12	19 22	19 37	20 29	20 37		21 37	22 22	22 37
Brundall Gardens	d	13 40		14 40		15 40		16 40		17 40				18 40			19 40		20 40		21 40		22 40
Norwich	a	13 50	14 33	14 50	15 33	15 50	16 33	16 50	17 33	17 50	18 23	18 23	18 33	18 50	19 23	19 33	19 50	20 40	20 50	21 33	21 50	22 35	22 50
London Liverpool Street [15] ⊖	a																						

		LE [1]	LE	LE
Lowestoft	d	22 48		23 30
Oulton Broad North	d	22 52		23 34
Somerleyton	d	22 58		
Haddiscoe	d	23 02		
Great Yarmouth	d		23 34	
Berney Arms	d			
Reedham (Norfolk)	d	23 11	23 47	23 52
Cantley	d	23 15		23 56
Buckenham	d			
Acle	d			
Lingwood	d			
Brundall	d	23 22	23 55	00 03
Brundall Gardens	d			
Norwich	a	23 33	00 07	00 14
London Liverpool Street [15] ⊖	a			

Saturdays

14 December to 17 May

		LE	LE	LE	LE [1]	LE	LE	LE	LE	LE	LE	LE	LE	LE	LE	LE	LE	LE	LE	LE	LE	LE	LE
Lowestoft	d		06 38			07 40			[illegible] 48		09 48		[illegible] 57		11 48		12 57		13 48		14 57		15 48
Oulton Broad North	d		06 42			07 44			08 52		09 52		11 01		11 52		13 01		[illegible]		15 01		15 52
Somerleyton	d		06 48			07 50			08 58		09 58				[illegible]				13 58				[illegible]
Haddiscoe	d		06 52			07 54			09 02		10 02				12 02				[illegible]				16 02
Great Yarmouth	d	06 17		07 17	07 45		08 17	08 47		09 17		10 17		11 17		12 17		13 17		14 17		15 12	
Berney Arms	d																					15x19	
Reedham (Norfolk)	d		07 01			08 03			09 11		10 11				12 11				14 11			15 27	16 11
Cantley	d		07 05			08 07			09 15		10 15				12 15				14 15			15 31	16 15
Buckenham	d																						16x19
Acle	d	06 28		07 28	07 56		08 28	08 58		09 28		10 28		11 28		12 28		13 28		14 28			
Lingwood	d	06 33		07 33	08 01		08 33	09 03		09 33		10 33		11 33		12 33		13 33		14 33			
Brundall	d	06 37	07 12	07 37	08 05	08 14	08 37		09 22	09 37	10 22	10 37		11 37	12 22	12 37		13 37	14 22	14 37		15 37	16 22
Brundall Gardens	d	06 40		07 40	08 08		08 40			09 40		10 40		11 40		12 40		13 40		14 40		15 40	
Norwich	a	06 50	07 24	07 50	08 18	08 25	08 50	09 17	09 33	09 50	10 33	10 52	11 33	11 50	12 33	12 50	13 33	13 52	14 33	14 50	15 33	15 50	16 33
London Liverpool Street [15] ⊖	a																						

A from 31 March

B until 28 March

Table 15R

Lowestoft and Great Yarmouth - Norwich

Saturdays
14 December to 17 May

Network Diagram - see first Page of Table 13

		LE	LE	LE	LE A	LE B	LE	LE ■1	LE	LE	LE	LE	LE	LE ■1	LE	LE	LE	LE ■1	LE	LE
Lowestoft	d		16 48				17 48			18 48		19 55		20 57		21 48		22 48		23 30
Oulton Broad North	d		16 52				17 52			18 52		19 59		21 01		21 52		22 52		23 34
Somerleyton	d		16 58				17 58			18 58		20 05				21 58		22 58		-
Haddiscoe	d		17 02				18 02			19 02		20 09				22 02		23 02		-
Great Yarmouth	d	16 17		17 17	17 47	17 47		18 17	18 47		19 17		20 17		21 17		22 17		23 34	-
Berney Arms	d				17x54															
Reedham (Norfolk)	d		17 11		18 01	18 01	18 11		19 01	19 11		20 18				22 11		23 11	23 47	23 52
Cantley	d		17 15		18 05	18 05	18 15		19 05	19 15		20 22				22 15		23 15		23 56
Buckenham	d																			-
Acle	d	16 28		17 28				18 28			19 28		20 28		21 28		22 28			-
Lingwood	d	16 33		17 33				18 33			19 33		20 33		21 33		22 33			
Brundall	d	16 37	17 22	17 37	18 12	18 12	18 22	18 37	19 12	19 22	19 37	20 29	20 37		21 37	22 22	22 37	23 22	23 55	00 03
Brundall Gardens	d	16 40		17 40				18 40			19 40		20 40		21 40		22 40			-
Norwich	a	16 50	17 33	17 50	18 23	18 23	18 33	18 50	19 23	19 33	19 50	20 40	20 50	21 33	21 50	22 35	22 50	23 33	00 07	00 14
London Liverpool Street 15 ⊖	a																			

Sundays
8 December to 11 May

		LE	LE	LE	LE	LE	LE ■1	LE	LE	LE ■1	LE	LE	LE	LE C	LE D	LE	LE ■1	LE	LE	LE ■1	LE	LE	LE ■1
Lowestoft	d			09 50			11 50			13 50			15 50				17 50			19 50			21 50
Oulton Broad North	d			09 54			11 54			13 54			15 54				17 54			19 54			21 54
Somerleyton	d			10 00			12 00			14 00			16 00				18 00			20 00			22 00
Haddiscoe	d			10 04			12 04			14 04			16 04				18 04			20 04			22 04
Great Yarmouth	d	08 20	09 22		10 18	11 22		12 18	13 22		14 20	15 22		16 18	16 18	17 22		18 18	19 22	-	20 20	21 22	
Berney Arms	d	08x27			10x25			12x25			14x27			16x25									
Reedham (Norfolk)	d	08 34		10 13	10 32		12 13	12 32		14 13	14 34		16 13	16 32	16 32		18 13	18 31		20 13	20 33		22 13
Cantley	d	08 38		10 17	10 36		12 17	12 36		14 17	14 38		16 17	16 36	16 36		18 17	18 35		20 17	20 37		22 17
Buckenham	d			10x21	10x40			12x40						16x40						-			
Acle	d		09 33			11 33			13 33			15 33				17 33			19 33			21 33	
Lingwood	d		09 38			11 38			13 38			15 38				17 38			19 38	-		21 38	
Brundall	d	08 45	09 42	10 24	10 44	11 42	12 24	12 44	13 42	14 24	14 45	15 42	16 24	16 44	16 44	17 42	18 24	18 41	19 42	20 24	20 43	21 42	22 24
Brundall Gardens	d		09 45			11 45			13 45			15 45				17 45			19 45	-		21 45	
Norwich	a	08 55	09 55	10 35	10 55	11 55	12 35	12 55	13 55	14 35	14 55	15 55	16 35	16 55	16 55	17 55	18 35	18 52	19 55	20 35	20 55	21 55	22 35
London Liverpool Street 15 ⊖	a																						

		LE	LE	LE ■1
Lowestoft	d			23 35
Oulton Broad North	d			23 39
Somerleyton	d			
Haddiscoe	d			
Great Yarmouth	d	22 20	23 20	
Berney Arms	d			
Reedham (Norfolk)	d	22 33	23 33	23 54
Cantley	d	22 37	23 37	
Buckenham	d			
Acle	d			
Lingwood	d			
Brundall	d	22 43	23 43	00 03
Brundall Gardens	d		23 46	
Norwich	a	22 55	23 55	00 13
London Liverpool Street 15 ⊖	a			

A from 5 April
B until 29 March
C from 30 March
D until 23 March

Table 16

Mondays to Saturdays

9 December to 17 May

Norwich - Cromer and Sheringham

Network Diagram - see first Page of Table 13

Miles			LE SX	LE SO	LE SX	LE SO	LE	LE	LE	LE	LE	LE	LE	LE	LE	LE	LE	LE	LE	LE	LE
0	**Norwich**	d	05 10	05 20	05 40	05 45	07 15	08 21	09 45	10 45	11 45	12 45	13 45	14 45	15 45	16 45	17 45	18 51	19 55	21 15	22 45
6	Salhouse	d			05 50	05 55	07 25	08 31	09 55		11 55		13 55		15 55	16 55	17 55		20 05	21 25	22 55
8¾	Hoveton & Wroxham	d	05 24	05 34	05 55	06 00	07 30	08 36	10 00	10 59	12 00	12 59	14 00	14 59	16 00	17 00	18 00	19 05	20 10	21 30	23 00
13	Worstead	d			06 02	06 07	07 37	08 43		11 05		13 05		15 05	16 07	17 07	18 07	19 11	20 17	21 37	23 07
—	**North Walsham**	a	05 34	05 44	06 07	06 12	07 42	08 48	10 10	11 11	12 10	13 11	14 10	15 11	16 12	17 12	18 12	19 17	20 22	21 42	23 12
16	**North Walsham**	d	05 34	05 44	06 10	06 13	07 45	08 51	10 13	11 13	12 13	13 13	14 13	15 13	16 15	17 15	18 17	19 20	20 25	21 43	23 13
19¾	Gunton	d			06 16	06 19	07 51	08 57	10 19		12 19		14 19		16 21	17 21	18 23	19 26	20 31	21 49	23 19
23½	Roughton Road	d			06 23	06 25	07 57	09 04		11 24		13 24		15 24	16 27	17 27	18 30	19 33	20 38	21 55	23 25
—	**Cromer**	a	05 49	05 59	06 28	06 31	08 03	09 09	10 30	11 30	12 30	13 30	14 30	15 30	16 33	17 33	18 36	19 39	20 43	22 01	23 31
26½	**Cromer**	d	05 56	06 01	06 46	06 36	08 05	09 12	10 32	11 32	12 32	13 32	14 32	15 32	16 35	17 35	18 38	19 41	20 46	22 03	23 33
28¾	West Runton	d	06 00	06 06	06 50	06 40	08 10	09 16	10 37	11 37	12 37	13 37	14 37	15 37	16 40	17 40	18 43	19 46	20 50	22 08	23 38
30½	**Sheringham**	a	06 07	06 12	06 56	06 46	08 15	09 22	10 43	11 43	12 43	13 43	14 43	15 43	16 46	17 46	18 49	19 52	20 56	22 14	23 44

Sundays

8 December to 11 May

		LE	LE	LE	LE	LE	LE	LE
Norwich	d	08 36	10 36	12 36	14 36	16 36	18 36	20 36
Salhouse	d	08 46	10 46	12 46	14 46	16 46	18 46	20 46
Hoveton & Wroxham	d	08 51	10 51	12 51	14 51	16 51	18 51	20 51
Worstead	d	08 58	10 58	12 58	14 58	16 58	18 58	20 58
North Walsham	a	09 03	11 03	13 03	15 03	17 03	19 03	21 03
North Walsham	d	09 04	11 06	13 06	15 06	17 06	19 06	21 06
Gunton	d	09 10	11 12	13 12	15 12	17 12	19 12	21 12
Roughton Road	d	09 16	11 19	13 19	15 19	17 19	19 19	21 19
Cromer	a	09 22	11 24	13 24	15 24	17 24	19 24	21 24
Cromer	d	09 25	11 27	13 27	15 27	17 27	19 27	21 27
West Runton	d	09 30	11 31	13 31	15 31	17 31	19 31	21 31
Sheringham	a	09 36	11 38	13 38	15 38	17 38	19 38	21 38

Table 16R

Mondays to Saturdays

9 December to 17 May

Sheringham and Cromer - Norwich

Network Diagram - see first Page of Table 13

Miles			LE SX	LE SO	LE SX	LE	LE	LE	LE	LE	LE	LE	LE	LE	LE	LE	LE	LE	LE	LE	LE
0	**Sheringham**	d		06 22	06 32	07 16	08 23	09 46	10 46	11 46	12 46	13 46	14 46	15 46	16 49	17 49	18 55	19 57	21 10	22 17	23 47
1¾	West Runton	d		06 26	06 36	07 20	08 27	09 50	10 50	11 50	12 50	13 50	14 50	15 50	16 53	17 53	18 59	20 01	21 14	22 21	23 51
—	**Cromer**	a		06 30	06 40	07 24	08 31	09 54	10 54	11 54	12 54	13 54	14 54	15 54	16 57	17 57	19 03	20 05	21 18	22 25	23 55
4	**Cromer**	d	05 53	06 33	06 43	07 27	08 34	09 57	10 57	11 57	12 57	13 57	14 57	15 57	17 00	18 00	19 06	20 08	21 21	22 28	23 58
7	Roughton Road	d	05 59	06 39	06 49	07 33	08 40	10 03		12 03		14 03	15 03	16 03		18 06		20 14	21 27	22 34	
10¾	Gunton	d	06 05	06 45	06 55	07 39	08 46		11 08		13 08			16 09		18 12		20 20	21 33	22 40	
—	**North Walsham**	a	06 10	06 50	07 00	07 45	08 51	10 13	11 13	12 13	13 13	14 13	15 13	16 15	17 15	18 17	19 20	20 25	21 38	22 45	00 12
14½	**North Walsham**	d	06 11	06 51	07 01	07 45	08 52	10 13	11 14	12 13	13 14	14 13	15 14	16 15	17 15	18 18	19 21	20 26	21 43	22 46	00 13
17½	Worstead	d	06 16	06 56	07 06	07 50	08 57	10 18		12 18		14 18		16 20		18 23		20 31	21 48	22 51	
21¾	Hoveton & Wroxham	d	06 23	07 03	07 13	07 57	09 04	10 25	11 24	12 25	13 24	14 25	15 24	16 27	17 25	18 30	19 31	20 38	21 55	22 58	00 22
24½	Salhouse	d	06 27	07 07	07 17	08 02	09 08		11 28		13 28		15 28	16 32		18 34		20 42	21 59	23 02	
30½	**Norwich**	a	06 40	07 20	07 30	08 14	09 21	10 41	11 41	12 41	13 41	14 41	15 41	16 44	17 41	18 47	19 46	20 55	22 12	23 15	00 37

Sundays

8 December to 11 May

		LE	LE	LE	LE	LE	LE	LE
Sheringham	d	09 42	11 42	13 42	15 42	17 42	19 42	21 42
West Runton	d	09 46	11 46	13 46	15 46	17 46	19 46	21 46
Cromer	a	09 50	11 50	13 50	15 50	17 50	19 50	21 50
Cromer	d	09 54	11 54	13 54	15 54	17 54	19 54	21 54
Roughton Road	d	10 00	12 00	14 00	16 00	18 00	20 00	22 00
Gunton	d	10 06	12 06	14 06	16 06	18 06	20 06	22 06
North Walsham	a	10 11	12 11	14 11	16 11	18 11	20 11	22 11
North Walsham	d	10 12	12 12	14 12	16 12	18 12	20 12	22 12
Worstead	d	10 17	12 17	14 17	16 17	18 17	20 17	22 17
Hoveton & Wroxham	d	10 24	12 24	14 24	16 24	18 24	20 24	22 24
Salhouse	d	10 28	12 28	14 28	16 28	18 28	20 28	22 28
Norwich	a	10 40	12 40	14 40	16 40	18 40	20 40	22 40

Table 17

Mondays to Fridays

9 December to 27 December

London and Cambridge - Ely, Kings Lynn, Peterborough and Norwich

Network Diagram - see first Page of Table 13

Miles	Miles	Miles			FC MO	FC MX	XC	XC	LE	FC	EM	LE	EM		FC	XC	LE	LE	EM	FC	XC	EM	FC		LE
					1	1	◇1	◇1	1	1	◇	1	◇		1	◇1	1	1	◇	1	◇1	◇	1		1
—	—	—	**London Liverpool Street**	d																					
—	—	0	**London Kings Cross**	d											05 45					06 45			07 15		
—	0	—	Ipswich	d								06 00													
—	—	—	Stansted Airport	d				05 16								06 12					07 21				
0	—	58	**Cambridge**	d	00 08	00 10	05 15	05 55	06 05	06 17					06 52	06 55	07 04	07 23		07 33	08 01		08 06		08 12
5¼	—	63¼	Waterbeach	d	00 15	00 16				06 23					06 58					07 39			08 12		
14¾	50¾	72¾	**Ely 6**	a	00 24	00 26	05 29	06 09	06 19	06 33		06 56			07 08	07 10	07 18	07 39		07 49	08 14		08 22		08 26
—	—	—		d	00 25	00 26	05 30	06 10	06 20	06 33	06 51	06 56	07 05		07 08	07 12	07 19		07 45	07 50	08 15	08 15	08 22		08 28
—	—	78¼	Littleport	d	00 32	00 33				06 42					07 15					07 58			08 29		
—	—	88½	Downham Market	d	00 41	00 42				06 53					07 25					08 07			08 38		
—	—	93¼	Watlington	d	00 46	00 48				06 59					07 32					08 12			08 44		
—	—	99¼	**Kings Lynn**	a	00 56	00 57				07 08					07 41					08 22			08 52		
—	—	—	Manea	d				06x20																	
—	66¼	—	March	d			05 46	06 28			07 07	07 13				07 29			08 01		08 32				
—	74	—	Whittlesea	d			05 58	06 39				07 24				07 40			08 13						
—	81¼	—	**Peterborough 8**	a			06 08	06 50			07 25	07 35				07 50			08 24		08 50				
—	—	—	Shippea Hill	d													07x28								
—	—	—	Lakenheath	d																					
30¾	—	—	Brandon	d					06 36				07 20				07 38								08 44
38	—	—	Thetford	d					06 44				07 29				07 47					08 37			08 53
45¾	—	—	Harling Road	d					06 53								07 55								
48¾	—	—	Eccles Road	d					06 58								08 00								
52¼	—	—	Attleborough	d					07 04				07 43				08 06					08 51			09 08
—	—	—	Spooner Row	d													08x11								
58¼	—	—	Wymondham	d					07 11				07 50				08 16					08 58			09 15
68¼	—	—	**Norwich**	a					07 27				08 13				08 30					09 13			09 30

		EM	FC	LE	XC	FC	LE	EM	EM		FC	XC	EM	LE	FC	EM	LE	XC	EM		LE	EM	FC	XC	EM
		◇	1	1	◇1	1	1	◇	◇		1	◇1	◇	1	1	◇	1	◇1	◇		1	◇	1	◇1	◇
London Liverpool Street	d																								
London Kings Cross	d		07 44			08 14					08 44				09 44								10 44		
Ipswich	d			08 03													10 00								
Stansted Airport	d				08 21							09 21						10 27						11 27	
Cambridge	d		08 38		09 01	09 07	09 12				09 35	10 01		10 12	10 35			11 01			11 12		11 35	12 01	
Waterbeach	d		08 44								09 41				10 41								11 41		
Ely 6	a		08 54	08 58	09 14	09 24	09 27				09 51	10 14		10 26	10 51		10 58	11 14			11 26		11 51	12 14	
	d	08 48	08 55	08 58	09 15		09 27	09 45	09 46		09 51	10 15	10 17	10 28	10 51	10 53	10 58	11 15	11 21		11 28	11 48	11 51	12 15	12 16
Littleport	d		09 02								09 58				10 58								11 58		
Downham Market	d		09 11								10 07				11 07								12 07		
Watlington	d		09 17								10 13				11 13								12 13		
Kings Lynn	a		09 26								10 22				11 22								12 22		
Manea	d																								
March	d	09 07		09 15	09 32							10 32					11 15	11 32						12 32	
Whittlesea	d			09 27													11 26								
Peterborough 8	a	09 25		09 37	09 50				10 26			10 50				11 27	11 37	11 50				12 24		12 50	
Shippea Hill	d																								
Lakenheath	d																								
Brandon	d						09 43							10 44							11 44				
Thetford	d						09 51	10 06					10 38	10 53					11 43		11 53				12 38
Harling Road	d																								
Eccles Road	d																								
Attleborough	d						10 06							11 08							12 08				
Spooner Row	d						10x11																		
Wymondham	d						10 16							11 15							12 15				
Norwich	a						10 30	10 44					11 12	11 30					12 15		12 30				13 13

		LE	EM	FC	LE		XC	EM	LE	EM	FC	XC	EM	LE	EM		FC	LE	XC	EM	LE	FC	EM	FC	XC
		1	◇	1	1		◇1	◇	1	◇	1	◇1	◇	1	◇		1	1	◇1	◇	1	1	◇	1	◇1
London Liverpool Street	d																								
London Kings Cross	d			11 44							12 44						13 44							14 44	
Ipswich	d				11 58													13 58							
Stansted Airport	d						12 27					13 27							14 27						15 27
Cambridge	d	12 12		12 35			13 01		13 12		13 35	14 01		14 12			14 35		15 01		15 12	15 23		15 35	16 01
Waterbeach	d			12 41							13 41						14 41					15 29		15 41	
Ely 6	a	12 26		12 51	12 58		13 14		13 26		13 51	14 14		14 26			14 51	14 58	15 14		15 26	15 40		15 51	16 14
	d	12 28	12 48	12 51	12 58		13 15	13 17	13 28	13 48	13 51	14 15	14 16	14 28	14 48		14 51	14 58	15 15	15 16	15 28		15 47	15 51	16 15
Littleport	d			12 58							13 58						14 58							15 58	
Downham Market	d			13 07							14 07						15 07							16 07	
Watlington	d			13 13							14 13						15 13							16 13	
Kings Lynn	a			13 22							14 22						15 22							16 22	
Manea	d																								
March	d				13 15		13 32					14 32						15 15	15 32						16 32
Whittlesea	d				13 26													15 26							
Peterborough 8	a		13 25		13 37		13 50			14 25		14 50			15 27			15 37	15 50				16 25		16 50
Shippea Hill	d																								
Lakenheath	d																								
Brandon	d	12 44							13 44					14 44							15 44				
Thetford	d	12 53						13 39	13 53				14 38	14 53						15 38	15 53				
Harling Road	d																								
Eccles Road	d																								
Attleborough	d	13 08							14 08					15 08							16 08				
Spooner Row	d																								
Wymondham	d	13 15							14 15					15 15							16 15				
Norwich	a	13 30						14 13	14 30				15 11	15 30						16 13	16 30				

Table 17

Mondays to Fridays

9 December to 27 December

London and Cambridge - Ely, Kings Lynn, Peterborough and Norwich

Network Diagram - see first Page of Table 13

			EM ◇	LE 1	FC 1	EM ◇	FC 1	LE 1	XC ◇1	EM ◇	LE 1		LE ◇1	EM ◇	FC 1	XC ◇1	EM ◇	FC 1	LE 1	LE ◇1 A	LE 1		EM ◇	LE 1	FC 1
London Liverpool Street	d												15 58							17 07					
London Kings Cross	d						15 44								16 44			17 14							17 44
Ipswich	d							16 00																17 49	
Stansted Airport	d								16 27							17 27									
Cambridge	d			16 12	16 19		16 35		17 01		17 12		17 22		17 40	18 01		18 06	18 12	18 17	18 23				18 39
Waterbeach	d				16 25		16 41						17 28		17 46					18 23	18 29				18 45
Ely 6	a			16 26	16 35		16 51	16 58	17 14		17 26		17 39		17 56	18 14		18 21	18 26	18 33	18 40			18 52	18 55
	d		16 16	16 28	16 35	16 47	16 52	16 58	17 15	17 16	17 28			17 52	17 56	18 15	18 18		18 28	18 33			18 52	18 58	18 55
Littleport	d						16 59								18 03					18 40				→	19 02
Downham Market	d				16a51		17 09								18 13					18 50					19 11
Watlington	d						17 15								18 18					18 56					19 17
Kings Lynn	a						17 24								18 28					19 08					19 26
Manea	d															18x26									
March	d							17 15	17 32							18 34							19 08		
Whittlesea	d							17 26																	
Peterborough 8	a					17 22		17 37	17 51					18 25		18 51							19 26		
Shippea Hill	d																								
Lakenheath	d																								
Brandon	d			16 44							17 44								18 44						
Thetford	d		16 37	16 53						17 38	17 53						18 40		18 53						
Harling Road	d																								
Eccles Road	d																								
Attleborough	d			17 08							18 08								19 08						
Spooner Row	d																								
Wymondham	d			17 15							18 15								19 15						
Norwich	a		17 13	17 29						18 13	18 29						19 15		19 29						

		LE 1	XC ◇1	FC 1	EM ◇	LE ◇1	LE 1		EM ◇	FC 1	XC ◇1	EM ◇	FC 1	LE ◇1	LE 1	FC 1	LE 1		XC ◇1	FC 1	LE 1	FC 1	EM ◇	FC 1	FC 1
London Liverpool Street	d					18 07								19 07											
London Kings Cross	d			18 14						18 44			19 14			19 44				20 14		20 44		21 14	21 44
Ipswich	d																20 00								
Stansted Airport	d		18 21								19 21								20 21						
Cambridge	d		19 01	19 09		19 19	19 25			19 39	20 01		20 07	20 14	20 20	20 40			21 01	21 10	21 15	21 40		22 08	22 38
Waterbeach	d	←				19 25				19 45				20 20		20 46				21 16		21 46		22 14	22 44
Ely 6	a	18 52	19 14	19 24		19 35	19 39			19 55	20 14		20 22	20 30	20 34	20 56	20 59		21 14	21 26	21 30	21 56		22 24	22 55
	d	18 58	19 15	19 24	19 28	19 35	19 40		19 52	19 56	20 15	20 16		20 30	20 37	20 56	20 59		21 15	21 26	21 30	21 56	22 16	22 24	
Littleport	d					19 42				20 03				20 37		21 03				21 33		22 03		22 31	
Downham Market	d			19 39		19 52				20 12				20 47		21 12				21 42		22 12		22 40	
Watlington	d					19 58				20 18				20 53		21 18				21 48		22 18		22 46	
Kings Lynn	a			19 52		20 10				20 26				21 05		21 27				21 57		22 27		22 55	
Manea	d																								
March	d	19 15	19 32								20 32						21 15		21 32						
Whittlesea	d	19 26															21 26								
Peterborough 8	a	19 37	19 50						20 25		20 50						21 37		21 50						
Shippea Hill	d																								
Lakenheath	d																								
Brandon	d						19 56								20 53						21 46				
Thetford	d				19 51		20 04					20 36			21 01						21 55		22 37		
Harling Road	d																								
Eccles Road	d																								
Attleborough	d						20 19								21 16						22 10		22 51		
Spooner Row	d																								
Wymondham	d						20 27								21 24						22 17		22 58		
Norwich	a				20 22		20 41					21 13			21 38						22 32		23 18		

		LE 1	FC 1		FC 1	FC 1
London Liverpool Street	d					
London Kings Cross	d		22 14		22 44	23 14
Ipswich	d					
Stansted Airport	d					
Cambridge	d	22 55	23 08		23 38	00 10
Waterbeach	d		23 14		23 44	00 16
Ely 6	a	23 09	23 24		23 55	00 26
	d	23 10	23 24			00 26
Littleport	d		23 31			00 33
Downham Market	d		23 40			00 42
Watlington	d		23 46			00 48
Kings Lynn	a		23 55			00 57
Manea	d					
March	d					
Whittlesea	d					
Peterborough 8	a					
Shippea Hill	d					
Lakenheath	d					
Brandon	d	23 26				
Thetford	d	23 34				
Harling Road	d					
Eccles Road	d					
Attleborough	d	23 49				
Spooner Row	d					
Wymondham	d	23 57				
Norwich	a	00 11				

A The Fenman

Table 17

Mondays to Fridays

30 December to 16 May

London and Cambridge - Ely, Kings Lynn, Peterborough and Norwich

Network Diagram - see first Page of Table 13

		FC	FC	FC	XC	XC	LE	FC	EM	LE		EM	FC	XC	LE	LE	EM	FC	XC	EM		FC	LE	EM	FC
		MO 1 A	MX 1	MO 1 B	◇1	◇1	1	1	◇	1		◇	1	◇1	1	1	◇	1	◇1	◇		1	1	◇	1
London Liverpool Street	d																								
London Kings Cross	d												05 45					06 45				07 15			07 44
Ipswich	d									06 00															
Stansted Airport	d					05 16								06 12					07 21						
Cambridge	d	00 08	00 10	00 28	05 15	05 55	06 05	06 17					06 52	06 55	07 04	07 23		07 33	08 01			08 06	08 12		08 38
Waterbeach	d	00 15	00 16	00 34				06 23					06 58					07 39				08 12			08 44
Ely 6	a	00 24	00 26	00 44	05 29	06 09	06 19	06 33		06 56			07 08	07 10	07 18	07 39		07 49	08 14			08 22	08 26		08 54
	d	00 25	00 26	00 44	05 30	06 10	06 20	06 33	06 51	06 56		07 05	07 08	07 12	07 19		07 45	07 50	08 15	08 15		08 22	08 28	08 48	08 55
Littleport	d	00 32	00 33	00 51				06 42					07 15					07 58				08 29			09 02
Downham Market	d	00 41	00 42	01 00				06 53					07 25					08 07				08 38			09 11
Watlington	d	00 46	00 48	01 06				06 59					07 32					08 12				08 44			09 17
Kings Lynn	a	00 56	00 57	01 14				07 08					07 41					08 22				08 52			09 26
Manea	d					06x20				07x07															
March	d				05 46	06 28			07 07	07 15				07 29			08 01		08 32					09 07	
Whittlesea	d				05 58	06 39				07 26				07 40			08 13								
Peterborough 8	a				06 08	06 50			07 25	07 37				07 50			08 24		08 50					09 25	
Shippea Hill	d														07x28										
Lakenheath	d																								
Brandon	d						06 36					07 20			07 38								08 44		
Thetford	d						06 44					07 29			07 47					08 37			08 53		
Harling Road	d						06 53								07 55										
Eccles Road	d						06 58								08 00										
Attleborough	d						07 04					07 43			08 06					08 51			09 08		
Spooner Row	d														08x11										
Wymondham	d						07 11					07 50			08 16					08 58			09 15		
Norwich	a						07 27					08 13			08 30					09 13			09 30		

		LE	XC	FC	LE	EM		EM	FC	XC	EM	LE	FC	EM	LE	XC		EM	LE	EM	FC	XC	EM	LE	EM
		1	◇1	1	1	◇		◇	1	◇1	◇	1	1	◇	1	◇1		◇	1	◇	1	◇1	◇	1	◇
London Liverpool Street	d																								
London Kings Cross	d			08 14					08 44				09 44								10 44				
Ipswich	d	08 03													10 00										
Stansted Airport	d		08 21							09 21						10 27						11 27			
Cambridge	d		09 01	09 07	09 12				09 35	10 01		10 12	10 35			11 01			11 12		11 35	12 01		12 12	
Waterbeach	d								09 41				10 41								11 41				
Ely 6	a	08 58	09 14	09 24	09 27				09 51	10 14		10 26	10 51		10 58	11 14			11 26		11 51	12 14		12 26	
	d	08 58	09 15		09 27	09 45		09 46	09 51	10 15	10 17	10 28	10 51	10 53	10 58	11 15		11 21	11 28	11 48	11 51	12 15	12 16	12 28	12 48
Littleport	d								09 58				10 58								11 58				
Downham Market	d								10 07				11 07								12 07				
Watlington	d								10 13				11 13								12 13				
Kings Lynn	a								10 22				11 22								12 22				
Manea	d	09x09													11x09										
March	d	09 17	09 32							10 32					11 17	11 32						12 32			
Whittlesea	d	09 28													11 28										
Peterborough 8	a	09 39	09 50					10 26		10 50				11 27	11 39	11 50				12 24		12 50			13 25
Shippea Hill	d																								
Lakenheath	d																								
Brandon	d				09 43							10 44							11 44					12 44	
Thetford	d				09 51	10 06					10 38	10 53						11 43	11 53				12 38	12 53	
Harling Road	d																								
Eccles Road	d																								
Attleborough	d				10 06							11 08							12 08					13 08	
Spooner Row	d				10x11																				
Wymondham	d				10 16							11 15							12 15					13 15	
Norwich	a				10 30	10 44					11 12	11 30						12 15	12 30				13 13	13 30	

		FC		LE	XC	EM	LE	EM	FC	XC	EM	LE		EM	FC	LE	XC	EM	LE	FC	EM	FC		XC	EM
		1		1	◇1	◇	1	◇	1	◇1	◇	1		◇	1	1	◇1	◇	1	1	◇	1		◇1	◇
London Liverpool Street	d																								
London Kings Cross	d	11 44							12 44						13 44							14 44			
Ipswich	d			11 58												13 58									
Stansted Airport	d				12 27					13 27							14 27							15 27	
Cambridge	d	12 35			13 01		13 12		13 35	14 01		14 12			14 35		15 01		15 12	15 23		15 35		16 01	
Waterbeach	d	12 41							13 41						14 41					15 29		15 41			
Ely 6	a	12 51		12 58	13 14		13 26		13 51	14 14		14 26			14 51	14 58	15 14		15 26	15 40		15 51		16 14	
	d	12 51		12 58	13 15	13 17	13 28	13 48	13 51	14 15	14 16	14 28		14 48	14 51	14 58	15 15	15 16	15 28		15 47	15 51		16 15	16 16
Littleport	d	12 58							13 58						14 58							15 58			
Downham Market	d	13 07							14 07						15 07							16 07			
Watlington	d	13 13							14 13						15 13							16 13			
Kings Lynn	a	13 22							14 22						15 22							16 22			
Manea	d			13x09												15x09									
March	d			13 17	13 32					14 32						15 17	15 32							16 32	
Whittlesea	d			13 28												15 28									
Peterborough 8	a			13 39	13 50			14 25		14 50				15 27		15 39	15 50				16 25			16 50	
Shippea Hill	d																								
Lakenheath	d																								
Brandon	d						13 44					14 44							15 44						
Thetford	d					13 39	13 53				14 38	14 53						15 38	15 53						16 37
Harling Road	d																								
Eccles Road	d																								
Attleborough	d						14 08					15 08							16 08						
Spooner Row	d																								
Wymondham	d						14 15					15 15							16 15						
Norwich	a					14 13	14 30				15 11	15 30						16 13	16 30						17 13

A from 31 March

B from 6 January until 24 March

Table 17

Mondays to Fridays

30 December to 16 May

London and Cambridge - Ely, Kings Lynn, Peterborough and Norwich

Network Diagram - see first Page of Table 13

		LE 1	FC 1	EM ◇	FC 1	LE 1	XC ◇1	EM ◇		LE 1	LE ◇1	EM ◇	FC 1	XC ◇1	EM ◇	FC 1	LE 1	LE ◇1 A		LE 1	EM ◇	LE 1	FC 1	LE 1	XC ◇1
London Liverpool Street	d										15 58							17 07							
London Kings Cross	d				15 44								16 44			17 14							17 44		
Ipswich	d					16 00																17 49			
Stansted Airport	d						16 27							17 27											18 21
Cambridge	d	16 12	16 19		16 35		17 01			17 12	17 22		17 40	18 01		18 06	18 12	18 17		18 23			18 39		19 01
Waterbeach	d		16 25		16 41						17 28		17 46					18 23		18 29			18 45	←	
Ely 6	a	16 26	16 35		16 51	16 58	17 14			17 26	17 39		17 56	18 14		18 21	18 26	18 33		18 40		18 52	18 55	18 52	19 14
	d	16 28	16 35	16 47	16 52	16 58	17 15	17 16		17 28		17 52	17 56	18 15	18 18		18 28	18 33			18 52	18 58	18 55	18 58	19 15
Littleport	d				16 59								18 03					18 40				→	19 02		
Downham Market	d		16a51		17 09								18 13					18 50					19 11		
Watlington	d				17 15								18 18					18 56					19 17		
Kings Lynn	a				17 24								18 28					19 08					19 26		
Manea	d					17x09								18x26										19x09	
March	d					17 17	17 32							18 34							19 08			19 17	19 32
Whittlesea	d					17 28																		19 28	
Peterborough 8	a			17 22		17 39	17 51					18 25		18 51							19 26			19 39	19 50
Shippea Hill	d																								
Lakenheath	d																								
Brandon	d	16 44								17 44							18 44								
Thetford	d	16 53						17 38		17 53					18 40		18 53								
Harling Road	d																								
Eccles Road	d																								
Attleborough	d	17 08								18 08							19 08								
Spooner Row	d																								
Wymondham	d	17 15								18 15							19 15								
Norwich	a	17 29						18 13		18 29					19 15		19 29								

		FC 1	EM ◇	LE ◇1		LE 1	EM ◇	FC 1	XC ◇1	EM ◇	FC 1	LE ◇1	LE 1	FC 1		LE 1	XC ◇1	FC 1	LE 1	FC 1	EM ◇	FC 1	FC 1	LE 1	
London Liverpool Street	d			18 07								19 07													
London Kings Cross	d	18 14						18 44			19 14			19 44				20 14		20 44		21 14	21 44		
Ipswich	d															20 00									
Stansted Airport	d								19 21								20 21								
Cambridge	d	19 09		19 19		19 25		19 39	20 01		20 07	20 14	20 20	20 40			21 01	21 10	21 15	21 40		22 08	22 38	22 55	
Waterbeach	d			19 25				19 45				20 20		20 46				21 16		21 46		22 14	22 44		
Ely 6	a	19 24		19 35		19 39		19 55	20 14		20 22	20 30	20 34	20 56		20 59	21 14	21 26	21 30	21 56		22 24	22 55	23 09	
	d	19 24	19 28	19 35		19 40	19 52	19 56	20 15	20 16		20 30	20 37	20 56		20 59	21 15	21 26	21 30	21 56	22 16	22 24		23 10	
Littleport	d			19 42				20 03				20 37		21 03				21 33		22 03		22 31			
Downham Market	d	19 39		19 52				20 12				20 47		21 12				21 42		22 12		22 40			
Watlington	d			19 58				20 18				20 53		21 18				21 48		22 18		22 46			
Kings Lynn	a	19 52		20 10				20 26				21 05		21 27				21 57		22 27		22 55			
Manea	d															21x09									
March	d								20 32							21 17	21 32								
Whittlesea	d															21 28									
Peterborough 8	a						20 25		20 50							21 39	21 50								
Shippea Hill	d																								
Lakenheath	d																								
Brandon	d					19 56							20 53						21 46					23 26	
Thetford	d		19 51			20 04				20 36			21 01						21 55		22 37			23 34	
Harling Road	d																								
Eccles Road	d																								
Attleborough	d					20 19							21 16						22 10		22 51			23 49	
Spooner Row	d																								
Wymondham	d					20 27							21 24						22 17		22 58			23 57	
Norwich	a		20 22			20 41				21 13			21 38						22 32		23 18			00 11	

		FC 1	FC 1	FC 1
London Liverpool Street	d			
London Kings Cross	d	22 14	22 44	23 14
Ipswich	d			
Stansted Airport	d			
Cambridge	d	23 08	23 38	00 10
Waterbeach	d	23 14	23 44	00 16
Ely 6	a	23 24	23 55	00 26
	d	23 24		00 26
Littleport	d	23 31		00 33
Downham Market	d	23 40		00 42
Watlington	d	23 46		00 48
Kings Lynn	a	23 55		00 57
Manea	d			
March	d			
Whittlesea	d			
Peterborough 8	a			
Shippea Hill	d			
Lakenheath	d			
Brandon	d			
Thetford	d			
Harling Road	d			
Eccles Road	d			
Attleborough	d			
Spooner Row	d			
Wymondham	d			
Norwich	a			

A The Fenman

Table 17

Saturdays

14 December to 21 December

London and Cambridge - Ely, Kings Lynn, Peterborough and Norwich

Network Diagram - see first Page of Table 13

		FC	XC	XC	LE	EM	FC	LE	EM	XC		LE	EM	FC	EM	XC	LE	EM	FC	LE		XC	LE	EM	EM
		1	◇1	◇1	1	◇	1	1	◇	◇1		1	◇	1	◇	◇1	1	◇	1	1		◇1	1	◇	◇
London Liverpool Street	d																								
London Kings Cross	d													06 44					07 44						
Ipswich	d							06 00												08 00					
Stansted Airport	d			05 25						06 27						07 27						08 27			
Cambridge	d	00 10	05 15	05 55	06 07		06 35			06 57		07 00		07 35		08 01	08 12		08 35			09 01	09 12		
Waterbeach	d	00 16					06 41							07 41					08 41						
Ely 6	a	00 26	05 29	06 09	06 21		06 51	06 56		07 11		07 15		07 51		08 14	08 26		08 51	08 58		09 14	09 26		
	d	00 26	05 30	06 10	06 22	06 48	06 51	06 56	07 06	07 12		07 16	07 48	07 51	08 14	08 15	08 28	08 48	08 51	08 58		09 15	09 28	09 45	09 46
Littleport	d	00 33					06 58							07 58					08 58						
Downham Market	d	00 42					07 07							08 07					09 07						
Watlington	d	00 48					07 13							08 13					09 13						
Kings Lynn	a	00 57					07 22							08 22					09 22						
Manea	d			06x20																					
March	d		05 46	06 28		07 07		07 13		07 29			08 04			08 32		09 05		09 15		09 32			
Whittlesea	d		05 58	06 39				07 24		07 40			08 14							09 26					
Peterborough 8	a		06 08	06 50		07 25		07 35		07 50			08 27			08 50		09 23		09 37		09 50			10 21
Shippea Hill	d											07x25													
Lakenheath	d																								
Brandon	d				06 38				07 22			07 35					08 44						09 44		
Thetford	d				06 47				07 30			07 43			08 36		08 53						09 53	10 07	
Harling Road	d				06 55							07 52													
Eccles Road	d				07 00							07 57													
Attleborough	d				07 06				07 44			08 03			08 50		09 08						10 08		
Spooner Row	d											08x08													
Wymondham	d				07 14				07 51			08 13			08 57		09 15						10 15		
Norwich	a				07 28				08 13			08 30			09 15		09 30						10 30	10 43	

		FC	XC	EM	LE	EM		FC	LE	XC	EM	LE	EM	FC	XC	EM		LE	EM	FC	LE	XC	EM	LE	EM
		1	◇1	◇	1	◇		1	1	◇1	◇	1	◇	1	◇1	◇		1	◇	1	1	◇1	◇	1	◇
London Liverpool Street	d																								
London Kings Cross	d	08 44						09 44						10 44						11 44					
Ipswich	d								09 58												11 58				
Stansted Airport	d		09 27							10 27					11 27							12 27			
Cambridge	d	09 35	10 01		10 12			10 35		11 01		11 12		11 35	12 01			12 12		12 35		13 01		13 12	
Waterbeach	d	09 41						10 41						11 41						12 41					
Ely 6	a	09 51	10 14		10 26			10 51	10 58	11 14		11 26		11 51	12 14			12 26		12 51	12 58	13 14		13 26	
	d	09 51	10 15	10 21	10 28	10 48		10 51	10 58	11 15	11 16	11 28	11 48	11 51	12 15	12 16		12 28	12 48	12 51	12 58	13 15	13 16	13 28	13 48
Littleport	d	09 58						10 58						11 58						12 58					
Downham Market	d	10 07						11 07						12 07						13 07					
Watlington	d	10 13						11 13						12 13						13 13					
Kings Lynn	a	10 22						11 22						12 22						13 22					
Manea	d																								
March	d		10 32						11 15	11 32					12 32						13 15	13 32			
Whittlesea	d								11 26												13 26				
Peterborough 8	a		10 50			11 19			11 37	11 50			12 22		12 49				13 26		13 37	13 50			14 25
Shippea Hill	d																								
Lakenheath	d																								
Brandon	d				10 44							11 44						12 44						13 44	
Thetford	d			10 43	10 53						11 37	11 53				12 38		12 53					13 37	13 53	
Harling Road	d																								
Eccles Road	d																								
Attleborough	d				11 08							12 08						13 08						14 08	
Spooner Row	d																								
Wymondham	d				11 15							12 15						13 15						14 15	
Norwich	a			11 15	11 30						12 13	12 30				13 13		13 30					14 13	14 30	

		FC		XC	EM	LE	EM	FC	LE	XC	EM	LE		EM	FC	XC	EM	LE	EM	FC	LE	XC		EM	LE
		1		◇1	◇	1	◇	1	1	◇1	◇	1		◇	1	◇1	◇	1	◇	1	1	◇1		◇	1
London Liverpool Street	d																								
London Kings Cross	d	12 44						13 44							14 44					15 44					
Ipswich	d								13 58												15 58				
Stansted Airport	d			13 27						14 27						15 27						16 27			
Cambridge	d	13 35		14 01		14 12		14 35		15 01		15 12			15 35	16 01		16 12		16 35		17 01			17 12
Waterbeach	d	13 41						14 41							15 41					16 41					
Ely 6	a	13 51		14 14		14 26		14 51	14 58	15 14		15 26			15 51	16 14		16 26		16 51	16 58	17 14			17 26
	d	13 51		14 15	14 16	14 28	14 48	14 51	14 58	15 15	15 21	15 27		15 47	15 51	16 15	16 16	16 28	16 47	16 51	16 58	17 15		17 16	17 28
Littleport	d	13 58						14 58							15 58					16 58					
Downham Market	d	14 07						15 07							16 07					17 07					
Watlington	d	14 13						15 13							16 13					17 13					
Kings Lynn	a	14 22						15 22							16 22					17 22					
Manea	d																								
March	d			14 32					15 15	15 32						16 32					17 15	17 32			
Whittlesea	d								15 26												17 26				
Peterborough 8	a			14 49			15 23		15 37	15 50				16 25		16 50			17 23		17 37	17 51			
Shippea Hill	d																								
Lakenheath	d											15x40													
Brandon	d					14 44						15 46						16 44							17 44
Thetford	d				14 37	14 53					15 42	15 54					16 38	16 53						17 37	17 53
Harling Road	d																								
Eccles Road	d																								
Attleborough	d					15 08						16 09						17 08							18 08
Spooner Row	d																								
Wymondham	d					15 15						16 17						17 15							18 15
Norwich	a				15 13	15 30					16 15	16 31					17 13	17 30						18 13	18 30

Table 17

Saturdays

14 December to 21 December

London and Cambridge - Ely, Kings Lynn, Peterborough and Norwich

Network Diagram - see first Page of Table 13

		EM	FC	XC	EM	LE	EM	FC		LE	XC	FC	EM	LE	EM	FC	XC	EM		LE	FC	LE	LE	FC	EM
		◇	1	◇1	◇	1	◇	1		1	◇1	1	◇	1	◇	1	◇1	◇		1	1	1	1	1	◇
London Liverpool Street	d																								
London Kings Cross	d		16 44					17 44				18 14				18 44					19 44			20 44	
Ipswich	d									17 58												19 58			
Stansted Airport	d			17 27							18 27						19 27								
Cambridge	d		17 35	18 01		18 12		18 35			19 01	19 04		19 12		19 35	20 01			20 12	20 35		21 12	21 40	
Waterbeach	d		17 41					18 41								19 41					20 41			21 46	
Ely 6	a		17 51	18 14		18 26		18 51		18 58	19 14	19 18		19 26		19 51	20 14			20 26	20 51	20 58	21 26	21 56	
	d	17 47	17 51	18 15	18 16	18 28	18 48	18 51		18 58	19 15	19 19	19 22	19 28	19 48	19 51	20 15	20 16		20 28	20 51	20 58	21 28	21 56	22 17
Littleport	d		17 58					18 58								19 58					20 58			22 03	
Downham Market	d		18 07					19 07				19 35				20 07					21 07			22 12	
Watlington	d		18 13					19 13								20 13					21 13			22 18	
Kings Lynn	a		18 22					19 22				19 52				20 22					21 22			22 27	
Manea	d			18x26																					
March	d			18 34			19 05			19 15	19 32						20 32					21 15			
Whittlesea	d									19 26												21 26			
Peterborough 8	a	18 23		18 52			19 24			19 37	19 50				20 23		20 50					21 37			
Shippea Hill	d																								
Lakenheath	d																								
Brandon	d					18 44								19 44						20 44			21 44		
Thetford	d				18 37	18 53							19 43	19 53				20 38		20 53			21 53		22 38
Harling Road	d																								
Eccles Road	d																								
Attleborough	d					19 08								20 08						21 08			22 08		22 52
Spooner Row	d																								
Wymondham	d					19 15								20 15						21 15			22 15		22 59
Norwich	a				19 13	19 30							20 16	20 30				21 13		21 30			22 32		23 19

		LE	FC	FC
		1	1	1
London Liverpool Street	d			
London Kings Cross	d		22 14	23 14
Ipswich	d			
Stansted Airport	d			
Cambridge	d	22 30	23 10	00 10
Waterbeach	d		23 16	00 16
Ely 6	a	22 44	23 26	00 26
	d	22 45	23 26	00 26
Littleport	d		23 33	00 33
Downham Market	d		23 42	00 42
Watlington	d		23 48	00 48
Kings Lynn	a		23 57	00 57
Manea	d			
March	d			
Whittlesea	d			
Peterborough 8	a			
Shippea Hill	d			
Lakenheath	d			
Brandon	d	23 01		
Thetford	d	23 09		
Harling Road	d			
Eccles Road	d			
Attleborough	d	23 24		
Spooner Row	d			
Wymondham	d	23 32		
Norwich	a	23 46		

Saturdays

28 December to 17 May

		FC	XC	XC	LE	EM	FC	LE	EM	XC		LE	EM	FC	EM	XC	LE	EM	FC	LE		XC	LE	EM	EM
		1	◇1	◇1	1	◇	1	1	◇	◇1		1	◇	1	◇	◇1	1	◇	1	1		◇1	1	◇	◇
London Liverpool Street	d																								
London Kings Cross	d													06 44					07 44						
Ipswich	d							06 00												08 00					
Stansted Airport	d			05 25						06 27						07 27						08 27			
Cambridge	d	00 10	05 15	05 55	06 07		06 35			06 57		07 00		07 35		08 01	08 12		08 35			09 01	09 12		
Waterbeach	d	00 16					06 41							07 41					08 41						
Ely 6	a	00 26	05 29	06 09	06 21		06 51	06 56		07 11		07 15		07 51		08 14	08 26		08 51	08 58		09 14	09 26		
	d	00 26	05 30	06 10	06 22	06 48	06 51	06 56	07 06	07 12		07 16	07 48	07 51	08 14	08 15	08 28	08 48	08 51	08 58		09 15	09 28	09 45	09 46
Littleport	d	00 33					06 58							07 58					08 58						
Downham Market	d	00 42					07 07							08 07					09 07						
Watlington	d	00 48					07 13							08 13					09 13						
Kings Lynn	a	00 57					07 22							08 22					09 22						
Manea	d			06x20				07x07												09x09					
March	d		05 46	06 28		07 07		07 15		07 29			08 04			08 32		09 05		09 17		09 32			
Whittlesea	d		05 58	06 39				07 26		07 40			08 14							09 28					
Peterborough 8	a		06 08	06 50		07 25		07 37		07 50			08 27			08 50		09 23		09 39		09 50			10 21
Shippea Hill	d											07x25													
Lakenheath	d																								
Brandon	d				06 38				07 22			07 35					08 44						09 44		
Thetford	d				06 47				07 30			07 43			08 36		08 53						09 53	10 07	
Harling Road	d				06 55							07 52													
Eccles Road	d				07 00							07 57													
Attleborough	d				07 06				07 44			08 03			08 50		09 08						10 08		
Spooner Row	d											08x08													
Wymondham	d				07 14				07 51			08 13			08 57		09 15						10 15		
Norwich	a				07 28				08 13			08 30			09 15		09 30						10 30	10 43	

Table 17

Saturdays

28 December to 17 May

London and Cambridge - Ely, Kings Lynn, Peterborough and Norwich

Network Diagram - see first Page of Table 13

		FC 1	XC ◇1	EM ◇	LE 1	EM ◇		FC 1	LE 1	XC ◇1	EM ◇	LE 1	EM ◇	FC 1	XC ◇1	EM ◇		LE 1	EM ◇	FC 1	LE 1	XC ◇1	EM ◇	LE 1	EM ◇
London Liverpool Street	d																								
London Kings Cross	d	08 44						09 44						10 44						11 44					
Ipswich	d								09 58												11 58				
Stansted Airport	d		09 27							10 27					11 27							12 27			
Cambridge	d	09 35	10 01		10 12			10 35		11 01		11 12		11 35	12 01			12 12		12 35		13 01		13 12	
Waterbeach	d	09 41						10 41						11 41						12 41					
Ely 6	a	09 51	10 14		10 26			10 51	10 58	11 14		11 26		11 51	12 14			12 26		12 51	12 58	13 14		13 26	
	d	09 51	10 15	10 21	10 28	10 48		10 51	10 58	11 15	11 16	11 28	11 48	11 51	12 15	12 16		12 28	12 48	12 51	12 58	13 15	13 16	13 28	13 48
Littleport	d	09 58						10 58						11 58						12 58					
Downham Market	d	10 07						11 07						12 07						13 07					
Watlington	d	10 13						11 13						12 13						13 13					
Kings Lynn	a	10 22						11 22						12 22						13 22					
Manea	d								11x09												13x09				
March	d		10 32						11 17	11 32					12 32						13 17	13 32			
Whittlesea	d								11 28												13 28				
Peterborough 8	a		10 50			11 19			11 39	11 50			12 23		12 49				13 26		13 39	13 50			14 25
Shippea Hill	d																								
Lakenheath	d																								
Brandon	d				10 44							11 44						12 44						13 44	
Thetford	d			10 43	10 53						11 37	11 53				12 38		12 53					13 37	13 53	
Harling Road	d																								
Eccles Road	d																								
Attleborough	d				11 08							12 08						13 08						14 08	
Spooner Row	d																								
Wymondham	d				11 15							12 15						13 15						14 15	
Norwich	a			11 15	11 30						12 13	12 30				13 13		13 30					14 13	14 30	

		FC 1		XC ◇1	EM ◇	LE 1	EM ◇	FC 1	LE 1	XC ◇1	EM ◇	LE 1		EM ◇	FC 1	XC ◇1	EM ◇	LE 1	EM ◇	FC 1	LE 1	XC ◇1		EM ◇	LE 1
London Liverpool Street	d																								
London Kings Cross	d	12 44						13 44							14 44					15 44					
Ipswich	d								13 58												15 58				
Stansted Airport	d			13 27						14 27						15 27						16 27			
Cambridge	d	13 35		14 01		14 12		14 35		15 01		15 12			15 35	16 01		16 12		16 35		17 01			17 12
Waterbeach	d	13 41						14 41							15 41					16 41					
Ely 6	a	13 51		14 14		14 26		14 51	14 58	15 14		15 26			15 51	16 14		16 26		16 51	16 58	17 14			17 26
	d	13 51		14 15	14 16	14 28	14 48	14 51	14 58	15 15	15 21	15 27		15 47	15 51	16 15	16 16	16 28	16 47	16 51	16 58	17 15		17 16	17 28
Littleport	d	13 58						14 58							15 58					16 58					
Downham Market	d	14 07						15 07							16 07					17 07					
Watlington	d	14 13						15 13							16 13					17 13					
Kings Lynn	a	14 22						15 22							16 22					17 22					
Manea	d								15x09												17x09				
March	d			14 32					15 17	15 32						16 32					17 17	17 32			
Whittlesea	d								15 28												17 28				
Peterborough 8	a			14 49			15 23		15 39	15 50				16 25		16 50			17 23		17 39	17 51			
Shippea Hill	d																								
Lakenheath	d											15x40													
Brandon	d					14 44						15 46						16 44							17 44
Thetford	d				14 37	14 53					15 42	15 54					16 38	16 53						17 37	17 53
Harling Road	d																								
Eccles Road	d																								
Attleborough	d					15 08						16 09						17 08							18 08
Spooner Row	d																								
Wymondham	d					15 15						16 17						17 15							18 15
Norwich	a				15 13	15 30					16 15	16 31					17 13	17 30						18 13	18 30

		EM ◇	FC 1	XC ◇1	EM ◇	LE 1	EM ◇	FC 1		LE 1	XC ◇1	FC 1	EM ◇	LE 1	EM ◇	FC 1	XC ◇1	EM ◇		LE 1	FC 1	LE 1	LE 1	FC 1	EM ◇
London Liverpool Street	d																								
London Kings Cross	d		16 44					17 44				18 14				18 44					19 44			20 44	
Ipswich	d									17 58												19 58			
Stansted Airport	d			17 27							18 27						19 27								
Cambridge	d		17 35	18 01		18 12		18 35			19 01	19 04		19 12		19 35	20 01			20 12	20 35		21 12	21 40	
Waterbeach	d		17 41					18 41								19 41					20 41			21 46	
Ely 6	a		17 51	18 14		18 26		18 51		18 58	19 14	19 18		19 26		19 51	20 14			20 26	20 51	20 58	21 26	21 56	
	d	17 47	17 51	18 15	18 16	18 28	18 48	18 51		18 58	19 15	19 19	19 22	19 28	19 48	19 51	20 15	20 16		20 28	20 51	20 58	21 28	21 56	22 17
Littleport	d		17 58					18 58								19 58					20 58			22 03	
Downham Market	d		18 07					19 07				19 35				20 07					21 07			22 12	
Watlington	d		18 13					19 13								20 13					21 13			22 18	
Kings Lynn	a		18 22					19 22				19 52				20 22					21 22			22 27	
Manea	d			18x26						19x09												21x09			
March	d			18 34			19 05			19 17	19 32						20 32					21 17			
Whittlesea	d									19 28												21 28			
Peterborough 8	a	18 23		18 52			19 24			19 39	19 50				20 23		20 50					21 39			
Shippea Hill	d																								
Lakenheath	d																								
Brandon	d					18 44								19 44						20 44			21 44		
Thetford	d				18 37	18 53							19 43	19 53				20 38		20 53			21 53		22 38
Harling Road	d																								
Eccles Road	d																								
Attleborough	d					19 08								20 08						21 08			22 08		22 52
Spooner Row	d																								
Wymondham	d					19 15								20 15						21 15			22 15		22 59
Norwich	a				19 13	19 30							20 16	20 30				21 13		21 30			22 32		23 19

Table 17

Saturdays

28 December to 17 May

London and Cambridge - Ely, Kings Lynn, Peterborough and Norwich

Network Diagram - see first Page of Table 13

Station		LE 1	FC 1	FC 1
London Liverpool Street	d			
London Kings Cross	d		22 14	23 14
Ipswich	d			
Stansted Airport	d			
Cambridge	d	22 30	23 10	00 10
Waterbeach	d		23 16	00 16
Ely 6	a	22 44	23 26	00 26
	d	22 45	23 26	00 26
Littleport	d		23 33	00 33
Downham Market	d		23 42	00 42
Watlington	d		23 48	00 48
Kings Lynn	a		23 57	00 57
Manea	d			
March	d			
Whittlesea	d			
Peterborough 8	a			
Shippea Hill	d			
Lakenheath	d			
Brandon	d	23 01		
Thetford	d	23 09		
Harling Road	d			
Eccles Road	d			
Attleborough	d	23 24		
Spooner Row	d			
Wymondham	d	23 32		
Norwich	a	23 46		

Sundays

8 December to 29 December

Station		FC 1	LE 1	FC 1	FC 1	LE 1	LE 1	XC ◇1	FC 1	EM ◇		LE 1	XC ◇1	FC 1	LE 1	LE 1	XC ◇1	FC 1	LE 1	XC ◇1		EM ◇	FC 1	EM ◇	LE 1
London Liverpool Street	d																								
London Kings Cross	d			07 53	09 15				10 15					11 15				12 15					13 15		
Ipswich	d					09 55									11 55										13 55
Stansted Airport	d							10 25					11 25				12 25			13 25					
Cambridge	d	00 10	08 48	09 06	10 06		10 48	11 00	11 06			11 52	12 00	12 06		12 52	13 00	13 06	13 52	14 00			14 06		
Waterbeach	d	00 16		09 12	10 12				11 12					12 12				13 12					14 12		
Ely 6	a	00 26	09 02	09 22	10 22	10 51	11 02	11 14	11 22			12 06	12 14	12 22	12 51	13 06	13 14	13 22	14 06	14 14			14 22		14 51
	d	00 26	09 03	09 22	10 22	10 52	11 03	11 15	11 22	11 39		12 07	12 15	12 22	12 52	13 07	13 15	13 22	14 07	14 15		14 20	14 22	14 45	14 52
Littleport	d	00 33		09 29	10 29				11 29					12 29				13 29					14 29		
Downham Market	d	00 42		09 38	10 38				11 38					12 38				13 38					14 38		
Watlington	d	00 48		09 44	10 44				11 44					12 44				13 44					14 44		
Kings Lynn	a	00 57		09 53	10 53				11 53					12 53				13 53					14 53		
Manea	d																								
March	d					11 09		11 32					12 32		13 09		13 32			14 32					15 09
Whittlesea	d					11 20									13 20										15 20
Peterborough 8	a					11 36		11 51		12 11			12 51		13 31		13 51			14 51				15 18	15 31
Shippea Hill	d																								
Lakenheath	d		09x17				11x17									13x20									
Brandon	d		09 22				11 22					12 23				13 25			14 23			14 35			
Thetford	d		09 31				11 31					12 31				13 34			14 31			14 44			
Harling Road	d																								
Eccles Road	d																								
Attleborough	d		09 46				11 46					12 46				13 49			14 46			14 58			
Spooner Row	d																								
Wymondham	d		09 53				11 53					12 54				13 56			14 54			15 05			
Norwich	a		10 13				12 13					13 13				14 13			15 13			15 22			

Station		LE 1	XC ◇1	FC 1	EM ◇	EM ◇		LE 1	XC ◇1	FC 1	EM ◇	LE 1	LE 1	XC ◇1	FC 1	EM ◇		EM ◇	LE 1	XC ◇1	FC 1	EM ◇	EM ◇	LE 1	LE 1
London Liverpool Street	d																								
London Kings Cross	d			14 15						15 15					16 15						17 15				
Ipswich	d											15 55												17 55	
Stansted Airport	d		14 25						15 25					16 25						17 25					
Cambridge	d	14 52	15 00	15 06				15 52	16 00	16 06			16 52	17 00	17 06				17 52	18 00	18 06				18 52
Waterbeach	d			15 12						16 12					17 12						18 12				
Ely 6	a	15 06	15 14	15 22				16 06	16 14	16 22		16 51	17 06	17 14	17 22				18 06	18 14	18 22			18 51	19 06
	d	15 07	15 15	15 22	15 34	15 46		16 07	16 15	16 22	16 34	16 52	17 07	17 15	17 22	17 36		17 48	18 07	18 15	18 22	18 36	18 48	18 52	19 07
Littleport	d			15 29						16 29					17 29						18 29				
Downham Market	d			15 38						16 38					17 38						18 38				
Watlington	d			15 44						16 44					17 44						18 44				
Kings Lynn	a			15 53						16 53					17 53						18 53				
Manea	d																								
March	d		15 32						16 32			17 09		17 32						18 32				19 09	
Whittlesea	d											17 20												19 20	
Peterborough 8	a		15 51			16 19			16 51			17 31		17 51				18 20		18 51			19 23	19 31	
Shippea Hill	d																								
Lakenheath	d							16x20																	
Brandon	d	15 23						16 25					17 23						18 23						19 23
Thetford	d	15 31			15 55			16 34			16 55		17 31			17 57			18 31			18 57			19 31
Harling Road	d																								
Eccles Road	d																								
Attleborough	d	15 46						16 49					17 46						18 46						19 46
Spooner Row	d																								
Wymondham	d	15 54						16 56					17 54						18 54						19 54
Norwich	a	16 13			16 35			17 13			17 26		18 13			18 30			19 10			19 29			20 13

Table 17

Sundays

8 December to 29 December

London and Cambridge - Ely, Kings Lynn, Peterborough and Norwich

Network Diagram - see first Page of Table 13

		XC ◇1		FC 1	EM ◇	EM ◇	LE 1	XC ◇1	FC 1	EM ◇	FC 1	EM ◇		LE 1	FC 1	EM ◇	FC 1	FC 1
London Liverpool Street	d																	
London Kings Cross	d			18 15					19 15		20 15				21 15		22 15	23 15
Ipswich	d																	
Stansted Airport	d	18 25						19 25										
Cambridge	d	19 00		19 06			19 52	20 00	20 07		21 06			21 52	22 06		23 06	00 08
Waterbeach	d			19 12					20 13		21 12				22 12		23 12	00 15
Ely 6	a	19 14		19 22			20 06	20 14	20 23		21 22			22 06	22 22		23 22	00 24
	d	19 15		19 22	19 26	19 48	20 07	20 15	20 23	20 36	21 22	21 44		22 07	22 22	22 29	23 22	00 25
Littleport	d			19 29					20 30		21 29				22 29		23 29	00 32
Downham Market	d			19 38					20 39		21 38				22 38		23 38	00 41
Watlington	d			19 44					20 45		21 44				22 44		23 44	00 46
Kings Lynn	a			19 53					20 53		21 53				22 53		23 53	00 56
Manea	d																	
March	d	19 32						20 32										
Whittlesea	d																	
Peterborough 8	a	19 51				20 23		20 51				22 16						
Shippea Hill	d																	
Lakenheath	d																	
Brandon	d						20 23							22 23				
Thetford	d				19 50		20 31			20 57				22 31		22 50		
Harling Road	d																	
Eccles Road	d																	
Attleborough	d						20 46			21 11				22 46		23 04		
Spooner Row	d																	
Wymondham	d						20 54			21 18				22 54		23 11		
Norwich	a				20 26		21 10			21 37				23 13		23 24		

Sundays

5 January to 23 March

		FC 1	LE 1	FC 1	FC 1	LE 1	LE 1	XC ◇1	FC 1	EM ◇		LE 1	XC ◇1	FC 1	LE 1	LE 1	XC ◇1	FC 1	LE 1	XC ◇1		EM ◇	FC 1	EM ◇	LE 1
London Liverpool Street	d																								
London Kings Cross	d			08 04	09 04				10 04					11 04				12 04					13 04		
Ipswich	d					09 55									11 55										13 55
Stansted Airport	d							10 25					11 25				12 25			13 25					
Cambridge	d	00 10	08 48	09 06	10 06		10 48	11 00	11 06			11 52	12 00	12 06		12 52	13 00	13 06	13 52	14 00			14 06		
Waterbeach	d	00 16		09 12	10 12				11 12					12 12				13 12					14 12		
Ely 6	a	00 26	09 02	09 22	10 22	10 51	11 02	11 14	11 22			12 06	12 14	12 22	12 51	13 06	13 14	13 22	14 06	14 14			14 22		14 51
	d	00 26	09 03	09 22	10 22	10 52	11 03	11 15	11 22	11 39		12 07	12 15	12 22	12 52	13 07	13 15	13 22	14 07	14 15		14 20	14 22	14 45	14 52
Littleport	d	00 33		09 29	10 29				11 29					12 29				13 29					14 29		
Downham Market	d	00 42		09 38	10 38				11 38					12 38				13 38					14 38		
Watlington	d	00 48		09 44	10 44				11 44					12 44				13 44					14 44		
Kings Lynn	a	00 57		09 53	10 53				11 53					12 53				13 53					14 53		
Manea	d																								
March	d					11 09		11 32					12 32		13 09		13 32			14 32					15 09
Whittlesea	d					11 20									13 20										15 20
Peterborough 8	a					11 36		11 51		12 11			12 51		13 31		13 51			14 51				15 18	15 31
Shippea Hill	d																								
Lakenheath	d		09x17				11x17									13x20									
Brandon	d		09 22				11 22					12 23				13 25			14 23			14 35			
Thetford	d		09 31				11 31					12 31				13 34			14 31			14 44			
Harling Road	d																								
Eccles Road	d																								
Attleborough	d		09 46				11 46					12 46				13 49			14 46			14 58			
Spooner Row	d																								
Wymondham	d		09 53				11 53					12 54				13 56			14 54			15 05			
Norwich	a		10 13				12 13					13 13				14 13			15 13			15 22			

		LE 1	XC ◇1	FC 1	EM ◇	EM ◇		LE 1	XC ◇1	FC 1	EM ◇	LE 1	LE 1	XC ◇1	FC 1	EM ◇		EM ◇	LE 1	XC ◇1	FC 1	EM ◇	EM ◇	LE 1	LE 1
London Liverpool Street	d																								
London Kings Cross	d			14 04						15 04					16 04						17 04				
Ipswich	d											15 55												17 55	
Stansted Airport	d		14 25						15 25					16 25						17 25					
Cambridge	d	14 52	15 00	15 06				15 52	16 00	16 06			16 52	17 00	17 06				17 52	18 00	18 06				18 52
Waterbeach	d			15 12						16 12					17 12						18 12				
Ely 6	a	15 06	15 14	15 22				16 06	16 14	16 22		16 51	17 06	17 14	17 22				18 06	18 14	18 22			18 51	19 06
	d	15 07	15 15	15 22	15 34	15 46		16 07	16 15	16 22	16 34	16 52	17 07	17 15	17 22	17 36		17 48	18 07	18 15	18 22	18 36	18 48	18 52	19 07
Littleport	d			15 29						16 29					17 29						18 29				
Downham Market	d			15 38						16 38					17 38						18 38				
Watlington	d			15 44						16 44					17 44						18 44				
Kings Lynn	a			15 53						16 53					17 53						18 53				
Manea	d																								
March	d		15 32						16 32			17 09		17 32						18 32				19 09	
Whittlesea	d											17 20												19 20	
Peterborough 8	a		15 51			16 19			16 51			17 31		17 51				18 20		18 51			19 23	19 31	
Shippea Hill	d																								
Lakenheath	d							16x20																	
Brandon	d	15 23						16 25					17 23						18 23						19 23
Thetford	d	15 31			15 55			16 34			16 55		17 31			17 57			18 31			18 57			19 31
Harling Road	d																								
Eccles Road	d																								
Attleborough	d	15 46						16 49					17 46						18 46						19 46
Spooner Row	d																								
Wymondham	d	15 54						16 56					17 54						18 54						19 54
Norwich	a	16 13			16 35			17 13			17 26		18 13			18 30			19 10			19 29			20 13

Table 17

London and Cambridge - Ely, Kings Lynn, Peterborough and Norwich

Network Diagram - see first Page of Table 13

Sundays

5 January to 23 March

		XC ◇1		FC 1	EM ◇	EM ◇	LE 1	XC ◇1	FC 1	EM ◇	FC 1	EM ◇		LE 1	FC 1	EM ◇	FC 1	FC 1
London Liverpool Street	d																	
London Kings Cross	d			18 04					19 04		20 04				21 04		22 15	23 15
Ipswich	d																	
Stansted Airport	d	18 25						19 25										
Cambridge	d	19 00		19 06			19 52	20 00	20 06		21 06			21 52	22 06		23 17	00 28
Waterbeach	d			19 12					20 12		21 12				22 12		23 23	00 34
Ely 6	a	19 14		19 22			20 06	20 14	20 22		21 22			22 06	22 22		23 33	00 44
	d	19 15		19 22	19 26	19 48	20 07	20 15	20 22	20 36	21 22	21 44		22 07	22 22	22 29	23 33	00 44
Littleport	d			19 29					20 29		21 29				22 29		23 40	00 51
Downham Market	d			19 38					20 38		21 38				22 38		23 49	01 00
Watlington	d			19 44					20 44		21 44				22 44		23 55	01 06
Kings Lynn	a			19 53					20 53		21 53				22 53		00 03	01 14
Manea	d																	
March	d	19 32						20 32										
Whittlesea	d																	
Peterborough 8	a	19 51				20 23		20 51				22 16						
Shippea Hill	d																	
Lakenheath	d																	
Brandon	d						20 23							22 23				
Thetford	d				19 50		20 31			20 57				22 31		22 50		
Harling Road	d																	
Eccles Road	d																	
Attleborough	d						20 46			21 11				22 46		23 04		
Spooner Row	d																	
Wymondham	d						20 54			21 18				22 54		23 11		
Norwich	a				20 26		21 10			21 37				23 13		23 24		

Sundays

30 March to 11 May

		FC 1	LE 1	FC 1	FC 1	LE 1	LE 1	XC ◇1	FC 1	EM ◇		LE 1	XC ◇1	FC 1	LE 1	LE 1	XC ◇1	FC 1	LE 1	XC ◇1		EM ◇	FC 1	EM ◇	LE 1
London Liverpool Street	d																								
London Kings Cross	d			07 53	09 15				10 15					11 15				12 15					13 15		
Ipswich	d					09 55									11 55										13 55
Stansted Airport	d							10 25					11 25				12 25			13 25					
Cambridge	d	00 10	08 48	09 06	10 06		10 48	11 00	11 06			11 52	12 00	12 06		12 52	13 00	13 06	13 52	14 00			14 06		
Waterbeach	d	00 16		09 12	10 12				11 12					12 12				13 12					14 12		
Ely 6	a	00 26	09 02	09 22	10 22	10 51	11 02	11 14	11 22			12 06	12 14	12 22	12 51	13 06	13 14	13 22	14 06	14 14			14 22		14 51
	d	00 26	09 03	09 22	10 22	10 52	11 03	11 15	11 22	11 39		12 07	12 15	12 22	12 52	13 07	13 15	13 22	14 07	14 15		14 20	14 22	14 45	14 52
Littleport	d	00 33		09 29	10 29				11 29					12 29				13 29					14 29		
Downham Market	d	00 42		09 38	10 38				11 38					12 38				13 38					14 38		
Watlington	d	00 48		09 44	10 44				11 44					12 44				13 44					14 44		
Kings Lynn	a	00 57		09 53	10 53				11 53					12 53				13 53					14 53		
Manea	d																								
March	d					11 09		11 32					12 32		13 09		13 32			14 32					15 09
Whittlesea	d					11 20									13 20										15 20
Peterborough 8	a					11 36		11 51		12 11			12 51		13 31		13 51			14 51				15 18	15 31
Shippea Hill	d																								
Lakenheath	d		09x17				11x17									13x20									
Brandon	d		09 22				11 22					12 23				13 25			14 23			14 35			
Thetford	d		09 31				11 31					12 31				13 34			14 31			14 44			
Harling Road	d																								
Eccles Road	d																								
Attleborough	d		09 46				11 46					12 46				13 49			14 46			14 58			
Spooner Row	d																								
Wymondham	d		09 53				11 53					12 54				13 56			14 54			15 05			
Norwich	a		10 13				12 13					13 13				14 13			15 13			15 22			

		LE 1	XC ◇1	FC 1	EM ◇	EM ◇		LE 1	XC ◇1	FC 1	EM ◇	LE 1	LE 1	XC ◇1	FC 1	EM ◇		EM ◇	LE 1	XC ◇1	FC 1	EM ◇	EM ◇	LE 1	LE 1
London Liverpool Street	d																								
London Kings Cross	d			14 15						15 15					16 15						17 15				
Ipswich	d											15 55												17 55	
Stansted Airport	d		14 25						15 25					16 25						17 25					
Cambridge	d	14 52	15 00	15 06				15 52	16 00	16 06			16 52	17 00	17 06				17 52	18 00	18 06				18 52
Waterbeach	d			15 12						16 12					17 12						18 12				
Ely 6	a	15 06	15 14	15 22				16 06	16 14	16 22		16 51	17 06	17 14	17 22				18 06	18 14	18 22			18 51	19 06
	d	15 07	15 15	15 22	15 34	15 46		16 07	16 15	16 22	16 34	16 52	17 07	17 15	17 22	17 36		17 48	18 07	18 15	18 22	18 36	18 48	18 52	19 07
Littleport	d			15 29						16 29					17 29						18 29				
Downham Market	d			15 38						16 38					17 38						18 38				
Watlington	d			15 44						16 44					17 44						18 44				
Kings Lynn	a			15 53						16 53					17 53						18 53				
Manea	d																								
March	d		15 32						16 32			17 09		17 32						18 32				19 09	
Whittlesea	d											17 20												19 20	
Peterborough 8	a		15 51			16 19			16 51			17 31		17 51				18 20		18 51			19 23	19 31	
Shippea Hill	d																								
Lakenheath	d							16x20																	
Brandon	d	15 23						16 25					17 23						18 23						19 23
Thetford	d	15 31			15 55			16 34			16 55		17 31			17 57			18 31			18 57			19 31
Harling Road	d																								
Eccles Road	d																								
Attleborough	d	15 46						16 49					17 46						18 46						19 46
Spooner Row	d																								
Wymondham	d	15 54						16 56					17 54						18 54						19 54
Norwich	a	16 13			16 35			17 13			17 26		18 13			18 30			19 10			19 29			20 13

Table 17

Sundays

30 March to 11 May

London and Cambridge - Ely, Kings Lynn, Peterborough and Norwich

Network Diagram - see first Page of Table 13

		XC ◇1		FC 1	EM ◇	EM ◇	LE 1	XC ◇1	FC 1	EM ◇	FC 1	EM ◇		LE 1	FC 1	EM ◇	FC 1	FC 1
London Liverpool Street	d																	
London Kings Cross	d			18 15					19 15		20 15				21 15		22 15	23 15
Ipswich	d																	
Stansted Airport	d	18 25						19 25										
Cambridge	d	19 00		19 06			19 52	20 00	20 07		21 06			21 52	22 06		23 06	00 08
Waterbeach	d			19 12					20 13		21 12				22 12		23 12	00 15
Ely 6	a	19 14		19 22			20 06	20 14	20 23		21 22			22 06	22 22		23 22	00 24
	d	19 15		19 22	19 26	19 48	20 07	20 15	20 23	20 36	21 22	21 44		22 07	22 22	22 29	23 22	00 25
Littleport	d			19 29					20 30		21 29				22 29		23 29	00 32
Downham Market	d			19 38					20 39		21 38				22 38		23 38	00 41
Watlington	d			19 44					20 45		21 44				22 44		23 44	00 46
Kings Lynn	a			19 53					20 53		21 53				22 53		23 53	00 56
Manea	d																	
March	d	19 32						20 32										
Whittlesea	d																	
Peterborough 8	a	19 51				20 23		20 51				22 16						
Shippea Hill	d																	
Lakenheath	d																	
Brandon	d						20 23							22 23				
Thetford	d				19 50		20 31			20 57				22 31		22 50		
Harling Road	d																	
Eccles Road	d																	
Attleborough	d						20 46			21 11				22 46		23 04		
Spooner Row	d																	
Wymondham	d						20 54			21 18				22 54		23 11		
Norwich	a				20 26		21 10			21 37				23 13		23 24		

Table 17

Mondays to Fridays

9 December to 27 December

Norwich, Peterborough, Kings Lynn and Ely - Cambridge and London

Network Diagram - see first Page of Table 13

Miles	Miles	Miles			FC	LE	FC	LE	FC	EM	LE	EM		FC	LE	LE	EM	XC	FC	FC	LE	EM		FC	LE
					■1	◇■1	■1	■1	■1	◇	◇■1	◇		■1	◇■1	■1	◇	◇■1	■1	■1	◇■1	◇		■1	■1
											A														
0	—	—	**Norwich**	d				05 33		05 50						06 33	06 51								
10	—	—	Wymondham	d				05 45		06 02						06 45									
—	—	—	Spooner Row	d																					
16	—	—	Attleborough	d				05 52		06 09						06 52									
—	—	—	Eccles Road	d																					
—	—	—	Harling Road	d																					
30½	—	—	Thetford	d				06 06		06 23						07 06	07 20								
37½	—	—	Brandon	d				06 14								07 14									
—	—	—	Lakenheath	d																					
—	—	—	Shippea Hill	d																					
—	0	—	**Peterborough** ■8	d								06 27						07 12				07 35			07 45
—	—	—	Whittlesea	d														07 20							07 53
—	15	—	March	d								06 43						07 31				07 51			08 04
—	—	—	Manea	d														07x38							
—	—	0	**Kings Lynn**	d	04 55	05 19	05 52		06 10		06 17			06 52					07 14	07 25				07 55	
—	—	6	Watlington	d	05 02	05 26	05 59				06 24			06 59					07 21					08 02	
—	—	10¾	Downham Market	d	05 08	05 33	06 05		06 21		06 31			07 05					07 28	07 37				08 08	
—	—	21	Littleport	d	05 17	05 42	06 14				06 40			07 14					07 37					08 17	
53½	30½	26½	**Ely** ■6	a	05 25	05 51	06 22	06 31	06 42	06 45	06 49	07 01		07 22		07 31	07 41	07 51	07 45	07 54		08 11		08 26	08 31
—	—	—		d	05 25	05 52	06 22	06 32	06 47		06 50			07 22	07 30	07 33		07 52	07 48	07 56	08 02			08 26	08 32
—	—	36	Waterbeach	d	05 35	06 01	06 32				06 59			07 32					07 57		08 11			08 36	
68¼	—	41¼	**Cambridge**	a	05 43	06 10	06 39	06 52	07 05		07 08			07 39	07 47	07 53		08 07	08 04	08 12	08 20			08 45	
—	—	—																							
—	55	—	Stansted Airport	a														08 39							
—	—	—	Ipswich	a																					09 28
—	—	99¼	**London Kings Cross**	a	06 39		07 38		08 07					08 38					09 09					09 44	
—	—	—	London Liverpool Street	a		07 25					08 25				09 20						09 50				

		LE	EM	XC	FC	FC	LE	EM		EM	XC	FC	EM	FC	LE	LE	EM	XC		EM	FC	LE	EM	XC	EM
		■1	◇	◇■1	■1	■1	■1	◇		◇	◇■1	■1	◇	■1	■1	■1	◇	◇■1		◇	■1	■1	◇	◇■1	◇
Norwich	d	07 37	07 57				08 40			08 57						09 40	09 57					10 40	10 57		
Wymondham	d	07 49					08 52									09 52						10 52			
Spooner Row	d																								
Attleborough	d	07 56					08 59									09 59						10 59			
Eccles Road	d																								
Harling Road	d																								
Thetford	d	08 10	08 24				09 13			09 24						10 13	10 24					11 13	11 24		
Brandon	d	08 18					09 21									10 21						11 21			
Lakenheath	d																								
Shippea Hill	d																								
Peterborough ■8	d			08 18				08 59			09 18		09 40		09 45			10 18		10 45				11 18	11 41
Whittlesea	d														09 53										
March	d			08 34							09 34				10 04			10 34						11 34	
Manea	d																								
Kings Lynn	d				08 28	08 58								09 55							10 55				
Watlington	d				08 35	09 05								10 02							11 02				
Downham Market	d				08 41	09 11								10 08							11 08				
Littleport	d				08 50	09 20								10 17							11 17				
Ely ■6	a	08 37	08 45	08 52	08 58	09 28	09 38	09 42		09 45	09 54		10 13	10 25	10 31	10 38	10 48	10 52		11 18	11 25	11 38	11 46	11 52	12 13
	d	08 39		08 52	08 58	09 28	09 39				09 55	10 11		10 25	10 32	10 39		10 52			11 25	11 39		11 52	
Waterbeach	d				09 08	09 38						10 20		10 35							11 35				
Cambridge	a	08 59		09 08	09 15	09 45	09 59				10 10	10 27		10 43		10 59		11 08			11 43	11 59		12 08	
Stansted Airport	a			09 40							10 40							11 40						12 40	
Ipswich	a														11 28										
London Kings Cross	a				10 13	10 44						11 32		11 35							12 37				
London Liverpool Street	a																								

		FC	LE	LE		EM	XC	EM	FC	LE	EM	XC	EM	FC		LE	LE	EM	XC	EM	FC	LE	EM	XC	
		■1	■1	■1		◇	◇■1	◇	■1	■1	◇	◇■1	◇	■1		■1	■1	◇	◇■1	◇	■1	■1	◇	◇■1	
Norwich	d			11 40		11 57				12 40	12 57						13 40	13 57				14 40	14 57		
Wymondham	d			11 52						12 52							13 52					14 52			
Spooner Row	d																								
Attleborough	d			11 59						12 59							13 59					14 59			
Eccles Road	d																								
Harling Road	d																								
Thetford	d			12 13		12 24				13 13	13 24						14 13	14 24				15 13	15 24		
Brandon	d			12 21						13 21							14 21					15 21			
Lakenheath	d																								
Shippea Hill	d																								
Peterborough ■8	d		11 45				12 18	12 42				13 18	13 41			13 45			14 18	14 41				15 18	
Whittlesea	d		11 53													13 53									
March	d		12 04				12 34					13 34				14 04			14 34					15 34	
Manea	d																								
Kings Lynn	d	11 55							12 55					13 55							14 55				
Watlington	d	12 02							13 02					14 02							15 02				
Downham Market	d	12 08							13 08					14 08							15 08				
Littleport	d	12 17							13 17					14 17							15 17				
Ely ■6	a	12 25	12 31	12 38		12 45	12 52	13 14	13 26	13 38	13 45	13 52	14 13	14 25		14 31	14 38	14 45	14 52	15 13	15 25	15 38	15 45	15 52	
	d	12 25	12 32	12 39			12 52		13 26	13 39		13 52		14 25		14 32	14 39		14 52		15 25	15 39		15 52	
Waterbeach	d	12 35							13 35					14 35							15 35				
Cambridge	a	12 43		12 59			13 08		13 44	13 59		14 08		14 43			14 59		15 08		15 43	15 59		16 08	
Stansted Airport	a						13 40					14 40							15 40					16 40	
Ipswich	a		13 28													15 28									
London Kings Cross	a	13 35							14 35					15 35							16 35				
London Liverpool Street	a																								

A The Fenman

Table 17

Mondays to Fridays

9 December to 27 December

Norwich, Peterborough, Kings Lynn and Ely - Cambridge and London

Network Diagram - see first Page of Table 13

		FC [1]	EM ◇	FC [1]	LE [1]	LE [1]	EM ◇	XC ◇[1]	FC [1]	EM ◇		FC [1]	LE [1]	EM ◇	XC ◇[1]	FC [1]	EM ◇	FC [1]	LE [1]	LE [1]		EM ◇	XC ◇[1]	FC [1]	EM ◇
Norwich	d					15 40	15 48						16 38	16 57						17 35		17 54			
Wymondham	d					15 52							16 50	17 09						17 47		18 06			
Spooner Row	d												16x54												
Attleborough	d					15 59	16 05						16 59							17 54		18 13			
Eccles Road	d						16 10													17 59					
Harling Road	d						16 14													18 03					
Thetford	d					16 13	16 23						17 13	17 27						18 13		18 27			
Brandon	d					16 21							17 21							18 21					
Lakenheath	d																								
Shippea Hill	d																								
Peterborough [8]	d		15 40		15 45			16 18		16 41					17 18		17 42		17 45				18 18		18 45
Whittlesea	d				15 53										17 26				17 53						
March	d				16 04			16 34							17 37				18 04				18 34		19 05
Manea	d														17x44										
Kings Lynn	d			15 55					16 37							17 37								18 37	
Watlington	d			16 02					16 44							17 44								18 44	
Downham Market	d			16 08					16 50			17 10				17 50								18 50	
Littleport	d			16 17					16 59							17 59								18 59	
Ely [6]	a		16 13	16 25	16 31	16 38	16 44	16 52	17 07	17 13		17 26	17 38	17 48	17 58	18 07	18 14		18 31	18 39		18 48	18 52	19 07	19 24
	d	16 06		16 25	16 32	16 39		16 52	17 08			17 26	17 39		17 59	18 08		18 28	18 32	18 39			18 52	19 08	
Waterbeach	d	16 16		16 35					17 17							18 17								19 17	
Cambridge	a	16 22		16 43		16 59		17 08	17 24			17 43	17 59		18 16	18 24		18 43		18 59			19 08	19 24	
Stansted Airport	a							17 40							18 54								19 40		
Ipswich	a				17 28														19 28						
London Kings Cross	a	17 35		17 38					18 34			18 35				19 41		19 35						20 33	
London Liverpool Street	a																								

		XC ◇[1]	LE [1]	EM ◇	XC ◇[1]	FC [1]		EM ◇	FC [1]	LE [1]	LE [1]	XC ◇[1]	FC [1]	XC ◇[1]	FC [1]	EM ◇		LE [1]	LE [1]	XC ◇[1]	FC [1]	LE [1]			
Norwich	d		18 40	18 57							19 40							21 15				22 40			
Wymondham	d		18 52								19 52							21 27				22 52			
Spooner Row	d																								
Attleborough	d		18 59								19 59							21 34				22 59			
Eccles Road	d																								
Harling Road	d																								
Thetford	d		19 13	19 24							20 13							21 48				23 13			
Brandon	d		19 21								20 21							21 56				23 21			
Lakenheath	d																								
Shippea Hill	d																								
Peterborough [8]	d	18 59			19 18			19 40		19 45		20 18		21 18		21 38			21 45	22 18					
Whittlesea	d									19 53									21 53						
March	d	19 15			19 34					20 04		20 34		21 34					22 04	22 34					
Manea	d																								
Kings Lynn	d					19 37							20 37		21 37						22 28				
Watlington	d					19 44							20 44		21 44						22 35				
Downham Market	d					19 50							20 50		21 50						22 41				
Littleport	d					19 59							20 59		21 59						22 50				
Ely [6]	a	19 33	19 38	19 48	19 52	20 08		20 13		20 31	20 39	20 52	21 07	21 52	22 07	22 13		22 16	22 25	22 52	22 58	23 38			
	d	19 34	19 39		19 52	20 08			20 29	20 32	20 39	20 52	21 08	21 52	22 08			22 16	22 26	22 52	22 58	23 39			
Waterbeach	d					20 17							21 17		22 17						23 08				
Cambridge	a	19 52	19 59		20 08	20 26			20 43		20 59	21 08	21 26	22 08	22 24			22 35		23 09	23 14	23 59			
Stansted Airport	a				20 40							21 40		22 52											
Ipswich	a									21 28									23 22						
London Kings Cross	a					21 32			21 35				22 32		23 32						00 40				
London Liverpool Street	a																								

Mondays to Fridays

30 December to 16 May

		FC [1]	LE ◇[1]	FC [1]	LE [1]	FC [1]	EM ◇	LE ◇[1] A	EM ◇	FC [1]		LE ◇[1]	LE [1]	EM ◇	XC ◇[1]	FC [1]	FC [1]	LE ◇[1]	EM ◇	FC [1]		LE [1]	LE [1]	EM ◇	XC ◇[1]
Norwich	d				05 33		05 50						06 33	06 51									07 37	07 57	
Wymondham	d				05 45		06 02						06 45										07 49		
Spooner Row	d																								
Attleborough	d				05 52		06 09						06 52										07 56		
Eccles Road	d																								
Harling Road	d																								
Thetford	d				06 06		06 23						07 06	07 20									08 10	08 24	
Brandon	d				06 14								07 14										08 18		
Lakenheath	d																								
Shippea Hill	d																								
Peterborough [8]	d								06 27						07 12				07 35			07 50			08 18
Whittlesea	d														07 20							07 58			
March	d								06 43						07 31				07 51			08 09			08 34
Manea	d														07x38							08x17			
Kings Lynn	d	04 55	05 19	05 52		06 10		06 17		06 52						07 14	07 25			07 55					
Watlington	d	05 02	05 26	05 59				06 24		06 59						07 21				08 02					
Downham Market	d	05 08	05 33	06 05		06 21		06 31		07 05						07 28	07 37			08 08					
Littleport	d	05 17	05 42	06 14				06 40		07 14						07 37				08 17					
Ely [6]	a	05 25	05 51	06 22	06 31	06 42	06 45	06 49	07 01	07 22			07 31	07 41	07 51	07 45	07 54		08 11	08 26		08 31	08 37	08 45	08 52
	d	05 25	05 52	06 22	06 32	06 47		06 50		07 22		07 30	07 33		07 52	07 48	07 56	08 02		08 26		08 32	08 39		08 52
Waterbeach	d	05 35	06 01	06 32				06 59		07 32						07 57		08 11		08 36					
Cambridge	a	05 43	06 10	06 39	06 52	07 05		07 08		07 39		07 47	07 53		08 07	08 04 }	08 12 }	08 20		08 45			08 59		09 08
Stansted Airport	a														08 39										09 40
Ipswich	a																					09 28			
London Kings Cross	a	06 39		07 38		08 07				08 38						09 09				09 44					
London Liverpool Street	a		07 25					08 25				09 20						09 50							

A The Fenman

Table 17

Mondays to Fridays

30 December to 16 May

Norwich, Peterborough, Kings Lynn and Ely - Cambridge and London

Network Diagram - see first Page of Table 13

		FC 1	FC 1	LE 1	EM ◇	EM ◇		XC ◇1	FC 1	EM ◇	FC 1	LE 1	LE 1	EM ◇	XC ◇1	EM ◇		FC 1	LE 1	EM ◇	XC ◇1	EM ◇	FC 1	LE 1	LE 1
Norwich	d			08 40		08 57							09 40	09 57					10 40	10 57					11 40
Wymondham	d			08 52									09 52						10 52						11 52
Spooner Row	d																								
Attleborough	d			08 59									09 59						10 59						11 59
Eccles Road	d																								
Harling Road	d																								
Thetford	d			09 13		09 24							10 13	10 24					11 13	11 24					12 13
Brandon	d			09 21									10 21						11 21						12 21
Lakenheath	d																								
Shippea Hill	d																								
Peterborough 8	d				08 59			09 18		09 40		09 50			10 18	10 45					11 18	11 41		11 50	
Whittlesea	d											09 58												11 58	
March	d							09 34				10 09			10 34						11 34			12 09	
Manea	d											10x17												12x17	
Kings Lynn	d	08 28	08 58								09 55							10 55					11 55		
Watlington	d	08 35	09 05								10 02							11 02					12 02		
Downham Market	d	08 41	09 11								10 08							11 08					12 08		
Littleport	d	08 50	09 20								10 17							11 17					12 17		
Ely 6	a	08 58	09 28	09 38	09 42	09 45		09 54		10 13	10 25	10 31	10 38	10 48	10 52	11 18		11 25	11 38	11 46	11 52	12 13	12 25	12 31	12 38
	d	08 58	09 28	09 39				09 55	10 11		10 25	10 32	10 39		10 52			11 25	11 39		11 52		12 25	12 32	12 39
Waterbeach	d	09 08	09 38						10 20		10 35							11 35					12 35		
Cambridge	a	09 15	09 45	09 59				10 10	10 27		10 43		10 59		11 08			11 43	11 59		12 08		12 43		12 59
Stansted Airport	a							10 40							11 40						12 40				
Ipswich	a											11 28												13 28	
London Kings Cross	a	10 13	10 44						11 32		11 35							12 37					13 35		
London Liverpool Street	a																								

		EM ◇		XC ◇1	EM ◇	FC 1	LE 1	EM ◇	XC ◇1	EM ◇	FC 1	LE 1		LE 1	EM ◇	XC ◇1	EM ◇	FC 1	LE 1	EM ◇	XC ◇1	FC 1		EM ◇	FC 1
Norwich	d	11 57					12 40	12 57						13 40	13 57				14 40	14 57					
Wymondham	d						12 52							13 52					14 52						
Spooner Row	d																								
Attleborough	d						12 59							13 59					14 59						
Eccles Road	d																								
Harling Road	d																								
Thetford	d	12 24					13 13	13 24						14 13	14 24				15 13	15 24					
Brandon	d						13 21							14 21					15 21						
Lakenheath	d																								
Shippea Hill	d																								
Peterborough 8	d			12 18	12 42				13 18	13 41		13 50				14 18	14 41				15 18			15 40	
Whittlesea	d											13 58													
March	d			12 34					13 34			14 09				14 34					15 34				
Manea	d											14x17													
Kings Lynn	d					12 55					13 55							14 55							15 55
Watlington	d					13 02					14 02							15 02							16 02
Downham Market	d					13 08					14 08							15 08							16 08
Littleport	d					13 17					14 17							15 17							16 17
Ely 6	a	12 45		12 52	13 14	13 26	13 38	13 45	13 52	14 13	14 25	14 31		14 38	14 45	14 52	15 13	15 25	15 38	15 45	15 52			16 13	16 25
	d			12 52		13 26	13 39		13 52		14 25	14 32		14 39		14 52		15 25	15 39		15 52	16 06			16 25
Waterbeach	d					13 35					14 35							15 35				16 16			16 35
Cambridge	a			13 08		13 44	13 59		14 08		14 43			14 59		15 08		15 43	15 59		16 08	16 22			16 43
Stansted Airport	a			13 40					14 40							15 40					16 40				
Ipswich	a											15 28													
London Kings Cross	a					14 35					15 35							16 35				17 35			17 38
London Liverpool Street	a																								

		LE 1	LE 1	EM ◇	XC ◇1	FC 1	EM ◇	FC 1		LE 1	EM ◇	XC ◇1	FC 1	EM ◇	FC 1	LE 1	LE 1	EM ◇		XC ◇1	FC 1	EM ◇	XC ◇1	LE 1	EM ◇
Norwich	d		15 40	15 48						16 38	16 57						17 35	17 54						18 40	18 57
Wymondham	d		15 52							16 50	17 09						17 47	18 06						18 52	
Spooner Row	d									16x54															
Attleborough	d		15 59	16 05						16 59							17 54	18 13						18 59	
Eccles Road	d			16 10													17 59								
Harling Road	d			16 14													18 03								
Thetford	d		16 13	16 23						17 13	17 27						18 13	18 27						19 13	19 24
Brandon	d		16 21							17 21							18 21							19 21	
Lakenheath	d																								
Shippea Hill	d																								
Peterborough 8	d	15 50			16 18		16 41					17 18		17 42		17 50				18 18		18 45	18 59		
Whittlesea	d	15 58										17 26				17 58									
March	d	16 09			16 34							17 37				18 09				18 34		19 05	19 15		
Manea	d	16x17										17x44				18x17									
Kings Lynn	d					16 37							17 37								18 37				
Watlington	d					16 44							17 44								18 44				
Downham Market	d					16 50		17 10					17 50								18 50				
Littleport	d					16 59							17 59								18 59				
Ely 6	a	16 31	16 38	16 44	16 52	17 07	17 13	17 26		17 38	17 48	17 58	18 07	18 14		18 31	18 39	18 48		18 52	19 07	19 24	19 33	19 38	19 48
	d	16 32	16 39		16 52	17 08		17 26		17 39		17 59	18 08		18 28	18 32	18 39			18 52	19 08		19 34	19 39	
Waterbeach	d					17 17							18 17								19 17				
Cambridge	a		16 59		17 08	17 24		17 43		17 59		18 16	18 24		18 43		18 59			19 08	19 24		19 52	19 59	
Stansted Airport	a				17 40							18 54								19 40					
Ipswich	a	17 28														19 28									
London Kings Cross	a					18 34		18 35					19 41		19 35						20 33				
London Liverpool Street	a																								

Table 17

Mondays to Fridays

30 December to 16 May

Norwich, Peterborough, Kings Lynn and Ely - Cambridge and London

Network Diagram - see first Page of Table 13

		XC ◇■	FC ■	EM ◇		FC ■	LE ■	LE ■	XC ◇■	FC ■	XC ◇■	FC ■	EM ◇	LE ■		LE ■	XC ◇■	FC ■	LE ■
Norwich	d							19 40						21 15					22 40
Wymondham	d							19 52						21 27					22 52
Spooner Row	d																		
Attleborough	d							19 59						21 34					22 59
Eccles Road	d																		
Harling Road	d																		
Thetford	d							20 13						21 48					23 13
Brandon	d							20 21						21 56					23 21
Lakenheath	d																		
Shippea Hill	d																		
Peterborough ■	d	19 18		19 40			19 50		20 18		21 18		21 38			21 45	22 18		
Whittlesea	d						19 58									21 53			
March	d	19 34					20 09		20 34		21 34					22 04	22 34		
Manea	d						20x17									22x12			
Kings Lynn	d		19 37							20 37		21 37						22 28	
Watlington	d		19 44							20 44		21 44						22 35	
Downham Market	d		19 50							20 50		21 50						22 41	
Littleport	d		19 59							20 59		21 59						22 50	
Ely ■	a	19 52	20 08	20 13			20 31	20 39	20 52	21 07	21 52	22 07	22 13	22 16		22 25	22 52	22 58	23 38
	d	19 52	20 08			20 29	20 32	20 39	20 52	21 08	21 52	22 08		22 16		22 26	22 52	22 58	23 39
Waterbeach	d		20 17							21 17		22 17						23 08	
Cambridge	a	20 08	20 26			20 43		20 59	21 08	21 26	22 08	22 24		22 35			23 09	23 14	23 59
Stansted Airport	a	20 40							21 40		22 52								
Ipswich	a						21 28									23 21			
London Kings Cross	a		21 32			21 35				22 32		23 32						00 40	
London Liverpool Street	a																		

Saturdays

14 December to 21 December

		FC ■	FC ■	LE ■	EM ◇	EM ◇	FC ■	LE ■	EM ◇	XC ◇■		EM ◇	FC ■	LE ■	LE ■	EM ◇	XC ◇■	FC ■	LE ■	EM ◇		EM ◇	XC ◇■	FC ■	EM ◇
Norwich	d			05 37	05 50			06 40	06 53						07 40	07 57			08 40			08 57			
Wymondham	d			05 49	06 02			06 52							07 52				08 52						
Spooner Row	d																								
Attleborough	d			05 56	06 09			06 59							07 59				08 59						
Eccles Road	d																								
Harling Road	d																								
Thetford	d			06 10	06 23			07 13	07 22						08 13	08 24			09 13			09 24			
Brandon	d			06 18				07 21							08 21				09 21						
Lakenheath	d																								
Shippea Hill	d																								
Peterborough ■	d					06 27				07 12		07 35		07 45			08 18			08 59			09 18		09 43
Whittlesea	d									07 20				07 53											
March	d					06 43				07 31		07 51		08 04			08 34						09 34		
Manea	d									07x38															
Kings Lynn	d		05 55				06 55						07 55					08 55						09 30	
Watlington	d		06 02				07 02						08 02					09 02							
Downham Market	d		06 08				07 08						08 08					09 08						09 41	
Littleport	d		06 17				07 17						08 17					09 17							
Ely ■	a		06 25	06 35	06 44	07 01	07 25	07 38	07 45	07 52		08 11	08 25	08 31	08 38	08 45	08 52	09 25	09 38	09 41		09 45	09 52	09 59	10 16
	d	05 26	06 25	06 36			07 25	07 39		07 52			08 25	08 32	08 39		08 52	09 25	09 39				09 53	09 59	
Waterbeach	d	05 35	06 35				07 35						08 35					09 35							
Cambridge	a	05 42	06 43	06 56			07 43	07 59		08 08			08 42		08 59		09 08	09 43	09 59				10 09	10 14	
Stansted Airport	a									08 39							09 40						10 40		
Ipswich	a													09 28											
London Kings Cross	a	06 39	07 36				08 36						09 36					10 35						11 04	
London Liverpool Street	a																								

		FC ■	LE ■	LE ■	EM ◇	XC ◇■		EM ◇	FC ■	LE ■	EM ◇	XC ◇■	EM ◇	FC ■	LE ■	LE ■		EM ◇	XC ◇■	EM ◇	FC ■	LE ■	EM ◇	XC ◇■	EM ◇
Norwich	d			09 38	09 57					10 40	10 57					11 40		11 57				12 40	12 57		
Wymondham	d			09 50						10 52						11 52						12 52			
Spooner Row	d																								
Attleborough	d			09 57						10 59						11 59						12 59			
Eccles Road	d																								
Harling Road	d																								
Thetford	d			10 11	10 24					11 13	11 24					12 13		12 24				13 13	13 24		
Brandon	d			10 19						11 21						12 21						13 21			
Lakenheath	d			10x24																					
Shippea Hill	d																								
Peterborough ■	d		09 47			10 18		10 40				11 18	11 41		11 45				12 18	12 40				13 18	13 40
Whittlesea	d		09 55												11 53										
March	d		10 06			10 34						11 34			12 04				12 34					13 34	
Manea	d																								
Kings Lynn	d	09 55							10 55					11 55							12 55				
Watlington	d	10 02							11 02					12 02							13 02				
Downham Market	d	10 08							11 08					12 08							13 08				
Littleport	d	10 17							11 17					12 17							13 17				
Ely ■	a	10 25	10 31	10 38	10 45	10 51		11 13	11 25	11 38	11 46	11 51	12 13	12 25	12 31	12 38		12 45	12 52	13 13	13 25	13 38	13 45	13 52	14 13
	d	10 25	10 32	10 39		10 52			11 25	11 39		11 52		12 25	12 32	12 39			12 52		13 25	13 39		13 52	
Waterbeach	d	10 35							11 35					12 35							13 35				
Cambridge	a	10 43		10 59		11 08			11 43	11 59		12 08		12 43		12 59			13 08		13 43	13 59		14 08	
Stansted Airport	a					11 40						12 40							13 40					14 40	
Ipswich	a		11 28												13 28										
London Kings Cross	a	11 37							12 34					13 34							14 34				
London Liverpool Street	a																								

Table 17

Saturdays

14 December to 21 December

Norwich, Peterborough, Kings Lynn and Ely - Cambridge and London

Network Diagram - see first Page of Table 13

		FC ■1		LE ■1	LE ■1	EM ◇	XC ◇■1	EM ◇	FC ■1	LE ■1	EM ◇	XC ◇■1		EM ◇	FC ■1	LE ■1	LE ■1	EM ◇	XC ◇■1	EM ◇	FC ■1	LE ■1		EM ◇	XC ◇■1
Norwich	d				13 40	13 57				14 40	14 57						15 35	15 52				16 38		16 54	
Wymondham	d				13 52					14 52							15 47					16 50		17 06	
Spooner Row	d																					16x54			
Attleborough	d				13 59					14 59							15 54	16 09				16 59			
Eccles Road	d																15 59								
Harling Road	d																16 03								
Thetford	d				14 13	14 24				15 13	15 24						16 13	16 23				17 13		17 24	
Brandon	d				14 21					15 21							16 21					17 21			
Lakenheath	d																								
Shippea Hill	d																								
Peterborough ■8	d			13 45			14 18	14 43				15 18		15 41		15 45			16 18	16 39					17 18
Whittlesea	d			13 53												15 53									17 26
March	d			14 04			14 34					15 34				16 04			16 34						17 37
Manea	d																								17x45
Kings Lynn	d	13 55							14 55						15 55						16 55				
Watlington	d	14 02							15 02						16 02						17 02				
Downham Market	d	14 08							15 08						16 08						17 08				
Littleport	d	14 17							15 17						16 17						17 17				
Ely ■6	a	14 25		14 31	14 38	14 45	14 52	15 18	15 25	15 38	15 45	15 52		16 13	16 25	16 31	16 38	16 45	16 52	17 13	17 25	17 38		17 45	18 00
	d	14 25		14 32	14 39		14 52		15 25	15 39		15 52			16 25	16 32	16 39		16 52		17 25	17 39			18 00
Waterbeach	d	14 35							15 35						16 35						17 35				
Cambridge	a	14 43			14 59		15 08		15 43	15 59		16 08			16 43		16 59		17 08		17 43	17 59			18 16
Stansted Airport	a						15 40					16 40							17 40						18 53
Ipswich	a			15 28												17 28									
London Kings Cross	a	15 34							16 34						17 35						18 35				
London Liverpool Street	a																								

		EM ◇	FC ■1	LE ■1	LE ■1	EM ◇	XC ◇■1	FC ■1		EM ◇	LE ■1	EM ◇	XC ◇■1	FC ■1	EM ◇	LE ■1	LE ■1	XC ◇■1		FC ■1	LE ■1	XC ◇■1	FC ■1	EM ◇	LE ■1
Norwich	d				17 35	17 50					18 38	18 57					19 40				20 40				
Wymondham	d				17 47	18 02					18 50						19 52				20 52				
Spooner Row	d																								
Attleborough	d				17 54	18 09					18 57						19 59				20 59				
Eccles Road	d				17 59																				
Harling Road	d				18 03																				
Thetford	d				18 13	18 23					19 11	19 24					20 13				21 13				
Brandon	d				18 21						19 19						20 21				21 21				
Lakenheath	d																								
Shippea Hill	d										19x27														
Peterborough ■8	d	17 40		17 45			18 18			18 44			19 18		19 41	19 45		20 18				21 18		21 40	21 45
Whittlesea	d			17 53												19 53									21 53
March	d			18 04			18 34			19 01			19 33			20 04		20 33				21 34			22 04
Manea	d																								
Kings Lynn	d		17 55					18 35						19 35						20 35			21 35		
Watlington	d		18 02					18 42						19 42						20 42			21 42		
Downham Market	d		18 08					18 48						19 48						20 48			21 48		
Littleport	d		18 17					18 57						19 57						20 57			21 57		
Ely ■6	a	18 13	18 25	18 31	18 38	18 45	18 52	19 05		19 19	19 38	19 45	19 52	20 05	20 14	20 31	20 38	20 51		21 05	21 38	21 52	22 05	22 13	22 25
	d		18 25	18 32	18 39		18 52	19 06			19 39		19 52	20 06		20 32	20 39	20 51		21 06	21 39	21 52	22 06		22 26
Waterbeach	d		18 35					19 15						20 15						21 15			22 15		
Cambridge	a		18 43		18 59		19 08	19 22			19 59		20 08	20 22			20 59	21 08		21 22	21 59	22 08	22 22		
Stansted Airport	a						19 40						20 40					21 40				22 40			
Ipswich	a			19 28												21 28									23 22
London Kings Cross	a		19 35					20 31						21 31						22 31			23 31		
London Liverpool Street	a																								

		XC ◇■1	LE ■1	FC ■1
Norwich	d		22 40	
Wymondham	d		22 52	
Spooner Row	d			
Attleborough	d		22 59	
Eccles Road	d			
Harling Road	d			
Thetford	d		23 13	
Brandon	d		23 21	
Lakenheath	d			
Shippea Hill	d			
Peterborough ■8	d	22 14		
Whittlesea	d			
March	d	22 29		
Manea	d			
Kings Lynn	d			23 11
Watlington	d			23 18
Downham Market	d			23 24
Littleport	d			23 33
Ely ■6	a	22 47	23 38	23 41
	d	22 48	23 39	23 43
Waterbeach	d			23 52
Cambridge	a	23 03	23 59	23 59
Stansted Airport	a			
Ipswich	a			
London Kings Cross	a			
London Liverpool Street	a			

Table 17

Saturdays

28 December to 17 May

Norwich, Peterborough, Kings Lynn and Ely - Cambridge and London

Network Diagram - see first Page of Table 13

		FC	FC	LE	EM	EM	FC	LE	EM	XC		EM	FC	LE	LE	EM	XC	FC	LE	EM		EM	XC	FC	EM
		1	1	1	◇	◇	1	1	◇	◇1		◇	1	1	1	◇	◇1	1	1	◇		◇	◇1	1	◇
Norwich	d			05 37	05 50			06 40	06 53						07 40	07 57			08 40			08 57			
Wymondham	d			05 49	06 02			06 52							07 52				08 52						
Spooner Row	d																								
Attleborough	d			05 56	06 09			06 59							07 59				08 59						
Eccles Road	d																								
Harling Road	d																								
Thetford	d			06 10	06 23			07 13	07 22						08 13	08 24			09 13			09 24			
Brandon	d			06 18				07 21							08 21				09 21						
Lakenheath	d																								
Shippea Hill	d																								
Peterborough 8	d					06 27				07 12		07 35		07 50			08 18			08 59			09 18		09 43
Whittlesea	d									07 20				07 58											
March	d					06 43				07 31		07 51		08 09			08 34						09 34		
Manea	d									07x38				08x17											
Kings Lynn	d		05 55				06 55						07 55					08 55						09 30	
Watlington	d		06 02				07 02						08 02					09 02							
Downham Market	d		06 08				07 08						08 08					09 08						09 41	
Littleport	d		06 17				07 17						08 17					09 17							
Ely 6	a		06 25	06 35	06 44	07 01	07 25	07 38	07 45	07 52		08 11	08 25	08 31	08 38	08 45	08 52	09 25	09 38	09 41		09 45	09 52	09 59	10 16
	d	05 26	06 25	06 36			07 25	07 39		07 52			08 25	08 32	08 39		08 52	09 25	09 39				09 53	09 59	
Waterbeach	d	05 35	06 35				07 35						08 35					09 35							
Cambridge	a	05 42	06 43	06 56			07 43	07 59		08 08			08 42		08 59		09 08	09 43	09 59				10 09	10 14	
Stansted Airport	a									08 39							09 40						10 40		
Ipswich	a													09 28											
London Kings Cross	a	06 39	07 36				08 36						09 36					10 35						11 04	
London Liverpool Street	a																								

		FC	LE	LE	EM	XC		EM	FC	LE	EM	XC	EM	FC	LE	LE		EM	XC	EM	FC	LE	EM	XC	EM
		1	1	1	◇	◇1		◇	1	1	◇	◇1	◇	1	1	1		◇	◇1	◇	1	1	◇	◇1	◇
Norwich	d			09 38	09 57					10 40	10 57					11 40		11 57				12 40	12 57		
Wymondham	d			09 50						10 52						11 52						12 52			
Spooner Row	d																								
Attleborough	d			09 57						10 59						11 59						12 59			
Eccles Road	d																								
Harling Road	d																								
Thetford	d			10 11	10 24					11 13	11 24					12 13		12 24				13 13	13 24		
Brandon	d			10 19						11 21						12 21						13 21			
Lakenheath	d			10x24																					
Shippea Hill	d																								
Peterborough 8	d		09 50			10 18		10 40				11 18	11 41		11 50				12 18	12 40				13 18	13 40
Whittlesea	d		09 58												11 58										
March	d		10 09			10 34						11 34			12 09				12 34					13 34	
Manea	d		10x17												12x17										
Kings Lynn	d	09 55							10 55					11 55							12 55				
Watlington	d	10 02							11 02					12 02							13 02				
Downham Market	d	10 08							11 08					12 08							13 08				
Littleport	d	10 17							11 17					12 17							13 17				
Ely 6	a	10 25	10 31	10 38	10 45	10 51		11 13	11 25	11 38	11 46	11 51	12 13	12 25	12 31	12 38		12 45	12 52	13 13	13 25	13 38	13 45	13 52	14 13
	d	10 25	10 32	10 39		10 52			11 25	11 39		11 52		12 25	12 32	12 39			12 52		13 25	13 39		13 52	
Waterbeach	d	10 35							11 35					12 35							13 35				
Cambridge	a	10 43		10 59		11 08			11 43	11 59		12 08		12 43		12 59			13 08		13 43	13 59		14 08	
Stansted Airport	a					11 40						12 40							13 40					14 40	
Ipswich	a		11 28												13 28										
London Kings Cross	a	11 37							12 34					13 34							14 34				
London Liverpool Street	a																								

		FC		LE	LE	EM	XC	EM	FC	LE	EM	XC		EM	FC	LE	LE	EM	XC	EM	FC	LE		EM	XC
		1		1	1	◇	◇1	◇	1	1	◇	◇1		◇	1	1	1	◇	◇1	◇	1	1		◇	◇1
Norwich	d				13 40	13 57				14 40	14 57						15 35	15 52				16 38		16 54	
Wymondham	d				13 52					14 52							15 47					16 50		17 06	
Spooner Row	d																					16x54			
Attleborough	d				13 59					14 59							15 54	16 09				16 59			
Eccles Road	d																15 59								
Harling Road	d																16 03								
Thetford	d				14 13	14 24				15 13	15 24						16 13	16 23				17 13		17 24	
Brandon	d				14 21					15 21							16 21					17 21			
Lakenheath	d																								
Shippea Hill	d																								
Peterborough 8	d			13 50			14 18	14 43				15 18		15 41		15 50			16 18	16 39					17 18
Whittlesea	d			13 58												15 58									17 26
March	d			14 09			14 34					15 34				16 09			16 34						17 37
Manea	d			14x17												16x17									17x45
Kings Lynn	d	13 55							14 55						15 55						16 55				
Watlington	d	14 02							15 02						16 02						17 02				
Downham Market	d	14 08							15 08						16 08						17 08				
Littleport	d	14 17							15 17						16 17						17 17				
Ely 6	a	14 25		14 31	14 38	14 45	14 52	15 18	15 25	15 38	15 45	15 52		16 13	16 25	16 31	16 38	16 45	16 52	17 13	17 25	17 38		17 45	18 00
	d	14 25		14 32	14 39		14 52		15 25	15 39		15 52			16 25	16 32	16 39		16 52		17 25	17 39			18 00
Waterbeach	d	14 35							15 35						16 35						17 35				
Cambridge	a	14 43			14 59		15 08		15 43	15 59		16 08			16 43		16 59		17 08		17 43	17 59			18 16
Stansted Airport	a						15 40					16 40							17 40						18 53
Ipswich	a			15 28												17 28									
London Kings Cross	a	15 34							16 34						17 35						18 35				
London Liverpool Street	a																								

Table 17

Saturdays

28 December to 17 May

Norwich, Peterborough, Kings Lynn and Ely - Cambridge and London

Network Diagram - see first Page of Table 13

		EM ◇	FC 1	LE 1	LE 1	EM ◇	XC ◇1	FC 1		EM ◇	LE 1	EM ◇	XC ◇1	FC 1	EM ◇	LE 1	LE 1	XC ◇1		FC 1	LE 1	XC ◇1	FC 1	EM ◇	LE 1
Norwich	d				17 35	17 50					18 38	18 57					19 40				20 40				
Wymondham	d				17 47	18 02					18 50						19 52				20 52				
Spooner Row	d																								
Attleborough	d				17 54	18 09					18 57						19 59				20 59				
Eccles Road	d				17 59																				
Harling Road	d				18 03																				
Thetford	d				18 13	18 23					19 11	19 24					20 13				21 13				
Brandon	d				18 21						19 19						20 21				21 21				
Lakenheath	d																								
Shippea Hill	d										19x27														
Peterborough 8	d	17 40		17 50			18 18			18 44			19 18		19 41	19 50		20 18				21 18		21 40	21 45
Whittlesea	d			17 58												19 58									21 53
March	d			18 09			18 34			19 01			19 33			20 09		20 33				21 34			22 04
Manea	d			18x17												20x17									22x12
Kings Lynn	d		17 55					18 35						19 35						20 35			21 35		
Watlington	d		18 02					18 42						19 42						20 42			21 42		
Downham Market	d		18 08					18 48						19 48						20 48			21 48		
Littleport	d		18 17					18 57						19 57						20 57			21 57		
Ely 6	a	18 13	18 25	18 31	18 38	18 45	18 52	19 05		19 19	19 38	19 45	19 52	20 05	20 14	20 31	20 38	20 51		21 05	21 38	21 52	22 05	22 13	22 25
	d		18 25	18 32	18 39		18 52	19 06			19 39		19 52	20 06		20 32	20 39	20 51		21 06	21 39	21 52	22 06		22 26
Waterbeach	d		18 35					19 15						20 15						21 15			22 15		
Cambridge	a		18 43		18 59		19 08	19 22			19 59		20 08	20 22			20 59	21 08		21 22	21 59	22 08	22 22		
Stansted Airport	a						19 40						20 40					21 40				22 40			
Ipswich	a			19 28												21 28									23 22
London Kings Cross	a		19 35					20 31						21 31						22 31			23 31		
London Liverpool Street	a																								

		XC ◇1	LE 1	FC 1
Norwich	d		22 40	
Wymondham	d		22 52	
Spooner Row	d			
Attleborough	d		22 59	
Eccles Road	d			
Harling Road	d			
Thetford	d		23 13	
Brandon	d		23 21	
Lakenheath	d			
Shippea Hill	d			
Peterborough 8	d	22 14		
Whittlesea	d			
March	d	22 29		
Manea	d			
Kings Lynn	d			23 11
Watlington	d			23 18
Downham Market	d			23 24
Littleport	d			23 33
Ely 6	a	22 47	23 38	23 41
	d	22 48	23 39	23 43
Waterbeach	d			23 52
Cambridge	a	23 03	23 59	23 59
Stansted Airport	a			
Ipswich	a			
London Kings Cross	a			
London Liverpool Street	a			

Sundays

8 December to 29 December

		FC 1	FC 1	LE 1	FC 1	LE 1	EM ◇	FC 1	LE 1	LE 1		FC 1	LE 1	XC ◇1	FC 1	LE 1	EM ◇	LE 1	EM ◇	XC ◇1		FC 1	LE 1	EM ◇	EM ◇
Norwich	d			09 03		10 03	10 47		11 03				12 03			13 03			13 53				14 03		14 53
Wymondham	d			09 15		10 15			11 15				12 15			13 15							14 15		
Spooner Row	d																								
Attleborough	d			09 22		10 22			11 22				12 22			13 22							14 22		
Eccles Road	d																								
Harling Road	d																								
Thetford	d			09 36		10 36	11 14		11 36				12 36			13 36			14 20				14 36		15 20
Brandon	d			09 44		10 44			11 44				12 44			13 44							14 44		
Lakenheath	d			09x49					11x49																
Shippea Hill	d																								
Peterborough 8	d									11 45				13 18			13 43	13 46		14 18				14 58	
Whittlesea	d									11 53								13 54							
March	d									12 04				13 34				14 05		14 34					
Manea	d																								
Kings Lynn	d	08 28	09 28		10 28			11 28				12 28			13 28							14 28			
Watlington	d	08 35	09 35		10 35			11 35				12 35			13 35							14 35			
Downham Market	d	08 41	09 41		10 41			11 41				12 41			13 41							14 41			
Littleport	d	08 50	09 50		10 50			11 50				12 50			13 50							14 50			
Ely 6	a	08 58	09 58	10 08	10 58	11 06	11 35	11 58	12 08	12 31		12 58	13 01	13 52	13 58	14 01	14 16	14 31	14 41	14 52		14 58	15 01	15 31	15 43
	d	08 58	09 58	10 09	10 58	11 07		11 58	12 09	12 32		12 58	13 04	13 52	13 58	14 04		14 32		14 52		14 58	15 04		
Waterbeach	d	09 08	10 08		11 08			12 08				13 08			14 08							15 08			
Cambridge	a	09 15	10 15	10 27	11 15	11 25		12 15	12 27			13 15	13 22	14 08	14 15	14 22				15 08		15 15	15 22		
Stansted Airport	a													14 45						15 45					
Ipswich	a									13 28								15 28							
London Kings Cross	a	10 10	11 08		12 08			13 08				14 08			15 08							16 08			
London Liverpool Street	a																								

Table 17

Sundays

8 December to 29 December

Norwich, Peterborough, Kings Lynn and Ely - Cambridge and London

Network Diagram - see first Page of Table 13

		XC ◇1	FC 1	LE 1	LE 1	EM ◇		XC ◇1	EM ◇	FC 1	LE 1	EM ◇	EM ◇	XC ◇1	FC 1	LE 1		LE 1	FC 1	EM ◇	EM ◇	XC ◇1	FC 1	LE 1	EM ◇
Norwich	d			15 03					15 54		16 03		16 54			17 03					17 54			18 03	
Wymondham	d			15 15							16 15					17 15								18 15	
Spooner Row	d																								
Attleborough	d			15 22							16 22					17 22								18 22	
Eccles Road	d																								
Harling Road	d																								
Thetford	d			15 36					16 21		16 36		17 21			17 36					18 21			18 36	
Brandon	d			15 44							16 44					17 44								18 44	
Lakenheath	d			15x49																					
Shippea Hill	d																								
Peterborough 8	d	15 18			15 45	15 58		16 18	17a12			16 59		17 18				17 45		17 57		18 18			18 49
Whittlesea	d				15 53													17 53							
March	d	15 34			16 04			16 34						17 34				18 04		18 13		18 34			
Manea	d																								
Kings Lynn	d		15 28							16 28					17 28				17 58				18 28		
Watlington	d		15 35							16 35					17 35								18 35		
Downham Market	d		15 41							16 41					17 41				18 09				18 41		
Littleport	d		15 50							16 50					17 50								18 50		
Ely 6	a	15 52	15 58	16 03	16 23	16 31		16 52		16 58	17 01	17 32	17 45	17 52	17 58	18 01		18 23	18 25	18 32	18 44	18 52	18 58	19 01	19 22
	d	15 52	15 58	16 04	16 29			16 52		16 58	17 04			17 52	17 58	18 04		18 29	18 26			18 52	18 58	19 04	
Waterbeach	d		16 08							17 08					18 08				18 35				19 08		
Cambridge	a	16 08	16 15	16 22				17 08		17 15	17 22			18 08	18 15	18 22			18 43			19 08	19 15	19 22	
Stansted Airport	a	16 45						17 45						18 45								19 45			
Ipswich	a				17 25													19 25							
London Kings Cross	a		17 08							18 10					19 11				19 36				20 12		
London Liverpool Street	a																								

		EM ◇		XC ◇1	FC 1	LE 1	EM ◇	XC ◇1	FC 1	LE 1	EM ◇	XC ◇1		FC 1	EM ◇	XC ◇1	FC 1	LE 1
Norwich	d	18 56								20 03	20 52							22 03
Wymondham	d									20 15								22 15
Spooner Row	d																	
Attleborough	d									20 22								22 22
Eccles Road	d																	
Harling Road	d																	
Thetford	d	19 23								20 36	21 19							22 36
Brandon	d									20 44								22 44
Lakenheath	d																	
Shippea Hill	d																	
Peterborough 8	d			19 18		19 45	19 59	20 18				21 18			21 53	22 16		
Whittlesea	d					19 53												
March	d			19 33		20 04		20 32				21 34				22 32		
Manea	d																	
Kings Lynn	d				19 28				20 28					21 28			22 28	
Watlington	d				19 35				20 35					21 35			22 35	
Downham Market	d				19 41				20 41					21 41			22 41	
Littleport	d				19 50				20 50					21 50			22 50	
Ely 6	a	19 44		19 51	19 58	20 23	20 32	20 50	20 58	21 01	21 40	21 52		21 58	22 26	22 51	22 58	23 01
	d			19 51	19 58	20 29		20 51	20 58	21 04		21 52		21 58		22 51	22 58	23 04
Waterbeach	d				20 08				21 08					22 08			23 08	
Cambridge	a			20 07	20 15			21 07	21 15	21 22		22 07		22 15		23 07	23 15	23 22
Stansted Airport	a			20 45				21 45				22 45						
Ipswich	a					21 25												
London Kings Cross	a				21 11				22 08					23 08			00 41	
London Liverpool Street	a																	

Sundays

5 January to 23 March

		FC 1	FC 1	LE 1	FC 1	LE 1	EM ◇	FC 1	LE 1	LE 1		FC 1	LE 1	XC ◇1	FC 1	LE 1	EM ◇	LE 1	EM ◇	XC ◇1		FC 1	LE 1	EM ◇ A	EM ◇ B
Norwich	d			09 03		10 03	10 47		11 03				12 03			13 03			13 53				14 03		
Wymondham	d			09 15		10 15			11 15				12 15			13 15							14 15		
Spooner Row	d																								
Attleborough	d			09 22		10 22			11 22				12 22			13 22							14 22		
Eccles Road	d																								
Harling Road	d																								
Thetford	d			09 36		10 36	11 14		11 36				12 36			13 36			14 20				14 36		
Brandon	d			09 44		10 44			11 44				12 44			13 44							14 44		
Lakenheath	d			09x49					11x49																
Shippea Hill	d																								
Peterborough 8	d									11 45				13 18			13 43	13 46		14 18				14 57	14 58
Whittlesea	d									11 53								13 54							
March	d									12 04				13 34				14 05		14 35					
Manea	d																								
Kings Lynn	d	08 28	09 28		10 28			11 28				12 28			13 28							14 28			
Watlington	d	08 35	09 35		10 35			11 35				12 35			13 35							14 35			
Downham Market	d	08 41	09 41		10 41			11 41				12 41			13 41							14 41			
Littleport	d	08 50	09 50		10 50			11 50				12 50			13 50							14 50			
Ely 6	a	08 58	09 58	10 08	10 58	11 06	11 35	11 58	12 08	12 31		12 58	13 01	13 52	13 58	14 01	14 16	14 31	14 41	14 52		14 58	15 01	15 31	15 31
	d	08 58	09 58	10 09	10 58	11 07		11 58	12 09	12 32		12 58	13 04	13 52	13 58	14 04		14 32		14 52		14 58	15 04		
Waterbeach	d	09 08	10 08		11 08			12 08				13 08			14 08							15 08			
Cambridge	a	09 15	10 15	10 27	11 15	11 25		12 15	12 27			13 15	13 22	14 08	14 15	14 22				15 08		15 15	15 22		
Stansted Airport	a													14 45						15 45					
Ipswich	a									13 28								15 28							
London Kings Cross	a	10 19	11 16		12 17			13 16				14 16			15 16							16 16			
London Liverpool Street	a																								

A until 9 February

B from 16 February

Table 17

Norwich, Peterborough, Kings Lynn and Ely - Cambridge and London

Sundays

5 January to 23 March

Network Diagram - see first Page of Table 13

		EM	XC	FC	LE	LE		EM	XC	EM	FC	LE	EM	EM	XC	FC		LE	LE	FC	EM	EM	XC	FC	LE
		◇	◇1	1	1	1		◇	◇1	◇	1	1	◇	◇	◇1	1		1	1	1	◇	◇	◇1	1	1
Norwich	d	14 53			15 03					15 54		16 03		16 54				17 03				17 54			18 03
Wymondham	d				15 15							16 15						17 15							18 15
Spooner Row	d																								
Attleborough	d				15 22							16 22						17 22							18 22
Eccles Road	d																								
Harling Road	d																								
Thetford	d	15 20			15 36					16 21		16 36		17 21				17 36				18 21			18 36
Brandon	d				15 44							16 44						17 44							18 44
Lakenheath	d				15x49																				
Shippea Hill	d																								
Peterborough 8	d		15 18			15 45		15 58	16 18	17a12			16 59		17 18				17 45		17 57		18 18		
Whittlesea	d					15 53													17 53						
March	d		15 34			16 04			16 34						17 34				18 04		18 13		18 34		
Manea	d																								
Kings Lynn	d			15 28							16 28					17 28				17 58				18 28	
Watlington	d			15 35							16 35					17 35								18 35	
Downham Market	d			15 41							16 41					17 41				18 09				18 41	
Littleport	d			15 50							16 50					17 50								18 50	
Ely 6	a	15 43	15 52	15 58	16 03	16 23		16 31	16 52		16 58	17 01	17 32	17 45	17 52	17 58		18 01	18 23	18 25	18 32	18 44	18 52	18 58	19 01
	d		15 52	15 58	16 04	16 29			16 52		16 58	17 04			17 52	17 58		18 04	18 29	18 26			18 52	18 58	19 04
Waterbeach	d			16 08							17 08					18 08				18 35				19 08	
Cambridge	a		16 08	16 15	16 22				17 08		17 15	17 22			18 08	18 15		18 22		18 43			19 08	19 15	19 22
Stansted Airport	a		16 45						17 45						18 45								19 45		
Ipswich	a					17 25													19 25						
London Kings Cross	a			17 17							18 19					19 20								20 21	
London Liverpool Street	a																								

		EM		EM	XC	FC	LE	EM	XC	FC	LE	EM		XC	FC	EM	XC	FC	LE
		◇		◇	◇1	1	1	◇	◇1	1	1	◇		◇1	1	◇	◇1	1	1
Norwich	d			18 56							20 03	20 52							22 03
Wymondham	d										20 15								22 15
Spooner Row	d																		
Attleborough	d										20 22								22 22
Eccles Road	d																		
Harling Road	d																		
Thetford	d			19 23							20 36	21 19							22 36
Brandon	d										20 44								22 44
Lakenheath	d																		
Shippea Hill	d																		
Peterborough 8	d	18 49			19 18		19 45	19 59	20 18					21 18		21 53	22 16		
Whittlesea	d						19 53												
March	d				19 33		20 04		20 33					21 34			22 32		
Manea	d																		
Kings Lynn	d					19 28				20 28					21 28			22 28	
Watlington	d					19 35				20 35					21 35			22 35	
Downham Market	d					19 41				20 41					21 41			22 41	
Littleport	d					19 50				20 50					21 50			22 50	
Ely 6	a	19 22		19 44	19 51	19 58	20 23	20 32	20 50	20 58	21 01	21 40		21 52	21 58	22 26	22 51	22 58	23 01
	d				19 51	19 58	20 29		20 51	20 58	21 04			21 52	21 58		22 51	22 58	23 04
Waterbeach	d					20 08				21 08					22 08			23 08	
Cambridge	a				20 07	20 15			21 07	21 15	21 22			22 07	22 15		23 07	23 15	23 22
Stansted Airport	a				20 45				21 45					22 45					
Ipswich	a						21 25												
London Kings Cross	a					21 17				22 22					23 22			00 39	
London Liverpool Street	a																		

Sundays

30 March to 11 May

		FC	FC	LE	FC	LE	EM	FC	LE	LE		FC	LE	XC	FC	LE	EM	LE	EM	XC		FC	LE	EM	EM
		1	1	1	1	1	◇	1	1	1		1	1	◇1	1	1	◇	1	◇	◇1		1	1	◇	◇
Norwich	d			09 03		10 03	10 47		11 03				12 03			13 03			13 53				14 03		14 53
Wymondham	d			09 15		10 15			11 15				12 15			13 15							14 15		
Spooner Row	d																								
Attleborough	d			09 22		10 22			11 22				12 22			13 22							14 22		
Eccles Road	d																								
Harling Road	d																								
Thetford	d			09 36		10 36	11 14		11 36				12 36			13 36			14 20				14 36		15 20
Brandon	d			09 44		10 44			11 44				12 44			13 44							14 44		
Lakenheath	d			09x49					11x49																
Shippea Hill	d																								
Peterborough 8	d									11 45				13 18			13 43	13 46		14 18				14 58	
Whittlesea	d									11 53								13 54							
March	d									12 04				13 34				14 05		14 34					
Manea	d																								
Kings Lynn	d	08 28	09 28		10 28			11 28				12 28			13 28							14 28			
Watlington	d	08 35	09 35		10 35			11 35				12 35			13 35							14 35			
Downham Market	d	08 41	09 41		10 41			11 41				12 41			13 41							14 41			
Littleport	d	08 50	09 50		10 50			11 50				12 50			13 50							14 50			
Ely 6	a	08 58	09 58	10 08	10 58	11 06	11 35	11 58	12 08	12 31		12 58	13 01	13 52	13 58	14 01	14 16	14 31	14 41	14 52		14 58	15 01	15 31	15 43
	d	08 58	09 58	10 09	10 58	11 07		11 58	12 09	12 32		12 58	13 04	13 52	13 58	14 04		14 32		14 52		14 58	15 04		
Waterbeach	d	09 08	10 08		11 08			12 08				13 08			14 08							15 08			
Cambridge	a	09 15	10 15	10 27	11 15	11 25		12 15	12 27			13 15	13 22	14 08	14 15	14 22				15 08		15 15	15 22		
Stansted Airport	a													14 45						15 45					
Ipswich	a									13 28								15 28							
London Kings Cross	a	10 10	11 08		12 08			13 08				14 08			15 08							16 08			
London Liverpool Street	a																								

Table 17

Sundays

30 March to 11 May

Norwich, Peterborough, Kings Lynn and Ely - Cambridge and London

Network Diagram - see first Page of Table 13

		XC ◇1	FC 1	LE 1	LE 1	EM ◇		XC ◇1	EM ◇	FC 1	LE 1	EM ◇	EM ◇	XC ◇1	FC 1	LE 1		LE 1	FC 1	EM ◇	EM ◇	XC ◇1	FC 1	LE 1	EM ◇
Norwich	d			15 03					15 54		16 03		16 54			17 03					17 54			18 03	
Wymondham	d			15 15							16 15					17 15								18 15	
Spooner Row	d																								
Attleborough	d			15 22							16 22					17 22								18 22	
Eccles Road	d																								
Harling Road	d																								
Thetford	d			15 36					16 21		16 36		17 21			17 36					18 21			18 36	
Brandon	d			15 44							16 44					17 44								18 44	
Lakenheath	d			15x49																					
Shippea Hill	d																								
Peterborough 8	d	15 18			15 45	15 58		16 18	17a12			16 59		17 18				17 45		17 57		18 18			18 49
Whittlesea	d				15 53													17 53							
March	d	15 34			16 04			16 34						17 34				18 04		18 13		18 34			
Manea	d																								
Kings Lynn	d		15 28							16 28					17 28				17 58				18 28		
Watlington	d		15 35							16 35					17 35								18 35		
Downham Market	d		15 41							16 41					17 41				18 09				18 41		
Littleport	d		15 50							16 50					17 50								18 50		
Ely 6	a	15 52	15 58	16 03	16 23	16 31		16 52		16 58	17 01	17 32	17 45	17 52	17 58	18 01		18 23	18 25	18 32	18 44	18 52	18 58	19 01	19 22
	d	15 52	15 58	16 04	16 29			16 52		16 58	17 04			17 52	17 58	18 04		18 29	18 26			18 52	18 58	19 04	
Waterbeach	d		16 08							17 08					18 08				18 35				19 08		
Cambridge	a	16 08	16 15	16 22				17 08		17 15	17 22			18 08	18 15	18 22			18 43			19 08	19 15	19 22	
Stansted Airport	a	16 45						17 45						18 45								19 45			
Ipswich	a				17 25													19 25							
London Kings Cross	a		17 08							18 10					19 11				19 36				20 12		
London Liverpool Street	a																								

		EM ◇		XC ◇1	FC 1	LE 1	EM ◇	XC ◇1	FC 1	LE 1	EM ◇	XC ◇1		FC 1	EM ◇	XC ◇1	FC 1	LE 1
Norwich	d	18 56								20 03	20 52							22 03
Wymondham	d									20 15								22 15
Spooner Row	d																	
Attleborough	d									20 22								22 22
Eccles Road	d																	
Harling Road	d																	
Thetford	d	19 23								20 36	21 19							22 36
Brandon	d									20 44								22 44
Lakenheath	d																	
Shippea Hill	d																	
Peterborough 8	d			19 18		19 45	19 59	20 18				21 18			21 53	22 16		
Whittlesea	d					19 53												
March	d			19 33		20 04		20 33				21 34				22 32		
Manea	d																	
Kings Lynn	d				19 28				20 28					21 28			22 28	
Watlington	d				19 35				20 35					21 35			22 35	
Downham Market	d				19 41				20 41					21 41			22 41	
Littleport	d				19 50				20 50					21 50			22 50	
Ely 6	a	19 44		19 51	19 58	20 23	20 32	20 51	20 58	21 01	21 40	21 52		21 58	22 26	22 51	22 58	23 01
	d			19 51	19 58	20 29		20 51	20 58	21 04		21 52		21 58		22 51	22 58	23 04
Waterbeach	d				20 08				21 08					22 08			23 08	
Cambridge	a			20 07	20 15			21 07	21 15	21 22		22 07		22 15		23 06	23 15	23 22
Stansted Airport	a			20 45				21 45				22 45						
Ipswich	a					21 25												
London Kings Cross	a				21 11				22 08					23 08			00 40	
London Liverpool Street	a																	

Network Diagram for Tables 18, 19, 27, 28, 29, 30

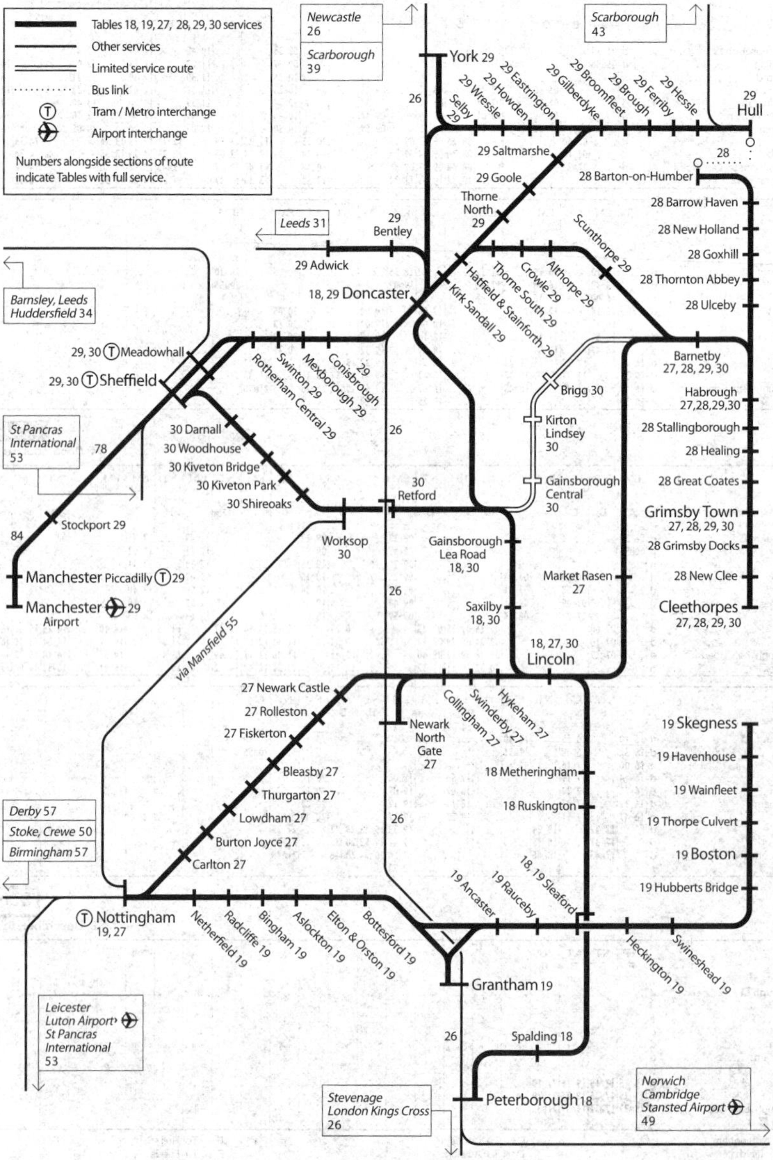
Tables 18, 19, 27, 28, 29, 30 services
Other services
Limited service route
Bus link
Tram / Metro interchange
Airport interchange
Numbers alongside sections of route indicate Tables with full service.
Newcastle 26
Scarborough 39
Scarborough 43
York 29
Selby 29
29 Wressle
29 Howden
29 Eastrington
29 Gilberdyke
29 Broomfleet
29 Brough
29 Ferriby
29 Hessle
29 Hull
29 Saltmarshe
29 Goole
Thorne North 29
28 Barton-on-Humber
28 Barrow Haven
28 New Holland
28 Goxhill
28 Thornton Abbey
28 Ulceby
Leeds 31
29 Bentley
29 Adwick
18, 29 Doncaster
Kirk Sandall 29
Hatfield & Stainforth 29
Thorne South 29
Crowle 29
Althorpe 29
Scunthorpe 29
Barnsley, Leeds Huddersfield 34
29, 30 Meadowhall
29, 30 Sheffield
Rotherham Central 29
Swinton 29
Mexborough 29
Conisbrough 29
Barnetby 27, 28, 29, 30
Brigg 30
Habrough 27,28,29,30
Kirton Lindsey 30
28 Stallingborough
28 Healing
St Pancras International 53
78
30 Darnall
30 Woodhouse
30 Kiveton Bridge
30 Kiveton Park
30 Shireoaks
30 Retford
Gainsborough Central 30
28 Great Coates
Grimsby Town 27, 28, 29, 30
Stockport 29
84
Worksop 30
Gainsborough Lea Road 18, 30
28 Grimsby Docks
Market Rasen 27
28 New Clee
Manchester Piccadilly 29
Manchester Airport 29
Saxilby 18, 30
Cleethorpes 27, 28, 29, 30
via Mansfield 55
18, 27, 30 Lincoln
27 Newark Castle
27 Rolleston
27 Fiskerton
Newark North Gate 27
Collingham 27
Swinderby 27
Hykeham 27
19 Skegness
19 Havenhouse
Bleasby 27
18 Metheringham
19 Wainfleet
Thurgarton 27
18 Ruskington
Lowdham 27
19 Thorpe Culvert
Derby 57
Stoke, Crewe 50
Birmingham 57
Burton Joyce 27
19 Boston
Carlton 27
19 Ancaster
19 Rauceby
18, 19 Sleaford
19 Hubberts Bridge
Nottingham 19, 27
Netherfield 19
Radcliffe 19
Bingham 19
Aslockton 19
Elton & Orston 19
Bottesford 19
Heckington 19
Swineshead 19
Grantham 19
Leicester Luton Airport St Pancras International 53
26
Spalding 18
Peterborough 18
Norwich Cambridge Stansted Airport 49
Stevenage London Kings Cross 26

TOCs operating on this network - East Midlands Trains (EM), Northern (NT), East Coast (GR), First TransPennine Express (TP), Cross Country (XC), Hull Trains (HT)

Table 18

Mondays to Fridays

9 December to 16 May

Peterborough - Sleaford, Lincoln and Doncaster

Network Diagram - refer to first Page of Table 18

Miles			EM	NT	EM	EM	EM	NT	EM	NT	EM		NT	EM	NT	EM	EM	NT	EM	NT	EM		NT	EM	NT
			A	B	C			D		D			D		D			B		D			D		D
0	**Peterborough 8**	d	06 30			07 30					08 33			09 35			10 40		11 49		12 41			13 40	
16½	Spalding	d	06a56			07a56					08 57			09 57			11 02		12 11		13 03			14 02	
35½	Sleaford	a									09 25			10 25			11 30		12 39		13 31			14 30	
—		d			06 50		07 43		08 40		09 25			10 25			11 31		12 42		13 32			14 31	
40	Ruskington	d			06 58		07 51		08 48		09 34			10 34			11 39		12 50		13 40			14 39	
47½	Metheringham	d			07 09		08 01		08 59		09 44			10 44			11 49		12 59		13 50			14 49	
56¾	**Lincoln**	a			07 22		08 15		09 13		09 59			10 59			12 05		13 14		14 05			15 05	
—		d		07 00				08 25	09 15	09 25			10 25		11 25	11 54		12 27	13 15	13 26			14 25		15 24
62¾	Saxilby	d		07 10				08 34	09 24	09 34			10 34		11 34	12 04		12 36	13 24	13 35			14 34		15 33
72¼	Gainsborough Lea Road	d		07a22				08 48	09 37	09 48			10 48		11 48	12 17		12a48	13 37	13 48			14 48		15 48
93½	**Doncaster 7**	a						10 32	10 03	11 32			12 32		13 33	12 47			14 06	15 33			16 32		17 31

		NT	EM	NT	EM	NT	EM		EM	EM	EM	NT	NT	EM	NT	EM
		E		B		B						B	B		B	
Peterborough 8	d		15 10		16 25		17 32			18 36						20 30
Spalding	d		15 32		16 48		17a58			19a02						20a56
Sleaford	a		16 00		17 16											
	d		16 14		17 19				17 56		19 00			20 05		
Ruskington	d		16 22		17 27				18 04		19 07			20 12		
Metheringham	d		16 32		17 37				18 14		19 17			20 22		
Lincoln	a		16 47		17 51				18 29		19 32			20 39		
	d	16 25		17 22		18 24			18 31		19 32	19 43	20 27		21 27	
Saxilby	d	16 35		17 31		18 33			18 42		19 41	19 52	20 36		21 36	
Gainsborough Lea Road	d	16 48		17a43		18a45			18 57		19 53	20a04	20a48		21a48	
Doncaster 7	a	18 34							19 25		20 23					

Saturdays

14 December to 17 May

		EM	NT	EM	EM	EM	NT	EM	NT	EM		NT	EM	NT	EM	NT	EM	NT	EM	EM		NT	EM	NT	NT
		A	B	C			D		D			D		D		D		D				D		D	E
Peterborough 8	d	06 30			07 30					08 33			09 32				11 49		12 41						
Spalding	d	06a56			07a56					08 57			09 57				12 11		13 03						
Sleaford	a									09 25			10 25				12 39		13 31						
	d			06 50		07 43				09 25			10 25				12 42		13 32						
Ruskington	d			06 58		07 51				09 34			10 34				12 50		13 40						
Metheringham	d			07 09		08 01				09 44			10 44				12 59		13 50						
Lincoln	a			07 22		08 15				09 59			10 59				13 14		14 05						
	d		07 00				08 25	09 15	09 25			10 25		11 25	11 54	12 27		13 25		14 10		14 25	15 10	15 24	16 25
Saxilby	d		07 10				08 34	09 24	09 34			10 34		11 34	12 04	12 36		13 34		14 19		14 34	15 20	15 33	16 35
Gainsborough Lea Road	d		07a22				08 48	09 37	09 48			10 48		11 48	12 17	12 49		13 48		14 32		14 48	15 32	15 48	16 48
Doncaster 7	a						10 32	10 11	11 32			12 33		13 32	12 47	14 32		15 34		15 01		16 32	16 01	17 32	18 37

		EM	NT	EM	NT	EM		EM	EM	EM	NT	NT	EM	NT	EM
			B		B						B	B		B	
Peterborough 8	d	15 10		16 25		17 30			18 36						20 30
Spalding	d	15 32		16 48		17a56			19a02						20a55
Sleaford	a	16 00		17 16											
	d	16 14		17 19				17 54		19 00			20 10		
Ruskington	d	16 22		17 27				18 02		19 07			20 17		
Metheringham	d	16 32		17 37				18 12		19 17			20 27		
Lincoln	a	16 47		17 51				18 27		19 32			20 40		
	d		17 22		18 24					19 32	19 43	20 27		21 27	
Saxilby	d		17 31		18 33					19 41	19 52	20 36		21 36	
Gainsborough Lea Road	d		17a43		18a45					19 54	20a04	20a48		21a48	
Doncaster 7	a									20 23					

Sundays

8 December to 11 May

		NT	NT	NT	NT
		F	B	B	B
Peterborough 8	d				
Spalding	d				
Sleaford	a				
	d				
Ruskington	d				
Metheringham	d				
Lincoln	a				
	d	15 15	17 15	19 15	21 10
Saxilby	d	15 25	17 25	19 25	21 20
Gainsborough Lea Road	d	15a37	17a37	19a37	21a32
Doncaster 7	a				

A From Nottingham
B To Sheffield
C To Leicester
D To Adwick
E To Hull
F To Leeds

For connections from London Kings Cross please see Table 25

Table 18R

Mondays to Fridays

9 December to 16 May

Doncaster, Lincoln and Sleaford - Peterborough

Network Diagram - refer to first Page of Table 18

Miles			NT	EM	EM	EM	EM	NT		NT	EM	NT	EM	NT	EM	EM	NT	EM		NT	EM	EM	EM	NT	EM
			A				B	A		A		A		C			C			C	D	E		C	F
0	**Doncaster 7**	d												09 01		10 24	10 03			11 03			13 01	12 03	
21¼	Gainsborough Lea Road	d	06 25					07 38		08 24		09 38		10 38		10 52	11 38			12 38			13 31	13 41	
30¾	Saxilby	d	06 38					07 51		08 37		09 51		10 51		11 05	11 51			12 51			13 44	13 54	
36¾	**Lincoln**	a	06 53					08 06		08 52		10 06		11 06		11 17	12 06			13 06			13 55	14 07	
—		d		07 05			08 00				09 10		10 15		11 10			12 10			13 30	13 30			14 41
46¼	Metheringham	d		07 18			08 12				09 22		10 28		11 23			12 22			13 43	13 43			14 54
53½	Ruskington	d		07 28			08 22				09 32		10 38		11 33			12 32			13 53	13 53			15 04
58	Sleaford	a		07 37			08 31				09 41		10 50		11 42			12 41			14 02	14 02			15 13
—		d					08 34				09 42		10 50		11 42			12 42			14 03	14 03			15 16
77	Spalding	d			07 00	08 00	09 01				10 07		11 17		12 07			13 07			14 28	14 29			15 43
93½	**Peterborough 8**	a			07 25	08 25	09 27				10 31		11 43		12 33			13 32			14 53	14 55			16 09

		EM	NT	EM		EM	EM	NT	NT	EM	NT	EM	NT	EM		EM	NT	EM	EM	EM	NT	EM	EM		
		G	C				H	C	C	I	C		C				A		J		A		K		
Doncaster 7	d		13 03			14 27		14 04	15 04		16 03		17 01					19 34				20 33			
Gainsborough Lea Road	d		14 38			14 54		15 39	16 38		17 38		18 40				19 39	20 00			20 42	21 00			
Saxilby	d		14 51			15 07		15 52	16 51		17 51		18 53				19 52	20 13			20 55	21 14			
Lincoln	a		15 06			15 22		16 10	17 06		18 06		19 07				20 06	20 25			21 10	21 26			
	d	14 41		15 12			16 01			17 19		18 10		19 10					20 48						
Metheringham	d	14 54		15 25			16 14			17 32		18 23		19 23					21 01						
Ruskington	d	15 04		15 35			16 24			17 42		18 33		19 33					21 10						
Sleaford	a	15 13		15 44			16 34			17 51		18 42		19 42					21 19						
	d	15 16					16 34																		
Spalding	d	15 46					16 59									18 02				19 56			21 00		
Peterborough 8	a	16 12					17 25									18 28				20 21			21 25		

Saturdays

14 December to 17 May

		NT	EM	EM	EM	EM	NT	NT	NT	EM		NT	EM	EM	NT	NT	EM	EM	NT	EM		NT	EM	EM	NT
		A				B	A	A	A			C			C	C	H		C			C		H	C
Doncaster 7	d											09 04		10 24	10 03	11 03		13 05	12 03			13 03	15 07		14 03
Gainsborough Lea Road	d	06 25					07 38	08 24	09 38			10 38		10 52	11 38	12 38		13 31	13 40			14 38	15 33		15 40
Saxilby	d	06 38					07 51	08 37	09 51			10 51		11 05	11 51	12 51		13 44	13 53			14 51	15 46		15 53
Lincoln	a	06 53					08 06	08 52	10 06			11 06		11 17	12 06	13 06		13 55	14 07			15 06	15 57		16 10
	d		07 05			08 00				10 15			11 10				13 30			14 41				16 01	
Metheringham	d		07 18			08 12				10 28			11 23				13 43			14 54				16 14	
Ruskington	d		07 28			08 22				10 38			11 33				13 53			15 04				16 24	
Sleaford	a		07 37			08 31				10 50			11 42				14 02			15 13				16 34	
	d					08 34				10 50			11 42				14 03			15 16				16 34	
Spalding	d			07 00	08 00	09 01				11 17			12 07				14 28			15 41				16 59	
Peterborough 8	a			07 25	08 25	09 27				11 43			12 33				14 53			16 07				17 25	

		NT	EM	EM	NT	EM		EM	EM	NT	NT	EM	EM	NT	EM	EM
		C			C					C	C	J		A		K
Doncaster 7	d	15 04		16 27	16 03					17 01	18 02				20 33	
Gainsborough Lea Road	d	16 38		16 56	17 38					18 40	19 39			20 42	21 00	
Saxilby	d	16 51		17 09	17 51					18 53	19 52			20 55	21 14	
Lincoln	a	17 06		17 20	18 06					19 07	20 06			21 11	21 26	
	d		17 15			18 10			19 05			20 49				
Metheringham	d		17 28			18 23			19 18			21 02				
Ruskington	d		17 38			18 33			19 28			21 11				
Sleaford	a		17 47			18 42			19 37			21 20				
	d															
Spalding	d							18 02					19 56			20 59
Peterborough 8	a							18 28					20 21			21 23

Sundays

8 December to 11 May

		NT	NT	NT	NT
		A	A	A	A
Doncaster 7	d				
Gainsborough Lea Road	d	14 27	16 36	18 36	20 25
Saxilby	d	14 39	16 48	18 48	20 37
Lincoln	a	14 54	17 02	19 03	20 51
	d				
Metheringham	d				
Ruskington	d				
Sleaford	a				
	d				
Spalding	d				
Peterborough 8	a				

A From Sheffield
B From Nottingham
C From Scunthorpe
D until 27 December. From Newark North Gate
E from 30 December. From Newark North Gate
F until 27 December
G from 30 December
H From Newark North Gate
I From Leicester
J To Boston
K To Nottingham

For connections to London Kings Cross please see Table 25

Table 19

Mondays to Fridays

9 December to 16 May

Nottingham and Grantham - Skegness

Network Diagram - refer to first Page of Table 18

Miles	Miles			EM	EM	EM	EM	EM	EM	EM	EM	EM	EM	EM	EM	EM	EM	EM	EM	EM	EM	EM	EM
				A					B	C		D		D		D		D		D		D	
0	—	**Nottingham 8**	d	05 10		05 50	06 41	07 34	07 52	08 35	08 50	09 34	09 55	10 34	10 45	11 34	11 45	12 34	12 45	13 34	13 45	14 34	14 45
4½	—	Netherfield	d								08 56												
5	—	Radcliffe (Notts)	d								09 01								12 55				
8½	—	Bingham	d	05 24		06 04	06 55	07 48			09 07		10 09		10 59		11 59		13 01		13 59		15 00
10¾	—	Aslockton	d	05 28				07 52			09 11				11 03						14 03		
14½	—	Elton & Orston	d																				
15	0	Bottesford	d	05 35		06 13	07 04	07 59			09 17				11 10				13 09				15 09
22½	—	**Grantham 7**	a	05 49		06 27	07 18	08 12	08 23	09 06	09 31	10 06		11 07	11 23	12 07	12 19	13 07	13 23	14 05	14 23	15 07	15 22
—	—		d			06 31	07 24	08 16			09 36				11 27		12 25		13 27		14 27		15 26
34	12¾	Ancaster	d					08 34											13 45				
37¾	—	Rauceby	d					08 40															
40	—	**Sleaford**	d			06 57	07 51	08 45			10 04		10 44		11 53		12 50		13 55		14 52		15 52
44½	—	Heckington	d			07 04	07 58	08 52			10 11		10 51		12 00		12 57		14 02		14 59		15 59
49½	—	Swineshead	d				08 04																16 05
52¾	—	Hubberts Bridge	d				08 09																16 10
56½	—	**Boston**	d		06 25	07 24	08 18	09 12			10 28		11 11		12 19		13 15		14 21		15 17		16 20
73¼	—	Thorpe Culvert	d			07 46																	
75¼	—	Wainfleet	d		06 49	07 51	08 43	09 36			10 52		11 35		12 44		13 40		14 46		15 42		16 45
77	—	Havenhouse	d			07 54																	
80¼	—	**Skegness**	a		07 03	08 05	08 56	09 49			11 05		11 50		12 58		13 54		15 00		15 56		16 59

		EM	EM	EM	EM	EM	EM	EM	EM	EM	EM	EM
		D		D		D		D		D	E	
Nottingham 8	d	15 34	15 45	16 35	16 45	17 34	17 45	18 37	18 44	20 34		20 51
Netherfield	d		15 51		16 51							
Radcliffe (Notts)	d		15 56		16 56		17 55					21 01
Bingham	d		16 02		17 02	17 48	18 01		18 58			21 07
Aslockton	d		16 06		17 06	17 52	18 05		19 03			21 11
Elton & Orston	d				17 10							
Bottesford	d		16 12		17 14		18 12		19 10			21 17
Grantham 7	a	16 08	16 25	17 08	17 28	18 09	18 25	19 07	19 23	21 07		21 32
	d		16 29		17 32		18 29		19 26			21 38
Ancaster	d				17 50				19 44			
Rauceby	d				17 56				19 50			
Sleaford	d		16 55		18 01		18 55		19 55		21 20	22 03
Heckington	d		17 02		18 08		19 02		20 02		21 28	22 10
Swineshead	d											
Hubberts Bridge	d											
Boston	d		17 21		18 26		19 21		20 19		21a53	22a29
Thorpe Culvert	d		17 43									
Wainfleet	d		17 48		18 51		19 46		20 43			
Havenhouse	d		17 51									
Skegness	a		18 00		19 05		20 00		20 57			

Saturdays

14 December to 17 May

		EM	EM	EM	EM	EM	EM	EM	EM	EM	EM	EM	EM	EM	EM	EM	EM	EM	EM	EM	EM	EM	EM
		A					C	C		D		D		D		D		D		D		D	
Nottingham 8	d	05 10		05 50	06 41	07 28	07 45	08 34	08 45	09 34	09 55	10 34	10 45	11 34	11 45	12 34	12 45	13 34	13 45	14 34	14 45	15 34	15 45
Netherfield	d								08 51														15 51
Radcliffe (Notts)	d								08 56								12 55						15 56
Bingham	d	05 24		06 04	06 55	07 42			09 02		10 09		10 59		11 59		13 01		13 59		14 59		16 02
Aslockton	d	05 28				07 46			09 06				11 03						14 03				16 06
Elton & Orston	d																						
Bottesford	d	05 35		06 13	07 04	07 53			09 12				11 10				13 09				15 08		16 12
Grantham 7	a	05 49		06 27	07 18	08 07	08 15	09 07	09 26	10 07		11 06	11 23	12 05	12 19	13 07	13 25	14 05	14 23	15 07	15 22	16 06	16 25
	d			06 31	07 24	08 16			09 30				11 27		12 25		13 29		14 27		15 26		16 29
Ancaster	d					08 34																	
Rauceby	d					08 40																	
Sleaford	d			06 57	07 51	08 45			09 56		10 44		11 53		12 50		13 55		14 52		15 52		16 55
Heckington	d			07 04	07 58	08 52			10 03		10 51		12 00		12 57		14 02		14 59		15 59		17 02
Swineshead	d				08 04																16 05		
Hubberts Bridge	d				08 09																16 10		
Boston	d		06 25	07 24	08 18	09 11			10 22		11 11		12 19		13 15		14 21		15 17		16 20		17 21
Thorpe Culvert	d			07 46																			17 43
Wainfleet	d		06 49	07 51	08 43	09 35			10 47		11 35		12 44		13 40		14 46		15 42		16 45		17 48
Havenhouse	d			07 54																			17 51
Skegness	a		07 03	08 05	08 56	09 48			11 00		11 50		12 58		13 54		15 00		15 56		16 59		18 00

A To Spalding
B From Mansfield Woodhouse to Norwich
C To Norwich
D From Liverpool Lime Street to Norwich
E From Lincoln

For connections from London Kings Cross please see Table 26

Table 19

Nottingham and Grantham - Skegness

Saturdays

14 December to 17 May

Network Diagram - refer to first Page of Table 18

		EM	EM	EM	EM	EM	EM	EM	EM	EM
		A		A		A		A	B	
Nottingham 8	d	16 34	16 45	17 34	17 45	18 37	18 45	20 34		20 51
Netherfield	d		16 51							
Radcliffe (Notts)	d		16 56		17 55					21 01
Bingham	d		17 02	17 48	18 01		18 59			21 07
Aslockton	d		17 06	17 52	18 05		19 03			21 11
Elton & Orston	d		17 10							
Bottesford	d		17 14		18 12		19 10			21 17
Grantham 7	a	17 04	17 28	18 10	18 25	19 08	19 23	21 05		21 31
	d		17 32		18 29		19 26			21 36
Ancaster	d		17 50				19 44			
Rauceby	d		17 56				19 50			
Sleaford	d		18 01		18 55		19 55		21 21	22 01
Heckington	d		18 08		19 02		20 02		21 29	22 08
Swineshead	d									
Hubberts Bridge	d									
Boston	d		18 26		19 21		20 19		21a53	22a29
Thorpe Culvert	d									
Wainfleet	d		18 51		19 46		20 43			
Havenhouse	d									
Skegness	a		19 05		20 00		20 57			

Sundays

8 December to 11 May

		EM	EM	EM	EM	EM	EM	EM	EM	EM	EM	EM	EM	EM
			C		D	E		A		A	A		A	A
Nottingham 8	d	11 55	12 37		13 47	14 45	14 56	15 50	16 23	16 45	17 36	18 31	18 46	20 45
Netherfield	d								16 29		17 42			
Radcliffe (Notts)	d								16 34		17 46			
Bingham	d	12 11	12 51				15 10		16 40		17 52	18 45	19 00	20 59
Aslockton	d								16 44		17 56			
Elton & Orston	d													
Bottesford	d								16 50		18 03			
Grantham 7	a	12 29	13 10		14 20	15 16	15 31	16 20	17 03	17 15	18 16	19 08	19 21	21 18
	d	12 33		13 50			15 36		17 07			19 13		
Ancaster	d													
Rauceby	d													
Sleaford	d	12 59		14 16			16 04		17 36			19 41		
Heckington	d	13 06		14 23			16 11		17 43			19 48		
Swineshead	d													
Hubberts Bridge	d													
Boston	d	13 24		14 45			16 31		18 02			20a10		
Thorpe Culvert	d													
Wainfleet	d	13 49		15 09			16 55		18 27					
Havenhouse	d													
Skegness	a	14 00		15 24			17 10		18 38					

A From Liverpool Lime Street to Norwich
B From Lincoln
C To Norwich
D From Sheffield to Norwich
E From Manchester Piccadilly to Norwich

For connections from London Kings Cross please see Table 26

Table 19R

Mondays to Fridays

9 December to 16 May

Skegness - Grantham and Nottingham

Network Diagram - refer to first Page of Table 18

Miles	Miles			EM	EM	EM A	EM	EM A	EM	EM A	EM	EM A	EM
0	—	**Skegness**	d				07 09		08 10		09 06		10 15
3¼	—	Havenhouse	d				07 15						
5	—	Wainfleet	d				07 19		08 18		09 14		10 23
7	—	Thorpe Culvert	d				07 23						
23¾	—	**Boston**	d		06 13		07 46		08 45		09 41		10 50
27½	—	Hubberts Bridge	d				07 52						
30¾	—	Swineshead	d				07 57						
35¾	—	Heckington	d		06 27		08 02		08 59		09 55		11 04
40¼	—	**Sleaford**	d		06 35		08 11		09 07		10 03		11 12
42½	—	Rauceby	d		06 39		08 15						
46¼	0	Ancaster	d		06 45		08 21						11 21
57¾	—	**Grantham** 7	a		07 04		08 42		09 35		10 31		11 41
—	—		d	06 10	07 10	07 58	08 45	08 55	09 40	09 58	10 36	11 00	11 45
65¼	12¾	Bottesford	d	06 21	07 21	08 11			09 52				11 56
67¾	—	Elton & Orston	d	06 25									
69½	—	Aslockton	d	06 29	07 27	08 18	09 00				10 52		
71¾	—	Bingham	d	06 33	07 31	08 22	09 05		10 00		10 57		12 04
75¼	—	Radcliffe (Notts)	d	06 39	07 37	08 28							12 09
77	—	Netherfield	d		07 42	08 33							
80¼	—	**Nottingham** 8	a	06 54	07 53	08 40	09 20	09 26	10 20	10 35	11 17	11 34	12 22

Miles	Miles			EM A	EM	EM A	EM	EM A	EM	EM A	EM	EM A	EM
0	—	**Skegness**	d		11 15		12 15		13 15		14 15		15 09
3¼	—	Havenhouse	d										
5	—	Wainfleet	d		11 23		12 23		13 23		14 23		15 17
7	—	Thorpe Culvert	d										
23¾	—	**Boston**	d		11 50		12 50		13 50		14 50		15 44
27½	—	Hubberts Bridge	d										15 50
30¾	—	Swineshead	d										15 55
35¾	—	Heckington	d		12 04		13 04		14 04		15 04		16 01
40¼	—	**Sleaford**	d		12 12		13 12		14 13		15 12		16 10
42½	—	Rauceby	d										16 14
46¼	0	Ancaster	d										16 20
57¾	—	**Grantham** 7	a		12 41		13 41		14 42		15 41		16 41
—	—		d	12 00	12 45	12 59	13 46	13 58	14 45	14 58	15 45	16 01	16 45
65¼	12¾	Bottesford	d				13 57				15 56		
67¾	—	Elton & Orston	d										
69½	—	Aslockton	d		13 00				15 00				
71¾	—	Bingham	d		13 04		14 05		15 05		16 04		17 02
75¼	—	Radcliffe (Notts)	d										
77	—	Netherfield	d										
80¼	—	**Nottingham** 8	a	12 35	13 23	13 36	14 22	14 35	15 23	15 32	16 22	16 35	17 17

		EM A	EM	EM A	EM	EM B	EM	EM C	EM	EM C	EM	EM
Skegness	d		16 11		17 30		18 14		19 14		20 15	21 02
Havenhouse	d		16 17									
Wainfleet	d		16 21		17 38		18 22		19 22		20 23	21 10
Thorpe Culvert	d		16 25									
Boston	d		16 48		18 05		18 49		19 49		20 50	21 37
Hubberts Bridge	d											
Swineshead	d											
Heckington	d		17 04		18 19		19 04		20 05		21 04	21 51
Sleaford	d		17 13		18 27		19 13		20 13		21 18	22 00
Rauceby	d											
Ancaster	d											
Grantham 7	a		17 42				19 41		20 40		21 45	
	d	16 58	17 45	17 57		18 57	19 45	19 59	20 44	20 59	21 49	
Bottesford	d		17 56				19 56				22 00	
Elton & Orston	d											
Aslockton	d		18 02				20 02				22 06	
Bingham	d		18 07		19 03	19 14	20 06		21 01		22 10	22 35
Radcliffe (Notts)	d						20 12					
Netherfield	d						20 16					
Nottingham 8	a	17 35	18 22	18 33	19 22	19 34	20 25	20 31	21 20	21 33	22 26	22 54

Saturdays

14 December to 17 May

		EM	EM	EM A	EM	EM A	EM	EM A	EM	EM A	EM	EM A
Skegness	d				07 09		08 15		09 15		10 15	
Havenhouse	d				07 15							
Wainfleet	d				07 19		08 23		09 23		10 23	
Thorpe Culvert	d				07 23							
Boston	d		06 13		07 46		08 50		09 50		10 50	
Hubberts Bridge	d				07 52							
Swineshead	d				07 57							
Heckington	d		06 27		08 02		09 04		10 05		11 04	
Sleaford	d		06 35		08 11		09 12		10 14		11 12	
Rauceby	d		06 39		08 15							
Ancaster	d		06 45		08 21						11 21	
Grantham 7	a		07 07		08 42		09 41		10 43		11 41	
	d	06 10	07 10	07 58	08 45	08 59	09 45	09 53	10 46	10 54	11 45	11 56
Bottesford	d	06 21	07 21	08 11			09 56				11 56	
Elton & Orston	d	06 25										
Aslockton	d	06 29	07 27	08 17	09 00				11 01			
Bingham	d	06 33	07 32	08 21	09 05		10 04		11 06		12 04	
Radcliffe (Notts)	d	06 39	07 37	08 27							12 09	
Netherfield	d		07 42	08 31								
Nottingham 8	a	06 54	07 52	08 39	09 20	09 35	10 22	10 36	11 23	11 35	12 22	12 36

		EM	EM A	EM	EM A	EM	EM A	EM	EM A	EM	EM A	EM
Skegness	d	11 15		12 15		13 15		14 15		15 09		16 11
Havenhouse	d											16 17
Wainfleet	d	11 23		12 23		13 23		14 23		15 17		16 21
Thorpe Culvert	d											16 25
Boston	d	11 50		12 50		13 50		14 50		15 44		16 48
Hubberts Bridge	d									15 50		
Swineshead	d									15 55		
Heckington	d	12 04		13 04		14 04		15 04		16 01		17 04
Sleaford	d	12 12		13 12		14 13		15 12		16 10		17 13
Rauceby	d									16 14		
Ancaster	d									16 20		
Grantham 7	a	12 41		13 41		14 42		15 41		16 41		17 42
	d	12 45	12 58	13 46	13 58	14 45	14 58	15 45	15 57	16 45	16 56	17 45
Bottesford	d			13 57				15 56				17 56
Elton & Orston	d											
Aslockton	d	13 00				15 00						18 02
Bingham	d	13 04		14 05		15 05		16 04		17 02		18 07
Radcliffe (Notts)	d											
Netherfield	d											
Nottingham 8	a	13 23	13 36	14 22	14 36	15 23	15 36	16 22	16 36	17 20	17 36	18 22

A From Norwich to Liverpool Lime Street **B** From Norwich to Manchester Piccadilly **C** From Norwich

For connections to London Kings Cross please see Table 26

Table 19R

Saturdays

14 December to 17 May

Skegness - Grantham and Nottingham

Network Diagram - refer to first Page of Table 18

		EM	EM	EM	EM	EM	EM	EM	EM	EM	EM
		A		B		C		C		D	
Skegness	d		17 30		18 14		19 19		20 15		21 02
Havenhouse	d										
Wainfleet	d		17 38		18 22		19 27		20 23		21 10
Thorpe Culvert	d										
Boston	d		18 05		18 49		19 54		20 50		21 37
Hubberts Bridge	d										
Swineshead	d										
Heckington	d		18 19		19 04		20 10		21 04		21 51
Sleaford	d		18 27		19 13		20 18		21 12		22 00
Rauceby	d										
Ancaster	d										
Grantham 7	a				19 41		20 45		21 43		
	d	17 59		18 58	19 45	20 03	20 48	20 58	21 47	22 02	
Bottesford	d				19 56				21 58		
Elton & Orston	d										
Aslockton	d				20 02				22 04		
Bingham	d		19 03	19 15	20 06		21 05		22 08		22 35
Radcliffe (Notts)	d				20 12						
Netherfield	d				20 16						
Nottingham 8	a	18 33	19 23	19 34	20 24	20 37	21 25	21 32	22 25	22 32	22 54

Sundays

8 December to 11 May

		EM	EM	EM	EM	EM	EM	EM	EM	EM	EM	EM	EM	EM	EM
		A		E		A	A		B	B		C		C	C
Skegness	d				14 10			16 17			18 07		19 15		
Havenhouse	d														
Wainfleet	d				14 18			16 25			18 15		19 23		
Thorpe Culvert	d														
Boston	d		12 13		14 45			16 52			18 42		19 50		
Hubberts Bridge	d														
Swineshead	d														
Heckington	d		12 27		14 59			17 06			18 56		20 04		
Sleaford	d		12 35		15 07			17 14			19 04		20 12		
Rauceby	d														
Ancaster	d														
Grantham 7	a		13 04		15 35			17 43			19 33		20 41		
	d	12 51		15 09	15 40	15 55	16 56	17 47	17 55	18 58	19 37	19 57	20 45	21 02	22 55
Bottesford	d	13 02													
Elton & Orston	d														
Aslockton	d	13 08													
Bingham	d	13 12			15 57			18 04	18 12		19 54		21 02		
Radcliffe (Notts)	d	13 18													
Netherfield	d	13 22													
Nottingham 8	a	13 29		15 39	16 17	16 24	17 25	18 22	18 27	19 33	20 12	20 31	21 20	21 34	23 28

A From Norwich to Liverpool Lime Street
B From Norwich to Manchester Piccadilly
C From Norwich
D From Spalding
E From Peterborough to Liverpool Lime Street

For connections to London Kings Cross please see Table 26

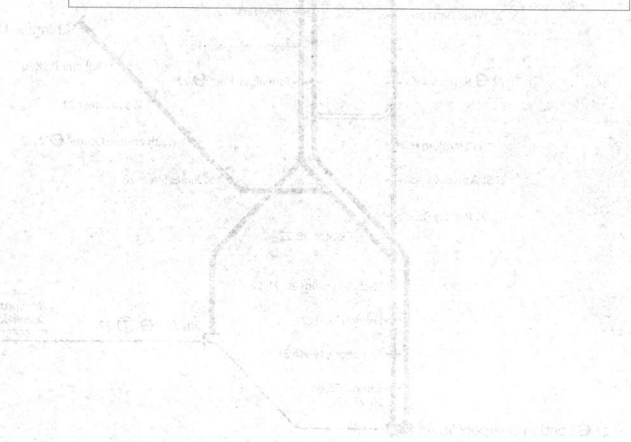

Network Diagram for Tables 20, 21, 22

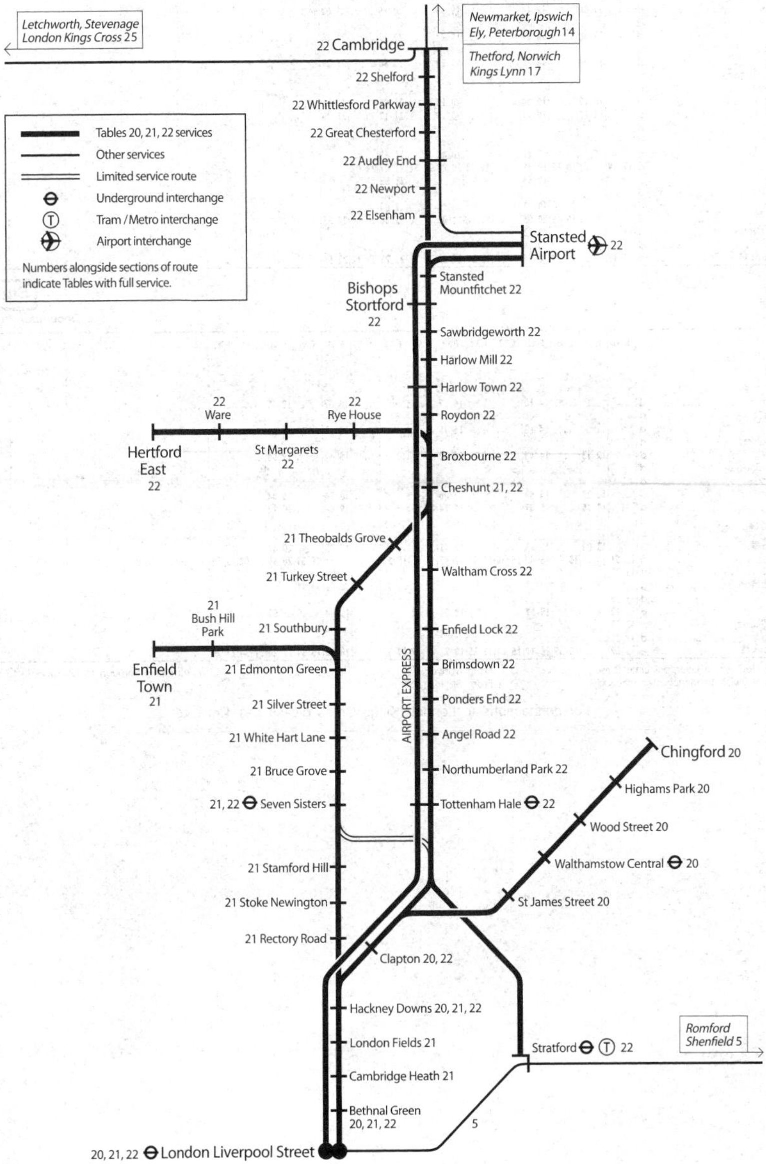

Letchworth, Stevenage
London Kings Cross 25
Newmarket, Ipswich
Ely, Peterborough 14
Thetford, Norwich
Kings Lynn 17
22 Cambridge
22 Shelford
22 Whittlesford Parkway
22 Great Chesterford
22 Audley End
22 Newport
22 Elsenham
Stansted Airport 22
Stansted Mountfitchet 22
Bishops Stortford 22
Sawbridgeworth 22
Harlow Mill 22
Harlow Town 22
Roydon 22
22 Ware
22 Rye House
Hertford East 22
St Margarets 22
Broxbourne 22
Cheshunt 21, 22
21 Theobalds Grove
21 Turkey Street
Waltham Cross 22
21 Bush Hill Park
21 Southbury
Enfield Lock 22
Enfield Town 21
21 Edmonton Green
Brimsdown 22
21 Silver Street
Ponders End 22
AIRPORT EXPRESS
21 White Hart Lane
Angel Road 22
Chingford 20
21 Bruce Grove
Northumberland Park 22
Highams Park 20
21, 22 Seven Sisters
Tottenham Hale 22
Wood Street 20
21 Stamford Hill
Walthamstow Central 20
21 Stoke Newington
St James Street 20
21 Rectory Road
Clapton 20, 22
Hackney Downs 20, 21, 22
London Fields 21
Stratford 22
Romford
Shenfield 5
Cambridge Heath 21
Bethnal Green 20, 21, 22
5
20, 21, 22 London Liverpool Street
Tables 20, 21, 22 services
Other services
Limited service route
Underground interchange
Tram / Metro interchange
Airport interchange
Numbers alongside sections of route indicate Tables with full service.

TOCs operating on this network - Greater Anglia (LE), Cross Country (XC)

Table 20

London - Chingford

Mondays to Fridays

9 December to 16 May

Network Diagram - see first Page of Table 20

Miles			LE	LE	LE	LE MX	LE	LE	LE	LE	LE		LE	LE	LE	LE	LE	LE	LE	LE	LE		LE	LE	LE
0	**London Liverpool Street** 15 ⊖	d	00 03	00 18	00 33	00 48	01 03	06 03	06 33	06 48	07 03		07 18	07 33	07 48	08 05	08 18	08 35	08 48	09 03	09 18		09 33	09 48	10 03
1¼	Bethnal Green	d	00 06	00 21	00 36			06 06	06 36	06 51	07 06		07 21	07 36	07 51		08 21		08 51	09 06	09 21		09 36	09 51	10 06
3	Hackney Downs	d	00 10	00 25	00 40	00 55	01 10	06 10	06 40	06 55	07 10		07 25	07 40	07 55	08 12	08 25	08 42	08 55	09 10	09 25		09 40	09 55	10 10
4	Clapton	d	00 13	00 28	00 43	00 58	01 13	06 13	06 43	06 58	07 13		07 28	07 43	07 58	08 15	08 28	08 45	08 58	09 13	09 28		09 43	09 58	10 13
5¾	St James Street	d	00 16	00 32	00 47	01 02	01 17	06 16	06 46	07 01	07 17		07 32	07 47	08 02	08 18	08 31	08 48	09 01	09 16	09 31		09 46	10 01	10 16
6¼	Walthamstow Central ⊖	d	00 18	00 34	00 49	01 04	01 19	06 18	06 48	07 03	07 19		07 34	07 49	08 04	08 20	08 33	08 50	09 03	09 18	09 33		09 48	10 03	10 18
7	Wood Street	d	00 20	00 36	00 51	01 06	01 21	06 20	06 50	07 05	07 21		07 36	07 51	08 06	08 22	08 35	08 52	09 05	09 20	09 35		09 50	10 05	10 20
8½	Highams Park	d	00 23	00 39	00 54	01 09	01 24	06 23	06 53	07 08	07 24		07 39	07 54	08 09	08 25	08 38	08 55	09 08	09 23	09 38		09 53	10 08	10 23
10½	**Chingford**	a	00 29	00 44	00 59	01 14	01 29	06 29	06 59	07 17	07 30		07 45	08 02	08 15	08 32	08 44	09 02	09 15	09 30	09 44		09 59	10 14	10 29

		LE	LE	LE	LE	LE	LE		LE	LE	LE	LE	LE	LE	LE	LE	LE		LE	LE	LE	LE	LE	LE	LE
London Liverpool Street 15 ⊖	d	10 18	10 33	10 48	11 03	11 18	11 33		11 48	12 03	12 18	12 33	12 48	13 03	13 18	13 33	13 48		14 03	14 18	14 33	14 48	15 03	15 18	15 33
Bethnal Green	d	10 21	10 36	10 51	11 06	11 21	11 36		11 51	12 06	12 21	12 36	12 51	13 06	13 21	13 36	13 51		14 06	14 21	14 36	14 51	15 06	15 21	15 36
Hackney Downs	d	10 25	10 40	10 55	11 10	11 25	11 40		11 55	12 10	12 25	12 40	12 55	13 10	13 25	13 40	13 55		14 10	14 25	14 40	14 55	15 10	15 25	15 40
Clapton	d	10 28	10 43	10 58	11 13	11 28	11 43		11 58	12 13	12 28	12 43	12 58	13 13	13 28	13 43	13 58		14 13	14 28	14 43	14 58	15 13	15 28	15 43
St James Street	d	10 31	10 46	11 01	11 16	11 31	11 46		12 01	12 16	12 31	12 46	13 01	13 16	13 31	13 46	14 01		14 16	14 31	14 46	15 01	15 16	15 31	15 46
Walthamstow Central ⊖	d	10 33	10 48	11 03	11 18	11 33	11 48		12 03	12 18	12 33	12 48	13 03	13 18	13 33	13 48	14 03		14 18	14 33	14 48	15 03	15 18	15 33	15 48
Wood Street	d	10 35	10 50	11 05	11 20	11 35	11 50		12 05	12 20	12 35	12 50	13 05	13 20	13 35	13 50	14 05		14 20	14 35	14 50	15 05	15 20	15 35	15 50
Highams Park	d	10 38	10 53	11 08	11 23	11 38	11 53		12 08	12 23	12 38	12 53	13 08	13 23	13 38	13 53	14 08		14 23	14 38	14 53	15 08	15 23	15 38	15 53
Chingford	a	10 44	10 59	11 14	11 29	11 44	11 59		12 14	12 30	12 45	13 00	13 15	13 30	13 45	14 00	14 15		14 30	14 44	14 59	15 14	15 29	15 44	15 59

		LE	LE		LE	LE	LE	LE	LE	LE	LE	LE	LE		LE	LE	LE	LE	LE	LE	LE			
London Liverpool Street 15 ⊖	d	15 48	16 03		16 18	16 33	16 48	17 03	17 18	17 33	17 48	18 03	18 18		18 33	18 48	19 03	19 18	19 33	19 48	20 03	and at the same minutes past each hour until		
Bethnal Green	d	15 51	16 06		16 21	16 36	16 51		17 21		17 51		18 21			18 51		19 21	19 36	19 51	20 06			
Hackney Downs	d	15 55	16 10		16 25	16 40	16 55	17 10	17 25	17 40	17 55	18 10	18 25		18 40	18 55	19 10	19 25	19 40	19 55	20 10			
Clapton	d	15 58	16 13		16 28	16 43	16 58	17 12	17 28	17 42	17 58	18 12	18 28		18 42	18 58	19 12	19 28	19 43	19 58	20 13			
St James Street	d	16 01	16 16		16 31	16 46	17 01	17 16	17 31	17 46	18 01	18 16	18 31		18 46	19 01	19 16	19 31	19 46	20 01	20 16			
Walthamstow Central ⊖	d	16 03	16 19		16 34	16 49	17 04	17 18	17 34	17 48	18 04	18 18	18 34		18 48	19 04	19 18	19 33	19 48	20 03	20 18			
Wood Street	d	16 05	16 21		16 36	16 51	17 06	17 20	17 36	17 50	18 06	18 20	18 36		18 50	19 06	19 20	19 35	19 50	20 05	20 20			
Highams Park	d	16 08	16 24		16 39	16 54	17 09	17 23	17 39	17 53	18 09	18 23	18 39		18 53	19 09	19 23	19 38	19 53	20 08	20 23			
Chingford	a	16 14	16 31		16 46	17 01	17 16	17 31	17 46	18 01	18 16	18 31	18 46		19 01	19 16	19 29	19 44	19 59	20 14	20 29			

		LE	LE	LE	LE		LE	LE	LE
London Liverpool Street 15 ⊖	d	22 18	22 33	22 48	23 03		23 18	23 33	23 48
Bethnal Green	d	22 21	22 36	22 51	23 06		23 21		23 51
Hackney Downs	d	22 25	22 40	22 55	23 10		23 25		23 55
Clapton	d	22 28	22 43	22 58	23 13		23 28		23 58
St James Street	d	22 31	22 46	23 01	23 16		23 31		00 01
Walthamstow Central ⊖	d	22 33	22 48	23 03	23 18		23 33	23 44	00 03
Wood Street	d	22 35	22 50	23 05	23 20		23 35		00 05
Highams Park	d	22 38	22 53	23 08	23 23		23 38		00 08
Chingford	a	22 44	22 59	23 14	23 29		23 44	23 54	00 14

Saturdays

14 December to 17 May

		LE	LE	LE	LE	LE	LE	LE	LE	LE	LE		LE	LE	LE	LE		LE	LE
London Liverpool Street 15 ⊖	d	00 03	00 18	00 33	00 48	01 03	06 03	06 33	06 48	07 03	07 18	and at the same minutes past each hour until	22 33	22 48	23 03	23 18		23 33	23 48
Bethnal Green	d	00 06	00 21	00 36			06 06	06 36	06 51	07 06	07 21		22 36	22 51	23 06	23 21			23 51
Hackney Downs	d	00 10	00 25	00 40	00 55	01 10	06 10	06 40	06 55	07 10	07 25		22 40	22 55	23 10	23 25			23 55
Clapton	d	00 13	00 28	00 43	00 58	01 13	06 13	06 43	06 58	07 13	07 28		22 43	22 58	23 13	23 28			23 58
St James Street	d	00 16	00 32	00 47	01 02	01 17	06 16	06 46	07 01	07 16	07 31		22 46	23 01	23 16	23 31			00 01
Walthamstow Central ⊖	d	00 18	00 34	00 49	01 04	01 19	06 18	06 48	07 03	07 18	07 33		22 48	23 03	23 18	23 33		23 44	00 03
Wood Street	d	00 20	00 36	00 51	01 06	01 21	06 20	06 50	07 05	07 20	07 35		22 50	23 05	23 20	23 35			00 05
Highams Park	d	00 23	00 39	00 54	01 09	01 24	06 23	06 53	07 08	07 23	07 38		22 53	23 08	23 23	23 38			00 08
Chingford	a	00 29	00 44	00 59	01 14	01 29	06 29	06 59	07 14	07 29	07 44		22 59	23 14	23 29	23 44		23 54	00 14

Sundays

8 December to 11 May

		LE	LE	LE	LE	LE	LE	LE	LE	LE		LE	LE	LE	LE	LE		LE	LE	LE	LE		LE	LE
London Liverpool Street 15 ⊖	d	00 03	00 18	00 33	00 48	01 03	07 33	08 03	08 33	08 48		09 03	09 18	09 33	09 48	10 03	and at the same minutes past each hour until	22 18	22 33	22 48	23 03		23 18	23 33
Bethnal Green	d	00 06	00 21	00 36									09 21	09 36	09 51	10 06		22 21	22 36	22 51	23 06		23 21	23 36
Hackney Downs	d	00 10	00 25	00 40	00 55	01 10	07 40	08 10	08 40	08 55		09 10	09 25	09 40	09 55	10 10		22 25	22 40	22 55	23 10		23 25	23 40
Clapton	d	00 13	00 28	00 43	00 58	01 13	07 43	08 13	08 43	08 58		09 13	09 28	09 43	09 58	10 13		22 28	22 43	22 58	23 13		23 28	23 43
St James Street	d	00 16	00 32	00 47	01 02	01 17	07 46	08 16	08 46	09 01		09 16	09 31	09 46	10 01	10 16		22 31	22 46	23 01	23 16		23 31	23 46
Walthamstow Central ⊖	d	00 18	00 34	00 49	01 04	01 19	07 48	08 18	08 48	09 03		09 18	09 33	09 48	10 03	10 18		22 33	22 48	23 03	23 18		23 33	23 48
Wood Street	d	00 20	00 36	00 51	01 06	01 21	07 50	08 20	08 50	09 05		09 20	09 35	09 50	10 05	10 20		22 35	22 50	23 05	23 20		23 35	23 50
Highams Park	d	00 23	00 39	00 54	01 09	01 24	07 53	08 23	08 53	09 08		09 23	09 38	09 53	10 08	10 23		22 38	22 53	23 08	23 23		23 38	23 53
Chingford	a	00 29	00 44	00 59	01 14	01 29	07 59	08 29	08 59	09 14		09 29	09 44	09 59	10 14	10 29		22 44	22 59	23 14	23 29		23 44	23 59

		LE
London Liverpool Street 15 ⊖	d	23 48
Bethnal Green	d	23 51
Hackney Downs	d	23 55
Clapton	d	23 58
St James Street	d	00 01
Walthamstow Central ⊖	d	00 03
Wood Street	d	00 05
Highams Park	d	00 08
Chingford	a	00 14

Table 20R

Mondays to Fridays

9 December to 16 May

Chingford - London

Network Diagram - see first Page of Table 20

Miles			LE	LE	LE	LE	LE	LE	LE	LE	LE	LE	LE	LE	LE	LE	LE	LE	LE	LE
0	**Chingford**	d	05 10	05 25	05 40	05 55	06 10	06 29	06 44	06 59	07 14	07 29	07 44	07 59	08 14	08 29	08 44	08 57	09 12	09 27
2	Highams Park	d	05 14	05 29	05 44	05 59	06 14	06 33	06 48	07 03	07 18	07 33	07 48	08 03	08 18	08 33	08 48	09 01	09 16	09 31
3½	Wood Street	d	05 17	05 32	05 47	06 02	06 17	06 37	06 52	07 07	07 22	07 37	07 52	08 07	08 22	08 37	08 52	09 05	09 20	09 35
4¼	Walthamstow Central ⊖	d	05 19	05 34	05 49	06 04	06 19	06 39	06 54	07 09	07 24	07 39	07 54	08 09	08 24	08 39	08 54	09 07	09 22	09 37
4¾	St James Street	d	05 21	05 36	05 51	06 06	06 21	06 42	06 56	07 12	07 26	07 42	07 56	08 12	08 26	08 42	08 56	09 10	09 25	09 40
6½	Clapton	d	05 24	05 39	05 54	06 09	06 24	06 45	07 00	07 15	07 30	07 45	08 00	08 15	08 30	08 45	09 00	09 13	09 28	09 43
7½	Hackney Downs	d	05 28	05 43	05 58	06 13	06 28	06 49	07 03	07 18	07 33	07 48	08 03	08 18	08 33	08 48	09 03	09 17	09 32	09 47
9¼	Bethnal Green	d	05 32	05 47	06 02	06 17	06 32	06 53	07 07		07 37		08 07		08 37		09 07	09 21	09 36	09 51
10½	**London Liverpool Street** 15 ⊖	a	05 36	05 51	06 07	06 21	06 36	06 58	07 13	07 28	07 43	07 58	08 13	08 28	08 43	08 57	09 13	09 27	09 42	09 57

		LE	LE	LE	LE		LE	LE	LE	LE	LE	LE	LE	LE	LE	LE	LE	LE	LE	LE	LE
Chingford	d	09 40	09 55	10 10	10 25	and at	15 40	15 55	16 10	16 25	16 40	16 55	17 10	17 25	17 39	17 55	18 09	18 25	18 39	18 55	19 09
Highams Park	d	09 44	09 59	10 14	10 29	the same	15 44	15 59	16 14	16 29	16 44	16 59	17 14	17 29	17 43	17 59	18 13	18 29	18 43	18 59	19 13
Wood Street	d	09 47	10 02	10 17	10 32	minutes	15 47	16 02	16 17	16 32	16 47	17 02	17 17	17 32	17 46	18 02	18 16	18 32	18 46	19 02	19 16
Walthamstow Central ⊖	d	09 49	10 04	10 19	10 34	past	15 49	16 04	16 19	16 34	16 49	17 04	17 19	17 34	17 48	18 04	18 18	18 34	18 48	19 04	19 18
St James Street	d	09 51	10 06	10 21	10 36	each	15 51	16 06	16 21	16 36	16 51	17 06	17 21	17 36	17 50	18 06	18 20	18 36	18 50	19 06	19 20
Clapton	d	09 54	10 09	10 24	10 39	hour until	15 54	16 09	16 24	16 39	16 54	17 09	17 24	17 39	17 54	18 09	18 24	18 39	18 54	19 09	19 24
Hackney Downs	d	09 58	10 13	10 28	10 43		15 58	16 13	16 28	16 43	16 58	17 13	17 28	17 43	17 57	18 13	18 27	18 43	18 57	19 13	19 27
Bethnal Green	d	10 02	10 17	10 32	10 47		16 02	16 17	16 32	16 47	17 02	17 17	17 32	17 47	18 01	18 17	18 31	18 47	19 01	19 17	19 31
London Liverpool Street 15 ⊖	a	10 06	10 21	10 36	10 51		16 06	16 21	16 36	16 51	17 06	17 21	17 36	17 52	18 06	18 22	18 36	18 51	19 06	19 22	19 36

		LE	LE	LE	LE		LE	LE	LE	LE	LE
Chingford	d	19 25	19 40	19 55	20 10	and at	22 25	22 40	22 55	23 10	23 25
Highams Park	d	19 29	19 44	19 59	20 14	the same	22 29	22 44	22 59	23 14	23 29
Wood Street	d	19 32	19 47	20 02	20 17	minutes	22 32	22 47	23 02	23 17	23 32
Walthamstow Central ⊖	d	19 34	19 49	20 04	20 19	past	22 34	22 49	23 04	23 19	23 34
St James Street	d	19 36	19 51	20 06	20 21	each	22 36	22 51	23 06	23 21	23 36
Clapton	d	19 39	19 54	20 09	20 24	hour until	22 39	22 54	23 09	23 24	23 39
Hackney Downs	d	19 43	19 58	20 13	20 28		22 43	22 58	23 13	23 28	23 43
Bethnal Green	d	19 47	20 02	20 17	20 32		22 47	23 02	23 17	23 32	23 47
London Liverpool Street 15 ⊖	a	19 51	20 06	20 21	20 36		22 51	23 06	23 21	23 36	23 51

Saturdays

14 December to 17 May

		LE	LE	LE	LE		LE	LE	LE	LE	LE	LE
Chingford	d	05 10	05 25	05 40	05 55	and at	22 10	22 25	22 40	22 55	23 10	23 25
Highams Park	d	05 14	05 29	05 44	05 59	the same	22 14	22 29	22 44	22 59	23 14	23 29
Wood Street	d	05 17	05 32	05 47	06 02	minutes	22 17	22 32	22 47	23 02	23 17	23 32
Walthamstow Central ⊖	d	05 19	05 34	05 49	06 04	past	22 19	22 34	22 49	23 04	23 19	23 34
St James Street	d	05 21	05 36	05 51	06 06	each	22 21	22 36	22 51	23 06	23 21	23 36
Clapton	d	05 24	05 39	05 54	06 09	hour until	22 24	22 39	22 54	23 09	23 24	23 39
Hackney Downs	d	05 28	05 43	05 58	06 13		22 28	22 43	22 58	23 13	23 28	23 43
Bethnal Green	d	05 32	05 47	06 02	06 17		22 32	22 47	23 02	23 17	23 32	23 47
London Liverpool Street 15 ⊖	a	05 36	05 51	06 06	06 21		22 36	22 51	23 06	23 21	23 36	23 51

Sundays

8 December to 11 May

		LE	LE	LE	LE	LE	LE	LE	LE	LE	LE	LE	LE	LE		LE	LE	LE	LE	LE	LE
Chingford	d	06 40	06 55	07 10	07 25	07 40	07 55	08 10	08 25	08 40	08 55	09 10	09 25	09 40	and at	21 55	22 10	22 25	22 40	22 55	23 10
Highams Park	d	06 44	06 59	07 14	07 29	07 44	07 59	08 14	08 29	08 44	08 59	09 14	09 29	09 44	the same	21 59	22 14	22 29	22 44	22 59	23 14
Wood Street	d	06 47	07 02	07 17	07 32	07 47	08 02	08 17	08 32	08 47	09 02	09 17	09 32	09 47	minutes	22 02	22 17	22 32	22 47	23 02	23 17
Walthamstow Central ⊖	d	06 49	07 04	07 19	07 34	07 49	08 04	08 19	08 34	08 49	09 04	09 19	09 34	09 49	past	22 04	22 19	22 34	22 49	23 04	23 19
St James Street	d	06 51	07 06	07 21	07 36	07 51	08 06	08 21	08 36	08 51	09 06	09 21	09 36	09 51	each	22 06	22 21	22 36	22 51	23 06	23 21
Clapton	d	06 54	07 09	07 24	07 39	07 54	08 09	08 24	08 39	08 54	09 09	09 24	09 39	09 54	hour until	22 09	22 24	22 39	22 54	23 09	23 24
Hackney Downs	d	06 58	07 13	07 28	07 43	07 58	08 13	08 28	08 43	08 58	09 13	09 28	09 43	09 58		22 13	22 28	22 43	22 58	23 13	23 28
Bethnal Green	d										09 17	09 32	09 47	10 02		22 17	22 32	22 47	23 02	23 17	23 32
London Liverpool Street 15 ⊖	a	07 06	07 21	07 36	07 51	08 06	08 21	08 36	08 51	09 06	09 21	09 36	09 51	10 06		22 21	22 36	22 51	23 06	23 21	23 36

Table 21

London - Cheshunt (via Seven Sisters) and Enfield Town

Mondays to Fridays

9 December to 16 May

Network Diagram - see first Page of Table 20

Miles	Miles			LE MX	LE	LE	LE	LE	LE	LE	LE	LE		LE	LE	LE	LE	LE	LE	LE	LE	LE		LE	LE
0	0	**London Liverpool Street** 15 ⊖	d	00 01	05 45	06 00	06 15	06 21	06 36	06 45	06 51	07 07		07 15	07 21	07 36	07 45	07 51	08 00	08 07	08 15	08 30		08 38	08 45
1¼	1¼	Bethnal Green	d	00 03	05 48	06 03		06 24	06 39		06 54	07 10			07 24	07 39		07 54		08 10	08 18	08 33			08 48
1¾	1¾	Cambridge Heath	d	00 05	05 50	06 05		06 26	06 41		06 56	07 12			07 26	07 41		07 56		08 12	08 20	08 35		08 43	08 50
2½	2½	London Fields	d	00 07	05 52	06 07		06 28	06 43		06 58	07 14			07 28	07 43		07 58		08 14	08 22	08 37		08 45	08 52
3	3	Hackney Downs	d	00 09	05 54	06 09	06 22	06 30	06 45	06 52	07 00	07 16		07 22	07 30	07 45	07 52	08 00	08 07	08 16	08 24	08 39		08 47	08 54
3¾	3¾	Rectory Road	d	00 12	05 57	06 12		06 33	06 48	06 55	07 03	07 19		07 25	07 33	07 48	07 55	08 03		08 19	08 27	08 42		08 49	08 57
4¼	4¼	Stoke Newington	d	00 13	05 58	06 13		06 34	06 49	06 56	07 04	07 20		07 26	07 34	07 49	07 56	08 04		08 20	08 28	08 43		08 51	08 58
5	5	Stamford Hill	d	00 15	06 00	06 15		06 36	06 51	06 58	07 06	07 22		07 28	07 36	07 51	07 58	08 06		08 22	08 30	08 45		08 53	09 00
5½	5½	Seven Sisters ⊖	d	00 17	06 02	06 17	06 27	06 38	06 53	07 00	07 08	07 24		07 30	07 38	07 53	08 00	08 08	08 15	08 24	08 32	08 47		08 55	09 02
6¼	6¼	Bruce Grove	d	00 19	06 04	06 19		06 40	06 55	07 02	07 10	07 26		07 32	07 40	07 55	08 02	08 10		08 26	08 34	08 49		08 57	09 04
7¼	7¼	White Hart Lane	d	00 21	06 06	06 21		06 42	06 57	07 04	07 12	07 28		07 34	07 42	07 57	08 04	08 12		08 28	08 36	08 51		08 59	09 06
8	8	Silver Street	d	00 23	06 08	06 23		06 44	06 59	07 06	07 14	07 30		07 36	07 44	07 59	08 06	08 14		08 30	08 38	08 53		09 01	09 08
8½	8½	Edmonton Green	d	00 25	06 10	06 25	06 32	06 46	07 01	07 08	07 16	07 32		07 38	07 46	08 01	08 08	08 16	08 20	08 32	08 44	08 55		09 03	09 10
—	9¾	Bush Hill Park	d	00 28		06 28		06 49		07 11	07 19			07 41	07 49		08 11	08 19		08 37		08 58			09 13
—	10¾	**Enfield Town**	a	00 33		06 33		06 54		07 16	07 24			07 46	07 54		08 16	08 24		08 41		09 03			09 18
10½	—	Southbury	d		06 14		06 36		07 05			07 36				08 05			08 24		08 48			09 07	
12¼	—	Turkey Street	d		06 17		06 39		07 08			07 39				08 08			08 27		08 51			09 10	
13½	—	Theobalds Grove	d		06 19		06 41		07 10			07 41				08 10			08 29		08 53			09 12	
14½	—	**Cheshunt**	a		06 24		06 46		07 15			07 46				08 15			08 34		08 58			09 17	

		LE	LE	LE	LE		LE	LE	LE	LE		LE	LE	LE	LE	LE	LE	LE	LE	LE		LE	LE	LE
London Liverpool Street 15 ⊖	d	09 00	09 15	09 30	09 45		15 00	15 15	15 30	15 45		16 00	16 15	16 21	16 30	16 41	16 45	16 52	17 00	17 11		17 15	17 22	17 30
Bethnal Green	d	09 03	09 18	09 33	09 48		15 03	15 18	15 33	15 48		16 03	16 18	16 24	16 33		16 48		17 03			17 18		17 33
Cambridge Heath	d	09 05	09 20	09 35	09 50		15 05	15 20	15 35	15 50		16 05	16 20	16 26	16 35		16 50	16 57	17 05			17 20	17 27	17 35
London Fields	d	09 07	09 22	09 37	09 52		15 07	15 22	15 37	15 52		16 07	16 22	16 28	16 37		16 52	16 59	17 07			17 22	17 29	17 37
Hackney Downs	d	09 09	09 24	09 39	09 54		15 09	15 24	15 39	15 54		16 09	16 24	16 30	16 39	16 48	16 54	17 01	17 09	17 18		17 24	17 31	17 39
Rectory Road	d	09 12	09 27	09 42	09 57	and at	15 12	15 27	15 42	15 57		16 12	16 27	16 33	16 42		16 57	17 03	17 12			17 27	17 33	17 42
Stoke Newington	d	09 13	09 28	09 43	09 58	the same	15 13	15 28	15 43	15 58		16 13	16 28	16 34	16 43		16 58	17 05	17 13			17 28	17 35	17 43
Stamford Hill	d	09 15	09 30	09 45	10 00	minutes	15 15	15 30	15 45	16 00		16 15	16 30	16 36	16 45		17 00		17 15			17 30		17 45
Seven Sisters ⊖	d	09 17	09 32	09 47	10 02	past	15 17	15 32	15 47	16 02		16 18	16 33	16 39	16 48	16 54	17 03	17 09	17 18	17 24		17 33	17 39	17 48
Bruce Grove	d	09 19	09 34	09 49	10 04	each	15 19	15 34	15 49	16 04		16 20	16 35	16 41	16 50		17 05	17 11	17 20			17 35	17 41	17 50
White Hart Lane	d	09 21	09 36	09 51	10 06	hour until	15 21	15 36	15 51	16 06		16 22	16 37	16 43	16 52		17 07	17 13	17 22			17 37	17 43	17 52
Silver Street	d	09 23	09 38	09 53	10 08		15 23	15 38	15 53	16 08		16 24	16 39	16 45	16 54		17 09	17 15	17 24			17 39	17 45	17 54
Edmonton Green	d	09 25	09 40	09 55	10 10		15 25	15 40	15 55	16 10		16 26	16 41	16 47	16 56	17 00	17 11	17 17	17 26	17 30		17 41	17 47	17 56
Bush Hill Park	d	09 28		09 58			15 28		15 58			16 29		16 50	16 59		17 14		17 29			17 44		17 59
Enfield Town	a	09 33		10 03			15 33		16 03			16 35		16 56	17 05		17 20		17 35			17 50		18 05
Southbury	d		09 44		10 14			15 44		16 14			16 45					17 21					17 51	
Turkey Street	d		09 47		10 17			15 47		16 17			16 48					17 24					17 54	
Theobalds Grove	d		09 49		10 19			15 49		16 19			16 50					17 26					17 56	
Cheshunt	a		09 54		10 24			15 54		16 24			16 56			17 09		17 32		17 39			18 02	

		LE	LE	LE	LE	LE	LE		LE	LE	LE	LE	LE	LE	LE	LE	LE	LE	LE		LE	LE	LE	LE
London Liverpool Street 15 ⊖	d	17 41	17 45	17 52	18 00	18 11	18 15		18 22	18 30	18 41	18 45	19 00	19 15	19 22	19 30	19 45	20 00	20 15		22 30	22 45	23 00	23 15
Bethnal Green	d		17 48		18 03		18 18			18 33		18 48	19 03	19 18		19 33	19 48	20 03	20 18		22 33	22 48	23 03	23 18
Cambridge Heath	d		17 50	17 57	18 05		18 20		18 27	18 35		18 50	19 05	19 20		19 35	19 50	20 05	20 20		22 35	22 50	23 05	23 20
London Fields	d		17 52	17 59	18 07		18 22		18 29	18 37		18 52	19 07	19 22	19 28	19 37	19 52	20 07	20 22		22 37	22 52	23 07	23 22
Hackney Downs	d	17 48	17 54	18 01	18 09	18 18	18 24		18 31	18 39	18 48	18 54	19 09	19 24	19 30	19 39	19 54	20 09	20 24		22 39	22 54	23 09	23 24
Rectory Road	d		17 57	18 03	18 12		18 27		18 33	18 42		18 57	19 12	19 27	19 32	19 42	19 57	20 12	20 27	and at	22 42	22 57	23 12	23 27
Stoke Newington	d		17 58	18 05	18 13		18 28		18 35	18 43		18 58	19 13	19 28	19 34	19 43	19 58	20 13	20 28	the same	22 43	22 58	23 13	23 28
Stamford Hill	d		18 00		18 15		18 30			18 45		19 00	19 15	19 30		19 45	20 00	20 15	20 30	minutes	22 45	23 00	23 15	23 30
Seven Sisters ⊖	d	17 54	18 03	18 09	18 18	18 24	18 33		18 39	18 48	18 54	19 03	19 17	19 32	19 37	19 47	20 02	20 17	20 32	past	22 47	23 02	23 17	23 32
Bruce Grove	d		18 05	18 11	18 20		18 35		18 41	18 50		19 05	19 19	19 34	19 39	19 49	20 04	20 19	20 34	each	22 49	23 04	23 19	23 34
White Hart Lane	d		18 07	18 13	18 22		18 37		18 43	18 52		19 07	19 21	19 36	19 41	19 51	20 06	20 21	20 36	hour until	22 51	23 06	23 21	23 36
Silver Street	d		18 09	18 15	18 24		18 39		18 45	18 54		19 09	19 23	19 38	19 43	19 53	20 08	20 23	20 38		22 53	23 08	23 23	23 38
Edmonton Green	d	18 00	18 11	18 17	18 26	18 30	18 41		18 47	18 56	19 00	19 11	19 25	19 40	19 45	19 55	20 10	20 25	20 40		22 55	23 10	23 25	23 40
Bush Hill Park	d		18 14		18 29		18 44			18 59			19 28		19 48	19 58		20 28			22 58		23 28	
Enfield Town	a		18 20		18 35		18 50			19 05			19 33		19 53	20 03		20 33			23 03		23 33	
Southbury	d			18 21					18 51			19 15		19 44			20 14		20 44			23 14		23 44
Turkey Street	d			18 24					18 54			19 18		19 47			20 17		20 47			23 17		23 47
Theobalds Grove	d			18 26					18 56			19 20		19 49			20 19		20 49			23 19		23 49
Cheshunt	a	18 09		18 32		18 39			19 02		19 09	19 26		19 54			20 24		20 54			23 24		23 54

			LE	LE
London Liverpool Street 15 ⊖	d		23 30	23 45
Bethnal Green	d		23 33	23 48
Cambridge Heath	d		23 35	23 50
London Fields	d		23 37	23 52
Hackney Downs	d		23 39	23 54
Rectory Road	d		23 42	23 57
Stoke Newington	d		23 43	23 58
Stamford Hill	d		23 45	23 59
Seven Sisters ⊖	d		23 47	00 02
Bruce Grove	d		23 49	00 04
White Hart Lane	d		23 51	00 06
Silver Street	d		23 53	00 08
Edmonton Green	d		23 55	00 10
Bush Hill Park	d		23 58	
Enfield Town	a		00 03	
Southbury	d			00 14
Turkey Street	d			00 17
Theobalds Grove	d			00 19
Cheshunt	a			00 22

Table 21

Saturdays

14 December to 17 May

London - Cheshunt (via Seven Sisters) and Enfield Town

Network Diagram - see first Page of Table 20

		LE	LE	LE	LE	LE	LE	LE		LE	LE	LE	LE	LE
London Liverpool Street 15 ⊖	d	00 01	05 15	05 31	05 45	06 00	06 15	06 30		22 45	23 00	23 15	23 30	23 45
Bethnal Green	d	00 03	05 18		05 48	06 03	06 18	06 33		22 48	23 03	23 18	23 33	23 48
Cambridge Heath	d	00 05	05 20		05 50	06 05	06 20	06 35		22 50	23 05	23 20	23 35	23 50
London Fields	d	00 07	05 22		05 52	06 07	06 22	06 37		22 52	23 07	23 22	23 37	23 52
Hackney Downs	d	00 09	05 24	05 38	05 54	06 09	06 24	06 39		22 54	23 09	23 24	23 39	23 54
Rectory Road	d	00 12	05 27		05 57	06 12	06 27	06 42	and at	22 57	23 12	23 27	23 42	23 57
Stoke Newington	d	00 13	05 28		05 58	06 13	06 28	06 43	the same	22 58	23 13	23 28	23 43	23 58
Stamford Hill	d	00 15	05 30		06 00	06 15	06 30	06 45	minutes	23 00	23 15	23 30	23 45	23 59
Seven Sisters ⊖	d	00 17	05 32	05 47	06 02	06 17	06 32	06 47	past	23 02	23 17	23 32	23 47	00 02
Bruce Grove	d	00 19	05 34	05 49	06 04	06 19	06 34	06 49	each	23 04	23 19	23 34	23 49	00 04
White Hart Lane	d	00 21	05 36	05 51	06 06	06 21	06 36	06 51	hour until	23 06	23 21	23 36	23 51	00 06
Silver Street	d	00 23	05 38	05 53	06 08	06 23	06 38	06 53		23 08	23 23	23 38	23 53	00 08
Edmonton Green	d	00 25	05 40	05 55	06 10	06 25	06 40	06 55		23 10	23 25	23 40	23 55	00 10
Bush Hill Park	d	00 28		05 58		06 28		06 58			23 28		23 58	
Enfield Town	a	00 33		06 03		06 33		07 03			23 33		00 03	
Southbury	d		05 44		06 14		06 44			23 14		23 44		00 14
Turkey Street	d		05 47		06 17		06 47			23 17		23 47		00 17
Theobalds Grove	d		05 49		06 19		06 49			23 19		23 49		00 19
Cheshunt	a		05 54		06 24		06 54			23 24		23 54		00 24

Sundays

8 December to 11 May

		LE	LE	LE	LE	LE	LE	LE	LE	LE	LE	LE	LE		LE	LE	LE	LE	LE	LE
London Liverpool Street 15 ⊖	d	00 01	07 30	07 52	08 00	08 22	08 30	08 52	09 00	09 22	09 30	09 52	10 00		22 22	22 30	22 52	23 00	23 22	23 30
Bethnal Green	d	00 03									09 33		10 03			22 33		23 03		23 33
Cambridge Heath	d	00 05									09 35		10 05			22 35		23 05		23 35
London Fields	d	00 07									09 37		10 07			22 37		23 07		23 37
Hackney Downs	d	00 09	07 39	07 59	08 09	08 29	08 39	08 59	09 09	09 29	09 39	09 59	10 09		22 29	22 39	22 59	23 09	23 29	23 39
Rectory Road	d	00 12	07 42		08 12		08 42		09 12		09 42		10 12	and at		22 42		23 12		23 42
Stoke Newington	d	00 13	07 43		08 13		08 43		09 13		09 43		10 13	the same		22 43		23 13		23 43
Stamford Hill	d	00 15	07 45		08 15		08 45		09 15		09 45		10 15	minutes		22 45		23 15		23 45
Seven Sisters ⊖	d	00 17	07 47	08 04	08 17	08 34	08 47	09 04	09 17	09 34	09 47	10 04	10 17	past	22 34	22 47	23 04	23 17	23 34	23 47
Bruce Grove	d	00 19	07 49		08 19		08 49		09 19		09 49		10 19	each		22 49		23 19		23 49
White Hart Lane	d	00 21	07 51		08 21		08 51		09 21		09 51		10 21	hour until		22 51		23 21		23 51
Silver Street	d	00 23	07 53		08 23		08 53		09 23		09 53		10 23			22 53		23 23		23 53
Edmonton Green	d	00 25	07 55	08 08	08 25	08 38	08 55	09 08	09 25	09 38	09 55	10 08	10 25		22 38	22 55	23 08	23 25	23 38	23 55
Bush Hill Park	d	00 28	07 58		08 28		08 58		09 28		09 58		10 28			22 58		23 28		23 58
Enfield Town	a	00 33	08 03		08 33		09 03		09 33		10 03		10 33			23 03		23 33		00 03
Southbury	d			08 12		08 42		09 12		09 42		10 12			22 42		23 12		23 42	
Turkey Street	d			08 15		08 45		09 15		09 45		10 15			22 45		23 15		23 45	
Theobalds Grove	d			08 17		08 47		09 17		09 47		10 17			22 47		23 17		23 47	
Cheshunt	a			08 20		08 52		09 20		09 52		10 20			22 52		23 20		23 50	

Table 21R

Mondays to Fridays

9 December to 16 May

Cheshunt (via Seven Sisters) and Enfield Town - London

Network Diagram - see first Page of Table 20

Miles	Miles			LE	LE	LE	LE	LE	LE	LE		LE	LE	LE	LE	LE	LE	LE	LE	LE		LE	LE	LE	LE
0	—	**Cheshunt**	d	05 16		06 01			06 33	06 47			06 52		07 17		07 22		07 47			07 52		08 17	
1	—	Theobalds Grove	d	05 19		06 04			06 36				06 55				07 25					07 55			
2¼	—	Turkey Street	d	05 21		06 06			06 38				06 57				07 27					07 57			
4	—	Southbury	d	05 24		06 09			06 41				07 00				07 30					08 00			
—	0	**Enfield Town**	d		05 52		06 18	06 33				06 53		07 08		07 23		07 38		07 53			08 08		08 23
—	1	Bush Hill Park	d		05 55		06 21	06 36				06 56		07 11		07 26		07 41		07 56			08 11		08 26
6	2¼	Edmonton Green	d	05 28	05 58	06 13	06 24	06 39	06 45	06 55		06 59	07 04	07 14	07 25	07 29	07 34	07 44	07 55	07 59		08 04	08 14	08 25	08 29
6½	2¾	Silver Street	d	05 30	06 00	06 15	06 26	06 41	06 47			07 01	07 06	07 16		07 31	07 36	07 46		08 01		08 06	08 16		08 31
7¼	3½	White Hart Lane	d	05 32	06 02	06 17	06 28	06 43	06 49			07 03	07 08	07 18		07 33	07 38	07 48		08 03		08 08	08 18		08 33
8¼	4½	Bruce Grove	d	05 34	06 04	06 19	06 30	06 45	06 51			07 05	07 10	07 20		07 35	07 40	07 50		08 05		08 10	08 20		08 35
9	5¼	Seven Sisters ⊖	d	05 36	06 06	06 21	06 33	06 48	06 54	07 02		07 08	07 13	07 23	07 32	07 38	07 43	07 53	08 02	08 08		08 13	08 23	08 32	08 38
9½	5¾	Stamford Hill	d	05 38	06 08	06 23	06 35	06 50	06 56			07 10		07 25		07 40		07 55		08 10			08 25		08 40
10¼	6½	Stoke Newington	d	05 40	06 10	06 25	06 37	06 52	06 58			07 12	07 16	07 27		07 42	07 46	07 57		08 12		08 16	08 27		08 42
10¾	7	Rectory Road	d	05 41	06 11	06 26	06 39	06 54	07 00			07 14	07 18	07 29		07 44	07 48	07 59		08 14		08 18	08 29		08 43
11½	7¾	Hackney Downs	d	05 44	06 14	06 29	06 43	06 58	07 04	07 08		07 18	07 22	07 33	07 38	07 48	07 52	08 03	08 08	08 18		08 22	08 33	08 38	08 48
12	8¼	London Fields	d	05 46	06 16	06 31	06 45	07 00	07 06			07 20	07 24	07 35		07 50	07 54	08 05		08 20		08 24	08 35		08 50
12¾	9	Cambridge Heath	d	05 48	06 18	06 33	06 47	07 02	07 08			07 22		07 37		07 52		08 07		08 22			08 37		08 52
13¼	9½	Bethnal Green	d	05 50	06 20	06 35	06 49		07 10			07 24		07 39		07 54		08 09		08 24			08 39		08 54
14½	10¾	**London Liverpool Street** 15 ⊖	a	05 55	06 25	06 40	06 54	07 10	07 16	07 18		07 31	07 33	07 46	07 48	08 01	08 03	08 16	08 18	08 31		08 33	08 46	08 48	08 59

		LE	LE	LE	LE	LE		LE	LE	LE	LE	LE	LE		LE	LE	LE	LE		LE	LE	LE	LE	LE
Cheshunt	d	08 22		08 43				09 07		09 31		10 01			15 31		16 01			16 31			17 03	
Theobalds Grove	d	08 25		08 46				09 10		09 34		10 04			15 34		16 04			16 34			17 06	
Turkey Street	d	08 27		08 48				09 12		09 36		10 06			15 36		16 06			16 36			17 08	
Southbury	d	08 30		08 51				09 15		09 39		10 09			15 39		16 09			16 39			17 11	
Enfield Town	d		08 38		08 53	09 08			09 23		09 52		10 22			15 52		16 22			16 52	17 06		17 21
Bush Hill Park	d		08 41		08 56	09 11			09 26		09 55		10 25	and at		15 55		16 25			16 55	17 09		17 24
Edmonton Green	d	08 34	08 44	08 55	08 59	09 14		09 19	09 29	09 43	09 58	10 13	10 28	the same	15 43	15 58	16 13	16 28		16 43	16 58	17 12	17 16	17 27
Silver Street	d	08 36	08 46		09 01	09 16		09 21	09 31	09 45	10 00	10 15	10 30	minutes	15 45	16 00	16 15	16 30		16 45	17 00	17 14	17 18	17 29
White Hart Lane	d	08 38	08 48		09 03	09 18		09 23	09 33	09 47	10 02	10 17	10 32	past	15 47	16 02	16 17	16 32		16 47	17 02	17 16	17 20	17 31
Bruce Grove	d	08 40	08 50		09 05	09 20		09 25	09 35	09 49	10 04	10 19	10 34	each	15 49	16 04	16 19	16 34		16 49	17 04	17 18	17 22	17 33
Seven Sisters ⊖	d	08 43	08 53	09 02	09 08	09 23		09 28	09 38	09 51	10 06	10 21	10 36	hour until	15 51	16 06	16 21	16 36		16 51	17 06	17 20	17 24	17 35
Stamford Hill	d		08 55		09 10	09 25			09 40	09 53	10 08	10 23	10 38		15 53	16 08	16 23	16 38		16 53	17 08	17 22	17 26	17 37
Stoke Newington	d	08 46	08 57		09 12	09 27		09 31	09 42	09 55	10 10	10 25	10 40		15 55	16 10	16 25	16 40		16 55	17 10	17 24	17 28	17 39
Rectory Road	d	08 48	08 59		09 14	09 29		09 33	09 44	09 56	10 11	10 26	10 41		15 56	16 11	16 26	16 41		16 56	17 11	17 26	17 30	17 41
Hackney Downs	d	08 52	09 03	09 08	09 18	09 33		09 37	09 48	09 59	10 14	10 29	10 44		15 59	16 14	16 29	16 44		16 59	17 14	17 29	17 33	17 44
London Fields	d	08 54	09 05		09 20	09 35		09 39	09 50	10 01	10 16	10 31	10 46		16 01	16 16	16 31	16 46		17 01	17 16	17 31		17 46
Cambridge Heath	d		09 07		09 22	09 37			09 52	10 03	10 18	10 33	10 48		16 03	16 18	16 33	16 48		17 03	17 18	17 33		17 48
Bethnal Green	d		09 09		09 24	09 39			09 54	10 05	10 20	10 35	10 50		16 05	16 20	16 35	16 50		17 05	17 20	17 35		17 50
London Liverpool Street 15 ⊖	a	09 03	09 16	09 18	09 31	09 46		09 48	10 01	10 10	10 25	10 40	10 55		16 10	16 25	16 40	16 55		17 10	17 25	17 40	17 42	17 55

		LE	LE	LE	LE		LE	LE	LE	LE	LE	LE	LE	LE	LE	LE	LE	LE	LE		LE	LE	LE	LE
Cheshunt	d		17 40				18 10			18 40			19 10		19 31		20 01		20 31			23 01		23 31
Theobalds Grove	d		17 43				18 13			18 43			19 13		19 34		20 04		20 34			23 04		23 34
Turkey Street	d		17 45				18 15			18 45			19 15		19 36		20 06		20 36			23 06		23 36
Southbury	d		17 48				18 18			18 48			19 18		19 39		20 09		20 39			23 09		23 39
Enfield Town	d	17 36		17 51	18 06			18 21	18 36		18 51	19 06		19 22		19 52		20 22			22 52		23 22	
Bush Hill Park	d	17 39		17 54	18 09			18 24	18 39		18 54	19 09		19 25		19 55		20 25		and at	22 55		23 25	
Edmonton Green	d	17 42	17 52	17 57	18 12		18 22	18 27	18 42	18 52	18 57	19 12	19 22	19 28	19 43	19 58	20 13	20 28	20 43	the same	22 58	23 13	23 28	23 43
Silver Street	d	17 44		17 59	18 14			18 29	18 44		18 59	19 14		19 30	19 45	20 00	20 15	20 30	20 45	minutes	23 00	23 15	23 30	23 45
White Hart Lane	d	17 46		18 01	18 16			18 31	18 46		19 01	19 16		19 32	19 47	20 02	20 17	20 32	20 47	past	23 02	23 17	23 32	23 47
Bruce Grove	d	17 48		18 03	18 18			18 33	18 48		19 03	19 18		19 34	19 49	20 04	20 19	20 34	20 49	each	23 04	23 19	23 34	23 49
Seven Sisters ⊖	d	17 50	17 58	18 05	18 20		18 28	18 35	18 50	18 58	19 05	19 20	19 28	19 36	19 51	20 06	20 21	20 36	20 51	hour until	23 06	23 21	23 36	23 51
Stamford Hill	d	17 52		18 07	18 22			18 37	18 52		19 07	19 22		19 38	19 53	20 08	20 23	20 38	20 53		23 08	23 23	23 38	23 53
Stoke Newington	d	17 54	18 01	18 09	18 24		18 31	18 39	18 54	19 01	19 09	19 24	19 31	19 40	19 55	20 10	20 25	20 40	20 55		23 10	23 25	23 40	23 55
Rectory Road	d	17 56		18 11	18 26			18 41	18 56		19 11	19 26		19 41	19 56	20 11	20 26	20 41	20 56		23 11	23 26	23 41	23 56
Hackney Downs	d	17 59	18 04	18 14	18 29		18 34	18 44	18 59	19 04	19 14	19 29	19 34	19 44	19 59	20 14	20 29	20 44	20 59		23 14	23 29	23 44	23 59
London Fields	d	18 01		18 16	18 31			18 46	19 01		19 16	19 31		19 46	20 01	20 16	20 31	20 46	21 01		23 16	23 31	23 46	00 01
Cambridge Heath	d	18 03		18 18	18 33			18 48	19 03		19 18	19 33		19 48	20 03	20 18	20 33	20 48	21 03		23 18	23 33	23 48	00 03
Bethnal Green	d	18 05		18 20	18 35			18 50	19 05		19 20	19 35		19 50	20 05	20 20	20 35	20 50	21 05		23 20	23 35	23 50	00 05
London Liverpool Street 15 ⊖	a	18 10	18 13	18 25	18 40		18 43	18 55	19 10	19 13	19 25	19 40	19 43	19 55	20 09	20 25	20 40	20 55	21 10		23 25	23 40	23 55	00 10

			LE	LE
			◇ 1	
Cheshunt	d		23 52	23 59
Theobalds Grove	d			
Turkey Street	d			
Southbury	d			
Enfield Town	d			
Bush Hill Park	d			
Edmonton Green	d			
Silver Street	d			
White Hart Lane	d			
Bruce Grove	d			
Seven Sisters ⊖	d		00 04	00 12
Stamford Hill	d			
Stoke Newington	d			
Rectory Road	d			
Hackney Downs	d			00 17
London Fields	d			
Cambridge Heath	d			
Bethnal Green	d			
London Liverpool Street 15 ⊖	a		00 18	00 26

Table 21R

Saturdays

14 December to 17 May

Cheshunt (via Seven Sisters) and Enfield Town - London

Network Diagram - see first Page of Table 20

		LE ◇1	LE	LE	LE	LE		LE	LE	LE	LE	LE	LE	LE	LE	LE	LE	LE	LE
Cheshunt	d	05 16	06 01		06 31		and at the same minutes past each hour until	21 01		21 31		22 01		22 31		23 01		23 31	
Theobalds Grove	d	05 19	06 04		06 34			21 04		21 34		22 04		22 34		23 04		23 34	
Turkey Street	d	05 21	06 06		06 36			21 06		21 36		22 06		22 36		23 06		23 36	
Southbury	d	05 24	06 09		06 39			21 09		21 39		22 09		22 39		23 09		23 39	
Enfield Town	d			06 22		06 52			21 22		21 52		22 22		22 52		23 22		23 52
Bush Hill Park	d			06 25		06 55			21 25		21 55		22 25		22 55		23 25		23 55
Edmonton Green	d	05 28	06 13	06 28	06 43	06 58		21 13	21 28	21 43	21 58	22 13	22 28	22 43	22 58	23 13	23 28	23 43	23 58
Silver Street	d	05 30	06 15	06 30	06 45	07 00		21 15	21 30	21 45	22 00	22 15	22 30	22 45	23 00	23 15	23 30	23 45	23 59
White Hart Lane	d	05 32	06 17	06 32	06 47	07 02		21 17	21 32	21 47	22 02	22 17	22 32	22 47	23 02	23 17	23 32	23 47	00 02
Bruce Grove	d	05 34	06 19	06 34	06 49	07 04		21 19	21 34	21 49	22 04	22 19	22 34	22 49	23 04	23 19	23 34	23 49	00 04
Seven Sisters ⊖	d	05 36	06 21	06 36	06 51	07 06		21 21	21 36	21 51	22 06	22 21	22 36	22 51	23 06	23 21	23 36	23 51	00 06
Stamford Hill	d	05 38	06 23	06 38	06 53	07 08		21 23	21 38	21 53	22 08	22 23	22 38	22 53	23 08	23 23	23 38	23 53	00 08
Stoke Newington	d	05 40	06 25	06 40	06 55	07 10		21 25	21 40	21 55	22 10	22 25	22 40	22 55	23 10	23 25	23 40	23 55	00 10
Rectory Road	d	05 41	06 26	06 41	06 56	07 11		21 26	21 41	21 56	22 11	22 26	22 41	22 56	23 11	23 26	23 41	23 56	00 11
Hackney Downs	d	05 45	06 29	06 44	06 59	07 14		21 29	21 44	21 59	22 14	22 29	22 44	22 59	23 14	23 29	23 44	23 59	00 14
London Fields	d		06 31	06 46	07 01	07 16		21 31	21 46	22 01	22 16	22 31	22 46	23 01	23 16	23 31	23 46	00 01	00 16
Cambridge Heath	d		06 33	06 48	07 03	07 18		21 33	21 48	22 03	22 18	22 33	22 48	23 03	23 18	23 33	23 48	00 03	00 18
Bethnal Green	d	05 49	06 35	06 50	07 05	07 20		21 35	21 50	22 05	22 20	22 35	22 50	23 05	23 20	23 35	23 50	00 05	00 20
London Liverpool Street 15 ⊖	a	05 54	06 40	06 55	07 10	07 25		21 40	21 55	22 10	22 25	22 40	22 55	23 10	23 24	23 40	23 55	00 10	00 25

Sundays

8 December to 11 May

		LE	LE	LE	LE	LE	LE	LE	LE		LE	LE	LE	LE	LE	LE	LE	LE
Cheshunt	d	07 45		08 15		08 45		09 15		and at the same minutes past each hour until	21 45		22 15		22 45		23 15	
Theobalds Grove	d	07 48		08 18		08 48		09 18			21 48		22 18		22 48		23 18	
Turkey Street	d	07 51		08 21		08 51		09 21			21 51		22 21		22 51		23 21	
Southbury	d	07 54		08 24		08 54		09 24			21 54		22 24		22 54		23 24	
Enfield Town	d		07 57		08 27		08 57		09 27			21 57		22 27		22 57		23 27
Bush Hill Park	d		08 00		08 30		09 00		09 30			22 00		22 30		23 00		23 30
Edmonton Green	d	07 57	08 03	08 27	08 33	08 57	09 03	09 27	09 33		21 57	22 03	22 27	22 33	22 57	23 03	23 27	23 33
Silver Street	d		08 05		08 35		09 05		09 35			22 05		22 35		23 05		23 35
White Hart Lane	d		08 07		08 37		09 07		09 37			22 07		22 37		23 07		23 37
Bruce Grove	d		08 09		08 39		09 09		09 39			22 09		22 39		23 09		23 39
Seven Sisters ⊖	d	08 03	08 11	08 33	08 41	09 03	09 11	09 33	09 41		22 03	22 11	22 33	22 41	23 03	23 11	23 33	23 41
Stamford Hill	d		08 13		08 43		09 13		09 43			22 13		22 43		23 13		23 43
Stoke Newington	d		08 15		08 45		09 15		09 45			22 15		22 45		23 15		23 45
Rectory Road	d		08 16		08 46		09 16		09 46			22 16		22 46		23 16		23 46
Hackney Downs	d	08 09	08 19	08 39	08 49	09 09	09 19	09 39	09 49		22 09	22 19	22 39	22 49	23 09	23 19	23 39	23 49
London Fields	d						09 21		09 51			22 21		22 51		23 21		23 51
Cambridge Heath	d						09 23		09 53			22 23		22 53		23 23		23 53
Bethnal Green	d						09 25		09 55			22 25		22 55		23 25		23 55
London Liverpool Street 15 ⊖	a	08 18	08 30	08 48	09 00	09 18	09 30	09 48	10 00		22 18	22 30	22 48	23 00	23 18	23 30	23 48	23 59

Table 22

Mondays to Fridays

9 December to 16 May

London - Broxbourne, Hertford East, Bishops Stortford, Stansted Airport and Cambridge

Network Diagram - see first Page of Table 20

Miles	Miles	Miles			LE MO ■1	LE MFO ■1	XC ◇■1 B	LE MTh FO ■1	LE TWO ■1	LE ■1	LE ■1	LE ■1	XC ◇■1 B	LE ◇■1	LE ■1	LE	LE C	LE ■1	LE ◇■1	LE A	LE ■1
0	—	—	**London Liverpool Street** [15] ⊖	d	03 40	04 10		04 40	04 40	05 10		05 25		05 28	05 40	05 42	05 52	05 55	05 58		06 10
1¼	—	—	Bethnal Green	d																	
3	—	—	Hackney Downs	d												05 48					
—	0	0	Stratford [7] ⊖	d													06 03				
4	—	—	Clapton	d																	
—	6¾	—	Seven Sisters ⊖	d																←	
6	—	4¼	Tottenham Hale ⊖	d				04 52	04 59	05 22		05 37		05 40	05 52	05 55	06 15	06 07	06 10	06 15	06 22
7	—	5¼	Northumberland Park	d													→			06 17	
7¾	—	6	Angel Road	d																06 19	
10	—	—	Ponders End	d												05 59					
10¾	—	—	Brimsdown	d												06 02					
11¾	—	—	Enfield Lock	d												06 04				06 24	
12¾	—	—	Waltham Cross	d												06 07					
14	—	12¼	Cheshunt	d				05 00	05 07					05 48		06 09			06 18	06 28	
17¼	—	15½	**Broxbourne** [3]	a				05 05	05 12					05 53		06 15			06 23	06 33	
—	0	—	**Broxbourne** [3]	d				05 05	05 12					05 53		06 15			06 25	06 37	
—	1¾	—	Rye House	d												06 18				06 40	
—	3	—	St Margarets (Herts)	d												06 21				06 43	
—	5	—	Ware	d												06 25				06 47	
—	7	—	**Hertford East**	a												06 31				06 53	
20	—	18½	Roydon	d										05 57					06 29		
22¾	—	21	Harlow Town	d				05 11	05 18	05 38		05 53		06 01				06 26	06 33		
24½	—	22¾	Harlow Mill	d										06 04					06 36		
26¾	—	25	Sawbridgeworth	d						05 43				06 08					06 39		
30¼	—	28½	**Bishops Stortford**	a				05 20	05 27	05 49		06 02		06 14	06 17				06 45		06 49
—	—	—		d				05 20	05 27	05 50	05 59	06 03		06 14	06 18				06 46		06 50
33¾	0	—	Stansted Mountfitchet	d				05 24	05 31		06 03			06 18	06 23				06 50		
—	—	—	**Stansted Airport**	a	04 30	05 00		05 39	05 39	05 59		06 12			06 30			06 43			06 59
—	3¾	—	**Stansted Airport**	d			05 16						06 12								
35½	8¼	—	Elsenham	d							06 07			06 22					06 54		
40	—	—	Newport (Essex)	d							06 12			06 27					06 59		
41¾	—	—	Audley End	d			05 37				06 15		06 24	06 30					07 02		
45¾	—	—	Great Chesterford	d							06 20			06 35					07 07		
49	—	—	Whittlesford Parkway	d							06 25			06 40					07 12		
52½	—	—	Shelford	d							06 29			06 44					07 16		
55¾	—	—	**Cambridge**	a			05 51				06 38		06 42	06 56					07 26		

		LE	LE ■1	XC ◇■1 B	LE ◇■1 D	LE ■1	LE ■1	LE ◇■1 A	LE	LE	LE ■1	LE ◇■1	LE ■1 🚲	LE	LE ■1 🚲	LE ◇■1	LE ■1	XC ◇■1 B	LE ■1 🚲	LE	LE ■1 🚲	LE ◇■1	LE ◇■1
London Liverpool Street [15] ⊖	d	06 12	06 25		06 28		06 40		06 42		06 55	06 58	07 10	07 12	07 25	07 28			07 40	07 42	07 55	07 58	08 03
Bethnal Green	d																						
Hackney Downs	d	06 18							06 48					07 18						07 48			
Stratford [7] ⊖	d					06 35				06 50							07 34						
Clapton	d																						
Seven Sisters ⊖	d																						
Tottenham Hale ⊖	d	06 25	06 37		06 40	06 44	06 52		06 55	07 00	07 07	07 10	07 22	07 25	07 37	07 41	07 47		07 52	07 55	08 07	08 11	08 15
Northumberland Park	d					06 47											07 49						
Angel Road	d																07 51						
Ponders End	d	06 29								07 04				07 29						07 59			
Brimsdown	d	06 32								07 07				07 32						08 02			
Enfield Lock	d	06 34							07 01					07 34						08 04			
Waltham Cross	d	06 37							07 04					07 37						08 07			
Cheshunt	d	06 39			06 51	06 54			07 06	07 11		07 21		07 39		07 51	07 58			08 09		08 21	
Broxbourne [3]	a	06 45			06 55	06 59			07 12	07 17		07 26		07 45		07 56	08 04			08 15		08 25	
Broxbourne [3]	d	06 45			06 55	06 59			07 15			07 26		07 45		07 56	08 10			08 15		08 25	
Rye House	d	06 48							07 18					07 48						08 18			
St Margarets (Herts)	d	06 51							07 21					07 51						08 21			
Ware	d	06 55							07 25					07 55						08 25			
Hertford East	a	07 01							07 31					08 02						08 32			
Roydon	d				07 00							07 30				08 00	08 14						
Harlow Town	d		06 55		07 11						07 25	07 34			07 56	08 04	08 18				08 26	08 36	
Harlow Mill	d				07 15							07 37				08 07	08 21						
Sawbridgeworth	d				07 18			←				07 41				08 11	08 25					08 42	
Bishops Stortford	a				07 24	07 14	07 17	07 24				07 47	07 50			08 17	08 32		08 20			08 47	
	d				07 28		07 18	07 28				07 47	07 51			08 17			08 21			08 47	
Stansted Mountfitchet	d				→			07 32			07 36	07 51				08 21					08 37	08 51	
Stansted Airport	a		07 12				07 30				07 43		08 00		08 13				08 30		08 45		
Stansted Airport	d			07 21														08 21					
Elsenham	d							07 36				07 55				08 25						08 55	
Newport (Essex)	d							07 41				08 00				08 30						09 00	
Audley End	d			07 37				07 44				08 03				08 33		08 38				09 03	
Great Chesterford	d							07 49				08 08				08 38						09 08	
Whittlesford Parkway	d							07 54				08 13				08 43						09 13	
Shelford	d							07 58				08 17				08 47						09 17	
Cambridge	a			07 58				08 08				08 29				08 55		08 58				09 26	09 08

A From London Liverpool Street
B To Birmingham New Street
C To Hertford East
D To Cambridge

Table 22

Mondays to Fridays

9 December to 16 May

London - Broxbourne, Hertford East, Bishops Stortford, Stansted Airport and Cambridge

Network Diagram - see first Page of Table 20

		LE 1	LE 1 🚲	LE	LE 1 🚲		LE ◇1	LE ◇1	LE 1	XC ◇1 A	LE 1 🚲	LE	LE 1 🚲	LE ◇1	LE 1		LE 1 🚲	LE	LE 1 🚲	LE ◇1	LE 1	LE 1 🚲	XC ◇1 A	LE	LE 1 🚲
London Liverpool Street 15 ⊖	d		08 10	08 12	08 25		08 28	08 33			08 40	08 42	08 55	08 58			09 10	09 12	09 25	09 28		09 40		09 42	09 55
Bethnal Green	d																								
Hackney Downs	d			08 18								08 48						09 18						09 48	
Stratford 7 ⊖	d	08 04							08 34						09 00						09 30				
Clapton	d																								
Seven Sisters ⊖	d																								
Tottenham Hale ⊖	d	08 18	08 22	08 25	08u37		08 40	08 45	08 48		08 52	08 55	09 07	09 10	09 13		09 22	09 25	09 37	09 40	09 43	09 52		09 55	10 07
Northumberland Park	d	08 20							08 50						09 15						09 46				
Angel Road	d								08 52												09 48				
Ponders End	d			08 29								08 59						09 29						09 59	
Brimsdown	d			08 32								09 02						09 32						10 02	
Enfield Lock	d	08 26		08 34								09 04			09 21			09 34						10 04	
Waltham Cross	d			08 37								09 07						09 37			09 53			10 07	
Cheshunt	d	08 29		08 39			08 48		08 59			09 09		09 18	09 25			09 39		09 48	09 56			10 09	
Broxbourne 3	a	08 35		08 45			08 53		09 05			09 15		09 23	09 31			09 45		09 53	10 01			10 15	
Broxbourne 3	d	08 39		08 45			08 53		09 09			09 15		09 23	09 34			09 45		09 53	10 05			10 15	
Rye House	d			08 48								09 18						09 48						10 18	
St Margarets (Herts)	d			08 51								09 21						09 51						10 21	
Ware	d			08 55								09 25						09 55						10 25	
Hertford East	a			09 02								09 32						10 01						10 31	
Roydon	d	08 43					08 57		09 13						09 39					09 57					
Harlow Town	d	08 47			08 55		09 05		09 17				09 25	09 29	09 43				09 55	10 01	10 11				10 25
Harlow Mill	d	08 50							09 20						09 46					10 04					
Sawbridgeworth	d	08 54					09 11		09 24						09 49					10 08	10 17				
Bishops Stortford	a	09 02	08 51				09 17		09 32		09 20			09 38	09 56		09 45			10 14	10 23	10 17			
	d		08 51				09 17				09 21			09 39			09 45			10 14		10 18			
Stansted Mountfitchet	d						09 21						09 37							10 18					10 36
Stansted Airport	a		09 01		09 14						09 31		09 45				09 55		10 12			10 27			10 44
Stansted Airport	d									09 21													10 27		
Elsenham	d						09 25													10 22					
Newport (Essex)	d						09 30													10 27					
Audley End	d						09 33	09 22		09 39				09 51						10 30			10 40		
Great Chesterford	d						09 38													10 35					
Whittlesford Parkway	d						09 43							09 58						10 40					
Shelford	d						09 47													10 44					
Cambridge	a						09 54	09 38		09 58				10 08						10 51			10 58		

			LE ◇1	LE 1	LE 1 🚲	LE	LE 1 🚲	LE ◇1	LE 1	LE 1 🚲	XC ◇1 A		LE	LE 1 🚲	LE ◇1	LE 1	LE 1 🚲	LE	LE 1 🚲	LE ◇1	LE 1		LE 1 🚲	XC ◇1 A	LE
London Liverpool Street 15 ⊖	d		09 58		10 10	10 12	10 25	10 28		10 40			10 42	10 55	10 58		11 10	11 12	11 25	11 28			11 40		11 42
Bethnal Green	d																								
Hackney Downs	d					10 18							10 48					11 18							11 48
Stratford 7 ⊖	d			10 00					10 30							11 00					11 30				
Clapton	d																								
Seven Sisters ⊖	d																								
Tottenham Hale ⊖	d		10 10	10 13	10 22	10 25	10 37	10 40	10 43	10 52			10 55	11 07	11 10	11 13	11 22	11 25	11 37	11 40	11 43		11 52		11 55
Northumberland Park	d			10 15												11 15									
Angel Road	d																								
Ponders End	d					10 29							10 59					11 29							11 59
Brimsdown	d					10 32							11 02					11 32							12 02
Enfield Lock	d			10 21		10 34							11 04			11 21		11 34							12 04
Waltham Cross	d					10 37			10 50				11 07					11 37			11 50				12 07
Cheshunt	d		10 18	10 25		10 39		10 48	10 52				11 09		11 18	11 25		11 39		11 48	11 52				12 09
Broxbourne 3	a		10 23	10 30		10 45		10 53	10 58				11 15		11 23	11 30		11 45		11 53	11 58				12 15
Broxbourne 3	d		10 23	10 34		10 45		10 53	10 58				11 15		11 23	11 34		11 45		11 53	11 58				12 15
Rye House	d					10 48							11 18					11 48							12 18
St Margarets (Herts)	d					10 51							11 21					11 51							12 21
Ware	d					10 55							11 25					11 55							12 25
Hertford East	a					11 01							11 31					12 01							12 31
Roydon	d			10 39				10 57								11 39				11 57					
Harlow Town	d		10 29	10 43			10 55	11 01	11 11					11 25	11 29	11 43			11 55	12 01	12 11				
Harlow Mill	d			10 46				11 04								11 46				12 04					
Sawbridgeworth	d			10 49				11 08	11 17							11 49				12 08	12 17				
Bishops Stortford	a		10 38	10 56	10 45			11 14	11 23	11 17					11 38	11 56	11 45			12 14	12 23		12 17		
	d		10 39		10 45			11 14		11 18					11 39		11 45			12 14			12 18		
Stansted Mountfitchet	d							11 18						11 36						12 18					
Stansted Airport	a				10 55		11 13			11 27				11 44			11 55		12 12				12 27		
Stansted Airport	d										11 27													12 27	
Elsenham	d							11 22												12 22					
Newport (Essex)	d							11 27												12 27					
Audley End	d		10 51					11 30			11 40				11 51					12 30				12 40	
Great Chesterford	d							11 35												12 35					
Whittlesford Parkway	d		10 58					11 40							11 58					12 40					
Shelford	d							11 44												12 44					
Cambridge	a		11 08					11 51			11 58				12 08					12 51				12 59	

A To Birmingham New Street

Table 22

Mondays to Fridays

9 December to 16 May

London - Broxbourne, Hertford East, Bishops Stortford, Stansted Airport and Cambridge

Network Diagram - see first Page of Table 20

		LE 1 🚲	LE ◇1	LE 1	LE 1 🚲	LE	LE 1 🚲		LE ◇1	LE 1	LE 1 🚲	XC ◇1 A	LE	LE 1 🚲	LE ◇1	LE 1	LE 1 🚲		LE	LE 1 🚲	LE ◇1	LE 1	LE 1 🚲	XC ◇1 A	LE
London Liverpool Street 15 ⊖	d	11 55	11 58		12 10	12 12	12 25		12 28		12 40		12 42	12 55	12 58		13 10		13 12	13 25	13 28		13 40		13 42
Bethnal Green	d																								
Hackney Downs	d					12 18							12 48						13 18						13 48
Stratford 7 ⊖	d			12 00						12 30						13 00						13 30			
Clapton	d																								
Seven Sisters ⊖	d																								
Tottenham Hale ⊖	d	12 07	12 10	12 13	12 22	12 25	12 37		12 40	12 43	12 52		12 55	13 07	13 10	13 13	13 22		13 25	13 37	13 40	13 43	13 52		13 55
Northumberland Park	d			12 15												13 15									
Angel Road	d																								
Ponders End	d					12 29							12 59						13 29						13 59
Brimsdown	d					12 32							13 02						13 32						14 02
Enfield Lock	d			12 21		12 34							13 04			13 21			13 34						14 04
Waltham Cross	d					12 37				12 50			13 07						13 37			13 50			14 07
Cheshunt	d		12 18	12 25		12 39			12 48	12 52			13 09		13 18	13 25			13 39		13 48	13 52			14 09
Broxbourne 3	a		12 23	12 30		12 45			12 53	12 58			13 15		13 23	13 30			13 45		13 53	13 58			14 15
Broxbourne 3	d		12 23	12 34		12 45			12 53	12 58			13 15		13 23	13 34			13 45		13 53	13 58			14 15
Rye House	d					12 48							13 18						13 48						14 18
St Margarets (Herts)	d					12 51							13 21						13 51						14 21
Ware	d					12 55							13 25						13 55						14 25
Hertford East	a					13 01							13 31						14 01						14 31
Roydon	d			12 39					12 57							13 39					13 57				
Harlow Town	d	12 25	12 29	12 43			12 55		13 01	13 11				13 25	13 29	13 43				13 55	14 01	14 11			
Harlow Mill	d			12 46					13 04							13 46					14 04				
Sawbridgeworth	d			12 49					13 08	13 17						13 49					14 08	14 17			
Bishops Stortford	a		12 38	12 56	12 45				13 14	13 23	13 17				13 38	13 56	13 45				14 14	14 23	14 17		
	d		12 39		12 45				13 14		13 18				13 39		13 45				14 14		14 18		
Stansted Mountfitchet	d	12 36							13 18					13 36							14 18				
Stansted Airport	a	12 44			12 55		13 12				13 27			13 44			13 55			14 12			14 27		
Stansted Airport	d											13 27												14 27	
Elsenham	d								13 22												14 22				
Newport (Essex)	d								13 27												14 27				
Audley End	d		12 51						13 30			13 40			13 51						14 30			14 40	
Great Chesterford	d								13 35												14 35				
Whittlesford Parkway	d		12 58						13 40						13 58						14 40				
Shelford	d								13 44												14 44				
Cambridge	a		13 08						13 51			13 58			14 08						14 51			14 58	

		LE 1 🚲	LE ◇1		LE 1	LE 1 🚲	LE	LE 1 🚲	LE ◇1	LE 1	LE 1 🚲	XC ◇1 A	LE		LE 1 🚲	LE ◇1	LE 1	LE 1 🚲	LE	LE 1 🚲	LE ◇1	LE 1	LE 1 🚲		XC ◇1 A
London Liverpool Street 15 ⊖	d	13 55	13 58			14 10	14 12	14 25	14 28		14 40		14 42		14 55	14 58		15 10	15 12	15 25	15 28		15 40		
Bethnal Green	d																								
Hackney Downs	d						14 18						14 48						15 18						
Stratford 7 ⊖	d				14 00					14 30							15 00					15 30			
Clapton	d																								
Seven Sisters ⊖	d																								
Tottenham Hale ⊖	d	14 07	14 10		14 13	14 22	14 25	14 37	14 40	14 43	14 52		14 55		15 07	15 10	15 13	15 22	15 25	15 37	15 40	15 43	15 52		
Northumberland Park	d				14 15												15 15								
Angel Road	d																								
Ponders End	d						14 29						14 59						15 29						
Brimsdown	d						14 32						15 02						15 32						
Enfield Lock	d				14 21		14 34						15 04				15 21		15 34						
Waltham Cross	d						14 37			14 50			15 07						15 37			15 50			
Cheshunt	d		14 18		14 25		14 39		14 48	14 52			15 09			15 18	15 25		15 39		15 48	15 52			
Broxbourne 3	a		14 23		14 30		14 45		14 53	14 58			15 15			15 23	15 30		15 45		15 53	15 58			
Broxbourne 3	d		14 23		14 34		14 45		14 53	14 58			15 15			15 23	15 34		15 45		15 53	15 58			
Rye House	d						14 48						15 18						15 48						
St Margarets (Herts)	d						14 51						15 21						15 51						
Ware	d						14 55						15 25						15 55						
Hertford East	a						15 01						15 31						16 01						
Roydon	d				14 39				14 57								15 39				15 57				
Harlow Town	d	14 25	14 29		14 43			14 55	15 01	15 11					15 25	15 29	15 43			15 55	16 01	16 11			
Harlow Mill	d				14 46				15 04								15 46				16 04				
Sawbridgeworth	d				14 49				15 08	15 17							15 49				16 08	16 17			
Bishops Stortford	a		14 38		14 56	14 45			15 14	15 23	15 17					15 38	15 56	15 45			16 14	16 23	16 17		
	d		14 39			14 45			15 14		15 18					15 41		15 45			16 14		16 18		
Stansted Mountfitchet	d	14 36							15 18						15 36	15 45					16 18				
Stansted Airport	a	14 44				14 55		15 13			15 27				15 44			15 55		16 12			16 27		
Stansted Airport	d											15 27													16 27
Elsenham	d								15 22							15 49					16 22				
Newport (Essex)	d								15 27							15 55					16 27				
Audley End	d		14 51						15 30			15 40				15 59					16 30				16 40
Great Chesterford	d								15 35							16 04					16 35				
Whittlesford Parkway	d		14 58						15 40							16 09					16 40				
Shelford	d								15 44							16 13					16 44				
Cambridge	a		15 09						15 51			15 58				16 20					16 51				16 58

A To Birmingham New Street

Table 22

Mondays to Fridays

9 December to 16 May

London - Broxbourne, Hertford East, Bishops Stortford, Stansted Airport and Cambridge

Network Diagram - see first Page of Table 20

		LE	LE 1 🚲	LE ◇1 A 🚲	LE 1	LE 1 🚲	LE	LE 1 🚲	LE 1	LE 1	XC ◇1 B	LE 1 🚲	LE C	LE ◇1	LE D	LE 1 E	LE 1 🚲	LE	LE ◇1 F	LE 1 🚲	LE 1 G	LE C	LE ◇1
London Liverpool Street 15 ⊖	d	15 42	15 55	15 58		16 10	16 12	16 25	16 28			16 39	16 41	16 43			16 54	16 56	17 07	17 09		17 11	17 13
Bethnal Green	d																						
Hackney Downs	d	15 48					16 19						16 48					17 03				17 18	
Stratford 7 ⊖	d				16 00					16 30						16 47							
Clapton	d																						
Seven Sisters ⊖	d												16 54									17 24	
Tottenham Hale ⊖	d	15 55	16 07	16 10	16 13	16 22	16 25	16 37	16 40	16 43		16 52		16 55		16 58	17 06	17 09	17 19	17 22			17 25
Northumberland Park	d				16 15											17 01							
Angel Road	d				16 17											17 03							
Ponders End	d	15 59					16 30			16 48								17 14					
Brimsdown	d	16 02					16 32			16 50								17 16					
Enfield Lock	d	16 04			16 22		16 35			16 53						17 08		17 19					
Waltham Cross	d	16 07					16 37			16 55					←	17 10		17 21					
Cheshunt	d	16 09		16 18	16 26		16 40			16 58			17 09	17 04	17 09	17 13		17 24				17 39	17 34
Broxbourne 3	a	16 15		16 23	16 31		16 45		16 53	17 03			→	17 10	17 15	17 18		17 31				→	17 39
Broxbourne 3	d	16 15		16 23	16 35		16 46		16 53	17 04				17 10	17 15	17 23							17 40
Rye House	d	16 18					16 49								17 19								
St Margarets (Herts)	d	16 21					16 52								17 22								
Ware	d	16 25					16 56								17 26								
Hertford East	a	16 31					17 04								17 33								
Roydon	d			16 27	16 39									17 14		17 28					←		17 44
Harlow Town	d		16 25	16 31	16 43			16 56	17 00	17 13				17 18		17 43	17 26			17 40	17 43		17 48
Harlow Mill	d			16 34	16 46									17 21		→					17 46		17 51
Sawbridgeworth	d			16 38	16 50				17 05					17 25							17 50		17 55
Bishops Stortford	a			16 44	16 58	16 47			17 11	17 25		17 17		17 31			17 35		17 43		17 58		18 01
	d			16 44		16 48			17 12			17 18		17 31			17 35		17 44				18 01
Stansted Mountfitchet	d		16 36	16 48					17 16					17 36						17 52			18 06
Stansted Airport	a		16 44			17 01		17 15				17 29					17 47			18 01			
Stansted Airport	d										17 27												
Elsenham	d			16 52										17 39									18 09
Newport (Essex)	d			16 57										17 45									18 15
Audley End	d			17 00					17 26		17 40			17 48					17 56				18 18
Great Chesterford	d			17 05										17 53									18 23
Whittlesford Parkway	d			17 10					17 33					17 58					18 04				18 28
Shelford	d			17 14										18 02									18 32
Cambridge	a			17 21					17 45		17 58			18 11					18 15				18 41

		LE D	LE	LE 1 🚲	LE	LE ◇1	XC ◇1 B	LE 1 🚲	LE C	LE ◇1	LE D	LE 1 E	LE 1 🚲	LE	LE ◇1 H	LE 1 🚲	LE 1 G	LE C	LE ◇1	LE D	LE	LE 1 🚲	LE
London Liverpool Street 15 ⊖	d			17 24	17 26	17 37		17 39	17 41	17 43			17 54	17 56	18 07	18 09		18 11	18 13			18 24	18 26
Bethnal Green	d																						
Hackney Downs	d				17 33				17 48					18 03				18 18					18 33
Stratford 7 ⊖	d		17 17									17 47									18 17		
Clapton	d																						
Seven Sisters ⊖	d								17 54									18 24					
Tottenham Hale ⊖	d		17 28	17 36	17 39	17 49		17 52		17 55		17 58	18 06	18 09	18 19	18 22			18 25		18 28	18 36	18 39
Northumberland Park	d		17 31									18 01									18 31		
Angel Road	d		17 33									18 03									18 33		
Ponders End	d				17 44									18 14									18 44
Brimsdown	d				17 46									18 16									18 46
Enfield Lock	d		17 38		17 49							18 08		18 19							18 38		18 49
Waltham Cross	d	←	17 40		17 51						←	18 10		18 21						←	18 40		18 51
Cheshunt	d	17 39	17 43		17 54				18 09	18 04	18 09	18 13		18 24				18 39	18 34	18 39	18 43		18 54
Broxbourne 3	a	17 45	17 48		18 01				→	18 09	18 15	18 18		18 31				→	18 39	18 45	18 48		19 01
Broxbourne 3	d	17 45	17 52							18 10	18 15	18 23							18 40	18 45	18 52		
Rye House	d	17 49	17 55								18 19									18 49	18 55		
St Margarets (Herts)	d	17 52	17 58								18 22									18 52	18 58		
Ware	d	17 56	18 02								18 26									18 56	19 02		
Hertford East	a	18 03	18 10								18 33									19 03	19 10		
Roydon	d									18 14		18 28					←		18 44				
Harlow Town	d			17 56				18 10		18 18		18 43	18 26			18 40	18 43		18 48			18 56	
Harlow Mill	d									18 21		→					18 46		18 51				
Sawbridgeworth	d							18 15		18 25							18 50		18 55				
Bishops Stortford	a			18 05		18 13				18 31			18 35		18 43		18 58		19 01			19 05	
	d			18 05		18 14				18 31			18 35		18 44				19 01			19 05	
Stansted Mountfitchet	d									18 36						18 52			19 06				
Stansted Airport	a			18 17				18 32					18 47			19 01						19 17	
Stansted Airport	d						18 21																
Elsenham	d									18 39									19 09				
Newport (Essex)	d									18 45									19 15				
Audley End	d					18 26	18 38			18 48					18 56				19 18				
Great Chesterford	d									18 53									19 23				
Whittlesford Parkway	d					18 34				18 58					19 04				19 28				
Shelford	d									19 02									19 32				
Cambridge	a					18 45	18 58			19 14					19 17				19 42				

A To Ely
B To Birmingham New Street
C To Hertford East
D From London Liverpool Street
E To Bishops Stortford
F To Kings Lynn. The Fenman
G From Stratford
H To Kings Lynn

Table 22

Mondays to Fridays

9 December to 16 May

London - Broxbourne, Hertford East, Bishops Stortford, Stansted Airport and Cambridge

Network Diagram - see first Page of Table 20

		LE ■1	XC ◇■1 A	LE ■1 🚲	LE B	LE ◇■1	LE C	LE ■1 D	LE ■1 🚲	LE	LE ◇■1 E	LE ■1 🚲	LE ■1 F	LE ◇■1	LE	LE ■1 🚲	LE ◇■1	LE ■1	XC ◇■1 A	LE ■1 🚲	LE	LE ■1 🚲
London Liverpool Street ■15 ⊖	d	18 37		18 39	18 41	18 43			18 54	18 56	19 07	19 09		19 11	19 13	19 25	19 28			19 40	19 42	19 55
Bethnal Green	d																					
Hackney Downs	d				18 48					19 03					19 19						19 48	
Stratford ■7 ⊖	d							18 47										19 30				
Clapton	d																					
Seven Sisters ⊖	d				18 54																	
Tottenham Hale ⊖	d	18 49		18 52		18 55		18 58	19 06	19 09	19 19	19 22		19 25	19 28	19 37	19 40	19 43		19 52	19 55	20 07
Northumberland Park	d							19 01										19 45				
Angel Road	d							19 03										19 47				
Ponders End	d									19 14					19 32						19 59	
Brimsdown	d									19 16					19 35						20 02	
Enfield Lock	d							19 08		19 19					19 37						20 04	
Waltham Cross	d						←	19 10		19 21					19 40			19 53			20 07	
Cheshunt	d				19 09	19 04	19 09	19 13		19 24				19 34	19 42		19 49	19 55			20 09	
Broxbourne ■3	a				→	19 09	19 15	19 18		19 31				19 39	19 48		19 55	20 01			20 15	
Broxbourne ■3	d					19 10	19 15	19 23		19 36				19 40	19 48		19 55	20 04			20 15	
Rye House	d						19 19			19 39					19 51						20 18	
St Margarets (Herts)	d						19 22			19 42					19 54						20 21	
Ware	d						19 26			19 47					19 58						20 25	
Hertford East	a						19 33			19 54					20 04						20 31	
Roydon	d					19 14		19 28					←	19 44			20 00	20 09				
Harlow Town	d			19 10		19 18		19 43	19 26			19 40	19 43	19 48		19 58	20 04	20 13				20 25
Harlow Mill	d					19 21		→					19 46	19 51			20 07	20 16				
Sawbridgeworth	d			19 15		19 25							19 50	19 55			20 10	20 19				
Bishops Stortford	a	19 13				19 31			19 35		19 43		19 56	20 01			20 16	20 28		20 20		
	d	19 14				19 31			19 35		19 44			20 01			20 17			20 21		
Stansted Mountfitchet	d					19 36						19 52		20 06			20 21					20 36
Stansted Airport	a			19 32					19 47			19 59				20 15				20 30		20 43
Stansted Airport	d		19 21																20 21			
Elsenham	d					19 39								20 09			20 25					
Newport (Essex)	d					19 45								20 15			20 30					
Audley End	d	19 26	19 38			19 48					19 56			20 18			20 33		20 39			
Great Chesterford	d					19 53								20 23			20 38					
Whittlesford Parkway	d	19 34				19 58					20 04			20 28			20 43					
Shelford	d					20 02								20 32			20 47					
Cambridge	a	19 45	19 58			20 12					20 13			20 41			20 56		20 59			

		LE ◇■1	LE ■1	LE ■1 🚲	LE	LE ■1 🚲	LE ◇■1	LE ■1	LE ■1 🚲	XC ■1	LE	LE ■1 🚲	LE ◇■1	LE ■1	LE ■1 🚲	LE	LE ■1 🚲	LE ◇■1	LE ■1	LE ■1 🚲	XC ■1	LE	LE ■1 🚲
London Liverpool Street ■15 ⊖	d	19 58		20 10	20 12	20 25	20 28		20 40		20 42	20 55	20 58		21 10	21 12	21 25	21 28		21 40		21 42	21 55
Bethnal Green	d																						
Hackney Downs	d				20 18						20 48					21 18						21 48	
Stratford ■7 ⊖	d		20 00					20 30						21 00					21 30				
Clapton	d																						
Seven Sisters ⊖	d																						
Tottenham Hale ⊖	d	20 10	20 13	20 22	20 25	20 37	20 40	20 43	20 52		20 55	21 07	21 10	21 13	21 22	21 25	21 37	21 40	21 43	21 52		21 55	22 07
Northumberland Park	d		20 15											21 15									
Angel Road	d																						
Ponders End	d				20 29						20 59					21 29						21 59	
Brimsdown	d				20 32						21 02					21 32						22 02	
Enfield Lock	d		20 21		20 34						21 04			21 21		21 34						22 04	
Waltham Cross	d				20 37			20 50			21 07					21 37			21 50			22 07	
Cheshunt	d	20 18	20 25		20 39		20 48	20 52			21 09		21 18	21 25		21 39		21 48	21 52			22 09	
Broxbourne ■3	a	20 23	20 30		20 45		20 53	20 58			21 15		21 23	21 30		21 45		21 53	21 58			22 15	
Broxbourne ■3	d	20 23	20 34		20 45		20 53	20 58			21 15		21 23	21 34		21 45		21 53	21 58			22 15	
Rye House	d				20 48						21 18					21 48						22 18	
St Margarets (Herts)	d				20 51						21 21					21 51						22 21	
Ware	d				20 55						21 25					21 55						22 25	
Hertford East	a				21 01						21 31					22 01						22 31	
Roydon	d		20 39				20 57							21 39				21 57					
Harlow Town	d	20 29	20 43			20 55	21 01	21 11				21 25	21 29	21 43			21 55	22 01	22 11				22 25
Harlow Mill	d		20 46				21 04							21 46				22 04					
Sawbridgeworth	d	20 34	20 49				21 08	21 17					21 34	21 49				22 08	22 17				
Bishops Stortford	a	20 40	20 56	20 45			21 14	21 23	21 17				21 40	21 56	21 45			22 14	22 23	22 17			
	d	20 40		20 45			21 14		21 18				21 40		21 45			22 14		22 18			
Stansted Mountfitchet	d						21 18					21 36						22 18					22 36
Stansted Airport	a			20 55		21 12			21 27			21 44			21 55		22 12			22 27			22 43
Stansted Airport	d									21 27											22 27		
Elsenham	d						21 22											22 22					
Newport (Essex)	d						21 27											22 27					
Audley End	d	20 52					21 30			21 40			21 52					22 30			22 40		
Great Chesterford	d						21 35											22 35					
Whittlesford Parkway	d	21 00					21 40						22 00					22 40					
Shelford	d						21 44											22 44					
Cambridge	a	21 09					21 51			21 58			22 09					22 51			22 56		

A To Birmingham New Street
B To Hertford East
C From London Liverpool Street
D To Bishops Stortford
E To Kings Lynn
F From Stratford

Table 22

London - Broxbourne, Hertford East, Bishops Stortford, Stansted Airport and Cambridge

Mondays to Fridays

9 December to 16 May

Network Diagram - see first Page of Table 20

		LE ◇1	LE 1	LE 1 🚲	XC 1	LE	LE 1 🚲	LE ◇1	LE 1	LE 1 🚲	LE	LE 1 🚲	LE ◇1	LE 1	LE	LE 1	LE ◇1	LE	LE A	LE FX 1	LE FO 1	LE B
London Liverpool Street 15 ⊖	d	21 58		22 10		22 12	22 25	22 28		22 40	22 42	22 55	22 58		23 12	23 25	23 28	23 40	23 45	23 58	23 58	
Bethnal Green	d																		23 48			
Hackney Downs	d					22 18					22 48				23 18			23 46	23 54			
Stratford 7 ⊖	d		22 00						22 30					23 00								
Clapton	d																	23 49				
Seven Sisters ⊖	d																		00 02			
Tottenham Hale ⊖	d	22 10	22 13	22 22		22 25	22 37	22 40	22 43	22 52	22 55	23 07	23 10	23 13	23 25	23 37	23 40	23 53		00 10	00 10	
Northumberland Park	d		22 15											23 15				23 55				
Angel Road	d																					
Ponders End	d					22 29					22 59				23 29			23 59				
Brimsdown	d					22 32					23 02				23 32			00 02				
Enfield Lock	d		22 21			22 34					23 04			23 21	23 34			00 04				
Waltham Cross	d					22 37			22 50		23 07				23 37			00 07				←
Cheshunt	d	22 18	22 25			22 39		22 48	22 52		23 09		23 18	23 25	23 39		23 48	00 09	00 22	00 18	00 18	00 22
Broxbourne 3	a	22 23	22 30			22 45		22 53	22 58		23 15		23 23	23 30	23 45		23 53	00 15	→	00 23	00 23	00 28
Broxbourne 3	d	22 23	22 34			22 45		22 53	22 59		23 15		23 23	23 30	23 45		23 53	00 15		00 23	00 23	00 28
Rye House	d					22 48					23 18				23 48			00 18				
St Margarets (Herts)	d					22 51					23 21				23 51			00 21				
Ware	d					22 55					23 25				23 55			00 25				
Hertford East	a					23 01					23 31				00 01			00 31				
Roydon	d		22 39					22 57						23 34			23 57			00 27	00 27	
Harlow Town	d	22 29	22 43				22 55	23 01	23 11			23 25	23 29	23 38		23 55	00 01			00 31	00 31	00 35
Harlow Mill	d		22 46					23 04						23 41			00 04			00 34	00 34	
Sawbridgeworth	d	22 34	22 49					23 08	23 17				23 34	23 45			00 08			00 38	00 38	
Bishops Stortford	a	22 40	22 56	22 45				23 14	23 23	23 17			23 40	23 51		00 04	00 14			00 44	00 44	00 47
	d	22 40		22 45				23 14		23 18			23 40			00 04	00 14				00 44	
Stansted Mountfitchet	d							23 18				23 36					00 18				00 48	
Stansted Airport	a			22 57			23 12			23 30		23 43				00 13						
Stansted Airport	d				22 57																	
Elsenham	d							23 22									00 22				00 52	
Newport (Essex)	d							23 27									00 27				00 57	
Audley End	d	22 52			23 10			23 30					23 52				00 30				01 00	
Great Chesterford	d							23 35									00 35				01 05	
Whittlesford Parkway	d	23 00						23 40					23 59				00 40				01 10	
Shelford	d							23 44									00 44					
Cambridge	a	23 09			23 30			23 51					00 09				00 51				01 19	

Saturdays

14 December to 17 May

		LE 1 B	LE 1	XC ◇1 C	LE 1	LE 1	LE ◇1 D	LE 1	LE ◇1 B	LE 1	XC ◇1 C	LE	LE 1 A	LE 1	LE ◇1	LE 1 B	LE 1	LE	LE 1 A	LE 1	LE ◇1	LE 1 B	LE 1
London Liverpool Street 15 ⊖	d		04 10		04 40	05 10	05 21	05 25		05 40		05 42	05 51	05 55	05 58		06 10	06 12	06 21	06 25	06 28		06 40
Bethnal Green	d																						
Hackney Downs	d											05 48						06 18					
Stratford 7 ⊖	d						05 30						06 00						06 30				
Clapton	d																						
Seven Sisters ⊖	d								←							←						←	
Tottenham Hale ⊖	d				04 52	05 22	05 40	05 37	05 40	05 52		05 55	06 13	06 07	06 10	06 13	06 22	06 25	06 43	06 37	06 40	06 43	06 52
Northumberland Park	d						→						→			06 15			→				
Angel Road	d																						
Ponders End	d											05 59						06 29					
Brimsdown	d											06 02						06 32					
Enfield Lock	d											06 04				06 21		06 34					
Waltham Cross	d											06 07						06 37				06 50	
Cheshunt	d				05 00				05 48			06 09			06 18	06 25		06 39			06 48	06 52	
Broxbourne 3	a				05 05				05 53			06 15			06 23	06 30		06 45			06 53	06 58	
Broxbourne 3	d				05 05				05 53			06 15			06 23	06 34		06 45			06 53	06 58	
Rye House	d											06 18						06 48					
St Margarets (Herts)	d											06 21						06 51					
Ware	d											06 25						06 55					
Hertford East	a											06 31						07 01					
Roydon	d								05 57							06 39					06 57		
Harlow Town	d				05 11	05 38		05 53	06 01					06 25	06 29	06 43				06 55	07 01	07 11	
Harlow Mill	d								06 04							06 46					07 04		
Sawbridgeworth	d					05 43			06 08							06 49					07 08	07 17	
Bishops Stortford	a				05 20	05 49		06 02	06 14	06 17					06 38	06 56	06 45				07 14	07 23	07 17
	d	00 04			05 20	05 50		06 02	06 14	06 18					06 39		06 45				07 14		07 18
Stansted Mountfitchet	d				05 24			06 06	06 18					06 36							07 18		
Stansted Airport	a	00 13	05 00		05 39	05 59		06 13		06 27				06 43			06 55			07 12			07 27
Stansted Airport	d			05 25							06 27												
Elsenham	d								06 22												07 22		
Newport (Essex)	d								06 27												07 27		
Audley End	d			05 37					06 30		06 40				06 51						07 30		
Great Chesterford	d								06 35												07 35		
Whittlesford Parkway	d								06 40						06 58						07 40		
Shelford	d								06 44												07 44		
Cambridge	a			05 52					06 51		06 56				07 08						07 51		

A To Bishops Stortford
B From London Liverpool Street
C To Birmingham New Street
D To Cambridge

Table 22

Saturdays

14 December to 17 May

London - Broxbourne, Hertford East, Bishops Stortford, Stansted Airport and Cambridge

Network Diagram - see first Page of Table 20

		XC ◇1 A	LE	LE 1	LE ◇1	LE 1		LE 1 🚲	LE	LE 1 🚲	LE ◇1	LE 1	LE 1 🚲	XC ◇1 A	LE	LE 1 🚲		LE ◇1	LE 1	LE 1 🚲	LE	LE 1 🚲	LE ◇1	LE 1	LE 1 🚲
London Liverpool Street 15 ⊖	d		06 42	06 55	06 58			07 10	07 12	07 25	07 28		07 40		07 42	07 55		07 58		08 10	08 12	08 25	08 28		08 40
Bethnal Green	d																								
Hackney Downs	d		06 48						07 18						07 48						08 18				
Stratford 7 ⊖	d					07 00						07 30							08 00					08 30	
Clapton	d																								
Seven Sisters ⊖	d																								
Tottenham Hale ⊖	d		06 55	07 07	07 10	07 13		07 22	07 25	07 37	07 40	07 43	07 52		07 55	08 07		08 10	08 13	08 22	08 25	08 37	08 40	08 43	08 52
Northumberland Park	d					07 15													08 15						
Angel Road	d																								
Ponders End	d		06 59						07 29						07 59						08 29				
Brimsdown	d		07 02						07 32						08 02						08 32				
Enfield Lock	d		07 04			07 21			07 34						08 04				08 21		08 34				
Waltham Cross	d		07 07						07 37			07 50			08 07						08 37			08 50	
Cheshunt	d		07 09		07 18	07 25			07 39		07 48	07 52			08 09			08 18	08 25		08 39		08 48	08 52	
Broxbourne 3	a		07 15		07 23	07 30			07 45		07 53	07 58			08 15			08 23	08 30		08 45		08 53	08 58	
Broxbourne 3	d		07 15		07 23	07 34			07 45		07 53	07 58			08 15			08 23	08 34		08 45		08 53	08 58	
Rye House	d		07 18						07 48						08 18						08 48				
St Margarets (Herts)	d		07 21						07 51						08 21						08 51				
Ware	d		07 25						07 55						08 25						08 55				
Hertford East	a		07 31						08 01						08 31						09 01				
Roydon	d					07 39					07 57								08 39				08 57		
Harlow Town	d			07 25	07 29	07 43				07 55	08 01	08 11				08 25		08 29	08 43			08 55	09 01	09 11	
Harlow Mill	d					07 46					08 04								08 46				09 04		
Sawbridgeworth	d					07 49					08 08	08 17							08 49				09 08	09 17	
Bishops Stortford	a				07 38	07 56		07 45			08 14	08 23	08 17					08 38	08 56	08 45			09 14	09 23	09 17
	d				07 39			07 45			08 14		08 18					08 39		08 45			09 14		09 18
Stansted Mountfitchet	d			07 36							08 18					08 36							09 18		
Stansted Airport	a			07 43				07 55		08 12			08 27			08 44				08 55		09 12			09 27
Stansted Airport	d	07 27												08 27											
Elsenham	d										08 22												09 22		
Newport (Essex)	d										08 27												09 27		
Audley End	d	07 40			07 51						08 30			08 40				08 51					09 30		
Great Chesterford	d										08 35												09 35		
Whittlesford Parkway	d				07 58						08 40							08 58					09 40		
Shelford	d										08 44												09 44		
Cambridge	a	07 58			08 08						08 51			08 58				09 08					09 51		

		XC ◇1 A		LE	LE 1 🚲	LE ◇1	LE 1	LE 1 🚲	LE	LE 1 🚲	LE ◇1	LE 1		LE 1 🚲	XC ◇1 A	LE	LE 1 🚲	LE ◇1	LE 1	LE 1 🚲	LE	LE 1 🚲		LE ◇1	LE 1
London Liverpool Street 15 ⊖	d			08 42	08 55	08 58		09 10	09 12	09 25	09 28			09 40		09 42	09 55	09 58		10 10	10 12	10 25		10 28	
Bethnal Green	d																								
Hackney Downs	d			08 48					09 18							09 48					10 18				
Stratford 7 ⊖	d						09 00					09 30							10 00						10 30
Clapton	d																								
Seven Sisters ⊖	d																								
Tottenham Hale ⊖	d			08 55	09 07	09 10	09 13	09 22	09 25	09 37	09 40	09 43		09 52		09 55	10 07	10 10	10 13	10 22	10 25	10 37		10 40	10 43
Northumberland Park	d						09 15												10 15						
Angel Road	d																								
Ponders End	d			08 59					09 29							09 59					10 29				
Brimsdown	d			09 02					09 32							10 02					10 32				
Enfield Lock	d			09 04			09 21		09 34							10 04			10 21		10 34				
Waltham Cross	d			09 07					09 37			09 50				10 07					10 37				10 50
Cheshunt	d			09 09		09 18	09 25		09 39		09 48	09 52				10 09		10 18	10 25		10 39			10 48	10 52
Broxbourne 3	a			09 15		09 23	09 30		09 45		09 53	09 58				10 15		10 23	10 30		10 45			10 53	10 58
Broxbourne 3	d			09 15		09 23	09 34		09 45		09 53	09 58				10 15		10 23	10 34		10 45			10 53	10 58
Rye House	d			09 18					09 48							10 18					10 48				
St Margarets (Herts)	d			09 21					09 51							10 21					10 51				
Ware	d			09 25					09 55							10 25					10 55				
Hertford East	a			09 31					10 01							10 31					11 01				
Roydon	d						09 39				09 57								10 39					10 57	
Harlow Town	d				09 25	09 29	09 43			09 55	10 01	10 11					10 25	10 29	10 43			10 55		11 01	11 11
Harlow Mill	d						09 46				10 04								10 46					11 04	
Sawbridgeworth	d						09 49				10 08	10 17							10 49					11 08	11 17
Bishops Stortford	a					09 38	09 56	09 45			10 14	10 23		10 17				10 38	10 56	10 45				11 14	11 23
	d					09 39		09 45			10 14			10 18				10 39		10 45				11 14	
Stansted Mountfitchet	d				09 36						10 18						10 36							11 18	
Stansted Airport	a				09 44			09 55		10 12				10 27			10 44			10 55		11 13			
Stansted Airport	d	09 27													10 27										
Elsenham	d										10 22													11 22	
Newport (Essex)	d										10 27													11 27	
Audley End	d	09 40				09 51					10 30				10 40			10 51						11 30	
Great Chesterford	d										10 35													11 35	
Whittlesford Parkway	d					09 58					10 40							10 58						11 40	
Shelford	d										10 44													11 44	
Cambridge	a	09 58				10 08					10 51				10 58			11 08						11 51	

A To Birmingham New Street

Table 22

Saturdays

14 December to 17 May

London - Broxbourne, Hertford East, Bishops Stortford, Stansted Airport and Cambridge

Network Diagram - see first Page of Table 20

		LE	XC	LE	LE	LE	LE	LE		LE	LE	LE	LE	LE	XC	LE	LE	LE	LE	LE	LE	LE	LE	LE	LE
		■1	◇■1		■1	◇■1	■1	■1			■1	◇■1	■1	■1	◇■1		■1	◇■1	■1	■1		■1	◇■1	■1	■1
			A												A										
		🛒			🛒			🛒			🛒			🛒			🛒			🛒		🛒			🛒
London Liverpool Street ■15 ⊖	d	10 40		10 42	10 55	10 58		11 10		11 12	11 25	11 28		11 40		11 42	11 55	11 58		12 10	12 12	12 25	12 28		12 40
Bethnal Green	d																								
Hackney Downs	d			10 48						11 18						11 48					12 18				
Stratford ■7 ⊖	d						11 00						11 30						12 00					12 30	
Clapton	d																								
Seven Sisters ⊖	d																								
Tottenham Hale ⊖	d	10 52		10 55	11 07	11 10	11 13	11 22		11 25	11 37	11 40	11 43	11 52		11 55	12 07	12 10	12 13	12 22	12 25	12 37	12 40	12 43	12 52
Northumberland Park	d						11 15												12 15						
Angel Road	d																								
Ponders End	d			10 59						11 29						11 59					12 29				
Brimsdown	d			11 02						11 32						12 02					12 32				
Enfield Lock	d			11 04			11 21			11 34						12 04			12 21		12 34				
Waltham Cross	d			11 07						11 37			11 50			12 07					12 37			12 50	
Cheshunt	d			11 09		11 18	11 25			11 39		11 48	11 52			12 09		12 18	12 25		12 39		12 48	12 52	
Broxbourne ■3	a			11 15		11 23	11 30			11 45		11 53	11 58			12 15		12 23	12 30		12 45		12 53	12 58	
Broxbourne ■3	d			11 15		11 23	11 34			11 45		11 53	11 58			12 15		12 23	12 34		12 45		12 53	12 58	
Rye House	d			11 18						11 48						12 18					12 48				
St Margarets (Herts)	d			11 21						11 51						12 21					12 51				
Ware	d			11 25						11 55						12 25					12 55				
Hertford East	a			11 31						12 01						12 31					13 01				
Roydon	d						11 39					11 57							12 39				12 57		
Harlow Town	d				11 25	11 29	11 43				11 55	12 01	12 11				12 25	12 29	12 43			12 55	13 01	13 11	
Harlow Mill	d						11 46					12 04							12 46				13 04		
Sawbridgeworth	d						11 49					12 08	12 17						12 49				13 08	13 17	
Bishops Stortford	a	11 17				11 38	11 56	11 45				12 14	12 23	12 17				12 38	12 56	12 45			13 14	13 23	13 17
	d	11 18				11 39		11 45				12 14		12 18				12 39		12 45			13 14		13 18
Stansted Mountfitchet	d				11 36							12 18					12 36						13 18		
Stansted Airport	a	11 27			11 44			11 55			12 12			12 27			12 44			12 55		13 12			13 27
Stansted Airport	d		11 27												12 27										
Elsenham	d											12 22											13 22		
Newport (Essex)	d											12 27											13 27		
Audley End	d		11 40			11 51						12 30			12 40			12 51					13 30		
Great Chesterford	d											12 35											13 35		
Whittlesford Parkway	d					11 58						12 40						12 58					13 40		
Shelford	d											12 44											13 44		
Cambridge	a		11 58			12 08						12 51			12 59			13 08					13 51		

		XC		LE	LE	LE	LE	LE	LE	LE	LE	LE	LE	XC		LE	LE	LE	LE	LE	LE	LE	LE	LE
		◇■1			■1	◇■1	■1	■1		■1	◇■1	■1	■1	◇■1			■1	◇■1	■1	■1		■1	◇■1	■1
		A												A										
					🛒			🛒		🛒			🛒				🛒			🛒		🛒		
London Liverpool Street ■15 ⊖	d			16 42	16 55	16 58		17 10	17 12	17 25	17 28		17 40			17 42	17 55	17 58		18 10	18 12	18 25	18 28	
Bethnal Green	d																							
Hackney Downs	d			16 48					17 18							17 48					18 18			
Stratford ■7 ⊖	d						17 00					17 30							18 00					18 30
Clapton	d																							
Seven Sisters ⊖	d																							
Tottenham Hale ⊖	d			16 55	17 07	17 10	17 13	17 22	17 25	17 37	17 40	17 43	17 52			17 55	18 07	18 10	18 13	18 22	18 25	18 37	18 40	18 43
Northumberland Park	d						17 15												18 15					
Angel Road	d																							
Ponders End	d			16 59					17 29							17 59					18 29			
Brimsdown	d			17 02					17 32							18 02					18 32			
Enfield Lock	d			17 04			17 21		17 34							18 04			18 21		18 34			
Waltham Cross	d		and at the same minutes past each hour until	17 07					17 37			17 50				18 07					18 37			18 50
Cheshunt	d			17 09		17 18	17 25		17 39		17 48	17 52				18 09		18 18	18 25		18 39		18 48	18 52
Broxbourne ■3	a			17 15		17 23	17 30		17 45		17 53	17 58				18 15		18 23	18 30		18 45		18 53	18 58
Broxbourne ■3	d			17 15		17 23	17 34		17 45		17 53	17 58				18 15		18 23	18 34		18 45		18 53	18 58
Rye House	d			17 18					17 48							18 18					18 48			
St Margarets (Herts)	d			17 21					17 51							18 21					18 51			
Ware	d			17 25					17 55							18 25					18 55			
Hertford East	a			17 31					18 01							18 31					19 01			
Roydon	d						17 39				17 57								18 39				18 57	
Harlow Town	d				17 25	17 29	17 43			17 55	18 01	18 11					18 25	18 29	18 43			18 55	19 01	19 11
Harlow Mill	d						17 46				18 04								18 46				19 04	
Sawbridgeworth	d						17 49				18 08	18 17							18 49				19 08	19 17
Bishops Stortford	a					17 38	17 56	17 45			18 14	18 23	18 17					18 38	18 56	18 45			19 14	19 23
	d					17 39		17 45			18 14		18 18					18 39		18 45			19 14	
Stansted Mountfitchet	d				17 36						18 18						18 36						19 18	
Stansted Airport	a				17 44			17 55		18 12			18 27				18 43			18 57		19 12		
Stansted Airport	d	13 27												18 27										
Elsenham	d										18 22												19 22	
Newport (Essex)	d										18 27												19 27	
Audley End	d	13 40				17 51					18 30			18 40				18 51					19 30	
Great Chesterford	d										18 35												19 35	
Whittlesford Parkway	d					17 58					18 40							18 58					19 40	
Shelford	d										18 44												19 44	
Cambridge	a	13 58				18 08					18 51			18 58				19 08					19 51	

A To Birmingham New Street

Table 22

Saturdays

14 December to 17 May

London - Broxbourne, Hertford East, Bishops Stortford, Stansted Airport and Cambridge

Network Diagram - see first Page of Table 20

			LE 1 🚲	XC ◇1 A	LE	LE 1 🚲	LE ◇1	LE 1	LE 1 🚲	LE	LE 1 🚲		LE ◇1	LE 1	LE 1 🚲	XC 1	LE	LE 1 🚲	LE ◇1	LE 1	LE 1 🚲		LE	LE 1 🚲	LE ◇1
London Liverpool Street 15 ⊖	d		18 40		18 42	18 55	18 58		19 10	19 12	19 25		19 28		19 40		19 42	19 55	19 58		20 10		20 12	20 25	20 28
Bethnal Green	d																								
Hackney Downs	d				18 48					19 18							19 48						20 18		
Stratford 7 ⊖	d							19 00						19 30						20 00					
Clapton	d																								
Seven Sisters ⊖	d																								
Tottenham Hale ⊖	d		18 52		18 55	19 07	19 10	19 13	19 22	19 25	19 37		19 40	19 43	19 52		19 55	20 07	20 10	20 13	20 22		20 25	20 37	20 40
Northumberland Park	d							19 15												20 15					
Angel Road	d																								
Ponders End	d				18 59					19 29							19 59						20 29		
Brimsdown	d				19 02					19 32							20 02						20 32		
Enfield Lock	d				19 04			19 21		19 34							20 04			20 21			20 34		
Waltham Cross	d				19 07					19 37				19 50			20 07						20 37		
Cheshunt	d				19 09		19 18	19 25		19 39			19 48	19 52			20 09		20 18	20 25			20 39		20 48
Broxbourne 3	a				19 15		19 23	19 30		19 45			19 53	19 58			20 15		20 23	20 30			20 45		20 53
Broxbourne 3	d				19 15		19 23	19 34		19 45			19 53	19 58			20 15		20 23	20 34			20 45		20 53
Rye House	d				19 18					19 48							20 18						20 48		
St Margarets (Herts)	d				19 21					19 51							20 21						20 51		
Ware	d				19 25					19 55							20 25						20 55		
Hertford East	a				19 31					20 01							20 31						21 01		
Roydon	d							19 39					19 57							20 39					20 57
Harlow Town	d					19 25	19 29	19 43			19 55		20 01	20 11				20 25	20 29	20 43				20 55	21 01
Harlow Mill	d							19 46					20 04							20 46					21 04
Sawbridgeworth	d							19 49					20 08	20 17						20 49					21 08
Bishops Stortford	a		19 17				19 38	19 56	19 45				20 14	20 23	20 17				20 38	20 56	20 45				21 14
	d		19 18				19 39		19 45				20 14		20 18				20 39		20 45				21 14
Stansted Mountfitchet	d					19 36							20 18					20 36							21 18
Stansted Airport	a		19 27			19 44			19 55		20 12				20 27			20 44			20 55			21 12	
Stansted Airport	d			19 27												20 27									
Elsenham	d												20 22												21 22
Newport (Essex)	d												20 27												21 27
Audley End	d			19 40			19 51						20 30			20 40			20 51						21 30
Great Chesterford	d												20 35												21 35
Whittlesford Parkway	d						19 58						20 40						20 58						21 40
Shelford	d												20 44												21 44
Cambridge	a			19 58			20 08						20 51			20 57			21 08						21 51

		LE 1	LE 1 🚲	XC 1	LE	LE 1 🚲	LE ◇1		LE 1	LE 1 🚲	LE	LE 1 🚲	LE ◇1	LE 1	LE 1 🚲	XC 1	LE		LE 1 🚲	LE ◇1	LE 1	LE 1 🚲	LE	LE 1 🚲	LE ◇1
London Liverpool Street 15 ⊖	d		20 40		20 42	20 55	20 58			21 10	21 12	21 25	21 28		21 40		21 42		21 55	21 58		22 10	22 12	22 25	22 28
Bethnal Green	d																								
Hackney Downs	d				20 48						21 18						21 48						22 18		
Stratford 7 ⊖	d	20 30							21 00					21 30							22 00				
Clapton	d																								
Seven Sisters ⊖	d																								
Tottenham Hale ⊖	d	20 43	20 52		20 55	21 07	21 10		21 13	21 22	21 25	21 37	21 40	21 43	21 52		21 55		22 07	22 10	22 13	22 22	22 25	22 37	22 40
Northumberland Park	d								21 15												22 15				
Angel Road	d																								
Ponders End	d				20 59						21 29						21 59						22 29		
Brimsdown	d				21 02						21 32						22 02						22 32		
Enfield Lock	d				21 04				21 21		21 34						22 04				22 21		22 34		
Waltham Cross	d	20 50			21 07						21 37			21 50			22 07						22 37		
Cheshunt	d	20 52			21 09		21 18		21 25		21 39		21 48	21 52			22 09			22 18	22 25		22 39		22 48
Broxbourne 3	a	20 58			21 15		21 23		21 30		21 45		21 53	21 58			22 15			22 23	22 30		22 45		22 53
Broxbourne 3	d	20 58			21 15		21 23		21 34		21 45		21 53	21 58			22 15			22 23	22 34		22 45		22 53
Rye House	d				21 18						21 48						22 18						22 48		
St Margarets (Herts)	d				21 21						21 51						22 21						22 51		
Ware	d				21 25						21 55						22 25						22 55		
Hertford East	a				21 31						22 01						22 31						23 01		
Roydon	d								21 39				21 57								22 39				22 57
Harlow Town	d	21 11				21 25	21 29		21 43			21 55	22 01	22 11					22 25	22 29	22 43			22 55	23 01
Harlow Mill	d								21 46				22 04								22 46				23 04
Sawbridgeworth	d	21 17							21 49				22 08	22 17							22 49				23 08
Bishops Stortford	a	21 23	21 17				21 38		21 56	21 45			22 14	22 23	22 17					22 38	22 56	22 45			23 14
	d		21 18				21 39			21 45			22 14		22 18					22 39		22 45			23 14
Stansted Mountfitchet	d					21 36							22 18						22 36						23 18
Stansted Airport	a		21 27			21 44				21 55		22 12			22 27				22 44			22 55		23 12	
Stansted Airport	d			21 27												22 27									
Elsenham	d												22 22												23 22
Newport (Essex)	d												22 27												23 27
Audley End	d			21 40			21 51						22 30			22 40				22 51					23 30
Great Chesterford	d												22 35												23 35
Whittlesford Parkway	d						21 58						22 40							22 58					23 40
Shelford	d												22 44												23 44
Cambridge	a			22 01			22 08						22 51			22 57				23 09					23 51

A To Birmingham New Street

Table 22

Saturdays

14 December to 17 May

London - Broxbourne, Hertford East, Bishops Stortford, Stansted Airport and Cambridge

Network Diagram - see first Page of Table 20

		LE	LE		XC	LE	LE	LE	LE	LE	LE	LE	LE		LE
		1	1		1		1	◇1	1		1	◇1			1
			🚲				🚲								
London Liverpool Street 15 ⊖	d		22 40			22 42	22 55	22 58		23 12	23 25	23 28	23 40		23 58
Bethnal Green	d														
Hackney Downs	d					22 48				23 18			23 46		
Stratford 7 ⊖	d	22 30							23 00						
Clapton	d												23 49		
Seven Sisters ⊖	d														
Tottenham Hale ⊖	d	22 43	22 52			22 55	23 07	23 10	23 13	23 25	23 37	23 40	23 53		00 10
Northumberland Park	d								23 15				23 55		
Angel Road	d														
Ponders End	d					22 59				23 29			23 59		
Brimsdown	d					23 02				23 32			00 02		
Enfield Lock	d					23 04			23 21	23 34			00 04		
Waltham Cross	d	22 50				23 07				23 37			00 07		
Cheshunt	d	22 52				23 09		23 18	23 25	23 39		23 48	00 09		00 18
Broxbourne 3	a	22 58				23 15		23 23	23 30	23 45		23 53	00 15		00 23
Broxbourne 3	d	22 58				23 15		23 23	23 30	23 45		23 53	00 15		00 23
Rye House	d					23 18				23 48			00 18		
St Margarets (Herts)	d					23 21				23 51			00 21		
Ware	d					23 25				23 55			00 25		
Hertford East	a					23 31				00 01			00 31		
Roydon	d								23 34			23 57			00 27
Harlow Town	d	23 11					23 25	23 29	23 38		23 55	00 01			00 31
Harlow Mill	d								23 41			00 04			00 34
Sawbridgeworth	d	23 17							23 45			00 08			00 38
Bishops Stortford	a	23 23	23 17					23 38	23 51		00 04	00 14			00 44
	d		23 18					23 39			00 04	00 14			00 44
Stansted Mountfitchet	d						23 36					00 18			00 48
Stansted Airport	a		23 27				23 43				00 13				
Stansted Airport	d				23 27										
Elsenham	d											00 22			00 52
Newport (Essex)	d											00 27			00 57
Audley End	d				23 40			23 51				00 30			01 00
Great Chesterford	d											00 35			01 05
Whittlesford Parkway	d							23 58				00 40			01 10
Shelford	d											00 44			
Cambridge	a				23 55			00 09				00 51			01 19

Sundays

8 December to 11 May

		LE	LE	LE	LE	LE	LE	LE	LE	LE		LE	LE	LE	LE	LE	LE	LE	LE	LE		LE	LE	LE	LE
		1	1	1	1	1	1	1	1	1		1	1	1	1		1	1	1			1	◇1		1
		A													B			C		D				C	
												🚲	🚲	🚲			🚲		🚲			🚲			🚲
London Liverpool Street 15 ⊖	d		04 10	04 40	05 10	05 40	06 10	06 25	06 40	06 55		07 10	07 25	07 40	07 43	07 52	07 55		08 10	08 22		08 25	08 28		08 40
Bethnal Green	d																								
Hackney Downs	d															07 59				08 29					
Stratford 7 ⊖	d																								
Clapton	d																								
Seven Sisters ⊖	d															08 04				08 34					
Tottenham Hale ⊖	d			04u52	05u22	05u52	06u22	06u37	06u52	07 07		07 22	07 37	07 52	07 55		08 07		08 22			08 37	08 40		08 52
Northumberland Park	d																								
Angel Road	d																								
Ponders End	d														07 59										
Brimsdown	d														08 02										
Enfield Lock	d														08 04										
Waltham Cross	d														08 07									⟵	
Cheshunt	d					06 00									08 09	08 20				08 52			08 49	08 52	
Broxbourne 3	a					06 05									08 15	08 26				⟶			08 54	08 58	
Broxbourne 3	d					06 05									08 19	08 26							08 54	08 58	
Rye House	d															08 29								09 01	
St Margarets (Herts)	d															08 32								09 04	
Ware	d															08 36								09 08	
Hertford East	a															08 42								09 14	
Roydon	d														08 24			⟵							
Harlow Town	d			05 08	05 38	06 11		06 53		07 23			07 53		08 28		08 23	08 28				08 53	09 00		
Harlow Mill	d														⟶			08 31							
Sawbridgeworth	d																	08 34					09 05		
Bishops Stortford	a			05 17	05 47	06 20	06 45		07 15			07 45		08 15				08 40	08 45				09 11		09 15
	d	00 04		05 18	05 48	06 21	06 46		07 16			07 46		08 16				08 41	08 45				09 12		09 16
Stansted Mountfitchet	d			05 22				07 04					08 04					08 45				09 04			
Stansted Airport	a	00 13	04 58	05 29	05 57	06 30	06 55	07 12	07 25	07 40		07 55	08 12	08 25			08 40		08 55			09 12			09 25
Stansted Airport	d																								
Elsenham	d																	08 49							
Newport (Essex)	d																	08 54							
Audley End	d																	08 57					09 24		
Great Chesterford	d																	09 02							
Whittlesford Parkway	d																	09 07					09 31		
Shelford	d																	09 11							
Cambridge	a																	09 19					09 41		

A not 8 December. From London Liverpool Street
B To Cambridge
C From London Liverpool Street
D To Hertford East

Table 22

Sundays

8 December to 11 May

London - Broxbourne, Hertford East, Bishops Stortford, Stansted Airport and Cambridge

Network Diagram - see first Page of Table 20

		LE	LE	LE	LE	LE	LE	LE	LE	LE	LE	XC	LE	LE	LE	LE
		1		1	1	1		1	◇1		1	◇1	1		1	1
		A			B		C			D		E	A			B
				🚲		🚲		🚲			🚲				🚲	
London Liverpool Street 15 ⊖	d		08 52	08 55		09 10	09 22	09 25	09 28		09 40			09 52	09 55	
Bethnal Green	d															
Hackney Downs	d		08 59				09 29							09 59		
Stratford 7 ⊖	d	08 45											09 45			
Clapton	d															
Seven Sisters ⊖	d		09 04				09 34							10 04		
Tottenham Hale ⊖	d	08 55		09 07		09 22		09 37	09 40		09 52		09 55		10 07	
Northumberland Park	d															
Angel Road	d															
Ponders End	d	08 59											09 59			
Brimsdown	d	09 02											10 02			
Enfield Lock	d	09 04											10 04			
Waltham Cross	d	09 07								←			10 07			
Cheshunt	d	09 09	09 20				09 52		09 49	09 52			10 09	10 20		
Broxbourne 3	a	09 15	09 26				→		09 54	09 58			10 15	10 26		
Broxbourne 3	d	09 19	09 26						09 54	09 58			10 19	10 26		
Rye House	d		09 29							10 01				10 29		
St Margarets (Herts)	d		09 32							10 04				10 32		
Ware	d		09 36							10 08				10 36		
Hertford East	a		09 42							10 14				10 42		
Roydon	d	09 24			←								10 24			←
Harlow Town	d	09 28		09 23	09 28			09 53	10 00				10 28		10 23	10 28
Harlow Mill	d	→			09 31								→			10 31
Sawbridgeworth	d				09 34				10 05							10 34
Bishops Stortford	a				09 40	09 45			10 11		10 15					10 40
	d				09 41	09 45			10 12		10 16					10 41
Stansted Mountfitchet	d				09 45			10 04								10 45
Stansted Airport	a			09 40		09 55		10 12			10 25				10 40	
Stansted Airport	d											10 25				
Elsenham	d				09 49											10 49
Newport (Essex)	d				09 54											10 54
Audley End	d				09 57				10 24			10 39				10 57
Great Chesterford	d				10 02											11 02
Whittlesford Parkway	d				10 07				10 31							11 07
Shelford	d				10 11											11 11
Cambridge	a				10 19				10 41			10 58				11 18

and at the same minutes past each hour until

		LE	LE	LE	LE	LE	LE	XC
		1		1	◇1		1	◇1
			C			D		E
		🚲		🚲			🚲	
London Liverpool Street 15 ⊖	d	18 10	18 22	18 25	18 28		18 40	
Bethnal Green	d							
Hackney Downs	d		18 29					
Stratford 7 ⊖	d							
Clapton	d							
Seven Sisters ⊖	d		18 34					
Tottenham Hale ⊖	d	18 22		18 37	18 40		18 52	
Northumberland Park	d							
Angel Road	d							
Ponders End	d							
Brimsdown	d							
Enfield Lock	d							
Waltham Cross	d					←		
Cheshunt	d		18 52		18 49	18 52		
Broxbourne 3	a		→		18 54	18 58		
Broxbourne 3	d				18 54	18 58		
Rye House	d					19 01		
St Margarets (Herts)	d					19 04		
Ware	d					19 08		
Hertford East	a					19 14		
Roydon	d							
Harlow Town	d			18 53	19 00			
Harlow Mill	d							
Sawbridgeworth	d				19 05			
Bishops Stortford	a	18 45			19 11		19 15	
	d	18 45			19 12		19 16	
Stansted Mountfitchet	d			19 04				
Stansted Airport	a	18 55		19 12			19 25	
Stansted Airport	d							19 25
Elsenham	d							
Newport (Essex)	d							
Audley End	d				19 24			19 39
Great Chesterford	d							
Whittlesford Parkway	d				19 31			
Shelford	d							
Cambridge	a				19 41			19 58

		LE	LE	LE	LE	LE	LE	LE	LE	LE	LE	XC	LE	LE
		1		1	1	1		1	◇1		1	1	1	
		A			B		C			D			A	
				🚲		🚲		🚲			🚲			
London Liverpool Street 15 ⊖	d		18 52	18 55		19 10	19 22	19 25	19 28		19 40			19 52
Bethnal Green	d													
Hackney Downs	d		18 59				19 29							19 59
Stratford 7 ⊖	d	18 45											19 45	
Clapton	d													
Seven Sisters ⊖	d		19 04				19 34							20 04
Tottenham Hale ⊖	d	18 55		19 07		19 22		19 37	19 40		19 52		19 55	
Northumberland Park	d													
Angel Road	d													
Ponders End	d	18 59											19 59	
Brimsdown	d	19 02											20 02	
Enfield Lock	d	19 04											20 04	
Waltham Cross	d	19 07								←			20 07	
Cheshunt	d	19 09	19 20				19 52		19 49	19 52			20 09	20 20
Broxbourne 3	a	19 15	19 26				→		19 54	19 58			20 15	20 26
Broxbourne 3	d	19 19	19 26						19 54	19 58			20 19	20 26
Rye House	d		19 29							20 01				20 29
St Margarets (Herts)	d		19 32							20 04				20 32
Ware	d		19 36							20 08				20 36
Hertford East	a		19 42							20 14				20 42
Roydon	d	19 24			←								20 24	
Harlow Town	d	19 28		19 23	19 28			19 53	20 00				20 28	
Harlow Mill	d	→			19 31								→	
Sawbridgeworth	d				19 34				20 05					
Bishops Stortford	a				19 40	19 45			20 11		20 15			
	d				19 41	19 45			20 12		20 16			
Stansted Mountfitchet	d				19 45			20 04						
Stansted Airport	a			19 40		19 55		20 12			20 25			
Stansted Airport	d											20 25		
Elsenham	d				19 49									
Newport (Essex)	d				19 54									
Audley End	d				19 57				20 24			20 39		
Great Chesterford	d				20 02									
Whittlesford Parkway	d				20 07				20 31					
Shelford	d				20 11									
Cambridge	a				20 18				20 41			20 57		

		LE	LE	LE	LE	LE	LE	LE	XC	LE
		1	1	1		1	◇1		1	1
			B		C			D		
		🚲		🚲		🚲				🚲
London Liverpool Street 15 ⊖	d	19 55		20 10	20 22	20 25	20 28			20 40
Bethnal Green	d									
Hackney Downs	d				20 29					
Stratford 7 ⊖	d									
Clapton	d									
Seven Sisters ⊖	d				20 34					
Tottenham Hale ⊖	d	20 07		20 22		20 37	20 40			20 52
Northumberland Park	d									
Angel Road	d									
Ponders End	d									
Brimsdown	d									
Enfield Lock	d									
Waltham Cross	d							←		
Cheshunt	d				20 52		20 49	20 52		
Broxbourne 3	a				→		20 54	20 58		
Broxbourne 3	d						20 54	20 58		
Rye House	d							21 01		
St Margarets (Herts)	d							21 04		
Ware	d							21 08		
Hertford East	a							21 14		
Roydon	d		←							
Harlow Town	d	20 23	20 28			20 53	21 00			
Harlow Mill	d		20 31							
Sawbridgeworth	d		20 34				21 05			
Bishops Stortford	a		20 40	20 45			21 11			21 15
	d		20 41	20 45			21 12			21 16
Stansted Mountfitchet	d		20 45			21 04				
Stansted Airport	a	20 40		20 55		21 12				21 28
Stansted Airport	d								21 19	
Elsenham	d		20 49							
Newport (Essex)	d		20 54							
Audley End	d		20 57				21 24		21 33	
Great Chesterford	d		21 02							
Whittlesford Parkway	d		21 07				21 31			
Shelford	d		21 11							
Cambridge	a		21 18				21 41		21 49	

A To Cambridge
B From Stratford
C To Hertford East
D From London Liverpool Street
E To Nuneaton

Table 22

Sundays

8 December to 11 May

London - Broxbourne, Hertford East, Bishops Stortford, Stansted Airport and Cambridge

Network Diagram - see first Page of Table 20

		LE	LE	LE	LE	LE	LE	LE	LE	LE	LE	XC	LE	LE	LE	LE	LE	XC	LE	LE	LE	LE
		1		1	1	1		1	◇1		1	1	1		1	1	1	1		1	◇1	
		A			B		C			D			A			B			C			D
				🚲		🚲		🚲			🚲				🚲		🚲			🚲		
London Liverpool Street 15 ⊖	d		20 52	20 55		21 10	21 22	21 25	21 28		21 40			21 52	21 55		22 10		22 22	22 25	22 28	
Bethnal Green	d																					
Hackney Downs	d		20 59				21 29							21 59					22 29			
Stratford 7 ⊖	d	20 45											21 45									
Clapton	d																					
Seven Sisters ⊖	d		21 04				21 34							22 04					22 34			
Tottenham Hale ⊖	d	20 55		21 07		21 22		21 37	21 40		21 52		21 55		22 07		22 22			22 37	22 40	
Northumberland Park	d																					
Angel Road	d																					
Ponders End	d	20 59											21 59									
Brimsdown	d	21 02											22 02									
Enfield Lock	d	21 04											22 04									
Waltham Cross	d	21 07								←			22 07									←
Cheshunt	d	21 09	21 20				21 52		21 49	21 52			22 09	22 20					22 52		22 49	22 52
Broxbourne 3	a	21 15	21 26				→		21 54	21 58			22 15	22 26					→		22 54	22 58
Broxbourne 3	d	21 19	21 26						21 54	21 58			22 19	22 26							22 54	22 58
Rye House	d		21 29							22 01				22 29								23 01
St Margarets (Herts)	d		21 32							22 04				22 32								23 04
Ware	d		21 36							22 08				22 36								23 08
Hertford East	a		21 42							22 14				22 42								23 14
Roydon	d	21 24			←								22 24			←						
Harlow Town	d	21 28		21 23	21 28			21 53	22 00				22 28		22 23	22 28				22 53	23 00	
Harlow Mill	d	→			21 31								→			22 31						
Sawbridgeworth	d				21 34				22 05							22 34					23 05	
Bishops Stortford	a				21 40	21 45			22 11		22 15					22 40	22 45				23 11	
	d				21 41	21 45			22 12		22 16					22 41	22 45				23 12	
Stansted Mountfitchet	d				21 45			22 04								22 45				23 04		
Stansted Airport	a			21 40		21 55		22 12			22 25				22 40		22 55			23 12		
Stansted Airport	d											22 25						23 04				
Elsenham	d				21 49											22 49						
Newport (Essex)	d				21 54											22 54						
Audley End	d				21 57				22 24			22 40				22 57		23 18			23 24	
Great Chesterford	d				22 02											23 02						
Whittlesford Parkway	d				22 07				22 31							23 07					23 31	
Shelford	d				22 11											23 11						
Cambridge	a				22 18				22 41			22 57				23 20		23 35			23 41	

		LE	LE	LE	LE	LE	LE	LE	LE	LE	LE	LE
		1	1		1	1			1	1		1
			A	E		B	D	C			D	
		🚲			🚲							
London Liverpool Street 15 ⊖	d	22 40		22 52	22 55			23 22	23 25	23 28		23 58
Bethnal Green	d											
Hackney Downs	d			22 59				23 29				
Stratford 7 ⊖	d		22 45									
Clapton	d											
Seven Sisters ⊖	d			23 04				23 34				
Tottenham Hale ⊖	d	22 52	22 55		23 07				23 37	23 40		00 10
Northumberland Park	d											
Angel Road	d											
Ponders End	d		22 59							23 44		
Brimsdown	d		23 02							23 47		
Enfield Lock	d		23 04							23 49		
Waltham Cross	d		23 07							23 52		
Cheshunt	d		23 09	23 20				23 50		23 54	←	00 18
Broxbourne 3	a		23 15	23 26				23 56		23 59	23 56	00 23
Broxbourne 3	d		23 19	23 26				00 03		23 59	00 03	00 23
Rye House	d							→			00 06	
St Margarets (Herts)	d										00 09	
Ware	d										00 13	
Hertford East	a										00 19	
Roydon	d		23 24			←	←					00 27
Harlow Town	d		23 28	23 32	23 23	23 28	23 32		23 53	00 06		00 31
Harlow Mill	d		→	→		23 31						00 34
Sawbridgeworth	d					23 34				00 11		00 38
Bishops Stortford	a	23 15				23 40	23 43		00 02	00 17		00 44
	d	23 16				23 41			00 03			
Stansted Mountfitchet	d					23 45						
Stansted Airport	a	23 25			23 40				00 12			
Stansted Airport	d											
Elsenham	d					23 49						
Newport (Essex)	d					23 54						
Audley End	d					23 57						
Great Chesterford	d					00 02						
Whittlesford Parkway	d					00 07						
Shelford	d					00 11						
Cambridge	a					00 18						

A To Cambridge
B From Stratford
C To Hertford East
D From London Liverpool Street
E To Bishops Stortford

Table 22R

Mondays to Fridays

9 December to 16 May

Cambridge, Stansted Airport, Bishops Stortford, Hertford East and Broxbourne - London

Network Diagram - see first Page of Table 20

Miles	Miles	Miles			LE	LE	LE	LE	XC	LE	LE	LE	LE	LE	XC	LE	LE	LE	LE	LE	LE	LE	LE
					MX		MFO	MFO					MFO										
					1	1	1	1	1	◇1		1	1	1	1	◇1	1	1		◇1	1		
												A		B									
																		🚲			🚲		
0	—	—	**Cambridge**	d					04 44	04 48					05 17	05 20	05 29			05 48			
3¼	—	—	Shelford	d												05 25							
6¾	—	—	Whittlesford Parkway	d						04 55						05 29	05 38			05 55			
10	—	—	Great Chesterford	d												05 33							
14	—	—	Audley End	d					04 58	05 03					05 35	05 39	05 47			06 04			
15¾	—	—	Newport (Essex)	d												05 42							
20¼	0	—	Elsenham	d												05 48							
—	—	—	**Stansted Airport**	a					05 12						05 49								
—	4½	—	**Stansted Airport**	d		00 30	01 00	01 30					05 30					06 00			06 15		
22½	8¼	—	Stansted Mountfitchet	d												05 51		06 06					
25½	—	0	**Bishops Stortford**	a		00 39				05 16			05 39			05 57	06 00	06 10		06 17	06 24		
—	—	—		d		00 39				05 16		05 30	05 39			05 57	06 00	06 10		06 18	06 24		
29	—	3¾	Sawbridgeworth	d						05 21		05 35				06 01	06 04						
31¼	—	5¾	Harlow Mill	d						05 24		05 38				06 05							
33	—	7½	Harlow Town	d		00 47				05 27		05 41	05 47			06 08	06 13	06 18		06 27	06 32		
35¾	—	10¼	Roydon	d						05 31		05 45				06 12							
—	0	—	**Hertford East**	d	00 07						05 25								06 06				06 27
—	2	—	Ware	d							05 29								06 10				06 31
—	4	—	St Margarets (Herts)	d							05 33								06 14				06 35
—	5¼	—	Rye House	d							05 36			←					06 17				06 38
38½	—	13¼	**Broxbourne 3**	a	00 19					05 36	05 40	05 50	05 53	05 50		06 16	06 19		06 22	06 34			06 43
—	7	—	**Broxbourne 3**	d	00 19					05 36	05 40	05 56	05 53	05 56		06 16	06 20		06 26	06 34		06 39	06 43
41¾	—	16¼	Cheshunt	d						05 41	05 44	→	05 57	06 01		06 20			06 30			06 44	06 47
43	—	—	Waltham Cross	d							05 47			06 03					06 33			06 46	
44	—	—	Enfield Lock	d							05 49			06 06					06 35			06 49	
45	—	—	Brimsdown	d							05 52			06 08					06 38			06 51	
45¾	—	—	Ponders End	d							05 54			06 10					06 40				
48	—	22¾	Angel Road	d							05 57			06 14									
48¾	—	23½	Northumberland Park	d							05 59			06 16								06 56	
49¾	—	24¼	Tottenham Hale ⊖	d						05 49	06 03		06 07	06 20		06 28	06 31	06 34	06 45	06 49	06 51	06 59	
—	0	—	Seven Sisters ⊖	d																			07 02
51¾	—	—	Clapton	d																			
—	6¾	28½	Stratford 7 ⊖	a										06 32			06 45					07 13	
52¾	—	—	Hackney Downs	d							06 08								06 52				07 08
54½	—	—	Bethnal Green	d																			
55¾	—	—	**London Liverpool Street 15 ⊖**	a	00 49	01 21	01 50	02 20		06 03	06 18		06 23			06 43		06 49	07 02	07 05	07 08		07 18

		LE	LE	LE	LE	LE	LE	LE	LE	LE	LE	LE	XC	LE	LE	LE	LE	LE	LE	LE	LE	LE	LE
		◇1		1	1	◇1		1	1		◇1	1	1	◇1		1			◇1		1	1	◇1
			C	A		D	E		B											C	A		F
					🚲			🚲				🚲				🚲						🚲	
Cambridge	d	05 51				06 18					06 21		06 32	06 47					06 51				07 17
Shelford	d	05 56									06 26								06 56				
Whittlesford Parkway	d	06 00				06 25					06 30			06 55					07 00				07 25
Great Chesterford	d	06 04									06 34								07 04				
Audley End	d	06 10				06 34					06 40		06 46	07 04					07 10				07 34
Newport (Essex)	d	06 13									06 43								07 13				
Elsenham	d	06 19									06 49								07 19				
Stansted Airport	a												07 09										
Stansted Airport	d				06 30			06 45				07 00				07 15						07 30	
Stansted Mountfitchet	d	06 22			06 36						06 52								07 22				
Bishops Stortford	a	06 28			06 40	06 47		06 54			06 58	07 09		07 17		07 24			07 28			07 39	07 47
	d	06 29		06 34	06 41	06 47		06 54			06 58	07 09		07 17		07 24			07 28		07 34	07 41	07 47
Sawbridgeworth	d	06 33		06 39							07 03	07 14							07 33		07 39		
Harlow Mill	d	06 37		06 42							07 06								07 36		07 42		
Harlow Town	d	06 40		06 56	06 49			07 02			07 10	07 19				07 32			07 40		07 56	07 49	
Roydon	d	06 44		07 00							07 14								07 44		08 00		
Hertford East	d									06 57							07 17	07 27					
Ware	d									07 01							07 21	07 31					
St Margarets (Herts)	d									07 05							07 25	07 35					
Rye House	d									07 08							07 28	07 38					
Broxbourne 3	a	06 48		07 05						07 13	07 18						07 33	07 43	07 48		08 05		
Broxbourne 3	d	06 49	07 00	07 09						07 13	07 18				07 30		07 39	07 43	07 48	08 00	08 09		
Cheshunt	d	06 53	07 05	07 14						07 17	07 23				07 35		07 44	07 47	07 53	08 05	08 14		
Waltham Cross	d		07 07	07 16				07 12							07 37		07 46			08 07	08 16		
Enfield Lock	d		07 10	07 19											07 40	07 43	07 49			08 10	08 19		
Brimsdown	d		07 12					07 16							07 42	07 46	07 51			08 12			
Ponders End	d		07 14												07 44					08 14			
Angel Road	d			07 24																	08 24		
Northumberland Park	d			07 26			←		←								07 56				08 26		
Tottenham Hale ⊖	d	07 02	07 20	07 29	07 05	07 08	07 20	07 23	07 29		07 32	07 35		07 38	07 50	07 53	07 59		08 02	08 20	08 29	08 05	08 08
Seven Sisters ⊖	d		→	→						07 32								08 02		→	→		
Clapton	d																						
Stratford 7 ⊖	a								07 43								08 13						
Hackney Downs	d						07 26			07 38					07 56			08 08					
Bethnal Green	d																						
London Liverpool Street 15 ⊖	a	07 20			07 23	07 25	07 38	07 41		07 48	07 50	07 53		07 55	08 08	08 10		08 18	08 20			08 23	08 25

A To Stratford
B From Bishops Stortford
C To London Liverpool Street
D From Kings Lynn
E From Broxbourne
F From Kings Lynn. The Fenman

Table 22R

Mondays to Fridays

9 December to 16 May

Cambridge, Stansted Airport, Bishops Stortford, Hertford East and Broxbourne - London

Network Diagram - see first Page of Table 20

		LE	LE	LE	LE	LE	LE	XC	LE	LE	LE	LE	LE	LE	XC	LE	LE	LE	LE	LE	LE	LE	LE
			1	1		◇1	1	1	◇1		1		◇1	1	◇1		1	◇1	1	1	◇1	1	
		A		B									C		D		E			B	C		
			🚲				🚲				🚲			🚲					🚲			🚲	
Cambridge	d					07 21		07 40	07 47				07 51		08 10			08 18			08 21		
Shelford	d					07 26							07 56								08 26		
Whittlesford Parkway	d					07 30			07 55				08 00					08 25			08 31		
Great Chesterford	d					07 34							08 04								08 35		
Audley End	d					07 40		07 54	08 04				08 10		08 25			08 34			08 40		
Newport (Essex)	d					07 43							08 13								08 43		
Elsenham	d					07 49							08 19								08 49		
Stansted Airport	a							08 09							08 39								
Stansted Airport	d		07 43				08 00				08 15			08 30					08 45			09 00	
Stansted Mountfitchet	d		07 49			07 52							08 22						08 51		08 53		
Bishops Stortford	a		07 53			07 58	08 09		08 17		08 24		08 28	08 39				08 48			08 58	09 09	
	d		07 54			07 58	08 09		08 17		08 24		08 28	08 39			08 43	08 49			08 58	09 09	
Sawbridgeworth	d					08 03	08 14						08 33				08 48				09 03		
Harlow Mill	d					08 06							08 36								09 06		
Harlow Town	d		08 02			08 10	08 19				08 32		08 40				08 53	08 57	09 02		09 10		
Roydon	d					08 14							08 44								09 14		
Hertford East	d				07 57							08 17				08 39							09 09
Ware	d				08 01							08 21				08 43							09 13
St Margarets (Herts)	d				08 05							08 25				08 47							09 17
Rye House	d				08 08							08 28				08 50				←			09 20
Broxbourne 3	a				08 13	08 18						08 36	08 48			08 55	09 00	09 03		09 00	09 18		09 25
Broxbourne 3	d				08 13	08 18				08 30		08 39	08 48			08 55	09 09	09 04		09 09	09 18		09 25
Cheshunt	d				08 17	08 23				08 35		08 44	08 53			09 00	→			09 14	09 23		09 30
Waltham Cross	d		08 12							08 37		08 46				09 02				09 16			09 32
Enfield Lock	d									08 40		08 49				09 05				09 19			09 35
Brimsdown	d		08 16							08 42		08 51				09 07							09 37
Ponders End	d									08 44						09 09							09 39
Angel Road	d																			09 24			
Northumberland Park	d	←		←								08 56								09 26			
Tottenham Hale ⊖	d	08 20	08 23	08 29		08 32	08 35		08 38	08 50	08 53	08 59	09 02	09 05		09 15		09 19	09 21	09 29	09 32	09 35	09 45
Seven Sisters ⊖	d				08 32																		
Clapton	d																						
Stratford 7 ⊖	a			08 43								09 13								09 43			
Hackney Downs	d	08 26			08 38					08 56						09 21							09 51
Bethnal Green	d																						
London Liverpool Street 15 ⊖	a	08 37	08 40		08 48	08 50	08 53		08 55	09 07	09 09		09 20	09 23		09 33		09 35	09 38		09 50	09 53	10 01

		LE	LE	LE	LE	XC	LE	LE	LE	LE	LE	LE	LE	LE	LE	LE	XC	LE	LE	LE	LE	LE
		1	1	◇1	1	◇1		1	1	◇1	1		1	1	◇1	1	◇1		1	1	◇1	1
						D											D					
		🚲			🚲			🚲			🚲		🚲			🚲			🚲			🚲
Cambridge	d			08 48		09 10				09 18					10 04		10 11				10 21	
Shelford	d			08 53						09 23											10 26	
Whittlesford Parkway	d			09 00						09 30					10 11						10 30	
Great Chesterford	d			09 04						09 34											10 34	
Audley End	d			09 10		09 25				09 40					10 19		10 25				10 40	
Newport (Essex)	d			09 13						09 43											10 43	
Elsenham	d			09 19						09 49											10 49	
Stansted Airport	a					09 40											10 40					
Stansted Airport	d	09 15			09 30			09 45			10 00		10 15			10 30			10 45			11 00
Stansted Mountfitchet	d	09 21		09 24						09 52			10 21								10 52	
Bishops Stortford	a			09 29	09 39					09 58	10 09				10 32	10 39					10 58	11 09
	d		09 13	09 29	09 39				09 47	09 58	10 09			10 15	10 32	10 39				10 47	10 58	11 09
Sawbridgeworth	d		09 18	09 33					09 52	10 03				10 20						10 52	11 03	
Harlow Mill	d		09 21	09 37						10 06				10 23							11 06	
Harlow Town	d	09 32	09 24	09 40				10 00	10 05	10 09			10 32	10 26	10 40				11 00	11 05	11 09	
Roydon	d		09 28							10 13				10 30							11 13	
Hertford East	d						09 39					10 09						10 39				
Ware	d						09 43					10 13						10 43				
St Margarets (Herts)	d						09 47					10 17						10 47				
Rye House	d						09 50					10 20						10 50				
Broxbourne 3	a		09 33	09 46			09 55		10 11	10 17		10 25		10 35	10 46			10 55		11 11	11 17	
Broxbourne 3	d		09 39	09 46			09 55		10 12	10 17		10 25		10 39	10 46			10 55		11 12	11 17	
Cheshunt	d		09 43	09 50			09 59		10 16	10 21		10 29		10 44	10 50			10 59		11 16	11 21	
Waltham Cross	d						10 01		10 19			10 31						11 01		11 19		
Enfield Lock	d		09 47				10 04					10 34		10 47				11 04				
Brimsdown	d						10 06					10 36						11 06				
Ponders End	d						10 08					10 38						11 08				
Angel Road	d		09 52																			
Northumberland Park	d		09 54											10 53								
Tottenham Hale ⊖	d	09 48	09 57	10 00	10 03		10 14	10 17	10 27	10 30	10 33	10 44	10 48	10 56	11 00	11 03		11 14	11 17	11 27	11 30	11 33
Seven Sisters ⊖	d																					
Clapton	d																					
Stratford 7 ⊖	a		10 08						10 40					11 10						11 40		
Hackney Downs	d						10 20					10 50						11 20				
Bethnal Green	d																					
London Liverpool Street 15 ⊖	a	10 03		10 14	10 17		10 28	10 31		10 44	10 47	10 58	11 02		11 14	11 17		11 28	11 31		11 44	11 47

A From Broxbourne
B From Bishops Stortford
C From Ely
D From Birmingham New Street
E To Stratford

Table 22R

Mondays to Fridays

9 December to 16 May

Cambridge, Stansted Airport, Bishops Stortford, Hertford East and Broxbourne - London

Network Diagram - see first Page of Table 20

		LE	LE 1 🛒	LE 1	LE ◇1	LE 1 🛒	XC ◇1 A		LE	LE 1 🛒	LE 1	LE ◇1	LE 1 🛒	LE	LE 1 🛒	LE 1	LE ◇1		LE 1 🛒	XC ◇1 B	LE	LE 1 🛒	LE 1	LE ◇1	LE 1 🛒
Cambridge	d				11 04		11 10					11 21					12 04			12 10				12 21	
Shelford	d											11 26												12 26	
Whittlesford Parkway	d				11 11							11 30					12 11							12 30	
Great Chesterford	d											11 34												12 34	
Audley End	d				11 19		11 25					11 40					12 19			12 25				12 40	
Newport (Essex)	d											11 43												12 43	
Elsenham	d											11 49												12 49	
Stansted Airport	a						11 40													12 40					
Stansted Airport	d		11 15			11 30				11 45			12 00		12 15				12 30			12 45			13 00
Stansted Mountfitchet	d		11 21									11 52			12 21									12 52	
Bishops Stortford	a				11 32	11 39						11 58	12 09				12 32		12 39					12 58	13 09
	d			11 15	11 32	11 39					11 47	11 58	12 09			12 15	12 32		12 39				12 47	12 58	13 09
Sawbridgeworth	d			11 20							11 52	12 03				12 20							12 52	13 03	
Harlow Mill	d			11 23								12 06				12 23								13 06	
Harlow Town	d		11 32	11 26	11 40					12 00	12 05	12 09			12 32	12 26	12 40					13 00	13 05	13 09	
Roydon	d			11 30								12 13				12 30								13 13	
Hertford East	d	11 09							11 39					12 09							12 39				
Ware	d	11 13							11 43					12 13							12 43				
St Margarets (Herts)	d	11 17							11 47					12 17							12 47				
Rye House	d	11 20							11 50					12 20							12 50				
Broxbourne 3	a	11 25		11 35	11 46				11 55		12 11	12 17		12 25		12 35	12 46				12 55		13 11	13 17	
Broxbourne 3	d	11 25		11 39	11 46				11 55		12 12	12 17		12 25		12 39	12 46				12 55		13 12	13 17	
Cheshunt	d	11 29		11 44	11 50				11 59		12 16	12 21		12 29		12 44	12 50				12 59		13 16	13 21	
Waltham Cross	d	11 31							12 01		12 19			12 31							13 01		13 19		
Enfield Lock	d	11 34		11 47					12 04					12 34		12 47					13 04				
Brimsdown	d	11 36							12 06					12 36							13 06				
Ponders End	d	11 38							12 08					12 38							13 08				
Angel Road	d																								
Northumberland Park	d			11 53												12 53									
Tottenham Hale ⊖	d	11 44	11 48	11 56	12 01	12 03			12 14	12 17	12 27	12 31	12 33	12 44	12 48	12 56	13 01		13 03		13 14	13 17	13 27	13 30	13 33
Seven Sisters ⊖	d																								
Clapton	d																								
Stratford 7 ⊖	a			12 10							12 40					13 10							13 40		
Hackney Downs	d	11 50							12 20					12 50							13 20				
Bethnal Green	d																								
London Liverpool Street 15 ⊖	a	11 58	12 02		12 14	12 17			12 31	12 33		12 44	12 47	13 01	13 03		13 14		13 17		13 31	13 33		13 44	13 47

		LE	LE 1 🛒		LE 1	LE ◇1	LE 1 🛒	XC ◇1 B	LE	LE 1 🛒	LE 1	LE ◇1	LE 1 🛒		LE	LE 1 🛒	LE 1	LE ◇1	LE 1 🛒	XC ◇1 B	LE	LE 1 🛒	LE 1		LE ◇1
Cambridge	d					13 04		13 10				13 21						14 04		14 10					14 21
Shelford	d											13 26													14 26
Whittlesford Parkway	d					13 11						13 30						14 11							14 30
Great Chesterford	d											13 34													14 34
Audley End	d					13 19		13 25				13 40						14 19		14 25					14 40
Newport (Essex)	d											13 43													14 43
Elsenham	d											13 49													14 49
Stansted Airport	a							13 40												14 40					
Stansted Airport	d		13 15				13 30			13 45			14 00			14 15			14 30			14 45			
Stansted Mountfitchet	d		13 21									13 52				14 21									14 52
Bishops Stortford	a					13 32	13 39					13 58	14 09					14 32	14 39						14 58
	d				13 15	13 32	13 39				13 47	13 58	14 09				14 15	14 32	14 39				14 47		14 58
Sawbridgeworth	d				13 20						13 52	14 03					14 20						14 52		15 03
Harlow Mill	d				13 23							14 06					14 23								15 06
Harlow Town	d		13 32		13 26	13 40				14 00	14 05	14 09				14 32	14 26	14 40				15 00	15 05		15 09
Roydon	d				13 30							14 13					14 30								15 13
Hertford East	d	13 09							13 39						14 09						14 39				
Ware	d	13 13							13 43						14 13						14 43				
St Margarets (Herts)	d	13 17							13 47						14 17						14 47				
Rye House	d	13 20							13 50						14 20						14 50				
Broxbourne 3	a	13 25			13 35	13 46			13 55		14 11	14 17			14 25		14 35	14 46			14 55		15 11		15 17
Broxbourne 3	d	13 25			13 39	13 46			13 55		14 12	14 17			14 25		14 39	14 46			14 55		15 12		15 17
Cheshunt	d	13 29			13 44	13 50			13 59		14 16	14 21			14 29		14 44	14 50			14 59		15 16		15 21
Waltham Cross	d	13 31							14 01		14 19				14 31						15 01		15 19		
Enfield Lock	d	13 34			13 47				14 04						14 34		14 47				15 04				
Brimsdown	d	13 36							14 06						14 36						15 06				
Ponders End	d	13 38							14 08						14 38						15 08				
Angel Road	d																								
Northumberland Park	d				13 53												14 53								
Tottenham Hale ⊖	d	13 44	13 48		13 56	14 00	14 03		14 14	14 17	14 27	14 30	14 33		14 44	14 48	14 56	15 01	15 03		15 14	15 17	15 27		15 31
Seven Sisters ⊖	d																								
Clapton	d																								
Stratford 7 ⊖	a				14 10						14 40						15 10						15 40		
Hackney Downs	d	13 50							14 20						14 50						15 20				
Bethnal Green	d																								
London Liverpool Street 15 ⊖	a	14 01	14 03			14 14	14 17		14 31	14 33		14 44	14 47		14 58	15 02		15 14	15 18		15 28	15 31			15 45

A From Gloucester

B From Birmingham New Street

Table 22R

Mondays to Fridays

9 December to 16 May

Cambridge, Stansted Airport, Bishops Stortford, Hertford East and Broxbourne - London

Network Diagram - see first Page of Table 20

		LE	LE	LE	LE	LE	LE	XC	LE	LE	LE	LE	LE	LE	LE	LE	LE	LE	XC	LE	LE	LE	LE
		1		1	1	◇1	1	◇1		1	1	◇1	1		1	1	◇1	1	◇1		1	1	◇1
								A											A				
		🚲		🚲			🚲			🚲			🚲		🚲			🚲			🚲		
Cambridge	d					15 04		15 10				15 21					15 51		16 10				16 21
Shelford	d											15 26					15 56						16 26
Whittlesford Parkway	d					15 11						15 30					16 00						16 30
Great Chesterford	d											15 34					16 04						16 34
Audley End	d					15 19		15 25				15 40					16 10		16 25				16 40
Newport (Essex)	d											15 43					16 13						16 43
Elsenham	d											15 49					16 19						16 49
Stansted Airport	a							15 40											16 40				
Stansted Airport	d	15 00		15 15			15 30			15 45			16 00		16 15			16 30			16 45		
Stansted Mountfitchet	d			15 21								15 52			16 21		16 24						16 52
Bishops Stortford	a	15 09				15 32	15 39					15 58	16 09				16 30	16 39					16 58
	d	15 09			15 15	15 32	15 39				15 47	15 58	16 09			16 15	16 30	16 39				16 43	16 58
Sawbridgeworth	d				15 20						15 52	16 03				16 20						16 48	17 03
Harlow Mill	d				15 23							16 06				16 23						16 51	
Harlow Town	d			15 32	15 26	15 40				16 00	16 03	16 09			16 32	16 26	16 38				17 00	16 54	17 08
Roydon	d				15 30							16 13				16 30						16 58	
Hertford East	d		15 09						15 39					16 09						16 39			
Ware	d		15 13						15 43					16 13						16 43			
St Margarets (Herts)	d		15 17						15 47					16 17						16 47			
Rye House	d		15 20						15 50					16 20						16 50			
Broxbourne 3	a		15 25		15 35	15 46			15 55		16 10	16 17		16 25		16 35	16 44			16 56		17 03	17 14
Broxbourne 3	d		15 25		15 39	15 46			15 55		16 10	16 17		16 25		16 39	16 44			16 56		17 07	17 14
Cheshunt	d		15 29		15 44	15 50			15 59		16 14	16 21		16 29		16 44	16 48			17 00		17 12	17 18
Waltham Cross	d		15 31						16 01		16 16			16 31						17 02		17 14	
Enfield Lock	d		15 34		15 47				16 04					16 34		16 47				17 05			
Brimsdown	d		15 36						16 06					16 36						17 07			
Ponders End	d		15 38						16 08					16 38						17 09			
Angel Road	d				15 52											16 52							
Northumberland Park	d				15 54						16 23					16 54						17 21	
Tottenham Hale ⊖	d	15 33	15 44	15 48	15 58	16 01	16 04		16 14	16 17	16 27	16 30	16 33	16 44	16 48	16 58	17 01	17 04		17 15	17 18	17 24	17 27
Seven Sisters ⊖	d																						
Clapton	d																						
Stratford 7 ⊖	a				16 10						16 37					17 08						17 35	
Hackney Downs	d		15 50						16 20					16 50						17 21			
Bethnal Green	d																						
London Liverpool Street 15 ⊖	a	15 47	15 59	16 03		16 15	16 18		16 31	16 33		16 44	16 47	16 59	17 02		17 16	17 18		17 30	17 32		17 44

		LE	LE	LE	LE	LE	LE	LE	XC	LE	LE	LE	LE	LE	LE	LE	LE	LE	LE	LE	LE	LE	XC
		◇1	1		1	1	◇1	1	◇1		1	1	◇1	1		1	1		◇1	1		1	◇1
									A														A
			🚲		🚲			🚲			🚲			🚲		🚲				🚲		🚲	
Cambridge	d	16 40					16 51		17 10				17 21						17 51				18 18
Shelford	d						16 56						17 26						17 56				
Whittlesford Parkway	d						17 00						17 30						18 00				
Great Chesterford	d						17 04						17 34						18 04				
Audley End	d	16 53					17 10		17 25				17 40						18 10				18 32
Newport (Essex)	d						17 13						17 43						18 13				
Elsenham	d						17 19						17 49						18 19				
Stansted Airport	a								17 40														18 54
Stansted Airport	d		17 00		17 15			17 30			17 45			18 00		18 15				18 30		18 45	
Stansted Mountfitchet	d				17 21		17 24						17 52			18 21			18 24				
Bishops Stortford	a		17 09				17 30	17 39					17 58	18 09					18 29	18 39			
	d		17 09			17 15	17 30	17 39				17 47	17 58	18 09			18 15		18 30	18 39			
Sawbridgeworth	d					17 20	17 35					17 52	18 03				18 20		18 35				
Harlow Mill	d					17 23	17 38						18 06				18 23						
Harlow Town	d				17 32	17 26	17 41				18 00	17 57	18 09			18 32	18 26		18 40			19 00	
Roydon	d					17 30							18 13				18 30						
Hertford East	d			17 09						17 39					18 09			18 25			18 39		
Ware	d			17 13						17 43					18 13			18 29			18 43		
St Margarets (Herts)	d			17 17						17 47					18 17			18 33			18 47		
Rye House	d			17 20						17 50					18 20			18 36			18 50		
Broxbourne 3	a			17 26		17 35	17 47			17 56		18 04	18 17		18 26		18 35	18 43	18 46		18 56		
Broxbourne 3	d			17 26		17 40	17 47			17 56		18 10	18 17		18 26		18 40		18 46		18 56		
Cheshunt	d			17 30		17 44	17 51			18 00		18 14	18 21		18 30		18 44		18 50		19 00		
Waltham Cross	d			17 32						18 02		18 17			18 32						19 02		
Enfield Lock	d			17 35		17 48				18 05					18 35		18 48				19 05		
Brimsdown	d			17 37						18 07					18 37						19 07		
Ponders End	d			17 39						18 09					18 39						19 09		
Angel Road	d					17 53											18 53						
Northumberland Park	d					17 55						18 23					18 55						
Tottenham Hale ⊖	d	17 30	17 33	17 45	17 51	17 58	18 01	18 04		18 15	18 21	18 27	18 30	18 33	18 45	18 51	18 58		19 01	19 04	19 15	19 21	
Seven Sisters ⊖	d																						
Clapton	d																						
Stratford 7 ⊖	a					18 09						18 38					19 09						
Hackney Downs	d			17 51						18 21					18 51						19 21		
Bethnal Green	d																						
London Liverpool Street 15 ⊖	a	17 46	17 48	17 59	18 08		18 16	18 18		18 29	18 38		18 45	18 47	18 59	19 08			19 16	19 18	19 29	19 38	

A From Birmingham New Street

Table 22R

Mondays to Fridays

9 December to 16 May

Cambridge, Stansted Airport, Bishops Stortford, Hertford East and Broxbourne - London

Network Diagram - see first Page of Table 20

		LE	LE	LE	LE	LE	LE	LE	LE	LE	XC	LE	LE	LE	LE	LE	LE	LE	LE	LE	LE	XC
			◇1	1		1	1		◇1	1	◇1		1		◇1	1		1	1	◇1	1	◇1
											A											A
				🛒		🛒				🛒			🛒			🛒		🛒			🛒	
Cambridge	d		18 21						18 51		19 10				19 21					20 04		20 10
Shelford	d		18 26						18 56						19 26							
Whittlesford Parkway	d		18 30						19 00						19 30					20 11		
Great Chesterford	d		18 34						19 04						19 34							
Audley End	d		18 40						19 10		19 25				19 40					20 19		20 25
Newport (Essex)	d		18 43						19 13						19 43							
Elsenham	d		18 49						19 19						19 49							
Stansted Airport	a										19 40											20 40
Stansted Airport	d			19 00		19 15				19 30			19 45			20 00		20 15			20 30	
Stansted Mountfitchet	d		18 52			19 21			19 24						19 52			20 21				
Bishops Stortford	a		18 58	19 09					19 29	19 39					19 58	20 09				20 32	20 39	
	d		18 58	19 09			19 15		19 30	19 39					19 58	20 09			20 15	20 32	20 39	
Sawbridgeworth	d		19 03				19 20		19 35						20 03				20 20			
Harlow Mill	d		19 06				19 23								20 06				20 23			
Harlow Town	d		19 09			19 32	19 26		19 40				20 00		20 09			20 32	20 26	20 40		
Roydon	d		19 13				19 30								20 13				20 30			
Hertford East	d				19 09			19 25				19 39					20 10					
Ware	d				19 13			19 29				19 43					20 14					
St Margarets (Herts)	d				19 17			19 33				19 47					20 18					
Rye House	d				19 20			19 36				19 50					20 21					
Broxbourne 3	a		19 17		19 26		19 35	19 42	19 46			19 55			20 17		20 25		20 35	20 46		
Broxbourne 3	d	19 10	19 17		19 26		19 39		19 46			19 55		20 12	20 17		20 25		20 39	20 46		
Cheshunt	d	19 14	19 21		19 30		19 43		19 50			19 59		20 16	20 21		20 29		20 44	20 50		
Waltham Cross	d	19 17			19 32							20 01		20 19			20 32					
Enfield Lock	d				19 35		19 47					20 04					20 34		20 47			
Brimsdown	d				19 37							20 06					20 37					
Ponders End	d				19 39							20 08					20 39					
Angel Road	d						19 52															
Northumberland Park	d	19 23					19 54												20 53			
Tottenham Hale ⊖	d	19 27	19 30	19 33	19 45	19 48	19 57		20 00	20 03		20 14	20 17	20 27	20 30	20 33	20 44	20 48	20 56	21 01	21 03	
Seven Sisters ⊖	d																					
Clapton	d																					
Stratford 7 ⊖	a	19 38					20 10							20 37					21 10			
Hackney Downs	d				19 51							20 20					20 50					
Bethnal Green	d																					
London Liverpool Street 15 ⊖	a		19 45	19 48	19 59	20 02			20 14	20 17		20 31	20 33		20 45	20 47	20 59	21 03		21 14	21 17	

		LE	LE	LE	LE	LE	LE	LE	LE	LE	LE	XC	LE	LE	LE	LE	LE	LE	LE	LE	LE	LE	LE
			1	1	◇1	1		1	1	◇1	1	◇1		1	1	◇1	1		1	◇1	1		1
												A											
			🛒			🛒		🛒			🛒			🛒									
Cambridge	d				20 21					21 04		21 10				21 21				22 04			
Shelford	d				20 26											21 26							
Whittlesford Parkway	d				20 30					21 11						21 30				22 11			
Great Chesterford	d				20 34											21 34							
Audley End	d				20 40					21 19		21 25				21 40				22 19			
Newport (Essex)	d				20 43											21 43							
Elsenham	d				20 49											21 49							
Stansted Airport	a											21 40											
Stansted Airport	d		20 45			21 00		21 15			21 30			21 45			22 00		22 15		22 30		22 45
Stansted Mountfitchet	d				20 52			21 21								21 52			22 21				
Bishops Stortford	a				20 58	21 09				21 32	21 39					21 58	22 09			22 32	22 39		
	d			20 47	20 58	21 09			21 15	21 32	21 39				21 47	21 58	22 09			22 32	22 39		
Sawbridgeworth	d			20 52	21 03				21 20						21 52	22 03							
Harlow Mill	d				21 06				21 23							22 06							
Harlow Town	d		21 00	20 57	21 09			21 32	21 26	21 40				22 00	22 05	22 09			22 32	22 40			23 00
Roydon	d				21 13				21 30							22 13							
Hertford East	d	20 39					21 09						21 39					22 09				22 39	
Ware	d	20 43					21 13						21 43					22 13				22 43	
St Margarets (Herts)	d	20 47					21 17						21 47					22 17				22 47	
Rye House	d	20 50					21 20						21 50					22 20				22 50	
Broxbourne 3	a	20 55		21 04	21 17		21 25		21 35	21 46			21 55		22 11	22 17		22 25		22 46		22 55	
Broxbourne 3	d	20 55		21 07	21 17		21 25		21 39	21 46			21 55		22 12	22 17		22 25		22 46		22 55	
Cheshunt	d	20 59		21 12	21 21		21 29		21 44	21 50			21 59		22 16	22 21		22 29		22 50		22 59	
Waltham Cross	d	21 01		21 14			21 31						22 01		22 19			22 31				23 01	
Enfield Lock	d	21 04					21 34		21 47				22 04					22 34				23 04	
Brimsdown	d	21 06					21 36						22 06					22 36				23 06	
Ponders End	d	21 08					21 38						22 08					22 38				23 08	
Angel Road	d																						
Northumberland Park	d								21 53														
Tottenham Hale ⊖	d	21 14	21 17	21 23	21 30	21 33	21 44	21 48	21 56	22 01	22 03		22 14	22 17	22 27	22 31	22 33	22 44	22 48	23 01	23 03	23 14	23 17
Seven Sisters ⊖	d																						
Clapton	d																						
Stratford 7 ⊖	a			21 40					22 10						22 40								
Hackney Downs	d	21 20					21 50						22 20					22 50				23 20	
Bethnal Green	d																						
London Liverpool Street 15 ⊖	a	21 28	21 31		21 44	21 47	21 58	22 02		22 14	22 17		22 28	22 31		22 45	22 47	22 58	23 02	23 14	23 17	23 28	23 31

A From Birmingham New Street

Table 22R

Mondays to Fridays

9 December to 16 May

Cambridge, Stansted Airport, Bishops Stortford, Hertford East and Broxbourne - London

Network Diagram - see first Page of Table 20

		XC ◇1 A	LE ◇1		LE 1	LE	LE 1	LE ◇1	LE 1	LE	LE 1	LE 1
Cambridge	d	22 10	22 21					22 51				
Shelford	d		22 26					22 56				
Whittlesford Parkway	d		22 30					23 00				
Great Chesterford	d		22 34					23 04				
Audley End	d	22 25	22 40					23 10				
Newport (Essex)	d		22 43					23 13				
Elsenham	d		22 49					23 19				
Stansted Airport	a	22 52										
Stansted Airport	d				23 00		23 15		23 30		23 45	23 59
Stansted Mountfitchet	d		22 52				23 21	23 24				
Bishops Stortford	a		22 58		23 09			23 29	23 39			00 08
	d		22 58		23 09			23 29	23 39			00 08
Sawbridgeworth	d		23 03					23 33				
Harlow Mill	d		23 06					23 37				
Harlow Town	d		23 09				23 32	23 40			23 59	00 16
Roydon	d		23 13					23 44				
Hertford East	d					23 09				23 39		
Ware	d					23 13				23 43		
St Margarets (Herts)	d					23 17				23 47		
Rye House	d					23 20				23 50		
Broxbourne 3	a		23 17			23 25		23 48		23 55		
Broxbourne 3	d		23 17			23 25		23 48		23 55		
Cheshunt	d		23 21			23 29		23 52		23 59		
Waltham Cross	d					23 31						
Enfield Lock	d					23 34						
Brimsdown	d					23 36						
Ponders End	d					23 38						
Angel Road	d											
Northumberland Park	d											
Tottenham Hale ⊖	d		23 30		23 33	23 44	23 48					
Seven Sisters ⊖	d							00 04	00 08	00 12	00 21	
Clapton	d											
Stratford 7 ⊖	a											
Hackney Downs	d					23 50				00 17		
Bethnal Green	d											
London Liverpool Street 15 ⊖	a		23 44		23 47	23 58	00 01	00 18	00 22	00 26	00 36	00 51

Saturdays

14 December to 17 May

		LE 1	LE 1	LE 1	LE 1	LE ◇1	XC 1	LE 1	LE	LE 1		LE ◇1	LE 1 [trolley]	XC 1	LE	LE 1 [trolley]	LE 1	LE ◇1	LE 1 [trolley]	LE		LE 1 [trolley]	LE 1	LE ◇1	LE 1 [trolley]
Cambridge	d					04 25	04 56					05 21		05 42				06 04						06 21	
Shelford	d											05 26												06 26	
Whittlesford Parkway	d					04 32						05 30						06 11						06 30	
Great Chesterford	d											05 34												06 34	
Audley End	d					04 40						05 40		05 56				06 19						06 40	
Newport (Essex)	d											05 43												06 43	
Elsenham	d											05 49												06 49	
Stansted Airport	a						05 20							06 08											
Stansted Airport	d		00 30	01 00	01 30			05 30					06 00			06 15			06 30			06 45			07 00
Stansted Mountfitchet	d											05 52				06 21								06 52	
Bishops Stortford	a		00 39			04 53		05 39				05 58	06 09					06 32	06 39					06 58	07 09
	d		00 39			04 53		05 39		05 47		05 58	06 09				06 15	06 32	06 39				06 47	06 58	07 09
Sawbridgeworth	d					04 58				05 52		06 03					06 20						06 52	07 03	
Harlow Mill	d					05 01						06 06					06 23							07 06	
Harlow Town	d		00 47			05 04				06 05		06 09				06 32	06 26	06 40				07 00	07 03	07 09	
Roydon	d					05 08						06 13					06 30							07 13	
Hertford East	d	00 07													06 09					06 39					
Ware	d														06 13					06 43					
St Margarets (Herts)	d														06 17					06 47					
Rye House	d														06 20					06 50					
Broxbourne 3	a	00 19				05 12				06 11		06 17			06 25		06 35	06 46		06 55			07 09	07 17	
Broxbourne 3	d	00 19				05 12			05 54	06 12		06 17			06 25		06 39	06 46		06 55			07 12	07 17	
Cheshunt	d					05 16			05 58	06 16		06 21			06 29		06 44	06 50		06 59			07 16	07 21	
Waltham Cross	d								06 01	06 19					06 31					07 01			07 19		
Enfield Lock	d								06 03						06 34		06 47			07 04					
Brimsdown	d								06 06						06 36					07 06					
Ponders End	d								06 08						06 38					07 08					
Angel Road	d																								
Northumberland Park	d																06 53								
Tottenham Hale ⊖	d							06 01	06 14	06 27		06 30	06 33		06 44	06 48	06 56	07 00	07 03	07 14		07 17	07 27	07 30	07 33
Seven Sisters ⊖	d					05 36																			
Clapton	d																								
Stratford 7 ⊖	a									06 40							07 10						07 40		
Hackney Downs	d					05 45			06 20						06 50					07 20					
Bethnal Green	d					05 49																			
London Liverpool Street 15 ⊖	a	00 49	01 21	01 50	02 20	05 54		06 14	06 28			06 44	06 47		06 58	07 01		07 14	07 17	07 28		07 31		07 44	07 47

A From Birmingham New Street

Table 22R

Saturdays

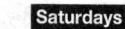

14 December to 17 May

Cambridge, Stansted Airport, Bishops Stortford, Hertford East and Broxbourne - London

Network Diagram - see first Page of Table 20

		XC ■1	LE	LE ■1 🚲	LE ■1	LE ◇■1		LE ■1 🚲	LE	LE ■1 🚲	LE ■1	LE ◇■1	LE ■1 🚲	XC ■1	LE	LE ■1 🚲		LE ■1	LE ◇■1	LE ■1 🚲	XC ◇■1 A	LE	LE ■1 🚲	LE ■1	LE ◇■1
Cambridge	d	06 40				07 04						07 21		07 40					08 04		08 11				08 21
Shelford	d											07 26													08 26
Whittlesford Parkway	d					07 11						07 30							08 11						08 30
Great Chesterford	d											07 34													08 34
Audley End	d	06 54				07 19						07 40		07 54					08 19		08 26				08 40
Newport (Essex)	d											07 43													08 43
Elsenham	d											07 49													08 49
Stansted Airport	a	07 09												08 08							08 39				
Stansted Airport	d			07 15				07 30		07 45			08 00			08 15				08 30			08 45		
Stansted Mountfitchet	d			07 21								07 52				08 21									08 52
Bishops Stortford	a					07 32		07 39				07 58	08 09						08 32	08 39					08 58
	d				07 15	07 32		07 39			07 47	07 58	08 09					08 15	08 32	08 39				08 47	08 58
Sawbridgeworth	d				07 20						07 52	08 03						08 20						08 52	09 03
Harlow Mill	d				07 23							08 06						08 23							09 06
Harlow Town	d			07 32	07 26	07 40				08 02	08 05	08 09				08 32		08 26	08 40				09 00	09 05	09 09
Roydon	d				07 30							08 13						08 30							09 13
Hertford East	d		07 09						07 39						08 09							08 39			
Ware	d		07 13						07 43						08 13							08 43			
St Margarets (Herts)	d		07 17						07 47						08 17							08 47			
Rye House	d		07 20						07 50						08 20							08 50			
Broxbourne ■3	a		07 25		07 35	07 46			07 55		08 11	08 17			08 25			08 35	08 46			08 55		09 11	09 17
Broxbourne ■3	d		07 25		07 39	07 46			07 55		08 12	08 17			08 25			08 39	08 46			08 55		09 12	09 17
Cheshunt	d		07 29		07 44	07 50			07 59		08 16	08 21			08 29			08 44	08 50			08 59		09 16	09 21
Waltham Cross	d		07 31						08 01		08 19				08 31							09 01		09 19	
Enfield Lock	d		07 34		07 47				08 04						08 34			08 47				09 04			
Brimsdown	d		07 36						08 06						08 36							09 06			
Ponders End	d		07 38						08 08						08 38							09 08			
Angel Road	d																								
Northumberland Park	d				07 53													08 53							
Tottenham Hale ⊖	d		07 44	07 48	07 56	08 00		08 03	08 14	08 17	08 27	08 30	08 33		08 44	08 48		08 56	09 00	09 03		09 14	09 17	09 27	09 30
Seven Sisters ⊖	d																								
Clapton	d																								
Stratford ■7 ⊖	a				08 10						08 40							09 10						09 40	
Hackney Downs	d		07 50						08 20						08 50							09 20			
Bethnal Green	d																								
London Liverpool Street ■15 ⊖	a		07 58	08 02		08 14		08 17	08 28	08 31		08 44	08 47		08 58	09 02			09 14	09 17		09 28	09 31		09 44

		LE ■1 🚲		LE	LE ■1 🚲	LE ■1	LE ◇■1	LE ■1 🚲	XC ◇■1 A	LE	LE ■1 🚲	LE ■1		LE ◇■1	LE ■1 🚲	LE	LE ■1 🚲	LE ■1	LE ◇■1	LE ■1 🚲	XC ◇■1 A	LE		LE ■1 🚲	LE ■1
Cambridge	d						09 04		09 10					09 21					10 04		10 10				
Shelford	d													09 26											
Whittlesford Parkway	d						09 11							09 30					10 11						
Great Chesterford	d													09 34											
Audley End	d						09 19		09 24					09 40					10 19		10 26				
Newport (Essex)	d													09 43											
Elsenham	d													09 49											
Stansted Airport	a								09 40												10 40				
Stansted Airport	d	09 00			09 15			09 30			09 45				10 00		10 15			10 30				10 45	
Stansted Mountfitchet	d				09 21									09 52			10 21								
Bishops Stortford	a	09 09					09 32	09 39						09 58	10 09				10 32	10 39					
	d	09 09				09 15	09 32	09 39				09 47		09 58	10 09			10 15	10 32	10 39					10 47
Sawbridgeworth	d					09 20						09 52		10 03				10 20							10 52
Harlow Mill	d					09 23								10 06				10 23							
Harlow Town	d				09 32	09 26	09 40				10 00	10 05		10 09			10 32	10 26	10 40					11 00	11 05
Roydon	d					09 30								10 13				10 30							
Hertford East	d			09 09						09 39						10 09						10 39			
Ware	d			09 13						09 43						10 13						10 43			
St Margarets (Herts)	d			09 17						09 47						10 17						10 47			
Rye House	d			09 20						09 50						10 20						10 50			
Broxbourne ■3	a			09 25		09 35	09 46			09 55		10 11		10 17		10 25		10 35	10 46			10 55			11 11
Broxbourne ■3	d			09 25		09 39	09 46			09 55		10 12		10 17		10 25		10 39	10 46			10 55			11 12
Cheshunt	d			09 29		09 44	09 50			09 59		10 16		10 21		10 29		10 44	10 50			10 59			11 16
Waltham Cross	d			09 31						10 01		10 19				10 31						11 01			11 19
Enfield Lock	d			09 34		09 47				10 04						10 34		10 47				11 04			
Brimsdown	d			09 36						10 06						10 36						11 06			
Ponders End	d			09 38						10 08						10 38						11 08			
Angel Road	d																								
Northumberland Park	d					09 53												10 53							
Tottenham Hale ⊖	d	09 33		09 44	09 48	09 56	10 00	10 03		10 14	10 17	10 27		10 30	10 33	10 44	10 48	10 56	11 00	11 03		11 14		11 17	11 27
Seven Sisters ⊖	d																								
Clapton	d																								
Stratford ■7 ⊖	a					10 10						10 40						11 10							11 40
Hackney Downs	d			09 50						10 20						10 50						11 20			
Bethnal Green	d																								
London Liverpool Street ■15 ⊖	a	09 47		09 58	10 02		10 14	10 17		10 28	10 31			10 44	10 47	10 58	11 02		11 14	11 17		11 28		11 31	

A From Birmingham New Street

Table 22R

Saturdays

14 December to 17 May

Cambridge, Stansted Airport, Bishops Stortford, Hertford East and Broxbourne - London

Network Diagram - see first Page of Table 20

		LE ◇1	LE 1 ⚲	LE	LE 1 ⚲	LE 1	LE ◇1	LE 1 ⚲		XC ◇1 A	LE	LE 1 ⚲	LE 1	LE ◇1	LE 1 ⚲	LE	LE 1 ⚲	LE 1		LE ◇1	LE 1 ⚲	XC ◇1 B	LE	LE 1 ⚲	LE 1
Cambridge	d	10 21					11 04			11 10				11 21						12 04		12 10			
Shelford	d	10 26												11 26											
Whittlesford Parkway	d	10 30					11 11							11 30						12 11					
Great Chesterford	d	10 34												11 34											
Audley End	d	10 40					11 19			11 25				11 40						12 19		12 25			
Newport (Essex)	d	10 43												11 43											
Elsenham	d	10 49												11 49											
Stansted Airport	a									11 40												12 40			
Stansted Airport	d		11 00		11 15			11 30				11 45			12 00		12 15				12 30			12 45	
Stansted Mountfitchet	d	10 52			11 21									11 52			12 21								
Bishops Stortford	a	10 58	11 09				11 32	11 39						11 58	12 09					12 32	12 39				
	d	10 58	11 09			11 15	11 32	11 39					11 47	11 58	12 09			12 15		12 32	12 39				12 47
Sawbridgeworth	d	11 03				11 20							11 52	12 03				12 20							12 52
Harlow Mill	d	11 06				11 23								12 06				12 23							
Harlow Town	d	11 09			11 32	11 26	11 40					12 00	12 05	12 09			12 32	12 26		12 40				13 00	13 05
Roydon	d	11 13				11 30								12 13				12 30							
Hertford East	d			11 09							11 39					12 09							12 39		
Ware	d			11 13							11 43					12 13							12 43		
St Margarets (Herts)	d			11 17							11 47					12 17							12 47		
Rye House	d			11 20							11 50					12 20							12 50		
Broxbourne 3	a	11 17		11 25		11 35	11 46				11 55		12 11	12 17		12 25		12 35		12 46			12 55		13 11
Broxbourne 3	d	11 17		11 25		11 39	11 46				11 55		12 12	12 17		12 25		12 39		12 46			12 55		13 12
Cheshunt	d	11 21		11 29		11 44	11 50				11 59		12 16	12 21		12 29		12 44		12 50			12 59		13 16
Waltham Cross	d			11 31							12 01		12 19			12 31							13 01		13 19
Enfield Lock	d			11 34		11 47					12 04					12 34		12 47					13 04		
Brimsdown	d			11 36							12 06					12 36							13 06		
Ponders End	d			11 38							12 08					12 38							13 08		
Angel Road	d																								
Northumberland Park	d					11 53												12 53							
Tottenham Hale ⊖	d	11 31	11 33	11 44	11 48	11 56	12 00	12 03			12 14	12 17	12 27	12 31	12 33	12 44	12 48	12 56		13 00	13 03		13 14	13 17	13 27
Seven Sisters ⊖	d																								
Clapton	d																								
Stratford 7 ⊖	a					12 10							12 40					13 10							13 40
Hackney Downs	d			11 50							12 20					12 50							13 20		
Bethnal Green	d																								
London Liverpool Street 15 ⊖	a	11 44	11 47	11 58	12 02		12 14	12 17			12 28	12 31		12 44	12 47	12 58	13 02			13 14	13 17		13 28	13 31	

		LE ◇1	LE 1 ⚲	LE		LE 1 ⚲	LE 1	LE ◇1	LE 1 ⚲	XC ◇1 B	LE	LE 1 ⚲	LE 1	LE ◇1	LE 1 ⚲	LE	LE 1 ⚲	LE 1	LE ◇1		LE 1 ⚲	XC ◇1 B	LE	LE 1 ⚲
Cambridge	d	12 21						13 04		13 10				13 21					14 04			16 10		
Shelford	d	12 26												13 26										
Whittlesford Parkway	d	12 30						13 11						13 30					14 11					
Great Chesterford	d	12 34												13 34										
Audley End	d	12 40						13 19		13 25				13 40					14 19			16 25		
Newport (Essex)	d	12 43												13 43										
Elsenham	d	12 49												13 49										
Stansted Airport	a									13 40												16 40		
Stansted Airport	d		13 00			13 15			13 30			13 45			14 00		14 15				16 30			16 45
Stansted Mountfitchet	d	12 52				13 21								13 52			14 21							
Bishops Stortford	a	12 58	13 09					13 32	13 39					13 58	14 09				14 32		16 39			
	d	12 58	13 09				13 15	13 32	13 39				13 47	13 58	14 09			14 15	14 32		16 39			
Sawbridgeworth	d	13 03					13 20						13 52	14 03				14 20		and at				
Harlow Mill	d	13 06					13 23							14 06				14 23		the same				
Harlow Town	d	13 09				13 32	13 26	13 40				14 00	14 05	14 09			14 32	14 26	14 40	minutes				17 00
Roydon	d	13 13					13 30							14 13				14 30		past				
Hertford East	d			13 09							13 39					14 09				each			16 39	
Ware	d			13 13							13 43					14 13				hour until			16 43	
St Margarets (Herts)	d			13 17							13 47					14 17							16 47	
Rye House	d			13 20							13 50					14 20							16 50	
Broxbourne 3	a	13 17		13 25			13 35	13 46			13 55		14 11	14 17		14 25		14 35	14 46				16 55	
Broxbourne 3	d	13 17		13 25			13 39	13 46			13 55		14 12	14 17		14 25		14 39	14 46				16 55	
Cheshunt	d	13 21		13 29			13 44	13 50			13 59		14 16	14 21		14 29		14 44	14 50				16 59	
Waltham Cross	d			13 31							14 01		14 19			14 31							17 01	
Enfield Lock	d			13 34			13 47				14 04					14 34		14 47					17 04	
Brimsdown	d			13 36							14 06					14 36							17 06	
Ponders End	d			13 38							14 08					14 38							17 08	
Angel Road	d																							
Northumberland Park	d						13 53											14 53						
Tottenham Hale ⊖	d	13 31	13 33	13 44		13 48	13 56	14 00	14 03		14 14	14 17	14 27	14 30	14 33	14 44	14 48	14 56	15 01		17 03		17 14	17 17
Seven Sisters ⊖	d																							
Clapton	d																							
Stratford 7 ⊖	a						14 10						14 40					15 10						
Hackney Downs	d			13 50							14 20					14 50							17 20	
Bethnal Green	d																							
London Liverpool Street 15 ⊖	a	13 44	13 47	13 58		14 02		14 14	14 17		14 28	14 31		14 44	14 47	14 58	15 02		15 14		17 17		17 28	17 31

A From Gloucester

B From Birmingham New Street

Table 22R

Saturdays

14 December to 17 May

Cambridge, Stansted Airport, Bishops Stortford, Hertford East and Broxbourne - London

Network Diagram - see first Page of Table 20

		LE	LE	LE	LE	LE	LE	LE	LE	XC	LE	LE	LE	LE	LE	LE	LE	LE	LE	LE	LE	LE	XC
		1	◇1	1		1	1	◇1	1	◇1		1	1	◇1	1		1	1	◇1	1		1	◇1
										A													A
				🚲		🚲			🚲			🚲			🚲		🚲			🚲		🚲	
Cambridge	d		16 21					17 04		17 10				17 21					18 04				18 18
Shelford	d		16 26											17 26									
Whittlesford Parkway	d		16 30					17 11						17 30					18 11				
Great Chesterford	d		16 34											17 34									
Audley End	d		16 40					17 19		17 25				17 40					18 19				18 35
Newport (Essex)	d		16 43											17 43									
Elsenham	d		16 49											17 49									
Stansted Airport	a									17 40													18 53
Stansted Airport	d			17 00		17 15			17 30			17 45			18 00		18 15			18 30		18 45	
Stansted Mountfitchet	d		16 52			17 21								17 52			18 21						
Bishops Stortford	a		16 58	17 09				17 32	17 39					17 58	18 09				18 32	18 39			
	d	16 47	16 58	17 09			17 15	17 32	17 39				17 47	17 58	18 09			18 15	18 32	18 39			
Sawbridgeworth	d	16 52	17 03				17 20						17 52	18 03				18 20					
Harlow Mill	d		17 06				17 23							18 06				18 23					
Harlow Town	d	17 05	17 09			17 32	17 26	17 40				18 00	18 05	18 09			18 32	18 26	18 40			19 00	
Roydon	d		17 13				17 30							18 13				18 30					
Hertford East	d				17 09						17 39					18 09					18 39		
Ware	d				17 13						17 43					18 13					18 43		
St Margarets (Herts)	d				17 17						17 47					18 17					18 47		
Rye House	d				17 20						17 50					18 20					18 50		
Broxbourne 3	a	17 11	17 17		17 25		17 35	17 46			17 55		18 11	18 17		18 25		18 35	18 46		18 55		
Broxbourne 3	d	17 12	17 17		17 25		17 39	17 46			17 55		18 12	18 17		18 25		18 39	18 46		18 55		
Cheshunt	d	17 16	17 21		17 29		17 44	17 50			17 59		18 16	18 21		18 29		18 44	18 50		18 59		
Waltham Cross	d	17 19			17 31						18 01		18 19			18 31					19 01		
Enfield Lock	d				17 34		17 47				18 04					18 34		18 47			19 04		
Brimsdown	d				17 36						18 06					18 36					19 06		
Ponders End	d				17 38						18 08					18 38					19 08		
Angel Road	d																						
Northumberland Park	d						17 53											18 53					
Tottenham Hale ⊖	d	17 27	17 30	17 33	17 44	17 48	17 56	18 01	18 03		18 14	18 17	18 27	18 30	18 33	18 44	18 48	18 56	19 00	19 03	19 14	19 17	
Seven Sisters ⊖	d																						
Clapton	d																						
Stratford 7 ⊖	a	17 40					18 10						18 40					19 10					
Hackney Downs	d				17 50						18 20					18 50					19 20		
Bethnal Green	d																						
London Liverpool Street 15 ⊖	a		17 44	17 47	17 58	18 02		18 14	18 17		18 28	18 31		18 44	18 47	18 58	19 02		19 14	19 17	19 28	19 31	

		LE	LE	LE	LE	LE	LE	LE	LE	XC	LE	LE	LE	LE	LE	LE	LE	LE	LE	LE	XC	LE
		1	◇1	1		1	1	◇1	1	◇1		1	1	◇1	1		1	1	◇1	1	◇1	
										A											A	
				🚲		🚲			🚲			🚲			🚲		🚲			🚲		
Cambridge	d		18 21					19 04		19 10				19 21					20 04		20 10	
Shelford	d		18 26											19 26								
Whittlesford Parkway	d		18 30					19 11						19 30					20 11			
Great Chesterford	d		18 34											19 34								
Audley End	d		18 40					19 19		19 25				19 40					20 19		20 25	
Newport (Essex)	d		18 43											19 43								
Elsenham	d		18 49											19 49								
Stansted Airport	a									19 40											20 40	
Stansted Airport	d			19 00		19 15			19 30			19 45			20 00		20 15			20 30		
Stansted Mountfitchet	d		18 52			19 21								19 52			20 21					
Bishops Stortford	a		18 58	19 09				19 32	19 39					19 58	20 09				20 32	20 39		
	d	18 47	18 58	19 09			19 15	19 32	19 39				19 47	19 58	20 09			20 15	20 32	20 39		
Sawbridgeworth	d	18 52	19 03				19 20						19 52	20 03				20 20				
Harlow Mill	d		19 06				19 23							20 06				20 23				
Harlow Town	d	19 05	19 09			19 32	19 26	19 40				20 00	20 05	20 09			20 32	20 26	20 40			
Roydon	d		19 13				19 30							20 13				20 30				
Hertford East	d				19 09						19 39					20 09						20 39
Ware	d				19 13						19 43					20 13						20 43
St Margarets (Herts)	d				19 17						19 47					20 17						20 47
Rye House	d				19 20						19 50					20 20						20 50
Broxbourne 3	a	19 11	19 17		19 25		19 35	19 46			19 55		20 11	20 17		20 25		20 35	20 46			20 55
Broxbourne 3	d	19 12	19 17		19 25		19 39	19 46			19 55		20 12	20 17		20 25		20 39	20 46			20 55
Cheshunt	d	19 16	19 21		19 29		19 44	19 50			19 59		20 16	20 21		20 29		20 44	20 50			20 59
Waltham Cross	d	19 19			19 31						20 01		20 19			20 31						21 01
Enfield Lock	d				19 34		19 47				20 04					20 34		20 47				21 04
Brimsdown	d				19 36						20 06					20 36						21 06
Ponders End	d				19 38						20 08					20 38						21 08
Angel Road	d																					
Northumberland Park	d						19 53											20 53				
Tottenham Hale ⊖	d	19 27	19 30	19 33	19 44	19 48	19 56	20 00	20 03		20 14	20 17	20 27	20 30	20 33	20 44	20 48	20 56	21 00	21 03		21 14
Seven Sisters ⊖	d																					
Clapton	d																					
Stratford 7 ⊖	a	19 40					20 10						20 40					21 10				
Hackney Downs	d				19 50						20 20					20 50						21 20
Bethnal Green	d																					
London Liverpool Street 15 ⊖	a		19 44	19 47	19 58	20 02		20 14	20 17		20 28	20 31		20 44	20 47	20 58	21 02		21 14	21 17		21 28

A From Birmingham New Street

Table 22R

Saturdays

14 December to 17 May

Cambridge, Stansted Airport, Bishops Stortford, Hertford East and Broxbourne - London

Network Diagram - see first Page of Table 20

		LE 1 🚌	LE 1	LE ◇1	LE 1 🚌	LE	LE 1 🚌	LE 1	LE ◇1	LE 1 🚌		XC ◇1 A	LE	LE 1 🚌	LE 1	LE ◇1	LE 1	LE	LE 1	LE ◇1		LE 1	XC ◇1 A	LE	LE 1
Cambridge	d			20 21					21 04			21 10				21 21				22 04			22 10		
Shelford	d			20 26												21 26									
Whittlesford Parkway	d			20 30					21 11							21 30				22 11					
Great Chesterford	d			20 34												21 34									
Audley End	d			20 40					21 19			21 25				21 40				22 19			22 25		
Newport (Essex)	d			20 43												21 43									
Elsenham	d			20 49												21 49									
Stansted Airport	a											21 40											22 40		
Stansted Airport	d	20 45			21 00		21 15			21 30				21 45			22 00		22 15			22 30			22 45
Stansted Mountfitchet	d			20 52			21 21									21 52			22 21						
Bishops Stortford	a			20 58	21 09				21 32	21 39						21 58	22 09			22 32		22 39			
	d		20 47	20 58	21 09			21 15	21 32	21 39					21 47	21 58	22 09			22 32		22 39			
Sawbridgeworth	d		20 52	21 03				21 20							21 52	22 03									
Harlow Mill	d			21 06				21 23								22 06									
Harlow Town	d	21 00	21 05	21 09			21 32	21 26	21 40					22 00	22 05	22 09			22 32	22 40					23 00
Roydon	d			21 13				21 30								22 13									
Hertford East	d					21 09							21 39					22 09						22 39	
Ware	d					21 13							21 43					22 13						22 43	
St Margarets (Herts)	d					21 17							21 47					22 17						22 47	
Rye House	d					21 20							21 50					22 20						22 50	
Broxbourne 3	a		21 11	21 17		21 25		21 35	21 46				21 55		22 11	22 17		22 25		22 46				22 55	
Broxbourne 3	d		21 12	21 17		21 25		21 39	21 46				21 55		22 12	22 17		22 25		22 46				22 55	
Cheshunt	d		21 16	21 21		21 29		21 44	21 50				21 59		22 16	22 21		22 29		22 50				22 59	
Waltham Cross	d		21 19			21 31							22 01		22 19			22 31						23 01	
Enfield Lock	d					21 34		21 47					22 04					22 34						23 04	
Brimsdown	d					21 36							22 06					22 36						23 06	
Ponders End	d					21 38							22 08					22 38						23 08	
Angel Road	d																								
Northumberland Park	d							21 53																	
Tottenham Hale ⊖	d	21 17	21 27	21 30	21 33	21 44	21 48	21 56	22 00	22 03			22 14	22 17	22 27	22 30	22 33	22 44	22 48	23 00		23 03		23 14	23 17
Seven Sisters ⊖	d																								
Clapton	d																								
Stratford 7 ⊖	a		21 40					22 10							22 40										
Hackney Downs	d					21 50							22 20					22 50						23 20	
Bethnal Green	d																								
London Liverpool Street 15 ⊖	a	21 31		21 44	21 47	21 58	22 02		22 14	22 17			22 28	22 31		22 44	22 47	22 58	23 02	23 14		23 17		23 28	23 31

		LE ◇1	LE 1	LE	LE 1	LE ◇1		LE 1	LE	LE 1	LE 1
Cambridge	d	22 21				22 51					
Shelford	d	22 26				22 56					
Whittlesford Parkway	d	22 30				23 00					
Great Chesterford	d	22 34				23 04					
Audley End	d	22 40				23 10					
Newport (Essex)	d	22 43				23 13					
Elsenham	d	22 49				23 19					
Stansted Airport	a										
Stansted Airport	d		23 00		23 15			23 30		23 45	23 59
Stansted Mountfitchet	d	22 52			23 21	23 24					
Bishops Stortford	a	22 58	23 09			23 29		23 39			00 08
	d	22 58	23 09			23 29		23 39			00 08
Sawbridgeworth	d	23 03				23 33					
Harlow Mill	d	23 06				23 37					
Harlow Town	d	23 09			23 32	23 40				23 59	00 16
Roydon	d	23 13				23 44					
Hertford East	d			23 09					23 39		
Ware	d			23 13					23 43		
St Margarets (Herts)	d			23 17					23 47		
Rye House	d			23 20					23 50		
Broxbourne 3	a	23 17		23 25		23 48			23 55		
Broxbourne 3	d	23 17		23 25		23 48			23 55		
Cheshunt	d	23 21		23 29		23 52			23 59		
Waltham Cross	d			23 31					00 01		
Enfield Lock	d			23 34					00 04		
Brimsdown	d			23 36					00 06		
Ponders End	d			23 38					00 08		
Angel Road	d										
Northumberland Park	d										
Tottenham Hale ⊖	d	23 30	23 33	23 44	23 48	00 01		00 04	00 14	00 17	
Seven Sisters ⊖	d										
Clapton	d										
Stratford 7 ⊖	a										
Hackney Downs	d			23 50					00 20		
Bethnal Green	d										
London Liverpool Street 15 ⊖	a	23 45	23 47	23 58	00 02	00 14		00 17	00 28	00 31	00 51

A From Birmingham New Street

Table 22R

Sundays

8 December to 11 May

Cambridge, Stansted Airport, Bishops Stortford, Hertford East and Broxbourne - London

Network Diagram - see first Page of Table 20

		LE	LE [1]	LE [1]	LE [1] 🚲	LE [1] 🚲	LE [1] 🚲	LE [1] 🚲	LE	LE [1] A	LE [1] 🚲	LE [1] B	LE [1] 🚲	LE	LE ◇[1]	LE [1] 🚲	LE [1] 🚲	LE	LE [1] A	LE [1] 🚲	LE [1] C
Cambridge	d														07 32				07 51		
Shelford	d																		07 56		
Whittlesford Parkway	d														07 39				08 00		
Great Chesterford	d																		08 04		
Audley End	d														07 47				08 10		
Newport (Essex)	d																		08 13		
Elsenham	d																		08 19		
Stansted Airport	a																				
Stansted Airport	d		00 30	05 30	06 00	06 30	07 00	07 15			07 30		07 45			08 00	08 15			08 30	
Stansted Mountfitchet	d												07 51						08 22		
Bishops Stortford	a		00 39	05 39	06 09	06 39	07 09				07 39				08 00	08 09			08 28	08 39	
	d		00 39	05 39	06 09	06 39	07 09			07 28	07 39				08 00	08 09			08 28	08 39	
Sawbridgeworth	d									07 32					08 05				08 32		
Harlow Mill	d									07 36									08 36		
Harlow Town	d		00 47	05 47	06 17	06 47	07 17	07 30		07 39			08 02		08 10		08 30		08 39		
Roydon	d									07 43									08 43		
Hertford East	d	00 07												07 55				08 25			
Ware	d													07 59				08 29			
St Margarets (Herts)	d													08 03				08 33			
Rye House	d													08 06				08 36			
Broxbourne [3]	a	00 19								07 48				08 11	08 16			08 41	08 48		
Broxbourne [3]	d								07 41	07 52				08 11	08 16			08 41	08 52		
Cheshunt	d								07 45	07 57				08 15	08 20			08 45	08 57		
Waltham Cross	d									07 59									08 59		
Enfield Lock	d									08 02									09 02		
Brimsdown	d									08 04									09 04		
Ponders End	d									08 06									09 06		
Angel Road	d																				
Northumberland Park	d											←									←
Tottenham Hale ⊖	d			06 04	06 33	07 03	07 33	07 46		08 12	08 01	08 12	08 17		08 29	08 32	08 46		09 12	09 01	09 12
Seven Sisters ⊖	d								08 03	→				08 33				09 03	→		
Clapton	d																				
Stratford [7] ⊖	a											08 23									09 23
Hackney Downs	d								08 09					08 39				09 09			
Bethnal Green	d																				
London Liverpool Street [15] ⊖	a		01 21	06 18	06 48	07 16	07 46	08 01	08 18		08 15		08 31	08 48	08 43	08 46	09 00	09 18		09 15	

		LE [1] 🚲	LE	LE ◇[1]	LE [1] 🚲	LE [1] 🚲	LE	LE [1] A	LE [1] 🚲	LE [1] C	XC [1]		LE [1] 🚲	LE	LE ◇[1]	LE [1] 🚲	LE [1] 🚲	LE	LE [1] A	LE [1] 🚲	LE [1] C	XC [1]
Cambridge	d			08 32				08 51			09 15				12 32				12 51			13 15
Shelford	d							08 56											12 56			
Whittlesford Parkway	d			08 39				09 00							12 39				13 00			
Great Chesterford	d							09 04											13 04			
Audley End	d			08 47				09 10			09 29				12 47				13 10			13 29
Newport (Essex)	d							09 13											13 13			
Elsenham	d							09 19											13 19			
Stansted Airport	a										09 45											13 45
Stansted Airport	d	08 45			09 00	09 15			09 30				12 45			13 00	13 15			13 30		
Stansted Mountfitchet	d	08 51						09 22					12 51						13 22			
Bishops Stortford	a			09 00	09 09			09 28	09 39						13 00	13 09			13 28	13 39		
	d			09 00	09 09			09 28	09 39						13 00	13 09			13 28	13 39		
Sawbridgeworth	d			09 05				09 32				and at the same minutes past each hour until			13 05				13 32			
Harlow Mill	d							09 36											13 36			
Harlow Town	d	09 02		09 10		09 30		09 39					13 02		13 10		13 30		13 39			
Roydon	d							09 43											13 43			
Hertford East	d		08 55				09 25							12 55				13 25				
Ware	d		08 59				09 29							12 59				13 29				
St Margarets (Herts)	d		09 03				09 33							13 03				13 33				
Rye House	d		09 06				09 36							13 06				13 36				
Broxbourne [3]	a		09 11	09 16			09 41	09 48						13 11	13 16			13 41	13 48			
Broxbourne [3]	d		09 11	09 16			09 41	09 52						13 11	13 16			13 41	13 52			
Cheshunt	d		09 15	09 20			09 45	09 57						13 15	13 20			13 45	13 57			
Waltham Cross	d							09 59											13 59			
Enfield Lock	d							10 02											14 02			
Brimsdown	d							10 04											14 04			
Ponders End	d							10 06											14 06			
Angel Road	d																					
Northumberland Park	d									←											←	
Tottenham Hale ⊖	d	09 17		09 29	09 32	09 46		10 12	10 01	10 12			13 17		13 29	13 32	13 46		14 12	14 01	14 12	
Seven Sisters ⊖	d		09 33				10 03	→						13 33				14 03	→			
Clapton	d																					
Stratford [7] ⊖	a									10 23											14 23	
Hackney Downs	d		09 39				10 09							13 39				14 09				
Bethnal Green	d																					
London Liverpool Street [15] ⊖	a	09 31	09 48	09 43	09 46	10 01	10 18		10 15				13 31	13 48	13 43	13 46	14 01	14 18		14 15		

A To Stratford
B From Bishops Stortford
C From Cambridge

Table 22R

Sundays

8 December to 11 May

Cambridge, Stansted Airport, Bishops Stortford, Hertford East and Broxbourne - London

Network Diagram - see first Page of Table 20

		LE	LE	LE	LE	LE	LE	LE	LE	LE	XC		LE	LE	LE	LE	LE	LE	LE	LE	LE	XC		LE
		1		◇1	1	1		1	1	1	◇1		1		◇1	1	1		1	1	1	◇1		1
								A		B	C								A		B	C		
		trolley			trolley	trolley			trolley				trolley			trolley	trolley			trolley				trolley
Cambridge	d			13 32				13 51			14 10	and at the same minutes past each hour until			18 32				18 51			19 10		
Shelford	d							13 56											18 56					
Whittlesford Parkway	d			13 39				14 00							18 39				19 00					
Great Chesterford	d							14 04											19 04					
Audley End	d			13 47				14 10			14 25				18 47				19 10			19 25		
Newport (Essex)	d							14 13											19 13					
Elsenham	d							14 19											19 19					
Stansted Airport	a										14 45											19 45		
Stansted Airport	d	13 45			14 00	14 15			14 30				18 45			19 00	19 15			19 30				19 45
Stansted Mountfitchet	d	13 51						14 22					18 51						19 22					19 51
Bishops Stortford	a			14 00	14 09			14 28	14 39						19 00	19 09			19 28	19 39				
	d			14 00	14 09			14 28	14 39						19 00	19 09			19 28	19 39				
Sawbridgeworth	d			14 05				14 32							19 05				19 32					
Harlow Mill	d							14 36											19 36					
Harlow Town	d	14 02		14 10		14 30		14 39					19 02		19 10		19 30		19 39					20 02
Roydon	d							14 43											19 43					
Hertford East	d		13 55				14 25							18 55				19 25						
Ware	d		13 59				14 29							18 59				19 29						
St Margarets (Herts)	d		14 03				14 33							19 03				19 33						
Rye House	d		14 06				14 36							19 06				19 36						
Broxbourne [3]	a		14 11	14 16			14 41	14 48						19 11	19 16			19 41	19 48					
Broxbourne [3]	d		14 11	14 16			14 41	14 52						19 11	19 16			19 41	19 52					
Cheshunt	d		14 15	14 20			14 45	14 57						19 15	19 20			19 45	19 57					
Waltham Cross	d							14 59											19 59					
Enfield Lock	d							15 02											20 02					
Brimsdown	d							15 04											20 04					
Ponders End	d							15 06											20 06					
Angel Road	d																							
Northumberland Park	d									←											←			
Tottenham Hale ⊖	d	14 17		14 29	14 32	14 46		15 12	15 01	15 12			19 17		19 29	19 32	19 46		20 12	20 01	20 12			20 17
Seven Sisters ⊖	d		14 33				15 03	→						19 33				20 03	→					
Clapton	d																							
Stratford [7] ⊖	a									15 23											20 23			
Hackney Downs	d		14 39				15 09							19 39				20 09						
Bethnal Green	d																							
London Liverpool Street [15] ⊖	a	14 31	14 48	14 43	14 46	15 01	15 18		15 15				19 31	19 48	19 43	19 46	20 01	20 18		20 15				20 31

		LE	LE	LE	LE	LE	LE	LE	LE		XC	LE	LE	LE	LE	LE	LE	LE	LE		LE	XC	LE	LE	LE
			◇1	1	1		1	1	1		◇1	1		◇1	1	1		1	1		1	◇1	1		◇1
							A		B		C							A			B	C			
				trolley	trolley			trolley				trolley			trolley	trolley			trolley				trolley		
Cambridge	d		19 32				19 51				20 09			20 32				20 51				21 10			21 32
Shelford	d						19 56											20 56							
Whittlesford Parkway	d		19 39				20 00							20 39				21 00							21 39
Great Chesterford	d						20 04											21 04							
Audley End	d		19 47				20 10				20 24			20 47				21 10				21 25			21 47
Newport (Essex)	d						20 13											21 13							
Elsenham	d						20 19											21 19							
Stansted Airport	a										20 45											21 45			
Stansted Airport	d			20 00	20 15			20 30				20 45			21 00	21 15			21 30				21 45		
Stansted Mountfitchet	d						20 22					20 51						21 22					21 51		
Bishops Stortford	a		20 00	20 09			20 28	20 39						21 00	21 09			21 28	21 39						22 00
	d		20 00	20 09			20 28	20 39						21 00	21 09			21 28	21 39						22 00
Sawbridgeworth	d		20 05				20 32							21 05				21 32							22 05
Harlow Mill	d						20 36											21 36							
Harlow Town	d		20 10		20 30		20 39					21 02		21 10		21 30		21 39					22 02		22 10
Roydon	d						20 43											21 43							
Hertford East	d	19 55				20 25							20 55				21 25							21 55	
Ware	d	19 59				20 29							20 59				21 29							21 59	
St Margarets (Herts)	d	20 03				20 33							21 03				21 33							22 03	
Rye House	d	20 06				20 36							21 06				21 36							22 06	
Broxbourne [3]	a	20 11	20 16			20 41	20 48						21 11	21 16			21 41	21 48						22 11	22 16
Broxbourne [3]	d	20 11	20 16			20 41	20 52						21 11	21 16			21 41	21 52						22 11	22 16
Cheshunt	d	20 15	20 20			20 45	20 57						21 15	21 20			21 45	21 57						22 15	22 20
Waltham Cross	d						20 59											21 59							
Enfield Lock	d						21 02											22 02							
Brimsdown	d						21 04											22 04							
Ponders End	d						21 06											22 06							
Angel Road	d																								
Northumberland Park	d								←												←				
Tottenham Hale ⊖	d		20 29	20 32	20 46		21 12	21 01	21 12			21 17		21 29	21 32	21 46		22 12	22 01		22 12		22 17		22 29
Seven Sisters ⊖	d	20 33				21 03	→						21 33				22 03	→						22 33	
Clapton	d																								
Stratford [7] ⊖	a								21 23												22 23				
Hackney Downs	d	20 39				21 09							21 39				22 09							22 39	
Bethnal Green	d																								
London Liverpool Street [15] ⊖	a	20 48	20 43	20 46	21 01	21 18		21 15				21 31	21 48	21 43	21 46	22 01	22 18		22 15				22 31	22 48	22 43

A To Stratford
B From Cambridge
C From Birmingham New Street

Table 22R

Sundays

8 December to 11 May

Cambridge, Stansted Airport, Bishops Stortford, Hertford East and Broxbourne - London

Network Diagram - see first Page of Table 20

		LE	LE	LE	LE		LE	LE	XC	LE	LE	LE	LE	LE	LE		LE	LE	LE
		1	1		1		1	1	◇1	1		◇1	1	1	1		1	1	1
					A			B	C										
Cambridge	d				21 51				22 10			22 32	22 51						
Shelford	d				21 56								22 56						
Whittlesford Parkway	d				22 00							22 39	23 00						
Great Chesterford	d				22 04								23 04						
Audley End	d				22 10				22 25			22 47	23 10						
Newport (Essex)	d				22 13								23 13						
Elsenham	d				22 19								23 19						
Stansted Airport	a								22 45										
Stansted Airport	d	22 00	22 15				22 30			22 45				23 00	23 15		23 30	23 45	23 59
Stansted Mountfitchet	d				22 22					22 51			23 22						
Bishops Stortford	a	22 09			22 28		22 39					23 00	23 28	23 09			23 39		00 08
	d	22 09			22 28		22 39					23 00		23 09			23 39		00 08
Sawbridgeworth	d				22 32							23 05							
Harlow Mill	d				22 36														
Harlow Town	d		22 30		22 39					23 02		23 10			23 30		23 47	23 59	00 16
Roydon	d				22 43														
Hertford East	d			22 25							22 55								
Ware	d			22 29							22 59								
St Margarets (Herts)	d			22 33							23 03								
Rye House	d			22 36							23 06								
Broxbourne 3	a			22 41	22 48						23 11	23 16							
Broxbourne 3	d			22 41	22 52						23 11	23 16							
Cheshunt	d			22 45	22 57						23 15	23 20							
Waltham Cross	d				22 59														
Enfield Lock	d				23 02														
Brimsdown	d				23 04														
Ponders End	d				23 06														
Angel Road	d																		
Northumberland Park	d							←											
Tottenham Hale ⊖	d	22 32	22 46		23 12		23 01	23 12		23 17		23 29		23 32	23 46				
Seven Sisters ⊖	d			23 03	→						23 33						00 08	00 21	
Clapton	d																		
Stratford 7 ⊖	a							23 23											
Hackney Downs	d			23 09							23 39								
Bethnal Green	d																		
London Liverpool Street 15 ⊖	a	22 46	23 01	23 18			23 15			23 31	23 48	23 43		23 46	00 01		00 22	00 35	00 51

A To Stratford

B From Cambridge

C From Birmingham New Street

Network Diagram for Tables 24, 25

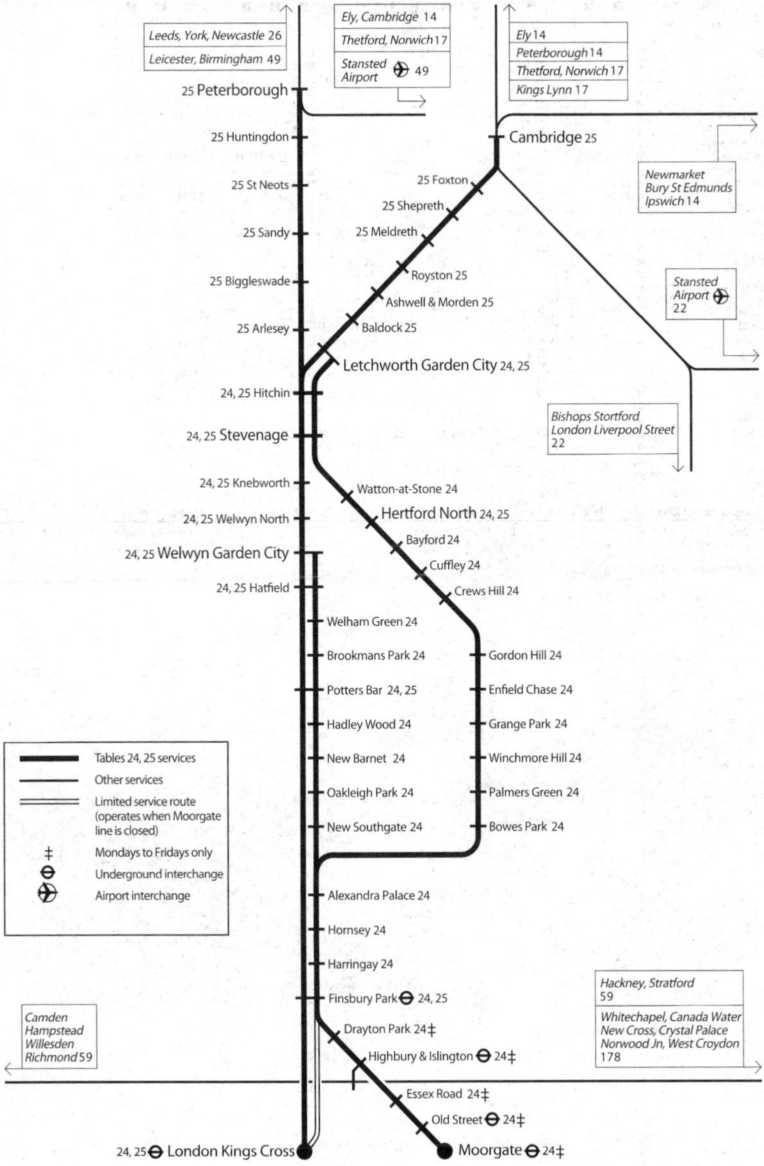

TOCs operating on this network - First Capital Connect (FC), East Coast (GR)

Table 24

Mondays to Fridays

9 December to 16 May

London - Welwyn Garden City, Hertford North and Letchworth Garden City

Network Diagram - see first Page of Table 24

Miles	Miles	Station		FC MX 1	FC MO	FC MX	FC MO A bus	FC MX	FC MO B	FC MO 1 A	FC MO A bus	FC MO A bus	FC MO 1 B	FC MX	FC MO B	FC MO A bus	FC MO A bus	FC MX	FC MO B	FC MO A bus	FC MO A bus	FC MO A	FC 1 C
0	—	London Kings Cross 15 ⊖	d							00 04			00 04	00 07	00 07			00 11	00 11			00 11	00 36
—	0	**Moorgate** ⊖	d																				
—	0½	Old Street ⊖	d																				
—	1¾	Essex Road	d																				
—	2¼	Highbury & Islington ⊖	d																				
—	2¾	Drayton Park	d																				
2½	3½	Finsbury Park ⊖	d							00 09			00 09	00 13	00 13			00 17	00 17			00 17	00 41
3½	4½	Harringay	d											00 15	00 15			00 19	00 19			00 19	
4	5	Hornsey	d											00 17	00 17			00 21	00 21			00 21	
5	6	Alexandra Palace	d							00 14				00 20	00 20			00 24	00 24		00 20	00 24	
6½	—	New Southgate	d															00 27	00 27				
8½	—	Oakleigh Park	d					00 01	00 01									00 30	00 30	00 04			
9¼	—	New Barnet	d					00 02	00 03									00 32	00 33	00 14			
10½	—	Hadley Wood	d					00 05	00 05		00 04							00 35	00 35	00 34			
12¾	—	Potters Bar	d					00 09	00 09		00 14	00 14	00 19					00 39	00 39	00 44	00 50		00 51
14½	—	Brookmans Park	d					00 12	00 12		00 22							00 42	00 42	00 52			
15½	—	Welham Green	d					00 14	00 14		00 26					←	←	00 44	00 44	00 56			
17¾	—	Hatfield	d					00 17	00 18		00 30	00 29	00 25			00 29	00 30	00 47	00 48	01 00	01 05		00 57
20¼	—	**Welwyn Garden City** 4	d	00 02			00 09	00a25	00a26		→	→	00 29			00 39	00a40	00a55	00a56	→	→		01 01
22	—	Welwyn North	d	00 05			00 19						00 32			00 49							01s04
25	—	Knebworth	d	00 09			00 29						00 36			00 59							01s08
—	6¾	Bowes Park	d											00 23	00 23							00 27	
—	7¾	Palmers Green	d											00 25	00 25							00 29	
—	8¾	Winchmore Hill	d											00 27	00 27							00 31	
—	9½	Grange Park	d											00 29	00 29							00 33	
—	10¼	Enfield Chase	d											00 31	00 31							00 35	
—	11	Gordon Hill	d											00 33	00 33							00 37	
—	12½	Crews Hill	d											00 36	00 36							00 40	
—	14¼	Cuffley	d											00 39	00 39							00 43	
—	17¾	Bayford	d		00 03	00 04								00 44	00 44							00 48	
—	20¾	**Hertford North**	d		00 08	00 09				00 30				00 49	00 49							00 53	
—	25	Watton-at-Stone	d		00 14	00 15								00 55	00 55							00 59	
27½	30	**Stevenage** 4	d	00 13	00 21	00 21	00a36			00 40			00 40	01 01	01 02	01a06						01 06	01 12
31¾	34¼	Hitchin 4	d	00 18	00 26	00 27				00 47			00 47	01 07	01 07							01 11	01a17
34¾	37¼	**Letchworth Garden City**	a	00 28	00 35	00 36				00 53			00 53	01 15	01 16							01 20	

Station		FC MO A bus	FC MO A bus	FC 1	FC MO A bus	FC MO A bus	FC 1 C	FC MO A bus	FC 1	FC	FC	FC	FC 1	FC	FC	FC 1	FC	FC	FC 1	FC	FC	FC	FC 1
London Kings Cross 15 ⊖	d			01 06			01 36		05 23		05 26	05 56	06 05	06 11	06 26	06 35			07 05				07 35
Moorgate ⊖	d																06 35	06 50		07 05	07 15	07 20	
Old Street ⊖	d																06 37	06 52		07 07	07 17	07 22	
Essex Road	d																06 40	06 55		07 10	07 20	07 25	
Highbury & Islington ⊖	d																06 43	06 58		07 13	07 23	07 28	
Drayton Park	d																06 44	06 59		07 14	07 24	07 29	
Finsbury Park ⊖	d			01 11			01 41		05 28		05 32	06 02	06 10	06 17	06 32	06 40	06 47	07 02	07 10	07 17	07 27	07 32	07 40
Harringay	d										05 35	06 05		06 20	06 35		06 50	07 05		07 20		07 35	
Hornsey	d										05 37	06 07		06 22	06 37		06 52	07 07		07 22		07 37	
Alexandra Palace	d			01 16	00 52	00 30	01 45	01 52			05 40	06 10		06 24	06 40		06 54	07 10		07 24	07 32	07 40	
New Southgate	d					00 40	01 48	02 02						06 27			06 57			07 27			
Oakleigh Park	d					00 50	01 51	02 12						06 31			07 01			07 31			
New Barnet	d					01 00	01 53	02 22						06 33			07 03			07 33			
Hadley Wood	d					01 20	01 56	02 42						06 35			07 05			07 35			
Potters Bar	d				01 22	01 30	01 59	02 52	05 38				06 21	06 39		06 51	07 09		07 21	07 39			07 51
Brookmans Park	d					01 38								06 42			07 12			07 42			
Welham Green	d	←	←			01 42								06 44			07 14			07 44			
Hatfield	d	01 00	01 05		01 37	01 46	02 05	03 07	05 44				06 27	06 48		06 57	07 18		07 27	07 48			07 57
Welwyn Garden City 4	d	01a10	01 15		01 47	01a56	02 09	03 17	05 48				06 32	06a53		07 02	07a23		07 32	07a53			08 02
Welwyn North	d		01 25		01s57		02s12	03s27	05 51				06 35			07 05			07 35				08 05
Knebworth	d		01 35		02s07		02s16	03s37	05 55				06 39			07 09			07 39				08 09
Bowes Park	d										05 42	06 12			06 42			07 12				07 42	
Palmers Green	d			01 19							05 44	06 14			06 44			07 14			07 36	07 44	
Winchmore Hill	d			01 21							05 47	06 17			06 47			07 17			07 39	07 47	
Grange Park	d										05 49	06 19			06 49			07 19				07 49	
Enfield Chase	d			01 24							05 51	06 21			06 51			07 21			07 42	07 51	
Gordon Hill	d			01 26							05 53	06 23			06 53			07 23			07 45	07 53	
Crews Hill	d										05 56	06 26			06 56			07 26				07 56	
Cuffley	d			01 30							05 59	06 29			06 59			07 29			07 49	07 59	
Bayford	d										06 04	06 34			07 04			07 34				08 04	
Hertford North	d			01 38						05 50	06a12	06 40			07 10			07 40			07a59	08 10	
Watton-at-Stone	d									05 55		06 45			07 15			07 45				08 15	
Stevenage 4	d		01a42	01 47	02a14		02 20	03a44	05 59	06a05		06a54	06 43		07a24	07 13		07a54	07 43			08a24	08 13
Hitchin 4	d			01 52			02a25		06a07				06 48			07a18			07 48				08a18
Letchworth Garden City	a			02s00									06 52						07 53				

A from 6 January until 24 March
B until 30 December, from 31 March
C until 3 January, MX from 7 January until 21 March, from 25 March

Table 24

Mondays to Fridays

9 December to 16 May

London - Welwyn Garden City, Hertford North and Letchworth Garden City

Network Diagram - see first Page of Table 24

		FC	FC	FC	FC 1	FC	FC	FC	FC	FC	FC	FC	FC 1	FC	FC	FC	FC	FC	FC	FC 1	FC	FC
London Kings Cross 15 ⊖	d				08 03								08 35							09 05		
Moorgate ⊖	d	07 33	07 38	07 50			07 58	08 03	08 08	08 18	08 23	08 28				08 33	08 38	08 43	08 52		09 02	09 12
Old Street ⊖	d	07 35	07 40	07 52			08 00	08 05	08 10	08 20	08 25	08 30				08 35	08 40	08 45	08 54		09 04	09 14
Essex Road	d	07 38	07 43	07 55			08 03	08 08	08 13	08 23	08 28	08 33				08 38	08 43	08 48	08 57		09 07	09 17
Highbury & Islington ⊖	d	07 41	07 46	07 58			08 06	08 11	08 16	08 26	08 31	08 36				08 41	08 46	08 51	09 00		09 10	09 20
Drayton Park	d	07 42	07 47	07 59			08 07	08 12	08 17	08 27	08 32	08 37				08 42	08 47	08 52	09 01		09 11	09 21
Finsbury Park ⊖	d	07 45	07 50	08 02	08 09		08 10	08 15	08 20	08 30	08 35	08 40	08 40			08 45	08 50	08 55	09 04	09 10	09 14	09 24
Harringay	d		07 53	08 05				08 18	08 23	08 33	08 38					08 48	08 53	08 58	09 07		09 17	09 27
Hornsey	d		07 55	08 07				08 20	08 25	08 35	08 40					08 50	08 55	09 00	09 09		09 19	09 29
Alexandra Palace	d	07 50	07 57	08 10			08 15	08 23	08 27	08 38	08 42	08 45				08 53	08 57	09 03	09 12		09 21	09 32
New Southgate	d		08 00						08 30		08 45						09 00				09 24	
Oakleigh Park	d		08 04						08 34		08 49						09 04				09 28	
New Barnet	d		08 06						08 36		08 51						09 06				09 30	
Hadley Wood	d		08 08						08 38		08 53				←		09 08				09 32	
Potters Bar	d		08 12		08 19				08 42		08 57		08 51		08 57		09 12			09 21	09 36	
Brookmans Park	d		08 15						08 45		↪				09 00		09 15				09 39	
Welham Green	d		08 17						08 47						09 02		09 17				09 41	
Hatfield	d		08 21		08 25				08 51				08 57		09 06		09 21			09 27	09 45	
Welwyn Garden City 4	d		08a26		08 29				08a56				09 02		09a11		09a28			09 32	09a50	
Welwyn North	d				08 32								09 05							09 35		
Knebworth	d				08 36								09 09							09 39		
Bowes Park	d			08 12			08 17			08 40		08 47						09 05	09 14			09 34
Palmers Green	d	07 54		08 14			08 19	08 26		08 42		08 49				08 56		09 07	09 16			09 36
Winchmore Hill	d	07 56		08 17			08 22	08 29		08 45		08 53				08 59		09 10	09 19			09 39
Grange Park	d			08 19			08 24			08 47		08 55						09 12	09 21			09 41
Enfield Chase	d	08 00		08 21			08 26	08 32		08 49		08 57				09 02		09 14	09 23			09 43
Gordon Hill	d	08 02		08 23			08a30	08 34		08 51		09a00				09 04		09a17	09 25			09 45
Crews Hill	d			08 26						08 54									09 28			09 48
Cuffley	d	08 07		08 29				08 39		08 57						09 09			09 31			09 51
Bayford	d			08 34						09 02									09 36			09 56
Hertford North	d	08a15		08 39				08 48		09 09						09a17			09 41			10 09
Watton-at-Stone	d			08 45		←				09 15				←					09 47			10 15
Stevenage 4	d			08 51	08 40	08 51		08a59		09 21			09 13	09 21					09a55	09 43		10 21
Hitchin 4	d			↪	08 44	08 57				↪			09a18	09 27						09 48		↪
Letchworth Garden City	a				08 49	09 03								09 34						09 53		

		FC	FC 1	FC	FC	FC	FC	FC	FC 1	FC	FC	FC	FC	FC 1		FC	FC	FC	FC	FC 1	FC	FC	FC	FC
London Kings Cross 15 ⊖	d		09 35						10 05					10 35						14 05				
Moorgate ⊖	d	09 20				09 30	09 40	09 50			10 00	10 10	10 20				13 30	13 40	13 50			14 00	14 10	14 20
Old Street ⊖	d	09 22				09 32	09 42	09 52			10 02	10 12	10 22				13 32	13 42	13 52			14 02	14 12	14 22
Essex Road	d	09 25				09 35	09 45	09 55			10 05	10 15	10 25				13 35	13 45	13 55			14 05	14 15	14 25
Highbury & Islington ⊖	d	09 28				09 38	09 48	09 58			10 08	10 18	10 28				13 38	13 48	13 58			14 08	14 18	14 28
Drayton Park	d	09 29				09 39	09 49	09 59			10 09	10 19	10 29				13 39	13 49	13 59			14 09	14 19	14 29
Finsbury Park ⊖	d	09 32	09 40			09 42	09 52	10 02	10 10		10 12	10 22	10 32	10 40			13 42	13 52	14 02	14 10		14 12	14 22	14 32
Harringay	d	09 35				09 45	09 55	10 05			10 15	10 25	10 35				13 45	13 55	14 05			14 15	14 25	14 35
Hornsey	d	09 37				09 47	09 57	10 07			10 17	10 27	10 37				13 47	13 57	14 07			14 17	14 27	14 37
Alexandra Palace	d	09 39				09 50	09 59	10 10			10 19	10 30	10 39				13 50	13 59	14 10			14 19	14 30	14 39
New Southgate	d	09 42					10 02				10 22		10 42					14 02				14 22		14 42
Oakleigh Park	d	09 46					10 06				10 26		10 46					14 06				14 26		14 46
New Barnet	d	09 48					10 08				10 28		10 48					14 08				14 28		14 48
Hadley Wood	d	09 50			←		10 10				10 30		10 50			←		14 10				14 30		14 50
Potters Bar	d	09 54	09 51		09 54		10 14		10 21		10 34		10 54	10 51	and at the same minutes past each hour until	13 54		14 14		14 21		14 34		14 54
Brookmans Park	d	↪			09 57		10 17				10 37		↪			13 57		14 17				14 37		↪
Welham Green	d				09 59		10 19				10 39					13 59		14 19				14 39		
Hatfield	d		09 57		10 03		10 23		10 27		10 43			10 57		14 03		14 23		14 27		14 43		
Welwyn Garden City 4	d		10 02		10a08		10a28		10 32		10a48			11 02		14a08		14a28		14 32		14a48		
Welwyn North	d		10 05						10 35					11 05						14 35				
Knebworth	d		10 09						10 39					11 09						14 39				
Bowes Park	d					09 52		10 12				10 32					13 52		14 12				14 32	
Palmers Green	d					09 54		10 14				10 34					13 54		14 14				14 34	
Winchmore Hill	d					09 57		10 17				10 37					13 57		14 17				14 37	
Grange Park	d					09 59		10 19				10 39					13 59		14 19				14 39	
Enfield Chase	d					10 01		10 21				10 41					14 01		14 21				14 41	
Gordon Hill	d					10 03		10 23				10 43					14 03		14 23				14 43	
Crews Hill	d					10 06		10 26				10 46					14 06		14 26				14 46	
Cuffley	d					10 09		10 29				10 49					14 09		14 29				14 49	
Bayford	d					10 14		10 34				10 54					14 14		14 34				14 54	
Hertford North	d					10a20		10 39				11a00					14a20		14 39				15a00	
Watton-at-Stone	d			←				10 45		←									14 45		←			
Stevenage 4	d		10 13	10 21				10 51	10 43	10 51				11 13					14 51	14 43	14 51			
Hitchin 4	d		10a18	10 27				↪	10 48	10 57				11a18					↪	14 48	14 57			
Letchworth Garden City	a			10 34					10 53	11 03										14 53	15 03			

Table 24

Mondays to Fridays

9 December to 16 May

London - Welwyn Garden City, Hertford North and Letchworth Garden City

Network Diagram - see first Page of Table 24

Station		FC 1		FC	FC	FC	FC	FC 1	FC	FC	FC	FC		FC 1	FC	FC	FC	FC	FC	FC 1	FC	FC		FC	FC
London Kings Cross 15 ⊖	d	14 35						15 05						15 35			15 44			16 06					
Moorgate ⊖	d				14 30	14 40	14 50			15 00	15 10	15 20				15 30		15 40	15 50		16 00	16 08		16 18	16 23
Old Street ⊖	d				14 32	14 42	14 52			15 02	15 12	15 22				15 32		15 42	15 52		16 02	16 10		16 20	16 25
Essex Road	d				14 35	14 45	14 55			15 05	15 15	15 25				15 35		15 45	15 55		16 05	16 13		16 23	16 28
Highbury & Islington ⊖	d				14 38	14 48	14 58			15 08	15 18	15 28				15 38		15 48	15 58		16 08	16 16		16 26	16 31
Drayton Park	d				14 39	14 49	14 59			15 09	15 19	15 29				15 39		15 49	15 59		16 09	16 17		16 27	16 32
Finsbury Park ⊖	d	14 40			14 42	14 52	15 02	15 10		15 12	15 22	15 32		15 40		15 42	15 50	15 52	16 02	16 11	16 12	16 20		16 30	16 35
Harringay	d				14 45	14 55	15 05			15 15	15 25	15 35				15 45		15 55	16 05		16 15	16 23		16 33	
Hornsey	d				14 47	14 57	15 07			15 17	15 27	15 37				15 47		15 57	16 07		16 17	16 25		16 35	
Alexandra Palace	d				14 50	14 59	15 10			15 19	15 30	15 39				15 50		15 59	16 10		16 19	16 28		16 38	16 41
New Southgate	d					15 02				15 22		15 42					15 55	16 02			16 22				
Oakleigh Park	d					15 06				15 26		15 46					15 58	16 06			16 26				
New Barnet	d					15 08				15 28		15 48					16 00	16 08			16 28				
Hadley Wood	d			←		15 10				15 30		15 50			←			16 10			16 30				
Potters Bar	d	14 51		14 54		15 14		15 21		15 34		15 54		15 51	15 54		16 05	16 14		16 21	16 34				
Brookmans Park	d			14 57		15 17				15 37		→			15 57			16 17			16 37				
Welham Green	d			14 59		15 19				15 39					15 59			16 19			16 39				
Hatfield	d	14 57		15 03		15 23		15 27		15 43				15 57	16 03		16 11	16 23		16 27	16 43				
Welwyn Garden City 4	d	15 02		15a08		15a28		15 32		15a48				16 02	16a08		16a16	16a28		16 31	16a48				
Welwyn North	d	15 05						15 35						16 05						16 34					
Knebworth	d	15 09						15 39						16 09						16 38					
Bowes Park	d				14 52		15 12				15 32					15 52			16 12			16 30			16 44
Palmers Green	d				14 54		15 14				15 34					15 54			16 14			16 32		16 41	16 46
Winchmore Hill	d				14 57		15 17				15 37					15 57			16 17			16 35		16 44	16 49
Grange Park	d				14 59		15 19				15 39					15 59			16 19			16 37			16 51
Enfield Chase	d				15 01		15 21				15 41					16 01			16 21			16 39		16 47	16 53
Gordon Hill	d				15 03		15 23				15 43					16 03			16 23			16 42		16a51	16 56
Crews Hill	d				15 06		15 26				15 46					16 06			16 26			16 45			
Cuffley	d				15 09		15 29				15 49					16 09			16 29			16 48			17 00
Bayford	d				15 14		15 34				15 54					16 14			16 34			16 53			
Hertford North	d				15a20		15 39				16 09					16a20			16 39			16a59			17 09
Watton-at-Stone	d						15 45		←		16 15								16 45						17 15
Stevenage 4	d	15 13					15 51	15 43	15 51		16a23			16 13					16a53	16 45					17a23
Hitchin 4	d	15a18					→	15 48	15 57					16a18						16 50					
Letchworth Garden City	a							15 53	16 03											16 55					

Station		FC 1	FC	FC	FC	FC 1	FC	FC		FC	FC	FC	FC	FC	FC 1	FC	FC	FC		FC	FC	FC	FC	FC	FC 1
London Kings Cross 15 ⊖	d	16 32				16 54		16 57							17 22			17 27							17 52
Moorgate ⊖	d		16 28	16 33	16 38		16 48			16 53	16 58	17 03	17 08	17 13			17 18			17 23	17 28	17 33	17 38	17 43	
Old Street ⊖	d		16 30	16 35	16 40		16 50			16 55	17 00	17 05	17 10	17 15			17 20			17 25	17 30	17 35	17 40	17 45	
Essex Road	d		16 33	16 38	16 43		16 53			16 58	17 03	17 08	17 13	17 18			17 23			17 28	17 33	17 38	17 43	17 48	
Highbury & Islington ⊖	d		16 36	16 41	16 46		16 56			17 01	17 06	17 11	17 16	17 21			17 26			17 31	17 36	17 41	17 46	17 51	
Drayton Park	d		16 37	16 42	16 47		16 57			17 02	17 07	17 12	17 17	17 22			17 27			17 32	17 37	17 42	17 47	17 52	
Finsbury Park ⊖	d	16 37	16 40	16 45	16 50	16 59	17 00	17 03		17 05	17 10	17 15	17 20	17 25	17 28		17 30	17 33		17 35	17 40	17 45	17 50	17 55	17 58
Harringay	d		16 43		16 53					17 08		17 18	17 23							17 38		17 48	17 53		
Hornsey	d		16 45		16 55					17 10		17 20	17 25							17 40		17 50	17 55		
Alexandra Palace	d		16 47	16 50	16 58					17 12	17 15	17 23	17 27	17 30						17 42	17 45	17 53	17 57	18 00	
New Southgate	d		16 50					17 08		17 15			17 30					17 38		17 45			18 00		
Oakleigh Park	d		16 54					17 11		17 19			17 34					17 41		17 49			18 04		
New Barnet	d		16 56					17 14		17 21			17 36					17 44		17 51			18 06		
Hadley Wood	d		16 58							17 24			17 39							17 54			18 09		
Potters Bar	d	16 47	17 02					17 19		17 28			17 43					17 49		17 58			18 13		
Brookmans Park	d		17 05							17 31			17 46							18 01			18 16		
Welham Green	d		17 07							17 33			17 48			←				18 03			18 18		
Hatfield	d	16 54	17 11			17 15		17 25		17 36			17 51		17 44	17 51		17 55		18 06			18 21		18 14
Welwyn Garden City 4	d	16 58	17a16			17 19		17a30		17a41			→		17 48	17a56		18a00		18a11			→		18 18
Welwyn North	d	17 01				17 22									17 52										18 22
Knebworth	d	17 06				17 26									17 56										18 26
Bowes Park	d				17 00		17 06					17 25					17 36					17 55			
Palmers Green	d			16 53	17 02		17 08				17 19	17 27		17 33			17 38				17 49	17 57		18 03	
Winchmore Hill	d			16 56	17 05		17 11				17 22	17 30		17 36			17 41				17 52	18 00		18 06	
Grange Park	d				17 07		17 13					17 32					17 43					18 02			
Enfield Chase	d			17 00	17 09		17 15				17 25	17 34		17 40			17 45				17 55	18 04		18 10	
Gordon Hill	d			17 02	17a12		17 18				17a31	17 37		17a43			17 48				17 58	18 07		18a13	
Crews Hill	d			17 05								17 40										18 10			
Cuffley	d			17 08			17 22					17 43					17 52				18 02	18 13			
Bayford	d			17 13								17 48										18 18			
Hertford North	d			17a19			17 31					17a53					18 01				18a11	18a23			
Watton-at-Stone	d						17 37										18 07								
Stevenage 4	d	17 10				17 35	17a44								18 02		18a14								18 31
Hitchin 4	d	17 16				17 40									18 09										18 37
Letchworth Garden City	a	17 21				17 46									18 14										18 43

Table 24

Mondays to Fridays

9 December to 16 May

London - Welwyn Garden City, Hertford North and Letchworth Garden City

Network Diagram - see first Page of Table 24

	FC	FC	FC		FC	FC	FC	FC	FC	FC 1	FC	FC	FC		FC	FC	FC	FC	FC	FC 1	FC	FC	FC	
London Kings Cross 15 ⊖ d			17 57							18 22			18 27							18 52			18 57	
Moorgate ⊖ d		17 48			17 53	17 58	18 03	18 08	18 13			18 18			18 23	18 28	18 33	18 38	18 43			18 50		
Old Street ⊖ d		17 50			17 55	18 00	18 05	18 10	18 15			18 20			18 25	18 30	18 35	18 40	18 45			18 52		
Essex Road d		17 53			17 58	18 03	18 08	18 13	18 18			18 23			18 28	18 33	18 38	18 43	18 48			18 55		
Highbury & Islington ⊖ d		17 56			18 01	18 06	18 11	18 16	18 21			18 26			18 31	18 36	18 41	18 46	18 51			18 58		
Drayton Park d		17 57			18 02	18 07	18 12	18 17	18 22			18 27			18 32	18 37	18 42	18 47	18 52			18 59		
Finsbury Park ⊖ d		18 00	18 03		18 05	18 10	18 15	18 20	18 25	18 28		18 30	18 33		18 35	18 40	18 45	18 51	18 55	18 58		19 02	19 03	
Harringay d					18 08		18 18	18 23							18 38		18 48		18 58					
Hornsey d					18 10		18 20	18 25							18 40		18 50		19 00					
Alexandra Palace d					18 12	18 15	18 23	18 27	18 30						18 42	18 45	18 53	18 57	19 02				19 07	
New Southgate d			18 08		18 15			18 30					18 38		18 45				19 05				19 10	
Oakleigh Park d			18 11		18 19			18 34					18 41		18 49				19 09				19 14	
New Barnet d					18 21			18 36					18 44		18 51				19 11				19 16	
Hadley Wood d			18 15		18 24			18 39							18 54				19 14		←		19 19	
Potters Bar d			18 19		18 28			18 43					18 49		18 58				19 18	19 08	19 18		19 23	
Brookmans Park d					18 31			18 46							19 01				→		19 21			
Welham Green d	←				18 33			18 48			←				19 03						19 23			
Hatfield d	18 21		18 25		18 36			18 51		18 44	18 51		18 55		19 06					19 15	19 26		19 29	
Welwyn Garden City 4 d	18a26		18a30		18a41			→		18 49	18a56		19a00		19a11					19 23	19a31		19a34	
Welwyn North d										18 51										19 32				
Knebworth d										18 55										19 36				
Bowes Park d		18 06					18 25					18 36					18 55	18 59				19 08		
Palmers Green d		18 08				18 19	18 27		18 33			18 38				18 49	18 57	19 02				19 10		
Winchmore Hill d		18 11				18 22	18 30		18 36			18 41				18 52	19 00	19 05				19 13		
Grange Park d		18 13					18 32					18 43					19 02	19 07				19 15		
Enfield Chase d		18 15				18 25	18 34		18 40			18 45				18 55	19 04	19 09				19 17		
Gordon Hill d		18 18				18 28	18 37		18a43			18 48				18 58	19 07	19a12				19 20		
Crews Hill d							18 40										19 10							
Cuffley d		18 22				18 32	18 43					18 52				19 02	19 13					19 24		
Bayford d							18 48										19 18							
Hertford North d		18 31				18a41	18a53					19 01				19a11	19a23					19 35		
Watton-at-Stone d		18 37										19 07										19 41		
Stevenage 4 d		18a44								19 01		19a14								19 40		19 51		
Hitchin 4 d										19 07										19 45		19 57		
Letchworth Garden City a										19 13										19 49		20 03		

	FC	FC	FC 1	FC	FC	FC 1	FC	FC	FC		FC	FC	FC	FC	FC 1	FC	FC	FC	FC 1		FC	FC	FC	FC
London Kings Cross 15 ⊖ d			19 18			19 33					19 40				20 06				20 36					
Moorgate ⊖ d	18 58	19 03		19 13	19 23				19 33			19 38	19 43	19 53		20 03	20 08	20 13				20 33	20 38	20 53
Old Street ⊖ d	19 00	19 05		19 15	19 25				19 35			19 40	19 45	19 55		20 05	20 10	20 15				20 35	20 40	20 55
Essex Road d	19 03	19 08		19 18	19 28				19 38			19 43	19 48	19 58		20 08	20 13	20 18				20 38	20 43	20 58
Highbury & Islington ⊖ d	19 06	19 11		19 21	19 31				19 41			19 46	19 51	20 01		20 11	20 16	20 21				20 41	20 46	21 01
Drayton Park d	19 07	19 12		19 22	19 32				19 42			19 47	19 52	20 02		20 12	20 17	20 22				20 42	20 47	21 02
Finsbury Park ⊖ d	19 10	19 15	19 23	19 25	19 35	19 39			19 45		19 46	19 50	19 55	20 05	20 11	20a15	20 20	20 25	20 41			20 45	20 50	21 05
Harringay d	19 13	19 18		19 28	19 38							19 53	19 58	20 08			20 23	20 28				20 48	20 53	21 08
Hornsey d	19 15	19 20		19 30	19 40							19 55	20 00	20 10			20 25	20 30				20 50	20 55	21 10
Alexandra Palace d	19 17	19 23		19 32	19 43				19 50			19 57	20 03	20 13			20 27	20 33				20 53	20 57	21 13
New Southgate d	19 20			19 35							19 51	20 00					20 30						21 00	
Oakleigh Park d	19 24			19 39							19 54	20 04					20 34						21 04	
New Barnet d	19 26			19 41							19 56	20 06					20 36						21 06	
Hadley Wood d	19 29			19 44								20 09					20 39						21 09	
Potters Bar d	19 33		19 37	19 48							20 02	20 13			20 21		20 43		20 51				21 13	
Brookmans Park d	19 36			19 51								20 16					20 46						21 16	
Welham Green d	19 38			19 53			←					20 18					20 48						21 18	
Hatfield d	19 41		19 45	19 56		19 52	19 56				20 08	20 21			20 27		20 51		20 57				21 21	
Welwyn Garden City 4 d	19a46		19 50	→		19 58	20a01				20a13	20a26			20 32		20a56		21 02				21a26	
Welwyn North d			19 53			20 02									20 35				21 05					
Knebworth d			19 57			20 06									20 39				21 09					
Bowes Park d		19 25			19 45				19 52				20 05	20 15				20 35				20 55		21 15
Palmers Green d		19 27			19 47				19 54				20 07	20 17				20 37				20 57		21 17
Winchmore Hill d		19 30			19 50				19 57				20 10	20 20				20 40				21 00		21 20
Grange Park d		19 32			19 52				19 59				20 12	20 22				20 42				21 02		21 22
Enfield Chase d		19 34			19 54				20 01				20 14	20 24				20 44				21 04		21 24
Gordon Hill d		19 37			19 57				20 04				20 17	20 26				20 46				21 06		21 26
Crews Hill d		19 40							20 07					20 29				20 49				21 09		21 29
Cuffley d		19 43			20 01				20 10				20 21	20 32				20 52				21 12		21 32
Bayford d		19 48							20 15					20 37				20 57				21 17		21 37
Hertford North d		19a53			20 10				20a20				20a31	20 42				21 09				21a23		21a43
Watton-at-Stone d					20 15			←						20 48				21 15			←			
Stevenage 4 d			20 02		20 22	20 10		20 22						20a56	20 43			21 21	21 13		21 21			
Hitchin 4 d			20 09		→	20 16		20 27							20 48			→	21 18		21 27			
Letchworth Garden City a			20 15			20 23		20 33							20 53				21 23		21 33			

Table 24

Mondays to Fridays

9 December to 16 May

London - Welwyn Garden City, Hertford North and Letchworth Garden City

Network Diagram - see first Page of Table 24

Station		FC 1	FC	FC	FC 1	FC	FC	FC	FC	FC 1	FC	FC	FC 1	FC	FC	FC	FC 1	FC	FC	FC 1	FC	FC
London Kings Cross 15 ⊖	d	21 06			21 36					22 06	22 11	22 26	22 36		22 41	22 56	23 06	23 11	23 26	23 36		23 41
Moorgate ⊖	d		21 08	21 13			21 33	21 38	21 53													
Old Street ⊖	d		21 10	21 15			21 35	21 40	21 55													
Essex Road	d		21 13	21 18			21 38	21 43	21 58													
Highbury & Islington ⊖	d		21 16	21 21			21 41	21 46	22 01													
Drayton Park	d		21 17	21 22			21 42	21 47	22 02													
Finsbury Park ⊖	d	21 11	21 20	21 25	21 41		21 45	21 50	22 05	22 12	22 17	22 32	22 41		22 47	23 02	23 11	23 17	23 32	23 41		23 47
Harringay	d		21 23	21 28			21 48	21 53	22 08		22 19	22 34			22 49	23 04		23 19	23 34			23 49
Hornsey	d		21 25	21 30			21 50	21 55	22 10		22 21	22 36			22 51	23 06		23 21	23 36			23 51
Alexandra Palace	d		21 27	21 33			21 53	21 57	22 13		22 24	22 39			22 54	23 09		23 24	23 39			23 54
New Southgate	d		21 30					22 00			22 27				22 57			23 27				23 57
Oakleigh Park	d		21 34					22 04			22 30				23 00			23 30				00 01
New Barnet	d		21 36					22 06			22 32				23 02			23 32				00 02
Hadley Wood	d		21 39					22 09			22 35				23 05			23 35				00 05
Potters Bar	d	21 22	21 43		21 51			22 13		22 22	22 39		22 52		23 09		23 21	23 39		23 51		00 09
Brookmans Park	d		21 46					22 16			22 42				23 12			23 42				00 12
Welham Green	d		21 48					22 18			22 44				23 14			23 44				00 14
Hatfield	d	21 28	21 51		21 57			22 21		22 28	22 47		22 58		23 17		23 27	23 47		23 57		00 17
Welwyn Garden City 4	d	21 32	21a56		22 02			22a26		22 32	22a52		23 02		23a22		23 32	23a52		00 02		00a25
Welwyn North	d	21 35			22 05					22 35			23 05				23 35			00 05		
Knebworth	d	21 39			22 09					22 39			23 09				23 39			00 09		
Bowes Park	d			21 35			21 55		22 15			22 42				23 12			23 42			
Palmers Green	d			21 37			21 57		22 17			22 44				23 14			23 44			
Winchmore Hill	d			21 40			22 00		22 20			22 46				23 16			23 46			
Grange Park	d			21 42			22 02		22 22			22 48				23 18			23 48			
Enfield Chase	d			21 44			22 04		22 24			22 50				23 20			23 50			
Gordon Hill	d			21 46			22 06		22 26			22 53				23 23			23 53			
Crews Hill	d			21 49			22 09		22 29			22 56				23 26			23 56			
Cuffley	d			21 52			22 12		22 32			22 59				23 29			23 59			
Bayford	d			21 57			22 17		22 37			23 04				23 34			00 04			
Hertford North	d			22 09			22a23		22a43			23 09				23a39			00 09			
Watton-at-Stone	d			22 15		←						23 15		←					00 15		←	
Stevenage 4	d	21 43		22 21	22 13	22 21				22 43		23 21	23 13	23 21			23 43		00 21	00 13	00 21	
Hitchin 4	d	21 48		→	22 18	22 27				22 48		→	23 18	23 27			23 48		→	00 18	00 27	
Letchworth Garden City	a	21 53			22 23	22 33				22 53			23 23	23 33			23 53			00 28	00 36	

Saturdays

14 December to 17 May

Station		FC 1	FC	FC	FC	FC	FC 1	FC 1	FC	FC 1	FC 1	FC	FC	FC 1	FC	FC	FC 1	FC		FC	FC 1	FC	FC
London Kings Cross 15 ⊖	d				00 07	00 11	00 36	01 06	01 11	01 36	05 23	05 26	05 56	06 06	06 11	06 26	06 36	06 41		20 56	21 06	21 11	21 26
Moorgate ⊖	d																						
Old Street ⊖	d																						
Essex Road	d																						
Highbury & Islington ⊖	d																						
Drayton Park	d																						
Finsbury Park ⊖	d				00 13	00 17	00 41	01 11	01 17	01 41	05 28	05 32	06 02	06 11	06 17	06 32	06 41	06 47		21 02	21 11	21 17	21 32
Harringay	d				00 15	00 19			01 19			05 34	06 04		06 19	06 34		06 49		21 04		21 19	21 34
Hornsey	d				00 17	00 21			01 21			05 36	06 06		06 21	06 36		06 51		21 06		21 21	21 36
Alexandra Palace	d				00 20	00 24		01 16	01 24	01 45		05 39	06 09		06 24	06 39		06 54		21 09		21 24	21 39
New Southgate	d					00 27			01 27	01 48					06 27			06 57				21 27	
Oakleigh Park	d		00 01			00 30			01 30	01 51					06 30			07 00				21 30	
New Barnet	d		00 02			00 32			01 32	01 53					06 33			07 03				21 33	
Hadley Wood	d		00 05			00 35			01 35	01 56					06 35			07 05	and at			21 35	
Potters Bar	d		00 09			00 39	00 51		01 39	01 59	05 38			06 21	06 39		06 51	07 09	the same		21 21	21 39	
Brookmans Park	d		00 12			00 42			01 42						06 42			07 12	minutes			21 42	
Welham Green	d		00 14			00 44			01 44						06 44			07 14	past			21 44	
Hatfield	d		00 17			00 47	00 57		01 47	02 05	05 44			06 27	06 48		06 57	07 18	each		21 27	21 48	
Welwyn Garden City 4	d	00 02	00a25			00a55	01 01		01a55	02 09	05 48			06 31	06a53		07 01	07a23	hour until		21 31	21a53	
Welwyn North	d	00 05					01s04			02s12	05 51			06 34			07 04				21 34		
Knebworth	d	00 09					01s08			02s16	05 55			06 38			07 08				21 38		
Bowes Park	d				00 23							05 42	06 12			06 42				21 12			21 42
Palmers Green	d				00 25			01 19				05 44	06 14			06 44				21 14			21 44
Winchmore Hill	d				00 27			01 21				05 46	06 16			06 46				21 16			21 46
Grange Park	d				00 29							05 48	06 18			06 48				21 18			21 48
Enfield Chase	d				00 31			01 24				05 50	06 20			06 50				21 20			21 50
Gordon Hill	d				00 33			01 26				05 52	06 22			06 52				21 22			21 52
Crews Hill	d				00 36							05 55	06 25			06 55				21 25			21 55
Cuffley	d				00 39			01 30				05 58	06 28			06 58				21 28			21 58
Bayford	d			00 04	00 44							06 03	06 33			07 03				21 33			22 03
Hertford North	d			00 09	00 49			01 38				06a08	06a38			07 08				21a38			22 08
Watton-at-Stone	d			00 15	00 55											07 14							22 14
Stevenage 4	d	00 13		00 21	01 01		01 12	01 47		02 20	05 59			06 42		07a21	07 12				21 42		22a21
Hitchin 4	d	00 18		00 27	01 07		01a17	01 52		02a25	06a07			06 47			07a17				21 47		
Letchworth Garden City	a	00 28		00 36	01 15			02s00						06 52							21 52		

Table 24

Saturdays

14 December to 17 May

London - Welwyn Garden City, Hertford North and Letchworth Garden City

Network Diagram - see first Page of Table 24

		FC 1	FC	FC	FC 1	FC	FC	FC 1	FC	FC	FC 1	FC	FC	FC 1	FC	FC	FC
London Kings Cross 15 ⊖	d	21 36	21 41	21 56	22 06	22 11	22 26	22 36	22 41	22 56	23 06	23 11	23 26	23 36		23 41	23 56
Moorgate ⊖	d																
Old Street ⊖	d																
Essex Road	d																
Highbury & Islington ⊖	d																
Drayton Park	d																
Finsbury Park ⊖	d	21 41	21 47	22 02	22 11	22 17	22 32	22 41	22 47	23 02	23 11	23 17	23 32	23 41		23 47	00 02
Harringay	d		21 49	22 04		22 19	22 34		22 49	23 04		23 19	23 34			23 49	00 04
Hornsey	d		21 51	22 06		22 21	22 36		22 51	23 06		23 21	23 36			23 51	00 06
Alexandra Palace	d		21 54	22 09		22 24	22 39		22 54	23 09		23 24	23 39			23 54	00 09
New Southgate	d		21 57			22 27			22 57			23 27				23 57	
Oakleigh Park	d		22 00			22 30			23 00			23 30				00 01	
New Barnet	d		22 03			22 33			23 03			23 33				00 03	
Hadley Wood	d		22 05			22 35			23 05			23 35				00 05	
Potters Bar	d	21 51	22 09		22 21	22 39		22 51	23 09		23 21	23 39		23 51		00 09	
Brookmans Park	d		22 12			22 42			23 12			23 42				00 12	
Welham Green	d		22 14			22 44			23 14			23 44				00 14	
Hatfield	d	21 57	22 18		22 27	22 48		22 57	23 18		23 27	23 48		23 57		00 18	
Welwyn Garden City 4	d	22 01	22a23		22 31	22a53		23 01	23a23		23 31	23a56		00 01		00a26	
Welwyn North	d	22 04			22 34			23 04			23 34			00 04			
Knebworth	d	22 08			22 38			23 08			23 38			00 08			
Bowes Park	d			22 12			22 42			23 12			23 42				00 12
Palmers Green	d			22 14			22 44			23 14			23 44				00 14
Winchmore Hill	d			22 16			22 46			23 16			23 46				00 16
Grange Park	d			22 18			22 48			23 18			23 48				00 18
Enfield Chase	d			22 20			22 50			23 20			23 50				00 20
Gordon Hill	d			22 22			22 52			23 22			23 52				00 22
Crews Hill	d			22 25			22 55			23 25			23 55				00 25
Cuffley	d			22 28			22 58			23 28			23 58				00 28
Bayford	d			22 33			23 03			23 33			00 03				00 33
Hertford North	d			22a38			23 08			23a38			00 08				00a41
Watton-at-Stone	d						23 14						00 14		←		
Stevenage 4	d	22 12			22 42		23a21	23 12			23 42		00 20	00 12	00 20		
Hitchin 4	d	22a17			22 47			23 17			23 47		↪	00 20	00 26		
Letchworth Garden City	a				22 52			23 24			23 52			00 27	00 35		

Sundays

8 December to 29 December

		FC 1 A	FC A	FC A	FC A	FC 1	FC	FC	FC 1	FC	FC	FC	FC	FC	FC	FC 1	FC 1 B	FC	FC	FC
London Kings Cross 15 ⊖	d					00 06	00 26	00 31	00 53	00 56	01 11	05 56	06 26	06 41	06 56	07 06	07 06	07 11	07 26	07 41
Moorgate ⊖	d																			
Old Street ⊖	d																			
Essex Road	d																			
Highbury & Islington ⊖	d																			
Drayton Park	d																			
Finsbury Park ⊖	d				00 02	00 11	00 32	00 37	00 58	01 02	01 17	06 02	06 32	06 47	07 02	07 11	07 11	07 17	07 32	07 47
Harringay	d				00 04		00 34	00 39		01 04	01 19	06 04	06 34	06 49	07 04			07 19	07 34	07 49
Hornsey	d				00 06		00 36	00 41		01 06	01 21	06 06	06 36	06 51	07 06			07 21	07 36	07 51
Alexandra Palace	d				00 09		00 39	00 44		01 09	01 24	06 09	06 39	06 54	07 09			07 24	07 39	07 54
New Southgate	d							00 47			01 27			06 57				07 27		07 57
Oakleigh Park	d		00 01					00 50			01 30			07 00				07 30		08 00
New Barnet	d		00 03					00 53			01 33			07 03				07 33		08 03
Hadley Wood	d		00 05					00 55			01 35			07 05				07 35		08 05
Potters Bar	d		00 09			00 21		00 59	01 08		01 39			07 09		07 21	07 21	07 39		08 09
Brookmans Park	d		00 12					01 02			01 42			07 12				07 42		08 12
Welham Green	d		00 14					01 04			01 44			07 14				07 44		08 14
Hatfield	d		00 18			00 27		01 08	01 14		01 48			07 18		07 27	07 27	07 48		08 18
Welwyn Garden City 4	d	00 01	00a26			00 38		01a16	01 18		01a56			07a26		07 31	07 31	07a56		08a26
Welwyn North	d	00 04				00 40			01s21							07 34	07 34			
Knebworth	d	00 08				00 44			01s24							07 38	07 38			
Bowes Park	d				00 12		00 42			01 12		06 12	06 42		07 12				07 42	
Palmers Green	d				00 14		00 44			01 14		06 14	06 44		07 14				07 44	
Winchmore Hill	d				00 16		00 46			01 16		06 16	06 46		07 16				07 46	
Grange Park	d				00 18		00 48			01 18		06 18	06 48		07 18				07 48	
Enfield Chase	d				00 20		00 50			01 20		06 20	06 50		07 20				07 50	
Gordon Hill	d				00 22		00 52			01 22		06 22	06 52		07 22				07 52	
Crews Hill	d				00 25		00 55			01 25		06 25	06 55		07 25				07 55	
Cuffley	d				00 28		00 58			01 28		06 28	06 58		07 28				07 58	
Bayford	d			00 03	00 33		01 03			01 33		06 33	07 03		07 33				08 03	
Hertford North	d			00 08	00a41		01a11			01 38		06a41	07 08		07a41				08 08	
Watton-at-Stone	d			00 14						01 44			07 14						08 14	
Stevenage 4	d	00 12		00 20		00 49			01 28	01 50			07a24			07 46	07 50		08a24	
Hitchin 4	d	00 20		00 26		00 55			01a33	01 56						07 54	07a58			
Letchworth Garden City	a	00 27		00 35		01 00				02 05						07 59				

A not 8 December
B until 28 December

Table 24

Sundays

8 December to 29 December

London - Welwyn Garden City, Hertford North and Letchworth Garden City

Network Diagram - see first Page of Table 24

		FC	FC 1	FC	FC	FC		FC	FC 1	FC	FC	FC	FC	FC 1	FC	FC	FC 1	FC	FC	FC 1	FC	FC
London Kings Cross 15 ⊖	d	07 56	08 06	08 11	08 26	08 41	and at the same minutes past each hour until	14 56	15 06	15 11	15 26	15 41	15 56	16 06	16 11	16 26	16 36	16 41	16 56	17 06	17 11	17 26
Moorgate ⊖	d																					
Old Street ⊖	d																					
Essex Road	d																					
Highbury & Islington ⊖	d																					
Drayton Park	d																					
Finsbury Park ⊖	d	08 02	08 11	08 17	08 32	08 47		15 02	15 11	15 17	15 32	15 47	16 02	16 11	16 17	16 32	16 41	16 47	17 02	17 11	17 17	17 32
Harringay	d	08 04		08 19	08 34	08 49		15 04		15 19	15 34	15 49	16 04		16 19	16 34		16 49	17 04		17 19	17 34
Hornsey	d	08 06		08 21	08 36	08 51		15 06		15 21	15 36	15 51	16 06		16 21	16 36		16 51	17 06		17 21	17 36
Alexandra Palace	d	08 09		08 24	08 39	08 54		15 09		15 24	15 39	15 54	16 09		16 24	16 39		16 54	17 09		17 24	17 39
New Southgate	d			08 27		08 57				15 27		15 57			16 27			16 57			17 27	
Oakleigh Park	d			08 30		09 00				15 30		16 00			16 30			17 00			17 30	
New Barnet	d			08 33		09 03				15 33		16 03			16 33			17 03			17 33	
Hadley Wood	d			08 35		09 05				15 35		16 05			16 35			17 05			17 35	
Potters Bar	d		08 21	08 39		09 09			15 21	15 39		16 09		16 21	16 39		16 51	17 09		17 21	17 39	
Brookmans Park	d			08 42		09 12				15 42		16 12			16 42			17 12			17 42	
Welham Green	d			08 44		09 14				15 44		16 14			16 44			17 14			17 44	
Hatfield	d		08 27	08 48		09 18			15 27	15 48		16 18		16 27	16 48		16 57	17 18		17 27	17 48	
Welwyn Garden City 4	d		08 31	08a53		09a23			15 31	15a53		16a23		16 31	16a53		17 01	17a23		17 31	17a53	
Welwyn North	d		08 34						15 34					16 34			17 04			17 34		
Knebworth	d		08 38						15 38					16 38			17 08			17 38		
Bowes Park	d	08 12			08 42			15 12			15 42		16 12			16 42			17 12			17 42
Palmers Green	d	08 14			08 44			15 14			15 44		16 14			16 44			17 14			17 44
Winchmore Hill	d	08 16			08 46			15 16			15 46		16 16			16 46			17 16			17 46
Grange Park	d	08 18			08 48			15 18			15 48		16 18			16 48			17 18			17 48
Enfield Chase	d	08 20			08 50			15 20			15 50		16 20			16 50			17 20			17 50
Gordon Hill	d	08 22			08 52			15 22			15 52		16 22			16 52			17 22			17 52
Crews Hill	d	08 25			08 55			15 25			15 55		16 25			16 55			17 25			17 55
Cuffley	d	08 28			08 58			15 28			15 58		16 28			16 58			17 28			17 58
Bayford	d	08 33			09 03			15 33			16 03		16 33			17 03			17 33			18 03
Hertford North	d	08a38			09 08			15a38			16 08		16a38			17 08			17a38			18 08
Watton-at-Stone	d				09 14						16 14					17 14						18 14
Stevenage 4	d		08 42		09a21				15 42		16a21			16 42		17a21	17 12			17 42		18a21
Hitchin 4	d		08 47						15 47					16 47			17a17			17 47		
Letchworth Garden City	a		08 52						15 52					16 52						17 52		

		FC 1	FC	FC	FC 1	FC	FC	FC 1	FC	FC	FC 1	FC	FC		FC	FC	FC 1	FC	FC	FC	FC	FC 1	FC
London Kings Cross 15 ⊖	d	17 36	17 41	17 56	18 06	18 11	18 26	18 36	18 41	18 56	19 06	19 11	19 26	and at the same minutes past each hour until	21 41	21 56	22 06	22 11	22 26	22 41	22 56	23 06	23 11
Moorgate ⊖	d																						
Old Street ⊖	d																						
Essex Road	d																						
Highbury & Islington ⊖	d																						
Drayton Park	d																						
Finsbury Park ⊖	d	17 41	17 47	18 02	18 11	18 17	18 32	18 41	18 47	19 02	19 11	19 17	19 32		21 47	22 02	22 11	22 17	22 32	22 47	23 02	23 11	23 17
Harringay	d		17 49	18 04		18 19	18 34		18 49	19 04		19 19	19 34		21 49	22 04		22 19	22 34	22 49	23 04		23 19
Hornsey	d		17 51	18 06		18 21	18 36		18 51	19 06		19 21	19 36		21 51	22 06		22 21	22 36	22 51	23 06		23 21
Alexandra Palace	d		17 54	18 09		18 24	18 39		18 54	19 09		19 24	19 39		21 54	22 09		22 24	22 39	22 54	23 09		23 24
New Southgate	d		17 57			18 27			18 57			19 27			21 57			22 27		22 57			23 27
Oakleigh Park	d		18 00			18 30			19 00			19 30			22 00			22 30		23 00			23 30
New Barnet	d		18 03			18 33			19 03			19 33			22 03			22 33		23 03			23 33
Hadley Wood	d		18 05			18 35			19 05			19 35			22 05			22 35		23 05			23 35
Potters Bar	d	17 51	18 09		18 21	18 39		18 51	19 09		19 21	19 39			22 09		22 21	22 39		23 09		23 21	23 39
Brookmans Park	d		18 12			18 42			19 12			19 42			22 12			22 42		23 12			23 42
Welham Green	d		18 14			18 44			19 14			19 44			22 14			22 44		23 14			23 44
Hatfield	d	17 57	18 18		18 27	18 48		18 57	19 18		19 27	19 48			22 18		22 27	22 48		23 18		23 27	23 48
Welwyn Garden City 4	d	18 01	18a23		18 31	18a53		19 01	19a23		19 31	19a53			22a23		22 31	22a53		23a23		23 31	23a53
Welwyn North	d	18 04			18 34			19 04			19 34						22 34					23 34	
Knebworth	d	18 08			18 38			19 08			19 38						22 38					23 38	
Bowes Park	d			18 12			18 42			19 12			19 42			22 12			22 42		23 12		
Palmers Green	d			18 14			18 44			19 14			19 44			22 14			22 44		23 14		
Winchmore Hill	d			18 16			18 46			19 16			19 46			22 16			22 46		23 16		
Grange Park	d			18 18			18 48			19 18			19 48			22 18			22 48		23 18		
Enfield Chase	d			18 20			18 50			19 20			19 50			22 20			22 50		23 20		
Gordon Hill	d			18 22			18 52			19 22			19 52			22 22			22 52		23 22		
Crews Hill	d			18 25			18 55			19 25			19 55			22 25			22 55		23 25		
Cuffley	d			18 28			18 58			19 28			19 58			22 28			22 58		23 28		
Bayford	d			18 33			19 03			19 33			20 03			22 33			23 03		23 33		
Hertford North	d			18a38			19 08			19a38			20 08			22a38			23 08		23a38		
Watton-at-Stone	d						19 14						20 14						23 14				
Stevenage 4	d	18 12			18 42		19a21	19 12			19 42		20a21				22 42		23a21			23 42	
Hitchin 4	d	18a17			18 47			19 17			19 47						22 47					23 47	
Letchworth Garden City	a				18 52			19 22			19 52						22 52					23 52	

Table 24

Sundays

8 December to 29 December

London - Welwyn Garden City, Hertford North and Letchworth Garden City

Network Diagram - see first Page of Table 24

Station		FC	FC
London Kings Cross 15 ⊖	d	23 26	23 41
Moorgate ⊖	d		
Old Street ⊖	d		
Essex Road	d		
Highbury & Islington ⊖	d		
Drayton Park	d		
Finsbury Park ⊖	d	23 32	23 47
Harringay	d	23 34	23 49
Hornsey	d	23 36	23 51
Alexandra Palace	d	23 39	23 54
New Southgate	d		23 57
Oakleigh Park	d		00 01
New Barnet	d		00 03
Hadley Wood	d		00 05
Potters Bar	d		00 09
Brookmans Park	d		00 12
Welham Green	d		00 14
Hatfield	d		00 18
Welwyn Garden City 4	d		00a26
Welwyn North	d		
Knebworth	d		
Bowes Park	d	23 42	
Palmers Green	d	23 44	
Winchmore Hill	d	23 46	
Grange Park	d	23 48	
Enfield Chase	d	23 50	
Gordon Hill	d	23 52	
Crews Hill	d	23 55	
Cuffley	d	23 58	
Bayford	d	00 03	
Hertford North	d	00 08	
Watton-at-Stone	d	00 14	
Stevenage 4	d	00 21	
Hitchin 4	d	00 26	
Letchworth Garden City	a	00 35	

Sundays

5 January to 23 March

Station		FC 1	FC	FC	FC	FC 1	FC	FC	FC 1	FC	FC	FC	FC 🚌	FC 🚌	FC 🚌	FC	FC	FC	FC 🚌	FC 🚌	FC 🚌	FC 🚌
London Kings Cross 15 ⊖	d					00 06	00 26	00 31	00 53	00 56	01 11	05 56				06 13	06 43					
Moorgate ⊖	d																					
Old Street ⊖	d																					
Essex Road	d																					
Highbury & Islington ⊖	d																					
Drayton Park	d																					
Finsbury Park ⊖	d				00 02	00 11	00 32	00 37	00 58	01 02	01 17	06 02				06 19	06 49					
Harringay	d				00 04		00 34	00 39		01 04	01 19	06 04				06 21	06 51					
Hornsey	d				00 06		00 36	00 41		01 06	01 21	06 06				06 23	06 53					
Alexandra Palace	d				00 09		00 39	00 44		01 09	01 24	06 09	06 14	06 33	06 14	06 26	06 56		07 03	06 33	07 33	07 03
New Southgate	d							00 47			01 27				06 24					06 43		07 13
Oakleigh Park	d		00 01					00 50			01 30				06 34					06 53		07 23
New Barnet	d		00 03					00 53			01 33				06 44					07 03		07 33
Hadley Wood	d		00 05					00 55			01 35				07 04					07 23		07 53
Potters Bar	d		00 09			00 21		00 59	01 08		01 39		06 44	07 03	07 14				07 33	07 33	08 03	08 03
Brookmans Park	d		00 12					01 02			01 42				07 22					07 41		08 11
Welham Green	d		00 14					01 04			01 44				07 26					07 45		08 15
Hatfield	d		00 18			00 27		01 08	01 14		01 48		06 59	07 18	07 30				07 48	07 49	08 18	08 19
Welwyn Garden City 4	d	00 01	00a26			00 38		01a16	01 18		01a56		07 09	07 28	07a40				07 58	07a59	08 28	08a29
Welwyn North	d	00 04				00 40			01s21				07 19	07 38					08 08		08 38	
Knebworth	d	00 08				00 44			01s24				07 29	07 48					08 18		08 48	
Bowes Park	d				00 12		00 42			01 12		06 12				06 29	06 59					
Palmers Green	d				00 14		00 44			01 14		06 14				06 31	07 01					
Winchmore Hill	d				00 16		00 46			01 16		06 16				06 33	07 03					
Grange Park	d				00 18		00 48			01 18		06 18				06 35	07 05					
Enfield Chase	d				00 20		00 50			01 20		06 20				06 37	07 07					
Gordon Hill	d				00 22		00 52			01 22		06 22				06 39	07 09					
Crews Hill	d				00 25		00 55			01 25		06 25				06 42	07 12					
Cuffley	d				00 28		00 58			01 28		06 28				06 45	07 15					
Bayford	d			00 03	00 33		01 03			01 33		06 33				06 50	07 20					
Hertford North	d			00 08	00a41		01a11			01 38		06 47				06a58	07a25	07 47				
Watton-at-Stone	d			00 14						01 44		06 52						07 52				
Stevenage 4	d	00 12		00 20		00 49			01 28	01 50		06 59	07a36	07a55				07 59	08a25		08a55	
Hitchin 4	d	00 20		00 26		00 55			01 33	01 56		07 05						08 05				
Letchworth Garden City	a	00 27		00 35		01 00			01 43	02 05		07 11						08 11				

Table 24

Sundays

5 January to 23 March

London - Welwyn Garden City, Hertford North and Letchworth Garden City

Network Diagram - see first Page of Table 24

Station		FC		FC	FC 🚌	FC 🚌	FC 🚌	FC 🚌	FC		FC	FC 🚌	FC 🚌	FC 🚌	FC 🚌	FC	FC	FC 🚌	FC 🚌		FC 🚌	FC 🚌	FC	FC
London Kings Cross [15] ⊖	d	07 13							17 13							18 16							19 13	
Moorgate ⊖	d																							
Old Street ⊖	d																							
Essex Road	d																							
Highbury & Islington ⊖	d																							
Drayton Park	d																							
Finsbury Park ⊖	d	07 19							17 19							18 22							19 19	
Harringay	d	07 21							17 21							18 24							19 21	
Hornsey	d	07 23							17 23							18 26							19 23	
Alexandra Palace	d	07 26			17 03	16 33	17 33	17 03	17 26			18 03	17 33	18 33	18 03	18 29		19 03	18 33		19 33	19 03	19 26	
New Southgate	d					16 43		17 13					17 43		18 13				18 43			19 13		
Oakleigh Park	d					16 53		17 23					17 53		18 23				18 53			19 23		
New Barnet	d					17 03		17 33					18 03		18 33				19 03			19 33		
Hadley Wood	d		and at the same minutes past each hour until			17 23		17 53					18 23		18 53				19 23			19 53		
Potters Bar	d				17 33	17 33	18 03	18 03				18 33	18 33	19 03	19 03			19 33	19 33		20 03	20 03		
Brookmans Park	d					17 41		18 11					18 41		19 11				19 41			20 11		
Welham Green	d					17 45		18 15					18 45		19 15				19 45			20 15		
Hatfield	d				17 48	17 49	18 18	18 19				18 48	18 49	19 18	19 19			19 48	19 49		20 18	20 19		
Welwyn Garden City [4]	d				17 58	17a59	18 28	18a29				18 58	18a59	19 28	19a29			19 58	19a59		20 28	20a29		
Welwyn North	d				18 08		18 38					19 08		19 38				20 08			20 38			
Knebworth	d				18 18		18 48					19 18		19 48				20 18			20 48			
Bowes Park	d	07 29							17 29							18 32							19 29	
Palmers Green	d	07 31							17 31							18 34							19 31	
Winchmore Hill	d	07 33							17 33							18 36							19 33	
Grange Park	d	07 35							17 35							18 38							19 35	
Enfield Chase	d	07 37							17 37							18 40							19 37	
Gordon Hill	d	07 39							17 39							18 42							19 39	
Crews Hill	d	07 42							17 42							18 45							19 42	
Cuffley	d	07 45							17 45							18 48							19 45	
Bayford	d	07 50							17 50							18 53							19 50	
Hertford North	d	07a55		17 47					17a55		18 50					18a58	19 47						19a55	20 47
Watton-at-Stone	d			17 52							18 55						19 52							20 52
Stevenage [4]	d			17 59	18a25		18a55				19 02	19a25		19a55			19 59	20a25			20a55			20 59
Hitchin [4]	d			18 05							19 08						20 05							21 05
Letchworth Garden City	a			18 11							19 14						20 11							21 11

Station		FC 🚌	FC 🚌	FC 🚌	FC 🚌	FC		FC	FC 🚌	FC 🚌	FC 🚌	FC 🚌	FC	FC	FC	FC 🚌		FC 🚌	FC 🚌	FC 🚌	FC 🚌	FC	FC 🚌	FC	FC
London Kings Cross [15] ⊖	d					20 13							21 13	21 43								22 26		22 55	23 26
Moorgate ⊖	d																								
Old Street ⊖	d																								
Essex Road	d																								
Highbury & Islington ⊖	d																								
Drayton Park	d																								
Finsbury Park ⊖	d					20 19							21 19	21 49								22 32		23 01	23 32
Harringay	d					20 21							21 21	21 51								22 34		23 03	23 34
Hornsey	d					20 23							21 23	21 53								22 36		23 05	23 36
Alexandra Palace	d	20 03	19 33	20 33	20 03	20 26			21 03	20 33	21 33	21 03	21 26	21 56		22 03		21 33	22 03	22 44	22 14	22 39	22 44	23 08	23 39
New Southgate	d		19 43		20 13					20 43		21 13						21 43	22 13		22 24		22 54		
Oakleigh Park	d		19 53		20 23					20 53		21 23						21 53	22 23		22 34		23 04		
New Barnet	d		20 03		20 33					21 03		21 33						22 03	22 33		22 44		23 14		
Hadley Wood	d		20 23		20 53					21 23		21 53						22 23	22 53		23 04		23 34		
Potters Bar	d	20 33	20 33	21 03	21 03				21 33	21 33	22 03	22 03				22 33		22 33	23 03	23 14	23 14		23 44		
Brookmans Park	d		20 41		21 11					21 41		22 11						22 41	23 11		23 22		23 52		
Welham Green	d		20 45		21 15					21 45		22 15						22 45	23 15		23 26		23 56		
Hatfield	d	20 48	20 49	21 18	21 19				21 48	21 49	22 18	22 19				22 48		22 49	23 19	23 29	23 30		23 59		
Welwyn Garden City [4]	d	20 58	20a59	21 28	21a29				21 58	21a59	22 28	22a29				22 58		22a59	23a29	23 39	23a40		00a10		
Welwyn North	d	21 08		21 38					22 08		22 38					23 08				23 49					
Knebworth	d	21 18		21 48					22 18		22 48					23 18				23 59					
Bowes Park	d					20 29							21 29	21 59								22 42		23 11	23 42
Palmers Green	d					20 31							21 31	22 01								22 44		23 13	23 44
Winchmore Hill	d					20 33							21 33	22 03								22 46		23 15	23 46
Grange Park	d					20 35							21 35	22 05								22 48		23 17	23 48
Enfield Chase	d					20 37							21 37	22 07								22 50		23 19	23 50
Gordon Hill	d					20 39							21 39	22 09								22 52		23 21	23 52
Crews Hill	d					20 42							21 42	22 12								22 55			23 55
Cuffley	d					20 45							21 45	22 15								22 58		23 26	23 58
Bayford	d					20 50							21 50	22 20								23 03			00 03
Hertford North	d					20a55		21 47					21a55	22a25	22 49							23a08		23a34	00 08
Watton-at-Stone	d							21 52							22 54										00 14
Stevenage [4]	d	21a25		21a55				21 59	22a25		22a55				23 01	23a25				00a06					00 21
Hitchin [4]	d							22 05							23 07										00 26
Letchworth Garden City	a							22 11							23 13										00 35

Table 24

Sundays
5 January to 23 March

London - Welwyn Garden City, Hertford North and Letchworth Garden City

Network Diagram - see first Page of Table 24

		FC (bus)		FC (bus)	FC (bus)	FC (bus)
London Kings Cross 15 ⊖	d					
Moorgate ⊖	d					
Old Street ⊖	d					
Essex Road	d					
Highbury & Islington ⊖	d					
Drayton Park	d					
Finsbury Park ⊖	d					
Harringay	d					
Hornsey	d					
Alexandra Palace	d	23 14		23 44	23 14	23 44
New Southgate	d				23 24	23 54
Oakleigh Park	d				23 34	00 04
New Barnet	d				23 44	00 14
Hadley Wood	d				00 04	00 34
Potters Bar	d	23 44		00 14	00 14	00 44
Brookmans Park	d				00 22	00 52
Welham Green	d				00 26	00 56
Hatfield	d	23 59		00 29	00 30	01 00
Welwyn Garden City 4	d	00 09		00 39	00a40	01a10
Welwyn North	d	00 19		00 49		
Knebworth	d	00 29		00 59		
Bowes Park	d					
Palmers Green	d					
Winchmore Hill	d					
Grange Park	d					
Enfield Chase	d					
Gordon Hill	d					
Crews Hill	d					
Cuffley	d					
Bayford	d					
Hertford North	d					
Watton-at-Stone	d					
Stevenage 4	d	00a36		01a06		
Hitchin 4	d					
Letchworth Garden City	a					

Sundays
30 March to 11 May

		FC 1	FC	FC	FC	FC 1	FC	FC	FC 1	FC		FC	FC	FC	FC	FC	FC 1		FC	FC		FC
London Kings Cross 15 ⊖	d					00 06	00 26	00 31	00 53	00 56		01 11	05 56	06 26	06 41	06 56	07 06		07 11	07 26		07 41
Moorgate ⊖	d																					
Old Street ⊖	d																					
Essex Road	d																					
Highbury & Islington ⊖	d																					
Drayton Park	d																					
Finsbury Park ⊖	d				00 02	00 11	00 32	00 37	00 58	01 02		01 17	06 02	06 32	06 47	07 02	07 11		07 17	07 32		07 47
Harringay	d				00 04		00 34	00 39		01 04		01 19	06 04	06 34	06 49	07 04			07 19	07 34		07 49
Hornsey	d				00 06		00 36	00 41		01 06		01 21	06 06	06 36	06 51	07 06			07 21	07 36		07 51
Alexandra Palace	d				00 09		00 39	00 44		01 09		01 24	06 09	06 39	06 54	07 09			07 24	07 39		07 54
New Southgate	d							00 47				01 27			06 57				07 27			07 57
Oakleigh Park	d		00 01					00 50				01 30			07 00				07 30			08 00
New Barnet	d		00 03					00 53				01 33			07 03				07 33			08 03
Hadley Wood	d		00 05					00 55				01 35			07 05				07 35			08 05
Potters Bar	d		00 09			00 21		00 59	01 08			01 39			07 09		07 21		07 39			08 09
Brookmans Park	d		00 12					01 02				01 42			07 12				07 42			08 12
Welham Green	d		00 14					01 04				01 44			07 14				07 44			08 14
Hatfield	d		00 18			00 27		01 08	01 14			01 48			07 18		07 27		07 48			08 18
Welwyn Garden City 4	d	00 01	00a26			00 38		01a16	01 18			01a56			07a26		07 31		07a56			08a26
Welwyn North	d	00 04				00 40			01s21								07 34					
Knebworth	d	00 08				00 44			01s24								07 38					
Bowes Park	d				00 12		00 42			01 12			06 12	06 42		07 12				07 42		
Palmers Green	d				00 14		00 44			01 14			06 14	06 44		07 14				07 44		
Winchmore Hill	d				00 16		00 46			01 16			06 16	06 46		07 16				07 46		
Grange Park	d				00 18		00 48			01 18			06 18	06 48		07 18				07 48		
Enfield Chase	d				00 20		00 50			01 20			06 20	06 50		07 20				07 50		
Gordon Hill	d				00 22		00 52			01 22			06 22	06 52		07 22				07 52		
Crews Hill	d				00 25		00 55			01 25			06 25	06 55		07 25				07 55		
Cuffley	d				00 28		00 58			01 28			06 28	06 58		07 28				07 58		
Bayford	d			00 03	00 33		01 03			01 33			06 33	07 03		07 33				08 03		
Hertford North	d			00 08	00a41		01a11			01 38			06a41	07 08		07a41				08 08		
Watton-at-Stone	d			00 14						01 44				07 14						08 14		
Stevenage 4	d	00 12		00 20		00 49			01 28	01 50				07a24			07 46	07 50		08a24		
Hitchin 4	d	00 20		00 26		00 55			01a33	01 56							07 54	07a58				
Letchworth Garden City	a	00 27		00 35		01 00				02 05							07 59					

Table 24

Sundays

30 March to 11 May

London - Welwyn Garden City, Hertford North and Letchworth Garden City

Network Diagram - see first Page of Table 24

Station		FC	FC 1	FC	FC	FC		FC	FC 1	FC	FC	FC	FC	FC 1	FC	FC	FC 1	FC	FC	FC 1	FC	FC
London Kings Cross 15 ⊖	d	07 56	08 06	08 11	08 26	08 41	and at the same minutes past each hour until	14 56	15 06	15 11	15 26	15 41	15 56	16 06	16 11	16 26	16 36	16 41	16 56	17 06	17 11	17 26
Moorgate ⊖	d																					
Old Street ⊖	d																					
Essex Road	d																					
Highbury & Islington ⊖	d																					
Drayton Park	d																					
Finsbury Park ⊖	d	08 02	08 11	08 17	08 32	08 47		15 02	15 11	15 17	15 32	15 47	16 02	16 11	16 17	16 32	16 41	16 47	17 02	17 11	17 17	17 32
Harringay	d	08 04		08 19	08 34	08 49		15 04		15 19	15 34	15 49	16 04		16 19	16 34		16 49	17 04		17 19	17 34
Hornsey	d	08 06		08 21	08 36	08 51		15 06		15 21	15 36	15 51	16 06		16 21	16 36		16 51	17 06		17 21	17 36
Alexandra Palace	d	08 09		08 24	08 39	08 54		15 09		15 24	15 39	15 54	16 09		16 24	16 39		16 54	17 09		17 24	17 39
New Southgate	d			08 27		08 57				15 27		15 57			16 27			16 57			17 27	
Oakleigh Park	d			08 30		09 00				15 30		16 00			16 30			17 00			17 30	
New Barnet	d			08 33		09 03				15 33		16 03			16 33			17 03			17 33	
Hadley Wood	d			08 35		09 05				15 35		16 05			16 35			17 05			17 35	
Potters Bar	d		08 21	08 39		09 09			15 21	15 39		16 09		16 21	16 39		16 51	17 09		17 21	17 39	
Brookmans Park	d			08 42		09 12				15 42		16 12			16 42			17 12			17 42	
Welham Green	d			08 44		09 14				15 44		16 14			16 44			17 14			17 44	
Hatfield	d		08 27	08 48		09 18			15 27	15 48		16 18		16 27	16 48		16 57	17 18		17 27	17 48	
Welwyn Garden City 4	d		08 31	08a53		09a23			15 31	15a53		16a23		16 31	16a53		17 01	17a23		17 31	17a53	
Welwyn North	d		08 34						15 34					16 34			17 04			17 34		
Knebworth	d		08 38						15 38					16 38			17 08			17 38		
Bowes Park	d	08 12			08 42			15 12			15 42		16 12			16 42			17 12			17 42
Palmers Green	d	08 14			08 44			15 14			15 44		16 14			16 44			17 14			17 44
Winchmore Hill	d	08 16			08 46			15 16			15 46		16 16			16 46			17 16			17 46
Grange Park	d	08 18			08 48			15 18			15 48		16 18			16 48			17 18			17 48
Enfield Chase	d	08 20			08 50			15 20			15 50		16 20			16 50			17 20			17 50
Gordon Hill	d	08 22			08 52			15 22			15 52		16 22			16 52			17 22			17 52
Crews Hill	d	08 25			08 55			15 25			15 55		16 25			16 55			17 25			17 55
Cuffley	d	08 28			08 58			15 28			15 58		16 28			16 58			17 28			17 58
Bayford	d	08 33			09 03			15 33			16 03		16 33			17 03			17 33			18 03
Hertford North	d	08a38			09 08			15a38			16 08		16a38			17 08			17a38			18 08
Watton-at-Stone	d				09 14						16 14					17 14						18 14
Stevenage 4	d		08 42		09a21				15 42		16a21			16 42		17a21	17 12			17 42		18a21
Hitchin 4	d		08 47						15 47					16 47			17a17			17 47		
Letchworth Garden City	a		08 52						15 52					16 52						17 52		

Station		FC 1	FC	FC	FC 1	FC	FC	FC 1	FC	FC	FC 1	FC	FC		FC	FC	FC 1	FC	FC	FC	FC	FC 1	FC
London Kings Cross 15 ⊖	d	17 36	17 41	17 56	18 06	18 11	18 26	18 36	18 41	18 56	19 06	19 11	19 26	and at the same minutes past each hour until	21 41	21 56	22 06	22 11	22 26	22 41	22 56	23 06	23 11
Moorgate ⊖	d																						
Old Street ⊖	d																						
Essex Road	d																						
Highbury & Islington ⊖	d																						
Drayton Park	d																						
Finsbury Park ⊖	d	17 41	17 47	18 02	18 11	18 17	18 32	18 41	18 47	19 02	19 11	19 17	19 32		21 47	22 02	22 11	22 17	22 32	22 47	23 02	23 11	23 17
Harringay	d		17 49	18 04		18 19	18 34		18 49	19 04		19 19	19 34		21 49	22 04		22 19	22 34	22 49	23 04		23 19
Hornsey	d		17 51	18 06		18 21	18 36		18 51	19 06		19 21	19 36		21 51	22 06		22 21	22 36	22 51	23 06		23 21
Alexandra Palace	d		17 54	18 09		18 24	18 39		18 54	19 09		19 24	19 39		21 54	22 09		22 24	22 39	22 54	23 09		23 24
New Southgate	d		17 57			18 27			18 57			19 27			21 57			22 27		22 57			23 27
Oakleigh Park	d		18 00			18 30			19 00			19 30			22 00			22 30		23 00			23 30
New Barnet	d		18 03			18 33			19 03			19 33			22 03			22 33		23 03			23 33
Hadley Wood	d		18 05			18 35			19 05			19 35			22 05			22 35		23 05			23 35
Potters Bar	d	17 51	18 09		18 21	18 39		18 51	19 09		19 21	19 39			22 09		22 21	22 39		23 09		23 21	23 39
Brookmans Park	d		18 12			18 42			19 12			19 42			22 12			22 42		23 12			23 42
Welham Green	d		18 14			18 44			19 14			19 44			22 14			22 44		23 14			23 44
Hatfield	d	17 57	18 18		18 27	18 48		18 57	19 18		19 27	19 48			22 18		22 27	22 48		23 18		23 27	23 48
Welwyn Garden City 4	d	18 01	18a23		18 31	18a53		19 01	19a23		19 31	19a53			22a23		22 31	22a53		23a23		23 31	23a53
Welwyn North	d	18 04			18 34			19 04			19 34						22 34					23 34	
Knebworth	d	18 08			18 38			19 08			19 38						22 38					23 38	
Bowes Park	d			18 12			18 42			19 12			19 42			22 12			22 42		23 12		
Palmers Green	d			18 14			18 44			19 14			19 44			22 14			22 44		23 14		
Winchmore Hill	d			18 16			18 46			19 16			19 46			22 16			22 46		23 16		
Grange Park	d			18 18			18 48			19 18			19 48			22 18			22 48		23 18		
Enfield Chase	d			18 20			18 50			19 20			19 50			22 20			22 50		23 20		
Gordon Hill	d			18 22			18 52			19 22			19 52			22 22			22 52		23 22		
Crews Hill	d			18 25			18 55			19 25			19 55			22 25			22 55		23 25		
Cuffley	d			18 28			18 58			19 28			19 58			22 28			22 58		23 28		
Bayford	d			18 33			19 03			19 33			20 03			22 33			23 03		23 33		
Hertford North	d			18a38			19 08			19a38			20 08			22a38			23 08		23a38		
Watton-at-Stone	d						19 14						20 14						23 14				
Stevenage 4	d	18 12			18 42		19a21	19 12			19 42		20a21				22 42		23a21			23 42	
Hitchin 4	d	18a17			18 47			19 17			19 47						22 47					23 47	
Letchworth Garden City	a				18 52			19 22			19 52						22 52					23 52	

Table 24

Sundays

30 March to 11 May

London - Welwyn Garden City, Hertford North and Letchworth Garden City

Network Diagram - see first Page of Table 24

Station		FC	FC
London Kings Cross 15 ⊖	d	23 26	23 41
Moorgate ⊖	d		
Old Street ⊖	d		
Essex Road	d		
Highbury & Islington ⊖	d		
Drayton Park	d		
Finsbury Park ⊖	d	23 32	23 47
Harringay	d	23 34	23 49
Hornsey	d	23 36	23 51
Alexandra Palace	d	23 39	23 54
New Southgate	d		23 57
Oakleigh Park	d		00 01
New Barnet	d		00 03
Hadley Wood	d		00 05
Potters Bar	d		00 09
Brookmans Park	d		00 12
Welham Green	d		00 14
Hatfield	d		00 18
Welwyn Garden City 4	d		00a26
Welwyn North	d		
Knebworth	d		
Bowes Park	d	23 42	
Palmers Green	d	23 44	
Winchmore Hill	d	23 46	
Grange Park	d	23 48	
Enfield Chase	d	23 50	
Gordon Hill	d	23 52	
Crews Hill	d	23 55	
Cuffley	d	23 58	
Bayford	d	00 03	
Hertford North	d	00 08	
Watton-at-Stone	d	00 14	
Stevenage 4	d	00 21	
Hitchin 4	d	00 26	
Letchworth Garden City	a	00 35	

Table 24

Mondays to Fridays

9 December to 16 May

Letchworth Garden City, Hertford North and Welwyn Garden City - London

Network Diagram - see first Page of Table 24

Miles	Miles			FC A	FC MO B 🚌	FC MO 1 B	FC MO B 🚌	FC 1 C	FC MO 1 D	FC MO B 🚌	FC MO B	FC MO B 🚌	FC	FC 1	FC	FC 1	FC	FC	FC	FC 1	FC	FC	FC
0	0	**Letchworth Garden City**	d												04 51				05 18	05 30			05 48
3	3	Hitchin 4	d											04 09	04 55	04 58			05 22	05 35			05 52
7¼	7¼	**Stevenage 4**	d									00 05		04 15	05 01	05 03			05 28	05 40			05 58
—	12¼	Watton-at-Stone	d			00 06									05 07				05 34				06 04
—	16½	**Hertford North**	d			00 12					00 20			04 25	05 14				05 41				06 11
—	19½	Bayford	d								00 25				05 18				05 45				06 15
—	23	Cuffley	d								00 29			04 32	05 23				05 50				06 20
—	24¾	Crews Hill	d								00 32				05 26				05 53				06 23
—	26¼	Gordon Hill	d								00 35			04 36	05 29				05 56				06 26
—	27	Enfield Chase	d	00 01							00 37			04 38	05 31				05 58				06 28
—	27¾	Grange Park	d	00 03							00 39				05 33				06 00				06 30
—	28½	Winchmore Hill	d	00 05							00 41			04 40	05 35				06 02				06 32
—	29½	Palmers Green	d	00 07							00 44			04 42	05 37				06 04				06 34
—	30½	Bowes Park	d	00 10							00 46				05 40				06 07				06 37
9¾	—	Knebworth	d					00 02	00 02			00 12				05 07				05 44			
12¾	—	Welwyn North	d					00 06	00 06			00 22				05 11				05 48			
14½	—	**Welwyn Garden City 4**	d					00 09	00 09			00 32	04 10			05 14		05 33		05 51		05 56	
17	—	Hatfield	d					00 13	00 13			00 42	04 14			05 17		05 37		05 55		06 00	
19¼	—	Welham Green	d															05 41				06 04	
20¼	—	Brookmans Park	d										04 19					05 43				06 06	
22	—	Potters Bar	d				00 12	00 18	00 18			00 57	04 22			05 23		05 46		06 01		06 09	
24¼	—	Hadley Wood	d										04 25					05 50				06 13	
25½	—	New Barnet	d							00 13			04 28			05 28		05 52				06 16	
26¼	—	Oakleigh Park	d							00 23			04 30			05 30		05 54				06 18	
28¼	—	New Southgate	d		00 03					00 33			04 33			05 33		05 57				06 21	
29¾	31¼	Alexandra Palace	d	00 12	00a13		00a42			00a43	00 49		04 36	04 45	05 42	05 36		06 00	06 09			06 24	06 39
30¾	32¼	Hornsey	d	00 14							00 51		04 38		05 44			06 03	06 11			06 26	06 41
31¼	32¾	Harringay	d	00 16							00 53		04 40		05 46		←	06 05	06 13		←	06 28	06 43
32¼	33¾	Finsbury Park ⊖	d	00 19		00s29		00s29	00s29		00 56	01s30	04 43	04s51	05 49	05 40	05 49	06 08	06 16	06 11	06 16	06 31	06 46
—	34½	Drayton Park	d												→				→		06 18	06 33	→
—	35	Highbury & Islington ⊖	d																		06 20	06 35	
—	35½	Essex Road	d																		06 22	06 37	
—	36¾	Old Street ⊖	d																		06 25	06 40	
—	37¼	**Moorgate** ⊖	a																		06 30	06 45	
34¾	—	London Kings Cross 15 ⊖	a	00 29		00 39		00 40	00 41		01 05	01 45	04 52	05 01		05 50	05 56	06 17		06 21			

		FC 1	FC	FC	FC 1	FC	FC	FC	FC	FC	FC	FC	FC	FC	FC	FC	FC 1	FC	FC	FC	FC	FC	FC
Letchworth Garden City	d	06 00			06 19				06 23				06 45				07 04					07 20	
Hitchin 4	d	06 05			06 24				06 27				06 50				07 09					07 24	
Stevenage 4	d	06 10		06 12	06 29				06 33				06 55		07 03		07 15					07 30	
Watton-at-Stone	d			06 19					06 40						07 10								
Hertford North	d			06 26				06 32	06 46					07 02	07 16				07 25	07 33			07 38
Bayford	d							06 36						07 06									07 42
Cuffley	d			06 34				06 41	06 54					07 11	07 24				07 32	07 41			07 47
Crews Hill	d							06 44						07 14									07 50
Gordon Hill	d			06 38				06 47	06 58		07 05			07 17	07 28			07 32	07 37	07 46			07 53
Enfield Chase	d			06 41				06 50	07 01		07 07			07 20	07 31			07 34	07 40	07 49			07 56
Grange Park	d							06 52			07 09			07 22				07 36	07 42				07 58
Winchmore Hill	d			06 44				06 54	07 04		07 12			07 24	07 34			07 39	07 44	07 52			08 00
Palmers Green	d			06 46				06 57	07 06		07 14			07 27	07 36			07 41	07 47	07 54			08 03
Bowes Park	d							06 59			07 17			07 29				07 44	07 49				08 05
Knebworth	d	06 14			06 33												07 19						
Welwyn North	d	06 18			06 37												07 24						
Welwyn Garden City 4	d	06 21			06 40	06 26	06 36			06 44		06 56	07 07			07 17	07 27				07 32	07 44	
Hatfield	d	06 25			06 44	06 30	06 40			06 48		07 00	07 11			07 21	07 31				07 36	07 48	
Welham Green	d					06 34				06 52		07 04				07 25					07 40		
Brookmans Park	d					06 36				06 54		07 06				07 27					07 42		
Potters Bar	d	06 31			06 50	06 39	06 47			06 57		07 09	07 17			07 30					07 45	07 54	
Hadley Wood	d					06 43	06 50			07 01		07 13				07 34					07 49		
New Barnet	d					06 46	06 53			07 04		07 16	07 22			07 37					07 52	07 59	
Oakleigh Park	d					06 48	06 55			07 06		07 18	07 24			07 39					07 54	08 01	
New Southgate	d					06 51	06 58			07 09		07 21	07 27			07 42					07 57	08 04	
Alexandra Palace	d			06 50		06 54		07 02		07 12	07 19	07 24		07 32				07 46	07 51		08 00		08 08
Hornsey	d					06 56		07 04		07 14	07 21	07 26		07 34				07 48	07 54		08 02		
Harringay	d		←			06 58		07 06		07 16	07 23	07 28		07 36				07 50	07 56		08 04		
Finsbury Park ⊖	d	06 40	06 46	06 55	06 59	07 01	07 04	07 09	07 14	07 19	07 26	07 31	07 34	07 39	07 43	07 48	07 49	07 53	07 59	08 03	08 08	08 10	08 13
Drayton Park	d		06 48	06 57		07 03		07 11	07 16	07 21	07 28	07 33		07 41	07 45	07 50		07 55	08 01	08 05	08 10		08 15
Highbury & Islington ⊖	d		06 50	06 59		07 05		07 13	07 18	07 23	07 30	07 35		07 43	07 47	07 52		07 57	08 03	08 07	08 12		08 17
Essex Road	d		06 52	07 01		07 07		07 15	07 20	07 25	07 32	07 37		07 45	07 49	07 54		07 59	08 05	08 09	08 14		08 19
Old Street ⊖	d		06 55	07 04		07 10		07 18	07 23	07 28	07 35	07 40		07 48	07 52	07 57		08 02	08 08	08 12	08 17		08 22
Moorgate ⊖	a		07 00	07 09		07 15		07 23	07 28	07 33	07 40	07 45		07 53	07 57	08 02		08 07	08 13	08 17	08 22		08 27
London Kings Cross 15 ⊖	a	06 48			07 06		07 10						07 40				07 57					08 17	

A until 3 January, MX from 7 January until 21 March, from 25 March

B from 6 January until 24 March

C MX until 21 March, from 25 March

D until 30 December

Table 24

Mondays to Fridays

9 December to 16 May

Letchworth Garden City, Hertford North and Welwyn Garden City - London

Network Diagram - see first Page of Table 24

		FC		FC	FC	FC	FC	FC	FC	FC	FC	FC		FC	FC	FC	FC	FC	FC 1	FC	FC	FC		FC	FC
Letchworth Garden City	d																		08 34						
Hitchin 4	d																		08 39						
Stevenage 4	d	07 35								08 05								08 35	08 45						09 04
Watton-at-Stone	d	07 42								08 12								08 42							09 11
Hertford North	d	07 50			07 54			08 07		08 20				08 30				08 50							09 17
Bayford	d							08 11						08 34				08 54							09 21
Cuffley	d	07 57			08 01			08 16		08 27				08 39				08 59							09 26
Crews Hill	d							08 19						08 42				09 02							09 29
Gordon Hill	d	08 02			08 06		08 16	08 22		08 32		08 37		08 45			08 57	09 05			09 12			09 27	09 32
Enfield Chase	d	08 04			08 08		08 18	08 25		08 34		08 39		08 47			08 59	09 07			09 14			09 29	09 34
Grange Park	d				08 10		08 20	08 27				08 41					09 01	09 09			09 16			09 31	09 36
Winchmore Hill	d				08 13		08 23	08 29				08 43					09 04	09 12			09 19			09 33	09 39
Palmers Green	d				08 15		08 25	08 32				08 46					09 06	09 14			09 21			09 36	09 41
Bowes Park	d	08 09			08 18		08 28	08 34		08 39		08 48		08 52			09 09	09 17			09 24			09 39	09 44
Knebworth	d																		08 49						
Welwyn North	d																		08 54						
Welwyn Garden City 4	d			07 47		07 59			08 14		08 17				08 34	08 44			08 59			09 04			
Hatfield	d			07 51		08 03			08 18		08 21				08 39	08 48			09 03			09 09			
Welham Green	d			07 55		08 07					08 25				08 42							09 12			
Brookmans Park	d			07 57		08 09					08 27				08 45							09 15			
Potters Bar	d			08 00		08 12			08 25		08 30				08 48	08 55			09 09			09 18			
Hadley Wood	d			08 04		08 16					08 34				08 51							09 21			
New Barnet	d			08 07		08 19			08 30		08 37				08 54	09 00						09 24			
Oakleigh Park	d			08 09		08 21			08 32		08 39				08 56	09 02						09 26			
New Southgate	d			08 12		08 24			08 35		08 42				08 59	09 05						09 29			
Alexandra Palace	d	08 11		08 15	08 20		08 30	08 37	08 38	08 41	08 45	08 51		08 54	09 02	09 08	09 11	09 19			09 26	09 32		09 41	09 46
Hornsey	d	08 13		08 18	08 22	08 28	08 32			08 43	08 47			08 56	09 05		09 14	09 21			09 28	09 35			09 48
Harringay	d	08 15		08 20	08 24	08 30	08 34			08 45	08 49			08 58	09 07		09 16	09 23		←	09 30	09 37			09 50
Finsbury Park ⊖	d	08 18		08 23	08 28	08 33	08 37	08 42	08 43	08 48	08 52	08 56		09 01	09 10	09 13	09 20	09 26	09 22	09 26	09 33	09 40		09 45	09 53
Drayton Park	d	08 20		08 25	08 30	08 35	08 39	08 44		08 50	08 54	08 58		09 03	09 12		09 22	→		09 28	09 35	09 42		→	→
Highbury & Islington ⊖	d	08 22		08 27	08 32	08 37	08 41	08 46		08 52	08 56	09 00		09 05	09 14		09 24			09 30	09 37	09 44			
Essex Road	d	08 24		08 29	08 34	08 39	08 43	08 48		08 54	08 58	09 02		09 07	09 16		09 26			09 32	09 39	09 46			
Old Street ⊖	d	08 27		08 32	08 37	08 42	08 46	08 51		08 57	09 01	09 05		09 10	09 19		09 29			09 35	09 42	09 49			
Moorgate ⊖	a	08 32		08 37	08 42	08 46	08 51	08 56		09 02	09 06	09 11		09 16	09 24		09 34			09 40	09 47	09 54			
London Kings Cross 15 ⊖	a								08 51							09 20			09 29						

		FC 1	FC	FC	FC	FC	FC	FC		FC	FC 1	FC	FC	FC	FC	FC 1	FC	FC	FC	FC 1	FC	FC	FC	FC	
Letchworth Garden City	d	08 59								09 22	09 29					10 00				10 29				10 51	
Hitchin 4	d	09 05								09 27	09 34					10 05				10 34				10 55	
Stevenage 4	d	09 10								09 33	09 40				10 00	10 10				10 40				11 01	
Watton-at-Stone	d									09 39					10 07									11 07	
Hertford North	d						09 34			09 54					10 14				10 34			10 54		11 14	
Bayford	d						09 38			09 58					10 18				10 38			10 58		11 18	
Cuffley	d						09 43			10 03					10 23				10 43			11 03		11 23	
Crews Hill	d						09 46			10 06					10 26				10 46			11 06		11 26	
Gordon Hill	d						09 49			10 09					10 29				10 49			11 09		11 29	
Enfield Chase	d						09 51			10 11					10 31				10 51			11 11		11 31	
Grange Park	d						09 53			10 13					10 33				10 53			11 13		11 33	
Winchmore Hill	d						09 55			10 15					10 35				10 55			11 15		11 35	
Palmers Green	d						09 57			10 17					10 37				10 57			11 17		11 37	
Bowes Park	d						10 00			10 20					10 40				11 00			11 20		11 40	
Knebworth	d	09 14									09 44					10 14				10 44					
Welwyn North	d	09 18									09 48					10 18				10 48					
Welwyn Garden City 4	d	09 21			09 24	09 40		09 44			09 51			10 04		10 21		10 24		10 51	10 44		11 04		
Hatfield	d	09 25			09 29	09 44		09 49			09 55			10 09		10 25		10 29		10 55	10 49		11 09		
Welham Green	d				09 32			09 52						10 12				10 32			10 52		11 12		
Brookmans Park	d				09 35			09 55						10 15				10 35			10 55		11 15		
Potters Bar	d	09 31			09 38	09 50		09 58			10 01			10 18		10 31		10 38		11 01	10 58		11 18		
Hadley Wood	d				09 41			10 01						10 21				10 41			11 01		11 21		
New Barnet	d				09 44	09 54		10 04						10 24				10 44			11 04		11 24		
Oakleigh Park	d				09 46			10 06						10 26				10 46			11 06		11 26		
New Southgate	d				09 49			10 09						10 29				10 49			11 09		11 29		
Alexandra Palace	d				09 52		10 02	10 12		10 22				10 32	10 42			10 52	11 02		11 12	11 22	11 32	11 42	
Hornsey	d				09 54		10 04	10 14		10 24				10 34	10 44			10 54	11 04		11 14	11 24	11 34	11 44	
Harringay	d		←	←	09 56		10 06	10 16		10 26		←	←	10 36	10 46		←	10 56	11 06		11 16	11 26	11 36	11 46	
Finsbury Park ⊖	d	09 41	09 45	09 53	09 59	10 03	10 09	10 19		10 29	10 11	10 19	10 29	10 39	10 49	10 41	10 49	10 59	11 09	11 11	11 19	11 29	11 39	11 49	
Drayton Park	d		09 47	09 55	10 01		10 11	→		→		10 21	10 31	10 41	→		10 51	11 01	11 11		11 21	11 31	11 41	→	
Highbury & Islington ⊖	d		09 49	09 57	10 03		10 13					10 23	10 33	10 43			10 53	11 03	11 13		11 23	11 33	11 43		
Essex Road	d		09 51	09 59	10 05		10 15					10 25	10 35	10 45			10 55	11 05	11 15		11 25	11 35	11 45		
Old Street ⊖	d		09 54	10 02	10 08		10 18					10 28	10 38	10 48			10 58	11 08	11 18		11 28	11 38	11 48		
Moorgate ⊖	a		09 59	10 07	10 13		10 23					10 33	10 43	10 53			11 03	11 13	11 23		11 33	11 43	11 53		
London Kings Cross 15 ⊖	a	09 50				10 09					10 20					10 50				11 20					

Table 24

Mondays to Fridays

9 December to 16 May

Letchworth Garden City, Hertford North and Welwyn Garden City - London

Network Diagram - see first Page of Table 24

		FC 1		FC	FC	FC	FC 1	FC	FC	FC	FC	FC 1		FC	FC	FC	FC 1	FC	FC	FC	FC	FC 1		FC
Letchworth Garden City	d						13 29				13 51						14 29				14 51			
Hitchin 4	d	11 04					13 34				13 55	14 04					14 34				14 55	15 04		
Stevenage 4	d	11 10					13 40				14 01	14 10					14 40				15 01	15 10		
Watton-at-Stone	d										14 07										15 07			
Hertford North	d					13 34			13 54		14 14					14 34			14 54		15 14			
Bayford	d					13 38			13 58		14 18					14 38			14 58		15 18			
Cuffley	d					13 43			14 03		14 23					14 43			15 03		15 23			
Crews Hill	d					13 46			14 06		14 26					14 46			15 06		15 26			
Gordon Hill	d					13 49			14 09		14 29					14 49			15 09		15 29			
Enfield Chase	d					13 51			14 11		14 31					14 51			15 11		15 31			
Grange Park	d					13 53			14 13		14 33					14 53			15 13		15 33			
Winchmore Hill	d					13 55			14 15		14 35					14 55			15 15		15 35			
Palmers Green	d					13 57			14 17		14 37					14 57			15 17		15 37			
Bowes Park	d		and at			14 00			14 20		14 40					15 00			15 20		15 40			
Knebworth	d	11 14	the same				13 44					14 14					14 44					15 14		
Welwyn North	d	11 18	minutes				13 48					14 18					14 48					15 18		
Welwyn Garden City 4	d	11 21	past		13 24		13 51	13 44		14 04		14 21			14 24		14 52	14 44		15 04		15 21		
Hatfield	d	11 25	each		13 29		13 55	13 49		14 09		14 25			14 29		14 55	14 49		15 09		15 25		
Welham Green	d		hour until		13 32			13 52		14 12					14 32			14 52		15 12				
Brookmans Park	d				13 35			13 55		14 15					14 35			14 55		15 15				
Potters Bar	d	11 31			13 38		14 01	13 58		14 18		14 31			14 38		15 01	14 58		15 18		15 31		
Hadley Wood	d				13 41			14 01		14 21					14 41			15 01		15 21				
New Barnet	d				13 44			14 04		14 24					14 44			15 04		15 24				
Oakleigh Park	d				13 46			14 06		14 26					14 46			15 06		15 26				
New Southgate	d				13 49			14 09		14 29					14 49			15 09		15 29				
Alexandra Palace	d				13 52	14 02		14 12	14 22	14 32	14 42				14 52	15 02		15 12	15 22	15 32	15 42			
Hornsey	d				13 54	14 04		14 14	14 24	14 34	14 44				14 54	15 04		15 14	15 24	15 34	15 44			
Harringay	d			←	13 56	14 06		14 16	14 26	14 36	14 46			←	14 56	15 06		15 16	15 26	15 36	15 46			←
Finsbury Park ⊖	d	11 41		13 49	13 59	14 09	14 11	14 19	14 29	14 39	14 49	14 41		14 49	14 59	15 09	15 11	15 19	15 29	15 39	15 49	15 41		15 49
Drayton Park	d			13 51	14 01	14 11		14 21	14 31	14 41	→			14 51	15 01	15 11		15 21	15 31	15 41	→			15 51
Highbury & Islington ⊖	d			13 53	14 03	14 13		14 23	14 33	14 43				14 53	15 03	15 13		15 23	15 33	15 43				15 53
Essex Road	d			13 55	14 05	14 15		14 25	14 35	14 45				14 55	15 05	15 15		15 25	15 35	15 45				15 55
Old Street ⊖	d			13 58	14 08	14 18		14 28	14 38	14 48				14 58	15 08	15 18		15 28	15 38	15 48				15 58
Moorgate ⊖	a			14 03	14 13	14 23		14 33	14 43	14 53				15 03	15 13	15 23		15 33	15 43	15 53				16 03
London Kings Cross 15 ⊖	a	11 50					14 20					14 50					15 20					15 50		

		FC	FC	FC	FC	FC 1	FC	FC	FC		FC	FC 1	FC	FC	FC	FC	FC	FC	FC 1		FC	FC	FC	FC	FC
Letchworth Garden City	d				15 21	15 29					15 51							16 21	16 29						
Hitchin 4	d				15 25	15 34					15 55	16 04						16 25	16 34						
Stevenage 4	d				15 31	15 40					16 01	16 10						16 31	16 40						
Watton-at-Stone	d				15 37						16 07							16 37							
Hertford North	d		15 34		15 54						16 14			16 27			16 34	16 44					16 54		
Bayford	d		15 38		15 58						16 18						16 38	16 48					16 58		
Cuffley	d		15 43		16 03						16 23			16 34			16 43	16 53					17 03		
Crews Hill	d		15 46		16 06						16 26						16 46	16 56					17 06		
Gordon Hill	d		15 49		16 09						16 29			16 39			16 49	16 59					17 09	17 19	
Enfield Chase	d		15 51		16 11						16 31			16 41			16 51	17 01					17 11	17 21	
Grange Park	d		15 53		16 13						16 33						16 53						17 13		
Winchmore Hill	d		15 55		16 15						16 35			16 43			16 55	17 03					17 15	17 23	
Palmers Green	d		15 57		16 17						16 37			16 46			16 57	17 06					17 17	17 26	
Bowes Park	d		16 00		16 20						16 40						17 00						17 20		
Knebworth	d					15 44						16 14							16 44						
Welwyn North	d					15 48						16 18							16 48						
Welwyn Garden City 4	d	15 24		15 44		15 51			16 04			16 21			16 24	16 40			16 51			16 44			17 04
Hatfield	d	15 29		15 49		15 55			16 09			16 25			16 29	16 44			16 55			16 49			17 09
Welham Green	d	15 32		15 52					16 12						16 32							16 52			17 12
Brookmans Park	d	15 35		15 55					16 15						16 35							16 55			17 15
Potters Bar	d	15 38		15 58		16 01			16 18			16 31			16 38	16 50			17 01			16 58			17 18
Hadley Wood	d	15 41		16 01					16 21						16 41							17 01			17 21
New Barnet	d	15 44		16 04					16 24						16 44							17 04			17 24
Oakleigh Park	d	15 46		16 06					16 26						16 46							17 06			17 26
New Southgate	d	15 49		16 09					16 29						16 49							17 09			17 29
Alexandra Palace	d	15 52	16 02	16 12	16 22				16 32		16 42			16 49	16 52		17 02	17 09				17 12	17 22	17 29	17 32
Hornsey	d	15 54	16 04	16 14	16 24				16 34		16 44				16 54		17 04					17 14	17 24		17 34
Harringay	d	15 56	16 06	16 16	16 26		←	←	16 36		16 46		←		16 56		17 06				←	17 16	17 26		17 36
Finsbury Park ⊖	d	15 59	16 09	16 19	16 29	16 11	16 19	16 29	16 39		16 49	16 41	16 49	16 54	16 59	17 02	17 09	17 14	17 11		17 14	17 19	17 29	17 34	17 39
Drayton Park	d	16 01	16 11	→	→		16 21	16 31	16 41		→		16 51	16 56	17 01		17 11	→			17 16	17 21	17 31	17 36	17 41
Highbury & Islington ⊖	d	16 03	16 13				16 23	16 33	16 43				16 53	16 58	17 03		17 13				17 18	17 23	17 33	17 38	17 43
Essex Road	d	16 05	16 15				16 25	16 35	16 45				16 55	17 00	17 05		17 15				17 20	17 25	17 35	17 40	17 45
Old Street ⊖	d	16 08	16 18				16 28	16 38	16 48				16 58	17 03	17 08		17 18				17 23	17 28	17 38	17 43	17 48
Moorgate ⊖	a	16 13	16 23				16 33	16 43	16 53				17 03	17 08	17 13		17 23				17 28	17 33	17 43	17 48	17 53
London Kings Cross 15 ⊖	a					16 20						16 50				17 09			17 20						

Table 24

Mondays to Fridays

9 December to 16 May

Letchworth Garden City, Hertford North and Welwyn Garden City - London

Network Diagram - see first Page of Table 24

		FC	FC 1	FC	FC		FC	FC	FC	FC	FC	FC 1	FC	FC	FC		FC	FC	FC	FC 1	FC	FC	FC	FC 1	FC
Letchworth Garden City	d											17 29												18 29	
Hitchin 4	d		17 04									17 34								18 12				18 34	
Stevenage 4	d	16 59	17 10								17 29	17 40			17 50					18 18		18 21		18 40	
Watton-at-Stone	d	17 06									17 36				17 57							18 28			
Hertford North	d	17 14					17 37				17 44				18 03						18 18	18 34			
Bayford	d	17 18									17 48										18 22				
Cuffley	d	17 23					17 44				17 53				18 11						18 27	18 42			
Crews Hill	d	17 26									17 56										18 30				
Gordon Hill	d	17 29			17 39		17 49			17 54	17 59				18 15				18 24		18 33	18 46			18 53
Enfield Chase	d	17 31			17 41		17 51			17 56	18 01				18 17				18 26		18 35	18 48			18 55
Grange Park	d	17 33			17 43					17 58	18 03								18 28		18 37				18 57
Winchmore Hill	d	17 35			17 45		17 53			18 00	18 05				18 20				18 30		18 39	18 51			18 59
Palmers Green	d	17 37			17 47		17 56			18 02	18 07				18 22				18 32		18 41	18 53			19 01
Bowes Park	d	17 40			17 50					18 05	18 10								18 35		18 44				19 04
Knebworth	d		17 14									17 44								18 22				18 44	
Welwyn North	d		17 18									17 48								18 26				18 48	
Welwyn Garden City 4	d		17 21					17 34	17 46			17 51					18 16	18 04		18 29			18 34	18 51	
Hatfield	d		17 25					17 38	17 50			17 55					18 20	18 08		18 33			18 38	18 55	
Welham Green	d							17 42										18 12					18 42		
Brookmans Park	d							17 44										18 14					18 44		
Potters Bar	d		17 31					17 47	17 57			18 01					18 27	18 17		18 40			18 47	19 01	
Hadley Wood	d							17 51										18 21					18 51		
New Barnet	d							17 54										18 24					18 54		
Oakleigh Park	d							17 56										18 26					18 56		
New Southgate	d							17 59										18 29					18 59		
Alexandra Palace	d	17 42			17 52		17 59	18 02		18 07	18 12							18 32	18 37		18 46		19 02		19 06
Hornsey	d	17 44			17 54			18 04		18 09	18 14							18 34	18 39		18 48		19 04		19 08
Harringay	d	17 46		←	17 56			18 06		18 11	18 16		←	←				18 36	18 41		18 50		19 06		19 10
Finsbury Park ⊖	d	17 49	17 41	17 49	17 59		18 04	18 09	18 09	18 14	18 19	18 11	18 14	18 19	18 29		18 38	18 39	18 44	18 49	18 53	19 00	19 09	19 11	19 13
Drayton Park	d	→		17 51	18 01		18 06	18 11		→	→		18 16	18 21	18 31			18 41	18 46		18 55	19 02	19 11		19 15
Highbury & Islington ⊖	d			17 53	18 03		18 08	18 13					18 18	18 23	18 33			18 43	18 48		18 57	19 04	19 13		19 17
Essex Road	d			17 55	18 05		18 10	18 15					18 20	18 25	18 35			18 45	18 50		18 59	19 06	19 15		19 19
Old Street ⊖	d			17 58	18 08		18 13	18 18					18 23	18 28	18 38			18 48	18 53		19 02	19 09	19 18		19 22
Moorgate ⊖	a			18 03	18 13		18 18	18 23					18 28	18 33	18 43			18 53	18 58		19 07	19 14	19 23		19 27
London Kings Cross 15 ⊖	a		17 50						18 17			18 20					18 47			18 58				19 20	

			FC	FC	FC	FC	FC 1	FC	FC	FC	FC 1		FC	FC	FC 1	FC	FC	FC	FC 1	FC	FC		FC	FC 1	FC
Letchworth Garden City	d										19 29							20 21	20 29						
Hitchin 4	d						19 11				19 34				20 04			20 25	20 34					21 04	
Stevenage 4	d			18 51			19 17		19 21		19 40				20 10			20 31	20 40				21 01	21 10	
Watton-at-Stone	d			18 58					19 28									20 37					21 08		
Hertford North	d		18 48	19 04				19 18	19 34				19 48			20 14		20 44					21 14		
Bayford	d		18 52					19 22					19 52			20 18		20 48					21 18		
Cuffley	d		18 57	19 12				19 27	19 42				19 57			20 23		20 53					21 23		
Crews Hill	d		19 00					19 30					20 00			20 26		20 56					21 26		
Gordon Hill	d		19 03	19 16		19 23		19 33	19 46				20 03			20 29		20 59					21 29		
Enfield Chase	d		19 05	19 18		19 25		19 35	19 48				20 05			20 31		21 01					21 31		
Grange Park	d		19 07			19 27		19 37					20 07			20 33		21 03					21 33		
Winchmore Hill	d		19 09	19 21		19 29		19 39	19 51				20 09			20 35		21 05					21 35		
Palmers Green	d		19 11	19 23		19 31		19 41	19 53				20 11			20 37		21 07					21 37		
Bowes Park	d		19 14			19 34		19 44					20 14			20 40		21 10					21 40		
Knebworth	d						19 21				19 44				20 14				20 44					21 14	
Welwyn North	d						19 25				19 48				20 18				20 48					21 18	
Welwyn Garden City 4	d				19 04		19 28			19 34	19 51			19 59	20 21		20 29		20 51		20 59			21 21	
Hatfield	d				19 08		19 32			19 38	19 55			20 03	20 25		20 33		20 55		21 03			21 25	
Welham Green	d				19 12					19 42				20 07			20 37				21 07				
Brookmans Park	d				19 14					19 44				20 09			20 39				21 09				
Potters Bar	d				19 17		19 38			19 47	20 01			20 12	20 31		20 42		21 01		21 12			21 31	
Hadley Wood	d				19 21					19 51				20 16			20 46				21 16				
New Barnet	d				19 24					19 54				20 19			20 49				21 19				
Oakleigh Park	d				19 26					19 56				20 21			20 51				21 21				
New Southgate	d				19 29					19 59				20 24			20 54				21 24				
Alexandra Palace	d		19 16		19 32	19 36		19 46		20 02			20 16	20 27		20 42	20 57	21 12			21 27		21 42		
Hornsey	d		19 18		19 34	19 38		19 48		20 04			20 18	20 29		20 44	20 59	21 14			21 29		21 44		
Harringay	d		19 20		19 36	19 40		19 50		20 06			20 20	20 31		20 46	21 01	21 16		←	21 31		21 46		←
Finsbury Park ⊖	d		19 23	19 30	19 39	19 43	19 48	19 53	20 00	20 09	20 11		20 23	20 34	20 41	20 49	21 04	21 19	21 11	21 19	21 34		21 49	21 41	21 49
Drayton Park	d		19 25	19 32	19 41	19 45		19 55	20 02	20 11			20 25	20 36		20 51	21 06	→		21 21	21 36		→		21 51
Highbury & Islington ⊖	d		19 27	19 34	19 43	19 47		19 57	20 04	20 13			20 27	20 38		20 53	21 08			21 23	21 38				21 53
Essex Road	d		19 29	19 36	19 45	19 49		19 59	20 06	20 15			20 29	20 40		20 55	21 10			21 25	21 40				21 55
Old Street ⊖	d		19 32	19 39	19 48	19 52		20 02	20 09	20 18			20 32	20 43		20 58	21 13			21 28	21 43				21 58
Moorgate ⊖	a		19 37	19 44	19 53	19 57		20 07	20 14	20 23			20 37	20 48		21 03	21 18			21 33	21 48				22 03
London Kings Cross 15 ⊖	a						19 55				20 19				20 50				21 18					21 50	

Table 24

Mondays to Fridays

9 December to 16 May

Letchworth Garden City, Hertford North and Welwyn Garden City - London

Network Diagram - see first Page of Table 24

		FC	FC	FC 1	FC	FC	FC 1		FC	FC	FC	FC 1	FC	FC	FC 1	FC	FC		FC 1					
Letchworth Garden City	d		21 21	21 29							22 21	22 29					23 21		23 48					
Hitchin 4	d		21 25	21 34			22 10				22 25	22 34			23 13		23 25		23 53					
Stevenage 4	d		21 31	21 40			22 16				22 31	22 40			23 19		23 31		23 59					
Watton-at-Stone	d		21 37								22 37						23 37							
Hertford North	d		21 44						22 14		22 44					23 14	23 44							
Bayford	d		21 48						22 18		22 48					23 18	23 48							
Cuffley	d		21 53						22 23		22 53					23 23	23 53							
Crews Hill	d		21 56						22 26		22 56					23 26	23 56							
Gordon Hill	d		21 59						22 29		22 59					23 29	23 59							
Enfield Chase	d		22 01						22 31		23 01					23 31	00 01							
Grange Park	d		22 03						22 33		23 03					23 33	00 03							
Winchmore Hill	d		22 05						22 35		23 05					23 35	00 05							
Palmers Green	d		22 07						22 37		23 07					23 37	00 07							
Bowes Park	d		22 10						22 40		23 10					23 40	00 10							
Knebworth	d			21 44			22 19					22 44			23 22				00 02					
Welwyn North	d			21 48			22 23					22 48			23 26				00 06					
Welwyn Garden City 4	d	21 29		21 51		21 59	22 26			22 29		22 51		22 59	23 29				00 09					
Hatfield	d	21 33		21 55		22 03	22 30			22 33		22 55		23 03	23 33				00 13					
Welham Green	d	21 37				22 07				22 37				23 07										
Brookmans Park	d	21 39				22 09				22 39				23 09										
Potters Bar	d	21 42		22 01		22 12	22 35			22 42		23 01		23 12	23 38				00 18					
Hadley Wood	d	21 46				22 16				22 46				23 16										
New Barnet	d	21 49				22 19				22 49				23 19										
Oakleigh Park	d	21 51				22 21				22 51				23 21										
New Southgate	d	21 54				22 24				22 54				23 24										
Alexandra Palace	d	21 57	22 12			22 27			22 42	22 57	23 12			23 27		23 42	00 12							
Hornsey	d	21 59	22 14			22 29			22 44	22 59	23 14			23 29		23 44	00 14							
Harringay	d	22 01	22 16		←	22 31			22 46	23 01	23 16		←	23 31		23 46	00 16							
Finsbury Park ⊖	d	22 04	22 19	22 11	22 19	22 34	22 44		22 49	23 04	23 19	23 11	23 19	23 34	23 47	23 49	00 19		00s29					
Drayton Park	d		↪								↪													
Highbury & Islington ⊖	d																							
Essex Road	d																							
Old Street ⊖	d																							
Moorgate ⊖	a																							
London Kings Cross 15 ⊖	a	22 11		22 20	22 26	22 41	22 51		22 56	23 11		23 19	23 26	23 41	23 55	23 56	00 29		00 40					

Saturdays

14 December to 17 May

		FC	FC 1	FC	FC 1	FC	FC 1	FC	FC	FC 1		FC	FC	FC 1	FC	FC	FC	FC 1	FC	FC		FC 1	FC	FC	FC
Letchworth Garden City	d					04 50			05 20	05 29							06 20	06 29							
Hitchin 4	d				04 09	04 54	04 58		05 25	05 34				06 04			06 24	06 34				07 04			
Stevenage 4	d				04 15	05 00	05 03		05 31	05 40				06 10			06 30	06 40				07 10			07 30
Watton-at-Stone	d					05 07			05 37								06 37								07 37
Hertford North	d				04 25	05 14			05 44						06 14		06 44						07 14		07 44
Bayford	d					05 18			05 48						06 18		06 48						07 18		07 48
Cuffley	d				04 32	05 23			05 53						06 23		06 53						07 23		07 53
Crews Hill	d					05 26			05 56						06 26		06 56						07 26		07 56
Gordon Hill	d				04 36	05 29			05 59						06 29		06 59						07 29		07 59
Enfield Chase	d	00 01			04 38	05 31			06 01						06 31		07 01						07 31		08 01
Grange Park	d	00 03				05 33			06 03						06 33		07 03						07 33		08 03
Winchmore Hill	d	00 05			04 40	05 35			06 05						06 35		07 05						07 35		08 05
Palmers Green	d	00 07			04 42	05 37			06 07						06 37		07 07						07 37		08 07
Bowes Park	d	00 10				05 40			06 10						06 40		07 10						07 40		08 10
Knebworth	d		00 02				05 07			05 44				06 14				06 44				07 14			
Welwyn North	d		00 06				05 11			05 48				06 18				06 48				07 18			
Welwyn Garden City 4	d		00 09	04 10			05 14			05 51			05 59	06 21		06 29		06 51		06 59		07 21		07 29	
Hatfield	d		00 13	04 14			05 17			05 55			06 03	06 25		06 33		06 55		07 03		07 25		07 33	
Welham Green	d												06 07			06 37				07 07				07 37	
Brookmans Park	d			04 19									06 09			06 39				07 09				07 39	
Potters Bar	d		00 18	04 22			05 23			06 01			06 12	06 31		06 42		07 01		07 12		07 31		07 42	
Hadley Wood	d			04 25									06 16			06 46				07 16				07 46	
New Barnet	d			04 28			05 28						06 19			06 49				07 19				07 49	
Oakleigh Park	d			04 30			05 30						06 21			06 51				07 21				07 51	
New Southgate	d			04 33			05 33						06 24			06 54				07 24				07 54	
Alexandra Palace	d	00 12		04 36	04 45	05 42	05 36		06 12				06 27		06 42	06 57	07 12			07 27			07 42	07 57	08 12
Hornsey	d	00 14		04 38		05 44			06 14				06 29		06 44	06 59	07 14			07 29			07 44	07 59	08 14
Harringay	d	00 16		04 40		05 46		←	06 16			←	06 31		06 46	07 01	07 16		←	07 31			07 46	08 01	08 16
Finsbury Park ⊖	d	00 19	00s29	04 43	04s51	05 49	05 40	05 49	06 19	06 10		06 19	06 34	06 40	06 49	07 04	07 19	07 10	07 19	07 34		07 40	07 49	08 04	08 19
Drayton Park	d					↪			↪								↪								↪
Highbury & Islington ⊖	d																								
Essex Road	d																								
Old Street ⊖	d																								
Moorgate ⊖	a																								
London Kings Cross 15 ⊖	a	00 29	00 40	04 52	05 01		05 50	05 56		06 19		06 26	06 41	06 49	06 56	07 11		07 19	07 26	07 41		07 49	07 56	08 11	

Table 24

Saturdays

14 December to 17 May

Letchworth Garden City, Hertford North and Welwyn Garden City - London

Network Diagram - see first Page of Table 24

		FC [1]	FC	FC	FC [1]	FC		FC	FC	FC [1]	FC	FC	FC [1]	FC	FC	FC		FC [1]	FC	FC	FC [1]	FC	FC	FC	FC [1]
Letchworth Garden City	d	07 29								08 29								09 29							10 29
Hitchin [4]	d	07 34			08 04					08 34			09 04					09 34			10 04				10 34
Stevenage [4]	d	07 40			08 10				08 30	08 40			09 10			09 30		09 40			10 10			10 30	10 40
Watton-at-Stone	d								08 37							09 37								10 37	
Hertford North	d					08 14			08 44					09 14		09 44						10 14		10 44	
Bayford	d					08 18			08 48					09 18		09 48						10 18		10 48	
Cuffley	d					08 23			08 53					09 23		09 53						10 23		10 53	
Crews Hill	d					08 26			08 56					09 26		09 56						10 26		10 56	
Gordon Hill	d					08 29			08 59					09 29		09 59						10 29		10 59	
Enfield Chase	d					08 31			09 01					09 31		10 01						10 31		11 01	
Grange Park	d					08 33			09 03					09 33		10 03						10 33		11 03	
Winchmore Hill	d					08 35			09 05					09 35		10 05						10 35		11 05	
Palmers Green	d					08 37			09 07					09 37		10 07						10 37		11 07	
Bowes Park	d					08 40			09 10					09 40		10 10						10 40		11 10	
Knebworth	d	07 44			08 14					08 44			09 14					09 44			10 14				10 44
Welwyn North	d	07 48			08 18					08 48			09 18					09 48			10 18				10 48
Welwyn Garden City [4]	d	07 51		07 59	08 21			08 29		08 51		08 59	09 21		09 29			09 52		09 59	10 21		10 29		10 51
Hatfield	d	07 55		08 03	08 25			08 33		08 55		09 03	09 25		09 33			09 55		10 03	10 25		10 33		10 55
Welham Green	d			08 07				08 37				09 07			09 37					10 07			10 37		
Brookmans Park	d			08 09				08 39				09 09			09 39					10 09			10 39		
Potters Bar	d	08 01		08 12	08 31			08 42		09 01		09 12	09 31		09 42			10 01		10 12	10 31		10 42		11 01
Hadley Wood	d			08 16				08 46				09 16			09 46					10 16			10 46		
New Barnet	d			08 19				08 49				09 19			09 49					10 19			10 49		
Oakleigh Park	d			08 21				08 51				09 21			09 51					10 21			10 51		
New Southgate	d			08 24				08 54				09 24			09 54					10 24			10 54		
Alexandra Palace	d			08 27		08 42		08 57	09 12			09 27		09 42	09 57	10 12				10 27		10 42	10 57	11 12	
Hornsey	d			08 29		08 44		08 59	09 14			09 29		09 44	09 59	10 14				10 29		10 44	10 59	11 14	
Harringay	d		←	08 31		08 46		09 01	09 16		←	09 31		09 46	10 01	10 16			←	10 31		10 46	11 01	11 16	
Finsbury Park ⊖	d	08 10	08 19	08 34	08 40	08 49		09 04	09 19	09 10	09 19	09 34	09 40	09 49	10 04	10 19		10 10	10 19	10 34	10 40	10 49	11 04	11 19	11 10
Drayton Park	d								↪							↪								↪	
Highbury & Islington ⊖	d																								
Essex Road	d																								
Old Street ⊖	d																								
Moorgate ⊖	a																								
London Kings Cross [15] ⊖	a	08 19	08 26	08 41	08 49	08 56		09 11		09 20	09 26	09 41	09 51	09 56	10 11			10 21	10 26	10 41	10 49	10 56	11 11		11 21

		FC		FC	FC [1]	FC	FC	FC	FC [1]	FC	FC	FC [1]		FC	FC	FC	FC [1]	FC	FC	FC [1]	FC	FC	FC	FC [1]	FC
Letchworth Garden City	d								11 29								12 29							13 29	
Hitchin [4]	d				11 04				11 34			12 04					12 34			13 04				13 34	
Stevenage [4]	d				11 10			11 30	11 40			12 10				12 30	12 40			13 10			13 30	13 40	
Watton-at-Stone	d							11 37								12 37							13 37		
Hertford North	d					11 14		11 44						12 14		12 44					13 14		13 44		
Bayford	d					11 18		11 48						12 18		12 48					13 18		13 48		
Cuffley	d					11 23		11 53						12 23		12 53					13 23		13 53		
Crews Hill	d					11 26		11 56						12 26		12 56					13 26		13 56		
Gordon Hill	d					11 29		11 59						12 29		12 59					13 29		13 59		
Enfield Chase	d					11 31		12 01						12 31		13 01					13 31		14 01		
Grange Park	d					11 33		12 03						12 33		13 03					13 33		14 03		
Winchmore Hill	d					11 35		12 05						12 35		13 05					13 35		14 05		
Palmers Green	d					11 37		12 07						12 37		13 07					13 37		14 07		
Bowes Park	d					11 40		12 10						12 40		13 10					13 40		14 10		
Knebworth	d				11 14				11 44			12 14					12 44			13 14				13 44	
Welwyn North	d				11 18				11 48			12 18					12 48			13 18				13 48	
Welwyn Garden City [4]	d			10 59	11 21		11 29		11 51		11 59	12 21			12 29		12 51		12 59	13 21		13 29		13 51	
Hatfield	d			11 03	11 25		11 33		11 55		12 03	12 25			12 33		12 55		13 03	13 25		13 33		13 55	
Welham Green	d			11 07			11 37				12 07				12 37				13 07			13 37			
Brookmans Park	d			11 09			11 39				12 09				12 39				13 09			13 39			
Potters Bar	d			11 12	11 31		11 42		12 01		12 12	12 31			12 42		13 01		13 12	13 31		13 42		14 01	
Hadley Wood	d			11 16			11 46				12 16				12 46				13 16			13 46			
New Barnet	d			11 19			11 49				12 19				12 49				13 19			13 49			
Oakleigh Park	d			11 21			11 51				12 21				12 51				13 21			13 51			
New Southgate	d			11 24			11 54				12 24				12 54				13 24			13 54			
Alexandra Palace	d			11 27		11 42	11 57	12 12			12 27			12 42	12 57	13 12			13 27		13 42	13 57	14 12		
Hornsey	d			11 29		11 44	11 59	12 14			12 29			12 44	12 59	13 14			13 29		13 44	13 59	14 14		
Harringay	d	←		11 31		11 46	12 01	12 16		←	12 31			12 46	13 01	13 16		←	13 31		13 46	14 01	14 16		←
Finsbury Park ⊖	d	11 19		11 34	11 40	11 49	12 04	12 19	12 10	12 19	12 34	12 40		12 49	13 04	13 19	13 10	13 19	13 34	13 40	13 49	14 04	14 19	14 10	14 19
Drayton Park	d							↪								↪							↪		
Highbury & Islington ⊖	d																								
Essex Road	d																								
Old Street ⊖	d																								
Moorgate ⊖	a																								
London Kings Cross [15] ⊖	a	11 26		11 41	11 49	11 56	12 11		12 19	12 26	12 41	12 49		12 56	13 11		13 19	13 26	13 41	13 50	13 56	14 11		14 19	14 26

Table 24

Saturdays

14 December to 17 May

Letchworth Garden City, Hertford North and Welwyn Garden City - London

Network Diagram - see first Page of Table 24

		FC	FC 1		FC	FC	FC	FC 1	FC	FC	FC 1		FC	FC	FC	FC 1	FC	FC	FC 1	FC	FC		FC	FC 1
Letchworth Garden City	d							16 29								17 29								18 29
Hitchin 4	d		14 04					16 34			17 04					17 34			18 04					18 34
Stevenage 4	d		14 10				16 30	16 40			17 10				17 30	17 40			18 10				18 30	18 40
Watton-at-Stone	d						16 37								17 37								18 37	
Hertford North	d				16 14		16 44						17 14		17 44					18 14			18 44	
Bayford	d				16 18		16 48						17 18		17 48					18 18			18 48	
Cuffley	d				16 23		16 53						17 23		17 53					18 23			18 53	
Crews Hill	d				16 26		16 56						17 26		17 56					18 26			18 56	
Gordon Hill	d				16 29		16 59						17 29		17 59					18 29			18 59	
Enfield Chase	d				16 31		17 01						17 31		18 01					18 31			19 01	
Grange Park	d				16 33		17 03						17 33		18 03					18 33			19 03	
Winchmore Hill	d				16 35		17 05						17 35		18 05					18 35			19 05	
Palmers Green	d				16 37		17 07						17 37		18 07					18 37			19 07	
Bowes Park	d				16 40		17 10						17 40		18 10					18 40			19 10	
Knebworth	d		14 14	and at the same minutes past each hour until				16 44			17 14					17 44			18 14					18 44
Welwyn North	d		14 18					16 48			17 18					17 48			18 18					18 48
Welwyn Garden City 4	d	13 59	14 21			16 29		16 51		16 59	17 21			17 29		17 51		17 59	18 21		18 29			18 51
Hatfield	d	14 03	14 25			16 33		16 55		17 03	17 25			17 33		17 55		18 03	18 25		18 33			18 55
Welham Green	d	14 07				16 37				17 07				17 37				18 07			18 37			
Brookmans Park	d	14 09				16 39				17 09				17 39				18 09			18 39			
Potters Bar	d	14 12	14 31			16 42		17 01		17 12	17 31			17 42		18 01		18 12	18 31		18 42			19 01
Hadley Wood	d	14 16				16 46				17 16				17 46				18 16			18 46			
New Barnet	d	14 19				16 49				17 19				17 49				18 19			18 49			
Oakleigh Park	d	14 21				16 51				17 21				17 51				18 21			18 51			
New Southgate	d	14 24				16 54				17 24				17 54				18 24			18 54			
Alexandra Palace	d	14 27			16 42	16 57	17 12			17 27			17 42	17 57	18 12			18 27		18 42	18 57		19 12	
Hornsey	d	14 29			16 44	16 59	17 14			17 29			17 44	17 59	18 14			18 29		18 44	18 59		19 14	
Harringay	d	14 31			16 46	17 01	17 16		←	17 31			17 46	18 01	18 16		←	18 31		18 46	19 01		19 16	
Finsbury Park	⊖ d	14 34	14 40		16 49	17 04	17 19	17 10	17 19	17 34	17 40		17 49	18 04	18 19	18 10	18 19	18 34	18 40	18 49	19 04		19 19	19 10
Drayton Park	d						→								→								→	
Highbury & Islington	⊖ d																							
Essex Road	d																							
Old Street	⊖ d																							
Moorgate	⊖ a																							
London Kings Cross 15	⊖ a	14 41	14 49		16 56	17 11		17 19	17 26	17 41	17 49		17 56	18 11		18 19	18 26	18 41	18 50	18 56	19 11			19 19

		FC	FC	FC 1	FC	FC	FC	FC 1		FC	FC	FC 1	FC	FC	FC	FC 1	FC	FC		FC 1	FC	FC	FC	FC 1	FC
Letchworth Garden City	d							19 29								20 29								21 29	
Hitchin 4	d			19 04				19 34				20 04				20 34				21 04				21 34	
Stevenage 4	d			19 10			19 30	19 40				20 10			20 30	20 40				21 10			21 30	21 40	
Watton-at-Stone	d						19 37								20 37								21 37		
Hertford North	d				19 14		19 44						20 14		20 44						21 14		21 44		
Bayford	d				19 18		19 48						20 18		20 48						21 18		21 48		
Cuffley	d				19 23		19 53						20 23		20 53						21 23		21 53		
Crews Hill	d				19 26		19 56						20 26		20 56						21 26		21 56		
Gordon Hill	d				19 29		19 59						20 29		20 59						21 29		21 59		
Enfield Chase	d				19 31		20 01						20 31		21 01						21 31		22 01		
Grange Park	d				19 33		20 03						20 33		21 03						21 33		22 03		
Winchmore Hill	d				19 35		20 05						20 35		21 05						21 35		22 05		
Palmers Green	d				19 37		20 07						20 37		21 07						21 37		22 07		
Bowes Park	d				19 40		20 10						20 40		21 10						21 40		22 10		
Knebworth	d			19 14				19 44				20 14				20 44				21 14				21 44	
Welwyn North	d			19 18				19 48				20 18				20 48				21 18				21 48	
Welwyn Garden City 4	d		18 59	19 21		19 29		19 51			19 59	20 21		20 29		20 51		20 59		21 21		21 29		21 51	
Hatfield	d		19 03	19 25		19 33		19 55			20 03	20 25		20 33		20 55		21 03		21 25		21 33		21 55	
Welham Green	d		19 07			19 37					20 07			20 37				21 07				21 37			
Brookmans Park	d		19 09			19 39					20 09			20 39				21 09				21 39			
Potters Bar	d		19 12	19 31		19 42		20 01			20 12	20 31		20 42		21 01		21 12		21 31		21 42		22 01	
Hadley Wood	d		19 16			19 46					20 16			20 46				21 16				21 46			
New Barnet	d		19 19			19 49					20 19			20 49				21 19				21 49			
Oakleigh Park	d		19 21			19 51					20 21			20 51				21 21				21 51			
New Southgate	d		19 24			19 54					20 24			20 54				21 24				21 54			
Alexandra Palace	d		19 27		19 42	19 57	20 12				20 27		20 42	20 57	21 12			21 27			21 42	21 57	22 12		
Hornsey	d		19 29		19 44	19 59	20 14				20 29		20 44	20 59	21 14			21 29			21 44	21 59	22 14		
Harringay	d	←	19 31		19 46	20 01	20 16			←	20 31		20 46	21 01	21 16		←	21 31			21 46	22 01	22 16		←
Finsbury Park	⊖ d	19 19	19 34	19 40	19 49	20 04	20 19	20 10		20 19	20 34	20 40	20 49	21 04	21 19	21 11	21 19	21 34		21 40	21 49	22 04	22 19	22 10	22 19
Drayton Park	d						→								→								→		
Highbury & Islington	⊖ d																								
Essex Road	d																								
Old Street	⊖ d																								
Moorgate	⊖ a																								
London Kings Cross 15	⊖ a	19 26	19 41	19 49	19 56	20 11		20 19		20 26	20 41	20 49	20 56	21 11		21 19	21 26	21 41		21 49	21 56	22 11		22 19	22 26

Table 24

Saturdays

14 December to 17 May

Letchworth Garden City, Hertford North and Welwyn Garden City - London

Network Diagram - see first Page of Table 24

		FC	FC 1	FC		FC	FC	FC 1	FC	FC	FC 1	FC	FC	FC 1
Letchworth Garden City	d							22 29						23 48
Hitchin 4	d		22 04					22 34			23 04			23 53
Stevenage 4	d		22 10				22 30	22 40			23 10		23 30	23 58
Watton-at-Stone	d						22 37						23 37	
Hertford North	d			22 14			22 44					23 14	23 44	
Bayford	d			22 18			22 48					23 18	23 48	
Cuffley	d			22 23			22 53					23 23	23 53	
Crews Hill	d			22 26			22 56					23 26	23 56	
Gordon Hill	d			22 29			22 59					23 29	23 59	
Enfield Chase	d			22 31			23 01					23 31	00 01	
Grange Park	d			22 33			23 03					23 33	00 03	
Winchmore Hill	d			22 35			23 05					23 35	00 05	
Palmers Green	d			22 37			23 07					23 37	00 07	
Bowes Park	d			22 40			23 10					23 40	00 10	
Knebworth	d		22 14					22 44			23 14			00 02
Welwyn North	d		22 18					22 48			23 18			00 05
Welwyn Garden City 4	d	21 59	22 21			22 29		22 51		22 59	23 21			00 09
Hatfield	d	22 03	22 25			22 33		22 55		23 03	23 25			00 12
Welham Green	d	22 07				22 37				23 07				
Brookmans Park	d	22 09				22 39				23 09				
Potters Bar	d	22 12	22 31			22 42		23 01		23 12	23 31			00 18
Hadley Wood	d	22 16				22 46				23 16				
New Barnet	d	22 19				22 49				23 19				
Oakleigh Park	d	22 21				22 51				23 21				
New Southgate	d	22 24				22 54				23 24				
Alexandra Palace	d	22 27		22 42		22 57	23 12			23 27		23 42	00 12	
Hornsey	d	22 29		22 44		22 59	23 14			23 29		23 44	00 14	
Harringay	d	22 31		22 46		23 01	23 16		←	23 31		23 46	00 16	
Finsbury Park ⊖	d	22 34	22 40	22 49		23 04	23 19	23 10	23 19	23 34	23 40	23 49	00 19	00s28
Drayton Park	d						→							
Highbury & Islington ⊖	d													
Essex Road	d													
Old Street ⊖	d													
Moorgate ⊖	a													
London Kings Cross 15 ⊖	a	22 41	22 49	22 56		23 11		23 19	23 26	23 41	23 49	23 59	00 29	00 40

Sundays

8 December to 29 December

		FC A	FC 1 A	FC	FC 1	FC	FC	FC	FC	FC		FC 1	FC	FC	FC	FC	FC	FC 1	FC	FC		FC	FC	FC	FC 1
Letchworth Garden City	d											07 29						08 29							09 29
Hitchin 4	d				06 33							07 33						08 33							09 34
Stevenage 4	d				06 39					07 30		07 39					08 30	08 39						09 30	09 40
Watton-at-Stone	d									07 37							08 37							09 37	
Hertford North	d					06 44		07 14		07 44					08 14		08 44					09 14		09 44	
Bayford	d					06 48		07 18		07 48					08 18		08 48					09 18		09 48	
Cuffley	d					06 53		07 23		07 53					08 23		08 53					09 23		09 53	
Crews Hill	d					06 56		07 26		07 56					08 26		08 56					09 26		09 56	
Gordon Hill	d					06 59		07 29		07 59					08 29		08 59					09 29		09 59	
Enfield Chase	d	00 01				07 01		07 31		08 01					08 31		09 01					09 31		10 01	
Grange Park	d	00 03				07 03		07 33		08 03					08 33		09 03					09 33		10 03	
Winchmore Hill	d	00 05				07 05		07 35		08 05					08 35		09 05					09 35		10 05	
Palmers Green	d	00 07				07 07		07 37		08 07					08 37		09 07					09 37		10 07	
Bowes Park	d	00 10				07 10		07 40		08 10					08 40		09 10					09 40		10 10	
Knebworth	d		00 02		06 43							07 43						08 43							09 43
Welwyn North	d		00 05		06 47							07 47						08 47							09 48
Welwyn Garden City 4	d		00 09	06 29	06 50		06 59		07 29			07 51		07 59		08 29		08 51		08 59			09 29		09 52
Hatfield	d		00 12	06 33	06 54		07 03		07 33			07 54		08 03		08 33		08 54		09 03			09 33		09 55
Welham Green	d			06 37			07 07		07 37					08 07		08 37				09 07			09 37		
Brookmans Park	d			06 39			07 09		07 39					08 09		08 39				09 09			09 39		
Potters Bar	d		00 18	06 42	07 00		07 12		07 42			08 00		08 12		08 42		09 00		09 12			09 42		10 01
Hadley Wood	d			06 46			07 16		07 46					08 16		08 46				09 16			09 46		
New Barnet	d			06 49			07 19		07 49					08 19		08 49				09 19			09 49		
Oakleigh Park	d			06 51			07 21		07 51					08 21		08 51				09 21			09 51		
New Southgate	d			06 54			07 24		07 54					08 24		08 54				09 24			09 54		
Alexandra Palace	d	00 12		06 57		07 12	07 27	07 42	07 57	08 12				08 27	08 42	08 57	09 12			09 27		09 42	09 57	10 12	
Hornsey	d	00 14		06 59		07 14	07 29	07 44	07 59	08 14				08 29	08 44	08 59	09 14			09 29		09 44	09 59	10 14	
Harringay	d	00 16		07 01		07 16	07 31	07 46	08 01	08 16			←	08 31	08 46	09 01	09 16		←	09 31		09 46	10 01	10 16	
Finsbury Park ⊖	d	00 19	00s28	07 04	07 10	07 19	07 34	07 49	08 04	08 19		08 10	08 19	08 34	08 49	09 04	09 19	09 10	09 19	09 34		09 49	10 04	10 19	10 10
Drayton Park	d									→							→							→	
Highbury & Islington ⊖	d																								
Essex Road	d																								
Old Street ⊖	d																								
Moorgate ⊖	a																								
London Kings Cross 15 ⊖	a	00 29	00 40	07 14	07 21	07 30	07 44	08 00	08 14			08 19	08 26	08 41	08 56	09 11		09 19	09 26	09 41		09 56	10 11		10 20

A not 8 December

Table 24

Sundays

8 December to 29 December

Letchworth Garden City, Hertford North and Welwyn Garden City - London

Network Diagram - see first Page of Table 24

		FC	FC	FC [1]	FC	FC		FC	FC [1]	FC	FC	FC [1]	FC	FC	FC	FC [1]	FC	FC		FC	FC	FC	FC [1]	FC
Letchworth Garden City	d			09 59					10 29			10 59				11 29							22 29	
Hitchin [4]	d			10 03					10 33			11 03				11 33							22 33	
Stevenage [4]	d			10 09				10 30	10 39			11 09			11 30	11 39						22 30	22 39	
Watton-at-Stone	d							10 37							11 37							22 37		
Hertford North	d				10 14			10 44					11 14		11 44					22 14		22 44		
Bayford	d				10 18			10 48					11 18		11 48					22 18		22 48		
Cuffley	d				10 23			10 53					11 23		11 53					22 23		22 53		
Crews Hill	d				10 26			10 56					11 26		11 56					22 26		22 56		
Gordon Hill	d				10 29			10 59					11 29		11 59					22 29		22 59		
Enfield Chase	d				10 31			11 01					11 31		12 01					22 31		23 01		
Grange Park	d				10 33			11 03					11 33		12 03					22 33		23 03		
Winchmore Hill	d				10 35			11 05					11 35		12 05					22 35		23 05		
Palmers Green	d				10 37			11 07					11 37		12 07					22 37		23 07		
Bowes Park	d				10 40			11 10					11 40		12 10				and at the same minutes past each hour until	22 40		23 10		
Knebworth	d			10 13					10 43			11 13				11 43							22 43	
Welwyn North	d			10 17					10 47			11 17				11 47							22 47	
Welwyn Garden City [4]	d		09 59	10 21		10 29			10 51		10 59	11 21		11 29		11 51		11 59			22 29		22 51	
Hatfield	d		10 03	10 24		10 33			10 54		11 03	11 24		11 33		11 54		12 03			22 33		22 54	
Welham Green	d		10 07			10 37					11 07			11 37				12 07			22 37			
Brookmans Park	d		10 09			10 39					11 09			11 39				12 09			22 39			
Potters Bar	d		10 12	10 30		10 42			11 00		11 12	11 30		11 42		12 00		12 12			22 42		23 00	
Hadley Wood	d		10 16			10 46					11 16			11 46				12 16			22 46			
New Barnet	d		10 19			10 49					11 19			11 49				12 19			22 49			
Oakleigh Park	d		10 21			10 51					11 21			11 51				12 21			22 51			
New Southgate	d		10 24			10 54					11 24			11 54				12 24			22 54			
Alexandra Palace	d		10 27		10 42	10 57		11 12			11 27		11 42	11 57	12 12			12 27		22 42	22 57	23 12		
Hornsey	d		10 29		10 44	10 59		11 14			11 29		11 44	11 59	12 14			12 29		22 44	22 59	23 14		
Harringay	d	←	10 31		10 46	11 01		11 16		←	11 31		11 46	12 01	12 16		←	12 31		22 46	23 01	23 16		←
Finsbury Park	⊖ d	10 19	10 34	10 40	10 49	11 04		11 19	11 10	11 19	11 34	11 40	11 49	12 04	12 19	12 10	12 19	12 34		22 49	23 04	23 19	23 10	23 19
Drayton Park	d							→							→							→		
Highbury & Islington	⊖ d																							
Essex Road	d																							
Old Street	⊖ d																							
Moorgate	⊖ a																							
London Kings Cross [15]	⊖ a	10 26	10 41	10 49	10 56	11 11			11 19	11 26	11 41	11 49	11 56	12 11		12 19	12 26	12 41		22 56	23 11		23 19	23 26

		FC		FC	FC	FC [1]
Letchworth Garden City	d					23 48
Hitchin [4]	d					23 53
Stevenage [4]	d				23 30	23 59
Watton-at-Stone	d				23 37	
Hertford North	d			23 14	23 44	
Bayford	d			23 18	23 48	
Cuffley	d			23 23	23 53	
Crews Hill	d			23 26	23 56	
Gordon Hill	d			23 29	23 59	
Enfield Chase	d			23 31	00 01	
Grange Park	d			23 33	00 03	
Winchmore Hill	d			23 35	00 05	
Palmers Green	d			23 37	00 07	
Bowes Park	d			23 40	00 10	
Knebworth	d					00 02
Welwyn North	d					00 06
Welwyn Garden City [4]	d	22 59				00 09
Hatfield	d	23 03				00 13
Welham Green	d	23 07				
Brookmans Park	d	23 09				
Potters Bar	d	23 12				00 18
Hadley Wood	d	23 16				
New Barnet	d	23 19				
Oakleigh Park	d	23 21				
New Southgate	d	23 24				
Alexandra Palace	d	23 27		23 42	00 12	
Hornsey	d	23 29		23 44	00 14	
Harringay	d	23 31		23 46	00 16	
Finsbury Park	⊖ d	23 34		23 49	00 19	00s29
Drayton Park	d					
Highbury & Islington	⊖ d					
Essex Road	d					
Old Street	⊖ d					
Moorgate	⊖ a					
London Kings Cross [15]	⊖ a	23 41		23 56	00 29	00 41

Table 24

Sundays

5 January to 23 March

Letchworth Garden City, Hertford North and Welwyn Garden City - London

Network Diagram - see first Page of Table 24

		FC	FC 1	FC 🚌	FC 🚌	FC 🚌	FC 🚌	FC 🚌	FC 🚌	FC	FC	FC	FC 🚌	FC 🚌	FC 🚌	FC 🚌	FC	FC	FC	FC 🚌	FC 🚌	FC 🚌	FC 🚌
Letchworth Garden City	d										06 44							07 44					
Hitchin 4	d										06 49							07 49					
Stevenage 4	d				05 45		06 15		06 45		06 55			07 15		07 45		07 55			08 15		08 45
Watton-at-Stone	d										07 01							08 01					
Hertford North	d									06 50	07a07	07 20					07 50	08a07	08 20				
Bayford	d									06 54		07 25					07 55		08 25				
Cuffley	d									06 59		07 29					07 59		08 29				
Crews Hill	d									07 02		07 32					08 02		08 32				
Gordon Hill	d									07 05		07 35					08 05		08 35				
Enfield Chase	d	00 01								07 07		07 37					08 07		08 37				
Grange Park	d	00 03								07 09		07 39					08 09		08 39				
Winchmore Hill	d	00 05								07 11		07 41					08 11		08 41				
Palmers Green	d	00 07								07 13		07 44					08 14		08 44				
Bowes Park	d	00 10								07 16		07 46					08 16		08 46				
Knebworth	d		00 02		05 52		06 22		06 52					07 22		07 52					08 22		08 52
Welwyn North	d		00 05		06 02		06 32		07 02					07 32		08 02					08 32		09 02
Welwyn Garden City 4	d		00 09	05 47	06 17	06 17	06 47	06 47	07 17				07 17	07 47	07 47	08 17				08 17	08 47	08 47	09 17
Hatfield	d		00 12	05 57	06 27	06 27	06 57	06 57	07 27				07 27	07 57	07 57	08 27				08 27	08 57	08 57	09 27
Welham Green	d			06 01		06 31		07 01					07 31		08 01					08 31		09 01	
Brookmans Park	d			06 05		06 35		07 05					07 35		08 05					08 35		09 05	
Potters Bar	d		00 18	06 13	06 42	06 43	07 12	07 13	07 42				07 43	08 12	08 13	08 42				08 43	09 12	09 13	09 42
Hadley Wood	d			06 23		06 53		07 23					07 53		08 23					08 53		09 23	
New Barnet	d			06 43		07 13		07 43					08 13		08 43					09 13		09 43	
Oakleigh Park	d			06 53		07 23		07 53					08 23		08 53					09 23		09 53	
New Southgate	d			07 03		07 33		08 03					08 33		09 03					09 33		10 03	
Alexandra Palace	d	00 12		07a13	07a12	07a43	07a42	08a13	08a12	07 18		07 49	08a43	08a42	09a13	09a12	08 19		08 49	09a43	09a42	10a13	10a12
Hornsey	d	00 14								07 20		07 51					08 21		08 51				
Harringay	d	00 16								07 22		07 53					08 23		08 53				
Finsbury Park ⊖	d	00 19	00s28							07 25		07 56					08 26		08 56				
Drayton Park	d																						
Highbury & Islington ⊖	d																						
Essex Road	d																						
Old Street ⊖	d																						
Moorgate ⊖	a																						
London Kings Cross 15 ⊖	a	00 29	00 40							07 35		08 05					08 33		09 03				

		FC	FC	FC 🚌	FC 🚌	FC 🚌	FC 🚌	FC 🚌	FC 🚌	FC	FC	FC	FC 🚌	FC 🚌	FC	FC 🚌	FC 🚌	FC 🚌	FC 🚌	FC	FC	and at the same minutes past each hour until
Letchworth Garden City	d	08 44									10 04				11 04					11 44		
Hitchin 4	d	08 49									10 09				11 09					11 49		
Stevenage 4	d	08 55			09 15		09 45		10 15		10 15			10 45	11 15		11 15		11 45	11 55		
Watton-at-Stone	d	09 01									10 21				11 21					12 01		
Hertford North	d	09a07	09 20							10 20	10a27	11 20			11a27					12a07	12 20	
Bayford	d		09 25							10 25		11 25									12 25	
Cuffley	d		09 29							10 29		11 29									12 29	
Crews Hill	d		09 32							10 32		11 32									12 32	
Gordon Hill	d		09 35							10 35		11 35									12 35	
Enfield Chase	d		09 37							10 37		11 37									12 37	
Grange Park	d		09 39							10 39		11 39									12 39	
Winchmore Hill	d		09 41							10 41		11 41									12 41	
Palmers Green	d		09 44							10 44		11 44									12 44	
Bowes Park	d		09 46							10 46		11 46									12 46	
Knebworth	d				09 22		09 52		10 22					10 52			11 22		11 52			
Welwyn North	d				09 32		10 02		10 32					11 02			11 32		12 02			
Welwyn Garden City 4	d			09 17	09 47	09 47	10 17	10 17	10 47				10 47	11 17		11 17	11 47	11 47	12 17			
Hatfield	d			09 27	09 57	09 57	10 27	10 27	10 57				10 57	11 27		11 27	11 57	11 57	12 27			
Welham Green	d			09 31		10 01		10 31					11 01			11 31		12 01				
Brookmans Park	d			09 35		10 05		10 35					11 05			11 35		12 05				
Potters Bar	d			09 43	10 12	10 13	10 42	10 43	11 12				11 13	11 42		11 43	12 12	12 13	12 42			
Hadley Wood	d			09 53		10 23		10 53					11 23			11 53		12 23				
New Barnet	d			10 13		10 43		11 13					11 43			12 13		12 43				
Oakleigh Park	d			10 23		10 53		11 23					11 53			12 23		12 53				
New Southgate	d			10 33		11 03		11 33					12 03			12 33		13 03				
Alexandra Palace	d		09 49	10a43	10a42	11a13	11a12	11a43	11a42	10 48		11 49	12a13	12a12		12a43	12a42	13a13	13a12		12 49	
Hornsey	d		09 51							10 51		11 51									12 51	
Harringay	d		09 53							10 53		11 53									12 53	
Finsbury Park ⊖	d		09 56							10 57		11 56									12 56	
Drayton Park	d																					
Highbury & Islington ⊖	d																					
Essex Road	d																					
Old Street ⊖	d																					
Moorgate ⊖	a																					
London Kings Cross 15 ⊖	a		10 03							11 03		12 03									13 03	

Table 24

Sundays

5 January to 23 March

Letchworth Garden City, Hertford North and Welwyn Garden City - London

Network Diagram - see first Page of Table 24

		FC 🚌	FC 🚌	FC 🚌	FC 🚌	FC	FC	FC 🚌	FC 🚌	FC 🚌	FC 🚌	FC 🚌	FC	FC	FC 🚌	FC 🚌	FC 🚌	FC	FC	FC 🚌	FC 🚌	FC 🚌	FC 🚌
Letchworth Garden City	d					15 44								17 02				17 44					
Hitchin 4	d					15 49								17 07				17 49					
Stevenage 4	d		15 15		15 45	15 55			16 15		16 45			17 13	17 15		17 45	17 55			18 15		18 45
Watton-at-Stone	d					16 01								17 19				18 01					
Hertford North	d					16a07	16 20						17 20	17a25				18a07	18 20				
Bayford	d						16 25						17 25						18 25				
Cuffley	d						16 29						17 29						18 29				
Crews Hill	d						16 32						17 32						18 32				
Gordon Hill	d						16 35						17 35						18 35				
Enfield Chase	d						16 37						17 37						18 37				
Grange Park	d						16 39						17 39						18 39				
Winchmore Hill	d						16 41						17 41						18 41				
Palmers Green	d						16 44						17 44						18 44				
Bowes Park	d						16 46						17 46						18 46				
Knebworth	d		15 22		15 52				16 22		16 52				17 22		17 52				18 22		18 52
Welwyn North	d		15 32		16 02				16 32		17 02				17 32		18 02				18 32		19 02
Welwyn Garden City 4	d	15 17	15 47	15 47	16 17			16 17	16 47	16 47	17 17	17 17			17 47	17 47	18 17			18 17	18 47	18 47	19 17
Hatfield	d	15 27	15 57	15 57	16 27			16 27	16 57	16 57	17 27	17 27			17 57	17 57	18 27			18 27	18 57	18 57	19 27
Welham Green	d	15 31		16 01				16 31		17 01		17 31				18 01				18 31		19 01	
Brookmans Park	d	15 35		16 05				16 35		17 05		17 35				18 05				18 35		19 05	
Potters Bar	d	15 43	16 12	16 13	16 42			16 43	17 12	17 13	17 42	17 43			18 12	18 13	18 42			18 43	19 12	19 13	19 42
Hadley Wood	d	15 53		16 23				16 53		17 23		17 53				18 23				18 53		19 23	
New Barnet	d	16 13		16 43				17 13		17 43		18 13				18 43				19 13		19 43	
Oakleigh Park	d	16 23		16 53				17 23		17 53		18 23				18 53				19 23		19 53	
New Southgate	d	16 33		17 03				17 33		18 03		18 33				19 03				19 33		20 03	
Alexandra Palace	d	16a43	16a42	17a13	17a12		16 49	17a43	17a42	18a13	18a12	18a43	17 49		18a42	19a13	19a12		18 49	19a43	19a42	20a13	20a12
Hornsey	d						16 51						17 51						18 51				
Harringay	d						16 53						17 53						18 53				
Finsbury Park ⊖	d						16 56						17 56						18 56				
Drayton Park	d																						
Highbury & Islington ⊖	d																						
Essex Road	d																						
Old Street ⊖	d																						
Moorgate ⊖	a																						
London Kings Cross 15 ⊖	a						17 03						18 03						19 03				

		FC 🚌	FC	FC	FC 🚌	FC 🚌	FC 🚌	FC	FC	FC 🚌	FC 🚌	FC 🚌	FC 🚌	FC 🚌	FC 🚌	FC	FC	FC 🚌	FC 🚌	FC	FC	FC 🚌
Letchworth Garden City	d			19 03				19 44									21 04			21 44		
Hitchin 4	d			19 08				19 49									21 09			21 49		
Stevenage 4	d			19 14	19 15		19 45	19 55			20 15		20 45		21 15		21 15		21 45	21 55		
Watton-at-Stone	d			19 20				20 01									21 21			22 01		
Hertford North	d		19 20	19a26				20a07	20 20							21 20	21a27			22a07	22 20	
Bayford	d		19 25						20 24							21 25					22 25	
Cuffley	d		19 29						20 29							21 29					22 29	
Crews Hill	d		19 32						20 32							21 32					22 32	
Gordon Hill	d		19 35						20 35							21 35					22 35	
Enfield Chase	d		19 37						20 37							21 37					22 37	
Grange Park	d		19 39						20 39							21 39					22 39	
Winchmore Hill	d		19 41						20 41							21 41					22 41	
Palmers Green	d		19 44						20 43							21 44					22 44	
Bowes Park	d		19 46						20 46							21 46					22 46	
Knebworth	d				19 22		19 52				20 22		20 52		21 22				21 52			
Welwyn North	d				19 32		20 02				20 32		21 02		21 32				22 02			
Welwyn Garden City 4	d	19 17			19 47	19 47	20 17			20 17	20 47	20 47	21 17	21 17	21 47			21 47	22 17			22 17
Hatfield	d	19 27			19 57	19 57	20 27			20 27	20 57	20 57	21 27	21 27	21 57			21 57	22 27			22 27
Welham Green	d	19 31				20 01				20 31		21 01		21 31				22 01				22 31
Brookmans Park	d	19 35				20 05				20 35		21 05		21 35				22 05				22 35
Potters Bar	d	19 43			20 12	20 13	20 42			20 43	21 12	21 13	21 42	21 43	22 12			22 13	22 42			22 43
Hadley Wood	d	19 53				20 23				20 53		21 23		21 53				22 23				22 53
New Barnet	d	20 13				20 43				21 13		21 43		22 13				22 43				23 13
Oakleigh Park	d	20 23				20 53				21 23		21 53		22 23				22 53				23 23
New Southgate	d	20 33				21 03				21 33		22 03		22 33				23 03				23 33
Alexandra Palace	d	20a43	19 49		20a42	21a13	21a12		20 49	21a43	21a42	22a13	22a12	22a43	22a42	21 49		23a13	23a12		22 49	23a43
Hornsey	d		19 51						20 51							21 51					22 51	
Harringay	d		19 53						20 53							21 53					22 53	
Finsbury Park ⊖	d		19 56						20 56							21 56					22 56	
Drayton Park	d																					
Highbury & Islington ⊖	d																					
Essex Road	d																					
Old Street ⊖	d																					
Moorgate ⊖	a																					
London Kings Cross 15 ⊖	a		20 03						21 03							22 03					23 03	

Table 24

Sundays

5 January to 23 March

Letchworth Garden City, Hertford North and Welwyn Garden City - London

Network Diagram - see first Page of Table 24

		FC	FC	FC	FC	FC	FC	FC	FC
		🚌	🚌	🚌	🚌			🚌	1
Letchworth Garden City	d						23 01		23 48
Hitchin 4	d						23 06		23 53
Stevenage 4	d	22 15		22 45			23 12	23 15	23 59
Watton-at-Stone	d						23 18		00 06
Hertford North	d					23 20	23a24		00 12
Bayford	d					23 25			
Cuffley	d					23 29			
Crews Hill	d					23 32			
Gordon Hill	d					23 35			
Enfield Chase	d					23 37			
Grange Park	d					23 39			
Winchmore Hill	d					23 41			
Palmers Green	d					23 44			
Bowes Park	d					23 46			
Knebworth	d	22 22		22 52				23 22	
Welwyn North	d	22 32		23 02				23 32	
Welwyn Garden City 4	d	22 47	22 47	23 17	23 17			23 47	
Hatfield	d	22 57	22 57	23 27	23 27			23 57	
Welham Green	d		23 01		23 31				
Brookmans Park	d		23 05		23 35				
Potters Bar	d	23 12	23 13	23 42	23 43			00 12	
Hadley Wood	d		23 23		23 53				
New Barnet	d		23 43		00 13				
Oakleigh Park	d		23 53		00 23				
New Southgate	d		00 03		00 33				
Alexandra Palace	d	23a42	00a13	00a12	00a43	23 49		00a42	
Hornsey	d					23 51			
Harringay	d					23 53			
Finsbury Park ⊖	d					23 56			00s29
Drayton Park	d								
Highbury & Islington ⊖	d								
Essex Road	d								
Old Street ⊖	d								
Moorgate ⊖	a								
London Kings Cross 15 ⊖	a					00 05			00 39

Sundays

30 March to 11 May

		FC	FC	FC	FC	FC	FC	FC	FC	FC		FC	FC	FC	FC	FC	FC	FC	FC	FC		FC	FC	FC	FC
			1		1							1						1							1
Letchworth Garden City	d											07 29						08 29							09 29
Hitchin 4	d				06 33							07 33						08 33							09 34
Stevenage 4	d				06 39					07 30		07 39					08 30	08 39						09 30	09 40
Watton-at-Stone	d									07 37							08 37							09 37	
Hertford North	d					06 44		07 14		07 44					08 14		08 44					09 14		09 44	
Bayford	d					06 48		07 18		07 48					08 18		08 48					09 18		09 48	
Cuffley	d					06 53		07 23		07 53					08 23		08 53					09 23		09 53	
Crews Hill	d					06 56		07 26		07 56					08 26		08 56					09 26		09 56	
Gordon Hill	d					06 59		07 29		07 59					08 29		08 59					09 29		09 59	
Enfield Chase	d	00 01				07 01		07 31		08 01					08 31		09 01					09 31		10 01	
Grange Park	d	00 03				07 03		07 33		08 03					08 33		09 03					09 33		10 03	
Winchmore Hill	d	00 05				07 05		07 35		08 05					08 35		09 05					09 35		10 05	
Palmers Green	d	00 07				07 07		07 37		08 07					08 37		09 07					09 37		10 07	
Bowes Park	d	00 10				07 10		07 40		08 10					08 40		09 10					09 40		10 10	
Knebworth	d		00 02		06 43							07 43						08 43							09 43
Welwyn North	d		00 05		06 47							07 47						08 47							09 48
Welwyn Garden City 4	d		00 09	06 29	06 50		06 59		07 29			07 51		07 59		08 29		08 51		08 59			09 29		09 52
Hatfield	d		00 12	06 33	06 54		07 03		07 33			07 54		08 03		08 33		08 54		09 03			09 33		09 55
Welham Green	d			06 37			07 07		07 37					08 07		08 37				09 07			09 37		
Brookmans Park	d			06 39			07 09		07 39					08 09		08 39				09 09			09 39		
Potters Bar	d		00 18	06 42	07 00		07 12		07 42			08 00		08 12		08 42		09 00		09 12			09 42		10 01
Hadley Wood	d			06 46			07 16		07 46					08 16		08 46				09 16			09 46		
New Barnet	d			06 49			07 19		07 49					08 19		08 49				09 19			09 49		
Oakleigh Park	d			06 51			07 21		07 51					08 21		08 51				09 21			09 51		
New Southgate	d			06 54			07 24		07 54					08 24		08 54				09 24			09 54		
Alexandra Palace	d	00 12		06 57		07 12	07 27	07 42	07 57	08 12				08 27	08 42	08 57	09 12			09 27		09 42	09 57	10 12	
Hornsey	d	00 14		06 59		07 14	07 29	07 44	07 59	08 14				08 29	08 44	08 59	09 14			09 29		09 44	09 59	10 14	
Harringay	d	00 16		07 01		07 16	07 31	07 46	08 01	08 16			←	08 31	08 46	09 01	09 16		←	09 31		09 46	10 01	10 16	
Finsbury Park ⊖	d	00 19	00s28	07 04	07 10	07 19	07 34	07 49	08 04	08 19		08 10	08 19	08 34	08 49	09 04	09 19	09 10	09 19	09 34		09 49	10 04	10 19	10 10
Drayton Park	d									↪							↪							↪	
Highbury & Islington ⊖	d																								
Essex Road	d																								
Old Street ⊖	d																								
Moorgate ⊖	a																								
London Kings Cross 15 ⊖	a	00 29	00 40	07 14	07 21	07 30	07 44	08 00	08 14			08 19	08 26	08 41	08 56	09 11		09 19	09 26	09 41		09 56	10 11		10 20

Table 24

Sundays

30 March to 11 May

Letchworth Garden City, Hertford North and Welwyn Garden City - London

Network Diagram - see first Page of Table 24

			FC	FC	FC 1	FC	FC		FC	FC 1	FC	FC	FC 1
Letchworth Garden City		d			09 59					10 29			10 59
Hitchin 4		d			10 03					10 33			11 03
Stevenage 4		d			10 09				10 30	10 39			11 09
Watton-at-Stone		d							10 37				
Hertford North		d				10 14			10 44				
Bayford		d				10 18			10 48				
Cuffley		d				10 23			10 53				
Crews Hill		d				10 26			10 56				
Gordon Hill		d				10 29			10 59				
Enfield Chase		d				10 31			11 01				
Grange Park		d				10 33			11 03				
Winchmore Hill		d				10 35			11 05				
Palmers Green		d				10 37			11 07				
Bowes Park		d				10 40			11 10				
Knebworth		d			10 13					10 43			11 13
Welwyn North		d			10 17					10 47			11 17
Welwyn Garden City 4		d		09 59	10 21		10 29			10 51		10 59	11 21
Hatfield		d		10 03	10 24		10 33			10 54		11 03	11 24
Welham Green		d		10 07			10 37					11 07	
Brookmans Park		d		10 09			10 39					11 09	
Potters Bar		d		10 12	10 30		10 42			11 00		11 12	11 30
Hadley Wood		d		10 16			10 46					11 16	
New Barnet		d		10 19			10 49					11 19	
Oakleigh Park		d		10 21			10 51					11 21	
New Southgate		d		10 24			10 54					11 24	
Alexandra Palace		d		10 27		10 42	10 57		11 12			11 27	
Hornsey		d		10 29		10 44	10 59		11 14			11 29	
Harringay		d	←	10 31		10 46	11 01		11 16		←	11 31	
Finsbury Park	⊖	d	10 19	10 34	10 40	10 49	11 04		11 19	11 10	11 19	11 34	11 40
Drayton Park		d							↪				
Highbury & Islington	⊖	d											
Essex Road		d											
Old Street	⊖	d											
Moorgate	⊖	a											
London Kings Cross 15	⊖	a	10 26	10 41	10 49	10 56	11 11			11 19	11 26	11 41	11 49

			FC	FC	FC	FC 1	FC	FC		FC	FC	FC	FC 1	FC
Letchworth Garden City		d				11 29							22 29	
Hitchin 4		d				11 33							22 33	
Stevenage 4		d			11 30	11 39						22 30	22 39	
Watton-at-Stone		d			11 37							22 37		
Hertford North		d	11 14		11 44					22 14		22 44		
Bayford		d	11 18		11 48					22 18		22 48		
Cuffley		d	11 23		11 53					22 23		22 53		
Crews Hill		d	11 26		11 56					22 26		22 56		
Gordon Hill		d	11 29		11 59					22 29		22 59		
Enfield Chase		d	11 31		12 01					22 31		23 01		
Grange Park		d	11 33		12 03					22 33		23 03		
Winchmore Hill		d	11 35		12 05					22 35		23 05		
Palmers Green		d	11 37		12 07					22 37		23 07		
Bowes Park		d	11 40		12 10				and at the same minutes past each hour until	22 40		23 10		
Knebworth		d				11 43							22 43	
Welwyn North		d				11 47							22 47	
Welwyn Garden City 4		d		11 29		11 51		11 59			22 29		22 51	
Hatfield		d		11 33		11 54		12 03			22 33		22 54	
Welham Green		d		11 37				12 07			22 37			
Brookmans Park		d		11 39				12 09			22 39			
Potters Bar		d		11 42		12 00		12 12			22 42		23 00	
Hadley Wood		d		11 46				12 16			22 46			
New Barnet		d		11 49				12 19			22 49			
Oakleigh Park		d		11 51				12 21			22 51			
New Southgate		d		11 54				12 24			22 54			
Alexandra Palace		d	11 42	11 57	12 12			12 27		22 42	22 57	23 12		
Hornsey		d	11 44	11 59	12 14			12 29		22 44	22 59	23 14		
Harringay		d	11 46	12 01	12 16		←	12 31		22 46	23 01	23 16		←
Finsbury Park	⊖	d	11 49	12 04	12 19	12 10	12 19	12 34		22 49	23 04	23 19	23 10	23 19
Drayton Park		d			↪							↪		
Highbury & Islington	⊖	d												
Essex Road		d												
Old Street	⊖	d												
Moorgate	⊖	a												
London Kings Cross 15	⊖	a	11 56	12 11		12 19	12 26	12 41		22 56	23 11		23 19	23 26

			FC		FC	FC	FC 1
Letchworth Garden City		d					23 48
Hitchin 4		d					23 53
Stevenage 4		d				23 30	23 59
Watton-at-Stone		d				23 37	
Hertford North		d			23 14	23 44	
Bayford		d			23 18	23 48	
Cuffley		d			23 23	23 53	
Crews Hill		d			23 26	23 56	
Gordon Hill		d			23 29	23 59	
Enfield Chase		d			23 31	00 01	
Grange Park		d			23 33	00 03	
Winchmore Hill		d			23 35	00 05	
Palmers Green		d			23 37	00 07	
Bowes Park		d			23 40	00 10	
Knebworth		d					00 02
Welwyn North		d					00 06
Welwyn Garden City 4		d	22 59				00 09
Hatfield		d	23 03				00 13
Welham Green		d	23 07				
Brookmans Park		d	23 09				
Potters Bar		d	23 12				00 18
Hadley Wood		d	23 16				
New Barnet		d	23 19				
Oakleigh Park		d	23 21				
New Southgate		d	23 24				
Alexandra Palace		d	23 27		23 42	00 12	
Hornsey		d	23 29		23 44	00 14	
Harringay		d	23 31		23 46	00 16	
Finsbury Park	⊖	d	23 34		23 49	00 19	00s29
Drayton Park		d					
Highbury & Islington	⊖	d					
Essex Road		d					
Old Street	⊖	d					
Moorgate	⊖	a					
London Kings Cross 15	⊖	a	23 41		23 56	00 29	00 40

Table 25

Mondays to Fridays

9 December to 16 May

London - Stevenage, Cambridge and Peterborough

Network Diagram - see first Page of Table 24

Miles	Miles			FC	FC	FC	FC	FC	FC	FC	FC	FC		FC	FC	FC	FC	FC	FC	FC	FC	FC		FC	FC
				MO	MX	MO	MX	MO	MO	MO	MX	MO		MX	MX	MO	MO	MO	MX	MO	MO	MO			MO
				1	1	1	1	1	1	1	1				1		1	1						1	1
				A	B	A	B	C	D	E	B	B		B		F	G	H		G	H	F		I	H
																bus						bus			
0	0	**London Kings Cross** 15 ⊖	d												00 04		00 04	00 04	00 07	00 07	00 11			00 36	00 36
2½	2½	Finsbury Park ⊖	d												00 09		00 09	00 09	00 13	00 13	00 17			00 41	00 41
12¾	12¾	Potters Bar	d														00 19					00 14		00 51	
17¾	17¾	Hatfield	d														00 25					00 29		00 57	
20¼	20¼	Welwyn Garden City 4	d								00 02					00 09	00 29					00 39		01 01	
22	22	Welwyn North	d								00 05					00 19	00 32					00 49		01s04	
25	25	Knebworth	d								00 09					00 29	00 36					00 59		01s08	
—	—	Hertford North	d									00 08		00 09				00 30	00 49	00 49	00 53				
27½	27½	**Stevenage** 4	d								00 13	00 21		00 21	00 35	00a36	00 40	00 40	01 01	01 02	01 06	01a06		01 12	01 12
31¾	31¾	Hitchin 4	d							00 04	00 18	00 26		00 27	00 40		00 47	00 47	01 07	01 07	01 11			01 17	01 17
34¾	—	Letchworth Garden City	d							00 09	00a28	00a35		00a36	00 45		00 53	00 53	01a15	01a16	01a20				
36¾	—	Baldock	d							00 12					00 48		00 56	00 56							
41	—	Ashwell & Morden	d	00 01	00 02					00 17					00 53		01 01	01 01							
45	—	Royston	d	00 05	00 06				00 08	00 22					00 58		01 06	01 06							
48	—	Meldreth	d	00 09	00 10					00 26					01 02		01 10	01 10							
50	—	Shepreth	d	00 12	00 13					00 29					01 05		01 13	01 13							
51	—	Foxton	d	00 15	00 16					00 31					01 07		01 15	01 15							
58	—	**Cambridge**	a	00 28	00 29				00 23	00 44					01 23		01 28	01 28							
—	37	Arlesey	d					00 04																01s25	01s25
—	41	Biggleswade	d			00 02	00 04	00 09																01s30	01s30
—	44	Sandy	d			00 06	00 08	00 13																01s34	01s34
—	51½	St Neots	d			00 13	00 15	00 20																01s42	01s42
—	58¾	Huntingdon	d			00 21	00 23	00 28																01s49	01s49
—	76¼	**Peterborough** 8	a			00 41	00 44	00 48																02 11	02 11

		FC	FC	FC	FC	FC	FC	FC		FC	FC	GR	FC	FC	GR	FC	FC	FC		GR	FC	FC	FC	FC	GR
		MO		MO		MO	MO																		
												R			R					R					R
			1		1	1		1			1	1		1	1	1	1			1	1	1	1	1	1
		F		F	I	H	F				J	K		L	M	B				K		J		L	N
		bus		bus			bus																		
London Kings Cross 15 ⊖	d		01 06		01 36	01 36		05 23			05 45	05 50	05 56	06 05	06 15		06 23	06 26		06 30	06 35	06 45	06 53	07 05	07 08
Finsbury Park ⊖	d		01 11		01 41	01 41		05 28			05 50		06 02	06 10			06 28	06 32			06 40		06 58	07 10	
Potters Bar	d	00 50		01 22	01 59		02 52	05 38						06 21							06 51			07 21	
Hatfield	d	01 05		01 37	02 05		03 07	05 44						06 27							06 57			07 27	
Welwyn Garden City 4	d	01 15		01 47	02 09		03 17	05 48						06 32							07 02			07 32	
Welwyn North	d	01 25		01s57	02s12		03s27	05 51						06 35							07 05			07 35	
Knebworth	d	01 35		02s07	02s16		03s37	05 55						06 39							07 09			07 39	
Hertford North	d		01 38							05 50			06 40			←		07 10							
Stevenage 4	d	01a42	01 47	02a14	02 20	02 20	03a44	05 59		06a05	06 08	06 12	06a54	06 43	06 35	06 43	06 47	07a24		06 50	07 13		07 17	07 43	07 28
Hitchin 4	d		01 52		02 25	02 25		06 07			06 12			→		06 48	06 52				07 18		07 22	→	
Letchworth Garden City	d		02s00								06 17					06 53							07 27		
Baldock	d		02s04								06 20					06 56							07 30		
Ashwell & Morden	d		02s09								06 25					07 01							07 35		
Royston	d		02a15								06 29					07 06							07 39		
Meldreth	d										06 33					07 11							07 43		
Shepreth	d										06 36					07 14							07 46		
Foxton	d										06 39					07 16							07 49		
Cambridge	a										06 50					07 29						07 32	08 03		
Arlesey	d							06 13									06 58				07 24				
Biggleswade	d				02s37	02s37		06 18									07 03				07 29				
Sandy	d							06 22									07 06				07 33				
St Neots	d				02s47	02s47		06 29									07 14				07 41				
Huntingdon	d				02s57	02s57		06 37									07 21				07 49				
Peterborough 8	a				03 16	03 16		06 54				06 41			07 04		07 38			07 19	08 06				07 57

A until 30 December, from 31 March. From London Kings Cross
B From London Kings Cross
C from 6 January until 24 March. From London Kings Cross
D from 6 January until 24 March. From London Kings Cross to Kings Lynn
E from 6 January until 24 March. From Stevenage
F from 6 January until 24 March. From Alexandra Palace
G until 30 December, from 31 March
H from 6 January until 24 March
I until 3 January, MX from 7 January until 21 March, from 25 March
J To Kings Lynn
K To Leeds
L To Cambridge
M To Newcastle
N To York

Table 25

London - Stevenage, Cambridge and Peterborough

Mondays to Fridays

9 December to 16 May

Network Diagram - see first Page of Table 24

		FC	FC	FC	GR	FC	FC	FC	FC	FC		FC	GR	FC	FC	FC	FC	GR	FC	FC		FC	GR	FC	FC
		A	B		C		A			D			C		A		E	F		B			C		A
London Kings Cross 15 ⊖	d	07 15		07 23	07 35	07 35	07 44	07 53	08 03	08 14		08 23	08 35	08 35	08 44	08 53	09 05	09 08	09 14			09 23	09 35	09 35	09 44
Finsbury Park ⊖	d			07 28		07 40		07 58	08 09			08 28		08 40		08 58	09 10					09 28		09 40	
Potters Bar	d					07 51			08 19					08 51			09 21							09 51	
Hatfield	d					07 57			08 25					08 57			09 27							09 57	
Welwyn Garden City 4	d					08 02			08 29					09 02			09 32							10 02	
Welwyn North	d					08 05			08 32					09 05			09 35							10 05	
Knebworth	d					08 09			08 36					09 09			09 39							10 09	
Hertford North	d		←																	←					
Stevenage 4	d		07 43	07 47	07a54	08 13		08 17	08 40			08 47	08a54	09 13		09 17	09 43	09 29		09 43		09 48	09a54	10 13	
Hitchin 4	d		07 48	07 52		08 18		08 22	08 44			08 52		09 18		09 22	→			09 48		09 53		10 18	
Letchworth Garden City	d		07 53					08 27	08 53							09 27				09 53					
Baldock	d		07 57					08 30	08 57							09 30				09 57					
Ashwell & Morden	d		08 02					08 35	09 02							09 35				10 02					
Royston	d		08 07					08 39	09 06							09 39				10 06					
Meldreth	d		08 11					08 43	09 10							09 43				10 10					
Shepreth	d		08 14					08 46	09 13							09 46				10 13					
Foxton	d		08 16					08 49	09 16							09 49				10 16					
Cambridge	a	08 04	08 31				08 34	09 03	09 29	09 03					09 30	10 03			10 05	10 29					10 30
Arlesey	d			07 58		08 24						08 58		09 24								09 58		10 24	
Biggleswade	d			08 03		08 29						09 03		09 29								10 03		10 29	
Sandy	d			08 06		08 33						09 06		09 33								10 06		10 33	
St Neots	d			08 14		08 41						09 14		09 41								10 14		10 41	
Huntingdon	d			08 21		08 49						09 21		09 49								10 21		10 49	
Peterborough 8	a			08 38		09 06						09 38		10 06				09 59				10 39		11 06	

		FC	FC	GR	FC	FC		FC	GR	FC	FC	FC	FC	GR	FC	FC		FC	GR	FC	FC	FC	FC	GR	FC
			E	G		B			C		A		E	F		B			C		A		E	G	
London Kings Cross 15 ⊖	d	09 53	10 05	10 08	10 14			10 23	10 35	10 35	10 44	10 53	11 05	11 08	11 14			11 23	11 35	11 35	11 44	11 53	12 05	12 08	12 14
Finsbury Park ⊖	d	09 58	10 10					10 28		10 40		10 58	11 10					11 28		11 40		11 58	12 10		
Potters Bar	d		10 21							10 51			11 21							11 51			12 21		
Hatfield	d		10 27							10 57			11 27							11 57			12 27		
Welwyn Garden City 4	d		10 32							11 02			11 32							12 02			12 32		
Welwyn North	d		10 35							11 05			11 35							12 05			12 35		
Knebworth	d		10 39							11 09			11 39							12 09			12 39		
Hertford North	d					←										←									
Stevenage 4	d	10 17	10 43	10 29		10 43		10 47	10a54	11 13		11 17	11 43	11 29		11 43		11 47	11a54	12 13		12 17	12 43	12 29	
Hitchin 4	d	10 22	→			10 48		10 52		11 18		11 22	→			11 48		11 52		12 18		12 22	→		
Letchworth Garden City	d	10 27				10 53						11 27				11 53						12 27			
Baldock	d	10 30				10 57						11 30				11 57						12 30			
Ashwell & Morden	d					11 02										12 02									
Royston	d	10 38				11 06						11 38				12 06						12 38			
Meldreth	d					11 10										12 10									
Shepreth	d					11 13										12 13									
Foxton	d					11 16										12 16									
Cambridge	a	10 55			11 02	11 29					11 30	11 55			12 03	12 29					12 30	12 55			13 03
Arlesey	d							10 58		11 24								11 58		12 24					
Biggleswade	d							11 03		11 29								12 03		12 29					
Sandy	d							11 06		11 33								12 06		12 33					
St Neots	d							11 14		11 41								12 14		12 41					
Huntingdon	d							11 21		11 49								12 21		12 49					
Peterborough 8	a			10 59				11 39		12 06				11 58				12 39		13 06				12 59	

		FC		FC	GR	FC	FC	FC	FC	GR	FC	FC		FC	GR	FC	FC	FC	FC	GR	FC	FC		FC	GR
		B			C		A		E	F		B			C		A		E	G		B			C
London Kings Cross 15 ⊖	d			12 23	12 35	12 35	12 44	12 53	13 05	13 08	13 14			13 23	13 35	13 35	13 44	13 53	14 05	14 08	14 14			14 23	14 35
Finsbury Park ⊖	d			12 28		12 40		12 58	13 10					13 28		13 40		13 58	14 10					14 28	
Potters Bar	d					12 51			13 21							13 51			14 21						
Hatfield	d					12 57			13 27							13 57			14 27						
Welwyn Garden City 4	d					13 02			13 32							14 02			14 32						
Welwyn North	d					13 05			13 35							14 05			14 35						
Knebworth	d					13 09			13 39							14 09			14 39						
Hertford North	d	←										←										←			
Stevenage 4	d	12 43		12 47	12a54	13 13		13 17	13 43	13 29		13 43		13 47	13a54	14 13		14 17	14 43	14 28		14 43		14 47	14a54
Hitchin 4	d	12 48		12 52		13 18		13 22	→			13 48		13 52		14 18		14 22	→			14 48		14 52	
Letchworth Garden City	d	12 53						13 27				13 53						14 27				14 53			
Baldock	d	12 57						13 30				13 57						14 30				14 57			
Ashwell & Morden	d	13 02										14 02										15 02			
Royston	d	13 06						13 38				14 06						14 38				15 06			
Meldreth	d	13 10										14 10										15 10			
Shepreth	d	13 13										14 13										15 13			
Foxton	d	13 16										14 16										15 16			
Cambridge	a	13 29					13 30	13 55			14 03	14 29					14 30	14 55			15 03	15 29			
Arlesey	d			12 58		13 24								13 58		14 24								14 58	
Biggleswade	d			13 03		13 29								14 03		14 29								15 03	
Sandy	d			13 06		13 33								14 06		14 33								15 06	
St Neots	d			13 14		13 41								14 14		14 41								15 14	
Huntingdon	d			13 21		13 49								14 21		14 49								15 21	
Peterborough 8	a			13 39		14 06				13 59				14 39		15 06				14 58				15 39	

A To Kings Lynn
B From London Kings Cross
C To Leeds
D To Ely
E To Cambridge
F To York
G To Newark North Gate

Table 25

London - Stevenage, Cambridge and Peterborough

Mondays to Fridays

9 December to 16 May

Network Diagram - see first Page of Table 24

		FC 1	FC 1 A	FC 1	FC 1 B	GR R 1 C	FC 1	FC 1 D		FC 1	GR R 1 E	FC 1	FC 1 A	FC 1	FC 1 B	GR R 1 F	FC 1	FC 1		FC 1 D	FC 1	FC 1 B	GR R 1 E	FC 1	FC 1 A
London Kings Cross 15 ⊖	d	14 35	14 44	14 53	15 05	15 08	15 14			15 23	15 35	15 35	15 44	15 53	16 06	16 09	16 14	16 17			16 22	16 32	16 33	16 40	16 44
Finsbury Park ⊖	d	14 40		14 58	15 10					15 28		15 40		15 58	16 11						16 27	16 37			
Potters Bar	d	14 51			15 21							15 51			16 21							16 47			
Hatfield	d	14 57			15 27							15 57			16 27							16 54			
Welwyn Garden City 4	d	15 02			15 32							16 02			16 31							16 58			
Welwyn North	d	15 05			15 35							16 05			16 34							17 01			
Knebworth	d	15 09			15 39							16 09			16 38						16 45	17 06			
Hertford North	d							←												←					
Stevenage 4	d	15 13		15 17	15 43	15 29		15 43		15 47	15a54	16 13		16 17	16 45	16 30		16 38		16 45	16 49	17 10	16a52		
Hitchin 4	d	15 18		15 22	→			15 48		15 52		16 18		16 22	→					16 50	16 55	17 16			
Letchworth Garden City	d			15 27				15 53						16 27				16 49		16 55		17 26			17 10
Baldock	d			15 30				15 57						16 30				16 52		16 59		→			
Ashwell & Morden	d							16 02										16 57		17 04					
Royston	d			15 38				16 06						16 38				17a04		17 08					17 20
Meldreth	d							16 10												17 12					
Shepreth	d							16 13												17 15					
Foxton	d							16 16												17 18					
Cambridge	a		15 30	15 55			16 03	16 29					16 30	16 55			17 04			17 31					17 35
Arlesey	d	15 24								15 58		16 24									17 00				
Biggleswade	d	15 29								16 03		16 29									17 06			17 07	
Sandy	d	15 33								16 06		16 33									17 10				
St Neots	d	15 41								16 14		16 41									17 21			17 17	
Huntingdon	d	15 49								16 21		16 49									17a30			17 25	
Peterborough 8	a	16 06				15 59				16 39		17 06				16 59								17 41	

		FC 1 D	FC 1	FC 1 B		FC 1	FC 1 G	FC 1 D	FC 1	FC 1 B	FC 1	GR R 1 H	FC 1	FC 1 A		FC 1 D	FC 1	FC 1 B	FC 1	FC 1	FC 1 A		FC 1 D	FC 1
London Kings Cross 15 ⊖	d		16 50	16 54		17 10	17 14		17 14	17 22	17 23	17 33	17 40	17 44			17 44	17 52	17 53	18 10	18 14			18 14
Finsbury Park ⊖	d		16 56	16 59					17 19	17 28							17 49	17 58						18 19
Potters Bar	d																							
Hatfield	d			17 15						17 44								18 14						
Welwyn Garden City 4	d			17 19						17 48								18 18						
Welwyn North	d		17 11	17 22						17 52								18 22						
Knebworth	d			17 26					17 36	17 56								18 26						
Hertford North	d															←							←	
Stevenage 4	d		17 18	17 35				←	17 40	18 02	17 43	17a53				18 02	18 09	18 31	18 13				18 31	18 40
Hitchin 4	d	←	17 23	17 40		17 34		17 40	17 45	→			18 04			18 09	18 14	→		18 34			18 37	18 46
Letchworth Garden City	d	17 26		→				17 47			17 52					18 14			18 23				18 44	
Baldock	d	17 30						17 50			17 55								18 26				18 48	
Ashwell & Morden	d	17 35						17 55			18 00								18 31				18 53	
Royston	d	17 40					17 49	18 00			18a07			18 19		18 28			18a37		18 52	18 57	19 01	
Meldreth	d	17 44						18 04								18 32						19 01		
Shepreth	d	17 47						18 07								18 35						19 04		
Foxton	d	17 49						18 10								18 38						19 06		
Cambridge	a	18 03					18 04	18 24						18 35		18 52					19 09	19 20	19 24	
Arlesey	d		17 29						17 51								18 20							18 52
Biggleswade	d		17 34						17 56								18 26							18 57
Sandy	d		17 38						18 00								18 30							19 02
St Neots	d		17 45			17 51			18 08				18 21				18 38			18 51				19 10
Huntingdon	d		17 53			17 59			18 16				18 29				18 46			18 59				19 18
Peterborough 8	a		18 12			18 20			18 32				18 51				19 03			19 21				19 39

A To Kings Lynn
B To Cambridge
C To York
D From London Kings Cross
E To Leeds
F To Newark North Gate
G To Ely
H To Harrogate

Table 25

London - Stevenage, Cambridge and Peterborough

Mondays to Fridays

9 December to 16 May

Network Diagram - see first Page of Table 24

		FC	FC	GR	FC	FC		FC	FC	FC	FC	GR	FC	FC	FC	FC		FC	GR	FC	FC	FC	FC	FC	FC
		1	1	R 1	1	1		1	1	1	1	R 1	1	1	1	1		1	R 1	1	1	1	1	1	1
		A		B		C		D		A		E		F	D	A			G	H		C	D		A
London Kings Cross 15 ⊖	d	18 22	18 23	18 33	18 40	18 44			18 44	18 52	18 53	19 06	19 10	19 14		19 18		19 23	19 33		19 33	19 44		19 53	20 06
Finsbury Park ⊖	d	18 28							18 49	18 58						19 23		19 28			19 39			19 58	20 11
Potters Bar	d									19 08						19 37									20 21
Hatfield	d	18 44								19 15						19 45					19 52				20 27
Welwyn Garden City 4	d	18 49								19 23						19 50					19 58				20 32
Welwyn North	d	18 51	18 41							19 32						19 53					20 02				20 35
Knebworth	d	18 55							19 05	19 36						19 57					20 06				20 39
Hertford North	d														←					←					
Stevenage 4	d	19 01		18a52				←	19 09	19 40	19 14	19 28			19 40	20 02		19 48	19a52	20 02	20 10			20 18	20 43
Hitchin 4	d	19 07	18 50					19 07	19 15	→	19 19		19 36		19 45	→		19 53		20 09	20 16		←	20 23	20 48
Letchworth Garden City	d	→	18 56					19 13			19 24			19 40	19 55					20 15	20a23	20 10	20 15		20 53
Baldock	d		19 00					19 17			19 28				19 58					→			20 19		→
Ashwell & Morden	d		19 05					19 22			19 33				20 03								20 24		
Royston	d		19a11			19 18		19 32			19a39			19 50	20 08							20 20	20 29		
Meldreth	d							19 36							20 12								20 33		
Shepreth	d							19 39							20 15								20 36		
Foxton	d							19 42							20 17								20 38		
Cambridge	a					19 34		19 56						20 06	20 30							20 35	20 52		
Arlesey	d								19 20									19 59						20 29	
Biggleswade	d				19 08				19 26									20 04						20 34	
Sandy	d								19 30									20 08						20 38	
St Neots	d				19 18				19 38				19 54					20 15						20 45	
Huntingdon	d				19 26				19 46				20 02					20 23						20 57	
Peterborough 8	a				19 44				20 03			19 57	20 21					20 41						21 20	

		FC		FC	FC	FC	GR	FC	FC	FC	FC	GR		FC	FC	FC	FC	FC	GR	FC	FC	FC		FC	FC
		1		1	1	1	R 1	1	1	1	1	R 1		1	1	1	1	1	R 1	1	1	1		1	1
				C	D		G	I	C	D		J		A		C	D		G	I	F	D			A
London Kings Cross 15 ⊖	d	20 10		20 14		20 23	20 35	20 36	20 44		20 53	21 00		21 06	21 10	21 14		21 23	21 35	21 36	21 44			21 53	22 06
Finsbury Park ⊖	d					20 28		20 41			20 58			21 11				21 28		21 41				21 58	22 12
Potters Bar	d							20 51						21 22						21 51					22 22
Hatfield	d							20 57						21 28						21 57					22 28
Welwyn Garden City 4	d							21 02						21 32						22 02					22 32
Welwyn North	d							21 05						21 35						22 05					22 35
Knebworth	d							21 09						21 39						22 09					22 39
Hertford North	d																								
Stevenage 4	d					20 48	20 55	21 13			21 17	21 21		21 43				21 49	21 56	22 13				22 17	22 43
Hitchin 4	d				←	20 53		21 18		←	21 22			21 48			←	21 54		22 18		←		22 22	22 48
Letchworth Garden City	d			20 40	20 53			21 23	21 10	21 23	21 27			21 53		21 40	21 53			22 23	22 10	22 23		22 27	22 53
Baldock	d				20 57			→			21 30			→			21 57			→				22 30	→
Ashwell & Morden	d				21 02						21 35						22 02							22 35	
Royston	d			20 50	21 06				21 20	21a34	21 40					21 50	22 06				22 20	22a34		22 40	
Meldreth	d				21 10						21 44						22 10							22 44	
Shepreth	d				21 13						21 47						22 13							22 47	
Foxton	d				21 16						21 49						22 16							22 49	
Cambridge	a			21 05	21 29				21 35		22 02					22 05	22 29				22 35			23 02	
Arlesey	d					20 59												22 00							
Biggleswade	d					21 04									21 37			22 05							
Sandy	d					21 08												22 09							
St Neots	d	20 45				21 15									21 46			22 16							
Huntingdon	d	20 53				21 23									21 53			22 24							
Peterborough 8	a	21 12				21 42	21 24					21 50			22 09			22 41	22 26						

		FC	FC	FC	FC	FC	FC	FC		FC	FC	FC	FC	FC	FC	FC	FC	FC		FC	FC
		1	1	1	1		1	1		1	1		1	1	1	1	1			1	
			C	D		K	I	F		D		D		A	C	D		K			D
London Kings Cross 15 ⊖	d	22 10	22 14		22 23	22 26	22 36	22 44			22 53		23 01	23 06	23 14		23 23	23 26		23 36	
Finsbury Park ⊖	d				22 28	22 32	22 41				22 58			23 11			23 28	23 32		23 41	
Potters Bar	d						22 52							23 21						23 51	
Hatfield	d						22 58							23 27						23 57	
Welwyn Garden City 4	d						23 02							23 32						00 02	
Welwyn North	d						23 05							23 35						00 05	
Knebworth	d						23 09							23 39						00 09	
Hertford North	d					23 09						←						00 09			←
Stevenage 4	d				22 48	23 21	23 13				23 17	23 21		23 43			23 48	00 21		00 13	00 21
Hitchin 4	d			←	22 53	→	23 18			←	23 22	23 27		23 48		←	23 53	→		00 18	00 27
Letchworth Garden City	d		22 40	22 53			23 23	23 10		23 23	23 27	23a33		23 53	23 40	23 53				00a28	00a36
Baldock	d			22 57			→				23 30			→		23 57					
Ashwell & Morden	d			23 02							23 35					00 02					
Royston	d		22 50	23 06				23 20		23a34	23 40				23 50	00 06					
Meldreth	d			23 10							23 44					00 10					
Shepreth	d			23 13							23 47					00 13					
Foxton	d			23 16							23 49					00 16					
Cambridge	a		23 05	23 29				23 35			00 02				00 05	00 29					
Arlesey	d				22 59												23 59				
Biggleswade	d	22 37			23 04								23 28				00 04				
Sandy	d				23 08												00 08				
St Neots	d	22 46			23 15								23 37				00 15				
Huntingdon	d	22 53			23 23								23 45				00 23				
Peterborough 8	a	23 09			23 44								00 11				00 44				

A To Cambridge
B To Bradford Forster Square
C To Kings Lynn
D From London Kings Cross
E To Lincoln
F To Ely
G To Leeds
H From London Kings Cross to Cambridge
I To Royston
J To Newcastle
K To Letchworth Garden City

Table 25

Saturdays

14 December to 17 May

London - Stevenage, Cambridge and Peterborough

Network Diagram - see first Page of Table 24

		FC	FC	FC	FC	FC	FC	FC	FC	FC		FC	FC	FC	FC	FC	FC	GR	FC	FC		FC	FC	FC	FC
		1	1	1	1		1		1			1	1	1	1	1	1	R 1	1	1			1	1	1
		A	A	A		A		B		A							C	D	A					E	
London Kings Cross 15 ⊖	d				00 01		00 04	00 07	00 31			00 36	01 06	01 36	05 23	05 45	06 06	06 15		06 23		06 26	06 36	06 44	06 53
Finsbury Park ⊖	d						00 09	00 13				00 41	01 11	01 41	05 28	05 50	06 11			06 28		06 32	06 41		06 58
Potters Bar	d											00 51		01 59	05 38		06 21						06 51		
Hatfield	d											00 57		02 05	05 44		06 27						06 57		
Welwyn Garden City 4	d		00 02									01 01		02 09	05 48		06 31						07 01		
Welwyn North	d		00 05									01s04		02s12	05 51		06 34						07 04		
Knebworth	d		00 09									01s08		02s16	05 55		06 38						07 08		
Hertford North	d					00 09		00 49		←			01 38						←			07 08			
Stevenage 4	d		00 13		00 21	00 21	00 35	01 01	00 50	01 01		01 12	01 47	02 20	05 59	06 08	06 42	06 35	06 42	06 47		07a21	07 12		07 17
Hitchin 4	d		00 18		00 25	00 27	00 40	→	00 55	01 07		01 17	01 52	02 25	06 07	06 13	→		06 47	06 52			07 17		07 22
Letchworth Garden City	d		00a28			00a36	00 45		01s00	01a15			02s00			06 17			06 53						07 27
Baldock	d						00 48		01s03				02s04			06 20			06 56						07 30
Ashwell & Morden	d	00 02					00 53						02s09			06 25			07 01						07 35
Royston	d	00 06					00 58		01s11				02a15			06 30			07 06						07 39
Meldreth	d	00 10					01 02									06 34			07 10						07 43
Shepreth	d	00 13					01 05									06 37			07 13						07 46
Foxton	d	00 16					01 07									06 39			07 15						07 49
Cambridge	a	00 29					01 23		01 26							06 55			07 28					07 30	08 02
Arlesey	d											01s25			06 13					06 57			07 23		
Biggleswade	d			00 04	00s34							01s30		02s37	06 18					07 02			07 28		
Sandy	d			00 08								01s34			06 22					07 06			07 32		
St Neots	d			00 15	00s43							01s42		02s47	06 29					07 13			07 39		
Huntingdon	d			00 23	00s54							01s49		02s57	06 37					07 21			07 47		
Peterborough 8	a			00 44	01 10							02 11		03 16	06 54			07 04		07 38			08 06		

		GR	GR	FC	FC	FC		FC	FC	FC	FC	FC	FC	FC	FC	FC		FC	GR	FC	FC	FC	FC	FC	FC
		R 1	R 1	1	1			1	1	1	1	1	1		1	1		1	R 1	1	1	1		1	1
		D	F						E							E			F						E
London Kings Cross 15 ⊖	d	07 00	07 03	07 06	07 23	07 26		07 36	07 44	07 53	08 06	08 14	08 23	08 26	08 36	08 44		08 53	09 03	09 06	09 14	09 23	09 26	09 36	09 44
Finsbury Park ⊖	d			07 11	07 28	07 32		07 41		07 58	08 11		08 28	08 32	08 41			08 58		09 11		09 28	09 32	09 41	
Potters Bar	d			07 21				07 51			08 21				08 51					09 21				09 51	
Hatfield	d			07 27				07 57			08 27				08 57					09 27				09 57	
Welwyn Garden City 4	d			07 31				08 01			08 31				09 01					09 31				10 01	
Welwyn North	d			07 34				08 04			08 34				09 04					09 34				10 04	
Knebworth	d			07 38				08 08			08 38				09 08					09 38				10 08	
Hertford North	d					08 08								09 08									10 08		
Stevenage 4	d	07a19	07 25	07 42	07 47	08a21		08 12		08 17	08 42		08 47	09a21	09 12			09 17	09 23	09 42		09 47	10a21	10 12	
Hitchin 4	d			07 47	07 52			08 17		08 22	08 47		08 52		09 17			09 22		09 47		09 52		10 17	
Letchworth Garden City	d			07 53						08 27	08 53							09 27		09 53					
Baldock	d			07 56						08 30	08 56							09 30		09 56					
Ashwell & Morden	d			08 01							09 01									10 01					
Royston	d			08 06						08 38	09 06							09 38		10 06					
Meldreth	d			08 10							09 10									10 10					
Shepreth	d			08 13							09 13									10 13					
Foxton	d			08 15							09 15									10 15					
Cambridge	a			08 28					08 30	08 55	09 28	09 03				09 30		09 55		10 28	10 03				10 30
Arlesey	d				07 57			08 23					08 57		09 23							09 57		10 23	
Biggleswade	d				08 02			08 28					09 02		09 28							10 02		10 28	
Sandy	d				08 06			08 32					09 06		09 32							10 06		10 32	
St Neots	d				08 13			08 39					09 13		09 39							10 13		10 39	
Huntingdon	d				08 21			08 47					09 21		09 47							10 21		10 47	
Peterborough 8	a		07 53		08 38			09 06					09 38		10 06				09 52			10 38		11 06	

		FC		FC	FC	FC	FC	FC	FC	FC	GR	FC		FC	FC	FC	FC	FC	FC	FC	FC	FC		FC	FC
		1		1	1	1		1	1	1	R 1	1		1	1		1	1	1	1	1	1			1
									E		F							E							
London Kings Cross 15 ⊖	d	09 53		10 06	10 14	10 23	10 26	10 36	10 44	10 53	11 03	11 06		11 14	11 23	11 26	11 36	11 44	11 53	12 06	12 14	12 23		12 26	12 36
Finsbury Park ⊖	d	09 58		10 11		10 28	10 32	10 41		10 58		11 11			11 28	11 32	11 41		11 58	12 11		12 28		12 32	12 41
Potters Bar	d			10 21				10 51				11 21					11 51			12 21					12 51
Hatfield	d			10 27				10 57				11 27					11 57			12 27					12 57
Welwyn Garden City 4	d			10 31				11 01				11 31					12 01			12 31					13 01
Welwyn North	d			10 34				11 04				11 34					12 04			12 34					13 04
Knebworth	d			10 38				11 08				11 38					12 08			12 38					13 08
Hertford North	d						11 08									12 08								13 08	
Stevenage 4	d	10 17		10 42		10 47	11a21	11 12		11 17	11 23	11 42			11 47	12a21	12 12		12 17	12 42		12 47		13a21	13 12
Hitchin 4	d	10 22		10 47		10 52		11 17		11 22		11 47			11 52		12 17		12 22	12 47		12 52			13 17
Letchworth Garden City	d	10 27		10 53						11 27		11 53							12 27	12 53					
Baldock	d	10 30		10 56						11 30		11 56							12 30	12 56					
Ashwell & Morden	d			11 01								12 01								13 01					
Royston	d	10 38		11 06						11 38		12 06							12 38	13 06					
Meldreth	d			11 10								12 10								13 10					
Shepreth	d			11 13								12 13								13 13					
Foxton	d			11 15								12 15								13 15					
Cambridge	a	10 55		11 28	11 03				11 30	11 55		12 28		12 03				12 30	12 55	13 28	13 03				
Arlesey	d					10 57		11 23							11 57		12 23					12 57			13 23
Biggleswade	d					11 02		11 28							12 02		12 28					13 02			13 28
Sandy	d					11 06		11 32							12 06		12 32					13 06			13 32
St Neots	d					11 13		11 39							12 13		12 39					13 13			13 39
Huntingdon	d					11 21		11 47							12 21		12 47					13 21			13 47
Peterborough 8	a					11 38		12 06			11 52				12 39		13 06					13 38			14 06

A From London Kings Cross
B To Letchworth Garden City
C To Cambridge
D To Edinburgh
E To Kings Lynn
F To Leeds

Table 25

Saturdays

14 December to 17 May

London - Stevenage, Cambridge and Peterborough

Network Diagram - see first Page of Table 24

		FC	FC	GR	FC	FC	FC	FC		FC	FC	FC	FC	FC	FC	FC	FC	FC		FC	GR	FC	FC	FC	FC
		1	1	R 1	1	1	1			1	1	1	1	1	1		1	1		1	R 1	1	1	1	
		A		B							A							A			B				
London Kings Cross 15 ⊖	d	12 44	12 53	13 03	13 06	13 14	13 23	13 26		13 36	13 44	13 53	14 06	14 14	14 23	14 26	14 36	14 44		14 53	15 03	15 06	15 14	15 23	15 26
Finsbury Park ⊖	d		12 58		13 11		13 28	13 32		13 41		13 58	14 11		14 28	14 32	14 41			14 58		15 11		15 28	15 32
Potters Bar	d				13 21					13 51			14 21				14 51					15 21			
Hatfield	d				13 27					13 57			14 27				14 57					15 27			
Welwyn Garden City 4	d				13 31					14 01			14 31				15 01					15 31			
Welwyn North	d				13 34					14 04			14 34				15 04					15 34			
Knebworth	d				13 38					14 08			14 38				15 08					15 38			
Hertford North	d							14 08								15 08									16 08
Stevenage 4	d		13 17	13 23	13 42		13 47	14a21		14 12		14 17	14 42		14 47	15a21	15 12			15 17	15 24	15 42		15 47	16a21
Hitchin 4	d		13 22		13 47		13 52			14 17		14 22	14 47		14 52		15 17			15 22		15 47		15 52	
Letchworth Garden City	d		13 27		13 53							14 27	14 53							15 27		15 53			
Baldock	d		13 30		13 56							14 30	14 56							15 30		15 56			
Ashwell & Morden	d				14 01								15 01									16 01			
Royston	d		13 38		14 06							14 38	15 06							15 38		16 06			
Meldreth	d				14 10								15 10									16 10			
Shepreth	d				14 13								15 13									16 13			
Foxton	d				14 15								15 15									16 15			
Cambridge	a	13 30	13 55		14 28	14 03					14 30	14 55	15 28	15 03				15 30		15 55		16 28	16 03		
Arlesey	d						13 57			14 23					14 57		15 23							15 57	
Biggleswade	d						14 02			14 28					15 02		15 28							16 02	
Sandy	d						14 06			14 32					15 06		15 32							16 06	
St Neots	d						14 13			14 39					15 13		15 39							16 13	
Huntingdon	d						14 21			14 47					15 21		15 47							16 21	
Peterborough 8	a			13 52			14 38			15 07					15 38		16 06				15 52			16 38	

		FC	FC	FC		FC	FC	FC	FC	FC	FC	FC	FC	GR		FC	FC	FC	FC	FC	FC	FC	FC	FC	
		1	1	1		1	1	1		1	1	1	1	R 1		1	1	1		1	1	1	1	1	
			A									A		B								A		C	
London Kings Cross 15 ⊖	d	15 36	15 44	15 53		16 06	16 14	16 23	16 26	16 36	16 40	16 44	16 53	17 03		17 06	17 14	17 23	17 26	17 36	17 40	17 44	17 53	18 06	
Finsbury Park ⊖	d	15 41		15 58		16 11		16 28	16 32	16 41			16 58			17 11		17 28	17 32	17 41			17 58	18 11	
Potters Bar	d	15 51				16 21				16 51						17 21				17 51				18 21	
Hatfield	d	15 57				16 27				16 57						17 27				17 57				18 27	
Welwyn Garden City 4	d	16 01				16 31				17 01						17 31				18 01				18 31	
Welwyn North	d	16 04				16 34				17 04						17 34				18 04				18 34	
Knebworth	d	16 08				16 38				17 08						17 38				18 08				18 38	
Hertford North	d								17 08										18 08						
Stevenage 4	d	16 12		16 17		16 42		16 47	17a21	17 12			17 17	17 24		17 42		17 47	18a21	18 12			18 17	18 42	
Hitchin 4	d	16 17		16 22		16 47		16 52		17 17			17 22			17 47		17 52		18 17			18 22	→	
Letchworth Garden City	d			16 27		16 53							17 27			17 53							18 27		
Baldock	d			16 30		16 56							17 30			17 56							18 30		
Ashwell & Morden	d					17 01										18 01									
Royston	d			16 38		17 06							17 38			18 06							18 38		
Meldreth	d					17 10										18 10									
Shepreth	d					17 13										18 13									
Foxton	d					17 15										18 15									
Cambridge	a		16 30	16 55		17 28	17 03					17 30	17 55			18 28	18 03					18 30	18 55		
Arlesey	d	16 23						16 57		17 23								17 57		18 23					
Biggleswade	d	16 28						17 02		17 28	17 08							18 02		18 28	18 08				
Sandy	d	16 32						17 06		17 32								18 06		18 32					
St Neots	d	16 39						17 13		17 39	17 18							18 13		18 39	18 18				
Huntingdon	d	16 47						17 21		17 47	17 26							18 21		18 47	18 25				
Peterborough 8	a	17 06						17 38		18 06	17 44			17 52				18 38		19 06	18 41				

A To Kings Lynn

B To Leeds

C To Cambridge

Table 25

Saturdays

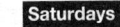

14 December to 17 May

London - Stevenage, Cambridge and Peterborough

Network Diagram - see first Page of Table 24

		GR	FC	FC	FC	FC		FC	FC	FC	FC	FC	FC	FC	FC	FC		GR	FC	FC	FC	FC	FC	FC	FC
		R 1 A	1 B	1 C	1			1	1 D	1 E	1 B	1	1	1	1			R 1 F	1	1 B	1	1	1		1
London Kings Cross 15 ⊖	d	18 08	18 14		18 23	18 26		18 36	18 40	18 40	18 44	18 53	19 06	19 14	19 23	19 26		19 30	19 36	19 44	19 53	20 06	20 23	20 26	20 36
Finsbury Park ⊖	d				18 28	18 32		18 41				18 58	19 11		19 28	19 32			19 41		19 58	20 11	20 28	20 32	20 41
Potters Bar	d							18 51					19 21						19 51			20 21			20 51
Hatfield	d							18 57					19 27						19 57			20 27			20 57
Welwyn Garden City 4	d							19 01					19 31						20 01			20 31			21 01
Welwyn North	d							19 04					19 34						20 04			20 34			21 04
Knebworth	d							19 08					19 38						20 08			20 38			21 08
Hertford North	d			←		19 08										20 08								21 08	
Stevenage 4	d	18 29		18 42	18 47	19a21		19 12				19 17	19 42		19 47	20a21		19 50	20 12		20 17	20 42	20 47	21a21	21 12
Hitchin 4	d			18 47	18 52			19 17				19 22	19 47		19 52				20 17		20 22	20 47	20 52		21 17
Letchworth Garden City	d			18 53								19 27	19 53								20 27	20 53			
Baldock	d			18 56								19 30	19 56								20 30	20 56			
Ashwell & Morden	d			19 01									20 01									21 01			
Royston	d			19 06								19 38	20 06								20 38	21 06			
Meldreth	d			19 10									20 10									21 10			
Shepreth	d			19 13									20 13									21 13			
Foxton	d			19 15									20 15									21 15			
Cambridge	a		19 04	19 28							19 30	19 55	20 28	20 03						20 30	20 56	21 28			
Arlesey	d				18 57			19 23							19 57				20 23				20 57		21 23
Biggleswade	d				19 02			19 28	19 08	19 08					20 02				20 28				21 02		21 28
Sandy	d				19 06			19 32							20 06				20 32				21 06		21 32
St Neots	d				19 13			19 39	19 18	19 18					20 13				20 39				21 13		21 39
Huntingdon	d				19 21			19 47	19 26	19 26					20 21				20 47				21 21		21 47
Peterborough 8	a	18 58			19 37			20 06	19 42	19 45					20 39			20 19	21 06				21 38		22 06

		FC		FC	FC	FC	FC	FC	FC	FC	FC	FC		FC	FC	FC	FC	FC	FC	FC	FC	FC		FC	FC
		1 B		1	1	1		1	1	1	1 G	1 B		1 C	1		1	1	1 G	1 B	1 C	1		H	1
London Kings Cross 15 ⊖	d	20 44		20 53	21 06	21 23	21 26	21 36	21 44	21 53	22 06	22 14			22 23	22 26	22 36	22 53	23 06	23 14		23 23		23 26	23 36
Finsbury Park ⊖	d			20 58	21 11	21 28	21 32	21 41		21 58	22 11				22 28	22 32	22 41	22 58	23 11			23 28		23 32	23 41
Potters Bar	d				21 21			21 51			22 21						22 51		23 21						23 51
Hatfield	d				21 27			21 57			22 27						22 57		23 27						23 57
Welwyn Garden City 4	d				21 31			22 01			22 31						23 01		23 31						00 01
Welwyn North	d				21 34			22 04			22 34						23 04		23 34						00 04
Knebworth	d				21 38			22 08			22 38						23 08		23 38						00 08
Hertford North	d						22 08									23 08								00 08	
Stevenage 4	d			21 17	21 42	21 47	22a21	22 12		22 17	22 42				22 47	23a21	23 12	23 17	23 42			23 47		00 20	00 12
Hitchin 4	d			21 22	21 47	21 52		22 17		22 22	22 47			←	22 52		23 17	23 22	23 47		←	23 52		→	00 20
Letchworth Garden City	d	21 10		21 27	21 53				22 10	22 27	22 53	22 40		22 53			23a24		23 53	23 40	23 53				00a27
Baldock	d			21 30	21 56					22 30	→			22 56					→		23 56				
Ashwell & Morden	d				22 01									23 01							00 01				
Royston	d	21 20		21 38	22 06				22 20	22 38		22 50		23 06						23 50	00 06				
Meldreth	d				22 10									23 10							00 10				
Shepreth	d				22 13									23 13							00 13				
Foxton	d				22 15									23 15							00 15				
Cambridge	a	21 35		21 55	22 28				22 35	22 55		23 05		23 28						00 05	00 28				
Arlesey	d					21 57		22 23							22 57			23 27				23 57			
Biggleswade	d					22 02		22 28							23 02			23 32				00 02			
Sandy	d					22 06		22 32							23 06			23 36				00 06			
St Neots	d					22 13		22 39							23 13			23 43				00 13			
Huntingdon	d					22 21		22 47							23 21			23 51				00 21			
Peterborough 8	a					22 38		23 06							23 38			00 12				00 42			

		FC	FC
		C	1
London Kings Cross 15 ⊖	d		23 53
Finsbury Park ⊖	d		23 58
Potters Bar	d		
Hatfield	d		
Welwyn Garden City 4	d		
Welwyn North	d		
Knebworth	d		
Hertford North	d	←	
Stevenage 4	d	00 20	00 25
Hitchin 4	d	00 26	00 31
Letchworth Garden City	d	00a35	
Baldock	d		
Ashwell & Morden	d		
Royston	d		
Meldreth	d		
Shepreth	d		
Foxton	d		
Cambridge	a		
Arlesey	d		00s39
Biggleswade	d		00s44
Sandy	d		00s48
St Neots	d		00s55
Huntingdon	d		01s03
Peterborough 8	a		01 24

A To Lincoln
B To Kings Lynn
C From London Kings Cross
D not until 21 December
E 14 December, 21 December
F To Bradford Forster Square
G To Cambridge
H To Letchworth Garden City

Table 25

Sundays

8 December to 29 December

London - Stevenage, Cambridge and Peterborough

Network Diagram - see first Page of Table 24

		FC [1] A	FC [1] A	FC [1] A	FC A	FC [1] A	FC [1] B	FC [1]	FC [1] C	FC [1]	FC [1]	FC	FC	FC [1]	FC [1]	FC [1] D	FC [1] E	FC	FC [1] F	FC [1]	FC [1]	FC	FC [1]
London Kings Cross [15] ⊖	d						00 06	00 15		00 23	00 53	00 56	06 26	06 38	07 06	07 06		07 26	07 53	08 06	08 23	08 26	08 53
Finsbury Park ⊖	d						00 11			00 28	00 58	01 02	06 32	06 43	07 11	07 11		07 32	07 58	08 11	08 28	08 32	08 58
Potters Bar	d						00 21				01 08				07 21	07 21				08 21			
Hatfield	d						00 27				01 14				07 27	07 27				08 27			
Welwyn Garden City [4]	d		00 01				00 38				01 18				07 31	07 31				08 31			
Welwyn North	d		00 04				00 40				01s21				07 34	07 34				08 34			
Knebworth	d		00 08				00 44				01s24				07 38	07 38				08 38			
Hertford North	d				00 08				←			01 38	07 08					08 08				09 08	
Stevenage [4]	d		00 12		00 20	00 25	00 49	00 41	00 49	00 55	01 28	01 50	07a24	07 06	07 46	07 50	07 50	08a24	08 17	08 42	08 47	09a21	09 17
Hitchin [4]	d		00 20		00 26	00 31	→	00 47	00 55	01 01	01 33	01 56		07 14	07 54	07 58	07 58		08 22	08 47	08 52		09 22
Letchworth Garden City	d		00a27		00a35			00s54	01 00			02a05		07 19	08 00				08 27	08 52			09 27
Baldock	d							00s57	01 04					07 22	08 03				08 30	08 56			09 30
Ashwell & Morden	d	00 01							01 09						08 08					09 01			
Royston	d	00 06						01s05	01 13					07 31	08 13				08 38	09 05			09 38
Meldreth	d	00 10							01 17						08 17					09 09			
Shepreth	d	00 13							01 20						08 20					09 12			
Foxton	d	00 15							01 23						08 22					09 15			
Cambridge	a	00 28						01 22	01 38					07 48	08 35				08 55	09 28			09 55
Arlesey	d					00s39				01s08	01s42					08 03	08 03				08 57		
Biggleswade	d			00 02		00s44				01s13	01s47					08 08	08 08				09 02		
Sandy	d			00 06		00s48				01s17	01s50					08 12	08 12				09 06		
St Neots	d			00 13		00s55				01s24	01s58					08 19	08 19				09 13		
Huntingdon	d			00 21		01s03				01s32	02s05					08 27	08 27				09 21		
Peterborough [8]	a			00 42		01 24				01 54	02 26					08 43	08 43				09 39		

		GR [R] [1] G 🍴	FC [1]	FC [1] F	FC [1]	FC	FC [1]	FC [1]	FC [1] F	FC [1]	FC	FC [1]	GR [R] [1] G 🍴	FC [1]	FC [1] F	FC [1]	FC	FC [1]	FC [1]	FC [1] F	FC [1]	FC	FC [1]
London Kings Cross [15] ⊖	d	09 03	09 06	09 15	09 23	09 26	09 53	10 06	10 15	10 23	10 26	10 53	11 03	11 06	11 15	11 23	11 26	11 53	12 06	12 15	12 23	12 26	12 53
Finsbury Park ⊖	d		09 11		09 28	09 32	09 58	10 11		10 28	10 32	10 58		11 11		11 28	11 32	11 58	12 11		12 28	12 32	12 58
Potters Bar	d		09 21					10 21						11 21					12 21				
Hatfield	d		09 27					10 27						11 27					12 27				
Welwyn Garden City [4]	d		09 31					10 31						11 31					12 31				
Welwyn North	d		09 34					10 34						11 34					12 34				
Knebworth	d		09 38					10 38						11 38					12 38				
Hertford North	d					10 08					11 08						12 08					13 08	
Stevenage [4]	d	09 23	09 42		09 47	10a21	10 17	10 42		10 47	11a21	11 17	11 23	11 42		11 47	12a21	12 17	12 42		12 47	13a21	13 17
Hitchin [4]	d		09 47		09 52		10 22	10 47		10 52		11 22		11 47		11 52		12 22	12 47		12 52		13 22
Letchworth Garden City	d		09 52				10 27	10 52				11 27		11 52				12 27	12 52				13 27
Baldock	d		09 56				10 30	10 56				11 30		11 56				12 30	12 56				13 30
Ashwell & Morden	d		10 01					11 01						12 01					13 01				
Royston	d		10 05				10 38	11 05				11 38		12 05				12 38	13 05				13 38
Meldreth	d		10 09					11 09						12 09					13 09				
Shepreth	d		10 12					11 12						12 12					13 12				
Foxton	d		10 15					11 15						12 15					13 15				
Cambridge	a		10 28	10 02			10 55	11 28	11 01			11 55		12 28	12 01			12 55	13 28	13 01			13 55
Arlesey	d				09 57					10 57						11 57					12 57		
Biggleswade	d				10 02					11 02						12 02					13 02		
Sandy	d				10 06					11 06						12 06					13 06		
St Neots	d				10 13					11 13						12 13					13 13		
Huntingdon	d				10 21					11 21						12 21					13 21		
Peterborough [8]	a	09 52			10 39					11 39			11 52			12 38					13 39		

		GR [R] [1] G 🍴	FC [1]	FC [1] F	FC [1]	FC	FC [1]	FC [1]	FC [1] F	FC [1]	FC	FC [1]	GR [R] [1] G 🍴	FC [1]	FC [1] F	FC [1]	FC	FC [1]	FC [1]	FC [1] F	FC [1]	FC
London Kings Cross [15] ⊖	d	13 03	13 06	13 15	13 23	13 26	13 53	14 06	14 15	14 23	14 26	14 53	15 03	15 06	15 15	15 23	15 26	15 53	16 06	16 15	16 23	16 26
Finsbury Park ⊖	d		13 11		13 28	13 32	13 58	14 11		14 28	14 32	14 58		15 11		15 28	15 32	15 58	16 11		16 28	16 32
Potters Bar	d		13 21					14 21						15 21					16 21			
Hatfield	d		13 27					14 27						15 27					16 27			
Welwyn Garden City [4]	d		13 31					14 31						15 31					16 31			
Welwyn North	d		13 34					14 34						15 34					16 34			
Knebworth	d		13 38					14 38						15 38					16 38			
Hertford North	d					14 08					15 08						16 08					17 08
Stevenage [4]	d	13 23	13 42		13 47	14a21	14 17	14 42		14 47	15a21	15 17	15 23	15 42		15 47	16a21	16 17	16 42		16 47	17a21
Hitchin [4]	d		13 47		13 52		14 22	14 47		14 52		15 22		15 47		15 52		16 22	16 47		16 52	
Letchworth Garden City	d		13 52				14 27	14 52				15 27		15 52				16 27	16 52			
Baldock	d		13 56				14 30	14 56				15 30		15 56				16 30	16 56			
Ashwell & Morden	d		14 01					15 01						16 01					17 01			
Royston	d		14 05				14 38	15 05				15 38		16 05				16 38	17 05			
Meldreth	d		14 09					15 09						16 09					17 09			
Shepreth	d		14 12					15 12						16 12					17 12			
Foxton	d		14 15					15 15						16 15					17 15			
Cambridge	a		14 28	14 01			14 55	15 28	15 01			15 55		16 28	16 01			16 55	17 28	17 01		
Arlesey	d				13 57					14 57						15 57					16 57	
Biggleswade	d				14 02					15 02						16 02					17 02	
Sandy	d				14 06					15 06						16 06					17 06	
St Neots	d				14 13					15 13						16 13					17 13	
Huntingdon	d				14 21					15 21						16 21					17 21	
Peterborough [8]	a	13 52			14 39					15 39			15 52			16 39					17 39	

A not 8 December. From London Kings Cross
B To Cambridge
C From London Kings Cross
D until 28 December
E 29 December
F To Kings Lynn
G To Leeds

Table 25

Sundays

8 December to 29 December

London - Stevenage, Cambridge and Peterborough

Network Diagram - see first Page of Table 24

		GR	FC	FC	FC	FC	FC	FC		GR	FC	FC	FC	FC	FC	FC	FC	GR		FC	FC	FC	GR	FC	FC
		R 1 A	1	1	1	1 B	1			R 1 A	1	1	1	1	1 B	1		R 1 C		1	1	1 D	R 1 E	1 B	1 F
London Kings Cross 15 ⊖	d	16 35	16 36	16 53	17 06	17 15	17 23	17 26		17 35	17 36	17 53	18 06	18 10	18 15	18 23	18 26	18 35		18 36	18 53	19 06	19 08	19 15	
Finsbury Park ⊖	d		16 41	16 58	17 11		17 28	17 32			17 41	17 58	18 11			18 28	18 32			18 41	18 58	19 11			
Potters Bar	d		16 51		17 21						17 51		18 21							18 51		19 21			
Hatfield	d		16 57		17 27						17 57		18 27							18 57		19 27			
Welwyn Garden City 4	d		17 01		17 31						18 01		18 31							19 01		19 31			
Welwyn North	d		17 04		17 34						18 04		18 34							19 04		19 34			
Knebworth	d		17 08		17 38						18 08		18 38							19 08		19 38			
Hertford North	d							18 08									19 08								←
Stevenage 4	d	16a54	17 12	17 17	17 42		17 47	18a21		17a54	18 12	18 17	18 42			18 47	19a21	18a54		19 12	19 17	19 42	19 29		19 42
Hitchin 4	d		17 17	17 22	17 47		17 52				18 17	18 22	18 47			18 52				19 17	19 22	↪			19 47
Letchworth Garden City	d			17 27	17 52							18 27	18 52							19 22	19 27				19 52
Baldock	d			17 30	17 56							18 30	18 56								19 30				19 56
Ashwell & Morden	d				18 01								19 01												20 01
Royston	d			17 38	18 05							18 38	19 05							19a34	19 38				20 05
Meldreth	d				18 09								19 09												20 09
Shepreth	d				18 12								19 12												20 12
Foxton	d				18 15								19 15												20 15
Cambridge	a			17 55	18 28	18 01						18 55	19 28		19 01						19 56			20 02	20 28
Arlesey	d		17 23				17 57				18 23					18 57									
Biggleswade	d		17 28				18 02				18 28			18 37		19 02									
Sandy	d		17 32				18 06				18 32					19 06									
St Neots	d		17 39				18 13				18 39			18 47		19 13									
Huntingdon	d		17 47				18 21				18 47			18 54		19 21									
Peterborough 8	a		18 06				18 39				19 06			19 12		19 39							19 59		

		FC	FC	GR		FC	FC	FC	FC	FC	GR	FC	FC	FC		FC	FC	GR	FC	FC	FC	FC	FC	FC	
		1		R 1 A		1	1	1 B	1		R 1 A	1	1	1 B		1		R 1 A	1	1	1 B	1		1	
London Kings Cross 15 ⊖	d	19 23	19 26	19 35		19 53	20 06	20 15	20 23	20 26	20 35	20 53	21 06	21 15		21 23	21 26	21 35	21 53	22 06	22 15	22 23	22 26	22 53	
Finsbury Park ⊖	d	19 28	19 32			19 58	20 11		20 28	20 32		20 58	21 11			21 28	21 32		21 58	22 11		22 28	22 32	22 58	
Potters Bar	d						20 21						21 21							22 21					
Hatfield	d						20 27						21 27							22 27					
Welwyn Garden City 4	d						20 31						21 31							22 31					
Welwyn North	d						20 34						21 34							22 34					
Knebworth	d						20 38						21 38							22 38					
Hertford North	d		20 08							21 08							22 08						23 08		
Stevenage 4	d	19 47	20a21	19 55		20 17	20 42		20 47	21a21	20 55	21 17	21 42			21 47	22a21	21 56	22 17	22 42		22 47	23a21	23 17	
Hitchin 4	d	19 52				20 22	20 47		20 52			21 22	21 47			21 52			22 22	22 47		22 52		23 22	
Letchworth Garden City	d					20 27	20 52					21 27	21 52						22 27	22 52				23 27	
Baldock	d					20 30	20 56					21 30	21 56						22 30	22 56				23 30	
Ashwell & Morden	d						21 01						22 01							23 01					
Royston	d					20 38	21 05					21 38	22 05						22 38	23 05				23 38	
Meldreth	d						21 09						22 09							23 09					
Shepreth	d						21 12						22 12							23 12					
Foxton	d						21 15						22 15							23 15					
Cambridge	a					20 55	21 28	21 01				21 55	22 28	22 01					22 55	23 28	23 01			23 55	
Arlesey	d	19 57							20 57							21 57						22 57			
Biggleswade	d	20 02							21 02							22 02						23 02			
Sandy	d	20 06							21 06							22 06						23 06			
St Neots	d	20 13							21 13							22 13						23 13			
Huntingdon	d	20 21							21 21							22 21						23 21			
Peterborough 8	a	20 39		20 24					21 39		21 24					22 39		22 25				23 41			

		FC	FC	FC	FC	FC
		1 D	1 B	1 F	1	
London Kings Cross 15 ⊖	d	23 06	23 15		23 23	23 26
Finsbury Park ⊖	d	23 11			23 28	23 32
Potters Bar	d	23 21				
Hatfield	d	23 27				
Welwyn Garden City 4	d	23 31				
Welwyn North	d	23 34				
Knebworth	d	23 38				
Hertford North	d					00 08
Stevenage 4	d	23 42			23 47	00 21
Hitchin 4	d	23 47		←	23 52	00 26
Letchworth Garden City	d	23 52	23 41	23 52		00a35
Baldock	d	↪		23 56		
Ashwell & Morden	d			00 01		
Royston	d		23 51	00 05		
Meldreth	d			00 09		
Shepreth	d			00 12		
Foxton	d			00 15		
Cambridge	a		00 07	00 28		
Arlesey	d				23 57	
Biggleswade	d				00 02	
Sandy	d				00 06	
St Neots	d				00 13	
Huntingdon	d				00 21	
Peterborough 8	a				00 41	

A To Leeds
B To Kings Lynn
C To Skipton
D To Cambridge
E To Lincoln
F From London Kings Cross

Table 25

Sundays

5 January to 23 March

London - Stevenage, Cambridge and Peterborough

Network Diagram - see first Page of Table 24

		FC	FC	FC	FC	FC	FC	FC	FC	FC	FC	FC	FC	FC	FC	FC	FC	FC	FC	FC	FC	FC	FC
		1	1	1		1	1	1	1	1	1				1		1	1			1		1
		A	A	A	A	A	B		A							C			C			C	D
												🚌				🚌			🚌			🚌	
London Kings Cross 15 ⊖	d						00 06	00 15		00 23	00 53		00 56	05 56	06 38			07 08			07 38		08 04
Finsbury Park ⊖	d						00 11			00 28	00 58		01 02	06 02	06 44			07 14			07 43		
Potters Bar	d						00 21				01 08					06 44			07 03			07 33	
Hatfield	d						00 27				01 14					06 59			07 18			07 48	
Welwyn Garden City 4	d		00 01				00 38				01 18					07 09			07 28			07 58	
Welwyn North	d		00 04				00 40				01s21					07 19			07 38			08 08	
Knebworth	d		00 08				00 44				01s24					07 29			07 48			08 18	
Hertford North	d				00 08				←				01 38	06 47						07 47			
Stevenage 4	d		00 12		00 20	00 25	00 49	00 41	00 49	00 55	01 28		01 50	06 59	07 10	07a36	07 48	07 52	07a55	07 59	08 09	08a25	
Hitchin 4	d		00 20		00 26	00 31	→	00 47	00 55	01 01	01 33		01 56	07 05	07 16		07 54	07 57		08 05	08 14		
Letchworth Garden City	d		00a27		00a35			00s54	01 00		01a43	01 49	02a05	07a11	07 21		07 59			08a11	08 19		
Baldock	d							00s57	01 04						07 24		08 03				08 22		
Ashwell & Morden	d	00 01							01 09								08 08						
Royston	d	00 06						01s05	01 13						07 32		08 12				08 31		
Meldreth	d	00 10							01 17								08 16						
Shepreth	d	00 13							01 20								08 19						
Foxton	d	00 15							01 23								08 22						
Cambridge	a	00 28						01 22	01 38						07 49		08 35				08 48		09 02
Arlesey	d					00s39				01s08		02s01						08 03					
Biggleswade	d			00 02		00s44				01s13		02s21						08 08					
Sandy	d			00 06		00s48				01s17		02s31						08 11					
St Neots	d			00 13		00s55				01s24		02s51						08 19					
Huntingdon	d			00 21		01s03				01s32		03s21						08 26					
Peterborough 8	a			00 42		01 24				01 54		04 01						08 43					

		FC	FC	FC	FC	FC	FC	GR	FC	FC	FC	FC	FC	FC	FC	FC	FC	FC	FC	FC	FC	FC	GR
								R															R
		1	1			1		1	1	1	1			1		1	1	1			1		1
				C			C	E	D			C			C	D			C			C	E
				🚌			🚌	🛒				🚌			🚌				🚌			🚌	🛒
London Kings Cross 15 ⊖	d	08 08				08 38		08 56	09 04	09 08				09 38		10 04	10 08				10 38		10 56
Finsbury Park ⊖	d	08 13				08 43				09 13				09 43			10 13				10 43		
Potters Bar	d			08 03			08 33					09 03			09 33				10 03			10 33	
Hatfield	d			08 18			08 48					09 18			09 48				10 18			10 48	
Welwyn Garden City 4	d			08 28			08 58					09 28			09 58				10 28			10 58	
Welwyn North	d			08 38			09 08					09 38			10 08				10 38			11 08	
Knebworth	d			08 48			09 18					09 48			10 18				10 48			11 18	
Hertford North	d				08 47								09 47							10 47			
Stevenage 4	d	08 40	08 48	08a55	08 59	09 09	09a25	09 26		09 40	09 48	09a55	09 59	10 09	10a25		10 40	10 48	10a55	10 59	11 09	11a25	11 26
Hitchin 4	d	08 45	08 54		09 05	09 14				09 45	09 54		10 05	10 14			10 45	10 54		11 05	11 14		
Letchworth Garden City	d		08 59		09a11	09 19					09 59		10a11	10 19				10 59		11a11	11 19		
Baldock	d		09 03			09 22					10 03			10 22				11 03			11 22		
Ashwell & Morden	d		09 08								10 08							11 08					
Royston	d		09 12			09 31					10 12			10 31				11 12			11 31		
Meldreth	d		09 16								10 16							11 16					
Shepreth	d		09 19								10 19							11 19					
Foxton	d		09 22								10 22							11 22					
Cambridge	a		09 35			09 48			10 02		10 35			10 48		11 01		11 35			11 48		
Arlesey	d	08 50								09 50							10 50						
Biggleswade	d	08 55								09 55							10 55						
Sandy	d	08 59								09 59							10 59						
St Neots	d	09 06								10 06							11 06						
Huntingdon	d	09 14								10 14							11 14						
Peterborough 8	a	09 32						09 55		10 32							11 32						11 55

		FC	FC	FC	FC	FC	FC	FC	FC	FC	FC	FC	FC	FC	FC	GR	FC	FC	FC	FC	FC	FC
																R						
		1	1	1			1		1	1	1			1		1	1	1	1			1
		D			C			C	D			C			C	E	D			C		
					🚌			🚌				🚌			🚌	🛒				🚌		
London Kings Cross 15 ⊖	d	11 04	11 08				11 38		12 04	12 08				12 38		12 56	13 04	13 08				13 38
Finsbury Park ⊖	d		11 13				11 43			12 13				12 43				13 13				13 43
Potters Bar	d				11 03			11 33				12 03			12 33					13 03		
Hatfield	d				11 18			11 48				12 18			12 48					13 18		
Welwyn Garden City 4	d				11 28			11 58				12 28			12 58					13 28		
Welwyn North	d				11 38			12 08				12 38			13 08					13 38		
Knebworth	d				11 48			12 18				12 48			13 18					13 48		
Hertford North	d					11 47							12 47								13 47	
Stevenage 4	d		11 40	11 48	11a55	11 59	12 09	12a25		12 40	12 48	12a55	12 59	13 09	13a25	13 28		13 40	13 48	13a55	13 59	14 09
Hitchin 4	d		11 45	11 54		12 05	12 14			12 45	12 54		13 05	13 14				13 45	13 54		14 05	14 14
Letchworth Garden City	d			11 59		12a11	12 19				12 59		13a11	13 19					13 59		14a11	14 19
Baldock	d			12 03			12 22				13 03			13 22					14 03			14 22
Ashwell & Morden	d			12 08							13 08								14 08			
Royston	d			12 12			12 31				13 12			13 31					14 12			14 31
Meldreth	d			12 16							13 16								14 16			
Shepreth	d			12 19							13 19								14 19			
Foxton	d			12 22							13 22								14 22			
Cambridge	a	12 01		12 35			12 48		13 01		13 35			13 48			14 01		14 35			14 48
Arlesey	d		11 50							12 50								13 50				
Biggleswade	d		11 55							12 55								13 55				
Sandy	d		11 59							12 59								13 59				
St Neots	d		12 06							13 06								14 06				
Huntingdon	d		12 14							13 14								14 14				
Peterborough 8	a		12 32							13 32						13 57		14 32				

A From London Kings Cross
B To Cambridge
C From Alexandra Palace
D To Kings Lynn
E To Leeds

Table 25

Sundays

5 January to 23 March

London - Stevenage, Cambridge and Peterborough

Network Diagram - see first Page of Table 24

		FC	FC	FC	FC	FC	FC	FC	GR	FC	FC	FC	FC	FC	FC	FC	FC	FC	FC	FC	FC	FC	FC
									R														
			1	1	1			1	1		1	1	1			1		1	1	1			1
		A	B			A			C	A	B			A			A	B			A		
London Kings Cross 15 ⊖	d		14 04	14 08				14 38	14 52		15 04	15 08				15 38		16 04	16 08				16 38
Finsbury Park ⊖	d			14 13				14 43				15 13				15 43			16 13				16 43
Potters Bar	d	13 33				14 03				14 33				15 03			15 33				16 03		
Hatfield	d	13 48				14 18				14 48				15 18			15 48				16 18		
Welwyn Garden City 4	d	13 58				14 28				14 58				15 28			15 58				16 28		
Welwyn North	d	14 08				14 38				15 08				15 38			16 08				16 38		
Knebworth	d	14 18				14 48				15 18				15 48			16 18				16 48		
Hertford North	d						14 47								15 47							16 47	
Stevenage 4	d	14a25		14 39	14 48	14a55	14 59	15 09	15 23	15a25		15 43	15 48	15a55	15 59	16 09	16a25		16 40	16 48	16a55	16 59	17 09
Hitchin 4	d			14 44	14 54		15 05	15 14				15 48	15 54		16 05	16 14			16 45	16 54		17 05	17 14
Letchworth Garden City	d				14 59		15a11	15 19					15 59		16a11	16 19				16 59		17a11	17 19
Baldock	d				15 03			15 22					16 03			16 22				17 03			17 22
Ashwell & Morden	d				15 08								16 08							17 08			
Royston	d				15 12			15 31					16 12			16 31				17 12			17 31
Meldreth	d				15 16								16 16							17 16			
Shepreth	d				15 19								16 19							17 19			
Foxton	d				15 22								16 22							17 22			
Cambridge	a		15 01		15 35			15 48			16 01		16 35			16 48		17 01		17 35			17 48
Arlesey	d			14 50								15 53							16 50				
Biggleswade	d			14 55								15 58							16 55				
Sandy	d			14 58								16 02							16 59				
St Neots	d			15 06								16 09							17 06				
Huntingdon	d			15 14								16 17							17 14				
Peterborough 8	a			15 33					15 52			16 33							17 32				

		FC	GR	FC	FC	FC	FC	GR	FC	FC	FC	FC	FC	FC	FC	FC	FC	GR	FC	FC	FC	FC
			R					R										R				
		1	1		1	1	1	1			1	1	1		1	1	1	1			1	
			C	A	B			C	A			B		A				D	A			A
London Kings Cross 15 ⊖	d		16 52		17 04	17 08		17 15			17 38	18 04			18 08	18 15		18 18			18 38	
Finsbury Park ⊖	d					17 13					17 43				18 13						18 43	
Potters Bar	d			16 33					17 03					17 33					18 03			18 33
Hatfield	d			16 48					17 18					17 48					18 18			18 48
Welwyn Garden City 4	d			16 58					17 28					17 58					18 28			18 58
Welwyn North	d			17 08					17 38					18 08					18 38			19 08
Knebworth	d			17 18					17 48					18 18					18 48			19 18
Hertford North	d									17 47										18 50		
Stevenage 4	d	17 13	17 22	17a25		17 40	17 48	17a50	17a55	17 59	18 09		18 13	18a25	18 40		18 50	18a53	18a55	19 02	19 12	19a25
Hitchin 4	d	17 18				17 45	17 54			18 05	18 14		18 18		18 45		18 56			19 08	19 17	
Letchworth Garden City	d						17 59			18a11	18 19						19 01			19a14	19 22	
Baldock	d						18 03				18 22						19 05				19 25	
Ashwell & Morden	d						18 08										19 10					
Royston	d						18 12				18 31						19 14				19 34	
Meldreth	d						18 16										19 18					
Shepreth	d						18 19										19 21					
Foxton	d						18 22										19 24					
Cambridge	a				18 01		18 35				18 48	19 01					19 37				19 50	
Arlesey	d	17 23				17 50							18 23		18 50							
Biggleswade	d	17 28				17 55							18 28		18 55	19 00						
Sandy	d	17 32				17 59							18 32		18 59							
St Neots	d	17 40				18 06							18 40		19 06	19 11						
Huntingdon	d	17 47				18 14							18 47		19 15	19 18						
Peterborough 8	a	18 06	17 51			18 32							19 06		19 33	19 34						

A From Alexandra Palace
B To Kings Lynn
C To Leeds
D To Skipton

Table 25

Sundays

5 January to 23 March

London - Stevenage, Cambridge and Peterborough

Network Diagram - see first Page of Table 24

		GR	FC	FC	FC	GR	FC	FC	FC	FC	FC	FC	FC	FC
		R 1	1	1	1	R 1			1		1	1	1	
		A	B			C	D			D	B			D
		trolley				trolley	bus			bus				bus
London Kings Cross 15 ⊖	d	18 56	19 04	19 08		19 15			19 38		20 04	20 08		
Finsbury Park ⊖	d			19 13					19 43			20 13		
Potters Bar	d						19 03			19 33				20 03
Hatfield	d						19 18			19 48				20 18
Welwyn Garden City 4	d						19 28			19 58				20 28
Welwyn North	d						19 38			20 08				20 38
Knebworth	d						19 48			20 18				20 48
Hertford North	d							19 47						
Stevenage 4	d	19 28		19 40	19 48	19a52	19a55	19 59	20 09	20a25		20 40	20 48	20a55
Hitchin 4	d			19 45	19 54			20 05	20 14			20 45	20 54	
Letchworth Garden City	d				19 59			20a11	20 19				20 59	
Baldock	d				20 03				20 22				21 03	
Ashwell & Morden	d				20 08								21 08	
Royston	d				20 12				20 31				21 12	
Meldreth	d				20 16								21 16	
Shepreth	d				20 19								21 19	
Foxton	d				20 22								21 22	
Cambridge	a		20 01		20 35				20 48		21 01		21 35	
Arlesey	d			19 50								20 50		
Biggleswade	d			19 55								20 55		
Sandy	d			19 59								20 59		
St Neots	d			20 06								21 06		
Huntingdon	d			20 14								21 14		
Peterborough 8	a	19 57		20 32								21 32		

		GR	FC	FC	FC	FC	FC	FC	GR	FC
		R 1		1		1	1	1	R 1	
		A			D	B			A	D
		trolley			bus				trolley	bus
London Kings Cross 15 ⊖	d	20 15		20 38		21 04	21 08		21 15	
Finsbury Park ⊖	d			20 43			21 13			
Potters Bar	d				20 33					21 03
Hatfield	d				20 48					21 18
Welwyn Garden City 4	d				20 58					21 28
Welwyn North	d				21 08					21 38
Knebworth	d				21 18					21 48
Hertford North	d		20 47							
Stevenage 4	d	20 55	20 59	21 09	21a25		21 40	21 48	21 54	21a55
Hitchin 4	d		21 05	21 14			21 45	21 54		
Letchworth Garden City	d		21a11	21 19				21 59		
Baldock	d			21 22				22 03		
Ashwell & Morden	d							22 08		
Royston	d			21 31				22 12		
Meldreth	d							22 16		
Shepreth	d							22 19		
Foxton	d							22 22		
Cambridge	a			21 48		22 01		22 35		
Arlesey	d						21 50			
Biggleswade	d						21 55			
Sandy	d						21 59			
St Neots	d						22 06			
Huntingdon	d						22 14			
Peterborough 8	a	21 24					22 32		22 25	

		FC	FC	FC	FC	FC	FC	FC	FC	FC	FC	FC	FC	FC	FC	FC	FC	FC
			1	1		1	1		1		1		1	1	1			
			E	F	D	B		D				D	B			D		D
					bus			bus				bus				bus		bus
London Kings Cross 15 ⊖	d		21 38	21 38		22 15	22 23				22 53		23 15	23 23			23 26	
Finsbury Park ⊖	d		21 43	21 43			22 28				22 58		23 20	23 28			23 32	
Potters Bar	d				21 33			22 03				22 33				23 14		23 44
Hatfield	d				21 48			22 18				22 48				23 29		23 59
Welwyn Garden City 4	d				21 58			22 28				22 58				23 39		00 09
Welwyn North	d				22 08			22 38				23 08				23 49		00 19
Knebworth	d				22 18			22 48				23 18				23 59		00 29
Hertford North	d	21 47								22 49							00 08	
Stevenage 4	d	21 59	22 09	22 13	22a25		22 54	22a55	22 58	23 01	23 24	23a25	23 48	23 54	23 58	00a06	00 21	00a36
Hitchin 4	d	22 05	22 14	22 18			22 59		23 04	23 07	23 29		23 53	23 59	00 04		00 26	
Letchworth Garden City	d	22a11	22 19	22 23					23 09	23a13	23 34		23 58		00 09		00a35	
Baldock	d		22 22	22 26					23 12		23 37				00 12			
Ashwell & Morden	d								23 17						00 17			
Royston	d		22 31	22 34					23 22		23 45		00 08		00 22			
Meldreth	d								23 26						00 26			
Shepreth	d								23 29						00 29			
Foxton	d								23 31						00 31			
Cambridge	a		22 48	22 51		23 12			23 44		00 01		00 23		00 44			
Arlesey	d						23 04							00 04				
Biggleswade	d						23 09							00 09				
Sandy	d						23 13							00 13				
St Neots	d						23 20							00 20				
Huntingdon	d						23 28							00 28				
Peterborough 8	a						23 48							00 48				

A To Leeds
B To Kings Lynn
C To Lincoln
D From Alexandra Palace
E until 9 February
F from 16 February

Table 25

Sundays
30 March to 11 May

London - Stevenage, Cambridge and Peterborough

Network Diagram - see first Page of Table 24

	FC	FC	FC	FC	FC		FC	FC	FC	FC	FC	FC	FC	FC	FC	FC		FC	FC	FC	FC	FC	FC	GR
	1	1	1		1		1	1	1	1	1			1	1				1	1	1		1	1
	A	A	A	A	A		B		A										C					D
London Kings Cross [15] ⊖ d							00 06	00 15		00 23	00 53	00 56	06 26	06 38	07 06			07 26	07 53	08 06	08 23	08 26	08 53	09 03
Finsbury Park ⊖ d							00 11			00 28	00 58	01 02	06 32	06 43	07 11			07 32	07 58	08 11	08 28	08 32	08 58	
Potters Bar d							00 21				01 08				07 21					08 21				
Hatfield d							00 27				01 14				07 27					08 27				
Welwyn Garden City [4] d		00 01					00 38				01 18				07 31					08 31				
Welwyn North d		00 04					00 40				01s21				07 34					08 34				
Knebworth d		00 08					00 44				01s24				07 38					08 38				
Hertford North d				00 08					←			01 38	07 08					08 08				09 08		
Stevenage [4] d		00 12		00 20	00 25		00 49	00 41	00 49	00 55	01 28	01 50	07a24	07 06	07 46	07 50		08a24	08 17	08 42	08 47	09a21	09 17	09 23
Hitchin [4] d		00 20		00 26	00 31		→	00 47	00 55	01 01	01 33	01 56		07 14	07 54	07 58			08 22	08 47	08 52		09 22	
Letchworth Garden City d		00a27		00a35				00s54	01 00			02a05		07 19	08 00				08 27	08 52			09 27	
Baldock d								00s57	01 04					07 22	08 03				08 30	08 56			09 30	
Ashwell & Morden d	00 01								01 09						08 08					09 01				
Royston d	00 06							01s05	01 13					07 31	08 13				08 38	09 05			09 38	
Meldreth d	00 10								01 17						08 17					09 09				
Shepreth d	00 13								01 20						08 20					09 12				
Foxton d	00 15								01 23						08 22					09 15				
Cambridge a	00 28							01 22	01 38					07 48	08 35				08 55	09 28			09 55	
Arlesey d					00s39					01s08	01s42					08 03					08 57			
Biggleswade d			00 02		00s44					01s13	01s47					08 08					09 02			
Sandy d			00 06		00s48					01s17	01s50					08 12					09 06			
St Neots d			00 13		00s55					01s24	01s58					08 19					09 13			
Huntingdon d			00 21		01s03					01s32	02s05					08 27					09 21			
Peterborough [8] a			00 42		01 24					01 54	02 26					08 43					09 39			09 52

	FC	FC		FC	FC	FC	FC	FC	FC	FC	FC	GR		FC	FC	FC	FC	FC	FC	FC	FC	FC		FC
	1	1		1		1	1	1	1		1	1		1	1	1		1	1	1	1			1
		C						C				D			C					C				
London Kings Cross [15] ⊖ d	09 06	09 15		09 23	09 26	09 53	10 06	10 15	10 23	10 26	10 53	11 03		11 06	11 15	11 23	11 26	11 53	12 06	12 15	12 23	12 26		12 53
Finsbury Park ⊖ d	09 11			09 28	09 32	09 58	10 11		10 28	10 32	10 58			11 11		11 28	11 32	11 58	12 11		12 28	12 32		12 58
Potters Bar d	09 21						10 21							11 21					12 21					
Hatfield d	09 27						10 27							11 27					12 27					
Welwyn Garden City [4] d	09 31						10 31							11 31					12 31					
Welwyn North d	09 34						10 34							11 34					12 34					
Knebworth d	09 38						10 38							11 38					12 38					
Hertford North d					10 08					11 08							12 08					13 08		
Stevenage [4] d	09 42			09 47	10a21	10 17	10 42		10 47	11a21	11 17	11 23		11 42		11 47	12a21	12 17	12 42		12 47	13a21		13 17
Hitchin [4] d	09 47			09 52		10 22	10 47		10 52		11 22			11 47		11 52		12 22	12 47		12 52			13 22
Letchworth Garden City d	09 52					10 27	10 52				11 27			11 52				12 27	12 52					13 27
Baldock d	09 56					10 30	10 56				11 30			11 56				12 30	12 56					13 30
Ashwell & Morden d	10 01						11 01							12 01					13 01					
Royston d	10 05					10 38	11 05				11 38			12 05				12 38	13 05					13 38
Meldreth d	10 09						11 09							12 09					13 09					
Shepreth d	10 12						11 12							12 12					13 12					
Foxton d	10 15						11 15							12 15					13 15					
Cambridge a	10 28	10 02				10 55	11 28	11 01			11 55			12 28	12 01			12 55	13 28	13 01				13 55
Arlesey d				09 57					10 57							11 57					12 57			
Biggleswade d				10 02					11 02							12 02					13 02			
Sandy d				10 06					11 06							12 06					13 06			
St Neots d				10 13					11 13							12 13					13 13			
Huntingdon d				10 21					11 21							12 21					13 21			
Peterborough [8] a				10 39					11 39			11 52				12 38					13 39			

	GR	FC	FC	FC	FC	FC	FC	FC		FC	FC	FC	GR	FC	FC	FC	FC	FC		FC	FC	FC	FC	GR
	1	1	1	1		1	1	1		1		1	1	1	1	1		1		1	1	1		1
	D		C					C					D		C						C			D
London Kings Cross [15] ⊖ d	13 03	13 06	13 15	13 23	13 26	13 53	14 06	14 15		14 23	14 26	14 53	15 03	15 06	15 15	15 23	15 26	15 53		16 06	16 15	16 23	16 26	16 35
Finsbury Park ⊖ d		13 11		13 28	13 32	13 58	14 11			14 28	14 32	14 58		15 11		15 28	15 32	15 58		16 11		16 28	16 32	
Potters Bar d		13 21					14 21							15 21						16 21				
Hatfield d		13 27					14 27							15 27						16 27				
Welwyn Garden City [4] d		13 31					14 31							15 31						16 31				
Welwyn North d		13 34					14 34							15 34						16 34				
Knebworth d		13 38					14 38							15 38						16 38				
Hertford North d					14 08						15 08						16 08						17 08	
Stevenage [4] d	13 23	13 42		13 47	14a21	14 17	14 42			14 47	15a21	15 17	15 23	15 42		15 47	16a21	16 17		16 42		16 47	17a21	16a54
Hitchin [4] d		13 47		13 52		14 22	14 47			14 52		15 22		15 47		15 52		16 22		16 47		16 52		
Letchworth Garden City d		13 52				14 27	14 52					15 27		15 52				16 27		16 52				
Baldock d		13 56				14 30	14 56					15 30		15 56				16 30		16 56				
Ashwell & Morden d		14 01					15 01							16 01						17 01				
Royston d		14 05				14 38	15 05					15 38		16 05				16 38		17 05				
Meldreth d		14 09					15 09							16 09						17 09				
Shepreth d		14 12					15 12							16 12						17 12				
Foxton d		14 15					15 15							16 15						17 15				
Cambridge a		14 28	14 01			14 55	15 28	15 01				15 55		16 28	16 01			16 55		17 28	17 01			
Arlesey d				13 57						14 57						15 57						16 57		
Biggleswade d				14 02						15 02						16 02						17 02		
Sandy d				14 06						15 06						16 06						17 06		
St Neots d				14 13						15 13						16 13						17 13		
Huntingdon d				14 21						15 21						16 21						17 21		
Peterborough [8] a	13 52			14 39						15 39			15 52			16 39						17 39		

A From London Kings Cross
B To Cambridge
C To Kings Lynn
D To Leeds

Table 25

Sundays

30 March to 11 May

London - Stevenage, Cambridge and Peterborough

Network Diagram - see first Page of Table 24

		FC	FC	FC	FC	FC	FC	GR	FC	FC	FC	FC	FC	FC	FC	GR	FC	FC	FC	GR	FC	FC	FC
		1	1	1	1 A	1		R 1 B	1	1	1	1	1 A	1		R 1 C	1	1	1 D	R 1 E	1 A	1 F	1
London Kings Cross 15 ⊖	d	16 36	16 53	17 06	17 15	17 23	17 26	17 35	17 36	17 53	18 06	18 10	18 15	18 23	18 26	18 35	18 36	18 53	19 06	19 08	19 15		19 23
Finsbury Park ⊖	d	16 41	16 58	17 11		17 28	17 32		17 41	17 58	18 11			18 28	18 32		18 41	18 58	19 11				19 28
Potters Bar	d	16 51		17 21					17 51		18 21						18 51		19 21				
Hatfield	d	16 57		17 27					17 57		18 27						18 57		19 27				
Welwyn Garden City 4	d	17 01		17 31					18 01		18 31						19 01		19 31				
Welwyn North	d	17 04		17 34					18 04		18 34						19 04		19 34				
Knebworth	d	17 08		17 38					18 08		18 38						19 08		19 38				
Hertford North	d						18 08								19 08							←	
Stevenage 4	d	17 12	17 17	17 42		17 47	18a21	17a54	18 12	18 17	18 42			18 47	19a21	18a54	19 12	19 17	19 42	19 29		19 42	19 47
Hitchin 4	d	17 17	17 22	17 47		17 52			18 17	18 22	18 47			18 52			19 17	19 22	→			19 47	19 52
Letchworth Garden City	d		17 27	17 52						18 27	18 52						19 22	19 27				19 52	
Baldock	d		17 30	17 56						18 30	18 56							19 30				19 56	
Ashwell & Morden	d			18 01							19 01											20 01	
Royston	d		17 38	18 05						18 38	19 05						19a34	19 38				20 05	
Meldreth	d			18 09							19 09											20 09	
Shepreth	d			18 12							19 12											20 12	
Foxton	d			18 15							19 15											20 15	
Cambridge	a		17 55	18 28	18 01					18 55	19 28		19 01					19 56			20 02	20 28	
Arlesey	d	17 23				17 57			18 23					18 57									19 57
Biggleswade	d	17 28				18 02			18 28			18 37		19 02									20 02
Sandy	d	17 32				18 06			18 32					19 06									20 06
St Neots	d	17 39				18 13			18 39			18 47		19 13									20 13
Huntingdon	d	17 47				18 21			18 47			18 54		19 21									20 21
Peterborough 8	a	18 06				18 39			19 06			19 12		19 39						19 59			20 39

		FC	GR	FC	FC	FC	FC	FC	GR	FC	FC	FC	FC	FC	GR	FC	FC	FC	FC	FC	FC	FC
			R 1 B	1	1	1 A	1		R 1 B	1	1	1 A	1		R 1 B	1	1	1 A	1		1	1 D
London Kings Cross 15 ⊖	d	19 26	19 35	19 53	20 06	20 15	20 23	20 26	20 35	20 53	21 06	21 15	21 23	21 26	21 35	21 53	22 06	22 15	22 23	22 26	22 53	23 06
Finsbury Park ⊖	d	19 32		19 58	20 11		20 28	20 32		20 58	21 11		21 28	21 32		21 58	22 11		22 28	22 32	22 58	23 11
Potters Bar	d				20 21						21 21						22 21					23 21
Hatfield	d				20 27						21 27						22 27					23 27
Welwyn Garden City 4	d				20 31						21 31						22 31					23 31
Welwyn North	d				20 34						21 34						22 34					23 34
Knebworth	d				20 38						21 38						22 38					23 38
Hertford North	d	20 08						21 08						22 08						23 08		
Stevenage 4	d	20a21	19 55	20 17	20 42		20 47	21a21	20 55	21 17	21 42		21 47	22a21	21 56	22 17	22 42		22 47	23a21	23 17	23 42
Hitchin 4	d			20 22	20 47		20 52			21 22	21 47		21 52			22 22	22 47		22 52		23 22	23 47
Letchworth Garden City	d			20 27	20 52					21 27	21 52					22 27	22 52				23 27	23 52
Baldock	d			20 30	20 56					21 30	21 56					22 30	22 56				23 30	→
Ashwell & Morden	d				21 01						22 01						23 01					
Royston	d			20 38	21 05					21 38	22 05					22 38	23 05				23 38	
Meldreth	d				21 09						22 09						23 09					
Shepreth	d				21 12						22 12						23 12					
Foxton	d				21 15						22 15						23 15					
Cambridge	a			20 55	21 28	21 01				21 55	22 28	22 01				22 55	23 28	23 01			23 55	
Arlesey	d						20 57						21 57						22 57			
Biggleswade	d						21 02						22 02						23 02			
Sandy	d						21 06						22 06						23 06			
St Neots	d						21 13						22 13						23 13			
Huntingdon	d						21 21						22 21						23 21			
Peterborough 8	a		20 24				21 39		21 24				22 39		22 25				23 41			

		FC	FC	FC	FC
		1 A	1 F	1	
London Kings Cross 15 ⊖	d	23 15		23 23	23 26
Finsbury Park ⊖	d			23 28	23 32
Potters Bar	d				
Hatfield	d				
Welwyn Garden City 4	d				
Welwyn North	d				
Knebworth	d				
Hertford North	d				00 08
Stevenage 4	d			23 47	00 21
Hitchin 4	d		←	23 52	00 26
Letchworth Garden City	d	23 41	23 52		00a35
Baldock	d		23 56		
Ashwell & Morden	d		00 01		
Royston	d	23 51	00 05		
Meldreth	d		00 09		
Shepreth	d		00 12		
Foxton	d		00 15		
Cambridge	a	00 07	00 28		
Arlesey	d			23 57	
Biggleswade	d			00 02	
Sandy	d			00 06	
St Neots	d			00 13	
Huntingdon	d			00 21	
Peterborough 8	a			00 41	

A To Kings Lynn
B To Leeds
C To Skipton
D To Cambridge
E To Lincoln
F From London Kings Cross

Table 25

Mondays to Fridays

9 December to 16 May

Peterborough, Cambridge and Stevenage - London

Network Diagram - see first Page of Table 24

Miles	Miles			FC	FC	FC	FC	FC	FC	FC	FC	FC		FC	FC	FC	FC	FC	FC	FC	FC	FC		FC	FC
						MO	MO																		
					1	1		1		1	1	1		1	1	1	1	1	1	1		1		1	1
				A	B	C	D											E							
0	—	**Peterborough** 8	d					03 25		04 10				05 10		05 40			05 50			06 15			
17½	—	Huntingdon	d					03 40		04 25				05 25		05 55			06 05			06 30			
24¾	—	St Neots	d					03 47		04 33				05 33		06 03			06 13			06 38			
32¼	—	Sandy	d							04 40				05 40					06 21						
35¼	—	Biggleswade	d					03 57		04 44				05 44					06 25			06 47			
39¼	—	Arlesey	d							04 49				05 49					06 30						
—	0	**Cambridge**	d								05 14						05 35	05 45		06 15					06 27
—	7	Foxton	d														05 44								06 36
—	8	Shepreth	d														05 47								06 39
—	10	Meldreth	d														05 50								06 43
—	13	Royston	d								05 29	05 16			05 46		06 05	05 59		06 29				06 42	06 50
—	17	Ashwell & Morden	d									05 21			05 51		06 09							06 47	06 55
—	21¼	Baldock	d									05 26			05 56		06 15							06 52	07 00
—	23¼	Letchworth Garden City	d						04 51		05 39	05 30			06 00		06 19	06 09		06 39	06 45			06 56	07 04
44½	26	Hitchin 4	d					04 09	04 55	04 58		05 35		05 58	06 05	06 19	06 24		06 36	06 43	06 50			07 01	07 09
48¾	30¼	**Stevenage** 4	d				00 05	04 15	05 01	05 03		05 40		06 03	06 10	06 25	06 29		06 42	06 49	06 55	06 59		07 07	07 15
—	—	Hertford North	a					04 25	05 13																
51¼	33	Knebworth	d		00 02	00 02	00 12			05 07		05 44			06 14		06 33		06 45					07 11	07 19
54¼	36	Welwyn North	d		00 06	00 06	00 22			05 11		05 48			06 18		06 37		06 49						07 24
56	37¾	Welwyn Garden City 4	d		00 09	00 09	00 32			05 14		05 51			06 21		06 40		06 54		07 07				07 27
58½	40¼	Hatfield	d		00 13	00 13	00 42			05 17		05 55			06 25		06 44				07 11				07 31
63½	45¼	Potters Bar	d		00 18	00 18	00 57			05 23		06 01			06 31		06 50				07 17				
73¾	55½	Finsbury Park ⊖	d	00 19	00s29	00s29	01s30	04s51	05 49	05 40		06 11		06 24	06 40	06 45	06 59		07 11	07 06	07 34			07 28	07 49
76¼	58	**London Kings Cross** 15 ⊖	a	00 29	00 40	00 41	01 45	05 01	05 56	05 50	06 10	06 21		06 31	06 48	06 53	07 06	06 39	07 19	07 14	07 40	07 24		07 35	07 57

		FC	FC	FC	FC	FC	FC	FC		FC	FC	FC	FC	FC	FC	FC	FC	FC		FC	FC	FC	FC	FC	FC
		1	1		1	1	1	1		1	1	1	1	1	1	1	1	1		1	1	1	1	1	1
		E						E			F		G				E					E			F
Peterborough 8	d		06 32		06 55						07 06	07 15		07 25				07 32		07 46					08 16
Huntingdon	d		06 46		07 11						07 25	07 33		07 40				07 50		08 05					08 31
St Neots	d		06 54		07 19						07 33	07 41		07 47				07 58		08 13					08 38
Sandy	d		07 02								07 41							08 06							08 46
Biggleswade	d		07 06								07 45			07 55				08 10							08 49
Arlesey	d		07 12								07 50							08 15							08 54
Cambridge	d	06 45					06 57	07 15								07 27	07 45				07 55	08 15			
Foxton	d						07 06									07 36					08 04				
Shepreth	d						07 09									07 39					08 07				
Meldreth	d						07 13									07 43					08 10				
Royston	d	06 59				07 12	07 21	07 29		07 32					07 42	07 50	07 59				08 14	08 29		08 34	
Ashwell & Morden	d					07 17				07 37					07 47						08 19			08 38	
Baldock	d					07 22				07 43					07 52						08 25			08 44	
Letchworth Garden City	d	07 09		07 20		07 26	07 31			07 46					07 56	08 01					08 29	08 39	08 34	08 47	
Hitchin 4	d		07 18	07 24		07 31	07 36			07 51	07 56		←		08 01	08 06		08 21			08 34		08 39	08 52	09 00
Stevenage 4	d		07 23	07 30	07 36	07 37	07 42				08 01	07 59	08 01		08 07	08 12		08 27		08 33			08 45	08 57	09 06
Hertford North	a										↦														↦
Knebworth	d						07 46								08 11	08 16							08 49		
Welwyn North	d						07 50			07 59						08 20							08 54		
Welwyn Garden City 4	d			07 44			07 54									08 24							08 59		
Hatfield	d			07 48																			09 03		
Potters Bar	d			07 54																			09 09		
Finsbury Park ⊖	d		07 42	08 10		07 57	08 10						08 19			08 40		08 48					09 22	09 16	
London Kings Cross 15 ⊖	a	07 38	07 49	08 17	08 01	08 05	08 17	08 07		08 20		08 21	08 28	08 30	08 35	08 48	08 38	08 56		08 58	09 02	09 09	09 29	09 23	

		GR	GR	FC		FC	FC	FC	FC	FC	FC	FC	GR	FC		FC	FC	FC	FC	FC	GR	FC	FC	FC
		R	R										R								R			
		1	1	1		1	1	1	1	1	1	1	1	1		1	1	1	1	1	1	1	1	1
		H	I	G			E			E			J	E							I	K	E	
Peterborough 8	d	08 27						08 46			09 16						09 26	09 46						10 16
Huntingdon	d							09 01			09 30						09 45	10 01						10 34
St Neots	d							09 08			09 38						09 52	10 08						10 42
Sandy	d							09 16									10 00	10 16						10 49
Biggleswade	d							09 19			09 47						10 04	10 19						10 53
Arlesey	d							09 24									10 09	10 24						10 58
Cambridge	d					08 25	08 50		08 55	09 20		09 30		09 50					09 55	10 15		10 30	10 45	
Foxton	d					08 34			09 04										10 04					
Shepreth	d					08 37			09 07										10 07					
Meldreth	d					08 40			09 10										10 10					
Royston	d					08 45	09 04		09 15	09 34		09 44		10 04					10 15			10 44		
Ashwell & Morden	d					08 50			09 20										10 20					
Baldock	d					08 55			09 25			09 52							10 25			10 52		
Letchworth Garden City	d					08 59	09 14		09 29	09 44		09 56		10 14		10 00			10 29			10 56		
Hitchin 4	d			←		09 05		09 30	09 34			10 00				10 05	10 15	10 30	10 34			11 00		11 04
Stevenage 4	d	08 59	09 03	09 06		09 10		09 36	09 40		09 58	10 06	10 09			10 10	10 21	10 36	10 40		11 02	11 06		11 10
Hertford North	a																							
Knebworth	d					09 14			09 44							10 14			10 44					11 14
Welwyn North	d					09 18			09 48							10 18			10 48					11 18
Welwyn Garden City 4	d					09 21			09 51							10 21			10 51					11 21
Hatfield	d					09 25			09 55							10 25			10 55					11 25
Potters Bar	d					09 31			10 01							10 31			11 01					11 31
Finsbury Park ⊖	d			09 27		09 41		09 57	10 11			10 24				10 41		10 55	11 11			11 24		11 41
London Kings Cross 15 ⊖	a	09 25	09 28	09 36		09 50	09 44	10 06	10 20	10 13	10 21	10 32	10 36	10 44		10 50	10 47	11 04	11 20	11 05	11 28	11 32	11 35	11 50

A until 3 January, MX from 7 January until 21 March, from 25 March. From Letchworth Garden City

B MX until 21 March, from 25 March. From Kings Lynn

C until 30 December. From Kings Lynn

D from 6 January until 24 March

E From Kings Lynn

F To London Kings Cross

G From Peterborough

H From Lincoln

I From Leeds

J From Harrogate

K From Ely

Table 25

Mondays to Fridays

9 December to 16 May

Peterborough, Cambridge and Stevenage - London

Network Diagram - see first Page of Table 24

		FC	FC	FC	FC	GR	GR	FC	FC	FC	FC	FC	FC	FC	GR	GR	FC	FC	FC	FC	FC	FC	FC
		1	1	1	1	R 1	R 1	1	1	1	1	1	1	1	R 1	R 1	1	1	1	1	1	1	1
					A	B	C		D	E				A	F	C		D	E				A
Peterborough 8	d	10 46			11 16	11 28					11 46			12 16	12 28					12 46			13 16
Huntingdon	d	11 01			11 34						12 01			12 34						13 01			13 34
St Neots	d	11 08			11 42						12 08			12 42						13 08			13 42
Sandy	d	11 16			11 49						12 16			12 49						13 16			13 49
Biggleswade	d	11 19			11 53						12 19			12 53						13 19			13 53
Arlesey	d	11 24			11 58						12 24			12 58						13 24			13 58
Cambridge	d		10 55	11 15				11 30	11 45			11 55	12 15				12 30	12 45			12 55	13 15	
Foxton	d		11 04									12 04									13 04		
Shepreth	d		11 07									12 07									13 07		
Meldreth	d		11 10									12 10									13 10		
Royston	d		11 15					11 44				12 15					12 44				13 15		
Ashwell & Morden	d		11 20									12 20									13 20		
Baldock	d		11 25					11 52				12 25					12 52				13 25		
Letchworth Garden City	d		11 29					11 56				12 29					12 56				13 29		
Hitchin 4	d	11 30	11 34		12 04			12 00		←	12 30	12 34		13 04			13 00		←	13 30	13 34		14 04
Stevenage 4	d	11 36	11 40		12 10	11 57	12 01	12 06		12 10	12 36	12 40		13 10	12 58	13 03	13 06		13 10	13 36	13 40		14 10
Hertford North	a				→									→									→
Knebworth	d		11 44							12 14		12 44							13 14		13 44		
Welwyn North	d		11 48							12 18		12 48							13 18		13 48		
Welwyn Garden City 4	d		11 51							12 21		12 51							13 21		13 51		
Hatfield	d		11 55							12 25		12 55							13 25		13 55		
Potters Bar	d		12 01							12 31		13 01							13 31		14 01		
Finsbury Park ⊖	d	11 55	12 11					12 24		12 41	12 55	13 11					13 24		13 41	13 55	14 11		
London Kings Cross 15 ⊖	a	12 03	12 20	12 05		12 23	12 28	12 34	12 37	12 50	13 03	13 20	13 06		13 26	13 28	13 32	13 35	13 50	14 03	14 20	14 06	

		GR	GR	FC	FC	FC	FC	FC	FC	FC	GR	GR	FC	FC	FC	FC	FC	FC	FC	GR	GR	FC	FC
		R 1	R 1	1	1	1	1	1	1	1	R 1	R 1	1	1	1	1	1	1	1	R 1	R 1	1	1
		B	C		D	E				A	F	C		D	E				A	B	C		D
Peterborough 8	d	13 29					13 46			14 16	14 27					14 46			15 16	15 29			
Huntingdon	d						14 01			14 34						15 01			15 34				
St Neots	d						14 08			14 42						15 08			15 42				
Sandy	d						14 16			14 49						15 16			15 49				
Biggleswade	d						14 19			14 53						15 19			15 53				
Arlesey	d						14 24			14 58						15 24			15 58				
Cambridge	d			13 30	13 45			13 55	14 15				14 30	14 45			14 55	15 15				15 30	15 45
Foxton	d							14 04									15 04						
Shepreth	d							14 07									15 07						
Meldreth	d							14 10									15 10						
Royston	d			13 44				14 15					14 44				15 15					15 44	
Ashwell & Morden	d							14 20									15 20						
Baldock	d			13 52				14 25					14 52				15 25					15 52	
Letchworth Garden City	d			13 56				14 29					14 56				15 29					15 56	
Hitchin 4	d			14 00		←	14 30	14 34		15 04			15 00		←	15 30	15 34		16 04			16 00	
Stevenage 4	d	13 59	14 03	14 06		14 10	14 36	14 40		15 10	14 57	15 02	15 06		15 10	15 36	15 40		16 10	15 58	16 03	16 06	
Hertford North	a									→									→				
Knebworth	d					14 14		14 44							15 14		15 44						
Welwyn North	d					14 18		14 48							15 18		15 48						
Welwyn Garden City 4	d					14 21		14 52							15 21		15 51						
Hatfield	d					14 25		14 55							15 25		15 55						
Potters Bar	d					14 31		15 01							15 31		16 01						
Finsbury Park ⊖	d			14 24		14 41	14 55	15 11					15 24		15 41	15 55	16 11					16 24	
London Kings Cross 15 ⊖	a	14 25	14 28	14 32	14 35	14 50	15 03	15 20	15 06		15 24	15 27	15 32	15 35	15 50	16 03	16 20	16 05		16 25	16 27	16 32	16 35

		FC	FC	FC	FC	FC	GR	GR	FC	FC	FC	FC	FC	FC	FC	GR	GR	FC	FC	FC	FC	FC
		1	1	1	1	1	R 1	R 1	1	1	1	1	1	1	1	R 1	R 1	1	1	1	1	1
		E				A	F	C	G	D	E				A	B	C	D	H	E		
Peterborough 8	d		15 46			16 16	16 26					16 46			17 21	17 29						
Huntingdon	d		16 01			16 34						17 01			17 41						18 04	
St Neots	d		16 08			16 42						17 08			17 49						18 11	
Sandy	d		16 16			16 49						17 16			17 56							
Biggleswade	d		16 19			16 53						17 19			18 00							
Arlesey	d		16 24			16 58						17 24			18 05							
Cambridge	d			15 55	16 15				16 25	16 45			16 55	17 15				17 25	17 45			17 55
Foxton	d			16 04					16 34				17 04					17 34				18 04
Shepreth	d			16 07					16 37				17 07					17 37				18 07
Meldreth	d			16 10					16 40				17 10					17 40				18 10
Royston	d			16 15					16 44				17 15					17 44				18 15
Ashwell & Morden	d			16 20					16 49				17 20					17 49				18 20
Baldock	d			16 25					16 54				17 25					17 54				18 25
Letchworth Garden City	d			16 29					16 57				17 29					17 57				18 29
Hitchin 4	d	←	16 30	16 34		17 04			17 01		←	17 30	17 34		18 12			18 01		←	18 29	18 34
Stevenage 4	d	16 10	16 36	16 40		17 10	16 57	17 03	17 06		17 10	17 36	17 40		18 18	17 59	18 04	18 07		18 18	18 35	18 40
Hertford North	a					→									→							
Knebworth	d	16 14		16 44							17 14		17 44							18 22		18 44
Welwyn North	d	16 18		16 48							17 18		17 48							18 26		18 48
Welwyn Garden City 4	d	16 21		16 51							17 21		17 51							18 29		18 51
Hatfield	d	16 25		16 55							17 25		17 55							18 33		18 55
Potters Bar	d	16 31		17 01							17 31		18 01							18 40		19 01
Finsbury Park ⊖	d	16 41	16 55	17 11					17 24		17 41	17 55	18 11					18 24		18 49	18 55	19 11
London Kings Cross 15 ⊖	a	16 50	17 03	17 20	17 04		17 21	17 28	17 35	17 38	17 50	18 03	18 20	18 05		18 26	18 29	18 34	18 35	18 58	19 03	19 20

A To London Kings Cross
B From York
C From Leeds
D From Kings Lynn
E From Peterborough
F From Newark North Gate
G From Ely
H From Downham Market

Table 25

Mondays to Fridays

9 December to 16 May

Peterborough, Cambridge and Stevenage - London

Network Diagram - see first Page of Table 24

		FC	FC	FC	GR	GR	FC	FC	FC	FC	FC	FC	FC	GR	GR	FC	FC	FC	FC	GR	GR	FC	FC
				A	B	C	D	E	F				A	G	C	D		F	A	H	I	F	
Peterborough 8	d		17 55	18 21	18 27					18 46			19 16	19 28					19 46	19 51			
Huntingdon	d		18 15	18 41						19 01			19 34						20 01				
St Neots	d		18 22	18 49						19 08			19 42						20 08				
Sandy	d		18 30	18 56						19 16			19 49						20 16				
Biggleswade	d		18 33	19 00						19 19			19 53						20 19				
Arlesey	d		18 38	19 05						19 24			19 58						20 24				
Cambridge	d	18 15					18 25	18 45			18 55	19 15				19 25	19 45						19 55
Foxton	d						18 35				19 04					19 34							20 04
Shepreth	d						18 37				19 07					19 37							20 07
Meldreth	d						18 40				19 10					19 40							20 10
Royston	d						18 46				19 15					19 44							20 15
Ashwell & Morden	d						18 51				19 20					19 49							20 20
Baldock	d						18 56				19 25					19 54							20 25
Letchworth Garden City	d						19 00				19 29					19 57							20 29
Hitchin 4	d		18 44	19 11			19 04		←	19 30	19 34		20 04			20 01		←	20 30			←	20 34
Stevenage 4	d		18 50	19 17	18 57	19 08	19 10		19 17	19 36	19 40		20 10	19 59	20 04	20 06		20 10	20 36	20 21	20 26	20 36	20 40
Hertford North	a			↪									↪						↪				
Knebworth	d								19 21		19 44							20 14					20 44
Welwyn North	d								19 25		19 48							20 18					20 48
Welwyn Garden City 4	d								19 28		19 51							20 21					20 51
Hatfield	d								19 32		19 55							20 25					20 55
Potters Bar	d								19 38		20 01							20 31					21 01
Finsbury Park ⊖	d		19 09				19 33		19 48	19 54	20 11					20 26		20 41				20 54	21 11
London Kings Cross 15 ⊖	a	19 11	19 16		19 24	19 34	19 41	19 35	19 55	20 02	20 19	20 11		20 25	20 28	20 33	20 36	20 50		20 47	20 52	21 02	21 18

		FC	GR	FC	FC	FC	FC	GR	FC	FC	FC	FC	GR	FC	FC	FC	FC	FC	FC	GR	FC	FC
			C	D	E		A	I		F			J	D						C	D	
Peterborough 8	d					20 16	20 42	20 47					21 18			21 27		21 46		22 17		22 27
Huntingdon	d					20 34	21 01									21 41		22 01				22 41
St Neots	d					20 41	21 08									21 49		22 08				22 49
Sandy	d					20 49	21 16									21 56		22 16				22 56
Biggleswade	d					20 53	21 19									22 00		22 19				23 00
Arlesey	d					20 58	21 24									22 05		22 24				23 05
Cambridge	d	20 15		20 30	20 45						20 55	21 15		21 30	21 45				21 55		22 30	
Foxton	d										21 04								22 04			
Shepreth	d										21 07								22 07			
Meldreth	d										21 10								22 10			
Royston	d			20 44							21 15			21 44					22 15		22 44	
Ashwell & Morden	d										21 20								22 20			
Baldock	d			20 52							21 25			21 52					22 25		22 52	
Letchworth Garden City	d			20 56					21 21		21 29			21 56			22 21		22 29		22 56	
Hitchin 4	d			21 00		21 04	21 30		21 25	←	21 34			22 00		22 10	22 25	22 30	22 34		23 00	23 13
Stevenage 4	d		21 00	21 06		21 10	21 36	21 18	21 31	21 36	21 40		21 50	22 06		22 16	22 31	22 36	22 40	22 48	23 06	23 19
Hertford North	a						↪		21 43								22 43					
Knebworth	d					21 14					21 44					22 19			22 44			23 22
Welwyn North	d					21 18					21 48					22 23			22 48			23 26
Welwyn Garden City 4	d					21 21					21 51					22 26			22 51			23 29
Hatfield	d					21 25					21 55					22 30			22 55			23 33
Potters Bar	d					21 31					22 01					22 35			23 01			23 38
Finsbury Park ⊖	d			21 24		21 41			22 19	21 54	22 11			22 24		22 44	23 19	22 54	23 11		23 24	23 47
London Kings Cross 15 ⊖	a	21 11	21 27	21 32	21 35	21 50		21 43	22 26	22 03	22 20	22 11	22 17	22 32	22 35	22 51	23 26	23 03	23 19	23 12	23 32	23 55

A To London Kings Cross
B From Newark North Gate
C From Leeds
D From Kings Lynn
E From Ely
F From Peterborough
G From York
H From Newcastle
I From Edinburgh
J From Aberdeen

Table 25

Mondays to Fridays

9 December to 16 May

Peterborough, Cambridge and Stevenage - London

Network Diagram - see first Page of Table 24

		FC	FC	GR
				R
			1	1
			A	B
				(catering symbol)
Peterborough [8]	d			23 46
Huntingdon	d			
St Neots	d			
Sandy	d			
Biggleswade	d			
Arlesey	d			
Cambridge	d		23 15	
Foxton	d		23 25	
Shepreth	d		23 28	
Meldreth	d		23 31	
Royston	d		23 35	
Ashwell & Morden	d		23 40	
Baldock	d		23 45	
Letchworth Garden City	d	23 21	23 48	
Hitchin [4]	d	23 25	23 53	
Stevenage [4]	d	23 31	23 59	00s26
Hertford North	a	23 43		
Knebworth	d		00 02	
Welwyn North	d		00 06	
Welwyn Garden City [4]	d		00 09	
Hatfield	d		00 13	
Potters Bar	d		00 18	
Finsbury Park ⊖	d	00 19	00s29	
London Kings Cross [15] ⊖	a	00 29	00 40	01 03

Saturdays

14 December to 17 May

		FC	FC	FC	FC	FC	FC	FC	FC	FC	FC	FC	FC	FC	FC	GR	FC	FC	FC	FC	FC	FC	FC
																R							
			1	1		1		1	1	1		1	1	1	1	1	1	1		1	1	1	1
		C	A						D						E	F	A	G					
																(catering symbol)							
Peterborough [8]	d			03 25		04 10				05 16		05 46			06 16	06 38				06 46			
Huntingdon	d			03 40		04 25				05 34		06 00			06 34					07 00			
St Neots	d			03 47		04 33				05 42		06 08			06 42					07 08			
Sandy	d					04 40				05 49		06 16			06 49					07 16			
Biggleswade	d			03 57		04 44				05 53		06 19			06 53					07 19			
Arlesey	d					04 49				05 58		06 24			06 58					07 24			
Cambridge	d								05 45				05 55	06 30			06 45				06 55	07 15	07 30
Foxton	d												06 04								07 04		
Shepreth	d												06 07								07 07		
Meldreth	d												06 10								07 10		
Royston	d							05 15	05 59				06 15	06 44							07 15		07 44
Ashwell & Morden	d							05 20					06 20								07 20		
Baldock	d							05 25					06 25	06 52							07 25		07 52
Letchworth Garden City	d				04 50		05 20	05 29	06 09		06 20		06 29	06 56							07 29		07 56
Hitchin [4]	d			04 09	04 54	04 58	05 25	05 34		06 04	06 24	06 30	06 34	07 00	07 04			←		07 30	07 34		08 00
Stevenage [4]	d			04 15	05 00	05 03	05 31	05 40		06 10	06 30	06 36	06 40	07 06	07 10	07 07		07 10	07 30	07 36	07 40		08 06
Hertford North	a			04 25	05 13		05 43				06 43				↪				07 43				
Knebworth	d		00 02			05 07		05 44		06 14			06 44					07 14			07 44		
Welwyn North	d		00 06			05 11		05 48		06 18			06 48					07 18			07 48		
Welwyn Garden City [4]	d		00 09			05 14		05 51		06 21			06 51					07 21			07 51		
Hatfield	d		00 13			05 17		05 55		06 25			06 55					07 25			07 55		
Potters Bar	d		00 18			05 23		06 01		06 31			07 01					07 31			08 01		
Finsbury Park ⊖	d	00 19	00s29	04s51	05 49	05 40	06 19	06 10		06 40	07 19	06 54	07 10	07 23				07 40	08 19	07 54	08 10		08 23
London Kings Cross [15] ⊖	a	00 29	00 40	05 01	05 56	05 50	06 26	06 19	06 39	06 49	07 26	07 01	07 19	07 31		07 35	07 36	07 49	08 26	08 01	08 19	08 04	08 31

A From Kings Lynn
B From Newcastle
C From Letchworth Garden City
D From Ely
E To London Kings Cross
F From Leeds
G From Peterborough

Table 25

Saturdays
14 December to 17 May

Peterborough, Cambridge and Stevenage - London

Network Diagram - see first Page of Table 24

		FC		GR	FC	FC	FC	FC	FC	FC	FC	FC		GR	FC	FC	FC	FC	FC	FC	FC	FC		FC	FC
		1		R 1	1	1		1	1	1	1	1		R 1	1	1	1		1	1	1	1		1	1
		A		B	C	D						A		B		C	D								C
Peterborough 8	d	07 18		07 38				07 46			08 09	08 18		08 33					08 46			09 09			
Huntingdon	d	07 34						08 00			08 24	08 34							09 00			09 23			
St Neots	d	07 42						08 08			08 33	08 42							09 08			09 31			
Sandy	d	07 49						08 16				08 49							09 16						
Biggleswade	d	07 53						08 19			08 42	08 53							09 19			09 39			
Arlesey	d	07 58						08 24				08 58							09 24						
Cambridge	d				07 45				07 55	08 15					08 30	08 45				08 55	09 15			09 30	09 45
Foxton	d								08 04											09 04					
Shepreth	d								08 07											09 07					
Meldreth	d								08 10											09 10					
Royston	d								08 15						08 44					09 15				09 44	
Ashwell & Morden	d								08 20											09 20					
Baldock	d								08 25						08 52					09 25				09 52	
Letchworth Garden City	d								08 29						08 56					09 29				09 56	
Hitchin 4	d	08 04				←		08 30	08 34			09 04			09 00		←		09 30	09 34				10 00	
Stevenage 4	d	08 10		08 07		08 10	08 30	08 36	08 40			09 10		09 02	09 06		09 10	09 30	09 36	09 40				10 06	
Hertford North	a	↪					08 43					↪						09 43							
Knebworth	d					08 14			08 44								09 14			09 44					
Welwyn North	d					08 18			08 48								09 18			09 48					
Welwyn Garden City 4	d					08 21			08 51								09 21			09 52					
Hatfield	d					08 25			08 55								09 25			09 55					
Potters Bar	d					08 31			09 01								09 31			10 01					
Finsbury Park ⊖	d					08 40	09 19	08 54	09 10						09 23		09 40	10 19	09 54	10 10				10 23	
London Kings Cross 15 ⊖	a			08 35	08 36	08 49	09 26	09 01	09 20	09 04	09 14			09 28	09 31	09 36	09 51	10 26	10 01	10 21	10 04	10 12		10 31	10 35

		FC	FC	FC	FC	FC	FC	FC		GR	FC	GR	FC	FC	FC	FC	FC	FC		FC	FC	FC	FC	FC	FC
		1		1	1	1	1	1		R 1	1	R 1	1	1		1	1	1		1	1	1		1	1
						C		A		E		F	C	D							C				
Peterborough 8	d			09 46			10 10	10 18		10 28		10 37				10 46						11 18		11 46	
Huntingdon	d	09 34		10 00			10 25	10 34								11 00						11 34		12 00	
St Neots	d	09 42		10 08			10 33	10 42								11 08						11 42		12 08	
Sandy	d	09 49		10 16				10 49								11 16						11 49		12 16	
Biggleswade	d	09 53		10 19			10 41	10 53								11 19						11 53		12 19	
Arlesey	d	09 58		10 24				10 58								11 24						11 58		12 24	
Cambridge	d				09 55	10 15					10 30		10 45				10 55	11 15		11 30	11 45				11 55
Foxton	d				10 04												11 04								12 04
Shepreth	d				10 07												11 07								12 07
Meldreth	d				10 10												11 10								12 10
Royston	d				10 15						10 44						11 15			11 44					12 15
Ashwell & Morden	d				10 20												11 20								12 20
Baldock	d				10 25						10 52						11 25			11 52					12 25
Letchworth Garden City	d				10 29						10 56						11 29			11 56					12 29
Hitchin 4	d	10 04		10 30	10 34			11 04			11 00			←		11 30	11 34			12 00		12 04		12 30	12 34
Stevenage 4	d	10 10	10 30	10 36	10 40			11 10		11 00	11 06	11 09		11 10	11 30	11 36	11 40			12 06		12 10	12 30	12 36	12 40
Hertford North	a		10 43					↪							11 43								12 43		
Knebworth	d	10 14			10 44									11 14			11 44					12 14			12 44
Welwyn North	d	10 18			10 48									11 18			11 48					12 18			12 48
Welwyn Garden City 4	d	10 21			10 51									11 21			11 51					12 21			12 51
Hatfield	d	10 25			10 55									11 25			11 55					12 25			12 55
Potters Bar	d	10 31			11 01									11 31			12 01					12 31			13 01
Finsbury Park ⊖	d	10 40	11 19	10 54	11 10						11 23			11 40	12 19	11 54	12 10			12 23		12 40	13 19	12 54	13 10
London Kings Cross 15 ⊖	a	10 49	11 26	11 01	11 21	11 04	11 15			11 26	11 31	11 36	11 37	11 49	12 26	12 01	12 19	12 04		12 32	12 34	12 49	13 26	13 01	13 19

		FC	FC	GR		FC	FC	FC	FC	FC	FC	FC	FC	FC		FC	FC	FC	FC	FC	FC	GR	FC	FC	
		1	1	R 1		1	1	1		1	1	1	1	1		1		1	1	1	1	R 1	1	1	
			A	B			C	D						C							A	B		C	
Peterborough 8	d		12 18	12 34						12 46						13 16		13 46			14 16	14 33			
Huntingdon	d		12 34							13 00						13 34		14 00			14 34				
St Neots	d		12 42							13 08						13 42		14 08			14 42				
Sandy	d		12 49							13 16						13 49		14 16			14 49				
Biggleswade	d		12 53							13 19						13 53		14 19			14 53				
Arlesey	d		12 58							13 24						13 58		14 24			14 58				
Cambridge	d	12 15				12 30	12 45				12 55	13 15	13 30	13 45					13 55	14 15			14 30	14 45	
Foxton	d										13 04								14 04						
Shepreth	d										13 07								14 07						
Meldreth	d										13 10								14 10						
Royston	d					12 44					13 15		13 44						14 15				14 44		
Ashwell & Morden	d										13 20								14 20						
Baldock	d					12 52					13 25		13 52						14 25				14 52		
Letchworth Garden City	d					12 56					13 29		13 56						14 29				14 56		
Hitchin 4	d		13 04			13 00		←		13 30	13 34		14 00			14 04		14 30	14 34		15 04		15 00		
Stevenage 4	d		13 10	13 03		13 06		13 10	13 30	13 36	13 40		14 06			14 10	14 30	14 36	14 40		15 10	15 02	15 06		
Hertford North	a		↪						13 43								14 43				↪				
Knebworth	d							13 14			13 44					14 14			14 44						
Welwyn North	d							13 18			13 48					14 18			14 48						
Welwyn Garden City 4	d							13 21			13 51					14 21			14 51						
Hatfield	d							13 25			13 55					14 25			14 55						
Potters Bar	d							13 31			14 01					14 31			15 01						
Finsbury Park ⊖	d					13 23		13 40	14 19	13 54	14 10		14 23			14 40	15 19	14 54	15 10				15 23		
London Kings Cross 15 ⊖	a	13 04		13 29		13 31	13 34	13 50	14 26	14 01	14 19	14 04	14 31	14 34		14 49	15 26	15 01	15 19	15 04		15 29	15 31	15 34	

A To London Kings Cross
B From Leeds
C From Kings Lynn
D From Peterborough
E From Lincoln
F From Harrogate

Table 25

Saturdays

14 December to 17 May

Peterborough, Cambridge and Stevenage - London

Network Diagram - see first Page of Table 24

		FC	FC	FC	FC	FC	FC	FC	FC	FC		FC	FC	FC	FC	GR	FC	FC	FC	FC		FC	FC	FC	FC
		1 A		1	1	1	1	1 B	1			1	1	1	1 C	R 1 D	1	1 B	1 A			1	1	1	1
Peterborough 8	d			14 46					15 18			15 46			16 16	16 34						16 46			
Huntingdon	d			15 00					15 34			16 00			16 34							17 00			
St Neots	d			15 08					15 42			16 08			16 42							17 08			
Sandy	d			15 16					15 49			16 16			16 49							17 16			
Biggleswade	d			15 19					15 53			16 19			16 53							17 19			
Arlesey	d			15 24					15 58			16 24			16 58							17 24			
Cambridge	d				14 55	15 15	15 30	15 45					15 55	16 15			16 30	16 45					16 55	17 15	17 30
Foxton	d				15 04								16 04										17 04		
Shepreth	d				15 07								16 07										17 07		
Meldreth	d				15 10								16 10										17 10		
Royston	d				15 15		15 44						16 15				16 44						17 15		17 44
Ashwell & Morden	d				15 20								16 20										17 20		
Baldock	d				15 25		15 52						16 25				16 52						17 25		17 52
Letchworth Garden City	d				15 29		15 56						16 29				16 56						17 29		17 56
Hitchin 4	d	←		15 30	15 34		16 00		16 04			16 30	16 34		17 04		17 00		←			17 30	17 34		18 01
Stevenage 4	d	15 10	15 30	15 36	15 40		16 06		16 10	16 30		16 36	16 40		17 10	17 04	17 06		17 10	17 30		17 36	17 40		18 07
Hertford North	a		15 43							16 43					→					17 43					
Knebworth	d	15 14			15 44				16 14				16 44						17 14				17 44		
Welwyn North	d	15 18			15 48				16 18				16 48						17 18				17 48		
Welwyn Garden City 4	d	15 21			15 51				16 21				16 51						17 21				17 51		
Hatfield	d	15 25			15 55				16 25				16 55						17 25				17 55		
Potters Bar	d	15 31			16 01				16 31				17 01						17 31				18 01		
Finsbury Park ⊖	d	15 40	16 19	15 54	16 10		16 23		16 40	17 19		16 54	17 10				17 23		17 40	18 19		17 54	18 10		18 24
London Kings Cross 15 ⊖	a	15 49	16 26	16 01	16 19	16 04	16 31	16 34	16 49	17 26		17 01	17 19	17 04		17 31	17 32	17 35	17 49	18 26		18 01	18 19	18 04	18 32

		FC	FC	FC	FC	FC		FC	FC	GR	FC	FC	FC	FC	FC	FC		FC	FC	FC	FC	FC	GR	FC	FC
		1 B	1		1	1		1	1 C	R 1 D	1	1 B	1 A		1	1		1	1 B	1	1	1 C	R 1 E		1 A
Peterborough 8	d		17 16		17 46				18 16	18 33					18 46						19 16	19 46	19 51		
Huntingdon	d		17 34		18 00				18 34						19 00						19 34	20 00			
St Neots	d		17 42		18 08				18 42						19 08						19 42	20 08			
Sandy	d		17 49		18 16				18 49						19 16						19 49	20 16			
Biggleswade	d		17 53		18 19				18 53						19 19						19 53	20 19			
Arlesey	d		17 58		18 24				18 58						19 24						19 58	20 24			
Cambridge	d	17 45				17 55		18 15			18 30	18 45				18 55		19 15	19 30	19 45					
Foxton	d					18 04										19 04									
Shepreth	d					18 07										19 07									
Meldreth	d					18 10										19 10									
Royston	d					18 15					18 44					19 15			19 44						
Ashwell & Morden	d					18 20										19 20									
Baldock	d					18 25					18 52					19 25			19 52						
Letchworth Garden City	d					18 29					18 56					19 29			19 56						
Hitchin 4	d		18 04		18 30	18 34			19 04		19 00		←		19 30	19 34			20 00		20 04	20 30			←
Stevenage 4	d		18 10	18 30	18 36	18 40			19 10	19 02	19 06		19 10	19 30	19 36	19 40			20 06		20 10	20 36	20 20	20 30	20 36
Hertford North	a			18 43					→					19 43								→		20 43	
Knebworth	d		18 14			18 44							19 14			19 44					20 14				
Welwyn North	d		18 18			18 48							19 18			19 48					20 18				
Welwyn Garden City 4	d		18 21			18 51							19 21			19 51					20 21				
Hatfield	d		18 25			18 55							19 25			19 55					20 25				
Potters Bar	d		18 31			19 01							19 31			20 01					20 31				
Finsbury Park ⊖	d		18 40	19 19	18 54	19 10					19 23		19 40	20 19	19 54	20 10			20 23		20 40			21 19	20 54
London Kings Cross 15 ⊖	a	18 35	18 50	19 26	19 01	19 19		19 04		19 28	19 31	19 35	19 49	20 26	20 01	20 19		20 03	20 31	20 34	20 49		20 46	21 26	21 01

		FC		FC	FC	GR	FC	FC	FC	FC	FC	FC		FC	GR	FC	FC	FC	FC	FC	FC	FC		FC	FC
		1		1	1 C	R 1 D	1 B	1	1 A		1	1		1 C	R 1 F	1 B	1	1 A		1	1	1 B		1	
Peterborough 8	d				20 16	20 34					20 46			21 16	21 22					21 46				22 16	
Huntingdon	d				20 34						21 00			21 34						22 00				22 34	
St Neots	d				20 42						21 08			21 42						22 08				22 42	
Sandy	d				20 49						21 16			21 49						22 16				22 49	
Biggleswade	d				20 53						21 19			21 53						22 19				22 53	
Arlesey	d				20 58						21 24			21 58						22 24				22 58	
Cambridge	d	19 55		20 15			20 30	20 45				20 55				21 30	21 45				21 55	22 30			
Foxton	d	20 04										21 04									22 04				
Shepreth	d	20 07										21 07									22 07				
Meldreth	d	20 10										21 10									22 10				
Royston	d	20 15					20 44					21 15				21 44					22 15	22 44			
Ashwell & Morden	d	20 20										21 20									22 20				
Baldock	d	20 25					20 52					21 25				21 52					22 25	22 52			
Letchworth Garden City	d	20 29					20 56					21 29				21 56					22 29	22 56			
Hitchin 4	d	20 34			21 04		21 00		←		21 30	21 34		22 04		22 00		←		22 30	22 34	23 00		23 04	
Stevenage 4	d	20 40			21 10	21 03	21 06		21 10	21 30	21 36	21 40		22 10	21 53	22 06		22 10	22 30	22 36	22 40	23 06		23 10	23 30
Hertford North	a				→					21 43				→					22 43						23 43
Knebworth	d	20 44							21 14			21 44						22 14			22 44			23 14	
Welwyn North	d	20 48							21 18			21 48						22 18			22 48			23 18	
Welwyn Garden City 4	d	20 51							21 21			21 51						22 21			22 51			23 21	
Hatfield	d	20 55							21 25			21 55						22 25			22 55			23 25	
Potters Bar	d	21 01							21 31			22 01						22 31			23 01			23 31	
Finsbury Park ⊖	d	21 11					21 23		21 40	22 19	21 54	22 10				22 23		22 40	23 19	22 54	23 10	23 23		23 40	00 19
London Kings Cross 15 ⊖	a	21 19		21 04		21 29	21 31	21 34	21 49	22 26	22 01	22 19			22 20	22 31	22 34	22 49	23 26	23 01	23 19	23 31		23 49	00 29

A From Peterborough
B From Kings Lynn
C To London Kings Cross
D From Leeds
E From Edinburgh
F From Aberdeen

Table 25

Saturdays
14 December to 17 May

Peterborough, Cambridge and Stevenage - London

Network Diagram - see first Page of Table 24

		FC 1	FC 1
Peterborough 8	d	22 46	
Huntingdon	d	23 00	
St Neots	d	23 08	
Sandy	d	23 16	
Biggleswade	d	23 19	
Arlesey	d	23 24	
Cambridge	d		23 15
Foxton	d		23 24
Shepreth	d		23 27
Meldreth	d		23 30
Royston	d		23 35
Ashwell & Morden	d		23 39
Baldock	d		23 44
Letchworth Garden City	d		23 48
Hitchin 4	d	23 30	23 53
Stevenage 4	d	23 36	23 58
Hertford North	a		
Knebworth	d		00 02
Welwyn North	d		00 05
Welwyn Garden City 4	d		00 09
Hatfield	d		00 12
Potters Bar	d		00 18
Finsbury Park ⊖	d	23 56	00s28
London Kings Cross 15 ⊖	a	00 10	00 40

Sundays
8 December to 29 December

		FC A	FC 1 B	FC 1	FC 1	FC	FC 1	FC 1	FC 1	FC		FC 1	FC 1	FC 1	FC	FC 1	GR R 1 C 🍴	FC 1	FC 1 D	FC 1		FC 1	FC 1	FC	FC 1
Peterborough 8	d			05 46			06 46					07 46				08 46	09 11			09 15					09 46
Huntingdon	d			06 00			07 00					08 00				09 00				09 30					10 00
St Neots	d			06 08			07 08					08 08				09 08				09 37					10 08
Sandy	d			06 15			07 15					08 15				09 15									10 15
Biggleswade	d			06 19			07 19					08 19				09 19				09 45					10 19
Arlesey	d			06 24			07 24					08 24				09 24									10 24
Cambridge	d				06 28			06 55	07 28				07 55	08 28				08 55	09 20			09 28			
Foxton	d							07 04					08 04					09 04							
Shepreth	d							07 07					08 07					09 07							
Meldreth	d							07 10					08 10					09 10							
Royston	d				06 42			07 15	07 42				08 15	08 42				09 15				09 42			
Ashwell & Morden	d							07 20					08 20					09 20							
Baldock	d				06 50			07 25	07 50				08 25	08 50				09 25				09 50			
Letchworth Garden City	d				06 53			07 29	07 53				08 29	08 53				09 29				09 53	09 59		
Hitchin 4	d			06 33	06 57		07 30	07 33	07 57			08 30	08 33	08 57		09 30		09 34				09 57	10 03		10 30
Stevenage 4	d			06 39	07 03	07 30	07 36	07 39	08 03	08 30		08 36	08 39	09 03	09 30	09 36	09 40	09 40				10 03	10 09	10 30	10 36
Hertford North	a					07 43				08 43					09 43									10 43	
Knebworth	d		00 02	06 43				07 43					08 43					09 43					10 13		
Welwyn North	d		00 05	06 47				07 47					08 47					09 48					10 17		
Welwyn Garden City 4	d		00 09	06 50				07 51					08 51					09 52					10 21		
Hatfield	d		00 12	06 54				07 54					08 54					09 55					10 24		
Potters Bar	d		00 18	07 00				08 00					09 00					10 01					10 30		
Finsbury Park ⊖	d	00 19	00s28	07 10	07s29	08 19	07 57	08 10	08 23	09 19		08 57	09 10	09 23	10 19	09 54		10 10				10 21	10 40	11 19	10 54
London Kings Cross 15 ⊖	a	00 29	00 40	07 21	07 40	08 26	08 09	08 19	08 32	09 26		09 05	09 19	09 32	10 26	10 01	10 07	10 20	10 10	10 15		10 28	10 49	11 26	11 01

		FC 1	FC 1 D	FC 1	FC 1	GR R 1 E 🍴		FC 1	FC	FC 1	FC 1	FC 1 D	FC 1	FC 1	FC	FC 1		FC 1	FC 1 D	FC 1	GR R 1 E 🍴	FC	FC 1	FC 1	FC 1 D
Peterborough 8	d			10 15		10 34				10 46			11 20			11 46					12 35		12 46		
Huntingdon	d			10 30						11 00			11 35			12 00							13 00		
St Neots	d			10 37						11 08			11 42			12 08							13 08		
Sandy	d									11 15						12 15							13 15		
Biggleswade	d			10 45						11 19			11 50			12 19							13 19		
Arlesey	d									11 24						12 24							13 24		
Cambridge	d	09 55	10 20		10 28						10 55	11 20		11 28				11 55	12 20	12 28				12 55	13 20
Foxton	d	10 04									11 04							12 04						13 04	
Shepreth	d	10 07									11 07							12 07						13 07	
Meldreth	d	10 10									11 10							12 10						13 10	
Royston	d	10 15			10 42						11 15			11 42				12 15		12 42				13 15	
Ashwell & Morden	d	10 20									11 20							12 20						13 20	
Baldock	d	10 25			10 50						11 25			11 50				12 25		12 50				13 25	
Letchworth Garden City	d	10 29			10 53			10 59			11 29			11 53				12 29		12 53				13 29	
Hitchin 4	d	10 33			10 57			11 03		11 30	11 33			11 57		12 30		12 33		12 57			13 30	13 33	
Stevenage 4	d	10 39			11 03	11 05		11 09	11 30	11 36	11 39			12 03	12 30	12 36		12 39		13 03	13 07	13 30	13 36	13 39	
Hertford North	a								11 43						12 43							13 43			
Knebworth	d	10 43						11 13			11 43							12 43						13 43	
Welwyn North	d	10 47						11 17			11 47							12 47						13 47	
Welwyn Garden City 4	d	10 51						11 21			11 51							12 51						13 51	
Hatfield	d	10 54						11 24			11 54							12 54						13 54	
Potters Bar	d	11 00						11 30			12 00							13 00						14 00	
Finsbury Park ⊖	d	11 10			11 21			11 40	12 19	11 54	12 10			12 21	13 19	12 54		13 10		13 21		14 19	13 54	14 10	
London Kings Cross 15 ⊖	a	11 19	11 08	11 15	11 28	11 32		11 49	12 26	12 01	12 19	12 08	12 20	12 28	13 26	13 01		13 19	13 08	13 28	13 33	14 26	14 01	14 19	14 08

A not 8 December. From Stevenage
B not 8 December. From Cambridge
C From York
D From Kings Lynn
E From Leeds

Table 25

Sundays

8 December to 29 December

Peterborough, Cambridge and Stevenage - London

Network Diagram - see first Page of Table 24

		FC		FC	FC	FC	FC	FC	GR	FC	FC	FC		FC	FC	FC	FC	FC	FC	FC	GR	FC		FC	FC
		1			1	1	1 A	1	R 1 B		1	1		1 A	1		1	1	1 A	1	R 1 B			1	1
Peterborough 8	d				13 46				14 34		14 46						15 46				16 35			16 46	
Huntingdon	d				14 00						15 00						16 00							17 00	
St Neots	d				14 08						15 08						16 08							17 08	
Sandy	d				14 15						15 15						16 15							17 15	
Biggleswade	d				14 19						15 19						16 19							17 19	
Arlesey	d				14 24						15 24						16 24							17 24	
Cambridge	d	13 28				13 55	14 20	14 28				14 55		15 20	15 28			15 55	16 20	16 28					16 55
Foxton	d					14 04						15 04						16 04							17 04
Shepreth	d					14 07						15 07						16 07							17 07
Meldreth	d					14 10						15 10						16 10							17 10
Royston	d	13 42				14 15		14 42				15 15			15 42			16 15		16 42					17 15
Ashwell & Morden	d					14 20						15 20						16 20							17 20
Baldock	d	13 50				14 25		14 50				15 25			15 50			16 25		16 50					17 25
Letchworth Garden City	d	13 53				14 29		14 53				15 29			15 53			16 29		16 53					17 29
Hitchin 4	d	13 57			14 30	14 33		14 57			15 30	15 33			15 57		16 30	16 33		16 57				17 30	17 33
Stevenage 4	d	14 03		14 30	14 36	14 39		15 03	15 07	15 30	15 36	15 39			16 03	16 30	16 36	16 39		17 03	17 05	17 30		17 36	17 39
Hertford North	a			14 43						15 43						16 43						17 43			
Knebworth	d					14 43						15 43						16 43							17 43
Welwyn North	d					14 47						15 47						16 47							17 47
Welwyn Garden City 4	d					14 51						15 51						16 51							17 51
Hatfield	d					14 54						15 54						16 54							17 54
Potters Bar	d					15 00						16 00						17 00							18 00
Finsbury Park ⊖	d	14 21		15 19	14 54	15 10		15 21		16 19	15 54	16 10			16 21	17 19	16 54	17 10		17 21		18 19		17 54	18 10
London Kings Cross 15 ⊖	a	14 28		15 26	15 01	15 19	15 08	15 28	15 32	16 26	16 01	16 19		16 08	16 28	17 26	17 01	17 19	17 08	17 28	17 32	18 26		18 01	18 19

		FC	FC	GR	FC	FC	FC	FC		FC	GR	FC	FC	FC	FC	FC	GR	FC		FC	FC	FC	FC	FC	GR
		1 A	1	R 1 B		1	1	1 A		1	R 1 B	1 A		1	1	1 A	R 1 B	1			1	1	1 A	1	R 1 B
Peterborough 8	d					17 46								18 46							19 46				
Huntingdon	d					18 00								19 00							20 00				
St Neots	d					18 08								19 08							20 08				
Sandy	d					18 15								19 15							20 15				
Biggleswade	d					18 19								19 19							20 19				
Arlesey	d					18 24								19 24							20 24				
Cambridge	d	17 20	17 28				17 55	18 20		18 28		18 45			18 55	19 20		19 28				19 55	20 20	20 28	
Foxton	d						18 04								19 04							20 04			
Shepreth	d						18 07								19 07							20 07			
Meldreth	d						18 10								19 10							20 10			
Royston	d		17 42				18 15			18 42					19 15			19 42				20 15		20 42	
Ashwell & Morden	d						18 20								19 20							20 20			
Baldock	d		17 50				18 25			18 50					19 25			19 50				20 25		20 50	
Letchworth Garden City	d		17 53				18 29			18 53					19 29			19 53				20 29		20 53	
Hitchin 4	d		17 57			18 30	18 33			18 57				19 30	19 33			19 57			20 30	20 33		20 57	
Stevenage 4	d		18 03	18 05	18 30	18 36	18 39			19 03	19 10		19 30	19 36	19 39		20 01	20 03		20 30	20 36	20 39		21 03	21 09
Hertford North	a				18 43								19 43							20 43					
Knebworth	d						18 43								19 43							20 43			
Welwyn North	d						18 47								19 47							20 47			
Welwyn Garden City 4	d						18 51								19 51							20 51			
Hatfield	d						18 54								19 54							20 54			
Potters Bar	d						19 00								20 00							21 00			
Finsbury Park ⊖	d		18 21		19 19	18 53	19 10			19 21			20 19	19 54	20 10			20 21		21 19	20 54	21 10		21 21	
London Kings Cross 15 ⊖	a	18 10	18 28	18 33	19 26	19 01	19 19	19 11		19 29	19 34	19 36	20 26	20 01	20 19	20 12	20 27	20 30		21 26	21 01	21 19	21 11	21 28	21 33

		FC	FC	FC		FC	FC	FC	FC	FC	FC	FC	GR	GR		FC	FC	GR	FC	FC
			1	1		1 A	1		1 C	1 D	1	1 A	R 1 B	R 1 E		1		R 1 E	1	1 A
Peterborough 8	d		20 46						21 46	21 46			22 14	22 23				22 54	23 01	
Huntingdon	d		21 00						22 00	22 00									23 15	
St Neots	d		21 08						22 08	22 08									23 22	
Sandy	d		21 15						22 15	22 15									23 30	
Biggleswade	d		21 19						22 19	22 19									23 33	
Arlesey	d		21 24						22 24	22 24									23 38	
Cambridge	d			20 55		21 20	21 28				21 55	22 20				22 28				23 15
Foxton	d			21 04							22 04									23 25
Shepreth	d			21 07							22 07									23 28
Meldreth	d			21 10							22 10									23 31
Royston	d			21 15			21 42				22 15					22 42				23 35
Ashwell & Morden	d			21 20							22 20									23 40
Baldock	d			21 25			21 50				22 25					22 50				23 45
Letchworth Garden City	d			21 29			21 53				22 29					22 53				23 48
Hitchin 4	d		21 30	21 33			21 57		22 30	22 30	22 33					22 57			23 45	23 53
Stevenage 4	d	21 30	21 36	21 39			22 03	22 30	22 36	22 36	22 39		22 47	22 55		23 03	23 30	23s32	23 50	23 59
Hertford North	a	21 43						22 43									23 43			
Knebworth	d			21 43							22 43									00 02
Welwyn North	d			21 47							22 47									00 06
Welwyn Garden City 4	d			21 51							22 51									00 09
Hatfield	d			21 54							22 54									00 13
Potters Bar	d			22 00							23 00									00 18
Finsbury Park ⊖	d	22 19	21 54	22 10			22 21	23 19	22 53	22 54	23 10					23 21	00 19		00s14	00s29
London Kings Cross 15 ⊖	a	22 26	22 02	22 19		22 08	22 28	23 26	23 01	23 02	23 19	23 08	23 14	23 19		23 28	00 29	23 59	00 25	00 41

A From Kings Lynn
B From Leeds
C 29 December
D until 28 December
E From Edinburgh

Table 25

Sundays

5 January to 23 March

Peterborough, Cambridge and Stevenage - London

Network Diagram - see first Page of Table 24

		FC	FC	FC	FC	FC	FC	FC	FC	FC		FC	FC	FC	FC	FC	FC	FC	FC	FC		FC	FC	FC	FC
			1				1			1				1	1			1				1	1		1
		A	B		C	C		C				C				C			C					C	
				bus	bus	bus		bus				bus	bus			bus			bus	bus				bus	
Peterborough 8	d			04 05									05 05							06 05			07 46		
Huntingdon	d			04 45									05 45							06 45			08 00		
St Neots	d			05 15									06 15							07 15			08 08		
Sandy	d			05 35									06 35							07 35			08 15		
Biggleswade	d			05 45									06 45							07 45			08 19		
Arlesey	d			06 05									07 05							08 05			08 24		
Cambridge	d									06 28				06 45				07 28				07 45			08 20
Foxton	d													06 55								07 55			
Shepreth	d													06 58								07 58			
Meldreth	d													07 01								08 01			
Royston	d									06 42				07 06				07 42				08 06			
Ashwell & Morden	d													07 11								08 11			
Baldock	d									06 50				07 16				07 50				08 16			
Letchworth Garden City	d						06 25		06 44	06 53				07 20	07 26		07 44	07 53				08 20			
Hitchin 4	d			06a23			06 30		06 49	06 57			07a23	07 24	07 30		07 49	07 57		08a23		08 24	08 30		
Stevenage 4	d				05 45	06 15	06 36	06 45	06 55	07 03		07 15		07a31	07 36	07 45	07 55	08 03	08 15			08a31	08 36	08 45	
Hertford North	a								07 07								08 07								
Knebworth	d		00 02		05 52	06 22		06 52				07 22				07 52			08 22					08 52	
Welwyn North	d		00 05		06 02	06 32		07 02				07 32				08 02			08 32					09 02	
Welwyn Garden City 4	d		00 09		06 17	06 47		07 17				07 47				08 17			08 47					09 17	
Hatfield	d		00 12		06 27	06 57		07 27				07 57				08 27			08 57					09 27	
Potters Bar	d		00 18		06a42	07a12		07a42				08a12				08a42			09a12					09a42	
Finsbury Park ⊖	d	00 19	00s28				07 02			07s29					08 02			08 29					09 02		
London Kings Cross 15 ⊖	a	00 29	00 40				07 08			07 40					08 08			08 35					09 08		09 18

		FC	FC	FC	FC	FC		GR	FC	FC	FC	FC	FC	FC	FC	FC		FC	FC	FC	FC	GR	FC	FC	FC
								R														R			
			1		1	1		1		1	1	1			1	1			1	1	1	1			1
				C				D	C	E			C					C	E			F	C		
				bus					bus				bus					bus					bus		
								trolley														trolley			
Peterborough 8	d					08 46		09 11			09 15					09 46				10 15		10 34			
Huntingdon	d					09 00					09 30					10 00				10 30					
St Neots	d					09 08					09 37					10 08				10 37					
Sandy	d					09 15										10 15									
Biggleswade	d					09 19					09 45					10 19				10 45					
Arlesey	d					09 24										10 24									
Cambridge	d		08 28		08 45					09 20		09 28			09 45				10 20		10 28				10 45
Foxton	d				08 55										09 55										10 55
Shepreth	d				08 58										09 58										10 58
Meldreth	d				09 01										10 01										11 01
Royston	d		08 42		09 06							09 42			10 06						10 42				11 06
Ashwell & Morden	d				09 11										10 11										11 11
Baldock	d		08 50		09 16							09 50			10 16						10 50				11 16
Letchworth Garden City	d	08 44	08 53		09 20							09 53		10 04	10 20						10 53			11 04	11 20
Hitchin 4	d	08 49	08 57		09 24	09 30						09 57		10 09	10 24	10 34					10 57			11 09	11 24
Stevenage 4	d	08 55	09 03	09 15	09a31	09 36		09 43	09 45			10 03	10 15	10 15	10a31	10 40		10 45			11 03	11 08	11 15	11 15	11a31
Hertford North	a	09 07												10 27										11 27	
Knebworth	d			09 22					09 52				10 22					10 52					11 22		
Welwyn North	d			09 32					10 02				10 32					11 02					11 32		
Welwyn Garden City 4	d			09 47					10 17				10 47					11 17					11 47		
Hatfield	d			09 57					10 27				10 57					11 27					11 57		
Potters Bar	d			10a12					10a42				11a12					11a42					12a12		
Finsbury Park ⊖	d		09 29			10 02						10 29				11 06					11 29				
London Kings Cross 15 ⊖	a		09 35			10 08		10 18		10 19	10 26	10 35				11 12			11 16	11 26	11 35	11 43			

		FC		FC	FC	FC	FC	FC	FC	FC	FC	FC		FC	FC	FC	GR	FC	FC	FC	FC	FC		FC	FC
																	R								
		1			1	1		1		1	1			1		1	1		1	1		1			1
				C	E				C			C		E			F	C			C	E			
				bus					bus			bus						bus			bus				
																	trolley								
Peterborough 8	d	10 46				11 11					11 46						12 39			12 46					
Huntingdon	d	11 00				11 25					12 00									13 00					
St Neots	d	11 08				11 32					12 08									13 08					
Sandy	d	11 15									12 15									13 15					
Biggleswade	d	11 19				11 40					12 19									13 19					
Arlesey	d	11 24									12 24									13 24					
Cambridge	d				11 20			11 28		11 45				12 20		12 28			12 45			13 20			13 28
Foxton	d									11 55									12 55						
Shepreth	d									11 58									12 58						
Meldreth	d									12 01									13 01						
Royston	d							11 42		12 06						12 42			13 06						13 42
Ashwell & Morden	d									12 11									13 11						
Baldock	d							11 50		12 16						12 50			13 16						13 50
Letchworth Garden City	d						11 44	11 53		12 20					12 44	12 53			13 20					13 44	13 53
Hitchin 4	d	11 36					11 49	11 57		12 24	12 32				12 49	12 57			13 24	13 31				13 49	13 57
Stevenage 4	d	11 42		11 45			11 55	12 03	12 15	12a31	12 38	12 45			12 55	13 03	13 08	13 15	13a31	13 37	13 45			13 55	14 03
Hertford North	a						12 07								13 07									14 07	
Knebworth	d			11 52					12 22			12 52						13 22			13 52				
Welwyn North	d			12 02					12 32			13 02						13 32			14 02				
Welwyn Garden City 4	d			12 17					12 47			13 17						13 47			14 17				
Hatfield	d			12 27					12 57			13 27						13 57			14 27				
Potters Bar	d			12a42					13a12			13a42						14a12			14a42				
Finsbury Park ⊖	d	12 08						12 29			13 05					13 29				14 04					14 29
London Kings Cross 15 ⊖	a	12 15			12 17	12 24		12 35			13 11			13 16		13 35	13 43			14 11		14 16			14 35

A From Stevenage
B From Cambridge
C To Alexandra Palace
D From York
E From Kings Lynn
F From Leeds

Table 25

Sundays

5 January to 23 March

Peterborough, Cambridge and Stevenage - London

Network Diagram - see first Page of Table 24

		FC	FC	FC	FC	FC	FC	FC		GR	FC	FC	FC	FC	FC	FC	FC	FC		FC	FC	FC	FC	FC	GR
		A (bus)	1	1	A (bus)	1 B		1		R 1 C (catering)	A (bus)	1	1	A (bus)	1 B		1	A (bus)		1	1	A (bus)	1 B	1	R 1 C (catering)
Peterborough 8	d			13 46						14 34			14 46								15 46				16 35
Huntingdon	d			14 00									15 00								16 00				
St Neots	d			14 08									15 08								16 08				
Sandy	d			14 15									15 15								16 15				
Biggleswade	d			14 19									15 19								16 19				
Arlesey	d			14 24									15 24								16 24				
Cambridge	d		13 45			14 20		14 28				14 45			15 20		15 28			15 45			16 20	16 28	
Foxton	d		13 55									14 55								15 55					
Shepreth	d		13 58									14 58								15 58					
Meldreth	d		14 01									15 01								16 01					
Royston	d		14 06					14 42				15 06					15 42			16 06				16 42	
Ashwell & Morden	d		14 11									15 11								16 11					
Baldock	d		14 16					14 50				15 16					15 50			16 16				16 50	
Letchworth Garden City	d		14 20				14 44	14 53				15 20				15 44	15 53			16 20				16 53	
Hitchin 4	d		14 24	14 31			14 49	14 57				15 24	15 31			15 49	15 57			16 24	16 31			16 57	
Stevenage 4	d	14 15	14a31	14 37	14 45		14 55	15 03		15 08	15 15	15a31	15 37	15 45		15 55	16 03	16 15		16a31	16 37	16 45		17 03	17 08
Hertford North	a						15 07									16 07									
Knebworth	d	14 22			14 52						15 22			15 52				16 22				16 52			
Welwyn North	d	14 32			15 02						15 32			16 02				16 32				17 02			
Welwyn Garden City 4	d	14 47			15 17						15 47			16 17				16 47				17 17			
Hatfield	d	14 57			15 27						15 57			16 27				16 57				17 27			
Potters Bar	d	15a12			15a42						16a12			16a42				17a12				17a42			
Finsbury Park ⊖	d			15 04				15 29					16 04				16 29				17 04			17 29	
London Kings Cross 15 ⊖	a			15 11		15 16		15 35		15 43			16 11		16 16		16 35				17 10		17 17	17 35	17 43

		FC	FC	FC		FC	FC	FC	FC	FC	GR	FC	FC	FC		FC	FC	FC	GR	FC	FC	FC	FC	FC	
			A (bus)	1		1	A (bus)	1 B		1	R 1 C (catering)	A (bus)	1	1		A (bus)	1 B	1	R 1 C (catering)		A (bus)	1 B	1	A (bus)	
Peterborough 8	d					16 46								17 46									18 46		
Huntingdon	d					17 00								18 00									19 00		
St Neots	d					17 08								18 08									19 08		
Sandy	d					17 15								18 15									19 15		
Biggleswade	d					17 19								18 19									19 19		
Arlesey	d					17 24								18 24									19 24		
Cambridge	d			16 45				17 20		17 28			17 45				18 20	18 28				18 45			
Foxton	d			16 55									17 55									18 55			
Shepreth	d			16 58									17 58									18 58			
Meldreth	d			17 01									18 01									19 01			
Royston	d			17 06						17 42			18 06					18 42				19 06			
Ashwell & Morden	d			17 11									18 11									19 11			
Baldock	d			17 16						17 50			18 16					18 50				19 16			
Letchworth Garden City	d	17 02		17 20					17 44	17 53			18 20					18 53		19 03		19 20			
Hitchin 4	d	17 07		17 24		17 32			17 49	17 57			18 24	18 31				18 57		19 08		19 24	19 30		
Stevenage 4	d	17 13	17 15	17a31		17 38	17 45		17 55	18 03	18 08	18 15	18a31	18 37		18 45		19 03	19 08	19 14	19 15	19a31	19 36	19 45	
Hertford North	a	17 25							18 07											19 26					
Knebworth	d		17 22				17 52					18 22				18 52					19 22			19 52	
Welwyn North	d		17 32				18 02					18 32				19 02					19 32			20 02	
Welwyn Garden City 4	d		17 47				18 17					18 47				19 17					19 47			20 17	
Hatfield	d		17 57				18 27					18 57				19 27					19 57			20 27	
Potters Bar	d		18a12				18a42					19a12				19a42					20a12			20a42	
Finsbury Park ⊖	d					18 04				18 29				19 04				19 29					20 03		
London Kings Cross 15 ⊖	a					18 11		18 19		18 35	18 43			19 11			19 20	19 35	19 43				20 10		

A To Alexandra Palace

B From Kings Lynn

C From Leeds

Table 25

Sundays

5 January to 23 March

Peterborough, Cambridge and Stevenage - London

Network Diagram - see first Page of Table 24

		FC 1 A	FC	FC 1	GR R 1 B (trolley)	FC C (bus)		FC 1	FC 1	FC C (bus)	FC 1 A	GR R 1 B (trolley)	FC 1	FC C (bus)	FC	FC 1		FC 1	FC C (bus)	FC 1 A	FC	FC 1	FC C (bus)	FC 1	FC 1
Peterborough 8	d								19 46			20 25						20 46							21 46
Huntingdon	d								20 00									21 00							22 00
St Neots	d								20 08									21 08							22 08
Sandy	d								20 15									21 15							22 15
Biggleswade	d								20 19									21 19							22 19
Arlesey	d								20 24									21 24							22 24
Cambridge	d	19 20		19 28				19 45			20 20		20 28			20 45				21 20		21 28		21 45	
Foxton	d							19 55								20 55								21 55	
Shepreth	d							19 58								20 58								21 58	
Meldreth	d							20 01								21 01								22 01	
Royston	d			19 42				20 06					20 42			21 06						21 42		22 06	
Ashwell & Morden	d							20 11								21 11								22 11	
Baldock	d			19 50				20 16					20 50			21 16						21 50		22 16	
Letchworth Garden City	d		19 44	19 53				20 20					20 53		21 04	21 20					21 44	21 53		22 20	
Hitchin 4	d		19 49	19 57				20 24	20 33				20 58		21 09	21 24		21 30			21 49	21 57		22 24	22 30
Stevenage 4	d		19 55	20 03	20 06	20 15		20a31	20 39	20 45		20 54	21 04	21 15	21 15	21a31		21 36	21 45		21 55	22 03	22 15	22a31	22 36
Hertford North	a		20 07												21 27						22 07				
Knebworth	d					20 22				20 52				21 22					21 52				22 22		
Welwyn North	d					20 32				21 02				21 32					22 02				22 32		
Welwyn Garden City 4	d					20 47				21 17				21 47					22 17				22 47		
Hatfield	d					20 57				21 27				21 57					22 27				22 57		
Potters Bar	d					21a12				21a42				22a12					22a42				23a12		
Finsbury Park ⊖	d			20 29					21 05				21 30					22 02				22 29			23 02
London Kings Cross 15 ⊖	a	20 21		20 35	20 43				21 11		21 17	21 29	21 37					22 08		22 22		22 35			23 08

		FC C (bus)		GR R 1 B (trolley)	FC 1 A	GR R 1 D (trolley)	FC 1	FC	FC C (bus)	FC 1	GR R 1 D (trolley)	FC 1		FC 1 A
Peterborough 8	d			22 14		22 23					22 54	23 01		
Huntingdon	d											23 15		
St Neots	d											23 22		
Sandy	d											23 30		
Biggleswade	d											23 33		
Arlesey	d											23 38		
Cambridge	d				22 20		22 28			22 45				23 15
Foxton	d									22 55				23 25
Shepreth	d									22 58				23 28
Meldreth	d									23 01				23 31
Royston	d						22 42			23 06				23 35
Ashwell & Morden	d									23 11				23 40
Baldock	d						22 50			23 16				23 45
Letchworth Garden City	d						22 53	23 01		23 20				23 48
Hitchin 4	d						22 57	23 06		23 24		23 45		23 53
Stevenage 4	d	22 45		22 46		22 55	23 03	23 12	23 15	23a31	23s35	23 50		23 59
Hertford North	a							23 24						00 12
Knebworth	d	22 52							23 22					
Welwyn North	d	23 02							23 32					
Welwyn Garden City 4	d	23 17							23 47					
Hatfield	d	23 27							23 57					
Potters Bar	d	23a42							00a12					
Finsbury Park ⊖	d						23 29					00s17		00s29
London Kings Cross 15 ⊖	a			23 21	23 22	23 30	23 35				00 15	00 26		00 39

A From Kings Lynn
B From Leeds
C To Alexandra Palace
D From Edinburgh

Table 25

Sundays

30 March to 11 May

Peterborough, Cambridge and Stevenage - London

Network Diagram - see first Page of Table 24

		FC	FC	FC	FC	FC	FC	FC	FC	FC	FC	FC	FC	FC	FC	GR	FC	FC	FC	FC	FC	FC	FC
		A	1 B	1	1		1	1	1		1	1	1		1	R 1 C	1	1 D	1	1	1		1
Peterborough 8	d			05 46			06 46				07 46				08 46	09 11			09 15				09 46
Huntingdon	d			06 00			07 00				08 00				09 00				09 30				10 00
St Neots	d			06 08			07 08				08 08				09 08				09 37				10 08
Sandy	d			06 15			07 15				08 15				09 15								10 15
Biggleswade	d			06 19			07 19				08 19				09 19				09 45				10 19
Arlesey	d			06 24			07 24				08 24				09 24								10 24
Cambridge	d				06 28			06 55	07 28			07 55	08 28				08 55	09 20		09 28			
Foxton	d							07 04				08 04					09 04						
Shepreth	d							07 07				08 07					09 07						
Meldreth	d							07 10				08 10					09 10						
Royston	d				06 42			07 15	07 42			08 15	08 42				09 15			09 42			
Ashwell & Morden	d							07 20				08 20					09 20						
Baldock	d				06 50			07 25	07 50			08 25	08 50				09 25			09 50			
Letchworth Garden City	d				06 53			07 29	07 53			08 29	08 53				09 29			09 53	09 59		
Hitchin 4	d			06 33	06 57		07 30	07 33	07 57		08 30	08 33	08 57		09 30		09 34			09 57	10 03		10 30
Stevenage 4	d			06 39	07 03	07 30	07 36	07 39	08 03	08 30	08 36	08 39	09 03	09 30	09 36	09 40	09 40			10 03	10 09	10 30	10 36
Hertford North	a					07 43				08 43				09 43								10 43	
Knebworth	d		00 02	06 43				07 43				08 43					09 43				10 13		
Welwyn North	d		00 05	06 47				07 47				08 47					09 48				10 17		
Welwyn Garden City 4	d		00 09	06 50				07 51				08 51					09 52				10 21		
Hatfield	d		00 12	06 54				07 54				08 54					09 55				10 24		
Potters Bar	d		00 18	07 00				08 00				09 00					10 01				10 30		
Finsbury Park ⊖	d	00 19	00s28	07 10	07s29	08 19	07 57	08 10	08 23	09 19	08 57	09 10	09 23	10 19	09 54		10 10			10 21	10 40	11 19	10 54
London Kings Cross 15 ⊖	a	00 29	00 40	07 21	07 40	08 26	08 09	08 19	08 32	09 26	09 05	09 19	09 32	10 26	10 01	10 07	10 20	10 10	10 15	10 28	10 49	11 26	11 01

		FC	FC	FC	FC	GR	FC	FC	FC	FC	FC	FC	FC	FC	FC	FC	FC	FC	GR	FC	FC	FC
		1	1 D	1	1	R 1 E	1		1	1	1 D	1	1		1	1	1 D	1	R 1 E		1	1
Peterborough 8	d			10 15		10 34			10 46			11 20			11 46				12 35		12 46	
Huntingdon	d			10 30					11 00			11 35			12 00						13 00	
St Neots	d			10 37					11 08			11 42			12 08						13 08	
Sandy	d								11 15						12 15						13 15	
Biggleswade	d			10 45					11 19			11 50			12 19						13 19	
Arlesey	d								11 24						12 24						13 24	
Cambridge	d	09 55	10 20		10 28					10 55	11 20		11 28			11 55	12 20	12 28				12 55
Foxton	d	10 04								11 04						12 04						13 04
Shepreth	d	10 07								11 07						12 07						13 07
Meldreth	d	10 10								11 10						12 10						13 10
Royston	d	10 15			10 42					11 15			11 42			12 15		12 42				13 15
Ashwell & Morden	d	10 20								11 20						12 20						13 20
Baldock	d	10 25			10 50					11 25			11 50			12 25		12 50				13 25
Letchworth Garden City	d	10 29			10 53		10 59			11 29			11 53			12 29		12 53				13 29
Hitchin 4	d	10 33			10 57		11 03		11 30	11 33			11 57		12 30	12 33		12 57			13 30	13 33
Stevenage 4	d	10 39			11 03	11 05	11 09	11 30	11 36	11 39			12 03	12 30	12 36	12 39		13 03	13 07	13 30	13 36	13 39
Hertford North	a							11 43						12 43						13 43		
Knebworth	d	10 43					11 13			11 43						12 43						13 43
Welwyn North	d	10 47					11 17			11 47						12 47						13 47
Welwyn Garden City 4	d	10 51					11 21			11 51						12 51						13 51
Hatfield	d	10 54					11 24			11 54						12 54						13 54
Potters Bar	d	11 00					11 30			12 00						13 00						14 00
Finsbury Park ⊖	d	11 10			11 21		11 40	12 19	11 54	12 10			12 21	13 19	12 54	13 10		13 21		14 19	13 54	14 10
London Kings Cross 15 ⊖	a	11 19	11 08	11 15	11 28	11 32	11 49	12 26	12 01	12 19	12 08	12 20	12 28	13 26	13 01	13 19	13 08	13 28	13 33	14 26	14 01	14 19

		FC	FC	FC	FC	FC	FC	FC	GR	FC	FC	FC	FC	FC	FC	FC	FC	FC	FC	GR	FC	FC	FC
		1 D	1		1	1	1 D	1	R 1 E		1	1	1 D	1		1	1	1 D	1	R 1 E		1	1
Peterborough 8	d				13 46				14 34		14 46					15 46				16 35		16 46	
Huntingdon	d				14 00						15 00					16 00						17 00	
St Neots	d				14 08						15 08					16 08						17 08	
Sandy	d				14 15						15 15					16 15						17 15	
Biggleswade	d				14 19						15 19					16 19						17 19	
Arlesey	d				14 24						15 24					16 24						17 24	
Cambridge	d	13 20	13 28			13 55	14 20	14 28				14 55	15 20	15 28			15 55	16 20	16 28				16 55
Foxton	d					14 04						15 04					16 04						17 04
Shepreth	d					14 07						15 07					16 07						17 07
Meldreth	d					14 10						15 10					16 10						17 10
Royston	d		13 42			14 15		14 42				15 15		15 42			16 15		16 42				17 15
Ashwell & Morden	d					14 20						15 20					16 20						17 20
Baldock	d		13 50			14 25		14 50				15 25		15 50			16 25		16 50				17 25
Letchworth Garden City	d		13 53			14 29		14 53				15 29		15 53			16 29		16 53				17 29
Hitchin 4	d		13 57		14 30	14 33		14 57			15 30	15 33		15 57		16 30	16 33		16 57			17 30	17 33
Stevenage 4	d		14 03	14 30	14 36	14 39		15 03	15 07	15 30	15 36	15 39		16 03	16 30	16 36	16 39		17 03	17 05	17 30	17 36	17 39
Hertford North	a			14 43						15 43					16 43						17 43		
Knebworth	d					14 43						15 43					16 43						17 43
Welwyn North	d					14 47						15 47					16 47						17 47
Welwyn Garden City 4	d					14 51						15 51					16 51						17 51
Hatfield	d					14 54						15 54					16 54						17 54
Potters Bar	d					15 00						16 00					17 00						18 00
Finsbury Park ⊖	d		14 21	15 19	14 54	15 10		15 21		16 19	15 54	16 10		16 21	17 19	16 54	17 10		17 21		18 19	17 54	18 10
London Kings Cross 15 ⊖	a	14 08	14 28	15 26	15 01	15 19	15 08	15 28	15 32	16 26	16 01	16 19	16 08	16 28	17 26	17 01	17 19	17 08	17 28	17 32	18 26	18 01	18 19

A From Stevenage
B From Cambridge
C From York
D From Kings Lynn
E From Leeds

Table 25

Sundays

30 March to 11 May

Peterborough, Cambridge and Stevenage - London

Network Diagram - see first Page of Table 24

		FC	FC	GR		FC	FC	FC	FC	FC	GR	FC	FC	FC		FC	FC	GR	FC	FC	FC	FC	FC	FC
				R							R							R						
		1	1	1			1	1	1	1	1	1		1		1	1	1	1		1	1	1	1
		A		B					A		B	A					A	B					A	
Peterborough 8	d						17 46							18 46							19 46			
Huntingdon	d						18 00							19 00							20 00			
St Neots	d						18 08							19 08							20 08			
Sandy	d						18 15							19 15							20 15			
Biggleswade	d						18 19							19 19							20 19			
Arlesey	d						18 24							19 24							20 24			
Cambridge	d	17 20	17 28					17 55	18 20	18 28		18 45				18 55	19 20		19 28			19 55	20 20	20 28
Foxton	d							18 04								19 04						20 04		
Shepreth	d							18 07								19 07						20 07		
Meldreth	d							18 10								19 10						20 10		
Royston	d		17 42					18 15		18 42						19 15			19 42			20 15		20 42
Ashwell & Morden	d							18 20								19 20						20 20		
Baldock	d		17 50					18 25		18 50						19 25			19 50			20 25		20 50
Letchworth Garden City	d		17 53					18 29		18 53						19 29			19 53			20 29		20 53
Hitchin 4	d		17 57				18 30	18 33		18 57				19 30		19 33			19 57		20 30	20 33		20 57
Stevenage 4	d		18 03	18 05		18 30	18 36	18 39		19 03	19 10		19 30	19 36		19 39		20 01	20 03	20 30	20 36	20 39		21 03
Hertford North	a					18 43							19 43							20 43				
Knebworth	d							18 43								19 43						20 43		
Welwyn North	d							18 47								19 47						20 47		
Welwyn Garden City 4	d							18 51								19 51						20 51		
Hatfield	d							18 54								19 54						20 54		
Potters Bar	d							19 00								20 00						21 00		
Finsbury Park ⊖	d		18 21			19 19	18 53	19 10		19 21			20 19	19 54		20 10			20 21	21 19	20 54	21 10		21 21
London Kings Cross 15 ⊖	a	18 10	18 28	18 33		19 26	19 01	19 19	19 11	19 29	19 34	19 36	20 26	20 01		20 19	20 12	20 27	20 30	21 26	21 01	21 19	21 11	21 28

		GR	FC	FC	FC	FC	FC	FC	FC	FC		FC	GR	GR	FC	FC	GR	FC	FC
		R											R	R			R		
		1		1	1	1	1		1	1		1	1	1	1		1	1	1
		B				A						A	B	C			C		A
Peterborough 8	d			20 46					21 46				22 14	22 23			22 54	23 01	
Huntingdon	d			21 00					22 00									23 15	
St Neots	d			21 08					22 08									23 22	
Sandy	d			21 15					22 15									23 30	
Biggleswade	d			21 19					22 19									23 33	
Arlesey	d			21 24					22 24									23 38	
Cambridge	d				20 55	21 20	21 28			21 55		22 20			22 28				23 15
Foxton	d				21 04					22 04									23 25
Shepreth	d				21 07					22 07									23 28
Meldreth	d				21 10					22 10									23 31
Royston	d				21 15		21 42			22 15					22 42				23 35
Ashwell & Morden	d				21 20					22 20									23 40
Baldock	d				21 25		21 50			22 25					22 50				23 45
Letchworth Garden City	d				21 29		21 53			22 29					22 53				23 48
Hitchin 4	d			21 30	21 33		21 57		22 30	22 33					22 57			23 45	23 53
Stevenage 4	d	21 09	21 30	21 36	21 39		22 03	22 30	22 36	22 39			22 47	22 55	23 03	23 30	23s32	23 50	23 59
Hertford North	a		21 43					22 43								23 43			
Knebworth	d				21 43					22 43									00 02
Welwyn North	d				21 47					22 47									00 06
Welwyn Garden City 4	d				21 51					22 51									00 09
Hatfield	d				21 54					22 54									00 13
Potters Bar	d				22 00					23 00									00 18
Finsbury Park ⊖	d		22 19	21 54	22 10		22 21	23 19	22 53	23 10					23 21	00 19		00s14	00s29
London Kings Cross 15 ⊖	a	21 33	22 26	22 02	22 19	22 08	22 28	23 26	23 01	23 19		23 08	23 14	23 19	23 28	00 29	23 59	00 25	00 40

A From Kings Lynn B From Leeds C From Edinburgh

Route Diagram for Table 26

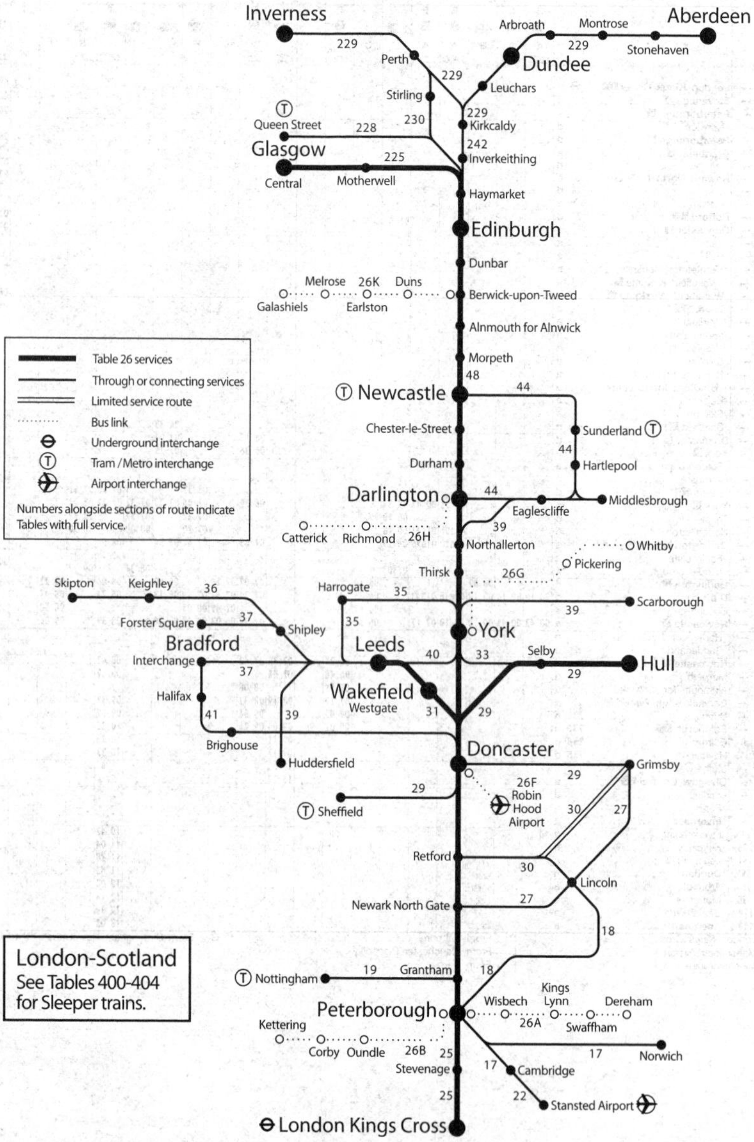

TOCs operating on this network - East Coast (GR), First TransPennine Express (TP), Northern (NT), Cross Country (XC), East Midlands Trains (EM), Grand Central (GC), Hull Trains (HT)

Table 26

Mondays to Fridays

9 December to 16 May

London - Humberside, Yorkshire, North East England and Scotland

Route Diagram - refer to first Page of Table 26

Miles	Miles	Miles	Station		GR	GR	TP	GR	GR	TP	NT	GR	XC	GR	NT	TP	XC	TP	GR	TP	NT	GR	XC
					MO	MX	MX	MO	MX														
					A	A	B	A	A		C				D	E	F			B	D		G
0	—	—	**London Kings Cross** 15 ⊖	d																		05 50	
27½	—	—	**Stevenage** 4	d																		06 12	
76¼	—	—	**Peterborough** 8	a																		06 41	
—	—	—	Norwich	d																			
—	—	—	**Peterborough** 8	d																		06 43	
105¼	—	—	**Grantham** 7	a																		07 02	
—	—	—		d																		07 03	
120	—	—	**Newark North Gate** 7	a																		07 14	
—	—	—		d																		07 15	
—	—	—	Lincoln	a																			
138½	—	—	**Retford** 10	d																		07 30	
156	0	—	**Doncaster** 7	a																		07 43	
—	—	—	Selby	a																			
—	—	—	Hull	a																			
—	—	—	Pontefract Monkhill	a																			
—	—	—	Wakefield Kirkgate 4	a																			
—	19¾	—	**Wakefield Westgate** 7	a																		08 01	
—	29¾	—	**Leeds** 10	a																		08 19	
—	—	—	Mirfield	a																			
—	—	—	Brighouse	a																			
—	—	—	Halifax	a																			
—	—	—	Shipley	a																			
—	—	—	Bradford Forster Square	a																			
—	—	—	**Bradford Interchange**	a																			
—	—	—	Keighley	a																			
—	—	—	Skipton	a																			
—	—	—	Sheffield 7	d													06 33						07 12
—	—	—	**Doncaster** 7	d										06 15			07 04						
188½	—	—	**York** 8	a										06 36			07 25						
—	—	—	Scarborough	a																			
—	—	—	Harrogate	a																			
—	—	—	Leeds 10	d												06 35			07 10	07 51			07 57
—	—	—	**York** 8	d				00 35	00 42	05 54				06 39		07 06	07 29	07 32	07 37	08 23			08 28
210¾	—	—	Thirsk	d						06 10						07 22		07 52		08 39			
218½	—	—	Northallerton	d				01s06	01s11	06 18						07 30		08 00		08 50			
232½	—	—	**Darlington** 7	a				01s20	01s25	06 29				07 05		07 41	07 54		08 04				08 57
—	—	—	Eaglescliffe	a																			
—	—	—	Middlesbrough	a						07 03								08 31		09 22			
—	—	—	**Darlington** 7	d			00 02				06 14			07 07	07 20	07 42	08 00		08 06		08 22		08 58
254½	—	—	**Durham**	d	00 10	00 14	00 19	01s38	01s43		06 35			07 24	07 42	07 59	08 18		08 24		08 43		09 15
260¼	—	—	Chester-le-Street	d							06 42				07 49	08 05					08 50		
268½	—	—	**Newcastle** 8	a	00 42	00 43	00 50	02 10	02 17		06 54			07 39	08 03	08 17	08 38		08 39		09 06		09 28
—	—	—	Hartlepool	a																			
—	—	—	Sunderland	a																			
—	—	—	**Newcastle** 8	d								06 25	07 35	07 42					08 42				09 35
285	—	—	Morpeth	d								06 40	07 48						08 57				
303¼	—	—	Alnmouth for Alnwick	d								06 55		08 08									10 00
335½	—	—	**Berwick-upon-Tweed**	d								07 19	08 19	08 32					09 32				10 21
363¾	—	—	Dunbar 238	d								07 43		08 56					09 57				
393	—	—	**Edinburgh** 10 238	a								08 07	09 04	09 21					10 20				11 06
—	—	0	**Edinburgh** 238	d									09 11						10 28				11 11
394¼	—	1¼	Haymarket 238	d									09 17						10 33				11 16
437¼	—	—	Motherwell	a									10 00										11 52
450¼	—	—	**Glasgow Central** 15	a									10 27										12 11
—	—	—	Stirling	a																			
—	—	—	Perth	a																			
—	—	—	**Inverness**	a																			
—	—	13¼	Inverkeithing	a															10 47				
—	—	26	Kirkcaldy	a															11 04				
—	—	51	Leuchars 8	a															11 28				
—	—	59¼	**Dundee**	a															11 43				
—	—	76¼	Arbroath	a															12 00				
—	—	90	Montrose	a															12 16				
—	—	114¼	Stonehaven	a															12 39				
—	—	130½	**Aberdeen**	a															13 03				

A From London Kings Cross
B From Manchester Airport
C From Middlesbrough
D From Saltburn
E From Manchester Piccadilly
F From Derby
G From Birmingham New Street. to Edinburgh

Table 26

Mondays to Fridays

9 December to 16 May

London - Humberside, Yorkshire, North East England and Scotland

Route Diagram - refer to first Page of Table 26

		GR	GR	TP	XC	EM	GR	GR	GR	HT	TP	TP	XC	GR	GR	XC FX	XC FO	GC	GR	GR	TP	GC	TP
		R 1	R 1	◇1	◇1 A	◇ B	R 1	R 1	R 1	◇1 ⊠	◇1 C	◇1 C	◇1 A	R 1	R 1	◇1 A	◇1 A	R 1 D	R 1	R 1	◇1 C	R 1 E	◇1 C
London Kings Cross 15 ⊖	d	06 15	06 30				07 00	07 05	07 08	07 22				07 30	07 35			07 52	08 00	08 03			
Stevenage 4	d	06 35	06 50						07 28						07 55								
Peterborough 8	a	07 04	07 19				07 45	07 51	07 57					08 15						08 48			
Norwich	d					05 50																	
Peterborough 8	d	07 06	07 21			07 27	07 46	07 52	07 59					08 16						08 50			
Grantham 7	a	07 25	07 39			07 58			08 18	08 26					08 39								
	d	07 26	07 40			07 58			08 19	08 27					08 40								
Newark North Gate 7	a	07 37							08 30					08 43									
	d	07 38							08 31					08 44									
Lincoln	a																						
Retford 10	d	07 54							08 45	08 50													
Doncaster 7	a	08 08	08 12					08 40	08 59	09 04				09 08	09 12					09 39			
Selby	a									09 20													
Hull	a									10 02													
Pontefract Monkhill	a																						
Wakefield Kirkgate 4	a																						
Wakefield Westgate 7	a		08 31					09 00							09 31					09 58			
Leeds 10	a		08 48					09 17							09 48					10 17			
Mirfield	a																						
Brighouse	a																						
Halifax	a																						
Shipley	a																						
Bradford Forster Square	a																						
Bradford Interchange	a																						
Keighley	a																						
Skipton	a																						
Sheffield 7 ⛴	d				07 54	09a37							08 22			08 48	08 48						
Doncaster 7	d	08 10			08 25				09 01					09 10		09 20	09 20						
York 8	a	08 31			08 47		08 50		09 27					09 32		09 42	09 43	09 47	09 50				
Scarborough	a																						
Harrogate	a																						
Leeds 10	d										08 28	08 57	09 05								09 28	←	09 57
York 8	d	08 35		08 42	08 50		08 55				08 58	09 26	09 32	09 36		09 48	09 48	10 01	09 54		09 58	10 01	10 26
Thirsk	d											09 46						↦				10 18	10 46
Northallerton	d	08 55									09 19	09 59									10 19	10 27	10 59
Darlington 7	a	09 06		09 12	09 16		09 21				09 30		09 57	10 03		10 13	10 13		10 20		10 30		
Eaglescliffe	a																					10 50	
Middlesbrough	a											10 30											11 30
Darlington 7	d	09 08		09 13	09 17		09 23				09 31		10 00	10 05		10 15	10 15		10 22		10 31		
Durham	d	09 25		09 29	09 34						09 47		10 18	10 23		10 32	10 32				10 47		
Chester-le-Street	d										09 53												
Newcastle 8 ⛴	a	09 42		09 44	09 47		09 51				10 07		10 30	10 39		10 45	10 45		10 50		11 05		
Hartlepool	a																					11 10	
Sunderland ⛴	a																					11 38	
Newcastle 8 ⛴	d						09 54						10 36	10 42					10 54				
Morpeth	d																						
Alnmouth for Alnwick	d													11 08									
Berwick-upon-Tweed	d						10 39												11 39				
Dunbar 238	d												11 39										
Edinburgh 10 238	a						11 22						12 03	12 12					12 22				
Edinburgh 238	d																						
Haymarket 238	d																						
Motherwell	a																						
Glasgow Central 15	a																						
Stirling	a																						
Perth	a																						
Inverness	a																						
Inverkeithing	a																						
Kirkcaldy	a																						
Leuchars 8	a																						
Dundee	a																						
Arbroath	a																						
Montrose	a																						
Stonehaven	a																						
Aberdeen	a																						

A From Birmingham New Street
B To Liverpool Lime Street
C From Manchester Airport
D To Sunderland
E From London Kings Cross

Table 26

Mondays to Fridays

9 December to 16 May

London - Humberside, Yorkshire, North East England and Scotland

Route Diagram - refer to first Page of Table 26

		XC	GR	GR	XC		EM	GR	GR	GR	TP	TP	XC	GR	GR		HT	XC	GR	TP	TP	XC	EM	GR	GR
		◇1	R 1	R 1	◇1		◇	R 1	R 1	R 1	◇1	◇1	◇1	R 1	R 1		◇1	◇1	R 1	◇1	◇1	◇1	◇	R 1	R 1
		A			B		C				D	D	E					F	G	D	D	H	C		
London Kings Cross 15 ⊖	d		08 30	08 35				09 00	09 03	09 08				09 30	09 35		09 48		10 00					10 03	10 08
Stevenage 4	d			08 55						09 29					09 55										10 29
Peterborough 8	a		09 15					09 45	09 51	09 59				10 15										10 49	10 59
Norwich	d						07 57																08 57		
Peterborough 8	d		09 16				09 27	09 46	09 52	10 00				10 16									10 28	10 51	11 00
Grantham 7	a			09 39			09 57			10 20					10 39		10 47						10 58		11 20
	d			09 40			09 58			10 21					10 40		10 48						11 00		11 22
Newark North Gate 7	a		09 43							10 32				10 43											11 35
	d		09 44							10 33				10 44											
Lincoln	a																								
Retford 10	d									10 49							11 09								
Doncaster 7	a		10 08	10 12					10 39	11 03				11 08	11 12		11 23							11 39	
Selby	a																11 39								
Hull	a																12 21								
Pontefract Monkhill	a																								
Wakefield Kirkgate 4	a																								
Wakefield Westgate 7	a			10 31					11 00						11 31									12 00	
Leeds 10	a			10 48					11 17						11 48									12 17	
Mirfield	a																								
Brighouse	a																								
Halifax	a																								
Shipley	a																								
Bradford Forster Square	a																								
Bradford Interchange	a																								
Keighley	a																								
Skipton	a																								
Sheffield 7	d	09 21			09 47		11a37						10 21					10 47				11 21	12a37		
Doncaster 7	d		10 09		10 19					11 04				11 10				11 19							
York 8	a		10 32		10 39			10 51		11 29				11 31				11 40	11 51						
Scarborough	a																								
Harrogate	a																								
Leeds 10	d	10 05									10 28	10 57	11 08							11 28	11 57	12 08			
York 8	d	10 32	10 35		10 48			10 54			10 58	11 26	11 32	11 36				11 48	11 54	11 58	12 26	12 32			
Thirsk	d											11 46									12 46				
Northallerton	d		10 55								11 19	11 59								12 19	12 59				
Darlington 7	a	10 57	11 06		11 13			11 20			11 30		11 57	12 03				12 13	12 21	12 30		12 57			
Eaglescliffe	a																								
Middlesbrough	a											12 30									13 30				
Darlington 7	d	11 00	11 08		11 15			11 22			11 31		12 00	12 07				12 15	12 22	12 31		13 00			
Durham	d	11 17	11 25		11 32						11 47		12 22	12 26				12 32		12 47		13 17			
Chester-le-Street	d										11 53														
Newcastle 8	a	11 29	11 42		11 45			11 50			12 06		12 34	12 41				12 44	12 51	13 03		13 29			
Hartlepool	a																								
Sunderland	a																								
Newcastle 8	d	11 40						11 53					12 39	12 45					12 53			13 38			
Morpeth	d																								
Alnmouth for Alnwick	d													13 11								14 02			
Berwick-upon-Tweed	d	12 22						12 38											13 40			14 23			
Dunbar 238	d												13 41												
Edinburgh 10 238	a	13 05						13 22					14 10	14 15					14 22			15 07			
Edinburgh 238	d	13 13																	14 28			15 11			
Haymarket 238	d	13 18																	14 33			15 16			
Motherwell	a	13 52																				15 52			
Glasgow Central 15	a	14 12																				16 12			
Stirling	a																								
Perth	a																								
Inverness	a																								
Inverkeithing	a																		14 46						
Kirkcaldy	a																		15 03						
Leuchars 3	a																		15 28						
Dundee	a																		15 46						
Arbroath	a																		16 04						
Montrose	a																		16 20						
Stonehaven	a																		16 43						
Aberdeen	a																		17 06						

A From Bath Spa. to Edinburgh
B From Guildford
C To Liverpool Lime Street
D From Manchester Airport
E From Plymouth
F From Reading
G The Northern Lights
H From Plymouth. to Edinburgh

Table 26

London - Humberside, Yorkshire, North East England and Scotland

Mondays to Fridays

9 December to 16 May

Route Diagram - refer to first Page of Table 26

		GR	GR	GC	XC	EM	GR	GR	GR	TP	GC	TP	XC	GR	GR	HT	XC	GR	TP	TP	XC	EM
		R 1	R 1	R 1	◇1 A	◇ B	R 1	R 1	R 1	◇1 C	R 1	◇1 C	◇1 D	R 1	R 1	◇1	◇1 E	R 1 F	◇1 C	◇1 C	◇1 G	◇ B
London Kings Cross 15 ⊖	d	10 30	10 35	10 48			11 00	11 05	11 08		11 21			11 30	11 35	11 48		12 00				
Stevenage 4	d		10 55						11 29						11 55							
Peterborough 8	a	11 15						11 51	11 58					12 15								
Norwich	d					09 57																10 57
Peterborough 8	d	11 16				11 28		11 52	11 59					12 16								12 26
Grantham 7	a		11 39			11 58			12 18						12 39	12 48						12 58
	d		11 40			12 00			12 19						12 40	12 49						12 59
Newark North Gate 7	a	11 43							12 30					12 43								
	d	11 44							12 31					12 44								
Lincoln	a																					
Retford 10	d								12 46							13 11						
Doncaster 7	a	12 08	12 12	12 23				12 41	13 03					13 08	13 12	13 23						
Selby	a															13 39						
Hull	a															14 21						
Pontefract Monkhill	a			12 47																		
Wakefield Kirkgate 4	a			13 06																		
Wakefield Westgate 7	a		12 31					13 00							13 31							
Leeds 10	a		12 48					13 17							13 48							
Mirfield	a			13 19																		
Brighouse	a			13 29																		
Halifax	a			13 39																		
Shipley	a																					
Bradford Forster Square	a																					
Bradford Interchange	a			13 55																		
Keighley	a																					
Skipton	a																					
Sheffield 7	d				11 47	13a39							12 21				12 47				13 21	14a37
Doncaster 7	d	12 09			12 19				13 05					13 10			13 19					
York 8	a	12 31			12 39		12 50		13 29		13 21			13 31			13 40	13 53				
Scarborough	a																					
Harrogate	a																					
Leeds 10	d									12 28		12 57	13 08						13 28	13 57	14 08	
York 8	d	12 35			12 48		12 53			12 58	13 23	13 26	13 32	13 36			13 48	13 55	13 58	14 26	14 32	
Thirsk	d										13 39	13 46								14 46		
Northallerton	d	12 55								13 19	13 47	13 59							14 19	14 59		
Darlington 7	a	13 06			13 13		13 19			13 30			14 00	14 05			14 13	14 22	14 30		14 57	
Eaglescliffe	a										14 04											
Middlesbrough	a											14 30								15 30		
Darlington 7	d	13 08			13 15		13 21			13 31			14 01	14 07			14 14	14 24	14 31		15 00	
Durham	d	13 25			13 32					13 47			14 18	14 25			14 31		14 47		15 17	
Chester-le-Street	d									13 53												
Newcastle 8	a	13 42			13 45		13 49			14 06			14 30	14 40			14 43	14 52	15 05		15 29	
Hartlepool	a										14 24											
Sunderland	a										14 51											
Newcastle 8	d						13 52						14 36	14 44				14 55			15 37	
Morpeth	d												14 50									
Alnmouth for Alnwick	d													15 10							16 02	
Berwick-upon-Tweed	d						14 37											15 41			16 22	
Dunbar 238	d												15 41									
Edinburgh 10 238	a						15 21						16 05	16 14				16 23			17 05	
Edinburgh 238	d																	16 33			17 11	
Haymarket 238	d																	16 39			17 15	
Motherwell	a																				17 52	
Glasgow Central 15	a																				18 11	
Stirling	a																	17 19				
Perth	a																	17 57				
Inverness	a																	20 06				
Inverkeithing	a																					
Kirkcaldy	a																					
Leuchars 3	a																					
Dundee	a																					
Arbroath	a																					
Montrose	a																					
Stonehaven	a																					
Aberdeen	a																					

A From Winchester
B To Liverpool Lime Street
C From Manchester Airport
D From Plymouth
E From Reading
F The Highland Chieftain
G From Penzance. 🍴 to Edinburgh

Table 26

Mondays to Fridays

9 December to 16 May

London - Humberside, Yorkshire, North East England and Scotland

Route Diagram - refer to first Page of Table 26

		GR	GR	GR	GR	XC	EM	GC	GR	GR	GR	TP	TP	XC	GR	GR	HT	XC	GR	TP	XC	EM	GR
		R	R	R	R			R	R	R	R				R	R			R				R
		1	1	1	1	◇1	◇	1	1	1	1	◇1	◇1	◇1	1	1	◇1	◇1	1	◇1	◇1	◇	1
						A	B					C	C	D				E		C	F	B	
		🍴🛒	🍴	🍴🛒	🍴🛒	🛒		🍴	🍴🛒	🍴🛒	🍴🛒	🛒	🛒	🛒	🍴🛒	🍴🛒	☒	🛒	🍴🛒	🛒	🛒		🍴🛒
London Kings Cross [15] ⊖	d	12 05	12 08	12 30	12 35			12 53	13 00	13 05	13 08				13 30	13 35	13 48		14 00				14 05
Stevenage [4]	d		12 29		12 55						13 29					13 55							
Peterborough [8]	a	12 50	12 59	13 15					13 46	13 51	13 59				14 15								14 50
Norwich	d						11 57															12 57	
Peterborough [8]	d	12 51	13 00	13 16			13 27		13 47	13 53	14 00				14 16							14 26	14 51
Grantham [7]	a		13 20		13 39		13 56				14 19					14 39	14 48					14 57	
	d		13 22		13 40		13 58				14 20					14 40	14 49					14 58	
Newark North Gate [7]	a		13 36	13 43							14 32				14 43								
	d			13 44							14 33				14 44								
Lincoln	a																						
Retford [10]	d										14 49						15 11						
Doncaster [7]	a	13 39		14 08	14 12					14 39	15 02				15 08	15 12	15 24						15 39
Selby	a																15 39						
Hull	a																16 21						
Pontefract Monkhill	a																						
Wakefield Kirkgate [4]	a																						
Wakefield Westgate [7]	a	13 59			14 31					14 59						15 31							15 59
Leeds [10]	a	14 17			14 48					15 17						15 48							16 17
Mirfield	a																						
Brighouse	a																						
Halifax	a																						
Shipley	a																						
Bradford Forster Square	a																						
Bradford Interchange	a																						
Keighley	a																						
Skipton	a																						
Sheffield [7] 🚌	d					13 47	15a37							14 21				14 47			15 21	16a37	
Doncaster [7]	d			14 09		14 19					15 04				15 10			15 20					
York [8]	a			14 31		14 39		14 47	14 50		15 30				15 31			15 44	15 51				
Scarborough	a																						
Harrogate	a																						
Leeds [10]	d											14 28	14 57	15 08						15 57	16 08		
York [8]	d			14 35		14 47		14 50	14 53			14 58	15 26	15 32	15 35			15 48	15 54	16 26	16 32		
Thirsk	d							15 12					15 46							16 46			
Northallerton	d			14 55				15 24				15 19	15 59		15 55					16 59			
Darlington [7]	a			15 06		15 12			15 19			15 30		15 57	16 06			16 13	16 21		16 58		
Eaglescliffe	a							15 49															
Middlesbrough	a												16 30							17 30			
Darlington [7]	d			15 08		15 15			15 21			15 31		16 00	16 08			16 15	16 22		17 00		
Durham	d			15 25		15 32						15 48		16 17	16 25			16 32			17 18		
Chester-le-Street	d											15 54											
Newcastle [8] 🚌	a			15 42		15 45			15 49			16 06		16 29	16 42			16 45	16 51		17 30		
Hartlepool	a							16 09															
Sunderland 🚌	a							16 39															
Newcastle [8] 🚌	d								15 52					16 37					16 53		17 37		
Morpeth	d																						
Alnmouth for Alnwick	d													17 02							18 02		
Berwick-upon-Tweed	d								16 37										17 40		18 22		
Dunbar 238	d													17 43									
Edinburgh [10] 238	a								17 22					18 07					18 23		19 05		
Edinburgh 238	d													18 11					18 33		19 11		
Haymarket 238	d													18 15					18 38		19 16		
Motherwell	a																				19 56		
Glasgow Central [15]	a																				20 15		
Stirling	a																						
Perth	a																						
Inverness	a																						
Inverkeithing	a													18 28					18 53				
Kirkcaldy	a													18 46					19 11				
Leuchars [3]	a													19 22					19 37				
Dundee	a													19 35					19 53				
Arbroath	a													19 51					20 11				
Montrose	a													20 05					20 27				
Stonehaven	a													20 26					20 50				
Aberdeen	a													20 48					21 13				

A From Southampton Central
B To Liverpool Lime Street
C From Manchester Airport
D From Plymouth. 🛒 to Edinburgh
E From Reading
F From Penzance. 🛒 to Edinburgh

Table 26

Mondays to Fridays

9 December to 16 May

London - Humberside, Yorkshire, North East England and Scotland

Route Diagram - refer to first Page of Table 26

		GR	GR		GR	GC	XC	GR	TP	XC	EM	GR	GR		GR	GR	HT	TP	XC	GR	GC	TP	XC		EM
		R 1	R 1		R 1	R 1	◇1	R 1	◇1	◇1	◇	R 1	R 1		R 1	R 1	◇1	◇1	◇1	R 1	R 1	◇1	◇1		◇
							A		B	C	D							E	F			B	C		D
London Kings Cross 15 ⊖	d	14 08	14 30		14 35	14 48		15 00				15 05	15 08		15 30	15 35	15 49			16 00	16 03				
Stevenage 4	d	14 28			14 55								15 29			15 55									
Peterborough 8	a	14 59	15 15									15 50	15 59		16 15										
Norwich	d										13 57														14 57
Peterborough 8	d	15 00	15 16								15 28	15 51	16 00		16 17										16 27
Grantham 7	a	15 19			15 39						15 59		16 20			16 40	16 48								16 57
	d	15 20			15 40						16 01		16 21			16 41	16 49								16 58
Newark North Gate 7	a	15 34	15 43										16 32		16 44										
	d		15 44										16 33		16 45										
Lincoln	a																								
Retford 10	d												16 49				17 10								
Doncaster 7	a		16 08		16 12	16 22						16 39	17 03		17 09	17 13	17 23				17 35				
Selby	a																17 39								
Hull	a																18 21								
Pontefract Monkhill	a					16 47																			
Wakefield Kirkgate 4	a					17 04															18 07				
Wakefield Westgate 7	a				16 31							17 00				17 31									
Leeds 10	a				16 50							17 17				17 48									
Mirfield	a					17 20															18 20				
Brighouse	a					17 29															18 28				
Halifax	a					17 40															18 40				
Shipley	a																								
Bradford Forster Square	a																								
Bradford Interchange	a					17 55															18 55				
Keighley	a																								
Skipton	a																								
Sheffield 7	d						15 47			16 21	17a36								16 47				17 21		18a36
Doncaster 7	d		16 10				16 19						17 05		17 10				17 19						
York 8	a		16 31				16 39	16 51					17 30		17 33				17 40	17 51					
Scarborough	a																								
Harrogate	a																								
Leeds 10	d								16 28	17 08								17 12				17 57	18 07		
York 8	d		16 35				16 48	16 53	16 58	17 32					17 36			17 41	17 48	17 54		18 25	18 33		
Thirsk	d								17 14									17 59							
Northallerton	d		16 55						17 22						17 56			18 09				18 46			
Darlington 7	a		17 06				17 14	17 20	17 33	17 58					18 07				18 13	18 21		18 57	19 01		
Eaglescliffe	a																								
Middlesbrough	a																	18 40							
Darlington 7	d		17 08				17 15	17 22	17 34	18 00					18 09				18 15	18 23		18 58	19 03		
Durham	d		17 25				17 32		17 51	18 17					18 26				18 33			19 14	19 22		
Chester-le-Street	d								17 57													19 20			
Newcastle 8	a		17 42				17 45	17 50	18 10	18 32					18 43				18 46	18 51		19 34	19 35		
Hartlepool	a																								
Sunderland	a																								
Newcastle 8	d							17 53		18 40					18 46					18 54			19 38		
Morpeth	d																								
Alnmouth for Alnwick	d														19 14								20 06		
Berwick-upon-Tweed	d							18 38		19 22										19 40			20 27		
Dunbar 238	d									19 45															
Edinburgh 10 238	a							19 23		20 09					20 14					20 22			21 11		
Edinburgh 238	d									20 14					20 17					20 32			21 14		
Haymarket 238	d									20 17					20 22					20 37			21 19		
Motherwell	a														21 03								22 04		
Glasgow Central 15	a														21 25								22 28		
Stirling	a																								
Perth	a																								
Inverness	a																								
Inverkeithing	a									20 30										20 51					
Kirkcaldy	a																			21 08					
Leuchars 3	a									21 25										21 36					
Dundee	a									21 41										21 50					
Arbroath	a																			22 08					
Montrose	a																			22 24					
Stonehaven	a																			22 47					
Aberdeen	a																			23 10					

A From Southampton Central
B From Manchester Airport
C From Plymouth. Trolley to Edinburgh
D To Liverpool Lime Street
E From Liverpool Lime Street
F From Reading

Table 26

Mondays to Fridays

9 December to 16 May

London - Humberside, Yorkshire, North East England and Scotland

Route Diagram - refer to first Page of Table 26

		GR	GR	GR	GR	GC	GR	TP FO	TP FX	XC	EM	GR	GR	TP	GR	GR	XC	XC	EM	GR	GR	GR	GR
		R 1	R 1	R 1	R 1	R 1	R 1	◇1	◇1	◇1	◇	R 1	R 1	◇1	R 1	R 1	◇1	◇1	◇	R 1	R 1	R 1	R 1
									A	B	C		D	A			E	F	G				
London Kings Cross 15 ⊖	d	16 06	16 09	16 30	16 33	16 50	17 00					17 03	17 19		17 30	17 33				17 49	18 00	18 03	18 19
Stevenage 4	d		16 30		16 53											17 55							
Peterborough 8	a	16 52	16 59	17 15								17 49	18 06		18 15					18 35		18 54	19 07
Norwich	d										15 48								16 57				
Peterborough 8	d	16 53	17 01	17 16							17 24	17 51	18 07		18 17				18 26	18 37		18 56	19 08
Grantham 7	a		17 21		17 39						17 56		18 27			18 41			18 55	19 05			19 27
	d		17 22		17 40						17 57		18 28			18 42			18 57	19 06			19 28
Newark North Gate 7	a		17 36	17 43									18 39		18 43							19 23	
	d			17 44									18 40		18 44							19 24	
Lincoln	a																						
Retford 10	d				18 02															19 28			
Doncaster 7	a	17 43		18 08	18 16							18 39	19 05			19 14				19 42		19 48	
Selby	a												19 23										
Hull	a												20 05										
Pontefract Monkhill	a																						
Wakefield Kirkgate 4	a																						
Wakefield Westgate 7	a	18 05			18 35							18 59				19 32				20 02		20 07	
Leeds 10	a	18 21			18 52							19 17				19 48				20 20		20 23	
Mirfield	a																						
Brighouse	a																						
Halifax	a																						
Shipley	a																						
Bradford Forster Square	a																						
Bradford Interchange	a																						
Keighley	a																					20s55	
Skipton	a																					21 13	
Sheffield 7	d									17 47	19a37						18 21	18 47	20a27				
Doncaster 7	d			18 10														19 17					
York 8	a			18 32		18 40	18 49								19 25			19 38			19 49		20 18
Scarborough	a																						
Harrogate	a															20 25							
Leeds 10	d								18 28	18 36				18 57			19 08						
York 8	d			18 36		18 42	18 53	18 57	18 57	19 04				19 26	19 29		19 33	19 45			19 52		20 20
Thirsk	d					18 58		19 14	19 14					19 46									
Northallerton	d			18 57		19 06		19 24	19 24					19 57									20 40
Darlington 7	a			19 08			19 19			19 29					19 55		20 00	20 10			20 19		20 51
Eaglescliffe	a					19 24																	
Middlesbrough	a							19 56	19 56					20 30									
Darlington 7	d			19 10			19 21			19 32					19 57		20 02	20 12			20 20		20 53
Durham	d			19 27						19 49					20 14		20 20	20 29					21 10
Chester-le-Street	d																						
Newcastle 8	a			19 42			19 49			20 01					20 31		20 33	20 42			20 49		21 27
Hartlepool	a					19 44																	
Sunderland	a					20 21																	
Newcastle 8	d			19 45			19 54			20 03							20 35				20 51		
Morpeth	d			20 01													20 49						
Alnmouth for Alnwick	d									20 27													
Berwick-upon-Tweed	d						20 40										21 22				21 38		
Dunbar 238	d																21 48				22 03		
Edinburgh 10 238	a			21 17			21 24			21 28							22 13				22 28		
Edinburgh 238	d																						
Haymarket 238	d																						
Motherwell	a																						
Glasgow Central 15	a																						
Stirling	a																						
Perth	a																						
Inverness	a																						
Inverkeithing	a																						
Kirkcaldy	a																						
Leuchars 8	a																						
Dundee	a																						
Arbroath	a																						
Montrose	a																						
Stonehaven	a																						
Aberdeen	a																						

- **A** From Manchester Airport
- **B** From Southampton Central
- **C** To Liverpool Lime Street
- **D** The Hull Executive
- **E** From Plymouth
- **F** From Reading
- **G** To Manchester Piccadilly

Table 26

Mondays to Fridays

9 December to 16 May

London - Humberside, Yorkshire, North East England and Scotland

Route Diagram - refer to first Page of Table 26

		TP	XC	GR	GR	HT	EM	XC	GR	GR	GR	TP	GC	GR FO	GR FX	GR	EM	GC	XC	GR	GR	HT	GR
		◇1	◇1	R 1	R 1	◇1	◇	◇1	R 1	R 1	R 1	◇1	R 1	R 1	R 1	R 1	◇	R ◇1	◇1	R 1	R 1	◇1	R 1
		A	B				C	D				A					C		F				
London Kings Cross 15 ⊖	d			18 30	18 33	18 50			19 00	19 03	19 06		19 18	19 30	19 30	19 33		19 52		20 00	20 05	20 30	20 35
Stevenage 4	d				18 53						19 28					19 53							20 55
Peterborough 8	a			19 17						19 49	19 57			20 15	20 15						20 50		21 24
Norwich	d						17 54										18 57						
Peterborough 8	d			19 18			19 26			19 52	20 00			20 16	20 16		20 27				20 51		21 26
Grantham 7	a				19 42	19 50	19 58				20 20					20 39	20 57					21 30	21 46
	d				19 43	19 51					20 22					20 40						21 31	21 47
Newark North Gate 7	a			19 45							20 33			20 43	20 43						21 18		21 58
	d			19 46							20 36			20 44	20 44						21 19		21 59
Lincoln	a										21 02												
Retford 10	d				20 05	20 12																21 52	
Doncaster 7	a			20 10	20 20	20 26				20 39				21 08	21 08	21 12		21 22			21 43	22 06	22 22
Selby	a					20 47																22 22	
Hull	a					21 29																23 06	
Pontefract Monkhill	a																						
Wakefield Kirkgate 4	a																	21 52					
Wakefield Westgate 7	a				20 38					21 00						21 31					22 07		22 40
Leeds 10	a				20 53					21 18						21 49					22 23		22 58
Mirfield	a																	22 08					
Brighouse	a																	22 16					
Halifax	a																	22 26					
Shipley	a				21s12																		
Bradford Forster Square	a				21 23																		
Bradford Interchange	a																	22 42					
Keighley	a																						
Skipton	a																						
Sheffield 7	d		19 26					19 54											20 53				
Doncaster 7	d			20 11				20 17						21 10	21 10				21 21				
York 8	a			20 32				20 38	20 50				21 17	21 31	21 31				21 44	21 50			
Scarborough	a																						
Harrogate	a																						
Leeds 10	d	19 57	20 08									20 45											
York 8	d	20 29	20 33	20 37				20 48	20 53			21 14	21 20	21 34	21 34				21 49	21 53			
Thirsk	d	20 49										21 31	21 37										
Northallerton	d	20 59										21 39	21 46	21 54	21 54								
Darlington 7	a		20 58	21 04				21 13	21 19			21 50		22 05	22 05				22 14	22 20			
Eaglescliffe	a												22 03										
Middlesbrough	a	21 30																					
Darlington 7	d		21 00	21 06				21 15	21 21			21 51		22 07	22 07				22 16	22 21			
Durham	d		21 18	21 23				21 32				22 07		22 24	22 24				22 34	22 39			
Chester-le-Street	d											22 13											
Newcastle 8	a		21 30	21 38				21 44	21 49			22 27		22 41	22 41				22 50	22 56			
Hartlepool	a												22 23										
Sunderland	a												22 51										
Newcastle 8	d		21 35	21 41					21 56					22 42									
Morpeth	d			21 57										22 57									
Alnmouth for Alnwick	d		22 01	22 13										23 13									
Berwick-upon-Tweed	d								22 39					23 39									
Dunbar 238	d																						
Edinburgh 10 238	a		23 03	23 17					23 30					00 28									
Edinburgh 238	d																						
Haymarket 238	d																						
Motherwell	a																						
Glasgow Central 15	a																						
Stirling	a																						
Perth	a																						
Inverness	a																						
Inverkeithing	a																						
Kirkcaldy	a																						
Leuchars 8	a																						
Dundee	a																						
Arbroath	a																						
Montrose	a																						
Stonehaven	a																						
Aberdeen	a																						

A From Manchester Airport
B From Plymouth. to Leeds
C To Nottingham
D From Southampton Central
F From Reading

Table 26

Mondays to Fridays

9 December to 16 May

London - Humberside, Yorkshire, North East England and Scotland

Route Diagram - refer to first Page of Table 26

		XC	GR	GR	TP	GR	GR
			R	R		R	R
		◇1	1	1	◇1	1	1
		A			B		
			🍴	🍴		☕	🍴
London Kings Cross 15 ⊖	d		21 00	21 35		22 00	23 30
Stevenage 4	d		21 21	21 56			
Peterborough 8	a		21 50	22 26		22 46	00s17
Norwich	d						
Peterborough 8	d		21 53	22 27		22 47	
Grantham 7	a			22 47		23 07	00s46
	d			22 49		23 08	
Newark North Gate 7	a		22 19	22 59		23 19	00s57
	d		22 20	23 01		23 20	
Lincoln	a						
Retford 10	d			23 17			
Doncaster 7	a		22 44	23 31		23 49	01s25
Selby	a						
Hull	a						
Pontefract Monkhill	a						
Wakefield Kirkgate 4	a						
Wakefield Westgate 7	a			23 53			
Leeds 10	a			00 10			02 36
Mirfield	a						
Brighouse	a						
Halifax	a						
Shipley	a						
Bradford Forster Square	a						
Bradford Interchange	a						
Keighley	a						
Skipton	a						
Sheffield 7 🚌	d	21 54					
Doncaster 7	d	22 31	22 46			23 50	
York 8	a	22 52	23 09			00 39	
Scarborough	a						
Harrogate	a						
Leeds 10	d				22 42		
York 8	d		23 12		23 20	00 42	
Thirsk	d				23 42		
Northallerton	d		23 44		23 50	01s11	
Darlington 7	a		23 55		00 01	01s25	
Eaglescliffe	a						
Middlesbrough	a						
Darlington 7	d		23 57		00 02		
Durham	d		00 14		00 19	01s43	
Chester-le-Street	d						
Newcastle 8 🚌	a		00 43		00 50	02 17	
Hartlepool	a						
Sunderland 🚌	a						
Newcastle 8 🚌	d						
Morpeth	d						
Alnmouth for Alnwick	d						
Berwick-upon-Tweed	d						
Dunbar 238	d						
Edinburgh 10 238	a						
Edinburgh 238	d						
Haymarket 238	d						
Motherwell	a						
Glasgow Central 15	a						
Stirling	a						
Perth	a						
Inverness	a						
Inverkeithing	a						
Kirkcaldy	a						
Leuchars 3	a						
Dundee	a						
Arbroath	a						
Montrose	a						
Stonehaven	a						
Aberdeen	a						

A From Southampton Central

B From Manchester Airport

Table 26

Saturdays

14 December to 17 May

London - Humberside, Yorkshire, North East England and Scotland

Route Diagram - refer to first Page of Table 26

		GR	TP	GR	TP	GR	XC	GR	NT	TP		TP	GR	XC	TP	NT	XC	GR	TP	XC		GR	TP	TP	XC
		R 1	◇1	R 1	◇1	R 1	◇1	R 1		◇1		◇1	R 1	◇1	◇1		◇1	R 1	◇1	◇1		R 1	◇1	◇1	◇1
		A	B	A					C	D				E	B	C	F			G			B	B	G
London Kings Cross 15 ⊖	d																	06 15				07 00			
Stevenage 4	d																	06 35				07 20			
Peterborough 8	a																	07 04							
Norwich	d																								
Peterborough 8	d																	07 06							
Grantham 7	a																	07 25							
	d																	07 26							
Newark North Gate 7	a																	07 37							
	d																	07 38							
Lincoln	a																								
Retford 10	d																	07 54							
Doncaster 7	a																	08 08							
Selby	a																								
Hull	a																								
Pontefract Monkhill	a																								
Wakefield Kirkgate 4	a																								
Wakefield Westgate 7	a																								
Leeds 10	a																								
Mirfield	a																								
Brighouse	a																								
Halifax	a																								
Shipley	a																								
Bradford Forster Square	a																								
Bradford Interchange	a																								
Keighley	a																								
Skipton	a																								
Sheffield 7	d													06 49			07 12			07 54					08 21
Doncaster 7	d							06 10						07 20				08 10		08 25					
York 8	a							06 30						07 43				08 31		08 47		08 51			
Scarborough	a																								
Harrogate	a																								
Leeds 10	d									06 35			07 10		07 51		07 57						08 28	08 57	09 08
York 8	d			00 42	05 54			06 33		07 06		07 32	07 37	07 48	08 23		08 29	08 35	08 42	08 50		08 55	08 59	09 26	09 32
Thirsk	d				06 10					07 22		07 52			08 39									09 46	
Northallerton	d			01s11	06 18			06 52		07 30		08 00			08 50			08 55					09 20	09 59	
Darlington 7	a			01s25	06 29			07 05		07 41			08 04	08 13			08 57	09 06	09 12	09 16		09 21	09 31		09 57
Eaglescliffe	a																								
Middlesbrough	a				07 03							08 31			09 22									10 32	
Darlington 7	d		00 02					07 06	07 20	07 42			08 06	08 15		08 22	08 58	09 08	09 13	09 17		09 23	09 32		10 00
Durham	d	00 14	00 19	01s43				07 24	07 42	07 59			08 24	08 32		08 43	09 15	09 25	09 29	09 34			09 48		10 17
Chester-le-Street	d								07 49	08 05						08 50							09 54		
Newcastle 8	a	00 43	00 50	02 17				07 39	08 03	08 17			08 37	08 45		09 06	09 27	09 40	09 46	09 47		09 51	10 08		10 30
Hartlepool	a																								
Sunderland	a																								
Newcastle 8	d					06 30	07 38	07 43					08 42				09 35	09 45				09 55			10 36
Morpeth	d					06 44	07 51						08 57												
Alnmouth for Alnwick	d					06 58		08 09									09 59								
Berwick-upon-Tweed	d					07 22	08 24	08 33					09 32				10 20					10 40			
Dunbar 238	d					07 50		08 57					09 57												11 39
Edinburgh 10 238	a					08 15	09 07	09 21					10 24				11 03	11 10				11 28			12 07
Edinburgh 238	d						09 11						10 28				11 11								
Haymarket 238	d						09 17						10 33				11 16								
Motherwell	a						09 52										11 52								
Glasgow Central 15	a						10 15										12 11								
Stirling	a																								
Perth	a																								
Inverness	a																								
Inverkeithing	a												10 47												
Kirkcaldy	a												11 04												
Leuchars 3	a												11 28												
Dundee	a												11 43												
Arbroath	a												12 00												
Montrose	a												12 16												
Stonehaven	a												12 39												
Aberdeen	a												13 03												

A From London Kings Cross
B From Manchester Airport
C From Saltburn
D From Manchester Piccadilly
E From Derby
F From Birmingham New Street, to Edinburgh
G From Birmingham New Street

Table 26

Saturdays

14 December to 17 May

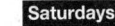

London - Humberside, Yorkshire, North East England and Scotland

Route Diagram - refer to first Page of Table 26

		EM	GR	GR	XC	GR	GR	TP	GC	EM	TP	XC	GR	XC	GR	TP	TP	XC	EM	GR	GR	HT	XC
		◇	R 1	R 1	◇1	R 1	R 1	◇1	R 1	◇1	◇1	◇1	R 1	◇1	R 1	◇1	◇1	◇1	◇	R 1	R 1	◇1	◇1
		A			B			C		D	C	E		F		C	C	G	A				H
London Kings Cross 15 ⊖	d		07 03	07 30		08 00	08 03		08 11				08 30		09 00					09 03	09 30	09 48	
Stevenage 4	d		07 25																	09 23			
Peterborough 8	a		07 53	08 15			08 48						09 15							09 52	10 15		
Norwich	d	05 50																	07 57				
Peterborough 8	d	07 27	07 55	08 16			08 49						09 16						09 25	09 54	10 16		
Grantham 7	a	07 55	08 13				09 08												09 53	10 14		10 47	
	d	07 58	08 14				09 09												09 53	10 15		10 48	
Newark North Gate 7	a		08 25				09 20						09 43							10 26			
	d		08 26				09 21						09 44							10 27			
Lincoln	a																						
Retford 10	d			08 55																	10 54	11 10	
Doncaster 7	a		08 49	09 10			09 47						10 08							10 50	11 08	11 23	
Selby	a																					11 39	
Hull	a																					12 19	
Pontefract Monkhill	a																						
Wakefield Kirkgate 4	a																						
Wakefield Westgate 7	a		09 07				10 07													11 07			
Leeds 10	a		09 24				10 24													11 25			
Mirfield	a																						
Brighouse	a																						
Halifax	a																						
Shipley	a																						
Bradford Forster Square	a																						
Bradford Interchange	a																						
Keighley	a																						
Skipton	a																						
Sheffield 7	d	09a38			08 48					09 21		09 21		09 47				10 21	11a37				10 47
Doncaster 7	d			09 12	09 20					09 55			10 10	10 19							11 10		11 19
York 8	a			09 32	09 43	09 50			10 12	10 16			10 32	10 39	10 50						11 31		11 40
Scarborough	a																						
Harrogate	a																						
Leeds 10	d							09 28			09 57	10 08				10 28	10 57	11 08					
York 8	d			09 36	09 48	09 53		09 58	10 15		10 26	10 32	10 35	10 48	10 53	10 58	11 26	11 32			11 36		11 48
Thirsk	d								10 32		10 46						11 46						
Northallerton	d							10 19	10 40		10 59		10 55			11 19	11 59						
Darlington 7	a			10 03	10 13	10 19		10 30				10 57	11 06	11 13	11 19	11 30		11 57			12 03		12 13
Eaglescliffe	a								10 57														
Middlesbrough	a										11 30						12 30						
Darlington 7	d			10 05	10 15	10 21		10 31				11 00	11 08	11 15	11 21	11 31		12 00			12 05		12 15
Durham	d			10 22	10 32			10 47				11 17	11 25	11 32		11 47		12 17			12 22		12 32
Chester-le-Street	d															11 53							
Newcastle 8	a			10 37	10 44	10 49		11 05				11 29	11 40	11 46	11 49	12 06		12 29			12 37		12 45
Hartlepool	a								11 20														
Sunderland	a								11 50														
Newcastle 8	d			10 40		10 55						11 36	11 45		11 55			12 36			12 41		
Morpeth	d																						
Alnmouth for Alnwick	d			11 06																	13 07		
Berwick-upon-Tweed	d					11 40						12 20			12 40								
Dunbar 238	d																	13 39					
Edinburgh 10 238	a			12 12		12 28						13 04	13 10		13 28			14 06			14 12		
Edinburgh 238	d											13 12											
Haymarket 238	d											13 16											
Motherwell	a											13 52											
Glasgow Central 15	a											14 12											
Stirling	a																						
Perth	a																						
Inverness	a																						
Inverkeithing	a																						
Kirkcaldy	a																						
Leuchars 3	a																						
Dundee	a																						
Arbroath	a																						
Montrose	a																						
Stonehaven	a																						
Aberdeen	a																						

A To Liverpool Lime Street
B From Birmingham New Street
C From Manchester Airport
D From St Pancras International
E From Bristol Temple Meads. ✠ to Edinburgh
F From Guildford
G From Plymouth
H From Bournemouth

Table 26

Saturdays

14 December to 17 May

London - Humberside, Yorkshire, North East England and Scotland

Route Diagram - refer to first Page of Table 26

		GR	TP	TP	XC	EM	GR	GR	GC	XC	EM	GR	GR	TP	GC	TP	XC	GR	GR	HT	XC	GR
		R 1	◇1	◇1	◇1	◇	R 1	R 1	R 1	◇1	◇	R 1	R 1	◇1	R 1	◇1	◇1	R 1	R 1	◇1	◇1	R 1
		A	B	B	C	D				E	D			B		B	F				G	H
London Kings Cross 15 ⊖	d	10 00					10 03	10 30	10 48			11 00	11 03		11 20			11 30	11 35	11 48		12 00
Stevenage 4	d												11 23									
Peterborough 8	a						10 50	11 15					11 52					12 15	12 21			
Norwich	d					08 57					09 57											
Peterborough 8	d					10 22	10 52	11 16			11 23		11 54					12 16	12 23			
Grantham 7	a					10 53	11 10				11 55		12 13							12 47		
	d					10 54	11 11				11 56		12 14							12 48		
Newark North Gate 7	a						11 23	11 43					12 25									
	d						11 24	11 44					12 26									
Lincoln	a																					
Retford 10	d																	12 54		13 10		
Doncaster 7	a						11 50	12 08	12 16				12 50					13 09	13 12	13 23		
Selby	a																			13 39		
Hull	a																			14 21		
Pontefract Monkhill	a																					
Wakefield Kirkgate 4	a								12 42													
Wakefield Westgate 7	a						12 07						13 07						13 31			
Leeds 10	a						12 25						13 25						13 48			
Mirfield	a								12 55													
Brighouse	a								13 05													
Halifax	a								13 23													
Shipley	a																					
Bradford Forster Square	a																					
Bradford Interchange	a								13 38													
Keighley	a																					
Skipton	a																					
Sheffield 7	d				11 21	12a37				11 47	13a37						12 21				12 47	
Doncaster 7	d							12 10		12 17								13 11			13 19	
York 8	a	11 51						12 32		12 39		12 47			13 13			13 32			13 39	13 51
Scarborough	a																					
Harrogate	a																					
Leeds 10	d		11 28	11 57	12 08									12 28		12 57	13 08					
York 8	d	11 54	11 58	12 26	12 32			12 35		12 48		12 53		12 58	13 16	13 26	13 32	13 36			13 48	13 54
Thirsk	d			12 46											13 33	13 46						
Northallerton	d		12 19	12 59				12 55						13 19	13 41	13 59						
Darlington 7	a	12 21	12 30		12 58			13 06		13 13		13 19		13 30			13 57	14 03			14 13	14 21
Eaglescliffe	a														13 58							
Middlesbrough	a			13 30												14 30						
Darlington 7	d	12 23	12 31		13 00			13 08		13 15		13 21		13 31			13 59	14 05			14 14	14 23
Durham	d		12 47		13 17			13 25		13 32				13 47			14 16	14 22			14 31	
Chester-le-Street	d													13 53								
Newcastle 8	a	12 51	13 03		13 29			13 40		13 45		13 49		14 06			14 28	14 37			14 43	14 51
Hartlepool	a														14 20							
Sunderland	a														14 50							
Newcastle 8	d	12 55			13 35			13 45				13 55					14 34	14 40				14 55
Morpeth	d																14 48					
Alnmouth for Alnwick	d				14 00													15 06				
Berwick-upon-Tweed	d	13 41			14 20							14 40										15 41
Dunbar 238	d																15 39					
Edinburgh 10 238	a	14 24			15 04			15 10				15 28					16 04	16 10				16 24
Edinburgh 238	d	14 28			15 11																	16 33
Haymarket 238	d	14 33			15 16																	16 39
Motherwell	a				15 52																	
Glasgow Central 15	a				16 12																	
Stirling	a																					17 19
Perth	a																					17 57
Inverness	a																					20 06
Inverkeithing	a	14 46																				
Kirkcaldy	a	15 03																				
Leuchars 3	a	15 28																				
Dundee	a	15 46																				
Arbroath	a	16 04																				
Montrose	a	16 20																				
Stonehaven	a	16 43																				
Aberdeen	a	17 06																				

A The Northern Lights
B From Manchester Airport
C From Plymouth. Trolley service to Edinburgh
D To Liverpool Lime Street
E From Southampton Central
F From Plymouth
G From Reading
H The Highland Chieftain

Table 26

Saturdays

14 December to 17 May

London - Humberside, Yorkshire, North East England and Scotland

Route Diagram - refer to first Page of Table 26

		TP	TP	TP	XC		EM	GR		GR	XC	EM	GR	GR		TP	GC	TP		XC	GR	XC	GR	TP	TP
		◇1 A	◇1 B	◇1 C	◇1 D		◇ F	1		1	◇1 G	◇ H	1	1		◇1 C	1	◇1 C		◇1 I	1	◇1 J	1	◇1 B	◇1 C
London Kings Cross 15 ⊖	d							12 03		12 30			13 00	13 03			13 20				13 30		14 00		
Stevenage 4	d													13 23											
Peterborough 8	a							12 49		13 15				13 52							14 15				
Norwich	d						10 57					11 57													
Peterborough 8	d						12 26	12 51		13 16		13 28		13 54							14 16				
Grantham 7	a						12 58	13 14				13 56	14 00	14 13											
	d						12 58	13 15				13 58	14 01	14 14											
Newark North Gate 7	a							13 25		13 43				14 25											
	d							13 26		13 44				14 26											
Lincoln	a																								
Retford 10	d																				14 55				
Doncaster 7	a							13 51		14 08				14 50							15 10				
Selby	a																								
Hull	a																								
Pontefract Monkhill	a																								
Wakefield Kirkgate 4	a																								
Wakefield Westgate 7	a							14 09						15 07											
Leeds 10	a							14 27						15 25											
Mirfield	a																								
Brighouse	a																								
Halifax	a																								
Shipley	a																								
Bradford Forster Square	a																								
Bradford Interchange	a																								
Keighley	a																								
Skipton	a																								
Sheffield 7	d				13 21		14a37				13 47	15a37								14 21		14 47			
Doncaster 7	d									14 10	14 19										15 12	15 19			
York 8	a									14 31	14 39		14 50				15 16				15 32	15 39	15 49		
Scarborough	a																								
Harrogate	a																								
Leeds 10	d	13 28	13 28	13 57	14 08											14 28		14 57		15 08				15 28	15 57
York 8	d	13 58	13 58	14 26	14 32					14 35	14 48		14 53			14 58	15 18	15 26		15 32	15 36	15 48	15 52	15 57	16 26
Thirsk	d			14 46													15 34	15 46							16 46
Northallerton	d	14 19	14 19	14 59						14 55						15 19	15 42	15 59							16 59
Darlington 7	a	14 30	14 30		14 57					15 06	15 13		15 19			15 30				15 57	16 03	16 13	16 19		
Eaglescliffe	a																15 59								
Middlesbrough	a			15 30														16 30							17 30
Darlington 7	d	14 31	14 31		15 00					15 08	15 15		15 21			15 31				16 00	16 05	16 15	16 21		
Durham	d	14 47	14 47		15 17					15 25	15 32					15 48				16 17	16 22	16 32			
Chester-le-Street	d															15 54									
Newcastle 8	a	15 05	15 05		15 29					15 40	15 45		15 49			16 06				16 29	16 37	16 45	16 49	16 57	
Hartlepool	a																16 20								
Sunderland	a																16 50								
Newcastle 8	d		15 08		15 35					15 45			15 55							16 34	16 40		16 55	16 58	
Morpeth	d																								
Alnmouth for Alnwick	d				16 00															16 58	17 06				
Berwick-upon-Tweed	d				16 20								16 40										17 41		
Dunbar 238	d																			17 39					
Edinburgh 10 238	a		16 40		17 07					17 12			17 29							18 03	18 10		18 26	18 37	
Edinburgh 238	d				17 11															18 11			18 33		
Haymarket 238	d				17 16															18 15			18 38		
Motherwell	a				17 52																				
Glasgow Central 15	a				18 11																				
Stirling	a																								
Perth	a																								
Inverness	a																								
Inverkeithing	a																			18 28			18 53		
Kirkcaldy	a																			18 43			19 11		
Leuchars 3	a																			19 13			19 37		
Dundee	a																			19 29			19 53		
Arbroath	a																			19 45			20 11		
Montrose	a																			20 02			20 27		
Stonehaven	a																			20 23			20 50		
Aberdeen	a																			20 42			21 13		

A from 15 February. From Manchester Airport
B from 4 January until 8 February. From Manchester Airport
C From Manchester Airport
D From Penzance. to Edinburgh
F To Liverpool Lime Street
G From Southampton Central
H To Liverpool Lime Street
I From Plymouth
J From Reading

Table 26

Saturdays

14 December to 17 May

London - Humberside, Yorkshire, North East England and Scotland

Route Diagram - refer to first Page of Table 26

		XC	EM	GR	GR	HT	XC	GR	TP	TP	XC	EM	GR	GR	GC	XC	GR	TP	TP	XC	EM	GR
				R	R			R					R	R	R		R					R
		◇1	◇	1	1	◇1	◇1	1	◇1	◇1	◇1	◇	1	1	1	◇1	1	◇1	◇1	◇1	◇	1
		A	B				C		D	D	E	B				F		G	D	E	B	
		🛒		🍽🛒	🍽🛒	⊠	🛒	🍽🛒			🛒		🍽🛒	🍽🛒	🍽	🛒	🍽🛒			🛒		🍽🛒
London Kings Cross [15] ⊖	d			14 03	14 30	14 48		15 00					15 03	15 30	15 48		16 00					16 03
Stevenage [4]	d												15 24									
Peterborough [8]	a			14 48	15 15								15 52	16 15								16 48
Norwich	d		12 57									13 57									14 57	
Peterborough [8]	d		14 26	14 50	15 16							15 24	15 54	16 16							16 27	16 50
Grantham [7]	a		14 57	15 08		15 47						15 55	16 13								16 55	17 11
	d		14 58	15 09		15 48						15 57	16 14								16 56	17 12
Newark North Gate [7]	a			15 21	15 43								16 25									17 24
	d			15 22	15 44								16 26									17 25
Lincoln	a																					
Retford [10]	d					16 09								16 54								
Doncaster [7]	a			15 47	16 08	16 23							16 50	17 08	17 20							17 49
Selby	a					16 41																
Hull	a					17 25																
Pontefract Monkhill	a																					
Wakefield Kirkgate [4]	a														17 44							
Wakefield Westgate [7]	a			16 07									17 07									18 08
Leeds [10]	a			16 25									17 25									18 25
Mirfield	a														17 57							
Brighouse	a														18 06							
Halifax	a														18 23							
Shipley	a																					
Bradford Forster Square	a																					
Bradford Interchange	a														18 38							
Keighley	a																					
Skipton	a																					
Sheffield [7] 🚌	d	15 21	16a37				15 47				16 21	17a34				16 47				17 22	18a33	
Doncaster [7]	d				16 10		16 19							17 10		17 19						
York [8]	a				16 31		16 39	16 52						17 31		17 37	17 49					
Scarborough	a																					
Harrogate	a																					
Leeds [10]	d	16 08							16 28	16 57	17 08							17 25	17 57	18 08		
York [8]	d	16 32			16 35		16 48	16 54	16 58	17 26	17 31			17 35		17 48	17 52	18 07	18 25	18 32		
Thirsk	d								17 14	17 46									18 46			
Northallerton	d				16 55				17 22	17 58									18 59			
Darlington [7]	a	16 58			17 06		17 13	17 21	17 33		17 56			18 01		18 13	18 19			18 59		
Eaglescliffe	a																					
Middlesbrough	a									18 30									19 31			
Darlington [7]	d	17 00			17 08		17 15	17 23	17 34		17 58			18 03		18 14	18 21			19 00		
Durham	d	17 17			17 25		17 31		17 51		18 14			18 20		18 31				19 18		
Chester-le-Street	d								17 57													
Newcastle [8] 🚌	a	17 29			17 40		17 45	17 51	18 10		18 29			18 35		18 43	18 49	19 03		19 31		
Hartlepool	a																					
Sunderland 🚌	a																					
Newcastle [8] 🚌	d	17 35			17 45			17 55			18 36			18 40			18 54	19 06		19 35		
Morpeth	d																					
Alnmouth for Alnwick	d	18 00												19 07						20 03		
Berwick-upon-Tweed	d	18 20						18 41			19 18						19 40			20 24		
Dunbar 238	d										19 41											
Edinburgh [10] 238	a	19 07			19 11			19 28			20 05			20 11			20 24	20 38		21 08		
Edinburgh 238	d	19 12									20 14							20 45		21 13		
Haymarket 238	d	19 16									20 18							20 50		21 18		
Motherwell	a	19 52																		21 56		
Glasgow Central [15]	a	20 09																21 55		22 21		
Stirling	a																					
Perth	a																					
Inverness	a																					
Inverkeithing	a										20 33											
Kirkcaldy	a										20 50											
Leuchars [3]	a										21 25											
Dundee	a										21 42											
Arbroath	a																					
Montrose	a																					
Stonehaven	a																					
Aberdeen	a																					

A From Penzance. 🛒 to Edinburgh
B To Liverpool Lime Street
C From Southampton Central
D From Manchester Airport
E From Plymouth. 🛒 to Edinburgh
F From Reading
G from 4 January until 8 February. From Manchester Airport

Table 26

Saturdays

14 December to 17 May

London - Humberside, Yorkshire, North East England and Scotland

Route Diagram - refer to first Page of Table 26

		GR	GC	GC	GR	TP	XC	TP	XC	EM	GR	GR	GR	GR	HT	XC	GR	TP	XC	EM	GR	GR	GR
		R 1	R 1	R 1	R 1	◇1	◇1	◇1	◇1	◇	R 1	R 1	R 1	R 1	◇1	◇1	R 1	◇1	◇1	◇	R 1	R 1	R 1
						A	B	A	C	D						E		A	F	G			
London Kings Cross 15 ⊖	d	16 30	16 36	16 48	17 00						17 03	17 10	17 30	17 35	17 48		18 00				18 03	18 08	18 30
Stevenage 4	d										17 24											18 29	
Peterborough 8	a	17 15									17 52	17 58	18 16	18 22							18 47	18 58	19 15
Norwich	d									15 52										16 54			
Peterborough 8	d	17 16								17 25	17 54	18 00	18 17	18 23						18 26	18 50	19 00	19 16
Grantham 7	a									17 57	18 13	18 20			18 47					18 55		19 19	
	d									17 59	18 14	18 21			18 49					18 58		19 21	
Newark North Gate 7	a	17 43									18 25		18 45								19 16	19 33	19 43
	d	17 44									18 26		18 46								19 17	19 34	19 44
Lincoln	a																					20 01	
Retford 10	d														19 11						19 33		
Doncaster 7	a	18 08	18 17								18 49	18 53	19 09	19 13	19 24						19 47		20 08
Selby	a											19 10			19 40								
Hull	a											19 53			20 21								
Pontefract Monkhill	a																						
Wakefield Kirkgate 4	a		18 45																				
Wakefield Westgate 7	a										19 07			19 31							20 06		
Leeds 10	a										19 24			19 48							20 22		
Mirfield	a		18 59																				
Brighouse	a		19 08																				
Halifax	a		19 22																				
Shipley	a																						
Bradford Forster Square	a																						
Bradford Interchange	a		19 37																				
Keighley	a																						
Skipton	a																						
Sheffield 7	d						17 47		18 22	19a37						18 47			19 22	20a28			
Doncaster 7	d	18 09											19 11			19 18							20 09
York 8	a	18 32		18 38	18 50								19 32			19 38	19 51						20 31
Scarborough	a																						
Harrogate	a													20 25									
Leeds 10	d					18 28	18 35	18 57	19 08									19 52	20 08				
York 8	d	18 36		18 42	18 53	18 58	19 08	19 26	19 32				19 36			19 45	19 54	20 29	20 33				20 36
Thirsk	d			18 58				19 46										20 49					
Northallerton	d	18 56		19 06		19 19		19 57										20 59					20 55
Darlington 7	a	19 07			19 20	19 30	19 34		19 57				20 03			20 10	20 20		20 58				21 07
Eaglescliffe	a			19 24																			
Middlesbrough	a							20 30										21 30					
Darlington 7	d	19 09			19 22	19 31	19 36		19 59				20 05			20 12	20 22		21 00				21 08
Durham	d	19 26				19 47	19 54		20 16				20 23			20 29			21 17				21 26
Chester-le-Street	d					19 53																	
Newcastle 8	a	19 41			19 50	20 06	20 07		20 28				20 40			20 42	20 50		21 29				21 43
Hartlepool	a			19 44																			
Sunderland	a			20 21																			
Newcastle 8	d	19 45			19 53				20 35								20 55		21 38				
Morpeth	d	20 01							20 48								21 10						
Alnmouth for Alnwick	d																21 26		22 02				
Berwick-upon-Tweed	d				20 40				21 20								21 50						
Dunbar 238	d								21 44								22 14						
Edinburgh 10 238	a	21 15			21 24				22 08								22 38		23 03				
Edinburgh 238	d																						
Haymarket 238	d																						
Motherwell	a																						
Glasgow Central 15	a																						
Stirling	a																						
Perth	a																						
Inverness	a																						
Inverkeithing	a																						
Kirkcaldy	a																						
Leuchars 3	a																						
Dundee	a																						
Arbroath	a																						
Montrose	a																						
Stonehaven	a																						
Aberdeen	a																						

A From Manchester Airport
B From Southampton Central
C From Plymouth
D To Liverpool Lime Street
E From Reading
F From Plymouth. to Leeds
G To Manchester Piccadilly

Table 26

Saturdays

14 December to 17 May

London - Humberside, Yorkshire, North East England and Scotland

Route Diagram - refer to first Page of Table 26

		GR	EM	XC	GR	GC	GC	GR	HT	EM	TP	XC	GR	GR	EM	GR	GR	XC
		R 1	◇	◇1	R 1	R 1	R 1	R 1	◇1	◇	◇1	◇1	R 1	R 1		R 1	R 1	◇1
			E	C			D			E	F	G			H			C
		catering		catering	catering	catering	catering	catering	⊠				catering	catering		catering	catering	
London Kings Cross 15 ⊖	d	18 35			19 00	19 11	19 23	19 30	19 48				20 00	20 30		21 00	22 00	
Stevenage 4	d							19 50										
Peterborough 8	a	19 21						20 19					20 46	21 15		21 45	22 45	
Norwich	d		17 50							18 57								
Peterborough 8	d	19 23	19 30					20 21		20 26			20 48	21 16	21 27	21 47	22 47	
Grantham 7	a		19 57					20 40	20 47	20 58				21 35	22 00		23 06	
	d							20 41	20 51					21 36			23 07	
Newark North Gate 7	a							20 52					21 14	21 47			23 18	
	d							20 53					21 15	21 48			23 19	
Lincoln	a																	
Retford 10	d								21 14					22 03			23 34	
Doncaster 7	a	20 12					20 51	21 16	21 27				21 39	22 17			23 48	
Selby	a								21 43									
Hull	a								22 25									
Pontefract Monkhill	a						21 14											
Wakefield Kirkgate 4	a						21 32											
Wakefield Westgate 7	a	20 32						21 34						22 35			00 05	
Leeds 10	a	20 47						21 53						22 53			00 23	
Mirfield	a						21 43											
Brighouse	a						21 53											
Halifax	a						22 08											
Shipley	a							22s11										
Bradford Forster Square	a							22 20										
Bradford Interchange	a						22 24											
Keighley	a	21s13																
Skipton	a	21 27																
Sheffield 7	d			19 54								20 53						22 09
Doncaster 7	d			20 19								21 23	21 41					22 34
York 8	a			20 39	20 47	20 59						21 43	22 02			22 51		22 55
Scarborough	a																	
Harrogate	a																	
Leeds 10	d										20 45							
York 8	d			20 48	20 53	21 01					21 14	21 48	22 06			22 53		
Thirsk	d					21 18					21 31							
Northallerton	d					21 26					21 39					23 14		
Darlington 7	a			21 13	21 19						21 50	22 13	22 32			23 25		
Eaglescliffe	a					21 45												
Middlesbrough	a																	
Darlington 7	d			21 15	21 21						21 51	22 15	22 34			23 27		
Durham	d			21 32							22 07	22 31	22 52			23 44		
Chester-le-Street	d										22 13							
Newcastle 8	a			21 44	21 51						22 27	22 47	23 09			00 01		
Hartlepool	a					22 04												
Sunderland	a					22 36												
Newcastle 8	d																	
Morpeth	d																	
Alnmouth for Alnwick	d																	
Berwick-upon-Tweed	d																	
Dunbar 238	d																	
Edinburgh 10 238	a																	
Edinburgh 238	d																	
Haymarket 238	d																	
Motherwell	a																	
Glasgow Central 15	a																	
Stirling	a																	
Perth	a																	
Inverness	a																	
Inverkeithing	a																	
Kirkcaldy	a																	
Leuchars 3	a																	
Dundee	a																	
Arbroath	a																	
Montrose	a																	
Stonehaven	a																	
Aberdeen	a																	

C From Southampton Central
D 1 catering R to Doncaster
E To Nottingham
F From Manchester Airport
G From Reading
H From Spalding to Nottingham

Table 26

Sundays

8 December to 29 December

London - Humberside, Yorkshire, North East England and Scotland

Route Diagram - refer to first Page of Table 26

		TP	GR	XC	GR	TP	XC	GR	TP	XC		TP	GR	GR	TP	XC	GR	GC	GR	GR		EM	TP	GR	XC
			R		R			R					R	R			R	R	R	R				R	
		◇1	1	◇1	1	◇1	◇1	1	◇1	◇1		◇1	1	1	◇1	◇1	1	1	1	1		◇1	◇1	1	◇1
		A				A			A	B					A	C			D			E	A		F
			🍽🛒	🛒	🍽🛒		🛒	🍽🛒		🛒			🍽🛒	🍽🛒		🛒	🍽🛒	🍽	🍽🛒	🍽🛒		🍽		🍽🛒	🛒
London Kings Cross [15] ⊖	d												09 00	09 03			09 30	09 48	10 00	10 03				10 20	
Stevenage [4]	d													09 23											
Peterborough [8]	a													09 52			10 15			10 48				11 08	
Norwich	d																								
Peterborough [8]	d													09 54			10 16			10 50				11 10	
Grantham [7]	a													10 13						11 09					
	d													10 14						11 10					
Newark North Gate [7]	a													10 25						11 21					
	d													10 26						11 22					
Lincoln	a																								
Retford [10]	d																10 55								
Doncaster [7]	a													10 50			11 09			11 46				11 57	
Selby	a																								
Hull	a																								
Pontefract Monkhill	a																								
Wakefield Kirkgate [4]	a																								
Wakefield Westgate [7]	a													11 08						12 04					
Leeds [10]	a													11 27						12 21					
Mirfield	a																								
Brighouse	a																								
Halifax	a																								
Shipley	a																								
Bradford Forster Square	a																								
Bradford Interchange	a																								
Keighley	a																								
Skipton	a																								
Sheffield [7] ⛴	d									09 21						10 21						11 31			11 21
Doncaster [7]	d							09 37									11 10					11 53		11 59	
York [8]	a							09 58					10 46				11 32	11 36	11 49			12 15		12 20	
Scarborough	a																								
Harrogate	a																								
Leeds [10]	d	07 37			08 30	08 40	09 08		09 38	10 08					10 35	11 05							11 40		12 05
York [8]	d	08 22			09 00	09 10	09 34	10 01	10 10	10 32		10 37	10 49		11 00	11 29	11 35	11 39	11 52				12 10	12 23	12 29
Thirsk	d	08 38										10 53						11 55							
Northallerton	d	08 46			09 21	09 31			10 31			11 01			11 21			12 03					12 31		
Darlington [7]	a	08 57			09 33	09 42	09 59	10 27	10 42	10 57			11 15		11 32	11 54	12 01		12 19				12 42	12 49	12 54
Eaglescliffe	a																	12 20							
Middlesbrough	a	09 26										11 33													
Darlington [7]	d				09 35	09 43	10 01	10 29	10 43	10 59			11 17		11 33	11 56	12 03		12 21				12 43	12 51	12 56
Durham	d				09 54	09 59	10 18	10 46	10 59	11 16					11 49	12 13	12 20						12 59		13 13
Chester-le-Street	d					10 05																			
Newcastle [8] ⛴	a				10 07	10 17	10 30	11 01	11 15	11 28			11 45		12 04	12 25	12 35		12 49				13 14	13 22	13 25
Hartlepool	a																	12 41							
Sunderland ⛴	a																	13 08							
Newcastle [8] ⛴	d		09 15	09 45	10 12		10 40	11 04		11 34			11 48			12 30	12 43		12 53						13 28
Morpeth	d			09 58	10 28																				
Alnmouth for Alnwick	d			10 12	10 44												13 09								13 52
Berwick-upon-Tweed	d		10 00		11 08		11 22	11 49		12 18			12 33						13 39						14 13
Dunbar 238	d				11 33											13 33	13 54								
Edinburgh [10] 238	a		10 45	11 13	11 58		12 07	12 32		12 59			13 16			13 57	14 18		14 21						14 56
Edinburgh 238	d						12 17			13 10									14 33						15 10
Haymarket 238	d						12 21			13 14									14 39						15 15
Motherwell	a						12 55			13 50															15 52
Glasgow Central [15]	a						13 14			14 09															16 13
Stirling	a																								
Perth	a																								
Inverness	a																								
Inverkeithing	a																		14 53						
Kirkcaldy	a																		15 10						
Leuchars [3]	a																		15 34						
Dundee	a																		15 49						
Arbroath	a																		16 06						
Montrose	a																		16 22						
Stonehaven	a																		16 45						
Aberdeen	a																		17 08						

A From Manchester Airport
B 🛒 from Leeds to Edinburgh
C From Birmingham New Street
D The Northern Lights
E From Leicester
F From Birmingham New Street. 🛒 to Edinburgh

Table 26

Sundays

8 December to 29 December

London - Humberside, Yorkshire, North East England and Scotland

Route Diagram - refer to first Page of Table 26

		GR	HT	TP	GR	GR	TP	GR	XC	EM	GR	GC	GR	GR	TP	GR	XC	GR	HT	TP	XC	GR	GR
		R 1	◇1	◇1	R 1	R 1	◇1	R 1	◇1	◇	R 1	R 1	R 1	R 1	◇1	R 1	◇1	R 1	◇1	◇1	◇1	R 1	R 1
				A			B		C	D		E	F		B		G			A	H		
London Kings Cross 15 ⊖	d	10 30	10 48		11 00	11 03		11 20			11 30	11 50	12 00	12 03		12 20		12 30	12 48			13 00	13 03
Stevenage 4	d					11 23																	13 23
Peterborough 8	a	11 15				11 52		12 08			12 15			12 48		13 08		13 15					13 52
Norwich	d									10 47													
Peterborough 8	d	11 16				11 54		12 09		12 16	12 16			12 50		13 09		13 16					13 54
Grantham 7	a		11 47			12 13				12 46				13 09					13 47				14 13
	d		11 48			12 14				12 51				13 10					13 48				14 14
Newark North Gate 7	a	11 43				12 25								13 21				13 43					14 25
	d	11 44				12 26								13 22				13 44					14 26
Lincoln	a																						
Retford 10	d		12 09								12 55								14 09				
Doncaster 7	a	12 08	12 22			12 50					13 09	13 19		13 46		13 56		14 08	14 22				14 50
Selby	a		12 43																14 43				
Hull	a		13 25																15 26				
Pontefract Monkhill	a																						
Wakefield Kirkgate 4	a											13 45											
Wakefield Westgate 7	a					13 08								14 04									15 08
Leeds 10	a					13 27								14 21									15 27
Mirfield	a											14 00											
Brighouse	a											14 08											
Halifax	a											14 19											
Shipley	a																						
Bradford Forster Square	a																						
Bradford Interchange	a											14 35											
Keighley	a																						
Skipton	a																						
Sheffield 7	d								12 21	14a34							13 21				13 51		
Doncaster 7	d	12 09									13 11					13 58		14 10			14 18		
York 8	a	12 31			12 49			13 14			13 32		13 49			14 20		14 32			14 38	14 46	
Scarborough	a																						
Harrogate	a																						
Leeds 10	d			12 12			12 40		13 05						13 40		14 05			14 12			
York 8	d	12 35		12 40	12 52		13 10	13 17	13 29		13 35		13 52		14 11	14 23	14 29	14 35		14 42	14 48	14 56	
Thirsk	d			12 56																14 58			
Northallerton	d	12 55		13 04			13 31	13 37							14 32			14 55		15 09			
Darlington 7	a	13 06			13 18		13 42	13 48	13 54		14 01		14 19		14 43	14 49	14 54	15 06			15 13	15 22	
Eaglescliffe	a																						
Middlesbrough	a			13 37																15 40			
Darlington 7	d	13 08			13 20		13 43	13 50	13 56		14 03		14 21		14 44	14 51	14 57	15 08			15 15	15 24	
Durham	d	13 25					13 59	14 07	14 13		14 20				15 00	15 08	15 14	15 25			15 32		
Chester-le-Street	d						14 05																
Newcastle 8	a	13 40			13 48		14 17	14 22	14 25		14 35		14 49		15 16	15 25	15 26	15 40			15 44	15 52	
Hartlepool	a																						
Sunderland	a																						
Newcastle 8	d	13 44			13 51			14 25	14 31		14 43		14 53				15 28	15 44				15 55	
Morpeth	d							14 40	14 46														
Alnmouth for Alnwick	d										15 10						15 53						
Berwick-upon-Tweed	d				14 36								15 39				16 13					16 40	
Dunbar 238	d								15 40														
Edinburgh 10 238	a	15 09			15 19			15 58	16 02		16 16		16 21				16 56	17 09				17 23	
Edinburgh 238	d												16 32				17 11						
Haymarket 238	d												16 37				17 15						
Motherwell	a																17 52						
Glasgow Central 15	a																18 12						
Stirling	a												17 18										
Perth	a												17 55										
Inverness	a												20 08										
Inverkeithing	a																						
Kirkcaldy	a																						
Leuchars 3	a																						
Dundee	a																						
Arbroath	a																						
Montrose	a																						
Stonehaven	a																						
Aberdeen	a																						

A From Liverpool Lime Street
B From Manchester Airport
C From Bristol Temple Meads
D To Liverpool Lime Street
E 1 to Doncaster
F The Highland Chieftain
G From Bristol Temple Meads. to Edinburgh
H From Birmingham New Street

Table 26

Sundays

8 December to 29 December

London - Humberside, Yorkshire, North East England and Scotland

Route Diagram - refer to first Page of Table 26

		TP		XC	GR	GC	XC	GR	TP	XC	EM	GR		GR	HT	TP	XC	GR	TP	XC	EM	GR		GR	GC
		◇1		◇1	■ 1	■ 1	◇1	■ 1	◇1	◇1	◇	■ 1		■ 1	◇1	◇1	◇1	■ 1	◇1	◇1	◇	■ 1		■ 1	■ 1
		A		B			C		A	B	D					E	F		A	G	D				H
				☕	🍴☕	🍴	☕	🍴☕		☕		🍴☕		🍴☕	⊠		☕	🍴☕		☕		🍴☕		🍴☕	🍴
London Kings Cross 15 ⊖	d				13 30	13 48		14 00				14 03		14 30	14 48			15 00				15 03		15 30	15 50
Stevenage 4	d																					15 23			
Peterborough 8	a				14 15							14 48		15 16								15 52		16 16	
Norwich	d																				13 53				
Peterborough 8	d				14 16						14 34	14 52		15 17							15 23	15 54		16 17	
Grantham 7	a										15 06	15 11			15 47						15 53	16 13		16 37	
	d										15 09	15 12			15 48						15 55	16 14		16 38	
Newark North Gate 7	a											15 23		15 45								16 25			
	d											15 24		15 46								16 26			
Lincoln	a																								
Retford 10	d				14 55										16 09							16 42			
Doncaster 7	a				15 09							15 48		16 10	16 23							16 56		17 10	17 17
Selby	a														16 45										
Hull	a														17 27										
Pontefract Monkhill	a																								
Wakefield Kirkgate 4	a																								17 45
Wakefield Westgate 7	a											16 08										17 15			
Leeds 10	a											16 27										17 31			
Mirfield	a																								18 00
Brighouse	a																								18 08
Halifax	a																								18 19
Shipley	a																								
Bradford Forster Square	a																								
Bradford Interchange	a																								18 33
Keighley	a																								
Skipton	a																								
Sheffield 7 ⛴	d			14 21			14 51			15 21	16a34						15 51			16 21	17a39				
Doncaster 7	d				15 10		15 22							16 11			16 18							17 11	
York 8	a				15 32	15 36	15 42	15 49						16 34			16 38	16 47						17 34	
Scarborough	a																								
Harrogate	a																								
Leeds 10	d	14 40		15 05					15 40	16 05						16 12			16 40	17 05					
York 8	d	15 10		15 29	15 35	15 39	15 45	15 52	16 10	16 29				16 36		16 41	16 47	16 54	17 10	17 29				17 36	
Thirsk	d					15 56										16 57									
Northallerton	d	15 31				16 06			16 31					16 58		17 07			17 31						
Darlington 7	a	15 42		15 54	16 01		16 10	16 19	16 42	16 54				17 09			17 14	17 21	17 42	17 54				18 03	
Eaglescliffe	a					16 23																			
Middlesbrough	a															17 39									
Darlington 7	d	15 43		15 56	16 03		16 12	16 21	16 43	16 56				17 11			17 17	17 23	17 43	17 56				18 05	
Durham	d	15 59		16 13	16 20		16 29		16 59	17 13				17 29			17 34		17 59	18 13				18 23	
Chester-le-Street	d	16 05																	18 05						
Newcastle 8 ⛴	a	16 18		16 25	16 35		16 42	16 49	17 14	17 25				17 44			17 47	17 51	18 18	18 25				18 38	
Hartlepool	a					16 50																			
Sunderland ⛴	a					17 21																			
Newcastle 8 ⛴	d			16 28	16 38			16 53		17 28				17 47				17 54		18 28				18 41	
Morpeth	d																								
Alnmouth for Alnwick	d			16 52	17 05					17 53														19 09	
Berwick-upon-Tweed	d							17 39		18 13								18 39		19 10					
Dunbar 238	d			17 33																19 35					
Edinburgh 10 238	a			17 57	18 09			18 21		18 56				19 14				19 22		19 57				20 13	
Edinburgh 238	d			18 13				18 36		19 18															
Haymarket 238	d			18 16				18 41		19 23															
Motherwell	a									19 58															
Glasgow Central 15	a									20 21															
Stirling	a																								
Perth	a																								
Inverness	a																								
Inverkeithing	a			18 28				18 54																	
Kirkcaldy	a			18 44				19 11																	
Leuchars 3	a			19 14				19 36																	
Dundee	a			19 29				19 50																	
Arbroath	a			19 46				20 08																	
Montrose	a			20 00				20 24																	
Stonehaven	a			20 22				20 47																	
Aberdeen	a			20 42				21 10																	

A From Manchester Airport
B From Plymouth. ☕ to Edinburgh
C From Birmingham New Street
D To Liverpool Lime Street
E From Liverpool Lime Street
F From Guildford
G From Penzance
H 1 to Doncaster

Table 26

Sundays

8 December to 29 December

London - Humberside, Yorkshire, North East England and Scotland

Route Diagram - refer to first Page of Table 26

		XC	GR	TP	XC	EM	GR	GR	GR	TP	GC	GR	TP	XC	XC	EM	GR	GR	GR	GR	HT	XC	EM
			R				R	R	R		R	R					R	R	R	R			
		◇1	1	◇1	◇1	◇	1	1	1	◇1	1	1	◇1	◇1	◇1	◇	1	1	1	1	◇1	◇1	◇
		A		B	C	D				E			B	A	F	G						A	G
		🛒	FP 🛒		🛒		FP 🛒	FP 🛒	FP 🛒		FP	FP 🛒		🛒	🛒		FP 🛒	FP 🛒	FP 🛒	FP 🛒	⊠	🛒	
London Kings Cross 15 ⊖	d		16 00				16 05	16 30	16 35		16 47	17 00					17 05	17 20	17 30	17 35	17 44		
Stevenage 4	d								16 55											17 55	18 04		
Peterborough 8	a						16 50	17 15									17 50		18 15				
Norwich	d					14 53										15 54							16 54
Peterborough 8	d					16 24	16 53	17 16								17 23	17 51		18 16				18 26
Grantham 7	a					16 54	17 12		17 39							17 53		18 24	18 35	18 41	18 47		18 56
	d					16 56	17 13		17 40							17 55		18 26	18 36	18 42	18 48		18 58
Newark North Gate 7	a						17 24	17 43									18 18	18 36					
	d						17 25	17 44									18 19	18 38					
Lincoln	a																						
Retford 10	d								18 03												19 09		
Doncaster 7	a						17 49	18 08	18 17								18 42	19 02	19 09	19 13	19 23		
Selby	a																	19 21			19 45		
Hull	a																	20 02			20 26		
Pontefract Monkhill	a																						
Wakefield Kirkgate 4	a																						
Wakefield Westgate 7	a						18 10		18 38								19 01			19 32			
Leeds 10	a						18 29		18 56								19 21			19 51			
Mirfield	a																						
Brighouse	a																						
Halifax	a																						
Shipley	a																						
Bradford Forster Square	a																						
Bradford Interchange	a																						
Keighley	a																						
Skipton	a																						
Sheffield 7 ⛴	d	16 51			17 21	18a33								17 51	18 21	19a31						18 51	20a31
Doncaster 7	d	17 19						18 10						18 16					19 12			19 19	
York 8	a	17 40	17 46					18 31			18 41	18 46							19 33			19 39	
Scarborough	a																						
Harrogate	a																						
Leeds 10	d			17 40	18 05					18 12			18 40	18 58	19 08								
York 8	d	17 45	17 49	18 10	18 29			18 35		18 40	18 44	18 54	19 10	19 22	19 32				19 38			19 45	
Thirsk	d									18 56	19 01												
Northallerton	d			18 31				18 55		19 04	19 09		19 31										
Darlington 7	a	18 10	18 15	18 42	18 54			19 06				19 22	19 42	19 47	19 59				20 04			20 10	
Eaglescliffe	a										19 29												
Middlesbrough	a									19 37													
Darlington 7	d	18 12	18 17	18 46	18 56			19 08				19 24	19 43	19 49	20 00				20 06			20 12	
Durham	d	18 29		19 02	19 13			19 25					19 59	20 06	20 18				20 23			20 29	
Chester-le-Street	d												20 05										
Newcastle 8 ⛴	a	18 41	18 45	19 17	19 25			19 40				19 52	20 18	20 19	20 31				20 38			20 41	
Hartlepool	a										19 48												
Sunderland ⛴	a										20 20												
Newcastle 8 ⛴	d		18 52		19 28			19 43				19 55			20 34				20 41			20 56	
Morpeth	d							19 58							20 48				20 56				
Alnmouth for Alnwick	d				19 53														21 12				
Berwick-upon-Tweed	d		19 37		20 13							20 40			21 22								
Dunbar 238	d							20 53							21 47								
Edinburgh 10 238	a		20 20		20 56			21 16				21 23			22 12				22 18			22 21	
Edinburgh 238	d				21 12			21 22															
Haymarket 238	d				21 17			21 26															
Motherwell	a				21 53			22 05															
Glasgow Central 15	a				22 14			22 26															
Stirling	a																						
Perth	a																						
Inverness	a																						
Inverkeithing	a																						
Kirkcaldy	a																						
Leuchars 3	a																						
Dundee	a																						
Arbroath	a																						
Montrose	a																						
Stonehaven	a																						
Aberdeen	a																						

A From Reading
B From Manchester Airport
C From Plymouth. 🛒 to Edinburgh
D To Liverpool Lime Street
E From Liverpool Lime Street
F From Plymouth
G To Manchester Piccadilly

Table 26

Sundays

8 December to 29 December

London - Humberside, Yorkshire, North East England and Scotland

Route Diagram - refer to first Page of Table 26

		GR	GR	TP		GC	XC	GR	GR	EM	GC	XC	GR	GR		GR	GC	TP	GR	GR	HT	EM	XC	GR
				A			B			C	D	E						A				C	E	
London Kings Cross 15 ⊖	d	18 00	18 05			18 23		18 30	18 35		18 45		19 00	19 05		19 08	19 23		19 30	19 35	19 50			20 00
Stevenage 4	d								18 55							19 29				19 55				
Peterborough 8	a		18 51					19 15						19 50		19 59			20 17	20 24				20 45
Norwich	d									17 54												18 56		
Peterborough 8	d		18 53					19 17		19 26				19 51		20 01			20 18	20 26		20 30		20 46
Grantham 7	a								19 40	19 56						20 21				20 45	20 50	21 00		
	d								19 41							20 23				20 46	20 51			
Newark North Gate 7	a		19 20					19 43						20 18		20 34			20 46					
	d		19 22					19 44						20 19		20 36			20 47					
Lincoln	a															21 02								
Retford 10	d								20 04												21 12			
Doncaster 7	a		19 47					20 08	20 18		20 23			20 43			20 58		21 13	21 17	21 24			
Selby	a																				21 41			
Hull	a																				22 23			
Pontefract Monkhill	a																							
Wakefield Kirkgate 4	a										20 53						21 20							
Wakefield Westgate 7	a		20 07						20 37					21 01						21 36				
Leeds 10	a		20 25						20 52					21 18						21 55				
Mirfield	a										21 09						21 35							
Brighouse	a										21 23						21 43							
Halifax	a										21 34						21 54							
Shipley	a																							
Bradford Forster Square	a																							
Bradford Interchange	a										21 49						22 08							
Keighley	a								21s19															
Skipton	a								21 40															
Sheffield 7	d						19 21					19 51											20 51	
Doncaster 7	d							20 10				20 18							21 15				21 22	
York 8	a	19 47				20 12		20 31				20 38	20 49						21 36				21 42	21 51
Scarborough	a																							
Harrogate	a		21 04																					
Leeds 10	d			19 40			20 08											20 40						
York 8	d	19 50		20 08		20 14	20 32	20 36				20 48	20 52					21 08	21 41				21 48	21 57
Thirsk	d			20 24		20 31												21 24						
Northallerton	d			20 33		20 39		20 56										21 32						
Darlington 7	a	20 16					20 59	21 07				21 13	21 19					21 43	22 17				22 23	22 37
Eaglescliffe	a					20 56																		
Middlesbrough	a			21 04																				
Darlington 7	d	20 18					21 00	21 09				21 15	21 22					21 44	22 19				22 25	22 39
Durham	d						21 18	21 26				21 32						22 01	22 37				22 42	22 56
Chester-le-Street	d																							
Newcastle 8	a	20 46					21 31	21 43				21 44	21 50					22 15	23 09				23 11	23 28
Hartlepool	a					21 16																		
Sunderland	a					21 51																		
Newcastle 8	d	20 59					21 34						21 53											
Morpeth	d												22 09											
Alnmouth for Alnwick	d						22 02						22 25											
Berwick-upon-Tweed	d	21 45											22 49											
Dunbar 238	d												23 14											
Edinburgh 10 238	a	22 28					23 04						23 39											
Edinburgh 238	d																							
Haymarket 238	d																							
Motherwell	a																							
Glasgow Central 15	a																							
Stirling	a																							
Perth	a																							
Inverness	a																							
Inverkeithing	a																							
Kirkcaldy	a																							
Leuchars 3	a																							
Dundee	a																							
Arbroath	a																							
Montrose	a																							
Stonehaven	a																							
Aberdeen	a																							

- **A** From Manchester Airport
- **B** From Plymouth. Trolley service to Newcastle
- **C** To Nottingham
- **D** 1 to Doncaster
- **E** From Reading

Table 26

Sundays

8 December to 29 December

London - Humberside, Yorkshire, North East England and Scotland

Route Diagram - refer to first Page of Table 26

		GR	GR	TP	GR	EM	GR	GR	GR
		R 1	R 1	◇1 A	R 1	◇ B	R 1	R 1	R 1
		🍴	🍴		🍴		🍴	🍴	🍴
London Kings Cross 15 ⊖	d	20 05	20 35		21 00		21 35	22 00	22 35
Stevenage 4	d		20 55				21 56		
Peterborough 8	a	20 50	21 24		21 45		22 25	22 46	23s23
Norwich	d					20 52			
Peterborough 8	d	20 51	21 26		21 46	22 23	22 27	22 47	
Grantham 7	a		21 45			22 53	22 47		23s44
	d		21 46				22 48		
Newark North Gate 7	a		21 57				22 59		23s55
	d		21 58				23 00		
Lincoln	a								
Retford 10	d	21 30					23 17		
Doncaster 7	a	21 44	22 22				23 35	23 40	00s24
Selby	a								
Hull	a								
Pontefract Monkhill	a								
Wakefield Kirkgate 4	a								
Wakefield Westgate 7	a	22 02	22 40				23 56		
Leeds 10	a	22 19	22 58				00 13		01 30
Mirfield	a								
Brighouse	a								
Halifax	a								
Shipley	a								
Bradford Forster Square	a								
Bradford Interchange	a								
Keighley	a								
Skipton	a								
Sheffield 7 ⛴	d								
Doncaster 7	d							23 42	
York 8	a				22 56			00 32	
Scarborough	a								
Harrogate	a								
Leeds 10	d			22 12					
York 8	d			22 43	23 04			00 35	
Thirsk	d			23 06					
Northallerton	d			23 16	23 40			01s06	
Darlington 7	a			23 27	23 51			01s20	
Eaglescliffe	a								
Middlesbrough	a								
Darlington 7	d			23 27	23 53				
Durham	d			23 44	00 10			01s38	
Chester-le-Street	d								
Newcastle 8 ⛴	a			00 14	00 42			02 10	
Hartlepool	a								
Sunderland ⛴	a								
Newcastle 8 ⛴	d								
Morpeth	d								
Alnmouth for Alnwick	d								
Berwick-upon-Tweed	d								
Dunbar 238	d								
Edinburgh 10 238	a								
Edinburgh 238	d								
Haymarket 238	d								
Motherwell	a								
Glasgow Central 15	a								
Stirling	a								
Perth	a								
Inverness	a								
Inverkeithing	a								
Kirkcaldy	a								
Leuchars 3	a								
Dundee	a								
Arbroath	a								
Montrose	a								
Stonehaven	a								
Aberdeen	a								

A From Liverpool Lime Street

B To Nottingham

Table 26

Sundays

5 January to 9 February

London - Humberside, Yorkshire, North East England and Scotland

Route Diagram - refer to first Page of Table 26

		TP	GR	XC	GR	TP	XC	GR	TP	XC	TP	GR	GR	TP	XC	GR	GR	GC	GR	TP	XC	EM
		◇1	R 1	◇1	R 1	◇1	◇1	R 1	◇1	◇1	◇1	R 1	R 1	◇1	◇1	R 1	R 1	R 1	R 1	◇1	◇1	◇1
		A				A			A	B				A	C		D			A	E	F
			⊡⊥	⊥	⊡⊥		⊥	⊡⊥		⊥		⊡⊥	⊡⊥		⊥	⊡⊥	⊡⊥	⊡	⊡⊥		⊥	⊥
London Kings Cross 15 ⊖	d											08 45	08 56			09 15	09 45	09 53	09 56			
Stevenage 4	d												09 26									
Peterborough 8	a												09 55			10 15			10 54			
Norwich	d																					
Peterborough 8	d												09 57			10 16			10 56			
Grantham 7	a												10 16						11 15			
	d												10 17						11 16			
Newark North Gate 7	a												10 28						11 27			
	d												10 29						11 28			
Lincoln	a																					
Retford 10	d															10 55						
Doncaster 7	a												10 53			11 09			11 52			
Selby	a																					
Hull	a																					
Pontefract Monkhill	a																					
Wakefield Kirkgate 4	a																					
Wakefield Westgate 7	a												11 11						12 11			
Leeds 10	a												11 28						12 27			
Mirfield	a																					
Brighouse	a																					
Halifax	a																					
Shipley	a																					
Bradford Forster Square	a																					
Bradford Interchange	a																					
Keighley	a																					
Skipton	a																					
Sheffield 7 ⇌	d									09 21					10 21						11 21	11 31
Doncaster 7	d							09 37								11 10						
York 8	a							09 58				10 46				11 32	11 47	11 52				12 20
Scarborough	a																					
Harrogate	a																					
Leeds 10	d	07 37			08 30	08 40	09 08		09 38	10 08				10 35	11 05					11 40	12 05	
York 8	d	08 22			09 00	09 10	09 34	10 01	10 10	10 32	10 37	10 49		11 00	11 29	11 35	11 52	11 56		12 10	12 29	
Thirsk	d	08 38									10 53							12 12				
Northallerton	d	08 46			09 21	09 31			10 31		11 01			11 21				12 20		12 31		
Darlington 7	a	08 57			09 33	09 42	09 59	10 27	10 42	10 57		11 15		11 32	11 54	12 01	12 19			12 42	12 54	
Eaglescliffe	a																	12 37				
Middlesbrough	a	09 26									11 33											
Darlington 7	d				09 35	09 43	10 01	10 29	10 43	10 59		11 17		11 32	11 56	12 03	12 21			12 43	12 56	
Durham	d				09 54	09 59	10 18	10 46	10 59	11 16				11 49	12 13	12 20				12 59	13 13	
Chester-le-Street	d					10 05																
Newcastle 8 ⇌	a				10 07	10 17	10 30	11 01	11 15	11 28		11 45		12 02	12 25	12 35	12 49			13 14	13 25	
Hartlepool	a																	12 57				
Sunderland ⇌	a																	13 24				
Newcastle 8 ⇌	d		09 15	09 45	10 12		10 40	11 04		11 34		11 48		12 03	12 30	12 43	12 53				13 28	
Morpeth	d			09 58	10 28																	
Alnmouth for Alnwick	d			10 12	10 44											13 09					13 52	
Berwick-upon-Tweed	d		10 00		11 08		11 22	11 49		12 18		12 33					13 39				14 13	
Dunbar 238	d				11 33										13 33	13 54						
Edinburgh 10 238	a		10 45	11 13	11 58		12 07	12 32		12 59		13 16		13 32	13 57	14 18	14 21				14 56	
Edinburgh 238	d						12 17			13 10							14 33				15 10	
Haymarket 238	d						12 21			13 14							14 39				15 15	
Motherwell	a						12 55			13 50											15 52	
Glasgow Central 15	a						13 14			14 09											16 13	
Stirling	a																					
Perth	a																					
Inverness	a																					
Inverkeithing	a																14 53					
Kirkcaldy	a																15 10					
Leuchars 3	a																15 34					
Dundee	a																15 49					
Arbroath	a																16 06					
Montrose	a																16 22					
Stonehaven	a																16 45					
Aberdeen	a																17 08					

A From Manchester Airport
B ⊥ from Leeds to Edinburgh
C From Derby
D The Northern Lights
E From Birmingham New Street. ⊥ to Edinburgh
F From Leicester

Table 26

Sundays

5 January to 9 February

London - Humberside, Yorkshire, North East England and Scotland

Route Diagram - refer to first Page of Table 26

		GR	HT	TP	GR	GR	TP	GR	XC	GR	GR	GC	TP	XC	EM	GR	GR	TP	XC	GR	HT	GR	TP
		1	◇1	◇1	1	1	◇1	1	◇1	1	1	1	◇1	◇1	◇	1	1	◇1	◇1	1	◇1	1	◇1
				A			B		C		D	E	B	F	G			A	H				B
London Kings Cross 15 ⊖	d	10 15	10 42		10 45	10 56				11 15	11 45	11 53				11 56	12 15			12 45	12 53	12 56	
Stevenage 4	d					11 26																13 28	
Peterborough 8	a	11 15				11 55				12 15						12 54	13 15					13 57	
Norwich	d														10 47								
Peterborough 8	d	11 16				11 57		12 10		12 16					12 18	12 56	13 17					13 59	
Grantham 7	a		11 55			12 16									12 48	13 14					14 06	14 17	
	d		11 56			12 17									12 51	13 15					14 07	14 18	
Newark North Gate 7	a	11 43				12 28										13 27	13 43					14 29	
	d	11 44				12 29										13 28	13 44					14 30	
Lincoln	a																						
Retford 10	d		12 22							12 55											14 27		
Doncaster 7	a	12 08	12 35			12 52				13 09		13 33				13 52	14 08				14 41	14 54	
Selby	a		12 53																		14 57		
Hull	a		13 37																		15 39		
Pontefract Monkhill	a																						
Wakefield Kirkgate 4	a											13 56											
Wakefield Westgate 7	a					13 10										14 10						15 13	
Leeds 10	a					13 27										14 27						15 29	
Mirfield	a											14 11											
Brighouse	a											14 19											
Halifax	a											14 36											
Shipley	a																						
Bradford Forster Square	a																						
Bradford Interchange	a											14 50											
Keighley	a																						
Skipton	a																						
Sheffield 7	d								12 21					13 21	14a34				13 45				
Doncaster 7	d	12 09								13 11							14 10						
York 8	a	12 31			12 49			13 14		13 32	13 49						14 32		14 38	14 49			
Scarborough	a																						
Harrogate	a																						
Leeds 10	d			12 12			12 40		13 05				13 40	14 05				14 12					14 40
York 8	d	12 35		12 40	12 52		13 07	13 17	13 29	13 35	13 52		14 11	14 29			14 35	14 42	14 48	14 56			15 10
Thirsk	d			12 56														14 58					
Northallerton	d	12 55		13 04			13 28	13 37					14 32				14 55	15 09					15 31
Darlington 7	a	13 06			13 18		13 39	13 49	13 54	14 01	14 19		14 43	14 54			15 06		15 13	15 23			15 42
Eaglescliffe	a																						
Middlesbrough	a			13 37														15 40					
Darlington 7	d	13 08			13 20		13 39	13 50	13 56	14 03	14 21		14 44	14 57			15 08		15 15	15 25			15 43
Durham	d	13 25					13 56	14 08	14 13	14 20			15 00	15 14			15 25		15 32				15 59
Chester-le-Street	d																						16 05
Newcastle 8	a	13 40			13 48		14 09	14 23	14 26	14 35	14 49		15 16	15 26			15 40		15 44	15 53			16 18
Hartlepool	a																						
Sunderland	a																						
Newcastle 8	d	13 44			13 51		14 14	14 25	14 31	14 43	14 53			15 28			15 44			15 56			
Morpeth	d							14 40	14 46														
Alnmouth for Alnwick	d									15 10				15 53									
Berwick-upon-Tweed	d				14 36						15 39			16 13						16 41			
Dunbar 238	d								15 40														
Edinburgh 10 238	a	15 09			15 19		15 42	15 56	16 02	16 16	16 21			16 56			17 09			17 24			
Edinburgh 238	d										16 32			17 11									
Haymarket 238	d										16 37			17 15									
Motherwell	a													17 52									
Glasgow Central 15	a													18 12									
Stirling	a										17 18												
Perth	a										17 55												
Inverness	a										20 08												
Inverkeithing	a																						
Kirkcaldy	a																						
Leuchars 3	a																						
Dundee	a																						
Arbroath	a																						
Montrose	a																						
Stonehaven	a																						
Aberdeen	a																						

A From Liverpool Lime Street
B From Manchester Airport
C From Birmingham New Street
D The Highland Chieftain
E 1 to Doncaster
F From Birmingham New Street, to Edinburgh
G To Liverpool Lime Street
H From Bristol Temple Meads

Table 26

Sundays

5 January to 9 February

London - Humberside, Yorkshire, North East England and Scotland

Route Diagram - refer to first Page of Table 26

		XC		GR	XC	GR	GC	TP	XC	EM	GR	GR		TP	XC	GR	TP	XC	EM	GR	HT	GR		XC	GR
		◇1		1	◇1	1	1	◇1	◇1	◇	1	1		◇1	◇1	1	◇1	◇1	◇	1	◇1	1		◇1	1
		A			B			C	A	D				E	B		C	F	D					G	
London Kings Cross 15 ⊖	d			13 15		13 45	13 53				13 56	14 15				14 45				14 52	14 58	15 15			15 45
Stevenage 4	d																			15 23					
Peterborough 8	a			14 15							14 55	15 16								15 52		16 21			
Norwich	d																		13 53						
Peterborough 8	d			14 16						14 34	14 57	15 17							15 23	15 54		16 23			
Grantham 7	a									15 06	15 15								15 53	16 13	16 17	16 43			
	d									15 09	15 16								15 55	16 14	16 18	16 44			
Newark North Gate 7	a										15 27	15 45								16 25					
	d										15 28	15 46								16 26					
Lincoln	a																								
Retford 10	d			14 55																16 42	16 47				
Doncaster 7	a			15 09							15 52	16 10								16 56	17 00	17 14			
Selby	a																				17 35				
Hull	a																				18 21				
Pontefract Monkhill	a																								
Wakefield Kirkgate 4	a																								
Wakefield Westgate 7	a										16 11									17 15					
Leeds 10	a										16 27									17 31					
Mirfield	a																								
Brighouse	a																								
Halifax	a																								
Shipley	a																								
Bradford Forster Square	a																								
Bradford Interchange	a																								
Keighley	a																								
Skipton	a																								
Sheffield 7	d	14 21			14 50				15 21	16a34					15 46			16 21	17a39					16 46	
Doncaster 7	d			15 11								16 11										17 16			
York 8	a			15 32	15 42	15 49	15 57					16 34			16 38	16 47						17 38		17 44	17 48
Scarborough	a																								
Harrogate	a																								
Leeds 10	d	15 05						15 40	16 05					16 12			16 40	17 05							
York 8	d	15 29		15 35	15 45	15 52	16 00	16 10	16 29			16 36		16 41	16 47	16 54	17 10	17 29				17 41		17 48	17 52
Thirsk	d						16 17							16 57											
Northallerton	d						16 25	16 31				16 58		17 07			17 31								
Darlington 7	a	15 54		16 01	16 10	16 19		16 42	16 54			17 09			17 14	17 24	17 42	17 54				18 08		18 13	18 18
Eaglescliffe	a						16 42																		
Middlesbrough	a													17 39											
Darlington 7	d	15 56		16 03	16 12	16 21		16 43	16 56			17 11			17 17	17 26	17 43	17 56				18 09		18 14	18 20
Durham	d	16 13		16 20	16 29			16 59	17 13			17 29			17 34		17 59	18 13				18 27		18 32	
Chester-le-Street	d																18 05								
Newcastle 8	a	16 25		16 35	16 42	16 49		17 14	17 25			17 44			17 47	17 54	18 18	18 25				18 42		18 45	18 49
Hartlepool	a						17 08																		
Sunderland	a						17 39																		
Newcastle 8	d	16 28		16 38		16 53			17 28			17 47				17 57		18 28				18 45			18 56
Morpeth	d																								
Alnmouth for Alnwick	d	16 52		17 05					17 53													19 13			
Berwick-upon-Tweed	d					17 39			18 13							18 42		19 10							19 41
Dunbar 238	d	17 33																19 35							
Edinburgh 10 238	a	17 57		18 09		18 21			18 56			19 14				19 25		19 57				20 17			20 24
Edinburgh 238	d	18 13				18 36			19 18																
Haymarket 238	d	18 16				18 41			19 23																
Motherwell	a								19 58																
Glasgow Central 15	a								20 21																
Stirling	a																								
Perth	a																								
Inverness	a																								
Inverkeithing	a	18 28				18 54																			
Kirkcaldy	a	18 44				19 11																			
Leuchars 3	a	19 14				19 36																			
Dundee	a	19 29				19 50																			
Arbroath	a	19 46				20 08																			
Montrose	a	20 00				20 24																			
Stonehaven	a	20 22				20 47																			
Aberdeen	a	20 42				21 10																			

A From Birmingham New Street. to Edinburgh
B From Plymouth
C From Manchester Airport
D To Liverpool Lime Street
E From Liverpool Lime Street
F From Reading
G From Penzance

Table 26

Sundays

5 January to 9 February

London - Humberside, Yorkshire, North East England and Scotland

Route Diagram - refer to first Page of Table 26

		TP	XC	EM	GR	GC	GR	GR		EM	TP	GR	GR	TP	GC	XC	XC	GR		GR	XC	GR	TP	XC	EM
					R	R	R	R				R	R		R			R		R		R			
		◇1	◇1	◇	1	1	1	1		◇	◇1	1	1	◇1	1	◇1	◇1	1		1	◇1	1	◇1	◇1	◇
		A	B	C		D				E	F			A		G	H				I		A	J	E
			🛒		FP🛒	FP	FP🛒	FP🛒				FP🛒	FP🛒		FP	🛒	🛒	FP🛒		FP🛒	🛒	FP🛒		🛒	
London Kings Cross [15] ⊖	d				15 52	15 58	16 15					16 45	16 52		16 58			17 12		17 15		17 45			
Stevenage [4]	d												17 22							17 52					
Peterborough [8]	a				16 50		17 13						17 51					18 15							
Norwich	d			14 53						15 54															16 54
Peterborough [8]	d			16 24	16 53		17 16	17 22		17 23			17 53					18 17							18 26
Grantham [7]	a			16 54	17 12			17 40		17 53								18 35		18 41					18 56
	d			16 56	17 13			17 41		17 55								18 36		18 42					18 58
Newark North Gate [7]	a				17 24		17 43						18 19												
	d				17 25		17 44						18 20												
Lincoln	a																								
Retford [10]	d							18 03																	
Doncaster [7]	a				17 49	17 53	18 08	18 17					18 42					19 09		19 13					
Selby	a																								
Hull	a																								
Pontefract Monkhill	a																								
Wakefield Kirkgate [4]	a					18 21																			
Wakefield Westgate [7]	a				18 10			18 38					19 01							19 32					
Leeds [10]	a				18 29			18 56					19 21							19 51					
Mirfield	a					18 39																			
Brighouse	a					18 47																			
Halifax	a					18 57																			
Shipley	a																								
Bradford Forster Square	a																								
Bradford Interchange	a					19 12																			
Keighley	a																								
Skipton	a																								
Sheffield [7] ⛴	d		17 21	18a33						19a31						17 46	18 21				18 51			19 21	20a31
Doncaster [7]	d						18 10											19 12							
York [8]	a						18 31					18 47			19 13			19 33			19 43	19 47			
Scarborough	a																								
Harrogate	a																								
Leeds [10]	d	17 40	18 05								18 12			18 40		18 58	19 08						19 40	20 08	
York [8]	d	18 10	18 29				18 35				18 40	18 54		19 10	19 15	19 22	19 32	19 38			19 45	19 51	20 08	20 32	
Thirsk	d										18 56				19 33								20 24		
Northallerton	d	18 31					18 55				19 04			19 31	19 45								20 33		
Darlington [7]	a	18 42	18 54				19 06					19 22		19 42		19 47	19 59	20 04			20 10	20 17		20 59	
Eaglescliffe	a														20 06										
Middlesbrough	a										19 37												21 04		
Darlington [7]	d	18 46	18 56				19 08					19 24		19 43		19 49	20 00	20 06			20 12	20 19		21 00	
Durham	d	19 02	19 13				19 25							19 59		20 06	20 18	20 23			20 29			21 18	
Chester-le-Street	d													20 05											
Newcastle [8] ⛴	a	19 17	19 25				19 40					19 52		20 18		20 19	20 31	20 38			20 41	20 48		21 31	
Hartlepool	a														20 25										
Sunderland ⛴	a														20 52										
Newcastle [8] ⛴	d		19 28				19 43					19 55				20 34		20 41			20 56	20 59		21 34	
Morpeth	d						19 58									20 48		20 56							
Alnmouth for Alnwick	d		19 53															21 12						22 02	
Berwick-upon-Tweed	d		20 13									20 40				21 22						21 45			
Dunbar 238	d						20 53									21 47									
Edinburgh [10] 238	a		20 56				21 16					21 23				22 12		22 18			22 21	22 26		23 04	
Edinburgh 238	d		21 12				21 22																		
Haymarket 238	d		21 17				21 26																		
Motherwell	a		21 53				22 05																		
Glasgow Central [15]	a		22 14				22 26																		
Stirling	a																								
Perth	a																								
Inverness	a																								
Inverkeithing	a																								
Kirkcaldy	a																								
Leuchars [3]	a																								
Dundee	a																								
Arbroath	a																								
Montrose	a																								
Stonehaven	a																								
Aberdeen	a																								

A From Manchester Airport
B From Reading. 🛒 to Edinburgh
C To Liverpool Lime Street
D 1 to Doncaster
E To Manchester Piccadilly
F From Liverpool Lime Street
G From Exeter St Davids
H From Reading
I From Plymouth
J From Reading. 🛒 to Newcastle

Table 26

Sundays

5 January to 9 February

London - Humberside, Yorkshire, North East England and Scotland

Route Diagram - refer to first Page of Table 26

		GR	HT	GR		GR	EM	XC	GR	GC	GR	TP	GR	GR		EM	GC	XC	GR	GR	HT	GC	GR	TP	
		R		R		R			R	R	R		R	R			R		R	R		R	R		
		1	◇1	1		1	◇	◇1	1	1	1	◇1	1	1		◇	1	◇1	1	1	◇1	1	1	◇1	
							A	B				C				A		B				D		E	
		🍴	☒	🍴		🍴		☕	🍴	🍴	🍴		🍴	🍴			🍴		🍴	🍴	☒	🍴	🍴		
London Kings Cross 15 ⊖	d	17 52	17 58	18 12		18 18			18 45	18 53	18 56		19 12	19 15			19 42		19 45	19 52	20 00	20 12	20 15		
Stevenage 4	d		18 28			18 55					19 28			19 53									20 55		
Peterborough 8	a	18 53		19 11							19 57		20 17						20 46	20 51			21 24		
Norwich	d						17 54									18 56									
Peterborough 8	d	18 55		19 17			19 26				19 58		20 18			20 30			20 48	20 53			21 26		
Grantham 7	a		19 19			19 40	19 56							20 42		21 00					21 15		21 45		
	d		19 22			19 41								20 44							21 16		21 46		
Newark North Gate 7	a	19 21		19 43							20 26		20 46	20 55									21 57		
	d	19 23		19 44							20 27		20 47	20 57									21 58		
Lincoln	a													21 24											
Retford 10	d		19 44			20 04														21 31	21 37				
Doncaster 7	a	19 47	19 57	20 08		20 18					20 51		21 13				21 24			21 45	21 51	21 56	22 22		
Selby	a		20 20																		22 10				
Hull	a		21 07																		22 52				
Pontefract Monkhill	a																								
Wakefield Kirkgate 4	a																21 50					22 38			
Wakefield Westgate 7	a	20 07				20 37					21 10									22 04			22 40		
Leeds 10	a	20 25				20 52					21 27									22 20			22 58		
Mirfield	a																22 05					22 53			
Brighouse	a																22 13					23 02			
Halifax	a																22 24					23 13			
Shipley	a																								
Bradford Forster Square	a																								
Bradford Interchange	a																22 39					23 27			
Keighley	a					21s19																			
Skipton	a					21 40																			
Sheffield 7	d							19 42										20 51							
Doncaster 7	d			20 10									21 15												
York 8	a			20 31				20 38	20 49	20 53			21 36					21 42	21 55						
Scarborough	a																								
Harrogate	a	21 04																							
Leeds 10	d											20 40												22 12	
York 8	d			20 36				20 48	20 52	20 56		21 08	21 40					21 48	21 58					22 43	
Thirsk	d									21 12		21 24												23 06	
Northallerton	d			20 56						21 20		21 32												23 16	
Darlington 7	a			21 07				21 13	21 19			21 43	22 18					22 23	22 37					23 27	
Eaglescliffe	a									21 37															
Middlesbrough	a																								
Darlington 7	d			21 09				21 15	21 22			21 44	22 20					22 25	22 38					23 27	
Durham	d			21 26				21 32				22 01	22 37					22 42	22 56					23 44	
Chester-le-Street	d																								
Newcastle 8	a			21 43				21 44	21 50			22 15	23 09					23 11	23 28					00 14	
Hartlepool	a									21 57															
Sunderland	a									22 24															
Newcastle 8	d								21 53																
Morpeth	d								22 09																
Alnmouth for Alnwick	d								22 25																
Berwick-upon-Tweed	d								22 49																
Dunbar 238	d								23 14																
Edinburgh 10 238	a								23 39																
Edinburgh 238	d																								
Haymarket 238	d																								
Motherwell	a																								
Glasgow Central 15	a																								
Stirling	a																								
Perth	a																								
Inverness	a																								
Inverkeithing	a																								
Kirkcaldy	a																								
Leuchars 3	a																								
Dundee	a																								
Arbroath	a																								
Montrose	a																								
Stonehaven	a																								
Aberdeen	a																								

A To Nottingham
B From Plymouth
C From Manchester Airport
D 1 to Doncaster
E From Liverpool Lime Street

Table 26

Sundays

5 January to 9 February

London - Humberside, Yorkshire, North East England and Scotland

Route Diagram - refer to first Page of Table 26

		GR	EM	GR	GR	GR
		R 1	◇ A	R 1	R 1	R 1
London Kings Cross 15 ⊖	d	20 45		21 15	21 45	22 10
Stevenage 4	d			21 54		
Peterborough 8	a	21 45		22 25	22 47	23s08
Norwich	d		20 52			
Peterborough 8	d	21 46	22 23	22 27	22 48	
Grantham 7	a		22 53	22 47		23s30
	d			22 48		
Newark North Gate 7	a			22 59		23s40
	d			23 00		
Lincoln	a					
Retford 10	d			23 17		
Doncaster 7	a			23 35	23 41	00s10
Selby	a					
Hull	a					
Pontefract Monkhill	a					
Wakefield Kirkgate 4	a					
Wakefield Westgate 7	a			23 56		
Leeds 10	a			00 13		01 15
Mirfield	a					
Brighouse	a					
Halifax	a					
Shipley	a					
Bradford Forster Square	a					
Bradford Interchange	a					
Keighley	a					
Skipton	a					
Sheffield 7	d					
Doncaster 7	d				23 42	
York 8	a	22 58			00 30	
Scarborough	a					
Harrogate	a					
Leeds 10	d					
York 8	d	23 04			00 35	
Thirsk	d					
Northallerton	d	23 39			01s06	
Darlington 7	a	23 51			01s20	
Eaglescliffe	a					
Middlesbrough	a					
Darlington 7	d	23 52				
Durham	d	00 10			01s38	
Chester-le-Street	d					
Newcastle 8	a	00 42			02 10	
Hartlepool	a					
Sunderland	a					
Newcastle 8	d					
Morpeth	d					
Alnmouth for Alnwick	d					
Berwick-upon-Tweed	d					
Dunbar 238	d					
Edinburgh 10 238	a					
Edinburgh 238	d					
Haymarket 238	d					
Motherwell	a					
Glasgow Central 15	a					
Stirling	a					
Perth	a					
Inverness	a					
Inverkeithing	a					
Kirkcaldy	a					
Leuchars 3	a					
Dundee	a					
Arbroath	a					
Montrose	a					
Stonehaven	a					
Aberdeen	a					

A To Nottingham

Table 26

Sundays

16 February to 23 March

London - Humberside, Yorkshire, North East England and Scotland

Route Diagram - refer to first Page of Table 26

		TP	GR	XC	GR	TP	XC	GR	TP	XC	TP	GR	GR	TP	GR	GR	GC	GR	TP	XC	EM	GR
		◇1	R 1	◇1	R 1	◇1	◇1	R 1	◇1	◇1	◇1	R 1	R 1	◇1	R 1	R 1	R 1	R 1	◇1	◇1	◇1	R 1
									A	B				C		D			C	E	F	
London Kings Cross 15 ⊖	d											08 45	08 56		09 15	09 45	09 53	09 56				10 15
Stevenage 4	d												09 26									
Peterborough 8	a												09 55		10 15			10 54				11 15
Norwich	d																					
Peterborough 8	d												09 57		10 16			10 56				11 16
Grantham 7	a												10 16					11 15				
	d												10 17					11 16				
Newark North Gate 7	a												10 28					11 27				11 43
	d												10 29					11 28				11 44
Lincoln	a																					
Retford 10	d														10 55							
Doncaster 7	a												10 53		11 09			11 52				12 08
Selby	a																					
Hull	a																					
Pontefract Monkhill	a																					
Wakefield Kirkgate 4	a																					
Wakefield Westgate 7	a												11 11					12 11				
Leeds 10	a												11 28					12 27				
Mirfield	a																					
Brighouse	a																					
Halifax	a																					
Shipley	a																					
Bradford Forster Square	a																					
Bradford Interchange	a																					
Keighley	a																					
Skipton	a																					
Sheffield 7	d									09 21										11 21	11 31	
Doncaster 7	d							09 37							11 10						11 56	12 09
York 8	a							09 58				10 46			11 32	11 47	11 52				12 17	12 31
Scarborough	a																					
Harrogate	a																					
Leeds 10	d				08 30	08 40	09 08		09 50	10 08				10 35					11 48	12 05		
York 8	d	08 22			09 00	09 10	09 34	10 01	10 15	10 32	10 37	10 49		11 00	11 35	11 52	11 56		12 12	12 29		12 35
Thirsk	d	08 38									10 53						12 12					
Northallerton	d	08 46			09 21	09 31			10 36		11 01			11 21			12 20		12 33			12 55
Darlington 7	a	08 57			09 33	09 42	09 59	10 27	10 47	10 57		11 15		11 32	12 01	12 19			12 44	12 54		13 06
Eaglescliffe	a																12 37					
Middlesbrough	a	09 26									11 33											
Darlington 7	d				09 35	09 43	10 01	10 29	10 48	10 59		11 17		11 33	12 03	12 21			12 45	12 56		13 08
Durham	d				09 54	09 59	10 18	10 46	11 04	11 16				11 49	12 20				13 02	13 13		13 25
Chester-le-Street	d					10 05																
Newcastle 8	a				10 07	10 17	10 30	11 01	11 19	11 28		11 45		12 04	12 35	12 49			13 16	13 25		13 40
Hartlepool	a																12 57					
Sunderland	a																13 24					
Newcastle 8	d		09 15	09 45	10 12		10 40	11 04		11 34		11 48			12 43	12 53				13 28		13 44
Morpeth	d			09 58	10 28																	
Alnmouth for Alnwick	d			10 12	10 44										13 09					13 52		
Berwick-upon-Tweed	d		10 00		11 08		11 22	11 49		12 18		12 33				13 39				14 13		
Dunbar 238	d				11 33										13 54							
Edinburgh 10 238	a		10 45	11 13	11 58		12 07	12 32		12 59		13 16			14 18	14 21				14 56		15 09
Edinburgh 238	d						12 17			13 10						14 33				15 10		
Haymarket 238	d						12 21			13 14						14 39				15 15		
Motherwell	a						12 55			13 50										15 52		
Glasgow Central 15	a						13 14			14 09										16 13		
Stirling	a																					
Perth	a																					
Inverness	a																					
Inverkeithing	a															14 53						
Kirkcaldy	a															15 10						
Leuchars 3	a															15 34						
Dundee	a															15 49						
Arbroath	a															16 06						
Montrose	a															16 22						
Stonehaven	a															16 45						
Aberdeen	a															17 08						

A From Manchester Piccadilly
B from Leeds to Edinburgh
C From Manchester Airport
D The Northern Lights
E From Birmingham New Street. to Edinburgh
F From Leicester

Table 26

Sundays

16 February to 23 March

London - Humberside, Yorkshire, North East England and Scotland

Route Diagram - refer to first Page of Table 26

		HT	TP	GR	GR	TP		GR	XC	GR	GR	GC	TP	XC	EM	GR		GR	TP	XC	GR	HT	GR	TP	XC
		◇1	◇1	R 1	R 1	◇1		R 1	◇1	R 1	R 1	R 1	◇1	◇1	◇	R 1		R 1	◇1	◇1	R 1	◇1	R 1	◇1	◇1
			A			B			C		D	E	B	F	G				A	H				B	F
London Kings Cross 15 ⊖	d	10 42		10 45	10 56					11 15	11 45	11 53				11 56		12 15			12 45	12 53	12 56		
Stevenage 4	d				11 26																		13 28		
Peterborough 8	a				11 55					12 15						12 54		13 15					13 57		
Norwich	d														10 47										
Peterborough 8	d				11 57			12 10		12 16					12 18	12 56		13 17					13 59		
Grantham 7	a	11 55			12 16										12 48	13 14						14 06	14 17		
	d	11 56			12 17										12 51	13 15						14 07	14 18		
Newark North Gate 7	a				12 28											13 27		13 43					14 29		
	d				12 29											13 28		13 44					14 30		
Lincoln	a																								
Retford 10	d	12 22								12 55												14 27			
Doncaster 7	a	12 35			12 52					13 09		13 33				13 52		14 08				14 41	14 54		
Selby	a	12 53																				14 57			
Hull	a	13 37																				15 39			
Pontefract Monkhill	a																								
Wakefield Kirkgate 4	a											13 56													
Wakefield Westgate 7	a				13 10											14 10							15 13		
Leeds 10	a				13 27											14 27							15 29		
Mirfield	a											14 11													
Brighouse	a											14 19													
Halifax	a											14 36													
Shipley	a																								
Bradford Forster Square	a																								
Bradford Interchange	a											14 50													
Keighley	a																								
Skipton	a																								
Sheffield 7 ⛴	d								12 21					13 21	14a34					13 51					14 21
Doncaster 7	d									13 11								14 10		14 18					
York 8	a			12 49				13 14		13 32	13 49							14 32		14 38	14 49				
Scarborough	a																								
Harrogate	a																								
Leeds 10	d		12 18			12 47			13 05				13 48	14 05					14 18					14 47	15 05
York 8	d		12 43	12 52		13 12		13 17	13 29	13 35	13 52		14 12	14 29				14 35	14 42	14 48	14 56			15 12	15 29
Thirsk	d		12 59																14 58						
Northallerton	d		13 13			13 33		13 37					14 33					14 55	15 10					15 33	
Darlington 7	a			13 18		13 44		13 49	13 54	14 01	14 19		14 44	14 54				15 06		15 14	15 23			15 44	15 54
Eaglescliffe	a																								
Middlesbrough	a		13 44																15 40						
Darlington 7	d			13 20		13 45		13 50	13 56	14 03	14 21		14 45	14 57				15 08		15 15	15 25			15 45	15 56
Durham	d					14 01		14 08	14 13	14 20			15 02	15 14				15 25		15 32				16 01	16 13
Chester-le-Street	d					14 07																		16 07	
Newcastle 8 ⛴	a			13 48		14 19		14 23	14 26	14 35	14 49		15 16	15 26				15 40		15 44	15 53			16 19	16 25
Hartlepool	a																								
Sunderland ⛴	a																								
Newcastle 8 ⛴	d			13 51				14 25	14 31	14 43	14 53			15 28				15 44			15 56				16 28
Morpeth	d							14 40	14 46																
Alnmouth for Alnwick	d									15 10				15 53											16 52
Berwick-upon-Tweed	d			14 36							15 39			16 13							16 41				
Dunbar 238	d								15 40																17 33
Edinburgh 10 238	a			15 19				15 56	16 02	16 16	16 21			16 56				17 09			17 24				17 57
Edinburgh 238	d										16 32			17 11											18 13
Haymarket 238	d										16 37			17 15											18 16
Motherwell	a													17 52											
Glasgow Central 15	a													18 12											
Stirling	a										17 18														
Perth	a										17 55														
Inverness	a										20 08														
Inverkeithing	a																								18 28
Kirkcaldy	a																								18 44
Leuchars 3	a																								19 14
Dundee	a																								19 29
Arbroath	a																								19 46
Montrose	a																								20 00
Stonehaven	a																								20 22
Aberdeen	a																								20 42

A From Liverpool Lime Street
B From Manchester Airport
C From Birmingham New Street
D The Highland Chieftain
E 1 to Doncaster
F From Birmingham New Street. to Edinburgh
G To Liverpool Lime Street
H From Bristol Temple Meads

Table 26

Sundays

16 February to 23 March

London - Humberside, Yorkshire, North East England and Scotland

Route Diagram - refer to first Page of Table 26

		GR	XC	GR	GC	TP	XC	EM	GR	GR	TP	XC	GR	TP	XC	EM	GR	HT	GR	XC	GR	TP
		R 1	◇1	R 1	R 1	◇1	◇1	◇	R 1	R 1	◇1	◇1	R 1	◇1	◇1	◇	R 1	◇1	R 1	◇1	R 1	◇1
			A			B	C	D			E	A		B	F	D				A		B
London Kings Cross 15 ⊖	d	13 15		13 45	13 53				13 56	14 15			14 45				14 52	14 58	15 15		15 45	
Stevenage 4	d																15 23					
Peterborough 8	a	14 15							14 55	15 16							15 52		16 21			
Norwich	d															13 53						
Peterborough 8	d	14 16						14 34	14 57	15 17						15 23	15 54		16 23			
Grantham 7	a							15 06	15 15							15 53	16 13	16 17	16 43			
	d							15 09	15 16							15 55	16 14	16 18	16 44			
Newark North Gate 7	a								15 27	15 45							16 25					
	d								15 28	15 46							16 26					
Lincoln	a																					
Retford 10	d	14 55															16 42	16 47				
Doncaster 7	a	15 09							15 52	16 10							16 56	17 00	17 14			
Selby	a																	17 35				
Hull	a																	18 21				
Pontefract Monkhill	a																					
Wakefield Kirkgate 4	a																					
Wakefield Westgate 7	a								16 11								17 15					
Leeds 10	a								16 27								17 31					
Mirfield	a																					
Brighouse	a																					
Halifax	a																					
Shipley	a																					
Bradford Forster Square	a																					
Bradford Interchange	a																					
Keighley	a																					
Skipton	a																					
Sheffield 7	d		14 51				15 21	16a34				15 51			16 21	17a39				16 51		
Doncaster 7	d	15 11	15 22							16 11		16 18							17 16	17 19		
York 8	a	15 32	15 42	15 49	15 57					16 34		16 38	16 47						17 38	17 42	17 48	
Scarborough	a																					
Harrogate	a																					
Leeds 10	d					15 48	16 05				16 18			16 47	17 05							17 48
York 8	d	15 35	15 45	15 52	16 00	16 12	16 29			16 36	16 43	16 47	16 54	17 12	17 29				17 41	17 48	17 52	18 10
Thirsk	d				16 17						17 00											
Northallerton	d				16 25	16 33				16 58	17 11			17 33								18 31
Darlington 7	a	16 01	16 10	16 19		16 44	16 54			17 09		17 15	17 24	17 44	17 54				18 08	18 13	18 18	18 44
Eaglescliffe	a				16 42																	
Middlesbrough	a										17 42											
Darlington 7	d	16 03	16 12	16 21		16 45	16 56			17 11		17 17	17 26	17 45	17 56				18 09	18 14	18 20	18 46
Durham	d	16 20	16 29			17 02	17 13			17 29		17 34		18 01	18 13				18 27	18 32		19 03
Chester-le-Street	d													18 07								
Newcastle 8	a	16 35	16 42	16 49		17 16	17 25			17 44		17 47	17 54	18 19	18 25				18 42	18 45	18 49	19 17
Hartlepool	a				17 08																	
Sunderland	a				17 39																	
Newcastle 8	d	16 38		16 53			17 28			17 47			17 57		18 28				18 45		18 56	
Morpeth	d																					
Alnmouth for Alnwick	d	17 05					17 53												19 13			
Berwick-upon-Tweed	d			17 39			18 13						18 42		19 10						19 41	
Dunbar 238	d														19 35							
Edinburgh 10 238	a	18 09		18 21			18 56			19 14			19 25		19 57				20 17		20 24	
Edinburgh 238	d			18 36			19 18															
Haymarket 238	d			18 41			19 23															
Motherwell	a						19 58															
Glasgow Central 15	a						20 21															
Stirling	a																					
Perth	a																					
Inverness	a																					
Inverkeithing	a			18 54																		
Kirkcaldy	a			19 11																		
Leuchars 3	a			19 36																		
Dundee	a			19 50																		
Arbroath	a			20 08																		
Montrose	a			20 24																		
Stonehaven	a			20 47																		
Aberdeen	a			21 10																		

A From Exeter St Davids
B From Manchester Airport
C From Birmingham New Street. to Edinburgh
D To Liverpool Lime Street
E From Liverpool Lime Street
F From Guildford

Table 26

Sundays

16 February to 23 March

London - Humberside, Yorkshire, North East England and Scotland

Route Diagram - refer to first Page of Table 26

		XC	EM	GR	GC	GR	GR	EM		TP	GR	GR	TP	GC	XC	XC	GR	GR		XC	GR	TP	XC	EM	GR
		◇1 A	◇ B	R 1	R 1 C	R 1	R 1	◇ D		◇1 E	R 1	R 1	◇1 F	R 1	◇1 G	◇1 H	R 1	R 1		◇1 G	R 1	◇1 F	◇1 I	◇ D	R 1
London Kings Cross 15 ⊖	d			15 52	15 58	16 15					16 45	16 52		16 58			17 12	17 15			17 45				17 52
Stevenage 4	d											17 22						17 52							
Peterborough 8	a			16 50		17 13						17 51					18 15								18 53
Norwich	d		14 53					15 54																16 54	
Peterborough 8	d		16 24	16 53		17 16	17 22	17 23				17 53					18 17							18 26	18 55
Grantham 7	a		16 54	17 12			17 40	17 53									18 35	18 41						18 56	
	d		16 56	17 13			17 41	17 55									18 36	18 42						18 58	
Newark North Gate 7	a			17 24		17 43						18 19													19 21
	d			17 25		17 44						18 20													19 23
Lincoln	a																								
Retford 10	d						18 03																		
Doncaster 7	a			17 49	17 53	18 08	18 17					18 42					19 09	19 13							19 47
Selby	a																								
Hull	a																								
Pontefract Monkhill	a																								
Wakefield Kirkgate 4	a				18 21																				
Wakefield Westgate 7	a			18 10			18 38					19 01						19 32							20 07
Leeds 10	a			18 29			18 56					19 21						19 51							20 25
Mirfield	a				18 39																				
Brighouse	a				18 47																				
Halifax	a				18 57																				
Shipley	a																								
Bradford Forster Square	a																								
Bradford Interchange	a				19 12																				
Keighley	a																								
Skipton	a																								
Sheffield 7	d	17 21	18a33					19a31							17 51	18 21				18 51			19 21	20a31	
Doncaster 7	d					18 10									18 15		19 12			19 19					
York 8	a					18 31					18 47			19 13			19 33			19 39	19 47				
Scarborough	a																								
Harrogate	a																								21 04
Leeds 10	d	18 05								18 18			18 47		18 58	19 08						19 48	20 08		
York 8	d	18 29				18 35				18 43	18 54		19 12	19 15	19 22	19 32	19 38			19 45	19 51	20 12	20 32		
Thirsk	d									19 00				19 33								20 29			
Northallerton	d					18 55				19 09			19 33	19 45								20 39			
Darlington 7	a	18 54				19 06					19 22		19 44		19 47	19 59	20 04			20 12	20 17		20 59		
Eaglescliffe	a													20 06											
Middlesbrough	a									19 40												21 10			
Darlington 7	d	18 56				19 08					19 24		19 45		19 49	20 00	20 06			20 13	20 19		21 00		
Durham	d	19 13				19 25							20 01		20 06	20 18	20 23			20 31			21 18		
Chester-le-Street	d												20 07												
Newcastle 8	a	19 25				19 40					19 52		20 18		20 21	20 31	20 38			20 44	20 48		21 31		
Hartlepool	a													20 25											
Sunderland	a													20 52											
Newcastle 8	d	19 28				19 43					19 55				20 34		20 41			20 56	20 59		21 34		
Morpeth	d					19 58									20 48		20 56								
Alnmouth for Alnwick	d	19 53															21 12						22 02		
Berwick-upon-Tweed	d	20 13									20 40				21 22						21 45				
Dunbar 238	d					20 53									21 47										
Edinburgh 10 238	a	20 56				21 16					21 23				22 12		22 18			22 21	22 26		23 04		
Edinburgh 238	d	21 12				21 22																			
Haymarket 238	d	21 17				21 26																			
Motherwell	a	21 53				22 05																			
Glasgow Central 15	a	22 14				22 26																			
Stirling	a																								
Perth	a																								
Inverness	a																								
Inverkeithing	a																								
Kirkcaldy	a																								
Leuchars 8	a																								
Dundee	a																								
Arbroath	a																								
Montrose	a																								
Stonehaven	a																								
Aberdeen	a																								

A From Reading. to Edinburgh
B To Liverpool Lime Street
C 1 to Doncaster
D To Manchester Piccadilly
E From Liverpool Lime Street
F From Manchester Airport
G From Exeter St Davids
H From Reading
I From Reading. to Newcastle

Table 26

Sundays

16 February to 23 March

London - Humberside, Yorkshire, North East England and Scotland

Route Diagram - refer to first Page of Table 26

		HT	GR	GR	EM	XC	GR	GC	GR	TP	XC	GR	GR	EM	GC	XC	GR	GR	HT	GC	GR	TP
		◇1	1	1	◇	◇1	1	1	1	◇1	◇1	1	1	◇	1	◇1	1	1	◇1	1	1	◇1
					A	B				C	D			A		B				E		F
London Kings Cross 15 ⊖	d	17 58	18 12	18 18			18 45	18 53	18 56			19 12	19 15		19 42		19 45	19 52	20 00	20 12	20 15	
Stevenage 4	d	18 28		18 55					19 28				19 53								20 55	
Peterborough 8	a		19 11						19 57			20 17					20 46	20 51			21 24	
Norwich	d				17 54									18 56								
Peterborough 8	d		19 17		19 26				19 58			20 18		20 30			20 48	20 53			21 26	
Grantham 7	a	19 19		19 40	19 56								20 42	21 00					21 15		21 45	
	d	19 22		19 41									20 44						21 16		21 46	
Newark North Gate 7	a		19 43						20 26			20 46	20 55								21 57	
	d		19 44						20 27			20 47	20 57								21 58	
Lincoln	a												21 24									
Retford 10	d	19 44		20 04														21 31	21 37			
Doncaster 7	a	19 57	20 08	20 18					20 51			21 13			21 24			21 45	21 51	21 56	22 22	
Selby	a	20 20																	22 10			
Hull	a	21 07																	22 52			
Pontefract Monkhill	a																					
Wakefield Kirkgate 4	a														21 50					22 38		
Wakefield Westgate 7	a			20 37					21 10									22 04			22 40	
Leeds 10	a			20 52					21 27									22 20			22 58	
Mirfield	a														22 05					22 53		
Brighouse	a														22 13					23 02		
Halifax	a														22 24					23 13		
Shipley	a																					
Bradford Forster Square	a																					
Bradford Interchange	a														22 39					23 27		
Keighley	a			21s19																		
Skipton	a			21 40																		
Sheffield 7	d					19 51					20 21					20 51						
Doncaster 7	d		20 10			20 18						21 15				21 22						
York 8	a		20 31			20 39	20 49	20 53				21 36				21 42	21 55					
Scarborough	a																					
Harrogate	a																					
Leeds 10	d									20 47	21 08											22 18
York 8	d		20 36				20 52	20 56		21 12	21 34	21 40				21 48	21 58					22 43
Thirsk	d							21 12		21 29												23 06
Northallerton	d		20 56					21 20		21 37												23 16
Darlington 7	a		21 07				21 19			21 48	22 01	22 18				22 23	22 37					23 27
Eaglescliffe	a							21 37														
Middlesbrough	a																					
Darlington 7	d		21 09				21 22			21 49	22 02	22 20				22 25	22 38					23 28
Durham	d		21 26							22 05	22 20	22 37				22 42	22 56					23 44
Chester-le-Street	d																					
Newcastle 8	a		21 43				21 50			22 19	22 33	23 09				23 11	23 28					00 14
Hartlepool	a							21 57														
Sunderland	a							22 24														
Newcastle 8	d						21 53															
Morpeth	d						22 09															
Alnmouth for Alnwick	d						22 25															
Berwick-upon-Tweed	d						22 49															
Dunbar 238	d						23 14															
Edinburgh 10 238	a						23 39															
Edinburgh 238	d																					
Haymarket 238	d																					
Motherwell	a																					
Glasgow Central 15	a																					
Stirling	a																					
Perth	a																					
Inverness	a																					
Inverkeithing	a																					
Kirkcaldy	a																					
Leuchars 8	a																					
Dundee	a																					
Arbroath	a																					
Montrose	a																					
Stonehaven	a																					
Aberdeen	a																					

A To Nottingham
B From Exeter St Davids
C From Manchester Airport
D From Reading
E 1 to Doncaster
F From Liverpool Lime Street

Table 26

Sundays

16 February to 23 March

London - Humberside, Yorkshire, North East England and Scotland

Route Diagram - refer to first Page of Table 26

		GR	EM	GR	GR	GR
		R		R	R	R
		1	◇	1	1	1
			A			
London Kings Cross 15 ⊖	d	20 45		21 15	21 45	22 10
Stevenage 4	d			21 54		
Peterborough 8	a	21 45		22 25	22 47	23s08
Norwich	d		20 52			
Peterborough 8	d	21 46	22 23	22 27	22 48	
Grantham 7	a		22 53	22 47		23s30
	d			22 48		
Newark North Gate 7	a			22 59		23s40
	d			23 00		
Lincoln	a					
Retford 10	d			23 17		
Doncaster 7	a			23 35	23 41	00s10
Selby	a					
Hull	a					
Pontefract Monkhill	a					
Wakefield Kirkgate 4	a					
Wakefield Westgate 7	a			23 56		
Leeds 10	a			00 13		01 15
Mirfield	a					
Brighouse	a					
Halifax	a					
Shipley	a					
Bradford Forster Square	a					
Bradford Interchange	a					
Keighley	a					
Skipton	a					
Sheffield 7	d					
Doncaster 7	d				23 42	
York 8	a	22 58			00 30	
Scarborough	a					
Harrogate	a					
Leeds 10	d					
York 8	d	23 04			00 35	
Thirsk	d					
Northallerton	d	23 39			01s06	
Darlington 7	a	23 51			01s20	
Eaglescliffe	a					
Middlesbrough	a					
Darlington 7	d	23 52				
Durham	d	00 10			01s38	
Chester-le-Street	d					
Newcastle 8	a	00 42			02 10	
Hartlepool	a					
Sunderland	a					
Newcastle 8	d					
Morpeth	d					
Alnmouth for Alnwick	d					
Berwick-upon-Tweed	d					
Dunbar 238	d					
Edinburgh 10 238	a					
Edinburgh 238	d					
Haymarket 238	d					
Motherwell	a					
Glasgow Central 15	a					
Stirling	a					
Perth	a					
Inverness	a					
Inverkeithing	a					
Kirkcaldy	a					
Leuchars 3	a					
Dundee	a					
Arbroath	a					
Montrose	a					
Stonehaven	a					
Aberdeen	a					

A To Nottingham

Table 26

Sundays

30 March to 11 May

London - Humberside, Yorkshire, North East England and Scotland

Route Diagram - refer to first Page of Table 26

		TP	GR	XC	GR	TP	XC	GR	TP	XC	TP	GR	GR	TP	XC	GR	GC	GR	GR	EM	TP	GR	XC
		◇1	R 1	◇1	R 1	◇1	◇1	R 1	◇1	◇1	◇1	R 1	R 1	◇1	◇1	R 1	R 1	R 1	R 1	◇1	◇1	R 1	◇1
		A				A			A	B				A	C			D		E	A		F
London Kings Cross 15 ⊖	d											09 00	09 03			09 30	09 48	10 00	10 03			10 20	
Stevenage 4	d												09 23										
Peterborough 8	a												09 52			10 15			10 48			11 08	
Norwich	d																						
Peterborough 8	d												09 54			10 16			10 50			11 10	
Grantham 7	a												10 13						11 09				
	d												10 14						11 10				
Newark North Gate 7	a												10 25						11 21				
	d												10 26						11 22				
Lincoln	a																						
Retford 10	d															10 55							
Doncaster 7	a												10 50			11 09			11 46			11 57	
Selby	a																						
Hull	a																						
Pontefract Monkhill	a																						
Wakefield Kirkgate 4	a																						
Wakefield Westgate 7	a												11 08						12 04				
Leeds 10	a												11 27						12 21				
Mirfield	a																						
Brighouse	a																						
Halifax	a																						
Shipley	a																						
Bradford Forster Square	a																						
Bradford Interchange	a																						
Keighley	a																						
Skipton	a																						
Sheffield 7	d									09 21					10 21					11 31			11 21
Doncaster 7	d							09 37								11 10				11 53		11 59	
York 8	a							09 58				10 46				11 32	11 36	11 49		12 15		12 20	
Scarborough	a																						
Harrogate	a																						
Leeds 10	d	07 40			08 30	08 40	09 08		09 40	10 08				10 35	11 05						11 40		12 05
York 8	d	08 22			09 00	09 10	09 34	10 01	10 10	10 32	10 37	10 49		11 00	11 29	11 35	11 39	11 52			12 10	12 23	12 29
Thirsk	d	08 38									10 53						11 55						
Northallerton	d	08 46			09 21	09 31			10 31		11 01			11 21			12 03				12 31		
Darlington 7	a	08 57			09 33	09 42	09 59	10 27	10 42	10 57		11 15		11 32	11 54	12 01		12 19			12 42	12 49	12 54
Eaglescliffe	a																12 20						
Middlesbrough	a	09 26									11 33												
Darlington 7	d				09 35	09 43	10 01	10 29	10 43	10 59		11 17		11 33	11 56	12 03		12 21			12 43	12 51	12 56
Durham	d				09 54	09 59	10 18	10 46	10 59	11 16				11 49	12 13	12 20					12 59		13 13
Chester-le-Street	d					10 05																	
Newcastle 8	a				10 07	10 17	10 30	11 01	11 15	11 28		11 45		12 04	12 25	12 35		12 49			13 14	13 22	13 25
Hartlepool	a																12 41						
Sunderland	a																13 08						
Newcastle 8	d		09 15	09 45	10 12		10 40	11 04		11 34		11 48			12 30	12 43		12 53					13 28
Morpeth	d			09 58	10 28																		
Alnmouth for Alnwick	d			10 12	10 44											13 09							13 52
Berwick-upon-Tweed	d		10 00		11 08		11 22	11 49		12 18		12 33						13 39					14 13
Dunbar 238	d				11 33										13 33	13 54							
Edinburgh 10 238	a		10 45	11 13	11 58		12 07	12 32		12 59		13 16			13 57	14 18		14 21					14 56
Edinburgh 238	d						12 17			13 10								14 33					15 10
Haymarket 238	d						12 21			13 14								14 39					15 15
Motherwell	a						12 55			13 50													15 52
Glasgow Central 15	a						13 14			14 09													16 13
Stirling	a																						
Perth	a																						
Inverness	a																						
Inverkeithing	a																	14 53					
Kirkcaldy	a																	15 10					
Leuchars 3	a																	15 34					
Dundee	a																	15 49					
Arbroath	a																	16 06					
Montrose	a																	16 22					
Stonehaven	a																	16 45					
Aberdeen	a																	17 08					

A From Manchester Airport
B from Leeds to Edinburgh
C From Birmingham New Street
D The Northern Lights
E From Leicester
F From Birmingham New Street. to Edinburgh

Table 26

Sundays

30 March to 11 May

London - Humberside, Yorkshire, North East England and Scotland

Route Diagram - refer to first Page of Table 26

		GR	HT	TP	GR	GR		TP	GR	XC	EM	GR	GC	GR	GR	TP		GR	XC	GR	HT	TP	XC	GR	GR
		R 1	◇1	◇1	R 1	R 1		◇1	R 1	◇1	◇	R 1	R 1	R 1	R 1	◇1		R 1	◇1	R 1	◇1	◇1	◇1	R 1	R 1
				A				B		C	D		E	F		B			G			A	H		
		RT	⊠		RT	RT			RT	T		RT	R	RT	RT			RT	T	RT	⊠		T	RT	RT
London Kings Cross 15 ⊖	d	10 30	10 48		11 00	11 03			11 20			11 30	11 50	12 00	12 03			12 20		12 30	12 48			13 00	13 03
Stevenage 4	d					11 23																			13 23
Peterborough 8	a	11 15				11 52			12 08			12 15			12 48			13 08		13 15					13 52
Norwich	d										10 47														
Peterborough 8	d	11 16				11 54			12 09		12 16	12 16			12 50			13 09		13 16					13 54
Grantham 7	a		11 47			12 13					12 46				13 09						13 47				14 13
	d		11 48			12 14					12 51				13 10						13 48				14 14
Newark North Gate 7	a	11 43				12 25									13 21					13 43					14 25
	d	11 44				12 26									13 22					13 44					14 26
Lincoln	a																								
Retford 10	d		12 09									12 55									14 09				
Doncaster 7	a	12 08	12 22			12 50						13 09	13 19		13 46			13 56		14 08	14 22				14 50
Selby	a		12 43																		14 43				
Hull	a		13 25																		15 26				
Pontefract Monkhill	a																								
Wakefield Kirkgate 4	a												13 45												
Wakefield Westgate 7	a					13 08									14 04										15 08
Leeds 10	a					13 27									14 21										15 27
Mirfield	a												14 00												
Brighouse	a												14 08												
Halifax	a												14 19												
Shipley	a																								
Bradford Forster Square	a																								
Bradford Interchange	a												14 35												
Keighley	a																								
Skipton	a																								
Sheffield 7	d									12 21	14a34								13 21				13 51		
Doncaster 7	d	12 09										13 11						13 58		14 10			14 18		
York 8	a	12 31			12 49				13 14			13 32		13 49				14 20		14 32			14 38	14 46	
Scarborough	a																								
Harrogate	a																								
Leeds 10	d			12 12				12 40		13 05						13 40			14 05			14 12			
York 8	d	12 35		12 40	12 52			13 10	13 17	13 29		13 35		13 52		14 11		14 23	14 29	14 35		14 42	14 48	14 56	
Thirsk	d			12 56																		14 58			
Northallerton	d	12 55		13 04				13 31	13 37							14 32				14 55		15 09			
Darlington 7	a	13 06			13 18			13 42	13 48	13 54		14 01		14 19		14 43		14 49	14 54	15 06			15 13	15 22	
Eaglescliffe	a																								
Middlesbrough	a			13 37																		15 40			
Darlington 7	d	13 08			13 20			13 43	13 50	13 56		14 03		14 21		14 44		14 51	14 57	15 08			15 15	15 24	
Durham	d	13 25						13 59	14 07	14 13		14 20				15 00		15 08	15 14	15 25			15 32		
Chester-le-Street	d							14 05																	
Newcastle 8	a	13 40			13 48			14 17	14 22	14 25		14 35		14 49		15 16		15 25	15 26	15 40			15 44	15 52	
Hartlepool	a																								
Sunderland	a																								
Newcastle 8	d	13 44			13 51				14 25	14 31		14 43		14 53					15 28	15 44				15 55	
Morpeth	d								14 40	14 46															
Alnmouth for Alnwick	d											15 10							15 53						
Berwick-upon-Tweed	d				14 36									15 39					16 13					16 40	
Dunbar 238	d									15 40															
Edinburgh 10 238	a	15 09			15 19				15 58	16 02		16 16		16 21					16 56	17 09				17 23	
Edinburgh 238	d													16 32					17 11						
Haymarket 238	d													16 37					17 15						
Motherwell	a																		17 52						
Glasgow Central 15	a																		18 12						
Stirling	a													17 18											
Perth	a													17 55											
Inverness	a													20 08											
Inverkeithing	a																								
Kirkcaldy	a																								
Leuchars 3	a																								
Dundee	a																								
Arbroath	a																								
Montrose	a																								
Stonehaven	a																								
Aberdeen	a																								

A From Liverpool Lime Street
B From Manchester Airport
C From Bristol Temple Meads
D To Liverpool Lime Street
E 1 to Doncaster
F The Highland Chieftain
G From Bristol Temple Meads. T to Edinburgh
H From Birmingham New Street

Table 26

Sundays

30 March to 11 May

London - Humberside, Yorkshire, North East England and Scotland

Route Diagram - refer to first Page of Table 26

		TP	XC	GR	GC	XC	GR	TP	XC	EM	GR	GR	HT	TP	XC	GR	TP	XC	EM	GR	GR	GC
		◇1 A	◇1 B	R 1	R 1	◇1 C	R 1	◇1 A	◇1 B	◇ D	R 1	R 1	◇1	◇1 E	◇1 F	R 1	◇1 A	◇1 G	◇ D	R 1	R 1	R 1 H
London Kings Cross 15 ⊖	d			13 30	13 48		14 00				14 03	14 30	14 48			15 00				15 03	15 30	15 50
Stevenage 4	d																			15 23		
Peterborough 8	a			14 15							14 48	15 16								15 52	16 16	
Norwich	d																		13 53			
Peterborough 8	d			14 16						14 34	14 52	15 17							15 23	15 54	16 17	
Grantham 7	a									15 06	15 11		15 47						15 53	16 13	16 37	
	d									15 09	15 12		15 48						15 55	16 14	16 38	
Newark North Gate 7	a										15 23	15 45								16 25		
	d										15 24	15 46								16 26		
Lincoln	a																					
Retford 10	d			14 55									16 09							16 42		
Doncaster 7	a			15 09							15 48	16 10	16 23							16 56	17 10	17 17
Selby	a												16 45									
Hull	a												17 27									
Pontefract Monkhill	a																					
Wakefield Kirkgate 4	a																					17 45
Wakefield Westgate 7	a										16 08									17 15		
Leeds 10	a										16 27									17 31		
Mirfield	a																					18 00
Brighouse	a																					18 08
Halifax	a																					18 19
Shipley	a																					
Bradford Forster Square	a																					
Bradford Interchange	a																					18 33
Keighley	a																					
Skipton	a																					
Sheffield 7	d		14 21			14 51			15 21	16a34					15 51			16 21	17a39			
Doncaster 7	d			15 10		15 22						16 11			16 18						17 11	
York 8	a			15 32	15 36	15 42	15 49					16 34			16 38	16 47					17 34	
Scarborough	a																					
Harrogate	a																					
Leeds 10	d	14 40	15 05					15 40	16 05					16 12			16 40	17 05				
York 8	d	15 10	15 29	15 35	15 39	15 45	15 52	16 10	16 29			16 36		16 41	16 47	16 54	17 10	17 29			17 36	
Thirsk	d				15 56									16 57								
Northallerton	d	15 31			16 06			16 31				16 58		17 07			17 31					
Darlington 7	a	15 42	15 54	16 01		16 10	16 19	16 42	16 54			17 09			17 14	17 21	17 42	17 54			18 03	
Eaglescliffe	a				16 23																	
Middlesbrough	a													17 39								
Darlington 7	d	15 43	15 56	16 03		16 12	16 21	16 43	16 56			17 11			17 17	17 23	17 43	17 56			18 05	
Durham	d	15 59	16 13	16 20		16 29		16 59	17 13			17 29			17 34		17 59	18 13			18 23	
Chester-le-Street	d	16 05															18 05					
Newcastle 8	a	16 18	16 25	16 35		16 42	16 49	17 14	17 25			17 44			17 47	17 51	18 18	18 25			18 38	
Hartlepool	a				16 50																	
Sunderland	a				17 21																	
Newcastle 8	d		16 28	16 38			16 53		17 28			17 47				17 54		18 28			18 41	
Morpeth	d																					
Alnmouth for Alnwick	d		16 52	17 05					17 53												19 09	
Berwick-upon-Tweed	d						17 39		18 13							18 39		19 10				
Dunbar 238	d		17 33															19 35				
Edinburgh 10 238	a		17 57	18 09			18 21		18 56			19 14				19 22		19 57			20 13	
Edinburgh 238	d		18 13				18 36		19 18													
Haymarket 238	d		18 16				18 41		19 23													
Motherwell	a								19 58													
Glasgow Central 15	a								20 21													
Stirling	a																					
Perth	a																					
Inverness	a																					
Inverkeithing	a		18 28				18 54															
Kirkcaldy	a		18 44				19 11															
Leuchars 3	a		19 14				19 36															
Dundee	a		19 29				19 50															
Arbroath	a		19 46				20 08															
Montrose	a		20 00				20 24															
Stonehaven	a		20 22				20 47															
Aberdeen	a		20 42				21 10															

A From Manchester Airport
B From Plymouth. to Edinburgh
C From Birmingham New Street
D To Liverpool Lime Street
E From Liverpool Lime Street
F From Guildford
G From Penzance
H 1 to Doncaster

Table 26

Sundays

30 March to 11 May

London - Humberside, Yorkshire, North East England and Scotland

Route Diagram - refer to first Page of Table 26

		XC	GR	TP	XC	EM	GR	GR	GR	TP	GC	GR	TP	XC	XC	EM	GR	GR	GR	GR	HT	XC	EM
		◇1	R 1	◇1	◇1	◇	R 1	R 1	R 1	◇1	R 1	R 1	◇1	◇1	◇1	◇	R 1	R 1	R 1	R 1	◇1	◇1	◇
		A		B	C	D				E			B	A	F	G						A	G
		trolley	rest.+trolley		trolley		rest.+trolley	rest.+trolley	rest.+trolley		rest.	rest.+trolley		trolley	trolley		rest.+trolley	rest.+trolley	rest.+trolley	rest.+trolley	⊠	trolley	
London Kings Cross 15 ⊖	d		16 00				16 05	16 30	16 35		16 47	17 00					17 05	17 20	17 30	17 35	17 44		
Stevenage 4	d								16 55											17 55	18 04		
Peterborough 8	a						16 50	17 15									17 50		18 15				
Norwich	d					14 53										15 54							16 54
Peterborough 8	d					16 24	16 53	17 16								17 23	17 51		18 16				18 26
Grantham 7	a					16 54	17 12		17 39							17 53		18 24	18 35	18 41	18 47		18 56
	d					16 56	17 13		17 40							17 55		18 26	18 36	18 42	18 48		18 58
Newark North Gate 7	a						17 24	17 43									18 18	18 36					
	d						17 25	17 44									18 19	18 38					
Lincoln	a																						
Retford 10	d								18 03												19 09		
Doncaster 7	a						17 49	18 08	18 17								18 42	19 02	19 09	19 13	19 23		
Selby	a																	19 21			19 45		
Hull	a																	20 02			20 26		
Pontefract Monkhill	a																						
Wakefield Kirkgate 4	a																						
Wakefield Westgate 7	a						18 10		18 38								19 01			19 32			
Leeds 10	a						18 29		18 56								19 21			19 51			
Mirfield	a																						
Brighouse	a																						
Halifax	a																						
Shipley	a																						
Bradford Forster Square	a																						
Bradford Interchange	a																						
Keighley	a																						
Skipton	a																						
Sheffield 7 🚊	d	16 51			17 21	18a33								17 51	18 21	19a31						18 51	20a31
Doncaster 7	d	17 19						18 10						18 16					19 12			19 19	
York 8	a	17 40	17 46					18 31			18 41	18 46							19 33			19 39	
Scarborough	a																						
Harrogate	a																						
Leeds 10	d			17 40	18 05					18 12			18 40	18 58	19 08								
York 8	d	17 45	17 49	18 10	18 29			18 35		18 40	18 44	18 54	19 10	19 22	19 32				19 38			19 45	
Thirsk	d									18 56	19 01												
Northallerton	d			18 31				18 55		19 04	19 09		19 31										
Darlington 7	a	18 10	18 15	18 42	18 54			19 06				19 22	19 42	19 47	19 59				20 04			20 10	
Eaglescliffe	a										19 29												
Middlesbrough	a									19 37													
Darlington 7	d	18 12	18 17	18 46	18 56			19 08				19 24	19 43	19 49	20 00				20 06			20 12	
Durham	d	18 29		19 02	19 13			19 25					19 59	20 06	20 18				20 23			20 29	
Chester-le-Street	d												20 05										
Newcastle 8 🚊	a	18 42	18 45	19 17	19 25			19 40				19 52	20 18	20 19	20 31				20 38			20 41	
Hartlepool	a										19 48												
Sunderland 🚊	a										20 20												
Newcastle 8 🚊	d		18 52		19 28			19 43				19 55			20 34				20 41			20 56	
Morpeth	d							19 58							20 48				20 56				
Alnmouth for Alnwick	d				19 53														21 12				
Berwick-upon-Tweed	d		19 37		20 13							20 40			21 22								
Dunbar 238	d							20 53							21 47								
Edinburgh 10 238	a		20 20		20 56			21 16				21 23			22 12				22 18			22 21	
Edinburgh 238	d				21 12			21 22															
Haymarket 238	d				21 17			21 26															
Motherwell	a				21 53			22 05															
Glasgow Central 15	a				22 14			22 26															
Stirling	a																						
Perth	a																						
Inverness	a																						
Inverkeithing	a																						
Kirkcaldy	a																						
Leuchars 3	a																						
Dundee	a																						
Arbroath	a																						
Montrose	a																						
Stonehaven	a																						
Aberdeen	a																						

A From Reading
B From Manchester Airport
C From Plymouth. trolley to Edinburgh
D To Liverpool Lime Street
E From Liverpool Lime Street
F From Plymouth. trolley to Newcastle
G To Manchester Piccadilly

Table 26

Sundays

30 March to 11 May

London - Humberside, Yorkshire, North East England and Scotland

Route Diagram - refer to first Page of Table 26

		GR	GR	TP	GC	XC	GR	GR	EM	GC	XC	GR	GR	GR	GC	TP	GR	GR	HT	EM	XC	GR
		R 1	R 1	◇1	R 1	◇1	R 1	R 1	◇	R 1	◇1	R 1	R 1	R 1	R 1	◇1	R 1	R 1	◇1	◇	◇1	R 1
				A		B			C	D	E					A				C	E	
London Kings Cross 15 ⊖	d	18 00	18 05		18 23		18 30	18 35		18 45		19 00	19 05	19 08	19 23		19 30	19 35	19 50			20 00
Stevenage 4	d							18 55						19 29				19 55				
Peterborough 8	a		18 51				19 15						19 50	19 59			20 17	20 24				20 45
Norwich	d								17 54											18 56		
Peterborough 8	d		18 53				19 17		19 26				19 51	20 01			20 18	20 26		20 30		20 46
Grantham 7	a							19 40	19 56					20 21				20 45	20 50	21 00		
	d							19 41						20 23				20 46	20 51			
Newark North Gate 7	a		19 20				19 43						20 18	20 34			20 46					
	d		19 22				19 44						20 19	20 36			20 47					
Lincoln	a													21 02								
Retford 10	d							20 04											21 12			
Doncaster 7	a		19 47				20 08	20 18		20 23			20 43		20 58		21 13	21 17	21 24			
Selby	a																		21 41			
Hull	a																		22 23			
Pontefract Monkhill	a																					
Wakefield Kirkgate 4	a									20 53					21 20							
Wakefield Westgate 7	a		20 07					20 37					21 01					21 36				
Leeds 10	a		20 25					20 52					21 18					21 55				
Mirfield	a									21 09					21 35							
Brighouse	a									21 23					21 43							
Halifax	a									21 34					21 54							
Shipley	a																					
Bradford Forster Square	a																					
Bradford Interchange	a									21 49					22 08							
Keighley	a							21s19														
Skipton	a							21 40														
Sheffield 7	d					19 21					19 51										20 51	
Doncaster 7	d						20 10				20 18						21 15				21 22	
York 8	a	19 47			20 12		20 31				20 38	20 49					21 36				21 42	21 51
Scarborough	a																					
Harrogate	a		21 04																			
Leeds 10	d			19 40		20 08										20 40						
York 8	d	19 50		20 08	20 14	20 32	20 36				20 48	20 52				21 08	21 41				21 48	21 57
Thirsk	d			20 24	20 31											21 24						
Northallerton	d			20 33	20 39		20 56									21 32						
Darlington 7	a	20 16				20 59	21 07				21 13	21 19				21 43	22 17				22 23	22 37
Eaglescliffe	a				20 56																	
Middlesbrough	a			21 04																		
Darlington 7	d	20 18				21 00	21 09				21 15	21 22				21 44	22 19				22 25	22 39
Durham	d					21 18	21 26				21 32					22 01	22 37				22 42	22 56
Chester-le-Street	d																					
Newcastle 8	a	20 46				21 31	21 43				21 44	21 50				22 15	23 09				23 11	23 28
Hartlepool	a				21 16																	
Sunderland	a				21 51																	
Newcastle 8	d	20 59				21 34						21 53										
Morpeth	d											22 09										
Alnmouth for Alnwick	d					22 02						22 25										
Berwick-upon-Tweed	d	21 45										22 49										
Dunbar 238	d											23 14										
Edinburgh 10 238	a	22 28				23 04						23 39										
Edinburgh 238	d																					
Haymarket 238	d																					
Motherwell	a																					
Glasgow Central 15	a																					
Stirling	a																					
Perth	a																					
Inverness	a																					
Inverkeithing	a																					
Kirkcaldy	a																					
Leuchars 3	a																					
Dundee	a																					
Arbroath	a																					
Montrose	a																					
Stonehaven	a																					
Aberdeen	a																					

A From Manchester Airport
B From Plymouth. to Newcastle
C To Nottingham
D 1 to Doncaster
E From Reading

Table 26

Sundays
30 March to 11 May

London - Humberside, Yorkshire, North East England and Scotland

Route Diagram - refer to first Page of Table 26

		GR	GR	TP	GR	EM	GR	GR	GR
		R	R		R		R	R	R
		1	1	◇1	1	◇	1	1	1
				A		B			
		🚃	🚃		🚃		🚃	🚃	🚃
London Kings Cross 15 ⊖	d	20 05	20 35		21 00		21 35	22 00	22 35
Stevenage 4	d		20 55				21 56		
Peterborough 8	a	20 50	21 24		21 45		22 25	22 46	23s23
Norwich	d					20 52			
Peterborough 8	d	20 51	21 26		21 46	22 23	22 27	22 47	
Grantham 7	a		21 45			22 53	22 47		23s44
	d		21 46				22 48		
Newark North Gate 7	a		21 57				22 59		23s55
	d		21 58				23 00		
Lincoln	a								
Retford 10	d	21 30					23 17		
Doncaster 7	a	21 44	22 22				23 35	23 40	00s24
Selby	a								
Hull	a								
Pontefract Monkhill	a								
Wakefield Kirkgate 4	a								
Wakefield Westgate 7	a	22 02	22 40				23 56		
Leeds 10	a	22 19	22 58				00 13		01 30
Mirfield	a								
Brighouse	a								
Halifax	a								
Shipley	a								
Bradford Forster Square	a								
Bradford Interchange	a								
Keighley	a								
Skipton	a								
Sheffield 7 ⛴	d								
Doncaster 7	d							23 42	
York 8	a				22 56			00 32	
Scarborough	a								
Harrogate	a								
Leeds 10	d			22 12					
York 8	d			22 43	23 04			00 35	
Thirsk	d			23 06					
Northallerton	d			23 16	23 40			01s06	
Darlington 7	a			23 27	23 51			01s20	
Eaglescliffe	a								
Middlesbrough	a								
Darlington 7	d			23 27	23 53				
Durham	d			23 44	00 10			01s38	
Chester-le-Street	d								
Newcastle 8 ⛴	a			00 14	00 42			02 10	
Hartlepool	a								
Sunderland ⛴	a								
Newcastle 8 ⛴	d								
Morpeth	d								
Alnmouth for Alnwick	d								
Berwick-upon-Tweed	d								
Dunbar 238	d								
Edinburgh 10 238	a								
Edinburgh 238	d								
Haymarket 238	d								
Motherwell	a								
Glasgow Central 15	a								
Stirling	a								
Perth	a								
Inverness	a								
Inverkeithing	a								
Kirkcaldy	a								
Leuchars 3	a								
Dundee	a								
Arbroath	a								
Montrose	a								
Stonehaven	a								
Aberdeen	a								

A From Liverpool Lime Street
B To Nottingham

Table 26R

Mondays to Fridays

9 December to 16 May

Scotland, North East England, Yorkshire and Humberside - London

Route Diagram - refer to first Page of Table 26

Miles	Miles	Miles	Station		GR	EM	GR	GR	GR	GR	GR	TP	GR		GR	XC	GR	TP	XC	HT	GR	GR	GR		EM
						A						B			C	D		E	F						G
—	—	0	**Aberdeen**	d																					
—	—	16¼	Stonehaven	d																					
—	—	40½	Montrose	d																					
—	—	54¼	Arbroath	d																					
—	—	71¼	**Dundee**	d																					
—	—	79½	Leuchars 3	d																					
—	—	104½	Kirkcaldy	d																					
—	—	117¼	Inverkeithing	d																					
—	—	—	**Inverness**	d																					
—	—	—	Perth	d																					
—	—	—	Stirling	d																					
0	—	—	**Glasgow Central** 15	d																					
12¾	—	—	Motherwell	d																					
56	—	129¼	Haymarket 238	d																					
57¼	—	130½	**Edinburgh** 10 238	a																					
—	—	—	**Edinburgh** 238	d																					
86½	—	—	Dunbar	d																					
114¾	—	—	**Berwick-upon-Tweed**	d																					
147	—	—	Alnmouth for Alnwick	d																					
165¼	—	—	Morpeth	d																					
181¾	—	—	**Newcastle** 8	a																					
—	—	—	Sunderland	d																					
—	—	—	Hartlepool	d																					
—	—	—	**Newcastle** 8	d					04 45		05 25						05 56	06 10	06 24				06 30		
190	—	—	Chester-le-Street	d														06 21							
195¾	—	—	**Durham**	d					05 00		05 39						06 10	06 27	06 37				06 43		
217¾	—	—	**Darlington** 7	a					05 16		05 56						06 27	06 44	06 52				07 00		
—	—	—	Middlesbrough	d								05 55													
—	—	—	Eaglescliffe	d																					
—	—	—	**Darlington** 7	d					05 18		05 58						06 29	06 45	06 54				07 01		
231¾	—	—	Northallerton	d					05 29		06 09	06 23						06 57					07 14		
239½	—	—	Thirsk	d								06 31						07 05							
261¾	—	—	**York** 8	a					05 57		06 28	06 48					06 56	07 28	07 20				07 33		
—	—	—	Leeds 10	a								07 20						08 04							
—	—	—	Harrogate	d																					
—	—	—	Scarborough	d																					
—	—	—	**York** 8	d					06 00		06 31					06 32	06 59		07 23				07 36		
294¼	—	—	**Doncaster** 7	a					06 21		06 52								07 48						
—	—	—	Skipton	d																					
—	—	—	Keighley	d																					
—	—	—	**Bradford Interchange**	d																					
—	—	—	Bradford Forster Square	d											06 30										
—	—	—	Shipley	d											06u36										
—	—	—	Halifax	d																					
—	—	—	Brighouse	d																					
—	—	—	Mirfield	d																					
—	0	—	**Leeds** 10	d			05 05	05 30		06 05			06 40		07 00	07 05						07 15			
—	10	—	**Wakefield Westgate** 7	d			05 18	05 43		06 18			06 53		07 13	07 19						07 28			
—	—	—	Wakefield Kirkgate 4	d																					
—	—	—	Pontefract Monkhill	d																					
—	—	—	Sheffield 7	a												07 50			08 18						
—	—	—	Hull	d																06 25					
—	—	—	Selby	d																07 00					
—	29¾	—	**Doncaster** 7	d			05 36	06 03	06 23	06 36	06 54		07 12							07 21		07 46			
311¾	—	—	**Retford** 10	d			05 51			06 51										07 41					
—	—	—	Lincoln	d																	07 20				
330¼	—	—	**Newark North Gate** 7	a			06 05	06 27	06 46	07 05			07 35								07 49				
—	—	—		d	05 35		06 06	06 28	06 47	07 06			07 36								07 56				
344¾	—	—	**Grantham** 7	a	05 46		06 17	06 40	06 59	07 18	07 25									08 01		08 16			
—	—	—		d	05 47	05 51	06 18	06 41	07 00	07 19	07 26									08 03		08 17			08 28
374	—	—	**Peterborough** 8	a	06 07	06 25	06 38	07 00	07 20	07 40	07 46						08 09				08 26		08 41		08 58
—	—	—	Norwich	a																					10 44
—	—	—	**Peterborough** 8	d	06 10		06 40	07 01	07 21	07 41	07 50						08 12				08 27		08 43		
422¾	—	—	**Stevenage** 4	a																	08 57	09 02			
450¼	—	—	**London Kings Cross** 15 ⊖	a	07 00		07 31	07 52	08 13	08 34	08 44		08 51		08 59		09 07			09 18	09 25	09 28	09 39		

A From Nottingham to Spalding
B To Manchester Airport
C West Riding Limited
D To Plymouth. from Leeds
E To Liverpool Lime Street. from York
F To Reading
G From Mansfield Woodhouse

Table 26R

Mondays to Fridays

9 December to 16 May

Scotland, North East England, Yorkshire and Humberside - London

Route Diagram - refer to first Page of Table 26

		GR	GR	XC	GR	GR	GC	TP	GC	XC	EM	GR	GR	TP	GR	XC	GR	HT	EM	GC	GR	GR	XC
				◇				◇		◇	◇			◇		◇		◇	◇				◇
		A		B		C		D		E	F			D		B			G				H
Aberdeen	d																						
Stonehaven	d																						
Montrose	d																						
Arbroath	d																						
Dundee	d																						
Leuchars 3	d																						
Kirkcaldy	d																						
Inverkeithing	d																						
Inverness	d																						
Perth	d																						
Stirling	d																						
Glasgow Central 15	d																						
Motherwell	d																						
Haymarket 238	d																						
Edinburgh 10 238	a																						
Edinburgh 238	d					05 40							05 48			06 06	06 25					06 55	07 00
Dunbar	d												06 09										
Berwick-upon-Tweed	d				06 00								06 34			06 47	07 08						07 39
Alnmouth for Alnwick	d				06 20								06 54			07 08							07 59
Morpeth	d				06 36								07 10										08 13
Newcastle 8	a				06 52	07 02							07 26			07 38	07 53					08 22	08 30
Sunderland	d								06 45														
Hartlepool	d								07 10														
Newcastle 8	d			06 45	06 55	07 04				07 25			07 29	07 33		07 41	07 56					08 25	08 35
Chester-le-Street	d													07 42									
Durham	d			06 58	07 08					07 37			07 42	07 49		07 55						08 38	08 48
Darlington 7	a			07 14	07 25					07 53			07 59	08 05		08 10	08 25					08 55	09 03
Middlesbrough	d							07 12															
Eaglescliffe	d								07 30														
Darlington 7	d			07 16	07 32					07 55			08 01	08 06		08 12	08 26					08 57	09 05
Northallerton	d							07 43	07 50					08 17								09 08	
Thirsk	d							07 51	07 59					08 25									
York 8	a			07 42	07 59			08 11	08 16	08 22			08 27	08 47		08 40	08 53					09 27	09 32
Leeds 10	a			08 08				08 52						09 23		09 08							
Harrogate	d											07 34											
Scarborough	d																						
York 8	d				08 02				08 20	08 26			08 30				08 56					09 30	09 35
Doncaster 7	a									08 49			08 52									09 52	09 57
Skipton	d		06 55																				
Keighley	d		07u08																				
Bradford Interchange	d						06 51													07 52			
Bradford Forster Square	d																						
Shipley	d		07u17																				
Halifax	d						07 07													08 06			
Brighouse	d						07 18													08 18			
Mirfield	d						07 28													08 28			
Leeds 10	d		07 40	08 11								08 15			08 45	09 11					09 15		
Wakefield Westgate 7	d		07 52	08 23								08 28			08 58	09 24					09 28		
Wakefield Kirkgate 4	d						07 42													08 56			
Pontefract Monkhill	d						08 01																
Sheffield 7	a			08 52						09 17						09 52							10 20
Hull	d	07 00																08 25					
Selby	d	07 36																09 01					
Doncaster 7	d	07 56	08 11				08 31					08 46	08 54		09 17			09 25		09 30	09 47	09 54	
Retford 10	d				08 34													09 39					
Lincoln	d																						
Newark North Gate 7	a	08 20	08 37										09 16									10 16	
	d	08 22	08 38										09 17									10 17	
Grantham 7	a	08 33										09 19						10 00			10 17		
	d	08 35									09 08	09 21						10 01	10 11		10 18		
Peterborough 8	a	09 01	09 06								09 38		09 48		10 08				10 40			10 47	
Norwich	a										11 12								12 15				
Peterborough 8	d	09 02	09 07										09 50		10 10							10 51	
Stevenage 4	a											10 08									11 01		
London Kings Cross 15 ⊖	a	09 55	10 00		10 03	09 40	10 12		10 25			10 36	10 42		11 01		10 51	11 12		11 15	11 28	11 42	

A The Hull Executive
B To Plymouth
C The Flying Scotsman
D To Manchester Airport
E To Southampton Central
F From Nottingham
G From Liverpool Lime Street
H To Reading

Table 26R

Mondays to Fridays

9 December to 16 May

Scotland, North East England, Yorkshire and Humberside - London

Route Diagram - refer to first Page of Table 26

		GR	XC	XC	TP	GR	GR	EM	GR	GC	TP	GR	XC	GR	XC	TP	GR	TP	HT	GR	EM	GR	GR
			FO	FX																			
		R 1	◇1	◇1	◇1	R 1	R 1	◇	R 1	R 1	◇1	R 1	◇1	R 1	◇1	◇1	R 1	◇1	◇1	R 1	◇	R 1	R 1
			A	A	B			C			B		D		A	B		B			C		
Aberdeen	d																						
Stonehaven	d																						
Montrose	d																						
Arbroath	d																						
Dundee	d														06 32								
Leuchars 3	d														06 46								
Kirkcaldy	d														07 21								
Inverkeithing	d														07 41								
Inverness	d																						
Perth	d																						
Stirling	d																						
Glasgow Central 15	d		06 01	06 01								06 50											
Motherwell	d		06 17	06 17								07 06											
Haymarket 238	d		06 57	06 57								07 48			07 59								
Edinburgh 10 238	a		07 02	07 02								07 52			08 04								
Edinburgh 238	d		07 07	07 07		07 30						08 00			08 10		08 30						
Dunbar	d		07 27	07 27																			
Berwick-upon-Tweed	d					08 12									08 51		09 12						
Alnmouth for Alnwick	d											08 59											
Morpeth	d																						
Newcastle 8	a		08 34	08 34		08 56						09 27			09 39		09 57						
Sunderland	d									08 42													
Hartlepool	d									09 09													
Newcastle 8	d		08 43	08 43		08 59					09 15	09 29	09 35		09 42		10 00	10 17					10 25
Chester-le-Street	d										09 24												
Durham	d		08 56	08 56							09 31	09 42	09 48		09 56			10 31					10 38
Darlington 7	a		09 11	09 11		09 25					09 47	09 59	10 04		10 11		10 27	10 46					10 55
Middlesbrough	d				08 50											09 50							
Eaglescliffe	d									09 30													
Darlington 7	d		09 13	09 13		09 27					09 48	10 00	10 05		10 13		10 29	10 48					10 57
Northallerton	d				09 18					09 50	09 59					10 18		10 59					11 08
Thirsk	d				09 28					10 00						10 28							
York 8	a		09 41	09 41	09 47	09 53				10 16	10 21	10 28	10 31		10 41	10 47	10 56	11 23					11 27
Leeds 10	a		10 08	10 08	10 22						10 52				11 08	11 22		11 52					
Harrogate	d																						
Scarborough	d																						
York 8	d					09 56	10 01			10 27		10 31	10 35				10 58						11 30
Doncaster 7	a						10 24					10 53	10 57										11 52
Skipton	d																						
Keighley	d																						
Bradford Interchange	d																						
Bradford Forster Square	d																						
Shipley	d																						
Halifax	d																						
Brighouse	d																						
Mirfield	d																						
Leeds 10	d	09 45	10 11	10 11					10 15					10 45	11 11							11 15	
Wakefield Westgate 7	d	09 58	10 23	10 23					10 28					10 58	11 24							11 28	
Wakefield Kirkgate 4	d																						
Pontefract Monkhill	d																						
Sheffield 7	a		10 51	10 52									11 20		11 52								
Hull	d																		10 30				
Selby	d																		11 06				
Doncaster 7	d	10 17					10 25		10 46			10 55		11 17					11 26			11 46	11 54
Retford 10	d						10 39												11 40				
Lincoln	d																						
Newark North Gate 7	a						10 53					11 17											12 16
	d						10 55					11 18								11 54			12 17
Grantham 7	a						11 06		11 16										12 00	12 05		12 16	
	d						11 07	11 10	11 17										12 01	12 06	12 11	12 17	
Peterborough 8	a	11 07					11 26	11 39				11 47		12 07						12 27	12 40		12 48
Norwich	a							13 13													14 13		
Peterborough 8	d	11 08					11 28					11 52		12 09						12 28			12 50
Stevenage 4	a						11 56		12 00											12 57		13 02	
London Kings Cross 15 ⊖	a	11 59				11 52	12 23		12 28	12 29		12 43		13 00			12 51		13 10	13 26		13 28	13 42

A To Plymouth. Trolley service from Edinburgh

B To Manchester Airport

C From Liverpool Lime Street

D To Southampton Central

Table 26R

Mondays to Fridays

9 December to 16 May

Scotland, North East England, Yorkshire and Humberside - London

Route Diagram - refer to first Page of Table 26

	GC	XC	GR	XC	TP	GR	GR	TP	EM	GR	GR	XC	GR	XC	TP	GR	TP	HT	HT	GR	EM
	R		R			R	R			R	R		R			R				R	
	1	◇1	1	◇1	◇1	1	1	◇1	◇	1	1	◇1	1	◇1	◇1	1	◇1	◇1	◇1	1	◇
		A		B	C			C	D			E		F	C		C	G	H		D
																		⊠	⊠		
Aberdeen d																07 52					
Stonehaven d																08 10					
Montrose d																08 33					
Arbroath d																08 49					
Dundee d																09 07					
Leuchars 8 d																09 21					
Kirkcaldy d																09 45					
Inverkeithing d																10 01					
Inverness d																					
Perth d																					
Stirling d																					
Glasgow Central 15 d				07 50										09 00							
Motherwell d				08 05										09 15							
Haymarket 238 d				08 51										09 58		10 20					
Edinburgh 10 238 a				08 56										10 04		10 24					
Edinburgh 238 d				09 08		09 30					10 00			10 10		10 30					
Dunbar d				09 28																	
Berwick-upon-Tweed d				09 51		10 12								10 49		11 12					
Alnmouth for Alnwick d											10 59										
Morpeth d														11 20							
Newcastle 8 ⛴ a				10 37		10 56					11 27			11 37		11 57					
Sunderland ⛴ d																					
Hartlepool d																					
Newcastle 8 ⛴ d		10 35		10 44		10 59		11 15			11 29	11 35		11 44		12 00	12 18				
Chester-le-Street d								11 24													
Durham d		10 48		10 56				11 31			11 42	11 48		11 56			12 31				
Darlington 7 a		11 04		11 12		11 25		11 46			11 59	12 04		12 12		12 27	12 47				
Middlesbrough d					10 50										11 50						
Eaglescliffe d																					
Darlington 7 d		11 05		11 13		11 27		11 48			12 00	12 05		12 13		12 29	12 48				
Northallerton d					11 18			11 59							12 18		12 59				
Thirsk d					11 28										12 28						
York 8 a		11 31		11 41	11 47	11 53		12 21			12 28	12 31		12 40	12 47	12 56	13 22				
Leeds 10 a				12 08	12 22			12 52						13 08	13 22		13 52				
Harrogate d																					
Scarborough d																					
York 8 d		11 34				11 56	12 01				12 30	12 35				12 58					
Doncaster 7 a		11 57					12 23				12 53	12 57									
Skipton d																					
Keighley d																					
Bradford Interchange d	10 22																				
Bradford Forster Square d																					
Shipley d																					
Halifax d	10 37																				
Brighouse d	10 48																				
Mirfield d	10 56																				
Leeds 10 d			11 45	12 11						12 15			12 45	13 11							
Wakefield Westgate 7 d			11 58	12 23						12 28			12 58	13 23							
Wakefield Kirkgate 4 d	11 11																				
Pontefract Monkhill d	11 36																				
Sheffield 7 ⛴ a		12 20		12 52								13 20		13 51							
Hull d																		12 30	12 30		
Selby d																		13 06	13 06		
Doncaster 7 d	12 08		12 17				12 25			12 47	12 54		13 17					13 25	13 25		
Retford 10 d							12 40											13 39	13 39		
Lincoln d																					
Newark North Gate 7 a							12 54				13 17										
d							12 55				13 18									13 54	
Grantham 7 a							13 06			13 17								14 00	14 00	14 05	
d							13 07		13 09	13 18								14 01	14 01	14 06	14 10
Peterborough 8 a			13 06				13 27		13 39		13 47		14 07							14 26	14 39
Norwich a									15 11												16 13
Peterborough 8 d			13 08				13 29				13 51		14 09							14 27	
Stevenage 4 a							13 58			14 02										14 56	
London Kings Cross 15 ⊖ a	13 43		13 58			13 48	14 25			14 28	14 43		15 01			14 51		15 08	15 09	15 24	

A To Reading
B To Plymouth. Trolley service from Edinburgh
C To Manchester Airport
D From Liverpool Lime Street
E To Southampton Central
F To Penzance. Trolley service from Edinburgh
G until 27 December
H from 30 December

Table 26R

Mondays to Fridays

9 December to 16 May

Scotland, North East England, Yorkshire and Humberside - London

Route Diagram - refer to first Page of Table 26

Station		GR	GR	XC	GR	XC	TP	GR	GR	GC	TP	TP	EM	GR	GR	XC	GR	XC	TP	TP	GR	TP	GR
											FO	FX							FX	FO			
		R	R		R	R		R	R	R				R	R		R				R		R
		1	1	◇1	1	◇1	◇1	1	1	1	◇1	◇1	◇	1	1	◇1	1	◇1	◇1	◇1	1	◇1	1
				A		B	C	D			C	C	E			F		G	C	C	H	C	
		restaurant, trolley	restaurant, trolley	trolley	restaurant, trolley	trolley	trolley	restaurant, trolley	restaurant, trolley	restaurant	trolley	trolley		restaurant, trolley	restaurant, trolley	trolley	restaurant, trolley	trolley	trolley	trolley	restaurant, trolley	trolley	restaurant
Aberdeen	d					08 20															09 52		
Stonehaven	d					08 38															10 10		
Montrose	d					08 59															10 33		
Arbroath	d					09 15															10 49		
Dundee	d					09 32															11 08		
Leuchars 3	d					09 47															11 23		
Kirkcaldy	d					10 17															11 47		
Inverkeithing	d					10 32															12 03		
Inverness	d							07 55															
Perth	d							09 57															
Stirling	d							10 32															
Glasgow Central 15	d																	11 00					
Motherwell	d																	11 14					
Haymarket 238	d					10 51		11 12										11 53			12 22		
Edinburgh 10 238	a					10 55		11 17										11 56			12 26		
Edinburgh 238	d					11 06		11 30							12 00			12 08			12 30		
Dunbar	d					11 27																	
Berwick-upon-Tweed	d					11 49									12 59			12 47			13 12		
Alnmouth for Alnwick	d					12 09																	
Morpeth	d																						
Newcastle 8	a					12 38		12 54							13 27			13 33			13 57		
Sunderland	d									12 28													
Hartlepool	d									12 52													
Newcastle 8	d		12 25	12 35		12 41		12 57			13 15	13 15			13 29	13 35		13 42			14 00	14 18	
Chester-le-Street	d										13 24	13 24											
Durham	d		12 38	12 48		12 54					13 31	13 31			13 42	13 48		13 55				14 31	
Darlington 7	a		12 55	13 04		13 09		13 25			13 46	13 46			13 59	14 04		14 10			14 27	14 46	
Middlesbrough	d						12 50												13 50	13 50			
Eaglescliffe	d									13 12													
Darlington 7	d		12 57	13 05		13 13		13 26			13 48	13 48			14 00	14 05		14 12			14 29	14 48	
Northallerton	d		13 08				13 18			13 31	13 58	13 59							14 18	14 18		14 59	
Thirsk	d						13 28			13 43									14 28	14 28			
York 8	a		13 27	13 31		13 40	13 47	13 53		14 00	14 22	14 22			14 28	14 31		14 40	14 47	14 47	14 56	15 22	
Leeds 10	a					14 08	14 22				14 52	14 52						15 08	15 22	15 23		15 52	
Harrogate	d																						
Scarborough	d																						
York 8	d		13 30	13 34				13 56	14 01	14 06					14 30	14 35					14 58		
Doncaster 7	a		13 52	13 57					14 24						14 53	14 57							
Skipton	d																						
Keighley	d																						
Bradford Interchange	d																						
Bradford Forster Square	d																						
Shipley	d																						
Halifax	d																						
Brighouse	d																						
Mirfield	d																						
Leeds 10	d	13 15			13 45	14 11								14 15			14 45	15 11					
Wakefield Westgate 7	d	13 28			13 58	14 23								14 28			14 58	15 24					
Wakefield Kirkgate 4	d																						
Pontefract Monkhill	d																						
Sheffield 7	a			14 20		14 52										15 20		15 52					
Hull	d																						
Selby	d																						
Doncaster 7	d	13 46	13 54		14 17				14 25					14 46	14 54		15 17						
Retford 10	d								14 41														
Lincoln	d																						
Newark North Gate 7	a		14 16						14 55						15 17								
	d		14 17						14 56						15 18								15 52
Grantham 7	a	14 16							15 07					15 16									16 03
	d	14 17							15 08				15 11	15 17									16 04
Peterborough 8	a		14 51		15 07				15 27				15 38		15 47		16 07						16 24
Norwich	a												17 13										
Peterborough 8	d		14 53		15 08				15 29						15 52		16 08						16 26
Stevenage 4	a	15 01							15 57					16 02									16 56
London Kings Cross 15 ⊖	a	15 27	15 44		16 01			15 50	16 25	16 11				16 27	16 43		16 59				16 51		17 22

A To Reading

B To Penzance. trolley ◇ from Edinburgh R to Edinburgh

C To Manchester Airport

D The Highland Chieftain

E From Liverpool Lime Street

F To Guildford

G To Penzance. trolley from Edinburgh

H The Northern Lights

Table 26R

Mondays to Fridays

9 December to 16 May

Scotland, North East England, Yorkshire and Humberside - London

Route Diagram - refer to first Page of Table 26

		EM	GR	GR	XC	HT	GR	XC FO	XC FX	TP FO	TP FX	GR	GC	GR	EM	GR	XC	TP	GR	GR	XC FO	XC FX
		◇ A			◇ B	◇		◇ C	◇ C	◇	◇ D				◇ A		◇ B	◇ E			◇ F	◇ F
Aberdeen	d																					
Stonehaven	d																					
Montrose	d																					
Arbroath	d																					
Dundee	d																					
Leuchars 3	d																					
Kirkcaldy	d																					
Inverkeithing	d																					
Inverness	d																					
Perth	d																					
Stirling	d																					
Glasgow Central 15	d																				13 00	13 00
Motherwell	d																				13 14	13 14
Haymarket 238	d																					
Edinburgh 10 238	a																				13 54	13 54
Edinburgh 238	d							13 06	13 06			13 30							14 00		14 08	14 08
Dunbar	d							13 28	13 28													
Berwick-upon-Tweed	d											14 12									14 49	14 49
Alnmouth for Alnwick	d							14 09	14 09										15 00			
Morpeth	d																					
Newcastle 8	a							14 38	14 38			14 56							15 27		15 33	15 33
Sunderland	d																					
Hartlepool	d																					
Newcastle 8	d			14 25	14 35			14 42	14 42			14 59					15 03	15 15	15 30		15 41	15 41
Chester-le-Street	d																	15 24				
Durham	d			14 38	14 48			14 56	14 56								15 16	15 31	15 44		15 54	15 54
Darlington 7	a			14 55	15 04			15 11	15 11			15 25					15 31	15 46	16 02		16 09	16 09
Middlesbrough	d									14 50	14 50											
Eaglescliffe	d																					
Darlington 7	d			14 57	15 05			15 13	15 13			15 27					15 33	15 48	16 03		16 12	16 12
Northallerton	d			15 08						15 18	15 18							15 59				
Thirsk	d									15 28	15 28											
York 8	a			15 27	15 31			15 41	15 41	15 47	15 47	15 53					15 59	16 21	16 31		16 40	16 40
Leeds 10	a							16 09	16 09		16 22						16 32	16 52			17 06	17 06
Harrogate	d																					
Scarborough	d																					
York 8	d			15 30	15 34							15 56		16 01					16 33			
Doncaster 7	a			15 52	15 57									16 23					16 55			
Skipton	d																					
Keighley	d																					
Bradford Interchange	d												14 22									
Bradford Forster Square	d																					
Shipley	d																					
Halifax	d												14 35									
Brighouse	d												14 47									
Mirfield	d												14 55									
Leeds 10	d		15 15				15 45	16 11	16 11							16 15	16 40			16 45	17 11	17 11
Wakefield Westgate 7	d		15 28				15 58	16 23	16 23							16 28	16 52			16 58	17 23	17 23
Wakefield Kirkgate 4	d												15 12									
Pontefract Monkhill	d												15 34									
Sheffield 7	a				16 20			16 51	16 52								17 20				17 52	17 53
Hull	d					15 10																
Selby	d					15 47																
Doncaster 7	d		15 46	15 54		16 05	16 16						16 20	16 25		16 46			16 56	17 17		
Retford 10	d					16 19								16 41								
Lincoln	d																					
Newark North Gate 7	a			16 18										16 54					17 19			
	d			16 19										16 55					17 20			
Grantham 7	a		16 17			16 39								17 07		17 16						
	d	16 10	16 18			16 40								17 08	17 12	17 17						
Peterborough 8	a	16 39		16 48			17 08							17 27	17 41				17 50	18 06		
Norwich	a	18 13													19 15							
Peterborough 8	d			16 50			17 09							17 29					17 51	18 08		
Stevenage 4	a		17 02											17 58		18 03						
London Kings Cross 15 ⊖	a		17 28	17 41		17 48	18 00					17 53	18 15	18 26		18 29			18 42	19 00		

A From Liverpool Lime Street
B To Reading
C To Plymouth
D To Manchester Piccadilly
E To Manchester Airport
F To Plymouth. Trolley service from Edinburgh

Table 26R

Mondays to Fridays

9 December to 16 May

Scotland, North East England, Yorkshire and Humberside - London

Route Diagram - refer to first Page of Table 26

		TP	GR	GC	TP	GR	EM	GR	GR		XC	HT	GR	XC	TP	GR	GR	TP	EM		GR	GR	XC	GR	XC
			R	R		R		R	R				R			R	R				R	R		R	
		◇1	1	1	◇1	1	◇	1	1		◇1	◇1	1	◇1	◇1	1	1	◇1	◇		1	1	◇1	1	◇1
		A			B		C				D			E	A			B	C				F		G
Aberdeen	d																								
Stonehaven	d																								
Montrose	d																								
Arbroath	d																								
Dundee	d																								
Leuchars 3	d																								
Kirkcaldy	d																								
Inverkeithing	d																								
Inverness	d																								
Perth	d																								
Stirling	d																								
Glasgow Central 15	d																								15 00
Motherwell	d																								15 14
Haymarket 238	d																								15 56
Edinburgh 10 238	a																								16 00
Edinburgh 238	d		14 30											15 08		15 30									16 05
Dunbar	d													15 28											
Berwick-upon-Tweed	d		15 12													16 12									
Alnmouth for Alnwick	d																								17 01
Morpeth	d																								17 16
Newcastle 8	a		15 56											16 34		16 56									17 33
Sunderland	d			15 18																					
Hartlepool	d			15 50																					
Newcastle 8	d		15 59		16 15				16 25		16 35			16 41		16 59		17 02				17 25	17 32		17 41
Chester-le-Street	d				16 24													17 11					17 41		
Durham	d				16 31				16 38		16 48			16 52				17 18				17 38	17 48		17 54
Darlington 7	a		16 25		16 46				16 55		17 04			17 09		17 25		17 34				17 55	18 04		18 09
Middlesbrough	d	15 50													16 50										
Eaglescliffe	d			16 11																					
Darlington 7	d		16 27		16 48				16 57		17 05			17 11		17 27		17 35				17 57	18 05		18 12
Northallerton	d	16 18		16 31	16 59				17 08						17 18			17 46				18 08			
Thirsk	d	16 28		16 43											17 28										
York 8	a	16 47	16 53	16 59	17 23				17 28		17 31			17 40	17 47	17 53		18 09				18 27	18 31		18 40
Leeds 10	a	17 22			17 52									18 08	18 22			18 37							19 08
Harrogate	d																								
Scarborough	d																								
York 8	d		16 56	17 02					17 31		17 35					17 56	18 01					18 30	18 34		
Doncaster 7	a								17 52		17 57						18 22					18 53	18 57		
Skipton	d																								
Keighley	d																								
Bradford Interchange	d																								
Bradford Forster Square	d																								
Shipley	d																								
Halifax	d																								
Brighouse	d																								
Mirfield	d																								
Leeds 10	d							17 15					17 45	18 11							18 15			18 45	19 11
Wakefield Westgate 7	d							17 28					17 58	18 23							18 28			18 57	19 24
Wakefield Kirkgate 4	d																								
Pontefract Monkhill	d																								
Sheffield 7	a										18 20			18 53									19 20		19 51
Hull	d											17 10													
Selby	d											17 45													
Doncaster 7	d							17 46	17 55			18 03	18 17				18 24				18 46	18 55		19 15	
Retford 10	d							18 00				18 17					18 39								
Lincoln	d																								
Newark North Gate 7	a								18 18								18 53					19 17			
	d					17 54			18 19								18 54					19 18			
Grantham 7	a					18 05		18 21				18 38					19 05				19 16				
	d					18 06	18 11	18 23				18 39					19 06		19 07		19 17				
Peterborough 8	a					18 26	18 38		18 48				19 07				19 27		19 38			19 50		20 05	
Norwich	a						20 22												21 13						
Peterborough 8	d					18 27			18 49				19 09				19 28					19 51		20 07	
Stevenage 4	a					18 56		19 07									19 58				20 03	20 20			
London Kings Cross 15 ⊖	a		18 51	19 06		19 24		19 34	19 42			19 47	20 00			19 50	20 25				20 28	20 47		20 59	

A To Manchester Piccadilly
B To Manchester Airport
C From Liverpool Lime Street
D To Reading
E To Plymouth
F To Southampton Central
G To Bristol Temple Meads. Trolley from Edinburgh

Table 26R

Mondays to Fridays

9 December to 16 May

Scotland, North East England, Yorkshire and Humberside - London

Route Diagram - refer to first Page of Table 26

		TP	TP	GR	GC	GR	GR	XC	HT	GR	XC	TP	TP	GR	XC	EM	GR	XC	TP	TP	GR	XC	GR
		FO	FX																FO	FX			
		◇1	◇1	R 1	R 1	R 1	R 1	◇1	◇1	R 1	◇1	◇1	◇1	R 1	◇1	◇	R 1	◇1	◇1	◇1	R 1	◇1	R 1
			A					B			C		D		B	E		F		D			
				FP ⚲	FP	FP ⚲	FP ⚲	⚲	⊠	FP ⚲	⚲			FP ⚲			FP ⚲	⚲			FP ⚲		FP
Aberdeen	d													14 52									
Stonehaven	d													15 10									
Montrose	d													15 33									
Arbroath	d													15 49									
Dundee	d													16 07									
Leuchars 3	d													16 22									
Kirkcaldy	d													16 46									
Inverkeithing	d													17 03									
Inverness	d																						
Perth	d																						
Stirling	d																						
Glasgow Central 15	d																	16 52				19 00	
Motherwell	d																	17 06				19 14	
Haymarket 238	d													17 21				17 53				19 53	
Edinburgh 10 238	a													17 26				17 57				19 57	
Edinburgh 238	d			16 30		17 00					17 08			17 31				18 05			18 30	20 02	
Dunbar	d										17 28			17 52				18 26			18 52	20 22	
Berwick-upon-Tweed	d			17 12							17 51			18 18				18 49			19 17	20 45	
Alnmouth for Alnwick	d					17 59												19 09			19 39	21 05	
Morpeth	d																				19 56		
Newcastle 8 ⛴	a			17 56		18 27					18 37			19 03				19 39			20 12	21 34	
Sunderland ⛴	d				17 31																		
Hartlepool	d				17 57																		
Newcastle 8 ⛴	d			17 59		18 29	18 35				18 43		18 52	19 06	19 35			19 42			20 15		21 15
Chester-le-Street	d												19 01										
Durham	d					18 42	18 48				18 56		19 08		19 50			19 55			20 28		21 28
Darlington 7	a			18 25		19 00	19 05				19 11		19 24	19 33	20 05			20 10			20 45		21 45
Middlesbrough	d	17 50	17 50									18 50							20 04	20 04			
Eaglescliffe	d				18 21																		
Darlington 7	d			18 27		19 01	19 06				19 14		19 25	19 35	20 07			20 13	20 33	20 33	20 47		21 47
Northallerton	d	18 18	18 18		18 41							19 19	19 36						20 44	20 44			21 58
Thirsk	d	18 28	18 28		18 50							19 29							20 52	20 52			
York 8	a	18 47	18 47	18 53	19 07	19 28	19 32				19 41	19 49	20 07	20 02	20 32			20 41	21 10	21 10	21 14		22 17
Leeds 10	a		19 35								20 08		20 35					21 08		21 37			
Harrogate	d																						
Scarborough	d																						
York 8	d			18 56	19 11	19 30	19 35							20 04	20 35						21 17		22 20
Doncaster 7	a					19 52	19 57							20 27	21 00						21 38		22 42
Skipton	d																						
Keighley	d																						
Bradford Interchange	d																						
Bradford Forster Square	d																						
Shipley	d																						
Halifax	d																						
Brighouse	d																						
Mirfield	d																						
Leeds 10	d					19 15				19 45	20 11						20 45	21 11					
Wakefield Westgate 7	d					19 28				19 58	20 23						20 58	21 25					
Wakefield Kirkgate 4	d																						
Pontefract Monkhill	d																						
Sheffield 7 ⛴	a							20 21			20 53				21 26			21 53					
Hull	d								19 10														
Selby	d								19 45														
Doncaster 7	d					19 46	19 54		20 03	20 17				20 28			21 17				21 40		22 43
Retford 10	d								20 17								21 34						
Lincoln	d																						
Newark North Gate 7	a						20 16														22 02		23 06
	d						20 17														22 04		23 07
Grantham 7	a					20 16			20 37								21 55				22 15		23 18
	d					20 17			20 38							21 10	21 56				22 16		23 19
Peterborough 8	a						20 46			21 03				21 16		21 37	22 15				22 35		23 45
Norwich	a															23 18							
Peterborough 8	d						20 47			21 05				21 18			22 17				22 37		23 46
Stevenage 4	a			20 25		20 59	21 17							21 48			22 47				23 08		00s26
London Kings Cross 15 ⊖	a			20 52	21 05	21 27	21 43		21 46	21 56				22 17			23 12				23 33		01 03

A To Manchester Airport
B To Birmingham New Street
C To Bristol Temple Meads. ⚲ to Leeds
D To Manchester Piccadilly
E From Liverpool Lime Street
F To Birmingham New Street. ⚲ from Edinburgh to Leeds

Table 26R

Mondays to Fridays

9 December to 16 May

Scotland, North East England, Yorkshire and Humberside - London

Route Diagram - refer to first Page of Table 26

		TP	TP	NT	GR
		◇1	◇1		R 1
			A		⊡
Aberdeen	d				18 18
Stonehaven	d				18 36
Montrose	d				18 59
Arbroath	d				19 15
Dundee	d				19 33
Leuchars 3	d				19 47
Kirkcaldy	d				20 11
Inverkeithing	d				20 27
Inverness	d				
Perth	d				
Stirling	d				
Glasgow Central 15	d				
Motherwell	d				
Haymarket 238	d				20 46
Edinburgh 10 238	a				20 50
Edinburgh 238	d				21 00
Dunbar	d				21 22
Berwick-upon-Tweed	d				21 48
Alnmouth for Alnwick	d				22 11
Morpeth	d				22 28
Newcastle 8 ⛴	a				22 43
Sunderland ⛴	d				
Hartlepool	d				
Newcastle 8 ⛴	d		21 56	22 21	22 46
Chester-le-Street	d			22 31	
Durham	d		22 10	22 39	23 00
Darlington 7	a		22 26	23 00	23 19
Middlesbrough	d	21 50			
Eaglescliffe	d				
Darlington 7	d	22 19	22 27		23 21
Northallerton	d	22 30	22 38		23s47
Thirsk	d	22 38			
York 8	a	22 56	23 01		00 14
Leeds 10	a		23 33		00 47
Harrogate	d				
Scarborough	d				
York 8	d				
Doncaster 7	a				
Skipton	d				
Keighley	d				
Bradford Interchange	d				
Bradford Forster Square	d				
Shipley	d				
Halifax	d				
Brighouse	d				
Mirfield	d				
Leeds 10	d				
Wakefield Westgate 7	d				
Wakefield Kirkgate 4	d				
Pontefract Monkhill	d				
Sheffield 7 ⛴	a				
Hull	d				
Selby	d				
Doncaster 7	d				
Retford 10	d				
Lincoln	d				
Newark North Gate 7	a				
	d				
Grantham 7	a				
	d				
Peterborough 8	a				
Norwich	a				
Peterborough 8	d				
Stevenage 4	a				
London Kings Cross 15 ⊖	a				

A To Manchester Piccadilly

Table 26R

Saturdays

14 December to 17 May

Scotland, North East England, Yorkshire and Humberside - London

Route Diagram - refer to first Page of Table 26

		EM	GR	GR	TP	GR	GR	XC	GR	TP	XC	GR	GR	EM	GR	GR	XC	GR	GC	TP	GC	EM	GR
			R	R		R	R		R			R	R		R	R		R	R		R		R
			1	1	◇1	1	1	◇1	1	◇1	◇1	1	1	◇	1	1	◇1	1	1	◇1	1	◇	1
		A			B			C		D	E			F			C			B		F	
Aberdeen	d																						
Stonehaven	d																						
Montrose	d																						
Arbroath	d																						
Dundee	d																						
Leuchars 8	d																						
Kirkcaldy	d																						
Inverkeithing	d																						
Inverness	d																						
Perth	d																						
Stirling	d																						
Glasgow Central 15	d																						
Motherwell	d																						
Haymarket 238	d																						
Edinburgh 10 238	a																						
Edinburgh 238	d																						
Dunbar	d																						
Berwick-upon-Tweed	d																						
Alnmouth for Alnwick	d																						
Morpeth	d																						
Newcastle 8	a																						
Sunderland	d																				06 43		
Hartlepool	d																				07 10		
Newcastle 8	d			04 45					06 00	06 10	06 22		06 30				06 45	06 55					07 22
Chester-le-Street	d									06 21													
Durham	d			05 00					06 13	06 27	06 37		06 43				06 58	07 08					07 36
Darlington 7	a			05 16					06 30	06 44	06 52		07 00				07 13	07 25					07 52
Middlesbrough	d				05 55															07 12			
Eaglescliffe	d																				07 30		
Darlington 7	d			05 18					06 31	06 45	06 54		07 02				07 15	07 27					07 54
Northallerton	d			05 29	06 23					06 57			07 13							07 43	07 50		08 07
Thirsk	d				06 31					07 05										07 51	07 59		
York 8	a			05 57	06 48				06 58	07 28	07 20		07 32				07 41	07 53		08 11	08 15		08 27
Leeds 10	a				07 20					08 04							08 08			08 52			
Harrogate	d																						
Scarborough	d																						
York 8	d			06 01				06 17	07 01		07 24		07 35					07 56			08 19		08 30
Doncaster 7	a			06 22					07 23		07 48		07 56					08 17					08 53
Skipton	d														06 55								
Keighley	d														07u09								
Bradford Interchange	d																		06 51				
Bradford Forster Square	d															07 33							
Shipley	d														07u19	07u40							
Halifax	d																		07 03				
Brighouse	d																		07 14				
Mirfield	d																		07 22				
Leeds 10	d		05 05			06 05	07 05	07 10							07 36	08 05	08 11						
Wakefield Westgate 7	d		05 18			06 18	07 17	07 22								08 18	08 24						
Wakefield Kirkgate 4	d																		07 38				
Pontefract Monkhill	d																		07 58				
Sheffield 7	a							07 51			08 18						08 52						
Hull	d											06 50											
Selby	d											07 25											
Doncaster 7	d		05 36	06 24		06 36	07 36		07 25			07 44	07 58		08 10	08 37		08 19	08 31				08 54
Retford 10	d		05 50			06 50										08 54							
Lincoln	d																						
Newark North Gate 7	a		06 04			07 04	07 59						08 21			09 08							09 17
	d		06 05			07 05	08 00						08 22			09 09							09 18
Grantham 7	a		06 17			07 17	08 11					08 17			08 41								09 30
	d	05 51	06 18			07 18	08 12					08 18		08 20	08 43							09 10	09 31
Peterborough 8	a	06 25	06 37	07 11		07 37	08 31		08 13			08 39	08 51	08 57		09 37						09 40	09 51
Norwich	a													10 43								11 15	
Peterborough 8	d		06 38	07 12		07 38	08 33		08 15			08 40	08 52			09 39							09 53
Stevenage 4	a		07 06			08 06	09 01																
London Kings Cross 15 ⊖	a		07 35	08 03		08 35	09 28		09 09			09 35	09 45		09 51	10 30		09 54	10 07		10 15		10 45

A From Nottingham to Spalding
B To Manchester Airport
C To Plymouth. from Leeds
D To Liverpool Lime Street
E To Reading
F From Nottingham

Table 26R

Saturdays

14 December to 17 May

Scotland, North East England, Yorkshire and Humberside - London

Route Diagram - refer to first Page of Table 26

		XC	GR	HT	GR	EM	GR	XC	TP	GR	GR	XC	GC	EM	GR	XC	TP	GR	GC	TP	GR	XC	HT
		◇1 A 🛒	R 1 🍴🛒	◇1 ⊠	R 1 🍴🛒	◇ B	R 1 🍴🛒	◇1 C 🛒	◇1 D	R 1 🍴🛒	R 1 🍴🛒	◇1 E 🛒	R 1 🍴	◇ B	R 1 🍴🛒	◇1 F 🛒	◇1 D	R 1 🍴🛒	R 1 🍴	◇1 D	R 1 🍴🛒	◇1 A 🛒	◇1 ⊠
Aberdeen	d																						
Stonehaven	d																						
Montrose	d																						
Arbroath	d																						
Dundee	d																						
Leuchars 3	d																						
Kirkcaldy	d																						
Inverkeithing	d																						
Inverness	d																						
Perth	d																						
Stirling	d																						
Glasgow Central 15	d															06 01					06 50		
Motherwell	d															06 17					07 06		
Haymarket 238	d															06 57					07 48		
Edinburgh 10 238	a															07 02					07 52		
Edinburgh 238	d							06 08		06 20	06 55	07 00				07 07		07 30			08 00		
Dunbar	d									06 41						07 27							
Berwick-upon-Tweed	d							06 47		07 06		07 40						08 13					
Alnmouth for Alnwick	d							07 07		07 27		08 00									08 59		
Morpeth	d									07 43		08 14											
Newcastle 8 ⛴	a							07 36		07 59	08 22	08 31				08 35		08 57			09 27		
Sunderland ⛴	d																		08 30				
Hartlepool	d																		08 55				
Newcastle 8 ⛴	d	07 35						07 40	07 43	08 02	08 25	08 35				08 42		09 00		09 15	09 29	09 35	
Chester-le-Street	d																			09 24			
Durham	d	07 48						07 53	07 57		08 38	08 48				08 55				09 31	09 42	09 48	
Darlington 7	a	08 03						08 08	08 13	08 28	08 55	09 03				09 10		09 26		09 47	09 59	10 04	
Middlesbrough	d																08 50						
Eaglescliffe	d																		09 18				
Darlington 7	d	08 05						08 10	08 14	08 30	08 57	09 05				09 12		09 28		09 48	10 00	10 05	
Northallerton	d								08 26		09 08						09 18		09 42	09 59			
Thirsk	d								08 34								09 28		09 51				
York 8	a	08 31						08 40	08 52	08 56	09 27	09 32				09 42	09 47	09 55	10 07	10 21	10 28	10 31	
Leeds 10	a							09 06	09 22							10 08	10 22			10 52			
Harrogate	d						08 13																
Scarborough	d																						
York 8	d	08 34								08 59	09 30	09 35						09 58	10 12		10 30	10 35	
Doncaster 7	a	08 57									09 52	09 57									10 52	10 57	
Skipton	d																						
Keighley	d																						
Bradford Interchange	d												08 38										
Bradford Forster Square	d																						
Shipley	d																						
Halifax	d												08 51										
Brighouse	d												09 06										
Mirfield	d												09 14										
Leeds 10	d		08 40				09 05	09 11							10 05	10 11							
Wakefield Westgate 7	d		08 53				09 18	09 24							10 18	10 24							
Wakefield Kirkgate 4	d												09 38										
Pontefract Monkhill	d												09 56										
Sheffield 7 ⛴	a	09 20						09 53				10 20				10 52						11 20	
Hull	d			08 25																			10 30
Selby	d			09 05																			11 06
Doncaster 7	d		09 13	09 24			09 36				09 53		10 24		10 37						10 54		11 26
Retford 10	d			09 38							10 08												11 40
Lincoln	d				09 30																		
Newark North Gate 7	a				09 52		09 59								11 00						11 17		
	d				09 53		10 00								11 01						11 18		
Grantham 7	a			09 59	10 06		10 12				10 29				11 13								12 00
	d			10 00	10 07	10 09	10 13				10 30			11 10	11 15								12 01
Peterborough 8	a		10 00		10 26	10 38	10 36			10 05	10 50			11 39	11 36						11 47		
Norwich	a					12 13								13 13									
Peterborough 8	d		10 01		10 28		10 37			10 07	10 52				11 37						11 52		
Stevenage 4	a				10 59		11 07																
London Kings Cross 15 ⊖	a		10 53	11 09	11 26		11 36			10 58	11 43		11 56		12 29			11 53	12 07		12 43		13 09

A To Southampton Central
B From Liverpool Lime Street
C To Plymouth
D To Manchester Airport
E To Reading
F To Plymouth. 🛒 from Edinburgh

Table 26R

Saturdays

14 December to 17 May

Scotland, North East England, Yorkshire and Humberside - London

Route Diagram - refer to first Page of Table 26

		EM	GR	XC	TP	GR	TP	GR	GC	XC	EM	GR	XC	TP	GR	TP	GR	XC	EM	GR	XC	XC
			R			R		R	R			R			R		R			R		
		◇	1	◇1	◇1	1	◇1	1	1	◇1	◇	1	◇1	◇1	1	◇1	1	◇1	◇	1	◇1	◇1
		A		B	C		C			D	A		B	C		C		E	A		F	G
			FP⊥	⊥		FP⊥		FP⊥	FP	⊥		FP⊥	⊥		FP⊥		FP⊥	⊥		FP⊥	⊥	⊥
Aberdeen	d																					
Stonehaven	d																					
Montrose	d																					
Arbroath	d																					
Dundee	d			06 32																		
Leuchars 3	d			06 46																		
Kirkcaldy	d			07 21																		
Inverkeithing	d			07 38																		
Inverness	d																					
Perth	d																					
Stirling	d																					
Glasgow Central 15	d												07 50								09 00	09 00
Motherwell	d												08 05								09 15	09 15
Haymarket 238	d			07 56									08 51								09 57	09 57
Edinburgh 10 238	a			08 01									08 56								10 02	10 02
Edinburgh 238	d			08 05		08 30		09 00					09 08		09 30		10 00				10 05	10 05
Dunbar	d												09 28									
Berwick-upon-Tweed	d			08 47		09 13							09 51		10 13						10 47	10 47
Alnmouth for Alnwick	d			09 09													10 59					
Morpeth	d																				11 19	11 19
Newcastle 8	a			09 39		09 58		10 23					10 38		10 58		11 27				11 38	11 38
Sunderland	d																					
Hartlepool	d																					
Newcastle 8	d			09 42		10 00	10 15	10 26		10 35			10 44		11 00	11 15	11 29	11 35			11 42	11 42
Chester-le-Street	d						10 24									11 24						
Durham	d			09 56			10 31	10 39		10 48			10 56			11 31	11 42	11 48			11 55	11 55
Darlington 7	a			10 11		10 28	10 47	10 55		11 03			11 12		11 28	11 46	11 59	12 04			12 11	12 11
Middlesbrough	d				09 50									10 50								
Eaglescliffe	d																					
Darlington 7	d			10 13		10 29	10 48	10 57		11 05			11 13		11 29	11 48	12 00	12 05			12 12	12 12
Northallerton	d				10 18		10 59	11 08						11 18		11 59						
Thirsk	d				10 28									11 28								
York 8	a			10 41	10 47	10 56	11 23	11 28		11 31			11 40	11 47	11 56	12 21	12 28	12 31			12 40	12 40
Leeds 10	a			11 08	11 22		11 52						12 08	12 22		12 52					13 08	13 08
Harrogate	d																					
Scarborough	d																					
York 8	d					10 59		11 31		11 35					11 59		12 30	12 35				
Doncaster 7	a							11 52		11 57							12 52	12 57				
Skipton	d																					
Keighley	d																					
Bradford Interchange	d								10 22													
Bradford Forster Square	d																					
Shipley	d																					
Halifax	d								10 38													
Brighouse	d								10 48													
Mirfield	d								10 56													
Leeds 10	d		11 05	11 11								12 05	12 11							13 05	13 11	13 11
Wakefield Westgate 7	d		11 18	11 24								12 18	12 24							13 18	13 23	13 23
Wakefield Kirkgate 4	d								11 13													
Pontefract Monkhill	d								11 37													
Sheffield 7	a			11 52						12 20			12 52					13 20			13 51	13 52
Hull	d																					
Selby	d																					
Doncaster 7	d		11 36					11 54	12 07			12 36					12 54			13 36		
Retford 10	d							12 08														
Lincoln	d																					
Newark North Gate 7	a		11 59									13 01					13 17			13 59		
	d		12 00									13 02					13 18			14 00		
Grantham 7	a		12 11									13 14								14 12		
	d	12 07	12 12								13 09	13 15							14 07	14 13		
Peterborough 8	a	12 37	12 32					12 47			13 38	13 35					13 46		14 41	14 32		
Norwich	a	14 13									15 13								16 15			
Peterborough 8	d		12 34					12 51				13 36					13 51			14 33		
Stevenage 4	a		13 02																	15 01		
London Kings Cross 15 ⊖	a		13 29			12 52		13 43	13 45			14 28			13 53		14 43			15 29		

A From Liverpool Lime Street
B To Plymouth. ⊥ from Edinburgh
C To Manchester Airport
D To Reading
E To Southampton Central
F 14 December, 21 December, 28 December. To Penzance. ⊥ from Edinburgh
G from 4 January. To Penzance. ⊥ from Edinburgh

Table 26R

Saturdays

14 December to 17 May

Scotland, North East England, Yorkshire and Humberside - London

Route Diagram - refer to first Page of Table 26

		TP	GR	TP	GR	XC	HT	EM	GR	XC	TP	GC	GR	TP	TP	GR	XC	GR	EM	GR	XC	TP	GR
		◇1	R 1	◇1	R 1	◇1	◇1	◇	R 1	◇1	◇1	R 1	R 1	◇1	◇1	R 1	◇1	R 1	◇	R 1	◇1	◇1	R 1
		A		A		B	⊠	C		D	A		E	F	G		H		C		D	A	I
Aberdeen	d		07 52							08 20													09 52
Stonehaven	d		08 10							08 38													10 10
Montrose	d		08 33							08 59													10 33
Arbroath	d		08 49							09 15													10 49
Dundee	d		09 07							09 32													11 08
Leuchars 3	d		09 21							09 47													11 23
Kirkcaldy	d		09 45							10 17													11 47
Inverkeithing	d		10 01							10 32													12 03
Inverness	d												07 55										
Perth	d												09 57										
Stirling	d												10 32										
Glasgow Central 15	d																				11 00		
Motherwell	d																				11 14		
Haymarket 238	d		10 20							10 52			11 12								11 52		12 22
Edinburgh 10 238	a		10 25							10 58			11 17								11 57		12 26
Edinburgh 238	d		10 30		11 00					11 08			11 30		11 40	12 00					12 05		12 30
Dunbar	d									11 28													
Berwick-upon-Tweed	d		11 13							11 51			12 13								12 45		13 13
Alnmouth for Alnwick	d									12 11						12 59							
Morpeth	d																						
Newcastle 8	a		11 58		12 23					12 40			12 58		13 16	13 27					13 32		13 58
Sunderland	d											12 18											
Hartlepool	d											12 45											
Newcastle 8	d		12 00	12 18	12 26	12 35				12 44			13 00	13 15	13 18	13 29	13 35				13 44		14 00
Chester-le-Street	d													13 24									
Durham	d			12 31	12 39	12 48				12 56				13 31	13 31	13 42	13 48				13 56		
Darlington 7	a		12 28	12 47	12 55	13 03				13 12			13 28	13 46	13 46	13 59	14 04				14 12		14 28
Middlesbrough	d	11 50									12 50											13 50	
Eaglescliffe	d											13 05											
Darlington 7	d		12 29	12 48	12 57	13 05				13 13			13 29	13 48	13 48	14 00	14 05				14 13		14 29
Northallerton	d	12 18		12 59	13 08						13 18	13 27		13 58	13 58							14 18	
Thirsk	d	12 28									13 28	13 36										14 28	
York 8	a	12 47	12 56	13 22	13 28	13 31				13 40	13 47	13 53	13 56	14 22	14 22	14 28	14 31				14 40	14 47	14 56
Leeds 10	a	13 22		13 52						14 08	14 22			14 52	14 52						15 08	15 22	
Harrogate	d																						
Scarborough	d																						
York 8	d		12 59		13 31	13 34						13 56	14 00			14 30	14 35						14 59
Doncaster 7	a				13 52	13 57										14 53	14 57						
Skipton	d																						
Keighley	d																						
Bradford Interchange	d																						
Bradford Forster Square	d																						
Shipley	d																						
Halifax	d																						
Brighouse	d																						
Mirfield	d																						
Leeds 10	d								14 05	14 11								14 40		15 05	15 11		
Wakefield Westgate 7	d								14 18	14 24								14 54		15 18	15 24		
Wakefield Kirkgate 4	d																						
Pontefract Monkhill	d																						
Sheffield 7	a					14 20				14 52							15 20				15 52		
Hull	d						13 30																
Selby	d						14 06																
Doncaster 7	d				13 54		14 26		14 36							14 54		15 12		15 36			
Retford 10	d				14 08		14 40																
Lincoln	d																						
Newark North Gate 7	a								15 03							15 17				15 59			
	d								15 04							15 18				16 00			
Grantham 7	a						15 01		15 16											16 12			
	d						15 02	15 10	15 17										16 07	16 13			
Peterborough 8	a				14 47			15 39	15 36							15 47		15 59	16 38	16 33			
Norwich	a							17 13											18 13				
Peterborough 8	d				14 51				15 37							15 51		16 01		16 34			
Stevenage 4	a																			17 03			
London Kings Cross 15 ⊖	a		14 52		15 43		16 10		16 29			15 49	15 54			16 43		16 53		17 31			16 56

A To Manchester Airport
B To Reading
C From Liverpool Lime Street
D To Penzance. Trolley service from Edinburgh
E The Highland Chieftain
F from 15 February. To Manchester Airport
G from 4 January until 8 February. To Manchester Airport
H To Southampton Central
I The Northern Lights

Table 26R

Saturdays

14 December to 17 May

Scotland, North East England, Yorkshire and Humberside - London

Route Diagram - refer to first Page of Table 26

Station		TP ◇1 A	GR 1	XC ◇1 B		HT ◇1	EM ◇ C	GR 1	XC ◇1 D	TP ◇1 E	GR 1	XC ◇1 B	TP ◇1 A	GR 1		GC 1	GR 1	XC ◇1 F	TP ◇1 A	GR 1	GC 1	TP ◇1 G	TP ◇1 H	EM ◇ C
Aberdeen	d																							
Stonehaven	d																							
Montrose	d																							
Arbroath	d																							
Dundee	d																							
Leuchars 3	d																							
Kirkcaldy	d																							
Inverkeithing	d																							
Inverness	d																							
Perth	d																							
Stirling	d																							
Glasgow Central 15	d																	13 00						
Motherwell	d																	13 14						
Haymarket 238	d																							
Edinburgh 10 238	a																	13 55						
Edinburgh 238	d		13 00						13 09		13 30			14 00				14 05		14 30			14 39	
Dunbar	d								13 29															
Berwick-upon-Tweed	d										14 12							14 47		15 12				
Alnmouth for Alnwick	d								14 09					15 00										
Morpeth	d																							
Newcastle 8	a		14 23						14 38		14 56			15 27				15 32		15 56			16 15	
Sunderland	d																							
Hartlepool	d																				15 29			
																					15 53			
Newcastle 8	d	14 18	14 26	14 35					14 44		14 59	15 08	15 15	15 31				15 41		15 59		16 15	16 21	
Chester-le-Street	d												15 24									16 24		
Durham	d	14 31	14 39	14 48					14 56			15 21	15 31	15 44				15 54				16 31		
Darlington 7	a	14 46	14 55	15 03					15 12		15 25	15 36	15 46	16 02				16 09		16 25		16 46	16 46	
Middlesbrough	d									14 50									15 50					
Eaglescliffe	d																				16 12			
Darlington 7	d	14 48	14 57	15 05					15 13		15 27	15 37	15 48	16 03				16 13		16 27		16 48	16 48	
Northallerton	d	14 59	15 08							15 18			15 59						16 18		16 31	16 59	16 59	
Thirsk	d									15 28									16 28		16 43			
York 8	a	15 22	15 28	15 31					15 40	15 47	15 53	16 03	16 21	16 30				16 40	16 47	16 53	16 59	17 23	17 23	
Leeds 10	a	15 52							16 08	16 22		16 32	16 52					17 08	17 22			17 52	17 52	
Harrogate	d																							
Scarborough	d																							
York 8	d		15 31	15 35							15 56			16 33						16 56	17 02			
Doncaster 7	a		15 52	15 57										16 54										
Skipton	d																							
Keighley	d																							
Bradford Interchange	d															15 22								
Bradford Forster Square	d																							
Shipley	d																							
Halifax	d															15 35								
Brighouse	d															15 46								
Mirfield	d															15 56								
Leeds 10	d							16 05	16 11			16 40					17 05	17 11						
Wakefield Westgate 7	d							16 18	16 24			16 52					17 18	17 23						
Wakefield Kirkgate 4	d															16 13								
Pontefract Monkhill	d															16 34								
Sheffield 7	a			16 20					16 52			17 20						17 52						
Hull	d					15 30																		
Selby	d					16 05																		
Doncaster 7	d		15 54			16 24		16 36						16 56		17 03	17 36							
Retford 10	d		16 08			16 38																		
Lincoln	d																							
Newark North Gate 7	a							16 59						17 18			17 59							
	d							17 00						17 20			18 00							
Grantham 7	a					16 59		17 11									18 11							
	d					17 00	17 06	17 12									18 12							18 15
Peterborough 8	a		16 47				17 37	17 31						17 49			18 31							18 42
Norwich	a						19 13																	20 16
Peterborough 8	d		16 51					17 33						17 51			18 33							
Stevenage 4	a																19 01							
London Kings Cross 15 ⊖	a		17 44			18 08		18 25			17 51			18 42		18 45	19 28			18 52	18 53			

A To Manchester Airport
B To Reading
C From Liverpool Lime Street
D To Plymouth
E To Manchester Piccadilly
F To Plymouth. from Edinburgh
G from 15 February. To Manchester Airport
H from 4 January until 8 February. To Manchester Airport

Table 26R

Saturdays

14 December to 17 May

Scotland, North East England, Yorkshire and Humberside - London

Route Diagram - refer to first Page of Table 26

		GR	XC	EM	EM	GR	XC	XC	TP	GR		TP	GR	XC	HT	GR	XC	TP	GR	GC		GR	XC	GR	TP
		R 1	◇1	◇1	◇	R 1	◇1	◇1	◇1	R 1		◇1	R 1	◇1	◇1	R 1	◇1	◇1	R 1	R 1		R 1	◇1	R 1	◇1
			A	B	C		D	E	F			G		H			I	G					J		K
Aberdeen	d																								
Stonehaven	d																								
Montrose	d																								
Arbroath	d																								
Dundee	d																								
Leuchars 3	d																								
Kirkcaldy	d																								
Inverkeithing	d																								
Inverness	d																								
Perth	d																								
Stirling	d																								
Glasgow Central 15	d																15 00								
Motherwell	d																15 14								
Haymarket 238	d																15 57								
Edinburgh 10 238	a																16 01								
Edinburgh 238	d	15 00					15 08	15 08		15 30			16 00				16 05		16 30			17 00			17 04
Dunbar	d						15 28	15 28																	
Berwick-upon-Tweed	d									16 12									17 12						
Alnmouth for Alnwick	d																17 03					17 59			
Morpeth	d																17 17								
Newcastle 8	a	16 23					16 34	16 34		16 56			17 23				17 34		17 56			18 27			18 37
Sunderland	d																			17 29					
Hartlepool	d																			17 53					
Newcastle 8	d	16 26	16 35				16 41	16 41		16 59		17 02	17 26	17 32			17 44		17 59			18 29	18 35		18 52
Chester-le-Street	d											17 11		17 41											19 01
Durham	d	16 39	16 48				16 54	16 54				17 18	17 39	17 48			17 56					18 42	18 49		19 08
Darlington 7	a	16 55	17 03				17 09	17 09		17 26		17 34	17 55	18 04			18 12		18 25			19 00	19 05		→
Middlesbrough	d								16 50									17 50							
Eaglescliffe	d																			18 12					
Darlington 7	d	16 57	17 05				17 13	17 13		17 28		17 35	17 57	18 05			18 13		18 27			19 01	19 06		
Northallerton	d	17 08							17 18			17 46	18 08					18 18		18 31					
Thirsk	d								17 28									18 28		18 42					
York 8	a	17 28	17 31				17 40	17 40	17 47	17 54		18 09	18 28	18 31			18 40	18 47	18 53	18 58		19 28	19 32		
Leeds 10	a						18 08	18 08	18 22			18 37					19 08	19 35							
Harrogate	d																								
Scarborough	d																								
York 8	d	17 31	17 35	17 50						17 57			18 31	18 34					18 56	19 02		19 30	19 35		
Doncaster 7	a	17 52	17 57	18 11									18 53	18 57								19 53	19 57		
Skipton	d																								
Keighley	d																								
Bradford Interchange	d																								
Bradford Forster Square	d																								
Shipley	d																								
Halifax	d																								
Brighouse	d																								
Mirfield	d																								
Leeds 10	d					18 05	18 11	18 11								19 05	19 11							20 05	
Wakefield Westgate 7	d					18 18	18 23	18 23								19 18	19 24							20 18	
Wakefield Kirkgate 4	d																								
Pontefract Monkhill	d																								
Sheffield 7	a		18 20	18 44			18 52	18 53						19 21			19 51						20 20		
Hull	d														18 30										
Selby	d														19 09										
Doncaster 7	d	17 54				18 39							18 55		19 28	19 37						19 55		20 36	
Retford 10	d	18 09													19 42									20 50	
Lincoln	d																								
Newark North Gate 7	a					19 02							19 17			20 00								21 04	
	d					19 03							19 18			20 01								21 05	
Grantham 7	a					19 15									20 03	20 12						20 26			
	d				19 08	19 16									20 05	20 13						20 27			
Peterborough 8	a	18 47			19 39	19 35							19 47			20 32						20 48		21 34	
Norwich	a				21 13																				
Peterborough 8	d	18 51				19 37							19 51			20 34						20 51		21 35	
Stevenage 4	a												20 19			21 02									
London Kings Cross 15 ⊖	a	19 43				20 28				19 52			20 46		21 13	21 29			20 52	20 56		21 42		22 27	

A To Reading
B To St Pancras International
C From Liverpool Lime Street
D from 4 January until 8 February. To Plymouth
E from 15 February. To Exeter St Davids
F To Manchester Piccadilly
G To Manchester Airport
H To Guildford
I To Bristol Temple Meads
J To Birmingham New Street
K from 4 January until 8 February. To Manchester Airport

Table 26R

Saturdays

14 December to 17 May

Scotland, North East England, Yorkshire and Humberside - London

Route Diagram - refer to first Page of Table 26

		XC	TP	TP	TP	GR	XC	XC	GR	TP	GR	NT	EM	TP
		◇1	◇1	◇1	◇1	R 1	◇1	◇1	R 1	◇1	R 1		◇	◇1
		A		B	C		D	E		F		G	H	I
		⚲				⚲		⚲	⚲		⚲			
Aberdeen	d					14 52								
Stonehaven	d					15 10								
Montrose	d					15 33								
Arbroath	d					15 49								
Dundee	d					16 07								
Leuchars 3	d					16 22								
Kirkcaldy	d					16 46								
Inverkeithing	d					17 03								
Inverness	d													
Perth	d													
Stirling	d													
Glasgow Central 15	d							16 52						
Motherwell	d							17 06						
Haymarket 238	d					17 21		17 53						
Edinburgh 10 238	a					17 26		17 57						
Edinburgh 238	d	17 08				17 30		18 08	18 30		19 00			
Dunbar	d	17 29				17 51		18 28			19 21			
Berwick-upon-Tweed	d	17 51				18 16		18 51	19 12		19 46			
Alnmouth for Alnwick	d							19 11			20 08			
Morpeth	d										20 25			
Newcastle 8 ⇌	a	18 37				19 01		19 40	19 58		20 41			
Sunderland ⇌	d													
Hartlepool	d													
Newcastle 8 ⇌	d	18 44			18 52	19 04	19 35	19 45			20 43	21 50		
Chester-le-Street	d			←	19 01							22 00		
Durham	d	18 57		19 08	19 08		19 50	19 57			20 56	22 08		
Darlington 7	a	19 12		19 24	19 24	19 31	20 05	20 13			21 14	22 29		
Middlesbrough	d		18 50							20 10				21 50
Eaglescliffe	d											22a48		
Darlington 7	d	19 14		19 25	19 25	19 33	20 07	20 14			21 15			22 20
Northallerton	d		19 19	19 36	19 36					20 39	21 28			22 31
Thirsk	d		19 29							20 47				22 39
York 8	a	19 41	19 49	20 07	20 07	20 00	20 33	20 41		21 05	21 47			22 57
Leeds 10	a	20 08		20 35	20 35			21 07		21 37				23 33
Harrogate	d													
Scarborough	d													
York 8	d					20 02	20 35				21 50			
Doncaster 7	a					20 25	20 57				22 15			
Skipton	d													
Keighley	d													
Bradford Interchange	d													
Bradford Forster Square	d													
Shipley	d													
Halifax	d													
Brighouse	d													
Mirfield	d													
Leeds 10	d	20 11						21 11						
Wakefield Westgate 7	d	20 23						21 23						
Wakefield Kirkgate 4	d													
Pontefract Monkhill	d													
Sheffield 7 ⇌	a	20 53					21 20	21 52						
Hull	d													
Selby	d													
Doncaster 7	d					20 26								
Retford 10	d													
Lincoln	d													
Newark North Gate 7	a													
	d													
Grantham 7	a					20 57								
	d					20 59							21 07	
Peterborough 8	a					21 19							21 39	
Norwich	a												23 19	
Peterborough 8	d					21 22								
Stevenage 4	a					21 51								
London Kings Cross 15 ⊖	a					22 20								

A To Birmingham New Street. ⚲ to Leeds
B from 4 January until 8 February. From Edinburgh to Manchester Airport
C from 15 February. To Manchester Airport
D To Birmingham New Street
E To Birmingham New Street. ⚲ from Edinburgh to Leeds
F To Manchester Airport
G To Middlesbrough
H From Liverpool Lime Street
I To Manchester Piccadilly

Table 26R

Sundays

8 December to 29 December

Scotland, North East England, Yorkshire and Humberside - London

Route Diagram - refer to first Page of Table 26

Station		GR	GR	GC	GR	TP	GR	HT	XC	GR	GR	GR	XC	TP	GC	GR	TP	GR	GR	HT	GR	XC	GR
						A			B				B	C			A					B	
Aberdeen	d																						
Stonehaven	d																						
Montrose	d																						
Arbroath	d																						
Dundee	d																						
Leuchars 3	d																						
Kirkcaldy	d																						
Inverkeithing	d																						
Inverness	d																						
Perth	d																						
Stirling	d																						
Glasgow Central 15	d																						
Motherwell	d																						
Haymarket 238	d																						
Edinburgh 10 238	a																						
Edinburgh 238	d																		09 00			09 08	09 30
Dunbar	d																						
Berwick-upon-Tweed	d																					09 49	10 13
Alnmouth for Alnwick	d																						
Morpeth	d																						
Newcastle 8	a																		10 23			10 36	10 58
Sunderland	d														09 18								
Hartlepool	d														09 43								
Newcastle 8	d				07 55	08 04				08 55		09 25	09 30	09 33		10 00			10 29			10 39	11 00
Chester-le-Street	d													09 43									
Durham	d				08 09	08 16				09 08		09 38	09 44	09 49					10 42			10 53	
Darlington 7	a				08 26	08 32				09 26		09 55	10 00	10 05		10 27			10 59			11 08	11 28
Middlesbrough	d																10 15						
Eaglescliffe	d														10 04								
Darlington 7	d				08 28	08 33				09 28		09 57	10 02	10 06		10 28			11 01			11 10	11 29
Northallerton	d					08 45						10 08		10 18	10 23		10 43		11 12				
Thirsk	d					08 53									10 32		10 51						
York 8	a				08 55	09 12				09 54		10 27	10 31	10 41	10 49	10 55	11 09		11 31			11 38	11 56
Leeds 10	a					09 38							10 56	11 08			11 38					12 05	
Harrogate	d																						
Scarborough	d																						
York 8	d	08 00			08 57				09 33	09 57		10 30			10 52	10 57			11 34				11 59
Doncaster 7	a	08 21										10 51							11 55				
Skipton	d																						
Keighley	d																						
Bradford Interchange	d			07 58																			
Bradford Forster Square	d																						
Shipley	d																						
Halifax	d			08 10																			
Brighouse	d			08 21																			
Mirfield	d			08 29																			
Leeds 10	d		08 05				09 05		10 00		10 05		11 00					11 05			12 05	12 10	
Wakefield Westgate 7	d		08 17				09 18		10 12		10 17		11 12					11 18			12 17	12 23	
Wakefield Kirkgate 4	d			08 46																			
Pontefract Monkhill	d																						
Sheffield 7	a																					12 54	
Hull	d							09 05												11 10			
Selby	d							09 40												11 45			
Doncaster 7	d	08 23	08 36	09 11			09 37	10 00	10a28		10 35	10 53	11a28					11 35	11 57	12 04	12 35		
Retford 10	d		08 50					10 14			10 50								12 11	12 18			
Lincoln	d																						
Newark North Gate 7	a		09 04				09 59				11 04	11 15						11 58			12 57		
	d		09 05				10 00				11 06	11 16						12 00			12 58		
Grantham 7	a		09 17				10 12	10 34			11 17							12 11		12 39	13 10		
	d		09 18				10 13	10 35			11 19							12 13		12 40	13 11		
Peterborough 8	a	09 10	09 38		10 03		10 33			11 01	11 39	11 47				12 02		12 33	12 50		13 31		
Norwich	a																						
Peterborough 8	d	09 11	09 41		10 05		10 34			11 04	11 41	11 51				12 03		12 35	12 51		13 32		
Stevenage 4	a	09 39					11 04											13 06					
London Kings Cross 15 ⊖	a	10 07	10 32	10 40	10 57		11 32	11 42		11 55	12 33	12 42			12 44	12 54		13 33	13 42	13 46	14 23		13 52

A To Manchester Airport **B** To Plymouth **C** To Liverpool Lime Street

Table 26R

Sundays

8 December to 29 December

Scotland, North East England, Yorkshire and Humberside - London

Route Diagram - refer to first Page of Table 26

		TP	EM	GR	GC	GR	XC	GR	TP	GR	EM	GR	XC	TP	GC	GR	TP	GR	GR	XC	EM	HT	GR
		◇1	◇	1	1	1	◇1	1	◇1	1	◇	1	◇1	◇1	1	1	◇1	1	1	◇1	◇	◇1	1
		A	B				C		A		D		E	F			A			G	H		
Aberdeen	d																						
Stonehaven	d																						
Montrose	d																						
Arbroath	d																						
Dundee	d																						
Leuchars 3	d																						
Kirkcaldy	d																						
Inverkeithing	d																						
Inverness	d																						
Perth	d																						
Stirling	d																						
Glasgow Central 15	d																						
Motherwell	d																						
Haymarket 238	d																						
Edinburgh 10 238	a																						
Edinburgh 238	d			10 00			10 08	10 30		11 00			11 05			11 30			12 00				
Dunbar	d												11 25										
Berwick-upon-Tweed	d							11 12					11 48			12 13							
Alnmouth for Alnwick	d			10 59			11 05						12 08						12 59				
Morpeth	d						11 19																
Newcastle 8	a			11 27			11 36	11 56		12 23			12 37			12 58			13 27				
Sunderland	d														12 12								
Hartlepool	d														12 36								
Newcastle 8	d	11 08		11 30			11 40	11 59	12 10	12 26			12 40			13 00	13 07	13 15	13 29	13 35			
Chester-le-Street	d																13 16						
Durham	d	11 20		11 43			11 53		12 22	12 39			12 52				13 23	13 29	13 42	13 48			
Darlington 7	a	11 36		12 01			12 08	12 25	12 38	12 56			13 08			13 28	13 39	13 46	13 59	14 04			
Middlesbrough	d													12 45									
Eaglescliffe	d														13 04								
Darlington 7	d	11 37		12 03			12 10	12 27	12 39	12 58			13 09			13 29	13 40	13 49	14 00	14 05			
Northallerton	d	11 49								13 10				13 14	13 23			14 00					
Thirsk	d													13 23	13 33								
York 8	a	12 11		12 29			12 37	12 55	13 11	13 29			13 36	13 42	13 49	13 56	14 12	14 19	14 28	14 32			
Leeds 10	a	12 38					13 05		13 38				14 03	14 08			14 38						
Harrogate	d																						
Scarborough	d																						
York 8	d			12 32				12 59		13 31					13 52	13 59		14 22	14 30	14 34			
Doncaster 7	a			12 53						13 53								14 43	14 52	14 57			
Skipton	d																						
Keighley	d																						
Bradford Interchange	d				12 00																		
Bradford Forster Square	d																						
Shipley	d																						
Halifax	d				12 14																		
Brighouse	d				12 25																		
Mirfield	d				12 33																		
Leeds 10	d					13 05	13 10					14 05	14 10										15 05
Wakefield Westgate 7	d					13 18	13 24					14 18	14 23										15 18
Wakefield Kirkgate 4	d				12 49																		
Pontefract Monkhill	d																						
Sheffield 7	a						13 53						14 52							15 21			
Hull	d																					14 35	
Selby	d																					15 10	
Doncaster 7	d			12 55	13 13	13 36				13 55		14 36						14 47	14 54			15 29	15 37
Retford 10	d									14 09												15 43	
Lincoln	d																						
Newark North Gate 7	a			13 17		13 59						14 58							15 16				15 59
	d			13 18		14 00						14 59							15 18				16 00
Grantham 7	a					14 11						15 11										16 04	16 12
	d		13 14			14 12					14 22	15 12									15 20	16 05	16 13
Peterborough 8	a		13 40	13 47		14 32				14 48	14 51	15 32						15 37	15 46		15 49		16 33
Norwich	a		15 22								16 35										17 26		
Peterborough 8	d			13 51		14 34				14 51		15 33						15 40	15 51				16 35
Stevenage 4	a					15 06																16 50	17 04
London Kings Cross 15 ⊖	a			14 42	14 45	15 32		14 50		15 42		16 24			15 44	15 52		16 32	16 42			17 14	17 32

A To Manchester Airport
B From Nottingham
C To Penzance
D From Sheffield
E To Plymouth
F To Liverpool Lime Street
G To Reading
H From Manchester Piccadilly

Table 26R

Sundays

8 December to 29 December

Scotland, North East England, Yorkshire and Humberside - London

Route Diagram - refer to first Page of Table 26

Station		XC	GR	GR	GR	TP	GR	GR	XC	XC	TP	GC	GR	TP	XC	GC	EM	GR	GR	GC	EM	GR
		◇1	R 1	R 1	R 1	◇1	R 1	R 1	◇1	◇1	◇1	R 1	R 1	◇1	◇1	R 1	◇	R 1	R 1	R 1	◇	R 1
		A	B	C	D	E			F	G	H		I	E	F		J				J	
Aberdeen	d				09 47																	
Stonehaven	d				10 05																	
Montrose	d				10 28																	
Arbroath	d				10 44																	
Dundee	d				11 03																	
Leuchars 3	d				11 17																	
Kirkcaldy	d				11 41																	
Inverkeithing	d				11 57																	
Inverness	d												09 40									
Perth	d												11 59									
Stirling	d												12 35									
Glasgow Central 15	d	10 55								11 51												
Motherwell	d	11 10								12 08												
Haymarket 238	d	11 51			12 16					12 49			13 15									
Edinburgh 10 238	a	11 56			12 20					12 54			13 20									
Edinburgh 238	d	12 08	12 20	12 20	12 30			13 00		13 08			13 30		13 55				14 00			
Dunbar	d									13 27												
Berwick-upon-Tweed	d	12 47			13 13								14 13		14 34							
Alnmouth for Alnwick	d									14 08									15 00			
Morpeth	d		13 33	13 33																		
Newcastle 8	a	13 33	13 49	13 49	13 58			14 24		14 37			14 58		15 20				15 27			
Sunderland	d											14 12										
Hartlepool	d											14 40										
Newcastle 8	d	13 40	13 52	13 52	14 00	14 08	14 15	14 27	14 35	14 40			15 00	15 07	15 23				15 30			
Chester-le-Street	d													15 16								
Durham	d	13 53	14 05	14 05		14 20	14 29	14 41	14 49	14 54				15 23	15 36				15 43			
Darlington 7	a	14 09			14 28	14 36	14 46	14 57	15 04	15 09			15 28	15 39	15 51				16 00			
Middlesbrough	d										14 43											
Eaglescliffe	d											15 04										
Darlington 7	d	14 10			14 29	14 37	14 49	14 59	15 06	15 11			15 29	15 40	15 53				16 02			
Northallerton	d					14 49	15 00				15 12	15 24										
Thirsk	d										15 20	15 33										
York 8	a	14 37	14 46	14 46	14 56	15 12	15 19	15 27	15 32	15 37	15 43	15 49	15 56	16 12	16 20				16 28			
Leeds 10	a	15 05				15 38				16 03	16 08			16 38								
Harrogate	d																					
Scarborough	d																					
York 8	d		14 48	14 48	14 59		15 22	15 29	15 35			15 51	15 59		16 24				16 31			
Doncaster 7	a						15 43	15 52	15 57						16 47				16 53			
Skipton	d																					
Keighley	d																					
Bradford Interchange	d															15 08				16 00		
Bradford Forster Square	d																					
Shipley	d																					
Halifax	d															15 23				16 14		
Brighouse	d															15 37				16 25		
Mirfield	d															15 45				16 33		
Leeds 10	d	15 10								16 10								16 16				16 45
Wakefield Westgate 7	d	15 23								16 22								16 28				16 58
Wakefield Kirkgate 4	d															16 02				16 49		
Pontefract Monkhill	d																					
Sheffield 7	a	15 51							16 21	16 51					17 15							
Hull	d																					
Selby	d																					
Doncaster 7	d						15 46	15 53								16 27		16 47	16 55	17 12		17 18
Retford 10	d							16 09														
Lincoln	d																					
Newark North Gate 7	a						16 08												17 17			17 45
	d						16 09												17 19			17 46
Grantham 7	a		15 38	15 38														17 17				
	d		15 39	15 39													16 22	17 18			17 21	
Peterborough 8	a						16 39	16 48									16 52		17 47		17 50	18 14
Norwich	a																18 30				19 29	
Peterborough 8	d						16 42	16 50											17 51			18 16
Stevenage 4	a																	18 04				
London Kings Cross 15 ⊖	a		16 45	16 47	16 52		17 35	17 43				17 45	17 52			17 57		18 33	18 42	18 43		19 10

A To Penzance. Trolley from Edinburgh
B 29 December
C until 28 December
D The Northern Lights
E To Manchester Airport
F To Reading
G To Plymouth. Trolley from Edinburgh
H To Liverpool Lime Street
I The Highland Chieftain
J From Liverpool Lime Street

Table 26R

Sundays

8 December to 29 December

Scotland, North East England, Yorkshire and Humberside - London

Route Diagram - refer to first Page of Table 26

		XC	GR	TP	HT	GR	EM	GR	GR	XC	GR	EM	XC	TP	GR	TP	GR	GR	XC	EM	GR	XC	GR
		◇1	1	◇1	◇1	1	◇	1	1	◇1	1	◇1	◇1	◇1	1	◇1	1	1	◇1	◇	1	◇1	1
		A		B			C			D		E	F	G		B			H	C		I	
Aberdeen	d	11 08	11 47																				
Stonehaven	d	11 25	12 05																				
Montrose	d	11 46	12 28																				
Arbroath	d	12 02	12 44																				
Dundee	d	12 21	13 02																				
Leuchars 3	d	12 34	13 17																				
Kirkcaldy	d	13 04	13 42																				
Inverkeithing	d	13 20	14 00																				
Inverness	d																						
Perth	d																						
Stirling	d																						
Glasgow Central 15	d												13 49									14 55	
Motherwell	d												14 04									15 11	
Haymarket 238	d	13 37	14 19										14 42									15 51	
Edinburgh 10 238	a	13 42	14 23										14 47									15 56	
Edinburgh 238	d	14 10	14 30						15 00				15 08		15 30			16 00				16 08	16 20
Dunbar	d												15 28										
Berwick-upon-Tweed	d	14 49	15 13												16 12								
Alnmouth for Alnwick	d																	16 59				17 05	
Morpeth	d																					17 19	
Newcastle 8	a	15 35	15 58						16 23				16 34		16 56			17 27				17 36	17 44
Sunderland	d																						
Hartlepool	d																						
Newcastle 8	d	15 40	16 00	16 08		16 15			16 26	16 35			16 40		16 59	17 05		17 29	17 35			17 40	17 49
Chester-le-Street	d															17 14							
Durham	d	15 53		16 20		16 29			16 39	16 48			16 53			17 21		17 42	17 48			17 54	
Darlington 7	a	16 08	16 28	16 36		16 46			16 56	17 03			17 08		17 26	17 37		18 00	18 05			18 10	18 15
Middlesbrough	d													16 43									
Eaglescliffe	d																						
Darlington 7	d	16 10	16 29	16 37		16 49			16 58	17 05			17 10		17 27	17 38		18 01	18 06			18 11	18 17
Northallerton	d			16 49		17 00								17 11		17 49							
Thirsk	d													17 20									
York 8	a	16 36	16 56	17 12		17 19			17 24	17 32			17 37	17 42	17 54	18 12		18 28	18 32			18 38	18 43
Leeds 10	a	17 06		17 38									18 04	18 08		18 38						19 03	
Harrogate	d										17 06												
Scarborough	d																						
York 8	d		16 59			17 22			17 30	17 34		17 49			17 58			18 30	18 35				18 48
Doncaster 7	a								17 51	17 57		18 11						18 52	18 57				
Skipton	d																						
Keighley	d																						
Bradford Interchange	d																						
Bradford Forster Square	d																						
Shipley	d																						
Halifax	d																						
Brighouse	d																						
Mirfield	d																						
Leeds 10	d	17 10						17 16			17 45		18 10				18 16				18 45	19 10	
Wakefield Westgate 7	d	17 23						17 29			17 58		18 22				18 28				18 58	19 22	
Wakefield Kirkgate 4	d																						
Pontefract Monkhill	d																						
Sheffield 7	a	17 52								18 23		18 39	18 51						19 21			19 50	
Hull	d				16 35																		
Selby	d				17 10																		
Doncaster 7	d				17 30			17 47	17 55		18 19						18 46	18 54			19 19		
Retford 10	d				17 44			18 01															
Lincoln	d																						
Newark North Gate 7	a					18 01					18 43							19 17			19 44		
	d					18 02					18 44							19 18			19 46		
Grantham 7	a				18 05			18 23	18 27								19 16						19 41
	d				18 06		18 17	18 24	18 28								19 17			19 28			19 42
Peterborough 8	a					18 31	18 47		18 50		19 13							19 46		19 57	20 15		
Norwich	a						20 26													21 37			
Peterborough 8	d					18 32			18 52		19 15							19 51			20 16		
Stevenage 4	a				18 49			19 09									20 00						
London Kings Cross 15 ⊖	a		18 53		19 18	19 23		19 34	19 43		20 10				19 49		20 27	20 42			21 10		20 48

A To Plymouth. Trolley from Edinburgh
B To Manchester Airport
C From Liverpool Lime Street
D To Reading
E To St Pancras International
F To Plymouth
G To Liverpool Lime Street
H To Guildford
I To Bristol Temple Meads. Trolley from Edinburgh

Table 26R

Sundays

8 December to 29 December

Scotland, North East England, Yorkshire and Humberside - London

Route Diagram - refer to first Page of Table 26

		TP	GR	XC		HT	GR	GR	GR	XC	TP	GC	GR	TP		XC	GR	EM	GR	XC	GR	TP	TP	GR
		◇1	R 1	◇1		◇1	R 1	R 1	R 1	◇1	◇1	R 1	R 1	◇1		◇1	R 1	◇	R 1	◇1	R 1	◇1	◇1	R 1
		A		B						C	D			E		B		F		G			A	
Aberdeen	d		13 47																					
Stonehaven	d		14 05																					
Montrose	d		14 28																					
Arbroath	d		14 44																					
Dundee	d		15 02																					
Leuchars 3	d		15 16																					
Kirkcaldy	d		15 40																					
Inverkeithing	d		15 56																					
Inverness	d																							
Perth	d																							
Stirling	d																							
Glasgow Central 15	d																			16 55				
Motherwell	d																			17 11				
Haymarket 238	d		16 17																	17 51				
Edinburgh 10 238	a		16 22																	17 56				
Edinburgh 238	d		16 30					17 00		17 08			17 30				18 00			18 08	18 30			19 00
Dunbar	d									17 28			17 51							18 28				19 21
Berwick-upon-Tweed	d		17 13							17 51			18 16							18 51	19 12			19 46
Alnmouth for Alnwick	d																18 59							
Morpeth	d																							
Newcastle 8	a		17 58					18 23		18 37			19 00				19 27			19 37	19 56			20 30
Sunderland	d											18 12												
Hartlepool	d											18 40												
Newcastle 8	d	17 53	18 00	18 21				18 26		18 40			19 03	19 10		19 26	19 30			19 40	20 01		20 08	20 33
Chester-le-Street	d																							
Durham	d	18 05		18 34				18 39		18 53				19 22		19 39	19 43			19 53			20 20	20 46
Darlington 7	a	18 21	18 28	18 49				18 56		19 08			19 30	19 38		19 54	20 01			20 08	20 27		20 36	21 03
Middlesbrough	d										18 45											20 06		
Eaglescliffe	d											19 04												
Darlington 7	d	18 22	18 29	18 52				18 58		19 10			19 31	19 39		19 56	20 02			20 10	20 29		20 37	21 05
Northallerton	d	18 34						19 10			19 14	19 22										20 34	20 49	
Thirsk	d										19 22	19 32										20 44		
York 8	a	19 03	18 56	19 19				19 29		19 37	19 42	19 49	19 58	20 11		20 22	20 29			20 37	20 56	21 02	21 12	21 31
Leeds 10	a	19 38								20 05	20 08			20 38						21 02			21 38	
Harrogate	d																							
Scarborough	d																							
York 8	d		18 59	19 24				19 31				19 52	20 00			20 24	20 31				20 59			21 34
Doncaster 7	a			19 47				19 53								20 47	20 53				21 20			21 55
Skipton	d																							
Keighley	d																							
Bradford Interchange	d																							
Bradford Forster Square	d																							
Shipley	d																							
Halifax	d																							
Brighouse	d																							
Mirfield	d																							
Leeds 10	d						19 16		19 45	20 10									20 45	21 10				
Wakefield Westgate 7	d						19 28		19 58	20 22									20 58	21 22				
Wakefield Kirkgate 4	d																							
Pontefract Monkhill	d																							
Sheffield 7	a			20 16						20 51						21 17				21 50				
Hull	d					18 45																		
Selby	d					19 20																		
Doncaster 7	d					19 39	19 46	19 55	20 20								20 54		21 16		21 25			21 57
Retford 10	d					19 54	20 00												21 30					
Lincoln	d																							
Newark North Gate 7	a							20 18	20 43								21 17				21 48			22 19
	d							20 19	20 44								21 18				21 49			22 20
Grantham 7	a					20 14	20 22						20 47						21 52		22 01			22 32
	d					20 15	20 23						20 48					21 20	21 53		22 02			22 33
Peterborough 8	a							20 48	21 13				21 08				21 46	21 51	22 13		22 22			22 53
Norwich	a																	23 24						
Peterborough 8	d							20 51	21 14				21 09				21 51		22 14		22 23			22 54
Stevenage 4	a						21 08												22 45		22 54			23s32
London Kings Cross 15 ⊖	a		20 54			21 21	21 33	21 42	22 07			21 44	22 00				22 42		23 14		23 19			23 59

A To Manchester Airport
B To Birmingham New Street
C To Bristol Temple Meads. ♀ to Leeds
D To Liverpool Lime Street
E To Manchester Piccadilly
F From Liverpool Lime Street
G To Birmingham New Street. ♀ from Edinburgh to Leeds

Table 26R

Sundays

8 December to 29 December

Scotland, North East England, Yorkshire and Humberside - London

Route Diagram - refer to first Page of Table 26

			NT	GR	XC	GR	TP
				R		R	
				1	◇1	1	◇1
			A				B
				🚃		🚃	
Aberdeen		d					
Stonehaven		d					
Montrose		d					
Arbroath		d					
Dundee		d					
Leuchars 3		d					
Kirkcaldy		d					
Inverkeithing		d					
Inverness		d					
Perth		d					
Stirling		d					
Glasgow Central 15		d			18 57		
Motherwell		d			19 11		
Haymarket	238	d			19 51		
Edinburgh 10	238	a			19 55		
Edinburgh	238	d		20 00	20 15	21 00	
Dunbar		d		20 22	20 35	21 22	
Berwick-upon-Tweed		d		20 48	21 01	21 47	
Alnmouth for Alnwick		d		21 11		22 09	
Morpeth		d		21 27			
Newcastle 8	⛴	a		21 43	21 46	22 39	
Sunderland	⛴	d					
Hartlepool		d					
Newcastle 8	⛴	d	21 06	21 45			
Chester-le-Street		d	21 15				
Durham		d	21 24	21 59			
Darlington 7		a	21 44	22 17			
Middlesbrough		d					22 08
Eaglescliffe		d	22a00				
Darlington 7		d		22 18			
Northallerton		d		22 32			22 36
Thirsk		d					22 44
York 8		a		23 03			23 09
Leeds 10		a		23 35			23 38
Harrogate		d					
Scarborough		d					
York 8		d					
Doncaster 7		a					
Skipton		d					
Keighley		d					
Bradford Interchange		d					
Bradford Forster Square		d					
Shipley		d					
Halifax		d					
Brighouse		d					
Mirfield		d					
Leeds 10		d					
Wakefield Westgate 7		d					
Wakefield Kirkgate 4		d					
Pontefract Monkhill		d					
Sheffield 7	⛴	a					
Hull		d					
Selby		d					
Doncaster 7		d					
Retford 10		d					
Lincoln		d					
Newark North Gate 7		a					
		d					
Grantham 7		a					
		d					
Peterborough 8		a					
Norwich		a					
Peterborough 8		d					
Stevenage 4		a					
London Kings Cross 15	⊖	a					

A To Saltburn
B To Manchester Airport

Table 26R

Sundays

5 January to 9 February

Scotland, North East England, Yorkshire and Humberside - London

Route Diagram - refer to first Page of Table 26

		GR	GR	GC	GR	TP	GR	HT	XC	GR	GR	GR	XC	TP	GC	GR	TP	GR	GR	HT	GR	XC	GR
		R	R	R	R		R			R	R	R			R	R		R	R		R		R
		1	1	1	1	◇1	1	◇1	◇1	1	1	1	◇1	◇1	1	1	◇1	1	1	◇1	1	◇1	1
						A			B				C	D			A					B	
Aberdeen	d																						
Stonehaven	d																						
Montrose	d																						
Arbroath	d																						
Dundee	d																						
Leuchars 8	d																						
Kirkcaldy	d																						
Inverkeithing	d																						
Inverness	d																						
Perth	d																						
Stirling	d																						
Glasgow Central 15	d																						
Motherwell	d																						
Haymarket 238	d																						
Edinburgh 10 238	a																						
Edinburgh 238	d																		09 00			09 08	09 30
Dunbar	d																						
Berwick-upon-Tweed	d																					09 49	10 13
Alnmouth for Alnwick	d																						
Morpeth	d																						
Newcastle 8	a																		10 23			10 36	10 58
Sunderland	d														09 18								
Hartlepool	d														09 43								
Newcastle 8	d				07 55	08 04				08 55		09 25	09 30	09 33		10 00			10 29			10 39	11 00
Chester-le-Street	d													09 43									
Durham	d				08 08	08 16				09 09		09 38	09 44	09 49					10 42			10 53	
Darlington 7	a				08 26	08 32				09 26		09 55	10 00	10 05		10 27			10 59			11 08	11 28
Middlesbrough	d																10 15						
Eaglescliffe	d														10 04								
Darlington 7	d				08 28	08 33				09 28		09 57	10 02	10 06		10 28			11 01			11 10	11 29
Northallerton	d					08 45						10 08		10 18	10 23		10 43		11 12				
Thirsk	d					08 53									10 32		10 51						
York 8	a				08 55	09 12				09 55		10 27	10 31	10 41	10 49	10 55	11 09		11 31			11 38	11 56
Leeds 10	a					09 38							10 56	11 08			11 38					12 05	
Harrogate	d																						
Scarborough	d																						
York 8	d	08 00			08 57				09 33	09 57		10 30			10 52	10 57			11 34				11 59
Doncaster 7	a	08 21										10 51							11 55				
Skipton	d																						
Keighley	d																						
Bradford Interchange	d			07 58																			
Bradford Forster Square	d																						
Shipley	d																						
Halifax	d			08 10																			
Brighouse	d			08 21																			
Mirfield	d			08 29																			
Leeds 10	d		08 05				09 05		10 00		10 05		11 00					11 05			12 05	12 10	
Wakefield Westgate 7	d		08 17				09 18		10 12		10 17		11 12					11 17			12 17	12 23	
Wakefield Kirkgate 4	d			08 46																			
Pontefract Monkhill	d																						
Sheffield 7	a								10 41				11 39									12 54	
Hull	d							09 05												11 10			
Selby	d							09 40												11 45			
Doncaster 7	d	08 23	08 35	09 12			09 37	10 00			10 35	10 53						11 38	11 57	12 03	12 35		
Retford 10	d		08 50					10 14			10 50								12 11	12 17			
Lincoln	d																						
Newark North Gate 7	a		09 04				09 59				11 04	11 15						12 00			12 57		
	d		09 06				10 00				11 06	11 16						12 01			12 58		
Grantham 7	a		09 17				10 12	10 34			11 17							12 13		12 38	13 10		
	d		09 19				10 13	10 35			11 19							12 14		12 39	13 11		
Peterborough 8	a	09 10	09 39		10 03		10 33			11 03	11 39	11 47				12 02		12 34	12 50		13 31		
Norwich	a																						
Peterborough 8	d	09 11	09 41		10 04		10 34			11 05	11 41	11 51				12 03		12 39	12 51		13 41		
Stevenage 4	a	09 42					11 06											13 07					
London Kings Cross 15 ⊖	a	10 18	10 44	11 01	11 09		11 43	12 02		12 10	12 44	13 03			13 05	13 09		13 43	14 02	14 05	14 43		14 08

A To Manchester Airport
B To Plymouth
C To Reading
D To Liverpool Lime Street

Table 26R

Sundays

5 January to 9 February

Scotland, North East England, Yorkshire and Humberside - London

Route Diagram - refer to first Page of Table 26

		TP	EM	GR	GC	GR		XC	GR	TP	GR	EM	GR	XC	TP	GC		TP	GR	TP	GR	XC	EM	HT	GR
		◇1	◇	R 1	R 1	R 1		◇1	R 1	◇1	R 1	◇	R 1	◇1	◇1	R 1		◇1	R 1	◇1	R 1	◇1	◇	◇1	R 1
		A	B					C		A		D		C	E			A		F		G	H		
Aberdeen	d																								
Stonehaven	d																								
Montrose	d																								
Arbroath	d																								
Dundee	d																								
Leuchars 3	d																								
Kirkcaldy	d																								
Inverkeithing	d																								
Inverness	d																								
Perth	d																								
Stirling	d																								
Glasgow Central 15	d																								
Motherwell	d																								
Haymarket 238	d																								
Edinburgh 10 238	a																								
Edinburgh 238	d			10 00				10 08	10 30		11 00			11 05				11 18	11 30		12 00				
Dunbar	d													11 25											
Berwick-upon-Tweed	d								11 12					11 48					12 13						
Alnmouth for Alnwick	d			10 59				11 05						12 08							12 59				
Morpeth	d							11 19																	
Newcastle 8	a			11 27				11 36	11 56		12 23			12 37				12 51	12 58		13 27				
Sunderland	d															12 12									
Hartlepool	d															12 36									
Newcastle 8	d	11 08		11 30				11 40	11 59	12 10	12 26			12 40				13 07	13 00		13 29	13 35			
Chester-le-Street	d																	13 16							
Durham	d	11 20		11 43				11 53		12 22	12 39			12 52				13 23			13 42	13 48			
Darlington 7	a	11 36		12 01				12 08	12 25	12 38	12 56			13 08				13 39	13 28		13 59	14 04			
Middlesbrough	d														12 45										
Eaglescliffe	d															13 04				←					
Darlington 7	d	11 37		12 03				12 10	12 27	12 39	12 58			13 09				13 40	13 29	13 40	14 00	14 05			
Northallerton	d	11 49									13 10				13 14	13 23		→							
Thirsk	d														13 23	13 33									
York 8	a	12 11		12 29				12 37	12 55	13 11	13 29			13 36	13 42	13 49			13 56	14 12	14 28	14 32			
Leeds 10	a	12 38						13 05		13 38				14 03	14 08					14 38					
Harrogate	d																								
Scarborough	d																								
York 8	d			12 32					12 59		13 31					13 52			13 59		14 30	14 34			
Doncaster 7	a			12 53							13 53										14 52				
Skipton	d																								
Keighley	d																								
Bradford Interchange	d				12 00																				
Bradford Forster Square	d																								
Shipley	d																								
Halifax	d				12 14																				
Brighouse	d				12 25																				
Mirfield	d				12 33																				
Leeds 10	d					13 05		13 10					14 05	14 10											15 05
Wakefield Westgate 7	d					13 18		13 24					14 18	14 23											15 18
Wakefield Kirkgate 4	d				12 49																				
Pontefract Monkhill	d																								
Sheffield 7	a							13 53						14 52								15 21			
Hull	d																							14 35	
Selby	d																							15 10	
Doncaster 7	d			12 55	13 13	13 36					13 55		14 36								14 54			15 29	15 37
Retford 10	d										14 09													15 43	
Lincoln	d																								
Newark North Gate 7	a			13 17		13 59							14 58								15 16				15 59
	d			13 18		14 00							14 59								15 18				16 00
Grantham 7	a					14 11							15 11											16 05	16 12
	d		13 14			14 12						14 22	15 12										15 20	16 06	16 13
Peterborough 8	a		13 40	13 47		14 32					14 48	14 50	15 32								15 46		15 49		16 33
Norwich	a		15 22									16 35											17 26		
Peterborough 8	d			13 51		14 34					14 51		15 33								15 51				16 35
Stevenage 4	a					15 06																		16 51	17 07
London Kings Cross 15 ⊖	a			15 02	15 03	15 43			15 08		16 02		16 43			16 03			16 08		17 02			17 27	17 43

A To Manchester Airport
B From Nottingham
C To Reading
D From Sheffield
E To Liverpool Lime Street
F From Edinburgh to Manchester Airport
G To Penzance
H From Manchester Piccadilly

Table 26R

Sundays

5 January to 9 February

Scotland, North East England, Yorkshire and Humberside - London

Route Diagram - refer to first Page of Table 26

		XC		GR	GR	TP	GR	GR	XC	XC	TP	GC		GR	TP	XC	GC	EM	GR	GR	GC	EM		EM	GR
		◇1		1	1	◇1	1	1	◇1	◇1	◇1	1		1	◇1	◇1	1	◇	1	1	1	◇1		◇	1
		A			B	C			D	A	E			F	C	D		G				H		G	
Aberdeen	d				09 47																				
Stonehaven	d				10 05																				
Montrose	d				10 28																				
Arbroath	d				10 44																				
Dundee	d				11 03																				
Leuchars 3	d				11 17																				
Kirkcaldy	d				11 41																				
Inverkeithing	d				11 57																				
Inverness	d													09 40											
Perth	d													11 59											
Stirling	d													12 35											
Glasgow Central 15	d	10 55								11 51															
Motherwell	d	11 10								12 08															
Haymarket 238	d	11 51			12 16					12 49				13 15											
Edinburgh 10 238	a	11 56			12 20					12 54				13 20											
Edinburgh 238	d	12 08		12 20	12 30			13 00		13 08				13 30		13 55				14 00					
Dunbar	d									13 27															
Berwick-upon-Tweed	d	12 47			13 13									14 13		14 34									
Alnmouth for Alnwick	d									14 08										15 00					
Morpeth	d			13 33																					
Newcastle 8	a	13 33		13 49	13 58			14 24		14 37				14 58		15 20				15 27					
Sunderland	d											14 12													
Hartlepool	d											14 40													
Newcastle 8	d	13 40		13 52	14 00	14 08	14 15	14 27	14 35	14 40				15 00	15 07	15 23				15 30					
Chester-le-Street	d														15 16										
Durham	d	13 53		14 05		14 20	14 29	14 41	14 49	14 54					15 23	15 36				15 43					
Darlington 7	a	14 09			14 28	14 36	14 46	14 57	15 04	15 09				15 28	15 39	15 51				16 00					
Middlesbrough	d										14 43														
Eaglescliffe	d											15 04													
Darlington 7	d	14 10			14 29	14 37	14 49	14 59	15 06	15 11				15 29	15 40	15 53				16 02					
Northallerton	d					14 49	15 00				15 12	15 24													
Thirsk	d										15 20	15 33													
York 8	a	14 37		14 46	14 56	15 12	15 19	15 27	15 32	15 37	15 43	15 49		15 56	16 12	16 20				16 28					
Leeds 10	a	15 05				15 38				16 04	16 08				16 38										
Harrogate	d																								
Scarborough	d																								
York 8	d			14 48	14 59		15 22	15 29	15 35			15 51		15 59		16 24				16 31		16 49			
Doncaster 7	a			15 12			15 43	15 52												16 53					
Skipton	d																								
Keighley	d																								
Bradford Interchange	d																15 08				16 00				
Bradford Forster Square	d																								
Shipley	d																								
Halifax	d																15 23				16 14				
Brighouse	d																15 37				16 25				
Mirfield	d																15 45				16 33				
Leeds 10	d	15 10								16 10									16 16						16 45
Wakefield Westgate 7	d	15 23								16 22									16 28						16 58
Wakefield Kirkgate 4	d																16 02				16 49				
Pontefract Monkhill	d																								
Sheffield 7	a	15 51							16 21	16 51						17 15						17 41			
Hull	d																								
Selby	d																								
Doncaster 7	d						15 46	15 54									16 27		16 47	16 55	17 12				17 18
Retford 10	d							16 09																	
Lincoln	d																								
Newark North Gate 7	a						16 08													17 17					17 45
	d						16 09													17 19					17 46
Grantham 7	a																		17 17						
	d																	16 22	17 18					17 21	
Peterborough 8	a						16 41	16 48										16 52		17 47				17 50	18 14
Norwich	a																	18 30						19 29	
Peterborough 8	d							16 51												17 51					18 16
Stevenage 4	a																		18 06						
London Kings Cross 15 ⊖	a				17 06			18 02				18 03		18 08			18 16		18 43	19 02	19 03				19 20

A To Reading. Trolley service from Edinburgh
B The Northern Lights
C To Manchester Airport
D To Plymouth
E To Liverpool Lime Street
F The Highland Chieftain
G From Liverpool Lime Street
H To St Pancras International

Table 26R

Sundays

5 January to 9 February

Scotland, North East England, Yorkshire and Humberside - London

Route Diagram - refer to first Page of Table 26

		XC	GR	TP	HT	EM	GR	GR	XC	GR	XC	TP	GR	TP	GR	GR	XC	EM	GR	XC	GR	TP	GR
		◇1	R 1	◇1	◇1	◇	R 1	R 1	◇1	R 1	◇1	◇1	R 1	◇1	R 1	R 1	◇1	◇	R 1	◇1	R 1	◇1	R 1
		A		B		C			D		E	F		B			G	C		H		B	
Aberdeen	d	11 08	11 47																				13 47
Stonehaven	d	11 25	12 05																				14 05
Montrose	d	11 46	12 28																				14 28
Arbroath	d	12 02	12 44																				14 44
Dundee	d	12 21	13 02																				15 02
Leuchars 3	d	12 34	13 17																				15 16
Kirkcaldy	d	13 04	13 42																				15 40
Inverkeithing	d	13 20	14 00																				15 56
Inverness	d																						
Perth	d																						
Stirling	d																						
Glasgow Central 15	d										13 49									14 55			
Motherwell	d										14 04									15 11			
Haymarket 238	d	13 37	14 19								14 42									15 51			16 17
Edinburgh 10 238	a	13 42	14 23								14 47									15 56			16 22
Edinburgh 238	d	14 10	14 30					15 00			15 08		15 30			16 00				16 08	16 20		16 30
Dunbar	d										15 28												
Berwick-upon-Tweed	d	14 49	15 13										16 12										17 13
Alnmouth for Alnwick	d															16 59				17 05			
Morpeth	d																			17 19			
Newcastle 8	a	15 35	15 58					16 23			16 34		16 56			17 27				17 36	17 44		17 58
Sunderland	d																						
Hartlepool	d																						
Newcastle 8	d	15 40	16 00	16 08				16 26	16 35		16 40		16 59	17 05		17 29	17 35			17 40	17 49	17 53	18 00
Chester-le-Street	d													17 14									
Durham	d	15 53		16 20				16 39	16 48		16 53			17 21		17 42	17 48			17 54		18 05	
Darlington 7	a	16 08	16 28	16 36				16 55	17 03		17 08		17 26	17 37		18 00	18 05			18 10	18 15	18 21	18 28
Middlesbrough	d											16 43											
Eaglescliffe	d																						
Darlington 7	d	16 10	16 29	16 37				16 57	17 05		17 10		17 27	17 38		18 01	18 06			18 11	18 17	18 22	18 29
Northallerton	d			16 49				17 08				17 12		17 49								18 34	
Thirsk	d											17 21											
York 8	a	16 36	16 56	17 12				17 28	17 32		17 37	17 43	17 54	18 12		18 28	18 32			18 38	18 43	19 03	18 56
Leeds 10	a	17 06		17 38							18 04	18 08		18 38						19 03		19 38	
Harrogate	d									17 06													
Scarborough	d																						
York 8	d		16 59					17 30	17 34				17 58			18 30	18 35				18 48		18 59
Doncaster 7	a							17 52								18 52							
Skipton	d																						
Keighley	d																						
Bradford Interchange	d																						
Bradford Forster Square	d																						
Shipley	d																						
Halifax	d																						
Brighouse	d																						
Mirfield	d																						
Leeds 10	d	17 10					17 16			17 45	18 10				18 16				18 45	19 10			
Wakefield Westgate 7	d	17 23					17 29			17 58	18 22				18 28				18 58	19 22			
Wakefield Kirkgate 4	d																						
Pontefract Monkhill	d																						
Sheffield 7	a	17 52							18 23		18 51						19 21			19 50			
Hull	d				16 35																		
Selby	d				17 10																		
Doncaster 7	d				17 29		17 47	17 55		18 19					18 47	18 54			19 19				
Retford 10	d				17 43		18 01												19 36				
Lincoln	d																						
Newark North Gate 7	a									18 43						19 17			19 50				
	d									18 44						19 18			19 51				
Grantham 7	a				18 03		18 23	18 27							19 18				20 02		19 41		
	d				18 04	18 17	18 24	18 28							19 19			19 28	20 03		19 42		
Peterborough 8	a					18 47		18 51		19 13						19 46		19 57	20 23				
Norwich	a					20 26												21 37					
Peterborough 8	d							18 52		19 15						19 51			20 25				
Stevenage 4	a				18 53		19 07								20 05				20 53				
London Kings Cross 15 ⊖	a		19 08		19 25		19 43	20 02		20 20			20 05		20 43	21 03			21 29		21 06		21 09

A To Reading. bicycle symbol from Edinburgh
B To Manchester Airport
C From Liverpool Lime Street
D To Plymouth
E To Guildford
F To Liverpool Lime Street
G To Bristol Temple Meads
H To Birmingham New Street. bicycle symbol from Edinburgh

Table 26R

Sundays

5 January to 9 February

Scotland, North East England, Yorkshire and Humberside - London

Route Diagram - refer to first Page of Table 26

		XC	HT	GR	GR	XC	TP	GC	GR	TP	XC	GR	EM	GR	XC	GR	TP	TP	GR	NT	GR	XC
		◇1 A	◇1	R 1	R 1	◇1 B	◇1 C	R 1	R 1	◇1 D	◇1 E	R 1	◇ F	R 1	◇1 G	R 1	◇1	◇1 H	R 1	I	R 1	◇1
Aberdeen	d																					
Stonehaven	d																					
Montrose	d																					
Arbroath	d																					
Dundee	d																					
Leuchars 3	d																					
Kirkcaldy	d																					
Inverkeithing	d																					
Inverness	d																					
Perth	d																					
Stirling	d																					
Glasgow Central 15	d														16 55							18 57
Motherwell	d														17 11							19 11
Haymarket 238	d														17 51							19 51
Edinburgh 10 238	a														17 56							19 55
Edinburgh 238	d			17 00		17 08			17 30			18 00			18 08	18 30			19 00		20 00	20 15
Dunbar	d					17 28			17 51						18 28				19 21		20 22	20 35
Berwick-upon-Tweed	d					17 51			18 16						18 51	19 12			19 46		20 48	21 01
Alnmouth for Alnwick	d											18 59									21 11	
Morpeth	d																				21 27	
Newcastle 8	a			18 23		18 37			19 00			19 27			19 37	19 56			20 30		21 43	21 46
Sunderland	d							18 12														
Hartlepool	d							18 40														
Newcastle 8	d	18 21		18 26		18 40			19 03	19 10	19 26	19 30			19 40	20 01		20 08	20 33	21 06	21 45	
Chester-le-Street	d																			21 15		
Durham	d	18 34		18 39		18 53				19 22	19 39	19 43			19 53			20 20	20 46	21 24	21 59	
Darlington 7	a	18 49		18 56		19 08			19 30	19 38	19 54	20 01			20 08	20 27		20 36	21 03	21 44	22 17	
Middlesbrough	d						18 45										20 06					
Eaglescliffe	d							19 04												22a00		
Darlington 7	d	18 52		18 58		19 10			19 31	19 39	19 56	20 02			20 10	20 29		20 37	21 05		22 18	
Northallerton	d			19 10			19 14	19 22									20 34	20 49			22 32	
Thirsk	d						19 22	19 32									20 44					
York 8	a	19 19		19 29		19 37	19 42	19 49	19 58	20 11	20 22	20 29			20 37	20 56	21 02	21 12	21 31		23 03	
Leeds 10	a					20 05	20 08			20 38					21 02			21 38			23 35	
Harrogate	d																					
Scarborough	d																					
York 8	d	19 24		19 31				19 52	20 00		20 24	20 31				20 59			21 34			
Doncaster 7	a			19 53								20 53				21 20			21 55			
Skipton	d																					
Keighley	d																					
Bradford Interchange	d																					
Bradford Forster Square	d																					
Shipley	d																					
Halifax	d																					
Brighouse	d																					
Mirfield	d																					
Leeds 10	d				19 45	20 10								20 45	21 10							
Wakefield Westgate 7	d				19 58	20 22								20 58	21 22							
Wakefield Kirkgate 4	d																					
Pontefract Monkhill	d																					
Sheffield 7	a	20 14				20 51					21 17				21 50							
Hull	d		18 45																			
Selby	d		19 20																			
Doncaster 7	d		19 39	19 55	20 20							20 54		21 16		21 25			21 57			
Retford 10	d		19 54											21 30								
Lincoln	d																					
Newark North Gate 7	a			20 18	20 43							21 17				21 48			22 19			
	d			20 19	20 44							21 18				21 49			22 20			
Grantham 7	a		20 14						20 47					21 52		22 01			22 32			
	d		20 15						20 48				21 20	21 53		22 02			22 33			
Peterborough 8	a			20 48	21 13				21 08			21 46	21 51	22 13		22 22			22 53			
Norwich	a												23 24									
Peterborough 8	d			20 51	21 14				21 09			21 51		22 14		22 23			22 54			
Stevenage 4	a													22 45		22 54			23s35			
London Kings Cross 15 ⊖	a		21 34	22 02	22 21			22 03	22 16			23 02		23 21		23 30			00 15			

A To Bristol Temple Meads
B To Birmingham New Street. ⚲ to Leeds
C To Liverpool Lime Street
D To Manchester Piccadilly
E To Birmingham New Street
F From Liverpool Lime Street
G To Birmingham New Street. ⚲ from Edinburgh to Leeds
H To Manchester Airport
I To Saltburn

Table 26R

Sundays

5 January to 9 February

Scotland, North East England, Yorkshire and Humberside - London

Route Diagram - refer to first Page of Table 26

			GR	TP
			R	
			[1]	◇[1]
				A
			🍴	
Aberdeen		d		
Stonehaven		d		
Montrose		d		
Arbroath		d		
Dundee		d		
Leuchars [3]		d		
Kirkcaldy		d		
Inverkeithing		d		
Inverness		d		
Perth		d		
Stirling		d		
Glasgow Central [15]		d		
Motherwell		d		
Haymarket	238	d		
Edinburgh [10]	238	a		
Edinburgh	238	d	21 00	
Dunbar		d	21 22	
Berwick-upon-Tweed		d	21 47	
Alnmouth for Alnwick		d	22 09	
Morpeth		d		
Newcastle [8]	⛴	a	22 39	
Sunderland	⛴	d		
Hartlepool		d		
Newcastle [8]	⛴	d		
Chester-le-Street		d		
Durham		d		
Darlington [7]		a		
Middlesbrough		d		22 08
Eaglescliffe		d		
Darlington [7]		d		
Northallerton		d		22 36
Thirsk		d		22 44
York [8]		a		23 09
Leeds [10]		a		23 38
Harrogate		d		
Scarborough		d		
York [8]		d		
Doncaster [7]		a		
Skipton		d		
Keighley		d		
Bradford Interchange		d		
Bradford Forster Square		d		
Shipley		d		
Halifax		d		
Brighouse		d		
Mirfield		d		
Leeds [10]		d		
Wakefield Westgate [7]		d		
Wakefield Kirkgate [4]		d		
Pontefract Monkhill		d		
Sheffield [7]	⛴	a		
Hull		d		
Selby		d		
Doncaster [7]		d		
Retford [10]		d		
Lincoln		d		
Newark North Gate [7]		a		
		d		
Grantham [7]		a		
		d		
Peterborough [8]		a		
Norwich		a		
Peterborough [8]		d		
Stevenage [4]		a		
London Kings Cross [15]	⊖	a		

A To Manchester Airport

Table 26R

Sundays

16 February to 23 March

Scotland, North East England, Yorkshire and Humberside - London

Route Diagram - refer to first Page of Table 26

Station		GR	GR	GR	TP	GR	HT	XC	GR	GR	GR	XC	TP	GC	GR	TP	GR	GR	HT	GR	XC	GR	TP
		1	1	1	◇1	1	◇1	◇1	1	1	1	◇1	◇1	1	1	◇1	1	1	◇1	1	◇1	1	◇1
					A			B				C	A			D					B		D
Aberdeen	d																						
Stonehaven	d																						
Montrose	d																						
Arbroath	d																						
Dundee	d																						
Leuchars 8	d																						
Kirkcaldy	d																						
Inverkeithing	d																						
Inverness	d																						
Perth	d																						
Stirling	d																						
Glasgow Central 15	d																						
Motherwell	d																						
Haymarket 238	d																						
Edinburgh 10 238	a																						
Edinburgh 238	d																	09 00			09 08	09 30	
Dunbar	d																						
Berwick-upon-Tweed	d																				09 49	10 13	
Alnmouth for Alnwick	d																						
Morpeth	d																						
Newcastle 8	a																	10 23			10 36	10 58	
Sunderland	d													09 18									
Hartlepool	d													09 43									
Newcastle 8	d			07 55	08 34				08 55		09 25	09 30	09 33		10 00			10 29			10 39	11 00	11 08
Chester-le-Street	d												09 43										
Durham	d			08 08	08 46				09 09		09 38	09 44	09 49					10 42			10 53		11 20
Darlington 7	a			08 26	09 02				09 26		09 55	10 00	10 05		10 27			10 59			11 08	11 28	11 36
Middlesbrough	d															10 15							
Eaglescliffe	d													10 04									
Darlington 7	d			08 28	09 04				09 28		09 57	10 02	10 06		10 28			11 01			11 10	11 29	11 37
Northallerton	d				09 15						10 08		10 18	10 23		10 43		11 12					11 49
Thirsk	d				09 23									10 32		10 51							
York 8	a			08 55	09 42				09 55		10 27	10 31	10 41	10 49	10 55	11 09		11 31			11 38	11 56	12 11
Leeds 10	a				10 12							10 56	11 08			11 38					12 05		12 38
Harrogate	d																						
Scarborough	d																						
York 8	d	08 00		08 57				09 33	09 57		10 30			10 52	10 57			11 34				11 59	
Doncaster 7	a	08 21									10 51							11 55					
Skipton	d																						
Keighley	d																						
Bradford Interchange	d																						
Bradford Forster Square	d																						
Shipley	d																						
Halifax	d																						
Brighouse	d																						
Mirfield	d																						
Leeds 10	d		08 05			09 05		10 00		10 05		11 00					11 05			12 05	12 10		
Wakefield Westgate 7	d		08 17			09 18		10 12		10 17		11 12					11 17			12 17	12 23		
Wakefield Kirkgate 4	d																						
Pontefract Monkhill	d																						
Sheffield 7	a																				12 54		
Hull	d						09 05												11 10				
Selby	d						09 40												11 45				
Doncaster 7	d	08 23	08 35			09 37	10 00	10a28		10 35	10 53	11a28					11 38	11 57	12 03	12 35			
Retford 10	d		08 50				10 14			10 50								12 11	12 17				
Lincoln	d																						
Newark North Gate 7	a		09 04			09 59				11 04	11 15						12 00			12 57			
	d		09 06			10 00				11 06	11 16						12 01			12 58			
Grantham 7	a		09 17			10 12	10 34			11 17							12 13		12 38	13 10			
	d		09 19			10 13	10 35			11 19							12 14		12 39	13 11			
Peterborough 8	a	09 10	09 39	10 03		10 33			11 03	11 39	11 47				12 02		12 34	12 50		13 31			
Norwich	a																						
Peterborough 8	d	09 11	09 41	10 04		10 34			11 05	11 41	11 51				12 03		12 39	12 51		13 41			
Stevenage 4	a	09 42				11 06											13 07						
London Kings Cross 15 ⊖	a	10 18	10 44	11 09		11 43	12 02		12 10	12 44	13 03			13 05	13 09		13 43	14 02	14 05	14 43		14 08	

A To Manchester Airport
B To Exeter St Davids
C To Reading
D To Liverpool Lime Street

Table 26R

Sundays

16 February to 23 March

Scotland, North East England, Yorkshire and Humberside - London

Route Diagram - refer to first Page of Table 26

Station		EM ◇ A	GR R 1	GC R 1	GR R 1	XC ◇1 B		GR R 1	TP ◇1 C	GR R 1	EM ◇ D	GR R 1	XC ◇1 B	TP ◇1 E	GC R 1	GR R 1		TP ◇1 C	GR R 1	XC ◇1 F	EM ◇ G	HT ◇1 ⊠	GR R 1	XC ◇1 H	GR R 1
Aberdeen	d																								
Stonehaven	d																								
Montrose	d																								
Arbroath	d																								
Dundee	d																								
Leuchars 3	d																								
Kirkcaldy	d																								
Inverkeithing	d																								
Inverness	d																								
Perth	d																								
Stirling	d																								
Glasgow Central 15	d																							10 55	
Motherwell	d																							11 10	
Haymarket 238	d																							11 51	
Edinburgh 10 238	a																							11 56	
Edinburgh 238	d		10 00			10 08		10 30		11 00			11 05			11 30			12 00					12 08	12 20
Dunbar	d												11 25												
Berwick-upon-Tweed	d							11 12					11 48			12 13								12 47	
Alnmouth for Alnwick	d		10 59			11 05							12 08						12 59						
Morpeth	d					11 19																			13 33
Newcastle 8	a		11 27			11 36		11 56		12 23			12 37			12 58			13 27					13 33	13 49
Sunderland	d														12 12										
Hartlepool	d														12 36										
Newcastle 8	d		11 30			11 40		11 59	12 10	12 26			12 40			13 00		13 07	13 29	13 35				13 40	13 52
Chester-le-Street	d																	13 16							
Durham	d		11 43			11 53			12 22	12 39			12 52					13 23	13 42	13 48				13 53	14 05
Darlington 7	a		12 01			12 08		12 25	12 38	12 56			13 08			13 28		13 39	13 59	14 04				14 09	
Middlesbrough	d													12 45											
Eaglescliffe	d														13 04										
Darlington 7	d		12 03			12 10		12 27	12 39	12 58			13 09			13 29		13 40	14 00	14 05				14 10	
Northallerton	d									13 10				13 14	13 23										
Thirsk	d													13 23	13 33										
York 8	a		12 29			12 37		12 55	13 11	13 29			13 36	13 42	13 49	13 56		14 12	14 28	14 32				14 37	14 46
Leeds 10	a					13 05			13 38				14 03	14 08				14 38						15 05	
Harrogate	d																								
Scarborough	d																								
York 8	d		12 32					12 59		13 31					13 52	13 59			14 30	14 34					14 48
Doncaster 7	a		12 53							13 53									14 52	14 57					15 12
Skipton	d																								
Keighley	d																								
Bradford Interchange	d			12 00																					
Bradford Forster Square	d																								
Shipley	d																								
Halifax	d			12 14																					
Brighouse	d			12 25																					
Mirfield	d			12 33																					
Leeds 10	d				13 05	13 10						14 05	14 10										15 05	15 10	
Wakefield Westgate 7	d				13 18	13 24						14 18	14 23										15 18	15 23	
Wakefield Kirkgate 4	d			12 49																					
Pontefract Monkhill	d																								
Sheffield 7	a					13 53							14 52							15 21				15 51	
Hull	d																					14 35			
Selby	d																					15 10			
Doncaster 7	d		12 55	13 13	13 36					13 55		14 36							14 54			15 29	15 37		
Retford 10	d									14 09												15 43			
Lincoln	d																								
Newark North Gate 7	a		13 17		13 59							14 58							15 16				15 59		
	d		13 18		14 00							14 59							15 18				16 00		
Grantham 7	a				14 11							15 11										16 05	16 12		
	d	13 14			14 12						14 22	15 12									15 20	16 06	16 13		
Peterborough 8	a	13 40	13 47		14 32					14 48	14 51	15 32							15 46		15 49		16 33		
Norwich	a	15 22									16 35										17 26				
Peterborough 8	d		13 51		14 34					14 51		15 33							15 51				16 35		
Stevenage 4	a				15 06																	16 51	17 07		
London Kings Cross 15 ⊖	a		15 02	15 03	15 43			15 08		16 02		16 43			16 03	16 08			17 02			17 27	17 43		

A From Nottingham
B To Reading
C To Liverpool Lime Street
D From Sheffield
E To Manchester Airport
F To Exeter St Davids
G From Manchester Piccadilly
H To Reading. Trolley service from Edinburgh

Table 26R

Sundays

16 February to 23 March

Scotland, North East England, Yorkshire and Humberside - London

Route Diagram - refer to first Page of Table 26

		GR		TP	GR	GR	XC	XC	TP	GC	GR	TP		XC	GC	EM	GR	GR	GC	EM	GR	XC		GR	TP
		R 1		◇1	R 1	R 1	◇1	◇1	◇1	R 1	R 1	◇1		◇1	R 1	◇	R 1	R 1	R 1	◇	R 1	◇1		R 1	◇1
		A		B			C	D	E		F	B		C		G				G		D			B
Aberdeen	d	09 47																				11 08		11 47	
Stonehaven	d	10 05																				11 25		12 05	
Montrose	d	10 28																				11 46		12 28	
Arbroath	d	10 44																				12 02		12 44	
Dundee	d	11 03																				12 21		13 02	
Leuchars 3	d	11 17																				12 34		13 17	
Kirkcaldy	d	11 41																				13 04		13 42	
Inverkeithing	d	11 57																				13 20		14 00	
Inverness	d										09 40														
Perth	d										11 59														
Stirling	d										12 35														
Glasgow Central 15	d							11 51																	
Motherwell	d							12 08																	
Haymarket 238	d	12 16						12 49			13 15											13 37		14 19	
Edinburgh 10 238	a	12 20						12 54			13 20											13 42		14 23	
Edinburgh 238	d	12 30				13 00		13 08			13 30			13 55				14 00				14 10		14 30	
Dunbar	d							13 27																	
Berwick-upon-Tweed	d	13 13									14 13			14 34								14 49		15 13	
Alnmouth for Alnwick	d							14 08										15 00							
Morpeth	d																								
Newcastle 8	a	13 58				14 24		14 37			14 58			15 20				15 27				15 35		15 58	
Sunderland	d									14 12															
Hartlepool	d									14 40															
Newcastle 8	d	14 00		14 08	14 15	14 27	14 35	14 40			15 00	15 07		15 23				15 30				15 40		16 00	16 08
Chester-le-Street	d											15 16													
Durham	d			14 20	14 29	14 41	14 49	14 54				15 23		15 36				15 43				15 53			16 20
Darlington 7	a	14 28		14 36	14 46	14 57	15 04	15 09			15 28	15 39		15 51				16 00				16 08		16 28	16 36
Middlesbrough	d								14 43																
Eaglescliffe	d									15 04															
Darlington 7	d	14 29		14 37	14 49	14 59	15 06	15 11			15 29	15 40		15 53				16 02				16 10		16 29	16 37
Northallerton	d			14 49	15 00				15 11	15 24															16 49
Thirsk	d								15 20	15 33															
York 8	a	14 56		15 12	15 19	15 27	15 32	15 37	15 42	15 49	15 56	16 12		16 20				16 28				16 36		16 56	17 12
Leeds 10	a			15 38				16 04	16 08			16 38										17 06			17 38
Harrogate	d																								
Scarborough	d																								
York 8	d	14 59			15 22	15 29	15 35			15 51	15 59			16 24				16 31						16 59	
Doncaster 7	a				15 43	15 52	15 57							16 47				16 53							
Skipton	d																								
Keighley	d																								
Bradford Interchange	d														15 08				16 00						
Bradford Forster Square	d																								
Shipley	d																								
Halifax	d														15 23				16 14						
Brighouse	d														15 37				16 25						
Mirfield	d														15 45				16 33						
Leeds 10	d							16 10									16 16				16 45	17 10			
Wakefield Westgate 7	d							16 22									16 28				16 58	17 23			
Wakefield Kirkgate 4	d														16 02				16 49						
Pontefract Monkhill	d																								
Sheffield 7	a						16 21	16 51						17 15								17 52			
Hull	d																								
Selby	d																								
Doncaster 7	d				15 46	15 54									16 27		16 47	16 55	17 12		17 18				
Retford 10	d					16 09																			
Lincoln	d																								
Newark North Gate 7	a				16 08													17 17			17 45				
	d				16 09													17 19			17 46				
Grantham 7	a																17 17								
	d															16 22	17 18			17 21					
Peterborough 8	a				16 41	16 48										16 52		17 47		17 50	18 14				
Norwich	a															18 30				19 29					
Peterborough 8	d					16 51												17 51			18 16				
Stevenage 4	a																18 06								
London Kings Cross 15 ⊖	a	17 06				18 02				18 03	18 08				18 16		18 43	19 02	19 03		19 20			19 08	

A The Northern Lights
B To Liverpool Lime Street
C To Exeter St Davids
D To Reading. from Edinburgh
E To Manchester Airport
F The Highland Chieftain
G From Liverpool Lime Street

Table 26R

Sundays

16 February to 23 March

Scotland, North East England, Yorkshire and Humberside - London

Route Diagram - refer to first Page of Table 26

	HT	EM	GR	GR	XC	GR	EM	XC	TP	GR	TP	GR	GR	XC	EM	GR	XC	GR	TP	GR	XC	HT
	◇1	◇	R 1	R 1	◇1	R 1	◇1	◇1	◇1	R 1	◇1	R 1	R 1	◇1	◇	R 1	◇1	R 1	◇1	R 1	◇1	◇1
		A			B		C	D	E		F			G	A		H		F		G	
Aberdeen d																				13 47		
Stonehaven d																				14 05		
Montrose d																				14 28		
Arbroath d																				14 44		
Dundee d																				15 02		
Leuchars 3 d																				15 16		
Kirkcaldy d																				15 40		
Inverkeithing d																				15 56		
Inverness d																						
Perth d																						
Stirling d																						
Glasgow Central 15 d								13 49									14 55					
Motherwell d								14 04									15 11					
Haymarket 238 d								14 42									15 51			16 17		
Edinburgh 10 238 a								14 47									15 56			16 22		
Edinburgh 238 d				15 00				15 08		15 30			16 00				16 08	16 20		16 30		
Dunbar d								15 28														
Berwick-upon-Tweed d										16 12										17 13		
Alnmouth for Alnwick d													16 59				17 05					
Morpeth d																	17 19					
Newcastle 8 a				16 23				16 34		16 56			17 27				17 36	17 44		17 58		
Sunderland d																						
Hartlepool d																						
Newcastle 8 d				16 26	16 35			16 40		16 59	17 05		17 29	17 35			17 40	17 49	17 53	18 00	18 21	
Chester-le-Street d											17 14											
Durham d				16 39	16 48			16 53			17 21		17 42	17 48			17 54		18 05		18 34	
Darlington 7 a				16 55	17 03			17 08		17 26	17 37		18 00	18 05			18 10	18 15	18 21	18 28	18 49	
Middlesbrough d									16 43													
Eaglescliffe d																						
Darlington 7 d				16 57	17 05			17 10		17 27	17 38		18 01	18 06			18 11	18 17	18 22	18 29	18 52	
Northallerton d				17 08					17 12		17 49								18 34			
Thirsk d									17 21													
York 8 a				17 28	17 32			17 37	17 43	17 54	18 12		18 28	18 32			18 38	18 43	19 03	18 56	19 19	
Leeds 10 a								18 04	18 08		18 38						19 03		19 38			
Harrogate d						17 06																
Scarborough d																						
York 8 d				17 30	17 34		17 49			17 58			18 30	18 35				18 48		18 59	19 24	
Doncaster 7 a				17 52	17 57		18 11						18 52	18 57							19 47	
Skipton d																						
Keighley d																						
Bradford Interchange d																						
Bradford Forster Square d																						
Shipley d																						
Halifax d																						
Brighouse d																						
Mirfield d																						
Leeds 10 d			17 16			17 45		18 10				18 16				18 45	19 10					
Wakefield Westgate 7 d			17 29			17 58		18 22				18 28				18 58	19 22					
Wakefield Kirkgate 4 d																						
Pontefract Monkhill d																						
Sheffield 7 a					18 23		18 39	18 51						19 21			19 50				20 16	
Hull d	16 35																					18 45
Selby d	17 10																					19 20
Doncaster 7 d	17 29		17 47	17 55		18 19						18 47	18 54			19 19						19 39
Retford 10 d	17 43		18 01													19 36						19 54
Lincoln d																						
Newark North Gate 7 a						18 43							19 17			19 50						
d						18 44							19 18			19 51						
Grantham 7 a	18 03		18 23	18 27								19 18				20 02		19 41				20 14
d	18 04	18 17	18 24	18 28								19 19			19 28	20 03		19 42				20 15
Peterborough 8 a		18 47		18 51		19 13							19 46		19 57	20 23						
Norwich a		20 26													21 37							
Peterborough 8 d				18 52		19 15							19 51			20 25						
Stevenage 4 a	18 53		19 07									20 05				20 53						
London Kings Cross 15 ⊖ a	19 25		19 43	20 02		20 20				20 05		20 43	21 03			21 29		21 06		21 09		21 34

A From Liverpool Lime Street
B To Exeter St Davids
C To St Pancras International
D To Guildford
E To Manchester Airport
F To Liverpool Lime Street
G To Bristol Temple Meads
H To Birmingham New Street. from Edinburgh

Table 26R

Sundays

16 February to 23 March

Scotland, North East England, Yorkshire and Humberside - London

Route Diagram - refer to first Page of Table 26

		GR	GR	XC	TP	GC	GR	TP	XC	GR	EM	GR	XC	GR	TP	TP	GR	NT	GR	XC	GR	TP
		R	R			R	R			R		R		R			R		R		R	
		1	1	◇1	◇1	1	1	◇1	◇1	1	◇	1	◇1	1	◇1	◇1	1		1	◇1	1	◇1
				A				B	C		D		E					F				G
Aberdeen	d																					
Stonehaven	d																					
Montrose	d																					
Arbroath	d																					
Dundee	d																					
Leuchars 3	d																					
Kirkcaldy	d																					
Inverkeithing	d																					
Inverness	d																					
Perth	d																					
Stirling	d																					
Glasgow Central 15	d												16 55							18 57		
Motherwell	d												17 11							19 11		
Haymarket 238	d												17 51							19 51		
Edinburgh 10 238	a												17 56							19 55		
Edinburgh 238	d	17 00		17 08			17 30			18 00			18 08	18 30			19 00		20 00	20 15	21 00	
Dunbar	d			17 28			17 51						18 28				19 21		20 22	20 35	21 22	
Berwick-upon-Tweed	d			17 51			18 16						18 51	19 12			19 46		20 48	21 01	21 47	
Alnmouth for Alnwick	d									18 59									21 11		22 09	
Morpeth	d																		21 27			
Newcastle 8	a	18 23		18 37			19 00			19 27			19 37	19 56			20 30		21 43	21 46	22 39	
Sunderland	d					18 12																
Hartlepool	d					18 40																
Newcastle 8	d	18 26		18 40			19 03	19 10	19 26	19 30			19 40	20 01		20 08	20 33	21 06	21 45			
Chester-le-Street	d																	21 15				
Durham	d	18 39		18 53				19 22	19 39	19 43			19 53			20 20	20 46	21 24	21 59			
Darlington 7	a	18 56		19 08			19 30	19 38	19 54	20 01			20 08	20 27		20 36	21 03	21 44	22 17			
Middlesbrough	d				18 45										20 06							22 08
Eaglescliffe	d					19 04												22a00				
Darlington 7	d	18 58		19 10			19 31	19 39	19 56	20 02			20 10	20 29		20 37	21 05		22 18			
Northallerton	d	19 10			19 14	19 22									20 34	20 49			22 32			22 36
Thirsk	d				19 22	19 32									20 44							22 44
York 8	a	19 29		19 37	19 42	19 49	19 58	20 11	20 22	20 29			20 37	20 56	21 02	21 12	21 31		23 03			23 09
Leeds 10	a			20 05	20 08			20 38					21 02			21 38			23 35			23 38
Harrogate	d																					
Scarborough	d																					
York 8	d	19 31				19 52	20 00		20 24	20 31				20 59			21 34					
Doncaster 7	a	19 53							20 47	20 53				21 20			21 55					
Skipton	d																					
Keighley	d																					
Bradford Interchange	d																					
Bradford Forster Square	d																					
Shipley	d																					
Halifax	d																					
Brighouse	d																					
Mirfield	d																					
Leeds 10	d		19 45	20 10								20 45	21 10									
Wakefield Westgate 7	d		19 58	20 22								20 58	21 22									
Wakefield Kirkgate 4	d																					
Pontefract Monkhill	d																					
Sheffield 7	a			20 51					21 17				21 50									
Hull	d																					
Selby	d																					
Doncaster 7	d	19 55	20 20							20 54		21 16		21 25			21 57					
Retford 10	d											21 30										
Lincoln	d																					
Newark North Gate 7	a	20 18	20 43							21 17				21 48			22 19					
	d	20 19	20 44							21 18				21 49			22 20					
Grantham 7	a						20 47					21 52		22 01			22 32					
	d						20 48				21 20	21 53		22 02			22 33					
Peterborough 8	a	20 48	21 13				21 08			21 46	21 51	22 13		22 22			22 53					
Norwich	a										23 24											
Peterborough 8	d	20 51	21 14				21 09			21 51		22 14		22 23			22 54					
Stevenage 4	a											22 45		22 54			23s35					
London Kings Cross 15 ⊖	a	22 02	22 21			22 03	22 16			23 02		23 21		23 30			00 15					

A To Birmingham New Street. ⊼ to Leeds
B To Liverpool Lime Street
C To Birmingham New Street
D From Liverpool Lime Street
E To Birmingham New Street. ⊼ from Edinburgh to Leeds
F To Saltburn
G To Manchester Airport

Table 26R

Sundays

30 March to 11 May

Scotland, North East England, Yorkshire and Humberside - London

Route Diagram - refer to first Page of Table 26

		GR	GR	GC	GR	TP	GR	HT	XC	GR	GR	GR	XC	TP	GC	GR	TP	GR	GR	HT	GR	XC	GR
		■	■	■	■		■			■	■	■			■	■		■	■		■		■
		1	1	1	1	◇1	1	◇1	◇1	1	1	1	◇1	◇1	1	1	◇1	1	1	◇1	1	◇1	1
						A			B				B	C			A					B	
Aberdeen	d																						
Stonehaven	d																						
Montrose	d																						
Arbroath	d																						
Dundee	d																						
Leuchars 8	d																						
Kirkcaldy	d																						
Inverkeithing	d																						
Inverness	d																						
Perth	d																						
Stirling	d																						
Glasgow Central 15	d																						
Motherwell	d																						
Haymarket 238	d																						
Edinburgh 10 238	a																						
Edinburgh 238	d																		09 00			09 08	09 30
Dunbar	d																						
Berwick-upon-Tweed	d																					09 49	10 13
Alnmouth for Alnwick	d																						
Morpeth	d																						
Newcastle 8	a																		10 23			10 36	10 58
Sunderland	d														09 18								
Hartlepool	d														09 43								
Newcastle 8	d				07 55	08 04				08 55		09 25	09 30	09 33		10 00			10 29			10 39	11 00
Chester-le-Street	d													09 43									
Durham	d				08 09	08 16				09 08		09 38	09 44	09 49					10 42			10 53	
Darlington 7	a				08 26	08 32				09 26		09 55	10 00	10 05		10 27			10 59			11 08	11 28
Middlesbrough	d																10 15						
Eaglescliffe	d														10 04								
Darlington 7	d				08 28	08 33				09 28		09 57	10 02	10 06		10 28			11 01			11 10	11 29
Northallerton	d					08 45						10 08		10 18	10 23		10 43		11 12				
Thirsk	d					08 53									10 32		10 51						
York 8	a				08 55	09 12				09 54		10 27	10 31	10 41	10 49	10 55	11 09		11 31			11 38	11 56
Leeds 10	a					09 38							10 56	11 08			11 38					12 05	
Harrogate	d																						
Scarborough	d																						
York 8	d	08 00			08 57				09 33	09 57		10 30			10 52	10 57			11 34				11 59
Doncaster 7	a	08 21										10 51							11 55				
Skipton	d																						
Keighley	d																						
Bradford Interchange	d			07 58																			
Bradford Forster Square	d																						
Shipley	d																						
Halifax	d			08 10																			
Brighouse	d			08 21																			
Mirfield	d			08 29																			
Leeds 10	d		08 05				09 05		10 00		10 05		11 00					11 05			12 05	12 10	
Wakefield Westgate 7	d		08 17				09 18		10 12		10 17		11 12					11 18			12 17	12 23	
Wakefield Kirkgate 4	d			08 46																			
Pontefract Monkhill	d																						
Sheffield 7	a																					12 54	
Hull	d							09 05												11 10			
Selby	d							09 40												11 45			
Doncaster 7	d	08 23	08 36	09 11			09 37	10 00	10a28		10 35	10 53	11a28					11 35	11 57	12 04	12 35		
Retford 10	d		08 50					10 14			10 50								12 11	12 18			
Lincoln	d																						
Newark North Gate 7	a		09 04				09 59				11 04	11 15						11 58			12 57		
	d		09 05				10 00				11 06	11 16						12 00			12 58		
Grantham 7	a		09 17				10 12	10 34			11 17							12 11		12 39	13 10		
	d		09 18				10 13	10 35			11 19							12 13		12 40	13 11		
Peterborough 8	a	09 10	09 38		10 03		10 33			11 01	11 39	11 47				12 02		12 33	12 50		13 31		
Norwich	a																						
Peterborough 8	d	09 11	09 41		10 05		10 34			11 04	11 41	11 51				12 03		12 35	12 51		13 32		
Stevenage 4	a	09 39					11 04											13 06					
London Kings Cross 15 ⊖	a	10 07	10 32	10 40	10 57		11 32	11 42		11 55	12 33	12 42			12 44	12 54		13 33	13 42	13 46	14 23		13 52

A To Manchester Airport
B To Plymouth
C To Liverpool Lime Street

Table 26R

Sundays
30 March to 11 May

Scotland, North East England, Yorkshire and Humberside - London

Route Diagram - refer to first Page of Table 26

	TP	EM	GR	GC	GR	XC	GR	TP	GR	EM	GR	XC	TP	GC	GR	TP	GR	GR	XC	EM	HT	GR
	◇1	◇	1	1	1	◇1	1	◇1	1	◇	1	◇1	◇1	1	1	◇1	1	1	◇1	◇	◇1	1
	A	B				C		A		D		E	F			A			G	H		
Aberdeen d																						
Stonehaven d																						
Montrose d																						
Arbroath d																						
Dundee d																						
Leuchars 3 d																						
Kirkcaldy d																						
Inverkeithing d																						
Inverness d																						
Perth d																						
Stirling d																						
Glasgow Central 15 d																						
Motherwell d																						
Haymarket 238 d																						
Edinburgh 10 238 a																						
Edinburgh 238 d			10 00			10 08	10 30		11 00			11 05			11 30			12 00				
Dunbar d												11 25										
Berwick-upon-Tweed d							11 12					11 48			12 13							
Alnmouth for Alnwick d			10 59			11 05						12 08						12 59				
Morpeth d						11 19																
Newcastle 8 a			11 27			11 36	11 56		12 23			12 37			12 58			13 27				
Sunderland d														12 12								
Hartlepool d														12 36								
Newcastle 8 d	11 08		11 30			11 40	11 59	12 10	12 26			12 40			13 00	13 07	13 15	13 29	13 35			
Chester-le-Street d																13 16						
Durham d	11 20		11 43			11 53		12 22	12 39			12 52				13 23	13 29	13 42	13 48			
Darlington 7 a	11 36		12 01			12 08	12 25	12 38	12 56			13 08			13 28	13 39	13 46	13 59	14 04			
Middlesbrough d													12 45									
Eaglescliffe d														13 04								
Darlington 7 d	11 37		12 03			12 10	12 27	12 39	12 58			13 09			13 29	13 40	13 49	14 00	14 05			
Northallerton d	11 49								13 10				13 14	13 23			14 00					
Thirsk d													13 23	13 33								
York 8 a	12 11		12 29			12 37	12 55	13 11	13 29			13 36	13 42	13 49	13 56	14 12	14 19	14 28	14 32			
Leeds 10 a	12 38					13 05		13 38				14 03	14 08			14 38						
Harrogate d																						
Scarborough d																						
York 8 d			12 32				12 59		13 31					13 52	13 59		14 22	14 30	14 34			
Doncaster 7 a			12 53						13 53								14 43	14 52	14 57			
Skipton d																						
Keighley d																						
Bradford Interchange d				12 00																		
Bradford Forster Square d																						
Shipley d																						
Halifax d				12 14																		
Brighouse d				12 25																		
Mirfield d				12 33																		
Leeds 10 d					13 05	13 10					14 05	14 10										15 05
Wakefield Westgate 7 d					13 18	13 24					14 18	14 23										15 18
Wakefield Kirkgate 4 d				12 49																		
Pontefract Monkhill d																						
Sheffield 7 a						13 53						14 52							15 21			
Hull d																					14 35	
Selby d																					15 10	
Doncaster 7 d			12 55	13 13	13 36				13 55		14 36						14 47	14 54			15 29	15 37
Retford 10 d									14 09												15 43	
Lincoln d																						
Newark North Gate 7 a			13 17		13 59						14 58							15 16				15 59
d			13 18		14 00						14 59							15 18				16 00
Grantham 7 a					14 11						15 11										16 04	16 12
d		13 14			14 12					14 22	15 12									15 20	16 05	16 13
Peterborough 8 a		13 40	13 47		14 32				14 48	14 51	15 32						15 37	15 46		15 49		16 33
Norwich a		15 22								16 35										17 26		
Peterborough 8 d			13 51		14 34				14 51		15 33						15 40	15 51				16 35
Stevenage 4 a					15 06																16 50	17 04
London Kings Cross 15 ⊖ a			14 42	14 45	15 32		14 50		15 42		16 24			15 44	15 52		16 32	16 42			17 14	17 32

A To Manchester Airport
B From Nottingham
C To Penzance
D From Sheffield
E To Plymouth
F To Liverpool Lime Street
G To Reading
H From Manchester Piccadilly

Table 26R

Sundays

30 March to 11 May

Scotland, North East England, Yorkshire and Humberside - London

Route Diagram - refer to first Page of Table 26

		XC ◇1 A	GR 1	GR 1 B	TP ◇1 C	GR 1	GR 1	XC ◇1 D	XC ◇1 E	TP ◇1 F	GC 1	GR 1 G	TP ◇1 C	XC ◇1 D	GC 1	EM ◇ H	GR 1	GR 1	GC 1	EM ◇ H	GR 1	XC ◇1 E
Aberdeen	d			09 47																		11 08
Stonehaven	d			10 05																		11 25
Montrose	d			10 28																		11 46
Arbroath	d			10 44																		12 02
Dundee	d			11 03																		12 21
Leuchars 3	d			11 17																		12 34
Kirkcaldy	d			11 41																		13 04
Inverkeithing	d			11 57																		13 20
Inverness	d											09 40										
Perth	d											11 59										
Stirling	d											12 35										
Glasgow Central 15	d	10 55							11 51													
Motherwell	d	11 10							12 08													
Haymarket 238	d	11 51		12 16					12 49			13 15										13 37
Edinburgh 10 238	a	11 56		12 20					12 54			13 20										13 42
Edinburgh 238	d	12 08	12 20	12 30			13 00		13 08			13 30		13 55				14 00				14 10
Dunbar	d								13 27													
Berwick-upon-Tweed	d	12 47		13 13								14 13		14 34								14 49
Alnmouth for Alnwick	d								14 08									15 00				
Morpeth	d		13 33																			
Newcastle 8	a	13 33	13 49	13 58			14 24		14 37			14 58		15 20				15 27				15 35
Sunderland	d										14 12											
Hartlepool	d										14 40											
Newcastle 8	d	13 40	13 52	14 00	14 08	14 15	14 27	14 35	14 40			15 00	15 07	15 23				15 30				15 40
Chester-le-Street	d												15 16									
Durham	d	13 53	14 05		14 20	14 29	14 41	14 49	14 54				15 23	15 36				15 43				15 53
Darlington 7	a	14 09		14 28	14 36	14 46	14 57	15 04	15 09			15 28	15 39	15 51				16 00				16 08
Middlesbrough	d									14 43												
Eaglescliffe	d										15 04											
Darlington 7	d	14 10		14 29	14 37	14 49	14 59	15 06	15 11			15 29	15 40	15 53				16 02				16 10
Northallerton	d				14 49	15 00				15 12	15 24											
Thirsk	d									15 20	15 33											
York 8	a	14 37	14 46	14 56	15 12	15 19	15 27	15 32	15 37	15 43	15 49	15 56	16 12	16 20				16 28				16 36
Leeds 10	a	15 05			15 38				16 03	16 08			16 38									17 06
Harrogate	d																					
Scarborough	d																					
York 8	d		14 48	14 59		15 22	15 29	15 35			15 51	15 59		16 24				16 31				
Doncaster 7	a					15 43	15 52	15 57						16 47				16 53				
Skipton	d																					
Keighley	d																					
Bradford Interchange	d														15 08				16 00			
Bradford Forster Square	d																					
Shipley	d																					
Halifax	d														15 23				16 14			
Brighouse	d														15 37				16 25			
Mirfield	d														15 45				16 33			
Leeds 10	d	15 10							16 10								16 16				16 45	17 10
Wakefield Westgate 7	d	15 23							16 22								16 28				16 58	17 23
Wakefield Kirkgate 4	d														16 02				16 49			
Pontefract Monkhill	d																					
Sheffield 7	a	15 51						16 21	16 51					17 15								17 52
Hull	d																					
Selby	d																					
Doncaster 7	d					15 46	15 53								16 27		16 47	16 55	17 12		17 18	
Retford 10	d						16 09															
Lincoln	d																					
Newark North Gate 7	a					16 08												17 17			17 45	
	d					16 09												17 19			17 46	
Grantham 7	a		15 38														17 17					
	d		15 39													16 22	17 18			17 21		
Peterborough 8	a					16 39	16 48									16 52		17 47		17 50	18 14	
Norwich	a															18 30				19 29		
Peterborough 8	d					16 42	16 50											17 51			18 16	
Stevenage 4	a																18 04					
London Kings Cross 15 ⊖	a		16 45	16 52		17 35	17 43				17 45	17 52			17 57		18 33	18 42	18 43		19 10	

A To Penzance. Trolley service from Edinburgh
B The Northern Lights
C To Manchester Airport
D To Reading
E To Plymouth. Trolley service from Edinburgh
F To Liverpool Lime Street
G The Highland Chieftain
H From Liverpool Lime Street

Table 26R

Sundays

30 March to 11 May

Scotland, North East England, Yorkshire and Humberside - London

Route Diagram - refer to first Page of Table 26

		GR	TP	HT	GR	EM	GR	GR	XC	GR	EM	XC	TP	GR	TP	GR	GR	XC	EM	GR	XC	GR	TP
		R			R		R	R		R				R		R	R			R		R	
		1	◇1	◇1	1	◇	1	1	◇1	1	◇1	◇1	◇1	1	◇1	1	1	◇1	◇	1	◇1	1	◇1
			A			B			C		D	E	F		A			G	B		H		A
Aberdeen	d	11 47																					
Stonehaven	d	12 05																					
Montrose	d	12 28																					
Arbroath	d	12 44																					
Dundee	d	13 02																					
Leuchars 3	d	13 17																					
Kirkcaldy	d	13 42																					
Inverkeithing	d	14 00																					
Inverness	d																						
Perth	d																						
Stirling	d																						
Glasgow Central 15	d											13 49									14 55		
Motherwell	d											14 04									15 11		
Haymarket	238 d	14 19										14 42									15 51		
Edinburgh 10	238 a	14 23										14 47									15 56		
Edinburgh	238 d	14 30						15 00				15 08		15 30			16 00				16 08	16 20	
Dunbar	d											15 28											
Berwick-upon-Tweed	d	15 13												16 12									
Alnmouth for Alnwick	d																16 59				17 05		
Morpeth	d																				17 19		
Newcastle 8	a	15 58						16 23				16 34		16 56			17 27				17 36	17 44	
Sunderland	d																						
Hartlepool	d																						
Newcastle 8	d	16 00	16 08		16 15			16 26	16 35			16 40		16 59	17 05		17 29	17 35			17 40	17 49	17 53
Chester-le-Street	d														17 14								
Durham	d		16 20		16 29			16 39	16 48			16 53			17 21		17 42	17 48			17 54		18 05
Darlington 7	a	16 28	16 36		16 46			16 56	17 03			17 08		17 26	17 37		18 00	18 05			18 10	18 15	18 21
Middlesbrough	d												16 43										
Eaglescliffe	d																						
Darlington 7	d	16 29	16 37		16 49			16 58	17 05			17 10		17 27	17 38		18 01	18 06			18 11	18 17	18 22
Northallerton	d		16 49		17 00								17 11		17 49								18 34
Thirsk	d												17 20										
York 8	a	16 56	17 12		17 19			17 24	17 32			17 37	17 42	17 54	18 12		18 28	18 32			18 38	18 43	19 03
Leeds 10	a		17 38									18 04	18 08		18 38						19 03		19 38
Harrogate	d									17 06													
Scarborough	d																						
York 8	d	16 59			17 22			17 30	17 34		17 49			17 58			18 30	18 35				18 48	
Doncaster 7	a							17 51	17 57		18 11						18 52	18 57					
Skipton	d																						
Keighley	d																						
Bradford Interchange	d																						
Bradford Forster Square	d																						
Shipley	d																						
Halifax	d																						
Brighouse	d																						
Mirfield	d																						
Leeds 10	d						17 16			17 45		18 10				18 16				18 45	19 10		
Wakefield Westgate 7	d						17 29			17 58		18 22				18 28				18 58	19 22		
Wakefield Kirkgate 4	d																						
Pontefract Monkhill	d																						
Sheffield 7	a								18 23		18 39	18 51						19 21			19 50		
Hull	d			16 35																			
Selby	d			17 10																			
Doncaster 7	d			17 30			17 47	17 55		18 19						18 46	18 54			19 19			
Retford 10	d			17 44			18 01																
Lincoln	d																						
Newark North Gate 7	a				18 01					18 43							19 17			19 44			
	d				18 02					18 44							19 18			19 46			
Grantham 7	a			18 05			18 23	18 27								19 16						19 41	
	d			18 06		18 17	18 24	18 28								19 17			19 28			19 42	
Peterborough 8	a				18 31	18 47		18 50		19 13							19 46		19 57	20 15			
Norwich	a					20 26													21 37				
Peterborough 8	d				18 32			18 52		19 15							19 51			20 16			
Stevenage 4	a			18 49			19 09									20 00							
London Kings Cross 15 ⊖	a	18 53		19 18	19 23		19 34	19 43		20 10				19 49		20 27	20 42			21 10		20 48	

A To Manchester Airport
B From Liverpool Lime Street
C To Reading
D To St Pancras International
E To Plymouth. Trolley from Edinburgh
F To Liverpool Lime Street
G To Guildford
H To Bristol Temple Meads. Trolley from Edinburgh

Table 26R

Sundays

30 March to 11 May

Scotland, North East England, Yorkshire and Humberside - London

Route Diagram - refer to first Page of Table 26

		GR	XC	HT		GR	GR	GR	XC	TP	GC	GR	TP	XC		GR	EM	GR	XC	GR	TP	TP	GR	NT	
		R 1	◇1	◇1		R 1	R 1	R 1	◇1	◇1	R 1	R 1	◇1	◇1		R 1	◇	R 1	◇1	R 1	◇1	◇1	R 1		
			A						B	C			D	A			E		F			G		H	
Aberdeen	d	13 47																							
Stonehaven	d	14 05																							
Montrose	d	14 28																							
Arbroath	d	14 44																							
Dundee	d	15 02																							
Leuchars 3	d	15 16																							
Kirkcaldy	d	15 40																							
Inverkeithing	d	15 56																							
Inverness	d																								
Perth	d																								
Stirling	d																								
Glasgow Central 15	d																		16 55						
Motherwell	d																		17 11						
Haymarket 238	d	16 17																	17 51						
Edinburgh 10 238	a	16 22																	17 56						
Edinburgh 238	d	16 30					17 00		17 08			17 30				18 00			18 08	18 30			19 00		
Dunbar	d								17 28			17 51							18 28				19 21		
Berwick-upon-Tweed	d	17 13							17 51			18 16							18 51	19 12			19 46		
Alnmouth for Alnwick	d															18 59									
Morpeth	d																								
Newcastle 8	a	17 58					18 23		18 37			19 00				19 27			19 37	19 56			20 30		
Sunderland	d										18 12														
Hartlepool	d										18 40														
Newcastle 8	d	18 00	18 21				18 26		18 40			19 03	19 10	19 26		19 30			19 40	20 01		20 08	20 33	21 06	
Chester-le-Street	d																							21 15	
Durham	d		18 34				18 39		18 53				19 22	19 39		19 43			19 53			20 20	20 46	21 24	
Darlington 7	a	18 28	18 49				18 56		19 08			19 30	19 38	19 54		20 01			20 08	20 27		20 36	21 03	21 44	
Middlesbrough	d									18 45											20 06				
Eaglescliffe	d										19 04													22a00	
Darlington 7	d	18 29	18 52				18 58		19 10			19 31	19 39	19 56		20 02			20 10	20 29		20 37	21 05		
Northallerton	d						19 10			19 14	19 22										20 34	20 49			
Thirsk	d									19 22	19 32										20 44				
York 8	a	18 56	19 19				19 29		19 37	19 42	19 49	19 58	20 11	20 22		20 29			20 37	20 56	21 02	21 12	21 31		
Leeds 10	a								20 05	20 08			20 38						21 02			21 38			
Harrogate	d																								
Scarborough	d																								
York 8	d	18 59	19 24				19 31				19 52	20 00		20 24		20 31				20 59			21 34		
Doncaster 7	a		19 47				19 53							20 47		20 53				21 20			21 55		
Skipton	d																								
Keighley	d																								
Bradford Interchange	d																								
Bradford Forster Square	d																								
Shipley	d																								
Halifax	d																								
Brighouse	d																								
Mirfield	d																								
Leeds 10	d					19 16		19 45	20 10									20 45	21 10						
Wakefield Westgate 7	d					19 28		19 58	20 22									20 58	21 22						
Wakefield Kirkgate 4	d																								
Pontefract Monkhill	d																								
Sheffield 7	a		20 16						20 51					21 17					21 50						
Hull	d			18 45																					
Selby	d			19 20																					
Doncaster 7	d			19 39		19 46	19 55	20 20								20 54		21 16		21 25			21 57		
Retford 10	d			19 54		20 00												21 30							
Lincoln	d																								
Newark North Gate 7	a						20 18	20 43								21 17				21 48			22 19		
	d						20 19	20 44								21 18				21 49			22 20		
Grantham 7	a			20 14		20 22						20 47						21 52		22 01			22 32		
	d			20 15		20 23						20 48					21 20	21 53		22 02			22 33		
Peterborough 8	a						20 48	21 13				21 08				21 46	21 51	22 13		22 22			22 53		
Norwich	a																23 24								
Peterborough 8	d						20 51	21 14				21 09				21 51		22 14		22 23			22 54		
Stevenage 4	a					21 08												22 45		22 54			23s32		
London Kings Cross 15 ⊖	a	20 54		21 21		21 33	21 42	22 07			21 44	22 00				22 42		23 14		23 19			23 59		

A To Birmingham New Street
B To Bristol Temple Meads. 🍴 to Leeds
C To Liverpool Lime Street
D To Manchester Piccadilly
E From Liverpool Lime Street
F To Birmingham New Street. 🍴 from Edinburgh to Leeds
G To Manchester Airport
H To Saltburn

Table 26R

Sundays
30 March to 11 May

Scotland, North East England, Yorkshire and Humberside - London

Route Diagram - refer to first Page of Table 26

		GR	XC	GR	TP
		■ 1 🍴	◇1	■ 1 🍴	◇1 A
Aberdeen	d				
Stonehaven	d				
Montrose	d				
Arbroath	d				
Dundee	d				
Leuchars 3	d				
Kirkcaldy	d				
Inverkeithing	d				
Inverness	d				
Perth	d				
Stirling	d				
Glasgow Central 15	d		18 57		
Motherwell	d		19 11		
Haymarket 238	d		19 51		
Edinburgh 10 238	a		19 55		
Edinburgh 238	d	20 00	20 15	21 00	
Dunbar	d	20 22	20 35	21 22	
Berwick-upon-Tweed	d	20 48	21 01	21 47	
Alnmouth for Alnwick	d	21 11		22 09	
Morpeth	d	21 27			
Newcastle 8	a	21 43	21 46	22 39	
Sunderland	d				
Hartlepool	d				
Newcastle 8	d	21 45			
Chester-le-Street	d				
Durham	d	21 59			
Darlington 7	a	22 17			
Middlesbrough	d				22 08
Eaglescliffe	d				
Darlington 7	d	22 18			
Northallerton	d	22 32			22 36
Thirsk	d				22 44
York 8	a	23 03			23 09
Leeds 10	a	23 35			23 38
Harrogate	d				
Scarborough	d				
York 8	d				
Doncaster 7	a				
Skipton	d				
Keighley	d				
Bradford Interchange	d				
Bradford Forster Square	d				
Shipley	d				
Halifax	d				
Brighouse	d				
Mirfield	d				
Leeds 10	d				
Wakefield Westgate 7	d				
Wakefield Kirkgate 4	d				
Pontefract Monkhill	d				
Sheffield 7	a				
Hull	d				
Selby	d				
Doncaster 7	d				
Retford 10	d				
Lincoln	d				
Newark North Gate 7	a				
	d				
Grantham 7	a				
	d				
Peterborough 8	a				
Norwich	a				
Peterborough 8	d				
Stevenage 4	a				
London Kings Cross 15 ⊖	a				

A To Manchester Airport

Table 26A

Mondays to Saturdays

9 December to 17 May

Peterborough - Wisbech, Kings Lynn, Swaffham and Dereham

Bus Service

Route Diagram - refer to first Page of Table 26

		GR SX	GR SX	GR SO	GR	GR	GR	GR	GR	GR	GR	GR	GR	GR	GR	GR	GR	GR	GR	GR	GR	GR	GR
Peterborough	d	07 07	07 37	07 42	08 12	08 42	09 12	09 42	10 12	10 42	11 12	11 42	12 12	12 42	13 12	13 42	14 12	14 42	15 12	15 42	16 12	16 42	17 17
Wisbech Bus Station	d	07 46	08 16	08 21	08 51	09 21	09 51	10 21	10 51	11 21	11 51	12 21	12 51	13 21	13 51	14 21	14 51	15 21	15 51	16 21	16 51	17 21	17 56
Kings Lynn Bus Station	d	08 25	08 55	08 55	09 25	09 55	10 25	10 55	11 25	11 55	12 25	12 55	13 25	13 55	14 25	14 55	15 25	15 55	16 25	16 55	17 25	17 55	18 29
Swaffham Market Place	d	09 04	09 34	09 34	10 04	10 34	11 04	11 34	12 04	12 34	13 04	13 34	14 04	14 34	15 04	15 34	16 04	16 34	17 04	17 34	18 04	18 34	19 06
Dereham Market Place	a	09 37	10 07	10 07	10 37	11 07	11 37	12 07	12 37	13 07	13 37	14 07	14 37	15 07	15 37	16 07	16 37	17 07	17 37	18 07	18 37	19 07	19 37

		GR	GR	GR	GR	GR		GR	GR	GR
Peterborough	d	17 47	18 17	18 47	19 18	20 18		21 18	22 18	23 18
Wisbech Bus Station	d	18 26	18 56	19 26	19 56	20 56		21 56	22 56	23 56
Kings Lynn Bus Station	d	18a59	19 29	19a58	20 28	21 28		22a28	23a28	00a28
Swaffham Market Place	d		20 06		21 06	22 06				
Dereham Market Place	a		20 37		21 37	22 37				

Sundays

8 December to 11 May

		GR	GR	GR	GR	GR	GR	GR	GR	GR	GR	GR	GR	GR	GR
Peterborough	d	09 18	10 18	11 18	12 18	13 18	14 18	15 18	16 18	17 18	18 18	19 18	20 18	21 18	23 18
Wisbech Bus Station	d	09 56	10 56	11 56	12 56	13 56	14 56	15 56	16 56	17 56	18 56	19 56	20 56	21 56	23 56
Kings Lynn Bus Station	d	10 28	11 28	12 28	13 28	14 28	15 28	16 28	17 28	18 28	19 28	20 28	21 28	22a28	00a28
Swaffham Market Place	d	11 06	12 06	13 06	14 06	15 06	16 06	17 06	18 06	19 06	20 06	21 06	22 06		
Dereham Market Place	a	11 37	12 37	13 37	14 37	15 37	16 37	17 37	18 37	19 37	20 37	21 37	22 37		

Table 26A-R

Mondays to Saturdays

9 December to 17 May

Dereham, Swaffham, Kings Lynn and Wisbech - Peterborough

Bus Service

Route Diagram - refer to first Page of Table 26

		GR SX 🚌	GR SX 🚌	GR SO 🚌	GR 🚌	GR 🚌		GR 🚌	GR 🚌	GR SX 🚌	GR SO 🚌	GR SX 🚌	GR SO 🚌	GR SX 🚌	GR SO 🚌	GR 🚌		GR 🚌	GR 🚌	GR 🚌	GR 🚌	GR 🚌	GR 🚌	GR 🚌	GR 🚌
Dereham Market Place	d								07 05	07 30	07 35	08 00	08 06	08 35	08 36	09 05		09 35	10 05	10 35	11 05	11 35	12 05	12 35	13 05
Swaffham Market Place	d								07 35	08 02	08 05	08 32	08 37	09 07	09 07	09 37		10 07	10 37	11 07	11 37	12 07	12 37	13 07	13 37
Kings Lynn Bus Station	d	05 42	06 12	06 12	06 42	07 12		07 42	08 12	08 42	08 42	09 12	09 12	09 42	09 42	10 12		10 42	11 12	11 42	12 12	12 42	13 12	13 42	14 12
Wisbech Bus Station	d	06 17	06 47	06 47	07 17	07 47		08 17	08 49	09 19	09 19	09 49	09 49	10 19	10 19	10 49		11 19	11 49	12 19	12 49	13 19	13 49	14 19	14 49
Peterborough	a	07 07	07 37	07 42	08 12	08 42		09 12	09 42	10 12	10 12	10 42	10 42	11 12	11 12	11 42		12 12	12 42	13 12	13 42	14 12	14 42	15 12	15 42

		GR 🚌		GR 🚌	GR 🚌	GR 🚌	GR 🚌	GR 🚌	GR 🚌	GR 🚌	GR 🚌	GR 🚌		GR 🚌
Dereham Market Place	d	13 35		14 05	14 35	15 05	15 35	16 05	16 35	17 45	18 45	19 49		20 49
Swaffham Market Place	d	14 07		14 37	15 07	15 37	16 07	16 37	17 07	18 17	19 17	20 19		21 19
Kings Lynn Bus Station	d	14 42		15 12	15 42	16 12	16 42	17 12	17 42	18 54	19 54	20 54		21 54
Wisbech Bus Station	d	15 19		15 49	16 19	16 49	17 19	17 49	18 19	19 27	20 27	21 27		22 27
Peterborough	a	16 12		16 42	17 17	17 47	18 17	18 47	19 18	20 18	21 18	22 18		23 18

Sundays

8 December to 11 May

		GR 🚌	GR 🚌	GR 🚌	GR 🚌	GR 🚌	GR 🚌	GR 🚌	GR 🚌	GR 🚌		GR 🚌	GR 🚌	GR 🚌	GR 🚌	GR 🚌
Dereham Market Place	d			08 49	09 49	10 49	11 49	12 49	13 49	14 49		15 49	16 49	17 49	18 49	20 49
Swaffham Market Place	d			09 19	10 19	11 19	12 19	13 19	14 19	15 19		16 19	17 19	18 19	19 19	21 19
Kings Lynn Bus Station	d	07 54	08 54	09 54	10 54	11 54	12 54	13 54	14 54	15 54		16 54	17 54	18 54	19 54	21 54
Wisbech Bus Station	d	08 27	09 27	10 27	11 27	12 27	13 27	14 27	15 27	16 27		17 27	18 27	19 27	20 27	22 27
Peterborough	a	09 18	10 18	11 18	12 18	13 18	14 18	15 18	16 18	17 18		18 18	19 18	20 18	21 18	23 18

Sunday service operates on Bank Holiday Monday

Table 26B

Mondays to Saturdays

9 December to 17 May

Peterborough - Oundle, Corby and Kettering

Bus Service

Route Diagram - refer to first Page of Table 26

		GR	GR	GR		GR	GR	GR	GR
Peterborough Queensgate	d	07 05	07 40	09 10	and hourly until	17 10	18 30	19 30	20 32
Oundle Market Place	a	07 30	08 20	09 35		17 35	18 57	19 57	20 58
Corby George Street	a	08 01	08 51	10 06		18 06	19 24	20 24	21 24
Kettering Library	a	08 30	09 30	10 30		18 30	19 50	20 50	21 50

Sundays

8 December to 11 May

		GR	GR	GR	GR	GR	GR
Peterborough Queensgate	d	10 10	12 10	14 10	16 10	18 10	20 10
Oundle Market Place	a	10 32	12 32	14 32	16 32	18 32	20 32
Corby George Street	a	11 02	13 02	15 02	17 02	19 02	21 02
Kettering Library	a	11 25	13 25	15 25	17 25	19 25	21 25

Table 26B-R

Mondays to Saturdays

9 December to 17 May

Kettering and Corby, Oundle - Peterborough

Bus Service

Route Diagram - refer to first Page of Table 26

		GR	GR	GR	GR		GR	GR	GR	GR
Kettering Library	d	05 28	05 58	06 58	08 43	and hourly until	15 43	16 48	17 55	18 55
Corby George Street	d	05 51	06 21	07 21	09 06		16 06	17 16	18 21	19 21
Oundle Market Place	d	06 25	06 55	07 55	09 40		16 40	17 50	18 55	19 55
Peterborough Queensgate	a	06 45	07 27	08 27	10 03		17 03	18 13	19 18	20 29

Sundays

8 December to 11 May

		GR	GR	GR	GR	GR	GR
Kettering Library	d	08 15	10 15	12 15	14 15	16 15	18 15
Corby George Street	d	08 37	10 37	12 37	14 37	16 37	18 37
Oundle Market Place	d	09 10	11 10	13 10	15 10	17 10	19 10
Peterborough Queensgate	a	09 42	11 42	13 42	15 42	17 42	19 42

Table 26G

Mondays to Fridays
9 December to 16 May

York - Pickering and Whitby

Bus Service

Route Diagram - refer to first Page of Table 26

		GR	GR	GR		GR	GR	GR		GR	GR	GR		GR
York	d	08 38	09 42	10 42		11 42	12 42	13 42		14 42	15 44	16 19		18 09
Eden Camp	a	09 42	10 42	11 42		12 42	13 42	14 42		15 42	16 52	17 27		19 07
Flamingo Land	a													
Pickering Eastgate	a	09 58	10 58	11 58		12 58	13 58	14 58		15 58	17 08	17 43		19 23
Whitby Bus Station	a	11 02		13 02						17 02				

Saturdays
14 December to 17 May

		GR	GR	GR		GR	GR	GR		GR	GR
York	d	08 42	10 42	11 42		13 42	14 42	15 42		16 42	17 42
Eden Camp	a	09 42	11 42	12 42		14 42	15 42	16 42		17 42	18 42
Flamingo Land	a										
Pickering Eastgate	a	09 58	11 58	12 58		14 58	15 58	16 58		17 58	18 58
Whitby Bus Station	a	11 02	13 02				17 02				

Sundays
8 December to 11 May

		GR	GR
York	d	12 52	14 52
Eden Camp	a	13 58	15 52
Flamingo Land	a		
Pickering Eastgate	a	14 14	16 08
Whitby Bus Station	a		

Table 26G-R

Mondays to Fridays
9 December to 16 May

Whitby and Pickering - York

Bus Service

Route Diagram - refer to first Page of Table 26

		GR		GR	GR	GR		GR	GR	GR		GR	GR	GR		GR
Whitby Bus Station	d							11 14		13 14				17 50		
Pickering Eastgate	d	06 47		08 47	09 17	11 17		12 17	13 17	14 17		15 37	17 25	18 53		19 35
Flamingo Land	d															
Eden Camp	d	07 03		09 03	09 33	11 33		12 33	13 27	14 33		16 09	17 41	19 09		19 45
York	a	08 10		10 05	10 35	12 35		13 35	14 35	15 35		17 37	19 08	20 08		20 50

Saturdays
14 December to 17 May

		GR	GR	GR		GR	GR	GR		GR	GR
Whitby Bus Station	d					11 14		13 14		17 50	
Pickering Eastgate	d	07 07	09 17	11 17		12 17	13 17	14 17		18 53	19 13
Flamingo Land	d										
Eden Camp	d	07 23	09 33	11 33		12 33	13 27	14 33		19 09	19 29
York	a	08 25	10 35	12 35		13 35	14 35	15 35		20 08	20 50

Sundays
8 December to 11 May

		GR	GR	GR
Whitby Bus Station	d			
Pickering Eastgate	d	08 52	14 27	16 27
Flamingo Land	d			
Eden Camp	d	09 08	14 43	16 43
York	a	10 25	15 45	18 05

Table 26H

Mondays to Saturdays

9 December to 17 May

Darlington - Richmond and Catterick

Bus Service

Route Diagram - refer to first Page of Table 26

		GR SX	GR SX	GR SX	GR SO	GR SX	GR SO	GR SX	GR	GR SO		GR SX	GR SO	GR SX	GR	GR SO		GR SX	GR SO	GR SX	GR	GR
Darlington	d	06 28	06 58	07 23	07 33	07 43	08 03	08 03	08 23	08 43	and at the same minutes past each hour until	15 43	16 03	16 03	16 23	16 43		16 43	17 03	17 03	17 23	17 43
Richmond (Market)	a	07 00	07 30	07 55	08 05	08 15	08 35	08 35	08 55	09 15		16 15	16 35	16 35	16 55	17 15		17 15	17 35	17 35	17 55	18 15
Catterick Garrison Tesco	a		07 43	08 08	08 18	08 28	08 48	08 48	09 08	09 28		16 28	16 48	16 48	17 08	17 28		17 28	17 48	17 48	18 08	18 28
Catterick Camp Centre	a		07 45		08 20	08 30	08 50	08 50		09 30		16 30	16 50	16 50		17 30		17 30	17 50	17 50		18 30
Catterick Garrison Kemmel	a		07 50	08 20	08 27	08 35		08 55	09 20			16 35		16 55	17 20			17 35		17 55	18 20	

		GR		GR
Darlington	d	18 03	and hourly until	21 03
Richmond (Market)	a	18 35		21 35
Catterick Garrison Tesco	a	18 48		21 48
Catterick Camp Centre	a	18 50		21 50
Catterick Garrison Kemmel	a	18 57		21 57

Sundays

8 December to 11 May

		GR		GR
Darlington	d	09 03	and hourly until	21 03
Richmond (Market)	a	09 35		21 35
Catterick Garrison Tesco	a	09 48		21 48
Catterick Camp Centre	a	09 50		21 50
Catterick Garrison Kemmel	a	09 57		21 57

Table 26H-R

Mondays to Saturdays

9 December to 17 May

Catterick and Richmond - Darlington

Bus Service

Route Diagram - refer to first Page of Table 26

		GR SX	GR SX	GR SX	GR	GR	GR		GR	GR	GR		GR	GR	GR		GR
Catterick Garrison Kemmel	d	06 22			07 20			and at the same minutes past each hour until	17 20				18 30		19 19	and hourly until	22 19
Catterick Camp Centre	d	06 28		07 08		07 48	08 08			17 48	18 08			19 08	19 25		22 25
Catterick Garrison Tesco	d	06 30		07 10	07 30	07 50	08 10		17 30	17 50	18 10		18 40	19 10	19 27		22 27
Richmond (Market)	d	06 41	07 01	07 21	07 41	08 01	08 21		17 41	18 01	18 21		18 51	19 21	19 38		22 38
Darlington	a	07 12	07 32	07 52	08 12	08 32	08 52		18 12	18 32	18 52		19 22	19 52	20 09		23 09

Sundays

8 December to 11 May

		GR		GR
Catterick Garrison Kemmel	d	09 19	and hourly until	22 19
Catterick Camp Centre	d	09 25		22 25
Catterick Garrison Tesco	d	09 27		22 27
Richmond (Market)	d	09 38		22 38
Darlington	a	10 09		23 09

Table 26K

Berwick-upon-Tweed - Scottish Border Towns

Bus Service

Mondays to Fridays

9 December to 16 May

This service is operated by First Lowland under contract to Scottish Borders Council. Telephone 01835 824000

Route Diagram - refer to first Page of Table 26

		XC	XC	XC	XC	XC	XC	XC	XC	XC
Berwick-upon-Tweed	d	06 57	08 12	09 52	10 52	12 52	15 07	17 52	18 52	20 22
Duns	a	07 30	08 45	10 25	11 25	13 25	15 40	18 25	19 25	20 55
Earlston	a	08 08	09 36	11 03	12 03	14 03	16 28	19 03	20 03	21 33
Melrose	a	08 22	09 50	11 15	12 15	14 15	16 40	19 15	20 15	21 45
Galashiels Bus Station	a	08 40	10 05	11 30	12 30	14 30	16 55	19 30	20 30	22 00

Saturdays

14 December to 17 May

		XC	XC	XC	XC	XC	XC
Berwick-upon-Tweed	d	08 22	10 52	12 52	15 17	17 17	19 17
Duns	a	08 55	11 25	13 25	15 50	17 50	19 50
Earlston	a	09 33	12 03	14 03	16 28	18 28	20 28
Melrose	a	09 47	12 15	14 15	16 40	18 40	20 40
Galashiels Bus Station	a	10 02	12 30	14 30	16 55	18 55	20 55

Sundays

15 December to 11 May

		XC	XC	XC	XC	XC	XC
Berwick-upon-Tweed	d	10 52	12 52	15 17	17 42	19 07	20 37
Duns	a	11 25	13 40	15 50	18 30	19 55	21 10
Earlston	a	12 03	14 18	16 28	19 08	20 33	21 48
Melrose	a	12 15	14 30	16 40	19 20	20 45	22 00
Galashiels Bus Station	a	12 30	14 45	16 55	19 35	21 00	22 15

Table 26K-R

Scottish Border Towns - Berwick-upon-Tweed

Bus Service

Mondays to Fridays

9 December to 16 May

This service is operated by First Lowland under contract to Scottish Borders Council. Telephone 01835 824000

Route Diagram - refer to first Page of Table 26

		XC	XC	XC	XC	XC	XC	XC	XC
Galashiels Bus Station	d	06 20	07 40	08 10	10 50	12 50	14 40	16 37	17 20
Melrose	d	06 35	07 55	08 28	11 05	13 05	14 55	16 55	17 35
Earlston	d	06 47	08 07	08 40	11 17	13 17	15 07	17 07	17 47
Duns	d	07 25	08 50	09 20	11 55	13 55	15 55	17 40	18 30
Berwick-upon-Tweed	a	07 56	09 26	09 56	12 26	14 26	16 26	18 11	19 01

Saturdays

14 December to 17 May

		XC	XC	XC	XC	XC	XC
Galashiels Bus Station	d	06 35	08 20	10 50	12 50	14 50	17 20
Melrose	d	06 50	08 35	11 05	13 05	15 05	17 35
Earlston	d	07 02	08 47	11 17	13 17	15 17	17 52
Duns	d	07 40	09 25	11 55	13 55	15 55	18 30
Berwick-upon-Tweed	a	08 11	09 56	12 26	14 26	16 26	19 01

Sundays

15 December to 11 May

		XC	XC	XC	XC	XC	XC
Galashiels Bus Station	d	08 50	10 50	12 35	14 50	16 35	18 35
Melrose	d	09 05	11 05	12 50	15 05	16 50	18 50
Earlston	d	09 17	11 17	13 02	15 17	17 02	19 02
Duns	d	09 55	11 55	13 40	15 55	17 40	19 40
Berwick-upon-Tweed	a	10 26	12 26	14 26	16 26	18 26	20 26

Table 27

Mondays to Fridays

9 December to 16 May

Nottingham - Newark - Lincoln - Cleethorpes

Network Diagram - refer to first Page of Table 18

Miles	Miles			EM	EM	EM	EM	EM	EM	EM	EM	EM		EM	EM	EM	EM	EM	EM	EM	EM	EM		EM	EM
						A			B	C				C	C		C	A	C		C	A		C	
0	—	**Nottingham** 8	d		05 55	06 55			08 06	09 21				10 29	11 17		12 29		13 16		14 29			15 29	
3	—	Carlton	d		06 01	07 01			08 12	09 28					11 23				13 23					15 35	
5	—	Burton Joyce	d		06 05	07 04			08 16						11 27				13 27						
9¼	—	Lowdham	d		06 10	07 09			08 20	09 34				10 40	11 32		12 40		13 32		14 40			15 41	
10	—	Thurgarton	d		06 14	07 13			08 24						11 36				13 36						
11	—	Bleasby	d		06 17	07 16			08 27						11 39				13 39						
12¾	—	Fiskerton	d		06 20	07 19			08 30						11 42				13 42						
13¾	—	Rolleston	d		06 22	07 21			08 33						11 45				13 44						
17¼	—	**Newark Castle**	d		06 30	07 28			08 40	09 51				11 00	11 52		12 54		13 53		14 53			15 54	
—	0	**Newark North Gate** 7	a																						
—	—		d				07 40	08 31			09 57	10 50				12 06		13 02				15 28			16 45
22¼	5	Collingham	d		06 40	07 36	07 49	08 40			10 05			11 10	12 01	12 15		13 11	14 01			15 37		16 03	
25	—	Swinderby	d		06 44		07 54	08 45						11 14		12 19			14 05					16 07	
29¾	—	Hykeham	d		06 50		08 00	08 51			10 14			11 20		12 26			14 11			15 46		16 13	17 02
33¾	—	**Lincoln**	a		07 03	07 56	08 10	09 02	09 06	10 14	10 23	11 14		11 32	12 20	12 36	13 20	13 30	14 23		15 18	15 55		16 25	17 13
—	—		d	05 57			08 15				10 25					12 37				14 37					17 23
48½	—	Market Rasen	d	06 13			08 32				10 42					12 54				14 53					17 39
63½	—	Barnetby	a	06 30			08 49				10 58					13 10				15 10					17 54
69½	—	Habrough	a	06 40			08 59				11 08					13 20				15 19					18 03
77½	—	**Grimsby Town**	a	06 55			09 13				11 22					13 35				15 34					18 15
80¾	—	**Cleethorpes**	a																						

		EM	EM	EM	EM	EM	EM	EM		EM	GR	EM	EM
											■ 1	◇1	
		D		C		C		C			E	F	
Nottingham 8	d	16 15		17 18	17 50	18 18		19 20				20 30	22 26
Carlton	d	16 21		17 24		18 24		19 26					22 32
Burton Joyce	d	16 24		17 27		18 27		19 30					22 35
Lowdham	d	16 29		17 32	18 01	18 32		19 35				20 41	22 40
Thurgarton	d	16 33		17 36		18 36							
Bleasby	d	16 36		17 39		18 39		19 40					22 45
Fiskerton	d	16 39		17 42		18 43		19 43					22 49
Rolleston	d	16 42		17 45		18 45		19 46					
Newark Castle	d	16 53		17 53	18 18	18 54		19 55				20 54	22 57
Newark North Gate 7	a												23 06
	d		17 28				19 34			20 03	20 36		23 09
Collingham	d	17 02	17 36	18 02	18 27	19 05	19 43			20 12		21 03	23 18
Swinderby	d			18 07	18 33	19 08							23 23
Hykeham	d			18 13	18 39	19 14							23 29
Lincoln	a	17 17	18 00	18 26	18 49	19 24	20 01	20 17		20 27	21 02	21 22	23 40
	d						20 02						
Market Rasen	d						20 19						
Barnetby	a						20 35						
Habrough	a						20 44						
Grimsby Town	a						20 56						
Cleethorpes	a						21 03						

Saturdays

14 December to 17 May

		EM	EM	EM	EM	EM	EM	EM	EM	EM		EM	EM	EM	EM	EM	EM	EM	EM	EM		EM	EM	EM	EM
				A					C			C	C		C	A	C		C	A		C	C		C
Nottingham 8	d		05 55	06 56			08 07		09 22			10 29	11 17		12 27		13 17		14 29			15 22	16 15		17 15
Carlton	d		06 01	07 02			08 13		09 28				11 23				13 23					15 29	16 21		17 21
Burton Joyce	d		06 05	07 06			08 17						11 27				13 27						16 24		17 24
Lowdham	d		06 10	07 10			08 22		09 35			10 40	11 32		12 38		13 32		14 40			15 36	16 29		17 29
Thurgarton	d		06 14	07 14			08 26						11 36				13 36						16 33		17 33
Bleasby	d		06 17	07 17			08 29						11 39				13 39						16 36		17 36
Fiskerton	d		06 20	07 21			08 32						11 42				13 42						16 39		17 39
Rolleston	d		06 22	07 23			08 35						11 45				13 44						16 42		17 42
Newark Castle	d		06 30	07 29			08 42		09 50			10 58	11 55		12 51		13 51		14 55			15 50	16 51		17 49
Newark North Gate 7	a																								
	d					08 20		09 35		10 52				12 06		13 02				15 29					
Collingham	d		06 40	07 39		08 29		09 43				11 09	12 08	12 15		13 11	14 00			15 38		15 59	17 00		17 58
Swinderby	d		06 44			08 34						11 13		12 19			14 05					16 03			18 03
Hykeham	d		06 50			08 41						11 19		12 26			14 11		15 11			16 09			18 09
Lincoln	a		07 04	07 58		08 55	09 08	09 59	10 14	11 20		11 31	12 26	12 36	13 18	13 30	14 23		15 22	15 56		16 21	17 16		18 22
	d	05 38			08 15			10 06						12 37				14 52						17 23	
Market Rasen	d	05 54			08 32			10 23						12 54				15 07						17 39	
Barnetby	a	06 11			08 49			10 39						13 10				15 23						17 54	
Habrough	a	06 21			08 59			10 48						13 20				15 33						18 03	
Grimsby Town	a	06 36			09 13			11 02						13 36				15 48						18 18	
Cleethorpes	a																								

A To Peterborough
B From Worksop
C From Leicester
D From Leicester to Sleaford
E From London Kings Cross
F From St Pancras International

For connections from London Kings Cross please see Table 26

Table 27

Saturdays

14 December to 17 May

Nottingham - Newark - Lincoln - Cleethorpes

Network Diagram - refer to first Page of Table 18

		EM	EM	GR	EM	EM	EM	EM
				■ 1	◇1			
			A	B	C		A	A
Nottingham 8	d		18 15		19 29		20 30	21 26
Carlton	d		18 21					
Burton Joyce	d		18 25					21 33
Lowdham	d		18 30		19 40		20 40	21 37
Thurgarton	d		18 34					
Bleasby	d		18 37					21 42
Fiskerton	d		18 40					21 46
Rolleston	d		18 43					
Newark Castle	d		18 53		19 53		20 56	21 57
Newark North Gate 7	a							22 06
	d	18 07		19 34		20 32		22 09
Collingham	d	18 16	19 02		20 08	20 41	21 04	22 18
Swinderby	d		19 07					22 22
Hykeham	d		19 13					22 28
Lincoln	a	18 35	19 25	20 01	20 26	20 56	21 23	22 40
	d	18 35				20 58		
Market Rasen	d	18 51				21a15		
Barnetby	a	19 07						
Habrough	a	19 16						
Grimsby Town	a	19 31						
Cleethorpes	a							

Sundays

8 December to 11 May

		EM	EM	EM	EM	EM	EM	EM	GR	GR	EM	EM	EM
									■ 1	■ 1			
									D	E			
Nottingham 8	d			16 33		17 26	18 36	19 35			20 39		22 28
Carlton	d					17 32							22 34
Burton Joyce	d					17 35							22 37
Lowdham	d			16 44		17 39	18 46	19 45			20 49		22 42
Thurgarton	d					17 43							22 46
Bleasby	d					17 46							22 49
Fiskerton	d					17 50							22 52
Rolleston	d					17 52							22 54
Newark Castle	d			16 59		18 00	18 59	19 58			21 03		23 03
Newark North Gate 7	a						19 09						23 13
	d	11 35	13 35		17 56		19 23		20 36	20 57		22 10	23 17
Collingham	d	11 43	13 43	17 08		18 09	19 31	20 07			21 12	22 19	23 25
Swinderby	d			17 12		18 14	19 36	20 12			21 17		23 30
Hykeham	d			17 18		18 20	19 42	20 18			21 23		23 36
Lincoln	a	12 02	14 02	17 31	18 20	18 33	19 54	20 30	21 02	21 24	21 35	22 37	23 48
	d												
Market Rasen	d												
Barnetby	a												
Habrough	a												
Grimsby Town	a												
Cleethorpes	a												

A From Leicester
B From London Kings Cross
C From St Pancras International
D until 29 December, from 30 March. From London Kings Cross
E from 5 January until 23 March. From London Kings Cross

For connections from London Kings Cross please see Table 26

Table 27R

Mondays to Fridays

9 December to 16 May

Cleethorpes - Lincoln - Newark - Nottingham

Network Diagram - refer to first Page of Table 18

Miles	Miles			EM	EM	EM	GR	EM	EM	EM	EM	EM	EM	EM	EM	EM	EM	EM	EM	EM	EM	EM	EM
						◇1	R 1																
						A	B	C		D		D		D		D		D	D	D		D	
0	—	**Cleethorpes**	d		05 49																		
3¼	—	**Grimsby Town**	d		05 56				07 03				09 20				11 28				13 49		
11¼	—	Habrough	d		06 06				07 13				09 30				11 38				13 59		
17¾	—	Barnetby	d		06 15				07 22				09 39				11 47				14 09		
32¼	—	Market Rasen	d		06 32				07 39				09 55				12 03				14 25		
47	—	**Lincoln**	a		06 51				07 57				10 14				12 22				14 44		
—	—		d	05 26	06 53	07 04	07 20	07 26	07 59	08 35	09 10	09 32	10 15	10 36	11 35	11 41	12 23	12 30	13 40	14 33	14 46	15 30	15 45
51	—	Hykeham	d	05 34	07 01			07 34		08 43				10 44				12 38				15 37	
55¾	—	Swinderby	d	05 40	07 07			07 40		08 49				10 50				12 44				15 43	
58½	0	Collingham	d	05 45	07 12	07 19		07 45	08 15	08 54	09 25		10 32	10 55			12 40	12 49			15 02	15 48	
—	5	**Newark North Gate 7**	a	05 56	07 22		07 49		08 25		09 35		10 44		12 01		12 52				15 11		16 11
—	—		d	05 59																			
63½	—	**Newark Castle**	d	06 10		07 29		07 57		09 04		09 56		11 05		12 04		12 58	14 05	14 59		15 58	
67	—	Rolleston	d	06 16				08 03				10 02						13 04				16 04	
68	—	Fiskerton	d	06 18				08 05				10 04						13 06				16 06	
69¾	—	Bleasby	d	06 22				08 09				10 08						13 10				16 10	
70¾	—	Thurgarton	d	06 25				08 12				10 11						13 13				16 12	
71½	—	Lowdham	d	06 29		07 42		08 16		09 18		10 15		11 18		12 17		13 18	14 17	15 12		16 16	
75¾	—	Burton Joyce	d	06 34				08 20				10 19						13 22		15 16			
77¾	—	Carlton	d	06 38				08 24				10 23				12 23				15 20		16 23	
80¾	—	**Nottingham 8**	a	06 47		07 56		08 31		09 30		10 30		11 30		12 30		13 31	14 30	15 27		16 30	

		EM	EM	EM	EM	EM	EM	EM	EM	EM	EM
		D		D		D					
Cleethorpes	d									21 16	
Grimsby Town	d		15 45				18 28			21 23	
Habrough	d		15 55				18 38			21 33	
Barnetby	d		16 04				18 47			21 42	
Market Rasen	d		16 19				19 02			21 57	
Lincoln	a		16 38				19 21			22 16	
	d	16 34	16 44	17 26	18 18	18 35	19 24	20 35	21 42		22 27
Hykeham	d	16 42		17 34	18 26		19 32				22 35
Swinderby	d	16 48		17 40			19 38				22 41
Collingham	d	16 53	16 59	17 45	18 36		19 43	20 50			22 46
Newark North Gate 7	a		17 12		18 46		19 53				
	d										
Newark Castle	d	17 04		17 55		19 03		20 59	22 09		22 57
Rolleston	d			18 01							
Fiskerton	d			18 03							23 04
Bleasby	d			18 07							23 07
Thurgarton	d			18 10							
Lowdham	d	17 16		18 14		19 16		21 13	22 22		23 12
Burton Joyce	d			18 18							23 16
Carlton	d	17 22		18 22							23 20
Nottingham 8	a	17 30		18 29		19 29		21 27	22 34		23 31

Saturdays

14 December to 17 May

		EM	EM	EM	EM	EM	EM	EM	GR	EM	EM	EM	EM	EM	EM	EM	EM	EM	EM	EM	EM	EM	EM
			◇1						R 1														
			A	C		D		D	B		D		D		D	D	D		D	D		D	D
Cleethorpes	d																						
Grimsby Town	d				06 50					09 20				11 28				13 49			16 00		
Habrough	d				07 00					09 30				11 38				13 59			16 09		
Barnetby	d				07 09					09 39				11 47				14 09			16 18		
Market Rasen	d				07 26					09 55				12 03				14 25			16 33		
Lincoln	a				07 44					10 14				12 22				14 44			16 52		
	d	05 26	07 04	07 26	07 46	08 35	09 01	09 19	09 30	10 15	10 36	11 35	11 41	12 23	12 30	13 40	14 35	14 46	15 27	16 34	16 54	17 26	18 34
Hykeham	d	05 34		07 34		08 43					10 44				12 38				15 34	16 42		17 34	
Swinderby	d	05 40		07 40		08 49					10 50				12 44				15 40	16 48		17 40	
Collingham	d	05 45	07 19	07 45	08 02	08 54	09 16			10 32	10 55			12 40	12 48			15 02	15 45	16 53	17 09	17 45	
Newark North Gate 7	a	05 56			08 12		09 25		09 52	10 44		12 00		12 52				15 11			17 22		
	d	05 59																					
Newark Castle	d	06 10	07 29	07 55		09 04		09 48			11 04		12 04		12 57	14 05	15 01		15 58	17 03		17 55	19 02
Rolleston	d	06 16		08 02				09 55							13 04				16 04			18 01	
Fiskerton	d	06 18		08 04				09 57							13 06				16 06			18 03	
Bleasby	d	06 22		08 07				10 01							13 09				16 10			18 07	
Thurgarton	d	06 25		08 10				10 04							13 12				16 12			18 10	
Lowdham	d	06 29	07 42	08 14		09 18		10 08			11 17		12 17		13 17	14 17	15 14		16 16	17 16		18 14	19 16
Burton Joyce	d	06 34		08 18				10 13							13 21		15 19					18 18	
Carlton	d	06 38		08 22				10 17					12 23				15 23		16 23	17 22		18 22	
Nottingham 8	a	06 47	07 57	08 30		09 30		10 25			11 30		12 31		13 30	14 30	15 30		16 30	17 30		18 29	19 28

A To St Pancras International
B To London Kings Cross
C From Sleaford to Leicester
D To Leicester

For connections to London Kings Cross please see Table 26

Table 27R

Saturdays

14 December to 17 May

Cleethorpes - Lincoln - Newark - Nottingham

Network Diagram - refer to first Page of Table 18

		EM		EM	EM	EM
Cleethorpes	d					
Grimsby Town	d	18 28			19 45	
Habrough	d	18 38			19 54	
Barnetby	d	18 47			20 03	
Market Rasen	d	19 02			20 18	
Lincoln	a	19 21			20 37	
	d	19 24		19 35		20 45
Hykeham	d	19 32				
Swinderby	d	19 38				
Collingham	d	19 43				21 00
Newark North Gate 7	a	19 53				
	d					
Newark Castle	d			20 03		21 10
Rolleston	d					
Fiskerton	d					
Bleasby	d					
Thurgarton	d					
Lowdham	d			20 16		21 23
Burton Joyce	d					
Carlton	d					
Nottingham 8	a			20 30		21 39

Sundays

8 December to 11 May

		EM	EM	EM	EM	EM	EM	EM	EM	EM		EM
Cleethorpes	d											
Grimsby Town	d											
Habrough	d											
Barnetby	d											
Market Rasen	d											
Lincoln	a											
	d	11 05	13 00	15 00	17 25	18 05	19 03	20 05	21 00	21 26		22 10
Hykeham	d			15 08		18 13	19 11	20 13	21 08	21 34		22 18
Swinderby	d			15 14		18 19	19 17	20 19	21 14	21 40		22 24
Collingham	d	11 20	13 15	15 18		18 23	19 22	20 23	21 18	21 45		22 28
Newark North Gate 7	a	11 30	13 25	15 28	17 49				21 27	21 55		
	d			15 32					21 31			
Newark Castle	d			15 42		18 34	19 33	20 35	21 40			22 39
Rolleston	d					18 40						22 45
Fiskerton	d					18 42						22 47
Bleasby	d					18 46						22 50
Thurgarton	d					18 49						22 53
Lowdham	d			15 55		18 53	19 45	20 47	21 53			22 58
Burton Joyce	d					18 57						23 02
Carlton	d					19 01						23 05
Nottingham 8	a			16 09		19 11	20 05	21 03	22 09			23 17

For connections to London Kings Cross please see Table 26

Table 28

Mondays to Fridays

9 December to 16 May

Cleethorpes - Barton-on-Humber, Barnetby

Network Diagram - refer to first Page of Table 18

Miles			TP	EM	NT	NT BHX	TP	EM	NT	NT BHX	TP		TP	NT	NT BHX	EM	TP	TP	NT	NT BHX	EM		TP	TP	NT
			◇1				◇1				◇1		◇1				◇1	◇1					◇1	◇1	
			A	B			A	B			A		A			B	A	A			B		A	A	
						🚌				🚌					🚌					🚌					
			🛒				🛒				🛒		🛒				🛒	🛒					🛒	🛒	
0	**Cleethorpes**	d	05 17	05 49	06 00		06 18		07 00		07 26		08 26	08 55			09 26	10 26	10 55				11 26	12 26	12 55
—	New Clee	d												08x58					10x58						12x58
—	Grimsby Docks	d			06 05				07 05					09 00					11 00						13 00
3¼	**Grimsby Town**	a	05 24	05 55	06 08		06 25		07 08		07 33		08 33	09 03			09 33	10 33	11 03				11 33	12 33	13 03
—		d	05 25	05 56	06 08		06 26	07 03	07 08		07 34		08 34	09 03		09 20	09 34	10 34	11 03		11 28		11 34	12 34	13 03
5¼	Great Coates	d			06 12				07 12					09 07					11 07						13 07
6½	Healing	d			06 15				07 15					09 10					11 10						13 10
7½	Stallingborough	d			06 18				07 18					09 13					11 13						13 13
11¼	Habrough	d	05 35	06 06	06 24		06 36	07 13	07 24		07 44		08 44	09 19		09 30		10 44	11 19		11 38				13 19
13	Ulceby	d			06 28				07 28					09 23					11 23						13 23
15½	Thornton Abbey	d			06 32				07 32					09 27					11 27						13 27
17¼	Goxhill	d			06 35				07 35					09 30					11 30						13 30
19¼	New Holland	d			06 40				07 40					09 35					11 35						13 35
20¾	Barrow Haven	d			06 43				07 43					09 38					11 38						13 38
22¾	**Barton-on-Humber**	a			06 48				07 48					09 43					11 43						13 43
—	**Barton-on-Humber**	d				06 53				08 10					10 00					12 00					
—	Hull Paragon Interchange	a				07 20				08 37					10 27					12 27					
—	**Barnetby**	a	05 44	06 15			06 45	07 22			07 53		08 53			09 39	09 53	10 53			11 47		11 53	12 53	

		NT BHX	TP	EM	TP	NT	NT BHX		TP	EM	TP	NT	NT BHX	TP	EM	TP	NT		NT BHX	TP	TP	NT	NT	EM
			◇1		◇1				◇1		◇1			◇1		◇1				◇1	◇1			
			A	B	A				A	B	A			A	B	C				D	C			E
		🚌					🚌						🚌						🚌				🚌	
			🛒		🛒				🛒		🛒			🛒										
Cleethorpes	d		13 26		14 26	14 55			15 26		16 26	16 55		17 26		18 26	19 00			19 26	20 26	21 03		21 16
New Clee	d					14x58																		
Grimsby Docks	d					15 00						17 00					19 05					21 08		
Grimsby Town	a		13 33		14 33	15 03			15 34		16 33	17 03		17 33		18 33	19 08			19 33	20 33	21 11		21 22
	d		13 34	13 49	14 34	15 03			15 34	15 45	16 34	17 04		17 34	18 28	18 34	19 08			19 34	20 34	21 11		21 23
Great Coates	d					15 07						17 08					19 12					21 15		
Healing	d					15 10						17 11					19 15					21 18		
Stallingborough	d					15 13						17 14					19 18					21 21		
Habrough	d			13 59	14 44	15 19				15 55	16 44	17 20		17 44	18 38		19 24			19 44		21 27		21 33
Ulceby	d					15 23						17 24					19 28					21 31		
Thornton Abbey	d					15 27						17 28					19 32					21 35		
Goxhill	d					15 30						17 31					19 35					21 38		
New Holland	d					15 35						17 36					19 40					21 43		
Barrow Haven	d					15 38						17 39					19 43					21 46		
Barton-on-Humber	a					15 43						17 44					19 48					21 51		
Barton-on-Humber	d	14 00					16 00						18 00						19 53				21 53	
Hull Paragon Interchange	a	14 27					16 27						18 27						20 20				22 20	
Barnetby	a		13 53	14 08	14 53				15 53	16 03	16 53			17 51	18 46	18 53				19 53	20 53			21 42

Saturdays

14 December to 17 May

		TP	NT	NT	TP	EM	NT	NT	TP	TP		NT	NT	EM	TP	TP	NT	NT	NT	EM		TP	TP	NT	NT
		◇1			◇1				◇1	◇1					◇1	◇1						◇1	◇1		
		A			A	B			A	A				B	A	A			F	B		A	A		
				🚌				🚌					🚌					🚌							🚌
Cleethorpes	d	05 17	06 00		06 18		07 00		07 26	08 26		08 55			09 26	10 26	10 55		11 10			11 26	12 26	12 55	
New Clee	d											08x58					10x58							12x58	
Grimsby Docks	d		06 05				07 05					09 00					11 00							13 00	
Grimsby Town	a	05 24	06 08		06 25		07 08		07 33	08 33		09 03			09 33	10 33	11 03		11 16			11 33	12 33	13 03	
	d	05 25	06 08		06 26	06 50	07 08		07 34	08 34		09 03		09 20	09 34	10 34	11 03		11 17	11 28		11 34	12 34	13 03	
Great Coates	d		06 12				07 12					09 07					11 07							13 07	
Healing	d		06 15				07 15					09 10					11 10							13 10	
Stallingborough	d		06 18				07 18					09 13					11 13							13 13	
Habrough	d	05 35	06 24		06 36	07 00	07 24		07 44	08 44		09 19		09 30		10 44	11 19		11 28	11 38				13 19	
Ulceby	d		06 28				07 28					09 23					11 23							13 23	
Thornton Abbey	d		06 32				07 32					09 27					11 27							13 27	
Goxhill	d		06 35				07 35					09 30					11 30							13 30	
New Holland	d		06 40				07 40					09 35					11 35							13 35	
Barrow Haven	d		06 43				07 43					09 38					11 38							13 38	
Barton-on-Humber	a		06 48				07 48					09 43					11 43							13 43	
Barton-on-Humber	d			08 10				10 00					12 00					14 00							16 00
Hull Paragon Interchange	a			08 37				10 27					12 27					14 27							16 27
Barnetby	a	05 44			06 45	07 09			07 53	08 53				09 39	09 53	10 53			11 37	11 47		11 53	12 53		

A To Manchester Airport
B To Newark North Gate
C To Manchester Piccadilly
D To Sheffield
E To Lincoln
F To Sheffield. via Retford

For Hull, Doncaster, Meadowhall, Sheffield, Manchester and Manchester Airport refer to Table 29

Table 28

Saturdays

14 December to 17 May

Cleethorpes - Barton-on-Humber, Barnetby

Network Diagram - refer to first Page of Table 18

		TP	EM		TP	NT	NT	NT	TP	EM	TP	NT	NT		TP	EM	TP	NT	NT	NT	TP	EM	TP		NT
		◇1			◇1				◇1		◇1				◇1		◇1				◇1		◇1		
		A	B		A			C	A	B	A				A	B	A	C			D	E	D		
							bus						bus							bus					
Cleethorpes	d	13 26			14 26	14 55		15 20	15 26		16 26	16 55			17 26		18 26	18 38	19 00		19 26		20 26		21 03
New Clee	d					14x58																			
Grimsby Docks	d					15 00						17 00							19 05						21 08
Grimsby Town	a	13 33			14 33	15 03		15 26	15 33		16 33	17 03			17 33		18 33	18 44	19 08		19 33		20 33		21 11
	d	13 34	13 49		14 34	15 03		15 27	15 34	16 00	16 34	17 04			17 34	18 28	18 34	18 45	19 08		19 34	19 45	20 34		21 11
Great Coates	d					15 07						17 08							19 12						21 15
Healing	d					15 10						17 11							19 15						21 18
Stallingborough	d					15 13						17 14							19 18						21 21
Habrough	d		13 59		14 44	15 19		15 37		16 09		17 20			17 44	18 38		18 55	19 24		19 44	19 54			21 27
Ulceby	d					15 23						17 24							19 28						21 31
Thornton Abbey	d					15 27						17 28							19 32						21 35
Goxhill	d					15 30						17 31							19 35						21 38
New Holland	d					15 35						17 36							19 40						21 43
Barrow Haven	d					15 38						17 39							19 43						21 46
Barton-on-Humber	a					15 43						17 44							19 48						21 51
Barton-on-Humber	d						18 00						19 53							21 53					
Hull Paragon Interchange	a						18 27						20 20							22 20					
Barnetby	a	13 53	14 08		14 53			15 46	15 53	16 18	16 53				17 50	18 46	18 53	19 04			19 53	20 03	20 52		

Sundays

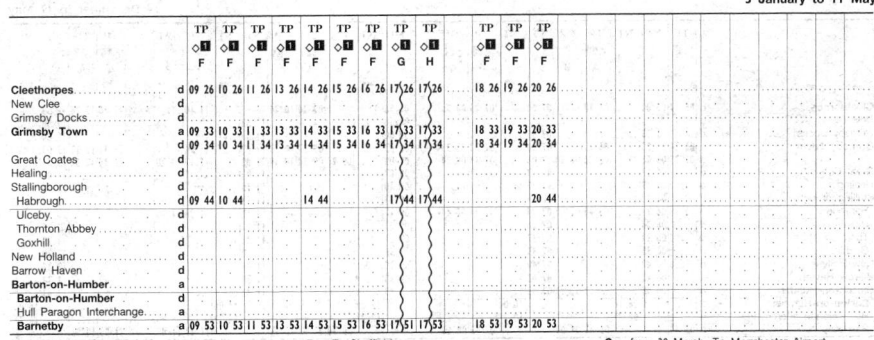

8 December to 29 December

		TP	TP	TP	TP	TP	TP	TP	TP	TP		TP	TP
		◇1	◇1	◇1	◇1	◇1	◇1	◇1	◇1	◇1		◇1	◇1
		A	A	A	A	A	A	A	A	A		A	D
Cleethorpes	d	09 26	10 26	11 26	13 26	14 26	15 26	16 26	17 26	18 26		19 26	20 26
New Clee	d												
Grimsby Docks	d												
Grimsby Town	a	09 33	10 33	11 33	13 33	14 33	15 33	16 33	17 33	18 33		19 33	20 33
	d	09 34	10 34	11 34	13 34	14 34	15 34	16 34	17 34	18 34		19 34	20 34
Great Coates	d												
Healing	d												
Stallingborough	d												
Habrough	d	09 44	10 44			14 44			17 44				20 44
Ulceby	d												
Thornton Abbey	d												
Goxhill	d												
New Holland	d												
Barrow Haven	d												
Barton-on-Humber	a												
Barton-on-Humber	d												
Hull Paragon Interchange	a												
Barnetby	a	09 53	10 53	11 53	13 53	14 53	15 53	16 53	17 51	18 53		19 53	20 53

Sundays

5 January to 11 May

		TP	TP	TP	TP	TP	TP	TP	TP	TP		TP	TP	TP
		◇1	◇1	◇1	◇1	◇1	◇1	◇1	◇1	◇1		◇1	◇1	◇1
		F	F	F	F	F	F	F	G	H		F	F	F
Cleethorpes	d	09 26	10 26	11 26	13 26	14 26	15 26	16 26	17 26	17 26		18 26	19 26	20 26
New Clee	d													
Grimsby Docks	d													
Grimsby Town	a	09 33	10 33	11 33	13 33	14 33	15 33	16 33	17 33	17 33		18 33	19 33	20 33
	d	09 34	10 34	11 34	13 34	14 34	15 34	16 34	17 34	17 34		18 34	19 34	20 34
Great Coates	d													
Healing	d													
Stallingborough	d													
Habrough	d	09 44	10 44			14 44			17 44	17 44				20 44
Ulceby	d													
Thornton Abbey	d													
Goxhill	d													
New Holland	d													
Barrow Haven	d													
Barton-on-Humber	a													
Barton-on-Humber	d													
Hull Paragon Interchange	a													
Barnetby	a	09 53	10 53	11 53	13 53	14 53	15 53	16 53	17 51	17 53		18 53	19 53	20 53

A To Manchester Airport
B To Newark North Gate
C To Sheffield. via Retford
D To Sheffield
E To Lincoln
F To Doncaster
G from 30 March. To Manchester Airport
H until 23 March. To Doncaster

For Hull, Doncaster, Meadowhall, Sheffield, Manchester and Manchester Airport refer to Table 29

Table 28R

Mondays to Fridays

9 December to 16 May

Barnetby - Barton-on-Humber - Cleethorpes

Network Diagram - refer to first Page of Table 18

Miles			TP	NT	NT	EM	NT	NT		TP	NT	EM	NT	TP	NT	TP	EM	NT		TP	NT	TP	NT	EM	TP
			MO		BHX			BHX					BHX					BHX					BHX		
			◇1							◇1				◇1		◇1				◇1		◇1			◇1
			A	B		C				D		E		D		D	E			D		D		E	D
					🚌			🚌					🚌					🚌					🚌		
														trolley		trolley				trolley		trolley			trolley
—	Barnetby	d		06 15		06 31				08 04		08 50		09 20		10 17	10 59			11 17		12 17		13 11	13 17
—	Hull Paragon Interchange	d			06 20			07 20					09 05					11 05					13 05		
—	Barton-on-Humber	a			06 52			07 52					09 40					11 40					13 40		
0	**Barton-on-Humber**	d					06 58				07 58				09 52						11 52				
2	Barrow Haven	d					07 03				08 03				09 57						11 57				
3½	New Holland	d					07 06				08 06				10 00						12 00				
5½	Goxhill	d					07 11				08 11				10 05						12 05				
7	Thornton Abbey	d					07 14				08 14				10 08						12 08				
9¾	Ulceby	d					07 18				08 18				10 12						12 12				
11½	Habrough	d		06 24		06 40	07 23			08 12	08 23	08 59		09 28	10 17		11 08				12 17	12 26		13 20	
15¼	Stallingborough	d		06 30			07 28				08 28				10 22						12 22				
16¼	Healing	d		06 33			07 31				08 31				10 25						12 25				
17¼	Great Coates	d		06 36			07 34				08 34				10 28						12 28				
19½	**Grimsby Town**	a		06 44		06 55	07 42			08 26	08 39	09 13		09 42	10 33	10 39	11 22			11 37	12 33	12 39		13 35	13 37
—		d	00 03	06 44						08 33	08 40			09 43	10 33	10 40				11 38	12 33	12 40			13 38
20½	Grimsby Docks	d		06 47							08 42				10 36						12 36				
—	New Clee	d									08x45				10x38						12x38				
22¾	**Cleethorpes**	a	00 10	06 52						08 44	08 49			09 55	10 43	10 51				11 50	12 43	12 52			13 50

		NT	TP	NT		EM	TP	NT	TP	NT	TP	EM	NT	TP		NT	TP	NT	TP	EM	NT	TP	NT	TP	
				BHX						BHX						BHX					BHX			FO	
			◇1				◇1		◇1		◇1			◇1			◇1		◇1			◇1		◇1	
			D			C	D		D		D	E		D			D		D	E		D		D	
				🚌						🚌						🚌					🚌				
			trolley				trolley		trolley		trolley			trolley			trolley		trolley						
Barnetby	d		14 17			15 11	15 17		16 17		17 17	17 55		18 27			19 27		20 27	20 35		21 26		22 22	
Hull Paragon Interchange	d			15 05						17 10						19 25					21 25				
Barton-on-Humber	a			15 40						17 45						19 52					21 52				
Barton-on-Humber	d	13 52						15 52					17 55					19 58					21 58		
Barrow Haven	d	13 57						15 57					18 00					20 03					22 03		
New Holland	d	14 00						16 00					18 03					20 06					22 06		
Goxhill	d	14 05						16 05					18 08					20 11					22 11		
Thornton Abbey	d	14 08						16 08					18 11					20 14					22 14		
Ulceby	d	14 12						16 12					18 15					20 18					22 18		
Habrough	d	14 17	14 26			15 19		16 17	16 26			18 03	18 20	18 35				20 23		20 44		21 35	22 23	22 31	
Stallingborough	d	14 22						16 22					18 25					20 28					22 28		
Healing	d	14 25						16 25					18 28					20 31					22 31		
Great Coates	d	14 28						16 28					18 31					20 34					22 34		
Grimsby Town	a	14 33	14 39			15 34	15 37	16 33	16 39		17 37	18 15	18 36	18 49			19 46	20 39	20 46	20 56		21 48	22 39	22 44	
	d	14 33	14 40				15 38	16 33	16 40		17 38		18 36	18 49			19 49	20 39	20 47	20 56		21 49	22 39	22 45	
Grimsby Docks	d	14 36						16 36					18 39					20 42					22 42		
New Clee	d	14x38																							
Cleethorpes	a	14 43	14 52				15 50	16 42	16 52		17 50		18 45	19 00			20 02	20 48	21 00	21 03		22 00	22 48	22 57	

		TP	TP
		FX	
		◇1	◇1
		F	D
Barnetby	d	22 46	23 32
Hull Paragon Interchange	d		
Barton-on-Humber	a		
Barton-on-Humber	d		
Barrow Haven	d		
New Holland	d		
Goxhill	d		
Thornton Abbey	d		
Ulceby	d		
Habrough	d	22 54	23 42
Stallingborough	d		
Healing	d		
Great Coates	d		
Grimsby Town	a	23 09	23 55
	d	23 10	23 56
Grimsby Docks	d		
New Clee	d		
Cleethorpes	a	23 20	00 09

A from 17 February until 24 March. From Doncaster
B From Scunthorpe
C From Lincoln
D From Manchester Airport
E From Newark North Gate
F From Sheffield

For Hull, Doncaster, Meadowhall, Sheffield, Manchester and Manchester Airport refer to Table 29

Table 28R

Saturdays

14 December to 17 May

Barnetby - Barton-on-Humber - Cleethorpes

Network Diagram - refer to first Page of Table 18

Station		EM	NT	NT	TP	NT		EM	NT	TP	NT	NT	TP	EM	NT	TP		NT	TP	NT	EM	TP	NT	NT	TP
					◇1					◇1			◇1			◇1			◇1			◇1			◇1
		A		(bus)	B			A	(bus)	B	C		B	D	(bus)	B			B	(bus)	D	B	C		B
Barnetby	d	06 12			08 04			08 50		09 20	09 39		10 17	10 39		11 17			12 17		13 11	13 17	13 38		14 17
Hull Paragon Interchange	d			07 20					09 05						11 05					13 05					
Barton-on-Humber	a			07 52					09 40						11 40					13 40					
Barton-on-Humber	d		06 58			07 58						09 52						11 52						13 52	
Barrow Haven	d		07 03			08 03						09 57						11 57						13 57	
New Holland	d		07 06			08 06						10 00						12 00						14 00	
Goxhill	d		07 11			08 11						10 05						12 05						14 05	
Thornton Abbey	d		07 14			08 14						10 08						12 08						14 08	
Ulceby	d		07 18			08 18						10 12						12 12						14 12	
Habrough	d	06 21	07 23			08 23		08 59		09 28	09 48	10 17		10 48				12 17	12 26		13 20		13 47	14 17	14 26
Stallingborough	d		07 28			08 28						10 22						12 22						14 22	
Healing	d		07 31			08 31						10 25						12 25						14 25	
Great Coates	d		07 34			08 34						10 28						12 28						14 28	
Grimsby Town	a	06 36	07 39		08 24	08 39		09 13		09 42	10 00	10 33	10 39	11 02		11 37		12 33	12 39		13 36	13 37	14 00	14 33	14 39
	d		07 39		08 33	08 40				09 43	10 01	10 33	10 40			11 38		12 33	12 40			13 38	14 00	14 33	14 40
Grimsby Docks	d		07 42			08 42						10 36						12 36						14 36	
New Clee	d					08x45						10x38						12x38						14x38	
Cleethorpes	a		07 51		08 44	08 49				09 55	10 13	10 43	10 51			11 50		12 43	12 52			13 50	14 11	14 43	14 52

Station		NT		TP	EM	NT	TP	NT	TP	NT	EM	NT		TP	EM	NT	TP	NT	TP	NT	TP	NT		TP	
				◇1			◇1		◇1					◇1			◇1		◇1		◇1			◇1	
		(bus)		B	A		B	(bus)	B	C	A			B	D	(bus)	B		B	(bus)	B			E	
Barnetby	d			15 17	15 25		16 17		17 17	17 38	17 55			18 23	19 08		19 27		20 27		21 47			23 13	
Hull Paragon Interchange	d	15 05						17 10								19 25				21 25					
Barton-on-Humber	a	15 40						17 45								19 52				21 52					
Barton-on-Humber	d					15 52						17 55						19 58				21 58			
Barrow Haven	d					15 57						18 00						20 03				22 03			
New Holland	d					16 00						18 03						20 06				22 06			
Goxhill	d					16 05						18 08						20 11				22 11			
Thornton Abbey	d					16 08						18 11						20 14				22 14			
Ulceby	d					16 12						18 15						20 18				22 18			
Habrough	d				15 33	16 17	16 26			17 47	18 03	18 20		18 32	19 16		19 35	20 23			21 56	22 23		23 22	
Stallingborough	d					16 22						18 25						20 28				22 28			
Healing	d					16 25						18 28						20 31				22 31			
Great Coates	d					16 28						18 31						20 34				22 34			
Grimsby Town	a			15 37	15 48	16 33	16 39		17 37	18 01	18 18	18 36		18 45	19 31		19 48	20 39	20 46		22 09	22 39		23 37	
	d			15 38		16 33	16 40		17 38	18 02		18 36		18 46			19 49	20 39	20 47		22 10	22 39		23 38	
Grimsby Docks	d					16 36						18 45						20 42				22 42			
New Clee	d																								
Cleethorpes	a			15 50		16 42	16 52		17 50	18 11		18 50		18 58			20 02	20 48	21 00		22 21	22 48		23 47	

Sundays

8 December to 29 December

Station		TP	TP	TP	TP	TP	TP	TP	TP	TP		TP	TP
		◇1	◇1	◇1	◇1	◇1	◇1	◇1	◇1	◇1		◇1	◇1
		E	B	B	B	B	B	B	B	B		B	E
Barnetby	d	11 09	13 18	15 19	16 17	17 17	18 17	19 17	20 17	21 18		22 17	23 38
Hull Paragon Interchange	d												
Barton-on-Humber	a												
Barton-on-Humber	d												
Barrow Haven	d												
New Holland	d												
Goxhill	d												
Thornton Abbey	d												
Ulceby	d												
Habrough	d	11 18			16 26			19 26		21 27		22 26	
Stallingborough	d												
Healing	d												
Great Coates	d												
Grimsby Town	a	11 31	13 38	15 38	16 39	17 37	18 37	19 39	20 37	21 39		22 39	23 57
	d	11 33	13 39	15 39	16 40	17 38	18 38	19 40	20 38	21 40		22 40	23 58
Grimsby Docks	d												
New Clee	d												
Cleethorpes	a	11 40	13 50	15 49	16 50	17 48	18 48	19 48	20 48	21 50		22 50	00 09

A From Lincoln
B From Manchester Airport
C From Sheffield. via Retford
D From Newark North Gate
E From Sheffield

For Hull, Doncaster, Meadowhall, Sheffield, Manchester and Manchester Airport refer to Table 29

Table 28R

Sundays

5 January to 23 March

Barnetby - Barton-on-Humber - Cleethorpes

Network Diagram - refer to first Page of Table 18

		TP	TP	TP	TP	TP	TP		TP	TP	TP	TP	TP	TP
		◇1	◇1	◇1	◇1	◇1	◇1		◇1	◇1	◇1	◇1	◇1	◇1
		A	A	A	A	A	A		A	A	A	A	A	B
Barnetby	d	11 26	13 18	14 40	15 43	16 42	17 40		18 42	19 51	20 40	21 40	22 44	23 40
Hull Paragon Interchange	d													
Barton-on-Humber	a													
Barton-on-Humber	d													
Barrow Haven	d													
New Holland	d													
Goxhill	d													
Thornton Abbey	d													
Ulceby	d													
Habrough	d	11 35				16 51				19 59		21 53	22 53	
Stallingborough	d													
Healing	d													
Great Coates	d													
Grimsby Town	a	11 48	13 38	15 00	16 02	17 04	18 00		19 02	20 11	21 00	22 04	23 04	00 02
	d	11 49	13 39	15 01	16 03	17 05	18 01		19 03	20 12	21 01	22 05	23 05	00 03
Grimsby Docks	d													
New Clee	d													
Cleethorpes	a	11 56	13 50	15 11	16 11	17 15	18 11		19 13	20 20	21 11	22 13	23 13	00 10

Sundays

30 March to 11 May

		TP	TP	TP	TP	TP	TP	TP	TP	TP		TP	TP
		◇1	◇1	◇1	◇1	◇1	◇1	◇1	◇1	◇1		◇1	◇1
		C	D	D	D	D	D	D	D	D		D	C
Barnetby	d	11 09	13 18	15 19	16 17	17 17	18 17	19 17	20 17	21 18		22 17	23 38
Hull Paragon Interchange	d												
Barton-on-Humber	a												
Barton-on-Humber	d												
Barrow Haven	d												
New Holland	d												
Goxhill	d												
Thornton Abbey	d												
Ulceby	d												
Habrough	d	11 18			16 26			19 26		21 27		22 26	
Stallingborough	d												
Healing	d												
Great Coates	d												
Grimsby Town	a	11 31	13 38	15 38	16 39	17 37	18 37	19 39	20 37	21 39		22 39	23 57
	d	11 33	13 39	15 39	16 40	17 38	18 38	19 40	20 38	21 40		22 40	23 58
Grimsby Docks	d												
New Clee	d												
Cleethorpes	a	11 40	13 50	15 49	16 50	17 48	18 48	19 48	20 48	21 50		22 50	00 09

A From Doncaster
B from 16 February. From Doncaster
C From Sheffield
D From Manchester Airport

For Hull, Doncaster, Meadowhall, Sheffield, Manchester and Manchester Airport refer to Table 29

Mondays to Fridays

9 December to 16 May

Airport, Manchester, Sheffield and Meadowhall-Doncaster and Hull

Network Diagram - refer to first Page of Table 18

Miles	Miles	Miles	Miles	Station			NT	TP	NT	NT	NT	NT	NT	NT	NT	XC	NT	NT	TP	TP	NT	XC	NT
							MO	MO												MX			
								◇1								◇1			◇1	◇1		◇1	
							A	B	C	D	C				C	E	C		F	G	C	H	C
0	—		—	**Manchester Airport**	85	d													05 20				
9¾	—	—	—	**Manchester Piccadilly 10**		d													05 44	05 44			
15¾	—	—	—	Stockport	78	d													05 52	05 52			
52½	—	—	—	**Sheffield 7**		a													06 40	06 40			
—	—	—	—			d			05 21	05 29				06 18	06 28	06 33		06 52	06 55	06 55		07 12	07 15
56	—	—	—	**Meadowhall**		d			05 27	05 35				06 24	06 34			06 58	07 01	07 01			07 21
58¾	—	—	—	Rotherham Central		d			05 33	05 41				06 30	06 40			07 05					07 27
63¼	—	—	—	Swinton (S.Yorks)		d			05a41	05 49				06 38	06a51			07 15					07a35
64½	—	—	—	Mexborough		d				05 52				06 41				07 18					
66¾	—	—	—	Conisbrough		d	00 02			05 56				06 45				07 22					
—	—	—	—	London Kings Cross		d																	
71½	—	—	—	**Doncaster 7**		a	00 13			06 06				06 56		06 57		07 32	07 22	07 22			
—	—	—	—	York 8	26	a										07 25						08 22	
—	0	0	0	**Doncaster**	31	d				06 12	06 26		06 39	06 59			07 08	07 34	07 24	07 24	07 26		
—	—	—	1¾	Bentley (S.Yorks)	31	a					06 29			07 02			07 11	07 37			07 29		
—	—	—	4	Adwick	31	a					06 33			07 08			07 15	07 43			07 33		
75½	—	4	—	Kirk Sandall		d				06 18			06 45										
78¼	—	6¾	—	Hatfield & Stainforth		d				06 23			06 50										
—	—	9¾	—	Thorne South		d							06 55										
—	—	15¾	—	Crowle		d							07 03										
—	—	19½	—	Althorpe		d							07 09										
—	—	23	—	**Scunthorpe**		a							07 18						07 49	07 49			
—	—	—	—			d						06 01							07 50	07 50			
—	—	—	—	Barnetby	28	d						06 15							08 04	08 04			
—	—	—	—	Habrough	28	d						06 24							08 12	08 12			
—	—	—	—	Grimsby Town	28	a						06 44							08 26	08 26			
—	—	—	—			d		00 03				06 44							08 33	08 33			
—	—	—	—	**Cleethorpes**	28	a		00 10				06 52							08 44	08 44			
81¼	—	—	—	Thorne North		d				06 28													
88¾	—	—	—	Goole		d				06 37													
92¼	—	—	—	Saltmarshe		d				06 42													
—	—	—	—	York 8	33	d																	
—	18¼	—	—	**Selby**		a																	
—	—	—	—			d																	
—	24½	—	—	Wressle		d																	
—	27	—	—	Howden		d																	
—	30	—	—	Eastrington		d																	
95½	32¼	—	—	Gilberdyke		d				06 49													
98	34¾	—	—	Broomfleet		d				06 53													
102	38¾	—	—	Brough		d				06 59													
105	41¾	—	—	Ferriby		d				07 03													
107¾	44½	—	—	Hessle		d				07 08													
112	49¼	—	—	**Hull**		a				07 21													

Station			NT	TP	NT	NT	NT	NT	NT	NT	NT	XC	TP	NT	TP	NT	XC	NT	NT
				◇1								◇1	◇1		◇1		◇1		
			I		D		C		J	K	C	L				C	M		
Manchester Airport	85	d											06 55						
Manchester Piccadilly 10		d		06 21									07 19		07 36				
Stockport	78	d											07 27						
Sheffield 7		a											08 11						
		d						07 24		07 41		07 54	08 11			08 16	08 22		
Meadowhall		d						07 30		07 47			08 17			08 22			
Rotherham Central		d						07 36		07 55						08 28			
Swinton (S.Yorks)		d						07 44		08 03						08a37			
Mexborough		d						07 47		08 06									
Conisbrough		d						07 51		08 10									
London Kings Cross		d																	
Doncaster 7		a						08 01		08 19		08 23	08 38						
York 8	26	a										08 47					09 26		
Doncaster	31	d			07 28		07 56	08 04	08 06	08 22	08 26		08 39	08 49					08 55
Bentley (S.Yorks)	31	a					07 59		08 09		08 29			08 52					
Adwick	31	a					08 03		08 13		08 33			08 58					
Kirk Sandall		d			07 34			08 10											09 01
Hatfield & Stainforth		d			07 39			08 15											09 06
Thorne South		d						08 20											
Crowle		d						08 29											
Althorpe		d						08 35											
Scunthorpe		a						08 43					09 05						
		d											09 06						
Barnetby	28	d											09 20						
Habrough	28	d											09 28						
Grimsby Town	28	a											09 42						
		d											09 43						
Cleethorpes	28	a											09 55						
Thorne North		d			07 44														09 11
Goole		d			07 53					08 43									09 20
Saltmarshe		d			07 58														
York 8	33	d				07 30												08 43	
Selby		a		07 43		07 50									08 57			09 06	
		d		07 43		07 50									08 58			09 07	
Wressle		d				07 58													
Howden		d		07 52		08 03												09 16	
Eastrington		d				08 08													
Gilberdyke		d	07 39		08 05	08 13													09 29
Broomfleet		d	07 43			08 17													
Brough		d	07 49	08 04	08 13	08 23				08 57								09 29	09 37
Ferriby		d	07 53		08 17	08 28													09 42
Hessle		d	07 58		08 22	08 32													09 46
Hull		a	08 10	08 20	08 34	08 46				09 13					09 31			09 47	09 59

A until 30 December, from 17 February. From Sheffield
B from 17 February until 24 March. From Doncaster
C To Leeds
D To Beverley
E From Derby to Newcastle
F until 30 December, MO from 6 January until 17 March, from 24 March
G from 31 December until 21 March
H From Birmingham New Street to Glasgow Central
I To Scarborough
J From Scunthorpe
K To Bridlington
L From Birmingham New Street to Newcastle
M From Birmingham New Street to Edinburgh

For all trains between Barnetby, Habrough, Grimsby Town and Cleethorpes see Table 28

Table 29

Mondays to Fridays

9 December to 16 May

Manchester Airport, Manchester, Sheffield and Meadowhall-Doncaster and Hull

Network Diagram - refer to first Page of Table 18

		HT	NT	NT	NT	XC FX	XC FO	NT	TP	TP	NT	XC		NT	NT	NT	NT	NT	XC	NT	TP
		◇1 ⊠		A	B	◇1 C 🛒	◇1 C 🛒	D	◇1 🛒	◇1 🛒	B	◇1 E 🛒				F	G	B	◇1 H 🛒	I	◇1 🛒
Manchester Airport 85 ✈	d								07 53												08 55
Manchester Piccadilly 10 ⇌	d								08 20	08 42											09 20
Stockport 78	d								08 28												09 28
Sheffield 7 ⇌	a								09 08												10 08
	d		08 25	08 41		08 48	08 48	08 54	09 10		09 15	09 21			09 24	09 29	09 41		09 47	09 53	10 10
Meadowhall ⇌	d		08 31	08 47				09 00	09 16		09 21				09 30	09 35	09 47			09 59	10 16
Rotherham Central	d		08 37					09 06			09 28				09 37	09 42				10 06	
Swinton (S.Yorks)	d		08 48					09 16			09a36				09 48	09 51				10 16	
Mexborough	d		08 52					09 19							09 51					10 19	
Conisbrough	d		08 56					09 23							09 55					10 23	
London Kings Cross	d	07 22																			
Doncaster 7	a	09 04	09 06	09 15		09 18	09 18	09 31	09 35						10 05		10 15		10 18	10 32	10 35
York 8 26	a					09 42	09 43					10 27				10 57			10 39		
Doncaster 31	d	09 06	09 08	09 19	09 26			09 34	09 37					09 52	10 07		10 19	10 26		10 34	10 37
Bentley (S.Yorks) 31	a				09 29			09 37										10 29		10 37	
Adwick 31	a				09 33			09 42										10 33		10 43	
Kirk Sandall	d		09 14											09 58	10 14						
Hatfield & Stainforth	d		09 19											10 03	10 19						
Thorne South	d		09 24												10 24						
Crowle	d		09 32												10 33						
Althorpe	d		09 38												10 39						
Scunthorpe	a		09 46						10 02						10 47						11 02
	d								10 03												11 03
Barnetby 28	d								10 17												11 17
Habrough 28	d																				
Grimsby Town 28	a								10 39												11 37
	d								10 40												11 38
Cleethorpes 28	a								10 51												11 50
Thorne North	d													10 08							
Goole	d			09 38										10 17			10 38				
Saltmarshe	d																				
York 8 33	d																				
Selby	a	09 20								09 57											
	d	09 21								09 58											
Wressle	d																				
Howden	d	09 31																			
Eastrington	d																				
Gilberdyke	d													10 25							
Broomfleet	d																				
Brough	d	09 44		09 53						10 17				10 33			10 53				
Ferriby	d													10 38							
Hessle	d													10 42							
Hull	a	10 02		10 09						10 35				10 55			11 09				

		NT	NT	TP	XC	NT	NT	NT		XC	HT	NT	NT	TP	TP	NT	XC	NT	NT	NT	NT
		B		◇1 🛒	◇1 J 🛒			A		◇1 K 🛒	◇1 ⊠	B	I	◇1 🛒	◇1 🛒	B	◇1 L 🛒				G
Manchester Airport 85 ✈	d													09 55							
Manchester Piccadilly 10 ⇌	d			09 42										10 20	10 42						
Stockport 78	d													10 28							
Sheffield 7 ⇌	a													11 08							
	d	10 14			10 21		10 24	10 41		10 47			10 53	11 10		11 14	11 21			11 24	11 41
Meadowhall ⇌	d	10 21					10 30	10 47					10 59	11 16		11 21				11 30	11 47
Rotherham Central	d	10 27					10 36						11 05			11 27				11 37	
Swinton (S.Yorks)	d	10a36					10 48						11 16			11a36				11 48	
Mexborough	d						10 51						11 19							11 51	
Conisbrough	d						10 55						11 23							11 55	
London Kings Cross	d										09 48										
Doncaster 7	a						11 04	11 15		11 18	11 23		11 32	11 35						12 04	12 14
York 8 26	a				11 30					11 40							12 30				
Doncaster 31	d					10 52	11 08	11 19			11 25	11 26	11 34	11 37					11 52	12 08	12 19
Bentley (S.Yorks) 31	a											11 29	11 37								
Adwick 31	a											11 33	11 43								
Kirk Sandall	d					10 58	11 14												11 58	12 14	
Hatfield & Stainforth	d					11 03	11 19												12 03	12 19	
Thorne South	d						11 24													12 24	
Crowle	d						11 32													12 32	
Althorpe	d						11 38													12 38	
Scunthorpe	a						11 46							12 02						12 46	
	d													12 03							
Barnetby 28	d													12 17							
Habrough 28	d													12 26							
Grimsby Town 28	a													12 39							
	d													12 40							
Cleethorpes 28	a													12 52							
Thorne North	d					11 08													12 08		
Goole	d					11 17		11 38											12 17		12 38
Saltmarshe	d																				
York 8 33	d		10 19															11 45			
Selby	a		10 39	10 56							11 39				11 57			12 04			
	d		10 39	10 58							11 40				11 58			12 05			
Wressle	d																				
Howden	d		10 49								11 50							12 14			
Eastrington	d																				
Gilberdyke	d		10 57			11 26												12 22	12 27		
Broomfleet	d					11 30															
Brough	d		11 05	11 17		11 36		11 53			12 03				12 17			12 30	12 35		12 53
Ferriby	d					11 40													12 40		
Hessle	d					11 45													12 44		
Hull	a		11 22	11 35		11 57		12 09			12 21				12 36			12 49	12 57		13 09

A To Bridlington
B To Leeds
C From Birmingham New Street to Newcastle
D From Worksop
E From Bath Spa to Glasgow Central
F via Pontefract Baghill
G To Scarborough
H From Guildford to Newcastle
I From Lincoln
J From Plymouth to Edinburgh
K From Reading to Newcastle
L From Plymouth to Glasgow Central

For all trains between Barnetby, Habrough, Grimsby Town and Cleethorpes see Table 28

Table 29

Mondays to Fridays

9 December to 16 May

Manchester Airport, Manchester, Sheffield and Meadowhall-Doncaster and Hull

Network Diagram - refer to first Page of Table 18

Station		NT	XC	NT	TP	TP	NT	XC	NT	NT	NT	NT	XC	HT	NT	NT	TP	TP	NT
			◇1	◇	◇1	◇1		◇1					◇1	◇1		◇	◇1	◇1	
		A	B	C			A	D				E	F		A	C			A
			🍴		🍴	🍴		🍴					🍴	⊠			🍴	🍴	
Manchester Airport 85 ✈	d				10 55												11 55		
Manchester Piccadilly 10	d				11 20	11 42											12 20	12 42	
Stockport 78	d				11 28												12 28		
Sheffield 7	a				12 08												13 08		
	d		11 47	11 53	12 10		12 14	12 21			12 25	12 41	12 47			12 53	13 10		13 14
Meadowhall	d			11 59	12 16		12 21				12 31	12 47				12 59	13 16		13 21
Rotherham Central	d			12 05			12 27				12 37					13 05			13 27
Swinton (S.Yorks)	d			12 16			12a36				12 48					13 16			13a36
Mexborough	d			12 19							12 51					13 19			
Conisbrough	d			12 23							12 55					13 23			
London Kings Cross	d													11 48					
Doncaster 7	a		12 18	12 32	12 35						13 04	13 15	13 18	13 23		13 33	13 35		
York 8 26	a		12 39					13 30					13 40						
Doncaster 31	d	12 26		12 34	12 37					12 52	13 08	13 19		13 25	13 26	13 34	13 37		
Bentley (S.Yorks) 31	a	12 29		12 38											13 29	13 37			
Adwick 31	a	12 33		12 43											13 33	13 43			
Kirk Sandall	d									12 58	13 14								
Hatfield & Stainforth	d									13 03	13 19								
Thorne South	d										13 24								
Crowle	d										13 33								
Althorpe	d										13 39								
Scunthorpe	a				13 02						13 46						14 02		
	d				13 03												14 03		
Barnetby 28	d				13 17												14 17		
Habrough 28	d																14 26		
Grimsby Town 28	a				13 37												14 39		
	d				13 38												14 40		
Cleethorpes 28	a				13 50												14 52		
Thorne North	d									13 08									
Goole	d									13 17		13 38							
Saltmarshe	d																		
York 8 33	d								12 47										
Selby	a					12 57			13 06					13 39				13 57	
	d					12 58			13 06					13 40				13 58	
Wressle	d																		
Howden	d								13 16					13 50					
Eastrington	d																		
Gilberdyke	d									13 27									
Broomfleet	d																		
Brough	d					13 17			13 29	13 35		13 53		14 03				14 17	
Ferriby	d									13 40									
Hessle	d									13 44									
Hull	a					13 35			13 47	13 56		14 09		14 21				14 35	

Station		XC	NT	NT	NT	NT	NT	NT	XC	NT	TP	TP	NT	XC	NT	NT	NT	NT	XC	HT
		◇1							◇1		◇1	◇1		◇1					◇1	◇1
		G				H	E	A	I				A	J		K		L	F	
		🍴							🍴		🍴	🍴		🍴					🍴	⊠
Manchester Airport 85 ✈	d										12 55									
Manchester Piccadilly 10	d										13 20	13 42								
Stockport 78	d										13 28									
Sheffield 7	a										14 08									
	d	13 21			13 24	13 29	13 41		13 47	13 53	14 10		14 14	14 21			14 24	14 41	14 47	
Meadowhall	d				13 30	13 35	13 46			13 59	14 16		14 21				14 30	14 47		
Rotherham Central	d				13 37	13 41				14 05			14 27				14 37			
Swinton (S.Yorks)	d				13 48	13 52				14 16			14a36				14 48			
Mexborough	d				13 51					14 19							14 51			
Conisbrough	d				13 55					14 23							14 55			
London Kings Cross	d																			13 48
Doncaster 7	a				14 04		14 15		14 18	14 31	14 35						15 04	15 17	15 18	15 24
York 8 26	a	14 30				14 55			14 39					15 30					15 44	
Doncaster 31	d			13 52	14 07		14 19	14 26		14 34	14 37					14 52	15 08	15 19		15 25
Bentley (S.Yorks) 31	a							14 29		14 37										
Adwick 31	a							14 33		14 43										
Kirk Sandall	d			13 58	14 14											14 58	15 14			
Hatfield & Stainforth	d			14 03	14 19											15 03	15 18			
Thorne South	d				14 26												15 24			
Crowle	d				14 34												15 32			
Althorpe	d				14 40												15 38			
Scunthorpe	a				14 47						15 02						15 46			
	d										15 03									
Barnetby 28	d										15 17									
Habrough 28	d																			
Grimsby Town 28	a										15 37									
	d										15 38									
Cleethorpes 28	a										15 50									
Thorne North	d			14 08												15 08				
Goole	d			14 17			14 38									15 17		15 38		
Saltmarshe	d			14 21																
York 8 33	d		13 44												14 47					
Selby	a		14 07									14 57			15 06					15 39
	d		14 08									14 58			15 06					15 40
Wressle	d																			
Howden	d		14 17												15 16					15 50
Eastrington	d																			
Gilberdyke	d			14 29												15 27				
Broomfleet	d																			
Brough	d		14 30	14 37			14 53					15 17			15 29	15 35		15 53		16 04
Ferriby	d			14 42												15 40				
Hessle	d			14 46												15 44				
Hull	a		14 52	14 57			15 09					15 35			15 47	15 56		16 09		16 21

A To Leeds
B From Winchester to Newcastle
C From Lincoln
D From Plymouth to Edinburgh
E To Bridlington
F From Reading to Newcastle
G From Penzance to Glasgow Central
H via Pontefract Baghill
I From Southampton Central to Newcastle
J From Plymouth to Aberdeen
K To Beverley
L To Scarborough

For all trains between Barnetby, Habrough, Grimsby Town and Cleethorpes see Table 28

Table 29

Mondays to Fridays

9 December to 16 May

Manchester Airport, Manchester, Sheffield and Meadowhall-Doncaster and Hull

Network Diagram - refer to first Page of Table 18

	NT A	NT ◇ B	TP ◇1	TP ◇1	NT A	XC ◇1 C	NT	NT	NT D	NT A	XC ◇1 E	NT ◇ B	TP ◇1	NT	TP ◇1	NT A	XC ◇1 F	NT
Manchester Airport 85 ✈ d			13 55										14 55					
Manchester Piccadilly 10 d			14 20	14 42									15 20		15 42			
Stockport 78 d			14 28										15 28					
Sheffield 7 a			15 08										16 08					
d		14 53	15 10		15 14	15 21		15 24	15 41		15 47	15 53	16 10			16 14	16 21	16 23
Meadowhall d		14 59	15 16		15 20			15 30	15 47			15 59	16 16			16 21		16 30
Rotherham Central d		15 05			15 26			15 37				16 05				16 27		16 37
Swinton (S.Yorks) d		15 16			15a36			15 48				16 16				16a36		16 48
Mexborough d		15 19						15 51				16 19						16 51
Conisbrough d		15 23						15 55				16 23						16 55
London Kings Cross d																		
Doncaster 7 a		15 33	15 35					16 04	16 15		16 18	16 32	16 35					17 07
York 8 26 a						16 30					16 39						17 30	
Doncaster 31 d	15 26	15 34	15 37				15 52	16 08	16 19	16 26		16 34	16 37					
Bentley (S.Yorks) 31 a	15 29	15 37								16 29		16 37						
Adwick 31 a	15 33	15 42								16 33		16 43						
Kirk Sandall d							15 58	16 14										
Hatfield & Stainforth d							16 03	16 19										
Thorne South d								16 24										
Crowle d								16 33										
Althorpe d								16 39										
Scunthorpe a			16 02					16 46					17 02					
d			16 03										17 03					
Barnetby 28 d			16 17										17 17					
Habrough 28 d			16 26															
Grimsby Town 28 a			16 39										17 37					
d			16 40										17 38					
Cleethorpes 28 a			16 52										17 50					
Thorne North d							16 08											
Goole d							16 17		16 38									
Saltmarshe d							16 22											
York 8 33 d														16 12				
Selby a				15 57										16 36	17 01			
d				15 58										16 36	17 01			
Wressle d														16 44				
Howden d														16 49				
Eastrington d																		
Gilberdyke d							16 28							16 55				
Broomfleet d																		
Brough d				16 17			16 36		16 53					17 03	17 20			
Ferriby d							16 40							17 08				
Hessle d							16 45							17 12				
Hull a				16 35			16 58		17 09					17 27	17 37			

	NT G	NT D	NT	XC ◇1 H	HT ◇1 ⊠	NT A	NT ◇ B	TP ◇1	NT A	NT	TP ◇1	XC ◇1 I	NT	NT	NT J	NT A	XC ◇1 K	NT	TP ◇1	NT L
Manchester Airport 85 ✈ d								15 55												
Manchester Piccadilly 10 d								16 20			16 42								17 42	
Stockport 78 d								16 28												
Sheffield 7 a								17 08												
d		16 41		16 47			16 53	17 10	17 14			17 21	17 27		17 41		17 47			
Meadowhall d		16 47					16 59	17 16	17 21				17 33		17 47					
Rotherham Central d							17 05		17 27				17 39							
Swinton (S.Yorks) d							17 15		17a37				17 48							
Mexborough d							17 18						17 51							
Conisbrough d							17 22						17 55							
London Kings Cross d					15 49															
Doncaster 7 a		17 14		17 18	17 23		17 31	17 37					18 07		18 12					
York 8 26 a				17 40								18 29					18 58			
Doncaster 31 d	16 52	17 19	17 22		17 25	17 26	17 32	17 46						17 56	18 19	18 26				18 30
Bentley (S.Yorks) 31 a						17 29	17 35									18 29				
Adwick 31 a						17 33	17 41									18 33				
Kirk Sandall d	16 58		17 29											18 02						18 37
Hatfield & Stainforth d	17 03		17 34											18 07						18 42
Thorne South d			17 39																	18 47
Crowle d			17 48																	18 55
Althorpe d			17 54																	19 01
Scunthorpe a			18 01					18 12												19 09
d								18 12												
Barnetby 28 d								18 27												
Habrough 28 d								18 35												
Grimsby Town 28 a								18 49												
d								18 49												
Cleethorpes 28 a								19 00												
Thorne North d	17 08	17 31												18 12						
Goole d	17 17	17 40												18 21	18 38					
Saltmarshe d														18 26						
York 8 33 d										17 19								18 18		
Selby a					17 39					17 45	17 59							18 42	19 00	
d					17 40					17 46	18 00							18 43	19 01	
Wressle d																		18 50		
Howden d					17 50					17 56	18 09							18 54		
Eastrington d																		18 59		
Gilberdyke d	17 25									18 04				18 33				19 04		
Broomfleet d														18 37						
Brough d	17 33	17 55			18 03					18 12	18 22			18 43	18 53			19 11	19 20	
Ferriby d	17 38													18 47						
Hessle d	17 42													18 52						
Hull a	17 56	18 11			18 21					18 30	18 39			19 04	19 09			19 29	19 38	

A To Leeds
B From Lincoln
C From Penzance to Glasgow Central
D To Bridlington
E From Southampton Central to Newcastle
F From Plymouth to Dundee
G To Beverley
H From Reading to Newcastle
I From Plymouth to Glasgow Central
J To Scarborough
K From Southampton Central to Edinburgh
L From Adwick

For all trains between Barnetby, Habrough, Grimsby Town and Cleethorpes see Table 28

Table 29

Mondays to Fridays

9 December to 16 May

Manchester Airport, Manchester, Sheffield and Meadowhall-Doncaster and Hull

Network Diagram - refer to first Page of Table 18

Station		NT	TP	NT	XC	NT	NT	NT	XC	NT	NT	TP	TP	NT	XC	NT	NT	NT	NT
		◇	◇1		◇1				◇1			◇1	◇1		◇1				
		A		B	C		D		E	F	B			B	C			G	
Manchester Airport 85 ✈	d		16 55									17 55							
Manchester Piccadilly 10	d		17 20									18 20	18 42						
Stockport 78	d		17 28									18 28							
Sheffield 7	a		18 10									19 09							
	d	17 53	18 10	18 16	18 21	18 29	18 41		18 47	19 00		19 12		19 19	19 26	19 31		19 44	
Meadowhall	d	17 59	18 18	18 22		18 36	18 47			19 06		19 18		19 25		19 37		19 50	
Rotherham Central	d	18 05		18 28		18 42				19 12				19 31		19 43			
Swinton (S.Yorks)	d	18 17		18a37		18 50				19 20				19a40		19 51			
Mexborough	d	18 20				18 53				19 23						19 55			
Conisbrough	d	18 24				18 57				19 27						19 59			
London Kings Cross	d																		
Doncaster 7	a	18 34	18 45			19 09	19 11		19 16	19 36		19 41				20 09		20 12	
York 8 26	a				19 30				19 38						20 30				
Doncaster 31	d	18 39	18 46				19 17	19 21			19 22	19 48					19 53	20 19	20 25
Bentley (S.Yorks) 31	a										19 25								
Adwick 31	a										19 29								
Kirk Sandall	d	18 45						19 27									19 59		20 31
Hatfield & Stainforth	d	18 50						19 32									20 04		20 36
Thorne South,	d							19 37											20 41
Crowle	d							19 46											20 50
Althorpe	d							19 52											20 56
Scunthorpe	a		19 11					20 00				20 12							21 04
	d		19 12									20 12							
Barnetby 28	d		19 27									20 27							
Habrough 28	d																		
Grimsby Town 28	a		19 46									20 46							
	d		19 49									20 47							
Cleethorpes 28	a		20 02									21 00							
Thorne North	d	18 55															20 09		
Goole	d	19 12					19 38										20 18	20 38	
Saltmarshe	d																		
York 8 33	d																		
Selby	a												20 00						
	d												20 01						
Wressle	d																		
Howden	d												20 10						
Eastrington	d																		
Gilberdyke	d	19 21															20 27		
Broomfleet	d																		
Brough	d	19 29					19 54						20 23				20 35	20 53	
Ferriby	d	19 34															20 40		
Hessle	d	19 38															20 44		
Hull	a	19 50					20 09						20 41				20 58	21 09	

Station		XC	NT	HT	NT	TP	TP	NT	NT	NT	NT	XC	TP FO	NT	NT	TP FX	HT	NT	XC	TP FO
		◇1		◇1		◇1	◇1					◇1	◇1			◇1	◇1		◇1	◇1
		H	B	⊠	D		I		B		B	E		G	B		⊠	B	J	
Manchester Airport 85 ✈	d					18 55							19 55							20 47
Manchester Piccadilly 10	d					19 18	20 11						20 20							21 20
Stockport 78	d					19 26							20 28							21 28
Sheffield 7	a					20 08							21 10							22 10
	d	19 54			19 58	20 10		20 15	20 27	20 38		20 53	21 10	21 16	21 30	21 34			21 54	22 10
Meadowhall	d				20 04	20 15		20 21	20 35	20 45			21 16	21 22	21 36	21 40				22 16
Rotherham Central	d				20 11			20 27	20 41	20 52				21 28	21 42					
Swinton (S.Yorks)	d				20 22			20 36	20a50	21 00				21 37	21a51					
Mexborough	d				20 25			20 39		21 03				21 40						
Conisbrough	d				20 29			20 43		21 07				21 44						
London Kings Cross	d			18 50													20 30			
Doncaster 7	a	20 15		20 26	20 37	20 44		20 55		21 18		21 19	21 40	21 54		22 02	22 06		22 29	22 42
York 8 26	a	20 38										21 44							22 52	
Doncaster 31	d		20 26	20 33	20 43	20 46		20 57		21 21	21 27		21 42	21 56		22 05	22 08	22 26		22 44
Bentley (S.Yorks) 31	a		20 29								21 30							22 29		
Adwick 31	a		20 33								21 34							22 33		
Kirk Sandall	d							21 03		21 27				22 02						22 49
Hatfield & Stainforth	d							21 08		21 32				22 07						22 54
Thorne South,	d									21 37										22 58
Crowle	d									21 46										23 07
Althorpe	d									21 52										23 12
Scunthorpe	a					21 11				22 00			22 07			22 30				23 17
	d					21 12							22 08			22 31				23 18
Barnetby 28	d					21 26							22 22			22 46				23 32
Habrough 28	d					21 35							22 31			22 54				23 42
Grimsby Town 28	a					21 48							22 44			23 09				23 55
	d					21 49							22 45			23 10				23 56
Cleethorpes 28	a					22 00							22 57			23 20				00 09
Thorne North	d							21 14						22 13						
Goole	d							21a23						22 22						
Saltmarshe	d													22 26						
York 8 33	d																			
Selby	a			20 47	21 01		21 33										22 22			
	d			20 48	21 02		21 33										22 22			
Wressle	d																			
Howden	d			20 58			21 43										22 32			
Eastrington	d																			
Gilberdyke	d				21 16									22 33						
Broomfleet	d																			
Brough	d			21 11	21 24		21 56							22 41			22 47			
Ferriby	d				21 29															
Hessle	d				21 33															
Hull	a			21 29	21 47		22 13							22 59			23 06			

A From Lincoln
B To Leeds
C From Plymouth to Edinburgh
D To Bridlington
E From Reading to Newcastle
F From Retford Low Level
G To Beverley
H From Southampton Central to Newcastle
I From Liverpool Lime Street
J From Southampton Central

For all trains between Barnetby, Habrough, Grimsby Town and Cleethorpes see Table 28

Table 29

Mondays to Fridays

9 December to 16 May

Manchester Airport, Manchester, Sheffield and Meadowhall-Doncaster and Hull

Network Diagram - refer to first Page of Table 18

Station	Table		TP FX ◇1	NT	NT A	NT	TP ◇1 B	NT A	NT
Manchester Airport	85 ✈	d	20 47						
Manchester Piccadilly 10	⇌	d	21 20						
Stockport	78	d	21 28						
Sheffield 7	⇌	a	22 09						
		d	22 10		22 24	22 34		23 15	23 27
Meadowhall	⇌	d	22 16		22 31	22 40		23 21	23 33
Rotherham Central		d			22 37	22 46		23 27	23 39
Swinton (S.Yorks)		d			22a46	22 54		23a36	23 48
Mexborough		d				22 57			23 51
Conisbrough		d				23 01			23 55
London Kings Cross		d							
Doncaster 7		a	22 42			23 12			00 07
York 8	26	a							
Doncaster	31	d	22 44			23 15			
Bentley (S.Yorks)	31	a							
Adwick	31	a							
Kirk Sandall		d	22 49			23 21			
Hatfield & Stainforth		d	22 54			23 26			
Thorne South		d	22 58						
Crowle		d	23 07						
Althorpe		d	23 12						
Scunthorpe		a	23 18						
		d	23 18						
Barnetby	28	d	23 32						
Habrough	28	d	23 42						
Grimsby Town	28	a	23 55						
		d	23 56						
Cleethorpes	28	a	00 09						
Thorne North		d				23 32			
Goole		d				23a43			
Saltmarshe		d							
York 8	33	d		22 13					
Selby		a		22 31					
		d		22 32			22 46		
Wressle		d							
Howden		d		22 41					
Eastrington		d							
Gilberdyke		d		22 49					
Broomfleet		d							
Brough		d		22 56			23 07		
Ferriby		d		23 01					
Hessle		d		23 06					
Hull		a		23 18			23 25		

A To Leeds

B From Leeds

For all trains between Barnetby, Habrough, Grimsby Town and Cleethorpes see Table 28

Table 29

Saturdays

14 December to 17 May

Manchester Airport, Manchester, Sheffield and Meadowhall-Doncaster and Hull

Network Diagram - refer to first Page of Table 18

Station			NT A	NT B	NT	NT	NT B	XC ◇1 C	NT	TP ◇1	NT B	XC ◇1 D 🍴	NT B	NT E	TP ◇1	NT A	NT
Manchester Airport ✈	85	d								05 20							
Manchester Piccadilly 10		d								05 44					06 21		
Stockport	78	d								05 52							
Sheffield 7		a								06 40							
		d	05 29			06 12	06 28	06 49	06 52	06 55		07 12	07 15				07 24
Meadowhall		d	05 35			06 18	06 34		06 58	07 01			07 21				07 30
Rotherham Central		d	05 41			06 24	06 40		07 04				07 27				07 36
Swinton (S.Yorks)		d	05 49			06 36	06a51		07 15				07a35				07 46
Mexborough		d	05 52			06 39			07 18								07 49
Conisbrough		d	05 56			06 43			07 22								07 53
London Kings Cross		d															
Doncaster 7		a	06 06			06 53		07 16	07 33	07 22							08 01
York 8	26	a						07 43				08 24					
Doncaster	31	d	06 12	06 26	06 47	06 55			07 34	07 24	07 26					07 28	08 04
Bentley (S.Yorks)	31	a		06 29		06 58			07 37		07 29						
Adwick	31	a		06 33		07 04			07 43		07 33						
Kirk Sandall		d	06 18		06 53											07 34	08 10
Hatfield & Stainforth		d	06 23		06 58											07 39	08 15
Thorne South		d			07 03												08 20
Crowle		d			07 11												08 29
Althorpe		d			07 17												08 35
Scunthorpe		a			07 26					07 49							08 43
		d								07 50							
Barnetby	28	d								08 04							
Habrough	28	d															
Grimsby Town	28	a								08 24							
		d								08 33							
Cleethorpes	28	a								08 44							
Thorne North		d	06 28													07 44	
Goole		d	06 37													07 53	
Saltmarshe		d	06 42													07 58	
York 8	33	d															
Selby		a													07 43		
		d													07 43		
Wressle		d															
Howden		d													07 52		
Eastrington		d															
Gilberdyke		d	06 49											07 39		08 05	
Broomfleet		d	06 53											07 43			
Brough		d	06 59											07 49	08 04	08 13	
Ferriby		d	07 03											07 53		08 17	
Hessle		d	07 08											07 58		08 22	
Hull		a	07 21											08 10	08 20	08 34	

Station			NT F	NT	NT G	NT B	XC ◇1 H 🍴	NT I	TP ◇1	NT	TP ◇1	NT B	XC ◇1 J 🍴	NT	NT	NT	NT G
Manchester Airport ✈	85	d							06 55								
Manchester Piccadilly 10		d							07 19		07 36						
Stockport	78	d							07 27								
Sheffield 7		a							08 11								
		d			07 41		07 54	08 03	08 11			08 14	08 21			08 25	08 41
Meadowhall		d			07 47				08 17			08 22				08 31	08 47
Rotherham Central		d			07 55							08 28				08 37	
Swinton (S.Yorks)		d			08 03							08a37				08 48	
Mexborough		d			08 06											08 51	
Conisbrough		d			08 10											08 55	
London Kings Cross		d															
Doncaster 7		a			08 19		08 23		08 38							09 06	09 14
York 8	26	a					08 47						09 30				
Doncaster	31	d	08 16		08 22	08 26			08 39	08 54					08 54	09 07	09 19
Bentley (S.Yorks)	31	a	08 19			08 29				08 57							
Adwick	31	a	08 23			08 33				09 02							
Kirk Sandall		d													09 00	09 14	
Hatfield & Stainforth		d													09 05	09 19	
Thorne South		d														09 24	
Crowle		d														09 32	
Althorpe		d														09 38	
Scunthorpe		a							09 05							09 46	
		d							09 06								
Barnetby	28	d						09 39	09 20								
Habrough	28	d						09 48	09 28								
Grimsby Town	28	a						10 00	09 42								
		d						10 01	09 43								
Cleethorpes	28	a						10 13	09 55								
Thorne North		d													09 10		
Goole		d			08 43										09 19		09 38
Saltmarshe		d															
York 8	33	d		07 38										08 43			
Selby		a		07 57							08 57			09 06			
		d		07 58							08 58			09 07			
Wressle		d		08 05													
Howden		d		08 10										09 16			
Eastrington		d		08 15													
Gilberdyke		d		08 18											09 28		
Broomfleet		d		08 23													
Brough		d		08 29	08 57									09 29	09 36		09 53
Ferriby		d		08 33											09 41		
Hessle		d		08 38											09 45		
Hull		a		08 52	09 13						09 31			09 47	09 58		10 09

Station			NT B	XC ◇1 H 🍴	NT	TP ◇1	TP ◇1	NT B	EM ◇1 K 🍴	XC ◇1 L 🍴
Manchester Airport ✈	85	d				07 53				
Manchester Piccadilly 10		d				08 20	08 42			
Stockport	78	d				08 28				
Sheffield 7		a				09 08				
		d		08 48	08 53	09 10		09 15	09 21	09 21
Meadowhall		d			09 00	09 16		09 21		
Rotherham Central		d			09 06			09 28		
Swinton (S.Yorks)		d			09 16			09a36		
Mexborough		d			09 19					
Conisbrough		d			09 23					
London Kings Cross		d								
Doncaster 7		a		09 18	09 33	09 35			09 53	
York 8	26	a		09 43					10 16	10 30
Doncaster	31	d	09 26		09 34	09 37				
Bentley (S.Yorks)	31	a	09 29		09 37					
Adwick	31	a	09 33		09 43					
Kirk Sandall		d								
Hatfield & Stainforth		d								
Thorne South		d								
Crowle		d								
Althorpe		d								
Scunthorpe		a				10 02				
		d				10 03				
Barnetby	28	d				10 17				
Habrough	28	d								
Grimsby Town	28	a				10 39				
		d				10 40				
Cleethorpes	28	a				10 51				
Thorne North		d								
Goole		d								
Saltmarshe		d								
York 8	33	d								
Selby		a					09 57			
		d					09 58			
Wressle		d								
Howden		d								
Eastrington		d								
Gilberdyke		d								
Broomfleet		d								
Brough		d					10 17			
Ferriby		d								
Hessle		d								
Hull		a					10 35			

A To Beverley
B To Leeds
C From Derby to Newcastle
D From Birmingham New Street to Glasgow Central
E To Scarborough
F From Scunthorpe
G To Bridlington
H From Birmingham New Street to Newcastle
I via Retford
J From Birmingham New Street to Edinburgh
K From St Pancras International
L From Bristol Temple Meads to Glasgow Central

For all trains between Barnetby, Habrough, Grimsby Town and Cleethorpes see Table 28

Table 29

Saturdays

14 December to 17 May

Manchester Airport, Manchester, Sheffield and Meadowhall-Doncaster and Hull

Network Diagram - refer to first Page of Table 18

Station			NT	NT	NT A	NT	NT B	NT C	XC ◇1 D	NT E	TP ◇1	TP ◇1	NT C	XC ◇1 F	NT	NT	NT	NT G	XC ◇1 H	HT ◇1 ⊠	NT C	NT E	TP ◇1	TP ◇1	NT C	XC ◇1 I	NT	NT	NT	NT B	NT C	XC ◇1 J	NT E	NT K	TP ◇1	TP ◇1	NT C	XC ◇1 F	NT
Manchester Airport	85	d									08 55												09 55												10 55				
Manchester Piccadilly 10		d									09 20	09 42											10 20	10 42											11 20	11 42			
Stockport	78	d									09 28												10 28												11 28				
Sheffield 7		a									10 08												11 08												12 08				
		d		09 27	09 32		09 41		09 47	09 53	10 10		10 14	10 21		10 24		10 41	10 47			10 53	11 10		11 14	11 21		11 24		11 41		11 47	11 53	12 00	12 10		12 14	12 21	
Meadowhall		d		09 35	09 39		09 47			09 59	10 16		10 21			10 30		10 47				10 59	11 16		11 21			11 30		11 47			11 59		12 16		12 21		
Rotherham Central		d		09 41	09 46					10 05			10 27			10 36						11 05			11 27			11 37					12 05				12 27		
Swinton (S.Yorks)		d		09 49	09 54					10 16			10a36			10 48						11 16			11a36			11 48					12 16				12a36		
Mexborough		d		09 52						10 19						10 51						11 19						11 51					12 19						
Conisbrough		d		09 56						10 23						10 55						11 23						11 55					12 23						
London Kings Cross		d																		09 48																			
Doncaster 7		a		10 07			10 14		10 17	10 32	10 35					11 04		11 11	11 15	11 23		11 32	11 35					12 04		12 14		12 15	12 33		12 35				
York 8	26	a			10 54				10 39					11 30					11 40							12 30						12 39						13 30	
Doncaster	31	d	09 42	10 07			10 19	10 26		10 34	10 37				10 42	11 08		11 19		11 25	11 26	11 34	11 37				11 42	12 08		12 19	12 26		12 34		12 37				12 42
Bentley (S.Yorks)	31	a						10 29		10 37											11 29	11 37									12 29		12 37						
Adwick	31	a						10 33		10 43											11 33	11 43									12 33		12 43						
Kirk Sandall		d	09 48	10 15											10 48	11 14											11 48	12 14											12 48
Hatfield & Stainforth		d	09 53	10 20											10 53	11 19											11 53	12 19											12 53
Thorne South		d		10 25												11 24												12 24											
Crowle		d		10 33												11 32												12 32											
Althorpe		d		10 39												11 38												12 38											
Scunthorpe		a		10 47							11 02					11 46							12 02					12 46							13 02				
		d									11 03												12 03												13 03				
Barnetby	28	d									11 17												12 17											13 38	13 17				
Habrough	28	d																					12 26											13 47					
Grimsby Town	28	a									11 37												12 39											14 00	13 37				
		d									11 38												12 40											14 00	13 38				
Cleethorpes	28	a									11 50												12 52											14 11	13 50				
Thorne North		d	09 58												10 58												11 58												12 58
Goole		d	10 07				10 38								11 07			11 38									12 07			12 38									13 07
Saltmarshe		d																																					
York 8	33	d				09 51											10 47												11 45										
Selby		a				10 09						10 57					11 06			11 39				11 57					12 04							12 57			
		d				10 09						10 58					11 07			11 40				11 58					12 05							12 58			
Wressle		d																																					
Howden		d				10 18											11 17			11 50									12 14										
Eastrington		d																																					
Gilberdyke		d	10 16			10 25									11 17		11 23										12 16		12 22										13 16
Broomfleet		d															11 27																						
Brough		d	10 24			10 33	10 52					11 17			11 25		11 33	11 53		12 03				12 17			12 24		12 30	12 52						13 17			13 24
Ferriby		d	10 29												11 29												12 29												13 29
Hessle		d	10 33												11 34												12 33												13 33
Hull		a	10 45			10 50	11 09					11 35			11 46		11 53	12 09		12 19				12 36			12 45		12 49	13 09						13 35			13 45

A via Pontefract Baghill
B To Scarborough
C To Leeds
D From Guildford to Newcastle
E From Lincoln
F From Plymouth to Edinburgh
G To Bridlington
H From Bournemouth to Newcastle
I From Plymouth to Glasgow Central
J From Southampton Central to Newcastle
K via Retford

For all trains between Barnetby, Habrough, Grimsby Town and Cleethorpes see Table 28

Table 29

Saturdays

14 December to 17 May

Manchester Airport, Manchester, Sheffield and Meadowhall-Doncaster and Hull

Network Diagram - refer to first Page of Table 18

	NT	NT	NT	XC	HT	NT	NT	TP	TP	NT	XC	NT	NT	NT	NT	NT	NT	XC	NT
			A	◇1 B	◇1	C	D	◇1	◇1	C	◇1 E					A	C	◇1 F	D
Manchester Airport 85 ✈ d								11 55											
Manchester Piccadilly 10 d								12 20	12 42										
Stockport 78 d								12 28											
Sheffield 7 a								13 08											
d	12 24		12 41	12 47			12 53	13 10		13 14	13 21		13 24	13 30		13 41		13 47	13 53
Meadowhall d	12 30		12 47				12 59	13 16		13 21			13 30	13 36		13 47			13 59
Rotherham Central d	12 37						13 05			13 27			13 37	13 42					14 05
Swinton (S.Yorks) d	12 47						13 16			13a36			13 48	13 52					14 17
Mexborough d	12 50						13 19						13 51						14 20
Conisbrough d	12 54						13 23						13 55						14 24
London Kings Cross d					11 48														
Doncaster 7 a	13 04		13 14	13 17	13 23		13 32	13 35					14 04			14 16		14 18	14 32
York 8 26 a				13 39							14 30			14 55				14 39	
Doncaster 31 d	13 08		13 19		13 25	13 26	13 33	13 37				13 42	14 08			14 19	14 26		14 34
Bentley (S.Yorks) 31 a						13 29	13 36										14 29		14 37
Adwick 31 a						13 33	13 42										14 33		14 43
Kirk Sandall d	13 14											13 48	14 14						
Hatfield & Stainforth d	13 19											13 53	14 19						
Thorne South d	13 24												14 24						
Crowle d	13 33												14 33						
Althorpe d	13 39												14 39						
Scunthorpe a	13 46							14 03					14 46						
d								14 03											
Barnetby 28 d								14 17											
Habrough 28 d								14 26											
Grimsby Town 28 a								14 39											
d								14 40											
Cleethorpes 28 a								14 52											
Thorne North d												13 58							
Goole d			13 38									14 07				14 38			
Saltmarshe d												14 12							
York 8 33 d		12 47													13 50				
Selby a		13 06			13 39				13 57						14 12				
d		13 06			13 40				13 58						14 13				
Wressle d																			
Howden d		13 16			13 50										14 22				
Eastrington d																			
Gilberdyke d												14 18							
Broomfleet d																			
Brough d		13 28	13 53		14 03				14 17			14 26			14 35	14 53			
Ferriby d												14 31							
Hessle d												14 35							
Hull a		13 48	14 09		14 21				14 35			14 49			14 55	15 09			

	TP	TP	NT	XC	NT	NT	NT	NT	NT	XC	NT	TP	TP	NT	XC	NT	NT	NT	NT
	◇1	◇1	C	◇1 G				H	C	◇1 B	D	◇1	◇1	C	◇1 E			A	C
Manchester Airport 85 ✈ d	12 55											13 55							
Manchester Piccadilly 10 d	13 20	13 42										14 20	14 42						
Stockport 78 d	13 28											14 28							
Sheffield 7 a	14 08											15 08							
d	14 10		14 14	14 21		14 24		14 41		14 47	14 53	15 10		15 14	15 21		15 24	15 41	
Meadowhall d	14 16		14 21			14 30		14 47			14 59	15 16		15 21			15 30	15 47	
Rotherham Central d			14 27			14 37					15 05			15 27			15 37		
Swinton (S.Yorks) d			14a36			14 48					15 17			15a36			15 47		
Mexborough d						14 51					15 20						15 50		
Conisbrough d						14 55					15 24						15 54		
London Kings Cross d																			
Doncaster 7 a	14 35					15 04		15 16		15 17	15 34	15 35					16 04	16 14	
York 8 26 a				15 30						15 39					16 30				
Doncaster 31 d	14 37				14 42	15 07		15 19	15 26		15 34	15 37				15 42	16 08	16 19	16 26
Bentley (S.Yorks) 31 a									15 29		15 37								16 29
Adwick 31 a									15 33		15 43								16 33
Kirk Sandall d					14 48	15 13										15 48	16 14		
Hatfield & Stainforth d					14 53	15 18										15 53	16 19		
Thorne South d						15 23											16 24		
Crowle d						15 31											16 33		
Althorpe d						15 37											16 39		
Scunthorpe a	15 02					15 46						16 02					16 46		
d	15 03											16 03							
Barnetby 28 d	15 17											16 17							
Habrough 28 d												16 26							
Grimsby Town 28 a	15 37											16 39							
d	15 38											16 40							
Cleethorpes 28 a	15 50											16 52							
Thorne North d					14 58											15 58			
Goole d					15 07			15 38								16 07		16 38	
Saltmarshe d																			
York 8 33 d							14 47												
Selby a		14 57					15 06						15 57						
d		14 58					15 06						15 58						
Wressle d																			
Howden d							15 16												
Eastrington d																			
Gilberdyke d					15 16											16 18			
Broomfleet d																			
Brough d		15 17			15 24		15 29	15 53					16 17			16 26		16 53	
Ferriby d					15 29											16 30			
Hessle d					15 33											16 35			
Hull a		15 35			15 45		15 48	16 09					16 35			16 48		17 09	

A To Bridlington
B From Reading to Newcastle
C To Leeds
D From Lincoln
E From Penzance to Glasgow Central
F From Southampton Central to Newcastle
G From Plymouth to Aberdeen
H To Scarborough

For all trains between Barnetby, Habrough, Grimsby Town and Cleethorpes see Table 28

Table 29

Saturdays

14 December to 17 May

Manchester Airport, Manchester, Sheffield and Meadowhall-Doncaster and Hull

Network Diagram - refer to first Page of Table 18

Station		XC ◇1 A	HT ◇1 ⊠	NT ◇ B	NT C	TP ◇1	NT	TP ◇1	NT D	XC ◇1 E	NT	NT F	NT G	NT	XC ◇1 H	NT	NT D	NT ◇ B	TP ◇1	TP ◇1
Manchester Airport 85 ✈	d					14 55													15 55	
Manchester Piccadilly 10	d					15 20		15 42											16 20	16 42
Stockport 78	d					15 28													16 28	
Sheffield 7	a					16 08													17 08	
	d	15 47		15 53	16 00	16 10			16 14	16 21	16 24		16 41		16 47			16 53	17 10	
Meadowhall	d			15 59		16 16			16 21		16 30		16 47					16 59	17 16	
Rotherham Central	d			16 05					16 27		16 37							17 05		
Swinton (S.Yorks)	d			16 16					16a36		16 47							17 16		
Mexborough	d			16 19							16 50							17 19		
Conisbrough	d			16 23							16 54							17 23		
London Kings Cross	d		14 48																	
Doncaster 7	a	16 18	16 23	16 32		16 35					17 06		17 12		17 16			17 32	17 35	
York 8 26	a	16 39								17 30					17 37					
Doncaster 31	d		16 26	16 34		16 37						16 42	17 19	17 22			17 26	17 34	17 43	
Bentley (S.Yorks) 31	a			16 37													17 29	17 37		
Adwick 31	a			16 43													17 33	17 43		
Kirk Sandall	d											16 48		17 29						
Hatfield & Stainforth	d											16 53		17 34						
Thorne South	d													17 39						
Crowle	d													17 48						
Althorpe	d													17 54						
Scunthorpe	a					17 02								18 02					18 08	
	d					17 03													18 08	
Barnetby 28	d				17 38	17 17													18 23	
Habrough 28	d				17 47														18 32	
Grimsby Town 28	a				18 01	17 37													18 45	
	d				18 02	17 38													18 46	
Cleethorpes 28	a				18 11	17 50													18 58	
Thorne North	d											16 58	17 31							
Goole	d											17 07	17 40							
Saltmarshe	d																			
York 8 33	d						16 12									17 19				
Selby	a		16 41				16 36	17 00								17 45				17 59
	d		16 44				16 36	17 00								17 46				17 59
Wressle	d						16 44													
Howden	d		16 54				16 49									17 56				18 08
Eastrington	d																			
Gilberdyke	d						16 55					17 17				18 04				
Broomfleet	d																			
Brough	d		17 09				17 03	17 19				17 25	17 56			18 12				18 21
Ferriby	d						17 08					17 30								
Hessle	d						17 12					17 34								
Hull	a		17 25				17 27	17 37				17 48	18 13			18 30				18 39

Station		NT D	XC ◇1 I	NT	NT	NT J	NT D	XC ◇1 A	NT	TP ◇1	NT K	NT B	TP ◇1	NT D	XC ◇1 L	NT	NT G	NT	XC ◇1 H
Manchester Airport 85 ✈	d												16 55						
Manchester Piccadilly 10	d									17 42			17 20						
Stockport 78	d												17 28						
Sheffield 7	a												18 10						
	d	17 14	17 22	17 27		17 41		17 47				17 53	18 11	18 16	18 22	18 30	18 41		18 47
Meadowhall	d	17 21		17 33		17 47						17 59	18 18	18 22		18 36	18 47		
Rotherham Central	d	17 27		17 39								18 05		18 28		18 42			
Swinton (S.Yorks)	d	17a37		17 47								18 16		18a37		18 50			
Mexborough	d			17 50								18 20				18 53			
Conisbrough	d			17 54								18 24				18 57			
London Kings Cross	d																		
Doncaster 7	a			18 11		18 12						18 37	18 45			19 08	19 12		19 16
York 8 26	a		18 30					18 57							19 30				19 38
Doncaster 31	d				17 47	18 19	18 26				18 30	18 39	18 46				19 17	19 21	
Bentley (S.Yorks) 31	a						18 29												
Adwick 31	a						18 33												
Kirk Sandall	d				17 53						18 37	18 43						19 27	
Hatfield & Stainforth	d				17 58						18 42	18 48						19 32	
Thorne South	d										18 47							19 37	
Crowle	d										18 55							19 46	
Althorpe	d										19 01							19 52	
Scunthorpe	a										19 09		19 11					20 00	
	d												19 12						
Barnetby 28	d												19 27						
Habrough 28	d												19 35						
Grimsby Town 28	a												19 48						
	d												19 49						
Cleethorpes 28	a												20 02						
Thorne North	d				18 03							18 53							
Goole	d				18 12	18 38						19 12					19 38		
Saltmarshe	d				18 17														
York 8 33	d								18 18										
Selby	a								18 42	19 00									
	d								18 43	19 01									
Wressle	d								18 50										
Howden	d								18 54										
Eastrington	d								18 59										
Gilberdyke	d				18 23				19 04			19 21							
Broomfleet	d				18 27														
Brough	d				18 33	18 53			19 11	19 20		19 29					19 54		
Ferriby	d				18 38							19 34							
Hessle	d				18 42							19 38							
Hull	a				18 55	19 07			19 29	19 38		19 50					20 09		

A From Southampton Central to Newcastle
B From Lincoln
C via Retford
D To Leeds
E From Plymouth to Dundee
F To Beverley
G To Bridlington
H From Reading to Newcastle
I From Plymouth to Glasgow Central
J To Scarborough
K From Adwick
L From Plymouth to Edinburgh

For all trains between Barnetby, Habrough, Grimsby Town and Cleethorpes see Table 28

Table 29

Saturdays

14 December to 17 May

Manchester Airport, Manchester, Sheffield and Meadowhall-Doncaster and Hull

Network Diagram - refer to first Page of Table 18

			NT A	HT ◇1 ☒	NT B	TP ◇1	TP ◇1	NT A	XC ◇1 C	NT	NT	NT	NT D	NT A	XC ◇1 E	NT F	TP ◇1 G	NT	XC ◇1 H	TP ◇1	NT A	NT	NT A	XC ◇1 I	HT ◇1 ☒	NT D	NT A	TP ◇1	NT A	XC ◇1 J	NT	NT A	XC ◇1 K	NT	TP ◇1 G	NT
Manchester Airport	85 ✈	d				17 55														18 55																
Manchester Piccadilly 10		d				18 20	18 42													19 18																
Stockport	78	d				18 28														19 26																
Sheffield 7		a				19 09														20 08																
		d			19 00	19 11		19 19	19 22			19 25	19 44		19 54	19 58		20 15	20 23	20 25	20 30	20 38		20 53		21 15	21 30	21 48		22 09		22 24	22 27	22 30		23 27
Meadowhall		d			19 06	19 18		19 25				19 31	19 50			20 04		20 21		20 32	20 36	20 45				21 21	21 36	21 54				22 30		22 36		23 33
Rotherham Central		d			19 12			19 31				19 37				20 11		20 27			20 42	20 53				21 27	21 42					22 36		22 45		23 39
Swinton (S.Yorks)		d			19 20			19a40				19 47				20 21		20 40			20a51	21 01				21 36	21a50					22a45		22 53		23 48
Mexborough		d			19 23							19 50				20 24		20 43				21 04				21 39								22 56		23 51
Conisbrough		d			19 27							19 54				20 28		20 47				21 08				21 43								23 00		23 55
London Kings Cross		d		17 48																					19 48											
Doncaster 7		a		19 24	19 39	19 41						20 02	20 14		20 18	20 36		20 55		21 01		21 18		21 21	21 27	21 54		22 13		22 30			22 51	23 09		00 08
York 8	26	a							20 30						20 39				21 57					21 43						22 55						
Doncaster	31	d	19 22	19 26		19 48					19 53	20 07	20 19	20 26		20 43		20 57		21 07		21 21	21 22		21 29	21 56		22 25	22 26					23 10		
Bentley (S.Yorks)	31	a	19 25											20 29									21 25						22 29							
Adwick	31	a	19 29											20 33									21 29						22 33							
Kirk Sandall		d									19 59	20 13						21 03				21 27				22 02		22 30						23 17		
Hatfield & Stainforth		d									20 04	20 18						21 08				21 32				22 07		22 35						23 22		
Thorne South		d										20 22										21 37						22 39								
Crowle		d										20 31										21 46						22 48								
Althorpe		d										20 37										21 52						22 53								
Scunthorpe		a				20 12						20 45								21 32		22 00						22 58								
		d				20 12														21 33								22 59								
Barnetby	28	d				20 27														21 47								23 13								
Habrough	28	d																		21 56								23 22								
Grimsby Town	28	a				20 46														22 09								23 37								
		d				20 47														22 10								23 38								
Cleethorpes	28	a				21 00														22 21								23 47								
Thorne North		d									20 09							21 14								22 13								23 27		
Goole		d									20 18		20 38					21a23								22 22								23a38		
Saltmarshe		d																								22 26										
York 8	33	d								19 47																					22 11					
Selby		a		19 40			20 00			20 05						21 01									21 43						22 29					
		d		19 41			20 01			20 06						21 02	21 30								21 44						22 30				22 46	
Wressle		d																																		
Howden		d		19 52			20 10			20 16							21 39								21 54						22 39					
Eastrington		d																																		
Gilberdyke		d									20 27					21 16										22 33					22 46					
Broomfleet		d																																		
Brough		d		20 05			20 23			20 30	20 35		20 53			21 24	21 52								22 07	22 41					22 54				23 07	
Ferriby		d									20 40					21 29															22 59					
Hessle		d									20 44					21 33															23 03					
Hull		a		20 21			20 41			20 48	20 58		21 09			21 47	22 10								22 25	22 59					23 16				23 25	

A To Leeds
B From Retford Low Level
C From Plymouth to Edinburgh
D To Beverley
E From Southampton Central to Newcastle
F To Bridlington
G From Leeds
H From Plymouth
I From Reading to Newcastle
J From Southampton Central
K From Plymouth to Leeds

For all trains between Barnetby, Habrough, Grimsby Town and Cleethorpes see Table 28

Table 29

Sundays

Manchester Airport, Manchester, Sheffield and Meadowhall-Doncaster and Hull

8 December to 29 December

Network Diagram - refer to first Page of Table 18

			NT	NT A	NT B	XC ◇1 C	NT A	NT D	TP ◇1 E	TP ◇1	XC ◇1 F ⊼	NT	NT B	NT A	NT	XC ◇1 G ⊼	EM ◇1 H ☕	NT A	NT	HT ◇1 ⊠	TP ◇1
Manchester Airport	85 ✈	d																			10 44
Manchester Piccadilly 10		d							09 12												11 18
Stockport	78	d																			11 27
Sheffield 7		a																			12 07
		d	08 00		08 45	09 21	09 36			09 52	10 21		10 28		11 05	11 21	11 31	11 36			12 10
Meadowhall		d	08 06		08 51		09 42			09 57			10 34		11 11			11 42			12 16
Rotherham Central		d	08 12		08 57		09 48			10 03					11 17			11 49			
Swinton (S.Yorks)		d	08 20		09 05		09a58			10 09					11 25			12a00			
Mexborough		d	08 23		09 08					10 13					11 28						
Conisbrough		d	08 27		09 12					10 17					11 32						
London Kings Cross		d																		10 48	
Doncaster 7		a	08 38		09 22					10 26			10 52		11 43		11 52			12 22	12 35
York 8	26	a				10 29					11 27					12 27	12 15				
Doncaster	31	d		09 12	09 26			10 19		10 28			10 57	11 12						12 28	12 37
Bentley (S.Yorks)	31	a		09 15										11 15							
Adwick	31	a		09 19										11 19							
Kirk Sandall		d																			
Hatfield & Stainforth		d																			
Thorne South		d																			
Crowle		d																			
Althorpe		d																			
Scunthorpe		a								10 54											13 03
		d								10 55											13 04
Barnetby	28	d								11 09											13 18
Habrough	28	d								11 18											
Grimsby Town	28	a								11 31											13 38
		d								11 33											13 39
Cleethorpes	28	a								11 40											13 50
Thorne North		d			09 38			10 31													
Goole		d			09 47			10 40					11 16								
Saltmarshe		d																			
York 8	33	d										10 40							12 05		
Selby		a							10 44			10 58							12 24	12 43	
		d							10 44			10 59							12 24	12 44	
Wressle		d																			
Howden		d										11 08							12 34	12 54	
Eastrington		d																			
Gilberdyke		d			09 55			10 48					11 25								
Broomfleet		d																			
Brough		d			10 03			10 56	11 05			11 19	11 33						12 47	13 07	
Ferriby		d						11 00													
Hessle		d						11 05													
Hull		a			10 21			11 17	11 21			11 41	11 49						13 05	13 25	

			XC ◇1 I ⊼	NT	NT B	NT A	TP ◇1	TP ◇1	XC ◇1 J ⊼	NT	NT D	NT A	XC ◇1 K ⊼	HT ◇1 ⊠	TP ◇1	XC ◇1 L ⊼	NT	NT	NT B	NT A	TP ◇1
Manchester Airport	85 ✈	d						11 55							12 55						
Manchester Piccadilly 10		d					12 01	12 18							13 20						14 02
Stockport	78	d						12 28							13 28						
Sheffield 7		a						13 08							14 08						
		d	12 21	12 24	12 28			13 10	13 21		13 24	13 36	13 51		14 10	14 21	14 22		14 28		
Meadowhall		d		12 30	12 34			13 16			13 30	13 42			14 16		14 28		14 34		
Rotherham Central		d		12 36							13 36	13 49					14 35				
Swinton (S.Yorks)		d		12 49							13 47	13a57					14 46				
Mexborough		d		12 52							13 50						14 49				
Conisbrough		d		12 56							13 54						14 53				
London Kings Cross		d												12 48							
Doncaster 7		a		13 04	12 55			13 34			14 02		14 13	14 22	14 35		15 03		14 56		
York 8	26	a	13 27						14 27				14 38			15 27					
Doncaster	31	d		13 06	12 58	13 12					14 06			14 29	14 37		15 07		15 03	15 12	
Bentley (S.Yorks)	31	a				13 15														15 15	
Adwick	31	a				13 19														15 19	
Kirk Sandall		d		13 12													15 13				
Hatfield & Stainforth		d		13 17													15 18				
Thorne South		d																			
Crowle		d																			
Althorpe		d																			
Scunthorpe		a													15 02						
		d													15 03						
Barnetby	28	d													15 19						
Habrough	28	d																			
Grimsby Town	28	a													15 38						
		d													15 39						
Cleethorpes	28	a													15 49						
Thorne North		d		13 22													15 25				
Goole		d		13a33	13 17						14 25						15a34		15 22		
Saltmarshe		d																			
York 8	33	d								13 45								14 52			
Selby		a					13 23			14 04				14 43				15 11			15 23
		d					13 23			14 04				14 44				15 11			15 23
Wressle		d																			
Howden		d								14 14				14 54				15 21			
Eastrington		d																			
Gilberdyke		d			13 26						14 33								15 32		
Broomfleet		d																			
Brough		d			13 34		13 42			14 26	14 41			15 08				15 34	15 40		15 41
Ferriby		d			13 39																
Hessle		d			13 43																
Hull		a			13 55		13 59			14 45	14 58			15 26				15 51	15 56		15 59

A To Leeds
B To Scarborough
C To Glasgow Central
D To Bridlington
E From Liverpool Lime Street
F From Birmingham New Street to Edinburgh
G From Birmingham New Street to Glasgow Central
H From Leicester
I From Bristol Temple Meads to Edinburgh
J From Bristol Temple Meads to Glasgow Central
K From Birmingham New Street to Newcastle
L From Plymouth to Aberdeen

For all trains between Barnetby, Habrough, Grimsby Town and Cleethorpes see Table 28

Table 29

Sundays

8 December to 29 December

Manchester Airport, Manchester, Sheffield and Meadowhall-Doncaster and Hull

Network Diagram - refer to first Page of Table 18

	XC	TP	XC	NT	NT	NT	XC	NT	HT	TP	XC	NT	NT
	◇1 A ✠	◇1	◇1 B ✠		C	D	◇1 E ✠		◇1 ⊠	◇1	◇1 F ✠		G
Manchester Airport 85 ✈ d		13 55								14 55			
Manchester Piccadilly 10 ⇌ d		14 20								15 20			
Stockport 78 d		14 28								15 28			
Sheffield 7 ⇌ a		15 08								16 09			
d	14 51	15 10	15 21	15 24	15 28	15 36	15 51			16 10	16 21	16 25	16 28
Meadowhall ⇌ d		15 16		15 30	15 34	15 42				16 16		16 31	16 34
Rotherham Central d				15 37		15 50						16 38	
Swinton (S.Yorks) d				15 47		15a58						16 48	
Mexborough d				15 50								16 51	
Conisbrough d				15 54								16 55	
London Kings Cross d									14 48				
Doncaster 7 a	15 13	15 35		16 04	15 53		16 15		16 23	16 35		17 04	16 56
York 8 26 a	15 42		16 27				16 38				17 27		
Doncaster 31 d		15 37			15 58				16 30	16 37		17 06	16 56
Bentley (S.Yorks) 31 a													
Adwick 31 a													
Kirk Sandall d												17 12	
Hatfield & Stainforth d												17 17	
Thorne South d													
Crowle d													
Althorpe d													
Scunthorpe a		16 02								17 02			
d		16 03								17 03			
Barnetby 28 d		16 17								17 17			
Habrough 28 d		16 26											
Grimsby Town 28 a		16 39								17 37			
d		16 40								17 38			
Cleethorpes 28 a		16 50								17 48			
Thorne North d					16 10							17 25	
Goole d					16 19							17a34	17 15
Saltmarshe d													
York 8 33 d								16 06					
Selby a								16 25	16 45				
d								16 25	16 46				
Wressle d													
Howden d								16 35	16 56				
Eastrington d													
Gilberdyke d					16 28								17 24
Broomfleet d													
Brough d					16 36			16 48	17 09				17 32
Ferriby d													
Hessle d													
Hull a					16 52			17 06	17 27				17 49

	NT	TP	NT	XC	TP	NT	XC	NT	NT	NT	XC	TP	XC
	D	◇1	H	◇1 I ✠	◇1		◇1 B ✠		C	D	◇1 I ✠	◇1	◇1 J ✠
Manchester Airport 85 ✈ d					15 55							16 55	
Manchester Piccadilly 10 ⇌ d		16 02			16 20							17 20	
Stockport 78 d					16 28							17 28	
Sheffield 7 ⇌ a					17 08							18 08	
d			16 36	16 51	17 10		17 21	17 25	17 28	17 36	17 51	18 10	18 21
Meadowhall ⇌ d			16 42		17 16			17 31	17 34	17 44		18 16	
Rotherham Central d			16 49					17 37		17 50			
Swinton (S.Yorks) d			16 58					17 47		17a58			
Mexborough d								17 50					
Conisbrough d								17 54					
London Kings Cross d													
Doncaster 7 a				17 13	17 35			18 05	17 55		18 13	18 35	
York 8 26 a			17 59	17 40			18 27				19 20		19 30
Doncaster 31 d	17 12				17 37				17 58			18 37	
Bentley (S.Yorks) 31 a	17 15												
Adwick 31 a	17 19												
Kirk Sandall d													
Hatfield & Stainforth d													
Thorne South d													
Crowle d													
Althorpe d													
Scunthorpe a					18 02							19 02	
d					18 03							19 03	
Barnetby 28 d					18 17							19 17	
Habrough 28 d												19 26	
Grimsby Town 28 a					18 37							19 39	
d					18 38							19 40	
Cleethorpes 28 a					18 48							19 48	
Thorne North d													
Goole d									18 17				
Saltmarshe d													
York 8 33 d						17 11							
Selby a		17 23				17 30							
d		17 23				17 30							
Wressle d													
Howden d						17 40							
Eastrington d													
Gilberdyke d									18 26				
Broomfleet d													
Brough d		17 41				17 53			18 34				
Ferriby d													
Hessle d													
Hull a		17 59				18 11			18 52				

	NT	NT	GR	NT	TP	XC	NT	NT	HT	TP	TP
		K	R 1 ✠	D	◇1	◇1 L ✠	H		◇1 ⊠	◇1	◇1
Manchester Airport 85 ✈ d										17 55	
Manchester Piccadilly 10 ⇌ d					18 02					18 20	19 02
Stockport 78 d										18 28	
Sheffield 7 ⇌ a										19 08	
d	18 25	18 28				18 51	18 57			19 10	
Meadowhall ⇌ d	18 31	18 34					19 05			19 16	
Rotherham Central d	18 37						19 11				
Swinton (S.Yorks) d	18 48						19 19				
Mexborough d	18 51										
Conisbrough d	18 55										
London Kings Cross d			17 20						17 44		
Doncaster 7 a	19 05	18 53	19 02			19 15			19 23	19 35	
York 8 26 a						19 39	20 18				
Doncaster 31 d		18 58	19 05	19 27					19 30	19 37	
Bentley (S.Yorks) 31 a				19 30							
Adwick 31 a				19 34							
Kirk Sandall d		19 04									
Hatfield & Stainforth d		19 09									
Thorne South d											
Crowle d											
Althorpe d											
Scunthorpe a										20 02	
d										20 03	
Barnetby 28 d										20 17	
Habrough 28 d											
Grimsby Town 28 a										20 37	
d										20 38	
Cleethorpes 28 a										20 48	
Thorne North d		19 14									
Goole d		19 23									
Saltmarshe d											
York 8 33 d								19 16			
Selby a			19 21		19 28			19 35	19 45		20 17
d			19 23		19 29			19 35	19 46		20 17
Wressle d											
Howden d								19 45	19 56		
Eastrington d											
Gilberdyke d		19 32									
Broomfleet d											
Brough d		19 40	19 46		19 48			19 58	20 08		20 37
Ferriby d											
Hessle d											
Hull a		19 57	20 02		20 05			20 16	20 26		20 54

A From Birmingham New Street to Newcastle
B From Plymouth to Glasgow Central
C To Bridlington
D To Leeds
E From Guildford to Newcastle
F From Penzance to Edinburgh
G To Scarborough
H via Pontefract Baghill
I From Reading to Newcastle
J From Plymouth to Edinburgh
K To Beverley
L From Reading to Edinburgh

For all trains between Barnetby, Habrough, Grimsby Town and Cleethorpes see Table 28

Table 29

Sundays

Manchester Airport, Manchester, Sheffield and Meadowhall-Doncaster and Hull

8 December to 29 December

Network Diagram - refer to first Page of Table 18

		XC	NT	NT	XC	NT	TP	TP	XC	NT	XC	HT	TP	NT	NT	NT	NT	TP	NT	NT	TP	NT
		◇1			◇1		◇1	◇1	◇1		◇1	◇1	◇1					◇1			◇1	
		A		B	C				D		C			B			B	E				
		🍴			🍴							⊠										
Manchester Airport 85 ✈	d						18 55						19 55									
Manchester Piccadilly 10 🚌	d						19 20	20 06					20 18									
Stockport 78	d						19 28						20 27									
Sheffield 7 🚌	a						20 08						21 08									
	d	19 21	19 29	19 36	19 51	20 02	20 10		20 21	20 28	20 51		21 10			21 25	21 36		22 13	22 26	22 30	23 34
Meadowhall 🚌	d		19 35	19 42		20 09	20 16			20 34			21 16			21 31	21 42		22 19	22 32	22 35	23 40
Rotherham Central	d		19 41	19 49						20 40						21 38	21 48			22 38		23 47
Swinton (S.Yorks)	d		19 49	19a57						20 48						21 47	21a56			22 48		23 55
Mexborough	d		19 52							20 51						21 50				22 51		23 58
Conisbrough	d		19 56							20 55						21 54				22 55		00 02
London Kings Cross	d											19 50										
Doncaster 7	a		20 07		20 16	20 27	20 35			21 05	21 19	21 24	21 35			22 03			22 38	23 05	22 56	00 13
York 8 26	a	20 30			20 38				21 31		21 42											
Doncaster 31	d					20 31	20 37			21 07		21 26	21 37	21 52		22 06			22 45		22 58	
Bentley (S.Yorks) 31	a													21 55								
Adwick 31	a													21 59								
Kirk Sandall	d									21 13												
Hatfield & Stainforth	d									21 18												
Thorne South	d																					
Crowle	d																					
Althorpe	d																					
Scunthorpe	a						21 02						22 02								23 23	
	d						21 03						22 03								23 24	
Barnetby 28	d						21 18						22 17								23 38	
Habrough 28	d						21 27						22 26									
Grimsby Town 28	a						21 39						22 39								23 57	
	d						21 40						22 40								23 58	
Cleethorpes 28	a						21 50						22 50								00 09	
Thorne North	d									21 24									22 57			
Goole	d					20 51				21a34						22 25			23 06			
Saltmarshe	d																					
York 8 33	d														21 41							
Selby	a							21 35				21 41			22 00							
	d							21 36				21 42			22 00			22 44				
Wressle	d																					
Howden	d											21 52			22 10							
Eastrington	d																					
Gilberdyke	d					20 59										22 34			23 15			
Broomfleet	d																					
Brough	d					21 07		21 55				22 05			22 23	22 42		23 03	23 23			
Ferriby	d																					
Hessle	d																					
Hull	a					21 23		22 09				22 23			22 41	23 00		23 19	23 39			

A From Plymouth to Edinburgh
B To Leeds
C From Reading to Newcastle
D From Plymouth
E From Leeds

For all trains between Barnetby, Habrough, Grimsby Town and Cleethorpes see Table 28

Table 29

Sundays

5 January to 9 February

Manchester Airport, Manchester, Sheffield and Meadowhall-Doncaster and Hull

Network Diagram - refer to first Page of Table 18

		NT	NT	NT	NT	TP	XC	NT	NT	TP	NT	NT	TP	XC	NT	TP
							◇1						◇1	◇1		◇1
					A		B	C	A			D	E	F		
		Bus				Bus				Bus	Bus			trolley		
Manchester Airport 85 ✈	d															
Manchester Piccadilly 10	d												09 12			
Stockport 78	d															
Sheffield 7	a															
	d	07 13	08 00	08 45		09 15	09 21		09 36	09 55	09 55			10 21		
Meadowhall	d	07 33	08 06	08 51		09 35			09 42		10 15					
Rotherham Central	d	07 43	08 12	08 57		09 45			09 48							
Swinton (S.Yorks)	d	07 55	08a20	09a05		09 57			09a58							
Mexborough	d	08 00				10 02										
Conisbrough	d	08 15				10 17										
London Kings Cross	d															
Doncaster 7	a	08 35				10 37				10 35	10 45					
York 8 26	a						10 29							11 27		
Doncaster 31	d				09 12			09 26				10 19				10 45
Bentley (S.Yorks) 31	a				09 15											
Adwick 31	a				09 19											
Kirk Sandall	d															
Hatfield & Stainforth	d															
Thorne South	d															
Crowle	d															
Althorpe	d															
Scunthorpe	a															11 11
	d															11 12
Barnetby 28	d															11 26
Habrough 28	d															11 35
Grimsby Town 28	a															11 48
	d															11 49
Cleethorpes 28	a															11 56
Thorne North	d							09 38				10 31				
Goole	d							09 47				10 40				
Saltmarshe	d															
York 8 33	d														10 40	
Selby	a												10 44		10 58	
	d												10 44		10 59	
Wressle	d															
Howden	d														11 08	
Eastrington	d															
Gilberdyke	d							09 55				10 48				
Broomfleet	d															
Brough	d							10 03				10 56	11 05		11 19	
Ferriby	d											11 00				
Hessle	d											11 05				
Hull	a							10 21				11 17	11 21		11 41	

		NT	NT	NT	XC	EM	TP	NT	NT	TP	HT	NT	NT	TP	XC	NT	TP	NT	NT	XC	NT	NT	XC	NT
					◇1	◇1				◇1	◇1			◇1	◇1					◇1			◇1	
		C		A	G	H		A				C			I				A	G		A	J	
					trolley	trolley	Bus				⊠		Bus		trolley		Bus	Bus		trolley			trolley	
Manchester Airport 85 ✈	d																							
Manchester Piccadilly 10	d													12 01										
Stockport 78	d																							
Sheffield 7	a																							
	d		11 05		11 21	11 31	11 35	11 36					11 55		12 21	12 24	13 00	13 05		13 21	13 24	13 36	13 45	
Meadowhall	d		11 11				11 55	11 42					12 15			12 30	13 20	13 25			13 30	13 42		
Rotherham Central	d		11 17					11 49								12 36					13 36	13 49		
Swinton (S.Yorks)	d		11a25					12a00								12a49					13a47	13a57		
Mexborough	d																							
Conisbrough	d																							
London Kings Cross	d										10 42													
Doncaster 7	a						12 25				12 35		12 45				13 50	13 55						
York 8 26	a				12 27	12 20									13 27					14 27			14 38	
Doncaster 31	d	10 57		11 12						12 37	12 39	12 58							13 12					
Bentley (S.Yorks) 31	a			11 15															13 15					
Adwick 31	a			11 19															13 19					
Kirk Sandall	d																							
Hatfield & Stainforth	d																							
Thorne South	d																							
Crowle	d																							
Althorpe	d																							
Scunthorpe	a									13 03														
	d									13 04														
Barnetby 28	d									13 18														
Habrough 28	d																							
Grimsby Town 28	a									13 38														
	d									13 39														
Cleethorpes 28	a									13 50														
Thorne North	d																							
Goole	d	11 16										13 17												
Saltmarshe	d																							
York 8 33	d								12 05															13 45
Selby	a								12 24		12 53			13 23										14 04
	d								12 24		12 54			13 23										14 04
Wressle	d																							
Howden	d								12 34		13 04													14 14
Eastrington	d																							
Gilberdyke	d	11 25										13 26												
Broomfleet	d																							
Brough	d	11 33							12 47		13 18	13 34		13 42										14 26
Ferriby	d											13 39												
Hessle	d											13 43												
Hull	a	11 49							13 05		13 37	13 55		13 59										14 45

A To Leeds
B To Glasgow Central
C To Scarborough
D To Bridlington
E From Liverpool Lime Street
F From Derby to Edinburgh
G From Birmingham New Street to Glasgow Central
H From Leicester
I From Birmingham New Street to Edinburgh
J From Bristol Temple Meads to Newcastle

For all trains between Barnetby, Habrough, Grimsby Town and Cleethorpes see Table 28

Table 29

Sundays

Manchester Airport, Manchester, Sheffield and Meadowhall-Doncaster and Hull

5 January to 9 February

Network Diagram - refer to first Page of Table 18

Station			TP	NT	HT	TP	NT	TP	XC	NT	XC	NT	NT	TP	NT	TP	NT	XC	NT	NT	XC	NT	NT	TP	TP	NT	XC	NT	NT	XC	NT	TP	TP	NT	HT	NT	NT	TP	XC
			◇1	A	◇1 ⊠	◇1	🚌	🚌	◇1 B 🍴		◇1 C 🍴		🚌	🚌	D	◇1	E	◇1 F 🍴		E	◇1 C 🍴	🚌	A	🚌	◇1		◇1 G 🍴		H	◇1 I 🍴	D	◇1	◇1		◇1 ⊠	E	🚌	🚌	◇1 J 🍴
Manchester Airport	85 ✈	d																																					
Manchester Piccadilly 10	🚆	d														14 02																16 02							
Stockport	78	d																																					
Sheffield 7	🚊	a																																					
		d					14 00	14 00	14 21	14 24	14 50		14 55	15 00				15 21	15 24	15 36	15 46	15 55		16 00			16 21	16 25	16 36	16 46							16 55	17 00	17 21
Meadowhall	🚊	d					14 20	14 20		14 28			15 15	15 20					15 30	15 42		16 15		16 20				16 31	16 42								17 15	17 20	
Rotherham Central		d								14 35									15 37	15 50								16 38	16 49										
Swinton (S.Yorks)		d								14a47									15a47	15a58								16a48	16 58										
Mexborough		d																																					
Conisbrough		d																																					
London Kings Cross		d			12 53																														14 58				
Doncaster 7		a			14 41		14 50	14 50					15 45	15 50								16 45		16 50											17 00		17 45	17 50	
York 8	26	a							15 27		15 42							16 27			16 38						17 27		17 59	17 44									18 27
Doncaster	31	d	14 00	14 06	14 43	15 00									15 03		15 12						15 58		16 00						16 56		17 00		17 06	17 12			
Bentley (S.Yorks)	31	a															15 15																			17 15			
Adwick	31	a															15 19																			17 19			
Kirk Sandall		d																																					
Hatfield & Stainforth		d																																					
Thorne South		d																																					
Crowle		d																																					
Althorpe		d																																					
Scunthorpe		a	14 25			15 25																			16 27								17 25						
		d	14 26			15 26																			16 28								17 26						
Barnetby	28	d	14 40			15 43																			16 42								17 40						
Habrough	28	d																							16 51														
Grimsby Town	28	a	15 00			16 02																			17 04								18 00						
		d	15 01			16 03																			17 05								18 01						
Cleethorpes	28	a	15 11			16 11																			17 15								18 11						
Thorne North		d																					16 10																
Goole		d		14 25											15 22								16 19								17 15								
Saltmarshe		d																																					
York 8	33	d										14 52														16 06								17 11					
Selby		a			14 57							15 11				15 23										16 25						17 23		17 30	17 35				
		d			14 58							15 11				15 23										16 25						17 23		17 30	17 37				
Wressle		d																																					
Howden		d			15 08							15 21														16 35								17 40	17 47				
Eastrington		d																																					
Gilberdyke		d		14 33											15 32								16 28								17 24								
Broomfleet		d																																					
Brough		d		14 41	15 21							15 34			15 40	15 41							16 36			16 48					17 32	17 41		17 53	18 00				
Ferriby		d																																					
Hessle		d																																					
Hull		a		14 58	15 39							15 51			15 56	15 59							16 52			17 06					17 49	17 59		18 11	18 21				

A To Bridlington
B From Birmingham New Street to Aberdeen
C From Plymouth to Newcastle
D To Scarborough
E To Leeds
F From Birmingham New Street to Glasgow Central
G From Reading to Edinburgh
H via Pontefract Baghill
I From Penzance to Newcastle
J From Reading to Glasgow Central

For all trains between Barnetby, Habrough, Grimsby Town and Cleethorpes see Table 28

Table 29

Sundays

5 January to 9 February

Manchester Airport, Manchester, Sheffield and Meadowhall-Doncaster and Hull

Network Diagram - refer to first Page of Table 18

	NT	NT	XC	NT	NT	TP	TP	XC	NT	XC	NT	NT	TP	TP	TP		NT	TP	XC	NT
			◇1			◇1		◇1		◇1			◇1		◇1			◇1	◇1	
		A	B		C			D		E	F	G							H	A
			🍴	🚌			🚌	🍴		🍴				🚌					🍴	
Manchester Airport 85 ✈ d																				
Manchester Piccadilly 10 d													18 02					19 02		
Stockport 78 d																				
Sheffield 7 a																				
d	17 25	17 36	17 46	17 55			18 05	18 21	18 25	18 51	18 57			19 00					19 21	
Meadowhall d	17 31	17 44		18 15			18 25		18 31		19 05			19 20						
Rotherham Central d	17 37	17 50							18 37		19 11									
Swinton (S.Yorks) d	17a47	17a58							18a48		19 19									
Mexborough d																				
Conisbrough d																				
London Kings Cross d																				
Doncaster 7 a				18 45			18 55							19 50						
York 8 26 a			19 20					19 31		19 43	20 18								20 30	
Doncaster 31 d					17 58	18 00						18 58			19 06					19 27
Bentley (S.Yorks) 31 a																				19 30
Adwick 31 a																				19 34
Kirk Sandall d												19 04								
Hatfield & Stainforth d												19 09								
Thorne South d																				
Crowle d																				
Althorpe d																				
Scunthorpe a						18 27									19 32					
d						18 28									19 32					
Barnetby 28 d						18 42									19 51					
Habrough 28 d															19 59					
Grimsby Town 28 a						19 02									20 11					
d						19 03									20 12					
Cleethorpes 28 a						19 13									20 20					
Thorne North d												19 14								
Goole d					18 17							19 23								
Saltmarshe d																				
York 8 33 d																	19 16			
Selby a													19 28				19 35	20 17		
d													19 29				19 35	20 17		
Wressle d																				
Howden d																	19 45			
Eastrington d																				
Gilberdyke d					18 26							19 32								
Broomfleet d																				
Brough d					18 34							19 40	19 48				19 58	20 37		
Ferriby d																				
Hessle d																				
Hull a					18 52							19 57	20 05				20 16	20 54		

	HT	TP	NT	NT	NT	XC	TP	XC	NT	NT	TP		XC	TP	TP	NT	NT	NT	NT	HT
	◇1	◇1				◇1		◇1			◇1		◇1		◇1					◇1
					A	I		J					I				A		A	
	⊠			🚌		🍴	🚌	🍴						🚌						⊠
Manchester Airport 85 ✈ d																				
Manchester Piccadilly 10 d											20 06									
Stockport 78 d																				
Sheffield 7 a																				
d			19 29	19 30	19 36	19 42	20 00	20 21	20 28				20 51	21 00		21 19	21 36			
Meadowhall d			19 35	19 50	19 42		20 20		20 34					21 20		21 25	21 42			
Rotherham Central d			19 41		19 49				20 40							21 32	21 48			
Swinton (S.Yorks) d			19a49		19a58				20a48							21a40	21a56			
Mexborough d																				
Conisbrough d																				
London Kings Cross d	17 58																			20 00
Doncaster 7 a	19 57			20 20			20 50							21 50						21 51
York 8 26 a						20 38		21 31					21 42							
Doncaster 31 d	19 59	20 00								20 31					21 00				21 52	21 55
Bentley (S.Yorks) 31 a																			21 55	
Adwick 31 a																			21 59	
Kirk Sandall d																				
Hatfield & Stainforth d																				
Thorne South d																				
Crowle d																				
Althorpe d																				
Scunthorpe a		20 25													21 25					
d		20 26													21 26					
Barnetby 28 d		20 40													21 40					
Habrough 28 d															21 53					
Grimsby Town 28 a		21 00													22 04					
d		21 01													22 05					
Cleethorpes 28 a		21 11													22 13					
Thorne North d																				
Goole d										20 51										
Saltmarshe d																				
York 8 33 d																		21 41		
Selby a	20 20										21 35							22 00		22 10
d	20 22										21 36							22 00		22 11
Wressle d																				
Howden d	20 32																	22 10		22 21
Eastrington d																				
Gilberdyke d										20 59										
Broomfleet d																				
Brough d	20 46									21 07	21 55							22 23		22 34
Ferriby d																				
Hessle d																				
Hull a	21 07									21 23	22 09							22 41		22 52

A To Leeds
B From Exeter St Davids to Edinburgh
C To Bridlington
D From Reading to Newcastle
E From Plymouth to Edinburgh
F via Pontefract Baghill
G To Beverley
H From Reading to Edinburgh
I From Plymouth to Newcastle
J From Reading

For all trains between Barnetby, Habrough, Grimsby Town and Cleethorpes see Table 28

Table 29

Sundays

5 January to 9 February

Manchester Airport, Manchester, Sheffield and Meadowhall-Doncaster and Hull

Network Diagram - refer to first Page of Table 18

			TP	NT	TP	NT	TP	NT	TP	NT	NT
			◇1						◇1		
									A		
				🚌	🚌		🚌				
Manchester Airport	85 ✈	d									
Manchester Piccadilly 10	🚌	d									
Stockport	78	d									
Sheffield 7	🚌	a									
		d		21 45	22 00		22 25	22 26			23 34
Meadowhall	🚌	d		22 05	22 20		22s45	22 32			23 40
Rotherham Central		d						22 38			23 47
Swinton (S.Yorks)		d						22a50			23a56
Mexborough		d									
Conisbrough		d									
London Kings Cross		d									
Doncaster 7		a		22 35	22 50		23s15				
York 8	26	a									
Doncaster	31	d	22 00			22 06				22 45	
Bentley (S.Yorks)	31	a									
Adwick	31	a									
Kirk Sandall		d									
Hatfield & Stainforth		d									
Thorne South		d									
Crowle		d									
Althorpe		d									
Scunthorpe		a	22 25				00s05				
		d	22 26								
Barnetby	28	d	22 44								
Habrough	28	d	22 53								
Grimsby Town	28	a	23 04				00s50				
		d	23 05								
Cleethorpes	28	a	23 13				01 10				
Thorne North		d								22 57	
Goole		d				22 25				23 06	
Saltmarshe		d									
York 8	33	d									
Selby		a									
		d							22 44		
Wressle		d									
Howden		d									
Eastrington		d									
Gilberdyke		d				22 34				23 15	
Broomfleet		d									
Brough		d				22 42			23 03	23 23	
Ferriby		d									
Hessle		d									
Hull		a				23 00			23 19	23 39	

A From Leeds

For all trains between Barnetby, Habrough, Grimsby Town and Cleethorpes see Table 28

Table 29

Sundays

16 February to 23 March

Manchester Airport, Manchester, Sheffield and Meadowhall-Doncaster and Hull

Network Diagram - refer to first Page of Table 18

	NT	NT A	NT B	TP (bus)	XC ◇1 C	NT A	TP (bus)	NT D	TP ◇1 E	NT	TP ◇1	NT B	NT A
Manchester Airport 85 ✈ d													
Manchester Piccadilly 10 d									09 12				
Stockport 78 d													
Sheffield 7 a													
d	08 00		08 45	09 15	09 21	09 36	09 55					10 28	
Meadowhall d	08 06		08 51	09 35		09 42						10 34	
Rotherham Central d	08 12		08 57	09 45		09 48							
Swinton (S.Yorks) d	08 20		09 05	09 57		09a58							
Mexborough d	08 23		09 08	10 02									
Conisbrough d	08 27		09 12	10 17									
London Kings Cross d													
Doncaster 7 a	08 38		09 22	10 37			10 35					10 52	
York 8 26 a					10 29								
Doncaster 31 d		09 12	09 26					10 19			10 45	10 57	11 12
Bentley (S.Yorks) 31 a		09 15											11 15
Adwick 31 a		09 19											11 19
Kirk Sandall d													
Hatfield & Stainforth d													
Thorne South d													
Crowle d													
Althorpe d													
Scunthorpe a											11 11		
d											11 12		
Barnetby 28 d											11 26		
Habrough 28 d											11 35		
Grimsby Town 28 a											11 48		
d											11 49		
Cleethorpes 28 a											11 56		
Thorne North d			09 38					10 31					
Goole d			09 47					10 40				11 16	
Saltmarshe d													
York 8 33 d										10 40			
Selby a									10 44	10 58			
d									10 44	10 59			
Wressle d													
Howden d										11 08			
Eastrington d													
Gilberdyke d			09 55					10 48				11 25	
Broomfleet d													
Brough d			10 03					10 56	11 04	11 19		11 33	
Ferriby d								11 00					
Hessle d								11 05					
Hull a			10 21					11 17	11 21	11 41		11 49	

	NT	XC ◇1 F (trolley)	EM ◇1 G	TP (bus)	NT A	NT	XC ◇1 H (trolley)	TP ◇1	HT ◇1 ⊠	NT	NT B	NT A	TP (bus)
Manchester Airport 85 ✈ d													
Manchester Piccadilly 10 d													
Stockport 78 d													
Sheffield 7 a													
d	11 05	11 21	11 31	11 35	11 36		12 21			12 24	12 28		13 00
Meadowhall d	11 11			11 55	11 42					12 30	12 34		13 20
Rotherham Central d	11 17				11 49					12 36			
Swinton (S.Yorks) d	11 25				12a00					12 49			
Mexborough d	11 28									12 52			
Conisbrough d	11 32									12 56			
London Kings Cross d									10 42				
Doncaster 7 a	11 43		11 52	12 25					12 35	13 04	12 55		13 50
York 8 26 a		12 27	12 17				13 27						
Doncaster 31 d								12 37	12 39	13 06	12 58	13 12	
Bentley (S.Yorks) 31 a												13 15	
Adwick 31 a												13 19	
Kirk Sandall d										13 12			
Hatfield & Stainforth d										13 17			
Thorne South d													
Crowle d													
Althorpe d													
Scunthorpe a								13 03					
d								13 04					
Barnetby 28 d								13 18					
Habrough 28 d													
Grimsby Town 28 a								13 38					
d								13 39					
Cleethorpes 28 a								13 50					
Thorne North d										13 22			
Goole d										13a33	13 17		
Saltmarshe d													
York 8 33 d						12 05							
Selby a						12 24			12 53				
d						12 24			12 54				
Wressle d													
Howden d						12 34			13 04				
Eastrington d													
Gilberdyke d											13 26		
Broomfleet d													
Brough d						12 47			13 18		13 34		
Ferriby d											13 39		
Hessle d											13 43		
Hull a						13 05			13 37		13 55		

	XC ◇1 F (trolley)	TP ◇1 I	NT	TP ◇1	NT D	NT A	XC ◇1 J (trolley)	HT ◇1 ⊠	TP ◇1	TP (bus)	XC ◇1 K (trolley)	NT
Manchester Airport 85 ✈ d												
Manchester Piccadilly 10 d												
Stockport 78 d												
Sheffield 7 a												
d	13 21				13 24	13 36	13 51			14 00	14 21	14 22
Meadowhall d					13 30	13 42				14 20		14 28
Rotherham Central d					13 36	13 49						14 35
Swinton (S.Yorks) d					13 47	13a57						14 46
Mexborough d					13 50							14 49
Conisbrough d					13 54							14 53
London Kings Cross d								12 53				
Doncaster 7 a					14 02		14 13	14 41		14 50		15 03
York 8 26 a	14 27						14 38				15 27	
Doncaster 31 d				14 00	14 06			14 43	15 00			15 07
Bentley (S.Yorks) 31 a												
Adwick 31 a												
Kirk Sandall d												15 13
Hatfield & Stainforth d												15 18
Thorne South d												
Crowle d												
Althorpe d												
Scunthorpe a				14 25					15 25			
d				14 26					15 26			
Barnetby 28 d				14 40					15 43			
Habrough 28 d												
Grimsby Town 28 a				15 00					16 02			
d				15 01					16 03			
Cleethorpes 28 a				15 11					16 11			
Thorne North d												15 25
Goole d					14 25							15a34
Saltmarshe d												
York 8 33 d			13 45									
Selby a			14 04					14 57				
d		13 23	14 04					14 58				
Wressle d												
Howden d			14 14					15 08				
Eastrington d												
Gilberdyke d					14 33							
Broomfleet d												
Brough d		13 42	14 26		14 41			15 21				
Ferriby d												
Hessle d												
Hull a		13 59	14 45		14 58			15 39				

A To Leeds
B To Scarborough
C To Glasgow Central
D To Bridlington
E From Liverpool Lime Street
F From Birmingham New Street to Glasgow Central
G From Leicester
H From Birmingham New Street to Edinburgh
I From Leeds
J From Bristol Temple Meads to Newcastle
K From Birmingham New Street to Aberdeen

For all trains between Barnetby, Habrough, Grimsby Town and Cleethorpes see Table 28

Table 29

Sundays

16 February to 23 March

Manchester Airport, Manchester, Sheffield and Meadowhall-Doncaster and Hull

Network Diagram - refer to first Page of Table 18

	NT	NT	NT	XC	TP	XC	TP	NT	NT	TP	NT	XC	TP	NT	XC	NT	NT	TP	NT	TP	NT	HT	NT	XC	TP	XC	NT	NT	TP	NT	XC	TP	XC	NT	NT	XC	NT
				◇1		◇1	◇1			◇1		◇1			◇1			◇1		◇1		◇1		◇1		◇1			◇1		◇1		◇1			◇1	
		A	B	C		D	E		F		B	C			G		A		H	E			B	C		I		F		B	J		K		L	J	H
				🛒	🚌	🛒						🛒	🚌		🛒							☒		🛒	🚌	🛒					🛒	🚌	🛒			🛒	
Manchester Airport 85 ✈ d																																					
Manchester Piccadilly 10 🚆 d																																					
Stockport 78 d																																					
Sheffield 7 🚆 a																																					
d		14 28		14 51	15 00	15 21		15 24	15 28		15 36	15 51	16 00		16 21	16 25	16 28		16 36					16 51	17 00	17 21	17 25	17 28		17 36	17 51	18 05	18 21	18 25	18 28	18 51	18 57
Meadowhall 🚆 d		14 34			15 20			15 30	15 34		15 42		16 20			16 31	16 34		16 42						17 20		17 31	17 34		17 44		18 25		18 31	18 34		19 05
Rotherham Central d								15 37			15 50					16 38			16 49								17 37			17 50				18 37			19 11
Swinton (S.Yorks) d								15 47			15a58					16 48			16 58								17 47			17a58				18 48			19 19
Mexborough d								15 50								16 51											17 50							18 51			
Conisbrough d								15 54								16 55											17 54							18 55			
London Kings Cross d																						14 58															
Doncaster 7 a		14 56		15 15	15 50			16 04	15 53			16 15	16 50			17 04	16 56					17 00		17 13	17 50		18 05	17 55			18 14	18 55		19 05	18 53	19 15	
York 8 26 a				15 42		16 27						16 38			17 27				17 59					17 42		18 27					19 20		19 30			19 39	20 18
Doncaster 31 d		15 03	15 12						15 58	16 00						17 06	16 56	17 00				17 06	17 12					17 58	18 00						18 58		
Bentley (S.Yorks) 31 a			15 15																				17 15														
Adwick 31 a			15 19																				17 19														
Kirk Sandall d																17 12																			19 04		
Hatfield & Stainforth d																17 17																			19 09		
Thorne South d																																					
Crowle d																																					
Althorpe d																																					
Scunthorpe a										16 27								17 25											18 27								
d										16 28								17 26											18 28								
Barnetby 28 d										16 42								17 40											18 42								
Habrough 28 d										16 51																											
Grimsby Town 28 a										17 04								18 00											19 02								
d										17 05								18 01											19 03								
Cleethorpes 28 a										17 15								18 11											19 13								
Thorne North d									16 10							17 25																			19 14		
Goole d		15 22							16 19							17a34	17 15											18 17							19 23		
Saltmarshe d																																					
York 8 33 d	14 52													16 06							17 11																
Selby a	15 11													16 25							17 30	17 35															
d	15 11						15 23							16 25						17 23	17 30	17 37															
Wressle d																																					
Howden d	15 21													16 35							17 40	17 47															
Eastrington d																																					
Gilberdyke d		15 32							16 28								17 24											18 26							19 32		
Broomfleet d																																					
Brough d	15 34	15 40					15 41		16 36					16 48			17 32			17 41	17 53	18 00						18 34							19 40		
Ferriby d																																					
Hessle d																																					
Hull a	15 51	15 56					15 59		16 52					17 06			17 49			17 59	18 11	18 21						18 52							19 57		

A To Scarborough
B To Leeds
C From Exeter St Davids to Newcastle
D From Birmingham New Street to Glasgow Central
E From Leeds
F To Bridlington
G From Guildford to Edinburgh
H via Pontefract Baghill
I From Reading to Glasgow Central
J From Exeter St Davids to Edinburgh
K From Reading to Newcastle
L To Beverley

For all trains between Barnetby, Habrough, Grimsby Town and Cleethorpes see Table 28

Table 29

Sundays

16 February to 23 March

Manchester Airport, Manchester, Sheffield and Meadowhall-Doncaster and Hull

Network Diagram - refer to first Page of Table 18

		TP	TP	XC	NT	TP	NT	HT	TP	NT	NT	XC	TP	TP	NT	TP	XC	NT	NT	XC	TP	TP	NT	HT	TP	NT	NT	TP	TP	NT	TP	TP	NT	NT
			◇1	◇1		◇1		◇1	◇1			◇1		◇1		◇1	◇1			◇1		◇1		◇1	◇1				◇1		◇1			
				A	B	C					B	D		C			E		B	F		C					B		C					
		🚌		🛒				☒				🛒	🚌				🛒				🚌			☒				🚌				🚌		
Manchester Airport 85 ✈	d																																	
Manchester Piccadilly 10	d																																	
Stockport 78	d																																	
Sheffield 7	a																																	
	d	19 00		19 21						19 29	19 36	19 51	20 00		20 02		20 21	20 28		20 51	21 00					21 25	21 36	22 00		22 13		22 25	22 26	23 34
Meadowhall	d	19 20								19 35	19 42		20 20		20 09			20 34			21 20					21 31	21 42	22 20		22 19		22s45	22 32	23 40
Rotherham Central	d									19 41	19 49							20 40								21 38	21 48						22 38	23 47
Swinton (S.Yorks)	d									19 49	19a57							20 48								21 47	21a56						22 48	23 55
Mexborough	d									19 52								20 51								21 50							22 51	23 58
Conisbrough	d									19 56								20 55								21 54							22 55	00 02
London Kings Cross	d							17 58																20 00										
Doncaster 7	a	19 50						19 57		20 07		20 16	20 50		20 27			21 05		21 19	21 50			21 51		22 03		22 50		22 38		23s15	23 05	00 13
York 8 26	a			20 30								20 39					21 31			21 42														
Doncaster 31	d		19 06		19 27			19 59	20 00						20 31	21 00		21 07	21 52					21 55	22 00	22 06				22 45	23 00			
Bentley (S.Yorks) 31	a				19 30														21 55															
Adwick 31	a				19 34														21 59															
Kirk Sandall	d																	21 13																
Hatfield & Stainforth	d																	21 18																
Thorne South	d																																	
Crowle	d																																	
Althorpe	d																																	
Scunthorpe	a		19 32						20 25							21 25									22 25						23 25	00s05		
	d		19 32						20 26							21 26									22 26						23 26			
Barnetby 28	d		19 51						20 40							21 40									22 44						23 40			
Habrough 28	d		19 59													21 53									22 53									
Grimsby Town 28	a		20 11						21 00							22 04									23 04						00 02	00s50		
	d		20 12						21 01							22 05									23 05						00 03			
Cleethorpes 28	a		20 20						21 11							22 13									23 13						00 10	01 10		
Thorne North	d																	21 24												22 57				
Goole	d														20 51			21a34								22 25				23 06				
Saltmarshe	d																																	
York 8 33	d						19 16																21 41											
Selby	a						19 35	20 20															22 00	22 10										
	d					19 29	19 35	20 22						20 35								21 36	22 00	22 11					22 44					
Wressle	d																																	
Howden	d						19 45	20 32															22 10	22 21										
Eastrington	d																																	
Gilberdyke	d														20 59											22 34				23 15				
Broomfleet	d																																	
Brough	d					19 48	19 58	20 46						20 55	21 07							21 55	22 23	22 34		22 42			23 03	23 23				
Ferriby	d																																	
Hessle	d																																	
Hull	a					20 05	20 16	21 07						21 11	21 23							22 09	22 41	22 52		23 00			23 19	23 39				

A From Reading to Edinburgh
B To Leeds
C From Leeds
D From Exeter St Davids
E From Reading to Newcastle
F From Exeter St Davids to Newcastle

For all trains between Barnetby, Habrough, Grimsby Town and Cleethorpes see Table 28

Table 29

Sundays

30 March to 11 May

Manchester Airport, Manchester, Sheffield and Meadowhall-Doncaster and Hull

Network Diagram - refer to first Page of Table 18

Station			NT	NT	NT	XC	NT	NT	TP	TP	XC	NT	NT	NT	NT	XC	EM	NT	NT	HT	TP	XC	NT	NT	NT	TP	TP	XC	NT	NT	NT	XC	HT	TP	XC	NT	NT	NT	NT	TP
						◇1			◇1	◇1	◇1					◇1	◇1			◇1	◇1	◇1				◇1	◇1	◇1				◇1	◇1	◇1	◇1					◇1
				A	B	C	A	D	E		F		B	A		G	H	A				I		B	A			J		D	A	K			L			B	A	
											☕					☕	🍴			☒		☕						☕				☕	☒		☕					
Manchester Airport	85 ✈	d																			10 44						11 55							12 55						
Manchester Piccadilly 10	🚉	d							09 12												11 18					12 01	12 18							13 20						14 02
Stockport	78	d																			11 27						12 28							13 28						
Sheffield 7	🚉	a																			12 07						13 08							14 08						
		d	08 00		08 45	09 21	09 36			09 52	10 21		10 28		11 05	11 21	11 31	11 36			12 10	12 21	12 24	12 28			13 10	13 21		13 24	13 36	13 51		14 10	14 21	14 22		14 28		
Meadowhall	🚉	d	08 06		08 51		09 42			09 57			10 34		11 11			11 42			12 16		12 30	12 34			13 16			13 30	13 42			14 16		14 28		14 34		
Rotherham Central		d	08 12		08 57		09 48			10 03					11 17			11 49					12 36							13 36	13 49					14 35				
Swinton (S.Yorks)		d	08 20		09 05		09a58			10 09					11 25			12a00					12 49							13 47	13a57					14 46				
Mexborough		d	08 23		09 08					10 13					11 28								12 52							13 50						14 49				
Conisbrough		d	08 27		09 12					10 17					11 32								12 56							13 54						14 53				
London Kings Cross		d																		10 48													12 48							
Doncaster 7		a	08 38		09 22					10 26			10 52		11 43		11 52			12 22	12 35		13 04	12 55			13 34			14 02		14 13	14 22	14 35		15 03		14 56		
York 8	26	a				10 29					11 27					12 27	12 15					13 27						14 27				14 38			15 27					
Doncaster	31	d		09 12	09 26			10 19		10 28			10 57	11 12						12 28	12 37		13 06	12 58	13 12					14 06			14 29	14 37		15 07		15 03	15 12	
Bentley (S.Yorks)	31	a		09 15										11 15											13 15														15 15	
Adwick	31	a		09 19										11 19											13 19														15 19	
Kirk Sandall		d																					13 12													15 13				
Hatfield & Stainforth		d																					13 17													15 18				
Thorne South		d																																						
Crowle		d																																						
Althorpe		d																																						
Scunthorpe		a								10 54											13 03													15 02						
		d								10 55											13 04													15 03						
Barnetby	28	d								11 09											13 18													15 19						
Habrough	28	d								11 18																														
Grimsby Town	28	a								11 31											13 38													15 38						
		d								11 33											13 39													15 39						
Cleethorpes	28	a								11 40											13 50													15 49						
Thorne North		d			09 38			10 31															13 22													15 25				
Goole		d			09 47			10 40					11 16										13a33	13 17						14 25						15a34		15 22		
Saltmarshe		d																																						
York 8	33	d										10 40							12 05										13 45								14 52			
Selby		a							10 44			10 58							12 24	12 43						13 23			14 04				14 43				15 11			15 23
		d							10 44			10 59							12 24	12 44						13 23			14 04				14 44				15 11			15 23
Wressle		d																																						
Howden		d										11 08							12 34	12 54									14 14				14 54				15 21			
Eastrington		d																																						
Gilberdyke		d			09 55			10 48					11 25											13 26						14 33								15 32		
Broomfleet		d																																						
Brough		d			10 03			10 56	11 05			11 19	11 33						12 47	13 07				13 34		13 42			14 26	14 41			15 08				15 34	15 40		15 41
Ferriby		d						11 00																13 39																
Hessle		d						11 05																13 43																
Hull		a			10 21			11 17	11 21			11 41	11 49						13 05	13 25				13 55		13 59			14 45	14 58			15 26				15 51	15 56		15 59

A To Leeds
B To Scarborough
C To Glasgow Central
D To Bridlington
E From Liverpool Lime Street
F From Birmingham New Street to Edinburgh
G From Birmingham New Street to Glasgow Central
H From Leicester
I From Bristol Temple Meads to Edinburgh
J From Bristol Temple Meads to Glasgow Central
K From Birmingham New Street to Newcastle
L From Plymouth to Aberdeen

For all trains between Barnetby, Habrough, Grimsby Town and Cleethorpes see Table 28

Table 29

Sundays

30 March to 11 May

Manchester Airport, Manchester, Sheffield and Meadowhall-Doncaster and Hull

Network Diagram - refer to first Page of Table 18

			XC	TP	XC	NT	NT	NT	XC	NT	HT	TP	XC	NT	NT	NT	TP	NT	XC	TP	NT
			◇1 A 🛒	◇1	◇1 B 🛒		C	D	◇1 E 🛒		◇1 ☒	◇1	◇1 F 🛒		G	D	◇1	H	◇1 I 🛒	◇1	
Manchester Airport	85 ✈	d		13 55								14 55								15 55	
Manchester Piccadilly 10	⇌	d		14 20								15 20					16 02			16 20	
Stockport	78	d		14 28								15 28								16 28	
Sheffield 7	⇌	a		15 08								16 09								17 08	
		d	14 51	15 10	15 21	15 24	15 28	15 36	15 51			16 10	16 21	16 25	16 28			16 36	16 51	17 10	
Meadowhall	⇌	d		15 16		15 30	15 34	15 42				16 16		16 31	16 34			16 42		17 16	
Rotherham Central		d				15 37		15 50						16 38				16 49			
Swinton (S.Yorks)		d				15 47		15a58						16 48				16 58			
Mexborough		d				15 50								16 51							
Conisbrough		d				15 54								16 55							
London Kings Cross		d									14 48										
Doncaster 7		a	15 13	15 35		16 04	15 53		16 15		16 23	16 35		17 04	16 56				17 13	17 35	
York 8	26	a	15 42		16 27				16 38				17 27					17 59	17 40		
Doncaster	31	d		15 37			15 58				16 30	16 37		17 06	16 56	17 12				17 37	
Bentley (S.Yorks)	31	a														17 15					
Adwick	31	a														17 19					
Kirk Sandall		d												17 12							
Hatfield & Stainforth		d												17 17							
Thorne South		d																			
Crowle		d																			
Althorpe		d																			
Scunthorpe		a		16 02								17 02								18 02	
		d		16 03								17 03								18 03	
Barnetby	28	d		16 17								17 17								18 17	
Habrough	28	d		16 26																	
Grimsby Town	28	a		16 39								17 37								18 37	
		d		16 40								17 38								18 38	
Cleethorpes	28	a		16 50								17 48								18 48	
Thorne North		d					16 10							17 25							
Goole		d					16 19							17a34	17 15						
Saltmarshe		d																			
York 8	33	d								16 06											17 11
Selby		a								16 25	16 45						17 23				17 30
		d								16 25	16 46						17 23				17 30
Wressle		d																			
Howden		d								16 35	16 56										17 40
Eastrington		d																			
Gilberdyke		d					16 28								17 24						
Broomfleet		d																			
Brough		d					16 36			16 48	17 09				17 32		17 41				17 53
Ferriby		d																			
Hessle		d																			
Hull		a					16 52			17 06	17 27				17 49		17 59				18 11

			XC	NT	NT	NT	XC	TP	XC	NT	NT	GR	NT	TP	XC	NT	NT	HT	TP	TP
			◇1 B 🛒		C	D	◇1 I 🛒	◇1	◇1 J 🛒		K	R 1 🍴	D	◇1	◇1 L 🛒	H		◇1 ☒	◇1	◇1
Manchester Airport	85 ✈	d						16 55											17 55	
Manchester Piccadilly 10	⇌	d						17 20						18 02					18 20	19 02
Stockport	78	d						17 28											18 28	
Sheffield 7	⇌	a						18 08											19 08	
		d	17 21	17 25	17 28	17 36	17 51	18 10	18 21	18 25	18 28				18 51	18 57			19 10	
Meadowhall	⇌	d		17 31	17 34	17 44		18 16		18 31	18 34					19 05			19 16	
Rotherham Central		d		17 37		17 50				18 37						19 11				
Swinton (S.Yorks)		d		17 47		17a58				18 48						19 19				
Mexborough		d		17 50						18 51										
Conisbrough		d		17 54						18 55										
London Kings Cross		d										17 20						17 44		
Doncaster 7		a		18 05	17 55		18 13	18 35		19 05	18 53	19 02			19 15			19 23	19 35	
York 8	26	a	18 27				19 20		19 30						19 39	20 18				
Doncaster	31	d			17 58			18 37			18 58	19 05	19 27					19 30	19 37	
Bentley (S.Yorks)	31	a											19 30							
Adwick	31	a											19 34							
Kirk Sandall		d									19 04									
Hatfield & Stainforth		d									19 09									
Thorne South		d																		
Crowle		d																		
Althorpe		d																		
Scunthorpe		a						19 02											20 02	
		d						19 03											20 03	
Barnetby	28	d						19 17											20 17	
Habrough	28	d						19 26												
Grimsby Town	28	a						19 39											20 37	
		d						19 40											20 38	
Cleethorpes	28	a						19 48											20 48	
Thorne North		d									19 14									
Goole		d			18 17						19 23									
Saltmarshe		d																		
York 8	33	d															19 16			
Selby		a										19 21		19 28			19 35	19 45		20 17
		d										19 23		19 29			19 35	19 46		20 17
Wressle		d																		
Howden		d															19 45	19 56		
Eastrington		d																		
Gilberdyke		d			18 26						19 32									
Broomfleet		d																		
Brough		d			18 34						19 40	19 46		19 48			19 58	20 08		20 37
Ferriby		d																		
Hessle		d																		
Hull		a			18 52						19 57	20 02		20 05			20 16	20 26		20 54

A From Birmingham New Street to Newcastle
B From Plymouth to Glasgow Central
C To Bridlington
D To Leeds
E From Guildford to Newcastle
F From Penzance to Edinburgh
G To Scarborough
H via Pontefract Baghill
I From Reading to Newcastle
J From Plymouth to Edinburgh
K To Beverley
L From Reading to Edinburgh

For all trains between Barnetby, Habrough, Grimsby Town and Cleethorpes see Table 28

Table 29

Sundays

30 March to 11 May

Manchester Airport, Manchester, Sheffield and Meadowhall-Doncaster and Hull

Network Diagram - refer to first Page of Table 18

Station		XC	NT	NT	XC	NT	TP	TP	XC	NT	XC	HT	TP	NT	NT	NT	NT	TP	NT	NT	TP	NT
		◇1			◇1		◇1	◇1	◇1		◇1	◇1	◇1					◇1			◇1	
		A		B	C				D		C			B			B	E				
		✠			✠				✠			⊠										
Manchester Airport 85 ✈	d						18 55						19 55									
Manchester Piccadilly 10 ⇌	d						19 20	20 06					20 18									
Stockport 78	d						19 28						20 27									
Sheffield 7 ⇌	a						20 08						21 08									
	d	19 21	19 29	19 36	19 51	20 02	20 10		20 21	20 28	20 51		21 10			21 25	21 36		22 13	22 26	22 30	23 34
Meadowhall ⇌	d		19 35	19 42		20 09	20 16			20 34			21 16			21 31	21 42		22 19	22 32	22 35	23 40
Rotherham Central	d		19 41	19 49						20 40						21 38	21 48			22 38		23 47
Swinton (S.Yorks)	d		19 49	19a57						20 48						21 47	21a56			22 48		23 55
Mexborough	d		19 52							20 51						21 50				22 51		23 58
Conisbrough	d		19 56							20 55						21 54				22 55		00 02
London Kings Cross	d											19 50										
Doncaster 7	a		20 07		20 16	20 27	20 35			21 05	21 19	21 24	21 35			22 03			22 38	23 05	22 56	00 13
York 8 26	a	20 30			20 38				21 31		21 42											
Doncaster 31	d					20 31	20 37			21 07		21 26	21 37	21 52		22 06			22 45		22 58	
Bentley (S.Yorks) 31	a													21 55								
Adwick 31	a													21 59								
Kirk Sandall	d									21 13												
Hatfield & Stainforth	d									21 18												
Thorne South	d																					
Crowle	d																					
Althorpe	d																					
Scunthorpe	a						21 02						22 02								23 23	
	d						21 03						22 03								23 24	
Barnetby 28	d						21 18						22 17								23 38	
Habrough 28	d						21 27						22 26									
Grimsby Town 28	a						21 39						22 39								23 57	
	d						21 40						22 40								23 58	
Cleethorpes 28	a						21 50						22 50								00 09	
Thorne North	d									21 24									22 57			
Goole	d					20 51				21a34						22 25			23 06			
Saltmarshe	d																					
York 8 33	d														21 41							
Selby	a							21 35				21 41			22 00							
	d							21 36				21 42			22 00			22 44				
Wressle	d																					
Howden	d											21 52			22 10							
Eastrington	d																					
Gilberdyke	d					20 59										22 34			23 15			
Broomfleet	d																					
Brough	d					21 07		21 55				22 05			22 23	22 42		23 03	23 23			
Ferriby	d																					
Hessle	d																					
Hull	a					21 23		22 09				22 23			22 41	23 00		23 19	23 39			

A From Plymouth to Edinburgh
B To Leeds
C From Reading to Newcastle
D From Plymouth
E From Leeds

For all trains between Barnetby, Habrough, Grimsby Town and Cleethorpes see Table 28

Table 29R

Mondays to Fridays

9 December to 16 May

Hull - Doncaster - Meadowhall, Sheffield, Manchester and Manchester Airport

Network Diagram - refer to first Page of Table 18

Miles	Miles	Miles	Miles	Station			NT MX	TP	EM	NT	NT	NT	TP	NT	TP	NT	HT	TP	XC	NT	XC
							A	◇1	◇1 B ⊠		A		◇1 ╤		◇1 C ╤		◇1 ⊠	◇1 ╤	◇1 D ╤	E	◇1 F
0	0	—	—	**Hull**		d						05 20			06 00	06 04	06 25	06 37			
4¾	4¾	—	—	Hessle		d										06 11					
7½	7½	—	—	Ferriby		d										06 16					
10½	10½	—	—	Brough		d						05 32			06 12	06 21	06 38	06 49			
14½	14½	—	—	Broomfleet		d															
17	17	—	—	Gilberdyke		d									06 19	06 29					
—	19¾	—	—	Eastrington		d															
—	22¼	—	—	Howden		d									06 26		06 49				
—	25	—	—	Wressle		d															
—	31	—	—	**Selby**		a									06 36		06 59	07 08			
—	—	—	—			d								06 18	06 36		07 00	07 08			
—	—	—	—	York 8	33	a															
20¾	—	—	—	Saltmarshe		d										06 35					
23¾	—	—	—	Goole		d						05 47				06 41					
31	—	—	—	Thorne North		d						05 55				06 50					
—	—	0	—	**Cleethorpes**	28	d							05 17								
—	—	3	—	Grimsby Town	28	d							05 25								
—	—	11	—	Habrough	28	d							05 35								
—	—	18	—	Barnetby	28	d							05 44								
—	—	29	—	**Scunthorpe**		a							05 59								
—	—	—	—			d							05 59								
—	—	32½	—	Althorpe		d							06 04								
—	—	36¼	—	Crowle		d							06 10								
—	—	42¼	—	Thorne South		d							06 19								
34¼	—	45¼	—	Hatfield & Stainforth		d						06 01	06 24			06 59					
37	—	48	—	Kirk Sandall		d						06 06				07 03					
—	—	—	0	Adwick	31	d															
—	—	—	2¼	Bentley (S.Yorks)	31	d															
41	49¼	52	4	**Doncaster 7**	31	a						06 15	06 37	06 38		07 12	07 17				
—	—	—	—	London Kings Cross 15	⊖26	a											09 18				
—	—	—	—	York 8	26	d															06 32
—	—	—	—	**Doncaster 7**		d		05 38	05 57	06 00		06 25	06 38						06 46	07 02	
45¾	—	—	—	Conisbrough		d				06 07		06 32								07 09	
48	—	—	—	Mexborough		d				06 11		06 36								07 13	
49¼	—	—	—	Swinton (S.Yorks)		d				06 14	06 23	06 39								07 17	
53¾	—	—	—	Rotherham Central		d	00 04			06 22	06 31	06 48								07 27	
56½	—	—	—	**Meadowhall**	⇌	d	00 09	05 58		06 27	06 37	06 54	06 58							07 33	
60	—	—	—	**Sheffield 7**	⇌	a	00 23	06 08	06 19	06 37	06 47	07 05	07 07						07 10	07 40	07 50
—	—	—	—			d		06 11					07 09								
96¼	—	—	—	Stockport	78	a		06 53					07 53								
102¼	—	—	—	**Manchester Piccadilly 10**	⇌	a		07 02					08 02		08 05			08 36			
112½	—	—	—	**Manchester Airport**	85 ✈	a		07 29					08 26								

Station			NT	TP	NT	NT	GR	NT	NT	XC	TP	XC	NT	NT	TP	XC	NT	NT	NT	NT	HT
			A	◇1 ╤			1 G ╤	H	I	1 J ╤	◇1 ╤	◇1 K ╤	A		◇1 ╤	◇1 L ╤		M	M	N	◇1 ⊠
Hull		d				06 40	07 00	07 07			07 37							07 40	08 03		08 25
Hessle		d				06 47												07 47			
Ferriby		d				06 52												07 52			
Brough		d				06 57	07 14	07 19			07 49							07 57	08 15		08 38
Broomfleet		d																08 03			
Gilberdyke		d				07 05		07 26										08 07			
Eastrington		d						07 31													
Howden		d						07 35			08 01										08 50
Wressle		d						07 40													
Selby		a					07 33	07 48			08 10										09 00
		d					07 36	07 48			08 11										09 01
York 8	33	a						08 21													
Saltmarshe		d				07 11												08 13			
Goole		d				07 16												08 18	08 30		
Thorne North		d				07 24												08 26			
Cleethorpes	28	d		06 18											07 26						
Grimsby Town	28	d		06 26											07 34						
Habrough	28	d		06 36											07 44						
Barnetby	28	d		06 45											07 53						
Scunthorpe		a		07 00											08 08						
		d		07 00					07 22						08 08					08 19	
Althorpe		d							07 27											08 24	
Crowle		d							07 33											08 30	
Thorne South		d							07 41											08 39	
Hatfield & Stainforth		d				07 30			07 47									08 32		08 45	
Kirk Sandall		d				07 35			07 51									08 36		08 50	
Adwick	31	d			07 29									08 15			08 31				
Bentley (S.Yorks)	31	d			07 33									08 19			08 35				
Doncaster 7	31	a		07 33	07 37	07 46	07 52		08 02					08 24	08 38		08 39	08 47	08 54	08 59	09 24
London Kings Cross 15	⊖26	a					09 55														11 12
York 8	26	d								07 23		07 45				08 26					
Doncaster 7		d		07 35	07 39	07 48				07 56				08 26	08 41	08 51			08 56	09 01	
Conisbrough		d			07 46	07 55								08 33						09 08	
Mexborough		d			07 50	07 59								08 37						09 12	
Swinton (S.Yorks)		d	07 30		07 54	08 03							08 34	08 43						09 16	
Rotherham Central		d	07 39		08 02	08 14							08 44	08 50						09 27	
Meadowhall	⇌	d	07 45	07 53	08 07	08 25							08 51	08 57	09 01				09 16	09 33	
Sheffield 7	⇌	a	07 56	08 00	08 18	08 33				08 18		08 52	08 59	09 05	09 08	09 17			09 26	09 41	
		d		08 05											09 11						
Stockport	78	a		08 53											09 53						
Manchester Piccadilly 10	⇌	a		09 02							09 36				10 02						
Manchester Airport	85 ✈	a		09 33											10 26						

A From Leeds
B From Leeds to St Pancras International
C To Liverpool Lime Street
D From Leeds to Southampton Central
E To Worksop
F To Plymouth
G The Hull Executive
H From Beverley
I To Adwick
J From Newcastle to Reading
K From Newcastle to Plymouth
L From Newcastle to Southampton Central
M From Bridlington
N To Lincoln

For all trains between Cleethorpes, Grimsby Town, Habrough and Barnetby refer to Table 28

Table 29R

Mondays to Fridays

9 December to 16 May

Hull - Doncaster - Meadowhall, Sheffield, Manchester and Manchester Airport

Network Diagram - refer to first Page of Table 18

		XC	NT	NT	NT	TP	TP	TP	NT	NT	XC	NT	XC	XC	NT	NT	NT	TP	TP	NT	NT	XC	NT	XC	NT	NT	NT	HT	TP	TP	NT	XC	NT	NT	XC	NT	NT	NT	TP
							FO						FO	FX																									
		◇1 A	B		C	◇1	◇1 D	◇1 E	F		◇1 G	H	◇1 I	◇1 I	B		J	◇1	◇1	F		◇1 K	◇ H	◇1 L	B			◇1 ⊠	◇1	◇1	F	◇1 M	N	◇ H	◇1 I	B			◇1
Hull	d				08 29	08 40			08 57	09 03							09 25	09 40		09 56	10 10						10 20	10 30	10 40		10 57							11 23	11 40
Hessle	d				08 36												09 32										10 27											11 30	
Ferriby	d				08 41												09 37										10 32											11 35	
Brough	d				08 46	08 52			09 09	09 15							09 42	09 52		10 08	10 22						10 37	10 43	10 52		11 09							11 40	11 52
Broomfleet	d																																					11 46	
Gilberdyke	d				08 54					09 21							09 50				10 28						10 45											11 50	
Eastrington	d																																						
Howden	d									09 29											10 36							10 56											
Wressle	d																																						
Selby	a					09 10				09 39								10 11			10 46							11 05	11 11										12 11
	d					09 11				09 39								10 11			10 46							11 06	11 11										12 11
York 8 33	a									10 10											11 18																		
Saltmarshe	d																										10 51												
Goole	d				09 02				09 24								10 01			10 23							11 01				11 24							12 01	
Thorne North	d				09 11												10 09										11 08											12 09	
Cleethorpes 28	d						08 26	08 26											09 26											10 26									
Grimsby Town 28	d						08 34	08 34											09 34											10 34									
Habrough 28	d						08 44	08 44																						10 44									
Barnetby 28	d						08 53	08 53											09 53											10 53									
Scunthorpe	a						09 08	09 08											10 08											11 08									
	d						09 08	09 08				09 19							10 08				10 19							11 08				11 19					
Althorpe	d											09 24											10 24											11 24					
Crowle	d											09 30											10 30											11 30					
Thorne South	d											09 39											10 39											11 39					
Hatfield & Stainforth	d				09 17							09 44					10 16						10 44				11 14							11 44				12 15	
Kirk Sandall	d				09 22							09 49					10 20						10 49				11 19							11 49				12 20	
Adwick 31	d			09 15												10 15										11 15											12 15		
Bentley (S.Yorks) 31	d			09 19												10 19										11 19											12 19		
Doncaster 7 31	a			09 24	09 32		09 38	09 38	09 48			10 00				10 24	10 30		10 38	10 47			11 00			11 24	11 30	11 24		11 38	11 47			11 59			12 25	12 30	
London Kings Cross 15 ⊖26	a																											13 10											
York 8 26	d	08 45									09 35		09 45	09 45								10 35		10 45								11 34	11 06		11 45				
Doncaster 7	d			09 26			09 42	09 42	09 50		09 58	10 03				10 26			10 42	10 50		10 59	11 03			11 26				11 42	11 49	11 58		12 03			12 26		
Conisbrough	d			09 33								10 11				10 33							11 11			11 33								12 11			12 33		
Mexborough	d			09 37								10 15				10 37							11 15			11 37								12 15			12 37		
Swinton (S.Yorks)	d		09 35	09 42								10 18			10 35	10 43							11 19		11 35	11 43							12 10	12 18		12 35	12 43		
Rotherham Central	d		09 44	09 50								10 27			10 44	10 52							11 27		11 44	11 52							12 19	12 27		12 44	12 52		
Meadowhall	d		09 51	09 57			10 01	10 01	10 08			10 33			10 51	10 58			11 01	11 07			11 33		11 51	11 58				12 01	12 09		12 24	12 33		12 51	12 58		
Sheffield 7	a	09 52	10 00	10 05			10 08	10 08	10 20		10 20	10 41	10 51	10 52	11 01	11 05			11 08	11 18		11 20	11 41	11 52	12 01	12 05				12 08	12 18	12 20	12 36	12 41	12 52	13 01	13 05		
	d						10 11	10 11											11 11											12 11									
Stockport 78	a						10 53	10 53											11 53											12 53									
Manchester Piccadilly 10	a					10 36	11 02	11 02										11 36	12 02										12 36	13 02									
Manchester Airport 85	a						11 26	11 34											12 26											13 26									13 36

- **A** From Edinburgh to Plymouth
- **B** From Leeds
- **C** From Scarborough
- **D** until 7 February
- **E** FX until 6 February, from 10 February
- **F** From Bridlington
- **G** From Edinburgh to Reading
- **H** To Lincoln
- **I** From Glasgow Central to Plymouth
- **J** From Beverley
- **K** From Newcastle to Southampton Central
- **L** From Dundee to Plymouth
- **M** From Newcastle to Reading
- **N** via Pontefract Baghill

For all trains between Cleethorpes, Grimsby Town, Habrough and Barnetby refer to Table 28

Table 29R

Mondays to Fridays

9 December to 16 May

Hull - Doncaster - Meadowhall, Sheffield, Manchester and Manchester Airport

Network Diagram - refer to first Page of Table 18

Station	Table		TP ◇1 ⚲	NT A	NT	XC ◇1 B ⚲	NT ◇ C	XC ◇1 D ⚲	NT E	NT	NT	HT ◇1 ☒	TP ◇1 ⚲	TP ◇1 ⚲	NT H	NT	XC ◇1 I ⚲	NT ◇ C	XC ◇1 J ⚲
Hull		d		11 57	12 03						12 20	12 30	12 40		12 57	13 12			
Hessle		d									12 27								
Ferriby		d									12 32								
Brough		d		12 09	12 15						12 37	12 43	12 52		13 09	13 24			
Broomfleet		d																	
Gilberdyke		d									12 45					13 32			
Eastrington		d														13 36			
Howden		d			12 27							12 56				13 42			
Wressle		d														13 47			
Selby		a			12 37							13 05	13 11			13 54			
		d			12 39							13 06	13 11			13 55			
York 8	33	a			13 04											14 25			
Saltmarshe		d									12 51								
Goole		d		12 24							13 01				13 24				
Thorne North		d									13 09								
Cleethorpes	28	d	11 26											12 26					
Grimsby Town	28	d	11 34											12 34					
Habrough	28	d																	
Barnetby	28	d	11 53											12 53					
Scunthorpe		a	12 08											13 08					
		d	12 08				12 19							13 08				13 19	
Althorpe		d					12 24											13 24	
Crowle		d					12 30											13 30	
Thorne South		d					12 39											13 39	
Hatfield & Stainforth		d					12 44				13 13							13 44	
Kirk Sandall		d					12 49				13 18							13 49	
Adwick	31	d								13 15									
Bentley (S.Yorks)	31	d								13 19									
Doncaster 7	31	a	12 38	12 47			12 59			13 24	13 30	13 24		13 38	13 47			13 59	
London Kings Cross 15	⊖26	a										15 09							
York 8	26	d				12 35		12 45									13 34		13 45
Doncaster 7		d	12 42	12 49		12 59	13 03			13 26				13 42	13 49		13 58	14 04	
Conisbrough		d					13 11			13 33								14 11	
Mexborough		d					13 15			13 37								14 15	
Swinton (S.Yorks)		d					13 18		13 35	13 43								14 18	
Rotherham Central		d					13 27		13 44	13 52								14 27	
Meadowhall	🚊	d	13 01	13 09			13 33		13 51	13 58				14 01	14 08			14 33	
Sheffield 7	🚊	a	13 08	13 18		13 20	13 41	13 51	14 01	14 05				14 08	14 18		14 20	14 40	14 52
		d	13 11											14 11					
Stockport	78	a	13 53											14 53					
Manchester Piccadilly 10	🚊	a	14 02										14 36	15 02					
Manchester Airport	85 ✈	a	14 26											15 26					

Station	Table		NT E	NT	NT	TP ◇1 ⚲	TP ◇1 ⚲	NT A	NT	XC ◇1 M ⚲	NT ◇ C	XC ◇1 D ⚲	NT E	NT	NT	TP ◇1 ⚲	TP ◇1 ⚲	NT H	NT	XC ◇1 I ⚲
Hull		d			13 25	13 40		13 57	14 20						14 25	14 40		14 57	15 03	
Hessle		d			13 32										14 32					
Ferriby		d			13 37										14 37					
Brough		d			13 42	13 52		14 09	14 32						14 42	14 52		15 09	15 15	
Broomfleet		d																		
Gilberdyke		d			13 50										14 50					
Eastrington		d																		
Howden		d							14 44										15 27	
Wressle		d																		
Selby		a				14 11			14 54							15 11			15 37	
		d				14 11			14 55							15 11			15 39	
York 8	33	a							15 25										16 06	
Saltmarshe		d																		
Goole		d			14 01			14 24							15 01			15 24		
Thorne North		d			14 09										15 09					
Cleethorpes	28	d					13 26										14 26			
Grimsby Town	28	d					13 34										14 34			
Habrough	28	d															14 44			
Barnetby	28	d					13 53										14 53			
Scunthorpe		a					14 08										15 08			
		d					14 08				14 19						15 08			
Althorpe		d									14 24									
Crowle		d									14 30									
Thorne South		d									14 39									
Hatfield & Stainforth		d			14 16						14 44				15 15					
Kirk Sandall		d			14 20						14 49				15 20					
Adwick	31	d		14 15										15 15						
Bentley (S.Yorks)	31	d		14 19										15 19						
Doncaster 7	31	a		14 24	14 30		14 38	14 47			14 59			15 24	15 30		15 38	15 47		
London Kings Cross 15	⊖26	a																		
York 8	26	d								14 35		14 45								15 34
Doncaster 7		d		14 26			14 42	14 49		14 59	15 04			15 26			15 42	15 49		15 58
Conisbrough		d		14 33							15 11			15 33						
Mexborough		d		14 37							15 15			15 37						
Swinton (S.Yorks)		d	14 35	14 43							15 18		15 35	15 43						
Rotherham Central		d	14 44	14 52							15 27		15 44	15 50						
Meadowhall	🚊	d	14 51	14 58			15 01	15 08			15 33		15 51	15 57			16 01	16 08		
Sheffield 7	🚊	a	15 01	15 05			15 08	15 18		15 20	15 41	15 52	16 01	16 05			16 08	16 18		16 20
		d					15 11										16 11			
Stockport	78	a					15 53										16 53			
Manchester Piccadilly 10	🚊	a				15 36	16 02									16 36	17 02			
Manchester Airport	85 ✈	a					16 34										17 33			

A From Bridlington
B From Newcastle to Southampton Central
C To Lincoln
D From Glasgow Central to Penzance
E From Leeds
H From Scarborough
I From Newcastle to Reading
J From Aberdeen to Penzance
M From Newcastle to Guildford

For all trains between Cleethorpes, Grimsby Town, Habrough and Barnetby refer to Table 28

Table 29R

Mondays to Fridays

Hull - Doncaster - Meadowhall, Sheffield, Manchester and Manchester Airport

9 December to 16 May

Network Diagram - refer to first Page of Table 18

Station			NT A	NT ◇ B	HT ◇1 ⊠	XC FO ◇1 C	XC FX ◇1 C	NT D	NT E	NT	TP ◇1	TP ◇1	NT F	XC ◇1 G	NT	NT ◇ B	NT H	TP ◇1	XC FO ◇1 I	XC FX ◇1 I	NT D	NT	TP ◇1	NT F	TP ◇1 J	XC ◇1 G	NT	HT ◇1 ⊠	NT	XC ◇1 C	NT K	NT D	NT	TP ◇1	NT L	NT H	TP ThX ◇1	TP ThO ◇1	XC ◇1 M	NT N
Hull		d			15 10					15 25	15 40		15 57		16 10		16 26	16 40						16 56	17 02			17 10	17 18						17 41	17 52	17 58	17 58		
Hessle		d								15 32							16 33												17 25						17 48					
Ferriby		d								15 37							16 38												17 30						17 53					
Brough		d			15 23					15 42	15 52		16 09		16 22		16 44	16 52						17 08	17 14			17 23	17 35						17 58	18 04	18 10	18 10		
Broomfleet		d															16 50												17 41											
Gilberdyke		d								15 50					16 29		16 53							17 15					17 45						18 06					
Eastrington		d																											17 49											
Howden		d			15 36										16 36													17 34	17 54											
Wressle		d																											17 59											
Selby		a			15 46						16 11				16 46			17 11							17 33			17 44	18 06							18 25	18 29	18 29		
		d			15 47						16 11				16 47			17 11										17 45	18 07							18 26	18 29	18 29		
York 8	33	a													17 13														18 33											
Saltmarshe		d															17 00																		18 12					
Goole		d								16 00			16 24				17 05							17 24											18 20					
Thorne North		d								16 09							17 12																		18 29					
Cleethorpes	28	d										15 26											16 26											17 26						
Grimsby Town	28	d										15 34											16 34											17 34						
Habrough	28	d																					16 44											17 44						
Barnetby	28	d										15 53											16 53											17 53						
Scunthorpe		a										16 08											17 08											18 08						
		d		15 19								16 08				16 19							17 08				17 18							18 08						
Althorpe		d		15 24												16 24											17 24													
Crowle		d		15 30												16 30											17 30													
Thorne South		d		15 39												16 39											17 39													
Hatfield & Stainforth		d		15 44						16 15						16 44	17 19										17 44								18 35					
Kirk Sandall		d		15 49						16 19						16 49	17 23										17 49								18 40					
Adwick	31	d							16 15																						18 16									
Bentley (S.Yorks)	31	d							16 19																						18 20									←
Doncaster 7	31	a		15 59	16 03				16 24	16 30		16 38	16 48			16 59	17 34						17 38	17 47			17 58	18 02			18 27			18 38	18 50	18 48				18 50
London Kings Cross 15	⊖26	a			17 48																							19 47							→					
York 8	26	d	15 02			15 44	15 44							16 05					16 45	16 45						17 35				17 45									18 34	
Doncaster 7		d		16 03					16 26			16 42	16 49			17 01						17 24	17 42	17 49		17 59	18 02						18 26	18 42		18 49			18 58	19 01
Conisbrough		d		16 11					16 33							17 08						17 31					18 09						18 33							19 09
Mexborough		d		16 15					16 37							17 12						17 35					18 13						18 37							19 13
Swinton (S.Yorks)		d	16 01	16 18				16 35	16 42							17 17					17 36	17 42					18 16					18 36	18 42							19 16
Rotherham Central		d	16 10	16 27				16 44	16 50							17 27					17 45	17 50					18 28					18 45	18 50							19 23
Meadowhall	⇌	d	16 17	16 33				16 51	16 57			17 01	17 07			17 33					17 51	17 57	18 01	18 09			18 34					18 51	18 58	19 01		19 09				19 29
Sheffield 7	⇌	a	16 27	16 41		16 51	16 52	17 00	17 05			17 08	17 18	17 20		17 41			17 52	17 53	18 02	18 05	18 08	18 18		18 20	18 41			18 53		19 00	19 06	19 08		19 18			19 20	19 39
		d										17 11											18 11											19 11						
Stockport	78	a										17 53											18 53											19 53						
Manchester Piccadilly 10	⇌	a									17 36	18 02						18 37					19 02											20 01			19 54	19 56		
Manchester Airport	85 ✈	a										18 26											19 28											20 39						

A via Pontefract Baghill
B To Lincoln
C From Edinburgh to Plymouth
D From Leeds
E To Retford Low Level
F From Bridlington
G From Newcastle to Reading
H From Scarborough
I From Glasgow Central to Plymouth
J To Huddersfield
K To Scunthorpe
L To Sheffield
M From Newcastle to Southampton Central
N From Hull

For all trains between Cleethorpes, Grimsby Town, Habrough and Barnetby refer to Table 28

Table 29R

Mondays to Fridays

9 December to 16 May

Hull - Doncaster - Meadowhall, Sheffield, Manchester and Manchester Airport

Network Diagram - refer to first Page of Table 18

Station			NT	NT	XC	NT	NT	TP	TP	NT	TP	NT	HT	NT	NT	XC	NT	XC	NT	TP
								FX												
					◇1			◇1	◇1		◇1		◇1			◇1		◇1		◇1
				A	B	C		D	E		F					G	H	I	C	
					⊥								☒			⊥				
Hull		d		18 23						18 54	19 00		19 10	19 18	19 25					
Hessle		d		18 30											19 32					
Ferriby		d		18 35											19 37					
Brough		d		18 40						19 06	19 12		19 23	19 30	19 42					
Broomfleet		d																		
Gilberdyke		d		18 48										19 37	19 50					
Eastrington		d																		
Howden		d											19 34	19 44						
Wressle		d																		
Selby		a									19 30		19 44	19 54						
		d											19 45	19 55						
York 8	33	a												20 24						
Saltmarshe		d																		
Goole		d		18 59						19 22					20 01					
Thorne North		d		19 08											20 09					
Cleethorpes	28	d						18 26	18 26											19 26
Grimsby Town	28	d						18 34	18 34											19 34
Habrough	28	d																		19 44
Barnetby	28	d						18 53	18 53											19 53
Scunthorpe		a						19 08	19 08											20 08
		d	18 19					19 08	19 08			19 15								20 08
Althorpe		d	18 24									19 20								
Crowle		d	18 30									19 26								
Thorne South		d	18 39									19 35								
Hatfield & Stainforth		d	18 46	19 15								19 40			20 15					
Kirk Sandall		d	18 50	19 19								19 45			20 20					
Adwick	31	d																		
Bentley (S.Yorks)	31	d																		
Doncaster 7	31	a	19 01	19 31				19 38	19 38	19 46		19 57	20 01		20 32					20 40
London Kings Cross 15 ⊖	26	a											21 46							
York 8	26	d			18 45											19 35		19 45		
Doncaster 7		d					19 28	19 42	19 42	19 49						19 59	20 03			20 42
Conisbrough		d					19 35										20 10			20 50
Mexborough		d					19 39										20 14			20 54
Swinton (S.Yorks)		d				19 35	19 43										20 17		20 35	20 57
Rotherham Central		d				19 46	19 50										20 28		20 45	21 03
Meadowhall		d				19 51	19 57	20 01	20 01	20 08							20 33		20 51	21 09
Sheffield 7		a			19 51	19 59	20 05	20 08	20 08	20 18						20 21	20 41	20 53	21 02	21 19
		d						20 11	20 11											
Stockport	78	a						20 53	20 53											
Manchester Piccadilly 10		a						21 02	21 02											
Manchester Airport	85	a							21 36											

Station			NT	XC	NT	TP	XC	TP	NT	NT	TP	TP	TP	NT	NT	NT	TP	NT	NT	NT	NT
						FO		FX			FX	FX									
				◇1		◇1	◇1	◇1			◇1	◇1	◇1				◇1				
				G	A		J	F	C		D	K	L						C		C
Hull		d			20 03	20 35		20 45						20 56			21 36			22 20	
Hessle		d			20 10															22 27	
Ferriby		d			20 15															22 32	
Brough		d			20 20	20 47		20 57						21 08			21 48			22 37	
Broomfleet		d																			
Gilberdyke		d			20 28												21 55				
Eastrington		d																			
Howden		d																			
Wressle		d																			
Selby		a				21 06		21 16									22 09				
		d				21 06											22 10				
York 8	33	a																			
Saltmarshe		d																			
Goole		d			20 36									21 23	21 35					22 52	
Thorne North		d			20 45										21 44					23 01	
Cleethorpes	28	d									20 26	20 26	20 26								
Grimsby Town	28	d									20 34	20 34	20 34								
Habrough	28	d																			
Barnetby	28	d									20 53	20 53	20 53								
Scunthorpe		a									21 08	21 08	21 08								
		d	20 21								21 08	21 08	21 08			21 31		22 21			
Althorpe		d	20 26													21 36		22 26			
Crowle		d	20 32													21 42		22 32			
Thorne South		d	20 41													21 51		22 41			
Hatfield & Stainforth		d	20 46		20 52										21 50	21 56		22 46		23 07	
Kirk Sandall		d	20 51		20 56										21 54	22 01		22 51		23 11	
Adwick	31	d																			
Bentley (S.Yorks)	31	d																			
Doncaster 7	31	a	21 01		21 06						21 40	21 40	21 40	21 46	22 06	22 11		23 02		23 22	
London Kings Cross 15 ⊖	26	a																			
York 8	26	d		20 35			20 45														
Doncaster 7		d		21 02	21 07					21 30	21 42	21 42	21 42	21 49		22 13				23 23	
Conisbrough		d			21 14					21 37						22 20				23 30	
Mexborough		d			21 18					21 41						22 24				23 34	
Swinton (S.Yorks)		d			21 21				21 36	21 44						22 29			22 35	23 37	23 56
Rotherham Central		d			21 29				21 44	21 55						22 38			22 47	23 49	00 04
Meadowhall		d			21 34				21 52	22 03	21 59	21 59	21 59	22 08		22 44			22 53	23 54	00 09
Sheffield 7		a		21 26	21 48		21 53		22 04	22 11	22 08	22 08	22 08	22 18		22 54			23 02	00 04	00 23
		d									22 11	22 11	22 11								
Stockport	78	a									22 53	22 53	22 53								
Manchester Piccadilly 10		a				22 36					23 02	23 02	23 02				23 37				
Manchester Airport	85	a				22 57						23 25	23 26								

A From Bridlington
B From Glasgow Central to Bristol Temple Meads
C From Leeds
D from 30 December until 20 March
E until 27 December, FO from 3 January until 14 March, from 21 March
F To Leeds
G From Newcastle to Birmingham New Street
H To Worksop
I From Edinburgh to Bristol Temple Meads
J From Glasgow Central to Birmingham New Street
K until 26 December
L FO until 14 March, from 21 March

For all trains between Cleethorpes, Grimsby Town, Habrough and Barnetby refer to Table 28

Table 29R

Saturdays

14 December to 17 May

Hull - Doncaster - Meadowhall, Sheffield, Manchester and Manchester Airport

Network Diagram - refer to first Page of Table 18

Station		NT	TP	NT	NT	TP	NT	TP	NT	TP	XC	NT	XC	NT	NT	NT	TP	NT	GR	NT
		A	◇1			◇1		◇1 B		◇1	◇1 C		◇1 D	A	E	E	◇1	F	1	G
Hull	d				05 20			06 00	06 06	06 37					06 40				06 50	
Hessle	d								06 13						06 47					
Ferriby	d								06 18						06 52					
Brough	d				05 32			06 12	06 23	06 49					06 57				07 03	
Broomfleet	d																			
Gilberdyke	d							06 19	06 32						07 05					
Eastrington	d																			
Howden	d							06 26												
Wressle	d																			
Selby	a							06 36		07 08									07 23	
	d						06 18	06 36		07 08									07 25	
York 8	33 a																			
Saltmarshe	d								06 38						07 11					
Goole	d				05 47				06 46						07 16					
Thorne North	d				05 55				06 55						07 24					
Cleethorpes	28 d					05 17											06 18			
Grimsby Town	28 d					05 25											06 26			
Habrough	28 d					05 35											06 36			
Barnetby	28 d					05 44											06 45			
Scunthorpe	a					05 59											07 00			
	d					05 59											07 00			
Althorpe	d					06 04														
Crowle	d					06 10														
Thorne South	d					06 19														
Hatfield & Stainforth	d				06 01	06 24			07 01						07 30					
Kirk Sandall	d				06 06				07 05						07 35					
Adwick	31 d															07 23				
Bentley (S.Yorks)	31 d															07 27				←
Doncaster 7	31 a				06 15	06 37	06 39		07 17						07 46	07 31	07 33		07 43	07 46
London Kings Cross 15	⊖26 a														→				09 35	
York 8	26 d												06 17					←		
Doncaster 7	d		05 38	06 00	06 25	06 38					06 47	07 02				07 39	07 35	07 39		07 48
Conisbrough	d			06 07	06 32							07 09				→		07 46		07 55
Mexborough	d			06 11	06 36							07 13						07 50		07 59
Swinton (S.Yorks)	d			06 14	06 39							07 17		07 30				07 53		08 02
Rotherham Central	d	00 04		06 25	06 48							07 27		07 40				08 01		08 14
Meadowhall	d	00 09	05 58	06 30	06 54	06 58						07 33		07 47			07 53	08 07		08 25
Sheffield 7	a	00 23	06 08	06 38	07 05	07 07					07 15	07 40	07 51	07 54			08 00	08 18		08 32
	d		06 11			07 09											08 05			
Stockport	78 a		06 53			07 53											08 53			
Manchester Piccadilly 10	a		07 02			08 02		08 05		08 36							09 02			
Manchester Airport	85 a		07 29			08 26											09 26			

Station		NT	XC	NT	TP	XC	NT	NT	TP	NT	NT	XC	NT	NT	HT	XC	NT	NT	NT	TP
		H	◇1 I	J	◇1	◇1 K	A		◇1			◇1 L	M	N	◇1	◇1 O	A		P	◇1
Hull	d	07 07			07 37						07 40		08 03		08 25				08 29	08 40
Hessle	d										07 47								08 36	
Ferriby	d										07 52								08 41	
Brough	d	07 19			07 49						07 57		08 15		08 38				08 46	08 52
Broomfleet	d										08 03									
Gilberdyke	d	07 26									08 07								08 54	
Eastrington	d	07 31																		
Howden	d	07 35			08 01										08 50					
Wressle	d	07 40																		
Selby	a	07 48			08 10										09 00					09 11
	d	07 48			08 11										09 05					09 11
York 8	33 a	08 21																		
Saltmarshe	d										08 13									
Goole	d										08 18		08 30						09 02	
Thorne North	d										08 26								09 11	
Cleethorpes	28 d								07 26											
Grimsby Town	28 d								07 34											
Habrough	28 d								07 44											
Barnetby	28 d								07 53											
Scunthorpe	a								08 08											
	d			07 30					08 08					08 19						
Althorpe	d			07 35										08 24						
Crowle	d			07 41										08 30						
Thorne South	d			07 49										08 39						
Hatfield & Stainforth	d			07 55							08 32			08 45					09 17	
Kirk Sandall	d			07 59							08 37			08 50					09 22	
Adwick	31 d							08 15		08 33								09 15		
Bentley (S.Yorks)	31 d							08 19		08 37								09 19		
Doncaster 7	31 a			08 10				08 23	08 38	08 42	08 48		08 57	09 02	09 23			09 24	09 32	
London Kings Cross 15	⊖26 a														11 09					
York 8	26 d		07 24			07 45						08 34				08 45				
Doncaster 7	d		07 56					08 26	08 41			08 58	09 01	09 04				09 26		
Conisbrough	d							08 33						09 12				09 33		
Mexborough	d							08 37						09 16				09 37		
Swinton (S.Yorks)	d						08 35	08 43						09 19			09 35	09 42		
Rotherham Central	d						08 44	08 50						09 27			09 44	09 51		
Meadowhall	d						08 51	08 56	09 01				09 24	09 33			09 51	09 57		
Sheffield 7	a		08 18			08 52	08 59	09 05	09 08			09 20	09 32	09 41		09 53	10 00	10 05		
	d								09 11											
Stockport	78 a								09 53											
Manchester Piccadilly 10	a				09 36				10 02											10 36
Manchester Airport	85 a								10 32											

A From Leeds
B To Liverpool Lime Street
C From Leeds to Southampton Central
D To Plymouth
E To Sheffield
F From Adwick
G From Hull
H From Beverley
I From Newcastle to Reading
J To Adwick
K From Newcastle to Plymouth
L From Newcastle to Southampton Central
M From Bridlington
N To Lincoln
O From Edinburgh to Plymouth
P From Scarborough

For all trains between Cleethorpes, Grimsby Town, Habrough and Barnetby refer to Table 28

Table 29R

Saturdays

14 December to 17 May

Hull - Doncaster - Meadowhall, Sheffield, Manchester and Manchester Airport

Network Diagram - refer to first Page of Table 18

	TP ◇1	NT A	NT	XC ◇1 B	NT C	XC ◇1 D	NT E	NT	NT F	TP ◇1	TP ◇1	NT A	NT	XC ◇1 G	NT C	XC ◇1 H	NT E	NT	NT
Hull d		08 57	09 03						09 25	09 40		09 57	10 10						10 20
Hessle d									09 32										10 27
Ferriby d									09 37										10 32
Brough d		09 09	09 15						09 42	09 52		10 09	10 22						10 37
Broomfleet d																			
Gilberdyke d			09 21						09 50				10 29						10 45
Eastrington d																			
Howden d			09 29										10 36						
Wressle d																			
Selby a			09 39							10 11			10 46						
d			09 39							10 11			10 46						
York 8 33 a			10 10										11 18						
Saltmarshe d																			10 51
Goole d		09 24							10 01			10 24							10 58
Thorne North d									10 09										11 06
Cleethorpes 28 d	08 26										09 26								
Grimsby Town 28 d	08 34										09 34								
Habrough 28 d	08 44																		
Barnetby 28 d	08 53										09 53								
Scunthorpe a	09 08										10 08								
d	09 08				09 19						10 08				10 19				
Althorpe d					09 24										10 24				
Crowle d					09 30										10 30				
Thorne South d					09 39										10 39				
Hatfield & Stainforth d					09 44				10 15						10 44				11 11
Kirk Sandall d					09 49				10 20						10 49				11 17
Adwick 31 d								10 15										11 15	
Bentley (S.Yorks) 31 d								10 19										11 19	
Doncaster 7 31 a	09 38	09 48			10 00			10 24	10 30		10 38	10 49			11 01			11 24	11 27
London Kings Cross 15 ⊖26 a																			
York 8 26 d				09 35		09 45								10 35		10 45			
Doncaster 7 d	09 42	09 49		09 58	10 03			10 26			10 42	10 50		10 59	11 03			11 26	
Conisbrough d					10 11			10 33							11 11			11 33	
Mexborough d					10 15			10 37							11 15			11 37	
Swinton (S.Yorks) d					10 18		10 35	10 43							11 19		11 35	11 43	
Rotherham Central d					10 27		10 44	10 52							11 27		11 44	11 52	
Meadowhall d	10 01	10 08			10 33		10 51	10 58			11 01	11 08			11 33		11 51	11 58	
Sheffield 7 a	10 08	10 18		10 20	10 41	10 52	11 00	11 05			11 08	11 18		11 20	11 41	11 52	12 00	12 05	
d	10 11										11 11								
Stockport 78 a	10 53										11 53								
Manchester Piccadilly 10 a	11 02									11 36	12 02								
Manchester Airport 85 ✈ a	11 32										12 26								

	HT ◇1 ☒	TP ◇1	TP ◇1	NT A	NT	XC ◇1 I	NT	NT C	XC ◇1 D	NT E	NT	NT	TP ◇1	TP ◇1	NT A	NT	XC ◇1 G	NT C
Hull d	10 30	10 40		10 57	11 05							11 23	11 40		11 55	12 03		
Hessle d												11 30						
Ferriby d												11 35						
Brough d	10 44	10 52		11 09	11 17							11 40	11 52		12 09	12 15		
Broomfleet d												11 46						
Gilberdyke d												11 50						
Eastrington d																		
Howden d	10 56				11 29											12 27		
Wressle d																		
Selby a	11 05	11 11			11 39								12 11			12 37		
d	11 06	11 11			11 40								12 11			12 39		
York 8 33 a					12 05											13 04		
Saltmarshe d																		
Goole d				11 24								12 01			12 24			
Thorne North d												12 09						
Cleethorpes 28 d			10 26											11 26				
Grimsby Town 28 d			10 34											11 34				
Habrough 28 d			10 44															
Barnetby 28 d			10 53											11 53				
Scunthorpe a			11 08											12 08				
d			11 08					11 19						12 08				12 19
Althorpe d								11 24										12 24
Crowle d								11 30										12 30
Thorne South d								11 39										12 39
Hatfield & Stainforth d								11 44				12 15						12 44
Kirk Sandall d								11 49				12 20						12 49
Adwick 31 d											12 15							
Bentley (S.Yorks) 31 d											12 19							
Doncaster 7 31 a	11 24		11 38	11 47				11 59			12 24	12 30		12 38	12 47			12 59
London Kings Cross 15 ⊖26 a	13 09																	
York 8 26 d						11 35	11 06		11 45								12 35	
Doncaster 7 d			11 42	11 49		11 59		12 03			12 26			12 42	12 49		12 59	13 03
Conisbrough d								12 11			12 33							13 11
Mexborough d								12 15			12 37							13 15
Swinton (S.Yorks) d							12 10	12 18		12 35	12 43							13 18
Rotherham Central d							12 19	12 27		12 44	12 52							13 27
Meadowhall d			12 01	12 08			12 25	12 33		12 51	12 58			13 01	13 08			13 33
Sheffield 7 a			12 08	12 20		12 20	12 36	12 41	12 52	13 00	13 05			13 08	13 18		13 20	13 41
d			12 11											13 11				
Stockport 78 a			12 53											13 53				
Manchester Piccadilly 10 a		12 36	13 02										13 36	14 02				
Manchester Airport 85 ✈ a			13 33											14 26				

A From Bridlington
B From Edinburgh to Reading
C To Lincoln
D From Glasgow Central to Plymouth
E From Leeds
F From Beverley
G From Newcastle to Southampton Central
H From Dundee to Plymouth
I From Newcastle to Reading

For all trains between Cleethorpes, Grimsby Town, Habrough and Barnetby refer to Table 28

Table 29R

Saturdays

Hull - Doncaster - Meadowhall, Sheffield, Manchester and Manchester Airport

14 December to 17 May

Network Diagram - refer to first Page of Table 18

		XC	NT	NT	NT	TP	TP	NT	NT	XC	NT	XC	NT	NT	NT
		◇1				◇1	◇1			◇1		◇1			
		A	C					D		E	F	G	C		
Hull	d				12 20	12 40		12 57	13 12						13 18
Hessle	d				12 27										13 25
Ferriby	d				12 32										13 30
Brough	d				12 38	12 52		13 09	13 24						13 36
Broomfleet	d														
Gilberdyke	d				12 45				13 32						13 43
Eastrington	d								13 36						
Howden	d								13 42						
Wressle	d								13 47						
Selby	a					13 11			13 54						
	d					13 11			13 55						
York 8	33 a								14 25						
Saltmarshe	d				12 51										
Goole	d				13 01			13 24							13 58
Thorne North	d				13 09										14 07
Cleethorpes	28 d						12 26								
Grimsby Town	28 d						12 34								
Habrough	28 d														
Barnetby	28 d						12 53								
Scunthorpe	a						13 08								
	d						13 08				13 19				
Althorpe	d										13 24				
Crowle	d										13 30				
Thorne South	d										13 39				
Hatfield & Stainforth	d				13 15						13 44				14 13
Kirk Sandall	d				13 20						13 49				14 17
Adwick	31 d			13 15										14 15	
Bentley (S.Yorks)	31 d			13 19										14 19	
Doncaster 7	31 a			13 24	13 30		13 38	13 47			13 59			14 24	14 30
London Kings Cross 15	⊖26 a														
York 8	26 d	12 45								13 34		13 45			
Doncaster 7	d			13 26			13 42	13 49		13 58	14 03			14 26	
Conisbrough	d			13 33							14 11			14 33	
Mexborough	d			13 37							14 15			14 37	
Swinton (S.Yorks)	d		13 35	13 43							14 18		14 35	14 43	
Rotherham Central	d		13 44	13 52							14 27		14 44	14 52	
Meadowhall	d		13 51	13 58			14 01	14 08			14 33		14 51	14 58	
Sheffield 7	a	13 52	14 00	14 05			14 08	14 18		14 20	14 40	14 52	15 00	15 05	
	d						14 11								
Stockport	78 a						14 53								
Manchester Piccadilly 10	a					14 36	15 02								
Manchester Airport	85 a						15 26								

		HT	TP	TP	NT	NT	XC	NT	XC	NT	NT	NT	TP	TP	NT	NT	XC	NT	NT	NT	HT	TP	XC	NT
		◇1	◇1	◇1			◇1	◇	◇1				◇1	◇1			◇1				◇1	◇1	◇1	
					H		I	F	J	C					D		E	K	F				L	C
Hull	d	13 30	13 40		13 57	14 20						14 25	14 40		14 57	15 03				15 18	15 30	15 40		
Hessle	d											14 32								15 25				
Ferriby	d											14 37								15 30				
Brough	d	13 43	13 52		14 09	14 32						14 42	14 52		15 09	15 15				15 35	15 43	15 52		
Broomfleet	d																							
Gilberdyke	d											14 50								15 43				
Eastrington	d																							
Howden	d	13 56				14 44										15 27					15 54			
Wressle	d																							
Selby	a	14 05	14 11			14 54							15 11			15 36					16 04	16 11		
	d	14 06	14 11			14 55							15 11			15 38					16 05	16 11		
York 8	33 a					15 25										16 04								
Saltmarshe	d																							
Goole	d				14 24							15 01			15 24					15 58				
Thorne North	d											15 09								16 06				
Cleethorpes	28 d			13 26										14 26										
Grimsby Town	28 d			13 34										14 34										
Habrough	28 d													14 44										
Barnetby	28 d			13 53										14 53										
Scunthorpe	a			14 08										15 08										
	d			14 08				14 19						15 08					15 19					
Althorpe	d							14 24											15 24					
Crowle	d							14 30											15 30					
Thorne South	d							14 39											15 39					
Hatfield & Stainforth	d							14 44				15 15							15 44	16 12				
Kirk Sandall	d							14 49				15 20							15 49	16 17				
Adwick	31 d										15 15													
Bentley (S.Yorks)	31 d										15 19													
Doncaster 7	31 a	14 25		14 38	14 47			14 59			15 24	15 30		15 38	15 47				15 59	16 27	16 23			
London Kings Cross 15	⊖26 a	16 10																			18 08			
York 8	26 d						14 35		14 45								15 35	15 02					15 45	
Doncaster 7	d			14 42	14 49		14 59	15 04			15 26			15 42	15 49		15 59		16 03					
Conisbrough	d							15 11			15 33								16 11					
Mexborough	d							15 15			15 37								16 15					
Swinton (S.Yorks)	d							15 18		15 35	15 42							16 01	16 18					16 35
Rotherham Central	d							15 27		15 44	15 50							16 09	16 27					16 44
Meadowhall	d			15 01	15 07			15 33		15 51	15 57			16 01	16 08			16 18	16 33					16 51
Sheffield 7	a			15 08	15 18		15 20	15 41	15 52	16 00	16 05			16 08	16 18		16 20	16 27	16 41				16 52	17 00
	d			15 11										16 11										
Stockport	78 a			15 53										16 53										
Manchester Piccadilly 10	a		15 36	16 02									16 36	17 02								17 36		
Manchester Airport	85 a			16 34										17 33										

A From Glasgow Central to Penzance
C From Leeds
D From Scarborough
E From Newcastle to Reading
F To Lincoln
G From Aberdeen to Penzance
H From Bridlington
I From Newcastle to Southampton Central
J From Glasgow Central to Penzance
K via Pontefract Baghill
L From Edinburgh to Plymouth

For all trains between Cleethorpes, Grimsby Town, Habrough and Barnetby refer to Table 28

Table 29R

Saturdays

14 December to 17 May

Hull - Doncaster - Meadowhall, Sheffield, Manchester and Manchester Airport

Network Diagram - refer to first Page of Table 18

		NT A	TP ◇1	NT D	XC ◇1 E	NT	NT F	NT	TP ◇1	XC ◇1 G	NT H	NT	TP ◇1	NT D	TP ◇1 I	NT	XC ◇1 E	NT F	EM ◇1 J
Hull	d			15 57		16 10		16 27	16 40					16 56	17 02	17 18			
Hessle	d							16 34								17 25			
Ferriby	d							16 39								17 30			
Brough	d			16 09		16 22		16 44	16 52					17 08	17 14	17 35			
Broomfleet	d							16 50								17 41			
Gilberdyke	d					16 29		16 54						17 15		17 45			
Eastrington	d															17 49			
Howden	d					16 36										17 54			
Wressle	d															17 59			
Selby	a					16 46			17 11						17 33	18 06			
	d					16 47			17 11							18 07			
York 8 33	a					17 13										18 33			
Saltmarshe	d							17 00											
Goole	d			16 24				17 05						17 24					
Thorne North	d							17 13											
Cleethorpes 28	d		15 26										16 26						
Grimsby Town 28	d		15 34										16 34						
Habrough 28	d																		
Barnetby 28	d		15 53										16 53						
Scunthorpe	a		16 08										17 08						
	d		16 08				16 19						17 08					17 18	
Althorpe	d						16 24											17 23	
Crowle	d						16 30											17 29	
Thorne South	d						16 39											17 38	
Hatfield & Stainforth	d						16 44	17 19										17 43	
Kirk Sandall	d						16 49	17 24										17 48	
Adwick 31	d	16 15																	
Bentley (S.Yorks) 31	d	16 19																	
Doncaster 7 31	a	16 24	16 38	16 47			16 59	17 35					17 38	17 47				17 58	
London Kings Cross 15 ⊖26	a																		
York 8 26	d				16 05					16 45							17 35		17 50
Doncaster 7	d	16 26	16 42	16 49			17 01					17 24	17 42	17 49			17 59	18 02	18 18
Conisbrough	d	16 33					17 08					17 31						18 09	
Mexborough	d	16 37					17 12					17 35						18 13	
Swinton (S.Yorks)	d	16 42					17 16				17 35	17 42						18 17	
Rotherham Central	d	16 50					17 27				17 45	17 50						18 27	
Meadowhall	d	16 57	17 01	17 08			17 33				17 50	17 57	18 01	18 08				18 33	
Sheffield 7	a	17 05	17 08	17 18	17 20		17 41			17 52	17 59	18 05	18 08	18 18			18 20	18 41	18 44
	d		17 11										18 11						
Stockport 78	a		17 53										18 53						
Manchester Piccadilly 10	a		18 02						18 37				19 02						
Manchester Airport 85	a		18 34										19 28						

		XC ◇1 K	XC ◇1 L	NT M	NT H	NT	TP ◇1	NT N	NT O	TP ◇1	XC ◇1 P	NT Q	NT	HT ◇1 ☒	NT D	XC ◇1 R	NT H	NT	TP ◇1
Hull	d							17 41	17 52	17 58				18 30	18 32				
Hessle	d							17 48							18 39				
Ferriby	d							17 53							18 44				
Brough	d							17 58	18 04	18 10				18 43	18 49				
Broomfleet	d																		
Gilberdyke	d							18 06							18 57				
Eastrington	d																		
Howden	d													18 56					
Wressle	d																		
Selby	a								18 23	18 29				19 05					
	d								18 26	18 29				19 09					
York 8 33	a																		
Saltmarshe	d							18 12											
Goole	d							18 19							19 05				
Thorne North	d							18 29							19 15				
Cleethorpes 28	d						17 26												18 26
Grimsby Town 28	d						17 34												18 34
Habrough 28	d						17 44												
Barnetby 28	d						17 53												18 53
Scunthorpe	a						18 08												19 08
	d						18 08						18 19						19 08
Althorpe	d												18 24						
Crowle	d												18 30						
Thorne South	d												18 39						
Hatfield & Stainforth	d							18 35					18 46		19 22				
Kirk Sandall	d							18 40					18 50		19 25				
Adwick 31	d			18 16															
Bentley (S.Yorks) 31	d			18 20								←							
Doncaster 7 31	a			18 27			18 38	18 50	18 47			18 50	19 01	19 27	19 37				19 38
London Kings Cross 15 ⊖26	a							→						21 13					
York 8 26	d	17 45	17 45								18 34					18 45			
Doncaster 7	d					18 26	18 42		18 49		18 59	19 01						19 28	19 42
Conisbrough	d					18 33						19 09						19 35	
Mexborough	d					18 37						19 13						19 39	
Swinton (S.Yorks)	d				18 36	18 42						19 16					19 35	19 43	
Rotherham Central	d				18 44	18 49						19 23					19 45	19 51	
Meadowhall	d				18 51	18 57	19 01		19 08			19 29					19 51	19 57	20 01
Sheffield 7	a	18 52	18 53		19 00	19 06	19 08		19 18		19 21	19 39				19 51	19 59	20 06	20 08
	d						19 11												20 11
Stockport 78	a						19 53												20 53
Manchester Piccadilly 10	a						20 01			19 57									21 02
Manchester Airport 85	a						20 39												21 36

A To Retford Low Level
D From Bridlington
E From Newcastle to Reading
F To Lincoln
G From Glasgow Central to Plymouth
H From Leeds
I To Leeds
J To St Pancras International
K from 4 January until 8 February. From Edinburgh to Plymouth
L from 15 February. From Edinburgh to Exeter St Davids
M To Scunthorpe
N To Sheffield
O From Scarborough
P From Newcastle to Guildford
Q From Hull
R From Glasgow Central to Bristol Temple Meads

For all trains between Cleethorpes, Grimsby Town, Habrough and Barnetby refer to Table 28

Table 29R

Saturdays

14 December to 17 May

Hull - Doncaster - Meadowhall, Sheffield, Manchester and Manchester Airport

Network Diagram - refer to first Page of Table 18

		NT	TP	NT	XC	NT	NT	XC	TP	NT	TP	NT	XC	NT	XC	NT	NT	TP	NT	NT	NT	NT	TP	NT	NT	NT	NT
			◇1		◇1			◇1	◇1		◇1		◇1		◇1			◇1					◇1				
			A		B ⚮	C		D	A	E			B	F	G	E									E	E	F
Hull	d	18 54	19 00	19 18			19 25		19 58					20 03					20 56		21 01		21 36				22 17
Hessle	d						19 32							20 10													22 24
Ferriby	d						19 37							20 15													22 29
Brough	d	19 06	19 12	19 30			19 42		20 10					20 20					21 08		21 13		21 48				22 34
Broomfleet	d																										
Gilberdyke	d			19 37			19 50							20 28									21 55				
Eastrington	d																										
Howden	d			19 44																	21 25						
Wressle	d																										
Selby	a		19 30	19 54					20 28												21 35		22 09				
	d			19 55																	21 35		22 10				
York 8 33	a			20 24																	21 57						
Saltmarshe	d																										
Goole	d	19 22					20 01							20 36					21 23	21 35							22 49
Thorne North	d						20 09							20 45						21 44							22 57
Cleethorpes 28	d										19 26							20 26									
Grimsby Town 28	d										19 34							20 34									
Habrough 28	d										19 44																
Barnetby 28	d										19 53							20 53									
Scunthorpe	a										20 08							21 08									
	d					19 19					20 08	20 21						21 08				21 31		22 21			
Althorpe	d					19 24						20 26										21 36		22 26			
Crowle	d					19 30						20 32										21 42		22 32			
Thorne South	d					19 39						20 41										21 51		22 41			
Hatfield & Stainforth	d					19 44	20 15					20 46		20 51						21 50		21 56		22 46			23 03
Kirk Sandall	d					19 49	20 20					20 51		20 56						21 54		22 01		22 51			23 08
Adwick 31	d																										
Bentley (S.Yorks) 31	d																										
Doncaster 7 31	a	19 46				19 59	20 32				20 40	21 01		21 05				21 40	21 46	22 06		22 11		23 02			23 18
London Kings Cross 15 ⊖26	a																										
York 8 26	d				19 35			19 45					20 35		20 45												
Doncaster 7	d	19 49			19 59	20 03					20 42		21 00	21 07			21 30	21 42	21 49			22 13					23 19
Conisbrough	d					20 10					20 50			21 14			21 37					22 20					23 26
Mexborough	d					20 14					20 54			21 18			21 41					22 24					23 30
Swinton (S.Yorks)	d					20 17				20 35	20 57			21 21		21 36	21 45					22 29			22 35	23 31	23 36
Rotherham Central	d					20 28				20 45	21 03			21 29		21 44	21 55					22 37			22 47	23 39	23 44
Meadowhall ⇌	d	20 07				20 33				20 51	21 09			21 35		21 52	22 03	21 59	22 08			22 43			22 53	23 45	23 50
Sheffield 7 ⇌	a	20 18			20 20	20 41		20 53		21 00	21 19		21 20	21 46	21 52	22 02	22 13	22 10	22 19			22 54			23 03	23 58	23 59
	d																										
Stockport 78	a																										
Manchester Piccadilly 10 ⇌	a																						23 37				
Manchester Airport 85 ✈	a																										

A To Leeds
B From Newcastle to Birmingham New Street
C To Worksop
D From Edinburgh to Birmingham New Street
E From Leeds
F From Bridlington
G From Glasgow Central to Birmingham New Street

For all trains between Cleethorpes, Grimsby Town, Habrough and Barnetby refer to Table 28

Table 29R

Sundays

8 December to 29 December

Hull - Doncaster - Meadowhall, Sheffield, Manchester and Manchester Airport

Network Diagram - refer to first Page of Table 18

	NT	NT	XC	NT	NT	NT	TP	HT	NT	NT	XC	TP	NT	XC	TP	NT	TP	HT	NT	NT	XC	NT	TP	NT	NT	TP	XC	NT	TP	NT	TP	NT	XC	NT	NT	TP	NT	XC
			◇1 A 🍴	B			◇1	◇1 ⊠			◇1 C 🍴	◇1		◇1 D 🍴	◇1	E	◇1	◇1 ⊠		B	◇1 F 🍴		◇1			◇1	◇1 G 🍴	H	◇1		◇1	B	◇1 F 🍴		H	◇1		◇1 I 🍴
Hull d					08 41	08 54	09 00	09 05		09 33						10 50	10 58	11 10	11 46						11 53	12 00		12 46	12 58	13 30					13 36		14 30	
Hessle d										09 40																									13 43			
Ferriby d										09 45																									13 48			
Brough d					08 53	09 06	09 12	09 17		09 50						11 02	11 10	11 23	11 58						12 05	12 12		12 58	13 10	13 42					13 53		14 42	
Broomfleet d																																						
Gilberdyke d					09 01					09 58						11 10									12 12			13 05							14 01			
Eastrington d																																						
Howden d						09 18		09 29										11 34	12 10											13 54							14 54	
Wressle d																																						
Selby a						09 27	09 32	09 39									11 28	11 44	12 19							12 31			13 28	14 03							15 03	
d						09 28	09 33	09 40									11 29	11 45	12 20							12 31			13 29	14 04							15 04	
York 8 33 a						09 52													12 45											14 29							15 28	
Saltmarshe d																																						
Goole d					09 09				09 43	10 06						11 18						11 43			12 21			13 14						13 43	14 09			
Thorne North d									09 51	10 15						11 27						11 51			12 29									13 51				
Cleethorpes 28 d												09 26			10 26								11 26													13 26		
Grimsby Town 28 d												09 34			10 34								11 34													13 34		
Habrough 28 d												09 44			10 44																							
Barnetby 28 d												09 53			10 53								11 53													13 53		
Scunthorpe a												10 08			11 08								12 08													14 08		
d												10 08			11 08								12 08													14 08		
Althorpe d																																						
Crowle d																																						
Thorne South d																																						
Hatfield & Stainforth d									09 57	10 21												11 57												13 57				
Kirk Sandall d									10 02	10 25												12 02												14 02				
Adwick 31 d																																						
Bentley (S.Yorks) 31 d																																						
Doncaster 7 31 a					09 29			09 57	10 11	10 36		10 40			11 38	11 44		12 03				12 11	12 40		12 46			13 38						14 11	14 32	14 37		
London Kings Cross 15 ⊖26 a								11 42										13 46																				
York 8 26 d											09 33			10 33							11 40						12 40						13 40					14 34
Doncaster 7 d	08 03	09 13	09 32		09 39				10 13		10 30	10 42	11 13	11 30	11 42	11 48						12 13	12 42	13 13				13 39			13 43			14 13	14 33	14 42		14 59
Conisbrough d	08 10	09 20							10 20				11 20									12 20		13 20										14 20				
Mexborough d	08 14	09 24							10 24				11 24									12 24		13 24										14 24				
Swinton (S.Yorks) d	08 17	09 28		09 35					10 27				11 27							12 07		12 27		13 27								14 07		14 30				
Rotherham Central d	08 25	09 35		09 48					10 35				11 35							12 15		12 38		13 36								14 15		14 43				
Meadowhall 🚋 d	08 30	09 41		09 54	10 00				10 40			11 00	11 40		12 00	12 08				12 24		12 43	13 00	13 44				13 57			14 00	14 21		14 48	14 52	15 00		
Sheffield 7 🚋 a	08 41	09 51	09 55	10 03	10 08				10 52		10 54	11 07	11 51	11 53	12 07	12 18				12 32	12 54	12 55	13 07	13 51			13 53	14 08			14 07	14 32	14 52	14 56	15 04	15 07		15 21
d												11 10			12 10								13 10								14 11					15 11		
Stockport 78 a												11 53			12 52								13 53								14 53					15 53		
Manchester Piccadilly 10 🚋 a							11 01					12 06			13 07		12 54						14 06			13 54			14 54		15 06					16 06		
Manchester Airport 85 ✈ a												12 27			13 28								14 27								15 28					16 27		

A From Leeds to Plymouth
B From Leeds
C To Plymouth
D From Newcastle to Plymouth
E From Bridlington
F From Edinburgh to Plymouth
G From Edinburgh to Penzance
H From Scarborough
I From Newcastle to Reading

For all trains between Cleethorpes, Grimsby Town, Habrough and Barnetby refer to Table 28

Table 29R

Sundays

8 December to 29 December

Hull - Doncaster - Meadowhall, Sheffield, Manchester and Manchester Airport

Network Diagram - refer to first Page of Table 18

		HT	XC	NT	NT	TP	TP	XC		NT	XC	NT	NT	TP	NT	XC	HT	XC	NT	NT
		◇1	◇1			◇1	◇1	◇1			◇1			◇1		◇1	◇1	◇1		
		☒	A		B			C		D	E		F			G	☒	H		B
Hull	d	14 35			14 41	14 58							15 41		16 02		16 35			16 41
Hessle	d																			
Ferriby	d																			
Brough	d	14 48			14 53	15 10							15 53		16 14		16 47			16 53
Broomfleet	d																			
Gilberdyke	d				15 00								16 00							17 00
Eastrington	d																			
Howden	d	15 00													16 26		16 59			
Wressle	d																			
Selby	a	15 09				15 28									16 35		17 09			
	d	15 10				15 29									16 37		17 10			
York 8	33 a														17 01					
Saltmarshe	d																			
Goole	d				15 09							15 43	16 09							17 09
Thorne North	d											15 51								
Cleethorpes	28 d						14 26							15 26						
Grimsby Town	28 d						14 34							15 34						
Habrough	28 d						14 44													
Barnetby	28 d						14 53							15 53						
Scunthorpe	a						15 08							16 08						
	d						15 08							16 08						
Althorpe	d																			
Crowle	d																			
Thorne South	d																			
Hatfield & Stainforth	d											15 57								
Kirk Sandall	d											16 02								
Adwick	31 d																			
Bentley (S.Yorks)	31 d																			
Doncaster 7	31 a	15 28			15 32		15 39					16 11	16 32	16 39			17 28			17 31
London Kings Cross 15	26 a	17 14															19 18			
York 8	26 d		14 40					15 35			15 41					16 24		16 40		
Doncaster 7	d			15 13	15 33		15 42	15 59				16 13	16 33	16 42		16 52			17 18	17 32
Conisbrough	d			15 20								16 20							17 26	
Mexborough	d			15 24								16 24							17 30	
Swinton (S.Yorks)	d			15 30						16 10		16 29							17 34	
Rotherham Central	d			15 41						16 17		16 41							17 42	
Meadowhall	d			15 48	15 52		16 00			16 23		16 47	16 53	17 00					17 48	17 53
Sheffield 7	a		15 51	15 55	16 03		16 07	16 21		16 32	16 51	16 55	17 03	17 07		17 15		17 52	17 56	18 01
	d						16 11							17 11						
Stockport	78 a						16 53							17 53						
Manchester Piccadilly 10	a					16 54	17 06							18 06						
Manchester Airport	85 a						17 27							18 27						

		TP	TP	NT	XC		NT	NT	EM	XC	NT	NT	TP	XC	NT	XC	NT	NT	HT	TP	TP
		◇1	◇1		◇1				◇1	◇1			◇1	◇1		◇1			◇1	◇1	◇1
					C			D	I	E		F		J	K	L		B	☒		
Hull	d	16 58		17 25								17 41						18 38	18 45	18 58	
Hessle	d																				
Ferriby	d																				
Brough	d	17 10		17 37								17 53						18 50	18 58	19 10	
Broomfleet	d																				
Gilberdyke	d											18 00						18 57			
Eastrington	d																				
Howden	d			17 49															19 10		
Wressle	d																				
Selby	a	17 28		17 58															19 19	19 28	
	d	17 29		17 59															19 20	19 29	
York 8	33 a			18 24																	
Saltmarshe	d																				
Goole	d						17 41					18 09						19 06			
Thorne North	d						17 49											19 14			
Cleethorpes	28 d		16 26										17 26								18 26
Grimsby Town	28 d		16 34										17 34								18 34
Habrough	28 d												17 44								
Barnetby	28 d		16 53										17 53								18 53
Scunthorpe	a		17 08										18 08								19 08
	d		17 08										18 08								19 08
Althorpe	d																				
Crowle	d																				
Thorne South	d																				
Hatfield & Stainforth	d						17 55											19 20			
Kirk Sandall	d						18 00											19 25			
Adwick	31 d																				
Bentley (S.Yorks)	31 d																				
Doncaster 7	31 a		17 38				18 10					18 33	18 38					19 35	19 38		19 40
London Kings Cross 15	26 a																		21 21		
York 8	26 d				17 34				17 49	17 40				18 35	18 10	18 40					
Doncaster 7	d		17 42		17 59				18 13		18 18	18 34	18 42	18 59			19 18	19 37			19 42
Conisbrough	d										18 25						19 25				
Mexborough	d										18 29						19 29				
Swinton (S.Yorks)	d							18 10			18 32				19 01		19 33				
Rotherham Central	d							18 17			18 41				19 13		19 41				
Meadowhall	d		18 00					18 25			18 47	18 53	19 00		19 18		19 48	19 57			20 00
Sheffield 7	a		18 07		18 23			18 34	18 39	18 51	18 56	19 03	19 07	19 21	19 27	19 50	19 56	20 07			20 07
	d		18 11										19 11								20 11
Stockport	78 a		18 53										19 53								20 53
Manchester Piccadilly 10	a	18 54	19 06										20 09							20 54	21 06
Manchester Airport	85 a		19 27										20 29								21 27

A From Glasgow Central to Penzance
B From Bridlington
C From Newcastle to Reading
D From Leeds
E From Glasgow Central to Plymouth
F From Scarborough
G From Edinburgh to Reading
H From Aberdeen to Plymouth
I To St Pancras International
J From Newcastle to Guildford
K via Pontefract Baghill
L From Glasgow Central to Bristol Temple Meads

For all trains between Cleethorpes, Grimsby Town, Habrough and Barnetby refer to Table 28

Table 29R

Sundays

8 December to 29 December

Hull - Doncaster - Meadowhall, Sheffield, Manchester and Manchester Airport

Network Diagram - refer to first Page of Table 18

		XC	NT	NT	XC	NT	TP	XC	NT	NT	XC	NT	TP	TP	NT	NT
		◇1			◇1		◇1	◇1			◇1		◇1	◇1		
		A		B	C			A	D		E	F		G	B	
		✠														
Hull	d		19 25						20 01	20 30				21 00		21 40
Hessle	d								20 08							
Ferriby	d								20 13							
Brough	d		19 37						20 18	20 42				21 12		21 52
Broomfleet	d															
Gilberdyke	d								20 26							21 59
Eastrington	d															
Howden	d		19 49							20 54						
Wressle	d															
Selby	a		19 58							21 03				21 30		
	d		19 59							21 04						
York 8 33	a		20 25							21 28						
Saltmarshe	d															
Goole	d								20 34							22 08
Thorne North	d								20 43							22 16
Cleethorpes 28	d						19 26						20 26			
Grimsby Town 28	d						19 34						20 34			
Habrough 28	d												20 44			
Barnetby 28	d						19 53						20 53			
Scunthorpe	a						20 08						21 08			
	d						20 08						21 08			
Althorpe	d															
Crowle	d															
Thorne South	d															
Hatfield & Stainforth	d															22 20
Kirk Sandall	d															22 25
Adwick 31	d															
Bentley (S.Yorks) 31	d															
Doncaster 7 31	a						20 40		20 59				21 40			22 37
London Kings Cross 15 ⊖26	a															
York 8 26	d	19 24			19 40			20 24			20 40	20 50				
Doncaster 7	d	19 52				20 18	20 42	20 51	21 01				21 42			22 40
Conisbrough	d					20 25			21 08							22 47
Mexborough	d					20 30			21 12							22 51
Swinton (S.Yorks)	d			20 09		20 33			21 15			21 45	21 53		22 29	22 53
Rotherham Central	d			20 17		20 42			21 22			21 52	21 59		22 38	22 58
Meadowhall 🚋	d			20 23		20 48	21 00		21 28			21 58	22 05		22 44	23 04
Sheffield 7 🚋	a	20 16		20 34	20 51	20 56	21 07	21 17	21 38		21 50	22 09	22 13		22 52	23 15
	d						21 11									
Stockport 78	a						21 53									
Manchester Piccadilly 10 🚋	a						22 06									
Manchester Airport 85 ✈	a						22 28									

A From Newcastle to Birmingham New Street
B From Leeds
C From Edinburgh to Bristol Temple Meads
D From Scarborough
E From Glasgow Central to Birmingham New Street
F via Pontefract Baghill
G To Leeds

For all trains between Cleethorpes, Grimsby Town, Habrough and Barnetby refer to Table 28

Table 29R

Sundays

5 January to 9 February

Hull - Doncaster - Meadowhall, Sheffield, Manchester and Manchester Airport

Network Diagram - refer to first Page of Table 18

			NT	NT	NT	NT	NT	NT	NT	TP	HT	NT	NT	NT	XC	NT	NT	TP	TP	NT	TP	XC	NT	NT	TP	NT	TP	HT	NT	NT	NT	NT	TP	NT	TP	NT	NT	XC	TP	NT
										◇1	◇1				◇1			◇1	◇1			◇1					◇1	◇1					◇1					◇1	◇1	
												A			B							C		D							A							E		
			🚌		🚌	🚌					⊠		🚌	🚌	🛒						🚌	🛒	🚌		🚌	🚌		⊠		🚌					🚌		🚌	🛒		
Hull		d						08 41	08 54	09 00	09 05						09 33							10 50			10 58	11 10						11 46		11 53			12 00	
Hessle		d															09 40																							
Ferriby		d															09 45																							
Brough		d						08 53	09 06	09 12	09 17						09 50							11 02			11 10	11 23						11 58		12 05			12 12	
Broomfleet		d																																						
Gilberdyke		d						09 01									09 58							11 10												12 12				
Eastrington		d																																						
Howden		d							09 18		09 29																	11 34						12 10						
Wressle		d																																						
Selby		a							09 27	09 32	09 39																11 28	11 44						12 19					12 31	
		d							09 28	09 33	09 40																11 29	11 45						12 20					12 31	
York 8	33	a							09 52																									12 45						
Saltmarshe		d																																						
Goole		d						09 09								09 43	10 06							11 18								11 43				12 21				
Thorne North		d														09 51	10 15							11 27								11 51				12 29				
Cleethorpes	28	d																09 26	10 26														11 26							
Grimsby Town	28	d																09 34	10 34														11 34							
Habrough	28	d																09 44	10 44																					
Barnetby	28	d																09 53	10 53														11 53							
Scunthorpe		a																10 08	11 08														12 08							
		d																10 08	11 08														12 08							
Althorpe		d																																						
Crowle		d																																						
Thorne South		d																																						
Hatfield & Stainforth		d														09 57	10 21															11 57								
Kirk Sandall		d														10 02	10 25															12 02								
Adwick	31	d																																						
Bentley (S.Yorks)	31	d																																						
Doncaster 7	31	a						09 29			09 57					10 08	10 36	10 40	11 38					11 44				12 01				12 11	12 42			12 46				
London Kings Cross 15	⊖26	a									12 02																	14 05												
York 8	26	d													09 33							10 33																11 40		
Doncaster 7		d	07 10		08 05	08 35							09 35	09 40							10 10		10 35		10 50	10 50				11 35					11 50		11 55			
Conisbrough		d	07 30		08 25	08 55							09 55										10 55							11 55										
Mexborough		d	07 45	08 14	08 40	09 10							10 10										11 10							12 10										
Swinton (S.Yorks)		d	07 50	08 17	08 45	09a15	09 27					09 35	10a15							10 28			11a15						11 29	12a15	12 07									12 27
Rotherham Central		d	08 10	08 25	09 05		09 35					09 48								10 35									11 36		12 15									12 38
Meadowhall	🚊	d	08 20	08 30	09 15		09 40					09 54		10 10						10 41	10 40				11 20	11 20			11 42		12 24				12 20		12 25			12 43
Sheffield 7	🚊	a	08 40	08 41	09 35		09 51					10 03		10 30	10 41					10 52	11 00	11 39			11 40	11 40			11 53		12 32				12 40		12 45	12 54		12 54
		d																																						
Stockport	78	a																																						
Manchester Piccadilly 10	🚊	a								11 01																	12 54												13 54	
Manchester Airport	85 ✈	a																																						

A From Leeds
B To Plymouth
C From Newcastle to Reading
D From Bridlington
E From Edinburgh to Plymouth

For all trains between Cleethorpes, Grimsby Town, Habrough and Barnetby refer to Table 28

Table 29R

Sundays

5 January to 9 February

Hull - Doncaster - Meadowhall, Sheffield, Manchester and Manchester Airport

Network Diagram - refer to first Page of Table 18

		NT	NT	NT	TP	NT	TP	NT	XC	NT	NT	TP	NT	NT	NT	XC	NT	TP	NT	XC
							◇1		◇1			◇1				◇1				◇1
			A						B		A			C		B				D
		🚌			🚌	🚌			🍴				🚌		🚌	🍴		🚌		🍴
Hull	d		12 46				12 58			13 30	13 36								14 30	
Hessle	d										13 43									
Ferriby	d										13 48									
Brough	d		12 58				13 10			13 42	13 53								14 42	
Broomfleet	d																			
Gilberdyke	d		13 05								14 01									
Eastrington	d																			
Howden	d									13 54									14 54	
Wressle	d																			
Selby	a						13 28			14 03									15 03	
	d						13 29			14 04									15 04	
York 8 33	a									14 29									15 28	
Saltmarshe	d																			
Goole	d		13 14	13 43							14 09									
Thorne North	d			13 51																
Cleethorpes 28	d											13 26								
Grimsby Town 28	d											13 34								
Habrough 28	d																			
Barnetby 28	d											13 53								
Scunthorpe	a											14 08								
	d											14 08								
Althorpe	d																			
Crowle	d																			
Thorne South	d																			
Hatfield & Stainforth	d			13 57																
Kirk Sandall	d			14 02																
Adwick 31	d																			
Bentley (S.Yorks) 31	d																			
Doncaster 7 31	a		13 38	14 11							14 32	14 38								
London Kings Cross 15 ⊖26	a																			
York 8 26	d								12 40							13 40				14 34
Doncaster 7	d	12 35			12 55	12 56							13 40		13 45			14 10		
Conisbrough	d	12 55											14 00							
Mexborough	d	13 10											14 15							
Swinton (S.Yorks)	d	13a15						13 27					14a20	14 07			14 30			
Rotherham Central	d							13 36						14 15			14 43			
Meadowhall ⇌	d				13 25	13 26		13 44						14 21	14 15		14 48	14 40		
Sheffield 7 ⇌	a				13 45	13 46		13 51	13 53					14 32	14 35	14 52	14 59	15 00		15 21
	d																			
Stockport 78	a																			
Manchester Piccadilly 10 ⇌	a						14 54													
Manchester Airport 85 ✈	a																			

		HT	NT	NT	TP	NT	TP	XC	TP	NT	XC	NT	NT	NT	NT	TP	NT	TP	XC
		◇1			◇1			◇1	◇1		◇1					◇1			◇1
				E				F			G		C		A				F
		⊠	🚌			🚌	🚌	🍴			🍴	🚌					🚌	🚌	🍴
Hull	d	14 35		14 41					14 58						15 41				
Hessle	d																		
Ferriby	d																		
Brough	d	14 48		14 53					15 10						15 53				
Broomfleet	d																		
Gilberdyke	d			15 00											16 00				
Eastrington	d																		
Howden	d	15 00																	
Wressle	d																		
Selby	a	15 09							15 28										
	d	15 10							15 29										
York 8 33	a																		
Saltmarshe	d																		
Goole	d			15 09										15 43	16 09				
Thorne North	d													15 51					
Cleethorpes 28	d				14 26											15 26			
Grimsby Town 28	d				14 34											15 34			
Habrough 28	d				14 44														
Barnetby 28	d				14 53											15 53			
Scunthorpe	a				15 08											16 08			
	d				15 08											16 08			
Althorpe	d																		
Crowle	d																		
Thorne South	d																		
Hatfield & Stainforth	d													15 57					
Kirk Sandall	d													16 02					
Adwick 31	d																		
Bentley (S.Yorks) 31	d																		
Doncaster 7 31	a	15 27		15 32	15 39									16 11	16 32	16 39			
London Kings Cross 15 ⊖26	a	17 27																	
York 8 26	d							14 40			15 35								15 40
Doncaster 7	d		14 40			14 45	14 50					15 40					15 45	15 50	
Conisbrough	d		15 00									16 00							
Mexborough	d		15 15									16 15							
Swinton (S.Yorks)	d		15a20							15 30		16a20	16 08						
Rotherham Central	d									15 41			16 15						
Meadowhall ⇌	d					15 15	15 20			15 48			16 23				16 15	16 20	
Sheffield 7 ⇌	a					15 35	15 40	15 51		15 55	16 21		16 32				16 35	16 40	16 51
	d																		
Stockport 78	a																		
Manchester Piccadilly 10 ⇌	a								16 54										
Manchester Airport 85 ✈	a																		

A From Scarborough
B From Edinburgh to Reading
C From Leeds
D From Newcastle to Penzance
E From Bridlington
F From Glasgow Central to Reading
G From Newcastle to Plymouth

For all trains between Cleethorpes, Grimsby Town, Habrough and Barnetby refer to Table 28

Table 29R

Sundays

Hull - Doncaster - Meadowhall, Sheffield, Manchester and Manchester Airport

5 January to 9 February

Network Diagram - refer to first Page of Table 18

Station		NT	NT	XC	HT	NT	NT	TP	NT	TP	EM	XC	TP	NT	NT	XC	NT	NT	NT	NT
				◇1 A	◇1	bus	B	◇1	bus	bus	◇1 C	◇1 D	◇1			◇1 E	bus	F		G
Hull	d	16 02			16 35		16 41						16 58	17 25						17 41
Hessle	d																			
Ferriby	d																			
Brough	d	16 14			16 47		16 53						17 10	17 37						17 53
Broomfleet	d																			
Gilberdyke	d						17 00													18 00
Eastrington	d																			
Howden	d	16 26			16 59									17 49						
Wressle	d																			
Selby	a	16 35			17 09								17 28	17 58						
	d	16 37			17 10								17 29	17 59						
York 8	33 a	17 01												18 24						
Saltmarshe	d																			
Goole	d						17 09												17 41	18 09
Thorne North	d																		17 49	
Cleethorpes	28 d							16 26												
Grimsby Town	28 d							16 34												
Habrough	28 d																			
Barnetby	28 d							16 53												
Scunthorpe	a							17 08												
	d							17 08												
Althorpe	d																			
Crowle	d																			
Thorne South	d																			
Hatfield & Stainforth	d																		17 55	
Kirk Sandall	d																		18 00	
Adwick	31 d																			
Bentley (S.Yorks)	31 d																			
Doncaster 7	31 a				17 27		17 31	17 38											18 10	18 33
London Kings Cross 15	⊖26 a				19 25															
York 8	26 d			16 24							16 49	16 40				17 34				
Doncaster 7	d					16 40			16 45	16 50							17 40			
Conisbrough	d					17 00											18 00			
Mexborough	d					17 15											18 15			
Swinton (S.Yorks)	d		16 29			17a20									17 34		18a20	18 07		
Rotherham Central	d		16 41												17 42			18 17		
Meadowhall	d		16 47						17 15	17 20					17 48			18 25		
Sheffield 7	a		16 55	17 15					17 35	17 40	17 41	17 52			17 56	18 23		18 34		
	d																			
Stockport	78 a																			
Manchester Piccadilly 10	a												18 54							
Manchester Airport	85 a																			

Station		TP	NT	TP	XC	NT	XC	NT	NT	NT	NT	HT	TP	TP	XC	TP	NT	TP	NT	XC
		◇1	bus	bus	◇1 H		◇1 I	J	B	bus	bus	◇1	◇1	bus	◇1 K	◇1		◇1		◇1 I
Hull	d								18 38			18 45				18 58	19 25			
Hessle	d																			
Ferriby	d																			
Brough	d								18 50			18 58				19 10	19 37			
Broomfleet	d																			
Gilberdyke	d								18 57											
Eastrington	d																			
Howden	d											19 10					19 49			
Wressle	d																			
Selby	a											19 19				19 28	19 58			
	d											19 20				19 29	19 59			
York 8	33 a																20 25			
Saltmarshe	d																			
Goole	d								19 06											
Thorne North	d								19 14											
Cleethorpes	28 d	17 26											18 26					19 26		
Grimsby Town	28 d	17 34											18 34					19 34		
Habrough	28 d	17 44																		
Barnetby	28 d	17 53											18 53					19 53		
Scunthorpe	a	18 08											19 08					20 08		
	d	18 08											19 08					20 08		
Althorpe	d																			
Crowle	d																			
Thorne South	d																			
Hatfield & Stainforth	d								19 20											
Kirk Sandall	d								19 25											
Adwick	31 d																			
Bentley (S.Yorks)	31 d																			
Doncaster 7	31 a	18 38							19 35			19 38	19 40					20 40		
London Kings Cross 15	⊖26 a											21 34								
York 8	26 d				17 40		18 35	18 10							18 40					19 24
Doncaster 7	d		17 45	17 50						18 40	18 45			18 50						
Conisbrough	d									19 00										
Mexborough	d									19 15										
Swinton (S.Yorks)	d					18 32		19 01		19a20									19 33	
Rotherham Central	d					18 41		19 13											19 41	
Meadowhall	d		18 15	18 20		18 47		19 18			19 15			19 20					19 48	
Sheffield 7	a		18 35	18 40	18 51	18 56	19 21	19 30			19 35			19 40	19 50				19 56	20 14
	d																			
Stockport	78 a																			
Manchester Piccadilly 10	a															20 54				
Manchester Airport	85 a																			

A From Edinburgh to Plymouth
B From Bridlington
C To St Pancras International
D From Aberdeen to Reading
E From Newcastle to Plymouth
F From Leeds
G From Scarborough
H From Glasgow Central to Guildford
I From Newcastle to Bristol Temple Meads
J via Pontefract Baghill
K From Glasgow Central to Birmingham New Street

For all trains between Cleethorpes, Grimsby Town, Habrough and Barnetby refer to Table 28

Table 29R

Sundays

5 January to 9 February

Hull - Doncaster - Meadowhall, Sheffield, Manchester and Manchester Airport

Network Diagram - refer to first Page of Table 18

		NT	NT	NT	TP	XC	NT	NT	NT	XC	TP	NT	TP	NT	TP	XC	NT	NT	NT	TP	NT	NT	NT	NT
						◇1				◇1	◇1		◇1			◇1								
			A			B	C			D			E			F	G					A		
Hull	d						20 01					20 30	21 00						21 40					
Hessle	d						20 08																	
Ferriby	d						20 13																	
Brough	d						20 18					20 42	21 12						21 52					
Broomfleet	d																							
Gilberdyke	d						20 26												21 59					
Eastrington	d																							
Howden	d											20 54												
Wressle	d																							
Selby	a											21 03	21 30											
	d											21 04												
York 8 33	a											21 28												
Saltmarshe	d																							
Goole	d						20 34												22 08					
Thorne North	d						20 43												22 16					
Cleethorpes 28	d										20 26													
Grimsby Town 28	d										20 34													
Habrough 28	d										20 44													
Barnetby 28	d										20 53													
Scunthorpe	a										21 08													
	d										21 08													
Althorpe	d																							
Crowle	d																							
Thorne South	d																							
Hatfield & Stainforth	d																		22 20					
Kirk Sandall	d																		22 25					
Adwick 31	d																							
Bentley (S.Yorks) 31	d																							
Doncaster 7 31	a						20 59				21 40								22 37					
London Kings Cross 15 ⊖26	a																							
York 8 26	d					19 40				20 24						20 40	20 50							
Doncaster 7	d	19 40		19 45	19 50			20 25							20 50			21 10		21 50	22 05			22 51
Conisbrough	d	20 00						20 45										21 30			22 25			23 10
Mexborough	d	20 15						21 00										21 45			22 40			23 25
Swinton (S.Yorks)	d	20a20	20 11					21a05	20 33					21 15			21 45	21 50		22 10	22a45	22 29	22 53	23s30
Rotherham Central	d		20 18						20 42					21 22			21 52	22 10		22 25		22 38	22 58	23s50
Meadowhall ⇌	d		20 24	20 15	20 20				20 48					21 28	21 20		21 58	22 20		22 35		22 44	23 04	23s59
Sheffield 7 ⇌	a		20 34	20 35	20 40	20 51			20 56	21 17				21 38	21 40	21 50	22 09	22 40		22 55		22 52	23 15	00 20
	d																							
Stockport 78	a																							
Manchester Piccadilly 10 ⇌	a																							
Manchester Airport 85 ✈	a																							

A From Leeds
B From Edinburgh to Birmingham New Street
C From Scarborough
D From Newcastle to Birmingham New Street
E To Leeds
F From Glasgow Central to Birmingham New Street
G via Pontefract Baghill

For all trains between Cleethorpes, Grimsby Town, Habrough and Barnetby refer to Table 28

Table 29R

Sundays

16 February to 23 March

Hull - Doncaster - Meadowhall, Sheffield, Manchester and Manchester Airport

Network Diagram - refer to first Page of Table 18

Station			NT	NT	XC ◇1 A	NT B	NT	TP ◇1	NT	HT ◇1 ☒	TP 🚌	NT	NT	TP ◇1	XC ◇1 C	TP 🚌	TP ◇1
Hull		d					08 41	08 48	08 54	09 05			09 33				
Hessle		d											09 40				
Ferriby		d											09 45				
Brough		d					08 53	09 00	09 06	09 17			09 50				
Broomfleet		d															
Gilberdyke		d					09 01						09 58				
Eastrington		d															
Howden		d							09 18	09 29							
Wressle		d															
Selby		a						09 19	09 27	09 39							
		d						09 20	09 28	09 40							
York 8	33	a							09 52								
Saltmarshe		d															
Goole		d					09 09					09 43	10 06				
Thorne North		d										09 51	10 15				
Cleethorpes	28	d												09 26			10 26
Grimsby Town	28	d												09 34			10 34
Habrough	28	d												09 44			10 44
Barnetby	28	d												09 53			10 53
Scunthorpe		a												10 08			11 08
		d												10 08			11 08
Althorpe		d															
Crowle		d															
Thorne South		d															
Hatfield & Stainforth		d										09 57	10 21				
Kirk Sandall		d										10 02	10 25				
Adwick	31	d															
Bentley (S.Yorks)	31	d															
Doncaster 7	31	a					09 29			09 57		10 11	10 36	10 40			11 38
London Kings Cross 15	⊖26	a								12 02							
York 8	26	d													09 33		
Doncaster 7		d	08 03	09 13	09 32		09 39				10 10	10 13			10 30	10 50	
Conisbrough		d	08 10	09 20								10 20					
Mexborough		d	08 14	09 24								10 24					
Swinton (S.Yorks)		d	08 17	09 28		09 35						10 27					
Rotherham Central		d	08 25	09 35		09 48						10 35					
Meadowhall	🚊	d	08 30	09 41		09 54	10 00				10 40	10 40				11 20	
Sheffield 7	🚊	a	08 41	09 51	09 55	10 03	10 08				11 00	10 52			10 54	11 40	
		d															
Stockport	78	a															
Manchester Piccadilly 10	🚊	a						11 01									
Manchester Airport	85 ✈	a															

Station			NT	XC ◇1 D	NT E	TP ◇1 F	HT ◇1 ☒	NT	NT B	TP 🚌	XC ◇1 G	NT	TP ◇1	NT	TP ◇1 F	TP 🚌	NT	XC ◇1 H	NT I	TP ◇1 F	NT	NT B	XC ◇1 H	TP 🚌	NT
Hull		d			10 50	10 58	11 10	11 46						11 53	12 00				12 46	12 58	13 30				
Hessle		d																							
Ferriby		d																							
Brough		d			11 02	11 10	11 23	11 58						12 05	12 12				12 58	13 10	13 42				
Broomfleet		d																							
Gilberdyke		d			11 10									12 12					13 05						
Eastrington		d																							
Howden		d					11 34	12 10													13 54				
Wressle		d																							
Selby		a				11 28	11 44	12 19							12 31					13 28	14 03				
		d					11 45	12 20													14 04				
York 8	33	a						12 45													14 29				
Saltmarshe		d																							
Goole		d			11 18							11 43		12 21					13 14						13 43
Thorne North		d			11 27							11 51		12 29											13 51
Cleethorpes	28	d											11 26												
Grimsby Town	28	d											11 34												
Habrough	28	d																							
Barnetby	28	d											11 53												
Scunthorpe		a											12 08												
		d											12 08												
Althorpe		d																							
Crowle		d																							
Thorne South		d																							
Hatfield & Stainforth		d										11 57													13 57
Kirk Sandall		d										12 02													14 02
Adwick	31	d																							
Bentley (S.Yorks)	31	d																							
Doncaster 7	31	a			11 44		12 01					12 11	12 42	12 46					13 38						14 11
London Kings Cross 15	⊖26	a					14 05																		
York 8	26	d		10 33							11 40							12 40					13 40		
Doncaster 7		d	11 13	11 30	11 48					11 50		12 13				12 55	13 13		13 39					14 10	14 13
Conisbrough		d	11 20									12 20					13 20								14 20
Mexborough		d	11 24									12 24					13 24								14 24
Swinton (S.Yorks)		d	11 27						12 07			12 27					13 27					14 07			14 30
Rotherham Central		d	11 35						12 15			12 38					13 36					14 15			14 43
Meadowhall	🚊	d	11 40		12 08				12 24	12 20		12 43				13 25	13 44		13 57			14 21		14 40	14 48
Sheffield 7	🚊	a	11 51	11 53	12 18				12 32	12 40	12 54	12 55				13 45	13 51	13 53	14 08			14 32	14 52	15 00	14 56
		d																							
Stockport	78	a																							
Manchester Piccadilly 10	🚊	a																							
Manchester Airport	85 ✈	a																							

A From Leeds to Exeter St Davids
B From Leeds
C To Exeter St Davids
D From Newcastle to Reading
E From Bridlington
F To Leeds
G From Edinburgh to Exeter St Davids
H From Edinburgh to Reading
I From Scarborough

For all trains between Cleethorpes, Grimsby Town, Habrough and Barnetby refer to Table 28

Table 29R

Sundays

16 February to 23 March

Hull - Doncaster - Meadowhall, Sheffield, Manchester and Manchester Airport

Network Diagram - refer to first Page of Table 18

Station		NT A	TP ◇1	NT	HT ◇1 ⊠	TP 🚌	XC ◇1 B 🛒	XC ◇1 C 🛒	NT	NT D	TP ◇1	TP ◇1 E	TP 🚌	XC ◇1 B 🛒	NT F	XC ◇1 C 🛒	NT	NT A	TP ◇1
Hull	d	13 36		14 30	14 35					14 41		14 58						15 41	
Hessle	d	13 43																	
Ferriby	d	13 48																	
Brough	d	13 53		14 42	14 48					14 53		15 10						15 53	
Broomfleet	d																		
Gilberdyke	d	14 01								15 00								16 00	
Eastrington	d																		
Howden	d			14 54	15 00														
Wressle	d																		
Selby	a			15 03	15 09							15 28							
	d			15 04	15 10														
York 8 33	a			15 28															
Saltmarshe	d																		
Goole	d	14 09								15 09							15 43	16 09	
Thorne North	d																15 51		
Cleethorpes 28	d		13 26								14 26								15 26
Grimsby Town 28	d		13 34								14 34								15 34
Habrough 28	d										14 44								
Barnetby 28	d		13 53								14 53								15 53
Scunthorpe	a		14 08								15 08								16 08
	d		14 08								15 08								16 08
Althorpe	d																		
Crowle	d																		
Thorne South	d																		
Hatfield & Stainforth	d																15 57		
Kirk Sandall	d																16 02		
Adwick 31	d																		
Bentley (S.Yorks) 31	d																		
Doncaster 7 31	a	14 32	14 38		15 27					15 32	15 39						16 11	16 32	16 39
London Kings Cross 15 ⊖26	a				17 27														
York 8 26	d						14 34	14 40						15 35		15 40			
Doncaster 7	d	14 33				14 50	14 59		15 13	15 33			15 50	15 59			16 13	16 33	
Conisbrough	d								15 20								16 20		
Mexborough	d								15 24								16 24		
Swinton (S.Yorks)	d								15 30						16 10		16 29		
Rotherham Central	d								15 41						16 17		16 41		
Meadowhall 🚋	d	14 52				15 20			15 48	15 52			16 20		16 23		16 47	16 53	
Sheffield 7 🚋	a	15 04				15 40	15 21	15 51	15 55	16 03			16 40	16 21	16 32	16 51	16 55	17 03	
	d																		
Stockport 78	a																		
Manchester Piccadilly 10 🚋	a																		
Manchester Airport 85 ✈	a																		

Station		NT	HT ◇1 ⊠	TP 🚌	XC ◇1 G 🛒	XC ◇1 H 🛒	NT	NT D	TP ◇1	TP ◇1 E	NT	NT	TP 🚌	XC ◇1 B 🛒	NT F	EM ◇1 I ☕	XC ◇1 J 🛒	NT	NT A	TP ◇1
Hull	d	16 02	16 35					16 41		16 58	17 25								17 41	
Hessle	d																			
Ferriby	d																			
Brough	d	16 14	16 47					16 53		17 10	17 37								17 53	
Broomfleet	d																			
Gilberdyke	d							17 00											18 00	
Eastrington	d																			
Howden	d	16 26	16 59								17 49									
Wressle	d																			
Selby	a	16 35	17 09							17 28	17 58									
	d	16 37	17 10								17 59									
York 8 33	a	17 01									18 24									
Saltmarshe	d																			
Goole	d							17 09				17 41							18 09	
Thorne North	d											17 49								
Cleethorpes 28	d								16 26											17 26
Grimsby Town 28	d								16 34											17 34
Habrough 28	d																			17 44
Barnetby 28	d								16 53											17 53
Scunthorpe	a								17 08											18 08
	d								17 08											18 08
Althorpe	d																			
Crowle	d																			
Thorne South	d																			
Hatfield & Stainforth	d											17 55								
Kirk Sandall	d											18 00								
Adwick 31	d																			
Bentley (S.Yorks) 31	d																			
Doncaster 7 31	a		17 27					17 31	17 38			18 10							18 33	18 38
London Kings Cross 15 ⊖26	a		19 25																	
York 8 26	d				16 24	16 40								17 34		17 49	17 40			
Doncaster 7	d			16 50	16 52		17 18	17 32					17 50	17 59		18 13		18 18	18 34	
Conisbrough	d						17 26											18 25		
Mexborough	d						17 30											18 29		
Swinton (S.Yorks)	d						17 34								18 10			18 32		
Rotherham Central	d						17 42								18 17			18 41		
Meadowhall 🚋	d			17 20			17 48	17 53					18 20		18 25			18 47	18 53	
Sheffield 7 🚋	a			17 40	17 15	17 52	17 56	18 01					18 40	18 23	18 34	18 39	18 51	18 56	19 03	
	d																			
Stockport 78	a																			
Manchester Piccadilly 10 🚋	a																			
Manchester Airport 85 ✈	a																			

A From Scarborough
B From Newcastle to Exeter St Davids
C From Glasgow Central to Reading
D From Bridlington
E To Leeds
F From Leeds
G From Edinburgh to Exeter St Davids
H From Aberdeen to Reading
I To St Pancras International
J From Glasgow Central to Guildford

For all trains between Cleethorpes, Grimsby Town, Habrough and Barnetby refer to Table 28

Table 29R

Sundays

16 February to 23 March

Hull - Doncaster - Meadowhall, Sheffield, Manchester and Manchester Airport

Network Diagram - refer to first Page of Table 18

		TP	XC	NT	XC	NT	NT	HT	TP	TP	NT	TP	TP	XC	NT	XC		NT	TP	XC	NT	TP	NT	XC	NT	TP	TP	NT	NT
			◇1		◇1			◇1	◇1	◇1		◇1		◇1		◇1				◇1		◇1		◇1		◇1			
			A	B	C		D			E				A	F	G				H	I			C	B	E		F	
		bus											bus						bus								bus		
			trolley		trolley			⊠						trolley															
Hull	d						18 38	18 45		18 58	19 25										20 01		20 30			21 00			21 40
Hessle	d																				20 08								
Ferriby	d																				20 13								
Brough	d						18 50	18 58		19 10	19 37										20 18		20 42			21 12			21 52
Broomfleet	d																												
Gilberdyke	d						18 57														20 26								21 59
Eastrington	d																												
Howden	d							19 10			19 49												20 54						
Wressle	d																												
Selby	a							19 19		19 28	19 58												21 03			21 30			
	d							19 20			19 59												21 04						
York 8	33 a										20 25												21 28						
Saltmarshe	d																												
Goole	d						19 06														20 34								22 08
Thorne North	d						19 14														20 43								22 16
Cleethorpes	28 d								18 26			19 26										20 26							
Grimsby Town	28 d								18 34			19 34										20 34							
Habrough	28 d																					20 44							
Barnetby	28 d								18 53			19 53										20 53							
Scunthorpe	a								19 08			20 08										21 08							
	d								19 08			20 08										21 08							
Althorpe	d																												
Crowle	d																												
Thorne South	d																												
Hatfield & Stainforth	d						19 20																						22 20
Kirk Sandall	d						19 25																						22 25
Adwick	31 d																												
Bentley (S.Yorks)	31 d																												
Doncaster 7	31 a						19 35	19 38	19 40			20 40									20 59	21 40							22 37
London Kings Cross 15	⊖26 a							21 34																					
York 8	26 d		18 35	18 10	18 40									19 24		19 40				20 24				20 40	20 50				
Doncaster 7	d	18 50	18 59			19 18	19 37						19 50	19 52				20 18	20 50	20 51	21 01						21 50		22 40
Conisbrough	d					19 25												20 25			21 08								22 47
Mexborough	d					19 29												20 30			21 12								22 51
Swinton (S.Yorks)	d			19 01		19 33									20 09			20 33			21 15				21 45		22 10	22 29	22 53
Rotherham Central	d			19 13		19 41									20 17			20 42			21 22				21 52		22 25	22 38	22 58
Meadowhall	tram d	19 20		19 18		19 48	19 57						20 20		20 23			20 48	21 20		21 28				21 58		22 35	22 44	23 04
Sheffield 7	tram a	19 40	19 21	19 27	19 50	19 56	20 07						20 40	20 16	20 34	20 51		20 56	21 40	21 17	21 38			21 50	22 09		22 55	22 52	23 15
	d																												
Stockport	78 a																												
Manchester Piccadilly 10	tram a																												
Manchester Airport	85 ✈ a																												

A From Newcastle to Bristol Temple Meads
B via Pontefract Baghill
C From Glasgow Central to Birmingham New Street
D From Bridlington
E To Leeds
F From Leeds
G From Edinburgh to Birmingham New Street
H From Newcastle to Birmingham New Street
I From Scarborough

For all trains between Cleethorpes, Grimsby Town, Habrough and Barnetby refer to Table 28

Table 29R

Sundays

30 March to 11 May

Hull - Doncaster - Meadowhall, Sheffield, Manchester and Manchester Airport

Network Diagram - refer to first Page of Table 18

Station		NT	NT	XC	NT	NT	NT	TP	HT	NT	NT	XC	TP	NT	XC	TP
				◇1				◇1	◇1			◇1	◇1		◇1	◇1
				A	B							C			D	
				trolley					☒			trolley			trolley	
Hull	d					08 41	08 54	09 00	09 05		09 33					
Hessle	d										09 40					
Ferriby	d										09 45					
Brough	d					08 53	09 06	09 12	09 17		09 50					
Broomfleet	d															
Gilberdyke	d					09 01					09 58					
Eastrington	d															
Howden	d						09 18		09 29							
Wressle	d															
Selby	a						09 27	09 32	09 39							
	d						09 28	09 33	09 40							
York 8 33	a						09 52									
Saltmarshe	d															
Goole	d					09 09				09 43	10 06					
Thorne North	d									09 51	10 15					
Cleethorpes 28	d												09 26			10 26
Grimsby Town 28	d												09 34			10 34
Habrough 28	d												09 44			10 44
Barnetby 28	d												09 53			10 53
Scunthorpe	a												10 08			11 08
	d												10 08			11 08
Althorpe	d															
Crowle	d															
Thorne South	d															
Hatfield & Stainforth	d									09 57	10 21					
Kirk Sandall	d									10 02	10 25					
Adwick 31	d															
Bentley (S.Yorks) 31	d															
Doncaster 7 31	a					09 29			09 57	10 11	10 36		10 40			11 38
London Kings Cross 15 ⊖26	a								11 42							
York 8 26	d											09 33			10 33	
Doncaster 7	d	08 03	09 13	09 32		09 39				10 13		10 30	10 42	11 13	11 30	11 42
Conisbrough	d	08 10	09 20							10 20				11 20		
Mexborough	d	08 14	09 24							10 24				11 24		
Swinton (S.Yorks)	d	08 17	09 28		09 35					10 27				11 27		
Rotherham Central	d	08 25	09 35		09 48					10 35				11 35		
Meadowhall ⇌	d	08 30	09 41		09 54	10 00				10 40			11 00	11 40		12 00
Sheffield 7 ⇌	a	08 41	09 51	09 55	10 03	10 08				10 52		10 54	11 07	11 51	11 53	12 07
	d												11 10			12 10
Stockport 78	a												11 53			12 52
Manchester Piccadilly 10 ⇌	a							11 01					12 06			13 07
Manchester Airport 85 ✈	a												12 27			13 28

Station		NT	TP	HT	NT	NT	XC	NT	TP	NT	NT	TP	XC	NT	TP	NT
			◇1	◇1			◇1		◇1			◇1	◇1		◇1	
		E				B	F						G	H		
				☒			trolley						trolley			
Hull	d	10 50	10 58	11 10	11 46						11 53	12 00		12 46	12 58	13 30
Hessle	d															
Ferriby	d															
Brough	d	11 02	11 10	11 23	11 58						12 05	12 12		12 58	13 10	13 42
Broomfleet	d															
Gilberdyke	d	11 10									12 12			13 05		
Eastrington	d															
Howden	d			11 34	12 10											13 54
Wressle	d															
Selby	a		11 28	11 44	12 19							12 31			13 28	14 03
	d		11 29	11 45	12 20							12 31			13 29	14 04
York 8 33	a				12 45											14 29
Saltmarshe	d															
Goole	d	11 18						11 43			12 21			13 14		
Thorne North	d	11 27						11 51			12 29					
Cleethorpes 28	d								11 26							
Grimsby Town 28	d								11 34							
Habrough 28	d															
Barnetby 28	d								11 53							
Scunthorpe	a								12 08							
	d								12 08							
Althorpe	d															
Crowle	d															
Thorne South	d															
Hatfield & Stainforth	d							11 57								
Kirk Sandall	d							12 02								
Adwick 31	d															
Bentley (S.Yorks) 31	d															
Doncaster 7 31	a	11 44		12 03				12 11	12 40		12 46			13 38		
London Kings Cross 15 ⊖26	a			13 46												
York 8 26	d						11 40						12 40			
Doncaster 7	d	11 48						12 13	12 42	13 13				13 39		
Conisbrough	d							12 20		13 20						
Mexborough	d							12 24		13 24						
Swinton (S.Yorks)	d					12 07		12 27		13 27						
Rotherham Central	d					12 15		12 38		13 36						
Meadowhall ⇌	d	12 08				12 24		12 43	13 00	13 44				13 57		
Sheffield 7 ⇌	a	12 18				12 32	12 54	12 55	13 07	13 51			13 53	14 08		
	d								13 10							
Stockport 78	a								13 53							
Manchester Piccadilly 10 ⇌	a		12 54						14 06			13 54			14 54	
Manchester Airport 85 ✈	a								14 27							

Station		TP	NT	XC	NT	NT	TP	NT	XC
		◇1		◇1			◇1		◇1
			B	F		H			I
				trolley					trolley
Hull	d					13 36		14 30	
Hessle	d					13 43			
Ferriby	d					13 48			
Brough	d					13 53		14 42	
Broomfleet	d								
Gilberdyke	d					14 01			
Eastrington	d								
Howden	d							14 54	
Wressle	d								
Selby	a							15 03	
	d							15 04	
York 8 33	a							15 28	
Saltmarshe	d								
Goole	d				13 43	14 09			
Thorne North	d				13 51				
Cleethorpes 28	d						13 26		
Grimsby Town 28	d						13 34		
Habrough 28	d								
Barnetby 28	d						13 53		
Scunthorpe	a						14 08		
	d						14 08		
Althorpe	d								
Crowle	d								
Thorne South	d								
Hatfield & Stainforth	d				13 57				
Kirk Sandall	d				14 02				
Adwick 31	d								
Bentley (S.Yorks) 31	d								
Doncaster 7 31	a				14 11	14 32	14 37		
London Kings Cross 15 ⊖26	a								
York 8 26	d			13 40					14 34
Doncaster 7	d	13 43			14 13	14 33	14 42		14 59
Conisbrough	d				14 20				
Mexborough	d				14 24				
Swinton (S.Yorks)	d		14 07		14 30				
Rotherham Central	d		14 15		14 43				
Meadowhall ⇌	d	14 00	14 21		14 48	14 52	15 00		
Sheffield 7 ⇌	a	14 07	14 32	14 52	14 56	15 04	15 07		15 21
	d	14 11					15 11		
Stockport 78	a	14 53					15 53		
Manchester Piccadilly 10 ⇌	a	15 06					16 06		
Manchester Airport 85 ✈	a	15 28					16 34		

A From Leeds to Plymouth
B From Leeds
C To Plymouth
D From Newcastle to Plymouth
E From Bridlington
F From Edinburgh to Plymouth
G From Edinburgh to Penzance
H From Scarborough
I From Newcastle to Reading

For all trains between Cleethorpes, Grimsby Town, Habrough and Barnetby refer to Table 28

Table 29R

Sundays

30 March to 11 May

Hull - Doncaster - Meadowhall, Sheffield, Manchester and Manchester Airport

Network Diagram - refer to first Page of Table 18

	HT	XC	NT	NT	TP	TP	XC	NT	XC	NT	NT	TP
	◇1	◇1			◇1	◇1	◇1		◇1			◇1
	⊠	A ⌶		B			C ⌶	D	E ⌶		F	
Hull d	14 35			14 41	14 58						15 41	
Hessle d												
Ferriby d												
Brough d	14 48			14 53	15 10						15 53	
Broomfleet d												
Gilberdyke d				15 00							16 00	
Eastrington d												
Howden d	15 00											
Wressle d												
Selby a	15 09				15 28							
d	15 10				15 29							
York 8 33 a												
Saltmarshe d												
Goole d				15 09						15 43	16 09	
Thorne North d										15 51		
Cleethorpes 28 d						14 26						15 26
Grimsby Town 28 d						14 34						15 34
Habrough 28 d						14 44						
Barnetby 28 d						14 53						15 53
Scunthorpe a						15 08						16 08
d						15 08						16 08
Althorpe d												
Crowle d												
Thorne South d												
Hatfield & Stainforth d										15 57		
Kirk Sandall d										16 02		
Adwick 31 d												
Bentley (S.Yorks) 31 d												
Doncaster 7 31 a	15 28			15 32		15 39				16 11	16 32	16 39
London Kings Cross 15 ⊖26 a	17 14											
York 8 26 d		14 40					15 35		15 41			
Doncaster 7 d			15 13	15 33		15 42	15 59			16 13	16 33	16 42
Conisbrough d			15 20							16 20		
Mexborough d			15 24							16 24		
Swinton (S.Yorks) d			15 30					16 10		16 29		
Rotherham Central d			15 41					16 17		16 41		
Meadowhall d			15 48	15 52		16 00		16 23		16 47	16 53	17 00
Sheffield 7 a		15 51	15 55	16 03		16 07	16 21	16 32	16 51	16 55	17 03	17 07
d						16 11						17 11
Stockport 78 a						16 53						17 53
Manchester Piccadilly 10 a					16 54	17 06						18 06
Manchester Airport 85 a						17 27						18 27

	NT	XC	HT	XC	NT	NT	TP	TP	NT	XC	NT	NT
		◇1	◇1	◇1			◇1	◇1		◇1		
		G ⌶	⊠	H ⌶		B				C ⌶		D
Hull d	16 02		16 35			16 41	16 58		17 25			
Hessle d												
Ferriby d												
Brough d	16 14		16 47			16 53	17 10		17 37			
Broomfleet d												
Gilberdyke d						17 00						
Eastrington d												
Howden d	16 26		16 59						17 49			
Wressle d												
Selby a	16 35		17 09				17 28		17 58			
d	16 37		17 10				17 29		17 59			
York 8 33 a	17 01								18 24			
Saltmarshe d												
Goole d						17 09					17 41	
Thorne North d											17 49	
Cleethorpes 28 d								16 26				
Grimsby Town 28 d								16 34				
Habrough 28 d												
Barnetby 28 d								16 53				
Scunthorpe a								17 08				
d								17 08				
Althorpe d												
Crowle d												
Thorne South d												
Hatfield & Stainforth d											17 55	
Kirk Sandall d											18 00	
Adwick 31 d												
Bentley (S.Yorks) 31 d												
Doncaster 7 31 a			17 28			17 31		17 38			18 10	
London Kings Cross 15 ⊖26 a			19 18									
York 8 26 d		16 24		16 40						17 34		
Doncaster 7 d		16 52			17 18	17 32		17 42		17 59		
Conisbrough d					17 26							
Mexborough d					17 30							
Swinton (S.Yorks) d					17 34							18 10
Rotherham Central d					17 42							18 17
Meadowhall d					17 48	17 53		18 00				18 25
Sheffield 7 a		17 15		17 52	17 56	18 01		18 07		18 23		18 34
d								18 11				
Stockport 78 a								18 53				
Manchester Piccadilly 10 a							18 54	19 06				
Manchester Airport 85 a								19 27				

	EM	XC	NT	NT	TP	XC	NT	XC	NT	NT	HT	TP	TP
	◇1	◇1			◇1	◇1		◇1			◇1	◇1	◇1
	I	E ⌶		F		J ⌶	K	L ⌶		B	⊠		
Hull d				17 41						18 38	18 45	18 58	
Hessle d													
Ferriby d													
Brough d				17 53						18 50	18 58	19 10	
Broomfleet d													
Gilberdyke d				18 00						18 57			
Eastrington d													
Howden d											19 10		
Wressle d													
Selby a											19 19	19 28	
d											19 20	19 29	
York 8 33 a													
Saltmarshe d													
Goole d				18 09						19 06			
Thorne North d										19 14			
Cleethorpes 28 d					17 26								18 26
Grimsby Town 28 d					17 34								18 34
Habrough 28 d					17 44								
Barnetby 28 d					17 53								18 53
Scunthorpe a					18 08								19 08
d					18 08								19 08
Althorpe d													
Crowle d													
Thorne South d													
Hatfield & Stainforth d										19 20			
Kirk Sandall d										19 25			
Adwick 31 d													
Bentley (S.Yorks) 31 d													
Doncaster 7 31 a				18 33	18 38					19 35	19 38		19 40
London Kings Cross 15 ⊖26 a											21 21		
York 8 26 d	17 49	17 40				18 35	18 10	18 40					
Doncaster 7 d	18 13		18 18	18 34	18 42	18 59			19 18	19 37			19 42
Conisbrough d			18 25						19 25				
Mexborough d			18 29						19 29				
Swinton (S.Yorks) d			18 32				19 01		19 33				
Rotherham Central d			18 41				19 13		19 41				
Meadowhall d			18 47	18 53	19 00		19 18		19 48	19 57			20 00
Sheffield 7 a	18 39	18 51	18 56	19 03	19 07	19 21	19 27	19 50	19 56	20 07			20 07
d					19 11								20 11
Stockport 78 a					19 53								20 53
Manchester Piccadilly 10 a					20 09							20 54	21 06
Manchester Airport 85 a					20 30								21 27

A From Glasgow Central to Penzance
B From Bridlington
C From Newcastle to Reading
D From Leeds
E From Glasgow Central to Plymouth
F From Scarborough
G From Edinburgh to Reading
H From Aberdeen to Plymouth
I To St Pancras International
J From Newcastle to Guildford
K via Pontefract Baghill
L From Glasgow Central to Bristol Temple Meads

For all trains between Cleethorpes, Grimsby Town, Habrough and Barnetby refer to Table 28

Table 29R

Sundays

30 March to 11 May

Hull - Doncaster - Meadowhall, Sheffield, Manchester and Manchester Airport

Network Diagram - refer to first Page of Table 18

		XC	NT	NT	XC	NT	TP	XC	NT	NT	XC	NT	TP	TP	NT	NT
		◇1			◇1		◇1	◇1			◇1		◇1	◇1		
		A		B	C			A	D		E	F		G	B	
		✠														
Hull	d		19 25						20 01	20 30				21 00		21 40
Hessle	d								20 08							
Ferriby	d								20 13							
Brough	d		19 37						20 18	20 42				21 12		21 52
Broomfleet	d															
Gilberdyke	d								20 26							21 59
Eastrington	d															
Howden	d		19 49							20 54						
Wressle	d															
Selby	a		19 58							21 03				21 30		
	d		19 59							21 04						
York 8 33	a		20 25							21 28						
Saltmarshe	d															
Goole	d								20 34							22 08
Thorne North	d								20 43							22 16
Cleethorpes 28	d						19 26						20 26			
Grimsby Town 28	d						19 34						20 34			
Habrough 28	d												20 44			
Barnetby 28	d						19 53						20 53			
Scunthorpe	a						20 08						21 08			
	d						20 08						21 08			
Althorpe	d															
Crowle	d															
Thorne South	d															
Hatfield & Stainforth	d															22 20
Kirk Sandall	d															22 25
Adwick 31	d															
Bentley (S.Yorks) 31	d															
Doncaster 7 31	a						20 40		20 59				21 40			22 37
London Kings Cross 15 ⊖26	a															
York 8 26	d	19 24			19 40			20 24			20 40	20 50				
Doncaster 7	d	19 52				20 18	20 42	20 51	21 01				21 42			22 40
Conisbrough	d					20 25			21 08							22 47
Mexborough	d					20 30			21 12							22 51
Swinton (S.Yorks)	d			20 09		20 33			21 15			21 45	21 53		22 29	22 53
Rotherham Central	d			20 17		20 42			21 22			21 52	21 59		22 38	22 58
Meadowhall 🚋	d			20 23		20 48	21 00		21 28			21 58	22 05		22 44	23 04
Sheffield 7 🚋	a	20 16		20 34	20 51	20 56	21 07	21 17	21 38		21 50	22 09	22 13		22 52	23 15
	d						21 11									
Stockport 78	a						21 53									
Manchester Piccadilly 10 🚋	a						22 06									
Manchester Airport 85 ✈	a						22 28									

A From Newcastle to Birmingham New Street
B From Leeds
C From Edinburgh to Bristol Temple Meads
D From Scarborough
E From Glasgow Central to Birmingham New Street
F via Pontefract Baghill
G To Leeds

For all trains between Cleethorpes, Grimsby Town, Habrough and Barnetby refer to Table 28

Table 30

Mondays to Fridays

9 December to 16 May

Lincoln and Retford - Sheffield

Network Diagram - refer to first Page of Table 18

Miles			NT	NT	NT	NT	NT	NT	NT	NT	NT	NT	NT	NT	NT	NT	NT	NT	NT	NT	NT FX	NT FO	NT	NT
									◇	◇	◇	◇	◇	◇	◇	◇		◇	◇	◇			◇	
			A	A		B	B	B	B	B		B	B	B	C		D							
0	**Lincoln**	18 d			07 00		08 25	09 25	10 25	11 25	12 27	13 26	14 25	15 24	16 25	17 22		18 24	19 43	20 27			21 27	
6	Saxilby	18 d			07 10		08 34	09 34	10 34	11 34	12 36	13 35	14 34	15 33	16 35	17 31		18 33	19 52	20 36			21 36	
15½	Gainsborough Lea Road	18 d			07 22		08 48	09 48	10 48	11 48	12 49	13 48	14 48	15 48	16 48	17 44		18 46	20 05	20 49			21 49	
25	**Retford Low Level** 10	a			07 36		09 02	10 02	11 02	12 02	13 03	14 02	15 02	16 02	17 02	17 58		19 04	20 18	21 03			22 03	
—		d		07b03	07 40		09 02	10 02	11 02	12 02	13 03	14 02	15 02	16 02	17 02	17 58	18 14	19 04	20 19	21 03			22 03	22b45
32¾	Worksop	d	06 30	07 16	07 52	08 14	09 14	10 14	11 14	12 14	13 15	14 14	15 14	16 14	17 14	18 10	18 25	19 16	20 31	21 15	21 26	21 26	22 15	22 58
34¾	Shireoaks	d	06 33	07 20	07 55	08 19	09 18	10 18	11 18	12 18	13 19	14 18	15 18	16 18	17 18		18 29	19 20	20 35		21 30	21 31	22 19	23 02
37¾	Kiveton Park	d	06 39	07 25	08 01	08 25	09 24	10 24	11 24	12 24	13 25	14 24	15 24	16 24	17 24		18 34	19 26	20 41	21 23	21 36	21 37	22 25	23 08
39	Kiveton Bridge	d	06 42	07 28	08 04	08 28	09 27	10 27	11 27	12 27	13 28	14 27	15 27	16 27	17 27		18 37	19 29	20 44		21 39	21 40	22 28	23 11
43¼	Woodhouse	d	06 48	07 35	08 10	08 34	09 33	10 33	11 33	12 33	13 34	14 33	15 33	16 33	17 33		18 43	19 35	20 50		21 46	21 50	22 34	23 17
46¼	Darnall	d	06 53	07 40	08 15	08 39	09 38	10 38	11 38	12 38	13 39	14 38	15 38	16 38	17 38		18 48	19 40	20 55		21 51	21 55	22 39	23 22
48½	**Sheffield** 7	a	07 02	07 48	08 24	08 48	09 47	10 47	11 47	12 48	13 48	14 48	15 48	16 48	17 49	18 35	18 57	19 54	21 05	21 41	22 04	22 04	22 50	23 33
—	Meadowhall	34 a	07 11	07 57		08 59	09 58	10 58	11 58	12 58		14 58	15 58	16 58	17 58		19 06							

		NT
Lincoln	18 d	
Saxilby	18 d	
Gainsborough Lea Road	18 d	
Retford Low Level 10	a	
	d	
Worksop	d	23 28
Shireoaks	d	23 32
Kiveton Park	d	23 38
Kiveton Bridge	d	23 41
Woodhouse	d	23 52
Darnall	d	23 57
Sheffield 7	a	00 04
Meadowhall	34 a	

A To Leeds
B To Adwick
C To Hull
D To Doncaster
b Retford

For connections from London Kings Cross please see Table 26

Table 30

Saturdays

14 December to 17 May

Lincoln and Retford - Sheffield

Network Diagram - refer to first Page of Table 18

			NT	NT	NT	NT		NT	NT	NT	NT	NT	NT	NT	NT	NT	NT	NT	NT	NT	NT	NT	NT
												◇	◇										
				A		B		B	C	B	B	B	B	C	D		E		C				
Cleethorpes	29	d							11 10					15 20					18 38				
Grimsby Town	29	d							11 17					15 27					18 45				
Habrough	29	d							11 28					15 37					18 55				
Barnetby	29	d							11 38					15 48					19 04				
Brigg		d							11 44					15 53					19 10				
Kirton Lindsey		d							11 53					16 02					19 19				
Gainsborough Central		d					and		12 20					16 20					19 37				
Lincoln	18	d			07 00	08 25	hourly	11 25		12 27	13 25	14 25	15 24		16 25	17 22		18 24		19 43	20 27		21 27
Saxilby	18	d			07 10	08 34	until	11 34		12 36	13 34	14 34	15 33		16 35	17 31		18 33		19 52	20 36		21 36
Gainsborough Lea Road	18	d			07 22	08 48		11 48		12 49	13 48	14 48	15 48		16 48	17 44		18 46		20 05	20 49		21 49
Retford Low Level 10		a			07 36	09 02		12 02	12 35	13 03	14 02	15 02	16 02	16 35	17 02	17 58		19 04	19 53	20 16	21 03		22 03
		d		07b03	07 40	09 02		12 02	12 35	13 03	14 02	15 02	16 02	16 35	17 02	17 58	18 14	19 04	19 53	20 18	21 03		22 03
Worksop		d	06 30	07 16	07 52	09 14		12 14	12 47	13 15	14 14	15 14	16 14	16 47	17 14	18 10	18 25	19 16	20 04	20 31	21 15	21 26	22 15
Shireoaks		d	06 33	07 20	07 55	09 18		12 18	12 51	13 19	14 18	15 18	16 18	16 51	17 18		18 29	19 20	20 08	20 35		21 31	22 19
Kiveton Park		d	06 39	07 25	08 01	09 24		12 24	12 57	13 25	14 24	15 24	16 24	16 57	17 24		18 34	19 26	20 12	20 41	21 23	21 37	22 25
Kiveton Bridge		d	06 42	07 28	08 04	09 27		12 27	13 00	13 28	14 27	15 27	16 27	17 00	17 27		18 37	19 29	20 17	20 44		21 40	22 28
Woodhouse		d	06 48	07 35	08 10	09 33		12 33	13 06	13 34	14 33	15 33	16 33	17 06	17 33		18 43	19 35	20 23	20 50		21 46	22 34
Darnall		d	06 53	07 40	08 15	09 38		12 38	13 11	13 39	14 38	15 38	16 38	17 11	17 38		18 48	19 40	20 28	20 55		21 51	22 39
Sheffield 7		a	07 02	07 48	08 24	09 48		12 48	13 23	13 48	14 48	15 48	16 48	17 23	17 49	18 35	18 57	19 54	20 36	21 05	21 46	22 00	22 50
Meadowhall	34	a		07 57		09 58		12 58		13 58	14 58	15 58	16 58		17 58		19 06						

			NT	NT
Cleethorpes	29	d		
Grimsby Town	29	d		
Habrough	29	d		
Barnetby	29	d		
Brigg		d		
Kirton Lindsey		d		
Gainsborough Central		d		
Lincoln	18	d		
Saxilby	18	d		
Gainsborough Lea Road	18	d		
Retford Low Level 10		a		
		d	22b45	
Worksop		d	22 58	23 28
Shireoaks		d	23 02	23 32
Kiveton Park		d	23 08	23 38
Kiveton Bridge		d	23 11	23 41
Woodhouse		d	23 17	23 47
Darnall		d	23 22	23 52
Sheffield 7		a	23 32	00 03
Meadowhall	34	a		

Sundays

8 December to 11 May

			NT	NT	NT	NT	NT	NT
			F	A				
Cleethorpes	29	d						
Grimsby Town	29	d						
Habrough	29	d						
Barnetby	29	d						
Brigg		d						
Kirton Lindsey		d						
Gainsborough Central		d						
Lincoln	18	d		15 15	17 15	19 15	21 10	
Saxilby	18	d		15 25	17 25	19 25	21 20	
Gainsborough Lea Road	18	d		15 37	17 37	19 37	21 32	
Retford Low Level 10		a		15 51	17 51	19 51	21 46	
		d	14 50	15 51	17 51	19 51	21 46	22 24
Worksop		d	15 01	16 03	18 03	20 03	21 58	22 35
Shireoaks		d	15 05	16 06	18 06	20 06	22 01	22 39
Kiveton Park		d	15 10	16 12	18 12	20 12	22 07	22 44
Kiveton Bridge		d	15 13	16 15	18 15	20 15	22 10	22 47
Woodhouse		d	15 19	16 21	18 21	20 21	22 16	22 53
Darnall		d	15 24	16 26	18 26	20 26	22 21	22 58
Sheffield 7		a	15 33	16 36	18 35	20 35	22 29	23 07
Meadowhall	34	a	15 42	16 44				

A To Leeds
B To Adwick
C via Retford
D To Hull
E To Doncaster
F To Huddersfield
b Retford

For connections from London Kings Cross please see Table 26

Table 30R

Mondays to Fridays

9 December to 16 May

Sheffield - Retford and Lincoln

Network Diagram - refer to first Page of Table 18

Miles			NT	NT	NT	NT	NT	NT	NT	NT	NT	NT	NT	NT	NT	NT	NT	NT	NT	NT	NT	NT	NT
							A		B	B	◇ B	◇ B	◇ B	◇ B	◇ B	◇ B	C	◇ B	◇	◇	A	D	
—	Meadowhall	34 d					07 33		09 33	10 33	11 33	12 33	13 33	14 33	15 33	16 33	16 57	17 33			20 33	21 31	
0	**Sheffield** 7	d	05 39	05 46	06 43	07 30	07 44	08 44	09 44	10 44	11 44	12 44	13 44	14 44	15 44	16 44	17 24	17 44	18 45	19 48	20 45	21 44	22 44
2¼	Darnall	d		05 51	06 48	07 35		08 49	09 49	10 49	11 49	12 49	13 49	14 50	15 49	16 49	17 30	17 49	18 50	19 53	20 50	21 50	22 49
5¼	Woodhouse	d		05 56	06 53	07 40		08 54	09 54	10 54	11 54	12 54	13 54	14 55	15 54	16 54	17 35	17 54	18 55	19 58	20 55	21 55	22 54
9½	Kiveton Bridge	d		06 03	07 00	07 47		09 01	10 01	11 01	12 01	13 01	14 01	15 02	16 01	17 01	17 41	18 04	19 03	20 05	21 02	22 01	23 01
10¾	Kiveton Park	d	05 54	06 06	07 03	07 50	07 59	09 04	10 04	11 04	12 04	13 04	14 04	15 05	16 04	17 04	17 44	18 07	19 06	20 08	21 05	22 04	23 04
13¾	Shireoaks	d		06 11	07 08	07 55		09 09	10 09	11 09	12 09	13 09	14 09	15 09	16 09	17 09	17 49	18 12	19 11	20 13	21 10	22 08	23 09
15¾	Worksop	d	06 01	06 23	07 14	08 00	08a10	09 14	10 14	11 14	12 14	13 14	14 14	15 14	16 14	17 14	17 53	18 17	19 16	20 18	21a21	22 15	23a21
23½	**Retford Low Level** 10	a	06 10	06b38	07 23	08 09		09 23	10 24	11 23	12 23	13 23	14 23	15 24	16 23	17 23	18 06	18 26	19 25	20 27		22b29	
—		d	06 11		07 24	08 10		09 24	10 24	11 24	12 24	13 24	14 24	15 24	16 24	17 24		18 27	19 26	20 28			
33	Gainsborough Lea Road	18 d	06 25		07 38	08 24		09 38	10 38	11 38	12 38	13 41	14 38	15 39	16 38	17 38		18 40	19 39	20 42			
42½	Saxilby	18 d	06 38		07 51	08 37		09 51	10 51	11 51	12 51	13 54	14 51	15 52	16 51	17 51		18 53	19 52	20 55			
48½	**Lincoln**	18 a	06 53		08 06	08 52		10 06	11 06	12 06	13 06	14 07	15 06	16 10	17 06	18 06		19 07	20 06	21 10			

A From Doncaster
B From Scunthorpe
C From Adwick
D From Huddersfield
b Retford

For connections to London Kings Cross please see Table 26

Table 30

Sheffield - Retford and Lincoln

Saturdays

14 December to 17 May

Network Diagram - refer to first Page of Table 18

		NT	NT	NT	NT	NT	NT	NT	NT	NT	NT	NT	NT	NT	NT	NT	NT	NT	NT	NT	NT	NT	NT
						A		B	B	B	A	B	B	B	◇ B	A	B	C	B	B		B	D
Meadowhall	34 d							09 33	10 33	11 33		12 33	13 33	14 33	15 33		16 33	16 57	17 33	18 33		20 33	21 31
Sheffield 7	d	05 39	05 46	06 44	07 30	08 03	08 44	09 44	10 44	11 44	12 00	12 44	13 44	14 44	15 44	16 00	16 44	17 24	17 44	18 45	19 48	20 45	21 44
Darnall	d		05 51	06 49	07 35	08 08	08 49	09 49	10 49	11 49	12 05	12 49	13 49	14 49	15 49	16 05	16 49	17 30	17 49	18 50	19 53	20 50	21 49
Woodhouse	d		05 56	06 54	07 40	08 13	08 54	09 54	10 54	11 54	12 10	12 54	13 54	14 54	15 54	16 10	16 54	17 35	17 54	18 55	19 58	20 55	21 54
Kiveton Bridge	d		06 03	07 01	07 47	08 20	09 01	10 01	11 01	12 01	12 17	13 01	14 01	15 01	16 01	16 17	17 01	17 41	18 04	19 02	20 05	21 02	22 01
Kiveton Park	d	05 54	06 06	07 04	07 50	08 23	09 04	10 04	11 04	12 04	12 20	13 04	14 04	15 04	16 04	16 20	17 04	17 44	18 07	19 05	20 08	21 05	22 04
Shireoaks	d		06 11	07 09	07 55	08 28	09 09	10 09	11 09	12 09	12 25	13 09	14 09	15 09	16 09	16 25	17 09	17 49	18 12	19 10	20 13	21 10	22 08
Worksop	d	06 01	06 23	07 14	08 00	08 33	09 14	10 14	11 14	12 14	12 35	13 14	14 14	15 14	16 14	16 36	17 14	17 53	18 17	19 15	20 18	21a24	22 15
Retford Low Level 10	a	06 10	06b38	07 23	08 09	08 42	09 23	10 23	11 23	12 23	12 44	13 23	14 23	15 23	16 23	16 46	17 23	18 06	18 26	19 24	20 27		22b29
	d	06 11		07 24	08 10	08 43	09 24	10 24	11 24	12 24	12 45	13 24	14 24	15 24	16 24	16 46	17 24		18 27	19 25	20 28		
Gainsborough Lea Road	18 d	06 25		07 38	08 24		09 38	10 38	11 38	12 38		13 40	14 38	15 40	16 38		17 38		18 40	19 39	20 42		
Saxilby	18 d	06 38		07 51	08 37		09 51	10 51	11 51	12 51		13 53	14 51	15 53	16 51		17 51		18 53	19 52	20 55		
Lincoln	18 a	06 53		08 06	08 52		10 06	11 06	12 06	13 06		14 07	15 06	16 10	17 06		18 06		19 07	20 06	21 11		
Gainsborough Central	d					08 58					13 00					17 01							
Kirton Lindsey	d					09 11					13 13					17 15							
Brigg	d					09 24					13 22					17 27							
Barnetby	29 a					09 38					13 37					17 37							
Habrough	29 a					09 48					13 47					17 47							
Grimsby Town	29 a					10 00					14 00					18 01							
Cleethorpes	29 a					10 13					14 11					18 11							

		NT
Meadowhall	34 d	
Sheffield 7	d	22 44
Darnall	d	22 49
Woodhouse	d	22 54
Kiveton Bridge	d	23 01
Kiveton Park	d	23 04
Shireoaks	d	23 09
Worksop	d	23a22
Retford Low Level 10	a	
	d	
Gainsborough Lea Road	18 d	
Saxilby	18 d	
Lincoln	18 a	
Gainsborough Central	d	
Kirton Lindsey	d	
Brigg	d	
Barnetby	29 a	
Habrough	29 a	
Grimsby Town	29 a	
Cleethorpes	29 a	

Sundays

8 December to 11 May

		NT	NT	NT	NT	NT	NT
Meadowhall	34 d						
Sheffield 7	d	13 42	13 57	15 43	17 43	19 32	21 06
Darnall	d		14 03	15 48	17 48	19 37	21 11
Woodhouse	d		14 08	15 53	17 53	19 42	21 16
Kiveton Bridge	d		14 14	16 00	18 00	19 49	21 23
Kiveton Park	d		14 17	16 03	18 03	19 52	21 26
Shireoaks	d		14 22	16 07	18 07	19 56	21 30
Worksop	d	14 03	14 26	16 12	18 12	20 01	21 37
Retford Low Level 10	a	14 12	14 39	16 21	18 21	20 10	21 48
	d	14 12		16 21	18 21	20 10	
Gainsborough Lea Road	18 d	14 27		16 36	18 36	20 25	
Saxilby	18 d	14 39		16 48	18 48	20 37	
Lincoln	18 a	14 54		17 02	19 03	20 51	
Gainsborough Central	d						
Kirton Lindsey	d						
Brigg	d						
Barnetby	29 a						
Habrough	29 a						
Grimsby Town	29 a						
Cleethorpes	29 a						

A via Retford
B From Scunthorpe
C From Adwick
D From Huddersfield
b Retford

For connections to London Kings Cross please see Table 26

Network Diagram for Tables 31, 32, 33, 34

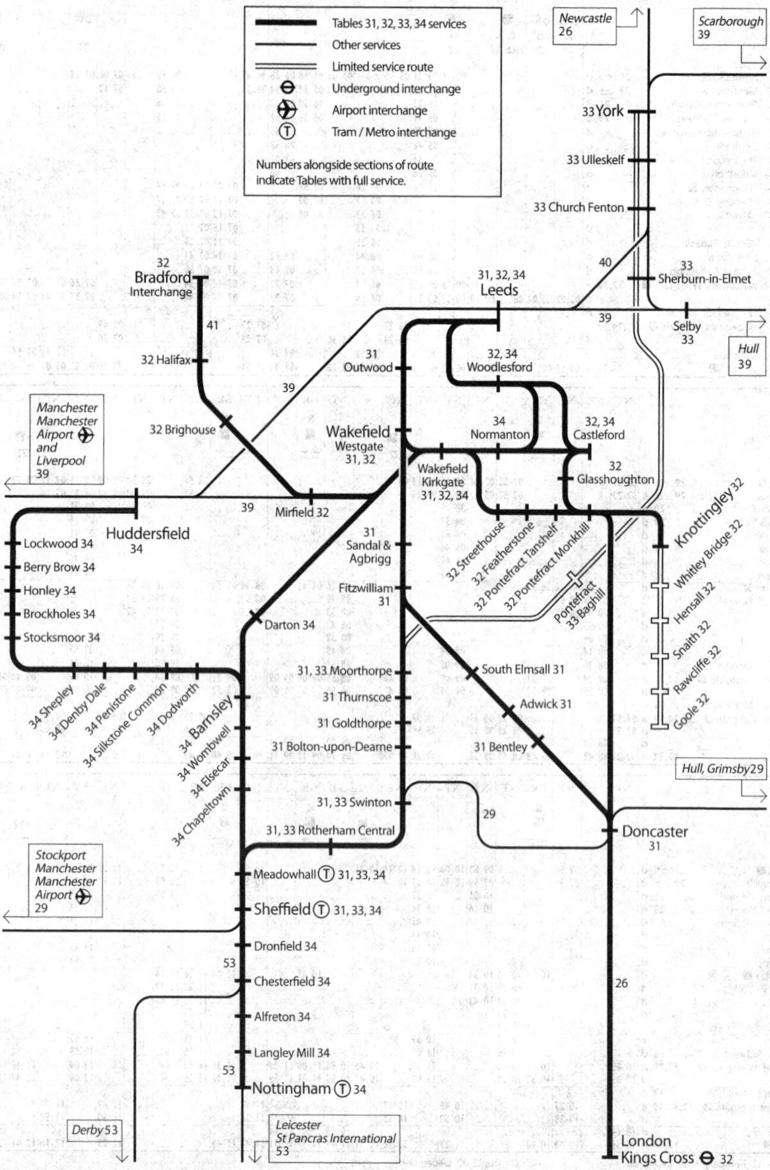

TOCs operating on this network - Northern (NT), East Coast (GR), Cross Country (XC), Grand Central (GC), East Midlands Trains (EM), First TransPennine Express (TP)

Table 31

Mondays to Fridays

9 December to 16 May

Sheffield, Doncaster and Wakefield - Leeds

Network Diagram - see first page of Table 31

Miles	Miles				EM MO	EM MO	EM MO	NT MX	EM MO	NT	NT	NT	NT	NT	NT	NT	NT	NT	NT		NT	XC	NT	NT	GR	NT
					◇1 A	◇1 B	◇1 C		◇1 D													◇1			R 1	
—	0	**Sheffield** 7	29	d					00 11	05 21	05 50		06 06	06 18	06 28	06 49			06 52		07 06	07 12				07 15
—	3½	Meadowhall	29	d						05 27	05 56		06 12	06 24	06 34	06 55			06 58		07 12					07 21
—	6¼	Rotherham Central	29	d						05 33				06 30	06 40				07 05							07 27
—	10¾	Swinton (S.Yorks)	29	d						05 41				06 38	06 51				07 15							07 35
—	13	Bolton-upon-Dearne		d						05 45					06 56											07 39
—	14¼	Goldthorpe		d						05 48					06 58											07 42
—	15	Thurnscoe		d						05 51					07 01											07 45
—	18½	Moorthorpe		d						05 56					07 06											07 54
0	—	**Doncaster** 7		d								06 26		06 59			07 08	07 26	07 34						07 45	
1¾	—	Bentley (S.Yorks)		d								06 29		07 02			07 11	07 29	07 37							
4	—	Adwick		a								06 33		07 08			07 15	07 33	07 43							
—	—			d								06 33					07 15	07 33								
8¾	—	South Elmsall		d								06 39					07 21	07 39								
13¼	22¼	Fitzwilliam		d						06 02		06 44			07 12		07 34	07 44								08 00
18	27	Sandal & Agbrigg		d						06 08		06 50			07 18		07 40	07 50					←	←		08 06
19¾	28¾	**Wakefield Westgate** 7	32,39	a					00 36	06 12		06 54			07 22		07 44	07 54				07 36	07 44	07 54	08 01	08 10
—	—			d	00 02	00 04	00 07	00 10	00 37	06 13		06 54			07 23		07 44	07 54				07 37	07 44	07 54	08 02	08 11
—	—	Pontefract Monkhill	32	d													→	→								
—	—	Wakefield Kirkgate 4	32,34,39	a							06 27		06 49			07 27					07 49					
—	—			d							06 28		06 50			07 28					07 50					
22¼	31¼	Outwood		d						06 18		06 59			07 28								07 49	07 59		08 16
29¾	38¾	**Leeds** 10	32,34	a	00 17	00 20	00 23	00 29	00 52	06 33	06 50	07 14	07 28		07 44	07 51					08 25	07 52	08 02	08 14	08 19	08 35

			NT	NT	NT	GR	NT	NT	NT	NT	XC		NT	GR	NT	NT	GR	NT	NT	NT	NT	NT	NT	XC	NT	GR
						R 1					◇1			R 1			R 1							◇1		R 1
Sheffield 7	29	d	07 21				07 51	08 06	08 16	08 19	08 22							08 51		08 54	09 06	09 15	09 18	09 21		
Meadowhall	29	d	07 27				07 57	08 12	08 22	08 25								08 57		09 00	09 12	09 21	09 24			
Rotherham Central	29	d							08 28											09 06		09 28				
Swinton (S.Yorks)	29	d							08 37											09 16		09 36				
Bolton-upon-Dearne		d							08 41													09 41				
Goldthorpe		d							08 44													09 43				
Thurnscoe		d							08 47													09 46				
Moorthorpe		d							08 52													09 51				
Doncaster 7		d		07 56	08 06	08 13							08 26	08 42		08 49	09 14		09 26	09 34						09 40
Bentley (S.Yorks)		d		07 59	08 09								08 29			08 52			09 29	09 37						
Adwick		a		08 03	08 13								08 33			08 58			09 33	09 42						
		d		08 03									08 33						09 33							
South Elmsall		d		08 09									08 39						09 39							
Fitzwilliam		d		08 14					08 59				08 45						09 44			09 59				
Sandal & Agbrigg		d		08 20					09 05				08 51		←				09 50			10 05			←	
Wakefield Westgate 7	32,39	a		08 24		08 31			09 09		08 46		08 55	09 00	09 09		09 31		09 54			10 09		09 46	09 54	09 58
		d		08 25		08 32			09 09		08 47		08 55	09 01	09 09		09 32		09 54			10 09		09 47	09 54	09 59
Pontefract Monkhill	32	d							→										→			→				
Wakefield Kirkgate 4	32,34,39	a	07 57				08 27	08 49		08 57								09 27			09 49		09 57			
		d	07 58				08 28	08 50		08 58								09 28			09 50		09 58			
Outwood		d		08 29									09 00		09 14										09 59	
Leeds 10	32,34	a	08 21	08 42		08 48	08 49	09 25		09 20	09 02		09 14	09 17	09 31		09 48	09 49			10 25		10 18	10 01	10 14	10 17

			NT		NT	GR	NT	NT	NT	NT	NT	XC	NT	GR	NT	NT	GR	NT	NT		NT	NT	NT	XC	NT	GR
						R 1						◇1		R 1			R 1						◇	◇1		R 1
Sheffield 7	29	d			09 50			09 53	10 06	10 14	10 18	10 21				10 50			10 53		11 06	11 14	11 18	11 21		
Meadowhall	29	d			09 56			09 59	10 12	10 21	10 24					10 56			10 59		11 12	11 21	11 24			
Rotherham Central	29	d						10 06		10 27									11 05			11 27				
Swinton (S.Yorks)	29	d						10 16		10 36									11 16			11 36				
Bolton-upon-Dearne		d								10 41												11 41				
Goldthorpe		d								10 43												11 43				
Thurnscoe		d								10 46												11 46				
Moorthorpe		d								10 53												11 53				
Doncaster 7		d				10 14	10 26	10 34						10 43			11 14	11 26	11 34							11 42
Bentley (S.Yorks)		d					10 29	10 37										11 29	11 37							
Adwick		a					10 33	10 43										11 33	11 43							
		d					10 33											11 33								
South Elmsall		d					10 39											11 39								
Fitzwilliam		d					10 44			10 59								11 45				11 59				
Sandal & Agbrigg		d	←				10 50			11 05			←		←			11 50				12 05			←	
Wakefield Westgate 7	32,39	a	10 09			10 31	10 54			11 09		10 46	10 54	11 00	11 09		11 31	11 54				12 09		11 46	11 54	12 00
		d	10 09			10 32	10 54			11 09		10 47	10 54	11 01	11 09		11 32	11 55				12 09		11 47	11 55	12 02
Pontefract Monkhill	32	d					→			→								→				→				
Wakefield Kirkgate 4	32,34,39	a			10 27				10 49		10 57					11 27					11 49		11 57			
		d			10 28				10 50		10 58					11 28					11 50		11 58			
Outwood		d	10 14										10 59		11 14										11 59	
Leeds 10	32,34	a	10 31		10 48	10 48			11 25		11 18	11 01	11 14	11 17	11 31	11 48	11 48				12 25		12 18	12 01	12 15	12 17

A from 17 February until 24 March

B from 31 March

C until 30 December

D from 6 January until 10 February

Table 31

Mondays to Fridays

9 December to 16 May

Sheffield, Doncaster and Wakefield - Leeds

Network Diagram - see first page of Table 31

		NT		NT	GR	GC	NT	NT	NT	NT	NT	XC	NT	GR	NT	GR	NT	NT		NT	NT	NT	NT	XC	NT
					R 1 ⊡🍴	R 1 ⊡		◇			◇	◇1 🍴		R 1 ⊡🍴		R 1 ⊡🍴				◇			◇	◇1 🍴	
Sheffield 7	29 🚊 d			11 50				11 53	12 06	12 14	12 18	12 21					12 50			12 53	13 06	13 14	13 18	13 21	
Meadowhall	29 🚊 d			11 56				11 59	12 12	12 21	12 24						12 56			12 59	13 12	13 21	13 24		
Rotherham Central	29 d							12 05		12 27										13 05		13 27			
Swinton (S.Yorks)	29 d							12 16		12 36										13 16		13 36			
Bolton-upon-Dearne	d									12 41												13 41			
Goldthorpe	d									12 43												13 43			
Thurnscoe	d									12 46												13 46			
Moorthorpe	d									12 53												13 53			
Doncaster 7	d				12 14	12 24	12 26	12 34						12 42		13 14		13 26		13 34					
Bentley (S.Yorks)	d						12 29	12 38										13 29		13 37					
Adwick	a						12 33	12 43										13 33		13 43					
	d						12 33											13 33							
South Elmsall	d						12 39											13 39							
Fitzwilliam	d						12 45			12 59								13 45				13 59			
Sandal & Agbrigg	d	←					12 50			13 05			←		←			13 50				14 05			←
Wakefield Westgate 7	32,39 a	12 09			12 31		12 54			13 09		12 46	12 54	13 00	13 09	13 31		13 54				14 09		13 46	13 54
	d	12 09			12 32		12 55			13 09		12 47	12 55	13 02	13 09	13 32		13 55				14 09		13 47	13 55
Pontefract Monkhill	32 d					12 49	→			→								→				→			
Wakefield Kirkgate 4	32,34,39 a			12 27		13 06			12 49		12 57						13 27				13 50		13 57		
	d			12 28					12 50		12 58						13 28				13 50		13 58		
Outwood	d	12 14											12 59		13 14										13 59
Leeds 10	32,34 a	12 31		12 48	12 48				13 25		13 18	13 02	13 13	13 17	13 29	13 48	13 49				14 25		14 18	14 01	14 14

		GR	NT	NT	GR	NT	NT	NT	NT	NT		XC	NT	GR	NT	GR	NT	NT	NT	NT	NT	NT	XC	NT	GR
		R 1 ⊡🍴			R 1 ⊡🍴					◇		◇1 🍴		R 1 ⊡🍴		R 1 ⊡🍴			◇			◇	◇1 🍴		R 1 ⊡🍴
Sheffield 7	29 🚊 d			13 50			13 53	14 06	14 14	14 18		14 21					14 50		14 53	15 06	15 14	15 18	15 21		
Meadowhall	29 🚊 d			13 56			13 59	14 12	14 21	14 24							14 56		14 59	15 12	15 20	15 24			
Rotherham Central	29 d						14 05		14 27										15 05		15 26				
Swinton (S.Yorks)	29 d						14 16		14 36										15 16		15 36				
Bolton-upon-Dearne	d								14 41												15 40				
Goldthorpe	d								14 43												15 43				
Thurnscoe	d								14 46												15 46				
Moorthorpe	d								14 53												15 53				
Doncaster 7	d	13 42			14 14	14 26	14 34							14 42		15 14		15 26	15 34						15 42
Bentley (S.Yorks)	d					14 29	14 37											15 29	15 37						
Adwick	a					14 33	14 43											15 33	15 42						
	d					14 33												15 33							
South Elmsall	d					14 39												15 39							
Fitzwilliam	d					14 45			14 59									15 44			15 59				
Sandal & Agbrigg	d		←			14 50			15 05				←		←			15 50			16 05			←	
Wakefield Westgate 7	32,39 a	13 59	14 09		14 31	14 54			15 09			14 46	14 54	14 59	15 09	15 31		15 54			16 10		15 46	15 54	15 59
	d	14 00	14 09		14 32	14 55			15 09			14 47	14 55	15 00	15 09	15 32		15 54			16 10		15 47	15 54	16 00
Pontefract Monkhill	32 d					→			→									→			→				
Wakefield Kirkgate 4	32,34,39 a			14 27				14 49		14 57							15 27			15 49		15 57			
	d			14 28				14 50		14 58							15 28			15 50		15 58			
Outwood	d		14 14										14 59		15 14									15 59	
Leeds 10	32,34 a	14 17	14 31	14 48	14 48			15 25		15 18		15 01	15 13	15 17	15 31	15 48	15 49			16 25		16 18	16 01	16 14	16 17

		NT		NT	GR	GC	NT	NT	NT	NT	NT	XC	NT	GR	NT	NT	GR	NT		NT	NT	NT	NT	XC	NT
					R 1 ⊡🍴	R 1 ⊡		◇			◇	◇1 🍴		R 1 ⊡🍴			R 1 ⊡🍴			◇			◇	◇1 🍴	
Sheffield 7	29 🚊 d			15 50				15 53	16 06	16 14	16 18	16 21				16 50				16 53	17 06	17 14	17 18	17 21	
Meadowhall	29 🚊 d			15 56				15 59	16 12	16 21	16 24					16 56				16 59	17 12	17 21	17 24		
Rotherham Central	29 d							16 05		16 27										17 05		17 27			
Swinton (S.Yorks)	29 d							16 16		16 36										17 15		17 37			
Bolton-upon-Dearne	d									16 41												17 41			
Goldthorpe	d									16 43												17 44			
Thurnscoe	d									16 46												17 47			
Moorthorpe	d									16 53												17 54			
Doncaster 7	d				16 13	16 24	16 26	16 34						16 42			17 14	17 26		17 32					
Bentley (S.Yorks)	d						16 29	16 37										17 29		17 36					
Adwick	a						16 33	16 43										17 33		17 41					
	d						16 33											17 33							
South Elmsall	d						16 39											17 39							
Fitzwilliam	d						16 44			16 59								17 45				18 01			
Sandal & Agbrigg	d	←					16 50			17 05			←		←			17 51				18 08			←
Wakefield Westgate 7	32,39 a	16 10			16 31		16 54			17 09		16 49	16 54	17 00	17 09		17 31	17 55				18 12		17 47	17 55
	d	16 10			16 32		16 54			17 09		16 50	16 54	17 01	17 09		17 32	17 55				18 12		17 49	17 55
Pontefract Monkhill	32 d					16 48	→			→								→				→			
Wakefield Kirkgate 4	32,34,39 a			16 27		17 04			16 49		16 57					17 28					17 49		17 57		
	d			16 28					16 50		16 58					17 28					17 50		17 58		
Outwood	d	16 15											16 59		17 14										18 00
Leeds 10	32,34 a	16 31		16 49	16 50				17 25		17 18	17 04	17 13	17 17	17 33	17 48	17 48				18 25		18 18	18 02	18 14

Table 31

Sheffield, Doncaster and Wakefield - Leeds

Mondays to Fridays

9 December to 16 May

Network Diagram - see first page of Table 31

Station		GC		GR	NT	XC	NT	GR	NT	NT	NT	XC	NT	GR	NT	GR	NT	NT		NT	NT	XC	NT	GR	GR
		R		R				R						R		R								R	R
		1		1		◇1		1			◇	◇1		1		1					◇	◇1		1	1
Sheffield 7	29 ⛴ d					17 47	17 50		18 06	18 16	18 19	18 21					18 50	19 06		19 19	19 22	19 26			
Meadowhall	29 ⛴ d						17 56		18 13	18 22	18 25						18 56	19 12		19 25	19 28				
Rotherham Central	29 d									18 28										19 31					
Swinton (S.Yorks)	29 d									18 37										19 40					
Bolton-upon-Dearne	d									18 42										19 45					
Goldthorpe	d									18 44										19 47					
Thurnscoe	d									18 47										19 50					
Moorthorpe	d									18 53										20 01					
Doncaster 7	d	17 38		17 45				18 18					18 26	18 41		19 15							19 22	19 44	19 50
Bentley (S.Yorks)	d												18 29										19 25		
Adwick	a												18 33										19 29		
	d												18 33										19 29		
South Elmsall	d												18 39										19 35		
Fitzwilliam	d									18 59			18 45							20 06			19 48		
Sandal & Agbrigg	d				←					19 05			18 51		←					20 12			19 53		
Wakefield Westgate 7	32,39 a			18 05	18 12	18 13		18 35		19 10		18 47	18 55	18 59	19 10	19 32				20 16		19 50	19 57	20 02	20 07
	d			18 06	18 12	18 15		18 36		19 10		18 48	18 55	19 00	19 10	19 33				20 17		19 51	19 58	20 03	20 08
Pontefract Monkhill	32 d									↪										↪					
Wakefield Kirkgate 4	32,34,39 a	18 07					18 28		18 50		18 59						19 30	19 50			19 57				
	d						18 32		18 50		18 59						19 32	19 50			19 58				
Outwood	d				18 17								19 00		19 15								20 02		
Leeds 10	32,34 a			18 21	18 31	18 32	18 51	18 52	19 26		19 23	19 03	19 14	19 17	19 30	19 48	19 55	20 26			20 18	20 05	20 17	20 20	20 23

Station		NT	NT	GR	NT	NT	XC	NT	GR	NT		GR	NT	XC	GC	NT	EM	GR	NT FO	NT FX	GR	NT FX	EM	NT	NT
				R					R			R						R			R				
				1		◇	◇1		1			1		◇1	◇1		◇1	1			1		◇1		
															⊠										
Sheffield 7	29 ⛴ d		19 51		20 07	20 18	20 21			20 27			21 09	21 21			21 27		21 30	21 30		22 06	22 19		22 24
Meadowhall	29 ⛴ d		19 57		20 13	20 24				20 35			21 15						21 36	21 36		22 12			22 31
Rotherham Central	29 d									20 41									21 42	21 42					22 37
Swinton (S.Yorks)	29 d									20 50									21 51	21 51					22 46
Bolton-upon-Dearne	d									20 55									21 56	21 56					22 51
Goldthorpe	d									20 57									21 58	21 58					22 53
Thurnscoe	d									21 00									22 01	22 01					22 56
Moorthorpe	d									21 06									22 06	22 06					23 01
Doncaster 7	d			20 21				20 26	20 41			21 14			21 23	21 27		21 44			22 23			22 26	
Bentley (S.Yorks)	d							20 29								21 30								22 29	
Adwick	a							20 33								21 34								22 33	
	d							20 33								21 34								22 33	
South Elmsall	d							20 39								21 40								22 39	
Fitzwilliam	d							20 45		21 12						21 47			22 12	22 12				22 45	23 07
Sandal & Agbrigg	d	←						20 51		21 18						21 53			22 18	22 18				22 51	23 13
Wakefield Westgate 7	32,39 a	20 16		20 38			20 47	20 55	21 00	21 22		21 31		21 47		21 57	22 00	22 07	22 22	22 22	22 40		22 46	22 55	23 17
	d	20 17		20 39			20 48	20 55	21 01	21 22		21 32		21 48		21 57	22 01	22 09	22 23	22 23	22 41		22 47	22 55	23 18
Pontefract Monkhill	32 d																								↪
Wakefield Kirkgate 4	32,34,39 a		20 29		20 50	20 58							21 52		21 52							22 54			
	d		20 29		20 51	20 59							21 52									22 54			
Outwood	d	20 22						21 00		21 27						22 02			22 28	22 28				23 00	
Leeds 10	32,34 a	20 35	20 48	20 53	21 26	21 20	21 06	21 14	21 18	21 47		21 49	22 29	22 02		22 15	22 17	22 23	22 44	22 46	22 58	23 30	23 05	23 14	

Station		XC		NT FO	NT	EM	GR	NT FO	NT FX	NT FX
							R			
		◇1				◇1	1			
Sheffield 7	29 ⛴ d	22 30				22 50		23 15	23 15	23 24
Meadowhall	29 ⛴ d							23 21	23 21	23 30
Rotherham Central	29 d							23 27	23 27	
Swinton (S.Yorks)	29 d							23 36	23 36	
Bolton-upon-Dearne	d							23 41	23 41	
Goldthorpe	d							23 44	23 44	
Thurnscoe	d							23 47	23 47	
Moorthorpe	d							23 52	23 52	
Doncaster 7	d						23 33			
Bentley (S.Yorks)	d									
Adwick	a									
	d									
South Elmsall	d									
Fitzwilliam	d									
Sandal & Agbrigg	d				←					
Wakefield Westgate 7	32,39 a	22 59			23 17	23 21	23 53		00 09	
	d	23 00			23 18	23 22	23 54		00 10	
Pontefract Monkhill	32 d									
Wakefield Kirkgate 4	32,34,39 a									00s10
	d			22 51						
Outwood	d				23 23					
Leeds 10	32,34 a	23 15		23 30	23 41	23 41	00 10	00 29	00 29	

Table 31

Saturdays

14 December to 17 May

Sheffield, Doncaster and Wakefield - Leeds

Network Diagram - see first page of Table 31

Station	Table		NT	NT	NT	NT	NT	NT	NT		XC	NT	NT	NT	NT	NT	NT	NT	XC	NT	GR	NT	NT	NT	NT	
											◇1								◇1		R 1					
Sheffield 7	29	d		06 06	06 12	06 28		06 52	07 06		07 12		07 15	07 51	08 06		08 14	08 19	08 21				08 51			
Meadowhall	29	d		06 12	06 18	06 34		06 58	07 12				07 21	07 57	08 12		08 22	08 25					08 57			
Rotherham Central	29	d			06 24	06 40		07 04					07 27				08 28									
Swinton (S.Yorks)	29	d			06 36	06 51		07 15					07 35				08 37									
Bolton-upon-Dearne		d				06 56							07 40				08 42									
Goldthorpe		d				06 58							07 42				08 44									
Thurnscoe		d				07 01							07 45				08 47									
Moorthorpe		d				07 06							07 54				08 53									
Doncaster 7		d	06 26		06 55		07 26	07 34								08 16				08 26	08 51			08 54	09 26	
Bentley (S.Yorks)		d	06 29		06 58		07 29	07 37								08 19				08 29				08 57	09 29	
Adwick		a	06 33		07 04		07 33	07 43								08 23				08 33				09 02	09 33	
		d	06 33				07 33													08 33					09 33	
South Elmsall		d	06 39				07 39													08 39					09 39	
Fitzwilliam		d	06 44			07 12	07 44						08 00				09 09			08 45					09 45	
Sandal & Agbrigg		d	06 50			07 18	07 50					←	08 06				09 15			08 50		←			09 50	
Wakefield Westgate 7	32,39	a	06 54			07 22	07 54				07 36	07 54	08 12				09 19		08 45	08 54	09 07	09 19			09 54	
		d	06 54			07 23	07 54				07 37	07 54	08 13				09 19		08 46	08 55	09 08	09 19			09 55	
Pontefract Monkhill	32	d					→										→								→	
Wakefield Kirkgate 4	32,34,39	a		06 49					07 49					08 27	08 49			08 57					09 27			
		d		06 50					07 50					08 28	08 50			08 58					09 28			
Outwood		d	06 59			07 28						07 59	08 18							08 59		09 24				
Leeds 10	32,34	a	07 14	07 28		07 44			08 25		07 51	08 14	08 32	08 49	09 25			09 20	09 03	09 14	09 24	09 40	09 49			

Station	Table		NT	NT	NT	NT	XC	NT	GR	NT	NT	NT	NT	NT	NT	NT	XC		NT	GR	NT	NT	NT	NT	NT	NT
							◇1		R 1								◇1			R 1						
Sheffield 7	29	d	08 53	09 06	09 15	09 18	09 21				09 50		09 53	10 06	10 14	10 18	10 21					10 50		10 53	11 06	11 14
Meadowhall	29	d	09 00	09 12	09 21	09 24					09 56		09 59	10 12	10 21	10 24						10 56		10 59	11 12	11 21
Rotherham Central	29	d	09 06		09 28								10 05		10 27									11 05		11 27
Swinton (S.Yorks)	29	d	09 16		09 36								10 16		10 36									11 16		11 36
Bolton-upon-Dearne		d			09 41										10 41											11 41
Goldthorpe		d			09 43										10 43											11 43
Thurnscoe		d			09 46										10 46											11 46
Moorthorpe		d			09 52										10 52											11 52
Doncaster 7		d	09 34						09 51			10 26	10 34							10 51			11 26	11 34		
Bentley (S.Yorks)		d	09 37									10 29	10 37										11 29	11 37		
Adwick		a	09 43									10 33	10 43										11 33	11 43		
		d										10 33											11 33			
South Elmsall		d										10 39											11 39			
Fitzwilliam		d			10 09							10 45			11 09								11 45			12 09
Sandal & Agbrigg		d			10 15			←		←		10 50			11 15				←		←		11 50			12 15
Wakefield Westgate 7	32,39	a			10 19		09 46	09 54	10 07	10 19		10 54			11 19		10 46		10 54	11 07	11 19		11 54			12 19
		d			10 19		09 47	09 55	10 08	10 19		10 55			11 19		10 47		10 55	11 08	11 19		11 55			12 19
Pontefract Monkhill	32	d			→							→			→								→			→
Wakefield Kirkgate 4	32,34,39	a		09 49		09 57					10 27			10 49		10 57						11 27			11 49	
		d		09 50		09 58					10 28			10 50		10 58						11 28			11 50	
Outwood		d						09 59		10 24									10 59		11 24					
Leeds 10	32,34	a		10 25		10 18	10 01	10 14	10 24	10 40	10 48			11 25		11 18	11 01		11 14	11 25	11 40	11 48			12 25	

Station	Table		NT	XC	NT	GR	NT	NT	GC		NT	NT	NT	NT	NT	XC	NT	GR	NT	GR	NT	NT	NT	NT	NT	
				◇1		R 1			R 1							◇1		R 1		R 1						
Sheffield 7	29	d	11 18	11 21				11 50				11 53	12 06	12 14	12 18	12 21					12 50		12 53	13 06	13 14	
Meadowhall	29	d	11 24					11 56				11 59	12 12	12 21	12 24						12 56		12 59	13 12	13 21	
Rotherham Central	29	d										12 05		12 27									13 05		13 27	
Swinton (S.Yorks)	29	d										12 16		12 36									13 16		13 36	
Bolton-upon-Dearne		d												12 41											13 41	
Goldthorpe		d												12 43											13 43	
Thurnscoe		d												12 46											13 46	
Moorthorpe		d												12 52											13 52	
Doncaster 7		d				11 51			12 20		12 26	12 34						12 51		13 14		13 26	13 33			
Bentley (S.Yorks)		d									12 29	12 37										13 29	13 37			
Adwick		a									12 33	12 43										13 33	13 42			
		d									12 33											13 33				
South Elmsall		d									12 39											13 39				
Fitzwilliam		d									12 45			13 09								13 45			14 09	
Sandal & Agbrigg		d			←		←				12 50			13 15			←		←			13 50			14 15	
Wakefield Westgate 7	32,39	a		11 46	11 54	12 07	12 19				12 54			13 19		12 46	12 54	13 07	13 19	13 31		13 54			14 19	
		d		11 47	11 55	12 08	12 19				12 55			13 19		12 47	12 55	13 08	13 19	13 32		13 55			14 19	
Pontefract Monkhill	32	d									→			→								→			→	
Wakefield Kirkgate 4	32,34,39	a	11 58					12 27	12 42				12 49		12 57						13 27			13 50		
		d	11 58					12 28					12 50		12 58						13 28			13 50		
Outwood		d			11 59		12 24										12 59		13 24							
Leeds 10	32,34	a	12 18	12 00	12 14	12 25	12 40	12 48					13 25		13 18	13 02	13 13	13 25	13 43	13 48	13 49			14 25		

Table 31

Saturdays

14 December to 17 May

Sheffield, Doncaster and Wakefield - Leeds

Network Diagram - see first page of Table 31

Station		NT	XC	NT	GR	NT	NT	NT		NT	NT	NT	NT	XC	NT	GR	NT	NT	NT	NT	NT	NT	NT	XC	
			◇1		R 1									◇1		R 1								◇1	
Sheffield 7 ... 29	d	13 18	13 21				13 50			13 53	14 06	14 14	14 18	14 21				14 50		14 53	15 06	15 14	15 18	15 21	
Meadowhall ... 29	d	13 24					13 56			13 59	14 12	14 21	14 24					14 56		14 59	15 12	15 21	15 24		
Rotherham Central ... 29	d									14 05		14 27								15 05		15 27			
Swinton (S.Yorks) ... 29	d									14 17		14 36								15 17		15 36			
Bolton-upon-Dearne	d											14 41										15 41			
Goldthorpe	d											14 43										15 43			
Thurnscoe	d											14 46										15 46			
Moorthorpe	d											14 52										15 52			
Doncaster 7	d				13 52			14 26		14 34						14 51			15 26	15 34					
Bentley (S.Yorks)	d							14 29		14 37									15 29	15 37					
Adwick	a							14 33		14 43									15 33	15 43					
	d							14 33											15 33						
South Elmsall	d							14 39											15 39						
Fitzwilliam	d							14 45				15 09							15 45			16 10			
Sandal & Agbrigg	d			←		←		14 50				15 15			←		←		15 50			16 16			
Wakefield Westgate 7 ... 32,39	a		13 46	13 54	14 09	14 19		14 54				15 19		14 46	14 54	15 07	15 19		15 54			16 20		15 46	
	d		13 47	13 55	14 10	14 19		14 55				15 19		14 47	14 55	15 08	15 19		15 55			16 20		15 47	
Pontefract Monkhill ... 32	d							→				→							→			→			
Wakefield Kirkgate 4 ... 32,34,39	a	13 57					14 27				14 49		14 57					15 27			15 49		15 57		
	d	13 58					14 28				14 50		14 58					15 28			15 50		15 58		
Outwood	d			13 59		14 24									14 59		15 24								
Leeds 10 ... 32,34	a	14 18	14 01	14 14	14 27	14 40	14 48				15 25		15 18	15 01	15 14	15 25	15 40	15 49			16 25		16 18	16 01	

Station		NT	GR	NT	NT	NT	NT	NT	NT	NT	XC	NT	GR	NT	NT	GC		NT	NT	NT	NT	NT	XC	NT	GR
			R 1				◇				◇1		R 1			R 1			◇				◇1		R 1
Sheffield 7 ... 29	d				15 50		15 53	16 06	16 14	16 18	16 21				16 50				16 53	17 06	17 14	17 18	17 22		
Meadowhall ... 29	d				15 56		15 59	16 12	16 21	16 24					16 56				16 59	17 12	17 21	17 24			
Rotherham Central ... 29	d						16 05		16 27										17 05		17 27				
Swinton (S.Yorks) ... 29	d						16 16		16 36										17 16		17 37				
Bolton-upon-Dearne	d								16 41												17 42				
Goldthorpe	d								16 43												17 44				
Thurnscoe	d								16 46												17 47				
Moorthorpe	d								16 52												17 52				
Doncaster 7	d		15 51			16 26	16 34						16 51			17 21		17 26	17 34						17 51
Bentley (S.Yorks)	d					16 29	16 37											17 29	17 37						
Adwick	a					16 33	16 43											17 33	17 43						
	d					16 33												17 33							
South Elmsall	d					16 39												17 39							
Fitzwilliam	d					16 44			17 09									17 45			18 13				
Sandal & Agbrigg	d	←		←		16 49			17 15			←		←				17 51			18 19			←	
Wakefield Westgate 7 ... 32,39	a	15 54	16 07	16 20		16 54			17 19		16 46	16 54	17 07	17 19				17 55			18 23		17 47	17 55	18 08
	d	15 55	16 08	16 20		16 54			17 19		16 47	16 54	17 08	17 19				17 55			18 23		17 47	17 55	18 09
Pontefract Monkhill ... 32	d					→			→									→			→				
Wakefield Kirkgate 4 ... 32,34,39	a				16 27			16 49		16 57					17 28	17 44				17 49		17 57			
	d				16 28			16 50		16 58					17 28					17 50		17 58			
Outwood	d	15 59		16 25								16 59		17 24										18 00	
Leeds 10 ... 32,34	a	16 13	16 25	16 41	16 49			17 25		17 18	17 01	17 13	17 25	17 41	17 48					18 25		18 18	18 02	18 14	18 25

Station		XC	NT	NT	GC	NT	NT	NT		XC	NT	GR	NT	GR	NT	NT	NT	NT	XC	NT	GR	NT	GR	NT	
		◇1			R 1					◇1		R 1		R 1					◇1		R 1		R 1		
Sheffield 7 ... 29	d	17 47		17 50		18 06	18 16	18 19		18 22					18 50	19 06	19 16	19 19	19 22					19 51	
Meadowhall ... 29	d			17 56		18 12	18 22	18 25							18 56	19 12	19 22	19 25						19 57	
Rotherham Central ... 29	d						18 28											19 31							
Swinton (S.Yorks) ... 29	d						18 37											19 40							
Bolton-upon-Dearne	d						18 41											19 45							
Goldthorpe	d						18 44											19 47							
Thurnscoe	d						18 47											19 50							
Moorthorpe	d						18 52											20 01							
Doncaster 7	d				18 20						18 26	18 51		19 15						19 22	19 49		20 13		
Bentley (S.Yorks)	d										18 29									19 25					
Adwick	a										18 33									19 29					
	d										18 33									19 29					
South Elmsall	d										18 39									19 35					
Fitzwilliam	d						19 09				18 45							20 07		19 48					
Sandal & Agbrigg	d		←				19 15				18 50		←					20 13		19 53		←			
Wakefield Westgate 7 ... 32,39	a	18 12	18 23				19 19			18 46	18 54	19 07	19 19	19 31				20 17	19 49	19 58	20 06	20 17	20 32		
	d	18 13	18 23				19 19			18 47	18 55	19 08	19 19	19 34				20 17	19 50	19 58	20 07	20 17	20 34		
Pontefract Monkhill ... 32	d						→											→							
Wakefield Kirkgate 4 ... 32,34,39	a			18 28	18 45	18 50		18 58							19 29	19 50	19 58							20 28	
	d			18 32		18 50		18 58							19 32	19 50	19 59							20 28	
Outwood	d		18 28								18 59		19 24							20 02		20 22			
Leeds 10 ... 32,34	a	18 31	18 44	18 51		19 27		19 23		19 00	19 14	19 24	19 43	19 48	19 55	20 26	20 20		20 04	20 17	20 22	20 38	20 47	20 48	

Table 31

Saturdays

14 December to 17 May

Sheffield, Doncaster and Wakefield - Leeds

Network Diagram - see first page of Table 31

			NT	NT	XC	NT	NT	GC	GR	NT	XC	NT	EM	NT	GR	EM	NT	NT	XC	NT	NT	GR
					◇1				R 1		◇1		◇1		R 1	◇1			◇1			R 1
Sheffield 7	29	d	20 07	20 18	20 23		20 30			21 06	21 21		21 25	21 30		22 19		22 24	22 27			
Meadowhall	29	d	20 13	20 26			20 36			21 12				21 36				22 30				
Rotherham Central	29	d					20 42							21 42				22 36				
Swinton (S.Yorks)	29	d					20 51							21 50				22 45				
Bolton-upon-Dearne		d					20 56							21 54				22 49				
Goldthorpe		d					20 58							21 57				22 52				
Thurnscoe		d					21 01							22 00				22 55				
Moorthorpe		d					21 07							22 05				23 00				
Doncaster 7		d				20 26		20 52	21 18			21 22			22 19		22 26		22 53			23 49
Bentley (S.Yorks)		d				20 29						21 25					22 29					
Adwick		a				20 33						21 29					22 33					
		d				20 33						21 29					22 33					
South Elmsall		d				20 40						21 37					22 39					
Fitzwilliam		d				20 46	21 13					21 45		22 11			22 45	23 10				
Sandal & Agbrigg		d				20 52	21 19					21 51		22 17			22 51	23 16			←	
Wakefield Westgate 7	32,39	a			20 48	20 56	21 23		21 34		21 48	21 55	21 59	22 21	22 35	22 44	22 55	23 20	23 09		23 20	00 05
		d			20 49	20 56	21 23		21 35		21 49	21 56	22 00	22 22	22 36	22 45	22 55	23 20	23 11		23 20	00 06
Pontefract Monkhill	32	d						21 16										→				
Wakefield Kirkgate 4	32,34,39	a	20 50	20 57				21 32		21 52												
		d	20 51	20 58						21 52										22 51		
Outwood		d				21 01	21 28					22 01		22 27			23 00				23 25	
Leeds 10	32,34	a	21 26	21 20	21 02	21 18	21 47		21 53	22 29	22 01	22 16	22 18	22 45	22 53	23 03	23 14		23 27	23 30	23 40	00 23

Sundays

8 December to 29 December

			GR	NT	NT	XC	NT	NT	XC	GR	NT	NT	NT	XC	GR	NT	NT	XC	GR	NT	NT	GC	NT	XC	GR
			R 1 A			◇1		◇	◇1	R 1				◇1	R 1			◇1	R 1			R		◇1	R 1
Sheffield 7	29	d			08 39	09 21	09 36	10 17	10 21			10 39	11 17	11 21		11 36	12 16	12 21			12 39		13 17	13 21	
Meadowhall	29	d			08 45		09 42	10 23				10 45	11 23			11 42	12 23				12 45		13 23		
Rotherham Central	29	d					09 48									11 49									
Swinton (S.Yorks)	29	d					09 58									12 00									
Bolton-upon-Dearne		d					10 03									12 04									
Goldthorpe		d					10 05									12 07									
Thurnscoe		d					10 08									12 10									
Moorthorpe		d					10 13									12 15									
Doncaster 7		d		09 12						10 51	11 12				11 47				12 51	13 12		13 22			13 47
Bentley (S.Yorks)		d		09 15							11 15									13 15					
Adwick		a		09 19							11 19									13 19					
		d		09 19							11 19									13 19					
South Elmsall		d		09 25							11 25									13 25					
Fitzwilliam		d		09 30			10 19				11 30					12 21				13 30					
Sandal & Agbrigg		d		09 36			10 25				11 36					12 27				13 36					
Wakefield Westgate 7	32,39	a		09 40		09 44	10 29		10 44	11 08	11 38			11 44	12 04	12 31		12 44	13 08	13 38				13 45	14 04
		d	00 06	09 40		09 45	10 30		10 45	11 10	11 39			11 45	12 05	12 31		12 45	13 10	13 39				13 46	14 05
Pontefract Monkhill	32	d																							
Wakefield Kirkgate 4	32,34,39	a			09 29			10 55				11 29	11 52				12 52				13 29	13 45	13 52		
		d			09 30			10 57				11 30	11 53				12 53				13 30		13 53		
Outwood		d		09 45			10 35				11 44					12 36				13 44					
Leeds 10	32,34	a	00 23	09 59	10 07	10 02	10 52	11 15	11 02	11 27	11 59	12 05	12 18	12 01	12 21	12 53	13 18	13 02	13 27	13 59	14 04		14 18	14 02	14 21

			NT	NT	XC	GR	NT	NT	NT	XC	GR	NT	NT	XC	GR	NT	NT	GC	NT	XC	EM	GR	NT	XC
					◇1	R 1				◇1	R 1			◇1	R 1			R		◇1	◇1	R 1		◇1
Sheffield 7	29	d	13 36	14 17	14 21			14 39	15 17	15 21		15 36	16 17	16 21			16 39		17 17	17 21	17 34		17 36	17 51
Meadowhall	29	d	13 42	14 23				14 45	15 23			15 42	16 23				16 45		17 23				17 44	
Rotherham Central	29	d	13 49									15 50											17 50	
Swinton (S.Yorks)	29	d	13 57									15 58											17 58	
Bolton-upon-Dearne		d	14 01									16 02											18 03	
Goldthorpe		d	14 04									16 05											18 05	
Thurnscoe		d	14 07									16 08											18 08	
Moorthorpe		d	14 12									16 13											18 13	
Doncaster 7		d				14 51	15 12				15 51				16 58	17 12		17 22				17 51		18 16
Bentley (S.Yorks)		d					15 15									17 15								
Adwick		a					15 19									17 19								
		d					15 19									17 19								
South Elmsall		d					15 25									17 25								
Fitzwilliam		d	14 17				15 30					16 19				17 30							18 19	
Sandal & Agbrigg		d	14 23				15 36					16 25				17 36							18 25	
Wakefield Westgate 7	32,39	a	14 27		14 44	15 08	15 39			15 44	16 08	16 29		16 44	17 15	17 39				17 44	18 05	18 10	18 29	18 33
		d	14 28		14 45	15 10	15 40			15 45	16 10	16 29		16 45	17 16	17 39				17 45	18 07	18 11	18 30	18 34
Pontefract Monkhill	32	d																						
Wakefield Kirkgate 4	32,34,39	a		14 52				15 29	15 52				16 52				17 29	17 45	17 52					
		d		14 53				15 30	15 53				16 53				17 30		17 53					
Outwood		d	14 33				15 45					16 34				17 45							18 35	
Leeds 10	32,34	a	14 47	15 18	15 02	15 27	15 59	16 04	16 18	16 02	16 27	16 54	17 16	17 02	17 31	17 59	18 05		18 18	18 02	18 24	18 29	18 50	18 51

A not 8 December

Table 31

Sundays

8 December to 29 December

Sheffield, Doncaster and Wakefield - Leeds

Network Diagram - see first page of Table 31

		GR	NT	XC	GR	GR	NT	NT		XC	NT	GR	NT	GR	NT	XC	GC	GR	GC	NT	EM	GR	XC	GR	
		R			R	R						R		R			R	R	R			R		R	
		1		◇1	1	1				◇1		1		1		◇1		1	1		◇1	1	◇1	1	
		🍽🛒		🛒	🍽🛒	🍽🛒				🛒		🍽🛒		🍽🛒		🛒	🍽	🍽🛒	🍽		🍽	🍽🛒	🛒	🍽🛒	
Sheffield 7	29 🚋 d		18 17	18 21			18 39	19 16		19 21			19 36		20 17	20 21				20 39	21 03		21 21		
Meadowhall	29 🚋 d		18 23				18 45	19 23					19 42		20 23					20 45					
Rotherham Central	29 d												19 49												
Swinton (S.Yorks)	29 d												19 57												
Bolton-upon-Dearne	d												20 02												
Goldthorpe	d												20 04												
Thurnscoe	d												20 07												
Moorthorpe	d												20 12												
Doncaster 7	d	18 20			18 44	19 15					19 27	19 50		20 20			20 28	20 44	20 59			21 19		21 45	
Bentley (S.Yorks)	d										19 30														
Adwick	a										19 34														
	d										19 34														
South Elmsall	d										19 41														
Fitzwilliam	d										19 47		20 18												
Sandal & Agbrigg	d										19 53		20 24												
Wakefield Westgate 7	32,39 a	18 38		18 47	19 01	19 32				19 48	19 57	20 07	20 28	20 37		20 49		21 01			21 27	21 36	21 47	22 02	
	d	18 39		18 49	19 02	19 33				19 50	19 57	20 09	20 28	20 38		20 51		21 02			21 29	21 37	21 48	22 04	
Pontefract Monkhill	32 d																								
Wakefield Kirkgate 4	32,34,39 a		18 52				19 29	19 52							20 52		20 53		21 20	21 29					
	d		18 53				19 30	19 53							20 53					21 30					
Outwood	d										20 02		20 33												
Leeds 10	32,34 a	18 56	19 18	19 04	19 21	19 51	20 05	20 18		20 05	20 16	20 25	20 52	20 52	21 16	21 06		21 18		22 04	21 44	21 55	22 04	22 19	

		NT	NT	GR	XC	NT	GR	EM
				R			R	
				1	◇1		1	◇1
				🍽🛒			🍽🛒	🍽
Sheffield 7	29 🚋 d		21 36		22 21	22 39		23 39
Meadowhall	29 🚋 d		21 42			22 45		
Rotherham Central	29 d		21 48					
Swinton (S.Yorks)	29 d		21 56					
Bolton-upon-Dearne	d		22 00					
Goldthorpe	d		22 03					
Thurnscoe	d		22 06					
Moorthorpe	d		22 11					
Doncaster 7	d	21 52		22 24			23 37	
Bentley (S.Yorks)	d	21 55						
Adwick	a	21 59						
	d	21 59						
South Elmsall	d	22 05						
Fitzwilliam	d	22 12	22 17					
Sandal & Agbrigg	d	22 18	22 23					
Wakefield Westgate 7	32,39 a	22 22	22 27	22 40	22 43		23 56	00 06
	d	22 23	22 28	22 41	22 43		23 57	00 07
Pontefract Monkhill	32 d							
Wakefield Kirkgate 4	32,34,39 a					23 26		
	d					23 27		
Outwood	d	22 28	22 33					
Leeds 10	32,34 a	22 42	22 50	22 58	23 01	00 05	00 13	00 23

Sundays

5 January to 9 February

		GR	NT	NT	XC	NT	NT	XC	GR	NT	NT	NT	XC	GR	NT	NT		XC	GR	NT	NT	NT	XC	GC	GR
		R							R					R					R					R	R
		1			◇1		◇	◇1	1				◇1	1				◇1	1				◇1		1
		🍽🛒						🛒	🍽🛒				🛒	🍽🛒				🛒	🍽🛒				🛒	🍽	🍽🛒
Sheffield 7	29 🚋 d			08 39	09 21	09 36	10 17	10 21			10 39	11 17	11 21		11 36	12 16		12 21			12 39	13 17	13 21		
Meadowhall	29 🚋 d			08 45		09 42	10 23				10 45	11 23			11 42	12 23					12 45	13 23			
Rotherham Central	29 d					09 48									11 49										
Swinton (S.Yorks)	29 d					09 58									12 00										
Bolton-upon-Dearne	d					10 03									12 04										
Goldthorpe	d					10 05									12 07										
Thurnscoe	d					10 08									12 10										
Moorthorpe	d					10 13									12 15										
Doncaster 7	d		09 12						10 54	11 12				11 54					12 53	13 12				13 35	13 53
Bentley (S.Yorks)	d		09 15							11 15										13 15					
Adwick	a		09 19							11 19										13 19					
	d		09 19							11 19										13 19					
South Elmsall	d		09 25							11 25										13 25					
Fitzwilliam	d		09 30			10 19				11 30					12 21					13 30					
Sandal & Agbrigg	d		09 36			10 25				11 36					12 27					13 36					
Wakefield Westgate 7	32,39 a		09 40		09 44	10 29		10 44	11 11	11 38			11 44	12 11	12 31			12 44	13 10	13 38			13 45		14 10
	d	00 06	09 40		09 45	10 30		10 45	11 13	11 39			11 45	12 12	12 31			12 45	13 11	13 39			13 46		14 12
Pontefract Monkhill	32 d																								
Wakefield Kirkgate 4	32,34,39 a			09 29			10 55				11 29	11 52				12 52					13 29	13 52		13 56	
	d			09 30			10 57				11 30	11 53				12 53					13 30	13 53			
Outwood	d		09 45			10 35				11 44					12 36					13 44					
Leeds 10	32,34 a	00 23	09 59	10 07	10 02	10 52	11 15	11 02	11 28	11 59	12 05	12 18	12 01	12 27	12 53	13 18		13 02	13 27	13 59	14 04	14 18	14 02		14 27

Table 31

Sundays

5 January to 9 February

Sheffield, Doncaster and Wakefield - Leeds

Network Diagram - see first page of Table 31

Station		NT	NT	XC	GR	NT	NT	NT	XC	GR	NT	NT	XC	GR	NT	NT		NT	XC	GR	GC	NT	XC	NT	GR
					R					R				R						R	R				R
				◇1	1				◇1	1			◇1	1					◇1	1			◇1		1
				⊥	⊡⊥				⊥	⊡⊥			⊥	⊡⊥					⊥	⊡⊥	⊡		⊥		⊡⊥
Sheffield 7	29 ⇌ d	13 36	14 17	14 21			14 39	15 17	15 21		15 36	16 17	16 21			16 39		17 17	17 21			17 36	17 46		
Meadowhall	29 ⇌ d	13 42	14 23				14 45	15 23			15 42	16 23				16 45		17 23				17 44			
Rotherham Central	29 d	13 49									15 50											17 50			
Swinton (S.Yorks)	29 d	13 57									15 58											17 58			
Bolton-upon-Dearne	d	14 01									16 02											18 03			
Goldthorpe	d	14 04									16 05											18 05			
Thurnscoe	d	14 07									16 08											18 08			
Moorthorpe	d	14 12									16 13											18 13			
Doncaster 7	d				14 56	15 12				15 54				16 58	17 12					17 51	17 55				18 20
Bentley (S.Yorks)	d					15 15									17 15										
Adwick	a					15 19									17 19										
	d					15 19									17 19										
South Elmsall	d					15 25									17 25										
Fitzwilliam	d	14 17				15 30					16 19				17 30							18 19			
Sandal & Agbrigg	d	14 23				15 36					16 25				17 36							18 25		←	
Wakefield Westgate 7	32,39 a	14 27		14 44	15 13	15 39			15 44	16 11	16 29		16 44	17 15	17 39				17 44	18 10		18 29	18 16	18 29	18 38
	d	14 28		14 45	15 14	15 40			15 45	16 12	16 29		16 45	17 16	17 39				17 45	18 11		18 30	18 17	18 30	18 39
Pontefract Monkhill	32 d																					↪			
Wakefield Kirkgate 4	32,34,39 a		14 52				15 29	15 52				16 52				17 29		17 52			18 21				
	d		14 53				15 30	15 53				16 53				17 30		17 53							
Outwood	d	14 33				15 45					16 34				17 45									18 35	
Leeds 10	32,34 a	14 47	15 18	15 02	15 29	15 59	16 04	16 18	16 02	16 27	16 55	17 16	17 02	17 31	17 59	18 05		18 18	18 02	18 29			18 34	18 50	18 56

Station		NT	XC	GR	NT	EM	GR	NT		XC	NT	GR	NT	GR	NT	XC	GR	NT	GC	GR	NT	XC	NT	NT
				R			R					R		R			R		R	R				
			◇1	1		◇1	1			◇1		1		1		◇1	1		1	1		◇1		
			⊥	⊡⊥		⊡	⊡⊥			⊥		⊡⊥		⊡⊥		⊥	⊡⊥		⊡	⊡⊥		⊥		
Sheffield 7	29 ⇌ d	18 17	18 21		18 39	18 44		19 16		19 21			19 36		20 17	20 21		20 39			21 36	21 39		
Meadowhall	29 ⇌ d	18 23			18 45			19 23					19 42		20 23			20 45			21 42			
Rotherham Central	29 d												19 49								21 48			
Swinton (S.Yorks)	29 d												19 58								21 56			
Bolton-upon-Dearne	d												20 02								22 00			
Goldthorpe	d												20 04								22 03			
Thurnscoe	d												20 07								22 06			
Moorthorpe	d												20 12								22 11			
Doncaster 7	d			18 44			19 15				19 27	19 50		20 20			20 53		21 28	21 47			21 52	
Bentley (S.Yorks)	d										19 30												21 55	
Adwick	a										19 34												21 59	
	d										19 34												21 59	
South Elmsall	d										19 41												22 05	
Fitzwilliam	d										19 47		20 18								22 17		22 12	
Sandal & Agbrigg	d										19 53		20 24								22 23		22 18	←
Wakefield Westgate 7	32,39 a		18 47	19 01		19 10	19 32			19 48	19 57	20 07	20 28	20 37		20 46	21 10			22 04	22 27	22 11	22 22	22 27
	d		18 49	19 02		19 12	19 33			19 50	19 57	20 09	20 28	20 38		20 50	21 11			22 05	22 28	22 11	22 23	22 28
Pontefract Monkhill	32 d																				↪			
Wakefield Kirkgate 4	32,34,39 a	18 52			19 29			19 52							20 52			21 29	21 50					
	d	18 53			19 30			19 53							20 53			21 30						
Outwood	d										20 02		20 33										22 28	22 33
Leeds 10	32,34 a	19 18	19 04	19 21	20 05	19 27	19 51	20 18		20 05	20 16	20 25	20 52	20 52	21 16	21 05	21 27	22 04		22 20		22 28	22 42	22 50

Station		GC	GR	EM	NT	XC	GR
		R	R				R
			1	◇1		◇1	1
		⊡	⊡⊥	⊡			⊡⊥
Sheffield 7	29 ⇌ d			22 24	22 39	22 42	
Meadowhall	29 ⇌ d				22 45		
Rotherham Central	29 d						
Swinton (S.Yorks)	29 d						
Bolton-upon-Dearne	d						
Goldthorpe	d						
Thurnscoe	d						
Moorthorpe	d						
Doncaster 7	d	22 05	22 24				23 37
Bentley (S.Yorks)	d						
Adwick	a						
	d						
South Elmsall	d						
Fitzwilliam	d						
Sandal & Agbrigg	d						
Wakefield Westgate 7	32,39 a		22 40	22 49		23 09	23 56
	d		22 41	22 50		23 10	23 57
Pontefract Monkhill	32 d						
Wakefield Kirkgate 4	32,34,39 a	22 38			23 26		
	d				23 27		
Outwood	d						
Leeds 10	32,34 a		22 58	23 09	00 05	23 26	00 13

Table 31

Sundays

16 February to 23 March

Sheffield, Doncaster and Wakefield - Leeds

Network Diagram - see first page of Table 31

			GR	NT	NT	XC	NT	NT	GR		NT	NT	NT	XC	GR	NT	NT	XC	GR	NT	NT	NT	XC	GC	GR	
			R						R						R				R					R	R	
			1			◇1		◇	1					◇1	1			◇1	1				◇1		1	
			🍴⊼						🍴⊼					⊼	🍴⊼			⊼	🍴⊼				⊼	🍴	🍴⊼	
Sheffield [7]	29 🚋	d			08 39	09 21	09 36	10 17				10 39	11 17	11 21		11 36	12 16	12 21			12 39	13 17	13 21			
Meadowhall	29 🚋	d			08 45		09 42	10 23				10 45	11 23			11 42	12 23				12 45	13 23				
Rotherham Central	29	d					09 48									11 49										
Swinton (S.Yorks)	29	d					09 58									12 00										
Bolton-upon-Dearne		d					10 03									12 04										
Goldthorpe		d					10 05									12 07										
Thurnscoe		d					10 08									12 10										
Moorthorpe		d					10 13									12 15										
Doncaster [7]		d		09 12					10 54		11 12				11 54				12 53	13 12				13 35	13 53	
Bentley (S.Yorks)		d		09 15							11 15									13 15						
Adwick		a		09 19							11 19									13 19						
		d		09 19							11 19									13 19						
South Elmsall		d		09 25							11 25									13 25						
Fitzwilliam		d		09 30			10 19				11 30					12 21				13 30						
Sandal & Agbrigg		d		09 36			10 25				11 36					12 27				13 36						
Wakefield Westgate [7]	32,39	a		09 40		09 44	10 29		11 11		11 38			11 44	12 11	12 31		12 44	13 10	13 38			13 45		14 10	
		d	00 06	09 40		09 45	10 30		11 13		11 39			11 45	12 12	12 31		12 45	13 11	13 39			13 46		14 12	
Pontefract Monkhill	32	d																								
Wakefield Kirkgate [4]	32,34,39	a			09 26			10 55				11 26	11 49				12 49				13 26	13 55		13 56		
		d			09 32			10 57				11 31	11 50				12 50				13 31	14 00				
Outwood		d		09 45			10 35				11 44					12 36				13 44						
Leeds [10]	32,34	a	00 23	09 59	10 06	10 02	10 52	11 15	11 28		11 59	12 05	12 15	12 01	12 27	12 53	13 15	13 02	13 27	13 59	14 05	14 23	14 02		14 27	

			NT	NT	XC	GR	NT	NT	NT	XC	GR	NT	NT	XC	GR	NT	NT		NT	XC	EM	GR	NT	GC	XC	GR
						R					R				R							R		R		R
					◇1	1				◇1	1			◇1	1					◇1	◇1	1			◇1	1
					⊼	🍴⊼				⊼	🍴⊼			⊼	🍴⊼					⊼	🍴	🍴⊼		🍴	⊼	🍴⊼
Sheffield [7]	29 🚋	d	13 36	14 17	14 21			14 39	15 17	15 21		15 36	16 17	16 21			16 39		17 17	17 21	17 34		17 36		17 51	
Meadowhall	29 🚋	d	13 42	14 23				14 45	15 23			15 42	16 23				16 45		17 23				17 44			
Rotherham Central	29	d	13 49									15 50											17 50			
Swinton (S.Yorks)	29	d	13 57									15 58											17 58			
Bolton-upon-Dearne		d	14 01									16 02											18 03			
Goldthorpe		d	14 04									16 05											18 05			
Thurnscoe		d	14 07									16 08											18 08			
Moorthorpe		d	14 12									16 13											18 13			
Doncaster [7]		d				14 56	15 12				15 54				16 58	17 12						17 51		17 55	18 15	18 20
Bentley (S.Yorks)		d					15 15									17 15										
Adwick		a					15 19									17 19										
		d					15 19									17 19										
South Elmsall		d					15 25									17 25										
Fitzwilliam		d	14 17				15 30					16 19				17 30							18 19			
Sandal & Agbrigg		d	14 23				15 36					16 25				17 36							18 25			
Wakefield Westgate [7]	32,39	a	14 27		14 44	15 13	15 39			15 44	16 11	16 29		16 44	17 15	17 39				17 44	18 05	18 10	18 29		18 33	18 38
		d	14 28		14 45	15 14	15 40			15 45	16 12	16 29		16 45	17 16	17 39				17 45	18 07	18 11	18 30		18 34	18 39
Pontefract Monkhill	32	d																								
Wakefield Kirkgate [4]	32,34,39	a		14 49				15 26	15 51				16 49				17 26		17 52					18 21		
		d		14 50				15 31	15 51				16 50				17 31		17 59							
Outwood		d	14 33				15 45					16 34				17 45							18 35			
Leeds [10]	32,34	a	14 47	15 15	15 02	15 29	15 59	16 04	16 16	16 02	16 27	16 54	17 13	17 02	17 31	17 59	18 05		18 24	18 02	18 24	18 29	18 50		18 51	18 56

			NT	XC	GR	GR	NT	NT	XC		NT	GR	NT	GR	NT	XC	GR	NT	EM	GC	GR	NT	XC	NT	NT	
					R	R						R		R			R			R	R					
				◇1	1	1			◇1			1		1		◇1	1		◇1	1	1		◇1			
				⊼	🍴⊼	🍴⊼			⊼			🍴⊼		🍴⊼		⊼	🍴⊼		🍴	🍴	🍴⊼		⊼			
Sheffield [7]	29 🚋	d	18 17	18 21			18 39	19 16	19 21				19 36		20 17	20 21		20 39	21 03			21 36	21 39			
Meadowhall	29 🚋	d	18 23				18 45	19 23					19 42		20 23			20 45				21 42				
Rotherham Central	29	d											19 49									21 48				
Swinton (S.Yorks)	29	d											19 57									21 56				
Bolton-upon-Dearne		d											20 02									22 00				
Goldthorpe		d											20 04									22 03				
Thurnscoe		d											20 07									22 06				
Moorthorpe		d											20 12									22 11				
Doncaster [7]		d			18 44	19 15					19 27	19 50		20 20			20 53			21 28	21 47			21 52		
Bentley (S.Yorks)		d									19 30													21 55		
Adwick		a									19 34													21 59		
		d									19 34													21 59		
South Elmsall		d									19 41													22 05		
Fitzwilliam		d									19 47		20 18									22 17		22 12		
Sandal & Agbrigg		d									19 53		20 24									22 23		22 18	←	
Wakefield Westgate [7]	32,39	a		18 47	19 01	19 32			19 48		19 57	20 07	20 28	20 37		20 46	21 10		21 27		22 04	22 27	22 11	22 22	22 27	
		d		18 49	19 02	19 33			19 50		19 57	20 09	20 28	20 38		20 50	21 11		21 29		22 05	22 28	22 11	22 23	22 28	
Pontefract Monkhill	32	d																				→				
Wakefield Kirkgate [4]	32,34,39	a	18 49				19 26	19 49							20 49			21 26		21 50						
		d	18 50				19 31	19 50							20 50			21 31								
Outwood		d									20 02		20 33											22 28	22 33	
Leeds [10]	32,34	a	19 15	19 04	19 21	19 51	20 05	20 15	20 05		20 16	20 25	20 52	20 52	21 13	21 05	21 27	22 04	21 44		22 20		22 28	22 42	22 50	

Table 31

Sheffield, Doncaster and Wakefield - Leeds

Sundays

16 February to 23 March

Network Diagram - see first page of Table 31

Station			GC	GR	NT	XC	GR	EM
			R	R 1		◇1	R 1	◇1
Sheffield 7	29	d			22 39	22 42		23 30
Meadowhall	29	d			22 45			
Rotherham Central	29	d						
Swinton (S.Yorks)	29	d						
Bolton-upon-Dearne		d						
Goldthorpe		d						
Thurnscoe		d						
Moorthorpe		d						
Doncaster 7		d	22 05	22 24			23 37	
Bentley (S.Yorks)		d						
Adwick		a						
		d						
South Elmsall		d						
Fitzwilliam		d						
Sandal & Agbrigg		d						
Wakefield Westgate 7	32,39	a		22 40		23 09	23 56	00 01
		d		22 41		23 10	23 57	00 02
Pontefract Monkhill	32	d						
Wakefield Kirkgate 4	32,34,39	a	22 38		23 26			
		d			23 27			
Outwood		d						
Leeds 10	32,34	a		22 58	00 05	23 26	00 13	00 17

Sundays

30 March to 11 May

Station			GR	NT	NT	XC	NT	NT	XC	GR	NT	NT	NT	XC	GR	NT	NT		XC	GR	NT	NT	GC	NT	XC	GR
			R 1			◇1		◇	◇1	R 1				◇1	R 1				◇1	R 1			R		◇1	R 1
Sheffield 7	29	d			08 39	09 21	09 36	10 17	10 21			10 39	11 17	11 21		11 36	12 16		12 21			12 39		13 17	13 21	
Meadowhall	29	d			08 45		09 42	10 23				10 45	11 23			11 42	12 23					12 45		13 23		
Rotherham Central	29	d					09 48									11 49										
Swinton (S.Yorks)	29	d					09 58									12 00										
Bolton-upon-Dearne		d					10 03									12 04										
Goldthorpe		d					10 05									12 07										
Thurnscoe		d					10 08									12 10										
Moorthorpe		d					10 13									12 15										
Doncaster 7		d		09 12						10 51	11 12				11 47					12 51	13 12		13 22			13 47
Bentley (S.Yorks)		d		09 15							11 15										13 15					
Adwick		a		09 19							11 19										13 19					
		d		09 19							11 19										13 19					
South Elmsall		d		09 25							11 25										13 25					
Fitzwilliam		d		09 30			10 19				11 30					12 21					13 30					
Sandal & Agbrigg		d		09 36			10 25				11 36					12 27					13 36					
Wakefield Westgate 7	32,39	a		09 40		09 44	10 29		10 44	11 08	11 38			11 44	12 04	12 31			12 44	13 08	13 38				13 45	14 04
		d	00 06	09 40		09 45	10 30		10 45	11 10	11 39			11 45	12 05	12 31			12 45	13 10	13 39				13 46	14 05
Pontefract Monkhill	32	d																								
Wakefield Kirkgate 4	32,34,39	a			09 29			10 55				11 29	11 52				12 52					13 29	13 45	13 52		
		d			09 30			10 57				11 30	11 53				12 53					13 30		13 53		
Outwood		d		09 45			10 35				11 44					12 36					13 44					
Leeds 10	32,34	a	00 23	09 59	10 07	10 02	10 52	11 15	11 02	11 27	11 59	12 05	12 18	12 01	12 21	12 53	13 18		13 02	13 27	13 59	14 04		14 18	14 02	14 21

Station			NT	NT	XC	GR	NT	NT	NT		XC	GR	NT	NT	XC	GR	NT	NT	GC	NT	XC	EM	GR	NT	XC	
					◇1	R 1					◇1	R 1			◇1	R 1			R		◇1	◇1	R 1		◇1	
Sheffield 7	29	d	13 36	14 17	14 21			14 39	15 17		15 21		15 36	16 17	16 21			16 39		17 17	17 21	17 34		17 36	17 51	
Meadowhall	29	d	13 42	14 23				14 45	15 23				15 42	16 23				16 45		17 23				17 44		
Rotherham Central	29	d	13 49										15 50											17 50		
Swinton (S.Yorks)	29	d	13 57										15 58											17 58		
Bolton-upon-Dearne		d	14 01										16 02											18 03		
Goldthorpe		d	14 04										16 05											18 05		
Thurnscoe		d	14 07										16 08											18 08		
Moorthorpe		d	14 12										16 13											18 13		
Doncaster 7		d				14 51	15 12					15 51				16 58	17 12		17 22				17 51		18 16	
Bentley (S.Yorks)		d					15 15										17 15									
Adwick		a					15 19										17 19									
		d					15 19										17 19									
South Elmsall		d					15 25										17 25									
Fitzwilliam		d	14 17				15 30						16 19				17 30							18 19		
Sandal & Agbrigg		d	14 23				15 36						16 25				17 36							18 25		
Wakefield Westgate 7	32,39	a	14 27		14 44	15 08	15 39				15 44	16 08	16 29		16 44	17 15	17 39				17 44	18 05	18 10	18 29	18 33	
		d	14 28		14 45	15 10	15 40				15 45	16 10	16 29		16 45	17 16	17 39				17 45	18 07	18 11	18 30	18 34	
Pontefract Monkhill	32	d																								
Wakefield Kirkgate 4	32,34,39	a		14 52				15 29	15 52					16 52				17 29	17 45	17 52						
		d		14 53				15 30	15 53					16 53				17 30		17 53						
Outwood		d	14 33				15 45						16 34				17 45							18 35		
Leeds 10	32,34	a	14 47	15 18	15 02	15 27	15 59	16 04	16 18		16 02	16 27	16 54	17 16	17 02	17 31	17 59	18 05		18 18	18 02	18 24	18 29	18 50	18 51	

Table 31

Sundays

30 March to 11 May

Sheffield, Doncaster and Wakefield - Leeds

Network Diagram - see first page of Table 31

			GR	NT	XC	GR	GR	NT	NT	XC	NT	GR	NT	GR	NT	XC	GC	GR	GC	NT	EM	GR	XC	GR
			R			R	R					R		R			R	R	R			R		R
			1		◇1	1	1			◇1		1		1		◇1		1	1		◇1	1	◇1	1
Sheffield 7	29	d		18 17	18 21			18 39	19 16	19 21			19 36		20 17	20 21				20 39	21 03		21 21	
Meadowhall	29	d		18 23				18 45	19 23				19 42		20 23					20 45				
Rotherham Central	29	d											19 49											
Swinton (S.Yorks)	29	d											19 57											
Bolton-upon-Dearne		d											20 02											
Goldthorpe		d											20 04											
Thurnscoe		d											20 07											
Moorthorpe		d											20 12											
Doncaster 7		d	18 20			18 44	19 15				19 27	19 50		20 20			20 28	20 44	20 59			21 19		21 45
Bentley (S.Yorks)		d									19 30													
Adwick		a									19 34													
		d									19 34													
South Elmsall		d									19 41													
Fitzwilliam		d									19 47		20 18											
Sandal & Agbrigg		d									19 53		20 24											
Wakefield Westgate 7	32,39	a	18 38		18 47	19 01	19 32			19 48	19 57	20 07	20 28	20 37		20 49		21 01			21 27	21 36	21 47	22 02
		d	18 39		18 49	19 02	19 33			19 50	19 57	20 09	20 28	20 38		20 50		21 02			21 29	21 37	21 48	22 04
Pontefract Monkhill	32	d																						
Wakefield Kirkgate 4	32,34,39	a		18 52				19 29	19 52						20 52		20 53		21 20	21 29				
		d		18 53				19 30	19 53						20 53					21 30				
Outwood		d									20 02		20 33											
Leeds 10	32,34	a	18 56	19 18	19 04	19 21	19 51	20 05	20 18	20 05	20 16	20 25	20 52	20 52	21 16	21 06		21 18		22 04	21 44	21 55	22 04	22 19

			NT	NT	GR	XC	NT	GR	EM
					R			R	
					1	◇1		1	◇1
Sheffield 7	29	d		21 36		22 21	22 39		23 38
Meadowhall	29	d		21 42			22 45		
Rotherham Central	29	d		21 48					
Swinton (S.Yorks)	29	d		21 56					
Bolton-upon-Dearne		d		22 00					
Goldthorpe		d		22 03					
Thurnscoe		d		22 06					
Moorthorpe		d		22 11					
Doncaster 7		d	21 52		22 24			23 37	
Bentley (S.Yorks)		d	21 55						
Adwick		a	21 59						
		d	21 59						
South Elmsall		d	22 05						
Fitzwilliam		d	22 12	22 17					
Sandal & Agbrigg		d	22 18	22 23					
Wakefield Westgate 7	32,39	a	22 22	22 27	22 40	22 43		23 56	00 03
		d	22 23	22 28	22 41	22 43		23 57	00 04
Pontefract Monkhill	32	d							
Wakefield Kirkgate 4	32,34,39	a					23 26		
		d					23 27		
Outwood		d	22 28	22 33					
Leeds 10	32,34	a	22 42	22 50	22 58	23 01	00 05	00 13	00 20

Table 31R

Mondays to Fridays

9 December to 16 May

Leeds - Wakefield, Doncaster and Sheffield

Network Diagram - see first page of Table 31

Miles	Miles	Station			GR	EM	GR	NT	XC	NT	NT	GR	XC		NT	EM	NT	GR	NT	GR	XC	NT	NT	NT	GR	NT
					R 1	◇1	R 1		◇1			R 1	◇1			◇1		R 1		R 1 A	◇1				R 1	
					🍽🍴	⊠	🍽🍴		🍴			🍽🍴	🍴			🍴		🍽🍴		🍽🍴	🍴				🍽🍴	
0	0	**Leeds** 10	32,34	d	05 05	05 25	05 30	05 33	06 00		06 05	06 05	06 16		06 19	06 34	06 38	06 40	06 43	07 00	07 05		07 05		07 15	07 20
7½	7½	Outwood		d				05 45							06 28				06 54							07 30
—	—	Wakefield Kirkgate 4	32,34,39	a							06 21						07 07						07 25			
—	—			d						06 04	06 21						07 08						07 25			
—	—	Pontefract Monkhill		d																						
10	10	**Wakefield Westgate** 7	32,39	a	05 17	05 36	05 42	05 49	06 11			06 17	06 27		06 32	06 45		06 52	06 58	07 12	07 17				07 27	07 34
—	—			d	05 18	05 38	05 43	05 50	06 12			06 18	06 28		06 33	06 47		06 53	06 59		07 19				07 28	07 34
11¾	11¾	Sandal & Agbrigg		d				05 53							06 36				07 02							07 37
16½	16½	Fitzwilliam		d				06 01							06 43				07 09							07 44
21	—	South Elmsall		d											06 49											07 49
25¾	—	Adwick		a											06 54											07 54
—	—			d											06 55									07 29		07 55
28	—	Bentley (S.Yorks)		d											06 59									07 33		07 59
29¾	—	**Doncaster** 7		a	05 35	05 55	06 01					06 34	06 44		07 08			07 10						07 37	07 45	08 07
—	20¼	Moorthorpe		d				06 07											07 15							
—	23¾	Thurnscoe		d				06 13											07 21							
—	24½	Goldthorpe		d				06 15											07 23							
—	25¾	Bolton-upon-Dearne		d				06 18											07 26							
—	28	Swinton (S.Yorks)	29	a				06 23											07 30					07 53		
—	32½	Rotherham Central	29	a				06 30											07 37			←		08 01		
—	35¼	Meadowhall	29 🚊	a				06 37		06 41	06 51						07 48		07 44			07 48	07 55	08 07		
—	38¾	**Sheffield** 7	29 🚊	a		06 19		06 47	06 41	06 55	07 00		07 10			07 25	→		07 56		07 50	07 58	08 05	08 18		

Station			GC	NT	NT		NT	GR	NT	NT	XC	NT	NT	GR	NT	NT	NT	GR	GC	NT	NT		NT	XC	NT	GR
			R 1					R 1			◇1			R 1				R 1	R 1					◇1		R 1
			🍽					🍽🍴			🍴			🍽🍴				🍽🍴	🍽					🍴		🍽🍴
Leeds 10	32,34	d		07 29	07 35			07 40	07 48	08 02	08 11			08 15	08 20	08 32	08 37	08 45			08 48		09 05	09 11		09 15
Outwood		d					←		07 59						08 29					←	08 59					
Wakefield Kirkgate 4	32,34,39	a		08 00	07 54		08 00			08 23						09 03	08 54			09 03			09 23			
		d	07 42	08 04	07 55		08 04			08 23						09 05	08 55		08 56	09 05			09 23			
Pontefract Monkhill		d	08 01	→												→										
Wakefield Westgate 7	32,39	a						07 51	08 03		08 22			08 27	08 33			08 57			09 03			09 22		09 27
		d						07 52	08 04		08 23			08 28	08 33			08 58			09 04			09 24		09 28
Sandal & Agbrigg		d							08 07						08 37						09 07					
Fitzwilliam		d							08 14						08 44						09 14					
South Elmsall		d													08 49											
Adwick		a													08 55											
		d										08 15	08 31		08 55										09 15	
Bentley (S.Yorks)		d										08 19	08 35		08 59										09 19	
Doncaster 7		a	08 29					08 09				08 24	08 39	08 45	09 07			09 15	09 28						09 24	09 45
Moorthorpe		d							08 20												09 20					
Thurnscoe		d							08 26												09 26					
Goldthorpe		d							08 28												09 28					
Bolton-upon-Dearne		d							08 31												09 31					
Swinton (S.Yorks)	29	a							08 34			08 43									09 35				09 42	
Rotherham Central	29	a							08 44			08 50									09 44				09 50	
Meadowhall	29 🚊	a			08 31		08 46		08 50	08 54		08 56					09 29			09 46	09 51		09 54		09 57	
Sheffield 7	29 🚊	a			08 39		08 56		08 59	09 02	08 52	09 05					09 37			09 56	10 00		10 02	09 52	10 05	

Station			NT	NT	NT	NT	GR	NT	NT	XC FO	XC FX	NT	GR		NT	NT	NT	NT	GR	NT	GC	NT	XC	NT	GR	NT
							R 1		◇	◇1	◇1		R 1						R 1		R 1	◇	◇1		R 1	
							🍽🍴			🍴	🍴		🍽🍴						🍽🍴		🍽		🍴		🍽🍴	
Leeds 10	32,34	d	09 20	09 32	09 37		09 45	09 48	10 05	10 11	10 11		10 15		10 20	10 32	10 37		10 45	10 48		11 05	11 11		11 15	11 20
Outwood		d	09 29			←		09 59							10 29			←		10 59						11 29
Wakefield Kirkgate 4	32,34,39	a		10 01	09 55	10 01			10 23							11 01	10 54	11 01				11 23				
		d		10 04	09 56	10 04			10 23							11 04	10 55	11 04			11 11	11 23				
Pontefract Monkhill		d		→												→					11 36					
Wakefield Westgate 7	32,39	a	09 33				09 57	10 03		10 22	10 22		10 27		10 33				10 57	11 03			11 22		11 27	11 33
		d	09 33				09 58	10 04		10 23	10 23		10 28		10 33				10 58	11 04			11 24		11 28	11 33
Sandal & Agbrigg		d	09 36					10 07							10 36					11 07						11 36
Fitzwilliam		d	09 45					10 14							10 44					11 14						11 44
South Elmsall		d	09 50												10 49											11 49
Adwick		a	09 55												10 54											11 54
		d	09 56									10 15			10 55									11 15		11 55
Bentley (S.Yorks)		d	10 00									10 19			10 59									11 19		11 59
Doncaster 7		a	10 07				10 15					10 24	10 44		11 07				11 15		12 07			11 24	11 45	12 07
Moorthorpe		d						10 20												11 20						
Thurnscoe		d						10 26												11 26						
Goldthorpe		d						10 28												11 28						
Bolton-upon-Dearne		d						10 31												11 31						
Swinton (S.Yorks)	29	a						10 35				10 42								11 35				11 43		
Rotherham Central	29	a						10 44				10 52								11 44				11 52		
Meadowhall	29 🚊	a			10 29	10 47		10 51	10 54			10 57					11 29	11 47		11 51		11 54		11 57		
Sheffield 7	29 🚊	a			10 37	10 56		11 01	11 02	10 51	10 52	11 05					11 37	11 57		12 01		12 02	11 52	12 05		

A West Riding Limited

Table 31R

Mondays to Fridays

9 December to 16 May

Leeds - Wakefield, Doncaster and Sheffield

Network Diagram - see first page of Table 31

		NT	NT	NT	NT	GR	NT	NT	XC	NT	GR	NT		NT	NT	NT	GR	NT	NT	XC	NT	GR	NT	NT	NT
		A				R 1		◇	◇1		R 1						R 1		◇	◇1		R 1			
Leeds 10 32,34	d		11 32	11 37		11 45	11 48	12 05	12 11		12 15	12 20		12 32	12 37		12 45	12 48	13 05	13 11		13 15	13 20	13 32	13 37
Outwood	d				←		11 59					12 29				←		12 59					13 29		
Wakefield Kirkgate 4 32,34,39	a		12 01	11 54	12 01			12 23						13 02	12 54	13 02			13 23					14 01	13 54
	d		12 04	11 55	12 04			12 23						13 04	12 55	13 04			13 23					14 04	13 55
Pontefract Monkhill	d		→											→										→	
Wakefield Westgate 7 32,39	a					11 57	12 03		12 22		12 27	12 33					12 57	13 03		13 22		13 27	13 33		
	d					11 58	12 04		12 23		12 28	12 33					12 58	13 04		13 23		13 28	13 33		
Sandal & Agbrigg	d						12 07					12 36						13 07					13 36		
Fitzwilliam	d						12 14					12 44						13 14					13 45		
South Elmsall	d											12 49											13 50		
Adwick	a											12 55											13 55		
	d									12 15		12 56									13 15		13 56		
Bentley (S.Yorks)	d									12 19		13 00									13 19		14 00		
Doncaster 7	a					12 15				12 25	12 45	13 07					13 15				13 24	13 44	14 07		
Moorthorpe	d	11 59					12 20											13 20							
Thurnscoe	d						12 26											13 26							
Goldthorpe	d						12 28											13 28							
Bolton-upon-Dearne	d						12 31											13 31							
Swinton (S.Yorks) 29	a	12 08					12 35			12 42								13 35			13 42				
Rotherham Central 29	a	12 18					12 44			12 52								13 44			13 52				
Meadowhall 29	a	12 24		12 29	12 47		12 51	12 54		12 57					13 27	13 47		13 51	13 54		13 57				14 29
Sheffield 7 29	a	12 36		12 37	12 56		13 01	13 02	12 52	13 05					13 37	13 56		14 01	14 02	13 51	14 05				14 37

		NT	GR	NT		NT	XC	NT	GR	NT	NT	NT	NT	GR	NT	GC	NT	XC	NT	GR		NT	NT	NT	NT
			R 1			◇	◇1		R 1					R 1		R 1	◇	◇1		R 1			A		
Leeds 10 32,34	d		13 45	13 48		14 05	14 11		14 15	14 20	14 32	14 37		14 45	14 48		15 05	15 11		15 15		15 20		15 32	15 37
Outwood	d	←		13 59						14 29			←		14 59							15 29			
Wakefield Kirkgate 4 32,34,39	a	14 01				14 23					15 01	14 54	15 01				15 23							16 01	15 54
	d	14 04				14 23					15 04	14 55	15 04			15 12	15 23							16 04	15 55
Pontefract Monkhill	d										→					15 34								→	
Wakefield Westgate 7 32,39	a		13 57	14 03			14 22		14 27	14 33				14 57	15 03			15 23		15 27		15 33			
	d		13 58	14 04			14 23		14 28	14 33				14 58	15 04			15 24		15 28		15 33			
Sandal & Agbrigg	d			14 07						14 36					15 07							15 36			
Fitzwilliam	d			14 14						14 44					15 14							15 44			
South Elmsall	d									14 49												15 49			
Adwick	a									14 54												15 54			
	d							14 15		14 55									15 15			15 55			
Bentley (S.Yorks)	d							14 19		14 59									15 19			15 59			
Doncaster 7	a		14 16					14 24	14 44	15 07				15 15		16 12			15 24	15 45		16 07			
Moorthorpe	d			14 20											15 20								15 51		
Thurnscoe	d			14 26											15 26										
Goldthorpe	d			14 28											15 28										
Bolton-upon-Dearne	d			14 31											15 31										
Swinton (S.Yorks) 29	a			14 35				14 42							15 35				15 42				16 00		
Rotherham Central 29	a			14 44				14 52							15 44				15 50				16 10		
Meadowhall 29	a	14 47		14 51		14 54		14 57				15 29	15 47		15 51		15 53		15 55				16 16		16 29
Sheffield 7 29	a	14 56		15 01		15 02	14 52	15 05				15 37	15 56		16 01		16 02	15 52	16 05				16 27		16 37

		NT	GR	NT	NT	XC FO	XC FX	NT	GR	NT	NT	NT		XC	NT	GR	NT	NT	NT	XC FO	XC FX	GR	NT	NT	NT
			R 1		◇	◇1	◇1		R 1					◇1		R 1			◇	◇1	◇1	R 1			
Leeds 10 32,34	d		15 45	15 48	16 05	16 11	16 11		16 15	16 20	16 32	16 37		16 40		16 45	16 48	16 57	17 05	17 11	17 11	17 15	17 20	17 32	17 37
Outwood	d	←		15 59						16 29					←		16 59	17 06					17 29		
Wakefield Kirkgate 4 32,34,39	a	16 01			16 23						17 01	16 54			17 01				17 22					18 01	17 54
	d	16 04			16 23						17 04	16 55			17 04				17 23					18 04	17 55
Pontefract Monkhill	d										→													→	
Wakefield Westgate 7 32,39	a		15 57	16 03		16 22	16 22		16 27	16 33				16 51		16 57	17 03	17 10		17 22	17 22	17 27	17 33		
	d		15 58	16 04		16 23	16 23		16 28	16 33				16 52		16 58	17 04	17 10		17 23	17 23	17 28	17 33		
Sandal & Agbrigg	d			16 07						16 36							17 08						17 36		
Fitzwilliam	d			16 14						16 44							17 15	17 20					17 44		
South Elmsall	d									16 49								17 26					17 49		
Adwick	a									16 54								17 31					17 54		
	d							16 15		16 55								17 32					17 55		
Bentley (S.Yorks)	d							16 19		16 59								17 36					17 59		
Doncaster 7	a		16 15					16 24	16 44	17 07						17 15		17 45				17 44	18 07		
Moorthorpe	d			16 20													17 21								
Thurnscoe	d			16 26													17 27								
Goldthorpe	d			16 28													17 29								
Bolton-upon-Dearne	d			16 31													17 32								
Swinton (S.Yorks) 29	a			16 35				16 40									17 36								
Rotherham Central 29	a			16 44				16 50									17 45								
Meadowhall 29	a	16 47		16 51	16 54			16 57				17 27			17 47		17 50		17 53						18 29
Sheffield 7 29	a	16 56		17 00	17 02	16 51	16 52	17 05				17 37		17 20	17 55		18 02		18 02	17 52	17 53				18 38

A via Pontefract Baghill

Table 31R

Leeds - Wakefield, Doncaster and Sheffield

Mondays to Fridays

9 December to 16 May

Network Diagram - see first page of Table 31

			NT	GR	NT	NT	XC	NT	GR	NT	NT	NT	NT		GR	NT	NT	XC	GR	NT	NT	NT	NT	GR	NT	XC
				R 1		◇	◇1		R 1						R 1		◇	◇1	R 1					R 1		◇1
Leeds 10	32,34	d		17 45	17 48	18 05	18 11		18 15	18 20	18 32	18 43			18 45	18 48	19 05	19 11	19 15	19 19	19 37	19 43		19 45	19 48	20 11
Outwood		d	←		17 59					18 29			←			18 59				19 28			←		19 59	
Wakefield Kirkgate 4	32,34,39	a	18 01			18 23					19 04	18 59	19 04				19 24				20 06	19 59	20 06			
		d	18 04			18 23					19 05	18 59	19 05				19 24				20 07	20 00	20 07			
Pontefract Monkhill		d									→										→					
Wakefield Westgate 7	32,39	a		17 57	18 03		18 22		18 27	18 33					18 56	19 03		19 23	19 27	19 32				19 57	20 03	20 22
		d		17 58	18 04		18 23		18 28	18 33					18 57	19 04		19 24	19 28	19 32				19 58	20 04	20 23
Sandal & Agbrigg		d			18 08					18 36						19 07				19 35					20 07	
Fitzwilliam		d			18 15					18 45						19 14				19 44					20 14	
South Elmsall		d								18 50										19 49						
Adwick		a								18 55										19 54						
		d						18 16		18 56										19 55						
Bentley (S.Yorks)		d						18 20		19 00										19 59						
Doncaster 7		a		18 15				18 27	18 45	19 08					19 13				19 45	20 07				20 16		
Moorthorpe		d			18 21											19 20									20 20	
Thurnscoe		d			18 27											19 26									20 26	
Goldthorpe		d			18 29											19 28									20 28	
Bolton-upon-Dearne		d			18 32											19 31									20 31	
Swinton (S.Yorks)	29	a			18 36											19 35									20 35	
Rotherham Central	29	a			18 44											19 45									20 44	
Meadowhall	29	a	18 47		18 51	18 54						19 35	19 47			19 51	19 54					20 35	20 47		20 51	
Sheffield 7	29	a	18 56		19 00	19 03	18 53					19 43	19 57			19 59	20 04	19 51				20 44	20 58		21 02	20 53

			NT	NT	NT		GR	NT	XC	NT	NT	NT	NT	NT	NT
							R 1		◇1						
Leeds 10	32,34	d	20 20	20 30	20 37		20 45	20 48	21 11	21 21	21 37	21 48	22 37	22 40	23 09
Outwood		d	20 29					20 59		21 30		21 59		22 49	23 20
Wakefield Kirkgate 4	32,34,39	a		20 46	21 06						22 06		23 10		
		d		20 46	21 07						22 07		23 10		
Pontefract Monkhill		d													
Wakefield Westgate 7	32,39	a	20 33				20 57	21 03	21 22	21 34		22 03		22 53	23 24
		d	20 33				20 58	21 04	21 25	21 34		22 04		22 53	23 25
Sandal & Agbrigg		d	20 36					21 07		21 37		22 07		22 56	23 28
Fitzwilliam		d	20 44					21 14		21 45		22 14		23 03	23 35
South Elmsall		d	20 49							21 50				23 08	
Adwick		a	20 54							21 55				23 13	
		d	20 55							21 56				23 14	
Bentley (S.Yorks)		d	20 59							22 00				23 18	
Doncaster 7		a	21 08				21 15			22 07				23 28	
Moorthorpe		d						21 21				22 20			23 41
Thurnscoe		d						21 27				22 26			23 47
Goldthorpe		d						21 29				22 28			23 49
Bolton-upon-Dearne		d						21 32				22 31			23 52
Swinton (S.Yorks)	29	a						21 36				22 35			23 56
Rotherham Central	29	a						21 44				22 47			00 03
Meadowhall	29	a		21 20	21 47			21 51			22 47	22 52	23 51		00 09
Sheffield 7	29	a		21 30	21 58			22 04	21 53		22 58	23 02	00 02		00 23

Saturdays

14 December to 17 May

			GR	XC	GR	XC	NT	EM	NT	NT	NT	NT	GR	XC	NT	NT	GC		NT	EM	NT	NT	NT	GR	NT	XC
			R 1	◇1	R 1	◇1		◇1					R 1	◇1			R 1			◇1				R 1		◇1
Leeds 10	32,34	d	05 05	06 00	06 05	06 16	06 20	06 34	06 38	06 43		07 05	07 05	07 10		07 20			07 29	07 34	07 35		07 48	08 05	08 05	08 11
Outwood		d					06 29			06 54						07 29						←	07 59			
Wakefield Kirkgate 4	32,34,39	a							07 07			07 25							08 00		07 54	08 00			08 23	
		d							07 08			07 25					07 38		08 04		07 55	08 04			08 23	
Pontefract Monkhill		d															07 58		→							
Wakefield Westgate 7	32,39	a	05 17	06 11	06 17	06 28	06 33	06 45		06 58			07 16	07 21		07 34				07 45			08 03	08 17		08 23
		d	05 18	06 12	06 18	06 29	06 33	06 46		06 59			07 17	07 22		07 34				07 46			08 04	08 18		08 24
Sandal & Agbrigg		d					06 36			07 02						07 37							08 07			
Fitzwilliam		d					06 44			07 09						07 44							08 14			
South Elmsall		d					06 49									07 49										
Adwick		a					06 54									07 54										
		d					06 55								07 23	07 55										
Bentley (S.Yorks)		d					06 59								07 27	07 59										
Doncaster 7		a	05 34		06 34	06 45	07 07						07 35		07 31	08 07	08 27							08 35		
Moorthorpe		d								07 15													08 20			
Thurnscoe		d								07 21													08 26			
Goldthorpe		d								07 23													08 28			
Bolton-upon-Dearne		d								07 26													08 31			
Swinton (S.Yorks)	29	a								07 30					07 53								08 35			
Rotherham Central	29	a								07 38	←				08 01								08 44			
Meadowhall	29	a							07 48	07 46	07 48	07 55			08 06						08 31	08 46	08 50		08 53	
Sheffield 7	29	a		06 45		07 15		07 22	→	07 54	07 58	08 05		07 51	08 18					08 21	08 39	08 56	08 59		09 02	08 52

Table 31R

Saturdays

14 December to 17 May

Leeds - Wakefield, Doncaster and Sheffield

Network Diagram - see first page of Table 31

		NT	NT	NT	NT	NT	NT	GR	NT	GR	NT	XC	NT	NT	GC	NT		NT	NT	NT	NT	GR	XC	NT	NT
								R 1		R 1		◇1			R 1							R 1	◇1		
Leeds 10 32,34	d			08 20	08 32	08 37		08 40	08 48	09 05	09 05	09 11		09 20		09 32		09 37		09 48	10 05	10 05	10 11		10 20
Outwood	d			08 29			←		08 59					09 29					←	09 59					10 29
Wakefield Kirkgate 4 32,34,39	a				09 03	08 54	09 03				09 23					10 01		09 54	10 01		10 23				
	d				09 05	08 55	09 05				09 23				09 38	10 04		09 55	10 04		10 23				
Pontefract Monkhill	d				→										09 56	→									
Wakefield Westgate 7 32,39	a			08 33				08 52	09 03	09 17		09 23		09 33						10 03		10 17	10 23		10 33
	d			08 33				08 53	09 04	09 18		09 24		09 33						10 04		10 18	10 24		10 33
Sandal & Agbrigg	d			08 36					09 07					09 36						10 07					10 36
Fitzwilliam	d			08 44					09 14					09 44						10 14					10 44
South Elmsall	d			08 49										09 49											10 49
Adwick	a			08 55										09 55											10 54
	d	08 15	08 33	08 55									09 15	09 55										10 15	10 55
Bentley (S.Yorks)	d	08 19	08 37	08 59									09 19	09 59										10 19	10 59
Doncaster 7	a	08 23	08 42	09 07				09 12		09 34			09 24	10 08	10 22							10 36		10 24	11 07
Moorthorpe	d								09 20											10 20					
Thurnscoe	d								09 26											10 26					
Goldthorpe	d								09 28											10 28					
Bolton-upon-Dearne	d								09 31											10 31					
Swinton (S.Yorks) 29	a	08 43							09 35				09 42							10 35				10 42	
Rotherham Central 29	a	08 50							09 44				09 50							10 44				10 52	
Meadowhall 29	a	08 56				09 29	09 46		09 51		09 54		09 57					10 29	10 46	10 51	10 54			10 57	
Sheffield 7 29	a	09 05				09 37	09 56		10 00		10 02	09 53	10 05					10 37	10 56	11 00	11 02		10 52	11 05	

		NT	NT	NT	NT	GR	GC	NT		XC	NT	NT	NT	NT	NT	NT	NT	NT	GR	XC	NT	NT	NT	NT	
						R 1	R 1			◇1									R 1	◇1					
Leeds 10 32,34	d	10 32	10 37		10 48	11 05		11 05		11 11		11 20		11 32	11 37		11 48	12 05	12 05	12 11		12 20	12 32	12 37	
Outwood	d			←	10 59							11 29				←	11 59					12 29			
Wakefield Kirkgate 4 32,34,39	a	11 01	10 54	11 01				11 23						12 01	11 54	12 01		12 23					13 02	12 54	
	d	11 04	10 55	11 04			11 13	11 23						12 04	11 55	12 04		12 23					13 04	12 55	
Pontefract Monkhill	d	→					11 37							→									→		
Wakefield Westgate 7 32,39	a				11 03	11 17				11 22		11 33					12 03		12 17	12 23		12 33			
	d				11 04	11 18				11 24		11 33					12 04		12 18	12 24		12 33			
Sandal & Agbrigg	d				11 07							11 36					12 07					12 36			
Fitzwilliam	d				11 14							11 44					12 14					12 44			
South Elmsall	d											11 49										12 49			
Adwick	a											11 54										12 54			
	d										11 15	11 55									12 15	12 55			
Bentley (S.Yorks)	d										11 19	11 59									12 19	12 59			
Doncaster 7	a					11 35	12 04				11 24	12 07							12 35		12 24	13 07			
Moorthorpe	d				11 20								11 59				12 20								
Thurnscoe	d				11 26												12 26								
Goldthorpe	d				11 28												12 28								
Bolton-upon-Dearne	d				11 31												12 31								
Swinton (S.Yorks) 29	a				11 35						11 42		12 08				12 35				12 42				
Rotherham Central 29	a				11 44						11 52		12 18				12 44				12 52				
Meadowhall 29	a		11 29	11 46	11 51			11 54			11 57		12 24		12 29	12 47	12 51	12 54			12 57			13 27	
Sheffield 7 29	a		11 37	11 57	12 00			12 02		11 52	12 05		12 36		12 37	12 56	13 00	13 02		12 52	13 05			13 37	

		NT	NT	NT	GR	XC	XC	NT	NT	NT	NT	NT	NT	NT	GR	XC		NT	NT	NT	NT	NT	GR	NT	NT
					R 1	◇1 A	◇1 B								R 1	◇1							R 1		
Leeds 10 32,34	d		12 48	13 05	13 05	13 11	13 11		13 20	13 32	13 37		13 48	14 05	14 05	14 11			14 20	14 32	14 37		14 40	14 48	15 05
Outwood	d	←	12 59						13 29			←	13 59						14 29			←		14 59	
Wakefield Kirkgate 4 32,34,39	a	13 02		13 23						14 01	13 54	14 01		14 23						15 01	14 54	15 01			15 23
	d	13 04		13 23						14 04	13 55	14 04		14 23						15 04	14 55	15 04			15 23
Pontefract Monkhill	d									→										→					
Wakefield Westgate 7 32,39	a		13 03		13 17	13 22	13 22		13 33				14 03		14 17	14 23			14 33				14 52	15 03	
	d		13 04		13 18	13 23	13 23		13 33				14 04		14 18	14 24			14 33				14 54	15 04	
Sandal & Agbrigg	d		13 07						13 36				14 07						14 36					15 07	
Fitzwilliam	d		13 14						13 44				14 14						14 44					15 14	
South Elmsall	d								13 49										14 49						
Adwick	a								13 54										14 54						
	d							13 15	13 55									14 15	14 55						
Bentley (S.Yorks)	d							13 19	13 59									14 19	14 59						
Doncaster 7	a				13 35			13 24	14 07						14 35			14 24	15 07				15 10		
Moorthorpe	d		13 20										14 20											15 20	
Thurnscoe	d		13 26										14 26											15 26	
Goldthorpe	d		13 28										14 28											15 28	
Bolton-upon-Dearne	d		13 31										14 31											15 31	
Swinton (S.Yorks) 29	a		13 35					13 42					14 35					14 43						15 35	
Rotherham Central 29	a		13 44					13 52					14 44					14 52						15 44	
Meadowhall 29	a	13 46	13 51	13 54				13 57			14 29	14 46	14 51	14 54				14 57			15 29	15 46		15 51	15 53
Sheffield 7 29	a	13 56	14 00	14 02		13 51	13 52	14 05			14 37	14 56	15 00	15 02		14 52		15 05			15 37	15 56		16 00	16 02

A 14 December, 21 December, 28 December **B** from 4 January

Table 31R

Saturdays

14 December to 17 May

Leeds - Wakefield, Doncaster and Sheffield

Network Diagram - see first page of Table 31

			GR	XC	NT	NT	NT	NT	NT	NT	NT	GR	GC	NT	XC	NT	NT		NT	NT	XC	NT	NT	NT	GR	XC
			R 1	◇1								R 1	R 1		◇1						◇1				R 1	◇1
							A																			
Leeds 10	32,34	d	15 05	15 11		15 20		15 32	15 37		15 48	16 05		16 05	16 11		16 20		16 32	16 37	16 40		16 48	17 05	17 05	17 11
Outwood		d				15 29				←	15 59						16 29					←	16 59			
Wakefield Kirkgate 4	32,34,39	a						16 01	15 54	16 01				16 23					17 01	16 54		17 01		17 22		
		d						16 04	15 55	16 04			16 13	16 23					17 04	16 55		17 04		17 23		
Pontefract Monkhill		d						→					16 34						→							
Wakefield Westgate 7	32,39	a	15 17	15 23		15 33					16 03	16 17			16 23		16 33				16 51		17 03		17 17	17 22
		d	15 18	15 24		15 33					16 04	16 18			16 24		16 33				16 52		17 04		17 18	17 23
Sandal & Agbrigg		d				15 36					16 07						16 36						17 07			
Fitzwilliam		d				15 44					16 14						16 44						17 14			
South Elmsall		d				15 49											16 49									
Adwick		a				15 54											16 54									
		d			15 15	15 55										16 15	16 55									
Bentley (S.Yorks)		d			15 19	15 59										16 19	16 59									
Doncaster 7		a	15 34		15 24	16 07						16 35	17 02			16 24	17 07								17 35	
Moorthorpe		d					15 51				16 20												17 20			
Thurnscoe		d									16 26												17 26			
Goldthorpe		d									16 28												17 28			
Bolton-upon-Dearne		d									16 31												17 31			
Swinton (S.Yorks)	29	a			15 42		16 01				16 35					16 40							17 35			
Rotherham Central	29	a			15 50		16 09				16 44					16 50							17 44			
Meadowhall	29	a			15 56		16 17		16 29	16 46	16 51			16 54		16 57				17 27		17 46	17 50	17 53		
Sheffield 7	29	a		15 52	16 05		16 27		16 37	16 56	17 00			17 02	16 52	17 05				17 37	17 20	17 55	17 59	18 02		17 52

			NT	NT	NT	NT	NT	NT	NT		GR	XC	XC	NT	NT	NT	NT	NT	NT	GR	XC	NT	NT	NT	NT	
											R 1	◇1	◇1							R 1	◇1					
												B	C													
Leeds 10	32,34	d	17 20		17 32	17 37		17 48	18 05		18 05	18 11	18 11	18 20	18 32	18 37		18 48	19 05	19 05	19 11	19 20	19 37	19 43		
Outwood		d	17 29				←	17 59						18 29			←	18 59				19 29			←	
Wakefield Kirkgate 4	32,34,39	a			18 01	17 54	18 01		18 23						19 04	18 54	19 04		19 24				20 06	19 59	20 06	
		d			18 04	17 55	18 04		18 23						19 05	18 55	19 05		19 24				20 07	20 00	20 07	
Pontefract Monkhill		d			→										→								→			
Wakefield Westgate 7	32,39	a	17 33					18 03			18 17	18 22	18 22	18 33				19 03		19 17	19 23	19 33				
		d	17 33					18 04			18 18	18 23	18 23	18 33				19 04		19 18	19 24	19 33				
Sandal & Agbrigg		d	17 36					18 08						18 36				19 07				19 36				
Fitzwilliam		d	17 44					18 15						18 44				19 14				19 44				
South Elmsall		d	17 49											18 49								19 49				
Adwick		a	17 54											18 54								19 54				
		d	17 55	18 16										18 55								19 55				
Bentley (S.Yorks)		d	17 59	18 20										18 59								19 59				
Doncaster 7		a	18 07	18 27							18 34			19 07						19 36		20 07				
Moorthorpe		d						18 21										19 20								
Thurnscoe		d						18 27										19 26								
Goldthorpe		d						18 29										19 28								
Bolton-upon-Dearne		d						18 32										19 31								
Swinton (S.Yorks)	29	a						18 36										19 35								
Rotherham Central	29	a						18 43										19 44								
Meadowhall	29	a				18 29	18 46	18 51	18 54							19 30	19 47	19 51	19 54					20 35	20 47	
Sheffield 7	29	a				18 38	18 56	19 00	19 03			18 52	18 53			19 40	19 57	19 59	20 04		19 51			20 44	20 58	

			NT	GR	XC	NT	NT	NT	NT	XC	NT	NT	NT	NT	NT	NT
				R 1	◇1					◇1						
Leeds 10	32,34	d	19 48	20 05	20 11	20 20	20 30	20 37	20 48	21 11	21 20	21 37	21 48	22 16	22 37	22 44
Outwood		d	19 59			20 29			20 59		21 29		21 59	22 25		22 55
Wakefield Kirkgate 4	32,34,39	a					20 46	21 06				22 06			23 10	
		d					20 46	21 07				22 07				
Pontefract Monkhill		d														
Wakefield Westgate 7	32,39	a	20 03	20 17	20 22	20 33			21 03	21 22	21 33		22 03	22 29		22 59
		d	20 04	20 18	20 23	20 33			21 04	21 23	21 33		22 04	22 30		23 00
Sandal & Agbrigg		d	20 07			20 36			21 07		21 36		22 07	22 33		23 03
Fitzwilliam		d	20 14			20 44			21 14		21 44		22 14	22 39		23 10
South Elmsall		d				20 49					21 49			22 44		
Adwick		a				20 54					21 54			22 50		
		d				20 55					21 55			22 50		
Bentley (S.Yorks)		d				20 59					21 59			22 54		
Doncaster 7		a		20 34		21 07					22 07			23 04		
Moorthorpe		d	20 20						21 21				22 20			23 16
Thurnscoe		d	20 26						21 27				22 26			23 22
Goldthorpe		d	20 28						21 29				22 28			23 24
Bolton-upon-Dearne		d	20 31						21 32				22 31			23 27
Swinton (S.Yorks)	29	a	20 35						21 36				22 35			23 31
Rotherham Central	29	a	20 44						21 44				22 47			23 38
Meadowhall	29	a	20 51				21 21	21 48	21 51			22 47	22 52			23 44
Sheffield 7	29	a	21 00		20 53		21 30	21 57	22 02	21 52		22 58	23 03			23 58

A via Pontefract Baghill

B from 4 January until 8 February

C from 15 February

Table 31R

Sundays

8 December to 29 December

Leeds - Wakefield, Doncaster and Sheffield

Network Diagram - see first page of Table 31

	GR	XC	GC	NT	NT	XC	NT	GR	EM	XC	NT	GR	NT	NT	EM	NT	XC	GR	NT	NT	NT	GR
	R 1	◇1	R 1			◇1		R 1	◇1	◇1		R 1			◇1		◇1	R 1				R 1
Leeds 10 32,34 d	08 05	08 10		08 34	08 48	09 00	09 05	09 05	09 45	10 00	10 02	10 05	10 17	10 20	10 51	10 57	11 00	11 05	11 20	11 29		12 05
Outwood d					08 59									10 29					11 31			
Wakefield Kirkgate 4 32,34,39 a				09 03			09 21				10 18		10 46			11 13				11 46		
d			08 46	09 03			09 21				10 18		10 46			11 13				11 46		
Pontefract Monkhill d																						
Wakefield Westgate 7 32,39 a	08 16	08 21			09 03	09 11		09 17	09 56	10 11		10 16		10 33	11 02		11 11	11 16	11 35			12 16
d	08 17	08 23			09 03	09 12		09 18	09 58	10 12		10 17		10 33	11 04		11 12	11 18	11 35			12 17
Sandal & Agbrigg d					09 07									10 36					11 39			
Fitzwilliam d					09 14									10 43					11 46			
South Elmsall d														10 48								
Adwick a														10 53								
d														10 54								
Bentley (S.Yorks) d														10 58								
Doncaster 7 a	08 34		09 06			09 31		09 35		10 28		10 33		11 06			11 28	11 34				12 33
Moorthorpe d					09 20														11 52			
Thurnscoe d					09 26														11 58			
Goldthorpe d					09 28														12 00			
Bolton-upon-Dearne d					09 31														12 03			
Swinton (S.Yorks) 29 a					09 35														12 07			
Rotherham Central 29 a					09 44														12 14		←	
Meadowhall 29 a				09 44	09 53		09 57				10 51		11 32			11 46			12 24	12 17	12 24	
Sheffield 7 29 a		08 51		09 55	10 03	09 55	10 04		10 25	10 54	11 02		11 44		11 36	11 56	11 53		→	12 29	12 32	

	XC	NT	NT	GC	NT	GR	XC	NT	NT	GR	XC	NT	NT	EM	GR	NT	GC	XC	NT	NT	XC	GR	NT
	◇1			R 1		R 1	◇1			R 1	◇1			◇1	R 1		R 1	◇1			◇1	R 1	
Leeds 10 32,34 d	12 10	12 20	12 29		12 34	13 05	13 10	13 20	14 05	14 05	14 10	14 17	14 20	14 39	15 05	15 05		15 10	15 20	16 04	16 10	16 16	16 17
Outwood d		12 29						13 31					14 29						15 31				
Wakefield Kirkgate 4 32,34,39 a			12 46		13 04				14 21			14 46				15 22				16 21			16 46
d			12 49	12 49	13 04				14 21			14 46				15 22	16 02			16 22			16 49
Pontefract Monkhill d																							
Wakefield Westgate 7 32,39 a	12 21	12 33				13 17	13 21	13 35		14 17	14 22		14 33	14 51	15 17			15 21	15 35		16 21	16 27	
d	12 23	12 33				13 18	13 24	13 35		14 18	14 23		14 33	14 53	15 18			15 23	15 35		16 22	16 28	
Sandal & Agbrigg d		12 36						13 39					14 36						15 39				
Fitzwilliam d		12 43						13 46					14 43						15 46				
South Elmsall d		12 48											14 48										
Adwick a		12 53											14 53										
d		12 54											14 54										
Bentley (S.Yorks) d		12 58											14 58										
Doncaster 7 a		13 06		13 10		13 35				14 34			15 06		15 35		16 23					16 44	
Moorthorpe d								13 52											15 52				
Thurnscoe d								13 58											15 58				
Goldthorpe d								14 00											16 00				
Bolton-upon-Dearne d								14 03											16 03				
Swinton (S.Yorks) 29 a								14 07											16 09				
Rotherham Central 29 a								14 14											16 17				
Meadowhall 29 a			13 19		13 48			14 21	14 54			15 35				15 55			16 22	16 56			17 34
Sheffield 7 29 a	12 54		13 30		13 58		13 53	14 32	15 06		14 52	15 44		15 24		16 05		15 51	16 32	17 05	16 51		17 44

	NT	GC	GR	NT	XC	GR	NT	GR	NT	XC	GR	NT	NT	NT	GR	NT	XC	GR	NT	GR	XC	NT
		R 1	R 1		◇1	R 1		R 1		◇1	R 1	A			R 1		◇1	R 1		R 1	◇1	
Leeds 10 32,34 d	16 19		16 45	17 05	17 10	17 16	17 20	17 45	18 03	18 10	18 16		18 17	18 19	18 45	19 04	19 10	19 16	19 20	19 45	20 10	20 17
Outwood d	16 28						17 31							18 28					19 31			
Wakefield Kirkgate 4 32,34,39 a				17 21					18 18				18 45			19 21						20 46
d		16 49		17 21					18 21				18 45			19 21						20 46
Pontefract Monkhill d																						
Wakefield Westgate 7 32,39 a	16 32		16 57		17 21	17 28	17 34	17 57		18 21	18 27			18 32	18 57		19 21	19 27	19 35	19 57	20 21	
d	16 32		16 58		17 23	17 29	17 34	17 58		18 22	18 28			18 32	18 58		19 22	19 28	19 35	19 58	20 22	
Sandal & Agbrigg d	16 35						17 38							18 35					19 39			
Fitzwilliam d	16 42						17 45							18 42					19 46			
South Elmsall d	16 47													18 47								
Adwick a	16 52													18 52								
d	16 53													18 53								
Bentley (S.Yorks) d	16 57													18 57								
Doncaster 7 a	17 06	17 10	17 17			17 45		18 15			18 44			19 06	19 17			19 44		20 16		
Moorthorpe d							17 52					18 52							19 52			
Thurnscoe d							17 58												19 58			
Goldthorpe d							18 00												20 00			
Bolton-upon-Dearne d							18 03												20 03			
Swinton (S.Yorks) 29 a							18 07					19 01							20 09			
Rotherham Central 29 a							18 17					19 12							20 16			
Meadowhall 29 a				17 55			18 24		18 56			19 18	19 32			19 54			20 22			21 33
Sheffield 7 29 a				18 05	17 52		18 34		19 06	18 51		19 27	19 43			20 04	19 50		20 34		20 51	21 42

A via Pontefract Baghill

Table 31R

Sundays

8 December to 29 December

Leeds - Wakefield, Doncaster and Sheffield

Network Diagram - see first page of Table 31

			NT	GR	XC	NT	NT	NT	NT
				R					
				1	◇1				
							A		
				⊡⊥					
Leeds 10	32,34	d	20 20	20 45	21 10	21 18		21 41	22 17
Outwood		d	20 29			21 27		21 52	
Wakefield Kirkgate 4	32,34,39	a							22 46
		d							22 46
Pontefract Monkhill		d							
Wakefield Westgate 7	32,39	a	20 33	20 57	21 21	21 31		21 56	
		d	20 33	20 58	21 22	21 31		21 56	
Sandal & Agbrigg		d	20 36			21 34		22 00	
Fitzwilliam		d	20 43			21 41		22 07	
South Elmsall		d	20 48			21 46			
Adwick		a	20 53			21 51			
		d	20 54			21 52			
Bentley (S.Yorks)		d	20 58			21 56			
Doncaster 7		a	21 06	21 14		22 04			
Moorthorpe		d					21 36	22 13	
Thurnscoe		d						22 19	
Goldthorpe		d						22 21	
Bolton-upon-Dearne		d						22 24	
Swinton (S.Yorks)	29	a					21 45	22 29	
Rotherham Central	29	a					21 52	22 38	
Meadowhall	29 🚋	a					21 57	22 43	23 30
Sheffield 7	29 🚋	a			21 50		22 09	22 52	23 43

Sundays

5 January to 9 February

			GR	XC	GC	NT	EM	NT	NT	GR	XC	EM	XC	NT	GR	NT	NT		NT	XC	GR	NT	NT	NT	GR	XC
			R		R					R					R						R				R	
			1	◇1	1		◇1			1	◇1	◇1	◇1		1					◇1	1				1	◇1
			⊡⊥	⊥	⊡		⊡			⊡⊥	⊥	⊡	⊥		⊡⊥					⊥	⊡⊥				⊡⊥	⊥
Leeds 10	32,34	d	08 05	08 10		08 34	08 43	08 48	09 05	09 05	09 15	09 51	10 00	10 02	10 05	10 17	10 20		10 57	11 00	11 05	11 20	11 29		12 05	12 10
Outwood		d						08 59									10 29					11 31				
Wakefield Kirkgate 4	32,34,39	a				09 03			09 21					10 18		10 46			11 13				11 46			
		d			08 46	09 03			09 21					10 18		10 46			11 13				11 46			
Pontefract Monkhill		d																								
Wakefield Westgate 7	32,39	a	08 16	08 21			08 56	09 03		09 17	09 26	10 05	10 11		10 16		10 33			11 11	11 16	11 35			12 16	12 21
		d	08 17	08 23			08 57	09 03		09 18	09 26	10 06	10 12		10 17		10 33			11 12	11 17	11 35			12 17	12 23
Sandal & Agbrigg		d						09 07									10 36					11 39				
Fitzwilliam		d						09 14									10 43					11 46				
South Elmsall		d															10 48									
Adwick		a															10 53									
		d															10 54									
Bentley (S.Yorks)		d															10 58									
Doncaster 7		a	08 33		09 10					09 35					10 33		11 06				11 36				12 33	
Moorthorpe		d						09 20														11 52				
Thurnscoe		d						09 26														11 58				
Goldthorpe		d						09 28														12 00				
Bolton-upon-Dearne		d						09 31														12 03				
Swinton (S.Yorks)	29	a						09 35														12 07				
Rotherham Central	29	a						09 44														12 14		←		
Meadowhall	29 🚋	a				09 44		09 53	09 57					10 51		11 32			11 46			12 24	12 17	12 24		
Sheffield 7	29 🚋	a		08 51		09 55	09 25	10 03	10 04		09 55	10 33	10 41	11 02		11 44			11 56	11 39		→	12 29	12 32		12 54

			NT	NT	GC	NT	GR	XC	NT		EM	NT	GR	XC	NT	NT	GR	NT	GC	XC	NT	NT	XC	GR	NT	
					R		R						R				R		R					R		
					1		1	◇1			◇1		1	◇1			1		1	◇1			◇1	1		
					⊡		⊡⊥	⊥			⊡		⊡⊥	⊥			⊡⊥		⊡	⊥			⊥	⊡⊥		
Leeds 10	32,34	d	12 20	12 29		12 34	13 05	13 10	13 20		13 41	14 05	14 05	14 10	14 17	14 20	15 05	15 05		15 10	15 20	16 04	16 10	16 16	16 17	
Outwood		d	12 29						13 31							14 29					15 31					
Wakefield Kirkgate 4	32,34,39	a		12 46		13 04						14 21			14 46			15 22				16 21			16 46	
		d		12 49	12 49	13 04						14 21			14 46			15 22	16 02			16 22			16 49	
Pontefract Monkhill		d																								
Wakefield Westgate 7	32,39	a	12 33				13 17	13 21	13 35		13 53		14 17	14 22		14 33	15 17			15 21	15 35		16 21	16 27		
		d	12 33				13 18	13 24	13 35		13 55		14 18	14 23		14 33	15 18			15 23	15 35		16 22	16 28		
Sandal & Agbrigg		d	12 36						13 39							14 36					15 39					
Fitzwilliam		d	12 43						13 46							14 43					15 46					
South Elmsall		d	12 48													14 48										
Adwick		a	12 53													14 53										
		d	12 54													14 54										
Bentley (S.Yorks)		d	12 58													14 58										
Doncaster 7		a	13 06		13 10		13 35						14 34			15 06	15 35		16 23					16 44		
Moorthorpe		d							13 52												15 52					
Thurnscoe		d							13 58												15 58					
Goldthorpe		d							14 00												16 00					
Bolton-upon-Dearne		d							14 03												16 03					
Swinton (S.Yorks)	29	a							14 07												16 07					
Rotherham Central	29	a							14 14												16 15					
Meadowhall	29 🚋	a		13 19		13 48			14 21			14 54			15 35			15 55			16 22	16 56			17 34	
Sheffield 7	29 🚋	a		13 30		13 58		13 53	14 32		14 23	15 06		14 52	15 44			16 05		15 51	16 32	17 05	16 51		17 44	

A via Pontefract Baghill

Table 31R

Sundays

5 January to 9 February

Leeds - Wakefield, Doncaster and Sheffield

Network Diagram - see first page of Table 31

		NT	GC	GR	NT	XC	GR	NT	GR	NT	XC	GR	NT	NT	NT	GR	NT	XC	NT	GR	XC	NT	NT
			R	R			R		R			R				R				R			
			1	1		◇1	1		1		◇1	1				1		◇1		1	◇1		
													A										
			🍴	🍴🛒		🛒	🍴🛒		🍴🛒		🛒	🍴🛒				🍴🛒		🛒		🍴🛒			
Leeds 10 ... 32,34	d	16 19		16 45	17 05	17 10	17 16	17 20	17 45	18 03	18 10	18 16		18 17	18 19	18 45	19 04	19 10	19 20	19 45	20 10	20 17	20 20
Outwood	d	16 28						17 31							18 28				19 31				20 29
Wakefield Kirkgate 4 . 32,34,39	a				17 21					18 18				18 45			19 21					20 46	
	d		16 49		17 21					18 21				18 45			19 21					20 46	
Pontefract Monkhill	d																						
Wakefield Westgate 7 32,39	a	16 32		16 57		17 21	17 28	17 34	17 57		18 21	18 27			18 32	18 57		19 21	19 35	19 57	20 21		20 33
	d	16 32		16 58		17 23	17 29	17 34	17 58		18 22	18 28			18 32	18 58		19 22	19 35	19 58	20 22		20 33
Sandal & Agbrigg	d	16 35						17 38							18 35				19 39				20 36
Fitzwilliam	d	16 42						17 45							18 42				19 46				20 43
South Elmsall	d	16 47													18 47								20 48
Adwick	a	16 52													18 52								20 53
	d	16 53													18 53								20 54
Bentley (S.Yorks)	d	16 57													18 57								20 58
Doncaster 7	a	17 06	17 10	17 15			17 45		18 15			18 44			19 06	19 17				20 16			21 06
Moorthorpe	d							17 52					18 52						19 54				
Thurnscoe	d							17 58											20 00				
Goldthorpe	d							18 00											20 02				
Bolton-upon-Dearne	d							18 03											20 05				
Swinton (S.Yorks) 29	a							18 07					19 01						20 11				
Rotherham Central 29	a							18 14					19 12						20 18				
Meadowhall 29 🚋	a				17 55			18 24		18 56			19 18	19 32			19 54		20 23			21 33	
Sheffield 7 29 🚋	a				18 05	17 52		18 34		19 06	18 51		19 30	19 43			20 04	19 50	20 34		20 51	21 42	

		GR	XC	NT	NT	NT	NT
		R					
		1	◇1				
					A		
		🍴🛒					
Leeds 10 ... 32,34	d	20 45	21 10	21 18		21 41	22 17
Outwood	d			21 27		21 52	
Wakefield Kirkgate 4 . 32,34,39	a						22 46
	d						22 46
Pontefract Monkhill	d						
Wakefield Westgate 7 32,39	a	20 57	21 21	21 31		21 56	
	d	20 58	21 22	21 31		21 56	
Sandal & Agbrigg	d			21 34		22 00	
Fitzwilliam	d			21 41		22 07	
South Elmsall	d			21 46			
Adwick	a			21 51			
	d			21 52			
Bentley (S.Yorks)	d			21 56			
Doncaster 7	a	21 14		22 04			
Moorthorpe	d				21 36	22 13	
Thurnscoe	d					22 19	
Goldthorpe	d					22 21	
Bolton-upon-Dearne	d					22 24	
Swinton (S.Yorks) 29	a				21 45	22 29	
Rotherham Central 29	a				21 52	22 38	
Meadowhall 29 🚋	a				21 57	22 43	23 30
Sheffield 7 29 🚋	a		21 50		22 09	22 52	23 43

Sundays

16 February to 23 March

		GR	XC	NT	NT	XC	NT	GR	EM	XC	NT	GR	EM	NT	NT	NT	XC	GR	NT	NT	NT	GR	XC	NT
		R						R				R						R				R		
		1	◇1			◇1		1	◇1	◇1		1	◇1				◇1	1				1	◇1	
		🍴🛒	🛒			🛒		🍴🛒	🍴	🛒		🍴🛒	🍴				🛒	🍴🛒				🍴🛒	🛒	
Leeds 10 ... 32,34	d	08 05	08 10	08 34	08 48	09 00	09 05	09 05	09 45	10 00	10 02	10 05	10 15	10 17	10 20	10 57	11 00	11 05	11 20	11 29		12 05	12 10	12 20
Outwood	d				08 59										10 29				11 31					12 29
Wakefield Kirkgate 4 . 32,34,39	a			09 03			09 21				10 18			10 46		11 13				11 46				
	d			09 03			09 21				10 18			10 46		11 13				11 46				
Pontefract Monkhill	d																							
Wakefield Westgate 7 32,39	a	08 16	08 21		09 03	09 11		09 17	09 56	10 11		10 16	10 26		10 33		11 11	11 16	11 35			12 16	12 21	12 33
	d	08 17	08 23		09 03	09 12		09 18	09 58	10 12		10 17	10 28		10 33		11 12	11 17	11 35			12 17	12 23	12 33
Sandal & Agbrigg	d				09 07										10 36				11 39					12 36
Fitzwilliam	d				09 14										10 43				11 46					12 43
South Elmsall	d														10 48									12 48
Adwick	a														10 53									12 53
	d														10 54									12 54
Bentley (S.Yorks)	d														10 58									12 58
Doncaster 7	a	08 33				09 31		09 35		10 28		10 33			11 06		11 28	11 36				12 33		13 06
Moorthorpe	d				09 20														11 52					
Thurnscoe	d				09 26														11 58					
Goldthorpe	d				09 28														12 00					
Bolton-upon-Dearne	d				09 31														12 03					
Swinton (S.Yorks) 29	a				09 35														12 07					
Rotherham Central 29	a				09 44														12 14		←			
Meadowhall 29 🚋	a			09 44	09 53		09 57				10 51			11 32		11 46			12 24	12 17	12 24			
Sheffield 7 29 🚋	a		08 51	09 55	10 03	09 55	10 04		10 25	10 54	11 02		10 57	11 44		11 56	11 53		→	12 29	12 32		12 54	

A via Pontefract Baghill

Table 31R

Sundays

16 February to 23 March

Leeds - Wakefield, Doncaster and Sheffield

Network Diagram - see first page of Table 31

	NT	GC	NT	GR	XC	NT	EM	NT	GR	XC	NT	NT	GR	NT	GC		XC	NT	NT	XC	GR	NT	NT	GC
		R 1		R 1	◇1		◇1		R 1	◇1			R 1		R 1		◇1			◇1	R 1			R 1
Leeds 10 32,34 d	12 29		12 34	13 05	13 10	13 20	13 59	14 05	14 05	14 10	14 17	14 20	15 05	15 05			15 10	15 20	16 04	16 10	16 16	16 17	16 19	
Outwood d						13 31						14 29						15 31					16 28	
Wakefield Kirkgate 4 32,34,39 a	12 46		13 04					14 21			14 46			15 22					16 21			16 46		
d	12 49	12 49	13 04					14 21			14 46			15 22	16 02				16 22			16 49		16 49
Pontefract Monkhill d																								
Wakefield Westgate 7 32,39 a				13 17	13 21	13 35	14 11		14 17	14 22		14 33	15 17				15 21	15 35		16 21	16 27		16 32	
d				13 18	13 24	13 35	14 13		14 18	14 23		14 33	15 18				15 23	15 35		16 22	16 28		16 32	
Sandal & Agbrigg d						13 39						14 36						15 39					16 35	
Fitzwilliam d						13 46						14 43						15 46					16 42	
South Elmsall d												14 48											16 47	
Adwick a												14 53											16 52	
d												14 54											16 53	
Bentley (S.Yorks) d												14 58											16 57	
Doncaster 7 a		13 10		13 35					14 34			15 06	15 35		16 23						16 44		17 06	17 10
Moorthorpe d						13 52												15 52						
Thurnscoe d						13 58												15 58						
Goldthorpe d						14 00												16 00						
Bolton-upon-Dearne d						14 03												16 03						
Swinton (S.Yorks) 29 a						14 07												16 09						
Rotherham Central 29 a						14 14												16 17						
Meadowhall 29 a	13 19		13 48			14 21		14 54			15 35			15 55				16 22	16 56			17 34		
Sheffield 7 29 a	13 30		13 58		13 53	14 32	14 44	15 06		14 52	15 44			16 05			15 51	16 32	17 05	16 51		17 44		

	GR	NT	XC	GR	NT	GR	NT		XC	GR	NT	NT	NT	GR	NT	XC	NT	GR	XC	NT	NT	GR	XC	
	R 1		◇1	R 1		R 1			◇1	R 1	A			R 1		◇1		R 1	◇1			R 1	◇1	
Leeds 10 32,34 d	16 45	17 05	17 10	17 16	17 20	17 45	18 03		18 10	18 16		18 17	18 19	18 45	19 04	19 10	19 20	19 45	20 10	20 17	20 20	20 45	21 10	
Outwood d					17 31								18 28				19 31				20 29			
Wakefield Kirkgate 4 32,34,39 a		17 21					18 18					18 45			19 21					20 46				
d		17 21					18 21					18 45			19 21					20 46				
Pontefract Monkhill d																								
Wakefield Westgate 7 32,39 a	16 57		17 21	17 28	17 34	17 57			18 21	18 27			18 32	18 57		19 21	19 35	19 57	20 21		20 33	20 57	21 21	
d	16 58		17 23	17 29	17 34	17 58			18 22	18 28			18 32	18 58		19 22	19 35	19 58	20 22		20 33	20 58	21 22	
Sandal & Agbrigg d					17 38								18 35				19 39				20 36			
Fitzwilliam d					17 45								18 42				19 46				20 43			
South Elmsall d													18 47								20 48			
Adwick a													18 52								20 53			
d													18 53								20 54			
Bentley (S.Yorks) d													18 57								20 58			
Doncaster 7 a	17 15			17 45		18 15				18 44			19 06	19 17				20 16			21 06	21 14		
Moorthorpe d					17 52						18 52						19 52							
Thurnscoe d					17 58												19 58							
Goldthorpe d					18 00												20 00							
Bolton-upon-Dearne d					18 03												20 03							
Swinton (S.Yorks) 29 a					18 07						19 01						20 09							
Rotherham Central 29 a					18 17						19 12						20 16							
Meadowhall 29 a		17 55			18 24		18 56				19 18	19 32			19 54		20 22			21 33				
Sheffield 7 29 a		18 05	17 52		18 34		19 06		18 51		19 27	19 43			20 04	19 50	20 34		20 51	21 42			21 50	

	NT	NT	NT	NT
		A		
Leeds 10 32,34 d	21 18		21 41	22 17
Outwood d	21 27		21 52	
Wakefield Kirkgate 4 32,34,39 a				22 46
d				22 46
Pontefract Monkhill d				
Wakefield Westgate 7 32,39 a	21 31		21 56	
d	21 31		21 56	
Sandal & Agbrigg d	21 34		22 00	
Fitzwilliam d	21 41		22 07	
South Elmsall d	21 46			
Adwick a	21 51			
d	21 52			
Bentley (S.Yorks) d	21 56			
Doncaster 7 a	22 04			
Moorthorpe d		21 36	22 13	
Thurnscoe d			22 19	
Goldthorpe d			22 21	
Bolton-upon-Dearne d			22 24	
Swinton (S.Yorks) 29 a		21 45	22 29	
Rotherham Central 29 a		21 52	22 38	
Meadowhall 29 a		21 57	22 43	23 30
Sheffield 7 29 a		22 09	22 52	23 43

A via Pontefract Baghill

Table 31R

Sundays

30 March to 11 May

Leeds - Wakefield, Doncaster and Sheffield

Network Diagram - see first page of Table 31

		GR	XC	GC	NT	NT	XC	NT		GR	EM	XC	NT	GR	NT	NT	EM	NT	XC	GR	NT	NT	NT	GR	
		R 1	◇1	R 1			◇1			R 1	◇1	◇1		R 1			◇1		◇1	R 1				R 1	
Leeds 10 32,34	d	08 05	08 10		08 34	08 48	09 00	09 05		09 05	09 45	10 00	10 02	10 05	10 17	10 20	10 51	10 57	11 00	11 05	11 20	11 29		12 05	
Outwood	d					08 59										10 29					11 31				
Wakefield Kirkgate 4 32,34,39	a				09 03			09 21					10 18		10 46			11 13				11 46			
	d			08 46	09 03			09 21					10 18		10 46			11 13				11 46			
Pontefract Monkhill	d																								
Wakefield Westgate 7 32,39	a	08 16	08 21			09 03	09 11			09 17	09 56	10 11		10 16		10 33	11 02		11 11	11 16	11 35			12 16	
	d	08 17	08 23			09 03	09 12			09 18	09 58	10 12		10 17		10 33	11 04		11 12	11 18	11 35			12 17	
Sandal & Agbrigg	d					09 07										10 36					11 39				
Fitzwilliam	d					09 14										10 43					11 46				
South Elmsall	d															10 48									
Adwick	a															10 53									
	d															10 54									
Bentley (S.Yorks)	d															10 58									
Doncaster 7	a	08 34		09 06			09 31			09 35		10 28		10 33		11 06			11 28	11 34				12 33	
Moorthorpe	d					09 20															11 52				
Thurnscoe	d					09 26															11 58				
Goldthorpe	d					09 28															12 00				
Bolton-upon-Dearne	d					09 31															12 03				
Swinton (S.Yorks) 29	a					09 35															12 07				
Rotherham Central 29	a					09 44															12 14		←		
Meadowhall 29	a				09 44	09 53		09 57					10 51		11 32			11 46			12 24	12 17	12 24		
Sheffield 7 29	a		08 51		09 55	10 03	09 55	10 04			10 25	10 54	11 02		11 44		11 36	11 56	11 53		→	12 29	12 32		

		XC	NT	NT	GC	NT	GR	XC	NT	NT	GR	XC	NT	NT	EM	GR		NT	GC	XC	NT	NT	XC	GR	NT
		◇1			R 1		R 1	◇1			R 1	◇1			◇1	R 1			R 1	◇1			◇1	R 1	
Leeds 10 32,34	d	12 10	12 20	12 29		12 34	13 05	13 10	13 20	14 05	14 05	14 10	14 17	14 20	14 39	15 05		15 05		15 10	15 20	16 04	16 10	16 16	16 17
Outwood	d		12 29						13 31					14 29							15 31				
Wakefield Kirkgate 4 32,34,39	a			12 46		13 04				14 21			14 46					15 22				16 21			16 46
	d			12 49	12 49	13 04				14 21			14 46					15 22	16 02			16 22			16 49
Pontefract Monkhill	d																								
Wakefield Westgate 7 32,39	a	12 21	12 33				13 17	13 21	13 35		14 17	14 22		14 33	14 51	15 17				15 21	15 35		16 21	16 27	
	d	12 23	12 33				13 18	13 24	13 35		14 18	14 23		14 33	14 53	15 18				15 23	15 35		16 22	16 28	
Sandal & Agbrigg	d		12 36						13 39					14 36							15 39				
Fitzwilliam	d		12 43						13 46					14 43							15 46				
South Elmsall	d		12 48											14 48											
Adwick	a		12 53											14 53											
	d		12 54											14 54											
Bentley (S.Yorks)	d		12 58											14 58											
Doncaster 7	a		13 06		13 10		13 35				14 34			15 06		15 35			16 23					16 44	
Moorthorpe	d								13 52												15 52				
Thurnscoe	d								13 58												15 58				
Goldthorpe	d								14 00												16 00				
Bolton-upon-Dearne	d								14 03												16 03				
Swinton (S.Yorks) 29	a								14 07												16 09				
Rotherham Central 29	a								14 14												16 17				
Meadowhall 29	a			13 19		13 48			14 21	14 54			15 35					15 55			16 22	16 56			17 34
Sheffield 7 29	a	12 54		13 30		13 58		13 53	14 32	15 06		14 52	15 44		15 24			16 05		15 51	16 32	17 05	16 51		17 44

		NT	GC	GR	NT	XC	GR	NT		GR	NT	XC	GR	NT	NT	NT	GR	NT	XC	GR	NT	GR	XC	NT	
			R 1	R 1		◇1	R 1			R 1		◇1	R 1	A			R 1		◇1	R 1		R 1	◇1		
Leeds 10 32,34	d	16 19		16 45	17 05	17 10	17 16	17 20		17 45	18 03	18 10	18 16		18 17	18 19	18 45	19 04	19 10	19 16	19 20	19 45	20 10	20 17	
Outwood	d	16 28						17 31								18 28					19 31				
Wakefield Kirkgate 4 32,34,39	a				17 21						18 18				18 45			19 21						20 46	
	d		16 49		17 21						18 21				18 45			19 21						20 46	
Pontefract Monkhill	d																								
Wakefield Westgate 7 32,39	a	16 32		16 57		17 21	17 28	17 34		17 57		18 21	18 27			18 32	18 57		19 21	19 27	19 35	19 57	20 21		
	d	16 32		16 58		17 23	17 29	17 34		17 58		18 22	18 28			18 32	18 58		19 22	19 28	19 35	19 58	20 22		
Sandal & Agbrigg	d	16 35						17 38								18 35					19 39				
Fitzwilliam	d	16 42						17 45								18 42					19 46				
South Elmsall	d	16 47														18 47									
Adwick	a	16 52														18 52									
	d	16 53														18 53									
Bentley (S.Yorks)	d	16 57														18 57									
Doncaster 7	a	17 06	17 10	17 17			17 45			18 15			18 44			19 06	19 17			19 44		20 16			
Moorthorpe	d							17 52						18 52							19 52				
Thurnscoe	d							17 58													19 58				
Goldthorpe	d							18 00													20 00				
Bolton-upon-Dearne	d							18 03													20 03				
Swinton (S.Yorks) 29	a							18 07						19 01							20 09				
Rotherham Central 29	a							18 17						19 12							20 16				
Meadowhall 29	a				17 55			18 24			18 56			19 18	19 32			19 54			20 22			21 33	
Sheffield 7 29	a				18 05	17 52		18 34			19 06	18 51		19 27	19 43			20 04	19 50		20 34		20 51	21 42	

A via Pontefract Baghill

Table 31R

Sundays

30 March to 11 May

Leeds - Wakefield, Doncaster and Sheffield

Network Diagram - see first page of Table 31

			NT	GR	XC	NT	NT	NT	NT
				R 1	◇1				
							A		
Leeds 10	32,34	d	20 20	20 45	21 10	21 18		21 41	22 17
Outwood		d	20 29			21 27		21 52	
Wakefield Kirkgate 4	32,34,39	a							22 46
		d							22 46
Pontefract Monkhill		d							
Wakefield Westgate 7	32,39	a	20 33	20 57	21 21	21 31		21 56	
		d	20 33	20 58	21 22	21 31		21 56	
Sandal & Agbrigg		d	20 36			21 34		22 00	
Fitzwilliam		d	20 43			21 41		22 07	
South Elmsall		d	20 48			21 46			
Adwick		a	20 53			21 51			
		d	20 54			21 52			
Bentley (S.Yorks)		d	20 58			21 56			
Doncaster 7		a	21 06	21 14		22 04			
Moorthorpe		d					21 36	22 13	
Thurnscoe		d						22 19	
Goldthorpe		d						22 21	
Bolton-upon-Dearne		d						22 24	
Swinton (S.Yorks)	29	a					21 45	22 29	
Rotherham Central	29	a					21 52	22 38	
Meadowhall	29	a					21 57	22 43	23 30
Sheffield 7	29	a			21 50		22 09	22 52	23 43

A via Pontefract Baghill

Table 32

Mondays to Saturdays

9 December to 17 May

Bradford, Leeds and Wakefield - Pontefract, Knottingley and Goole

Network Diagram - see first page of Table 31

Miles	Miles		NT SX	NT	NT	NT SX	NT SO	NT	GC SO R 1 ☕	GC SX R 1 ☕	NT		NT SO	NT SX	NT SX	NT SO	NT	NT	NT	GC SO R 1 ☕	NT		NT	NT
—	—	Bradford Interchange 41 d							06 51	06 51										08 38				
—	—	Halifax 41 d							07 03	07 07										08 51				
—	—	Brighouse 41 d							07 14	07 18										09 06				
—	—	Mirfield d							07 22	07 28										09 14				
0	—	**Leeds** 10 31,34 d	05 46		06 38	07 00	07 00				07 29		08 00	08 05			08 32	09 00			09 32		10 00	
6	—	Woodlesford 34 d	05 54		06 46	07 08	07 08				07 37		08 08	08 15			08 40	09 08			09 40		10 08	
10¾	—	Castleford 34 a	06 03		06 54	07 17	07 19				07 45		08 17	08 24			08 48	09 17			09 48		10 17	
—	—	d	06 05		06 57	07 19	07 19				07 48		08 19	08 26			08 51	09 19			09 51		10 19	
12¼	—	Glasshoughton d	06 09			07 24	07 24						08 24	08 31				09 24					10 24	
—	0	**Wakefield Westgate** 7 31,39 d		06 24																				
—	1	Wakefield Kirkgate 4 31,34,39 a		06 29	07 07				07 36	07 40	08 00						09 03			09 35	10 01			
—	—	d		06 29				07 31	07 38	07 42					08 31	08 31			09 31	09 38				10 31
—	5¼	Streethouse d		06 36				07 39							08 39	08 39			09 39					10 39
—	7	Featherstone d		06 40				07 43							08 43	08 43			09 43					10 43
—	9	Pontefract Tanshelf d		06 44				07 46							08 46	08 46			09 46					10 46
14	9¾	Pontefract Monkhill a	06 14	06 46		07 28	07 28	07 50	07 56	07 58			08 28	08 35	08 49	08 49		09 28	09 49	09 54			10 28	10 49
—	—	d	06 14	06 47		07 28	07 28	07 50	07 58	08 01			08 28	08 35	08 49	08 49		09 28	09 49	09 56			10 28	10 49
—	—	London Kings Cross 15 ⊖26 a							10 07	10 12										11 56				
16	—	**Knottingley** a	06 20	06 55		07 36	07 36	07 56					08 36	08 44	08 55	08 56		09 37	09 56				10 36	10 56
—	—	d																						
20¼	—	Whitley Bridge d																						
22	—	Hensall d																						
25¾	—	Snaith d																						
28½	—	Rawcliffe d																						
32½	—	**Goole** a																						

	NT	NT	GC SX R 1 ☕	GC SO R 1 ☕	NT	NT	NT		NT	NT	NT	NT	NT	NT	NT	NT	NT		GC SX R 1 ☕	NT	NT	NT	GC SO R 1 ☕	NT
Bradford Interchange 41 d			10 22	10 22															14 22				15 22	
Halifax 41 d			10 37	10 38															14 35				15 35	
Brighouse 41 d			10 48	10 48															14 47				15 46	
Mirfield d			10 56	10 56															14 55				15 56	
Leeds 10 31,34 d	10 32	11 00				11 32	12 00			12 32	13 00		13 32	14 00		14 32	15 00				15 32	16 00		
Woodlesford 34 d	10 40	11 08				11 40	12 08			12 40	13 08		13 40	14 08		14 40	15 08				15 40	16 08		
Castleford 34 a	10 48	11 17				11 48	12 17			12 48	13 17		13 48	14 17		14 48	15 17				15 48	16 17		
d	10 51	11 19				11 51	12 19			12 51	13 19		13 51	14 19		14 51	15 19				15 51	16 19		
Glasshoughton d		11 24					12 24				13 24			14 24			15 24					16 24		
Wakefield Westgate 7 31,39 d																								
Wakefield Kirkgate 4 31,34,39 a	11 01		11 10	11 11		12 01				13 02			14 01			15 01			15 10		16 01		16 11	
d			11 11	11 13	11 31				12 31			13 31			14 31				15 12	15 31			16 13	16 31
Streethouse d					11 39				12 39			13 39			14 39					15 39				16 39
Featherstone d					11 43				12 43			13 43			14 43					15 43				16 43
Pontefract Tanshelf d					11 46				12 46			13 46			14 46					15 46				16 46
Pontefract Monkhill a		11 29	11 34	11 35	11 49		12 28		12 49		13 28	13 49		14 28	14 49		15 28		15 33	15 49		16 28	16 32	16 49
d		11 29	11 36	11 37	11 49		12 28		12 49		13 28	13 49		14 28	14 49		15 28		15 34	15 49		16 28	16 34	16 49
London Kings Cross 15 ⊖26 a			13 43	13 45															18 15				18 45	
Knottingley a		11 35			11 56		12 35		12 56		13 35	13 56		14 35	14 56		15 36			15 56		16 36		16 56
d																								
Whitley Bridge d																								
Hensall d																								
Snaith d																								
Rawcliffe d																								
Goole a																								

	NT	NT SO	NT SX		NT	NT	NT	NT	NT	NT SO	NT SX	NT	NT		NT	NT	NT	NT	NT	NT	NT	NT SX	NT SO	
Bradford Interchange 41 d																								
Halifax 41 d																								
Brighouse 41 d																								
Mirfield d																								
Leeds 10 31,34 d	16 32	17 16	17 16			17 32	18 00		18 32	18 59	18 59		19 37		20 05		20 37	21 05		21 37	22 08			
Woodlesford 34 d	16 40	17 24	17 24			17 40	18 08		18 40	19 08	19 08		19 45		20 13		20 45	21 13		21 45	22 16			
Castleford 34 a	16 48	17 33	17 34			17 48	18 17		18 48	19 17	19 18		19 53		20 22		20 53	21 22		21 53	22 27			
d	16 51	17 36	17 36			17 51	18 19		18 51	19 19	19 19		19 56		20 24		20 56	21 24		21 56	22 27			
Glasshoughton d		17 40	17 40				18 24			19 24	19 24				20 29			21 29			22 32			
Wakefield Westgate 7 31,39 d																			21 57			23 04	23 04	
Wakefield Kirkgate 4 31,34,39 a	17 01					18 01			19 04				20 06				21 06		22 00	22 06		23 07	23 07	
d					17 31			18 33				19 33				20 54			22 00			23 07	23 07	
Streethouse d					17 39			18 41				19 41				21 02			22 08			23 15	23 15	
Featherstone d					17 43			18 45				19 45				21 06			22 12			23 19	23 19	
Pontefract Tanshelf d					17 46			18 48				19 48				21 09			22 16			23 23	23 23	
Pontefract Monkhill a		17 44	17 44		17 49		18 28	18 51		19 28	19 28	19 51			20 33	21 12		21 33	22 18		22 36	23 25	23 29	
d		17 44	17 44		17 49		18 28	18 51		19 28	19 28	19 51			20 33	21 12		21 33	22 19		22 36	23 26		
London Kings Cross 15 ⊖26 a																								
Knottingley a		17 51	17 51		17 57		18 35	18 58		19 35	19 35	19 58			20 40	21 19		21 40	22 25		22 44	23 32		
d		17 53	17 53																					
Whitley Bridge d		17 59	17 59																					
Hensall d		18 03	18 03																					
Snaith d		18 10	18 10																					
Rawcliffe d		18 15	18 15																					
Goole a		18 26	18 26																					

Table 32

Bradford, Leeds and Wakefield - Pontefract, Knottingley and Goole

Mondays to Saturdays

9 December to 17 May

Network Diagram - see first page of Table 31

Station	Table		NT
Bradford Interchange	41	d	
Halifax	41	d	
Brighouse	41	d	
Mirfield		d	
Leeds 10	31,34	d	22 37
Woodlesford	34	d	22 45
Castleford	34	a	22 53
		d	22 56
Glasshoughton		d	
Wakefield Westgate 7	31,39	d	
Wakefield Kirkgate 4	31,34,39	a	23 10
		d	
Streethouse		d	
Featherstone		d	
Pontefract Tanshelf		d	
Pontefract Monkhill		a	
		d	
London Kings Cross 15 ⊖	26	a	
Knottingley		a	
		d	
Whitley Bridge		d	
Hensall		d	
Snaith		d	
Rawcliffe		d	
Goole		a	

Sundays

8 December to 11 May

Station	Table		NT	NT	NT	NT	NT	NT	NT	NT	NT		NT	NT	NT	NT	NT	NT
Bradford Interchange	41	d																
Halifax	41	d																
Brighouse	41	d																
Mirfield		d																
Leeds 10	31,34	d	08 34	09 34	10 17	11 17	12 34	13 17	14 17	15 17	16 17		17 17	18 17	19 17	20 17	21 17	22 17
Woodlesford	34	d	08 42	09 42	10 25	11 25	12 42	13 25	14 25	15 25	16 25		17 25	18 25	19 25	20 25	21 25	22 25
Castleford	34	a	08 50	09 50	10 33	11 33	12 50	13 33	14 33	15 33	16 33		17 33	18 33	19 35	20 33	21 33	22 33
		d	08 53	09 53	10 36	11 36	12 53	13 36	14 36	15 36	16 36		17 36	18 36	19 36	20 36	21 36	22 36
Glasshoughton		d		09 57		11 40		13 40		15 40			17 40		19 40		21 40	
Wakefield Westgate 7	31,39	d																
Wakefield Kirkgate 4	31,34,39	a	09 03		10 46		13 04		14 46		16 46			18 45		20 46		22 46
		d																
Streethouse		d																
Featherstone		d																
Pontefract Tanshelf		d																
Pontefract Monkhill		a		10 02		11 45		13 45		15 45			17 45		19 45		21 45	
		d		10 02		11 45		13 45		15 45			17 45		19 45		21 45	
London Kings Cross 15 ⊖	26	a																
Knottingley		a		10 08		11 52		13 52		15 52			17 52		19 52		21 52	
		d																
Whitley Bridge		d																
Hensall		d																
Snaith		d																
Rawcliffe		d																
Goole		a																

Table 32R

Mondays to Saturdays

9 December to 17 May

Goole, Knottingley and Pontefract - Wakefield and Leeds, Bradford

Network Diagram - see first page of Table 31

Miles	Miles			NT SX	NT SX	NT SO	NT	NT SX	NT SO	NT SX		NT SX	NT SO	NT	NT	NT	NT	NT	NT	NT		NT	NT	NT	NT
0	—	**Goole**	d						07 04	07 04															
4	—	Rawcliffe	d						07 11	07 11															
6¾	—	Snaith	d						07 16	07 16															
10½	—	Hensall	d						07 23	07 23															
12¼	—	Whitley Bridge	d						07 30	07 30															
16½	—	**Knottingley**	a						07 37	07 38															
—	—		d	06 25			06 56		07 38	07 38				07 53	08 16		08 53	09 16		09 53		10 16		10 53	11 16
—	—	London Kings Cross 15 ⊖26	d																						
18½	0	Pontefract Monkhill	a	06 29			07 00		07 42	07 42				07 57	08 20		08 57	09 20		09 57		10 20		10 57	11 20
—	—		d	06 29			07 00		07 42	07 42				07 57	08 20		08 57	09 20		09 57		10 20		10 57	11 20
—	0¾	Pontefract Tanshelf	d				07 03							08 00			09 00			10 00				11 00	
—	2¾	Featherstone	d				07 06							08 03			09 03			10 03				11 03	
—	4½	Streethouse	d				07 10							08 07			09 07			10 07				11 07	
—	8¾	Wakefield Kirkgate 4 31,34,39	a				07 21							08 18			09 18			10 20				11 18	
—	—		d		06 50	06 50						07 50	07 50			08 50			09 50				10 50		
—	9¾	**Wakefield Westgate** 7 31,39	a																						
20	—	Glasshoughton 34	d	06 34					07 48	07 48					08 25			09 25				10 25			11 25
21½	—	Castleford	a	06 38	06 59	07 00			07 52	07 52		08 00	08 00		08 30	09 00		09 29	10 00			10 29	11 00		11 29
—	—		d	06 41	07 02	07 02		07 38	07 55	07 55		08 02	08 03		08 32	09 02		09 32	10 02			10 32	11 02		11 32
26½	—	Woodlesford 34	d	06 50	07 12	07 12		07 47	08 04	08 04		08 12	08 12		08 41	09 12		09 41	10 12			10 41	11 12		11 41
32½	—	**Leeds** 10 31,34	a	07 04	07 28	07 28		08 01	08 18	08 18		08 25	08 25		08 54	09 25		09 53	10 25			10 55	11 25		11 54
—	—	Mirfield	a																						
—	—	Brighouse 41	a																						
—	—	Halifax 41	a																						
—	—	Bradford Interchange 41	a																						

		NT	NT	NT	NT	GC SX R 1		NT	NT	NT	NT	NT SO	NT SX	NT	NT	NT		NT	NT	NT	NT	GC SX R 1	NT	NT	NT
Goole	d																								
Rawcliffe	d																								
Snaith	d																								
Hensall	d																								
Whitley Bridge	d																								
Knottingley	a																								
	d		11 53	12 16				12 53	13 16		13 53	14 16	14 16		14 53	15 16			15 53	16 16			16 53	17 15	
London Kings Cross 15 ⊖26	d					10 48																14 48			
Pontefract Monkhill	a		11 57	12 20		12 47		12 57	13 20		13 57	14 20	14 20		14 57	15 20			15 57	16 20		16 47	16 57	17 19	
	d		11 57	12 20		12 49		12 57	13 20		13 57	14 20	14 20		14 57	15 20			15 57	16 20		16 48	16 57	17 19	
Pontefract Tanshelf	d		12 00					13 00			14 00				15 00				16 00				17 00		
Featherstone	d		12 03					13 03			14 03				15 03				16 03				17 03		
Streethouse	d		12 07					13 07			14 07				15 07				16 07				17 07		
Wakefield Kirkgate 4 31,34,39	a		12 18			13 06		13 18			14 18				15 18				16 19			17 04	17 18		
	d	11 50			12 50	13 08				13 50				14 50				15 50			16 50	17 08			17 50
Wakefield Westgate 7 31,39	a																								
Glasshoughton 34	d			12 25					13 25			14 25	14 25			15 25				16 25				17 24	
Castleford	a	12 00		12 29	13 00				13 29	14 00		14 28	14 29	15 00		15 29		16 00		16 29	17 00			17 28	18 00
	d	12 02		12 32	13 02				13 32	14 02		14 32	14 32	15 02		15 32		16 02		16 32	17 02			17 31	18 02
Woodlesford 34	d	12 12		12 41	13 12				13 41	14 12		14 41	14 41	15 12		15 41		16 12		16 41	17 12			17 41	18 12
Leeds 10 31,34	a	12 25		12 54	13 25				13 53	14 25		14 53	14 53	15 25		15 54		16 25		16 54	17 25			17 54	18 25
Mirfield	a					13 19																17 20			
Brighouse 41	a					13 29																17 29			
Halifax 41	a					13 39																17 40			
Bradford Interchange 41	a					13 55																17 55			

		NT		NT	NT SX	NT SO	NT	NT	NT	NT	NT	NT		GC SO	NT	NT SX	NT SO	NT	NT	NT FO	NT SO	NT FSX		NT	NT
Goole	d							18 49																	
Rawcliffe	d							18 56																	
Snaith	d							19 01																	
Hensall	d							19 08																	
Whitley Bridge	d							19 12																	
Knottingley	a							19 20																	
	d	18 02		18 39			19 02	19 21		19 55	20 16				21 16	21 23	21 23		22 16					22 30	23 05
London Kings Cross 15 ⊖26	d													19 23											
Pontefract Monkhill	a	18 06		18 43			19 06	19 25		19 59	20 20			21 14	21 20	21 27	21 27		22 22					22 34	23 09
	d	18 06		18 43			19 06	19 25		19 59	20 20			21 16	21 20	21 27	21 27		22 22					22 34	23 09
Pontefract Tanshelf	d	18 09					19 09			20 02						21 30	21 30							22 37	
Featherstone	d	18 12					19 12			20 05						21 33	21 33							22 40	
Streethouse	d	18 16					19 16			20 09						21 37	21 37							22 44	
Wakefield Kirkgate 4 31,34,39	a	18 27					19 28			20 20				21 32		21 47	21 47							22 55	
	d				18 50	18 50			19 50			20 51		21 33		21 47	21 48	21 52		22 51	22 51	22 54		22 55	
Wakefield Westgate 7 31,39	a															21 53	21 53							23 01	
Glasshoughton 34	d			18 48				19 30			20 25				21 25				22 27						23 14
Castleford	a			18 54	19 00	19 00		19 34	20 00		20 29	21 01			21 29			22 04	22 31	23 01	23 02	23 01			23 18
	d			18 57	19 03	19 03		19 37	20 02		20 32	21 03			21 32			22 05	22 34	23 04	23 04	23 04			23 21
Woodlesford 34	d			19 06	19 13	19 13		19 46	20 12		20 44	21 13			21 41			22 15	22 43	23 14	23 14	23 14			23 30
Leeds 10 31,34	a			19 20	19 26	19 27		20 00	20 26		20 57	21 26			21 53			22 29	22 57	23 30	23 30	23 30			23 44
Mirfield	a													21 43											
Brighouse 41	a													21 53											
Halifax 41	a													22 08											
Bradford Interchange 41	a													22 24											

Table 32R

Sundays

8 December to 9 February

Goole, Knottingley and Pontefract - Wakefield and Leeds, Bradford

Network Diagram - see first page of Table 31

		NT	NT	NT	NT	NT	NT	NT	NT	NT	NT	NT	NT	NT	NT
Goole	d														
Rawcliffe	d														
Snaith	d														
Hensall	d														
Whitley Bridge	d														
Knottingley	a														
	d		10 26		12 26		14 26		16 26		18 26		20 26		22 26
London Kings Cross 15 ⊖26	d														
Pontefract Monkhill	a		10 30		12 30		14 30		16 30		18 30		20 30		22 30
	d		10 30		12 30		14 30		16 30		18 30		20 30		22 30
Pontefract Tanshelf	d														
Featherstone	d														
Streethouse	d														
Wakefield Kirkgate 4 31,34,39	a														
	d	09 30		11 30		13 30		15 30		17 30		19 30		21 30	
Wakefield Westgate 7 31,39	a														
Glasshoughton 34	d		10 35		12 35		14 35		16 35		18 35		20 35		22 35
Castleford	a	09 40	10 39	11 40	12 39	13 40	14 39	15 40	16 39	17 40	18 39	19 41	20 39	21 40	22 39
	d	09 45	10 42	11 41	12 42	13 42	14 42	15 41	16 42	17 42	18 42	19 44	20 42	21 42	22 42
Woodlesford 34	d	09 55	10 51	11 51	12 52	13 51	14 51	15 51	16 51	17 51	18 51	19 53	20 51	21 51	22 51
Leeds 10 31,34	a	10 07	11 04	12 05	13 05	14 04	15 04	16 04	17 04	18 05	19 04	20 05	21 03	22 04	23 04
Mirfield	a														
Brighouse 41	a														
Halifax 41	a														
Bradford Interchange 41	a														

Sundays

16 February to 23 March

		NT	NT	NT	NT	NT	NT	NT	NT	NT	NT	NT	NT	NT	NT
Goole	d														
Rawcliffe	d														
Snaith	d														
Hensall	d														
Whitley Bridge	d														
Knottingley	a														
	d		10 26		12 26		14 26		16 26		18 26		20 26		22 26
London Kings Cross 15 ⊖26	d														
Pontefract Monkhill	a		10 30		12 30		14 30		16 30		18 30		20 30		22 30
	d		10 30		12 30		14 30		16 30		18 30		20 30		22 30
Pontefract Tanshelf	d														
Featherstone	d														
Streethouse	d														
Wakefield Kirkgate 4 31,34,39	a														
	d	09 32		11 31		13 31		15 31		17 31		19 31		21 31	
Wakefield Westgate 7 31,39	a														
Glasshoughton 34	d		10 35		12 35		14 35		16 35		18 35		20 35		22 35
Castleford	a	09 42	10 39	11 41	12 39	13 43	14 39	15 41	16 39	17 41	18 39	19 42	20 39	21 41	22 39
	d	09 44	10 42	11 42	12 42	13 45	14 42	15 42	16 42	17 43	18 42	19 45	20 42	21 43	22 42
Woodlesford 34	d	09 54	10 51	11 52	12 52	13 54	14 51	15 52	16 51	17 52	18 51	19 54	20 51	21 52	22 51
Leeds 10 31,34	a	10 06	11 04	12 05	13 05	14 05	15 04	16 04	17 04	18 05	19 04	20 05	21 03	22 04	23 04
Mirfield	a														
Brighouse 41	a														
Halifax 41	a														
Bradford Interchange 41	a														

Sundays

30 March to 11 May

		NT	NT	NT	NT	NT	NT	NT	NT	NT	NT	NT	NT	NT	NT
Goole	d														
Rawcliffe	d														
Snaith	d														
Hensall	d														
Whitley Bridge	d														
Knottingley	a														
	d		10 26		12 26		14 26		16 26		18 26		20 26		22 26
London Kings Cross 15 ⊖26	d														
Pontefract Monkhill	a		10 30		12 30		14 30		16 30		18 30		20 30		22 30
	d		10 30		12 30		14 30		16 30		18 30		20 30		22 30
Pontefract Tanshelf	d														
Featherstone	d														
Streethouse	d														
Wakefield Kirkgate 4 31,34,39	a														
	d	09 30		11 30		13 30		15 30		17 30		19 30		21 30	
Wakefield Westgate 7 31,39	a														
Glasshoughton 34	d		10 35		12 35		14 35		16 35		18 35		20 35		22 35
Castleford	a	09 40	10 39	11 40	12 39	13 40	14 39	15 40	16 39	17 40	18 39	19 41	20 39	21 40	22 39
	d	09 45	10 42	11 41	12 42	13 42	14 42	15 41	16 42	17 42	18 42	19 44	20 42	21 42	22 42
Woodlesford 34	d	09 55	10 51	11 51	12 52	13 51	14 51	15 51	16 51	17 51	18 51	19 53	20 51	21 51	22 51
Leeds 10 31,34	a	10 07	11 04	12 05	13 05	14 04	15 04	16 04	17 04	18 05	19 04	20 05	21 03	22 04	23 04
Mirfield	a														
Brighouse 41	a														
Halifax 41	a														
Bradford Interchange 41	a														

Table 33

Mondays to Fridays

9 December to 16 May

Sheffield and Selby - York

Local services only

Network Diagram - see first page of Table 31

Miles	Miles	Station	NT	NT A	NT B	NT A	NT	NT C	NT D	NT E	NT		NT	NT A	NT	NT C	NT D	NT	NT E	NT	NT		NT A	NT
0	—	**Sheffield** 7 29,31 🚌 d								09 29									13 29					
3½	—	Meadowhall 29,31 🚌 d								09 35									13 35					
6¼	—	Rotherham Central 29,31 d								09 42									13 41					
10¾	—	Swinton (S.Yorks) 29,31 d								09 51									13 52					
18½	—	Moorthorpe 31 d								10 01									14 02					
25½	—	Pontefract Baghill d								10 10									14 11					
—	—	Hull 29 d			07 07		09 03				10 10				12 03			13 12		14 20	15 03			16 10
—	0	**Selby** d	06 47		07 48		09 39				10 46		11 40		12 39			13 55		14 55	15 39			16 47
33¾	8¼	Sherburn-in-Elmet d	06 59		08 03		09 53			10 25	10 59		11 52					14 09	14 28	15 07				
36	10½	Church Fenton d	07 03	08 00		09 05		10 05	10 06	10 29				12 06		14 05	14 06		14 34				16 06	
38	12½	Ulleskelf d			08 09					10 33									14 38					
46¾	21	**York** 8 29 a	07 19	08 16	08 21	09 21	10 10	10 21	10 21	10 57	11 18		12 10	12 21	13 04	14 20	14 21	14 25	14 55	15 25	16 06		16 21	17 13

Station	NT F	NT	NT A	NT	NT D	NT C	NT		NT A
Sheffield 7 29,31 🚌 d									
Meadowhall 29,31 🚌 d									
Rotherham Central 29,31 d									
Swinton (S.Yorks) 29,31 d									
Moorthorpe 31 d									
Pontefract Baghill d									
Hull 29 d		17 18		19 18					
Selby d		18 07		19 55			21 21		
Sherburn-in-Elmet d									
Church Fenton d	17 53		19 05		21 12	21 13			23 26
Ulleskelf d	17 58				21 16	21 17			
York 8 29 a	18 10	18 33	19 21	20 24	21 30	21 30	21 43		23 42

Saturdays

14 December to 17 May

Station	NT	NT B	NT A	NT A	NT	NT G	NT H	NT E	NT		NT	NT A	NT	NT A	NT	NT	NT	NT	NT G		NT H	NT	NT H	NT G
Sheffield 7 29,31 🚌 d								09 32								13 30								
Meadowhall 29,31 🚌 d								09 39								13 36								
Rotherham Central 29,31 d								09 46								13 42								
Swinton (S.Yorks) 29,31 d								09 54								13 52								
Moorthorpe 31 d								10 04								14 02								
Pontefract Baghill d								10 13								14 11								
Hull 29 d		07 07			09 03				10 10		11 05		12 03		13 12		14 20	15 03				16 10		
Selby d	06 47	07 48			09 39				10 46		11 40		12 39		13 55		14 55	15 38				16 47		
Sherburn-in-Elmet d	06 59	08 03			09 53			10 30	10 59						14 09	14 28	15 06							
Church Fenton d	07 03		08 05	09 05		10 05	10 06	10 35				12 06		14 06		14 32			16 05		16 06		18 06	18 06
Ulleskelf d		08 09						10 42								14 36							18 11	18 11
York 8 29 a	07 19	08 21	08 21	09 21	10 10	10 21	10 21	10 54	11 18		12 05	12 21	13 04	14 21	14 25	14 55	15 25	16 04	16 21		16 21	17 13	18 24	18 25

Station	NT	NT A	NT	NT A	NT		NT A
Sheffield 7 29,31 🚌 d							
Meadowhall 29,31 🚌 d							
Rotherham Central 29,31 d							
Swinton (S.Yorks) 29,31 d							
Moorthorpe 31 d							
Pontefract Baghill d							
Hull 29 d	17 18		19 18		21 01		
Selby d	18 07		19 55		21 35		
Sherburn-in-Elmet d							
Church Fenton d		19 06		21 12			23 20
Ulleskelf d				21 17			
York 8 29 a	18 33	19 21	20 24	21 30	21 57		23 36

Sundays

8 December to 11 May

Station	NT I	NT	NT J	NT	NT A	NT	NT A	NT	NT		NT A	NT E	NT	NT A	NT E	NT	NT A	NT		NT K
Sheffield 7 29,31 🚌 d												16 36			18 57					
Meadowhall 29,31 🚌 d												16 42			19 05					
Rotherham Central 29,31 d												16 49			19 11					
Swinton (S.Yorks) 29,31 d												16 58			19 19					
Moorthorpe 31 d												17 13			19 29					
Pontefract Baghill d												17 21			19 38					
Hull 29 d		08 54		11 46		13 30		14 30	16 02				17 25			19 25		20 30		
Selby d		09 28		12 20		14 04		15 04	16 37				17 59			19 59		21 04		
Sherburn-in-Elmet d												17 38			19 56					
Church Fenton d	09 18		11 02		12 49		14 49				16 49	17 43		18 49	20 00		20 49			23 07
Ulleskelf d																				
York 8 29 a	09 34	09 52	11 17	12 45	13 02	14 29	15 02	15 28	17 01		17 02	17 59	18 24	19 02	20 18	20 25	21 02	21 28		23 23

A From Blackpool North
B From Beverley
C from 24 March. From Blackpool North
D until 21 March. From Hebden Bridge
E via Pontefract Baghill
F From Leeds
G from 29 March. From Blackpool North
H until 22 March. From Hebden Bridge
I From Bradford Interchange
J From Huddersfield
K From Leeds

Table 33R

York - Selby and Sheffield

Local services only

Mondays to Fridays

9 December to 16 May

Network Diagram - see first page of Table 31

Miles	Miles				NT	NT A	NT	NT B	NT	NT A	NT	NT	NT C	NT A	NT	NT	NT A	NT	NT	NT C	NT A	NT A	NT	NT
0	0	**York** 8	29	d	05 44	07 06	07 30	07 48	08 43	09 11	10 19	11 02	11 06	11 09	11 45	12 47	13 09	13 44	14 47	15 02	15 08	16 08	16 12	17 19
8¾	8¾	Ulleskelf		d		07 15							11 16							15 12				
10¾	10¾	Church Fenton		a		07 20		08 00		09 22			11 20	11 20			13 20			15 16	15 20	16 20		17 30
—	—			d									11 21							15 16				17 30
12¾	12¾	Sherburn-in-Elmet		d					08 55			11 16	11 25					13 56		15 20			16 25	17 34
—	21	**Selby**		a	06 08		07 50		09 06		10 39	11 27			12 04	13 06		14 07	15 06				16 36	17 45
—	—	Hull	29	a			08 46		09 47		11 22				12 49	13 47		14 52	15 47				17 27	18 30
21¼	—	Pontefract Baghill		d									11 43							15 39				
28¼	—	Moorthorpe	31	a									11 59							15 51				
36	—	Swinton (S.Yorks)	29,31	a									12 08							16 00				
40½	—	Rotherham Central	29,31	a									12 18							16 10				
43¼	—	Meadowhall	29,31 🚋	a									12 24							16 16				
46¾	—	**Sheffield** 7	29,31 🚋	a									12 36							16 27				

			NT A	NT	NT B	NT	NT B	NT B	NT	NT B
York 8	29	d	18 05	18 18	19 04	20 17	21 23	22 09	22 13	23 13
Ulleskelf		d	18 15					22 19		
Church Fenton		a	18 21		19 17		21 33	22 23		23 28
		d								
Sherburn-in-Elmet		d		18 31		20 29				
Selby		a		18 42		20 42			22 31	
Hull	29	a		19 29					23 18	
Pontefract Baghill		d								
Moorthorpe	31	a								
Swinton (S.Yorks)	29,31	a								
Rotherham Central	29,31	a								
Meadowhall	29,31 🚋	a								
Sheffield 7	29,31 🚋	a								

Saturdays

14 December to 17 May

			NT	NT A	NT	NT A	NT	NT A	NT	NT	NT	NT A	NT	NT	NT A	NT	NT	NT C	NT A	NT A	NT	NT	NT A	NT
York 8	29	d	06 09	07 06	07 38	08 09	08 43	09 11	09 51	10 47	11 06	11 09	11 45	12 47	13 09	13 50	14 47	15 02	15 09	16 08	16 12	17 19	18 05	18 18
Ulleskelf		d		07 15							11 16							15 12					18 16	
Church Fenton		a		07 20		08 20		09 22			11 20	11 20			13 20			15 16	15 21	16 20		17 30	18 21	
		d									11 20							15 16				17 30		
Sherburn-in-Elmet		d					08 55				11 24					14 01		15 20			16 25	17 34		18 31
Selby		a	06 30		07 57		09 06		10 09	11 06			12 04	13 06		14 12	15 06				16 36	17 45		18 42
Hull	29	a			08 52		09 47		10 50	11 53			12 49	13 48		14 55	15 48				17 27	18 30		19 29
Pontefract Baghill		d									11 43							15 40						
Moorthorpe	31	a									11 59							15 51						
Swinton (S.Yorks)	29,31	a									12 08							16 01						
Rotherham Central	29,31	a									12 18							16 09						
Meadowhall	29,31 🚋	a									12 24							16 17						
Sheffield 7	29,31 🚋	a									12 36							16 27						

			NT B	NT	NT B	NT	NT B
York 8	29	d	19 04	19 47	21 18	22 11	23 13
Ulleskelf		d			21 27		
Church Fenton		a	19 17		21 33		23 28
		d					
Sherburn-in-Elmet		d					
Selby		a		20 05		22 29	
Hull	29	a		20 48		23 16	
Pontefract Baghill		d					
Moorthorpe	31	a					
Swinton (S.Yorks)	29,31	a					
Rotherham Central	29,31	a					
Meadowhall	29,31 🚋	a					
Sheffield 7	29,31 🚋	a					

Sundays

8 December to 11 May

			NT A	NT A	NT	NT A	NT	NT	NT A	NT	NT A	NT	NT	NT A	NT D	NT	NT A	NT C	NT	NT B
York 8	29	d	08 50	09 52	10 40	11 52	12 05	13 45	13 52	14 52	15 52	16 06	17 11	17 52	18 10	19 16	19 52	20 50	21 41	21 52
Ulleskelf		d																		
Church Fenton		a	09 01	10 03		12 03			14 03		16 03			18 03	18 21		20 03	21 01		22 04
		d													18 21			21 01		
Sherburn-in-Elmet		d													18 25			21 05		
Selby		a			10 58		12 24	14 04		15 11		16 25	17 30			19 35			22 00	
Hull	29	a			11 41		13 05	14 45		15 51		17 06	18 11			20 16			22 41	
Pontefract Baghill		d													18 40			21 20		
Moorthorpe	31	a													18 51			21 35		
Swinton (S.Yorks)	29,31	a													19 01			21 45		
Rotherham Central	29,31	a													19 12			21 52		
Meadowhall	29,31 🚋	a													19 18			21 57		
Sheffield 7	29,31 🚋	a													19 30			22 09		

A To Hebden Bridge
B To Leeds
C via Pontefract Baghill
D until 29 December, from 5 January. via Pontefract Baghill

Table 34

Mondays to Fridays

9 December to 16 May

Nottingham, Sheffield - Barnsley - Huddersfield and Leeds

Network Diagram - see first page of Table 31

Miles	Miles	Station			NT	NT	NT	NT	NT	NT	NT	NT	NT	NT	NT	TP	NT	NT	NT	NT	EM	NT	NT	NT
																◇1					◇			
							A				B				B	C	D			E	F		G	H
0	—	**Nottingham** 8	🚌	d															06 21		06 39			
12	—	Langley Mill		d															06 40					
18¼	—	Alfreton		d															06 48		07 00			
28¼	—	Chesterfield		d										06 26					06 58		07 10			
33½	—	Dronfield		d										06 34					07 05		07 18			
40½	—	**Sheffield** 7	29,31 🚌	a										06 46					07 18		07 28			
—	—			d	05 17	05 21	05 29	05 36	05 50	06 06	06 18	06 28	06 36	06 49	06 52	06 55	07 06	07 15	07 21	07 24		07 36	07 41	07 51
44	3½	**Meadowhall** 4	29,31 🚌	a	05 22	05 26	05 34	05 41	05 55	06 11	06 23	06 33	06 41	06 54	06 57	07 00	07 11	07 20	07 26	07 30		07 41	07 46	07 57
—	—			d	05 23	05 27		05 42	05 56	06 12		06 34	06 42	06 55			07 12	07 21	07 27			07 42		07 57
47¾	7¼	Chapeltown		d	05 29			05 48		06 18			06 48				07 18					07 48		
51	10½	Elsecar		d	05 34					06 23							07 23							
52½	12	Wombwell		d	05 38			05 55		06 27			06 55				07 27					07 55		
56½	16	**Barnsley**		a	05 44			06 00	06 10	06 32			07 00	07 09			07 32		07 42			08 00		08 11
—	—			d				06 01	06 10	06 33			07 01	07 12			07 33		07 42			08 01		08 12
—	19	Dodworth		d				06 07					07 07									08 07		
—	20¼	Silkstone Common		d				06 11					07 11									08 11		
—	23½	Penistone		d				06 18					07 18									08 18		
—	27½	Denby Dale		d				06 24					07 24									08 24		
—	29¾	Shepley		d				06 29					07 29									08 29		
—	30¾	Stocksmoor		d				06 32					07 32									08 32		
—	32¾	Brockholes		d				06 36					07 36									08 36		
—	33¾	Honley		d				06 38					07 38									08 38		
—	34¾	Berry Brow		d				06 41					07 41									08 41		
—	35¾	Lockwood		d				06 44					07 44									08 44		
—	37	**Huddersfield**		a				06 50					07 49									08 49		
60	—	Darton		d						06 38							07 38							
67½	—	**Wakefield Kirkgate** 4	31	a					06 27	06 49				07 27			07 49		07 57					08 27
—	—			d					06 28	06 50				07 28			07 50		07 58					08 28
70½	—	Normanton		d					06 33	06 54				07 33			07 54							
74	—	Castleford		a						06 59							08 00							
78¾	—	Woodlesford		a						07 12							08 12							
84¾	—	**Leeds** 10	31	a		06 33			06 50	07 28		07 44		07 51			08 25	08 35	08 21					08 49

Station			EM	NT	TP	NT	NT	NT	NT	EM	NT	NT	NT	NT	TP	NT	NT	NT	NT	NT	EM	NT	NT	NT
			◇1		◇1					◇					◇1						◇			
			I		C			E		F	G		J		C			E	K		L	M		N
			🍴		🍴										🍴									
Nottingham 8	🚌	d					07 12			07 47							08 18				08 47			
Langley Mill		d					07 31										08 36							
Alfreton		d					07 39			08 08							08 44				09 08			
Chesterfield		d	07 43				07 49			08 20							08 55				09 20			
Dronfield		d	07 49							08 27							09 02							
Sheffield 7	29,31 🚌	a	08 00				08 04			08 37							09 15				09 37			
		d		08 06	08 11	08 16	08 19	08 25	08 36		08 41	08 51	08 54	09 06	09 10	09 15	09 18	09 24	09 29	09 36		09 41	09 50	09 53
Meadowhall 4	29,31 🚌	a		08 11	08 17	08 21	08 24	08 30	08 41		08 46	08 56	08 59	09 11	09 16	09 20	09 23	09 29	09 34	09 41		09 46	09 55	09 58
		d		08 12		08 22	08 25		08 42			08 57		09 12		09 21	09 24			09 42			09 56	
Chapeltown		d		08 18					08 48					09 18						09 48				
Elsecar		d		08 23										09 23										
Wombwell		d		08 27					08 55					09 27						09 55				
Barnsley		a		08 32			08 42		09 00			09 11		09 32			09 42			10 00			10 11	
		d		08 33			08 42		09 01			09 12		09 33			09 42			10 01			10 12	
Dodworth		d							09 07											10 07				
Silkstone Common		d							09 11											10 11				
Penistone		d							09 18											10 18				
Denby Dale		d							09 24											10 24				
Shepley		d							09 29											10 29				
Stocksmoor		d							09 32											10 32				
Brockholes		d							09 36											10 36				
Honley		d							09 38											10 38				
Berry Brow		d							09 41											10 41				
Lockwood		d							09 44											10 44				
Huddersfield		a							09 49											10 49				
Darton		d		08 38										09 38										
Wakefield Kirkgate 4	31	a		08 49			08 57					09 27		09 49			09 57						10 27	
		d		08 50			08 58					09 28		09 50			09 58						10 28	
Normanton		d		08 54										09 54										
Castleford		a		09 00										10 00										
Woodlesford		a		09 12										10 12										
Leeds 10	31	a		09 25		09 31	09 20					09 49		10 25		10 31	10 18						10 48	

A To Beverley
B To Adwick
C From Manchester Airport to Cleethorpes
D From Worksop
E To Scunthorpe
F To Liverpool Lime Street
G To Bridlington
H From Retford
I From Derby
J From Worksop to Adwick
K To York, via Pontefract Baghill
L From Norwich to Liverpool Lime Street
M To Scarborough
N From Lincoln to Adwick

Table 34

Mondays to Fridays

9 December to 16 May

Nottingham, Sheffield - Barnsley - Huddersfield and Leeds

Network Diagram - see first page of Table 31

		NT	TP ◇1 A	NT		NT	NT B	NT	EM ◇ C	NT D	NT	NT E	NT	TP ◇1 A		NT	NT ◇	NT B	NT	EM ◇ C	NT F	NT	NT ◇ E	NT
Nottingham 8	d					09 17			09 47								10 17			10 47				
Langley Mill	d					09 36											10 36							
Alfreton	d					09 44			10 08								10 44			11 08				
Chesterfield	d					09 55			10 20								10 55			11 20				
Dronfield	d					10 02											11 02							
Sheffield 7 29,31	a					10 15			10 37								11 15			11 37				
	d	10 06	10 10	10 14		10 18	10 24	10 36		10 41	10 50	10 53	11 06	11 10		11 14	11 18	11 24	11 36		11 41	11 50	11 53	12 06
Meadowhall 4 29,31	a	10 11	10 16	10 20		10 23	10 29	10 41		10 46	10 55	10 58	11 11	11 16		11 20	11 23	11 29	11 41		11 46	11 55	11 58	12 11
	d	10 12		10 21		10 24		10 42			10 56		11 12			11 21	11 24		11 42			11 56		12 12
Chapeltown	d	10 18						10 48					11 18						11 48					12 18
Elsecar	d	10 23											11 23											12 23
Wombwell	d	10 27						10 55					11 27						11 55					12 27
Barnsley	a	10 32				10 42		11 00			11 11		11 32				11 42		12 00			12 10		12 32
	d	10 33				10 42		11 01			11 12		11 33				11 42		12 01			12 11		12 33
Dodworth	d							11 07											12 07					
Silkstone Common	d							11 11											12 11					
Penistone	d							11 18											12 18					
Denby Dale	d							11 24											12 24					
Shepley	d							11 29											12 29					
Stocksmoor	d							11 32											12 32					
Brockholes	d							11 36											12 36					
Honley	d							11 38											12 38					
Berry Brow	d							11 41											12 41					
Lockwood	d							11 44											12 44					
Huddersfield	a							11 49											12 49					
Darton	d	10 38											11 38											12 38
Wakefield Kirkgate 4 31	a	10 49				10 57					11 27		11 49				11 57					12 27		12 49
	d	10 50				10 58					11 28		11 50				11 58					12 28		12 50
Normanton	d	10 54											11 54											12 54
Castleford	a	11 00											12 00											13 00
Woodlesford	a	11 12											12 12											13 12
Leeds 10 31	a	11 25		11 31		11 18					11 48		12 25			12 31	12 18					12 48		13 25

		TP ◇1 A	NT	NT ◇	NT B	NT	EM ◇ C	NT D	NT	NT ◇ E		NT	TP ◇1 A	NT	NT ◇	NT B	NT G	NT	EM ◇ C	NT D		NT	NT H	NT	TP ◇1 A
Nottingham 8	d			11 17			11 47								12 17				12 47						
Langley Mill	d			11 36											12 36										
Alfreton	d			11 44			12 08								12 44				13 08						
Chesterfield	d			11 55			12 20								12 55				13 20						
Dronfield	d			12 02											13 02										
Sheffield 7 29,31	a			12 15			12 37								13 15				13 39						
	d	12 10	12 14	12 18	12 25	12 36		12 41	12 50	12 53		13 06	13 10	13 14	13 18	13 24	13 29	13 36		13 41		13 50	13 53	14 06	14 10
Meadowhall 4 29,31	a	12 15	12 20	12 23	12 30	12 41		12 46	12 55	12 58		13 11	13 16	13 20	13 23	13 29	13 34	13 41		13 46		13 55	13 58	14 11	14 16
	d		12 21	12 24		12 42			12 56			13 12		13 21	13 24			13 42				13 56		14 12	
Chapeltown	d					12 48						13 18						13 48						14 18	
Elsecar	d											13 23												14 23	
Wombwell	d					12 55						13 27						13 55						14 27	
Barnsley	a			12 42		13 00			13 11			13 32			13 42			14 00				14 11		14 32	
	d			12 42		13 01			13 12			13 33			13 42			14 01				14 12		14 33	
Dodworth	d					13 07												14 07							
Silkstone Common	d					13 11												14 11							
Penistone	d					13 18												14 18							
Denby Dale	d					13 24												14 24							
Shepley	d					13 29												14 29							
Stocksmoor	d					13 32												14 32							
Brockholes	d					13 36												14 36							
Honley	d					13 38												14 38							
Berry Brow	d					13 41												14 41							
Lockwood	d					13 44												14 44							
Huddersfield	a					13 49												14 49							
Darton	d											13 38												14 38	
Wakefield Kirkgate 4 31	a			12 57					13 27			13 50			13 57							14 27		14 49	
	d			12 58					13 28			13 50			13 58							14 28		14 50	
Normanton	d											13 54												14 54	
Castleford	a											14 00												15 00	
Woodlesford	a											14 12												15 12	
Leeds 10 31	a		13 29	13 18					13 49			14 25		14 31	14 18							14 48		15 25	

A From Manchester Airport to Cleethorpes
B To Scunthorpe
C From Norwich to Liverpool Lime Street
D To Bridlington
E From Lincoln to Adwick
F To Scarborough
G To York. via Pontefract Baghill
H To Adwick

Table 34

Mondays to Fridays

9 December to 16 May

Nottingham, Sheffield - Barnsley - Huddersfield and Leeds

Network Diagram - see first page of Table 31

		NT	NT	NT	NT	EM		NT	NT	NT	NT	TP	NT	NT	NT	NT		EM	NT	NT	NT	NT	TP	NT	NT
			◇			◇				◇		◇1		◇				◇			◇		◇1		◇
				A		B		C		D		E			A			B	F		D		E		
Nottingham 8	d		13 17			13 47								14 17				14 47							15 17
Langley Mill	d		13 36											14 36											15 36
Alfreton	d		13 44			14 08								14 44				15 08							15 44
Chesterfield	d		13 55			14 20								14 55				15 21							15 55
Dronfield	d		14 02											15 02											16 02
Sheffield 7 29,31	a		14 15			14 37								15 15				15 37							16 15
	d	14 14	14 18	14 24	14 36			14 41	14 50	14 53	15 06	15 10	15 14	15 18	15 24	15 36			15 41	15 50	15 53	16 06	16 10	16 14	16 18
Meadowhall 4 29,31	a	14 20	14 23	14 29	14 41			14 46	14 55	14 58	15 11	15 16	15 20	15 23	15 29	15 41			15 46	15 55	15 58	16 11	16 16	16 20	16 24
	d	14 21	14 24		14 42				14 56		15 12		15 20	15 24		15 42				15 56		16 12		16 21	16 24
Chapeltown	d				14 48						15 18					15 48						16 18			
Elsecar	d										15 23											16 23			
Wombwell	d				14 55						15 27					15 55						16 27			
Barnsley	a		14 42		15 00				15 11		15 32			15 42		16 00				16 11		16 32			16 42
	d		14 42		15 01				15 12		15 33			15 42		16 01				16 12		16 33			16 42
Dodworth	d				15 07											16 07									
Silkstone Common	d				15 11											16 11									
Penistone	d				15 18											16 18									
Denby Dale	d				15 24											16 24									
Shepley	d				15 29											16 29									
Stocksmoor	d				15 32											16 32									
Brockholes	d				15 36											16 36									
Honley	d				15 38											16 38									
Berry Brow	d				15 41											16 41									
Lockwood	d				15 44											16 44									
Huddersfield	a				15 49											16 49									
Darton	d										15 38											16 38			
Wakefield Kirkgate 4 31	a		14 57						15 27		15 49			15 57						16 27		16 49			16 57
	d		14 58						15 28		15 50			15 58						16 28		16 50			16 58
Normanton	d										15 54											16 54			
Castleford	a										16 00											17 00			
Woodlesford	a										16 12											17 12			
Leeds 10 31	a	15 31	15 18						15 49		16 25		16 31	16 18						16 49		17 25		17 33	17 18

		NT		NT	EM	NT	NT	NT	NT	TP	NT	NT		NT	EM	NT	NT	NT	NT	NT	TP	NT		NT	NT
					◇			◇		◇1		◇			◇				◇		◇1			◇	
		G			B	F		D		E				G	B		C		H		E				G
Nottingham 8	d				15 47							16 17			16 47									17 17	
Langley Mill	d											16 38												17 36	
Alfreton	d				16 08							16 46			17 08									17 44	
Chesterfield	d				16 21							16 57			17 18									17 55	
Dronfield	d											17 04												18 02	
Sheffield 7 29,31	a				16 37							17 15			17 36									18 15	
	d	16 23		16 36		16 41	16 50	16 53	17 06	17 10	17 14	17 18		17 27		17 36	17 41	17 50	17 53	18 06	18 10	18 16		18 19	18 29
Meadowhall 4 29,31	a	16 30		16 41		16 46	16 55	16 58	17 11	17 16	17 20	17 23		17 32		17 41	17 46	17 55	17 58	18 13	18 18	18 21		18 24	18 35
	d			16 42			16 56		17 12		17 21	17 24				17 42		17 56		18 13		18 22		18 25	
Chapeltown	d			16 48					17 18							17 48				18 19					
Elsecar	d			16 53					17 23							17 53				18 25					
Wombwell	d			16 57					17 27							17 57				18 28					
Barnsley	a			17 02			17 11		17 32			17 42				18 02		18 12		18 34				18 42	
	d			17 03			17 12		17 33			17 42				18 03		18 13		18 34				18 42	
Dodworth	d			17 09												18 09									
Silkstone Common	d			17 13												18 13									
Penistone	d			17 20												18 27									
Denby Dale	d			17 26												18 33									
Shepley	d			17 31												18 38									
Stocksmoor	d			17 34												18 41									
Brockholes	d			17 38												18 45									
Honley	d			17 40												18 47									
Berry Brow	d			17 43												18 50									
Lockwood	d			17 46												18 53									
Huddersfield	a			17 50												18 57									
Darton	d								17 38											18 39					
Wakefield Kirkgate 4 31	a						17 28		17 49			17 57						18 28		18 50				18 59	
	d						17 28		17 50			17 58						18 32		18 50				18 59	
Normanton	d								17 54											18 54					
Castleford	a								18 00											19 00					
Woodlesford	a								18 12											19 13					
Leeds 10 31	a						17 48		18 25		18 31	18 18						18 51		19 26		19 30		19 23	

A To Scunthorpe
B From Norwich to Liverpool Lime Street
C To Scarborough
D From Lincoln to Adwick
E From Manchester Airport to Cleethorpes
F To Bridlington
G To Doncaster
H From Lincoln to Hull

Table 34

Mondays to Fridays

9 December to 16 May

Nottingham, Sheffield - Barnsley - Huddersfield and Leeds

Network Diagram - see first page of Table 31

Station			EM ◇ A	NT	NT B	NT	NT C	NT	TP ◇1 D (trolley)	NT	NT ◇	NT E	EM ◇ A	NT	NT F	NT	NT B	NT	TP ◇1 D	NT G	NT ◇	EM ◇ H	NT	NT I
Nottingham 8	⇌	d	17 45								18 17		18 47								19 17	19 41		
Langley Mill		d	18 01								18 36										19 36			
Alfreton		d	18 08								18 44		19 08								19 44	20 02		
Chesterfield		d	18 20								18 55		19 21								19 56	20 13		
Dronfield		d									19 02										20 03			
Sheffield 7	29,31 ⇌	a	18 36								19 15		19 37								20 15	20 27		
		d		18 36	18 41	18 50	19 00	19 06	19 12	19 19	19 22	19 31		19 37	19 44	19 51	19 58	20 07	20 10	20 15	20 18		20 27	20 38
Meadowhall 4	29,31 ⇌	a		18 41	18 46	18 56	19 06	19 12	19 18	19 24	19 27	19 36		19 42	19 49	19 56	20 03	20 12	20 15	20 20	20 24		20 34	20 44
		d		18 42		18 56		19 12		19 25	19 28			19 43		19 57		20 13			20 24		20 35	
Chapeltown		d		18 48				19 18						19 49				20 19						
Elsecar		d		18 53				19 23						19 54				20 24						
Wombwell		d		18 57				19 27						19 58				20 28						
Barnsley		a		19 02		19 14		19 33			19 42			20 03		20 12		20 33			20 43			
		d		19 10		19 14		19 33			19 43			20 08		20 12		20 34			20 43			
Dodworth		d		19 16										20 14										
Silkstone Common		d		19 20										20 18										
Penistone		d		19 27										20 25										
Denby Dale		d		19 33										20 31										
Shepley		d		19 38										20 36										
Stocksmoor		d		19 41										20 39										
Brockholes		d		19 45										20 43										
Honley		d		19 47										20 45										
Berry Brow		d		19 50										20 48										
Lockwood		d		19 53										20 51										
Huddersfield		a		19 58										20 55										
Darton		d						19 38										20 39						
Wakefield Kirkgate 4	31	a				19 30		19 50			19 57					20 29		20 50			20 58			
		d				19 32		19 50			19 58					20 29		20 51			20 59			
Normanton		d						19 54										20 55						
Castleford		a						20 00										21 01						
Woodlesford		a						20 12										21 13						
Leeds 10	31	a				19 55		20 26		20 35	20 18					20 48		21 26			21 20		21 47	

Station			NT	NT	TP FO ◇1 D	NT F	EM ◇1 J (trolley)	NT FO	NT FX	TP FX ◇1 K	NT	NT FO	NT FO	NT FX	TP ◇1 D	NT	NT	NT G	NT	EM ◇1 J (trolley)	NT	NT FX L	NT E
Nottingham 8	⇌	d					20 34									21 15				21 33			
Langley Mill		d					20 51									21 40				21 56			
Alfreton		d					20 59									21 48				22 04			
Chesterfield		d					21 10									22 00				22 15			
Dronfield		d														22 07							
Sheffield 7	29,31 ⇌	a					21 25									22 19				22 34			
		d	20 42	21 09	21 10	21 16	21 27	21 30	21 30	21 34	21 41	22 06		22 06	22 10		22 24	22 34	22 41	22 50	23 15	23 24	23 27
Meadowhall 4	29,31 ⇌	a	20 47	21 14	21 16	21 21		21 35	21 35	21 39	21 46	22 11		22 11	22 16		22 30	22 39	22 46		23 20	23 29	23 32
		d	20 48	21 15				21 36	21 36		21 47	22 12		22 12			22 31		22 47		23 21	23 30	
Chapeltown		d	20 54	21 21							21 53	22 18		22 18					22 53			23 36	
Elsecar		d		21 26								22 23		22 23					22 58			23 41	
Wombwell		d	21 01	21 30							22 00	22 27		22 27					23 02			23 45	
Barnsley		a	21 07	21 35							22 05	22 32		22 32					23 07			23 50	
		d	21 08	21 36							22 08			22 33					23 08			23 51	
Dodworth		d	21 14								22 14								23 14				
Silkstone Common		d	21 18								22 18								23 18				
Penistone		d	21 25								22 25								23 25				
Denby Dale		d	21 31								22 31								23 31				
Shepley		d	21 36								22 36								23 36				
Stocksmoor		d	21 39								22 39								23 39				
Brockholes		d	21 43								22 43								23 43				
Honley		d	21 45								22 45								23 45				
Berry Brow		d	21 48								22 48								23 48				
Lockwood		d	21 51								22 51								23 51				
Huddersfield		a	21 56								22 57								23 55				
Darton		d		21 41										22 38								23 56	
Wakefield Kirkgate 4	31	a		21 52										22 54								00s10	
		d		21 52									22 51	22 54									
Normanton		d		21 57									22 56	22 56									
Castleford		a		22 04									23 01	23 01									
Woodlesford		a		22 14									23 14	23 14									
Leeds 10	31	a		22 29			22 17	22 44	22 46				23 30	23 30			23 41			23 41	00 29		

A From Norwich to Liverpool Lime Street
B To Bridlington
C From Retford Low Level to Doncaster
D From Manchester Airport to Cleethorpes
E To Doncaster
F To Beverley
G To Goole
H From Norwich to Manchester Piccadilly
I To Scunthorpe
J From St Pancras International
K To Cleethorpes
L To Wakefield Westgate

Table 34

Saturdays

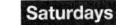

14 December to 17 May

Nottingham, Sheffield - Barnsley - Huddersfield and Leeds

Network Diagram - see first page of Table 31

		NT	NT	NT	NT	NT	NT	NT	NT	TP		NT	NT	NT	EM	NT	NT	NT	EM	NT		TP	NT	NT	NT
										◇1					◇				◇1			◇1			
			A			B			B	C				D	E		F	G	H			C			D
Nottingham 8	d														06 40									07 11	
Langley Mill	d																							07 30	
Alfreton	d														07 01									07 38	
Chesterfield	d														07 11				07 43					07 48	
Dronfield	d														07 18				07 49						
Sheffield 7 29,31	a														07 28				07 59					08 11	
	d	05 17	05 29	05 43	06 06	06 12	06 28	06 36	06 52	06 55		07 06	07 15	07 24		07 36	07 41	07 51		08 06		08 11	08 14	08 19	08 25
Meadowhall 4 29,31	a	05 22	05 34	05 48	06 11	06 17	06 33	06 41	06 57	07 00		07 11	07 20	07 29		07 41	07 46	07 57		08 11		08 17	08 21	08 24	08 30
	d	05 23		05 49	06 12		06 34	06 42				07 12	07 21			07 42		07 57		08 12			08 22	08 25	
Chapeltown	d	05 29		05 55	06 18			06 48				07 18				07 48				08 18					
Elsecar	d	05 34		06 01	06 23							07 23								08 23					
Wombwell	d	05 38		06 05	06 27			06 55				07 27				07 55				08 27					
Barnsley	a	05 44		06 11	06 32			07 00				07 32				08 00		08 11		08 32				08 42	
	d				06 33			07 01				07 33				08 01		08 12		08 33				08 42	
Dodworth	d							07 07								08 07									
Silkstone Common	d							07 11								08 11									
Penistone	d							07 18								08 18									
Denby Dale	d							07 24								08 24									
Shepley	d							07 29								08 29									
Stocksmoor	d							07 32								08 32									
Brockholes	d							07 36								08 36									
Honley	d							07 38								08 38									
Berry Brow	d							07 41								08 41									
Lockwood	d							07 44								08 44									
Huddersfield	a							07 49								08 49									
Darton	d				06 38							07 38								08 38					
Wakefield Kirkgate 4 31	a				06 49							07 49						08 27		08 49				08 57	
	d				06 50							07 50						08 28		08 50				08 58	
Normanton	d				06 54							07 54								08 54					
Castleford	a				07 00							08 00								09 00					
Woodlesford	a				07 12							08 12								09 12					
Leeds 10 31	a				07 28		07 44					08 25	08 32					08 49		09 25			09 40	09 20	

		NT	EM	NT	NT	NT		NT	TP	NT	NT	NT	NT	NT	EM	NT		NT	NT	NT	TP	NT	NT	NT	NT
			◇						◇1						◇						◇1				
			E	F		B			C			D	I		J	K			L		C			D	
Nottingham 8	d		07 47								08 17				08 48								09 17		
Langley Mill	d										08 36												09 36		
Alfreton	d		08 09								08 44				09 10								09 44		
Chesterfield	d		08 20								08 55				09 21								09 55		
Dronfield	d		08 27								09 02												10 02		
Sheffield 7 29,31	a		08 37								09 15				09 38								10 15		
	d	08 36		08 41	08 51	08 53		09 06	09 10	09 15	09 18	09 27	09 32	09 36		09 41		09 50	09 53	10 06	10 10	10 14	10 18	10 24	10 36
Meadowhall 4 29,31	a	08 41		08 46	08 56	08 59		09 11	09 15	09 20	09 23	09 34	09 38	09 41		09 46		09 55	09 58	10 11	10 16	10 20	10 23	10 29	10 41
	d	08 42			08 57			09 12		09 21	09 24			09 42				09 56		10 12		10 21	10 24		10 42
Chapeltown	d	08 48						09 18						09 48						10 18					10 48
Elsecar	d							09 23												10 23					
Wombwell	d	08 55						09 27						09 55						10 27					10 55
Barnsley	a	09 00			09 11			09 32			09 42			10 00				10 11		10 32			10 42		11 00
	d	09 01			09 12			09 33			09 42			10 01				10 12		10 33			10 42		11 01
Dodworth	d	09 07												10 07											11 07
Silkstone Common	d	09 11												10 11											11 11
Penistone	d	09 18												10 18											11 18
Denby Dale	d	09 24												10 24											11 24
Shepley	d	09 29												10 29											11 29
Stocksmoor	d	09 32												10 32											11 32
Brockholes	d	09 36												10 36											11 36
Honley	d	09 38												10 38											11 38
Berry Brow	d	09 41												10 41											11 41
Lockwood	d	09 44												10 44											11 44
Huddersfield	a	09 49												10 49											11 49
Darton	d							09 38												10 38					
Wakefield Kirkgate 4 31	a				09 27			09 49			09 57							10 27		10 49			10 57		
	d				09 28			09 50			09 58							10 28		10 50			10 58		
Normanton	d							09 54												10 54					
Castleford	a							10 00												11 00					
Woodlesford	a							10 12												11 12					
Leeds 10 31	a				09 49			10 25		10 40	10 18							10 48		11 25		11 40	11 18		

A To Beverley
B To Adwick
C From Manchester Airport to Cleethorpes
D To Scunthorpe
E To Liverpool Lime Street
F To Bridlington
G From Retford
H From Derby
I To York. via Pontefract Baghill
J From Norwich to Liverpool Lime Street
K To Scarborough
L From Lincoln to Adwick

Table 34

Saturdays

14 December to 17 May

Nottingham, Sheffield - Barnsley - Huddersfield and Leeds

Network Diagram - see first page of Table 31

		EM		NT	NT	NT	NT	TP	NT	NT	NT	NT		EM	NT	NT	NT	NT	TP	NT	NT	NT		NT	EM
		◇						◇1						◇					◇1						◇
		A		B		C		D			E			A	F		C		D			E			A
Nottingham 8	d	09 47								10 17				10 47							11 17				11 47
Langley Mill	d									10 36											11 36				
Alfreton	d	10 10								10 44				11 10							11 44				12 10
Chesterfield	d	10 20								10 55				11 20							11 55				12 21
Dronfield	d									11 02											12 02				
Sheffield 7 29,31	a	10 37								11 15				11 37							12 15				12 37
	d			10 41	10 50	10 53	11 06	11 10	11 14	11 18	11 24	11 36			11 41	11 50	11 53	12 06	12 10	12 14	12 18	12 24		12 36	
Meadowhall 4 29,31	a			10 46	10 55	10 58	11 11	11 16	11 20	11 23	11 29	11 41			11 46	11 55	11 58	12 11	12 16	12 20	12 23	12 29		12 41	
	d				10 56		11 12		11 21	11 24		11 42				11 56		12 12		12 21	12 24			12 42	
Chapeltown	d						11 18					11 48						12 18						12 48	
Elsecar	d						11 23											12 23							
Wombwell	d						11 27					11 55						12 27						12 55	
Barnsley	a				11 11		11 32			11 42		12 00				12 10		12 32			12 42			13 00	
	d				11 12		11 33			11 42		12 01				12 11		12 33			12 42			13 01	
Dodworth	d											12 07												13 07	
Silkstone Common	d											12 11												13 11	
Penistone	d											12 18												13 18	
Denby Dale	d											12 24												13 24	
Shepley	d											12 29												13 29	
Stocksmoor	d											12 32												13 32	
Brockholes	d											12 36												13 36	
Honley	d											12 38												13 38	
Berry Brow	d											12 41												13 41	
Lockwood	d											12 44												13 44	
Huddersfield	a											12 49												13 49	
Darton	d						11 38											12 38							
Wakefield Kirkgate 4 31	a				11 27		11 49			11 58						12 27		12 49			12 57				
	d				11 28		11 50			11 58						12 28		12 50			12 58				
Normanton	d						11 54											12 54							
Castleford	a						12 00											13 00							
Woodlesford	a						12 12											13 12							
Leeds 10 31	a				11 48		12 25		12 40	12 18						12 48		13 25		13 43	13 18				

		NT	NT	NT	NT	TP	NT	NT		NT	NT	NT	EM	NT	NT	NT	NT	TP		NT	NT	NT	NT	EM	NT
						◇1							◇					◇1						◇	
		B		C		D				E	G		A	B		C		D				E		A	F
Nottingham 8	d							12 17					12 47								13 17			13 47	
Langley Mill	d							12 36													13 36				
Alfreton	d							12 44					13 10								13 44			14 10	
Chesterfield	d							12 55					13 20								13 55			14 20	
Dronfield	d							13 02													14 02				
Sheffield 7 29,31	a							13 15					13 37								14 15			14 37	
	d	12 41	12 50	12 53	13 06	13 10	13 14	13 18		13 24	13 30	13 36		13 41	13 50	13 53	14 06	14 10		14 14	14 18	14 24	14 36		14 41
Meadowhall 4 29,31	a	12 46	12 55	12 58	13 11	13 16	13 20	13 23		13 29	13 35	13 41		13 46	13 55	13 58	14 11	14 16		14 20	14 23	14 29	14 41		14 46
	d		12 56		13 12		13 21	13 24				13 42			13 56		14 12			14 21	14 24		14 42		
Chapeltown	d				13 18							13 48					14 18						14 48		
Elsecar	d				13 23												14 23								
Wombwell	d				13 27							13 55					14 27						14 55		
Barnsley	a		13 11		13 32			13 42				14 00			14 11		14 32				14 42		15 00		
	d		13 12		13 33			13 42				14 01			14 12		14 33				14 42		15 01		
Dodworth	d											14 07											15 07		
Silkstone Common	d											14 11											15 11		
Penistone	d											14 18											15 18		
Denby Dale	d											14 24											15 24		
Shepley	d											14 29											15 29		
Stocksmoor	d											14 32											15 32		
Brockholes	d											14 36											15 36		
Honley	d											14 38											15 38		
Berry Brow	d											14 41											15 41		
Lockwood	d											14 44											15 44		
Huddersfield	a											14 49											15 49		
Darton	d				13 38												14 38								
Wakefield Kirkgate 4 31	a		13 27		13 50			13 57							14 27		14 49				14 57				
	d		13 28		13 50			13 58							14 28		14 50				14 58				
Normanton	d				13 54												14 54								
Castleford	a				14 00												15 00								
Woodlesford	a				14 12												15 12								
Leeds 10 31	a		13 49		14 25		14 40	14 18							14 48		15 25			15 40	15 18				

A From Norwich to Liverpool Lime Street
B To Bridlington
C From Lincoln to Adwick
D From Manchester Airport to Cleethorpes
E To Scunthorpe
F To Scarborough
G To York

Table 34

Saturdays

14 December to 17 May

Nottingham, Sheffield - Barnsley - Huddersfield and Leeds

Network Diagram - see first page of Table 31

		NT	NT A	NT		TP ◇1 B	NT	NT	NT C	NT	EM ◇ D	NT E	NT	NT ◇ A		NT	TP ◇1 B	NT	NT	NT F	NT	EM ◇ D	NT E	NT
Nottingham 8	d							14 17			14 47								15 17			15 47		
Langley Mill	d							14 36											15 36					
Alfreton	d							14 44			15 10								15 44			16 10		
Chesterfield	d							14 55			15 20								15 55			16 20		
Dronfield	d							15 02											16 02					
Sheffield 7 29,31	a							15 15			15 37								16 15			16 37		
	d	14 50	14 53	15 06		15 10	15 14	15 18	15 24	15 36		15 41	15 50	15 53		16 06	16 10	16 14	16 18	16 24	16 36		16 41	16 50
Meadowhall 4 29,31	a	14 55	14 58	15 11		15 16	15 20	15 23	15 29	15 41		15 46	15 55	15 58		16 11	16 16	16 20	16 23	16 29	16 41		16 46	16 55
	d	14 56		15 12			15 21	15 24		15 42			15 56			16 12		16 21	16 24		16 42			16 56
Chapeltown	d			15 18						15 48						16 18					16 48			
Elsecar	d			15 23												16 23					16 53			
Wombwell	d			15 27						15 55						16 27					16 57			
Barnsley	a	15 11		15 32				15 42		16 00			16 11			16 32			16 42		17 02			17 11
	d	15 12		15 33				15 42		16 01			16 12			16 33			16 42		17 03			17 12
Dodworth	d									16 07											17 09			
Silkstone Common	d									16 11											17 13			
Penistone	d									16 18											17 20			
Denby Dale	d									16 24											17 26			
Shepley	d									16 29											17 31			
Stocksmoor	d									16 32											17 34			
Brockholes	d									16 36											17 38			
Honley	d									16 38											17 40			
Berry Brow	d									16 41											17 43			
Lockwood	d									16 44											17 46			
Huddersfield	a									16 49											17 50			
Darton	d			15 38												16 38								
Wakefield Kirkgate 4 31	a	15 27		15 49				15 57					16 27			16 49			16 57					17 28
	d	15 28		15 50				15 58					16 28			16 50			16 58					17 28
Normanton	d			15 54												16 54								
Castleford	a			16 00												17 00								
Woodlesford	a			16 12												17 12								
Leeds 10 31	a	15 49		16 25			16 41	16 18					16 49			17 25		17 41	17 18					17 48

		NT ◇ A	NT	TP ◇1 B	NT	NT	NT F	EM ◇ D	NT	NT G		NT	NT H	NT	TP ◇1 B	NT	NT	NT F	EM ◇ D	NT		NT E	NT	NT I	NT
Nottingham 8	d					16 17		16 44									17 17		17 44						
Langley Mill	d					16 36											17 36		18 00						
Alfreton	d					16 44		17 05									17 44		18 07						
Chesterfield	d					16 55		17 15									17 55		18 18						
Dronfield	d					17 02											18 02								
Sheffield 7 29,31	a					17 15		17 34									18 15		18 33						
	d	16 53	17 06	17 10	17 14	17 18	17 27		17 36	17 41		17 50	17 53	18 06	18 11	18 16	18 19	18 30		18 36		18 41	18 50	19 00	19 06
Meadowhall 4 29,31	a	16 58	17 11	17 16	17 21	17 23	17 32		17 41	17 46		17 55	17 58	18 12	18 18	18 21	18 24	18 35		18 41		18 46	18 55	19 06	19 11
	d		17 12		17 21	17 24			17 42			17 56		18 12		18 22	18 25			18 42			18 56		19 12
Chapeltown	d		17 18						17 48					18 18						18 48					19 18
Elsecar	d		17 23						17 53					18 23						18 53					19 23
Wombwell	d		17 27						17 57					18 27						18 57					19 27
Barnsley	a		17 32			17 42			18 02			18 11		18 33			18 42			19 02			19 14		19 33
	d		17 33			17 42			18 03			18 12		18 33			18 42			19 03			19 14		19 33
Dodworth	d								18 09											19 09					
Silkstone Common	d								18 13											19 13					
Penistone	d								18 20											19 20					
Denby Dale	d								18 26											19 26					
Shepley	d								18 31											19 31					
Stocksmoor	d								18 34											19 34					
Brockholes	d								18 38											19 38					
Honley	d								18 40											19 41					
Berry Brow	d								18 43											19 44					
Lockwood	d								18 46											19 46					
Huddersfield	a								18 51											19 51					
Darton	d		17 38											18 38											19 38
Wakefield Kirkgate 4 31	a		17 49			17 57						18 28		18 50			18 58						19 29		19 50
	d		17 50			17 58						18 32		18 50			18 58						19 32		19 50
Normanton	d		17 54											18 54											19 54
Castleford	a		18 00											19 00											20 00
Woodlesford	a		18 12											19 13											20 12
Leeds 10 31	a		18 25		18 44	18 18						18 51		19 27		19 43	19 23						19 55		20 26

A From Lincoln to Adwick
B From Manchester Airport to Cleethorpes
C To Scunthorpe
D From Norwich to Liverpool Lime Street
E To Bridlington
F To Doncaster
G To Scarborough
H From Lincoln to Hull
I From Retford Low Level to Doncaster

Table 34

Saturdays

14 December to 17 May

Nottingham, Sheffield - Barnsley - Huddersfield and Leeds

Network Diagram - see first page of Table 31

Station			TP	NT	NT	NT	EM	NT	NT	NT	NT	NT	NT	NT	TP	EM	NT	NT	NT	NT	NT	EM	NT	NT
			◇1				◇								◇1	◇						◇1		
			A			B	C		D		E		F		A	G		B			D	H		
Nottingham 8		d		18 17			18 47							19 17		19 39						20 16		
Langley Mill		d		18 36										19 36								20 33		
Alfreton		d		18 44			19 10							19 44		20 00						20 41		
Chesterfield		d		18 55			19 21							19 55		20 10						20 52		
Dronfield		d		19 02										20 02										
Sheffield 7	29,31	a		19 15			19 37							20 15		20 28						21 05		
		d	19 11	19 16	19 19	19 25		19 37	19 44	19 51	19 58	20 07	20 15	20 18	20 25		20 30	20 38	20 43	21 06	21 15	21 25	21 30	21 41
Meadowhall 4	29,31	a	19 18	19 22	19 24	19 30		19 42	19 49	19 56	20 03	20 12	20 20	20 26	20 32		20 35	20 44	20 48	21 11	21 21		21 36	21 46
		d		19 22	19 25			19 43		19 57		20 13		20 26			20 36		20 49	21 12			21 36	21 47
Chapeltown		d						19 49				20 19							20 55	21 18				21 53
Elsecar		d						19 54				20 24								21 23				
Wombwell		d						19 58				20 28							21 02	21 27				22 00
Barnsley		a		19 43				20 03		20 12		20 33		20 42					21 07	21 33				22 05
		d		19 43				20 08		20 12		20 34		20 42					21 08	21 33				22 08
Dodworth		d						20 14											21 14					22 14
Silkstone Common		d						20 18											21 18					22 18
Penistone		d						20 25											21 25					22 25
Denby Dale		d						20 31											21 31					22 31
Shepley		d						20 36											21 36					22 36
Stocksmoor		d						20 39											21 39					22 39
Brockholes		d						20 43											21 43					22 43
Honley		d						20 45											21 45					22 45
Berry Brow		d						20 48											21 48					22 48
Lockwood		d						20 51											21 51					22 51
Huddersfield		a						20 55											21 56					22 56
Darton		d										20 39								21 38				
Wakefield Kirkgate 4	31	a		19 58						20 28		20 50		20 57						21 52				
		d		19 59						20 28		20 51		20 58						21 52				
Normanton		d										20 55								21 57				
Castleford		a										21 01								22 04				
Woodlesford		a										21 13								22 14				
Leeds 10	31	a		20 20	20 38					20 48		21 26		21 20			21 47			22 29		22 18	22 45	

Station			NT	TP	NT	NT	NT	NT	NT	NT	NT
				◇1							
				I					F		J
Nottingham 8		d	20 43			21 17					
Langley Mill		d	21 08			21 36					
Alfreton		d	21 16			21 44					
Chesterfield		d	21 26			21 55					
Dronfield		d				22 02					
Sheffield 7	29,31	a	21 43			22 14					
		d		21 48	22 06			22 24	22 30	22 41	23 27
Meadowhall 4	29,31	a		21 54	22 11			22 30	22 35	22 46	23 32
		d			22 12			22 30		22 47	
Chapeltown		d			22 18					22 53	
Elsecar		d			22 23					22 58	
Wombwell		d			22 27					23 02	
Barnsley		a			22 32					23 07	
		d								23 08	
Dodworth		d								23 14	
Silkstone Common		d								23 18	
Penistone		d								23 25	
Denby Dale		d								23 31	
Shepley		d								23 36	
Stocksmoor		d								23 39	
Brockholes		d								23 43	
Honley		d								23 45	
Berry Brow		d								23 48	
Lockwood		d								23 51	
Huddersfield		a								23 59	
Darton		d									
Wakefield Kirkgate 4	31	a									
		d					22 51				
Normanton		d					22 56				
Castleford		a					23 02				
Woodlesford		a					23 14				
Leeds 10	31	a					23 30	23 40			

A From Manchester Airport to Cleethorpes
B To Scunthorpe
C From Norwich to Liverpool Lime Street
D To Beverley
E To Bridlington
F To Goole
G From Norwich to Manchester Piccadilly
H From St Pancras International
I To Cleethorpes
J To Doncaster

Table 34

Sundays

8 December to 29 December

Nottingham, Sheffield - Barnsley - Huddersfield and Leeds

Network Diagram - see first page of Table 31

		NT A	NT	NT B	NT	NT	TP ◇1 C	NT ◇ D	NT B	EM ◇ E		NT	NT A	NT	EM ◇ E	NT	NT	TP ◇1 F	NT	NT G		NT B	EM ◇ E	NT	NT
Nottingham 8	d									09 47				10 12	10 48				11 16				11 44		
Langley Mill	d													10 36					11 35						
Alfreton	d									10 05				10 44	11 09				11 43				12 05		
Chesterfield	d									10 18				10 55	11 19				11 53				12 15		
Dronfield	d									10 25				11 02					12 00						
Sheffield 7 29,31	a									10 37				11 14	11 35				12 15				12 32		
	d	08 00	08 39	08 45	09 36	09 39	09 52	10 17	10 28			10 39	11 05	11 17		11 36	11 49	12 10	12 16	12 24		12 28		12 35	12 39
Meadowhall 4 29,31	a	08 05	08 44	08 50	09 41	09 44	09 57	10 22	10 33			10 44	11 10	11 22		11 41	11 54	12 16	12 22	12 29		12 33		12 40	12 44
	d		08 45		09 42	09 45		10 23				10 45		11 23		11 42	11 55		12 23					12 41	12 45
Chapeltown	d		08 51			09 51						10 51					12 01								12 55
Elsecar	d		08 56			09 56						10 56					12 06								13 00
Wombwell	d		09 00			10 00						11 00					12 10								13 04
Barnsley	a		09 05			10 05		10 37				11 05		11 37			12 15		12 37					12 55	13 09
	d		09 10			10 06		10 37				11 10		11 37			12 16		12 37					13 06	13 10
Dodworth	d					10 12											12 22							13 12	
Silkstone Common	d					10 16											12 26							13 16	
Penistone	d					10 23											12 33							13 23	
Denby Dale	d					10 29											12 39							13 29	
Shepley	d					10 34											12 44							13 34	
Stocksmoor	d					10 37											12 47							13 37	
Brockholes	d					10 41											12 51							13 41	
Honley	d					10 43											12 53							13 43	
Berry Brow	d					10 46											12 56							13 46	
Lockwood	d					10 49											12 59							13 49	
Huddersfield	a					10 53											13 04							13 53	
Darton	d		09 15									11 15													13 15
Wakefield Kirkgate 4 31	a		09 29					10 55				11 29		11 52					12 52						13 29
	d		09 30					10 57				11 30		11 53					12 53						13 30
Normanton	d		09 34									11 34													13 34
Castleford	a		09 40									11 40													13 40
Woodlesford	a		09 55									11 51													13 51
Leeds 10 31	a		10 07		10 52			11 15				12 05		12 18		12 53			13 18						14 04

		TP ◇1 H	NT	NT I	EM ◇ E	NT		NT	TP ◇1 F	NT	NT G	NT B	EM ◇ J	NT	TP ◇1 F	NT		NT A	NT I	NT	EM ◇ E	NT K	TP ◇1 F	NT	NT G
Nottingham 8	d		12 15		12 41					13 13			13 42			14 15					14 47			15 12	
Langley Mill	d		12 34		12 57					13 34			13 58			14 34					15 03			15 36	
Alfreton	d		12 42		13 05					13 42			14 06			14 42					15 11			15 44	
Chesterfield	d		12 52		13 15					13 52			14 16			14 53					15 21			15 56	
Dronfield	d		12 59							13 59						15 00								16 03	
Sheffield 7 29,31	a		13 15		13 32					14 15			14 34			15 15					15 39			16 15	
	d	13 10	13 17	13 24		13 36		13 39	14 10	14 17	14 22	14 28		14 39	15 10	15 17		15 24	15 28	15 36		15 39	16 10	16 17	16 25
Meadowhall 4 29,31	a	13 16	13 22	13 29		13 41		13 44	14 16	14 22	14 27	14 33		14 44	15 16	15 22		15 29	15 33	15 41		15 42	16 16	16 22	16 30
	d		13 23			13 42		13 45		14 23				14 45		15 23				15 42		15 43		16 23	
Chapeltown	d							13 51						14 51								15 49			
Elsecar	d							13 56						14 56								15 54			
Wombwell	d							14 00						15 00								15 58			
Barnsley	a		13 37					14 05		14 37				15 05		15 37						16 03		16 37	
	d		13 37					14 06		14 37				15 10		15 37						16 04		16 37	
Dodworth	d							14 12														16 10			
Silkstone Common	d							14 16														16 14			
Penistone	d							14 23														16 21			
Denby Dale	d							14 29														16 27			
Shepley	d							14 34														16 32			
Stocksmoor	d							14 37														16 35			
Brockholes	d							14 41														16 39			
Honley	d							14 43														16 41			
Berry Brow	d							14 46														16 44			
Lockwood	d							14 49														16 47			
Huddersfield	a							14 53														16 53			
Darton	d													15 15											
Wakefield Kirkgate 4 31	a		13 52							14 52				15 29		15 52								16 52	
	d		13 53							14 53				15 30		15 53								16 53	
Normanton	d													15 34											
Castleford	a													15 40											
Woodlesford	a													15 51											
Leeds 10 31	a		14 18			14 47				15 18				16 04		16 18				16 54				17 16	

A To Doncaster
B To Scarborough
C To Cleethorpes
D To Carlisle
E To Liverpool Lime Street
F From Manchester Airport to Cleethorpes
G To Goole
H From Manchester Airport to Doncaster
I To Bridlington
J From Norwich to Liverpool Lime Street
K From Retford Low Level

Table 34

Sundays

8 December to 29 December

Nottingham, Sheffield - Barnsley - Huddersfield and Leeds

Network Diagram - see first page of Table 31

		NT		EM	NT	NT	NT	TP	NT	NT	NT	NT		EM	NT	TP	NT	NT	NT	EM	NT	NT		TP	NT
				◇				◇1						◇		◇1				◇				◇1	
		A		B	C	D		E		F	G			H		E		F	I	H		C		E	
Nottingham 8	d			15 47					16 15					16 42			17 15			17 41					18 15
Langley Mill	d								16 34					17 01			17 34			17 57					18 34
Alfreton	d			16 08					16 42					17 09			17 42			18 05					18 42
Chesterfield	d			16 18					16 52					17 19			17 52			18 16					18 52
Dronfield	d								16 59								17 59								18 58
Sheffield 7 29,31	a			16 34					17 15					17 39			18 15			18 33					19 15
	d	16 28			16 36	16 39	16 54	17 10	17 17	17 25	17 28	17 36			17 39	18 10	18 17	18 25	18 28		18 39	18 57		19 10	19 16
Meadowhall 4 29,31	a	16 33			16 41	16 44	16 59	17 16	17 22	17 30	17 33	17 44			17 46	18 16	18 22	18 30	18 33		18 44	19 04		19 16	19 22
	d					16 45	17 00		17 23			17 44			17 46		18 23				18 45				19 23
Chapeltown	d					16 51									17 52						18 51				
Elsecar	d					16 56									17 58						18 56				
Wombwell	d					17 00									18 01						19 00				
Barnsley	a					17 05	17 14		17 37						18 08		18 37				19 05				19 37
	d					17 10	17 15		17 37						18 10		18 37				19 10				19 37
Dodworth	d						17 21								18 16										
Silkstone Common	d						17 25								18 20										
Penistone	d						17 32								18 27										
Denby Dale	d						17 38								18 34										
Shepley	d						17 43								18 39										
Stocksmoor	d						17 46								18 41										
Brockholes	d						17 50								18 45										
Honley	d						17 52								18 48										
Berry Brow	d						17 55								18 51										
Lockwood	d						17 58								18 53										
Huddersfield	a						18 05								18 58										
Darton	d					17 15															19 15				
Wakefield Kirkgate 4 31	a					17 29			17 52								18 52				19 29				19 52
	d					17 30			17 53								18 53				19 30				19 53
Normanton	d					17 34															19 34				
Castleford	a					17 40															19 41				
Woodlesford	a					17 51															19 53				
Leeds 10 31	a					18 05			18 18			18 50					19 18				20 05				20 18

		NT	EM	NT	NT	NT	TP	NT		NT	EM	NT	TP	NT	NT	NT	NT	NT		NT	TP	NT	NT		
			◇				◇1				◇		◇1								◇1				
		F	J			K	E			L	J		E		K			K		F	M		F		
Nottingham 8	d		18 40					19 15			19 43			20 15								21 33			
Langley Mill	d		18 56					19 34						20 34								21 57			
Alfreton	d		19 04					19 42			20 04			20 42								22 05			
Chesterfield	d		19 15					19 52			20 14			20 52								22 16			
Dronfield	d							19 59														22 23			
Sheffield 7 29,31	a		19 31					20 15			20 31			21 14								22 36			
	d	19 29		19 36	19 39	20 02	20 10	20 17		20 28		20 39	21 10		21 25	21 36	21 43	22 13		22 26	22 30	22 39	23 34		
Meadowhall 4 29,31	a	19 34		19 41	19 44	20 08	20 16	20 22		20 33		20 44	21 16		21 30	21 41	21 48	22 18		22 31	22 35	22 44	23 39		
	d			19 42	19 45			20 23				20 45				21 42	21 49					22 45			
Chapeltown	d				19 51							20 51					21 55					22 51			
Elsecar	d				19 56							20 56					22 00					22 56			
Wombwell	d				20 00							21 00					22 04					23 00			
Barnsley	a				20 05			20 37				21 06					22 09					23 05			
	d				20 06			20 37				21 10										23 10			
Dodworth	d				20 12																				
Silkstone Common	d				20 16																				
Penistone	d				20 23																				
Denby Dale	d				20 29																				
Shepley	d				20 34																				
Stocksmoor	d				20 37																				
Brockholes	d				20 41																				
Honley	d				20 44																				
Berry Brow	d				20 47																				
Lockwood	d				20 49																				
Huddersfield	a				20 57																				
Darton	d											21 15										23 15			
Wakefield Kirkgate 4 31	a							20 52				21 29										23 26			
	d							20 53				21 30										23 27			
Normanton	d											21 34										23 34			
Castleford	a											21 40										23 40			
Woodlesford	a											21 51										23 53			
Leeds 10 31	a			20 52				21 16				22 04				22 50						00 05			

A To Scarborough
B From Peterborough to Liverpool Lime Street
C To York, via Pontefract Baghill
D From Lincoln
E From Manchester Airport to Cleethorpes
F To Doncaster
G To Bridlington
H From Norwich to Liverpool Lime Street
I To Beverley
J From Norwich to Manchester Piccadilly
K To Hull
L To Goole
M To Cleethorpes

Table 34

Sundays

5 January to 9 February

Nottingham, Sheffield - Barnsley - Huddersfield and Leeds

Network Diagram - see first page of Table 31

			NT A 🚌	NT B	NT	NT B	TP A 🚌	NT	NT	NT A 🚌	NT ◇ C	EM ◇ D	NT	NT B	NT	EM ◇ D	TP A 🚌	NT	NT	NT A 🚌	NT	NT B	EM ◇ D	NT
Nottingham 8		d										09 47			10 12	10 48					11 16		11 44	
Langley Mill		d													10 36						11 35			
Alfreton		d										10 05			10 44	11 09					11 43		12 05	
Chesterfield		d										10 18			10 55	11 19					11 53		12 15	
Dronfield		d										10 25			11 02						12 00			
Sheffield 7	29,31	a										10 37			11 14	11 35					12 15		12 32	
		d	07 13	08 00	08 39	08 45	09 15	09 36	09 39	09 55	10 17		10 39	11 05	11 17		11 35	11 36	11 49	11 55	12 16	12 24		12 35
Meadowhall 4	29,31	a	07 33	08 05	08 44	08 50	09 35	09 41	09 44	10 15	10 22		10 44	11 10	11 22		11 55	11 41	11 54	12 15	12 22	12 29		12 40
		d			08 45			09 42	09 45		10 23		10 45		11 23			11 42	11 55		12 23			12 41
Chapeltown		d			08 51				09 51				10 51						12 01					
Elsecar		d			08 56				09 56				10 56						12 06					
Wombwell		d			09 00				10 00				11 00						12 10					
Barnsley		a			09 05				10 05		10 37		11 05		11 37				12 15		12 37			12 55
		d			09 10				10 06		10 37		11 10		11 37				12 16		12 37			13 06
Dodworth		d							10 12										12 22					13 12
Silkstone Common		d							10 16										12 26					13 16
Penistone		d							10 23										12 33					13 23
Denby Dale		d							10 29										12 39					13 29
Shepley		d							10 34										12 44					13 34
Stocksmoor		d							10 37										12 47					13 37
Brockholes		d							10 41										12 51					13 41
Honley		d							10 43										12 53					13 43
Berry Brow		d							10 46										12 56					13 46
Lockwood		d							10 49										12 59					13 49
Huddersfield		a							10 53										13 04					13 53
Darton		d			09 15								11 15											
Wakefield Kirkgate 4	31	a			09 29						10 55		11 29		11 52						12 52			
		d			09 30						10 57		11 30		11 53						12 53			
Normanton		d			09 34								11 34											
Castleford		a			09 40								11 40											
Woodlesford		a			09 55								11 51											
Leeds 10	31	a			10 07			10 52			11 15		12 05		12 18			12 53			13 18			

			NT	TP A 🚌	NT A 🚌	NT	NT B	EM ◇ D	NT	NT	NT A 🚌	TP A 🚌	NT	NT B	EM ◇ E	NT	NT A 🚌	TP A 🚌	NT	NT B	NT	EM ◇ D	NT F	NT A 🚌
Nottingham 8		d				12 15		12 41					13 13		13 42				14 15			14 47		
Langley Mill		d				12 34		12 57					13 34		13 58				14 34			15 03		
Alfreton		d				12 42		13 05					13 42		14 06				14 42			15 11		
Chesterfield		d				12 52		13 15					13 52		14 16				14 53			15 21		
Dronfield		d				12 59							13 59						15 00					
Sheffield 7	29,31	a				13 15		13 32					14 15		14 34				15 15			15 39		
		d	12 39	13 00	13 05	13 17	13 24		13 36	13 39	14 00	14 00	14 17	14 24		14 39	14 55	15 00	15 17	15 24	15 36		15 39	15 55
Meadowhall 4	29,31	a	12 44	13 20	13 25	13 22	13 29		13 41	13 44	14 20	14 20	14 22	14 27		14 44	15 15	15 20	15 22	15 29	15 41		15 42	16 15
		d	12 45			13 23			13 42	13 45			14 23			14 45			15 23		15 42		15 43	
Chapeltown		d	12 55							13 51						14 51							15 49	
Elsecar		d	13 00							13 56						14 56							15 54	
Wombwell		d	13 04							14 00						15 00							15 58	
Barnsley		a	13 09			13 37				14 05			14 37			15 05			15 37				16 03	
		d	13 10			13 37				14 06			14 37			15 10			15 37				16 04	
Dodworth		d								14 12													16 10	
Silkstone Common		d								14 16													16 14	
Penistone		d								14 23													16 21	
Denby Dale		d								14 29													16 27	
Shepley		d								14 34													16 32	
Stocksmoor		d								14 37													16 35	
Brockholes		d								14 41													16 39	
Honley		d								14 43													16 41	
Berry Brow		d								14 46													16 44	
Lockwood		d								14 49													16 47	
Huddersfield		a								14 53													16 53	
Darton		d	13 15													15 15								
Wakefield Kirkgate 4	31	a	13 29			13 52							14 52			15 29			15 52					
		d	13 30			13 53							14 53			15 30			15 53					
Normanton		d	13 34													15 34								
Castleford		a	13 40													15 40								
Woodlesford		a	13 51													15 51								
Leeds 10	31	a	14 04			14 18			14 47				15 18			16 04			16 18		16 55			

A To Doncaster
B To Swinton (S.Yorks)
C To Carlisle
D To Liverpool Lime Street
E From Norwich to Liverpool Lime Street
F From Retford Low Level

Table 34

Sundays

5 January to 9 February

Nottingham, Sheffield - Barnsley - Huddersfield and Leeds

Network Diagram - see first page of Table 31

		TP A 🚌	NT	NT B	EM ◇ C	NT D	NT E	NT	NT A 🚌	TP A 🚌	NT	NT B	NT	EM ◇ F	NT	NT A 🚌	TP A 🚌	NT	NT B	EM ◇ F	NT	NT D
Nottingham 8	d		15 12		15 47						16 15			16 42				17 15		17 41		
Langley Mill	d		15 36								16 34			17 01				17 34		17 57		
Alfreton	d		15 44		16 08						16 42			17 09				17 42		18 05		
Chesterfield	d		15 56		16 18						16 52			17 19				17 52		18 16		
Dronfield	d		16 03								16 59							17 59				
Sheffield 7 29,31	a		16 15		16 34						17 15			17 39				18 15		18 33		
	d	16 00	16 17	16 25		16 36	16 39	16 54	16 55	17 00	17 17	17 25	17 36		17 39	17 55	18 05	18 17	18 25		18 39	18 57
Meadowhall 4 29,31	a	16 20	16 22	16 30		16 41	16 44	16 59	17 15	17 20	17 22	17 30	17 44		17 46	18 15	18 25	18 22	18 30		18 44	19 04
	d		16 23				16 45	17 00			17 23		17 44		17 46			18 23			18 45	
Chapeltown	d						16 51								17 52						18 51	
Elsecar	d						16 56								17 58						18 56	
Wombwell	d						17 00								18 01						19 00	
Barnsley	a		16 37				17 05	17 14			17 37				18 08			18 37			19 05	
	d		16 37				17 10	17 15			17 37				18 10			18 37			19 10	
Dodworth	d							17 21							18 16							
Silkstone Common	d							17 25							18 20							
Penistone	d							17 32							18 27							
Denby Dale	d							17 38							18 34							
Shepley	d							17 43							18 39							
Stocksmoor	d							17 46							18 41							
Brockholes	d							17 50							18 45							
Honley	d							17 52							18 48							
Berry Brow	d							17 55							18 51							
Lockwood	d							17 58							18 53							
Huddersfield	a							18 05							18 58							
Darton	d						17 15														19 15	
Wakefield Kirkgate 4 31	a		16 52				17 29				17 52							18 52			19 29	
	d		16 53				17 30				17 53							18 53			19 30	
Normanton	d						17 34														19 34	
Castleford	a						17 40														19 41	
Woodlesford	a						17 51														19 53	
Leeds 10 31	a		17 16				18 05				18 18		18 50					19 18			20 05	

		TP A 🚌	NT	NT B	NT A 🚌	EM ◇ G	NT	NT	TP A 🚌	NT	NT B	EM ◇ G	NT	TP A 🚌	NT	NT B	NT	NT	NT A 🚌	TP A 🚌	TP H 🚌	NT B	NT
Nottingham 8	d		18 15			18 40				19 15		19 43			20 15								21 33
Langley Mill	d		18 34			18 56				19 34					20 34								21 57
Alfreton	d		18 42			19 04				19 42		20 04			20 42								22 05
Chesterfield	d		18 52			19 15				19 52		20 14			20 52								22 16
Dronfield	d		18 58							19 59													22 23
Sheffield 7 29,31	a		19 15			19 31				20 15		20 31			21 14								22 36
	d	19 00	19 16	19 29	19 30		19 36	19 39	20 00	20 17	20 28		20 39	21 00		21 19	21 36	21 43	21 45	22 00	22 25	22 26	22 39
Meadowhall 4 29,31	a	19 20	19 22	19 34	19 50		19 41	19 44	20 20	20 22	20 33		20 44	21 20		21 25	21 41	21 48	22 05	22 20	22s45	22 31	22 44
	d		19 23				19 42	19 45		20 23			20 45				21 42	21 49					22 45
Chapeltown	d							19 51					20 51					21 55					22 51
Elsecar	d							19 56					20 56					22 00					22 56
Wombwell	d							20 00					21 00					22 04					23 00
Barnsley	a		19 37					20 05		20 37			21 06					22 09					23 05
	d		19 37					20 06		20 37			21 10										23 10
Dodworth	d							20 12															
Silkstone Common	d							20 16															
Penistone	d							20 23															
Denby Dale	d							20 29															
Shepley	d							20 34															
Stocksmoor	d							20 37															
Brockholes	d							20 41															
Honley	d							20 44															
Berry Brow	d							20 47															
Lockwood	d							20 49															
Huddersfield	a							20 57															
Darton	d												21 15										23 15
Wakefield Kirkgate 4 31	a		19 52							20 52			21 29										23 26
	d		19 53							20 53			21 30										23 27
Normanton	d												21 34										23 34
Castleford	a												21 40										23 40
Woodlesford	a												21 51										23 53
Leeds 10 31	a		20 18				20 52			21 16			22 04				22 50						00 05

A To Doncaster
B To Swinton (S.Yorks)
C From Peterborough to Liverpool Lime Street
D To York. via Pontefract Baghill
E From Lincoln
F From Norwich to Liverpool Lime Street
G From Norwich to Manchester Piccadilly
H To Cleethorpes

Table 34

Sundays

5 January to 9 February

Nottingham, Sheffield - Barnsley - Huddersfield and Leeds

Network Diagram - see first page of Table 31

Station		NT A
Nottingham 8	d	
Langley Mill	d	
Alfreton	d	
Chesterfield	d	
Dronfield	d	
Sheffield 7 29,31	a	
	d	23 34
Meadowhall 4 29,31	a	23 39
	d	
Chapeltown	d	
Elsecar	d	
Wombwell	d	
Barnsley	a	
	d	
Dodworth	d	
Silkstone Common	d	
Penistone	d	
Denby Dale	d	
Shepley	d	
Stocksmoor	d	
Brockholes	d	
Honley	d	
Berry Brow	d	
Lockwood	d	
Huddersfield	a	
Darton	d	
Wakefield Kirkgate 4 31	a	
	d	
Normanton	d	
Castleford	a	
Woodlesford	a	
Leeds 10 31	a	

Sundays

16 February to 23 March

Station		NT	NT	NT	TP	NT	NT	NT	NT	EM	NT	NT	NT	EM	TP	NT	NT	NT	NT	NT	EM	NT	NT
								◇		◇				◇							◇		
		B		C	B			D	C	E		B		E	B				F	C	E		
Nottingham 8	d									09 47			10 12	10 48				11 16			11 44		
Langley Mill	d												10 36					11 35					
Alfreton	d									10 05			10 44	11 09				11 43			12 05		
Chesterfield	d									10 18			10 55	11 19				11 53			12 15		
Dronfield	d									10 25			11 02					12 00					
Sheffield 7 29,31	a									10 37			11 14	11 35				12 15			12 32		
	d	08 00	08 39	08 45	09 15	09 36	09 39	10 17	10 28		10 39	11 05	11 17		11 35	11 36	11 49	12 16	12 24	12 28		12 35	12 39
Meadowhall 4 29,31	a	08 05	08 44	08 50	09 35	09 41	09 44	10 22	10 33		10 44	11 10	11 22		11 55	11 41	11 54	12 22	12 29	12 33		12 40	12 44
	d		08 45			09 42	09 45	10 23			10 45		11 23			11 42	11 55	12 23				12 41	12 45
Chapeltown	d		08 51				09 51				10 51						12 01						12 55
Elsecar	d		08 56				09 56				10 56						12 06						13 00
Wombwell	d		09 00				10 00				11 00						12 10						13 04
Barnsley	a		09 05				10 05	10 37			11 05		11 37				12 15	12 37				12 55	13 09
	d		09 10				10 06	10 37			11 10		11 37				12 16	12 37				13 06	13 10
Dodworth	d						10 12										12 22					13 12	
Silkstone Common	d						10 16										12 26					13 16	
Penistone	d						10 23										12 33					13 23	
Denby Dale	d						10 29										12 39					13 29	
Shepley	d						10 34										12 44					13 34	
Stocksmoor	d						10 37										12 47					13 37	
Brockholes	d						10 41										12 51					13 41	
Honley	d						10 43										12 53					13 43	
Berry Brow	d						10 46										12 56					13 46	
Lockwood	d						10 49										12 59					13 49	
Huddersfield	a						10 53										13 04					13 53	
Darton	d		09 15								11 15												13 15
Wakefield Kirkgate 4 31	a		09 26					10 55			11 26		11 49					12 49					13 26
	d		09 32					10 57			11 31		11 50					12 50					13 31
Normanton	d		09 36								11 35												13 35
Castleford	a		09 42								11 41												13 43
Woodlesford	a		09 54								11 52												13 54
Leeds 10 31	a		10 06			10 52		11 15			12 05		12 15			12 53		13 15					14 05

A To Swinton (S.Yorks)
B To Doncaster
C To Scarborough
D To Carlisle
E To Liverpool Lime Street
F To Goole

Table 34

Sundays

16 February to 23 March

Nottingham, Sheffield - Barnsley - Huddersfield and Leeds

Network Diagram - see first page of Table 31

		TP	NT	NT	EM	NT		NT	TP	NT	NT	NT	EM	NT	TP	NT		NT	NT	NT	EM	NT	TP	NT	NT
		A		B	◇ C				A		D	E	◇ F		A			A	B		◇ C	G	A		D
Nottingham 8	d		12 15		12 41					13 13			13 42			14 15					14 47			15 12	
Langley Mill	d		12 34		12 57					13 34			13 58			14 34					15 03			15 36	
Alfreton	d		12 42		13 05					13 42			14 06			14 42					15 11			15 44	
Chesterfield	d		12 52		13 15					13 52			14 16			14 52					15 21			15 56	
Dronfield	d		12 59							13 59						14 59								16 03	
Sheffield 7 29,31	a		13 15		13 32					14 15			14 34			15 15					15 39			16 15	
	d	13 00	13 17	13 24		13 36		13 39	14 00	14 17	14 22	14 28		14 39	15 00	15 17		15 24	15 28	15 36		15 39	16 00	16 17	16 25
Meadowhall 4 29,31	a	13 20	13 22	13 29		13 41		13 44	14 20	14 22	14 27	14 33		14 44	15 20	15 22		15 29	15 33	15 41		15 42	16 20	16 22	16 30
	d		13 23			13 42		13 45		14 23				14 45		15 23				15 42		15 43		16 23	
Chapeltown	d							13 51						14 51								15 49			
Elsecar	d							13 56						14 56								15 54			
Wombwell	d							14 00						15 00								15 58			
Barnsley	a		13 37					14 05		14 37				15 05		15 37						16 03		16 37	
	d		13 37					14 06		14 37				15 10		15 37						16 04		16 37	
Dodworth	d							14 12														16 10			
Silkstone Common	d							14 16														16 14			
Penistone	d							14 23														16 21			
Denby Dale	d							14 29														16 27			
Shepley	d							14 34														16 32			
Stocksmoor	d							14 37														16 35			
Brockholes	d							14 41														16 39			
Honley	d							14 43														16 41			
Berry Brow	d							14 46														16 44			
Lockwood	d							14 49														16 47			
Huddersfield	a							14 53														16 53			
Darton	d													15 15											
Wakefield Kirkgate 4 31	a		13 55							14 49				15 26		15 51								16 49	
	d		14 00							14 50				15 31		15 51								16 50	
Normanton	d													15 35											
Castleford	a													15 41											
Woodlesford	a													15 52											
Leeds 10 31	a		14 23			14 47				15 15				16 04		16 16				16 54				17 13	

		NT		EM	NT	NT	NT	TP	NT	NT	NT	NT		EM	NT	TP	NT	NT	NT	EM	NT	NT		TP	NT
		E		◇ H	I	J		A		A	B			◇ F		A		A	K	◇ F		I		A	
Nottingham 8	d			15 47					16 15					16 42			17 15			17 41					18 15
Langley Mill	d								16 34					17 01			17 34			17 57					18 34
Alfreton	d			16 08					16 42					17 09			17 42			18 05					18 42
Chesterfield	d			16 18					16 52					17 19			17 52			18 16					18 52
Dronfield	d								16 59								17 59								18 58
Sheffield 7 29,31	a			16 34					17 15					17 39			18 15			18 33					19 15
	d	16 28			16 36	16 39	16 54	17 00	17 17	17 25	17 28	17 36			17 39	18 05	18 17	18 25	18 28		18 39	18 57		19 00	19 16
Meadowhall 4 29,31	a	16 33			16 41	16 44	16 59	17 20	17 22	17 30	17 33	17 44			17 46	18 25	18 22	18 30	18 33		18 44	19 04		19 20	19 22
	d					16 45	17 00		17 23			17 44			17 46		18 23				18 45				19 23
Chapeltown	d					16 51									17 52						18 51				
Elsecar	d					16 56									17 58						18 56				
Wombwell	d					17 00									18 01						19 00				
Barnsley	a					17 05	17 14		17 37						18 08		18 37				19 05				19 37
	d					17 10	17 15		17 37						18 10		18 37				19 10				19 37
Dodworth	d						17 21								18 16										
Silkstone Common	d						17 25								18 20										
Penistone	d						17 32								18 27										
Denby Dale	d						17 38								18 34										
Shepley	d						17 43								18 39										
Stocksmoor	d						17 46								18 41										
Brockholes	d						17 50								18 45										
Honley	d						17 52								18 48										
Berry Brow	d						17 55								18 51										
Lockwood	d						17 58								18 53										
Huddersfield	a						18 05								18 58										
Darton	d					17 15															19 15				
Wakefield Kirkgate 4 31	a					17 26			17 52								18 49				19 26				19 49
	d					17 31			17 59								18 50				19 31				19 50
Normanton	d					17 35															19 35				
Castleford	a					17 41															19 42				
Woodlesford	a					17 52															19 54				
Leeds 10 31	a					18 05			18 24			18 50					19 15				20 05				20 15

A To Doncaster
B To Bridlington
C To Liverpool Lime Street
D To Goole
E To Scarborough
F From Norwich to Liverpool Lime Street
G From Retford Low Level
H From Peterborough to Liverpool Lime Street
I To York. via Pontefract Baghill
J From Lincoln
K To Beverley

Table 34

Sundays

16 February to 23 March

Nottingham, Sheffield - Barnsley - Huddersfield and Leeds

Network Diagram - see first page of Table 31

Station		NT A	EM ◇ B	NT	NT	TP A	NT C	NT	NT D	EM ◇ B	NT	TP A	NT	NT C	NT	NT	TP A	NT C	TP E	NT A	NT	NT A
Nottingham 8	d		18 40					19 15		19 43			20 15								21 33	
Langley Mill	d		18 56					19 34					20 34								21 57	
Alfreton	d		19 04					19 42		20 04			20 42								22 05	
Chesterfield	d		19 15					19 52		20 14			20 52								22 16	
Dronfield	d							19 59													22 23	
Sheffield 7 29,31	a		19 31					20 15		20 31			21 14								22 36	
	d	19 29		19 36	19 39	20 00	20 02	20 17	20 28		20 39	21 00		21 25	21 36	21 43	22 00	22 13	22 25	22 26	22 39	23 34
Meadowhall 4 29,31	a	19 34		19 41	19 44	20 20	20 08	20 22	20 33		20 44	21 20		21 30	21 41	21 48	22 20	22 18	22s45	22 31	22 44	23 39
	d			19 42	19 45			20 23			20 45				21 42	21 49					22 45	
Chapeltown	d				19 51						20 51					21 55					22 51	
Elsecar	d				19 56						20 56					22 00					22 56	
Wombwell	d				20 00						21 00					22 04					23 00	
Barnsley	a				20 05			20 37			21 06					22 09					23 05	
	d				20 06			20 37			21 10										23 10	
Dodworth	d				20 12																	
Silkstone Common	d				20 16																	
Penistone	d				20 23																	
Denby Dale	d				20 29																	
Shepley	d				20 34																	
Stocksmoor	d				20 37																	
Brockholes	d				20 41																	
Honley	d				20 44																	
Berry Brow	d				20 47																	
Lockwood	d				20 49																	
Huddersfield	a				20 57																	
Darton	d										21 15										23 15	
Wakefield Kirkgate 4 31	a							20 49			21 26										23 26	
	d							20 50			21 31										23 27	
Normanton	d										21 35										23 34	
Castleford	a										21 41										23 40	
Woodlesford	a										21 52										23 53	
Leeds 10 31	a			20 52				21 13			22 04				22 50						00 05	

Sundays

30 March to 11 May

Station		NT A	NT	NT F	NT	NT	TP ◇1 E	NT ◇ G	NT F	EM ◇ H	NT	NT A	NT	EM ◇ H	NT	NT	TP ◇1 I	NT	NT D	NT F	EM ◇ H	NT	NT
Nottingham 8	d									09 47			10 12	10 48				11 16			11 44		
Langley Mill	d												10 36					11 35					
Alfreton	d									10 05			10 44	11 09				11 43			12 05		
Chesterfield	d									10 18			10 55	11 19				11 53			12 15		
Dronfield	d									10 25			11 02					12 00					
Sheffield 7 29,31	a									10 37			11 14	11 35				12 15			12 32		
	d	08 00	08 39	08 45	09 36	09 39	09 52	10 17	10 28		10 39	11 05	11 17		11 36	11 49	12 10	12 16	12 24	12 28		12 35	12 39
Meadowhall 4 29,31	a	08 05	08 44	08 50	09 41	09 44	09 57	10 22	10 33		10 44	11 10	11 22		11 41	11 54	12 16	12 22	12 29	12 33		12 40	12 44
	d		08 45		09 42	09 45		10 23			10 45		11 23		11 42	11 55		12 23				12 41	12 45
Chapeltown	d		08 51			09 51					10 51					12 01							12 55
Elsecar	d		08 56			09 56					10 56					12 06							13 00
Wombwell	d		09 00			10 00					11 00					12 10							13 04
Barnsley	a		09 05			10 05		10 37			11 05		11 37			12 15		12 37				12 55	13 09
	d		09 10			10 06		10 37			11 10		11 37			12 16		12 37				13 06	13 10
Dodworth	d					10 12										12 22						13 12	
Silkstone Common	d					10 16										12 26						13 16	
Penistone	d					10 23										12 33						13 23	
Denby Dale	d					10 29										12 39						13 29	
Shepley	d					10 34										12 44						13 34	
Stocksmoor	d					10 37										12 47						13 37	
Brockholes	d					10 41										12 51						13 41	
Honley	d					10 43										12 53						13 43	
Berry Brow	d					10 46										12 56						13 46	
Lockwood	d					10 49										12 59						13 49	
Huddersfield	a					10 53										13 04						13 53	
Darton	d		09 15								11 15												13 15
Wakefield Kirkgate 4 31	a		09 29					10 55			11 29		11 52					12 52					13 29
	d		09 30					10 57			11 30		11 53					12 53					13 30
Normanton	d		09 34								11 34												13 34
Castleford	a		09 40								11 40												13 40
Woodlesford	a		09 55								11 51												13 51
Leeds 10 31	a		10 07		10 52			11 15			12 05		12 18		12 53			13 18					14 04

A To Doncaster
B From Norwich to Manchester Piccadilly
C To Hull
D To Goole
E To Cleethorpes
F To Scarborough
G To Carlisle
H To Liverpool Lime Street
I From Manchester Airport to Cleethorpes

Table 34

Sundays

30 March to 11 May

Nottingham, Sheffield - Barnsley - Huddersfield and Leeds

Network Diagram - see first page of Table 31

			TP	NT	NT	EM	NT	NT	TP	NT	NT	NT	EM	NT	TP	NT	NT	NT	NT	EM	NT	TP	NT	NT
			◇1			◇			◇1				◇		◇1					◇		◇1		
			A		B	C			D		E	F	G		D		H	B		C	I	D		E
Nottingham 8		d		12 15		12 41				13 13			13 42			14 15				14 47			15 12	
Langley Mill		d		12 34		12 57				13 34			13 58			14 34				15 03			15 36	
Alfreton		d		12 42		13 05				13 42			14 06			14 42				15 11			15 44	
Chesterfield		d		12 52		13 15				13 52			14 16			14 53				15 21			15 56	
Dronfield		d		12 59						13 59						15 00							16 03	
Sheffield 7	29,31	a		13 15		13 32				14 15			14 34			15 15				15 39			16 15	
		d	13 10	13 17	13 24		13 36	13 39	14 10	14 17	14 22	14 28		14 39	15 10	15 17	15 24	15 28	15 36		15 39	16 10	16 17	16 25
Meadowhall 4	29,31	a	13 16	13 22	13 29		13 41	13 44	14 16	14 22	14 27	14 33		14 44	15 16	15 22	15 29	15 33	15 41		15 42	16 16	16 22	16 30
		d		13 23			13 42	13 45		14 23				14 45		15 23			15 42		15 43		16 23	
Chapeltown		d						13 51						14 51							15 49			
Elsecar		d						13 56						14 56							15 54			
Wombwell		d						14 00						15 00							15 58			
Barnsley		a		13 37				14 05		14 37				15 05		15 37					16 03		16 37	
		d		13 37				14 06		14 37				15 10		15 37					16 04		16 37	
Dodworth		d						14 12													16 10			
Silkstone Common		d						14 16													16 14			
Penistone		d						14 23													16 21			
Denby Dale		d						14 29													16 27			
Shepley		d						14 34													16 32			
Stocksmoor		d						14 37													16 35			
Brockholes		d						14 41													16 39			
Honley		d						14 43													16 41			
Berry Brow		d						14 46													16 44			
Lockwood		d						14 49													16 47			
Huddersfield		a						14 53													16 53			
Darton		d												15 15										
Wakefield Kirkgate 4	31	a		13 52						14 52				15 29		15 52							16 52	
		d		13 53						14 53				15 30		15 53							16 53	
Normanton		d												15 34										
Castleford		a												15 40										
Woodlesford		a												15 51										
Leeds 10	31	a		14 18			14 47			15 18				16 04		16 18			16 54				17 16	

			NT	EM	NT	NT	NT	TP	NT	NT	NT	NT	EM	NT	TP	NT	NT	NT	EM	NT	NT	TP	NT
				◇				◇1					◇		◇1				◇			◇1	
			F	J	K	L		D		H	B		G		D		H	M	G		K	D	
Nottingham 8		d		15 47					16 15				16 42			17 15			17 41				18 15
Langley Mill		d							16 34				17 01			17 34			17 57				18 34
Alfreton		d		16 08					16 42				17 09			17 42			18 05				18 42
Chesterfield		d		16 18					16 52				17 19			17 52			18 16				18 52
Dronfield		d							16 59							17 59							18 58
Sheffield 7	29,31	a		16 34					17 15				17 39			18 15			18 33				19 15
		d	16 28		16 36	16 39	16 54	17 10	17 17	17 25	17 28	17 36		17 39	18 10	18 17	18 25	18 28		18 39	18 57	19 10	19 16
Meadowhall 4	29,31	a	16 33		16 41	16 44	16 59	17 16	17 22	17 30	17 33	17 44		17 46	18 16	18 22	18 30	18 33		18 44	19 04	19 16	19 22
		d				16 45	17 00		17 23			17 44		17 46		18 23				18 45			19 23
Chapeltown		d				16 51								17 52						18 51			
Elsecar		d				16 56								17 58						18 56			
Wombwell		d				17 00								18 01						19 00			
Barnsley		a				17 05	17 14		17 37					18 08		18 37				19 05			19 37
		d				17 10	17 15		17 37					18 10		18 37				19 10			19 37
Dodworth		d					17 21							18 16									
Silkstone Common		d					17 25							18 20									
Penistone		d					17 32							18 27									
Denby Dale		d					17 38							18 34									
Shepley		d					17 43							18 39									
Stocksmoor		d					17 46							18 41									
Brockholes		d					17 50							18 45									
Honley		d					17 52							18 48									
Berry Brow		d					17 55							18 51									
Lockwood		d					17 58							18 53									
Huddersfield		a					18 05							18 58									
Darton		d				17 15														19 15			
Wakefield Kirkgate 4	31	a				17 29			17 52							18 52				19 29			19 52
		d				17 30			17 53							18 53				19 30			19 53
Normanton		d				17 34														19 34			
Castleford		a				17 40														19 41			
Woodlesford		a				17 51														19 53			
Leeds 10	31	a				18 05			18 18			18 50				19 18				20 05			20 18

A From Manchester Airport to Doncaster
B To Bridlington
C To Liverpool Lime Street
D From Manchester Airport to Cleethorpes
E To Goole
F To Scarborough
G From Norwich to Liverpool Lime Street
H To Doncaster
I From Retford Low Level
J From Peterborough to Liverpool Lime Street
K To York. via Pontefract Baghill
L From Lincoln
M To Beverley

Table 34

Sundays

30 March to 11 May

Nottingham, Sheffield - Barnsley - Huddersfield and Leeds

Network Diagram - see first page of Table 31

		NT	EM	NT	NT	NT	TP	NT		NT	EM	NT	TP	NT	NT	NT	NT	NT		NT	TP	NT	NT		
			◇				◇1				◇		◇1								◇1				
		A	B			C	D			E	B		D		C			C		A	F		A		
Nottingham 8 ⇌	d		18 40					19 15			19 43			20 15								21 33			
Langley Mill	d		18 56					19 34						20 34								21 57			
Alfreton	d		19 04					19 42			20 04			20 42								22 05			
Chesterfield	d		19 15					19 52			20 14			20 52								22 16			
Dronfield	d							19 59														22 23			
Sheffield 7 29,31 ⇌	a		19 31					20 15			20 31			21 14								22 36			
	d	19 29		19 36	19 39	20 02	20 10	20 17		20 28		20 39	21 10		21 25	21 36	21 43	22 13		22 26	22 30	22 39	23 34		
Meadowhall 4 29,31 ⇌	a	19 34		19 41	19 44	20 08	20 16	20 22		20 33		20 44	21 16		21 30	21 41	21 48	22 18		22 31	22 35	22 44	23 39		
	d			19 42	19 45			20 23				20 45				21 42	21 49					22 45			
Chapeltown	d				19 51							20 51					21 55					22 51			
Elsecar	d				19 56							20 56					22 00					22 56			
Wombwell	d				20 00							21 00					22 04					23 00			
Barnsley	a				20 05			20 37				21 06					22 09					23 05			
	d				20 06			20 37				21 10										23 10			
Dodworth	d				20 12																				
Silkstone Common	d				20 16																				
Penistone	d				20 23																				
Denby Dale	d				20 29																				
Shepley	d				20 34																				
Stocksmoor	d				20 37																				
Brockholes	d				20 41																				
Honley	d				20 44																				
Berry Brow	d				20 47																				
Lockwood	d				20 49																				
Huddersfield	a				20 57																				
Darton	d											21 15										23 15			
Wakefield Kirkgate 4 31	a							20 52				21 29										23 26			
	d							20 53				21 30										23 27			
Normanton	d											21 34										23 34			
Castleford	a											21 40										23 40			
Woodlesford	a											21 51										23 53			
Leeds 10 31	a			20 52				21 16				22 04				22 50						00 05			

A To Doncaster
B From Norwich to Manchester Piccadilly
C To Hull
D From Manchester Airport to Cleethorpes
E To Goole
F To Cleethorpes

Table 34R

Mondays to Fridays

9 December to 16 May

Leeds and Huddersfield - Barnsley - Sheffield, Nottingham

Network Diagram - see first page of Table 31

Miles	Miles	Station		EM MX ◇ A	NT MX B	NT	NT	NT	TP ◇1 C	NT		NT D	NT	NT	NT	NT E	TP ◇1 F	EM ◇1 G	NT	NT H		NT	NT	TP ◇1 F	NT
0	—	**Leeds 10** 31	d										05 33		06 05			06 34				06 38	06 43		07 05
6	—	Woodlesford	d																			06 46			
10¾	—	Castleford	d																			06 57			
14¼	—	Normanton	d																			07 03			
17¼	—	Wakefield Kirkgate 4 31	a												06 21							07 07			07 25
—	—		d											06 04	06 21							07 08			07 25
24¾	—	Darton	d											06 15								07 19			
—	0	**Huddersfield**	d																06 10						
—	1¼	Lockwood	d																06 13						
—	2¼	Berry Brow	d																06 16						
—	3¼	Honley	d																06 19						
—	4¼	Brockholes	d																06 22						
—	6¼	Stocksmoor	d																06 26						
—	7¼	Shepley	d																06 28						
—	9½	Denby Dale	d																06 34						
—	13½	Penistone	d																06 42						
—	16¾	Silkstone Common	d																06 47						
—	18	Dodworth	d																06 51						
28¼	21	**Barnsley**	a											06 20	06 37				06 57			07 25			07 41
—	—		d				05 23			05 53				06 21	06 38				06 58			07 26			07 42
32¼	25	Wombwell	d				05 28			05 58				06 26					07 03			07 31			
33¾	26½	Elsecar	d				05 32			06 02				06 30					07 07			07 35			
37	29¾	Chapeltown	d				05 37			06 07				06 35					07 12			07 40			
40¾	33½	**Meadowhall** 29,31	a				05 45			06 15			06 37	06 41	06 51				07 20			07 48	07 44		07 55
—	—		d		00 09		05 45		05 58	06 18		06 27	06 37	06 42	06 51	06 54	06 58		07 22	07 33		07 50	07 45	07 53	07 56
44¼	37	**Sheffield 7** 29,31	a		00 23		05 54		06 08	06 25		06 37	06 47	06 55	07 00	07 05	07 07	07 25	07 29	07 40		07 58	07 56	08 00	08 05
—	—		d			05 05		06 03							07 03			07 37							08 08
51¼	—	Dronfield	d					06 13							07 13										08 18
56½	—	Chesterfield	d	00 02		05 20		06 19							07 20			07 50							08 24
66½	—	Alfreton	d					06 30							07 31			08 01							08 34
72¾	—	Langley Mill	d					06 37							07 39			08 09							08 42
84¾	—	**Nottingham**	a	00 39		06 11		07 02							07 59			08 25							09 02

Station		NT I	NT	NT E	EM ◇ J	NT K		NT	NT B	NT	NT	NT I	TP ◇1 F	NT L	NT	EM ◇ J		NT K	NT	NT M	NT B	NT	NT	NT I	TP ◇1 F
Leeds 10 31	d					07 29		07 35		07 48	08 02							08 32	08 37			08 48	09 05		
Woodlesford	d					07 37												08 40							
Castleford	d					07 48												08 51							
Normanton	d					07 54			←									08 57			←				
Wakefield Kirkgate 4 31	a					08 00		07 54	08 00		08 23							09 03	08 54		09 03		09 23		
	d					08 04		07 55	08 04		08 23							09 05	08 55		09 05		09 23		
Darton	d					→			08 15									→			09 17				
Huddersfield	d		07 10												08 10										
Lockwood	d		07 13												08 13										
Berry Brow	d		07 16												08 16										
Honley	d		07 19												08 19										
Brockholes	d		07 22												08 22										
Stocksmoor	d		07 26												08 26										
Shepley	d		07 28												08 28										
Denby Dale	d		07 34												08 34										
Penistone	d		07 42												08 42										
Silkstone Common	d		07 47												08 47										
Dodworth	d		07 51												08 51										
Barnsley	a		07 57					08 11	08 21		08 39				08 57				09 11		09 23		09 39		
	d		07 58					08 14	08 24		08 40				08 58				09 14		09 24		09 40		
Wombwell	d		08 03						08 29						09 03						09 29				
Elsecar	d		08 07						08 33						09 07						09 33				
Chapeltown	d		08 12						08 38						09 12						09 38				
Meadowhall 29,31	a		08 20					08 31	08 46	08 50	08 54				09 20				09 29		09 46	09 51	09 54		
	d	08 07	08 22	08 25				08 31	08 48	08 51	08 54	08 57	09 01	09 16	09 21				09 30	09 33	09 48	09 51	09 54	09 57	10 01
Sheffield 7 29,31	a	08 18	08 29	08 33				08 39	08 56	08 59	09 02	09 05	09 08	09 26	09 28				09 37	09 41	09 56	10 00	10 02	10 05	10 08
	d				08 38						09 05					09 36							10 05		
Dronfield	d										09 15												10 15		
Chesterfield	d				08 53						09 21					09 52							10 21		
Alfreton	d				09 03						09 32					10 02							10 31		
Langley Mill	d										09 39												10 39		
Nottingham	a				09 26						10 02					10 27							11 02		

A From Liverpool Lime Street
B From Leeds
C From Doncaster to Manchester Airport
D From Doncaster
E From Hull
F From Cleethorpes to Manchester Airport
G To St Pancras International
H From Doncaster to Worksop
I From Adwick
J From Liverpool Lime Street to Norwich
K To Sheffield
L From Bridlington
M From Scunthorpe to Lincoln

Table 34R

Mondays to Fridays

9 December to 16 May

Leeds and Huddersfield - Barnsley - Sheffield, Nottingham

Network Diagram - see first page of Table 31

		NT		NT	NT	NT	EM	NT	NT	NT	NT	NT		TP	NT	NT	EM	NT	NT	NT	NT	NT		NT	NT
							◇				◇			◇1			◇			◇				◇	
		A			B		C	D	E			F		G	A		C	B		D	E				F
Leeds 10 31	d				09 32	09 37				09 48	10 05							10 32	10 37			10 48		11 05	
Woodlesford	d				09 40													10 40							
Castleford	d				09 51													10 51							
Normanton	d				09 57				←									10 57			←				
Wakefield Kirkgate 4 31	a				10 01	09 55			10 01		10 23							11 01	10 54		11 01			11 23	
	d				10 04	09 56			10 04		10 23							11 04	10 55		11 04			11 23	
Darton	d				→				10 15									→			11 15				
Huddersfield	d			09 13												10 13									
Lockwood	d			09 16												10 16									
Berry Brow	d			09 19												10 19									
Honley	d			09 22												10 22									
Brockholes	d			09 25												10 25									
Stocksmoor	d			09 29												10 29									
Shepley	d			09 31												10 31									
Denby Dale	d			09 36												10 36									
Penistone	d			09 44												10 44									
Silkstone Common	d			09 49												10 49									
Dodworth	d			09 53												10 53									
Barnsley	a			10 00		10 12			10 21		10 39					11 00			11 11		11 21			11 39	
	d			10 01		10 14			10 24		10 40					11 01			11 14		11 24			11 40	
Wombwell	d			10 06					10 29							11 06					11 29				
Elsecar	d								10 33												11 33				
Chapeltown	d			10 13					10 38							11 13					11 38				
Meadowhall 29,31	a			10 20		10 29			10 47	10 51	10 54					11 20			11 29		11 47	11 51		11 54	
	d	10 08		10 21		10 30		10 33	10 48	10 51	10 54	10 58		11 01	11 07	11 21			11 30	11 33	11 48	11 51		11 54	11 58
Sheffield 7 29,31	a	10 20		10 30		10 37		10 41	10 56	11 01	11 02	11 05		11 08	11 18	11 29			11 37	11 41	11 57	12 01		12 02	12 05
	d						10 38				11 05						11 37							12 05	
Dronfield	d										11 15													12 15	
Chesterfield	d						10 52				11 21						11 52							12 21	
Alfreton	d						11 03				11 31						12 02							12 31	
Langley Mill	d										11 39													12 39	
Nottingham	a						11 27				12 02						12 27							13 02	

		TP	NT	NT	EM	NT	NT	NT		NT	NT	NT	NT	NT	TP	NT	NT	NT		NT	EM	NT	NT	NT	NT
		◇1			◇					◇			◇		◇1						◇	◇			◇
		G	A		C	H	B			D	E			F	G	A		B			C	D	E		
Leeds 10 31	d						11 32	11 37				11 48	12 05					12 32		12 37				12 48	13 05
Woodlesford	d						11 40											12 40							
Castleford	d						11 51											12 51							
Normanton	d						11 57				←							12 57					←		
Wakefield Kirkgate 4 31	a						12 01	11 54			12 01		12 23					13 02		12 54			13 02		13 23
	d						12 04	11 55			12 04		12 23					13 04		12 55			13 04		13 23
Darton	d						→				12 15							→					13 17		
Huddersfield	d			11 13													12 13								
Lockwood	d			11 16													12 16								
Berry Brow	d			11 19													12 19								
Honley	d			11 22													12 22								
Brockholes	d			11 25													12 25								
Stocksmoor	d			11 29													12 29								
Shepley	d			11 31													12 31								
Denby Dale	d			11 36													12 36								
Penistone	d			11 44													12 44								
Silkstone Common	d			11 49													12 49								
Dodworth	d			11 53													12 53								
Barnsley	a			12 00				12 11			12 21		12 39				13 00			13 11			13 22		13 39
	d			12 01				12 14			12 24		12 40				13 01			13 14			13 24		13 40
Wombwell	d			12 06							12 29						13 06						13 29		
Elsecar	d										12 33												13 33		
Chapeltown	d			12 13							12 38						13 13						13 38		
Meadowhall 29,31	a			12 20				12 29			12 47	12 51	12 54				13 20			13 27			13 47	13 51	13 54
	d	12 01	12 09	12 21		12 24		12 30		12 33	12 48	12 51	12 54	12 58	13 01	13 09	13 21			13 28		13 33	13 48	13 51	13 54
Sheffield 7 29,31	a	12 08	12 18	12 30		12 36		12 37		12 41	12 56	13 01	13 02	13 05	13 08	13 18	13 29			13 37		13 41	13 56	14 01	14 02
	d				12 36								13 05								13 38				14 05
Dronfield	d												13 15												14 15
Chesterfield	d				12 52								13 21								13 54				14 22
Alfreton	d				13 02								13 33								14 05				14 32
Langley Mill	d												13 40												14 40
Nottingham	a				13 27								14 02								14 27				15 02

A From Bridlington
B To Sheffield
C From Liverpool Lime Street to Norwich
D From Scunthorpe to Lincoln
E From Leeds
F From Adwick
G From Cleethorpes to Manchester Airport
H From York. via Pontefract Baghill

Table 34R

Mondays to Fridays

9 December to 16 May

Leeds and Huddersfield - Barnsley - Sheffield, Nottingham

Network Diagram - see first page of Table 31

			NT	TP	NT		NT	EM	NT	NT	NT	NT	NT	NT	NT		TP	NT	NT	NT	NT	EM	NT	NT	NT
				◇1				◇			◇			◇			◇1					◇	◇		
			A	B	C			D	E		F	G			A		B	H		E		D	F	G	
				🛒													🛒								
Leeds 10	31	d							13 32	13 37			13 48	14 05						14 32	14 37				14 48
Woodlesford		d							13 40											14 40					
Castleford		d							13 51											14 51					
Normanton		d							13 57			←								14 57				←	
Wakefield Kirkgate 4	31	a							14 01	13 54		14 01		14 23						15 01	14 54			15 01	
		d							14 04	13 55		14 04		14 23						15 04	14 55			15 04	
Darton		d							→			14 15								→				15 15	
Huddersfield		d					13 13												14 13						
Lockwood		d					13 16												14 16						
Berry Brow		d					13 19												14 19						
Honley		d					13 22												14 22						
Brockholes		d					13 25												14 25						
Stocksmoor		d					13 29												14 29						
Shepley		d					13 31												14 31						
Denby Dale		d					13 36												14 36						
Penistone		d					13 44												14 44						
Silkstone Common		d					13 49												14 49						
Dodworth		d					13 53												14 53						
Barnsley		a					14 00			14 11		14 21		14 39					15 00		15 13			15 21	
		d					14 01			14 14		14 24		14 40					15 01		15 14			15 24	
Wombwell		d					14 06					14 29							15 06					15 29	
Elsecar		d										14 33												15 33	
Chapeltown		d					14 13					14 38							15 13					15 38	
Meadowhall	29,31 🚊	a					14 20			14 29		14 47	14 51	14 54					15 20		15 29			15 47	15 51
		d	13 58	14 01	14 08		14 21			14 30	14 33	14 48	14 51	14 54	14 58		15 01	15 08	15 21		15 30		15 33	15 48	15 51
Sheffield 7	29,31 🚊	a	14 05	14 08	14 18		14 29			14 37	14 40	14 56	15 01	15 02	15 05		15 08	15 18	15 29		15 37		15 41	15 56	16 01
		d						14 36						15 05								15 38			
Dronfield		d												15 15											
Chesterfield		d						14 52						15 21								15 52			
Alfreton		d						14 59						15 31								16 02			
Langley Mill		d												15 39											
Nottingham		a						15 25						16 02								16 26			

			NT	NT	TP	NT	NT	NT	NT	NT	EM		NT	NT	NT	NT	NT	TP	NT	NT	NT		NT	NT	EM	NT
			◇		◇1						◇		◇			◇		◇1						◇	◇	
				A	B	C	I		E		D		F	G			J	B	H		E			F	D	G
					🛒													🛒								
Leeds 10	31	d	15 05						15 32	15 37					15 48	16 05					16 32		16 37			
Woodlesford		d							15 40												16 40					
Castleford		d							15 51												16 51					
Normanton		d							15 57					←							16 57					←
Wakefield Kirkgate 4	31	a	15 23						16 01	15 54				16 01		16 23					17 01		16 54			17 01
		d	15 23						16 04	15 55				16 04		16 23					17 04		16 55			17 04
Darton		d							→					16 15							→					17 15
Huddersfield		d						15 13												16 13						
Lockwood		d						15 16												16 16						
Berry Brow		d						15 19												16 19						
Honley		d						15 22												16 22						
Brockholes		d						15 25												16 25						
Stocksmoor		d						15 29												16 29						
Shepley		d						15 31												16 31						
Denby Dale		d						15 36												16 36						
Penistone		d						15 44												16 44						
Silkstone Common		d						15 49												16 49						
Dodworth		d						15 53												16 53						
Barnsley		a	15 39					16 00		16 11				16 21		16 39				17 00			17 11			17 21
		d	15 40					16 01		16 14				16 24		16 40				17 01			17 14			17 24
Wombwell		d						16 06						16 29						17 06						17 29
Elsecar		d												16 33												17 33
Chapeltown		d						16 13						16 38						17 13						17 38
Meadowhall	29,31 🚊	a	15 53					16 20		16 29				16 47	16 51	16 54				17 20			17 27			17 47
		d	15 54	15 57	16 01	16 08	16 17	16 21		16 30			16 33	16 48	16 51	16 54	16 57	17 01	17 07	17 21			17 28	17 33		17 48
Sheffield 7	29,31 🚊	a	16 02	16 05	16 08	16 18	16 27	16 29		16 37			16 41	16 56	17 00	17 02	17 05	17 08	17 18	17 32			17 37	17 41		17 55
		d	16 05								16 38					17 05									17 45	
Dronfield		d	16 15								16 48					17 15									17 55	
Chesterfield		d	16 21								16 53					17 21									18 01	
Alfreton		d	16 31								17 04					17 31									18 11	
Langley Mill		d	16 39													17 39										
Nottingham		a	17 02								17 27					18 02									18 31	

A From Adwick
B From Cleethorpes to Manchester Airport
C From Scarborough
D From Liverpool Lime Street to Norwich
E To Sheffield
F From Scunthorpe to Lincoln
G From Leeds
H From Bridlington
I From York, via Pontefract Baghill
J From Adwick to Retford Low Level

Table 34R

Mondays to Fridays

9 December to 16 May

Leeds and Huddersfield - Barnsley - Sheffield, Nottingham

Network Diagram - see first page of Table 31

		NT	NT ◇	NT A	TP ◇1 B	NT C		NT	NT D	NT	NT E	EM ◇ F	NT G	NT D	NT D	NT		NT ◇	NT A	TP ◇1 B	NT H	NT I	EM ◇ J	NT K	NT G
Leeds 10 31	d	16 48	17 05						17 32	17 37					17 43	17 48		18 05							
Woodlesford	d								17 40																
Castleford	d								17 51																
Normanton	d		17 18						17 57				←												
Wakefield Kirkgate 4 31	a		17 22						18 01	17 54			18 01					18 23							
	d		17 23						18 04	17 55			18 04					18 23							
Darton	d								→				18 15												
Huddersfield	d							17 13						17 56	18 23										
Lockwood	d							17 16						17 59	18 26										
Berry Brow	d							17 19						18 02	18 29										
Honley	d							17 22						18 05	18 32										
Brockholes	d							17 25						18 08	18 35										
Stocksmoor	d							17 29						18 12	18 39										
Shepley	d							17 31						18 14	18 41										
Denby Dale	d							17 36						18 19	18 46										
Penistone	d							17 44						18 31	18 54										
Silkstone Common	d							17 49						18 36	18 59										
Dodworth	d							17 53						18 40	19 03							←			←
Barnsley	a		17 39					18 00		18 11			18 21	18 47	19 09			18 39				18 47			19 09
	d		17 40					18 01		18 14			18 24	18 55	19 10			18 40				18 55			19 10
Wombwell	d							18 06					18 29	→	→							19 00			19 15
Elsecar	d												18 33									19 04			
Chapeltown	d							18 13					18 38									19 09			19 22
Meadowhall 29,31 ⇌	a	17 50	17 53					18 21		18 29			18 47			18 51		18 54				19 17			19 30
	d	17 51	17 54	17 57	18 01	18 09		18 22		18 29	18 34		18 48			18 51		18 55	18 58	19 01	19 09	19 18		19 29	19 32
Sheffield 7 29,31 ⇌	a	18 02	18 02	18 05	18 08	18 18		18 31		18 38	18 41		18 56			19 00		19 03	19 06	19 08	19 18	19 27		19 39	19 42
	d		18 05									18 51						19 06					19 37		
Dronfield	d		18 15															19 16							
Chesterfield	d		18 21									19 06						19 22					19 51		
Alfreton	d		18 31									19 16						19 32					20 03		
Langley Mill	d		18 39															19 40							
Nottingham	a		19 02									19 41						20 02					20 29		

		NT D		NT	NT G	NT	NT ◇	NT A	TP ◇1 L	NT K	NT	EM ◇ F		NT M	NT D	NT	NT G	NT	TP ◇1 N	NT	EM ◇ F	NT O		NT C	NT
Leeds 10 31	d	18 32		18 43		18 48	19 05								19 37	19 43		19 48		20 30					20 37
Woodlesford	d	18 40													19 45										20 45
Castleford	d	18 51													19 56										20 56
Normanton	d	19 00			←										20 02		←								21 02
Wakefield Kirkgate 4 31	a	19 04		18 59	19 04		19 24								20 06	19 59	20 06			20 46					21 06
	d	19 05		18 59	19 05		19 24								20 07	20 00	20 07			20 46					21 07
Darton	d	→			19 19										→		20 19								21 18
Huddersfield	d										19 18											20 18			
Lockwood	d										19 21											20 21			
Berry Brow	d										19 24											20 24			
Honley	d										19 27											20 27			
Brockholes	d										19 30											20 30			
Stocksmoor	d										19 34											20 34			
Shepley	d										19 36											20 36			
Denby Dale	d										19 43											20 41			
Penistone	d										19 50											20 49			
Silkstone Common	d										19 56											20 54			
Dodworth	d										19 59											20 58			
Barnsley	a			19 15	19 26		19 40				20 07					20 16	20 26			21 02		21 08			21 24
	d			19 19	19 26		19 41				20 07					20 16	20 27			21 03		21 12			21 25
Wombwell	d				19 31						20 12						20 32					21 17			21 30
Elsecar	d				19 35												20 36								21 34
Chapeltown	d				19 38						20 19						20 41					21 24			21 39
Meadowhall 29,31 ⇌	a			19 35	19 47	19 51	19 54				20 28					20 35	20 47	20 51		21 20		21 30			21 47
	d			19 36	19 48	19 51	19 54	19 57	20 01	20 08	20 29			20 33		20 37	20 48	20 51	21 09	21 22		21 31		21 34	21 49
Sheffield 7 29,31 ⇌	a			19 43	19 57	19 59	20 04	20 05	20 08	20 18	20 36			20 41		20 44	20 58	21 02	21 19	21 30		21 40		21 48	21 58
	d						20 05					20 41									21 39				
Dronfield	d						20 15														21 49				
Chesterfield	d						20 23					20 56									21 55				
Alfreton	d						20 33					21 08									22 05				
Langley Mill	d						20 41														22 13				
Nottingham	a						21 02					21 33									22 35				

A From Doncaster
B From Cleethorpes to Manchester Airport
C From Bridlington
D To Sheffield
E From Scunthorpe
F From Liverpool Lime Street
G From Leeds
H From Scarborough
I From Huddersfield
J From Liverpool Lime Street to Norwich
K From Hull
L From Cleethorpes to Manchester Piccadilly
M From Doncaster to Worksop
N From Cleethorpes
O To Retford

Table 34R

Mondays to Fridays

9 December to 16 May

Leeds and Huddersfield - Barnsley - Sheffield, Nottingham

Network Diagram - see first page of Table 31

			NT	TP	NT	NT	NT	NT	NT		NT	NT	EM	NT	NT	NT
				◇1									◇			
				A	B	C		D					E		C	
Leeds 10	31	d	20 48						21 37		21 48			22 37		23 09
Woodlesford		d							21 45					22 45		
Castleford		d							21 56					22 56		
Normanton		d							22 02					23 01		
Wakefield Kirkgate 4	31	a							22 06					23 10		
		d							22 07					23 10		
Darton		d							22 21					23 24		
Huddersfield		d					21 18					22 18				
Lockwood		d					21 21					22 21				
Berry Brow		d					21 24					22 24				
Honley		d					21 27					22 27				
Brockholes		d					21 30					22 30				
Stocksmoor		d					21 34					22 34				
Shepley		d					21 36					22 36				
Denby Dale		d					21 41					22 41				
Penistone		d					21 49					22 49				
Silkstone Common		d					21 54					22 54				
Dodworth		d					21 58					22 58				
Barnsley		a					22 05		22 27			23 05		23 31		
		d					22 06		22 28			23 06		23 31		
Wombwell		d					22 11		22 33			23 11		23 36		
Elsecar		d							22 37			23 15		23 40		
Chapeltown		d					22 18		22 42			23 20		23 45		
Meadowhall	29,31 🚋	a	21 51				22 25		22 47		22 52	23 26		23 51		00 09
		d	21 52	21 59	22 03	22 08	22 26	22 44	22 48		22 53	23 27		23 51	23 54	00 09
Sheffield 7	29,31 🚋	a	22 04	22 08	22 11	22 18	22 36	22 54	22 58		23 02	23 36		00 02	00 04	00 23
		d											23 37			
Dronfield		d														
Chesterfield		d											00 02			
Alfreton		d														
Langley Mill		d														
Nottingham		a											00 39			

Saturdays

14 December to 17 May

			EM	NT	NT	NT	TP	NT	NT	NT	NT		TP	EM	NT	NT	NT	NT	TP	NT	NT		NT	EM	NT	NT
			◇				◇1						◇1	◇1					◇1					◇1		
			E	F			G		B		C		H	I		B			H		J		K	I		C
														✕										🚲		
Leeds 10	31	d												06 34			06 38	06 43		07 05			07 29	07 34		
Woodlesford		d															06 46						07 37			
Castleford		d															06 57						07 48			
Normanton		d															07 03						07 54			
Wakefield Kirkgate 4	31	a															07 07			07 25			08 00			
		d															07 08			07 25			08 04			
Darton		d															07 19						↪			
Huddersfield		d													06 10										07 10	
Lockwood		d													06 13										07 13	
Berry Brow		d													06 16										07 16	
Honley		d													06 19										07 19	
Brockholes		d													06 22										07 22	
Stocksmoor		d													06 26										07 26	
Shepley		d													06 28										07 28	
Denby Dale		d													06 34										07 34	
Penistone		d													06 42										07 42	
Silkstone Common		d													06 47										07 47	
Dodworth		d													06 51										07 51	
Barnsley		a													06 57		07 25			07 41					07 57	
		d				05 23		05 50		06 23					06 58		07 26			07 42					07 58	
Wombwell		d				05 28		05 55		06 29					07 03		07 31								08 03	
Elsecar		d				05 32		05 59		06 32					07 07		07 35								08 07	
Chapeltown		d				05 37		06 04		06 38					07 12		07 40								08 12	
Meadowhall	29,31 🚋	a				05 45		06 10		06 43					07 20		07 48	07 46		07 55					08 20	
		d		00 09		05 45	05 58	06 10	06 30	06 43	06 54		06 58		07 22	07 33	07 50	07 47	07 53	07 56	08 07				08 22	08 25
Sheffield 7	29,31 🚋	a		00 23		05 54	06 08	06 25	06 38	06 55	07 05		07 07	07 22	07 29	07 40	07 58	07 54	08 00	08 05	08 18			08 21	08 29	08 32
		d			05 54					07 03				07 37						08 08				08 34		
Dronfield		d								07 13										08 18						
Chesterfield		d	00 02		06 20					07 19				07 50						08 24				08 47		
Alfreton		d			06 30					07 29				08 01						08 34				08 57		
Langley Mill		d			06 38					07 37				08 09						08 42						
Nottingham		a	00 39		07 02					08 00				08 27						09 02				09 19		

A From Cleethorpes to Manchester Piccadilly
B From Doncaster
C From Hull
D From Scunthorpe
E From Liverpool Lime Street
F From Leeds
G From Doncaster to Manchester Airport
H From Cleethorpes to Manchester Airport
I To St Pancras International
J From Adwick
K To Sheffield

Table 34R

Saturdays

14 December to 17 May

Leeds and Huddersfield - Barnsley - Sheffield, Nottingham

Network Diagram - see first page of Table 31

Station	Table		EM	NT	NT	NT	NT		NT	TP	NT	NT	EM	NT	NT	NT	NT		NT	NT	NT	TP	NT	NT	NT	NT
			◇							◇[1]			◇									◇[1]				
			A		B				C	D		E	A	F		G	B				C	D	E		F	
Leeds [10]	31	d		07 35		07 48	08 05							08 32	08 37				08 48	09 05					09 32	09 37
Woodlesford		d												08 40											09 40	
Castleford		d												08 51											09 51	
Normanton		d			←									08 57			←								09 57	
Wakefield Kirkgate [4]	31	a		07 54	08 00		08 23							09 03	08 54		09 03			09 23					10 01	09 54
		d		07 55	08 04		08 23							09 05	08 55		09 05			09 23					10 04	09 55
Darton		d			08 15									→			09 17								→	
Huddersfield		d									08 10													09 13		
Lockwood		d									08 13													09 16		
Berry Brow		d									08 16													09 19		
Honley		d									08 19													09 22		
Brockholes		d									08 22													09 25		
Stocksmoor		d									08 26													09 29		
Shepley		d									08 28													09 31		
Denby Dale		d									08 34													09 36		
Penistone		d									08 42													09 44		
Silkstone Common		d									08 47													09 49		
Dodworth		d									08 51													09 53		
Barnsley		a		08 11	08 21		08 39				08 57				09 11		09 23			09 39				10 00		10 11
		d		08 14	08 24		08 40				08 58				09 14		09 24			09 40				10 01		10 14
Wombwell		d			08 29						09 03						09 29							10 06		
Elsecar		d			08 33						09 07						09 33									
Chapeltown		d			08 38						09 12						09 38							10 13		
Meadowhall	29,31	a		08 31	08 46	08 50	08 53				09 19				09 29		09 46		09 51	09 54				10 20		10 29
		d		08 31	08 48	08 51	08 53		08 56	09 01	09 21	09 24			09 30	09 33	09 48		09 51	09 54	09 57	10 01	10 08	10 21		10 30
Sheffield [7]	29,31	a		08 39	08 56	08 59	09 02		09 05	09 08	09 28	09 32			09 37	09 41	09 56		10 00	10 02	10 05	10 08	10 18	10 30		10 37
		d	08 38				09 05						09 37							10 05						
Dronfield		d					09 15													10 15						
Chesterfield		d	08 53				09 21						09 52							10 21						
Alfreton		d	09 03				09 32						10 02							10 31						
Langley Mill		d					09 40													10 39						
Nottingham		a	09 27				10 00						10 27							11 00						

Station	Table		EM		NT	NT	NT	NT	NT	TP	NT	NT	EM		NT	NT	NT	NT	NT	NT	NT	TP	NT		NT	NT
			◇							◇[1]			◇									◇[1]				
			A		G	B			C	D	E		A		F		G	B			C	D	E			H
Leeds [10]	31	d					09 48	10 05							10 32	10 37			10 48	11 05						
Woodlesford		d													10 40											
Castleford		d													10 51											
Normanton		d				←									10 57			←								
Wakefield Kirkgate [4]	31	a				10 01		10 23							11 01	10 54		11 01		11 23						
		d				10 04		10 23							11 04	10 55		11 04		11 23						
Darton		d				10 15									→			11 15								
Huddersfield		d										10 13													11 13	
Lockwood		d										10 16													11 16	
Berry Brow		d										10 19													11 19	
Honley		d										10 22													11 22	
Brockholes		d										10 25													11 25	
Stocksmoor		d										10 29													11 29	
Shepley		d										10 31													11 31	
Denby Dale		d										10 36													11 36	
Penistone		d										10 44													11 44	
Silkstone Common		d										10 49													11 49	
Dodworth		d										10 53													11 53	
Barnsley		a				10 21		10 39				11 00				11 11		11 21		11 39					12 00	
		d				10 24		10 40				11 01				11 14		11 24		11 40					12 01	
Wombwell		d				10 29						11 06						11 29							12 06	
Elsecar		d				10 33												11 33								
Chapeltown		d				10 38						11 13						11 38							12 13	
Meadowhall	29,31	a				10 46	10 51	10 54				11 20				11 29		11 46	11 51	11 54					12 20	
		d			10 33	10 48	10 51	10 54	10 58	11 01	11 08	11 21				11 30	11 33	11 48	11 51	11 54	11 58	12 01	12 08		12 21	12 25
Sheffield [7]	29,31	a			10 41	10 56	11 00	11 02	11 05	11 08	11 18	11 30				11 37	11 41	11 57	12 00	12 02	12 05	12 08	12 20		12 30	12 36
		d	10 38					11 05					11 37							12 05						
Dronfield		d						11 15												12 15						
Chesterfield		d	10 53					11 21					11 52							12 22						
Alfreton		d	11 03					11 31					12 02							12 32						
Langley Mill		d						11 39												12 40						
Nottingham		a	11 27					12 00					12 28							13 00						

A From Liverpool Lime Street to Norwich
B From Leeds
C From Adwick
D From Cleethorpes to Manchester Airport
E From Bridlington
F To Sheffield
G From Scunthorpe to Lincoln
H From York

Table 34R

Saturdays

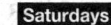

14 December to 17 May

Leeds and Huddersfield - Barnsley - Sheffield, Nottingham

Network Diagram - see first page of Table 31

			EM	NT	NT	NT	NT	NT	NT		NT	TP	NT	NT	EM	NT	NT	NT	NT		NT	NT	NT	TP	NT	NT
			◇									◇1			◇									◇1		
			A	B		C	D				E	F	G		A	B		C	D				E	F	H	
Leeds 10	31	d		11 32	11 37			11 48	12 05							12 32	12 37				12 48	13 05				
Woodlesford		d		11 40												12 40										
Castleford		d		11 51												12 51										
Normanton		d		11 57			←									12 57			←							
Wakefield Kirkgate 4	31	a		12 01	11 54		12 01		12 23							13 02	12 54		13 02			13 23				
		d		12 04	11 55		12 04		12 23							13 04	12 55		13 04			13 23				
Darton		d		↪			12 15									↪			13 17							
Huddersfield		d												12 13												13 13
Lockwood		d												12 16												13 16
Berry Brow		d												12 19												13 19
Honley		d												12 22												13 22
Brockholes		d												12 25												13 25
Stocksmoor		d												12 29												13 29
Shepley		d												12 31												13 31
Denby Dale		d												12 36												13 36
Penistone		d												12 44												13 44
Silkstone Common		d												12 49												13 49
Dodworth		d												12 53												13 53
Barnsley		a			12 11		12 21		12 39					13 00			13 11		13 22			13 39				14 00
		d			12 14		12 24		12 40					13 01			13 14		13 24			13 40				14 01
Wombwell		d					12 29							13 06					13 29							14 06
Elsecar		d					12 33												13 33							
Chapeltown		d					12 38							13 13					13 38							14 13
Meadowhall	29,31	a			12 29		12 47	12 51	12 54					13 20			13 27		13 46		13 51	13 54				14 20
		d			12 30	12 33	12 48	12 51	12 54		12 58	13 01	13 08	13 21			13 28	13 33	13 48		13 51	13 54	13 58	14 01	14 08	14 21
Sheffield 7	29,31	a			12 37	12 41	12 56	13 00	13 02		13 05	13 08	13 18	13 29			13 37	13 41	13 56		14 00	14 02	14 05	14 08	14 18	14 29
		d	12 37						13 05						13 37							14 05				
Dronfield		d							13 15													14 15				
Chesterfield		d	12 52						13 21						13 52							14 21				
Alfreton		d	13 02						13 31						14 02							14 31				
Langley Mill		d							13 40													14 39				
Nottingham		a	13 27						14 00						14 27							15 00				

			EM	NT	NT		NT	NT	NT	NT	NT	TP	NT	NT	EM		NT	NT	NT	NT	NT	NT	NT	TP	NT	
			◇									◇1			◇				◇					◇1		
			A	B			C	D			E	F	G		A		B		C	D			E	F	H	
Leeds 10	31	d		13 32	13 37				13 48	14 05							14 32	14 37			14 48	15 05				
Woodlesford		d		13 40													14 40									
Castleford		d		13 51													14 51									
Normanton		d		13 57				←									14 57			←						
Wakefield Kirkgate 4	31	a		14 01	13 54			14 01		14 23							15 01	14 54		15 01		15 23				
		d		14 04	13 55			14 04		14 23							15 04	14 55		15 04		15 23				
Darton		d		↪				14 15									↪			15 15						
Huddersfield		d												14 13												
Lockwood		d												14 16												
Berry Brow		d												14 19												
Honley		d												14 22												
Brockholes		d												14 25												
Stocksmoor		d												14 29												
Shepley		d												14 31												
Denby Dale		d												14 36												
Penistone		d												14 44												
Silkstone Common		d												14 49												
Dodworth		d												14 53												
Barnsley		a			14 11			14 21		14 39				15 00				15 13		15 21		15 39				
		d			14 14			14 24		14 40				15 01				15 14		15 24		15 40				
Wombwell		d						14 29						15 06						15 29						
Elsecar		d						14 33												15 33						
Chapeltown		d						14 38						15 13						15 38						
Meadowhall	29,31	a			14 29			14 46	14 51	14 54				15 20				15 29		15 46	15 51	15 53				
		d			14 30		14 33	14 48	14 51	14 54	14 58	15 01	15 07	15 21				15 30	15 33	15 48	15 51	15 54	15 57	16 01	16 08	
Sheffield 7	29,31	a			14 37		14 40	14 56	15 00	15 02	15 05	15 08	15 18	15 29				15 37	15 41	15 56	16 00	16 02	16 05	16 08	16 18	
		d	14 37							15 05					15 37							16 05				
Dronfield		d								15 15												16 15				
Chesterfield		d	14 52							15 21					15 52							16 21				
Alfreton		d	15 02							15 32					16 03							16 31				
Langley Mill		d								15 39												16 39				
Nottingham		a	15 27							16 00					16 27							17 00				

A From Liverpool Lime Street to Norwich
B To Sheffield
C From Scunthorpe to Lincoln
D From Leeds
E From Adwick
F From Cleethorpes to Manchester Airport
G From Bridlington
H From Scarborough

Table 34R

Saturdays

14 December to 17 May

Leeds and Huddersfield - Barnsley - Sheffield, Nottingham

Network Diagram - see first page of Table 31

Station			NT	NT	NT	NT	EM	NT	NT	NT	NT		NT	TP	NT	NT	NT	NT	EM	NT	NT		NT	NT	NT	TP
							◇							◇1					◇							◇1
			A		B		C	D	E				F	G	H		B		C	D	E				I	G
Leeds 10	31	d			15 32	15 37				15 48	16 05						16 32	16 37					16 48	17 05		
Woodlesford		d			15 40												16 40									
Castleford		d			15 51												16 51									
Normanton		d			15 57				←								16 57				←			17 18		
Wakefield Kirkgate 4	31	a			16 01	15 54			16 01		16 23						17 01	16 54			17 01			17 22		
		d			16 04	15 55			16 04		16 23						17 04	16 55			17 04			17 23		
Darton		d			→				16 15								→				17 15					
Huddersfield		d		15 13												16 13										
Lockwood		d		15 16												16 16										
Berry Brow		d		15 19												16 19										
Honley		d		15 22												16 22										
Brockholes		d		15 25												16 25										
Stocksmoor		d		15 29												16 29										
Shepley		d		15 31												16 31										
Denby Dale		d		15 36												16 36										
Penistone		d		15 44												16 44										
Silkstone Common		d		15 49												16 49										
Dodworth		d		15 53												16 53										
Barnsley		a		16 00		16 11			16 21		16 39					17 00		17 11			17 21			17 39		
		d		16 01		16 14			16 24		16 40					17 01		17 14			17 24			17 40		
Wombwell		d		16 06					16 29							17 06					17 29					
Elsecar		d							16 33												17 33					
Chapeltown		d		16 13					16 38							17 13					17 38					
Meadowhall	29,31	a		16 20		16 29			16 46	16 51	16 54					17 20		17 27			17 46		17 50	17 53		
		d	16 18	16 21		16 30		16 33	16 47	16 51	16 54		16 57	17 01	17 08	17 21		17 28		17 33	17 48		17 50	17 54	17 57	18 01
Sheffield 7	29,31	a	16 27	16 29		16 37		16 41	16 56	17 00	17 02		17 05	17 08	17 18	17 32		17 37		17 41	17 55		17 59	18 02	18 05	18 08
		d					16 38				17 05								17 41					18 05		
Dronfield		d					16 48				17 15								17 52					18 15		
Chesterfield		d					16 53				17 21								17 59					18 21		
Alfreton		d					17 04				17 31								18 09					18 31		
Langley Mill		d									17 39													18 39		
Nottingham		a					17 27				18 00								18 31					19 00		

Station			NT	NT	NT	NT	NT		EM	NT	NT	NT	NT	TP	NT	NT	EM		NT	NT	NT	NT	NT	NT	NT	TP
									◇					◇1			◇									◇1
			H		B		D		J	E			I	G	K		C		L	B		E			I	G
Leeds 10	31	d			17 32	17 37					17 48	18 05								18 32	18 37		18 48	19 05		
Woodlesford		d			17 40															18 40						
Castleford		d			17 51															18 51						
Normanton		d			17 57					←										19 00		←				
Wakefield Kirkgate 4	31	a			18 01	17 54				18 01		18 23								19 04	18 54	19 04		19 24		
		d			18 04	17 55				18 04		18 23								19 05	18 55	19 05		19 24		
Darton		d			→					18 15										→		19 19				
Huddersfield		d		17 13												18 13										
Lockwood		d		17 16												18 16										
Berry Brow		d		17 19												18 19										
Honley		d		17 22												18 22										
Brockholes		d		17 25												18 25										
Stocksmoor		d		17 29												18 29										
Shepley		d		17 31												18 31										
Denby Dale		d		17 36												18 36										
Penistone		d		17 44												18 44										
Silkstone Common		d		17 49												18 49										
Dodworth		d		17 53												18 53										
Barnsley		a		18 00		18 11				18 21		18 39				19 01					19 11	19 26		19 40		
		d		18 01		18 14				18 24		18 40				19 01					19 14	19 26		19 41		
Wombwell		d		18 06						18 29						19 06						19 31				
Elsecar		d								18 33												19 35				
Chapeltown		d		18 13						18 38						19 13						19 40				
Meadowhall	29,31	a		18 21		18 29				18 46	18 51	18 54				19 20					19 30	19 47	19 51	19 54		
		d	18 08	18 22		18 30	18 33			18 48	18 51	18 54	18 57	19 01	19 08	19 21			19 29		19 32	19 48	19 51	19 54	19 57	20 01
Sheffield 7	29,31	a	18 18	18 31		18 38	18 41			18 56	19 00	19 03	19 06	19 08	19 18	19 30			19 39		19 40	19 57	19 59	20 04	20 06	20 08
		d							18 50			19 05					19 37							20 05		
Dronfield		d										19 15												20 15		
Chesterfield		d							19 04			19 21					19 52							20 21		
Alfreton		d							19 15			19 32					20 03							20 31		
Langley Mill		d										19 39												20 39		
Nottingham		a							19 39			20 00					20 31							21 00		

A From York, via Pontefract Baghill
B To Sheffield
C From Liverpool Lime Street to Norwich
D From Scunthorpe to Lincoln
E From Leeds
F From Adwick to Retford Low Level
G From Cleethorpes to Manchester Airport
H From Bridlington
I From Doncaster
J From Liverpool Lime Street
K From Scarborough
L From Hull

Table 34R

Saturdays

14 December to 17 May

Leeds and Huddersfield - Barnsley - Sheffield, Nottingham

Network Diagram - see first page of Table 31

			NT		NT	EM	NT	NT	NT	NT	NT	TP	NT		EM	NT	NT	NT	NT	TP	NT	NT	EM		NT	NT
						◇						◇1			◇					◇1			◇			
			A			B	C	D		E		F			B	G	H			F	I	A	B			J
Leeds 10	31	d						19 37	19 43		19 48		20 30					20 37	20 48							
Woodlesford		d						19 45										20 45								
Castleford		d						19 56										20 56								
Normanton		d						20 02		←								21 02								
Wakefield Kirkgate 4	31	a						20 06	19 59	20 06			20 46					21 06								
		d						20 07	20 00	20 07			20 46					21 07								
Darton		d						→		20 19								21 18								
Huddersfield		d			19 18											20 18									21 18	
Lockwood		d			19 21											20 21									21 21	
Berry Brow		d			19 24											20 24									21 24	
Honley		d			19 27											20 27									21 27	
Brockholes		d			19 30											20 30									21 30	
Stocksmoor		d			19 34											20 34									21 34	
Shepley		d			19 36											20 36									21 36	
Denby Dale		d			19 41											20 41									21 41	
Penistone		d			19 49											20 52									21 49	
Silkstone Common		d			19 54											20 57									21 54	
Dodworth		d			19 58											21 01									21 58	
Barnsley		a			20 05				20 16	20 26			21 02			21 09		21 25							22 05	
		d			20 06				20 16	20 27			21 03			21 12		21 26							22 06	
Wombwell		d			20 11					20 32						21 17		21 31							22 11	
Elsecar		d								20 36								21 35								
Chapeltown		d			20 18					20 41						21 24		21 40							22 18	
Meadowhall	29,31 ⛴	a			20 24				20 35	20 47	20 51		21 21			21 30		21 48	21 51						22 24	
		d	20 07		20 24		20 33		20 37	20 48	20 51	21 09	21 21			21 31	21 35	21 49	21 52	21 59	22 03	22 08			22 25	22 43
Sheffield 7	29,31 ⛴	a	20 18		20 36		20 41		20 44	20 58	21 00	21 19	21 30			21 41	21 46	21 57	22 02	22 10	22 13	22 19			22 36	22 54
		d				20 39									21 38								22 35			
Dronfield		d													21 48											
Chesterfield		d				20 54									21 54								22 51			
Alfreton		d				21 05									22 04								23 02			
Langley Mill		d													22 11											
Nottingham		a				21 33									22 33								23 32			

			NT	NT	NT	EM	NT	NT
						◇		
						B		H
Leeds 10	31	d	21 37	21 48			22 44	
Woodlesford		d	21 45					
Castleford		d	21 56					
Normanton		d	22 02					
Wakefield Kirkgate 4	31	a	22 06					
		d	22 07					
Darton		d	22 21					
Huddersfield		d			22 18			
Lockwood		d			22 21			
Berry Brow		d			22 24			
Honley		d			22 27			
Brockholes		d			22 30			
Stocksmoor		d			22 34			
Shepley		d			22 36			
Denby Dale		d			22 41			
Penistone		d			22 49			
Silkstone Common		d			22 54			
Dodworth		d			22 58			
Barnsley		a	22 27		23 05			
		d	22 28		23 06			
Wombwell		d	22 33		23 11			
Elsecar		d	22 37		23 15			
Chapeltown		d	22 42		23 20			
Meadowhall	29,31 ⛴	a	22 47	22 52	23 26		23 44	
		d	22 48	22 53	23 27		23 45	23 50
Sheffield 7	29,31 ⛴	a	22 58	23 03	23 36		23 58	23 59
		d				23 38		
Dronfield		d						
Chesterfield		d				23 53		
Alfreton		d						
Langley Mill		d						
Nottingham		a				00 30		

A From Hull
B From Liverpool Lime Street
C From Scunthorpe to Worksop
D To Sheffield
E From Leeds
F From Cleethorpes
G To Retford
H From Bridlington
I From Doncaster
J From Scunthorpe

Table 34R

Sundays

8 December to 29 December

Leeds and Huddersfield - Barnsley - Sheffield, Nottingham

Network Diagram - see first page of Table 31

Station			NT	NT	NT	NT	NT	NT	NT	EM	NT		NT	NT	TP	NT	NT	NT	NT	TP	NT		NT	NT	EM	NT
										◇1					◇1					◇1					◇	
			A		A				B	C			D		E			A		E	F				G	
Leeds [10]	31	d				08 34	08 48	09 05		09 45				10 02			10 17		10 57				11 20	11 29		
Woodlesford		d				08 42											10 25									
Castleford		d				08 53											10 36									
Normanton		d				08 58											10 41									
Wakefield Kirkgate [4]	31	a				09 03		09 21						10 18			10 46		11 13					11 46		
		d				09 03		09 21						10 18			10 46		11 13					11 46		
Darton		d				09 17											11 00									
Huddersfield		d									09 19					10 15										11 29
Lockwood		d									09 22					10 18										11 32
Berry Brow		d									09 25					10 21										11 35
Honley		d									09 28					10 24										11 38
Brockholes		d									09 31					10 27										11 41
Stocksmoor		d									09 35					10 31										11 45
Shepley		d									09 37					10 33										11 47
Denby Dale		d									09 42					10 39										11 52
Penistone		d									09 50					10 46										12 00
Silkstone Common		d									09 55					10 52										12 05
Dodworth		d									09 59					10 55										12 09
Barnsley		a				09 24		09 40			10 06			10 37		11 03	11 08		11 32					12 05		12 16
		d				09 24		09 41			10 12			10 38		11 03	11 12		11 33					12 06		12 17
Wombwell		d				09 29					10 17						11 17									12 22
Elsecar		d				09 33					10 21						11 21									12 26
Chapeltown		d				09 38					10 26						11 26									12 31
Meadowhall	29,31	a				09 44	09 53	09 57			10 32			10 51		11 20	11 32		11 46				12 24	12 17		12 34
		d	08 30		09 41	09 44	09 54	09 57	10 00		10 33		10 40	10 51	11 00	11 20	11 35	11 40	11 46	12 00	12 08		12 24	12 17		12 35
Sheffield [7]	29,31	a	08 41		09 51	09 55	10 03	10 04	10 08	10 25	10 44		10 52	11 02	11 07	11 28	11 44	11 51	11 56	12 07	12 18		12 32	12 29		12 47
		d		09 05				10 07		10 31				11 03					12 06					12 31	12 41	
Dronfield		d		09 15				10 17						11 13					12 16					12 42		
Chesterfield		d		09 21				10 23		10 47				11 20					12 23					12 48	12 56	
Alfreton		d		09 32				10 33						11 30					12 33					12 58	13 07	
Langley Mill		d		09 39				10 41						11 38					12 41					13 06		
Nottingham		a		09 58				10 59		11 17				11 57					12 59					13 24	13 28	

Station			NT	TP	NT	EM	NT		NT	NT	TP	NT	EM	NT	NT	NT	NT		TP	NT	EM	NT	NT	NT	NT	TP
				◇1		◇					◇1		◇						◇1		◇					◇1
			D	E		H	A			I	J		K		D	I			E		K		A	F		E
Leeds [10]	31	d			12 29				12 34			13 20					14 05					14 17			15 05	
Woodlesford		d							12 42													14 25				
Castleford		d							12 53													14 36				
Normanton		d							12 58													14 41				
Wakefield Kirkgate [4]	31	a			12 46				13 04								14 21					14 46			15 22	
		d			12 49				13 04								14 21					14 46			15 22	
Darton		d							13 18													15 00				
Huddersfield		d												13 19						14 15						
Lockwood		d												13 22						14 18						
Berry Brow		d												13 25						14 21						
Honley		d												13 28						14 24						
Brockholes		d												13 31						14 27						
Stocksmoor		d												13 35						14 31						
Shepley		d												13 37						14 33						
Denby Dale		d												13 42						14 39						
Penistone		d												13 50						14 46						
Silkstone Common		d												13 55						14 52						
Dodworth		d												13 59						14 55						
Barnsley		a			13 08				13 24					14 06			14 40			15 03		15 07			15 41	
		d			13 08				13 24					14 12			14 41			15 03		15 12			15 42	
Wombwell		d							13 29					14 17								15 17				
Elsecar		d							13 33					14 21								15 21				
Chapeltown		d							13 38					14 26								15 26				
Meadowhall	29,31	a			13 19				13 48			14 21		14 32			14 54			15 20		15 35			15 55	
		d	12 43	13 00	13 20		13 44		13 51	13 57	14 00	14 21		14 33	14 48	14 52	14 56		15 00	15 21		15 35	15 48	15 52	15 56	16 00
Sheffield [7]	29,31	a	12 55	13 07	13 30		13 51		13 58	14 08	14 07	14 32		14 48	14 56	15 04	15 06		15 07	15 28		15 44	15 55	16 03	16 05	16 07
		d			13 31	13 48							14 43				15 07				15 39				16 07	
Dronfield		d			13 42												15 16								16 17	
Chesterfield		d			13 48	14 02							14 57				15 23				15 53				16 23	
Alfreton		d			13 59	14 12							15 08				15 33				16 03				16 33	
Langley Mill		d			14 06								15 15				15 41				16 11				16 41	
Nottingham		a			14 25	14 33							15 32				15 59				16 28				16 59	

A From Doncaster
B From Hull
C To St Pancras International
D From Goole
E From Cleethorpes to Manchester Airport
F From Bridlington
G To Norwich
H From Manchester Piccadilly to Norwich
I From Scarborough
J From Doncaster to Manchester Airport
K From Liverpool Lime Street to Norwich

Table 34R

Sundays

8 December to 29 December

Leeds and Huddersfield - Barnsley - Sheffield, Nottingham

Network Diagram - see first page of Table 31

Station		NT		EM ◇ A	NT	NT B	NT C	NT	TP ◇1 D	EM ◇ A	NT	NT E		NT F	NT	TP ◇1 D	NT	EM ◇ G	NT	NT E	NT C	NT H		TP ◇1 D	NT I
Leeds 10 31	d	15 20						16 04			16 17				17 05		17 20					18 03			
Woodlesford	d										16 25														
Castleford	d										16 36														
Normanton	d										16 41														
Wakefield Kirkgate 4 31	a							16 21			16 46				17 21							18 18			
	d							16 22			16 49				17 21							18 21			
Darton	d										17 03														
Huddersfield	d				15 19														17 19						
Lockwood	d				15 22														17 22						
Berry Brow	d				15 25														17 25						
Honley	d				15 28														17 28						
Brockholes	d				15 31														17 31						
Stocksmoor	d				15 35														17 35						
Shepley	d				15 37														17 37						
Denby Dale	d				15 42														17 47						
Penistone	d				15 50														17 54						
Silkstone Common	d				15 55														18 00						
Dodworth	d				15 59														18 03						
Barnsley	a				16 06			16 41			17 09				17 40				18 11			18 41			
	d				16 12			16 42			17 12				17 41				18 12			18 42			
Wombwell	d				16 17						17 17								18 17						
Elsecar	d				16 21						17 21								18 21						
Chapeltown	d				16 26						17 26								18 26						
Meadowhall 29,31 🚋	a	16 22			16 32			16 56			17 34				17 55		18 24		18 32			18 56			
	d	16 23			16 34	16 47	16 53	16 56	17 00		17 35	17 48		17 53	17 56	18 00	18 25		18 33	18 47	18 53	18 56		19 00	19 18
Sheffield 7 29,31 🚋	a	16 32			16 44	16 55	17 03	17 05	17 07		17 44	17 56		18 01	18 05	18 07	18 34		18 44	18 56	19 03	19 06		19 07	19 27
	d			16 41				17 07		17 40					18 07			18 40				19 07			
Dronfield	d							17 17							18 17							19 17			
Chesterfield	d			16 55				17 23		17 54					18 23			18 55				19 23			
Alfreton	d			17 05				17 33		18 05					18 33			19 05				19 33			
Langley Mill	d			17 13				17 44		18 12					18 41			19 13				19 41			
Nottingham	a			17 28				17 59		18 28					18 59			19 33				19 59			

Station		EM ◇ A	NT	NT E	NT	NT F	TP ◇1 D	NT		EM ◇ G	NT	NT E	TP ◇1 D	NT C	EM ◇ G	NT	NT I	TP ◇1 J		NT	NT	NT K	EM ◇ G	NT
Leeds 10 31	d		18 17		19 04			19 20								20 17					21 41			22 17
Woodlesford	d		18 25													20 25								22 25
Castleford	d		18 36													20 36								22 36
Normanton	d		18 40													20 41								22 41
Wakefield Kirkgate 4 31	a		18 45		19 21											20 46								22 46
	d		18 45		19 21											20 46								22 46
Darton	d		18 59													21 00								23 00
Huddersfield	d										19 19													
Lockwood	d										19 22													
Berry Brow	d										19 25													
Honley	d										19 28													
Brockholes	d										19 31													
Stocksmoor	d										19 35													
Shepley	d										19 37													
Denby Dale	d										19 42													
Penistone	d										19 50													
Silkstone Common	d										19 55													
Dodworth	d										19 59													
Barnsley	a		19 05		19 40						20 06					21 07								23 07
	d		19 11		19 40						20 12					21 12				22 21				23 12
Wombwell	d		19 17								20 17					21 17				22 26				23 17
Elsecar	d		19 21								20 21					21 21				22 30				23 21
Chapeltown	d		19 26								20 26					21 26				22 35				23 26
Meadowhall 29,31 🚋	a		19 32		19 54			20 22			20 34					21 33				22 40	22 43			23 30
	d		19 33	19 48	19 54	19 57	20 00	20 23			20 34	20 48	21 00	21 28		21 33	21 58	22 05		22 41	22 44	23 04		23 32
Sheffield 7 29,31 🚋	a		19 43	19 56	20 04	20 07	20 07	20 34			20 43	20 56	21 07	21 38		21 42	22 09	22 13		22 51	22 52	23 15		23 43
	d	19 40			20 07					20 40					21 40								23 27	
Dronfield	d				20 16										21 50									
Chesterfield	d	19 54			20 23					20 54					21 56								23 42	
Alfreton	d	20 05			20 33					21 05					22 06								23 52	
Langley Mill	d	20 12			20 41					21 12					22 14								23 59	
Nottingham	a	20 30			20 59					21 33					22 36								00 21	

A From Liverpool Lime Street to Norwich
B From Goole
C From Scarborough
D From Cleethorpes to Manchester Airport
E From Doncaster
F From Bridlington
G From Liverpool Lime Street
H From Carlisle
I From York. via Pontefract Baghill
J From Cleethorpes
K From Hull

Table 34R

Sundays

5 January to 9 February

Leeds and Huddersfield - Barnsley - Sheffield, Nottingham

Network Diagram - see first page of Table 31

			NT	NT	NT	NT	NT	NT	EM	NT	NT	NT	NT	TP	NT	NT	NT	TP	NT	NT	NT	NT	NT	NT
			A	B		A	C		◇1 D			A		A	C			A	A		C			
Leeds 10	31	d						08 34	08 43	08 48	09 05					10 02				10 17		10 57	11 20	11 29
Woodlesford		d						08 42												10 25				
Castleford		d						08 53												10 36				
Normanton		d						08 58												10 41				
Wakefield Kirkgate 4	31	a						09 03			09 21					10 18				10 46		11 13		11 46
		d						09 03			09 21					10 18				10 46		11 13		11 46
Darton		d						09 17												11 00				
Huddersfield		d											09 19				10 15							
Lockwood		d											09 22				10 18							
Berry Brow		d											09 25				10 21							
Honley		d											09 28				10 24							
Brockholes		d											09 31				10 27							
Stocksmoor		d											09 35				10 31							
Shepley		d											09 37				10 33							
Denby Dale		d											09 42				10 39							
Penistone		d											09 50				10 46							
Silkstone Common		d											09 55				10 52							
Dodworth		d											09 59				10 55							
Barnsley		a						09 24			09 40		10 06			10 37	11 03			11 08		11 32		12 05
		d						09 24			09 41		10 12			10 38	11 03			11 12		11 33		12 06
Wombwell		d						09 29					10 17							11 17				
Elsecar		d						09 33					10 21							11 21				
Chapeltown		d						09 38					10 26							11 26				
Meadowhall	29,31	a						09 44		09 53	09 57		10 32			10 51	11 20			11 32		11 46	12 24	12 17
		d	08 20	08 30		09 15	09 40	09 44		09 54	09 57	10 10	10 34	10 40	10 41	10 51	11 20	11 20	11 20	11 35	11 42	11 46	12 24	12 17
Sheffield 7	29,31	a	08 40	08 41		09 35	09 51	09 55	09 25	10 03	10 04	10 30	10 44	11 00	10 52	11 02	11 28	11 40	11 40	11 44	11 53	11 56	12 32	12 29
		d			09 05				09 41		10 07					11 03						12 06		12 31
Dronfield		d			09 15						10 17					11 13						12 16		12 42
Chesterfield		d			09 21				09 56		10 23					11 20						12 23		12 48
Alfreton		d			09 32						10 33					11 30						12 33		12 58
Langley Mill		d			09 39						10 41					11 38						12 41		13 06
Nottingham		a			09 58				10 25		10 59					11 57						12 59		13 24

			TP	EM	NT	NT	NT	NT	TP	NT	EM	NT	NT	NT	NT	EM	NT	TP	NT	NT	NT	TP	NT	EM
			A	◇ E	A		C		A	A	◇ F	C		A		◇ G		A	C		A	A		◇ G
Leeds 10	31	d						12 29					12 34		13 20					14 05				
Woodlesford		d											12 42											
Castleford		d											12 53											
Normanton		d											12 58											
Wakefield Kirkgate 4	31	a						12 46					13 04							14 21				
		d						12 49					13 04							14 21				
Darton		d											13 18											
Huddersfield		d				11 29											13 19						14 15	
Lockwood		d				11 32											13 22						14 18	
Berry Brow		d				11 35											13 25						14 21	
Honley		d				11 38											13 28						14 24	
Brockholes		d				11 41											13 31						14 27	
Stocksmoor		d				11 45											13 35						14 31	
Shepley		d				11 47											13 37						14 33	
Denby Dale		d				11 52											13 42						14 39	
Penistone		d				12 00											13 50						14 46	
Silkstone Common		d				12 05											13 55						14 52	
Dodworth		d				12 09											13 59						14 55	
Barnsley		a				12 16		13 08					13 24				14 06			14 40			15 03	
		d				12 17		13 08					13 24				14 12			14 41			15 03	
Wombwell		d				12 22							13 29				14 17							
Elsecar		d				12 26							13 33				14 21							
Chapeltown		d				12 31							13 38				14 26							
Meadowhall	29,31	a				12 34		13 19					13 48		14 21		14 32			14 54			15 20	
		d	12 20		12 25	12 35	12 43	13 20	13 25	13 26		13 44	13 51	14 15	14 21		14 33	14 40	14 48	14 56	15 15	15 20	15 21	
Sheffield 7	29,31	a	12 40		12 45	12 47	12 54	13 30	13 45	13 46		13 51	13 58	14 35	14 32		14 48	15 00	14 59	15 06	15 35	15 40	15 28	
		d		12 41				13 31			13 48					14 43				15 07				15 39
Dronfield		d						13 42												15 16				
Chesterfield		d		12 56				13 48			14 02					14 57				15 23				15 53
Alfreton		d		13 07				13 59			14 12					15 08				15 33				16 03
Langley Mill		d						14 06								15 15				15 41				16 11
Nottingham		a		13 28				14 25			14 33					15 32				15 59				16 28

A From Doncaster
B From Mexborough
C From Swinton (S.Yorks)
D To St Pancras International
E To Norwich
F From Manchester Piccadilly to Norwich
G From Liverpool Lime Street to Norwich

Table 34R

Sundays

5 January to 9 February

Leeds and Huddersfield - Barnsley - Sheffield, Nottingham

Network Diagram - see first page of Table 31

		NT		NT	NT	NT	TP	NT	EM	NT	NT	NT		NT	EM	TP	NT	NT	NT	NT	TP	NT		EM	NT
									◇						◇									◇	
				A		B	B		C		A			B	C	B		A		B	B			D	
						🚌	🚌							🚌		🚌				🚌	🚌				
Leeds 10 31	d	14 17			15 05			15 20				16 04					16 17		17 05			17 20			
Woodlesford	d	14 25															16 25								
Castleford	d	14 36															16 36								
Normanton	d	14 41															16 41								
Wakefield Kirkgate 4 31	a	14 46			15 22							16 21					16 46		17 21						
	d	14 46			15 22							16 22					16 49		17 21						
Darton	d	15 00															17 03								
Huddersfield	d									15 19															17 19
Lockwood	d									15 22															17 22
Berry Brow	d									15 25															17 25
Honley	d									15 28															17 28
Brockholes	d									15 31															17 31
Stocksmoor	d									15 35															17 35
Shepley	d									15 37															17 37
Denby Dale	d									15 42															17 47
Penistone	d									15 50															17 54
Silkstone Common	d									15 55															18 00
Dodworth	d									15 59															18 03
Barnsley	a	15 07			15 41					16 06		16 41					17 09		17 40						18 11
	d	15 12			15 42					16 12		16 42					17 12		17 41						18 12
Wombwell	d	15 17								16 17							17 17								18 17
Elsecar	d	15 21								16 21							17 21								18 21
Chapeltown	d	15 26								16 26							17 26								18 26
Meadowhall 29,31 🚋	a	15 35			15 55			16 22		16 32		16 56					17 34		17 55			18 24			18 32
	d	15 35		15 48	15 56	16 15	16 20	16 23		16 34	16 47	16 56		17 15		17 20	17 35	17 48	17 56	18 15	18 20	18 25			18 33
Sheffield 7 29,31 🚋	a	15 44		15 55	16 05	16 35	16 40	16 32		16 44	16 55	17 05		17 35		17 40	17 44	17 56	18 05	18 35	18 40	18 34			18 44
	d				16 07				16 41			17 07			17 40				18 07					18 40	
Dronfield	d				16 17							17 17							18 17						
Chesterfield	d				16 23				16 55			17 23			17 54				18 23					18 55	
Alfreton	d				16 33				17 05			17 33			18 05				18 33					19 05	
Langley Mill	d				16 41				17 13			17 44			18 12				18 41					19 13	
Nottingham	a				16 59				17 28			17 59			18 28				18 59					19 33	

		NT	NT	NT	NT	EM	TP	NT		NT	NT	NT	TP	NT	EM	NT	NT	TP		NT	EM	NT	NT	NT	TP
						◇									◇						◇				
		A	E	B	F	C	B			A		B	B		D		A	B		A	D		F	B	B
				🚌			🚌					🚌	🚌					🚌						🚌	🚌
Leeds 10 31	d		18 03					18 17			19 04			19 20								20 17			
Woodlesford	d							18 25														20 25			
Castleford	d							18 36														20 36			
Normanton	d							18 40														20 41			
Wakefield Kirkgate 4 31	a		18 18					18 45			19 21											20 46			
	d		18 21					18 45			19 21											20 46			
Darton	d							18 59														21 00			
Huddersfield	d															19 19									
Lockwood	d															19 22									
Berry Brow	d															19 25									
Honley	d															19 28									
Brockholes	d															19 31									
Stocksmoor	d															19 35									
Shepley	d															19 37									
Denby Dale	d															19 42									
Penistone	d															19 50									
Silkstone Common	d															19 55									
Dodworth	d															19 59									
Barnsley	a		18 41					19 05			19 40					20 06						21 07			
	d		18 42					19 11			19 40					20 12						21 12			
Wombwell	d							19 17								20 17						21 17			
Elsecar	d							19 21								20 21						21 21			
Chapeltown	d							19 26								20 26						21 26			
Meadowhall 29,31 🚋	a		18 56					19 32			19 54			20 23		20 34						21 33			
	d	18 47	18 56	19 15	19 18		19 20	19 33		19 48	19 54	20 15	20 20	20 24		20 34	20 48	21 20		21 28		21 33	21 58	22 20	22 35
Sheffield 7 29,31 🚋	a	18 56	19 06	19 35	19 30		19 40	19 43		19 56	20 04	20 35	20 40	20 34		20 43	20 56	21 40		21 38		21 42	22 09	22 40	22 55
	d		19 07			19 40					20 07				20 40						21 40				
Dronfield	d		19 17								20 16										21 50				
Chesterfield	d		19 23			19 54					20 23				20 54						21 56				
Alfreton	d		19 33			20 05					20 33				21 05						22 06				
Langley Mill	d		19 41			20 12					20 41				21 12						22 14				
Nottingham	a		19 59			20 30					20 59				21 33						22 36				

A From Swinton (S.Yorks)
B From Doncaster
C From Liverpool Lime Street to Norwich
D From Liverpool Lime Street
E From Carlisle
F From York. via Pontefract Baghill

Table 34R

Sundays

5 January to 9 February

Leeds and Huddersfield - Barnsley - Sheffield, Nottingham

Network Diagram - see first page of Table 31

		NT	NT	NT	EM	NT
					◇	
				A	B	
Leeds 10 — 31	d		21 41			22 17
Woodlesford	d					22 25
Castleford	d					22 36
Normanton	d					22 41
Wakefield Kirkgate 4 — 31	a					22 46
	d					22 46
Darton	d					23 00
Huddersfield	d					
Lockwood	d					
Berry Brow	d					
Honley	d					
Brockholes	d					
Stocksmoor	d					
Shepley	d					
Denby Dale	d					
Penistone	d					
Silkstone Common	d					
Dodworth	d					
Barnsley	a					23 07
	d	22 21				23 12
Wombwell	d	22 26				23 17
Elsecar	d	22 30				23 21
Chapeltown	d	22 35				23 26
Meadowhall — 29,31	a	22 40	22 43			23 30
	d	22 41	22 44	23 04		23 32
Sheffield 7 — 29,31	a	22 51	22 52	23 15		23 43
	d				23 27	
Dronfield	d					
Chesterfield	d				23 42	
Alfreton	d				23 52	
Langley Mill	d				23 59	
Nottingham	a				00 21	

Sundays

16 February to 23 March

		NT	NT	NT	NT	NT	NT	NT	EM	NT		NT	TP	NT	NT	TP	NT	NT	NT	NT		NT	NT	TP	EM
									◇1																◇
		C		C				D	E			F	C			C		C		G				C	H
Leeds 10 — 31	d				08 34	08 48	09 05		09 45					10 02			10 17		10 57			11 20	11 29		
Woodlesford	d				08 42												10 25								
Castleford	d				08 53												10 36								
Normanton	d				08 58												10 41								
Wakefield Kirkgate 4 — 31	a				09 03		09 21							10 18			10 46		11 13				11 46		
	d				09 03		09 21							10 18			10 46		11 13				11 46		
Darton	d				09 17												11 00								
Huddersfield	d									09 19					10 15										
Lockwood	d									09 22					10 18										
Berry Brow	d									09 25					10 21										
Honley	d									09 28					10 24										
Brockholes	d									09 31					10 27										
Stocksmoor	d									09 35					10 31										
Shepley	d									09 37					10 33										
Denby Dale	d									09 42					10 39										
Penistone	d									09 50					10 46										
Silkstone Common	d									09 55					10 52										
Dodworth	d									09 59					10 55										
Barnsley	a				09 24		09 40			10 06				10 37	11 03		11 08		11 32				12 05		
	d				09 24		09 41			10 12				10 38	11 03		11 12		11 33				12 06		
Wombwell	d				09 29					10 17							11 17								
Elsecar	d				09 33					10 21							11 21								
Chapeltown	d				09 38					10 26							11 26								
Meadowhall — 29,31	a				09 44	09 53	09 57			10 32				10 51	11 20		11 32		11 46			12 24	12 17		
	d	08 30		09 41	09 44	09 54	09 57	10 00		10 33		10 40	10 40	10 51	11 20	11 20	11 35	11 40	11 46	12 08		12 24	12 17	12 20	
Sheffield 7 — 29,31	a	08 41		09 51	09 55	10 03	10 04	10 08	10 25	10 44		10 52	11 00	11 02	11 28	11 40	11 44	11 51	11 56	12 18		12 32	12 29	12 40	
	d		09 05				10 07		10 34					11 03					12 06				12 31		12 47
Dronfield	d		09 15				10 17							11 13					12 16				12 42		
Chesterfield	d		09 21				10 23		10 47					11 20					12 23				12 48		13 01
Alfreton	d		09 32				10 33							11 30					12 33				12 58		13 12
Langley Mill	d		09 39				10 41							11 38					12 41				13 06		
Nottingham	a		09 58				10 59		11 17					11 57					12 59				13 24		13 33

A From Swinton (S.Yorks)
B From Liverpool Lime Street
C From Doncaster
D From Hull
E To St Pancras International
F From Goole
G From Bridlington
H To Norwich

Table 34R

Sundays

16 February to 23 March

Leeds and Huddersfield - Barnsley - Sheffield, Nottingham

Network Diagram - see first page of Table 31

		NT	NT	NT	TP	EM		NT	NT	NT	NT	EM	NT	TP	NT	NT		NT	TP	NT	EM	NT	NT	NT	NT
			A		B	◇ C		B		D		◇ E		B	A	D			B		◇ E		B	F	
Leeds 10 31	d			12 29					12 34		13 20							14 05				14 17			15 05
Woodlesford	d								12 42													14 25			
Castleford	d								12 53													14 36			
Normanton	d								12 58													14 41			
Wakefield Kirkgate 4 31	a			12 46					13 04									14 21				14 46			15 22
	d			12 49					13 04									14 21				14 46			15 22
Darton	d								13 18													15 00			
Huddersfield	d	11 29											13 19							14 15					
Lockwood	d	11 32											13 22							14 18					
Berry Brow	d	11 35											13 25							14 21					
Honley	d	11 38											13 28							14 24					
Brockholes	d	11 41											13 31							14 27					
Stocksmoor	d	11 45											13 35							14 31					
Shepley	d	11 47											13 37							14 33					
Denby Dale	d	11 52											13 42							14 39					
Penistone	d	12 00											13 50							14 46					
Silkstone Common	d	12 05											13 55							14 52					
Dodworth	d	12 09											13 59							14 55					
Barnsley	a	12 16		13 08					13 24				14 06					14 40		15 03		15 07			15 41
	d	12 17		13 08					13 24				14 12					14 41		15 03		15 12			15 42
Wombwell	d	12 22							13 29				14 17									15 17			
Elsecar	d	12 26							13 33				14 21									15 21			
Chapeltown	d	12 31							13 38				14 26									15 26			
Meadowhall 29,31	a	12 34		13 19					13 48		14 21		14 32					14 54		15 20		15 35			15 55
	d	12 35	12 43	13 20	13 25			13 44	13 51	13 57	14 21		14 33	14 40	14 48	14 52		14 56	15 20	15 21		15 35	15 48	15 52	15 56
Sheffield 7 29,31	a	12 47	12 55	13 30	13 45			13 51	13 58	14 08	14 32		14 48	15 00	14 56	15 04		15 06	15 40	15 28		15 44	15 55	16 03	16 05
	d			13 31		13 48						14 46						15 07			15 39				16 07
Dronfield	d			13 42														15 16							16 17
Chesterfield	d			13 48		14 02						15 00						15 23			15 53				16 23
Alfreton	d			13 59		14 12						15 11						15 33			16 03				16 33
Langley Mill	d			14 06								15 18						15 41			16 11				16 41
Nottingham	a			14 25		14 33						15 35						15 59			16 28				16 59

		TP		NT	EM	NT	NT	NT	NT	TP	NT	EM		NT	NT	NT	TP	NT	NT	EM	NT	NT		NT	NT
		B			◇ E		A	D		B		◇ E		B	F		B			◇ G	B	D		H	I
Leeds 10 31	d			15 20					16 04		16 17					17 05		17 20						18 03	
Woodlesford	d										16 25														
Castleford	d										16 36														
Normanton	d										16 41														
Wakefield Kirkgate 4 31	a								16 21		16 46					17 21								18 18	
	d								16 22		16 49					17 21								18 21	
Darton	d										17 03														
Huddersfield	d					15 19													17 19						
Lockwood	d					15 22													17 22						
Berry Brow	d					15 25													17 25						
Honley	d					15 28													17 28						
Brockholes	d					15 31													17 31						
Stocksmoor	d					15 35													17 35						
Shepley	d					15 37													17 37						
Denby Dale	d					15 42													17 47						
Penistone	d					15 50													17 54						
Silkstone Common	d					15 55													18 00						
Dodworth	d					15 59													18 03						
Barnsley	a					16 06			16 41		17 09					17 40			18 11					18 41	
	d					16 12			16 42		17 12					17 41			18 12					18 42	
Wombwell	d					16 17					17 17								18 17						
Elsecar	d					16 21					17 21								18 21						
Chapeltown	d					16 26					17 26								18 26						
Meadowhall 29,31	a			16 22		16 32			16 56		17 34					17 55		18 24	18 32					18 56	
	d	16 20		16 23		16 34	16 47	16 53	16 56	17 20	17 35			17 48	17 53	17 56	18 20	18 25	18 33		18 47	18 53		18 56	19 18
Sheffield 7 29,31	a	16 40		16 32		16 44	16 55	17 03	17 05	17 40	17 44			17 56	18 01	18 05	18 40	18 34	18 44		18 56	19 03		19 06	19 27
	d				16 42				17 07			17 48				18 07				18 45				19 07	
Dronfield	d								17 17							18 17								19 17	
Chesterfield	d				16 56				17 23			18 02				18 23				19 00				19 23	
Alfreton	d				17 07				17 33			18 13				18 33				19 10				19 33	
Langley Mill	d				17 14				17 44			18 20				18 41				19 18				19 41	
Nottingham	a				17 30				17 59			18 36				18 59				19 38				19 59	

A From Goole
B From Doncaster
C From Manchester Piccadilly to Norwich
D From Scarborough
E From Liverpool Lime Street to Norwich
F From Bridlington
G From Liverpool Lime Street
H From Carlisle
I From York. via Pontefract Baghill

Table 34R

Sundays

16 February to 23 March

Leeds and Huddersfield - Barnsley - Sheffield, Nottingham

Network Diagram - see first page of Table 31

		EM ◇ A	TP B 🚌	NT	NT B	NT	NT C	TP B 🚌	NT	EM ◇ D	NT	NT B	TP B 🚌	NT E	EM ◇ D	NT	NT F	TP B 🚌	NT	NT	NT G	EM ◇ D	NT
Leeds 10	31 d			18 17		19 04			19 20							20 17				21 41			22 17
Woodlesford	d			18 25												20 25							22 25
Castleford	d			18 36												20 36							22 36
Normanton	d			18 40												20 41							22 41
Wakefield Kirkgate 4	31 a			18 45		19 21										20 46							22 46
	d			18 45		19 21										20 46							22 46
Darton	d			18 59												21 00							23 00
Huddersfield	d										19 19												
Lockwood	d										19 22												
Berry Brow	d										19 25												
Honley	d										19 28												
Brockholes	d										19 31												
Stocksmoor	d										19 35												
Shepley	d										19 37												
Denby Dale	d										19 42												
Penistone	d										19 50												
Silkstone Common	d										19 55												
Dodworth	d										19 59												
Barnsley	a			19 05		19 40					20 06					21 07							23 07
	d			19 11		19 40					20 12					21 12			22 21				23 12
Wombwell	d			19 17							20 17					21 17			22 26				23 17
Elsecar	d			19 21							20 21					21 21			22 30				23 21
Chapeltown	d			19 26							20 26					21 26			22 35				23 26
Meadowhall	29,31 🚊 a			19 32		19 54			20 22		20 34					21 33			22 40	22 43			23 30
	d		19 20	19 33	19 48	19 54	19 57	20 20	20 23		20 34	20 48	21 20	21 28		21 33	21 58	22 35	22 41	22 44	23 04		23 32
Sheffield 7	29,31 🚊 a		19 40	19 43	19 56	20 04	20 07	20 40	20 34		20 43	20 56	21 40	21 38		21 42	22 09	22 55	22 51	22 52	23 15		23 43
	d	19 40				20 07				20 40					21 40							23 27	
Dronfield	d					20 16									21 50								
Chesterfield	d	19 54				20 23				20 54					21 56							23 42	
Alfreton	d	20 05				20 33				21 05					22 06							23 52	
Langley Mill	d	20 12				20 41				21 12					22 14							23 59	
Nottingham	a	20 30				20 59				21 33					22 36							00 21	

Sundays

30 March to 11 May

		NT B	NT	NT B	NT	NT	NT	NT G	EM ◇1 H 🍴	NT	NT I	NT	TP ◇1 J	NT	NT	NT B	NT	TP ◇1 J	NT C	NT	NT	EM ◇ K	NT
Leeds 10	31 d				08 34	08 48	09 05		09 45			10 02			10 17		10 57			11 20	11 29		
Woodlesford	d				08 42										10 25								
Castleford	d				08 53										10 36								
Normanton	d				08 58										10 41								
Wakefield Kirkgate 4	31 a				09 03		09 21					10 18			10 46		11 13				11 46		
	d				09 03		09 21					10 18			10 46		11 13				11 46		
Darton	d				09 17										11 00								
Huddersfield	d									09 19				10 15									11 29
Lockwood	d									09 22				10 18									11 32
Berry Brow	d									09 25				10 21									11 35
Honley	d									09 28				10 24									11 38
Brockholes	d									09 31				10 27									11 41
Stocksmoor	d									09 35				10 31									11 45
Shepley	d									09 37				10 33									11 47
Denby Dale	d									09 42				10 39									11 52
Penistone	d									09 50				10 46									12 00
Silkstone Common	d									09 55				10 52									12 05
Dodworth	d									09 59				10 55									12 09
Barnsley	a				09 24		09 40			10 06		10 37		11 03	11 08		11 32				12 05		12 16
	d				09 24		09 41			10 12		10 38		11 03	11 12		11 33				12 06		12 17
Wombwell	d				09 29					10 17					11 17								12 22
Elsecar	d				09 33					10 21					11 21								12 26
Chapeltown	d				09 38					10 26					11 26								12 31
Meadowhall	29,31 🚊 a				09 44	09 53	09 57			10 32		10 51		11 20	11 32		11 46			12 24	12 17		12 34
	d	08 30		09 41	09 44	09 54	09 57	10 00		10 33	10 40	10 51	11 00	11 20	11 35	11 40	11 46	12 00	12 08	12 24	12 17		12 35
Sheffield 7	29,31 🚊 a	08 41		09 51	09 55	10 03	10 04	10 08	10 25	10 44	10 52	11 02	11 07	11 28	11 44	11 51	11 56	12 07	12 18	12 32	12 29		12 47
	d		09 05				10 07		10 31			11 03					12 06				12 31	12 41	
Dronfield	d		09 15				10 17					11 13					12 16				12 42		
Chesterfield	d		09 21				10 23		10 47			11 20					12 23				12 48	12 56	
Alfreton	d		09 32				10 33					11 30					12 33				12 58	13 07	
Langley Mill	d		09 39				10 41					11 38					12 41				13 06		
Nottingham	a		09 58				10 59		11 17			11 57					12 59				13 24	13 28	

A From Liverpool Lime Street to Norwich
B From Doncaster
C From Bridlington
D From Liverpool Lime Street
E From Scarborough
F From York. via Pontefract Baghill
G From Hull
H To St Pancras International
I From Goole
J From Cleethorpes to Manchester Airport
K To Norwich

Table 34R

Sundays

30 March to 11 May

Leeds and Huddersfield - Barnsley - Sheffield, Nottingham

Network Diagram - see first page of Table 31

		NT	TP	NT	EM	NT		NT	NT	TP	NT	EM	NT	NT	NT	NT		TP	NT	EM	NT	NT	NT	NT	TP
			◇1		◇					◇1		◇						◇1		◇					◇1
		A	B		C	D			E	F		G		A	E			B		G		D	H		B
Leeds 10 31	d			12 29				12 34			13 20					14 05					14 17			15 05	
Woodlesford	d							12 42													14 25				
Castleford	d							12 53													14 36				
Normanton	d							12 58													14 41				
Wakefield Kirkgate 4 31	a			12 46				13 04								14 21					14 46			15 22	
	d			12 49				13 04								14 21					14 46			15 22	
Darton	d							13 18													15 00				
Huddersfield	d												13 19						14 15						
Lockwood	d												13 22						14 18						
Berry Brow	d												13 25						14 21						
Honley	d												13 28						14 24						
Brockholes	d												13 31						14 27						
Stocksmoor	d												13 35						14 31						
Shepley	d												13 37						14 33						
Denby Dale	d												13 42						14 39						
Penistone	d												13 50						14 46						
Silkstone Common	d												13 55						14 52						
Dodworth	d												13 59						14 55						
Barnsley	a			13 08				13 24					14 06			14 40			15 03		15 07			15 41	
	d			13 08				13 24					14 12			14 41			15 03		15 12			15 42	
Wombwell	d							13 29					14 17								15 17				
Elsecar	d							13 33					14 21								15 21				
Chapeltown	d							13 38					14 26								15 26				
Meadowhall 29,31	a			13 19				13 48			14 21		14 32			14 54			15 20		15 35			15 55	
	d	12 43	13 00	13 20		13 44		13 51	13 57	14 00	14 21		14 33	14 48	14 52	14 56		15 00	15 21		15 35	15 48	15 52	15 56	16 00
Sheffield 7 29,31	a	12 55	13 07	13 30		13 51		13 58	14 08	14 07	14 32		14 48	14 56	15 04	15 06		15 07	15 28		15 44	15 55	16 03	16 05	16 07
	d			13 31	13 48							14 43				15 07				15 39				16 07	
Dronfield	d			13 42												15 16								16 17	
Chesterfield	d			13 48	14 02							14 57				15 23				15 53				16 23	
Alfreton	d			13 59	14 12							15 08				15 33				16 03				16 33	
Langley Mill	d			14 06								15 15				15 41				16 11				16 41	
Nottingham	a			14 25	14 33							15 32				15 59				16 28				16 59	

		NT		EM	NT	NT	NT	NT	TP	EM	NT	NT		NT	NT	TP	NT	EM	NT	NT	NT	NT		TP	NT
				◇					◇1	◇						◇1		◇						◇1	
				G		A	E		B	G		D		H		B		I		D	E	J		B	K
Leeds 10 31	d	15 20						16 04			16 17				17 05		17 20					18 03			
Woodlesford	d										16 25														
Castleford	d										16 36														
Normanton	d										16 41														
Wakefield Kirkgate 4 31	a							16 21			16 46				17 21							18 18			
	d							16 22			16 49				17 21							18 21			
Darton	d										17 03														
Huddersfield	d				15 19														17 19						
Lockwood	d				15 22														17 22						
Berry Brow	d				15 25														17 25						
Honley	d				15 28														17 28						
Brockholes	d				15 31														17 31						
Stocksmoor	d				15 35														17 35						
Shepley	d				15 37														17 37						
Denby Dale	d				15 42														17 47						
Penistone	d				15 50														17 54						
Silkstone Common	d				15 55														18 00						
Dodworth	d				15 59														18 03						
Barnsley	a				16 06			16 41			17 09				17 40				18 11			18 41			
	d				16 12			16 42			17 12				17 41				18 12			18 42			
Wombwell	d				16 17						17 17								18 17						
Elsecar	d				16 21						17 21								18 21						
Chapeltown	d				16 26						17 26								18 26						
Meadowhall 29,31	a	16 22			16 32			16 56			17 34				17 55		18 24		18 32			18 56			
	d	16 23			16 34	16 47	16 53	16 56	17 00		17 35	17 48		17 53	17 56	18 00	18 25		18 33	18 47	18 53	18 56		19 00	19 18
Sheffield 7 29,31	a	16 32			16 44	16 55	17 03	17 05	17 07		17 44	17 56		18 01	18 05	18 07	18 34		18 44	18 56	19 03	19 06		19 07	19 27
	d			16 41				17 07		17 40					18 07			18 40				19 07			
Dronfield	d							17 17							18 17							19 17			
Chesterfield	d			16 55				17 23		17 54					18 23			18 55				19 23			
Alfreton	d			17 05				17 33		18 05					18 33			19 05				19 33			
Langley Mill	d			17 13				17 44		18 12					18 41			19 13				19 41			
Nottingham	a			17 28				17 59		18 28					18 59			19 33				19 59			

A From Goole
B From Cleethorpes to Manchester Airport
C From Manchester Piccadilly to Norwich
D From Doncaster
E From Scarborough
F From Doncaster to Manchester Airport
G From Liverpool Lime Street to Norwich
H From Bridlington
I From Liverpool Lime Street
J From Carlisle
K From York. via Pontefract Baghill

Table 34R

Sundays

30 March to 11 May

Leeds and Huddersfield - Barnsley - Sheffield, Nottingham

Network Diagram - see first page of Table 31

Station			EM	NT	NT	NT	NT	TP	NT	EM	NT	NT	TP	NT	EM	NT	NT	TP	NT	NT	NT	EM	NT
			◇					◇[1]		◇			◇[1]		◇			◇[1]				◇	
			A		B		C	D		E		B	D	F	E		G	H			I	E	
Leeds [10]	31	d		18 17		19 04			19 20							20 17				21 41			22 17
Woodlesford		d		18 25												20 25							22 25
Castleford		d		18 36												20 36							22 36
Normanton		d		18 40												20 41							22 41
Wakefield Kirkgate [4]	31	a		18 45		19 21										20 46							22 46
		d		18 45		19 21										20 46							22 46
Darton		d		18 59												21 00							23 00
Huddersfield		d									19 19												
Lockwood		d									19 22												
Berry Brow		d									19 25												
Honley		d									19 28												
Brockholes		d									19 31												
Stocksmoor		d									19 35												
Shepley		d									19 37												
Denby Dale		d									19 42												
Penistone		d									19 50												
Silkstone Common		d									19 55												
Dodworth		d									19 59												
Barnsley		a		19 05		19 40					20 06					21 07							23 07
		d		19 11		19 40					20 12					21 12			22 21				23 12
Wombwell		d		19 17							20 17					21 17			22 26				23 17
Elsecar		d		19 21							20 21					21 21			22 30				23 21
Chapeltown		d		19 26							20 26					21 26			22 35				23 26
Meadowhall	29,31 🚋	a		19 32		19 54			20 22		20 34					21 33			22 40	22 43			23 30
		d		19 33	19 48	19 54	19 57	20 00	20 23		20 34	20 48	21 00	21 28		21 33	21 58	22 05	22 41	22 44	23 04		23 32
Sheffield [7]	29,31 🚋	a		19 43	19 56	20 04	20 07	20 07	20 34		20 43	20 56	21 07	21 38		21 42	22 09	22 13	22 51	22 52	23 15		23 43
		d	19 40			20 07				20 40					21 40							23 27	
Dronfield		d				20 16									21 50								
Chesterfield		d	19 54			20 23				20 54					21 56							23 42	
Alfreton		d	20 05			20 33				21 05					22 06							23 52	
Langley Mill		d	20 12			20 41				21 12					22 14							23 59	
Nottingham		a	20 30			20 59				21 33					22 36							00 21	

A From Liverpool Lime Street to Norwich
B From Doncaster
C From Bridlington
D From Cleethorpes to Manchester Airport
E From Liverpool Lime Street
F From Scarborough
G From York. via Pontefract Baghill
H From Cleethorpes
I From Hull

Network Diagram for Tables 35, 36, 37, 38

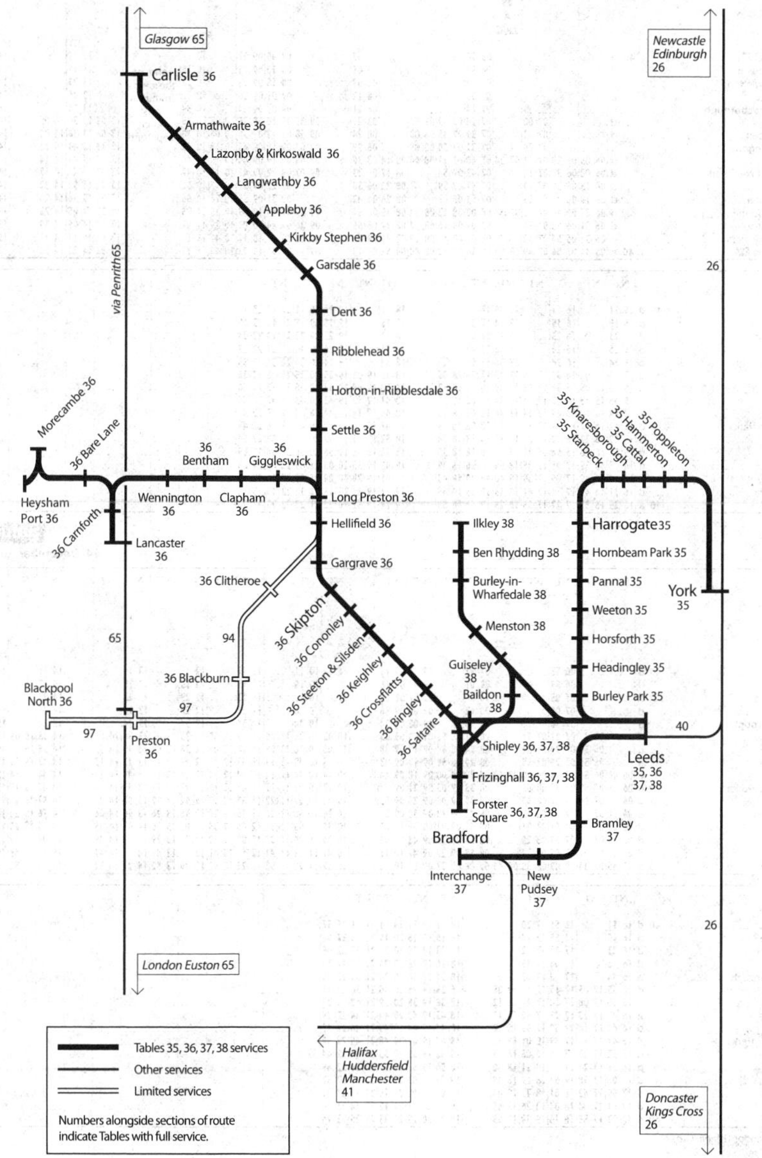

Glasgow 65
Carlisle 36
Armathwaite 36
Lazonby & Kirkoswald 36
Langwathby 36
Appleby 36
Kirkby Stephen 36
Garsdale 36
Dent 36
Ribblehead 36
Horton-in-Ribblesdale 36
Settle 36
Long Preston 36
Hellifield 36
Gargrave 36
via Penrith 65
Morecambe 36
36 Bare Lane
Heysham Port 36
36 Carnforth
Lancaster 36
Wennington 36
36 Bentham
Clapham 36
36 Giggleswick
36 Clitheroe
65
94
36 Blackburn
97
Blackpool North 36
97
Preston 36
36 Skipton
36 Cononley
36 Steeton & Silsden
36 Keighley
36 Crossflatts
36 Bingley
36 Saltaire
Ilkley 38
Ben Rhydding 38
Burley-in-Wharfedale 38
Menston 38
Guiseley 38
Baildon 38
Shipley 36, 37, 38
Frizinghall 36, 37, 38
Forster Square 36, 37, 38
Bradford
Interchange 37
New Pudsey 37
Bramley 37
Leeds 35, 36 37, 38
40
Newcastle Edinburgh 26
26
35 Knaresborough
35 Starbeck
35 Hammerton
35 Cattal
35 Poppleton
Harrogate 35
Hornbeam Park 35
Pannal 35
Weeton 35
Horsforth 35
Headingley 35
Burley Park 35
York 35
26
London Euston 65
Halifax Huddersfield Manchester 41
Doncaster Kings Cross 26
Tables 35, 36, 37, 38 services
Other services
Limited services
Numbers alongside sections of route indicate Tables with full service.

TOCs operating on this network - Northern (NT), East Coast (GR)

Table 35

Mondays to Fridays

9 December to 16 May

York - Harrogate - Leeds

Network Diagram - see first page of Table 35

Miles	Station			NT	NT	NT	GR	NT	NT	NT	NT	NT	NT	NT	NT	NT	NT		NT	NT	NT	NT	NT
							R 1 A																
0	**York** 8	40	d					06 50				07 57		08 45	09 11		10 11	and at the same minutes past each hour until		13 11		14 11	
3	Poppleton		d					06 55				08 01		08 50	09 15		10 15			13 15		14 15	
8¾	Hammerton		d					07 02				08 09		08 58	09 23		10 23			13 23		14 23	
10¼	Cattal		d					07 06				08 12		09 01	09 26		10 26			13 26		14 26	
16¾	**Knaresborough**		a					07 14				08 21		09 09	09 34		10 34			13 34		14 34	
—			d			07 00		07 24	07 42	07 57		08 21	08 55	09 10	09 35	10 05	10 35		13 05	13 35	14 05	14 35	15 05
18¼	Starbeck		d			07 03		07 27	07 45	08 00		08 24	08 58	09 13	09 38	10 08	10 38		13 08	13 38	14 08	14 38	15 08
20½	**Harrogate**		a			07 08		07 32	07 50	08 05		08 29	09 03	09 18	09 43	10 13	10 43		13 13	13 43	14 13	14 43	15 13
—			d	06 05	06 28	07 11	07 34	07 40	07 51	08 06	08 14	08 30	09 04	09 19	09 44	10 14	10 44		13 14	13 44	14 14	14 44	15 14
21½	Hornbeam Park		d	06 08	06 30	07 14		07 43	07 54		08 17	08 33	09 07	09 22	09 47	10 17	10 47		13 17	13 47	14 17	14 47	15 17
23¾	Pannal		d	06 13	06 35	07 19		07 47	07 59		08 22	08 38		09 27	09 52	10 22	10 52		13 22	13 52	14 22	14 52	15 22
27	Weeton		d	06 18	06 40	07 23		07 52	08 03		08 26	08 42		09 31	09 56	10 26	10 56		13 26	13 56	14 26	14 56	15 26
33	Horsforth		d	06 27	06 48	07 32	07u53	08 00	08 12	08 23	08 35	08 51	09 22	09 40	10 05	10 35	11 05		13 35	14 05	14 35	15 05	15 35
35¾	Headingley		d	06 31	06 52	07 36		08 04	08 16	08 27	08 39	08 55	09 26	09 44	10 09	10 39	11 09		13 39	14 09	14 39	15 09	15 39
36½	Burley Park		d	06 34	06 54	07 38		08 07	08 18	08 29	08 41	08 57	09 27	09 47	10 11	10 41	11 11		13 41	14 11	14 41	15 11	15 41
38¾	**Leeds** 10	40	a	06 44	07 06	07 49	08 06	08 16	08 32	08 40	08 52	09 12	09 37	09 56	10 22	10 52	11 23		13 52	14 23	14 52	15 24	15 52

Station			NT	NT	NT	NT	NT	NT	NT	NT	NT	NT	NT	NT	NT
York 8	40	d	15 11		16 11		17 09	17 29		18 11		19 11	20 11	21 11	22 11
Poppleton		d	15 15		16 15		17 14	17 36		18 15		19 15	20 15	21 16	22 15
Hammerton		d	15 23		16 23		17 22	17 43		18 23		19 23	20 23	21 23	22 23
Cattal		d	15 26		16 26		17 26	17 47		18 26		19 26	20 26	21 27	22 27
Knaresborough		a	15 34		16 34		17 35	17 56		18 34		19 34	20 34	21 34	22 35
		d	15 35	16 05	16 35	17 05	17 35	17 56	18 05	18 35	19 05	19 35	20 35	21 35	22 36
Starbeck		d	15 38	16 08	16 38	17 08	17 39	18 00	18 12	18 38	19 08	19 38	20 38	21 39	22 40
Harrogate		a	15 43	16 13	16 43	17 13	17 44	18 05	18 17	18 43	19 13	19 43	20 43	21 43	22 45
		d	15 44	16 14	16 44	17 14	17 46	18 06	18 18	18 44	19 14	19 44	20 44	21 45	22 47
Hornbeam Park		d	15 47	16 17	16 47	17 17	17 48	18 08	18 21	18 47	19 17	19 47	20 47	21 48	22 49
Pannal		d	15 52	16 22	16 52	17 22	17 53	18 13	18 26	18 52	19 22	19 52	20 52	21 53	22 54
Weeton		d	15 56	16 26	16 56	17 26	17 58	18 18	18 30	18 56	19 26	19 56	20 56	21 58	22 59
Horsforth		d	16 05	16 35	17 05	17 35	18 06	18 26	18 39	19 05	19 35	20 05	21 05	22 06	23 08
Headingley		d	16 09	16 39	17 09	17 39	18 10	18 30	18 43	19 09	19 39	20 09	21 09	22 10	23 12
Burley Park		d	16 11	16 41	17 11	17 41	18 13	18 33	18 45	19 11	19 41	20 11	21 11	22 13	23 15
Leeds 10	40	a	16 23	16 52	17 22	17 55	18 25	18 43	18 55	19 24	19 52	20 22	21 23	22 23	23 24

Saturdays

14 December to 17 May

Station			NT	NT	NT	NT	GR	NT	NT	NT	NT	NT	NT	NT	NT	NT	NT	NT	NT	NT	NT	NT	NT	NT
							R 1 A																	
York 8	40	d			06 53			07 57		08 45	09 11		10 11		11 11		12 11		13 11		14 11		15 11	
Poppleton		d			06 57			08 01		08 49	09 15		10 15		11 15		12 15		13 15		14 15		15 15	
Hammerton		d			07 05			08 09		08 57	09 23		10 23		11 23		12 23		13 23		14 23		15 23	
Cattal		d			07 08			08 12		09 00	09 26		10 26		11 26		12 26		13 26		14 26		15 26	
Knaresborough		a			07 16			08 20		09 08	09 34		10 34		11 34		12 34		13 34		14 34		15 34	
		d		06 47	07 21	07 51		08 21	08 51	09 09	09 35	10 05	10 35	11 05	11 35	12 05	12 35	13 05	13 35	14 05	14 35	15 05	15 35	16 05
Starbeck		d		06 50	07 24	07 54		08 24	08 54	09 12	09 38	10 08	10 38	11 08	11 38	12 08	12 38	13 08	13 38	14 08	14 38	15 08	15 38	16 08
Harrogate		a		06 55	07 29	07 59		08 29	08 59	09 17	09 43	10 13	10 43	11 13	11 43	12 13	12 43	13 13	13 43	14 13	14 43	15 13	15 43	16 13
		d	06 06	06 56	07 31	08 00	08 13	08 30	09 00	09 18	09 44	10 14	10 44	11 14	11 44	12 14	12 44	13 14	13 44	14 14	14 44	15 14	15 44	16 14
Hornbeam Park		d	06 08	06 59	07 33	08 03		08 33	09 03	09 21	09 47	10 17	10 47	11 17	11 47	12 17	12 47	13 17	13 47	14 17	14 47	15 17	15 47	16 17
Pannal		d	06 13	07 04	07 38	08 08		08 38	09 08	09 26	09 52	10 22	10 52	11 22	11 52	12 22	12 52	13 22	13 52	14 22	14 52	15 22	15 52	16 22
Weeton		d	06 18	07 08	07 42	08 12		08 42	09 12	09 30	09 56	10 26	10 56	11 26	11 56	12 26	12 56	13 26	13 56	14 26	14 56	15 26	15 56	16 26
Horsforth		d	06 28	07 17	07 51	08 21		08 51	09 21	09 39	10 05	10 35	11 05	11 35	12 05	12 35	13 05	13 35	14 05	14 35	15 05	15 35	16 05	16 35
Headingley		d	06 32	07 21	07 55	08 25		08 55	09 25	09 43	10 09	10 39	11 09	11 39	12 09	12 39	13 09	13 39	14 09	14 39	15 09	15 39	16 09	16 39
Burley Park		d	06 34	07 23	07 57	08 27		08 57	09 27	09 47	10 11	10 41	11 11	11 41	12 11	12 41	13 11	13 41	14 11	14 41	15 11	15 41	16 11	16 41
Leeds 10	40	a	06 45	07 34	08 08	08 38	08 45	09 08	09 37	09 55	10 22	10 52	11 22	11 52	12 23	12 52	13 20	13 52	14 22	14 52	15 22	15 52	16 23	16 52

Station			NT	NT	NT	NT	NT	NT	NT	NT	NT	NT
York 8	40	d	16 11		16 51	17 20		18 11	19 11	20 11	21 11	21 57
Poppleton		d	16 15		16 55	17 24		18 15	19 15	20 15	21 16	22 01
Hammerton		d	16 23		17 03	17 32		18 23	19 23	20 23	21 23	22 09
Cattal		d	16 26		17 06	17 35		18 26	19 26	20 26	21 27	22 12
Knaresborough		a	16 34		17 14	17 43		18 34	19 34	20 34	21 35	22 20
		d	16 35	17 05	17 15	17 44	18 05	18 35	19 35	20 36	21 36	22 21
Starbeck		d	16 38	17 08	17 18	17 47	18 12	18 38	19 38	20 39	21 40	22 24
Harrogate		a	16 43	17 13	17 23	17 52	18 17	18 43	19 43	20 44	21 44	22 29
		d	16 44	17 14	17 37	17 59	18 18	18 44	19 44	20 45	21 46	22 37
Hornbeam Park		d	16 47	17 17	17 39	18 01	18 21	18 47	19 47	20 48	21 49	22 39
Pannal		d	16 52	17 22	17 44	18 06	18 26	18 52	19 52	20 53	21 54	22 44
Weeton		d	16 56	17 26	17 49	18 11	18 30	18 56	19 56	20 57	21 59	22 49
Horsforth		d	17 05	17 38	17 57	18 19	18 39	19 05	20 05	21 06	22 07	22 57
Headingley		d	17 09	17 42	18 01	18 23	18 43	19 09	20 09	21 10	22 12	23 01
Burley Park		d	17 11	17 44	18 04	18 26	18 45	19 11	20 11	21 12	22 14	23 04
Leeds 10	40	a	17 23	17 55	18 16	18 39	18 55	19 22	20 22	21 23	22 25	23 14

A To London Kings Cross

Table 35

Sundays

8 December to 11 May

York - Harrogate - Leeds

Network Diagram - see first page of Table 35

			NT	NT	NT		NT	NT	NT	NT	NT	GR R 1 A	NT	NT	NT		NT	NT	NT
York 8	40	d			11 17		12 17	13 20	14 17	15 17	16 17		17 17	18 17	19 17		20 17	21 26	
Poppleton		d			11 22		12 21	13 25	14 21	15 21	16 21		17 21	18 21	19 21		20 21	21 30	
Hammerton		d			11 29		12 29	13 32	14 29	15 29	16 29		17 29	18 29	19 29		20 29	21 38	
Cattal		d			11 33		12 32	13 36	14 32	15 32	16 32		17 32	18 32	19 32		20 32	21 41	
Knaresborough		a			11 41		12 40	13 44	14 42	15 41	16 41		17 41	18 41	19 42		20 41	21 49	
		d			11 42		12 42	13 44	14 42	15 42	16 42		17 42	18 42	19 42		20 42	21 50	
Starbeck		d			11 45		12 45	13 48	14 45	15 45	16 45		17 45	18 45	19 45		20 45	21 53	
Harrogate		a			11 50		12 50	13 52	14 50	15 50	16 50		17 50	18 50	19 50		20 50	21 58	
		d	09 53	10 53	11 53		12 53	13 54	14 53	15 53	16 53	17 06	17 53	18 53	19 53		20 53	22 02	23 12
Hornbeam Park		d	09 56	10 56	11 56		12 56	13 56	14 56	15 55	16 56		17 56	18 56	19 56		20 56	22 04	23 15
Pannal		d	10 01	11 01	12 01		13 01	14 01	15 01	16 00	17 01		18 01	19 01	20 01		21 01	22 09	23 20
Weeton		d	10 05	11 05	12 05		13 05	14 06	15 05	16 05	17 05		18 05	19 05	20 05		21 05	22 14	23 24
Horsforth		d	10 14	11 14	12 14		13 14	14 14	15 14	16 13	17 14		18 14	19 14	20 14		21 14	22 23	23 33
Headingley		d	10 18	11 18	12 18		13 18	14 18	15 18	16 17	17 18		18 18	19 18	20 18		21 18	22 27	23 37
Burley Park		d	10 20	11 20	12 20		13 20	14 21	15 20	16 20	17 20		18 20	19 20	20 20		21 20	22 30	23 39
Leeds 10	40	a	10 30	11 30	12 30		13 30	14 29	15 30	16 28	17 30	17 32	18 30	19 30	20 30		21 30	22 39	23 54

A To London Kings Cross

Table 35R

Mondays to Fridays

9 December to 16 May

Leeds - Harrogate - York

Network Diagram - see first page of Table 35

Miles				NT	NT	NT	NT	NT	NT	NT	NT	NT	NT	NT	NT	NT	NT	NT	NT	NT	NT	NT	NT	NT
0	**Leeds** 10	40	d	06 09	06 29	07 13	07 43	07 59	08 29	08 59	09 29	09 59	10 29	10 59	11 29	11 59	12 29	12 59	13 29	13 59	14 29	14 59	15 29	15 59
2¼	Burley Park		d	06 14	06 34	07 18	07 48	08 04	08 34	09 04	09 34	10 04	10 34	11 04	11 34	12 04	12 34	13 04	13 34	14 04	14 34	15 04	15 34	16 04
3	Headingley		d	06 16	06 36	07 20	07 50	08 06	08 36	09 06	09 36	10 06	10 36	11 06	11 36	12 06	12 36	13 06	13 36	14 06	14 36	15 06	15 36	16 06
5¾	Horsforth		d	06 22	06 42	07 26	07 56	08 12	08 42	09 12	09 42	10 12	10 42	11 12	11 42	12 12	12 42	13 12	13 42	14 12	14 42	15 12	15 42	16 12
11¾	Weeton		d	06 29	06 49	07 33	08 03	08 19	08 49	09 19	09 49	10 19	10 49	11 19	11 49	12 19	12 49	13 19	13 49	14 19	14 49	15 19	15 49	16 19
15	Pannal		d	06 35	06 55	07 39	08 09	08 25	08 55	09 25	09 55	10 25	10 55	11 25	11 55	12 25	12 55	13 25	13 55	14 25	14 55	15 25	15 55	16 25
17¼	Hornbeam Park		d	06 40	07 00	07 44	08 14	08 30	09 00	09 30	10 00	10 30	11 00	11 30	12 00	12 30	13 00	13 30	14 00	14 30	15 00	15 30	16 00	16 30
18¼	**Harrogate**		a	06 43	07 05	07 49	08 17	08 33	09 03	09 33	10 03	10 33	11 03	11 33	12 03	12 33	13 05	13 33	14 03	14 33	15 03	15 33	16 03	16 33
—			d	06 45	07 05	07 49	08 19	08 34	09 05	09 35	10 05	10 35	11 05	11 35	12 05	12 35	13 07	13 35	14 05	14 35	15 05	15 35	16 05	16 35
20½	Starbeck		d	06 49	07 08	07 52	08 22	08 38	09 08	09 38	10 08	10 38	11 08	11 38	12 08	12 38	13 10	13 38	14 08	14 38	15 08	15 38	16 08	16 38
22	**Knaresborough**		a	06 54	07 16	07 59	08 28	08 45	09 14	09 45	10 14	10 45	11 14	11 45	12 14	12 45	13 16	13 45	14 14	14 45	15 14	15 45	16 14	16 45
—			d	06 55	07 19	07 59	08 28		09 15		10 14		11 14		12 14		13 16		14 14		15 14		16 14	
28½	Cattal		d	07 03	07 27	08 07	08 36		09 23		10 22		11 22		12 22		13 24		14 22		15 22		16 22	
30	Hammerton		d	07 06	07 30	08 11	08 40		09 27		10 26		11 26		12 26		13 28		14 26		15 26		16 26	
35¾	Poppleton		d	07 14	07 37	08 18	08 47		09 34		10 33		11 33		12 33		13 35		14 33		15 33		16 33	
38¾	**York** 8	40	a	07 22	07 48	08 32	08 58		09 45		10 45		11 44		12 45		13 44		14 44		15 46		16 45	

			NT	NT	NT	NT	NT	NT	NT	NT	NT	NT	GR 1 A	NT	NT	NT	NT
Leeds 10	40	d	16 29	16 42	16 59	17 13	17 29	17 44	17 59	18 29	18 59	19 29	19 59	20 29	21 29	22 34	23 29
Burley Park		d	16 34	16 47	17 04	17 18	17 34	17 49	18 04	18 34	19 04	19 34		20 34	21 34	22 39	23 34
Headingley		d	16 36	16 49	17 06	17 20	17 36	17 51	18 06	18 36	19 06	19 36		20 36	21 36	22 41	23 36
Horsforth		d	16 42	16a55	17 12	17 26	17 42	17 57	18 12	18 42	19 12	19 42		20 42	21 42	22 47	23 42
Weeton		d	16 49		17 19	17 33	17 49		18 19	18 49	19 19	19 49		20 49	21 49	22 55	23 49
Pannal		d	16 55		17 25	17 39	17 55		18 25	18 55	19 25	19 55		20 55	21 55	23 01	23 55
Hornbeam Park		d	17 00		17 30	17 44	18 00		18 30	19 00	19 30	20 00		21 00	22 00	23 06	23 58
Harrogate		a	17 04		17 33	17 47	18 03	18 15	18 33	19 03	19 33	20 03	20 25	21 03	22 03	23 12	00 06
		d	17 05		17 35	17 49	18 05	18 16	18 35	19 05	19 35	20 05		21 05	22 05		
Starbeck		d	17 08		17 38	17 52	18 08	18 20	18 39	19 08	19 38	20 08		21 08	22 08		
Knaresborough		a	17 14		17 45	18 01	18 14	18 26	18 45	19 14	19 45	20 14		21 14	22 16		
		d	17 14				18 14			19 14		20 14		21 14			
Cattal		d	17 22				18 22			19 22		20 22		21 22			
Hammerton		d	17 26				18 26			19 26		20 26		21 26			
Poppleton		d	17 33				18 33			19 33		20 33		21 33			
York 8	40	a	17 47				18 45			19 48		20 45		21 47			

Saturdays

14 December to 17 May

			NT	NT	NT	NT	NT	NT	NT	NT	NT	NT	NT	NT	NT	NT	NT	NT	NT	NT	NT	NT	NT	NT
Leeds 10	40	d	06 09	06 36	07 13	07 39	07 54	08 29	08 59	09 29	09 59	10 29	10 59	11 29	11 59	12 29	12 59	13 29	13 59	14 29	14 59	15 29	15 59	16 29
Burley Park		d	06 14	06 41	07 18	07 44	07 59	08 34	09 04	09 34	10 04	10 34	11 04	11 34	12 04	12 34	13 04	13 34	14 04	14 34	15 04	15 34	16 04	16 34
Headingley		d	06 16	06 43	07 20	07 46	08 01	08 36	09 06	09 36	10 06	10 36	11 06	11 36	12 06	12 36	13 06	13 36	14 06	14 36	15 06	15 36	16 06	16 36
Horsforth		d	06 22	06 49	07 26	07 52	08 07	08 42	09 12	09 42	10 12	10 42	11 12	11 42	12 12	12 42	13 12	13 42	14 12	14 42	15 12	15 42	16 12	16 42
Weeton		d	06 29	06 56	07 33	07 59	08 14	08 49	09 19	09 49	10 19	10 49	11 19	11 49	12 19	12 49	13 19	13 49	14 19	14 49	15 19	15 49	16 19	16 49
Pannal		d	06 35	07 02	07 39	08 09	08 23	08 55	09 25	09 55	10 25	10 55	11 25	11 55	12 25	12 55	13 25	13 55	14 25	14 55	15 25	15 55	16 25	16 55
Hornbeam Park		d	06 40	07 07	07 44	08 14	08 28	09 00	09 30	10 00	10 30	11 00	11 30	12 00	12 30	13 00	13 30	14 00	14 30	15 00	15 30	16 00	16 30	17 00
Harrogate		a	06 43	07 10	07 47	08 17	08 31	09 03	09 33	10 03	10 33	11 03	11 33	12 03	12 33	13 03	13 33	14 03	14 33	15 03	15 33	16 03	16 33	17 03
		d	06 45	07 12	07 49	08 19	08 31	09 05	09 35	10 05	10 35	11 05	11 35	12 05	12 35	13 05	13 35	14 05	14 35	15 05	15 35	16 05	16 35	17 08
Starbeck		d	06 49	07 15	07 52	08 22	08 36	09 08	09 38	10 08	10 38	11 08	11 38	12 08	12 38	13 08	13 38	14 08	14 38	15 08	15 38	16 08	16 38	17 11
Knaresborough		a	06 54	07 21	07 59	08 28	08 42	09 14	09 45	10 14	10 45	11 14	11 45	12 14	12 45	13 14	13 45	14 14	14 45	15 14	15 45	16 14	16 45	17 17
		d	06 55	07 21	07 59	08 28		09 15		10 14		11 14		12 14		13 14		14 14		15 14		16 14		17 21
Cattal		d	07 03	07 29	08 07	08 36		09 23		10 22		11 22		12 22		13 22		14 22		15 22		16 22		17 29
Hammerton		d	07 06	07 33	08 11	08 40		09 27		10 26		11 26		12 26		13 26		14 26		15 26		16 26		17 34
Poppleton		d	07 13	07 40	08 19	08 47		09 34		10 33		11 33		12 33		13 33		14 33		15 33		16 33		17 41
York 8	40	a	07 21	07 46	08 26	08 59		09 44		10 45		11 45		12 45		13 48		14 44		15 46		16 44		17 52

			NT	NT	NT	NT	NT	NT	GR 1 A	NT	NT	NT	NT
Leeds 10	40	d	16 59	17 13	17 29	17 59	18 29	19 29	19 59	20 29	21 20	22 34	23 21
Burley Park		d	17 04	17 18	17 34	18 04	18 34	19 34		20 34	21 25	22 39	23 26
Headingley		d	17 06	17 20	17 36	18 06	18 36	19 36		20 36	21 27	22 41	23 28
Horsforth		d	17 12	17 26	17 42	18 12	18 42	19 42		20 42	21 33	22 47	23 34
Weeton		d	17 19	17 33	17 49	18 19	18 49	19 49		20 49	21 40	22 54	23 41
Pannal		d	17 25	17 39	17 55	18 25	18 55	19 55		20 55	21 46	23 00	23 47
Hornbeam Park		d	17 30	17 44	18 00	18 30	19 00	20 00		21 00	21 51	23 05	23 52
Harrogate		a	17 33	17 47	18 03	18 33	19 03	20 04	20 25	21 03	21 54	23 11	23 58
		d	17 35	17 49	18 05	18 35	19 05	20 04		21 05	21 56		
Starbeck		d	17 38	17 52	18 08	18 38	19 08	20 08		21 08	21 59		
Knaresborough		a	17 45	18 00	18 14	18 45	19 14	20 14		21 14	22 06		
		d			18 14		19 14	20 14		21 14			
Cattal		d			18 22		19 22	20 22		21 22			
Hammerton		d			18 26		19 26	20 26		21 27			
Poppleton		d			18 33		19 33	20 33		21 34			
York 8	40	a			18 44		19 45	20 47		21 48			

A From London Kings Cross

Table 35R

Leeds - Harrogate - York

Sundays

8 December to 11 May

Network Diagram - see first page of Table 35

		NT		NT	NT	NT	NT	NT	NT	NT	NT	NT		NT	NT	NT	GR	NT	NT	NT
												A		B			R 1 C [symbol]			
Leeds 10	40 d	09 54			10 54	11 54	12 54	13 58	14 54	15 54	16 54	17 54		17 54	18 54	19 54	20 38	21 16	22 26	23 23
Burley Park	d	09 59			10 59	11 59	12 59	14 03	14 59	15 59	16 59	17 59		17 59	18 59	19 59		21 21	22 31	23 28
Headingley	d	10 01			11 01	12 01	13 01	14 05	15 01	16 01	17 01	18 01		18 01	19 01	20 01		21 23	22 33	23 30
Horsforth	d	10 07			11 07	12 07	13 07	14 11	15 07	16 07	17 07	18 07		18 07	19 07	20 07		21 29	22 39	23 36
Weeton	d	10 14			11 14	12 14	13 14	14 18	15 14	16 14	17 14	18 14		18 14	19 14	20 14		21 37	22 46	23 43
Pannal	d	10 20			11 20	12 20	13 20	14 24	15 20	16 20	17 20	18 20		18 20	19 20	20 20		21 43	22 52	23 49
Hornbeam Park	d	10 25			11 25	12 25	13 25	14 29	15 25	16 25	17 25	18 25		18 25	19 25	20 25		21 48	22 57	23 54
Harrogate	a	10 31			11 28	12 28	13 28	14 32	15 28	16 28	17 28	18 28		18 28	19 28	20 28	21 04	21 51	23 03	23 59
	d			10 46	11 33	12 33	13 33	14 33	15 33	16 30	17 33	18 30		18 33	19 33	20 33		21 53		
Starbeck	d			10 49	11 36	12 36	13 36	14 36	15 36	16 34	17 36	18 34		18 36	19 36	20 36		21 57		
Knaresborough	a			10 55	11 42	12 42	13 42	14 42	15 42	16 39	17 42	18 39		18 42	19 42	20 42		22 03		
	d			10 55	11 44	12 44	13 47	14 44	15 44	16 44	17 44	18 44		18 44	19 44	20 44				
Cattal	d			11 03	11 52	12 52	13 55	14 52	15 52	16 52	17 52	18 52		18 52	19 52	20 52				
Hammerton	d			11 07	11 56	12 55	13 59	14 55	15 55	16 55	17 55	18 55		18 55	19 55	20 55				
Poppleton	d			11 14	12 03	13 02	14 06	15 02	16 02	17 02	18 02	19 02		19 02	20 02	21 02				
York 8	40 a			11 21	12 11	13 10	14 13	15 13	16 10	17 11	18 10	19 12		19 12	20 13	21 15				

A from 5 January until 23 March

B until 29 December, from 30 March

C From London Kings Cross

Table 36

Mondays to Fridays

9 December to 16 May

Leeds and Bradford - Skipton, Lancaster, Morecambe and Carlisle

Network Diagram - see first page of Table 35

Miles	Miles	Miles				NT	NT	NT	NT	NT	NT	NT	NT	NT		NT	NT	NT	NT	NT	NT	NT	NT	NT		NT
							◇														◇					
—	—	—	London Kings Cross 15	⊖26	d																					
0	0	—	**Leeds 10**	37	d		05 29		06 16		06 56		07 25			07 51		08 18	08 25		08 50	08 56		09 26		
—	—	0	**Bradford Forster Square**	37	d			06 04		06 39		07 15		07 41			08 09			08 41			09 11			09 41
—	—	1¾	Frizinghall	37	d			06 07		06 43		07 18		07 44			08 12			08 44			09 14			09 44
10¾	10¾	2¾	Shipley	37	a		05 41	06 11	06 29	06 47	07 08	07 22	07 36	07 48		08 02	08 16	08 30	08 37	08 48	09 02	09 07	09 18	09 37		09 48
—	—	—			d		05 42	06 12	06 29	06 48	07 08	07 23	07 37	07 49		08 03	08 17	08 31	08 37	08 49	09 03	09 09	09 19	09 38		09 49
11½	—	—	Saltaire		d		05 44	06 14	06 31	06 50	07 10	07 25	07 39	07 51		08 05	08 20		08 40	08 52		09 11	09 22	09 40		09 52
13¾	13¾	—	Bingley		d		05 49	06 18	06 35	06 54	07 14	07 29	07 43	07 55		08 09	08 24	08 36	08 44	08 56	09 07	09 14	09 26	09 44		09 56
14½	—	—	Crossflatts		d		05 51	06 20	06 37	06 56	07 17	07 31	07 46	07 57		08 11	08 26		08 46	08 58		09 17	09 28	09 47		09 58
17	17	—	Keighley		d		05 56	06 25	06 42	07 01	07 21	07 36	07 50	08 02		08 15	08 31	08 41	08 50	09 03	09 13	09 21	09 33	09 51		10 03
20	—	—	Steeton & Silsden		d		06 00	06 29	06 46	07 05	07 26	07 40	07 55	08 06		08 19	08 35		08 54	09 07		09 26	09 37	09 56		10 07
23¼	—	—	Cononley		d		06 05	06 33	06 51	07 09	07 30	07 44	07 59	08 10		08 23	08 40		08 59	09 12		09 30	09 42	10 00		10 12
26¼	26¼	—	**Skipton**		a		06 12	06 42	06 59	07 18	07 39	07 52	08 08	08 19		08 31	08 48	08 55	09 09	09 20	09 25	09 40	09 50	10 11		10 20
—	—	—			d	05 41	06 15											08 55			09 27					
30	30	—	Gargrave		d	05 47												09 01			09 33					
—	—	—	Blackpool North	94	d																					
—	—	—	Preston		d																					
—	—	—	Blackburn	97	d																					
—	—	—	Clitheroe	94	d																					
36¼	36	—	Hellifield		d	05 56	06 27											09 10			09 41					
37½	37¼	—	Long Preston		d	05 59												09 13			09 44					
—	41	—	Giggleswick		d	06 07												09 20								
—	47¾	—	Clapham (Nth Yorkshire)		d	06 15												09 28								
—	51	—	Bentham		d	06 21												09 34								
—	54¼	—	Wennington		d	06 26												09 40								
—	64	—	Carnforth	82	a	06 42												09 56								
—	70	—	**Lancaster 6**	65,82,98	a	06 52												10 08								
—	72¾	—	Bare Lane	98	a													10 26								
—	74¼	—	**Morecambe**	98	a													10 31								
—	78½	—	Heysham Harbour	⛴	a																					
41¼	—	—	Settle		d		06 35														09 51					
47½	—	—	Horton-in-Ribblesdale		d																09 59					
52¼	—	—	Ribblehead		d		06 50														10 07					
58¼	—	—	Dent		d																10 17					
61¾	—	—	Garsdale		d		07 05														10 22					
71½	—	—	Kirkby Stephen		d		07 18														10 35					
82¼	—	—	Appleby		d		07 31														10 48					
93¼	—	—	Langwathby		d		07 45														11 02					
97½	—	—	Lazonby & Kirkoswald		d		07 51														11 08					
103	—	—	Armathwaite		d		07 59														11 16					
113	—	—	**Carlisle 8**	65	a		08 17														11 35					

			NT	NT	NT	NT	NT	NT	NT	NT		NT	NT	NT	NT	NT	NT	NT	NT	NT		NT	NT	NT	NT	NT
			◇						◇										◇							
London Kings Cross 15	⊖26	d																								
Leeds 10	37	d	09 47	09 56		10 18	10 26		10 49	10 56			11 26		11 56		12 26		12 49	12 56			13 14	13 26		13 56
Bradford Forster Square	37	d			10 11			10 41				11 11		11 41		12 11		12 41				13 11			13 41	
Frizinghall	37	d			10 14			10 44				11 14		11 44		12 14		12 44				13 14			13 44	
Shipley	37	a	10 01	10 07	10 18	10 30	10 37	10 48	11 01	11 07		11 18	11 38	11 48	12 07	12 18	12 37	12 48	13 01	13 07		13 18	13 28	13 38	13 48	14 07
		d	10 02	10 08	10 19	10 31	10 38	10 49	11 02	11 08		11 19	11 39	11 49	12 08	12 19	12 38	12 49	13 02	13 08		13 19	13 29	13 38	13 49	14 08
Saltaire		d		10 10	10 22		10 40	10 52		11 10		11 21	11 40	11 51	12 10	12 22	12 40	12 52		13 10		13 22		13 40	13 52	14 10
Bingley		d	10 06	10 14	10 26	10 36	10 44	10 56	11 06	11 14		11 25	11 44	11 55	12 14	12 26	12 44	12 56	13 06	13 14		13 26	13 34	13 44	13 56	14 14
Crossflatts		d		10 17	10 28		10 47	10 58		11 17		11 27	11 47	11 57	12 17	12 28	12 47	12 58		13 17		13 28		13 47	13 58	14 17
Keighley		d	10 12	10 21	10 33	10 41	10 51	11 03	11 12	11 21		11 32	11 51	12 02	12 21	12 33	12 51	13 03	13 12	13 21		13 33	13 39	13 51	14 03	14 21
Steeton & Silsden		d		10 26	10 37		10 56	11 07		11 26		11 36	11 56	12 06	12 26	12 37	12 56	13 07		13 26		13 37		13 56	14 07	14 26
Cononley		d		10 30	10 42		11 00	11 12		11 30		11 40	12 00	12 10	12 30	12 42	13 00	13 12		13 30		13 42		14 00	14 11	14 30
Skipton		a	10 24	10 39	10 50	10 55	11 11	11 20	11 24	11 40		11 50	12 11	12 20	12 40	12 50	13 10	13 20	13 24	13 40		13 50	13 56	14 10	14 20	14 40
		d	10 26			11 00			11 26										13 26				14 01			
Gargrave		d				11 05													13 31				14 06			
Blackpool North	94	d																								
Preston		d																								
Blackburn	97	d																								
Clitheroe	94	d																								
Hellifield		d				11 14			11 37										13 40				14 15			
Long Preston		d				11 17													13 42				14 18			
Giggleswick		d				11 24																	14 25			
Clapham (Nth Yorkshire)		d				11 33																	14 34			
Bentham		d				11 39																	14 40			
Wennington		d				11 44																	14 45			
Carnforth	82	a				12 00																	15 01			
Lancaster 6	65,82,98	a				12 11																	15 15			
Bare Lane	98	a				12 26																	15 30			
Morecambe	98	a				12 30																	15 35			
Heysham Harbour	⛴	a				12 48																				
Settle		d	10 44						11 46										13 48							
Horton-in-Ribblesdale		d							11 54										13 57							
Ribblehead		d							12 02										14 05							
Dent		d							12 12										14 14							
Garsdale		d							12 17										14 20							
Kirkby Stephen		d	11 22						12 30										14 32							
Appleby		d	11 36						12 43										14 45							
Langwathby		d							12 57										14 59							
Lazonby & Kirkoswald		d							13 03										15 04							
Armathwaite		d							13 11										15 12							
Carlisle 8	65	a	12 17						13 29										15 32							

Table 36

Mondays to Fridays

9 December to 16 May

Leeds and Bradford - Skipton, Lancaster, Morecambe and Carlisle

Network Diagram - see first page of Table 35

Station	Table		NT	NT	NT	NT	NT	NT	NT	NT	NT	NT	NT	NT	NT	NT	NT	NT	NT	NT	NT	NT	NT	NT
						◇																◇		
London Kings Cross 15	⊖26	d																						
Leeds 10	37	d		14 26		14 49	14 56		15 26		15 56		16 26		16 39	16 56		17 26		17 41	17 56	18 06		18 26
Bradford Forster Square	37	d	14 11		14 41			15 11		15 41		16 11		16 40			17 11		17 38				18 16	
Frizinghall	37	d	14 14		14 44			15 14		15 44		16 14		16 43			17 14		17 41				18 19	
Shipley	37	a	14 18	14 37	14 48	15 01	15 07	15 18	15 37	15 48	16 07	16 18	16 37	16 48	16 53	17 07	17 18	17 37	17 45	17 53	18 07	18 18	18 23	18 38
		d	14 19	14 38	14 49	15 02	15 08	15 19	15 38	15 49	16 08	16 19	16 38	16 49	16 55	17 08	17 19	17 38	17 46	17 54	18 08	18 18	18 23	18 38
Saltaire		d	14 22	14 40	14 52		15 10	15 22	15 40	15 52	16 10	16 22	16 40	16 52		17 10	17 22	17 40	17 49	17 56	18 10		18 27	18 40
Bingley		d	14 26	14 44	14 56	15 06	15 14	15 26	15 44	15 56	16 14	16 26	16 44	16 56	17 03	17 14	17 26	17 44	17 53	18 00	18 14	18 24	18 31	18 44
Crossflatts		d	14 28	14 47	14 58		15 17	15 28	15 47	15 58	16 17	16 28	16 47	16 58		17 17	17 28	17 47	17 55	18 03	18 17		18 33	18 47
Keighley		d	14 33	14 51	15 03	15 12	15 21	15 33	15 51	16 03	16 21	16 33	16 51	17 03	17 10	17 21	17 33	17 51	18 00	18 07	18 21	18 29	18 38	18 51
Steeton & Silsden		d	14 37	14 56	15 07		15 26	15 37	15 56	16 07	16 26	16 37	16 56	17 07		17 26	17 37	17 56	18 04	18 12	18 26	18 34	18 42	18 56
Cononley		d	14 41	15 00	15 12		15 30	15 42	16 00	16 11	16 30	16 41	17 00	17 11		17 30	17 42	18 00	18 09	18 16	18 30		18 47	19 00
Skipton		a	14 50	15 10	15 20	15 24	15 40	15 50	16 10	16 20	16 40	16 50	17 10	17 19	17 24	17 40	17 50	18 10	18 17	18 24	18 40	18 45	18 55	19 10
		d				15 26									17 26							18 46		
Gargrave		d													17 31							18 51		
Blackpool North	94	d																						
Preston		d																						
Blackburn	97	d																						
Clitheroe	94	d																						
Hellifield		d				15 37									17 40							19 00		
Long Preston		d													17 43							19 02		
Giggleswick		d													17 51									
Clapham (Nth Yorkshire)		d													17 59									
Bentham		d													18 05									
Wennington		d													18 10									
Carnforth	82	a													18 26									
Lancaster 6	65,82,98	a													18 40									
Bare Lane	98	a													18 55									
Morecambe	98	a													19 01									
Heysham Harbour	⛴	a																						
Settle		d				15 45																19 08		
Horton-in-Ribblesdale		d				15 53																19 17		
Ribblehead		d				16 01																19 25		
Dent		d				16 11																19 34		
Garsdale		d				16 16																19 40		
Kirkby Stephen		d				16 29																19 52		
Appleby		d				16 41																20 05		
Langwathby		d				16 55																20 19		
Lazonby & Kirkoswald		d				17 01																20 24		
Armathwaite		d				17 09																20 32		
Carlisle 8	65	a				17 28																20 52		

Station	Table		NT	NT	NT	NT	NT	NT	NT	NT	NT	GR	NT	NT	NT	NT	NT	NT	NT	NT	NT
												R 1 🚲									
London Kings Cross 15	⊖26	d										18 03									
Leeds 10	37	d		18 54		19 19	19 26		19 56		20 26	20 34	20 56		21 26	21 56		22 26	22 56		23 18
Bradford Forster Square	37	d	18 41		19 07			19 36		20 07				21 05			22 05			23 09	
Frizinghall	37	d	18 44		19 10			19 39		20 10				21 08			22 08			23 12	
Shipley	37	a	18 48	19 05	19 14	19 31	19 37	19 43	20 07	20 15	20 37		21 07	21 12	21 38	22 07	22 12	22 37	23 08	23 16	23 31
		d	18 49	19 06	19 15	19 32	19 38	19 44	20 08	20 15	20 38		21 08	21 14	21 38	22 08	22 14	22 38	23 09	23 17	23 32
Saltaire		d	18 51	19 08	19 18		19 40	19 47	20 10	20 17	20 40		21 10	21 17	21 40	22 10	22 16	22 40	23 11	23 20	23 34
Bingley		d	18 55	19 12	19 22	19 36	19 44	19 51	20 14	20 21	20 44		21 14	21 21	21 44	22 14	22 20	22 44	23 15	23 24	23 38
Crossflatts		d	18 57	19 15	19 24		19 47	19 53	20 17	20 23	20 47		21 17	21 23	21 47	22 17	22 22	22 47	23 18	23 26	23 40
Keighley		d	19 02	19 19	19 29	19 42	19 51	19 58	20 21	20 28	20 51	20s55	21 21	21 28	21 51	22 21	22 27	22 51	23 22	23 31	23 44
Steeton & Silsden		d	19 06	19 24	19 33		19 56	20 02	20 26	20 32	20 56		21 26	21 32	21 56	22 26	22 31	22 56	23 27	23 35	23 48
Cononley		d	19 10	19 28	19 38		20 00	20 07	20 30	20 36	21 00		21 30	21 35	22 00	22 30	22 35	23 00	23 31	23 40	23 52
Skipton		a	19 19	19 35	19 46	19 57	20 10	20 15	20 40	20 46	21 10	21 13	21 40	21 44	22 10	22 40	22 42	23 10	23 40	23 48	00 02
		d				20 00															
Gargrave		d				20 06															
Blackpool North	94	d																			
Preston		d																			
Blackburn	97	d																			
Clitheroe	94	d																			
Hellifield		d				20 15															
Long Preston		d				20 17															
Giggleswick		d																			
Clapham (Nth Yorkshire)		d																			
Bentham		d																			
Wennington		d																			
Carnforth	82	a																			
Lancaster 6	65,82,98	a																			
Bare Lane	98	a																			
Morecambe	98	a																			
Heysham Harbour	⛴	a																			
Settle		d				20 23															
Horton-in-Ribblesdale		d				20 32															
Ribblehead		d				20a41															
Dent		d																			
Garsdale		d																			
Kirkby Stephen		d																			
Appleby		d																			
Langwathby		d																			
Lazonby & Kirkoswald		d																			
Armathwaite		d																			
Carlisle 8	65	a																			

Table 36

Saturdays

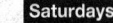

14 December to 17 May

Leeds and Bradford - Skipton, Lancaster, Morecambe and Carlisle

Network Diagram - see first page of Table 35

Station	Table		NT	NT	NT	NT	NT	NT	NT	NT	NT	NT	NT	NT	NT	NT	NT	NT	NT	NT	NT	NT	NT	NT
London Kings Cross 15	⊖26	d																						
Leeds 10	37	d	05 54		06 19	06 56		07 56		08 19	08 25		08 49	08 56		09 26		09 47	09 56		10 19	10 26		10 49
Bradford Forster Square	37	d		06 10			07 11		08 11			08 41			09 11		09 41			10 11			10 41	
Frizinghall	37	d		06 13			07 14		08 14			08 44			09 14		09 44			10 14			10 44	
Shipley	37	a	06 06	06 17	06 31	07 08	07 18	08 08	08 18	08 31	08 37	08 48	09 01	09 07	09 18	09 37	09 48	10 01	10 07	10 18	10 31	10 37	10 48	11 01
		d	06 07	06 19	06 32	07 08	07 19	08 08	08 19	08 32	08 37	08 49	09 02	09 09	09 19	09 38	09 49	10 02	10 08	10 19	10 32	10 38	10 49	11 02
Saltaire		d	06 09	06 22		07 10	07 22	08 10	08 22		08 40	08 52		09 11	09 22	09 40	09 52		10 10	10 22		10 40	10 52	
Bingley		d	06 14	06 26	06 36	07 14	07 26	08 14	08 26	08 37	08 44	08 56	09 06	09 14	09 26	09 44	09 56	10 06	10 14	10 26	10 37	10 44	10 56	11 06
Crossflatts		d	06 16	06 28		07 17	07 28	08 16	08 28		08 46	08 58		09 17	09 28	09 47	09 58		10 17	10 28		10 47	10 58	
Keighley		d	06 21	06 33	06 42	07 21	07 33	08 20	08 33	08 43	08 50	09 03	09 12	09 21	09 33	09 51	10 03	10 12	10 21	10 33	10 42	10 51	11 03	11 12
Steeton & Silsden		d	06 25	06 37		07 26	07 37	08 24	08 37		08 54	09 07		09 26	09 37	09 56	10 07		10 26	10 37		10 56	11 07	
Cononley		d	06 30	06 42		07 30	07 42	08 28	08 42		08 59	09 12		09 30	09 42	10 00	10 12		10 30	10 42		11 00	11 12	
Skipton		a	06 37	06 49	06 55	07 39	07 50	08 39	08 50	08 56	09 09	09 20	09 24	09 40	09 50	10 11	10 20	10 24	10 39	10 50	10 55	11 11	11 20	11 24
		d	06 38		06 56					09 00			09 26					10 26			11 00			11 26
Gargrave		d	06 43							09 05			09 32								11 05			
Blackpool North	94	d																						
Preston		d																						
Blackburn	97	d																						
Clitheroe	94	d																						
Hellifield		d	06 52		07 08					09 14			09 40								11 14			11 37
Long Preston		d	06 55							09 17			09 43								11 17			
Giggleswick		d	07 03							09 25											11 25			
Clapham (Nth Yorkshire)		d	07 11							09 33											11 33			
Bentham		d	07 17							09 39											11 39			
Wennington		d	07 22							09 44											11 44			
Carnforth	82	a	07 38							10 00											12 00			
Lancaster 6	65,82,98	a	07 50							10 13											12 11			
Bare Lane	98	a								10 24											12 32			
Morecambe	98	a								10 31											12 36			
Heysham Harbour	⛴	a																			12 54			
Settle		d			07 15								09 50					10 44						11 46
Horton-in-Ribblesdale		d			07 24								09 58											11 54
Ribblehead		d			07 32								10 06											12 02
Dent		d			07 41								10 16											12 12
Garsdale		d			07 47								10 21											12 17
Kirkby Stephen		d			07 59								10 34					11 22						12 30
Appleby		d			08 12								10 47					11 36						12 43
Langwathby		d			08 26								11 01											12 57
Lazonby & Kirkoswald		d			08 31								11 07											13 03
Armathwaite		d			08 39								11 15											13 11
Carlisle 8	65	a			08 58								11 34					12 17						13 29

Station	Table		NT	NT	NT	NT	NT	NT	NT	NT	NT	NT	NT	NT	NT	NT	NT	NT	NT	NT	NT	NT	NT	NT
London Kings Cross 15	⊖26	d																						
Leeds 10	37	d	10 56		11 26		11 56		12 26		12 49	12 56		13 26		13 49	13 56		14 26		14 49	14 56		15 26
Bradford Forster Square	37	d		11 11		11 41		12 11		12 41			13 11		13 41			14 11		14 41			15 11	
Frizinghall	37	d		11 14		11 44		12 14		12 44			13 14		13 44			14 14		14 44			15 14	
Shipley	37	a	11 07	11 18	11 38	11 48	12 07	12 18	12 37	12 48	13 01	13 07	13 18	13 37	13 48	14 03	14 07	14 18	14 37	14 48	15 01	15 07	15 18	15 37
		d	11 08	11 19	11 39	11 49	12 08	12 19	12 38	12 49	13 02	13 08	13 19	13 38	13 49	14 03	14 08	14 19	14 38	14 49	15 02	15 08	15 19	15 38
Saltaire		d	11 10	11 21	11 40	11 51	12 10	12 22	12 40	12 52		13 10	13 22	13 40	13 52		14 10	14 22	14 40	14 52		15 10	15 22	15 40
Bingley		d	11 14	11 25	11 44	11 55	12 14	12 26	12 44	12 56	13 06	13 14	13 26	13 44	13 56	14 08	14 14	14 26	14 44	14 56	15 06	15 14	15 26	15 44
Crossflatts		d	11 17	11 27	11 47	11 57	12 17	12 28	12 47	12 58		13 17	13 28	13 47	13 58		14 17	14 28	14 47	14 58		15 17	15 28	15 47
Keighley		d	11 21	11 32	11 51	12 02	12 21	12 33	12 51	13 03	13 12	13 21	13 33	13 51	14 03	14 14	14 21	14 33	14 51	15 03	15 12	15 21	15 33	15 51
Steeton & Silsden		d	11 26	11 36	11 56	12 06	12 26	12 37	12 56	13 07		13 26	13 37	13 56	14 07		14 26	14 37	14 56	15 07		15 26	15 37	15 56
Cononley		d	11 30	11 40	12 00	12 10	12 30	12 42	13 00	13 12		13 30	13 42	14 00	14 11		14 30	14 41	15 00	15 12		15 30	15 42	16 00
Skipton		a	11 40	11 50	12 11	12 20	12 40	12 50	13 10	13 20	13 24	13 40	13 50	14 10	14 20	14 26	14 40	14 50	15 10	15 20	15 24	15 40	15 50	16 10
		d									13 26					14 34					15 26			
Gargrave		d									13 31					14 39								
Blackpool North	94	d																						
Preston		d																						
Blackburn	97	d																						
Clitheroe	94	d																						
Hellifield		d									13 40					14 48					15 37			
Long Preston		d									13 42					14 51								
Giggleswick		d														14 59								
Clapham (Nth Yorkshire)		d														15 07								
Bentham		d														15 13								
Wennington		d														15 18								
Carnforth	82	a														15 34								
Lancaster 6	65,82,98	a														15 45								
Bare Lane	98	a														15 55								
Morecambe	98	a														16 02								
Heysham Harbour	⛴	a																						
Settle		d									13 48										15 45			
Horton-in-Ribblesdale		d									13 57										15 53			
Ribblehead		d									14 05										16 01			
Dent		d									14 14										16 11			
Garsdale		d									14 20										16 16			
Kirkby Stephen		d									14 32										16 29			
Appleby		d									14 45										16 41			
Langwathby		d									14 59										16 55			
Lazonby & Kirkoswald		d									15 04										17 01			
Armathwaite		d									15 12										17 09			
Carlisle 8	65	a									15 27										17 28			

Table 36

Saturdays

14 December to 17 May

Leeds and Bradford - Skipton, Lancaster, Morecambe and Carlisle

Network Diagram - see first page of Table 35

		NT		NT	NT	NT	NT	NT	NT	NT	NT	NT		NT	NT	NT	NT	NT	NT	NT	NT	NT		NT	NT
London Kings Cross 15	⊖26 d																								
Leeds 10	37 d			15 56		16 26		16 39	16 56		17 26			17 50	17 56		18 26		18 56		19 19	19 26			19 56
Bradford Forster Square	37 d	15 41			16 11		16 40			17 11		17 41				18 11		18 41		19 07				19 36	
Frizinghall	37 d	15 44			16 14		16 43			17 14		17 44				18 14		18 44		19 10				19 39	
Shipley	37 a	15 48		16 07	16 18	16 37	16 48	16 53	17 07	17 18	17 37	17 48		18 02	18 07	18 18	18 38	18 48	19 07	19 14	19 31	19 37		19 43	20 07
	d	15 49		16 08	16 19	16 38	16 49	16 55	17 08	17 19	17 38	17 49		18 03	18 08	18 19	18 38	18 49	19 08	19 15	19 32	19 38		19 44	20 08
Saltaire	d	15 52		16 10	16 22	16 40	16 52		17 10	17 22	17 40	17 51			18 10	18 22	18 40	18 51	19 10	19 18		19 40		19 47	20 10
Bingley	d	15 56		16 14	16 26	16 44	16 56	17 03	17 14	17 26	17 44	17 55		18 08	18 14	18 26	18 44	18 55	19 14	19 22	19 36	19 44		19 51	20 14
Crossflatts	d	15 58		16 17	16 28	16 47	16 58		17 17	17 28	17 47	17 57			18 17	18 28	18 47	18 57	19 17	19 24		19 47		19 53	20 17
Keighley	d	16 03		16 21	16 33	16 51	17 03	17 10	17 21	17 33	17 51	18 02		18 14	18 21	18 33	18 51	19 02	19 21	19 29	19 42	19 51		19 58	20 21
Steeton & Silsden	d	16 07		16 26	16 37	16 56	17 07		17 26	17 37	17 56	18 06		18 19	18 26	18 37	18 56	19 06	19 26	19 33		19 56		20 02	20 26
Cononley	d	16 11		16 30	16 41	17 00	17 11		17 30	17 42	18 00	18 10			18 30	18 42	19 00	19 10	19 30	19 38		20 00		20 07	20 30
Skipton	a	16 20		16 40	16 50	17 10	17 19	17 24	17 40	17 50	18 10	18 17		18 29	18 40	18 50	19 10	19 19	19 40	19 46	19 57	20 10		20 15	20 40
	d							17 24						18 35							20 00				
Gargrave	d							17 30						18 40							20 06				
Blackpool North	94 d																								
Preston	d																								
Blackburn	97 d																								
Clitheroe	94 d																								
Hellifield	d							17 39						18 49							20 15				
Long Preston	d							17 42						18 51							20 17				
Giggleswick	d							17 49																	
Clapham (Nth Yorkshire)	d							17 57																	
Bentham	d							18 04																	
Wennington	d							18 09																	
Carnforth	82 a							18 26																	
Lancaster 6	65,82,98 a							18 38																	
Bare Lane	98 a							18 53																	
Morecambe	98 a							18 59																	
Heysham Harbour	⛴ a																								
Settle	d													18 57							20 23				
Horton-in-Ribblesdale	d													19 06							20 32				
Ribblehead	d													19 14							20a41				
Dent	d													19 23											
Garsdale	d													19 29											
Kirkby Stephen	d													19 41											
Appleby	d													19 54											
Langwathby	d													20 08											
Lazonby & Kirkoswald	d													20 13											
Armathwaite	d													20 21											
Carlisle 8	65 a													20 41											

		NT	NT	GR R 1 🚃	NT	NT	NT	NT		NT	NT	NT	NT	NT
London Kings Cross 15	⊖26 d			18 35										
Leeds 10	37 d		20 26	20 55	20 56		21 26			22 03	22 26	22 56		23 18
Bradford Forster Square	37 d	20 07				21 05		22 01					23 05	
Frizinghall	37 d	20 10				21 08		22 04					23 08	
Shipley	37 a	20 15	20 37		21 07	21 12	21 38	22 08		22 15	22 37	23 08	23 12	23 31
	d	20 15	20 38		21 08	21 17	21 38	22 09		22 16	22 38	23 09	23 14	23 32
Saltaire	d	20 17	20 40		21 10	21 20	21 40	22 12		22 18	22 40	23 11	23 17	23 34
Bingley	d	20 21	20 44		21 14	21 24	21 44	22 16		22 22	22 44	23 15	23 21	23 38
Crossflatts	d	20 23	20 47		21 17	21 26	21 47	22 18		22 25	22 47	23 18	23 23	23 40
Keighley	d	20 28	20 51	21s13	21 21	21 31	21 51	22 23		22 29	22 51	23 22	23 28	23 44
Steeton & Silsden	d	20 32	20 56		21 26	21 35	21 56	22 27		22 34	22 56	23 27	23 32	23 48
Cononley	d	20 36	21 00		21 30	21 40	22 00	22 31		22 38	23 00	23 31	23 37	23 52
Skipton	a	20 46	21 10	21 27	21 40	21 47	22 10	22 39		22 47	23 10	23 40	23 44	00 02
	d													
Gargrave	d													
Blackpool North	94 d													
Preston	d													
Blackburn	97 d													
Clitheroe	94 d													
Hellifield	d													
Long Preston	d													
Giggleswick	d													
Clapham (Nth Yorkshire)	d													
Bentham	d													
Wennington	d													
Carnforth	82 a													
Lancaster 6	65,82,98 a													
Bare Lane	98 a													
Morecambe	98 a													
Heysham Harbour	⛴ a													
Settle	d													
Horton-in-Ribblesdale	d													
Ribblehead	d													
Dent	d													
Garsdale	d													
Kirkby Stephen	d													
Appleby	d													
Langwathby	d													
Lazonby & Kirkoswald	d													
Armathwaite	d													
Carlisle 8	65 a													

Table 36

Sundays

8 December to 11 May

Leeds and Bradford - Skipton, Lancaster, Morecambe and Carlisle

Network Diagram - see first page of Table 35

			NT	NT	NT	NT	NT	NT	NT	NT	NT	NT	NT	NT	NT	NT	NT	NT	NT	NT	NT	NT	NT	NT
			A	B							◇ C													
London Kings Cross 15	⊖26	d																						
Leeds 10	37	d	08 40	08 40		09 00	10 08		10 51	11 08	11 20	12 08		13 08		13 55	14 08		14 57	15 08	16 08		17 08	17 21
Bradford Forster Square	37	d						10 48					12 48					14 48				16 48		
Frizinghall	37	d						10 51					12 51					14 51				16 51		
Shipley	37	a	08 52	08 52		09 15	10 19	10 54	11 03	11 19	11 32	12 19	12 54	13 19		14 07	14 19	14 54	15 09	15 19	16 19	16 54	17 19	17 33
		d	08 53	08 53		09 16	10 20	10 55	11 04	11 20	11 32	12 20	12 55	13 20		14 08	14 20	14 55	15 10	15 20	16 20	16 55	17 20	17 34
Saltaire		d	08 55	08 55		09 18	10 22	10 57		11 22		12 22	12 57	13 22			14 22	14 57		15 22	16 22	16 57	17 22	
Bingley		d	09 00	09 00		09 23	10 26	11 01	11 09	11 26	11 37	12 26	13 01	13 26		14 12	14 26	15 01	15 15	15 26	16 26	17 01	17 26	17 39
Crossflatts		d	09 02	09 02		09 25	10 28	11 03		11 28		12 28	13 03	13 28			14 28	15 03		15 28	16 28	17 03	17 28	
Keighley		d	09 07	09 07		09 30	10 32	11 08	11 15	11 32	11 42	12 32	13 08	13 32		14 18	14 32	15 08	15 20	15 32	16 32	17 08	17 32	17 44
Steeton & Silsden		d	09 11	09 11		09 34	10 36	11 12		11 36		12 36	13 12	13 36			14 36	15 12		15 36	16 36	17 12	17 36	
Cononley		d	09 16	09 16		09 39	10 40	11 16		11 40		12 40	13 16	13 40			14 40	15 16		15 40	16 40	17 16	17 40	
Skipton		a	09 23	09 23		09 46	10 48	11 23	11 28	11 48	11 53	12 48	13 23	13 48		14 30	14 48	15 23	15 33	15 48	16 48	17 23	17 48	17 57
		d	09 26	09 26		09 48			11 30		11 55					14 33			15 36					18 00
Gargrave		d	09 31	09 31		09 53			11 35							14 38			15 41					18 05
Blackpool North	94	d			08 10																			
Preston		d			08 39										13 18									
Blackburn	97	d			09 04										13 39									
Clitheroe	94	d			09 27										14 02									
Hellifield		d	09 40	09 40	09a52	10 02			11 44						14a27	14 47			15 50					18 14
Long Preston		d	09 43	09 43					11 46							14 50			15 53					18 18
Giggleswick		d	09 52	09 52					11 54										16 00					18 25
Clapham (Nth Yorkshire)		d	10 00	10 00					12 02										16 08					18 33
Bentham		d	10 06	10 06					12 08										16 15					18 39
Wennington		d	10 11	10 11					12 13										16 20					18 44
Carnforth	82	a	10 27	10 30					12 30										16 36					19 00
Lancaster 6	65,82,98	a		10 40					12 44										16 46					19 13
Bare Lane	98	a		10 51					13 06										16 56					19 31
Morecambe	98	a		10 57					13 12										17 03					19 37
Heysham Harbour	⛴	a																						
Settle		d				10 10					12 14					14 56								
Horton-in-Ribblesdale		d				10 19										15 05								
Ribblehead		d				10 27										15 13								
Dent		d				10 37										15 23								
Garsdale		d				10 43										15 28								
Kirkby Stephen		d				10 56					12 51					15 41								
Appleby		d				11 09					13 05					15 54								
Langwathby		d				11 23										16 08								
Lazonby & Kirkoswald		d				11 29										16 14								
Armathwaite		d				11 37										16 22								
Carlisle 8	65	a				11 56					13 47					16 39								

			NT	NT	NT	NT	NT	NT	GR	GR	NT	NT	NT	NT
									R 1 D	R 1 E				
London Kings Cross 15	⊖26	d							18 18	18 35				
Leeds 10	37	d	17 40	18 08		19 08	20 08		21 01	21 01	21 08	22 08		23 20
Bradford Forster Square	37	d			18 48			20 48					22 48	
Frizinghall	37	d			18 51			20 51					22 51	
Shipley	37	a	17 52	18 19	18 54	19 19	20 19	20 54			21 19	22 19	22 54	23 31
		d	17 53	18 20	18 55	19 20	20 20	20 55			21 20	22 20	22 55	23 32
Saltaire		d		18 22	18 57	19 22	20 22	20 57			21 22	22 22	22 57	23 34
Bingley		d	17 57	18 26	19 01	19 26	20 26	21 01			21 26	22 26	23 01	23 38
Crossflatts		d		18 28	19 03	19 28	20 28	21 03			21 28	22 28	23 03	23 40
Keighley		d	18 03	18 32	19 08	19 32	20 32	21 08	21s19	21s19	21 32	22 32	23 08	23 44
Steeton & Silsden		d		18 36	19 12	19 36	20 36	21 12			21 36	22 36	23 12	23 48
Cononley		d		18 40	19 16	19 40	20 40	21 16			21 40	22 40	23 16	23 52
Skipton		a	18 17	18 48	19 23	19 48	20 48	21 23	21 40	21 40	21 48	22 48	23 23	23 59
		d	18 17											
Gargrave		d												
Blackpool North	94	d												
Preston		d												
Blackburn	97	d												
Clitheroe	94	d												
Hellifield		d	18 28											
Long Preston		d												
Giggleswick		d												
Clapham (Nth Yorkshire)		d												
Bentham		d												
Wennington		d												
Carnforth	82	a												
Lancaster 6	65,82,98	a												
Bare Lane	98	a												
Morecambe	98	a												
Heysham Harbour	⛴	a												
Settle		d	18 36											
Horton-in-Ribblesdale		d	18 45											
Ribblehead		d	18 53											
Dent		d	19 03											
Garsdale		d	19 08											
Kirkby Stephen		d	19 21											
Appleby		d	19 34											
Langwathby		d	19 48											
Lazonby & Kirkoswald		d	19 54											
Armathwaite		d	20 02											
Carlisle 8	65	a	20 21											

A from 30 March
B until 23 March
C From Sheffield
D from 5 January until 23 March
E until 29 December, from 30 March

Table 36R

Mondays to Fridays

9 December to 16 May

Carlisle, Morecambe, Lancaster and Skipton - Bradford and Leeds

Network Diagram - see first page of Table 35

Miles	Miles	Miles				NT	NT	NT	NT	NT	GR R 1	NT	NT	NT		NT	NT	NT	NT ◇	NT	NT	NT	NT	NT		NT
0	—	—	**Carlisle 8**	65	d														05 50							
10	—	—	Armathwaite		d														06 04							
15½	—	—	Lazonby & Kirkoswald		d														06 11							
19¾	—	—	Langwathby		d														06 18							
30¾	—	—	Appleby		d														06 32							
41½	—	—	Kirkby Stephen		d														06 46							
51¼	—	—	Garsdale		d														06 59							
54¾	—	—	Dent		d																					
60¾	—	—	Ribblehead		d														07 16							
65½	—	—	Horton-in-Ribblesdale		d														07 22							
71¾	—	—	Settle		d														07 30							
—	0	—	Heysham Harbour ⛴		d																					
—	2	—	**Morecambe**	98	d																					
—	3¼	—	Bare Lane	98	d																					
—	5¾	—	**Lancaster 6**	65,82,98	d																	07 08				
—	12	—	Carnforth	82	d																	07 18				
—	21½	—	Wennington		d																	07 31				
—	25	—	Bentham		d																	07 37				
—	28	—	Clapham (Nth Yorkshire)		d																	07 43				
—	34¾	—	Giggleswick		d																	07 52				
75½	38¾	—	Long Preston		d														07 36			08 00				
76¾	40	—	Hellifield		d														07 39			08 03				
—	—	—	Clitheroe	94	a																					
—	—	—	Blackburn	94,97	a																					
—	—	—	Preston 8	97	a																					
—	—	—	Blackpool North	97	a																					
83	46	—	Gargrave		d														07 47			08 11				
86¾	49¾	—	**Skipton**		a														07 55			08 21				
—	—	—			d	05 47	06 01	06 15	06 27	06 41	06 55	07 01	07 07	07 20		07 27	07 34	07 46	07 57	08 02	08 14	08 26	08 31	08 41		09 01
89¾	—	—	Cononley		d	05 51	06 05	06 19	06 31	06 45		07 05	07 11	07 24		07 31	07 38	07 50		08 06	08 18		08 35	08 45		09 05
93	—	—	Steeton & Silsden		d	05 55	06 09	06 24	06 35	06 50		07 10	07 16	07 29		07 36	07 43	07 55	08 04	08 11	08 23		08 39	08 50		09 09
96	59	—	Keighley		d	06 00	06 14	06 28	06 40	06 55	07u08	07 15	07 20	07 33		07 40	07 47	07 59	08 09	08 15	08 27	08 37	08 44	08 54		09 14
98½	—	—	Crossflatts		d	06 03	06 17	06 32	06 43	06 59		07 18	07 25	07 37		07 44	07 51	08 03		08 19	08 31		08 47	08 58		09 17
99¼	62	—	Bingley		d	06 06	06 20	06 34	06 46	07 01		07 21	07 27	07 40		07 47	07 54	08 06	08 14	08 22	08 34	08 42	08 50	09 00		09 20
101½	—	—	Saltaire		d	06 10	06 24	06 39	06 50	07 06		07 26	07 32	07 45		07 52	07 59	08 11		08 27	08 39		08 54	09 05		09 24
102¼	65	0	Shipley		a	06 12	06 27	06 41	06 53	07 08		07 28	07 34	07 47		07 55	08 01	08 13	08 19	08 29	08 41	08 46	08 57	09 07		09 27
—	—	—			d	06 13	06 28	06 42	06 53	07 09	07u17	07 29	07 35	07 47		07 56	08 02	08 13	08 19	08 30	08 41	08 47	08 58	09 07		09 28
—	—	1	Frizinghall	37	a		06 32		06 57			07 32				07 59				08 33			09 02			09 32
—	—	2¾	**Bradford Forster Square**	37	a		06 38		07 03			07 39				08 05				08 39			09 09			09 38
113	76	—	**Leeds 10**	37	a	06 27		06 57		07 23	07 31		07 49	08 03			08 17	08 30	08 37		08 56	09 06		09 22		
—	—	—	London Kings Cross 15	⊖26	a						10 00															

			NT	NT	NT	NT	NT	NT	NT	NT ◇		NT	NT	NT	NT	NT	NT	NT	NT	NT		NT	NT	NT	NT	NT ◇
Carlisle 8	65	d								08 53																11 55
Armathwaite		d								09 07																12 09
Lazonby & Kirkoswald		d								09 14																12 16
Langwathby		d								09 20																12 22
Appleby		d								09 35																12 37
Kirkby Stephen		d								09 48																12 50
Garsdale		d								10 02																13 03
Dent		d								10 07																13 08
Ribblehead		d								10 17																13 18
Horton-in-Ribblesdale		d								10 24																13 24
Settle		d								10 32																13 32
Heysham Harbour ⛴		d																								
Morecambe	98	d															10 34									
Bare Lane	98	d															10 38									
Lancaster 6	65,82,98	d															10 49									
Carnforth	82	d															11 07									
Wennington		d															11 20									
Bentham		d															11 26									
Clapham (Nth Yorkshire)		d															11 33									
Giggleswick		d															11 42									
Long Preston		d															11 50									13 38
Hellifield		d								10 39							11 53									13 41
Clitheroe	94	a																								
Blackburn	94,97	a																								
Preston 8	97	a																								
Blackpool North	97	a																								
Gargrave		d															12 01									13 49
Skipton		a								10 54							12 11									13 57
		d	09 17	09 31	09 47	10 01	10 17	10 31	10 47	10 58		11 01	11 17	11 32	11 47	12 01	12 13	12 17	12 31	12 47		13 01	13 17	13 31	13 47	13 58
Cononley		d	09 21	09 35	09 51	10 05	10 21	10 35	10 51			11 05	11 21	11 36	11 51	12 05		12 21	12 35	12 51		13 05	13 21	13 35	13 51	
Steeton & Silsden		d	09 25	09 39	09 55	10 09	10 25	10 39	10 55			11 09	11 25	11 40	11 55	12 09		12 25	12 39	12 55		13 09	13 25	13 39	13 55	
Keighley		d	09 30	09 44	10 00	10 14	10 30	10 44	11 00	11 08		11 14	11 30	11 45	12 00	12 14	12 23	12 30	12 44	13 00		13 14	13 30	13 44	14 00	14 09
Crossflatts		d	09 33	09 47	10 03	10 17	10 33	10 47	11 03			11 17	11 33	11 48	12 03	12 17		12 33	12 47	13 03		13 17	13 33	13 47	14 03	
Bingley		d	09 36	09 50	10 06	10 20	10 36	10 50	11 06	11 13		11 20	11 36	11 51	12 06	12 20		12 36	12 50	13 06		13 20	13 36	13 50	14 06	14 13
Saltaire		d	09 40	09 54	10 10	10 24	10 40	10 54	11 10			11 24	11 40	11 55	12 10	12 24		12 40	12 54	13 10		13 24	13 40	13 54	14 10	
Shipley		a	09 43	09 58	10 12	10 27	10 42	10 57	11 12	11 18		11 27	11 43	11 58	12 14	12 27	12 33	12 44	12 57	13 12		13 27	13 42	13 57	14 12	14 18
		d	09 44	09 58	10 14	10 28	10 44	10 58	11 14	11 18		11 28	11 44	11 58	12 14	12 28	12 33	12 45	12 58	13 14		13 28	13 44	13 58	14 14	14 18
Frizinghall	37	a		10 02		10 32		11 02				11 32		12 02		12 32			13 02			13 32		14 02		
Bradford Forster Square	37	a		10 08		10 38		11 08				11 38		12 10		12 38			13 08			13 38		14 08		
Leeds 10	37	a	09 59		10 28		10 58		11 29	11 36			11 58		12 29		12 52	12 59		13 28			13 58		14 29	14 37
London Kings Cross 15	⊖26	a																								

Table 36R

Mondays to Fridays

9 December to 16 May

Carlisle, Morecambe, Lancaster and Skipton - Bradford and Leeds

Network Diagram - see first page of Table 35

Station			NT	NT	NT	NT	NT	NT	NT	NT	NT	NT	NT	NT	NT	NT	NT	NT	NT	NT	NT	NT	NT	NT
													◇											
																					A			
Carlisle 8	65	d											14 04				15 05							
Armathwaite		d											14 18											
Lazonby & Kirkoswald		d											14 25											
Langwathby		d											14 31											
Appleby		d											14 47				15 42							
Kirkby Stephen		d											15 00				15 55							
Garsdale		d											15 13											
Dent		d											15 18											
Ribblehead		d											15 27											
Horton-in-Ribblesdale		d											15 34											
Settle		d											15 43				16 35							
Heysham Harbour		d						13 15																
Morecambe	98	d						13 31													16 19			
Bare Lane	98	d						13 36													16 23			
Lancaster 6	65,82,98	d						13 48																
Carnforth	82	d						13 58													16 32			
Wennington		d						14 12													16 46			
Bentham		d						14 18													16 52			
Clapham (Nth Yorkshire)		d						14 24													16 59			
Giggleswick		d						14 33													17 08			
Long Preston		d						14 40													17 16			
Hellifield		d						14 44					15 50								17 20			
Clitheroe	94	a																						
Blackburn	94,97	a																						
Preston 8	97	a																						
Blackpool North	97	a																						
Gargrave		d						14 52													17 28			
Skipton		a						15 03					16 05				16 55				17 37			
		d	14 01	14 17	14 31	14 47	15 00	15 10	15 17	15 31	15 47	16 01	16 10	16 17	16 35	16 47	16 57	17 01	17 19	17 26	17 38	17 47	18 01	18 16
Cononley		d	14 05	14 21	14 35	14 51	15 04		15 21	15 35	15 51	16 05		16 21	16 39	16 51		17 05	17 23	17 30		17 51	18 05	18 20
Steeton & Silsden		d	14 09	14 26	14 39	14 55	15 08		15 25	15 39	15 55	16 09		16 25	16 43	16 55		17 09	17 27	17 34		17 55	18 09	18 25
Keighley		d	14 14	14 30	14 44	15 00	15 13	15 20	15 30	15 44	16 00	16 14	16 21	16 30	16 48	17 00	17 07	17 14	17 32	17 39	17 48	18 00	18 14	18 29
Crossflatts		d	14 17	14 34	14 47	15 03	15 16		15 34	15 47	16 03	16 17		16 33	16 51	17 03		17 17	17 35	17 42		18 03	18 17	18 33
Bingley		d	14 20	14 37	14 50	15 06	15 19	15 25	15 36	15 50	16 06	16 20	16 26	16 36	16 54	17 06	17 14	17 20	17 38	17 45		18 06	18 20	18 35
Saltaire		d	14 24	14 42	14 55	15 10	15 23		15 41	15 54	16 10	16 24		16 40	16 59	17 10		17 24	17 42	17 49		18 10	18 24	18 40
Shipley		a	14 28	14 44	14 57	15 12	15 27	15 30	15 43	15 57	16 12	16 27	16 31	16 44	17 02	17 14	17 20	17 27	17 44	17 54	17 58	18 13	18 28	18 43
		d	14 28	14 45	14 58	15 14	15 28	15 30	15 44	15 58	16 14	16 28	16 31	16 45	17 02	17 15	17 23	17 28	17 45	17 55	17 58	18 14	18 28	18 44
Frizinghall	37	a	14 32		15 01		15 32			16 02		16 31			17 06			17 32		17 58			18 32	
Bradford Forster Square	37	a	14 39		15 08		15 38			16 08		16 38			17 12			17 38		18 04			18 38	
Leeds 10	37	a		15 00		15 28		15 47	15 58		16 28		16 53	16 59		17 29	17 40		18 00		18 15	18 29		18 59
London Kings Cross 15	⊖26	a																						

Station			NT	NT	NT	NT	NT	NT	NT	NT	NT	NT	NT	NT	NT	NT	NT	NT	NT
			◇								◇								
Carlisle 8	65	d	16 18								18 14								
Armathwaite		d	16 32								18 28								
Lazonby & Kirkoswald		d	16 39								18 35								
Langwathby		d	16 45								18 41								
Appleby		d	17 01								18 56								
Kirkby Stephen		d	17 14								19 09								
Garsdale		d	17 27								19 22								
Dent		d	17 32								19 27								
Ribblehead		d	17 42								19 37						21 00		
Horton-in-Ribblesdale		d	17 48								19 43						21 06		
Settle		d	17 57								19 51						21 14		
Heysham Harbour		d																	
Morecambe	98	d											19 08						
Bare Lane	98	d											19 12						
Lancaster 6	65,82,98	d											19 24						
Carnforth	82	d											19 34						
Wennington		d											19 48						
Bentham		d											19 54						
Clapham (Nth Yorkshire)		d											20 00						
Giggleswick		d											20 09						
Long Preston		d	18 03										20 17				21 20		
Hellifield		d	18 06								19 59		20 21				21 23		
Clitheroe	94	a																	
Blackburn	94,97	a																	
Preston 8	97	a																	
Blackpool North	97	a																	
Gargrave		d	18 14										20 29				21 31		
Skipton		a	18 23								20 14		20 38				21 38		
		d	18 27	18 31	18 47	18 59	19 17	19 31	19 47	19 54	20 15	20 23	20 42	20 47	20 54	21 17	21 48	21 54	22 17
Cononley		d		18 35	18 51	19 03	19 21	19 35	19 51	19 58		20 29		20 51	20 58	21 21	21 52	21 59	22 21
Steeton & Silsden		d		18 39	18 55	19 07	19 25	19 39	19 55	20 02		20 33		20 55	21 02	21 25	21 57	22 03	22 25
Keighley		d	18 38	18 44	19 00	19 12	19 30	19 44	20 00	20 07	20 25	20 38	20 52	21 00	21 07	21 30	22 02	22 08	22 30
Crossflatts		d		18 47	19 03	19 15	19 33	19 47	20 03	20 10		20 41		21 03	21 10	21 33	22 06	22 11	22 33
Bingley		d	18 42	18 50	19 06	19 18	19 36	19 50	20 06	20 13	20 30	20 44		21 06	21 13	21 36	22 08	22 14	22 36
Saltaire		d		18 54	19 10	19 22	19 40	19 54	20 10	20 17		20 48		21 10	21 17	21 40	22 12	22 18	22 40
Shipley		a	18 48	18 57	19 12	19 25	19 43	19 57	20 12	20 19	20 34	20 50	20 59	21 12	21 20	21 42	22 15	22 21	22 42
		d	18 48	18 57	19 14	19 26	19 44	19 58	20 14	20 20	20 35	20 51	20 59	21 14	21 20	21 43	22 16	22 22	22 43
Frizinghall	37	a		19 01		19 29		20 01		20 24					21 24			22 25	
Bradford Forster Square	37	a		19 08		19 35		20 08		20 32					21 31			22 31	
Leeds 10	37	a	19 06		19 31		19 59		20 28		20 54	21 05	21 17	21 30		21 59	22 33		23 01
London Kings Cross 15	⊖26	a																	

A From Lancaster

Table 36R

Saturdays

14 December to 17 May

Carlisle, Morecambe, Lancaster and Skipton - Bradford and Leeds

Network Diagram - see first page of Table 35

		NT	NT	NT	GR	NT	NT	NT	NT	NT		NT	NT	NT	NT	NT	NT	NT	NT	NT		NT	NT	NT	NT
Carlisle 8	65 d																			07 52					
Armathwaite	d																			08 06					
Lazonby & Kirkoswald	d																			08 13					
Langwathby	d																			08 19					
Appleby	d																			08 34					
Kirkby Stephen	d																			08 47					
Garsdale	d																			09 00					
Dent	d																			09 05					
Ribblehead	d								07 16											09 15					
Horton-in-Ribblesdale	d								07 22											09 21					
Settle	d								07 30											09 29					
Heysham Harbour	d																								
Morecambe	98 d																								
Bare Lane	98 d																								
Lancaster 6	65,82,98 d																	08 23							
Carnforth	82 d																	08 33							
Wennington	d																	08 47							
Bentham	d																	08 52							
Clapham (Nth Yorkshire)	d																	08 59							
Giggleswick	d																	09 07							
Long Preston	d								07 36									09 15							
Hellifield	d								07 39									09 19		09 37					
Clitheroe	94 a																								
Blackburn	94,97 a																								
Preston 8	97 a																								
Blackpool North	97 a																								
Gargrave	d								07 47									09 27							
Skipton	a								07 55									09 36		09 53					
	d	05 47	06 01	06 46	06 55	07 06	07 29	07 46	07 57	08 01		08 17	08 31	08 47	09 01	09 17	09 31	09 42	09 47	09 56		10 01	10 17	10 31	10 47
Cononley	d	05 51	06 05	06 50		07 10	07 33	07 50		08 05		08 21	08 35	08 51	09 05	09 21	09 35		09 51			10 05	10 21	10 35	10 51
Steeton & Silsden	d	05 55	06 09	06 55		07 14	07 38	07 55	08 04	08 10		08 26	08 39	08 55	09 09	09 25	09 39		09 55			10 09	10 25	10 39	10 55
Keighley	d	06 00	06 14	06 59	07u09	07 19	07 42	07 59	08 09	08 14		08 30	08 44	09 00	09 14	09 30	09 44	09 52	10 00	10 08		10 14	10 30	10 44	11 00
Crossflatts	d	06 03	06 17	07 03		07 22	07 46	08 03		08 18		08 34	08 47	09 03	09 17	09 33	09 47		10 03			10 17	10 33	10 47	11 03
Bingley	d	06 06	06 20	07 06		07 25	07 49	08 06	08 14	08 21		08 37	08 50	09 06	09 20	09 36	09 50	09 58	10 06	10 12		10 20	10 36	10 50	11 06
Saltaire	d	06 10	06 24	07 11		07 29	07 54	08 11		08 26		08 42	08 54	09 10	09 24	09 40	09 54		10 10			10 24	10 40	10 54	11 10
Shipley	a	06 12	06 27	07 13		07 32	07 56	08 13	08 19	08 28		08 44	08 57	09 12	09 27	09 43	09 58	10 02	10 12	10 19		10 27	10 42	10 57	11 12
	d	06 13	06 28	07 13	07u19	07 32	07 57	08 13	08 19	08 29		08 44	08 58	09 14	09 28	09 44	09 58	10 02	10 14	10 19		10 28	10 44	10 58	11 14
Frizinghall	37 a		06 32			07 36	08 00			08 32			09 02		09 32		10 02					10 32		11 02	
Bradford Forster Square	37 a		06 38			07 42	08 06			08 39			09 09		09 38		10 08					10 38		11 08	
Leeds 10	37 a	06 27		07 27	07 33			08 28	08 37			08 58		09 28		09 59		10 20	10 28	10 34			10 58		11 29
London Kings Cross 15	⊖26 a				09 51																				

		NT	NT	NT	NT	NT		NT	NT	NT	NT	NT	NT	NT	NT	NT		NT	NT	NT	NT	NT	NT	NT	NT
Carlisle 8	65 d			09 26														11 51							
Armathwaite	d			09 40														12 05							
Lazonby & Kirkoswald	d			09 47														12 12							
Langwathby	d			09 53														12 18							
Appleby	d			10 08														12 33							
Kirkby Stephen	d			10 21														12 46							
Garsdale	d			10 35														12 59							
Dent	d			10 40														13 04							
Ribblehead	d			10 49														13 14							
Horton-in-Ribblesdale	d			10 56														13 20							
Settle	d			11 04														13 28							
Heysham Harbour	d																							13 15	
Morecambe	98 d								10 34															13 31	
Bare Lane	98 d								10 38															13 36	
Lancaster 6	65,82,98 d								10 49															13 48	
Carnforth	82 d								11 07															13 58	
Wennington	d								11 20															14 12	
Bentham	d								11 26															14 18	
Clapham (Nth Yorkshire)	d								11 33															14 25	
Giggleswick	d								11 42															14 33	
Long Preston	d								11 50									13 34						14 40	
Hellifield	d			11 11					11 53									13 37						14 44	
Clitheroe	94 a																								
Blackburn	94,97 a																								
Preston 8	97 a																								
Blackpool North	97 a																								
Gargrave	d								12 01									13 45						14 52	
Skipton	a			11 26					12 11									13 55						15 03	
	d	11 01	11 17	11 28	11 32	11 47		12 01	12 13	12 17	12 31	12 47	13 01	13 17	13 31	13 47		13 57	14 01	14 17	14 31	14 47	15 00	15 10	15 17
Cononley	d	11 05	11 21		11 36	11 51		12 05		12 21	12 35	12 51	13 05	13 21	13 35	13 51			14 05	14 21	14 35	14 51	15 04		15 21
Steeton & Silsden	d	11 09	11 25		11 40	11 55		12 09		12 25	12 39	12 55	13 09	13 25	13 39	13 55			14 09	14 26	14 39	14 55	15 08		15 25
Keighley	d	11 14	11 30	11 38	11 45	12 00		12 14	12 23	12 29	12 44	13 00	13 14	13 30	13 44	14 00		14 09	14 14	14 30	14 44	15 00	15 13	15 20	15 30
Crossflatts	d	11 17	11 33		11 48	12 03		12 17		12 33	12 47	13 03	13 17	13 33	13 47	14 03			14 17	14 34	14 47	15 03	15 16		15 34
Bingley	d	11 20	11 36	11 42	11 51	12 06		12 20		12 36	12 50	13 06	13 20	13 36	13 50	14 06		14 13	14 20	14 37	14 50	15 06	15 19	15 25	15 36
Saltaire	d	11 24	11 40		11 55	12 10		12 24		12 40	12 54	13 10	13 24	13 40	13 54	14 10			14 24	14 42	14 54	15 10	15 23		15 41
Shipley	a	11 27	11 43	11 49	11 58	12 14		12 28	12 33	12 44	12 57	13 12	13 27	13 42	13 57	14 12		14 18	14 28	14 44	14 58	15 12	15 27	15 30	15 43
	d	11 28	11 44	11 49	11 58	12 14		12 28	12 33	12 45	12 58	13 14	13 28	13 44	13 58	14 14		14 18	14 28	14 45	14 58	15 14	15 28	15 30	15 44
Frizinghall	37 a	11 32			12 02			12 32			13 02		13 32		14 02				14 32		15 02		15 32		
Bradford Forster Square	37 a	11 38			12 10			12 38			13 08		13 38		14 08				14 38		15 08		15 38		
Leeds 10	37 a		11 58	12 07		12 29			12 48	12 59		13 28		13 58		14 29		14 37		15 00		15 28		15 47	15 58
London Kings Cross 15	⊖26 a																								

Table 36R

Saturdays

14 December to 17 May

Carlisle, Morecambe, Lancaster and Skipton - Bradford and Leeds

Network Diagram - see first page of Table 35

			VT A 🚌		VT A 🚌	VT A 🚌	NT	NT	NT	NT	NT	NT	VT A 🚌		NT	NT	NT	NT	NT	NT	NT	NT	NT		NT	NT
Carlisle 8	65	d	12 20		13 00	14 20					14 26		15 00						15 49						16 18	
Armathwaite		d									14 40														16 32	
Lazonby & Kirkoswald		d									14 47														16 39	
Langwathby		d									14 53														16 45	
Appleby		d									15 09								16 26						17 01	
Kirkby Stephen		d									15 22								16 39						17 14	
Garsdale		d									15 35														17 27	
Dent		d									15 40														17 32	
Ribblehead		d									15 49														17 42	
Horton-in-Ribblesdale		d									15 56														17 48	
Settle		d									16 04								17 16						17 57	
Heysham Harbour	⛴	d																								
Morecambe	98	d																			16 21					
Bare Lane	98	d																			16 25					
Lancaster 6	65,82,98	d	14a25		15a25	16a25							17a25								16 40					
Carnforth	82	d																			16 50					
Wennington		d																			17 04					
Bentham		d																			17 09					
Clapham (Nth Yorkshire)		d																			17 16					
Giggleswick		d																			17 25					
Long Preston		d																			17 33				18 03	
Hellifield		d									16 11										17 36				18 06	
Clitheroe	94	a																								
Blackburn	94,97	a																								
Preston 8	97	a																								
Blackpool North	97	a																								
Gargrave		d																			17 44				18 14	
Skipton		a									16 26								17 38		17 54				18 23	
		d					15 31	15 47	16 01	16 17	16 28	16 33			16 47	17 01	17 19	17 29	17 41	17 47	17 58	18 01	18 16		18 27	18 31
Cononley		d					15 35	15 51	16 05	16 21		16 37			16 51	17 05	17 23	17 33		17 51		18 05	18 20			18 35
Steeton & Silsden		d					15 39	15 55	16 09	16 25		16 41			16 55	17 09	17 27	17 37		17 55		18 09	18 25			18 39
Keighley		d					15 44	16 00	16 14	16 30	16 38	16 46			17 00	17 14	17 32	17 42	17 51	18 00	18 08	18 14	18 29		18 38	18 44
Crossflatts		d					15 47	16 03	16 17	16 33		16 49			17 03	17 17	17 35	17 45		18 03		18 17	18 33			18 47
Bingley		d					15 50	16 06	16 20	16 36	16 42	16 52			17 06	17 20	17 38	17 48	17 55	18 06	18 14	18 20	18 35		18 42	18 50
Saltaire		d					15 54	16 10	16 24	16 40		16 56			17 10	17 24	17 42	17 52		18 10		18 24	18 40			18 54
Shipley		a					15 57	16 12	16 27	16 44	16 49	16 59			17 14	17 27	17 44	17 55	18 00	18 13	18 19	18 28	18 43		18 48	18 57
		d					15 58	16 14	16 28	16 45	16 49	16 59			17 15	17 28	17 45	17 56	18 00	18 14	18 19	18 28	18 44		18 48	18 57
Frizinghall	37	a					16 02		16 31			17 03				17 32		18 00				18 32				19 01
Bradford Forster Square	37	a					16 08		16 38			17 08				17 38		18 06				18 38				19 08
Leeds 10	37	a						16 28		16 59	17 07				17 29		18 00		18 17	18 29	18 42		18 59		19 07	
London Kings Cross 15	⊖26	a																								

			VT A 🚌	VT A 🚌	NT	NT	NT	NT	NT		NT	NT	NT	NT	NT	NT	NT	NT	NT		NT	NT				
Carlisle 8	65	d	16 20	16 40								18 07														
Armathwaite		d										18 21														
Lazonby & Kirkoswald		d										18 28														
Langwathby		d										18 34														
Appleby		d										18 49														
Kirkby Stephen		d										19 02														
Garsdale		d										19 15														
Dent		d										19 20														
Ribblehead		d										19 30						21 00								
Horton-in-Ribblesdale		d										19 36						21 06								
Settle		d										19 44						21 14								
Heysham Harbour	⛴	d																								
Morecambe	98	d												19 09												
Bare Lane	98	d												19 13												
Lancaster 6	65,82,98	d	18a25	18a30										19 24												
Carnforth	82	d												19 34												
Wennington		d												19 47												
Bentham		d												19 53												
Clapham (Nth Yorkshire)		d												20 00												
Giggleswick		d												20 09												
Long Preston		d												20 17				21 20								
Hellifield		d										19 52		20 20				21 23								
Clitheroe	94	a																								
Blackburn	94,97	a																								
Preston 8	97	a																								
Blackpool North	97	a																								
Gargrave		d												20 28				21 31								
Skipton		a										20 07		20 37				21 38								
		d			18 47	18 59	19 17	19 31	19 47		19 54	20 07	20 17	20 38	20 47	20 54	21 17		21 47		21 54	22 17				
Cononley		d			18 51	19 03	19 21	19 35	19 51		19 58		20 21		20 51	20 58	21 21		21 51		21 59	22 21				
Steeton & Silsden		d			18 55	19 07	19 25	19 39	19 55		20 02		20 25		20 55	21 02	21 25		21 55		22 03	22 25				
Keighley		d			19 00	19 12	19 30	19 44	20 00		20 07	20 17	20 30	20 48	21 00	21 07	21 30		22 00		22 08	22 30				
Crossflatts		d			19 03	19 15	19 33	19 47	20 03		20 10		20 32		21 03	21 10	21 33		22 03		22 11	22 33				
Bingley		d			19 06	19 18	19 36	19 50	20 06		20 13	20 22	20 36	20 53	21 06	21 13	21 36		22 06		22 14	22 36				
Saltaire		d			19 10	19 22	19 40	19 54	20 10		20 17		20 39		21 10	21 17	21 40		22 10		22 18	22 40				
Shipley		a			19 12	19 25	19 43	19 57	20 12		20 20	20 27	20 42	20 58	21 12	21 20	21 42		22 13		22 21	22 42				
		d			19 14	19 26	19 44	19 58	20 14		20 20	20 28	20 43	20 58	21 14	21 20	21 43		22 14		22 22	22 43				
Frizinghall	37	a				19 29		20 01			20 24					21 24					22 25					
Bradford Forster Square	37	a				19 35		20 08			20 32					21 31					22 31					
Leeds 10	37	a			19 29		19 59		20 28			20 46	21 00	21 16	21 30		21 59		22 32			23 01				
London Kings Cross 15	⊖26	a																								

A from 4 January until 8 February

Table 36R

Sundays

8 December to 11 May

Carlisle, Morecambe, Lancaster and Skipton - Bradford and Leeds

Network Diagram - see first page of Table 35

Station		NT	NT	NT	NT	NT	NT	NT	NT	NT	NT	NT	NT	NT	VT	VT	NT	NT	VT	NT	NT	NT	NT
															A 🚌	A 🚌			A 🚌			B	
Carlisle 8	65 d							09 25							12 13	12 20	12 59		13 00				
Armathwaite	d							09 39									13 13						
Lazonby & Kirkoswald	d							09 46									13 20						
Langwathby	d							09 53									13 27						
Appleby	d							10 07									13 41						
Kirkby Stephen	d							10 21									13 55						
Garsdale	d							10 34									14 08						
Dent	d							10 40									14 14						
Ribblehead	d							10 49									14 23						
Horton-in-Ribblesdale	d							10 56									14 30						
Settle	d							11 04									14 38						
Heysham Harbour	⛴ d																						
Morecambe	98 d												12 20									14 46	
Bare Lane	98 d												12 24									14 50	
Lancaster 8	65,82,98 d												12 48		14a18	14a10			15a25				
Carnforth	82 d												12 58									15 00	
Wennington	d												13 12									15 14	
Bentham	d												13 17									15 20	
Clapham (Nth Yorkshire)	d												13 24									15 26	
Giggleswick	d												13 32									15 35	
Long Preston	d							11 10					13 40				14 44					15 45	
Hellifield	d					10 30		11 13					13 44				14 47			14 55		15 49	
Clitheroe	94 a					10 53														15 16			
Blackburn	94,97 a					11 20														15 43			
Preston 8	97 a					11 46														16 04			
Blackpool North	97 a																			16 33			
Gargrave	d							11 21					13 52				14 55					15 57	
Skipton	a							11 30					14 01				15 04					16 06	
	d	08 34	09 14	09 36	10 14		11 14	11 30	11 36	12 14	13 14	13 36	14 02	14 14			15 06	15 14			15 36	16 08	16 14
Cononley	d	08 38	09 18	09 40	10 18		11 18		11 40	12 18	13 18	13 40		14 18				15 18			15 40		16 18
Steeton & Silsden	d	08 43	09 22	09 44	10 22		11 22		11 44	12 22	13 22	13 44		14 22				15 22			15 44		16 22
Keighley	d	08 47	09 27	09 49	10 27		11 27	11 40	11 49	12 27	13 27	13 49	14 12	14 27			15 16	15 27			15 49	16 18	16 27
Crossflatts	d	08 51	09 30	09 52	10 30		11 30		11 52	12 30	13 30	13 52		14 30				15 30			15 52		16 30
Bingley	d	08 53	09 33	09 55	10 33		11 33	11 44	11 55	12 33	13 33	13 55	14 16	14 33			15 20	15 33			15 55	16 23	16 33
Saltaire	d	08 58	09 37	09 59	10 37		11 37		11 59	12 37	13 37	13 59		14 37				15 37			15 59		16 37
Shipley	a	09 00	09 39	10 02	10 39		11 39	11 49	12 02	12 39	13 39	14 02	14 21	14 39			15 25	15 39			16 02	16 27	16 39
	d	09 00	09 40	10 02	10 40		11 40	11 49	12 02	12 40	13 40	14 02	14 21	14 40			15 25	15 40			16 02	16 29	16 40
Frizinghall	37 a			10 06					12 06			14 06									16 06		
Bradford Forster Square	37 a			10 12					12 12			14 12									16 12		
Leeds 10	37 a	09 14	09 54		10 54		11 54	12 06		12 54	13 54		14 39	14 54			15 44	15 54				16 47	16 54
London Kings Cross 15	⊖26 a																						

Station		NT	NT	NT	NT	NT	NT	NT	NT	NT	NT	NT	NT	NT	NT
		C													
Carlisle 8	65 d	15 20				17 00									
Armathwaite	d					17 14									
Lazonby & Kirkoswald	d					17 21									
Langwathby	d					17 28									
Appleby	d	15 57				17 43									
Kirkby Stephen	d	16 10				17 57									
Garsdale	d					18 10									
Dent	d					18 16									
Ribblehead	d					18 25									
Horton-in-Ribblesdale	d					18 32									
Settle	d	16 46				18 41									
Heysham Harbour	⛴ d														
Morecambe	98 d						17 45					20 00			
Bare Lane	98 d						17 49					20 04			
Lancaster 8	65,82,98 d						18 04					20 20			
Carnforth	82 d						18 14					20 30			
Wennington	d						18 28					20 44			
Bentham	d						18 33					20 49			
Clapham (Nth Yorkshire)	d						18 40					20 56			
Giggleswick	d						18 49					21 05			
Long Preston	d						18 57					21 13			
Hellifield	d					18 49	19 00					21 16			
Clitheroe	94 a														
Blackburn	94,97 a														
Preston 8	97 a														
Blackpool North	97 a														
Gargrave	d						19 09					21 24			
Skipton	a	17 07				19 04	19 17					21 33			
	d	17 09	17 14	17 36	18 14	19 05	19 18	19 23	19 36	20 14	21 14	21 33	21 39	22 14	23 14
Cononley	d		17 18	17 40	18 18			19 27	19 40	20 18	21 18		21 43	22 18	23 18
Steeton & Silsden	d		17 22	17 44	18 22			19 31	19 44	20 22	21 22		21 47	22 22	23 22
Keighley	d	17 19	17 27	17 49	18 27	19 15	19 28	19 36	19 49	20 27	21 27	21 43	21 52	22 27	23 28
Crossflatts	d		17 30	17 52	18 30			19 39	19 52	20 30	21 30		21 55	22 30	23 30
Bingley	d	17 24	17 33	17 55	18 33	19 20	19 32	19 42	19 55	20 33	21 33	21 48	21 58	22 33	23 33
Saltaire	d		17 37	17 59	18 37			19 46	19 59	20 37	21 37		22 02	22 37	23 36
Shipley	a	17 28	17 39	18 02	18 39	19 24	19 37	19 48	20 02	20 39	21 39	21 53	22 05	22 40	23 40
	d	17 29	17 40	18 02	18 40	19 25	19 38	19 49	20 02	20 40	21 40	21 54	22 05	22 40	23 40
Frizinghall	37 a			18 06					20 06				22 09		
Bradford Forster Square	37 a			18 12					20 12				22 15		
Leeds 10	37 a	17 45	17 54		18 54	19 42	19 56	20 03		20 54	21 54	22 10		22 54	23 57
London Kings Cross 15	⊖26 a														

A from 5 January until 9 February　**B** From Lancaster　**C** To Nottingham

Table 37

Mondays to Fridays

9 December to 16 May

Leeds - Shipley and Bradford

Network Diagram - see first page of Table 35

Miles	Miles			NT	NT ◇	NT	NT	NT	NT	NT	NT	NT		NT	NT	NT	NT	NT	NT	NT	NT	NT		NT	NT
0	0	**Leeds** 10	d	05 08	05 29		05 51	06 03	06 16		06 22	06 37			06 49	06 51	06 56		07 08	07 23		07 25			07 37
10¾	—	**Shipley**	a		05 41				06 29						07 01		07 08					07 36			
—	—		d			06 28				06 41				06 53	07 02			07 15			07 29			07 47	
11¾	—	Frizinghall	d			06 32				06 44				06 57	07 04			07 17			07 32			07 49	
—	4	Bramley	d	05 15			05 58				06 29	06 44							07 15	07 29					07 44
—	5¾	New Pudsey	d	05 20			06 02	06 13			06 34	06 49				07 01			07 20	07 34					07 49
—	9½	**Bradford Interchange**	a	05 28			06 13	06 21			06 42	06 57				07 11			07 28	07 43					07 57
13½	—	**Bradford Forster Square**	a			06 38				06 50				07 03	07 10			07 22			07 39			07 56	

		NT	NT	NT	NT	NT	NT	NT		NT	NT	NT	NT	NT	NT	NT	NT	NT ◇		NT	NT	NT	NT	NT	NT
Leeds 10	d	07 39	07 51		07 51		08 08	08 10		08 18		08 23	08 25		08 37	08 40		08 50		08 51	08 56		09 07	09 10	09 23
Shipley	a	07 50			08 02			08 22		08 30			08 37			08 51		09 02			09 07			09 21	
	d	07 51		07 56		08 13		08 23			08 30			08 48		08 52	08 58					09 18		09 22	
Frizinghall	d	07 53		07 59		08 15		08 25			08 33			08 51		08 54	09 02					09 21		09 24	
Bramley	d						08 15					08 30			08 44								09 14		09 30
New Pudsey	d		08 01				08 20					08 35			08 49					09 00			09 19		09 35
Bradford Interchange	a		08 09				08 28					08 43			08 57					09 12			09 28		09 43
Bradford Forster Square	a	07 59		08 05		08 21		08 31			08 39			08 57		09 00	09 09					09 27		09 31	

		NT	NT	NT		NT	NT	NT	NT ◇	NT	NT	NT	NT ◇	NT		NT	NT	NT	NT	NT	NT ◇	NT	NT	NT ◇	
Leeds 10	d		09 26			09 37	09 40		09 47	09 53	09 56		10 07	10 10			10 18	10 23	10 26		10 37	10 40		10 49	
Shipley	a		09 37				09 52		10 01		10 07			10 21			10 30		10 37			10 51		11 01	
	d	09 28		09 44			09 52	09 58				10 14		10 22		10 28				10 44		10 52	10 58		
Frizinghall	d	09 32		09 47			09 54	10 02				10 17		10 24		10 32				10 47		10 54	11 02		
Bramley	d					09 44							10 14					10 30			10 44				
New Pudsey	d					09 49				10 02			10 20					10 35			10 49				
Bradford Interchange	a					09 57				10 12			10 28					10 43			10 57				
Bradford Forster Square	a	09 38		09 53			10 02	10 08				10 23		10 30		10 38				10 53		11 00	11 08		

		NT	NT	NT	NT ◇	NT	NT	NT	NT	NT		NT ◇	NT	NT	NT	NT	NT	NT ◇	NT	NT		NT	NT	NT	NT
Leeds 10	d	10 53	10 56		11 07	11 10	11 23		11 26			11 37	11 40	11 53		11 56		12 07	12 10	12 23			12 26		12 37
Shipley	a		11 07			11 21			11 38				11 51			12 07			12 21				12 37		12 51
	d			11 14		11 22		11 28		11 44			11 52		11 58		12 14		12 22			12 28		12 44	12 52
Frizinghall	d			11 17		11 24		11 32		11 47			11 54		12 02		12 17		12 24			12 32		12 47	12 54
Bramley	d				11 14		11 30					11 44						12 14		12 30					
New Pudsey	d	11 02			11 19		11 35					11 49		12 02				12 19		12 35					
Bradford Interchange	a	11 11			11 28		11 43					11 57		12 11				12 28		12 43					
Bradford Forster Square	a			11 23		11 30		11 38		11 53			12 00		12 10		12 24		12 31			12 38		12 53	13 00

		NT ◇	NT	NT ◇	NT	NT		NT	NT ◇	NT	NT	NT	NT	NT	NT	NT ◇		NT	NT	NT	NT	NT	NT ◇	NT	NT
Leeds 10	d	12 37		12 49	12 53	12 56			13 07	13 10	13 14		13 23	13 26		13 37		13 40	13 53		13 56		14 07	14 10	14 23
Shipley	a			13 01		13 07				13 21	13 28			13 38				13 51			14 07			14 21	
	d		12 58					13 14		13 22		13 28			13 44			13 52		13 58		14 14		14 22	
Frizinghall	d		13 02					13 17		13 24		13 32			13 47			13 54		14 02		14 17		14 24	
Bramley	d	12 44							13 14				13 30			13 44							14 14		14 30
New Pudsey	d	12 49			13 02				13 19				13 35			13 49			14 02				14 19		14 35
Bradford Interchange	a	12 57			13 12				13 28				13 43			13 58			14 12				14 28		14 43
Bradford Forster Square	a		13 08					13 23		13 30		13 38			13 53			14 00		14 08		14 23		14 30	

		NT		NT	NT	NT ◇	NT	NT	NT ◇	NT	NT	NT		NT ◇	NT	NT	NT	NT	NT	NT ◇	NT	NT		NT	NT
Leeds 10	d			14 26		14 37	14 40		14 49	14 53	14 56			15 07	15 10	15 23		15 26		15 37	15 40	15 52			15 56
Shipley	a			14 37			14 51		15 01		15 07				15 21			15 37			15 52				16 07
	d	14 28			14 44		14 52	14 58				15 14			15 22		15 28		15 44		15 52			15 58	
Frizinghall	d	14 32			14 47		14 54	15 01				15 17			15 24		15 32		15 47		15 55			16 02	
Bramley	d					14 44								15 14		15 30				15 44					
New Pudsey	d					14 49				15 02				15 19		15 35				15 49		16 01			
Bradford Interchange	a					14 57				15 12				15 28		15 43				15 57		16 10			
Bradford Forster Square	a	14 39			14 53		15 00	15 08				15 23			15 30		15 38		15 53		16 01			16 08	

		NT	NT ◇	NT	NT	NT	NT	NT		NT	NT ◇	NT	NT	NT	NT	NT	NT	NT		NT	NT	NT	NT	NT	NT
Leeds 10	d		16 07	16 10	16 23		16 26			16 35	16 37	16 39		16 51	16 56		17 07	17 10		17 23		17 26		17 37	17 37
Shipley	a			16 21			16 37			16 49		16 53			17 07			17 21				17 37		17 49	
	d	16 14		16 22		16 28		16 44		16 49			17 02			17 15		17 22			17 28		17 44	17 50	
Frizinghall	d	16 17		16 24		16 31		16 47		16 52			17 06			17 17		17 24			17 32		17 46	17 52	
Bramley	d		16 14		16 30						16 44						17 14			17 30					17 44
New Pudsey	d		16 19		16 35						16 49			17 00			17 19			17 35					17 49
Bradford Interchange	a		16 28		16 43						16 57			17 10			17 28			17 43					17 57
Bradford Forster Square	a	16 23		16 30		16 38		16 53		16 58			17 12			17 23		17 30			17 38		17 53	17 58	

Table 37

Leeds - Shipley and Bradford

Mondays to Fridays

9 December to 16 May

Network Diagram - see first page of Table 35

		NT	NT	NT	NT	NT	NT	NT	NT	NT		NT	NT	NT	NT	NT	NT	NT	NT	NT		NT	NT	NT	NT
							◇								◇							◇			
Leeds 10	d	17 41		17 51	17 56		18 06	18 08	18 10	18 23			18 26		18 36	18 40	18 51		18 54			19 08	19 10		19 19
Shipley	a	17 53			18 07		18 18		18 22				18 38			18 51			19 05				19 21		19 31
	d		17 55			18 14			18 22			18 28		18 44		18 52		18 57		19 14			19 22	19 26	
Frizinghall	d		17 58			18 17			18 24			18 32		18 46		18 56		19 01		19 17			19 24	19 29	
Bramley	d							18 15		18 30					18 45							19 15			
New Pudsey	d			18 01				18 20		18 35					18 49		19 01					19 20			
Bradford Interchange	a			18 10				18 28		18 43					18 58		19 09					19 28			
Bradford Forster Square	a		18 04			18 23			18 31			18 38		18 52		19 02		19 08		19 23			19 30	19 35	

		NT	NT	NT	NT	NT		NT	NT	NT	NT	NT	NT	NT	NT	NT		NT	GR	NT	NT	NT	NT	NT	NT
					◇									◇					R 1					◇	
Leeds 10	d	19 23	19 26		19 37			19 56		20 08		20 26		20 37	20 51			20 56	21 01		21 08	21 26		21 37	
Shipley	a		19 37					20 07				20 37						21 07	21s12			21 38			
	d			19 44		19 58			20 20		20 28		20 48			21 03				21 20			21 48		22 03
Frizinghall	d			19 47		20 01			20 24		20 30		20 51			21 05				21 24			21 51		22 05
Bramley	d	19 30			19 44					20 15				20 44							21 15			21 44	
New Pudsey	d	19 35			19 49					20 20				20 49	21 01						21 20			21 49	
Bradford Interchange	a	19 44			19 57					20 28				20 57	21 10						21 28			21 57	
Bradford Forster Square	a			19 53		20 08			20 32		20 36		20 57			21 12			21 23	21 31			21 57		22 11

		NT		NT	NT	NT	NT	NT	NT	NT	NT	NT
								◇				
Leeds 10	d	21 56			22 08	22 26		22 37		22 56	23 08	23 18
Shipley	a	22 07				22 37				23 08		23 31
	d			22 22			22 48		23 03			
Frizinghall	d			22 25			22 51		23 05			
Bramley	d				22 15			22 44			23 15	
New Pudsey	d				22 20			22 49			23 20	
Bradford Interchange	a				22 28			22 57			23 29	
Bradford Forster Square	a			22 31			22 57		23 13			

Saturdays

14 December to 17 May

		NT	NT	NT	NT	NT	NT	NT	NT	NT		NT	NT	NT	NT	NT	NT	NT	NT	NT		NT	NT	NT	NT
Leeds 10	d	05 37	05 51	05 54		06 16	06 19		06 37	06 51		06 56	07 08	07 10	07 23		07 37		07 51			07 56	08 08	08 10	
Shipley	a			06 06			06 31					07 08		07 21								08 08		08 22	
	d				06 28			06 44						07 22		07 32		07 47		07 57				08 23	08 29
Frizinghall	d				06 32			06 47						07 24		07 36		07 49		08 00				08 25	08 32
Bramley	d	05 44	05 58			06 23			06 44				07 15		07 30		07 44						08 15		
New Pudsey	d	05 49	06 02			06 28			06 49	07 01			07 20		07 35		07 49		08 01				08 20		
Bradford Interchange	a	05 57	06 13			06 36			06 57	07 11			07 28		07 43		07 57		08 09				08 28		
Bradford Forster Square	a				06 38			06 55						07 30		07 42		07 56		08 06				08 31	08 39

		NT	NT	NT	NT	NT		NT	NT	NT	NT	NT	NT	NT	NT	NT		NT	NT	NT	NT	NT	NT	NT	NT
Leeds 10	d	08 19	08 23	08 25		08 37		08 40		08 49	08 51	08 56		09 07	09 10	09 23			09 26		09 37	09 40		09 47	09 53
Shipley	a	08 31		08 37				08 51		09 01		09 07			09 21				09 37			09 52		10 01	
	d				08 44			08 52	08 58				09 14		09 22			09 28		09 44		09 52	09 58		
Frizinghall	d				08 46			08 54	09 02				09 17		09 24			09 32		09 47		09 54	10 02		
Bramley	d		08 30			08 44								09 14		09 30					09 44				
New Pudsey	d		08 35			08 49					09 00			09 19		09 35					09 49				10 02
Bradford Interchange	a		08 43			08 57					09 12			09 28		09 43					09 57				10 11
Bradford Forster Square	a				08 53			09 00	09 09				09 24		09 31			09 38		09 53		10 02	10 08		

		NT		NT	NT	NT	NT	NT	NT	NT	NT	NT		NT	NT	NT	NT	NT	NT	NT	NT	NT		NT	NT
Leeds 10	d	09 56			10 07	10 10		10 19	10 23	10 26		10 37		10 40		10 49	10 53	10 56		11 07	11 10	11 23			11 26
Shipley	a	10 07				10 21		10 31		10 37				10 51		11 01		11 07			11 21				11 38
	d			10 14		10 22	10 28				10 44			10 52	10 58				11 14		11 22			11 28	
Frizinghall	d			10 17		10 24	10 32				10 47			10 54	11 02				11 17		11 24			11 32	
Bramley	d				10 14				10 30			10 44								11 14		11 30			
New Pudsey	d				10 19				10 35			10 49					11 02			11 19		11 35			
Bradford Interchange	a				10 28				10 43			10 57					11 12			11 28		11 43			
Bradford Forster Square	a			10 23		10 30	10 38				10 53			11 00	11 08				11 23		11 30			11 38	

		NT	NT	NT	NT	NT	NT	NT		NT	NT	NT	NT	NT	NT	NT	NT	NT		NT	NT	NT	NT	NT	NT
Leeds 10	d		11 37	11 40	11 53		11 56			12 07	12 10	12 23		12 26		12 37	12 40			12 49	12 53	12 56		13 07	13 10
Shipley	a			11 51			12 07				12 21			12 37			12 51			13 01		13 07			13 21
	d	11 44		11 52		11 58		12 14			12 22		12 28		12 44		12 52	12 58					13 14		13 22
Frizinghall	d	11 47		11 54		12 02		12 17			12 24		12 32		12 47		12 54	13 02					13 17		13 24
Bramley	d		11 44							12 14		12 30				12 44								13 14	
New Pudsey	d		11 49		12 02					12 19		12 35				12 49					13 02			13 19	
Bradford Interchange	a		11 57		12 12					12 28		12 43				12 57					13 12			13 28	
Bradford Forster Square	a	11 53		12 00		12 10		12 24			12 31		12 38		12 53		13 00	13 08					13 23		13 30

		NT	NT	NT		NT	NT	NT	NT	NT	NT	NT	NT	NT		NT	NT	NT	NT	NT	NT	NT	NT	NT	
Leeds 10	d	13 23		13 26			13 37	13 40		13 49	13 53	13 56		14 07		14 10	14 23		14 26		14 37	14 40		14 49	
Shipley	a			13 37				13 51		14 03		14 07				14 21			14 37			14 51		15 01	
	d		13 28			13 44		13 52	13 58				14 14			14 22		14 28		14 44		14 52	14 58		
Frizinghall	d		13 32			13 47		13 54	14 02				14 17			14 24		14 32		14 47		14 54	15 02		
Bramley	d	13 30					13 44							14 14			14 30				14 44				
New Pudsey	d	13 35					13 49				14 02			14 19			14 35				14 49				
Bradford Interchange	a	13 43					13 58				14 12			14 28			14 43				14 57				
Bradford Forster Square	a		13 38			13 53		14 00	14 08				14 23			14 30		14 38		14 53		15 00	15 08		

Table 37

Saturdays

14 December to 17 May

Leeds - Shipley and Bradford

Network Diagram - see first page of Table 35

		NT	NT	NT	NT	NT		NT	NT	NT	NT	NT	NT	NT	NT	NT		NT	NT	NT	NT	NT	NT	NT	NT
Leeds 10	d	14 53	14 56		15 07	15 10		15 23		15 26		15 37	15 40	15 52		15 56			16 07	16 10	16 23		16 26		16 35
Shipley	a		15 07			15 21				15 37			15 52			16 07				16 21			16 37		16 49
	d			15 14		15 22			15 28		15 44		15 52		15 58			16 14		16 22		16 28		16 44	16 49
Frizinghall	d			15 17		15 24			15 32		15 47		15 55		16 02			16 17		16 24		16 31		16 47	16 52
Bramley	d				15 14			15 30				15 44							16 14		16 30				
New Pudsey	d	15 02			15 19			15 35				15 49		16 01					16 19		16 35				
Bradford Interchange	a	15 12			15 28			15 43				15 57		16 10					16 28		16 43				
Bradford Forster Square	a			15 23		15 30			15 38		15 53		16 01		16 08			16 23		16 30		16 38		16 53	16 58

		NT		NT	NT	NT	NT	NT	NT	NT	NT	NT		NT	NT	NT	NT	NT	NT	NT	NT	NT		NT	NT
Leeds 10	d	16 37		16 39		16 51	16 56		17 07	17 10	17 23			17 26		17 37	17 40		17 50	17 51	17 56			18 08	18 10
Shipley	a			16 53			17 07			17 21				17 37			17 51		18 02		18 07				18 22
	d				16 59			17 15		17 22		17 28			17 44		17 52	17 56				18 14			18 22
Frizinghall	d				17 03			17 17		17 24		17 32			17 46		17 54	18 00				18 17			18 24
Bramley	d	16 44							17 14		17 30					17 44								18 15	
New Pudsey	d	16 49				17 00			17 19		17 35					17 49				18 01				18 20	
Bradford Interchange	a	16 57				17 10			17 28		17 43					17 57				18 09				18 28	
Bradford Forster Square	a				17 08			17 23		17 30		17 38			17 53		18 00	18 06				18 23			18 31

		NT	NT	NT	NT	NT	NT	NT		NT	NT	NT	NT	NT	NT	NT	NT	NT		NT	NT	NT	NT	NT	NT
Leeds 10	d	18 23		18 26		18 37	18 40	18 51			18 56		19 08	19 10		19 19	19 23	19 26			19 37		19 56		20 08
Shipley	a			18 38			18 52				19 07			19 21		19 31		19 37					20 07		
	d		18 28		18 44		18 52			18 57		19 14		19 22	19 26					19 44		19 58		20 20	
Frizinghall	d		18 32		18 46		18 55			19 01		19 17		19 24	19 29					19 47		20 01		20 24	
Bramley	d	18 30				18 44							19 15				19 30				19 44				20 15
New Pudsey	d	18 35				18 49		19 01					19 20				19 35				19 49				20 20
Bradford Interchange	a	18 43				18 58		19 09					19 28				19 44				19 57				20 28
Bradford Forster Square	a		18 38		18 52		19 01			19 08		19 23		19 30	19 35					19 53		20 08		20 32	

		NT	NT	NT		NT	NT	NT	NT	NT	NT	NT	NT	NT		NT	GR R 1	NT	NT	NT	NT	NT	NT	NT	
Leeds 10	d		20 26			20 37	20 51		20 56		21 08	21 26		21 37			22 00	22 03		22 08	22 26		22 37		
Shipley	a		20 37						21 07			21 38					22s11	22 15			22 37				
	d	20 28		20 48				21 03		21 20			21 48			22 03			22 22			22 48		23 03	
Frizinghall	d	20 30		20 51				21 05		21 24			21 51			22 05			22 25			22 51		23 05	
Bramley	d					20 44					21 15			21 44						22 15			22 44		
New Pudsey	d					20 49	21 01				21 20			21 49						22 20			22 49		
Bradford Interchange	a					20 57	21 10				21 28			21 57						22 28			22 57		
Bradford Forster Square	a	20 36		20 57				21 12		21 31			21 57			22 11	22 20		22 31			22 57		23 13	

		NT	NT	NT
Leeds 10	d	22 56	23 00	23 18
Shipley	a	23 08		23 31
	d			
Frizinghall	d			
Bramley	d		23 07	
New Pudsey	d		23 12	
Bradford Interchange	a		23 21	
Bradford Forster Square	a			

Sundays

8 December to 11 May

		NT A	NT	NT	NT	NT	NT	NT	NT	NT		NT	NT	NT	NT	NT	NT	NT	NT	NT		NT	NT	NT	NT
Leeds 10	d	07 40	08 02	08 21	08 34	08 40	08 45	09 00	09 02	09 18		09 34	09 35	09 54			10 08	10 12	10 34	10 35		10 51	10 54	11 08	11 12
Shipley	a				08 45	08 52		09 15				09 45					10 19		10 45			11 03		11 19	
	d				08 46							09 46			10 02	10 15			10 46						
Frizinghall	d				08 48							09 48			10 06	10 18			10 48						
Bramley	d		08 09	08 28					09 09	09 25				10 01				10 19					11 01		11 19
New Pudsey	d	08 00	08 14	08 33			08 54		09 14	09 30			09 44	10 06				10 24		10 44			11 06		11 24
Bradford Interchange	a	08 10	08 22	08 41			09 03		09 22	09 38			09 53	10 14				10 32		10 53			11 14		11 32
Bradford Forster Square	a				08 54							09 54			10 12	10 24			10 54						

		NT ◇	NT	NT	NT	NT		NT	NT	NT	NT	NT	NT	NT	NT	NT		NT	NT	NT	NT	NT	NT	NT	NT
Leeds 10	d	11 20	11 34	11 35	11 54				12 08	12 13	12 34	12 35	12 54	13 08	13 13	13 34		13 35	13 54		13 55		14 08	14 12	14 34
Shipley	a	11 32	11 45						12 19		12 45			13 19		13 45					14 07		14 19		14 45
	d		11 46			12 02		12 15			12 46					13 46				14 02		14 15			14 46
Frizinghall	d		11 48			12 06		12 18			12 48					13 48				14 06		14 18			14 48
Bramley	d				12 01					12 20				13 01	13 20				14 01					14 19	
New Pudsey	d			11 44	12 06					12 25			12 44	13 06	13 25			13 44	14 06					14 24	
Bradford Interchange	a			11 53	12 14					12 33			12 53	13 14	13 33			13 53	14 14					14 32	
Bradford Forster Square	a		11 54			12 12		12 24			12 54					13 54				14 12		14 24			14 54

A until 23 March

Table 37

Sundays

8 December to 11 May

Leeds - Shipley and Bradford

Network Diagram - see first page of Table 35

		NT	NT	NT	NT	NT	NT	NT		NT	NT	NT	NT	NT	NT	NT	NT	NT		NT	NT	NT	NT	NT	NT
Leeds 10	d	14 35	14 54	14 57	15 08	15 12	15 34	15 35		15 54			16 08	16 13	16 35	16 35	16 54	17 08		17 12	17 21	17 34	17 35	17 40	
Shipley	a			15 09	15 19		15 45						16 19			16 46		17 19			17 33	17 45		17 52	
	d						15 46				16 02	16 15				16 46						17 46			18 02
Frizinghall	d						15 48				16 06	16 18				16 48						17 48			18 06
Bramley	d		15 01			15 19				16 01				16 20			17 01			17 19					
New Pudsey	d	14 44	15 06			15 24		15 44		16 06				16 25	16 44		17 06			17 24			17 44		
Bradford Interchange	a	14 53	15 14			15 32		15 53		16 14				16 33	16 53		17 14			17 32			17 53		
Bradford Forster Square	a						15 54				16 12	16 24				16 55						17 54			18 12

		NT	NT	NT		NT	NT	NT	NT	NT	NT	NT	NT	NT		NT	NT	NT	NT	NT	NT	NT	NT	NT	
Leeds 10	d	17 54		18 08		18 13	18 34	18 35	19 03	19 08	19 34	19 35	19 54				20 08	20 12	20 34	20 35	21 04	21 08	21 34	21 35	
Shipley	a			18 19			18 45			19 19	19 45						20 19		20 45			21 19	21 45		
	d		18 15				18 46				19 46			20 02		20 15			20 46				21 46		
Frizinghall	d		18 18				18 48				19 48			20 06		20 18			20 48				21 48		
Bramley	d	18 01				18 20			19 10				20 01					20 19			21 12			21 43	
New Pudsey	d	18 06				18 25		18 44	19 15			19 44	20 06					20 24		20 44	21 17			21 47	
Bradford Interchange	a	18 14				18 33		18 53	19 24			19 53	20 14					20 34		20 53	21 25			21 56	
Bradford Forster Square	a		18 24				18 54				19 54			20 12		20 24			20 54				21 54		

		NT	NT	NT	NT	NT	NT	NT	NT
Leeds 10	d		22 05		22 08	22 34	22 38	23 20	23 22
Shipley	a				22 19	22 46		23 31	
	d	22 05		22 15		22 47			
Frizinghall	d	22 09		22 18		22 49			
Bramley	d		22 12				22 45		23 29
New Pudsey	d		22 17				22 50		23 34
Bradford Interchange	a		22 27				22 58		23 43
Bradford Forster Square	a	22 15		22 24		22 56			

Table 37R

Mondays to Fridays

9 December to 16 May

Bradford and Shipley - Leeds

Network Diagram - see first page of Table 35

Miles	Miles			NT MX	NT	NT	NT	NT	NT	GR R 1 A		NT	NT	NT	NT	NT	NT	NT	NT	GR R 1		NT	NT	NT	NT
0	—	**Bradford Forster Square**	d		05 59	06 04		06 15		06 30		06 39		06 44		06 55			07 11			07 15			
—	0	**Bradford Interchange**	d	00 37					06 18						06 47			07 02					07 20		07 34
—	3½	New Pudsey	d						06 27						06 56			07 11					07 28		07 42
—	5½	Bramley	d						06 31						07 00			07 15							07 46
1¾	—	Frizinghall	d		06 02	06 07		06 18				06 43		06 47		06 58			07 14			07 18			
2¾	—	**Shipley**	a		06 06	06 11		06 22				06 47		06 51		07 02			07 18			07 22			
—	—		d		06 08		06 13			06u36			06 42			07 02	07 09			07u17				07 35	
13½	9½	**Leeds** 10	a	00 55	06 22		06 27		06 41	06 52			06 57		07 09	07 16	07 23	07 26		07 31			07 39	07 49	07 57

		NT	NT	NT	NT	NT		NT	NT	NT	NT	NT	NT ◇	NT	NT	NT		NT	NT	NT	NT	NT	NT	NT	NT
Bradford Forster Square	d	07 41		07 45				07 59		08 09		08 16			08 26				08 41		08 46			09 01	
Bradford Interchange	d				07 50				08 05					08 20				08 34				08 50			09 04
New Pudsey	d				07 58				08 13					08 28				08 42				08 58			09 12
Bramley	d				08 02				08 18									08 46				09 02			09 16
Frizinghall	d	07 44		07 49				08 02		08 12		08 19			08 29				08 44		08 49			09 04	
Shipley	a	07 48		07 52				08 06		08 16		08 23			08 33				08 48		08 53			09 08	
	d		07 47			08 02		08 07			08 13		08 19		08 33	08 41				08 47			09 07	09 09	
Leeds 10	a		08 03		08 12	08 17		08 24	08 29		08 30		08 37	08 39	08 49	08 56		08 57		09 06		09 12	09 22	09 25	09 27

		NT		NT	NT	NT	NT	NT	NT	NT	NT	NT		NT	NT	NT	NT	NT	NT	NT	NT	NT		NT	NT
Bradford Forster Square	d	09 11		09 16		09 31		09 41		09 46		10 01		10 11			10 16		10 31		10 41			10 46	
Bradford Interchange	d				09 20		09 34				09 50					10 05		10 18		10 34					10 50
New Pudsey	d				09 27		09 42				09 58					10 14		10 28		10 42					10 58
Bramley	d						09 46				10 02					10 18				10 46					11 02
Frizinghall	d	09 14		09 19		09 34		09 44		09 49		10 04		10 14			10 19		10 34		10 44			10 49	
Shipley	a	09 18		09 23		09 38		09 48		09 53		10 08		10 18			10 23		10 38		10 48			10 53	
	d					09 39			09 44			10 09			10 14				10 39			10 44			
Leeds 10	a				09 39	09 53	09 57		09 59		10 12	10 24			10 28	10 29		10 38	10 53	10 57		10 58			11 12

		NT	NT	NT	NT	NT	NT ◇	NT		NT	NT ◇	NT	NT	NT	NT ◇	NT	NT	NT		NT	NT	NT B	NT C	NT	NT
Bradford Forster Square	d	11 01		11 11		11 16				11 31		11 41		11 46		12 01		12 11			12 16				12 31
Bradford Interchange	d		11 05					11 20			11 34				11 50		12 05					12 19	12 19		
New Pudsey	d		11 13					11 28			11 42				11 58		12 13					12 28	12 28		
Bramley	d		11 17								11 46				12 02		12 17								
Frizinghall	d	11 04		11 14		11 19				11 34		11 44		11 49		12 04		12 14			12 19				12 34
Shipley	a	11 08		11 18		11 23				11 38		11 48		11 53		12 08		12 18			12 23				12 38
	d	11 09			11 14		11 18			11 39			11 44			12 09				12 14				12 33	12 39
Leeds 10	a	11 24	11 27		11 29		11 36	11 39		11 55	11 57		11 58		12 14	12 24	12 27			12 29		12 37	12 39	12 52	12 54

		NT ◇	NT	NT		NT	NT ◇	NT	NT	NT	NT	NT	NT	NT		NT ◇	NT	NT	NT	NT ◇	NT	NT	NT	NT	
Bradford Forster Square	d		12 41			12 46		13 01		13 11		13 15		13 31			13 41		13 46		14 01		14 11		
Bradford Interchange	d	12 34					12 50		13 05				13 19			13 34				13 50		14 05			
New Pudsey	d	12 42					12 58		13 13				13 28			13 42				13 58		14 13			
Bramley	d	12 46					13 02		13 17							13 46				14 02		14 17			
Frizinghall	d		12 44			12 49		13 04		13 14		13 19		13 34			13 44		13 49		14 04		14 14		
Shipley	a		12 48			12 53		13 08		13 18		13 22		13 38			13 48		13 53		14 08		14 18		
	d			12 45				13 09			13 14			13 39				13 44			14 09			14 14	
Leeds 10	a	12 57		12 59			13 13	13 24	13 27		13 28		13 40	13 54		13 57		13 58		14 14	14 24	14 27		14 29	

		NT	NT ◇	NT	NT	NT ◇	NT	NT	NT	NT ◇		NT	NT	NT	NT	NT	NT	NT	NT	NT ◇		NT	NT	NT	NT ◇
Bradford Forster Square	d	14 16			14 31		14 41		14 46			15 01		15 11		15 16			15 31			15 41		15 46	
Bradford Interchange	d			14 19		14 34				14 50			15 05				15 19			15 34					15 50
New Pudsey	d			14 28		14 42				14 58			15 13				15 28			15 42					15 58
Bramley	d					14 46				15 02			15 17							15 46					16 02
Frizinghall	d	14 19			14 34		14 44		14 49			15 04		15 14		15 19			15 34			15 44		15 49	
Shipley	a	14 23			14 38		14 48		14 53			15 08		15 18		15 23			15 38			15 48		15 53	
	d		14 18		14 39			14 45				15 09			15 14			15 30	15 39				15 44		
Leeds 10	a		14 37	14 39	14 52	14 57		15 00		15 13		15 24	15 27		15 28		15 39	15 47	15 54	15 57			15 58		16 13

		NT	NT	NT	NT	NT		NT	NT ◇	NT	NT ◇	NT	NT	NT	NT ◇	NT		NT	NT	NT	NT	NT	NT	NT	NT ◇
Bradford Forster Square	d	16 01		16 11		16 16				16 31		16 40		16 44		17 01			17 11		17 16			17 31	
Bradford Interchange	d		16 05					16 19			16 34				16 50			17 05				17 19			17 34
New Pudsey	d		16 13					16 28			16 42				16 58			17 13				17 28			17 42
Bramley	d		16 17								16 46				17 02			17 17							17 46
Frizinghall	d	16 04		16 14		16 19				16 34		16 43		16 48		17 04			17 14		17 19			17 34	
Shipley	a	16 08		16 18		16 23				16 38		16 48		16 52		17 08			17 18		17 23			17 38	
	d	16 09			16 14				16 31	16 39			16 45			17 09				17 15			17 23	17 39	
Leeds 10	a	16 25	16 27		16 28			16 39	16 53	16 53	16 57		16 59		17 13	17 24		17 27		17 29		17 39	17 40	17 55	17 57

A West Riding Limited

B from 24 March

C until 21 March

Table 37R

Mondays to Fridays

9 December to 16 May

Bradford and Shipley - Leeds

Network Diagram - see first page of Table 35

		NT	NT	NT	NT	NT	NT	NT		NT	NT	NT	NT	NT	NT	NT	NT	NT		NT	NT	NT	NT	NT	NT
																				◇					
Bradford Forster Square	d	17 38		17 47			18 01	18 11				18 16		18 27		18 41		18 46				19 01		19 07	
Bradford Interchange	d				17 50						18 07		18 19		18 34						18 52		19 05		
New Pudsey	d				17 58						18 15		18 28		18 43						19 00		19 14		
Bramley	d				18 02						18 19				18 47						19 04		19 18		
Frizinghall	d	17 41		17 50			18 04	18 14				18 19		18 30		18 44		18 49				19 04		19 10	
Shipley	a	17 45		17 54			18 08	18 18				18 23		18 34		18 48		18 53				19 08		19 14	
	d		17 45			17 58	18 09			18 14				18 34			18 44			18 48		19 09			19 14
Leeds 10	a		18 00		18 12	18 15	18 24			18 29	18 31		18 39	18 49	18 57		18 59			19 06	19 13	19 26	19 27		19 31

		NT	NT	NT		NT	NT	NT	NT	NT	NT	NT	NT	NT		NT	NT	NT	NT	NT	NT	NT	NT	NT	
																◇	◇							A 🚌	
Bradford Forster Square	d		19 31			19 36		19 41		20 07				20 25				20 38				21 05			
Bradford Interchange	d	19 19		19 34					19 50			20 04	20 19				20 37				21 04			21 10	
New Pudsey	d	19 27		19 42					19 59			20 13	20 28				20 46				21 13			21 20	
Bramley	d			19 46					20 03			20 17					20 50				21 17				
Frizinghall	d		19 34			19 39		19 44		20 10				20 28				20 41				21 08			
Shipley	a		19 38			19 43		19 48		20 15				20 32				20 45				21 12			
	d		19 39				19 44				20 14					20 35			20 51	20 59			21 14		
Leeds 10	a	19 39	19 55	19 57			19 59		20 14		20 28	20 30	20 38			20 54	20 59		21 05	21 17	21 25		21 30	21 40	

		NT	NT	NT	NT	NT	NT	NT	NT	NT		NT	NT	NT	NT	NT	NT	NT	NT						
				◇								◇					A 🚌								
Bradford Forster Square	d	21 25			21 38		22 05			22 25			22 38			23 09		23 20							
Bradford Interchange	d			21 37		22 04			22 17			22 37			23 04		23 10		23 46						
New Pudsey	d			21 46		22 13			22 26			22 46			23 13		23 20		23 54						
Bramley	d			21 50		22 17						22 50			23 17				23 58						
Frizinghall	d	21 28			21 41		22 08			22 28			22 41			23 12		23 23							
Shipley	a	21 32			21 45		22 12			22 32			22 45			23 16		23 27							
	d		21 43					22 16						22 43											
Leeds 10	a		21 59	22 01		22 25		22 33	22 36			23 00		23 01	23 26		23 40		00 08						

Saturdays

14 December to 17 May

		NT	NT	NT	NT	NT	NT	NT	NT	NT		NT	NT	GR	NT	GR	NT	NT	NT	NT		NT	NT	NT	NT
														R 1		R 1									
Bradford Forster Square	d		06 01	06 10		06 15		07 01		07 11			07 15			07 33			07 59	08 11				08 16	
Bradford Interchange	d	00 37					06 26		07 05						07 20		07 34	07 50					08 05		
New Pudsey	d						06 35		07 14						07 28		07 42	07 58					08 14		
Bramley	d						06 39		07 18								07 46	08 02					08 18		
Frizinghall	d		06 04	06 13		06 18		07 04		07 14			07 18						08 02	08 14				08 19	
Shipley	a		06 08	06 17		06 22		07 08		07 18			07 23						08 06	08 18				08 23	
	d		06 08		06 13			07 09				07 13		07u19		07u40			08 07			08 13			08 19
Leeds 10	a	00 55	06 22		06 27		06 49	07 23	07 27			07 27		07 33	07 39	07 54	07 57	08 11	08 24			08 28	08 30		08 37

		NT	NT	NT	NT	NT		NT	NT	NT	NT	NT	NT	NT	NT	NT		NT	NT	NT	NT	NT	NT	NT	NT
Bradford Forster Square	d		08 31		08 41			08 46		09 01		09 11		09 16		09 31			09 41		09 46			10 01	
Bradford Interchange	d	08 20		08 34					08 50		09 04				09 20			09 34				09 50			10 05
New Pudsey	d	08 28		08 42					08 58		09 12				09 27			09 42				09 58			10 13
Bramley	d			08 46					09 02		09 16							09 46				10 02			10 17
Frizinghall	d		08 34		08 44			08 49		09 04		09 14		09 19		09 34			09 44		09 49			10 04	
Shipley	a		08 38		08 48			08 53		09 08		09 18		09 23		09 38			09 48		09 53			10 08	
	d		08 38			08 44				09 09			09 14			09 39				09 44			10 02	10 09	
Leeds 10	a	08 39	08 54	08 56		08 58			09 12	09 25	09 27		09 28		09 39	09 53		09 57		09 59		10 12	10 20	10 25	10 27

		NT		NT	NT	NT	NT	NT	NT	NT	NT	NT		NT	NT	NT	NT	NT	NT	NT	NT	NT		NT	NT
Bradford Forster Square	d	10 11			10 16			10 31		10 41		10 46			11 01		11 11		11 16		11 31			11 41	
Bradford Interchange	d						10 18		10 34					10 50		11 05				11 20		11 34			
New Pudsey	d						10 28		10 42					10 58		11 13				11 28		11 42			
Bramley	d								10 46					11 02		11 17						11 46			
Frizinghall	d	10 14			10 19			10 34		10 44		10 49			11 04		11 14		11 19		11 34			11 44	
Shipley	a	10 18			10 23			10 38		10 48		10 53			11 08		11 18		11 23		11 38			11 48	
	d			10 14		10 19		10 39			10 44				11 09			11 14			11 39				11 44
Leeds 10	a			10 28		10 34	10 38	10 53	10 57		10 58			11 13	11 24	11 27		11 29		11 39	11 55	11 57			11 58

		NT	NT	NT	NT	NT	NT	NT		NT	NT	NT	NT	NT	NT	NT	NT	NT		NT	NT	NT	NT	NT	NT
Bradford Forster Square	d	11 46			12 01		12 11			12 16			12 31		12 41		12 46			13 01		13 11		13 15	
Bradford Interchange	d			11 50		12 05					12 19			12 34				12 50			13 05				13 19
New Pudsey	d			11 58		12 13					12 28			12 42				12 58			13 13				13 28
Bramley	d			12 02		12 17								12 46				13 02			13 17				
Frizinghall	d	11 49			12 04		12 14			12 19			12 34		12 44		12 49			13 04		13 14		13 19	
Shipley	a	11 53			12 08		12 18			12 23			12 38		12 48		12 53			13 08		13 18		13 23	
	d		11 49		12 09			12 14				12 33	12 39			12 45				13 09			13 14		
Leeds 10	a		12 07	12 12	12 24	12 27		12 29			12 39	12 48	12 55	12 57		12 59		13 12		13 24	13 27		13 28		13 39

A until 21 March

Table 37R

Saturdays

14 December to 17 May

Bradford and Shipley - Leeds

Network Diagram - see first page of Table 35

		NT	NT	NT	NT	NT	NT	NT	NT	NT		NT	NT	NT	NT	NT	NT	NT	NT	NT		NT	NT	NT	NT
Bradford Forster Square	d	13 31		13 41		13 46		14 01		14 11			14 16			14 31		14 41		14 46			15 01		15 11
Bradford Interchange	d		13 34				13 50		14 05						14 19		14 34					14 50		15 05	
New Pudsey	d		13 42				13 58		14 13						14 28		14 42					14 58		15 13	
Bramley	d		13 46				14 02		14 17								14 46					15 02		15 17	
Frizinghall	d	13 34		13 44		13 49		14 04		14 14			14 19			14 34		14 44		14 49			15 04		15 14
Shipley	a	13 38		13 48		13 53		14 08		14 18			14 23			14 38		14 48		14 53			15 08		15 18
	d	13 39			13 44			14 09				14 14		14 18		14 39			14 45				15 09		
Leeds 10	a	13 54	13 57		13 58		14 14	14 24	14 27			14 29		14 37	14 39	14 53	14 57		15 00			15 13	15 24	15 27	

		NT	NT	NT	NT	NT		NT	NT	NT	NT	NT	NT	NT	NT	NT		NT	NT	NT	NT	NT	NT	NT	NT
Bradford Forster Square	d		15 16			15 31			15 41		15 46		16 01		16 11			16 16		16 31		16 40		16 44	
Bradford Interchange	d			15 19				15 34				15 50		16 05					16 19		16 34				
New Pudsey	d			15 28				15 42				15 58		16 13					16 28		16 42				
Bramley	d							15 46				16 02		16 17							16 46				
Frizinghall	d		15 19			15 34			15 44		15 49		16 04		16 14			16 19		16 34		16 43		16 48	
Shipley	a		15 23			15 38			15 48		15 53		16 08		16 18			16 23		16 38		16 48		16 52	
	d	15 14			15 30	15 39				15 44			16 09			16 14				16 39			16 45		16 49
Leeds 10	a	15 28		15 39	15 47	15 54		15 57		15 58		16 13	16 24	16 27		16 28			16 39	16 53	16 57		16 59		17 07

		NT		NT	NT	NT	NT	NT	NT	NT	NT	NT		NT	NT	NT	NT	NT	NT	NT	NT	NT		NT	NT
Bradford Forster Square	d			17 01		17 11		17 16		17 31		17 41			17 46			18 01		18 11		18 16			
Bradford Interchange	d	16 50			17 04				17 19		17 34					17 50			18 04					18 19	
New Pudsey	d	16 58			17 13				17 28		17 42					17 58			18 13					18 28	
Bramley	d	17 02			17 17						17 46					18 02			18 17						
Frizinghall	d			17 04		17 14		17 19		17 34		17 44			17 49			18 04		18 14		18 19			
Shipley	a			17 08		17 18		17 23		17 38		17 48			17 53			18 08		18 18		18 23			
	d			17 09			17 15			17 39				17 45			18 00	18 09			18 14				18 19
Leeds 10	a	17 13		17 24	17 27		17 29		17 39	17 55	17 57			18 00		18 12	18 17	18 24	18 29		18 29			18 39	18 42

		NT	NT	NT	NT	NT	NT	NT		NT	NT	NT	NT	NT	NT	NT	NT	NT		NT	NT	NT	NT	NT	NT
Bradford Forster Square	d	18 31		18 41		18 46				19 01		19 07			19 31		19 36			19 41		20 07			
Bradford Interchange	d		18 34					18 52			19 05			19 18		19 34					19 50			20 04	20 19
New Pudsey	d		18 43					19 00			19 13			19 28		19 42					19 59			20 13	20 28
Bramley	d		18 47					19 04			19 17					19 46					20 03			20 17	
Frizinghall	d	18 34		18 44		18 49				19 04		19 10			19 34		19 39			19 44		20 10			
Shipley	a	18 38		18 48		18 53				19 08		19 14			19 38		19 43			19 48		20 15			
	d	18 38			18 44		18 48			19 09			19 14		19 39			19 44					20 14		
Leeds 10	a	18 52	18 57		18 59		19 07	19 13		19 26	19 28		19 29	19 38	19 55	19 55		19 59			20 14		20 28	20 30	20 38

		NT	NT	NT		NT	NT	NT	NT	NT	NT	NT A (bus)	NT	NT		NT	NT	NT	NT	NT	NT	NT	NT	NT	
Bradford Forster Square	d	20 25				20 38				21 05			21 25				21 38	22 01				22 25			
Bradford Interchange	d			20 37					21 04			21 10				21 37			22 04		22 17			22 37	
New Pudsey	d			20 46					21 13			21 20				21 46			22 13		22 26			22 46	
Bramley	d			20 50					21 17							21 50			22 17					22 50	
Frizinghall	d	20 28				20 41				21 08			21 28				21 41	22 04				22 28			
Shipley	a	20 32				20 45				21 12			21 32				21 45	22 08				22 32			
	d		20 28				20 43	20 58			21 14			21 43						22 14			22 43		
Leeds 10	a		20 46	20 59			21 00	21 16	21 25		21 30	21 40		21 59		21 59			22 25	22 32	22 35		23 01	23 01	

		NT	NT	NT	NT A (bus)	NT
Bradford Forster Square	d	22 38		23 05		23 20
Bradford Interchange	d		23 04		23 10	
New Pudsey	d		23 13		23 20	
Bramley	d		23 17			
Frizinghall	d	22 41		23 08		23 23
Shipley	a	22 45		23 12		23 27
	d					
Leeds 10	a		23 26		23 40	

Sundays

8 December to 11 May

		NT B	NT	NT	NT	NT	NT	NT	NT	NT		NT	NT	NT	NT	NT	NT	NT	NT	NT		NT	NT	NT	NT
Bradford Forster Square	d				09 02			10 02				10 38		10 48		11 02							12 02		12 38
Bradford Interchange	d	00 04	08 31			09 20			10 04	10 25					11 02		11 25		11 44			12 02		12 25	
New Pudsey	d	00 12	08 39			09 29			10 12	10 33					11 10		11 33		11 53			12 10		12 33	
Bramley	d	00 16	08 43			09 33			10 16	10 37							11 37		11 57					12 37	
Frizinghall	d				09 05			10 05				10 41		10 51		11 05							12 05		12 41
Shipley	a				09 08			10 08				10 44		10 54		11 09							12 08		12 44
	d			09 00	09 10		09 40	10 08					10 40			11 10		11 40		11 49			12 08		
Leeds 10	a	00 27	08 51	09 14	09 24	09 42	09 54	10 22	10 25	10 46			10 54		11 21	11 24	11 48	11 54	12 05	12 06		12 22	12 22	12 46	

		NT	NT	NT	NT	NT		NT	NT	NT	NT	NT	NT	NT	NT	NT		NT	NT	NT	NT	NT	NT	NT	NT
Bradford Forster Square	d			12 48		13 02						14 02			14 38				14 48		15 02				
Bradford Interchange	d		12 44		13 02			13 25		13 44	14 02			14 25				14 44		15 03			15 25		15 44
New Pudsey	d		12 53		13 10			13 33		13 53	14 11			14 33				14 53		15 11			15 33		15 53
Bramley	d		12 57					13 37		13 57				14 37				14 57					15 37		15 57
Frizinghall	d			12 51		13 05						14 05			14 41				14 51		15 05				
Shipley	a			12 54		13 08						14 08			14 44				14 54		15 08				
	d	12 40				13 08			13 40			14 08	14 21			14 40					15 08	15 25		15 40	
Leeds 10	a	12 54	13 06		13 22	13 22		13 46	13 54	14 06	14 22	14 22	14 39	14 48		14 54		15 06		15 22	15 24	15 44	15 46	15 54	16 06

A until 22 March

B not 8 December

Table 37R

Sundays

8 December to 11 May

Bradford and Shipley - Leeds

Network Diagram - see first page of Table 35

		NT	NT	NT	NT	NT	NT	NT		NT	NT	NT	NT	NT	NT	NT	NT	NT		NT	NT	NT	NT	NT	NT
Bradford Forster Square	d	16 02				16 38				16 48		17 02						18 02			18 38			18 48	
Bradford Interchange	d		16 03	16 25				16 44			17 02			17 25		17 43	18 02			18 25			18 44		19 02
New Pudsey	d		16 11	16 33				16 53			17 10			17 33		17 52	18 10			18 33			18 53		19 11
Bramley	d			16 37				16 57						17 37		17 56				18 37			18 57		
Frizinghall	d	16 05				16 41				16 51		17 05						18 05			18 41			18 51	
Shipley	a	16 08				16 44				16 54		17 08						18 08			18 44			18 54	
	d	16 08			16 29		16 40					17 09	17 29		17 40			18 08				18 40			
Leeds 10	a	16 22	16 22	16 46	16 47		16 54	17 05			17 22	17 23	17 45	17 48	17 54	18 07	18 22	18 23		18 46		18 54	19 08		19 22

		NT	NT	NT		NT	NT	NT	NT	NT	NT	NT	NT	NT		NT	NT	NT	NT	NT	NT	NT	NT	NT	
Bradford Forster Square	d	19 02								20 02		20 38		20 48			21 02						22 02		
Bradford Interchange	d			19 25				19 44	20 02		20 25					21 02		21 26		21 44		22 02		22 26	
New Pudsey	d			19 33				19 53	20 10		20 33					21 10		21 34		21 53		22 10		22 35	
Bramley	d			19 37				19 57			20 37							21 38		21 57				22 39	
Frizinghall	d	19 05								20 05		20 41		20 51			21 05						22 05		
Shipley	a	19 08								20 08		20 44		20 54			21 08						22 09		
	d	19 08	19 25			19 38	19 49			20 08			20 40				21 08		21 40		21 54		22 09		
Leeds 10	a	19 22	19 42	19 46		19 56	20 03	20 08	20 22	20 22	20 47		20 54			21 22	21 24	21 48	21 54	22 05	22 10	22 21	22 24	22 47	

		NT	NT	NT	NT	NT	NT	NT	NT
Bradford Forster Square	d	22 38		22 48		23 05			
Bradford Interchange	d				23 04		23 25		23 47
New Pudsey	d				23 12		23 33		23 55
Bramley	d						23 37		23 59
Frizinghall	d	22 41		22 51		23 08			
Shipley	a	22 44		22 54		23 11			
	d		22 40			23 11		23 40	
Leeds 10	a		22 54		23 23	23 28	23 46	23 57	00 08

Table 38

Leeds and Bradford - Ilkey

Mondays to Saturdays

9 December to 17 May

Network Diagram - see first page of Table 35

Miles	Miles		NT	NT	NT SX	NT SX	NT SO	NT SX	NT SX	NT SO	NT SX		NT SX	NT SX	NT	NT	NT SO	NT SX	NT	NT	NT		NT	NT
0	—	**Leeds** 10 d	06 02		06 34		07 02	07 03			07 29		07 35		08 02		08 32	08 35		09 02			09 32	
—	0	**Bradford Forster Square** 37 d		06 15		06 44			07 11	07 15				07 45		08 16			08 46		09 16			09 46
—	1¾	Frizinghall 37 d		06 18		06 47			07 14	07 18				07 49		08 19			08 49		09 19			09 49
—	2¾	Shipley 37 d		06 22		06 51			07 19	07 23				07 53		08 23			08 53		09 23			09 53
—	4¼	Baildon d		06 25		06 54			07 22	07 26				07 56		08 26			08 56		09 26			09 56
10¼	7½	Guiseley d	06 14	06 31	06 48	07 00	07 14	07 15	07 28	07 32	07 42		07 50	08 02	08 14	08 32	08 44	08 48	09 02	09 14	09 32		09 45	10 02
11½	8¾	Menston d	06 17	06 34	06 51	07 03	07 17	07 18	07 31	07 35	07 45		07 53	08 05	08 17	08 35	08 47	08 51	09 05	09 17	09 35		09 48	10 05
13	10¼	Burley-in-Wharfedale d	06 20	06 37	06 54	07 06	07 20	07 21	07 34	07 38	07 48		07 56	08 09	08 20	08 38	08 50	08 54	09 08	09 20	09 38		09 52	10 08
15¼	12½	Ben Rhydding d	06 23	06 40	06 57	07 09	07 24	07 24	07 37	07 41	07 52		07 59	08 12	08 23	08 41	08 53	08 57	09 11	09 24	09 41		09 55	10 11
16¼	13½	**Ilkley** a	06 29	06 46	07 03	07 15	07 29	07 30	07 42	07 47	07 57		08 05	08 17	08 29	08 49	09 02	09 03	09 17	09 33	09 47		10 01	10 17

	NT	NT	NT	NT	NT SX	NT SO	NT		NT	NT	NT	NT	NT	NT	NT	NT SX	NT SO		NT	NT	NT	NT	NT	NT
Leeds 10 d	10 02		10 32		11 02	11 02			11 32		12 02		12 32		13 02				13 32		14 02		14 32	
Bradford Forster Square 37 d		10 16		10 46			11 16			11 46		12 16		12 46		13 15	13 15			13 46		14 16		14 46
Frizinghall 37 d		10 19		10 49			11 19			11 49		12 19		12 49		13 19	13 19			13 49		14 19		14 49
Shipley 37 d		10 23		10 53			11 23			11 53		12 23		12 53		13 23	13 23			13 53		14 23		14 53
Baildon d		10 26		10 56			11 26			11 56		12 26		12 56		13 25	13 26			13 56		14 26		14 56
Guiseley d	10 14	10 32	10 44	11 02	11 14	11 14	11 32		11 44	12 02	12 14	12 32	12 44	13 02	13 14	13 32	13 32		13 44	14 02	14 14	14 32	14 44	15 02
Menston d	10 17	10 35	10 47	11 05	11 17	11 17	11 35		11 47	12 05	12 17	12 35	12 47	13 05	13 17	13 35	13 35		13 47	14 05	14 17	14 35	14 47	15 05
Burley-in-Wharfedale d	10 20	10 38	10 50	11 08	11 20	11 20	11 38		11 50	12 08	12 20	12 38	12 50	13 08	13 20	13 38	13 38		13 50	14 08	14 20	14 38	14 50	15 08
Ben Rhydding d	10 23	10 41	10 53	11 11	11 23	11 23	11 41		11 53	12 11	12 23	12 41	12 53	13 11	13 23	13 40	13 41		13 53	14 11	14 23	14 41	14 53	15 11
Ilkley a	10 30	10 47	10 59	11 17	11 29	11 31	11 47		12 00	12 17	12 29	12 47	13 01	13 17	13 29	13 47	13 47		13 59	14 17	14 29	14 47	14 59	15 17

	NT	NT	NT		NT	NT	NT	NT	NT	NT	NT SX	NT SO	NT SX		NT SO	NT SX	NT SX	NT SO	NT SX	NT SO	NT SX	NT SX	NT SO	
Leeds 10 d	15 02		15 32			16 02		16 32		17 02	17 16				17 32	17 34	17 47			18 02	18 02			
Bradford Forster Square 37 d		15 16			15 46		16 16		16 44			17 16	17 16					17 46	17 47			18 11	18 16	
Frizinghall 37 d		15 19			15 49		16 19		16 48			17 19	17 19					17 49	17 50			18 14	18 19	
Shipley 37 d		15 23			15 53		16 23		16 52			17 23	17 25					17 53	17 55			18 19	18 23	
Baildon d		15 26			15 56		16 26		16 55			17 26	17 28					17 57	17 59			18 22	18 26	
Guiseley d	15 14	15 32	15 44		16 02	16 14	16 32	16 44	17 01	17 14	17 28	17 32	17 35		17 44	17 46	17 59	18 02	18 07	18 14	18 19	18 27	18 32	
Menston d	15 17	15 35	15 47		16 05	16 17	16 35	16 47	17 04	17 17	17 31	17 35	17 38		17 47	17 49	18 02	18 05	18 10	18 17	18 22	18 30	18 35	
Burley-in-Wharfedale d	15 20	15 38	15 50		16 08	16 20	16 38	16 50	17 07	17 20	17 34	17 38	17 42		17 51	17 52	18 05	18 08	18 17	18 20	18 26	18 35	18 38	
Ben Rhydding d	15 23	15 41	15 53		16 11	16 23	16 41	16 53	17 10	17 23	17 37	17 41	17 46		17 54	17 56	18 09	18 12	18 20	18 23	18 29	18 39	18 41	
Ilkley a	15 31	15 47	15 59		16 17	16 31	16 47	17 00	17 17	17 29	17 42	17 47	17 51		17 59	18 01	18 16	18 17	18 26	18 28	18 35	18 44	18 47	

	NT	NT	NT	NT	NT	NT	NT	NT	NT		NT	NT	NT	NT
Leeds 10 d	18 32		19 02	19 33		20 03		21 06			22 06		23 15	
Bradford Forster Square 37 d		18 46			19 41		20 38		21 38			22 38		23 20
Frizinghall 37 d		18 49			19 44		20 41		21 41			22 41		23 23
Shipley 37 d		18 53			19 48		20 46		21 45			22 45		23 27
Baildon d		18 56			19 51		20 49		21 48			22 48		23 30
Guiseley d	18 44	19 02	19 14	19 45	19 56	20 15	20 54	21 18	21 54		22 18	22 54	23 27	23 36
Menston d	18 47	19 05	19 17	19 48	19 59	20 18	20 57	21 21	21 57		22 21	22 57	23 30	23 39
Burley-in-Wharfedale d	18 50	19 08	19 20	19 51	20 02	20 21	21 00	21 24	22 00		22 24	23 00	23 33	23 42
Ben Rhydding d	18 53	19 11	19 24	19 54	20 06	20 24	21 04	21 27	22 03		22 27	23 03	23 36	23 45
Ilkley a	19 00	19 17	19 29	20 00	20 12	20 33	21 10	21 33	22 09		22 33	23 09	23 42	23 51

Sundays

8 December to 11 May

	NT	NT	NT	NT	NT	NT	NT	NT	NT		NT	NT	NT	NT	NT	NT	NT	NT	NT		NT	NT	NT	NT
Leeds 10 d	09 12	10 12		11 12	12 12		13 12	14 12			15 12	16 12		17 12	18 12		19 12	20 12			21 12	22 12		23 16
Bradford Forster Square 37 d			10 38			12 38			14 38				16 38			18 38			20 38				22 38	
Frizinghall 37 d			10 41			12 41			14 41				16 41			18 41			20 41				22 41	
Shipley 37 d			10 44			12 44			14 44				16 44			18 44			20 44				22 44	
Baildon d			10 47			12 47			14 47				16 47			18 47			20 47				22 47	
Guiseley d	09 23	10 23	10 52	11 23	12 23	12 52	13 23	14 23	14 52		15 23	16 23	16 52	17 23	18 23	18 52	19 23	20 23	20 52		21 23	22 23	22 52	23 27
Menston d	09 26	10 26	10 55	11 26	12 26	12 55	13 26	14 26	14 55		15 26	16 26	16 55	17 26	18 26	18 55	19 26	20 26	20 55		21 26	22 26	22 55	23 30
Burley-in-Wharfedale d	09 29	10 29	10 58	11 29	12 29	12 58	13 29	14 29	14 58		15 29	16 29	16 58	17 29	18 29	18 58	19 29	20 29	20 58		21 29	22 29	22 58	23 33
Ben Rhydding d	09 33	10 33	11 02	11 33	12 33	13 02	13 33	14 33	15 02		15 33	16 33	17 02	17 33	18 33	19 02	19 33	20 33	21 02		21 33	22 33	23 02	23 37
Ilkley a	09 38	10 38	11 07	11 38	12 38	13 07	13 38	14 38	15 07		15 38	16 38	17 07	17 38	18 38	19 07	19 38	20 38	21 07		21 38	22 38	23 07	23 42

Table 38R

Ilkley - Bradford and Leeds

Mondays to Saturdays

9 December to 17 May

Network Diagram - see first page of Table 35

Miles	Miles			NT SX	NT SO	NT SX	NT SO	NT SX	NT SX	NT	NT	NT SX	NT SX	NT SX	NT SX	NT SO	NT SX	NT SO	NT SX	NT	NT SO	NT SX	NT
0	0	**Ilkley**	d	06 02	06 10	06 17	06 19	06 34	06 50	07 10	07 22	07 37	07 48	07 57	08 05	08 10	08 15	08 21	08 24	08 40	08 51	08 54	09 10
1	1	Ben Rhydding	d	06 04	06 11	06 19	06 21	06 36	06 52	07 12	07 24	07 40	07 51	08 00	08 08	08 12	08 18	08 23	08 27	08 42	08 53	08 56	09 12
3¼	3¼	Burley-in-Wharfedale	d	06 10	06 17	06 25	06 27	06 42	06 58	07 18	07 30	07 45	07 56	08 05	08 13	08 18	08 23	08 29	08 32	08 48	08 59	09 02	09 18
4¾	4¾	Menston	d	06 13	06 20	06 28	06 30	06 45	07 01	07 21	07 33	07 49	08 00	08 08	08 17	08 21	08 27	08 32	08 35	08 51	09 02	09 05	09 21
6	6	Guiseley	d	06 16	06 23	06 31	06 34	06 48	07 04	07 24	07 36	07 52	08 03	08 12	08 20	08 24	08 30	08 35	08 39	08 54	09 05	09 08	09 24
—	9¼	Baildon	d			06 36	06 39		07 09		07 41		08 08					08 40	08 44		09 10	09 13	
—	10¾	Shipley	37 a			06 41	06 43		07 14		07 47		08 12					08 43	08 48		09 14	09 18	
—	11¾	Frizinghall	37 a			06 44	06 47		07 17		07 49		08 15					08 46	08 51		09 17	09 21	
—	13½	**Bradford Forster Square**	37 a			06 50	06 55		07 22		07 56		08 21					08 53	08 57		09 24	09 27	
16¼	—	**Leeds** 10	a	06 30	06 39			07 02		07 38		08 09		08 26	08 35	08 39	08 44			09 11			09 39

		NT	NT	NT	NT	NT	NT	NT	NT	NT	NT	NT	NT	NT	NT	NT	NT	NT	NT	NT	NT	NT	NT
Ilkley	d	09 21	09 40	09 51	10 10	10 21	10 40	10 51	11 10	11 21	11 40	11 51	12 10	12 21	12 40	12 51	13 10	13 21	13 40	13 51	14 10	14 21	14 40
Ben Rhydding	d	09 23	09 42	09 53	10 12	10 23	10 42	10 53	11 12	11 23	11 42	11 53	12 12	12 23	12 42	12 53	13 12	13 23	13 42	13 53	14 12	14 23	14 42
Burley-in-Wharfedale	d	09 29	09 48	09 59	10 18	10 29	10 48	10 59	11 18	11 29	11 48	11 59	12 18	12 29	12 48	12 59	13 18	13 29	13 48	13 58	14 18	14 29	14 48
Menston	d	09 32	09 51	10 02	10 21	10 32	10 51	11 02	11 21	11 32	11 51	12 02	12 21	12 32	12 51	13 02	13 21	13 32	13 51	14 01	14 21	14 32	14 51
Guiseley	d	09 35	09 54	10 05	10 25	10 35	10 54	11 05	11 24	11 35	11 54	12 05	12 24	12 35	12 54	13 05	13 24	13 35	13 54	14 05	14 24	14 35	14 54
Baildon	d	09 40		10 10		10 40		11 10		11 40		12 10		12 40		13 10		13 40		14 10		14 40	
Shipley	37 a	09 44		10 14		10 44		11 14		11 44		12 14		12 44		13 14		13 44		14 14		14 44	
Frizinghall	37 a	09 47		10 17		10 47		11 17		11 47		12 17		12 47		13 17		13 47		14 17		14 47	
Bradford Forster Square	37 a	09 53		10 23		10 53		11 23		11 53		12 24		12 53		13 23		13 53		14 23		14 53	
Leeds 10	a		10 11		10 41		11 08		11 39		12 08		12 41		13 08		13 38		14 09		14 39		15 10

		NT	NT	NT	NT	NT	NT SO	NT SX	NT	NT	NT	NT SO	NT SX	NT	NT SO	NT SX	NT	NT SX	NT SO	NT SX	NT	NT
Ilkley	d	14 51	15 10	15 21	15 40	15 51	16 10	16 12	16 21	16 40	16 51	17 10	17 14	17 21	17 40	17 42	17 51	18 04	18 10	18 12	18 21	18 40
Ben Rhydding	d	14 53	15 12	15 23	15 42	15 53	16 12	16 14	16 23	16 42	16 53	17 12	17 16	17 23	17 42	17 44	17 53	18 06	18 12	18 14	18 23	18 42
Burley-in-Wharfedale	d	14 59	15 18	15 29	15 48	15 59	16 18	16 20	16 29	16 48	16 59	17 18	17 22	17 29	17 48	17 50	17 59	18 12	18 18	18 20	18 29	18 48
Menston	d	15 02	15 21	15 32	15 51	16 02	16 21	16 23	16 32	16 51	17 02	17 21	17 25	17 32	17 51	17 53	18 02	18 15	18 21	18 23	18 32	18 51
Guiseley	d	15 05	15 24	15 35	15 54	16 05	16 24	16 27	16 35	16 54	17 05	17 24	17 29	17 35	17 54	17 56	18 05	18 18	18 24	18 26	18 35	18 54
Baildon	d	15 10		15 40		16 10			16 40		17 10			17 40			18 10				18 40	
Shipley	37 a	15 14		15 44		16 14			16 44		17 14			17 43			18 14				18 43	
Frizinghall	37 a	15 17		15 47		16 17			16 47		17 17			17 46			18 17				18 46	
Bradford Forster Square	37 a	15 23		15 53		16 23			16 53		17 23			17 53			18 23				18 52	
Leeds 10	a		15 40		16 10		16 39	16 46		17 09		17 38	17 44		18 09	18 16		18 35	18 40	18 47		19 09

		NT	NT	NT	NT	NT	NT SO	NT SX	NT	NT	NT	NT	NT	NT
Ilkley	d	18 51	19 10	19 21	19 41	20 05	20 21	20 29	20 40	21 21	21 40	22 21	22 40	23 21
Ben Rhydding	d	18 53	19 12	19 23	19 43	20 07	20 23	20 31	20 42	21 23	21 42	22 23	22 42	23 23
Burley-in-Wharfedale	d	18 59	19 18	19 29	19 49	20 13	20 29	20 36	20 48	21 29	21 48	22 29	22 48	23 29
Menston	d	19 02	19 21	19 32	19 52	20 16	20 32	20 39	20 51	21 32	21 51	22 32	22 51	23 32
Guiseley	d	19 05	19 24	19 35	19 55	20 19	20 35	20 43	20 54	21 35	21 54	22 35	22 54	23 35
Baildon	d	19 10		19 40		20 24			20 59		21 59		22 59	
Shipley	37 a	19 14		19 44		20 27			21 03		22 02		23 02	
Frizinghall	37 a	19 17		19 47		20 30			21 05		22 05		23 05	
Bradford Forster Square	37 a	19 23		19 53		20 36			21 12		22 11		23 13	
Leeds 10	a		19 40		20 12		20 49	21 00		21 49		22 49		23 49

Sundays

8 December to 11 May

		NT	NT	NT	NT	NT	NT	NT	NT	NT	NT	NT	NT	NT	NT	NT	NT	NT	NT	NT	NT	NT	NT
Ilkley	d	09 21	09 53	10 21	11 21	11 53	12 21	13 21	13 53	14 21	15 21	15 53	16 21	17 21	17 53	18 21	19 21	19 53	20 21	21 21	21 53	22 21	23 21
Ben Rhydding	d	09 23	09 55	10 23	11 23	11 55	12 23	13 23	13 55	14 23	15 23	15 55	16 23	17 23	17 55	18 23	19 23	19 55	20 23	21 23	21 55	22 23	23 23
Burley-in-Wharfedale	d	09 29	10 01	10 29	11 29	12 01	12 29	13 29	14 01	14 29	15 29	16 01	16 29	17 29	18 01	18 29	19 29	20 01	20 29	21 29	22 01	22 29	23 29
Menston	d	09 32	10 04	10 32	11 32	12 04	12 32	13 32	14 04	14 32	15 32	16 04	16 32	17 32	18 04	18 32	19 32	20 04	20 32	21 32	22 04	22 32	23 32
Guiseley	d	09 35	10 07	10 35	11 35	12 07	12 35	13 35	14 07	14 35	15 35	16 07	16 35	17 35	18 07	18 35	19 35	20 07	20 35	21 35	22 07	22 35	23 35
Baildon	d		10 12			12 12			14 12			16 12			18 12			20 12			22 12		
Shipley	37 a		10 15			12 15			14 15			16 15			18 15			20 15			22 15		
Frizinghall	37 a		10 18			12 18			14 18			16 18			18 18			20 18			22 18		
Bradford Forster Square	37 a		10 24			12 24			14 24			16 24			18 24			20 24			22 24		
Leeds 10	a	09 50		10 49	11 49		12 49	13 49		14 49	15 49		16 49	17 49		18 49	19 49		20 49	21 49		22 49	23 50

Network Diagram for Tables 39, 40, 41, 43

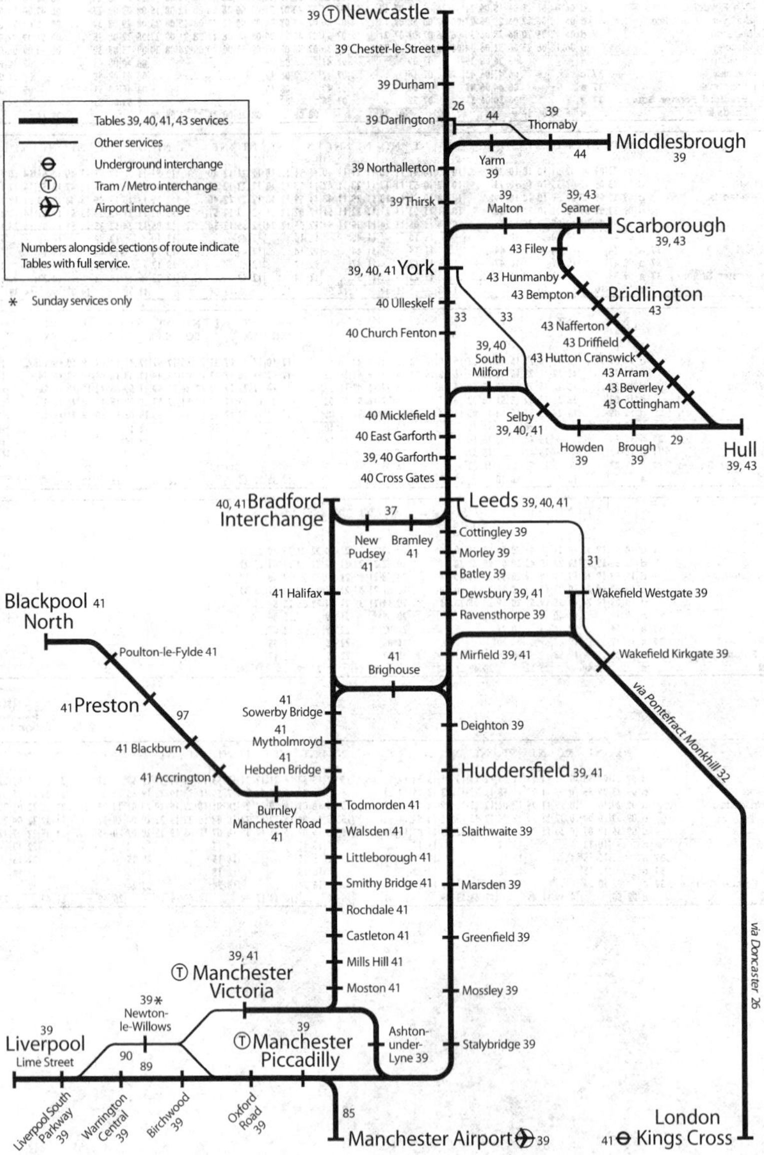
Tables 39, 40, 41, 43 services
Other services
Underground interchange
Tram / Metro interchange
Airport interchange
Numbers alongside sections of route indicate Tables with full service.
* Sunday services only
39 Newcastle
39 Chester-le-Street
39 Durham
39 Darlington
26
44
39 Thornaby
Middlesbrough 39
44
Yarm 39
39 Northallerton
39 Thirsk
39 Malton
39, 43 Seamer
Scarborough 39, 43
43 Filey
39, 40, 41 York
43 Hunmanby
43 Bempton
Bridlington 43
40 Ulleskelf
33
33
40 Church Fenton
43 Nafferton
43 Driffield
39, 40 South Milford
43 Hutton Cranswick
43 Arram
43 Beverley
43 Cottingham
Selby 39, 40, 41
40 Micklefield
40 East Garforth
39, 40 Garforth
40 Cross Gates
Howden 39
Brough 39
29
Hull 39, 43
40, 41 Bradford Interchange
37
Leeds 39, 40, 41
New Pudsey 41
Bramley 41
Cottingley 39
Morley 39
Batley 39
31
41 Halifax
Dewsbury 39, 41
Wakefield Westgate 39
Ravensthorpe 39
Blackpool North 41
Poulton-le-Fylde 41
Mirfield 39, 41
Wakefield Kirkgate 39
41 Brighouse
41 Preston
97
41 Sowerby Bridge
via Pontefract Monkhill 32
41 Mytholmroyd
41 Blackburn
Deighton 39
41 Hebden Bridge
41 Accrington
Huddersfield 39, 41
Burnley Manchester Road 41
Todmorden 41
Walsden 41
Slaithwaite 39
Littleborough 41
Smithy Bridge 41
Marsden 39
Rochdale 41
Castleton 41
Greenfield 39
via Doncaster 26
39, 41 Manchester Victoria
Mills Hill 41
Moston 41
Mossley 39
39* Newton-le-Willows
39 Liverpool Lime Street
90
89
39 Manchester Piccadilly
Ashton-under-Lyne 39
Stalybridge 39
Liverpool South Parkway 39
Warrington Central 39
Birchwood 39
Oxford Road 39
85
Manchester Airport 39
London 41 Kings Cross

TOCs operating on this network - Grand Central (GC), East Coast (GR), Northern (NT), First TransPennine Express (TP), Cross Country (XC)

Table 39

Mondays to Fridays

9 December to 16 May

Liverpool, Manchester Airport and Manchester - Huddersfield - Wakefield, Leeds, Hull, York, Scarborough, Middlesbrough and Newcastle

Network Diagram - refer to first Page of Table 39

Miles	Miles	Miles	Miles	Miles			TP MX ◇1	TP ◇1	TP MO ◇1 A	TP MO ◇1 B	TP MX ◇1	TP MX ◇1 C	TP MX ◇1 D	TP ◇1 E	NT	TP ◇1 F	TP MX ◇1 D	TP ◇1	TP ◇1 F	TP MX ◇1 D	NT	NT	TP ◇1	GR R 1	TP ◇1	NT	NT	TP ◇1	NT	NT	XC ◇1	NT	TP ◇1	NT	NT	TP ◇1	TP ◇1	NT
0	—	—	—	—	**Liverpool Lime Street** 10	d																											06 15					
5½	—	—	—	—	Liverpool South Parkway 7	d																											06 25					
18½	—	—	—	—	Warrington Central	d																											06 38					
21¾	—	—	—	—	Birchwood	d																											06 43					
34¼	—	—	—	—	Manchester Oxford Road	d																											07 06					
—	—	—	—	—	**Manchester Airport**	d						00 38		00 48		04 13			05 37									06 30									07 06	
34¾	—	—	—	—	**Manchester Piccadilly** 10	a						00 51		01 01		04 27			05 51									06 44					07 08				07 22	
—	—	—	—	—		d						00 53	00 53	01 03		04 30	04 30	05 39	05 57	05 57					06 21			06 54					07 11				07 27	
—	—	—	—	0	**Manchester Victoria**	d																							06 55									06 58
—	—	—	—	6½	Ashton-under-Lyne	d																							07 05									
42¼	—	—	—	7¾	**Stalybridge**	a												05 52										07 07	07 10				07 23					
—	—	—	—	—		d												05 52									06 41	07 07	07 11				07 23					
45	—	—	—	10½	Mossley (Grtr Manchester)	d																					06 45		07 15									
47½	—	—	—	12¾	Greenfield	d																					06 49		07 19									
53¼	—	—	—	18¾	Marsden	d																				06 48	06 58		07 28									
55¾	—	—	—	21¼	Slaithwaite	d																				06 52	07 02		07 32									
60¼	—	—	—	25¾	**Huddersfield**	a										05 31	05 31	06 10	06 26	06 26					06 54	07 00	07 10	07 25	07 41				07 44				07 56	
—	—	—	—	—		d			00 11	00 12	00 26				05 32	05 39	05 39	06 11	06 27	06 27	06 31	06 41			06 56	07 00		07 26				07 30	07 45	07 49			07 57	
62¼	—	—	—	27¾	Deighton	d									05 36						06 34	06 45				07 03								07 53				
65¼	—	—	—	30¾	Mirfield	d									05 41						06 39	06 50				07 08				07 20				07 58				08 06
66¾	—	—	—	—	Ravensthorpe	d															06 42					07 11				07 23								
68¼	—	—	—	—	**Dewsbury**	a					00s35								06 36	06 36	06 46				07 05	07 15				07 27			07 54				08 06	08 11
—	—	—	—	—		d													06 37	06 37	06 46				07 06	07 15				07 35			07 55				08 07	08 12
69¾	—	—	—	—	Batley	d															06 49					07 18				07 38								08 15
73	—	—	—	—	Morley	d															06 55					07 24				07 44								08 21
74½	—	—	—	—	Cottingley	d															06 59					07 28				07 47								08 24
77½	0	—	0	—	**Leeds** 10	a			00 47	00 51	00 51	02 01	02 01	02 32		06 01	06 01	06 32	06 52	06 52	07 09				07 19	07 38		07 47		07 56		08 29	08 10				08 24	08 33
—	—	—	—	—		d	00 32		00 48	00 54	00 54	02 08	02 08	02 34		06 04	06 04	06 35	06 55	06 55				07 10	07 23			07 51			07 57		08 12				08 28	
84¾	7¼	—	7¼	—	Garforth	d																						08 00										
—	12¾	—	—	—	South Milford	a																																
—	20¾	—	—	—	Selby	a																			07 43													
—	29½	—	—	—	Howden	a																			07 52													
—	—	—	—	—		d																			07 52										08 03			
—	41¼	—	—	—	Brough	a																			08 04										08 23			
—	51¾	—	—	—	**Hull**	a																			08 20										08 46			
—	—	—	—	—	Wakefield Kirkgate	a									05 58							07 03												08 13				
—	—	—	—	—	**Wakefield Westgate**	a									06 05							07 10												08 20				
103	—	0	25½	—	**York** 8	a	01 11		01 17	01 21	01 30	02 46	02 46	03 04		06 27	06 27	07 00	07 21	07 21				07 33				08 20			08 22		08 35				08 52	
—	—	—	—	—		d		05 54								06 40	06 40	07 06	07 25	07 25			07 32	07 37				08 23			08 28		08 40			08 42	08 58	
—	—	—	46½	—	Malton	d										07 03	07 03		07 48	07 48													09 03					
—	—	—	64¾	—	Seamer	a										07 20	07 20		08 05	08 05													09 20					
—	—	—	67½	—	**Scarborough**	a										07 29	07 29		08 14	08 14													09 29					
125½	—	22¼	—	—	Thirsk	a		06 10										07 22					07 52					08 39										
133	—	30½	—	—	Northallerton	a		06 18										07 30					08 00					08 50									09 18	
147	—	—	—	—	**Darlington** 7	a		06 29										07 41						08 04							08 57					09 12	09 30	
—	—	42¼	—	—	Yarm	d																	08 14					09 04										
—	—	47½	—	—	Thornaby	a		06 52															08 24					09 12										
—	—	50¾	—	—	**Middlesbrough**	a		07 03															08 31					09 22										
169	—	—	—	—	Durham	a												07 58						08 22							09 13					09 29	09 47	
174¾	—	—	—	—	Chester-le-Street	a												08 04																			09 53	
183	—	—	—	—	**Newcastle** 8	a												08 17						08 39							09 28					09 44	10 07	

A from 17 February until 24 March
B until 10 February, from 31 March
C until 27 December, from 25 March
D from 31 December until 21 March
E 9 December, 16 December, 23 December
F until 30 December, MO from 6 January until 17 March, from 24 March

Table 39

Mondays to Fridays

9 December to 16 May

Liverpool, Manchester Airport and Manchester - Huddersfield - Wakefield, Leeds, Hull, York, Scarborough, Middlesbrough and Newcastle

Network Diagram - refer to first Page of Table 39

		TP	NT	XC	NT	NT	TP	NT	NT	TP	TP	NT	NT	NT	NT	NT	TP	XC	NT	TP	NT	NT	TP	TP	NT	NT	NT	NT	NT	TP	XC	NT	TP	NT	NT	TP	TP
		◇1 ✠		◇1 ✠			◇1 ✠			◇1 ✠	◇1 ✠						◇1 ✠	◇1 ✠		◇1 ✠			◇1 ✠	◇1 ✠						◇1 ✠	◇1 ✠		◇1 ✠			◇1 ✠	◇1 ✠
Liverpool Lime Street 10	d									07 15				07 16									08 22					08 44								09 22	
Liverpool South Parkway 7 ✈	d									07 25													08 32													09 32	
Warrington Central	d									07 40													08 45													09 45	
Birchwood	d									07 45													08 50													09 50	
Manchester Oxford Road	d									08 06													09 07													10 07	
Manchester Airport ✈	d						07 35				08 06									08 35				09 06									09 35				10 06
Manchester Piccadilly 10	a						07 49			08 08	08 22									08 49			09 09	09 22									09 52			10 09	10 22
	d	07 36					07 57			08 10	08 26						08 42			08 57			09 11	09 27						09 42			09 57			10 11	10 27
Manchester Victoria	d				07 40							08 00	08 02	08 27	08 57										09 00	09 13	09 27	09 57									
Ashton-under-Lyne	d				07 49								08 12	08 37	09 07											09 23	09 37	10 07									
Stalybridge	a	07 49			07 54		08 10			08 26			08 18	08 41	09 13								09 26			09 29	09 42	10 13								10 26	
	d	07 49			07 54		08 10			08 26				08 42									09 26				09 42									10 26	
Mossley (Grtr Manchester)	d				07 59									08 46													09 47										
Greenfield	d				08 03									08 50													09 51										
Marsden	d				08 11									08 59													09 59										
Slaithwaite	d				08 16									09 03													10 04										
Huddersfield	a	08 09			08 24		08 28			08 44	08 56			09 12			09 15			09 26			09 44	09 56			10 12			10 15			10 26			10 44	10 56
	d	08 10	08 13			08 22	08 30	08 34	08 38	08 45	08 57						09 16		09 23	09 27	09 31	09 38	09 45	09 57						10 16		10 23	10 27	10 31	10 35	10 45	10 57
Deighton	d		08 16					08 37	08 41												09 34	09 41												10 34	10 38		
Mirfield	d		08 21					08 42	08 46			09 07									09 39	09 46			10 07									10 39	10 43		
Ravensthorpe	d		08 24					08 45													09 42													10 42			
Dewsbury	a	08 19	08 27				08 39	08 49			09 07	09 12								09 36	09 46			10 06	10 12								10 36	10 46			11 06
	d	08 20	08 27				08 39	08 53			09 07	09 12								09 37	09 46			10 07	10 12								10 37	10 46			11 07
Batley	d		08 30					08 56				09 15									09 49				10 15									10 49			
Morley	d		08 36					09 02				09 21									09 55				10 21									10 55			
Cottingley	d		08 39					09 06													09 59													10 59			
Leeds 10	a	08 36	08 52			09 27	08 54	09 17		09 09	09 22	09 32					09 36		10 29	09 52	10 08		10 09	10 22	10 32					10 36		11 27	10 52	11 08		11 09	11 22
	d	08 38		09 05			08 57			09 12	09 28						09 38	10 05		09 57			10 12	10 28						10 38	11 08		10 57			11 12	11 28
Garforth	d						09 05													10 05													11 05				
South Milford	a																																				
Selby	a	08 57															09 57													10 56							
Howden	a																																				
	d															09 16													10 49								
Brough	a															09 29	10 15												11 04	11 15							
Hull	a	09 31														09 47	10 35												11 22	11 35							
Wakefield Kirkgate	a								09 03													10 03													11 02		
Wakefield Westgate	a								09 10													10 10													11 10		
York 8	a			09 26			09 22			09 35	09 52							10 27		10 22			10 35	10 52							11 30		11 22			11 35	11 52
	d			09 32			09 26			09 40	09 58							10 32		10 26			10 40	10 58							11 32		11 26			11 40	11 58
Malton	d									10 03													11 03													12 03	
Seamer	a									10 20													11 20													12 20	
Scarborough	a									10 29													11 29													12 29	
Thirsk	a						09 45													10 45													11 45				
Northallerton	a						09 58				10 18									10 58				11 18									11 58				12 18
Darlington 7	a			09 57							10 30							10 57						11 30							11 57						12 30
Yarm	d						10 12													11 13													12 13				
Thornaby	a						10 21													11 21													12 21				
Middlesbrough	a						10 30													11 30													12 30				
Durham	a			10 17							10 47							11 15						11 47							12 21						12 47
Chester-le-Street	a																							11 53													
Newcastle 8	a			10 30							11 05							11 29						12 06							12 34						13 03

Table 39

Mondays to Fridays

9 December to 16 May

Liverpool, Manchester Airport and Manchester - Huddersfield - Wakefield, Leeds, Hull, York, Scarborough, Middlesbrough and Newcastle

Network Diagram - refer to first Page of Table 39

		NT ◇	NT	NT	NT	TP ◇1	XC ◇1	NT	TP ◇1	NT	NT	TP ◇1	TP ◇1	NT ◇
Liverpool Lime Street 10	d				09 46							10 22		
Liverpool South Parkway 7 ✈	d											10 32		
Warrington Central	d											10 45		
Birchwood	d											10 50		
Manchester Oxford Road	d											11 07		
Manchester Airport ✈	d								10 35				11 06	
Manchester Piccadilly 10	a								10 52			11 09	11 22	
	d					10 42			10 57			11 11	11 27	
Manchester Victoria	d	10 00	10 13	10 27	10 57									11 00
Ashton-under-Lyne	d		10 23	10 37	11 07									
Stalybridge	a		10 29	10 42	11 13							11 26		
	d			10 42								11 26		
Mossley (Grtr Manchester)	d			10 47										
Greenfield	d			10 51										
Marsden	d			10 59										
Slaithwaite	d			11 04										
Huddersfield	a			11 12		11 15			11 26			11 44	11 56	
	d					11 16		11 23	11 27	11 31	11 35	11 45	11 57	
Deighton	d									11 34	11 38			
Mirfield	d	11 07								11 39	11 43			12 07
Ravensthorpe	d									11 42				
Dewsbury	a	11 12							11 36	11 46			12 06	12 12
	d	11 12							11 37	11 46			12 07	12 12
Batley	d	11 15								11 49				12 15
Morley	d	11 21								11 55				12 21
Cottingley	d									11 59				
Leeds 10	a	11 33				11 36		12 27	11 52	12 08		12 09	12 22	12 31
	d					11 38	12 08		11 57			12 12	12 28	
Garforth	d								12 06					
South Milford	a													
Selby	a					11 57								
Howden	a													
	d													
Brough	a					12 16								
Hull	a					12 36								
Wakefield Kirkgate	a										12 02			
Wakefield Westgate	a										12 10			
York 8	a						12 30		12 23			12 35	12 52	
	d						12 32		12 26			12 40	12 58	
Malton	d											13 03		
Seamer	a											13 20		
Scarborough	a											13 29		
Thirsk	a								12 45					
Northallerton	a								12 58				13 18	
Darlington 7	a						12 57						13 30	
Yarm	d								13 13					
Thornaby	a								13 21					
Middlesbrough	a								13 30					
Durham	a						13 15						13 47	
Chester-le-Street	a												13 53	
Newcastle 8	a						13 29						14 06	

		NT	NT	NT	NT	TP ◇1	XC ◇1	NT	TP ◇1	NT
Liverpool Lime Street 10	d			10 46						
Liverpool South Parkway 7 ✈	d									
Warrington Central	d									
Birchwood	d									
Manchester Oxford Road	d									
Manchester Airport ✈	d								11 35	
Manchester Piccadilly 10	a								11 52	
	d					11 42			11 57	
Manchester Victoria	d	11 13	11 27	11 57						
Ashton-under-Lyne	d	11 23	11 37	12 07						
Stalybridge	a	11 29	11 42	12 13						
	d		11 42							
Mossley (Grtr Manchester)	d		11 47							
Greenfield	d		11 51							
Marsden	d		11 59							
Slaithwaite	d		12 04							
Huddersfield	a		12 12			12 15			12 26	
	d					12 16		12 23	12 27	12 31
Deighton	d									12 34
Mirfield	d									12 39
Ravensthorpe	d									12 42
Dewsbury	a								12 36	12 46
	d								12 37	12 46
Batley	d									12 49
Morley	d									12 55
Cottingley	d									12 59
Leeds 10	a					12 36		13 27	12 52	13 08
	d					12 38	13 08		12 57	
Garforth	d								13 05	
South Milford	a									
Selby	a					12 57				
Howden	a									
	d				12 14					
Brough	a				12 30	13 16				
Hull	a				12 49	13 35				
Wakefield Kirkgate	a									
Wakefield Westgate	a									
York 8	a						13 30		13 22	
	d						13 32		13 26	
Malton	d									
Seamer	a									
Scarborough	a									
Thirsk	a								13 45	
Northallerton	a								13 58	
Darlington 7	a						14 00			
Yarm	d								14 13	
Thornaby	a								14 21	
Middlesbrough	a								14 30	
Durham	a						14 17			
Chester-le-Street	a									
Newcastle 8	a						14 30			

		NT	TP ◇1	TP ◇1	NT ◇	NT	NT	NT	NT	TP ◇1	XC ◇1	NT	TP ◇1	NT	NT
Liverpool Lime Street 10	d		11 22					11 46							
Liverpool South Parkway 7 ✈	d		11 32												
Warrington Central	d		11 45												
Birchwood	d		11 50												
Manchester Oxford Road	d		12 07												
Manchester Airport ✈	d			12 06									12 35		
Manchester Piccadilly 10	a		12 09	12 22									12 52		
	d		12 11	12 27						12 42			12 57		
Manchester Victoria	d				12 00	12 13	12 27	12 57							
Ashton-under-Lyne	d					12 23	12 37	13 07							
Stalybridge	a		12 26			12 29	12 42	13 13							
	d		12 26				12 42								
Mossley (Grtr Manchester)	d						12 47								
Greenfield	d						12 51								
Marsden	d						12 59								
Slaithwaite	d						13 04								
Huddersfield	a		12 44	12 56			13 12			13 15			13 26		
	d	12 38	12 45	12 57						13 16		13 23	13 27	13 31	13 36
Deighton	d	12 41												13 34	13 39
Mirfield	d	12 46			13 07									13 39	13 44
Ravensthorpe	d													13 42	
Dewsbury	a			13 06	13 12								13 36	13 46	
	d			13 07	13 12								13 37	13 46	
Batley	d				13 15									13 49	
Morley	d				13 21									13 55	
Cottingley	d													13 59	
Leeds 10	a		13 09	13 22	13 32					13 36		14 27	13 51	14 08	
	d		13 12	13 28						13 38	14 08		13 57		
Garforth	d												14 05		
South Milford	a														
Selby	a									13 57					
Howden	a														
	d								13 16						
Brough	a								13 28	14 16					
Hull	a								13 47	14 35					
Wakefield Kirkgate	a	13 02													14 00
Wakefield Westgate	a	13 10													14 10
York 8	a		13 35	13 52							14 30		14 22		
	d		13 40	13 58							14 32		14 26		
Malton	d		14 03												
Seamer	a		14 20												
Scarborough	a		14 29												
Thirsk	a												14 45		
Northallerton	a			14 18									14 58		
Darlington 7	a			14 30							14 57				
Yarm	d												15 13		
Thornaby	a												15 21		
Middlesbrough	a												15 30		
Durham	a			14 47							15 15				
Chester-le-Street	a														
Newcastle 8	a			15 05							15 29				

Table 39

Mondays to Fridays

9 December to 16 May

Liverpool, Manchester Airport and Manchester - Huddersfield - Wakefield, Leeds, Hull, York, Scarborough, Middlesbrough and Newcastle

Network Diagram - refer to first Page of Table 39

		TP	TP	NT	NT	NT	NT	NT	TP	XC	NT	TP	NT	NT	TP	TP	NT	NT	NT	NT	NT	TP	XC	NT	TP	NT	NT	TP	TP	NT	NT	NT	NT	NT	TP	XC	NT
		◇1 ᅲ	◇1 ᅲ	◇					◇1 ᅲ	◇1 ᅲ		◇1 ᅲ			◇1 ᅲ	◇1 ᅲ	◇					◇1 ᅲ	◇1 ᅲ		◇1 ᅲ			◇1 ᅲ	◇1 ᅲ	◇					◇1 ᅲ	◇1 ᅲ	
Liverpool Lime Street 10	d	12 22					12 46								13 22						13 46								14 22					14 46				
Liverpool South Parkway 7 ✈	d	12 32													13 32														14 32									
Warrington Central	d	12 45													13 45														14 45									
Birchwood	d	12 50													13 50														14 50									
Manchester Oxford Road	d	13 07													14 07														15 07									
Manchester Airport ✈	d		13 06									13 35				14 06									14 35					15 06							
Manchester Piccadilly 10	a	13 09	13 22									13 52			14 09	14 22									14 52			15 09	15 22								
	d	13 11	13 27						13 42			13 57			14 11	14 27						14 42			14 57			15 11	15 27						15 42		
Manchester Victoria	d			13 00	13 13	13 27	13 57										14 00	14 13	14 27	14 57										15 00	15 13	15 27	15 57				
Ashton-under-Lyne	d				13 23	13 37	14 07											14 23	14 37	15 07											15 23	15 37	16 07				
Stalybridge	a	13 26			13 29	13 42	14 13								14 26			14 29	14 42	15 13								15 26			15 29	15 42	16 13				
	d	13 26				13 42									14 26				14 42									15 26				15 42					
Mossley (Grtr Manchester)	d					13 47													14 47													15 47					
Greenfield	d					13 51													14 51													15 51					
Marsden	d					13 59													14 59													15 59					
Slaithwaite	d					14 04													15 04													16 04					
Huddersfield	a	13 44	13 56			14 12			14 15			14 26			14 44	14 56			15 12			15 15			15 26			15 44	15 56			16 12			16 15		
	d	13 45	13 57						14 16		14 23	14 27	14 31	14 38	14 45	14 57						15 16		15 23	15 27	15 31	15 38	15 45	15 57						16 16		16 23
Deighton	d												14 34	14 41												15 34	15 41										
Mirfield	d			14 07									14 39	14 46			15 07									15 39	15 46			16 07							
Ravensthorpe	d												14 42													15 42											
Dewsbury	a		14 06	14 12								14 36	14 46			15 06	15 12								15 36	15 46			16 06	16 12							
	d		14 07	14 12								14 37	14 46			15 07	15 12								15 37	15 46			16 07	16 12							
Batley	d			14 15									14 49				15 15									15 49				16 15							
Morley	d			14 21									14 55				15 21									15 55				16 21							
Cottingley	d												14 59													15 59											
Leeds 10	a	14 09	14 22	14 32					14 36		15 27	14 52	15 08		15 09	15 22	15 32					15 36		16 27	15 52	16 08		16 08	16 22	16 32					16 36		17 27
	d	14 12	14 28						14 38	15 08		14 57			15 12	15 28						15 38	16 08		15 57			16 12	16 28						16 38	17 08	
Garforth	d											15 05													16 05												
South Milford	a																																				
Selby	a								14 57													15 57													17 01		
Howden	a																																				
	d							14 17													15 16													16 49			
Brough	a							14 30	15 15												15 28	16 16												17 03	17 20		
Hull	a							14 52	15 35												15 47	16 35												17 27	17 37		
Wakefield Kirkgate	a													15 02													16 02										
Wakefield Westgate	a													15 10													16 10										
York 8	a	14 35	14 52							15 30		15 22			15 35	15 52							16 30		16 22			16 35	16 52							17 30	
	d	14 40	14 58							15 32		15 26			15 40								16 32		16 26			16 40	16 58							17 32	
Malton	d	15 03													16 03													17 03									
Seamer	a	15 20													16 20													17 20									
Scarborough	a	15 29													16 29													17 29									
Thirsk	a											15 45													16 45				17 14								
Northallerton	a		15 18									15 58													16 59				17 22								
Darlington 7	a		15 30							15 57													16 58						17 33							17 58	
Yarm	d											16 13													17 13												
Thornaby	a											16 21													17 21												
Middlesbrough	a											16 30													17 30												
Durham	a		15 48							16 15													17 15						17 50							18 15	
Chester-le-Street	a		15 54																										17 56								
Newcastle 8	a		16 06							16 29													17 30						18 10							18 32	

Table 39

Mondays to Fridays

9 December to 16 May

Liverpool, Manchester Airport and Manchester - Huddersfield - Wakefield, Leeds, Hull, York, Scarborough, Middlesbrough and Newcastle

Network Diagram - refer to first Page of Table 39

		TP	NT	NT	TP	TP	NT	NT	NT	TP	XC	NT	TP	TP	NT	NT	NT	TP	NT	TP	TP	TP	NT	XC	NT	NT	TP	XC	NT	TP	NT	NT	NT	TP	TP	NT	NT
													FO	FX						FX	FO	FO															
		◇1 ⊼			◇1 ⊼	◇1 ⊼	◇			◇1 ⊼	◇1 ⊼		◇1 ⊼	◇1 ⊼				◇1 ⊼		◇1 ⊼	◇1 ⊼	◇1 ⊼		◇1 ⊼			◇1 ⊼	◇1 ⊼		◇1 ⊼				◇1 ⊼	◇1 ⊼		
Liverpool Lime Street 10	d				15 22											15 46		16 22														16 46		17 22			
Liverpool South Parkway 7 ✈	d				15 32													16 32																17 32			
Warrington Central	d				15 45													16 45																17 45			
Birchwood	d				15 50													16 50																17 50			
Manchester Oxford Road	d				16 07													17 07																18 07			
Manchester Airport ✈	d	15 35				16 06							16 34	16 35						17 06										17 35							
Manchester Piccadilly 10 ⛴	a	15 52			16 09	16 22							16 52	16 52				17 09		17 22										17 52				18 09			
	d	15 57			16 11	16 27				16 42			16 56	16 56				17 11		17 26	17 26						17 42			17 56				18 11	18 27		
Manchester Victoria ⛴	d						16 00	16 17	16 27							16 57			17 15				17 00		17 27							17 57				18 00	18 27
Ashton-under-Lyne	d							16 27	16 37							17 07			17 24						17 37							18 07					18 37
Stalybridge	a				16 26			16 33	16 42				17 08	17 08		17 12		17 26	17 29	17 38	17 38				17 42					18 08		18 12		18 26			18 42
	d				16 26				16 42				17 08	17 08		17 12		17 26	17 29	17 38	17 38				17 43					18 08		18 12		18 26			18 42
Mossley (Grtr Manchester)	d								16 47							17 17			17 34						17 47							18 17					18 47
Greenfield	d								16 51							17 21			17 38						17 51							18 21					18 51
Marsden	d								16 59							17 29									18 00							18 29					18 59
Slaithwaite	d								17 04							17 34																18 34					19 04
Huddersfield	a	16 26			16 44	16 56			17 12	17 15			17 26	17 26		17 42		17 44	17 54	17 56	17 57				18 11		18 15			18 26		18 43		18 44	18 56		19 12
	d	16 27	16 31	16 38	16 45	16 57				17 16		17 23	17 27	17 27	17 31		17 38	17 45		17 57	17 57						18 16		18 25	18 27	18 37		18 41	18 45	18 57		
Deighton	d		16 34	16 41											17 34		17 41														18 40		18 44				
Mirfield	d		16 39	16 46			17 07								17 39		17 46						18 07								18 45		18 49			19 08	
Ravensthorpe	d		16 42												17 42																18 48						
Dewsbury	a	16 36	16 46			17 06	17 12						17 36	17 36	17 46					18 06	18 07		18 13							18 36	18 52				19 06	19 13	
	d	16 37	16 46			17 07	17 12						17 37	17 37	17 46					18 07	18 07		18 13							18 37	18 56				19 07	19 13	
Batley	d		16 49				17 15								17 49								18 17								18 59					19 16	
Morley	d		16 55				17 21								17 55								18 22								19 05					19 22	
Cottingley	d		16 59												17 59																19 09						
Leeds 10	a	16 52	17 08		17 09	17 22	17 31			17 36		18 31	17 52	17 52	18 08			18 09		18 22	18 22		18 34				18 36		19 27	18 52	19 20			19 09	19 23	19 33	
	d	16 57			17 12	17 25				17 38	18 07		17 57	17 57				18 12		18 28	18 28			18 36			18 38	19 08		18 57				19 12	19 28		
Garforth	d	17 05				17 34							18 05	18 05																19 05							
South Milford	a																										18 51										
Selby	a									17 59																	19 00										
Howden	a									18 08																											
	d									18 09																18 54											
Brough	a									18 21																19 11	19 19										
Hull	a									18 39																19 29	19 38										
Wakefield Kirkgate	a			17 02													18 02																19 02				
Wakefield Westgate	a			17 15													18 10																19 12				
York 8	a	17 21			17 36	17 54					18 29		18 23	18 23				18 35		18 52	18 52			18 58				19 30		19 22				19 35	19 54		
	d	17 24			17 41	18 00					18 33		18 25	18 25				18 40		18 57		18 57		19 04				19 33		19 26				19 40			
Malton	d	17 47				18 23												19 03																20 03			
Seamer	a	18 04				18 40												19 20																20 20			
Scarborough	a	18 13				18 49												19 29																20 29			
Thirsk	a				17 57															19 13		19 13								19 45							
Northallerton	a				18 08								18 45	18 45						19 24		19 24								19 56							
Darlington 7	a										19 01		18 57	18 57										19 29				20 00									
Yarm	d				18 23															19 38		19 38								20 11							
Thornaby	a				18 32															19 46		19 46								20 21							
Middlesbrough	a				18 40															19 56		19 56								20 30							
Durham	a										19 19		19 14	19 14										19 47				20 18									
Chester-le-Street	a												19 20	19 20																							
Newcastle 8 ⛴	a										19 35		19 34	19 34										20 01				20 33									

Table 39

Mondays to Fridays

9 December to 16 May

Liverpool, Manchester Airport and Manchester - Huddersfield - Wakefield, Leeds, Hull, York, Scarborough, Middlesbrough and Newcastle

Network Diagram - refer to first Page of Table 39

Station		TP FX ◇1	TP FO ◇1	XC ◇1	NT	TP ◇1	NT	NT	TP ◇1	NT ◇	TP ◇1	NT	NT	NT
Liverpool Lime Street 10	d								18 22					
Liverpool South Parkway 7 ✈	d								18 32					
Warrington Central	d								18 45					
Birchwood	d								18 50					
Manchester Oxford Road	d								19 07					
Manchester Airport ✈	d					18 35					19 20			
Manchester Piccadilly 10	a					18 52			19 09		19 36			
	d	18 42	18 42			18 57			19 11		19 42			
Manchester Victoria	d									19 00		19 27		
Ashton-under-Lyne	d											19 37		
Stalybridge	a								19 26			19 42		
	d								19 26			19 42		
Mossley (Grtr Manchester)	d											19 47		
Greenfield	d											19 51		
Marsden	d											19 59		
Slaithwaite	d											20 04		
Huddersfield	a	19 15	19 15			19 26			19 44		20 15	20 12		
	d	19 16	19 16		19 23	19 27	19 31	19 38	19 45		20 16		20 25	20 31
Deighton	d						19 34	19 41						20 34
Mirfield	d						19 39	19 46		20 07				20 39
Ravensthorpe	d						19 42							20 42
Dewsbury	a					19 36	19 46			20 12	20 25			20 46
	d					19 37	19 46			20 12	20 26			20 46
Batley	d						19 49			20 15				20 49
Morley	d						19 55			20 21				20 55
Cottingley	d						19 59							20 59
Leeds 10	a	19 36	19 36		20 30	19 52	20 08		20 09	20 31	20 41		21 25	21 08
	d	19 38	19 38	20 08		19 57			20 12		20 45			
Garforth	d					20 05								
South Milford	a	19 50	19 51											
Selby	a	20 00	20 00											
Howden	a	20 09	20 09											
	d	20 10	20 10											
Brough	a	20 22	20 22											
Hull	a	20 41	20 41											
Wakefield Kirkgate	a							20 03						
Wakefield Westgate	a							20 10						
York 8	a			20 30		20 22			20 35		21 08			
	d			20 33		20 29			20 40		21 14			
Malton	d								21 02					
Seamer	a								21 20					
Scarborough	a								21 28					
Thirsk	a					20 48					21 30			
Northallerton	a					20 59					21 38			
Darlington 7	a			20 58							21 50			
Yarm	d					21 13								
Thornaby	a					21 21								
Middlesbrough	a					21 30								
Durham	a			21 16							22 07			
Chester-le-Street	a										22 13			
Newcastle 8	a			21 30							22 27			

Station		NT	TP ◇1	TP ◇1	NT	NT	NT	NT	TP ◇1	NT	NT	TP ThFO ◇1	TP MT WO ◇1
Liverpool Lime Street 10	d		19 22						20 22				
Liverpool South Parkway 7 ✈	d		19 32						20 32				
Warrington Central	d		19 45						20 45				
Birchwood	d		19 50						20 50				
Manchester Oxford Road	d		20 07						21 07				
Manchester Airport ✈	d			20 20									
Manchester Piccadilly 10	a		20 09	20 36					21 09				
	d		20 11	20 42					21 11				
Manchester Victoria	d				20 27					21 27			
Ashton-under-Lyne	d				20 37					21 37			
Stalybridge	a		20 26		20 42				21 26	21 41			
	d		20 26		20 42				21 26	21 42			
Mossley (Grtr Manchester)	d				20 47					21 46			
Greenfield	d				20 51					21 50			
Marsden	d				20 59					21 59			
Slaithwaite	d				21 04					22 03			
Huddersfield	a		20 44	21 15	21 12				21 44	22 12			
	d	20 38	20 45	21 16		21 27	21 31	21 38	21 45				
Deighton	d	20 41					21 34	21 42					
Mirfield	d	20 46					21 39	21 47					
Ravensthorpe	d						21 42						
Dewsbury	a			21 25			21 46						
	d			21 26			21 46						
Batley	d						21 49						
Morley	d						21 55						
Cottingley	d						21 59						
Leeds 10	a		21 09	21 41		22 25	22 08		22 09				
	d		21 12	21 42					22 12			22 22	22 22
Garforth	d												
South Milford	a		21 23									22 35	22 36
Selby	a		21 33									22 46	22 46
Howden	a		21 42										
	d		21 43								22 41		
Brough	a		21 55								22 56	23 06	23 06
Hull	a		22 13								23 18	23 25	23 25
Wakefield Kirkgate	a	21 03						22 01					
Wakefield Westgate	a	21 10						22 10					
York 8	a			22 06					22 38				
	d			22 10									
Malton	d			22 33									
Seamer	a			22 50									
Scarborough	a			22 59									
Thirsk	a												
Northallerton	a												
Darlington 7	a												
Yarm	d												
Thornaby	a												
Middlesbrough	a												
Durham	a												
Chester-le-Street	a												
Newcastle 8	a												

Station		TP ◇1	NT	NT	NT	TP FO ◇1	TP FX ◇1 A	TP FX ◇1 B	NT	TP FX ◇1	TP FO ◇1	TP FO ◇1
Liverpool Lime Street 10	d									22 30	22 30	
Liverpool South Parkway 7 ✈	d									22 40	22 40	
Warrington Central	d									22 53	22 53	
Birchwood	d									22 58	22 58	
Manchester Oxford Road	d									23 17	23 17	
Manchester Airport ✈	d	21 20				22 18		22 22				23 24
Manchester Piccadilly 10	a	21 36				22 31		22 35		23 19	23 19	23 38
	d	21 42				22 42	22 42	22 42		23 21	23 21	23 40
Manchester Victoria	d		22 08						23 00			
Ashton-under-Lyne	d		22 18						23 10			
Stalybridge	a	21 55	22 22			22 55	22 55	22 55	23 14	23 34	23 34	
	d	21 55	22 23			22 55	22 55	22 55	23 15	23 34	23 34	
Mossley (Grtr Manchester)	d		22 27						23 19			
Greenfield	d		22 31						23 23			
Marsden	d		22 40						23 32			
Slaithwaite	d		22 44						23 36			
Huddersfield	a	22 15	22 53			23 15	23 15	23 15	23 44	23 52	23 52	00 10
	d	22 16		22 25	22 31	23 16	23 16	23 16		23 53	23 53	00 10
Deighton	d				22 34							
Mirfield	d				22 39							
Ravensthorpe	d				22 42							
Dewsbury	a	22 25			22 46	23 25	23 25	23 25				00s19
	d	22 26			22 46	23 26	23 26	23 26				
Batley	d				22 49							
Morley	d				22 55							
Cottingley	d				22 59							
Leeds 10	a	22 41		23 26	23 08	23 41	23 41	23 41		00 30	00 31	00 35
	d	22 42				23 42	23 42	23 42		00 32	00 34	00 37
Garforth	d											
South Milford	a											
Selby	a											
Howden	a											
	d											
Brough	a											
Hull	a											
Wakefield Kirkgate	a											
Wakefield Westgate	a											
York 8	a	23 09				00 09	00 09	00 09		01 11	01 16	01 04
	d	23 20										
Malton	d											
Seamer	a											
Scarborough	a											
Thirsk	a	23 42										
Northallerton	a	23 50										
Darlington 7	a	00 01										
Yarm	d											
Thornaby	a											
Middlesbrough	a											
Durham	a	00 18										
Chester-le-Street	a											
Newcastle 8	a	00 50										

A from 30 December until 20 March

B until 26 December, from 24 March

Table 39

Mondays to Fridays

9 December to 16 May

Liverpool, Manchester Airport and Manchester - Huddersfield - Wakefield, Leeds, Hull, York, Scarborough, Middlesbrough and Newcastle

Network Diagram - refer to first Page of Table 39

		TP FX ◇1 A	TP FX ◇1 B
Liverpool Lime Street 10	d		
Liverpool South Parkway 7 ✈	d		
Warrington Central	d		
Birchwood	d		
Manchester Oxford Road	d		
Manchester Airport ✈	d	23 24	
Manchester Piccadilly 10	a	23 37	
	d	23 40	23 40
Manchester Victoria	d		
Ashton-under-Lyne	d		
Stalybridge	a		
	d		
Mossley (Grtr Manchester)	d		
Greenfield	d		
Marsden	d		
Slaithwaite	d		
Huddersfield	a	00 25	00 25
	d	00 26	00 26
Deighton	d		
Mirfield	d		
Ravensthorpe	d		
Dewsbury	a	00s35	00s35
	d		
Batley	d		
Morley	d		
Cottingley	d		
Leeds 10	a	00 51	00 51
	d	00 54	00 54
Garforth	d		
South Milford	a		
Selby	a		
Howden	a		
	d		
Brough	a		
Hull	a		
Wakefield Kirkgate	a		
Wakefield Westgate	a		
York 8	a	01 30	01 30
	d		
Malton	d		
Seamer	a		
Scarborough	a		
Thirsk	a		
Northallerton	a		
Darlington 7	a		
Yarm	d		
Thornaby	a		
Middlesbrough	a		
Durham	a		
Chester-le-Street	a		
Newcastle 8	a		

A until 26 December, from 24 March

B from 30 December until 20 March

Table 39

Saturdays

14 December to 17 May

Liverpool, Manchester Airport and Manchester - Huddersfield - Wakefield, Leeds, Hull, York, Scarborough, Middlesbrough and Newcastle

Network Diagram - refer to first Page of Table 39

Station		TP	TP	TP	TP	TP	TP	TP	TP	NT
		◇1	◇1	◇1	◇1	◇1	◇1	◇1	◇1	
Liverpool Lime Street 10	d									
Liverpool South Parkway 7 ✈	d									
Warrington Central	d									
Birchwood	d									
Manchester Oxford Road	d									
Manchester Airport ✈	d					00 38	04 13		05 37	
Manchester Piccadilly 10	a					00 51	04 27		05 51	
	d					00 53	04 30	05 39	05 57	
Manchester Victoria	d									
Ashton-under-Lyne	d									
Stalybridge	a							05 52		
	d							05 52		
Mossley (Grtr Manchester)	d									
Greenfield	d									
Marsden	d									
Slaithwaite	d									
Huddersfield	a					01 34	05 10	06 10	06 26	
	d			00 10		01 35	05 11	06 11	06 27	06 31
Deighton	d									06 34
Mirfield	d									06 39
Ravensthorpe	d									06 42
Dewsbury	a			00s19					06 36	06 46
	d								06 37	06 46
Batley	d									06 49
Morley	d									06 55
Cottingley	d									06 59
Leeds 10	a			00 35		02 13	05 32	06 32	06 52	07 07
	d	00 34		00 37		02 16	05 34	06 35	06 55	
Garforth	d									
South Milford	a									
Selby	a									
Howden	a									
	d									
Brough	a									
Hull	a									
Wakefield Kirkgate	a									
Wakefield Westgate	a									
York 8	a	01 16		01 04		02 42	06 00	07 00	07 21	
	d		05 54		06 40			07 06	07 25	
Malton	d				07 03				07 48	
Seamer	a				07 20				08 05	
Scarborough	a				07 29				08 14	
Thirsk	a		06 10					07 22		
Northallerton	a		06 18					07 30		
Darlington 7	a		06 29					07 41		
Yarm	d									
Thornaby	a		06 53							
Middlesbrough	a		07 03							
Durham	a							07 58		
Chester-le-Street	a							08 04		
Newcastle 8	a							08 17		

Station		NT	NT	TP	GR	TP	TP	NT	XC	NT
				◇1	B 1	◇1	◇1		◇1	
Liverpool Lime Street 10	d									
Liverpool South Parkway 7 ✈	d									
Warrington Central	d									
Birchwood	d									
Manchester Oxford Road	d									
Manchester Airport ✈	d						06 30			
Manchester Piccadilly 10	a						06 44			
	d					06 21	06 54			
Manchester Victoria	d							06 55		
Ashton-under-Lyne	d							07 05		
Stalybridge	a						07 07	07 10		
	d						07 07	07 11		
Mossley (Grtr Manchester)	d							07 15		
Greenfield	d							07 19		
Marsden	d		07 00					07 28		
Slaithwaite	d		07 04					07 32		
Huddersfield	a		07 12			06 54	07 25	07 41		
	d	06 41				06 56	07 26			07 30
Deighton	d	06 45								
Mirfield	d	06 50								
Ravensthorpe	d									
Dewsbury	a					07 05				
	d					07 06				
Batley	d									
Morley	d									
Cottingley	d									
Leeds 10	a					07 19	07 47			08 30
	d				07 10	07 23	07 51		07 57	
Garforth	d						08 00			
South Milford	a									
Selby	a					07 43				
Howden	a					07 52				
	d					07 52				
Brough	a					08 04				
Hull	a					08 20				
Wakefield Kirkgate	a	07 03								
Wakefield Westgate	a	07 10								
York 8	a				07 32		08 20		08 24	
	d			07 32	07 37		08 23		08 29	
Malton	d									
Seamer	a									
Scarborough	a									
Thirsk	a			07 52			08 39			
Northallerton	a			08 00			08 50			
Darlington 7	a				08 04				08 57	
Yarm	d			08 14			09 04			
Thornaby	a			08 24			09 12			
Middlesbrough	a			08 31			09 22			
Durham	a				08 22				09 13	
Chester-le-Street	a									
Newcastle 8	a				08 37				09 27	

Station		NT	TP	NT	TP	TP	NT	TP	NT	XC
			◇1		◇1	◇1		◇1		◇1
Liverpool Lime Street 10	d		06 15							
Liverpool South Parkway 7 ✈	d		06 25							
Warrington Central	d		06 38							
Birchwood	d		06 43							
Manchester Oxford Road	d		07 06							
Manchester Airport ✈	d					07 06				
Manchester Piccadilly 10	a		07 08			07 22				
	d		07 11			07 27		07 36		
Manchester Victoria	d						06 58			
Ashton-under-Lyne	d									
Stalybridge	a		07 23					07 49		
	d		07 23					07 49		
Mossley (Grtr Manchester)	d									
Greenfield	d									
Marsden	d									
Slaithwaite	d									
Huddersfield	a		07 44			07 56		08 09		
	d	07 34	07 45			07 57		08 10	08 14	
Deighton	d	07 38							08 17	
Mirfield	d	07 43					08 06		08 22	
Ravensthorpe	d								08 25	
Dewsbury	a		07 54			08 06	08 11	08 19	08 29	
	d		07 55			08 07	08 12	08 20	08 29	
Batley	d						08 15		08 32	
Morley	d						08 21		08 38	
Cottingley	d						08 24		08 42	
Leeds 10	a		08 10			08 24	08 31	08 36	08 52	
	d		08 12			08 28		08 38		09 08
Garforth	d									
South Milford	a									
Selby	a							08 57		
Howden	a									
	d			08 10						
Brough	a			08 28						
Hull	a			08 52				09 31		
Wakefield Kirkgate	a	07 57								
Wakefield Westgate	a	08 10								
York 8	a		08 35			08 52				09 30
	d		08 40		08 42	08 59				09 32
Malton	d		09 03							
Seamer	a		09 20							
Scarborough	a		09 29							
Thirsk	a									
Northallerton	a					09 19				
Darlington 7	a				09 12	09 31				09 57
Yarm	d									
Thornaby	a									
Middlesbrough	a									
Durham	a				09 28	09 48				10 15
Chester-le-Street	a					09 54				
Newcastle 8	a				09 46	10 08				10 30

Station		NT	NT	NT	TP	NT	NT	TP	TP	NT
					◇1			◇1	◇1	
Liverpool Lime Street 10	d			06 46				07 15		
Liverpool South Parkway 7 ✈	d							07 25		
Warrington Central	d							07 40		
Birchwood	d							07 45		
Manchester Oxford Road	d							08 06		
Manchester Airport ✈	d				07 35				08 06	
Manchester Piccadilly 10	a				07 49			08 08	08 22	
	d				07 57			08 10	08 26	
Manchester Victoria	d	07 40		07 57						08 00
Ashton-under-Lyne	d	07 49		08 07						
Stalybridge	a	07 54		08 13	08 09			08 26		
	d	07 54			08 10			08 26		
Mossley (Grtr Manchester)	d	07 59								
Greenfield	d	08 03								
Marsden	d	08 11								
Slaithwaite	d	08 16								
Huddersfield	a	08 24			08 28			08 44	08 56	
	d		08 21		08 30	08 34	08 38	08 45	08 57	
Deighton	d					08 37	08 41			
Mirfield	d					08 42	08 46			09 07
Ravensthorpe	d					08 45				
Dewsbury	a				08 39	08 49			09 06	09 12
	d				08 39	08 53			09 07	09 12
Batley	d					08 56				09 15
Morley	d					09 02				09 21
Cottingley	d					09 06				
Leeds 10	a		09 27		08 54	09 16		09 09	09 22	09 32
	d				08 57			09 12	09 28	
Garforth	d				09 05					
South Milford	a									
Selby	a									
Howden	a									
	d									
Brough	a									
Hull	a									
Wakefield Kirkgate	a						09 02			
Wakefield Westgate	a						09 10			
York 8	a				09 22			09 35	09 52	
	d				09 26			09 40	09 58	
Malton	d							10 03		
Seamer	a							10 20		
Scarborough	a							10 29		
Thirsk	a				09 45					
Northallerton	a				09 58				10 18	
Darlington 7	a								10 30	
Yarm	d				10 14					
Thornaby	a				10 22					
Middlesbrough	a				10 32					
Durham	a								10 47	
Chester-le-Street	a									
Newcastle 8	a								11 05	

Table 39

Saturdays

14 December to 17 May

Liverpool, Manchester Airport and Manchester - Huddersfield - Wakefield, Leeds, Hull, York, Scarborough, Middlesbrough and Newcastle

Network Diagram - refer to first Page of Table 39

		NT	NT	NT	TP ◇1	XC ◇1	NT	TP ◇1	NT	NT	TP ◇1	TP ◇1	NT	NT	NT	NT	TP ◇1	XC ◇1	NT
Liverpool Lime Street 10	d	07 16									08 22				08 44				
Liverpool South Parkway 7 ✈	d										08 32								
Warrington Central	d										08 45								
Birchwood	d										08 50								
Manchester Oxford Road	d										09 07								
Manchester Airport ✈	d							08 35				09 06							
Manchester Piccadilly 10	a							08 49			09 09	09 22							
	d				08 42			08 57			09 11	09 27					09 42		
Manchester Victoria	d	08 27	08 57										09 00	09 27	09 57				
Ashton-under-Lyne	d	08 37	09 07											09 37	10 07				
Stalybridge	a	08 41	09 13								09 26			09 42	10 13				
	d	08 42									09 26			09 42					
Mossley (Grtr Manchester)	d	08 46												09 47					
Greenfield	d	08 50												09 51					
Marsden	d	08 59												09 59					
Slaithwaite	d	09 03												10 04					
Huddersfield	a	09 12			09 15			09 26			09 44	09 56		10 12			10 15		
	d				09 16		09 23	09 27	09 31	09 38	09 45	09 57					10 16		10 23
Deighton	d								09 34	09 41									
Mirfield	d								09 39	09 46			10 07						
Ravensthorpe	d								09 42										
Dewsbury	a							09 36	09 46			10 06	10 12						
	d							09 37	09 46			10 07	10 12						
Batley	d								09 49				10 15						
Morley	d								09 55				10 21						
Cottingley	d								09 59										
Leeds 10	a				09 36		10 27	09 52	10 08		10 09	10 22	10 32				10 36		11 27
	d				09 38	10 08		09 57			10 12	10 28					10 38	11 08	
Garforth	d							10 05											
South Milford	a																		
Selby	a				09 57												10 57		
Howden	a																		
	d			09 16												10 18			
Brough	a			09 29	10 16											10 32	11 16		
Hull	a			09 47	10 35											10 50	11 35		
Wakefield Kirkgate	a									10 02									
Wakefield Westgate	a									10 10									
York 8	a					10 30		10 22			10 35	10 52						11 30	
	d					10 32		10 26			10 40	10 58						11 32	
Malton	d										11 03								
Seamer	a										11 20								
Scarborough	a										11 29								
Thirsk	a							10 45											
Northallerton	a							10 58				11 18							
Darlington 7	a					10 57						11 30						11 57	
Yarm	d							11 13											
Thornaby	a							11 21											
Middlesbrough	a							11 30											
Durham	a					11 15						11 47						12 15	
Chester-le-Street	a											11 53							
Newcastle 8	a					11 29						12 06						12 29	

		TP ◇1	NT	NT	TP ◇1	TP ◇1	NT	NT	NT	NT	TP ◇1	XC ◇1	NT	TP ◇1	NT	NT	TP ◇1	TP ◇1	NT
Liverpool Lime Street 10	d				09 22				09 46								10 22		
Liverpool South Parkway 7 ✈	d				09 32												10 32		
Warrington Central	d				09 45												10 45		
Birchwood	d				09 50												10 50		
Manchester Oxford Road	d				10 07												11 07		
Manchester Airport ✈	d	09 35				10 06								10 35				11 06	
Manchester Piccadilly 10	a	09 52			10 09	10 22								10 52			11 09	11 22	
	d	09 57			10 11	10 27					10 42			10 57			11 11	11 27	
Manchester Victoria	d						10 00	10 27	10 57										11 00
Ashton-under-Lyne	d							10 37	11 07										
Stalybridge	a				10 26			10 42	11 13								11 26		
	d				10 26			10 42									11 26		
Mossley (Grtr Manchester)	d							10 47											
Greenfield	d							10 51											
Marsden	d							10 59											
Slaithwaite	d							11 04											
Huddersfield	a	10 26			10 44	10 56		11 12			11 15			11 26			11 44	11 56	
	d	10 27	10 31	10 38	10 45	10 57					11 16		11 23	11 27	11 31	11 38	11 45	11 57	
Deighton	d		10 34	10 41											11 34	11 41			
Mirfield	d		10 39	10 46			11 07								11 39	11 46			12 07
Ravensthorpe	d		10 42												11 42				
Dewsbury	a	10 36	10 46			11 06	11 12							11 36	11 46			12 06	12 12
	d	10 37	10 46			11 07	11 12							11 37	11 46			12 07	12 12
Batley	d		10 49				11 15								11 49				12 15
Morley	d		10 55				11 21								11 55				12 21
Cottingley	d		10 59												11 59				
Leeds 10	a	10 52	11 08		11 09	11 22	11 35				11 36		12 27	11 52	12 08		12 09	12 22	12 32
	d	10 57			11 12	11 28					11 38	12 08		11 57			12 12	12 28	
Garforth	d	11 05												12 05					
South Milford	a																		
Selby	a										11 57								
Howden	a																		
	d									11 17									
Brough	a									11 32	12 16								
Hull	a									11 53	12 36								
Wakefield Kirkgate	a			11 02												12 02			
Wakefield Westgate	a			11 10												12 10			
York 8	a	11 22			11 35	11 52						12 30		12 22			12 35	12 52	
	d	11 26			11 40	11 58						12 32		12 26			12 40	12 58	
Malton	d				12 03												13 03		
Seamer	a				12 20												13 20		
Scarborough	a				12 29												13 29		
Thirsk	a	11 45												12 45					
Northallerton	a	11 58				12 18								12 59				13 18	
Darlington 7	a					12 30						12 58						13 30	
Yarm	d	12 13												13 13					
Thornaby	a	12 21												13 21					
Middlesbrough	a	12 30												13 30					
Durham	a					12 47						13 15						13 47	
Chester-le-Street	a																	13 53	
Newcastle 8	a					13 03						13 29						14 06	

Table 39

Saturdays

14 December to 17 May

Liverpool, Manchester Airport and Manchester - Huddersfield - Wakefield, Leeds, Hull, York, Scarborough, Middlesbrough and Newcastle

Network Diagram - refer to first Page of Table 39

		NT	NT	NT	TP	XC	NT	TP	NT	NT	TP	TP	NT	NT	NT	NT	TP	XC	NT	TP	NT	NT	TP	TP	TP	NT	NT	NT	NT	TP	XC	NT	TP	NT	NT	TP	TP
					◇1	◇1		◇1			◇1	◇1					◇1	◇1		◇1			◇1	◇1	◇1					◇1	◇1		◇1			◇1	◇1
																								A	B												B
Liverpool Lime Street 10	d		10 46								11 22				11 46								12 22					12 46								13 22	
Liverpool South Parkway 7	d										11 32												12 32													13 32	
Warrington Central	d										11 45												12 45													13 45	
Birchwood	d										11 50												12 50													13 50	
Manchester Oxford Road	d										12 07												13 07													14 07	
Manchester Airport	d							11 35				12 06								12 35				13 05	13 06								13 35				14 06
Manchester Piccadilly 10	a							11 52			12 09	12 22								12 52			13 09	13 22	13 22								13 52			14 09	14 22
	d				11 42			11 57			12 11	12 27					12 42			12 57			13 11	13 27	13 27					13 42			13 57			14 11	14 27
Manchester Victoria	d	11 27	11 57										12 00	12 27	12 57											13 00	13 27	13 57									
Ashton-under-Lyne	d	11 37	12 07											12 37	13 07												13 37	14 07									
Stalybridge	a	11 42	12 13								12 26			12 42	13 13								13 26				13 42	14 13								14 26	
	d	11 42									12 26			12 42									13 26				13 42									14 26	
Mossley (Grtr Manchester)	d	11 47												12 47													13 47										
Greenfield	d	11 51												12 51													13 51										
Marsden	d	11 59												12 59													13 59										
Slaithwaite	d	12 04												13 04													14 04										
Huddersfield	a	12 12			12 15			12 26			12 44	12 56		13 12			13 15			13 26			13 44	13 56	13 56		14 12			14 15			14 26			14 44	14 56
	d				12 16		12 23	12 27	12 31	12 38	12 45	12 57					13 16		13 23	13 27	13 31	13 38	13 45	13 57	13 57					14 16		14 23	14 27	14 31	14 38	14 45	14 57
Deighton	d								12 34	12 41											13 34	13 41												14 34	14 41		
Mirfield	d								12 39	12 46			13 07								13 39	13 46				14 07								14 39	14 46		
Ravensthorpe	d								12 42												13 42													14 42			
Dewsbury	a							12 36	12 46			13 06	13 12							13 36	13 46			14 06	14 06	14 12							14 36	14 46			15 06
	d							12 37	12 46			13 07	13 12							13 37	13 46			14 07	14 07	14 12							14 37	14 46			15 07
Batley	d								12 49				13 15								13 49					14 15								14 49			
Morley	d								12 55				13 21								13 55					14 21								14 55			
Cottingley	d								12 59												13 59													14 59			
Leeds 10	a				12 36		13 27	12 52	13 08		13 09	13 22	13 32				13 36		14 27	13 52	14 08		14 09	14 22	14 22	14 32				14 36		15 27	14 52	15 08		15 09	15 22
	d				12 38	13 08		12 57			13 12	13 28					13 38	14 08		13 57			14 12	14 28	14 28					14 38	15 08		14 57			15 12	15 28
Garforth	d							13 05												14 05													15 05				
South Milford	a																																				
Selby	a				12 57												13 57													14 57							
Howden	a																																				
	d			12 14												13 16													14 22								
Brough	a			12 30	13 16											13 28	14 16												14 35	15 16							
Hull	a			12 49	13 35											13 48	14 35												14 55	15 35							
Wakefield Kirkgate	a									13 02												14 02													15 02		
Wakefield Westgate	a									13 10												14 10													15 10		
York 8	a					13 30		13 22			13 35	13 52						14 30		14 22			14 35	14 51	14 52						15 30		15 22			15 35	15 52
	d					13 32		13 26			13 40	13 58						14 32		14 26			14 40	14 58	14 58						15 32		15 26			15 40	
Malton	d										14 03												15 03													16 03	
Seamer	a										14 20												15 20													16 20	
Scarborough	a										14 29												15 29													16 29	
Thirsk	a							13 45												14 45													15 45				
Northallerton	a							13 58				14 18								14 58				15 18	15 18								15 58				
Darlington 7	a					13 57						14 30						14 57						15 30	15 30						15 57						
Yarm	d							14 13												15 13													16 13				
Thornaby	a							14 21												15 21													16 21				
Middlesbrough	a							14 30												15 30													16 30				
Durham	a					14 14						14 47						15 15						15 47	15 48						16 15						
Chester-le-Street	a																							15 53	15 54												
Newcastle 8	a					14 28						15 05						15 29						16 09	16 06						16 29						

A from 4 January until 8 February

B from 15 February

Table 39

Saturdays
14 December to 17 May

Liverpool, Manchester Airport and Manchester - Huddersfield - Wakefield, Leeds, Hull, York, Scarborough, Middlesbrough and Newcastle

Network Diagram - refer to first Page of Table 39

Station		TP ◇1 A	NT	NT	NT	NT	TP ◇1	XC ◇1	NT	TP ◇1	NT	NT	TP ◇1	TP ◇1	NT	NT	NT	NT	TP ◇1
Liverpool Lime Street 10	d				13 46								14 22				14 46		
Liverpool South Parkway 7 ✈	d												14 32						
Warrington Central	d												14 45						
Birchwood	d												14 50						
Manchester Oxford Road	d												15 07						
Manchester Airport ✈	d	14 06								14 35				15 06					
Manchester Piccadilly 10	a	14 22								14 52			15 09	15 22					
	d	14 27					14 42			14 57			15 11	15 27					15 42
Manchester Victoria	d		14 00	14 27	14 57										15 00	15 27	15 57		
Ashton-under-Lyne	d			14 37	15 07											15 37	16 07		
Stalybridge	a			14 42	15 13								15 26			15 42	16 13		
	d			14 42									15 26			15 42			
Mossley (Grtr Manchester)	d			14 47												15 47			
Greenfield	d			14 51												15 51			
Marsden	d			14 59												15 59			
Slaithwaite	d			15 04												16 04			
Huddersfield	a	14 56		15 12			15 15			15 26			15 44	15 56		16 12			16 15
	d	14 57					15 16		15 23	15 27	15 31	15 38	15 45	15 57					16 16
Deighton	d										15 34	15 41							
Mirfield	d		15 07								15 39	15 46			16 07				
Ravensthorpe	d										15 42								
Dewsbury	a	15 06	15 12							15 36	15 46			16 06	16 12				
	d	15 07	15 12							15 37	15 46			16 07	16 12				
Batley	d		15 15								15 49				16 15				
Morley	d		15 21								15 55				16 21				
Cottingley	d										15 59								
Leeds 10	a	15 22	15 32				15 36		16 27	15 52	16 08		16 09	16 22	16 31				16 36
	d	15 28					15 38	16 08		15 57			16 12	16 28					16 38
Garforth	d									16 05									
South Milford	a																		
Selby	a						15 57												17 00
Howden	a																		
	d					15 16												16 49	
Brough	a					15 29	16 16											17 03	17 19
Hull	a					15 48	16 35											17 27	17 37
Wakefield Kirkgate	a											16 02							
Wakefield Westgate	a											16 10							
York 8	a	15 52						16 30		16 22			16 35	16 52					
	d	15 57						16 32		16 26			16 40	16 58					
Malton	d												17 03						
Seamer	a												17 20						
Scarborough	a												17 29						
Thirsk	a									16 45				17 14					
Northallerton	a									16 58				17 22					
Darlington 7	a							16 58						17 33					
Yarm	d									17 13									
Thornaby	a									17 21									
Middlesbrough	a									17 30									
Durham	a							17 15						17 50					
Chester-le-Street	a													17 56					
Newcastle 8	a	16 57						17 29						18 10					

Station		XC ◇1	NT	TP ◇1	NT	NT	TP ◇1	TP ◇1 B	TP ◇1 A	NT	NT	NT	TP ◇1	NT	XC ◇1	NT	TP ◇1	NT	NT
Liverpool Lime Street 10	d						15 22					15 46							
Liverpool South Parkway 7 ✈	d						15 32												
Warrington Central	d						15 45												
Birchwood	d						15 50												
Manchester Oxford Road	d						16 07												
Manchester Airport ✈	d			15 35				16 06	16 06								16 35		
Manchester Piccadilly 10	a			15 52			16 09	16 22	16 22								16 52		
	d			15 57			16 11	16 27	16 27				16 42				16 56		
Manchester Victoria	d									16 00	16 27	16 57							
Ashton-under-Lyne	d										16 37	17 07							
Stalybridge	a						16 26				16 42	17 13					17 08		
	d						16 26				16 42						17 08		
Mossley (Grtr Manchester)	d										16 47								
Greenfield	d										16 51								
Marsden	d										16 59			17 29					
Slaithwaite	d										17 04			17 34					
Huddersfield	a			16 26			16 44	16 56	16 56		17 12		17 15	17 42			17 26		
	d		16 23	16 27	16 31	16 38	16 45	16 57	16 57				17 16			17 23	17 27	17 31	17 38
Deighton	d				16 34	16 41												17 34	17 41
Mirfield	d				16 39	16 46				17 07								17 39	17 46
Ravensthorpe	d				16 42													17 42	
Dewsbury	a			16 36	16 46			17 06	17 06	17 12							17 36	17 46	
	d			16 37	16 46			17 07	17 07	17 12							17 37	17 46	
Batley	d				16 49					17 15								17 49	
Morley	d				16 55					17 21								17 55	
Cottingley	d				16 59													17 59	
Leeds 10	a		17 27	16 52	17 08		17 09	17 22	17 22	17 31			17 36			18 29	17 52	18 08	
	d	17 08		16 57			17 12	17 25	17 25				17 38		18 08		17 57		
Garforth	d			17 05				17 34	17 34								18 05		
South Milford	a																		
Selby	a												17 59						
Howden	a												18 08						
	d												18 08						
Brough	a												18 21						
Hull	a												18 39						
Wakefield Kirkgate	a					17 02													18 02
Wakefield Westgate	a					17 10													18 10
York 8	a	17 30		17 22			17 35	17 55	17 55						18 30		18 23		
	d	17 31		17 26			17 40		18 07						18 32		18 25		
Malton	d						18 03												
Seamer	a						18 20												
Scarborough	a						18 29												
Thirsk	a			17 45													18 45		
Northallerton	a			17 56													18 58		
Darlington 7	a	17 56													18 59				
Yarm	d			18 13													19 13		
Thornaby	a			18 21													19 21		
Middlesbrough	a			18 30													19 31		
Durham	a	18 13													19 17				
Chester-le-Street	a																		
Newcastle 8	a	18 29							19 03						19 31				

A from 4 January until 8 February
B from 15 February

Table 39

Saturdays

14 December to 17 May

Liverpool, Manchester Airport and Manchester - Huddersfield - Wakefield, Leeds, Hull, York, Scarborough, Middlesbrough and Newcastle

Network Diagram - refer to first Page of Table 39

		TP	TP	NT	XC	NT	NT	NT	TP	XC	NT	TP	NT	NT	TP	NT	NT	TP	XC	NT	TP	NT	NT	TP	NT	TP	NT	NT	TP	NT	NT	NT	TP	NT	XC	TP	NT
		◇1	◇1		◇1 ⚮				◇1	◇1 ⚮		◇1			◇1			◇1	◇1		◇1			◇1		◇1			◇1				◇1		◇1	◇1	
Liverpool Lime Street 10	d	16 22					16 46								17 22									18 22									19 22				
Liverpool South Parkway 7 ✈	d	16 32													17 32									18 32									19 32				
Warrington Central	d	16 45													17 45									18 45									19 45				
Birchwood	d	16 50													17 50									18 50									19 50				
Manchester Oxford Road	d	17 07													18 07									19 07									20 07				
Manchester Airport ✈	d		17 06									17 35									18 35					19 20										20 20	
Manchester Piccadilly 10 🚋	a	17 09	17 22									17 52			18 09						18 52			19 09		19 36							20 09			20 36	
	d	17 11	17 26						17 42			17 56			18 11			18 42			18 57			19 11		19 42							20 11			20 42	
Manchester Victoria 🚋	d			17 00		17 27	17 57									18 00	18 27								19 00		19 27							20 27			
Ashton-under-Lyne	d					17 37	18 07										18 37										19 37							20 37			
Stalybridge	a	17 26	17 38			17 42	18 13					18 08			18 26		18 42							19 26			19 42						20 26	20 42			
	d	17 26	17 38			17 42						18 08			18 26		18 42							19 26			19 42						20 26	20 42			
Mossley (Grtr Manchester)	d					17 47											18 47										19 47							20 47			
Greenfield	d					17 51											18 51										19 51							20 51			
Marsden	d					17 59											18 59										19 59							20 59			
Slaithwaite	d					18 04											19 04										20 04							21 04			
Huddersfield	a	17 44	17 56			18 12			18 15			18 26			18 44		19 12	19 15			19 26			19 44		20 15	20 12						20 44	21 12		21 15	
	d	17 45	17 57						18 16		18 25	18 27	18 31	18 37	18 45			19 16		19 23	19 27	19 31	19 38	19 45		20 16				20 25	20 31	20 38	20 45			21 16	21 27
Deighton	d												18 34	18 40								19 34	19 41								20 34	20 41					
Mirfield	d			18 07									18 39	18 45		19 08						19 39	19 46		20 07						20 39	20 46					
Ravensthorpe	d												18 42									19 42									20 42						
Dewsbury	a		18 06	18 12								18 36	18 46		18 55	19 13					19 36	19 46			20 12	20 25					20 46					21 25	
	d		18 07	18 13								18 37	18 46		18 55	19 13					19 37	19 46			20 12	20 26					20 46					21 26	
Batley	d			18 16									18 49			19 16						19 49			20 15						20 49						
Morley	d			18 22									18 55			19 22						19 55			20 21						20 55						
Cottingley	d												18 59									19 59									20 59						
Leeds 10	a	18 09	18 22	18 31					18 36		19 28	18 52	19 08		19 10	19 33		19 36		20 30	19 52	20 08		20 09	20 33	20 41				21 25	21 08		21 09			21 41	22 25
	d	18 12	18 28		18 35				18 38	19 08		18 57			19 12			19 38	20 08		19 52			20 12		20 45			21 08				21 12		21 15	21 42	
Garforth	d											19 05									20 00																
South Milford	a								18 51									19 51											21 20								
Selby	a								19 00									20 00											21 30								
Howden	a																	20 09											21 39								
	d							18 54										20 10										20 16	21 39								
Brough	a							19 11	19 19									20 22										20 29	21 52								
Hull	a							19 29	19 38									20 41										20 48	22 10								
Wakefield Kirkgate	a													19 02									20 02									21 03					
Wakefield Westgate	a													19 10									20 10									21 10					
York 8	a	18 35	18 52		18 57					19 30		19 22			19 35				20 30		20 22			20 35		21 08							21 40		21 57	22 06	
	d	18 40	18 58		19 08					19 32		19 26			19 40				20 33		20 29			20 40		21 14										22 10	
Malton	d	19 03													20 03									21 04												22 33	
Seamer	a	19 20													20 20									21 20												22 50	
Scarborough	a	19 29													20 29									21 29												22 59	
Thirsk	a											19 45									20 48					21 30											
Northallerton	a		19 17									19 56									20 58					21 38											
Darlington 7	a		19 30		19 34					19 57									20 58							21 50											
Yarm	d											20 11									21 13																
Thornaby	a											20 21									21 21																
Middlesbrough	a											20 30									21 30																
Durham	a		19 47		19 51					20 14									21 15							22 07											
Chester-le-Street	a		19 53																							22 13											
Newcastle 8 🚋	a		20 06		20 07					20 28									21 29							22 27											

Table 39

Saturdays

14 December to 17 May

Liverpool, Manchester Airport and Manchester - Huddersfield - Wakefield, Leeds, Hull, York, Scarborough, Middlesbrough and Newcastle

Network Diagram - refer to first Page of Table 39

		NT	NT	TP ◇1	NT	NT	TP ◇1	NT	TP ◇1	NT	NT	NT	TP ◇1	NT	TP ◇1 A	TP ◇1 B	TP B (bus)	TP ◇1 A
Liverpool Lime Street 10	d			20 22											22 30	22 30		
Liverpool South Parkway 7 ✈	d			20 32											22 40	22 40		
Warrington Central	d			20 45											22 53	22 53		
Birchwood	d			20 50											22 58	22 58		
Manchester Oxford Road	d			21 07											23 17	23 17		
Manchester Airport ✈	d								21 20				22 22					23 24
Manchester Piccadilly 10 ⛴	a			21 09					21 36				22 37		23 19	23 19		23 38
	d			21 11					21 42				22 42		23 21	23 21		23 41
Manchester Victoria ⛴	d				21 27						22 08			23 00				
Ashton-under-Lyne	d				21 37						22 18			23 10				
Stalybridge	a			21 26	21 41				21 55		22 22		22 55	23 14	23 34	23 34		
	d			21 26	21 42				21 55		22 23		22 55	23 15	23 34	23 34		
Mossley (Grtr Manchester)	d				21 46						22 27			23 19				
Greenfield	d				21 50						22 31			23 23				
Marsden	d	21 19			21 59						22 40			23 32				
Slaithwaite	d	21 23			22 03						22 44			23 36				
Huddersfield	a	21 30		21 44	22 12				22 15		22 53		23 15	23 43	23 52	23 53		00 10
	d	21 31	21 38	21 45					22 16	22 20		22 25	23 16		23 53		23 59	00 11
Deighton	d	21 34	21 41							22 23								
Mirfield	d	21 39	21 46							22 28								
Ravensthorpe	d	21 42								22 31								
Dewsbury	a	21 46							22 25	22 35			23 25					00s20
	d	21 46							22 26	22 35			23 26					
Batley	d	21 49								22 38								
Morley	d	21 55								22 44								
Cottingley	d	21 59								22 48								
Leeds 10	a	22 08		22 09					22 41	22 57		23 26	23 41		00 14		00 23	00 35
	d			22 12			22 22	22 37	22 42				23 42		00 15			00 38
Garforth	d																	
South Milford	a						22 36											
Selby	a						22 46											
Howden	a																	
	d					22 39												
Brough	a					22 53	23 06											
Hull	a					23 16	23 25											
Wakefield Kirkgate	a		22 02					23 10										
Wakefield Westgate	a		22 10															
York 8	a			22 38					23 09				00 09		00 42			01 06
	d																	
Malton	d																	
Seamer	a																	
Scarborough	a																	
Thirsk	a																	
Northallerton	a																	
Darlington 7	a																	
Yarm	d																	
Thornaby	a																	
Middlesbrough	a																	
Durham	a																	
Chester-le-Street	a																	
Newcastle 8 ⛴	a																	

A until 8 February, from 29 March
B from 15 February until 22 March

NRT DEC 13 EDITION

Table 39

Sundays

8 December to 29 December

Liverpool, Manchester Airport and Manchester - Huddersfield, Leeds, Hull, York, Scarborough, Middlesbrough and Newcastle

Network Diagram - refer to first Page of Table 39

Station		TP ◇1 A	TP ◇1 A	TP ◇1	TP ◇1	TP ◇1	NT	GR R 1	TP ◇1	XC ◇1
Liverpool Lime Street 10	d									
Liverpool South Parkway 7	d									
Warrington Central	d									
Birchwood	d									
Newton-le-Willows	d									
Manchester Oxford Road	d									
Manchester Airport	d			01 22	04 43	06 24			07 24	
Manchester Piccadilly 10	a			01 36	04 57	06 38			07 37	
	d			01 42	05 02	06 42			07 42	
Manchester Victoria	a									
	d									
Ashton-under-Lyne	d									
Stalybridge	a					06 53			07 54	
	d					06 54			07 54	
Mossley (Grtr Manchester)	d									
Greenfield	d									
Marsden	d									
Slaithwaite	d									
Huddersfield	a			02 11	05 31	07 11			08 11	
	d		00 11	02 12	05 32	07 12	07 51		08 12	
Deighton	d						07 54			
Mirfield	d						07 59			
Ravensthorpe	d						08 02			
Dewsbury	a		00s20			07 21	08 06		08 21	
	d					07 22	08 06		08 22	
Batley	d						08 09			
Morley	d						08 15			
Cottingley	d						08 19			
Leeds 10	a		00 35	02 33	05 53	07 36	08 27		08 37	
	d	00 15	00 38	02 35	05 55	07 37		08 30	08 40	09 08
Garforth	d									
South Milford	a									
Selby	a									
Howden	a									
Brough	a									
Hull	a									
York 8	a	00 42	01 06	03 18	06 38	08 19		08 55	09 02	09 31
	d					08 22		09 00	09 10	09 34
Malton	d									
Seamer	a									
Scarborough	a									
Thirsk	a					08 38				
Northallerton	a					08 46		09 19	09 30	
Darlington 7	a					08 57		09 33	09 42	09 59
Yarm	d									
Thornaby	a					09 17				
Middlesbrough	a					09 26				
Durham	a							09 51	09 59	10 16
Chester-le-Street	a								10 05	
Newcastle 8	a							10 07	10 17	10 30

Station		TP ◇1	TP ◇1	TP ◇1	NT	TP ◇1	NT	TP ◇1	NT	TP ◇1
Liverpool Lime Street 10	d					08 22				09 22
Liverpool South Parkway 7	d					08 32				09 32
Warrington Central	d					08 45				09 45
Birchwood	d					08 50				09 50
Newton-le-Willows	d									
Manchester Oxford Road	d					09 08				10 07
Manchester Airport	d		08 20					09 03		
Manchester Piccadilly 10	a		08 37			09 10		09 17		10 09
	d		08 42			09 12		09 27		10 11
Manchester Victoria	a									
	d				08 43				09 43	
Ashton-under-Lyne	d				08 53				09 53	
Stalybridge	a		08 54		08 57	09 24			09 57	10 24
	d		08 54		08 58	09 24			09 58	10 24
Mossley (Grtr Manchester)	d				09 03				10 02	
Greenfield	d				09 07				10 06	
Marsden	d				09 16				10 15	
Slaithwaite	d				09 20				10 19	
Huddersfield	a		09 12		09 28	09 42		09 55	10 28	10 42
	d		09 12			09 43	09 47	10 01		10 43
Deighton	d						09 50			
Mirfield	d						09 55			
Ravensthorpe	d						09 58			
Dewsbury	a		09 21				10 02	10 10		
	d		09 22				10 03	10 10		
Batley	d						10 06			
Morley	d						10 12			
Cottingley	d						10 15			
Leeds 10	a		09 36			10 04	10 23	10 26		11 04
	d	09 12	09 38			10 22		10 35		11 12
Garforth	d									
South Milford	a					10 34				
Selby	a					10 44				
Howden	a									
Brough	a					11 04				
Hull	a					11 21				
York 8	a	09 37	10 03					10 58		11 39
	d	09 42	10 10	10 37				11 00		11 42
Malton	d	10 06								12 06
Seamer	a	10 22								12 23
Scarborough	a	10 31								12 32
Thirsk	a			10 53						
Northallerton	a		10 30	11 01				11 20		
Darlington 7	a		10 42					11 32		
Yarm	d			11 15						
Thornaby	a			11 23						
Middlesbrough	a			11 33						
Durham	a		10 59					11 49		
Chester-le-Street	a									
Newcastle 8	a		11 15					12 04		

Station		TP ◇1	NT	TP ◇1	NT	TP ◇1	NT	TP ◇1	TP ◇1	TP ◇1
Liverpool Lime Street 10	d			10 22					11 22	
Liverpool South Parkway 7	d			10 32					11 32	
Warrington Central	d			10 45					11 45	
Birchwood	d			10 50					11 50	
Newton-le-Willows	d									
Manchester Oxford Road	d			11 07					12 07	
Manchester Airport	d	10 20				11 20				12 20
Manchester Piccadilly 10	a	10 37		11 09		11 34			12 09	12 34
	d	10 42		11 11		11 42		12 01	12 11	12 42
Manchester Victoria	a									
	d		10 43				11 43			
Ashton-under-Lyne	d		10 53				11 53			
Stalybridge	a		10 57	11 23			11 57		12 24	
	d		10 58	11 23			11 58		12 24	
Mossley (Grtr Manchester)	d		11 02				12 02			
Greenfield	d		11 06				12 06			
Marsden	d		11 15				12 15			
Slaithwaite	d		11 19				12 19			
Huddersfield	a	11 11	11 28	11 42		12 11	12 28	12 32	12 42	13 11
	d	11 12		11 43	11 58	12 12		12 33	12 43	13 12
Deighton	d				12 01					
Mirfield	d				12 06					
Ravensthorpe	d				12 09					
Dewsbury	a	11 21			12 13	12 21				13 21
	d	11 22			12 13	12 22				13 22
Batley	d				12 16					
Morley	d				12 22					
Cottingley	d				12 26					
Leeds 10	a	11 37		12 04	12 34	12 37		12 54	13 04	13 37
	d	11 40		12 12		12 40		13 01	13 12	13 40
Garforth	d									
South Milford	a							13 13		
Selby	a							13 23		
Howden	a									
Brough	a							13 42		
Hull	a							13 59		
York 8	a	12 03		12 35		13 06			13 35	14 04
	d	12 10		12 40		13 10			13 42	14 11
Malton	d								14 06	
Seamer	a								14 23	
Scarborough	a								14 32	
Thirsk	a			12 56						
Northallerton	a	12 30		13 04		13 30				14 31
Darlington 7	a	12 42				13 42				14 43
Yarm	d			13 18						
Thornaby	a			13 27						
Middlesbrough	a			13 37						
Durham	a	12 59				13 59				15 00
Chester-le-Street	a					14 05				
Newcastle 8	a	13 14				14 17				15 16

Station		NT	TP ◇1	TP ◇1	NT	TP ◇1	NT	TP ◇1	TP ◇1	TP ◇1
Liverpool Lime Street 10	d			12 22					13 22	
Liverpool South Parkway 7	d			12 32					13 32	
Warrington Central	d			12 45					13 45	
Birchwood	d			12 50					13 50	
Newton-le-Willows	d									
Manchester Oxford Road	d			13 07					14 07	
Manchester Airport	d					13 20				14 20
Manchester Piccadilly 10	a			13 09		13 37			14 09	14 37
	d		13 02	13 11		13 42		14 02	14 11	14 42
Manchester Victoria	a									
	d	12 43					13 43			
Ashton-under-Lyne	d	12 53					13 53			
Stalybridge	a	12 57		13 24			13 57		14 24	
	d	12 58		13 24			13 58		14 24	
Mossley (Grtr Manchester)	d	13 02					14 02			
Greenfield	d	13 06					14 06			
Marsden	d	13 15					14 15			
Slaithwaite	d	13 19					14 19			
Huddersfield	a	13 28	13 32	13 42		14 11	14 28	14 32	14 42	15 11
	d		13 33	13 43	13 58	14 12		14 33	14 43	15 12
Deighton	d				14 01					
Mirfield	d				14 06					
Ravensthorpe	d				14 09					
Dewsbury	a				14 13	14 21				15 21
	d				14 13	14 22				15 22
Batley	d				14 16					
Morley	d				14 22					
Cottingley	d				14 26					
Leeds 10	a		13 54	14 04	14 34	14 37		14 53	15 05	15 37
	d		13 57	14 12		14 40		15 01	15 12	15 40
Garforth	d									
South Milford	a							15 14		
Selby	a							15 23		
Howden	a									
Brough	a							15 41		
Hull	a							15 59		
York 8	a		14 23	14 35		15 06			15 40	16 04
	d			14 42		15 10			15 42	16 10
Malton	d								16 06	
Seamer	a								16 23	
Scarborough	a								16 32	
Thirsk	a			14 58						
Northallerton	a			15 08		15 30				16 30
Darlington 7	a					15 42				16 42
Yarm	d			15 23						
Thornaby	a			15 31						
Middlesbrough	a			15 40						
Durham	a					15 59				16 59
Chester-le-Street	a					16 05				
Newcastle 8	a					16 18				17 14

A not 8 December

Table 39

Sundays

8 December to 29 December

Liverpool, Manchester Airport and Manchester - Huddersfield, Leeds, Hull, York, Scarborough, Middlesbrough and Newcastle

Network Diagram - refer to first Page of Table 39

		NT	TP ◇1	TP ◇1	NT	TP ◇1	NT	TP ◇1	TP ◇1	TP ◇1	NT	TP ◇1	TP ◇1	NT	TP ◇1	NT	TP ◇1	TP ◇1	TP ◇1
Liverpool Lime Street 10	d			14 22					15 22				16 22					17 22	
Liverpool South Parkway 7 ✈	d			14 32					15 32				16 32					17 32	
Warrington Central	d			14 45					15 45				16 45					17 45	
Birchwood	d			14 50					15 50				16 50					17 50	
Newton-le-Willows	d																		
Manchester Oxford Road	d			15 07					16 07				17 07					18 07	
Manchester Airport ✈	d					15 20				16 20					17 20				18 20
Manchester Piccadilly 10	a			15 09		15 37			16 09	16 37			17 09		17 37			18 09	18 37
	d		15 02	15 11		15 42		16 02	16 11	16 42		17 02	17 11		17 42		18 02	18 11	18 42
Manchester Victoria	a																		
	d	14 43					15 43				16 43					17 43			
Ashton-under-Lyne	d	14 53					15 53				16 53					17 53			
Stalybridge	a	14 57		15 25			15 57		16 24		16 57		17 24			17 57		18 24	
	d	14 58		15 25			15 58		16 24		16 58		17 24			17 58		18 24	
Mossley (Grtr Manchester)	d	15 02					16 02				17 02					18 02			
Greenfield	d	15 06					16 06				17 06					18 06			
Marsden	d	15 15					16 15				17 15					18 15			
Slaithwaite	d	15 19					16 19				17 19					18 19			
Huddersfield	a	15 28	15 32	15 43		16 11	16 28	16 32	16 42	17 11	17 28	17 32	17 42		18 11	18 28	18 32	18 42	19 11
	d		15 33	15 44	15 58	16 12		16 33	16 43	17 12		17 33	17 43	17 58	18 12		18 33	18 43	19 12
Deighton	d				16 01									18 01					
Mirfield	d				16 06									18 06					
Ravensthorpe	d				16 09									18 09					
Dewsbury	a				16 13	16 22				17 21				18 13	18 21				19 21
	d				16 13	16 22				17 22				18 13	18 22				19 22
Batley	d				16 16									18 16					
Morley	d				16 22									18 22					
Cottingley	d				16 26									18 26					
Leeds 10	a		15 54	16 05	16 34	16 37		16 54	17 05	17 37		17 54	18 04	18 34	18 37		18 54	19 04	19 37
	d		15 57	16 12		16 40		17 01	17 12	17 40		17 57	18 12		18 40		19 01	19 12	19 40
Garforth	d																		
South Milford	a							17 14									19 16		
Selby	a							17 23									19 28		
Howden	a																		
Brough	a							17 41									19 48		
Hull	a							17 59									20 05		
York 8	a		16 23	16 35		17 08			17 37	18 06		18 23	18 35		19 06			19 36	20 04
	d			16 41		17 10			17 42	18 10			18 40		19 10			19 42	20 08
Malton	d								18 06									20 06	
Seamer	a								18 23									20 23	
Scarborough	a								18 32									20 32	
Thirsk	a			16 57									18 56						20 24
Northallerton	a			17 07		17 30				18 30			19 04		19 30				20 32
Darlington 7	a					17 42				18 42					19 42				
Yarm	d			17 21									19 18						20 47
Thornaby	a			17 30									19 27						20 55
Middlesbrough	a			17 39									19 37						21 04
Durham	a					17 59				19 02					19 59				
Chester-le-Street	a					18 05									20 05				
Newcastle 8	a					18 18				19 17					20 18				

		NT	TP ◇1	TP ◇1	NT	TP ◇1	NT	TP ◇1	TP ◇1	TP ◇1	NT	TP ◇1	TP ◇1	NT	NT	TP ◇1	TP ◇1	TP ◇1
Liverpool Lime Street 10	d			18 22					19 22			20 22					21 52	
Liverpool South Parkway 7 ✈	d			18 32					19 32			20 32					22 02	
Warrington Central	d			18 45					19 45			20 45					22 15	
Birchwood	d			18 50					19 50			20 50					22 20	
Newton-le-Willows	d																	
Manchester Oxford Road	d			19 07					20 07			21 07					22 37	
Manchester Airport ✈	d					19 20				20 20						21 20		23 20
Manchester Piccadilly 10	a			19 09		19 37			20 09	20 37		21 09				21 37	22 39	23 37
	d		19 02	19 11		19 42		20 06	20 11	20 42		21 11				21 42	22 42	23 42
Manchester Victoria	a																	
	d	18 43					19 43				20 43			21 43				
Ashton-under-Lyne	d	18 53					19 53				20 53			21 53				
Stalybridge	a	18 57		19 24			19 57		20 24		20 57	21 24		21 57			22 54	
	d	18 58		19 24			19 58		20 24		20 58	21 24					22 54	
Mossley (Grtr Manchester)	d	19 02					20 02				21 02							
Greenfield	d	19 06					20 06				21 06							
Marsden	d	19 15					20 15				21 15				21 47			
Slaithwaite	d	19 19					20 19				21 19				21 51			
Huddersfield	a	19 28	19 32	19 42		20 11	20 28	20 36	20 42	21 11	21 28	21 42			21 57	22 11	23 12	00 11
	d		19 33	19 43	19 58	20 12		20 37	20 43	21 12		21 43			21 57	22 12	23 13	00 12
Deighton	d				20 01										22 01			
Mirfield	d				20 06										22 06			
Ravensthorpe	d				20 09										22 09			
Dewsbury	a				20 13	20 21				21 21					22 13	22 21	23 23	
	d				20 13	20 22				21 22					22 13	22 22	23 23	
Batley	d				20 16										22 16			
Morley	d				20 22										22 22			
Cottingley	d				20 26										22 26			
Leeds 10	a		19 54	20 04	20 34	20 37		20 58	21 05	21 37		22 05			22 34	22 37	23 39	00 51
	d		19 57	20 12		20 40		21 04	21 12	21 40		22 12	22 22			22 40	23 43	00 54
Garforth	d																	
South Milford	a												22 34					
Selby	a		20 17					21 35					22 44					
Howden	a																	
Brough	a		20 37					21 55					23 03					
Hull	a		20 54					22 09					23 19					
York 8	a			20 34		21 04			21 37	22 07		22 38				23 06	00 25	01 21
	d			20 42		21 08				22 10		22 43						
Malton	d			21 06						22 34								
Seamer	a			21 23						22 51								
Scarborough	a			21 32						22 58								
Thirsk	a					21 24						23 05						
Northallerton	a					21 32						23 15						
Darlington 7	a					21 43						23 27						
Yarm	d																	
Thornaby	a																	
Middlesbrough	a																	
Durham	a					22 00						23 44						
Chester-le-Street	a																	
Newcastle 8	a					22 15						00 14						

Table 39

Sundays
5 January to 9 February

Liverpool, Manchester Airport and Manchester - Huddersfield, Leeds, Hull, York, Scarborough, Middlesbrough and Newcastle

Network Diagram - refer to first Page of Table 39

Station		TP	TP	TP	TP	TP	NT	GR	TP	XC
		◇1	◇1	◇1	◇1	◇1		R 1	◇1	◇1
Liverpool Lime Street 10	d									
Liverpool South Parkway 7 ✈	d									
Warrington Central	d									
Birchwood	d									
Newton-le-Willows	d									
Manchester Oxford Road	d									
Manchester Airport ✈	d			01 22	04 43	06 24			07 24	
Manchester Piccadilly 10	a			01 36	04 57	06 38			07 37	
	d			01 42	05 02	06 42			07 42	
Manchester Victoria	a									
	d									
Ashton-under-Lyne	d									
Stalybridge	a					06 53			07 54	
	d					06 54			07 54	
Mossley (Grtr Manchester)	d									
Greenfield	d									
Marsden	d									
Slaithwaite	d									
Huddersfield	a			02 11	05 31	07 11			08 11	
	d		00 11	02 12	05 32	07 12	07 51		08 12	
Deighton	d						07 54			
Mirfield	d						07 59			
Ravensthorpe	d						08 02			
Dewsbury	a		00s20			07 21	08 06		08 21	
	d					07 22	08 06		08 22	
Batley	d						08 09			
Morley	d						08 15			
Cottingley	d						08 19			
Leeds 10	a		00 35	02 33	05 53	07 36	08 27		08 37	
	d	00 15	00 38	02 35	05 55	07 37		08 30	08 40	09 08
Garforth	d									
South Milford	a									
Selby	a									
Howden	a									
Brough	a									
Hull	a									
York 8	a	00 42	01 06	03 18	06 38	08 19		08 55	09 02	09 31
	d					08 22		09 00	09 10	09 34
Malton	d									
Seamer	a									
Scarborough	a									
Thirsk	a					08 38				
Northallerton	a					08 46		09 19	09 30	
Darlington 7	a					08 57		09 33	09 42	09 59
Yarm	d									
Thornaby	a					09 17				
Middlesbrough	a					09 26				
Durham	a							09 51	09 59	10 16
Chester-le-Street	a								10 05	
Newcastle 8	a							10 07	10 17	10 30

Station		TP	TP	TP	TP	NT	TP	TP	TP	TP
		◇1	◇1	◇1	◇1		◇1	◇1	◇1	◇1
Liverpool Lime Street 10	d				08 22			09 22		10 22
Liverpool South Parkway 7 ✈	d				08 32			09 32		10 32
Warrington Central	d				08 45			09 45		10 45
Birchwood	d				08 50			09 50		10 50
Newton-le-Willows	d									
Manchester Oxford Road	d				09 08			10 07		11 07
Manchester Airport ✈	d		08 20				09 22		10 20	
Manchester Piccadilly 10	a		08 37		09 10		09 36	10 09	10 37	11 09
	d		08 42		09 12		09 41	10 11	10 42	11 11
Manchester Victoria	a									
	d									
Ashton-under-Lyne	d									
Stalybridge	a		08 54		09 24			10 24		11 23
	d		08 54		09 24			10 24		11 23
Mossley (Grtr Manchester)	d									
Greenfield	d									
Marsden	d									
Slaithwaite	d									
Huddersfield	a		09 12		09 42		10 10	10 42	11 11	11 42
	d		09 12		09 43	09 47	10 11	10 43	11 12	11 43
Deighton	d					09 50				
Mirfield	d					09 55				
Ravensthorpe	d					09 58				
Dewsbury	a		09 21			10 02	10 20		11 21	
	d		09 22			10 03	10 21		11 22	
Batley	d					10 06				
Morley	d					10 12				
Cottingley	d					10 15				
Leeds 10	a		09 36		10 04	10 23	10 34	11 04	11 37	12 04
	d	09 12	09 38		10 22		10 35	11 12	11 40	12 12
Garforth	d									
South Milford	a				10 34					
Selby	a				10 44					
Howden	a									
Brough	a				11 04					
Hull	a				11 21					
York 8	a	09 37	10 03				10 58	11 39	12 03	12 35
	d	09 42	10 10	10 37			11 00	11 42	12 10	12 40
Malton	d	10 06						12 06		
Seamer	a	10 22						12 23		
Scarborough	a	10 31						12 32		
Thirsk	a			10 53						12 56
Northallerton	a		10 30	11 01			11 20		12 30	13 04
Darlington 7	a		10 42				11 32		12 42	
Yarm	d			11 15						13 18
Thornaby	a			11 23						13 27
Middlesbrough	a			11 33						13 37
Durham	a		10 59				11 48		12 59	
Chester-le-Street	a									
Newcastle 8	a		11 15				12 02		13 14	

Station		NT	TP	TP	GR	TP	TP	TP	TP	NT
			◇1	◇1	R 1	◇1	◇1	◇1	◇1	
Liverpool Lime Street 10	d					11 22			12 22	
Liverpool South Parkway 7 ✈	d					11 32			12 32	
Warrington Central	d					11 45			12 45	
Birchwood	d					11 50			12 50	
Newton-le-Willows	d									
Manchester Oxford Road	d					12 07			13 07	
Manchester Airport ✈	d		11 20				12 20			
Manchester Piccadilly 10	a		11 34			12 09	12 34		13 09	
	d		11 42	12 01		12 11	12 42	13 02	13 11	
Manchester Victoria	a									
	d									
Ashton-under-Lyne	d									
Stalybridge	a					12 24			13 24	
	d					12 24			13 24	
Mossley (Grtr Manchester)	d									
Greenfield	d									
Marsden	d									
Slaithwaite	d									
Huddersfield	a		12 11	12 32		12 42	13 11	13 32	13 42	
	d	11 58	12 12	12 33		12 43	13 12	13 33	13 43	13 58
Deighton	d	12 01								14 01
Mirfield	d	12 06								14 06
Ravensthorpe	d	12 09								14 09
Dewsbury	a	12 13	12 21				13 21			14 13
	d	12 13	12 22				13 22			14 13
Batley	d	12 16								14 16
Morley	d	12 22								14 22
Cottingley	d	12 26								14 26
Leeds 10	a	12 34	12 37	12 54		13 04	13 37	13 54	14 04	14 34
	d		12 40	13 01		13 12	13 40	13 57	14 12	
Garforth	d									
South Milford	a			13 13						
Selby	a			13 23						
Howden	a									
Brough	a			13 42						
Hull	a			13 59						
York 8	a		13 05			13 35	14 04	14 23	14 35	
	d		13 07		13 17	13 42	14 11		14 42	
Malton	d					14 06				
Seamer	a					14 23				
Scarborough	a					14 32				
Thirsk	a								14 58	
Northallerton	a		13 27		13 36		14 31		15 08	
Darlington 7	a		13 39		13 49		14 43			
Yarm	d								15 23	
Thornaby	a								15 31	
Middlesbrough	a								15 40	
Durham	a		13 55		14 07		15 00			
Chester-le-Street	a									
Newcastle 8	a		14 09		14 23		15 16			

Station		TP	TP	TP	TP	TP	TP	NT	TP	TP
		◇1	◇1	◇1	◇1	◇1	◇1		◇1	◇1
Liverpool Lime Street 10	d			13 22			14 22			
Liverpool South Parkway 7 ✈	d			13 32			14 32			
Warrington Central	d			13 45			14 45			
Birchwood	d			13 50			14 50			
Newton-le-Willows	d									
Manchester Oxford Road	d			14 07			15 07			
Manchester Airport ✈	d	13 20			14 20				15 20	
Manchester Piccadilly 10	a	13 37		14 09	14 37		15 09		15 37	
	d	13 42	14 02	14 11	14 42	15 02	15 11		15 42	16 02
Manchester Victoria	a									
	d									
Ashton-under-Lyne	d									
Stalybridge	a			14 24			15 25			
	d			14 24			15 25			
Mossley (Grtr Manchester)	d									
Greenfield	d									
Marsden	d									
Slaithwaite	d									
Huddersfield	a	14 11	14 32	14 42	15 11	15 32	15 43		16 11	16 32
	d	14 12	14 33	14 43	15 12	15 33	15 44	15 58	16 12	16 33
Deighton	d							16 01		
Mirfield	d							16 06		
Ravensthorpe	d							16 09		
Dewsbury	a	14 21			15 21			16 13	16 22	
	d	14 22			15 22			16 13	16 22	
Batley	d							16 16		
Morley	d							16 22		
Cottingley	d							16 26		
Leeds 10	a	14 37	14 53	15 05	15 37	15 54	16 05	16 34	16 37	16 54
	d	14 40	15 01	15 12	15 40	15 57	16 12		16 40	17 01
Garforth	d									
South Milford	a		15 14							17 14
Selby	a		15 23							17 23
Howden	a									
Brough	a		15 41							17 41
Hull	a		15 59							17 59
York 8	a	15 06		15 40	16 04	16 23	16 35		17 08	
	d	15 10		15 42	16 10		16 41		17 10	
Malton	d			16 06						
Seamer	a			16 23						
Scarborough	a			16 32						
Thirsk	a						16 57			
Northallerton	a	15 30			16 30		17 07		17 30	
Darlington 7	a	15 42			16 42				17 42	
Yarm	d						17 21			
Thornaby	a						17 30			
Middlesbrough	a						17 39			
Durham	a	15 59			16 59				17 59	
Chester-le-Street	a	16 05							18 05	
Newcastle 8	a	16 18			17 14				18 18	

Table 39

Sundays

5 January to 9 February

Liverpool, Manchester Airport and Manchester - Huddersfield, Leeds, Hull, York, Scarborough, Middlesbrough and Newcastle

Network Diagram - refer to first Page of Table 39

		TP	TP	TP	TP	NT	TP	TP	TP	TP	TP	TP	NT	TP	TP	TP	TP	TP	TP	NT	TP	TP	TP
		◇1	◇1	◇1	◇1		◇1	◇1	◇1	◇1	◇1	◇1		◇1	◇1	◇1	◇1	◇1	◇1		◇1	◇1	◇1
Liverpool Lime Street 10	d	15 22			16 22				17 22			18 22				19 22		20 22				21 52	
Liverpool South Parkway 7 ✈	d	15 32			16 32				17 32			18 32				19 32		20 32				22 02	
Warrington Central	d	15 45			16 45				17 45			18 45				19 45		20 45				22 15	
Birchwood	d	15 50			16 50				17 50			18 50				19 50		20 50				22 20	
Newton-le-Willows	d																						
Manchester Oxford Road	d	16 07			17 07				18 07			19 07				20 07		21 07				22 37	
Manchester Airport ✈	d		16 20				17 20			18 20				19 20			20 20				21 20		23 20
Manchester Piccadilly 10 🚋	a	16 09	16 37		17 09		17 37		18 09	18 37		19 09		19 37		20 09	20 37	21 09			21 37	22 39	23 37
	d	16 11	16 42	17 02	17 11		17 42	18 02	18 11	18 42	19 02	19 11		19 42	20 06	20 11	20 42	21 11			21 42	22 42	23 42
Manchester Victoria 🚋	a																						
	d																						
Ashton-under-Lyne	d																						
Stalybridge	a	16 24			17 24				18 24			19 24				20 24		21 24				22 54	
	d	16 24			17 24				18 24			19 24				20 24		21 24				22 54	
Mossley (Grtr Manchester)	d																						
Greenfield	d																						
Marsden	d																			21 47			
Slaithwaite	d																			21 51			
Huddersfield	a	16 42	17 11	17 32	17 42		18 11	18 32	18 42	19 11	19 32	19 42		20 11	20 36	20 42	21 11	21 42		21 57	22 11	23 12	00 11
	d	16 43	17 12	17 33	17 43	17 58	18 12	18 33	18 43	19 12	19 33	19 43	19 58	20 12	20 37	20 43	21 12	21 43		21 57	22 12	23 13	00 12
Deighton	d					18 01							20 01							22 01			
Mirfield	d					18 06							20 06							22 06			
Ravensthorpe	d					18 09							20 09							22 09			
Dewsbury	a		17 21			18 13	18 21			19 21			20 13	20 21			21 21			22 13	22 21	23 23	
	d		17 22			18 13	18 22			19 22			20 13	20 22			21 22			22 13	22 22	23 23	
Batley	d					18 16							20 16							22 16			
Morley	d					18 22							20 22							22 22			
Cottingley	d					18 26							20 26							22 26			
Leeds 10	a	17 05	17 37	17 54	18 04	18 34	18 37	18 54	19 04	19 37	19 54	20 04	20 34	20 37	20 58	21 05	21 37	22 05		22 34	22 37	23 39	00 51
	d	17 12	17 40	17 57	18 12		18 40	19 01	19 12	19 40	19 57	20 12		20 40	21 04	21 12	21 40	22 12	22 22		22 40	23 43	00 54
Garforth	d																						
South Milford	a							19 16											22 34				
Selby	a							19 28			20 17				21 35				22 44				
Howden	a																						
Brough	a							19 48			20 37				21 55				23 03				
Hull	a							20 05			20 54				22 09				23 19				
York 8	a	17 35	18 06	18 23	18 35		19 06		19 36	20 04		20 34		21 04		21 37	22 07	22 38			23 06	00 25	01 21
	d	17 47	18 10		18 40		19 10		19 42	20 08		20 42		21 08			22 10	22 43					
Malton	d	18 11							20 06			21 06					22 34						
Seamer	a	18 28							20 23			21 23					22 51						
Scarborough	a	18 37							20 32			21 32					22 58						
Thirsk	a				18 56					20 24				21 24				23 05					
Northallerton	a		18 30		19 04		19 30			20 32				21 32				23 15					
Darlington 7	a		18 42				19 42							21 43				23 27					
Yarm	d				19 18					20 47													
Thornaby	a				19 27					20 55													
Middlesbrough	a				19 37					21 04													
Durham	a		19 02				19 59							22 00				23 44					
Chester-le-Street	a						20 05																
Newcastle 8 🚋	a		19 17				20 18							22 15				00 14					

Table 39

Sundays
16 February to 23 March

Liverpool, Manchester Airport and Manchester - Huddersfield, Leeds, Hull, York, Scarborough, Middlesbrough and Newcastle

Network Diagram - refer to first Page of Table 39

Station		TP	GR	TP	TP	XC	TP	TP	TP	TP	NT	TP	TP	TP	TP	TP	TP	NT	TP
		◇1	R 1 restaurant	◇1	bus	◇1 trolley	◇1	◇1	◇1	bus	bus	◇1	◇1	bus	◇1	◇1	bus	bus	◇1
Liverpool Lime Street 10	d											08 22			09 22				10 22
Liverpool South Parkway 7 ✈	d											08 32			09 32				10 32
Warrington Central	d											08 45			09 45				10 45
Birchwood	d											08 50			09 50				10 50
Newton-le-Willows	d																		
Manchester Oxford Road	d											09 08			10 07				11 07
Manchester Airport ✈	d												09 00			10 20			
Manchester Piccadilly 10	a											09 10	09 13		10 09	10 37			11 09
	d							08 42				09 12	09 27		10 11	10 42			11 11
Manchester Victoria	a																		
	d																		
Ashton-under-Lyne	d																		
Stalybridge	a							08 54				09 24			10 24				11 24
	d							08 54				09 24			10 24				11 24
Mossley (Grtr Manchester)	d																		
Greenfield	d																		
Marsden	d																		
Slaithwaite	d																		
Huddersfield	a							09 12				09 42	09 55		10 42	11 10			11 42
	d				08 20			09 13		09 20	09 25	09 43	09 56	10 20	10 43	11 11	11 20	11 25	11 43
Deighton	d										09 34							11 34	
Mirfield	d										09 44							11 44	
Ravensthorpe	d										09 49							11 49	
Dewsbury	a										09 57							11 57	
	d										09 57							11 57	
Batley	d										10 05							12 05	
Morley	d										10 17							12 17	
Cottingley	d										10 27							12 27	
Leeds 10	a				08 43			09 48		09 43	10 42	10 17	10 30	10 43	11 17	11 46	11 43	12 42	12 17
	d		08 30	08 40		09 08	09 12	09 50				10 22	10 35		11 18	11 48			12 18
Garforth	d																		
South Milford	a											10 34							
Selby	a											10 44							
Howden	a																		
Brough	a											11 03							
Hull	a											11 21							
York 8	a		08 55	09 02		09 31	09 37	10 13					10 59		11 41	12 11			12 41
	d	08 22	09 00	09 10		09 34	09 42	10 15	10 37				11 00		11 42	12 12			12 43
Malton	d						10 06								12 06				
Seamer	a						10 22								12 23				
Scarborough	a						10 31								12 32				
Thirsk	a	08 38							10 53										12 59
Northallerton	a	08 46	09 19	09 30				10 35	11 01				11 20			12 33			13 12
Darlington 7	a	08 57	09 33	09 42		09 59		10 47					11 32			12 44			
Yarm	d								11 15										13 27
Thornaby	a	09 17							11 23										13 35
Middlesbrough	a	09 26							11 33										13 44
Durham	a		09 51	09 59		10 16		11 04					11 49			13 01			
Chester-le-Street	a			10 05															
Newcastle 8	a		10 07	10 17		10 30		11 19					12 04			13 16			

Station		TP	TP	TP	GR	TP	TP	TP	NT	TP	TP	TP	TP	TP	TP	TP	TP	NT	TP
		◇1	bus	◇1	R 1 restaurant	◇1	◇1	bus	bus	◇1	◇1	◇1	bus	◇1	◇1	◇1	bus	bus	◇1
Liverpool Lime Street 10	d					11 22					12 22				13 22				
Liverpool South Parkway 7 ✈	d					11 32					12 32				13 32				
Warrington Central	d					11 45					12 45				13 45				
Birchwood	d					11 50					12 50				13 50				
Newton-le-Willows	d																		
Manchester Oxford Road	d					12 07					13 07				14 07				
Manchester Airport ✈	d	11 20					12 20					13 20				14 20			
Manchester Piccadilly 10	a	11 36				12 09	12 37				13 09	13 37			14 09	14 37			
	d	11 42				12 11	12 42			13 02	13 11	13 42			14 11	14 42			15 02
Manchester Victoria	a																		
	d																		
Ashton-under-Lyne	d																		
Stalybridge	a					12 24					13 24				14 24				
	d					12 24					13 24				14 24				
Mossley (Grtr Manchester)	d																		
Greenfield	d																		
Marsden	d																		
Slaithwaite	d																		
Huddersfield	a	12 10				12 42	13 10			13 32	13 42	14 10			14 42	15 10			15 32
	d	12 11	12 20			12 43	13 11	13 20	13 25	13 33	13 43	14 11	14 20		14 43	15 11	15 20	15 25	15 33
Deighton	d								13 34									15 34	
Mirfield	d								13 44									15 44	
Ravensthorpe	d								13 49									15 49	
Dewsbury	a								13 57									15 57	
	d								13 57									15 57	
Batley	d								14 05									16 05	
Morley	d								14 17									16 17	
Cottingley	d								14 27									16 27	
Leeds 10	a	12 45	12 43			13 17	13 46	13 43	14 42	14 09	14 17	14 45	14 43		15 17	15 46	15 43	16 42	16 09
	d	12 47		13 01		13 18	13 48				14 18	14 47		15 01	15 18	15 48			
Garforth	d																		
South Milford	a			13 13										15 14					
Selby	a			13 23										15 23					
Howden	a																		
Brough	a			13 42										15 41					
Hull	a			13 59										15 59					
York 8	a	13 10				13 41	14 11				14 40	15 10			15 40	16 11			
	d	13 12			13 17	13 42	14 12				14 42	15 12			15 42	16 12			
Malton	d					14 06									16 06				
Seamer	a					14 23									16 23				
Scarborough	a					14 32									16 32				
Thirsk	a										14 58								
Northallerton	a	13 32			13 36		14 33				15 09	15 32				16 33			
Darlington 7	a	13 44			13 49		14 44					15 44				16 44			
Yarm	d										15 23								
Thornaby	a										15 32								
Middlesbrough	a										15 40								
Durham	a	14 01			14 07		15 01					16 01				17 01			
Chester-le-Street	a	14 07										16 07							
Newcastle 8	a	14 19			14 23		15 16					16 19				17 16			

Table 39

Sundays

16 February to 23 March

Liverpool, Manchester Airport and Manchester - Huddersfield, Leeds, Hull, York, Scarborough, Middlesbrough and Newcastle

Network Diagram - refer to first Page of Table 39

		TP	TP	TP	TP	TP	TP	TP	NT	TP	TP	TP	TP	TP	TP	TP	TP	TP
		◇1	◇1		◇1	◇1	◇1			◇1	◇1	◇1		◇1	◇1	◇1		◇1
				bus				bus	bus				bus				bus	
Liverpool Lime Street 10	d	14 22				15 22					16 22				17 22			
Liverpool South Parkway 7 ✈	d	14 32				15 32					16 32				17 32			
Warrington Central	d	14 45				15 45					16 45				17 45			
Birchwood	d	14 50				15 50					16 50				17 50			
Newton-le-Willows	d																	
Manchester Oxford Road	d	15 07				16 07					17 07				18 07			
Manchester Airport ✈	d		15 20				16 20					17 20				18 20		
Manchester Piccadilly 10	a	15 09	15 37			16 09	16 37				17 09	17 37			18 09	18 37		
	d	15 11	15 42			16 11	16 42			17 02	17 11	17 42			18 11	18 42		
Manchester Victoria	a																	
	d																	
Ashton-under-Lyne	d																	
Stalybridge	a	15 23				16 24					17 23				18 24			
	d	15 24				16 24					17 24				18 24			
Mossley (Grtr Manchester)	d																	
Greenfield	d																	
Marsden	d																	
Slaithwaite	d																	
Huddersfield	a	15 42	16 10			16 42	17 10			17 32	17 42	18 10			18 42	19 10		
	d	15 43	16 11	16 20		16 43	17 11	17 20	17 25	17 33	17 43	18 11	18 20		18 43	19 11	19 20	
Deighton	d								17 34									
Mirfield	d								17 44									
Ravensthorpe	d								17 49									
Dewsbury	a								17 57									
	d								17 57									
Batley	d								18 05									
Morley	d								18 17									
Cottingley	d								18 27									
Leeds 10	a	16 17	16 45	16 43		17 17	17 46	17 43	18 42	18 10	18 17	18 45	18 43		19 17	19 46	19 43	
	d	16 18	16 47		17 01	17 22	17 48				18 18	18 47		19 01	19 18	19 48		20 15
Garforth	d																	
South Milford	a				17 14									19 16				
Selby	a				17 23									19 28				20 34
Howden	a																	
Brough	a				17 41									19 48				20 55
Hull	a				17 59									20 05				21 11
York 8	a	16 41	17 10			17 45	18 10				18 41	19 10			19 41	20 11		
	d	16 43	17 12			17 47	18 10				18 43	19 12			19 42	20 12		
Malton	d					18 11									20 06			
Seamer	a					18 28									20 23			
Scarborough	a					18 37									20 32			
Thirsk	a	16 59									18 59					20 28		
Northallerton	a	17 10	17 32				18 31				19 07	19 32				20 36		
Darlington 7	a		17 44				18 44					19 44						
Yarm	d	17 25									19 23					20 53		
Thornaby	a	17 33									19 31					21 01		
Middlesbrough	a	17 42									19 40					21 10		
Durham	a		18 01				19 02					20 01						
Chester-le-Street	a		18 07									20 07						
Newcastle 8	a		18 19				19 17					20 18						

		NT	TP	TP	TP	TP	TP	TP	TP	TP	NT	TP	NT	TP	TP	TP	TP	TP
			◇1	◇1		◇1	◇1	◇1		◇1		◇1		◇1		◇1		◇1
		bus			bus				bus		bus				bus		bus	
Liverpool Lime Street 10	d		18 22				19 22					20 22				21 52		
Liverpool South Parkway 7 ✈	d		18 32				19 32					20 32				22 02		
Warrington Central	d		18 45				19 45					20 45				22 15		
Birchwood	d		18 50				19 50					20 50				22 20		
Newton-le-Willows	d																	
Manchester Oxford Road	d		19 07				20 07					21 07				22 37		
Manchester Airport ✈	d			19 20				20 20						21 20				23 24
Manchester Piccadilly 10	a		19 09	19 37			20 09	20 37				21 09		21 37		22 39		23 38
	d		19 11	19 42			20 11	20 42				21 11		21 42		22 42		23 42
Manchester Victoria	a																	
	d																	
Ashton-under-Lyne	d																	
Stalybridge	a		19 24				20 24					21 24				22 54		
	d		19 24				20 24					21 24				22 54		
Mossley (Grtr Manchester)	d																	
Greenfield	d																	
Marsden	d												21 47					
Slaithwaite	d												21 51					
Huddersfield	a		19 42	20 10			20 42	21 10				21 42	21 56	22 10		23 12		00 10
	d	19 25	19 43	20 11	20 20		20 43	21 11	21 20		21 25	21 43		22 11	22 20	23 12	23 20	00 11
Deighton	d	19 34									21 34							
Mirfield	d	19 44									21 44							
Ravensthorpe	d	19 49									21 49							
Dewsbury	a	19 57									21 57							
	d	19 57									21 57							
Batley	d	20 05									22 05							
Morley	d	20 17									22 17							
Cottingley	d	20 27									22 27							
Leeds 10	a	20 42	20 17	20 45	20 43		21 18	21 46	21 43		22 42	22 18		22 47	22 43	23 51	23 43	00 47
	d		20 22	20 47		21 04	21 23	21 48		22 22		22 18		22 59		23 52		00 48
Garforth	d																	
South Milford	a									22 34								
Selby	a					21 35				22 44								
Howden	a																	
Brough	a					21 55				23 03								
Hull	a					22 09				23 19								
York 8	a		20 45	21 10			21 46	22 15				22 42		23 27		00 36		01 17
	d		20 47	21 12				22 17				22 43						
Malton	d		21 11					22 41										
Seamer	a		21 28					22 58										
Scarborough	a		21 38					23 05										
Thirsk	a			21 28								23 05						
Northallerton	a			21 36								23 15						
Darlington 7	a			21 48								23 27						
Yarm	d																	
Thornaby	a																	
Middlesbrough	a																	
Durham	a			22 05								23 44						
Chester-le-Street	a																	
Newcastle 8	a			22 19								00 14						

Table 39

Sundays
30 March to 11 May

Liverpool, Manchester Airport and Manchester - Huddersfield, Leeds, Hull, York, Scarborough, Middlesbrough and Newcastle

Network Diagram - refer to first Page of Table 39

		TP	TP	TP	TP	NT	TP	NT	GR	TP	XC	TP	TP	TP	TP	NT	TP	TP	TP
		◇1	◇1	◇1	◇1		◇1		1	◇1	◇1	◇1	◇1	◇1	◇1		◇1	◇1	◇1
Liverpool Lime Street 10	d														08 22			09 22	
Liverpool South Parkway 7	d														08 32			09 32	
Warrington Central	d														08 45			09 45	
Birchwood	d														08 50			09 50	
Newton-le-Willows	d																		
Manchester Oxford Road	d														09 08			10 07	
Manchester Airport	d			01 22	04 43		06 24			07 24			08 10				09 22		10 20
Manchester Piccadilly 10	a			01 36	04 57		06 38			07 37			08 24		09 10		09 36	10 09	10 37
	d			01 42	05 02		06 42			07 42			08 30		09 12		09 40	10 11	10 42
Manchester Victoria	a																		
	d																		
Ashton-under-Lyne	d																		
Stalybridge	a						06 53			07 54			08 42		09 24			10 24	
	d						06 54			07 54			08 42		09 24			10 24	
Mossley (Grtr Manchester)	d																		
Greenfield	d																		
Marsden	d																		
Slaithwaite	d																		
Huddersfield	a			02 11	05 31		07 11			08 11			09 00		09 42		10 08	10 42	11 11
	d		00 11	02 12	05 32		07 12	07 51		08 12			09 01		09 43	09 47	10 09	10 43	11 12
Deighton	d							07 54								09 50			
Mirfield	d							07 59								09 55			
Ravensthorpe	d							08 02								09 58			
Dewsbury	a		00s20				07 21	08 06		08 21			09 10			10 02	10 18		11 21
	d						07 22	08 06		08 22			09 10			10 03	10 19		11 22
Batley	d							08 09								10 06			
Morley	d							08 15								10 12			
Cottingley	d							08 19								10 15			
Leeds 10	a		00 35	02 33	05 53		07 38	08 27		08 37			09 25		10 04	10 23	10 34	11 04	11 37
	d	00 15	00 38	02 35	05 55		07 40		08 30	08 40	09 08	09 12	09 40		10 22		10 35	11 12	11 40
Garforth	d																		
South Milford	a														10 34				
Selby	a														10 44				
Howden	a																		
Brough	a														11 04				
Hull	a														11 21				
York 8	a	00 42	01 06	03 03	06 23		08 06		08 55	09 02	09 31	09 37	10 03				10 58	11 39	12 03
	d						08 22		09 00	09 10	09 34	09 42	10 10	10 37			11 00	11 42	12 10
Malton	d											10 06						12 06	
Seamer	a											10 22						12 23	
Scarborough	a											10 31						12 32	
Thirsk	a						08 38							10 53					
Northallerton	a						08 46		09 19	09 30			10 30	11 01			11 20		12 30
Darlington 7	a						08 57		09 33	09 42	09 59		10 42				11 32		12 42
Yarm	d													11 15					
Thornaby	a					08d38	09 17							11 23					
Middlesbrough	a					08 43	09 26							11 33					
Durham	a								09 51	09 59	10 16		10 59				11 49		12 59
Chester-le-Street	a									10 05									
Newcastle 8	a								10 07	10 17	10 30		11 15				12 04		13 14

		TP	NT	TP	TP	TP	TP	TP	TP	NT	TP	TP	TP	TP	TP	NT	TP	NT	TP
		◇1		◇1	◇1	◇1	◇1	◇1	◇1		◇1	◇1	◇1	◇1	◇1		◇1		◇1
Liverpool Lime Street 10	d	10 22				11 22			12 22				13 22				14 22		
Liverpool South Parkway 7	d	10 32				11 32			12 32				13 32				14 32		
Warrington Central	d	10 45				11 45			12 45				13 45				14 45		
Birchwood	d	10 50				11 50			12 50				13 50				14 50		
Newton-le-Willows	d																		
Manchester Oxford Road	d	11 07				12 07			13 07				14 07				15 07		
Manchester Airport	d			11 20			12 20				13 20			14 20					15 20
Manchester Piccadilly 10	a	11 09		11 34		12 09	12 34		13 09		13 37		14 09	14 37			15 09		15 37
	d	11 11		11 42	12 01	12 11	12 42	13 02	13 11		13 42	14 02	14 11	14 42	15 02		15 11		15 42
Manchester Victoria	a																		
	d																		
Ashton-under-Lyne	d																		
Stalybridge	a	11 23				12 24			13 24				14 24				15 25		
	d	11 23				12 24			13 24				14 24				15 25		
Mossley (Grtr Manchester)	d																		
Greenfield	d																		
Marsden	d																		
Slaithwaite	d																		
Huddersfield	a	11 42		12 11	12 32	12 42	13 11	13 32	13 42		14 11	14 32	14 42	15 11	15 32		15 43		16 11
	d	11 43	11 58	12 12	12 33	12 43	13 12	13 33	13 43	13 58	14 12	14 33	14 43	15 12	15 33		15 44	15 58	16 12
Deighton	d		12 01							14 01								16 01	
Mirfield	d		12 06							14 06								16 06	
Ravensthorpe	d		12 09							14 09								16 09	
Dewsbury	a		12 13	12 21			13 21			14 13	14 21			15 21				16 13	16 22
	d		12 13	12 22			13 22			14 13	14 22			15 22				16 13	16 22
Batley	d		12 16							14 16								16 16	
Morley	d		12 22							14 22								16 22	
Cottingley	d		12 26							14 26								16 26	
Leeds 10	a	12 04	12 34	12 37	12 54	13 04	13 37	13 54	14 04	14 34	14 37	14 53	15 05	15 37	15 54		16 05	16 34	16 37
	d	12 12		12 40	13 01	13 12	13 40	13 57	14 12		14 40	15 01	15 12	15 40	15 57		16 12		16 40
Garforth	d																		
South Milford	a				13 13							15 14							
Selby	a				13 23							15 23							
Howden	a																		
Brough	a				13 42							15 41							
Hull	a				13 59							15 59							
York 8	a	12 35		13 06		13 35	14 04	14 23	14 35		15 06		15 40	16 04	16 23		16 35		17 08
	d	12 40		13 10		13 42	14 11		14 42		15 10		15 42	16 10			16 41		17 10
Malton	d					14 06							16 06						
Seamer	a					14 23							16 23						
Scarborough	a					14 32							16 32						
Thirsk	a	12 56							14 58								16 57		
Northallerton	a	13 04		13 30			14 31		15 08		15 30			16 30			17 07		17 30
Darlington 7	a			13 42			14 43				15 42			16 42					17 42
Yarm	d	13 18							15 23								17 21		
Thornaby	a	13 27							15 31							16d18	17 30		
Middlesbrough	a	13 37							15 40							16 23	17 39		
Durham	a			13 59			15 00				15 59			16 59					17 59
Chester-le-Street	a			14 05							16 05								18 05
Newcastle 8	a			14 17			15 16				16 18			17 14					18 18

Table 39

Sundays
30 March to 11 May

Liverpool, Manchester Airport and Manchester - Huddersfield, Leeds, Hull, York, Scarborough, Middlesbrough and Newcastle

Network Diagram - refer to first Page of Table 39

		TP	TP	TP	TP	TP	NT	TP	TP	TP	TP	TP	TP	NT	TP	TP	TP	TP	TP	TP	NT	TP	TP	TP
		◇1	◇1	◇1	◇1	◇1		◇1	◇1	◇1	◇1	◇1	◇1		◇1	◇1	◇1	◇1	◇1	◇1		◇1	◇1	◇1
Liverpool Lime Street 10	d		15 22			16 22				17 22			18 22				19 22		20 22				21 52	
Liverpool South Parkway 7 ✈	d		15 32			16 32				17 32			18 32				19 32		20 32				22 02	
Warrington Central	d		15 45			16 45				17 45			18 45				19 45		20 45				22 15	
Birchwood	d		15 50			16 50				17 50			18 50				19 50		20 50				22 20	
Newton-le-Willows	d																							
Manchester Oxford Road	d		16 07			17 07				18 07			19 07				20 07		21 07				22 37	
Manchester Airport ✈	d			16 20				17 20			18 20				19 20			20 20				21 20		23 20
Manchester Piccadilly 10 🚋	a		16 09	16 37		17 09		17 37		18 09	18 37		19 09		19 37		20 09	20 37	21 09			21 37	22 39	23 37
	d	16 02	16 11	16 42	17 02	17 11		17 42	18 02	18 11	18 42	19 02	19 11		19 42	20 06	20 11	20 42	21 11			21 42	22 42	23 42
Manchester Victoria 🚋	a																							
	d																							
Ashton-under-Lyne	d																							
Stalybridge	a		16 24			17 24				18 24			19 24				20 24		21 24				22 54	
	d		16 24			17 24				18 24			19 24				20 24		21 24				22 54	
Mossley (Grtr Manchester)	d																							
Greenfield	d																							
Marsden	d																				21 47			
Slaithwaite	d																				21 51			
Huddersfield	a	16 32	16 42	17 11	17 32	17 42		18 11	18 32	18 42	19 11	19 32	19 42		20 11	20 36	20 42	21 11	21 42		21 57	22 11	23 12	00 11
	d	16 33	16 43	17 12	17 33	17 43	17 58	18 12	18 33	18 43	19 12	19 33	19 43	19 58	20 12	20 37	20 43	21 12	21 43		21 57	22 12	23 13	00 12
Deighton	d						18 01							20 01							22 01			
Mirfield	d						18 06							20 06							22 06			
Ravensthorpe	d						18 09							20 09							22 09			
Dewsbury	a			17 21			18 13	18 21			19 21			20 13	20 21			21 21			22 13	22 21	23 23	
	d			17 22			18 13	18 22			19 22			20 13	20 22			21 22			22 13	22 22	23 23	
Batley	d						18 16							20 16							22 16			
Morley	d						18 22							20 22							22 22			
Cottingley	d						18 26							20 26							22 26			
Leeds 10	a	16 54	17 05	17 37	17 54	18 04	18 34	18 37	18 54	19 04	19 37	19 54	20 04	20 34	20 37	20 58	21 05	21 37	22 05		22 34	22 37	23 39	00 51
	d	17 01	17 12	17 40	17 57	18 12		18 40	19 01	19 12	19 40	19 57	20 12		20 40	21 04	21 12	21 40	22 12	22 22		22 40	23 43	00 54
Garforth	d																							
South Milford	a	17 14							19 16											22 34				
Selby	a	17 23							19 28			20 17				21 35				22 44				
Howden	a																							
Brough	a	17 41							19 48			20 37				21 55				23 03				
Hull	a	17 59							20 05			20 54				22 09				23 19				
York 8	a		17 37	18 06	18 23	18 35		19 06		19 36	20 04		20 34		21 04		21 37	22 07	22 38			23 06	00 25	01 21
	d		17 42	18 10		18 40		19 10		19 42	20 08		20 42		21 08			22 10	22 43					
Malton	d		18 06							20 06			21 06					22 34						
Seamer	a		18 23							20 23			21 23					22 51						
Scarborough	a		18 32							20 32			21 32					22 58						
Thirsk	a					18 56					20 24				21 24				23 05					
Northallerton	a			18 30		19 04		19 30			20 32				21 32				23 15					
Darlington 7	a			18 42				19 42							21 43				23 27					
Yarm	d					19 18					20 47													
Thornaby	a					19 27					20 55													
Middlesbrough	a					19 37					21 04													
Durham	a			19 02				19 59							22 00				23 44					
Chester-le-Street	a							20 05																
Newcastle 8 🚋	a			19 17				20 18							22 15				00 14					

Table 39R

Mondays to Fridays

9 December to 16 May

Newcastle, Middlesbrough, Scarborough, York, Hull, Leeds and Wakefield - Huddersfield - Manchester, Manchester Airport and Liverpool

Network Diagram - refer to first Page of Table 39

Miles	Miles	Miles	Miles	Miles			TP MO	GR MX	TP MX	TP MO	TP MO	TP MO	TP MX	TP MX	TP MO	TP MX	TP MX	TP MX	TP MO	TP MO	TP	NT	NT	TP	NT	NT	NT	TP	TP	NT	NT	TP	NT	TP	NT	NT	NT	NT
							◇1	1	◇1	◇1	◇1	◇1	◇1	◇1	◇1	◇1	◇1	◇1	◇1	◇1	◇1			◇1				◇1	◇1			◇1		◇1				
							A		B	C	D		E	B		E	B		F	G																		
0	—	—	—	—	**Newcastle** 8	d																																
8¼	—	—	—	—	Chester-le-Street	d																																
14	—	—	—	—	Durham	d																																
—	—	0	—	—	**Middlesbrough**	d																									05 55						
—	—	3¼	—	—	Thornaby	d																									06 00						
—	—	8½	—	—	Yarm	d																									06 08						
36	—	—	—	—	**Darlington** 7	d																															
50	—	20¾	—	—	Northallerton	d																									06 23						
57¾	—	28½	—	—	Thirsk	d																									06 31						
—	—	—	0	—	**Scarborough**	d																															
—	—	—	2¾	—	Seamer	d																															
—	—	—	21	—	Malton	d																															
80	—	50¾	42	—	**York** 8	a																									06 48						
—	—	—	—	—		d		00 18				01 38	01 38	01 38	02 47	02 52	02 52	04 00	04 23	04 23	05 26			05 57				06 28				06 55						
—	—	—	—	0	**Wakefield Westgate**	d																				06 41										07 41	
—	—	—	—	1	Wakefield Kirkgate	d																				06 46										07 46	
—	0	—	—	—	**Hull**	d																							06 00					06 37				
—	10½	—	—	—	Brough	d																							06 12					06 49				
—	22¼	—	—	—	Howden	a																							06 26									
—	—	—	—	—		d																							06 26									
—	31	—	—	—	Selby	d																							06 36					07 08				
—	38¾	—	—	—	South Milford	d																																
98¼	44½	—	60¼	—	Garforth	d																		06 12								07 10		07 24				
105½	51¾	—	67½	—	**Leeds** 10	a		00 47				02 04	02 19	02 19	03 13	03 33	03 33	04 42	04 49	04 49	05 52			06 22				06 52	07 00			07 20		07 35				
—	—	—	—	—		d						02 05	02 20	02 20	03 15	03 35	03 35	04 50	04 50	04 50	05 55		06 13	06 25			06 43	06 55	07 08		07 13	07 23		07 38				07 43
108½	—	—	—	—	Cottingley	d																					06 48											07 48
110	—	—	—	—	Morley	d																	06 21				06 52				07 21							07 52
113½	—	—	—	—	Batley	d																	06 26				06 57				07 26							07 57
114¾	—	—	—	—	**Dewsbury**	a															06 06		06 29	06 36			07 00	07 06			07 29	07 34						08 00
—	—	—	—	—		d															06 06		06 29	06 36			07 01	07 06			07 29	07 34						08 01
116	—	—	—	—	Ravensthorpe	d																					07 04											08 04
117¾	—	—	—	10½	Mirfield	d																	06 35			06 59	07 08				07 36						07 59	08 08
120¾	—	—	—	13½	Deighton	d																				07 06	07 16										08 04	08 13
122¾	—	—	—	15½	**Huddersfield**	a						02 42	02 42	02 42	03 56	03 56	03 56	05 27	05 27	05 27	06 14			06 44		07 12	07 20	07 15	07 25			07 43		07 56			08 11	08 21
—	—	—	—	—		d	00 01			00 01	00 14	02 45	02 45	02 45	03 59	03 59	03 59	05 28	05 28	05 28	06 15	06 29		06 45	06 57			07 16	07 26	07 33		07 44		07 57		08 02		
127¾	—	—	—	20	Slaithwaite	d																06 36			07 04					07 40						08 09		
129¾	—	—	—	22½	Marsden	d																06 42			07 12					07 55						08 15		
135¾	—	—	—	28½	Greenfield	d																06 50			07 20					08 03						08 23		
138	—	—	—	30¾	Mossley (Grtr Manchester)	d																06 54			07 24					08 08			←			08 27		
140¾	—	—	—	33½	**Stalybridge**	a															06 33	06 59		07 02	07 29			07 34	07 43	08 12		08 01	08 12	08 17		08 32		
—	—	—	—	—		d															06 33	07 00		07 03	07 30			07 34	07 46	08 13		08 02	08 13	08 17	08 22	08 33		
—	—	—	—	34¾	Ashton-under-Lyne	d																07 04			07 34					→			08 17		08 26	08 37		
—	—	—	—	41¼	**Manchester Victoria**	a																07 17	07 53		07 47						08 53		08 31		08 35	08 52		
148¾	—	—	—	—	**Manchester Piccadilly** 10	a	00 30			00 43	00 43	03 44	03 45	03 44	04 58	04 58	04 58	06 00	06 00	06 00	06 50			07 19				07 51	08 05			08 19		08 36				
—	—	—	—	—		d	00 34		00 42	00 44	00 47	03 44		03 44	05 00		05 00	06 08	06 08	06 08	06 54			07 22				07 54	08 07			08 24						
—	—	—	—	—	**Manchester Airport**	a	00 48		00 57	00 57	01 01	04 00		04 00	05 19		05 19	06 24	06 24	06 26	07 12			07 41				08 12				08 42						
148¾	—	—	—	—	Manchester Oxford Road	a																							08 09									
161¾	—	—	—	—	Birchwood	a																							08 25									
164½	—	—	—	—	Warrington Central	a																							08 30									
177¾	—	—	—	—	Liverpool South Parkway 7	a																							08 47									
183	—	—	—	—	**Liverpool Lime Street** 10	a																							08 58						09 43			

A from 6 January until 10 February, from 31 March
B until 27 December, from 25 March
C until 30 December
D from 17 February until 24 March
E from 31 December until 21 March
F until 3 February, from 24 March
G from 10 February until 17 March

Table 39R

Mondays to Fridays

9 December to 16 May

Newcastle, Middlesbrough, Scarborough, York, Hull, Leeds and Wakefield - Huddersfield - Manchester, Manchester Airport and Liverpool

Network Diagram - refer to first Page of Table 39

Station		TP ◇1 ✠	TP ◇1 A ✠	NT	NT	NT	TP ◇1 ✠	TP ◇1 ✠	NT	NT	TP ◇1 ✠	TP ◇1 ✠	NT	NT	NT	NT	TP ◇1 ✠
Newcastle 8	d		06 10														07 33
Chester-le-Street	d		06 21														07 42
Durham	d		06 27														07 49
Middlesbrough	d										07 12						
Thornaby	d										07 17						
Yarm	d										07 27						
Darlington 7	d		06 45														08 06
Northallerton	d		06 57								07 43						08 17
Thirsk	d		07 05								07 51						08 25
Scarborough	d	06 30					07 00					07 40					
Seamer	d	06 35					07 05					07 45					
Malton	d	06 53					07 23					08 03					
York 8	a	07 23	07 28				07 50				08 11	08 30					08 47
	d	07 26	07 40				07 55				08 26	08 40					08 57
Wakefield Westgate	d								08 39								
Wakefield Kirkgate	d								08 45								
Hull	d							07 37									
Brough	d							07 49									
Howden	a							08 00									
	d							08 01									
Selby	d							08 11									
South Milford	d																
Garforth	d						08 12				08 41						09 12
Leeds 10	a	07 52	08 04				08 22	08 36			08 52	09 04					09 23
	d	07 55	08 08			08 13	08 25	08 40		08 43	08 55	09 08				09 13	09 25
Cottingley	d					08 18				08 48						09 18	
Morley	d					08 22				08 52						09 22	
Batley	d					08 27				08 57						09 27	
Dewsbury	a	08 06				08 30	08 36			09 00	09 06					09 30	09 36
	d	08 06				08 31	08 36			09 01	09 06					09 31	09 36
Ravensthorpe	d					08 34				09 04							
Mirfield	d					08 38			08 58	09 08						09 37	
Deighton	d								09 05	09 17							
Huddersfield	a	08 15	08 25				08 44	08 58	09 10	09 22	09 15	09 25					09 45
	d	08 16	08 26	08 30			08 45	08 59			09 16	09 26		09 30			09 46
Slaithwaite	d			08 37										09 37			
Marsden	d			08 43										09 43			
Greenfield	d			08 51										09 51			
Mossley (Grtr Manchester)	d			08 55										09 55			
Stalybridge	a		08 44	09 00								09 43		10 00			
	d		08 46	09 01	09 22							09 46	09 51	10 01	10 22		
Ashton-under-Lyne	d			09 05	09 26								09 55	10 05	10 26		
Manchester Victoria	a			09 20	09 37	09 53							10 04	10 20	10 36	10 53	
Manchester Piccadilly 10	a	08 51	09 05				09 19	09 36			09 49	10 05					10 19
	d	08 54	09 07				09 24				09 54	10 07					10 24
Manchester Airport ✈	a	09 12					09 42				10 12						10 42
Manchester Oxford Road	a		09 09									10 09					
Birchwood	a		09 25									10 25					
Warrington Central	a		09 30									10 30					
Liverpool South Parkway 7 ✈	a		09 47									10 47					
Liverpool Lime Street 10	a		09 58		10 43							10 58			11 43		

Station		TP ◇1 ✠	NT	NT	TP ◇1 ✠	TP ◇1 ✠	NT	NT	NT	NT ◇	TP ◇1 ✠	TP ◇1 ✠	NT	NT	TP ◇1 ✠	TP ◇1 ✠	NT	NT	NT	NT ◇	TP ◇1 ✠
Newcastle 8	d														09 15						
Chester-le-Street	d														09 24						
Durham	d														09 31						
Middlesbrough	d										08 50										09 50
Thornaby	d										08 55										09 55
Yarm	d										09 03										10 03
Darlington 7	d														09 48						
Northallerton	d										09 18				09 59						10 18
Thirsk	d										09 28										10 28
Scarborough	d					08 48										09 48					
Seamer	d					08 53										09 53					
Malton	d					09 11										10 11					
York 8	a					09 38					09 47				10 21	10 38					10 47
	d				09 26	09 40					09 57				10 26	10 40					10 57
Wakefield Westgate	d		09 39										10 39								
Wakefield Kirkgate	d		09 45										10 45								
Hull	d	08 40										09 40									
Brough	d	08 52										09 52									
Howden	a																				
	d																				
Selby	d	09 11										10 11									
South Milford	d																				
Garforth	d										10 12										11 12
Leeds 10	a	09 36			09 52	10 04					10 22	10 36			10 52	11 04					11 22
	d	09 40		09 43	09 55	10 08				10 13	10 25	10 40		10 43	10 55	11 08				11 13	11 25
Cottingley	d			09 48										10 48							
Morley	d			09 52						10 21				10 52						11 21	
Batley	d			09 57						10 26				10 57						11 26	
Dewsbury	a			10 00	10 06					10 29	10 36			11 00	11 06					11 29	11 36
	d			10 01	10 06					10 29	10 36			11 01	11 06					11 29	11 36
Ravensthorpe	d			10 04										11 04							
Mirfield	d		09 59	10 08						10 35			10 58	11 08						11 35	
Deighton	d		10 06	10 14									11 02	11 14							
Huddersfield	a	09 58	10 12	10 21	10 15	10 25					10 45	10 58	11 12	11 21	11 15	11 25					11 45
	d	09 59			10 16	10 26		10 30			10 46	10 59			11 16	11 26		11 30			11 46
Slaithwaite	d							10 37										11 37			
Marsden	d							10 43										11 43			
Greenfield	d							10 51										11 51			
Mossley (Grtr Manchester)	d							10 55										11 55			
Stalybridge	a					10 43		11 00								11 43		12 00			
	d					10 46	10 51	11 01	11 22							11 46	11 51	12 01	12 22		
Ashton-under-Lyne	d						10 55	11 05	11 26								11 55	12 05	12 26		
Manchester Victoria	a						11 04	11 18	11 35	11 53							12 04	12 20	12 35	12 53	
Manchester Piccadilly 10	a	10 36			10 49	11 05					11 19	11 36			11 49	12 05					12 19
	d				10 54	11 07					11 32				11 54	12 07					12 24
Manchester Airport ✈	a				11 12						11 50				12 12						12 42
Manchester Oxford Road	a					11 09										12 09					
Birchwood	a					11 25										12 25					
Warrington Central	a					11 30										12 30					
Liverpool South Parkway 7 ✈	a					11 47										12 47					
Liverpool Lime Street 10	a					11 58			12 43							12 58			13 43		

A ✠ from York

Table 39R

Mondays to Fridays

9 December to 16 May

Newcastle, Middlesbrough, Scarborough, York, Hull, Leeds and Wakefield - Huddersfield - Manchester, Manchester Airport and Liverpool

Network Diagram - refer to first Page of Table 39

Station		TP	NT	NT	TP	TP	NT	NT	NT	NT	TP	TP	NT	NT	TP	TP	NT	NT	NT
		◇1 ✠			◇1 ✠	◇1 ✠				◇	◇1 ✠	◇1 ✠			◇1 ✠	◇1 ✠			
Newcastle 8	d				10 17										11 15				
Chester-le-Street	d														11 24				
Durham	d				10 31										11 31				
Middlesbrough	d										10 50								
Thornaby	d										10 55								
Yarm	d										11 03								
Darlington 7	d				10 48										11 48				
Northallerton	d				10 59						11 18				11 59				
Thirsk	d										11 28								
Scarborough	d					10 48										11 48			
Seamer	d					10 53										11 53			
Malton	d					11 11										12 11			
York 8	a				11 23	11 38					11 47				12 21	12 38			
	d				11 26	11 40					11 57				12 26	12 40			
Wakefield Westgate	d		11 39										12 39						
Wakefield Kirkgate	d		11 45										12 45						
Hull	d	10 40										11 40							
Brough	d	10 52										11 52							
Howden	a																		
	d																		
Selby	d	11 11										12 11							
South Milford	d																		
Garforth	d										12 12								
Leeds 10	a	11 36			11 52	12 04					12 22	12 36			12 52	13 04			
	d	11 40		11 43	11 55	12 08				12 13	12 25	12 40		12 43	12 55	13 08			
Cottingley	d			11 48										12 48					
Morley	d			11 52						12 21				12 52					
Batley	d			11 57						12 26				12 57					
Dewsbury	a			12 00	12 06					12 29	12 36			13 00	13 06				
	d			12 01	12 06					12 29	12 36			13 01	13 06				
Ravensthorpe	d			12 04										13 04					
Mirfield	d		11 58	12 08						12 35			12 58	13 08					
Deighton	d		12 02	12 17									13 02	13 14					
Huddersfield	a	11 58	12 12	12 21	12 15	12 25					12 45	12 58	13 12	13 21	13 15	13 25			
	d	11 59			12 16	12 26		12 30			12 46	12 59			13 16	13 26		13 30	
Slaithwaite	d							12 37										13 37	
Marsden	d							12 43										13 43	
Greenfield	d							12 51										13 51	
Mossley (Grtr Manchester)	d							12 55										13 55	
Stalybridge	a					12 43		13 00								13 43		14 00	
	d					12 46	12 51	13 01	13 22							13 46	13 51	14 01	14 22
Ashton-under-Lyne	d						12 55	13 05	13 26								13 55	14 05	14 26
Manchester Victoria	a						13 04	13 19	13 35	13 53							14 04	14 20	14 35
Manchester Piccadilly 10	a	12 36			12 49	13 05					13 19	13 36			13 49	14 05			
	d				12 54	13 07					13 24				13 54	14 07			
Manchester Airport	a				13 12						13 42				14 12				
Manchester Oxford Road	a					13 09										14 09			
Birchwood	a					13 25										14 25			
Warrington Central	a					13 30										14 30			
Liverpool South Parkway 7	a					13 47										14 47			
Liverpool Lime Street 10	a					13 58			14 43							14 58			15 43

Station		NT	TP	TP	NT	NT	TP	TP	NT	NT	NT	NT	TP	TP	NT	NT	TP FO	TP FX	TP
		◇	◇1 ✠	◇1 ✠			◇1 ✠	◇1 ✠				◇	◇1 ✠	◇1 ✠			◇1 ✠	◇1 ✠	◇1 ✠
Newcastle 8	d						12 18										13 15	13 15	
Chester-le-Street	d																13 24	13 24	
Durham	d						12 31										13 31	13 31	
Middlesbrough	d		11 50										12 50						
Thornaby	d		11 55										12 55						
Yarm	d		12 03										13 03						
Darlington 7	d						12 48										13 48	13 48	
Northallerton	d		12 18				12 59						13 18				13 58	13 59	
Thirsk	d		12 28										13 28						
Scarborough	d							12 48											13 48
Seamer	d							12 53											13 53
Malton	d							13 11											14 11
York 8	a		12 47				13 22	13 38					13 47				14 22	14 22	14 38
	d		12 57				13 26	13 40					13 57				14 26	14 26	14 40
Wakefield Westgate	d				13 39										14 39				
Wakefield Kirkgate	d				13 45										14 45				
Hull	d			12 40										13 40					
Brough	d			12 52										13 52					
Howden	a																		
	d																		
Selby	d			13 11										14 11					
South Milford	d																		
Garforth	d		13 12										14 12						
Leeds 10	a		13 22	13 36			13 52	14 04					14 22	14 36			14 52	14 52	15 04
	d	13 13	13 25	13 40		13 43	13 55	14 08				14 13	14 25	14 40		14 43	14 55	14 55	15 08
Cottingley	d					13 48										14 48			
Morley	d	13 21				13 52						14 21				14 52			
Batley	d	13 26				13 57						14 26				14 57			
Dewsbury	a	13 29	13 36			14 00	14 06					14 29	14 36			15 00	15 06	15 06	
	d	13 29	13 36			14 01	14 06					14 29	14 36			15 01	15 06	15 06	
Ravensthorpe	d					14 04										15 04			
Mirfield	d	13 35			13 58	14 08						14 35			14 58	15 08			
Deighton	d				14 02	14 14									15 02	15 16			
Huddersfield	a		13 45	13 58	14 12	14 21	14 15	14 25					14 45	14 58	15 12	15 21	15 15	15 15	15 25
	d		13 46	13 59			14 16	14 26		14 30			14 46	14 59			15 16	15 16	15 26
Slaithwaite	d									14 37									
Marsden	d									14 43									
Greenfield	d									14 51									
Mossley (Grtr Manchester)	d									14 55									
Stalybridge	a							14 43		15 00									15 43
	d							14 46	14 51	15 01	15 22								15 46
Ashton-under-Lyne	d								14 55	15 05	15 26								
Manchester Victoria	a	14 52							15 04	15 20	15 35	15 53							
Manchester Piccadilly 10	a		14 19	14 36			14 49	15 05					15 19	15 36			15 49	15 49	16 05
	d		14 24				14 54	15 07					15 24				15 54	15 54	16 07
Manchester Airport	a		14 42				15 12						15 42				16 12	16 12	
Manchester Oxford Road	a							15 09											16 09
Birchwood	a							15 25											16 25
Warrington Central	a							15 30											16 30
Liverpool South Parkway 7	a							15 47											16 47
Liverpool Lime Street 10	a							15 58			16 43								16 58

Table 39R

Mondays to Fridays

9 December to 16 May

Newcastle, Middlesbrough, Scarborough, York, Hull, Leeds and Wakefield - Huddersfield - Manchester, Manchester Airport and Liverpool

Network Diagram - refer to first Page of Table 39

		NT	NT	NT	NT	TP	TP	TP	TP	NT	NT	TP	NT	TP	NT	TP	NT	TP	TP	TP	TP	NT	NT	TP	TP	NT	NT	TP	TP	TP	NT	NT	NT	TP	TP	TP	TP
						FX	FO	FO								FO		FX	FO	FO	FX							FO	FX						FX		
						◇1	◇1	◇1	◇1			◇1		◇1		◇1	◇	◇1	◇1	◇1	◇1			◇1	◇1			◇1	◇1	◇1				◇1	◇1	◇1	◇1
							A	B																										C	D		
						✠	✠	✠	✠			✠		✠				✠	✠	✠	✠			✠	✠			✠	✠	✠				✠	✠		✠
Newcastle 8 ⛴	d											14 18												15 15										16 15	16 15		
Chester-le-Street	d																							15 24										16 24	16 24		
Durham	d											14 31												15 31										16 31	16 31		
Middlesbrough	d					13 50	13 50	13 50								14 50		14 50										15 50	15 50								
Thornaby	d					13 55	13 55	13 55								14 55		14 55										15 55	15 55								
Yarm	d					14 03	14 03	14 03								15 03		15 03										16 03	16 03								
Darlington 7	d											14 48												15 48										16 48	16 48		
Northallerton	d					14 18	14 18	14 18				14 59				15 18		15 18						15 59				16 18	16 18					16 59	16 59		
Thirsk	d					14 28	14 28	14 28								15 28		15 28										16 28	16 28								
Scarborough	d													14 48											15 48												16 48
Seamer	d													14 53											15 53												16 53
Malton	d													15 11											16 11												17 11
York 8	a					14 47	14 47	14 47				15 22		15 38		15 47		15 47						16 21	16 38			16 47	16 47					17 23	17 23		17 38
	d					14 57	14 57	14 57				15 26		15 40				15 57	15 57					16 26	16 40			16 57	16 57					17 26	17 26		17 40
Wakefield Westgate	d									15 39												16 39										17 39					
Wakefield Kirkgate	d									15 45												16 45										17 45					
Hull	d								14 40											15 40	15 40									16 40						17 02	
Brough	d								14 52											15 52	15 52									16 52						17 14	
Howden	a																																				
	d																																				
Selby	d								15 11											16 11	16 11									17 11						17 33	
South Milford	d																																				
Garforth	d					15 12	15 12	15 12										16 12		16 22								17 12	17 12								
Leeds 10	a					15 22	15 23	15 23	15 36			15 52		16 07				16 22	16 22	16 36	16 36			16 52	17 07			17 22	17 22	17 37				17 52	17 52	17 58	18 04
	d				15 13	15 25	15 25	15 25	15 40		15 43	15 55		16 08			16 13	16 25	16 25	16 40	16 40		16 43	16 55	17 08		17 13	17 26	17 26	17 40			17 43	17 55	17 55	18 02	18 08
Cottingley	d										15 48						16 18						16 48				17 18						17 48				
Morley	d				15 21						15 52						16 22						16 52				17 22						17 52				
Batley	d				15 26						15 57						16 27						16 57				17 27						17 57				
Dewsbury	a				15 29	15 36	15 36	15 36			16 00	16 06					16 30	16 36	16 36				17 00	17 06			17 30	17 37	17 37				18 00	18 06	18 06	18 13	
	d				15 29	15 36	15 36	15 36			16 01	16 06					16 31	16 36	16 36				17 01	17 06			17 31	17 37	17 37				18 01	18 06	18 06	18 13	
Ravensthorpe	d										16 04						16 34						17 04				17 34						18 04				
Mirfield	d				15 35					15 58	16 08						16 38					16 58	17 08				17 38					17 59	18 08				
Deighton	d									16 02	16 14											17 02	17 14									18 03	18 13				
Huddersfield	a					15 45	15 45	15 45	15 58	16 12	16 21	16 15		16 25				16 45	16 45	16 58	16 58	17 12	17 21	17 15	17 25			17 46	17 46	17 58		18 12	18 20	18 15	18 15	18 23	18 25
	d		15 30			15 46	15 46	15 46	15 59			16 16		16 26	16 30			16 46	16 46	16 59	16 59			17 16	17 26	17 30		17 46	17 46	17 59	18 04			18 16	18 16		18 26
Slaithwaite	d		15 37												16 37											17 37					18 11						
Marsden	d		15 43												16 43											17 43					18 17						
Greenfield	d		15 51												16 51											17 51											
Mossley (Grtr Manchester)	d		15 55												16 55											17 55											
Stalybridge	a		16 00											16 43	17 00					17 18	17 18				17 43	18 00				18 18	18 30						18 43
	d	15 51	16 01	16 22									16 42	16 46	17 01					17 18	17 18				17 46	18 01				18 18	18 31						18 46
Ashton-under-Lyne	d	15 55	16 05	16 26									16 46		17 05											18 05					18 35						
Manchester Victoria ⛴	a	16 04	16 21	16 35	16 52								16 55		17 19		17 53									18 19	18 54				18 48						
Manchester Piccadilly 10 ⛴	a					16 19	16 19	16 19	16 36			16 49		17 05				17 21	17 21	17 36	17 36			17 49	18 05			18 19	18 19	18 37				18 49	18 49		19 05
	d					16 24	16 24	16 24				16 54		17 07										17 54	18 07				18 24					18 54	18 56		19 07
Manchester Airport ✈	a					16 42	16 41	16 46				17 12												18 12					18 42					19 13	19 15		
Manchester Oxford Road	a													17 09											18 09												19 09
Birchwood	a													17 25											18 25												19 25
Warrington Central	a													17 30											18 30												19 30
Liverpool South Parkway 7 ✈	a													17 47											18 47												19 47
Liverpool Lime Street 10	a			17 43										18 01											19 01												20 01

A from 14 February
B until 7 February
C until 7 February, FO from 14 February
D from 10 February

Table 39R

Mondays to Fridays

9 December to 16 May

Newcastle, Middlesbrough, Scarborough, York, Hull, Leeds and Wakefield - Huddersfield - Manchester, Manchester Airport and Liverpool

Network Diagram - refer to first Page of Table 39

		NT	NT	TP	TP	NT	NT	TP	TP	TP	NT	TP	NT	TP	TP	TP	NT	TP	NT
								ThX	ThO			FO		FX	FO				
				◇1	◇1			◇1	◇1	◇1		◇1		◇1	◇1	◇1		◇1	
				🚌	🚌			🚌	🚌										
Newcastle 8	d				17 02														
Chester-le-Street	d				17 11														
Durham	d				17 18														
Middlesbrough	d			16 50								17 50		17 50					
Thornaby	d			16 55								17 55		17 55					
Yarm	d			17 03								18 03		18 03					
Darlington 7	d				17 35														
Northallerton	d			17 18	17 46							18 18		18 18					
Thirsk	d			17 28								18 28		18 28					
Scarborough	d									17 48								18 48	
Seamer	d									17 53								18 53	
Malton	d									18 11								19 11	
York 8	a			17 47	18 09					18 38		18 47		18 47				19 38	
	d			17 57	18 12					18 40				19 08	19 08			19 40	
Wakefield Westgate	d					18 39											19 42		
Wakefield Kirkgate	d					18 45											19 47		
Hull	d							17 58	17 58							19 00			
Brough	d							18 10	18 10							19 12			
Howden	a																		
	d																		
Selby	d							18 29	18 29							19 31			
South Milford	d																		
Garforth	d			18 12										19 22	19 22				
Leeds 10	a			18 22	18 37			18 52	18 52	19 04				19 35	19 35	19 56		20 04	
	d		18 13	18 25	18 40		18 43	18 55	18 55	19 08			19 13	19 40	19 40			20 08	
Cottingley	d		18 18				18 48						19 18						
Morley	d		18 22				18 52						19 22						
Batley	d		18 27				18 57						19 27						
Dewsbury	a		18 30	18 36			19 00	19 06	19 06				19 30	19 51	19 51				
	d		18 31	18 36			19 01	19 06	19 06				19 31	19 51	19 51				
Ravensthorpe	d		18 34				19 04						19 34						
Mirfield	d		18 38			18 58	19 08						19 38				20 00		
Deighton	d					19 03	19 16						19 45				20 05		
Huddersfield	a			18 45	18 58	19 12	19 21	19 15	19 15	19 25			19 52	19 59	19 59		20 16	20 25	
	d	18 31		18 46	18 59			19 16	19 16	19 26	19 30			20 00	20 00			20 26	20 30
Slaithwaite	d	18 38									19 37								20 37
Marsden	d	18 43									19 43								20 43
Greenfield	d	18 51									19 51								20 51
Mossley (Grtr Manchester)	d	18 55									19 55								20 55
Stalybridge	a	19 01								19 43	20 00							20 43	21 00
	d	19 01								19 46	20 01							20 46	21 01
Ashton-under-Lyne	d	19 05									20 05								21 05
Manchester Victoria	a	19 20	19 53								20 20								21 20
Manchester Piccadilly 10	a			19 21	19 33			19 54	19 56	20 05				20 33	20 33			21 05	
	d				19 40					20 07				20 40	20 40			21 07	
Manchester Airport	a				19 59									20 57	20 57				
Manchester Oxford Road	a									20 09								21 09	
Birchwood	a									20 25								21 25	
Warrington Central	a									20 30								21 30	
Liverpool South Parkway 7	a									20 47								21 47	
Liverpool Lime Street 10	a									21 01								22 00	

		TP	NT	TP	TP	NT	TP	NT	TP	NT	TP	TP	TP	TP	TP	NT	TP	NT	TP
				FX					FO		FO	FX	FX	FX					
		◇1		◇1	◇1		◇1		◇1		◇1	◇1	◇1	◇1	◇1		◇1		◇1
				A	B							A	C						
Newcastle 8	d			18 52	18 52														
Chester-le-Street	d			19 01	19 01														
Durham	d			19 08	19 08														
Middlesbrough	d	18 50							20 04			20 04	20 04				20 50		21 50
Thornaby	d	18 55							20 09			20 09	20 09				20 55		21 55
Yarm	d	19 03															21 03		
Darlington 7	d			19 25	19 25				20 33			20 33	20 33						22 19
Northallerton	d	19 19		19 36	19 36				20 44			20 44	20 44				21 18		22 30
Thirsk	d	19 29							20 52			20 52	20 52						22 38
Scarborough	d						19 48								20 48				
Seamer	d						19 53								20 53				
Malton	d						20 11								21 11				
York 8	a	19 49		20 07	20 07		20 38		21 10			21 10	21 10		21 38		21 43		22 56
	d			20 10	20 10		20 40					21 14	21 14				21 46		
Wakefield Westgate	d					20 50										21 41			
Wakefield Kirkgate	d					20 56										21 47			
Hull	d										20 35			20 45					
Brough	d										20 47			20 57					
Howden	a																		
	d																		
Selby	d										21 06			21 16					
South Milford	d										21 16			21 26					
Garforth	d																		
Leeds 10	a			20 35	20 35		21 04				21 35	21 37	21 37	21 44			22 07		
	d		20 13	20 40	20 40		21 08			21 13	21 40	21 40	21 40				22 10		
Cottingley	d		20 18							21 18									
Morley	d		20 22							21 22									
Batley	d		20 27							21 27									
Dewsbury	a		20 30	20 51	20 51					21 30	21 51	21 51	21 51						
	d		20 31	20 51	20 51					21 31	21 51	21 51	21 51						
Ravensthorpe	d		20 34							21 34									
Mirfield	d		20 37			21 09				21 38						22 03			
Deighton	d		20 45			21 16				21 45						22 10			
Huddersfield	a		20 52	20 59	20 59	21 21	21 25			21 52	21 59	21 59	21 59			22 16	22 27		
	d			21 00	21 00		21 26	21 30			22 00	22 00	22 00				22 28	22 34	
Slaithwaite	d							21 37										22 41	
Marsden	d							21 43										22 47	
Greenfield	d							21 51										22 55	
Mossley (Grtr Manchester)	d							21 55										22 59	
Stalybridge	a						21 43	22 00									22 45	23 04	
	d						21 46	22 01									22 46	23 05	
Ashton-under-Lyne	d							22 05										23 09	
Manchester Victoria	a							22 20										23 24	
Manchester Piccadilly 10	a			21 33	21 33		22 05				22 36	22 37	22 33				23 05		
	d				21 40		22 07				22 40		22 40						
Manchester Airport	a				21 57						22 57		22 57						
Manchester Oxford Road	a						22 09												
Birchwood	a						22 25												
Warrington Central	a						22 30												
Liverpool South Parkway 7	a						22 47												
Liverpool Lime Street 10	a						23 01												

A from 30 December until 20 March

B until 27 December, FO from 3 January until 14 March, from 21 March

C until 26 December, from 24 March

Table 39R

Mondays to Fridays

9 December to 16 May

Newcastle, Middlesbrough, Scarborough, York, Hull, Leeds and Wakefield - Huddersfield - Manchester, Manchester Airport and Liverpool

Network Diagram - refer to first Page of Table 39

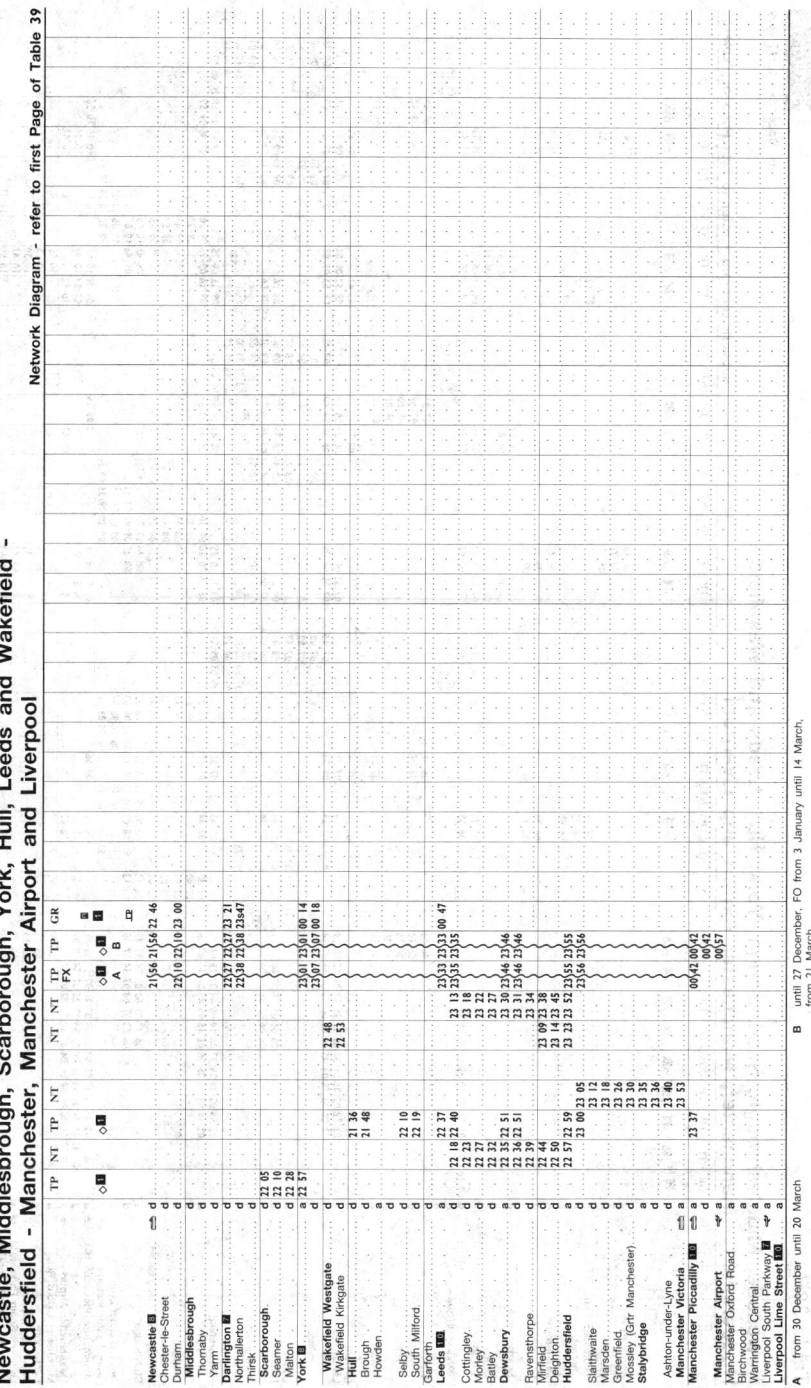

		TP	NT	TP	NT	NT	NT	TP FX	TP	GR
		◇1		◇1				◇1 A	◇1 B	B 1 ☕
Newcastle 8 🚢	d							21 56	21 56	22 46
Chester-le-Street	d									
Durham	d							22 10	22 10	23 00
Middlesbrough	d									
Thornaby	d									
Yarm	d									
Darlington 7	d							22 27	22 27	23 21
Northallerton	d							22 38	22 38	23s47
Thirsk	d									
Scarborough	d	22 05								
Seamer	d	22 10								
Malton	d	22 28								
York 8	a	22 57						23 01	23 01	00 14
	d							23 07	23 07	00 18
Wakefield Westgate	d					22 48				
Wakefield Kirkgate	d					22 53				
Hull	d			21 36						
Brough	d			21 48						
Howden	a									
	d									
Selby	d			22 10						
South Milford	d			22 19						
Garforth	d									
Leeds 10	a			22 37				23 33	23 33	00 47
	d		22 18	22 40			23 13	23 35	23 35	
Cottingley	d		22 23				23 18			
Morley	d		22 27				23 22			
Batley	d		22 32				23 27			
Dewsbury	a		22 35	22 51			23 30	23 46	23 46	
	d		22 36	22 51			23 31	23 46	23 46	
Ravensthorpe	d		22 39				23 34			
Mirfield	d		22 44			23 09	23 38			
Deighton	d		22 50			23 14	23 45			
Huddersfield	a		22 57	22 59		23 23	23 52	23 55	23 55	
	d			23 00	23 05			23 56	23 56	
Slaithwaite	d				23 12					
Marsden	d				23 18					
Greenfield	d				23 26					
Mossley (Grtr Manchester)	d				23 30					
Stalybridge	a				23 35					
	d				23 36					
Ashton-under-Lyne	d				23 40					
Manchester Victoria 🚢	a				23 53					
Manchester Piccadilly 10 🚢	a			23 37				00 42	00 42	
	d								00 42	
Manchester Airport ✈	a								00 57	
Manchester Oxford Road	a									
Birchwood	a									
Warrington Central	a									
Liverpool South Parkway 7 ✈	a									
Liverpool Lime Street 10	a									

A from 30 December until 20 March

B until 27 December, FO from 3 January until 14 March, from 21 March

Table 39R

Saturdays

14 December to 17 May

Newcastle, Middlesbrough, Scarborough, York, Hull, Leeds and Wakefield - Huddersfield - Manchester, Manchester Airport and Liverpool

Network Diagram - refer to first Page of Table 39

		GR	TP	TP	TP	TP	TP	TP	TP	TP	NT	NT	TP	NT	TP	NT	NT	NT	NT
		1	◇1	◇1	◇1	◇1	◇1	◇1	◇1	◇1			◇1		◇1				
Newcastle 8	d																		
Chester-le-Street	d																		
Durham	d																		
Middlesbrough	d												05 55						
Thornaby	d												06 00						
Yarm	d												06 08						
Darlington 7	d																		
Northallerton	d												06 23						
Thirsk	d												06 31						
Scarborough	d																		
Seamer	d																		
Malton	d																		
York 8	a												06 48						
	d	00 18		01 52	02 40	03 52	05 26	05 57	06 28				06 55						
Wakefield Westgate	d																	07 29	
Wakefield Kirkgate	d																	07 35	
Hull	d									06 00					06 37				
Brough	d									06 12					06 49				
Howden	a									06 26									
	d									06 26									
Selby	d									06 36					07 08				
South Milford	d																		
Garforth	d							06 12					07 10		07 24				
Leeds 10	a	00 47		02 18	03 06	04 34	05 52	06 22	06 52	06 59			07 20		07 35				
	d			02 20	03 10	04 45	05 55	06 25	06 55	07 08		07 13	07 23		07 38				07 43
Cottingley	d																		07 48
Morley	d											07 21							07 52
Batley	d											07 26							07 57
Dewsbury	a						06 06	06 36	07 06			07 29	07 34						08 00
	d						06 06	06 36	07 06			07 29	07 34						08 01
Ravensthorpe	d																		08 04
Mirfield	d											07 35						07 50	08 08
Deighton	d																	07 56	08 13
Huddersfield	a			02 56	03 49	05 27	06 14	06 44	07 15	07 25			07 43		07 56			08 03	08 21
	d			02 56	03 59	05 28	06 15	06 45	07 16	07 26	07 33		07 44		07 57		08 02		
Slaithwaite	d										07 40						08 09		
Marsden	d										07 55						08 15		
Greenfield	d										08 03						08 23		
Mossley (Grtr Manchester)	d										08 08			←			08 27		
Stalybridge	a						06 33	07 03	07 34	07 43	08 12		08 01	08 12	08 17		08 32		
	d						06 33	07 04	07 34	07 46	08 13		08 02	08 13	08 17	08 22	08 33		
Ashton-under-Lyne	d										→			08 17		08 26	08 37		
Manchester Victoria	a											08 53		08 31		08 35	08 52		
Manchester Piccadilly 10	a			03 44	04 51	06 00	06 50	07 20	07 51	08 05			08 19		08 36				
	d		00 42	03 44	04 53	06 08	06 54	07 23	07 54	08 07			08 24						
Manchester Airport ✈	a		00 57	04 00	05 08	06 24	07 12	07 42	08 12				08 42						
Manchester Oxford Road	a									08 09									
Birchwood	a									08 25									
Warrington Central	a									08 30									
Liverpool South Parkway 7 ✈	a									08 47									
Liverpool Lime Street 10	a									08 58						09 43			

		TP	TP	NT	NT	NT	TP	TP	NT	NT	TP	TP	NT	NT	NT	TP	TP	NT	NT
		◇1	◇1				◇1	◇1			◇1	◇1				◇1	◇1		
Newcastle 8	d		06 10													07 43			
Chester-le-Street	d		06 21																
Durham	d		06 27													07 57			
Middlesbrough	d										07 12								
Thornaby	d										07 17								
Yarm	d										07 27								
Darlington 7	d		06 45													08 14			
Northallerton	d		06 57								07 43					08 26			
Thirsk	d		07 05								07 51					08 34			
Scarborough	d	06 30					06 58					07 48							
Seamer	d	06 35					07 03					07 53							
Malton	d	06 53					07 21					08 11							
York 8	a	07 23	07 28				07 47				08 11	08 38				08 52			
	d	07 26	07 40				07 53				08 26	08 40				08 57			
Wakefield Westgate	d								08 29									09 29	
Wakefield Kirkgate	d								08 35									09 35	
Hull	d							07 37									08 40		
Brough	d							07 49									08 52		
Howden	a							08 00											
	d							08 01											
Selby	d							08 11									09 11		
South Milford	d																		
Garforth	d						08 12				08 41					09 12			
Leeds 10	a	07 52	08 04				08 22	08 36			08 52	09 04				09 22	09 36		
	d	07 55	08 08			08 13	08 25	08 40		08 43	08 55	09 08			09 13	09 25	09 40		09 43
Cottingley	d					08 18				08 48					09 18				09 48
Morley	d					08 22				08 52					09 22				09 52
Batley	d					08 27				08 57					09 27				09 57
Dewsbury	a	08 06				08 30	08 36			09 00	09 06				09 30	09 36			10 00
	d	08 06				08 31	08 36			09 01	09 06				09 31	09 36			10 01
Ravensthorpe	d					08 34				09 04									10 04
Mirfield	d					08 38			08 51	09 08					09 37			09 51	10 08
Deighton	d								08 58	09 17								09 58	10 14
Huddersfield	a	08 15	08 25				08 44	08 58	09 05	09 21	09 15	09 25				09 45	09 58	10 05	10 21
	d	08 16	08 26	08 30			08 45	08 59			09 16	09 26	09 30			09 46	09 59		
Slaithwaite	d			08 37									09 37						
Marsden	d			08 43									09 43						
Greenfield	d			08 51									09 51						
Mossley (Grtr Manchester)	d			08 55									09 55						
Stalybridge	a		08 44	09 00								09 43	10 00						
	d		08 46	09 01	09 22							09 46	10 01	10 22					
Ashton-under-Lyne	d			09 05	09 26								10 05	10 26					
Manchester Victoria	a			09 20	09 35	09 53							10 20	10 35	10 53				
Manchester Piccadilly 10	a	08 51	09 05				09 19	09 36			09 49	10 05				10 19	10 36		
	d	08 54	09 07				09 24				09 54	10 07				10 24			
Manchester Airport ✈	a	09 12					09 42				10 12					10 42			
Manchester Oxford Road	a		09 09									10 09							
Birchwood	a		09 25									10 25							
Warrington Central	a		09 30									10 30							
Liverpool South Parkway 7 ✈	a		09 47									10 47							
Liverpool Lime Street 10	a		09 58		10 43							10 58		11 43					

Table 39R

Saturdays

14 December to 17 May

Newcastle, Middlesbrough, Scarborough, York, Hull, Leeds and Wakefield - Huddersfield - Manchester, Manchester Airport and Liverpool

Network Diagram - refer to first Page of Table 39

Station		TP ◇1	TP ◇1	NT	NT	NT	TP ◇1	TP ◇1	NT	NT
Newcastle 8	d									
Chester-le-Street	d									
Durham	d									
Middlesbrough	d						08 50			
Thornaby	d						08 55			
Yarm	d						09 03			
Darlington 7	d									
Northallerton	d						09 18			
Thirsk	d						09 28			
Scarborough	d		08 48							
Seamer	d		08 53							
Malton	d		09 11							
York 8	a		09 38				09 47			
	d	09 26	09 40				09 57			
Wakefield Westgate	d								10 29	
Wakefield Kirkgate	d								10 35	
Hull	d							09 40		
Brough	d							09 52		
Howden	a									
	d									
Selby	d							10 11		
South Milford	d									
Garforth	d						10 12			
Leeds 10	a	09 52	10 04				10 22	10 36		
	d	09 55	10 08			10 13	10 25	10 40		10 43
Cottingley	d									10 48
Morley	d					10 21				10 52
Batley	d					10 26				10 57
Dewsbury	a	10 06				10 29	10 36			11 00
	d	10 06				10 29	10 36			11 01
Ravensthorpe	d									11 04
Mirfield	d					10 35			10 51	11 08
Deighton	d								10 58	11 14
Huddersfield	a	10 15	10 25				10 45	10 58	11 05	11 21
	d	10 16	10 26	10 30			10 46	10 59		
Slaithwaite	d			10 37						
Marsden	d			10 43						
Greenfield	d			10 51						
Mossley (Grtr Manchester)	d			10 55						
Stalybridge	a		10 43	11 00						
	d		10 46	11 01	11 22					
Ashton-under-Lyne	d			11 05	11 26					
Manchester Victoria	a			11 18	11 35	11 53				
Manchester Piccadilly 10	a	10 49	11 05				11 19	11 36		
	d	10 54	11 07				11 24			
Manchester Airport	a	11 12					11 42			
Manchester Oxford Road	a		11 09							
Birchwood	a		11 25							
Warrington Central	a		11 30							
Liverpool South Parkway 7	a		11 47							
Liverpool Lime Street 10	a		11 58		12 43					

Station		TP ◇1	TP ◇1	NT	NT	NT	TP ◇1	TP ◇1	NT	NT
Newcastle 8	d	09 15								
Chester-le-Street	d	09 24								
Durham	d	09 31								
Middlesbrough	d						09 50			
Thornaby	d						09 55			
Yarm	d						10 03			
Darlington 7	d	09 48								
Northallerton	d	09 59					10 18			
Thirsk	d						10 28			
Scarborough	d		09 48							
Seamer	d		09 53							
Malton	d		10 11							
York 8	a	10 21	10 38				10 47			
	d	10 26	10 40				10 57			
Wakefield Westgate	d								11 29	
Wakefield Kirkgate	d								11 35	
Hull	d							10 40		
Brough	d							10 52		
Howden	a									
	d									
Selby	d							11 11		
South Milford	d									
Garforth	d						11 12			
Leeds 10	a	10 52	11 04				11 22	11 36		
	d	10 55	11 08			11 13	11 25	11 40		11 43
Cottingley	d									11 48
Morley	d					11 21				11 52
Batley	d					11 26				11 57
Dewsbury	a	11 06				11 29	11 36			12 00
	d	11 06				11 29	11 36			12 01
Ravensthorpe	d									12 04
Mirfield	d					11 35			11 49	12 08
Deighton	d								11 58	12 14
Huddersfield	a	11 15	11 25				11 45	11 58	12 05	12 21
	d	11 16	11 26	11 30			11 46	11 59		
Slaithwaite	d			11 37						
Marsden	d			11 43						
Greenfield	d			11 51						
Mossley (Grtr Manchester)	d			11 55						
Stalybridge	a		11 43	12 00						
	d		11 46	12 01	12 22					
Ashton-under-Lyne	d			12 05	12 26					
Manchester Victoria	a			12 20	12 36	12 53				
Manchester Piccadilly 10	a	11 49	12 05				12 19	12 36		
	d	11 54	12 07				12 24			
Manchester Airport	a	12 12					12 42			
Manchester Oxford Road	a		12 09							
Birchwood	a		12 25							
Warrington Central	a		12 30							
Liverpool South Parkway 7	a		12 47							
Liverpool Lime Street 10	a		12 58		13 43					

Station		TP ◇1	TP ◇1	NT	NT	NT	TP ◇1	TP ◇1	NT	NT
Newcastle 8	d	10 15								
Chester-le-Street	d	10 24								
Durham	d	10 31								
Middlesbrough	d						10 50			
Thornaby	d						10 55			
Yarm	d						11 03			
Darlington 7	d	10 48								
Northallerton	d	10 59					11 18			
Thirsk	d						11 28			
Scarborough	d		10 48							
Seamer	d		10 53							
Malton	d		11 11							
York 8	a	11 23	11 38				11 47			
	d	11 26	11 40				11 57			
Wakefield Westgate	d								12 29	
Wakefield Kirkgate	d								12 35	
Hull	d							11 40		
Brough	d							11 52		
Howden	a									
	d									
Selby	d							12 11		
South Milford	d									
Garforth	d						12 12			
Leeds 10	a	11 52	12 04				12 22	12 36		
	d	11 55	12 08			12 13	12 25	12 40		12 43
Cottingley	d									12 48
Morley	d					12 21				12 52
Batley	d					12 26				12 57
Dewsbury	a	12 06				12 29	12 36			13 00
	d	12 06				12 29	12 36			13 01
Ravensthorpe	d									13 04
Mirfield	d					12 35			12 49	13 08
Deighton	d								12 58	13 14
Huddersfield	a	12 15	12 25				12 45	12 58	13 05	13 21
	d	12 16	12 26	12 30			12 46	12 59		
Slaithwaite	d			12 37						
Marsden	d			12 43						
Greenfield	d			12 51						
Mossley (Grtr Manchester)	d			12 55						
Stalybridge	a		12 43	13 00						
	d		12 46	13 01	13 22					
Ashton-under-Lyne	d			13 05	13 26					
Manchester Victoria	a			13 19	13 35	13 53				
Manchester Piccadilly 10	a	12 49	13 05				13 19	13 36		
	d	12 54	13 07				13 24			
Manchester Airport	a	13 12					13 42			
Manchester Oxford Road	a		13 09							
Birchwood	a		13 25							
Warrington Central	a		13 30							
Liverpool South Parkway 7	a		13 47							
Liverpool Lime Street 10	a		13 58		14 43					

Station		TP ◇1	TP ◇1	NT	NT	NT	TP ◇1	TP ◇1	NT	NT
Newcastle 8	d	11 15								
Chester-le-Street	d	11 24								
Durham	d	11 31								
Middlesbrough	d						11 50			
Thornaby	d						11 55			
Yarm	d						12 03			
Darlington 7	d	11 48								
Northallerton	d	11 59					12 18			
Thirsk	d						12 28			
Scarborough	d		11 48							
Seamer	d		11 53							
Malton	d		12 11							
York 8	a	12 21	12 38				12 47			
	d	12 26	12 40				12 57			
Wakefield Westgate	d								13 39	
Wakefield Kirkgate	d								13 45	
Hull	d							12 40		
Brough	d							12 52		
Howden	a									
	d									
Selby	d							13 11		
South Milford	d									
Garforth	d						13 12			
Leeds 10	a	12 52	13 04				13 22	13 36		
	d	12 55	13 08			13 13	13 25	13 40		13 43
Cottingley	d									13 48
Morley	d					13 21				13 52
Batley	d					13 26				13 57
Dewsbury	a	13 06				13 29	13 36			14 00
	d	13 06				13 29	13 36			14 01
Ravensthorpe	d									14 04
Mirfield	d					13 35			13 58	14 08
Deighton	d								14 05	14 14
Huddersfield	a	13 15	13 25				13 45	13 58	14 12	14 21
	d	13 16	13 26	13 30			13 46	13 59		
Slaithwaite	d			13 37						
Marsden	d			13 43						
Greenfield	d			13 51						
Mossley (Grtr Manchester)	d			13 55						
Stalybridge	a		13 43	14 00						
	d		13 46	14 01	14 22					
Ashton-under-Lyne	d			14 05	14 26					
Manchester Victoria	a			14 20	14 35	14 53				
Manchester Piccadilly 10	a	13 49	14 05				14 19	14 36		
	d	13 54	14 07				14 24			
Manchester Airport	a	14 12					14 42			
Manchester Oxford Road	a		14 09							
Birchwood	a		14 25							
Warrington Central	a		14 30							
Liverpool South Parkway 7	a		14 47							
Liverpool Lime Street 10	a		14 58		15 43					

Table 39R

Saturdays

14 December to 17 May

Newcastle, Middlesbrough, Scarborough, York, Hull, Leeds and Wakefield - Huddersfield - Manchester, Manchester Airport and Liverpool

Network Diagram - refer to first Page of Table 39

		TP	TP	NT	NT	NT	TP	TP	NT	NT	TP	TP	TP	NT	NT	NT	TP	TP	NT	NT	TP	TP	NT	NT	TP	TP	NT	NT	NT	NT	TP	TP	NT	NT	TP	TP	NT
		◇1	◇1				◇1	◇1			◇1 A	◇1 B	◇1				◇1	◇1			◇1	◇1			◇1	◇1					◇1	◇1			◇1	◇1	
Newcastle 8	d	12 18									13 15	13 18									14 18										15 15						
Chester-le-Street	d										13 24																				15 24						
Durham	d	12 31									13 31	13 31									14 31										15 31						
Middlesbrough	d						12 50										13 50								14 50										15 50		
Thornaby	d						12 55										13 55								14 55										15 55		
Yarm	d						13 03										14 03								15 03										16 03		
Darlington 7	d	12 48									13 48	13 48									14 48										15 48						
Northallerton	d	12 59					13 18				13 58	13 58					14 18				14 59				15 18						15 59				16 18		
Thirsk	d						13 28										14 28								15 28										16 28		
Scarborough	d		12 48										13 48									14 48										15 48					
Seamer	d		12 53										13 53									14 53										15 53					
Malton	d		13 11										14 11									15 11										16 11					
York 8	a	13 22	13 38				13 47				14 22	14 22	14 38				14 47				15 22	15 38			15 47						16 21	16 38			16 47		
	d	13 26	13 40				13 57				14 26	14 26	14 40				14 57				15 26	15 40			15 57						16 26	16 40			16 57		
Wakefield Westgate	d								14 39										15 29										16 29								
Wakefield Kirkgate	d								14 45										15 35										16 35								
Hull	d							13 40										14 40								15 40										16 40	
Brough	d							13 52										14 52								15 52										16 52	
Howden	a																																				
	d																																				
Selby	d							14 11										15 11								16 11										17 11	
South Milford	d																																				
Garforth	d						14 12										15 12								16 12										17 12		
Leeds 10	a	13 52	14 04				14 22	14 36			14 52	14 52	15 04				15 22	15 36			15 52	16 04			16 22	16 36					16 52	17 04			17 22	17 36	
	d	13 55	14 08			14 13	14 25	14 37		14 43	14 55	14 55	15 08			15 13	15 25	15 40		15 43	15 55	16 08		16 13	16 25	16 40				16 43	16 55	17 08		17 13	17 26	17 40	
Cottingley	d									14 48										15 48				16 18						16 48				17 18			
Morley	d					14 21				14 52						15 21				15 52				16 22						16 52				17 22			
Batley	d					14 26				14 57						15 26				15 57				16 27						16 57				17 27			
Dewsbury	a	14 06				14 29	14 36			15 00	15 06	15 06				15 29	15 36			16 00	16 06			16 30	16 36					17 00	17 06			17 30	17 37		
	d	14 06				14 29	14 36			15 01	15 06	15 06				15 29	15 36			16 01	16 06			16 31	16 36					17 01	17 06			17 31	17 37		
Ravensthorpe	d									15 04										16 04				16 34						17 04				17 34			
Mirfield	d					14 35			14 58	15 08						15 35			15 51	16 08				16 38					16 51	17 08				17 38			
Deighton	d								15 05	15 14									15 58	16 17									16 58	17 14							
Huddersfield	a	14 15	14 25				14 45	14 55	15 12	15 21	15 15	15 15	15 25				15 45	15 58	16 05	16 21	16 15	16 25			16 45	16 58			17 05	17 21	17 15	17 25			17 46	17 58	
	d	14 16	14 26	14 30			14 46	14 56			15 16	15 16	15 26	15 30			15 46	15 59			16 16	16 26	16 30		16 46	16 59		17 04			17 16	17 26	17 30		17 46	17 59	
Slaithwaite	d			14 37										15 37									16 37					17 11					17 37				
Marsden	d			14 43										15 43									16 43					17a17					17 43				
Greenfield	d			14 51										15 51									16 51										17 51				
Mossley (Grtr Manchester)	d			14 55										15 55									16 55										17 55				
Stalybridge	a		14 43	15 00									15 43	16 00								16 43	17 00			17 18						17 43	18 00			18 18	
	d		14 46	15 01	15 22								15 46	16 01	16 22							16 46	17 01			17 18	17 22					17 46	18 01			18 18	18 22
Ashton-under-Lyne	d			15 05	15 26									16 05	16 26								17 05				17 26						18 05				18 26
Manchester Victoria	a			15 20	15 35	15 53								16 20	16 35	16 53							17 20	17 54			17 35						18 19	18 54			18 35
Manchester Piccadilly 10	a	14 49	15 05				15 19	15 36			15 49	15 49	16 05				16 19	16 36			16 49	17 05			17 21	17 36					17 49	18 05			18 19	18 37	
	d	14 54	15 07				15 24				15 54	15 54	16 07				16 24				16 54	17 07									17 54	18 07			18 24		
Manchester Airport	a	15 12					15 42				16 12	16 12					16 42				17 12										18 12				18 42		
Manchester Oxford Road	a		15 09										16 09									17 09										18 09					
Birchwood	a		15 25										16 25									17 25										18 25					
Warrington Central	a		15 30										16 30									17 30										18 30					
Liverpool South Parkway 7	a		15 47										16 47									17 47										18 47					
Liverpool Lime Street 10	a		15 58		16 43								16 58		17 43							18 01					18 43					19 01					19 43

A from 15 February

B from 4 January until 8 February

Table 39R

Saturdays

14 December to 17 May

Newcastle, Middlesbrough, Scarborough, York, Hull, Leeds and Wakefield - Huddersfield - Manchester, Manchester Airport and Liverpool

Network Diagram - refer to first Page of Table 39

Station		NT	NT	TP ◇1 A	TP ◇1 B	TP ◇1	TP ◇1	NT	NT	TP ◇1	TP ◇1	NT	NT	TP ◇1	TP ◇1	NT	NT	TP ◇1	TP ◇1
Newcastle 8	d			16 15	16 21						17 02								
Chester-le-Street	d			16 24							17 11								
Durham	d			16 31							17 18								
Middlesbrough	d									16 50								17 50	
Thornaby	d									16 55								17 55	
Yarm	d									17 03								18 03	
Darlington 7	d			16 48	16 48						17 35								
Northallerton	d			16 59	16 59					17 18	17 46							18 18	
Thirsk	d									17 28								18 28	
Scarborough	d						16 48								17 48				
Seamer	d						16 53								17 53				
Malton	d						17 11								18 11				
York 8	a			17 23	17 23		17 38			17 47	18 09				18 38			18 47	
	d			17 26	17 26		17 40			17 57	18 12				18 40			19 08	
Wakefield Westgate	d	17 29										18 29							
Wakefield Kirkgate	d	17 34										18 37							
Hull	d					17 02								17 58					19 00
Brough	d					17 14								18 10					19 12
Howden	a																		
	d																		
Selby	d					17 33								18 29					19 31
South Milford	d																		
Garforth	d									18 12								19 22	
Leeds 10	a			17 52	17 52	17 58	18 05			18 22	18 37			18 52	19 04			19 35	19 56
	d		17 43	17 55	17 55		18 08		18 13	18 25	18 40		18 43	18 55	19 08		19 13	19 40	
Cottingley	d		17 48						18 18				18 48				19 18		
Morley	d		17 52						18 22				18 52				19 22		
Batley	d		17 57						18 27				18 57				19 27		
Dewsbury	a		18 00	18 06	18 06				18 30	18 36			19 00	19 06			19 30	19 51	
	d		18 01	18 06	18 06				18 31	18 36			19 01	19 06			19 31	19 51	
Ravensthorpe	d		18 04						18 34				19 04				19 34		
Mirfield	d	17 50	18 08						18 38			18 51	19 08				19 38		
Deighton	d	17 57	18 16									19 00	19 16				19 45		
Huddersfield	a	18 04	18 21	18 15	18 15		18 25			18 45	18 58	19 06	19 21	19 15	19 25		19 52	19 59	
	d			18 16	18 16		18 26	18 30		18 46	18 59			19 16	19 26	19 29		20 00	
Slaithwaite	d							18 37								19 36			
Marsden	d							18 43								19 42			
Greenfield	d							18 51								19 50			
Mossley (Grtr Manchester)	d							18 55								19 54			
Stalybridge	a						18 43	19 00							19 43	19 59			
	d						18 46	19 00							19 46	20 00			
Ashton-under-Lyne	d							19 04								20 04			
Manchester Victoria	a							19 19	19 54							20 19			
Manchester Piccadilly 10	a			18 49	18 49		19 05			19 21	19 33			19 57	20 05			20 33	
	d			18 54	18 54		19 07				19 40				20 07			20 40	
Manchester Airport	a			19 13	19 13						19 59							20 57	
Manchester Oxford Road	a						19 09								20 09				
Birchwood	a						19 25								20 25				
Warrington Central	a						19 30								20 30				
Liverpool South Parkway 7	a						19 47								20 47				
Liverpool Lime Street 10	a						20 00								21 00				

Station		NT	TP ◇1	NT	TP ◇1	NT	TP ◇1	TP ◇1	NT	TP ◇1	NT	NT	TP ◇1	NT	TP ◇1	NT	TP ◇1	NT	TP ◇1
Newcastle 8	d						18 52												
Chester-le-Street	d						19 01												
Durham	d						19 08												
Middlesbrough	d				18 50								20 10		20 50				
Thornaby	d				18 55								20 15		20 55				
Yarm	d				19 03								20 23		21 03				
Darlington 7	d						19 25												
Northallerton	d				19 19		19 36						20 39		21 18				
Thirsk	d				19 29								20 47						
Scarborough	d		18 48							19 48							22 05		
Seamer	d		18 53							19 53							22 10		
Malton	d		19 11							20 11							22 28		
York 8	a		19 38		19 49		20 07			20 38			21 05		21 43		22 56		
	d		19 40				20 10			20 40			21 14		21 46				
Wakefield Westgate	d	19 41							20 50					21 41					
Wakefield Kirkgate	d	19 45							20 56					21 50					
Hull	d							19 58											21 36
Brough	d							20 10											21 48
Howden	a																		
	d																		
Selby	d							20 29											22 10
South Milford	d							20 38											22 19
Garforth	d																		
Leeds 10	a		20 04				20 35	20 56		21 04			21 37		22 07				22 37
	d		20 08			20 13	20 40			21 08		21 13	21 40		22 10			22 17	22 40
Cottingley	d					20 18						21 18						22 22	
Morley	d					20 22						21 22						22 26	
Batley	d					20 27						21 27						22 31	
Dewsbury	a					20 30	20 51					21 30	21 51					22 34	22 51
	d					20 31	20 51					21 31	21 51					22 35	22 51
Ravensthorpe	d					20 34						21 34						22 38	
Mirfield	d	19 59				20 38			21 09			21 38		22 03				22 42	
Deighton	d	20 08				20 44			21 16			21 45		22 10				22 49	
Huddersfield	a	20 13	20 25			20 48	20 59		21 20	21 25		21 52	21 59	22 14	22 27			22 56	22 59
	d		20 26	20 30		20 48	21 00			21 26	21 30		22 00		22 28	22 34			23 00
Slaithwaite	d			20 37		20 55					21 37					22 41			
Marsden	d			20 43		21a02					21 42					22 47			
Greenfield	d			20 51							21 50					22 55			
Mossley (Grtr Manchester)	d			20 55							21 54					22 59			
Stalybridge	a		20 43	21 00						21 43	22 00				22 45	23 04			
	d		20 46	21 01						21 46	22 00				22 46	23 05			
Ashton-under-Lyne	d			21 05							22 05					23 09			
Manchester Victoria	a			21 20							22 19					23 24			
Manchester Piccadilly 10	a		21 05				21 33			22 05			22 33		23 05				23 37
	d		21 07				21 40			22 07			22 40						
Manchester Airport	a						21 57						22 57						
Manchester Oxford Road	a		21 09							22 09									
Birchwood	a		21 25							22 25									
Warrington Central	a		21 30							22 30									
Liverpool South Parkway 7	a		21 47							22 47									
Liverpool Lime Street 10	a		22 00							23 00									

A from 15 February

B from 4 January until 8 February

Table 39R

Saturdays

14 December to 17 May

Newcastle, Middlesbrough, Scarborough, York, Hull, Leeds and Wakefield - Huddersfield - Manchester, Manchester Airport and Liverpool

Network Diagram - refer to first Page of Table 39

		NT	NT	NT	TP	TP
					◇1	◇1
					A	B
Newcastle 8	d					
Chester-le-Street	d					
Durham	d					
Middlesbrough	d				21 50	21 50
Thornaby	d				21 55	21 55
Yarm	d					
Darlington 7	d				22 20	22 20
Northallerton	d				22 31	22 31
Thirsk	d				22 39	22 39
Scarborough	d					
Seamer	d					
Malton	d					
York 8	a				22 57	22 57
	d				23 07	23 07
Wakefield Westgate	d		22 42			
Wakefield Kirkgate	d		22 47			
Hull	d					
Brough	d					
Howden	a					
	d					
Selby	d					
South Milford	d					
Garforth	d					
Leeds 10	a				23 33	23 33
	d			23 05	23 35	23 35
Cottingley	d			23 10		
Morley	d			23 14		
Batley	d			23 19		
Dewsbury	a			23 22	23 46	23 46
	d			23 23	23 46	23 46
Ravensthorpe	d			23 26		
Mirfield	d		23 00	23 30		
Deighton	d		23 08	23 37		
Huddersfield	a		23 15	23 44	23 55	23 55
	d	23 05			23 56	23 56
Slaithwaite	d	23 12				
Marsden	d	23 18				
Greenfield	d	23 26				
Mossley (Grtr Manchester)	d	23 30				
Stalybridge	a	23 35				
	d	23 36				
Ashton-under-Lyne	d	23 40				
Manchester Victoria	a	23 53				
Manchester Piccadilly 10	a				00 27	00 27
	d					00 31
Manchester Airport	a					00 46
Manchester Oxford Road	a					
Birchwood	a					
Warrington Central	a					
Liverpool South Parkway 7	a					
Liverpool Lime Street 10	a					

A from 15 February until 22 March

B until 8 February, from 29 March

Table 39

Sundays

8 December to 29 December

Newcastle, Middlesbrough, Scarborough, York, Hull and Leeds - Huddersfield - Manchester, Manchester Airport and Liverpool

Network Diagram - refer to first Page of Table 39

		TP	TP	TP	TP	TP	TP	TP	TP	NT	TP	NT	TP	TP	TP	NT	TP	NT	TP
		◇1	◇1	◇1	◇1	◇1	◇1	◇1	◇1		◇1		◇1	◇1	◇1		◇1		◇1
		A																	
Newcastle 8	d												08 04						09 33
Chester-le-Street	d																		09 43
Durham	d												08 16						09 49
Middlesbrough	d																		
Thornaby	d																		
Yarm	d																		
Darlington 7	d												08 33						10 06
Northallerton	d												08 45						10 18
Thirsk	d												08 53						
Scarborough	d																09 20		
Seamer	d																09 25		
Malton	d																09 43		
York 8	a												09 12				10 09		10 41
	d		02 29	03 44	04 57	05 57	06 54		08 10		08 45		09 15				10 15		10 45
Hull	d													09 00					
Brough	d													09 12					
Howden	d																		
Selby	d													09 33					
South Milford	d													09 42					
Garforth	d																		
Leeds 10	a		03 10	04 25	05 38	06 38	07 34		08 36		09 08		09 38	10 02			10 38		11 08
	d		03 10	04 25	05 40	06 40	07 40		08 40	08 47	09 15		09 40	10 08			10 40	10 44	11 10
Cottingley	d									08 52								10 49	
Morley	d									08 56								10 53	
Batley	d									09 01								10 58	
Dewsbury	a				05 51	06 51	07 51		08 51	09 04			09 51				10 51	11 01	
	d				05 51	06 51	07 51		08 51	09 05			09 51				10 51	11 02	
Ravensthorpe	d									09 08								11 05	
Mirfield	d									09 12								11 09	
Deighton	d									09 19								11 15	
Huddersfield	a		03 29	04 44	06 00	07 00	08 00		09 00	09 23	09 32		10 00	10 25			11 00	11 21	11 27
	d		03 30	04 45	06 01	07 01	08 01		09 01		09 33	09 37	10 01	10 26		10 37	11 01		11 28
Slaithwaite	d											09 44				10 44			
Marsden	d											09 50				10 50			
Greenfield	d											09 58				10 58			
Mossley (Grtr Manchester)	d											10 02				11 02			
Stalybridge	a					07 18	08 18		09 18		09 52	10 07		10 45		11 07			11 45
	d					07 19	08 19		09 19		09 53	10 08		10 46		11 08			11 46
Ashton-under-Lyne	d											10 12				11 12			
Manchester Victoria	a											10 27				11 27			
	d																		
Manchester Piccadilly 10	a		04 02	05 17	06 34	07 34	08 34		09 34		10 09		10 34	11 01			11 34		12 05
	d	00 31	04 06	05 21	06 38	07 38	08 38	09 12	09 38		10 10		10 38		11 10		11 38		12 07
Manchester Airport	a	00 46	04 23	05 38	06 55	07 55	08 53		09 55				10 54				11 54		
Manchester Oxford Road	a							09 14			10 12				11 12				12 09
Newton-le-Willows	a																		
Birchwood	a							09 28			10 27				11 26				12 25
Warrington Central	a							09 33			10 32				11 31				12 30
Liverpool South Parkway 7	a							09 46			10 48				11 45				12 47
Liverpool Lime Street 10	a							10 00			10 59				11 58				12 58

		NT	TP	TP	TP	NT	TP	NT	TP	TP	NT	TP	TP	TP	NT	TP	NT	TP	TP
			◇1	◇1	◇1		◇1		◇1	◇1		◇1	◇1	◇1		◇1		◇1	◇1
Newcastle 8	d						11 08					12 10				13 07			
Chester-le-Street	d															13 16			
Durham	d						11 20					12 22				13 23			
Middlesbrough	d		10 15											12 45					
Thornaby	d		10 20											12 50					
Yarm	d		10 28											12 59					
Darlington 7	d						11 37					12 39				13 40			
Northallerton	d		10 43				11 49							13 14					
Thirsk	d		10 51											13 23					
Scarborough	d				10 52					11 52									13 52
Seamer	d				10 57					11 57									13 57
Malton	d				11 15					12 15									14 15
York 8	a		11 09		11 41		12 11			12 41		13 11		13 42		14 12			14 40
	d		11 15		11 45		12 15			12 45		13 15		13 45		14 15		14 33	14 45
Hull	d			10 58					12 00				12 58						
Brough	d			11 10					12 12				13 10						
Howden	d																		
Selby	d			11 29					12 31				13 29						
South Milford	d			11 38									13 38						
Garforth	d																		
Leeds 10	a		11 38	11 56	12 09		12 38		12 56	13 08		13 38	13 56	14 08		14 38		14 56	15 08
	d		11 40	11 59	12 10		12 40	12 44	12 59	13 10		13 40	13 59	14 10		14 40	14 44	14 59	15 10
Cottingley	d							12 49									14 49		
Morley	d							12 53									14 53		
Batley	d							12 58									14 58		
Dewsbury	a		11 51				12 51	13 01				13 51				14 51	15 01		
	d		11 51				12 51	13 02				13 51				14 51	15 02		
Ravensthorpe	d							13 05									15 05		
Mirfield	d							13 09									15 09		
Deighton	d							13 20									15 20		
Huddersfield	a		12 00	12 16	12 27		13 00	13 24	13 16	13 27		14 00	14 16	14 27		15 00	15 24	15 16	15 27
	d	11 37	12 01	12 17	12 28	12 37	13 01		13 17	13 28	13 37	14 01	14 17	14 28	14 37	15 01		15 17	15 28
Slaithwaite	d	11 44				12 44					13 44				14 44				
Marsden	d	11 50				12 50					13 50				14 50				
Greenfield	d	11 58				12 58					13 58				14 58				
Mossley (Grtr Manchester)	d	12 02				13 02					14 02				15 02				
Stalybridge	a	12 07			12 45	13 07				13 45	14 07			14 45	15 07				15 45
	d	12 08			12 46	13 08				13 45	14 08			14 46	15 08				15 46
Ashton-under-Lyne	d	12 12				13 12					14 12				15 12				
Manchester Victoria	a	12 27				13 27					14 27				15 27				
	d																		
Manchester Piccadilly 10	a		12 34	12 54	13 05		13 34		13 54	14 05		14 34	14 54	15 05		15 34		15 54	16 05
	d		12 38		13 07		13 38			14 06		14 38		15 07		15 38			16 07
Manchester Airport	a		12 52				13 52					14 52				15 52			
Manchester Oxford Road	a				13 09					14 08				15 09					16 09
Newton-le-Willows	a																		
Birchwood	a				13 25					14 24				15 25					16 25
Warrington Central	a				13 30					14 29				15 30					16 30
Liverpool South Parkway 7	a				13 47					14 47				15 47					16 47
Liverpool Lime Street 10	a				13 58					14 57				15 58					16 58

A not 8 December

Table 39

Sundays

8 December to 29 December

Newcastle, Middlesbrough, Scarborough, York, Hull and Leeds - Huddersfield - Manchester, Manchester Airport and Liverpool

Network Diagram - refer to first Page of Table 39

Station		NT	TP	TP	TP	NT	TP	NT	TP	TP	NT	TP	TP	TP	NT	TP	NT	TP	TP
			◇1	◇1	◇1		◇1		◇1	◇1		◇1	◇1	◇1		◇1		◇1	◇1
Newcastle 8 ⇌	d		14 08				15 07					16 08				17 05			
Chester-le-Street	d						15 16									17 14			
Durham	d		14 20				15 23					16 20				17 21			
Middlesbrough	d				14 43									16 43					
Thornaby	d				14 48									16 48					
Yarm	d				14 56									16 56					
Darlington 7	d		14 37				15 40					16 37				17 38			
Northallerton	d		14 49		15 12							16 49		17 11		17 49			
Thirsk	d				15 20									17 20					
Scarborough	d									15 52									17 52
Seamer	d									15 57									17 57
Malton	d									16 15									18 15
York 8	a		15 12		15 43		16 12			16 41		17 12		17 42		18 12			18 41
	d		15 15		15 45		16 15		16 33	16 45		17 15		17 45		18 15		18 33	18 45
Hull	d			14 58									16 58						
Brough	d			15 10									17 10						
Howden	d																		
Selby	d			15 29									17 29						
South Milford	d			15 38									17 38						
Garforth	d																		
Leeds 10	a		15 38	15 56	16 08		16 38		16 56	17 08		17 38	17 56	18 08		18 38		18 57	19 08
	d		15 40	15 59	16 10		16 40	16 44	16 59	17 11		17 40	17 59	18 10		18 40	18 44	18 59	19 10
Cottingley	d							16 49									18 49		
Morley	d							16 53									18 53		
Batley	d							16 58									18 58		
Dewsbury	a		15 51				16 51	17 01				17 51				18 51	19 01		
	d		15 51				16 51	17 02				17 51				18 51	19 02		
Ravensthorpe	d							17 05									19 05		
Mirfield	d							17 09									19 09		
Deighton	d							17 20									19 20		
Huddersfield	a		16 00	16 16	16 27		17 00	17 24	17 16	17 28		18 00	18 16	18 27		19 00	19 24	19 16	19 27
	d	15 37	16 01	16 17	16 28	16 37	17 01		17 17	17 29	17 37	18 01	18 17	18 28	18 37	19 01		19 17	19 28
Slaithwaite	d	15 44				16 44					17 44				18 44				
Marsden	d	15 50				16 50					17 50				18 50				
Greenfield	d	15 58				16 58					17 58				18 58				
Mossley (Grtr Manchester)	d	16 02				17 02					18 02				19 02				
Stalybridge	a	16 07			16 45	17 07				17 45	18 07			18 45	19 07				19 45
	d	16 08			16 46	17 08				17 47	18 08			18 46	19 08				19 46
Ashton-under-Lyne	d	16 12				17 12					18 12				19 12				
Manchester Victoria ⇌	a	16 27				17 27					18 27				19 27				
	d																		
Manchester Piccadilly 10 ⇌	a		16 34	16 54	17 05		17 34		17 54	18 05		18 34	18 54	19 05		19 34		19 54	20 05
	d		16 38		17 07		17 38			18 07		18 38		19 07		19 38			20 07
Manchester Airport ✈	a		16 52				17 52					18 52				19 52			
Manchester Oxford Road	a				17 09					18 09				19 09					20 09
Newton-le-Willows	a																		
Birchwood	a				17 25					18 25				19 25					20 25
Warrington Central	a				17 30					18 30				19 30					20 30
Liverpool South Parkway 7 ✈	a				17 47					18 47				19 47					20 47
Liverpool Lime Street 10	a				17 58					18 58				19 58					20 58

Station		NT	TP	TP	TP	NT	TP	NT	TP	NT	TP	TP	TP	TP	NT	GR	TP
			◇1	◇1	◇1		◇1		◇1		◇1	◇1	◇1	◇1		1	◇1
Newcastle 8 ⇌	d		17 53				19 10					20 08				21 45	
Chester-le-Street	d																
Durham	d		18 05				19 22					20 20				21 59	
Middlesbrough	d				18 45						20 06						22 08
Thornaby	d				18 50						20 11						22 13
Yarm	d				18 58						20 19						22 21
Darlington 7	d		18 22				19 39					20 37				22 18	
Northallerton	d		18 34		19 14						20 34	20 49				22 32	22 36
Thirsk	d				19 22						20 44						22 44
Scarborough	d								19 52					21 20			
Seamer	d								19 57					21 25			
Malton	d								20 15					21 43			
York 8	a		19 03		19 42		20 11		20 41		21 02	21 12		22 09		23 03	23 09
	d		19 15		19 45		20 15		20 45			21 15		22 12		23 05	23 12
Hull	d			18 58									21 00				
Brough	d			19 10									21 12				
Howden	d																
Selby	d			19 29									21 31				
South Milford	d			19 38									21 40				
Garforth	d																
Leeds 10	a		19 38	19 56	20 08		20 38		21 08			21 38	21 59	22 36		23 35	23 38
	d		19 40	19 59	20 10		20 40	20 44	21 10			21 40		22 40	22 44		23 40
Cottingley	d							20 49							22 49		
Morley	d							20 53							22 53		
Batley	d							20 58							22 58		
Dewsbury	a		19 51				20 50	21 01				21 51			23 01		23 51
	d		19 51				20 51	21 02				21 51			23 02		23 51
Ravensthorpe	d							21 05							23 05		
Mirfield	d							21 09							23 09		
Deighton	d							21 15							23 16		
Huddersfield	a		20 00	20 16	20 27		21 00	21 19	21 27			22 00		22 57	23 20		23 59
	d	19 37	20 01	20 17	20 28	20 37	21 01	21 19	21 28	21 37		22 01		22 58			00 01
Slaithwaite	d	19 44				20 44		21 26		21 44							
Marsden	d	19 50				20 50		21a33		21 50							
Greenfield	d	19 58				20 58				21 58							
Mossley (Grtr Manchester)	d	20 02				21 02				22 02							
Stalybridge	a	20 07			20 45	21 07	21 18			22 07		22 18		23 18			
	d	20 08			20 46	21 08	21 19			22 08		22 19		23 19			
Ashton-under-Lyne	d	20 12				21 12				22 12							
Manchester Victoria ⇌	a	20 27				21 27				22 27							
	d																
Manchester Piccadilly 10 ⇌	a		20 34	20 54	21 05		21 34		22 05			22 36		23 34			00 43
	d		20 38		21 07				22 07			22 38					00 44
Manchester Airport ✈	a		20 52									22 52					00 57
Manchester Oxford Road	a				21 09				22 09								
Newton-le-Willows	a																
Birchwood	a				21 25				22 25								
Warrington Central	a				21 30				22 30								
Liverpool South Parkway 7 ✈	a				21 46				22 47								
Liverpool Lime Street 10	a				21 58				22 58								

Table 39

Sundays

5 January to 9 February

Newcastle, Middlesbrough, Scarborough, York, Hull and Leeds - Huddersfield - Manchester, Manchester Airport and Liverpool

Network Diagram - refer to first Page of Table 39

		TP ◇1	TP ◇1	TP ◇1	TP ◇1	TP ◇1	TP ◇1	TP ◇1	NT	TP ◇1	NT	TP ◇1	NT	TP ◇1	TP ◇1	TP ◇1	NT	TP ◇1	NT
Newcastle 8 ⛴	d													08 04					
Chester-le-Street	d																		
Durham	d													08 16					
Middlesbrough	d																		
Thornaby	d																		
Yarm	d																		
Darlington 7	d													08 33					
Northallerton	d													08 45					
Thirsk	d													08 53					
Scarborough	d																	09 20	
Seamer	d																	09 25	
Malton	d																	09 43	
York 8	a													09 12				10 09	
	d		02 29	03 44	04 57	05 57	06 54			08 10		08 45		09 15				10 15	
Hull	d														09 00				
Brough	d														09 12				
Howden	d																		
Selby	d														09 33				
South Milford	d														09 42				
Garforth	d																		
Leeds 10	a		03 10	04 25	05 38	06 38	07 34			08 36		09 08		09 38	10 02			10 38	
	d		03 10	04 25	05 40	06 40	07 40			08 40	08 47	09 15		09 40	10 08			10 40	10 44
Cottingley	d										08 52								10 49
Morley	d										08 56								10 53
Batley	d										09 01								10 58
Dewsbury	a				05 51	06 51	07 51			08 51	09 04			09 51				10 51	11 01
	d				05 51	06 51	07 51			08 51	09 05			09 51				10 51	11 02
Ravensthorpe	d										09 08								11 05
Mirfield	d										09 12								11 09
Deighton	d										09 19								11 15
Huddersfield	a		03 29	04 44	06 00	07 00	08 00			09 00	09 23	09 32		10 00	10 25			11 00	11 21
	d		03 30	04 45	06 01	07 01	08 01			09 01		09 33		10 01	10 26			11 01	
Slaithwaite	d																		
Marsden	d																		
Greenfield	d																		
Mossley (Grtr Manchester)	d																		
Stalybridge	a					07 18	08 18			09 18		09 52			10 45				
	d					07 19	08 19			09 19		09 53			10 46				
Ashton-under-Lyne	d																		
Manchester Victoria ⛴	a																		
	d																		
Manchester Piccadilly 10 ⛴	a		04 02	05 17	06 34	07 34	08 34			09 34		10 09		10 34	11 01			11 34	
	d	00 31	04 06	05 21	06 38	07 38	08 38	09 12	09 18	09 38		10 10	10 19	10 38		11 10	11 18	11 38	
Manchester Airport ✈	a	00 46	04 23	05 38	06 55	07 55	08 53			09 55				10 54				11 54	
Manchester Oxford Road	a							09 14	09 20			10 12	10 21			11 12	11 20		
Newton-le-Willows	a																		
Birchwood	a							09 28				10 27				11 26			
Warrington Central	a							09 33				10 32				11 31			
Liverpool South Parkway 7 ✈	a							09 46				10 48				11 45			
Liverpool Lime Street 10	a							10 00	10 03			10 59	11 03			11 58	12 02		

		TP ◇1	NT	TP ◇1	TP ◇1	TP ◇1	NT	TP ◇1	NT	TP ◇1	TP ◇1	NT	TP ◇1	TP ◇1	TP ◇1	NT	TP ◇1	NT	TP ◇1
Newcastle 8 ⛴	d	09 33						11 08					12 10				13 07		
Chester-le-Street	d	09 43															13 16		
Durham	d	09 49						11 20					12 22				13 23		
Middlesbrough	d			10 15											12 45				
Thornaby	d			10 20											12 50				
Yarm	d			10 28											12 59				
Darlington 7	d	10 06						11 37					12 39				13 40		
Northallerton	d	10 18		10 43				11 49							13 14				
Thirsk	d			10 51											13 23				
Scarborough	d					10 52					11 52								
Seamer	d					10 57					11 57								
Malton	d					11 15					12 15								
York 8	a	10 41		11 09		11 41		12 11			12 41		13 11		13 42		14 12		
	d	10 45		11 15		11 45		12 15			12 45		13 15		13 45		14 15		14 33
Hull	d				10 58					12 00				12 58					
Brough	d				11 10					12 12				13 10					
Howden	d																		
Selby	d				11 29					12 31				13 29					
South Milford	d				11 38									13 38					
Garforth	d																		
Leeds 10	a	11 08		11 38	11 56	12 09		12 38		12 56	13 08		13 38	13 56	14 08		14 38		14 56
	d	11 10		11 40	11 59	12 10		12 40	12 44	12 59	13 10		13 40	13 59	14 10		14 40	14 44	14 59
Cottingley	d								12 49									14 49	
Morley	d								12 53									14 53	
Batley	d								12 58									14 58	
Dewsbury	a			11 51				12 51	13 01				13 51				14 51	15 01	
	d			11 51				12 51	13 02				13 51				14 51	15 02	
Ravensthorpe	d								13 05									15 05	
Mirfield	d								13 09									15 09	
Deighton	d								13 20									15 20	
Huddersfield	a	11 27		12 00	12 16	12 27		13 00	13 24	13 16	13 27		14 00	14 16	14 27		15 00	15 24	15 16
	d	11 28		12 01	12 17	12 28		13 01		13 17	13 28		14 01	14 17	14 28		15 01		15 17
Slaithwaite	d																		
Marsden	d																		
Greenfield	d																		
Mossley (Grtr Manchester)	d																		
Stalybridge	a	11 45				12 45					13 45				14 45				
	d	11 46				12 46					13 45				14 46				
Ashton-under-Lyne	d																		
Manchester Victoria ⛴	a																		
	d																		
Manchester Piccadilly 10 ⛴	a	12 05		12 34	12 54	13 05		13 34		13 54	14 05		14 34	14 54	15 05		15 34		15 54
	d	12 07	12 18	12 38		13 07	13 18	13 38			14 06	14 18	14 38		15 07	15 18	15 38		
Manchester Airport ✈	a			12 52				13 52					14 52				15 52		
Manchester Oxford Road	a	12 09	12 20			13 09	13 20				14 08	14 20			15 09	15 20			
Newton-le-Willows	a																		
Birchwood	a	12 25				13 25					14 24				15 25				
Warrington Central	a	12 30				13 30					14 29				15 30				
Liverpool South Parkway 7 ✈	a	12 47				13 47					14 47				15 47				
Liverpool Lime Street 10	a	12 58	13 03			13 58	14 03				14 57	15 03			15 58	16 03			

Table 39

Sundays
5 January to 9 February

Newcastle, Middlesbrough, Scarborough, York, Hull and Leeds - Huddersfield - Manchester, Manchester Airport and Liverpool

Network Diagram - refer to first Page of Table 39

Station		TP	NT	TP	TP	TP	NT	TP	NT	TP	TP	NT	TP	TP	TP	NT	TP	NT	TP
		◇1		◇1	◇1	◇1		◇1		◇1	◇1		◇1	◇1	◇1		◇1		◇1
Newcastle 8	d			14 08				15 07					16 08				17 05		
Chester-le-Street	d							15 16									17 14		
Durham	d			14 20				15 23					16 20				17 21		
Middlesbrough	d					14 43									16 43				
Thornaby	d					14 48									16 48				
Yarm	d					14 56									16 56				
Darlington 7	d			14 37				15 40					16 37				17 38		
Northallerton	d			14 49		15 12							16 49		17 12		17 49		
Thirsk	d					15 20									17 21				
Scarborough	d	13 52									15 52								
Seamer	d	13 57									15 57								
Malton	d	14 15									16 15								
York 8	a	14 40		15 12		15 43		16 12			16 41		17 12		17 43		18 12		
	d	14 45		15 15		15 45		16 15		16 33	16 45		17 15		17 45		18 15		18 33
Hull	d				14 58									16 58					
Brough	d				15 10									17 10					
Howden	d																		
Selby	d				15 29									17 29					
South Milford	d				15 38									17 38					
Garforth	d																		
Leeds 10	a	15 08		15 38	15 56	16 08		16 38		16 56	17 08		17 38	17 56	18 08		18 38		18 57
	d	15 10		15 40	15 59	16 10		16 40	16 44	16 59	17 11		17 40	17 59	18 10		18 40	18 44	18 59
Cottingley	d								16 49									18 49	
Morley	d								16 53									18 53	
Batley	d								16 58									18 58	
Dewsbury	a			15 51				16 51	17 01				17 51				18 51	19 01	
	d			15 51				16 51	17 02				17 51				18 51	19 02	
Ravensthorpe	d								17 05									19 05	
Mirfield	d								17 09									19 09	
Deighton	d								17 20									19 20	
Huddersfield	a	15 27		16 00	16 16	16 27		17 00	17 24	17 16	17 28		18 00	18 16	18 27		19 00	19 24	19 16
	d	15 28		16 01	16 17	16 28		17 01		17 17	17 29		18 01	18 17	18 28		19 01		19 17
Slaithwaite	d																		
Marsden	d																		
Greenfield	d																		
Mossley (Grtr Manchester)	d																		
Stalybridge	a	15 45				16 45					17 45				18 45				
	d	15 46				16 46					17 47				18 46				
Ashton-under-Lyne	d																		
Manchester Victoria	a																		
	d																		
Manchester Piccadilly 10	a	16 05		16 34	16 54	17 05		17 34		17 54	18 05		18 34	18 54	19 05		19 34		19 54
	d	16 07	16 18	16 38		17 07	17 18	17 38			18 07	18 18	18 38		19 07	19 18	19 38		
Manchester Airport ✈	a			16 52				17 52					18 52				19 52		
Manchester Oxford Road	a	16 09	16 20			17 09	17 20				18 09	18 20			19 09	19 20			
Newton-le-Willows	a																		
Birchwood	a	16 25				17 25					18 25				19 25				
Warrington Central	a	16 30				17 30					18 30				19 30				
Liverpool South Parkway 7 ✈	a	16 47				17 47					18 47				19 47				
Liverpool Lime Street 10	a	16 58	17 03			17 58	18 03				18 58	19 02			19 58	20 02			

Station		TP	NT	TP	TP	TP	TP	NT	NT	TP	TP	TP	TP	TP	NT	GR	TP
		◇1		◇1	◇1	◇1	◇1			◇1	◇1	◇1	◇1	◇1		1	◇1
Newcastle 8	d			17 53			19 10					20 08				21 45	
Chester-le-Street	d																
Durham	d			18 05			19 22					20 20				21 59	
Middlesbrough	d					18 45					20 06						22 08
Thornaby	d					18 50					20 11						22 13
Yarm	d					18 58					20 19						22 21
Darlington 7	d			18 22			19 39					20 37				22 18	
Northallerton	d			18 34		19 14					20 34	20 49				22 32	22 36
Thirsk	d					19 22					20 44						22 44
Scarborough	d	17 52								19 52				21 20			
Seamer	d	17 57								19 57				21 25			
Malton	d	18 15								20 15				21 43			
York 8	a	18 41		19 03		19 42	20 11			20 41	21 02	21 12		22 09		23 03	23 09
	d	18 45		19 15		19 45	20 15			20 45		21 15		22 12		23 05	23 12
Hull	d				18 58								21 00				
Brough	d				19 10								21 12				
Howden	d																
Selby	d				19 29								21 31				
South Milford	d				19 38								21 40				
Garforth	d																
Leeds 10	a	19 08		19 38	19 56	20 08	20 38			21 08		21 38	21 59	22 36		23 35	23 38
	d	19 10		19 40	19 59	20 10	20 40		20 44	21 10		21 40		22 40	22 44		23 40
Cottingley	d								20 49						22 49		
Morley	d								20 53						22 53		
Batley	d								20 58						22 58		
Dewsbury	a			19 51			20 50		21 01			21 51			23 01		23 51
	d			19 51			20 51		21 02			21 51			23 02		23 51
Ravensthorpe	d								21 05						23 05		
Mirfield	d								21 09						23 09		
Deighton	d								21 15						23 16		
Huddersfield	a	19 27		20 00	20 16	20 27	21 00		21 19	21 27		22 00		22 57	23 20		23 59
	d	19 28		20 01	20 17	20 28	21 01		21 19	21 28		22 01		22 58			00 01
Slaithwaite	d								21 26								
Marsden	d								21a33								
Greenfield	d																
Mossley (Grtr Manchester)	d																
Stalybridge	a	19 45				20 45	21 18					22 18		23 18			
	d	19 46				20 46	21 19					22 19		23 19			
Ashton-under-Lyne	d																
Manchester Victoria	a																
	d																
Manchester Piccadilly 10	a	20 05		20 34	20 54	21 05	21 34			22 05		22 36		23 34			00 30
	d	20 07	20 17	20 38		21 07		21 17		22 07		22 38					00 34
Manchester Airport ✈	a			20 52								22 52					00 48
Manchester Oxford Road	a	20 09	20 19			21 09		21 19		22 09							
Newton-le-Willows	a																
Birchwood	a	20 25				21 25				22 25							
Warrington Central	a	20 30				21 30				22 30							
Liverpool South Parkway 7 ✈	a	20 47				21 46				22 47							
Liverpool Lime Street 10	a	20 58	21 03			21 58		22 03		22 58							

Table 39

Sundays

16 February to 23 March

Newcastle, Middlesbrough, Scarborough, York, Hull and Leeds - Huddersfield - Manchester, Manchester Airport and Liverpool

Network Diagram - refer to first Page of Table 39

		TP 🚌	TP ◇1	NT	TP ◇1	TP ◇1	TP 🚌	NT	TP ◇1	TP ◇1	TP ◇1	TP 🚌	NT	TP ◇1	NT 🚌	TP ◇1	TP 🚌	NT	TP ◇1
Newcastle 8 🚊	d													08 34					09 33
Chester-le-Street	d																		09 43
Durham	d													08 46					09 49
Middlesbrough	d																		
Thornaby	d																		
Yarm	d																		
Darlington 7	d													09 04					10 06
Northallerton	d													09 15					10 18
Thirsk	d													09 23					
Scarborough	d															09 20			
Seamer	d															09 25			
Malton	d															09 43			
York 8	a													09 42		10 09			10 41
	d					08 30			08 45					09 45		10 15			10 45
Hull	d									08 48									
Brough	d									09 00									
Howden	d																		
Selby	d									09 20									
South Milford	d									09 29									
Garforth	d																		
Leeds 10	a					08 53			09 08	09 49				10 12		10 38			11 08
	d	08 00				08 55	09 00		09 22	09 54		10 00		10 25	10 45	10 50	11 00		11 21
Cottingley	d														11 00				
Morley	d														11 10				
Batley	d														11 20				
Dewsbury	a														11 28				
	d														11 28				
Ravensthorpe	d														11 35				
Mirfield	d														11 40				
Deighton	d														11 50				
Huddersfield	a	08 22				09 32	09 22		09 57	10 25		10 22		11 00	11 59	11 22	11 22		11 56
	d					09 33			10 01	10 26				11 01		11 28			12 01
Slaithwaite	d																		
Marsden	d																		
Greenfield	d																		
Mossley (Grtr Manchester)	d																		
Stalybridge	a					09 52				10 45						11 45			
	d				09 19	09 53				10 46						11 46			
Ashton-under-Lyne	d																		
Manchester Victoria 🚊	a																		
	d																		
Manchester Piccadilly 10 🚊	a				09 34	10 09			10 34	11 01				11 34		12 05			12 34
	d		09 12	09 18	09 38	10 10		10 19	10 38		11 10		11 18	11 38		12 07		12 18	12 38
Manchester Airport ✈	a				09 55				10 54					11 54					12 52
Manchester Oxford Road	a		09 14	09 20		10 12		10 21			11 12		11 20			12 09		12 20	
Newton-le-Willows	a																		
Birchwood	a		09 28			10 27					11 26					12 25			
Warrington Central	a		09 33			10 32					11 31					12 30			
Liverpool South Parkway 7 ✈	a		09 46			10 48					11 45					12 47			
Liverpool Lime Street 10	a		10 00	10 03		10 59		11 03			11 58		12 02			12 58		13 03	

		TP ◇1	TP ◇1	TP 🚌	NT	TP ◇1	NT 🚌	TP ◇1	TP ◇1	TP 🚌	NT	TP ◇1	TP ◇1	TP ◇1	TP 🚌	NT	TP ◇1	TP ◇1	NT 🚌
Newcastle 8 🚊	d							11 08					12 10						
Chester-le-Street	d																		
Durham	d							11 20					12 22						
Middlesbrough	d	10 15															12 45		
Thornaby	d	10 20															12 50		
Yarm	d	10 28															12 59		
Darlington 7	d							11 37					12 39						
Northallerton	d	10 43						11 49									13 14		
Thirsk	d	10 51															13 23		
Scarborough	d					10 52						11 52							
Seamer	d					10 57						11 57							
Malton	d					11 15						12 15							
York 8	a	11 09				11 41		12 11				12 41	13 11				13 42		
	d	11 15				11 45		12 15				12 45	13 15				13 45		
Hull	d		10 58						12 00					12 58					
Brough	d		11 10						12 12					13 10					
Howden	d																		
Selby	d		11 29						12 31					13 29					
South Milford	d		11 38											13 38					
Garforth	d																		
Leeds 10	a	11 38	11 56			12 09		12 38	12 56			13 08	13 38	13 56			14 08		
	d	11 50		12 00		12 21	12 45	12 50		13 00		13 21	13 50		14 00		14 21	14 44	14 45
Cottingley	d						13 00												15 00
Morley	d						13 10												15 10
Batley	d						13 20												15 20
Dewsbury	a						13 28												15 28
	d						13 28												15 28
Ravensthorpe	d						13 35												15 35
Mirfield	d						13 40												15 40
Deighton	d						13 50												15 50
Huddersfield	a	12 22		12 22		12 56	13 59	13 25		13 22		13 56	14 22		14 22		14 56	15 16	15 59
	d	12 28				13 01		13 28				14 01	14 28				15 01	15 17	
Slaithwaite	d																		
Marsden	d																		
Greenfield	d																		
Mossley (Grtr Manchester)	d																		
Stalybridge	a	12 45						13 45					14 45						
	d	12 46						13 45					14 46						
Ashton-under-Lyne	d																		
Manchester Victoria 🚊	a																		
	d																		
Manchester Piccadilly 10 🚊	a	13 05				13 34		14 05				14 34	15 05				15 34	15 54	
	d	13 07			13 18	13 38		14 06			14 18	14 38	15 07			15 18	15 38		
Manchester Airport ✈	a					13 52						14 52					15 52		
Manchester Oxford Road	a	13 09			13 20			14 08			14 20		15 09			15 20			
Newton-le-Willows	a																		
Birchwood	a	13 25						14 24					15 25						
Warrington Central	a	13 30						14 29					15 30						
Liverpool South Parkway 7 ✈	a	13 47						14 47					15 47						
Liverpool Lime Street 10	a	13 58			14 03			14 57			15 03		15 58			16 03			

Table 39

Sundays

16 February to 23 March

Newcastle, Middlesbrough, Scarborough, York, Hull and Leeds - Huddersfield - Manchester, Manchester Airport and Liverpool

Network Diagram - refer to first Page of Table 39

Station		TP ◇1	TP 🚌	NT	TP ◇1	TP ◇1	TP ◇1	TP 🚌	NT	TP ◇1	TP ◇1	NT 🚌	TP ◇1	TP 🚌	NT	TP ◇1	TP ◇1	TP ◇1	TP 🚌
Newcastle 8 🚢	d	13 07				14 08							15 07				16 08		
Chester-le-Street	d	13 16											15 16						
Durham	d	13 23				14 20							15 23				16 20		
Middlesbrough	d									14 43									
Thornaby	d									14 48									
Yarm	d									14 56									
Darlington 7	d	13 40				14 37							15 40				16 37		
Northallerton	d					14 49				15 11							16 49		
Thirsk	d									15 20									
Scarborough	d				13 52											15 52			
Seamer	d				13 57											15 57			
Malton	d				14 15											16 15			
York 8	a	14 12			14 40	15 12				15 42			16 12			16 41	17 12		
	d	14 15			14 45	15 15				15 44			16 15			16 45	17 15		
Hull	d						14 58											16 58	
Brough	d						15 10											17 10	
Howden	d																		
Selby	d						15 29											17 29	
South Milford	d						15 38											17 38	
Garforth	d																		
Leeds 10	a	14 38			15 08	15 38	15 56			16 08			16 38			17 08	17 38	17 56	
	d	14 50	15 00		15 21	15 50		16 00		16 21	16 44	16 45	16 50	17 00		17 21	17 50		18 00
Cottingley	d											17 00							
Morley	d											17 10							
Batley	d											17 20							
Dewsbury	a											17 28							
	d											17 28							
Ravensthorpe	d											17 35							
Mirfield	d											17 40							
Deighton	d											17 50							
Huddersfield	a	15 24	15 22		15 58	16 25		16 22		16 58	17 16	17 59	17 25	17 22		17 58	18 25		18 22
	d	15 28			16 01	16 28				17 01	17 17		17 29			18 01	18 28		
Slaithwaite	d																		
Marsden	d																		
Greenfield	d																		
Mossley (Grtr Manchester)	d																		
Stalybridge	a	15 45				16 45							17 45				18 45		
	d	15 46				16 46							17 47				18 46		
Ashton-under-Lyne	d																		
Manchester Victoria 🚢	a																		
	d																		
Manchester Piccadilly 10 🚢	a	16 05			16 34	17 05				17 34	17 54		18 05			18 34	19 05		
	d	16 07		16 18	16 38	17 07			17 18	17 38			18 07		18 18	18 38	19 07		
Manchester Airport ✈	a				16 52					17 52						18 52			
Manchester Oxford Road	a	16 09		16 20		17 09			17 20				18 09		18 20		19 09		
Newton-le-Willows	a																		
Birchwood	a	16 25				17 25							18 25				19 25		
Warrington Central	a	16 30				17 30							18 30				19 30		
Liverpool South Parkway 7 ✈	a	16 47				17 47							18 47				19 47		
Liverpool Lime Street 10	a	16 58		17 03		17 58			18 03				18 58		19 02		19 58		

Station		NT	TP ◇1	TP ◇1	NT 🚌	TP ◇1	TP 🚌	NT	TP ◇1	TP ◇1	TP ◇1	TP 🚌	NT	TP ◇1	NT 🚌	NT	TP ◇1	TP 🚌	TP ◇1
Newcastle 8 🚢	d					17 05				17 53							19 10		
Chester-le-Street	d					17 14													
Durham	d					17 21				18 05							19 22		
Middlesbrough	d		16 43											18 45					
Thornaby	d		16 48											18 50					
Yarm	d		16 57											18 58					
Darlington 7	d					17 38				18 22							19 39		
Northallerton	d		17 12			17 49				18 34				19 14					
Thirsk	d		17 21											19 22					
Scarborough	d								17 52										19 52
Seamer	d								17 57										19 57
Malton	d								18 15										20 15
York 8	a		17 43			18 12			18 41	19 03				19 42			20 11		20 41
	d		17 45			18 15			18 45	19 15				19 45			20 15		20 45
Hull	d										18 58								
Brough	d										19 10								
Howden	d																		
Selby	d										19 29								
South Milford	d										19 38								
Garforth	d																		
Leeds 10	a		18 08			18 38			19 08	19 38	19 54			20 08			20 38		21 08
	d		18 21	18 44	18 45	18 50	19 00		19 21	19 50		20 00			20 45		20 50	21 00	21 21
Cottingley	d				19 00										21 00				
Morley	d				19 10										21 10				
Batley	d				19 20										21 20				
Dewsbury	a				19 28										21 28				
	d				19 28										21 28				
Ravensthorpe	d				19 35										21 35				
Mirfield	d				19 40										21 40				
Deighton	d				19 50										21 50				
Huddersfield	a		18 59	19 16	19 59	19 25	19 22		19 59	20 25		20 22			21 59		21 25	21 22	21 59
	d		19 01	19 17		19 28			20 01	20 28			21 19				21 28		22 01
Slaithwaite	d												21 27						
Marsden	d												21a33						
Greenfield	d																		
Mossley (Grtr Manchester)	d																		
Stalybridge	a					19 45				20 45									22 18
	d					19 46				20 46									22 19
Ashton-under-Lyne	d																		
Manchester Victoria 🚢	a																		
	d																		
Manchester Piccadilly 10 🚢	a		19 34	19 54		20 05			20 34	21 05							22 05		22 36
	d	19 18	19 38			20 07		20 17	20 38	21 07						21 17	22 07		22 38
Manchester Airport ✈	a		19 52						20 52										22 52
Manchester Oxford Road	a	19 20				20 09		20 19		21 09						21 19	22 09		
Newton-le-Willows	a																		
Birchwood	a					20 25				21 25							22 25		
Warrington Central	a					20 30				21 30							22 30		
Liverpool South Parkway 7 ✈	a					20 47				21 47							22 47		
Liverpool Lime Street 10	a	20 02				20 58		21 03		21 58						22 03	22 58		

Table 39

Sundays

16 February to 23 March

Newcastle, Middlesbrough, Scarborough, York, Hull and Leeds - Huddersfield - Manchester, Manchester Airport and Liverpool

Network Diagram - refer to first Page of Table 39

		TP	TP	TP	TP	TP	NT	TP	GR	TP	TP
		◇1	◇1	◇1		◇1			1		◇1
					[train]		[train]	[train]	[trolley]	[train]	
Newcastle 8	d		20 08						21 45		
Chester-le-Street	d										
Durham	d		20 20						21 59		
Middlesbrough	d	20 06									22 08
Thornaby	d	20 11									22 13
Yarm	d	20 19									22 21
Darlington 7	d		20 37						22 18		
Northallerton	d	20 34	20 49						22 32		22 36
Thirsk	d	20 44									22 44
Scarborough	d					21 20					
Seamer	d					21 25					
Malton	d					21 43					
York 8	a	21 02	21 12			22 09			23 03		23 09
	d		21 15			22 12			23 05		23 12
Hull	d			21 00							
Brough	d			21 12							
Howden	d										
Selby	d			21 31							
South Milford	d			21 40							
Garforth	d										
Leeds 10	a		21 38	21 59		22 36			23 35		23 38
	d				22 00	22 40	22 45	23 00		23 40	23 40
Cottingley	d						23 00				
Morley	d						23 10				
Batley	d						23 20				
Dewsbury	a						23 28				
	d						23 28				
Ravensthorpe	d						23 35				
Mirfield	d						23 40				
Deighton	d						23 50				
Huddersfield	a				22 22	23 13	23 59	23 22		00 02	00 12
	d					23 14					00 14
Slaithwaite	d										
Marsden	d										
Greenfield	d										
Mossley (Grtr Manchester)	d										
Stalybridge	a					23 34					
	d					23 35					
Ashton-under-Lyne	d										
Manchester Victoria	a										
	d										
Manchester Piccadilly 10	a					23 50					00 43
	d										00 47
Manchester Airport	a										01 01
Manchester Oxford Road	a										
Newton-le-Willows	a										
Birchwood	a										
Warrington Central	a										
Liverpool South Parkway 7	a										
Liverpool Lime Street 10	a										

Table 39

Sundays

30 March to 11 May

Newcastle, Middlesbrough, Scarborough, York, Hull and Leeds - Huddersfield - Manchester, Manchester Airport and Liverpool

Network Diagram - refer to first Page of Table 39

		TP ◇1	TP ◇1	TP ◇1	TP ◇1	TP ◇1	TP ◇1	TP ◇1	NT	TP ◇1
Newcastle 8 ⇌	d									
Chester-le-Street	d									
Durham	d									
Middlesbrough	d									
Thornaby	d									
Yarm	d									
Darlington 7	d									
Northallerton	d									
Thirsk	d									
Scarborough	d									
Seamer	d									
Malton	d									
York 8	a									
	d		02 44	03 59	05 12	06 12	07 12			08 10
Hull	d									
Brough	d									
Howden	d									
Selby	d									
South Milford	d									
Garforth	d									
Leeds 10	a		03 10	04 25	05 39	06 38	07 38			08 36
	d		03 10	04 25	05 40	06 40	07 40			08 40
Cottingley	d									
Morley	d									
Batley	d									
Dewsbury	a				05 51	06 51	07 51			08 51
	d				05 51	06 51	07 51			08 51
Ravensthorpe	d									
Mirfield	d									
Deighton	d									
Huddersfield	a		03 29	04 44	06 00	07 00	08 00			09 00
	d		03 30	04 45	06 01	07 01	08 01			09 01
Slaithwaite	d									
Marsden	d									
Greenfield	d									
Mossley (Grtr Manchester)	d									
Stalybridge	a					07 18	08 18			09 18
	d					07 19	08 19			09 19
Ashton-under-Lyne	d									
Manchester Victoria ⇌	a									
	d									
Manchester Piccadilly 10 ⇌	a		04 02	05 17	06 34	07 34	08 34			09 34
	d	00 31	04 06	05 21	06 38	07 38	08 38	09 12	09 18	09 38
Manchester Airport ✈	a	00 46	04 23	05 38	06 55	07 55	08 53			09 55
Manchester Oxford Road	a							09 14	09 20	
Newton-le-Willows	a									
Birchwood	a							09 28		
Warrington Central	a							09 33		
Liverpool South Parkway 7 ✈	a							09 46		
Liverpool Lime Street 10	a							10 00	10 03	

		NT	TP ◇1	NT	TP ◇1	TP ◇1	TP ◇1	NT	TP ◇1	NT
Newcastle 8 ⇌	d				08 04					
Chester-le-Street	d									
Durham	d				08 16					
Middlesbrough	d									
Thornaby	d									
Yarm	d									
Darlington 7	d				08 33					
Northallerton	d				08 45					
Thirsk	d				08 53					
Scarborough	d								09 20	
Seamer	d								09 25	
Malton	d								09 43	
York 8	a				09 12				10 09	
	d		08 45		09 15				10 15	
Hull	d					09 00				
Brough	d					09 12				
Howden	d									
Selby	d					09 33				
South Milford	d					09 42				
Garforth	d									
Leeds 10	a		09 08		09 38	10 02			10 38	
	d	08 47	09 15		09 40	10 08			10 40	10 44
Cottingley	d	08 52								10 49
Morley	d	08 56								10 53
Batley	d	09 01								10 58
Dewsbury	a	09 04			09 51				10 51	11 01
	d	09 05			09 51				10 51	11 02
Ravensthorpe	d	09 08								11 05
Mirfield	d	09 12								11 09
Deighton	d	09 19								11 15
Huddersfield	a	09 23	09 32		10 00	10 25			11 00	11 21
	d		09 33		10 01	10 26			11 01	
Slaithwaite	d									
Marsden	d									
Greenfield	d									
Mossley (Grtr Manchester)	d									
Stalybridge	a		09 52			10 45				
	d		09 53			10 46				
Ashton-under-Lyne	d									
Manchester Victoria ⇌	a									
	d									
Manchester Piccadilly 10 ⇌	a		10 09		10 34	11 01			11 34	
	d		10 10	10 19	10 38		11 10	11 18	11 38	
Manchester Airport ✈	a				10 54				11 54	
Manchester Oxford Road	a		10 12	10 21			11 12	11 20		
Newton-le-Willows	a									
Birchwood	a		10 27				11 26			
Warrington Central	a		10 32				11 31			
Liverpool South Parkway 7 ✈	a		10 48				11 45			
Liverpool Lime Street 10	a		10 59	11 03			11 58	12 02		

		TP ◇1	NT	TP ◇1	TP ◇1	TP ◇1	NT	TP ◇1	NT	TP ◇1
Newcastle 8 ⇌	d	09 33						11 08		
Chester-le-Street	d	09 43								
Durham	d	09 49						11 20		
Middlesbrough	d			10 15						
Thornaby	d			10 20						
Yarm	d			10 28						
Darlington 7	d	10 06						11 37		
Northallerton	d	10 18		10 43				11 49		
Thirsk	d			10 51						
Scarborough	d					10 52				
Seamer	d					10 57				
Malton	d					11 15				
York 8	a	10 41		11 09		11 41		12 11		
	d	10 45		11 15		11 45		12 15		
Hull	d				10 58					12 00
Brough	d				11 10					12 12
Howden	d									
Selby	d				11 29					12 31
South Milford	d				11 38					
Garforth	d									
Leeds 10	a	11 08		11 38	11 56	12 09		12 38		12 56
	d	11 10		11 40	11 59	12 10		12 40	12 44	12 59
Cottingley	d								12 49	
Morley	d								12 53	
Batley	d								12 58	
Dewsbury	a			11 51				12 51	13 01	
	d			11 51				12 51	13 02	
Ravensthorpe	d								13 05	
Mirfield	d								13 09	
Deighton	d								13 20	
Huddersfield	a	11 27		12 00	12 16	12 27		13 00	13 24	13 16
	d	11 28		12 01	12 17	12 28		13 01		13 17
Slaithwaite	d									
Marsden	d									
Greenfield	d									
Mossley (Grtr Manchester)	d									
Stalybridge	a	11 45				12 45				
	d	11 46				12 46				
Ashton-under-Lyne	d									
Manchester Victoria ⇌	a									
	d									
Manchester Piccadilly 10 ⇌	a	12 05		12 34	12 54	13 05		13 34		13 54
	d	12 07	12 18	12 38		13 07	13 18	13 38		
Manchester Airport ✈	a			12 52				13 52		
Manchester Oxford Road	a	12 09	12 20			13 09	13 20			
Newton-le-Willows	a									
Birchwood	a	12 25				13 25				
Warrington Central	a	12 30				13 30				
Liverpool South Parkway 7 ✈	a	12 47				13 47				
Liverpool Lime Street 10	a	12 58	13 03			13 58	14 03			

		TP ◇1	NT	TP ◇1	TP ◇1	TP ◇1	NT	TP ◇1	NT	TP ◇1
Newcastle 8 ⇌	d			12 10				13 07		
Chester-le-Street	d							13 16		
Durham	d			12 22				13 23		
Middlesbrough	d					12 45				
Thornaby	d					12 50				
Yarm	d					12 59				
Darlington 7	d			12 39				13 40		
Northallerton	d					13 14				
Thirsk	d					13 23				
Scarborough	d	11 52								
Seamer	d	11 57								
Malton	d	12 15								
York 8	a	12 41		13 11		13 42		14 12		
	d	12 45		13 15		13 45		14 15		14 33
Hull	d				12 58					
Brough	d				13 10					
Howden	d									
Selby	d				13 29					
South Milford	d				13 38					
Garforth	d									
Leeds 10	a	13 08		13 38	13 56	14 08		14 38		14 56
	d	13 10		13 40	13 59	14 10		14 40	14 44	14 59
Cottingley	d								14 49	
Morley	d								14 53	
Batley	d								14 58	
Dewsbury	a			13 51				14 51	15 01	
	d			13 51				14 51	15 02	
Ravensthorpe	d								15 05	
Mirfield	d								15 09	
Deighton	d								15 20	
Huddersfield	a	13 27		14 00	14 16	14 27		15 00	15 24	15 16
	d	13 28		14 01	14 17	14 28		15 01		15 17
Slaithwaite	d									
Marsden	d									
Greenfield	d									
Mossley (Grtr Manchester)	d									
Stalybridge	a	13 45				14 45				
	d	13 45				14 46				
Ashton-under-Lyne	d									
Manchester Victoria ⇌	a									
	d									
Manchester Piccadilly 10 ⇌	a	14 05		14 34	14 54	15 05		15 34		15 54
	d	14 06	14 18	14 38		15 07	15 18	15 38		
Manchester Airport ✈	a			14 52				15 52		
Manchester Oxford Road	a	14 08	14 20			15 09	15 20			
Newton-le-Willows	a									
Birchwood	a	14 24				15 25				
Warrington Central	a	14 29				15 30				
Liverpool South Parkway 7 ✈	a	14 47				15 47				
Liverpool Lime Street 10	a	14 57	15 03			15 58	16 03			

Table 39

Sundays

30 March to 11 May

Newcastle, Middlesbrough, Scarborough, York, Hull and Leeds - Huddersfield - Manchester, Manchester Airport and Liverpool

Network Diagram - refer to first Page of Table 39

		TP	NT	TP	NT	TP	TP	NT	TP	NT	TP	TP	NT	TP	TP	TP	NT	TP	NT	TP	TP	NT	TP	TP	TP	TP	NT	NT	TP	TP	TP	TP	TP	NT	GR	TP
		◇1		◇1		◇1	◇1		◇1		◇1	◇1		◇1	◇1	◇1		◇1		◇1	◇1		◇1	◇1	◇1	◇1			◇1	◇1	◇1	◇1	◇1		R 1	◇1
Newcastle 8	d			14 08					15 07					16 08				17 05					17 53			19 10					20 08				21 45	
Chester-le-Street	d								15 16									17 14																		
Durham	d			14 20					15 23					16 20				17 21					18 05			19 22					20 20				21 59	
Middlesbrough	d				14 17		14 43									16 43									18 45					20 06						22 08
Thornaby	d				14 22		14 48									16 48									18 50					20 11						22 13
Yarm	d						14 56									16 56									18 58					20 19						22 21
Darlington 7	d			14 37	14a42				15 40					16 37				17 38					18 22			19 39					20 37				22 18	
Northallerton	d			14 49			15 12							16 49		17 11		17 49					18 34		19 14					20 34	20 49				22 32	22 36
Thirsk	d						15 20									17 20									19 22					20 44						22 44
Scarborough	d	13 52										15 52									17 52								19 52				21 20			
Seamer	d	13 57										15 57									17 57								19 57				21 25			
Malton	d	14 15										16 15									18 15								20 15				21 43			
York 8	a	14 40		15 12			15 43		16 12			16 41		17 12		17 42		18 12			18 41		19 03		19 42	20 11			20 41	21 02	21 12		22 09		23 03	23 09
	d	14 45		15 15			15 45		16 15		16 33	16 45		17 15		17 45		18 15		18 33	18 45		19 15		19 45	20 15			20 45		21 15		22 12		23 05	23 12
Hull	d					14 58									16 58									18 58								21 00				
Brough	d					15 10									17 10									19 10								21 12				
Howden	d																																			
Selby	d					15 29									17 29									19 29								21 31				
South Milford	d					15 38									17 38									19 38								21 40				
Garforth	d																																			
Leeds 10	a	15 08		15 38		15 56	16 08		16 38		16 56	17 08		17 38	17 56	18 08		18 38		18 57	19 08		19 38	19 56	20 08	20 38			21 08		21 38	21 59	22 36		23 35	23 38
	d	15 10		15 40		15 59	16 10		16 40	16 44	16 59	17 11		17 40	17 59	18 10		18 40	18 44	18 59	19 10		19 40	19 59	20 10	20 40		20 44	21 10		21 40		22 40	22 44		23 40
Cottingley	d									16 49									18 49									20 49						22 49		
Morley	d									16 53									18 53									20 53						22 53		
Batley	d									16 58									18 58									20 58						22 58		
Dewsbury	a			15 51					16 51	17 01				17 51				18 51	19 01				19 51			20 50		21 01			21 51			23 01		23 51
	d			15 51					16 51	17 02				17 51				18 51	19 02				19 51			20 51		21 02			21 51			23 02		23 51
Ravensthorpe	d									17 05									19 05									21 05						23 05		
Mirfield	d									17 09									19 09									21 09						23 09		
Deighton	d									17 20									19 20									21 15						23 16		
Huddersfield	a	15 27		16 00		16 16	16 27		17 00	17 24	17 16	17 28		18 00	18 16	18 27		19 00	19 24	19 16	19 27		20 00	20 16	20 27	21 00		21 19	21 27		22 00		22 57	23 20		23 59
	d	15 28		16 01		16 17	16 28		17 01		17 17	17 29		18 01	18 17	18 28		19 01		19 17	19 28		20 01	20 17	20 28	21 01		21 19	21 28		22 01		22 58			00 01
Slaithwaite	d																											21 26								
Marsden	d																											21a33								
Greenfield	d																																			
Mossley (Grtr Manchester)	d																																			
Stalybridge	a	15 45					16 45					17 45				18 45					19 45				20 45	21 18					22 18		23 18			
	d	15 46					16 46					17 47				18 46					19 46				20 46	21 19					22 19		23 19			
Ashton-under-Lyne	d																																			
Manchester Victoria	a																																			
	d																																			
Manchester Piccadilly 10	a	16 05		16 34		16 54	17 05		17 34		17 54	18 05		18 34	18 54	19 05		19 34		19 54	20 05		20 34	20 54	21 05	21 34			22 05		22 36		23 34			00 30
	d	16 07	16 18	16 38			17 07	17 18	17 38			18 07	18 18	18 38		19 07	19 18	19 38			20 07	20 17	20 38		21 07		21 17		22 07		22 38					00 34
Manchester Airport	a			16 52					17 52					18 52				19 52					20 52								22 52					00 48
Manchester Oxford Road	a	16 09	16 20				17 09	17 20				18 09	18 20			19 09	19 20				20 09	20 19			21 09		21 19		22 09							
Newton-le-Willows	a																																			
Birchwood	a	16 25					17 25					18 25				19 25					20 25				21 25				22 25							
Warrington Central	a	16 30					17 30					18 30				19 30					20 30				21 30				22 30							
Liverpool South Parkway 7	a	16 47					17 47					18 47				19 47					20 47				21 46				22 47							
Liverpool Lime Street 10	a	16 58	17 03				17 58	18 03				18 58	19 02			19 58	20 02				20 58	21 03			21 58		22 03		22 58							

Table 40

York and Selby - Leeds

Mondays to Fridays

9 December to 16 May

Network Diagram - refer to first Page of Table 39

Miles	Miles			GR	TP	TP	TP	TP	TP	TP	TP	NT	TP		NT		TP	XC	TP	NT	TP	TP	NT	TP	NT
				MX	MO	MX	MO	MX	MX	MO															
				[R] [1] 🍴	◇[1]	◇[1]	◇[1]	◇[1]	◇[1]	◇[1]	◇[1]		◇[1]				◇[1] 🛒	◇[1]	◇[1] 🛒		◇[1] 🛒	◇[1] 🛒		◇[1] 🛒	
0	—	**York** [8]	33 d	00 18	01 38	01 38	02 47	02 52	04 00	04 23	05 26	05 40	05 57		06 13		06 28	06 32			06 55		07 06	07 26	
8¾	—	Ulleskelf	33 d																				07 15		
10¾	—	Church Fenton	33 d																				07 21		
—	0	**Selby**	d																06 36	06 43		07 08			07 23
—	7¾	South Milford	d																	06 53					07 32
15¾	11	Micklefield	d									05 59			06 28					06 58			07 28		07 41
17½	12¾	East Garforth	d									06 03			06 32					07 03			07 32		07 46
18	13¼	Garforth	d									06 05	06 12		06 35					07 05	07 10	07 24	07 35		07 48
21	16¼	Cross Gates	d									06 10			06 40					07 09			07 40	07 45	07 53
25½	20¾	**Leeds** [10]	a	00 47	02 04	02 19	03 13	03 33	04 42	04 49	05 52	06 21	06 22		06 48		06 52	06 55	07 00	07 19	07 20	07 35	07 49	07 52	08 01
—	—	Bradford Interchange	37 a												07 11					07 43			08 09		08 28

		TP	XC	NT		NT	TP	NT	TP	NT	TP	NT	TP	XC	NT	TP	TP		NT	TP	TP	XC	NT	TP	TP
		◇[1] 🛒	◇[1] 🛒				◇[1] 🛒		◇[1] 🛒		◇[1] 🛒		◇[1] 🛒	◇[1] 🛒		◇[1] 🛒	◇[1] 🛒			◇[1] 🛒	◇[1] 🛒	◇[1] 🛒		◇[1] 🛒	◇[1] 🛒
York [8]	33 d	07 40	07 45			07 48	07 55			08 12	08 26		08 40	08 45		08 57			09 11	09 26	09 40	09 45		09 57	
Ulleskelf	33 d																								
Church Fenton	33 d					08 06													09 23						
Selby	d			07 43					08 11			08 24			08 43		09 11						09 43		10 11
South Milford	d			07 53								08 34			08 53								09 53		
Micklefield	d			08 00		08 13				08 27		08 42			09 00				09 30				10 00		
East Garforth	d			08 05		08 18		←		08 31		08 46			09 05				09 34				10 05		
Garforth	d			08 07		08 20	08 12	08 20		08 33	08 41	08 48			09 07	09 12			09 37				10 07	10 12	
Cross Gates	d			08 12		→		08 25		08 38		08 53			09 11				09 42				10 11		
Leeds [10]	a	08 04	08 08	08 19			08 22	08 35	08 36	08 48	08 52	09 02	09 04	09 08	09 19	09 23	09 36		09 51	09 52	10 04	10 08	10 19	10 22	10 36
Bradford Interchange	37 a			08 43						09 12					09 43				10 12				10 43		

		NT	TP	TP	XC	NT		TP	TP	NT	TP	TP	XC	NT	TP	TP	NT	TP	TP		XC	NT	TP	TP	NT
			◇[1] 🛒	◇[1] 🛒	◇[1] 🛒			◇[1] 🛒	◇[1] 🛒		◇[1] 🛒	◇[1] 🛒	◇[1] 🛒		◇[1] 🛒	◇[1] 🛒		◇[1] 🛒	◇[1] 🛒		◇[1] 🛒		◇[1] 🛒	◇[1] 🛒	
York [8]	33 d	10 11	10 26	10 40	10 45			10 57		11 09	11 26	11 40	11 45		11 57		12 13	12 26	12 40		12 45		12 57		13 09
Ulleskelf	33 d																								
Church Fenton	33 d									11 21															13 21
Selby	d					10 43			11 11					11 43		12 11						12 43		13 11	
South Milford	d					10 53								11 53								12 53			
Micklefield	d	10 29				11 00				11 29				12 00			12 29					13 00			13 29
East Garforth	d	10 33				11 05				11 33				12 05			12 33					13 05			13 33
Garforth	d	10 36				11 07		11 12		11 36				12 07	12 12		12 35					13 07	13 12		13 36
Cross Gates	d	10 41				11 11				11 41				12 11			12 40					13 11			13 41
Leeds [10]	a	10 49	10 52	11 04	11 08	11 19		11 22	11 36	11 49	11 52	12 04	12 08	12 19	12 22	12 36	12 49	12 52	13 04		13 08	13 20	13 22	13 36	13 49
Bradford Interchange	37 a	11 11				11 43				12 11				12 43			13 12					13 43			14 12

		TP	TP	XC	NT	TP	TP	NT		TP	TP	XC	NT	TP	TP	TP	NT	TP	TP	XC	NT		TP	TP	XC
														FX	FO								FX	FO	
		◇[1] 🛒	◇[1] 🛒	◇[1] 🛒		◇[1] 🛒	◇[1] 🛒			◇[1] 🛒	◇[1] 🛒	◇[1] 🛒		◇[1] 🛒	◇[1] 🛒	◇[1] 🛒		◇[1] 🛒	◇[1] 🛒	◇[1] 🛒			◇[1] 🛒	◇[1] 🛒	◇[1] 🛒
York [8]	33 d	13 26	13 40	13 45		13 57		14 13		14 26	14 40	14 45		14 57	14 57		15 08	15 26	15 40	15 44			15 57	15 57	16 05
Ulleskelf	33 d																								
Church Fenton	33 d																15 21								
Selby	d				13 43		14 11						14 43			15 11					15 43				
South Milford	d				13 53								14 53								15 53				
Micklefield	d				14 00			14 29					15 00				15 29				16 00				
East Garforth	d				14 05			14 33					15 05				15 33				16 05				
Garforth	d				14 07	14 12		14 36					15 07	15 12	15 12		15 36				16 07		16 12		
Cross Gates	d				14 11			14 41					15 11				15 41				16 11				
Leeds [10]	a	13 52	14 04	14 08	14 19	14 22	14 36	14 49		14 52	15 04	15 08	15 19	15 22	15 23	15 36	15 49	15 52	16 07	16 09	16 19		16 22	16 22	16 32
Bradford Interchange	37 a				14 43			15 12					15 43				16 10				16 43				

		TP	TP	NT	TP	TP	XC	NT	TP	TP		NT	TP	TP	TP	XC	NT	TP	NT	NT	TP	TP	TP		XC
		FO	FX																						
		◇[1] 🛒	◇[1] 🛒		◇[1] 🛒	◇[1] 🛒	◇[1] 🛒		◇[1] 🛒	◇[1] 🛒			◇[1] 🛒	◇[1]	◇[1] 🛒	◇[1] 🛒		◇[1] 🛒	◇		◇[1] 🛒	◇[1] 🛒	◇[1]		◇[1] 🛒
York [8]	33 d			16 08	16 26	16 40	16 45		16 57			17 13	17 26		17 40	17 45		17 57		18 05	18 12		18 40		18 45
Ulleskelf	33 d																			18 15					
Church Fenton	33 d			16 20																18 23					
Selby	d	16 11	16 11					16 43		17 11				17 33			17 40		18 02			18 29			
South Milford	d							16 53									17 51								
Micklefield	d			16 29				17 00				17 30					18 00			18 30					
East Garforth	d			16 33				17 05				17 34					18 05			18 34					
Garforth	d	16 22		16 35				17 07	17 12			17 36					18 07	18 12	18 21	18 36					
Cross Gates	d			16 40				17 11				17 41					18 11			18 41					
Leeds [10]	a	16 36	16 36	16 49	16 52	17 07	17 06	17 19	17 22	17 37		17 49	17 52	17 58	18 04	18 08	18 19	18 22	18 32	18 49	18 37	18 52	19 04		19 08
Bradford Interchange	37 a			17 10								18 10					18 43		18 58	19 09					

Table 40

York and Selby - Leeds

Mondays to Fridays

9 December to 16 May

Network Diagram - refer to first Page of Table 39

		NT		NT ◇	NT	TP ◇1	NT	TP ◇1	TP ◇1	XC ◇1 trolley	TP ◇1	NT	TP ◇1	XC ◇1 trolley	TP FO ◇1		TP FX ◇1	TP FX ◇1	NT	TP ◇1	TP ◇1		NT B	TP ◇1	NT
York [8]	33 d				19 04	19 08			19 40	19 45	20 10	20 13	20 40	20 45			21 14		21 23	21 46			22 09	23 07	23 13
Ulleskelf	33 d																						22 19		
Church Fenton	33 d				19 20														21 33				22 23		23 28
Selby	d	18 43		19 00				19 31							21 06			21 16			22 10				
South Milford	d	18 53													21 16			21 26			22 19				
Micklefield	d	19 00			19 28							20 28							21 41				22 31		23 35
East Garforth	d	19 05			19 32		←					20 32							21 45				22 35		23 39
Garforth	d	19 07		19 15	19 34	19 22	19 34					20 34							21 47				22 37		23 42
Cross Gates	d	19 11			→		19 39					20 39							21 52				22 42		23 47
Leeds [10]	a	19 19		19 27		19 35	19 48	19 56	20 04	20 08	20 35	20 48	21 04	21 08	21 35		21 37	21 44	22 03	22 07	22 37		22 51	23 33	23 56
Bradford Interchange	37 a	19 44		19 57								21 10													

Saturdays

14 December to 17 May

		GR R 1 restaurant	TP ◇1	TP ◇1	TP ◇1	TP ◇1	TP ◇1	NT	XC ◇1	TP ◇1	TP ◇1	NT	TP ◇1		TP ◇1	NT	TP ◇1	TP ◇1	XC ◇1	NT	TP ◇1	TP ◇1	NT	TP ◇1	TP ◇1
York [8]	33 d	00 18	01 52	02 40	03 52	05 26	05 57	06 13	06 17	06 28			06 55			07 06	07 26	07 40	07 45		07 53		08 09	08 26	08 40
Ulleskelf	33 d															07 15									
Church Fenton	33 d															07 21							08 21		
Selby	d										06 36	06 43			07 08					07 43		08 11			
South Milford	d											06 53								07 53					
Micklefield	d							06 28				06 58				07 28				08 00			08 28		
East Garforth	d							06 32				07 03				07 32				08 05			08 32		
Garforth	d						06 12	06 35				07 05	07 10		07 24	07 35				08 07	08 12		08 35	08 41	
Cross Gates	d							06 40				07 09				07 40	07 45			08 12			08 40		
Leeds [10]	a	00 47	02 18	03 06	04 34	05 52	06 22	06 49	06 58	06 52	06 59	07 19	07 20		07 35	07 49	07 52	08 04	08 08	08 19	08 22	08 36	08 49	08 52	09 04
Bradford Interchange	37 a							07 11				07 43				08 09				08 43			09 12		

		XC ◇1 trolley		NT	TP ◇1	TP ◇1	NT	TP ◇1	TP ◇1	XC ◇1 trolley	NT	TP ◇1	TP ◇1	NT	TP ◇1		TP ◇1	XC ◇1 trolley	NT	TP ◇1	TP ◇1	NT	TP ◇1	TP ◇1	XC ◇1 trolley
York [8]	33 d	08 45			08 57		09 11	09 26	09 40	09 45		09 57		10 11	10 26		10 40	10 45		10 57		11 09	11 26	11 40	11 45
Ulleskelf	33 d																								
Church Fenton	33 d						09 23															11 21			
Selby	d			08 43		09 11					09 43		10 11						10 43		11 11				
South Milford	d			08 53							09 53								10 53						
Micklefield	d			09 00			09 30				10 00			10 29					11 00			11 29			
East Garforth	d			09 05			09 34				10 05			10 33					11 05			11 33			
Garforth	d			09 07	09 12		09 37				10 07	10 12		10 36					11 07	11 12		11 36			
Cross Gates	d			09 11			09 42				10 11			10 41					11 11			11 41			
Leeds [10]	a	09 06		09 19	09 22	09 36	09 51	09 52	10 04	10 08	10 19	10 22	10 36	10 49	10 52		11 04	11 08	11 19	11 22	11 36	11 49	11 52	12 04	12 08
Bradford Interchange	37 a			09 43			10 11				10 43			11 12					11 43			12 12			

		NT	TP ◇1	TP ◇1		NT	TP ◇1	TP ◇1	XC ◇1 trolley	NT	TP ◇1	TP ◇1	NT	TP ◇1	TP ◇1	XC ◇1 trolley	NT		TP ◇1	TP ◇1	NT	TP ◇1	TP ◇1	XC ◇1 trolley	NT
York [8]	33 d		11 57			12 13	12 26	12 40	12 45		12 57		13 09	13 26	13 40	13 45			13 57		14 13	14 26	14 40	14 45	
Ulleskelf	33 d																								
Church Fenton	33 d												13 21												
Selby	d	11 43		12 11						12 43		13 11					13 43			14 11					14 43
South Milford	d	11 53								12 53							13 53								14 53
Micklefield	d	12 00				12 29				13 00			13 29				14 00				14 29				15 00
East Garforth	d	12 05				12 33				13 05			13 33				14 05				14 33				15 05
Garforth	d	12 07	12 12			12 35				13 07	13 12		13 36				14 07		14 12		14 36				15 07
Cross Gates	d	12 11				12 40				13 11			13 41				14 11				14 41				15 11
Leeds [10]	a	12 19	12 22	12 36		12 49	12 52	13 04	13 08	13 20	13 22	13 36	13 49	13 52	14 04	14 08	14 19		14 22	14 36	14 49	14 52	15 04	15 08	15 19
Bradford Interchange	37 a	12 43				13 12				13 43			14 12				14 43				15 12				15 43

		TP ◇1	TP ◇1	NT	TP ◇1	TP ◇1		XC ◇1 trolley	NT	TP ◇1	XC ◇1 trolley	TP ◇1	NT	TP ◇1	TP ◇1	XC ◇1 trolley	NT	TP ◇1	TP ◇1		NT	TP ◇1	TP ◇1	TP ◇1	XC ◇1 trolley
York [8]	33 d	14 57		15 09	15 26	15 40		15 45		15 57	16 05		16 08	16 26	16 40	16 45		16 57			17 13	17 26		17 40	17 45
Ulleskelf	33 d																								
Church Fenton	33 d			15 21									16 20												
Selby	d		15 11						15 43			16 11					16 43		17 11				17 33		
South Milford	d								15 53								16 53								
Micklefield	d			15 29					16 00				16 29				17 00				17 29				
East Garforth	d			15 33					16 05				16 33				17 05				17 33				
Garforth	d	15 12		15 36					16 07	16 12			16 35				17 07	17 12			17 35				
Cross Gates	d			15 41					16 11				16 40				17 11				17 40				
Leeds [10]	a	15 22	15 36	15 49	15 52	16 04		16 08	16 19	16 22	16 32	16 36	16 49	16 52	17 04	17 08	17 19	17 22	17 36		17 49	17 52	17 58	18 05	18 08
Bradford Interchange	37 a			16 10					16 43				17 10				17 43				18 09				

Table 40

Saturdays

14 December to 17 May

York and Selby - Leeds

Network Diagram - refer to first Page of Table 39

			NT	TP	NT	TP	TP	TP	XC	NT	NT		NT	TP	NT	TP	TP	XC	TP	NT	TP	TP	XC	TP		NT
				◇1		◇1	◇1	◇1	◇1					◇1		◇1	◇1	◇1	◇1		◇1	◇1	◇1	◇1		
									🛒									🛒					🛒			
York 8	33	d		17 57	18 05	18 12		18 40	18 45				19 04	19 08			19 40	19 45	20 10	20 13		20 40	20 45	21 14		21 18
Ulleskelf	33	d			18 16																					21 27
Church Fenton	33	d			18 22								19 20													21 33
Selby		d	17 40				18 29			18 43	19 00					19 31					20 29					
South Milford		d	17 51							18 53											20 38					
Micklefield		d	18 00		18 30					19 00			19 28							20 28						21 41
East Garforth		d	18 05		18 34					19 05			19 32		←					20 32						21 45
Garforth		d	18 07	18 12	18 36					19 07	19 15		19 34	19 22	19 34					20 34						21 47
Cross Gates		d	18 11		18 41					19 11			→		19 39					20 39						21 52
Leeds 10		a	18 19	18 22	18 49	18 37	18 52	19 04	19 08	19 19	19 27			19 35	19 48	19 56	20 04	20 08	20 35	20 48	20 56	21 04	21 07	21 37		22 01
Bradford Interchange	37	a	18 43		19 09					19 44										21 10						

			TP	TP	NT	TP	NT
			◇1	◇1		◇1	
York 8	33	d	21 46		22 13	23 07	23 13
Ulleskelf	33	d					
Church Fenton	33	d					23 28
Selby		d		22 10			
South Milford		d		22 19			
Micklefield		d			22 30		23 35
East Garforth		d			22 34		23 39
Garforth		d			22 36		23 42
Cross Gates		d			22 41		23 47
Leeds 10		a	22 07	22 37	22 50	23 33	23 56
Bradford Interchange	37	a					

Sundays

8 December to 9 February

			TP	TP	TP	TP	TP	TP	TP	NT	TP	XC	TP	NT		TP	XC	TP	NT	TP	TP	XC	TP	NT	TP	TP
			◇1	◇1	◇1	◇1	◇1	◇1	◇1		◇1	◇1	◇1			◇1	◇1	◇1		◇1	◇1	◇1	◇1		◇1	◇1
												🛒					🛒					🛒				
York 8	33	d	02 29	03 44	04 57	05 57	06 54	08 10	08 45	08 50	09 15	09 33		09 52		10 15	10 33	10 45	10 57	11 15		11 40	11 45	11 52	12 15	
Ulleskelf	33	d																								
Church Fenton	33	d								09 02				10 04										12 04		
Selby		d											09 33								11 29					12 31
South Milford		d											09 42								11 38					
Micklefield		d								09 09				10 12					11 12					12 11		
East Garforth		d								09 13				10 16					11 16					12 15		
Garforth		d								09 16				10 18					11 18					12 18		
Cross Gates		d								09 21				10 23					11 23					12 23		
Leeds 10		a	03 10	04 25	05 38	06 38	07 34	08 36	09 08	09 30	09 38	09 56	10 02	10 32		10 38	10 56	11 08	11 32	11 38	11 56	12 05	12 09	12 32	12 38	12 56
Bradford Interchange	37	a								09 53				10 53					11 53					12 53		

			XC		TP	NT	TP	TP	XC	TP	NT	TP	TP	XC	TP	NT		TP	TP		XC	TP	NT	TP	TP	XC
			◇1		◇1		◇1	◇1	◇1	◇1		◇1	◇1	◇1	◇1			◇1	◇1		◇1	◇1		◇1	◇1	◇1
																					B					
			🛒						🛒					🛒							🛒					🛒
York 8	33	d	12 40		12 45	12 52	13 15		13 40	13 45	13 52	14 15	14 33	14 40	14 45	14 52		15 15			15 41	15 45	15 52	16 15	16 33	16 40
Ulleskelf	33	d																								
Church Fenton	33	d									14 04												16 04			
Selby		d						13 29											15 29							
South Milford		d						13 38											15 38							
Micklefield		d				13 07					14 11					15 07							16 11			
East Garforth		d				13 11					14 15					15 11							16 15			
Garforth		d				13 13					14 18					15 13							16 18			
Cross Gates		d				13 18					14 23					15 18							16 23			
Leeds 10		a	13 05		13 08	13 27	13 38	13 56	14 03	14 08	14 32	14 38	14 56	15 05	15 08	15 27		15 38	15 56		16 04	16 08	16 32	16 38	16 56	17 06
Bradford Interchange	37	a				13 53					14 53					15 53							16 53			

			TP	NT	TP		TP	XC	TP	NT	TP	TP	XC	TP	NT	TP	TP	XC		TP	NT	TP	XC	TP	NT	TP
			◇1		◇1		◇1	◇1	◇1		◇1	◇1	◇1	◇1		◇1	◇1	◇1		◇1		◇1	◇1	◇1		◇1
								🛒					🛒					🛒					🛒			
York 8	33	d	16 45	16 52	17 15			17 40	17 45	17 52	18 15	18 33	18 40	18 45	18 52	19 15		19 40		19 45	19 52	20 15	20 40	20 45	20 57	21 15
Ulleskelf	33	d																								
Church Fenton	33	d								18 04											20 04					
Selby		d					17 29										19 29									
South Milford		d					17 38										19 38									
Micklefield		d		17 07						18 11					19 07						20 12				21 12	
East Garforth		d		17 11						18 15					19 11						20 16				21 17	
Garforth		d		17 13						18 18					19 13						20 18				21 19	
Cross Gates		d		17 18						18 23					19 18						20 23				21 24	
Leeds 10		a	17 08	17 27	17 38		17 56	18 04	18 08	18 32	18 38	18 57	19 03	19 08	19 27	19 38	19 56	20 05		20 08	20 32	20 38	21 02	21 08	21 33	21 38
Bradford Interchange	37	a		17 53						18 53					19 53						20 53				21 56	

A from 5 January

B until 29 December

Table 40

York and Selby - Leeds

Sundays

8 December to 9 February

Network Diagram - refer to first Page of Table 39

		TP	NT	TP	GR	TP
		◇1		◇1	1	◇1
York 8	33 d		21 52	22 12	23 05	23 12
Ulleskelf	33 d					
Church Fenton	33 d		22 04			
Selby	d	21 31				
South Milford	d	21 40				
Micklefield	d		22 12			
East Garforth	d		22 16			
Garforth	d		22 19			
Cross Gates	d		22 23			
Leeds 10	a	21 59	22 32	22 36	23 35	23 38
Bradford Interchange	37 a					

Sundays

16 February to 23 March

		TP	TP	TP	NT	TP	XC	TP	NT	TP	XC	TP	NT		TP	TP	XC	TP	NT	TP	TP	XC	TP	NT	TP
		◇1	◇1	◇1		◇1	◇1	◇1		◇1	◇1	◇1			◇1	◇1	◇1	◇1		◇1	◇1	◇1	◇1		◇1
York 8	33 d	08 10	08 30	08 45	08 50		09 33	09 45	09 52	10 15	10 33	10 45	10 57		11 15		11 40	11 45	11 52	12 15		12 40	12 45	12 52	13 15
Ulleskelf	33 d																								
Church Fenton	33 d				09 02				10 04										12 04						
Selby	d					09 20										11 29					12 31				
South Milford	d					09 29										11 38									
Micklefield	d				09 09				10 12				11 12						12 11					13 07	
East Garforth	d				09 13				10 16				11 16						12 15					13 11	
Garforth	d				09 16				10 18				11 18						12 18					13 13	
Cross Gates	d				09 21				10 23				11 23						12 23					13 18	
Leeds 10	a	08 36	08 53	09 08	09 30	09 49	09 56	10 12	10 32	10 38	10 56	11 08	11 32		11 38	11 56	12 05	12 09	12 32	12 38	12 56	13 05	13 08	13 27	13 38
Bradford Interchange	37 a				09 53				10 53				11 53						12 53					13 53	

		TP		XC	TP	NT	TP	XC	TP	NT	TP	TP	XC	TP	NT		TP	XC	TP	NT	TP	TP	XC	TP	NT
		◇1		◇1	◇1		◇1	◇1	◇1		◇1	◇1	◇1	◇1			◇1	◇1	◇1		◇1	◇1	◇1	◇1	
York 8	33 d			13 40	13 45	13 52	14 15	14 40	14 45	14 52	15 15		15 40	15 44	15 52		16 15	16 40	16 45	16 52	17 15		17 40	17 45	17 52
Ulleskelf	33 d																								
Church Fenton	33 d					14 04									16 04										18 04
Selby	d	13 29										15 29										17 29			
South Milford	d	13 38										15 38										17 38			
Micklefield	d					14 11				15 07					16 11					17 07					18 11
East Garforth	d					14 15				15 11					16 15					17 11					18 15
Garforth	d					14 18				15 13					16 18					17 13					18 18
Cross Gates	d					14 23				15 18					16 23					17 18					18 23
Leeds 10	a	13 56		14 03	14 08	14 32	14 38	15 05	15 08	15 27	15 38	15 56	16 04	16 08	16 32		16 38	17 06	17 08	17 27	17 38	17 56	18 04	18 08	18 32
Bradford Interchange	37 a					14 53				15 53					16 53					17 53					18 53

		TP	XC	TP		NT	TP	TP	XC	TP	NT	TP	XC	TP	NT	TP	TP		NT	TP	GR	TP			
		◇1	◇1	◇1			◇1	◇1	◇1	◇1		◇1	◇1	◇1		◇1	◇1			◇1	1	◇1			
York 8	33 d	18 15	18 40	18 45		18 52	19 15		19 40	19 45	19 52	20 15	20 40	20 45	20 57	21 15			21 52	22 12	23 05	23 12			
Ulleskelf	33 d																								
Church Fenton	33 d										20 04								22 04						
Selby	d							19 29									21 31								
South Milford	d							19 38									21 40								
Micklefield	d					19 07					20 12				21 12				22 12						
East Garforth	d					19 11					20 16				21 17				22 16						
Garforth	d					19 13					20 18				21 19				22 19						
Cross Gates	d					19 18					20 23				21 24				22 23						
Leeds 10	a	18 38	19 03	19 08		19 27	19 38	19 54	20 05	20 08	20 32	20 38	21 02	21 08	21 33	21 38	21 59		22 32	22 36	23 35	23 38			
Bradford Interchange	37 a					19 53					20 53				21 56										

Sundays

30 March to 11 May

		TP	TP	TP	TP	TP	TP	TP	NT	TP	XC	TP	NT		TP	XC	TP	NT	TP	TP	XC	TP	NT	TP	TP
		◇1	◇1	◇1	◇1	◇1	◇1	◇1		◇1	◇1	◇1			◇1	◇1	◇1		◇1	◇1	◇1	◇1		◇1	◇1
York 8	33 d	02 44	03 59	05 12	06 12	07 12	08 10	08 45	08 50	09 15	09 33		09 52		10 15	10 33	10 45	10 57	11 15		11 40	11 45	11 52	12 15	
Ulleskelf	33 d																								
Church Fenton	33 d								09 02				10 04										12 04		
Selby	d											09 33								11 29					12 31
South Milford	d											09 42								11 38					
Micklefield	d								09 09				10 12					11 12					12 11		
East Garforth	d								09 13				10 16					11 16					12 15		
Garforth	d								09 16				10 18					11 18					12 18		
Cross Gates	d								09 21				10 23					11 23					12 23		
Leeds 10	a	03 10	04 25	05 39	06 38	07 38	08 36	09 08	09 30	09 38	09 56	10 02	10 32		10 38	10 56	11 08	11 32	11 38	11 56	12 05	12 09	12 32	12 38	12 56
Bradford Interchange	37 a								09 53				10 53					11 53					12 53		

Table 40

Sundays

30 March to 11 May

York and Selby - Leeds

Network Diagram - refer to first Page of Table 39

		XC	TP	NT		TP	TP	XC	TP	NT	TP	TP	XC	TP	NT	TP	TP		XC	TP	NT	TP	TP	XC	TP
		◇1	◇1			◇1	◇1	◇1	◇1		◇1	◇1	◇1	◇1		◇1	◇1		◇1	◇1		◇1	◇1	◇1	◇1
		🍴						🍴					🍴						🍴					🍴	
York 8	33 d	12 40	12 45	12 52		13 15		13 40	13 45	13 52	14 15	14 33	14 40	14 45	14 52	15 15			15 41	15 45	15 52	16 15	16 33	16 40	16 45
Ulleskelf	33 d																								
Church Fenton	33 d									14 04											16 04				
Selby	d						13 29										15 29								
South Milford	d						13 38										15 38								
Micklefield	d			13 07						14 11					15 07						16 11				
East Garforth	d			13 11						14 15					15 11						16 15				
Garforth	d			13 13						14 18					15 13						16 18				
Cross Gates	d			13 18						14 23					15 18						16 23				
Leeds 10	a	13 05	13 08	13 27		13 38	13 56	14 03	14 08	14 32	14 38	14 56	15 05	15 08	15 27	15 38	15 56		16 03	16 08	16 32	16 38	16 56	17 06	17 08
Bradford Interchange	37 a			13 53						14 53					15 53						16 53				

		NT	TP	TP	XC	TP		NT	TP	TP	XC	TP	NT	TP	TP	XC	TP	NT	TP		XC	TP	NT	TP	TP
			◇1	◇1	◇1	◇1			◇1	◇1	◇1	◇1		◇1	◇1	◇1	◇1		◇1		◇1	◇1		◇1	◇1
					🍴						🍴					🍴					🍴				
York 8	33 d	16 52	17 15		17 40	17 45		17 52	18 15	18 33	18 40	18 45	18 52	19 15		19 40	19 45	19 52	20 15		20 40	20 45	20 57	21 15	
Ulleskelf	33 d																								
Church Fenton	33 d							18 04										20 04							
Selby	d			17 29											19 29										21 31
South Milford	d			17 38											19 38										21 40
Micklefield	d	17 07						18 11					19 07					20 12					21 12		
East Garforth	d	17 11						18 15					19 11					20 16					21 17		
Garforth	d	17 13						18 18					19 13					20 18					21 19		
Cross Gates	d	17 18						18 23					19 18					20 23					21 24		
Leeds 10	a	17 27	17 38	17 56	18 04	18 08		18 32	18 38	18 57	19 03	19 08	19 27	19 38	19 56	20 05	20 08	20 32	20 38		21 02	21 08	21 33	21 38	21 59
Bradford Interchange	37 a	17 53						18 53					19 53					20 53					21 56		

		NT	TP	GR	TP
				8	
			◇1	1	◇1
				🍴	
York 8	33 d	21 52	22 12	23 05	23 12
Ulleskelf	33 d				
Church Fenton	33 d	22 04			
Selby	d				
South Milford	d				
Micklefield	d	22 12			
East Garforth	d	22 16			
Garforth	d	22 19			
Cross Gates	d	22 23			
Leeds 10	a	22 32	22 36	23 35	23 38
Bradford Interchange	37 a				

Table 40R

Mondays to Fridays

9 December to 16 May

Leeds - Selby and York

Network Diagram - refer to first Page of Table 39

Miles	Miles			TP MX	TP MO	TP MO		TP MX	TP MX	TP	TP	TP	NT	NT	TP	NT	GR	TP	NT		NT	NT	TP	XC	NT
				◇1	◇1	◇1		◇1	◇1	◇1	◇1	◇1			◇1		R 1	◇1					◇1	◇1	
					A	B				C											D	E			
—	—	Bradford Interchange	37 d																07 02		07 20	07 20			07 34
0	0	**Leeds** 10	d	00 32	00 48	00 54		00 54	02 08	02 34	06 04	06 35	06 38	06 48	06 55	06 58	07 10	07 23	07 29		07 41	07 42	07 51	07 57	08 00
4¼	4¼	Cross Gates	d										06 44			07 05			07 36						08 06
7¼	7¼	Garforth	d										06 50	06 58		07 10			07 41		07 51	07 51	08 00		08 12
8	8	East Garforth	d										06 52			07 13			07 43						08 14
9	9	Micklefield	d										06 56			07 17			07 47						08 18
—	12¾	South Milford	d													07 21									08 22
—	20¾	**Selby**	a											07 18		07 33		07 43							08 37
14¾	—	Church Fenton	33 a																		07 59	07 59			
16½	—	Ulleskelf	33 a																						
25½	—	**York** 8	33 a	01 11	01 17	01 21		01 30	02 46	03 04	06 27	07 00	07 15		07 21		07 33		08 06		08 16	08 16	08 20	08 22	

		TP	NT	TP	TP	NT	TP	XC		TP	NT	TP	NT	TP	NT	NT	TP	XC	TP	NT	TP		TP	NT	TP
		◇1		◇1	◇1		◇1	◇1		◇1		◇1		◇1			◇1	◇1	◇1		◇1		◇1		◇1
															D	E									
Bradford Interchange	37 d		07 50			08 20					08 50				09 20	09 20				09 50				10 18	
Leeds 10	d	08 12	08 15	08 28	08 38	08 41	08 57	09 05		09 12	09 15	09 28	09 33	09 38	09 41	09 42	09 57	10 05	10 12	10 15	10 28		10 38	10 41	10 57
Cross Gates	d		08 22			08 48					09 22				09 48	09 49				10 22				10 48	
Garforth	d		08 27			08 53	09 05				09 27				09 53	09 54	10 05			10 27				10 53	11 05
East Garforth	d		08 29			08 56					09 29				09 56	09 56				10 29				10 56	
Micklefield	d		08 33			08 59					09 34				09 59	10 00				10 33				10 59	
South Milford	d		08 38								09 38									10 38					
Selby	a		08 53		08 57						09 53			09 57						10 54			10 56		
Church Fenton	33 a					09 05									10 05	10 05									
Ulleskelf	33 a																								
York 8	33 a	08 35		08 52		09 21	09 22	09 26		09 35		09 52	10 06		10 21	10 21	10 22	10 27	10 35		10 52			11 18	11 22

		XC	TP	NT	TP	TP	NT	TP	XC	TP		NT	TP	TP	NT	TP	XC	TP	NT	TP	TP	NT	NT		TP
		◇1	◇1		◇1	◇1		◇1	◇1	◇1		◇	◇1	◇1		◇1	◇1	◇1	◇	◇1	◇1				◇1
																						D	E		
Bradford Interchange	37 d			10 50			11 20					11 50			12 19				12 50			13 19	13 19		
Leeds 10	d	11 08	11 12	11 15	11 28	11 38	11 42	11 57	12 08	12 12		12 15	12 28	12 38	12 42	12 57	13 08	13 12	13 15	13 28	13 38	13 41	13 42		13 57
Cross Gates	d			11 22			11 49					12 22			12 49				13 22			13 48	13 49		
Garforth	d			11 27			11 54	12 06				12 27			12 54	13 05			13 27			13 53	13 54		14 05
East Garforth	d			11 29			11 56					12 29			12 56				13 29			13 55	13 56		
Micklefield	d			11 33			12 00					12 33			13 00				13 33			13 59	14 00		
South Milford	d			11 38								12 38							13 38						
Selby	a			11 54		11 57						12 53		12 57					13 53		13 57				
Church Fenton	33 a						12 05															14 04	14 05		
Ulleskelf	33 a																								
York 8	33 a	11 30	11 35		11 52		12 21	12 23	12 30	12 35			12 52		13 18	13 22	13 30	13 35		13 52		14 20	14 21		14 22

		XC	TP	NT	TP	TP	NT	TP	XC	TP	NT	TP		TP	NT	TP	XC	TP	NT	TP	TP	NT	NT	TP	XC
		◇1	◇1	◇	◇1	◇1		◇1	◇1	◇1	◇	◇1		◇1		◇1	◇1	◇1	◇	◇1	◇1			◇1	◇1
																						E	D		
Bradford Interchange	37 d			13 50			14 19				14 50				15 19				15 50			16 19	16 19		
Leeds 10	d	14 08	14 12	14 15	14 28	14 38	14 42	14 57	15 08	15 12	15 15	15 28		15 38	15 42	15 57	16 08	16 12	16 15	16 28	16 38	16 42	16 42	16 57	17 08
Cross Gates	d			14 22			14 49				15 22				15 49				16 22			16 49	16 49		
Garforth	d			14 27			14 54	15 05			15 27				15 54	16 05			16 28			16 54	16 54	17 05	
East Garforth	d			14 29			14 56				15 29				15 56				16 30			16 56	16 56		
Micklefield	d			14 33			15 00				15 33				16 00				16 34			17 00	17 00		
South Milford	d			14 38							15 38								16 39						
Selby	a			14 53		14 57					15 53			15 57					16 54		17 01				
Church Fenton	33 a														16 05										
Ulleskelf	33 a																								
York 8	33 a	14 30	14 35		14 52		15 18	15 22	15 30	15 35		15 52			16 21	16 22	16 30	16 35		16 52		17 18	17 20	17 21	17 30

			TP	NT	TP	NT	TP	NT	NT	TP	XC	TP	NT	TP		XC	TP	NT	TP	XC	TP	NT	TP	TP	NT
			◇1	◇	◇1		◇1			◇1	◇1	◇1		◇1		◇1	◇1		◇1	◇1	◇1		◇1	◇1	
Bradford Interchange	37 d			16 50				17 19					17 50					18 19				18 52			19 19
Leeds 10	d		17 12	17 15	17 25	17 28	17 38	17 42	17 46	17 57	18 07	18 12	18 15	18 28		18 36	18 38	18 41	18 57	19 08	19 12	19 15	19 28	19 38	19 41
Cross Gates	d		17 18	17 22		17 35		17 49	17 53				18 22					18 48				19 22			19 48
Garforth	d			17 28	17 34	17 40		17 54	17 58	18 05			18 28					18 53	19 05			19 27			19 53
East Garforth	d			17 30		17 42		17 56	18 01				18 30					18 56				19 29			19 55
Micklefield	d			17 34		17 46		18 00	18 05				18 34					18 59				19 33			19 59
South Milford	d			17 39					18 09				18 39				18 51							19 51	
Selby	a			17 53			17 59		18 23				18 53				19 00							20 00	
Church Fenton	33 a					17 51												19 05							
Ulleskelf	33 a					17 57																			
York 8	33 a		17 36		17 54	18 10		18 18		18 23	18 29	18 35		18 52		18 58		19 21	19 22	19 30	19 35	19 52	19 54		20 22

A from 17 February until 24 March
B until 10 February, from 31 March
C 9 December, 16 December, 23 December
D from 24 March
E until 21 March

Table 40R

Leeds - Selby and York

Mondays to Fridays

9 December to 16 May

Network Diagram - refer to first Page of Table 39

	TP ◇1	XC ◇1	TP ◇1	TP ◇1	NT A	NT B	TP ◇1	TP ◇1	NT	TP ◇1	TP ◇1	TP ◇1		NT	TP ◇1
Bradford Interchange 37 d					20 19	20 19								22 17	
Leeds 10 d	19 57	20 08	20 12	20 45	20 49	20 49	21 12	21 42	21 56	22 12	22 22	22 42		23 02	23 42
Cross Gates d					20 56	20 56			22 02					23 09	
Garforth d	20 05				21 01	21 01			22 08					23 14	
East Garforth d					21 03	21 03			22 10					23 16	
Micklefield d					21 07	21 07			22 14					23 20	
South Milford d							21 24				22 36				
Selby a							21 33				22 46				
Church Fenton 33 a					21 11	21 12								23 25	
Ulleskelf 33 a					21 15	21 16									
York 8 33 a	20 22	20 30	20 35	21 08	21 30	21 30		22 06	22 32	22 38		23 09		23 42	00 09

Saturdays

14 December to 17 May

	TP ◇1	TP ◇1	TP ◇1	TP ◇1	TP ◇1	NT	TP ◇1	GR R 1	NT	TP ◇1	NT	TP ◇1		XC ◇1	NT	TP ◇1	NT	TP ◇1	TP ◇1	NT	TP ◇1	XC ◇1	TP ◇1	NT
Bradford Interchange 37 d											07 20				07 34					08 20				08 50
Leeds 10 d	00 34	00 37	02 16	05 34	06 35	06 38	06 55	07 10	07 14	07 23	07 41	07 51		07 57	08 00	08 12	08 15	08 28	08 38	08 41	08 57	09 08	09 12	09 15
Cross Gates d						06 44					07 48				08 06		08 22			08 48				09 22
Garforth d						06 50					07 53	08 00			08 12		08 27			08 53	09 05			09 27
East Garforth d						06 52					07 56				08 14		08 29			08 56				09 29
Micklefield d						06 56					07 59				08 18		08 33			08 59				09 34
South Milford d															08 22		08 38							09 38
Selby a									07 37	07 43					08 37		08 53		08 57					09 53
Church Fenton 33 a											08 05									09 05				
Ulleskelf 33 a																								
York 8 33 a	01 16	01 04	02 42	06 00	07 00	07 15	07 21	07 32			08 21	08 20		08 24		08 35		08 52		09 21	09 22	09 30	09 35	

	TP ◇1		TP ◇1	NT C	NT D	TP ◇1	XC ◇1	TP ◇1	NT	TP ◇1	TP ◇1	NT C	NT D	TP ◇1		XC ◇1	TP ◇1	NT	TP ◇1	TP ◇1	NT	TP ◇1	XC ◇1	TP ◇1
Bradford Interchange 37 d				09 20	09 20				09 50			10 18	10 18					10 50			11 20			
Leeds 10 d	09 28		09 38	09 41	09 42	09 57	10 08	10 12	10 15	10 28	10 38	10 41	10 42	10 57		11 08	11 12	11 15	11 28	11 38	11 42	11 57	12 08	12 12
Cross Gates d				09 48	09 49				10 22			10 48	10 49					11 22			11 49			
Garforth d				09 53	09 54	10 05			10 27			10 53	10 54	11 05				11 27			11 54	12 05		
East Garforth d				09 56	09 56				10 29			10 56	10 56					11 29			11 56			
Micklefield d				09 59	10 00				10 33			10 59	11 00					11 33			12 00			
South Milford d									10 38									11 38						
Selby a			09 57						10 54		10 57							11 54		11 57				
Church Fenton 33 a				10 05	10 05																12 05			
Ulleskelf 33 a																								
York 8 33 a	09 52			10 21	10 21	10 22	10 30	10 35		10 52		11 18	11 18	11 22		11 30	11 35		11 52		12 21	12 22	12 30	12 35

	NT	TP ◇1	TP ◇1		NT	TP ◇1	XC ◇1	TP ◇1	NT	TP ◇1	TP ◇1	NT	TP ◇1	XC ◇1	TP ◇1	NT		TP ◇1 E	TP ◇1 F	TP ◇1	NT	TP ◇1	XC ◇1	TP ◇1
Bradford Interchange 37 d	11 50				12 19				12 50			13 19				13 50					14 19			
Leeds 10 d	12 15	12 28	12 38		12 42	12 57	13 08	13 12	13 15	13 28	13 38	13 42	13 57	14 08	14 12	14 15		14 28	14 28	14 38	14 42	14 57	15 08	15 12
Cross Gates d	12 22				12 49				13 22			13 49				14 22					14 49			
Garforth d	12 27				12 54	13 05			13 27			13 54	14 05			14 27					14 54	15 05		
East Garforth d	12 29				12 56				13 29			13 56				14 29					14 56			
Micklefield d	12 33				13 00				13 33			14 00				14 33					15 00			
South Milford d	12 38								13 38							14 38								
Selby a	12 53		12 57						13 53		13 57					14 53				14 57				
Church Fenton 33 a												14 05												
Ulleskelf 33 a																								
York 8 33 a		12 52			13 18	13 22	13 30	13 35		13 52		14 21	14 22	14 30	14 35			14 51	14 52		15 18	15 22	15 30	15 35

	NT	TP ◇1	TP ◇1	NT C	NT D		TP ◇1	XC ◇1	TP ◇1	NT	TP ◇1	TP ◇1	NT D	NT C	TP ◇1	XC ◇1	TP ◇1	NT		TP ◇1	TP ◇1	NT D	NT C	TP ◇1
Bradford Interchange 37 d	14 50			15 19	15 19					15 50			16 19	16 19				16 50				17 19	17 19	
Leeds 10 d	15 15	15 28	15 38	15 41	15 42		15 57	16 08	16 12	16 15	16 28	16 38	16 42	16 42	16 57	17 08	17 12	17 15		17 25	17 38	17 42	17 42	17 57
Cross Gates d	15 22			15 48	15 49					16 22			16 49	16 49				17 22				17 49	17 49	
Garforth d	15 27			15 53	15 54		16 05			16 28			16 54	16 54	17 05			17 28		17 34		17 54	17 54	18 05
East Garforth d	15 29			15 56	15 56					16 30			16 56	16 56				17 30				17 56	17 56	
Micklefield d	15 33			15 59	16 00					16 34			17 00	17 00				17 34				18 00	18 00	
South Milford d	15 38									16 39								17 39						
Selby a	15 53		15 57							16 54		17 00						17 53			17 59			
Church Fenton 33 a				16 05	16 05																	18 05	18 05	
Ulleskelf 33 a																						18 09	18 09	
York 8 33 a		15 52		16 21	16 21		16 22	16 30	16 35		16 52		17 18	17 21	17 22	17 30	17 35			17 55		18 24	18 25	18 23

A until 21 March
B from 24 March
C from 29 March
D until 22 March
E from 4 January until 8 February
F from 15 February

Table 40R

Saturdays

Leeds - Selby and York

14 December to 17 May

Network Diagram - refer to first Page of Table 39

			XC	TP	NT	TP	XC	TP	NT	TP	XC		TP	NT	TP	NT	TP	XC	TP	TP	NT	TP	TP	XC		TP
			◇1 🛒	◇1		◇1	◇1 🛒	◇1		◇1	◇1 🛒		◇1		◇1		◇1	◇1	◇1	◇1		◇1	◇1	◇1		◇1
Bradford Interchange	37	d			17 50				18 19					18 52		19 18					20 19					
Leeds 10		d	18 08	18 12	18 15	18 28	18 35	18 38	18 42	18 57	19 08		19 12	19 15	19 38	19 42	19 52	20 08	20 12	20 45	20 49	21 08	21 12	21 15		21 42
Cross Gates		d			18 22				18 49					19 22		19 49					20 56					
Garforth		d			18 28				18 54	19 05				19 27		19 54	20 00				21 01					
East Garforth		d			18 30				18 56					19 29		19 56					21 03					
Micklefield		d			18 34				19 00					19 33		20 00					21 07					
South Milford		d			18 39			18 51							19 51							21 21				
Selby		a			18 53			19 00							20 00							21 30				
Church Fenton	33	a							19 05												21 12					
Ulleskelf	33	a																			21 17					
York 8	33	a	18 30	18 35		18 52	18 57		19 21	19 22	19 30		19 35	19 53		20 18	20 22	20 30	20 35	21 08	21 30		21 40	21 57		22 06

			NT	TP	TP	TP	NT	TP
				◇1	◇1	◇1		◇1
Bradford Interchange	37	d					22 17	
Leeds 10		d	22 00	22 12	22 22	22 42	22 56	23 42
Cross Gates		d	22 07				23 03	
Garforth		d	22 12				23 08	
East Garforth		d	22 14				23 10	
Micklefield		d	22 18				23 14	
South Milford		d			22 36			
Selby		a			22 46			
Church Fenton	33	a					23 19	
Ulleskelf	33	a						
York 8	33	a	22 36	22 38		23 09	23 36	00 09

Sundays

8 December to 9 February

			TP	TP	TP	TP	TP	GR	TP	NT	XC	TP	TP	NT		XC	TP	TP	NT	XC	TP	NT	TP	XC	TP	NT
			◇1 A	◇1 A	◇1	◇1	◇1	1 🍴🛒	◇1		◇1 🛒	◇1	◇1			◇1 🛒	◇1	◇1		◇1 🛒	◇1		◇1	◇1 🛒	◇1	
Bradford Interchange	37	d								08 31				09 20					10 04			11 02				12 02
Leeds 10		d	00 15	00 38	02 35	05 55	07 37	08 30	08 40	08 54	09 08	09 12	09 38	09 50		10 08	10 22	10 35	10 38	11 05	11 12	11 25	11 40	12 05	12 12	12 25
Cross Gates		d								09 00				09 56					10 44			11 32				12 32
Garforth		d								09 06				10 02					10 50			11 37				12 37
East Garforth		d								09 08				10 04					10 52			11 39				12 39
Micklefield		d								09 12				10 08					10 56			11 43				12 43
South Milford		d															10 35									
Selby		a															10 44									
Church Fenton	33	a								09 18									11 02							12 48
Ulleskelf	33	a																								
York 8	33	a	00 42	01 06	03 18	06 38	08 19	08 55	09 02	09 34	09 31	09 37	10 03	10 27		10 29		10 58	11 17	11 27	11 39	11 59	12 03	12 27	12 35	13 02

			TP		TP	TP	XC	TP	NT	TP	TP	XC	TP	NT	TP	TP		XC	TP	NT	TP	TP	XC	TP	NT	TP
			◇1 B		◇1 C	◇1	◇1 🛒	◇1		◇1	◇1	◇1 🛒	◇1		◇1	◇1		◇1 🛒	◇1		◇1	◇1	◇1 🛒	◇1		◇1
Bradford Interchange	37	d							13 02					14 02						15 03					16 03	
Leeds 10		d	12 40		12 40	13 01	13 05	13 12	13 25	13 40	13 57	14 05	14 12	14 25	14 40	15 01		15 05	15 12	15 25	15 40	15 57	16 05	16 12	16 25	16 40
Cross Gates		d							13 32					14 32						15 32					16 32	
Garforth		d							13 37					14 37						15 37					16 37	
East Garforth		d							13 39					14 39						15 39					16 39	
Micklefield		d							13 43					14 43						15 43					16 43	
South Milford		d				13 14										15 14										
Selby		a				13 23										15 23										
Church Fenton	33	a												14 48											16 48	
Ulleskelf	33	a																								
York 8	33	a	13 05		13 06		13 27	13 35	13 59	14 04	14 23	14 27	14 35	15 02	15 06			15 27	15 40	15 59	16 04	16 23	16 27	16 35	17 02	17 08

			TP	XC	TP		TP	NT	TP	TP	XC	TP	NT	TP	XC	TP	XC	XC		TP	NT	TP	TP	XC	TP	NT
			◇1	◇1 🛒	◇1 B		◇1 C		◇1	◇1	◇1 🛒	◇1		◇1	◇1 🛒	◇1	◇1 C 🛒	◇1 B 🛒		◇1		◇1	◇1	◇1 🛒	◇1	
Bradford Interchange	37	d						17 02					18 02								19 02					20 02
Leeds 10		d	17 01	17 05	17 12		17 12	17 25	17 40	17 57	18 05	18 12	18 25	18 40	18 58	19 01	19 08	19 08		19 12	19 25	19 40	19 57	20 08	20 12	20 25
Cross Gates		d						17 32					18 32								19 32					20 32
Garforth		d						17 37					18 37								19 37					20 37
East Garforth		d						17 39					18 39								19 39					20 39
Micklefield		d						17 43					18 43								19 43					20 43
South Milford		d	17 14													19 16										
Selby		a	17 23													19 28							20 17			
Church Fenton	33	a											18 48													20 48
Ulleskelf	33	a																								
York 8	33	a		17 27	17 35		17 37	18 02	18 06	18 23	18 27	18 35	19 02	19 06	19 20		19 30	19 31		19 36	19 59	20 04		20 30	20 34	21 02

A not 8 December

B from 5 January

C until 29 December

Table 40R

Sundays

8 December to 9 February

Leeds - Selby and York

Network Diagram - refer to first Page of Table 39

			TP ◇1	TP ◇1	XC ◇1 A	XC ◇1 B 🛒	TP ◇1		NT	TP ◇1	TP ◇1	TP ◇1	TP ◇1	NT	TP ◇1
Bradford Interchange	37	d							21 02						
Leeds 10		d	20 40	21 04	21 08	21 08	21 12		21 26	21 40	22 12	22 22	22 40	22 43	23 43
Cross Gates		d							21 33					22 49	
Garforth		d							21 38					22 55	
East Garforth		d							21 40					22 57	
Micklefield		d							21 44					23 01	
South Milford		d										22 35			
Selby		a		21 35								22 44			
Church Fenton	33	a												23 07	
Ulleskelf	33	a													
York 8	33	a	21 04		21 31	21 31	21 37		22 00	22 07	22 38		23 06	23 23	00 25

Sundays

16 February to 23 March

			GR R 1 🛒	TP ◇1	NT	XC ◇1 🛒	TP ◇1	TP ◇1	NT	XC ◇1 🛒	TP ◇1	TP ◇1	NT	TP ◇1		NT	TP ◇1	XC ◇1 🛒	TP ◇1	NT	TP ◇1	TP ◇1	XC ◇1 🛒	TP ◇1	NT	TP ◇1
Bradford Interchange	37	d			08 31				09 20				10 04			11 02				12 02					13 02	
Leeds 10		d	08 30	08 40	08 54	09 08	09 12	09 50	09 53	10 08	10 22	10 35	10 38	11 18		11 25	11 48	12 05	12 18	12 25	12 47	13 01	13 05	13 18	13 25	13 48
Cross Gates		d			09 00				09 59				10 44			11 32				12 32					13 32	
Garforth		d			09 06				10 05				10 50			11 37				12 37					13 37	
East Garforth		d			09 08				10 07				10 52			11 39				12 39					13 39	
Micklefield		d			09 12				10 11				10 56			11 43				12 43					13 43	
South Milford		d									10 35											13 14				
Selby		a									10 44											13 23				
Church Fenton	33	a			09 18								11 02							12 48						
Ulleskelf	33	a																								
York 8	33	a	08 55	09 02	09 34	09 31	09 37	10 13	10 30	10 29		10 59	11 17	11 41		11 59	12 11	12 27	12 41	13 02	13 10		13 27	13 41	13 59	14 11

			XC ◇1 🛒		TP ◇1	NT	TP ◇1	TP ◇1	XC ◇1 🛒	TP ◇1	NT	TP ◇1	XC ◇1 🛒	TP ◇1	NT	TP ◇1		TP ◇1	XC ◇1 🛒	TP ◇1	NT	TP ◇1	XC ◇1 🛒	TP ◇1	NT	TP ◇1
Bradford Interchange	37	d				14 02					15 03				16 03						17 02				18 02	
Leeds 10		d	14 05		14 18	14 25	14 47	15 01	15 05	15 18	15 25	15 48	16 05	16 18	16 25	16 47		17 01	17 05	17 22	17 25	17 48	18 05	18 18	18 25	18 47
Cross Gates		d				14 32					15 32				16 32						17 32				18 32	
Garforth		d				14 37					15 37				16 37						17 37				18 37	
East Garforth		d				14 39					15 39				16 39						17 39				18 39	
Micklefield		d				14 43					15 43				16 43						17 43				18 43	
South Milford		d						15 14										17 14								
Selby		a						15 23										17 23								
Church Fenton	33	a				14 48									16 48										18 48	
Ulleskelf	33	a																								
York 8	33	a	14 27		14 40	15 02	15 10		15 27	15 40	15 59	16 11	16 27	16 41	17 02	17 10			17 27	17 45	18 02	18 10	18 27	18 41	19 02	19 10

			XC ◇1 🛒	TP ◇1	XC ◇1 🛒		TP ◇1	NT	TP ◇1	XC ◇1 🛒	TP ◇1	TP ◇1	NT	TP ◇1	TP ◇1	XC ◇1 🛒	TP ◇1	NT		TP ◇1	TP ◇1	TP ◇1	NT	TP ◇1	TP ◇1
Bradford Interchange	37	d						19 02					20 02					21 02							
Leeds 10		d	18 58	19 01	19 08		19 18	19 25	19 48	20 08	20 15	20 22	20 25	20 47	21 04	21 08	21 23	21 26		21 48	22 18	22 22	22 43	22 59	23 52
Cross Gates		d						19 32					20 32					21 33					22 49		
Garforth		d						19 37					20 37					21 38					22 55		
East Garforth		d						19 39					20 39					21 40					22 57		
Micklefield		d						19 43					20 43					21 44					23 01		
South Milford		d		19 16																		22 35			
Selby		a		19 28							20 34				21 35							22 44			
Church Fenton	33	a											20 48										23 07		
Ulleskelf	33	a																							
York 8	33	a	19 20		19 30		19 41	19 59	20 11	20 30		20 45	21 02	21 10		21 31	21 46	22 00		22 15	22 42		23 22	23 27	00 36

Sundays

30 March to 11 May

			TP ◇1	TP ◇1	TP ◇1	TP ◇1	TP ◇1	GR R 1 🛒	TP ◇1	NT	XC ◇1 🛒	TP ◇1	TP ◇1	NT		XC ◇1 🛒	TP ◇1	TP ◇1	NT	XC ◇1 🛒	TP ◇1	NT	TP ◇1	XC ◇1 🛒	TP ◇1	NT
Bradford Interchange	37	d								08 31				09 20					10 04			11 02				12 02
Leeds 10		d	00 15	00 38	02 35	05 55	07 40	08 30	08 40	08 54	09 08	09 12	09 40	09 50		10 08	10 22	10 35	10 38	11 05	11 12	11 25	11 40	12 05	12 12	12 25
Cross Gates		d								09 00				09 56					10 44			11 32				12 32
Garforth		d								09 06				10 02					10 50			11 37				12 37
East Garforth		d								09 08				10 04					10 52			11 39				12 39
Micklefield		d								09 12				10 08					10 56			11 43				12 43
South Milford		d															10 35									
Selby		a															10 44									
Church Fenton	33	a								09 18									11 02							12 48
Ulleskelf	33	a																								
York 8	33	a	00 42	01 06	03 03	06 23	08 06	08 55	09 02	09 34	09 31	09 37	10 03	10 27		10 29		10 58	11 17	11 27	11 39	11 59	12 03	12 27	12 35	13 02

A until 29 December

B from 5 January

Table 40R

Sundays

30 March to 11 May

Leeds - Selby and York

Network Diagram - refer to first Page of Table 39

	TP ◇1	TP ◇1	XC ◇1 trolley		TP ◇1	NT	TP ◇1	TP ◇1	XC ◇1 trolley	TP ◇1	NT	TP ◇1	TP ◇1	XC ◇1 trolley	TP ◇1	NT		TP ◇1	TP ◇1	XC ◇1 trolley	TP ◇1	NT	TP ◇1	TP ◇1
Bradford Interchange 37 d						13 02					14 02					15 03						16 03		
Leeds 10 d	12 40	13 01	13 05		13 12	13 25	13 40	13 57	14 05	14 12	14 25	14 40	15 01	15 05	15 12	15 25		15 40	15 57	16 05	16 12	16 25	16 40	17 01
Cross Gates d						13 32					14 32					15 32						16 32		
Garforth d						13 37					14 37					15 37						16 37		
East Garforth d						13 39					14 39					15 39						16 39		
Micklefield d						13 43					14 43					15 43						16 43		
South Milford d		13 14											15 14											17 14
Selby a		13 23											15 23											17 23
Church Fenton 33 a											14 48											16 48		
Ulleskelf 33 a																								
York 8 33 a	13 06		13 27		13 35	13 59	14 04	14 23	14 27	14 35	15 02	15 06		15 27	15 40	15 59		16 04	16 23	16 27	16 35	17 02	17 08	

	XC ◇1 trolley	TP ◇1	NT	TP ◇1	TP ◇1		XC ◇1 trolley	TP ◇1	NT	TP ◇1	XC ◇1 trolley	TP ◇1	XC ◇1 trolley	TP ◇1	NT	TP ◇1	TP ◇1	XC ◇1 trolley		TP ◇1	NT	TP ◇1	TP ◇1	XC ◇1 trolley
Bradford Interchange 37 d			17 02						18 02						19 02						20 02			
Leeds 10 d	17 05	17 12	17 25	17 40	17 57		18 05	18 12	18 25	18 40	18 58	19 01	19 08	19 12	19 25	19 40	19 57	20 08		20 12	20 25	20 40	21 04	21 08
Cross Gates d			17 32						18 32						19 32						20 32			
Garforth d			17 37						18 37						19 37						20 37			
East Garforth d			17 39						18 39						19 39						20 39			
Micklefield d			17 43						18 43						19 43						20 43			
South Milford d												19 16												
Selby a												19 28					20 17						21 35	
Church Fenton 33 a									18 48												20 48			
Ulleskelf 33 a																								
York 8 33 a	17 27	17 37	18 02	18 06	18 23		18 27	18 35	19 02	19 06	19 20		19 30	19 36	19 59	20 04		20 30		20 34	21 02	21 04		21 31

	TP ◇1	NT	TP ◇1	TP ◇1	TP ◇1	TP ◇1	NT		TP ◇1
Bradford Interchange 37 d		21 02							
Leeds 10 d	21 12	21 26	21 40	22 12	22 22	22 40	22 43		23 43
Cross Gates d		21 33					22 49		
Garforth d		21 38					22 55		
East Garforth d		21 40					22 57		
Micklefield d		21 44					23 01		
South Milford d					22 35				
Selby a					22 44				
Church Fenton 33 a							23 07		
Ulleskelf 33 a									
York 8 33 a	21 37	22 00	22 07	22 38		23 06	23 23		00 25

Table 41

Mondays to Fridays

9 December to 21 March

Manchester Victoria, Rochdale, Blackpool North and Huddersfield - Bradford and Leeds via Brighouse and Halifax

Network Diagram - refer to first Page of Table 39

Miles	Miles	Miles	Miles			NT MX A	NT 🚌	NT	NT	NT	NT B 🚌	NT	NT	NT	NT	NT	NT	NT 🚌	NT	NT	NT	NT C	NT
0	—	—	—	**Manchester Victoria** 🚊	d					05 51				06 17	06 43		06 58			07 17	07 48		08 00
4	—	—	—	Moston	d									06 23			07 04			07 23			08 06
6	—	—	—	Mills Hill	d									06 28			07 09			07 28			08 11
8¾	—	—	—	Castleton	d									06 33			07 14			07 33			08 16
10½	—	—	—	**Rochdale**	a					06 05				06 36	06 56		07 17			07 36	08 01		08 19
—	—	—	—		d					06 05				06 37	06 56		07 18			07 37	08 01		08 20
12¾	—	—	—	Smithy Bridge	d					06 09				06 41			07 22			07 41			08 24
13¾	—	—	—	Littleborough	d					06 13				06 44			07 25			07 44			08 27
17¾	—	—	—	Walsden	d					06 19				06 50			07 31			07 50			
19¼	—	—	—	Todmorden	d					06 22				06 54	07 08		07 35			07 54	08 13		08 34
—	0	—	—	**Blackpool North** 97	d																		
—	3	—	—	Poulton-le-Fylde 97	d																		
—	17½	—	—	**Preston** 8 97	d		04 57																
—	29½	—	—	Blackburn 97	d		05 27																
—	35¾	—	—	Accrington 97	d		05 45																
—	42	—	—	Burnley Manchester Road 97	d		06 05				06 35							07 36					
23½	54¾	—	0	**Hebden Bridge**	a		06 40			06 29	07 10			07 00	07 14		07 41	08 16		08 00	08 19		08 41
—	—	—	—		d	00 04		05 47	06 16	06 29			06 50	07 00	07 16		07 41		07 50	08 00	08 21		08 41
24¾	56	—	1¼	Mytholmroyd	d	00 08		05 50	06 19	06 32				07 03	07 19		07 45			08 04			08 44
28¾	60	—	5¼	Sowerby Bridge	d	00 13		05 56	06 25	06 38			06 57	07 09	07 25		07 50		07 57	08 09			08 50
—	—	0	—	**Huddersfield** 39	d											07 30						08 22	
—	—	—	—	London Kings Cross 15 ⊖26	d																		
—	—	5¾	11	Brighouse	d											07 40	07 59					08 33	08 58
—	—	—	15	Mirfield 39	a												08 06						09 06
—	—	—	—		d												08 06						09 07
—	—	—	18	Dewsbury 39	a												08 11						09 12
32¼	63½	10½	—	**Halifax**	a	00 20		06 02	06 32	06 45			07 03	07 16	07 32	07 50			08 03	08 16	08 33	08 43	
—	—	—	—		d	00 20		06 03	06 32	06 46		07 02	07 03	07 17	07 33	07 50			08 03	08 17	08 33	08 48	
40¼	71½	—	—	**Bradford Interchange**	a	00 34		06 16	06 45	07 00			07 17	07 31	07 47	08 03			08 17	08 31	08 47	09 01	
—	—	—	—		d	00 37		06 18	06 47	07 02			07 20	07 34	07 50	08 05			08 20	08 34	08 50	09 04	
43¾	75	—	—	New Pudsey 37	a			06 27	06 56	07 11			07 28	07 42	07 58	08 13			08 28	08 42	08 58	09 12	
45¾	77	—	—	Bramley 37	a			06 30	06 59	07 14				07 46	08 02	08 18				08 46	09 02	09 16	
49¾	81	—	27¼	**Leeds** 10 37,39	a	00 55		06 41	07 09	07 26		07 56	07 39	07 57	08 12	08 29	08 33		08 39	08 57	09 12	09 27	09 32
—	—	—	—	Selby 40	a									08 37	08 53						09 53		
—	—	—	—	York 8 40	a					08 06			08 16						09 21				

		NT 🚌	NT	NT	NT D	NT	NT C	NT	NT 🚌	NT	NT	NT	NT	NT	NT ◇	NT 🚌	NT	NT ◇	NT E	NT ◇	NT	NT ◇	NT 🚌
Manchester Victoria 🚊	d			08 22	08 30	08 48		09 00			09 22	09 33	09 48		10 00			10 21	10 30	10 48		11 00	
Moston	d				08 36			09 06				09 39			10 06				10 36			11 06	
Mills Hill	d				08 40			09 11				09 44			10 11				10 40			11 11	
Castleton	d				08 45			09 16				09 49			10 16				10 45			11 16	
Rochdale	a			08 34	08 51	09 02		09 19			09 35	09 54	10 02		10 19			10 34	10 51	11 02		11 19	
	d			08 35		09 02		09 20			09 36		10 02		10 20			10 35		11 02		11 20	
Smithy Bridge	d			08 39				09 24			09 40				10 24			10 39				11 24	
Littleborough	d			08 42				09 27			09 43				10 27			10 42				11 27	
Walsden	d			08 48							09 49							10 48					
Todmorden	d			08 52		09 14		09 34			09 53		10 14		10 34			10 52		11 14		11 34	
Blackpool North 97	d																						
Poulton-le-Fylde 97	d																						
Preston 8 97	d																						
Blackburn 97	d																						
Accrington 97	d																						
Burnley Manchester Road 97	d	08 35							09 37							10 38							11 35
Hebden Bridge	a	09 15		08 58		09 20		09 41	10 17		09 59		10 20		10 41	11 18		10 58		11 20		11 41	12 15
	d		08 50	09 00		09 21		09 41		09 50	10 00		10 21		10 41		10 50	11 00		11 21		11 41	
Mytholmroyd	d			09 03				09 44			10 03				10 44			11 03				11 44	
Sowerby Bridge	d		08 57	09 09				09 50			10 09				10 50			11 09				11 50	
Huddersfield 39	d						09 23							10 23							11 23		
London Kings Cross 15 ⊖26	d																						
Brighouse	d						09 34	09 58						10 33	10 58						11 33	11 58	
Mirfield 39	a							10 06							11 06							12 06	
	d							10 07							11 07							12 07	
Dewsbury 39	a							10 12							11 12							12 12	
Halifax	a		09 03	09 15		09 33	09 44			10 02	10 15		10 33	10 43			11 02	11 15		11 33	11 43		
	d		09 03	09 17		09 33	09 49			10 03	10 17		10 33	10 49			11 03	11 17		11 33	11 49		
Bradford Interchange	a		09 17	09 31		09 47	10 03			10 17	10 31		10 47	11 02			11 17	11 31		11 47	12 02		
	d		09 20	09 34		09 50	10 05			10 18	10 34		10 50	11 05			11 20	11 34		11 50	12 05		
New Pudsey 37	a		09 27	09 42		09 58	10 14			10 27	10 42		10 58	11 13			11 28	11 42		11 58	12 13		
Bramley 37	a			09 46		10 02	10 17				10 46		11 02	11 17				11 46		12 02	12 17		
Leeds 10 37,39	a		09 39	09 57		10 12	10 29	10 32		10 38	10 57		11 12	11 27	11 33		11 39	11 57		12 14	12 27	12 31	
Selby 40	a					10 54							11 54							12 53			
York 8 40	a		10 21							11 18							12 21						

A From Manchester Victoria
B not 25 December, 26 December
C From Wakefield Westgate
D From Kirkby
E From Wigan Wallgate

For connections from Liverpool Lime Street please see Table 90

Table 41

Mondays to Fridays

9 December to 21 March

Manchester Victoria, Rochdale, Blackpool North and Huddersfield - Bradford and Leeds via Brighouse and Halifax

Network Diagram - refer to first Page of Table 39

		NT	NT	NT	NT	NT		NT	NT	NT	NT	NT	NT	GC	NT	NT		NT	NT	NT	NT	NT	NT	NT	NT
			◇	A	◇			◇	(bus)		◇	A	◇	R 1		◇		(bus)		◇	A	◇		◇	(bus)
Manchester Victoria	d		11 21	11 30	11 48			12 00			12 21	12 30	12 48			13 00				13 21	13 30	13 48		14 00	
Moston	d			11 36				12 06				12 36				13 06					13 36			14 06	
Mills Hill	d			11 40				12 11				12 40				13 11					13 40			14 11	
Castleton	d			11 45				12 16				12 45				13 16					13 45			14 16	
Rochdale	a		11 34	11 51	12 02			12 19			12 34	12 51	13 02			13 19				13 34	13 51	14 02		14 19	
	d		11 35		12 02			12 20			12 35		13 02			13 20				13 35		14 02		14 20	
Smithy Bridge	d		11 39					12 24			12 39					13 24				13 39				14 24	
Littleborough	d		11 42					12 27			12 42					13 27				13 42				14 27	
Walsden	d		11 48								12 48									13 48					
Todmorden	d		11 52		12 14			12 34			12 52		13 14			13 34				13 52		14 14		14 34	
Blackpool North	97 d																								
Poulton-le-Fylde	97 d																								
Preston 8	97 d																								
Blackburn	97 d																								
Accrington	97 d																								
Burnley Manchester Road	97 d								12 35									13 35							14 36
Hebden Bridge	a		11 58		12 20			12 41	13 15		12 58		13 20			13 41		14 15		13 58		14 20		14 41	15 16
	d	11 50	12 00		12 21			12 41		12 50	13 00		13 21			13 41			13 50	14 00		14 21		14 41	
Mytholmroyd	d		12 03					12 44			13 03					13 44				14 03				14 44	
Sowerby Bridge	d		12 09					12 50			13 09					13 50				14 09				14 50	
Huddersfield	39 d					12 23									13 23								14 23		
London Kings Cross 15 ⊖26	d													10 48											
Brighouse	d					12 33		12 58						13 30	13 35	13 58							14 33	14 58	
Mirfield	39 a							13 06								14 06								15 06	
	d							13 07								14 07								15 07	
Dewsbury	39 a							13 12								14 12								15 12	
Halifax	a	12 02	12 15		12 33	12 43				13 02	13 15		13 33	13 39	13 46				14 02	14 15		14 33	14 43		
	d	12 03	12 17		12 33	12 49				13 03	13 17		13 33	13 41	13 49				14 03	14 17		14 33	14 49		
Bradford Interchange	a	12 17	12 31		12 47	13 02				13 17	13 31		13 47	13 55	14 02				14 17	14 31		14 47	15 02		
	d	12 19	12 34		12 50	13 05				13 19	13 34		13 50		14 05				14 19	14 34		14 50	15 05		
New Pudsey	37 a	12 27	12 42		12 58	13 13				13 27	13 42		13 58		14 13				14 28	14 42		14 58	15 13		
Bramley	37 a		12 46		13 02	13 17					13 46		14 02		14 17					14 46		15 02	15 17		
Leeds 10	37,39 a	12 39	12 57		13 13	13 27		13 32		13 40	13 57		14 14		14 27	14 32			14 39	14 57		15 13	15 27	15 32	
Selby	40 a				13 53								14 53									15 53			
York 8	40 a	13 18								14 21									15 18						

		NT		NT	NT	NT	NT	NT	NT	NT	NT	NT		NT	NT	NT	NT	NT	NT	NT	NT	GC		NT	NT
				◇	A	◇		◇	(bus)		◇	A		◇		◇	(bus)		◇	A		R 1			
Manchester Victoria	d			14 21	14 30	14 48		15 00			15 21	15 30		15 48		16 00			16 24	16 30	16 48				17 00
Moston	d				14 36			15 06				15 36				16 06				16 36					17 06
Mills Hill	d				14 40			15 11				15 40				16 11				16 40					17 11
Castleton	d				14 45			15 16				15 45				16 16				16 45					17 16
Rochdale	a			14 34	14 51	15 02		15 19			15 34	15 51		16 02		16 19			16 37	16 51	17 02				17 19
	d			14 35		15 02		15 20			15 35			16 02		16 20			16 37		17 02				17 20
Smithy Bridge	d			14 39				15 24			15 39					16 24			16 41						17 24
Littleborough	d			14 42				15 27			15 42					16 27			16 45						17 27
Walsden	d			14 48							15 48								16 51						
Todmorden	d			14 52		15 14		15 34			15 52			16 14		16 34			16 54		17 14				17 34
Blackpool North	97 d																								
Poulton-le-Fylde	97 d																								
Preston 8	97 d																								
Blackburn	97 d																								
Accrington	97 d																								
Burnley Manchester Road	97 d								15 36								16 36								
Hebden Bridge	a			14 58		15 20		15 41	16 16		16 00			16 20		16 41	17 16		17 01		17 20				17 41
	d	14 50		15 00		15 21		15 41		15 50	16 01			16 21		16 41		16 50	17 01		17 21				17 41
Mytholmroyd	d			15 03				15 44			16 04					16 44			17 04						17 44
Sowerby Bridge	d			15 09				15 50			16 10					16 50			17 10						17 50
Huddersfield	39 d						15 23								16 23									17 23	
London Kings Cross 15 ⊖26	d																					14 48			
Brighouse	d						15 33	15 58							16 33	16 58						17 30		17 42	17 58
Mirfield	39 a							16 06								17 06									18 07
	d							16 07								17 07									18 07
Dewsbury	39 a							16 12								17 12									18 13
Halifax	a	15 02		15 15		15 33	15 43			16 02	16 16			16 33	16 46			17 02	17 17		17 33	17 40		17 53	
	d	15 03		15 17		15 33	15 49			16 03	16 17			16 33	16 49			17 03	17 17		17 33	17 41		17 53	
Bradford Interchange	a	15 17		15 31		15 47	16 02			16 17	16 31			16 47	17 02			17 17	17 31		17 47	17 55		18 06	
	d	15 19		15 34		15 50	16 05			16 19	16 34			16 50	17 05			17 19	17 34		17 50			18 07	
New Pudsey	37 a	15 27		15 42		15 58	16 13			16 27	16 42			16 58	17 13			17 28	17 42		17 58			18 15	
Bramley	37 a			15 46		16 02	16 17				16 46			17 02	17 17				17 46		18 02			18 19	
Leeds 10	37,39 a	15 39		15 57		16 13	16 27	16 32		16 39	16 57			17 13	17 27	17 31		17 39	17 57		18 12			18 31	18 34
Selby	40 a					16 54								17 53							18 53				
York 8	40 a	16 21								17 18								18 18							

A From Wigan Wallgate

For connections from Liverpool Lime Street please see Table 90

Table 41

Mondays to Fridays

9 December to 21 March

Manchester Victoria, Rochdale, Blackpool North and Huddersfield - Bradford and Leeds via Brighouse and Halifax

Network Diagram - refer to first Page of Table 39

Station		NT	NT	NT	NT	NT	GC	NT		NT	NT	NT	NT
							R 1						
					A								
		🚌									🚌		
Manchester Victoria	d			17 18	17 30	17 43				18 00			18 21
Moston	d			17 24	17 36	17 49							
Mills Hill	d			17 29	17 40	17 54				18 09			
Castleton	d			17 34	17 45	17 59				18 14			
Rochdale	a			17 37	17 51	18 02				18 18			18 35
	d			17 38		18 03				18 18			18 36
Smithy Bridge	d			17 42						18 22			18 40
Littleborough	d			17 46		18 08				18 26			18 43
Walsden	d			17 52						18 32			18 49
Todmorden	d			17 55		18 16				18 35			18 53
Blackpool North	97 d												
Poulton-le-Fylde	97 d												
Preston 8	97 d												
Blackburn	97 d												
Accrington	97 d												
Burnley Manchester Road	97 d	17 36									18 36		
Hebden Bridge	a	18 16		18 00		18 22				18 42	19 16		18 59
	d		17 50	18 00		18 23				18 42		18 50	19 00
Mytholmroyd	d			18 05						18 45			19 03
Sowerby Bridge	d			18 11						18 51			19 09
Huddersfield	39 d							18 25					
London Kings Cross 15	⊖26 d						16 03						
Brighouse	d						18 29	18 34		18 59			
Mirfield	39 a									19 07			
	d									19 08			
Dewsbury	39 a									19 13			
Halifax	a		18 02	18 17		18 35	18 40	18 47				19 03	19 15
	d		18 03	18 18		18 35	18 41	18 49				19 03	19 17
Bradford Interchange	a		18 17	18 32		18 49	18 55	19 02				19 17	19 31
	d		18 19	18 34		18 52		19 05				19 19	19 34
New Pudsey	37 a		18 28	18 43		19 00		19 14				19 27	19 42
Bramley	37 a			18 46		19 04		19 17					19 46
Leeds 10	37,39 a		18 39	18 57		19 13		19 27		19 33		19 39	19 57
Selby	40 a												
York 8	40 a		19 21			19 52						20 22	

Station		NT	NT	NT	NT	NT		NT	NT	NT	NT	NT	NT
					◇			◇				◇	
		B											
									🚌				
Manchester Victoria	d	18 26	18 48		19 00			19 21		19 55		20 21	20 55
Moston	d	18 32			19 06			19 27		20 01		20 27	21 01
Mills Hill	d	18 36			19 11			19 32		20 05		20 32	21 06
Castleton	d	18 41			19 16			19 37		20 10		20 37	21 11
Rochdale	a	18 47	19 01		19 19			19 40		20 14		20 40	21 16
	d		19 01		19 19			19 41				20 41	
Smithy Bridge	d				19 23			19 45				20 45	
Littleborough	d				19 27			19 48				20 48	
Walsden	d							19 54				20 54	
Todmorden	d		19 13		19 34			19 58				20 58	
Blackpool North	97 d												
Poulton-le-Fylde	97 d												
Preston 8	97 d												
Blackburn	97 d												
Accrington	97 d												
Burnley Manchester Road	97 d								19 37				
Hebden Bridge	a		19 20		19 41			20 04	20 17			21 04	
	d		19 20		19 41	19 50		20 05	20 17			21 05	
Mytholmroyd	d				19 44			20 08				21 08	
Sowerby Bridge	d				19 50			20 14				21 14	
Huddersfield	39 d			19 23							20 25		
London Kings Cross 15	⊖26 d												
Brighouse	d			19 33	19 58						20 35		
Mirfield	39 a				20 07								
	d				20 07								
Dewsbury	39 a				20 12								
Halifax	a		19 34	19 43		20 03		20 20	20 45		20 45	21 20	
	d		19 34	19 49		20 03		20 21	20 45		20 49	21 21	
Bradford Interchange	a		19 48	20 02		20 17		20 35	21 10		21 02	21 35	
	d		19 50	20 04		20 19		20 37	21 10		21 04	21 37	
New Pudsey	37 a		19 59	20 13		20 28		20 46	21 20		21 13	21 46	
Bramley	37 a		20 03	20 16				20 49			21 16	21 49	
Leeds 10	37,39 a		20 14	20 30	20 31	20 38		20 59	21 40		21 25	22 01	
Selby	40 a												
York 8	40 a					21 30							

Station		NT	NT	NT		GC	NT	NT	NT	NT
				◇		◇1				
		C				D		C		
						⊠	🚌			
Manchester Victoria	d			21 21					22 28	23 20
Moston	d			21 27					22 34	23 27
Mills Hill	d			21 32					22 39	23 32
Castleton	d			21 37					22 44	23 37
Rochdale	a			21 40					22 47	23 40
	d			21 41					22 48	23 41
Smithy Bridge	d			21 45					22 52	23 45
Littleborough	d			21 48					22 55	23 48
Walsden	d			21 54					23 01	23 54
Todmorden	d			21 58					23 05	23 58
Blackpool North	97 d									
Poulton-le-Fylde	97 d									
Preston 8	97 d									
Blackburn	97 d									
Accrington	97 d									
Burnley Manchester Road	97 d						21 37			
Hebden Bridge	a			22 04			22 17		23 11	00 04
	d		21 49	22 05			22 17		23 11	00 04
Mytholmroyd	d			22 08					23 15	00 08
Sowerby Bridge	d			22 14					23 20	00 13
Huddersfield	39 d	21 27						22 25		
London Kings Cross 15	⊖26 d					19 52				
Brighouse	d	21 37				22 17		22 35		
Mirfield	39 a									
	d									
Dewsbury	39 a									
Halifax	a	21 47	22 01	22 20		22 26	22 45	22 45	23 29	00 20
	d	21 49	22 01	22 21		22 29	22 45	22 49	23 29	00 20
Bradford Interchange	a	22 02	22 15	22 35		22 42	23 10	23 02	23 43	00 34
	d	22 04	22 17	22 37			23 10	23 04	23 46	00 37
New Pudsey	37 a	22 13	22 26	22 46			23 20	23 13	23 54	
Bramley	37 a	22 16		22 49				23 16	23 58	
Leeds 10	37,39 a	22 25	22 36	23 00			23 40	23 26	00 08	00 55
Selby	40 a									
York 8	40 a		23 42							

A From Wigan Wallgate
B From Clitheroe
C From Wakefield Westgate
D ⊠ ◇ from Brighouse

For connections from Liverpool Lime Street please see Table 90

Table 41

Mondays to Fridays

24 March to 16 May

Manchester Victoria, Rochdale, Blackpool North and Huddersfield - Bradford and Leeds via Brighouse and Halifax

Network Diagram - refer to first Page of Table 39

		NT MX A	NT	NT	NT	NT	NT	NT	NT	NT	NT	NT	NT	NT	NT B	NT	NT	NT	NT C	NT	NT B	NT	NT
Manchester Victoria ⇌	d				05 51			06 17	06 43		06 58		07 17	07 48		08 00		08 22	08 30	08 48		09 00	
Moston	d							06 23			07 04		07 23			08 06			08 36			09 06	
Mills Hill	d							06 28			07 09		07 28			08 11			08 40			09 11	
Castleton	d							06 33			07 14		07 33			08 16			08 45			09 16	
Rochdale	a				06 05			06 36	06 56		07 17		07 36	08 01		08 19		08 34	08 51	09 02		09 19	
	d				06 05			06 37	06 56		07 18		07 37	08 01		08 20		08 35		09 02		09 20	
Smithy Bridge	d				06 09			06 41			07 22		07 41			08 24		08 39				09 24	
Littleborough	d				06 13			06 44			07 25		07 44			08 27		08 42				09 27	
Walsden	d				06 19			06 50			07 31		07 50					08 48					
Todmorden	d				06 22			06 54	07 08		07 35		07 54	08 13		08 34		08 52		09 14		09 34	
Blackpool North	97 d						05 29					06 28					07 29						08 29
Poulton-le-Fylde	97 d						05 35					06 34					07 35						08 35
Preston 8	97 d						05 54					06 54					07 54						08 54
Blackburn	97 d						06 10					07 10					08 10						09 10
Accrington	97 d						06 17					07 17					08 18						09 17
Burnley Manchester Road	97 d						06 26					07 26					08 27						09 26
Hebden Bridge	a				06 29		06 49	07 00	07 14		07 41	07 49	08 00	08 19		08 41	08 49	08 58		09 20		09 41	09 49
	d	00 04	05 47	06 16	06 29		06 50	07 00	07 16		07 41	07 50	08 00	08 21		08 41	08 50	09 00		09 21		09 41	09 50
Mytholmroyd	d	00 08	05 50	06 19	06 32			07 03	07 19		07 45		08 04			08 44		09 03				09 44	
Sowerby Bridge	d	00 13	05 56	06 25	06 38		06 57	07 09	07 25		07 50	07 57	08 09			08 50	08 57	09 09				09 50	
Huddersfield	39 d									07 30					08 22						09 23		
London Kings Cross 15 ⊖	26 d																						
Brighouse	d									07 40	07 59				08 33	08 58					09 34	09 58	
Mirfield	39 a										08 06					09 06						10 06	
	d										08 06					09 07						10 07	
Dewsbury	39 a										08 11					09 12						10 12	
Halifax	a	00 20	06 02	06 32	06 45		07 03	07 16	07 32	07 50		08 03	08 16	08 33	08 43		09 03	09 15		09 33	09 44		10 02
	d	00 20	06 03	06 32	06 46	07 02	07 03	07 17	07 33	07 50		08 03	08 17	08 33	08 48		09 03	09 17		09 33	09 49		10 03
Bradford Interchange	a	00 34	06 16	06 45	07 00		07 17	07 31	07 47	08 03		08 17	08 31	08 47	09 01		09 17	09 31		09 47	10 03		10 17
	d	00 37	06 18	06 47	07 02		07 20	07 34	07 50	08 05		08 20	08 34	08 50	09 04		09 20	09 34		09 50	10 05		10 18
New Pudsey	37 a		06 27	06 56	07 11		07 28	07 42	07 58	08 13		08 28	08 42	08 58	09 12		09 27	09 42		09 58	10 14		10 27
Bramley	37 a		06 30	06 59	07 14			07 46	08 02	08 18			08 46	09 02	09 16			09 46		10 02	10 17		
Leeds 10	37,39 a	00 55	06 41	07 09	07 26	07 56	07 39	07 57	08 12	08 29	08 33	08 39	08 57	09 12	09 27	09 32	09 39	09 57		10 12	10 29	10 32	10 38
Selby	40 a							08 37	08 53					09 53						10 54			
York 8	40 a				08 06		08 16					09 21					10 21						11 18

		NT	NT	NT	NT	NT ◇	NT	NT ◇	NT ◇ D	NT ◇	NT	NT ◇	NT	NT ◇	NT D	NT ◇	NT	NT ◇	NT	NT ◇	NT D	NT ◇	GC R 1 ☕
Manchester Victoria ⇌	d	09 22	09 33	09 48		10 00		10 21	10 30	10 48		11 00		11 21	11 30	11 48		12 00		12 21	12 30	12 48	
Moston	d		09 39			10 06			10 36			11 06			11 36			12 06			12 36		
Mills Hill	d		09 44			10 11			10 40			11 11			11 40			12 11			12 40		
Castleton	d		09 49			10 16			10 45			11 16			11 45			12 16			12 45		
Rochdale	a	09 35	09 54	10 02		10 19		10 34	10 51	11 02		11 19		11 34	11 51	12 02		12 19		12 34	12 51	13 02	
	d	09 36		10 02		10 20		10 35		11 02		11 20		11 35		12 02		12 20		12 35		13 02	
Smithy Bridge	d	09 40				10 24		10 39				11 24		11 39				12 24		12 39			
Littleborough	d	09 43				10 27		10 42				11 27		11 42				12 27		12 42			
Walsden	d	09 49						10 48						11 48						12 48			
Todmorden	d	09 53		10 14		10 34		10 52		11 14		11 34		11 52		12 14		12 34		12 52		13 14	
Blackpool North	97 d						09 29						10 29						11 29				
Poulton-le-Fylde	97 d						09 35						10 35						11 35				
Preston 8	97 d						09 54						10 54						11 54				
Blackburn	97 d						10 10						11 10						12 10				
Accrington	97 d						10 17						11 17						12 17				
Burnley Manchester Road	97 d						10 26						11 28						12 26				
Hebden Bridge	a	09 59		10 20		10 41	10 49	10 58		11 20		11 41	11 49	11 58		12 20		12 41	12 49	12 58		13 20	
	d	10 00		10 21		10 41	10 50	11 00		11 21		11 41	11 50	12 00		12 21		12 41	12 50	13 00		13 21	
Mytholmroyd	d	10 03				10 44		11 03				11 44		12 03				12 44		13 03			
Sowerby Bridge	d	10 09				10 50		11 09				11 50		12 09				12 50		13 09			
Huddersfield	39 d				10 23						11 23						12 23						
London Kings Cross 15 ⊖	26 d																						10 48
Brighouse	d				10 33	10 58					11 33	11 58					12 33	12 58					13 30
Mirfield	39 a					11 06						12 06						13 06					
	d					11 07						12 07						13 07					
Dewsbury	39 a					11 12						12 12						13 12					
Halifax	a	10 15		10 33	10 43		11 02	11 15		11 33	11 43		12 02	12 15		12 33	12 43		13 02	13 15		13 33	13 39
	d	10 17		10 33	10 49		11 03	11 17		11 33	11 49		12 03	12 17		12 33	12 49		13 03	13 17		13 33	13 41
Bradford Interchange	a	10 31		10 47	11 02		11 17	11 31		11 47	12 02		12 17	12 31		12 47	13 02		13 17	13 31		13 47	13 55
	d	10 34		10 50	11 05		11 20	11 34		11 50	12 05		12 19	12 34		12 50	13 05		13 19	13 34		13 50	
New Pudsey	37 a	10 42		10 58	11 13		11 28	11 42		11 58	12 13		12 27	12 42		12 58	13 13		13 27	13 42		13 58	
Bramley	37 a	10 46		11 02	11 17			11 46		12 02	12 17			12 46		13 02	13 17			13 46		14 02	
Leeds 10	37,39 a	10 57		11 12	11 27	11 33	11 39	11 57		12 14	12 27	12 31	12 37	12 57		13 13	13 27	13 32	13 40	13 57		14 14	
Selby	40 a			11 54						12 53						13 53						14 53	
York 8	40 a						12 21						13 18						14 20				

A From Manchester Victoria
B From Wakefield Westgate
C From Kirkby
D From Wigan Wallgate

For connections from Liverpool Lime Street please see Table 90

Table 41

Mondays to Fridays

24 March to 16 May

Manchester Victoria, Rochdale, Blackpool North and Huddersfield - Bradford and Leeds via Brighouse and Halifax

Network Diagram - refer to first Page of Table 39

			NT		NT	NT	NT	NT	NT	NT	NT	NT	NT		NT	NT	NT	NT	NT	NT	NT	NT	NT		NT	NT
					◇		◇		◇		◇		◇			◇		◇		◇		◇			◇	
								A							A						A					
Manchester Victoria		d			13 00		13 21	13 30	13 48		14 00		14 21		14 30	14 48		15 00		15 21	15 30	15 48			16 00	
Moston		d			13 06			13 36			14 06				14 36			15 06			15 36				16 06	
Mills Hill		d			13 11			13 40			14 11				14 40			15 11			15 40				16 11	
Castleton		d			13 16			13 45			14 16				14 45			15 16			15 45				16 16	
Rochdale		a			13 19		13 34	13 51	14 02		14 19		14 34		14 51	15 02		15 19		15 34	15 51	16 02			16 19	
		d			13 20		13 35		14 02		14 20		14 35			15 02		15 20		15 35		16 02			16 20	
Smithy Bridge		d			13 24		13 39				14 24		14 39					15 24		15 39					16 24	
Littleborough		d			13 27		13 42				14 27		14 42					15 27		15 42					16 27	
Walsden		d					13 48						14 48							15 48						
Todmorden		d			13 34		13 52		14 14		14 34		14 52			15 14		15 34		15 52		16 14			16 34	
Blackpool North	97	d				12 29						13 29							14 29							15 29
Poulton-le-Fylde	97	d				12 35						13 35							14 35							15 35
Preston 8	97	d				12 54						13 54							14 54							15 54
Blackburn	97	d				13 10						14 10							15 10							16 10
Accrington	97	d				13 17						14 17							15 17							16 17
Burnley Manchester Road	97	d				13 26						14 26							15 26							16 26
Hebden Bridge		a			13 41	13 49	13 58		14 20		14 41	14 49	14 58			15 20		15 41	15 49	16 00		16 20			16 41	16 49
		d			13 41	13 50	14 00		14 21		14 41	14 50	15 00			15 21		15 41	15 50	16 01		16 21			16 41	16 50
Mytholmroyd		d			13 44		14 03				14 44		15 03					15 44		16 04					16 44	
Sowerby Bridge		d			13 50		14 09				14 50		15 09					15 50		16 10					16 50	
Huddersfield	39	d	13 23							14 23							15 23						16 23			
London Kings Cross 15 ⊖	26	d																								
Brighouse		d	13 35		13 58					14 33	14 58						15 33	15 58					16 33		16 58	
Mirfield	39	a			14 06						15 06							16 06							17 06	
		d			14 07						15 07							16 07							17 07	
Dewsbury	39	a			14 12						15 12							16 12							17 12	
Halifax		a	13 46			14 02	14 15		14 33	14 43		15 02	15 15			15 33	15 43		16 02	16 16		16 33	16 46			17 02
		d	13 49			14 03	14 17		14 33	14 49		15 03	15 17			15 33	15 49		16 03	16 17		16 33	16 49			17 03
Bradford Interchange		a	14 02			14 17	14 31		14 47	15 02		15 17	15 31			15 47	16 02		16 17	16 31		16 47	17 02			17 17
		d	14 05			14 19	14 34		14 50	15 05		15 19	15 34			15 50	16 05		16 19	16 34		16 50	17 05			17 19
New Pudsey	37	a	14 13			14 28	14 42		14 58	15 13		15 27	15 42			15 58	16 13		16 27	16 42		16 58	17 13			17 28
Bramley	37	a	14 17				14 46		15 02	15 17			15 46			16 02	16 17			16 46		17 02	17 17			
Leeds 10	37,39	a	14 27		14 32	14 39	14 57		15 13	15 27	15 32	15 39	15 57			16 13	16 27	16 32	16 39	16 57		17 13	17 27		17 31	17 39
Selby	40	a							15 53							16 54						17 53				
York 8	40	a				15 18						16 21							17 20							18 18

			NT	NT	NT	GC	NT	NT	NT		NT	NT	NT	GC	NT	NT	NT	NT	NT		NT	NT	NT	NT	NT	NT
						R								R												
						1								1												
			◇																				◇		◇	
				A								A							B							
						☕								☕												
Manchester Victoria		d	16 24	16 30	16 48			17 00			17 18	17 30	17 43			18 00		18 21	18 26		18 48		19 00		19 21	19 55
Moston		d		16 36				17 06			17 24	17 36	17 49						18 32				19 06		19 27	20 01
Mills Hill		d		16 40				17 11			17 29	17 40	17 54			18 09			18 36				19 11		19 32	20 05
Castleton		d		16 45				17 16			17 34	17 45	17 59			18 14			18 41				19 16		19 37	20 10
Rochdale		a	16 37	16 51	17 02			17 19			17 37	17 51	18 02			18 18		18 35	18 47		19 01		19 19		19 40	20 14
		d	16 37		17 02			17 20			17 38		18 03			18 18		18 36			19 01		19 19		19 41	
Smithy Bridge		d	16 41					17 24			17 42					18 22		18 40					19 23		19 45	
Littleborough		d	16 45					17 27			17 46		18 08			18 26		18 43					19 27		19 48	
Walsden		d	16 51								17 52					18 32		18 49							19 54	
Todmorden		d	16 54		17 14			17 34			17 55		18 16			18 35		18 53			19 13		19 34		19 58	
Blackpool North	97	d							16 29								17 14							18 29		
Poulton-le-Fylde	97	d							16 35								17 20							18 35		
Preston 8	97	d							16 54								17 44							18 54		
Blackburn	97	d							17 10								18 11							19 10		
Accrington	97	d							17 17								18 19							19 17		
Burnley Manchester Road	97	d							17 26								18 28							19 26		
Hebden Bridge		a	17 01		17 20			17 41	17 49		18 00		18 22			18 42	18 49	18 59			19 20		19 41	19 49	20 04	
		d	17 01		17 21			17 41	17 50		18 00		18 23			18 42	18 50	19 00			19 20		19 41	19 50	20 05	
Mytholmroyd		d	17 04					17 44			18 05					18 45		19 03					19 44		20 08	
Sowerby Bridge		d	17 10					17 50			18 11					18 51		19 09					19 50		20 14	
Huddersfield	39	d					17 23								18 25							19 23				
London Kings Cross 15 ⊖	26	d				14 48								16 03												
Brighouse		d				17 30	17 42	17 58						18 29	18 34	18 59						19 33	19 58			
Mirfield	39	a						18 07								19 07							20 07			
		d						18 07								19 08							20 07			
Dewsbury	39	a						18 13								19 13							20 12			
Halifax		a	17 17		17 33	17 40	17 53		18 02		18 17		18 35	18 40	18 47		19 03	19 15			19 34	19 43		20 03	20 20	
		d	17 17		17 33	17 41	17 53		18 03		18 18		18 35	18 41	18 49		19 03	19 17			19 34	19 49		20 03	20 21	
Bradford Interchange		a	17 31		17 47	17 55	18 06		18 17		18 32		18 49	18 55	19 02		19 17	19 31			19 48	20 02		20 17	20 35	
		d	17 34		17 50		18 07		18 19		18 34		18 52		19 05		19 19	19 34			19 50	20 04		20 19	20 37	
New Pudsey	37	a	17 42		17 58		18 15		18 28		18 43		19 00		19 14		19 27	19 42			19 59	20 13		20 28	20 46	
Bramley	37	a	17 46		18 02		18 19				18 46		19 04		19 17			19 46			20 03	20 16			20 49	
Leeds 10	37,39	a	17 57		18 12		18 31	18 34	18 39		18 57		19 13		19 27	19 33	19 39	19 57			20 14	20 30	20 31	20 38	20 59	
Selby	40	a			18 53																					
York 8	40	a							19 21				19 52				20 22							21 30		

A From Wigan Wallgate

B From Clitheroe

For connections from Liverpool Lime Street please see Table 90

Table 41

Mondays to Fridays

24 March to 16 May

Manchester Victoria, Rochdale, Blackpool North and Huddersfield - Bradford and Leeds via Brighouse and Halifax

Network Diagram - refer to first Page of Table 39

		NT	NT	NT	NT	NT	NT	GC	NT	NT	NT
			◇		A		◇	◇ 1 B ⊠	A		
Manchester Victoria	d		20 21	20 55			21 21			22 28	23 20
Moston	d		20 27	21 01			21 27			22 34	23 27
Mills Hill	d		20 32	21 06			21 32			22 39	23 32
Castleton	d		20 37	21 11			21 37			22 44	23 37
Rochdale	a		20 40	21 16			21 40			22 47	23 40
	d		20 41				21 41			22 48	23 41
Smithy Bridge	d		20 45				21 45			22 52	23 45
Littleborough	d		20 48				21 48			22 55	23 48
Walsden	d		20 54				21 54			23 01	23 54
Todmorden	d		20 58				21 58			23 05	23 58
Blackpool North 97	d					20 29					
Poulton-le-Fylde 97	d					20 35					
Preston 8 97	d					20 54					
Blackburn 97	d					21 10					
Accrington 97	d					21 18					
Burnley Manchester Road 97	d					21 27					
Hebden Bridge	a		21 04			21 49	22 04			23 11	00 04
	d		21 05			21 49	22 05			23 11	00 04
Mytholmroyd	d		21 08				22 08			23 15	00 08
Sowerby Bridge	d		21 14				22 14			23 20	00 13
Huddersfield 39	d	20 25			21 27				22 25		
London Kings Cross 15 ⊖26	d							19 52			
Brighouse	d	20 35			21 37			22 17	22 35		
Mirfield 39	a										
	d										
Dewsbury 39	a										
Halifax	a	20 45	21 20		21 47	22 01	22 20	22 26	22 45	23 29	00 20
	d	20 49	21 21		21 49	22 01	22 21	22 29	22 49	23 29	00 20
Bradford Interchange	a	21 02	21 35		22 02	22 15	22 35	22 42	23 02	23 43	00 34
	d	21 04	21 37		22 04	22 17	22 37		23 04	23 46	00 37
New Pudsey 37	a	21 13	21 46		22 13	22 26	22 46		23 13	23 54	
Bramley 37	a	21 16	21 49		22 16		22 49		23 16	23 58	
Leeds 10 37,39	a	21 25	22 01		22 25	22 36	23 00		23 26	00 08	00 55
Selby 40	a										
York 8 40	a					23 42					

Saturdays

14 December to 22 March

		NT	NT	NT	NT	NT	NT	NT	NT	NT	NT	NT	NT	NT	NT	NT	NT	NT	NT	NT	NT	NT	NT
		C	🚌			🚌						🚌				A		🚌			D		
Manchester Victoria	d				05 54			06 17	06 43		06 58			07 17	07 48		08 00			08 22	08 30	08 48	
Moston	d							06 23			07 04			07 23			08 06				08 36		
Mills Hill	d							06 28			07 09			07 28			08 11				08 40		
Castleton	d							06 33			07 14			07 33			08 16				08 45		
Rochdale	a				06 08			06 36	06 56		07 17			07 36	08 01		08 19			08 35	08 51	09 02	
	d				06 09			06 37	06 56		07 18			07 37	08 01		08 20			08 35		09 02	
Smithy Bridge	d				06 13			06 41			07 22			07 41			08 24			08 39			
Littleborough	d				06 16			06 44			07 25			07 44			08 27			08 42			
Walsden	d				06 22			06 50			07 31			07 50						08 48			
Todmorden	d				06 26			06 54	07 08		07 35			07 54	08 13		08 34			08 52		09 14	
Blackpool North 97	d																						
Poulton-le-Fylde 97	d																						
Preston 8 97	d		04 57																				
Blackburn 97	d		05 27																				
Accrington 97	d		05 45																				
Burnley Manchester Road 97	d		06 05			06 35						07 36						08 35					
Hebden Bridge	a		06 40		06 32	07 10		07 00	07 14		07 41	08 16		08 00	08 19		08 41	09 15		09 00		09 20	
	d	00 04		05 55	06 33		06 50	07 00	07 16		07 41		07 50	08 00	08 21		08 41		08 50	09 00		09 21	
Mytholmroyd	d	00 08		05 58	06 36			07 04	07 19		07 45			08 04			08 44			09 03			
Sowerby Bridge	d	00 13		06 04	06 42		06 57	07 09	07 25		07 50		07 57	08 09			08 50		08 57	09 09			
Huddersfield 39	d									07 30						08 21							09 23
London Kings Cross 15 ⊖26	d																						
Brighouse	d									07 40	07 59					08 33	08 58						09 33
Mirfield 39	a										08 06						09 06						
	d										08 06						09 07						
Dewsbury 39	a										08 11						09 12						
Halifax	a	00 20		06 10	06 48		07 03	07 16	07 32	07 50			08 03	08 16	08 33	08 43			09 03	09 16		09 33	09 45
	d	00 20		06 11	06 49		07 03	07 17	07 33	07 50			08 03	08 17	08 33	08 48			09 03	09 17		09 33	09 49
Bradford Interchange	a	00 34		06 24	07 03		07 17	07 31	07 47	08 03			08 17	08 31	08 47	09 02			09 17	09 31		09 47	10 02
	d	00 37		06 26	07 05		07 20	07 34	07 50	08 05			08 20	08 34	08 50	09 04			09 20	09 34		09 50	10 05
New Pudsey 37	a			06 35	07 14		07 28	07 42	07 58	08 14			08 28	08 42	08 58	09 12			09 27	09 42		09 58	10 13
Bramley 37	a			06 38	07 17			07 46	08 02	08 18				08 46	09 02	09 16				09 46		10 02	10 17
Leeds 10 37,39	a	00 55		06 49	07 27		07 39	07 57	08 11	08 30	08 31		08 39	08 56	09 12	09 27	09 32		09 39	09 57		10 12	10 27
Selby 40	a							08 37							09 53							10 54	
York 8 40	a						08 21						09 21						10 21				

A From Wakefield Westgate

B ⊠ ◇ from Brighouse

C From Manchester Victoria

D From Kirkby

For connections from Liverpool Lime Street please see Table 90

Table 41

Saturdays

14 December to 22 March

Manchester Victoria, Rochdale, Blackpool North and Huddersfield - Bradford and Leeds via Brighouse and Halifax

Network Diagram - refer to first Page of Table 39

		NT	NT	NT	NT	NT		NT	NT	NT	NT	NT	NT	NT	NT	NT		NT	NT	NT	NT	NT	NT	NT	NT
			Bus			A					Bus			B					Bus			B			
Manchester Victoria	d	09 00			09 22	09 33		09 48		10 00			10 21	10 30	10 48			11 00			11 21	11 30	11 48		12 00
Moston	d	09 06				09 39				10 06				10 36				11 06				11 36			12 06
Mills Hill	d	09 11				09 44				10 11				10 40				11 11				11 40			12 11
Castleton	d	09 16				09 49				10 16				10 45				11 16				11 45			12 16
Rochdale	a	09 19			09 35	09 54		10 02		10 19			10 34	10 51	11 02			11 19			11 34	11 51	12 02		12 19
	d	09 20			09 36			10 02		10 20			10 35		11 02			11 20			11 35		12 02		12 20
Smithy Bridge	d	09 24			09 40					10 24			10 39					11 24			11 39				12 24
Littleborough	d	09 27			09 43					10 27			10 42					11 27			11 42				12 27
Walsden	d				09 49								10 48								11 48				
Todmorden	d	09 34			09 53			10 14		10 34			10 52		11 14			11 34			11 52		12 14		12 34
Blackpool North	97 d																								
Poulton-le-Fylde	97 d																								
Preston 8	97 d																								
Blackburn	97 d																								
Accrington	97 d																								
Burnley Manchester Road	97 d		09 37								10 38								11 35						
Hebden Bridge	a	09 41	10 17		09 59			10 20		10 41	11 18		10 58		11 20			11 41	12 15		11 58		12 20		12 41
	d	09 41		09 50	10 00			10 21		10 41		10 50	11 00		11 21			11 41		11 50	12 00		12 21		12 41
Mytholmroyd	d	09 44			10 03					10 44			11 03					11 44			12 03				12 44
Sowerby Bridge	d	09 50			10 09					10 50			11 09					11 50			12 09				12 50
Huddersfield	39 d								10 23							11 23								12 23	
London Kings Cross 15 ⊖26	d																								
Brighouse	d	09 58							10 33	10 58						11 33		11 58						12 33	12 58
Mirfield	39 a	10 06								11 06								12 06							13 06
	d	10 07								11 07								12 07							13 07
Dewsbury	39 a	10 12								11 12								12 12							13 12
Halifax	a			10 02	10 15			10 33	10 43			11 02	11 15		11 33	11 43				12 02	12 15		12 33	12 43	
	d			10 03	10 17			10 33	10 49			11 03	11 17		11 33	11 49				12 03	12 17		12 33	12 49	
Bradford Interchange	a			10 17	10 31			10 47	11 02			11 17	11 31		11 47	12 02				12 17	12 31		12 47	13 02	
	d			10 18	10 34			10 50	11 05			11 20	11 34		11 50	12 05				12 19	12 34		12 50	13 05	
New Pudsey	37 a			10 27	10 42			10 58	11 13			11 28	11 42		11 58	12 13				12 27	12 42		12 58	13 13	
Bramley	37 a				10 46			11 02	11 17				11 46		12 02	12 17					12 46		13 02	13 17	
Leeds 10	37,39 a	10 32		10 38	10 57			11 13	11 27	11 35		11 39	11 57		12 12	12 27		12 32		12 39	12 57		13 12	13 27	13 32
Selby	40 a							11 54							12 53								13 53		
York 8	40 a			11 18								12 21								13 18					

		NT		NT	NT	GC	NT	NT	NT	NT	NT	NT		NT	NT	NT	NT	NT	NT	NT	NT	NT		NT	NT
		Bus				R 1 ☕	B				Bus				B				Bus			B			
Manchester Victoria	d				12 21		12 30	12 48		13 00				13 21	13 30	13 48		14 00			14 21	14 30		14 48	
Moston	d						12 36			13 06					13 36			14 06				14 36			
Mills Hill	d						12 40			13 11					13 40			14 11				14 40			
Castleton	d						12 45			13 16					13 45			14 16				14 45			
Rochdale	a				12 34		12 51	13 02		13 19				13 34	13 51	14 02		14 19			14 34	14 51		15 02	
	d				12 35			13 02		13 20				13 35		14 02		14 20			14 35			15 02	
Smithy Bridge	d				12 39					13 24				13 39				14 24			14 39				
Littleborough	d				12 42					13 27				13 42				14 27			14 42				
Walsden	d				12 48									13 48							14 48				
Todmorden	d				12 52			13 14		13 34				13 52		14 14		14 34			14 52			15 14	
Blackpool North	97 d																								
Poulton-le-Fylde	97 d																								
Preston 8	97 d																								
Blackburn	97 d																								
Accrington	97 d																								
Burnley Manchester Road	97 d	12 35									13 35								14 36						
Hebden Bridge	a	13 15			12 58			13 20		13 41	14 15			13 58		14 20		14 41	15 16		14 58			15 20	
	d			12 50	13 00			13 21		13 41		13 50		14 00		14 21		14 41		14 50	15 00			15 21	
Mytholmroyd	d				13 03					13 44				14 03				14 44			15 03				
Sowerby Bridge	d				13 09					13 50				14 09				14 50			15 09				
Huddersfield	39 d								13 23								14 23								15 23
London Kings Cross 15 ⊖26	d					10 48																			
Brighouse	d					13 06			13 33	13 58							14 33	14 58							15 33
Mirfield	39 a									14 06								15 06							
	d									14 07								15 07							
Dewsbury	39 a									14 12								15 12							
Halifax	a			13 02	13 15	13 23		13 33	13 45			14 02		14 15		14 33	14 43			15 02	15 15			15 33	15 43
	d			13 03	13 17	13 24		13 33	13 49			14 03		14 17		14 33	14 49			15 03	15 17			15 33	15 49
Bradford Interchange	a			13 17	13 31	13 38		13 47	14 02			14 17		14 31		14 47	15 02			15 17	15 31			15 47	16 02
	d			13 19	13 34			13 50	14 05			14 19		14 34		14 50	15 05			15 19	15 34			15 50	16 05
New Pudsey	37 a			13 27	13 42			13 58	14 13			14 28		14 42		14 58	15 13			15 27	15 42			15 58	16 13
Bramley	37 a				13 46			14 02	14 17					14 46		15 02	15 17				15 46			16 02	16 17
Leeds 10	37,39 a			13 39	13 57			14 14	14 27	14 32		14 39		14 57		15 13	15 27	15 32		15 39	15 57			16 13	16 27
Selby	40 a							14 53								15 53								16 54	
York 8	40 a			14 21								15 18								16 21					

A From Blackburn

B From Wigan Wallgate

For connections from Liverpool Lime Street please see Table 90

Table 41

Saturdays

14 December to 22 March

Manchester Victoria, Rochdale, Blackpool North and Huddersfield - Bradford and Leeds via Brighouse and Halifax

Network Diagram - refer to first Page of Table 39

Station			NT	NT	NT	NT	NT	NT	NT		NT	NT	NT	NT	NT	NT	NT	NT	NT		NT	NT	GC	NT	NT	NT
				(bus)			A					(bus)			A				(bus)				R 1 (restaurant)	A		
Manchester Victoria (tram)		d	15 00			15 21	15 30	15 48			16 00			16 24	16 30	16 48		17 00				17 18		17 30	17 43	
Moston		d	15 06				15 36				16 06				16 36			17 06				17 24		17 36	17 49	
Mills Hill		d	15 11				15 40				16 11				16 40			17 11				17 29		17 40	17 54	
Castleton		d	15 16				15 45				16 16				16 45			17 16				17 34		17 45	17 59	
Rochdale		a	15 19			15 34	15 51	16 02			16 19			16 37	16 51	17 02		17 19				17 37		17 51	18 02	
		d	15 20			15 35		16 02			16 20			16 37		17 02		17 20				17 38			18 03	
Smithy Bridge		d	15 24			15 39					16 24			16 41				17 24				17 42				
Littleborough		d	15 27			15 42					16 27			16 45				17 27				17 46			18 08	
Walsden		d				15 48								16 51								17 52				
Todmorden		d	15 34			15 52		16 14			16 34			16 54		17 14		17 34				17 55			18 16	
Blackpool North	97	d																								
Poulton-le-Fylde	97	d																								
Preston 8	97	d																								
Blackburn	97	d																								
Accrington	97	d																								
Burnley Manchester Road	97	d		15 36								16 36							17 36							
Hebden Bridge		a	15 41	16 16		16 00		16 20			16 41	17 16		17 01		17 20		17 41	18 16			18 02			18 22	
		d	15 41		15 50	16 01		16 21			16 41		16 50	17 01		17 21		17 41			17 50	18 02			18 23	
Mytholmroyd		d	15 44			16 04					16 44			17 04				17 44				18 05				
Sowerby Bridge		d	15 50			16 10					16 50			17 10				17 50				18 11				
Huddersfield	39	d							16 23								17 23									18 25
London Kings Cross 15 ⊖	26	d																					15 48			
Brighouse		d	15 58						16 33		16 58						17 33	17 58					18 07			18 33
Mirfield	39	a	16 06								17 06							18 07								
		d	16 07								17 07							18 07								
Dewsbury	39	a	16 12								17 12							18 12								
Halifax		a			16 02	16 16		16 33	16 46				17 02	17 17		17 33	17 49				18 02	18 17	18 23		18 35	18 46
		d			16 03	16 17		16 33	16 49				17 03	17 17		17 33	17 49				18 03	18 18	18 24		18 35	18 49
Bradford Interchange		a			16 17	16 31		16 47	17 02				17 17	17 31		17 47	18 04				18 17	18 32	18 38		18 49	19 02
		d			16 19	16 34		16 50	17 04				17 19	17 34		17 50	18 04				18 19	18 34			18 52	19 05
New Pudsey	37	a			16 27	16 42		16 58	17 13				17 28	17 42		17 58	18 13				18 28	18 43			19 00	19 13
Bramley	37	a				16 46		17 02	17 17					17 46		18 02	18 17					18 46			19 04	19 17
Leeds 10	37,39	a	16 31		16 39	16 57		17 13	17 27		17 31		17 39	17 57		18 12	18 29	18 31			18 39	18 57			19 13	19 28
Selby	40	a						17 53								18 53										
York 8	40	a			17 18								18 24								19 21				19 53	

Station			NT	NT	NT		NT	GC	NT	NT	NT	NT	NT	NT	NT		NT	NT	NT	NT	NT	NT	GC	NT	NT	
				(bus)				R 1 (restaurant)	B						(bus)						C				(bus)	
Manchester Victoria (tram)		d	18 00				18 21		18 26	18 48		19 00		19 21			19 55		20 21	20 55				21 21		
Moston		d							18 32			19 06		19 27			20 01		20 27	21 01				21 27		
Mills Hill		d	18 09						18 36			19 10		19 32			20 05		20 32	21 06				21 32		
Castleton		d	18 14						18 41			19 15		19 37			20 10		20 37	21 11				21 37		
Rochdale		a	18 18				18 35		18 47	19 01		19 19		19 40			20 14		20 40	21 16				21 40		
		d	18 18				18 36			19 01		19 19		19 41					20 41					21 41		
Smithy Bridge		d	18 22				18 40					19 23		19 45					20 45					21 45		
Littleborough		d	18 26				18 43					19 27		19 48					20 48					21 48		
Walsden		d	18 32				18 49							19 54					20 54					21 54		
Todmorden		d	18 35				18 53			19 13		19 34		19 58					20 58					21 58		
Blackpool North	97	d																								
Poulton-le-Fylde	97	d																								
Preston 8	97	d																								
Blackburn	97	d																								
Accrington	97	d																								
Burnley Manchester Road	97	d		18 36											19 37										21 37	
Hebden Bridge		a	18 42	19 16			18 59			19 19		19 41		20 04	20 17				21 04					22 04	22 17	
		d	18 42		18 50		19 00			19 20		19 41	19 50	20 05	20 17				21 05			21 49		22 05	22 17	
Mytholmroyd		d	18 45				19 03					19 44		20 08					21 08					22 08		
Sowerby Bridge		d	18 51				19 09					19 50		20 14					21 14					22 14		
Huddersfield	39	d									19 23							20 25			21 27					
London Kings Cross 15 ⊖	26	d						16 36															19 23			
Brighouse		d	18 59					19 09			19 33	19 58						20 35			21 38		21 59			
Mirfield	39	a	19 07									20 07														
		d	19 08									20 07														
Dewsbury	39	a	19 13									20 12														
Halifax		a			19 02		19 15	19 22		19 34	19 43		20 03	20 20	20 45			20 45	21 20		21 47	22 01	22 08	22 20	22 45	
		d			19 03		19 17	19 23		19 34	19 49		20 03	20 21	20 45			20 49	21 21		21 48	22 01	22 10	22 21	22 45	
Bradford Interchange		a			19 17		19 31	19 37		19 48	20 02		20 17	20 35	21 10			21 02	21 35		22 02	22 15	22 24	22 35	23 10	
		d			19 18		19 34			19 50	20 04		20 19	20 37	21 10			21 04	21 37		22 04	22 17		22 37	23 10	
New Pudsey	37	a			19 27		19 42			19 59	20 13		20 28	20 46	21 20			21 13	21 46		22 13	22 26		22 46	23 20	
Bramley	37	a					19 46			20 03	20 16			20 49				21 16	21 49		22 16			22 49		
Leeds 10	37,39	a	19 33		19 38		19 55			20 14	20 30	20 33	20 38	20 59	21 40			21 25	21 59		22 25	22 35		23 01	23 40	
Selby	40	a																								
York 8	40	a			20 18								21 30									23 36				

A From Wigan Wallgate
B From Clitheroe
C From Wakefield Westgate

For connections from Liverpool Lime Street please see Table 90

Table 41

Saturdays

14 December to 22 March

Manchester Victoria, Rochdale, Blackpool North and Huddersfield - Bradford and Leeds via Brighouse and Halifax

Network Diagram - refer to first Page of Table 39

Station			NT	NT	NT	NT
Manchester Victoria ⛴		d	22 21		22 54	23 20
Moston		d	22 27			23 26
Mills Hill		d	22 32			23 31
Castleton		d	22 37			23 36
Rochdale		a	22 42		23 07	23 41
		d			23 07	
Smithy Bridge		d			23 11	
Littleborough		d			23 15	
Walsden		d			23 21	
Todmorden		d			23 24	
Blackpool North	97	d				
Poulton-le-Fylde	97	d				
Preston 8	97	d				
Blackburn	97	d				
Accrington	97	d				
Burnley Manchester Road	97	d				
Hebden Bridge		a			23 31	
		d			23 31	
Mytholmroyd		d			23 34	
Sowerby Bridge		d			23 40	
Huddersfield	39	d		22 25		
London Kings Cross 15 ⊖	26	d				
Brighouse		d		22 35		
Mirfield	39	a				
		d				
Dewsbury	39	a				
Halifax		a		22 45	23 46	
		d		22 49	23 47	
Bradford Interchange		a		23 02	00 02	
		d		23 04	00 04	
New Pudsey	37	a		23 13	00 12	
Bramley	37	a		23 16	00 15	
Leeds 10	37,39	a		23 26	00 27	
Selby	40	a				
York 8	40	a				

Saturdays

29 March to 17 May

Station			NT A	NT	NT	NT	NT	NT	NT	NT	NT
Manchester Victoria ⛴		d			05 54		06 17	06 43		06 58	
Moston		d					06 23			07 04	
Mills Hill		d					06 28			07 09	
Castleton		d					06 33			07 14	
Rochdale		a			06 08		06 36	06 56		07 17	
		d			06 09		06 37	06 56		07 18	
Smithy Bridge		d			06 13		06 41			07 22	
Littleborough		d			06 16		06 44			07 25	
Walsden		d			06 22		06 50			07 31	
Todmorden		d			06 26		06 54	07 08		07 35	
Blackpool North	97	d				05 29					06 28
Poulton-le-Fylde	97	d				05 35					06 34
Preston 8	97	d				05 54					06 54
Blackburn	97	d				06 10					07 10
Accrington	97	d				06 17					07 17
Burnley Manchester Road	97	d				06 26					07 26
Hebden Bridge		a			06 32	06 49	07 00	07 14		07 41	07 49
		d	00 04	05 55	06 33	06 50	07 00	07 16		07 41	07 50
Mytholmroyd		d	00 08	05 58	06 36		07 04	07 19		07 45	
Sowerby Bridge		d	00 13	06 04	06 42	06 57	07 09	07 25		07 50	07 57
Huddersfield	39	d							07 30		
London Kings Cross 15 ⊖	26	d									
Brighouse		d							07 40	07 59	
Mirfield	39	a								08 06	
		d								08 06	
Dewsbury	39	a								08 11	
Halifax		a	00 20	06 10	06 48	07 03	07 16	07 32	07 50		08 03
		d	00 20	06 11	06 49	07 03	07 17	07 33	07 50		08 03
Bradford Interchange		a	00 34	06 24	07 03	07 17	07 31	07 47	08 03		08 17
		d	00 37	06 26	07 05	07 20	07 34	07 50	08 05		08 20
New Pudsey	37	a		06 35	07 14	07 28	07 42	07 58	08 14		08 28
Bramley	37	a		06 38	07 17		07 46	08 02	08 18		
Leeds 10	37,39	a	00 55	06 49	07 27	07 39	07 57	08 11	08 30	08 31	08 39
Selby	40	a					08 37				
York 8	40	a				08 21					09 21

Station			NT	NT	NT B	NT	NT	NT	NT C	NT	NT	NT	NT	NT	NT D
Manchester Victoria ⛴		d	07 17	07 48		08 00		08 22	08 30	08 48		09 00		09 22	09 33
Moston		d	07 23			08 06			08 36			09 06			09 39
Mills Hill		d	07 28			08 11			08 40			09 11			09 44
Castleton		d	07 33			08 16			08 45			09 16			09 49
Rochdale		a	07 36	08 01		08 19		08 35	08 51	09 02		09 19		09 35	09 54
		d	07 37	08 01		08 20		08 35		09 02		09 20		09 36	
Smithy Bridge		d	07 41			08 24		08 39				09 24		09 40	
Littleborough		d	07 44			08 27		08 42				09 27		09 43	
Walsden		d	07 50					08 48						09 49	
Todmorden		d	07 54	08 13		08 34		08 52		09 14		09 34		09 53	
Blackpool North	97	d					07 29						08 29		
Poulton-le-Fylde	97	d					07 35						08 35		
Preston 8	97	d					07 54						08 54		
Blackburn	97	d					08 10						09 10		
Accrington	97	d					08 17						09 17		
Burnley Manchester Road	97	d					08 26						09 26		
Hebden Bridge		a	08 00	08 19		08 41	08 49	09 00		09 20		09 41	09 49	09 59	
		d	08 00	08 21		08 41	08 50	09 00		09 21		09 41	09 50	10 00	
Mytholmroyd		d	08 04			08 44		09 03				09 44		10 03	
Sowerby Bridge		d	08 09			08 50	08 57	09 09				09 50		10 09	
Huddersfield	39	d			08 21						09 23				
London Kings Cross 15 ⊖	26	d													
Brighouse		d			08 33	08 58					09 33	09 58			
Mirfield	39	a				09 06						10 06			
		d				09 07						10 07			
Dewsbury	39	a				09 12						10 12			
Halifax		a	08 16	08 33	08 43		09 03	09 16		09 33	09 45		10 02	10 15	
		d	08 17	08 33	08 48		09 03	09 17		09 33	09 49		10 03	10 17	
Bradford Interchange		a	08 31	08 47	09 02		09 17	09 31		09 47	10 02		10 17	10 31	
		d	08 34	08 50	09 04		09 20	09 34		09 50	10 05		10 18	10 34	
New Pudsey	37	a	08 42	08 58	09 12		09 27	09 42		09 58	10 13		10 27	10 42	
Bramley	37	a	08 46	09 02	09 16			09 46		10 02	10 17			10 46	
Leeds 10	37,39	a	08 56	09 12	09 27	09 32	09 39	09 57		10 12	10 27	10 32	10 38	10 57	
Selby	40	a		09 53						10 54					
York 8	40	a					10 21						11 18		

A From Manchester Victoria
B From Wakefield Westgate
C From Kirkby
D From Blackburn

For connections from Liverpool Lime Street please see Table 90

Table 41

Saturdays
29 March to 17 May

Manchester Victoria, Rochdale, Blackpool North and Huddersfield - Bradford and Leeds via Brighouse and Halifax

Network Diagram - refer to first Page of Table 39

		NT	NT	NT	NT	NT	NT	NT	NT	NT	NT	NT	NT	NT	NT	NT	NT	NT	GC	NT	NT	NT	NT
							A						A						R 1	A			
Manchester Victoria	d	09 48		10 00		10 21	10 30	10 48		11 00		11 21	11 30	11 48		12 00		12 21		12 30	12 48		13 00
Moston	d			10 06			10 36			11 06			11 36			12 06				12 36			13 06
Mills Hill	d			10 11			10 40			11 11			11 40			12 11				12 40			13 11
Castleton	d			10 16			10 45			11 16			11 45			12 16				12 45			13 16
Rochdale	a	10 02		10 19		10 34	10 51	11 02		11 19		11 34	11 51	12 02		12 19		12 34		12 51	13 02		13 19
	d	10 02		10 20		10 35		11 02		11 20		11 35		12 02		12 20		12 35			13 02		13 20
Smithy Bridge	d			10 24		10 39				11 24		11 39				12 24		12 39					13 24
Littleborough	d			10 27		10 42				11 27		11 42				12 27		12 42					13 27
Walsden	d					10 48						11 48						12 48					
Todmorden	d	10 14		10 34		10 52		11 14		11 34		11 52		12 14		12 34		12 52			13 14		13 34
Blackpool North 97	d				09 29						10 29						11 29						
Poulton-le-Fylde 97	d				09 35						10 35						11 35						
Preston 8 97	d				09 54						10 54						11 54						
Blackburn 97	d				10 10						11 10						12 10						
Accrington 97	d				10 18						11 17						12 17						
Burnley Manchester Road 97	d				10 26						11 28						12 26						
Hebden Bridge	a	10 20		10 41	10 50	10 58		11 20		11 41	11 49	11 58		12 20		12 41	12 49	12 58			13 20		13 41
	d	10 21		10 41	10 50	11 00		11 21		11 41	11 50	12 00		12 21		12 41	12 50	13 00			13 21		13 41
Mytholmroyd	d			10 44		11 03				11 44		12 03				12 44		13 03					13 44
Sowerby Bridge	d			10 50		11 09				11 50		12 09				12 50		13 09					13 50
Huddersfield 39	d		10 23						11 23						12 23							13 23	
London Kings Cross 15 ⊖26	d																		10 48				
Brighouse	d		10 33	10 58					11 33	11 58					12 33	12 58			13 06			13 33	13 58
Mirfield 39	a			11 06						12 06						13 06							14 06
	d			11 07						12 07						13 07							14 07
Dewsbury 39	a			11 12						12 12						13 12							14 12
Halifax	a	10 33	10 43		11 02	11 15		11 33	11 43		12 02	12 15		12 33	12 43		13 02	13 15	13 23		13 33	13 45	
	d	10 33	10 49		11 03	11 17		11 33	11 49		12 03	12 17		12 33	12 49		13 03	13 17	13 24		13 33	13 49	
Bradford Interchange	a	10 47	11 02		11 17	11 31		11 47	12 02		12 17	12 31		12 47	13 02		13 17	13 31	13 38		13 47	14 02	
	d	10 50	11 05		11 20	11 34		11 50	12 05		12 19	12 34		12 50	13 05		13 19	13 34			13 50	14 05	
New Pudsey 37	a	10 58	11 13		11 28	11 42		11 58	12 13		12 27	12 42		12 58	13 13		13 27	13 42			13 58	14 13	
Bramley 37	a	11 02	11 17			11 46		12 02	12 17			12 46		13 02	13 17			13 46			14 02	14 17	
Leeds 10 37,39	a	11 13	11 27	11 35	11 39	11 57		12 12	12 27	12 32	12 39	12 57		13 12	13 27	13 32	13 39	13 57			14 14	14 27	14 32
Selby 40	a	11 54						12 53						13 53							14 53		
York 8 40	a				12 21						13 18						14 21						

		NT	NT	NT	NT	NT	NT	NT	NT	NT	NT	NT	NT	NT	NT	NT	NT	NT	NT	NT	NT	NT
				A						A						A						A
Manchester Victoria	d		13 21	13 30	13 48		14 00		14 21	14 30	14 48		15 00		15 21	15 30	15 48		16 00		16 24	16 30
Moston	d			13 36			14 06			14 36			15 06			15 36			16 06			16 36
Mills Hill	d			13 40			14 11			14 40			15 11			15 40			16 11			16 40
Castleton	d			13 45			14 16			14 45			15 16			15 45			16 16			16 45
Rochdale	a		13 34	13 51	14 02		14 19		14 34	14 51	15 02		15 19		15 34	15 51	16 02		16 19		16 37	16 51
	d		13 35		14 02		14 20		14 35		15 02		15 20		15 35		16 02		16 20		16 37	
Smithy Bridge	d		13 39				14 24		14 39				15 24		15 39				16 24		16 41	
Littleborough	d		13 42				14 27		14 42				15 27		15 42				16 27		16 45	
Walsden	d		13 48						14 48						15 48						16 51	
Todmorden	d		13 52		14 14		14 34		14 52		15 14		15 34		15 52		16 14		16 34		16 54	
Blackpool North 97	d	12 29						13 29						14 29						15 29		
Poulton-le-Fylde 97	d	12 35						13 35						14 35						15 35		
Preston 8 97	d	12 53						13 54						14 54						15 54		
Blackburn 97	d	13 09						14 10						15 10						16 10		
Accrington 97	d	13 16						14 17						15 17						16 17		
Burnley Manchester Road 97	d	13 25						14 26						15 26						16 26		
Hebden Bridge	a	13 49	13 58		14 20		14 41	14 49	14 58		15 20		15 41	15 49	16 00		16 20		16 41	16 49	17 01	
	d	13 50	14 00		14 21		14 41	14 50	15 00		15 21		15 41	15 50	16 01		16 21		16 41	16 50	17 01	
Mytholmroyd	d		14 03				14 44		15 03				15 44		16 04				16 44		17 04	
Sowerby Bridge	d		14 09				14 50		15 09				15 50		16 10				16 50		17 10	
Huddersfield 39	d					14 23						15 23						16 23				
London Kings Cross 15 ⊖26	d																					
Brighouse	d					14 33	14 58					15 33	15 58					16 33	16 58			
Mirfield 39	a						15 06						16 06						17 06			
	d						15 07						16 07						17 07			
Dewsbury 39	a						15 12						16 12						17 12			
Halifax	a	14 02	14 15		14 33	14 43		15 02	15 15		15 33	15 43		16 02	16 16		16 33	16 46		17 02	17 17	
	d	14 03	14 17		14 33	14 49		15 03	15 17		15 33	15 49		16 03	16 17		16 33	16 49		17 03	17 17	
Bradford Interchange	a	14 17	14 31		14 47	15 02		15 17	15 31		15 47	16 02		16 17	16 31		16 47	17 02		17 17	17 31	
	d	14 19	14 34		14 50	15 05		15 19	15 34		15 50	16 05		16 19	16 34		16 50	17 04		17 19	17 34	
New Pudsey 37	a	14 28	14 42		14 58	15 13		15 27	15 42		15 58	16 13		16 27	16 42		16 58	17 13		17 28	17 42	
Bramley 37	a		14 46		15 02	15 17			15 46		16 02	16 17			16 46		17 02	17 17			17 46	
Leeds 10 37,39	a	14 39	14 57		15 13	15 27	15 32	15 39	15 57		16 13	16 27	16 31	16 39	16 57		17 13	17 27	17 31	17 39	17 57	
Selby 40	a				15 53						16 54						17 53					
York 8 40	a	15 18						16 21						17 21						18 25		

A From Wigan Wallgate

For connections from Liverpool Lime Street please see Table 90

Table 41

Saturdays

29 March to 17 May

Manchester Victoria, Rochdale, Blackpool North and Huddersfield - Bradford and Leeds via Brighouse and Halifax

Network Diagram - refer to first Page of Table 39

		NT	NT	NT	NT	NT	GC	NT		NT	NT	NT	NT	NT	GC	NT	NT	NT		NT	NT	NT	NT	NT	NT
							■ 1 ⌶	A							■ 1 ⌶	B									
Manchester Victoria ⛴	d	16 48		17 00		17 18		17 30		17 43		18 00		18 21		18 26	18 48			19 00		19 21	19 55		20 21
Moston	d			17 06		17 24		17 36		17 49						18 32				19 06		19 27	20 01		20 27
Mills Hill	d			17 11		17 29		17 40		17 54		18 09				18 36				19 10		19 32	20 05		20 32
Castleton	d			17 16		17 34		17 45		17 59		18 14				18 41				19 15		19 37	20 10		20 37
Rochdale	a	17 02		17 19		17 37		17 51		18 02		18 18		18 35		18 47	19 01			19 19		19 40	20 14		20 40
	d	17 02		17 20		17 38				18 03		18 18		18 36			19 01			19 19		19 41			20 41
Smithy Bridge	d			17 24		17 42						18 22		18 40						19 23		19 45			20 45
Littleborough	d			17 27		17 46				18 08		18 26		18 43						19 27		19 48			20 48
Walsden	d					17 52						18 32		18 49								19 54			20 54
Todmorden	d	17 14		17 34		17 55				18 16		18 35		18 53			19 13			19 34		19 58			20 58
Blackpool North 97	d				16 29								17 14								18 29				
Poulton-le-Fylde 97	d				16 35								17 20								18 35				
Preston 8 97	d				16 54								17 44								18 54				
Blackburn 97	d				17 10								18 11								19 10				
Accrington 97	d				17 17								18 19								19 17				
Burnley Manchester Road 97	d				17 26								18 28								19 26				
Hebden Bridge	a	17 20		17 41	17 49	18 02				18 22		18 42	18 49	18 59			19 19			19 41	19 49	20 04			21 04
	d	17 21		17 41	17 50	18 02				18 23		18 42	18 50	19 00			19 20			19 41	19 50	20 05			21 05
Mytholmroyd	d			17 44		18 05						18 45		19 03						19 44		20 08			21 08
Sowerby Bridge	d			17 50		18 11						18 51		19 09						19 50		20 14			21 14
Huddersfield 39	d		17 23								18 25							19 23						20 25	
London Kings Cross 15 ⊖26	d						15 48								16 36										
Brighouse	d		17 33	17 58			18 07				18 33	18 59			19 09			19 33		19 58				20 35	
Mirfield 39	a			18 07								19 07								20 07					
	d			18 07								19 08								20 07					
Dewsbury 39	a			18 12								19 13								20 12					
Halifax	a	17 33	17 49		18 02	18 17	18 23			18 35	18 46		19 02	19 15	19 22		19 34	19 43			20 03	20 20		20 45	21 20
	d	17 33	17 49		18 03	18 18	18 24			18 35	18 49		19 03	19 17	19 23		19 34	19 49			20 03	20 21		20 49	21 21
Bradford Interchange	a	17 47	18 04		18 17	18 32	18 38			18 49	19 02		19 17	19 31	19 37		19 48	20 02			20 17	20 35		21 02	21 35
	d	17 50	18 04		18 19	18 34				18 52	19 05		19 18	19 34			19 50	20 04			20 19	20 37		21 04	21 37
New Pudsey 37	a	17 58	18 13		18 28	18 43				19 00	19 13		19 27	19 42			19 59	20 13			20 28	20 46		21 13	21 46
Bramley 37	a	18 02	18 17			18 46				19 04	19 17			19 46			20 03	20 16				20 49		21 16	21 49
Leeds 10 37,39	a	18 12	18 29	18 31	18 39	18 57				19 13	19 28	19 33	19 38	19 55			20 14	20 30		20 33	20 38	20 59		21 25	21 59
Selby 40	a	18 53																							
York 8 40	a				19 21					19 53			20 18								21 30				

		NT	NT	NT		GC	NT	NT	NT	NT	NT
			C								
Manchester Victoria ⛴	d	20 55					21 21	22 21		22 54	23 20
Moston	d	21 01					21 27	22 27			23 26
Mills Hill	d	21 06					21 32	22 32			23 31
Castleton	d	21 11					21 37	22 37			23 36
Rochdale	a	21 16					21 40	22 42		23 07	23 41
	d						21 41			23 07	
Smithy Bridge	d						21 45			23 11	
Littleborough	d						21 48			23 15	
Walsden	d						21 54			23 21	
Todmorden	d						21 58			23 24	
Blackpool North 97	d			20 29							
Poulton-le-Fylde 97	d			20 35							
Preston 8 97	d			20 54							
Blackburn 97	d			21 10							
Accrington 97	d			21 18							
Burnley Manchester Road 97	d			21 27							
Hebden Bridge	a			21 49			22 04			23 31	
	d			21 49			22 05			23 31	
Mytholmroyd	d						22 08			23 34	
Sowerby Bridge	d						22 14			23 40	
Huddersfield 39	d		21 27						22 25		
London Kings Cross 15 ⊖26	d					19 23					
Brighouse	d		21 38			21 59			22 35		
Mirfield 39	a										
	d										
Dewsbury 39	a										
Halifax	a		21 47	22 01		22 08	22 20		22 45	23 46	
	d		21 48	22 01		22 10	22 21		22 49	23 47	
Bradford Interchange	a		22 02	22 15		22 24	22 35		23 02	00 02	
	d		22 04	22 17			22 37		23 04	00 04	
New Pudsey 37	a		22 13	22 26			22 46		23 13	00 12	
Bramley 37	a		22 16				22 49		23 16	00 15	
Leeds 10 37,39	a		22 25	22 35			23 01		23 26	00 27	
Selby 40	a										
York 8 40	a			23 36							

A From Wigan Wallgate **B** From Clitheroe **C** From Wakefield Westgate

For connections from Liverpool Lime Street please see Table 90

Table 41

Sundays

8 December to 29 December

Manchester Victoria, Rochdale, Blackpool North and Huddersfield - Bradford and Leeds via Brighouse and Halifax

Network Diagram - refer to first Page of Table 39

Station	Table	a/d	NT	NT	NT	NT	NT	NT	NT	NT	NT		NT	NT	NT	NT	NT	NT	NT	NT	NT		NT	NT	NT	NT
			A							Bus								Bus						Bus		
Manchester Victoria		d			08 32			09 14	09 48				10 14	10 48			11 15			11 48			12 14		12 48	
Moston		d							09 54					10 54						11 54					12 54	
Mills Hill		d							09 59					10 58						11 58					12 58	
Castleton		d							10 04					11 03						12 03					13 03	
Rochdale		a			08 48			09 27	10 10				10 27	11 09			11 27			12 09			12 28		13 09	
		d						09 28					10 28				11 28						12 28			
Smithy Bridge		d						09 32					10 32				11 32						12 32			
Littleborough		d						09 36					10 36				11 36						12 36			
Walsden		d						09 42					10 42				11 42						12 42			
Todmorden		d						09 45					10 45				11 45						12 45			
Blackpool North	97	d																								
Poulton-le-Fylde	97	d																								
Preston 8	97	d																								
Blackburn	97	d																								
Accrington	97	d																								
Burnley Manchester Road	97	d								10 12								11 20						12 20		
Hebden Bridge		a						09 52					10 52				11 52	12 00					12 52	13 00		
		d						09 52			10 22		10 52			11 32	11 52	12 00			12 32		12 52	13 00		
Mytholmroyd		d						09 55					10 55				11 55						12 55			
Sowerby Bridge		d						10 01					11 01				12 01						13 01			
Huddersfield	39	d					09 27								11 08											13 08
London Kings Cross 15 ⊖	26	d																								
Brighouse		d					09 37								11 18											13 18
Mirfield	39	a																								
		d																								
Dewsbury	39	a																								
Halifax		a					09 48	10 08		11 12	10 34		11 08		11 28	11 44	12 08	12 20			12 44		13 08	13 20		13 28
		d				09 05	09 48	10 08			10 45		11 08		11 29	11 45	12 08		12 29		12 45		13 08			13 29
Bradford Interchange		a				09 18	10 01	10 22			11 00		11 22		11 42	11 59	12 22		12 42		12 59		13 22			13 42
		d	00 04	08 31		09 20	10 04	10 25			11 02		11 25		11 44	12 02	12 25		12 44		13 02		13 25			13 44
New Pudsey	37	a	00 12	08 39		09 29	10 12	10 33			11 10		11 33		11 53	12 10	12 33		12 53		13 10		13 33			13 53
Bramley	37	a	00 15	08 43		09 32	10 16	10 37					11 37		11 56		12 37		12 56				13 37			13 56
Leeds 10	37,39	a	00 27	08 51		09 42	10 25	10 46			11 21		11 48		12 05	12 22	12 46		13 06		13 22		13 46			14 06
Selby	40	a																								
York 8	40	a		09 34		10 27	11 17				11 59					13 02					13 59					

Station	Table	a/d	NT	NT	GC	NT	NT		NT	NT	NT	NT	NT	NT	NT	NT	NT		NT	NT	NT	NT	NT	NT	NT	NT
					R	Bus						Bus					Bus						Bus			
Manchester Victoria		d		13 15					13 48		14 15		14 48			15 15				15 48		16 15		16 48		
Moston		d							13 54				14 54							15 54				16 54		
Mills Hill		d							13 58				14 58							15 58				16 58		
Castleton		d							14 03				15 03							16 03				17 03		
Rochdale		a		13 27					14 09		14 27		15 09			15 27				16 09		16 27		17 09		
		d		13 28							14 28					15 28						16 28				
Smithy Bridge		d		13 32							14 32					15 32						16 32				
Littleborough		d		13 36							14 36					15 36						16 36				
Walsden		d		13 42							14 42					15 42						16 42				
Todmorden		d		13 45							14 45					15 45						16 45				
Blackpool North	97	d																								
Poulton-le-Fylde	97	d																								
Preston 8	97	d																								
Blackburn	97	d																								
Accrington	97	d																								
Burnley Manchester Road	97	d				13 20						14 20					15 20						16 20			
Hebden Bridge		a		13 52		14 00					14 52	15 00				15 52	16 00					16 52	17 00			
		d	13 32	13 52		14 00				14 32	14 52	15 00			15 32	15 52	16 00				16 32	16 52	17 00			17 32
Mytholmroyd		d		13 55							14 55					15 55						16 55				
Sowerby Bridge		d		14 01							15 01					16 01						17 01				
Huddersfield	39	d												15 08											17 08	
London Kings Cross 15 ⊖	26	d			11 50																					
Brighouse		d			14 09									15 18											17 18	
Mirfield	39	a																								
		d																								
Dewsbury	39	a																								
Halifax		a	13 44	14 08	14 19	14 20				14 44	15 08	15 20		15 28	15 44	16 08	16 20				16 44	17 08	17 20		17 26	17 44
		d	13 46	14 08	14 22		14 29			14 45	15 08			15 29	15 46	16 08			16 29		16 45	17 08			17 26	17 45
Bradford Interchange		a	14 00	14 22	14 35		14 42			15 00	15 22			15 42	16 00	16 22			16 42		16 59	17 22			17 41	17 59
		d	14 02	14 25			14 44			15 03	15 25			15 44	16 03	16 25			16 44		17 02	17 25			17 43	18 02
New Pudsey	37	a	14 10	14 33			14 53			15 11	15 33			15 53	16 11	16 33			16 53		17 10	17 33			17 52	18 10
Bramley	37	a		14 37			14 56				15 37			15 56		16 37			16 56			17 37			17 56	
Leeds 10	37,39	a	14 22	14 48			15 06			15 22	15 46			16 06	16 22	16 46			17 05		17 22	17 48			18 07	18 22
Selby	40	a																								
York 8	40	a	15 02							15 59					17 02						18 02					19 02

A not 8 December. From Manchester Victoria

For connections from Liverpool Lime Street please see Table 90

Table 41

Sundays

8 December to 29 December

Manchester Victoria, Rochdale, Blackpool North and Huddersfield - Bradford and Leeds via Brighouse and Halifax

Network Diagram - refer to first Page of Table 39

		NT		GC	NT	NT	NT	NT	NT	NT	NT	NT	
				R ☕	🚌					🚌			
Manchester Victoria ⛴	d	17 15					17 48		18 09				
Moston	d						17 54		18 15				
Mills Hill	d						17 58		18 19				
Castleton	d						18 03		18 24				
Rochdale	a	17 27					18 09		18 28				
	d	17 28							18 28				
Smithy Bridge	d	17 32							18 32				
Littleborough	d	17 36							18 36				
Walsden	d	17 42							18 42				
Todmorden	d	17 45							18 45				
Blackpool North 97	d												
Poulton-le-Fylde 97	d												
Preston 8 97	d												
Blackburn 97	d												
Accrington 97	d												
Burnley Manchester Road 97	d				17 20					18 20			
Hebden Bridge	a	17 52			18 00				18 52	19 00			
	d	17 52			18 00			18 32	18 52	19 00		19 32	
Mytholmroyd	d	17 55							18 55				
Sowerby Bridge	d	18 01							19 01				
Huddersfield 39	d										19 08		
London Kings Cross 15 ⊖26	d			15 50									
Brighouse	d			18 09							19 18		
Mirfield 39	a												
	d												
Dewsbury 39	a												
Halifax	a	18 08		18 19	18 20			18 44	19 08	19 20	19 28	19 44	
	d	18 08		18 20		18 29		18 45	19 08		19 29	19 45	
Bradford Interchange	a	18 22		18 33		18 42		19 00	19 24		19 42	19 59	
	d	18 25				18 44		19 02	19 25		19 44	20 02	
New Pudsey 37	a	18 33				18 53		19 10	19 33		19 53	20 10	
Bramley 37	a	18 37				18 56			19 37		19 56		
Leeds 10 37,39	a	18 46				19 08		19 22	19 46		20 08	20 22	
Selby 40	a												
York 8 40	a							19 59				21 02	

		NT	NT	NT	NT	NT	NT	GC	NT	GC		NT	NT
			🚌			🚌		R ☕		R 1 ☕			🚌
Manchester Victoria ⛴	d	19 09			20 09							21 09	
Moston	d	19 15			20 15							21 15	
Mills Hill	d	19 19			20 19							21 19	
Castleton	d	19 24			20 24							21 24	
Rochdale	a	19 28			20 28							21 28	
	d	19 28			20 28							21 28	
Smithy Bridge	d	19 32			20 32							21 32	
Littleborough	d	19 36			20 36							21 36	
Walsden	d	19 42			20 42							21 42	
Todmorden	d	19 45			20 45							21 45	
Blackpool North 97	d												
Poulton-le-Fylde 97	d												
Preston 8 97	d												
Blackburn 97	d												
Accrington 97	d												
Burnley Manchester Road 97	d		19 20			20 20							21 20
Hebden Bridge	a	19 52	20 00		20 52	21 00						21 52	22 00
	d	19 52	20 00	20 32	20 52	21 00			21 32			21 52	22 00
Mytholmroyd	d	19 55			20 55							21 55	
Sowerby Bridge	d	20 01			21 01							22 01	
Huddersfield 39	d						21 08						
London Kings Cross 15 ⊖26	d							18 45		19 23			
Brighouse	d						21 18	21 25		21 44			
Mirfield 39	a												
	d												
Dewsbury 39	a												
Halifax	a	20 08	20 20	20 44	21 08	21 20	21 28	21 34	21 44	21 54		22 08	22 20
	d	20 08		20 45	21 08		21 30	21 35	21 45	21 55		22 09	
Bradford Interchange	a	20 22		20 59	21 22		21 42	21 49	21 59	22 08		22 23	
	d	20 25		21 02	21 26		21 44		22 02			22 26	
New Pudsey 37	a	20 33		21 10	21 34		21 53		22 10			22 34	
Bramley 37	a	20 37			21 38		21 56					22 38	
Leeds 10 37,39	a	20 47		21 22	21 48		22 05		22 21			22 47	
Selby 40	a												
York 8 40	a			22 00									

		NT	NT	NT	NT
					🚌
Manchester Victoria ⛴	d		22 09		
Moston	d		22 15		
Mills Hill	d		22 19		
Castleton	d		22 24		
Rochdale	a		22 28		
	d		22 28		
Smithy Bridge	d		22 32		
Littleborough	d		22 36		
Walsden	d		22 42		
Todmorden	d		22 45		
Blackpool North 97	d				
Poulton-le-Fylde 97	d				
Preston 8 97	d				
Blackburn 97	d				
Accrington 97	d				
Burnley Manchester Road 97	d				22 20
Hebden Bridge	a		22 52		23 00
	d	22 34	22 52		23 00
Mytholmroyd	d		22 55		
Sowerby Bridge	d		23 01		
Huddersfield 39	d				
London Kings Cross 15 ⊖26	d				
Brighouse	d				
Mirfield 39	a				
	d				
Dewsbury 39	a				
Halifax	a	22 46	23 08		
	d	22 47	23 08		
Bradford Interchange	a	23 01	23 22		
	d	23 04	23 25	23 47	
New Pudsey 37	a	23 12	23 33	23 55	
Bramley 37	a		23 37	23 59	
Leeds 10 37,39	a	23 23	23 46	00 08	00 15
Selby 40	a				
York 8 40	a				

For connections from Liverpool Lime Street please see Table 90

Table 41

Sundays

5 January to 9 February

Manchester Victoria, Rochdale, Blackpool North and Huddersfield - Bradford and Leeds via Brighouse and Halifax

Network Diagram - refer to first Page of Table 39

Station		NT	NT	NT	NT	NT	NT	NT	NT	NT	NT	NT	NT	NT	NT	NT	NT	NT	NT	NT	NT	NT	NT
		A						🚌								🚌					🚌		
Manchester Victoria	d				09 14				10 14		10 48			11 14				12 14					
Moston	d										10 54												
Mills Hill	d										10 58												
Castleton	d										11 03												
Rochdale	a				09 28				10 27		11 09			11 27				12 28					
	d																						
Smithy Bridge	d																						
Littleborough	d																						
Walsden	d																						
Todmorden	d																						
Blackpool North 97	d																						
Poulton-le-Fylde 97	d																						
Preston 8 97	d																						
Blackburn 97	d																						
Accrington 97	d																						
Burnley Manchester Road 97	d							10 12								11 20					12 20		
Hebden Bridge	a															12 00					13 00		
	d									10 22					11 32	12 00				12 32	13 00		
Mytholmroyd	d																						
Sowerby Bridge	d																						
Huddersfield 39	d					09 27							11 08										13 08
London Kings Cross 15 ⊖26	d																						
Brighouse	d					09 37							11 18										13 18
Mirfield 39	a																						
	d																						
Dewsbury 39	a																						
Halifax	a					09 48		11 12		10 34			11 28		11 44	12 20				12 44	13 20		13 28
	d			09 05		09 48	10 08			10 45		11 08	11 29		11 45		12 08		12 29	12 45		13 08	13 29
Bradford Interchange	a			09 18		10 01	10 22			11 00		11 22	11 42		11 59		12 22		12 42	12 59		13 22	13 42
	d	00 04	08 31	09 20		10 04	10 25			11 02		11 25	11 44		12 02		12 25		12 44	13 02		13 25	13 44
New Pudsey 37	a	00 12	08 39	09 29		10 12	10 33			11 10		11 33	11 53		12 10		12 33		12 53	13 10		13 33	13 53
Bramley 37	a	00 15	08 43	09 32		10 16	10 37					11 37	11 56				12 37		12 56			13 37	13 56
Leeds 10 37,39	a	00 27	08 51	09 42		10 25	10 46			11 21		11 48	12 05		12 22		12 46		13 06	13 22		13 46	14 06
Selby 40	a																						
York 8 40	a		09 34	10 27		11 17				11 59					13 02					13 59			

Station		NT	NT	NT	NT	NT	NT	GC	NT	NT	NT	NT	NT	NT	NT	NT	NT	NT	NT	NT	NT	NT	NT
				🚌				8		🚌					🚌					🚌			
Manchester Victoria	d	13 14				14 14							15 14				16 14						17 14
Moston	d																						
Mills Hill	d																						
Castleton	d																						
Rochdale	a	13 27				14 27							15 27				16 27						17 27
	d																						
Smithy Bridge	d																						
Littleborough	d																						
Walsden	d																						
Todmorden	d																						
Blackpool North 97	d																						
Poulton-le-Fylde 97	d																						
Preston 8 97	d																						
Blackburn 97	d																						
Accrington 97	d																						
Burnley Manchester Road 97	d			13 20						14 20					15 20					16 20			
Hebden Bridge	a			14 00						15 00					16 00					17 00			
	d		13 32	14 00					14 32	15 00				15 32	16 00				16 32	17 00			
Mytholmroyd	d																						
Sowerby Bridge	d																						
Huddersfield 39	d											15 08										17 08	
London Kings Cross 15 ⊖26	d							11 53															
Brighouse	d							14 20				15 18										17 18	
Mirfield 39	a																						
	d																						
Dewsbury 39	a																						
Halifax	a		13 44	14 20				14 36	14 44	15 20		15 28		15 44	16 20				16 44	17 20		17 26	
	d		13 46		14 08		14 29	14 37	14 45		15 08	15 29		15 46		16 08		16 29	16 45		17 08	17 26	
Bradford Interchange	a		14 00		14 22		14 42	14 50	15 00		15 22	15 42		16 00		16 22		16 42	16 59		17 22	17 41	
	d		14 02		14 25		14 44		15 03		15 25	15 44		16 03		16 25		16 44	17 02		17 25	17 43	
New Pudsey 37	a		14 10		14 33		14 53		15 11		15 33	15 53		16 11		16 33		16 53	17 10		17 33	17 52	
Bramley 37	a				14 37		14 56				15 37	15 56				16 37		16 56			17 37	17 56	
Leeds 10 37,39	a		14 22		14 48		15 06		15 22		15 46	16 06		16 22		16 46		17 05	17 22		17 48	18 07	
Selby 40	a																						
York 8 40	a		15 02						15 59					17 02					18 02				

A From Manchester Victoria

For connections from Liverpool Lime Street please see Table 90

Table 41

Sundays

5 January to 9 February

Manchester Victoria, Rochdale, Blackpool North and Huddersfield - Bradford and Leeds via Brighouse and Halifax

Network Diagram - refer to first Page of Table 39

		NT	NT	NT	NT	NT	NT	GC	NT	NT	NT	NT	NT	NT	NT	NT	NT	NT	NT	NT	NT	NT
								R														
			🚌						🚌					🚌				🚌				
								☕														
Manchester Victoria 🚢	d				18 08						19 08					20 08				21 08		
Moston	d				18 15						19 15					20 15				21 15		
Mills Hill	d				18 19						19 19					20 19				21 19		
Castleton	d				18 24						19 24					20 24				21 24		
Rochdale	a				18 28						19 28					20 28				21 28		
	d																					
Smithy Bridge	d																					
Littleborough	d																					
Walsden	d																					
Todmorden	d																					
Blackpool North 97	d																					
Poulton-le-Fylde 97	d																					
Preston 8 97	d																					
Blackburn 97	d																					
Accrington 97	d																					
Burnley Manchester Road 97	d		17 20						18 20					19 20				20 20				
Hebden Bridge	a		18 00						19 00					20 00				21 00				
	d	17 32	18 00				18 32		19 00				19 32	20 00			20 32	21 00				21 32
Mytholmroyd	d																					
Sowerby Bridge	d																					
Huddersfield 39	d											19 08									21 08	
London Kings Cross 15 ⊖26	d							15 58														
Brighouse	d							18 48				19 18									21 18	
Mirfield 39	a																					
	d																					
Dewsbury 39	a																					
Halifax	a	17 44	18 20				18 44	18 57	19 20			19 28	19 44	20 20			20 44	21 20			21 28	21 44
	d	17 45		18 08		18 29	18 45	18 58		19 08		19 29	19 45		20 08		20 45		21 08		21 30	21 45
Bradford Interchange	a	17 59		18 22		18 42	19 00	19 12		19 24		19 42	19 59		20 22		20 59		21 22		21 42	21 59
	d	18 02		18 25		18 44	19 02			19 25		19 44	20 02		20 25		21 02		21 26		21 44	22 02
New Pudsey 37	a	18 10		18 33		18 53	19 10			19 33		19 53	20 10		20 33		21 10		21 34		21 53	22 10
Bramley 37	a			18 37		18 56				19 37		19 56			20 37				21 38		21 56	
Leeds 10 37,39	a	18 22		18 46		19 08	19 22			19 46		20 08	20 22		20 47		21 22		21 48		22 05	22 21
Selby 40	a																					
York 8 40	a	19 02					19 59						21 02				22 00					

		NT	NT	GC	NT	NT	NT	GC	NT	NT
				R				R		
				1						
		🚌								🚌
				☕				☕		
Manchester Victoria 🚢	d				22 08					
Moston	d				22 15					
Mills Hill	d				22 19					
Castleton	d				22 24					
Rochdale	a				22 28					
	d									
Smithy Bridge	d									
Littleborough	d									
Walsden	d									
Todmorden	d									
Blackpool North 97	d									
Poulton-le-Fylde 97	d									
Preston 8 97	d									
Blackburn 97	d									
Accrington 97	d									
Burnley Manchester Road 97	d	21 20								22 20
Hebden Bridge	a	22 00								23 00
	d	22 00				22 34				23 00
Mytholmroyd	d									
Sowerby Bridge	d									
Huddersfield 39	d									
London Kings Cross 15 ⊖26	d			19 42				20 12		
Brighouse	d			22 14				23 03		
Mirfield 39	a									
	d									
Dewsbury 39	a									
Halifax	a	22 20		22 24		22 46		23 13		
	d		22 09	22 25		22 47	23 08	23 14		
Bradford Interchange	a		22 23	22 39		23 01	23 22	23 27		
	d		22 26			23 04	23 25		23 47	
New Pudsey 37	a		22 34			23 12	23 33		23 55	
Bramley 37	a		22 38				23 37		23 59	
Leeds 10 37,39	a		22 47			23 23	23 46		00 08	00 15
Selby 40	a									
York 8 40	a									

For connections from Liverpool Lime Street please see Table 90

Table 41

Sundays

16 February to 23 March

Manchester Victoria, Rochdale, Blackpool North and Huddersfield - Bradford and Leeds via Brighouse and Halifax

Network Diagram - refer to first Page of Table 39

		NT A	NT	NT	NT	NT	NT 🚌	NT	NT	NT		NT	NT	NT	NT 🚌	NT	NT	NT	NT 🚌	NT		NT	NT	NT 🚌	NT
Manchester Victoria 🚊	d					09 14			10 14	10 48				11 15				12 14					13 15		
Moston	d									10 54															
Mills Hill	d									10 58															
Castleton	d									11 03															
Rochdale	a					09 27			10 27	11 09				11 27				12 28					13 27		
	d					09 28			10 28					11 28				12 28					13 28		
Smithy Bridge	d					09 32			10 32					11 32				12 32					13 32		
Littleborough	d					09 36			10 36					11 36				12 36					13 36		
Walsden	d					09 42			10 42					11 42				12 42					13 42		
Todmorden	d					09 45			10 45					11 45				12 45					13 45		
Blackpool North 97	d																								
Poulton-le-Fylde 97	d																								
Preston 8 97	d																								
Blackburn 97	d																								
Accrington 97	d																								
Burnley Manchester Road 97	d						10 12								11 20				12 20					13 20	
Hebden Bridge	a					09 52			10 52					11 52	12 00			12 52	13 00				13 52	14 00	
	d					09 52		10 22	10 52				11 32	11 52	12 00		12 32	12 52	13 00			13 32	13 52	14 00	
Mytholmroyd	d					09 55			10 55					11 55				12 55					13 55		
Sowerby Bridge	d					10 01			11 01					12 01				13 01					14 01		
Huddersfield 39	d				09 27							11 08								13 08					
London Kings Cross 15 ⊖26	d																								
Brighouse	d				09 37							11 18								13 18					
Mirfield 39	a																								
	d																								
Dewsbury 39	a																								
Halifax	a				09 48	10 08	11 12	10 34	11 08			11 28	11 44	12 08	12 20		12 44	13 08	13 20	13 28		13 44	14 08	14 20	
	d			09 05	09 48	10 08		10 45	11 08			11 29	11 45	12 08		12 29	12 45	13 08		13 29		13 46	14 08		14 29
Bradford Interchange	a			09 18	10 01	10 22		11 00	11 22			11 42	11 59	12 22		12 42	12 59	13 22		13 42		14 00	14 22		14 42
	d	00 04	08 31	09 20	10 04	10 25		11 02	11 25			11 44	12 02	12 25		12 44	13 02	13 25		13 44		14 02	14 25		14 44
New Pudsey 37	a	00 12	08 39	09 29	10 12	10 33		11 10	11 33			11 53	12 10	12 33		12 53	13 10	13 33		13 53		14 10	14 33		14 53
Bramley 37	a	00 15	08 43	09 32	10 16	10 37			11 37			11 56		12 37		12 56		13 37		13 56			14 37		14 56
Leeds 10 37,39	a	00 27	08 51	09 42	10 25	10 46		11 21	11 48			12 05	12 22	12 46		13 06	13 22	13 46		14 06		14 22	14 48		15 06
Selby 40	a																								
York 8 40	a		09 34	10 30	11 17			11 59					13 02				13 59					15 02			

		GC ■ ☕	NT	NT	NT 🚌	NT		NT	NT	NT 🚌	NT	NT	NT	NT 🚌	NT	NT		NT	NT 🚌	NT	NT	GC ■ ☕	NT	NT 🚌	NT
Manchester Victoria 🚊	d			14 15					15 15				16 15					17 15					18 09		
Moston	d																						18 15		
Mills Hill	d																						18 19		
Castleton	d																						18 24		
Rochdale	a			14 27					15 27				16 27					17 27					18 28		
	d			14 28					15 28				16 28					17 28					18 28		
Smithy Bridge	d			14 32					15 32				16 32					17 32					18 32		
Littleborough	d			14 36					15 36				16 36					17 36					18 36		
Walsden	d			14 42					15 42				16 42					17 42					18 42		
Todmorden	d			14 45					15 45				16 45					17 45					18 45		
Blackpool North 97	d																								
Poulton-le-Fylde 97	d																								
Preston 8 97	d																								
Blackburn 97	d																								
Accrington 97	d																								
Burnley Manchester Road 97	d				14 20					15 20				16 20					17 20					18 20	
Hebden Bridge	a			14 52	15 00				15 52	16 00			16 52	17 00				17 52	18 00				18 52	19 00	
	d		14 32	14 52	15 00			15 32	15 52	16 00		16 32	16 52	17 00		17 32		17 52	18 00		18 32		18 52	19 00	
Mytholmroyd	d			14 55					15 55				16 55					17 55					18 55		
Sowerby Bridge	d			15 01					16 01				17 01					18 01					19 01		
Huddersfield 39	d					15 08									17 08										19 08
London Kings Cross 15 ⊖26	d	11 53																				15 58			
Brighouse	d	14 20				15 18									17 18							18 48			19 18
Mirfield 39	a																								
	d																								
Dewsbury 39	a																								
Halifax	a	14 36	14 44	15 08	15 20	15 28		15 44	16 08	16 20		16 44	17 08	17 20	17 26	17 44		18 08	18 20		18 44	18 57	19 08	19 20	19 28
	d	14 37	14 45	15 08		15 29		15 46	16 08		16 29	16 45	17 08		17 26	17 45		18 08		18 29	18 45	18 58	19 08		19 29
Bradford Interchange	a	14 50	15 00	15 22		15 42		16 00	16 22		16 42	16 59	17 22		17 41	17 59		18 22		18 42	19 00	19 12	19 24		19 42
	d		15 03	15 25		15 44		16 03	16 25		16 44	17 02	17 25		17 43	18 02		18 25		18 44	19 02		19 25		19 44
New Pudsey 37	a		15 11	15 33		15 53		16 11	16 33		16 53	17 10	17 33		17 52	18 10		18 33		18 53	19 10		19 33		19 53
Bramley 37	a			15 37		15 56			16 37		16 56		17 37		17 56			18 37		18 56			19 37		19 56
Leeds 10 37,39	a		15 22	15 46		16 06		16 22	16 46		17 05	17 22	17 48		18 07	18 22		18 46		19 08	19 22		19 46		20 08
Selby 40	a																								
York 8 40	a		15 59					17 02				18 02				19 02					19 59				

A From Manchester Victoria

For connections from Liverpool Lime Street please see Table 90

Table 41

Sundays

16 February to 23 March

Manchester Victoria, Rochdale, Blackpool North and Huddersfield - Bradford and Leeds via Brighouse and Halifax

Network Diagram - refer to first Page of Table 39

			NT		NT	NT	NT	NT	NT	NT	NT	NT	GC		NT	NT	NT	GC	NT	NT
						[bus]			[bus]				■ 1 ⊡		[bus]			■ ⊡		[bus]
Manchester Victoria		d			19 09			20 09				21 09					22 09			
Moston		d			19 15			20 15				21 15					22 15			
Mills Hill		d			19 19			20 19				21 19					22 19			
Castleton		d			19 24			20 24				21 24					22 24			
Rochdale		a			19 28			20 28				21 28					22 28			
		d			19 28			20 28				21 28					22 28			
Smithy Bridge		d			19 32			20 32				21 32					22 32			
Littleborough		d			19 36			20 36				21 36					22 36			
Walsden		d			19 42			20 42				21 42					22 42			
Todmorden		d			19 45			20 45				21 45					22 45			
Blackpool North	97	d																		
Poulton-le-Fylde	97	d																		
Preston ■	97	d																		
Blackburn	97	d																		
Accrington	97	d																		
Burnley Manchester Road	97	d				19 20			20 20						21 20					22 20
Hebden Bridge		a			19 52	20 00		20 52	21 00			21 52			22 00		22 52			23 00
		d	19 32		19 52	20 00	20 32	20 52	21 00		21 32	21 52			22 00	22 34	22 52			23 00
Mytholmroyd		d			19 55			20 55				21 55					22 55			
Sowerby Bridge		d			20 01			21 01				22 01					23 01			
Huddersfield	39	d								21 08										
London Kings Cross ■ ⊖	26	d											19 42					20 12		
Brighouse		d								21 18			22 14					23 03		
Mirfield	39	a																		
		d																		
Dewsbury	39	a																		
Halifax		a	19 44		20 08	20 20	20 44	21 08	21 20	21 28	21 44	22 08	22 24		22 20	22 46	23 08	23 13		
		d	19 45		20 08		20 45	21 08		21 30	21 45	22 09	22 25			22 47	23 08	23 14		
Bradford Interchange		a	19 59		20 22		20 59	21 22		21 42	21 59	22 23	22 39			23 01	23 22	23 27		
		d	20 02		20 25		21 02	21 26		21 44	22 02	22 26				23 04	23 25		23 47	
New Pudsey	37	a	20 10		20 33		21 10	21 34		21 53	22 10	22 34				23 12	23 33		23 55	
Bramley	37	a			20 37			21 38		21 56		22 38					23 37		23 59	
Leeds ■	37,39	a	20 22		20 47		21 22	21 48		22 05	22 21	22 47				23 23	23 46		00 08	00 15
Selby	40	a																		
York ■	40	a	21 02				22 00													

Sundays

30 March to 11 May

			NT	NT	NT	NT	NT	NT	NT	NT	NT		NT	NT	NT	NT	NT	NT	NT	NT	GC		NT	NT	NT	NT
			A																		■ ⊡					
Manchester Victoria		d					09 14		10 14	10 48				11 15			12 14			13 15					14 15	
Moston		d								10 54																
Mills Hill		d								10 58																
Castleton		d								11 03																
Rochdale		a					09 27		10 27	11 09				11 27			12 28			13 27					14 27	
		d					09 28		10 28					11 28			12 28			13 28					14 28	
Smithy Bridge		d					09 32		10 32					11 32			12 32			13 32					14 32	
Littleborough		d					09 36		10 36					11 36			12 36			13 36					14 36	
Walsden		d					09 42		10 42					11 42			12 42			13 42					14 42	
Todmorden		d					09 45		10 45					11 45			12 45			13 45					14 45	
Blackpool North	97	d						09 01					10 11			11 13			12 11					13 13		
Poulton-le-Fylde	97	d						09 07					10 17			11 19			12 17					13 19		
Preston ■	97	d						09 27					10 37			11 37			12 37					13 37		
Blackburn	97	d						09 44					10 54			11 54			12 54					13 54		
Accrington	97	d						09 51					11 01			12 01			13 01					14 01		
Burnley Manchester Road	97	d						10 00					11 10			12 10			13 10					14 10		
Hebden Bridge		a					09 52	10 22	10 52				11 32	11 52		12 32	12 52		13 32	13 52				14 32	14 52	
		d					09 52	10 22	10 52				11 32	11 52		12 32	12 52		13 32	13 52				14 32	14 52	
Mytholmroyd		d					09 55		10 55					11 55			12 55			13 55					14 55	
Sowerby Bridge		d					10 01		11 01					12 01			13 01			14 01					15 01	
Huddersfield	39	d				09 27					11 08							13 08								15 08
London Kings Cross ■ ⊖	26	d																			11 50					
Brighouse		d				09 37					11 18							13 18			14 09					15 18
Mirfield	39	a																								
		d																								
Dewsbury	39	a																								
Halifax		a				09 48	10 08	10 34	11 08		11 28		11 44	12 08		12 44	13 08	13 28	13 44	14 08	14 19			14 44	15 08	15 28
		d			09 05	09 48	10 08	10 45	11 08		11 29		11 45	12 08	12 29	12 45	13 08	13 29	13 46	14 08	14 22		14 29	14 45	15 08	15 29
Bradford Interchange		a			09 18	10 01	10 22	11 00	11 22		11 42		11 59	12 22	12 42	12 59	13 22	13 42	14 00	14 22	14 35		14 42	15 00	15 22	15 42
		d	00 04	08 31	09 20	10 04	10 25	11 02	11 25		11 44		12 02	12 25	12 44	13 02	13 25	13 44	14 02	14 25			14 44	15 03	15 25	15 44
New Pudsey	37	a	00 12	08 39	09 29	10 12	10 33	11 10	11 33		11 53		12 10	12 33	12 53	13 10	13 33	13 53	14 10	14 33			14 53	15 11	15 33	15 53
Bramley	37	a	00 15	08 43	09 32	10 16	10 37		11 37		11 56			12 37	12 56		13 37	13 56		14 37			14 56		15 37	15 56
Leeds ■	37,39	a	00 27	08 51	09 42	10 25	10 46	11 21	11 48		12 05		12 22	12 46	13 06	13 22	13 46	14 06	14 22	14 48			15 06	15 22	15 46	16 06
Selby	40	a																								
York ■	40	a		09 34	10 27	11 17		11 59					13 02			13 59			15 02					15 59		

A From Manchester Victoria

For connections from Liverpool Lime Street please see Table 90

Table 41

Sundays

30 March to 11 May

Manchester Victoria, Rochdale, Blackpool North and Huddersfield - Bradford and Leeds via Brighouse and Halifax

Network Diagram - refer to first Page of Table 39

Station	Table		NT	NT	NT	NT	NT	NT	NT	NT	GC	NT	NT	NT	NT	NT	NT	NT	NT	NT	GC	NT	GC	NT
											R ☕										R ☕		R 1 ☕	
Manchester Victoria ⛴		d		15 15			16 15			17 15				18 09			19 09		20 09					21 09
Moston		d												18 15			19 15		20 15					21 15
Mills Hill		d												18 19			19 19		20 19					21 19
Castleton		d												18 24			19 24		20 24					21 24
Rochdale		a		15 27			16 27			17 27				18 28			19 28		20 28					21 28
		d		15 28			16 28			17 28				18 28			19 28		20 28					21 28
Smithy Bridge		d		15 32			16 32			17 32				18 32			19 32		20 32					21 32
Littleborough		d		15 36			16 36			17 36				18 36			19 36		20 36					21 36
Walsden		d		15 42			16 42			17 42				18 42			19 42		20 42					21 42
Todmorden		d		15 45			16 45			17 45				18 45			19 45		20 45					21 45
Blackpool North	97	d	14 11			15 13			16 11				17 11			18 11		19 13				20 11		
Poulton-le-Fylde	97	d	14 17			15 19			16 17				17 17			18 17		19 19				20 17		
Preston 8	97	d	14 37			15 37			16 37				17 37			18 37		19 37				20 37		
Blackburn	97	d	14 54			15 54			16 54				17 54			18 54		19 54				20 54		
Accrington	97	d	15 01			16 01			17 01				18 01			19 01		20 01				21 01		
Burnley Manchester Road	97	d	15 10			16 10			17 10				18 10			19 10		20 10				21 10		
Hebden Bridge		a	15 32	15 52		16 32	16 52		17 32	17 52			18 32	18 52		19 32	19 52	20 32	20 52			21 32		21 52
		d	15 32	15 52		16 32	16 52		17 32	17 52			18 32	18 52		19 32	19 52	20 32	20 52			21 32		21 52
Mytholmroyd		d		15 55			16 55			17 55				18 55			19 55		20 55					21 55
Sowerby Bridge		d		16 01			17 01			18 01				19 01			20 01		21 01					22 01
Huddersfield	39	d						17 08							19 08					21 08				
London Kings Cross 15 ⊖	26	d									15 50										18 45		19 23	
Brighouse		d						17 18			18 09				19 18					21 18	21 25		21 44	
Mirfield	39	a																						
		d																						
Dewsbury	39	a																						
Halifax		a	15 44	16 08		16 44	17 08	17 26	17 44	18 08	18 19		18 44	19 08	19 28	19 44	20 08	20 44	21 08	21 28	21 34	21 44	21 54	22 08
		d	15 46	16 08	16 29	16 45	17 08	17 26	17 45	18 08	18 20	18 29	18 45	19 08	19 29	19 45	20 08	20 45	21 08	21 30	21 35	21 45	21 55	22 09
Bradford Interchange		a	16 00	16 22	16 42	16 59	17 22	17 41	17 59	18 22	18 33	18 42	19 00	19 24	19 42	19 59	20 22	20 59	21 22	21 42	21 49	21 59	22 08	22 23
		d	16 03	16 25	16 44	17 02	17 25	17 43	18 02	18 25		18 44	19 02	19 25	19 44	20 02	20 25	21 02	21 26	21 44		22 02		22 26
New Pudsey	37	a	16 11	16 33	16 53	17 10	17 33	17 52	18 10	18 33		18 53	19 10	19 33	19 53	20 10	20 33	21 10	21 34	21 53		22 10		22 34
Bramley	37	a		16 37	16 56		17 37	17 56		18 37		18 56		19 37	19 56		20 37		21 38	21 56				22 38
Leeds 10	37,39	a	16 22	16 46	17 05	17 22	17 48	18 07	18 22	18 46		19 08	19 22	19 46	20 08	20 22	20 47	21 22	21 48	22 05		22 21		22 47
Selby	40	a																						
York 8	40	a	17 02			18 02			19 02				19 59			21 02		22 00						

Station	Table		NT	NT	NT
Manchester Victoria ⛴		d		22 09	
Moston		d		22 15	
Mills Hill		d		22 19	
Castleton		d		22 24	
Rochdale		a		22 28	
		d		22 28	
Smithy Bridge		d		22 32	
Littleborough		d		22 36	
Walsden		d		22 42	
Todmorden		d		22 45	
Blackpool North	97	d	21 13		
Poulton-le-Fylde	97	d	21 19		
Preston 8	97	d	21 39		
Blackburn	97	d	21 55		
Accrington	97	d	22 02		
Burnley Manchester Road	97	d	22 12		
Hebden Bridge		a	22 34	22 52	
		d	22 34	22 52	
Mytholmroyd		d		22 55	
Sowerby Bridge		d		23 01	
Huddersfield	39	d			
London Kings Cross 15 ⊖	26	d			
Brighouse		d			
Mirfield	39	a			
		d			
Dewsbury	39	a			
Halifax		a	22 46	23 08	
		d	22 47	23 08	
Bradford Interchange		a	23 01	23 22	
		d	23 04	23 25	23 47
New Pudsey	37	a	23 12	23 33	23 55
Bramley	37	a		23 37	23 59
Leeds 10	37,39	a	23 23	23 46	00 08
Selby	40	a			
York 8	40	a			

For connections from Liverpool Lime Street please see Table 90

Table 41R

Mondays to Fridays

9 December to 21 March

Leeds and Bradford - Huddersfield, Blackpool North, Rochdale and Manchester Victoria via Halifax and Brighouse

Network Diagram - refer to first Page of Table 39

Miles	Miles	Miles	Miles			NT	NT	NT	NT	NT	NT	NT	NT	GC	NT	NT	NT	NT	NT	NT	NT	GC	NT
							🚌			🚌			A	R 1 ☕			B		🚌		C	R 1 ☕	
—	—	—	—	York [8] 40	d											06 13							
—	—	—	—	Selby 40	d																06 43		
0	0	—	0	**Leeds [10]** 37,39	d	05 08		05 51	06 03		06 13	06 22			06 37	06 51		07 08		07 13	07 23		07 37
4	4	—	—	Bramley 37	d	05 15		05 58				06 29			06 44			07 15			07 29		07 44
5¾	5¾	—	—	New Pudsey 37	d	05 20		06 02	06 13			06 34			06 49	07 01		07 20			07 34		07 49
9½	9½	—	—	**Bradford Interchange** 37	a	05 28		06 13	06 21			06 42			06 57	07 11		07 28			07 43		07 57
—	—	—	—		d	05 32		06 14	06 24			06 45		06 51	07 00	07 14		07 31			07 45	07 52	08 00
17½	17½	0	—	**Halifax**	a	05 44		06 25	06 36			06 58		07 06	07 12	07 25		07 43			07 59	08 05	08 12
—	—	—	—		d	05 44		06 26	06 36				07 02	07 07	07 12	07 26		07 44			08 00	08 06	08 12
—	—	—	9¼	Dewsbury 39	d						06 29									07 29			
—	—	—	12¼	Mirfield 39	a						06 35									07 35			
—	—	—	—		d						06 35									07 36			
—	—	5¼	16¼	Brighouse	d						06 49		07a12	07 18						07 49	08 09	08 18	
—	—	—	—	London Kings Cross [15] ⊖26	a									10 12								11 15	
—	—	10½	—	**Huddersfield** 39	a																08 29		
21	21	—	22	Sowerby Bridge	d	05 51			06 43		06 59				07 19					07 59			08 19
25	25	—	26	Mytholmroyd	d	05 57			06 49		07 05				07 25					08 05			08 25
26¼	26¼	—	27¼	**Hebden Bridge**	a	06 00		06 38	06 52		07 08				07 28	07 38		07 55		08 08			08 28
—	—	—	—		d	06 00	06 05		06 52	06 57	07 08				07 28			07 56	08 01	08 08			08 28
—	39	—	—	Burnley Manchester Road 97	a		06 45			07 37									08 41				
—	45¼	—	—	Accrington 97	a																		
—	51½	—	—	Blackburn 97	a																		
—	63½	—	—	**Preston [8]** 97	a																		
—	78	—	—	Poulton-le-Fylde 97	a																		
—	81	—	—	**Blackpool North** 97	a																		
30½	—	—	—	Todmorden	d	06 08			07 00		07 15				07 36		07 44	08 04		08 15			08 36
32	—	—	—	Walsden	d	06 11			07 03						07 39		07 47						08 39
36	—	—	—	Littleborough	d	06 17			07 09		07 23				07 45		07 53	08 11		08 23			08 45
37	—	—	—	Smithy Bridge	d	06 20			07 12		07 25				07 48		07 56			08 25			08 48
39¼	—	—	—	**Rochdale**	a	06 24			07 16		07 29				07 52		08 00	08 16		08 29			08 51
—	—	—	—		d	06 24			07 18		07 30				07 54		08 00	08 17		08 30			08 51
41	—	—	—	Castleton	d	06 27			07 21		07 33				07 57		08 03	08 20		08 33			
43¾	—	—	—	Mills Hill	d	06 32			07 26		07 38				08 02		08 08	08 25		08 37			
45¾	—	—	—	Moston	d	06 35			07 29		07 41				08 05		08 11			08 40			
49¾	—	—	—	**Manchester Victoria** 🚋	a	06 48			07 43		07 53				08 17		08 22	08 37		08 53			09 08

		NT	NT	NT	NT	NT	NT	NT	NT	NT	NT	NT	NT	NT	NT	NT	NT	GC	NT	NT	NT	NT	NT
		B			🚌		C		B			🚌				B		R 1 ☕	◇	🚌	◇		◇
York [8] 40	d		07 06							08 12							09 11						
Selby 40	d			07 23			07 43							08 43								09 43	
Leeds [10] 37,39	d		07 51	08 08		08 13	08 23	08 37		08 51	09 07		09 13	09 23	09 37		09 53		10 07		10 13	10 23	10 37
Bramley 37	d			08 15			08 30	08 44			09 14			09 30	09 44				10 14			10 30	10 44
New Pudsey 37	d		08 01	08 20			08 35	08 49		09 00	09 19			09 35	09 49		10 02		10 20			10 35	10 49
Bradford Interchange 37	a		08 09	08 28			08 43	08 57		09 12	09 28			09 43	09 57		10 12		10 28			10 43	10 57
	d		08 12	08 32			08 46	09 00		09 13	09 32			09 46	10 00		10 14	10 22	10 32			10 46	11 00
Halifax	a		08 23	08 44			09 01	09 12		09 25	09 44			10 01	10 12		10 25	10 33	10 44			11 01	11 12
	d		08 24	08 44			09 06	09 12		09 25	09 44			10 06	10 12		10 26	10 37	10 44			11 06	11 12
Dewsbury 39	d					08 31							09 31								10 29		
Mirfield 39	a					08 37							09 36								10 35		
	d					08 38							09 37								10 35		
Brighouse	d					08 49	09 16						09 49	10 16				10 48			10 49	11 16	
London Kings Cross [15] ⊖26	a																	13 43					
Huddersfield 39	a						09 29							10 30								11 30	
Sowerby Bridge	d					08 59		09 19					09 59		10 19						10 59		11 19
Mytholmroyd	d					09 05		09 25					10 05		10 25						11 05		11 25
Hebden Bridge	a		08 36	08 56		09 08		09 28		09 38	09 56		10 08		10 28		10 38		10 56		11 08		11 28
	d			08 56	09 01	09 08		09 28			09 56	10 01	10 08		10 28				10 56	11 01	11 08		11 28
Burnley Manchester Road 97	a				09 41							10 41								11 41			
Accrington 97	a																						
Blackburn 97	a																						
Preston [8] 97	a																						
Poulton-le-Fylde 97	a																						
Blackpool North 97	a																						
Todmorden	d			09 04		09 15		09 36			10 04		10 15		10 36				11 04		11 15		11 36
Walsden	d							09 39							10 39								11 39
Littleborough	d					09 23		09 45					10 23		10 45						11 23		11 45
Smithy Bridge	d					09 25		09 48					10 25		10 48						11 25		11 48
Rochdale	a			09 14		09 29		09 51			10 14		10 29		10 51				11 14		11 29		11 51
	d	09 04		09 14		09 30		09 51	10 05		10 14		10 30		10 51	11 04			11 14		11 30		11 51
Castleton	d	09 07				09 33			10 08				10 33			11 07					11 33		
Mills Hill	d	09 12				09 37			10 13				10 38			11 12					11 38		
Moston	d	09 15				09 40			10 16				10 41			11 15					11 41		
Manchester Victoria 🚋	a	09 26		09 30		09 53		10 08	10 25		10 32		10 53		11 08	11 26			11 30		11 53		12 08

A To Leeds **B** To Wigan Wallgate **C** To Wakefield Westgate

For connections to Liverpool Lime Street please see Table 90

Table 41R

Mondays to Fridays

9 December to 21 March

Leeds and Bradford - Huddersfield, Blackpool North, Rochdale and Manchester Victoria via Halifax and Brighouse

Network Diagram - refer to first Page of Table 39

			NT	NT	NT	NT	NT		NT	NT	NT	NT	NT	NT	NT	NT	NT		NT	NT	NT	NT	NT	NT	NT	NT
			A		◇	🚌	◇			◇	A		◇	🚌	◇		◇		A		◇	🚌	◇		◇	A
York 8	40	d		10 11								11 09								12 13						
Selby	40	d							10 43							11 43								12 43		
Leeds 10	37,39	d		10 53	11 07		11 13		11 23	11 37		11 53	12 07		12 13	12 23	12 37			12 53	13 07		13 13	13 23	13 37	
Bramley	37	d			11 14				11 30	11 44			12 14			12 30	12 44				13 14			13 30	13 44	
New Pudsey	37	d		11 02	11 19				11 35	11 49		12 02	12 19			12 35	12 49			13 02	13 19			13 35	13 49	
Bradford Interchange	37	a		11 11	11 28				11 43	11 57		12 11	12 28			12 43	12 57			13 12	13 28			13 43	13 58	
		d		11 12	11 31				11 46	12 00		12 14	12 32			12 46	13 00			13 14	13 32			13 46	14 00	
Halifax		a		11 25	11 43				11 59	12 12		12 25	12 44			13 01	13 12			13 25	13 44			14 01	14 12	
		d		11 25	11 44				12 06	12 12		12 26	12 44			13 06	13 12			13 26	13 44			14 06	14 13	
Dewsbury	39	d					11 29								12 29								13 29			
Mirfield	39	a					11 35								12 35								13 35			
		d					11 35								12 35								13 35			
Brighouse		d					11 49		12 16						12 49	13 16							13 49	14 16		
London Kings Cross 15	⊖26	a																								
Huddersfield	39	a							12 30							13 30								14 30		
Sowerby Bridge		d					11 59			12 19					12 59		13 19						13 59		14 19	
Mytholmroyd		d					12 05			12 25					13 05		13 25						14 05		14 25	
Hebden Bridge		a		11 38	11 55		12 08			12 28		12 38	12 56		13 08		13 28			13 38	13 56		14 08		14 28	
		d			11 56	12 01	12 08			12 28			12 56	13 01	13 08		13 28				13 56	14 01	14 08		14 29	
Burnley Manchester Road	97	a				12 41								13 41								14 41				
Accrington	97	a																								
Blackburn	97	a																								
Preston 8	97	a																								
Poulton-le-Fylde	97	a																								
Blackpool North	97	a																								
Todmorden		d			12 03		12 15			12 36			13 04		13 15		13 36				14 04		14 15		14 36	
Walsden		d								12 39							13 39								14 39	
Littleborough		d					12 23			12 45					13 23		13 45						14 23		14 46	
Smithy Bridge		d					12 25			12 48					13 25		13 48						14 25		14 48	
Rochdale		a			12 13		12 29			12 51			13 14		13 29		13 51				14 14		14 29		14 51	
		d	12 04		12 14		12 30			12 51	13 04		13 14		13 30		13 51		14 04		14 14		14 30		14 52	15 04
Castleton		d	12 07				12 33				13 07				13 33				14 07				14 33			15 07
Mills Hill		d	12 12				12 38				13 12				13 38				14 12				14 38			15 12
Moston		d	12 15				12 41				13 15				13 41				14 15				14 41			15 15
Manchester Victoria ⛴		a	12 25		12 30		12 53			13 08	13 25		13 32		13 53		14 08		14 25		14 30		14 52		15 08	15 25

			NT		GC	NT	NT	NT	NT	NT	NT	NT	NT		NT	NT	NT	NT	NT	NT	NT	NT	NT		NT	NT
					B 1 ☕	◇	🚌	◇		◇	A		◇		🚌			◇	B		◇	🚌	◇			◇
York 8	40	d	13 09									14 13								15 08						
Selby	40	d							13 43								14 43								15 43	
Leeds 10	37,39	d	13 53			14 07		14 13	14 23	14 37		14 53	15 07			15 13	15 23	15 37		15 52	16 07		16 13		16 23	16 37
Bramley	37	d				14 14			14 30	14 44			15 14				15 30	15 44			16 14				16 30	16 44
New Pudsey	37	d	14 02			14 19			14 35	14 49		15 02	15 19				15 35	15 49		16 01	16 19				16 35	16 49
Bradford Interchange	37	a	14 12			14 28			14 43	14 57		15 12	15 28				15 43	15 57		16 10	16 28				16 43	16 57
		d	14 14		14 22	14 32			14 46	15 00		15 14	15 32				15 46	16 00		16 13	16 32				16 46	17 00
Halifax		a	14 25		14 33	14 44			15 00	15 12		15 25	15 44				16 01	16 12		16 24	16 44				17 01	17 12
		d	14 26		14 35	14 44			15 06	15 12		15 26	15 44				16 06	16 12		16 25	16 44				17 06	17 12
Dewsbury	39	d						14 29								15 29							16 31			
Mirfield	39	a						14 35								15 35							16 37			
		d						14 35								15 35							16 38			
Brighouse		d			14 47			14 49	15 16							15 49	16 16						16 49		17 16	
London Kings Cross 15	⊖26	a			18 15																					
Huddersfield	39	a							15 30								16 30								17 30	
Sowerby Bridge		d						14 59		15 19						15 59		16 19		16 32			16 59			17 19
Mytholmroyd		d						15 05		15 25						16 05		16 25					17 05			17 25
Hebden Bridge		a	14 38			14 56		15 08		15 28		15 38	15 56			16 08		16 28		16 39	16 56		17 08			17 28
		d				14 56	15 01	15 08		15 28			15 56		16 01	16 08		16 28			16 56	17 01	17 08			17 28
Burnley Manchester Road	97	a					15 41								16 41							17 41				
Accrington	97	a																								
Blackburn	97	a																								
Preston 8	97	a																								
Poulton-le-Fylde	97	a																								
Blackpool North	97	a																								
Todmorden		d				15 04		15 15		15 36			16 04			16 15		16 36			17 04		17 15			17 36
Walsden		d								15 39								16 39								17 39
Littleborough		d						15 23		15 45						16 23		16 45					17 23			17 45
Smithy Bridge		d						15 25		15 48						16 25		16 48					17 25			17 48
Rochdale		a				15 14		15 29		15 51			16 14			16 29		16 51			17 14		17 29			17 51
		d				15 14		15 30		15 51	16 04		16 14			16 30		16 51	17 03		17 14		17 30			17 51
Castleton		d						15 33			16 07					16 33			17 06				17 33			
Mills Hill		d						15 38			16 12					16 38			17 11				17 38			
Moston		d						15 41			16 15					16 41			17 14				17 41			
Manchester Victoria ⛴		a				15 31		15 53		16 08	16 27		16 32			16 52		17 08	17 23		17 32		17 53			18 08

A To Wigan Wallgate

B To Blackburn

For connections to Liverpool Lime Street please see Table 90

Table 41R

Mondays to Fridays

9 December to 21 March

Leeds and Bradford - Huddersfield, Blackpool North, Rochdale and Manchester Victoria via Halifax and Brighouse

Network Diagram - refer to first Page of Table 39

Station	Table		NT	NT	NT	NT	NT	NT	NT	NT	NT	NT	NT	NT	NT	NT	NT	NT	NT	NT	NT	NT	NT	NT
																◇		◇				◇		
			A												B						C			
						Bus							Bus								Bus			
York 8	40	d		16 08							17 13						18 05							
Selby	40	d													17 40	18 02				18 43		19 00		
Leeds 10	37,39	d		16 51	17 07		17 13	17 23	17 37		17 51	18 08		18 13	18 23	18 36	18 51	19 08		19 23		19 37	20 08	
Bramley	37	d			17 14			17 30	17 44			18 15			18 30	18 45		19 15		19 30		19 44	20 15	
New Pudsey	37	d		17 00	17 19			17 35	17 49		18 01	18 20			18 35	18 49	19 01	19 20		19 35		19 49	20 20	
Bradford Interchange	37	a		17 10	17 28			17 43	17 57		18 10	18 28			18 43	18 58	19 09	19 28		19 44		19 57	20 28	
		d		17 12	17 31			17 46	18 00		18 12	18 32			18 46	19 00	19 12	19 32		19 46		20 00	20 31	
Halifax		a		17 23	17 43			17 59	18 12		18 24	18 44			19 00	19 12	19 24	19 44		20 00		20 12	20 44	
		d		17 24	17 44			18 06	18 12		18 24	18 44			19 06	19 13	19 25	19 44		20 06		20 12	20 44	
Dewsbury	39	d					17 31							18 31										
Mirfield	39	a					17 37							18 37										
		d					17 38							18 38										
Brighouse		d					17 49	18 16						18 49	19 16					20 16			20 55	
London Kings Cross 15 ⊖26		a																						
Huddersfield	39	a						18 31							19 29					20 30			21 10	
Sowerby Bridge		d		17 31			17 59		18 19		18 31			18 59		19 19						20 19		
Mytholmroyd		d					18 05		18 25					19 05		19 25						20 25		
Hebden Bridge		a		17 38	17 56		18 08		18 28		18 38	18 56		19 08		19 28	19 37	19 56				20 28		
		d			17 56	18 01	18 08		18 28			18 56	19 01	19 08		19 29		19 56			20 01	20 28		
Burnley Manchester Road	97	a				18 41							19 41								20 40			
Accrington	97	a																						
Blackburn	97	a																						
Preston 8	97	a																			21 48			
Poulton-le-Fylde	97	a																						
Blackpool North	97	a																						
Todmorden		d			18 04		18 15		18 36			19 04		19 15		19 36		20 04				20 36		
Walsden		d					18 19		18 39					19 19		19 39						20 39		
Littleborough		d					18 25		18 45					19 25		19 46						20 45		
Smithy Bridge		d					18 28		18 48					19 28		19 48						20 48		
Rochdale		a			18 14		18 32		18 51			19 15		19 32		19 52		20 14				20 52		
		d	18 02		18 14		18 32		18 51	19 00		19 15		19 32		19 53		20 14	20 25			20 52		21 25
Castleton		d	18 05				18 35			19 03				19 35		19 56			20 28			20 55		21 28
Mills Hill		d	18 10				18 40			19 08				19 40		20 01			20 33			21 00		21 33
Moston		d	18 13				18 43			19 11				19 43		20 04			20 36			21 03		21 36
Manchester Victoria		a	18 21		18 32		18 54		19 09	19 21		19 32		19 53		20 15		20 32	20 46			21 12		21 46

Station	Table		NT	NT	NT	NT	NT	NT	NT	NT
			◇				◇		◇	
					Bus					
York 8	40	d		20 13						
Selby	40	d								
Leeds 10	37,39	d	20 37	20 51		21 08	21 37	22 08	22 37	23 08
Bramley	37	d	20 44			21 15	21 44	22 15	22 44	23 15
New Pudsey	37	d	20 49	21 01		21 20	21 49	22 20	22 49	23 20
Bradford Interchange	37	a	20 57	21 10		21 28	21 57	22 28	22 57	23 29
		d	21 00	21 13		21 31	22 00	22 31	23 00	23 31
Halifax		a	21 12	21 24		21 44	22 12	22 44	23 12	23 44
		d	21 12	21 25		21 44	22 12	22 44	23 12	23 44
Dewsbury	39	d								
Mirfield	39	a								
		d								
Brighouse		d				21 55		22 55		23 55
London Kings Cross 15 ⊖26		a								
Huddersfield	39	a				22 10		23 10		00 10
Sowerby Bridge		d	21 19				22 19		23 19	
Mytholmroyd		d	21 25				22 25		23 25	
Hebden Bridge		a	21 28	21 39			22 28		23 28	
		d	21 28		21 43		22 28		23 28	
Burnley Manchester Road	97	a			22 18					
Accrington	97	a								
Blackburn	97	a								
Preston 8	97	a								
Poulton-le-Fylde	97	a								
Blackpool North	97	a								
Todmorden		d	21 36				22 36		23 36	
Walsden		d	21 39				22 39		23 39	
Littleborough		d	21 45				22 45		23 45	
Smithy Bridge		d	21 48				22 48		23 48	
Rochdale		a	21 52				22 52		23 52	
		d	21 52				22 52		23 52	
Castleton		d	21 55				22 55			
Mills Hill		d	22 00				23 00			
Moston		d	22 03				23 03			
Manchester Victoria		a	22 15				23 15		00 10	

A To Blackburn

B To Wakefield Westgate

C not 25 December, 26 December

For connections to Liverpool Lime Street please see Table 90

Table 41R

Mondays to Fridays

24 March to 16 May

Leeds and Bradford - Huddersfield, Blackpool North, Rochdale and Manchester Victoria via Halifax and Brighouse

Network Diagram - refer to first Page of Table 39

Station	Table		NT	NT	NT	NT	NT	NT A	GC R 1 ☕	NT	NT		NT B	NT	NT	NT C	GC R 1 ☕	NT	NT B	NT	NT		NT	NT C	NT	NT B
York 8	40	d									06 13									07 06						
Selby	40	d														06 43					07 23			07 43		
Leeds 10	37,39	d	05 08	05 51	06 03	06 13	06 22			06 37	06 51			07 08	07 13	07 23		07 37		07 51	08 08		08 13	08 23	08 37	
Bramley	37	d	05 15	05 58			06 29			06 44				07 15		07 29		07 44			08 15			08 30	08 44	
New Pudsey	37	d	05 20	06 02	06 13		06 34			06 49	07 01			07 20		07 34		07 49		08 01	08 20			08 35	08 49	
Bradford Interchange	37	a	05 28	06 13	06 21		06 42			06 57	07 11			07 28		07 43		07 57		08 09	08 28			08 43	08 57	
		d	05 32	06 14	06 24		06 45		06 51	07 00	07 14			07 31		07 45	07 52	08 00		08 12	08 32			08 46	09 00	
Halifax		a	05 44	06 25	06 36		06 58		07 06	07 12	07 25			07 43		07 59	08 05	08 12		08 23	08 44			09 01	09 12	
		d	05 44	06 26	06 36			07 02	07 07	07 12	07 26			07 44		08 00	08 06	08 12		08 24	08 44			09 06	09 12	
Dewsbury	39	d				06 29									07 29								08 31			
Mirfield	39	a				06 35									07 35								08 37			
		d				06 35									07 36								08 38			
Brighouse		d				06 49		07a12	07 18						07 49	08 09	08 18						08 49	09 16		
London Kings Cross 15 ⊖	26	a							10 12								11 15									
Huddersfield	39	a														08 29								09 29		
Sowerby Bridge		d	05 51		06 43	06 59				07 19					07 59			08 19					08 59		09 19	
Mytholmroyd		d	05 57		06 49	07 05				07 25					08 05			08 25					09 05		09 25	
Hebden Bridge		a	06 00	06 37	06 52	07 08				07 28	07 37			07 55	08 08			08 28		08 35	08 56		09 08		09 28	
		d	06 00	06 38	06 52	07 08				07 28	07 38			07 56	08 08			08 28		08 36	08 56		09 08		09 28	
Burnley Manchester Road	97	a		06 57							07 57									08 57						
Accrington	97	a		07 06							08 06									09 06						
Blackburn	97	a		07 16							08 16									09 14						
Preston 8	97	a		07 36							08 39									09 32						
Poulton-le-Fylde	97	a		07 54							08 57									09 50						
Blackpool North	97	a		08 05							09 05									10 01						
Todmorden		d	06 08		07 00	07 15				07 36			07 44	08 04	08 15			08 36			09 04		09 15		09 36	
Walsden		d	06 11		07 03					07 39			07 47					08 39							09 39	
Littleborough		d	06 17		07 09	07 23				07 45			07 53	08 11	08 23			08 45					09 23		09 45	
Smithy Bridge		d	06 20		07 12	07 25				07 48			07 56		08 25			08 48					09 25		09 48	
Rochdale		a	06 24		07 16	07 29				07 52			08 00	08 16	08 29			08 51			09 14		09 29		09 51	
		d	06 24		07 18	07 30				07 54			08 00	08 17	08 30			08 51	09 04		09 14		09 30		09 51	10 05
Castleton		d	06 27		07 21	07 33				07 57			08 03	08 20	08 33				09 07				09 33			10 08
Mills Hill		d	06 32		07 26	07 38				08 02			08 08	08 25	08 37				09 12				09 37			10 13
Moston		d	06 35		07 29	07 41				08 05			08 11		08 40				09 15				09 40			10 16
Manchester Victoria		a	06 48		07 43	07 53				08 17			08 22	08 37	08 53			09 08	09 26		09 30		09 53		10 08	10 25

Station	Table		NT	NT	NT	NT	NT		NT B	NT	GC R 1 ☕	NT ◇	NT ◇	NT	NT ◇	NT B	NT		NT ◇	NT ◇	NT	NT ◇	NT B	NT	NT ◇	NT ◇
York 8	40	d	08 12							09 11							10 11							11 09		
Selby	40	d				08 43								09 43							10 43					
Leeds 10	37,39	d	08 51	09 07	09 13	09 23	09 37			09 53		10 07	10 13	10 23	10 37		10 53		11 07	11 13	11 23	11 37		11 53	12 07	12 13
Bramley	37	d		09 14		09 30	09 44					10 14		10 30	10 44				11 14		11 30	11 44			12 14	
New Pudsey	37	d	09 00	09 19		09 35	09 49			10 02		10 20		10 35	10 49		11 02		11 19		11 35	11 49		12 02	12 19	
Bradford Interchange	37	a	09 12	09 28		09 43	09 57			10 12		10 28		10 43	10 57		11 11		11 28		11 43	11 57		12 11	12 28	
		d	09 13	09 32		09 46	10 00			10 14	10 22	10 32		10 46	11 00		11 12		11 31		11 46	12 00		12 14	12 32	
Halifax		a	09 25	09 44		10 01	10 12			10 25	10 33	10 44		11 01	11 12		11 25		11 43		11 59	12 12		12 25	12 44	
		d	09 25	09 44		10 06	10 12			10 26	10 37	10 44		11 06	11 12		11 25		11 44		12 06	12 12		12 26	12 44	
Dewsbury	39	d			09 31								10 29							11 29						12 29
Mirfield	39	a			09 36								10 35							11 35						12 35
		d			09 37								10 35							11 35						12 35
Brighouse		d			09 49	10 16					10 48		10 49	11 16						11 49	12 16					12 49
London Kings Cross 15 ⊖	26	a									13 43															
Huddersfield	39	a				10 30								11 30							12 30					
Sowerby Bridge		d			09 59		10 19						10 59		11 19					11 59		12 19				12 59
Mytholmroyd		d			10 05		10 25						11 05		11 25					12 05		12 25				13 05
Hebden Bridge		a	09 37	09 56	10 08		10 28			10 37		10 56	11 08		11 28		11 37		11 55	12 08		12 28		12 37	12 56	13 08
		d	09 37	09 56	10 08		10 28			10 38		10 56	11 08		11 28		11 38		11 56	12 08		12 28		12 38	12 56	13 08
Burnley Manchester Road	97	a	09 56							10 57							11 57							12 57		
Accrington	97	a	10 06							11 06							12 06							13 06		
Blackburn	97	a	10 14							11 14							12 14							13 14		
Preston 8	97	a	10 32							11 32							12 32							13 32		
Poulton-le-Fylde	97	a	10 50							11 50							12 50							13 50		
Blackpool North	97	a	11 01							12 00							13 00							14 00		
Todmorden		d		10 04	10 15		10 36					11 04	11 15		11 36				12 03	12 15		12 36			13 04	13 15
Walsden		d					10 39								11 39							12 39				
Littleborough		d			10 23		10 45						11 23		11 45					12 23		12 45				13 23
Smithy Bridge		d			10 25		10 48						11 25		11 48					12 25		12 48				13 25
Rochdale		a		10 14	10 29		10 51					11 14	11 29		11 51				12 13	12 29		12 51			13 14	13 29
		d		10 14	10 30		10 51		11 04			11 14	11 30		11 51	12 04			12 14	12 30		12 51	13 04		13 14	13 30
Castleton		d			10 33				11 07				11 33			12 07				12 33			13 07			13 33
Mills Hill		d			10 38				11 12				11 38			12 12				12 38			13 12			13 38
Moston		d			10 41				11 15				11 41			12 15				12 41			13 15			13 41
Manchester Victoria		a		10 32	10 53		11 08		11 26			11 30	11 53		12 08	12 25			12 30	12 53		13 08	13 25		13 32	13 53

A To Leeds

B To Wigan Wallgate

C To Wakefield Westgate

For connections to Liverpool Lime Street please see Table 90

Table 41R

Mondays to Fridays

24 March to 16 May

Leeds and Bradford - Huddersfield, Blackpool North, Rochdale and Manchester Victoria via Halifax and Brighouse

Network Diagram - refer to first Page of Table 39

Station	Table		NT		NT	NT	NT	NT	NT	NT	NT	NT	NT		GC	NT	NT	NT	NT	NT	NT	NT	NT		NT	NT
					◇	A		◇	◇		◇	A			1 ☕	◇	◇		◇	A		◇				◇
York 8	40	d					12 13						13 09								14 13					
Selby	40	d	11 43							12 43								13 43							14 43	
Leeds 10	37,39	d	12 23		12 37		12 53	13 07	13 13	13 23	13 37		13 53			14 07	14 13	14 23	14 37		14 53	15 07	15 13		15 23	15 37
Bramley	37	d	12 30		12 44			13 14		13 30	13 44					14 14		14 30	14 44			15 14			15 30	15 44
New Pudsey	37	d	12 35		12 49		13 02	13 19		13 35	13 49		14 02			14 19		14 35	14 49		15 02	15 19			15 35	15 49
Bradford Interchange	37	a	12 43		12 57		13 12	13 28		13 43	13 58		14 12			14 28		14 43	14 57		15 12	15 28			15 43	15 57
		d	12 46		13 00		13 14	13 32		13 46	14 00		14 14		14 22	14 32		14 46	15 00		15 14	15 32			15 46	16 00
Halifax		a	13 01		13 12		13 25	13 44		14 01	14 12		14 25		14 33	14 44		15 00	15 12		15 25	15 44			16 01	16 12
		d	13 06		13 12		13 26	13 44		14 06	14 13		14 26		14 35	14 44		15 06	15 12		15 26	15 44			16 06	16 12
Dewsbury	39	d							13 29								14 29						15 29			
Mirfield	39	a							13 35								14 35						15 35			
		d							13 35								14 35						15 35			
Brighouse		d	13 16						13 49	14 16					14 47		14 49	15 16					15 49		16 16	
London Kings Cross 15 ⊖	26	a													18 15											
Huddersfield	39	a	13 30							14 30								15 30							16 30	
Sowerby Bridge		d			13 19				13 59		14 19						14 59		15 19				15 59			16 19
Mytholmroyd		d			13 25				14 05		14 25						15 05		15 25				16 05			16 25
Hebden Bridge		a			13 28		13 37	13 56	14 08		14 28		14 37			14 56	15 08		15 28		15 37	15 56	16 08			16 28
		d			13 28		13 38	13 56	14 08		14 29		14 38			14 56	15 08		15 28		15 38	15 56	16 08			16 28
Burnley Manchester Road	97	a					13 57						14 57								15 57					
Accrington	97	a					14 06						15 06								16 06					
Blackburn	97	a					14 14						15 14								16 14					
Preston 8	97	a					14 32						15 32								16 32					
Poulton-le-Fylde	97	a					14 50						15 50								16 50					
Blackpool North	97	a					15 00						16 00								17 00					
Todmorden		d			13 36			14 04	14 15		14 36					15 04	15 15		15 36			16 04	16 15			16 36
Walsden		d			13 39						14 39								15 39							16 39
Littleborough		d			13 45				14 23		14 46						15 23		15 45				16 23			16 45
Smithy Bridge		d			13 48				14 25		14 48						15 25		15 48				16 25			16 48
Rochdale		a			13 51			14 14	14 29		14 51					15 14	15 29		15 51			16 14	16 29			16 51
		d			13 51	14 04		14 14	14 30		14 52	15 04				15 14	15 30		15 51	16 04		16 14	16 30			16 51
Castleton		d				14 07			14 33			15 07					15 33			16 07			16 33			
Mills Hill		d				14 12			14 38			15 12					15 38			16 12			16 38			
Moston		d				14 15			14 41			15 15					15 41			16 15			16 41			
Manchester Victoria		a			14 08	14 25		14 30	14 52		15 08	15 25				15 31	15 53		16 08	16 27		16 32	16 52			17 08

Station	Table		NT	NT	NT	NT	NT	NT	NT		NT	NT	NT	NT	NT	NT	NT	NT	NT		NT	NT	NT	NT	NT	NT
			B		◇	◇		◇	B												C	◇		◇		
York 8	40	d		15 08							16 08						17 13						18 05			
Selby	40	d					15 43														17 40	18 02				18 43
Leeds 10	37,39	d		15 52	16 07	16 13	16 23	16 37			16 51	17 07	17 13	17 23	17 37		17 51	18 08	18 13		18 23	18 36	18 51	19 08		19 23
Bramley	37	d			16 14		16 30	16 44				17 14		17 30	17 44			18 15			18 30	18 45		19 15		19 30
New Pudsey	37	d		16 01	16 19		16 35	16 49			17 00	17 19		17 35	17 49		18 01	18 20			18 35	18 49	19 01	19 20		19 35
Bradford Interchange	37	a		16 10	16 28		16 43	16 57			17 10	17 28		17 43	17 57		18 10	18 28			18 43	18 58	19 09	19 28		19 44
		d		16 13	16 32		16 46	17 00			17 12	17 31		17 46	18 00		18 12	18 32			18 46	19 00	19 12	19 32		19 46
Halifax		a		16 24	16 44		17 01	17 12			17 23	17 43		17 59	18 12		18 24	18 44			19 00	19 12	19 24	19 44		20 00
		d		16 25	16 44		17 06	17 12			17 24	17 44		18 06	18 12		18 24	18 44			19 06	19 13	19 24	19 44		20 06
Dewsbury	39	d				16 31							17 31						18 31							
Mirfield	39	a				16 37							17 37						18 37							
		d				16 38							17 38						18 38							
Brighouse		d				16 49	17 16						17 49	18 16					18 49		19 16					20 16
London Kings Cross 15 ⊖	26	a																								
Huddersfield	39	a					17 30							18 31							19 29					20 30
Sowerby Bridge		d		16 32		16 59		17 19			17 31		17 59		18 19		18 31		18 59			19 19				
Mytholmroyd		d				17 05		17 25					18 05		18 25				19 05			19 25				
Hebden Bridge		a		16 38	16 56	17 08		17 28			17 37	17 56	18 08		18 28		18 37	18 56	19 08			19 28	19 37	19 56		
		d		16 39	16 56	17 08		17 28			17 38	17 56	18 08		18 28		18 38	18 56	19 08			19 29	19 37	19 56		
Burnley Manchester Road	97	a		16 57							17 57						18 57						19 56			
Accrington	97	a		17 06							18 06						19 06						20 05			
Blackburn	97	a		17 14							18 14						19 14						20 14			
Preston 8	97	a		17 32							18 33						19 32						20 32			
Poulton-le-Fylde	97	a		17 56							18 50						19 50						20 50			
Blackpool North	97	a		18 06							19 00						20 00						21 00			
Todmorden		d			17 04	17 15		17 36				18 04	18 15		18 36			19 04	19 15			19 36		20 04		
Walsden		d						17 39					18 19		18 39				19 19			19 39				
Littleborough		d				17 23		17 45					18 25		18 45				19 25			19 46				
Smithy Bridge		d				17 25		17 48					18 28		18 48				19 28			19 48				
Rochdale		a			17 14	17 29		17 51				18 14	18 32		18 51			19 15	19 32			19 52		20 14		
		d	17 03		17 14	17 30		17 51	18 02			18 14	18 32		18 51	19 00		19 15	19 32			19 53		20 14	20 25	
Castleton		d	17 06			17 33			18 05				18 35			19 03			19 35			19 56			20 28	
Mills Hill		d	17 11			17 38			18 10				18 40			19 08			19 40			20 01			20 33	
Moston		d	17 14			17 41			18 13				18 43			19 11			19 43			20 04			20 36	
Manchester Victoria		a	17 23		17 32	17 53		18 08	18 21			18 32	18 54		19 09	19 21		19 32	19 53			20 15		20 32	20 46	

A To Wigan Wallgate
B To Blackburn
C To Wakefield Westgate

For connections to Liverpool Lime Street please see Table 90

Table 41R

Mondays to Fridays

24 March to 16 May

Leeds and Bradford - Huddersfield, Blackpool North, Rochdale and Manchester Victoria via Halifax and Brighouse

Network Diagram - refer to first Page of Table 39

Station	Table		NT	NT	NT	NT	NT	NT	NT	NT	NT	NT
			◇			◇			◇		◇	
York 8	40	d					20 13					
Selby	40	d	19 00									
Leeds 10	37,39	d	19 37	20 08		20 37	20 51	21 08	21 37	22 08	22 37	23 08
Bramley	37	d	19 44	20 15		20 44		21 15	21 44	22 15	22 44	23 15
New Pudsey	37	d	19 49	20 20		20 49	21 01	21 20	21 49	22 20	22 49	23 20
Bradford Interchange	37	a	19 57	20 28		20 57	21 10	21 28	21 57	22 28	22 57	23 29
		d	20 00	20 31		21 00	21 13	21 31	22 00	22 31	23 00	23 31
Halifax		a	20 12	20 44		21 12	21 24	21 44	22 12	22 44	23 12	23 44
		d	20 12	20 44		21 12	21 25	21 44	22 12	22 44	23 12	23 44
Dewsbury	39	d										
Mirfield	39	a										
		d										
Brighouse		d		20 55				21 55		22 55		23 55
London Kings Cross 15	⊖26	a										
Huddersfield	39	a		21 10				22 10		23 10		00 10
Sowerby Bridge		d	20 19			21 19			22 19		23 19	
Mytholmroyd		d	20 25			21 25			22 25		23 25	
Hebden Bridge		a	20 28			21 28	21 36		22 28		23 28	
		d	20 28			21 28	21 37		22 28		23 28	
Burnley Manchester Road	97	a					21 56					
Accrington	97	a					22 05					
Blackburn	97	a					22 13					
Preston 8	97	a					22 31					
Poulton-le-Fylde	97	a					22 49					
Blackpool North	97	a					22 59					
Todmorden		d	20 36			21 36			22 36		23 36	
Walsden		d	20 39			21 39			22 39		23 39	
Littleborough		d	20 45			21 45			22 45		23 45	
Smithy Bridge		d	20 48			21 48			22 48		23 48	
Rochdale		a	20 52			21 52			22 52		23 52	
		d	20 52		21 25	21 52			22 52		23 52	
Castleton		d	20 55		21 28	21 55			22 55			
Mills Hill		d	21 00		21 33	22 00			23 00			
Moston		d	21 03		21 36	22 03			23 03			
Manchester Victoria	⛴	a	21 12		21 46	22 15			23 15		00 10	

Saturdays

14 December to 22 March

Station	Table		NT	NT	NT	NT	NT	GC	NT	NT	NT	NT	NT
			🚌			🚌		■ 1 ☕		A			🚌
York 8	40	d									06 13		
Selby	40	d											
Leeds 10	37,39	d		05 37	05 51		06 16		06 37		06 51	07 08	
Bramley	37	d		05 44	05 58		06 23		06 44			07 15	
New Pudsey	37	d		05 49	06 02		06 28		06 49		07 01	07 20	
Bradford Interchange	37	a		05 57	06 13		06 36		06 57		07 11	07 28	
		d		06 00	06 14		06 40	06 51	07 00		07 14	07 31	
Halifax		a		06 12	06 25		06 52	07 02	07 12		07 25	07 43	
		d		06 12	06 26		06 52	07 03	07 12		07 26	07 44	
Dewsbury	39	d											
Mirfield	39	a											
		d											
Brighouse		d						07 14					
London Kings Cross 15	⊖26	a						10 07					
Huddersfield	39	a											
Sowerby Bridge		d		06 19			06 59		07 19				
Mytholmroyd		d		06 25			07 05		07 25				
Hebden Bridge		a		06 28	06 38		07 08		07 28		07 38	07 55	
		d	06 05	06 28		06 57	07 08		07 28	07 33		07 56	08 01
Burnley Manchester Road	97	a	06 45			07 37							08 41
Accrington	97	a											
Blackburn	97	a											
Preston 8	97	a											
Poulton-le-Fylde	97	a											
Blackpool North	97	a											
Todmorden		d		06 35			07 15		07 36	07 44		08 04	
Walsden		d		06 38					07 39	07 47			
Littleborough		d		06 45			07 23		07 45	07 53		08 11	
Smithy Bridge		d		06 47			07 25		07 48	07 56			
Rochdale		a		06 54			07 29		07 52	08 00		08 16	
		d		06 55			07 30		07 54	08 00		08 17	
Castleton		d		06 58			07 33		07 57	08 03		08 20	
Mills Hill		d		07 03			07 38		08 02	08 08		08 25	
Moston		d		07 06			07 41		08 05	08 11			
Manchester Victoria	⛴	a		07 17			07 53		08 17	08 22		08 37	

Station	Table		NT	NT	NT	NT	NT	NT	NT	NT	GC	NT	NT
						A			🚌		■ 1 ☕		
York 8	40	d					07 06						
Selby	40	d		06 43								07 43	
Leeds 10	37,39	d	07 13	07 23	07 37		07 51	08 08		08 13		08 23	08 37
Bramley	37	d		07 30	07 44			08 15				08 30	08 44
New Pudsey	37	d		07 35	07 49		08 01	08 20				08 35	08 49
Bradford Interchange	37	a		07 43	07 57		08 09	08 28				08 43	08 57
		d		07 46	08 00		08 12	08 32			08 38	08 46	09 00
Halifax		a		07 59	08 12		08 23	08 44			08 50	08 59	09 12
		d		08 06	08 12		08 24	08 44			08 51	09 06	09 12
Dewsbury	39	d	07 29							08 31			
Mirfield	39	a	07 35							08 37			
		d	07 35							08 38			
Brighouse		d	07 49	08 16						08 49	09 06	09 16	
London Kings Cross 15	⊖26	a									11 56		
Huddersfield	39	a		08 30								09 30	
Sowerby Bridge		d	07 59		08 19					08 59			09 19
Mytholmroyd		d	08 05		08 25					09 05			09 25
Hebden Bridge		a	08 08		08 28		08 36	08 56		09 08			09 28
		d	08 08		08 28			08 56	09 01	09 08			09 28
Burnley Manchester Road	97	a							09 41				
Accrington	97	a											
Blackburn	97	a											
Preston 8	97	a											
Poulton-le-Fylde	97	a											
Blackpool North	97	a											
Todmorden		d	08 15		08 36			09 04		09 15			09 36
Walsden		d			08 39								09 39
Littleborough		d	08 23		08 45					09 23			09 45
Smithy Bridge		d	08 25		08 48					09 25			09 48
Rochdale		a	08 29		08 51			09 14		09 29			09 51
		d	08 30		08 51	09 04		09 14		09 30			09 51
Castleton		d	08 33			09 07				09 33			
Mills Hill		d	08 37			09 12				09 37			
Moston		d	08 40			09 15				09 40			
Manchester Victoria	⛴	a	08 53		09 08	09 26		09 32		09 53			10 07

A To Wigan Wallgate

For connections to Liverpool Lime Street please see Table 90

Table 41R

Saturdays

14 December to 22 March

Leeds and Bradford - Huddersfield, Blackpool North, Rochdale and Manchester Victoria via Halifax and Brighouse

Network Diagram - refer to first Page of Table 39

Station	Table		NT	NT	NT	NT	NT	NT	NT	NT	NT	GC	NT	NT	NT	NT	NT	NT	NT	NT	NT	NT	NT	NT
			A			🚌				A		R 1 ☕		🚌				A			🚌			
York 8	40	d		08 09							09 11								10 11					
Selby	40	d						08 43								09 43							10 43	
Leeds 10	37,39	d		08 51	09 07		09 13	09 23	09 37		09 53		10 07		10 13	10 23	10 37		10 53	11 07		11 13	11 23	11 37
Bramley	37	d			09 14			09 30	09 44				10 14			10 30	10 44			11 14			11 30	11 44
New Pudsey	37	d		09 00	09 19			09 35	09 49		10 02		10 19			10 35	10 49		11 02	11 19			11 35	11 49
Bradford Interchange	37	a		09 12	09 28			09 43	09 57		10 11		10 28			10 43	10 57		11 12	11 28			11 43	11 57
		d		09 13	09 32			09 46	10 00		10 14	10 22	10 32			10 46	11 00		11 14	11 31			11 46	12 00
Halifax		a		09 24	09 44			10 01	10 12		10 25	10 34	10 44			10 59	11 12		11 24	11 43			11 59	12 12
		d		09 25	09 44			10 06	10 12		10 26	10 38	10 44			11 06	11 12		11 26	11 44			12 06	12 12
Dewsbury	39	d					09 31								10 29							11 29		
Mirfield	39	a					09 36								10 35							11 35		
		d					09 37								10 35							11 35		
Brighouse		d					09 49	10 16				10 48			10 49	11 16						11 49	12 16	
London Kings Cross 15 ⊖	26	a										13 45												
Huddersfield	39	a						10 30								11 30							12 30	
Sowerby Bridge		d					09 59		10 19						10 59		11 19					11 59		12 19
Mytholmroyd		d					10 05		10 25						11 05		11 25					12 05		12 25
Hebden Bridge		a		09 38	09 56		10 08		10 28		10 38		10 56		11 08		11 28		11 38	11 55		12 08		12 28
		d			09 56	10 01	10 08		10 28				10 56	11 01	11 08		11 28			11 56	12 01	12 08		12 28
Burnley Manchester Road	97	a				10 41								11 41							12 41			
Accrington	97	a																						
Blackburn	97	a																						
Preston 8	97	a																						
Poulton-le-Fylde	97	a																						
Blackpool North	97	a																						
Todmorden		d			10 04		10 15		10 36				11 04		11 15		11 36			12 03		12 15		12 36
Walsden		d							10 39								11 39							12 39
Littleborough		d					10 23		10 45						11 23		11 45					12 23		12 45
Smithy Bridge		d					10 25		10 48						11 25		11 48					12 25		12 48
Rochdale		a			10 14		10 29		10 51				11 14		11 29		11 51			12 13		12 29		12 51
		d	10 05		10 14		10 30		10 51	11 04			11 14		11 30		11 51	12 04		12 14		12 30		12 51
Castleton		d	10 08				10 33			11 07					11 33			12 07				12 33		
Mills Hill		d	10 13				10 38			11 12					11 38			12 12				12 38		
Moston		d	10 16				10 41			11 15					11 41			12 15				12 41		
Manchester Victoria 🚊		a	10 25		10 32		10 53		11 07	11 26			11 32		11 53		12 07	12 25		12 31		12 53		13 07

Station	Table		NT	NT	NT	NT	NT	NT	NT	NT	NT	NT	NT	NT	NT	NT	NT	NT	NT	NT	NT	NT	NT
			A			🚌				A			🚌				A			🚌			
York 8	40	d		11 09							12 13							13 09					
Selby	40	d						11 43							12 43							13 43	
Leeds 10	37,39	d		11 53	12 07		12 13	12 23	12 37		12 53	13 07		13 13	13 23	13 37		13 53	14 07		14 13	14 23	14 37
Bramley	37	d			12 14			12 30	12 44			13 14			13 30	13 44			14 14			14 30	14 44
New Pudsey	37	d		12 02	12 19			12 35	12 49		13 02	13 19			13 35	13 49		14 02	14 19			14 35	14 49
Bradford Interchange	37	a		12 12	12 28			12 43	12 57		13 12	13 28			13 43	13 58		14 12	14 28			14 43	14 57
		d		12 14	12 32			12 46	13 00		13 14	13 32			13 46	14 00		14 14	14 32			14 46	15 00
Halifax		a		12 25	12 44			12 59	13 12		13 25	13 44			13 59	14 12		14 25	14 44			14 59	15 12
		d		12 26	12 44			13 06	13 12		13 26	13 44			14 06	14 13		14 26	14 44			15 06	15 12
Dewsbury	39	d					12 29							13 29							14 29		
Mirfield	39	a					12 35							13 35							14 35		
		d					12 35							13 35							14 35		
Brighouse		d					12 49	13 16						13 49	14 16						14 49	15 16	
London Kings Cross 15 ⊖	26	a																					
Huddersfield	39	a						13 30							14 30							15 30	
Sowerby Bridge		d					12 59		13 19					13 59		14 19					14 59		15 19
Mytholmroyd		d					13 05		13 25					14 05		14 25					15 05		15 25
Hebden Bridge		a		12 38	12 56		13 08		13 28		13 38	13 56		14 08		14 28		14 38	14 56		15 08		15 28
		d			12 56	13 01	13 08		13 28			13 56	14 01	14 08		14 29			14 56	15 01	15 08		15 28
Burnley Manchester Road	97	a				13 41							14 41							15 41			
Accrington	97	a																					
Blackburn	97	a																					
Preston 8	97	a																					
Poulton-le-Fylde	97	a																					
Blackpool North	97	a																					
Todmorden		d			13 04		13 15		13 36			14 04		14 15		14 36			15 04		15 15		15 36
Walsden		d							13 39							14 39							15 39
Littleborough		d					13 23		13 45					14 23		14 46					15 23		15 45
Smithy Bridge		d					13 25		13 48					14 25		14 48					15 25		15 48
Rochdale		a			13 14		13 29		13 51			14 14		14 29		14 51			15 14		15 29		15 51
		d	13 04		13 14		13 30		13 51	14 04		14 14		14 30		14 52	15 04		15 14		15 30		15 51
Castleton		d	13 07				13 33			14 07				14 33			15 07				15 33		
Mills Hill		d	13 12				13 38			14 12				14 38			15 12				15 38		
Moston		d	13 15				13 41			14 15				14 41			15 15				15 41		
Manchester Victoria 🚊		a	13 25		13 32		13 53		14 07	14 25		14 32		14 53		15 08	15 25		15 32		15 53		16 08

A To Wigan Wallgate

For connections to Liverpool Lime Street please see Table 90

Table 41R

Saturdays

14 December to 22 March

Leeds and Bradford - Huddersfield, Blackpool North, Rochdale and Manchester Victoria via Halifax and Brighouse

Network Diagram - refer to first Page of Table 39

			NT	NT	GC	NT	NT	NT	NT	NT	NT	NT	NT	NT	NT	NT	NT	NT	NT	NT	NT	NT	NT	NT
			A		1st class, catering		bus				B			bus		C		B			bus			
York 8	40	d		14 13								15 09							16 08					
Selby	40	d							14 43							15 43							16 43	
Leeds 10	37,39	d		14 53		15 07		15 13	15 23	15 37		15 52	16 07		16 13	16 23	16 37		16 51	17 07		17 13	17 23	17 37
Bramley	37	d				15 14			15 30	15 44			16 14			16 30	16 44			17 14			17 30	17 44
New Pudsey	37	d		15 02		15 19			15 35	15 49		16 01	16 19			16 35	16 49		17 00	17 19			17 35	17 49
Bradford Interchange	37	a		15 12		15 28			15 43	15 57		16 10	16 28			16 43	16 57		17 10	17 28			17 43	17 57
		d		15 14	15 22	15 32			15 46	16 00		16 13	16 32			16 46	17 00		17 12	17 32			17 46	18 00
Halifax		a		15 25	15 33	15 44			15 59	16 12		16 24	16 44			16 59	17 12		17 23	17 44			17 59	18 12
		d		15 26	15 35	15 44			16 06	16 12		16 25	16 44			17 06	17 12		17 24	17 44			18 06	18 12
Dewsbury	39	d						15 29							16 31							17 31		
Mirfield	39	a						15 35							16 37							17 37		
		d						15 35							16 38							17 38		
Brighouse		d			15 46			15 49	16 16						16 49	17 16						17 49	18 16	
London Kings Cross 15 ⊖	26	a			18 45																			
Huddersfield	39	a							16 30							17 29							18 31	
Sowerby Bridge		d						15 59		16 19		16 31			16 59		17 19		17 31			17 59		18 19
Mytholmroyd		d						16 05		16 25					17 05		17 25					18 05		18 25
Hebden Bridge		a		15 38		15 56		16 08		16 28		16 39	16 56		17 08		17 28		17 37	17 56		18 08		18 28
		d				15 56	16 01	16 08		16 28			16 56	17 01	17 08		17 28			17 56	18 01	18 08		18 28
Burnley Manchester Road	97	a					16 41							17 41							18 41			
Accrington	97	a																						
Blackburn	97	a																						
Preston 8	97	a																						
Poulton-le-Fylde	97	a																						
Blackpool North	97	a																						
Todmorden		d				16 04		16 15		16 36			17 04		17 15		17 36			18 04		18 15		18 36
Walsden		d								16 39							17 39					18 19		18 39
Littleborough		d						16 23		16 45					17 23		17 45					18 25		18 45
Smithy Bridge		d						16 25		16 48					17 25		17 48					18 28		18 48
Rochdale		a				16 14		16 29		16 51			17 14		17 29		17 51			18 14		18 32		18 51
		d	16 04			16 14		16 30		16 51	17 03		17 14		17 30		17 51	18 02		18 14		18 32		18 51
Castleton		d	16 07					16 33			17 06				17 33			18 05				18 35		
Mills Hill		d	16 12					16 38			17 11				17 38			18 10				18 40		
Moston		d	16 15					16 41			17 14				17 41			18 13				18 43		
Manchester Victoria ⇌		a	16 26			16 32		16 53		17 07	17 23		17 33		17 54		18 07	18 22		18 32		18 54		19 10

			NT	NT	NT	NT	NT	NT	NT	NT	NT	NT	NT	NT	NT	NT	NT	NT	NT	NT	NT	NT	NT
						bus								bus						bus			
York 8	40	d		17 13						18 05									20 13				
Selby	40	d						17 40					18 43										
Leeds 10	37,39	d		17 51	18 08		18 13	18 23	18 37	18 51	19 08		19 23		19 37	20 08		20 37	20 51		21 08	21 37	22 08
Bramley	37	d			18 15			18 30	18 44		19 15		19 30		19 44	20 15		20 44			21 15	21 44	22 15
New Pudsey	37	d		18 01	18 20			18 35	18 49	19 01	19 20		19 35		19 49	20 20		20 49	21 01		21 20	21 49	22 20
Bradford Interchange	37	a		18 09	18 28			18 43	18 58	19 09	19 28		19 44		19 57	20 28		20 57	21 10		21 28	21 57	22 28
		d		18 12	18 32			18 46	19 00	19 12	19 32		19 46		20 00	20 31		21 00	21 13		21 31	22 00	22 31
Halifax		a		18 23	18 44			18 59	19 12	19 24	19 44		19 59		20 12	20 44		21 12	21 24		21 44	22 12	22 44
		d		18 24	18 44			19 06	19 13	19 25	19 44		20 06		20 12	20 44		21 12	21 25		21 44	22 12	22 44
Dewsbury	39	d					18 31																
Mirfield	39	a					18 37																
		d					18 38																
Brighouse		d					18 49	19 16					20 16			20 55					21 55		22 55
London Kings Cross 15 ⊖	26	a																					
Huddersfield	39	a						19 30					20 30			21 10					22 10		23 10
Sowerby Bridge		d		18 31			18 59		19 19						20 19			21 19				22 19	
Mytholmroyd		d					19 05		19 25						20 25			21 25				22 25	
Hebden Bridge		a		18 38	18 56		19 08		19 28	19 37	19 56				20 28			21 28	21 39			22 28	
		d			18 56	19 01	19 08		19 28		19 56			20 01	20 28			21 28		21 43		22 28	
Burnley Manchester Road	97	a				19 41								20 40						22 18			
Accrington	97	a																					
Blackburn	97	a																					
Preston 8	97	a												21 48									
Poulton-le-Fylde	97	a																					
Blackpool North	97	a																					
Todmorden		d			19 04		19 15		19 36		20 04				20 36			21 36				22 36	
Walsden		d					19 19		19 39						20 39			21 39				22 39	
Littleborough		d					19 25		19 45						20 45			21 45				22 45	
Smithy Bridge		d					19 28		19 48						20 48			21 48				22 48	
Rochdale		a			19 15		19 32		19 52		20 14				20 52			21 52				22 52	
		d	19 00		19 15		19 32		19 52		20 14	20 25			20 52		21 25	21 52				22 52	
Castleton		d	19 03				19 35		19 55			20 28			20 55		21 28	21 55				22 55	
Mills Hill		d	19 08				19 40		20 00			20 33			21 00		21 33	22 00				23 00	
Moston		d	19 11				19 43		20 03			20 36			21 03		21 36	22 03				23 03	
Manchester Victoria ⇌		a	19 20		19 32		19 54		20 15		20 32	20 46			21 13		21 46	22 14				23 14	

A To Wigan Wallgate
B To Blackburn
C To Wakefield Westgate

For connections to Liverpool Lime Street please see Table 90

Table 41R

Saturdays
14 December to 22 March

Leeds and Bradford - Huddersfield, Blackpool North, Rochdale and Manchester Victoria via Halifax and Brighouse

Network Diagram - refer to first Page of Table 39

Station			NT	NT	NT
York ■	40	d			
Selby	40	d			
Leeds ■	37,39	d		22 37	23 00
Bramley	37	d		22 44	23 07
New Pudsey	37	d		22 49	23 12
Bradford Interchange	37	a		22 57	23 21
		d		23 00	23 23
Halifax		a		23 12	23 36
		d		23 12	23 36
Dewsbury	39	d			
Mirfield	39	a			
		d			
Brighouse		d			23 47
London Kings Cross ■ ⊖	26	a			
Huddersfield	39	a			00 01
Sowerby Bridge		d		23 19	
Mytholmroyd		d		23 25	
Hebden Bridge		a		23 28	
		d		23 28	
Burnley Manchester Road	97	a			
Accrington	97	a			
Blackburn	97	a			
Preston ■	97	a			
Poulton-le-Fylde	97	a			
Blackpool North	97	a			
Todmorden		d		23 36	
Walsden		d		23 39	
Littleborough		d		23 45	
Smithy Bridge		d		23 48	
Rochdale		a		23 52	
		d	23 04	23 52	
Castleton		d	23 07		
Mills Hill		d	23 12		
Moston		d	23 15		
Manchester Victoria		a	23 27	00 08	

Saturdays
29 March to 17 May

Station			NT	NT	NT	GC ■ 1	NT	NT A	NT	NT	NT	NT	NT
York ■	40	d							06 13				
Selby	40	d										06 43	
Leeds ■	37,39	d	05 37	05 51	06 16		06 37		06 51	07 08	07 13	07 23	07 37
Bramley	37	d	05 44	05 58	06 23		06 44			07 15		07 30	07 44
New Pudsey	37	d	05 49	06 02	06 28		06 49		07 01	07 20		07 35	07 49
Bradford Interchange	37	a	05 57	06 13	06 36		06 57		07 11	07 28		07 43	07 57
		d	06 00	06 14	06 40	06 51	07 00		07 14	07 31		07 46	08 00
Halifax		a	06 12	06 25	06 52	07 02	07 12		07 25	07 43		07 59	08 12
		d	06 12	06 26	06 52	07 03	07 12		07 26	07 44		08 06	08 12
Dewsbury	39	d									07 29		
Mirfield	39	a									07 35		
		d									07 35		
Brighouse		d				07 14					07 49	08 16	
London Kings Cross ■ ⊖	26	a				10 07							
Huddersfield	39	a										08 30	
Sowerby Bridge		d	06 19		06 59		07 19				07 59		08 19
Mytholmroyd		d	06 25		07 05		07 25				08 05		08 25
Hebden Bridge		a	06 28	06 37	07 08		07 28		07 37	07 55	08 08		08 28
		d	06 28	06 38	07 08		07 28	07 33	07 38	07 56	08 08		08 28
Burnley Manchester Road	97	a		06 57					07 57				
Accrington	97	a		07 06					08 06				
Blackburn	97	a		07 16					08 14				
Preston ■	97	a		07 36					08 38				
Poulton-le-Fylde	97	a		07 54					08 56				
Blackpool North	97	a		08 05					09 05				
Todmorden		d	06 35		07 15		07 36	07 44		08 04	08 15		08 36
Walsden		d	06 38				07 39	07 47					08 39
Littleborough		d	06 45		07 23		07 45	07 53		08 11	08 23		08 45
Smithy Bridge		d	06 47		07 25		07 48	07 56			08 25		08 48
Rochdale		a	06 54		07 29		07 52	08 00		08 16	08 29		08 51
		d	06 55		07 30		07 54	08 00		08 17	08 30		08 51
Castleton		d	06 58		07 33		07 57	08 03		08 20	08 33		
Mills Hill		d	07 03		07 38		08 02	08 08		08 25	08 37		
Moston		d	07 06		07 41		08 05	08 11			08 40		
Manchester Victoria		a	07 17		07 53		08 17	08 22		08 37	08 53		09 08

Station			NT A	NT	NT	NT	GC ■ 1	NT	NT	NT A	NT	NT	NT
York ■	40	d		07 06							08 09		
Selby	40	d						07 43					
Leeds ■	37,39	d		07 51	08 08	08 13		08 23	08 37		08 51	09 07	09 13
Bramley	37	d			08 15			08 30	08 44			09 14	
New Pudsey	37	d		08 01	08 20			08 35	08 49		09 00	09 19	
Bradford Interchange	37	a		08 09	08 28			08 43	08 57		09 12	09 28	
		d		08 12	08 32		08 38	08 46	09 00		09 13	09 32	
Halifax		a		08 23	08 44		08 50	08 59	09 12		09 24	09 44	
		d		08 24	08 44		08 51	09 06	09 12		09 24	09 44	
Dewsbury	39	d				08 31							09 31
Mirfield	39	a				08 37							09 36
		d				08 38							09 37
Brighouse		d				08 49	09 06	09 16					09 49
London Kings Cross ■ ⊖	26	a					11 56						
Huddersfield	39	a						09 30					
Sowerby Bridge		d				08 59			09 19				09 59
Mytholmroyd		d				09 05			09 25				10 05
Hebden Bridge		a		08 35	08 56	09 08			09 28		09 37	09 56	10 08
		d		08 36	08 56	09 08			09 28		09 37	09 56	10 08
Burnley Manchester Road	97	a		08 57							09 56		
Accrington	97	a		09 06							10 06		
Blackburn	97	a		09 14							10 14		
Preston ■	97	a		09 32							10 32		
Poulton-le-Fylde	97	a		09 50							10 50		
Blackpool North	97	a		10 01							11 01		
Todmorden		d			09 04	09 15			09 36			10 04	10 15
Walsden		d							09 39				
Littleborough		d				09 23			09 45				10 23
Smithy Bridge		d				09 25			09 48				10 25
Rochdale		a			09 14	09 29			09 51			10 14	10 29
		d	09 04		09 14	09 30			09 51	10 05		10 14	10 30
Castleton		d	09 07			09 33				10 08			10 33
Mills Hill		d	09 12			09 37				10 13			10 38
Moston		d	09 15			09 40				10 16			10 41
Manchester Victoria		a	09 26		09 32	09 53			10 07	10 25		10 32	10 53

A To Wigan Wallgate

For connections to Liverpool Lime Street please see Table 90

Table 41R

Saturdays

29 March to 17 May

Leeds and Bradford - Huddersfield, Blackpool North, Rochdale and Manchester Victoria via Halifax and Brighouse

Network Diagram - refer to first Page of Table 39

	NT	NT	NT	NT	GC	NT	NT	NT	NT	NT	NT	NT	NT	NT	NT	NT	NT	NT	NT	NT	NT	NT
			A		R 1					A						A						A
York 8 40 d				09 11							10 11						11 09					
Selby 40 d	08 43							09 43						10 43						11 43		
Leeds 10 37,39 d	09 23	09 37		09 53		10 07	10 13	10 23	10 37		10 53	11 07	11 13	11 23	11 37		11 53	12 07	12 13	12 23	12 37	
Bramley 37 d	09 30	09 44				10 14		10 30	10 44			11 14		11 30	11 44			12 14		12 30	12 44	
New Pudsey 37 d	09 35	09 49		10 02		10 19		10 35	10 49		11 02	11 19		11 35	11 49		12 02	12 19		12 35	12 49	
Bradford Interchange 37 a	09 43	09 57		10 11		10 28		10 43	10 57		11 12	11 28		11 43	11 57		12 12	12 28		12 43	12 57	
d	09 46	10 00		10 14	10 22	10 32		10 46	11 00		11 14	11 31		11 46	12 00		12 14	12 32		12 46	13 00	
Halifax a	10 01	10 12		10 25	10 34	10 44		10 59	11 12		11 24	11 43		11 59	12 12		12 25	12 44		12 59	13 12	
d	10 06	10 12		10 26	10 38	10 44		11 06	11 12		11 26	11 44		12 06	12 12		12 26	12 44		13 06	13 12	
Dewsbury 39 d							10 29						11 29						12 29			
Mirfield 39 a							10 35						11 35						12 35			
d							10 35						11 35						12 35			
Brighouse d	10 16				10 48		10 49	11 16					11 49	12 16					12 49	13 16		
London Kings Cross 15 ⊖26 a					13 45																	
Huddersfield 39 a	10 30							11 30						12 30						13 30		
Sowerby Bridge d		10 19					10 59		11 19				11 59		12 19				12 59		13 19	
Mytholmroyd d		10 25					11 05		11 25				12 05		12 25				13 05		13 25	
Hebden Bridge a		10 28		10 37		10 56	11 08		11 28		11 36	11 55	12 08		12 28		12 37	12 56	13 08		13 28	
d		10 28		10 38		10 56	11 08		11 28		11 38	11 56	12 08		12 28		12 38	12 56	13 08		13 28	
Burnley Manchester Road 97 a				10 57							11 57						12 57					
Accrington 97 a				11 06							12 06						13 06					
Blackburn 97 a				11 14							12 14						13 14					
Preston 8 97 a				11 32							12 32						13 32					
Poulton-le-Fylde 97 a				11 50							12 50						13 50					
Blackpool North 97 a				12 00							13 00						14 00					
Todmorden d		10 36				11 04	11 15		11 36			12 03	12 15		12 36			13 04	13 15		13 36	
Walsden d		10 39							11 39						12 39						13 39	
Littleborough d		10 45					11 23		11 45				12 23		12 45				13 23		13 45	
Smithy Bridge d		10 48					11 25		11 48				12 25		12 48				13 25		13 48	
Rochdale a		10 51				11 14	11 29		11 51			12 13	12 29		12 51			13 14	13 29		13 51	
d		10 51	11 04			11 14	11 30		11 51	12 04		12 14	12 30		12 51	13 04		13 14	13 30		13 51	14 04
Castleton d			11 07				11 33			12 07			12 33			13 07			13 33			14 07
Mills Hill d			11 12				11 38			12 12			12 38			13 12			13 38			14 12
Moston d			11 15				11 41			12 15			12 41			13 15			13 41			14 15
Manchester Victoria a		11 07	11 26			11 32	11 53		12 07	12 25		12 31	12 53		13 07	13 25		13 32	13 53		14 07	14 25

	NT	NT	NT	NT	NT	NT	NT	NT	NT	NT	NT	NT	NT	GC	NT	NT	NT	NT	NT	NT	NT
						A						A		R 1					B		
York 8 40 d	12 13						13 09						14 13							15 09	
Selby 40 d				12 43						13 43							14 43				
Leeds 10 37,39 d	12 53	13 07	13 13	13 23	13 37		13 53	14 07	14 13	14 23	14 37		14 53		15 07	15 13	15 23	15 37		15 52	16 07
Bramley 37 d		13 14		13 30	13 44			14 14		14 30	14 44				15 14		15 30	15 44			16 14
New Pudsey 37 d	13 02	13 19		13 35	13 49		14 02	14 19		14 35	14 49		15 02		15 19		15 35	15 49		16 01	16 19
Bradford Interchange 37 a	13 12	13 28		13 43	13 58		14 12	14 28		14 43	14 57		15 12		15 28		15 43	15 57		16 10	16 28
d	13 14	13 32		13 46	14 00		14 14	14 32		14 46	15 00		15 14	15 22	15 32		15 46	16 00		16 13	16 32
Halifax a	13 25	13 44		13 59	14 12		14 25	14 44		14 59	15 12		15 25	15 33	15 44		15 59	16 12		16 24	16 44
d	13 26	13 44		14 06	14 13		14 26	14 44		15 06	15 12		15 26	15 35	15 44		16 06	16 12		16 25	16 44
Dewsbury 39 d			13 29						14 29							15 29					
Mirfield 39 a			13 35						14 35							15 35					
d			13 35						14 35							15 35					
Brighouse d			13 49	14 16					14 49	15 16				15 46		15 49	16 16				
London Kings Cross 15 ⊖26 a														18 45							
Huddersfield 39 a				14 30						15 30							16 30				
Sowerby Bridge d			13 59		14 19				14 59		15 19					15 59		16 19		16 31	
Mytholmroyd d			14 05		14 25				15 05		15 25					16 05		16 25			
Hebden Bridge a	13 37	13 56	14 08		14 28		14 37	14 56	15 08		15 28		15 37		15 56	16 08		16 28		16 37	16 56
d	13 38	13 56	14 08		14 29		14 38	14 56	15 08		15 28		15 38		15 56	16 08		16 28		16 38	16 56
Burnley Manchester Road 97 a	13 57						14 57						15 57							16 57	
Accrington 97 a	14 06						15 06						16 06							17 06	
Blackburn 97 a	14 14						15 14						16 14							17 14	
Preston 8 97 a	14 32						15 32						16 32							17 32	
Poulton-le-Fylde 97 a	14 50						15 50						16 50							17 50	
Blackpool North 97 a	15 00						16 00						17 00							17 58	
Todmorden d		14 04	14 15		14 36			15 04	15 15		15 36				16 04	16 15		16 36			17 04
Walsden d					14 39						15 39							16 39			
Littleborough d			14 23		14 46				15 23		15 45					16 23		16 45			
Smithy Bridge d			14 25		14 48				15 25		15 48					16 25		16 48			
Rochdale a		14 14	14 29		14 51			15 14	15 29		15 51				16 14	16 29		16 51			17 14
d		14 14	14 30		14 52	15 04		15 14	15 30		15 51	16 04			16 14	16 30		16 51	17 03		17 14
Castleton d			14 33			15 07			15 33			16 07				16 33			17 06		
Mills Hill d			14 38			15 12			15 38			16 12				16 38			17 11		
Moston d			14 41			15 15			15 41			16 15				16 41			17 14		
Manchester Victoria a		14 32	14 53		15 08	15 25		15 32	15 53		16 08	16 26			16 32	16 53		17 07	17 23		17 33

A To Wigan Wallgate

B To Blackburn

For connections to Liverpool Lime Street please see Table 90

Table 41R

Saturdays
29 March to 17 May

Leeds and Bradford - Huddersfield, Blackpool North, Rochdale and Manchester Victoria via Halifax and Brighouse

Network Diagram - refer to first Page of Table 39

		NT	NT A	NT	NT B	NT	NT	NT		NT	NT	NT	NT	NT	NT	NT	NT	NT		NT	NT	NT	NT	NT	NT
York 8	40 d					16 08							17 13					18 05							
Selby	40 d		15 43							16 43						17 40						18 43			
Leeds 10	37,39 d	16 13	16 23	16 37		16 51	17 07	17 13		17 23	17 37		17 51	18 08	18 13	18 23	18 37	18 51		19 08		19 23	19 37	20 08	
Bramley	37 d		16 30	16 44			17 14			17 30	17 44			18 15		18 30	18 44			19 15		19 30	19 44	20 15	
New Pudsey	37 d		16 35	16 49		17 00	17 19			17 35	17 49		18 01	18 20		18 35	18 49	19 01		19 20		19 35	19 49	20 20	
Bradford Interchange	37 a		16 43	16 57		17 10	17 28			17 43	17 57		18 09	18 28		18 43	18 58	19 09		19 28		19 44	19 57	20 28	
	d		16 46	17 00		17 12	17 32			17 46	18 00		18 12	18 32		18 46	19 00	19 12		19 32		19 46	20 00	20 31	
Halifax	a		16 59	17 12		17 23	17 44			17 59	18 12		18 23	18 44		18 59	19 12	19 24		19 44		19 59	20 12	20 44	
	d		17 06	17 12		17 24	17 44			18 06	18 12		18 24	18 44		19 06	19 13	19 24		19 44		20 06	20 12	20 44	
Dewsbury	39 d	16 31						17 31							18 31										
Mirfield	39 a	16 37						17 37							18 37										
	d	16 38						17 38							18 38										
Brighouse	d	16 49	17 16					17 49		18 16					18 49	19 16						20 16		20 55	
London Kings Cross 15 ⊖26	a																								
Huddersfield	39 a		17 29							18 31						19 30						20 30		21 10	
Sowerby Bridge	d	16 59		17 19		17 31		17 59			18 19		18 31		18 59		19 19						20 19		
Mytholmroyd	d	17 05		17 25				18 05			18 25				19 05		19 25						20 25		
Hebden Bridge	a	17 08		17 28		17 37	17 56	18 08			18 28		18 37	18 56	19 08		19 28	19 36		19 56			20 28		
	d	17 08		17 28		17 38	17 56	18 08			18 28		18 38	18 56	19 08		19 28	19 36		19 56			20 28		
Burnley Manchester Road	97 a					17 57							18 57					19 56							
Accrington	97 a					18 06							19 06					20 05							
Blackburn	97 a					18 14							19 14					20 14							
Preston 8	97 a					18 33							19 32					20 32							
Poulton-le-Fylde	97 a					18 50							19 50					20 50							
Blackpool North	97 a					19 00							20 00					21 00							
Todmorden	d	17 15		17 36			18 04	18 15			18 36			19 04	19 15		19 36			20 04			20 36		
Walsden	d			17 39				18 19			18 39				19 19		19 39						20 39		
Littleborough	d	17 23		17 45				18 25			18 45				19 25		19 45						20 45		
Smithy Bridge	d	17 25		17 48				18 28			18 48				19 28		19 48						20 48		
Rochdale	a	17 29		17 51			18 14	18 32			18 51			19 15	19 32		19 52			20 14			20 52		
	d	17 30		17 51	18 02		18 14	18 32			18 51	19 00		19 15	19 32		19 52			20 14	20 25		20 52		21 25
Castleton	d	17 33			18 05			18 35				19 03			19 35		19 55				20 28		20 55		21 28
Mills Hill	d	17 38			18 10			18 40				19 08			19 40		20 00				20 33		21 00		21 33
Moston	d	17 41			18 13			18 43				19 11			19 43		20 03				20 36		21 03		21 36
Manchester Victoria ⛴	a	17 54		18 07	18 22		18 32	18 54			19 10	19 20		19 32	19 54		20 15			20 32	20 46		21 13		21 46

		NT	NT	NT		NT	NT	NT	NT	NT
York 8	40 d		20 13							
Selby	40 d									
Leeds 10	37,39 d	20 37	20 51	21 08		21 37	22 08		22 37	23 00
Bramley	37 d	20 44		21 15		21 44	22 15		22 44	23 07
New Pudsey	37 d	20 49	21 01	21 20		21 49	22 20		22 49	23 12
Bradford Interchange	37 a	20 57	21 10	21 28		21 57	22 28		22 57	23 21
	d	21 00	21 13	21 31		22 00	22 31		23 00	23 23
Halifax	a	21 12	21 24	21 44		22 12	22 44		23 12	23 36
	d	21 12	21 25	21 44		22 12	22 44		23 12	23 36
Dewsbury	39 d									
Mirfield	39 a									
	d									
Brighouse	d			21 55			22 55			23 47
London Kings Cross 15 ⊖26	a									
Huddersfield	39 a			22 10			23 10			00 01
Sowerby Bridge	d	21 19				22 19			23 19	
Mytholmroyd	d	21 25				22 25			23 25	
Hebden Bridge	a	21 28	21 36			22 28			23 28	
	d	21 28	21 37			22 28			23 28	
Burnley Manchester Road	97 a		21 56							
Accrington	97 a		22 05							
Blackburn	97 a		22 13							
Preston 8	97 a		22 31							
Poulton-le-Fylde	97 a		22 49							
Blackpool North	97 a		22 59							
Todmorden	d	21 36				22 36			23 36	
Walsden	d	21 39				22 39			23 39	
Littleborough	d	21 45				22 45			23 45	
Smithy Bridge	d	21 48				22 48			23 48	
Rochdale	a	21 52				22 52			23 52	
	d	21 52				22 52		23 04	23 52	
Castleton	d	21 55				22 55		23 07		
Mills Hill	d	22 00				23 00		23 12		
Moston	d	22 03				23 03		23 15		
Manchester Victoria ⛴	a	22 14				23 14		23 27	00 08	

A To Wakefield Westgate
B To Blackburn

For connections to Liverpool Lime Street please see Table 90

Table 41R

Sundays

8 December to 29 December

Leeds and Bradford - Huddersfield, Blackpool North, Rochdale and Manchester Victoria via Halifax and Brighouse

Network Diagram - refer to first Page of Table 39

		GC	NT	NT	NT	NT	NT	NT	NT	NT		NT	NT	NT	NT	NT	NT	NT	NT	NT		NT	NT	NT	NT
		■ 1 ⊡	bus					bus						bus					bus						bus
York 8	40 d												08 50					09 52						10 57	
Selby	40 d																								
Leeds 10	37,39 d		07 40	08 02		08 21	08 45		09 02			09 18	09 35		09 54		10 12	10 35		10 54			11 12	11 35	
Bramley	37 d			08 09		08 28			09 09			09 25			10 01		10 19			11 01			11 19		
New Pudsey	37 d		08 00	08 14		08 33	08 54		09 14			09 30	09 44		10 06		10 24	10 44		11 06			11 24	11 44	
Bradford Interchange	37 a		08 10	08 22		08 41	09 03		09 22			09 38	09 53		10 14		10 32	10 53		11 14			11 32	11 53	
	d	07 58	08 10			08 45	09 05		09 25			09 44	09 55		10 17		10 35	10 55		11 17			11 35	11 55	
Halifax	a	08 09	08 35			08 57	09 17		09 37			09 57	10 07		10 29		10 48	11 07		11 29			11 48	12 07	
	d	08 10	08 35			09 01	09 17		09 37			09 59	10 07		10 29		10 48	11 07		11 29				12 07	
Dewsbury	39 d																								
Mirfield	39 a																								
	d																								
Brighouse	d	08 21										10 09					10 58								
London Kings Cross 15 ⊖26	a	10 40																							
Huddersfield	39 a											10 24					11 14								
Sowerby Bridge	d					09 06			09 44						10 36					11 36					
Mytholmroyd	d					09 12			09 50						10 42					11 42					
Hebden Bridge	a		08 55			09 17	09 29		09 53				10 19		10 45			11 19		11 45				12 19	
	d		08 55			09 17		09 40	09 53					10 40	10 45				11 40	11 45					12 40
Burnley Manchester Road	97 a		09 30					10 20						11 20					12 20						13 20
Accrington	97 a																								
Blackburn	97 a																								
Preston 8	97 a																								
Poulton-le-Fylde	97 a																								
Blackpool North	97 a																								
Todmorden	d					09 24			10 00						10 52					11 52					
Walsden	d					09 27			10 03						10 55					11 55					
Littleborough	d					09 34			10 10						11 02					12 02					
Smithy Bridge	d					09 36			10 12						11 04					12 04					
Rochdale	a					09 41			10 17						11 09					12 09					
	d				08 58	09 41			10 17	10 22					11 09	11 22				12 09		12 22			
Castleton	d				09 01					10 25						11 25						12 25			
Mills Hill	d				09 06					10 30						11 30						12 30			
Moston	d				09 09					10 33						11 33						12 33			
Manchester Victoria ⛴	a				09 20	09 56			10 31	10 43					11 23	11 43				12 23		12 43			

		GC	NT	NT	NT	NT		NT	NT	NT	NT	NT	NT	NT	NT	NT		NT	NT	GC	NT	NT	NT	NT	NT
		■ 1 ⊡						bus					bus						bus	■ 1 ⊡					bus
York 8	40 d					11 52						12 52						13 52						14 52	
Selby	40 d																								
Leeds 10	37,39 d		11 54		12 13	12 35			12 54		13 13	13 35		13 54		14 12		14 35			14 54		15 12	15 35	
Bramley	37 d		12 01		12 20				13 01		13 20			14 01		14 19					15 01		15 19		
New Pudsey	37 d		12 06		12 25	12 44			13 06		13 25	13 44		14 06		14 24		14 44			15 06		15 24	15 44	
Bradford Interchange	37 a		12 14		12 33	12 53			13 14		13 33	13 53		14 14		14 32		14 53			15 14		15 32	15 53	
	d	12 00	12 17		12 36	12 55			13 17		13 36	13 55		14 17		14 35		14 55		15 08	15 17		15 35	15 55	
Halifax	a	12 13	12 29		12 49	13 07			13 29		13 49	14 07		14 29		14 48		15 07		15 19	15 29		15 48	16 07	
	d	12 14	12 29		12 49	13 07			13 29			14 07		14 29		14 48		15 07		15 23	15 29			16 07	
Dewsbury	39 d																								
Mirfield	39 a																								
	d																								
Brighouse	d	12 25			12 59											14 58				15 37					
London Kings Cross 15 ⊖26	a	14 45																		17 57					
Huddersfield	39 a				13 14											15 14									
Sowerby Bridge	d		12 36						13 36					14 36							15 36				
Mytholmroyd	d		12 42						13 42					14 42							15 42				
Hebden Bridge	a		12 45			13 19			13 45			14 19		14 45				15 19			15 45			16 19	
	d		12 45					13 40	13 45				14 40	14 45					15 40		15 45				16 40
Burnley Manchester Road	97 a							14 20					15 20						16 20						17 20
Accrington	97 a																								
Blackburn	97 a																								
Preston 8	97 a																								
Poulton-le-Fylde	97 a																								
Blackpool North	97 a																								
Todmorden	d		12 52						13 52					14 52							15 52				
Walsden	d		12 55						13 55					14 55							15 54				
Littleborough	d		13 02						14 02					15 02							16 02				
Smithy Bridge	d		13 04						14 04					15 04							16 03				
Rochdale	a		13 09						14 09					15 09							16 08				
	d		13 09	13 22					14 09	14 22				15 09	15 22						16 09	16 22			
Castleton	d			13 25						14 25					15 25							16 25			
Mills Hill	d			13 30						14 30					15 30							16 30			
Moston	d			13 33						14 33					15 33							16 33			
Manchester Victoria ⛴	a		13 23	13 43					14 23	14 43				15 23	15 43						16 23	16 43			

For connections to Liverpool Lime Street please see Table 90

Table 41R

Sundays

8 December to 29 December

Leeds and Bradford - Huddersfield, Blackpool North, Rochdale and Manchester Victoria via Halifax and Brighouse

Network Diagram - refer to first Page of Table 39

			GC	NT	NT	NT	NT	NT	NT	NT	NT	NT	NT	NT	NT	NT	NT	NT	NT	NT	NT	NT	NT
			■ 1					bus					bus				bus			bus			
York ■	40	d					15 52					16 52				17 52			18 52				19 52
Selby	40	d																					
Leeds ■10	37,39	d		15 54		16 13	16 35		16 54		17 12	17 35		17 54	18 13	18 35		19 03	19 35		19 54	20 12	20 35
Bramley	37	d		16 01		16 20			17 01		17 19			18 01	18 20			19 10			20 01	20 19	
New Pudsey	37	d		16 06		16 25	16 44		17 06		17 24	17 44		18 06	18 25	18 44		19 15	19 44		20 06	20 24	20 44
Bradford Interchange	37	a		16 14		16 33	16 53		17 14		17 32	17 53		18 14	18 33	18 53		19 24	19 53		20 14	20 34	20 53
		d	16 00	16 17		16 36	16 55		17 17		17 35	17 55		18 17	18 36	18 55		19 27	19 55		20 19	20 35	20 55
Halifax		a	16 13	16 29		16 49	17 07		17 29		17 49	18 07		18 29	18 49	19 07		19 39	20 07		20 31	20 47	21 07
		d	16 14	16 29		16 49	17 07		17 29			18 07		18 29	18 49	19 07		19 39	20 07		20 31	20 48	21 07
Dewsbury	39	d																					
Mirfield	39	a																					
		d																					
Brighouse		d	16 25			16 59									18 59							20 58	
London Kings Cross ■15 ⊖	26	a	18 43																				
Huddersfield	39	a				17 14									19 14							21 14	
Sowerby Bridge		d		16 36					17 36					18 40				19 46			20 38		
Mytholmroyd		d		16 42					17 42					18 46				19 52			20 44		
Hebden Bridge		a		16 45			17 19		17 45			18 19		18 49		19 19		19 55	20 19		20 47		21 19
		d		16 45				17 40	17 45				18 40	18 49			19 40	19 55		20 40	20 47		
Burnley Manchester Road	97	a						18 20					19 20				20 20			21 20			
Accrington	97	a																					
Blackburn	97	a																					
Preston ■	97	a																					
Poulton-le-Fylde	97	a																					
Blackpool North	97	a																					
Todmorden		d		16 52					17 52					18 57				20 02			20 54		
Walsden		d		16 55					17 55					19 00				20 05			20 57		
Littleborough		d		17 02					18 02					19 06				20 11			21 03		
Smithy Bridge		d		17 04					18 04					19 09				20 14			21 06		
Rochdale		a		17 09					18 09					19 13				20 18			21 10		
		d		17 09	17 22				18 09	18 22				19 13				20 19			21 11		
Castleton		d			17 25					18 25				19 16				20 22			21 14		
Mills Hill		d			17 30					18 30				19 21				20 27			21 19		
Moston		d			17 33					18 33				19 24				20 30			21 22		
Manchester Victoria		a		17 23	17 43				18 23	18 43				19 36				20 40			21 32		

			NT	NT	NT	NT	NT	NT
			bus					
York ■	40	d			20 57			
Selby	40	d						
Leeds ■10	37,39	d		21 04	21 35	22 05	22 38	23 22
Bramley	37	d		21 12	21 43	22 12	22 45	23 29
New Pudsey	37	d		21 17	21 47	22 17	22 50	23 34
Bradford Interchange	37	a		21 25	21 56	22 27	22 58	23 43
		d		21 28	22 00	22 29	23 01	
Halifax		a		21 40	22 12	22 42	23 14	
		d		21 40	22 12	22 42	23 14	
Dewsbury	39	d						
Mirfield	39	a						
		d						
Brighouse		d				22 52	23a25	
London Kings Cross ■15 ⊖	26	a						
Huddersfield	39	a				23 06		
Sowerby Bridge		d		21 47	22 19			
Mytholmroyd		d		21 53	22 25			
Hebden Bridge		a		21 57	22 28			
		d	21 30		22 28			
Burnley Manchester Road	97	a	22 10					
Accrington	97	a	22 30					
Blackburn	97	a	22 48					
Preston ■	97	a	23 18					
Poulton-le-Fylde	97	a	23 58					
Blackpool North	97	a	00 13					
Todmorden		d			22 35			
Walsden		d			22 38			
Littleborough		d			22 45			
Smithy Bridge		d			22 47			
Rochdale		a			22 52			
		d			22 52			
Castleton		d			22 55			
Mills Hill		d			22 59			
Moston		d			23 02			
Manchester Victoria		a			23 12			

For connections to Liverpool Lime Street please see Table 90

Table 41R

Sundays

5 January to 9 February

Leeds and Bradford - Huddersfield, Blackpool North, Rochdale and Manchester Victoria via Halifax and Brighouse

Network Diagram - refer to first Page of Table 39

			GC	NT	NT	NT	NT	NT	NT	NT	NT		NT	NT	NT	NT	NT	NT	NT	NT	NT		NT	NT	NT	GC
			■ 1 ☕	🚌				🚌					🚌					🚌							🚌	■ 1 ☕
York ■	40	d									08 50						09 52							10 57		
Selby	40	d																								
Leeds ■	37,39	d		07 40	08 02	08 21	08 45		09 02	09 18	09 35				09 54	10 12	10 35			10 54			11 12	11 35		
Bramley	37	d			08 09	08 28			09 09	09 25					10 01	10 19				11 01			11 19			
New Pudsey	37	d		08 00	08 14	08 33	08 54		09 14	09 30	09 44				10 06	10 24	10 44			11 06			11 24	11 44		
Bradford Interchange	37	a		08 10	08 22	08 41	09 03		09 22	09 38	09 53				10 14	10 32	10 53			11 14			11 32	11 53		
		d	07 58	08 10		08 45	09 05		09 25	09 44	09 55				10 17	10 35	10 55			11 17			11 35	11 55		12 00
Halifax		a	08 09	08 35		08 57	09 17		09 37	09 57	10 07				10 29	10 48	11 07			11 29			11 48	12 07		12 13
		d	08 10	08 35			09 17			09 59	10 07					10 48	11 07							12 07		12 14
Dewsbury	39	d																								
Mirfield	39	a																								
		d																								
Brighouse		d	08 21							10 09						10 58										12 25
London Kings Cross ■ ⊖26		a	11 01																							15 03
Huddersfield	39	a								10 24						11 14										
Sowerby Bridge		d																								
Mytholmroyd		d																								
Hebden Bridge		a		08 55			09 29				10 19						11 19							12 19		
		d		08 55				09 40					10 40					11 40							12 40	
Burnley Manchester Road	97	a		09 30				10 20					11 20					12 20							13 20	
Accrington	97	a																								
Blackburn	97	a																								
Preston ■	97	a																								
Poulton-le-Fylde	97	a																								
Blackpool North	97	a																								
Todmorden		d																								
Walsden		d																								
Littleborough		d																								
Smithy Bridge		d																								
Rochdale		a																								
		d												09 41					10 17		11 09					
Castleton		d																								
Mills Hill		d																								
Moston		d																								
Manchester Victoria	🚢	a												09 56					10 32		11 24					

			NT	NT	NT	NT	NT		NT	NT	NT	NT	NT	NT	NT	NT	NT		NT	GC	NT	NT	NT	NT	NT	GC
							🚌						🚌						🚌	■ 1 ☕					🚌	■ 1 ☕
York ■	40	d				11 52						12 52					13 52							14 52		
Selby	40	d																								
Leeds ■	37,39	d	11 54		12 13	12 35			12 54		13 13	13 35		13 54		14 12	14 35				14 54		15 12	15 35		
Bramley	37	d	12 01		12 20				13 01		13 20			14 01		14 19					15 01		15 19			
New Pudsey	37	d	12 06		12 25	12 44			13 06		13 25	13 44		14 06		14 24	14 44				15 06		15 24	15 44		
Bradford Interchange	37	a	12 14		12 33	12 53			13 14		13 33	13 53		14 14		14 32	14 53				15 14		15 32	15 53		
		d	12 17		12 36	12 55			13 17		13 36	13 55		14 17		14 35	14 55			15 08	15 17		15 35	15 55		16 00
Halifax		a	12 29		12 49	13 07			13 29		13 49	14 07		14 29		14 48	15 07			15 19	15 29		15 48	16 07		16 13
		d			12 49	13 07						14 07				14 48	15 07			15 23				16 07		16 14
Dewsbury	39	d																								
Mirfield	39	a																								
		d																								
Brighouse		d			12 59											14 58				15 37						16 25
London Kings Cross ■ ⊖26		a																		18 16						19 03
Huddersfield	39	a			13 14											15 14										
Sowerby Bridge		d																								
Mytholmroyd		d																								
Hebden Bridge		a				13 19						14 19					15 19							16 19		
		d					13 40						14 40						15 40						16 40	
Burnley Manchester Road	97	a					14 20						15 20						16 20						17 20	
Accrington	97	a																								
Blackburn	97	a																								
Preston ■	97	a																								
Poulton-le-Fylde	97	a																								
Blackpool North	97	a																								
Todmorden		d																								
Walsden		d																								
Littleborough		d																								
Smithy Bridge		d																								
Rochdale		a																								
		d		12 09						13 09					14 09							15 09				
Castleton		d																								
Mills Hill		d																								
Moston		d																								
Manchester Victoria	🚢	a		12 24						13 24					14 24							15 24				

For connections to Liverpool Lime Street please see Table 90

Table 41R

Sundays

5 January to 9 February

Leeds and Bradford - Huddersfield, Blackpool North, Rochdale and Manchester Victoria via Halifax and Brighouse

Network Diagram - refer to first Page of Table 39

Station	Table		NT		NT	NT	NT	NT (bus)	NT	NT	NT	NT	NT (bus)		NT	NT	NT	NT	NT (bus)	NT	NT	NT (bus)	NT		NT	NT
York 8	40	d					15 52					16 52						17 52			18 52					
Selby	40	d																								
Leeds 10	37,39	d	15 54			16 13	16 35		16 54		17 12	17 35			17 54		18 13	18 35		19 03	19 35				19 54	20 12
Bramley	37	d	16 01			16 20			17 01		17 19				18 01		18 20			19 10					20 01	20 19
New Pudsey	37	d	16 06			16 25	16 44		17 06		17 24	17 44			18 06		18 25	18 44		19 15	19 44				20 06	20 24
Bradford Interchange	37	a	16 14			16 33	16 53		17 14		17 32	17 53			18 14		18 33	18 53		19 24	19 53				20 14	20 34
		d	16 17			16 36	16 55		17 17		17 35	17 55			18 17		18 36	18 55		19 27	19 55				20 19	20 35
Halifax		a	16 29			16 49	17 07		17 29		17 49	18 07			18 29		18 49	19 07		19 39	20 07				20 31	20 47
		d				16 49	17 07					18 07					18 49	19 07			20 07					20 48
Dewsbury	39	d																								
Mirfield	39	a																								
		d																								
Brighouse		d				16 59											18 59									20 58
London Kings Cross 15 ⊖	26	a																								
Huddersfield	39	a				17 14											19 14									21 14
Sowerby Bridge		d																								
Mytholmroyd		d																								
Hebden Bridge		a					17 19					18 19						19 19			20 19					
		d						17 40					18 40						19 40			20 40				
Burnley Manchester Road	97	a						18 20					19 20						20 20			21 20				
Accrington	97	a																								
Blackburn	97	a																								
Preston 8	97	a																								
Poulton-le-Fylde	97	a																								
Blackpool North	97	a																								
Todmorden		d																								
Walsden		d																								
Littleborough		d																								
Smithy Bridge		d																								
Rochdale		a																								
		d			16 09					17 09						18 09							19 13			
Castleton		d																					19 16			
Mills Hill		d																					19 21			
Moston		d																					19 24			
Manchester Victoria		a			16 25					17 24						18 24							19 37			

Station	Table		NT	NT (bus)	NT	NT	NT	NT	NT		NT	NT	NT
York 8	40	d	19 52				20 57						
Selby	40	d											
Leeds 10	37,39	d	20 35			21 04	21 35		22 05		22 38		23 22
Bramley	37	d				21 12	21 43		22 12		22 45		23 29
New Pudsey	37	d	20 44			21 17	21 47		22 17		22 50		23 34
Bradford Interchange	37	a	20 53			21 25	21 56		22 27		22 58		23 43
		d	20 55			21 28	22 00		22 29		23 01		
Halifax		a	21 07			21 40	22 12		22 42		23 14		
		d	21 07			21 40			22 42		23 14		
Dewsbury	39	d											
Mirfield	39	a											
		d											
Brighouse		d							22 52		23a25		
London Kings Cross 15 ⊖	26	a											
Huddersfield	39	a							23 06				
Sowerby Bridge		d				21 47							
Mytholmroyd		d				21 53							
Hebden Bridge		a	21 19			21 57							
		d		21 30									
Burnley Manchester Road	97	a		22 10									
Accrington	97	a		22 30									
Blackburn	97	a		22 48									
Preston 8	97	a		23 18									
Poulton-le-Fylde	97	a		23 58									
Blackpool North	97	a		00 13									
Todmorden		d											
Walsden		d											
Littleborough		d											
Smithy Bridge		d											
Rochdale		a											
		d			20 19			21 11				22 52	
Castleton		d			20 22			21 14				22 55	
Mills Hill		d			20 27			21 19				22 59	
Moston		d			20 30			21 22				23 02	
Manchester Victoria		a			20 41			21 33				23 12	

For connections to Liverpool Lime Street please see Table 90

Table 41R

Sundays
16 February to 23 March

Leeds and Bradford - Huddersfield, Blackpool North, Rochdale and Manchester Victoria via Halifax and Brighouse

Network Diagram - refer to first Page of Table 39

Station	Table		NT	NT	NT	NT	NT	NT	NT	NT	NT		NT	NT	NT	NT	NT	NT	NT	NT	GC		NT	NT	NT	NT
			🚌				🚌				🚌					🚌				🚌	R 1 ☕					🚌
York 8	40	d								08 50					09 52				10 57						11 52	
Selby	40	d																								
Leeds 10	37,39	d	07 40	08 02	08 21	08 45		09 02	09 18	09 35			09 54	10 12	10 35		10 54	11 12	11 35				11 54	12 13	12 35	
Bramley	37	d		08 09	08 28			09 09	09 25				10 01	10 19			11 01	11 19					12 01	12 20		
New Pudsey	37	d	08 00	08 14	08 33	08 54		09 14	09 30	09 44			10 06	10 24	10 44		11 06	11 24	11 44				12 06	12 25	12 44	
Bradford Interchange	37	a	08 10	08 22	08 41	09 03		09 22	09 38	09 53			10 14	10 32	10 53		11 14	11 32	11 53				12 14	12 33	12 53	
		d	08 10		08 45	09 05		09 25	09 44	09 55			10 17	10 35	10 55		11 17	11 35	11 55		12 00		12 17	12 36	12 55	
Halifax		a	08 35		08 57	09 17		09 37	09 57	10 07			10 29	10 48	11 07		11 29	11 48	12 07		12 13		12 29	12 49	13 07	
		d	08 35		09 01	09 17		09 37	09 59	10 07			10 29	10 48	11 07		11 29		12 07		12 14		12 29	12 49	13 07	
Dewsbury	39	d																								
Mirfield	39	a																								
		d																								
Brighouse		d							10 09					10 58							12 25			12 59		
London Kings Cross 15 ⊖	26	a																			15 03					
Huddersfield	39	a							10 24					11 14										13 14		
Sowerby Bridge		d			09 06			09 44					10 36				11 36						12 36			
Mytholmroyd		d			09 12			09 50					10 42				11 42						12 42			
Hebden Bridge		a	08 55		09 17	09 29		09 53		10 19			10 45		11 19		11 45		12 19				12 45		13 19	
		d	08 55		09 17		09 40	09 53			10 40		10 45			11 40	11 45			12 40			12 45			13 40
Burnley Manchester Road	97	a	09 30				10 20				11 20					12 20				13 20						14 20
Accrington	97	a																								
Blackburn	97	a																								
Preston 8	97	a																								
Poulton-le-Fylde	97	a																								
Blackpool North	97	a																								
Todmorden		d			09 24			10 00					10 52				11 52						12 52			
Walsden		d			09 27			10 03					10 55				11 55						12 55			
Littleborough		d			09 34			10 10					11 02				12 02						13 02			
Smithy Bridge		d			09 36			10 12					11 04				12 04						13 04			
Rochdale		a			09 41			10 17					11 09				12 09						13 09			
		d			09 41			10 17					11 09				12 09						13 09			
Castleton		d																								
Mills Hill		d																								
Moston		d																								
Manchester Victoria ⇌		a			09 56			10 31					11 23				12 23						13 23			

Station	Table		NT	NT	NT	NT	NT		NT	NT	NT	GC	NT	NT	NT	NT	GC		NT	NT	NT	NT	NT	NT	NT	NT
						🚌					🚌	R 1 ☕				🚌	R 1 ☕					🚌				🚌
York 8	40	d			12 52					13 52					14 52						15 52				16 52	
Selby	40	d																								
Leeds 10	37,39	d	12 54	13 13	13 35		13 54		14 12	14 35			14 54	15 12	15 35				15 54	16 13	16 35		16 54	17 12	17 35	
Bramley	37	d	13 01	13 20			14 01		14 19				15 01	15 19					16 01	16 20			17 01	17 19		
New Pudsey	37	d	13 06	13 25	13 44		14 06		14 24	14 44			15 06	15 24	15 44				16 06	16 25	16 44		17 06	17 24	17 44	
Bradford Interchange	37	a	13 14	13 33	13 53		14 14		14 32	14 53			15 14	15 32	15 53				16 14	16 33	16 53		17 14	17 32	17 53	
		d	13 17	13 36	13 55		14 17		14 35	14 55		15 08	15 17	15 35	15 55		16 00		16 17	16 36	16 55		17 17	17 35	17 55	
Halifax		a	13 29	13 49	14 07		14 29		14 48	15 07		15 19	15 29	15 48	16 07		16 13		16 29	16 49	17 07		17 29	17 49	18 07	
		d	13 29		14 07		14 29		14 48	15 07		15 23	15 29		16 07		16 14		16 29	16 49	17 07		17 29		18 07	
Dewsbury	39	d																								
Mirfield	39	a																								
		d																								
Brighouse		d							14 58			15 37					16 25			16 59						
London Kings Cross 15 ⊖	26	a										18 16					19 03									
Huddersfield	39	a							15 14											17 14						
Sowerby Bridge		d	13 36				14 36						15 36						16 36				17 36			
Mytholmroyd		d	13 42				14 42						15 42						16 42				17 42			
Hebden Bridge		a	13 45		14 19		14 45			15 19			15 45		16 19				16 45		17 19		17 45		18 19	
		d	13 45			14 40	14 45				15 40		15 45			16 40			16 45			17 40	17 45			18 40
Burnley Manchester Road	97	a				15 20					16 20					17 20						18 20				19 20
Accrington	97	a																								
Blackburn	97	a																								
Preston 8	97	a																								
Poulton-le-Fylde	97	a																								
Blackpool North	97	a																								
Todmorden		d	13 52				14 52						15 52						16 52				17 52			
Walsden		d	13 55				14 55						15 54						16 55				17 55			
Littleborough		d	14 02				15 02						16 02						17 02				18 02			
Smithy Bridge		d	14 04				15 04						16 03						17 04				18 04			
Rochdale		a	14 09				15 09						16 08						17 09				18 09			
		d	14 09				15 09						16 09						17 09				18 09			
Castleton		d																								
Mills Hill		d																								
Moston		d																								
Manchester Victoria ⇌		a	14 23				15 23						16 23						17 23				18 23			

For connections to Liverpool Lime Street please see Table 90

Table 41R

Sundays

16 February to 23 March

Leeds and Bradford - Huddersfield, Blackpool North, Rochdale and Manchester Victoria via Halifax and Brighouse

Network Diagram - refer to first Page of Table 39

		NT	NT	NT	NT (bus)	NT	NT	NT (bus)	NT	NT	NT	NT (bus)	NT	NT	NT	NT	NT
York 8	40 d			17 52			18 52				19 52			20 57			
Selby	40 d																
Leeds 10	37,39 d	17 54	18 13	18 35		19 03	19 35		19 54	20 12	20 35		21 04	21 35	22 05	22 38	23 22
Bramley	37 d	18 01	18 20			19 10			20 01	20 19			21 12	21 43	22 12	22 45	23 29
New Pudsey	37 d	18 06	18 25	18 44		19 15	19 44		20 06	20 24	20 44		21 17	21 47	22 17	22 50	23 34
Bradford Interchange	37 a	18 14	18 33	18 53		19 24	19 53		20 14	20 34	20 53		21 25	21 56	22 27	22 58	23 43
	d	18 17	18 36	18 55		19 27	19 55		20 19	20 35	20 55		21 28	22 00	22 29	23 01	
Halifax	a	18 29	18 49	19 07		19 39	20 07		20 31	20 47	21 07		21 40	22 12	22 42	23 14	
	d	18 29	18 49	19 07		19 39	20 07		20 31	20 48	21 07		21 40	22 12	22 42	23 14	
Dewsbury	39 d																
Mirfield	39 a																
	d																
Brighouse	d		18 59							20 58					22 52	23a25	
London Kings Cross 15 ⊖26	a																
Huddersfield	39 a		19 14							21 14					23 06		
Sowerby Bridge	d	18 40				19 46			20 38				21 47	22 19			
Mytholmroyd	d	18 46				19 52			20 44				21 53	22 25			
Hebden Bridge	a	18 49		19 19		19 55	20 19		20 47		21 19		21 57	22 28			
	d	18 49			19 40	19 55		20 40	20 47			21 30		22 28			
Burnley Manchester Road	97 a				20 20			21 20				22 10					
Accrington	97 a											22 30					
Blackburn	97 a											22 48					
Preston 8	97 a											23 18					
Poulton-le-Fylde	97 a											23 58					
Blackpool North	97 a											00 13					
Todmorden	d	18 57				20 02			20 54					22 35			
Walsden	d	19 00				20 05			20 57					22 38			
Littleborough	d	19 06				20 11			21 03					22 45			
Smithy Bridge	d	19 09				20 14			21 06					22 47			
Rochdale	a	19 13				20 18			21 10					22 52			
	d	19 13				20 19			21 11					22 52			
Castleton	d	19 16				20 22			21 14					22 55			
Mills Hill	d	19 21				20 27			21 19					22 59			
Moston	d	19 24				20 30			21 22					23 02			
Manchester Victoria	⇌ a	19 36				20 40			21 32					23 12			

Sundays

30 March to 11 May

		GC R 1	NT	NT	NT	NT	NT	NT	NT	NT	NT	NT	NT	NT	GC R 1	NT	NT	NT	NT	NT	NT	NT	NT
York 8	40 d							08 50			09 52			10 57				11 52			12 52		
Selby	40 d																						
Leeds 10	37,39 d		08 02	08 21	08 45	09 02	09 18	09 35	09 54	10 12	10 35	10 54	11 12	11 35		11 54	12 13	12 35	12 54	13 13	13 35	13 54	14 12
Bramley	37 d		08 09	08 28		09 09	09 25		10 01	10 19		11 01	11 19			12 01	12 20		13 01	13 20		14 01	14 19
New Pudsey	37 d		08 14	08 33	08 54	09 14	09 30	09 44	10 06	10 24	10 44	11 06	11 24	11 44		12 06	12 25	12 44	13 06	13 25	13 44	14 06	14 24
Bradford Interchange	37 a		08 22	08 41	09 03	09 22	09 38	09 53	10 14	10 32	10 53	11 14	11 32	11 53		12 14	12 33	12 53	13 14	13 33	13 53	14 14	14 32
	d	07 58		08 45	09 05	09 25	09 44	09 55	10 17	10 35	10 55	11 17	11 35	11 55	12 00	12 17	12 36	12 55	13 17	13 36	13 55	14 17	14 35
Halifax	a	08 09		08 57	09 17	09 37	09 57	10 07	10 29	10 48	11 07	11 29	11 48	12 07	12 13	12 29	12 49	13 07	13 29	13 49	14 07	14 29	14 48
	d	08 10		09 01	09 17	09 37	09 59	10 07	10 29	10 48	11 07	11 29		12 07	12 14	12 29	12 49	13 07	13 29		14 07	14 29	14 48
Dewsbury	39 d																						
Mirfield	39 a																						
	d																						
Brighouse	d	08 21					10 09			10 58					12 25		12 59						14 58
London Kings Cross 15 ⊖26	a	10 40													14 45								
Huddersfield	39 a						10 24			11 14							13 14						15 14
Sowerby Bridge	d			09 06		09 44			10 36			11 36				12 36			13 36			14 36	
Mytholmroyd	d			09 12		09 50			10 42			11 42				12 42			13 42			14 42	
Hebden Bridge	a			09 17	09 29	09 53		10 19	10 45		11 19	11 45		12 19		12 45		13 19	13 45		14 19	14 45	
	d			09 17	09 29	09 53		10 19	10 45		11 19	11 45		12 19		12 45		13 19	13 45		14 19	14 45	
Burnley Manchester Road	97 a				09 50			10 38			11 38			12 38				13 38			14 38		
Accrington	97 a				09 59			10 47			11 47			12 47				13 47			14 47		
Blackburn	97 a				10 07			10 56			11 55			12 55				13 55			14 55		
Preston 8	97 a				10 27			11 13			12 13			13 13				14 13			15 13		
Poulton-le-Fylde	97 a				10 45			11 31			12 31			13 31				14 30			15 32		
Blackpool North	97 a				10 53			11 39			12 38			13 38				14 38			15 39		
Todmorden	d			09 24		10 00			10 52			11 52				12 52			13 52			14 52	
Walsden	d			09 27		10 03			10 55			11 55				12 55			13 55			14 55	
Littleborough	d			09 34		10 10			11 02			12 02				13 02			14 02			15 02	
Smithy Bridge	d			09 36		10 12			11 04			12 04				13 04			14 04			15 04	
Rochdale	a			09 41		10 17			11 09			12 09				13 09			14 09			15 09	
	d			09 41		10 17			11 09			12 09				13 09			14 09			15 09	
Castleton	d																						
Mills Hill	d																						
Moston	d																						
Manchester Victoria	⇌ a			09 56		10 31			11 23			12 23				13 23			14 23			15 23	

For connections to Liverpool Lime Street please see Table 90

Table 41R

Sundays
30 March to 11 May

Leeds and Bradford - Huddersfield, Blackpool North, Rochdale and Manchester Victoria via Halifax and Brighouse

Network Diagram - refer to first Page of Table 39

Station			NT	GC	NT	NT	NT	GC	NT	NT	NT	NT	NT	NT	NT	NT	NT	NT	NT	NT	NT	NT	NT	NT
				B 1 ⊡				B 1 ⊡																
York 8	40	d	13 52				14 52				15 52			16 52			17 52		18 52			19 52		20 57
Selby	40	d																						
Leeds 10	37,39	d	14 35		14 54	15 12	15 35		15 54	16 13	16 35	16 54	17 12	17 35	17 54	18 13	18 35	19 03	19 35	19 54	20 12	20 35	21 04	21 35
Bramley	37	d			15 01	15 19			16 01	16 20		17 01	17 19		18 01	18 20		19 10		20 01	20 19		21 12	21 43
New Pudsey	37	d	14 44		15 06	15 24	15 44		16 06	16 25	16 44	17 06	17 24	17 44	18 06	18 25	18 44	19 15	19 44	20 06	20 24	20 44	21 17	21 47
Bradford Interchange	37	a	14 53		15 14	15 32	15 53		16 14	16 33	16 53	17 14	17 32	17 53	18 14	18 33	18 53	19 24	19 53	20 14	20 34	20 53	21 25	21 56
		d	14 55	15 08	15 17	15 35	15 55	16 00	16 17	16 36	16 55	17 17	17 35	17 55	18 17	18 36	18 55	19 27	19 55	20 19	20 35	20 55	21 28	22 00
Halifax		a	15 07	15 19	15 29	15 48	16 07	16 13	16 29	16 49	17 07	17 29	17 49	18 07	18 29	18 49	19 07	19 39	20 07	20 31	20 47	21 07	21 40	22 12
		d	15 07	15 23	15 29		16 07	16 14	16 29	16 49	17 07	17 29		18 07	18 29	18 49	19 07	19 39	20 07	20 31	20 48	21 07	21 40	22 12
Dewsbury	39	d																						
Mirfield	39	a																						
		d																						
Brighouse		d		15 37				16 25		16 59						18 59					20 58			
London Kings Cross 15	⊖26	a		17 57				18 43																
Huddersfield	39	a								17 14						19 14					21 14			
Sowerby Bridge		d			15 36				16 36			17 36			18 40			19 46		20 38			21 47	22 19
Mytholmroyd		d			15 42				16 42			17 42			18 46			19 52		20 44			21 53	22 25
Hebden Bridge		a	15 19		15 45		16 19		16 45		17 19	17 45		18 19	18 49		19 19	19 55	20 19	20 47		21 19	21 57	22 28
		d	15 19		15 45		16 19		16 45		17 19	17 45		18 19	18 49		19 19	19 55	20 19	20 47		21 19		22 28
Burnley Manchester Road	97	a	15 38				16 38				17 38			18 38			19 38		20 38			21 38		
Accrington	97	a	15 47				16 47				17 47			18 47			19 47		20 47			21 47		
Blackburn	97	a	15 55				16 55				17 55			18 55			19 56		20 55			21 55		
Preston 8	97	a	16 13				17 13				18 13			19 13			20 14		21 13			22 13		
Poulton-le-Fylde	97	a	16 31				17 31				18 31			19 31			20 32		21 31			22 31		
Blackpool North	97	a	16 38				17 38				18 38			19 38			20 39		21 38			22 38		
Todmorden		d			15 52				16 52			17 52			18 57			20 02		20 54				22 35
Walsden		d			15 54				16 55			17 55			19 00			20 05		20 57				22 38
Littleborough		d			16 02				17 02			18 02			19 06			20 11		21 03				22 45
Smithy Bridge		d			16 03				17 04			18 04			19 09			20 14		21 06				22 47
Rochdale		a			16 08				17 09			18 09			19 13			20 18		21 10				22 52
		d			16 09				17 09			18 09			19 13			20 19		21 11				22 52
Castleton		d													19 16			20 22		21 14				22 55
Mills Hill		d													19 21			20 27		21 19				22 59
Moston		d													19 24			20 30		21 22				23 02
Manchester Victoria	⇌	a			16 23				17 23			18 23			19 36			20 40		21 32				23 12

Station			NT	NT	NT
York 8	40	d			
Selby	40	d			
Leeds 10	37,39	d	22 05	22 38	23 22
Bramley	37	d	22 12	22 45	23 29
New Pudsey	37	d	22 17	22 50	23 34
Bradford Interchange	37	a	22 27	22 58	23 43
		d	22 29	23 01	
Halifax		a	22 42	23 14	
		d	22 42	23 14	
Dewsbury	39	d			
Mirfield	39	a			
		d			
Brighouse		d	22 52	23a25	
London Kings Cross 15	⊖26	a			
Huddersfield	39	a	23 06		
Sowerby Bridge		d			
Mytholmroyd		d			
Hebden Bridge		a			
		d			
Burnley Manchester Road	97	a			
Accrington	97	a			
Blackburn	97	a			
Preston 8	97	a			
Poulton-le-Fylde	97	a			
Blackpool North	97	a			
Todmorden		d			
Walsden		d			
Littleborough		d			
Smithy Bridge		d			
Rochdale		a			
		d			
Castleton		d			
Mills Hill		d			
Moston		d			
Manchester Victoria	⇌	a			

For connections to Liverpool Lime Street please see Table 90

Table 43

Mondays to Saturdays

9 December to 17 May

Hull - Beverley, Bridlington and Scarborough

Network Diagram - refer to first Page of Table 39

Miles			NT	NT	NT	NT	NT A	NT	NT B	NT C	NT A		NT	NT A	NT	NT A	NT	NT A	NT	NT A	NT		NT A	NT	NT A
0	**Hull**	d	05 57	06 23	06 54	07 14	07 36	07 52	08 14	08 37	09 17		09 47	10 14	10 44	11 14	11 44	12 14	12 44	13 14	13 44		14 14	14 44	15 14
4	Cottingham	d		06 30	07 01	07 21	07 43	07 59	08 21	08 44	09 24		09 54	10 21	10 51	11 21	11 51	12 21	12 51	13 21	13 51		14 21	14 51	15 21
8¼	**Beverley**	d	06 08	06 36	07 07	07 27	07a49	08 05	08 27	08a50	09 30		10 00	10 27	10 57	11 28	11 57	12 27	12 57	13 28	13 58		14 27	14 57	15 27
11¼	Arram	d			07 12			08 10											13 02						
16¼	Hutton Cranswick	d			07 19	07 36		08 17	08 36		09 39		10 09		11 06		12 06		13 09		14 07			15 06	
19½	Driffield	d	06 20	06 48	07 24	07 42		08 22	08 42		09 45		10 15	10 39	11 12	11 40	12 12	12 39	13 14	13 40	14 13		14 39	15 12	15 39
21½	Nafferton	d			07 28	07 46		08 26	08 46		09 49		10 19		11 16		12 16		13 18		14 17			15 16	
31	**Bridlington**	a	06 36	07 06	07 40	07 59		08 40	08 57		10 02		10 31	10 56	11 29	11 55	12 29	12 56	13 33	13 55	14 30		14 56	15 27	15 56
—		d			07 49				09 00				10 37			12 05				14 05				15 31	
34½	Bempton	d			07 56				09 07				10 44			12 12				14 12				15 38	
41¾	Hunmanby	d			08 06				09 17				10 54			12 22				14 22				15 48	
44½	Filey	d			08 11				09 22				10 59			12 27				14 27				15 53	
51	Seamer	39 d			08 22				09 34				11 11			12 38				14 38				16 05	
53¾	**Scarborough**	39 a			08 30				09 41				11 18			12 46				14 46				16 12	

		NT	NT SX C	NT SO A	NT SX A	NT	NT A		NT	NT C	NT A	NT	NT SX A	NT SO A	NT A	NT A	NT A		NT A
Hull	d	15 44	16 00	16 14	16 20	16 44	17 14		17 38	17 57	18 15	18 44	19 15	19 15	20 15	21 15	21 48		23 00
Cottingham	d	15 52	16 07	16 21	16 27	16 51	17 21		17 45	18 04	18 22	18 51	19 22	19 22	20 22	21 22	21 55		23 07
Beverley	d	15 58	16a14	16 27	16 33	16 57	17 27		17 51	18a12	18 28	18a58	19 28	19 28	20 28	21a30	22 01		23a13
Arram	d	16 03							17 56						20 33				
Hutton Cranswick	d	16 10		16 36	16 42		17 36		18 03		18 37		19 37	19 37	20 40		22 10		
Driffield	d	16 15		16 42	16 48	17 09	17 42		18 08		18 43		19 43	19 43	20 45		22 16		
Nafferton	d	16 19		16 46	16 52		17 46		18 12		18 47		19 47	19 47	20 49		22 20		
Bridlington	a	16 34		16 57	17 03	17 26	18 00		18 24		19 01		19 58	19 58	21 04		22 33		
	d			17 05	17 06				18 30				20 03	20 21					
Bempton	d			17 12	17 13				18 37				20 10	20 28					
Hunmanby	d			17 22	17 23				18 47				20 20	20 38					
Filey	d			17 27	17 28				18 52				20 25	20 43					
Seamer	39 d			17 38	17 39				19 03				20 36	20 54					
Scarborough	39 a			17 45	17 46				19 11				20 43	21 01					

Sundays

8 December to 11 May

		NT	NT	NT A	NT C	NT A	NT	NT A	NT A	NT A		NT A	NT	NT A	NT A	NT A
Hull	d	09 00	09 25	10 25	11 25	12 00	13 00	14 05	15 05	16 05		16 55	17 15	18 00	19 00	20 00
Cottingham	d	09 07	09 32	10 32	11 32	12 07	13 07	14 12	15 12	16 12		17 02	17 22	18 07	19 07	20 06
Beverley	d	09 13	09 38	10 38	11 38	12 13	13 13	14 18	15 18	16 18		17 08	17 28	18 13	19 13	20a12
Arram	d		09 43													
Hutton Cranswick	d		09 50	10 47		12 22		14 27		16 27			17 37		19 22	
Driffield	d	09 25	09 55	10 53	11 50	12 28	13 25	14 33	15 30	16 33		17 20	17 43	18 25	19 28	
Nafferton	d		09 59	10 57		12 32		14 37		16 37			17 47		19 32	
Bridlington	a	09 41	10 11	11 08	12 06	12 43	13 42	14 48	15 46	16 48		17 37	18 00	18 39	19 45	
	d		10 13	11 11		12 46		14 51		16 53				18 45		
Bempton	d		10 20	11 18		12 53		14 58		17 00				18 52		
Hunmanby	d		10 30	11 28		13 03		15 08		17 10				19 02		
Filey	d		10 35	11 33		13 08		15 13		17 15				19 07		
Seamer	39 d		10 46	11 44		13 20		15 24		17 26				19 19		
Scarborough	39 a		10 54	11 50		13 25		15 30		17 32				19 24		

A From Sheffield

B From Gilberdyke

C From Doncaster

Table 43R

Mondays to Saturdays

9 December to 17 May

Scarborough, Bridlington and Beverley - Hull

Network Diagram - refer to first Page of Table 39

Miles			NT SO A	NT SX A	NT SX	NT SO	NT SX B	NT C		NT	NT SO B	NT SX B	NT C	NT B	NT C	NT	NT C	NT		NT C	NT	NT SO C	NT SX C	NT	NT C
0	**Scarborough**	39 d									06 50	06 50				09 02		10 00				11 28	11 28		
2¾	Seamer	39 d									06 55	06 55				09 07		10 05				11 33	11 33		
9¼	Filey	d									07 04	07 04				09 16		10 14				11 42	11 42		
12	Hunmanby	d									07 09	07 09				09 21		10 19				11 47	11 47		
19¼	Bempton	d									07 19	07 19				09 31		10 29				11 57	11 57		
22¾	**Bridlington**	a									07 26	07 25				09 38		10 36				12 04	12 04		
—		d				06 46	06 46	07 14			07 32	07 32	08 08		09 05	09 41	10 11	10 41		11 11	11 41	12 09	12 09	12 41	13 11
32¼	Nafferton	d				06 56	06 56	07 24			07 43	07 43	08 19		09 16	09 52		10 52			11 52			12 52	
24¼	Driffield	d				07 01	07 01	07 29			07 47	07 47	08 23		09 20	09 56	10 24	10 56		11 24	11 56	12 22	12 22	12 56	13 24
37½	Hutton Cranswick	d				07 05	07 05	07 33			07 52	07 52	08 28		09 25	10 01		11 01			12 01			13 01	
42½	Arram	d									07 59	07 59			09 32						12 08				
45½	**Beverley**	d	06 30	06 38	06 58	07 15	07 15	07 43		07 57	08 05	08 05	08 38	09 00	09 37	10 11	10 37	11 11		11 37	12 13	12 36	12 36	13 11	13 37
49¾	Cottingham	d	06 36	06 44	07 03	07 21	07 21	07 49		08 03	08 11	08 11	08 44	09 06	09 43	10 17	10 43	11 17		11 43	12 19	12 42	12 42	13 17	13 43
53¾	**Hull**	a	06 44	06 53	07 13	07 31	07 33	07 59		08 13	08 21	08 21	08 54	09 15	09 53	10 27	10 53	11 27		11 54	12 29	12 52	12 53	13 27	13 53

		NT	NT C	NT		NT C	NT SX B	NT SO	NT C	NT	NT C	NT SO B	NT SX B	NT		NT	NT	NT C	NT SO	NT SX	NT	NT SO C	NT SX	NT	
Scarborough	39 d		13 28				14 54	14 54			16 23						17 54		19 40	20 03					
Seamer	39 d		13 33				14 59	14 59			16 28						17 59		19 45	20 08					
Filey	d		13 42				15 08	15 08			16 37						18 08		19 54	20 17					
Hunmanby	d		13 47				15 13	15 13			16 42						18 13		19 59	20 25					
Bempton	d		13 57				15 23	15 23			16 52						18 23		20 09	20 34					
Bridlington	a		14 04				15 30	15 31			16 59						18 30		20 17	20 42					
	d	13 41	14 11	14 41		15 11	15 36	15 36	16 09	16 41	17 04	17 34	17 34			18 15	18 41	19 10	20 27	20 44		21 28	21 28	22 42	
Nafferton	d	13 52		14 52			15 47	15 47		16 52		17 45	17 45				18 52	19 21	20 38	20 55		21 39	21 39	22 53	
Driffield	d	13 56	14 24	14 56		15 24	15 51	15 51	16 22	16 56	17 17	17 49	17 49			18 28	18 56	19 25	20 42	21 00		21 43	21 43	22 58	
Hutton Cranswick	d	14 01		15 01			15 56	15 56		17 01		17 54	17 54				19 01	19 30	20 47	21 05		21 48	21 48	23 03	
Arram	d									17 08															
Beverley	d	14 11	14 37	15 11		15 37	16 06	16 06	16 35	17 13	17 29	18 04	18 04	18 20		18 41	19 11	19 40	20 57	21 14	21 42	21 58	21 58	23 13	
Cottingham	d	14 17	14 43	15 17		15 43	16 12	16 12	16 41	17 19	17 35	18 10	18 10	18 25		18 47	19 17	19 46	21 03	21 20	21 46	22 04	22 04	23 19	
Hull	a	14 27	14 53	15 27		15 53	16 24	16 25	16 51	17 28	17 46	18 20	18 22	18 35		18 58	19 27	19 58	21 15	21 30	21 56	22 14	22 15	23 28	

Sundays

8 December to 11 May

		NT B	NT B	NT B	NT B	NT B	NT B	NT B	NT	NT B		NT	NT B	NT	NT
Scarborough	39 d		11 12	12 08		14 08		16 08					18 08		19 40
Seamer	39 d		11 17	12 13		14 13		16 13					18 13		19 45
Filey	d		11 26	12 22		14 22		16 22					18 22		19 54
Hunmanby	d		11 30	12 27		14 27		16 27					18 27		19 59
Bempton	d		11 40	12 37		14 37		16 37					18 37		20 09
Bridlington	a		11 48	12 44		14 44		16 44					18 44		20 16
	d	09 51	11 51	12 51	13 51	14 51	15 51	16 51	17 21	17 51		18 11	18 57	19 57	20 19
Nafferton	d	10 02	12 01		14 02		16 02		17 32				19 08	20 08	
Driffield	d	10 06	12 06	13 04	14 06	15 04	16 06	17 04	17 36	18 04		18 24	19 12	20 12	20 32
Hutton Cranswick	d	10 11	12 10		14 11		16 11		17 41				19 17	20 17	
Arram	d												19 24		
Beverley	d	10 21	12 20	13 17	14 21	15 17	16 21	17 17	17 51	18 17		18 37	19 29	20 27	20 45
Cottingham	d	10 27	12 25	13 23	14 27	15 23	16 27	17 23	17 57	18 23		18 43	19 35	20 33	20 51
Hull	a	10 37	12 35	13 33	14 37	15 33	16 37	17 34	18 06	18 33		18 53	19 45	20 43	21 00

A To York **B** To Doncaster **C** To Sheffield

Network Diagram for Tables 44, 45, 48

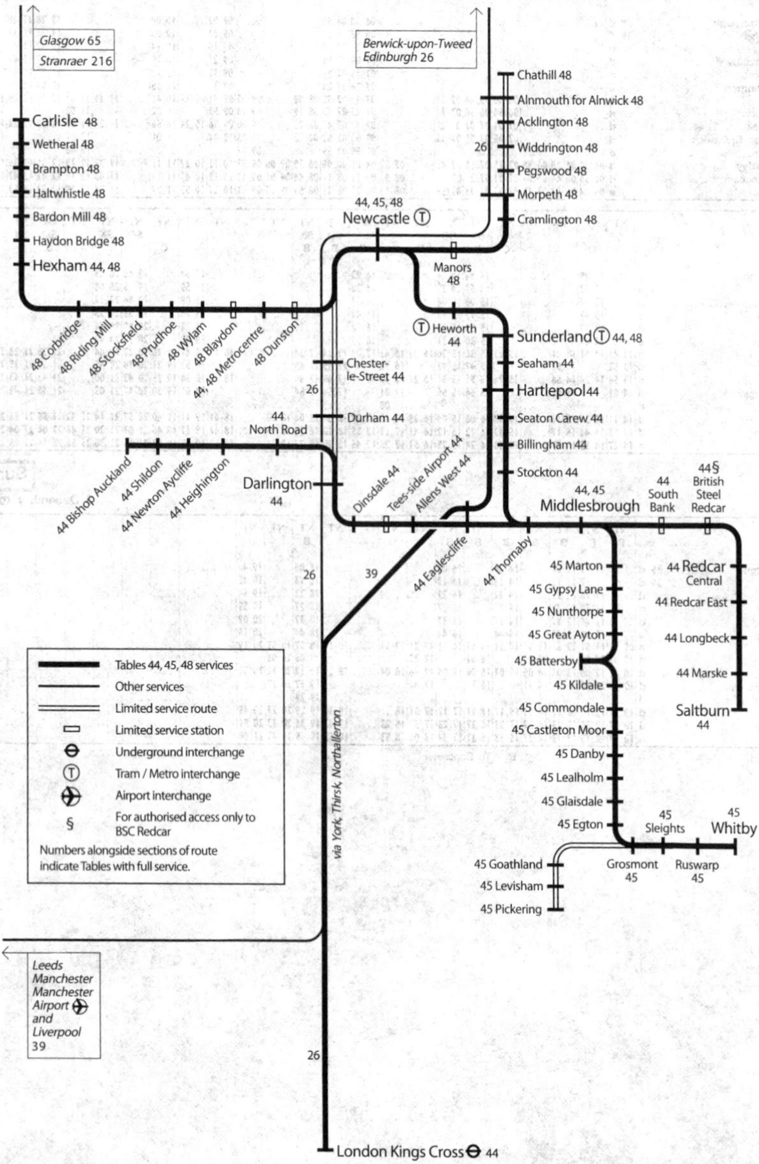

TOCs operating on this network - Northern (NT), Grand Central (GC), First TransPennine Express (TP), North Yorkshire Moors Railway (NY), East Coast (GR), Cross Country (XC)

Table 44

Mondays to Fridays

9 December to 16 May

Saltburn and Middlesbrough - Darlington, Bishop Auckland, Sunderland and Newcastle

Network Diagram - refer to first Page of Table 44

Miles	Miles			NT	NT	TP	NT	NT	NT	NT	TP	NT		NT	NT	NT	NT	NT	TP	NT	NT	TP		NT	NT
						◇1					◇1								◇1			◇1			
0	—	**Saltburn**	d					06 21						07 11	07 25	07 56				08 31				09 31	09 58
2	—	Marske	d					06 25						07 15	07 29	08 00				08 35				09 35	10 02
2½	—	Longbeck	d					06 28						07 18	07 32	08 03				08 38				09 38	10 05
4	—	Redcar East	d					06 31						07 21	07 35	08 06				08 41				09 41	10 08
5	—	**Redcar Central**	d					06 34						07 24	07 38	08 09				08 44				09 44	10 11
6¾	—	British Steel Redcar §	d																						
10	—	South Bank	d					06 41						07 31	07 45					08 51					10 18
12½	0	**Middlesbrough**	a					06 46						07 37	07 50	08 18				08 56				09 55	10 24
—	—		d	05 45		05 55		06 47		06 55	07 12	07 32		07 37	07 50	08 19	08 32	08 45	08 50	09 08	09 32	09 50		09 55	10 24
15¾	3¼	Thornaby	d	05 50		06a00		06 52		07 00	07a17	07 37		07 42	07 55	08 24	08 37	08 50	08a55	09 13	09 37	09a55		10 00	10 29
—	—	London Kings Cross 15 ⊖26	d																						
18¾	—	Eaglescliffe	a	05 55				06 57						07 47	08 00	08 30		08 55		09 18				10 05	10 34
—	—		d	05 55				06 57						07 47	08 01	08 30		08 55		09 18				10 06	10 34
19½	—	Allens West	d	05 58				07 00						07 50	08 03	08 32		08 58		09 21				10 08	10 37
22	—	Tees-side Airport	d																						
23¾	—	Dinsdale	d	06 04				07 06						07 56	08 10	08 39		09 04		09 27				10 15	10 43
27½	—	**Darlington 7** 26	a	06 14				07 17						08 07	08 20	08 50		09 13		09 39				10 25	10 52
—	—		d	06 14	06 47			07 20	07 48						08 22	08 52									10 54
28¾	—	North Road	d		06 50				07 51							08 55									10 57
33¼	—	Heighington	d		06 58				07 59							09 03									11 05
34½	—	Newton Aycliffe	d		07 02				08 03							09 07									11 08
36¾	—	Shildon	d		07 06				08 07							09 11									11 13
39½	—	**Bishop Auckland**	a		07 14				08 15							09 18									11 20
—	5½	Stockton	d							07 06		07 43					08 43				09 43				
—	10	Billingham	d							07 13		07 50					08 50				09 50				
—	15	Seaton Carew	d							07 19		07 56					08 56				09 56				
—	17¼	**Hartlepool**	d				07 03			07 25		08 02					09 01				10 02				
—	30	Seaham	d				07 18			07 40		08 17					09 15				10 17				
—	35¼	**Sunderland**	a				07 28			07 50		08 28					09 27				10 28				
—	—		d				07 30			07 55		08 30					09 30				10 30				
—	44½	Heworth	d				07 41			08 08		08 42					09 42				10 42				
—	47¼	**Newcastle 8** 26	a	06 54			07 51	08 03		08 17		08 52			09 06		09 51				10 51				
—	—	Metrocentre 48	a				08 01										10 01				11 01				
—	—	Hexham 48	a				08 38										10 38				11 37				

		NT	GC	TP	NT	NT	NT	TP		NT	NT		NT	TP	NT	NT	NT	GC		TP	NT	NT	NT	TP FO	TP FX
			R 1	◇1				◇1						◇1				R 1		◇1				◇1	◇1
Saltburn	d				10 31	10 58				11 31	11 58				12 31	12 58					13 31	13 58			
Marske	d				10 35	11 02				11 35	12 02				12 35	13 02					13 35	14 02			
Longbeck	d				10 38	11 05				11 38	12 05				12 38	13 05					13 38	14 05			
Redcar East	d				10 41	11 08				11 41	12 08				12 41	13 08					13 41	14 08			
Redcar Central	d				10 44	11 11				11 44	12 11				12 44	13 11					13 44	14 11			
British Steel Redcar §	d																								
South Bank	d					11 18					12 18					13 18						14 18			
Middlesbrough	a				10 54	11 23				11 56	12 23				12 54	13 23					13 54	14 23			
	d	10 32		10 50	10 55	11 23	11 31	11 50		11 56	12 23		12 32	12 50	12 55	13 23	13 32			13 50	13 55	14 23	14 32	14 50	14 50
Thornaby	d	10 37		10a55	11 00	11 28	11 36	11a55		12 01	12 28		12 37	12a55	13 00	13 28	13 37			13a55	14 00	14 28	14 37	14a55	14a55
London Kings Cross 15 ⊖26	d		07 52															11 21							
Eaglescliffe	a		10 50		11 05	11 33				12 06	12 33				13 05	13 33		14 04			14 05	14 33			
	d		10 51		11 06	11 34				12 07	12 34				13 06	13 34		14 05			14 06	14 34			
Allens West	d				11 08	11 36				12 09	12 36				13 08	13 36					14 08	14 36			
Tees-side Airport	d																								
Dinsdale	d				11 15	11 43				12 16	12 43				13 15	13 43					14 15	14 43			
Darlington 7 26	a				11 25	11 52				12 25	12 52				13 26	13 52					14 25	14 52			
	d										12 54											14 54			
North Road	d										12 57											14 57			
Heighington	d										13 05											15 05			
Newton Aycliffe	d										13 08											15 08			
Shildon	d										13 13											15 13			
Bishop Auckland	a										13 20											15 20			
Stockton	d	10 43					11 42						12 43				13 43						14 43		
Billingham	d	10 50					11 50						12 50				13 50						14 50		
Seaton Carew	d	10 56					11 56						12 56				13 56						14 56		
Hartlepool	d	11 02	11 11				12 02						13 02				14 02	14 25					15 02		
Seaham	d	11 17					12 17						13 17				14 17						15 17		
Sunderland	a	11 27	11 38				12 27						13 28				14 27	14 51					15 27		
	d	11 30					12 30						13 30				14 30						15 30		
Heworth	d	11 42					12 42						13 42				14 42						15 42		
Newcastle 8 26	a	11 51					12 52						13 51				14 51						15 51		
Metrocentre 48	a	12 01					13 01						14 01				15 01						16 01		
Hexham 48	a	12 38					13 37						14 38				15 37						16 38		

§ For authorised access only to BSC Redcar   **A** from 24 March   **B** until 21 March

Table 44

Mondays to Fridays

9 December to 16 May

Saltburn and Middlesbrough - Darlington, Bishop Auckland, Sunderland and Newcastle

Network Diagram - refer to first Page of Table 44

		NT	NT	NT		GC	TP	NT	NT	NT	TP	NT	NT	NT		TP	NT	NT	NT	NT	TP	NT	GC	NT
						R 1	◇1				◇1					◇1					◇1		R 1	
Saltburn	d	14 31	14 59					15 31	15 58			16 29	16 58				17 31	17 58				18 31		18 58
Marske	d	14 35	15 03					15 35	16 02			16 33	17 02				17 35	18 02				18 35		19 02
Longbeck	d	14 38	15 06					15 38	16 05			16 36	17 05				17 38	18 05				18 38		19 05
Redcar East	d	14 41	15 09					15 41	16 08			16 39	17 08				17 41	18 08				18 41		19 08
Redcar Central	d	14 44	15 12					15 44	16 11			16 42	17 11				17 44	18 11				18 44		19 11
British Steel Redcar §	d											16 45												
South Bank	d		15 19						16 18			16 51	17 18					18 18						19 18
Middlesbrough	a	14 54	15 24					15 54	16 23			16 56	17 23				17 54	18 23				18 54		19 23
	d	14 55	15 25	15 32			15 50	15 55	16 23	16 32	16 50	16 57	17 24	17 39		17 50	17 55	18 23	18 32	18 45	18 50	18 55		19 23
Thornaby	d	15 00	15 30	15 37			15a55	16 00	16 28	16 37	16a55	17 02	17 29	17 44		17a55	18 00	18 28	18 37	18 50	18a55	19 00		19 28
London Kings Cross 15 ⊖26	d					12 53																	16 50	
Eaglescliffe	a	15 05	15 35			15 49		16 05	16 34			17 07	17 34				18 05	18 34				19 05	19 24	19 33
	d	15 06	15 36			15 50		16 06	16 34			17 07	17 35				18 06	18 34				19 06	19 26	19 34
Allens West	d	15 08	15 38					16 08	16 36			17 10	17 37				18 08	18 36				19 08		19 36
Tees-side Airport	d																							
Dinsdale	d	15 15	15 45					16 15	16 43			17 16	17 44				18 15	18 43				19 15		19 43
Darlington 7 26	a	15 25	15 54					16 25	16 52			17 26	17 53				18 25	18 53		19 11		19 25		19 52
	d		15 54									17 28					18 32							
North Road	d		15 57									17 31					18 35							
Heighington	d		16 05									17 39					18 43							
Newton Aycliffe	d		16 08									17 42					18 46							
Shildon	d		16 13									17 47					18 51							
Bishop Auckland	a		16 19									17 54					18 56							
Stockton	d			15 43						16 44				17 50					18 43					
Billingham	d			15 50						16 51				17 57					18 50					
Seaton Carew	d			15 56						16 57				18 03					18 56					
Hartlepool	d			16 02		16 10				17 03				18 09					19 02				19 54	
Seaham	d			16 17						17 18				18 24					19 17					
Sunderland 🚇	a			16 27		16 39				17 28				18 38					19 27				20 21	
	d			16 30						17 30				18 42					19 29					
Heworth 🚇	d			16 42						17 42				18 55					19 42					
Newcastle 8 26 🚇	a			16 51						17 51				19 05					19 51					
Metrocentre 48	a			17 01						18 01									20 04					
Hexham 48	a			17 37						18 32														

		NT	NT	TP	TP	NT	NT	GC	TP	NT		NT
				◇1	◇1			R 1	◇1			
Saltburn	d		19 31			20 31				21 31		22 39
Marske	d		19 35			20 35				21 35		22 43
Longbeck	d		19 38			20 38				21 38		22 46
Redcar East	d		19 41			20 41				21 41		22 49
Redcar Central	d		19 44			20 44				21 44		22 52
British Steel Redcar §	d											
South Bank	d									21 51		
Middlesbrough	a		19 54			20 54				21 55		23 02
	d	19 40	19 55	20 04	20 50	20 55	21 01		21 50	21 55		23 03
Thornaby	d	19 45	20 00	20 09	20a55	21 00	21 06		21 55	22 00		23 08
London Kings Cross 15 ⊖26	d							19 18				
Eaglescliffe	a		20 05			21 06		22 03		22 05		23 13
	d		20 06			21 06		22 05		22 06		23 13
Allens West	d		20 08			21 08				22 08		23 16
Tees-side Airport	d											
Dinsdale	d		20 15			21 15				22 15		23 22
Darlington 7 26	a		20 26	20 29		21 26			22 15	22 26		23 33
	d		20 33									
North Road	d		20 36									
Heighington	d		20 44									
Newton Aycliffe	d		20 47									
Shildon	d		20 52									
Bishop Auckland	a		20 59									
Stockton	d	19 51					21 12					
Billingham	d	19 58					21 19					
Seaton Carew	d	20 04					21 25					
Hartlepool	d	20 10					21 31	22 25				
Seaham	d	20 27					21 46					
Sunderland 🚇	a	20 37					21 57	22 51				
	d	20 42					21 58					
Heworth 🚇	d	20 53					22 09					
Newcastle 8 26 🚇	a	21 02					22 19					
Metrocentre 48	a	21 14										
Hexham 48	a											

§ For authorised access only to BSC Redcar

Table 44

Saturdays

14 December to 17 May

Saltburn and Middlesbrough - Darlington, Bishop Auckland, Sunderland and Newcastle

Network Diagram - refer to first Page of Table 44

		NT	NT	TP	NT	NT	NT	NT	TP	NT		NT	NT	NT	NT	NT	TP	NT	NT	TP		NT	NT	NT	GC
				◇1					◇1								◇1			◇1					R 1 ⊐P
Saltburn	d					06 21						07 11	07 25	07 55				08 31				09 31	09 58		
Marske	d					06 25						07 15	07 29	07 59				08 35				09 35	10 02		
Longbeck	d					06 28						07 18	07 32	08 02				08 38				09 38	10 05		
Redcar East	d					06 31						07 21	07 35	08 05				08 41				09 41	10 08		
Redcar Central	d					06 34						07 24	07 38	08 08				08 44				09 44	10 11		
British Steel Redcar §	d																								
South Bank	d					06 41							07 45					08 51					10 18		
Middlesbrough	a					06 46						07 37	07 50	08 20				08 56				09 55	10 24		
	d	05 45		05 55		06 47		06 55	07 12	07 32		07 37	07 50	08 20	08 32	08 45	08 50	09 08	09 32	09 50		09 55	10 24	10 32	
Thornaby	d	05 50		06a00		06 52		07 00	07a17	07 37		07 42	07 55	08 25	08 37	08 50	08a55	09 13	09 37	09a55		10 00	10 29	10 37	
London Kings Cross 15 ⊖26	d																								08 11
Eaglescliffe	a	05 55				06 57						07 47	08 00	08 30		08 55		09 21				10 05	10 34		10 57
	d	05 55				06 57						07 47	08 01	08 31		08 55		09 22				10 06	10 34		11 00
Allens West	d	05 58				07 00						07 50	08 03	08 33		08 58		09 24				10 08	10 37		
Tees-side Airport	d																								
Dinsdale	d	06 04				07 06						07 56	08 10	08 40		09 04		09 31				10 15	10 43		
Darlington 7 26	a	06 14				07 19						08 07	08 20	08 50		09 13		09 39				10 25	10 52		
	d		06 47			07 20	07 48						08 22	08 52									10 54		
North Road	d		06 50				07 51							08 55									10 57		
Heighington	d		06 58				07 59							09 03									11 05		
Newton Aycliffe	d		07 01				08 03							09 07									11 08		
Shildon	d		07 06				08 07							09 11									11 13		
Bishop Auckland	a		07 14				08 15							09 18									11 20		
Stockton	d							07 06		07 43					08 43				09 43					10 43	
Billingham	d							07 13		07 50					08 50				09 50					10 50	
Seaton Carew	d							07 19		07 56					08 56				09 56					10 56	
Hartlepool	d				07 03			07 25		08 02					09 02				10 02					11 02	11 24
Seaham	d				07 18			07 41		08 17					09 16				10 17					11 17	
Sunderland ⛴	a				07 28			07 51		08 28					09 27				10 28					11 27	11 50
	d				07 30			07 56		08 30					09 30				10 30					11 30	
Heworth ⛴	d				07 41			08 08		08 42					09 42				10 42					11 42	
Newcastle 8 26 ⛴	a				07 51	08 03		08 17		08 52			09 06		09 51				10 51					11 51	
Metrocentre 48	a				08 01										10 01				11 01					12 01	
Hexham 48	a				08 38										10 38				11 37					12 38	

		TP	NT	NT	NT	TP		NT	NT	NT	TP	NT	NT	NT	GC	TP		NT	NT	NT	TP	NT	NT	NT	GC
		◇1				◇1					◇1				R 1 ⊐P	◇1					◇1				R 1 ⊐P
Saltburn	d		10 31	10 58				11 31	11 58			12 31	12 58					13 31	13 58			14 31	14 58		
Marske	d		10 35	11 02				11 35	12 02			12 35	13 02					13 35	14 02			14 35	15 02		
Longbeck	d		10 38	11 05				11 38	12 05			12 38	13 05					13 38	14 05			14 38	15 05		
Redcar East	d		10 41	11 08				11 41	12 08			12 41	13 08					13 41	14 08			14 41	15 08		
Redcar Central	d		10 44	11 11				11 44	12 11			12 44	13 11					13 44	14 11			14 44	15 11		
British Steel Redcar §	d																								
South Bank	d			11 18					12 18				13 18						14 18				15 18		
Middlesbrough	a		10 54	11 23				11 56	12 23			12 54	13 23					13 54	14 23			14 54	15 23		
	d	10 50	10 55	11 23	11 32	11 50		11 56	12 23	12 32	12 50	12 55	13 23	13 32		13 50		13 55	14 23	14 32	14 50	14 55	15 24	15 32	
Thornaby	d	10a55	11 00	11 28	11 36	11a55		12 01	12 28	12 37	12a55	13 00	13 28	13 37		13a55		14 00	14 28	14 37	14a55	15 00	15 29	15 37	
London Kings Cross 15 ⊖26	d														11 20										13 20
Eaglescliffe	a		11 05	11 33				12 06	12 33			13 09	13 33		13 58			14 05	14 33			15 05	15 34		15 59
	d		11 06	11 34				12 07	12 34			13 09	13 34		14 00			14 06	14 34			15 06	15 34		16 02
Allens West	d		11 08	11 36				12 09	12 36			13 12	13 36					14 08	14 36			15 08	15 37		
Tees-side Airport	d																								
Dinsdale	d		11 15	11 43				12 16	12 43			13 18	13 43					14 15	14 43			15 15	15 43		
Darlington 7 26	a		11 25	11 52				12 25	12 52			13 26	13 52					14 25	14 52			15 25	15 52		
	d								12 54										14 54				15 54		
North Road	d								12 57										14 57				15 57		
Heighington	d								13 05										15 05				16 05		
Newton Aycliffe	d								13 08										15 08				16 08		
Shildon	d								13 13										15 13				16 13		
Bishop Auckland	a								13 20										15 20				16 20		
Stockton	d				11 42					12 42				13 43						14 43				15 43	
Billingham	d				11 50					12 50				13 50						14 50				15 50	
Seaton Carew	d				11 56					12 56				13 56						14 56				15 56	
Hartlepool	d				12 02					13 02				14 02	14 24					15 02				16 02	16 22
Seaham	d				12 17					13 17				14 17						15 17				16 17	
Sunderland ⛴	a				12 27					13 28				14 27	14 50					15 29				16 27	16 50
	d				12 30					13 30				14 30						15 30				16 30	
Heworth ⛴	d				12 42					13 42				14 42						15 42				16 42	
Newcastle 8 26 ⛴	a				12 51					13 51				14 51						15 51				16 51	
Metrocentre 48	a				13 01					14 01				15 01						16 01				17 01	
Hexham 48	a				13 37					14 38				15 37						16 38				17 37	

§ For authorised access only to BSC Redcar

Table 44

Saturdays

14 December to 17 May

Saltburn and Middlesbrough - Darlington, Bishop Auckland, Sunderland and Newcastle

Network Diagram - refer to first Page of Table 44

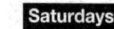

		TP		NT	NT	NT	TP	NT	NT	NT	TP	NT		NT	NT	TP	NT	GC	NT	NT	NT	TP		NT	TP
		◇1					◇1				◇1					◇1		1				◇1			◇1
Saltburn	d			15 31	15 58			16 29	16 58			17 31		17 58			18 31		18 58		19 31				
Marske	d			15 35	16 02			16 33	17 02			17 35		18 02			18 35		19 02		19 35				
Longbeck	d			15 38	16 05			16 36	17 05			17 38		18 05			18 38		19 05		19 38				
Redcar East	d			15 41	16 08			16 39	17 08			17 41		18 08			18 41		19 08		19 41				
Redcar Central	d			15 44	16 11			16 42	17 11			17 44		18 11			18 44		19 11		19 44				
British Steel Redcar §	d							16 45																	
South Bank	d				16 18			16 51	17 18					18 18					19 18						
Middlesbrough	a			15 54	16 23			16 56	17 23			17 54		18 23			18 54		19 23		19 54				
	d	15 50		15 55	16 23	16 32	16 50	16 57	17 23	17 39	17 50	17 55		18 23	18 32	18 50	18 55		19 23	19 40	19 57	20 10		20 45	20 50
Thornaby	d	15a55		16 00	16 28	16 37	16a55	17 02	17 28	17 44	17a55	18 00		18 28	18 37	18a55	19 00		19 28	19 45	20 02	20a15		20 50	20a55
London Kings Cross 15 ⊖26	d																	16 48							
Eaglescliffe	a			16 05	16 33			17 07	17 33			18 05		18 33			19 05	19 24	19 33		20 07				
	d			16 06	16 34			17 07	17 34			18 06		18 34			19 06	19 26	19 34		20 07				
Allens West	d			16 08	16 36			17 10	17 36			18 08		18 36			19 08		19 36		20 10				
Tees-side Airport	d																								
Dinsdale	d			16 15	16 43			17 16	17 43			18 15		18 43			19 15		19 43		20 16				
Darlington 7 26	a			16 25	16 52			17 26	17 53			18 25		18 53			19 25		19 52		20 26				
	d							17 28				18 32									20 32				
North Road	d							17 31				18 35									20 35				
Heighington	d							17 39				18 43									20 43				
Newton Aycliffe	d							17 42				18 46									20 46				
Shildon	d							17 47				18 51									20 51				
Bishop Auckland	a							17 54				18 56									20 58				
Stockton	d					16 43				17 50					18 43					19 51				20 56	
Billingham	d					16 50				17 57					18 50					19 58				21 03	
Seaton Carew	d					16 56				18 03					18 56					20 04				21 09	
Hartlepool	d					17 02				18 09					19 02			19 54		20 10				21 15	
Seaham	d					17 17				18 24					19 17					20 27				21 30	
Sunderland ⛴	a					17 29				18 38					19 27			20 21		20 37				21 40	
	d					17 30				18 42					19 28					20 42				21 43	
Heworth ⛴	d					17 42				18 55					19 42					20 53				21 54	
Newcastle 8 26 ⛴	a					17 51				19 04					19 51					21 04				22 04	
Metrocentre 48	a					18 01									20 04										
Hexham 48	a					18 32																			

		NT	GC	TP	NT	NT
			1	◇1		
Saltburn	d	20 31			21 31	22 39
Marske	d	20 35			21 35	22 43
Longbeck	d	20 38			21 38	22 46
Redcar East	d	20 41			21 41	22 49
Redcar Central	d	20 44			21 44	22 52
British Steel Redcar §	d					
South Bank	d				21 51	
Middlesbrough	a	20 54			21 55	23 02
	d	20 55		21 50	21 55	23 03
Thornaby	d	21 00		21 55	22 00	23 08
London Kings Cross 15 ⊖26	d		19 11			
Eaglescliffe	a	21 05	21 45		22 05	23 13
	d	21 06	21 46		22 06	23 13
Allens West	d	21 08			22 08	23 16
Tees-side Airport	d					
Dinsdale	d	21 15			22 15	23 22
Darlington 7 26	a	21 26		22 15	22 26	23 33
	d					
North Road	d					
Heighington	d					
Newton Aycliffe	d					
Shildon	d					
Bishop Auckland	a					
Stockton	d					
Billingham	d					
Seaton Carew	d					
Hartlepool	d		22 10			
Seaham	d					
Sunderland ⛴	a		22 36			
	d					
Heworth ⛴	d					
Newcastle 8 26 ⛴	a					
Metrocentre 48	a					
Hexham 48	a					

§ For authorised access only to BSC Redcar

Table 44

Sundays

8 December to 29 December

Saltburn and Middlesbrough - Darlington, Bishop Auckland, Sunderland and Newcastle

Network Diagram - refer to first Page of Table 44

	NT	NT	NT	NT	NT	TP	NT	NT	NT		NT	NT	GC	NT	TP	NT	NT	NT	TP		NT	NT	NT	NT
						◇1							R 1 ☕		◇1				◇1					
				A					A															
Saltburn d					09 43			10 43				11 43				12 43		13 43			14 43			15 43
Marske d					09 47			10 47				11 47				12 47		13 47			14 47			15 47
Longbeck d					09 50			10 50				11 50				12 50		13 50			14 50			15 50
Redcar East d					09 53			10 53				11 53				12 53		13 53			14 53			15 53
Redcar Central d					09 56			10 56				11 56				12 56		13 56			14 56			15 56
British Steel Redcar § d																								
South Bank d					10 03			11 03				12 03				13 03		14 03			15 03			16 03
Middlesbrough a					10 08			11 08				12 08				13 08		14 08			15 08			16 08
d	08 39	09 09		09 31	10 09	10 15		11 08	11 31			12 09			12 45	13 09	13 31	14 09	14 43		15 09		15 31	16 09
Thornaby d	08 44	09 14		09 36	10 14	10a20		11 13	11 36			12 14			12a50	13 14	13 36	14 14	14a48		15 14		15 36	16 14
London Kings Cross 15 ⊖26 d													09 48											
Eaglescliffe a	08 49	09 19			10 19			11 18				12 19	12 20			13 19		14 19			15 19			16 19
d	08 49	09 19			10 19		10 36	11 19			12 11	12 19	12 21			13 19		14 19			15 19			16 19
Allens West d	08 52	09 22			10 22			11 21			12 14	12 22				13 22		14 22			15 22			16 22
Tees-side Airport d											12 18													
Dinsdale d	08 58	09 28			10 28			11 28			12 22	12 28				13 28		14 28			15 28			16 28
Darlington 7 26 a	09 08	09 38			10 38			11 37			12 31	12 38				13 38		14 38			15 38			16 38
d		09 39						11 38										14 39						16 40
North Road d		09 42						11 41										14 42						16 43
Heighington d		09 50						11 50										14 50						16 51
Newton Aycliffe d		09 53						11 53										14 53						16 54
Shildon d		09 58						11 57										14 58						16 59
Bishop Auckland a		10 04						12 04										15 04						17 05
Stockton d				09 42			10 41		11 42								13 42						15 42	
Billingham d				09 49			10 49		11 49								13 49						15 49	
Seaton Carew d				09 55			10 55		11 55								13 55						15 55	
Hartlepool d				10 01			11 00		12 01				12 42				14 01						16 01	
Seaham d				10 16			11 16		12 16								14 16						16 16	
Sunderland ⛴ a				10 26			11 26		12 26				13 08				14 26						16 26	
d			09 28	10 28			11 28		12 28					13 28			14 28					15 28	16 28	
Heworth ⛴ d			09 39	10 38			11 38		12 38					13 40			14 39					15 39	16 39	
Newcastle 8 26 ⛴ a			09 48	10 48			11 48		12 48					13 49			14 48					15 48	16 48	
Metrocentre 48 a			09 59	10 59			11 59		12 59					13 59			14 59					15 59	16 59	
Hexham 48 a																								

	GC	NT	TP	NT	NT		NT	NT	TP	NT	NT	GC	NT	TP	NT		GC	NT	NT	TP	NT			
	R 1 ☕		◇1						◇1			R 1 ☕		◇1			R 1 ☕			◇1				
Saltburn d				16 43				17 43		18 43					19 43			20 43	21 37		22 43			
Marske d				16 47				17 47		18 47					19 47			20 47	21 41		22 47			
Longbeck d				16 50				17 50		18 50					19 50			20 50	21 44		22 50			
Redcar East d				16 53				17 53		18 53					19 53			20 53	21 47		22 53			
Redcar Central d				16 56				17 56		18 56					19 56			20 56	21 50		22 56			
British Steel Redcar § d																								
South Bank d				17 03				18 03		19 03					20 03			21 03	21 57		23 03			
Middlesbrough a				17 08				18 08		19 08					20 11			21 08	22 02		23 08			
d			16 43	17 10	17 45			18 09	18 45	19 09			19 32	20 06	20 12			21 09	22 03	22 08	23 08			
Thornaby d			16a48	17 15	17 50			18 14	18a50	19 14			19 37	20a11	20 17			21 14	22 08	22a13	23 13			
London Kings Cross 15 ⊖26 d	13 48											16 47					18 23							
Eaglescliffe a	16 23			17 20				18 19		19 19		19 29			20 22		20 56	21 19	22 13		23 18			
d	16 26	16 37		17 20			18 12	18 19		19 19		19 30			20 23		20 58	21 19	22 14		23 19			
Allens West d				17 23			18 14	18 22		19 22					20 25			21 22	22 16		23 21			
Tees-side Airport d																								
Dinsdale d				17 29			18 21	18 28		19 28					20 32			21 28	22 23		23 28			
Darlington 7 26 a				17 40			18 31	18 37		19 38					20 44			21 38	22 33		23 38			
d								18 43																
North Road d								18 46																
Heighington d								18 54																
Newton Aycliffe d								18 57																
Shildon d								19 02																
Bishop Auckland a								19 08																
Stockton d		16 43			17 56								19 43											
Billingham d		16 50			18 03								19 50											
Seaton Carew d		16 56			18 09								19 56											
Hartlepool d	16 51	17 03			18 15							19 49	20 02				21 25							
Seaham d		17 19			18 30								20 17											
Sunderland ⛴ a	17 21	17 28			18 41							20 20	20 27				21 51							
d		17 28			18 43						19 28		20 28											
Heworth ⛴ d		17 39			18 54						19 39		20 43											
Newcastle 8 26 ⛴ a		17 48			19 05						19 52		20 50											
Metrocentre 48 a		17 59																						
Hexham 48 a																								

§ For authorised access only to BSC Redcar

A 8 December

Table 44

Sundays

5 January to 23 March

Saltburn and Middlesbrough - Darlington, Bishop Auckland, Sunderland and Newcastle

Network Diagram - refer to first Page of Table 44

		NT	NT	NT	NT	TP	NT	NT	NT	NT		GC	NT	TP	NT	NT	NT	TP	NT	NT		NT	NT	NT	GC
						◇1						R 1 ☕		◇1				◇1							R 1 ☕
Saltburn	d				09 43			10 43		11 43					12 43		13 43		14 43				15 43		
Marske	d				09 47			10 47		11 47					12 47		13 47		14 47				15 47		
Longbeck	d				09 50			10 50		11 50					12 50		13 50		14 50				15 50		
Redcar East	d				09 53			10 53		11 53					12 53		13 53		14 53				15 53		
Redcar Central	d				09 56			10 56		11 56					12 56		13 56		14 56				15 56		
British Steel Redcar §	d																								
South Bank	d				10 03			11 03		12 03					13 03		14 03		15 03				16 03		
Middlesbrough	a				10 08			11 08		12 08					13 08		14 08		15 08				16 08		
	d	08 39	09 09		10 09	10 15		11 08		12 09				12 45	13 09	13 31	14 09	14 43	15 09			15 31	16 09		
Thornaby	d	08 44	09 14		10 14	10a20		11 13		12 14				12a50	13 14	13 36	14 14	14a48	15 14			15 36	16 14		
London Kings Cross 15 ⊖26	d											09 53													13 53
Eaglescliffe	a	08 49	09 19		10 19			11 18		12 19		12 37			13 19		14 19		15 19				16 19		16 42
	d	08 49	09 19		10 19		10 36	11 19	12 11	12 19		12 39			13 19		14 19		15 19				16 19	16 37	16 47
Allens West	d	08 52	09 22		10 22			11 21	12 14	12 22					13 22		14 22		15 22				16 22		
Tees-side Airport	d								12 18																
Dinsdale	d	08 58	09 28		10 28			11 28	12 22	12 28					13 28		14 28		15 28				16 28		
Darlington 7 26	a	09 08	09 38		10 38			11 37	12 31	12 38					13 38		14 38		15 38				16 38		
	d		09 39					11 38									14 39						16 40		
North Road	d		09 42					11 41									14 42						16 43		
Heighington	d		09 50					11 50									14 50						16 51		
Newton Aycliffe	d		09 53					11 53									14 53						16 54		
Shildon	d		09 58					11 57									14 58						16 59		
Bishop Auckland	a		10 04					12 04									15 04						17 05		
Stockton	d						10 41									13 42						15 42		16 43	
Billingham	d						10 49									13 49						15 49		16 50	
Seaton Carew	d						10 55									13 55						15 55		16 56	
Hartlepool	d						11 00					12 58				14 01						16 01		17 03	17 13
Seaham	d						11 16									14 16						16 16		17 19	
Sunderland 🚇	a						11 26					13 24				14 26						16 26		17 28	17 39
	d			09 28			11 28						13 28			14 28				15 28		16 28		17 28	
Heworth 🚇	d			09 39			11 38						13 40			14 39				15 39		16 39		17 39	
Newcastle 8 26 🚇	a			09 48			11 48						13 49			14 48				15 48		16 48		17 48	
Metrocentre 48	a			09 59			11 59						13 59			14 59				15 59		16 59		17 59	
Hexham 48	a																								

		TP	NT	NT	NT	NT		TP	NT	NT	NT	GC	TP	NT	NT	GC		NT	TP	NT					
		◇1						◇1				R 1 ☕	◇1			R 1 ☕			◇1						
Saltburn	d		16 43			17 43			18 43					19 43	20 43			21 37		22 43					
Marske	d		16 47			17 47			18 47					19 47	20 47			21 41		22 47					
Longbeck	d		16 50			17 50			18 50					19 50	20 50			21 44		22 50					
Redcar East	d		16 53			17 53			18 53					19 53	20 53			21 47		22 53					
Redcar Central	d		16 56			17 56			18 56					19 56	20 56			21 50		22 56					
British Steel Redcar §	d																								
South Bank	d		17 03			18 03			19 03					20 03	21 03			21 57		23 03					
Middlesbrough	a		17 08			18 08			19 08					20 11	21 08			22 02		23 08					
	d	16 43	17 10	17 45		18 09		18 45	19 09		19 32		20 06	20 12	21 09			22 03	22 08	23 08					
Thornaby	d	16a48	17 15	17 50		18 14		18a50	19 14		19 37		20a11	20 17	21 14			22 08	22a13	23 13					
London Kings Cross 15 ⊖26	d											16 58				18 53									
Eaglescliffe	a		17 20			18 19			19 19			20 06		20 22	21 19	21 37		22 13		23 18					
	d		17 20		18 12	18 19			19 19			20 07		20 23	21 19	21 39		22 14		23 19					
Allens West	d		17 23		18 14	18 22			19 22					20 25	21 22			22 16		23 21					
Tees-side Airport	d																								
Dinsdale	d		17 29		18 21	18 28			19 28					20 32	21 28			22 23		23 28					
Darlington 7 26	a		17 40		18 31	18 37			19 38					20 44	21 38			22 33		23 38					
	d					18 43																			
North Road	d					18 46																			
Heighington	d					18 54																			
Newton Aycliffe	d					18 57																			
Shildon	d					19 02																			
Bishop Auckland	a					19 08																			
Stockton	d			17 56							19 43														
Billingham	d			18 03							19 50														
Seaton Carew	d			18 09							19 56														
Hartlepool	d			18 15							20 02	20 26				21 58									
Seaham	d			18 30							20 17														
Sunderland 🚇	a			18 41							20 27	20 52				22 24									
	d			18 43						19 28	20 28														
Heworth 🚇	d			18 54						19 39	20 43														
Newcastle 8 26 🚇	a			19 05						19 52	20 50														
Metrocentre 48	a																								
Hexham 48	a																								

§ For authorised access only to BSC Redcar

Table 44

Sundays
30 March to 11 May

Saltburn and Middlesbrough - Darlington, Bishop Auckland, Sunderland and Newcastle

Network Diagram - refer to first Page of Table 44

		NT	NT	NT	NT	NT	TP	NT	NT	NT		NT	GC	NT	TP	NT	NT	NT	NT	TP		NT	NT	NT	NT
		A					◇1						R 1 ☕		◇1					◇1					
Saltburn	d					09 43			10 43			11 43				12 43		13 43				14 43			15 43
Marske	d					09 47			10 47			11 47				12 47		13 47				14 47			15 47
Longbeck	d					09 50			10 50			11 50				12 50		13 50				14 50			15 50
Redcar East	d					09 53			10 53			11 53				12 53		13 53				14 53			15 53
Redcar Central	d					09 56			10 56			11 56				12 56		13 56				14 56			15 56
British Steel Redcar §	d																								
South Bank	d					10 03			11 03			12 03				13 03		14 03				15 03			16 03
Middlesbrough	a					10 08			11 08			12 08				13 08		14 08				15 08			16 08
	d		08 39	09 09		10 09	10 15		11 08			12 09			12 45	13 09	13 31	14 09	14 17	14 43		15 09		15 31	16 09
Thornaby	d		08 44	09 14		10 14	10a20		11 13			12 14			12a50	13 14	13 36	14 14	14 22	14a48		15 14		15 36	16 14
London Kings Cross 15 ⊖26	d												09 48												
Eaglescliffe	a		08 49	09 19		10 19			11 18			12 19	12 20			13 19		14 19				15 19			16 19
	d		08 49	09 19		10 19		10 36	11 19	12 11		12 19	12 21			13 19		14 19				15 19			16 19
Allens West	d		08 52	09 22		10 22			11 21	12 14		12 22				13 22		14 22				15 22			16 22
Tees-side Airport	d									12 18															
Dinsdale	d		08 58	09 28		10 28			11 28	12 22		12 28				13 28		14 28				15 28			16 28
Darlington 7	26 a		09 08	09 38		10 38			11 37	12 31		12 38				13 38		14 38	14 42			15 38			16 38
	d	07 20		09 39					11 38									14 39							16 40
North Road	d	07 23		09 42					11 41									14 42							16 43
Heighington	d	07 31		09 50					11 50									14 50							16 51
Newton Aycliffe	d	07 34		09 53					11 53									14 53							16 54
Shildon	d	07 39		09 58					11 57									14 58							16 59
Bishop Auckland	a	07 46		10 04					12 04									15 04							17 05
Stockton	d							10 41									13 42							15 42	
Billingham	d							10 49									13 49							15 49	
Seaton Carew	d							10 55									13 55							15 55	
Hartlepool	d							11 00					12 42				14 01							16 01	
Seaham	d							11 16									14 16							16 16	
Sunderland ⛴	a							11 26					13 08				14 26							16 26	
	d				09 28			11 28						13 28			14 28						15 28	16 28	
Heworth ⛴	d				09 39			11 38						13 40			14 39						15 39	16 39	
Newcastle 8	26 ⛴ a				09 48			11 48						13 49			14 48						15 48	16 48	
Metrocentre	48 a				09 59			11 59						13 59			14 59						15 59	16 59	
Hexham	48 a																								

		GC	NT	TP	NT	NT		NT	NT	NT	TP	NT	NT	GC	NT	TP		NT	GC	NT	NT	TP	NT		
		R 1 ☕		◇1							◇1			R 1 ☕		◇1			R 1 ☕			◇1			
Saltburn	d					16 43				17 43		18 43						19 43		20 43	21 37		22 43		
Marske	d					16 47				17 47		18 47						19 47		20 47	21 41		22 47		
Longbeck	d					16 50				17 50		18 50						19 50		20 50	21 44		22 50		
Redcar East	d					16 53				17 53		18 53						19 53		20 53	21 47		22 53		
Redcar Central	d					16 56				17 56		18 56						19 56		20 56	21 50		22 56		
British Steel Redcar §	d																								
South Bank	d					17 03				18 03		19 03						20 03		21 03	21 57		23 03		
Middlesbrough	a					17 08				18 08		19 08						20 11		21 08	22 02		23 08		
	d			16 43	16 55	17 10		17 45		18 09	18 45	19 09			19 32	20 06		20 12		21 09	22 03	22 08	23 08		
Thornaby	d			16a48	17 00	17 15		17 50		18 14	18a50	19 14			19 37	20a11		20 17		21 14	22 08	22a13	23 13		
London Kings Cross 15 ⊖26	d	13 48												16 47					18 23						
Eaglescliffe	a	16 23			17 05	17 20				18 19		19 19		19 29				20 22	20 56	21 19	22 13		23 18		
	d	16 26	16 37		17 05	17 20			18 12	18 19		19 19		19 30				20 23	20 58	21 19	22 14		23 19		
Allens West	d				17 08	17 23			18 14	18 22		19 22						20 25		21 22	22 16		23 21		
Tees-side Airport	d																								
Dinsdale	d				17 14	17 29			18 21	18 28		19 28						20 32		21 28	22 23		23 28		
Darlington 7	26 a				17 24	17 46			18 31	18 37		19 38						20 44		21 38	22 33		23 38		
	d					17 46				18 43															
North Road	d					17 49				18 46															
Heighington	d					17 57				18 54															
Newton Aycliffe	d					18 00				18 57															
Shildon	d					18 05				19 02															
Bishop Auckland	a					18 11				19 08															
Stockton	d		16 43					17 56							19 43										
Billingham	d		16 50					18 03							19 50										
Seaton Carew	d		16 56					18 09							19 56										
Hartlepool	d	16 51	17 03					18 15						19 49	20 02				21 25						
Seaham	d		17 19					18 30							20 17										
Sunderland ⛴	a	17 21	17 28					18 41						20 20	20 27				21 51						
	d		17 28					18 43					19 28		20 28										
Heworth ⛴	d		17 39					18 54					19 39		20 43										
Newcastle 8	26 ⛴ a		17 48					19 05					19 52		20 50										
Metrocentre	48 a		17 59																						
Hexham	48 a																								

§ For authorised access only to BSC Redcar

A from 20 April

Table 44R

Mondays to Fridays

9 December to 16 May

Newcastle, Sunderland, Bishop Auckland and Darlington - Middlesbrough and Saltburn

Network Diagram - refer to first Page of Table 44

Miles	Miles			NT	NT	NT	TP	NT	GC	NT	NT	NT	TP	NT	NT	TP	NT	GC	NT	NT	NT	TP	NT
							◇1		R 1 🍴				◇1			◇1 🚲		R 1 🍴				◇1 🚲	
—	—	Hexham 48	d									06 12							07 42				08 45
—	—	Metrocentre 48	d									06 45							08 15				09 16
—	0	**Newcastle** 8 26 ⛴	d	06 00								07 00		07 30					08 30				09 30
—	2¾	Heworth ⛴	d	06 07								07 07		07 37					08 37				09 37
—	12	**Sunderland** ⛴	a	06 19								07 18		07 49					08 50				09 49
—	—		d	06 20					06 45			07 19		07 50				08 42	08 51				09 50
—	17¼	Seaham	d	06 28								07 27		07 58					08 58				09 57
—	30	**Hartlepool**	d	06a46					07 10			07 45		08 15				09 09	09 15				10 15
—	32¼	Seaton Carew	d									07 49		08 19					09 19				10 19
—	37¼	Billingham	d									07 56		08 26					09 26				10 26
—	41¾	Stockton	d									08 04		08 33					09 34				10 33
0	—	**Bishop Auckland**	d								07 20						08 21				09 26		
2¾	—	Shildon	d								07 25						08 26				09 31		
5	—	Newton Aycliffe	d								07 30						08 31				09 36		
6¼	—	Heighington	d								07 33						08 34				09 39		
10¾	—	North Road	d								07 42						08 43				09 48		
—	—	Chester-le-Street 26	d																				
—	—	Durham 26	d																				
12	—	**Darlington** 7 26	a								07 46						08 47				09 53		
—	—		d			06 30	06 36	06 58		07 25	07 48				08 30		08 59			09 30	09 55		
15¾	—	Dinsdale	d			06 37		07 03		07 30	07 53				08 35		09 04			09 35	10 01		
17½	—	Tees-side Airport	d																				
20	—	Allens West	d			06 43		07 10		07 37	08 00				08 42		09 11			09 42	10 07		
20¾	—	Eaglescliffe	a			06 45		07 12	07 29	07 39	08 02				08 44		09 13	09 27		09 44	10 09		
—	—		d			06 46		07 12	07 30	07 39	08 02				08 44		09 13	09 30		09 44	10 10		
—	—	London Kings Cross 15 ⊖26	a						10 25									12 29					
23¾	44	Thornaby	d			06 51	06 53	07 17		07 46	08 08	08 11	08 24	08 39	08 50	09 13	09 20		09 39	09 50	10 15	10 21	10 39
27	47¼	**Middlesbrough**	a			06 57	07 03	07 23		07 52	08 14	08 21	08 31	08 47	08 56	09 22	09 26		09 50	09 57	10 21	10 30	10 48
—	—		d		06 34	06 59		07 24		07 54					08 57		09 27			09 57	10 22		
29½	—	South Bank	d		06 41					07 58					09 01						10 27		
32¾	—	British Steel Redcar §	d							08 04													
34½	—	**Redcar Central**	d		06 48	07 09		07 34		08 07					09 09		09 37			10 07	10 34		
35½	—	Redcar East	d		06 51			07 37		08 10					09 11		09 40			10 10	10 37		
37	—	Longbeck	d		06 55			07 41		08 14					09 15		09 44			10 14	10 41		
37½	—	Marske	d		06 56			07 42		08 15					09 17		09 45			10 15	10 42		
39½	—	**Saltburn**	a		07 03	07 21		07 51		08 23					09 26		09 53			10 25	10 50		

		NT	NT	TP	NT	NT	NT	TP	NT	NT	NT	GC	TP	NT	NT	NT	TP	NT	NT	NT	TP	NT	NT
				◇1 🚲				◇1 🚲				R 1 🍴	◇1 🚲				◇1 🚲				◇1 🚲		
Hexham 48	d				09 43				10 45					11 43				12 45				13 43	
Metrocentre 48	d				10 16				11 16					12 16				13 16				14 16	
Newcastle 8 26 ⛴	d				10 30				11 30					12 30				13 30				14 30	
Heworth ⛴	d				10 37				11 37					12 37				13 37				14 37	
Sunderland ⛴	a				10 49				11 49					12 49				13 49				14 50	
	d				10 50				11 50			12 28		12 50				13 50				14 51	
Seaham	d				10 58				11 58					12 58				13 57				14 59	
Hartlepool	d				11 12				12 15			12 52		13 15				14 15				15 15	
Seaton Carew	d				11 16				12 19					13 19				14 19				15 19	
Billingham	d				11 23				12 26					13 26				14 26				15 26	
Stockton	d				11 30				12 33					13 33				14 33				15 33	
Bishop Auckland	d						11 25									13 25							
Shildon	d						11 30									13 30							
Newton Aycliffe	d						11 35									13 35							
Heighington	d						11 38									13 38							
North Road	d						11 47									13 47							
Chester-le-Street 26	d																						
Durham 26	d																						
Darlington 7 26	a						11 51									13 51							
	d	10 32	10 53			11 30	11 53			12 32	12 53				13 30	13 53			14 30	14 53			15 30
Dinsdale	d	10 37	10 58			11 35	11 58			12 37	12 58				13 35	13 58			14 36	14 58			15 36
Tees-side Airport	d																						
Allens West	d	10 44	11 05			11 42	12 05			12 44	13 05				13 42	14 05			14 42	15 05			15 42
Eaglescliffe	a	10 46	11 07			11 44	12 07			12 46	13 07	13 11			13 44	14 07			14 44	15 07			15 44
	d	10 46	11 07			11 44	12 07			12 46	13 08	13 12			13 44	14 07			14 45	15 07			15 45
London Kings Cross 15 ⊖26	a											16 11											
Thornaby	d	10 52	11 13	11 22	11 36	11 50	12 13	12 22	12 39	12 52	13 13		13 22	13 39	13 50	14 14	14 22	14 39	14 50	15 13	15 22	15 39	15 50
Middlesbrough	a	10 58	11 19	11 30	11 46	11 57	12 19	12 30	12 50	12 58	13 19		13 30	13 48	13 56	14 20	14 30	14 45	14 57	15 19	15 30	15 48	15 56
	d	10 59	11 20			11 58	12 20			12 59	13 20				13 57	14 21			14 57	15 20			15 57
South Bank	d		11 25				12 25				13 26					14 25				15 25			
British Steel Redcar §	d																						
Redcar Central	d	11 09	11 32			12 08	12 32			13 09	13 32				14 07	14 33			15 07	15 32			16 07
Redcar East	d	11 12	11 35			12 11	12 35			13 12	13 35				14 10	14 35			15 10	15 35			16 10
Longbeck	d	11 16	11 39			12 15	12 39			13 16	13 39				14 14	14 39			15 14	15 39			16 14
Marske	d	11 17	11 40			12 16	12 40			13 17	13 40				14 15	14 41			15 15	15 40			16 15
Saltburn	a	11 25	11 49			12 25	12 49			13 27	13 50				14 25	14 50			15 25	15 49			16 25

§ For authorised access only to BSC Redcar

Table 44R

Mondays to Fridays

9 December to 16 May

Newcastle, Sunderland, Bishop Auckland and Darlington - Middlesbrough and Saltburn

Network Diagram - refer to first Page of Table 44

Station			NT	GC	TP	NT	NT	NT	TP	NT	NT	NT	NT	GC	TP	NT	NT	NT	TP	NT	NT	TP	NT
				R 1	◇1				◇1			◇		R 1	◇1			A	◇1			◇1	
Hexham	48	d				14 45				15 43		16 15				16 45		17 43					18 43
Metrocentre	48	d				15 16				16 16		16 39				17 16		18 16					19 16
Newcastle 8	26	d				15 30				16 30		16 53				17 30		18 30					19 30
Heworth		d				15 37				16 37		17 00				17 37		18 37					19 37
Sunderland		a				15 49				16 49		17 14				17 50		18 49					19 50
		d		15 18		15 50				16 50		17 15		17 31		17 50		18 50					19 50
Seaham		d				15 57				16 58		17 21				17 57		18 57					19 57
Hartlepool		d		15 50		16 15				17 15		17 39		17 57		18 15		19 14					20 14
Seaton Carew		d				16 19				17 19		17 43				18 19		19 19					20 19
Billingham		d				16 26				17 26		17 50				18 26		19 26					20 26
Stockton		d				16 33				17 33		17 57				18 33		19 33					20 33
Bishop Auckland		d	15 25					16 23									18 04			19 02			
Shildon		d	15 30					16 28									18 09			19 07			
Newton Aycliffe		d	15 35					16 33									18 14			19 12			
Heighington		d	15 38					16 36									18 17			19 16			
North Road		d	15 47					16 45									18 26			19 24			
Chester-le-Street	26	d																					
Durham	26	d																					
Darlington 7	26	a	15 51					16 50									18 31			19 28			
		d	15 53				16 29	16 53			17 30		18 00				18 33			19 30	19 53		
Dinsdale		d	15 58				16 35	16 58			17 36		18 06				18 38			19 35	19 58		
Tees-side Airport		d																					
Allens West		d	16 05				16 42	17 05			17 42		18 12				18 45			19 42	20 05		
Eaglescliffe		a	16 07	16 10			16 44	17 07			17 44		18 14	18 16			18 47			19 45	20 07		
		d	16 07	16 11			16 44	17 07			17 45		18 15	18 21			18 47			19 45	20 07		
London Kings Cross 15 ⊖	26	a		19 06										21 05									
Thornaby		d	16 13		16 22	16 39	16 50	17 13	17 22	17 39	17 52	18 03	18 21		18 32	18 39	18 53	19 36	19 47	19 53	20 13	20 21	20 38
Middlesbrough		a	16 19		16 30	16 46	16 56	17 19	17 30	17 48	17 58	18 15	18 26		18 40	18 48	18 59	19 47	19 56	19 59	20 21	20 30	20 47
		d	16 20				16 58	17 20			17 59		18 27				18 59			20 00			
South Bank		d	16 25					17 25					18 32							20 04			
British Steel Redcar §		d																					
Redcar Central		d	16 32				17 08	17 32			18 10		18 39				19 10			20 12			
Redcar East		d	16 35				17 11	17 35			18 12		18 42				19 12			20 14			
Longbeck		d	16 39				17 15	17 39			18 16		18 46				19 16			20 18			
Marske		d	16 40				17 16	17 40			18 18		18 47				19 18			20 20			
Saltburn		a	16 49				17 25	17 50			18 25		18 56				19 26			20 28			

Station			NT	TP	NT	NT	NT	NT
				◇1				
Hexham	48	d						
Metrocentre	48	d						
Newcastle 8	26	d			20 30		21 18	
Heworth		d			20 37		21 25	
Sunderland		a			20 49		21 37	
		d			20 50		21 38	
Seaham		d			20 58		21 46	
Hartlepool		d			21 15		22 03	
Seaton Carew		d			21 19		22 07	
Billingham		d			21 26		22 14	
Stockton		d			21 33		22 21	
Bishop Auckland		d				21 10		
Shildon		d				21 15		
Newton Aycliffe		d				21 20		
Heighington		d				21 23		
North Road		d				21 32		
Chester-le-Street	26	d						
Durham	26	d						
Darlington 7	26	a				21 36		
		d	20 30			21 38		22 38
Dinsdale		d	20 36			21 43		22 43
Tees-side Airport		d						
Allens West		d	20 42			21 50		22 50
Eaglescliffe		a	20 44			21 52		22 52
		d	20 45			21 52		22 52
London Kings Cross 15 ⊖	26	a						
Thornaby		d	20 50	21 22	21 40	21 58	22 30	22 58
Middlesbrough		a	20 57	21 30	21 47	22 06	22 36	23 04
		d	20 59			22 06		
South Bank		d	21 03			22 11		
British Steel Redcar §		d						
Redcar Central		d	21 11			22 18		
Redcar East		d	21 13			22 21		
Longbeck		d	21 17			22 25		
Marske		d	21 19			22 26		
Saltburn		a	21 26			22 36		

§ For authorised access only to BSC Redcar

A from 24 March

Table 44R

Saturdays

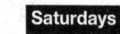

14 December to 17 May

Newcastle, Sunderland, Bishop Auckland and Darlington - Middlesbrough and Saltburn

Network Diagram - refer to first Page of Table 44

Station			NT	NT	NT	TP	NT	GC	NT	NT	NT		TP	NT	NT	TP	NT	GC	NT	NT	NT		TP	NT	NT	NT
						◇1		R 1 ☕					◇1			◇1		R 1 ☕					◇1			
Hexham	48	d									06 12								07 42					08 45		
Metrocentre	48	d									06 45								08 15					09 16		
Newcastle 8	26 ⛴	d	06 00								07 00			07 30					08 30					09 30		
Heworth	⛴	d	06 07								07 07			07 37					08 37					09 37		
Sunderland	⛴	a	06 27								07 18			07 49					08 49					09 49		
		d	06 28					06 43			07 19			07 50				08 30	08 50					09 50		
Seaham		d	06 35								07 27			07 58					08 58					09 57		
Hartlepool		d	06a53					07 10			07 45			08 15				08 55	09 14					10 14		
Seaton Carew		d									07 49			08 19					09 19					10 19		
Billingham		d									07 56			08 26					09 26					10 26		
Stockton		d									08 04			08 33					09 33					10 33		
Bishop Auckland		d								07 20							08 21				09 26					
Shildon		d								07 25							08 26				09 31					
Newton Aycliffe		d								07 30							08 31				09 36					
Heighington		d								07 33							08 34				09 40					
North Road		d								07 42							08 43				09 48					
Chester-le-Street	26	d																								
Durham	26	d																								
Darlington 7	26	a								07 46							08 47				09 54					
		d			06 28	06 36	06 58		07 30	07 48					08 23		08 59			09 31	09 55				10 32	10 53
Dinsdale		d			06 34		07 03		07 35	07 53					08 28		09 04			09 36	10 01				10 37	10 58
Tees-side Airport		d																								
Allens West		d			06 40		07 10		07 42	08 00					08 35		09 11			09 43	10 08				10 44	11 05
Eaglescliffe		a			06 42		07 12	07 28	07 43	08 02					08 37		09 13	09 14		09 45	10 10				10 46	11 07
		d			06 43		07 12	07 30	07 43	08 02					08 37		09 13	09 18		09 45	10 10				10 46	11 07
London Kings Cross 15	⊖26	a						10 15										12 07								
Thornaby		d			06 49	06 53	07 17		07 49	08 08	08 13		08 24	08 39	08 45	09 13	09 20		09 38	09 51	10 15		10 23	10 39	10 52	11 13
Middlesbrough		a			06 55	07 03	07 23		07 55	08 14	08 22		08 31	08 47	08 51	09 22	09 26		09 49	09 56	10 20		10 32	10 48	10 58	11 19
		d		06 34	06 59		07 24		07 56						08 53		09 27			09 57	10 23				10 59	11 20
South Bank		d		06 38					08 00						08 57						10 28					11 25
British Steel Redcar §		d																								
Redcar Central		d		06 46	07 09		07 35		08 08						09 05		09 37			10 07	10 35				11 09	11 32
Redcar East		d		06 48			07 38		08 10						09 07		09 40			10 10	10 38				11 12	11 35
Longbeck		d		06 52			07 41		08 14						09 11		09 44			10 14	10 42				11 16	11 39
Marske		d		06 54			07 43		08 16						09 13		09 45			10 15	10 43				11 17	11 40
Saltburn		a		07 01	07 21		07 51		08 24						09 23		09 53			10 25	10 51				11 25	11 49

Station			TP	NT	NT	NT	TP		NT	NT	GC	NT	TP	NT	NT	NT	TP		NT	NT	NT	TP	NT	NT	NT	GC
			◇1				◇1				R 1 ☕		◇1				◇1					◇1				R 1 ☕
Hexham	48	d		09 43					10 45					11 43					12 45				13 43			
Metrocentre	48	d		10 16					11 16					12 16					13 16				14 16			
Newcastle 8	26 ⛴	d		10 30					11 30					12 30					13 30				14 30			
Heworth	⛴	d		10 37					11 37					12 37					13 37				14 37			
Sunderland	⛴	a		10 49					11 49					12 49					13 49				14 49			
		d		10 50					11 50		12 18			12 50					13 50				14 50			15 29
Seaham		d		10 58					11 58					12 58					13 57				14 58			
Hartlepool		d		11 14					12 15		12 45			13 15					14 14				15 15			15 53
Seaton Carew		d		11 18					12 19					13 19					14 19				15 19			
Billingham		d		11 25					12 26					13 26					14 26				15 26			
Stockton		d		11 32					12 33					13 33					14 33				15 33			
Bishop Auckland		d				11 25										13 25									15 25	
Shildon		d				11 30										13 30									15 30	
Newton Aycliffe		d				11 35										13 35									15 35	
Heighington		d				11 38										13 38									15 38	
North Road		d				11 47										13 47									15 47	
Chester-le-Street	26	d																								
Durham	26	d																								
Darlington 7	26	a				11 51										13 51									15 51	
		d			11 32	11 53				12 32		12 53			13 33	13 53				14 32	14 53			15 30	15 53	
Dinsdale		d			11 37	11 58				12 37		12 58			13 38	13 58				14 38	14 58			15 36	15 58	
Tees-side Airport		d																								
Allens West		d			11 44	12 05				12 44		13 05			13 45	14 05				14 44	15 05			15 42	16 05	
Eaglescliffe		a			11 46	12 07				12 46	13 04	13 07			13 47	14 07				14 46	15 07			15 44	16 07	16 11
		d			11 46	12 07				12 46	13 05	13 07			13 47	14 07				14 47	15 07			15 45	16 07	16 12
London Kings Cross 15	⊖26	a									15 49															18 53
Thornaby		d	11 22	11 38	11 52	12 13	12 22		12 39	12 52		13 15	13 22	13 39	13 53	14 13	14 22		14 38	14 53	15 13	15 22	15 39	15 50	16 14	
Middlesbrough		a	11 30	11 46	11 58	12 19	12 30		12 49	12 58		13 21	13 30	13 48	13 59	14 19	14 30		14 46	14 58	15 19	15 30	15 48	15 56	16 20	
		d			11 59	12 20				12 59		13 22			14 00	14 20				14 59	15 20			15 57	16 20	
South Bank		d				12 25						13 26				14 25					15 25				16 25	
British Steel Redcar §		d																								
Redcar Central		d			12 09	12 32				13 09		13 34			14 10	14 32				15 09	15 32			16 07	16 32	
Redcar East		d			12 12	12 35				13 12		13 36			14 13	14 35				15 12	15 35			16 10	16 35	
Longbeck		d			12 16	12 39				13 16		13 40			14 17	14 39				15 16	15 39			16 14	16 39	
Marske		d			12 17	12 40				13 17		13 42			14 18	14 40				15 17	15 40			16 15	16 40	
Saltburn		a			12 25	12 49				13 25		13 50			14 25	14 50				15 25	15 49			16 25	16 49	

§ For authorised access only to BSC Redcar

Table 44R

Saturdays

14 December to 17 May

Newcastle, Sunderland, Bishop Auckland and Darlington - Middlesbrough and Saltburn

Network Diagram - refer to first Page of Table 44

		TP		NT	NT	NT	TP	NT	NT	NT	GC	NT		TP	NT	NT	TP	NT	NT	NT	TP	NT		NT	TP
		◇1					◇1				B 1 ☕			◇1			◇1				◇1				◇1
Hexham	48 d			14 45				15 43		16 15					16 45			17 43				18 44			
Metrocentre	48 d			15 16				16 16		16 39					17 16			18 16				19 17			
Newcastle 8	26 ⛴ d			15 30				16 30		16 53					17 30			18 30				19 30			
Heworth	⛴ d			15 37				16 37		17 00					17 37			18 37				19 37			
Sunderland	⛴ a			15 49				16 49		17 14					17 50			18 49				19 50			
	d			15 50				16 50		17 15	17 29				17 50			18 50				19 50			
Seaham	d			15 57				16 58		17 22					17 57			18 57				19 57			
Hartlepool	d			16 14				17 15		17 39	17 53				18 14			19 14				20 14			
Seaton Carew	d			16 19				17 19		17 44					18 19			19 19				20 19			
Billingham	d			16 26				17 26		17 51					18 26			19 26				20 26			
Stockton	d			16 33				17 33		17 58					18 33			19 33				20 33			
Bishop Auckland	d					16 23										18 04				19 16					
Shildon	d					16 28										18 09				19 21					
Newton Aycliffe	d					16 33										18 14				19 26					
Heighington	d					16 36										18 17				19 29					
North Road	d					16 45										18 26				19 38					
Chester-le-Street	26 d																								
Durham	26 d																								
Darlington 7	26 a					16 50										18 31				19 42					
	d				16 30	16 53			17 30			18 00				18 33			19 30	19 53				20 30	
Dinsdale	d				16 36	16 58			17 36			18 06				18 38			19 35	19 58				20 36	
Tees-side Airport	d																								
Allens West	d				16 42	17 05			17 42			18 12				18 45			19 42	20 05				20 42	
Eaglescliffe	a				16 44	17 07			17 44		18 11	18 14				18 47			19 44	20 07				20 44	
	d				16 45	17 07			17 45		18 12	18 15				18 47			19 44	20 07				20 45	
London Kings Cross 15	⊖26 a										20 56														
Thornaby	d	16 22		16 39	16 50	17 13	17 22	17 39	17 52	18 07		18 20		18 24	18 38	18 53	19 22	19 38	19 50	20 13	20 21	20 38		20 50	21 22
Middlesbrough	a	16 30		16 46	16 56	17 19	17 30	17 48	17 58	18 13		18 26		18 30	18 48	18 59	19 31	19 48	19 56	20 21	20 30	20 47		20 56	21 30
	d				16 58	17 20			17 59			18 27				18 59			19 56					20 58	
South Bank	d					17 25						18 32							20 01					21 02	
British Steel Redcar §	d																								
Redcar Central	d				17 08	17 32			18 10			18 39				19 10			20 08					21 10	
Redcar East	d				17 11	17 35			18 12			18 42				19 12			20 11					21 12	
Longbeck	d				17 15	17 39			18 16			18 46				19 16			20 15					21 16	
Marske	d				17 16	17 40			18 18			18 47				19 18			20 16					21 18	
Saltburn	a				17 25	17 50			18 25			18 56				19 26			20 25					21 26	

		NT	NT	NT
Hexham	48 d			
Metrocentre	48 d		20 47	
Newcastle 8	26 ⛴ d		21 00	21 50
Heworth	⛴ d		21 08	
Sunderland	⛴ a		21 20	
	d		21 20	
Seaham	d		21 28	
Hartlepool	d		21 45	
Seaton Carew	d		21 49	
Billingham	d		21 56	
Stockton	d		22 03	
Bishop Auckland	d	21 10		
Shildon	d	21 15		
Newton Aycliffe	d	21 20		
Heighington	d	21 23		
North Road	d	21 32		
Chester-le-Street	26 d			22 00
Durham	26 d			22 08
Darlington 7	26 a	21 36		22 29
	d	21 38		22 34
Dinsdale	d	21 43		22 39
Tees-side Airport	d			
Allens West	d	21 50		22 46
Eaglescliffe	a	21 52		22 48
	d	21 52		22 48
London Kings Cross 15	⊖26 a			
Thornaby	d	21 58	22 10	22 54
Middlesbrough	a	22 06	22 18	23 02
	d	22 06		
South Bank	d	22 11		
British Steel Redcar §	d			
Redcar Central	d	22 18		
Redcar East	d	22 21		
Longbeck	d	22 25		
Marske	d	22 26		
Saltburn	a	22 36		

§ For authorised access only to BSC Redcar

Table 44R

Sundays

8 December to 29 December

Newcastle, Sunderland, Bishop Auckland and Darlington - Middlesbrough and Saltburn

Network Diagram - refer to first Page of Table 44

	NT	TP	NT	GC	NT	NT	NT	NT	TP		NT	NT	NT	GC	NT	NT	TP	NT	GC		NT	NT	NT	TP
		◇1		R 1 ☕					◇1					R 1 ☕			◇1		R 1 ☕					◇1
Hexham 48 d																								
Metrocentre 48 d												10 48			11 50	12 48						13 50	14 48	
Newcastle 8 26 ⛴ d					09 00	09 45						11 00			12 00	13 00						14 00	15 00	
Heworth ⛴ d					09 07	09 52						11 06			12 06	13 06						14 06	15 06	
Sunderland ⛴ a					09 22	10 05						11 21			12 21	13 22						14 22	15 21	
d				09 18		10 06						11 22		12 12	12 21				14 12			14 22		
Seaham d						10 14						11 29			12 29							14 29		
Hartlepool d				09 43		10 31						11 46		12 36	12 45				14 40			14 46		
Seaton Carew d						10 35						11 50			12 50							14 50		
Billingham d						10 42						11 57			12 57							14 57		
Stockton d						10 49						12 04			13 04							15 04		
Bishop Auckland d								10 17					12 17											
Shildon d								10 22					12 22											
Newton Aycliffe d								10 27					12 27											
Heighington d								10 30					12 30											
North Road d								10 39					12 39											
Chester-le-Street 26 d																								
Durham 26 d																								
Darlington 7 26 a								10 43					12 43											
d	08 45	09 01	09 45				10 20	10 45			11 46		12 45					13 45			14 45			
Dinsdale d	08 50		09 50				10 25	10 50			11 51		12 50					13 50			14 50			
Tees-side Airport d							10 29																	
Allens West d	08 57		09 57				10 34	10 57			11 58		12 57					13 57			14 57			
Eaglescliffe a	08 59		09 59	10 01			10 36	10 59			12 00	12 11	12 59	12 59				13 59	14 58		14 59			
d	08 59		09 59	10 04				10 59			12 00		12 59	13 04				13 59	15 04		14 59			
London Kings Cross 15 ⊖26 a				12 44										15 44					17 45					
Thornaby d	09 05	09 17	10 05			10 55		11 05	11 24		12 06		13 05		13 09		13 28	14 05			15 05	15 10		15 32
Middlesbrough a	09 10	09 26	10 10			11 04		11 12	11 33		12 11		13 10		13 18		13 37	14 10			15 10	15 18		15 40
d	09 11		10 11					11 13			12 12		13 11					14 11			15 11			
South Bank d	09 15		10 15					11 17			12 16		13 15					14 15			15 15			
British Steel Redcar § d																								
Redcar Central d	09 23		10 23					11 25			12 24		13 23					14 23			15 23			
Redcar East d	09 25		10 25					11 27			12 26		13 25					14 25			15 25			
Longbeck d	09 29		10 29					11 31			12 30		13 29					14 29			15 29			
Marske d	09 31		10 31					11 33			12 32		13 31					14 31			15 31			
Saltburn a	09 38		10 38					11 40			12 39		13 38					14 38			15 38			

	NT	NT	NT	NT	TP		NT	NT	NT	GC	NT	NT	TP	NT	NT		TP	NT	NT	NT				
					◇1					R 1 ☕			◇1				◇1							
Hexham 48 d																								
Metrocentre 48 d				15 50				16 48			17 50	18 48												
Newcastle 8 26 ⛴ d				16 00				17 00			18 00	19 00						20 00	21 06					
Heworth ⛴ d				16 06				17 06			18 06	19 06						20 07						
Sunderland ⛴ a				16 22				17 20			18 21	19 22						20 21						
d				16 22				17 21		18 12	18 22							20 21						
Seaham d				16 29				17 30			18 29							20 28						
Hartlepool d				16 46				17 46		18 40	18 46							20 45						
Seaton Carew d				16 50				17 51			18 50							20 49						
Billingham d				16 57				17 58			18 57							20 57						
Stockton d				17 04				18 05			19 04							21 04						
Bishop Auckland d	15 17						17 16							19 17										
Shildon d	15 22						17 21							19 22										
Newton Aycliffe d	15 27						17 26							19 27										
Heighington d	15 30						17 29							19 30										
North Road d	15 39						17 38							19 39										
Chester-le-Street 26 d																			21 15					
Durham 26 d																			21 24					
Darlington 7 26 a	15 43						17 42							19 46					21 44					
d	15 45	16 23	16 45				17 45		18 45					19 48	20 32				21 45	22 45				
Dinsdale d	15 50	16 28	16 50				17 50		18 50					19 53	20 37				21 51					
Tees-side Airport d																								
Allens West d	15 57	16 35	16 57				17 57		18 57					20 00	20 44				21 58					
Eaglescliffe a	15 59	16 37	16 59				17 59	18 11	18 59	18 59				20 02	20 46				22 00	22 56				
d	15 59		16 59				17 59		18 59	19 04				20 02	20 46				22 00	22 56				
London Kings Cross 15 ⊖26 a										21 44														
Thornaby d	16 05		17 05	17 10	17 30		18 05		19 05		19 10		19 28	20 08	20 52		20 56	21 09	22 05	23 02				
Middlesbrough a	16 10		17 10	17 18	17 39		18 10		19 10		19 19		19 37	20 13	20 57		21 04	21 20	22 10	23 10				
d	16 11		17 11				18 11		19 11					20 14	20 58				22 11					
South Bank d	16 15		17 15				18 15		19 15					20 18	21 02				22 15					
British Steel Redcar § d																								
Redcar Central d	16 23		17 23				18 23		19 23					20 26	21 10				22 23					
Redcar East d	16 25		17 25				18 25		19 25					20 28	21 12				22 25					
Longbeck d	16 29		17 29				18 29		19 29					20 32	21 16				22 29					
Marske d	16 31		17 31				18 31		19 31					20 34	21 18				22 31					
Saltburn a	16 38		17 38				18 38		19 38					20 41	21 25				22 38					

§ For authorised access only to BSC Redcar

Table 44R

Sundays

5 January to 23 March

Newcastle, Sunderland, Bishop Auckland and Darlington - Middlesbrough and Saltburn

Network Diagram - refer to first Page of Table 44

	NT	TP	NT	GC	NT	NT	NT	NT	TP		NT	NT	NT	GC	NT	NT	TP	TP	NT		GC	NT	NT	NT
		◇1		1					◇1					1			◇1 A	◇1 B			1			
Hexham 48 d																								
Metrocentre 48 d												10 48			11 50	12 48							13 50	14 48
Newcastle 26 d					09 00	09 45						11 00			12 00	13 00							14 00	15 00
Heworth d					09 07	09 52						11 06			12 06	13 06							14 06	15 06
Sunderland a					09 22	10 05						11 21			12 21	13 22							14 22	15 21
d				09 18		10 06						11 22		12 12	12 21						14 12		14 22	
Seaham d						10 14						11 29			12 29								14 29	
Hartlepool d				09 43		10 31						11 46		12 36	12 45						14 40		14 46	
Seaton Carew d						10 35						11 50			12 50								14 50	
Billingham d						10 42						11 57			12 57								14 57	
Stockton d						10 49						12 04			13 04								15 04	
Bishop Auckland d								10 17					12 17											
Shildon d								10 22					12 22											
Newton Aycliffe d								10 27					12 27											
Heighington d								10 30					12 30											
North Road d								10 39					12 39											
Chester-le-Street 26 d																								
Durham 26 d																								
Darlington 26 a								10 43					12 43											
d	08 45	09 01	09 45				10 20	10 45			11 46		12 45						13 45			14 45		
Dinsdale d	08 50		09 50				10 25	10 50			11 51		12 50						13 50			14 50		
Tees-side Airport d							10 29																	
Allens West d	08 57		09 57				10 34	10 57			11 58		12 57						13 57			14 57		
Eaglescliffe a	08 59		09 59	10 01			10 36	10 59			12 00	12 11	12 59	12 59					13 59		14 58	14 59		
d	08 59		09 59	10 04				10 59			12 00		12 59	13 04					13 59		15 04	14 59		
London Kings Cross 15 ⊖26 a				13 05										16 03							18 03			
Thornaby d	09 05	09 17	10 05			10 55		11 05	11 24		12 06		13 05		13 09		13 28	13 35	14 05			15 05	15 10	
Middlesbrough a	09 10	09 26	10 10			11 04		11 12	11 33		12 11		13 10		13 18		13 37	13 44	14 10			15 10	15 18	
d	09 11		10 11					11 13			12 12		13 11						14 11			15 11		
South Bank d	09 15		10 15					11 17			12 16		13 15						14 15			15 15		
British Steel Redcar § d																								
Redcar Central d	09 23		10 23					11 25			12 24		13 23						14 23			15 23		
Redcar East d	09 25		10 25					11 27			12 26		13 25						14 25			15 25		
Longbeck d	09 29		10 29					11 31			12 30		13 29						14 29			15 29		
Marske d	09 31		10 31					11 33			12 32		13 31						14 31			15 31		
Saltburn a	09 38		10 38					11 40			12 39		13 38						14 38			15 38		

	TP	NT	NT	NT	NT		TP	TP	NT	NT	NT	GC	NT	NT	TP		TP	NT	NT	TP	TP	NT	NT	NT
	◇1						◇1 A	◇1 B				1			◇1 A		◇1 B			◇1 A	◇1 B			
Hexham 48 d																								
Metrocentre 48 d					15 50					16 48			17 50	18 48										
Newcastle 26 d					16 00					17 00			18 00	19 00								20 00	21 06	
Heworth d					16 06					17 06			18 06	19 06								20 07		
Sunderland a					16 22					17 20			18 21	19 22								20 21		
d					16 22					17 21		18 12	18 22									20 21		
Seaham d					16 29					17 30			18 29									20 28		
Hartlepool d					16 46					17 46		18 40	18 46									20 45		
Seaton Carew d					16 50					17 51			18 50									20 49		
Billingham d					16 57					17 58			18 57									20 57		
Stockton d					17 04					18 05			19 04									21 04		
Bishop Auckland d		15 17							17 16									19 17						
Shildon d		15 22							17 21									19 22						
Newton Aycliffe d		15 27							17 26									19 27						
Heighington d		15 30							17 29									19 30						
North Road d		15 39							17 38									19 39						
Chester-le-Street 26 d																							21 15	
Durham 26 d																							21 24	
Darlington 26 a		15 43							17 42									19 46					21 44	
d		15 45	16 23	16 45					17 45		18 45							19 48	20 32				21 45	22 45
Dinsdale d		15 50	16 28	16 50					17 50		18 50							19 53	20 37				21 51	
Tees-side Airport d																								
Allens West d		15 57	16 35	16 57					17 57		18 57							20 00	20 44				21 58	
Eaglescliffe a		15 59	16 37	16 59					17 59	18 11	18 59	18 59						20 02	20 46				22 00	22 56
d		15 59		16 59					17 59		18 59	19 04						20 02	20 46				22 00	22 56
London Kings Cross 15 ⊖26 a												22 03												
Thornaby d	15 32	16 05		17 05	17 10		17 30	17 33	18 05		19 05		19 10		19 28		19 31	20 08	20 52	20 56	21 02	21 09	22 05	23 02
Middlesbrough a	15 40	16 10		17 10	17 18		17 39	17 42	18 10		19 10		19 19		19 37		19 40	20 13	20 57	21 04	21 10	21 20	22 10	23 10
d		16 11		17 11					18 11		19 11							20 14	20 58				22 11	
South Bank d		16 15		17 15					18 15		19 15							20 18	21 02				22 15	
British Steel Redcar § d																								
Redcar Central d		16 23		17 23					18 23		19 23							20 26	21 10				22 23	
Redcar East d		16 25		17 25					18 25		19 25							20 28	21 12				22 25	
Longbeck d		16 29		17 29					18 29		19 29							20 32	21 16				22 29	
Marske d		16 31		17 31					18 31		19 31							20 34	21 18				22 31	
Saltburn a		16 38		17 38					18 38		19 38							20 41	21 25				22 38	

§ For authorised access only to BSC Redcar

A until 9 February

B from 16 February

Table 44R

Sundays

30 March to 11 May

Newcastle, Sunderland, Bishop Auckland and Darlington - Middlesbrough and Saltburn

Network Diagram - refer to first Page of Table 44

	NT	NT	TP	NT	GC	NT	NT	NT	NT		TP	NT	NT	NT	GC	NT	NT	TP	NT		GC	NT	NT	NT
			◇1		R 1 ☕						◇1				R 1 ☕			◇1			R 1 ☕			
Hexham 48 d																								
Metrocentre 48 d													10 48			11 50	12 48						13 50	14 48
Newcastle 8 26 d						09 00	09 45						11 00			12 00	13 00						14 00	15 00
Heworth d						09 07	09 52						11 06			12 06	13 06						14 06	15 06
Sunderland a						09 22	10 05						11 21			12 21	13 22						14 22	15 21
d					09 18		10 06						11 22		12 12	12 21					14 12		14 22	
Seaham d							10 14						11 29			12 29							14 29	
Hartlepool d					09 43		10 31						11 46		12 36	12 45					14 40		14 46	
Seaton Carew d							10 35						11 50			12 50							14 50	
Billingham d							10 42						11 57			12 57							14 57	
Stockton d							10 49						12 04			13 04							15 04	
Bishop Auckland d	07 50								10 17					12 17										
Shildon d	07 55								10 22					12 22										
Newton Aycliffe d	08 00								10 27					12 27										
Heighington d	08 04								10 30					12 30										
North Road d	08 12								10 39					12 39										
Chester-le-Street 26 d																								
Durham 26 d																								
Darlington 7 26 a	08 16								10 43					12 43										
d	08 18	08 45	09 01	09 45				10 20	10 45			11 46		12 45					13 45			14 45		
Dinsdale d	08 23	08 50		09 50				10 25	10 50			11 51		12 50					13 50			14 50		
Tees-side Airport d								10 29																
Allens West d	08 30	08 57		09 57				10 34	10 57			11 58		12 57					13 57			14 57		
Eaglescliffe a	08 32	08 59		09 59	10 01			10 36	10 59			12 00	12 11	12 59	12 59				13 59		14 58	14 59		
d	08 32	08 59		09 59	10 04				10 59			12 00		12 59	13 04				13 59		15 04	14 59		
London Kings Cross 15 ⊖26 a					12 44										15 44						17 45			
Thornaby d	08 38	09 05	09 17	10 05			10 55		11 05		11 24	12 06		13 05		13 09		13 28	14 05			15 05	15 10	
Middlesbrough a	08 43	09 10	09 26	10 10			11 02		11 12		11 33	12 11		13 10		13 18		13 37	14 10			15 10	15 18	
d		09 11		10 11					11 13			12 12		13 11					14 11			15 11		
South Bank d		09 15		10 15					11 17			12 16		13 15					14 15			15 15		
British Steel Redcar § d																								
Redcar Central d		09 23		10 23					11 25			12 24		13 23					14 23			15 23		
Redcar East d		09 25		10 25					11 27			12 26		13 25					14 25			15 25		
Longbeck d		09 29		10 29					11 31			12 30		13 29					14 29			15 29		
Marske d		09 31		10 31					11 33			12 32		13 31					14 31			15 31		
Saltburn a		09 38		10 38					11 40			12 39		13 38					14 38			15 38		

	TP	NT	NT	NT	NT		NT	TP	NT	NT	NT	GC	NT	NT	TP		NT	NT	TP	NT	NT	NT		
	◇1							◇1				R 1 ☕			◇1				◇1					
Hexham 48 d																								
Metrocentre 48 d							15 50			16 48			17 50	18 48										
Newcastle 8 26 d							16 00			17 00			18 00	19 00						20 00	21 06			
Heworth d							16 06			17 06			18 06	19 06						20 07				
Sunderland a							16 22			17 20			18 21	19 22						20 21				
d							16 22			17 21		18 12	18 22							20 21				
Seaham d							16 29			17 30			18 29							20 28				
Hartlepool d							16 46			17 46		18 40	18 46							20 45				
Seaton Carew d							16 50			17 51			18 50							20 49				
Billingham d							16 57			17 58			18 57							20 57				
Stockton d							17 04			18 05			19 04							21 04				
Bishop Auckland d		15 17							17 16		18 17						19 17							
Shildon d		15 22							17 21		18 22						19 22							
Newton Aycliffe d		15 27							17 26		18 27						19 27							
Heighington d		15 30							17 29		18 31						19 30							
North Road d		15 39							17 38		18 39						19 39							
Chester-le-Street 26 d																					21 15			
Durham 26 d																					21 24			
Darlington 7 26 a		15 43							17 42		18 43						19 46				21 44			
d		15 45	15 58	16 23	16 45				17 45		18 45						19 48	20 32			21 45	22 45		
Dinsdale d		15 50	16 03	16 28	16 50				17 50		18 50						19 53	20 37			21 51			
Tees-side Airport d																								
Allens West d		15 57	16 10	16 35	16 57				17 57		18 57						20 00	20 44			21 58			
Eaglescliffe a		15 59	16 12	16 37	16 59				17 59	18 11	18 59	18 59					20 02	20 46			22 00	22 56		
d		15 59	16 12		16 59				17 59		18 59	19 04					20 02	20 46			22 00	22 56		
London Kings Cross 15 ⊖26 a												21 44												
Thornaby d	15 32	16 05	16 18		17 05		17 10	17 30	18 05		19 05		19 10		19 28		20 08	20 52	20 56	21 09	22 05	23 02		
Middlesbrough a	15 40	16 10	16 23		17 10		17 18	17 39	18 10		19 10		19 19		19 37		20 13	20 57	21 04	21 20	22 10	23 10		
d		16 11			17 11				18 11		19 11						20 14	20 58			22 11			
South Bank d		16 15			17 15				18 15		19 15						20 18	21 02			22 15			
British Steel Redcar § d																								
Redcar Central d		16 23			17 23				18 23		19 23						20 26	21 10			22 23			
Redcar East d		16 25			17 25				18 25		19 25						20 28	21 12			22 25			
Longbeck d		16 29			17 29				18 29		19 29						20 32	21 16			22 29			
Marske d		16 31			17 31				18 31		19 31						20 34	21 18			22 31			
Saltburn a		16 38			17 38				18 38		19 38						20 41	21 25			22 38			

§ For authorised access only to BSC Redcar

Table 45

Middlesbrough and Pickering - Whitby

Mondays to Fridays

9 December to 21 March

Network Diagram - refer to first Page of Table 44

Miles			NT	NT	NT	NT	NT	NT	NT	NT	NT	NT
—	Newcastle 8 44	d			07 30		10 30		13 30	15 30		16 30
0	**Middlesbrough**	d	07 04	08 14	08 47	10 36	11 49	14 14	14 47	16 47	17 38	17 54
—	James Cook Uni Hosptl Stn	d										
3	Marton	d	07 11	08 21	08 54	10 43	11 56	14 21	14 54	16 54	17 45	18 01
4	Gypsy Lane	d	07 14	08 24	08 57	10 46	11 59	14 24	14 57	16 57	17 48	18 04
4½	Nunthorpe	d	07 17	08a30	08a59	10 49	12a01	14 27	14a59	17a02	17 51	18a08
8½	Great Ayton	d	07 23			10 55		14 33			17 57	
11	Battersby	a	07 29			11 01		14 39			18 03	
—		d	07 36			11 05		14 43			18 07	
12¾	Kildale	d	07 41			11 10		14 48			18 12	
16¾	Commondale	d	07 48			11 17		14 55			18 19	
18½	Castleton Moor	d	07 52			11 20		14 58			18 22	
20	Danby	d	07 55			11 23		15 01			18 25	
23½	Lealholm	d	08 02			11 30		15 08			18 32	
25½	Glaisdale	a	08 07			11 34		15 12			18 36	
—		d	08 09			11 37		15 15			18 39	
27¼	Egton	d	08 13			11 40		15 18			18 42	
—	**Pickering §**	d										
—	Levisham §	d										
—	Goathland §	d										
28¾	Grosmont	d	08 17			11 44		15 22			18 46	
32	Sleights	d	08 26			11 53		15 31			18 55	
33½	Ruswarp	d	08 31			11 58		15 36			19 00	
35	**Whitby**	a	08 38			12 04		15 42			19 07	

Mondays to Fridays

24 March to 16 May

		NT	NT	NT	NY D	NT	NT	NY B	NT	NT	NT	NY C	NY A	NT	NT	NT
Newcastle 8 44	d			07 30			10 30			13 30	15 30				16 30	18 30
Middlesbrough	d	07 04	08 14	08 47		10 36	11 49		14 14	14 47	16 47			17 38	17 54	19 49
James Cook Uni Hosptl Stn	d	07 08	08 18	08 51		10 40	11 53		14 18	14 51	16 51			17 42	17 58	19 53
Marton	d	07 11	08 21	08 54		10 43	11 56		14 21	14 54	16 54			17 45	18 01	19 56
Gypsy Lane	d	07 14	08 24	08 57		10 46	11 59		14 24	14 57	16 57			17 48	18 04	19 59
Nunthorpe	d	07 17	08a30	08a59		10 49	12a01		14 27	14a59	17a02			17 51	18a08	20a02
Great Ayton	d	07 23				10 55			14 33					17 57		
Battersby	a	07 29				11 01			14 39					18 03		
	d	07 36				11 05			14 43					18 07		
Kildale	d	07 41				11 10			14 48					18 12		
Commondale	d	07 48				11 17			14 55					18 19		
Castleton Moor	d	07 52				11 20			14 58					18 22		
Danby	d	07 55				11 23			15 01					18 25		
Lealholm	d	08 02				11 30			15 08					18 32		
Glaisdale	a	08 07				11 34			15 12					18 36		
	d	08 09				11 37			15 15					18 39		
Egton	d	08 13				11 40			15 18					18 42		
Pickering §	d				09 00			12 00				15c00	16 00			
Levisham §	d				09 20			12 20				15c20	16 20			
Goathland §	d				09 45			12 50				16c10	16 50			
Grosmont	d	08 17			10 10	11 44		13 10	15 22			16 35	17 10	18 46		
Sleights	d	08 26				11 53			15 31					18 55		
Ruswarp	d	08 31				11 58			15 36					19 00		
Whitby	a	08 38			10 35	12 04		13 35	15 42			17 00	17 35	19 07		

North Yorkshire Moors Railway trains commence from 7 April

Saturdays

14 December to 22 March

		NT	NT	NT	NT	NT	NT	NT	NT	NT	NT	NT
Newcastle 8 44	d			07 30		10 30		13 30	15 30		16 30	18 30
Middlesbrough	d	07 04	08 14	08 47	10 36	11 49	14 14	14 47	16 47	17 38	17 54	19 49
James Cook Uni Hosptl Stn	d											
Marton	d	07 11	08 21	08 54	10 43	11 56	14 21	14 54	16 54	17 45	18 01	19 56
Gypsy Lane	d	07 14	08 24	08 57	10 46	11 59	14 24	14 57	16 57	17 48	18 04	19 59
Nunthorpe	d	07 17	08a28	08a59	10 49	12a01	14 27	14a59	17a01	17 51	18a08	20a02
Great Ayton	d	07 23			10 55		14 33			17 57		
Battersby	a	07 29			11 01		14 39			18 03		
	d	07 36			11 05		14 43			18 07		
Kildale	d	07 41			11 10		14 48			18 12		
Commondale	d	07 48			11 17		14 55			18 19		
Castleton Moor	d	07 52			11 20		14 58			18 22		
Danby	d	07 55			11 23		15 01			18 25		
Lealholm	d	08 02			11 30		15 08			18 32		
Glaisdale	a	08 07			11 34		15 12			18 36		
	d	08 09			11 37		15 15			18 39		
Egton	d	08 13			11 40		15 18			18 42		
Pickering §	d											
Levisham §	d											
Goathland §	d											
Grosmont	d	08 17			11 44		15 22			18 46		
Sleights	d	08 26			11 53		15 31			18 55		
Ruswarp	d	08 31			11 58		15 36			19 00		
Whitby	a	08 38			12 04		15 42			19 07		

§ North Yorkshire Moors Railway. For full service between Grosmont and Pickering please see separate publicity

A The Moors Explorer, 25 April, 2 May, 5 May

B The Yorkshire Coast Express, from 7 April

C The Moors Explorer, not 25 April, 2 May, 5 May

D from 7 April

For connections to Darlington please see Table 44

Table 45

Saturdays

29 March to 17 May

Middlesbrough and Pickering - Whitby

Network Diagram - refer to first Page of Table 44

		NT	NT	NT	NY	NT	NT	NY	NT	NT		NT	NY	NY	NT	NT
					1			1					1	1		
					D			B					C	A		
Newcastle 8 44	d			07 30			10 30			13 30		15 30			16 30	18 30
Middlesbrough	d	07 04	08 14	08 47		10 36	11 49		14 14	14 47		16 47			17 54	19 49
James Cook Uni Hosptl Stn	d	07 08	08 18	08 51		10 40	11 53		14 18	14 51		16 51			17 58	19 53
Marton	d	07 11	08 21	08 54		10 43	11 56		14 21	14 54		16 54			18 01	19 56
Gypsy Lane	d	07 14	08 24	08 57		10 46	11 59		14 24	14 57		16 57			18 04	19 59
Nunthorpe	d	07 17	08a28	08a59		10 49	12a01		14 27	14a59		17a01			18a08	20a02
Great Ayton	d	07 23				10 55			14 33							
Battersby	a	07 29				11 01			14 39							
	d	07 36				11 05			14 43							
Kildale	d	07 41				11 10			14 48							
Commondale	d	07 48				11 17			14 55							
Castleton Moor	d	07 52				11 20			14 58							
Danby	d	07 55				11 23			15 01							
Lealholm	d	08 02				11 30			15 08							
Glaisdale	a	08 07				11 34			15 12							
	d	08 09				11 37			15 15							
Egton	d	08 13				11 40			15 18							
Pickering §	d				09 00			12 00					15c00	16 00		
Levisham §	d				09 20			12 20					15c20	16 20		
Goathland §	d				09 45			12 50					16c10	16 50		
Grosmont	d	08 17			10 10	11 44		13 10	15 22				16 35	17 10		
Sleights	d	08 26				11 53			15 31							
Ruswarp	d	08 31				11 58			15 36							
Whitby	a	08 38			10 35	12 04		13 35	15 42				17 00	17 35		

§ North Yorkshire Moors Railway. For full service between Grosmont and Pickering please see separate publicity

A The Moors Explorer, 26 April, 3 May from 5 April

B The Yorkshire Coast Express, from 5 April

C The Moors Explorer, not 26 April, 3 May

D From 5 April

For connections to Darlington please see Table 44

North Yorkshire Moors Railway trains commence from 5 April

Table 45

Sundays

8 December to 11 May

Middlesbrough and Pickering - Whitby

Network Diagram - refer to first Page of Table 44

		NT	NY	NT	NY	NT	NY	NT
			☕ 1		☕ 1		☕ 1	
			B		A		B	
Newcastle 8 44 ⛴	d			09 45				
Middlesbrough	d	08 43		11 03		13 43		16 24
James Cook Uni Hosptl Stn	d	08 47		11 07		13 47		16 28
Marton	d	08 50		11 10		13 50		16 31
Gypsy Lane	d	08 53		11 13		13 53		16 34
Nunthorpe	d	08 56		11 16		13 59		16 40
Great Ayton	d	09 02		11 23		14 06		16 47
Battersby	a	09 08		11 28		14 11		16 52
	d	09 12		11 33		14 16		16 57
Kildale	d	09 17		11 37		14 20		17 01
Commondale	d	09 24		11 44		14 27		17 08
Castleton Moor	d	09 27		11 48		14 31		17 12
Danby	d	09 30		11 51		14 34		17 15
Lealholm	d	09 37		11 58		14 40		17 21
Glaisdale	a	09 41		12 02		14 45		17 26
	d	09 44		12 07		14 47		17 28
Egton	d	09 47		12 10		14 51		17 32
Pickering §	d		09 40		11 45		*15c00*	
Levisham §	d		10 00		12 05		*15c20*	
Goathland §	d		10 28		12 35		*15c50*	
Grosmont	d	09 51	10 50	12 14	13 12	14 55	16 10	17 36
Sleights	d	10 00		12 23		15 04		17 45
Ruswarp	d	10 05		12 28		15 08		17 49
Whitby	a	10 13	11 15	12 35	13 35	15 15	16 30	17 56

§ North Yorkshire Moors Railway. For full service between Grosmont and Pickering please see separate publicity

A The Yorkshire Coast Express, from 6 April

B From 6 April

For connections to Darlington please see Table 44

North Yorkshire Moors Railway trains commence from 6 April

Table 45R

Whitby - Pickering and Middlesbrough

Mondays to Fridays

9 December to 21 March

Network Diagram - refer to first Page of Table 44

Miles			NT	NT	NT	NT	NT	NT	NT	NT	NT	NT	NT
0	**Whitby**	d				08 50		12 41			16 00		19 15
1½	Ruswarp	d				08 54		12 45			16 04		19 19
3	Sleights	d				08 59		12 50			16 09		19 24
6¼	Grosmont	d				09 07		12 58			16 17		19 32
—	Goathland §	a											
—	Levisham §	a											
—	**Pickering** §	a											
7¾	Egton	d				09 10		13 01			16 21		19 35
9½	Glaisdale	a				09 14		13 05			16 25		19 39
—		d				09 17		13 08			16 28		19 42
11½	Lealholm	d				09 22		13 13			16 33		19 47
15	Danby	d				09 28		13 19			16 40		19 53
16½	Castleton Moor	d				09 31		13 22			16 44		19 56
18¾	Commondale	d				09 35		13 26			16 47		20 00
22¼	Kildale	d				09 42		13 33			16 54		20 07
24	Battersby	a				09 47		13 38			16 59		20 12
—		d				09 51		13 42			17 04		20 16
26½	Great Ayton	d				09 56		13 47			17 09		20 21
30½	Nunthorpe	d	07 20	08 31	09 16	10 03	12 16	13 54	15 16	17 03	17 16	18 24	20 28
31	Gypsy Lane	d	07 22	08 33	09 18	10 05	12 18	13 56	15 18	17 05	17 18	18 26	20 30
32	Marton	d	07 24	08 36	09 21	10 08	12 21	13 59	15 21	17 08	17 20	18 29	20 33
—	James Cook Uni Hosptl Stn	d											
35	**Middlesbrough**	a	07 31	08 44	09 30	10 17	12 28	14 07	15 28	17 15	17 30	18 36	20 40
—	Newcastle 8 44	a	08 52		10 51		13 51		16 51				

Mondays to Fridays

24 March to 16 May

		NT	NT	NT	NT	NY	NT	NT	NY	NT	NT	NT	NY	NY	NT	NT
Notes						B			A				C	D		
Whitby	d				08 50	11 00		12 41	14 00			16 00	17 30	18 00		19 15
Ruswarp	d				08 54			12 45				16 04				19 19
Sleights	d				08 59			12 50				16 09				19 24
Grosmont	d				09 07	11 30		12 58	14 30			16 17	18 00	18 30		19 32
Goathland §	a					11 45			14 45				18 15	18 45		
Levisham §	a					12 16			15 16				18 40	19 10		
Pickering §	a					12 40			15 40				19 00	19 30		
Egton	d				09 10			13 01				16 21				19 35
Glaisdale	a				09 14			13 05				16 25				19 39
	d				09 17			13 08				16 28				19 42
Lealholm	d				09 22			13 13				16 33				19 47
Danby	d				09 28			13 19				16 40				19 53
Castleton Moor	d				09 31			13 22				16 44				19 56
Commondale	d				09 35			13 26				16 47				20 00
Kildale	d				09 42			13 33				16 54				20 07
Battersby	a				09 47			13 38				16 59				20 12
	d				09 51			13 42				17 04				20 16
Great Ayton	d				09 56			13 47				17 09				20 21
Nunthorpe	d	07 20	08 31	09 16	10 03		12 16	13 54		15 16	17 03	17 16			18 24	20 28
Gypsy Lane	d	07 22	08 33	09 18	10 05		12 18	13 56		15 18	17 05	17 18			18 26	20 30
Marton	d	07 24	08 36	09 21	10 08		12 21	13 59		15 21	17 08	17 20			18 29	20 33
James Cook Uni Hosptl Stn	d	07 27	08 38	09 23	10 10		12 23	14 01		15 23	17 10	17 23			18 31	20 35
Middlesbrough	a	07 31	08 44	09 30	10 17		12 28	14 07		15 28	17 15	17 30			18 36	20 40
Newcastle 8 44	a	08 52		10 51			13 51			16 51						

North Yorkshire Moors Railway trains commence from 7 April

Saturdays

14 December to 22 March

		NT	NT	NT	NT	NT	NT	NT	NT	NT	NT	NT
Whitby	d				08 50		12 41			16 00		19 15
Ruswarp	d				08 54		12 45			16 04		19 19
Sleights	d				08 59		12 50			16 09		19 24
Grosmont	d				09 07		12 58			16 17		19 32
Goathland §	a											
Levisham §	a											
Pickering §	a											
Egton	d				09 10		13 01			16 21		19 35
Glaisdale	a				09 14		13 05			16 25		19 39
	d				09 17		13 08			16 28		19 42
Lealholm	d				09 22		13 13			16 33		19 47
Danby	d				09 28		13 19			16 40		19 53
Castleton Moor	d				09 31		13 22			16 44		19 56
Commondale	d				09 35		13 26			16 47		20 00
Kildale	d				09 42		13 33			16 54		20 07
Battersby	a				09 47		13 38			16 59		20 12
	d				09 51		13 42			17 04		20 16
Great Ayton	d				09 56		13 47			17 09		20 21
Nunthorpe	d	07 20	08 31	09 16	10 03	12 16	13 54	15 16	17 03	17 16	18 24	20 28
Gypsy Lane	d	07 22	08 33	09 18	10 05	12 18	13 56	15 18	17 05	17 18	18 26	20 30
Marton	d	07 24	08 36	09 21	10 08	12 21	13 59	15 21	17 08	17 20	18 29	20 33
James Cook Uni Hosptl Stn	d											
Middlesbrough	a	07 31	08 44	09 29	10 17	12 28	14 07	15 29	17 15	17 30	18 36	20 41
Newcastle 8 44	a	08 52		10 51			13 51	16 51				22 04

§ North Yorkshire Moors Railway. For full service between Grosmont and Pickering please see separate publicity

A The Yorkshire Coast Express, from 7 April
B The Moors Explorer, from 7 April
C From 7 April, not 25 April, 2 May, 5 May
D 25 April, 2 May, 5 May

For connections to Darlington please see Table 44

Table 45R

Saturdays

29 March to 17 May

Whitby - Pickering and Middlesbrough

Network Diagram - refer to first Page of Table 44

		NT	NT	NT	NT	NY	NT	NT	NY	NT		NT	NT	NY	NY	NT	NT
						☕1			☕1					☕1	☕1		
						D			C					A	B		
Whitby	d				08 50	11 00		12 41	14 00				16 00	17 30	18 00		19 15
Ruswarp	d				08 54			12 45					16 04				19 19
Sleights	d				08 59			12 50					16 09				19 24
Grosmont	d				09 07	11 30		12 58	14 30				16 17	18 00	18 30		19 32
Goathland §	a					11 45			14 45					18 15	18 45		
Levisham §	a					12 16			15 16					18 40	19 10		
Pickering §	a					12 40			15 40					19 00	19 30		
Egton	d				09 10			13 01					16 21				19 35
Glaisdale	a				09 14			13 05					16 25				19 39
	d				09 17			13 08					16 28				19 42
Lealholm	d				09 22			13 13					16 33				19 47
Danby	d				09 28			13 19					16 40				19 53
Castleton Moor	d				09 31			13 22					16 44				19 56
Commondale	d				09 35			13 26					16 47				20 00
Kildale	d				09 42			13 33					16 54				20 07
Battersby	a				09 47			13 38					16 59				20 12
	d				09 51			13 42					17 04				20 16
Great Ayton	d				09 56			13 47					17 09				20 21
Nunthorpe	d	07 20	08 31	09 16	10 03		12 16	13 54		15 16		17 03	17 16			18 24	20 28
Gypsy Lane	d	07 22	08 33	09 18	10 05		12 18	13 56		15 18		17 05	17 18			18 26	20 30
Marton	d	07 24	08 36	09 21	10 08		12 21	13 59		15 21		17 08	17 20			18 29	20 33
James Cook Uni Hosptl Stn	d	07 27	08 38	09 23	10 10		12 23	14 01		15 23		17 10	17 23			18 31	20 35
Middlesbrough	a	07 31	08 44	09 29	10 17		12 28	14 07		15 29		17 15	17 30			18 36	20 41
Newcastle 8 44 ⛴	a	08 52		10 51			13 51			16 51							22 04

§ North Yorkshire Moors Railway. For full service between Grosmont and Pickering please see separate publicity

A From 5 April, not 26 April, 3 May

B 26 April, 3 May,

C **The Yorkshire Coast Express**, from 5 April

D **The Moors Explorer**, from 5 April

For connections to Darlington please see Table 44

North Yorkshire Moors Railway trains commence from 5 April

Table 45R

Sundays

8 December to 11 May

Whitby - Pickering and Middlesbrough

Network Diagram - refer to first Page of Table 44

		NT	NY	NT	NY	NT	NY	NT
			1		1		1	
			B		A		B	
Whitby	d	10 25	11 40	12 46	14 00	15 27	17 00	18 05
Ruswarp	d	10 29		12 50		15 31		18 09
Sleights	d	10 34		12 55		15 36		18 14
Grosmont	d	10 42	12 10	13 03	14 32	15 44	17 20	18 22
Goathland §	a		12 25		14 47		17 50	
Levisham §	a		12 56		15 18		18 20	
Pickering §	a		13 20		15 42		18 40	
Egton	d	10 45		13 06		15 47		18 25
Glaisdale	a	10 49		13 10		15 51		18 29
	d	10 52		13 13		15 54		18 32
Lealholm	d	10 57		13 18		15 59		18 37
Danby	d	11 04		13 24		16 05		18 43
Castleton Moor	d	11 07		13 27		16 08		18 46
Commondale	d	11 11		13 31		16 12		18 50
Kildale	d	11 18		13 38		16 19		18 57
Battersby	a	11 23		13 43		16 24		19 02
	d	11 38		13 47		16 28		19 06
Great Ayton	d	11 43		13 52		16 33		19 11
Nunthorpe	d	11 50		14 00		16 40		19 18
Gypsy Lane	d	11 52		14 02		16 42		19 20
Marton	d	11 55		14 05		16 45		19 23
James Cook Uni Hosptl Stn	d	11 57		14 07		16 48		19 25
Middlesbrough	a	12 03		14 14		16 54		19 31
Newcastle 8 44	a							20 50

§ North Yorkshire Moors Railway. For full service between Grosmont and Pickering please see separate publicity

A The Yorkshire Coast Express, from 6 April

B From 6 April

For connections to Darlington please see Table 44

North Yorkshire Moors Railway trains commence from 6 April

Table 48

Mondays to Fridays

9 December to 16 May

Chathill and Morpeth - Newcastle - Metrocentre, Hexham and Carlisle

Network Diagram - refer to first Page of Table 44

Miles	Miles	Station		GR	NT	NT	GR	XC	NT	NT	XC	NT		NT	NT	GR	NT	NT	NT	NT	NT	NT		NT	NT
				R 1 🍴			R 1 🍴	◇1 🍴			◇1 🍴					R 1 🍴	◇				◇				
0	—	**Chathill**	d						07 08																
11¼	—	Alnmouth for Alnwick 26	d	06 20			06 54	07 08	07 20		07 59					08 59									
17½	—	Acklington	d						07 37																
22¾	—	Widdrington	d						07 44																
27½	—	Pegswood	d						07 50																
39½	—	**Morpeth** 26	d	06 36			07 10		07 54		08 13	08 49								09 49					10 49
36¼	—	Cramlington	d						08 03			08 57								09 57					10 57
45½	—	Manors	d						08 16			09 11								10 11					11 11
46	—	**Newcastle** 8 26 ⛴	a	06 52			07 26	07 38	08 20		08 30	09 14				09 27				10 13					11 14
—	—	Sunderland 26,44 ⛴	d							07 30									09 30					10 30	
—	—	**Newcastle** 8 ⛴	d		06 28	06 47				07 53				08 24	08 54		09 26	09 44	09 54	10 15	10 22	10 44		10 54	11 15
48¼	2¼	Dunston	d							07 58					08 59			09 49				10 50			
49½	3½	**Metrocentre**	a		06 35	06 54				08 01				08 32	09 02		09 33	09 54	10 01	10 23	10 30	10 54		11 01	11 23
—	—		d		06 36	06 55				08 02				08 32	09 03		09 34		10 02		10 32			11 02	
—	5½	Blaydon	d		06 40					08 06									10 06						
—	9¾	Wylam	d		06 46					08 12				08 40	09 11				10 12					11 10	
—	12	Prudhoe	d		06 50	07 05				08 16				08 45	09 15		09 43		10 16		10 42			11 14	
—	14½	Stocksfield	d		06 55					08 21				08 49	09 20				10 21					11 19	
—	16¾	Riding Mill	d		06 59					08 25					09 24				10 25					11 23	
—	19¼	Corbridge	d		07 04					08 30					09 29				10 30					11 27	
—	22¼	**Hexham**	a		07 12	07 17				08 38				08 58	09 38		09 57		10 38		10 55			11 37	
—	—		d			07 17								08 59			09 57				10 55				
—	30	Haydon Bridge	d			07 26								09 08							11 04				
—	33¾	Bardon Mill	d			07 33								09 14							11 11				
—	38½	Haltwhistle	d			07 40								09 21			10 17				11 18				
—	50¾	Brampton (Cumbria)	d			07 55								09 37							11 33				
—	57½	Wetheral	d			08 04								09 46							11 42				
—	61¾	**Carlisle** 8	a			08 13								09 57			10 50				11 57				

Station		GR	XC	NT	NT	NT	NT	XC		NT	NT	NT	NT	GR	NT	NT	NT	NT		XC	NT	NT	NT	NT	GR
		R 1 🍴	◇1 🍴	◇				◇1 🍴		◇				R 1 🍴						◇1 🍴	◇				R 1 🍴
Chathill	d																								
Alnmouth for Alnwick 26	d	10 59						12 09						12 59						14 09					15 00
Acklington	d																								
Widdrington	d																								
Pegswood	d																								
Morpeth 26	d		11 20				11 49						12 49					13 49						14 49	
Cramlington	d						11 57						12 57					13 57						14 57	
Manors	d						12 11						13 11					14 11						15 11	
Newcastle 8 26 ⛴	a	11 27	11 37				12 13	12 38					13 13	13 27				14 13		14 38				15 14	15 27
Sunderland 26,44 ⛴	d					11 30						12 30					13 30						14 30		
Newcastle 8 ⛴	d			11 22	11 44	11 54	12 15			12 22	12 44	12 54	13 15		13 22	13 44	13 54	14 15			14 24	14 44	14 54	15 15	
Dunston	d				11 49						12 49					13 49						14 49			
Metrocentre	a			11 31	11 54	12 01	12 23			12 31	12 54	13 01	13 23		13 32	13 54	14 01	14 23			14 32	14 54	15 01	15 23	
	d			11 32		12 02				12 32		13 02			13 32		14 02				14 32		15 02		
Blaydon	d					12 06											14 06								
Wylam	d					12 12						13 10					14 12						15 10		
Prudhoe	d			11 42		12 16				12 42		13 14			13 43		14 16				14 43		15 14		
Stocksfield	d					12 21						13 19					14 21						15 19		
Riding Mill	d					12 25						13 23					14 25						15 23		
Corbridge	d					12 30						13 27					14 30						15 27		
Hexham	a			11 55		12 38				12 55		13 37			13 56		14 38				14 55		15 37		
	d			11 55						12 55					13 56						14 56				
Haydon Bridge	d									13 04											15 05				
Bardon Mill	d									13 11											15 11				
Haltwhistle	d			12 16						13 18					14 17						15 18				
Brampton (Cumbria)	d									13 33											15 34				
Wetheral	d									13 42											15 42				
Carlisle 8	a			12 49						13 52					14 51						15 57				

For connections from London Kings Cross please see Table 26

Table 48

Mondays to Fridays

9 December to 16 May

Chathill and Morpeth - Newcastle - Metrocentre, Hexham and Carlisle

Network Diagram - refer to first Page of Table 44

Station			NT	NT	NT	NT	NT	NT	NT	NT	XC		NT	NT	NT	NT	NT	NT	GR	NT	XC		NT	NT	NT	GR
			◇								◇ 1								R 1		◇ 1			◇		R 1
Chathill		d																					19 10			
Alnmouth for Alnwick	26	d									17 01								17 59		19 09		19 22			19 39
Acklington		d																					19 30			
Widdrington		d																					19 37			
Pegswood		d																					19 43			
Morpeth	26	d				15 49				16 49	17 16		17 48							19 01			19 47			19 56
Cramlington		d				15 57				16 57			17 56							19 09			19 56			
Manors		d				16 11				17 11																
Newcastle 8	26	a				16 14				17 14	17 33		18 11						18 27	19 25	19 39		20 08			20 12
Sunderland	26,44	d			15 30				16 30								17 30								19 29	
Newcastle 8		d	15 24	15 44	15 54	16 15	16 22	16 44	16 54					17 16	17 24	17 44	17 54	18 24						19 25	19 54	
Dunston		d		15 49				16 49								17 49		18 29							19 59	
Metrocentre		a	15 31	15 54	16 01	16 23	16 31	16 54	17 01					17 24	17 31	17 54	18 01	18 32						19 33	20 04	
		d	15 32		16 02		16 32		17 02					17 24	17 32		18 02	18 33						19 34		
Blaydon		d			16 06										17 36			18 37								
Wylam		d			16 12		16 40		17 10					17 33	17 42		18 10	18 43						19 42		
Prudhoe		d	15 42		16 16		16 45		17 14					17 37	17 46		18 14	18 47						19 46		
Stocksfield		d			16 21		16 49		17 19						17 51		18 19	18 52						19 51		
Riding Mill		d			16 25		16 54		17 23						17 55		18 23	18 56						19 55		
Corbridge		d			16 30		16 58		17 27						18 00		18 27	19 01						19 59		
Hexham		a	15 56		16 38		17 03		17 37					17 51	18 08		18 32	19 06						20 04		
		d	15 56				17 03							17 52			18 33	19 06						20 05		
Haydon Bridge		d	16 06				17 13							18 01			18 42							20 14		
Bardon Mill		d					17 19							18 07			18 48							20 20		
Haltwhistle		d	16 20				17 26							18 14			18 55	19 27						20 27		
Brampton (Cumbria)		d					17 41							18 30			19 11							20 43		
Wetheral		d					17 50							18 39			19 20							20 52		
Carlisle 8		a	16 52				18 00							18 54			19 32	19 59						21 03		

Station			NT	NT	XC	NT	NT		GR	NT	NT
					◇ 1	◇			R 1		
Chathill		d									
Alnmouth for Alnwick	26	d			21 05				22 11		
Acklington		d									
Widdrington		d									
Pegswood		d									
Morpeth	26	d							22 28	22 45	
Cramlington		d								22 53	
Manors		d									
Newcastle 8	26	a			21 34				22 43	23 07	
Sunderland	26,44	d		20 42							
Newcastle 8		d	20 15	21 04		21 18	21 54				22 33
Dunston		d		21 09			21 59				
Metrocentre		a	20 22	21 14		21 25	22 04				22 40
		d	20 23			21 26					22 41
Blaydon		d	20 27								22 45
Wylam		d	20 33			21 34					22 51
Prudhoe		d	20 37			21 38					22 55
Stocksfield		d	20 42			21 43					23 00
Riding Mill		d	20 46			21 47					23 04
Corbridge		d	20 51			21 51					23 09
Hexham		a	20 59			21 56					23 17
		d				21 57					
Haydon Bridge		d				22 06					
Bardon Mill		d				22 12					
Haltwhistle		d				22 19					
Brampton (Cumbria)		d				22 35					
Wetheral		d				22 43					
Carlisle 8		a				22 56					

For connections from London Kings Cross please see Table 26

Table 48

Saturdays

14 December to 17 May

Chathill and Morpeth - Newcastle - Metrocentre, Hexham and Carlisle

Network Diagram - refer to first Page of Table 44

		NT	XC	GR	NT	NT		XC	NT	NT	NT	GR	XC	NT	NT	NT		NT	NT	NT	NT	NT	GR	XC	NT
			◇1	1				◇1				1	◇1										1	◇1	
Chathill	d				07 10																				
Alnmouth for Alnwick 26	d		07 07	07 27	07 22			08 00				08 59	09 09										10 59		
Acklington	d				07 37																				
Widdrington	d				07 44																				
Pegswood	d				07 50																				
Morpeth 26	d			07 43	07 54			08 14	08 49									09 49				10 49		11 19	
Cramlington	d				08 03				08 57									09 57				10 57			
Manors	d				08 16				09 11									10 11				11 11			
Newcastle 8 26	a		07 36	07 59	08 21			08 31	09 14			09 27	09 39					10 14				11 14	11 27	11 38	
Sunderland 26,44	d					07 30										09 30					10 30				
Newcastle 8	d	06 30				07 53				08 24	08 54			09 26	09 44	09 54		10 15	10 22	10 44	10 54	11 15			11 22
Dunston	d					07 58					08 59				09 49					10 49					
Metrocentre	a	06 38				08 01				08 32	09 02			09 33	09 54	10 01		10 23	10 31	10 54	11 01	11 23			11 31
	d	06 38				08 02				08 32	09 03			09 34		10 02			10 32		11 02				11 32
Blaydon	d					08 06										10 06									
Wylam	d	06 46				08 12				08 40	09 11					10 12					11 10				
Prudhoe	d	06 51				08 16				08 45	09 15			09 43		10 16			10 42		11 14				11 42
Stocksfield	d	06 55				08 21				08 49	09 20					10 21					11 19				
Riding Mill	d	07 00				08 25					09 24					10 25					11 23				
Corbridge	d	07 04				08 30					09 29					10 30					11 27				
Hexham	a	07 09				08 38				08 58	09 38			09 57		10 38			10 55		11 37				11 55
	d	07 09								08 59				09 57					10 55						11 55
Haydon Bridge	d	07 18								09 08									11 04						
Bardon Mill	d	07 25								09 14									11 11						
Haltwhistle	d	07 32								09 21				10 17					11 18						12 16
Brampton (Cumbria)	d	07 47								09 37									11 33						
Wetheral	d	07 56								09 46									11 42						
Carlisle 8	a	08 05								09 57				10 50					11 57						12 49

		NT		NT	NT	XC	NT	NT	NT	NT	GR	NT		NT	NT	NT	XC	NT	NT	NT	NT	GR		NT	NT
						◇1					1						◇1					1			
Chathill	d																								
Alnmouth for Alnwick 26	d					12 11					12 59						14 09					15 00			
Acklington	d																								
Widdrington	d																								
Pegswood	d																								
Morpeth 26	d				11 49					12 49						13 49					14 49				
Cramlington	d				11 57					12 57						13 57					14 57				
Manors	d				12 10					13 11						14 11					15 11				
Newcastle 8 26	a				12 14	12 40				13 14	13 27					14 14	14 38				15 14	15 27			
Sunderland 26,44	d			11 30					12 30						13 30					14 30					
Newcastle 8	d	11 44		11 54	12 15		12 22	12 44	12 54	13 15		13 22		13 44	13 54	14 15		14 24	14 44	14 54	15 15			15 24	15 44
Dunston	d	11 49						12 49						13 49					14 49						15 49
Metrocentre	a	11 54		12 01	12 23		12 31	12 54	13 01	13 23		13 32		13 54	14 01	14 23		14 31	14 54	15 01	15 23			15 31	15 54
	d			12 02			12 32		13 02			13 32			14 02			14 32		15 02				15 32	
Blaydon	d			12 06											14 06										
Wylam	d			12 12					13 10						14 12					15 10					
Prudhoe	d			12 16			12 42		13 14			13 43			14 16			14 42		15 14				15 42	
Stocksfield	d			12 21					13 19						14 21					15 19					
Riding Mill	d			12 25					13 23						14 25					15 23					
Corbridge	d			12 30					13 27						14 30					15 27					
Hexham	a			12 38			12 55		13 37			13 56			14 38			14 55		15 37				15 56	
	d						12 55					13 56						14 55						15 56	
Haydon Bridge	d						13 04											15 04						16 06	
Bardon Mill	d						13 11											15 11							
Haltwhistle	d						13 18					14 17						15 18						16 20	
Brampton (Cumbria)	d						13 33											15 33							
Wetheral	d						13 42											15 42							
Carlisle 8	a						13 56					14 51						15 55						16 50	

For connections from London Kings Cross please see Table 26

Table 48

Saturdays

14 December to 17 May

Chathill and Morpeth - Newcastle - Metrocentre, Hexham and Carlisle

Network Diagram - refer to first Page of Table 44

Station		NT	NT	NT	NT	NT	NT	XC	NT	NT	NT	NT	NT	NT	GR	NT	NT	XC	NT	NT	GR	NT
								◇1							R 1			◇1			R 1	
Chathill	d																18 36					
Alnmouth for Alnwick 26	d							17 03							17 59		18 48	19 11			20 08	
Acklington	d																18 56					
Widdrington	d																19 03					
Pegswood	d																19 09					
Morpeth 26	d		15 49				16 49	17 17	17 52							18 50	19 13				20 25	21 15
Cramlington	d		15 57				16 57		18 00							18 58	19 22					21 23
Manors	d		16 10				17 11															
Newcastle 8 26 ⛴	a		16 14				17 14	17 34	18 15						18 27	19 13	19 35	19 40			20 41	21 39
Sunderland 26,44 ⛴	d	15 30				16 30							17 30							19 28		
Newcastle 8 ⛴	d	15 54	16 15	16 22	16 44	16 54				17 16	17 24	17 44	17 54	18 24					19 25	19 54		
Dunston	d				16 50							17 49		18 29						19 59		
Metrocentre	a	16 01	16 23	16 31	16 55	17 01				17 24	17 31	17 54	18 01	18 32					19 33	20 04		
	d	16 02		16 32		17 02				17 24	17 32		18 02	18 33					19 34			
Blaydon	d	16 06									17 36			18 37								
Wylam	d	16 12		16 40		17 10				17 33	17 42		18 10	18 43					19 42			
Prudhoe	d	16 16		16 45		17 14				17 37	17 46		18 14	18 47					19 46			
Stocksfield	d	16 21		16 49		17 19					17 51		18 19	18 52					19 51			
Riding Mill	d	16 25		16 54		17 23					17 55		18 23	18 56					19 55			
Corbridge	d	16 30		16 58		17 27					18 00		18 27	19 01					19 59			
Hexham	a	16 38		17 03		17 37				17 51	18 08		18 32	19 06					20 04			
	d			17 03						17 52			18 33	19 06					20 05			
Haydon Bridge	d			17 13						18 01			18 42						20 14			
Bardon Mill	d			17 19						18 07			18 48						20 20			
Haltwhistle	d			17 26						18 14			18 55	19 27					20 27			
Brampton (Cumbria)	d			17 41						18 30			19 11						20 43			
Wetheral	d			17 50						18 39			19 20						20 52			
Carlisle 8	a			18 00						18 54			19 32	19 59					21 03			

Station		NT	NT	NT	NT
Chathill	d				
Alnmouth for Alnwick 26	d				
Acklington	d				
Widdrington	d				
Pegswood	d				
Morpeth 26	d				
Cramlington	d				
Manors	d				
Newcastle 8 26 ⛴	a				
Sunderland 26,44 ⛴	d				
Newcastle 8 ⛴	d	20 15	20 30	21 18	21 53
Dunston	d		20 35		21 58
Metrocentre	a	20 22	20 40	21 25	22 02
	d	20 23		21 26	22 02
Blaydon	d	20 27			22 06
Wylam	d	20 33		21 34	22 12
Prudhoe	d	20 37		21 38	22a18
Stocksfield	d	20 42		21 43	
Riding Mill	d	20 46		21 47	
Corbridge	d	20 51		21 51	
Hexham	a	20 59		21 56	
	d			21 57	
Haydon Bridge	d			22 06	
Bardon Mill	d			22 12	
Haltwhistle	d			22 19	
Brampton (Cumbria)	d			22 35	
Wetheral	d			22 43	
Carlisle 8	a			22 56	

For connections from London Kings Cross please see Table 26

Table 48

Sundays

8 December to 11 May

Chathill and Morpeth - Newcastle - Metrocentre, Hexham and Carlisle

Network Diagram - refer to first Page of Table 44

		NT	NT	NT	NT	NT		GR	XC	NT	NT	NT	XC	NT	NT	NT		GR	NT	NT	NT	GR	XC	NT	NT
								R 1	◇1				◇1					R 1				R 1	◇1		
						A										A									
Chathill	d																								
Alnmouth for Alnwick 26	d							10 59	11 05				12 08					12 59					14 08		
Acklington	d																								
Widdrington	d																								
Pegswood	d																								
Morpeth 26	d								11 19													13 33			
Cramlington	d																								
Manors	d																								
Newcastle 8 26	a							11 27	11 36				12 37					13 27				13 49	14 37		
Sunderland 26,44	d		09 28			10 28						11 28				12 28					13 28				
Newcastle 8	d	09 10	09 50	10 10	10 30	10 50				11 10	11 30	11 50		12 10	12 30	12 50			13 10	13 30	13 51			14 10	14 30
Dunston	d				10 35						11 35				12 35					13 35					14 35
Metrocentre	a	09 17	09 59	10 17	10 40	10 59				11 17	11 40	11 59		12 17	12 40	12 59			13 17	13 40	13 59			14 17	14 40
	d	09 18		10 18						11 18				12 18					13 18					14 18	
Blaydon	d			10 22										12 22										14 22	
Wylam	d	09 26		10 28						11 26				12 28					13 26					14 28	
Prudhoe	d	09 30		10 32						11 30				12 32					13 30					14 32	
Stocksfield	d	09 35		10 37						11 35				12 37					13 35					14 37	
Riding Mill	d	09 39		10 41						11 39				12 41					13 39					14 41	
Corbridge	d	09 43		10 46						11 43				12 46					13 43					14 46	
Hexham	a	09 48		10 51						11 48				12 51					13 48					14 51	
	d	09 49		10 51						11 49				12 51					13 49					14 51	
Haydon Bridge	d	09 58		11 00										13 00											
Bardon Mill	d	10 04		11 07										13 07											
Haltwhistle	d	10 11		11 14						12 10				13 14					14 10					15 12	
Brampton (Cumbria)	d	10 27		11 29										13 29											
Wetheral	d	10 35		11 38										13 38											
Carlisle 8	a	10 44		11 49						12 40				13 48					14 40					15 44	

		NT		GR	NT	NT	NT	NT	NT	NT	GR	XC		NT	NT	NT	NT	NT	NT	GR	NT	GR		GR	
				R 1							R 1	◇1								R 1		R 1		R 1	
Chathill	d																								
Alnmouth for Alnwick 26	d			15 00							16 59	17 05								18 59		21 11		22 09	
Acklington	d																								
Widdrington	d																								
Pegswood	d																								
Morpeth 26	d											17 19										21 27			
Cramlington	d																								
Manors	d																								
Newcastle 8 26	a			15 27							17 27	17 36								19 27		21 43		22 39	
Sunderland 26,44	d	14 28					15 28			16 28						17 28									
Newcastle 8	d	14 50			15 10	15 30	15 50	16 10	16 30	16 50				17 10	17 30	17 50	18 10	18 30	18 54		20 15				
Dunston	d					15 35			16 35						17 35			18 35			20 20				
Metrocentre	a	14 59			15 17	15 40	15 59	16 18	16 40	16 59				17 17	17 40	17 59	18 17	18 40	19 03		20 23				
	d				15 18			16 18						17 18			18 18				20 24				
Blaydon	d							16 22									18 22				20 28				
Wylam	d				15 26			16 29						17 26			18 28				20 34				
Prudhoe	d				15 30			16 33						17 30			18 32				20 38				
Stocksfield	d				15 35			16 38						17 35			18 37				20 43				
Riding Mill	d				15 39			16 42						17 39			18 41				20 47				
Corbridge	d				15 43			16 46						17 43			18 46				20 52				
Hexham	a				15 48			16 51						17 48			18 51				20 57				
	d				15 49			16 52						17 49			18 51				20 57				
Haydon Bridge	d				15 58												19 00				21 06				
Bardon Mill	d				16 04												19 07				21 13				
Haltwhistle	d				16 11			17 13						18 10			19 14				21 20				
Brampton (Cumbria)	d				16 27												19 29				21 35				
Wetheral	d				16 35												19 38				21 44				
Carlisle 8	a				16 45			17 46						18 40			19 49				21 55				

A 8 December

For connections from London Kings Cross please see Table 26

Table 48R

Mondays to Fridays

9 December to 16 May

Carlisle, Hexham and Metrocentre - Newcastle - Morpeth and Chathill

Network Diagram - refer to first Page of Table 44

Miles	Miles			NT	NT	NT	GR	XC	GR	NT		SR	NT	GR	NT	SR	NT	XC	NT	NT		NT	SR	GR	NT
							R 1	◇1	R 1					R 1				◇1						R 1	
0	—	**Carlisle** 8	d			06 25						07 17				08 28							09 37		
4¼	—	Wetheral	d			06 33						07 25				08 36									
11	—	Brampton (Cumbria)	d			06 43						07 35				08 46									
23¼	—	Haltwhistle	d			06 57						07 49				09 00							10 08		
28	—	Bardon Mill	d			07 05						07 57				09 08									
31¾	—	Haydon Bridge	d			07 10						08 02				09 13									
39½	—	**Hexham**	a			07 19						08 11				09 22							10 26		
—	—		d		06 12	07 19				07 42		08 12			08 45	09 22				09 43			10 26		
42½	—	Corbridge	d		06 17	07 24				07 47		08 16			08 50					09 47					
45	—	Riding Mill	d		06 21	07 28				07 51		08 21			08 54					09 52					
47¼	—	Stocksfield	d		06 25	07 32				07 55		08 25			08 58					09 56					
49¾	—	Prudhoe	d		06 30	07 37				08 00		08 29			09 03	09 34				10 00			10 38		
52	—	Wylam	d		06 34	07 41				08 04		08 34			09 07					10 05					
56¼	—	Blaydon	d		06 40					08 10		08 40								10 11					
58¼	—	**Metrocentre**	a		06 45	07 50				08 15		08 45			09 16	09 46				10 16			10 50		
—	—		d		06 45	07 50				08 15		08 45			09 16	09 46			10 02	10 16		10 31	10 51		11 02
59½	1¼	Dunston	d			07 53						08 48			09 19							10 34			
61¾	3½	**Newcastle** 8	a		06 55	08 04				08 27		08 58			09 28	09 59			10 10	10 27		10 41	11 07		11 11
—	—	Sunderland 26,44	a		07 18					08 50					09 49					10 49					
—	—	**Newcastle** 8 26	d	05 55			06 25	07 35	07 42				07 58	08 42			09 15	09 35	10 15					10 42	11 15
—	4	Manors	d														09 17		10 17						11 17
—	13¼	Cramlington	d	06 07									08 07				09 28		10 28						11 28
—	20	**Morpeth** 26	d	06 15			06 40	07a47					08a19	08a55			09a35		10a36						11a36
—	22	Pegswood	d																						
—	26¾	Widdrington	d																						
—	32	Acklington	d																						
—	38¼	Alnmouth for Alnwick 26	d	06 32			06a54		08a07									09a58						11a07	
—	49½	**Chathill**	a	06 46																					

		NT	NT	NT	NT	NT		NT	NT	GR	NT	NT	NT	NT	XC	NT		NT	NT	NT	XC	GR	NT	NT	NT
				◇					◇	R 1				◇	◇1					◇	◇1	R 1			
Carlisle 8	d			10 28					11 34					12 28						13 30					
Wetheral	d			10 36										12 36						13 38					
Brampton (Cumbria)	d			10 46										12 46						13 48					
Haltwhistle	d			11 00					12 03					13 00						14 02					
Bardon Mill	d			11 08										13 08						14 10					
Haydon Bridge	d			11 13										13 13						14 15					
Hexham	a			11 22					12 21					13 22						14 24					
	d	10 45		11 22		11 43			12 22			12 45		13 22				13 43		14 24				14 45	
Corbridge	d	10 50				11 48						12 50						13 48						14 50	
Riding Mill	d	10 54				11 52						12 54						13 52						14 54	
Stocksfield	d	10 58				11 56						12 58						13 56						14 58	
Prudhoe	d	11 03		11 34		12 01			12 33			13 03		13 34				14 01		14 36				15 03	
Wylam	d	11 07				12 05						13 07						14 05						15 07	
Blaydon	d					12 11												14 11							
Metrocentre	a	11 16		11 45		12 16			12 46			13 16		13 45				14 16		14 47				15 16	
	d	11 16	11 31	11 46	12 02	12 16		12 31	12 46		13 02	13 16	13 31	13 46		14 02		14 16	14 31	14 48			15 02	15 16	15 31
Dunston	d		11 34					12 34					13 34						14 34						15 34
Newcastle 8	a	11 27	11 41	11 59	12 11	12 28		12 41	12 58		13 12	13 27	13 41	13 59		14 11		14 28	14 41	15 01			15 12	15 28	15 41
Sunderland 26,44	a	11 49				12 49						13 49						14 50						15 49	
Newcastle 8 26	d				12 15					12 45	13 15				13 38	14 15					14 36	14 44	15 15		
Manors	d				12 17						13 17					14 17							15 17		
Cramlington	d				12 28						13 28					14 28							15 28		
Morpeth 26	d				12a36						13a36					14a36					14a48		15a36		
Pegswood	d																								
Widdrington	d																								
Acklington	d																								
Alnmouth for Alnwick 26	d									13a10					14a01							15a09			
Chathill	a																								

For connections to London Kings Cross please see Table 26

Table 48R

Mondays to Fridays

9 December to 16 May

Carlisle, Hexham and Metrocentre - Newcastle - Morpeth and Chathill

Network Diagram - refer to first Page of Table 44

		SR	XC	NT	NT	NT	NT	XC		NT	NT	XC	NT	NT	NT	NT	NT	NT		SR	NT	GR	XC	NT	NT
			◇1				◇	◇1				◇1		◇			◇					R 1	◇1	◇	
																A									
Carlisle 8	d	14 36					15 28							16 28			17 28			18 37				19 41	
Wetheral	d													16 36			17 36			18 45					
Brampton (Cumbria)	d													16 46			17 46			18 54					
Haltwhistle	d	15 05					15 56							17 00			18 01			19 09				20 10	
Bardon Mill	d													17 08			18 08			19 16					
Haydon Bridge	d													17 13			18 13			19 21					
Hexham	a	15 23					16 14							17 22			18 22			19 30				20 28	
	d	15 23			15 43		16 15				16 45			17 22		17 43	18 23	18 43		19 31				20 28	
Corbridge	d				15 48						16 50					17 48	18 27	18 48		19 35				20 33	
Riding Mill	d				15 52						16 54					17 52	18 32	18 52		19 40				20 37	
Stocksfield	d				15 56						16 58					17 56	18 36	18 56		19 44				20 41	
Prudhoe	d	15 34			16 01		16 26				17 03			17 34		18 01	18 40	19 01		19 48				20 46	
Wylam	d				16 05											18 05	18 45	19 06		19 53				20 50	
Blaydon	d				16 11											18 11		19 11							
Metrocentre	a	15 45			16 16		16 39				17 16			17 45		18 16	18 56	19 16		20 01				20 59	
	d	15 46		16 02	16 16	16 31	16 39			17 02	17 16		17 27	17 46	18 06	18 16	18 56	19 16		20 02	20 31			20 59	21 22
Dunston	d					16 34							17 30		18 09			19 19			20 34				21 25
Newcastle 8 ⛴	a	15 57		16 11	16 27	16 41	16 49			17 11	17 28		17 36	17 58	18 16	18 26	19 09	19 27		20 16	20 41			21 11	21 32
Sunderland 26,44 ⛴	a				16 49		17 14				17 50					18 49		19 50							
Newcastle 8 26 ⛴	d		15 37	16 15				16 37		17 15		17 37	17 38		18 25							18 46	19 38		
Manors	d			16 17						17 17			17 41		18 27										
Cramlington	d			16 28						17 28			17 52		18 38										
Morpeth 26	d			16a36						17a36			18 00		18a46										
Pegswood	d												18 12												
Widdrington	d												18 18												
Acklington	d												18 25												
Alnmouth for Alnwick 26	d		16a00					17a00				18a00	18 34									19a11	20a03		
Chathill	a												18 46												

		GR	XC	XC		XC	GR	NT	NT	NT	GR FO	NT
		R 1	◇1	◇1		◇1	R 1			◇	R 1	
Carlisle 8	d									21 28		
Wetheral	d									21 35		
Brampton (Cumbria)	d									21 45		
Haltwhistle	d									22 00		
Bardon Mill	d									22 07		
Haydon Bridge	d									22 12		
Hexham	a									22 21		
	d							21 12		22 22		23 21
Corbridge	d							21 17		22 26		23 26
Riding Mill	d							21 21		22 31		23 30
Stocksfield	d							21 25		22 35		23 34
Prudhoe	d							21 30		22 39		23 39
Wylam	d							21 34		22 44		23 43
Blaydon	d							21 40				
Metrocentre	a							21 45		22 52		23 52
	d							21 45	22 15	22 53		23 52
Dunston	d								22 18			
Newcastle 8 ⛴	a							21 56	22 26	23 05		00 03
Sunderland 26,44 ⛴	a											
Newcastle 8 26 ⛴	d	19 45	20 03	20 35		21 35	21 41	22 00			22 42	
Manors	d											
Cramlington	d							22 12				
Morpeth 26	d	19a58		20a49			21 57	22a21			22 57	
Pegswood	d											
Widdrington	d											
Acklington	d											
Alnmouth for Alnwick 26	d		20a26			21a58	22a10				23a11	
Chathill	a											

A from 24 March

For connections to London Kings Cross please see Table 26

Table 48R

Saturdays

14 December to 17 May

Carlisle, Hexham and Metrocentre - Newcastle - Morpeth and Chathill

Network Diagram - refer to first Page of Table 44

Station		NT	NT	NT	GR	XC	NT	SR	GR	NT	GR	NT	NT	NT	XC	NT	NT	NT	SR	GR	NT	NT	NT
					1	◇1			1		1				◇1					1			
Carlisle (8)	d			06 25				07 17					08 28						09 37				
Wetheral	d			06 33				07 25					08 36										
Brampton (Cumbria)	d			06 43				07 35					08 46										
Haltwhistle	d			06 57				07 49					09 00						10 08				
Bardon Mill	d			07 05				07 57					09 08										
Haydon Bridge	d			07 10				08 02					09 13										
Hexham	a			07 19				08 11					09 22						10 26				
	d		06 12	07 19			07 42	08 12				08 45	09 22				09 43		10 26			10 45	
Corbridge	d		06 17	07 24			07 47	08 16				08 50					09 48					10 50	
Riding Mill	d		06 21	07 28			07 51	08 21				08 54					09 52					10 54	
Stocksfield	d		06 25	07 32			07 55	08 25				08 58					09 56					10 58	
Prudhoe	d		06 30	07 37			08 00	08 29				09 03	09 34				10 01		10 38			11 03	
Wylam	d		06 34	07 41			08 04	08 34				09 07					10 05					11 07	
Blaydon	d		06 40				08 10	08 40									10 11						
Metrocentre	a		06 45	07 50			08 15	08 45				09 16	09 46				10 16		10 50			11 16	
	d		06 45	07 50			08 15	08 45				09 16	09 46			10 02	10 16	10 31	10 51		11 02	11 16	11 31
Dunston	d			07 53				08 48				09 19						10 34					11 34
Newcastle (8)	a		06 55	08 04			08 27	08 58				09 28	09 59			10 10	10 27	10 41	11 07		11 11	11 27	11 41
Sunderland 26,44	a		07 18				08 49					09 49					10 49					11 49	
Newcastle (8) 26	d	05 55			06 30	07 38			07 43	07 58	08 42			09 15	09 35	10 15				10 40	11 15		
Manors	d													09 17		10 17					11 17		
Cramlington	d	06 07								08 07				09 28		10 28					11 28		
Morpeth 26	d	06 15			06 44	07a50				08a19	08a55			09a36		10a36					11a36		
Pegswood	d																						
Widdrington	d																						
Acklington	d																						
Alnmouth for Alnwick 26	d	06 35			06a57				08a08						09a58					11a05			
Chathill	a	06 50																					

Station		NT	NT	NT	NT	NT	GR	NT	NT	NT	NT	XC	NT	NT	NT	NT	XC	GR	NT	NT	NT	SR
							1					◇1					◇1	1				
Carlisle (8)	d	10 28				11 34					12 28					13 30						14 36
Wetheral	d	10 36									12 36					13 38						
Brampton (Cumbria)	d	10 46									12 46					13 48						
Haltwhistle	d	11 00				12 03					13 00					14 02						15 05
Bardon Mill	d	11 08									13 08					14 10						
Haydon Bridge	d	11 13									13 13					14 15						
Hexham	a	11 22				12 21					13 22					14 24						15 23
	d	11 22		11 43		12 22			12 45		13 22			13 43		14 24				14 45		15 23
Corbridge	d			11 48					12 50					13 48						14 50		
Riding Mill	d			11 52					12 54					13 52						14 54		
Stocksfield	d			11 56					12 58					13 56						14 58		
Prudhoe	d	11 34		12 01		12 33			13 03		13 34			14 01		14 36				15 03		15 34
Wylam	d			12 05					13 07					14 05						15 07		
Blaydon	d			12 11										14 11								
Metrocentre	a	11 46		12 16		12 45			13 16		13 45			14 16		14 47				15 16		15 45
	d	11 46	12 02	12 16	12 31	12 45		13 02	13 16	13 31	13 46		14 02	14 16	14 31	14 48			15 02	15 16	15 31	15 46
Dunston	d				12 34					13 34					14 34						15 34	
Newcastle (8)	a	11 59	12 11	12 28	12 41	12 58		13 12	13 27	13 41	13 59		14 11	14 28	14 41	15 01			15 12	15 28	15 41	15 57
Sunderland 26,44	a			12 49					13 49					14 49						15 49		
Newcastle (8) 26	d		12 15				12 41	13 15				13 35	14 15				14 34	14 40	15 15			
Manors	d		12 17					13 17					14 17						15 17			
Cramlington	d		12 28					13 28					14 28						15 28			
Morpeth 26	d		12a36					13a36					14a36				14a46		15a36			
Pegswood	d																					
Widdrington	d																					
Acklington	d																					
Alnmouth for Alnwick 26	d						13a06					13a58						15a05				
Chathill	a																					

For connections to London Kings Cross please see Table 26

Table 48R

Saturdays

14 December to 17 May

Carlisle, Hexham and Metrocentre - Newcastle - Morpeth and Chathill

Network Diagram - refer to first Page of Table 44

		XC	NT	NT	NT	NT	XC	GR	NT	NT	NT	NT	XC	NT	NT	NT	GR	NT	SR	NT	XC
		◇1					◇1	R 1					◇1				R 1				◇1
Carlisle 8	d					15 28						16 28				17 28			18 37		
Wetheral	d											16 36				17 36			18 45		
Brampton (Cumbria)	d											16 46				17 46			18 54		
Haltwhistle	d					15 56						17 00				18 01			19 09		
Bardon Mill	d											17 08				18 08			19 16		
Haydon Bridge	d											17 13				18 13			19 21		
Hexham	a					16 14						17 22				18 22			19 30		
	d			15 43		16 15					16 45	17 22			17 43	18 23		18 44	19 31		
Corbridge	d			15 48							16 50				17 48	18 27		18 49	19 35		
Riding Mill	d			15 52							16 54				17 52	18 32		18 53	19 40		
Stocksfield	d			15 56							16 58				17 56	18 36		18 57	19 44		
Prudhoe	d			16 01		16 26					17 03	17 34			18 01	18 40		19 02	19 48		
Wylam	d			16 05							17 07				18 05	18 45		19 06	19 53		
Blaydon	d			16 11											18 11			19 12			
Metrocentre	a			16 16		16 39					17 16	17 45			18 16	18 53		19 17	20 01		
	d		16 02	16 16	16 31	16 39			16 50	17 07	17 16	17 46		18 06	18 16	18 54		19 17	20 02	20 15	
Dunston	d				16 34					17 10				18 09				19 20		20 18	
Newcastle 8	a		16 11	16 26	16 41	16 49			16 57	17 17	17 28	17 59		18 16	18 26	19 07		19 28	20 16	20 25	
Sunderland 26,44	a			16 49		17 14					17 50				18 49			19 50			
Newcastle 8 26	d	15 35	16 15				16 34	16 40	17 00	17 22			17 35	18 19			18 40				19 35
Manors	d		16 17						17 03	17 24				18 21							
Cramlington	d		16 28						17 14	17 35				18 32							
Morpeth 26	d		16a36						17 22	17a43				18a40							
Pegswood	d								17 25												
Widdrington	d								17 31												
Acklington	d								17 38												
Alnmouth for Alnwick 26	d	15a58					16a57	17a05	17 46				17a59				19a05				20a00
Chathill	a								17 59												

		GR	NT	XC	NT	NT	GR	NT	XC	NT	NT
		R 1		◇1			R 1		◇1		
Carlisle 8	d					19 41					21 28
Wetheral	d										21 35
Brampton (Cumbria)	d										21 45
Haltwhistle	d					20 10					22 00
Bardon Mill	d										22 07
Haydon Bridge	d										22 12
Hexham	a					20 28					22 21
	d					20 28		21 12			22 22
Corbridge	d					20 33		21 17			22 26
Riding Mill	d					20 37		21 21			22 31
Stocksfield	d					20 41		21 25			22 35
Prudhoe	d					20 46		21 30			22 39
Wylam	d					20 50		21 34			22 44
Blaydon	d							21 40			
Metrocentre	a					20 59		21 45			22 52
	d				20 47	20 59		21 45		22 33	22 53
Dunston	d							21 48		22 36	
Newcastle 8	a				20 56	21 11		21 58		22 44	23 05
Sunderland 26,44	a				21 20						
Newcastle 8 26	d	19 45	20 20	20 35			20 55		21 38		
Manors	d										
Cramlington	d		20 32								
Morpeth 26	d	19a58	20a41	20a47			21 10				
Pegswood	d										
Widdrington	d										
Acklington	d										
Alnmouth for Alnwick 26	d						21a24		22a01		
Chathill	a										

For connections to London Kings Cross please see Table 26

Table 48R

Sundays

8 December to 11 May

Carlisle, Hexham and Metrocentre - Newcastle - Morpeth and Chathill

Network Diagram - refer to first Page of Table 44

		XC	NT	NT	GR	NT		NT	NT	NT	NT	NT	GR	NT	NT	NT		XC	NT	NT	NT	GR	XC	GR	NT
					R								R									R		R	
		◇1			1								1					◇1				1	◇1	1	
Carlisle 8	d			09 05					10 05			11 12				12 05					13 12				
Wetheral	d			09 12					10 12							12 12									
Brampton (Cumbria)	d			09 22					10 22							12 22									
Haltwhistle	d			09 37					10 36			11 40				12 36					13 40				
Bardon Mill	d			09 44					10 44							12 44									
Haydon Bridge	d			09 49					10 49							12 49									
Hexham	a			09 58					10 58			11 58				12 58					13 58				
	d			09 59					10 59			11 59				12 59					13 59				
Corbridge	d			10 03					11 03			12 03				13 03					14 03				
Riding Mill	d			10 08					11 08			12 08				13 08					14 08				
Stocksfield	d			10 12					11 12			12 12				13 12					14 12				
Prudhoe	d			10 16					11 16			12 16				13 16					14 16				
Wylam	d			10 21					11 21			12 21				13 21					14 21				
Blaydon	d			10 27								12 27									14 27				
Metrocentre	a			10 31					11 29			12 32				13 29					14 31				
	d		10 10	10 32		10 48		11 10	11 30	11 50	12 10	12 33		12 48	13 15	13 30			13 50	14 10	14 32				14 48
Dunston	d		10 13					11 13			12 13				13 18					14 13					
Newcastle 8	a		10 20	10 45		10 56		11 20	11 42	11 58	12 20	12 45		12 56	13 25	13 42			13 58	14 20	14 45				14 56
Sunderland 26,44	a					11 21				12 21				13 22					14 22						15 21
Newcastle 8 26	d	09 45			10 12								12 43					13 28				14 25	14 31	14 43	
Manors	d																								
Cramlington	d																								
Morpeth 26	d	09 58			10 28																	14a38	14a44		
Pegswood	d																								
Widdrington	d																								
Acklington	d																								
Alnmouth for Alnwick 26	d	10a11			10a42								13a08					13a51						15a08	
Chathill	a																								

		NT		NT	XC	NT	NT	NT	XC	GR	NT	NT		NT	XC	NT	NT	NT	GR	GR	NT	NT		NT	XC
										R									R	R					
					◇1				◇1	1					◇1				1	1					◇1
																			A	B					
Carlisle 8	d			14 12				15 05						16 12				17 12						18 05	
Wetheral	d							15 12																18 12	
Brampton (Cumbria)	d							15 22																18 22	
Haltwhistle	d			14 40				15 36						16 40				17 40						18 36	
Bardon Mill	d							15 44																18 44	
Haydon Bridge	d							15 49																18 49	
Hexham	a			14 58				15 58						16 58				17 58						18 58	
	d			14 59				15 59						16 59				17 59						18 59	
Corbridge	d			15 03				16 03						17 03				18 03						19 03	
Riding Mill	d			15 08				16 08						17 08				18 08						19 08	
Stocksfield	d			15 12				16 12						17 12				18 12						19 12	
Prudhoe	d			15 16				16 16						17 16				18 16						19 16	
Wylam	d			15 21				16 21						17 21				18 21						19 21	
Blaydon	d							16 27										18 27							
Metrocentre	a			15 29				16 32						17 29				18 31						19 29	
	d	15 10		15 30		15 50	16 10	16 33			16 48	17 10		17 30		17 50	18 10	18 32			18 48	19 10		19 30	
Dunston	d	15 13					16 13					17 13					18 13					19 13			
Newcastle 8	a	15 20		15 42		15 58	16 20	16 45			16 56	17 20		17 42		17 58	18 20	18 45			18 56	19 20		19 42	
Sunderland 26,44	a					16 22					17 20					18 21					19 22				
Newcastle 8 26	d				15 28				16 28	16 38					17 28				18 41	18 45					19 28
Manors	d																								
Cramlington	d																								
Morpeth 26	d																								
Pegswood	d																								
Widdrington	d																								
Acklington	d																								
Alnmouth for Alnwick 26	d				15a52				16a51	17a03					17a51				19a06	19a10					19a51
Chathill	a																								

A until 29 December, from 30 March   **B** from 5 January until 23 March

For connections to London Kings Cross please see Table 26

Table 48R

Sundays

8 December to 11 May

Carlisle, Hexham and Metrocentre - Newcastle - Morpeth and Chathill

Network Diagram - refer to first Page of Table 44

		GR	NT	XC	XC	GR	XC	GR
		R 1		◇1	◇1	R 1	◇1	R 1
				A	B			
Carlisle 8	d		20 15					
Wetheral	d							
Brampton (Cumbria)	d							
Haltwhistle	d		20 43					
Bardon Mill	d							
Haydon Bridge	d							
Hexham	a		21 01					
	d		21 02					
Corbridge	d		21 06					
Riding Mill	d		21 11					
Stocksfield	d		21 15					
Prudhoe	d		21 19					
Wylam	d		21 24					
Blaydon	d		21 30					
Metrocentre	a		21 34					
	d		21 35					
Dunston	d		21 38					
Newcastle 8	a		21 48					
Sunderland 26,44	a							
Newcastle 8 26	d	19 43		20 34	20 34	20 41	21 34	21 53
Manors	d							
Cramlington	d							
Morpeth 26	d	19a56		20a47	20a47	20 56		22 09
Pegswood	d							
Widdrington	d							
Acklington	d							
Alnmouth for Alnwick 26	d					21a10	21a59	22a23
Chathill	a							

A until 23 March

B from 30 March

For connections to London Kings Cross please see Table 26

Route Diagram for Table 49

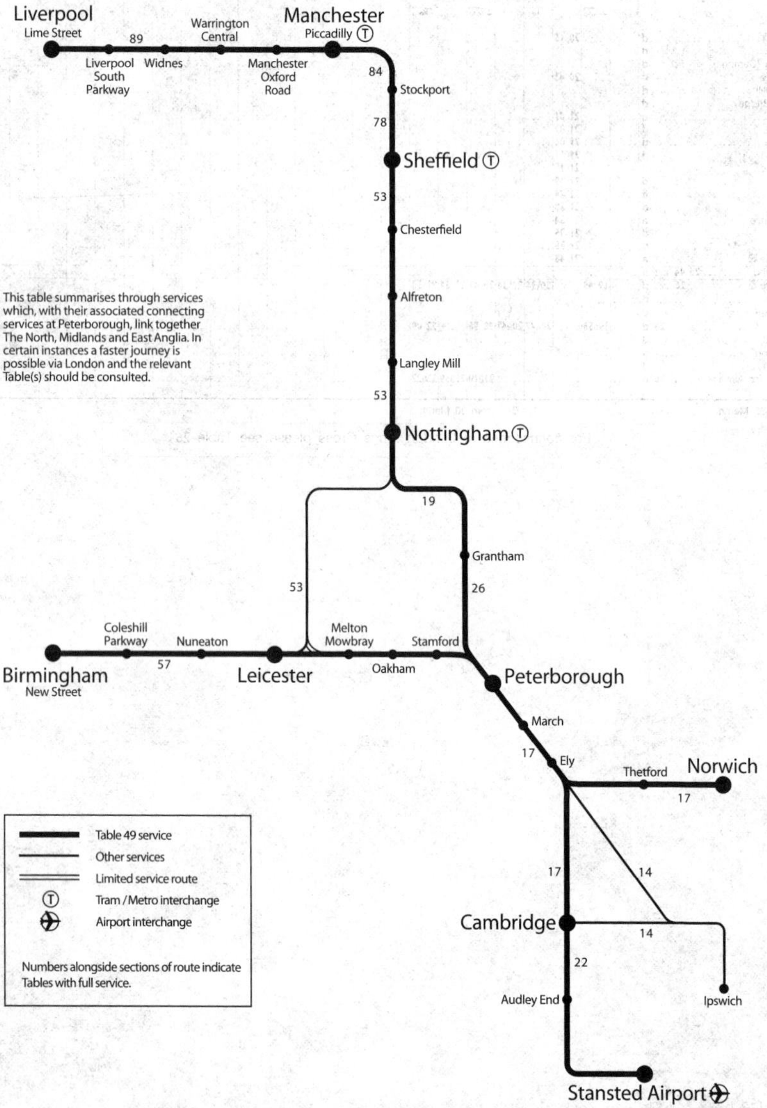

This table summarises through services which, with their associated connecting services at Peterborough, link together The North, Midlands and East Anglia. In certain instances a faster journey is possible via London and the relevant Table(s) should be consulted.

TOCs operating on this network - East Midlands (EM), Cross Country (XC)

Table 49

Mondays to Fridays

9 December to 16 May

Stansted Airport - East Anglia - East Midlands - Birmingham and North West England

Route Diagram - refer to first Page of Table 49

Miles	Miles	Miles	Miles			XC	XC	EM	EM	EM	EM	XC	EM	XC	EM	EM	XC	EM	XC	EM	XC	EM	XC
						◇1	◇1	◇	◇	◇	◇	◇1	◇	◇1	◇	◇	◇1	◇	◇1	◇	◇1	◇	◇1
														A		B	A		A		A		A
														🚲		🚲	🚲		🚲		🚲		🚲
0	0	—	0	**Norwich**	d						05 50		06 51		07 57			08 57		09 57		10 57	
30½	30½	—	30½	Thetford	d						06 23		07 20		08 24			09 24		10 24		11 24	
—	—	0	—	**Stansted Airport** ✈	d		05 16					06 12		07 21			08 21		09 21		10 27		11 27
—	—	10¾	—	Audley End	d		05 37					06 24		07 37			08 38		09 39		10 40		11 40
—	—	24¾	—	**Cambridge**	d	05 15	05 55					06 55		08 01			09 01		10 01		11 01		12 01
53¾	53¾	39½	53¾	Ely 6	d	05 30	06 10				06 51	07 12	07 45	08 15	08 48		09 15	09 46	10 15	10 53	11 15	11 48	12 15
69	69	—	69	March	d	05 46	06 28				07 07	07 29	08 01	08 32	09 07		09 32		10 32		11 32		12 32
82¾	82¾	—	82¾	**Peterborough 8**	a	06 08	06 50				07 25	07 50	08 24	08 50	09 25		09 50	10 26	10 50	11 27	11 50	12 24	12 50
—	—	—	—		d	06 10	06 52				07 27	07 52	08 26	08 52	09 27		09 52	10 28	10 52	11 28	11 52	12 26	12 52
95¼	—	—	—	Stamford	d	06 23	07 05					08 05		09 05			10 05		11 05		12 05		13 05
108¾	—	—	—	Oakham	d	06 37	07 19					08 19		09 19		09 48	10 19		11 19		12 19		13 19
120¼	—	—	—	Melton Mowbray	d	06 48	07 30					08 30		09 30		10 01	10 30		11 30		12 30		13 30
135¼	—	—	—	**Leicester**	d	07 10	07 51					08 48		09 48			10 48		11 48		12 48		13 48
154	—	—	—	Nuneaton	a	07 28	08 16					09 07		10 06			11 06		12 06		13 06		14 06
165½	—	—	—	Coleshill Parkway	a	07 44	08 32					09 25		10 25			11 25		12 25		13 25		14 25
175	—	—	—	**Birmingham New Street 12**	a	07 58	08 45					09 38		10 38			11 38		12 38		13 38		14 38
—	112	—	—	Grantham 7	d						07 58		08 55		09 58			11 00		12 00		12 59	
—	—	—	—	East Midlands Parkway	d											10a30							
—	134¾	—	152½	**Nottingham 8** 🚊	a						08 40		09 26		10 35			11 34		12 35		13 36	
—	—	—	—		d			05 21	06 39	07 47	08 47		09 47		10 47			11 47		12 47		13 47	
—	146¾	—	164½	Langley Mill	d																		
—	153	—	170¾	Alfreton	d				07 00	08 08	09 08		10 08		11 08			12 08		13 08		14 08	
—	162¾	—	180¾	Chesterfield	d			05 49	07 10	08 20	09 20		10 20		11 20			12 20		13 20		14 20	
—	174¾	—	193	**Sheffield 7** 🚊	a			06 15	07 28	08 37	09 37		10 37		11 37			12 37		13 39		14 37	
—	—	—	—		d			06 20	07 32	08 41	09 41		10 41		11 41			12 40		13 43		14 40	
—	212	—	229¾	Stockport	a			07 22	08 24	09 25	10 25		11 25		12 24			13 25		14 25		15 25	
—	218	—	232¾	**Manchester Piccadilly 10** 🚊	a			07 34	08 36	09 36	10 36		11 36		12 36			13 36		14 36		15 36	
—	218½	—	236¼	Manchester Oxford Road	a			07 37	08 40	09 40	10 40		11 40		12 40			13 40		14 40		15 40	
—	234¼	—	252	Warrington Central	a			07 53	08 57	09 57	10 57		11 57		12 57			13 57		14 57		15 57	
—	240½	—	258¼	Widnes	a			08 01	09 05	10 05	11 05		12 05		13 05			14 05		15 05		16 05	
—	247¼	—	265	Liverpool South Parkway 7 ✈	a			08 18	09 15	10 15	11 15		12 15		13 15			14 15		15 15		16 15	
—	252¾	—	270½	**Liverpool Lime Street 10**	a			08 31	09 31	10 31	11 31		12 31		13 31			14 31		15 31		16 31	

		EM	XC	EM	XC	EM	XC	EM	XC	EM	XC	EM	XC	EM	EM	XC	EM	XC	EM	XC
		◇	◇1	◇	◇1	◇	◇1	◇	◇1	◇	◇1	◇	◇1	◇	◇1	◇1	◇	◇1		◇1
			C		C		C		A		A		A		D				E	
			🚲		🚲		🚲		🚲		🚲		🚲		🚲					
Norwich	d	11 57		12 57		13 57		14 57		15 48		16 57		17 54			18 57			
Thetford	d	12 24		13 24		14 24		15 24		16 23		17 27		18 27			19 24			
Stansted Airport ✈	d		12 27		13 27		14 27		15 27		16 27		17 27			18 21		19 21		20 21
Audley End	d		12 40		13 40		14 40		15 40		16 40		17 40			18 38		19 38		20 39
Cambridge	d		13 01		14 01		15 01		16 01		17 01		18 01			19 01		20 01		21 01
Ely 6	d	12 48	13 15	13 48	14 15	14 48	15 15	15 47	16 15	16 47	17 15	17 52	18 15	18 52		19 15	19 52	20 15		21 15
March	d		13 32		14 32		15 32		16 32		17 32		18 34	19 08		19 32		20 32		21 32
Peterborough 8	a	13 25	13 50	14 25	14 50	15 27	15 50	16 25	16 50	17 22	17 51	18 25	18 51	19 26		19 50	20 25	20 50		21 50
	d	13 27	13 52	14 26	14 52	15 28	15 52	16 27	16 52	17 24	17 52	18 26	18 52	19 26		19 52	20 27	20 52	21 31	21 52
Stamford	d		14 05		15 05		16 05		17 05		18 05		19 05			20 05		21 05	21 45	22 05
Oakham	d		14 19		15 19		16 19		17 19		18 19		19 19		19 37	20 19		21 19	22 01	22 19
Melton Mowbray	d		14 30		15 30		16 30		17 30		18 30		19 30		19a48	20 30		21 30	22 14	22 30
Leicester	d		14 48		15 48		16 48		17 48		18 48		19 48			20 48		21 48		22 48
Nuneaton	a		15 06		16 06		17 08		18 14		19 06		20 06			21 07		22 06		23 06
Coleshill Parkway	a		15 25		16 24		17 24		18 32		19 25		20 25			21 24		22 25		23 25
Birmingham New Street 12	a		15 38		16 38		17 38		18 46		19 38		20 38			21 37		22 38		23 38
Grantham 7	d	13 58		14 58		16 01		16 58		17 57		18 57		19 59			20 59			
East Midlands Parkway	d																			
Nottingham 8 🚊	a	14 35		15 32		16 35		17 35		18 33		19 34		20 31			21 33		22 54	
	d	14 47		15 47		16 47		17 45		18 47		19 41								
Langley Mill	d							18 01												
Alfreton	d	15 08		16 08		17 08		18 08		19 08		20 02								
Chesterfield	d	15 21		16 21		17 18		18 20		19 21		20 13								
Sheffield 7 🚊	a	15 37		16 37		17 36		18 36		19 37		20 27								
	d	15 41		16 41		17 41		18 42		19 40		20 31								
Stockport	a	16 25		17 25		18 25		19 25		20 25		21 20								
Manchester Piccadilly 10 🚊	a	16 36		17 37		18 36		19 36		20 36		21 32								
Manchester Oxford Road	a	16 40		17 40		18 40		19 40		20 40										
Warrington Central	a	16 57		18 03		18 57		19 57		20 57										
Widnes	a	17 05		18 11		19 05		20 05		21 05										
Liverpool South Parkway 7 ✈	a	17 15		18 21		19 18		20 16		21 19										
Liverpool Lime Street 10	a	17 31		18 35		19 34		20 35		21 35										

A 🚲 from Peterborough
B From Corby, to Derby
C 🚲 from Peterborough
D From St Pancras International
E From Spalding

For connections from Ipswich please see Table 14

Table 49

Saturdays

14 December to 21 December

Stansted Airport - East Anglia - East Midlands - Birmingham and North West England

Route Diagram - refer to first Page of Table 49

		XC	EM	XC	EM	EM	EM	XC	EM	XC	EM	XC	EM	XC	EM	XC	EM	XC	EM	XC	EM	XC	EM
		◇1	◇	◇1	◇	◇	◇	◇1	◇	◇1	◇	◇1	◇	◇1	◇	◇1	◇	◇1	◇	◇1	◇	◇1	◇
										A 🛒		A 🛒		A 🛒		A 🛒		A 🛒		A 🛒		A 🛒	
Norwich	d						05 50		06 53		07 57		08 57		09 57		10 57		11 57		12 57		13 57
Thetford	d						06 23		07 22		08 24		09 24		10 24		11 24		12 24		13 24		14 24
Stansted Airport ✈	d			05 25				06 27		07 27		08 27		09 27		10 27		11 27		12 27		13 27	
Audley End	d			05 37				06 40		07 40		08 40		09 40		10 40		11 40		12 40		13 40	
Cambridge	d	05 15		05 55				06 57		08 01		09 01		10 01		11 01		12 01		13 01		14 01	
Ely 6	d	05 30		06 10			06 48	07 12	07 48	08 15	08 48	09 15	09 46	10 15	10 48	11 15	11 48	12 15	12 48	13 15	13 48	14 15	14 48
March	d	05 46		06 28			07 07	07 29	08 04	08 32	09 05	09 32		10 32		11 32		12 32		13 32		14 32	
Peterborough 8	a	06 08		06 50			07 25	07 50	08 27	08 50	09 23	09 50	10 21	10 50	11 19	11 50	12 22	12 49	13 26	13 50	14 25	14 49	15 23
	d	06 10		06 52			07 27	07 52	08 28	08 52	09 25	09 52	10 22	10 52	11 23	11 52	12 25	12 52	13 28	13 52	14 26	14 52	15 24
Stamford	d	06 23		07 05				08 05		09 05		10 05		11 05		12 05		13 05		14 05		15 05	
Oakham	d	06 39		07 21				08 19		09 19		10 19		11 19		12 19		13 19		14 19		15 19	
Melton Mowbray	d	06 50		07 32				08 30		09 30		10 30		11 30		12 30		13 30		14 30		15 30	
Leicester	d	07 16		07 49				08 48		09 48		10 48		11 48		12 48		13 48		14 48		15 48	
Nuneaton	a	07 34		08 07				09 07		10 06		11 06		12 06		13 06		14 06		15 06		16 06	
Coleshill Parkway	a	07 50		08 23				09 25		10 24		11 24		12 24		13 24		14 24		15 24		16 24	
Birmingham New Street 12	a	08 02		08 38				09 38		10 38		11 38		12 38		13 38		14 38		15 38		16 38	
Grantham 7	d						07 58		08 59		09 53		10 54		11 56		12 58		13 58		14 58		15 57
East Midlands Parkway	d																						
Nottingham 8 🚌	a						08 39		09 35		10 36		11 35		12 36		13 36		14 36		15 36		16 36
	d		05 20		06 40	07 47	08 48		09 47		10 47		11 47		12 47		13 47		14 47		15 47		16 44
Langley Mill	d																						
Alfreton	d				07 01	08 09	09 10		10 10		11 10		12 10		13 10		14 10		15 10		16 10		17 05
Chesterfield	d		05 49		07 11	08 20	09 21		10 20		11 20		12 21		13 20		14 20		15 20		16 20		17 15
Sheffield 7 🚌	a		06 15		07 28	08 37	09 38		10 37		11 37		12 37		13 37		14 37		15 37		16 37		17 34
	d		06 20		07 32	08 41	09 41		10 41		11 41		12 41		13 41		14 41		15 41		16 41		17 38
Stockport	a		07 22		08 24	09 25	10 25		11 25		12 24		13 25		14 25		15 25		16 25		17 25		18 26
Manchester Piccadilly 10 🚌	a		07 34		08 36	09 36	10 36		11 36		12 36		13 36		14 36		15 36		16 36		17 37		18 37
Manchester Oxford Road	a		07 37		08 40	09 40	10 40		11 40		12 40		13 40		14 40		15 40		16 40		17 40		18 40
Warrington Central	a		07 53		08 57	09 57	10 57		11 57		12 57		13 57		14 57		15 57		16 57		18 03		18 57
Widnes	a		08 01		09 05	10 05	11 05		12 05		13 05		14 05		15 05		16 05		17 05		18 11		19 05
Liverpool South Parkway 7 ✈	a		08 18		09 15	10 15	11 15		12 15		13 15		14 15		15 15		16 15		17 15		18 21		19 18
Liverpool Lime Street 10	a		08 31		09 31	10 31	11 31		12 31		13 31		14 31		15 31		16 31		17 31		18 35		19 35

		XC	EM	XC	EM	XC	EM	XC	EM	XC	EM	XC	EM
		◇1	◇	◇1	◇	◇1	◇	◇1	◇	◇1	◇	◇1	
		A 🛒		A 🛒		A 🛒		A 🛒					B
Norwich	d		14 57		15 52		16 54		17 50		18 57		
Thetford	d		15 24		16 23		17 24		18 23		19 24		
Stansted Airport ✈	d	14 27		15 27		16 27		17 27		18 27		19 27	
Audley End	d	14 40		15 40		16 40		17 40		18 40		19 40	
Cambridge	d	15 01		16 01		17 01		18 01		19 01		20 01	
Ely 6	d	15 15	15 47	16 15	16 47	17 15	17 47	18 15	18 48	19 15	19 48	20 15	
March	d	15 32		16 32		17 32		18 34	19 05	19 32		20 32	
Peterborough 8	a	15 50	16 25	16 50	17 23	17 51	18 23	18 52	19 24	19 50	20 23	20 50	
	d	15 52	16 27	16 52	17 25	17 52	18 26	18 54	19 29	19 52	20 26	20 52	21 27
Stamford	d	16 05		17 05		18 05		19 06		20 05		21 05	
Oakham	d	16 19		17 19		18 19		19 19		20 19		21 19	
Melton Mowbray	d	16 30		17 30		18 30		19 30		20 30		21 30	
Leicester	d	16 48		17 48		18 48		19 48		20 48		21 48	
Nuneaton	a	17 06		18 07		19 06		20 07		21 07		22 06	
Coleshill Parkway	a	17 24		18 24		19 24		20 24		21 24		22 24	
Birmingham New Street 12	a	17 38		18 38		19 38		20 38		21 38		22 38	
Grantham 7	d		16 56		17 59		18 58		20 03		20 58		22 02
East Midlands Parkway	d												
Nottingham 8 🚌	a		17 36		18 33		19 34		20 37		21 32		22 32
	d		17 44		18 47		19 39						
Langley Mill	d		18 00										
Alfreton	d		18 07		19 10		20 00						
Chesterfield	d		18 18		19 21		20 10						
Sheffield 7 🚌	a		18 33		19 37		20 28						
	d		18 38		19 40		20 32						
Stockport	a		19 24		20 25		21 20						
Manchester Piccadilly 10 🚌	a		19 35		20 36		21 32						
Manchester Oxford Road	a		19 39		20 40								
Warrington Central	a		19 57		20 57								
Widnes	a		20 05		21 05								
Liverpool South Parkway 7 ✈	a		20 15		21 19								
Liverpool Lime Street 10	a		20 30		21 32								

A 🛒 from Peterborough

B From Spalding

For connections from Ipswich please see Table 14

Table 49

Saturdays

28 December to 17 May

Stansted Airport - East Anglia - East Midlands - Birmingham and North West England

Route Diagram - refer to first Page of Table 49

Station		XC	EM	XC	EM	EM	EM	XC	EM	XC
		◇1	◇	◇1	◇	◇	◇	◇1	◇	◇1
										A 🚲
Norwich	d						05 50		06 53	
Thetford	d						06 23		07 22	
Stansted Airport ✈	d			05 25				06 27		07 27
Audley End	d			05 37				06 40		07 40
Cambridge	d	05 15		05 55				06 57		08 01
Ely 6	d	05 30		06 10			06 48	07 12	07 48	08 15
March	d	05 46		06 28			07 07	07 29	08 04	08 32
Peterborough 8	a	06 08		06 50			07 25	07 50	08 27	08 50
	d	06 10		06 52			07 27	07 52	08 28	08 52
Stamford	d	06 23		07 05				08 05		09 05
Oakham	d	06 39		07 21				08 19		09 19
Melton Mowbray	d	06 50		07 32				08 30		09 30
Leicester	d	07 16		07 49				08 48		09 48
Nuneaton	a	07 34		08 07				09 07		10 06
Coleshill Parkway	a	07 50		08 23				09 24		10 25
Birmingham New Street 12	a	08 02		08 38				09 38		10 38
Grantham 7	d						07 58		08 59	
East Midlands Parkway	d									
Nottingham 8 🚌	a						08 39		09 35	
	d		05 20		06 40	07 47	08 48		09 47	
Langley Mill	d									
Alfreton	d				07 01	08 09	09 10		10 10	
Chesterfield	d		05 49		07 11	08 20	09 21		10 20	
Sheffield 7 🚌	a		06 15		07 28	08 37	09 38		10 37	
	d		06 20		07 32	08 41	09 41		10 41	
Stockport	a		07 22		08 24	09 25	10 25		11 25	
Manchester Piccadilly 10 🚌	a		07 34		08 36	09 36	10 36		11 36	
Manchester Oxford Road	a		07 37		08 40	09 40	10 40		11 40	
Warrington Central	a		07 53		08 57	09 57	10 57		11 57	
Widnes	a		08 01		09 05	10 05	11 05		12 05	
Liverpool South Parkway 7 ✈	a		08 18		09 15	10 15	11 15		12 15	
Liverpool Lime Street 10	a		08 31		09 31	10 31	11 31		12 31	

Station		EM	XC	EM	XC	EM	XC	EM	XC	EM	XC	EM	XC	EM
		◇	◇1	◇	◇1	◇	◇1	◇	◇1	◇	◇1	◇	◇1	◇
			A 🚲		A 🚲		A 🚲		A 🚲		A 🚲		A 🚲	
Norwich	d	07 57		08 57		09 57		10 57		11 57		12 57		13 57
Thetford	d	08 24		09 24		10 24		11 24		12 24		13 24		14 24
Stansted Airport ✈	d		08 27		09 27		10 27		11 27		12 27		13 27	
Audley End	d		08 40		09 40		10 40		11 40		12 40		13 40	
Cambridge	d		09 01		10 01		11 01		12 01		13 01		14 01	
Ely 6	d	08 48	09 15	09 46	10 15	10 48	11 15	11 48	12 15	12 48	13 15	13 48	14 15	14 48
March	d	09 05	09 32		10 32		11 32		12 32		13 32		14 32	
Peterborough 8	a	09 23	09 50	10 21	10 50	11 19	11 50	12 23	12 49	13 26	13 50	14 25	14 49	15 23
	d	09 25	09 52	10 22	10 52	11 23	11 52	12 26	12 52	13 28	13 52	14 26	14 52	15 24
Stamford	d		10 05		11 05		12 05		13 05		14 05		15 05	
Oakham	d		10 19		11 17		12 19		13 19		14 19		15 19	
Melton Mowbray	d		10 30		11 28		12 30		13 30		14 30		15 30	
Leicester	d		10 48		11 48		12 48		13 48		14 48		15 48	
Nuneaton	a		11 06		12 06		13 06		14 06		15 06		16 06	
Coleshill Parkway	a		11 24		12 24		13 24		14 24		15 24		16 24	
Birmingham New Street 12	a		11 38		12 38		13 38		14 38		15 38		16 38	
Grantham 7	d	09 53		10 54		11 56		12 58		13 58		14 58		15 57
East Midlands Parkway	d													
Nottingham 8 🚌	a	10 36		11 35		12 36		13 36		14 36		15 36		16 36
	d	10 47		11 47		12 47		13 47		14 47		15 47		16 44
Langley Mill	d													
Alfreton	d	11 10		12 10		13 10		14 10		15 10		16 10		17 05
Chesterfield	d	11 20		12 21		13 20		14 20		15 20		16 20		17 15
Sheffield 7 🚌	a	11 37		12 37		13 37		14 37		15 37		16 37		17 34
	d	11 41		12 41		13 41		14 41		15 41		16 41		17 38
Stockport	a	12 24		13 25		14 25		15 25		16 25		17 25		18 26
Manchester Piccadilly 10 🚌	a	12 36		13 36		14 36		15 36		16 36		17 37		18 37
Manchester Oxford Road	a	12 40		13 40		14 40		15 40		16 40		17 40		18 40
Warrington Central	a	12 57		13 57		14 57		15 57		16 57		18 03		18 57
Widnes	a	13 05		14 05		15 05		16 05		17 05		18 11		19 05
Liverpool South Parkway 7 ✈	a	13 15		14 15		15 15		16 15		17 15		18 21		19 18
Liverpool Lime Street 10	a	13 31		14 31		15 31		16 31		17 31		18 35		19 35

Station		XC	EM	XC	EM	XC	EM	XC	EM	XC	EM	XC	EM
		◇1	◇	◇1	◇	◇1	◇	◇1	◇	◇1	◇	◇1	
		A 🚲		A 🚲		A 🚲		A 🚲					B
Norwich	d		14 57		15 52		16 54		17 50		18 57		
Thetford	d		15 24		16 23		17 24		18 23		19 24		
Stansted Airport ✈	d	14 27		15 27		16 27		17 27		18 27		19 27	
Audley End	d	14 40		15 40		16 40		17 40		18 40		19 40	
Cambridge	d	15 01		16 01		17 01		18 01		19 01		20 01	
Ely 6	d	15 15	15 47	16 15	16 47	17 15	17 47	18 15	18 48	19 15	19 48	20 15	
March	d	15 32		16 32		17 32		18 34	19 05	19 32		20 32	
Peterborough 8	a	15 50	16 25	16 50	17 23	17 51	18 23	18 52	19 24	19 50	20 23	20 50	
	d	15 52	16 27	16 52	17 25	17 52	18 26	18 54	19 30	19 52	20 26	20 52	21 27
Stamford	d	16 05		17 05		18 05		19 06		20 05		21 05	
Oakham	d	16 19		17 19		18 19		19 19		20 19		21 17	
Melton Mowbray	d	16 30		17 30		18 30		19 30		20 30		21 28	
Leicester	d	16 48		17 48		18 48		19 48		20 48		21 48	
Nuneaton	a	17 06		18 07		19 06		20 07		21 07		22 06	
Coleshill Parkway	a	17 24		18 24		19 24		20 24		21 24		22 24	
Birmingham New Street 12	a	17 38		18 38		19 38		20 38		21 38		22 38	
Grantham 7	d		16 56		17 59		18 58		20 03		20 58		22 02
East Midlands Parkway	d												
Nottingham 8 🚌	a		17 36		18 33		19 34		20 37		21 32		22 32
	d		17 44		18 47		19 39						
Langley Mill	d		18 00										
Alfreton	d		18 07		19 10		20 00						
Chesterfield	d		18 18		19 21		20 10						
Sheffield 7 🚌	a		18 33		19 37		20 28						
	d		18 38		19 40		20 32						
Stockport	a		19 24		20 25		21 20						
Manchester Piccadilly 10 🚌	a		19 35		20 36		21 32						
Manchester Oxford Road	a		19 39		20 40								
Warrington Central	a		19 57		20 57								
Widnes	a		20 05		21 05								
Liverpool South Parkway 7 ✈	a		20 15		21 19								
Liverpool Lime Street 10	a		20 30		21 32								

A 🚲 from Peterborough

B From Spalding

For connections from Ipswich please see Table 14

Table 49

Sundays

8 December to 29 December

Stansted Airport - East Anglia - East Midlands - Birmingham and North West England

Route Diagram - refer to first Page of Table 49

		EM	XC	EM	EM	EM	EM	XC	XC	EM		EM	XC	EM	XC	EM	XC	EM	XC	EM		XC	EM	XC	EM
		◇	◇1	◇	◇	◇	◇	◇1	◇1	◇		◇	◇1	◇	◇1	◇	◇1	◇	◇1	◇		◇1	◇	◇1	◇
									A				A		A		A		A						
Norwich	d						10 47							13 53		14 53		15 54		16 54			17 54		18 56
Thetford	d						11 14							14 20		15 20		16 21		17 21			18 21		19 23
Stansted Airport ✈	d		10 25					11 25	12 25				13 25		14 25		15 25		16 25			17 25		18 25	
Audley End	d		10 39					11 39	12 39				13 39		14 39		15 39		16 39			17 39		18 39	
Cambridge	d		11 00					12 00	13 00				14 00		15 00		16 00		17 00			18 00		19 00	
Ely 6	d		11 15				11 39	12 15	13 15				14 15	14 45	15 15	15 46	16 15		17 15	17 48		18 15	18 48	19 15	19 48
March	d		11 32					12 32	13 32				14 32		15 32		16 32		17 32			18 32		19 32	
Peterborough 8	a		11 51				12 11	12 51	13 51				14 51	15 18	15 51	16 19	16 51	17 12	17 51	18 20		18 51	19 23	19 51	20 23
	d		11 53				12 16	12 53	13 53			14 34	14 53	15 23	15 53	16 24	16 53	17 23	17 53	18 26		18 53	19 26	19 53	20 30
Stamford	d		12 06					13 06	14 06				15 06		16 06		17 06		18 06			19 06		20 06	
Oakham	d		12 20					13 20	14 20				15 20		16 20		17 20		18 20			19 20		20 20	
Melton Mowbray	d		12 32					13 32	14 32				15 32		16 32		17 30		18 32			19 32		20 32	
Leicester	d		12 50					13 50	14 50				15 50		16 50		17 50		18 50			19 50		20 50	
Nuneaton	a		13 09					14 09	15 09				16 09		17 09		18 09		19 09			20 09		21 08	
Coleshill Parkway	a		13 25					14 24	15 24				16 24		17 24		18 25		19 24			20 25		21 25	
Birmingham New Street 12	a		13 38					14 38	15 38				16 38		17 38		18 40		19 38			20 38		21 38	
Grantham 7	d						12 51					15 09		15 55		16 56		17 55		18 58			19 57		21 02
East Midlands Parkway	d																								
Nottingham 8	a						13 29					15 39		16 24		17 25		18 27		19 33			20 31		21 34
	d	09 47		10 48	11 44	12 41	13 42			14 47		15 47		16 42		17 41		18 40		19 43					
Langley Mill	d					12 57	13 58			15 03				17 01		17 57		18 56							
Alfreton	d	10 05		11 09	12 05	13 05	14 06			15 11		16 08		17 09		18 05		19 04		20 04					
Chesterfield	d	10 18		11 19	12 15	13 15	14 16			15 21		16 18		17 19		18 16		19 15		20 14					
Sheffield 7	a	10 37		11 35	12 32	13 32	14 34			15 39		16 34		17 39		18 33		19 31		20 31					
	d	10 41		11 39	12 37	13 39	14 37			15 43		16 39		17 44		18 37		19 35		20 35					
Stockport	a	11 25		12 25	13 25	14 25	15 25			16 25		17 28		18 25		19 25		20 25		21 24					
Manchester Piccadilly 10	a	11 37		12 37	13 37	14 37	15 37			16 37		17 37		18 37		19 37		20 38		21 36					
Manchester Oxford Road	a	11 41		12 41	13 41	14 41	15 41			16 41		17 41		18 41		19 41									
Warrington Central	a	11 58		12 58	13 58	14 58	15 58			16 58		17 58		18 58		19 58									
Widnes	a	12 06		13 06	14 06	15 06	16 06			17 06		18 06		19 06		20 06									
Liverpool South Parkway 7 ✈	a	12 16		13 16	14 16	15 16	16 16			17 16		18 16		19 16		20 16									
Liverpool Lime Street 10	a	12 30		13 30	14 30	15 30	16 30			17 30		18 30		19 30		20 30									

		XC	EM
		◇1	◇
Norwich	d		20 52
Thetford	d		21 19
Stansted Airport ✈	d	19 25	
Audley End	d	19 39	
Cambridge	d	20 00	
Ely 6	d	20 15	21 44
March	d	20 32	
Peterborough 8	a	20 51	22 16
	d	20 53	22 23
Stamford	d	21 06	
Oakham	d	21 20	
Melton Mowbray	d	21 31	
Leicester	d	21 50	
Nuneaton	a	22 09	
Coleshill Parkway	a	22 25	
Birmingham New Street 12	a	22 38	
Grantham 7	d		22 55
East Midlands Parkway	d		
Nottingham 8	a		23 28
	d		
Langley Mill	d		
Alfreton	d		
Chesterfield	d		
Sheffield 7	a		
	d		
Stockport	a		
Manchester Piccadilly 10	a		
Manchester Oxford Road	a		
Warrington Central	a		
Widnes	a		
Liverpool South Parkway 7 ✈	a		
Liverpool Lime Street 10	a		

A from Peterborough

For connections from Ipswich please see Table 14

Table 49

Sundays

5 January to 23 March

Stansted Airport - East Anglia - East Midlands - Birmingham and North West England

Route Diagram - refer to first Page of Table 49

		EM	XC	EM	EM	EM	EM	XC	XC	EM	EM	XC	EM	XC	EM	XC	EM	XC	EM	XC	EM	XC	EM
		◇	◇1	◇	◇	◇	◇	◇1	◇1	◇	◇	◇1	◇	◇1	◇	◇1	◇	◇1	◇	◇1	◇	◇1	◇
									A 🚲			A 🚲		A 🚲		A 🚲		A 🚲					
Norwich	d						10 47						13 53		14 53		15 54		16 54		17 54		18 56
Thetford	d						11 14						14 20		15 20		16 21		17 21		18 21		19 23
Stansted Airport ✈	d		10 25					11 25	12 25			13 25		14 25		15 25		16 25		17 25		18 25	
Audley End	d		10 39					11 39	12 39			13 39		14 39		15 39		16 39		17 39		18 39	
Cambridge	d		11 00					12 00	13 00			14 00		15 00		16 00		17 00		18 00		19 00	
Ely 6	d		11 15				11 39	12 15	13 15			14 15	14 45	15 15	15 46	16 15		17 15	17 48	18 15	18 48	19 15	19 48
March	d		11 32					12 32	13 32			14 32		15 32		16 32		17 32		18 32		19 32	
Peterborough 8	a		11 51				12 11	12 51	13 51			14 51	15 18	15 51	16 19	16 51	17 12	17 51	18 20	18 51	19 23	19 51	20 23
	d		11 53				12 18	12 53	13 53		14 34	14 53	15 23	15 53	16 24	16 53	17 23	17 53	18 26	18 53	19 26	19 53	20 30
Stamford	d		12 06					13 06	14 06			15 06		16 06		17 06		18 06		19 06		20 06	
Oakham	d		12 20					13 20	14 20			15 20		16 20		17 20		18 20		19 20		20 20	
Melton Mowbray	d		12 31					13 32	14 32			15 32		16 32		17 30		18 33		19 31		20 32	
Leicester	d		12 50					13 50	14 50			15 50		16 50		17 50		18 50		19 50		20 50	
Nuneaton	a		13 15					14 15	15 15			16 15		17 15		18 15		19 15		20 15		21 15	
Coleshill Parkway	a																						
Birmingham New Street 12	a																						
Grantham 7	d						12 51				15 09		15 55		16 56		17 55		18 58		19 57		21 02
East Midlands Parkway	d																						
Nottingham 8 🚊	a						13 29				15 39		16 24		17 25		18 27		19 33		20 31		21 34
	d	09 47		10 48	11 44	12 41	13 42			14 47	15 47		16 42		17 41		18 40		19 43				
Langley Mill	d					12 57	13 58			15 03			17 01		17 57		18 56						
Alfreton	d	10 05		11 09	12 05	13 05	14 06			15 11	16 08		17 09		18 05		19 04		20 04				
Chesterfield	d	10 18		11 19	12 15	13 15	14 16			15 21	16 18		17 19		18 16		19 15		20 14				
Sheffield 7 🚊	a	10 37		11 35	12 32	13 32	14 34			15 39	16 34		17 39		18 33		19 31		20 31				
	d	10 41		11 39	12 37	13 39	14 37			15 43	16 39		17 44		18 37		19 35		20 35				
Stockport	a	11 25		12 25	13 25	14 25	15 25			16 25	17 28		18 25		19 25		20 25		21 24				
Manchester Piccadilly 10 🚊	a	11 37		12 37	13 37	14 37	15 37			16 37	17 37		18 37		19 37		20 38		21 36				
Manchester Oxford Road	a	11 41		12 41	13 41	14 41	15 41			16 41	17 41		18 41		19 41								
Warrington Central	a	11 58		12 58	13 58	14 58	15 58			16 58	17 58		18 58		19 58								
Widnes	a	12 06		13 06	14 06	15 06	16 06			17 06	18 06		19 06		20 06								
Liverpool South Parkway 7 ✈	a	12 16		13 16	14 16	15 16	16 16			17 16	18 16		19 16		20 16								
Liverpool Lime Street 10	a	12 30		13 30	14 30	15 30	16 30			17 30	18 30		19 30		20 30								

		XC	EM
		◇1	◇
Norwich	d		20 52
Thetford	d		21 19
Stansted Airport ✈	d	19 25	
Audley End	d	19 39	
Cambridge	d	20 00	
Ely 6	d	20 15	21 44
March	d	20 32	
Peterborough 8	a	20 51	22 16
	d	20 53	22 23
Stamford	d	21 06	
Oakham	d	21 20	
Melton Mowbray	d	21 31	
Leicester	d	21 50	
Nuneaton	a	22 09	
Coleshill Parkway	a		
Birmingham New Street 12	a		
Grantham 7	d		22 55
East Midlands Parkway	d		
Nottingham 8 🚊	a		23 28
	d		
Langley Mill	d		
Alfreton	d		
Chesterfield	d		
Sheffield 7 🚊	a		
	d		
Stockport	a		
Manchester Piccadilly 10 🚊	a		
Manchester Oxford Road	a		
Warrington Central	a		
Widnes	a		
Liverpool South Parkway 7 ✈	a		
Liverpool Lime Street 10	a		

A 🚲 from Peterborough

For connections from Ipswich please see Table 14

Table 49

Sundays

30 March to 11 May

Stansted Airport - East Anglia - East Midlands - Birmingham and North West England

Route Diagram - refer to first Page of Table 49

		EM	XC	EM	EM	EM	EM	XC	XC	EM	EM	XC	EM	XC	EM	XC	EM	XC	EM	XC	EM	XC	EM
		◇	◇[1]	◇	◇	◇	◇	◇[1]	◇[1]	◇	◇	◇[1]	◇	◇[1]	◇	◇[1]	◇	◇[1]	◇	◇[1]	◇	◇[1]	◇
									A 🛒			A 🛒		A 🛒		A 🛒		A 🛒					
Norwich	d						10 47						13 53		14 53		15 54		16 54		17 54		18 56
Thetford	d						11 14						14 20		15 20		16 21		17 21		18 21		19 23
Stansted Airport ✈	d		10 25					11 25	12 25			13 25		14 25		15 25		16 25		17 25		18 25	
Audley End	d		10 39					11 39	12 39			13 39		14 39		15 39		16 39		17 39		18 39	
Cambridge	d		11 00					12 00	13 00			14 00		15 00		16 00		17 00		18 00		19 00	
Ely [6]	d		11 15				11 39	12 15	13 15			14 15	14 45	15 15	15 46	16 15		17 15	17 48	18 15	18 48	19 15	19 48
March	d		11 32					12 32	13 32			14 32		15 32		16 32		17 32		18 32		19 32	
Peterborough [8]	a		11 51				12 11	12 51	13 51			14 51	15 18	15 51	16 19	16 51	17 12	17 51	18 20	18 51	19 23	19 51	20 23
	d		11 53				12 16	12 53	13 53		14 34	14 53	15 23	15 53	16 24	16 53	17 23	17 53	18 26	18 53	19 26	19 53	20 30
Stamford	d		12 06					13 06	14 06			15 06		16 06		17 06		18 06		19 06		20 06	
Oakham	d		12 20					13 20	14 20			15 20		16 20		17 20		18 20		19 20		20 20	
Melton Mowbray	d		12 31					13 32	14 32			15 32		16 32		17 30		18 32		19 31		20 32	
Leicester	d		12 50					13 50	14 50			15 50		16 50		17 50		18 50		19 50		20 50	
Nuneaton	a		13 09					14 09	15 09			16 09		17 09		18 09		19 09		20 09		21 08	
Coleshill Parkway	a		13 25					14 24	15 24			16 24		17 24		18 25		19 24		20 25		21 25	
Birmingham New Street [12]	a		13 38					14 38	15 38			16 38		17 38		18 40		19 38		20 38		21 38	
Grantham [7]	d						12 51				15 09		15 55		16 56		17 55		18 58		19 57		21 02
East Midlands Parkway	d																						
Nottingham [8] 🚌	a						13 29				15 39		16 24		17 25		18 27		19 33		20 31		21 34
	d	09 47		10 48	11 44	12 41	13 42			14 47	15 47		16 42		17 41		18 40		19 43				
Langley Mill	d					12 57	13 58			15 03			17 01		17 57		18 56						
Alfreton	d	10 05		11 09	12 05	13 05	14 06			15 11	16 08		17 09		18 05		19 04		20 04				
Chesterfield	d	10 18		11 19	12 15	13 15	14 16			15 21	16 18		17 19		18 16		19 15		20 14				
Sheffield [7] 🚌	a	10 37		11 35	12 32	13 32	14 34			15 39	16 34		17 39		18 33		19 31		20 31				
	d	10 41		11 39	12 37	13 39	14 37			15 43	16 39		17 44		18 37		19 35		20 35				
Stockport	a	11 25		12 25	13 25	14 25	15 25			16 25	17 28		18 25		19 25		20 25		21 24				
Manchester Piccadilly [10] 🚌	a	11 37		12 37	13 37	14 37	15 37			16 37	17 37		18 37		19 37		20 38		21 36				
Manchester Oxford Road	a	11 41		12 41	13 41	14 41	15 41			16 41	17 41		18 41		19 41								
Warrington Central	a	11 58		12 58	13 58	14 58	15 58			16 58	17 58		18 58		19 58								
Widnes	a	12 06		13 06	14 06	15 06	16 06			17 06	18 06		19 06		20 06								
Liverpool South Parkway [7] ✈	a	12 16		13 16	14 16	15 16	16 16			17 16	18 16		19 16		20 16								
Liverpool Lime Street [10]	a	12 30		13 30	14 30	15 30	16 30			17 30	18 30		19 30		20 30								

		XC	EM
		◇[1]	◇
Norwich	d		20 52
Thetford	d		21 19
Stansted Airport ✈	d	19 25	
Audley End	d	19 39	
Cambridge	d	20 00	
Ely [6]	d	20 15	21 44
March	d	20 32	
Peterborough [8]	a	20 51	22 16
	d	20 53	22 23
Stamford	d	21 06	
Oakham	d	21 20	
Melton Mowbray	d	21 31	
Leicester	d	21 50	
Nuneaton	a	22 09	
Coleshill Parkway	a	22 25	
Birmingham New Street [12]	a	22 38	
Grantham [7]	d		22 55
East Midlands Parkway	d		
Nottingham [8] 🚌	a		23 28
	d		
Langley Mill	d		
Alfreton	d		
Chesterfield	d		
Sheffield [7] 🚌	a		
	d		
Stockport	a		
Manchester Piccadilly [10] 🚌	a		
Manchester Oxford Road	a		
Warrington Central	a		
Widnes	a		
Liverpool South Parkway [7] ✈	a		
Liverpool Lime Street [10]	a		

A 🛒 from Peterborough

For connections from Ipswich please see Table 14

Table 49R

Mondays to Fridays

9 December to 16 May

North West England and Birmingham - East Midlands - East Anglia - Stansted Airport

Route Diagram - refer to first Page of Table 49

Miles	Miles	Miles	Miles	Station		EM MX	EM	EM	EM	XC	EM	XC	EM	EM	XC	EM	XC	EM	XC	EM	XC	EM	XC
						◇	◇		◇ 1	◇ 1	◇	◇ 1		◇	◇ 1	◇	◇ 1	◇	◇ 1	◇	◇ 1	◇	◇ 1
						A		B	C [trolley]			D [trolley]		E	D [trolley]		F [trolley]		D [trolley]		D [trolley]		D [trolley]
—	0	—	0	**Liverpool Lime Street 10**	d													06 47		07 42		08 52	
—	5½	—	5½	Liverpool South Parkway 7 ✈	d													06 57		07 53		09 03	
—	12¼	—	12¼	Widnes	d													07 07		08 05		09 11	
—	18½	—	18½	Warrington Central	d													07 15		08 13		09 19	
—	34¼	—	34¼	Manchester Oxford Road	d													07 38		08 39		09 39	
—	34¾	—	34¾	**Manchester Piccadilly 10**	d													07 42		08 43		09 43	
—	40¾	—	40¾	Stockport	d													07 54		08 54		09 54	
—	77½	—	77½	**Sheffield 7**	a													08 34		09 34		10 34	
—	—	—	—		d													08 38		09 36		10 38	
—	89¾	—	89¾	Chesterfield	d	00 02												08 53		09 52		10 52	
—	99¾	—	99¾	Alfreton	d													09 03		10 02		11 03	
—	106	—	106	Langley Mill	d																		
—	118	—	118	**Nottingham 8**	a	00 39												09 26		10 27		11 27	
—	—	—	—		d		04 56	05 10			06 10		06 55	07 52		08 35		09 34		10 34		11 34	
—	—	—	—	East Midlands Parkway	d						06 21												
—	140¾	—	—	Grantham 7	d			05 51						08 28		09 08		10 11		11 10		12 11	
0	—	—	—	**Birmingham New Street 12**	d					05 22		06 22			07 22		08 22		09 22		10 22		11 22
9½	—	—	—	Coleshill Parkway	d					05 36		06 36			07 35		08 36		09 36		10 36		11 36
21	—	—	—	Nuneaton	d					05 52		06 52			07 51		08 52		09 52		10 52		11 52
39¾	—	—	—	**Leicester**	d					06 15		07 18			08 18		09 18		10 18		11 18		12 18
54¾	—	—	—	Melton Mowbray	d		05 36		06 00	06 32	06 53	07 35			08 35		09 35		10 35		11 35		12 35
66¼	—	—	—	Oakham	d		05 48		06a11	06 43	07 05	07 46			08 46		09 46		10 46		11 46		12 46
79¾	—	—	—	Stamford	d		06 03			06 57	07 19	08 00			09 00		10 00		11 00		12 00		13 00
92¼	170	—	187¾	**Peterborough 8**	a		06 19	06 25		07 10	07 33	08 13	09 27	08 58	09 14	09 38	10 14	10 40	11 14	11 39	12 13	12 40	13 15
—	—	—	—		d		06 27			07 12	07 35	08 18		08 59	09 18	09 40	10 18	10 45	11 18	11 41	12 18	12 42	13 18
106¼	184	—	201¾	March	a		06 42			07 30	07 50	08 33			09 33		10 33		11 33		12 33		13 33
121½	206¾	0	217	Ely 6	a		07 01			07 51	08 11	08 52		09 42	09 54	10 13	10 52	11 18	11 52	12 13	12 52	13 14	13 52
—	—	14¾	—	**Cambridge**	a					08 07		09 08			10 10		11 08		12 08		13 08		14 08
—	—	28¾	—	Audley End	a					08 24		09 24			10 24		11 23		12 23		13 23		14 23
—	—	39½	—	**Stansted Airport** ✈	a					08 39		09 40			10 40		11 40		12 40		13 40		14 40
144½	222¼	—	240¼	Thetford	a		07 28				08 36			10 06		10 37		11 43		12 38		13 39	
152	252¾	—	270½	**Norwich**	a		08 13				09 13			10 44		11 12		12 15		13 13		14 13	

Station		EM	XC	EM	XC	EM	XC	EM	XC	EM	EM	XC	EM	XC	XC	EM	EM	XC	XC	EM	EM	EM
		◇	◇ 1	◇	◇ 1	◇	◇ 1	◇	◇ 1	◇	◇ 1	◇ 1	◇	◇ 1	◇ 1	◇	◇	◇ 1	◇ 1	◇	◇	◇
			[trolley]		D [trolley]		D [trolley]		D [trolley]		[trolley]											
Liverpool Lime Street 10	d	09 52		10 52		11 52		12 52		13 52			14 52			15 52	16 52			17 52	18 52	19 52
Liverpool South Parkway 7 ✈	d	10 03		11 03		12 03		13 03		14 03			15 03			16 03	17 03			18 03	19 03	20 03
Widnes	d	10 11		11 11		12 11		13 11		14 11			15 11			16 11	17 11			18 11	19 11	20 11
Warrington Central	d	10 19		11 19		12 19		13 19		14 19			15 19			16 19	17 19			18 19	19 19	20 19
Manchester Oxford Road	d	10 39		11 39		12 39		13 39		14 39			15 39			16 39	17 39			18 39	19 39	20 39
Manchester Piccadilly 10	d	10 43		11 43		12 43		13 43		14 43			15 43			16 43	17 43			18 43	19 43	20 43
Stockport	d	10 54		11 54		12 54		13 54		14 54			15 54			16 54	17 54			18 54	19 54	20 54
Sheffield 7	a	11 33		12 34		13 35		14 34		15 34			16 34			17 39	18 47			19 33	20 35	21 34
	d	11 37		12 36		13 38		14 36		15 38			16 38			17 45	18 51			19 37	20 41	21 39
Chesterfield	d	11 52		12 52		13 54		14 52		15 52			16 53			18 01	19 06			19 51	20 56	21 55
Alfreton	d	12 02		13 02		14 05		14 59		16 02			17 04			18 11	19 16			20 03	21 08	22 05
Langley Mill	d																					22 13
Nottingham 8	a	12 27		13 27		14 27		15 25		16 26			17 27			18 31	19 41			20 29	21 33	22 35
	d	12 34		13 34		14 34		15 34		16 35			17 34			18 37				20 34		
East Midlands Parkway	d										16 47											
Grantham 7	d	13 09		14 10		15 11		16 10		17 12			18 11			19 07				21 10		
Birmingham New Street 12	d		12 22		13 22		14 22		15 22			16 22		16 52	17 22			18 22	19 22			
Coleshill Parkway	d		12 36		13 36		14 36		15 36			16 36		17 06	17 36			18 36	19 36			
Nuneaton	d		12 52		13 52		14 52		15 52			16 52		17 20	17 52			18 52	19 52			
Leicester	d		13 18		14 18		15 18		16 18			17 18		17 55	18 18			19 18	20 18			
Melton Mowbray	d		13 35		14 35		15 35		16 35		17 14	17 35		18 13	18 35			19 35	20 35			
Oakham	d		13 46		14 46		15 46		16 46		17a25	17 46		18 25	18 46			19 46	20 46			
Stamford	d		14 00		15 00		16 00		17 00			18 00		18 39	19 00			20 00	21 00			
Peterborough 8	a	13 39	14 13	14 39	15 14	15 38	16 14	16 39	17 14	17 41		18 16	18 38	18 58	19 16	19 38		20 13	21 13	21 37		
	d	13 41	14 18	14 41	15 18	15 40	16 18	16 41	17 18	17 42		18 18	18 45	18 59	19 18	19 40		20 18	21 18	21 38		
March	a		14 33		15 33		16 33		17 36			18 33	19 04	19 14	19 33			20 33	21 33			
Ely 6	a	14 13	14 52	15 13	15 52	16 13	16 52	17 13	17 58	18 14		18 52	19 24	19 33	19 52	20 13		20 52	21 52	22 13		
Cambridge	a		15 08		16 08		17 08		18 16			19 08		19 52	20 08			21 08	22 08			
Audley End	a		15 23		16 23		17 23		18 31			19 23			20 23			21 23	22 23			
Stansted Airport ✈	a		15 40		16 40		17 40		18 54			19 40			20 40			21 40	22 52			
Thetford	a	14 38		15 38		16 37		17 38		18 39			19 50			20 36				22 37		
Norwich	a	15 11		16 13		17 13		18 13		19 15			20 22			21 13				23 18		

A From Liverpool Lime Street
B To Spalding
C To St Pancras International
D [trolley] to Peterborough
E From Mansfield Woodhouse
F From Gloucester. [trolley] to Peterborough

For connections to Ipswich please see Table 14

Table 49R

Mondays to Fridays

9 December to 16 May

North West England and Birmingham - East Midlands - East Anglia - Stansted Airport

Route Diagram - refer to first Page of Table 49

		XC ◇1	EM ◇
Liverpool Lime Street 10	d		21 37
Liverpool South Parkway 7 ✈	d		21 47
Widnes	d		21 55
Warrington Central	d		22 03
Manchester Oxford Road	d		22 24
Manchester Piccadilly 10 ⛴	d		22 28
Stockport	d		22 38
Sheffield 7 ⛴	a		23 35
	d		23 37
Chesterfield	d		00 02
Alfreton	d		
Langley Mill	d		
Nottingham 8 ⛴	a		00 39
	d		
East Midlands Parkway	d		
Grantham 7	d		
Birmingham New Street 12	d	20 22	
Coleshill Parkway	d	20 36	
Nuneaton	d	20 52	
Leicester	d	21 18	
Melton Mowbray	d	21 35	
Oakham	d	21 46	
Stamford	d	22 00	
Peterborough 8	a	22 13	
	d	22 18	
March	a	22 33	
Ely 6	a	22 52	
Cambridge	a	23 09	
Audley End	a		
Stansted Airport ✈	a		
Thetford	a		
Norwich	a		

Saturdays

14 December to 21 December

		EM ◇ A	EM ◇	EM B	XC ◇1	EM ◇	XC ◇1 C 🍴	EM	EM ◇	XC ◇1 C 🍴	EM ◇	XC ◇1 D 🍴	EM ◇	XC ◇1 C 🍴	EM ◇	XC ◇1 C 🍴	EM ◇	XC ◇1 C 🍴	EM ◇	XC ◇1 C 🍴	EM ◇	XC ◇1 C 🍴	EM ◇
Liverpool Lime Street 10	d												06 49		07 42		08 52		09 52		10 52		11 52
Liverpool South Parkway 7 ✈	d												06 59		07 52		09 03		10 03		11 03		12 03
Widnes	d												07 07		08 05		09 11		10 11		11 11		12 11
Warrington Central	d												07 15		08 13		09 19		10 19		11 19		12 19
Manchester Oxford Road	d												07 38		08 39		09 39		10 39		11 39		12 39
Manchester Piccadilly 10 ⛴	d												07 42		08 43		09 43		10 43		11 43		12 43
Stockport	d												07 54		08 54		09 54		10 54		11 54		12 54
Sheffield 7 ⛴	a												08 34		09 34		10 34		11 34		12 34		13 34
	d												08 38		09 37		10 38		11 37		12 37		13 37
Chesterfield	d	00 02											08 53		09 52		10 53		11 52		12 52		13 52
Alfreton	d												09 03		10 02		11 03		12 02		13 02		14 02
Langley Mill	d																						
Nottingham 8 ⛴	a	00 39											09 27		10 27		11 27		12 28		13 27		14 27
	d		05 06	05 10		06 10		06 56	07 45		08 34		09 34		10 34		11 34		12 34		13 34		14 34
East Midlands Parkway	d					06 22																	
Grantham 7	d			05 51					08 20		09 10		10 09		11 10		12 07		13 09		14 07		15 10
Birmingham New Street 12	d				05 22		06 22			07 22		08 22		09 22		10 22		11 22		12 22		13 22	
Coleshill Parkway	d				05 36		06 36			07 36		08 36		09 36		10 36		11 36		12 36		13 36	
Nuneaton	d				05 52		06 52			07 52		08 52		09 52		10 52		11 52		12 52		13 52	
Leicester	d				06 15		07 18			08 18		09 18		10 18		11 18		12 18		13 18		14 18	
Melton Mowbray	d		05 38		06 32	06 53	07 35			08 35		09 35		10 35		11 35		12 35		13 35		14 35	
Oakham	d		05 50		06 44	07 05	07 46			08 46		09 46		10 46		11 46		12 46		13 46		14 46	
Stamford	d		06 05		06 58	07 19	08 00			09 00		10 00		11 00		12 00		13 00		14 00		15 00	
Peterborough 8	a		06 19	06 25	07 12	07 33	08 12	09 27	08 57	09 12	09 40	10 16	10 38	11 17	11 39	12 12	12 37	13 12	13 38	14 12	14 41	15 12	15 39
	d		06 27		07 12	07 35	08 18		08 59	09 18	09 43	10 18	10 40	11 18	11 41	12 18	12 40	13 18	13 40	14 18	14 43	15 18	15 41
March	a		06 42		07 30	07 50	08 33			09 33		10 33		11 33		12 33		13 33		14 33		15 33	
Ely 6	a		07 01		07 52	08 11	08 52		09 41	09 52	10 16	10 51	11 13	11 51	12 13	12 52	13 13	13 52	14 13	14 52	15 18	15 52	16 13
Cambridge	a				08 08		09 08			10 09		11 08		12 08		13 08		14 08		15 08		16 08	
Audley End	a				08 25		09 24			10 24		11 24		12 24		13 24		14 24		15 24		16 23	
Stansted Airport ✈	a				08 39		09 40			10 40		11 40		12 40		13 40		14 40		15 40		16 40	
Thetford	a		07 30			08 36			10 06		10 43		11 37		12 38		13 37		14 37		15 42		16 38
Norwich	a		08 13			09 15			10 43		11 15		12 13		13 13		14 13		15 13		16 15		17 13

A From Liverpool Lime Street
B To Spalding
C 🍴 to Peterborough
D From Gloucester. 🍴 to Peterborough

For connections to Ipswich please see Table 14

Table 49R

Saturdays

14 December to 21 December

North West England and Birmingham - East Midlands - East Anglia - Stansted Airport

Route Diagram - refer to first Page of Table 49

		XC	EM	XC	EM	XC		EM	XC	EM	EM	XC	XC	EM	EM	EM		XC	EM	EM
		◇1	◇	◇1	◇	◇1		◇	◇1	◇	◇	◇1	◇1	◇	◇	◇		◇1	◇	◇
		A		A		A														
		⚲		⚲		⚲														
Liverpool Lime Street 10	d		12 52		13 52			14 52		15 52	16 52			17 52	18 52	19 52			20 52	21 37
Liverpool South Parkway 7 ✈	d		13 03		14 03			15 03		16 03	17 03			18 03	19 03	20 03			21 03	21 47
Widnes	d		13 11		14 11			15 11		16 11	17 11			18 11	19 11	20 11			21 11	21 55
Warrington Central	d		13 19		14 19			15 19		16 19	17 19			18 19	19 19	20 19			21 19	22 03
Manchester Oxford Road	d		13 39		14 39			15 39		16 39	17 39			18 39	19 39	20 39			21 39	22 24
Manchester Piccadilly 10 ⛴	d		13 43		14 43			15 43		16 43	17 43			18 43	19 43	20 43			21 43	22 28
Stockport	d		13 54		14 54			15 54		16 54	17 54			18 54	19 54	20 54			21 52	22 38
Sheffield 7 ⛴	a		14 34		15 34			16 34		17 37	18 36			19 33	20 36	21 34			22 31	23 35
	d		14 37		15 37			16 38		17 41	18 50			19 37	20 39	21 38			22 35	23 38
Chesterfield	d		14 52		15 52			16 53		17 59	19 04			19 52	20 54	21 54			22 51	23 53
Alfreton	d		15 02		16 03			17 04		18 09	19 15			20 03	21 05	22 04			23 02	
Langley Mill	d															22 11				
Nottingham 8 ⛴	a		15 27		16 27			17 27		18 31	19 39			20 31	21 33	22 33			23 32	00 30
	d		15 34		16 34			17 34		18 37				20 34						
East Midlands Parkway	d																			
Grantham 7	d		16 07		17 06			18 15		19 08				21 07						
Birmingham New Street 12	d	14 22		15 22		16 22			17 22			18 22	19 22					20 22		
Coleshill Parkway	d	14 36		15 36		16 36			17 36			18 36	19 36					20 36		
Nuneaton	d	14 52		15 52		16 52			17 52			18 52	19 52					20 52		
Leicester	d	15 18		16 18		17 18			18 18			19 18	20 18					21 18		
Melton Mowbray	d	15 35		16 35		17 35			18 35			19 35	20 35					21 35		
Oakham	d	15 46		16 46		17 46			18 46			19 46	20 46					21 46		
Stamford	d	16 00		17 00		18 00			19 00			20 00	21 00					22 00		
Peterborough 8	a	16 12	16 38	17 11	17 37	18 12		18 42	19 12	19 39		20 12	21 12	21 39				22 12		
	d	16 18	16 39	17 18	17 40	18 18		18 44	19 18	19 41		20 18	21 18	21 40				22 14		
March	a	16 33		17 37		18 33		19 00	19 32			20 32	21 33					22 29		
Ely 6	a	16 52	17 13	18 00	18 13	18 52		19 19	19 52	20 14		20 51	21 52	22 13				22 47		
Cambridge	a	17 08		18 16		19 08			20 08			21 08	22 08					23 03		
Audley End	a	17 24		18 34		19 24			20 24			21 24	22 23							
Stansted Airport ✈	a	17 40		18 53		19 40			20 40			21 40	22 40							
Thetford	a		17 37		18 37			19 43		20 38				22 37						
Norwich	a		18 13		19 13			20 16		21 13				23 19						

Saturdays

28 December to 17 May

		EM	EM	EM	XC	EM	XC	EM	EM	XC		EM	XC	EM	XC	EM	XC	EM	XC	EM		XC	EM	XC	EM
		◇	◇		◇1	◇	◇1		◇	◇1		◇	◇1	◇	◇1	◇	◇1	◇	◇1	◇		◇1	◇	◇1	◇
		B		C			A			A			D		A		A		A			A		A	
							⚲			⚲			⚲		⚲		⚲		⚲			⚲		⚲	
Liverpool Lime Street 10	d													06 49		07 42		08 52		09 52			10 52		11 52
Liverpool South Parkway 7 ✈	d													06 59		07 52		09 03		10 03			11 03		12 03
Widnes	d													07 07		08 05		09 11		10 11			11 11		12 11
Warrington Central	d													07 15		08 13		09 19		10 19			11 19		12 19
Manchester Oxford Road	d													07 38		08 39		09 39		10 39			11 39		12 39
Manchester Piccadilly 10 ⛴	d													07 42		08 43		09 43		10 43			11 43		12 43
Stockport	d													07 54		08 54		09 54		10 54			11 54		12 54
Sheffield 7 ⛴	a													08 34		09 34		10 34		11 34			12 34		13 34
	d													08 38		09 37		10 38		11 37			12 37		13 37
Chesterfield	d	00 02												08 53		09 52		10 53		11 52			12 52		13 52
Alfreton	d													09 03		10 02		11 03		12 02			13 02		14 02
Langley Mill	d																								
Nottingham 8 ⛴	a	00 39												09 27		10 27		11 27		12 28			13 27		14 27
	d		05 06	05 10		06 10		06 56	07 45			08 34		09 34		10 34		11 34		12 34			13 34		14 34
East Midlands Parkway	d					06 22																			
Grantham 7	d			05 51					08 20			09 10		10 09		11 10		12 07		13 09			14 07		15 10
Birmingham New Street 12	d				05 22		06 22			07 22			08 22		09 22		10 22		11 22			12 22		13 22	
Coleshill Parkway	d				05 36		06 36			07 36			08 36		09 36		10 36		11 36			12 36		13 36	
Nuneaton	d				05 52		06 52			07 52			08 52		09 52		10 52		11 52			12 52		13 52	
Leicester	d				06 15		07 18			08 18			09 18		10 18		11 18		12 18			13 18		14 18	
Melton Mowbray	d		05 38		06 32	06 53	07 35			08 35			09 35		10 35		11 35		12 35			13 35		14 35	
Oakham	d		05 50		06 44	07 05	07 46			08 46			09 46		10 46		11 46		12 46			13 46		14 46	
Stamford	d		06 05		06 58	07 19	08 00			09 00			10 00		11 00		12 00		13 00			14 00		15 00	
Peterborough 8	a		06 19	06 25	07 12	07 33	08 12	09 27	08 57	09 12		09 40	10 16	10 38	11 17	11 39	12 12	12 37	13 12	13 38		14 12	14 41	15 12	15 39
	d		06 27		07 12	07 35	08 18		08 59	09 18		09 43	10 18	10 40	11 18	11 41	12 18	12 40	13 18	13 40		14 18	14 43	15 18	15 41
March	a		06 42		07 30	07 50	08 33			09 33			10 33		11 33		12 33		13 33			14 33		15 33	
Ely 6	a		07 01		07 52	08 11	08 52		09 41	09 52		10 16	10 51	11 13	11 51	12 13	12 52	13 13	13 52	14 13		14 52	15 18	15 52	16 13
Cambridge	a				08 08		09 08			10 09			11 08		12 08		13 08		14 08			15 08		16 08	
Audley End	a				08 25		09 24			10 24			11 24		12 24		13 24		14 24			15 24		16 23	
Stansted Airport ✈	a				08 39		09 40			10 40			11 40		12 40		13 40		14 40			15 40		16 40	
Thetford	a		07 30			08 36			10 06			10 43		11 37		12 38		13 37		14 37			15 42		16 38
Norwich	a		08 13			09 15			10 43			11 15		12 13		13 13		14 13		15 13			16 15		17 13

A ⚲ to Peterborough
B From Liverpool Lime Street
C To Spalding
D From Gloucester. ⚲ to Peterborough

For connections to Ipswich please see Table 14

Table 49R

Saturdays

28 December to 17 May

North West England and Birmingham - East Midlands - East Anglia - Stansted Airport

Route Diagram - refer to first Page of Table 49

		XC	EM	XC	EM	XC		EM	XC	EM	EM	XC	XC	EM	EM	EM		XC	EM	EM
		◇1	◇	◇1	◇	◇1		◇	◇1	◇	◇	◇1	◇1	◇	◇	◇		◇1	◇	◇
		A 🛒		A 🛒		A 🛒														
Liverpool Lime Street 10	d		12 52		13 52			14 52		15 52	16 52			17 52	18 52	19 52			20 52	21 37
Liverpool South Parkway 7 ✈	d		13 03		14 03			15 03		16 03	17 03			18 03	19 03	20 03			21 03	21 47
Widnes	d		13 11		14 11			15 11		16 11	17 11			18 11	19 11	20 11			21 11	21 55
Warrington Central	d		13 19		14 19			15 19		16 19	17 19			18 19	19 19	20 19			21 19	22 03
Manchester Oxford Road	d		13 39		14 39			15 39		16 39	17 39			18 39	19 39	20 39			21 39	22 24
Manchester Piccadilly 10 ⛴	d		13 43		14 43			15 43		16 43	17 43			18 43	19 43	20 43			21 43	22 28
Stockport	d		13 54		14 54			15 54		16 54	17 54			18 54	19 54	20 54			21 52	22 38
Sheffield 7 ⛴	a		14 34		15 34			16 34		17 37	18 36			19 33	20 36	21 34			22 31	23 35
	d		14 37		15 37			16 38		17 41	18 50			19 37	20 39	21 38			22 35	23 38
Chesterfield	d		14 52		15 52			16 53		17 59	19 04			19 52	20 54	21 54			22 51	23 53
Alfreton	d		15 02		16 03			17 04		18 09	19 15			20 03	21 05	22 04			23 02	
Langley Mill	d															22 11				
Nottingham 8 ⛴	a		15 27		16 27			17 27		18 31	19 39			20 31	21 33	22 33			23 32	00 30
	d		15 34		16 34			17 34		18 37				20 34						
East Midlands Parkway	d																			
Grantham 7	d		16 07		17 06			18 15		19 08				21 07						
Birmingham New Street 12	d	14 22		15 22		16 22			17 22			18 22	19 22					20 22		
Coleshill Parkway	d	14 36		15 36		16 36			17 36			18 36	19 36					20 36		
Nuneaton	d	14 52		15 52		16 52			17 52			18 52	19 52					20 52		
Leicester	d	15 18		16 18		17 18			18 18			19 18	20 18					21 18		
Melton Mowbray	d	15 35		16 35		17 35			18 35			19 35	20 35					21 35		
Oakham	d	15 46		16 46		17 46			18 46			19 46	20 46					21 46		
Stamford	d	16 00		17 00		18 00			19 00			20 00	21 00					22 00		
Peterborough 8	a	16 12	16 38	17 11	17 37	18 12		18 42	19 12	19 39		20 12	21 12	21 39				22 12		
	d	16 18	16 39	17 18	17 40	18 18		18 44	19 18	19 41		20 18	21 18	21 40				22 14		
March	a	16 33		17 37		18 33		19 00	19 32			20 32	21 33					22 29		
Ely 6	a	16 52	17 13	18 00	18 13	18 52		19 19	19 52	20 14		20 51	21 52	22 13				22 47		
Cambridge	a	17 08		18 16		19 08			20 08			21 08	22 08					23 03		
Audley End	a	17 24		18 34		19 24			20 24			21 24	22 23							
Stansted Airport ✈	a	17 40		18 53		19 40			20 40			21 40	22 40							
Thetford	a		17 37		18 37			19 43		20 38				22 37						
Norwich	a		18 13		19 13			20 16		21 13				23 19						

Sundays

8 December to 29 December

		XC	EM	XC	EM	XC	EM	XC	EM	XC		EM	XC	EM	XC	EM	EM	XC	XC	EM		EM	EM	XC	EM
		◇1	◇	◇1	◇	◇1	◇	◇1	◇	◇1		◇	◇1	◇	◇1	◇	◇	◇1	◇1	◇		◇	◇	◇1	◇
		A 🛒		A 🛒		A 🛒		A 🛒		A 🛒															
Liverpool Lime Street 10	d								12 52			13 52		14 52		15 52	16 52			17 52		18 52	19 52		21 21
Liverpool South Parkway 7 ✈	d								13 03			14 03		15 03		16 03	17 03			18 03		19 03	20 03		21 31
Widnes	d								13 11			14 11		15 11		16 11	17 11			18 11		19 11	20 11		21 39
Warrington Central	d								13 19			14 19		15 19		16 19	17 19			18 19		19 19	20 19		21 47
Manchester Oxford Road	d								13 39			14 39		15 39		16 39	17 39			18 39		19 39	20 39		22 07
Manchester Piccadilly 10 ⛴	d						12 44		13 44			14 44		15 44		16 44	17 44			18 44		19 44	20 44		22 11
Stockport	d						12 55		13 54			14 54		15 54		16 54	17 54			18 54		19 54	20 54		22 28
Sheffield 7 ⛴	a						13 38		14 37			15 35		16 37		17 34	18 36			19 35		20 35	21 34		23 24
	d				12 41		13 48		14 43			15 39		16 41		17 40	18 40			19 40		20 40	21 40		23 27
Chesterfield	d				12 56		14 02		14 57			15 53		16 55		17 54	18 55			19 54		20 54	21 56		23 42
Alfreton	d				13 07		14 12		15 08			16 03		17 05		18 05	19 05			20 05		21 05	22 06		23 52
Langley Mill	d								15 15			16 11		17 13		18 12	19 13			20 12		21 12	22 14		23 59
Nottingham 8 ⛴	a				13 28		14 33		15 32			16 28		17 28		18 28	19 33			20 30		21 33	22 36		00 21
	d		12 37		13 47		14 45		15 50			16 45		17 36		18 46				20 45					
East Midlands Parkway	d																								
Grantham 7	d		13 14		14 22		15 20		16 22			17 21		18 17		19 28				21 20					
Birmingham New Street 12	d	11 22		12 22		13 22		14 22		15 22			16 22		17 22			18 22	19 22					20 22	
Coleshill Parkway	d	11 36		12 36		13 36		14 36		15 36			16 36		17 36			18 36	19 36					20 36	
Nuneaton	d	11 52		12 52		13 52		14 52		15 52			16 52		17 52			18 52	19 52					20 52	
Leicester	d	12 19		13 19		14 19		15 19		16 19			17 19		18 19			19 19	20 19					21 19	
Melton Mowbray	d	12 36		13 36		14 36		15 36		16 36			17 36		18 36			19 36	20 36					21 36	
Oakham	d	12 47		13 47		14 47		15 47		16 47			17 48		18 48			19 48	20 48					21 47	
Stamford	d	13 01		14 01		15 01		16 01		17 01			18 01		19 02			20 01	21 01					22 01	
Peterborough 8	a	13 17	13 40	14 17	14 51	15 17	15 49	16 17	16 52	17 17		17 50	18 17	18 47	19 15	19 57		20 15	21 15	21 51				22 15	
	d	13 18	13 43	14 18	14 58	15 18	15 58	16 18	16 59	17 18		17 57	18 18	18 49	19 18	19 59		20 18	21 18	21 53				22 16	
March	a	13 34		14 34		15 33		16 33		17 33		18 12	18 33		19 32			20 32	21 33					22 32	
Ely 6	a	13 52	14 16	14 52	15 31	15 52	16 31	16 52	17 32	17 52		18 32	18 52	19 22	19 51	20 32		20 50	21 52	22 26				22 51	
Cambridge	a	14 08		15 08		16 08		17 08		18 08			19 08		20 07			21 07	22 07					23 07	
Audley End	a	14 24		15 24		16 25		17 24		18 24			19 24		20 23			21 24	22 25						
Stansted Airport ✈	a	14 45		15 45		16 45		17 45		18 45			19 45		20 45			21 45	22 45						
Thetford	a		14 43		15 55		16 55		17 56			18 56		19 49		20 56				22 50					
Norwich	a		15 22		16 35		17 26		18 30			19 29		20 26		21 37				23 24					

A 🛒 to Peterborough

For connections to Ipswich please see Table 14

Table 49R

Sundays
5 January to 23 March

North West England and Birmingham - East Midlands - East Anglia - Stansted Airport

Route Diagram - refer to first Page of Table 49

		XC	EM	XC	EM	EM	XC	EM	XC	EM	EM	XC
		◇1	◇	◇1	◇	◇	◇1	◇	◇1	◇	◇	◇1
		A		A	B	C	A		A	B	C	A
		trolley		trolley			trolley		trolley			trolley
Liverpool Lime Street 10	d									12 52	12 52	
Liverpool South Parkway 7 ✈	d									13 03	13 03	
Widnes	d									13 11	13 11	
Warrington Central	d									13 19	13 19	
Manchester Oxford Road	d									13 39	13 39	
Manchester Piccadilly 10	d							12 44		13 44	13 44	
Stockport	d							12 55		13 54	13 54	
Sheffield 7	a							13 38		14 37	14 37	
	d				12 41	12 47		13 48		14 43	14 46	
Chesterfield	d				12 56	13 01		14 02		14 57	15 00	
Alfreton	d				13 07	13 12		14 12		15 08	15 11	
Langley Mill	d									15 15	15 18	
Nottingham 8	a				13 28	13 33		14 33		15 32	15 35	
	d		12 37		13 47	13 47		14 45		15 50	15 50	
East Midlands Parkway	d											
Grantham 7	d		13 14		14 22	14 22		15 20		16 22	16 22	
Birmingham New Street 12	d											
Coleshill Parkway	d											
Nuneaton	d	11 52		12 52			13 52		14 52			15 52
Leicester	d	12 19		13 19			14 19		15 19			16 19
Melton Mowbray	d	12 36		13 37			14 36		15 36			16 36
Oakham	d	12 47		13 48			14 47		15 47			16 47
Stamford	d	13 01		14 01			15 01		16 01			17 01
Peterborough 8	a	13 17	13 40	14 17	14 50	14 51	15 17	15 49	16 17	16 52	16 52	17 17
	d	13 18	13 43	14 18	14 57	14 58	15 18	15 58	16 18	16 59	16 59	17 18
March	a	13 34		14 35			15 33		16 33			17 33
Ely 6	a	13 52	14 16	14 52	15 31	15 31	15 52	16 31	16 52	17 32	17 32	17 52
Cambridge	a	14 08		15 08			16 08		17 08			18 08
Audley End	a	14 24		15 24			16 25		17 24			18 24
Stansted Airport ✈	a	14 45		15 45			16 45		17 45			18 45
Thetford	a		14 43		15 55	15 55		16 55		17 56	17 56	
Norwich	a		15 22		16 35	16 35		17 26		18 30	18 30	

		EM	XC	EM	EM	XC	EM	EM	EM	EM	XC	XC
		◇	◇1	◇	◇	◇1	◇	◇	◇	◇	◇1	◇1
				B	C		B	C	B	C		
Liverpool Lime Street 10	d	13 52		14 52	14 52		15 52	15 52	16 52	16 52		
Liverpool South Parkway 7 ✈	d	14 03		15 03	15 03		16 03	16 03	17 03	17 03		
Widnes	d	14 11		15 11	15 11		16 11	16 11	17 11	17 11		
Warrington Central	d	14 19		15 19	15 19		16 19	16 19	17 19	17 19		
Manchester Oxford Road	d	14 39		15 39	15 39		16 39	16 39	17 39	17 39		
Manchester Piccadilly 10	d	14 44		15 44	15 44		16 44	16 44	17 44	17 44		
Stockport	d	14 54		15 54	15 54		16 54	16 54	17 54	17 54		
Sheffield 7	a	15 35		16 37	16 39		17 34	17 34	18 36	18 41		
	d	15 39		16 41	16 42		17 40	17 48	18 40	18 45		
Chesterfield	d	15 53		16 55	16 56		17 54	18 02	18 55	19 00		
Alfreton	d	16 03		17 05	17 07		18 05	18 13	19 05	19 10		
Langley Mill	d	16 11		17 13	17 14		18 12	18 20	19 13	19 18		
Nottingham 8	a	16 28		17 28	17 30		18 28	18 36	19 33	19 38		
	d	16 45		17 36	17 36		18 46	18 46				
East Midlands Parkway	d											
Grantham 7	d	17 21		18 17	18 17		19 28	19 28				
Birmingham New Street 12	d											
Coleshill Parkway	d											
Nuneaton	d		16 52			17 52					18 52	19 52
Leicester	d		17 19			18 19					19 19	20 19
Melton Mowbray	d		17 36			18 36					19 36	20 36
Oakham	d		17 48			18 48					19 48	20 48
Stamford	d		18 01			19 02					20 01	21 01
Peterborough 8	a	17 50	18 17	18 47	18 47	19 15	19 57	19 57			20 15	21 15
	d	17 57	18 18	18 49	18 49	19 18	19 59	19 59			20 18	21 18
March	a	18 12	18 33			19 32					20 32	21 33
Ely 6	a	18 32	18 52	19 22	19 22	19 51	20 32	20 32			20 50	21 52
Cambridge	a		19 08			20 07					21 07	22 07
Audley End	a		19 24			20 23					21 24	22 25
Stansted Airport ✈	a		19 45			20 45					21 45	22 45
Thetford	a	18 56		19 49	19 49		20 56	20 56				
Norwich	a	19 29		20 26	20 26		21 37	21 37				

		EM	EM	EM	XC	EM
		◇	◇	◇	◇1	◇
Liverpool Lime Street 10	d	17 52	18 52	19 52		21 21
Liverpool South Parkway 7 ✈	d	18 03	19 03	20 03		21 31
Widnes	d	18 11	19 11	20 11		21 39
Warrington Central	d	18 19	19 19	20 19		21 47
Manchester Oxford Road	d	18 39	19 39	20 39		22 07
Manchester Piccadilly 10	d	18 44	19 44	20 44		22 11
Stockport	d	18 54	19 54	20 54		22 28
Sheffield 7	a	19 35	20 35	21 34		23 24
	d	19 40	20 40	21 40		23 27
Chesterfield	d	19 54	20 54	21 56		23 42
Alfreton	d	20 05	21 05	22 06		23 52
Langley Mill	d	20 12	21 12	22 14		23 59
Nottingham 8	a	20 30	21 33	22 36		00 21
	d	20 45				
East Midlands Parkway	d					
Grantham 7	d	21 20				
Birmingham New Street 12	d					
Coleshill Parkway	d					
Nuneaton	d				20 52	
Leicester	d				21 18	
Melton Mowbray	d				21 35	
Oakham	d				21 47	
Stamford	d				22 01	
Peterborough 8	a	21 51			22 14	
	d	21 53			22 16	
March	a				22 31	
Ely 6	a	22 26			22 51	
Cambridge	a				23 07	
Audley End	a					
Stansted Airport ✈	a					
Thetford	a	22 50				
Norwich	a	23 24				

A trolley to Peterborough   B until 9 February   C from 16 February

For connections to Ipswich please see Table 14

Table 49R

Sundays
30 March to 11 May

North West England and Birmingham - East Midlands - East Anglia - Stansted Airport

Route Diagram - refer to first Page of Table 49

		XC	EM	XC	EM	XC	EM	XC	EM	XC	EM	XC	EM	XC	EM	EM	XC	XC	EM	EM	EM	XC	EM
		◇1	◇	◇1	◇	◇1	◇	◇1	◇	◇1	◇	◇1	◇	◇1	◇	◇	◇1	◇1	◇	◇	◇	◇1	◇
		A		A		A		A		A													
		🚲		🚲		🚲		🚲		🚲													
Liverpool Lime Street 10	d								12 52		13 52		14 52		15 52	16 52			17 52	18 52	19 52		21 21
Liverpool South Parkway 7 ✈	d								13 03		14 03		15 03		16 03	17 03			18 03	19 03	20 03		21 31
Widnes	d								13 11		14 11		15 11		16 11	17 11			18 11	19 11	20 11		21 39
Warrington Central	d								13 19		14 19		15 19		16 19	17 19			18 19	19 19	20 19		21 47
Manchester Oxford Road	d								13 39		14 39		15 39		16 39	17 39			18 39	19 39	20 39		22 07
Manchester Piccadilly 10 ⛴	d						12 44		13 44		14 44		15 44		16 44	17 44			18 44	19 44	20 44		22 11
Stockport	d						12 55		13 54		14 54		15 54		16 54	17 54			18 54	19 54	20 54		22 28
Sheffield 7 ⛴	a						13 38		14 37		15 35		16 37		17 34	18 36			19 35	20 35	21 34		23 24
	d				12 41		13 48		14 43		15 39		16 41		17 40	18 40			19 40	20 40	21 40		23 27
Chesterfield	d				12 56		14 02		14 57		15 53		16 55		17 54	18 55			19 54	20 54	21 56		23 42
Alfreton	d				13 07		14 12		15 08		16 03		17 05		18 05	19 05			20 05	21 05	22 06		23 52
Langley Mill	d								15 15		16 11		17 13		18 12	19 13			20 12	21 12	22 14		23 59
Nottingham 8 ⛴	a				13 28		14 33		15 32		16 28		17 28		18 28	19 33			20 30	21 33	22 36		00 21
	d		12 37		13 47		14 45		15 50		16 45		17 36		18 46				20 45				
East Midlands Parkway	d																						
Grantham 7	d		13 14		14 22		15 20		16 22		17 21		18 17		19 28				21 20				
Birmingham New Street 12	d	11 22		12 22		13 22		14 22		15 22		16 22		17 22			18 22	19 22				20 22	
Coleshill Parkway	d	11 36		12 36		13 36		14 36		15 36		16 36		17 36			18 36	19 36				20 36	
Nuneaton	d	11 52		12 52		13 52		14 52		15 52		16 52		17 52			18 52	19 52				20 52	
Leicester	d	12 19		13 19		14 19		15 19		16 19		17 19		18 19			19 19	20 19				21 19	
Melton Mowbray	d	12 36		13 36		14 36		15 36		16 36		17 36		18 36			19 36	20 36				21 35	
Oakham	d	12 47		13 47		14 47		15 47		16 47		17 48		18 48			19 48	20 48				21 47	
Stamford	d	13 01		14 01		15 01		16 01		17 01		18 01		19 02			20 01	21 01				22 02	
Peterborough 8	a	13 17	13 40	14 17	14 51	15 17	15 49	16 17	16 52	17 17	17 50	18 17	18 47	19 15	19 57		20 15	21 15	21 51			22 14	
	d	13 18	13 43	14 18	14 58	15 18	15 58	16 18	16 59	17 18	17 57	18 18	18 49	19 18	19 59		20 18	21 18	21 53			22 16	
March	a	13 34		14 34		15 33		16 33		17 33	18 12	18 33		19 32			20 32	21 33				22 31	
Ely 6	a	13 52	14 16	14 52	15 31	15 52	16 31	16 52	17 32	17 52	18 32	18 52	19 22	19 51	20 32		20 51	21 52	22 26			22 51	
Cambridge	a	14 08		15 08		16 08		17 08		18 08		19 08		20 07			21 07	22 07				23 07	
Audley End	a	14 24		15 24		16 25		17 24		18 24		19 24		20 23			21 24	22 25					
Stansted Airport ✈	a	14 45		15 45		16 45		17 45		18 45		19 45		20 45			21 45	22 45					
Thetford	a		14 43		15 55		16 55		17 56		18 56		19 49		20 56				22 50				
Norwich	a		15 22		16 35		17 26		18 30		19 29		20 26		21 37				23 24				

A 🚲 to Peterborough

For connections to Ipswich please see Table 14

Network Diagram for Tables 50, 55, 56, 57

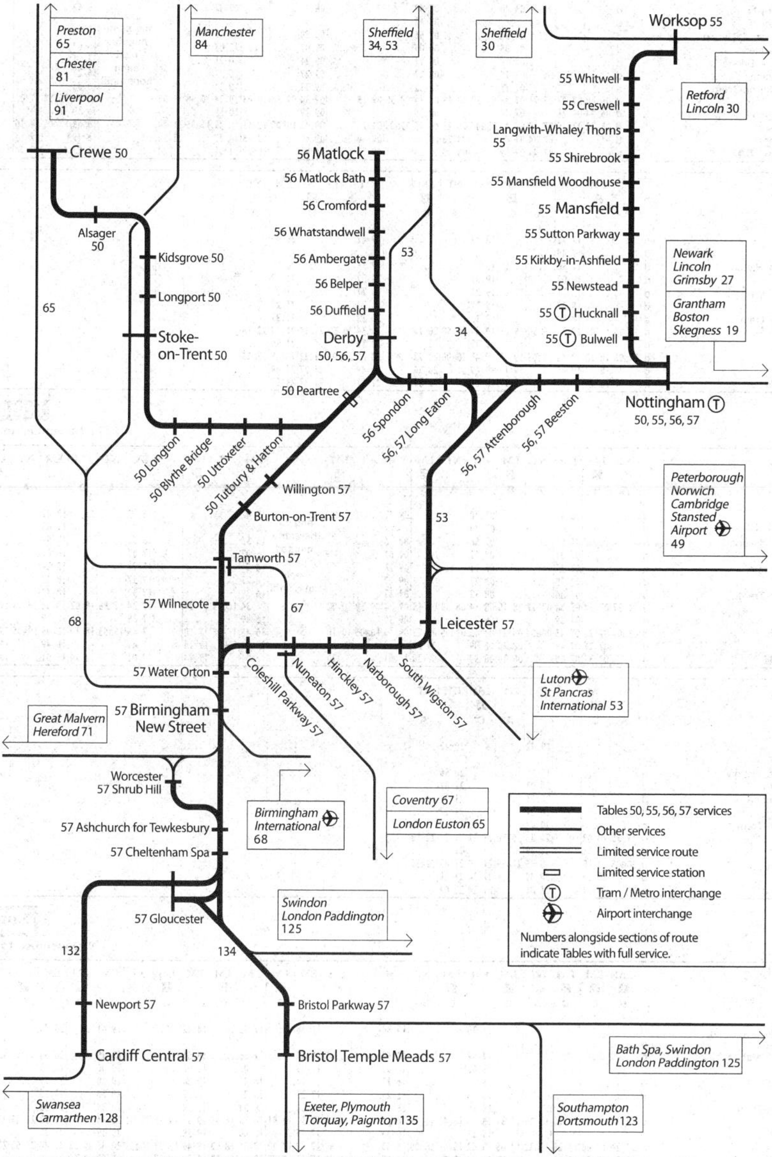

TOCs operating on this network - East Midlands Trains (EM), Northern (NT), London Midland (LM), Cross Country (XC), Arriva Trains Wales (AW), First Great Western (GW)

Table 50

Mondays to Fridays

9 December to 16 May

Derby - Stoke-on-Trent and Crewe

Network Diagram - refer to first Page of Table 50

Miles			NT	NT	LM	EM	NT	LM	EM	NT	LM		EM	NT	LM	EM	NT	LM		EM	NT	LM		EM
					1			1			1				1			1				1		
			A	A	B		A	B		A	C			A	C		A	C			A	C		
0	**Derby 6**	d				06 40			07 40				08 42			09 42			and at the same minutes past each hour until	15 42				16 42
1¼	Peartree	d							07 43															16 44
11¼	Tutbury & Hatton	d				06 54			07 56				08 56			09 56				15 56				16 55
19	Uttoxeter	d				07 05			08 07				09 07			10 07				16 07				17 06
30	Blythe Bridge	d				07 19			08 21				09 21			10 21				16 21				17 21
33½	Longton	d				07 25			08 27				09 27			10 27				16 27				17 27
36	**Stoke-on-Trent**	a				07 31			08 32				09 33			10 33				16 33				17 33
—		d	06 30	07 17	07 21	07 33	07 57	08 15	08 34	08 58	09 15		09 34	09 58	10 03	10 34	10 58	11 02		16 34	16 58	17 02		17 34
38¾	Longport	d	06 34	07 21		07 38			08 39				09 39			10 39				16 39				17 39
42¼	Kidsgrove	d	06a38	07a25	07 30	07 44	08a04	08 23	08 45	09a05	09 24		09 45	10a05	10 11	10 45	11a05	11 10		16 45	17a05	17 10		17 46
44½	Alsager	d			07 34	07 48		08 28	08 49		09 28		09 49		10 15	10 49		11 14		16 49		17 14		17 50
51	**Crewe 10**	a			07 44	07 59		08 38	08 59		09 38		10 01		10 29	11 01		11 24		17 01		17 24		18 01

		NT	LM	EM	NT	LM	EM	NT	LM		EM	NT	LM	EM	NT
			1			1			1				1		
		A	C		A	C		A	C			A	C		A
Derby 6	d			17 42			18 42				19 42			20 40	
Peartree	d			17 44											
Tutbury & Hatton	d			17 56			18 56				19 56			20 56	
Uttoxeter	d			18 07			19 07				20 07			21 07	
Blythe Bridge	d			18 21			19 21				20 21			21 21	
Longton	d			18 27			19 27				20 27			21 27	
Stoke-on-Trent	a			18 32			19 33				20 33			21 33	
	d	17 58	18 02	18 34	18 58	19 05	19 34	19 58	20 14		20 34	20 58	21 14	21 34	22 18
Longport	d			18 39			19 39				20 39			21 39	
Kidsgrove	d	18a05	18 10	18 45	19a05	19 13	19 45	20a05	20 22		20 45	21a05	21 23	21 45	22a25
Alsager	d		18 14	18 49		19 17	19 49		20 26		20 49		21 27	21 49	
Crewe 10	a		18 24	19 01		19 27	20 01		20 37		21 01		21 37	21 59	

Saturdays

14 December to 17 May

		NT	LM	EM	NT	LM	EM	NT	LM	EM	NT	LM		EM	NT	LM		EM	NT	LM	EM	NT	LM	EM
			1			1			1			1				1				1			1	
		A	B		A	B		A	C		A	C			A	C			A	C		A	C	
Derby 6	d			06 40			07 40			08 42			and at the same minutes past each hour until	15 42				16 42			17 42			18 42
Peartree	d						07 44														17 45			
Tutbury & Hatton	d			06 56			07 56			08 56				15 56				16 56			17 57			18 56
Uttoxeter	d			07 07			08 07			09 07				16 07				17 07			18 07			19 07
Blythe Bridge	d			07 21			08 21			09 21				16 21				17 21			18 21			19 21
Longton	d			07 28			08 27			09 27				16 27				17 27			18 27			19 27
Stoke-on-Trent	a			07 34			08 32			09 33				16 33				17 32			18 32			19 33
	d	06 57	07 14	07 34	07 57	08 15	08 34	08 58	09 15	09 34	09 58	10 02		16 34	16 58	17 02		17 34	17 58	18 02	18 34	18 58	19 02	19 34
Longport	d			07 39			08 39			09 39				16 39				17 39			18 39			19 39
Kidsgrove	d	07a04	07 23	07 45	08a04	08 23	08 45	09a05	09 23	09 45	10a05	10 10		16 45	17a05	17 10		17 45	18a05	18 10	18 45	19a05	19 10	19 45
Alsager	d		07 27	07 49		08 28	08 49		09 28	09 49		10 14		16 49		17 14		17 49		18 14	18 49		19 14	19 49
Crewe 10	a		07 37	07 59		08 38	08 59		09 38	10 01		10 24		17 01		17 24		18 01		18 24	19 01		19 24	20 01

		NT	LM		EM	NT	LM	EM	NT
			1				1		
		A	C			A	C		A
Derby 6	d				19 42			20 42	
Peartree	d								
Tutbury & Hatton	d				19 56			20 56	
Uttoxeter	d				20 07			21 07	
Blythe Bridge	d				20 21			21 21	
Longton	d				20 27			21 27	
Stoke-on-Trent	a				20 33			21 33	
	d	19 58	20 02		20 34	20 58	21 02	21 34	22 18
Longport	d				20 39			21 39	
Kidsgrove	d	20a05	20 10		20 45	21a05	21 10	21 45	22a25
Alsager	d		20 14		20 49		21 14	21 49	
Crewe 10	a		20 24		21 01		21 24	22 01	

Sundays

8 December to 11 May

		LM	LM	LM	NT	LM	EM	LM	NT	EM		LM	EM	LM	EM	LM	EM	LM	NT	EM	LM	EM	LM	NT	LM
		1	1	1		1		1				1		1		1		1			1		1		1
		B	C	C	A	C		C	A			C		C		C		C	A		C		C	A	A
Derby 6	d						14 38			15 38			16 38		17 42		18 42			19 41		20 40			
Peartree	d																								
Tutbury & Hatton	d						14 52			15 52			16 52		17 56		18 56			19 55		20 54			
Uttoxeter	d						15 03			16 03			17 03		18 06		19 06			20 06		21 05			
Blythe Bridge	d						15 17			16 17			17 17		18 21		19 20			20 20		21 19			
Longton	d						15 23			16 23			17 23		18 27		19 27			20 26		21 25			
Stoke-on-Trent	a						15 30			16 31			17 30		18 34		19 34			20 34		21 33			
	d	11 16	12 40	13 20	13 25	14 37	15 30	15 41	16 01	16 31		16 41	17 30	17 41	18 35	18 45	19 34	19 45	20 01	20 34	20 45	21 33	21 45	22 39	22 45
Longport	d						15 35			16 36			17 35		18 40		19 39			20 39		21 38			
Kidsgrove	d	11 24	12 48	13 28	13a32	14 45	15 42	15 49	16a08	16 43		16 49	17 42	17 49	18 46	18 53	19 46	19 53	20a08	20 46	20 53	21 44	21 53	22a46	22 53
Alsager	d	11 28	12 52	13 32		14 50	15 46	15 53		16 47		16 53	17 46	17 53	18 50	18 57	19 50	19 57		20 50	20 57	21 49	21 57		22 57
Crewe 10	a	11 43	13 02	13 43		15 00	16 00	16 03		17 00		17 03	18 02	18 03	19 02	19 07	20 03	20 07		21 00	21 07	22 00	22 07		23 07

A To Manchester Piccadilly
B From Northampton
C From London Euston

Table 50R

Crewe and Stoke-on-Trent - Derby

Mondays to Fridays

9 December to 16 May

Network Diagram - refer to first Page of Table 50

Miles	Station		NT A	EM	LM 1 B	EM	LM 1 B	EM	NT C	LM 1 B		EM	NT C	LM 1 B	EM	NT C	LM 1 B	EM	NT C	LM 1 B	EM	NT C
0	**Crewe** 10	d		06 07	06 52	06 58	07 55	08 07		09 02	and at the same minutes past each hour until	14 07		15 02	15 07		16 02	16 07		17 02	17 07	
6¼	Alsager	d		06 16	07 01	07 07	08 05	08 16		09 11		14 16		15 11	15 16		16 11	16 16		17 11	17 16	
8½	Kidsgrove	d	06 16	06 21	07 08	07 12	08 09	08 21	08 32	09 15		14 21	14 32	15 15	15 21	15 32	16 15	16 21	16 32	17 15	17 21	17 31
12	Longport	d		06 27		07 18		08 27				14 27			15 27			16 27			17 27	
15	**Stoke-on-Trent**	a	06 26	06 31	07 16	07 23	08 17	08 31	08 42	09 23		14 31	14 42	15 23	15 31	15 42	16 23	16 31	16 42	17 23	17 31	17 41
—		d		06 33		07 24		08 33				14 33			15 33			16 33			17 33	
17½	Longton	d		06 39		07 30		08 39				14 39			15 39			16 39			17 39	
20¾	Blythe Bridge	d		06 45		07 36		08 45				14 45			15 45			16 45			17 45	
31¾	Uttoxeter	d		06 58		07 49		08 58				14 58			15 58			16 58			17 58	
39½	Tutbury & Hatton	d		07 07		07 58		09 07				15 07			16 07			17 07			18 07	
49½	Peartree	d		07 19											16 19							
51	**Derby** 6	a		07 25		08 16		09 26				15 26			16 26			17 26			18 26	

Station		LM 1 B	EM	NT C	LM 1 D	EM	NT C	LM 1 D	NT C	EM	NT C	NT C
Crewe 10	d	18 02	18 07		19 02	19 07		20 15		20 45		
Alsager	d	18 11	18 16		19 11	19 16		20 24		20 58		
Kidsgrove	d	18 15	18 21	18 32	19 15	19 21	19 32	20 28	20 32	21 07	21 32	22 32
Longport	d		18 27			19 27				21 12		
Stoke-on-Trent	a	18 25	18 31	18 42	19 23	19 31	19 42	20 36	20 42	21 16	21 42	22 42
	d		18 33			19 33				21 18		
Longton	d		18 39			19 39				21 24		
Blythe Bridge	d		18 45			19 45				21 30		
Uttoxeter	d		18 58			19 58				21 42		
Tutbury & Hatton	d		19 07			20 07				21 51		
Peartree	d											
Derby 6	a		19 26			20 25				22 09		

Saturdays

14 December to 17 May

Station		NT A	EM	LM 1 B	EM	NT C	LM 1 B	EM	NT C		LM 1 B	EM	NT C	LM 1 B	EM	NT C	LM 1 B	EM	NT C	LM 1 B	EM	NT C
Crewe 10	d		06 07	06 59	07 07		08 02	08 07		and at the same minutes past each hour until	14 02	14 07		15 02	15 07		16 02	16 07		17 02	17 07	
Alsager	d		06 16	07 07	07 16		08 11	08 16			14 11	14 16		15 11	15 16		16 11	16 16		17 11	17 16	
Kidsgrove	d	06 16	06 21	07 12	07 21	07 28	08 15	08 21	08 32		14 15	14 21	14 32	15 15	15 21	15 32	16 15	16 21	16 32	17 15	17 21	17 31
Longport	d		06 27		07 27			08 27				14 27			15 27			16 27			17 27	
Stoke-on-Trent	a	06 26	06 31	07 20	07 31	07 40	08 23	08 31	08 42		14 23	14 31	14 42	15 23	15 31	15 42	16 23	16 31	16 42	17 23	17 31	17 41
	d		06 33		07 33			08 33				14 33			15 33			16 33			17 33	
Longton	d		06 39		07 39			08 39				14 39			15 39			16 39			17 39	
Blythe Bridge	d		06 45		07 45			08 45				14 45			15 45			16 45			17 45	
Uttoxeter	d		06 58		07 58			08 58				14 58			15 58			16 58			17 58	
Tutbury & Hatton	d		07 07		08 07			09 07				15 07			16 07			17 07			18 07	
Peartree	d		07 19												16 19							
Derby 6	a		07 25		08 25			09 25				15 25			16 25			17 25			18 25	

Station		LM 1 D	EM	NT C	LM 1 D	EM	NT C	NT C	EM	NT C	NT C
Crewe 10	d	18 02	18 07		19 02	19 07			20 45		
Alsager	d	18 11	18 16		19 11	19 16			20 54		
Kidsgrove	d	18 15	18 21	18 32	19 15	19 21	19 32	20 32	21 08	21 32	22 32
Longport	d		18 27			19 27			21 14		
Stoke-on-Trent	a	18 25	18 31	18 42	19 25	19 31	19 42	20 42	21 18	21 42	22 42
	d		18 33			19 33			21 19		
Longton	d		18 39			19 39			21 25		
Blythe Bridge	d		18 45			19 45			21 31		
Uttoxeter	d		18 58			19 58			21 44		
Tutbury & Hatton	d		19 07			20 07			21 53		
Peartree	d										
Derby 6	a		19 25			20 25			22 11		

Sundays

8 December to 11 May

Station		LM 1 B	LM 1 B	LM 1 B	NT C	LM 1 B	LM 1 B	EM	LM 1 B	EM	NT C	LM 1 B	EM	LM 1 B	EM	LM 1 B	EM	LM 1 B	EM	NT C	LM 1 B	EM F
Crewe 10	d	09 30	10 37	11 37		12 37	13 37	14 04	14 33	15 05		15 37	16 08	16 33	17 08	17 37	18 08	18 37	19 08		19 37	20 15
Alsager	d	09 38	10 46	11 46		12 46	13 46	14 13	14 42	15 14		15 46	16 17	16 42	17 17	17 46	18 17	18 46	19 17		19 46	20 24
Kidsgrove	d	09 43	10 50	11 50	12 25	12 50	13 50	14 18	14 46	15 21	15 25	15 50	16 22	16 46	17 22	17 50	18 22	18 50	19 22	19 28	19 50	20 30
Longport	d							14 24		15 26			16 29		17 29		18 29		19 29			20 35
Stoke-on-Trent	a	09 51	10 58	11 58	12 35	12 58	13 58	14 29	14 54	15 30	15 37	15 58	16 35	16 54	17 33	17 58	18 34	18 58	19 33	19 40	19 58	20 40
	d							14 29		15 32			16 35		17 35		18 35		19 35			20 40
Longton	d							14 35		15 38			16 41		17 41		18 41		19 41			20 46
Blythe Bridge	d							14 41		15 44			16 47		17 47		18 47		19 47			20 52
Uttoxeter	d							14 54		15 56			16 59		17 59		18 59		19 59			21 05
Tutbury & Hatton	d							15 03		16 06			17 08		18 08		19 08		20 08			21 14
Peartree	d																					
Derby 6	a							15 19		16 24			17 27		18 28		19 28		20 28			21 34

A From Macclesfield
B To London Euston
C From Manchester Piccadilly
D To Northampton
F Arrives Derby 3 minutes later from 16 February until 23 March

Table 50R

Sundays

8 December to 11 May

Crewe and Stoke-on-Trent - Derby

Network Diagram - refer to first Page of Table 50

		LM 1 A	EM C	NT D
Crewe 10	d	20 44	21 16	
Alsager	d	20 53	21 25	
Kidsgrove	d	20 59	21 30	22 26
Longport	d		21 36	
Stoke-on-Trent	a	21 06	21 40	22 36
	d		21 42	
Longton	d		21 48	
Blythe Bridge	d		21 54	
Uttoxeter	d		22 06	
Tutbury & Hatton	d		22 15	
Peartree	d			
Derby 6	a		22 36	

A To Northampton

C Arrives Derby 2 minutes later from 16 February until 23 March

D From Manchester Piccadilly

Route Diagram for Table 51

This Table summarises through services which, with their associated connecting services at Birmingham New Street, link centres in the North and South of the country. In certain instances a faster journey is possible via London and the relevant Table(s) should be consulted.

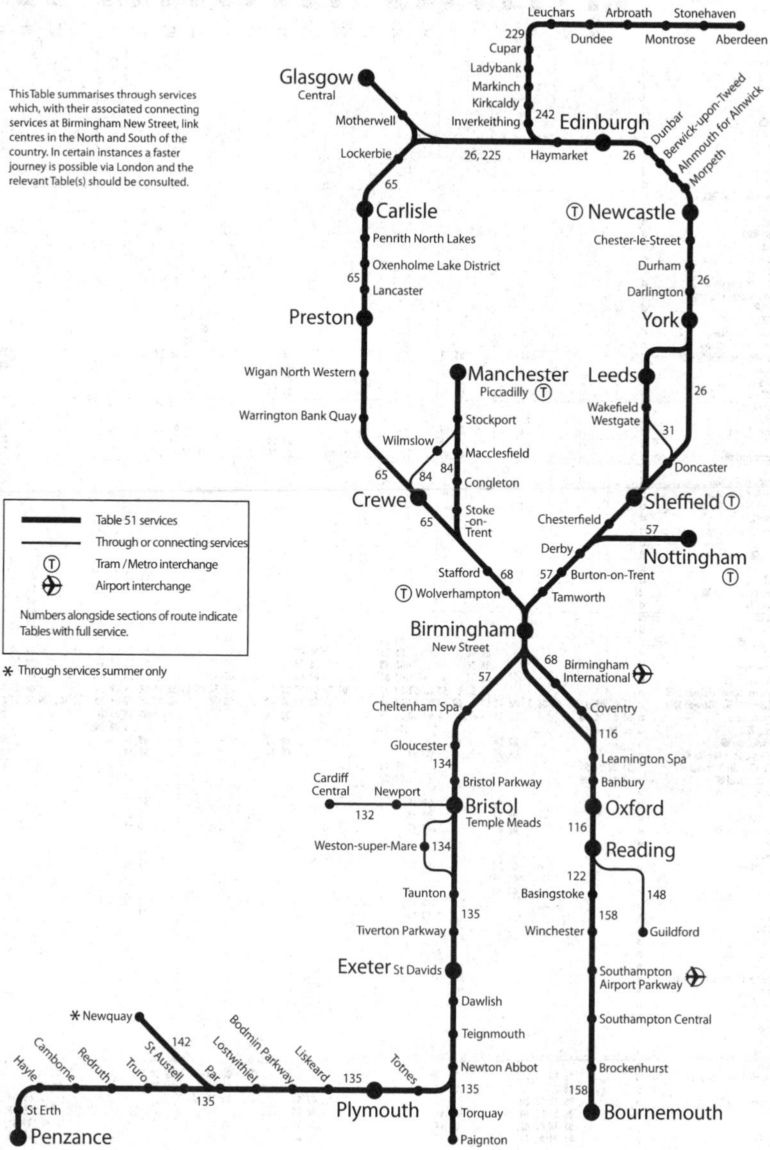

* Through services summer only

TOCs operating on this network - Cross Country (XC), Virgin Trains (VT)

Table 51

Mondays to Fridays

9 December to 16 May

Scotland, The North East, North West England - The South West and South Coast

Route Diagram - see first Page of Table 51

XC in W.of England & S. Wales 132, 134, 135

		XC	XC	XC	XC	XC	XC	XC	XC	XC	VT	XC	XC	VT	XC	VT	VT	XC	XC	VT	XC	XC	XC
		◇1	◇1	◇1	◇1	◇1	◇1	◇1	◇1	◇1	◇1	◇1	◇1	◇1	◇1	◇1	◇1	◇1	◇1	◇1	◇1	◇1	1
										A					B								
				⊥		⊥		⊥	⊥	⊥	⊠		⊥	⊠	⊥	⊠	⊠	⊥		⊠	⊥	⊥	
Aberdeen	d																						
Stonehaven	d																						
Montrose	d																						
Arbroath	d																						
Dundee	d																						
Leuchars 3	d																						
Cupar	d																						
Ladybank	d																						
Markinch	d																						
Kirkcaldy	d																						
Inverkeithing	d																						
Glasgow Central 15	d																						
Motherwell	d																						
Haymarket	d																						
Edinburgh 10	d																						
Haymarket	d																						
Lockerbie	d																						
Carlisle 8	d																						
Penrith North Lakes	d																						
Oxenholme Lake District	d																						
Lancaster 6	d																						
Preston 8	d																06 16							
Wigan North Western	d																06 27							
Warrington Bank Quay	d																06 38							
M'chester Piccadilly 10	d							05 11					06 00				06 27					07 07	
Stockport	d												06 08				06 35					07 16	
Wilmslow	d												06 16										
Crewe 10	d							05 47					06 38			07 01							
Macclesfield	d																06 48						
Congleton	d																						
Stoke-on-Trent	d							06 07									07 06					07 44	
Stafford	d							06 25					06 58				07 28					08 02	
Wolverhampton 7	d							06 41			07 05		07 16			07 37	07 45					08 16	
Dunbar	d																						
Berwick-upon-Tweed	d																						
Alnmouth for Alnwick	d																						
Morpeth	d																						
Newcastle 8	d																						
Chester-le-Street	d																						
Durham	d																						
Darlington 7	d																						
York 8	d																						
Leeds 10	d																	06 00			06 16		
Wakefield Westgate 7	d																	06 12			06 28		
Doncaster 7	d																				06 46		
Sheffield 7	d											06 01						06 52			07 18		
Chesterfield	d											06 26						07 06			07 30		
Nottingham 8	d									06 00					06 37				07 04				07 37
Derby 6	d						06 10			06 36		06 48			07 06			07 27	07 36		07 50		08 06
Burton-on-Trent	d						06 20			06 48		06 58			07 17			07 38	07 50		08 00		08 18
Tamworth	d						06 31		←	07 01		07 09			07 30			07 50	08 03		08 11		08 30
Birmingham New Street 12	a						06 52	06 57	06 52	07 25	07 25	07 27	07 33		07 54	08 01	08 05	08 09	08 24		08 27	08 34	08 54
Birmingham New Street 12	d	05 00	05 37	06 04	06 33	06 42	07 12	07 04	07 12	07 30		07 33	07 42		08 04		08 10	08 12	08 30	08 30	08 33	08 42	
Cheltenham Spa	a	06 01	06 36			07 21	→		07 50	08 13			08 24					08 49	09 10			09 24	
Gloucester 7	a	06 16	06 53							08 23									09 20				
Bristol Parkway 7	a					07 54			08 25				08 53					09 24				09 53	
Bristol Temple Meads 10	a					08 05			08 39				09 14					09 38				10 08	
Newport (South Wales)	a	07 08	07 52							09 12									10 11				
Cardiff Central 7	a	07 26	08 08							09 30									10 27				
Weston-super-Mare	a																						
Taunton	a					08 41			09 15									10 17					
Tiverton Parkway	a					08 53			09 27									10 29					
Exeter St Davids 6	a					09 07			09 42									10 45					
Dawlish	a																						
Teignmouth	a																						
Newton Abbot	a					09 28			10 01									11 06					
Torquay	a					09 39																	
Paignton	a					09 46																	
Totnes	a								10 16									11 20					
Plymouth	a								10 46									11 47					
Liskeard 6	a																						
Bodmin Parkway	a																						
Lostwithiel	a																						
Par	a																						
Newquay (Summer Only)	a																						
St Austell	a																						
Truro	a																						
Redruth	a																						
Camborne	a																						
Hayle	a																						
St Erth	a																						
Penzance	a																						
Birmingham International ✈	d			06 14				07 14						07 41	08 14		08 20			08 40			
Coventry	d			06 25				07 25						07a51	08 25		08a30			08a50			
Leamington Spa 8	d			06 37	07 00			07 38				07 59			08 38						09 00		
Banbury	a			06 53	07 18			07 55				08 15			08 54						09 18		
Oxford	a			07 14	07 41			08 14				08 39			09 14						09 41		
Reading 7	a			07 41	08 13			08 39				09 08			09 39						10 12		
Guildford	a																						
Basingstoke	a			08 08	08 40			09 09							10 08						10 38		
Winchester	a			08 24	08 56			09 24							10 24						10 54		
Southampton Airport Pkway ✈	a			08 32	09 08			09 32							10 32						11 07		
Southampton Central ⛴	a			08 44	09 17			09 41							10 43						11 17		
Brockenhurst 3	a			08 59				09 56							10 58								
Bournemouth	a			09 14				10 12							11 12								

A ⊥ from Birmingham New Street to Newport (South Wales)

B ⊥ from Birmingham New Street

Table 51

Mondays to Fridays

9 December to 16 May

Scotland, The North East, North West England - The South West and South Coast

Route Diagram - see first Page of Table 51
XC in W.of England & S. Wales 132, 134, 135

		XC	VT	XC	XC	VT	XC	XC	XC	XC	VT	XC	XC	VT	XC	XC	XC	XC	XC	VT	XC	XC	VT
																		FX	FO				
		R					R																
		◇1	◇1	◇1	◇1	◇1	◇1	◇1	1	◇1	◇1	◇1	◇1	◇1	◇1	◇1	1	◇1	◇1	◇1	◇1	◇1	◇1
		A		B	C		A																
		trolley	⊠	trolley	trolley	⊠	trolley	trolley		trolley	⊠	trolley	trolley	⊠	trolley	trolley		trolley	trolley	⊠	trolley	trolley	restaurant
Aberdeen	d																						
Stonehaven	d																						
Montrose	d																						
Arbroath	d																						
Dundee	d																						
Leuchars 3	d																						
Cupar	d																						
Ladybank	d																						
Markinch	d																						
Kirkcaldy	d																						
Inverkeithing	d																						
Glasgow Central 15	d										05 50												
Motherwell	d										06 04												
Haymarket	d																						
Edinburgh 10	d																			06 52	06 06		
Haymarket	d																			06 56			
Lockerbie	d																						
Carlisle 8	d										07 02									08 06			
Penrith North Lakes	d										07 18									08 21			
Oxenholme Lake District	d										07 41												
Lancaster 6	d		06 58								07 56									08 57			
Preston 8	d		07 17								08 17									09 16			
Wigan North Western	d		07 28								08 28									09 28			
Warrington Bank Quay	d		07 39								08 39									09 39			
M'chester Piccadilly 10	d	07 27						08 07		08 27						09 07		09 27	09 27				
Stockport	d	07 35						08 16		08 35						09 16		09 35	09 35				
Wilmslow	d																						
Crewe 10	d		08 01								09 01									10 01			
Macclesfield	d	07 49								08 49								09 49	09 49				
Congleton	d																						
Stoke-on-Trent	d	08 07						08 44		09 07						09 44		10 07	10 07				
Stafford	d	08 25						09 03		09 25						10 03		10 25	10 25				
Wolverhampton 7	d	08 41	08 45					09 16		09 41	09 45					10 17		10 41	10 41	10 45			
Dunbar	d																						
Berwick-upon-Tweed	d																				06 47		
Alnmouth for Alnwick	d																				07 08		
Morpeth	d																						
Newcastle 8	d						06 24					06 45			07 25						07 41		
Chester-le-Street	d																						
Durham	d						06 37					06 58			07 37						07 55		
Darlington 7	d						06 54					07 16			07 55						08 12		
York 8	d			06 32			07 23					07 45			08 26						08 45		
Leeds 10	d			07 05								08 11									09 11		
Wakefield Westgate 7	d			07 19								08 23									09 24		
Doncaster 7	d						07 56								08 51								
Sheffield 7	d			07 53			08 20					08 56			09 24						09 55		
Chesterfield	d			08 06			08 32					09 08									10 06		
Nottingham 8	d				08 12				08 41				09 10				09 41					10 10	
Derby 6	d			08 28	08 37		08 53		09 11			09 28	09 36		09 53		10 11				10 28	10 36	
Burton-on-Trent	d			08 38	08 49				09 22			09 38	09 50				10 22					10 49	
Tamworth	d			08 50	09 02				09 34				10 02				10 34				10 48	11 02	
Birmingham New Street 12	a	08 58	09 05	09 10	09 24		09 27	09 32	09 56	09 58	10 05	10 06	10 24		10 27	10 33	10 56	10 58	10 58	11 05	11 09	11 25	
Birmingham New Street 12	d	09 04	09 10	09 20	09 30	09 30	09 33	09 42		10 04	10 10	10 20	10 30	10 30	10 33	10 42		11 04	11 04	11 10	11 20	11 30	11 30
Cheltenham Spa	a			09 59	10 10			10 24				11 01	11 10			11 24					11 59	12 10	
Gloucester 7	a				10 20								11 20									12 20	
Bristol Parkway 7	a			10 29				10 53				11 30				11 53					12 30		
Bristol Temple Meads 10	a			10 42				11 10				11 40				12 05					12 41		
Newport (South Wales)	a				11 11								12 10									13 11	
Cardiff Central 7	a				11 27								12 26									13 29	
Weston-super-Mare	a							11 32															
Taunton	a			11 16				12 00				12 15									13 16		
Tiverton Parkway	a			11 29				12 12				12 27									13 29		
Exeter St Davids 6	a			11 44				12 26				12 42									13 44		
Dawlish	a							12 39															
Teignmouth	a							12 44															
Newton Abbot	a			12 04				12 51				13 01									14 04		
Torquay	a							13 02															
Paignton	a							13 10															
Totnes	a			12 18								13 14									14 18		
Plymouth	a			12 47								13 41									14 46		
Liskeard 6	a																						
Bodmin Parkway	a																						
Lostwithiel	a																						
Par	a																						
Newquay (Summer Only)	a																						
St Austell	a																						
Truro	a																						
Redruth	a																						
Camborne	a																						
Hayle	a																						
St Erth	a																						
Penzance	a																						
Birmingham International ✈	d	09 14	09 20			09 40				10 14	10 20			10 40				11 14	11 14	11 20			11 40
Coventry	d	09 25	09a30			09a50				10 25	10a30			10a50				11 25	11 25	11a30			11a50
Leamington Spa 8	d	09 38					10 00			10 38					11 00			11 38	11 38				
Banbury	a	09 54					10 17			10 54					11 17			11 54	11 56				
Oxford	a	10 13					10 41			11 14					11 41			12 14	12 14				
Reading 7	a	10 39					11 09			11 39					12 12			12 39	12 39				
Guildford	a																						
Basingstoke	a	11 08								12 08					12 39			13 08	13 08				
Winchester	a	11 24								12 24					12 54			13 24	13 24				
Southampton Airport Pkwy ✈	a	11 32								12 32					13 08			13 32	13 32				
Southampton Central	a	11 43								12 41					13 17			13 41	13 41				
Brockenhurst 3	a	11 58								12 56								13 56	13 56				
Bournemouth	a	12 12								13 10								14 10	14 10				

A ◇ from Birmingham New Street R to Birmingham New Street

B trolley from Leeds

C trolley from Birmingham New Street

Table 51

Mondays to Fridays

9 December to 16 May

Scotland, The North East, North West England - The South West and South Coast

Route Diagram - see first Page of Table 51
XC in W.of England & S. Wales 132, 134, 135

		XC		XC	XC	XC	VT	XC	XC	VT	XC	XC		XC	XC	VT	XC	XC	VT	XC	XC	XC		XC	VT
		◇1		◇1	1	◇1	◇1	◇1	◇1	◇1	◇1	◇1		1	◇1	◇1	◇1	◇1	◇1	◇1	◇1	1		◇1	◇1
								A									A								
		🛒		🛒		🛒	⊠	🛒	🛒	☕	🛒	🛒			🛒	⊠	🛒	🛒	☕	🛒	🛒			🛒	⊠
Aberdeen	d																								
Stonehaven	d																								
Montrose	d																								
Arbroath	d																								
Dundee	d																06 32								
Leuchars 3	d																06 46								
Cupar	d																06 54								
Ladybank	d																07 03								
Markinch	d																07 11								
Kirkcaldy	d																07 21								
Inverkeithing	d																07 41								
Glasgow Central 15	d						08 00	06 01																	10 00
Motherwell	d							06 17																	
Haymarket	d							06 57									07 59								
Edinburgh 10	d	07 00						07 07								08 52	08 10								
Haymarket	d															08 57									
Lockerbie	d																								
Carlisle 8	d						09 10									10 08									11 10
Penrith North Lakes	d																								11 25
Oxenholme Lake District	d															10 43									
Lancaster 6	d						09 56									10 57									
Preston 8	d						10 17									11 17									12 17
Wigan North Western	d						10 28									11 28									12 28
Warrington Bank Quay	d						10 39									11 39									12 39
M'chester Piccadilly 10 ⛴	d			10 07		10 27						11 07			11 27						12 07			12 27	
Stockport	d			10 16		10 35						11 16			11 35						12 16			12 35	
Wilmslow	d																								
Crewe 10	d						11 01									12 01									13 01
Macclesfield	d					10 49									11 49									12 49	
Congleton	d																								
Stoke-on-Trent	d			10 44		11 07						11 44			12 07						12 44			13 07	
Stafford	d			11 02		11 25						12 03			12 25						13 02			13 25	
Wolverhampton 7 ⛴	d			11 16		11 41	11 45					12 16			12 41	12 45					13 17			13 41	13 45
Dunbar	d							07 27																	
Berwick-upon-Tweed	d	07 39															08 51								
Alnmouth for Alnwick	d	07 59																							
Morpeth	d	08 13																							
Newcastle 8	d	08 35						08 43			09 35						09 42			10 35					
Chester-le-Street	d																								
Durham	d	08 48						08 56			09 48						09 56			10 48					
Darlington 7	d	09 05						09 13			10 05						10 13			11 05					
York 8	d	09 35						09 45			10 35						10 45			11 34					
Leeds 10	d							10 11									11 11								
Wakefield Westgate 7	d							10 23									11 24								
Doncaster 7	d	09 58									10 59									11 58					
Sheffield 7 ⛴	d	10 24						10 55			11 24						11 55			12 24					
Chesterfield	d							11 07									12 06								
Nottingham 8 ⛴	d				10 41				11 10					11 41				12 10				12 41			
Derby 6	d	10 53			11 11			11 28	11 37		11 53			12 11			12 28	12 37		12 53		13 11			
Burton-on-Trent	d				11 22				11 49					12 22				12 49				13 25			
Tamworth	d				11 34				12 02					12 34			12 48	13 02				13 36			
Birmingham New Street 12	a	11 27		11 33	11 56	11 58	12 05	12 07	12 24		12 27	12 33		12 56	12 58	13 05	13 08	13 24		13 27	13 33	13 56		13 58	14 05
Birmingham New Street 12	d	11 33		11 42		12 04	12 10	12 20	12 30	12 30	12 33	12 42			13 04	13 10	13 20	13 30	13 30	13 33	13 42			14 04	14 10
Cheltenham Spa	a			12 24				13 01	13 10			13 24					13 58	14 10			14 24				
Gloucester 7	a								13 20									14 23							
Bristol Parkway 7	a			12 53				13 31				13 57					14 30				14 53				
Bristol Temple Meads 10	a			13 09				13 41				14 08					14 41				15 10				
Newport (South Wales)	a								14 10									15 10							
Cardiff Central 7	a								14 27									15 30							
Weston-super-Mare	a																								
Taunton	a							14 15									15 16				15 44				
Tiverton Parkway	a							14 27									15 29				15 56				
Exeter St Davids 6	a							14 42									15 45				16 12				
Dawlish	a																								
Teignmouth	a																								
Newton Abbot	a							15 01									16 05								
Torquay	a																								
Paignton	a																								
Totnes	a							15 14									16 19								
Plymouth	a							15 41									16 48								
Liskeard 6	a																								
Bodmin Parkway	a																								
Lostwithiel	a																								
Par	a																								
Newquay (Summer Only)	a																								
St Austell	a																								
Truro	a																								
Redruth	a																								
Camborne	a																								
Hayle	a																								
St Erth	a																								
Penzance	a																								
Birmingham International ✈	d					12 14	12 20			12 40					13 14	13 20			13 40					14 14	14 20
Coventry	d					12 25	12a30			12a50					13 25	13a30			13a50					14 24	14a29
Leamington Spa 8	d	12 01				12 38					13 00				13 38					14 00				14 38	
Banbury	a	12 17				12 54					13 21				13 54					14 17				14 54	
Oxford	a	12 41				13 14					13 41				14 13					14 40				15 13	
Reading 7	a	13 07				13 39					14 11				14 39					15 08				15 40	
Guildford	a																								
Basingstoke	a					14 08					14 39				15 08									16 08	
Winchester	a					14 24					14 54				15 24									16 24	
Southampton Airport Pkway ✈	a					14 34					15 08				15 32									16 32	
Southampton Central ⛴	a					14 42					15 17				15 41									16 41	
Brockenhurst 3	a					14 56									15 56									16 56	
Bournemouth	a					15 11									16 10									17 10	

A 🛒 from Edinburgh

Table 51

Mondays to Fridays

9 December to 16 May

Scotland, The North East, North West England - The South West and South Coast

Route Diagram - see first Page of Table 51
XC in W.of England & S. Wales 132, 134, 135

		XC	XC	VT	XC	XC	XC	XC	VT	XC	XC	VT	XC	XC	XC	XC	XC	VT	XC	XC	VT	XC	XC
																	R						
		◇1	◇1	◇1	◇1	◇1	1	◇1	◇1	◇1	◇1	◇1	◇1	◇1	1	◇1	◇1	◇1	◇1	◇1	◇1	◇1	◇1
		A								B				C			D		E				
		🛒	🛒	🍴	🛒	🛒	🛒	🛒	🍴	🛒	🛒	🍴	🛒	🛒		🛒	🛒	🍴	🛒	🛒	🍴	🛒	🛒
Aberdeen	d																08 20						
Stonehaven	d																08 38						
Montrose	d																08 59						
Arbroath	d																09 15						
Dundee	d																09 32						
Leuchars 3	d																09 47						
Cupar	d																09 54						
Ladybank	d																10 01						
Markinch	d																10 09						
Kirkcaldy	d																10 17						
Inverkeithing	d																10 32						
Glasgow Central 15	d	07 50								09 00								12 00					
Motherwell	d	08 05								09 15													
Haymarket	d	08 51								09 58							10 51						
Edinburgh 10	d	09 08							10 51	10 10							11 06						
Haymarket	d								10 57														
Lockerbie	d																						
Carlisle 8	d								12 08									13 11					
Penrith North Lakes	d																						
Oxenholme Lake District	d								12 43														
Lancaster 6	d								12 57									13 57					
Preston 8	d								13 17									14 17					
Wigan North Western	d								13 28									14 28					
Warrington Bank Quay	d								13 39									14 39					
M'chester Piccadilly 10	d					13 07		13 27						14 07		14 27							15 07
Stockport	d					13 16		13 35						14 16		14 35							15 16
Wilmslow	d																						
Crewe 10	d								14 01									15 01					
Macclesfield	d							13 49								14 49							
Congleton	d																						
Stoke-on-Trent	d					13 44		14 07						14 44		15 08							15 44
Stafford	d					14 02		14 25						15 03		15 25							16 03
Wolverhampton 7	d					14 16		14 41	14 45					15 17		15 41		15 45					16 16
Dunbar	d	09 28															11 27						
Berwick-upon-Tweed	d	09 51								10 49							11 49						
Alnmouth for Alnwick	d																12 09						
Morpeth	d									11 20													
Newcastle 8	d	10 44			11 35					11 44			12 35				12 41					13 35	
Chester-le-Street	d																						
Durham	d	10 56			11 48					11 56			12 48				12 54					13 48	
Darlington 7	d	11 13			12 05					12 13			13 05				13 13					14 05	
York 8	d	11 45			12 35					12 45			13 34				13 45					14 35	
Leeds 10	d	12 11								13 11							14 11						
Wakefield Westgate 7	d	12 23								13 23							14 23						
Doncaster 7	d				12 59								13 58									14 59	
Sheffield 7	d	12 55			13 24					13 55			14 24				14 55					15 24	
Chesterfield	d	13 07								14 07							15 07						
Nottingham 8	d		13 10				13 41				14 10				14 41					15 10			
Derby 6	d	13 28	13 37		13 53		14 11			14 28	14 36		14 53		15 11		15 28			15 37		15 53	
Burton-on-Trent	d	13 38	13 49				14 22				14 50				15 25		15 38			15 49			
Tamworth	d		14 02				14 33			14 47	15 02				15 36				←	16 02			
Birmingham New Street 12	a	14 06	14 24		14 27	14 33	14 56	14 58	15 05	15 07	15 24		15 27	15 33	15 56	15 58	16 03	16 05	16 03	16 24		16 27	16 33
Birmingham New Street 12	d	14 20	14 30	14 30	14 33	14 42		15 04	15 10	15 20	15 30	15 30	15 33	15 42		16 04	16 12	16 10	16 12	16 30	16 30	16 33	16 42
Cheltenham Spa	a	15 01	15 10			15 24				16 00	16 10			16 24			→		16 50	17 13			17 24
Gloucester 7	a		15 20								16 20									17 23			
Bristol Parkway 7	a	15 30				15 55				16 33				16 53					17 25				17 54
Bristol Temple Meads 10	a	15 41				16 10				16 44				17 10					17 39				18 07
Newport (South Wales)	a		16 11								17 11									18 12			
Cardiff Central 7	a		16 29								17 28									18 28			
Weston-super-Mare	a																						
Taunton	a	16 15								17 17				17 44					18 15				
Tiverton Parkway	a	16 27								17 29				17 56					18 27				
Exeter St Davids 6	a	16 41								17 44				18 11					18 42				
Dawlish	a													18 23									
Teignmouth	a													18 28									
Newton Abbot	a	17 02								18 10				18 35					19 06				
Torquay	a													18 47									
Paignton	a													18 55									
Totnes	a	17 15								18 23									19 20				
Plymouth	a	17 42								18 50									19 46				
Liskeard 6	a									19 23									20 11				
Bodmin Parkway	a									19 35									20 23				
Lostwithiel	a																						
Par	a									19 46									20 34				
Newquay (Summer Only)	a																						
St Austell	a									19 52									20 41				
Truro	a									20 09									21 00				
Redruth	a									20 25									21 15				
Camborne	a									20 31									21 22				
Hayle	a																						
St Erth	a									20 42									21 33				
Penzance	a									20 52									21 42				
Birmingham International ✈	d			14 40				15 14	15 20			15 40				16 14		16 20			16 40		
Coventry	d			14a50				15 24	15a30			15a50				16 24		16a30			16a50		
Leamington Spa 8	d				15 00			15 38					16 01			16 38						17 00	
Banbury	a				15 17			15 54					16 17			16 54						17 17	
Oxford	a				15 41			16 13					16 40			17 13						17 40	
Reading 7	a				16 11			16 39					17 07			17 39						18 08	
Guildford	a																					18 59	
Basingstoke	a				16 39			17 08								18 08							
Winchester	a				16 59			17 24								18 24							
Southampton Airport Pkway ✈	a				17 07			17 32								18 32							
Southampton Central	a				17 17			17 41								18 44							
Brockenhurst 3	a							17 56								18 58							
Bournemouth	a							18 15								19 13							

A 🛒 from Edinburgh
B 🛒 from Edinburgh to Plymouth
C 🛒 to Newton Abbot
D 🛒 ◇ from Edinburgh R to Edinburgh
E 🛒 to Plymouth

Table 51

Mondays to Fridays

9 December to 16 May

Scotland, The North East, North West England - The South West and South Coast

Route Diagram - see first Page of Table 51
XC in W.of England & S. Wales 132, 134, 135

		XC	XC	VT	XC	XC	VT	XC	XC	XC	XC	VT	XC	XC	XC	VT	XC	XC	XC	XC	VT	XC
													FO	FX								
		1	◇1	◇1	◇1	◇1	◇1	◇1	◇1	1	◇1	◇1	◇1	◇1	◇1	◇1	◇1	◇1	◇1	1	1	◇1
					A													B	C			D
Aberdeen	d																					
Stonehaven	d																					
Montrose	d																					
Arbroath	d																					
Dundee	d																					
Leuchars [8]	d																					
Cupar	d																					
Ladybank	d																					
Markinch	d																					
Kirkcaldy	d																					
Inverkeithing	d																					
Glasgow Central [15]	d				11 00							14 00										13 00
Motherwell	d				11 14																	13 14
Haymarket	d				11 53																	
Edinburgh [10]	d			12 51	12 08								13 06	13 06							14 51	14 08
Haymarket	d			12 57																	14 57	
Lockerbie	d																					
Carlisle [8]	d			14 08								15 10									16 08	
Penrith North Lakes	d			14 22																	16 21	
Oxenholme Lake District	d											15 44										
Lancaster [6]	d			14 57																	16 57	
Preston [8]	d			15 17								16 17									17 17	
Wigan North Western	d			15 28								16 28									17 28	
Warrington Bank Quay	d			15 39								16 39									17 39	
M'chester Piccadilly [10]	d		15 27						16 07		16 27							17 05	17 27			
Stockport	d		15 35						16 16		16 35							17 13	17 35			
Wilmslow	d																		17 44			
Crewe [10]	d			16 01								17 01							18 07		18 01	
Macclesfield	d		15 49								16 49							17 27				
Congleton	d																					
Stoke-on-Trent	d		16 07						16 44		17 07							17 44				
Stafford	d		16 25						17 03		17 25							18 04	18 28			
Wolverhampton [7]	d		16 41	16 45					17 16		17 41	17 45						18 15	18 41		18 45	
Dunbar	d												13 28	13 28								
Berwick-upon-Tweed	d				12 47																	14 49
Alnmouth for Alnwick	d												14 09	14 09								
Morpeth	d																					
Newcastle [8]	d				13 42			14 35					14 42	14 42			15 03					15 41
Chester-le-Street	d																					
Durham	d				13 55			14 48					14 56	14 56			15 16					15 54
Darlington [7]	d				14 12			15 05					15 13	15 13			15 33					16 12
York [8]	d				14 45			15 34					15 44	15 44			16 05					16 45
Leeds [10]	d				15 11								16 11	16 11			16 40					17 11
Wakefield Westgate [7]	d				15 24								16 23	16 23			16 52					17 23
Doncaster [7]	d							15 58														
Sheffield [7]	d				15 55			16 24					16 54	16 54			17 24					17 58
Chesterfield	d				16 07								17 05	17 07								18 10
Nottingham [8]	d	15 41				16 10				16 41					17 10					17 41		
Derby [6]	d	16 11			16 28	16 36		16 53		17 11			17 27	17 28	17 37		17 53			18 11		18 29
Burton-on-Trent	d	16 22				16 49				17 25			17 38	17 38	17 49					18 24		
Tamworth	d	16 34			16 47	17 02				17 36					18 02					18 36		18 48
Birmingham New Street [12]	a	16 56	16 58	17 05	17 09	17 24		17 28	17 33	17 56	17 58	18 05	18 05	18 05	18 26		18 27	18 32	18 58	18 58	19 05	19 08
Birmingham New Street [12]	d		17 04	17 10	17 12	17 30	17 30	17 33	17 42		18 04	18 10	18 12	18 12	18 30	18 30	18 33	18 42	19 04		19 10	19 12
Cheltenham Spa	a				17 51	18 18			18 24				18 51	18 52	19 14			19 24				19 50
Gloucester [7]	a					18 29									19 24							
Bristol Parkway [7]	a				18 28				18 53				19 26	19 26				19 58				20 28
Bristol Temple Meads [10]	a				18 41				19 05				19 38	19 38				20 09				20 42
Newport (South Wales)	a					19 16									20 11			20 47				
Cardiff Central [7]	a					19 33									20 27			21 02				
Weston-super-Mare	a																					
Taunton	a				19 15								20 16	20 16								21 16
Tiverton Parkway	a				19 27								20 28	20 28								21 28
Exeter St Davids [6]	a				19 42								20 42	20 42								21 43
Dawlish	a																					
Teignmouth	a																					
Newton Abbot	a				20 04								21 01	21 01								22 04
Torquay	a																					
Paignton	a																					
Totnes	a				20 17								21 15	21 15								22 16
Plymouth	a				20 44								21 46	21 46								22 43
Liskeard [6]	a				21 12																	
Bodmin Parkway	a				21 24																	
Lostwithiel	a				21 30																	
Par	a				21 37																	
Newquay (Summer Only)	a																					
St Austell	a				21 44																	
Truro	a				22 01																	
Redruth	a				22 13																	
Camborne	a				22 19																	
Hayle	a				22 27																	
St Erth	a				22 32																	
Penzance	a				22 42																	
Birmingham International ✈	d		17 14	17 20			17 40				18 14	18 20				18 40			19 14		19 20	
Coventry	d		17 24	17a30			17a50				18 24	18a30				18a50			19 24		19a30	
Leamington Spa [8]	d		17 38					18 00			18 37						19 00		19 38			
Banbury	a		17 54					18 18			18 54						19 17		19 54			
Oxford	a		18 15					18 40			19 13						19 39		20 13			
Reading [7]	a		18 40					19 10			19 41						20 08		20 39			
Guildford	a																					
Basingstoke	a		19 08								20 09								21 09			
Winchester	a		19 24								20 24								21 24			
Southampton Airport Pkway ✈	a		19 32								20 32								21 32			
Southampton Central	a		19 41								20 41								21 40			
Brockenhurst [3]	a		19 56								20 58								21 55			
Bournemouth	a		20 12								21 15								22 15			

A from Edinburgh to Plymouth
B to Bristol Temple Meads
C to Reading
D from Edinburgh to Bristol Temple Meads

Table 51

Mondays to Fridays

9 December to 16 May

Scotland, The North East, North West England - The South West and South Coast

Route Diagram - see first Page of Table 51
XC in W.of England & S. Wales 132, 134, 135

		XC	XC	XC	XC	XC	VT	XC	XC	XC	XC	XC	XC	VT	XC	XC	XC	VT	XC	XC	XC	XC	XC
		◇1	◇1	◇1	1	◇1	◇1	◇1	◇1	◇1	◇1	1	◇1	R 1	◇1	◇1	◇1	◇1	1	◇1	◇1	◇1	◇1
						A		B		C	C		A		D							E	
			trolley	trolley	trolley	trolley	⊠	trolley		trolley	trolley	trolley	trolley	⊠	trolley	trolley		⊠				trolley	
Aberdeen	d																						
Stonehaven	d																						
Montrose	d																						
Arbroath	d																						
Dundee	d																						
Leuchars 3	d																						
Cupar	d																						
Ladybank	d																						
Markinch	d																						
Kirkcaldy	d																						
Inverkeithing	d																						
Glasgow Central 15	d						16 00								15 00			17 40					
Motherwell	d														15 14								
Haymarket	d														15 56								
Edinburgh 10	d							15 08						16 52	16 05							17 08	
Haymarket	d													16 57									
Lockerbie	d																	18 35					
Carlisle 8	d						17 09							18 08				18 57					
Penrith North Lakes	d																						
Oxenholme Lake District	d						17 44							18 42				19 32					
Lancaster 6	d													18 57				19 47					
Preston 8	d						18 17							19 16				20 07					
Wigan North Western	d						18 28							19 29				20 19					
Warrington Bank Quay	d						18 39							19 39				20 31					
M'chester Piccadilly 10	d			18 05		18 27					19 07		19 27				20 07			20 27			
Stockport	d			18 13		18 35					19 16		19 35				20 16			20 35			
Wilmslow	d																						
Crewe 10	d						19 01							20 01				20 53					
Macclesfield	d			18 26									19 49							20 49			
Congleton	d					18 54																	
Stoke-on-Trent	d			18 44		19 07					19 44		20 07				20 44			21 07			
Stafford	d			19 02		19 25					20 04		20 28				21 03	21 13		21 25			
Wolverhampton 7	d			19 16		19 41	19 45				20 17		20 44	20 47			21 16	21 32		21 41			
Dunbar	d							15 28														17 28	
Berwick-upon-Tweed	d																					17 51	
Alnmouth for Alnwick	d														17 01								
Morpeth	d														17 16								
Newcastle 8	d		16 35					16 41		17 32					17 41	18 35						18 43	19 35
Chester-le-Street	d									17 41													
Durham	d		16 48					16 52		17 48					17 54	18 48						18 56	19 50
Darlington 7	d		17 05					17 11		18 05					18 12	19 06						19 14	20 07
York 8	d		17 35					17 45		18 34					18 45	19 35						19 45	20 35
Leeds 10	d							18 11							19 11							20 11	
Wakefield Westgate 7	d							18 23							19 24							20 23	
Doncaster 7	d		17 59							18 58						19 59							21 02
Sheffield 7	d		18 24					18 58		19 24					19 54	20 24						20 57	21 29
Chesterfield	d							19 10							20 06							21 09	21 41
Nottingham 8	d	18 10			18 41				19 10			19 40							20 40				
Derby 6	d	18 37	18 53		19 10			19 29	19 36	19 54		20 10			20 28	20 54			21 10			21 29	22 02
Burton-on-Trent	d	18 49			19 21			19 38	19 49			20 21							21 24			21 40	
Tamworth	d	19 02			19 33				20 03			20 33			20 47				21 35			21 50	
Birmingham New Street 12	a	19 24	19 27	19 33	19 55	19 58	20 05	20 09	20 24	20 27	20 33	20 56	21 00	21 05	21 07	21 29	21 33	21 50	21 58	22 00		22 09	22 51
Birmingham New Street 12	d	19 30	19 33	19 42		20 04	20 10	20 12	20 30	20 33	20 42		21 04	21 10	21 12						22 04	22 12	
Cheltenham Spa	a	20 10		20 24				20 51	21 10		21 26				21 51							22 51	
Gloucester 7	a	20 20							21 20						22 01								
Bristol Parkway 7	a			20 55				21 25			22 01				22 32							23 20	
Bristol Temple Meads 10	a			21 05				21 36			22 13				22 43							23 40	
Newport (South Wales)	a	21 10							22 14														
Cardiff Central 7	a	21 28							22 35														
Weston-super-Mare	a																						
Taunton	a			21 44				22 15															
Tiverton Parkway	a			21 56				22 27															
Exeter St Davids 6	a			22 11				22 42															
Dawlish	a																						
Teignmouth	a																						
Newton Abbot	a			22 30				23 06															
Torquay	a																						
Paignton	a																						
Totnes	a			22 43				23 19															
Plymouth	a			23 13				23 45															
Liskeard 6	a																						
Bodmin Parkway	a																						
Lostwithiel	a																						
Par	a																						
Newquay (Summer Only)	a																						
St Austell	a																						
Truro	a																						
Redruth	a																						
Camborne	a																						
Hayle	a																						
St Erth	a																						
Penzance	a																						
Birmingham International	d					20 14	20 20						21 14	21 20							22 14		
Coventry	d					20 24	20a30						21 24	21a30							22 25		
Leamington Spa 8	d		20 04			20 38				21 00			21 38								22 38		
Banbury	a		20 21			20 54				21 17			21 54								22 54		
Oxford	a		20 39			21 13				21 40			22 14								23 14		
Reading 7	a		21 07			21 41				22 17			22 41								23 49		
Guildford	a																						
Basingstoke	a					22 09				22 39			23 05										
Winchester	a					22 24				22 56			23 24										
Southampton Airport Pkway	a					22 32				23 12			23 36										
Southampton Central	a					22 42				23 20			23 43										
Brockenhurst 3	a					22 56																	
Bournemouth	a					23 21																	

A trolley to Reading
B trolley to Bristol Temple Meads
C trolley to Birmingham New Street
D trolley from Edinburgh to Birmingham New Street
E trolley to Leeds

Table 51

Mondays to Fridays

9 December to 16 May

Scotland, The North East, North West England - The South West and South Coast

Route Diagram - see first Page of Table 51

XC in W.of England & S. Wales 132, 134, 135

		VT	XC	XC	XC	XC
		◇1	◇1	1	◇1	◇1
					A	
		☒			✠	
Aberdeen	d					
Stonehaven	d					
Montrose	d					
Arbroath	d					
Dundee	d					
Leuchars 3	d					
Cupar	d					
Ladybank	d					
Markinch	d					
Kirkcaldy	d					
Inverkeithing	d					
Glasgow Central 15	d				16 52	
Motherwell	d				17 06	
Haymarket	d				17 53	
Edinburgh 10	d	18 52			18 05	
Haymarket	d	18 56				
Lockerbie	d					
Carlisle 8	d	20 06				
Penrith North Lakes	d					
Oxenholme Lake District	d	20 41				
Lancaster 6	d	20 56				
Preston 8	d	21 16				
Wigan North Western	d	21 28				
Warrington Bank Quay	d	21 39				
M'chester Piccadilly 10 🚌	d		21 27			22 07
Stockport	d		21 35			22 16
Wilmslow	d					
Crewe 10	d	22 01				
Macclesfield	d		21 49			22 29
Congleton	d					
Stoke-on-Trent	d		22 08			22 47
Stafford	d		22 26			23 07
Wolverhampton 7 🚌	d	22 33	22 41			23 21
Dunbar	d				18 26	
Berwick-upon-Tweed	d				18 49	
Alnmouth for Alnwick	d				19 09	
Morpeth	d					
Newcastle 8	d				19 42	
Chester-le-Street	d					
Durham	d				19 55	
Darlington 7	d				20 13	
York 8	d				20 45	
Leeds 10	d				21 11	
Wakefield Westgate 7	d				21 25	
Doncaster 7	d					
Sheffield 7 🚌	d				22 00	
Chesterfield	d				22 24	
Nottingham 8 🚌	d			21 39		
Derby 6	d			22 11	22 45	
Burton-on-Trent	d			22 22	22 55	
Tamworth	d			22 34	23 06	
Birmingham New Street 12	a	22 58	22 58	23 01	23 25	23 39
Birmingham New Street 12	d					
Cheltenham Spa	a					
Gloucester 7	a					
Bristol Parkway 7	a					
Bristol Temple Meads 10	a					
Newport (South Wales)	a					
Cardiff Central 7	a					
Weston-super-Mare	a					
Taunton	a					
Tiverton Parkway	a					
Exeter St Davids 6	a					
Dawlish	a					
Teignmouth	a					
Newton Abbot	a					
Torquay	a					
Paignton	a					
Totnes	a					
Plymouth	a					
Liskeard 6	a					
Bodmin Parkway	a					
Lostwithiel	a					
Par	a					
Newquay (Summer Only)	a					
St Austell	a					
Truro	a					
Redruth	a					
Camborne	a					
Hayle	a					
St Erth	a					
Penzance	a					
Birmingham International ✈	d					
Coventry	d					
Leamington Spa 8	d					
Banbury	a					
Oxford	a					
Reading 7	a					
Guildford	a					
Basingstoke	a					
Winchester	a					
Southampton Airport Pkway ✈	a					
Southampton Central ⛴	a					
Brockenhurst 3	a					
Bournemouth	a					

A ✠ from Edinburgh to Leeds

Table 51

Saturdays

14 December to 28 December

Scotland, The North East, North West England - The South West and South Coast

Route Diagram - see first Page of Table 51

		XC	XC	XC	XC	XC	XC	XC	XC	XC		XC	XC	XC	VT	XC	XC	VT	XC	XC		XC	XC	VT	XC
		◇1	◇1	◇1	◇1	◇1	◇1	◇1	◇1	◇1		◇1	◇1	◇1	◇1	◇1	◇1	◇1	◇1	◇1		1	◇1	◇1	◇1
										A		B		C											D
				🛒		🛒		🛒	🛒	🛒		🛒	🛒	🛒	🍴	🛒		🍴	🛒	🛒			🛒	🍴	🛒
Aberdeen	d																								
Stonehaven	d																								
Montrose	d																								
Arbroath	d																								
Dundee	d																								
Leuchars 3	d																								
Cupar	d																								
Ladybank	d																								
Markinch	d																								
Kirkcaldy	d																								
Inverkeithing	d																								
Glasgow Central 15	d																								
Motherwell	d																								
Haymarket	d																								
Edinburgh 10	d																								
Haymarket	d																								
Lockerbie	d																								
Carlisle 8	d																								
Penrith North Lakes	d																								
Oxenholme Lake District	d																								
Lancaster 6	d																							06 58	
Preston 8	d														06 17									07 17	
Wigan North Western	d														06 28									07 28	
Warrington Bank Quay	d														06 39									07 39	
M'chester Piccadilly 10 ⇌	d							05 11					06 00							07 07			07 27		
Stockport	d												06 08							07 16			07 35		
Wilmslow	d																								
Crewe 10	d							05 47							07 01									08 01	
Macclesfield	d												06 21										07 49		
Congleton	d																								
Stoke-on-Trent	d							06 08					06 39							07 44			08 07		
Stafford	d							06 26					06 58							08 03			08 26		
Wolverhampton 7 ⇌	d							06 41					07 16		07 45					08 16			08 41	08 45	
Dunbar	d																								
Berwick-upon-Tweed	d																								
Alnmouth for Alnwick	d																								
Morpeth	d																								
Newcastle 8	d																								
Chester-le-Street	d																								
Durham	d																								
Darlington 7	d																								
York 8	d																								06 17
Leeds 10	d															06 00			06 16						07 10
Wakefield Westgate 7	d															06 12			06 29						07 22
Doncaster 7	d																		06 47						
Sheffield 7 ⇌	d															06 50			07 18						07 56
Chesterfield	d															07 03			07 30						08 08
Nottingham 8 ⇌	d									05 58				06 37			06 58					07 38			
Derby 6	d						06 10			06 36		06 48		07 06		07 26	07 36		07 50			08 06			08 28
Burton-on-Trent	d						06 20			06 48		06 59		07 17		07 37	07 50		08 00			08 18			08 38
Tamworth	d						06 31		←	07 01		07 09		07 29		07 48	08 02		08 11			08 30			08 49
Birmingham New Street 12	a						06 50	06 57	06 50	07 24		07 27	07 33	07 52	08 05	08 08	08 24		08 28	08 34		08 54	08 58	09 05	09 08
Birmingham New Street 12	d	05 00	05 42	06 04	06 33	06 42	07 12	07 04	07 12	07 30		07 33	07 42	08 04	08 10	08 12	08 30	08 30	08 33	08 42			09 04	09 10	09 12
Cheltenham Spa	a	06 02	06 42			07 24	→		07 51	08 10			08 24			08 51	09 10			09 24					09 51
Gloucester 7	a	06 12	06 52							08 20							09 20								
Bristol Parkway 7	a					07 53			08 24				08 53			09 24				09 53					10 29
Bristol Temple Meads 10	a					08 05			08 38				09 06			09 38				10 04					10 42
Newport (South Wales)	a	07 05	07 48							09 06							10 05								
Cardiff Central 7	a	07 21	08 04							09 22							10 21								
Weston-super-Mare	a																								
Taunton	a					08 42			09 16							10 17									11 15
Tiverton Parkway	a					08 54			09 28							10 30									11 28
Exeter St Davids 6	a					09 08			09 41							10 45									11 41
Dawlish	a																								
Teignmouth	a																								
Newton Abbot	a					09 28			10 02							11 09									12 03
Torquay	a					09 39																			
Paignton	a					09 47																			
Totnes	a								10 15							11 23									12 16
Plymouth	a								10 41							11 51									12 42
Liskeard 6	a																								
Bodmin Parkway	a																								
Lostwithiel	a																								
Par	a																								
Newquay (Summer Only)	a																								
St Austell	a																								
Truro	a																								
Redruth	a																								
Camborne	a																								
Hayle	a																								
St Erth	a																								
Penzance	a																								
Birmingham International ✈	d			06 14				07 14						08 14	08 20			08 40					09 14	09 20	
Coventry	d			06 25				07 25						08 25	08a29			08a50					09 25	09a30	
Leamington Spa 8	d			06 38	07 00			07 38				08 00		08 38					09 00				09 38		
Banbury	a			06 54	07 17			07 54				08 17		08 54					09 17				09 54		
Oxford	a			07 14	07 40			08 14				08 40		09 14					09 40				10 14		
Reading 7	a			07 39	08 06			08 39				09 07		09 39					10 06				10 41		
Guildford	a																								
Basingstoke	a			08 08	08 40			09 08						10 08					10 39				11 08		
Winchester	a			08 24	08 55			09 24						10 24					10 54				11 24		
Southampton Airport Pkway ✈	a			08 32	09 08			09 32						10 32					11 08				11 32		
Southampton Central ⛴	a			08 41	09 17			09 40						10 41					11 17				11 41		
Brockenhurst 3	a			08 56				09 57						10 57									11 57		
Bournemouth	a			09 14				10 11						11 12									12 11		

A 🛒 from Birmingham New Street to Newport (South Wales)

B 🛒 from Birmingham New Street

C 🛒 from Derby

D 🛒 from Leeds

Table 51

Saturdays

14 December to 28 December

Scotland, The North East, North West England - The South West and South Coast

Route Diagram - see first Page of Table 51

		XC	VT	XC	XC	XC		XC	XC	VT	XC	XC	VT	XC	XC	XC		XC	XC	VT	XC	XC	VT	XC	XC
		◇1	◇1	◇1	◇1	1		◇1	◇1	◇1	◇1	◇1	◇1	◇1	◇1	1		◇1	◇1	◇1	◇1	◇1	◇1	◇1	◇1
		A							B																
		🛒	🍽	🛒	🛒			🛒	🛒	🍽	🛒	🛒	🍽	🛒	🛒			🛒	🛒	🍽	🛒	🛒	🍽	🛒	🛒
Aberdeen	d																								
Stonehaven	d																								
Montrose	d																								
Arbroath	d																								
Dundee	d																								
Leuchars 3	d																								
Cupar	d																								
Ladybank	d																								
Markinch	d																								
Kirkcaldy	d																								
Inverkeithing	d																								
Glasgow Central 15	d									05 50															
Motherwell	d									06 04															
Haymarket	d																								
Edinburgh 10	d																		06 08	06 52				07 00	
Haymarket	d																			06 56					
Lockerbie	d																								
Carlisle 8	d									07 02										08 07					
Penrith North Lakes	d									07 18										08 22					
Oxenholme Lake District	d									07 42															
Lancaster 6	d									07 57										08 57					
Preston 8	d									08 17										09 17					
Wigan North Western	d									08 28										09 28					
Warrington Bank Quay	d									08 39										09 39					
M'chester Piccadilly 10 ⇌	d				08 07			08 27							09 07			09 27							10 07
Stockport	d				08 16			08 35							09 16			09 35							10 16
Wilmslow	d																								
Crewe 10	d									09 01										10 01					
Macclesfield	d							08 49										09 49							
Congleton	d																								
Stoke-on-Trent	d				08 44			09 07							09 44			10 07							10 44
Stafford	d				09 03			09 26							10 03			10 26							11 03
Wolverhampton 7 ⇌	d				09 16			09 41		09 45					10 17			10 41		10 45					11 16
Dunbar	d																								
Berwick-upon-Tweed	d																		06 47					07 40	
Alnmouth for Alnwick	d																		07 07					08 00	
Morpeth	d																							08 14	
Newcastle 8	d			06 22					06 45					07 35					07 40					08 35	
Chester-le-Street	d																								
Durham	d			06 37					06 58					07 48					07 53					08 48	
Darlington 7	d			06 54					07 15					08 05					08 10					09 05	
York 8	d			07 24					07 45					08 34					08 45					09 35	
Leeds 10	d								08 11										09 11						
Wakefield Westgate 7	d								08 24										09 24						
Doncaster 7	d			07 56										08 58										09 58	
Sheffield 7 ⇌	d			08 20					08 54					09 23					09 54					10 24	
Chesterfield	d			08 32					09 06										10 06						
Nottingham 8 ⇌	d	08 12				08 41						09 10				09 41						10 10			
Derby 6	d	08 37		08 53		09 10			09 27			09 36		09 52		10 11			10 27			10 37		10 52	
Burton-on-Trent	d	08 49				09 21			09 37			09 50				10 22						10 49			
Tamworth	d	09 02				09 33					←	10 02				10 34			10 48		←	11 02			
Birmingham New Street 12	a	09 25		09 27	09 33	09 54		09 58	10 03	10 05	10 03	10 24		10 27	10 33	10 55		10 58	11 04	11 05	11 04	11 24		11 27	11 33
Birmingham New Street 12	d	09 30	09 30	09 33	09 42			10 04	10 12	10 10	10 12	10 30	10 30	10 33	10 42			11 04	11 12	11 10	11 12	11 30	11 30	11 33	11 42
Cheltenham Spa	a	10 10			10 24				→		10 51	11 10			11 24				→		11 51	12 10			12 24
Gloucester 7	a	10 20										11 20										12 20			
Bristol Parkway 7	a				10 54						11 24				11 53						12 29				12 53
Bristol Temple Meads 10	a				11 09						11 38				12 04						12 42				13 07
Newport (South Wales)	a	11 06										12 05										13 05			
Cardiff Central 7	a	11 24										12 23										13 21			
Weston-super-Mare	a				11 29																				
Taunton	a				11 59						12 16										13 15				
Tiverton Parkway	a				12 11						12 28										13 28				
Exeter St Davids 6	a				12 26						12 41										13 42				
Dawlish	a				12 39																				
Teignmouth	a				12 44																				
Newton Abbot	a				12 51						13 02										14 02				
Torquay	a				13 03																				
Paignton	a				13 11																				
Totnes	a										13 15										14 15				
Plymouth	a										13 41										14 41				
Liskeard 6	a																								
Bodmin Parkway	a																								
Lostwithiel	a																								
Par	a																								
Newquay (Summer Only)	a																								
St Austell	a																								
Truro	a																								
Redruth	a																								
Camborne	a																								
Hayle	a																								
St Erth	a																								
Penzance	a																								
Birmingham International ✈	d		09 40					10 14		10 20			10 40					11 14		11 20			11 40		
Coventry	d		09a50					10 25		10a30			10a50					11 25		11a30			11a49		
Leamington Spa 8	d			10 00				10 38						11 00				11 38						12 00	
Banbury	a			10 17				10 54						11 17				11 54						12 17	
Oxford	a			10 40				11 14						11 40				12 14						12 40	
Reading 7	a			11 11				11 39						12 07				12 40						13 07	
Guildford	a																								
Basingstoke	a							12 08						12 40				13 08							
Winchester	a							12 24						12 55				13 24							
Southampton Airport Pkwy ✈	a							12 32						13 08				13 32							
Southampton Central ⛴	a							12 41						13 17				13 41							
Brockenhurst 3	a							12 57										13 57							
Bournemouth	a							13 11										14 11							

A 🛒 from Birmingham New Street **B** 🛒 from Leeds

Table 51

Saturdays

14 December to 28 December

Scotland, The North East, North West England - The South West and South Coast

Route Diagram - see first Page of Table 51

		XC	XC	VT	XC	XC	VT	XC	XC	XC	XC	VT	XC	XC	VT	XC	XC	XC	XC	XC	VT	XC
		1	◇1	◇1	◇1	◇1	◇1	◇1	◇1	1	◇1	◇1	◇1	◇1	◇1	◇1	◇1	1	◇1	◇1	◇1	◇1
					A								A							A		
			trolley	buffet	trolley	trolley	buffet	trolley	trolley		trolley	buffet	trolley	trolley	buffet	trolley	trolley		trolley	trolley	buffet	trolley
Aberdeen	d																					
Stonehaven	d																					
Montrose	d																					
Arbroath	d																					
Dundee	d												06 32									
Leuchars [3]	d												06 46									
Cupar	d												06 54									
Ladybank	d												07 03									
Markinch	d												07 11									
Kirkcaldy	d												07 21									
Inverkeithing	d												07 38									
Glasgow Central [15]	d			08 00	06 01															07 50	10 00	
Motherwell	d				06 17															08 05		
Haymarket	d				06 57								07 56							08 51		
Edinburgh [10]	d				07 07							08 52	08 05							09 08		
Haymarket	d											08 57										
Lockerbie	d																					
Carlisle [8]	d			09 09								10 08									11 11	
Penrith North Lakes	d																				11 25	
Oxenholme Lake District	d											10 42										
Lancaster [6]	d			09 56								10 57										
Preston [8]	d			10 17								11 18									12 17	
Wigan North Western	d			10 28								11 28									12 28	
Warrington Bank Quay	d			10 39								11 40									12 39	
M'chester Piccadilly [10]	d		10 27						11 07		11 27						12 07		12 27			
Stockport	d		10 35						11 16		11 35						12 16		12 35			
Wilmslow	d																					
Crewe [10]	d			11 01								12 01									13 01	
Macclesfield	d		10 49								11 49								12 49			
Congleton	d																					
Stoke-on-Trent	d		11 07						11 44		12 07						12 44		13 07			
Stafford	d		11 26						12 03		12 25						13 03		13 26			
Wolverhampton [7]	d		11 41	11 45					12 16		12 41	12 45					13 16		13 41		13 45	
Dunbar	d				07 27															09 28		
Berwick-upon-Tweed	d												08 47							09 51		
Alnmouth for Alnwick	d												09 09									
Morpeth	d																					
Newcastle [8]	d				08 42			09 35					09 42			10 35				10 44		
Chester-le-Street	d																					
Durham	d				08 55			09 48					09 56			10 48				10 56		
Darlington [7]	d				09 12			10 05					10 13			11 05				11 13		
York [8]	d				09 45			10 35					10 45			11 35				11 45		
Leeds [10]	d				10 11								11 11							12 11		
Wakefield Westgate [7]	d				10 24								11 24							12 24		
Doncaster [7]	d							10 59								11 59						
Sheffield [7]	d				10 54			11 23					11 54			12 23				12 54		
Chesterfield	d				11 06								12 07							13 06		
Nottingham [8]	d	10 41				11 10				11 41				12 10				12 41				
Derby [6]	d	11 11			11 26	11 36		11 52		12 11			12 29	12 36		12 52		13 11		13 27		
Burton-on-Trent	d	11 22			11 39	11 49				12 22				12 49				13 25		13 38		
Tamworth	d	11 34				12 02				12 34			12 49	13 02				13 36				←
Birmingham New Street [12]	a	11 56	11 59	12 05	12 08	12 24		12 27	12 33	12 56	12 58	13 05	13 08	13 23		13 26	13 32	13 55	13 58	14 04	14 05	14 04
Birmingham New Street [12]	d		12 04	12 10	12 12	12 30	12 30	12 33	12 42		13 04	13 10	13 12	13 30	13 30	13 33	13 42		14 04	14 12	14 10	14 12
Cheltenham Spa	a				12 51	13 10			13 25				13 51	14 10			14 24			→		14 51
Gloucester [7]	a					13 20								14 20								
Bristol Parkway [7]	a				13 24				13 55				14 26				14 57					15 24
Bristol Temple Meads [10]	a				13 38				14 05				14 40				15 09					15 38
Newport (South Wales)	a					14 06								15 10								
Cardiff Central [7]	a					14 22								15 26								
Weston-super-Mare	a																					
Taunton	a				14 15								15 17				15 43					16 15
Tiverton Parkway	a				14 28								15 29				15 55					16 28
Exeter St Davids [6]	a				14 42								15 44				16 10					16 41
Dawlish	a																					
Teignmouth	a																					
Newton Abbot	a				15 02								16 04									17 02
Torquay	a																					
Paignton	a																					
Totnes	a				15 15								16 18									17 15
Plymouth	a				15 42								16 46									17 41
Liskeard [8]	a																					
Bodmin Parkway	a																					
Lostwithiel	a																					
Par	a																					
Newquay (Summer Only)	a																					
St Austell	a																					
Truro	a																					
Redruth	a																					
Camborne	a																					
Hayle	a																					
St Erth	a																					
Penzance	a																					
Birmingham International ✈	d		12 14	12 20			12 40				13 14	13 20			13 40				14 14		14 20	
Coventry	d		12 25	12a30			12a49				13 25	13a30			13a50				14 25		14a30	
Leamington Spa [8]	d		12 38					13 02			13 38					14 00			14 38			
Banbury	a		12 54					13 19			13 54					14 16			14 54			
Oxford	a		13 14					13 40			14 14					14 40			15 14			
Reading [7]	a		13 39					14 09			14 40					15 08			15 39			
Guildford	a																					
Basingstoke	a		14 08					14 40			15 08								16 08			
Winchester	a		14 24					14 55			15 24								16 24			
Southampton Airport Pkway ✈	a		14 32					15 08			15 32								16 32			
Southampton Central	a		14 41					15 17			15 41								16 41			
Brockenhurst [3]	a		14 57								15 57								16 57			
Bournemouth	a		15 11								16 11								17 11			

A trolley from Edinburgh

Table 51

Saturdays

14 December to 28 December

Scotland, The North East, North West England - The South West and South Coast

Route Diagram - see first Page of Table 51

		XC	VT	XC	XC	XC	XC	VT	XC	XC	VT	XC	XC	XC	XC	XC	VT	XC	XC	VT	XC	XC	XC
		◇1	◇1	◇1	◇1	1	◇1	◇1	◇1	◇1	◇1	◇1	◇1	1	◇1	◇1	◇1	◇1	◇1	◇1	◇1	◇1	1
									A							B		C					
		🛒	🍴	🛒	🛒	🛒	🛒	🍴	🛒	🛒	🍴	🛒	🛒		🛒	🛒	🍴	🛒	🛒	🍴	🛒	🛒	🛒
Aberdeen	d															08 20							
Stonehaven	d															08 38							
Montrose	d															08 59							
Arbroath	d															09 15							
Dundee	d															09 32							
Leuchars 3	d															09 47							
Cupar	d															09 54							
Ladybank	d															10 01							
Markinch	d															10 09							
Kirkcaldy	d															10 17							
Inverkeithing	d															10 32							
Glasgow Central 15	d								09 00								12 00						
Motherwell	d								09 15														
Haymarket	d								09 57							10 52							
Edinburgh 10	d							10 52	10 05							11 08							
Haymarket	d							10 57															
Lockerbie	d																						
Carlisle 8	d							12 08									13 11						
Penrith North Lakes	d																						
Oxenholme Lake District	d							12 43															
Lancaster 6	d							12 57									13 58						
Preston 8	d							13 17									14 17						
Wigan North Western	d							13 28									14 28						
Warrington Bank Quay	d							13 39									14 39						
M'chester Piccadilly 10 ⛴	d				13 07		13 27						14 07		14 27							15 07	
Stockport	d				13 16		13 35						14 16		14 35							15 16	
Wilmslow	d																						
Crewe 10	d							14 01									15 01						
Macclesfield	d						13 49								14 49								
Congleton	d																						
Stoke-on-Trent	d				13 44		14 07						14 44		15 07							15 44	
Stafford	d				14 03		14 26						15 03		15 26							16 03	
Wolverhampton 7 ⛴	d				14 16		14 41	14 45					15 17		15 41		15 45					16 17	
Dunbar	d															11 28							
Berwick-upon-Tweed	d								10 47							11 51							
Alnmouth for Alnwick	d															12 11							
Morpeth	d								11 19														
Newcastle 8	d			11 35					11 42			12 35				12 44					13 35		
Chester-le-Street	d																						
Durham	d			11 48					11 55			12 48				12 56					13 48		
Darlington 7	d			12 05					12 12			13 05				13 13					14 05		
York 8	d			12 35					12 45			13 34				13 45					14 35		
Leeds 10	d								13 11							14 11							
Wakefield Westgate 7	d								13 23							14 24							
Doncaster 7	d			12 59								13 58									14 59		
Sheffield 7 ⛴	d			13 23					13 54			14 23				14 54					15 23		
Chesterfield	d								14 07							15 06							
Nottingham 8 ⛴	d	13 10				13 41				14 10				14 41					15 10				15 41
Derby 6	d	13 36		13 52		14 11			14 30	14 36		14 53		15 11		15 27			15 37		15 52		16 11
Burton-on-Trent	d	13 49				14 22				14 49				15 25		15 38			15 49				16 22
Tamworth	d	14 02				14 34			14 49	15 02				15 34				←	16 02				16 34
Birmingham New Street 12	a	14 23		14 25	14 33	14 55	14 58	15 05	15 08	15 24		15 27	15 33	15 55	15 58	16 04	16 05	16 04	16 24		16 27	16 33	16 55
Birmingham New Street 12	d	14 30	14 30	14 33	14 42		15 04	15 10	15 12	15 30	15 30	15 33	15 42		16 04	16 12	16 10	16 12	16 30	16 30	16 33	16 42	
Cheltenham Spa	a	15 10			15 24				15 51	16 10			16 24			→		16 50	17 10			17 24	
Gloucester 7	a	15 20								16 20									17 20				
Bristol Parkway 7	a				15 54				16 29				16 53					17 25				17 53	
Bristol Temple Meads 10	a				16 07				16 42				17 07					17 38				18 07	
Newport (South Wales)	a	16 06								17 08									18 06				
Cardiff Central 7	a	16 25								17 24									18 22				
Weston-super-Mare	a																						
Taunton	a								17 17				17 41					18 15					
Tiverton Parkway	a								17 29				17 53					18 28					
Exeter St Davids 6	a								17 45				18 07					18 41					
Dawlish	a												18 20										
Teignmouth	a												18 25										
Newton Abbot	a								18 10				18 32					19 04					
Torquay	a												18 43										
Paignton	a												18 51										
Totnes	a								18 24									19 17					
Plymouth	a								18 52									19 43					
Liskeard 6	a								19 17									20 10					
Bodmin Parkway	a								19 32									20 22					
Lostwithiel	a																	20 27					
Par	a								19 44									20 35					
Newquay (Summer Only)	a																						
St Austell	a								19 52									20 41					
Truro	a								20 10									21 00					
Redruth	a								20 26									21 12					
Camborne	a								20 33									21 18					
Hayle	a																	21 26					
St Erth	a								20 45									21 31					
Penzance	a								20 56									21 43					
Birmingham International ✈	d		14 40				15 14	15 20			15 40				16 14		16 20			16 40			
Coventry	d		14a49				15 25	15a30			15a50				16 25		16a30			16a50			
Leamington Spa 8	d			15 00			15 38					16 02			16 38						17 00		
Banbury	a			15 19			15 54					16 19			16 54						17 17		
Oxford	a			15 40			16 14					16 40			17 14						17 41		
Reading 7	a			16 09			16 40					17 08			17 39						18 08		
Guildford	a																						
Basingstoke	a			16 40			17 08								18 08						18 40		
Winchester	a			16 55			17 24								18 24						18 55		
Southampton Airport Pkway ✈	a			17 08			17 32								18 32						19 08		
Southampton Central ⛴	a			17 17			17 41								18 40						19 17		
Brockenhurst 3	a						17 57								18 57								
Bournemouth	a						18 11								19 11								

A 🛒 from Edinburgh to Plymouth

B 🛒 from Edinburgh

C 🛒 to Plymouth

Table 51

Saturdays

14 December to 28 December

Scotland, The North East, North West England - The South West and South Coast

Route Diagram - see first Page of Table 51

		XC	VT	XC	XC	VT	XC	XC	XC	XC	VT	XC	XC	VT	XC	XC	XC	XC	XC	XC	XC	XC
		◇1	◇1	◇1	◇1	◇1	◇1	◇1	1	◇1	◇1	◇1	◇1	◇1	◇1	◇1	1	◇1	◇1	◇1	◇1	◇1
				A												B		C	D			B
		🛒	🍽	🛒		🍽	🛒	🛒	🛒	🛒	🍽	🛒		🍽	🛒	🛒	🛒	🛒	🛒		🛒	🛒
Aberdeen	d																					
Stonehaven	d																					
Montrose	d																					
Arbroath	d																					
Dundee	d																					
Leuchars 3	d																					
Cupar	d																					
Ladybank	d																					
Markinch	d																					
Kirkcaldy	d																					
Inverkeithing	d																					
Glasgow Central 15	d			11 00							14 00								13 00			
Motherwell	d			11 14															13 14			
Haymarket	d			11 52																		
Edinburgh 10	d		12 52	12 05								13 09							14 05			
Haymarket	d		12 57																			
Lockerbie	d																					
Carlisle 8	d		14 08								15 10											
Penrith North Lakes	d		14 22																			
Oxenholme Lake District	d										15 44											
Lancaster 6	d		14 56																			
Preston 8	d		15 17								16 17											
Wigan North Western	d		15 28								16 28											
Warrington Bank Quay	d		15 39								16 39											
M'chester Piccadilly 10 🚊	d	15 27						16 07		16 27						17 06		17 27				18 05
Stockport	d	15 35						16 16		16 35						17 15		17 36				18 13
Wilmslow	d																					
Crewe 10	d		16 01								17 01											
Macclesfield	d	15 49								16 49						17 27						18 26
Congleton	d																	17 54				
Stoke-on-Trent	d	16 07						16 44		17 07						17 45		18 07				18 44
Stafford	d	16 25						17 03		17 26						18 04		18 26				19 03
Wolverhampton 7 🚊	d	16 41	16 45					17 17		17 41	17 45					18 16		18 41				19 16
Dunbar	d											13 29										
Berwick-upon-Tweed	d			12 45															14 47			
Alnmouth for Alnwick	d											14 09										
Morpeth	d																					
Newcastle 8	d			13 44			14 35					14 44			15 08				15 41		16 35	
Chester-le-Street	d																					
Durham	d			13 56			14 48					14 56			15 21				15 54		16 48	
Darlington 7	d			14 13			15 05					15 13			15 37				16 13		17 05	
York 8	d			14 45			15 35					15 45			16 05				16 45		17 35	
Leeds 10	d			15 11								16 11			16 40				17 11			
Wakefield Westgate 7	d			15 24								16 24			16 52				17 23			
Doncaster 7	d						15 59														17 59	
Sheffield 7 🚊	d			15 54			16 23					16 54			17 23				17 54		18 23	
Chesterfield	d			16 07								17 06							18 07			
Nottingham 8 🚊	d				16 10				16 41				17 10				17 41			18 10		
Derby 6	d			16 27	16 36		16 53		17 11			17 27	17 36		17 52		18 11		18 27	18 36	18 52	
Burton-on-Trent	d				16 49				17 25			17 38	17 49				18 23			18 49		
Tamworth	d			16 48	17 02				17 36				18 02				18 35		18 46	19 02		
Birmingham New Street 12	a	16 58	17 05	17 07	17 24		17 27	17 33	17 55	17 58	18 05	18 07	18 24		18 27	18 33	18 57	18 58	19 06	19 22	19 26	19 33
Birmingham New Street 12	d	17 04	17 10	17 12	17 30	17 30	17 33	17 42		18 04	18 10	18 12	18 30	18 30	18 33	18 42		19 04	19 12	19 30	19 33	19 42
Cheltenham Spa	a			17 51	18 16			18 24				18 51	19 10			19 24			19 51	20 10		20 24
Gloucester 7	a				18 26								19 20							20 20		
Bristol Parkway 7	a			18 29				18 53				19 25				19 55			20 29			20 53
Bristol Temple Meads 10	a			18 42				19 04				19 38				20 05			20 42			21 04
Newport (South Wales)	a				19 11								20 03			20 44				21 09		
Cardiff Central 7	a				19 30								20 20			21 00				21 26		
Weston-super-Mare	a																					
Taunton	a			19 15								20 15							21 15			21 42
Tiverton Parkway	a			19 28								20 28							21 28			21 54
Exeter St Davids 6	a			19 43								20 41							21 42			22 09
Dawlish	a																					
Teignmouth	a																					
Newton Abbot	a			20 03								21 02							22 04			22 28
Torquay	a																					
Paignton	a																					
Totnes	a			20 16								21 15							22 20			22 41
Plymouth	a			20 43								21 41							22 47			23 08
Liskeard 6	a			21 24																		
Bodmin Parkway	a			21 36																		
Lostwithiel	a																					
Par	a			21 47																		
Newquay (Summer Only)	a																					
St Austell	a			21 54																		
Truro	a			22 11																		
Redruth	a			22 27																		
Camborne	a			22 34																		
Hayle	a																					
St Erth	a			22 45																		
Penzance	a			22 54																		
Birmingham International ✈	d	17 14	17 20			17 40				18 14	18 20			18 40				19 14				
Coventry	d	17 25	17a30			17a49				18 25	18a30			18a49				19 25				
Leamington Spa 8	d	17 38					18 02			18 38					19 00			19 38			20 03	
Banbury	a	17 54					18 18			18 54					19 17			19 54			20 18	
Oxford	a	18 14					18 40			19 14					19 40			20 14			20 40	
Reading 7	a	18 40					19 08			19 39					20 08			20 40			21 08	
Guildford	a																					
Basingstoke	a	19 08								20 08								21 08				
Winchester	a	19 24								20 24								21 24				
Southampton Airport Pkway ✈	a	19 32								20 32								21 32				
Southampton Central ⛴	a	19 41								20 41								21 41				
Brockenhurst 3	a	19 57								20 57								21 57				
Bournemouth	a	20 11								21 11								22 15				

A 🛒 from Edinburgh to Plymouth
B 🛒 to Bristol Temple Meads
C 🛒 to Reading
D 🛒 from Edinburgh to Bristol Temple Meads

Table 51

Saturdays

14 December to 28 December

Scotland, The North East, North West England - The South West and South Coast

Route Diagram - see first Page of Table 51

		XC	XC	XC	XC	XC	XC	XC	XC	XC	XC	XC	VT	XC	XC	XC	XC	XC	VT	VT	XC	XC	XC
		[1]	◇[1]	◇[1]	◇[1]	◇[1]	◇[1]	[1]	◇[1]	◇[1]	◇[1]	◇[1]	◇[1]	[1]	◇[1]	◇[1]	◇[1]	◇[1]	◇[1]	◇[1]	◇[1]	[1]	◇[1]
			A	B			C		C	C						D							E
		⊼	⊼	⊼		⊼	⊼	⊼	⊼	⊼	⊼		⊡			⊼			⊡	⊡			⊼
Aberdeen	d																						
Stonehaven	d																						
Montrose	d																						
Arbroath	d																						
Dundee	d																						
Leuchars [3]	d																						
Cupar	d																						
Ladybank	d																						
Markinch	d																						
Kirkcaldy	d																						
Inverkeithing	d																						
Glasgow Central [15]	d									15 00			18 00						18 40				16 52
Motherwell	d									15 14													17 06
Haymarket	d									15 57													17 53
Edinburgh [10]	d			15 08						16 05						17 08				18 52			18 08
Haymarket	d																			18 56			
Lockerbie	d																						
Carlisle [8]	d												19 09						19 48	20 08			
Penrith North Lakes	d																		20 02	20 22			
Oxenholme Lake District	d																		20 25	20 45			
Lancaster [6]	d												19 57						20 40	21 00			
Preston [8]	d												20 17						21 00	21 21			
Wigan North Western	d												20 28						21 11	21 32			
Warrington Bank Quay	d												20 39						21 22	21 43			
M'chester Piccadilly [10]	d		18 27				19 07		19 27			20 07			20 27		21 07				21 27		
Stockport	d		18 35				19 16		19 35			20 16			20 35						21 35		
Wilmslow	d																						
Crewe [10]	d												21 01						21 43	22 04			
Macclesfield	d								19 49						20 49						21 49		
Congleton	d		18 54																				
Stoke-on-Trent	d		19 07				19 44		20 07			20 44			21 07		21 45				22 07		
Stafford	d		19 25				20 03		20 26			21 03			21 27		22 03		22 08	22 23	22 29		
Wolverhampton [7]	d		19 41				20 16		20 41			21 16	21 34		21 41		22 16		22 23	22 40	22 44		
Dunbar	d			15 28												17 29							18 28
Berwick-upon-Tweed	d															17 51							18 51
Alnmouth for Alnwick	d									17 03													19 11
Morpeth	d									17 17													
Newcastle [8]	d			16 41		17 32				17 44	18 35					18 44		19 35					19 45
Chester-le-Street	d					17 41																	
Durham	d			16 54		17 48				17 56	18 49					18 57		19 50					19 57
Darlington [7]	d			17 13		18 05				18 13	19 06					19 14		20 07					20 14
York [8]	d			17 45		18 34				18 45	19 35					19 45		20 35					20 45
Leeds [10]	d			18 11						19 11						20 11							21 11
Wakefield Westgate [7]	d			18 23						19 24						20 23							21 23
Doncaster [7]	d					18 59					19 59							21 00					
Sheffield [7]	d			18 58		19 24				19 54	20 23					20 54		21 23					21 54
Chesterfield	d			19 10						20 06						21 06		21 35					22 06
Nottingham [8]	d	18 41			19 10			19 41						20 37								21 39	
Derby [6]	d	19 11		19 29	19 36	19 53		20 10		20 27	20 52			21 10		21 27		21 54				22 11	22 26
Burton-on-Trent	d	19 22		19 37	19 49			20 21						21 24		21 38						22 21	22 37
Tamworth	d	19 34			20 02			20 33		20 46				21 35		21 49						22 33	22 47
Birmingham New Street [12]	a	19 55	19 59	20 06	20 24	20 27	20 33	20 56	20 58	21 03	21 25	21 32	21 55	21 57	21 58	22 06	22 32	22 43	22 46	22 59	23 01	23 02	23 06
Birmingham New Street [12]	d		20 04	20 12	20 30	20 33	20 42		21 04	21 12													
Cheltenham Spa	a			20 51	21 10		21 24			21 50													
Gloucester [7]	a				21 20					21 59													
Bristol Parkway [7]	a			21 20			21 58			22 30													
Bristol Temple Meads [10]	a			21 35			22 12			22 41													
Newport (South Wales)	a				22 19																		
Cardiff Central [7]	a				22 45																		
Weston-super-Mare	a																						
Taunton	a			22 15																			
Tiverton Parkway	a			22 28																			
Exeter St Davids [6]	a			22 43																			
Dawlish	a																						
Teignmouth	a																						
Newton Abbot	a			23 10																			
Torquay	a																						
Paignton	a																						
Totnes	a			23 25																			
Plymouth	a			23 53																			
Liskeard [6]	a																						
Bodmin Parkway	a																						
Lostwithiel	a																						
Par	a																						
Newquay (Summer Only)	a																						
St Austell	a																						
Truro	a																						
Redruth	a																						
Camborne	a																						
Hayle	a																						
St Erth	a																						
Penzance	a																						
Birmingham International ✈	d		20 14						21 14														
Coventry	d		20 25						21 25														
Leamington Spa [8]	d		20 38			21 00			21 38														
Banbury	a		20 54			21 19			21 54														
Oxford	a		21 14			21 41			22 16														
Reading [7]	a		21 38			22 08			22 41														
Guildford	a					22 59																	
Basingstoke	a		22 09						23 07														
Winchester	a		22 24						23 24														
Southampton Airport Pkway ✈	a		22 32						23 32														
Southampton Central ⛴	a		22 40						23 41														
Brockenhurst [3]	a		22 56																				
Bournemouth	a		23 20																				

A ⊼ to Reading
B ⊼ to Bristol Temple Meads
C ⊼ to Birmingham New Street
D ⊼ to Leeds
E ⊼ from Edinburgh to Leeds

Table 51

Saturdays
4 January to 8 February

Scotland, The North East, North West England - The South West and South Coast

Route Diagram - see first Page of Table 51

		XC ◇1	XC ◇1	XC ◇1 ⊼	XC ◇1	XC ◇1 ⊼	XC ◇1	XC ◇1 ⊼	XC ◇1 ⊼	XC ◇1 A ⊼	XC ◇1 B ⊼	XC ◇1 ⊼	XC ◇1 C ⊼	VT ◇1 ⊓	XC ◇1 ⊼	XC ◇1	VT ◇1 ⊓	XC ◇1 ⊼	XC ◇1 ⊼	XC 1	XC ◇1 ⊼	VT ◇1 ⊓	XC ◇1 D ⊼
Aberdeen	d																						
Stonehaven	d																						
Montrose	d																						
Arbroath	d																						
Dundee	d																						
Leuchars 8	d																						
Cupar	d																						
Ladybank	d																						
Markinch	d																						
Kirkcaldy	d																						
Inverkeithing	d																						
Glasgow Central 15	d																						
Motherwell	d																						
Haymarket	d																						
Edinburgh 10	d																						
Haymarket	d																						
Lockerbie	d																						
Carlisle 8	d																						
Penrith North Lakes	d																						
Oxenholme Lake District	d																						
Lancaster 6	d																					06 58	
Preston 8	d													06 17								07 17	
Wigan North Western	d													06 28								07 28	
Warrington Bank Quay	d													06 39								07 39	
M'chester Piccadilly 10	d							05 11				06 00							07 07		07 27		
Stockport	d											06 08							07 16		07 35		
Wilmslow	d																						
Crewe 10	d							05 47						07 01								08 01	
Macclesfield	d											06 21									07 49		
Congleton	d																						
Stoke-on-Trent	d							06 08				06 39							07 44		08 07		
Stafford	d							06 26				06 58							08 03		08 26		
Wolverhampton 7	d							06 41				07 16		07 45					08 16		08 41	08 45	
Dunbar	d																						
Berwick-upon-Tweed	d																						
Alnmouth for Alnwick	d																						
Morpeth	d																						
Newcastle 8	d																						
Chester-le-Street	d																						
Durham	d																						
Darlington 7	d																						
York 8	d																						06 17
Leeds 10	d														06 00			06 16					07 10
Wakefield Westgate 7	d														06 12			06 29					07 22
Doncaster 7	d																	06 47					
Sheffield 7	d														06 50			07 18					07 56
Chesterfield	d														07 03			07 30					08 08
Nottingham 8	d									05 58			06 37			06 58				07 38			
Derby 6	d						06 10			06 36	06 48		07 06		07 26	07 36		07 50		08 06			08 28
Burton-on-Trent	d						06 20			06 48	06 59		07 17		07 37	07 50		08 00		08 18			08 38
Tamworth	d						06 31		←	07 01	07 09		07 29		07 48	08 02		08 11		08 30			08 49
Birmingham New Street 12	a						06 50	06 57	06 50	07 24	07 27	07 33	07 52	08 05	08 08	08 24		08 28	08 34	08 54	08 58	09 05	09 08
Birmingham New Street 12	d	05 00	05 42	06 04	06 33	06 42	07 12	07 04	07 12	07 30	07 33	07 42	08 04	08 10	08 12	08 30	08 30	08 33	08 42		09 04	09 10	09 12
Cheltenham Spa	a	06 02	06 42			07 24	→		07 51	08 10		08 24			08 51	09 10			09 24				09 51
Gloucester 7	a	06 12	06 52							08 20						09 20							
Bristol Parkway 7	a					07 53			08 24			08 53			09 24				09 53				10 29
Bristol Temple Meads 10	a					08 05			08 38			09 06			09 38				10 04				10 42
Newport (South Wales)	a	07 05	07 48							09 06						10 05							
Cardiff Central 7	a	07 21	08 04							09 22						10 21							
Weston-super-Mare	a																						
Taunton	a					08 42			09 16						10 17								11 15
Tiverton Parkway	a					08 54			09 28						10 30								11 28
Exeter St Davids 6	a					09 08			09 41						10 45								11 41
Dawlish	a																						
Teignmouth	a																						
Newton Abbot	a					09 28			10 02						11 09								12 03
Torquay	a					09 39																	
Paignton	a					09 47																	
Totnes	a								10 15						11 23								12 16
Plymouth	a								10 41						11 51								12 42
Liskeard 6	a																						
Bodmin Parkway	a																						
Lostwithiel	a																						
Par	a																						
Newquay (Summer Only)	a																						
St Austell	a																						
Truro	a																						
Redruth	a																						
Camborne	a																						
Hayle	a																						
St Erth	a																						
Penzance	a																						
Birmingham International	d			06 14				07 14					08 14	08 20			08 40				09 14	09 20	
Coventry	d			06 25				07 25					08 25	08a29			08a50				09 25	09a30	
Leamington Spa 8	d			06 38	07 00			07 38			08 00		08 38					09 00			09 38		
Banbury	a			06 54	07 17			07 54			08 17		08 54					09 17			09 54		
Oxford	a			07 14	07 40			08 14			08 40		09 14					09 40			10 14		
Reading 7	a			07 39	08 06			08 39			09 07		09 39					10 06			10 41		
Guildford	a																						
Basingstoke	a			08 08	08 40			09 08					10 08					10 39			11 08		
Winchester	a			08 24	08 55			09 24					10 24					10 54			11 24		
Southampton Airport Pkwy	a			08 32	09 08			09 32					10 32					11 08			11 32		
Southampton Central	a			08 41	09 17			09 40					10 41					11 17			11 41		
Brockenhurst 3	a			08 56				09 57					10 57								11 57		
Bournemouth	a			09 14				10 11					11 12								12 11		

A ⊼ from Birmingham New Street to Newport (South Wales)

B ⊼ from Birmingham New Street

C ⊼ from Derby

D ⊼ from Leeds

Table 51

Saturdays

4 January to 8 February

Scotland, The North East, North West England - The South West and South Coast

Route Diagram - see first Page of Table 51

		XC	VT	XC	XC	XC		XC	XC	VT	XC	XC	VT	XC	XC	XC		XC	XC	VT	XC	XC	VT	XC	XC
		◇1	◇1	◇1	◇1	1		◇1	◇1	◇1	◇1	◇1	◇1	◇1	◇1	1		◇1	◇1	◇1	◇1	◇1	◇1	◇1	◇1
		A							B																
Aberdeen	d																								
Stonehaven	d																								
Montrose	d																								
Arbroath	d																								
Dundee	d																								
Leuchars 3	d																								
Cupar	d																								
Ladybank	d																								
Markinch	d																								
Kirkcaldy	d																								
Inverkeithing	d																								
Glasgow Central 15	d									05 50															
Motherwell	d									06 04															
Haymarket	d																								
Edinburgh 10	d																		06 08	06 52				07 00	
Haymarket	d																			06 56					
Lockerbie	d																								
Carlisle 8	d									07 02										08 07					
Penrith North Lakes	d									07 18										08 22					
Oxenholme Lake District	d									07 42															
Lancaster 6	d									07 57										08 57					
Preston 8	d									08 17										09 17					
Wigan North Western	d									08 28										09 28					
Warrington Bank Quay	d									08 39										09 39					
M'chester Piccadilly 10	d				08 07			08 27							09 07			09 27							10 07
Stockport	d				08 16			08 35							09 16			09 35							10 16
Wilmslow	d																								
Crewe 10	d									09 01										10 01					
Macclesfield	d							08 49										09 49							
Congleton	d																								
Stoke-on-Trent	d				08 44			09 07							09 44			10 07							10 44
Stafford	d				09 03			09 26							10 03			10 26							11 03
Wolverhampton 7	d				09 16			09 41		09 45					10 17			10 41		10 45					11 16
Dunbar	d																								
Berwick-upon-Tweed	d																		06 47					07 40	
Alnmouth for Alnwick	d																		07 07					08 00	
Morpeth	d																							08 14	
Newcastle 8	d			06 22					06 45					07 35					07 40					08 35	
Chester-le-Street	d																								
Durham	d			06 37					06 58					07 48					07 53					08 48	
Darlington 7	d			06 54					07 15					08 05					08 10					09 05	
York 8	d			07 24					07 45					08 34					08 45					09 35	
Leeds 10	d								08 11										09 11						
Wakefield Westgate 7	d								08 24										09 24						
Doncaster 7	d			07 56										08 58										09 58	
Sheffield 7	d			08 20					08 54					09 23					09 54					10 24	
Chesterfield	d			08 32					09 06										10 06						
Nottingham 8	d	08 12				08 41						09 10				09 41						10 10			
Derby 6	d	08 37		08 53		09 10			09 27			09 36		09 52		10 11			10 27			10 37		10 52	
Burton-on-Trent	d	08 49				09 21			09 37			09 50				10 22						10 49			
Tamworth	d	09 02				09 33					←	10 02				10 34			10 48		←	11 02			
Birmingham New Street 12	a	09 25		09 27	09 33	09 54		09 58	10 03	10 05	10 03	10 24		10 27	10 33	10 55		10 58	11 04	11 05	11 04	11 24		11 27	11 33
Birmingham New Street 12	d	09 30	09 30	09 33	09 42			10 04	10 12	10 10	10 12	10 30	10 30	10 33	10 42			11 04	11 12	11 10	11 12	11 30	11 30	11 33	11 42
Cheltenham Spa	a	10 10			10 24				→		10 51	11 10			11 24				→		11 51	12 10			12 24
Gloucester 7	a	10 20										11 20										12 20			
Bristol Parkway 7	a				10 54						11 24				11 53						12 29				12 53
Bristol Temple Meads 10	a				11 09						11 38				12 04						12 42				13 07
Newport (South Wales)	a	11 06										12 05										13 05			
Cardiff Central 7	a	11 24										12 23										13 21			
Weston-super-Mare	a				11 29																				
Taunton	a				11 59						12 16										13 15				
Tiverton Parkway	a				12 11						12 28										13 28				
Exeter St Davids 6	a				12 26						12 41										13 42				
Dawlish	a				12 39																				
Teignmouth	a				12 44																				
Newton Abbot	a				12 51						13 02										14 02				
Torquay	a				13 03																				
Paignton	a				13 11																				
Totnes	a										13 15										14 17				
Plymouth	a										13 41										14 44				
Liskeard 6	a																								
Bodmin Parkway	a																								
Lostwithiel	a																								
Par	a																								
Newquay (Summer Only)	a																								
St Austell	a																								
Truro	a																								
Redruth	a																								
Camborne	a																								
Hayle	a																								
St Erth	a																								
Penzance	a																								
Birmingham International	d		09 40					10 14		10 20			10 40					11 14		11 20			11 40		
Coventry	d		09a50					10 25		10a30			10a50					11 25		11a30			11a49		
Leamington Spa 8	d			10 00				10 38						11 00				11 38						12 00	
Banbury	a			10 17				10 54						11 17				11 54						12 17	
Oxford	a			10 40				11 14						11 40				12 14						12 40	
Reading 7	a			11 11				11 39						12 07				12 40						13 07	
Guildford	a																								
Basingstoke	a							12 08						12 40				13 08							
Winchester	a							12 24						12 55				13 24							
Southampton Airport Pkway	a							12 32						13 08				13 32							
Southampton Central	a							12 41						13 17				13 41							
Brockenhurst 3	a							12 57										13 57							
Bournemouth	a							13 11										14 11							

A from Birmingham New Street

B from Leeds

Table 51

Saturdays

4 January to 8 February

Scotland, The North East, North West England - The South West and South Coast

Route Diagram - see first Page of Table 51

		XC		XC	VT	XC	XC	VT	XC	XC	XC	XC		VT	XC	XC	VT	XC	XC	XC	XC	XC		VT	XC
		1		◇1	◇1	◇1	◇1	◇1	◇1	◇1	1	◇1		◇1	◇1	◇1	◇1	◇1	◇1	1	◇1	◇1		◇1	◇1
						A									A							A			
				⌶	⊏	⌶	⌶	⊏	⌶	⌶		⌶		⊏	⌶	⌶	⊏	⌶	⌶		⌶	⌶		⊏	⌶
Aberdeen	d																								
Stonehaven	d																								
Montrose	d																								
Arbroath	d																								
Dundee	d														06 32										
Leuchars 3	d														06 46										
Cupar	d														06 54										
Ladybank	d														07 03										
Markinch	d														07 11										
Kirkcaldy	d														07 21										
Inverkeithing	d														07 38										
Glasgow Central 15	d				08 00	06 01																07 50		10 00	
Motherwell	d					06 17																08 05			
Haymarket	d					06 57									07 56							08 51			
Edinburgh 10	d					07 07								08 52	08 05							09 08			
Haymarket	d													08 57											
Lockerbie	d																								
Carlisle 8	d				09 09									10 08										11 11	
Penrith North Lakes	d																							11 25	
Oxenholme Lake District	d													10 42											
Lancaster 6	d				09 56									10 57											
Preston 8	d				10 17									11 18										12 17	
Wigan North Western	d				10 28									11 28										12 28	
Warrington Bank Quay	d				10 39									11 40										12 39	
M'chester Piccadilly 10	d			10 27						11 07		11 27							12 07		12 27				
Stockport	d			10 35						11 16		11 35							12 16		12 35				
Wilmslow	d																								
Crewe 10	d				11 01									12 01										13 01	
Macclesfield	d			10 49								11 49									12 49				
Congleton	d																								
Stoke-on-Trent	d			11 07						11 44		12 07							12 44		13 07				
Stafford	d			11 26						12 03		12 25							13 03		13 26				
Wolverhampton 7	d			11 41	11 45					12 16		12 41		12 45					13 16		13 41			13 45	
Dunbar	d					07 27																09 28			
Berwick-upon-Tweed	d														08 47							09 51			
Alnmouth for Alnwick	d														09 09										
Morpeth	d																								
Newcastle 8	d					08 42			09 35						09 42			10 35				10 44			
Chester-le-Street	d																								
Durham	d					08 55			09 48						09 56			10 48				10 56			
Darlington 7	d					09 12			10 05						10 13			11 05				11 13			
York 8	d					09 45			10 35						10 45			11 35				11 45			
Leeds 10	d					10 11									11 11							12 11			
Wakefield Westgate 7	d					10 24									11 24							12 24			
Doncaster 7	d								10 59									11 59							
Sheffield 7	d					10 54			11 23						11 54			12 23				12 54			
Chesterfield	d					11 06									12 07							13 06			
Nottingham 8	d	10 41					11 10				11 41					12 10				12 41					
Derby 6	d	11 11				11 26	11 36		11 52		12 11				12 29	12 36		12 52		13 11		13 27			
Burton-on-Trent	d	11 22				11 39	11 49				12 22					12 49				13 25		13 38			
Tamworth	d	11 34					12 02				12 34				12 49	13 02				13 36					←
Birmingham New Street 12	a	11 56		11 59	12 05	12 08	12 24		12 27	12 33	12 56	12 58		13 05	13 08	13 23		13 26	13 32	13 55	13 58	14 04		14 05	14 04
Birmingham New Street 12	d			12 04	12 10	12 12	12 30	12 30	12 33	12 42		13 04		13 10	13 12	13 30	13 30	13 33	13 42		14 04	14 12		14 10	14 12
Cheltenham Spa	a					12 51	13 10			13 25					13 51	14 10			14 24			→			14 51
Gloucester 7	a						13 20									14 20									
Bristol Parkway 7	a					13 24				13 55					14 26				14 57						15 24
Bristol Temple Meads 10	a					13 38				14 05					14 40				15 09						15 38
Newport (South Wales)	a						14 06									15 10									
Cardiff Central 7	a						14 22									15 26									
Weston-super-Mare	a																								
Taunton	a					14 15									15 17				15 43						16 15
Tiverton Parkway	a					14 28									15 29				15 55						16 28
Exeter St Davids 6	a					14 42									15 44				16 10						16 41
Dawlish	a																								
Teignmouth	a																								
Newton Abbot	a					15 02									16 04										17 02
Torquay	a																								
Paignton	a																								
Totnes	a					15 15									16 18										17 15
Plymouth	a					15 42									16 46										17 41
Liskeard 6	a																								
Bodmin Parkway	a																								
Lostwithiel	a																								
Par	a																								
Newquay (Summer Only)	a																								
St Austell	a																								
Truro	a																								
Redruth	a																								
Camborne	a																								
Hayle	a																								
St Erth	a																								
Penzance	a																								
Birmingham International ✈	d			12 14	12 20			12 40				13 14		13 20			13 40				14 14			14 20	
Coventry	d			12 25	12a30			12a49				13 25		13a30			13a50				14 25			14a30	
Leamington Spa 8	d			12 38					13 02			13 38						14 00			14 38				
Banbury	a			12 54					13 19			13 54						14 16			14 54				
Oxford	a			13 14					13 40			14 14						14 40			15 14				
Reading 7	a			13 39					14 09			14 40						15 08			15 39				
Guildford	a																								
Basingstoke	a			14 08					14 40			15 08									16 08				
Winchester	a			14 24					14 55			15 24									16 24				
Southampton Airport Pkway ✈	a			14 32					15 08			15 32									16 32				
Southampton Central ⛴	a			14 41					15 17			15 41									16 41				
Brockenhurst 3	a			14 57								15 57									16 57				
Bournemouth	a			15 11								16 11									17 11				

A ⌶ from Edinburgh

Table 51

Saturdays

4 January to 8 February

Scotland, The North East, North West England - The South West and South Coast

Route Diagram - see first Page of Table 51

		XC	VT	XC	XC	XC	XC	VT	XC	XC	VT	XC	XC	XC	XC	XC	VT	XC	XC	VT	XC	XC	XC
		◇[1]	◇[1]	◇[1]	◇[1]	[1]	◇[1]	◇[1]	◇[1]	◇[1]	◇[1]	◇[1]	◇[1]	[1]	◇[1]	◇[1]	◇[1]	◇[1]	◇[1]	◇[1]	◇[1]	◇[1]	[1]
									A							B		C					
		⊼	⊡	⊼	⊼	⊼	⊼	⊡	⊼	⊼	⊡	⊼	⊼		⊼	⊼	⊡	⊼	⊼	⊡	⊼	⊼	⊼
Aberdeen	d															08 20							
Stonehaven	d															08 38							
Montrose	d															08 59							
Arbroath	d															09 15							
Dundee	d															09 32							
Leuchars [3]	d															09 47							
Cupar	d															09 54							
Ladybank	d															10 01							
Markinch	d															10 09							
Kirkcaldy	d															10 17							
Inverkeithing	d															10 32							
Glasgow Central [15]	d								09 00														
Motherwell	d								09 15														
Haymarket	d								09 57							10 52							
Edinburgh [10]	d								10 05							11 08							
Haymarket	d																						
Lockerbie	d																						
Carlisle [8]	d																						
Penrith North Lakes	d																						
Oxenholme Lake District	d																						
Lancaster [6]	d																						
Preston [8]	d							13 17									14 17						
Wigan North Western	d							13 28									14 28						
Warrington Bank Quay	d							13 39									14 39						
M'chester Piccadilly [10]	d				13 07		13 27						14 07		14 27							15 07	
Stockport	d				13 16		13 35						14 16		14 35							15 16	
Wilmslow	d																						
Crewe [10]	d							14 01									15 01						
Macclesfield	d						13 49								14 49								
Congleton	d																						
Stoke-on-Trent	d				13 44		14 07						14 44		15 07							15 44	
Stafford	d				14 03		14 26						15 03		15 26							16 03	
Wolverhampton [7]	d				14 16		14 41	14 45					15 17		15 41		15 45					16 17	
Dunbar	d															11 28							
Berwick-upon-Tweed	d								10 47							11 51							
Alnmouth for Alnwick	d															12 11							
Morpeth	d								11 19														
Newcastle [8]	d			11 35					11 42			12 35				12 44					13 35		
Chester-le-Street	d																						
Durham	d			11 48					11 55			12 48				12 56					13 48		
Darlington [7]	d			12 05					12 12			13 05				13 13					14 05		
York [8]	d			12 35					12 45			13 34				13 45					14 35		
Leeds [10]	d								13 11							14 11							
Wakefield Westgate [7]	d								13 23							14 24							
Doncaster [7]	d			12 59								13 58									14 59		
Sheffield [7]	d			13 23					13 54			14 23				14 54					15 23		
Chesterfield	d								14 07							15 06							
Nottingham [8]	d	13 10				13 41				14 10				14 41					15 10				15 41
Derby [6]	d	13 36		13 52		14 11			14 30	14 36		14 53		15 11		15 27			15 37		15 52		16 11
Burton-on-Trent	d	13 49				14 22				14 49				15 25		15 38			15 49				16 22
Tamworth	d	14 02				14 34			14 49	15 02				15 34				⟵	16 02				16 34
Birmingham New Street [12]	a	14 23		14 25	14 33	14 55	14 58	15 05	15 08	15 24		15 27	15 33	15 55	15 58	16 04	16 05	16 04	16 24		16 27	16 33	16 55
Birmingham New Street [12]	d	14 30	14 30	14 33	14 42		15 04	15 10	15 12	15 30	15 30	15 33	15 42		16 04	16 12	16 10	16 12	16 30	16 30	16 33	16 42	
Cheltenham Spa	a	15 10			15 24				15 51	16 10			16 24			⟶		16 50	17 10			17 24	
Gloucester [7]	a	15 20								16 20									17 20				
Bristol Parkway [7]	a				15 54				16 29				16 53					17 25				17 53	
Bristol Temple Meads [10]	a				16 07				16 42				17 07					17 38				18 07	
Newport (South Wales)	a	16 06								17 08									18 06				
Cardiff Central [7]	a	16 25								17 24									18 22				
Weston-super-Mare	a																						
Taunton	a								17 17				17 41					18 15					
Tiverton Parkway	a								17 29				17 53					18 28					
Exeter St Davids [6]	a								17 45				18 07					18 41					
Dawlish	a												18 20										
Teignmouth	a												18 25										
Newton Abbot	a								18 10				18 32					19 04					
Torquay	a												18 43										
Paignton	a												18 51										
Totnes	a								18 24									19 17					
Plymouth	a								18 52									19 43					
Liskeard [6]	a								19 20									20 10					
Bodmin Parkway	a								19 34									20 22					
Lostwithiel	a																	20 27					
Par	a								19 46									20 35					
Newquay (Summer Only)	a																						
St Austell	a								19 54									20 41					
Truro	a								20 12									21 00					
Redruth	a								20 26									21 12					
Camborne	a								20 33									21 18					
Hayle	a																	21 26					
St Erth	a								20 45									21 31					
Penzance	a								20 56									21 43					
Birmingham International ✈	d		14 40				15 14	15 20			15 40				16 14		16 20			16 40			
Coventry	d		14a49				15 25	15a30			15a50				16 25		16a30			16a50			
Leamington Spa [8]	d			15 00			15 38					16 02			16 38						17 00		
Banbury	a			15 19			15 54					16 19			16 54						17 17		
Oxford	a			15 40			16 14					16 40			17 14						17 41		
Reading [7]	a			16 09			16 40					17 08			17 39						18 08		
Guildford	a																						
Basingstoke	a			16 40			17 08								18 08						18 40		
Winchester	a			16 55			17 24								18 24						18 55		
Southampton Airport Pkway ✈	a			17 08			17 32								18 32						19 08		
Southampton Central ⛴	a			17 17			17 41								18 40						19 17		
Brockenhurst [3]	a						17 57								18 57								
Bournemouth	a						18 11								19 11								

A ⊼ from Edinburgh to Plymouth

B ⊼ from Edinburgh

C ⊼ to Plymouth

Table 51

Saturdays

4 January to 8 February

Scotland, The North East, North West England - The South West and South Coast

Route Diagram - see first Page of Table 51

		XC	VT	XC	XC	VT	XC	XC	XC	XC	VT	XC	XC	VT	XC	XC	XC	XC	XC	XC	XC	XC
		◇[1]	◇[1]	◇[1]	◇[1]	◇[1]	◇[1]	◇[1]	[1]	◇[1]	◇[1]	◇[1]	◇[1]	◇[1]	◇[1]	◇[1]	[1]	◇[1]	◇[1]	◇[1]	◇[1]	◇[1]
				A												B		C	D			B
		trolley	catering	trolley		catering	trolley	trolley	trolley	trolley	catering	trolley		catering	trolley	trolley	trolley	trolley	trolley		trolley	trolley
Aberdeen	d																					
Stonehaven	d																					
Montrose	d																					
Arbroath	d																					
Dundee	d																					
Leuchars [3]	d																					
Cupar	d																					
Ladybank	d																					
Markinch	d																					
Kirkcaldy	d																					
Inverkeithing	d																					
Glasgow Central [15]	d			11 00															13 00			
Motherwell	d			11 14															13 14			
Haymarket	d			11 52																		
Edinburgh [10]	d			12 05								13 09							14 05			
Haymarket	d																					
Lockerbie	d																					
Carlisle [8]	d																					
Penrith North Lakes	d																					
Oxenholme Lake District	d																					
Lancaster [6]	d																					
Preston [8]	d		15 17								16 17											
Wigan North Western	d		15 28								16 28											
Warrington Bank Quay	d		15 39								16 39											
M'chester Piccadilly [10] ⛴	d	15 27						16 07		16 27						17 06		17 27				18 05
Stockport	d	15 35						16 16		16 35						17 15		17 36				18 13
Wilmslow	d																					
Crewe [10]	d		16 01								17 01											
Macclesfield	d	15 49								16 49						17 27						18 26
Congleton	d																	17 54				
Stoke-on-Trent	d	16 07						16 44		17 07						17 45		18 07				18 44
Stafford	d	16 25						17 03		17 26						18 04		18 26				19 03
Wolverhampton [7] ⛴	d	16 41	16 45					17 17		17 41	17 45					18 16		18 41				19 16
Dunbar	d											13 29										
Berwick-upon-Tweed	d			12 45															14 47			
Alnmouth for Alnwick	d											14 09										
Morpeth	d																					
Newcastle [8]	d			13 44			14 35					14 44			15 08				15 41		16 35	
Chester-le-Street	d																					
Durham	d			13 56			14 48					14 56			15 21				15 54		16 48	
Darlington [7]	d			14 13			15 05					15 13			15 37				16 13		17 05	
York [8]	d			14 45			15 35					15 45			16 05				16 45		17 35	
Leeds [10]	d			15 11								16 11			16 40				17 11			
Wakefield Westgate [7]	d			15 24								16 24			16 52				17 23			
Doncaster [7]	d						15 59														17 59	
Sheffield [7] ⛴	d			15 54			16 23					16 54			17 23				17 54		18 23	
Chesterfield	d			16 07								17 06							18 07			
Nottingham [8] ⛴	d				16 10				16 41				17 10				17 41			18 10		
Derby [6]	d			16 27	16 36		16 53		17 11			17 27	17 36		17 52		18 11		18 27	18 36	18 52	
Burton-on-Trent	d				16 49				17 25			17 38	17 49				18 23			18 49		
Tamworth	d			16 48	17 02				17 36				18 02				18 35		18 46	19 02		
Birmingham New Street [12]	a	16 58	17 05	17 07	17 24		17 27	17 33	17 55	17 58	18 05	18 07	18 24		18 27	18 33	18 57	18 58	19 06	19 22	19 26	19 33
Birmingham New Street [12]	d	17 04	17 10	17 12	17 30	17 30	17 33	17 42		18 04	18 10	18 12	18 30	18 30	18 33	18 42		19 04	19 12	19 30	19 33	19 42
Cheltenham Spa	a			17 51	18 16			18 24				18 51	19 10			19 24			19 51	20 10		20 24
Gloucester [7]	a				18 26								19 20							20 20		
Bristol Parkway [7]	a			18 29				18 53				19 25				19 55			20 29			20 53
Bristol Temple Meads [10]	a			18 42				19 04				19 38				20 05			20 42			21 04
Newport (South Wales)	a				19 11								20 03			20 44				21 12		
Cardiff Central [7]	a				19 30								20 20			21 00				21 29		
Weston-super-Mare	a																					
Taunton	a			19 15								20 15							21 15			21 42
Tiverton Parkway	a			19 28								20 28							21 28			21 54
Exeter St Davids [6]	a			19 43								20 41							21 44			22 09
Dawlish	a																					
Teignmouth	a																					
Newton Abbot	a			20 04								21 02							22 08			22 28
Torquay	a																					
Paignton	a																					
Totnes	a			20 18								21 15							22 23			22 41
Plymouth	a			20 45								21 41							22 50			23 08
Liskeard [6]	a			21 24																		
Bodmin Parkway	a			21 36																		
Lostwithiel	a																					
Par	a			21 47																		
Newquay (Summer Only)	a																					
St Austell	a			21 54																		
Truro	a			22 11																		
Redruth	a			22 29																		
Camborne	a			22 36																		
Hayle	a																					
St Erth	a			22 47																		
Penzance	a			22 56																		
Birmingham International ✈	d	17 14	17 20			17 40				18 14	18 20			18 40				19 14				
Coventry	d	17 25	17a30			17a49				18 25	18a30			18a49				19 25				
Leamington Spa [8]	d	17 38					18 02			18 38					19 00			19 38			20 03	
Banbury	a	17 54					18 18			18 54					19 17			19 54			20 18	
Oxford	a	18 14					18 40			19 14					19 40			20 14			20 40	
Reading [7]	a	18 40					19 08			19 39					20 08			20 40			21 08	
Guildford	a																					
Basingstoke	a	19 08								20 08								21 08				
Winchester	a	19 24								20 24								21 24				
Southampton Airport Pkway ✈	a	19 32								20 32								21 32				
Southampton Central ⛴	a	19 41								20 41								21 41				
Brockenhurst [3]	a	19 57								20 57								21 57				
Bournemouth	a	20 11								21 11								22 15				

A trolley from Edinburgh to Plymouth
B trolley to Bristol Temple Meads
C trolley to Reading
D trolley from Edinburgh to Bristol Temple Meads

Table 51

Saturdays

4 January to 8 February

Scotland, The North East, North West England - The South West and South Coast

Route Diagram - see first Page of Table 51

		XC	XC	XC	XC	XC	XC	XC	XC	XC	XC	XC	VT	XC	XC	XC	XC	XC	VT	XC	XC	XC
		1	◇1	◇1	◇1	◇1	◇1	1	◇1	◇1	◇1	◇1	◇1	1	◇1	◇1	◇1	◇1	◇1	◇1	1	◇1
			A	B			C		C	C						D						E
		🛒	🛒	🛒		🛒	🛒	🛒	🛒	🛒	🛒		☕			🛒			☕			🛒
Aberdeen	d																					
Stonehaven	d																					
Montrose	d																					
Arbroath	d																					
Dundee	d																					
Leuchars 3	d																					
Cupar	d																					
Ladybank	d																					
Markinch	d																					
Kirkcaldy	d																					
Inverkeithing	d																					
Glasgow Central 15	d									15 00												16 52
Motherwell	d									15 14												17 06
Haymarket	d									15 57												17 53
Edinburgh 10	d			15 08						16 05						17 08						18 08
Haymarket	d																					
Lockerbie	d																					
Carlisle 8	d																					
Penrith North Lakes	d																					
Oxenholme Lake District	d																					
Lancaster 6	d																					
Preston 8	d																					
Wigan North Western	d																		21 32			
Warrington Bank Quay	d												20 39						21 43			
M'chester Piccadilly 10 🚊	d		18 27				19 07		19 27			20 07			20 27		21 07			21 27		
Stockport	d		18 35				19 16		19 35			20 16			20 35					21 35		
Wilmslow	d																					
Crewe 10	d												21 01						22 04			
Macclesfield	d								19 49						20 49					21 49		
Congleton	d		18 54																			
Stoke-on-Trent	d		19 07				19 44		20 07			20 44			21 07		21 45			22 07		
Stafford	d		19 25				20 03		20 26			21 03			21 27		22 03		22 23	22 29		
Wolverhampton 7 🚊	d		19 41				20 16		20 41			21 16	21 34		21 41		22 16		22 40	22 44		
Dunbar	d			15 28												17 29						18 28
Berwick-upon-Tweed	d															17 51						18 51
Alnmouth for Alnwick	d									17 03												19 11
Morpeth	d									17 17												
Newcastle 8	d			16 41		17 32				17 44	18 35					18 44		19 35				19 45
Chester-le-Street	d					17 41																
Durham	d			16 54		17 48				17 56	18 49					18 57		19 50				19 57
Darlington 7	d			17 13		18 05				18 13	19 06					19 14		20 07				20 14
York 8	d			17 45		18 34				18 45	19 35					19 45		20 35				20 45
Leeds 10	d			18 11						19 11						20 11						21 11
Wakefield Westgate 7	d			18 23						19 24						20 23						21 23
Doncaster 7	d					18 59					19 59							21 00				
Sheffield 7 🚊	d			18 58		19 24				19 54	20 23					20 54		21 23				21 54
Chesterfield	d			19 10						20 06						21 06		21 35				22 06
Nottingham 8 🚊	d	18 41			19 10			19 41						20 37							21 39	
Derby 6	d	19 11		19 29	19 36	19 53		20 10		20 27	20 52			21 10		21 27		21 54			22 11	22 26
Burton-on-Trent	d	19 22		19 37	19 49			20 21						21 24		21 38					22 21	22 37
Tamworth	d	19 34			20 02			20 33		20 46				21 35		21 49					22 33	22 47
Birmingham New Street 12	a	19 55	19 59	20 06	20 24	20 27	20 33	20 56	20 58	21 03	21 25	21 32	21 55	21 57	21 58	22 06	22 32	22 43	22 59	23 01	23 02	23 06
Birmingham New Street 12	d		20 04	20 12	20 30	20 33	20 42		21 04	21 12												
Cheltenham Spa	a			20 51	21 10		21 24			21 50												
Gloucester 7	a				21 20					21 59												
Bristol Parkway 7	a			21 20			21 58			22 30												
Bristol Temple Meads 10	a			21 35			22 12			22 41												
Newport (South Wales)	a				22 19																	
Cardiff Central 7	a				22 45																	
Weston-super-Mare	a																					
Taunton	a			22 15																		
Tiverton Parkway	a			22 28																		
Exeter St Davids 6	a			22 43																		
Dawlish	a																					
Teignmouth	a																					
Newton Abbot	a			23 11																		
Torquay	a																					
Paignton	a																					
Totnes	a			23 27																		
Plymouth	a			23 55																		
Liskeard 6	a																					
Bodmin Parkway	a																					
Lostwithiel	a																					
Par	a																					
Newquay (Summer Only)	a																					
St Austell	a																					
Truro	a																					
Redruth	a																					
Camborne	a																					
Hayle	a																					
St Erth	a																					
Penzance	a																					
Birmingham International ✈	d		20 14						21 14													
Coventry	d		20 25						21 25													
Leamington Spa 8	d		20 38			21 00			21 38													
Banbury	a		20 54			21 19			21 54													
Oxford	a		21 14			21 41			22 16													
Reading 7	a		21 38			22 08			22 47													
Guildford	a					22 59																
Basingstoke	a		22 09						23 12													
Winchester	a		22 24						23 27													
Southampton Airport Pkway ✈	a		22 32						23 35													
Southampton Central ⛴	a		22 40						23 43													
Brockenhurst 3	a		22 56																			
Bournemouth	a		23 20																			

A 🛒 to Reading
B 🛒 to Bristol Temple Meads
C 🛒 to Birmingham New Street
D 🛒 to Leeds
E 🛒 from Edinburgh to Leeds

Table 51

Saturdays

15 February to 17 May

Scotland, The North East, North West England - The South West and South Coast

Route Diagram - see first Page of Table 51

		XC	XC	XC	XC	XC	XC	XC	XC	XC	XC	XC	XC	VT	XC	XC	VT	XC	XC	XC	XC	VT	XC
		◇1	◇1	◇1	◇1	◇1	◇1	◇1	◇1	◇1	◇1	◇1	◇1	◇1	◇1	◇1	◇1	◇1	◇1	1	◇1	◇1	◇1
										A	B		C										D
				trolley		trolley		trolley	trolley	trolley	trolley	trolley	trolley	catering	trolley		catering	trolley	trolley		trolley	catering	trolley
Aberdeen	d																						
Stonehaven	d																						
Montrose	d																						
Arbroath	d																						
Dundee	d																						
Leuchars 8	d																						
Cupar	d																						
Ladybank	d																						
Markinch	d																						
Kirkcaldy	d																						
Inverkeithing	d																						
Glasgow Central 15	d																						
Motherwell	d																						
Haymarket	d																						
Edinburgh 10	d																						
Haymarket	d																						
Lockerbie	d																						
Carlisle 8	d																						
Penrith North Lakes	d																						
Oxenholme Lake District	d																						
Lancaster 6	d																					06 58	
Preston 8	d													06 17								07 17	
Wigan North Western	d													06 28								07 28	
Warrington Bank Quay	d													06 39								07 39	
M'chester Piccadilly 10	d							05 11				06 00							07 07		07 27		
Stockport	d											06 08							07 16		07 35		
Wilmslow	d																						
Crewe 10	d							05 47						07 01								08 01	
Macclesfield	d											06 21									07 49		
Congleton	d																						
Stoke-on-Trent	d							06 08				06 39							07 44		08 07		
Stafford	d							06 26				06 58							08 03		08 26		
Wolverhampton 7	d							06 41				07 16		07 45					08 16		08 41	08 45	
Dunbar	d																						
Berwick-upon-Tweed	d																						
Alnmouth for Alnwick	d																						
Morpeth	d																						
Newcastle 8	d																						
Chester-le-Street	d																						
Durham	d																						
Darlington 7	d																						
York 8	d																						06 17
Leeds 10	d														06 00			06 16					07 10
Wakefield Westgate 7	d														06 12			06 29					07 22
Doncaster 7	d																	06 47					
Sheffield 7	d														06 50			07 18					07 56
Chesterfield	d														07 03			07 30					08 08
Nottingham 8	d									05 58			06 37			06 58				07 38			
Derby 6	d						06 10			06 36	06 48		07 06		07 26	07 36		07 50		08 06			08 28
Burton-on-Trent	d						06 20			06 48	06 59		07 17		07 37	07 50		08 00		08 18			08 38
Tamworth	d						06 31		←	07 01	07 09		07 29		07 48	08 02		08 11		08 30			08 49
Birmingham New Street 12	a						06 50	06 57	06 50	07 24	07 27	07 33	07 52	08 05	08 08	08 24		08 28	08 34	08 54	08 58	09 05	09 08
Birmingham New Street 12	d	05 00	05 42	06 04	06 33	06 42	07 12	07 04	07 12	07 30	07 33	07 42	08 04	08 10	08 12	08 30	08 30	08 33	08 42		09 04	09 10	09 12
Cheltenham Spa	a	06 02	06 42			07 24	↪		07 51	08 10		08 24			08 51	09 10			09 24				09 51
Gloucester 7	a	06 12	06 52							08 20						09 20							
Bristol Parkway 7	a					07 53			08 24			08 53			09 24				09 53				10 29
Bristol Temple Meads 10	a					08 05			08 38			09 06			09 38				10 04				10 42
Newport (South Wales)	a	07 05	07 48							09 06						10 05							
Cardiff Central 7	a	07 21	08 04							09 22						10 21							
Weston-super-Mare	a																						
Taunton	a					08 42			09 16						10 17								11 15
Tiverton Parkway	a					08 54			09 28						10 30								11 28
Exeter St Davids 6	a					09 08			09 41						10 45								11 41
Dawlish	a																						
Teignmouth	a																						
Newton Abbot	a					09 28			10 02						11 09								12 03
Torquay	a					09 39																	
Paignton	a					09 47																	
Totnes	a								10 15						11 23								12 16
Plymouth	a								10 41						11 51								12 42
Liskeard 6	a																						
Bodmin Parkway	a																						
Lostwithiel	a																						
Par	a																						
Newquay (Summer Only)	a																						
St Austell	a																						
Truro	a																						
Redruth	a																						
Camborne	a																						
Hayle	a																						
St Erth	a																						
Penzance	a																						
Birmingham International ✈	d			06 14				07 14					08 14	08 20			08 40				09 14	09 20	
Coventry	d			06 25				07 25					08 25	08a29			08a50				09 25	09a30	
Leamington Spa 8	d			06 38	07 00			07 38			08 00		08 38					09 00			09 38		
Banbury	a			06 54	07 17			07 54			08 17		08 54					09 17			09 54		
Oxford	a			07 14	07 40			08 14			08 40		09 14					09 40			10 14		
Reading 7	a			07 39	08 06			08 39			09 07		09 39					10 06			10 41		
Guildford	a																						
Basingstoke	a			08 08	08 40			09 08					10 08					10 39			11 08		
Winchester	a			08 24	08 55			09 24					10 24					10 54			11 24		
Southampton Airport Pkway ✈	a			08 32	09 08			09 32					10 32					11 08			11 32		
Southampton Central	a			08 41	09 17			09 40					10 41					11 17			11 41		
Brockenhurst 3	a			08 56				09 57					10 57								11 57		
Bournemouth	a			09 14				10 11					11 12								12 11		

A trolley from Birmingham New Street to Newport (South Wales)

B trolley from Birmingham New Street

C trolley from Derby

D trolley from Leeds

Table 51

Saturdays

15 February to 17 May

Scotland, The North East, North West England - The South West and South Coast

Route Diagram - see first Page of Table 51

		XC	VT	XC	XC	XC		XC	XC	VT	XC	XC	VT	XC	XC	XC		XC	XC	VT	XC	XC	VT	XC	XC
		◇1	◇1	◇1	◇1	1		◇1	◇1	◇1	◇1	◇1	◇1	◇1	◇1	1		◇1	◇1	◇1	◇1	◇1	◇1	◇1	◇1
		A							B																
Aberdeen	d																								
Stonehaven	d																								
Montrose	d																								
Arbroath	d																								
Dundee	d																								
Leuchars 3	d																								
Cupar	d																								
Ladybank	d																								
Markinch	d																								
Kirkcaldy	d																								
Inverkeithing	d																								
Glasgow Central 15	d									05 50															
Motherwell	d									06 04															
Haymarket	d																								
Edinburgh 10	d																		06 08	06 52				07 00	
Haymarket	d																			06 56					
Lockerbie	d																								
Carlisle 8	d									07 02										08 07					
Penrith North Lakes	d									07 18										08 22					
Oxenholme Lake District	d									07 42															
Lancaster 6	d									07 57										08 57					
Preston 8	d									08 17										09 17					
Wigan North Western	d									08 28										09 28					
Warrington Bank Quay	d									08 39										09 39					
M'chester Piccadilly 10	d				08 07			08 27							09 07			09 27							10 07
Stockport	d				08 16			08 35							09 16			09 35							10 16
Wilmslow	d																								
Crewe 10	d									09 01										10 01					
Macclesfield	d							08 49										09 49							
Congleton	d																								
Stoke-on-Trent	d				08 44			09 07							09 44			10 07							10 44
Stafford	d				09 03			09 26							10 03			10 26							11 03
Wolverhampton 7	d				09 16			09 41		09 45					10 17			10 41		10 45					11 16
Dunbar	d																								
Berwick-upon-Tweed	d																		06 47					07 40	
Alnmouth for Alnwick	d																		07 07					08 00	
Morpeth	d																							08 14	
Newcastle 8	d			06 22					06 45					07 35					07 40					08 35	
Chester-le-Street	d																								
Durham	d			06 37					06 58					07 48					07 53					08 48	
Darlington 7	d			06 54					07 15					08 05					08 10					09 05	
York 8	d			07 24					07 45					08 34					08 45					09 35	
Leeds 10	d								08 11										09 11						
Wakefield Westgate 7	d								08 24										09 24						
Doncaster 7	d			07 56										08 58										09 58	
Sheffield 7	d			08 20					08 54					09 23					09 54					10 24	
Chesterfield	d			08 32					09 06										10 06						
Nottingham 8	d	08 12				08 41						09 10				09 41						10 10			
Derby 6	d	08 37		08 53		09 10			09 27			09 36		09 52		10 11			10 27			10 37		10 52	
Burton-on-Trent	d	08 49				09 21			09 37			09 50				10 22						10 49			
Tamworth	d	09 02				09 33					←	10 02				10 34			10 48		←	11 02			
Birmingham New Street 12	a	09 25		09 27	09 33	09 54		09 58	10 03	10 05	10 03	10 24		10 27	10 33	10 55		10 58	11 04	11 05	11 04	11 24		11 27	11 33
Birmingham New Street 12	d	09 30	09 30	09 33	09 42			10 04	10 12	10 10	10 12	10 30	10 30	10 33	10 42			11 04	11 12	11 10	11 12	11 30	11 30	11 33	11 42
Cheltenham Spa	a	10 10			10 24				→		10 51	11 10			11 24				→		11 51	12 10			12 24
Gloucester 7	a	10 20										11 20										12 20			
Bristol Parkway 7	a				10 54						11 24				11 53						12 29				12 53
Bristol Temple Meads 10	a				11 09						11 38				12 04						12 42				13 07
Newport (South Wales)	a	11 06										12 05										13 05			
Cardiff Central 7	a	11 24										12 23										13 21			
Weston-super-Mare	a				11 29																				
Taunton	a				11 59						12 16										13 15				
Tiverton Parkway	a				12 11						12 28										13 28				
Exeter St Davids 6	a				12 26						12 41										13 42				
Dawlish	a				12 39																				
Teignmouth	a				12 44																				
Newton Abbot	a				12 51						13 02										14 02				
Torquay	a				13 03																				
Paignton	a				13 11																				
Totnes	a										13 15										14 15				
Plymouth	a										13 41										14 41				
Liskeard 6	a																								
Bodmin Parkway	a																								
Lostwithiel	a																								
Par	a																								
Newquay (Summer Only)	a																								
St Austell	a																								
Truro	a																								
Redruth	a																								
Camborne	a																								
Hayle	a																								
St Erth	a																								
Penzance	a																								
Birmingham International	d		09 40					10 14		10 20			10 40					11 14		11 20			11 40		
Coventry	d		09a50					10 25		10a30			10a50					11 25		11a30			11a49		
Leamington Spa 8	d			10 00				10 38						11 00				11 38						12 00	
Banbury	a			10 17				10 54						11 17				11 54						12 17	
Oxford	a			10 40				11 14						11 40				12 14						12 40	
Reading 7	a			11 11				11 39						12 07				12 40						13 07	
Guildford	a																								
Basingstoke	a							12 08						12 40				13 08							
Winchester	a							12 24						12 55				13 24							
Southampton Airport Pkway	a							12 32						13 08				13 32							
Southampton Central	a							12 41						13 17				13 41							
Brockenhurst 3	a							12 57										13 57							
Bournemouth	a							13 11										14 11							

A from Birmingham New Street

B from Leeds

Table 51

Saturdays

15 February to 17 May

Scotland, The North East, North West England - The South West and South Coast

Route Diagram - see first Page of Table 51

		XC	XC	VT	XC	XC	VT	XC	XC	XC	XC	VT	XC	XC	VT	XC	XC	XC	XC	XC	VT	XC
		1	◇1	◇1	◇1	◇1	◇1	◇1	◇1	1	◇1	◇1	◇1	◇1	◇1	◇1	◇1	1	◇1	◇1	◇1	◇1
					A								A							A		
Aberdeen	d																					
Stonehaven	d																					
Montrose	d																					
Arbroath	d																					
Dundee	d												06 32									
Leuchars 3	d												06 46									
Cupar	d												06 54									
Ladybank	d												07 03									
Markinch	d												07 11									
Kirkcaldy	d												07 21									
Inverkeithing	d												07 38									
Glasgow Central 15	d			08 00	06 01															07 50	10 00	
Motherwell	d				06 17															08 05		
Haymarket	d				06 57								07 56							08 51		
Edinburgh 10	d				07 07							08 52	08 05							09 08		
Haymarket	d											08 57										
Lockerbie	d																					
Carlisle 8	d			09 09								10 08									11 11	
Penrith North Lakes	d																				11 25	
Oxenholme Lake District	d											10 42										
Lancaster 6	d			09 56								10 57										
Preston 8	d			10 17								11 18									12 17	
Wigan North Western	d			10 28								11 28									12 28	
Warrington Bank Quay	d			10 39								11 40									12 39	
M'chester Piccadilly 10	d		10 27						11 07		11 27						12 07		12 27			
Stockport	d		10 35						11 16		11 35						12 16		12 35			
Wilmslow	d																					
Crewe 10	d			11 01								12 01									13 01	
Macclesfield	d		10 49								11 49								12 49			
Congleton	d																					
Stoke-on-Trent	d		11 07						11 44		12 07						12 44		13 07			
Stafford	d		11 26						12 03		12 25						13 03		13 26			
Wolverhampton 7	d		11 41	11 45					12 16		12 41	12 45					13 16		13 41		13 45	
Dunbar	d				07 27															09 28		
Berwick-upon-Tweed	d												08 47							09 51		
Alnmouth for Alnwick	d												09 09									
Morpeth	d																					
Newcastle 8	d				08 42			09 35					09 42			10 35				10 44		
Chester-le-Street	d																					
Durham	d				08 55			09 48					09 56			10 48				10 56		
Darlington 7	d				09 12			10 05					10 13			11 05				11 13		
York 8	d				09 45			10 35					10 45			11 35				11 45		
Leeds 10	d				10 11								11 11							12 11		
Wakefield Westgate 7	d				10 24								11 24							12 24		
Doncaster 7	d							10 59								11 59						
Sheffield 7	d				10 54			11 23					11 54			12 23				12 54		
Chesterfield	d				11 06								12 07							13 06		
Nottingham 8	d	10 41				11 10				11 41				12 10				12 41				
Derby 6	d	11 11			11 26	11 36		11 52		12 11			12 29	12 36		12 52		13 11		13 27		
Burton-on-Trent	d	11 22			11 39	11 49				12 22				12 49				13 25		13 38		
Tamworth	d	11 34				12 02				12 34			12 49	13 02				13 36				←
Birmingham New Street 12	a	11 56	11 59	12 05	12 08	12 24		12 27	12 33	12 56	12 58	13 05	13 08	13 23		13 26	13 32	13 55	13 58	14 04	14 05	14 04
Birmingham New Street 12	d		12 04	12 10	12 12	12 30	12 30	12 33	12 42		13 04	13 10	13 12	13 30	13 30	13 33	13 42		14 04	14 12	14 10	14 12
Cheltenham Spa	a				12 51	13 10			13 25				13 51	14 10			14 24			→		14 51
Gloucester 7	a					13 20								14 20								
Bristol Parkway 7	a				13 24				13 55				14 26				14 57					15 24
Bristol Temple Meads 10	a				13 38				14 05				14 40				15 09					15 38
Newport (South Wales)	a					14 06								15 10								
Cardiff Central 7	a					14 22								15 26								
Weston-super-Mare	a																					
Taunton	a				14 15								15 17				15 43					16 15
Tiverton Parkway	a				14 28								15 29				15 55					16 28
Exeter St Davids 6	a				14 42								15 44				16 10					16 41
Dawlish	a																					
Teignmouth	a																					
Newton Abbot	a				15 02								16 04									17 02
Torquay	a																					
Paignton	a																					
Totnes	a				15 15								16 18									17 15
Plymouth	a				15 42								16 46									17 41
Liskeard 6	a																					
Bodmin Parkway	a																					
Lostwithiel	a																					
Par	a																					
Newquay (Summer Only)	a																					
St Austell	a																					
Truro	a																					
Redruth	a																					
Camborne	a																					
Hayle	a																					
St Erth	a																					
Penzance	a																					
Birmingham International	d		12 14	12 20			12 40				13 14	13 20			13 40				14 14		14 20	
Coventry	d		12 25	12a30			12a49				13 25	13a30			13a50				14 25		14a30	
Leamington Spa 8	d		12 38					13 02			13 38					14 00			14 38			
Banbury	a		12 54					13 19			13 54					14 16			14 54			
Oxford	a		13 14					13 40			14 14					14 40			15 14			
Reading 7	a		13 39					14 09			14 40					15 08			15 39			
Guildford	a																					
Basingstoke	a		14 08					14 40			15 08								16 08			
Winchester	a		14 24					14 55			15 24								16 24			
Southampton Airport Pkway	a		14 32					15 08			15 32								16 32			
Southampton Central	a		14 41					15 17			15 41								16 41			
Brockenhurst 3	a		14 57								15 57								16 57			
Bournemouth	a		15 11								16 11								17 11			

A from Edinburgh

Table 51

Saturdays

15 February to 17 May

Scotland, The North East, North West England - The South West and South Coast

Route Diagram - see first Page of Table 51

		XC	VT	XC	XC	XC	XC	VT		XC	XC	VT	XC	XC	XC	XC	XC	VT		XC	XC	VT	XC	XC	XC
		◇1	◇1	◇1	◇1	1	◇1	◇1		◇1	◇1	◇1	◇1	◇1	1	◇1	◇1	◇1		◇1	◇1	◇1	◇1	◇1	1
										A							B			C					
		trolley	buffet	trolley	trolley	trolley	trolley	buffet		trolley	trolley	buffet	trolley	trolley		trolley	trolley	buffet		trolley	trolley	buffet	trolley	trolley	trolley
Aberdeen	d																08 20								
Stonehaven	d																08 38								
Montrose	d																08 59								
Arbroath	d																09 15								
Dundee	d																09 32								
Leuchars 3	d																09 47								
Cupar	d																09 54								
Ladybank	d																10 01								
Markinch	d																10 09								
Kirkcaldy	d																10 17								
Inverkeithing	d																10 32								
Glasgow Central 15	d									09 00								12 00							
Motherwell	d									09 15															
Haymarket	d									09 57							10 52								
Edinburgh 10	d							10 52		10 05							11 08								
Haymarket	d							10 57																	
Lockerbie	d																								
Carlisle 8	d							12 08										13 11							
Penrith North Lakes	d																								
Oxenholme Lake District	d							12 43																	
Lancaster 6	d							12 57										13 58							
Preston 8	d							13 17										14 17							
Wigan North Western	d							13 28										14 28							
Warrington Bank Quay	d							13 39										14 39							
M'chester Piccadilly 10	d				13 07		13 27							14 07		14 27								15 07	
Stockport	d				13 16		13 35							14 16		14 35								15 16	
Wilmslow	d																								
Crewe 10	d							14 01										15 01							
Macclesfield	d						13 49									14 49									
Congleton	d																								
Stoke-on-Trent	d				13 44		14 07							14 44		15 07								15 44	
Stafford	d				14 03		14 26							15 03		15 26								16 03	
Wolverhampton 7	d				14 16		14 41	14 45						15 17		15 41		15 45						16 17	
Dunbar	d																11 28								
Berwick-upon-Tweed	d									10 47							11 51								
Alnmouth for Alnwick	d																12 11								
Morpeth	d									11 19															
Newcastle 8	d			11 35						11 42			12 35				12 44						13 35		
Chester-le-Street	d																								
Durham	d			11 48						11 55			12 48				12 56						13 48		
Darlington 7	d			12 05						12 12			13 05				13 13						14 05		
York 8	d			12 35						12 45			13 34				13 45						14 35		
Leeds 10	d									13 11							14 11								
Wakefield Westgate 7	d									13 23							14 24								
Doncaster 7	d			12 59									13 58										14 59		
Sheffield 7	d			13 23						13 54			14 23				14 54						15 23		
Chesterfield	d									14 07							15 06								
Nottingham 8	d	13 10				13 41					14 10				14 41						15 10				15 41
Derby 6	d	13 36		13 52		14 11				14 30	14 36		14 53		15 11		15 27				15 37		15 52		16 11
Burton-on-Trent	d	13 49				14 22					14 49				15 25		15 38				15 49				16 22
Tamworth	d	14 02				14 34				14 49	15 02				15 34					←	16 02				16 34
Birmingham New Street 12	a	14 23		14 25	14 33	14 55	14 58	15 05		15 08	15 24		15 27	15 33	15 55	15 58	16 04	16 05		16 04	16 24		16 27	16 33	16 55
Birmingham New Street 12	d	14 30	14 30	14 33	14 42		15 04	15 10		15 12	15 30	15 30	15 33	15 42		16 04	16 12	16 10		16 12	16 30	16 30	16 33	16 42	
Cheltenham Spa	a	15 10			15 24					15 51	16 10			16 24			→			16 50	17 10			17 24	
Gloucester 7	a	15 20									16 20										17 20				
Bristol Parkway 7	a				15 54					16 29				16 53						17 25				17 53	
Bristol Temple Meads 10	a				16 07					16 42				17 07						17 38				18 07	
Newport (South Wales)	a	16 06									17 08										18 06				
Cardiff Central 7	a	16 25									17 24										18 22				
Weston-super-Mare	a																								
Taunton	a									17 17				17 41						18 15					
Tiverton Parkway	a									17 29				17 53						18 28					
Exeter St Davids 6	a									17 45				18 07						18 41					
Dawlish	a													18 20											
Teignmouth	a													18 25											
Newton Abbot	a									18 10				18 32						19 04					
Torquay	a													18 43											
Paignton	a													18 51											
Totnes	a									18 24										19 17					
Plymouth	a									18 52										19 43					
Liskeard 6	a									19 17										20 10					
Bodmin Parkway	a									19 32										20 22					
Lostwithiel	a																			20 27					
Par	a									19 44										20 35					
Newquay (Summer Only)	a																								
St Austell	a									19 52										20 41					
Truro	a									20 10										21 00					
Redruth	a									20 26										21 12					
Camborne	a									20 33										21 18					
Hayle	a																			21 26					
St Erth	a									20 45										21 31					
Penzance	a									20 56										21 43					
Birmingham International	d		14 40				15 14	15 20				15 40				16 14		16 20				16 40			
Coventry	d		14a49				15 25	15a30				15a50				16 25		16a30				16a50			
Leamington Spa 8	d			15 00			15 38						16 02			16 38							17 00		
Banbury	a			15 19			15 54						16 19			16 54							17 17		
Oxford	a			15 40			16 14						16 40			17 14							17 41		
Reading 7	a			16 09			16 40						17 08			17 39							18 08		
Guildford	a																								
Basingstoke	a			16 40			17 08									18 08							18 40		
Winchester	a			16 55			17 24									18 24							18 55		
Southampton Airport Pkway	a			17 08			17 32									18 32							19 08		
Southampton Central	a			17 17			17 41									18 40							19 17		
Brockenhurst 3	a						17 57									18 57									
Bournemouth	a						18 11									19 11									

A trolley from Edinburgh to Plymouth

B trolley from Edinburgh

C trolley to Plymouth

Table 51

Saturdays

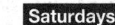

15 February to 17 May

Scotland, The North East, North West England - The South West and South Coast

Route Diagram - see first Page of Table 51

		XC	VT	XC	XC	VT	XC	XC	XC	XC	VT	XC	XC	VT	XC	XC	XC	XC	XC	XC	XC	XC
		◇1	◇1	◇1	◇1	◇1	◇1	◇1	1	◇1	◇1	◇1	◇1	◇1	◇1	◇1	1	◇1	◇1	◇1	◇1	◇1
				A												B		C	D			E
		🛒	🍽	🛒		🍽	🛒	🛒	🛒	🛒	🍽	🛒		🍽	🛒	🛒	🛒	🛒	🛒		🛒	🛒
Aberdeen	d																					
Stonehaven	d																					
Montrose	d																					
Arbroath	d																					
Dundee	d																					
Leuchars 3	d																					
Cupar	d																					
Ladybank	d																					
Markinch	d																					
Kirkcaldy	d																					
Inverkeithing	d																					
Glasgow Central 15	d			11 00							14 00								13 00			
Motherwell	d			11 14															13 14			
Haymarket	d			11 52																		
Edinburgh 10	d		12 52	12 05								13 09							14 05			
Haymarket	d		12 57																			
Lockerbie	d																					
Carlisle 8	d		14 08								15 10											
Penrith North Lakes	d		14 22																			
Oxenholme Lake District	d										15 44											
Lancaster 6	d		14 56																			
Preston 8	d		15 17								16 17											
Wigan North Western	d		15 28								16 28											
Warrington Bank Quay	d		15 39								16 39											
M'chester Piccadilly 10 ⛴	d	15 27						16 07		16 27						17 06		17 27				18 05
Stockport	d	15 35						16 16		16 35						17 15		17 36				18 13
Wilmslow	d																					
Crewe 10	d		16 01								17 01											
Macclesfield	d	15 49								16 49						17 27						18 26
Congleton	d																	17 54				
Stoke-on-Trent	d	16 07						16 44		17 07						17 45		18 07				18 44
Stafford	d	16 25						17 03		17 26						18 04		18 26				19 03
Wolverhampton 7 ⛴	d	16 41	16 45					17 17		17 41	17 45					18 16		18 41				19 16
Dunbar	d											13 29										
Berwick-upon-Tweed	d			12 45															14 47			
Alnmouth for Alnwick	d											14 09										
Morpeth	d																					
Newcastle 8	d			13 44			14 35					14 44			15 08				15 41		16 35	
Chester-le-Street	d																					
Durham	d			13 56			14 48					14 56			15 21				15 54		16 48	
Darlington 7	d			14 13			15 05					15 13			15 37				16 13		17 05	
York 8	d			14 45			15 35					15 45			16 05				16 45		17 35	
Leeds 10	d			15 11								16 11			16 40				17 11			
Wakefield Westgate 7	d			15 24								16 24			16 52				17 23			
Doncaster 7	d						15 59														17 59	
Sheffield 7 ⛴	d			15 54			16 23					16 54			17 23				17 54		18 23	
Chesterfield	d			16 07								17 06							18 07			
Nottingham 8 ⛴	d				16 10				16 41				17 10				17 41			18 10		
Derby 6	d			16 27	16 36		16 53		17 11			17 27	17 36		17 52		18 11		18 27	18 36	18 52	
Burton-on-Trent	d				16 49				17 25			17 38	17 49				18 23			18 49		
Tamworth	d			16 48	17 02				17 36				18 02				18 35		18 46	19 02		
Birmingham New Street 12	a	16 58	17 05	17 07	17 24		17 27	17 33	17 55	17 58	18 05	18 07	18 24		18 27	18 33	18 57	18 58	19 06	19 22	19 26	19 33
Birmingham New Street 12	d	17 04	17 10	17 12	17 30	17 30	17 33	17 42		18 04	18 10	18 12	18 30	18 30	18 33	18 42		19 04	19 12	19 30	19 33	19 42
Cheltenham Spa	a			17 51	18 16			18 24				18 51	19 10			19 24			19 51	20 10		20 24
Gloucester 7	a				18 26								19 20							20 20		
Bristol Parkway 7	a			18 29				18 53				19 25				19 55			20 29			20 53
Bristol Temple Meads 10	a			18 42				19 04				19 38				20 05			20 42			21 04
Newport (South Wales)	a				19 11								20 03			20 44				21 09		
Cardiff Central 7	a				19 30								20 20			21 00				21 26		
Weston-super-Mare	a																					
Taunton	a			19 15								20 15							21 15			
Tiverton Parkway	a			19 28								20 28							21 28			
Exeter St Davids 6	a			19 43								20 41							21 42			
Dawlish	a																					
Teignmouth	a																					
Newton Abbot	a			20 03								21 02							22 04			
Torquay	a																					
Paignton	a																					
Totnes	a			20 16								21 15							22 20			
Plymouth	a			20 43								21 41							22 47			
Liskeard 6	a			21 24																		
Bodmin Parkway	a			21 36																		
Lostwithiel	a																					
Par	a			21 47																		
Newquay (Summer Only)	a																					
St Austell	a			21 54																		
Truro	a			22 11																		
Redruth	a			22 27																		
Camborne	a			22 34																		
Hayle	a																					
St Erth	a			22 45																		
Penzance	a			22 54																		
Birmingham International ✈	d	17 14	17 20			17 40				18 14	18 20			18 40				19 14				
Coventry	d	17 25	17a30			17a49				18 25	18a30			18a49				19 25				
Leamington Spa 8	d	17 38					18 02			18 38					19 00			19 38			20 03	
Banbury	a	17 54					18 18			18 54					19 17			19 54			20 18	
Oxford	a	18 14					18 40			19 14					19 40			20 14			20 40	
Reading 7	a	18 40					19 08			19 39					20 08			20 40			21 08	
Guildford	a																					
Basingstoke	a	19 08								20 08								21 08				
Winchester	a	19 24								20 24								21 24				
Southampton Airport Pkwy ✈	a	19 32								20 32								21 32				
Southampton Central ⛴	a	19 41								20 41								21 41				
Brockenhurst 3	a	19 57								20 57								21 57				
Bournemouth	a	20 11								21 11								22 15				

A 🛒 from Edinburgh to Plymouth
B 🛒 to Bristol Temple Meads
C 🛒 to Reading
D 🛒 from Edinburgh to Bristol Temple Meads
E until 22 March

Table 51

Saturdays

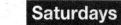

15 February to 17 May

Scotland, The North East, North West England - The South West and South Coast

Route Diagram - see first Page of Table 51

		XC	XC	XC	XC	XC	XC	XC	XC	XC	XC	XC	XC	XC	XC	VT	XC	XC	XC	XC	XC	VT	VT
		◇1	1	◇1	◇1	◇1	◇1	◇1	◇1	1	◇1	◇1	◇1	◇1	◇1	◇1	1	◇1	◇1	◇1	◇1	◇1	◇1
		A		B	A	C			D		E	F	D						G				
		trolley	trolley	trolley	trolley	trolley		trolley	trolley	trolley	trolley	trolley	trolley	trolley		buffet			trolley			buffet	buffet
Aberdeen	d																						
Stonehaven	d																						
Montrose	d																						
Arbroath	d																						
Dundee	d																						
Leuchars 3	d																						
Cupar	d																						
Ladybank	d																						
Markinch	d																						
Kirkcaldy	d																						
Inverkeithing	d																						
Glasgow Central 15	d												15 00			18 00						18 40	
Motherwell	d												15 14										
Haymarket	d												15 57										
Edinburgh 10	d				15 08	15 08							16 05						17 08				18 52
Haymarket	d																						18 56
Lockerbie	d																						
Carlisle 8	d															19 09						19 48	20 08
Penrith North Lakes	d																					20 02	20 22
Oxenholme Lake District	d																					20 25	20 45
Lancaster 6	d															19 57						20 40	21 00
Preston 8	d															20 17						21 00	21 21
Wigan North Western	d															20 28						21 11	21 32
Warrington Bank Quay	d															20 39						21 22	21 43
M'chester Piccadilly 10	d	18 05		18 27					19 07		19 27	19 27			20 07			20 27		21 07			
Stockport	d	18 13		18 35					19 16		19 35	19 35			20 16			20 35					
Wilmslow	d																						
Crewe 10	d															21 01						21 43	22 04
Macclesfield	d	18 26									19 49	19 49						20 49					
Congleton	d			18 54																			
Stoke-on-Trent	d	18 44		19 07					19 44		20 07	20 07			20 44			21 07		21 45			
Stafford	d	19 03		19 25					20 03		20 26	20 26			21 03			21 27		22 03		22 08	22 23
Wolverhampton 7	d	19 16		19 41					20 16		20 41	20 41			21 16	21 34		21 41		22 16		22 23	22 40
Dunbar	d				15 28	15 28													17 29				
Berwick-upon-Tweed	d																		17 51				
Alnmouth for Alnwick	d												17 03										
Morpeth	d												17 17										
Newcastle 8	d				16 41	16 41		17 32					17 44	18 35					18 44		19 35		
Chester-le-Street	d							17 41															
Durham	d				16 54	16 54		17 48					17 56	18 49					18 57		19 50		
Darlington 7	d				17 13	17 13		18 05					18 13	19 06					19 14		20 07		
York 8	d				17 45	17 45		18 34					18 45	19 35					19 45		20 35		
Leeds 10	d				18 11	18 11							19 11						20 11				
Wakefield Westgate 7	d				18 23	18 23							19 24						20 23				
Doncaster 7	d							18 59						19 59							21 00		
Sheffield 7	d				18 58	18 58		19 24					19 54	20 23					20 54		21 23		
Chesterfield	d				19 10	19 10							20 06						21 06		21 35		
Nottingham 8	d		18 41				19 10			19 41							20 37						
Derby 6	d		19 11		19 29	19 29	19 36	19 53		20 10			20 27	20 52			21 10		21 27		21 54		
Burton-on-Trent	d		19 22		19 37	19 37	19 49			20 21							21 24		21 38				
Tamworth	d		19 34				20 02			20 33			20 46				21 35		21 49				
Birmingham New Street 12	a	19 33	19 55	19 59	20 06	20 06	20 24	20 27	20 33	20 56	20 58	20 58	21 03	21 25	21 32	21 55	21 57	21 58	22 06	22 32	22 43	22 46	22 59
Birmingham New Street 12	d	19 42		20 04	20 12	20 12	20 30	20 33	20 42		21 04	21 04	21 12										
Cheltenham Spa	a	20 24			20 51	20 51	21 10		21 24				21 50										
Gloucester 7	a						21 20						21 59										
Bristol Parkway 7	a	20 53			21 20	21 20			21 58				22 30										
Bristol Temple Meads 10	a	21 04			21 35	21 35			22 12				22 41										
Newport (South Wales)	a						22 19																
Cardiff Central 7	a						22 45																
Weston-super-Mare	a																						
Taunton	a	21 42			22 15	22 15																	
Tiverton Parkway	a	21 54			22 28	22 29																	
Exeter St Davids 6	a	22 09			22 43	22 44																	
Dawlish	a																						
Teignmouth	a																						
Newton Abbot	a	22 28			23 10																		
Torquay	a																						
Paignton	a																						
Totnes	a	22 41			23 24																		
Plymouth	a	23 08			23 53																		
Liskeard 6	a																						
Bodmin Parkway	a																						
Lostwithiel	a																						
Par	a																						
Newquay (Summer Only)	a																						
St Austell	a																						
Truro	a																						
Redruth	a																						
Camborne	a																						
Hayle	a																						
St Erth	a																						
Penzance	a																						
Birmingham International	d			20 14							21 14	21 14											
Coventry	d			20 25							21 25	21 25											
Leamington Spa 8	d			20 38				21 00			21 38	21 38											
Banbury	a			20 54				21 19			21 54	21 54											
Oxford	a			21 14				21 41			22 16	22 16											
Reading 7	a			21 38				22 08			22 44	22 45											
Guildford	a							22 59															
Basingstoke	a			22 09							23 13	23 12											
Winchester	a			22 24							23 28	23 27											
Southampton Airport Pkway	a			22 32							23 37	23 35											
Southampton Central	a			22 40							23 44	23 43											
Brockenhurst 3	a			22 56																			
Bournemouth	a			23 20																			

A from 29 March. trolley to Bristol Temple Meads
B trolley to Reading
C until 22 March. trolley to Bristol Temple Meads
D trolley to Birmingham New Street
E until 22 March. trolley to Birmingham New Street
F from 29 March. trolley to Birmingham New Street
G trolley to Leeds

Table 51

Saturdays

15 February to 17 May

Scotland, The North East, North West England - The South West and South Coast

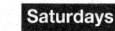

Route Diagram - see first Page of Table 51

		XC ◇1	XC 1	XC ◇1 A 🚲
Aberdeen	d			
Stonehaven	d			
Montrose	d			
Arbroath	d			
Dundee	d			
Leuchars 3	d			
Cupar	d			
Ladybank	d			
Markinch	d			
Kirkcaldy	d			
Inverkeithing	d			
Glasgow Central 15	d			16 52
Motherwell	d			17 06
Haymarket	d			17 53
Edinburgh 10	d			18 08
Haymarket	d			
Lockerbie	d			
Carlisle 8	d			
Penrith North Lakes	d			
Oxenholme Lake District	d			
Lancaster 6	d			
Preston 8	d			
Wigan North Western	d			
Warrington Bank Quay	d			
M'chester Piccadilly 10 ⇌	d	21 27		
Stockport	d	21 35		
Wilmslow	d			
Crewe 10	d			
Macclesfield	d	21 49		
Congleton	d			
Stoke-on-Trent	d	22 07		
Stafford	d	22 29		
Wolverhampton 7 ⇌	d	22 44		
Dunbar	d			18 28
Berwick-upon-Tweed	d			18 51
Alnmouth for Alnwick	d			19 11
Morpeth	d			
Newcastle 8	d			19 45
Chester-le-Street	d			
Durham	d			19 57
Darlington 7	d			20 14
York 8	d			20 45
Leeds 10	d			21 11
Wakefield Westgate 7	d			21 23
Doncaster 7	d			
Sheffield 7 ⇌	d			21 54
Chesterfield	d			22 06
Nottingham 8 ⇌	d		21 39	
Derby 6	d		22 11	22 26
Burton-on-Trent	d		22 21	22 37
Tamworth	d		22 33	22 47
Birmingham New Street 12	a	23 01	23 02	23 06
Birmingham New Street 12	d			
Cheltenham Spa	a			
Gloucester 7	a			
Bristol Parkway 7	a			
Bristol Temple Meads 10	a			
Newport (South Wales)	a			
Cardiff Central 7	a			
Weston-super-Mare	a			
Taunton	a			
Tiverton Parkway	a			
Exeter St Davids 6	a			
Dawlish	a			
Teignmouth	a			
Newton Abbot	a			
Torquay	a			
Paignton	a			
Totnes	a			
Plymouth	a			
Liskeard 6	a			
Bodmin Parkway	a			
Lostwithiel	a			
Par	a			
Newquay (Summer Only)	a			
St Austell	a			
Truro	a			
Redruth	a			
Camborne	a			
Hayle	a			
St Erth	a			
Penzance	a			
Birmingham International ✈	d			
Coventry	d			
Leamington Spa 8	d			
Banbury	a			
Oxford	a			
Reading 7	a			
Guildford	a			
Basingstoke	a			
Winchester	a			
Southampton Airport Pkwy ✈	a			
Southampton Central ⛴	a			
Brockenhurst 3	a			
Bournemouth	a			

A 🚲 from Edinburgh to Leeds

Table 51

Sundays

8 December to 29 December

Scotland, The North East, North West England - The South West and South Coast

Route Diagram - see first Page of Table 51

		XC	XC	XC	XC	XC	XC	XC	XC	VT		XC	XC	XC	VT	XC	VT	XC	XC	XC		VT	XC	XC	XC
		◇1	◇1	◇1	◇1	◇1	◇1	◇1	◇1	◇1		◇1	◇1	◇1	◇1	◇1	◇1	◇1	◇1	◇1		◇1	◇1	◇1	◇1
			A	B			B											B							B
		🛒	🛒	🍴🛒	🛒	🛒	🍴🛒	🛒	🛒	🍴		🛒	🛒		🍴	🛒	🍴	🍴🛒	🛒			🍴	🛒	🛒	🍴🛒
Aberdeen	d																								
Stonehaven	d																								
Montrose	d																								
Arbroath	d																								
Dundee	d																								
Leuchars 8	d																								
Cupar	d																								
Ladybank	d																								
Markinch	d																								
Kirkcaldy	d																								
Inverkeithing	d																								
Glasgow Central 15	d																								
Motherwell	d																								
Haymarket	d																								
Edinburgh 10	d																								
Haymarket	d																								
Lockerbie	d																								
Carlisle 8	d																								
Penrith North Lakes	d																								
Oxenholme Lake District	d																								
Lancaster 6	d																								
Preston 8	d									10 17							11 17								
Wigan North Western	d									10 28							11 28								
Warrington Bank Quay	d									10 39							11 39								
M'chester Piccadilly 10 ⛴	d			08 27			09 27					10 27						11 27							12 26
Stockport	d			08 36			09 36					10 36						11 36							12 35
Wilmslow	d			08 43																					
Crewe 10	d			09 05						11 01							12 01								
Macclesfield	d						09 49					10 49						11 49							12 49
Congleton	d																								
Stoke-on-Trent	d						10 07					11 07						12 07							13 07
Stafford	d			09 26			10 27					11 28						12 25							13 25
Wolverhampton 7 ⛴	d			09 41			10 43			11 32		11 42					12 32	12 41							13 41
Dunbar	d																								
Berwick-upon-Tweed	d																								
Alnmouth for Alnwick	d																								
Morpeth	d																								
Newcastle 8	d																		09 30						
Chester-le-Street	d																								
Durham	d																		09 44						
Darlington 7	d																		10 02						
York 8	d												09 33						10 33						
Leeds 10	d					08 10			09 00				10 00						11 00						
Wakefield Westgate 7	d					08 23			09 12				10 12						11 12						
Doncaster 7	d								09 32				10 30						11 30						
Sheffield 7 ⛴	d					08 54			09 57				10 57						11 57						
Chesterfield	d					09 07			10 09				11 09						12 09						
Nottingham 8 ⛴	d													11 11						12 10					
Derby 6	d					09 28			10 33				11 29	11 36					12 29	12 36					
Burton-on-Trent	d												11 40	11 47						12 47					
Tamworth	d								10 53					12 00					12 48	13 00					
Birmingham New Street 12	a			09 58		10 19	10 59		11 21	11 55		11 59	12 05	12 22			12 54	12 58	13 06	13 21					13 58
Birmingham New Street 12	d	09 04	09 12	10 04	10 12	10 30	11 04	11 12	11 30			12 04	12 12	12 30	12 30	12 33		13 04	13 12	13 30		13 30	13 33	13 42	14 04
Cheltenham Spa	a		09 50		10 52	11 09		11 52	12 09				12 51	13 10					13 51	14 10				14 23	
Gloucester 7	a				11 02			12 02						13 21						14 20					
Bristol Parkway 7	a		10 20			11 39			12 40				13 20						14 20					14 53	
Bristol Temple Meads 10	a		10 31			11 51			12 51				13 31						14 31					15 08	
Newport (South Wales)	a				11 48			12 52						14 06						15 08					
Cardiff Central 7	a				12 08			13 12						14 26						15 31					
Weston-super-Mare	a																								
Taunton	a		11 15			12 26			13 26				14 15						15 15						
Tiverton Parkway	a		11 27			12 36			13 37				14 27						15 27						
Exeter St Davids 6	a		11 41			12 54			13 54				14 42						15 41						
Dawlish	a																								
Teignmouth	a																								
Newton Abbot	a		12 01			13 14			14 14				15 01						16 01						
Torquay	a																								
Paignton	a																								
Totnes	a		12 14			13 28			14 28				15 14						16 14						
Plymouth	a		12 40			13 56			14 55				15 41						16 40						
Liskeard 6	a		13 17																						
Bodmin Parkway	a		13 29																						
Lostwithiel	a																								
Par	a		13 40																						
Newquay (Summer Only)	a																								
St Austell	a		13 46																						
Truro	a		14 06																						
Redruth	a		14 18																						
Camborne	a		14 24																						
Hayle	a																								
St Erth	a		14 35																						
Penzance	a		14 49																						
Birmingham International ✈	d	09 14		10 14			11 14					12 14			12 40			13 14				13 40			14 14
Coventry	d	09 25		10 25			11 25					12 25			12a50			13 25				13a50			14 25
Leamington Spa 8	d	09 38		10 38			11 38					12 38				13 00		13 38					13 59		14 38
Banbury	a	09 54		10 54			11 54					12 54				13 17		13 54					14 17		14 54
Oxford	a	10 14		11 14			12 14					13 14				13 37		14 14					14 37		15 14
Reading 7	a	10 42		11 39			12 42					13 45				14 07		14 39					15 07		15 39
Guildford	a																								
Basingstoke	a	11 09		12 09			13 09					14 09						15 09							16 09
Winchester	a	11 24		12 24			13 24					14 24						15 24							16 24
Southampton Airport Pkwy ✈	a	11 33		12 33			13 33					14 33						15 33							16 33
Southampton Central ⛴	a	11 42		12 42			13 42					14 42						15 42							16 42
Brockenhurst 3	a	12 02		13 02			14 01					15 02						16 02							17 02
Bournemouth	a	12 26		13 26			14 26					15 26						16 26							17 26

A 🛒 to Plymouth

B 🍴 from Birmingham New Street 🛒 to Birmingham New Street

Table 51

Sundays

8 December to 29 December

Scotland, The North East, North West England - The South West and South Coast

Route Diagram - see first Page of Table 51

		VT	XC	XC	VT	XC	XC	XC	XC	VT	XC	XC	VT	XC	XC	XC	XC	VT	XC	XC	VT	XC	XC
		◇1	◇1	◇1	◇1	◇1	◇1	◇1	◇1	◇1	◇1	◇1	◇1	◇1	◇1	◇1	◇1	◇1	◇1	◇1	◇1	◇1	◇1
								A			B					A							
		🍽	🛒		🍽	🛒	🛒	🍽🛒	🛒	🍽	🛒	🛒	🍽	🛒	🛒	🍽🛒	🛒	🍽	🛒	🛒	🍽	🛒	🛒
Aberdeen	d																						
Stonehaven	d																						
Montrose	d																						
Arbroath	d																						
Dundee	d																						
Leuchars 3	d																						
Cupar	d																						
Ladybank	d																						
Markinch	d																						
Kirkcaldy	d																						
Inverkeithing	d																						
Glasgow Central 15	d																	11 58					
Motherwell	d																						
Haymarket	d																						
Edinburgh 10	d		09 08						10 08	10 51							11 05						
Haymarket	d									10 55													
Lockerbie	d																						
Carlisle 8	d									12 07								13 10					
Penrith North Lakes	d																						
Oxenholme Lake District	d									12 43													
Lancaster 6	d	11 58								12 57								13 58					
Preston 8	d	12 17								13 17								14 17					
Wigan North Western	d	12 28								13 28								14 28					
Warrington Bank Quay	d	12 39								13 39								14 39					
M'chester Piccadilly 10 ⛴	d						13 07	13 27							14 07	14 27							15 07
Stockport	d							13 36								14 36							
Wilmslow	d																						
Crewe 10	d	13 01								14 01								15 01					
Macclesfield	d							13 49								14 49							
Congleton	d																						
Stoke-on-Trent	d						13 43	14 07							14 43	15 07							15 43
Stafford	d							14 25								15 25							
Wolverhampton 7 ⛴	d	13 45					14 15	14 41		14 45					15 15	15 41		15 45					16 15
Dunbar	d																11 25						
Berwick-upon-Tweed	d		09 49														11 48						
Alnmouth for Alnwick	d								11 05								12 08						
Morpeth	d								11 19														
Newcastle 8	d		10 39						11 40								12 40					13 35	
Chester-le-Street	d																						
Durham	d		10 53						11 53								12 52					13 48	
Darlington 7	d		11 10						12 10								13 09					14 05	
York 8	d		11 40						12 40								13 40					14 34	
Leeds 10	d		12 10						13 10								14 10						
Wakefield Westgate 7	d		12 23						13 24								14 23						
Doncaster 7	d																					14 59	
Sheffield 7 ⛴	d		12 57						13 57					14 22			14 54					15 24	
Chesterfield	d		13 09						14 09					14 32			15 06						
Nottingham 8 ⛴	d			13 10								14 10								15 10			
Derby 6	d		13 32	13 36		13 55			14 29			14 35		14 53			15 26			15 35		15 53	
Burton-on-Trent	d		13 43	13 47								14 47					15 37			15 47			
Tamworth	d			14 00					14 48		←	15 00							←	16 00			
Birmingham New Street 12	a	14 06	14 09	14 22		14 27	14 31	14 58	15 05	15 06	15 05	15 21		15 26	15 31	15 58	16 02	16 07	16 02	16 22		16 26	16 31
Birmingham New Street 12	d	14 10	14 12	14 30	14 30	14 33	14 42	15 04	15 12	15 10	15 12	15 30	15 30	15 33	15 42	16 04	16 12	16 10	16 12	16 30	16 30	16 33	16 42
Cheltenham Spa	a		14 50	15 10			15 24		→		15 51	16 10			16 24		→		16 50	17 10			17 24
Gloucester 7	a			15 21								16 20								17 20			
Bristol Parkway 7	a		15 23				15 59				16 20				16 54				17 20				18 02
Bristol Temple Meads 10	a		15 34				16 11				16 35				17 08				17 33				18 13
Newport (South Wales)	a			16 06								17 06								18 06			
Cardiff Central 7	a			16 26								17 27								18 28			
Weston-super-Mare	a																						
Taunton	a		16 14				16 45				17 15								18 18				
Tiverton Parkway	a		16 24				16 57				17 27								18 30				
Exeter St Davids 6	a		16 42				17 11				17 41								18 45				
Dawlish	a						17 24																
Teignmouth	a						17 29																
Newton Abbot	a		17 02				17 36				18 01								19 04				
Torquay	a						17 48																
Paignton	a						17 56																
Totnes	a		17 16								18 14								19 17				
Plymouth	a		17 43								18 40								19 44				
Liskeard 6	a										19 15												
Bodmin Parkway	a										19 27												
Lostwithiel	a																						
Par	a										19 38												
Newquay (Summer Only)	a																						
St Austell	a										19 44												
Truro	a										20 02												
Redruth	a										20 13												
Camborne	a										20 20												
Hayle	a																						
St Erth	a										20 32												
Penzance	a										20 41												
Birmingham International ✈	d	14 20			14 40			15 14		15 20			15 40			16 14		16 21			16 40		
Coventry	d	14a30			14a50			15 25		15a30			15a50			16 25		16a31			16a50		
Leamington Spa 8	d					15 00		15 38						16 00		16 38						17 00	
Banbury	a					15 18		15 54						16 17		16 54						17 17	
Oxford	a					15 40		16 14						16 37		17 14						17 37	
Reading 7	a					16 07		16 39						17 08		17 38						18 07	
Guildford	a																						
Basingstoke	a							17 09								18 09							
Winchester	a							17 24								18 24							
Southampton Airport Pkwy ✈	a							17 33								18 33							
Southampton Central ⛴	a							17 40								18 42							
Brockenhurst 3	a							18 02								19 01							
Bournemouth	a							18 26								19 26							

A 🍽 from Birmingham New Street 🛒 to Birmingham New Street

B 🛒 to Plymouth

Table 51

Sundays

8 December to 29 December

Scotland, The North East, North West England - The South West and South Coast

Route Diagram - see first Page of Table 51

		XC	XC	VT	XC	XC	VT	XC	XC	XC	XC	VT	XC	XC	VT	XC	XC	XC	XC	VT	XC	XC
		◇1	◇1	◇1	◇1	◇1	◇1	◇1	◇1	◇1	◇1	◇1	◇1	◇1	◇1	◇1	◇1	◇1	◇1	◇1	◇1	◇1
		A	B		C	D				A	B			D				E	B		F	D
		🍴🛒	🛒	🍴	🛒	🛒	🍴	🛒	🛒	🍴🛒	🛒	🍴	🛒	🛒	🍴	🛒	🛒	🍴🛒	🛒	🍴	🛒	🛒
Aberdeen	d																		11 08			
Stonehaven	d																		11 25			
Montrose	d																		11 46			
Arbroath	d																		12 02			
Dundee	d																		12 21			
Leuchars 3	d																		12 34			
Cupar	d																		12 41			
Ladybank	d																		12 48			
Markinch	d																		12 56			
Kirkcaldy	d																		13 04			
Inverkeithing	d																		13 20			
Glasgow Central 15	d		10 55								11 51	13 55										
Motherwell	d		11 10								12 08											
Haymarket	d		11 51								12 49								13 37			
Edinburgh 10	d		12 08	12 51							13 08					13 55			14 10	14 51		
Haymarket	d			12 55																14 56		
Lockerbie	d																					
Carlisle 8	d			14 07								15 12								16 07		
Penrith North Lakes	d			14 22																16 22		
Oxenholme Lake District	d											15 47										
Lancaster 6	d			14 57																16 57		
Preston 8	d			15 17								16 17								17 18		
Wigan North Western	d			15 28								16 29								17 29		
Warrington Bank Quay	d			15 39								16 40								17 40		
M'chester Piccadilly 10 🚊	d	15 27							16 07	16 27							17 07	17 27				
Stockport	d	15 36								16 36								17 36				
Wilmslow	d																					
Crewe 10	d			16 01								17 00								18 01		
Macclesfield	d	15 49								16 49								17 49				
Congleton	d																					
Stoke-on-Trent	d	16 07							16 43	17 08							17 43	18 08				
Stafford	d	16 25								17 26								18 27				
Wolverhampton 7 🚊	d	16 41		16 45					17 15	17 41		17 45					18 15	18 41		18 45		
Dunbar	d										13 27											
Berwick-upon-Tweed	d		12 47													14 34			14 49			
Alnmouth for Alnwick	d										14 08											
Morpeth	d																					
Newcastle 8	d		13 40					14 35			14 40					15 23			15 40			
Chester-le-Street	d																					
Durham	d		13 53					14 49			14 54					15 36			15 53			
Darlington 7	d		14 10					15 06			15 11					15 53			16 10			
York 8	d		14 40					15 35			15 41					16 24			16 40			
Leeds 10	d		15 10								16 10								17 10			
Wakefield Westgate 7	d		15 23								16 22								17 23			
Doncaster 7	d							15 59								16 52						
Sheffield 7 🚊	d		15 54					16 24			16 54					17 24			17 54			
Chesterfield	d		16 06								17 06								18 06			
Nottingham 8 🚊	d					16 10								17 10								18 10
Derby 6	d		16 27			16 35		16 54			17 26			17 36		17 54			18 26			18 35
Burton-on-Trent	d					16 47					17 37			17 47								18 47
Tamworth	d		16 48		←	17 00							←	18 00					18 45		←	19 00
Birmingham New Street 12	a	16 58	17 05	17 06	17 05	17 20		17 26	17 31	17 58	18 02	18 07	18 02	18 20		18 26	18 31	18 58	19 04	19 06	19 04	19 21
Birmingham New Street 12	d	17 04	17 12	17 10	17 12	17 30	17 30	17 33	17 42	18 04	18 12	18 10	18 12	18 30	18 30	18 33	18 42	19 04	19 12	19 10	19 12	19 30
Cheltenham Spa	a		↪		17 51	18 10			18 24		↪		18 51	19 11			19 24		↪		19 51	20 10
Gloucester 7	a					18 20								19 26								20 21
Bristol Parkway 7	a				18 20				18 54				19 21				20 03				20 20	
Bristol Temple Meads 10	a				18 36				19 08				19 32				20 14				20 31	
Newport (South Wales)	a					19 06								20 11								21 06
Cardiff Central 7	a					19 27								20 31								21 26
Weston-super-Mare	a																20 36					
Taunton	a				19 15								20 17				20 58				21 15	
Tiverton Parkway	a				19 28								20 29				21 11				21 27	
Exeter St Davids 6	a				19 47								20 44				21 27				21 41	
Dawlish	a																21 41					
Teignmouth	a																21 46					
Newton Abbot	a				20 07								21 02				21 54				22 01	
Torquay	a																					
Paignton	a																					
Totnes	a				20 20								21 15								22 18	
Plymouth	a				20 46								21 43				22 37				22 45	
Liskeard 6	a				21 12																	
Bodmin Parkway	a				21 24																	
Lostwithiel	a																					
Par	a				21 35																	
Newquay (Summer Only)	a																					
St Austell	a				21 41																	
Truro	a				21 58																	
Redruth	a				22 10																	
Camborne	a				22 16																	
Hayle	a																					
St Erth	a				22 30																	
Penzance	a				22 43																	
Birmingham International ✈	d	17 14		17 20			17 40			18 14		18 21			18 40			19 14		19 20		
Coventry	d	17 25		17a29			17a50			18 25		18a31			18a50			19 25		19a30		
Leamington Spa 8	d	17 38						18 01		18 38						19 00		19 38				
Banbury	a	17 54						18 19		18 54						19 17		19 54				
Oxford	a	18 14						18 41		19 14						19 37		20 14				
Reading 7	a	18 39						19 07		19 39						20 07		20 39				
Guildford	a																					
Basingstoke	a	19 09								20 09								21 09				
Winchester	a	19 24								20 24								21 24				
Southampton Airport Pkway ✈	a	19 33								20 33								21 33				
Southampton Central ⛴	a	19 40								20 42								21 43				
Brockenhurst 3	a	20 02								21 02								22 02				
Bournemouth	a	20 26								21 26								22 26				

A 🍴 from Birmingham New Street 🛒 to Birmingham New Street
B 🛒 from Edinburgh
C 🛒 to Plymouth
D 🛒 to Birmingham New Street
E 🍴 from Birmingham New Street to Reading 🛒 to Birmingham New Street
F 🛒 to Bristol Temple Meads

Table 51

Sundays

8 December to 29 December

Scotland, The North East, North West England - The South West and South Coast

Route Diagram - see first Page of Table 51

		VT	XC	XC	XC	XC	VT	XC		XC	XC	XC	VT	XC	XC	XC	XC	XC		XC	XC	XC	VT	XC	VT
		◇1	◇1	◇1	◇1	◇1	◇1	◇1		◇1	◇1	◇1	◇1	◇1	◇1	◇1	◇1	◇1		◇1	◇1	◇1	◇1	◇1	◇1
					A			B			C	D			E					F					
		🍽	🛒	🛒	🍽🛒	🛒	🍽	🛒		🛒	🛒	🛒	🍽	🛒	🛒		🛒			🛒			🍽		🍽
Aberdeen	d																								
Stonehaven	d																								
Montrose	d																								
Arbroath	d																								
Dundee	d																								
Leuchars 3	d																								
Cupar	d																								
Ladybank	d																								
Markinch	d																								
Kirkcaldy	d																								
Inverkeithing	d																								
Glasgow Central 15	d					13 49	15 57								14 55								18 30		
Motherwell	d					14 04									15 11										
Haymarket	d					14 42									15 51										
Edinburgh 10	d					15 08							16 51		16 08					17 08					18 51
Haymarket	d												16 55												18 56
Lockerbie	d																								
Carlisle 8	d						17 09						18 07										19 44		20 07
Penrith North Lakes	d																								20 22
Oxenholme Lake District	d						17 44						18 42										20 19		
Lancaster 6	d												18 57										20 34		20 57
Preston 8	d						18 17						19 17										20 55		21 17
Wigan North Western	d						18 28						19 28										21 07		21 29
Warrington Bank Quay	d						18 39						19 39										21 18		21 39
M'chester Piccadilly 10 ⛴	d			18 07	18 27							19 07		19 27				20 07						21 07	
Stockport	d				18 36									19 36				20 16						21 16	
Wilmslow	d																								
Crewe 10	d						19 01						20 01										21 40		22 01
Macclesfield	d				18 49									19 49				20 29						21 29	
Congleton	d																								
Stoke-on-Trent	d			18 43	19 07							19 43		20 07				20 47						21 47	
Stafford	d				19 25									20 27				21 09					22 02	22 06	
Wolverhampton 7 ⛴	d			19 15	19 41		19 42					20 15	20 33	20 41				21 22					22 18	22 22	22 34
Dunbar	d					15 28														17 28					
Berwick-upon-Tweed	d																			17 51					
Alnmouth for Alnwick	d														17 05										
Morpeth	d														17 19										
Newcastle 8	d		16 35			16 40					17 35				17 40		18 21			18 40		19 26			
Chester-le-Street	d																								
Durham	d		16 48			16 53					17 48				17 54		18 34			18 53		19 39			
Darlington 7	d		17 05			17 10					18 06				18 11		18 52			19 10		19 56			
York 8	d		17 34			17 40					18 35				18 40		19 24			19 40		20 24			
Leeds 10	d					18 10									19 10					20 10					
Wakefield Westgate 7	d					18 22									19 22					20 22					
Doncaster 7	d		17 59								18 59						19 52					20 51			
Sheffield 7 ⛴	d		18 24			18 54					19 24				19 54		20 20			20 54		21 20			
Chesterfield	d					19 06									20 06					21 06		21 32			
Nottingham 8 ⛴	d									19 10						20 10					21 10				
Derby 6	d		18 54			19 27				19 36	19 56				20 27	20 36	20 54			21 26	21 36	21 53			
Burton-on-Trent	d					19 38				19 47						20 48				21 37	21 48	22 03			
Tamworth	d							←		20 00					20 45	21 00				21 47	21 59	22 14			
Birmingham New Street 12	a		19 28	19 31	19 58	20 05	20 06	20 05		20 23	20 27	20 31	20 51	20 58	21 03	21 20	21 25	21 39		22 05	22 23	22 30	22 38	22 40	22 55
Birmingham New Street 12	d	19 30	19 33	19 42	20 04	20 12	20 10	20 12			20 33	20 42		21 04	21 12			21 43		22 12					
Cheltenham Spa	a			20 24		→		20 51				21 24			21 51			22 23		22 52					
Gloucester 7	a														22 03										
Bristol Parkway 7	a			20 56				21 20				21 59			22 33			22 52		23 22					
Bristol Temple Meads 10	a			21 06				21 29				22 10			22 44			23 06		23 33					
Newport (South Wales)	a																								
Cardiff Central 7	a																								
Weston-super-Mare	a																								
Taunton	a							22 15																	
Tiverton Parkway	a							22 27																	
Exeter St Davids 6	a							22 45																	
Dawlish	a																								
Teignmouth	a																								
Newton Abbot	a							23 04																	
Torquay	a																								
Paignton	a																								
Totnes	a							23 19																	
Plymouth	a							23 47																	
Liskeard 6	a																								
Bodmin Parkway	a																								
Lostwithiel	a																								
Par	a																								
Newquay (Summer Only)	a																								
St Austell	a																								
Truro	a																								
Redruth	a																								
Camborne	a																								
Hayle	a																								
St Erth	a																								
Penzance	a																								
Birmingham International ✈	d	19 40			20 14		20 20							21 14											
Coventry	d	19a50			20 25		20a30							21 24											
Leamington Spa 8	d		20 00		20 38						21 00			21 35											
Banbury	a		20 18		20 54						21 17														
Oxford	a		20 40		21 14						21 37			22 08											
Reading 7	a		21 07		21 46						22 08			22 35											
Guildford	a										22 42														
Basingstoke	a				22 09																				
Winchester	a				22 24																				
Southampton Airport Pkway ✈	a				22 33																				
Southampton Central ⛴	a				22 42																				
Brockenhurst 3	a																								
Bournemouth	a																								

A 🍽 from Birmingham New Street to Reading 🛒 to Birmingham New Street

B 🛒 to Bristol Temple Meads

C 🛒 to Reading

D 🛒 to Birmingham New Street

E 🛒 from Edinburgh to Birmingham New Street

F 🛒 to Leeds

Table 51

Sundays

8 December to 29 December

Scotland, The North East, North West England - The South West and South Coast

Route Diagram - see first Page of Table 51

		XC ◇1 A 🍴	XC ◇1
Aberdeen	d		
Stonehaven	d		
Montrose	d		
Arbroath	d		
Dundee	d		
Leuchars 3	d		
Cupar	d		
Ladybank	d		
Markinch	d		
Kirkcaldy	d		
Inverkeithing	d		
Glasgow Central 15	d	16 55	
Motherwell	d	17 11	
Haymarket	d	17 51	
Edinburgh 10	d	18 08	
Haymarket	d		
Lockerbie	d		
Carlisle 8	d		
Penrith North Lakes	d		
Oxenholme Lake District	d		
Lancaster 6	d		
Preston 8	d		
Wigan North Western	d		
Warrington Bank Quay	d		
M'chester Piccadilly 10 ⇌	d		22 07
Stockport	d		22 16
Wilmslow	d		
Crewe 10	d		
Macclesfield	d		22 29
Congleton	d		
Stoke-on-Trent	d		22 47
Stafford	d		23 05
Wolverhampton 7 ⇌	d		23 19
Dunbar	d	18 28	
Berwick-upon-Tweed	d	18 51	
Alnmouth for Alnwick	d		
Morpeth	d		
Newcastle 8	d	19 40	
Chester-le-Street	d		
Durham	d	19 53	
Darlington 7	d	20 10	
York 8	d	20 40	
Leeds 10	d	21 10	
Wakefield Westgate 7	d	21 22	
Doncaster 7	d		
Sheffield 7 ⇌	d	21 54	
Chesterfield	d	22 06	
Nottingham 8 ⇌	d		
Derby 6	d	22 26	
Burton-on-Trent	d	22 37	
Tamworth	d	22 47	
Birmingham New Street 12	a	23 04	23 36
Birmingham New Street 12	d		
Cheltenham Spa	a		
Gloucester 7	a		
Bristol Parkway 7	a		
Bristol Temple Meads 10	a		
Newport (South Wales)	a		
Cardiff Central 7	a		
Weston-super-Mare	a		
Taunton	a		
Tiverton Parkway	a		
Exeter St Davids 6	a		
Dawlish	a		
Teignmouth	a		
Newton Abbot	a		
Torquay	a		
Paignton	a		
Totnes	a		
Plymouth	a		
Liskeard 6	a		
Bodmin Parkway	a		
Lostwithiel	a		
Par	a		
Newquay (Summer Only)	a		
St Austell	a		
Truro	a		
Redruth	a		
Camborne	a		
Hayle	a		
St Erth	a		
Penzance	a		
Birmingham International ✈	d		
Coventry	d		
Leamington Spa 8	d		
Banbury	a		
Oxford	a		
Reading 7	a		
Guildford	a		
Basingstoke	a		
Winchester	a		
Southampton Airport Pkway ✈	a		
Southampton Central ⛴	a		
Brockenhurst 3	a		
Bournemouth	a		

A 🍴 from Edinburgh to Leeds

Table 51

Sundays

5 January to 9 February

Scotland, The North East, North West England - The South West and South Coast

Route Diagram - see first Page of Table 51

		XC	XC	XC	XC	XC	XC	XC	XC	VT	XC	XC	VT	XC	XC	VT	XC	XC	VT	XC	XC	XC	XC
		◇1	◇1	◇1	◇1	◇1	◇1	◇1	◇1	◇1	◇1	◇1	◇1	◇1	◇1	◇1	◇1	◇1	◇1	◇1	◇1	◇1	◇1
			A	B			B										B						B
		🛒	🛒	🍽🛒	🛒	🛒	🍽🛒	🛒	🛒	🍽	🛒	🛒	🍽	🛒		🍽	🍽🛒	🛒	🍽		🛒	🛒	🍽🛒
Aberdeen	d																						
Stonehaven	d																						
Montrose	d																						
Arbroath	d																						
Dundee	d																						
Leuchars 3	d																						
Cupar	d																						
Ladybank	d																						
Markinch	d																						
Kirkcaldy	d																						
Inverkeithing	d																						
Glasgow Central 15	d																						
Motherwell	d																						
Haymarket	d																						
Edinburgh 10	d																						
Haymarket	d																						
Lockerbie	d																						
Carlisle 8	d																						
Penrith North Lakes	d																						
Oxenholme Lake District	d																						
Lancaster 6	d																						
Preston 8	d																						
Wigan North Western	d									10 28						11 28							
Warrington Bank Quay	d									10 39						11 40							
M'chester Piccadilly 10	d			08 27			09 27				10 27						11 27						12 26
Stockport	d			08 36			09 36				10 36						11 36						12 35
Wilmslow	d			08 43																			
Crewe 10	d			09 05						11 01						12 01							
Macclesfield	d						09 49				10 49						11 49						12 49
Congleton	d																						
Stoke-on-Trent	d						10 07				11 07						12 07						13 07
Stafford	d			09 26			10 27				11 28						12 25						13 25
Wolverhampton 7	d			09 41			10 43			11 32	11 42					12 34	12 41						13 41
Dunbar	d																						
Berwick-upon-Tweed	d																						
Alnmouth for Alnwick	d																						
Morpeth	d																						
Newcastle 8	d																				09 30		
Chester-le-Street	d																						
Durham	d																				09 44		
Darlington 7	d																				10 02		
York 8	d											09 33									10 33		
Leeds 10	d					08 10			09 15			10 00									11 00		
Wakefield Westgate 7	d					08 23			09 26			10 12									11 12		
Doncaster 7	d																						
Sheffield 7	d					08 54			09 57			10 57									11 57		
Chesterfield	d					09 07			10 09			11 09									12 09		
Nottingham 8	d																						
Derby 6	d					09 28			10 33			11 31									12 29		
Burton-on-Trent	d											11 41									12 40		
Tamworth	d																						
Birmingham New Street 12	a			09 58		10 19	10 59		11 26	11 55	11 59	12 27				12 56	12 58				13 20		13 58
Birmingham New Street 12	d	09 04	09 12	10 04	10 12	10 30	11 04	11 12	11 30		12 04	12 30	12 30	12 33	12 33		13 04	13 12	13 30	13 30	13 33	13 42	14 04
Cheltenham Spa	a		09 50		10 52	11 09		11 52	12 09			13 07			13 12			13 51		14 10		14 23	
Gloucester 7	a				11 02			12 02							13 22					14 20			
Bristol Parkway 7	a		10 20			11 39			12 40			13 39						14 20				14 53	
Bristol Temple Meads 10	a		10 31			11 51			12 51			13 50						14 31				15 08	
Newport (South Wales)	a				11 48			12 52							14 08					15 08			
Cardiff Central 7	a				12 08			13 12							14 28					15 31			
Weston-super-Mare	a																						
Taunton	a		11 15			12 26			13 26			14 24						15 15					
Tiverton Parkway	a		11 27			12 36			13 37			14 37						15 27					
Exeter St Davids 6	a		11 41			12 54			13 54			14 52						15 41					
Dawlish	a																						
Teignmouth	a																						
Newton Abbot	a		12 01						14 14			15 12						16 01					
Torquay	a																						
Paignton	a																						
Totnes	a		12 14						14 28			15 26						16 14					
Plymouth	a		12 40						14 55			15 54						16 40					
Liskeard 6	a		13 17																				
Bodmin Parkway	a		13 29																				
Lostwithiel	a																						
Par	a		13 40																				
Newquay (Summer Only)	a																						
St Austell	a		13 46																				
Truro	a		14 06																				
Redruth	a		14 18																				
Camborne	a		14 24																				
Hayle	a																						
St Erth	a		14 35																				
Penzance	a		14 49																				
Birmingham International ✈	d	09 14		10 14			11 14				12 14		12 40				13 14		13 40				14 14
Coventry	d	09 25		10 25			11 25				12 25		12a50				13 25		13a50				14 25
Leamington Spa 8	d	09 38		10 38			11 38				12 38			13 00			13 38				14 00		14 38
Banbury	a	09 54		10 54			11 54				12 54			13 17			13 54				14 17		14 54
Oxford	a	10 14		11 14			12 14				13 14			13 37			14 14				14 37		15 14
Reading 7	a	10 45		11 45			12 45				13 45			14 14			14 45				15 13		15 45
Guildford	a																						
Basingstoke	a	11 09		12 09			13 09				14 09						15 09						16 09
Winchester	a	11 24		12 24			13 24				14 24						15 24						16 24
Southampton Airport Pkway ✈	a	11 33		12 33			13 33				14 33						15 33						16 33
Southampton Central ⛴	a	11 42		12 42			13 42				14 42						15 42						16 42
Brockenhurst 3	a	12 02		13 02			14 01				15 02						16 02						17 02
Bournemouth	a	12 26		13 26			14 26				15 26						16 26						17 26

A 🛒 to Plymouth

B 🍽 from Birmingham New Street 🛒 to Birmingham New Street

Table 51

Sundays

5 January to 9 February

Scotland, The North East, North West England - The South West and South Coast

Route Diagram - see first Page of Table 51

		VT	XC	VT	XC	XC	XC	XC	XC	VT	XC	VT	XC	XC	XC	XC	XC	VT	XC	VT	XC	XC	XC
		◇1	◇1	◇1	◇1	◇1	◇1	◇1	◇1	◇1	◇1	◇1	◇1	◇1	◇1	◇1	◇1	◇1	◇1	◇1	◇1	◇1	◇1
									A		B						A						
		🍴	☕	🍴	☕		☕	☕	🍴☕	🍴	☕	🍴	☕	☕	☕	☕	🍴☕	🍴	☕	🍴	☕	☕	☕
Aberdeen	d																						
Stonehaven	d																						
Montrose	d																						
Arbroath	d																						
Dundee	d																						
Leuchars 8	d																						
Cupar	d																						
Ladybank	d																						
Markinch	d																						
Kirkcaldy	d																						
Inverkeithing	d																						
Glasgow Central 15	d																						
Motherwell	d																						
Haymarket	d																						
Edinburgh 10	d		09 08											10 08								11 05	
Haymarket	d																						
Lockerbie	d																						
Carlisle 8	d																						
Penrith North Lakes	d																						
Oxenholme Lake District	d																						
Lancaster 6	d																						
Preston 8	d																						
Wigan North Western	d	12 28								13 28								14 28					
Warrington Bank Quay	d	12 40								13 39								14 39					
M'chester Piccadilly 10	d						13 07		13 27						14 07		14 27						15 07
Stockport	d								13 36								14 36						
Wilmslow	d																						
Crewe 10	d	13 01								14 01								15 01					
Macclesfield	d								13 49								14 49						
Congleton	d																						
Stoke-on-Trent	d						13 43		14 07						14 43		15 07						15 43
Stafford	d								14 25								15 25						
Wolverhampton 7	d	13 45					14 15		14 41	14 45					15 15		15 41	15 45					16 15
Dunbar	d																					11 25	
Berwick-upon-Tweed	d		09 49																			11 48	
Alnmouth for Alnwick	d													11 05								12 08	
Morpeth	d													11 19									
Newcastle 8	d		10 39											11 40								12 40	
Chester-le-Street	d																						
Durham	d		10 53											11 53								12 52	
Darlington 7	d		11 10											12 10								13 09	
York 8	d		11 40											12 40								13 40	
Leeds 10	d		12 10											13 10								14 10	
Wakefield Westgate 7	d		12 23											13 24								14 23	
Doncaster 7	d																						
Sheffield 7	d		12 57											13 57		14 22						14 54	
Chesterfield	d		13 09											14 09		14 32						15 06	
Nottingham 8	d																						
Derby 6	d		13 32					13 55						14 29		14 53						15 25	
Burton-on-Trent	d		13 43											14 39								15 37	
Tamworth	d										←								←				
Birmingham New Street 12	a	14 06	14 27				14 31	14 50	14 58	15 06	14 50			15 21	15 31	15 50	15 58	16 07	15 50			16 21	16 31
Birmingham New Street 12	d	14 10	14 30	14 30	14 33	14 33	14 42	15 12	15 04	15 10	15 12	15 30	15 30	15 33	15 42	16 12	16 04	16 10	16 12	16 30	16 30	16 33	16 42
Cheltenham Spa	a		15 08			15 15	15 24	↪			15 51		16 10		16 24	↪			16 50		17 10		17 24
Gloucester 7	a					15 25							16 20								17 20		
Bristol Parkway 7	a		15 39				15 59				16 20				16 54				17 20				18 02
Bristol Temple Meads 10	a		15 50				16 11				16 35				17 08				17 33				18 13
Newport (South Wales)	a					16 10							17 06								18 06		
Cardiff Central 7	a					16 30							17 27								18 28		
Weston-super-Mare	a																						
Taunton	a		16 24				16 45				17 15								18 18				
Tiverton Parkway	a		16 37				16 57				17 27								18 30				
Exeter St Davids 6	a		16 52				17 11				17 41								18 45				
Dawlish	a						17 24																
Teignmouth	a						17 29																
Newton Abbot	a		17 12				17 36				18 01								19 04				
Torquay	a						17 48																
Paignton	a						17 56																
Totnes	a		17 26								18 14								19 17				
Plymouth	a		17 54								18 40								19 44				
Liskeard 6	a										19 15												
Bodmin Parkway	a										19 27												
Lostwithiel	a																						
Par	a										19 38												
Newquay (Summer Only)	a																						
St Austell	a										19 44												
Truro	a										20 02												
Redruth	a										20 13												
Camborne	a										20 20												
Hayle	a																						
St Erth	a										20 32												
Penzance	a										20 41												
Birmingham International ✈	d	14 20		14 40					15 14	15 20		15 40					16 14	16 21		16 40			
Coventry	d	14a30		14a50					15 25	15a30		15a50					16 25	16a31		16a50			
Leamington Spa 8	d				15 00				15 38					15 59			16 38					17 00	
Banbury	a				15 18				15 54					16 17			16 54					17 17	
Oxford	a				15 40				16 14					16 37			17 14					17 37	
Reading 7	a				16 13				16 46					17 14			17 44					18 13	
Guildford	a																						
Basingstoke	a								17 09								18 09						
Winchester	a								17 24								18 24						
Southampton Airport Pkway ✈	a								17 33								18 33						
Southampton Central ⛴	a								17 40								18 42						
Brockenhurst 3	a								18 02								19 01						
Bournemouth	a								18 26								19 26						

A 🍴 from Birmingham New Street ☕ to Birmingham New Street

B ☕ to Plymouth

Table 51

Sundays

5 January to 9 February

Scotland, The North East, North West England - The South West and South Coast

Route Diagram - see first Page of Table 51

		XC	XC	VT	XC	VT	XC	XC	XC	XC	XC	VT	XC	VT	XC	XC	XC	XC	XC	VT	XC	VT
		◇1	◇1	◇1	◇1	◇1	◇1	◇1	◇1	◇1	◇1	◇1	◇1	◇1	◇1	◇1	◇1	◇1	◇1	◇1	◇1	◇1
			A		B			C			A					C			D		E	
		🛒	🍽🛒	🍽	🛒	🍽	🛒	🛒	🛒	🛒	🍽🛒	🍽	🛒	🍽	🛒	🛒	🛒	🛒	🍽🛒	🍽	🛒	🍽
Aberdeen	d																					
Stonehaven	d																					
Montrose	d																					
Arbroath	d																					
Dundee	d																					
Leuchars 8	d																					
Cupar	d																					
Ladybank	d																					
Markinch	d																					
Kirkcaldy	d																					
Inverkeithing	d																					
Glasgow Central 15	d							10 55								11 51						
Motherwell	d							11 10								12 08						
Haymarket	d							11 51								12 49						
Edinburgh 10	d							12 08								13 08		13 55		14 51		
Haymarket	d																			14 56		
Lockerbie	d																					
Carlisle 8	d																			16 07		
Penrith North Lakes	d																			16 22		
Oxenholme Lake District	d																					
Lancaster 8	d																			16 57		
Preston 8	d			15 17								16 17								17 18		
Wigan North Western	d			15 29								16 29								17 29		
Warrington Bank Quay	d			15 40								16 40								17 40		
M'chester Piccadilly 10	d		15 27						16 07		16 27						17 07		17 27			
Stockport	d		15 36								16 36								17 36			
Wilmslow	d																					
Crewe 10	d			16 01								17 00								18 01		
Macclesfield	d		15 49								16 49								17 49			
Congleton	d																					
Stoke-on-Trent	d		16 07						16 43		17 08						17 43		18 08			
Stafford	d		16 25								17 26								18 27			
Wolverhampton 7	d		16 41	16 45					17 15		17 41	17 45					18 15		18 41	18 45		
Dunbar	d															13 27						
Berwick-upon-Tweed	d							12 47										14 34				
Alnmouth for Alnwick	d															14 08						
Morpeth	d																					
Newcastle 8	d	13 35						13 40		14 35						14 40		15 23				
Chester-le-Street	d																					
Durham	d	13 48						13 53		14 49						14 54		15 36				
Darlington 7	d	14 05						14 10		15 06						15 11		15 53				
York 8	d	14 34						14 40		15 35						15 40		16 24				
Leeds 10	d							15 10								16 10						
Wakefield Westgate 7	d							15 23								16 22						
Doncaster 7	d																					
Sheffield 7	d	15 24						15 54		16 25						16 54		17 24				
Chesterfield	d							16 06								17 06						
Nottingham 8	d																					
Derby 6	d	15 53						16 27		16 55						17 26		17 54				
Burton-on-Trent	d							16 37								17 37						
Tamworth	d																					
Birmingham New Street 12	a	16 49	16 58	17 06	← 16 49			17 17	17 31	17 50	17 58	18 07	← 17 50			18 21	18 31	18 50	18 58	19 06	← 18 50	
Birmingham New Street 12	d	17 12	17 04	17 10	17 12	17 30	17 30	17 33	17 42	18 12	18 04	18 10	18 12	18 30	18 30	18 33	18 42	19 12	19 04	19 10	19 12	19 30
Cheltenham Spa	a	→			17 51		18 10		18 24	→			18 51		19 11		19 24	→			19 51	
Gloucester 7	a						18 20								19 26							
Bristol Parkway 7	a				18 20				18 54				19 21				20 03				20 20	
Bristol Temple Meads 10	a				18 36				19 08				19 32				20 14				20 31	
Newport (South Wales)	a						19 06								20 11							
Cardiff Central 7	a						19 27								20 31							
Weston-super-Mare	a																20 36					
Taunton	a				19 15								20 17				20 58				21 15	
Tiverton Parkway	a				19 28								20 29				21 11				21 27	
Exeter St Davids 6	a				19 47								20 44				21 27				21 41	
Dawlish	a																21 41					
Teignmouth	a																21 46					
Newton Abbot	a				20 07								21 02				21 54				22 01	
Torquay	a																					
Paignton	a																					
Totnes	a				20 20								21 15								22 18	
Plymouth	a				20 46								21 43				22 37				22 45	
Liskeard 6	a				21 12																	
Bodmin Parkway	a				21 24																	
Lostwithiel	a																					
Par	a				21 35																	
Newquay (Summer Only)	a																					
St Austell	a				21 41																	
Truro	a				21 58																	
Redruth	a				22 10																	
Camborne	a				22 16																	
Hayle	a																					
St Erth	a				22 30																	
Penzance	a				22 43																	
Birmingham International ✈	d		17 14	17 20		17 40					18 14	18 21		18 40					19 14	19 20		19 40
Coventry	d		17 25	17a30		17a50					18 25	18a31		18a50					19 25	19a30		19a50
Leamington Spa 8	d		17 38					18 00			18 38					19 00			19 38			
Banbury	a		17 54					18 18			18 54					19 17			19 54			
Oxford	a		18 14					18 40			19 14					19 37			20 14			
Reading 7	a		18 46					19 12			19 45					20 13			20 47			
Guildford	a																					
Basingstoke	a		19 09								20 09								21 09			
Winchester	a		19 24								20 24								21 24			
Southampton Airport Pkway ✈	a		19 33								20 33								21 33			
Southampton Central ⛴	a		19 40								20 42								21 43			
Brockenhurst 3	a		20 02								21 02								22 02			
Bournemouth	a		20 26								21 26								22 26			

A 🍽 from Birmingham New Street 🛒 to Birmingham New Street

B 🛒 to Plymouth

C 🛒 from Edinburgh

D 🍽 from Birmingham New Street to Reading 🛒 to Birmingham New Street

E 🛒 to Bristol Temple Meads

Table 51

Sundays

5 January to 9 February

Scotland, The North East, North West England - The South West and South Coast

Route Diagram - see first Page of Table 51

Station		XC	XC	XC	XC	XC	VT	XC		XC	XC	VT	XC	XC	XC	XC	XC	XC		XC	VT	XC	XC	VT	XC
		◇1	◇1	◇1	◇1	◇1	◇1	◇1		◇1	◇1	◇1	◇1	◇1	◇1	◇1	◇1	◇1		◇1	◇1	◇1	◇1	◇1	◇1
			A			B		C		D	E					A		E		F					G
		🛒	🛒	🛒	🛒	🍽🛒	🍽	🛒		🛒	🛒	🍽	🛒	🛒		🛒		🛒		🛒	🍽			🍽	🛒
Aberdeen	d		11 08																						
Stonehaven	d		11 25																						
Montrose	d		11 46																						
Arbroath	d		12 02																						
Dundee	d		12 21																						
Leuchars 3	d		12 34																						
Cupar	d		12 41																						
Ladybank	d		12 48																						
Markinch	d		12 56																						
Kirkcaldy	d		13 04																						
Inverkeithing	d		13 20																						
Glasgow Central 15	d						15 57			13 49						14 55					18 30				16 55
Motherwell	d									14 04						15 11									17 11
Haymarket	d		13 37							14 42						15 51									17 51
Edinburgh 10	d		14 10							15 08		16 51				16 08				17 08				18 51	18 08
Haymarket	d											16 55												18 56	
Lockerbie	d																								
Carlisle 8	d						17 09					18 07									19 44			20 07	
Penrith North Lakes	d																							20 22	
Oxenholme Lake District	d						17 44					18 42									20 19				
Lancaster 6	d											18 57									20 34			20 57	
Preston 8	d						18 17					19 17									20 55			21 17	
Wigan North Western	d						18 28					19 28									21 07			21 29	
Warrington Bank Quay	d						18 39					19 39									21 18			21 39	
M'chester Piccadilly 10	d			18 07		18 27					19 07			19 27			20 07					21 07			
Stockport	d					18 36								19 36			20 16					21 16			
Wilmslow	d																								
Crewe 10	d						19 01					20 01									21 40			22 01	
Macclesfield	d					18 49								19 49			20 29					21 29			
Congleton	d																								
Stoke-on-Trent	d			18 43		19 07					19 43			20 07			20 47					21 47			
Stafford	d					19 25								20 27			21 09				22 02	22 06			
Wolverhampton 7	d			19 15		19 41	19 42				20 15	20 33		20 41			21 22				22 18	22 22		22 34	
Dunbar	d									15 28										17 28					18 28
Berwick-upon-Tweed	d		14 49																	17 51					18 51
Alnmouth for Alnwick	d															17 05									
Morpeth	d															17 19									
Newcastle 8	d		15 40		16 35					16 40			17 35			17 40		18 21		18 40			19 26		19 40
Chester-le-Street	d																								
Durham	d		15 53		16 48					16 53			17 48			17 54		18 34		18 53			19 39		19 53
Darlington 7	d		16 10		17 05					17 10			18 06			18 11		18 52		19 10			19 56		20 10
York 8	d		16 40		17 34					17 40			18 35			18 40		19 24		19 40			20 24		20 40
Leeds 10	d		17 10							18 10						19 10				20 10					21 10
Wakefield Westgate 7	d		17 23							18 22						19 22				20 22					21 22
Doncaster 7	d																								
Sheffield 7	d		17 54		18 24					18 54			19 24			19 54		20 20		20 54			21 20		21 54
Chesterfield	d		18 06							19 06						20 06				21 06			21 32		22 06
Nottingham 8	d																								
Derby 6	d		18 26		18 55					19 27			19 56			20 27		20 54		21 27			21 52		22 26
Burton-on-Trent	d		18 37							19 37						20 37				21 37			22 03		22 37
Tamworth	d							←							←										
Birmingham New Street 12	a		19 21	19 31	19 50	19 58	20 06	19 50		20 21	20 31	20 51	20 52	20 58	20 52	21 21	21 39	21 51		22 18	22 38	22 40	22 44	22 55	23 17
Birmingham New Street 12	d	19 30	19 33	19 42	20 12	20 04	20 10	20 12		20 33	20 42		21 12	21 04	21 12		21 43	22 12							
Cheltenham Spa	a	20 10		20 24	→			20 51			21 24		→		21 51		22 23	22 52							
Gloucester 7	a	20 21													22 03										
Bristol Parkway 7	a			20 56				21 20			21 59				22 33		22 52	23 22							
Bristol Temple Meads 10	a			21 06				21 29			22 10				22 44		23 06	23 33							
Newport (South Wales)	a	21 06																							
Cardiff Central 7	a	21 26																							
Weston-super-Mare	a																								
Taunton	a							22 15																	
Tiverton Parkway	a							22 27																	
Exeter St Davids 6	a							22 45																	
Dawlish	a																								
Teignmouth	a																								
Newton Abbot	a							23 04																	
Torquay	a																								
Paignton	a																								
Totnes	a							23 19																	
Plymouth	a							23 47																	
Liskeard 6	a																								
Bodmin Parkway	a																								
Lostwithiel	a																								
Par	a																								
Newquay (Summer Only)	a																								
St Austell	a																								
Truro	a																								
Redruth	a																								
Camborne	a																								
Hayle	a																								
St Erth	a																								
Penzance	a																								
Birmingham International ✈	d					20 14	20 20							21 14											
Coventry	d					20 25	20a30							21 24											
Leamington Spa 8	d		20 00			20 38				21 00				21 35											
Banbury	a		20 18			20 54				21 17															
Oxford	a		20 40			21 14				21 37				22 08											
Reading 7	a		21 13			21 44				22 10				22 38											
Guildford	a									22 42															
Basingstoke	a					22 09																			
Winchester	a					22 24																			
Southampton Airport Pkway ✈	a					22 33																			
Southampton Central ⛴	a					22 42																			
Brockenhurst 3	a																								
Bournemouth	a																								

A 🛒 from Edinburgh
B 🍽 from Birmingham New Street to Reading 🛒 to Birmingham New Street
C 🛒 to Bristol Temple Meads
D 🛒 to Reading
E 🛒 to Birmingham New Street
F 🛒 to Leeds
G 🛒 from Edinburgh to Leeds

Table 51

Sundays

5 January to 9 February

Scotland, The North East, North West England - The South West and South Coast

Route Diagram - see first Page of Table 51

Station		XC
		◇1
Aberdeen	d	
Stonehaven	d	
Montrose	d	
Arbroath	d	
Dundee	d	
Leuchars 3	d	
Cupar	d	
Ladybank	d	
Markinch	d	
Kirkcaldy	d	
Inverkeithing	d	
Glasgow Central 15	d	
Motherwell	d	
Haymarket	d	
Edinburgh 10	d	
Haymarket	d	
Lockerbie	d	
Carlisle 8	d	
Penrith North Lakes	d	
Oxenholme Lake District	d	
Lancaster 6	d	
Preston 8	d	
Wigan North Western	d	
Warrington Bank Quay	d	
M'chester Piccadilly 10 ⇌	d	22 07
Stockport	d	22 16
Wilmslow	d	
Crewe 10	d	
Macclesfield	d	22 29
Congleton	d	
Stoke-on-Trent	d	22 47
Stafford	d	23 05
Wolverhampton 7 ⇌	d	23 19
Dunbar	d	
Berwick-upon-Tweed	d	
Alnmouth for Alnwick	d	
Morpeth	d	
Newcastle 8	d	
Chester-le-Street	d	
Durham	d	
Darlington 7	d	
York 8	d	
Leeds 10	d	
Wakefield Westgate 7	d	
Doncaster 7	d	
Sheffield 7 ⇌	d	
Chesterfield	d	
Nottingham 8 ⇌	d	
Derby 6	d	
Burton-on-Trent	d	
Tamworth	d	
Birmingham New Street 12	a	23 36
Birmingham New Street 12	d	
Cheltenham Spa	a	
Gloucester 7	a	
Bristol Parkway 7	a	
Bristol Temple Meads 10	a	
Newport (South Wales)	a	
Cardiff Central 7	a	
Weston-super-Mare	a	
Taunton	a	
Tiverton Parkway	a	
Exeter St Davids 6	a	
Dawlish	a	
Teignmouth	a	
Newton Abbot	a	
Torquay	a	
Paignton	a	
Totnes	a	
Plymouth	a	
Liskeard 6	a	
Bodmin Parkway	a	
Lostwithiel	a	
Par	a	
Newquay (Summer Only)	a	
St Austell	a	
Truro	a	
Redruth	a	
Camborne	a	
Hayle	a	
St Erth	a	
Penzance	a	
Birmingham International ✈	d	
Coventry	d	
Leamington Spa 8	d	
Banbury	a	
Oxford	a	
Reading 7	a	
Guildford	a	
Basingstoke	a	
Winchester	a	
Southampton Airport Pkway ✈	a	
Southampton Central ⛴	a	
Brockenhurst 3	a	
Bournemouth	a	

Table 51

Sundays

16 February to 23 March

Scotland, The North East, North West England - The South West and South Coast

Route Diagram - see first Page of Table 51

		XC	XC	XC	XC	XC	XC	XC	XC	VT		XC	XC	VT	XC	XC	VT	XC	XC	VT		XC	XC	XC	XC
		◇1	◇1	◇1	◇1	◇1	◇1	◇1	◇1	◇1		◇1	◇1	◇1	◇1	◇1	◇1	◇1	◇1	◇1		◇1	◇1	◇1	◇1
				A			A											A							A
		🛒	🛒	🍽🛒	🛒	🛒	🍽🛒	🛒	🛒	🍽		🛒	🛒	🍽	🛒		🍽	🍽🛒	🛒	🍽			🛒	🛒	🍽🛒
Aberdeen	d																								
Stonehaven	d																								
Montrose	d																								
Arbroath	d																								
Dundee	d																								
Leuchars [8]	d																								
Cupar	d																								
Ladybank	d																								
Markinch	d																								
Kirkcaldy	d																								
Inverkeithing	d																								
Glasgow Central [15]	d																								
Motherwell	d																								
Haymarket	d																								
Edinburgh [10]	d																								
Haymarket	d																								
Lockerbie	d																								
Carlisle [8]	d																								
Penrith North Lakes	d																								
Oxenholme Lake District	d																								
Lancaster [6]	d																								
Preston [8]	d									10 14							11 14								
Wigan North Western	d									10 28							11 28								
Warrington Bank Quay	d									10 39							11 39								
M'chester Piccadilly [10]	d			08 27			09 27					10 27						11 27							12 26
Stockport	d			08 36			09 36					10 36						11 36							12 35
Wilmslow	d			08 43																					
Crewe [10]	d			09 05						11 01							12 01								
Macclesfield	d						09 49					10 49						11 49							12 49
Congleton	d																								
Stoke-on-Trent	d						10 07					11 07						12 07							13 07
Stafford	d			09 26			10 27					11 28						12 25							13 25
Wolverhampton [7]	d			09 41			10 43			11 32		11 42					12 32	12 41							13 41
Dunbar	d																								
Berwick-upon-Tweed	d																								
Alnmouth for Alnwick	d																								
Morpeth	d																								
Newcastle [8]	d																						09 30		
Chester-le-Street	d																								
Durham	d																						09 44		
Darlington [7]	d																						10 02		
York [8]	d												09 33										10 33		
Leeds [10]	d					08 10			09 00				10 00										11 00		
Wakefield Westgate [7]	d					08 23			09 12				10 12										11 12		
Doncaster [7]	d								09 32				10 30										11 30		
Sheffield [7]	d					08 54			09 57				10 57										11 57		
Chesterfield	d					09 07			10 09				11 10										12 10		
Nottingham [8]	d																								
Derby [6]	d					09 28			10 33				11 33										12 30		
Burton-on-Trent	d												11 44										12 40		
Tamworth	d																								
Birmingham New Street [12]	a			09 58		10 19	10 59		11 24	11 55		11 59	12 24				12 54	12 58					13 20		13 58
Birmingham New Street [12]	d	09 04	09 12	10 04	10 12	10 30	11 04	11 12	11 30			12 04	12 30	12 30	12 33	12 33		13 04	13 12	13 30		13 30	13 33	13 42	14 04
Cheltenham Spa	a		09 50		10 52	11 09		11 52	12 09				13 07			13 13			13 51			14 10		14 23	
Gloucester [7]	a				11 02			12 02								13 23						14 20			
Bristol Parkway [7]	a		10 20			11 39			12 40				13 39						14 20					14 53	
Bristol Temple Meads [10]	a		10 31			11 51			12 51				13 49						14 31					15 08	
Newport (South Wales)	a				11 48			12 52								14 08						15 08			
Cardiff Central [7]	a				12 08			13 12								14 28						15 31			
Weston-super-Mare	a																								
Taunton	a		11 15			12 26			13 26				14 24						15 15						
Tiverton Parkway	a		11 27			12 36			13 37				14 36						15 27						
Exeter St Davids [6]	a		11 41			12 54			13 54				14 52						15 41						
Dawlish	a																								
Teignmouth	a																								
Newton Abbot	a																								
Torquay	a																								
Paignton	a																								
Totnes	a																								
Plymouth	a																								
Liskeard [6]	a																								
Bodmin Parkway	a																								
Lostwithiel	a																								
Par	a																								
Newquay (Summer Only)	a																								
St Austell	a																								
Truro	a																								
Redruth	a																								
Camborne	a																								
Hayle	a																								
St Erth	a																								
Penzance	a																								
Birmingham International ✈	d	09 14		10 14			11 14					12 14		12 40				13 14		13 40					14 14
Coventry	d	09 25		10 25			11 25					12 25		12a50				13 25		13a50					14 25
Leamington Spa [8]	d	09 38		10 38			11 38					12 38			13 00			13 38					14 00		14 38
Banbury	a	09 54		10 54			11 54					12 54			13 17			13 54					14 17		14 54
Oxford	a	10 14		11 14			12 14					13 14			13 37			14 14					14 37		15 14
Reading [7]	a	10 40		11 40			12 40					13 40			14 07			14 40					15 07		15 40
Guildford	a																								
Basingstoke	a	11 09		12 10			13 09					14 09						15 09							16 09
Winchester	a	11 24		12 25			13 24					14 24						15 24							16 24
Southampton Airport Pkway ✈	a	11 33		12 33			13 33					14 33						15 33							16 33
Southampton Central ⛴	a	11 42		12 42			13 42					14 42						15 42							16 42
Brockenhurst [3]	a	12 02		13 02			14 01					15 02						16 02							17 02
Bournemouth	a	12 26		13 26			14 26					15 26						16 26							17 26

A 🍽 from Birmingham New Street 🛒 to Birmingham New Street

Table 51

Sundays

16 February to 23 March

Scotland, The North East, North West England - The South West and South Coast

Route Diagram - see first Page of Table 51

		VT	XC	VT	XC	XC		XC	XC	XC	VT	XC	VT	XC	XC	XC		XC	XC	VT	XC	VT	XC	XC	XC
		◇1	◇1	◇1	◇1	◇1		◇1	◇1	◇1	◇1	◇1	◇1	◇1	◇1	◇1		◇1	◇1	◇1	◇1	◇1	◇1	◇1	◇1
										A									A						
		☕	🛒	☕	🛒			🛒	🛒	☕🛒	☕	🛒	☕	🛒	🛒	🛒		🛒	☕🛒	☕	🛒	☕	🛒	🛒	🛒
Aberdeen	d																								
Stonehaven	d																								
Montrose	d																								
Arbroath	d																								
Dundee	d																								
Leuchars 3	d																								
Cupar	d																								
Ladybank	d																								
Markinch	d																								
Kirkcaldy	d																								
Inverkeithing	d																								
Glasgow Central 15	d																			11 58					
Motherwell	d																								
Haymarket	d																								
Edinburgh 10	d		09 08								10 51				10 08									11 05	
Haymarket	d										10 55														
Lockerbie	d																								
Carlisle 8	d										12 07									13 10					
Penrith North Lakes	d																								
Oxenholme Lake District	d										12 43														
Lancaster 6	d	11 58									12 57									13 58					
Preston 8	d	12 17									13 17									14 17					
Wigan North Western	d	12 28									13 28									14 28					
Warrington Bank Quay	d	12 39									13 39									14 39					
M'chester Piccadilly 10 🚊	d							13 07		13 27						14 07			14 27						15 07
Stockport	d									13 36									14 36						
Wilmslow	d																								
Crewe 10	d	13 01									14 01									15 01					
Macclesfield	d									13 49									14 49						
Congleton	d																								
Stoke-on-Trent	d							13 43		14 07						14 43			15 07						15 43
Stafford	d									14 25									15 25						
Wolverhampton 7 🚊	d	13 45						14 15		14 41	14 45					15 15			15 41	15 45					16 15
Dunbar	d																							11 25	
Berwick-upon-Tweed	d		09 49																					11 48	
Alnmouth for Alnwick	d														11 05									12 08	
Morpeth	d														11 19										
Newcastle 8	d		10 39												11 40									12 40	
Chester-le-Street	d																								
Durham	d		10 53												11 53									12 52	
Darlington 7	d		11 10												12 10									13 09	
York 8	d		11 40												12 40									13 40	
Leeds 10	d		12 10												13 10									14 10	
Wakefield Westgate 7	d		12 23												13 24									14 23	
Doncaster 7	d																								
Sheffield 7 🚊	d		12 57												13 57			14 22						14 54	
Chesterfield	d		13 09												14 09			14 32						15 06	
Nottingham 8 🚊	d																								
Derby 6	d		13 32						13 55						14 29			14 53						15 25	
Burton-on-Trent	d		13 43												14 39									15 37	
Tamworth	d											←									←				
Birmingham New Street 12	a	14 06	14 24					14 31	14 50	14 58	15 06	14 50			15 21	15 31		15 50	15 58	16 07	15 50			16 21	16 31
Birmingham New Street 12	d	14 10	14 30	14 30	14 33	14 33		14 42	15 12	15 04	15 10	15 12	15 30	15 30	15 33	15 42		16 12	16 04	16 10	16 12	16 30	16 30	16 33	16 42
Cheltenham Spa	a		15 08			15 15		15 24	→			15 51		16 10		16 24		→			16 50		17 10		17 24
Gloucester 7	a					15 25								16 20									17 20		
Bristol Parkway 7	a		15 39					15 59				16 20				16 54					17 20				18 02
Bristol Temple Meads 10	a		15 50					16 11				16 35				17 08					17 33				18 13
Newport (South Wales)	a					16 10								17 06									18 06		
Cardiff Central 7	a					16 30								17 27									18 28		
Weston-super-Mare	a																								
Taunton	a		16 24									17 15									18 18				
Tiverton Parkway	a		16 37									17 27									18 30				
Exeter St Davids 6	a		16 52									17 41									18 45				
Dawlish	a																								
Teignmouth	a																								
Newton Abbot	a																								
Torquay	a																								
Paignton	a																								
Totnes	a																								
Plymouth	a																								
Liskeard 6	a																								
Bodmin Parkway	a																								
Lostwithiel	a																								
Par	a																								
Newquay (Summer Only)	a																								
St Austell	a																								
Truro	a																								
Redruth	a																								
Camborne	a																								
Hayle	a																								
St Erth	a																								
Penzance	a																								
Birmingham International ✈	d	14 20		14 40						15 14	15 20		15 40						16 14	16 21		16 40			
Coventry	d	14a30		14a50						15 25	15a30		15a50						16 25	16a31		16a50			
Leamington Spa 8	d				15 00					15 38					15 59				16 38					17 00	
Banbury	a				15 18					15 54					16 17				16 54					17 17	
Oxford	a				15 40					16 14					16 37				17 14					17 37	
Reading 7	a				16 07					16 40					17 08				17 40					18 07	
Guildford	a																								
Basingstoke	a									17 09									18 09						
Winchester	a									17 24									18 24						
Southampton Airport Pkway ✈	a									17 33									18 33						
Southampton Central ⛴	a									17 40									18 42						
Brockenhurst 3	a									18 02									19 01						
Bournemouth	a									18 26									19 26						

A ☕ from Birmingham New Street 🛒 to Birmingham New Street

Table 51

Sundays

16 February to 23 March

Scotland, The North East, North West England - The South West and South Coast

Route Diagram - see first Page of Table 51

		XC		XC	VT	XC	VT	XC	XC	XC	XC	XC		VT	XC	VT	XC	XC	XC	XC	XC	VT		XC	VT
		◇1		◇1	◇1	◇1	◇1	◇1	◇1	◇1	◇1	◇1		◇1	◇1	◇1	◇1	◇1	◇1	◇1	◇1	◇1		◇1	◇1
				A					B			A						B			A			C	
Aberdeen	d																								
Stonehaven	d																								
Montrose	d																								
Arbroath	d																								
Dundee	d																								
Leuchars 3	d																								
Cupar	d																								
Ladybank	d																								
Markinch	d																								
Kirkcaldy	d																								
Inverkeithing	d																								
Glasgow Central 15	d								10 55					13 55				11 51							
Motherwell	d								11 10									12 08							
Haymarket	d								11 51									12 49							
Edinburgh 10	d				12 51				12 08									13 08		13 55		14 51			
Haymarket	d				12 55																	14 56			
Lockerbie	d																								
Carlisle 8	d				14 07									15 12								16 07			
Penrith North Lakes	d				14 22																	16 22			
Oxenholme Lake District	d													15 47											
Lancaster 6	d				14 57																	16 57			
Preston 8	d				15 17									16 17								17 18			
Wigan North Western	d				15 28									16 29								17 29			
Warrington Bank Quay	d				15 39									16 40								17 40			
M'chester Piccadilly 10	d			15 27						16 07		16 27							17 07		17 27				
Stockport	d			15 36								16 36									17 36				
Wilmslow	d																								
Crewe 10	d				16 01									17 00								18 01			
Macclesfield	d			15 49								16 49									17 49				
Congleton	d																								
Stoke-on-Trent	d			16 07						16 43		17 08							17 43		18 08				
Stafford	d			16 25								17 26									18 27				
Wolverhampton 7	d			16 41	16 45					17 15		17 41		17 45					18 15		18 41	18 45			
Dunbar	d																	13 27							
Berwick-upon-Tweed	d								12 47											14 34					
Alnmouth for Alnwick	d																	14 08							
Morpeth	d																								
Newcastle 8	d	13 35							13 40		14 35							14 40		15 23					
Chester-le-Street	d																								
Durham	d	13 48							13 53		14 49							14 54		15 36					
Darlington 7	d	14 05							14 10		15 06							15 11		15 53					
York 8	d	14 34							14 40		15 35							15 40		16 24					
Leeds 10	d								15 10									16 10							
Wakefield Westgate 7	d								15 23									16 22							
Doncaster 7	d	14 59									15 59									16 52					
Sheffield 7	d	15 24							15 54		16 24							16 54		17 24					
Chesterfield	d								16 06									17 06							
Nottingham 8	d																								
Derby 6	d	15 54							16 27		16 55							17 26		17 54					
Burton-on-Trent	d								16 37									17 37							
Tamworth	d					←									←									←	
Birmingham New Street 12	a	16 49		16 58	17 06	16 49			17 17	17 31	17 50	17 58		18 07	17 50			18 21	18 31	18 50	18 58	19 06		18 50	
Birmingham New Street 12	d	17 12		17 04	17 10	17 12	17 30	17 30	17 33	17 42	18 12	18 04		18 10	18 12	18 30	18 30	18 33	18 42	19 12	19 04	19 10		19 12	19 30
Cheltenham Spa	a	→				17 51		18 10		18 24	→				18 51		19 11		19 24	→				19 51	
Gloucester 7	a							18 20									19 26								
Bristol Parkway 7	a					18 20				18 54					19 21				20 03					20 20	
Bristol Temple Meads 10	a					18 36				19 08					19 32				20 14					20 31	
Newport (South Wales)	a							19 06									20 11								
Cardiff Central 7	a							19 27									20 31								
Weston-super-Mare	a																								
Taunton	a					19 15									20 17									21 15	
Tiverton Parkway	a					19 28									20 29									21 27	
Exeter St Davids 6	a					19 47									20 44									21 41	
Dawlish	a																								
Teignmouth	a																								
Newton Abbot	a																								
Torquay	a																								
Paignton	a																								
Totnes	a																								
Plymouth	a																								
Liskeard 6	a																								
Bodmin Parkway	a																								
Lostwithiel	a																								
Par	a																								
Newquay (Summer Only)	a																								
St Austell	a																								
Truro	a																								
Redruth	a																								
Camborne	a																								
Hayle	a																								
St Erth	a																								
Penzance	a																								
Birmingham International	d			17 14	17 20		17 40					18 14		18 21		18 40					19 14	19 20			19 40
Coventry	d			17 25	17a29		17a50					18 25		18a31		18a50					19 25	19a30			19a50
Leamington Spa 6	d			17 38					18 00			18 38						19 00			19 38				
Banbury	a			17 54					18 18			18 54						19 17			19 54				
Oxford	a			18 14					18 40			19 14						19 37			20 14				
Reading 7	a			18 40					19 06			19 40						20 07			20 40				
Guildford	a																								
Basingstoke	a			19 09								20 09									21 09				
Winchester	a			19 24								20 24									21 24				
Southampton Airport Pkwy	a			19 33								20 33									21 33				
Southampton Central	a			19 40								20 42									21 43				
Brockenhurst 3	a			20 02								21 02									22 02				
Bournemouth	a			20 26								21 26									22 26				

A from Birmingham New Street to Birmingham New Street

B from Edinburgh

C to Bristol Temple Meads

Table 51

Sundays

16 February to 23 March

Scotland, The North East, North West England - The South West and South Coast

Route Diagram - see first Page of Table 51

		XC	XC	XC	XC	XC	VT	XC	XC	XC	VT	XC	XC	XC	XC	XC	XC	XC	VT	XC	XC	VT	XC
		◇1	◇1	◇1	◇1	◇1	◇1	◇1	◇1	◇1	◇1	◇1	◇1	◇1	◇1	◇1	◇1	◇1	◇1	◇1	◇1	◇1	◇1
			A			B		C	D	E					A		E	F					G
		🛒	🛒	🛒	🛒	🍽🛒	🍽	🛒	🛒	🛒	🍽	🛒	🛒		🛒		🛒	🛒	🍽			🍽	🛒
Aberdeen	d		11 08																				
Stonehaven	d		11 25																				
Montrose	d		11 46																				
Arbroath	d		12 02																				
Dundee	d		12 21																				
Leuchars [8]	d		12 34																				
Cupar	d		12 41																				
Ladybank	d		12 48																				
Markinch	d		12 56																				
Kirkcaldy	d		13 04																				
Inverkeithing	d		13 20																				
Glasgow Central [15]	d						15 57		13 49						14 55				18 30				16 55
Motherwell	d								14 04						15 11								17 11
Haymarket	d		13 37						14 42						15 51								17 51
Edinburgh [10]	d		14 10						15 08		16 51				16 08			17 08				18 51	18 08
Haymarket	d										16 55											18 56	
Lockerbie	d																						
Carlisle [8]	d						17 09				18 07								19 44			20 07	
Penrith North Lakes	d																					20 22	
Oxenholme Lake District	d						17 44				18 42								20 19				
Lancaster [6]	d										18 57								20 34			20 57	
Preston [8]	d						18 17				19 17								20 55			21 17	
Wigan North Western	d						18 28				19 28								21 07			21 29	
Warrington Bank Quay	d						18 39				19 39								21 18			21 39	
M'chester Piccadilly [10]	d			18 07		18 27				19 07			19 27			20 07				21 07			
Stockport	d					18 36							19 36			20 16				21 16			
Wilmslow	d																						
Crewe [10]	d						19 01				20 01								21 40			22 01	
Macclesfield	d					18 49							19 49			20 29				21 29			
Congleton	d																						
Stoke-on-Trent	d			18 43		19 07				19 43			20 07			20 47				21 47			
Stafford	d					19 25							20 27			21 09			22 02	22 06			
Wolverhampton [7]	d			19 15		19 41	19 42			20 15	20 33		20 41			21 22			22 18	22 22		22 34	
Dunbar	d								15 28									17 28					18 28
Berwick-upon-Tweed	d		14 49															17 51					18 51
Alnmouth for Alnwick	d														17 05								
Morpeth	d														17 19								
Newcastle [8]	d		15 40		16 35				16 40			17 35			17 40		18 21	18 40			19 26		19 40
Chester-le-Street	d																						
Durham	d		15 53		16 48				16 53			17 48			17 54		18 34	18 53			19 39		19 53
Darlington [7]	d		16 10		17 05				17 10			18 06			18 11		18 52	19 10			19 56		20 10
York [8]	d		16 40		17 34				17 40			18 35			18 40		19 24	19 40			20 24		20 40
Leeds [10]	d		17 10						18 10						19 10			20 10					21 10
Wakefield Westgate [7]	d		17 23						18 22						19 22			20 22					21 22
Doncaster [7]	d				17 59							18 59					19 52				20 51		
Sheffield [7]	d		17 54		18 24				18 54			19 24			19 54		20 20	20 54			21 20		21 54
Chesterfield	d		18 06						19 06						20 06			21 06			21 32		22 06
Nottingham [8]	d																						
Derby [6]	d		18 25		18 55				19 27			19 56			20 27		20 54	21 27			21 52		22 26
Burton-on-Trent	d		18 37						19 37						20 37			21 37			22 03		22 37
Tamworth	d							←						←									
Birmingham New Street [12]	a		19 21	19 31	19 50	19 58	20 06	19 50	20 21	20 31	20 51	20 52	20 58	20 52	21 21	21 39	21 48	22 18	22 38	22 40	22 44	22 55	23 17
Birmingham New Street [12]	d	19 30	19 33	19 42	20 12	20 04	20 10	20 12	20 33	20 42		21 12	21 04	21 12		21 43	22 12						
Cheltenham Spa	a	20 10		20 24	→			20 51		21 24		→		21 51		22 23	22 52						
Gloucester [7]	a	20 21												22 03									
Bristol Parkway [7]	a			20 56				21 20		21 59				22 33		22 52	23 22						
Bristol Temple Meads [10]	a			21 06				21 29		22 10				22 44		23 06	23 33						
Newport (South Wales)	a	21 06																					
Cardiff Central [7]	a	21 26																					
Weston-super-Mare	a																						
Taunton	a							22 15															
Tiverton Parkway	a							22 27															
Exeter St Davids [6]	a							22 46															
Dawlish	a																						
Teignmouth	a																						
Newton Abbot	a																						
Torquay	a																						
Paignton	a																						
Totnes	a																						
Plymouth	a																						
Liskeard [6]	a																						
Bodmin Parkway	a																						
Lostwithiel	a																						
Par	a																						
Newquay (Summer Only)	a																						
St Austell	a																						
Truro	a																						
Redruth	a																						
Camborne	a																						
Hayle	a																						
St Erth	a																						
Penzance	a																						
Birmingham International ✈	d					20 14	20 20						21 14										
Coventry	d					20 25	20a30						21 24										
Leamington Spa [8]	d		20 00			20 38			21 00				21 35										
Banbury	a		20 18			20 54			21 17														
Oxford	a		20 40			21 14			21 37				22 08										
Reading [7]	a		21 07						22 04				22 33										
Guildford	a								22 42														
Basingstoke	a					22 10																	
Winchester	a					22 24																	
Southampton Airport Pkway ✈	a					22 33																	
Southampton Central ⛴	a					22 42																	
Brockenhurst [3]	a																						
Bournemouth	a																						

A 🛒 from Edinburgh
B 🍽 from Birmingham New Street 🛒 to Birmingham New Street
C 🛒 to Bristol Temple Meads
D 🛒 to Reading
E 🛒 to Birmingham New Street
F 🛒 to Leeds
G 🛒 from Edinburgh to Leeds

Table 51

Sundays

16 February to 23 March

Scotland, The North East, North West England - The South West and South Coast

Route Diagram - see first Page of Table 51

Station		XC ◇1
Aberdeen	d	
Stonehaven	d	
Montrose	d	
Arbroath	d	
Dundee	d	
Leuchars 8	d	
Cupar	d	
Ladybank	d	
Markinch	d	
Kirkcaldy	d	
Inverkeithing	d	
Glasgow Central 15	d	
Motherwell	d	
Haymarket	d	
Edinburgh 10	d	
Haymarket	d	
Lockerbie	d	
Carlisle 8	d	
Penrith North Lakes	d	
Oxenholme Lake District	d	
Lancaster 6	d	
Preston 8	d	
Wigan North Western	d	
Warrington Bank Quay	d	
M'chester Piccadilly 10	d	22 07
Stockport	d	22 16
Wilmslow	d	
Crewe 10	d	
Macclesfield	d	22 29
Congleton	d	
Stoke-on-Trent	d	22 47
Stafford	d	23 05
Wolverhampton 7	d	23 19
Dunbar	d	
Berwick-upon-Tweed	d	
Alnmouth for Alnwick	d	
Morpeth	d	
Newcastle 8	d	
Chester-le-Street	d	
Durham	d	
Darlington 7	d	
York 8	d	
Leeds 10	d	
Wakefield Westgate 7	d	
Doncaster 7	d	
Sheffield 7	d	
Chesterfield	d	
Nottingham 8	d	
Derby 6	d	
Burton-on-Trent	d	
Tamworth	d	
Birmingham New Street 12	a	23 36
Birmingham New Street 12	d	
Cheltenham Spa	a	
Gloucester 7	a	
Bristol Parkway 7	a	
Bristol Temple Meads 10	a	
Newport (South Wales)	a	
Cardiff Central 7	a	
Weston-super-Mare	a	
Taunton	a	
Tiverton Parkway	a	
Exeter St Davids 6	a	
Dawlish	a	
Teignmouth	a	
Newton Abbot	a	
Torquay	a	
Paignton	a	
Totnes	a	
Plymouth	a	
Liskeard 6	a	
Bodmin Parkway	a	
Lostwithiel	a	
Par	a	
Newquay (Summer Only)	a	
St Austell	a	
Truro	a	
Redruth	a	
Camborne	a	
Hayle	a	
St Erth	a	
Penzance	a	
Birmingham International	d	
Coventry	d	
Leamington Spa 8	d	
Banbury	a	
Oxford	a	
Reading 7	a	
Guildford	a	
Basingstoke	a	
Winchester	a	
Southampton Airport Pkway	a	
Southampton Central	a	
Brockenhurst 3	a	
Bournemouth	a	

Table 51

Sundays

30 March to 11 May

Scotland, The North East, North West England - The South West and South Coast

Route Diagram - see first Page of Table 51

		XC	XC	XC	XC	XC	XC	XC	XC	VT		XC	XC	XC	VT	XC	VT	XC	XC	XC		VT	XC	XC	XC
		◇1	◇1	◇1	◇1	◇1	◇1	◇1	◇1	◇1		◇1	◇1	◇1	◇1	◇1	◇1	◇1	◇1	◇1		◇1	◇1	◇1	◇1
			A	B			B											B							B
		🛒	🛒	⊓🛒	🛒	🛒	⊓🛒	🛒	🛒	⊓		🛒	🛒		⊓	🛒	⊓	⊓🛒	🛒			⊓	🛒	🛒	⊓🛒
Aberdeen	d																								
Stonehaven	d																								
Montrose	d																								
Arbroath	d																								
Dundee	d																								
Leuchars 3	d																								
Cupar	d																								
Ladybank	d																								
Markinch	d																								
Kirkcaldy	d																								
Inverkeithing	d																								
Glasgow Central 15	d																								
Motherwell	d																								
Haymarket	d																								
Edinburgh 10	d																								
Haymarket	d																								
Lockerbie	d																								
Carlisle 8	d																								
Penrith North Lakes	d																								
Oxenholme Lake District	d																								
Lancaster 6	d																								
Preston 8	d									10 17							11 17								
Wigan North Western	d									10 28							11 28								
Warrington Bank Quay	d									10 39							11 39								
M'chester Piccadilly 10	d			08 27			09 27					10 27						11 27							12 26
Stockport	d			08 36			09 36					10 37						11 36							12 35
Wilmslow	d			08 43																					
Crewe 10	d			09 05						11 01							12 01								
Macclesfield	d						09 49					10 50						11 49							12 49
Congleton	d																								
Stoke-on-Trent	d						10 07					11 08						12 07							13 07
Stafford	d			09 26			10 27					11 28						12 25							13 25
Wolverhampton 7	d			09 41			10 43			11 32		11 42					12 32	12 41							13 41
Dunbar	d																								
Berwick-upon-Tweed	d																								
Alnmouth for Alnwick	d																								
Morpeth	d																								
Newcastle 8	d																		09 30						
Chester-le-Street	d																								
Durham	d																		09 44						
Darlington 7	d																		10 02						
York 8	d												09 33						10 33						
Leeds 10	d					08 10			09 00				10 00						11 00						
Wakefield Westgate 7	d					08 23			09 12				10 12						11 12						
Doncaster 7	d								09 32				10 30						11 30						
Sheffield 7	d					08 54			09 57				10 57						11 57						
Chesterfield	d					09 07			10 09				11 09						12 09						
Nottingham 8	d													11 11						12 10					
Derby 6	d					09 28			10 33				11 29	11 36					12 29	12 36					
Burton-on-Trent	d												11 40	11 47						12 47					
Tamworth	d								10 53					12 00					12 48	13 00					
Birmingham New Street 12	a			09 58		10 19	10 59		11 21	11 55		11 59	12 05	12 22			12 54	12 58	13 06	13 21					13 58
Birmingham New Street 12	d	09 04	09 12	10 04	10 12	10 30	11 04	11 12	11 30			12 04	12 12	12 30	12 30	12 33		13 04	13 12	13 30		13 30	13 33	13 42	14 04
Cheltenham Spa	a		09 50		10 52	11 09		11 52	12 09				12 51	13 10					13 51	14 10				14 23	
Gloucester 7	a				11 02			12 02						13 21						14 20					
Bristol Parkway 7	a		10 20			11 39			12 40				13 20						14 20					14 53	
Bristol Temple Meads 10	a		10 31			11 51			12 51				13 31						14 31					15 08	
Newport (South Wales)	a				11 48			12 52						14 06						15 08					
Cardiff Central 7	a				12 08			13 12						14 26						15 31					
Weston-super-Mare	a																								
Taunton	a		11 15			12 26			13 26				14 15						15 15						
Tiverton Parkway	a		11 27			12 36			13 37				14 27						15 27						
Exeter St Davids 6	a		11 41			12 54			13 54				14 42						15 41						
Dawlish	a																								
Teignmouth	a																								
Newton Abbot	a		12 01			13 14			14 14				15 01						16 01						
Torquay	a																								
Paignton	a																								
Totnes	a		12 14			13 28			14 28				15 14						16 14						
Plymouth	a		12 40			13 56			14 55				15 41						16 40						
Liskeard 6	a		13 17																						
Bodmin Parkway	a		13 29																						
Lostwithiel	a																								
Par	a		13 40																						
Newquay (Summer Only)	a																								
St Austell	a		13 46																						
Truro	a		14 06																						
Redruth	a		14 18																						
Camborne	a		14 24																						
Hayle	a																								
St Erth	a		14 35																						
Penzance	a		14 49																						
Birmingham International ✈	d	09 14		10 14			11 14					12 14			12 40			13 14				13 40			14 14
Coventry	d	09 25		10 25			11 25					12 25			12a50			13 25				13a50			14 25
Leamington Spa 8	d	09 38		10 38			11 38					12 38				13 00		13 38					13 59		14 38
Banbury	a	09 54		10 54			11 54					12 54				13 17		13 54					14 17		14 54
Oxford	a	10 14		11 14			12 14					13 14				13 37		14 14					14 37		15 14
Reading 7	a	10 43		11 44			12 43					13 44				14 07		14 45					15 07		15 42
Guildford	a																								
Basingstoke	a	11 09		12 09			13 09					14 09						15 09							16 09
Winchester	a	11 24		12 24			13 24					14 24						15 24							16 24
Southampton Airport Pkway ✈	a	11 33		12 33			13 33					14 33						15 33							16 33
Southampton Central ⛴	a	11 42		12 42			13 42					14 42						15 42							16 42
Brockenhurst 3	a	12 02		13 02			14 01					15 02						16 02							17 02
Bournemouth	a	12 26		13 26			14 26					15 26						16 26							17 26

A 🛒 to Plymouth

B ⊓ from Birmingham New Street 🛒 to Birmingham New Street

Table 51

Sundays
30 March to 11 May

Scotland, The North East, North West England - The South West and South Coast

Route Diagram - see first Page of Table 51

		VT	XC	XC	VT	XC	XC	XC	XC	VT	XC	XC	VT	XC	XC	XC	XC	VT	XC	XC	VT	XC	XC
		◇1	◇1	◇1	◇1	◇1	◇1	◇1	◇1	◇1	◇1	◇1	◇1	◇1	◇1	◇1	◇1	◇1	◇1	◇1	◇1	◇1	◇1
								A			B					A							
		ꝑ	⊼		ꝑ	⊼	⊼	ꝑ⊼	⊼	ꝑ	⊼	⊼	ꝑ	⊼	⊼	ꝑ⊼	⊼	ꝑ	⊼	⊼	ꝑ	⊼	⊼
Aberdeen	d																						
Stonehaven	d																						
Montrose	d																						
Arbroath	d																						
Dundee	d																						
Leuchars 3	d																						
Cupar	d																						
Ladybank	d																						
Markinch	d																						
Kirkcaldy	d																						
Inverkeithing	d																						
Glasgow Central 15	d																	11 58					
Motherwell	d																						
Haymarket	d																						
Edinburgh 10	d		09 08						10 08	10 51							11 05						
Haymarket	d									10 55													
Lockerbie	d																						
Carlisle 8	d									12 07								13 10					
Penrith North Lakes	d																						
Oxenholme Lake District	d									12 43													
Lancaster 6	d	11 58								12 57								13 58					
Preston 8	d	12 17								13 17								14 17					
Wigan North Western	d	12 28								13 28								14 28					
Warrington Bank Quay	d	12 39								13 39								14 39					
M'chester Piccadilly 10	d						13 07	13 27							14 07	14 27							15 07
Stockport	d							13 36								14 36							
Wilmslow	d																						
Crewe 10	d	13 01								14 01								15 01					
Macclesfield	d							13 49								14 49							
Congleton	d																						
Stoke-on-Trent	d						13 43	14 07							14 43	15 07							15 43
Stafford	d							14 25								15 25							
Wolverhampton 7	d	13 45					14 15	14 41		14 45					15 15	15 41		15 45					16 15
Dunbar	d																11 25						
Berwick-upon-Tweed	d		09 49														11 48						
Alnmouth for Alnwick	d								11 05								12 08						
Morpeth	d								11 19														
Newcastle 8	d		10 39						11 40								12 40					13 35	
Chester-le-Street	d																						
Durham	d		10 53						11 53								12 52					13 48	
Darlington 7	d		11 10						12 10								13 09					14 05	
York 8	d		11 40						12 40								13 40					14 34	
Leeds 10	d		12 10						13 10								14 10						
Wakefield Westgate 7	d		12 23						13 24								14 23						
Doncaster 7	d																					14 59	
Sheffield 7	d		12 57						13 57					14 22			14 54					15 24	
Chesterfield	d		13 09						14 09					14 32			15 06						
Nottingham 8	d			13 10								14 10								15 10			
Derby 6	d		13 32	13 36		13 55			14 29			14 35		14 53			15 25			15 35		15 53	
Burton-on-Trent	d		13 43	13 47								14 47					15 37			15 47			
Tamworth	d			14 00					14 48		←	15 00							←	16 00			
Birmingham New Street 12	a	14 06	14 09	14 22		14 27	14 31	14 58	15 05	15 06	15 05	15 21		15 26	15 31	15 58	16 02	16 07	16 02	16 22		16 26	16 31
Birmingham New Street 12	d	14 10	14 12	14 30	14 30	14 33	14 42	15 04	15 12	15 10	15 12	15 30	15 30	15 33	15 42	16 04	16 12	16 10	16 12	16 30	16 30	16 33	16 42
Cheltenham Spa	a		14 50	15 10			15 24		→		15 51	16 10			16 24		→		16 50	17 10			17 24
Gloucester 7	a			15 21								16 20								17 20			
Bristol Parkway 7	a		15 23				15 59				16 20				16 54				17 20				18 02
Bristol Temple Meads 10	a		15 34				16 11				16 35				17 08				17 33				18 13
Newport (South Wales)	a			16 06								17 06								18 06			
Cardiff Central 7	a			16 26								17 27								18 28			
Weston-super-Mare	a																						
Taunton	a		16 14				16 45				17 15								18 18				
Tiverton Parkway	a		16 24				16 57				17 27								18 30				
Exeter St Davids 6	a		16 42				17 11				17 41								18 45				
Dawlish	a						17 24																
Teignmouth	a						17 29																
Newton Abbot	a		17 02				17 36				18 01								19 04				
Torquay	a						17 48																
Paignton	a						17 56																
Totnes	a		17 16								18 14								19 17				
Plymouth	a		17 43								18 40								19 44				
Liskeard 6	a										19 15												
Bodmin Parkway	a										19 27												
Lostwithiel	a																						
Par	a										19 38												
Newquay (Summer Only)	a																						
St Austell	a										19 44												
Truro	a										20 02												
Redruth	a										20 13												
Camborne	a										20 20												
Hayle	a																						
St Erth	a										20 32												
Penzance	a										20 41												
Birmingham International ✈	d	14 20			14 40			15 14		15 20			15 40			16 14		16 21			16 40		
Coventry	d	14a30			14a50			15 25		15a30			15a50			16 25		16a31			16a50		
Leamington Spa 8	d					15 00		15 38						15 59		16 38						17 00	
Banbury	a					15 18		15 54						16 17		16 54						17 17	
Oxford	a					15 40		16 14						16 37		17 14						17 37	
Reading 7	a					16 07		16 46						17 08		17 45						18 07	
Guildford	a																						
Basingstoke	a							17 09								18 09							
Winchester	a							17 24								18 24							
Southampton Airport Pkway ✈	a							17 33								18 33							
Southampton Central ⛴	a							17 40								18 42							
Brockenhurst 3	a							18 02								19 01							
Bournemouth	a							18 26								19 26							

A ꝑ from Birmingham New Street ⊼ to Birmingham New Street

B ⊼ to Plymouth

Table 51

Sundays

30 March to 11 May

Scotland, The North East, North West England - The South West and South Coast

Route Diagram - see first Page of Table 51

		XC	XC	VT	XC	XC	VT	XC	XC	XC	XC	VT	XC	XC	VT	XC	XC	XC	XC	VT	XC	XC
		◇1	◇1	◇1	◇1	◇1	◇1	◇1	◇1	◇1	◇1	◇1	◇1	◇1	◇1	◇1	◇1	◇1	◇1	◇1	◇1	◇1
		A	B		C	D				A	B			D				E	B		F	D
		⊡🛒	🛒	⊡	🛒	🛒	⊡	🛒	🛒	⊡🛒	🛒	⊡	🛒	🛒	⊡	🛒	🛒	⊡🛒	🛒	⊡	🛒	🛒
Aberdeen	d																		11 08			
Stonehaven	d																		11 25			
Montrose	d																		11 46			
Arbroath	d																		12 02			
Dundee	d																		12 21			
Leuchars [3]	d																		12 34			
Cupar	d																		12 41			
Ladybank	d																		12 48			
Markinch	d																		12 56			
Kirkcaldy	d																		13 04			
Inverkeithing	d																		13 20			
Glasgow Central [15]	d		10 55								11 51	13 55										
Motherwell	d		11 10								12 08											
Haymarket	d		11 51								12 49								13 37			
Edinburgh [10]	d		12 08	12 51							13 08					13 55			14 10	14 51		
Haymarket	d			12 55																14 56		
Lockerbie	d																					
Carlisle [8]	d			14 07								15 12								16 07		
Penrith North Lakes	d			14 22																16 22		
Oxenholme Lake District	d											15 47										
Lancaster [6]	d			14 57																16 57		
Preston [8]	d			15 17								16 17								17 18		
Wigan North Western	d			15 28								16 29								17 29		
Warrington Bank Quay	d			15 39								16 40								17 40		
M'chester Piccadilly [10] ⇌	d	15 27							16 07	16 27							17 07	17 27				
Stockport	d	15 36								16 36								17 36				
Wilmslow	d																					
Crewe [10]	d			16 01								17 00								18 01		
Macclesfield	d	15 49								16 49								17 49				
Congleton	d																					
Stoke-on-Trent	d	16 07							16 43	17 08							17 43	18 08				
Stafford	d	16 25								17 26								18 27				
Wolverhampton [7] ⇌	d	16 41		16 45					17 15	17 41		17 45					18 15	18 41		18 45		
Dunbar	d										13 27											
Berwick-upon-Tweed	d		12 47													14 34			14 49			
Alnmouth for Alnwick	d										14 08											
Morpeth	d																					
Newcastle [8]	d		13 40					14 35			14 40					15 23			15 40			
Chester-le-Street	d																					
Durham	d		13 53					14 49			14 54					15 36			15 53			
Darlington [7]	d		14 10					15 06			15 11					15 53			16 10			
York [8]	d		14 40					15 35			15 41					16 24			16 40			
Leeds [10]	d		15 10								16 10								17 10			
Wakefield Westgate [7]	d		15 23								16 22								17 23			
Doncaster [7]	d							15 59								16 52						
Sheffield [7] ⇌	d		15 54					16 24			16 54					17 24			17 54			
Chesterfield	d		16 06								17 06								18 06			
Nottingham [8] ⇌	d					16 10								17 10								18 10
Derby [6]	d		16 26			16 35		16 54			17 26			17 36		17 54			18 25			18 35
Burton-on-Trent	d					16 47					17 37			17 47								18 47
Tamworth	d		16 48		←	17 00							←	18 00					18 45		←	19 00
Birmingham New Street [12]	a	16 58	17 05	17 06	17 05	17 20		17 26	17 31	17 58	18 02	18 07	18 02	18 20		18 26	18 31	18 58	19 04	19 06	19 04	19 21
Birmingham New Street [12]	d	17 04	17 12	17 10	17 12	17 30	17 30	17 33	17 42	18 04	18 12	18 10	18 12	18 30	18 30	18 33	18 42	19 04	19 12	19 10	19 12	19 30
Cheltenham Spa	a		↪		17 51	18 10			18 24		↪		18 51	19 11			19 24		↪		19 51	20 10
Gloucester [7]	a					18 20								19 26								20 21
Bristol Parkway [7]	a				18 20				18 54				19 21				20 03				20 20	
Bristol Temple Meads [10]	a				18 36				19 08				19 32				20 14				20 31	
Newport (South Wales)	a					19 06								20 11								21 06
Cardiff Central [7]	a					19 27								20 31								21 26
Weston-super-Mare	a																20 36					
Taunton	a				19 15								20 17				20 58				21 15	
Tiverton Parkway	a				19 28								20 29				21 11				21 27	
Exeter St Davids [6]	a				19 47								20 44				21 27				21 41	
Dawlish	a																21 41					
Teignmouth	a																21 46					
Newton Abbot	a				20 07								21 02				21 54				22 01	
Torquay	a																					
Paignton	a																					
Totnes	a				20 20								21 15								22 18	
Plymouth	a				20 46								21 43				22 37				22 45	
Liskeard [6]	a				21 12																	
Bodmin Parkway	a				21 24																	
Lostwithiel	a																					
Par	a				21 35																	
Newquay (Summer Only)	a																					
St Austell	a				21 41																	
Truro	a				21 58																	
Redruth	a				22 10																	
Camborne	a				22 16																	
Hayle	a																					
St Erth	a				22 30																	
Penzance	a				22 43																	
Birmingham International ✈	d	17 14		17 20			17 40			18 14		18 21			18 40			19 14		19 20		
Coventry	d	17 25		17a29			17a50			18 25		18a31			18a50			19 25		19a30		
Leamington Spa [3]	d	17 38						18 00		18 38						19 00		19 38				
Banbury	a	17 54						18 19		18 54						19 17		19 54				
Oxford	a	18 14						18 41		19 14						19 37		20 14				
Reading [7]	a	18 45						19 07		19 45						20 07		20 45				
Guildford	a																					
Basingstoke	a	19 09								20 09								21 09				
Winchester	a	19 24								20 24								21 24				
Southampton Airport Pkway ✈	a	19 33								20 33								21 33				
Southampton Central ⛴	a	19 40								20 42								21 43				
Brockenhurst [3]	a	20 02								21 02								22 02				
Bournemouth	a	20 26								21 26								22 26				

A ⊡ from Birmingham New Street 🛒 to Birmingham New Street
B 🛒 from Edinburgh
C 🛒 to Plymouth
D 🛒 to Birmingham New Street
E ⊡ from Birmingham New Street to Reading 🛒 to Birmingham New Street
F 🛒 to Bristol Temple Meads

Table 51

Sundays

30 March to 11 May

Scotland, The North East, North West England - The South West and South Coast

Route Diagram - see first Page of Table 51

		VT	XC	XC	XC	XC	VT	XC		XC	XC	XC	VT	XC	XC	XC	XC	XC		XC	XC	XC	VT	XC	VT
		◇1	◇1	◇1	◇1	◇1	◇1	◇1		◇1	◇1	◇1	◇1	◇1	◇1	◇1	◇1	◇1		◇1	◇1	◇1	◇1	◇1	◇1
					A	B		C			D	E			F					G					
		[R]	[T]	[T]	[R][T]	[T]	[R]	[T]		[T]	[T]	[T]	[R]	[T]	[T]		[T]			[T]			[R]		[R]
Aberdeen	d																								
Stonehaven	d																								
Montrose	d																								
Arbroath	d																								
Dundee	d																								
Leuchars 3	d																								
Cupar	d																								
Ladybank	d																								
Markinch	d																								
Kirkcaldy	d																								
Inverkeithing	d																								
Glasgow Central 15	d					13 49	15 57								14 55								18 30		
Motherwell	d					14 04									15 11										
Haymarket	d					14 42									15 51										
Edinburgh 10	d					15 08							16 51		16 08					17 08					18 51
Haymarket	d												16 55												18 56
Lockerbie	d																								
Carlisle 8	d						17 09						18 07										19 44		20 07
Penrith North Lakes	d																								20 22
Oxenholme Lake District	d						17 44						18 42										20 19		
Lancaster 6	d												18 57										20 34		20 57
Preston 8	d						18 17						19 17										20 55		21 17
Wigan North Western	d						18 28						19 28										21 07		21 29
Warrington Bank Quay	d						18 39						19 39										21 18		21 39
M'chester Piccadilly 10	d			18 07	18 27							19 07		19 27				20 07						21 07	
Stockport	d				18 36									19 36				20 16						21 16	
Wilmslow	d																								
Crewe 10	d						19 01						20 01										21 40		22 01
Macclesfield	d				18 49									19 49				20 29						21 29	
Congleton	d																								
Stoke-on-Trent	d			18 43	19 07							19 43		20 07				20 47						21 47	
Stafford	d				19 25									20 27				21 09					22 02	22 06	
Wolverhampton 7	d			19 15	19 41		19 42					20 15	20 33	20 41				21 22					22 18	22 22	22 34
Dunbar	d					15 28														17 28					
Berwick-upon-Tweed	d																			17 51					
Alnmouth for Alnwick	d														17 05										
Morpeth	d														17 19										
Newcastle 8	d		16 35			16 40					17 35				17 40		18 21			18 40		19 26			
Chester-le-Street	d																								
Durham	d		16 48			16 53					17 48				17 54		18 34			18 53		19 39			
Darlington 7	d		17 05			17 10					18 06				18 11		18 52			19 10		19 56			
York 8	d		17 34			17 40					18 35				18 40		19 24			19 40		20 24			
Leeds 10	d					18 10									19 10					20 10					
Wakefield Westgate 7	d					18 22									19 22					20 22					
Doncaster 7	d		17 59								18 59						19 52					20 51			
Sheffield 7	d		18 24			18 54					19 24				19 54		20 20			20 54		21 20			
Chesterfield	d					19 06									20 06					21 06		21 32			
Nottingham 8	d									19 10						20 10					21 10				
Derby 6	d		18 54			19 27				19 36	19 56				20 26	20 36	20 54			21 26	21 36	21 52			
Burton-on-Trent	d					19 38				19 47						20 48				21 37	21 48	22 03			
Tamworth	d							⟵		20 00					20 45	21 00				21 47	21 59	22 14			
Birmingham New Street 12	a		19 28	19 31	19 58	20 05	20 06	20 05		20 23	20 27	20 31	20 51	20 58	21 03	21 20	21 25	21 39		22 05	22 23	22 30	22 38	22 40	22 55
Birmingham New Street 12	d	19 30	19 33	19 42	20 04	20 12	20 10	20 12			20 33	20 42		21 04	21 12			21 43		22 12					
Cheltenham Spa	a			20 24		⟶		20 51				21 24			21 51			22 23		22 52					
Gloucester 7	a														22 03										
Bristol Parkway 7	a			20 56				21 20				21 59			22 33			22 52		23 22					
Bristol Temple Meads 10	a			21 06				21 29				22 10			22 44			23 06		23 33					
Newport (South Wales)	a																								
Cardiff Central 7	a																								
Weston-super-Mare	a																								
Taunton	a							22 15																	
Tiverton Parkway	a							22 27																	
Exeter St Davids 6	a							22 45																	
Dawlish	a																								
Teignmouth	a																								
Newton Abbot	a							23 04																	
Torquay	a																								
Paignton	a																								
Totnes	a							23 19																	
Plymouth	a							23 47																	
Liskeard 6	a																								
Bodmin Parkway	a																								
Lostwithiel	a																								
Par	a																								
Newquay (Summer Only)	a																								
St Austell	a																								
Truro	a																								
Redruth	a																								
Camborne	a																								
Hayle	a																								
St Erth	a																								
Penzance	a																								
Birmingham International ✈	d	19 40			20 14		20 20							21 14											
Coventry	d	19a50			20 25		20a30							21 24											
Leamington Spa 8	d		20 00		20 38						21 00			21 35											
Banbury	a		20 18		20 54						21 17														
Oxford	a		20 40		21 14						21 37			22 08											
Reading 7	a		21 07		21 44						22 08			22 33											
Guildford	a										22 42														
Basingstoke	a				22 09																				
Winchester	a				22 24																				
Southampton Airport Pkwy ✈	a				22 33																				
Southampton Central	a				22 42																				
Brockenhurst 3	a																								
Bournemouth	a																								

A [R] from Birmingham New Street to Reading [T] to Birmingham New Street
B [T] from Edinburgh
C [T] to Bristol Temple Meads
D [T] to Reading
E [T] to Birmingham New Street
F [T] from Edinburgh to Birmingham New Street
G [T] to Leeds

Table 51

Sundays
30 March to 11 May

Scotland, The North East, North West England - The South West and South Coast

Route Diagram - see first Page of Table 51

		XC	XC
		◇1	◇1
		A	
		🍴	
Aberdeen	d		
Stonehaven	d		
Montrose	d		
Arbroath	d		
Dundee	d		
Leuchars 8	d		
Cupar	d		
Ladybank	d		
Markinch	d		
Kirkcaldy	d		
Inverkeithing	d		
Glasgow Central 15	d	16 55	
Motherwell	d	17 11	
Haymarket	d	17 51	
Edinburgh 10	d	18 08	
Haymarket	d		
Lockerbie	d		
Carlisle 8	d		
Penrith North Lakes	d		
Oxenholme Lake District	d		
Lancaster 6	d		
Preston 8	d		
Wigan North Western	d		
Warrington Bank Quay	d		
M'chester Piccadilly 10 ⇌	d		22 07
Stockport	d		22 16
Wilmslow	d		
Crewe 10	d		
Macclesfield	d		22 29
Congleton	d		
Stoke-on-Trent	d		22 47
Stafford	d		23 05
Wolverhampton 7 ⇌	d		23 19
Dunbar	d	18 28	
Berwick-upon-Tweed	d	18 51	
Alnmouth for Alnwick	d		
Morpeth	d		
Newcastle 8	d	19 40	
Chester-le-Street	d		
Durham	d	19 53	
Darlington 7	d	20 10	
York 8	d	20 40	
Leeds 10	d	21 10	
Wakefield Westgate 7	d	21 22	
Doncaster 7	d		
Sheffield 7 ⇌	d	21 54	
Chesterfield	d	22 06	
Nottingham 8 ⇌	d		
Derby 6	d	22 26	
Burton-on-Trent	d	22 37	
Tamworth	d	22 47	
Birmingham New Street 12	a	23 04	23 36
Birmingham New Street 12	d		
Cheltenham Spa	a		
Gloucester 7	a		
Bristol Parkway 7	a		
Bristol Temple Meads 10	a		
Newport (South Wales)	a		
Cardiff Central 7	a		
Weston-super-Mare	a		
Taunton	a		
Tiverton Parkway	a		
Exeter St Davids 6	a		
Dawlish	a		
Teignmouth	a		
Newton Abbot	a		
Torquay	a		
Paignton	a		
Totnes	a		
Plymouth	a		
Liskeard 6	a		
Bodmin Parkway	a		
Lostwithiel	a		
Par	a		
Newquay (Summer Only)	a		
St Austell	a		
Truro	a		
Redruth	a		
Camborne	a		
Hayle	a		
St Erth	a		
Penzance	a		
Birmingham International ✈	d		
Coventry	d		
Leamington Spa 8	d		
Banbury	a		
Oxford	a		
Reading 7	a		
Guildford	a		
Basingstoke	a		
Winchester	a		
Southampton Airport Pkway ✈	a		
Southampton Central ⛴	a		
Brockenhurst 3	a		
Bournemouth	a		

A 🍴 from Edinburgh to Leeds

Table 51R

Mondays to Fridays

9 December to 16 May

South Coast and the South West - North West England, The North East and Scotland

Route Diagram - see first Page of Table 51

		VT	XC	XC	VT	XC	XC	XC	XC	XC	XC	VT	XC	XC	XC	XC	XC	XC	XC	XC	VT	XC	XC
		MO												FX	FO								
		◇1	◇1	◇1	◇1	1	◇1	◇1	1	◇1	◇1	◇1	1	◇1	◇1	◇1	1	◇1	◇1	◇1	◇1	1	◇1
				A														B	A				B
		◫		⊼	⊠		⊼	⊼		⊼	⊼	⊠	⊼	⊼	⊼	⊼		⊼	⊼		⊠	⊼	⊼
Bournemouth	d																						
Brockenhurst 3	d																						
Southampton Central	d																	05 15					
Southampton Airport Pkway	d																	05 22					
Winchester	d																	05 31					
Basingstoke	d																	05 47					
Guildford	d																						06 02
Reading 7	d																	06 10					06 40
Oxford	d																	06 36					07 08
Banbury	d																	06 54					07 26
Leamington Spa 8	d																	07 12					07 43
Coventry	d																	07 27			07 42		
Birmingham International	d	00 09																07 38			07 53		
Penzance	d																						
St Erth	d																						
Hayle	d																						
Camborne	d																						
Redruth	d																						
Truro	d																						
St Austell	d																						
Newquay (Summer Only)	d																						
Par	d																						
Lostwithiel	d																						
Bodmin Parkway	d																						
Liskeard 6	d																						
Plymouth	d																						
Totnes	d																						
Paignton	d																						
Torquay	d																						
Newton Abbot	d																						
Teignmouth	d																						
Dawlish	d																						
Exeter St Davids 6	d																						
Tiverton Parkway	d																						
Taunton	d																						
Weston-super-Mare	d																						
Cardiff Central 7	d																						
Newport (South Wales)	d																						
Bristol Temple Meads 10	d																		06 27				
Bristol Parkway 7	d																		06 38				
Gloucester 7	d																			07 10			
Cheltenham Spa	d																		07 10	07 21			
Birmingham New Street 12	a	00 21																07 48	07 55	08 15	08 08		08 14
Birmingham New Street 12	d	00 24	05 57	06 00	06 15	06 19	06 22	06 30	06 49	06 57	07 03	07 15	07 19	07 30	07 30	07 31	07 49	07 57	08 03		08 15	08 19	08 30
Tamworth	d					06 39			07 07		07 19		07 39				08 07		08 19			08 36	
Burton-on-Trent	d					06 51			07 20		07 31		07 50				08 19		08 29			08 48	
Derby 6	a			06 33		07 04		07 11	07 34		07 42		08 05	08 09	08 09		08 36		08 41			09 00	09 06
Nottingham 8	a					07 38			08 09				08 34				09 06					09 28	
Chesterfield	a			06 53				07 31			08 02			08 32	08 32				09 02				
Sheffield 7	a			07 06				07 45			08 16			08 45	08 45				09 17				09 44
Doncaster 7	a							08 23						09 18	09 18								10 18
Wakefield Westgate 7	a			07 36							08 46								09 46				
Leeds 10	a			07 52							09 02								10 01				
York 8	a			08 22				08 47			09 26			09 42	09 43				10 27				10 39
Darlington 7	a			08 57				09 16			09 57			10 13	10 13				10 57				11 13
Durham	a			09 13				09 33			10 17			10 30	10 30				11 15				11 30
Chester-le-Street	a																						
Newcastle 8	a			09 28				09 47			10 30			10 45	10 45				11 29				11 45
Morpeth	a																						
Alnmouth for Alnwick	a			09 58																			
Berwick-upon-Tweed	a			10 19															12 21				
Dunbar	a										11 37												
Wolverhampton 7	d	00a43	06 16		06 37		06 41			07 15		07 37				07 49		08 15			08 37		
Stafford	a		06 29				06 53			07 29						08 00		08 29					
Stoke-on-Trent	a		06 50				07 13									08 19		08 54					
Congleton	a		07 02																				
Macclesfield	a		07 11				07 30									08 36		09 11					
Crewe 10	a				07 07					07 50		08 06									09 07		
Wilmslow	a									08 08													
Stockport	a		07 25				07 45			08 20						08 50		09 27					
M'chester Piccadilly 10	a		07 34				07 59			08 34						08 59		09 38					
Warrington Bank Quay	a				07 26							08 26									09 26		
Wigan North Western	a				07 37							08 37									09 37		
Preston 8	a				07 51							08 51									09 51		
Lancaster 6	a				08 07							09 08									10 07		
Oxenholme Lake District	a				08 20																10 21		
Penrith North Lakes	a											09 45											
Carlisle 8	a				08 59							10 00									10 59		
Lockerbie	a																						
Haymarket	a				10 16																12 16		
Edinburgh 10	a			11 06	10 21						12 03								13 05		12 21		
Haymarket	a			11 14															13 17				
Motherwell	a			11 52															13 52				
Glasgow Central 15	a			12 11								11 16							14 12				
Inverkeithing	a																						
Kirkcaldy	a																						
Markinch	a																						
Ladybank	a																						
Cupar	a																						
Leuchars 3	a																						
Dundee	a																						
Arbroath	a																						
Montrose	a																						
Stonehaven	a																						
Aberdeen	a																						

A ⊼ to Edinburgh

B ⊼ from Reading

Table 51R

Mondays to Fridays

9 December to 16 May

South Coast and the South West - North West England, The North East and Scotland

Route Diagram - see first Page of Table 51

		XC	XC	XC	XC	VT	XC	XC	XC	XC	XC	XC	VT	XC	XC	XC	XC	XC	XC	VT	XC	XC	XC
		◇1	◇1	◇1	◇1	◇1	1	◇1	◇1	◇1	◇1	◇1	◇1	1	◇1	◇1	◇1	◇1	◇1	◇1	1	◇1	◇1
				A					B			C			A	D							
		⍑		⍑	⍑	⊠	⍑	⍑	⍑		⍑	⍑	⊡	⍑	⍑	⍑		⍑	⍑	⊡	⍑	⍑	⍑
Bournemouth	d										06 30							07 30					
Brockenhurst 3	d										06 49							07 49					
Southampton Central	d			06 15							07 15							08 15					
Southampton Airport Pkwy	d			06 22							07 22							08 22					
Winchester	d			06 31							07 31				08 01			08 31					
Basingstoke	d			06 47							07 47				08 18			08 47					
Guildford	d																						
Reading 7	d			07 09				07 41			08 09				08 40			09 09				09 40	
Oxford	d			07 36				08 09			08 36				09 07			09 36				10 07	
Banbury	d			07 56				08 27			08 54				09 26			09 56				10 29	
Leamington Spa 8	d			08 14				08 44			09 12				09 43			10 13				10 47	
Coventry	d			08 27		08 42					09 27		09 42					10 27		10 42			
Birmingham International	d			08 38		08 53					09 38		09 53					10 38		10 53			
Penzance	d																						
St Erth	d																						
Hayle	d																						
Camborne	d																						
Redruth	d																						
Truro	d																						
St Austell	d																						
Newquay (Summer Only)	d																						
Par	d																						
Lostwithiel	d																						
Bodmin Parkway	d																						
Liskeard 6	d																						
Plymouth	d				05 20							06 25							07 25				
Totnes	d				05 45							06 50							07 50				
Paignton	d															07 02							
Torquay	d															07 08							
Newton Abbot	d				06 02							07 03				07 19			08 03				
Teignmouth	d															07 26							
Dawlish	d															07 31							
Exeter St Davids 6	d				06 22							07 23				07 45			08 23				
Tiverton Parkway	d				06 36							07 37				07 58			08 37				
Taunton	d				06 50							07 51				08 12			08 51				
Weston-super-Mare	d															08 33							
Cardiff Central 7	d		06 40						07 00	07 45							08 45						
Newport (South Wales)	d		06 55						07 15	08 02							09 00						
Bristol Temple Meads 10	d	07 00			07 30				08 00			08 30				09 00			09 30				10 00
Bristol Parkway 7	d	07 09			07 39				08 09			08 39				09 09			09 39				10 09
Gloucester 7	d		07 46							08 49							09 46						
Cheltenham Spa	d	07 40	07 57		08 11				08 40	09 01		09 12				09 42	09 56		10 11				10 41
Birmingham New Street 12	a	08 26	08 45	08 48	08 55	09 08		09 18	09 26	09 45	09 48	09 56	10 08		10 18	10 25	10 45	10 48	10 55	11 10		11 18	11 26
Birmingham New Street 12	d	08 31	08 49	08 57	09 03	09 15	09 19	09 30	09 31	09 49	09 57	10 03	10 15	10 19	10 30	10 31	10 49	10 57	11 03	11 15	11 19	11 30	11 31
Tamworth	d		09 09				09 36			10 07		10 19		10 36			11 09				11 36		
Burton-on-Trent	d		09 21		09 27		09 48			10 19				10 48			11 21		11 26		11 48		
Derby 6	a		09 34		09 39		10 00	10 06		10 34		10 38		11 00	11 06		11 34		11 38		12 00	12 06	
Nottingham 8	a		10 03				10 28			11 03				11 28			12 03				12 28		
Chesterfield	a				10 02							11 02							12 02				
Sheffield 7	a				10 17			10 44				11 16			11 42				12 17			12 44	
Doncaster 7	a							11 18							12 18							13 18	
Wakefield Westgate 7	a				10 46							11 46							12 46				
Leeds 10	a				11 01							12 01							13 02				
York 8	a				11 30			11 40				12 30			12 39				13 30			13 40	
Darlington 7	a				11 57			12 13				12 57			13 13				14 00			14 13	
Durham	a				12 21			12 30				13 15			13 30				14 17			14 30	
Chester-le-Street	a																						
Newcastle 8	a				12 34			12 44				13 29			13 45				14 30			14 43	
Morpeth	a																		14 48				
Alnmouth for Alnwick	a											14 01											
Berwick-upon-Tweed	a											14 22											
Dunbar	a				13 39														15 40				
Wolverhampton 7	d	08 49		09 15		09 37			09 49		10 15		10 37			10 49		11 15		11 37			11 49
Stafford	a	09 00		09 29					10 00		10 29					11 00		11 28					12 00
Stoke-on-Trent	a	09 19		09 54					10 19		10 54					11 19		11 54					12 19
Congleton	a																						
Macclesfield	a			10 11							11 11							12 11					
Crewe 10	a					10 07							11 07							12 07			
Wilmslow	a																						
Stockport	a	09 49		10 27					10 49		11 27					11 49		12 26					12 49
M'chester Piccadilly 10	a	09 59		10 38					10 59		11 38					11 59		12 38					12 59
Warrington Bank Quay	a					10 26							11 26							12 26			
Wigan North Western	a					10 37							11 37							12 37			
Preston 8	a					10 51							11 51							12 51			
Lancaster 6	a					11 07							12 07							13 07			
Oxenholme Lake District	a												12 21							13 21			
Penrith North Lakes	a					11 44																	
Carlisle 8	a					12 00							12 59							14 00			
Lockerbie	a																						
Haymarket	a												14 15										
Edinburgh 10	a				14 10							15 07	14 22						16 05				
Haymarket	a											15 14											
Motherwell	a											15 52											
Glasgow Central 15	a					13 17						16 12								15 16			
Inverkeithing	a																						
Kirkcaldy	a																						
Markinch	a																						
Ladybank	a																						
Cupar	a																						
Leuchars 8	a																						
Dundee	a																						
Arbroath	a																						
Montrose	a																						
Stonehaven	a																						
Aberdeen	a																						

A ⍑ from Reading
B ⍑ from Bristol Temple Meads
C ⍑ to Edinburgh
D ⍑ from Newton Abbot

Table 51R

Mondays to Fridays

9 December to 16 May

South Coast and the South West - North West England, The North East and Scotland

Route Diagram - see first Page of Table 51

		XC	XC	XC	VT	XC	XC	XC	XC	XC	XC	VT	XC	XC	XC	XC	XC	XC	VT	XC	XC	XC
			R															R			R	
		◇1	◇1	◇1	◇1	1	◇1	◇1	◇1	◇1	◇1	◇1	1	◇1	◇1	◇1	◇1	◇1	◇1	1	◇1	◇1
			A	B							C							D			A	
		trolley	trolley	trolley	shop		trolley	trolley		trolley	trolley	shop	trolley	trolley	trolley	trolley	trolley	trolley	shop		trolley	trolley
Bournemouth	d		08 45							09 45							10 45					
Brockenhurst [3]	d		09 00							10 00							11 00					
Southampton Central	d		09 15				09 46			10 15							11 15				11 46	
Southampton Airport Pkway	d		09 22				09 55			10 22							11 22				11 53	
Winchester	d		09 31				10 03			10 31							11 31				12 02	
Basingstoke	d		09 47				10 19			10 47							11 47				12 18	
Guildford	d																					
Reading [7]	d		10 10				10 40			11 10				11 40			12 10				12 40	
Oxford	d		10 36				11 07			11 36				12 07			12 36				13 07	
Banbury	d		10 54				11 25			11 53				12 25			12 54				13 26	
Leamington Spa [8]	d		11 12				11 43			12 11				12 43			13 12				13 44	
Coventry	d		11 27		11 42					12 27		12 42					13 28		13 42			
Birmingham International	d		11 38		11 53					12 38		12 53					13 39		13 53			
Penzance	d			06 28														08 28				
St Erth	d			06 36														08 36				
Hayle	d																					
Camborne	d			06 46														08 46				
Redruth	d			06 52														08 52				
Truro	d			07 04														09 04				
St Austell	d			07 20														09 20				
Newquay (Summer Only)	d																					
Par	d			07 28														09 28				
Lostwithiel	d																					
Bodmin Parkway	d			07 38														09 38				
Liskeard [6]	d			07 53														09 51				
Plymouth	d			08 25							09 25							10 25				
Totnes	d			08 50							09 50							10 50				
Paignton	d														10 07							
Torquay	d														10 13							
Newton Abbot	d			09 03							10 03				10 24			11 03				
Teignmouth	d														10 31							
Dawlish	d														10 36							
Exeter St Davids [6]	d			09 23							10 23				10 50			11 23				
Tiverton Parkway	d			09 37							10 37				11 03			11 37				
Taunton	d			09 51							10 51				11 17			11 51				
Weston-super-Mare	d																					
Cardiff Central [7]	d	09 45							10 45							11 45						
Newport (South Wales)	d	10 00							11 00							12 02						
Bristol Temple Meads [10]	d			10 30				11 00			11 30				12 00			12 30				13 00
Bristol Parkway [7]	d			10 39				11 09			11 39				12 09			12 39				13 09
Gloucester [7]	d	10 50							11 50							12 48						
Cheltenham Spa	d	11 01		11 11				11 42	12 01		12 11				12 40	12 58		13 11				13 42
Birmingham New Street [12]	a	11 45	11 48	11 58	12 08		12 18	12 26	12 45	12 48	12 55	13 08		13 18	13 26	13 45	13 49	13 56	14 08		14 18	14 25
Birmingham New Street [12]	d	11 49	11 57	12 03	12 15	12 19	12 30	12 31	12 49	12 57	13 03	13 15	13 19	13 30	13 31	13 49	13 57	14 03	14 15	14 19	14 30	14 31
Tamworth	d	12 07		12 19		12 35			13 09				13 36			14 09		14 19		14 36		
Burton-on-Trent	d	12 19				12 47			13 19		13 28		13 48			14 21				14 48		
Derby [6]	a	12 32		12 38		13 00	13 06		13 34		13 40		14 00	14 06		14 34		14 40		15 00	15 06	
Nottingham [8]	a	13 03				13 28			14 03				14 28			15 03				15 28		
Chesterfield	a			13 02							14 02							15 02				
Sheffield [7]	a			13 17			13 42				14 17			14 44				15 17			15 44	
Doncaster [7]	a						14 18							15 18							16 18	
Wakefield Westgate [7]	a			13 46							14 46							15 46				
Leeds [10]	a			14 01							15 01							16 01				
York [8]	a			14 30			14 39				15 30			15 44				16 30			16 39	
Darlington [7]	a			14 57			15 12				15 57			16 13				16 58			17 14	
Durham	a			15 15			15 30				16 15			16 30				17 15			17 31	
Chester-le-Street	a																					
Newcastle [8]	a			15 29			15 45				16 29			16 45				17 30			17 45	
Morpeth	a																					
Alnmouth for Alnwick	a			16 00							17 00							18 00				
Berwick-upon-Tweed	a			16 21														18 21				
Dunbar	a										17 42											
Wolverhampton [7]	d		12 15		12 37			12 49		13 15		13 37			13 49		14 15		14 37			14 49
Stafford	a		12 29					13 00		13 29					14 00		14 29					15 00
Stoke-on-Trent	a		12 54					13 19		13 54					14 19		14 54					15 19
Congleton	a																					
Macclesfield	a		13 11							14 11							15 11					
Crewe [10]	a				13 07							14 07							15 07			
Wilmslow	a																					
Stockport	a		13 27					13 49		14 27					14 49		15 27					15 49
M'chester Piccadilly [10]	a		13 38					13 59		14 38					14 59		15 38					15 59
Warrington Bank Quay	a				13 26							14 26							15 26			
Wigan North Western	a				13 37							14 37							15 37			
Preston [8]	a				13 51							14 51							15 52			
Lancaster [6]	a				14 07							15 08							16 08			
Oxenholme Lake District	a											15 22										
Penrith North Lakes	a				14 42														16 44			
Carlisle [8]	a				14 58							16 00							17 00			
Lockerbie	a																					
Haymarket	a				16 16														18 17			
Edinburgh [10]	a			17 05	16 24						18 07							19 05	18 26			
Haymarket	a			17 14							18 14							19 14				
Motherwell	a			17 52														19 56				
Glasgow Central [15]	a			18 11								17 17						20 15				
Inverkeithing	a										18 28											
Kirkcaldy	a										18 46											
Markinch	a										18 56											
Ladybank	a										19 03											
Cupar	a										19 15											
Leuchars [3]	a										19 22											
Dundee	a										19 35											
Arbroath	a										19 51											
Montrose	a										20 05											
Stonehaven	a										20 26											
Aberdeen	a										20 48											

A ◇ from Birmingham New Street R to Birmingham New Street

B trolley from Plymouth to Edinburgh

C trolley to Edinburgh

D trolley from Plymouth to Edinburgh ◇ from Plymouth R to Plymouth

Table 51R

Mondays to Fridays

9 December to 16 May

South Coast and the South West - North West England, The North East and Scotland

Route Diagram - see first Page of Table 51

		XC	XC	XC	VT	XC	XC	XC	XC	XC	XC	VT	XC	XC	XC	XC	XC	XC	VT	XC	XC	XC	XC
								■				■							■				
		◇1	◇1	◇1	◇1	1	◇1	◇1	◇1	◇1	◇1	1	1	◇1	◇1	◇1	◇1	◇1	1	1	◇1	◇1	1
				A				B			A												
		🛒	🛒	🛒	☕		🛒	🛒	🛒	🛒	🛒	⊠		🛒	🛒	🛒	🛒	🛒	⊠		🛒	🛒	
Bournemouth	d		11 45							12 45							13 45						
Brockenhurst 3	d		12 00							13 00							14 00						
Southampton Central	d		12 15							13 15				13 46			14 15						
Southampton Airport Pkwy	d		12 22							13 22				13 53			14 22						
Winchester	d		12 31							13 31				14 03			14 31						
Basingstoke	d		12 47							13 47				14 19			14 47						
Guildford	d																						
Reading 7	d		13 10				13 40			14 10				14 40			15 09				15 40		
Oxford	d		13 36				14 07			14 36				15 07			15 36				16 07		
Banbury	d		13 54				14 26			14 57				15 25			15 55				16 24		
Leamington Spa 8	d		14 12				14 42			15 14				15 43			16 12				16 43		
Coventry	d		14 27		14 42					15 27		15 42					16 27		16 42				
Birmingham International	d		14 38		14 53					15 38		15 53					16 38		16 53				
Penzance	d							09 40															
St Erth	d							09 48															
Hayle	d							09 52															
Camborne	d							10 01															
Redruth	d							10 08															
Truro	d							10 19															
St Austell	d							10 35															
Newquay (Summer Only)	d																						
Par	d							10 43															
Lostwithiel	d							10 50															
Bodmin Parkway	d							10 56															
Liskeard 6	d							11 09															
Plymouth	d			11 25				11 50			12 24							13 24					
Totnes	d			11 50				12 15			12 50							13 50					
Paignton	d																					14 01	
Torquay	d																					14 07	
Newton Abbot	d			12 03				12 28			13 03							14 03				14 18	
Teignmouth	d																					14 25	
Dawlish	d																					14 30	
Exeter St Davids 6	d			12 23				12 48			13 24							14 24				14 44	
Tiverton Parkway	d			12 37				13 02			13 38							14 38				14 57	
Taunton	d			12 51				13 16			13 52							14 52				15 11	
Weston-super-Mare	d																					15 38	
Cardiff Central 7	d	12 45							13 45							14 45							
Newport (South Wales)	d	13 01							14 00							15 01							
Bristol Temple Meads 10	d			13 30				14 00			14 30				15 00			15 30				16 00	
Bristol Parkway 7	d			13 39				14 09			14 40				15 09			15 40				16 09	
Gloucester 7	d	13 50							14 50							15 50							
Cheltenham Spa	d	14 01		14 10				14 41	15 01		15 11				15 42	16 01		16 11				16 41	
Birmingham New Street 12	a	14 45	14 48	14 55	15 08		15 18	15 23	15 45	15 48	15 56	16 08		16 18	16 26	16 45	16 48	16 56	17 08		17 18	17 23	
Birmingham New Street 12	d	14 49	14 57	15 03	15 15	15 19	15 30	15 31	15 49	15 57	16 03	16 15	16 19	16 30	16 31	16 49	16 57	17 03	17 15	17 19	17 30	17 31	17 39
Tamworth	d	15 09				15 36			16 09		16 19		16 36			17 09				17 36			18 03
Burton-on-Trent	d	15 21		15 26		15 48			16 21				16 48			17 21		17 26		17 48			18 14
Derby 6	a	15 35		15 40		16 00	16 06		16 34		16 40		17 00	17 06		17 34		17 39		18 00	18 06		18 29
Nottingham 8	a	16 03				16 28			17 03				17 31			18 03				18 31			
Chesterfield	a			16 02							17 03							18 02					
Sheffield 7	a			16 17			16 44				17 18			17 42				18 18			18 43		
Doncaster 7	a						17 18														19 16		
Wakefield Westgate 7	a			16 49							17 47			18 13				18 47					
Leeds 10	a			17 04							18 02			18 32				19 03					
York 8	a			17 30			17 40				18 29			18 58				19 30			19 38		
Darlington 7	a			17 58			18 13				19 01			19 29				20 00			20 10		
Durham	a			18 15			18 30				19 19			19 47				20 18			20 27		
Chester-le-Street	a																						
Newcastle 8	a			18 32			18 46				19 35			20 01				20 33			20 42		
Morpeth	a																	20 49					
Alnmouth for Alnwick	a										20 03			20 26									
Berwick-upon-Tweed	a			19 21							20 26							21 21					
Dunbar	a			19 44														21 47					
Wolverhampton 7	d		15 15		15 37			15 50		16 15		16 37			16 49		17 15		17 37			17 50	
Stafford	a		15 29					16 01		16 30					17 00		17 29					18 01	
Stoke-on-Trent	a		15 54					16 20		16 54					17 18		17 54					18 20	
Congleton	a																						
Macclesfield	a		16 11							17 11							18 11						
Crewe 10	a				16 07							17 07							18 07				
Wilmslow	a																						
Stockport	a		16 27					16 49		17 27					17 49		18 27					18 49	
M'chester Piccadilly 10	a		16 38					16 59		17 38					17 58		18 38					18 59	
Warrington Bank Quay	a				16 26							17 26							18 26				
Wigan North Western	a				16 37							17 37							18 37				
Preston 8	a				16 51							17 51							18 51				
Lancaster 6	a				17 08							18 07							19 07				
Oxenholme Lake District	a				17 21							18 21							19 21				
Penrith North Lakes	a				17 46							18 46											
Carlisle 8	a				18 05							19 02							20 00				
Lockerbie	a																						
Haymarket	a											20 20											
Edinburgh 10	a			20 09							21 11	20 27		21 28				22 13					
Haymarket	a			20 16							21 17												
Motherwell	a										22 04												
Glasgow Central 15	a				19 23						22 28								21 17				
Inverkeithing	a			20 30																			
Kirkcaldy	a																						
Markinch	a			21 01																			
Ladybank	a			21 09																			
Cupar	a			21 17																			
Leuchars 3	a			21 25																			
Dundee	a			21 41																			
Arbroath	a																						
Montrose	a																						
Stonehaven	a																						
Aberdeen	a																						

A 🛒 to Edinburgh

B 🛒 ◇ from Plymouth ■ to Plymouth

Table 51R

Mondays to Fridays

9 December to 16 May

South Coast and the South West - North West England, The North East and Scotland

Route Diagram - see first Page of Table 51

		XC	XC	XC		XC	VT	XC	XC	XC	XC	XC	XC	VT		XC	XC	XC	XC	XC	XC	VT	XC	XC
			FX	FO																				
		◇1	◇1	◇1		◇1	◇1	1	◇1	◇1	◇1	◇1	◇1	◇1		1	◇1	◇1	◇1	◇1	◇1	◇1	◇1	◇1
						A					B						B		B		B		B	
		🍴	🍴	🍴		🍴	⊠		🍴	🍴	🍴	🍴	🍴	⊡			🍴	🍴	🍴	🍴	🍴	⊠	🍴	🍴
Bournemouth	d		14 45	14 45								15 45								16 45				
Brockenhurst 3	d		15 00	15 00								16 00								17 00				
Southampton Central	d		15 15	15 15					15 46			16 15								17 15			17 46	
Southampton Airport Pkwy ✈	d		15 22	15 22					15 53			16 22								17 22			17 53	
Winchester	d		15 31	15 31					16 02			16 31								17 31			18 02	
Basingstoke	d		15 47	15 47					16 18			16 47								17 47			18 18	
Guildford	d																							
Reading 7	d		16 10	16 10					16 40			17 09					17 40			18 10			18 40	
Oxford	d		16 35	16 36					17 07			17 36					18 07			18 36			19 13	
Banbury	d		16 55	16 55					17 29			17 55					18 26			18 55			19 31	
Leamington Spa 8	d		17 13	17 13					17 47			18 12					18 46			19 12			19 50	
Coventry	d		17 28	17 28			17 42					18 27		18 42						19 27		19 42		
Birmingham International ✈	d		17 39	17 39			17 53					18 38		18 53						19 38		19 53		
Penzance	d																							
St Erth	d																							
Hayle	d																							
Camborne	d																							
Redruth	d																							
Truro	d																							
St Austell	d																							
Newquay (Summer Only)	d																							
Par	d																							
Lostwithiel	d																							
Bodmin Parkway	d																							
Liskeard 6	d																							
Plymouth	d					14 25							15 24								16 25			
Totnes	d					14 50							15 50								16 50			
Paignton	d																							
Torquay	d																							
Newton Abbot	d					15 03							16 03								17 03			
Teignmouth	d																							
Dawlish	d																							
Exeter St Davids 6	d					15 23							16 24					16 54			17 23			
Tiverton Parkway	d					15 37							16 38					17 08			17 37			
Taunton	d					15 51							16 52					17 22			17 51			
Weston-super-Mare	d																							
Cardiff Central 7	d	15 45									16 45								17 45					
Newport (South Wales)	d	16 00									17 00								18 00					
Bristol Temple Meads 10	d					16 30				17 00			17 30					18 00			18 30			19 00
Bristol Parkway 7	d					16 39				17 09			17 40					18 09			18 39			19 09
Gloucester 7	d	16 50									17 50								18 46					
Cheltenham Spa	d	17 01				17 11				17 42	18 01		18 11					18 41	18 57		19 11			19 40
Birmingham New Street 12	a	17 45	17 49	17 49		17 55	18 08		18 18	18 24	18 45	18 49	18 55	19 08			19 18	19 23	19 45	19 48	19 56	20 08	20 18	20 23
Birmingham New Street 12	d	17 49	17 57	17 57		18 03	18 15	18 19	18 30	18 31	18 49	18 57	19 03	19 15		19 19	19 30	19 31	19 49	19 57	20 03	20 15	20 30	20 31
Tamworth	d	18 09				18 19		18 36			19 09					19 36			20 09		20 19			
Burton-on-Trent	d	18 21						18 48			19 21		19 25			19 48			20 21					
Derby 6	a	18 34				18 38		19 00	19 05		19 34		19 40			20 00	20 04		20 34		20 38		21 09	
Nottingham 8 🚌	a	19 03						19 30			20 03					20 28			21 03					
Chesterfield	a					19 02			19 27				20 04								21 02		21 37	
Sheffield 7 🚌	a					19 18			19 41				20 19				20 39				21 15		21 50	
Doncaster 7	a								20 15								21 19						22 29	
Wakefield Westgate 7	a					19 50							20 47								21 47			
Leeds 10	a					20 05							21 06								22 02			
York 8	a					20 30			20 38								21 44						22 52	
Darlington 7	a					20 58			21 13								22 14							
Durham	a					21 16			21 30								22 33							
Chester-le-Street	a																							
Newcastle 8	a					21 30			21 44								22 50							
Morpeth	a																							
Alnmouth for Alnwick	a					21 58																		
Berwick-upon-Tweed	a																							
Dunbar	a																							
Wolverhampton 7 🚌	d		18 15	18 15			18 37			18 49		19 15		19 37				19 49		20 16		20 37		20 49
Stafford	a		18 29	18 29						19 00		19 27						20 00		20 29		20 49		
Stoke-on-Trent	a		18 54	18 54						19 19		19 54						20 19		20 54				21 18
Congleton	a																							
Macclesfield	a		19 11	19 11								20 11								21 11				
Crewe 10	a						19 07							20 07								21 16		
Wilmslow	a																							
Stockport	a		19 27	19 27						19 48		20 27						20 48		21 25				21 47
M'chester Piccadilly 10 🚌	a		19 38	19 38						19 59		20 37						20 58		21 39				21 59
Warrington Bank Quay	a						19 26							20 26										
Wigan North Western	a						19 37							20 37										
Preston 8	a						19 51							20 51										
Lancaster 6	a						20 08							21 07										
Oxenholme Lake District	a													21 21										
Penrith North Lakes	a						20 44																	
Carlisle 8	a						21 00							22 00										
Lockerbie	a																							
Haymarket	a						22 13																	
Edinburgh 10	a					23 03	22 22																	
Haymarket	a																							
Motherwell	a																							
Glasgow Central 15	a													23 18										
Inverkeithing	a																							
Kirkcaldy	a																							
Markinch	a																							
Ladybank	a																							
Cupar	a																							
Leuchars 3	a																							
Dundee	a																							
Arbroath	a																							
Montrose	a																							
Stonehaven	a																							
Aberdeen	a																							

A 🍴 to Leeds

B 🍴 to Birmingham New Street

Table 51R

Mondays to Fridays

9 December to 16 May

South Coast and the South West - North West England, The North East and Scotland

Route Diagram - see first Page of Table 51

		XC	XC	XC	XC	XC	XC	XC	VT	XC	XC	XC	XC	XC	XC	XC	XC	XC	XC
		◇1	◇1	◇1	◇1	◇1	◇1	◇1	◇1	◇1	1	◇1	◇1	◇1	1	◇1	◇1	◇1	◇1
		A	A	A				B		C									
		🛒	🛒	🛒				🛒	🍽	🛒									
Bournemouth	d		17 45							18 45				19 45					
Brockenhurst 3	d		18 00							19 00				20 00					
Southampton Central	d		18 15							19 15				20 15					
Southampton Airport Pkway ✈	d		18 22							19 22				20 22					
Winchester	d		18 31							19 31				20 31					
Basingstoke	d		18 47							19 47				20 47					
Guildford	d																		
Reading 7	d		19 09		19 40					20 10		20 40		21 10				21 46	
Oxford	d		19 36		20 07					20 36		21 09		21 36				22 30	
Banbury	d		19 56		20 28					20 54		21 33		21 54				22 53	
Leamington Spa 8	d		20 13		20 46					21 12		21 52		22 11				23 11	
Coventry	d		20 27						20 42	21 28				22 24				23 25	
Birmingham International ✈	d		20 38						20 53	21 39				22 34				23 36	
Penzance	d																		
St Erth	d																		
Hayle	d																		
Camborne	d																		
Redruth	d																		
Truro	d																		
St Austell	d																		
Newquay (Summer Only)	d																		
Par	d																		
Lostwithiel	d																		
Bodmin Parkway	d																		
Liskeard 6	d																		
Plymouth	d			17 24				18 25											
Totnes	d			17 50				18 50											
Paignton	d																20 14		
Torquay	d																20 20		
Newton Abbot	d			18 03				19 03									20 31		
Teignmouth	d																		
Dawlish	d																		
Exeter St Davids 6	d			18 25				19 23									20 52		
Tiverton Parkway	d			18 39				19 37									21 04		
Taunton	d			18 53				19 51									21 18		
Weston-super-Mare	d																		
Cardiff Central 7	d	18 45					19 50									21 05			21 50
Newport (South Wales)	d	19 01					20 05									21 21			22 05
Bristol Temple Meads 10	d			19 30		20 00		20 30									22 00		
Bristol Parkway 7	d			19 40		20 09		20 40									22 10		
Gloucester 7	d	19 46				20 46	20 58									22 04			22 47
Cheltenham Spa	d	19 58		20 11		20 56	21 09	21 17								22 15	22 41		22 58
Birmingham New Street 12	a	20 41	20 48	20 52	21 22	21 40	21 51	22 04	21 08	21 49		22 17		22 45		23 05	23 43	00 02	23 59
Birmingham New Street 12	d	20 49	20 57	21 03					21 15	21 57	22 03		22 30		23 09				
Tamworth	d	21 09		21 19							22 27				23 28				
Burton-on-Trent	d	21 21		21 30							22 39				23 40				
Derby 6	a	21 33		21 43							22 52				23 54				
Nottingham 8	a	22 08									23 27				00 17				
Chesterfield	a			22 06															
Sheffield 7	a			22 24															
Doncaster 7	a																		
Wakefield Westgate 7	a			22 59															
Leeds 10	a			23 15															
York 8	a																		
Darlington 7	a																		
Durham	a																		
Chester-le-Street	a																		
Newcastle 8	a																		
Morpeth	a																		
Alnmouth for Alnwick	a																		
Berwick-upon-Tweed	a																		
Dunbar	a																		
Wolverhampton 7	d		21 16						21 37	22 16			22 48						
Stafford	a		21 31						21 52	22 29			23 00						
Stoke-on-Trent	a		21 54							22 53			23 20						
Congleton	a																		
Macclesfield	a		22 11							23 11									
Crewe 10	a								22 16										
Wilmslow	a																		
Stockport	a		22 25							23 25									
M'chester Piccadilly 10	a		22 34							23 34			00 12						
Warrington Bank Quay	a								22 35										
Wigan North Western	a								22 46										
Preston 8	a								23 00										
Lancaster 6	a																		
Oxenholme Lake District	a																		
Penrith North Lakes	a																		
Carlisle 8	a																		
Lockerbie	a																		
Haymarket	a																		
Edinburgh 10	a																		
Haymarket	a																		
Motherwell	a																		
Glasgow Central 15	a																		
Inverkeithing	a																		
Kirkcaldy	a																		
Markinch	a																		
Ladybank	a																		
Cupar	a																		
Leuchars 3	a																		
Dundee	a																		
Arbroath	a																		
Montrose	a																		
Stonehaven	a																		
Aberdeen	a																		

A 🛒 to Birmingham New Street

B 🛒 to Bristol Temple Meads

C 🛒 to Reading

Table 51R

Saturdays

14 December to 28 December

South Coast and the South West - North West England, The North East and Scotland

Route Diagram - see first Page of Table 51

		XC	XC	VT	XC	XC	XC	XC	XC	XC	VT	XC	XC	XC	XC	XC	XC	XC	VT	XC	XC	XC	XC
		◇1	◇1	◇1	1	◇1	◇1	1	◇1	◇1	◇1	1	◇1	◇1	1	◇1	◇1	◇1	◇1	1	◇1	◇1	◇1
			A													B	A				B		
			🛒	☕		🛒	🛒		🛒	🛒	⊠	🛒	🛒	🛒		🛒	🛒		☕	🛒	🛒	🛒	
Bournemouth	d																						
Brockenhurst 3	d																						
Southampton Central	d															05 09							
Southampton Airport Pkway	d															05 16							
Winchester	d															05 25							
Basingstoke	d															05 41							
Guildford	d																				06 09		
Reading 7	d															06 10					06 45		
Oxford	d															06 38					07 12		
Banbury	d															06 56					07 33		
Leamington Spa 8	d															07 14					07 51		
Coventry	d															07 27							
Birmingham International	d															07 38							
Penzance	d																						
St Erth	d																						
Hayle	d																						
Camborne	d																						
Redruth	d																						
Truro	d																						
St Austell	d																						
Newquay (Summer Only)	d																						
Par	d																						
Lostwithiel	d																						
Bodmin Parkway	d																						
Liskeard 8	d																						
Plymouth	d																						
Totnes	d																						
Paignton	d																						
Torquay	d																						
Newton Abbot	d																						
Teignmouth	d																						
Dawlish	d																						
Exeter St Davids 6	d																						
Tiverton Parkway	d																						
Taunton	d																						
Weston-super-Mare	d																						
Cardiff Central 7	d																						06 40
Newport (South Wales)	d																						06 55
Bristol Temple Meads 10	d																06 15					07 00	
Bristol Parkway 7	d																06 24					07 09	
Gloucester 7	d																07 00	07 07					07 46
Cheltenham Spa	d																07 11	07 18				07 41	07 57
Birmingham New Street 12	a															07 48	07 56	08 08			08 17	08 25	08 45
Birmingham New Street 12	d	05 57	05 57	06 15	06 19	06 30	06 31	06 49	06 57	07 03	07 15	07 19	07 30	07 31	07 49	07 57	08 03		08 15	08 19	08 30	08 31	08 49
Tamworth	d		06 13		06 39	06 46		07 07		07 19		07 39	07 46		08 07		08 19			08 36			09 09
Burton-on-Trent	d		06 24		06 51	06 56		07 19		07 29		07 50	07 56		08 19		08 29			08 48			09 21
Derby 6	a		06 35		07 05	07 09		07 34		07 42		08 05	08 09		08 34		08 42			09 00	09 08		09 34
Nottingham 8	a				07 38			08 08				08 34			09 06					09 28			10 04
Chesterfield	a		06 56			07 30				08 02			08 30				09 02						
Sheffield 7	a		07 09			07 48				08 16			08 45				09 17				09 44		
Doncaster 7	a					08 23							09 18								10 17		
Wakefield Westgate 7	a		07 36							08 45							09 46						
Leeds 10	a		07 51							09 03							10 01						
York 8	a		08 24			08 47				09 30			09 43				10 30				10 39		
Darlington 7	a		08 57			09 16				09 57			10 13				10 57				11 13		
Durham	a		09 13			09 33				10 15			10 30				11 15				11 30		
Chester-le-Street	a																						
Newcastle 8	a		09 27			09 47				10 30			10 44				11 29				11 46		
Morpeth	a																						
Alnmouth for Alnwick	a		09 58																				
Berwick-upon-Tweed	a		10 19														12 19						
Dunbar	a									11 37													
Wolverhampton 7	d	06 16		06 37			06 49		07 15		07 37			07 49		08 15			08 37			08 49	
Stafford	a	06 29					07 00		07 29					08 00		08 29						09 00	
Stoke-on-Trent	a	06 50					07 18							08 19		08 54						09 19	
Congleton	a	07 02																					
Macclesfield	a	07 11					07 36							08 36		09 11							
Crewe 10	a			07 07					07 50		08 06								09 07				
Wilmslow	a								08 08														
Stockport	a	07 25					07 49		08 20					08 49		09 27						09 49	
M'chester Piccadilly 10	a	07 34					07 59		08 34					08 59		09 38						09 59	
Warrington Bank Quay	a			07 26							08 26								09 26				
Wigan North Western	a			07 37							08 37								09 37				
Preston 8	a			07 51							08 51								09 51				
Lancaster 6	a			08 07							09 08								10 07				
Oxenholme Lake District	a			08 21															10 21				
Penrith North Lakes	a										09 45												
Carlisle 8	a			09 00							10 00								10 59				
Lockerbie	a																						
Haymarket	a			10 16															12 16				
Edinburgh 10	a		11 03	10 25						12 07							13 04		12 22				
Haymarket	a		11 15														13 15						
Motherwell	a		11 52														13 52						
Glasgow Central 15	a		12 11								11 16						14 12						
Inverkeithing	a																						
Kirkcaldy	a																						
Markinch	a																						
Ladybank	a																						
Cupar	a																						
Leuchars 3	a																						
Dundee	a																						
Arbroath	a																						
Montrose	a																						
Stonehaven	a																						
Aberdeen	a																						

A 🛒 to Edinburgh

B 🛒 from Reading

Table 51R

Saturdays

14 December to 28 December

South Coast and the South West - North West England, The North East and Scotland

Route Diagram - see first Page of Table 51

		XC	XC	VT	XC	XC	XC	XC	XC	XC	VT	XC	XC	XC	XC	XC	XC	VT	XC	XC	XC	XC	XC
		◇1	◇1	◇1	1	◇1	◇1	◇1	◇1	◇1	◇1	1	◇1	◇1	◇1	◇1	◇1	◇1	1	◇1	◇1	◇1	◇1
						A	B			C			A	D									
		⊤	⊤	⊠	⊤	⊤	⊤		⊤	⊤	⊡	⊤	⊤	⊤		⊤	⊤	⊡	⊤	⊤	⊤	⊤	⊤
Bournemouth	d					06 25			06 37							07 45							08 45
Brockenhurst 3	d					06 39			06 55							08 00							09 00
Southampton Central ⛴	d	06 15				06 53			07 15				07 47			08 15							09 15
Southampton Airport Pkway ✈	d	06 22				07 01			07 22				07 54			08 21							09 22
Winchester	d	06 31				07 09			07 31				08 03			08 31							09 31
Basingstoke	d	06 47				07 25			07 47				08 19			08 47							09 47
Guildford	d																						
Reading 7	d	07 10				07 47			08 10				08 40			09 10				09 40			10 10
Oxford	d	07 36				08 15			08 36				09 07			09 36				10 07			10 36
Banbury	d	07 54				08 33			08 54				09 24			09 54				10 24			10 54
Leamington Spa 8	d	08 12				08 50			09 12				09 42			10 12				10 42			11 12
Coventry	d	08 27		08 42					09 27		09 42					10 27		10 42					11 27
Birmingham International ✈	d	08 38		08 53					09 38		09 53					10 38		10 53					11 38
Penzance	d																						
St Erth	d																						
Hayle	d																						
Camborne	d																						
Redruth	d																						
Truro	d																						
St Austell	d																						
Newquay (Summer Only)	d																						
Par	d																						
Lostwithiel	d																						
Bodmin Parkway	d																						
Liskeard 6	d																						
Plymouth	d		05 25							06 25							07 25						
Totnes	d		05 50							06 50							07 50						
Paignton	d													07 02									
Torquay	d													07 08									
Newton Abbot	d		06 03							07 03				07 19			08 03						
Teignmouth	d													07 26									
Dawlish	d													07 31									
Exeter St Davids 6	d		06 23							07 23				07 45			08 23						
Tiverton Parkway	d		06 37							07 37				07 58			08 37						
Taunton	d		06 51							07 51				08 12			08 51						
Weston-super-Mare	d																						
Cardiff Central 7	d						07 00	07 45							08 45							09 45	
Newport (South Wales)	d						07 15	08 00							09 00							10 00	
Bristol Temple Meads 10	d		07 30				08 00			08 30				09 00			09 30				10 00		
Bristol Parkway 7	d		07 39				08 09			08 39				09 09			09 39				10 09		
Gloucester 7	d							08 49							09 50							10 50	
Cheltenham Spa	d		08 13				08 41	09 00		09 10				09 41	10 01		10 11				10 41	11 01	
Birmingham New Street 12	a	08 48	08 56	09 08		09 20	09 26	09 45	09 48	09 55	10 08		10 18	10 25	10 45	10 48	10 56	11 08		11 18	11 26	11 45	11 48
Birmingham New Street 12	d	08 57	09 03	09 15	09 19	09 30	09 31	09 49	09 57	10 03	10 15	10 19	10 30	10 31	10 49	10 57	11 03	11 15	11 19	11 30	11 31	11 49	11 57
Tamworth	d				09 36			10 07		10 19		10 36			11 09				11 36			12 07	
Burton-on-Trent	d		09 28		09 48			10 19				10 48			11 21		11 28		11 48			12 19	
Derby 6	a		09 41		10 00	10 06		10 35		10 41		11 00	11 09		11 34		11 41		12 00	12 06		12 35	
Nottingham 8 ⛴	a				10 28			11 06				11 28			12 04				12 28			13 04	
Chesterfield	a		10 02							11 02							12 02						
Sheffield 7 ⛴	a		10 17			10 44				11 17			11 42				12 17			12 44			
Doncaster 7	a					11 15							12 15							13 17			
Wakefield Westgate 7	a		10 46							11 46							12 46						
Leeds 10	a		11 01							12 00							13 02						
York 8	a		11 30			11 40				12 30			12 39				13 30			13 39			
Darlington 7	a		11 57			12 13				12 58			13 13				13 57			14 13			
Durham	a		12 15			12 30				13 15			13 30				14 14			14 30			
Chester-le-Street	a																						
Newcastle 8	a		12 29			12 45				13 29			13 45				14 28			14 43			
Morpeth	a																14 46						
Alnmouth for Alnwick	a									13 58													
Berwick-upon-Tweed	a									14 19													
Dunbar	a		13 37														15 38						
Wolverhampton 7 ⛴	d	09 15		09 37			09 49		10 15		10 37			10 49		11 15		11 37			11 49		12 15
Stafford	a	09 29					10 00		10 29					11 00		11 29					12 00		12 29
Stoke-on-Trent	a	09 54					10 19		10 54					11 19		11 54					12 19		12 54
Congleton	a																						
Macclesfield	a	10 11							11 11							12 11							13 11
Crewe 10	a			10 07							11 07							12 07					
Wilmslow	a																						
Stockport	a	10 27					10 49		11 27					11 49		12 26					12 49		13 27
M'chester Piccadilly 10 ⛴	a	10 38					10 59		11 38					11 59		12 38					12 59		13 38
Warrington Bank Quay	a			10 26							11 26							12 26					
Wigan North Western	a			10 37							11 37							12 37					
Preston 8	a			10 51							11 51							12 51					
Lancaster 6	a			11 07							12 07							13 07					
Oxenholme Lake District	a										12 20							13 21					
Penrith North Lakes	a			11 44																			
Carlisle 8	a			12 00							12 59							14 00					
Lockerbie	a																						
Haymarket	a										14 15												
Edinburgh 10	a		14 06							15 04	14 22						16 04						
Haymarket	a									15 15													
Motherwell	a									15 52													
Glasgow Central 15	a			13 17						16 12								15 17					
Inverkeithing	a																						
Kirkcaldy	a																						
Markinch	a																						
Ladybank	a																						
Cupar	a																						
Leuchars 3	a																						
Dundee	a																						
Arbroath	a																						
Montrose	a																						
Stonehaven	a																						
Aberdeen	a																						

A ⊤ from Reading
B ⊤ from Bristol Temple Meads
C ⊤ to Edinburgh
D ⊤ from Newton Abbot

Table 51R

Saturdays

14 December to 28 December

South Coast and the South West - North West England, The North East and Scotland

Route Diagram - see first Page of Table 51

		XC	VT	XC	XC	XC	XC	XC	XC	VT	XC	XC	XC	XC	XC	XC	VT	XC	XC	XC	XC	XC
		◇1	◇1	1	◇1	◇1	◇1	◇1	◇1	◇1	1	◇1	◇1	◇1	◇1	◇1	◇1	1	◇1	◇1	◇1	◇1
		A														A						
		🛒	🍴		🛒	🛒		🛒	🛒	🍴	🛒	🛒	🛒	🛒	🛒	🛒	🍴		🛒	🛒	🛒	🛒
Bournemouth	d							09 45							10 45							11 45
Brockenhurst 3	d							10 00							11 00							12 00
Southampton Central	d				09 47			10 15							11 15				11 47			12 15
Southampton Airport Pkway	d				09 54			10 22							11 22				11 54			12 22
Winchester	d				10 03			10 31							11 31				12 03			12 31
Basingstoke	d				10 19			10 47							11 47				12 19			12 47
Guildford	d																					
Reading 7	d				10 39			11 09				11 40			12 09				12 39			13 10
Oxford	d				11 07			11 36				12 07			12 36				13 07			13 36
Banbury	d				11 24			11 54				12 24			12 54				13 24			13 54
Leamington Spa 8	d				11 42			12 12				12 42			13 12				13 42			14 12
Coventry	d		11 42					12 27		12 42					13 27		13 42					14 27
Birmingham International	d		11 53					12 38		12 53					13 38		13 53					14 38
Penzance	d	06 30														08 28						
St Erth	d	06 38														08 36						
Hayle	d	06 41																				
Camborne	d	06 51														08 46						
Redruth	d	06 57														08 52						
Truro	d	07 09														09 04						
St Austell	d	07 25														09 20						
Newquay (Summer Only)	d																					
Par	d	07 32														09 28						
Lostwithiel	d	07 39																				
Bodmin Parkway	d	07 46														09 38						
Liskeard 6	d	07 58														09 51						
Plymouth	d	08 25							09 25							10 25						
Totnes	d	08 50							09 50							10 50						
Paignton	d												10 07									
Torquay	d												10 13									
Newton Abbot	d	09 03							10 03				10 24			11 03						
Teignmouth	d												10 31									
Dawlish	d												10 36									
Exeter St Davids 6	d	09 23							10 23				10 50			11 23						
Tiverton Parkway	d	09 37							10 37				11 03			11 37						
Taunton	d	09 51							10 51				11 17			11 51						
Weston-super-Mare	d																					
Cardiff Central 7	d						10 45							11 45							12 45	
Newport (South Wales)	d						11 00							12 00							13 00	
Bristol Temple Meads 10	d	10 30				11 00			11 30				12 00			12 30				13 00		
Bristol Parkway 7	d	10 39				11 09			11 39				12 09			12 39				13 09		
Gloucester 7	d						11 50							12 48							13 50	
Cheltenham Spa	d	11 11				11 41	12 01		12 11				12 41	12 59		13 11				13 41	14 01	
Birmingham New Street 12	a	11 55	12 08		12 18	12 26	12 45	12 48	12 55	13 08		13 18	13 26	13 45	13 48	13 55	14 08		14 18	14 26	14 45	14 48
Birmingham New Street 12	d	12 03	12 15	12 19	12 30	12 31	12 49	12 57	13 03	13 15	13 19	13 30	13 31	13 49	13 57	14 03	14 15	14 19	14 30	14 31	14 49	14 57
Tamworth	d	12 19		12 36			13 09				13 36			14 09		14 19		14 36			15 09	
Burton-on-Trent	d			12 48			13 21		13 27		13 48			14 21				14 47			15 21	
Derby 6	a	12 41		13 00	13 06		13 34		13 41		14 00	14 06		14 35		14 41		15 00	15 06		15 36	
Nottingham 8	a			13 28			14 04				14 28			15 04				15 28			16 04	
Chesterfield	a	13 02							14 02							15 02						
Sheffield 7	a	13 17			13 43				14 17			14 44				15 17			15 44			
Doncaster 7	a				14 18							15 17							16 18			
Wakefield Westgate 7	a	13 46							14 46							15 46						
Leeds 10	a	14 01							15 01							16 01						
York 8	a	14 30			14 39				15 30			15 39				16 30			16 39			
Darlington 7	a	14 57			15 13				15 57			16 13				16 58			17 13			
Durham	a	15 15			15 30				16 15			16 30				17 15			17 30			
Chester-le-Street	a																					
Newcastle 8	a	15 29			15 45				16 29			16 45				17 29			17 45			
Morpeth	a																					
Alnmouth for Alnwick	a	15 58							16 57							17 59						
Berwick-upon-Tweed	a	16 19														18 19						
Dunbar	a								17 38													
Wolverhampton 7	d		12 37			12 49		13 15		13 37			13 49		14 15		14 37			14 49		15 15
Stafford	a					13 00		13 29					14 00		14 29					15 00		15 29
Stoke-on-Trent	a					13 18		13 54					14 19		14 54					15 19		15 54
Congleton	a																					
Macclesfield	a							14 11							15 11							16 11
Crewe 10	a		13 07							14 07							15 07					
Wilmslow	a																					
Stockport	a					13 49		14 27					14 49		15 27					15 49		16 27
M'chester Piccadilly 10	a					13 59		14 38					14 59		15 38					15 59		16 38
Warrington Bank Quay	a		13 26							14 26							15 26					
Wigan North Western	a		13 37							14 37							15 37					
Preston 8	a		13 51							14 51							15 51					
Lancaster 6	a		14 07							15 07							16 08					
Oxenholme Lake District	a									15 21												
Penrith North Lakes	a		14 42														16 44					
Carlisle 8	a		14 58							15 59							17 00					
Lockerbie	a																					
Haymarket	a		16 17														18 16					
Edinburgh 10	a	17 07	16 22						18 03							19 07	18 24					
Haymarket	a	17 15							18 14							19 15						
Motherwell	a	17 52														19 52						
Glasgow Central 15	a	18 11								17 17						20 09						
Inverkeithing	a								18 28													
Kirkcaldy	a								18 43													
Markinch	a								18 52													
Ladybank	a								18 59													
Cupar	a								19 06													
Leuchars 3	a								19 13													
Dundee	a								19 29													
Arbroath	a								19 45													
Montrose	a								20 02													
Stonehaven	a								20 23													
Aberdeen	a								20 42													

A 🛒 from Plymouth to Edinburgh

Table 51R

Saturdays

14 December to 28 December

South Coast and the South West - North West England, The North East and Scotland

Route Diagram - see first Page of Table 51

		XC	VT	XC	XC	XC	XC	XC		XC	VT	XC	XC	XC	XC	XC	XC	VT		XC	XC	XC	XC	XC	XC
		◇1	◇1	1	◇1	◇1	◇1	◇1		◇1	R 1	1	◇1	◇1	◇1	◇1	◇1	R 1		1	◇1	◇1	◇1	◇1	◇1
		A				B				A															C
		🍴	🍽		🍴	🍽🍴	🍴	🍴		🍴	⊠		🍴	🍴	🍴	🍴	🍴	⊠			🍴	🍴	🍴	🍴	🍴
Bournemouth	d							12 45								13 45								14 45	
Brockenhurst 3	d							13 00								14 00								15 00	
Southampton Central	d							13 15					13 47			14 15								15 15	
Southampton Airport Pkwy ✈	d							13 22					13 54			14 22								15 22	
Winchester	d							13 31					14 03			14 31								15 31	
Basingstoke	d							13 47					14 19			14 47								15 47	
Guildford	d																								
Reading 7	d				13 40			14 10					14 39			15 09					15 40			16 10	
Oxford	d				14 07			14 36					15 07			15 36					16 07			16 36	
Banbury	d				14 24			14 54					15 24			15 54					16 24			16 54	
Leamington Spa 8	d				14 42			15 12					15 42			16 12					16 42			17 12	
Coventry	d		14 42					15 27			15 42					16 27		16 42						17 27	
Birmingham International ✈	d		14 53					15 38			15 53					16 38		16 53						17 38	
Penzance	d					09 43																			
St Erth	d					09 51																			
Hayle	d																								
Camborne	d					10 01																			
Redruth	d					10 07																			
Truro	d					10 19																			
St Austell	d					10 35																			
Newquay (Summer Only)	d																								
Par	d					10 42																			
Lostwithiel	d					10 49																			
Bodmin Parkway	d					10 56																			
Liskeard 6	d					11 08																			
Plymouth	d	11 25				11 48				12 24							13 25								14 25
Totnes	d	11 50				12 13				12 50							13 50								14 50
Paignton	d																					13 53			
Torquay	d																					13 59			
Newton Abbot	d	12 03				12 25				13 03							14 03					14 10			15 03
Teignmouth	d																					14 17			
Dawlish	d																					14 22			
Exeter St Davids 6	d	12 23				12 48				13 24							14 23					14 36			15 23
Tiverton Parkway	d	12 37				13 02				13 38							14 37					14 49			15 37
Taunton	d	12 51				13 16				13 52							14 51					15 03			15 51
Weston-super-Mare	d																					15 29			
Cardiff Central 7	d						13 45								14 45								15 45		
Newport (South Wales)	d						14 00								15 00								16 00		
Bristol Temple Meads 10	d	13 30				14 00				14 30				15 00			15 30					16 00			16 30
Bristol Parkway 7	d	13 39				14 09				14 40				15 09			15 39					16 09			16 39
Gloucester 7	d						14 50								15 50								16 50		
Cheltenham Spa	d	14 11				14 41	15 01			15 11				15 40	16 01		16 11					16 40	17 01		17 11
Birmingham New Street 12	a	14 55	15 08		15 18	15 26	15 45	15 48		15 55	16 08		16 18	16 26	16 45	16 48	16 55	17 08			17 18	17 26	17 45	17 48	17 55
Birmingham New Street 12	d	15 03	15 15	15 19	15 30	15 31	15 49	15 57		16 03	16 15	16 19	16 30	16 31	16 49	16 57	17 03	17 15		17 19	17 30	17 31	17 49	17 57	18 03
Tamworth	d			15 36			16 09			16 19		16 36			17 09					17 36			18 09		18 19
Burton-on-Trent	d	15 27		15 48			16 21					16 48	16 54		17 21		17 26			17 48			18 21		
Derby 6	a	15 41		16 00	16 06		16 34			16 40		17 00	17 06		17 34		17 41			18 00	18 06		18 36		18 41
Nottingham 8	a			16 28			17 04					17 31			18 04					18 31			19 04		
Chesterfield	a	16 02								17 03							18 02								19 02
Sheffield 7	a	16 17			16 44					17 18			17 44				18 18				18 43				19 18
Doncaster 7	a				17 16																19 16				
Wakefield Westgate 7	a	16 46								17 47			18 12				18 46								19 49
Leeds 10	a	17 01								18 02			18 31				19 00								20 04
York 8	a	17 30			17 37					18 30			18 57				19 30				19 38				20 30
Darlington 7	a	17 56			18 13					18 59			19 34				19 57				20 10				20 58
Durham	a	18 13			18 30					19 17			19 51				20 14				20 27				21 15
Chester-le-Street	a																								
Newcastle 8	a	18 29			18 43					19 31			20 07				20 28				20 42				21 29
Morpeth	a																20 47								
Alnmouth for Alnwick	a									20 00															22 01
Berwick-upon-Tweed	a	19 17								20 23							21 18								
Dunbar	a	19 40															21 42								
Wolverhampton 7	d		15 37			15 49		16 15			16 37			16 49		17 15		17 37				17 49		18 15	
Stafford	a					16 00		16 29						17 00		17 29						18 00		18 29	
Stoke-on-Trent	a					16 19		16 54						17 19		17 54						18 19		18 54	
Congleton	a																								
Macclesfield	a							17 11								18 11								19 11	
Crewe 10	a		16 06								17 07							18 07							
Wilmslow	a																								
Stockport	a					16 49		17 27						17 49		18 27						18 49		19 27	
M'chester Piccadilly 10	a					16 59		17 38						17 59		18 38						18 59		19 38	
Warrington Bank Quay	a		16 27								17 26							18 27							
Wigan North Western	a		16 38								17 37							18 38							
Preston 8	a		16 51								17 51							18 51							
Lancaster 6	a		17 08								18 07							19 07							
Oxenholme Lake District	a		17 21								18 21							19 21							
Penrith North Lakes	a										18 47														
Carlisle 8	a		18 00								19 02							20 00							
Lockerbie	a																								
Haymarket	a										20 14														
Edinburgh 10	a	20 05								21 08	20 20						22 08								23 03
Haymarket	a	20 17								21 16															
Motherwell	a									21 56															
Glasgow Central 15	a		19 16							22 21								21 19							
Inverkeithing	a	20 33																							
Kirkcaldy	a	20 50																							
Markinch	a	21 00																							
Ladybank	a	21 08																							
Cupar	a	21 17																							
Leuchars 3	a	21 25																							
Dundee	a	21 42																							
Arbroath	a																								
Montrose	a																								
Stonehaven	a																								
Aberdeen	a																								

A 🍴 to Edinburgh

B 🍽 from Birmingham New Street 🍴 from Plymouth to Birmingham New Street

C 🍴 to Leeds

Table 51R

Saturdays

14 December to 28 December

South Coast and the South West - North West England, The North East and Scotland

Route Diagram - see first Page of Table 51

		VT	XC	XC		XC	XC	XC	XC	VT	XC	XC	XC	XC		XC	XC	VT	XC	XC	XC	XC	XC	XC	
		◇1	1	◇1		◇1	◇1	◇1	◇1	◇1	1	◇1	◇1	◇1		◇1	◇1	◇1	◇1	◇1	◇1	◇1	◇1	◇1	
							A		B			A		A		A	A		A	A	A	A	A		
		🍽		🛒		🛒	🛒	🛒	🛒	🍽		🛒	🛒	🛒		🛒	🛒	🍽	🛒	🛒	🛒	🛒	🛒		
Bournemouth	d							15 45								16 45						17 45			
Brockenhurst 3	d							16 00								17 00						18 00			
Southampton Central	d			15 47				16 15								17 15			17 47			18 15			
Southampton Airport Pkway	d			15 54				16 22								17 22			17 54			18 22			
Winchester	d			16 03				16 31								17 31			18 03			18 31			
Basingstoke	d			16 18				16 47								17 47			18 18			18 47			
Guildford	d																								
Reading 7	d			16 39				17 09				17 40				18 09			18 39			19 09		19 40	
Oxford	d			17 07				17 36				18 07				18 36			19 07			19 36		20 07	
Banbury	d			17 24				17 54				18 24				18 54			19 24			19 54		20 29	
Leamington Spa 8	d			17 42				18 12				18 42				19 12			19 42			20 12		20 46	
Coventry	d	17 42						18 27		18 42						19 27		19 42				20 27			
Birmingham International	d	17 53						18 38		18 53						19 38		19 53				20 38			
Penzance	d																								
St Erth	d																								
Hayle	d																								
Camborne	d																								
Redruth	d																								
Truro	d																								
St Austell	d																								
Newquay (Summer Only)	d																								
Par	d																								
Lostwithiel	d																								
Bodmin Parkway	d																								
Liskeard 6	d																								
Plymouth	d								15 25								16 25						17 24		
Totnes	d								15 50								16 50						17 50		
Paignton	d																								
Torquay	d																								
Newton Abbot	d								16 03								17 03						18 03		
Teignmouth	d																								
Dawlish	d																								
Exeter St Davids 6	d								16 23				16 53				17 23						18 24		
Tiverton Parkway	d								16 37				17 07				17 37						18 38		
Taunton	d								16 51				17 21				17 51						18 52		
Weston-super-Mare	d																								
Cardiff Central 7	d						16 45							17 45							18 45				
Newport (South Wales)	d						17 00							18 00							19 00				
Bristol Temple Meads 10	d					17 00			17 30				18 00				18 30			19 00			19 30		
Bristol Parkway 7	d					17 09			17 39				18 09				18 39			19 09			19 40		
Gloucester 7	d						17 50							18 46							19 46				
Cheltenham Spa	d					17 41	18 01		18 13				18 41	18 57			19 11			19 41	19 57		20 11		
Birmingham New Street 12	a	18 08		18 18		18 26	18 45	18 48	18 55	19 08		19 18	19 26	19 45		19 48	19 58	20 08	20 18	20 26	20 42	20 48	20 52	21 15	
Birmingham New Street 12	d	18 15	18 19	18 30		18 31	18 49	18 57	19 03	19 15	19 19	19 30	19 31	19 49		19 57	20 03	20 15	20 30	20 31	20 49	20 57	21 03		
Tamworth	d		18 36				19 09				19 36			20 09			20 19				21 09		21 19		
Burton-on-Trent	d		18 47				19 21		19 27		19 48			20 21							21 21		21 30		
Derby 6	a		19 00	19 05			19 35		19 39		20 00	20 06		20 34			20 42		21 24		21 34		21 43		
Nottingham 8	a		19 34				20 04				20 28			21 04							22 08				
Chesterfield	a			19 30					20 04			20 30					21 04		21 46				22 04		
Sheffield 7	a			19 44					20 21			20 49					21 19		22 05				22 22		
Doncaster 7	a			20 18								21 21							22 30				22 51		
Wakefield Westgate 7	a								20 48								21 48						23 09		
Leeds 10	a								21 02								22 01						23 27		
York 8	a			20 39					21 57			21 43							22 55						
Darlington 7	a			21 13								22 13													
Durham	a			21 30								22 30													
Chester-le-Street	a																								
Newcastle 8	a			21 44								22 47													
Morpeth	a																								
Alnmouth for Alnwick	a																								
Berwick-upon-Tweed	a																								
Dunbar	a																								
Wolverhampton 7	d	18 37				18 49		19 15		19 37			19 49			20 15		20 37		20 49		21 15			
Stafford	a					19 00		19 29					20 00			20 29		20 51		21 00		21 29			
Stoke-on-Trent	a					19 19		19 54					20 19			20 54				21 20		21 52			
Congleton	a																								
Macclesfield	a							20 11					20 36			21 11				21 38		22 11			
Crewe 10	a	19 07								20 07								21 10							
Wilmslow	a																								
Stockport	a					19 49		20 27					20 49			21 25				21 53		22 25			
M'chester Piccadilly 10	a					19 59		20 37					20 59			21 39				22 04		22 34			
Warrington Bank Quay	a	19 26								20 26															
Wigan North Western	a	19 37								20 37															
Preston 8	a	19 54								20 59															
Lancaster 6	a																								
Oxenholme Lake District	a																								
Penrith North Lakes	a																								
Carlisle 8	a																								
Lockerbie	a																								
Haymarket	a																								
Edinburgh 10	a																								
Haymarket	a																								
Motherwell	a																								
Glasgow Central 15	a																								
Inverkeithing	a																								
Kirkcaldy	a																								
Markinch	a																								
Ladybank	a																								
Cupar	a																								
Leuchars 3	a																								
Dundee	a																								
Arbroath	a																								
Montrose	a																								
Stonehaven	a																								
Aberdeen	a																								

A 🛒 to Birmingham New Street **B** 🛒 to Leeds

Table 51R

Saturdays

14 December to 28 December

South Coast and the South West - North West England, The North East and Scotland

Route Diagram - see first Page of Table 51

		XC	XC	XC	XC	XC	XC	XC	XC	XC	XC
		◇1	◇1	◇1	◇1	◇1	◇1	◇1	1	◇1	◇1
		A		B							
		⚹		⚹							
Bournemouth	d	18 45						19 45			
Brockenhurst 3	d	19 00						20 00			
Southampton Central	d	19 15						20 15			
Southampton Airport Pkway ✈	d	19 22						20 22			
Winchester	d	19 31						20 31			
Basingstoke	d	19 47						20 47			
Guildford	d										
Reading 7	d	20 09				20 40		21 09			21 40
Oxford	d	20 36				21 07		21 36			22 07
Banbury	d	20 54				21 25		21 55			22 29
Leamington Spa 8	d	21 12				21 44		22 12			22 46
Coventry	d	21 27				21 56		22 27			
Birmingham International ✈	d	21 38				22 11		22 38			
Penzance	d										
St Erth	d										
Hayle	d										
Camborne	d										
Redruth	d										
Truro	d										
St Austell	d										
Newquay (Summer Only)	d										
Par	d										
Lostwithiel	d										
Bodmin Parkway	d										
Liskeard 6	d										
Plymouth	d			18 25							
Totnes	d			18 50							
Paignton	d										
Torquay	d										
Newton Abbot	d			19 03							
Teignmouth	d										
Dawlish	d										
Exeter St Davids 6	d			19 23							
Tiverton Parkway	d			19 37							
Taunton	d			19 51							
Weston-super-Mare	d										
Cardiff Central 7	d				20 00					20 50	
Newport (South Wales)	d				20 15					21 05	
Bristol Temple Meads 10	d		20 00	20 30							
Bristol Parkway 7	d		20 09	20 39							
Gloucester 7	d				21 07					21 49	
Cheltenham Spa	d		20 41	21 11	21 18					22 00	
Birmingham New Street 12	a	21 48	21 38	21 52	22 07	22 21		22 48		22 42	23 16
Birmingham New Street 12	d	21 57			22 10		22 31		22 49		
Tamworth	d				22 27				23 08		
Burton-on-Trent	d				22 39				23 20		
Derby 6	a				22 55				23 33		
Nottingham 8 🚌	a				23 28						
Chesterfield	a										
Sheffield 7 🚌	a										
Doncaster 7	a										
Wakefield Westgate 7	a										
Leeds 10	a										
York 8	a										
Darlington 7	a										
Durham	a										
Chester-le-Street	a										
Newcastle 8	a										
Morpeth	a										
Alnmouth for Alnwick	a										
Berwick-upon-Tweed	a										
Dunbar	a										
Wolverhampton 7 🚌	d	22 15					22 49				
Stafford	a	22 29					23 01				
Stoke-on-Trent	a	22 50					23 20				
Congleton	a										
Macclesfield	a	23 07					23 38				
Crewe 10	a										
Wilmslow	a										
Stockport	a	23 20					23 53				
M'chester Piccadilly 10 🚌	a	23 30					00 10				
Warrington Bank Quay	a										
Wigan North Western	a										
Preston 8	a										
Lancaster 6	a										
Oxenholme Lake District	a										
Penrith North Lakes	a										
Carlisle 8	a										
Lockerbie	a										
Haymarket	a										
Edinburgh 10	a										
Haymarket	a										
Motherwell	a										
Glasgow Central 15	a										
Inverkeithing	a										
Kirkcaldy	a										
Markinch	a										
Ladybank	a										
Cupar	a										
Leuchars 3	a										
Dundee	a										
Arbroath	a										
Montrose	a										
Stonehaven	a										
Aberdeen	a										

A ⚹ to Reading

B ⚹ to Bristol Temple Meads

Table 51R

Saturdays

4 January to 8 February

South Coast and the South West - North West England, The North East and Scotland

Route Diagram - see first Page of Table 51

		XC	XC	VT	XC	XC	XC	XC	XC	XC		VT	XC	XC	XC	XC	XC	XC	XC	VT		XC	XC	XC	XC
		◇1	◇1	◇1	1	◇1	◇1	1	◇1	◇1		◇1	1	◇1	◇1	1	◇1	◇1	◇1	◇1		1	◇1	◇1	◇1
			A														B	A					B		
			🛒	🍽		🛒	🛒		🛒	🛒		⊠	🛒	🛒	🛒		🛒	🛒		🍽		🛒	🛒	🛒	
Bournemouth	d																								
Brockenhurst 3	d																								
Southampton Central ⛴	d																05 09								
Southampton Airport Pkwy ✈	d																05 16								
Winchester	d																05 25								
Basingstoke	d																05 41								
Guildford	d																						06 09		
Reading 7	d																06 10						06 45		
Oxford	d																06 38						07 12		
Banbury	d																06 56						07 33		
Leamington Spa 8	d																07 14						07 51		
Coventry	d																07 27								
Birmingham International ✈	d																07 38								
Penzance	d																								
St Erth	d																								
Hayle	d																								
Camborne	d																								
Redruth	d																								
Truro	d																								
St Austell	d																								
Newquay (Summer Only)	d																								
Par	d																								
Lostwithiel	d																								
Bodmin Parkway	d																								
Liskeard 6	d																								
Plymouth	d																								
Totnes	d																								
Paignton	d																								
Torquay	d																								
Newton Abbot	d																								
Teignmouth	d																								
Dawlish	d																								
Exeter St Davids 6	d																								
Tiverton Parkway	d																								
Taunton	d																								
Weston-super-Mare	d																								
Cardiff Central 7	d																								06 40
Newport (South Wales)	d																								06 55
Bristol Temple Meads 10	d																	06 15						07 00	
Bristol Parkway 7	d																	06 24						07 09	
Gloucester 7	d																	07 00	07 07						07 46
Cheltenham Spa	d																	07 11	07 18					07 41	07 57
Birmingham New Street 12	a																07 48	07 56	08 08				08 17	08 25	08 45
Birmingham New Street 12	d	05 57	05 57	06 15	06 19	06 30	06 31	06 49	06 57	07 03		07 15	07 19	07 30	07 31	07 49	07 57	08 03		08 15		08 19	08 30	08 31	08 49
Tamworth	d		06 13		06 39	06 46		07 07		07 19			07 39	07 46		08 07		08 19				08 36			09 09
Burton-on-Trent	d		06 24		06 51	06 56		07 19		07 29			07 50	07 56		08 19		08 29				08 48			09 21
Derby 6	a		06 35		07 05	07 09		07 34		07 42			08 05	08 09		08 34		08 42				09 00	09 08		09 34
Nottingham 8 🚊	a				07 38			08 08					08 34			09 06						09 28			10 04
Chesterfield	a		06 56			07 30				08 02				08 30				09 02							
Sheffield 7 🚊	a		07 09			07 48				08 16				08 45				09 17					09 44		
Doncaster 7	a					08 23								09 18									10 17		
Wakefield Westgate 7	a		07 36							08 45								09 46							
Leeds 10	a		07 51							09 03								10 01							
York 8	a		08 24			08 47				09 30				09 43				10 30					10 39		
Darlington 7	a		08 57			09 16				09 57				10 13				10 57					11 13		
Durham	a		09 13			09 33				10 15				10 30				11 15					11 30		
Chester-le-Street	a																								
Newcastle 8	a		09 27			09 47				10 30				10 44				11 29					11 46		
Morpeth	a																								
Alnmouth for Alnwick	a		09 58																						
Berwick-upon-Tweed	a		10 19															12 19							
Dunbar	a									11 37															
Wolverhampton 7 🚊	d	06 16		06 37			06 49		07 15			07 37			07 49		08 15			08 37				08 49	
Stafford	a	06 29					07 00		07 29						08 00		08 29							09 00	
Stoke-on-Trent	a	06 50					07 18								08 19		08 54							09 19	
Congleton	a	07 02																							
Macclesfield	a	07 11					07 36								08 36		09 11								
Crewe 10	a			07 07					07 50			08 06								09 07					
Wilmslow	a								08 08																
Stockport	a	07 25					07 49		08 20						08 49		09 27							09 49	
M'chester Piccadilly 10 🚊	a	07 34					07 59		08 34						08 59		09 38							09 59	
Warrington Bank Quay	a			07 26								08 26								09 26					
Wigan North Western	a			07 37								08 37								09 37					
Preston 8	a			07 51								08 51								09 51					
Lancaster 6	a			08 07								09 08								10 08					
Oxenholme Lake District	a			08 21																10 22					
Penrith North Lakes	a											09 45													
Carlisle 8	a			09 00								10 00								11 00					
Lockerbie	a																								
Haymarket	a			10 16																12 16					
Edinburgh 10	a		11 03	10 25						12 07								13 04		12 22					
Haymarket	a		11 15															13 15							
Motherwell	a		11 52															13 52							
Glasgow Central 15	a		12 11									11 16						14 12							
Inverkeithing	a																								
Kirkcaldy	a																								
Markinch	a																								
Ladybank	a																								
Cupar	a																								
Leuchars 3	a																								
Dundee	a																								
Arbroath	a																								
Montrose	a																								
Stonehaven	a																								
Aberdeen	a																								

A 🛒 to Edinburgh

B 🛒 from Reading

Table 51R

Saturdays

4 January to 8 February

South Coast and the South West - North West England, The North East and Scotland

Route Diagram - see first Page of Table 51

		XC	XC	VT	XC	XC	XC	XC	XC	XC	VT	XC	XC	XC	XC	XC	XC	VT	XC	XC	XC	XC	XC
		◇1	◇1	◇1	1	◇1	◇1	◇1	◇1	◇1	◇1	1	◇1	◇1	◇1	◇1	◇1	◇1	1	◇1	◇1	◇1	◇1
						A	B			C			A	D									
		🛒	🛒	☒	🛒	🛒	🛒		🛒	🛒	🍴	🛒	🛒	🛒		🛒	🛒	🍴	🛒	🛒	🛒	🛒	🛒
Bournemouth	d					06 25			06 37							07 45							08 45
Brockenhurst 3	d					06 39			06 55							08 00							09 00
Southampton Central	d	06 15				06 53			07 15				07 47			08 15							09 15
Southampton Airport Pkwy	d	06 22				07 01			07 22				07 54			08 21							09 22
Winchester	d	06 31				07 09			07 31				08 03			08 31							09 31
Basingstoke	d	06 47				07 25			07 47				08 19			08 47							09 47
Guildford	d																						
Reading 7	d	07 10				07 47			08 10				08 40			09 10				09 40			10 10
Oxford	d	07 36				08 15			08 36				09 07			09 36				10 07			10 36
Banbury	d	07 54				08 33			08 54				09 24			09 54				10 24			10 54
Leamington Spa 8	d	08 12				08 50			09 12				09 42			10 12				10 42			11 12
Coventry	d	08 27		08 42					09 27		09 42					10 27		10 42					11 27
Birmingham International	d	08 38		08 53					09 38		09 53					10 38		10 53					11 38
Penzance	d																						
St Erth	d																						
Hayle	d																						
Camborne	d																						
Redruth	d																						
Truro	d																						
St Austell	d																						
Newquay (Summer Only)	d																						
Par	d																						
Lostwithiel	d																						
Bodmin Parkway	d																						
Liskeard 6	d																						
Plymouth	d		05 25							06 25							07 25						
Totnes	d		05 50							06 50							07 50						
Paignton	d													07 02									
Torquay	d													07 08									
Newton Abbot	d		06 03							07 03				07 19			08 03						
Teignmouth	d													07 26									
Dawlish	d													07 31									
Exeter St Davids 6	d		06 23							07 23				07 45			08 23						
Tiverton Parkway	d		06 37							07 37				07 58			08 37						
Taunton	d		06 51							07 51				08 12			08 51						
Weston-super-Mare	d																						
Cardiff Central 7	d						07 00	07 45							08 45							09 45	
Newport (South Wales)	d						07 15	08 00							09 00							10 00	
Bristol Temple Meads 10	d		07 30				08 00			08 30				09 00			09 30				10 00		
Bristol Parkway 7	d		07 39				08 09			08 39				09 09			09 39				10 09		
Gloucester 7	d							08 49							09 50							10 50	
Cheltenham Spa	d		08 13				08 41	09 00		09 10				09 41	10 01		10 11				10 41	11 01	
Birmingham New Street 12	a	08 48	08 56	09 08		09 20	09 26	09 45	09 48	09 55	10 08		10 18	10 25	10 45	10 48	10 56	11 08		11 18	11 26	11 45	11 48
Birmingham New Street 12	d	08 57	09 03	09 15	09 19	09 30	09 31	09 49	09 57	10 03	10 15	10 19	10 30	10 31	10 49	10 57	11 03	11 15	11 19	11 30	11 31	11 49	11 57
Tamworth	d				09 36			10 07		10 19		10 36			11 09				11 36			12 07	
Burton-on-Trent	d		09 28		09 48			10 19				10 48			11 21		11 28		11 48			12 19	
Derby 6	a		09 41		10 00	10 06		10 35		10 41		11 00	11 09		11 34		11 41		12 00	12 06		12 35	
Nottingham 8	a				10 28			11 06				11 28			12 04				12 28			13 04	
Chesterfield	a		10 02							11 02							12 02						
Sheffield 7	a		10 17			10 44				11 17			11 42				12 17			12 44			
Doncaster 7	a					11 15							12 15							13 17			
Wakefield Westgate 7	a		10 46							11 46							12 46						
Leeds 10	a		11 01							12 00							13 02						
York 8	a		11 30			11 40				12 30			12 39				13 30			13 39			
Darlington 7	a		11 57			12 13				12 58			13 13				13 57			14 13			
Durham	a		12 15			12 30				13 15			13 30				14 14			14 30			
Chester-le-Street	a																						
Newcastle 8	a		12 29			12 45				13 29			13 45				14 28			14 43			
Morpeth	a																14 46						
Alnmouth for Alnwick	a									13 58													
Berwick-upon-Tweed	a									14 19													
Dunbar	a		13 37														15 38						
Wolverhampton 7	d	09 15		09 37			09 49		10 15		10 37			10 49		11 15		11 37			11 49		12 15
Stafford	a	09 29					10 00		10 29					11 00		11 29					12 00		12 29
Stoke-on-Trent	a	09 54					10 19		10 54					11 19		11 54					12 19		12 54
Congleton	a																						
Macclesfield	a	10 11							11 11							12 11							13 11
Crewe 10	a			10 07							11 07							12 07					
Wilmslow	a																						
Stockport	a	10 27					10 49		11 27					11 49		12 26					12 49		13 27
M'chester Piccadilly 10	a	10 38					10 59		11 38					11 59		12 38					12 59		13 38
Warrington Bank Quay	a			10 26							11 26							12 26					
Wigan North Western	a			10 37							11 37							12 37					
Preston 8	a			10 51							11 51							12 51					
Lancaster 6	a			11 07																			
Oxenholme Lake District	a																						
Penrith North Lakes	a			11 44																			
Carlisle 8	a			12 00																			
Lockerbie	a																						
Haymarket	a																						
Edinburgh 10	a		14 06							15 04							16 04						
Haymarket	a									15 15													
Motherwell	a									15 52													
Glasgow Central 15	a			13 17						16 12													
Inverkeithing	a																						
Kirkcaldy	a																						
Markinch	a																						
Ladybank	a																						
Cupar	a																						
Leuchars 3	a																						
Dundee	a																						
Arbroath	a																						
Montrose	a																						
Stonehaven	a																						
Aberdeen	a																						

A 🛒 from Reading

B 🛒 from Bristol Temple Meads

C 🛒 to Edinburgh

D 🛒 from Newton Abbot

Table 51R

Saturdays

4 January to 8 February

South Coast and the South West - North West England, The North East and Scotland

Route Diagram - see first Page of Table 51

		XC		VT	XC	XC	XC	XC	XC	XC	VT	XC		XC	XC	XC	XC	XC	VT	XC	XC	XC		XC	XC
		◇1		◇1	1	◇1	◇1	◇1	◇1	◇1	◇1	1		◇1	◇1	◇1	◇1	◇1	◇1	1	◇1	◇1		◇1	◇1
		A																A							
Bournemouth	d								09 45								10 45								11 45
Brockenhurst 3	d								10 00								11 00								12 00
Southampton Central	d					09 47			10 15								11 15				11 47				12 15
Southampton Airport Pkway	d					09 54			10 22								11 22				11 54				12 22
Winchester	d					10 03			10 31								11 31				12 03				12 31
Basingstoke	d					10 19			10 47								11 47				12 19				12 47
Guildford	d																								
Reading 7	d					10 39			11 09					11 40			12 10				12 39				13 10
Oxford	d					11 07			11 36					12 07			12 36				13 07				13 36
Banbury	d					11 24			11 54					12 24			12 54				13 24				13 54
Leamington Spa 8	d					11 42			12 12					12 42			13 12				13 42				14 12
Coventry	d			11 42					12 27		12 42						13 27		13 42						14 27
Birmingham International	d			11 53					12 38		12 53						13 38		13 53						14 38
Penzance	d	06 30																08 28							
St Erth	d	06 38																08 36							
Hayle	d	06 41																							
Camborne	d	06 51																08 46							
Redruth	d	06 57																08 52							
Truro	d	07 09																09 04							
St Austell	d	07 25																09 20							
Newquay (Summer Only)	d																								
Par	d	07 32																09 28							
Lostwithiel	d	07 39																							
Bodmin Parkway	d	07 46																09 38							
Liskeard 6	d	07 58																09 51							
Plymouth	d	08 25								09 25								10 25							
Totnes	d	08 50								09 50								10 50							
Paignton	d														10 07										
Torquay	d														10 13										
Newton Abbot	d	09 03								10 03					10 24			11 03							
Teignmouth	d														10 31										
Dawlish	d														10 36										
Exeter St Davids 6	d	09 23								10 23					10 50			11 23							
Tiverton Parkway	d	09 37								10 37					11 03			11 37							
Taunton	d	09 51								10 51					11 17			11 51							
Weston-super-Mare	d																								
Cardiff Central 7	d							10 45								11 45								12 45	
Newport (South Wales)	d							11 00								12 00								13 00	
Bristol Temple Meads 10	d	10 30					11 00			11 30					12 00			12 30				13 00			
Bristol Parkway 7	d	10 39					11 09			11 39					12 09			12 39				13 09			
Gloucester 7	d							11 50								12 48								13 50	
Cheltenham Spa	d	11 11					11 41	12 01		12 11					12 41	12 59		13 11				13 41		14 01	
Birmingham New Street 12	a	11 55		12 08		12 18	12 26	12 45	12 48	12 55	13 08			13 18	13 26	13 45	13 48	13 55	14 08		14 18	14 26		14 45	14 48
Birmingham New Street 12	d	12 03		12 15	12 19	12 30	12 31	12 49	12 57	13 03	13 15	13 19		13 30	13 31	13 49	13 57	14 03	14 15	14 19	14 30	14 31		14 49	14 57
Tamworth	d	12 19			12 36			13 09				13 36				14 09		14 19		14 36				15 09	
Burton-on-Trent	d				12 48			13 21		13 27		13 48				14 21				14 47				15 21	
Derby 6	a	12 41			13 00	13 06		13 34		13 41		14 00		14 06		14 35		14 41		15 00	15 06			15 36	
Nottingham 8	a				13 28			14 04				14 28				15 04				15 28				16 04	
Chesterfield	a	13 02								14 02								15 02							
Sheffield 7	a	13 17				13 43				14 17				14 44				15 17			15 44				
Doncaster 7	a					14 18								15 17							16 18				
Wakefield Westgate 7	a	13 46								14 46								15 46							
Leeds 10	a	14 01								15 01								16 01							
York 8	a	14 30				14 39				15 30				15 39				16 30			16 39				
Darlington 7	a	14 57				15 13				15 57				16 13				16 58			17 13				
Durham	a	15 15				15 30				16 15				16 30				17 15			17 30				
Chester-le-Street	a																								
Newcastle 8	a	15 29				15 45				16 29				16 45				17 29			17 45				
Morpeth	a																								
Alnmouth for Alnwick	a	15 58								16 57								17 59							
Berwick-upon-Tweed	a	16 19																18 19							
Dunbar	a									17 38															
Wolverhampton 7	d			12 37			12 49		13 15		13 37				13 49		14 15		14 37			14 49			15 15
Stafford	a						13 00		13 29						14 00		14 29					15 00			15 29
Stoke-on-Trent	a						13 18		13 54						14 19		14 54					15 19			15 54
Congleton	a																								
Macclesfield	a								14 11								15 11								16 11
Crewe 10	a			13 07							14 07								15 07						
Wilmslow	a																								
Stockport	a						13 49		14 27						14 49		15 27					15 49			16 27
M'chester Piccadilly 10	a						13 59		14 38						14 59		15 38					15 59			16 38
Warrington Bank Quay	a			13 26							14 26								15 26						
Wigan North Western	a			13 37							14 37								15 37						
Preston 8	a			13 51							14 51								15 51						
Lancaster 6	a																								
Oxenholme Lake District	a																								
Penrith North Lakes	a																								
Carlisle 8	a																								
Lockerbie	a																								
Haymarket	a																								
Edinburgh 10	a	17 07								18 03								19 07							
Haymarket	a	17 15								18 14								19 15							
Motherwell	a	17 52																19 52							
Glasgow Central 15	a	18 11																20 09							
Inverkeithing	a									18 28															
Kirkcaldy	a									18 43															
Markinch	a									18 52															
Ladybank	a									18 59															
Cupar	a									19 06															
Leuchars 3	a									19 13															
Dundee	a									19 29															
Arbroath	a									19 45															
Montrose	a									20 02															
Stonehaven	a									20 23															
Aberdeen	a									20 42															

A from Plymouth to Edinburgh

Table 51R

Saturdays

4 January to 8 February

South Coast and the South West - North West England, The North East and Scotland

Route Diagram - see first Page of Table 51

		XC	VT	XC	XC	XC	XC	XC	XC	VT	XC	XC	XC	XC	XC	XC	VT	XC	XC	XC	XC	XC	XC
		◇1	◇1	1	◇1	◇1	◇1	◇1	◇1	R 1	1	◇1	◇1	◇1	◇1	◇1	R 1	1	◇1	◇1	◇1	◇1	◇1
		A				B			A														C
		[trolley]	[restaurant]		[trolley]	[restaurant] [trolley]	[trolley]	[trolley]	[trolley]	☒		[trolley]	[trolley]	[trolley]	[trolley]	[trolley]	☒		[trolley]	[trolley]	[trolley]	[trolley]	[trolley]
Bournemouth	d							12 45							13 45							14 45	
Brockenhurst 3	d							13 00							14 00							15 00	
Southampton Central	d							13 15				13 47			14 15							15 15	
Southampton Airport Pkway	d							13 22				13 54			14 22							15 22	
Winchester	d							13 31				14 03			14 31							15 31	
Basingstoke	d							13 47				14 19			14 47							15 47	
Guildford	d																						
Reading 7	d				13 40			14 10				14 39			15 10				15 40			16 10	
Oxford	d				14 07			14 36				15 07			15 36				16 07			16 36	
Banbury	d				14 24			14 54				15 24			15 54				16 24			16 54	
Leamington Spa 8	d				14 42			15 12				15 42			16 12				16 42			17 12	
Coventry	d		14 42					15 27		15 42					16 27		16 42					17 27	
Birmingham International	d		14 53					15 38		15 53					16 38		16 53					17 38	
Penzance	d					09 43																	
St Erth	d					09 51																	
Hayle	d																						
Camborne	d					10 01																	
Redruth	d					10 07																	
Truro	d					10 19																	
St Austell	d					10 35																	
Newquay (Summer Only)	d																						
Par	d					10 42																	
Lostwithiel	d					10 49																	
Bodmin Parkway	d					10 56																	
Liskeard 6	d					11 08																	
Plymouth	d	11 25				11 48			12 24							13 25							14 25
Totnes	d	11 50				12 13			12 50							13 50							14 50
Paignton	d																			13 53			
Torquay	d																			13 59			
Newton Abbot	d	12 03				12 25			13 03							14 03				14 10			15 03
Teignmouth	d																			14 17			
Dawlish	d																			14 22			
Exeter St Davids 6	d	12 23				12 48			13 24							14 23				14 36			15 23
Tiverton Parkway	d	12 37				13 02			13 38							14 37				14 49			15 37
Taunton	d	12 51				13 16			13 52							14 51				15 03			15 51
Weston-super-Mare	d																			15 29			
Cardiff Central 7	d						13 45							14 45							15 45		
Newport (South Wales)	d						14 00							15 00							16 00		
Bristol Temple Meads 10	d	13 30				14 00			14 30				15 00			15 30				16 00			16 30
Bristol Parkway 7	d	13 39				14 09			14 40				15 09			15 39				16 09			16 39
Gloucester 7	d						14 50							15 50							16 50		
Cheltenham Spa	d	14 11				14 41	15 01		15 11				15 40	16 01		16 11				16 40	17 01		17 11
Birmingham New Street 12	a	14 55	15 08		15 18	15 26	15 45	15 48	15 55	16 08		16 18	16 26	16 45	16 48	16 55	17 08		17 18	17 26	17 45	17 48	17 55
Birmingham New Street 12	d	15 03	15 15	15 19	15 30	15 31	15 49	15 57	16 03	16 15	16 19	16 30	16 31	16 49	16 57	17 03	17 15	17 19	17 30	17 31	17 49	17 57	18 03
Tamworth	d			15 36			16 09		16 19		16 36			17 09				17 36			18 09		18 19
Burton-on-Trent	d	15 27		15 48			16 21				16 48	16 54		17 21		17 26		17 48			18 21		
Derby 6	a	15 41		16 00	16 06		16 34		16 40		17 00	17 06		17 34		17 41		18 00	18 06		18 36		18 41
Nottingham 8	a			16 28			17 04				17 31			18 04				18 31			19 04		
Chesterfield	a	16 02							17 03							18 02							19 02
Sheffield 7	a	16 17			16 44				17 18			17 44				18 18			18 43				19 18
Doncaster 7	a				17 16														19 16				
Wakefield Westgate 7	a	16 46							17 47			18 12				18 46							19 49
Leeds 10	a	17 01							18 02			18 31				19 00							20 04
York 8	a	17 30			17 37				18 30			18 57				19 30			19 38				20 30
Darlington 7	a	17 56			18 13				18 59			19 34				19 57			20 10				20 58
Durham	a	18 13			18 30				19 17			19 51				20 14			20 27				21 15
Chester-le-Street	a																						
Newcastle 8	a	18 29			18 43				19 31			20 07				20 28			20 42				21 29
Morpeth	a															20 47							
Alnmouth for Alnwick	a								20 00														22 01
Berwick-upon-Tweed	a	19 17							20 23							21 18							
Dunbar	a	19 40														21 42							
Wolverhampton 7	d		15 37			15 49		16 15		16 37			16 49		17 15		17 37			17 49		18 15	
Stafford	a					16 00		16 29					17 00		17 29					18 00		18 29	
Stoke-on-Trent	a					16 19		16 54					17 19		17 54					18 19		18 54	
Congleton	a																						
Macclesfield	a							17 11							18 11							19 11	
Crewe 10	a		16 06							17 07							18 07						
Wilmslow	a																						
Stockport	a					16 49		17 27					17 49		18 27					18 49		19 27	
M'chester Piccadilly 10	a					16 59		17 38					17 59		18 38					18 59		19 38	
Warrington Bank Quay	a		16 27							17 26							18 26						
Wigan North Western	a		16 38							17 37							18 37						
Preston 8	a		16 51							17 51							18 51						
Lancaster 6	a																						
Oxenholme Lake District	a																						
Penrith North Lakes	a																						
Carlisle 8	a																						
Lockerbie	a																						
Haymarket	a																						
Edinburgh 10	a	20 05							21 08							22 08							23 03
Haymarket	a	20 17							21 16														
Motherwell	a								21 56														
Glasgow Central 15	a								22 21														
Inverkeithing	a	20 33																					
Kirkcaldy	a	20 50																					
Markinch	a	21 00																					
Ladybank	a	21 08																					
Cupar	a	21 17																					
Leuchars 3	a	21 25																					
Dundee	a	21 42																					
Arbroath	a																						
Montrose	a																						
Stonehaven	a																						
Aberdeen	a																						

A [trolley] to Edinburgh

B [restaurant] from Birmingham New Street [trolley] from Plymouth to Birmingham New Street

C [trolley] to Leeds

Table 51R

Saturdays

4 January to 8 February

South Coast and the South West - North West England, The North East and Scotland

Route Diagram - see first Page of Table 51

		VT	XC	XC	XC	XC	XC	XC	VT	XC	XC	XC	XC	XC	XC	VT	XC	XC	XC	XC	XC	XC
		◇[1]	[1]	◇[1]	◇[1]	◇[1]	◇[1]	◇[1]	◇[1]	[1]	◇[1]	◇[1]	◇[1]	◇[1]	◇[1]	◇[1]	◇[1]	◇[1]	◇[1]	◇[1]	◇[1]	◇[1]
						A		B			A		A	A	A		A	A	A	A	A	
		[buffet]		[trolley]	[trolley]	[trolley]	[trolley]	[trolley]	[buffet]		[trolley]	[trolley]	[trolley]	[trolley]	[trolley]	[buffet]	[trolley]	[trolley]	[trolley]	[trolley]	[trolley]	
Bournemouth	d						15 45							16 45						17 45		
Brockenhurst [3]	d						16 00							17 00						18 00		
Southampton Central ⛴	d			15 47			16 15							17 15			17 47			18 15		
Southampton Airport Pkway ✈	d			15 54			16 22							17 22			17 54			18 22		
Winchester	d			16 03			16 31							17 31			18 03			18 31		
Basingstoke	d			16 18			16 47							17 47			18 18			18 47		
Guildford	d																					
Reading [7]	d			16 39			17 10				17 40			18 09			18 39			19 09		19 40
Oxford	d			17 07			17 36				18 07			18 36			19 07			19 36		20 07
Banbury	d			17 24			17 54				18 24			18 54			19 24			19 54		20 29
Leamington Spa [8]	d			17 42			18 12				18 42			19 12			19 42			20 12		20 46
Coventry	d	17 42					18 27		18 42					19 27		19 42				20 27		
Birmingham International ✈	d	17 53					18 38		18 53					19 38		19 53				20 38		
Penzance	d																					
St Erth	d																					
Hayle	d																					
Camborne	d																					
Redruth	d																					
Truro	d																					
St Austell	d																					
Newquay (Summer Only)	d																					
Par	d																					
Lostwithiel	d																					
Bodmin Parkway	d																					
Liskeard [6]	d																					
Plymouth	d							15 25							16 25						17 24	
Totnes	d							15 50							16 50						17 50	
Paignton	d																					
Torquay	d																					
Newton Abbot	d							16 03							17 03						18 03	
Teignmouth	d																					
Dawlish	d																					
Exeter St Davids [6]	d							16 23				16 53			17 23						18 24	
Tiverton Parkway	d							16 37				17 07			17 37						18 38	
Taunton	d							16 51				17 21			17 51						18 52	
Weston-super-Mare	d																					
Cardiff Central [7]	d					16 45							17 45						18 45			
Newport (South Wales)	d					17 00							18 00						19 00			
Bristol Temple Meads [10]	d				17 00			17 30				18 00			18 30			19 00			19 30	
Bristol Parkway [7]	d				17 09			17 39				18 09			18 39			19 09			19 40	
Gloucester [7]	d					17 50							18 46						19 46			
Cheltenham Spa	d				17 41	18 01		18 13				18 41	18 57		19 11			19 41	19 57		20 11	
Birmingham New Street [12]	a	18 08		18 18	18 26	18 45	18 48	18 55	19 08		19 18	19 26	19 45	19 48	19 58	20 08	20 18	20 26	20 42	20 48	20 52	21 15
Birmingham New Street [12]	d	18 15	18 19	18 30	18 31	18 49	18 57	19 03	19 15	19 19	19 30	19 31	19 49	19 57	20 03	20 15	20 30	20 31	20 49	20 57	21 03	
Tamworth	d		18 36			19 09				19 36			20 09		20 19				21 09		21 19	
Burton-on-Trent	d		18 47			19 21		19 27		19 48			20 21						21 21		21 30	
Derby [6]	a		19 00	19 05		19 35		19 39		20 00	20 06		20 34		20 42		21 24		21 34		21 43	
Nottingham [8] 🚋	a		19 34			20 04				20 28			21 04						22 08			
Chesterfield	a			19 30				20 04			20 30				21 04		21 46				22 04	
Sheffield [7] 🚋	a			19 44				20 21			20 49				21 19		22 05				22 22	
Doncaster [7]	a			20 18							21 21						22 30				22 51	
Wakefield Westgate [7]	a							20 48							21 48						23 09	
Leeds [10]	a							21 02							22 01						23 27	
York [8]	a			20 39				21 57			21 43						22 55					
Darlington [7]	a			21 13							22 13											
Durham	a			21 30							22 30											
Chester-le-Street	a																					
Newcastle [8]	a			21 44							22 47											
Morpeth	a																					
Alnmouth for Alnwick	a																					
Berwick-upon-Tweed	a																					
Dunbar	a																					
Wolverhampton [7] 🚋	d	18 37			18 49		19 15		19 37			19 49		20 15		20 37		20 49		21 15		
Stafford	a				19 00		19 29					20 00		20 29		20 49		21 00		21 29		
Stoke-on-Trent	a				19 19		19 54					20 19		20 54				21 20		21 52		
Congleton	a																					
Macclesfield	a						20 11					20 36		21 11				21 38		22 11		
Crewe [10]	a	19 07							20 07							21 10						
Wilmslow	a																					
Stockport	a				19 49		20 27					20 49		21 25				21 53		22 25		
M'chester Piccadilly [10] 🚋	a				19 59		20 37					20 59		21 39				22 04		22 34		
Warrington Bank Quay	a	19 26							20 26													
Wigan North Western	a	19 37							20 37													
Preston [8]	a	19 54																				
Lancaster [6]	a																					
Oxenholme Lake District	a																					
Penrith North Lakes	a																					
Carlisle [8]	a																					
Lockerbie	a																					
Haymarket	a																					
Edinburgh [10]	a																					
Haymarket	a																					
Motherwell	a																					
Glasgow Central [15]	a																					
Inverkeithing	a																					
Kirkcaldy	a																					
Markinch	a																					
Ladybank	a																					
Cupar	a																					
Leuchars [8]	a																					
Dundee	a																					
Arbroath	a																					
Montrose	a																					
Stonehaven	a																					
Aberdeen	a																					

A [trolley] to Birmingham New Street

B [trolley] to Leeds

Table 51R

Saturdays
4 January to 8 February

South Coast and the South West - North West England, The North East and Scotland

Route Diagram - see first Page of Table 51

		XC ◇1 A ⚲	XC ◇1	XC ◇1 B ⚲	XC ◇1	XC ◇1	XC ◇1	XC ◇1	XC 1	XC ◇1	XC ◇1
Bournemouth	d	18 45						19 45			
Brockenhurst 3	d	19 00						20 00			
Southampton Central ⛴	d	19 15						20 15			
Southampton Airport Pkway ✈	d	19 22						20 22			
Winchester	d	19 31						20 31			
Basingstoke	d	19 47						20 47			
Guildford	d										
Reading 7	d	20 09				20 40		21 09			21 40
Oxford	d	20 36				21 07		21 36			22 07
Banbury	d	20 54				21 25		21 55			22 29
Leamington Spa 8	d	21 12				21 44		22 12			22 46
Coventry	d	21 27				21 56		22 27			
Birmingham International ✈	d	21 38				22 11		22 38			
Penzance	d										
St Erth	d										
Hayle	d										
Camborne	d										
Redruth	d										
Truro	d										
St Austell	d										
Newquay (Summer Only)	d										
Par	d										
Lostwithiel	d										
Bodmin Parkway	d										
Liskeard 6	d										
Plymouth	d			18 25							
Totnes	d			18 50							
Paignton	d										
Torquay	d										
Newton Abbot	d			19 03							
Teignmouth	d										
Dawlish	d										
Exeter St Davids 6	d			19 23							
Tiverton Parkway	d			19 37							
Taunton	d			19 51							
Weston-super-Mare	d										
Cardiff Central 7	d				20 00					20 50	
Newport (South Wales)	d				20 15					21 05	
Bristol Temple Meads 10	d		20 00	20 30							
Bristol Parkway 7	d		20 09	20 39							
Gloucester 7	d				21 07					21 49	
Cheltenham Spa	d		20 41	21 11	21 18					22 00	
Birmingham New Street 12	a	21 48	21 38	21 52	22 07	22 21		22 48		22 42	23 16
Birmingham New Street 12	d	21 57			22 10		22 31		22 49		
Tamworth	d				22 27				23 08		
Burton-on-Trent	d				22 39				23 20		
Derby 6	a				22 55				23 33		
Nottingham 8 🚌	a				23 28						
Chesterfield	a										
Sheffield 7 🚌	a										
Doncaster 7	a										
Wakefield Westgate 7	a										
Leeds 10	a										
York 8	a										
Darlington 7	a										
Durham	a										
Chester-le-Street	a										
Newcastle 8	a										
Morpeth	a										
Alnmouth for Alnwick	a										
Berwick-upon-Tweed	a										
Dunbar	a										
Wolverhampton 7 🚌	d	22 15					22 49				
Stafford	a	22 29					23 01				
Stoke-on-Trent	a	22 50					23 20				
Congleton	a										
Macclesfield	a	23 07					23 38				
Crewe 10	a										
Wilmslow	a										
Stockport	a	23 20					23 53				
M'chester Piccadilly 10 🚌	a	23 30					00 10				
Warrington Bank Quay	a										
Wigan North Western	a										
Preston 8	a										
Lancaster 6	a										
Oxenholme Lake District	a										
Penrith North Lakes	a										
Carlisle 8	a										
Lockerbie	a										
Haymarket	a										
Edinburgh 10	a										
Haymarket	a										
Motherwell	a										
Glasgow Central 15	a										
Inverkeithing	a										
Kirkcaldy	a										
Markinch	a										
Ladybank	a										
Cupar	a										
Leuchars 8	a										
Dundee	a										
Arbroath	a										
Montrose	a										
Stonehaven	a										
Aberdeen	a										

A ⚲ to Reading

B ⚲ to Bristol Temple Meads

Table 51R

Saturdays

15 February to 17 May

South Coast and the South West - North West England, The North East and Scotland

Route Diagram - see first Page of Table 51

		XC	XC	VT	XC	XC	XC	XC	XC	XC	VT	XC	XC	XC	XC	XC	XC	XC	VT	XC	XC	XC	XC
		◇1	◇1	◇1	1	◇1	◇1	1	◇1	◇1	◇1	1	◇1	◇1	1	◇1	◇1	◇1	◇1	1	◇1	◇1	◇1
			A													B	A				B		
			⚲	⊐		⚲	⚲		⚲	⚲	⊠	⚲	⚲	⚲		⚲	⚲		⊐	⚲	⚲	⚲	
Bournemouth	d																						
Brockenhurst 3	d																						
Southampton Central	d															05 09							
Southampton Airport Pkway	d															05 16							
Winchester	d															05 25							
Basingstoke	d															05 41							
Guildford	d																				06 09		
Reading 7	d															06 10					06 45		
Oxford	d															06 38					07 12		
Banbury	d															06 56					07 33		
Leamington Spa 8	d															07 14					07 51		
Coventry	d															07 27							
Birmingham International	d															07 38							
Penzance	d																						
St Erth	d																						
Hayle	d																						
Camborne	d																						
Redruth	d																						
Truro	d																						
St Austell	d																						
Newquay (Summer Only)	d																						
Par	d																						
Lostwithiel	d																						
Bodmin Parkway	d																						
Liskeard 6	d																						
Plymouth	d																						
Totnes	d																						
Paignton	d																						
Torquay	d																						
Newton Abbot	d																						
Teignmouth	d																						
Dawlish	d																						
Exeter St Davids 6	d																						
Tiverton Parkway	d																						
Taunton	d																						
Weston-super-Mare	d																						
Cardiff Central 7	d																						06 40
Newport (South Wales)	d																						06 55
Bristol Temple Meads 10	d																06 15					07 00	
Bristol Parkway 7	d																06 24					07 09	
Gloucester 7	d																07 00	07 07					07 46
Cheltenham Spa	d																07 11	07 18				07 41	07 57
Birmingham New Street 12	a															07 48	07 56	08 08			08 17	08 25	08 45
Birmingham New Street 12	d	05 57	05 57	06 15	06 19	06 30	06 31	06 49	06 57	07 03	07 15	07 19	07 30	07 31	07 49	07 57	08 03		08 15	08 19	08 30	08 31	08 49
Tamworth	d		06 13		06 39	06 46		07 07		07 19		07 39	07 46		08 07		08 19			08 36			09 09
Burton-on-Trent	d		06 24		06 51	06 56		07 19		07 29		07 50	07 56		08 19		08 29			08 48			09 21
Derby 6	a		06 35		07 05	07 09		07 34		07 42		08 05	08 09		08 34		08 42			09 00	09 08		09 34
Nottingham 8	a				07 38			08 08				08 34			09 06					09 28			10 04
Chesterfield	a		06 56			07 30				08 02			08 30				09 02						
Sheffield 7	a		07 09			07 48				08 16			08 45				09 17				09 44		
Doncaster 7	a					08 23							09 18								10 17		
Wakefield Westgate 7	a		07 36							08 45							09 46						
Leeds 10	a		07 51							09 03							10 01						
York 8	a		08 24			08 47				09 30			09 43				10 30				10 39		
Darlington 7	a		08 57			09 16				09 57			10 13				10 57				11 13		
Durham	a		09 13			09 33				10 15			10 30				11 15				11 30		
Chester-le-Street	a																						
Newcastle 8	a		09 27			09 47				10 30			10 44				11 29				11 46		
Morpeth	a																						
Alnmouth for Alnwick	a		09 58																				
Berwick-upon-Tweed	a		10 19														12 19						
Dunbar	a									11 37													
Wolverhampton 7	d	06 16		06 37			06 49		07 15		07 37			07 49		08 15			08 37			08 49	
Stafford	a	06 29					07 00		07 29					08 00		08 29						09 00	
Stoke-on-Trent	a	06 50					07 18							08 19		08 54						09 19	
Congleton	a	07 02																					
Macclesfield	a	07 11					07 36							08 36		09 11							
Crewe 10	a			07 07					07 50		08 06								09 07				
Wilmslow	a								08 08														
Stockport	a	07 25					07 49		08 20					08 49		09 27						09 49	
M'chester Piccadilly 10	a	07 34					07 59		08 34					08 59		09 38						09 59	
Warrington Bank Quay	a			07 26							08 26								09 26				
Wigan North Western	a			07 37							08 37								09 37				
Preston 8	a			07 51							08 51								09 51				
Lancaster 6	a			08 07							09 08								10 07				
Oxenholme Lake District	a			08 21															10 21				
Penrith North Lakes	a										09 45												
Carlisle 8	a			09 00							10 00								10 59				
Lockerbie	a																						
Haymarket	a			10 16															12 16				
Edinburgh 10	a		11 03	10 25						12 07							13 04		12 22				
Haymarket	a		11 15														13 15						
Motherwell	a		11 52														13 52						
Glasgow Central 15	a		12 11								11 16						14 12						
Inverkeithing	a																						
Kirkcaldy	a																						
Markinch	a																						
Ladybank	a																						
Cupar	a																						
Leuchars 3	a																						
Dundee	a																						
Arbroath	a																						
Montrose	a																						
Stonehaven	a																						
Aberdeen	a																						

A ⚲ to Edinburgh **B** ⚲ from Reading

Table 51R

Saturdays

15 February to 17 May

South Coast and the South West - North West England, The North East and Scotland

Route Diagram - see first Page of Table 51

		XC	XC	VT	XC	XC	XC	XC	XC	XC	VT	XC	XC	XC	XC	XC	XC	VT	XC	XC	XC	XC	XC
		◇1	◇1	◇1	1	◇1	◇1	◇1	◇1	◇1	◇1	1	◇1	◇1	◇1	◇1	◇1	◇1	1	◇1	◇1	◇1	◇1
						A	B			C			A	D									
		T	T	☒	T	T	T		T	T	⊐	T	T	T		T	T	⊐	T	T	T	T	T
Bournemouth	d					06 25			06 37							07 45							08 45
Brockenhurst 3	d					06 39			06 55							08 00							09 00
Southampton Central	d	06 15				06 53			07 15				07 47			08 15							09 15
Southampton Airport Pkway	d	06 22				07 01			07 22				07 54			08 21							09 22
Winchester	d	06 31				07 09			07 31				08 03			08 31							09 31
Basingstoke	d	06 47				07 25			07 47				08 19			08 47							09 47
Guildford	d																						
Reading 7	d	07 10				07 47			08 10				08 40			09 10				09 40			10 10
Oxford	d	07 36				08 15			08 36				09 07			09 36				10 07			10 36
Banbury	d	07 54				08 33			08 54				09 24			09 54				10 24			10 54
Leamington Spa 8	d	08 12				08 50			09 12				09 42			10 12				10 42			11 12
Coventry	d	08 27		08 42					09 27		09 42					10 27		10 42					11 27
Birmingham International	d	08 38		08 53					09 38		09 53					10 38		10 53					11 38
Penzance	d																						
St Erth	d																						
Hayle	d																						
Camborne	d																						
Redruth	d																						
Truro	d																						
St Austell	d																						
Newquay (Summer Only)	d																						
Par	d																						
Lostwithiel	d																						
Bodmin Parkway	d																						
Liskeard 6	d																						
Plymouth	d		05 25							06 25							07 25						
Totnes	d		05 50							06 50							07 50						
Paignton	d													07 02									
Torquay	d													07 08									
Newton Abbot	d		06 03							07 03				07 19			08 03						
Teignmouth	d													07 26									
Dawlish	d													07 31									
Exeter St Davids 6	d		06 23							07 23				07 45			08 23						
Tiverton Parkway	d		06 37							07 37				07 58			08 37						
Taunton	d		06 51							07 51				08 12			08 51						
Weston-super-Mare	d																						
Cardiff Central 7	d						07 00	07 45							08 45							09 45	
Newport (South Wales)	d						07 15	08 00							09 00							10 00	
Bristol Temple Meads 10	d		07 30				08 00			08 30				09 00			09 30				10 00		
Bristol Parkway 7	d		07 39				08 09			08 39				09 09			09 39				10 09		
Gloucester 7	d							08 49							09 50							10 50	
Cheltenham Spa	d		08 13				08 41	09 00		09 10				09 41	10 01		10 11				10 41	11 01	
Birmingham New Street 12	a	08 48	08 56	09 08		09 20	09 26	09 45	09 48	09 55	10 08		10 18	10 25	10 45	10 48	10 56	11 08		11 18	11 26	11 45	11 48
Birmingham New Street 12	d	08 57	09 03	09 15	09 19	09 30	09 31	09 49	09 57	10 03	10 15	10 19	10 30	10 31	10 49	10 57	11 03	11 15	11 19	11 30	11 31	11 49	11 57
Tamworth	d				09 36			10 07		10 19		10 36			11 09				11 36			12 07	
Burton-on-Trent	d		09 28		09 48			10 19				10 48			11 21		11 28		11 48			12 19	
Derby 6	a		09 41		10 00	10 06		10 35		10 41		11 00	11 09		11 34		11 41		12 00	12 06		12 35	
Nottingham 8	a				10 28			11 06				11 28			12 04				12 28			13 04	
Chesterfield	a		10 02							11 02							12 02						
Sheffield 7	a		10 17			10 44				11 17			11 42				12 17			12 44			
Doncaster 7	a					11 15							12 15							13 17			
Wakefield Westgate 7	a		10 46							11 46							12 46						
Leeds 10	a		11 01							12 00							13 02						
York 8	a		11 30			11 40				12 30			12 39				13 30			13 39			
Darlington 7	a		11 57			12 13				12 58			13 13				13 57			14 13			
Durham	a		12 15			12 30				13 15			13 30				14 14			14 30			
Chester-le-Street	a																						
Newcastle 8	a		12 29			12 45				13 29			13 45				14 28			14 43			
Morpeth	a																14 46						
Alnmouth for Alnwick	a									13 58													
Berwick-upon-Tweed	a									14 19													
Dunbar	a		13 37														15 38						
Wolverhampton 7	d	09 15		09 37			09 49		10 15		10 37			10 49		11 15		11 37			11 49		12 15
Stafford	a	09 29					10 00		10 29					11 00		11 29					12 00		12 29
Stoke-on-Trent	a	09 54					10 19		10 54					11 19		11 54					12 19		12 54
Congleton	a																						
Macclesfield	a	10 11							11 11							12 11							13 11
Crewe 10	a			10 07							11 07							12 07					
Wilmslow	a																						
Stockport	a	10 27					10 49		11 27					11 49		12 26					12 49		13 27
M'chester Piccadilly 10	a	10 38					10 59		11 38					11 59		12 38					12 59		13 38
Warrington Bank Quay	a			10 26							11 26							12 26					
Wigan North Western	a			10 37							11 37							12 37					
Preston 8	a			10 51							11 51							12 51					
Lancaster 6	a			11 07							12 07							13 07					
Oxenholme Lake District	a										12 20							13 21					
Penrith North Lakes	a			11 44																			
Carlisle 8	a			12 00							12 59							14 00					
Lockerbie	a																						
Haymarket	a										14 15												
Edinburgh 10	a		14 06							15 04	14 22						16 04						
Haymarket	a									15 15													
Motherwell	a									15 52													
Glasgow Central 15	a			13 17						16 12								15 17					
Inverkeithing	a																						
Kirkcaldy	a																						
Markinch	a																						
Ladybank	a																						
Cupar	a																						
Leuchars 8	a																						
Dundee	a																						
Arbroath	a																						
Montrose	a																						
Stonehaven	a																						
Aberdeen	a																						

A T from Reading
B T from Bristol Temple Meads
C T to Edinburgh
D T from Newton Abbot

Table 51R

Saturdays

15 February to 17 May

South Coast and the South West - North West England, The North East and Scotland

Route Diagram - see first Page of Table 51

		XC		VT	XC	XC	XC	XC	XC	XC	VT	XC		XC	XC	XC	XC	XC	VT	XC	XC	XC		XC	XC
		◇■1		◇■1	■1	◇■1	◇■1	◇■1	◇■1	◇■1	◇■1	■1		◇■1	◇■1	◇■1	◇■1	◇■1	◇■1	■1	◇■1	◇■1		◇■1	◇■1
		A																A							
		🛒		🍴		🛒	🛒		🛒	🛒	🍴	🛒		🛒	🛒	🛒	🛒	🛒	🍴		🛒	🛒		🛒	🛒
Bournemouth	d								09 45								10 45								11 45
Brockenhurst ■3	d								10 00								11 00								12 00
Southampton Central ⛴	d					09 47			10 15								11 15				11 47				12 15
Southampton Airport Pkway ✈	d					09 54			10 22								11 22				11 54				12 22
Winchester	d					10 03			10 31								11 31				12 03				12 31
Basingstoke	d					10 19			10 47								11 47				12 19				12 47
Guildford	d																								
Reading ■7	d					10 39			11 09					11 40			12 09				12 39				13 10
Oxford	d					11 07			11 36					12 07			12 36				13 07				13 36
Banbury	d					11 24			11 54					12 24			12 54				13 24				13 54
Leamington Spa ■8	d					11 42			12 12					12 42			13 12				13 42				14 12
Coventry	d			11 42					12 27		12 42						13 27		13 42						14 27
Birmingham International ✈	d			11 53					12 38		12 53						13 38		13 53						14 38
Penzance	d	06 30																08 28							
St Erth	d	06 38																08 36							
Hayle	d	06 41																							
Camborne	d	06 51																08 46							
Redruth	d	06 57																08 52							
Truro	d	07 09																09 04							
St Austell	d	07 25																09 20							
Newquay (Summer Only)	d																								
Par	d	07 32																09 28							
Lostwithiel	d	07 39																							
Bodmin Parkway	d	07 46																09 38							
Liskeard ■6	d	07 58																09 51							
Plymouth	d	08 25								09 25								10 25							
Totnes	d	08 50								09 50								10 50							
Paignton	d														10 07										
Torquay	d														10 13										
Newton Abbot	d	09 03								10 03					10 24			11 03							
Teignmouth	d														10 31										
Dawlish	d														10 36										
Exeter St Davids ■6	d	09 23								10 23					10 50			11 23							
Tiverton Parkway	d	09 37								10 37					11 03			11 37							
Taunton	d	09 51								10 51					11 17			11 51							
Weston-super-Mare	d																								
Cardiff Central ■7	d							10 45								11 45								12 45	
Newport (South Wales)	d							11 00								12 00								13 00	
Bristol Temple Meads ■10	d	10 30					11 00			11 30					12 00			12 30				13 00			
Bristol Parkway ■7	d	10 39					11 09			11 39					12 09			12 39				13 09			
Gloucester ■7	d							11 50								12 48								13 50	
Cheltenham Spa	d	11 11					11 41	12 01		12 11					12 41	12 59		13 11				13 41		14 01	
Birmingham New Street ■12	a	11 55		12 08		12 18	12 26	12 45	12 48	12 55	13 08			13 18	13 26	13 45	13 48	13 55	14 08		14 18	14 26		14 45	14 48
Birmingham New Street ■12	d	12 03		12 15	12 19	12 30	12 31	12 49	12 57	13 03	13 15	13 19		13 30	13 31	13 49	13 57	14 03	14 15	14 19	14 30	14 31		14 49	14 57
Tamworth	d	12 19			12 36			13 09				13 36				14 09		14 19		14 36				15 09	
Burton-on-Trent	d				12 48			13 21		13 27		13 48				14 21				14 47				15 21	
Derby ■6	a	12 41			13 00	13 06		13 34		13 41		14 00		14 06		14 35		14 41		15 00	15 06			15 36	
Nottingham ■8 ⇌	a				13 28			14 04				14 28				15 04				15 28				16 04	
Chesterfield	a	13 02								14 02								15 02							
Sheffield ■7 ⇌	a	13 17				13 43				14 17				14 44				15 17			15 44				
Doncaster ■7	a					14 18								15 17							16 18				
Wakefield Westgate ■7	a	13 46								14 46								15 46							
Leeds ■10	a	14 01								15 01								16 01							
York ■8	a	14 30				14 39				15 30				15 39				16 30			16 39				
Darlington ■7	a	14 57				15 13				15 57				16 13				16 58			17 13				
Durham	a	15 15				15 30				16 15				16 30				17 15			17 30				
Chester-le-Street	a																								
Newcastle ■8	a	15 29				15 45				16 29				16 45				17 29			17 45				
Morpeth	a																								
Alnmouth for Alnwick	a	15 58								16 57								17 59							
Berwick-upon-Tweed	a	16 19																18 19							
Dunbar	a									17 38															
Wolverhampton ■7 ⇌	d			12 37			12 49		13 15		13 37				13 49		14 15		14 37			14 49			15 15
Stafford	a						13 00		13 29						14 00		14 29					15 00			15 29
Stoke-on-Trent	a						13 18		13 54						14 19		14 54					15 19			15 54
Congleton	a																								
Macclesfield	a								14 11								15 11								16 11
Crewe ■10	a			13 07							14 07								15 07						
Wilmslow	a																								
Stockport	a						13 49		14 27						14 49		15 27					15 49			16 27
M'chester Piccadilly ■10 ⇌	a						13 59		14 38						14 59		15 38					15 59			16 38
Warrington Bank Quay	a			13 26							14 26								15 26						
Wigan North Western	a			13 37							14 37								15 37						
Preston ■8	a			13 51							14 51								15 51						
Lancaster ■6	a			14 07							15 07								16 08						
Oxenholme Lake District	a										15 21														
Penrith North Lakes	a			14 42															16 44						
Carlisle ■8	a			14 58							15 59								17 00						
Lockerbie	a																								
Haymarket	a			16 17															18 16						
Edinburgh ■10	a	17 07		16 22						18 03								19 07	18 24						
Haymarket	a	17 15								18 14								19 15							
Motherwell	a	17 52																19 52							
Glasgow Central ■15	a	18 11									17 17							20 09							
Inverkeithing	a									18 28															
Kirkcaldy	a									18 43															
Markinch	a									18 52															
Ladybank	a									18 59															
Cupar	a									19 06															
Leuchars ■3	a									19 13															
Dundee	a									19 29															
Arbroath	a									19 45															
Montrose	a									20 02															
Stonehaven	a									20 23															
Aberdeen	a									20 42															

A 🛒 from Plymouth to Edinburgh

Table 51R

Saturdays

15 February to 17 May

South Coast and the South West - North West England, The North East and Scotland

Route Diagram - see first Page of Table 51

		XC	VT	XC	XC	XC	XC	XC	XC	VT	XC	XC	XC	XC	XC	XC	VT	XC	XC	XC	XC	XC	XC
										R							R						
		◇1	◇1	1	◇1	◇1	◇1	◇1	◇1	1	1	◇1	◇1	◇1	◇1	◇1	1	1	◇1	◇1	◇1	◇1	◇1
		A				B			A														C
		🛒	☕		🛒	☕🛒	🛒	🛒	🛒	⊠		🛒	🛒	🛒	🛒	🛒	⊠		🛒	🛒	🛒	🛒	🛒
Bournemouth	d							12 45							13 45							14 45	
Brockenhurst [3]	d							13 00							14 00							15 00	
Southampton Central ⛴	d							13 15				13 47			14 15							15 15	
Southampton Airport Pkway ✈	d							13 22				13 54			14 22							15 22	
Winchester	d							13 31				14 03			14 31							15 31	
Basingstoke	d							13 47				14 19			14 47							15 47	
Guildford	d																						
Reading [7]	d				13 40			14 10				14 39			15 09				15 40			16 10	
Oxford	d				14 07			14 36				15 07			15 36				16 07			16 36	
Banbury	d				14 24			14 54				15 24			15 54				16 24			16 54	
Leamington Spa [8]	d				14 42			15 12				15 42			16 12				16 42			17 12	
Coventry	d		14 42					15 27		15 42					16 27		16 42					17 27	
Birmingham International ✈	d		14 53					15 38		15 53					16 38		16 53					17 38	
Penzance	d					09 43																	
St Erth	d					09 51																	
Hayle	d																						
Camborne	d					10 01																	
Redruth	d					10 07																	
Truro	d					10 19																	
St Austell	d					10 35																	
Newquay (Summer Only)	d																						
Par	d					10 42																	
Lostwithiel	d					10 49																	
Bodmin Parkway	d					10 56																	
Liskeard [6]	d					11 08																	
Plymouth	d	11 25				11 48			12 24							13 25							14 25
Totnes	d	11 50				12 13			12 50							13 50							14 50
Paignton	d																			13 53			
Torquay	d																			13 59			
Newton Abbot	d	12 03				12 25			13 03							14 03				14 10			15 03
Teignmouth	d																			14 17			
Dawlish	d																			14 22			
Exeter St Davids [6]	d	12 23				12 48			13 24							14 23				14 36			15 23
Tiverton Parkway	d	12 37				13 02			13 38							14 37				14 49			15 37
Taunton	d	12 51				13 16			13 52							14 51				15 03			15 51
Weston-super-Mare	d																			15 29			
Cardiff Central [7]	d						13 45							14 45							15 45		
Newport (South Wales)	d						14 00							15 00							16 00		
Bristol Temple Meads [10]	d	13 30				14 00			14 30				15 00			15 30				16 00			16 30
Bristol Parkway [7]	d	13 39				14 09			14 40				15 09			15 39				16 09			16 39
Gloucester [7]	d						14 50							15 50							16 50		
Cheltenham Spa	d	14 11				14 41	15 01		15 11				15 40	16 01		16 11				16 40	17 01		17 11
Birmingham New Street [12]	a	14 55	15 08		15 18	15 26	15 45	15 48	15 55	16 08		16 18	16 26	16 45	16 48	16 55	17 08		17 18	17 26	17 45	17 48	17 55
Birmingham New Street [12]	d	15 03	15 15	15 19	15 30	15 31	15 49	15 57	16 03	16 15	16 19	16 30	16 31	16 49	16 57	17 03	17 15	17 19	17 30	17 31	17 49	17 57	18 03
Tamworth	d			15 36			16 09		16 19		16 36			17 09				17 36			18 09		18 19
Burton-on-Trent	d	15 27		15 48			16 21				16 48	16 54		17 21		17 26		17 48			18 21		
Derby [6]	a	15 41		16 00	16 06		16 34		16 40		17 00	17 06		17 34		17 41		18 00	18 06		18 36		18 41
Nottingham [8] 🚋	a			16 28			17 04				17 31			18 04				18 31			19 04		
Chesterfield	a	16 02							17 03							18 02							19 02
Sheffield [7] 🚋	a	16 17			16 44				17 18			17 44				18 18			18 43				19 18
Doncaster [7]	a				17 16														19 16				
Wakefield Westgate [7]	a	16 46							17 47			18 12				18 46							19 49
Leeds [10]	a	17 01							18 02			18 31				19 00							20 04
York [8]	a	17 30			17 37				18 30			18 57				19 30			19 38				20 30
Darlington [7]	a	17 56			18 13				18 59			19 34				19 57			20 10				20 58
Durham	a	18 13			18 30				19 17			19 51				20 14			20 27				21 15
Chester-le-Street	a																						
Newcastle [8]	a	18 29			18 43				19 31			20 07				20 28			20 42				21 29
Morpeth	a															20 47							
Alnmouth for Alnwick	a								20 00														22 01
Berwick-upon-Tweed	a	19 17							20 23							21 18							
Dunbar	a	19 40														21 42							
Wolverhampton [7] 🚋	d		15 37			15 49		16 15		16 37			16 49		17 15		17 37			17 49		18 15	
Stafford	a					16 00		16 29					17 00		17 29					18 00		18 29	
Stoke-on-Trent	a					16 19		16 54					17 19		17 54					18 19		18 54	
Congleton	a																						
Macclesfield	a							17 11							18 11							19 11	
Crewe [10]	a		16 06							17 07							18 07						
Wilmslow	a																						
Stockport	a					16 49		17 27					17 49		18 27					18 49		19 27	
M'chester Piccadilly [10] 🚋	a					16 59		17 38					17 59		18 38					18 59		19 38	
Warrington Bank Quay	a		16 27							17 26							18 27						
Wigan North Western	a		16 38							17 37							18 38						
Preston [8]	a		16 51							17 51							18 51						
Lancaster [6]	a		17 08							18 07							19 07						
Oxenholme Lake District	a		17 21							18 21							19 21						
Penrith North Lakes	a									18 47													
Carlisle [8]	a		18 00							19 02							20 00						
Lockerbie	a																						
Haymarket	a									20 14													
Edinburgh [10]	a	20 05							21 08	20 20						22 08							23 03
Haymarket	a	20 17							21 16														
Motherwell	a								21 56														
Glasgow Central [15]	a		19 16						22 21								21 19						
Inverkeithing	a	20 33																					
Kirkcaldy	a	20 50																					
Markinch	a	21 00																					
Ladybank	a	21 08																					
Cupar	a	21 17																					
Leuchars [3]	a	21 25																					
Dundee	a	21 42																					
Arbroath	a																						
Montrose	a																						
Stonehaven	a																						
Aberdeen	a																						

A 🛒 to Edinburgh

B ☕ from Birmingham New Street 🛒 from Plymouth to Birmingham New Street

C 🛒 to Leeds

Table 51R

Saturdays

15 February to 17 May

South Coast and the South West - North West England, The North East and Scotland

Route Diagram - see first Page of Table 51

		VT	XC	XC	XC	XC	XC	XC	VT	XC	XC	XC	XC	XC	XC	VT	XC	XC	XC	XC	XC	XC
		◇1	1	◇1	◇1	◇1	◇1	◇1	◇1	1	◇1	◇1	◇1	◇1	◇1	◇1	◇1	◇1	◇1	◇1	◇1	◇1
						A		B			A		A	A	A		A	A	A	A	A	
		🍽		🛒	🛒	🛒	🛒	🛒	🍽		🛒	🛒	🛒	🛒	🛒	🍽	🛒	🛒	🛒	🛒	🛒	
Bournemouth	d						15 45							16 45						17 45		
Brockenhurst [3]	d						16 00							17 00						18 00		
Southampton Central	d			15 47			16 15							17 15			17 47			18 15		
Southampton Airport Pkwy	d			15 54			16 22							17 22			17 54			18 22		
Winchester	d			16 03			16 31							17 31			18 03			18 31		
Basingstoke	d			16 18			16 47							17 47			18 18			18 47		
Guildford	d																					
Reading [7]	d			16 39			17 09				17 40			18 09			18 39			19 09		19 40
Oxford	d			17 07			17 36				18 07			18 36			19 07			19 36		20 07
Banbury	d			17 24			17 54				18 24			18 54			19 24			19 54		20 29
Leamington Spa [8]	d			17 42			18 12				18 42			19 12			19 42			20 12		20 46
Coventry	d	17 42					18 27		18 42					19 27		19 42				20 27		
Birmingham International	d	17 53					18 38		18 53					19 38		19 53				20 38		
Penzance	d																					
St Erth	d																					
Hayle	d																					
Camborne	d																					
Redruth	d																					
Truro	d																					
St Austell	d																					
Newquay (Summer Only)	d																					
Par	d																					
Lostwithiel	d																					
Bodmin Parkway	d																					
Liskeard [6]	d																					
Plymouth	d							15 25							16 25						17 24	
Totnes	d							15 50							16 50						17 50	
Paignton	d																					
Torquay	d																					
Newton Abbot	d							16 03							17 03						18 03	
Teignmouth	d																					
Dawlish	d																					
Exeter St Davids [6]	d							16 23				16 53			17 23						18 24	
Tiverton Parkway	d							16 37				17 07			17 37						18 38	
Taunton	d							16 51				17 21			17 51						18 52	
Weston-super-Mare	d																					
Cardiff Central [7]	d					16 45							17 45						18 45			
Newport (South Wales)	d					17 00							18 00						19 00			
Bristol Temple Meads [10]	d				17 00			17 30				18 00			18 30			19 00			19 30	
Bristol Parkway [7]	d				17 09			17 39				18 09			18 39			19 09			19 40	
Gloucester [7]	d					17 50							18 46						19 46			
Cheltenham Spa	d				17 41	18 01		18 13				18 41	18 57		19 11			19 41	19 57		20 11	
Birmingham New Street [12]	a	18 08		18 18	18 26	18 45	18 48	18 55	19 08		19 18	19 26	19 45	19 48	19 58	20 08	20 18	20 26	20 42	20 48	20 52	21 15
Birmingham New Street [12]	d	18 15	18 19	18 30	18 31	18 49	18 57	19 03	19 15	19 19	19 30	19 31	19 49	19 57	20 03	20 15	20 30	20 31	20 49	20 57	21 03	
Tamworth	d		18 36			19 09				19 36			20 09		20 19				21 09		21 19	
Burton-on-Trent	d		18 47			19 21		19 27		19 48			20 21						21 21		21 30	
Derby [6]	a		19 00	19 05		19 35		19 39		20 00	20 06		20 34		20 42		21 24		21 34		21 43	
Nottingham [8]	a		19 34			20 04				20 28			21 04						22 08			
Chesterfield	a			19 30				20 04			20 30				21 04		21 46				22 04	
Sheffield [7]	a			19 44				20 21			20 49				21 19		22 05				22 22	
Doncaster [7]	a			20 18							21 21						22 30				22 51	
Wakefield Westgate [7]	a							20 48							21 48						23 09	
Leeds [10]	a							21 02							22 01						23 27	
York [8]	a			20 39				21 57			21 43						22 55					
Darlington [7]	a			21 13							22 13											
Durham	a			21 30							22 30											
Chester-le-Street	a																					
Newcastle [8]	a			21 44							22 47											
Morpeth	a																					
Alnmouth for Alnwick	a																					
Berwick-upon-Tweed	a																					
Dunbar	a																					
Wolverhampton [7]	d	18 37			18 49		19 15		19 37			19 49		20 15		20 37		20 49		21 15		
Stafford	a				19 00		19 29					20 00		20 29		20 51		21 00		21 29		
Stoke-on-Trent	a				19 19		19 54					20 19		20 54				21 20		21 52		
Congleton	a																					
Macclesfield	a						20 11					20 36		21 11				21 38		22 11		
Crewe [10]	a	19 07							20 07							21 10						
Wilmslow	a																					
Stockport	a				19 49		20 27					20 49		21 25				21 53		22 25		
M'chester Piccadilly [10]	a				19 59		20 37					20 59		21 39				22 04		22 34		
Warrington Bank Quay	a	19 26							20 26													
Wigan North Western	a	19 37							20 37													
Preston [8]	a	19 54							20 59													
Lancaster [6]	a																					
Oxenholme Lake District	a																					
Penrith North Lakes	a																					
Carlisle [8]	a																					
Lockerbie	a																					
Haymarket	a																					
Edinburgh [10]	a																					
Haymarket	a																					
Motherwell	a																					
Glasgow Central [15]	a																					
Inverkeithing	a																					
Kirkcaldy	a																					
Markinch	a																					
Ladybank	a																					
Cupar	a																					
Leuchars [3]	a																					
Dundee	a																					
Arbroath	a																					
Montrose	a																					
Stonehaven	a																					
Aberdeen	a																					

A 🛒 to Birmingham New Street

B 🛒 to Leeds

Table 51R

Saturdays

15 February to 17 May

South Coast and the South West - North West England, The North East and Scotland

Route Diagram - see first Page of Table 51

		XC	XC	XC	XC	XC	XC	XC	XC	XC		XC
		◇1	◇1	◇1	◇1	◇1	◇1	◇1	1	◇1		◇1
		A		B								
		⚲		⚲								
Bournemouth	d	18 45						19 45				
Brockenhurst 3	d	19 00						20 00				
Southampton Central	d	19 15						20 15				
Southampton Airport Pkway	d	19 22						20 22				
Winchester	d	19 31						20 31				
Basingstoke	d	19 47						20 47				
Guildford	d											
Reading 7	d	20 09				20 40		21 09				21 40
Oxford	d	20 36				21 07		21 36				22 07
Banbury	d	20 54				21 25		21 55				22 29
Leamington Spa 8	d	21 12				21 44		22 12				22 46
Coventry	d	21 27				21 56		22 27				
Birmingham International	d	21 38				22 11		22 38				
Penzance	d											
St Erth	d											
Hayle	d											
Camborne	d											
Redruth	d											
Truro	d											
St Austell	d											
Newquay (Summer Only)	d											
Par	d											
Lostwithiel	d											
Bodmin Parkway	d											
Liskeard 6	d											
Plymouth	d			18 25								
Totnes	d			18 50								
Paignton	d											
Torquay	d											
Newton Abbot	d			19 03								
Teignmouth	d											
Dawlish	d											
Exeter St Davids 6	d			19 23								
Tiverton Parkway	d			19 37								
Taunton	d			19 51								
Weston-super-Mare	d											
Cardiff Central 7	d				20 00					20 50		
Newport (South Wales)	d				20 15					21 05		
Bristol Temple Meads 10	d		20 00	20 30								
Bristol Parkway 7	d		20 09	20 39								
Gloucester 7	d				21 07					21 49		
Cheltenham Spa	d		20 41	21 11	21 18					22 00		
Birmingham New Street 12	a	21 48	21 38	21 52	22 07	22 21		22 48		22 42		23 16
Birmingham New Street 12	d	21 57			22 10		22 31		22 49			
Tamworth	d				22 27				23 08			
Burton-on-Trent	d				22 39				23 20			
Derby 6	a				22 55				23 33			
Nottingham 8	a				23 28							
Chesterfield	a											
Sheffield 7	a											
Doncaster 7	a											
Wakefield Westgate 7	a											
Leeds 10	a											
York 8	a											
Darlington 7	a											
Durham	a											
Chester-le-Street	a											
Newcastle 8	a											
Morpeth	a											
Alnmouth for Alnwick	a											
Berwick-upon-Tweed	a											
Dunbar	a											
Wolverhampton 7	d	22 15					22 49					
Stafford	a	22 29					23 01					
Stoke-on-Trent	a	22 50					23 20					
Congleton	a											
Macclesfield	a	23 07					23 38					
Crewe 10	a											
Wilmslow	a											
Stockport	a	23 20					23 53					
M'chester Piccadilly 10	a	23 30					00 10					
Warrington Bank Quay	a											
Wigan North Western	a											
Preston 8	a											
Lancaster 6	a											
Oxenholme Lake District	a											
Penrith North Lakes	a											
Carlisle 8	a											
Lockerbie	a											
Haymarket	a											
Edinburgh 10	a											
Haymarket	a											
Motherwell	a											
Glasgow Central 15	a											
Inverkeithing	a											
Kirkcaldy	a											
Markinch	a											
Ladybank	a											
Cupar	a											
Leuchars 8	a											
Dundee	a											
Arbroath	a											
Montrose	a											
Stonehaven	a											
Aberdeen	a											

A ⚲ to Reading

B ⚲ to Bristol Temple Meads

Table 51R

Sundays

8 December to 29 December

South Coast and the South West - North West England, The North East and Scotland

Route Diagram - see first Page of Table 51

		VT	XC	XC	VT	XC	XC	VT	XC	XC	VT	XC	XC	XC	VT	XC	XC	XC	XC	VT	XC	XC	XC
		◇1	◇1	◇1	◇1	◇1	◇1	◇1	◇1	◇1	◇1	◇1	◇1	◇1	◇1	◇1	◇1	◇1	◇1	◇1	◇1	◇1	◇1
							A							A			B		A				C
		⊡	☕	☕	⊡	☕	☕	⊡	☕	☕		☕	☕	☕	⊡	☕	☕	☕	☕	⊡	☕	☕	☕
Bournemouth	d																	09 40					
Brockenhurst [3]	d																	09 57					
Southampton Central ⛴	d												09 15					10 15					
Southampton Airport Pkwy ✈	d												09 22					10 22					
Winchester	d												09 31					10 31					
Basingstoke	d												09 47					10 47					
Guildford	d																						
Reading [7]	d								09 11				10 11					11 11					
Oxford	d								09 37				10 37					11 37					
Banbury	d								09 55				10 55					11 55					
Leamington Spa [8]	d								10 12				11 12					12 12					
Coventry	d								10 28				11 29					12 28					
Birmingham International ✈	d								10 40				11 40					12 40					
Penzance	d																						
St Erth	d																						
Hayle	d																						
Camborne	d																						
Redruth	d																						
Truro	d																						
St Austell	d																						
Newquay (Summer Only)	d																						
Par	d																						
Lostwithiel	d																						
Bodmin Parkway	d																						
Liskeard [6]	d																						
Plymouth	d																		09 25				
Totnes	d																		09 50				
Paignton	d																						
Torquay	d																						
Newton Abbot	d																		10 03				
Teignmouth	d																						
Dawlish	d																						
Exeter St Davids [6]	d																		10 23				
Tiverton Parkway	d																		10 37				
Taunton	d																		10 51				
Weston-super-Mare	d																						
Cardiff Central [7]	d																10 45						11 45
Newport (South Wales)	d																10 59						11 59
Bristol Temple Meads [10]	d									09 15				10 30					11 30				
Bristol Parkway [7]	d									09 24				10 39					11 39				
Gloucester [7]	d									10 00							11 51						12 47
Cheltenham Spa	d									10 12				11 10			12 03		12 10				12 58
Birmingham New Street [12]	a								10 50	10 49			11 51	11 48			12 45	12 50	12 49				13 41
Birmingham New Street [12]	d	08 45	09 01	09 03	09 20	10 01	10 03	10 20	11 01	11 03	11 20	11 49	12 01	12 03	12 20	12 30	12 49	13 01	13 03	13 20	13 30	13 31	13 49
Tamworth	d			09 19			10 18					12 07		12 19			13 07						14 07
Burton-on-Trent	d			09 28			10 29			11 25		12 19					13 19		13 26				14 19
Derby [6]	a			09 41			10 40			11 37		12 34		12 41		13 01	13 33		13 37		14 01		14 34
Nottingham [8] 🚊	a											13 00					14 00						15 00
Chesterfield	a			10 02			11 02			12 01				13 02		13 29			14 02		14 29		
Sheffield [7] 🚊	a			10 16			11 17			12 18				13 18		13 43			14 17		14 45		
Doncaster [7]	a															14 13					15 13		
Wakefield Westgate [7]	a			10 44			11 44			12 44				13 45					14 44				
Leeds [10]	a			11 02			12 01			13 02				14 02					15 02				
York [8]	a			11 27			12 27			13 27				14 27		14 38			15 27		15 42		
Darlington [7]	a			11 54			12 54			13 54				14 54		15 13			15 54		16 10		
Durham	a			12 11			13 11			14 11				15 12		15 30			16 11		16 27		
Chester-le-Street	a																						
Newcastle [8]	a			12 25			13 25			14 25				15 26		15 44			16 25		16 42		
Morpeth	a									14 44													
Alnmouth for Alnwick	a						13 51							15 52					16 51				
Berwick-upon-Tweed	a						14 12							16 12									
Dunbar	a			13 32						15 39									17 32				
Wolverhampton [7] 🚊	d	09 04	09 19		09 38	10 19		10 38	11 19		11 38		12 19		12 37			13 19		13 37		13 49	
Stafford	a	09 17	09 32			10 32			11 32				12 32					13 33					
Stoke-on-Trent	a					10 51			11 51				12 52					13 56				14 19	
Congleton	a																						
Macclesfield	a					11 08			12 09				13 10					14 14					
Crewe [10]	a	09 35	09 54		10 08			11 07			12 07				13 07					14 07			
Wilmslow	a		10 12																				
Stockport	a		10 21			11 22			12 22				13 28					14 28					
M'chester Piccadilly [10] 🚊	a		10 37			11 31			12 40				13 40					14 40				14 57	
Warrington Bank Quay	a	09 54			10 27			11 26			12 26				13 26					14 26			
Wigan North Western	a	10 05			10 38			11 37			12 37				13 37					14 37			
Preston [8]	a	10 22			10 51			11 51			12 51				13 51					14 50			
Lancaster [6]	a				11 07			12 08			13 07				14 08					15 08			
Oxenholme Lake District	a				11 21			12 22			13 21									15 22			
Penrith North Lakes	a														14 44								
Carlisle [8]	a				11 59			13 01			14 00				15 00					16 01			
Lockerbie	a																						
Haymarket	a							14 14							16 14								
Edinburgh [10]	a			13 57			14 56	14 22		16 02				16 56	16 23				17 57				
Haymarket	a						15 14							17 14					18 16				
Motherwell	a						15 52							17 52									
Glasgow Central [15]	a				13 20		16 13				15 16			18 12						17 17			
Inverkeithing	a																		18 28				
Kirkcaldy	a																		18 44				
Markinch	a																		18 53				
Ladybank	a																		19 01				
Cupar	a																		19 07				
Leuchars [3]	a																		19 14				
Dundee	a																		19 29				
Arbroath	a																		19 46				
Montrose	a																		20 00				
Stonehaven	a																		20 22				
Aberdeen	a																		20 42				

A ☕ to Edinburgh   **B** ☕ from Newport (South Wales)   **C** ☕ from Birmingham New Street

Table 51R

Sundays

8 December to 29 December

South Coast and the South West - North West England, The North East and Scotland

Route Diagram - see first Page of Table 51

		XC	XC	VT	XC	XC	XC	XC	XC	VT	XC	XC	XC	XC	XC	VT	XC	XC	XC	XC	XC	VT	XC
		◇1	◇1	◇1	◇1	◇1	◇1	◇1	◇1	◇1	◇1	◇1	◇1	◇1	◇1	◇1	◇1	◇1	◇1	◇1	◇1	◇1	◇1
			A						B				C		A								
		⊼	⊼	⊡	⊼	⊼	⊼	⊼	⊼	⊡	⊼	⊼	⊼	⊼	⊼	⊡	⊼	⊼	⊼	⊼	⊼	⊡	⊼
Bournemouth	d	10 40						11 40						12 40						13 40			
Brockenhurst 3	d	10 57						11 57						12 57						13 57			
Southampton Central ⛴	d	11 15						12 15						13 15						14 15			
Southampton Airport Pkway ✈	d	11 22						12 22						13 22						14 22			
Winchester	d	11 31						12 31						13 31						14 31			
Basingstoke	d	11 47						12 47						13 47						14 47			
Guildford	d				12 14																		
Reading 7	d	12 11			12 54			13 11			13 41			14 09			14 40			15 09			15 40
Oxford	d	12 37			13 17			13 37			14 06			14 37			15 06			15 37			16 06
Banbury	d	12 55			13 35			13 55			14 24			14 55			15 25			15 55			16 25
Leamington Spa 8	d	13 12			13 52			14 12			14 42			15 12			15 43			16 12			16 43
Coventry	d	13 26		13 42				14 26		14 44				15 26		15 42				16 26		16 42	
Birmingham International ✈	d	13 38		13 53				14 38		14 54				15 38		15 53				16 38		16 53	
Penzance	d								09 30														
St Erth	d								09 38														
Hayle	d																						
Camborne	d								09 48														
Redruth	d								09 54														
Truro	d								10 06														
St Austell	d								10 22														
Newquay (Summer Only)	d																						
Par	d								10 30														
Lostwithiel	d																						
Bodmin Parkway	d								10 40														
Liskeard 6	d								10 53														
Plymouth	d		10 25						11 25			12 00			12 25			12 52			13 24		
Totnes	d		10 50						11 50						12 50						13 50		
Paignton	d					10 50																	
Torquay	d					10 56																	
Newton Abbot	d		11 03			11 08			12 03			12 36			13 03			13 27			14 03		
Teignmouth	d					11 15																	
Dawlish	d					11 20																	
Exeter St Davids 6	d		11 23			11 33			12 23			12 57			13 23			13 48			14 24		
Tiverton Parkway	d		11 37			11 47			12 37			13 11			13 37						14 38		
Taunton	d		11 52			12 01			12 51			13 25			13 51						14 52		
Weston-super-Mare	d					12 22																	
Cardiff Central 7	d						12 45						13 45						14 45				
Newport (South Wales)	d						12 59						13 59						14 59				
Bristol Temple Meads 10	d		12 30			13 00			13 30			14 00			14 30			15 00			15 30		
Bristol Parkway 7	d		12 39			13 09			13 39			14 09			14 39			15 09			15 40		
Gloucester 7	d						13 49						14 47						15 47				
Cheltenham Spa	d		13 10			13 41	14 00		14 10			14 41	14 58		15 10			15 41	15 58		16 11		
Birmingham New Street 12	a	13 48	13 48	14 05	14 19	14 27	14 44	14 48	14 48	15 06	15 09	15 27	15 41	15 48	15 48	16 05	16 09	16 26	16 41	16 48	16 49	17 05	17 10
Birmingham New Street 12	d	14 01	14 03	14 16	14 30	14 31	14 49	15 01	15 03	15 17	15 30	15 31	15 49	16 01	16 03	16 16	16 30	16 31	16 49	17 01	17 03	17 16	17 30
Tamworth	d		14 19				15 09						16 07		16 19				17 07				
Burton-on-Trent	d						15 21		15 25				16 19						17 19		17 28		
Derby 6	a		14 39		15 01		15 33		15 37		16 01		16 34		16 38		17 01		17 34		17 40		18 01
Nottingham 8 ⛴	a						16 00						17 00						18 00				
Chesterfield	a		15 02						16 02						17 02						18 03		
Sheffield 7 ⛴	a		15 17		15 47				16 18		16 48				17 17		17 48				18 19		18 46
Doncaster 7	a				16 15						17 13						18 13						19 15
Wakefield Westgate 7	a		15 44						16 44						17 44		18 33				18 47		
Leeds 10	a		16 02						17 02						18 02		18 51				19 04		
York 8	a		16 27		16 38				17 27		17 40				18 27		19 20				19 30		19 39
Darlington 7	a		16 54		17 14				17 54		18 10				18 54		19 47				19 59		20 10
Durham	a		17 11		17 32				18 11		18 27				19 11		20 04				20 17		20 27
Chester-le-Street	a																						
Newcastle 8	a		17 25		17 47				18 25		18 41				19 25		20 19				20 31		20 41
Morpeth	a																				20 47		
Alnmouth for Alnwick	a		17 51												19 51								
Berwick-upon-Tweed	a		18 12						19 09						20 12						21 21		
Dunbar	a								19 34												21 45		
Wolverhampton 7 ⛴	d	14 19		14 37		14 49		15 19		15 38		15 49		16 19		16 37		16 49		17 19		17 37	
Stafford	a	14 33						15 33						16 34						17 35			
Stoke-on-Trent	a	14 56				15 19		15 56				16 19		16 56				17 19		17 56			
Congleton	a																						
Macclesfield	a	15 14						16 14						17 14						18 14			
Crewe 10	a			15 07						16 07						17 07						18 07	
Wilmslow	a																						
Stockport	a	15 28						16 28						17 28						18 28			
M'chester Piccadilly 10 ⛴	a	15 40				15 59		16 40				16 59		17 40				17 56		18 40			
Warrington Bank Quay	a			15 26						16 26						17 26						18 26	
Wigan North Western	a			15 37						16 37						17 37						18 37	
Preston 8	a			15 51						16 51						17 51						18 51	
Lancaster 6	a			16 08						17 08						18 07						19 07	
Oxenholme Lake District	a									17 22						18 21						19 21	
Penrith North Lakes	a			16 44												18 46							
Carlisle 8	a			17 00						18 01						19 03						20 00	
Lockerbie	a																						
Haymarket	a			18 13												20 16							
Edinburgh 10	a		18 56	18 22					19 57						20 56	20 21					22 12		22 21
Haymarket	a		19 22												21 16								
Motherwell	a		19 58												21 53								
Glasgow Central 15	a		20 21							19 17					22 14							21 15	
Inverkeithing	a																						
Kirkcaldy	a																						
Markinch	a																						
Ladybank	a																						
Cupar	a																						
Leuchars 3	a																						
Dundee	a																						
Arbroath	a																						
Montrose	a																						
Stonehaven	a																						
Aberdeen	a																						

A ⊼ to Edinburgh

B ⊼ from Plymouth

C ⊼ from Birmingham New Street

Table 51R

Sundays

8 December to 29 December

South Coast and the South West - North West England, The North East and Scotland

Route Diagram - see first Page of Table 51

		XC	XC	XC	XC	VT	XC	XC	XC	XC	XC	VT	XC	XC	XC	XC	XC	VT	XC	XC	XC	XC
		◇1	◇1	◇1	◇1	◇1	◇1	◇1	◇1	◇1	◇1	1	◇1	◇1	◇1	◇1	◇1	◇1	◇1	◇1	◇1	◇1
			A		B			C	A		D		E		A					A	A	A
Bournemouth	d			14 40						15 40						16 40						17 40
Brockenhurst 3	d			14 57						15 57						16 57						17 57
Southampton Central	d			15 15						16 15						17 15						18 15
Southampton Airport Pkwy	d			15 22						16 22						17 22						18 22
Winchester	d			15 31						16 31						17 31						18 31
Basingstoke	d			15 47						16 47						17 47						18 47
Guildford	d																					
Reading 7	d			16 09			16 41			17 09			17 40			18 10			18 41			19 11
Oxford	d			16 37			17 06			17 37			18 07			18 37			19 06			19 37
Banbury	d			16 55			17 25			17 54			18 25			18 55			19 24			19 55
Leamington Spa 8	d			17 12			17 43			18 12			18 43			19 12			19 42			20 12
Coventry	d			17 26		17 44				18 26		18 44				19 26		19 42	19 54			20 26
Birmingham International	d			17 38		17 54				18 38		18 54				19 38		19 53	20 04			20 38
Penzance	d							12 30														
St Erth	d							12 40														
Hayle	d							12 44														
Camborne	d							12 56														
Redruth	d							13 02														
Truro	d							13 14														
St Austell	d							13 30														
Newquay (Summer Only)	d																					
Par	d							13 38														
Lostwithiel	d							13 45														
Bodmin Parkway	d							13 51														
Liskeard 6	d							14 04														
Plymouth	d				14 24			14 35			15 24						16 25					
Totnes	d				14 50			15 00			15 50						16 48					
Paignton	d																					
Torquay	d																					
Newton Abbot	d				15 03			15 12			16 03						17 01					
Teignmouth	d																					
Dawlish	d																					
Exeter St Davids 6	d				15 24			15 33			16 24						17 24					
Tiverton Parkway	d				15 37			15 46			16 37						17 38					
Taunton	d				15 52			16 00			16 52						17 52					
Weston-super-Mare	d							16 30														
Cardiff Central 7	d		15 45						16 45						17 45						18 45	
Newport (South Wales)	d		15 59						16 59						17 59						18 59	
Bristol Temple Meads 10	d	16 00			16 30			17 00			17 30			18 00			18 30			19 00		
Bristol Parkway 7	d	16 09			16 40			17 09			17 40			18 09			18 39			19 09		
Gloucester 7	d		16 47						17 47						18 47						19 52	
Cheltenham Spa	d	16 40	16 58		17 12			17 41	17 58		18 11			18 40	18 58		19 10			19 41	20 02	
Birmingham New Street 12	a	17 26	17 41	17 48	17 48	18 06	18 09	18 28	18 41	18 48	18 48	19 06	19 11	19 26	19 41	19 48	19 48	20 05	20 15	20 27	20 44	20 48
Birmingham New Street 12	d	17 31	17 49	18 01	18 03	18 16	18 30	18 31	18 49	19 01	19 03	19 16	19 30	19 31	19 49	20 01	20 03	20 16		20 31	20 49	21 01
Tamworth	d		18 07		18 19				19 09						20 07		20 19				21 06	
Burton-on-Trent	d		18 19						19 21		19 26				20 19						21 19	
Derby 6	a		18 33		18 39		19 02		19 33		19 40		20 01		20 34		20 38				21 33	
Nottingham 8	a		19 00						20 00						21 00						22 00	
Chesterfield	a				19 04						20 02						21 02					
Sheffield 7	a				19 20		19 39				20 18		20 40				21 16					
Doncaster 7	a						20 16						21 19									
Wakefield Westgate 7	a				19 48						20 49						21 47					
Leeds 10	a				20 05						21 06						22 04					
York 8	a				20 30		20 38				21 31		21 42									
Darlington 7	a				20 59		21 13						22 23									
Durham	a				21 17		21 30						22 40									
Chester-le-Street	a																					
Newcastle 8	a				21 31		21 44						23 11									
Morpeth	a																					
Alnmouth for Alnwick	a				21 59																	
Berwick-upon-Tweed	a																					
Dunbar	a																					
Wolverhampton 7	d	17 49		18 19		18 37		18 49		19 19		19 37		19 49		20 19		20 38		20 53		21 19
Stafford	a			18 35						19 37						20 36		20 52				21 36
Stoke-on-Trent	a	18 19		18 56				19 19		19 56				20 19		20 56				21 20		21 56
Congleton	a																					
Macclesfield	a			19 15						20 14						21 15						22 14
Crewe 10	a					19 06						20 07						21 10				
Wilmslow	a																					
Stockport	a			19 28						20 28						21 28						22 27
M'chester Piccadilly 10	a	18 56		19 40				19 58		20 40				21 00		21 40				21 57		22 39
Warrington Bank Quay	a					19 25						20 26										
Wigan North Western	a					19 36						20 37										
Preston 8	a					19 51						20 51										
Lancaster 6	a					20 07						21 08										
Oxenholme Lake District	a											21 22										
Penrith North Lakes	a					20 44																
Carlisle 8	a					20 59						22 01										
Lockerbie	a											22 20										
Haymarket	a					22 14																
Edinburgh 10	a				23 04	22 20																
Haymarket	a																					
Motherwell	a											23 03										
Glasgow Central 15	a											23 20										
Inverkeithing	a																					
Kirkcaldy	a																					
Markinch	a																					
Ladybank	a																					
Cupar	a																					
Leuchars 3	a																					
Dundee	a																					
Arbroath	a																					
Montrose	a																					
Stonehaven	a																					
Aberdeen	a																					

A to Birmingham New Street
B to Newcastle
C from Plymouth
D to Leeds
E to Sheffield

Table 51R

Sundays

8 December to 29 December

South Coast and the South West - North West England, The North East and Scotland

Route Diagram - see first Page of Table 51

		XC	XC	XC	VT	XC	XC	XC		XC	XC	XC	XC	XC
		◇1	◇1	◇1	◇1	◇1	◇1	◇1		◇1	◇1	◇1	◇1	◇1
		A	B				C	C						
		⚲	⚲		☕	⚲	⚲	⚲						
Bournemouth	d						18 40				19 40			
Brockenhurst 3	d						18 57				19 57			
Southampton Central ⛴	d						19 15				20 15			
Southampton Airport Pkway ✈	d						19 22				20 22			
Winchester	d						19 31				20 31			
Basingstoke	d						19 47				20 47			
Guildford	d													
Reading 7	d					19 40	20 11			20 40	21 11		21 35	
Oxford	d					20 06	20 37			21 06	21 37		22 06	
Banbury	d					20 24	20 55			21 24	21 54		22 24	
Leamington Spa 8	d					20 42	21 12			21 41	22 12		22 42	
Coventry	d				20 41	20 54	21 26			21 53	22 23		22 53	
Birmingham International ✈	d				20 52	21 04	21 38			22 03	22 33		23 03	
Penzance	d	15 30												
St Erth	d	15 38												
Hayle	d													
Camborne	d	15 49												
Redruth	d	15 55												
Truro	d	16 07												
St Austell	d	16 23												
Newquay (Summer Only)	d													
Par	d	16 31												
Lostwithiel	d													
Bodmin Parkway	d	16 41												
Liskeard 6	d	16 53												
Plymouth	d	17 25						18 24						
Totnes	d	17 50						18 50						
Paignton	d		18 20											
Torquay	d		18 26											
Newton Abbot	d	18 02	18 37					19 03						
Teignmouth	d													
Dawlish	d													
Exeter St Davids 6	d	18 22	18 58					19 24						
Tiverton Parkway	d	18 36	19 11					19 37						
Taunton	d	18 49	19 24					19 52						
Weston-super-Mare	d													
Cardiff Central 7	d			19 45								20 45		
Newport (South Wales)	d			20 00								20 59		
Bristol Temple Meads 10	d	19 30	20 00					20 30						22 10
Bristol Parkway 7	d	19 39	20 09					20 40						22 20
Gloucester 7	d			20 49								21 48		
Cheltenham Spa	d	20 10	20 40	21 00				21 11				21 59		22 49
Birmingham New Street 12	a	20 49	21 18	21 44	21 03	21 15	21 48	21 48		22 14	22 43	22 42	23 13	23 40
Birmingham New Street 12	d	21 03			21 13		22 01	22 03						
Tamworth	d	21 19						22 19						
Burton-on-Trent	d	21 29												
Derby 6	a	21 41						22 40						
Nottingham 8 🚌	a													
Chesterfield	a	22 02						23 04						
Sheffield 7 🚌	a	22 18						23 20						
Doncaster 7	a													
Wakefield Westgate 7	a	22 43												
Leeds 10	a	23 01						00 16						
York 8	a													
Darlington 7	a													
Durham	a													
Chester-le-Street	a													
Newcastle 8	a													
Morpeth	a													
Alnmouth for Alnwick	a													
Berwick-upon-Tweed	a													
Dunbar	a													
Wolverhampton 7 🚌	d				21 38		22 20							
Stafford	a				21 55		22 36							
Stoke-on-Trent	a						22 55							
Congleton	a													
Macclesfield	a						23 12							
Crewe 10	a				22 15									
Wilmslow	a													
Stockport	a						23 27							
M'chester Piccadilly 10 🚌	a						23 41							
Warrington Bank Quay	a				22 34									
Wigan North Western	a				22 45									
Preston 8	a				23 05									
Lancaster 6	a													
Oxenholme Lake District	a													
Penrith North Lakes	a													
Carlisle 8	a													
Lockerbie	a													
Haymarket	a													
Edinburgh 10	a													
Haymarket	a													
Motherwell	a													
Glasgow Central 15	a													
Inverkeithing	a													
Kirkcaldy	a													
Markinch	a													
Ladybank	a													
Cupar	a													
Leuchars 3	a													
Dundee	a													
Arbroath	a													
Montrose	a													
Stonehaven	a													
Aberdeen	a													

A ⚲ from Plymouth to Birmingham New Street **B** ⚲ to Bristol Temple Meads **C** ⚲ to Birmingham New Street

Table 51R

Sundays

5 January to 9 February

South Coast and the South West - North West England, The North East and Scotland

Route Diagram - see first Page of Table 51

		VT	XC	XC	VT	XC	XC	VT	XC	XC	VT	XC	XC	XC	XC	VT	XC	XC	XC	XC	VT	XC	XC
		◇1	◇1	◇1	◇1	◇1	◇1	◇1	◇1	◇1	◇1	◇1	◇1	◇1	◇1	◇1	◇1	◇1	◇1	◇1	◇1	◇1	◇1
						A						A			B		A					A	
Bournemouth	d																	09 40					
Brockenhurst 3	d																	09 57					
Southampton Central	d												09 15					10 15					
Southampton Airport Pkwy	d												09 22					10 22					
Winchester	d												09 31					10 31					
Basingstoke	d												09 47					10 47					
Guildford	d																						
Reading 7	d									09 11			10 11					11 11					
Oxford	d									09 37			10 37					11 37					
Banbury	d									09 55			10 55					11 55					
Leamington Spa 8	d									10 12			11 12					12 12					
Coventry	d									10 28			11 29					12 28					
Birmingham International	d									10 40			11 40					12 40					
Penzance	d																						
St Erth	d																						
Hayle	d																						
Camborne	d																						
Redruth	d																						
Truro	d																						
St Austell	d																						
Newquay (Summer Only)	d																						
Par	d																						
Lostwithiel	d																						
Bodmin Parkway	d																						
Liskeard 6	d																						
Plymouth	d																		09 25				
Totnes	d																		09 50				
Paignton	d																						
Torquay	d																						
Newton Abbot	d																		10 03				
Teignmouth	d																						
Dawlish	d																						
Exeter St Davids 6	d																		10 23				
Tiverton Parkway	d																		10 37				
Taunton	d																		10 51				
Weston-super-Mare	d																						
Cardiff Central 7	d														10 45					11 45			
Newport (South Wales)	d														10 59					11 59			
Bristol Temple Meads 10	d			09 15										10 30					11 30				
Bristol Parkway 7	d			09 24										10 39					11 39				
Gloucester 7	d			10 00											11 51					12 47			
Cheltenham Spa	d			10 12										11 10	12 03				12 10	12 58			
Birmingham New Street 12	a			10 49						10 50			11 51	11 48	12 45			12 50	12 49	13 41			
Birmingham New Street 12	d	08 45	09 01		09 20	09 30	10 01	10 20	10 30	11 01	11 20	11 30	12 01	12 03		12 20	12 30	13 01	13 03		13 20	13 30	13 31
Tamworth	d																						
Burton-on-Trent	d					10 15			11 15			12 15					13 14					14 15	
Derby 6	a					10 27			11 27			12 27		12 55			13 26		13 55			14 27	
Nottingham 8	a																						
Chesterfield	a					11 02			12 02			13 02		13 29			14 02		14 29			15 02	
Sheffield 7	a					11 17			12 18			13 18		13 43			14 17		14 45			15 17	
Doncaster 7	a																						
Wakefield Westgate 7	a					11 44			12 44			13 45					14 44					15 44	
Leeds 10	a					12 01			13 02			14 02					15 02					16 02	
York 8	a					12 27			13 27			14 27		14 38			15 27		15 42			16 27	
Darlington 7	a					12 54			13 54			14 54		15 13			15 54		16 10			16 54	
Durham	a					13 11			14 11			15 12		15 30			16 11		16 27			17 11	
Chester-le-Street	a																						
Newcastle 8	a					13 25			14 26			15 26		15 44			16 25		16 42			17 25	
Morpeth	a								14 44														
Alnmouth for Alnwick	a					13 51						15 52					16 51					17 51	
Berwick-upon-Tweed	a					14 12						16 12										18 12	
Dunbar	a								15 39								17 32						
Wolverhampton 7	d	09 04	09 19		09 38		10 19	10 38		11 19	11 38		12 19			12 38		13 19			13 38		13 49
Stafford	a	09 17	09 32				10 32			11 32			12 32					13 33					
Stoke-on-Trent	a						10 51			11 51			12 52					13 56					14 19
Congleton	a																						
Macclesfield	a						11 08			12 09			13 10					14 14					
Crewe 10	a	09 35	09 54		10 08			11 07			12 07					13 07					14 07		
Wilmslow	a		10 12																				
Stockport	a		10 21				11 22			12 22			13 28					14 28					
M'chester Piccadilly 10	a		10 37				11 31			12 40			13 40					14 40					14 57
Warrington Bank Quay	a	09 54			10 27			11 26			12 26					13 26					14 27		
Wigan North Western	a	10 05			10 38			11 37			12 37					13 37					14 38		
Preston 8	a																				14 51		
Lancaster 6	a																						
Oxenholme Lake District	a																						
Penrith North Lakes	a																						
Carlisle 8	a																						
Lockerbie	a																						
Haymarket	a																						
Edinburgh 10	a					14 56			16 02			16 56					17 57					18 56	
Haymarket	a					15 14						17 14					18 16					19 22	
Motherwell	a					15 52						17 52										19 58	
Glasgow Central 15	a					16 13						18 12										20 21	
Inverkeithing	a																18 28						
Kirkcaldy	a																18 44						
Markinch	a																18 53						
Ladybank	a																19 01						
Cupar	a																19 07						
Leuchars 3	a																19 14						
Dundee	a																19 29						
Arbroath	a																19 46						
Montrose	a																20 00						
Stonehaven	a																20 22						
Aberdeen	a																20 42						

A to Edinburgh

B from Newport (South Wales)

Table 51R

Sundays

5 January to 9 February

South Coast and the South West - North West England, The North East and Scotland

Route Diagram - see first Page of Table 51

Station		XC	XC	VT	XC	XC	XC	XC	XC	VT	XC	XC	XC	XC	XC	VT	XC	XC	XC	XC	XC	VT	XC
		◇1	◇1	◇1	◇1	◇1	◇1	◇1	◇1	◇1	◇1	◇1	◇1	◇1	◇1	◇1	◇1	◇1	◇1	◇1	◇1	◇1	◇1
											A												B
Bournemouth	d	10 40					11 40						12 40						13 40				
Brockenhurst 3	d	10 57					11 57						12 57						13 57				
Southampton Central	d	11 15					12 15						13 15						14 15				
Southampton Airport Pkway	d	11 22					12 22						13 22						14 22				
Winchester	d	11 31					12 31						13 31						14 31				
Basingstoke	d	11 47					12 47						13 47						14 47				
Guildford	d																						
Reading 7	d	12 11			12 43		13 11				13 36		14 09				14 40		15 09				15 36
Oxford	d	12 37			13 17		13 37				14 06		14 37				15 06		15 37				16 06
Banbury	d	12 55			13 35		13 55				14 24		14 55				15 25		15 55				16 25
Leamington Spa 8	d	13 12			13 52		14 12				14 42		15 12				15 43		16 12				16 43
Coventry	d	13 26		13 42			14 26			14 44			15 26			15 42			16 26			16 42	
Birmingham International	d	13 38		13 53			14 38			14 54			15 38			15 53			16 38			16 53	
Penzance	d								09 30														
St Erth	d								09 38														
Hayle	d																						
Camborne	d								09 48														
Redruth	d								09 54														
Truro	d								10 06														
St Austell	d								10 22														
Newquay (Summer Only)	d																						
Par	d								10 30														
Lostwithiel	d																						
Bodmin Parkway	d								10 40														
Liskeard 6	d								10 53														
Plymouth	d		10 25						11 25			12 00						12 52			13 24		
Totnes	d		10 50						11 50												13 50		
Paignton	d					10 50																	
Torquay	d					10 56																	
Newton Abbot	d		11 03			11 08			12 03			12 36						13 27			14 03		
Teignmouth	d					11 15																	
Dawlish	d					11 20																	
Exeter St Davids 6	d		11 23			11 33			12 23			12 57			13 23			13 48			14 24		
Tiverton Parkway	d		11 37			11 47			12 37			13 11			13 37						14 38		
Taunton	d		11 52			12 01			12 51			13 25			13 51						14 52		
Weston-super-Mare	d					12 22																	
Cardiff Central 7	d							12 45						13 45						14 45			
Newport (South Wales)	d							12 59						13 59						14 59			
Bristol Temple Meads 10	d		12 30			13 00			13 30			14 00			14 30			15 00			15 30		
Bristol Parkway 7	d		12 39			13 09			13 39			14 09			14 39			15 09			15 40		
Gloucester 7	d							13 49						14 47						15 47			
Cheltenham Spa	d		13 10			13 41		14 00	14 10			14 41		14 58	15 10			15 41		15 58	16 11		
Birmingham New Street 12	a	13 48	13 48	14 05	14 19	14 27	14 48	14 44	14 48	15 06	15 09	15 27	15 48	15 41	15 48	16 05	16 09	16 26	16 48	16 41	16 49	17 05	17 10
Birmingham New Street 12	d	14 01	14 03	14 16	14 30	14 31	15 01		15 03	15 17	15 30	15 31	16 01		16 03	16 16	16 30	16 31	17 01		17 03	17 16	17 30
Tamworth	d																						
Burton-on-Trent	d				15 15						16 15						17 16						18 16
Derby 6	a		14 55		15 27				15 55		16 26				16 55		17 29				17 55		18 29
Nottingham 8	a																						
Chesterfield	a				16 02						17 02						18 03						19 04
Sheffield 7	a		15 42		16 18				16 41		17 17				17 42		18 19				18 46		19 20
Doncaster 7	a																						
Wakefield Westgate 7	a				16 44						17 44				18 16		18 47						19 48
Leeds 10	a				17 02						18 02				18 34		19 04						20 05
York 8	a		16 38		17 27				17 44		18 27				19 20		19 31				19 43		20 30
Darlington 7	a		17 14		17 54				18 13		18 54				19 47		19 59				20 10		20 59
Durham	a		17 32		18 11				18 31		19 11				20 04		20 17				20 27		21 17
Chester-le-Street	a																						
Newcastle 8	a		17 47		18 25				18 45		19 25				20 19		20 31				20 41		21 31
Morpeth	a														20 47								
Alnmouth for Alnwick	a										19 51												21 59
Berwick-upon-Tweed	a				19 09						20 12				21 21								
Dunbar	a				19 34										21 45								
Wolverhampton 7	d	14 19		14 37		14 49	15 19			15 38		15 49	16 19			16 37		16 49	17 19			17 37	
Stafford	a	14 33					15 33						16 34						17 35				
Stoke-on-Trent	a	14 56				15 19	15 56					16 19	16 56					17 19	17 56				
Congleton	a																						
Macclesfield	a	15 14					16 14						17 14						18 14				
Crewe 10	a			15 07						16 07						17 07						18 07	
Wilmslow	a																						
Stockport	a	15 28					16 28						17 28						18 28				
M'chester Piccadilly 10	a	15 40				15 59	16 40					16 59	17 40					17 56	18 40				
Warrington Bank Quay	a			15 26						16 26						17 26						18 26	
Wigan North Western	a			15 37						16 37						17 37						18 37	
Preston 8	a			15 51						16 51						17 51						18 51	
Lancaster 6	a			16 08						17 08						18 07						19 07	
Oxenholme Lake District	a									17 22						18 21						19 21	
Penrith North Lakes	a			16 44												18 46							
Carlisle 8	a			17 00						18 01						19 03						20 00	
Lockerbie	a																						
Haymarket	a			18 13												20 16							
Edinburgh 10	a			18 22	19 57						20 56				22 12	20 21					22 21		23 04
Haymarket	a										21 16												
Motherwell	a										21 53												
Glasgow Central 15	a									19 17	22 14											21 15	
Inverkeithing	a																						
Kirkcaldy	a																						
Markinch	a																						
Ladybank	a																						
Cupar	a																						
Leuchars 8	a																						
Dundee	a																						
Arbroath	a																						
Montrose	a																						
Stonehaven	a																						
Aberdeen	a																						

A to Edinburgh

B to Newcastle

Table 51R

Sundays

5 January to 9 February

South Coast and the South West - North West England, The North East and Scotland

Route Diagram - see first Page of Table 51

		XC	XC	XC	XC	VT	XC	XC	XC	XC	XC	XC	VT	XC	XC	XC	XC	VT	XC	XC	XC	XC
													R									
		◇1	◇1	◇1	◇1	◇1	◇1	◇1	◇1	◇1	◇1	◇1	1	◇1	◇1	◇1	◇1	◇1	◇1	◇1	◇1	◇1
								A			B									C	C	
		⊼	⊼	⊼	⊼	⊡	⊼	⊼	⊼	⊼	⊼	⊼	⊡	⊼	⊼	⊼	⊼	⊡	⊼	⊼	⊼	⊼
Bournemouth	d		14 40						15 40						16 40						17 40	
Brockenhurst 3	d		14 57						15 57						16 57						17 57	
Southampton Central	d		15 15						16 15						17 15						18 15	
Southampton Airport Pkway	d		15 22						16 22						17 22						18 22	
Winchester	d		15 31						16 31						17 31						18 31	
Basingstoke	d		15 47						16 47						17 47						18 47	
Guildford	d																					
Reading 7	d		16 09				16 36		17 09			17 35			18 10				18 36		19 11	
Oxford	d		16 37				17 06		17 37			18 07			18 37				19 06		19 37	
Banbury	d		16 55				17 25		17 54			18 25			18 55				19 24		19 55	
Leamington Spa 8	d		17 12				17 43		18 12			18 43			19 12				19 42		20 12	
Coventry	d		17 26			17 43			18 26				18 44		19 26			19 42	19 54		20 26	
Birmingham International	d		17 38			17 54			18 38				18 54		19 38			19 53	20 04		20 38	
Penzance	d							12 30														
St Erth	d							12 40														
Hayle	d							12 44														
Camborne	d							12 56														
Redruth	d							13 02														
Truro	d							13 14														
St Austell	d							13 30														
Newquay (Summer Only)	d																					
Par	d							13 38														
Lostwithiel	d							13 45														
Bodmin Parkway	d							13 51														
Liskeard 6	d							14 04														
Plymouth	d				14 24			14 35			15 24						16 25					
Totnes	d				14 50			15 00			15 50						16 49					
Paignton	d																					
Torquay	d																					
Newton Abbot	d				15 03			15 12			16 03						17 02					
Teignmouth	d																					
Dawlish	d																					
Exeter St Davids 6	d				15 24			15 33			16 24						17 24					
Tiverton Parkway	d				15 37			15 46			16 37						17 38					
Taunton	d				15 52			16 00			16 52						17 52					
Weston-super-Mare	d							16 30														
Cardiff Central 7	d			15 45						16 45						17 45						18 45
Newport (South Wales)	d			15 59						16 59						17 59						18 59
Bristol Temple Meads 10	d	16 00			16 30			17 00			17 30			18 00			18 30			19 00		
Bristol Parkway 7	d	16 09			16 40			17 09			17 40			18 09			18 40			19 09		
Gloucester 7	d			16 47						17 47						18 47						19 52
Cheltenham Spa	d	16 40		16 58	17 12			17 41		17 58	18 11			18 40		18 58	19 11			19 41		20 02
Birmingham New Street 12	a	17 26	17 48	17 41	17 48	18 06	18 09	18 28	18 48	18 41	18 48	19 11	19 06	19 26	19 48	19 41	19 49	20 05	20 15	20 27	20 48	20 44
Birmingham New Street 12	d	17 31	18 01		18 03	18 16	18 30	18 31	19 01		19 03		19 16	19 31	20 01		20 03	20 16		20 31	21 01	
Tamworth	d																					
Burton-on-Trent	d						19 16															
Derby 6	a				18 55		19 29				19 55						20 57					
Nottingham 8	a																					
Chesterfield	a						20 02										21 19					
Sheffield 7	a				19 40		20 18				20 40						21 38					
Doncaster 7	a																					
Wakefield Westgate 7	a						20 46										22 11					
Leeds 10	a						21 05										22 28					
York 8	a				20 38		21 31				21 42											
Darlington 7	a				21 13						22 23											
Durham	a				21 30						22 40											
Chester-le-Street	a																					
Newcastle 8	a				21 44						23 11											
Morpeth	a																					
Alnmouth for Alnwick	a																					
Berwick-upon-Tweed	a																					
Dunbar	a																					
Wolverhampton 7	d	17 49	18 19			18 38		18 49	19 19				19 37	19 49	20 19			20 38		20 53	21 19	
Stafford	a		18 35						19 37						20 36			20 52			21 36	
Stoke-on-Trent	a	18 19	18 56					19 19	19 56					20 19	20 56					21 20	21 56	
Congleton	a																					
Macclesfield	a		19 15						20 14						21 15						22 14	
Crewe 10	a					19 06							20 07					21 10				
Wilmslow	a																					
Stockport	a		19 28						20 28						21 28						22 27	
M'chester Piccadilly 10	a	18 56	19 40					19 58	20 40					21 00	21 40					21 57	22 39	
Warrington Bank Quay	a					19 26							20 26									
Wigan North Western	a					19 37							20 37									
Preston 8	a					19 51							20 51									
Lancaster 6	a					20 07							21 08									
Oxenholme Lake District	a												21 22									
Penrith North Lakes	a					20 44																
Carlisle 8	a					20 59							22 01									
Lockerbie	a												22 20									
Haymarket	a					22 14																
Edinburgh 10	a					22 20																
Haymarket	a																					
Motherwell	a												23 03									
Glasgow Central 15	a												23 20									
Inverkeithing	a																					
Kirkcaldy	a																					
Markinch	a																					
Ladybank	a																					
Cupar	a																					
Leuchars 3	a																					
Dundee	a																					
Arbroath	a																					
Montrose	a																					
Stonehaven	a																					
Aberdeen	a																					

A ⊼ from Plymouth **B** ⊼ to Sheffield **C** ⊼ to Birmingham New Street

Table 51R

Sundays
5 January to 9 February

South Coast and the South West - North West England, The North East and Scotland

Route Diagram - see first Page of Table 51

		XC	XC	XC	VT	XC	XC	XC	XC	XC	XC	XC	XC
		◇1	◇1	◇1	◇1	◇1	◇1	◇1	◇1	◇1	◇1	◇1	◇1
		A	B				C	C					
		⚲	⚲		⊡	⚲	⚲	⚲					
Bournemouth	d						18 40			19 40			
Brockenhurst 3	d						18 57			19 57			
Southampton Central	d						19 15			20 15			
Southampton Airport Pkway	d						19 22			20 22			
Winchester	d						19 31			20 31			
Basingstoke	d						19 47			20 47			
Guildford	d												
Reading 7	d					19 36	20 11		20 36	21 11		21 36	
Oxford	d					20 06	20 37		21 06	21 37		22 06	
Banbury	d					20 24	20 55		21 24	21 54		22 24	
Leamington Spa 8	d					20 42	21 12		21 41	22 12		22 42	
Coventry	d				20 42	20 54	21 26		21 53	22 23		22 53	
Birmingham International	d				20 53	21 04	21 38		22 03	22 33		23 03	
Penzance	d	15 30											
St Erth	d	15 38											
Hayle	d												
Camborne	d	15 49											
Redruth	d	15 55											
Truro	d	16 07											
St Austell	d	16 23											
Newquay (Summer Only)	d												
Par	d	16 31											
Lostwithiel	d												
Bodmin Parkway	d	16 41											
Liskeard 6	d	16 53											
Plymouth	d	17 25						18 24					
Totnes	d	17 50						18 50					
Paignton	d		18 20										
Torquay	d		18 26										
Newton Abbot	d	18 02	18 37					19 03					
Teignmouth	d												
Dawlish	d												
Exeter St Davids 6	d	18 22	18 58					19 24					
Tiverton Parkway	d	18 36	19 11					19 37					
Taunton	d	18 49	19 24					19 52					
Weston-super-Mare	d												
Cardiff Central 7	d			19 45							20 45		
Newport (South Wales)	d			20 00							20 59		
Bristol Temple Meads 10	d	19 30	20 00					20 30					22 10
Bristol Parkway 7	d	19 39	20 09					20 40					22 20
Gloucester 7	d			20 49							21 48		
Cheltenham Spa	d	20 10	20 40	21 00				21 11			21 59		22 49
Birmingham New Street 12	a	20 49	21 18	21 44	21 04	21 15	21 48	21 48	22 14	22 43	22 42	23 13	23 40
Birmingham New Street 12	d	21 03			21 16		22 01	22 03					
Tamworth	d												
Burton-on-Trent	d	21 47						22 46					
Derby 6	a	21 58						22 59					
Nottingham 8	a												
Chesterfield	a	22 23						23 20					
Sheffield 7	a	22 38						23 36					
Doncaster 7	a												
Wakefield Westgate 7	a	23 09											
Leeds 10	a	23 26						00 27					
York 8	a												
Darlington 7	a												
Durham	a												
Chester-le-Street	a												
Newcastle 8	a												
Morpeth	a												
Alnmouth for Alnwick	a												
Berwick-upon-Tweed	a												
Dunbar	a												
Wolverhampton 7	d				21 37		22 20						
Stafford	a				21 56		22 36						
Stoke-on-Trent	a						22 55						
Congleton	a												
Macclesfield	a						23 12						
Crewe 10	a				22 16								
Wilmslow	a												
Stockport	a						23 27						
M'chester Piccadilly 10	a						23 41						
Warrington Bank Quay	a				22 35								
Wigan North Western	a				22 46								
Preston 8	a				23 05								
Lancaster 6	a												
Oxenholme Lake District	a												
Penrith North Lakes	a												
Carlisle 8	a												
Lockerbie	a												
Haymarket	a												
Edinburgh 10	a												
Haymarket	a												
Motherwell	a												
Glasgow Central 15	a												
Inverkeithing	a												
Kirkcaldy	a												
Markinch	a												
Ladybank	a												
Cupar	a												
Leuchars 3	a												
Dundee	a												
Arbroath	a												
Montrose	a												
Stonehaven	a												
Aberdeen	a												

A ⚲ from Plymouth to Birmingham New Street **B** ⚲ to Bristol Temple Meads **C** ⚲ to Birmingham New Street

Table 51R

Sundays

16 February to 23 March

South Coast and the South West - North West England, The North East and Scotland

Route Diagram - see first Page of Table 51

		VT	XC	XC	VT	XC	XC	VT	XC	XC	VT	XC	XC	XC	XC	VT	XC	XC	XC	XC	VT	XC	XC
		◇1	◇1	◇1	◇1	◇1	◇1	◇1	◇1	◇1	◇1	◇1	◇1	◇1	◇1	◇1	◇1	◇1	◇1	◇1	◇1	◇1	◇1
						A						A			B		A					A	
		🍽	🛒	🛒	🍽	🛒	🛒	🍽	🛒	🛒	🍽	🛒	🛒	🛒	🛒	🍽	🛒	🛒	🛒		🍽	🛒	🛒
Bournemouth	d																	09 40					
Brockenhurst [3]	d																	09 57					
Southampton Central	d												09 15					10 15					
Southampton Airport Pkway	d												09 22					10 22					
Winchester	d												09 31					10 31					
Basingstoke	d												09 47					10 47					
Guildford	d																						
Reading [7]	d									09 11			10 16					11 16					
Oxford	d									09 37			10 41					11 41					
Banbury	d									09 55			10 59					11 59					
Leamington Spa [8]	d									10 12			11 16					12 15					
Coventry	d									10 28			11 29					12 28					
Birmingham International	d									10 40			11 40					12 39					
Penzance	d																						
St Erth	d																						
Hayle	d																						
Camborne	d																						
Redruth	d																						
Truro	d																						
St Austell	d																						
Newquay (Summer Only)	d																						
Par	d																						
Lostwithiel	d																						
Bodmin Parkway	d																						
Liskeard [6]	d																						
Plymouth	d																						
Totnes	d																						
Paignton	d																						
Torquay	d																						
Newton Abbot	d																						
Teignmouth	d																						
Dawlish	d																						
Exeter St Davids [6]	d																		10 23				
Tiverton Parkway	d																		10 37				
Taunton	d																		10 51				
Weston-super-Mare	d																						
Cardiff Central [7]	d														10 45					11 45			
Newport (South Wales)	d														10 59					11 59			
Bristol Temple Meads [10]	d			09 15										10 30					11 30				
Bristol Parkway [7]	d			09 24										10 39					11 39				
Gloucester [7]	d			10 00											11 51					12 47			
Cheltenham Spa	d			10 12										11 10	12 03				12 10	12 58			
Birmingham New Street [12]	a			10 49						10 50			11 51	11 48	12 45			12 49	12 49	13 41			
Birmingham New Street [12]	d	08 45	09 01		09 20	09 30	10 01	10 20	10 30	11 01	11 20	11 30	12 01	12 03		12 20	12 30	13 00	13 03		13 20	13 30	13 31
Tamworth	d																						
Burton-on-Trent	d					10 15			11 15			12 15					13 14					14 15	
Derby [6]	a					10 27			11 27			12 27		12 55			13 26		13 55			14 27	
Nottingham [8]	a																						
Chesterfield	a					11 02			12 02			13 02		13 29			14 02		14 29			15 02	
Sheffield [7]	a					11 17			12 18			13 18		13 43			14 17		14 45			15 17	
Doncaster [7]	a													14 13					15 15				
Wakefield Westgate [7]	a					11 44			12 44			13 45					14 44					15 44	
Leeds [10]	a					12 01			13 02			14 02					15 02					16 02	
York [8]	a					12 27			13 27			14 27		14 38			15 27		15 42			16 27	
Darlington [7]	a					12 54			13 54			14 54		15 14			15 54		16 10			16 54	
Durham	a					13 11			14 11			15 12		15 31			16 11		16 27			17 11	
Chester-le-Street	a																						
Newcastle [8]	a					13 25			14 26			15 26		15 44			16 25		16 42			17 25	
Morpeth	a								14 44														
Alnmouth for Alnwick	a					13 51						15 52					16 51					17 51	
Berwick-upon-Tweed	a					14 12						16 12										18 12	
Dunbar	a								15 39								17 32						
Wolverhampton [7]	d	09 04	09 19		09 38		10 19	10 38		11 19	11 38		12 19			12 37		13 18			13 37		13 49
Stafford	a	09 17	09 32				10 32			11 32			12 32					13 32					
Stoke-on-Trent	a						10 51			11 51			12 52					13 55					14 19
Congleton	a																						
Macclesfield	a						11 08			12 09			13 10					14 13					
Crewe [10]	a	09 35	09 54		10 08			11 07			12 07					13 07					14 07		
Wilmslow	a		10 12																				
Stockport	a		10 21				11 22			12 22			13 28					14 27					
M'chester Piccadilly [10]	a		10 37				11 31			12 40			13 40					14 39					14 57
Warrington Bank Quay	a	09 54			10 27			11 26			12 26					13 26					14 26		
Wigan North Western	a	10 05			10 38			11 37			12 37					13 37					14 37		
Preston [8]	a	10 25			10 54			11 52			12 51					13 51					14 50		
Lancaster [6]	a				11 18			12 08			13 07					14 08					15 08		
Oxenholme Lake District	a				11 32			12 22			13 21										15 22		
Penrith North Lakes	a															14 44							
Carlisle [8]	a				12 10			13 01			14 00					15 00					16 01		
Lockerbie	a																						
Haymarket	a							14 14								16 14							
Edinburgh [10]	a					14 56		14 22	16 02			16 56				16 23	17 57					18 56	
Haymarket	a					15 14						17 14					18 16					19 22	
Motherwell	a					15 52						17 52										19 58	
Glasgow Central [15]	a				13 29	16 13					15 16	18 12									17 17	20 21	
Inverkeithing	a																18 28						
Kirkcaldy	a																18 44						
Markinch	a																18 53						
Ladybank	a																19 01						
Cupar	a																19 07						
Leuchars [8]	a																19 14						
Dundee	a																19 29						
Arbroath	a																19 46						
Montrose	a																20 00						
Stonehaven	a																20 22						
Aberdeen	a																20 42						

A 🛒 to Edinburgh

B 🛒 from Newport (South Wales)

Table 51R

Sundays

16 February to 23 March

South Coast and the South West - North West England, The North East and Scotland

Route Diagram - see first Page of Table 51

		XC	XC	VT	XC	XC	XC	XC	XC	XC	VT	XC	XC	XC	XC	VT	XC	XC	XC	XC	XC	VT	XC
		◇1	◇1	◇1	◇1	◇1	◇1	◇1	◇1	◇1	◇1	◇1	◇1	◇1	◇1	◇1	◇1	◇1	◇1	◇1	◇1	◇1	◇1
					A							B											C
Bournemouth	d	10 40					11 40							12 40					13 40				
Brockenhurst 3	d	10 57					11 57							12 57					13 57				
Southampton Central	d	11 15					12 15							13 15					14 15				
Southampton Airport Pkwy	d	11 22					12 22							13 22					14 22				
Winchester	d	11 31					12 31							13 31					14 31				
Basingstoke	d	11 47					12 47							13 47					14 47				
Guildford	d				12 14																		
Reading 7	d	12 16			12 49		13 17					13 36		14 17			14 36		15 17				15 36
Oxford	d	12 41			13 17		13 41					14 06		14 41			15 06		15 41				16 06
Banbury	d	12 59			13 35		13 59					14 24		14 59			15 25		15 59				16 25
Leamington Spa 8	d	13 15			13 52		14 15					14 42		15 15			15 43		16 15				16 43
Coventry	d	13 28		13 42			14 28				14 44			15 27		15 42			16 28			16 42	
Birmingham International	d	13 39		13 53			14 38				14 54			15 39		15 53			16 39			16 53	
Penzance	d																						
St Erth	d																						
Hayle	d																						
Camborne	d																						
Redruth	d																						
Truro	d																						
St Austell	d																						
Newquay (Summer Only)	d																						
Par	d																						
Lostwithiel	d																						
Bodmin Parkway	d																						
Liskeard 6	d																						
Plymouth	d																						
Totnes	d																						
Paignton	d																						
Torquay	d																						
Newton Abbot	d																						
Teignmouth	d																						
Dawlish	d																						
Exeter St Davids 6	d		11 23						12 23						13 23						14 24		
Tiverton Parkway	d		11 37						12 37						13 37						14 38		
Taunton	d		11 52						12 51						13 51						14 52		
Weston-super-Mare	d																						
Cardiff Central 7	d							12 45		13 45										14 45			
Newport (South Wales)	d							12 59		13 59										14 59			
Bristol Temple Meads 10	d		12 30			13 00			13 30						14 30			15 00			15 30		
Bristol Parkway 7	d		12 39			13 09			13 39						14 39			15 09			15 40		
Gloucester 7	d							13 49		14 47										15 47			
Cheltenham Spa	d		13 10			13 41		14 00	14 10	14 58					15 10			15 41		15 58	16 11		
Birmingham New Street 12	a	13 50	13 48	14 05	14 19	14 27	14 48	14 44	14 48	15 41	15 06	15 09		15 50	15 48	16 05	16 09	16 26	16 50	16 41	16 49	17 05	17 10
Birmingham New Street 12	d	14 01	14 03	14 16	14 30	14 31	15 00		15 03		15 17	15 30	15 31	16 01	16 03	16 16	16 30	16 31	17 01		17 03	17 16	17 30
Tamworth	d																						
Burton-on-Trent	d				15 15							16 15					17 16						18 16
Derby 6	a		14 55		15 27				15 55			16 27			16 55		17 29				17 57		18 29
Nottingham 8	a																						
Chesterfield	a				16 02							17 02					18 03						19 04
Sheffield 7	a		15 47		16 18				16 48			17 17			17 48		18 19				18 46		19 20
Doncaster 7	a		16 15						17 13						18 14						19 15		
Wakefield Westgate 7	a				16 44							17 44			18 33		18 47						19 48
Leeds 10	a				17 02							18 02			18 51		19 04						20 05
York 8	a		16 38		17 27				17 42			18 27			19 20		19 30				19 39		20 30
Darlington 7	a		17 15		17 54				18 13			18 54			19 47		19 59				20 12		20 59
Durham	a		17 32		18 11				18 31			19 11			20 04		20 17				20 30		21 17
Chester-le-Street	a																						
Newcastle 8	a		17 47		18 25				18 45			19 25			20 21		20 31				20 44		21 31
Morpeth	a														20 47								
Alnmouth for Alnwick	a											19 51											21 59
Berwick-upon-Tweed	a				19 09							20 12			21 21								
Dunbar	a				19 34										21 45								
Wolverhampton 7	d	14 19		14 37		14 49	15 18				15 38		15 49	16 19		16 37		16 49	17 19			17 37	
Stafford	a	14 33					15 32							16 34					17 35				
Stoke-on-Trent	a	14 56				15 19	15 55						16 19	16 56				17 19	17 56				
Congleton	a																						
Macclesfield	a	15 14					16 13							17 14					18 14				
Crewe 10	a			15 07							16 07					17 07						18 07	
Wilmslow	a																						
Stockport	a	15 28					16 27							17 28					18 28				
M'chester Piccadilly 10	a	15 40				15 59	16 39						16 59	17 40				17 56	18 40				
Warrington Bank Quay	a			15 26							16 26					17 26						18 26	
Wigan North Western	a			15 37							16 37					17 37						18 37	
Preston 8	a			15 51							16 51					17 51						18 51	
Lancaster 6	a			16 08							17 08					18 07						19 07	
Oxenholme Lake District	a										17 22					18 21						19 21	
Penrith North Lakes	a			16 44												18 46							
Carlisle 8	a			17 00							18 01					19 03						20 00	
Lockerbie	a																						
Haymarket	a			18 13												20 16							
Edinburgh 10	a			18 22	19 57							20 56			22 12	20 21					22 21		23 04
Haymarket	a											21 16											
Motherwell	a											21 53											
Glasgow Central 15	a										19 17	22 14										21 15	
Inverkeithing	a																						
Kirkcaldy	a																						
Markinch	a																						
Ladybank	a																						
Cupar	a																						
Leuchars 8	a																						
Dundee	a																						
Arbroath	a																						
Montrose	a																						
Stonehaven	a																						
Aberdeen	a																						

A from Reading

B to Edinburgh

C to Newcastle

Table 51R

Sundays

16 February to 23 March

South Coast and the South West - North West England, The North East and Scotland

Route Diagram - see first Page of Table 51

		XC		XC	XC	XC	VT	XC	XC	XC	XC	XC		XC	VT	XC	XC	XC	XC	VT	XC	XC		XC	XC
															R										
		◇1		◇1	◇1	◇1	◇1	◇1	◇1	◇1	◇1	◇1		◇1	1	◇1	◇1	◇1	◇1	◇1	◇1	◇1		◇1	◇1
												A										B		B	
		🛒		🛒	🛒	🛒	🍽	🛒	🛒	🛒	🛒	🛒		🛒	🍽	🛒	🛒	🛒	🛒	🍽	🛒	🛒		🛒	🛒
Bournemouth	d			14 40						15 40							16 40							17 40	
Brockenhurst 3	d			14 57						15 57							16 57							17 57	
Southampton Central	d			15 15						16 15							17 15							18 15	
Southampton Airport Pkway	d			15 22						16 22							17 22							18 22	
Winchester	d			15 31						16 31							17 31							18 31	
Basingstoke	d			15 47						16 47							17 47							18 47	
Guildford	d																								
Reading 7	d			16 17				16 36		17 17				17 36			18 17				18 41			19 17	
Oxford	d			16 41				17 06		17 41				18 07			18 41				19 06			19 41	
Banbury	d			16 59				17 25		17 59				18 25			18 59				19 24			19 59	
Leamington Spa 8	d			17 15				17 43		18 15				18 43			19 15				19 42			20 15	
Coventry	d			17 28			17 44			18 28					18 44		19 28			19 42	19 54			20 28	
Birmingham International	d			17 39			17 54			18 39					18 54		19 40			19 53	20 04			20 40	
Penzance	d																								
St Erth	d																								
Hayle	d																								
Camborne	d																								
Redruth	d																								
Truro	d																								
St Austell	d																								
Newquay (Summer Only)	d																								
Par	d																								
Lostwithiel	d																								
Bodmin Parkway	d																								
Liskeard 6	d																								
Plymouth	d																								
Totnes	d																								
Paignton	d																								
Torquay	d																								
Newton Abbot	d																								
Teignmouth	d																								
Dawlish	d																								
Exeter St Davids 6	d					15 24						16 24							17 23						
Tiverton Parkway	d					15 37						16 37							17 37						
Taunton	d					15 52						16 52							17 51						
Weston-super-Mare	d																								
Cardiff Central 7	d				15 45						16 45							17 45							18 45
Newport (South Wales)	d				15 59						16 59							17 59							18 59
Bristol Temple Meads 10	d	16 00				16 30			17 00			17 30				18 00			18 30			19 00			
Bristol Parkway 7	d	16 09				16 40			17 09			17 40				18 09			18 40			19 09			
Gloucester 7	d				16 47						17 47							18 47							19 52
Cheltenham Spa	d	16 40			16 58	17 12			17 41		17 58	18 11				18 40		18 58	19 11			19 41			20 02
Birmingham New Street 12	a	17 26		17 50	17 41	17 48	18 06	18 09	18 27	18 50	18 41	18 48		19 11	19 06	19 26	19 50	19 41	19 49	20 05	20 15	20 27		20 50	20 44
Birmingham New Street 12	d	17 31		18 01		18 03	18 16	18 30	18 31	19 01		19 03			19 16	19 31	20 01		20 03	20 16		20 31		21 01	
Tamworth	d																								
Burton-on-Trent	d							19 16																	
Derby 6	a					18 56		19 29				19 55							20 57						
Nottingham 8	a																								
Chesterfield	a							20 02											21 19						
Sheffield 7	a					19 39		20 18				20 40							21 38						
Doncaster 7	a					20 16						21 19													
Wakefield Westgate 7	a							20 46											22 11						
Leeds 10	a							21 05											22 28						
York 8	a					20 39		21 31				21 42													
Darlington 7	a							22 01				22 23													
Durham	a							22 19				22 40													
Chester-le-Street	a																								
Newcastle 8	a							22 33				23 11													
Morpeth	a																								
Alnmouth for Alnwick	a																								
Berwick-upon-Tweed	a																								
Dunbar	a																								
Wolverhampton 7	d	17 49		18 19			18 37		18 49	19 19					19 37	19 49	20 19			20 38		20 53		21 19	
Stafford	a			18 35						19 37							20 36			20 52				21 36	
Stoke-on-Trent	a	18 19		18 56					19 19	19 56						20 19	20 56					21 20		21 56	
Congleton	a																								
Macclesfield	a			19 15						20 14							21 15							22 14	
Crewe 10	a						19 06								20 07					21 10					
Wilmslow	a																								
Stockport	a			19 28						20 28							21 28							22 27	
M'chester Piccadilly 10	a	18 56		19 40					19 58	20 40						21 00	21 40					21 57		22 39	
Warrington Bank Quay	a						19 25								20 26										
Wigan North Western	a						19 36								20 37										
Preston 8	a						19 51								20 51										
Lancaster 6	a						20 07								21 08										
Oxenholme Lake District	a														21 22										
Penrith North Lakes	a						20 44																		
Carlisle 8	a						20 59								22 01										
Lockerbie	a														22 20										
Haymarket	a						22 14																		
Edinburgh 10	a						22 20																		
Haymarket	a																								
Motherwell	a														23 03										
Glasgow Central 15	a														23 20										
Inverkeithing	a																								
Kirkcaldy	a																								
Markinch	a																								
Ladybank	a																								
Cupar	a																								
Leuchars 3	a																								
Dundee	a																								
Arbroath	a																								
Montrose	a																								
Stonehaven	a																								
Aberdeen	a																								

A 🛒 to Sheffield

B 🛒 to Birmingham New Street

Table 51R

Sundays

16 February to 23 March

South Coast and the South West - North West England, The North East and Scotland

Route Diagram - see first Page of Table 51

		XC	XC	XC	XC	VT	XC	XC		XC	XC	XC	XC	XC	XC
		◇[1]	◇[1]	◇[1]	◇[1]	◇[1]	◇[1]	◇[1]		◇[1]	◇[1]	◇[1]	◇[1]	◇[1]	◇[1]
								A							
		🛒				🍴	🛒	🛒		🛒					
Bournemouth	d							18 40				19 40			
Brockenhurst [3]	d							18 57				19 57			
Southampton Central ⛴	d							19 15				20 15			
Southampton Airport Pkway ✈	d							19 22				20 22			
Winchester	d							19 31				20 31			
Basingstoke	d							19 47				20 47			
Guildford	d														
Reading [7]	d						19 36	20 17			20 36	21 17			21 36
Oxford	d						20 07	20 42			21 06	21 41			22 06
Banbury	d						20 26	21 00			21 24	21 59			22 24
Leamington Spa [6]	d						20 43	21 17			21 41	22 16			22 42
Coventry	d					20 41	20 55	21 29			21 53	22 29			22 53
Birmingham International ✈	d					20 52	21 05	21 40			22 03	22 39			23 03
Penzance	d														
St Erth	d														
Hayle	d														
Camborne	d														
Redruth	d														
Truro	d														
St Austell	d														
Newquay (Summer Only)	d														
Par	d														
Lostwithiel	d														
Bodmin Parkway	d														
Liskeard [6]	d														
Plymouth	d														
Totnes	d														
Paignton	d														
Torquay	d														
Newton Abbot	d														
Teignmouth	d														
Dawlish	d														
Exeter St Davids [6]	d	18 23			19 23									20 44	
Tiverton Parkway	d	18 36			19 35									20 58	
Taunton	d	18 49			19 50									21 11	
Weston-super-Mare	d														
Cardiff Central [7]	d			19 45									20 45		
Newport (South Wales)	d			20 00									20 59		
Bristol Temple Meads [10]	d	19 30	20 00		20 30									22 10	
Bristol Parkway [7]	d	19 39	20 09		20 40									22 20	
Gloucester [7]	d			20 49									21 48		
Cheltenham Spa	d	20 10	20 40	21 00	21 11								21 59	22 49	
Birmingham New Street [12]	a	20 49	21 18	21 44	21 49	21 03	21 16	21 50			22 14	22 49	22 42	23 40	23 13
Birmingham New Street [12]	d	21 03				21 14		22 01		22 03					
Tamworth	d														
Burton-on-Trent	d	21 47								22 46					
Derby [6]	a	21 58								22 59					
Nottingham [8] ⛴	a														
Chesterfield	a	22 19								23 20					
Sheffield [7] ⛴	a	22 38								23 36					
Doncaster [7]	a														
Wakefield Westgate [7]	a	23 09													
Leeds [10]	a	23 26								00 27					
York [8]	a														
Darlington [7]	a														
Durham	a														
Chester-le-Street	a														
Newcastle [8]	a														
Morpeth	a														
Alnmouth for Alnwick	a														
Berwick-upon-Tweed	a														
Dunbar	a														
Wolverhampton [7] ⛴	d					21 38		22 20							
Stafford	a					21 55		22 36							
Stoke-on-Trent	a							22 55							
Congleton	a														
Macclesfield	a							23 12							
Crewe [10]	a					22 15									
Wilmslow	a														
Stockport	a							23 27							
M'chester Piccadilly [10] ⛴	a							23 41							
Warrington Bank Quay	a					22 34									
Wigan North Western	a					22 45									
Preston [8]	a					23 05									
Lancaster [6]	a														
Oxenholme Lake District	a														
Penrith North Lakes	a														
Carlisle [8]	a														
Lockerbie	a														
Haymarket	a														
Edinburgh [10]	a														
Haymarket	a														
Motherwell	a														
Glasgow Central [15]	a														
Inverkeithing	a														
Kirkcaldy	a														
Markinch	a														
Ladybank	a														
Cupar	a														
Leuchars [8]	a														
Dundee	a														
Arbroath	a														
Montrose	a														
Stonehaven	a														
Aberdeen	a														

A 🛒 to Birmingham New Street

Table 51R

Sundays

30 March to 11 May

South Coast and the South West - North West England, The North East and Scotland

Route Diagram - see first Page of Table 51

		VT	XC	XC	VT	XC	XC	VT	XC	XC	VT	XC	XC	XC	VT	XC	XC	XC	XC	VT	XC	XC	XC
		◇1	◇1	◇1	◇1	◇1	◇1	◇1	◇1	◇1	◇1	◇1	◇1	◇1	◇1	◇1	◇1	◇1	◇1	◇1	◇1	◇1	◇1
							A							A			B		A				C
Bournemouth	d																	09 40					
Brockenhurst 3	d																	09 57					
Southampton Central	d												09 15					10 15					
Southampton Airport Pkwy	d												09 22					10 22					
Winchester	d												09 31					10 31					
Basingstoke	d												09 47					10 47					
Guildford	d																						
Reading 7	d								09 11				10 11					11 11					
Oxford	d								09 37				10 37					11 37					
Banbury	d								09 55				10 55					11 55					
Leamington Spa 8	d								10 12				11 12					12 12					
Coventry	d								10 28				11 29					12 28					
Birmingham International	d								10 40				11 40					12 40					
Penzance	d																						
St Erth	d																						
Hayle	d																						
Camborne	d																						
Redruth	d																						
Truro	d																						
St Austell	d																						
Newquay (Summer Only)	d																						
Par	d																						
Lostwithiel	d																						
Bodmin Parkway	d																						
Liskeard 8	d																						
Plymouth	d																		09 25				
Totnes	d																		09 50				
Paignton	d																						
Torquay	d																						
Newton Abbot	d																		10 03				
Teignmouth	d																						
Dawlish	d																						
Exeter St Davids 6	d																		10 23				
Tiverton Parkway	d																		10 37				
Taunton	d																		10 51				
Weston-super-Mare	d																						
Cardiff Central 7	d																10 45						11 45
Newport (South Wales)	d																10 59						11 59
Bristol Temple Meads 10	d									09 15				10 30					11 30				
Bristol Parkway 7	d									09 24				10 39					11 39				
Gloucester 7	d									10 00							11 51						12 47
Cheltenham Spa	d									10 12				11 10			12 03		12 10				12 58
Birmingham New Street 12	a								10 50	10 49			11 51	11 48			12 45	12 50	12 49				13 41
Birmingham New Street 12	d	08 45	09 01	09 03	09 20	10 01	10 03	10 20	11 01	11 03	11 20	11 49	12 01	12 03	12 20	12 30	12 49	13 01	13 03	13 20	13 30	13 31	13 49
Tamworth	d			09 19			10 18					12 07		12 19			13 07						14 07
Burton-on-Trent	d			09 28			10 29			11 25		12 19					13 19		13 26				14 19
Derby 6	a			09 41			10 40			11 37		12 34		12 41		13 01	13 33		13 37		14 01		14 34
Nottingham 8	a											13 00					14 00						15 00
Chesterfield	a			10 02			11 02			12 01				13 02		13 29			14 02		14 29		
Sheffield 7	a			10 16			11 17			12 18				13 18		13 43			14 17		14 45		
Doncaster 7	a															14 13					15 13		
Wakefield Westgate 7	a			10 44			11 44			12 44				13 45					14 44				
Leeds 10	a			11 02			12 01			13 02				14 02					15 02				
York 8	a			11 27			12 27			13 27				14 27		14 38			15 27		15 42		
Darlington 7	a			11 54			12 54			13 54				14 54		15 13			15 54		16 10		
Durham	a			12 11			13 11			14 11				15 12		15 30			16 11		16 27		
Chester-le-Street	a																						
Newcastle 8	a			12 25			13 25			14 25				15 26		15 44			16 25		16 42		
Morpeth	a									14 44													
Alnmouth for Alnwick	a						13 51							15 52					16 51				
Berwick-upon-Tweed	a						14 12							16 12									
Dunbar	a			13 32						15 39									17 32				
Wolverhampton 7	d	09 04	09 19		09 38	10 19		10 38	11 19		11 38		12 19		12 37			13 19		13 37		13 49	
Stafford	a	09 17	09 32			10 32			11 32				12 32					13 33					
Stoke-on-Trent	a					10 51			11 51				12 52					13 56				14 19	
Congleton	a																						
Macclesfield	a					11 08			12 09				13 10					14 14					
Crewe 10	a	09 35	09 54		10 08			11 07			12 07				13 07					14 07			
Wilmslow	a		10 12																				
Stockport	a		10 21			11 22			12 22				13 28					14 28					
M'chester Piccadilly 10	a		10 37			11 31			12 40				13 40					14 40				14 57	
Warrington Bank Quay	a	09 54			10 27			11 26			12 26				13 26					14 26			
Wigan North Western	a	10 05			10 38			11 37			12 37				13 37					14 37			
Preston 8	a	10 22			10 51			11 51			12 51				13 51					14 50			
Lancaster 6	a				11 18			12 08			13 07				14 08					15 08			
Oxenholme Lake District	a				11 32			12 22			13 21									15 22			
Penrith North Lakes	a														14 44								
Carlisle 8	a				12 10			13 01			14 00				15 00					16 01			
Lockerbie	a																						
Haymarket	a							14 14							16 14								
Edinburgh 10	a			13 57			14 56	14 22		16 02				16 56	16 23				17 57				
Haymarket	a						15 14							17 14					18 16				
Motherwell	a						15 52							17 52									
Glasgow Central 15	a				13 29		16 13				15 16			18 12						17 17			
Inverkeithing	a																		18 28				
Kirkcaldy	a																		18 44				
Markinch	a																		18 53				
Ladybank	a																		19 01				
Cupar	a																		19 07				
Leuchars 3	a																		19 14				
Dundee	a																		19 29				
Arbroath	a																		19 46				
Montrose	a																		20 00				
Stonehaven	a																		20 22				
Aberdeen	a																		20 42				

A to Edinburgh **B** from Newport (South Wales) **C** from Birmingham New Street

Table 51R

Sundays

30 March to 11 May

South Coast and the South West - North West England, The North East and Scotland

Route Diagram - see first Page of Table 51

		XC	XC	VT	XC	XC	XC	XC	XC	VT	XC	XC	XC	XC	XC	VT	XC	XC	XC	XC	XC	VT	XC
		◇1	◇1	◇1	◇1	◇1	◇1	◇1	◇1	◇1	◇1	◇1	◇1	◇1	◇1	◇1	◇1	◇1	◇1	◇1	◇1	◇1	◇1
			A						B				C		A						D		
Bournemouth	d	10 40						11 40						12 40						13 40			
Brockenhurst 3	d	10 57						11 57						12 57						13 57			
Southampton Central	d	11 15						12 15						13 15						14 15			
Southampton Airport Pkway	d	11 22						12 22						13 22						14 22			
Winchester	d	11 31						12 31						13 31						14 31			
Basingstoke	d	11 47						12 47						13 47						14 47			
Guildford	d				12 14																		
Reading 7	d	12 11			12 54			13 11			13 41			14 09			14 40			15 09			15 40
Oxford	d	12 37			13 19			13 37			14 06			14 37			15 06			15 37			16 06
Banbury	d	12 55			13 37			13 55			14 24			14 55			15 25			15 55			16 25
Leamington Spa 8	d	13 12			13 53			14 12			14 42			15 12			15 43			16 12			16 43
Coventry	d	13 26		13 42				14 26		14 44				15 26		15 42				16 26		16 42	
Birmingham International	d	13 38		13 53				14 38		14 54				15 38		15 53				16 38		16 53	
Penzance	d								09 30														
St Erth	d								09 38														
Hayle	d																						
Camborne	d								09 48														
Redruth	d								09 54														
Truro	d								10 06														
St Austell	d								10 22														
Newquay (Summer Only)	d																						
Par	d								10 30														
Lostwithiel	d																						
Bodmin Parkway	d								10 40														
Liskeard 6	d								10 53														
Plymouth	d		10 25						11 25			12 00			12 25			12 52			13 24		
Totnes	d		10 50						11 50						12 50						13 50		
Paignton	d					10 50																	
Torquay	d					10 56																	
Newton Abbot	d		11 03			11 08			12 03			12 36			13 03			13 27			14 03		
Teignmouth	d					11 15																	
Dawlish	d					11 20																	
Exeter St Davids 6	d		11 23			11 33			12 23			12 57			13 23			13 48			14 24		
Tiverton Parkway	d		11 37			11 47			12 37			13 11			13 37						14 38		
Taunton	d		11 52			12 01			12 51			13 25			13 51						14 52		
Weston-super-Mare	d					12 22																	
Cardiff Central 7	d						12 45						13 45						14 45				
Newport (South Wales)	d						12 59						13 59						14 59				
Bristol Temple Meads 10	d		12 30			13 00			13 30			14 00			14 30			15 00			15 30		
Bristol Parkway 7	d		12 39			13 09			13 39			14 09			14 39			15 09			15 40		
Gloucester 7	d						13 49						14 47						15 47				
Cheltenham Spa	d		13 10			13 41	14 00		14 10			14 41	14 58		15 10			15 41	15 58		16 11		
Birmingham New Street 12	a	13 48	13 48	14 05	14 19	14 27	14 44	14 48	14 48	15 06	15 09	15 27	15 41	15 48	15 48	16 05	16 09	16 26	16 41	16 48	16 49	17 05	17 10
Birmingham New Street 12	d	14 01	14 03	14 16	14 30	14 31	14 49	15 01	15 03	15 17	15 30	15 31	15 49	16 01	16 03	16 16	16 30	16 31	16 49	17 01	17 03	17 16	17 30
Tamworth	d		14 19				15 09						16 07		16 19				17 07				
Burton-on-Trent	d						15 21		15 25				16 19						17 19		17 28		
Derby 6	a		14 39		15 01		15 33		15 37		16 01		16 34		16 38		17 01		17 34		17 40		18 01
Nottingham 8	a						16 00						17 00						18 00				
Chesterfield	a		15 02						16 02						17 02						18 03		
Sheffield 7	a		15 17		15 47				16 18		16 48				17 17		17 48				18 19		18 46
Doncaster 7	a				16 15						17 13						18 13						19 15
Wakefield Westgate 7	a		15 44						16 44						17 44		18 33				18 47		
Leeds 10	a		16 02						17 02						18 02		18 51				19 04		
York 8	a		16 27		16 38				17 27		17 40				18 27		19 20				19 30		19 39
Darlington 7	a		16 54		17 14				17 54		18 10				18 54		19 47				19 59		20 10
Durham	a		17 11		17 32				18 11		18 27				19 11		20 04				20 17		20 27
Chester-le-Street	a																						
Newcastle 8	a		17 25		17 47				18 25		18 42				19 25		20 19				20 31		20 41
Morpeth	a																				20 47		
Alnmouth for Alnwick	a		17 51												19 51								
Berwick-upon-Tweed	a		18 12						19 09						20 12						21 21		
Dunbar	a								19 34												21 45		
Wolverhampton 7	d	14 19		14 37		14 49		15 19		15 38		15 49		16 19		16 37		16 49		17 19		17 37	
Stafford	a	14 33						15 33						16 34						17 35			
Stoke-on-Trent	a	14 56				15 19		15 56				16 19		16 56				17 19		17 56			
Congleton	a																						
Macclesfield	a	15 14						16 14						17 14						18 14			
Crewe 10	a			15 07						16 07						17 07						18 07	
Wilmslow	a																						
Stockport	a	15 28						16 28						17 28						18 28			
M'chester Piccadilly 10	a	15 40				15 59		16 40				16 59		17 40				17 56		18 40			
Warrington Bank Quay	a			15 26						16 26						17 26						18 26	
Wigan North Western	a			15 37						16 37						17 37						18 37	
Preston 8	a			15 51						16 51						17 51						18 51	
Lancaster 6	a			16 08						17 08						18 07						19 07	
Oxenholme Lake District	a									17 22						18 21						19 21	
Penrith North Lakes	a			16 44												18 46							
Carlisle 8	a			17 00						18 01						19 03						20 00	
Lockerbie	a																						
Haymarket	a			18 13												20 16							
Edinburgh 10	a		18 56	18 22					19 57						20 56	20 21					22 12		22 21
Haymarket	a		19 22												21 16								
Motherwell	a		19 58												21 53								
Glasgow Central 15	a		20 21							19 17					22 14							21 15	
Inverkeithing	a																						
Kirkcaldy	a																						
Markinch	a																						
Ladybank	a																						
Cupar	a																						
Leuchars 3	a																						
Dundee	a																						
Arbroath	a																						
Montrose	a																						
Stonehaven	a																						
Aberdeen	a																						

A to Edinburgh
B from Plymouth
C from Birmingham New Street
D to Newcastle

Table 51R

Sundays
30 March to 11 May

South Coast and the South West - North West England, The North East and Scotland

Route Diagram - see first Page of Table 51

		XC	XC	XC	XC	VT	XC	XC	XC	XC	XC	VT	XC	XC	XC	XC	XC	VT	XC	XC	XC	XC
												R										
		◇1	◇1	◇1	◇1	◇1	◇1	◇1	◇1	◇1	◇1	1	◇1	◇1	◇1	◇1	◇1	◇1	◇1	◇1	◇1	◇1
			A		B			C	A				D		A					A	A	A
		🛒	🛒	🛒	🛒	🍴	🛒	🛒	🛒	🛒	🛒	🍴	🛒	🛒	🛒	🛒	🛒	🍴	🛒	🛒	🛒	🛒
Bournemouth	d			14 40						15 40						16 40						17 40
Brockenhurst 3	d			14 57						15 57						16 57						17 57
Southampton Central	d			15 15						16 15						17 15						18 15
Southampton Airport Pkway	d			15 22						16 22						17 22						18 22
Winchester	d			15 31						16 31						17 31						18 31
Basingstoke	d			15 47						16 47						17 47						18 47
Guildford	d																					
Reading 7	d			16 09			16 41			17 09			17 40			18 10			18 41			19 09
Oxford	d			16 37			17 06			17 37			18 07			18 37			19 06			19 37
Banbury	d			16 55			17 25			17 54			18 25			18 55			19 24			19 55
Leamington Spa 8	d			17 12			17 43			18 12			18 43			19 12			19 42			20 12
Coventry	d			17 26		17 44				18 26		18 44				19 26		19 42	19 54			20 26
Birmingham International	d			17 38		17 54				18 38		18 54				19 38		19 53	20 04			20 38
Penzance	d							12 30														
St Erth	d							12 40														
Hayle	d							12 44														
Camborne	d							12 56														
Redruth	d							13 02														
Truro	d							13 14														
St Austell	d							13 30														
Newquay (Summer Only)	d																					
Par	d							13 38														
Lostwithiel	d							13 45														
Bodmin Parkway	d							13 51														
Liskeard 6	d							14 04														
Plymouth	d				14 24			14 35			15 24						16 25					
Totnes	d				14 50			15 00			15 50						16 48					
Paignton	d																					
Torquay	d																					
Newton Abbot	d				15 03			15 12			16 03						17 01					
Teignmouth	d																					
Dawlish	d																					
Exeter St Davids 6	d				15 24			15 33			16 24						17 24					
Tiverton Parkway	d				15 37			15 46			16 37						17 38					
Taunton	d				15 52			16 00			16 52						17 52					
Weston-super-Mare	d							16 30														
Cardiff Central 7	d		15 45						16 45						17 45						18 45	
Newport (South Wales)	d		15 59						16 59						17 59						18 59	
Bristol Temple Meads 10	d	16 00			16 30			17 00			17 30			18 00			18 30			19 00		
Bristol Parkway 7	d	16 09			16 40			17 09			17 40			18 09			18 39			19 09		
Gloucester 7	d		16 47						17 47						18 47						19 52	
Cheltenham Spa	d	16 40	16 58		17 12			17 41	17 58		18 11			18 40	18 58		19 10			19 41	20 02	
Birmingham New Street 12	a	17 26	17 41	17 48	17 48	18 06	18 09	18 28	18 41	18 48	18 48	19 06	19 11	19 26	19 41	19 48	19 48	20 05	20 15	20 27	20 44	20 48
Birmingham New Street 12	d	17 31	17 49	18 01	18 03	18 16	18 30	18 31	18 49	19 01	19 03	19 16	19 30	19 31	19 49	20 01	20 03	20 16		20 31	20 49	21 01
Tamworth	d		18 07		18 19				19 09						20 07		20 19				21 06	
Burton-on-Trent	d		18 19						19 21		19 26				20 19						21 19	
Derby 6	a		18 33		18 39		19 02		19 33		19 40		20 01		20 34		20 38				21 33	
Nottingham 8	a		19 00						20 00						21 00						22 00	
Chesterfield	a				19 04						20 02						21 02					
Sheffield 7	a				19 20		19 39				20 18		20 40				21 16					
Doncaster 7	a						20 16						21 19									
Wakefield Westgate 7	a				19 48						20 49						21 47					
Leeds 10	a				20 05						21 06						22 04					
York 8	a				20 30		20 38				21 31		21 42									
Darlington 7	a				20 59		21 13						22 23									
Durham	a				21 17		21 30						22 40									
Chester-le-Street	a																					
Newcastle 8	a				21 31		21 44						23 11									
Morpeth	a																					
Alnmouth for Alnwick	a				21 59																	
Berwick-upon-Tweed	a																					
Dunbar	a																					
Wolverhampton 7	d	17 49		18 19		18 37		18 49		19 19		19 37		19 49		20 19		20 38		20 53		21 19
Stafford	a			18 35						19 37						20 36		20 52				21 36
Stoke-on-Trent	a	18 19		18 56				19 19		19 56				20 19		20 56				21 20		21 56
Congleton	a																					
Macclesfield	a			19 15						20 14						21 15						22 14
Crewe 10	a					19 06						20 07						21 10				
Wilmslow	a																					
Stockport	a			19 28						20 28						21 28						22 27
M'chester Piccadilly 10	a	18 56		19 40				19 58		20 40				21 00		21 40				21 57		22 39
Warrington Bank Quay	a					19 25						20 26										
Wigan North Western	a					19 36						20 37										
Preston 8	a					19 51						20 51										
Lancaster 6	a					20 07						21 08										
Oxenholme Lake District	a											21 22										
Penrith North Lakes	a					20 44																
Carlisle 8	a					20 59						22 01										
Lockerbie	a											22 20										
Haymarket	a					22 14																
Edinburgh 10	a				23 04	22 20																
Haymarket	a																					
Motherwell	a											23 03										
Glasgow Central 15	a											23 20										
Inverkeithing	a																					
Kirkcaldy	a																					
Markinch	a																					
Ladybank	a																					
Cupar	a																					
Leuchars 3	a																					
Dundee	a																					
Arbroath	a																					
Montrose	a																					
Stonehaven	a																					
Aberdeen	a																					

A 🛒 to Birmingham New Street
B 🛒 to Newcastle
C 🛒 from Plymouth
D 🛒 to Sheffield

Table 51R

Sundays
30 March to 11 May

South Coast and the South West - North West England, The North East and Scotland

Route Diagram - see first Page of Table 51

		XC	XC	XC	VT	XC	XC	XC	XC	XC	XC	XC	XC
		◇1	◇1	◇1	◇1	◇1	◇1	◇1	◇1	◇1	◇1	◇1	◇1
		A	B				C	C					
		trolley	trolley		buffet	trolley	trolley	trolley					
Bournemouth	d						18 40			19 40			
Brockenhurst 3	d						18 57			19 57			
Southampton Central ⛴	d						19 15			20 15			
Southampton Airport Pkway ✈	d						19 22			20 22			
Winchester	d						19 31			20 31			
Basingstoke	d						19 47			20 47			
Guildford	d												
Reading 7	d					19 40	20 09		20 41	21 09		21 35	
Oxford	d					20 06	20 37		21 06	21 37		22 06	
Banbury	d					20 24	20 55		21 24	21 54		22 24	
Leamington Spa 8	d					20 42	21 12		21 41	22 12		22 42	
Coventry	d				20 41	20 54	21 26		21 53	22 23		22 53	
Birmingham International ✈	d				20 52	21 04	21 38		22 03	22 33		23 03	
Penzance	d	15 30											
St Erth	d	15 38											
Hayle	d												
Camborne	d	15 49											
Redruth	d	15 55											
Truro	d	16 07											
St Austell	d	16 23											
Newquay (Summer Only)	d												
Par	d	16 31											
Lostwithiel	d												
Bodmin Parkway	d	16 41											
Liskeard 6	d	16 53											
Plymouth	d	17 25						18 24					
Totnes	d	17 50						18 50					
Paignton	d		18 20										
Torquay	d		18 26										
Newton Abbot	d	18 02	18 37					19 03					
Teignmouth	d												
Dawlish	d												
Exeter St Davids 6	d	18 22	18 58					19 24					
Tiverton Parkway	d	18 36	19 11					19 37					
Taunton	d	18 49	19 24					19 52					
Weston-super-Mare	d												
Cardiff Central 7	d			19 45							20 45		
Newport (South Wales)	d			20 00							20 59		
Bristol Temple Meads 10	d	19 30	20 00					20 30					22 10
Bristol Parkway 7	d	19 39	20 09					20 40					22 20
Gloucester 7	d			20 49							21 48		
Cheltenham Spa	d	20 10	20 40	21 00				21 11			21 59		22 49
Birmingham New Street 12	a	20 49	21 18	21 44	21 03	21 15	21 48	21 48	22 14	22 43	22 42	23 13	23 40
Birmingham New Street 12	d	21 03			21 14		22 01	22 03					
Tamworth	d	21 19						22 19					
Burton-on-Trent	d	21 29											
Derby 6	a	21 41						22 40					
Nottingham 8 🚌	a												
Chesterfield	a	22 02						23 04					
Sheffield 7 🚌	a	22 18						23 20					
Doncaster 7	a												
Wakefield Westgate 7	a	22 43											
Leeds 10	a	23 01						00 16					
York 8	a												
Darlington 7	a												
Durham	a												
Chester-le-Street	a												
Newcastle 8	a												
Morpeth	a												
Alnmouth for Alnwick	a												
Berwick-upon-Tweed	a												
Dunbar	a												
Wolverhampton 7 🚌	d				21 38		22 20						
Stafford	a				21 55		22 36						
Stoke-on-Trent	a						22 55						
Congleton	a												
Macclesfield	a						23 12						
Crewe 10	a				22 15								
Wilmslow	a												
Stockport	a						23 27						
M'chester Piccadilly 10 🚌	a						23 41						
Warrington Bank Quay	a				22 34								
Wigan North Western	a				22 45								
Preston 8	a				23 05								
Lancaster 6	a												
Oxenholme Lake District	a												
Penrith North Lakes	a												
Carlisle 8	a												
Lockerbie	a												
Haymarket	a												
Edinburgh 10	a												
Haymarket	a												
Motherwell	a												
Glasgow Central 15	a												
Inverkeithing	a												
Kirkcaldy	a												
Markinch	a												
Ladybank	a												
Cupar	a												
Leuchars 3	a												
Dundee	a												
Arbroath	a												
Montrose	a												
Stonehaven	a												
Aberdeen	a												

A trolley from Plymouth to Birmingham New Street
B trolley to Bristol Temple Meads
C trolley to Birmingham New Street

Network Diagram for Table 52

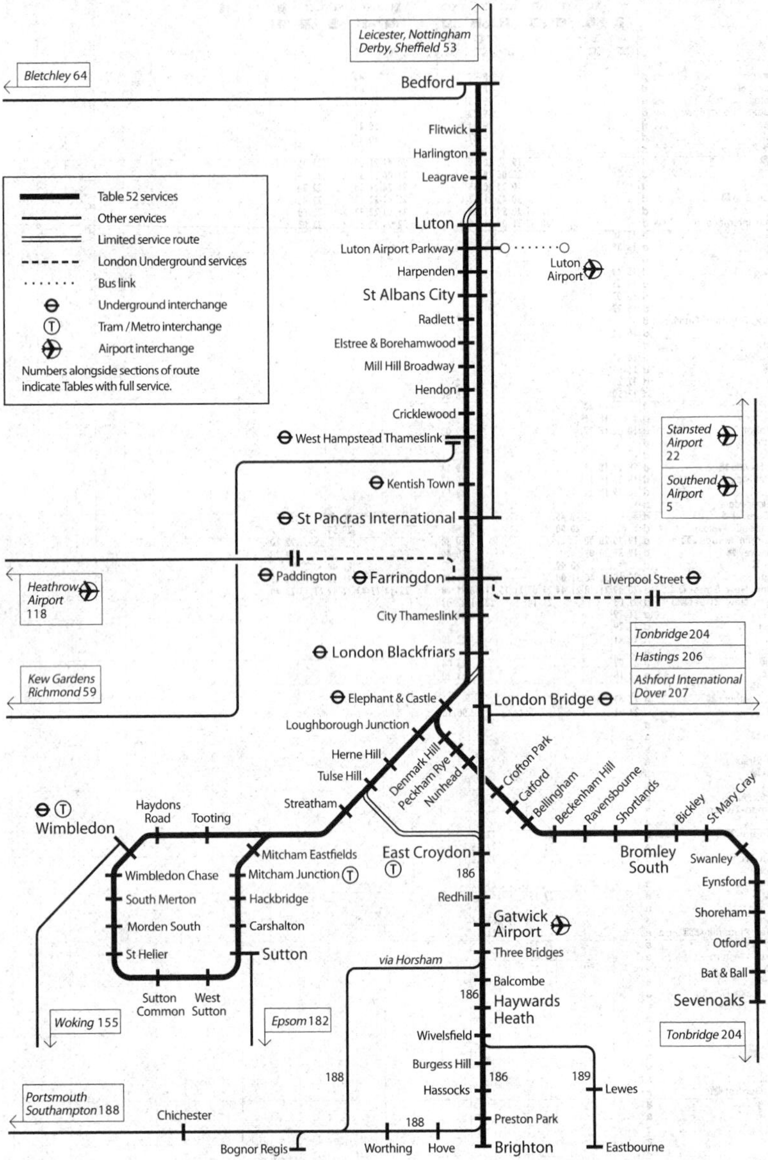

Leicester, Nottingham Derby, Sheffield 53
Bletchley 64
Bedford
Flitwick
Harlington
Leagrave
Luton
Luton Airport Parkway
Luton Airport
Harpenden
St Albans City
Radlett
Elstree & Borehamwood
Mill Hill Broadway
Hendon
Cricklewood
West Hampstead Thameslink
Kentish Town
St Pancras International
Paddington
Farringdon
Liverpool Street
City Thameslink
London Blackfriars
Elephant & Castle
London Bridge
Loughborough Junction
Herne Hill
Tulse Hill
Denmark Hill
Peckham Rye
Nunhead
Crofton Park
Catford
Bellingham
Beckenham Hill
Ravensbourne
Shortlands
Bickley
St Mary Cray
Bromley South
Swanley
Eynsford
Shoreham
Otford
Bat & Ball
Sevenoaks
Tonbridge 204
Streatham
Wimbledon
Haydons Road
Tooting
Mitcham Eastfields
Mitcham Junction
Wimbledon Chase
South Merton
Morden South
St Helier
Hackbridge
Carshalton
Sutton
Sutton Common
West Sutton
Woking 155
Epsom 182
East Croydon
186
Redhill
Gatwick Airport
Three Bridges
via Horsham
Balcombe
186
Haywards Heath
Wivelsfield
Burgess Hill
Hassocks
186
188
189
Lewes
Preston Park
Brighton
Eastbourne
Hove
Worthing
188
Bognor Regis
Chichester
Portsmouth Southampton 188
Stansted Airport 22
Southend Airport 5
Heathrow Airport 118
Kew Gardens Richmond 59
Tonbridge 204
Hastings 206
Ashford International Dover 207
Table 52 services
Other services
Limited service route
London Underground services
Bus link
Underground interchange
Tram / Metro interchange
Airport interchange
Numbers alongside sections of route indicate Tables with full service.

TOCs operating on this network - First Capital Connect (FC), Southeastern (SE), East Midlands Trains (EM)

Table 52

Mondays to Fridays

9 December to 16 May

Bedford, Luton, St Albans and City of London - South London, Gatwick Airport and Brighton

Network Diagram - refer to first Page of Table 52

Miles	Miles	Miles	Miles	Miles			FC	SE	SE	FC	FC	FC	SE	FC	FC	FC		FC	FC	FC	FC		FC	FC	FC
							MX	MO	MX	MO	MX	MX		MX	MO			MO	MO						
										1		1		1	1	1		1	1	1	1		1	1	1
							A	B	B	C	A	C	B	C	C	D		E	E	D	C				
0	—	—	—	0	**Bedford** 7	d																	00 42	01 42	
9½	—	—	—	—	Flitwick	d																	00 52	01 52	
12½	—	—	—	—	Harlington	d																	00 56	01 56	
17	—	—	—	—	Leagrave	d															00 02		01 02	02 02	
19½	—	—	—	19½	**Luton** 10	d															00 06		01 06	02 06	
20½	—	—	—	20½	Luton Airport Parkway 7 ✈	d															00 09		01 09	02 09	
25	—	—	—	—	Harpenden	d															00 15		01 15	02 15	
29¾	—	—	—	—	**St Albans City**	d															00 21		01 21	02 21	
34¼	—	—	—	—	Radlett	d															00 26		01 26	02 26	
37¼	—	—	—	—	Elstree & Borehamwood	d														00 01	00 31		01 31	02 31	
40½	—	—	—	—	Mill Hill Broadway	d														00 05	00 35		01 35	02 35	
42¾	—	—	—	—	Hendon	d														00 08	00 38		01 38	02 38	
44¾	—	—	—	—	Cricklewood	d													00 02	00 12	00 42		01 42	02 42	
45¾	—	—	—	—	West Hampstead Thameslink ⊖	d													00 05	00 15	00 45		01 45	02 45	
48¼	—	—	—	—	Kentish Town ⊖	d													00 10	00 20	00 50		01 50	02 50	
49¾	—	—	—	50	**St Pancras International** 15 ⊖	a													00 13	00 23	00 53		01 53	02 53	
—	—	—	—	—		d													00 14	00 24	00 54		01 54	02 54	03 25
51	—	—	—	—	Farringdon 3 ⊖	d													00 19	00 29					
51¾	—	—	—	—	City Thameslink 3	d																			
52¼	0	0	0	—	**London Blackfriars** 3 ⊖	d										00 05			00 25	00 35	01 05		02 05	03 05	03 36
—	1	1	1¼	—	Elephant & Castle ⊖173,179	d																			
—	3	3	—	—	Loughborough Jn 173,179	d																			
—	4	4	—	—	Herne Hill 4 173,179	d																			
53	—	—	—	—	**London Bridge** 4	a										00 11				00 41					
—	—	—	—	—		d										00 12				00 42					
—	5	5	—	—	Tulse Hill 3	d					00 02														
—	6½	6½	—	—	Streatham 4	d					00 06														
—	—	8	—	—	Mitcham Eastfields 173	d																			
—	—	9¼	—	—	Mitcham Junction 173 🚊	d																			
—	—	10½	—	—	Hackbridge 173	d																			
—	—	11¼	—	—	Carshalton 173	d																			
—	8	—	—	—	Tooting 173	d					00 10														
—	9¼	—	—	—	Haydons Road 173	d					00 13														
—	10½	—	—	—	**Wimbledon** 6 ⊖173,179 🚊	d					00 19														
—	11½	—	—	—	Wimbledon Chase 179	d					00 22														
—	12	—	—	—	South Merton 179	d					00 24														
—	12½	—	—	—	Morden South 179	d					00 26														
—	13	—	—	—	St Helier 179	d					00 28														
—	14	—	—	—	Sutton Common 179	d	00 01				00 30														
—	15	—	—	—	West Sutton 179	d	00 04				00 33														
—	16	12½	—	—	**Sutton (Surrey)** 4 179	a	00 09				00 39														
—	—	—	3¾	—	Denmark Hill 4 195	d																			
—	—	—	4¾	—	Peckham Rye 4 195	d																			
—	—	—	5½	—	Nunhead 4 195	d																			
—	—	—	6¾	—	Crofton Park 195	d																			
—	—	—	7½	—	Catford 195	d							00 03												
—	—	—	8½	—	Bellingham 195	d							00 05												
—	—	—	9	—	Beckenham Hill 195	d							00 07												
—	—	—	10	—	Ravensbourne 195	d							00 09												
—	—	—	10¾	—	Shortlands 195	d							00 11												
—	—	—	11½	—	Bromley South 4 195	d							00 14												
—	—	—	12½	—	Bickley 4 195	d							00 17												
—	—	—	15½	—	St Mary Cray 195	d							00 21												
—	—	—	18	—	Swanley 4 195	d							00 26												
—	—	—	21	—	Eynsford 195	d		00 01					00 30												
—	—	—	23¼	—	Shoreham (Kent) 195	d		00 04	00 04				00 34												
—	—	—	24¾	—	Otford 4 195	d		00 07	00 07				00 37												
—	—	—	26¼	—	Bat & Ball 195	d		00 10	00 10				00 40												
—	—	—	27½	—	Sevenoaks 4 195	a		00 13	00 13				00 43												
63¼	—	—	—	—	**East Croydon** 🚊	d										00 29		00 29	00 57	00 57	01 36		02 36	03 36	04 06
73¾	—	—	—	—	Redhill	d																			
79½	—	—	—	—	**Gatwick Airport** 10 ✈	d								00 19	00 20	00 49		00 49	01 19	01 19	01 55		02 56	03 56	04 26
82¼	—	—	—	—	Three Bridges 4	d								00a24	00 25	00a54		00a54	01a24	01a24	02a02		03a02	04a02	04a32
86¾	—	—	—	—	Balcombe	d																			
90¾	—	—	—	—	**Haywards Heath** 3	d									00 36										
93¾	—	—	—	—	Wivelsfield 4	d						00 03													
94½	—	—	—	—	Burgess Hill 4	d				00 02		00 05			00 42										
96½	—	—	—	—	Hassocks 4	d				00 06		00 08			00 45										
102¼	—	—	—	—	Preston Park	d						00 15													
103¾	—	—	—	—	**Brighton** 10	a				00 15		00 19			00 55										

A From Luton
B From London Blackfriars
C From Bedford
D until 3 January, MX from 7 January. From Bedford
E from 6 January. From Bedford

The trains that operate to and from Sevenoaks, Orpington and Rochester (and a few other destinations at peak times) are operated jointly by First Capital Connect (north of Blackfriars) and Southeastern (south of Blackfriars)

Table 52 shows the complete service between Bedford and London, whilst services between London, Sevenoaks, Sutton and Brighton only show through Thameslink services. Other Tables should be consulted for additional journey opportunities.

Table 52

Mondays to Fridays

9 December to 16 May

Bedford, Luton, St Albans and City of London - South London, Gatwick Airport and Brighton

Network Diagram - refer to first Page of Table 52

		FC	FC	FC	SE	FC	FC	FC	FC	FC	FC	FC	FC	SE	EM	FC	FC	FC	FC	EM	FC	FC
		1	1	1		1	1				1		1		◇1		1		1	◇1		1
															A			B		C	D	
Bedford 7	d	02 42		03 42		04 08	04 20				05 00		05 20		05 37		05 40		05 54			05 58
Flitwick	d	02 52		03 52		04 18	04 30				05 10		05 30				05 50		06 04			06 08
Harlington	d	02 56		03 56		04 22	04 34				05 14		05 34				05 54					06 12
Leagrave	d	03 02		04 02		04 28	04 40				05 20		05 39				05 59					06 17
Luton 10	d	03 06		04 06		04 32	04 44		05 08		05 24		05 44			05 48	06 04	06 06	06 14	06 25		06 22
Luton Airport Parkway 7 ✈	d	03 09		04 09		04 35	04 47		05 10		05 27		05 46		05 56	05 50	06 06	06 08				06 24
Harpenden	d	03 15		04 15		04 41	04 53		05 16		05 33		05 52			05 56	06 12	06 14	06 20			06 30
St Albans City	d	03 21		04 21		04 47	04 59		05 22		05 39		05 58			06 02	06 18	06 20	06 26			06 36
Radlett	d	03 26		04 26			05 04		05 28							06 07		06 25				
Elstree & Borehamwood	d	03 31		04 31			05 09		05 32							06 12		06 30				
Mill Hill Broadway	d	03 35		04 35			05 13		05 36							06 16		06 34				
Hendon	d	03 38		04 38			05 16		05 40							06 19		06 37				
Cricklewood	d	03 42		04 42			05 20		05 43							06 23		06 41				
West Hampstead Thameslink ⊖	d	03 45		04 45		05 05	05 23		05 46		05 54	06 04	06 13			06 26	06 30	06 44				06 50
Kentish Town ⊖	d	03 50		04 50			05 28		05 50	05 54		06 08				06 30		06 48			←	
St Pancras International 15 ⊖	a	03 53		04 53		05 12	05 32		05 54	05 58	06 01	06 12	06 20		06 19	06 34	06 38	06 52	06 44	06 49	06 52	06 57
	d	03 54	04 24	04 54		05 12	05 32	05 36	05 54	05 58	06 02	06 12	06 22			06 34	06 38	06 52	06 44		06 52	06 58
Farringdon 3 ⊖	d			04 59		05 18	05 38	05 42	06 00	06 04	06 08	06 18	06 28			06 40	06 44	→	06 50		06 58	07 04
City Thameslink 3	d					05 21	05 41	05 44	06 03	06 07	06 11	06 21	06 31			06 43	06 47		06 53		07 01	07 07
London Blackfriars 3 ⊖	d	04 05	04 35	05 05	05 24	05 24	05 44	05 47	06 06	06 10	06 14	06 24	06 34	06 42		06 46	06 50		06 58		07 04	07 09
Elephant & Castle ⊖173,179	d				05 28			05 50	06 09	06 16		06 27		06 46		06 49			07 02		07 07	
Loughborough Jn 173,179	d								06 13			06 31				06 53					07 11	
Herne Hill 4 173,179	d							05 57	06 17			06 35				06 57					07 15	
London Bridge 4	a					05 30	05 50				06 20		06 41				06 56					07 15
	d					05 30	05 50				06 20		06 42				07 00					07 16
Tulse Hill 3	d							06 02	06 22			06 42				07 02					07 20	
Streatham 4	d							06 05	06 25			06 45				07 05					07 23	
Mitcham Eastfields 173	d								06 29			06 49									07 27	
Mitcham Junction 173 🚋	d								06 32			06 52									07 30	
Hackbridge 173	d								06 35			06 55									07 33	
Carshalton 173	d								06 38			06 58									07 36	
Tooting 173	d							06 10								07 11						
Haydons Road 173	d							06 13								07 14						
Wimbledon 6 ⊖173,179 🚋	d							06 16								07 17						
Wimbledon Chase 179	d							06 19								07 20						
South Merton 179	d							06 21								07 22						
Morden South 179	d							06 23								07 24						
St Helier 179	d							06 25								07 26						
Sutton Common 179	d							06 27								07 28						
West Sutton 179	d							06 30								07 31						
Sutton (Surrey) 4 179	a							06 33	06 43			07 03				07 35					07 39	
Denmark Hill 4 195	d				05 34					06 22				06 52					07 09			
Peckham Rye 4 195	d				05 37					06 25				06 55					07 12			
Nunhead 4 195	d				05 39					06 27				06 57					07 14			
Crofton Park 195	d				05 42					06 30				07 00					07 17			
Catford 195	d				05 45					06 33				07 03					07 20			
Bellingham 195	d				05 47					06 35				07 05					07 22			
Beckenham Hill 195	d				05 49					06 37				07 07					07 24			
Ravensbourne 195	d				05 51					06 39				07 09					07 26			
Shortlands 195	d				05 53					06 41				07 11					07 28			
Bromley South 4 195	d				05 57					06 44				07 14					07 31			
Bickley 4 195	d				05 59					06 47				07 17					07 34			
St Mary Cray 195	d				06 04					06 51				07 21					07 38			
Swanley 4 195	d				06 09					06 56				07 26					07 46			
Eynsford 195	d				06 14					07 00				07 30					07 50			
Shoreham (Kent) 195	d				06 17					07 04				07 34					07 54			
Otford 4 195	d				06 20					07 07				07 37					07 58			
Bat & Ball 195	d				06 23					07 10				07 40					08 01			
Sevenoaks 4 195	a				06 27					07 14				07 43					08 04			
East Croydon 🚋	d	04 36	05 06	05 32		05 48	06 06				06 35		06 55				07 15					07 31
Redhill	d																					
Gatwick Airport 10 ✈	d	04 56	05 26	05 48		06 04	06 23				06 52		07 11				07 31					07 47
Three Bridges 4	d	05 02	05 32	05 52		06 08	06 27				06 56		07 15				07 35					07 51
Balcombe	d					06 14	06 34						07 21									07 57
Haywards Heath 3	d	05 12	05 41	06 02		06 19	06 39				07 06		07 26				07 45					08 02
Wivelsfield 4	d		05 45			06 23	06 43				07 10						07 49					08 06
Burgess Hill 4	d		05 47	06 07		06 25	06 45				07 12		07 31				07 51					08 08
Hassocks 4	d		05 51	06 10		06 29	06 49				07 16		07 35				07 54					08 12
Preston Park	d		05 57	06 18		06 35	06 55				07 22						08 01					08 18
Brighton 10	a	05 30	06 02	06 22		06 40	06 59				07 27		07 44				08 05					08 23

A From Leicester
B To Sutton (Surrey)
C From Derby
D From Luton

The trains that operate to and from Sevenoaks, Orpington and Rochester (and a few other destinations at peak times) are operated jointly by First Capital Connect (north of Blackfriars) and Southeastern (south of Blackfriars)

Table 52 shows the complete service between Bedford and London, whilst services between London, Sevenoaks, Sutton and Brighton only show through Thameslink services. Other Tables should be consulted for additional journey opportunities.

Table 52

Mondays to Fridays

9 December to 16 May

Bedford, Luton, St Albans and City of London - South London, Gatwick Airport and Brighton

Network Diagram - refer to first Page of Table 52

		FC A	FC ■1	FC ■1 B	FC C	FC ■1 D	EM ◇■1 E 🚲	FC F	FC ■1 G	FC ■1 H	FC B	FC ■1 I	FC J	FC K	FC A	EM ◇■1 L 🚲	FC M	FC B	FC ■1	FC J	FC C	FC ■1 D
Bedford ■7	d		06 14	06 18		06 22	06 30					06 34					06 40		06 54			06 58
Flitwick	d		06 24			06 32					06 36	06 44					06 50		07 04			07 08
Harlington	d					06 36					06 40						06 54					07 12
Leagrave	d			06 34		06 41					06 45						06 59					07 18
Luton ■10	d		06 34	06 39	06 43	06 46					06 50	06 54			07 00		07 04	07 10	07 14			07 22
Luton Airport Parkway ■7 ✈	d			06 41	06 45	06 48					06 52				07 02	07 05	07 06	07 12				07 25
Harpenden	d		06 40	06 47	06 51	06 54					06 58	07 00			07 08		07 12	07 18	07 20			07 31
St Albans City	d	06 40	06 46	06 53	06 57	07 00					07 04	07 06			07 16		07 18	07 24	07 26		07 34	07 38
Radlett	d	06 45			07 02						07 09				07 21			07 29			07 39	
Elstree & Borehamwood	d	06 50			07 06						07 13				07 25			07 33			07 43	
Mill Hill Broadway	d	06 54			07 10						07 17				07 30			07 37			07 48	
Hendon	d	06 57			07 13										07 33						07 51	
Cricklewood	d	07 01			07 17										07 37						07 55	
West Hampstead Thameslink ⊖	d	07 04		07 08	07 20						07 24				07 40			07 44			08 00	
Kentish Town ⊖	d	07 08			07 24			←	←	←			←	←	07 44					←	08 04	
St Pancras International ■15 ⊖	a	07 12	07 04	07 16	07 28	07 20	07 08	07 12	07 16	07 20	07 31	07 24	07 28	07 31	07 48	07 31	07 37	07 51	07 43	07 48	08 08	07 54
	d	07 12	07 04	07 16	07 28	07 20		07 12	07 16	07 20	07 32	07 24	07 28	07 32	07 48		07 38	07 52	07 44	07 48	08 08	07 56
Farringdon ■3 ⊖	d	→	07 10	→	→	→		07 18	07 22	07 26	→	07 30	07 34	07 38	→		07 44	→	07 50	07 54	→	→
City Thameslink ■3	d		07 13					07 21	07 25	07 29		07 33	07 37	07 41			07 47		07 53	07 57		
London Blackfriars ■3 ⊖	d		07 16					07 24	07 28	07 32		07 36	07 40	07 44			07 50		07 56	08 00		
Elephant & Castle ⊖173,179	d		07 19					07 28	07 33			07a39	07 44	07 47			07 54			08 04		
Loughborough Jn 173,179	d		07 23						07 37					07 51								
Herne Hill ■4 173,179	d		07 27						07 41					07 57								
London Bridge ■4	a									07 41												
	d									07 42												
Tulse Hill ■3	d		07 31						07 45					08 05					08 10			
Streatham ■4	d		07 34						07 48					08 08								
Mitcham Eastfields 173	d								07 52													
Mitcham Junction 173 🚋	d								07 55													
Hackbridge 173	d								07 58													
Carshalton 173	d								08 01													
Tooting 173	d		07 38											08 13								
Haydons Road 173	d		07 41											08 16								
Wimbledon ■6 ⊖173,179 🚋	d		07 47											08 19								
Wimbledon Chase 179	d		07 50											08 22								
South Merton 179	d		07 52											08 24								
Morden South 179	d		07 54											08 26								
St Helier 179	d		07 56											08 28								
Sutton Common 179	d		07 58											08 30								
West Sutton 179	d		08 01											08 33								
Sutton (Surrey) ■4 179	a		08 07						08 04					08 37								
Denmark Hill ■4 195	d							07 34					07 50				08 00			08 10		
Peckham Rye ■4 195	d							07 36					07 53				08 03			08 13		
Nunhead ■4 195	d							07 39					07 56				08 06			08 15		
Crofton Park 195	d							07 42									08 09			08 18		
Catford 195	d							07 44					08 00				08 12			08 21		
Bellingham 195	d							07 47					08 02				08 15			08 23		
Beckenham Hill 195	d							07 49									08 17			08 25		
Ravensbourne 195	d							07 51									08 19			08 27		
Shortlands 195	d							07 54									08 22			08 30		
Bromley South ■4 195	d							07 57					08a10				08 25			08 33		
Bickley ■4 195	d							08 00									08a28			08 35		
St Mary Cray 195	d							08 04												08 40		
Swanley ■4 195	d							08 10												08 44		
Eynsford 195	d							08 15												08 49		
Shoreham (Kent) 195	d							08 18												08 52		
Otford ■4 195	d							08 22												08 55		
Bat & Ball 195	d							08 25												08 58		
Sevenoaks ■4 195	a							08 28												09 01		
East Croydon 🚋	d									07 55									08 26			
Redhill	d																					
Gatwick Airport ■10 ✈	d									08 12									08 42			
Three Bridges ■4	d									08 16									08 46			
Balcombe	d									08 22									08 52			
Haywards Heath ■3	d									08 27									08 58			
Wivelsfield ■4	d									08 31									09 02			
Burgess Hill ■4	d									08 33									09 04			
Hassocks ■4	d									08 37									09 07			
Preston Park	d									08 43									09 14			
Brighton ■10	a									08 48									09 18			

A To Sevenoaks
B To Sutton (Surrey)
C To Bromley South
D To Brighton
E From Derby
F From St Albans City
G From Bedford. ■1 to London Blackfriars
H From Bedford
I To Beckenham Junction
J From Luton
K From Flitwick
L From Nottingham
M To Orpington

The trains that operate to and from Sevenoaks, Orpington and Rochester (and a few other destinations at peak times) are operated jointly by First Capital Connect (north of Blackfriars) and Southeastern (south of Blackfriars)

Table 52 shows the complete service between Bedford and London, whilst services between London, Sevenoaks, Sutton and Brighton only show through Thameslink services. Other Tables should be consulted for additional journey opportunities.

Table 52

Mondays to Fridays

9 December to 16 May

Bedford, Luton, St Albans and City of London - South London, Gatwick Airport and Brighton

Network Diagram - refer to first Page of Table 52

	EM	FC	FC	FC	EM	FC	FC	FC	FC	FC	FC	EM	FC	FC	FC	FC	FC	FC	FC	FC	EM	FC
	◇1		1	1	◇1				1		1	◇1				1	1			1	◇1	
	A	B	C	D	E ⊠	F		G	H	I		J	F	C	I			G	G	K	E ⊠	F
Bedford 7 d	07 09			07 12					07 16	07 22	07 30					07 34	07 44			07 48	07 54	
Flitwick d									07 26	07 32	07 40					07 44				07 58		
Harlington d									07 30	07 36						07 48				08 02		
Leagrave d				07 28					07 35	07 41						07 53	08 00			08 08		
Luton 10 d	07 24			07 32			07 30		07 40	07 46	07 50	07 59				07 58	08 04	08 02		08 12		
Luton Airport Parkway 7 ✈ d					07 41		07 32		07 42	07 48						08 00		08 04		08 15	08 11	
Harpenden d				07 38			07 38		07 48	07 54	07 56					08 05	08 10	08 10		08 21		
St Albans City d				07 44			07 44	07 52	07 55	08 00	08 02				08 07	08 11	08 16	08 16	08 23	08 28		
Radlett d							07 49	07 57		08 05					08 12			08 21	08 28			
Elstree & Borehamwood d							07 53	08 01		08 09					08 16			08 25	08 32			
Mill Hill Broadway d							07 57	08 06		08 13					08 21			08 29	08 37			
Hendon d								08 09							08 24				08 40			
Cricklewood d								08 13							08 28				08 44			
West Hampstead Thameslink ⊖ d							08 04	08 16		08 20					08 32			08 36	08 48			
Kentish Town ⊖ d		←	←			←		08 20					←	←	08 36				08 52			←
St Pancras International 15 ⊖ a	07 48	07 51	07 54	08 04	08 07	08 08	08 11	08 24	08 15	08 27	08 19	08 23	08 24	08 27	08 40	08 31	08 35	08 44	08 56	08 47	08 39	08 40
d		07 52	07 56	08 04		08 08	08 12	08 24	08 16	08 28	08 20		08 24	08 28	08 40	08 32	08 36	08 44	08 56	08 48		08 40
Farringdon 3 ⊖ d		07 58	08 02	08 10		08 14	08 18	↪	08 22	↪	08 26		08 30	08 34	↪	08 38	08 42	↪	↪	↪		08 46
City Thameslink 3 d		08 01	08 05	08 13		08 17	08 21		08 25		08 29		08 33	08 37		08 41	08 45					08 49
London Blackfriars 3 ⊖ d		08 04	08 08	08a16		08 20	08 24		08 28		08 32		08 36	08 40		08 44	08 48					08 52
Elephant & Castle ⊖173,179 d		08 07					08 27		08 32				08 39	08 45								08 56
Loughborough Jn 173,179 d		08 11					08 31															
Herne Hill 4 173,179 d		08 17					08 36						08 46				08 57					
London Bridge 4 a			08 16																			
d			08 18																			
Tulse Hill 3 d		08 21					08 40						08 51				09 01					
Streatham 4 d		08 24					08 44						08 54				09 05					
Mitcham Eastfields 173 d		08 28											08 58									
Mitcham Junction 173 🚋 d		08 31											09 01									
Hackbridge 173 d		08 34											09 04									
Carshalton 173 d		08 37											09 07									
Tooting 173 d							08 48										09 10					
Haydons Road 173 d							08 51										09 13					
Wimbledon 6 ⊖173,179 🚋 d							08 55										09 17					
Wimbledon Chase 179 d							08 58										09 20					
South Merton 179 d							09 00										09 22					
Morden South 179 d							09 02										09 24					
St Helier 179 d							09 04										09 26					
Sutton Common 179 d							09 06										09 28					
West Sutton 179 d							09 09										09 31					
Sutton (Surrey) 4 179 a		08 40					09 12						09 10				09 37					
Denmark Hill 4 195 d									08 38					08 52								09 02
Peckham Rye 4 195 d									08 41					08 55								
Nunhead 4 195 d									08 43					08 57								
Crofton Park 195 d									08 46					09 00								
Catford 195 d									08 49					09 03								09 09
Bellingham 195 d									08 51					09 05								
Beckenham Hill 195 d									08 53					09 07								
Ravensbourne 195 d									08 55					09 09								
Shortlands 195 d									08 57					09 11								
Bromley South 4 195 d						08a37			09 00					09 14								09 18
Bickley 4 195 d									09 03					09 17								09 20
St Mary Cray 195 d									09 07					09 21								09 25
Swanley 4 195 d									09 12					09 26								09 36
Eynsford 195 d									09 16					09 30								09 40
Shoreham (Kent) 195 d									09 20					09 34								09 44
Otford 4 195 d									09 23					09 37								09 47
Bat & Ball 195 d									09 26					09 40								09 50
Sevenoaks 4 195 a									09 29					09 45								09 53
East Croydon 🚋 d			08 37								08 58					09 12						
Redhill d																						
Gatwick Airport 10 ✈ d			08 53								09 13					09 28						
Three Bridges 4 d			08 58								09 17					09 32						
Balcombe d																						
Haywards Heath 3 d			09 08								09 27					09 41						
Wivelsfield 4 d																						
Burgess Hill 4 d			09 13								09 32											
Hassocks 4 d											09 35											
Preston Park d											09 42											
Brighton 10 a			09 25								09 46					09 55						

A From Melton Mowbray
B From Luton
C From Bedford
D To Kent House
E From Sheffield
F From St Albans City
G To Sutton (Surrey)
H 1 from London Blackfriars
I To Sevenoaks
J From Nottingham
K To Brighton

The trains that operate to and from Sevenoaks, Orpington and Rochester (and a few other destinations at peak times) are operated jointly by First Capital Connect (north of Blackfriars) and Southeastern (south of Blackfriars)

Table 52 shows the complete service between Bedford and London, whilst services between London, Sevenoaks, Sutton and Brighton only show through Thameslink services. Other Tables should be consulted for additional journey opportunities.

Table 52

Mondays to Fridays

9 December to 16 May

Bedford, Luton, St Albans and City of London - South London, Gatwick Airport and Brighton

Network Diagram - refer to first Page of Table 52

		FC A	FC [1] B	EM ◇[1] C ♿	FC [1]	FC D	FC	FC E		FC [1]	FC F	FC [1] G	EM ◇[1] C ☒	FC D	FC [1] B	FC D	FC	FC E	FC [1]		FC F	FC E	FC [1] G	EM ◇[1] H ♿	FC D
Bedford [7]	d				07 58					08 04		08 24	08 29						08 40				08 54	09 05	
Flitwick	d				08 08					08 14		08 34							08 50				09 04		
Harlington	d									08 18		08 38							08 54				09 08		
Leagrave	d									08 23		08 43							08 59				09 13		
Luton [10]	d			08 15	08 20		08 20			08 28		08 48					08 54		09 04			09 14	09 18	09 19	
Luton Airport Parkway [7] ✈	d						08 22			08 30		08 50					08 56		09 06			09 16	09 20		
Harpenden	d				08 26		08 28			08 36		08 56					09 02		09 12			09 22	09 26		
St Albans City	d				08 33		08 34	08 43		08 44	08 58	09 02					09 08	09 14	09 18			09 29	09 32		
Radlett	d						08 39	08 48			09 03						09 13	09 19				09 34			
Elstree & Borehamwood	d						08 43	08 52			09 07						09 17	09 23				09 38			
Mill Hill Broadway	d							08 57			09 12							09 28				09 43			
Hendon	d							09 00			09 15							09 31				09 46			
Cricklewood	d							09 04			09 19							09 35				09 50			
West Hampstead Thameslink ⊖	d						08 52	09 08			09 22	09 15					09 26	09 39				09 54	09 45		
Kentish Town ⊖	d	←	←			←		09 12			09 26			←	←	←		09 44			09 54	10 00			←
St Pancras International [15] ⊖	a	08 44	08 47	08 42	08 51	08 56	08 59	09 16		09 03	09 30	09 21	09 06	09 16	09 21	09 30	09 33	09 47	09 39		09 58	10 03	09 52	09 45	09 47
	d	08 44	08 48		08 52	08 56	09 00	09 16		09 04	09 30	09 22		09 16	09 22	09 30	09 34	09 48	09 40		10 00	10 04	09 54		09 48
Farringdon [3] ⊖	d	08 50	08 54		08 58	09 02	09 06	→		09 10	→	→		09 22	09 28	09 36	09 40	→	09 45		→	→	→		09 53
City Thameslink [3]	d	08 53	08 57		09 01	09 05	09 09			09 13				09 25	09 31	09 39	09 43		09 48						09 57
London Blackfriars [3] ⊖	d	08 56	09 00		09 04	09 08	09 12			09 16				09 28	09 34	09 42	09 46		09 50						10 00
Elephant & Castle ⊖173,179	d	09 00			09a09	09 12	09 16							09 31		09 46	09 49								10 03
Loughborough Jn 173,179	d	09 04				09 16								09 35			09 53								10 07
Herne Hill [4] 173,179	d	09 11				09 25								09 41			09 57								10 11
London Bridge [4]	a		09 11							09 26					09 41				09 56						
	d		09 12							09 27					09 42				09 57						
Tulse Hill [3]	d	09 16				09 31								09 46			10 01								10 16
Streatham [4]	d	09 20				09 35								09 50			10 05								10 20
Mitcham Eastfields 173	d	09 24												09 54											10 24
Mitcham Junction 173 🚊	d	09 27												09 57											10 27
Hackbridge 173	d	09 30												10 00											10 30
Carshalton 173	d	09 33												10 03											10 33
Tooting 173	d					09 40											10 10								
Haydons Road 173	d					09 43											10 13								
Wimbledon [6] ⊖173,179 🚊	d					09 47											10 17								
Wimbledon Chase 179	d					09 50											10 20								
South Merton 179	d					09 52											10 22								
Morden South 179	d					09 54											10 24								
St Helier 179	d					09 56											10 26								
Sutton Common 179	d					09 58											10 28								
West Sutton 179	d					10 01											10 31								
Sutton (Surrey) [4] 179	a	09 36				10 05								10 06			10 35								10 36
Denmark Hill [4] 195	d						09 22									09 52									
Peckham Rye [4] 195	d						09 25									09 55									
Nunhead [4] 195	d						09 27									09 57									
Crofton Park 195	d						09 30									10 00									
Catford 195	d						09 33									10 03									
Bellingham 195	d						09 35									10 05									
Beckenham Hill 195	d						09 37									10 07									
Ravensbourne 195	d						09 39									10 09									
Shortlands 195	d						09 41									10 11									
Bromley South [4] 195	d						09 44									10 14									
Bickley [4] 195	d						09 47									10 17									
St Mary Cray 195	d						09 51									10 21									
Swanley [4] 195	d						09 56									10 26									
Eynsford 195	d						10 00									10 30									
Shoreham (Kent) 195	d						10 04									10 34									
Otford [4] 195	d						10 07									10 37									
Bat & Ball 195	d						10 10									10 40									
Sevenoaks [4] 195	a						10 13									10 43									
East Croydon 🚊	d		09 25							09 41					09 55				10 11						
Redhill	d																								
Gatwick Airport [10] ✈	d		09 41							09 57					10 11				10 27						
Three Bridges [4]	d		09 45							10 02					10 15				10 32						
Balcombe	d		09 51												10 21										
Haywards Heath [3]	d		09 56							10 11					10 27				10 41						
Wivelsfield [4]	d		10 00												10 31										
Burgess Hill [4]	d		10 02												10 33										
Hassocks [4]	d		10 06												10 36										
Preston Park	d		10 12												10 43										
Brighton [10]	a		10 17							10 25					10 47				10 55						

A From Luton
B From Bedford
C From Nottingham
D From St Albans City
E To Sutton (Surrey)
F To Sevenoaks
G To Brighton
H From Derby

The trains that operate to and from Sevenoaks, Orpington and Rochester (and a few other destinations at peak times) are operated jointly by First Capital Connect (north of Blackfriars) and Southeastern (south of Blackfriars)

Table 52 shows the complete service between Bedford and London, whilst services between London, Sevenoaks, Sutton and Brighton only show through Thameslink services. Other Tables should be consulted for additional journey opportunities.

Table 52

Mondays to Fridays

9 December to 16 May

Bedford, Luton, St Albans and City of London - South London, Gatwick Airport and Brighton

Network Diagram - refer to first Page of Table 52

Station		FC 1	FC	FC 1	EM ◇1	FC	FC	FC 1	FC 1	FC	FC	FC	FC 1	FC	FC 1	EM ◇1	FC	FC	FC 1	FC	FC	FC	FC
		A	B	C	D (bike)	E	F	A		G	H	B		B	C	I (bike)	E	F	A		G	H	B
Bedford 7	d			09 10	09 16				09 20				09 24		09 40	09 47				09 50			
Flitwick	d			09 20					09 30				09 34		09 50					10 00			
Harlington	d			09 24									09 38		09 54								
Leagrave	d			09 29									09 43		09 59								
Luton 10	d			09 34					09 40			09 44	09 48		10 04	10 02				10 10			10 14
Luton Airport Parkway 7 ✈	d			09 36	09 31				09 43			09 46	09 50		10 06					10 13			10 16
Harpenden	d			09 42					09 48			09 52	09 56		10 12					10 18			10 22
St Albans City	d		09 44	09 48					09 54			09 59	10 02	10 14	10 18					10 24			10 29
Radlett	d		09 49									10 04		10 19									10 34
Elstree & Borehamwood	d		09 53									10 08		10 23									10 38
Mill Hill Broadway	d		09 58									10 13		10 28									10 43
Hendon	d		10 01									10 16		10 31									10 46
Cricklewood	d		10 05									10 20		10 35									10 50
West Hampstead Thameslink ⊖	d		10 10									10 24	10 15	10 40									10 54
Kentish Town ⊖	d	←	10 15			←	←	←		←	10 26	10 30		10 45			←	←	←		←	10 56	11 00
St Pancras International 15 ⊖	a	09 52	10 19	10 09	09 56	09 58	10 03	10 09	10 15	10 19	10 29	10 33	10 22	10 49	10 39	10 26	10 29	10 33	10 39	10 45	10 49	10 59	11 03
	d	09 54	10 19	10 10		10 00	10 04	10 10	10 15	10 19	10 30	10 34	10 24	10 49	10 40		10 30	10 34	10 40	10 45	10 49	11 00	11 04
Farringdon 3 ⊖	d	09 59	→	→		10 05	10 09	10 15	10 21	10 25	→	→	10 29	→	→		10 35	10 39	10 45	10 51	10 55	→	→
City Thameslink 3	d	10 03				10 09	10 13	10 18	10 24	10 27			10 33				10 39	10 43	10 48	10 54	10 57		
London Blackfriars 3 ⊖	d	10 05				10 12	10 16	10 20	10 27	10 30			10 35				10 42	10 46	10 50	10 57	11 00		
Elephant & Castle ⊖173,179	d					10 16	10 19		10a30	10 33							10 46	10 49		11a00	11 03		
Loughborough Jn 173,179	d						10 23			10 37								10 53			11 07		
Herne Hill 4 173,179	d						10 27			10 41								10 57			11 11		
London Bridge 4	a	10 11						10 26					10 41						10 56				
	d	10 12						10 27					10 42						10 57				
Tulse Hill 3	d						10 31			10 46								11 01			11 16		
Streatham 4	d						10 35			10 50								11 05			11 20		
Mitcham Eastfields 173	d									10 54											11 24		
Mitcham Junction 173 🚋	d									10 57											11 27		
Hackbridge 173	d									11 00											11 30		
Carshalton 173	d									11 03											11 33		
Tooting 173	d						10 40											11 10					
Haydons Road 173	d						10 43											11 13					
Wimbledon 6 ⊖173,179 🚋	d						10 47											11 17					
Wimbledon Chase 179	d						10 50											11 20					
South Merton 179	d						10 52											11 22					
Morden South 179	d						10 54											11 24					
St Helier 179	d						10 56											11 26					
Sutton Common 179	d						10 58											11 28					
West Sutton 179	d						11 01											11 31					
Sutton (Surrey) 4 179	a						11 05			11 06								11 35			11 36		
Denmark Hill 4 195	d					10 22											10 52						
Peckham Rye 4 195	d					10 25											10 55						
Nunhead 4 195	d					10 27											10 57						
Crofton Park 195	d					10 30											11 00						
Catford 195	d					10 33											11 03						
Bellingham 195	d					10 35											11 05						
Beckenham Hill 195	d					10 37											11 07						
Ravensbourne 195	d					10 39											11 09						
Shortlands 195	d					10 41											11 11						
Bromley South 4 195	d					10 44											11 14						
Bickley 4 195	d					10 47											11 17						
St Mary Cray 195	d					10 51											11 21						
Swanley 4 195	d					10 56											11 26						
Eynsford 195	d					11 00											11 30						
Shoreham (Kent) 195	d					11 04											11 34						
Otford 4 195	d					11 07											11 37						
Bat & Ball 195	d					11 10											11 40						
Sevenoaks 4 195	a					11 13											11 43						
East Croydon 🚋	d	10 25						10 41					10 55						11 11				
Redhill	d																						
Gatwick Airport 10 ✈	d	10 41						10 57					11 11						11 27				
Three Bridges 4	d	10 45						11 02					11 15						11 32				
Balcombe	d												11 21										
Haywards Heath 3	d	10 55						11 11					11 27						11 41				
Wivelsfield 4	d	10 59											11 31										
Burgess Hill 4	d	11 01											11 33										
Hassocks 4	d	11 04											11 36										
Preston Park	d	11 11											11 43										
Brighton 10	a	11 15						11 25					11 47						11 55				

A From Bedford
B To Sutton (Surrey)
C To Brighton
D From Lincoln
E From Kentish Town
F From Luton
G From St Albans City
H To Sevenoaks
I From Corby.

The trains that operate to and from Sevenoaks, Orpington and Rochester (and a few other destinations at peak times) are operated jointly by First Capital Connect (north of Blackfriars) and Southeastern (south of Blackfriars)

Table 52 shows the complete service between Bedford and London, whilst services between London, Sevenoaks, Sutton and Brighton only show through Thameslink services. Other Tables should be consulted for additional journey opportunities.

Table 52

Mondays to Fridays

9 December to 16 May

Bedford, Luton, St Albans and City of London - South London, Gatwick Airport and Brighton

Network Diagram - refer to first Page of Table 52

Station		FC 1	FC A	FC 1 B	EM ◇1 C	FC D	FC E	FC 1 F	FC	FC G	FC H	FC A	FC 1	FC A	FC 1 B	EM ◇1 I	FC D	FC E	FC 1 F	FC G	FC H	FC A	FC 1
Bedford 7	d	09 54		10 10	10 16				10 20				10 24		10 40	10 47							10 54
Flitwick	d	10 04		10 20					10 30				10 34		10 50								11 04
Harlington	d	10 08		10 24									10 38		10 54								11 08
Leagrave	d	10 13		10 29									10 43		10 59								11 13
Luton 10	d	10 18		10 34					10 40			10 44	10 48		11 04	11 02						11 14	11 18
Luton Airport Parkway 7 ✈	d	10 20		10 36	10 31				10 43			10 46	10 50		11 06							11 16	11 20
Harpenden	d	10 26		10 42					10 48			10 52	10 56		11 12							11 22	11 26
St Albans City	d	10 32	10 44	10 48					10 54			10 59	11 02	11 14	11 18							11 29	11 32
Radlett	d		10 49									11 04		11 19								11 34	
Elstree & Borehamwood	d		10 53									11 08		11 23								11 38	
Mill Hill Broadway	d		10 58									11 13		11 28								11 43	
Hendon	d		11 01									11 16		11 31								11 46	
Cricklewood	d		11 05									11 20		11 35								11 50	
West Hampstead Thameslink ⊖	d	10 45	11 10									11 24	11 15	11 39								11 54	11 45
Kentish Town ⊖	d		11 15			←	←	←		←	11 26	11 30		11 44			←	←	←	←	11 56	12 00	
St Pancras International 15 ⊖	a	10 52	11 19	11 09	10 56	10 59	11 03	11 09	11 15	11 19	11 29	11 33	11 22	11 47	11 39	11 26	11 29	11 33	11 39	11 47	11 59	12 03	11 52
	d	10 54	11 19	11 10		11 00	11 04	11 10	11 15	11 19	11 30	11 34	11 24	11 48	11 40		11 30	11 34	11 40	11 48	12 00	12 04	11 54
Farringdon 3 ⊖	d	10 59	→	→		11 05	11 09	11 15	11 21	11 25	→	→	11 29	→	→		11 35	11 39	11 45	11 53	→	→	11 59
City Thameslink 3	d	11 03				11 09	11 13	11 18	11 24	11 27			11 33				11 39	11 43	11 48	11 57			12 03
London Blackfriars 3 ⊖	d	11 05				11 12	11 16	11 20	11 27	11 30			11 35				11 42	11 46	11 50	12 00			12 05
Elephant & Castle ⊖173,179	d					11 16	11 19		11a30	11 33							11 46	11 49		12 03			
Loughborough Jn 173,179	d						11 23			11 37								11 53		12 07			
Herne Hill 4 173,179	d						11 27			11 41								11 57		12 11			
London Bridge 4	a	11 11						11 26					11 41						11 56				12 11
	d	11 12						11 27					11 42						11 57				12 12
Tulse Hill 3	d						11 31			11 46								12 01		12 16			
Streatham 4	d						11 35			11 50								12 05		12 20			
Mitcham Eastfields 173	d									11 54										12 24			
Mitcham Junction 173	d									11 57										12 27			
Hackbridge 173	d									12 00										12 30			
Carshalton 173	d									12 03										12 33			
Tooting 173	d						11 40											12 10					
Haydons Road 173	d						11 43											12 13					
Wimbledon 6 ⊖173,179	d						11 47											12 17					
Wimbledon Chase 179	d						11 50											12 20					
South Merton 179	d						11 52											12 22					
Morden South 179	d						11 54											12 24					
St Helier 179	d						11 56											12 26					
Sutton Common 179	d						11 58											12 28					
West Sutton 179	d						12 01											12 31					
Sutton (Surrey) 4 179	a						12 05			12 06								12 35		12 36			
Denmark Hill 4 195	d					11 22											11 52						
Peckham Rye 4 195	d					11 25											11 55						
Nunhead 4 195	d					11 27											11 57						
Crofton Park 195	d					11 30											12 00						
Catford 195	d					11 33											12 03						
Bellingham 195	d					11 35											12 05						
Beckenham Hill 195	d					11 37											12 07						
Ravensbourne 195	d					11 39											12 09						
Shortlands 195	d					11 41											12 11						
Bromley South 4 195	d					11 44											12 14						
Bickley 4 195	d					11 47											12 17						
St Mary Cray 195	d					11 51											12 21						
Swanley 4 195	d					11 56											12 26						
Eynsford 195	d					12 00											12 30						
Shoreham (Kent) 195	d					12 04											12 34						
Otford 4 195	d					12 07											12 37						
Bat & Ball 195	d					12 10											12 40						
Sevenoaks 4 195	a					12 13											12 43						
East Croydon	d	11 25						11 41					11 55						12 11				12 25
Redhill	d																						
Gatwick Airport 10 ✈	d	11 41						11 57					12 11						12 27				12 41
Three Bridges 4	d	11 45						12 02					12 15						12 32				12 45
Balcombe	d												12 21										
Haywards Heath 3	d	11 55						12 11					12 27						12 41				12 55
Wivelsfield 4	d	11 59											12 31										12 59
Burgess Hill 4	d	12 01											12 33										13 01
Hassocks 4	d	12 04											12 36										13 04
Preston Park	d	12 11											12 43										13 11
Brighton 10	a	12 15						12 25					12 47						12 55				13 15

A To Sutton (Surrey)
B To Brighton
C From Nottingham
D From Kentish Town
E From Luton
F From Bedford
G From St Albans City
H To Sevenoaks
I From Corby.

The trains that operate to and from Sevenoaks, Orpington and Rochester (and a few other destinations at peak times) are operated jointly by First Capital Connect (north of Blackfriars) and Southeastern (south of Blackfriars)

Table 52 shows the complete service between Bedford and London, whilst services between London, Sevenoaks, Sutton and Brighton only show through Thameslink services. Other Tables should be consulted for additional journey opportunities.

Table 52

Mondays to Fridays

9 December to 16 May

Bedford, Luton, St Albans and City of London - South London, Gatwick Airport and Brighton

Network Diagram - refer to first Page of Table 52

Station		FC	FC	EM	FC	FC	FC	FC	FC	FC	FC	FC	FC	EM	FC	FC	FC	FC	FC	FC	FC	FC
			1	◇1			1				1		1	◇1			1				1	
		A	B	C	D	E	F	G	H	A		A	B	I	D	E	F	G	H	A		A
Bedford 7	d		11 10	11 16							11 24		11 40	11 47							11 54	
Flitwick	d		11 20								11 34		11 50								12 04	
Harlington	d		11 24								11 38		11 54								12 08	
Leagrave	d		11 29								11 43		11 59								12 13	
Luton 10	d		11 34							11 44	11 48		12 04	12 02						12 14	12 18	
Luton Airport Parkway 7 ✈	d		11 36	11 31						11 46	11 50		12 06							12 16	12 20	
Harpenden	d		11 42							11 52	11 56		12 12							12 22	12 26	
St Albans City	d	11 44	11 48							11 59	12 02	12 14	12 18							12 29	12 32	12 44
Radlett	d	11 49								12 04		12 19								12 34		12 49
Elstree & Borehamwood	d	11 53								12 08		12 23								12 38		12 53
Mill Hill Broadway	d	11 58								12 13		12 28								12 43		12 58
Hendon	d	12 01								12 16		12 31								12 46		13 01
Cricklewood	d	12 05								12 20		12 35								12 50		13 05
West Hampstead Thameslink ⊖	d	12 09								12 24	12 15	12 39								12 54	12 45	13 09
Kentish Town ⊖	d	12 14			←	←	←	←	12 26	12 30		12 44			←	←	←	←	12 56	13 00		13 14
St Pancras International 15 ⊖	a	12 17	12 09	11 56	11 59	12 03	12 09	12 17	12 29	12 33	12 22	12 47	12 39	12 26	12 29	12 33	12 39	12 47	12 59	13 03	12 52	13 17
	d	12 18	12 10		12 00	12 04	12 10	12 18	12 30	12 34	12 24	12 48	12 40		12 30	12 34	12 40	12 48	13 00	13 04	12 54	13 18
Farringdon 3 ⊖	d	→	→		12 05	12 09	12 15	12 23	→	→	12 29	→	→		12 35	12 39	12 45	12 53	→	→	12 59	→
City Thameslink 3	d				12 09	12 13	12 18	12 27			12 33				12 39	12 43	12 48	12 57			13 03	
London Blackfriars 3 ⊖	d				12 12	12 16	12 20	12 30			12 35				12 42	12 46	12 50	13 00			13 05	
Elephant & Castle ⊖173,179	d				12 16	12 19		12 33							12 46	12 49		13 03				
Loughborough Jn 173,179	d					12 23		12 37								12 53		13 07				
Herne Hill 4 173,179	d					12 27		12 41								12 57		13 11				
London Bridge 4	a						12 26				12 41						12 56				13 11	
	d						12 27				12 42						12 57				13 12	
Tulse Hill 3	d					12 31		12 46								13 01		13 16				
Streatham 4	d					12 35		12 50								13 05		13 20				
Mitcham Eastfields 173	d							12 54										13 24				
Mitcham Junction 173 ⛴	d							12 57										13 27				
Hackbridge 173	d							13 00										13 30				
Carshalton 173	d							13 03										13 33				
Tooting 173	d					12 40										13 10						
Haydons Road 173	d					12 43										13 13						
Wimbledon 6 ⊖173,179 ⛴	d					12 47										13 17						
Wimbledon Chase 179	d					12 50										13 20						
South Merton 179	d					12 52										13 22						
Morden South 179	d					12 54										13 24						
St Helier 179	d					12 56										13 26						
Sutton Common 179	d					12 58										13 28						
West Sutton 179	d					13 01										13 31						
Sutton (Surrey) 4 179	a					13 05		13 06								13 35		13 36				
Denmark Hill 4 195	d				12 22										12 52							
Peckham Rye 4 195	d				12 25										12 55							
Nunhead 4 195	d				12 27										12 57							
Crofton Park 195	d				12 30										13 00							
Catford 195	d				12 33										13 03							
Bellingham 195	d				12 35										13 05							
Beckenham Hill 195	d				12 37										13 07							
Ravensbourne 195	d				12 39										13 09							
Shortlands 195	d				12 41										13 11							
Bromley South 4 195	d				12 44										13 14							
Bickley 4 195	d				12 47										13 17							
St Mary Cray 195	d				12 51										13 21							
Swanley 4 195	d				12 56										13 26							
Eynsford 195	d				13 00										13 30							
Shoreham (Kent) 195	d				13 04										13 34							
Otford 4 195	d				13 07										13 37							
Bat & Ball 195	d				13 10										13 40							
Sevenoaks 4 195	a				13 13										13 43							
East Croydon ⛴	d						12 41				12 55						13 11				13 25	
Redhill	d																					
Gatwick Airport 10 ✈	d						12 57				13 11						13 27				13 41	
Three Bridges 4	d						13 02				13 15						13 32				13 45	
Balcombe	d										13 21											
Haywards Heath 3	d						13 11				13 27						13 41				13 55	
Wivelsfield 4	d										13 31										13 59	
Burgess Hill 4	d										13 33										14 01	
Hassocks 4	d										13 36										14 04	
Preston Park	d										13 43										14 11	
Brighton 10	a						13 25				13 47						13 55				14 15	

A To Sutton (Surrey)
B To Brighton
C From Nottingham
D From Kentish Town
E From Luton
F From Bedford
G From St Albans City
H To Sevenoaks
I From Corby.

The trains that operate to and from Sevenoaks, Orpington and Rochester (and a few other destinations at peak times) are operated jointly by First Capital Connect (north of Blackfriars) and Southeastern (south of Blackfriars)

Table 52 shows the complete service between Bedford and London, whilst services between London, Sevenoaks, Sutton and Brighton only show through Thameslink services. Other Tables should be consulted for additional journey opportunities.

Table 52

Mondays to Fridays

9 December to 16 May

Bedford, Luton, St Albans and City of London - South London, Gatwick Airport and Brighton

Network Diagram - refer to first Page of Table 52

	FC 1 A	EM ◇1 B 🚲	FC C	FC D	FC 1 E	FC F	FC G	FC H	FC 1	FC H	FC 1 A	EM ◇1 I 🚲	FC C	FC D	FC 1 E	FC F	FC G	FC H	FC 1	FC H	FC 1 A	EM ◇1 B 🚲
Bedford 7 d	12 10	12 16							12 24		12 40	12 47							12 54		13 10	13 16
Flitwick d	12 20								12 34		12 50								13 04		13 20	
Harlington d	12 24								12 38		12 54								13 08		13 24	
Leagrave d	12 29								12 43		12 59								13 13		13 29	
Luton 10 d	12 34							12 44	12 48		13 04	13 02						13 14	13 18		13 34	
Luton Airport Parkway 7 ✈ d	12 36	12 31						12 46	12 50		13 06							13 16	13 20		13 36	13 31
Harpenden d	12 42							12 52	12 56		13 12							13 22	13 26		13 42	
St Albans City d	12 48							12 59	13 02	13 14	13 18							13 29	13 32	13 44	13 48	
Radlett d								13 04		13 19								13 34		13 49		
Elstree & Borehamwood d								13 08		13 23								13 38		13 53		
Mill Hill Broadway d								13 13		13 28								13 43		13 58		
Hendon d								13 16		13 31								13 46		14 01		
Cricklewood d								13 20		13 35								13 50		14 05		
West Hampstead Thameslink ⊖ d								13 24	13 15	13 39								13 54	13 45	14 09		
Kentish Town ⊖ d			←	←	←	←	13 26	13 30		13 44			←	←	←	←	13 56	14 00		14 14		
St Pancras International 15 ⊖ a	13 09	12 56	12 59	13 03	13 09	13 17	13 29	13 33	13 22	13 47	13 39	13 26	13 29	13 33	13 39	13 47	13 59	14 03	13 52	14 17	14 09	13 56
d	13 10		13 00	13 04	13 10	13 18	13 30	13 34	13 24	13 48	13 40		13 30	13 34	13 40	13 48	14 00	14 04	13 54	14 18	14 09	
Farringdon 3 ⊖ d	→		13 05	13 09	13 15	13 23	→	→	13 29	→	→		13 35	13 39	13 45	13 53	→	→	13 59	→	→	
City Thameslink 3 d			13 09	13 13	13 18	13 27			13 33				13 39	13 43	13 48	13 57			14 03			
London Blackfriars 3 ⊖ d			13 12	13 16	13 20	13 30			13 35				13 42	13 46	13 50	14 00			14 05			
Elephant & Castle ⊖173,179 d			13 16	13 19		13 33							13 46	13 49		14 03						
Loughborough Jn 173,179 d				13 23		13 37								13 53		14 07						
Herne Hill 4 173,179 d				13 27		13 41								13 57		14 11						
London Bridge 4 a					13 26				13 41						13 56				14 11			
d					13 27				13 42						13 57				14 12			
Tulse Hill 3 d				13 31		13 46								14 01		14 16						
Streatham 4 d				13 35		13 50								14 05		14 20						
Mitcham Eastfields 173 d						13 54										14 24						
Mitcham Junction 173 🚌 d						13 57										14 27						
Hackbridge 173 d						14 00										14 30						
Carshalton 173 d						14 03										14 33						
Tooting 173 d				13 40										14 10								
Haydons Road 173 d				13 43										14 13								
Wimbledon 6 ⊖173,179 🚌 d				13 47										14 17								
Wimbledon Chase 179 d				13 50										14 20								
South Merton 179 d				13 52										14 22								
Morden South 179 d				13 54										14 24								
St Helier 179 d				13 56										14 26								
Sutton Common 179 d				13 58										14 28								
West Sutton 179 d				14 01										14 31								
Sutton (Surrey) 4 179 a				14 05		14 06								14 35		14 36						
Denmark Hill 4 195 d			13 22										13 52									
Peckham Rye 4 195 d			13 25										13 55									
Nunhead 4 195 d			13 27										13 57									
Crofton Park 195 d			13 30										14 00									
Catford 195 d			13 33										14 03									
Bellingham 195 d			13 35										14 05									
Beckenham Hill 195 d			13 37										14 07									
Ravensbourne 195 d			13 39										14 09									
Shortlands 195 d			13 41										14 11									
Bromley South 4 195 d			13 44										14 14									
Bickley 4 195 d			13 47										14 17									
St Mary Cray 195 d			13 51										14 21									
Swanley 4 195 d			13 56										14 26									
Eynsford 195 d			14 00										14 30									
Shoreham (Kent) 195 d			14 04										14 34									
Otford 4 195 d			14 07										14 37									
Bat & Ball 195 d			14 10										14 40									
Sevenoaks 4 195 a			14 13										14 43									
East Croydon 🚌 d					13 41				13 55						14 11				14 25			
Redhill d																						
Gatwick Airport 10 ✈ d					13 57				14 11						14 27				14 41			
Three Bridges 4 d					14 02				14 15						14 32				14 45			
Balcombe d									14 21													
Haywards Heath 3 d					14 11				14 27						14 41				14 55			
Wivelsfield 4 d									14 31										14 59			
Burgess Hill 4 d									14 33										15 01			
Hassocks 4 d									14 36										15 04			
Preston Park d									14 43										15 11			
Brighton 10 a					14 25				14 47						14 55				15 15			

A To Brighton
B From Nottingham
C From Kentish Town
D From Luton
E From Bedford
F From St Albans City
G To Sevenoaks
H To Sutton (Surrey)
I From Corby.

The trains that operate to and from Sevenoaks, Orpington and Rochester (and a few other destinations at peak times) are operated jointly by First Capital Connect (north of Blackfriars) and Southeastern (south of Blackfriars)

Table 52 shows the complete service between Bedford and London, whilst services between London, Sevenoaks, Sutton and Brighton only show through Thameslink services. Other Tables should be consulted for additional journey opportunities.

Table 52

Mondays to Fridays

9 December to 16 May

Bedford, Luton, St Albans and City of London - South London, Gatwick Airport and Brighton

Network Diagram - refer to first Page of Table 52

		FC	FC	FC	FC	FC	FC	FC	FC	FC	EM	FC	FC	FC	FC	FC	FC	FC	FC	FC	EM	FC	FC
				1				1		1	◇1			1				1		1	◇1		
		A	B	C	D	E	F		F	G	H	A	B	C	D	E	F		F	G	I	A	B
Bedford 7	d							13 24		13 40	13 47							13 54		14 10	14 16		
Flitwick	d							13 34		13 50								14 04		14 20			
Harlington	d							13 38		13 54								14 08		14 24			
Leagrave	d							13 43		13 59								14 13		14 29			
Luton 10	d						13 44	13 48		14 04	14 02						14 14	14 18		14 34			
Luton Airport Parkway 7 ✈	d						13 46	13 50		14 06							14 16	14 20		14 36	14 31		
Harpenden	d						13 52	13 56		14 12							14 22	14 26		14 42			
St Albans City	d						13 59	14 02	14 14	14 18							14 29	14 32	14 44	14 48			
Radlett	d						14 04		14 19								14 34		14 49				
Elstree & Borehamwood	d						14 08		14 23								14 38		14 53				
Mill Hill Broadway	d						14 13		14 28								14 43		14 58				
Hendon	d						14 16		14 31								14 46		15 01				
Cricklewood	d						14 20		14 35								14 50		15 05				
West Hampstead Thameslink ⊖	d						14 24	14 15	14 39								14 54	14 45	15 09				
Kentish Town ⊖	d	←	←	←	←	14 26	14 30		14 44			←	←	←	←	14 56	15 00		15 14			←	←
St Pancras International 15 ⊖	a	13 59	14 03	14 09	14 17	14 29	14 33	14 22	14 47	14 39	14 26	14 29	14 33	14 39	14 47	14 59	15 03	14 52	15 17	15 09	14 56	14 59	15 03
	d	14 00	14 04	14 09	14 18	14 30	14 34	14 24	14 48	14 40		14 30	14 34	14 40	14 48	15 00	15 04	14 54	15 18	15 10		15 00	15 04
Farringdon 3 ⊖	d	14 05	14 09	14 14	14 23	→	→	14 29	→	→		14 35	14 39	14 45	14 53	→	→	14 59	→	→		15 05	15 09
City Thameslink 3	d	14 09	14 13	14 18	14 27			14 33				14 39	14 43	14 48	14 57			15 03				15 09	15 13
London Blackfriars 3 ⊖	d	14 12	14 16	14 20	14 30			14 35				14 42	14 46	14 50	15 00			15 05				15 12	15 16
Elephant & Castle ⊖173,179	d	14 16	14 19		14 33							14 46	14 49		15 03							15 16	15 19
Loughborough Jn 173,179	d		14 23		14 37								14 53		15 07								15 23
Herne Hill 4 173,179	d		14 27		14 41								14 57		15 11								15 27
London Bridge 4	a			14 26				14 41						14 56				15 11					
	d			14 27				14 42						14 57				15 12					
Tulse Hill 3	d		14 31		14 46								15 01		15 16								15 31
Streatham 4	d		14 35		14 50								15 05		15 20								15 35
Mitcham Eastfields 173	d				14 54										15 24								
Mitcham Junction 173 🚌	d				14 57										15 27								
Hackbridge 173	d				15 00										15 30								
Carshalton 173	d				15 03										15 33								
Tooting 173	d		14 40										15 10										15 40
Haydons Road 173	d		14 43										15 13										15 43
Wimbledon 6 ⊖173,179 🚌	d		14 47										15 17										15 47
Wimbledon Chase 179	d		14 50										15 20										15 50
South Merton 179	d		14 52										15 22										15 52
Morden South 179	d		14 54										15 24										15 54
St Helier 179	d		14 56										15 26										15 56
Sutton Common 179	d		14 58										15 28										15 58
West Sutton 179	d		15 01										15 31										16 01
Sutton (Surrey) 4 179	a		15 05		15 06								15 35		15 36								16 05
Denmark Hill 4 195	d	14 22										14 52										15 22	
Peckham Rye 4 195	d	14 25										14 55										15 25	
Nunhead 4 195	d	14 27										14 57										15 27	
Crofton Park 195	d	14 30										15 00										15 30	
Catford 195	d	14 33										15 03										15 33	
Bellingham 195	d	14 35										15 05										15 35	
Beckenham Hill 195	d	14 37										15 07										15 37	
Ravensbourne 195	d	14 39										15 09										15 39	
Shortlands 195	d	14 41										15 11										15 41	
Bromley South 4 195	d	14 44										15 14										15 44	
Bickley 4 195	d	14 47										15 17										15 47	
St Mary Cray 195	d	14 51										15 21										15 51	
Swanley 4 195	d	14 56										15 26										15 56	
Eynsford 195	d	15 00										15 30										16 00	
Shoreham (Kent) 195	d	15 04										15 34										16 04	
Otford 4 195	d	15 07										15 37										16 07	
Bat & Ball 195	d	15 10										15 40										16 10	
Sevenoaks 4 195	a	15 13										15 43										16 13	
East Croydon 🚌	d			14 41				14 55						15 11				15 25					
Redhill	d																						
Gatwick Airport 10 ✈	d			14 57				15 11						15 27				15 41					
Three Bridges 4	d			15 02				15 15						15 32				15 45					
Balcombe	d							15 21															
Haywards Heath 3	d			15 11				15 27						15 41				15 55					
Wivelsfield 4	d							15 31										15 59					
Burgess Hill 4	d							15 33										16 01					
Hassocks 4	d							15 36										16 04					
Preston Park	d							15 43										16 11					
Brighton 10	a			15 25				15 47						15 55				16 15					

A From Kentish Town
B From Luton
C From Bedford
D From St Albans City
E To Sevenoaks
F To Sutton (Surrey)
G To Brighton
H From Corby.
I From Nottingham

The trains that operate to and from Sevenoaks, Orpington and Rochester (and a few other destinations at peak times) are operated jointly by First Capital Connect (north of Blackfriars) and Southeastern (south of Blackfriars)

Table 52 shows the complete service between Bedford and London, whilst services between London, Sevenoaks, Sutton and Brighton only show through Thameslink services. Other Tables should be consulted for additional journey opportunities.

Table 52

Mondays to Fridays

9 December to 16 May

Bedford, Luton, St Albans and City of London - South London, Gatwick Airport and Brighton

Network Diagram - refer to first Page of Table 52

		FC	FC	FC	FC	FC	FC	FC	EM	FC	FC	FC	FC	FC	FC	FC	FC	FC	FC	EM	FC	FC	FC
		[1]				[1]		[1]	◇[1]			[1]				[1]			[1]	◇[1]			[1]
		A	B	C	D		D	E	F	G	H	A	B	C	D		I	D	E	J	G	H	A
									🚲											🚲			
Bedford [7]	d					14 24		14 40	14 47							14 54			15 10	15 16			
Flitwick	d					14 34		14 50								15 04			15 20				
Harlington	d					14 38		14 54								15 08			15 24				
Leagrave	d					14 43		14 59								15 13			15 29				
Luton [10]	d				14 44	14 48		15 04	15 02						15 14	15 18			15 34				
Luton Airport Parkway [7] ✈	d				14 46	14 50		15 06							15 16	15 20			15 36	15 31			
Harpenden	d				14 52	14 56		15 12							15 22	15 26			15 42				
St Albans City	d				14 59	15 02	15 14	15 18							15 29	15 32		15 44	15 48				
Radlett	d				15 04		15 19								15 34			15 49					
Elstree & Borehamwood	d				15 08		15 23								15 38			15 53					
Mill Hill Broadway	d				15 13		15 28								15 43			15 58					
Hendon	d				15 16		15 31								15 46			16 01					
Cricklewood	d				15 20		15 35								15 50			16 05					
West Hampstead Thameslink ⊖	d				15 24	15 15	15 39								15 54	15 45		16 09					
Kentish Town ⊖	d	←	←	15 26	15 30		15 44			←	←	←	←	15 56	16 00		16 10	16 14			←	←	←
St Pancras International [15] ⊖	a	15 09	15 17	15 29	15 33	15 22	15 47	15 39	15 26	15 29	15 33	15 39	15 47	15 59	16 03	15 52	16 13	16 17	16 09	15 56	15 59	16 03	16 09
	d	15 10	15 18	15 30	15 34	15 24	15 48	15 40		15 30	15 34	15 40	15 48	16 00	16 04	15 54	16 14	16 18	16 10		16 00	16 04	16 10
Farringdon [3] ⊖	d	15 15	15 23	→	→	15 29	→	→		15 35	15 39	15 45	15 53	→	→	15 59	→	→	→		16 05	16 09	16 15
City Thameslink [3]	d	15 18	15 27			15 33				15 39	15 43	15 48	15 57			16 03					16 09	16 13	16 18
London Blackfriars [3] ⊖	d	15 20	15 30			15 35				15 42	15 46	15 50	16 00			16 05					16 12	16 16	16 20
Elephant & Castle ⊖173,179	d		15 33							15 46	15 49		16 03								16 16	16 19	
Loughborough Jn 173,179	d		15 37								15 53		16 07									16 23	
Herne Hill [4] 173,179	d		15 41								15 57		16 11									16 27	
London Bridge [4]	a	15 26				15 41						15 56				16 11							16 26
	d	15 27				15 42						15 57				16 12							16 27
Tulse Hill [3]	d		15 46								16 01		16 16									16 32	
Streatham [4]	d		15 50								16 05		16 20									16 36	
Mitcham Eastfields 173	d		15 54										16 24										
Mitcham Junction 173 🚊	d		15 57										16 27										
Hackbridge 173	d		16 00										16 30										
Carshalton 173	d		16 03										16 33										
Tooting 173	d										16 10											16 40	
Haydons Road 173	d										16 13											16 43	
Wimbledon [6] ⊖173,179 🚊	d										16 17											16 47	
Wimbledon Chase 179	d										16 20											16 50	
South Merton 179	d										16 22											16 52	
Morden South 179	d										16 24											16 54	
St Helier 179	d										16 26											16 56	
Sutton Common 179	d										16 28											16 58	
West Sutton 179	d										16 31											17 01	
Sutton (Surrey) [4] 179	a		16 06								16 35		16 36									17 05	
Denmark Hill [4] 195	d									15 52											16 22		
Peckham Rye [4] 195	d									15 55											16 25		
Nunhead [4] 195	d									15 57											16 27		
Crofton Park 195	d									16 00											16 30		
Catford 195	d									16 03											16 33		
Bellingham 195	d									16 05											16 35		
Beckenham Hill 195	d									16 07											16 37		
Ravensbourne 195	d									16 09											16 39		
Shortlands 195	d									16 11											16 41		
Bromley South [4] 195	d									16 14											16 44		
Bickley [4] 195	d									16 17											16 47		
St Mary Cray 195	d									16 21											16 51		
Swanley [4] 195	d									16 26											16 56		
Eynsford 195	d									16 30											17 00		
Shoreham (Kent) 195	d									16 34											17 04		
Otford [4] 195	d									16 37											17 07		
Bat & Ball 195	d									16 40											17 10		
Sevenoaks [4] 195	a									16 43											17 14		
East Croydon 🚊	d	15 41				15 55						16 11				16 25							16 41
Redhill	d																						
Gatwick Airport [10] ✈	d	15 57				16 11						16 27				16 41							16 57
Three Bridges [4]	d	16 02				16 15						16 32				16 45							17 02
Balcombe	d					16 21																	
Haywards Heath [3]	d	16 11				16 27						16 41				16 55							17 11
Wivelsfield [4]	d					16 31										16 59							
Burgess Hill [4]	d					16 33										17 01							17 17
Hassocks [4]	d					16 36										17 04							17 21
Preston Park	d					16 43										17 11							
Brighton [10]	a	16 25				16 47						16 55				17 15							17 30

A From Bedford
B From St Albans City
C To Sevenoaks
D To Sutton (Surrey)
E To Brighton
F From Corby.
G From Kentish Town
H From Luton
I To Orpington
J From Nottingham

The trains that operate to and from Sevenoaks, Orpington and Rochester (and a few other destinations at peak times) are operated jointly by First Capital Connect (north of Blackfriars) and Southeastern (south of Blackfriars)

Table 52 shows the complete service between Bedford and London, whilst services between London, Sevenoaks, Sutton and Brighton only show through Thameslink services. Other Tables should be consulted for additional journey opportunities.

Table 52

Mondays to Fridays

9 December to 16 May

Bedford, Luton, St Albans and City of London - South London, Gatwick Airport and Brighton

Network Diagram - refer to first Page of Table 52

	FC	FC	FC	FC	FC [1]	FC	FC [1]	EM ◇[1]	FC	FC	FC [1]	FC [1]	FC	FC	FC	FC	FC [1]	EM ◇[1]	FC	FC [1]	FC [1]	FC
	A	B	C	D		D	E	F 🚃	G	H	I		B	D		D	J	K 🚃	H	L	M	B
Bedford [7] d					15 24		15 40	15 47				15 50			15 54		16 08	16 16			16 20	
Flitwick d					15 34		15 50					16 00			16 04		16 18				16 30	
Harlington d					15 38		15 54								16 08		16 22					
Leagrave d					15 43		15 59								16 13		16 27					
Luton [10] d				15 44	15 48		16 04	16 02				16 10		16 14	16 18		16 32				16 40	
Luton Airport Parkway [7] ✈ d				15 46	15 50		16 06					16 13		16 16	16 20		16 34	16 31			16 42	
Harpenden d				15 52	15 56		16 12					16 18		16 22	16 26		16 41					
St Albans City d				15 59	16 02	16 14	16 18					16 24		16 29	16 32	16 44	16 47				16 53	
Radlett d				16 04		16 19								16 34		16 49						
Elstree & Borehamwood d				16 08		16 23								16 38		16 53						
Mill Hill Broadway d				16 13		16 28								16 43		16 58						
Hendon d				16 16		16 31								16 46		17 01						
Cricklewood d				16 20		16 35								16 50		17 05						
West Hampstead Thameslink ⊖ d				16 24	16 15	16 40								16 54	16 44	17 08						
Kentish Town ⊖ d	←	←	16 24	16 30		16 45			←	←	←		←	16 58		17 12			←	←		←
St Pancras International [15] ⊖ a	16 13	16 17	16 27	16 33	16 21	16 49	16 39	16 26	16 27	16 33	16 39	16 44	16 49	17 02	16 53	17 17	17 07	16 56	17 02	17 07	17 11	17 17
d	16 14	16 18	16 28	16 34	16 22	16 50	16 40		16 28	16 34	16 40	16 46	16 50	17 02	16 58	17 18	17 08		17 02	17 08	17 14	17 18
Farringdon [3] ⊖ d	16 19	16 23	→	→	16 27	→	→		16 33	16 39	16 45	16 51	16 55	→	17 03	→	→		17 07	17 13	17 19	17 23
City Thameslink [3] d	16 23	16 27			16 31				16 37	16 43	16 49	16 55	16 59		17 07				17 11	17 17	17 22	17 27
London Blackfriars [3] ⊖ d	16 26	16 30			16 36				16 42	16 46	16 52	16 58	17 02		17 10				17 14	17 20	17 25	17 30
Elephant & Castle ⊖173,179 d	16 30	16 33							16 46	16 49	16 56	17 02	17 06		17 14				17 18		17 29	17 34
Loughborough Jn 173,179 d		16 37								16 53	17 00		17 10						17 22			17 38
Herne Hill [4] 173,179 d		16 41								16 57	17a04		17 16						17 26		17 36	17 43
London Bridge [4] a					16 42																	
d					16 43																	
Tulse Hill [3] d		16 47								17 02			17 20						17 32			17 48
Streatham [4] d		16 51								17 06			17 24						17 36			17 52
Mitcham Eastfields 173 d		16 55											17 28									17 55
Mitcham Junction 173 🚌 d		16 58											17 31									17 58
Hackbridge 173 d		17 01											17 34									18 02
Carshalton 173 d		17 04											17 37									18 04
Tooting 173 d										17 10									17 40			
Haydons Road 173 d										17 13									17 43			
Wimbledon [6] ⊖173,179 🚌 d										17 19									17 49			
Wimbledon Chase 179 d										17 22									17 52			
South Merton 179 d										17 24									17 54			
Morden South 179 d										17 26									17 56			
St Helier 179 d										17 28									17 58			
Sutton Common 179 d										17 30									18 00			
West Sutton 179 d										17 33									18 03			
Sutton (Surrey) [4] 179 a		17 08								17 37			17 40						18 07			18 08
Denmark Hill [4] 195 d	16 39								16 52						17 20							
Peckham Rye [4] 195 d	16 42								16 55						17 23							
Nunhead [4] 195 d	16 44								16 57						17 26							
Crofton Park 195 d	16 47								17 00						17 29							
Catford 195 d	16 50								17 03						17 32							
Bellingham 195 d	16 52								17 05						17 35							
Beckenham Hill 195 d	16 54								17 07						17 37							
Ravensbourne 195 d	16 56								17 09						17 39							
Shortlands 195 d	16 58								17 11						17 43							
Bromley South [4] 195 d	17 01								17 14						17 46						17 48	
Bickley [4] 195 d	17a04								17 17												17 50	
St Mary Cray 195 d									17 21												17 55	
Swanley [4] 195 d									17 26						17 55						17a59	
Eynsford 195 d									17 30						18 00							
Shoreham (Kent) 195 d									17 34						18 03							
Otford [4] 195 d									17 37						18 06							
Bat & Ball 195 d									17 40						18 14							
Sevenoaks [4] 195 a									17 45						18 23							
East Croydon 🚌 d					17 00							17 26								17 47		
Redhill d																				18 03		
Gatwick Airport [10] ✈ d					17 16							17 42								18 14		
Three Bridges [4] d					17 21							17 46								18 19		
Balcombe d					17 27							17 52								18 25		
Haywards Heath [3] d					17 32							17 58								18 31		
Wivelsfield [4] d					17 37																	
Burgess Hill [4] d					17 39							18 03								18 36		
Hassocks [4] d					17 43							18 07								18 40		
Preston Park d					17 50							18 14								18 47		
Brighton [10] a					17 54							18 18								18 53		

A From Kentish Town to Orpington
B From St Albans City
C To Sevenoaks
D To Sutton (Surrey)
E To Beckenham Junction
F From Corby.
G From Kentish Town
H From Luton
I From Bedford to Beckenham Junction
J To Brighton
K From Nottingham
L From Bedford
M To Rochester

The trains that operate to and from Sevenoaks, Orpington and Rochester (and a few other destinations at peak times) are operated jointly by First Capital Connect (north of Blackfriars) and Southeastern (south of Blackfriars)

Table 52 shows the complete service between Bedford and London, whilst services between London, Sevenoaks, Sutton and Brighton only show through Thameslink services. Other Tables should be consulted for additional journey opportunities.

Table 52

Mondays to Fridays

9 December to 16 May

Bedford, Luton, St Albans and City of London - South London, Gatwick Airport and Brighton

Network Diagram - refer to first Page of Table 52

Station		FC	FC	FC	FC	FC	EM	FC	FC	FC	FC	FC	FC	FC	FC	FC	FC	FC	EM	FC	FC	EM	FC
				[1]	[1]	[1]	◇[1]		[1]	[1]					[1]			[1]	◇[1]			◇[1]	[1]
			A		B	C	D 🚲	E	F	G	A	H		I	J		K		L 🚲	I	K	L 🚲	
Bedford [7]	d			16 24	16 34	16 40	16 47								16 54			17 07	17 16				17 20
Flitwick	d			16 34	16 44	16 51									17 04			17 17					17 30
Harlington	d			16 38	16 48										17 08			17 21					17 34
Leagrave	d			16 43	16 53										17 13			17 26					17 39
Luton [10]	d		16 44	16 48	16 58	17 02	17 02					17 10			17 18	17 22		17 31			17 38	17 49	17 44
Luton Airport Parkway [7] ✈	d		16 46	16 50	17 00	17 04						17 12			17 20	17 24		17 34	17 31		17 40		17 46
Harpenden	d		16 52	16 56	17 06	17 10						17 18			17 26	17 30		17 39			17 46		17 52
St Albans City	d		17 00	17 02	17 12	17 16					17 20	17 24			17 32	17 36	17 40	17 45			17 52		17 58
Radlett	d		17 05								17 25					17 41	17 45				17 57		
Elstree & Borehamwood	d		17 09								17 29					17 45	17 49				18 01		
Mill Hill Broadway	d		17 14								17 34					17 49	17 53				18 06		
Hendon	d		17 17								17 37						17 57				18 09		
Cricklewood	d		17 21								17 41						18 00				18 13		
West Hampstead Thameslink ⊖	d		17 24	17 15	17 28						17 44		17 40		17 48	17 56	18 04				18 19		
Kentish Town ⊖	d	17 16	17 28					←	←	←	17 48			←			18 08			←	18 23		
St Pancras International [15] ⊖	a	17 21	17 32	17 25	17 35	17 39	17 26	17 32	17 35	17 39	17 52	17 43	17 47	17 52	17 55	18 03	18 12	18 07	17 56	18 12	18 27	18 15	18 17
	d	17 22	17 32	17 28	17 36	17 40		17 32	17 36	17 40	17 52	17 44	17 48	17 52	17 56	18 04	18 12	18 08		18 12	18 28		18 18
Farringdon [3] ⊖	d	17 27	→	17 33	→	→		17 37	17 41	17 45	→	17 49	17 53	17 57	18 01	18 09	→	18 13		18 17	→		18 23
City Thameslink [3]	d	17 31		17 37				17 41	17 45	17 49		17 53	17 57	18 01	18 05	18 13		18 17		18 21			18 27
London Blackfriars [3] ⊖	d	17 36		17 40				17 44	17 48	17 52		17 56	18 00	18 04	18 10	18 16		18 20		18 24			18 30
Elephant & Castle ⊖173,179	d	17 40						17 48	17 52	17 56		18 00	18 05	18 08	18 14	18 20				18 28			18 34
Loughborough Jn 173,179	d							17 52						18 12		18 24							
Herne Hill [4] 173,179	d							17 57				18a06		18 17	18 21	18 28							
London Bridge [4]	a																	18 27					
	d																	18 28					
Tulse Hill [3]	d							18 02						18 22		18 32							
Streatham [4]	d							18 06						18 26		18 36							
Mitcham Eastfields 173	d													18 29									
Mitcham Junction 173 🚋	d													18 32									
Hackbridge 173	d													18 36									
Carshalton 173	d													18 38									
Tooting 173	d							18 10								18 40							
Haydons Road 173	d							18 13								18 43							
Wimbledon [6] ⊖173,179 🚋	d							18 17								18 47							
Wimbledon Chase 179	d							18 22								18 52							
South Merton 179	d							18 24								18 54							
Morden South 179	d							18 26								18 56							
St Helier 179	d							18 28								18 58							
Sutton Common 179	d							18 30								19 00							
West Sutton 179	d							18 33								19 03							
Sutton (Surrey) [4] 179	a							18 37						18 42		19 07							
Denmark Hill [4] 195	d	17 47											18 15							18 34			
Peckham Rye [4] 195	d	17 50											18 18							18 38			
Nunhead [4] 195	d	17 52											18 20							18 40			
Crofton Park 195	d	17 55											18 23							18 43			
Catford 195	d	17 58											18 26							18 46			
Bellingham 195	d	18 01											18 29							18 49			
Beckenham Hill 195	d	18 03											18 31							18 51			
Ravensbourne 195	d	18 05											18 33							18 53			
Shortlands 195	d	18 07											18 35							18 58			
Bromley South [4] 195	d	18 10							18 10				18 38		18 31					19 01			
Bickley [4] 195	d	18 12											18 40							19 04			
St Mary Cray 195	d	18 22							18 17				18 45		18 38					19 10			
Swanley [4] 195	d	18 26							18 22				18 53		18a42					19 15			
Eynsford 195	d	18 31											18 57							19 19			
Shoreham (Kent) 195	d	18 34											19 01							19 23			
Otford [4] 195	d	18 38							18a30				19 04							19 26			
Bat & Ball 195	d	18 41											19 07							19 29			
Sevenoaks [4] 195	a	18 50											19 12							19 37			
East Croydon 🚋	d			18 09						18 26								18 43					19 01
Redhill	d									18 39													
Gatwick Airport [10] ✈	d			18 24						18 49								18 59					19 18
Three Bridges [4]	d			18 29						18a56								19 03					
Balcombe	d																	19 10					
Haywards Heath [3]	d			18 38														19 15					19 30
Wivelsfield [4]	d			18 43																			
Burgess Hill [4]	d			18 45														19 21					19 35
Hassocks [4]	d			18 49														19 25					19 39
Preston Park	d			18 56																			19 46
Brighton [10]	a			19 01														19 34					19 52

A To Sutton (Surrey)
B To Ashford International
C To Three Bridges
D From Corby.
E From Luton
F From Bedford to Ashford International
G From Bedford
H To Kent House
I From St Albans City
J To Rochester
K To Sevenoaks
L From Nottingham

The trains that operate to and from Sevenoaks, Orpington and Rochester (and a few other destinations at peak times) are operated jointly by First Capital Connect (north of Blackfriars) and Southeastern (south of Blackfriars)

Table 52 shows the complete service between Bedford and London, whilst services between London, Sevenoaks, Sutton and Brighton only show through Thameslink services. Other Tables should be consulted for additional journey opportunities.

Table 52

Mondays to Fridays

9 December to 16 May

Bedford, Luton, St Albans and City of London - South London, Gatwick Airport and Brighton

Network Diagram - refer to first Page of Table 52

		FC [1]	FC A	FC [1] B	EM ◇[1] C bike	FC D	FC [1] E	EM ◇[1] F bike	FC G	FC	FC H	FC [1]	FC A	FC [1] B	EM ◇[1] I bike	FC G	FC E	FC [1] E	FC	FC H	FC [1]	FC A
Bedford [7]	d	17 30		17 34	17 47							17 54	18 02	18 10	18 16						18 24	18 36
Flitwick	d			17 44								18 04		18 20							18 34	
Harlington	d			17 48								18 08		18 24							18 38	
Leagrave	d			17 53								18 13		18 29							18 43	
Luton [10]	d	17 49		17 58	18 02			18 11		18 06		18 18	18 22	18 34						18 44	18 48	18 54
Luton Airport Parkway [7] ✈	d	17 52		18 00						18 08		18 20	18 24	18 36	18 31					18 46	18 50	18 57
Harpenden	d			18 06						18 14		18 26	18 30	18 42						18 52	18 56	19 02
St Albans City	d	18 03	18 06	18 12						18 20	18 26	18 32	18 36	18 48					18 52	18 58	19 02	19 08
Radlett	d		18 11							18 25	18 31		18 41						18 57	19 03		19 13
Elstree & Borehamwood	d		18 15							18 29	18 35		18 45						19 01	19 07		19 17
Mill Hill Broadway	d		18 20							18 33	18 40		18 49							19 12		
Hendon	d		18 23								18 43									19 15		
Cricklewood	d		18 27								18 47									19 19		
West Hampstead Thameslink ⊖	d	18 15	18 30							18 40	18 50	18 44	18 56	19 02					19 10	19 22		19 26
Kentish Town ⊖	d		18 34			←	←		←		18 54					←	←	←		19 26		
St Pancras International [15] ⊖	a	18 22	18 38	18 32	18 26	18 27	18 32	18 35	18 38	18 47	18 58	18 52	19 04	19 08	18 56	18 58	19 04	19 08	19 17	19 30	19 22	19 33
	d	18 22	18 38	18 34		18 28	18 34		18 38	18 48	19 00	18 54	19 04	19 09		19 00	19 04	19 09	19 18	19 30	19 24	19 34
Farringdon [3] ⊖	d	18 27	↪	↪		18 33	18 39		18 43	18 53	↪	18 59	↪	↪		19 05	19 09	19 14	19 23	↪	19 29	↪
City Thameslink [3]	d	18 31				18 37	18 43		18 47	18 57		19 03				19 09	19 13	19 18	19 27		19 33	
London Blackfriars [3] ⊖	d	18 34				18 42	18 46		18 50	19 00		19 05				19 12	19 16	19 20	19 30		19 35	
Elephant & Castle ⊖173,179	d	18 38				18 46			18 54	19 04						19 16	19 19		19 33			
Loughborough Jn 173,179	d	18 42							18 58	19 08							19 23		19 37			
Herne Hill [4] 173,179	d	18 48							19 02	19 12							19 27		19 41			
London Bridge [4]	a						18 54					19 11						19 26			19 41	
	d						18 57					19 12						19 27			19 42	
Tulse Hill [3]	d	18 52							19 06	19 16							19 31		19 46			
Streatham [4]	d	18 56							19 10	19 20							19 35		19 50			
Mitcham Eastfields 173	d	18 59								19 24									19 54			
Mitcham Junction 173 ⛴	d	19 02								19 27									19 57			
Hackbridge 173	d	19 06								19 30									20 00			
Carshalton 173	d	19 08								19 33									20 03			
Tooting 173	d								19 18								19 40					
Haydons Road 173	d								19 21								19 43					
Wimbledon [6] ⊖173,179 ⛴	d								19 24								19 49					
Wimbledon Chase 179	d								19 27								19 52					
South Merton 179	d								19 29								19 54					
Morden South 179	d								19 31								19 56					
St Helier 179	d								19 33								19 58					
Sutton Common 179	d								19 35								20 00					
West Sutton 179	d								19 38								20 03					
Sutton (Surrey) [4] 179	a	19 12							19 41	19 36							20 07		20 06			
Denmark Hill [4] 195	d					18 52										19 22						
Peckham Rye [4] 195	d					18 55										19 25						
Nunhead [4] 195	d					18 57										19 27						
Crofton Park 195	d					19 00										19 30						
Catford 195	d					19 03										19 33						
Bellingham 195	d					19 05										19 35						
Beckenham Hill 195	d					19 07										19 37						
Ravensbourne 195	d					19 09										19 39						
Shortlands 195	d					19 13										19 41						
Bromley South [4] 195	d					19 16										19 44						
Bickley [4] 195	d					19 19										19 47						
St Mary Cray 195	d					19 23										19 51						
Swanley [4] 195	d					19 29										19 56						
Eynsford 195	d					19 33										20 00						
Shoreham (Kent) 195	d					19 37										20 04						
Otford [4] 195	d					19 40										20 07						
Bat & Ball 195	d					19 43										20 10						
Sevenoaks [4] 195	a					19 50										20 13						
East Croydon ⛴	d						19 11					19 25						19 41			19 55	
Redhill	d																					
Gatwick Airport [10] ✈	d						19 26					19 41						19 57			20 11	
Three Bridges [4]	d						19 31					19 45						20 02			20 15	
Balcombe	d						19 37					19 51										
Haywards Heath [3]	d						19 42					19 57						20 11			20 25	
Wivelsfield [4]	d											20 01									20 29	
Burgess Hill [4]	d						19 48					20 03						20 16			20 31	
Hassocks [4]	d						19 51					20 06						20 20			20 34	
Preston Park	d											20 13									20 41	
Brighton [10]	a						20 01					20 17						20 29			20 45	

A To Sutton (Surrey)
B To Brighton
C From Corby.
D From Luton
E From Bedford
F From Sheffield
G From St Albans City
H To Sevenoaks
I From Nottingham

The trains that operate to and from Sevenoaks, Orpington and Rochester (and a few other destinations at peak times) are operated jointly by First Capital Connect (north of Blackfriars) and Southeastern (south of Blackfriars)

Table 52 shows the complete service between Bedford and London, whilst services between London, Sevenoaks, Sutton and Brighton only show through Thameslink services. Other Tables should be consulted for additional journey opportunities.

Table 52

Mondays to Fridays

9 December to 16 May

Bedford, Luton, St Albans and City of London - South London, Gatwick Airport and Brighton

Network Diagram - refer to first Page of Table 52

	FC	EM	FC	FC	FC	FC	FC	FC	FC	FC	EM	FC	FC	FC	FC	FC	FC	EM	FC	FC	FC	FC
	1	◇1			1			1			◇1						1	◇1				1
	A	B	C	D	D		E		F	F	G	C	C	D	E	F		H	I	C		
Bedford 7 d	18 40	18 47						18 54		19 12	19 16						19 25	19 47				19 52
Flitwick d	18 50							19 04									19 35					20 02
Harlington d	18 54							19 08									19 39					20 06
Leagrave d	18 59							19 13									19 44					20 11
Luton 10 d	19 04	19 02					19 14	19 18	19 24	19 32						19 44	19 49	20 02				20 16
Luton Airport Parkway 7 ✈ d	19 06						19 16	19 20	19 27	19 34	19 31					19 46	19 51					20 18
Harpenden d	19 12						19 22	19 26	19 32	19 40						19 52	19 57					20 24
St Albans City d	19 18					19 22	19 28	19 32	19 38	19 46						20 00	20 03				20 22	20 30
Radlett d						19 27	19 33		19 43	19 51						20 05					20 27	
Elstree & Borehamwood d						19 31	19 37		19 47	19 55						20 09					20 31	
Mill Hill Broadway d							19 42			19 59						20 14						
Hendon d							19 45			20 03						20 17						
Cricklewood d							19 49			20 06						20 21						
West Hampstead Thameslink ⊖ d	19 32					19 40	19 52	19 45	19 56	20 09						20 24	20 16				20 40	20 45
Kentish Town ⊖ d			←	←	←		19 56			20 14		←	←	←	20 26	20 30			←	←		
St Pancras International 15 ⊖ a	19 38	19 26	19 30	19 33	19 38	19 47	20 00	19 52	20 03	20 17	19 56	20 00	20 03	20 17	20 29	20 33	20 23	20 26	20 29	20 33	20 47	20 52
d	19 39		19 30	19 34	19 39	19 48	20 00	19 54	20 04	20 18		20 00	20 04	20 18	20 30	20 34	20 24		20 30	20 34	20 48	20 54
Farringdon 3 ⊖ d	↦		19 36	19 39	19 44	19 53	↦	19 59	↦	↦		20 05	20 09	20 23	↦	↦	20 29		20 35	20 39	20 53	20 59
City Thameslink 3 d			19 39	19 43	19 48	19 57		20 03				20 09	20 13	20 27			20 33		20 39	20 43	20 57	21 03
London Blackfriars 3 ⊖ d			19 42	19 46	19 50	20 00		20 05				20 12	20 16	20 30			20 35		20 42	20 46	21 00	21 05
Elephant & Castle ⊖173,179 d			19 46	19 49		20 03						20 16	20 19	20 33					20 46	20 49	21 03	
Loughborough Jn 173,179 d				19 53		20 07							20 23	20 37						20 53	21 07	
Herne Hill 4 173,179 d				19 57		20 11							20 27	20 41						20 57	21 11	
London Bridge 4 a					19 56			20 11									20 41					21 11
d					19 57			20 12									20 42					21 12
Tulse Hill 3 d				20 01		20 16							20 31	20 50						21 01	21 20	
Streatham 4 d				20 05		20 20							20 35	20 53						21 05	21 23	
Mitcham Eastfields 173 d						20 24								20 57							21 27	
Mitcham Junction 173 d						20 27								21 00							21 30	
Hackbridge 173 d						20 30								21 03							21 33	
Carshalton 173 d						20 33								21 06							21 36	
Tooting 173 d				20 10									20 40							21 10		
Haydons Road 173 d				20 13									20 43							21 13		
Wimbledon 6 ⊖173,179 d				20 19									20 49							21 19		
Wimbledon Chase 179 d				20 22									20 52							21 22		
South Merton 179 d				20 24									20 54							21 24		
Morden South 179 d				20 26									20 56							21 26		
St Helier 179 d				20 28									20 58							21 28		
Sutton Common 179 d				20 30									21 00							21 30		
West Sutton 179 d				20 33									21 03							21 33		
Sutton (Surrey) 4 179 a				20 39		20 36							21 09	21 10						21 39	21 40	
Denmark Hill 4 195 d			19 52									20 22							20 52			
Peckham Rye 4 195 d			19 55									20 25							20 55			
Nunhead 4 195 d			19 57									20 27							20 57			
Crofton Park 195 d			20 00									20 30							21 00			
Catford 195 d			20 03									20 33							21 03			
Bellingham 195 d			20 05									20 35							21 05			
Beckenham Hill 195 d			20 07									20 37							21 07			
Ravensbourne 195 d			20 09									20 39							21 09			
Shortlands 195 d			20 11									20 41							21 11			
Bromley South 4 195 d			20 14									20 44							21 14			
Bickley 4 195 d			20 17									20 47							21 17			
St Mary Cray 195 d			20 21									20 51							21 21			
Swanley 4 195 d			20 26									20 56							21 26			
Eynsford 195 d			20 30									21 00							21 30			
Shoreham (Kent) 195 d			20 34									21 04							21 34			
Otford 4 195 d			20 37									21 07							21 37			
Bat & Ball 195 d			20 40									21 10							21 40			
Sevenoaks 4 195 a			20 43									21 13							21 43			
East Croydon d					20 11			20 25									20 55					21 25
Redhill d																						
Gatwick Airport 10 ✈ d					20 27			20 41									21 11					21 41
Three Bridges 4 d					20 32			20 45									21 15					21 45
Balcombe d								20 51														21 53
Haywards Heath 3 d					20 41			20 57									21 25					21 59
Wivelsfield 4 d								21 01									21 29					22 03
Burgess Hill 4 d					20 46			21 03									21 31					22 05
Hassocks 4 d								21 06									21 34					22 08
Preston Park d								21 13									21 41					22 15
Brighton 10 a					20 57			21 17									21 45					22 19

A To Brighton
B From Derby
C From Luton
D From Bedford
E To Sevenoaks
F To Sutton (Surrey)
G From Nottingham
H From Corby.
I From Kentish Town

The trains that operate to and from Sevenoaks, Orpington and Rochester (and a few other destinations at peak times) are operated jointly by First Capital Connect (north of Blackfriars) and Southeastern (south of Blackfriars)

Table 52 shows the complete service between Bedford and London, whilst services between London, Sevenoaks, Sutton and Brighton only show through Thameslink services. Other Tables should be consulted for additional journey opportunities.

Table 52

Mondays to Fridays

9 December to 16 May

Bedford, Luton, St Albans and City of London - South London, Gatwick Airport and Brighton

Network Diagram - refer to first Page of Table 52

		EM	FC	FC	FC	SE	EM	FC		FC	SE	EM	FC	FC	SE	EM	EM	FC	FC		SE	FC	EM	FC	SE
		◇1			1		◇1			1		◇1		1		◇1	◇1		1				◇1	1	
		A					B					A				C	D						A		
Bedford 7	d	20 16			20 22		20 47			20 52		21 18		21 22		21 42	21 42		21 52				22 19	22 22	
Flitwick	d				20 32					21 02				21 32					22 02					22 32	
Harlington	d				20 36					21 06				21 36					22 06					22 36	
Leagrave	d				20 41					21 11				21 41					22 11					22 41	
Luton 10	d			20 20	20 46		21 02	20 50		21 16			21 20	21 46		21 59	21 59	21 50	22 16			22 20	22 36	22 46	
Luton Airport Parkway 7 ✈	d	20 31		20 22	20 48			20 52		21 18		21 34	21 22	21 48				21 52	22 18			22 22	22 39	22 48	
Harpenden	d			20 28	20 54			20 58		21 24			21 28	21 54				21 58	22 24			22 28		22 54	
St Albans City	d			20 34	21 00			21 04		21 30			21 34	22 00				22 04	22 30			22 34		23 00	
Radlett	d			20 39				21 09					21 39					22 09				22 39			
Elstree & Borehamwood	d			20 43				21 13					21 43					22 13				22 43			
Mill Hill Broadway	d			20 47				21 17					21 47					22 17				22 47			
Hendon	d			20 50				21 20					21 50					22 20				22 50			
Cricklewood	d			20 54				21 24					21 54					22 24				22 54			
West Hampstead Thameslink ⊖	d			20 56	21 15			21 26		21 45			21 56	22 15				22 26	22 45			22 56		23 16	
Kentish Town ⊖	d		20 56	21 01				21 31					22 01					22 31				23 01			
St Pancras International 15 ⊖	a	20 56	20 59	21 05	21 22		21 26	21 35		21 52		21 57	22 05	22 22		22 24	22 28	22 35	22 52			23 05	23 06	23 24	
	d		21 00	21 06	21 24			21 36		21 54			22 06	22 24				22 36	22 54			23 06		23 24	
Farringdon 3 ⊖	d		21 05	21 10	21 29			21 40		21 59			22 10	22 29				22 40	22 59			23 10		23 29	
City Thameslink 3	d		21 09	21 13	21 33			21 43		22 03			22 13	22 33				22 43	23 03						
London Blackfriars 3 ⊖	d		21 12	21 16	21 35	21 42		21 46		22 05	22 12		22 16	22 35	22 42			22 46	23 05		23 12	23 16		23 35	23 42
Elephant & Castle ⊖173,179	d		21 16	21 19		21 46		21 49			22 16		22 19		22 46			22 49			23 16	23 19			23 46
Loughborough Jn 173,179	d			21 23				21 53					22 23					22 53				23s23			
Herne Hill 4 173,179	d			21 27				21 57					22 27					22 57				23 27			
London Bridge 4	a				21 41					22 11				22 41					23 11					23 41	
	d				21 42					22 12				22 42					23 12					23 42	
Tulse Hill 3	d			21 31				22 01					22 31					23 01				23 31			
Streatham 4	d			21 35				22 05					22 35					23 05				23 35			
Mitcham Eastfields 173	d																								
Mitcham Junction 173 🚊	d																								
Hackbridge 173	d																								
Carshalton 173	d																								
Tooting 173	d			21 40				22 10					22 40					23 10				23 40			
Haydons Road 173	d			21 43				22 13					22 43					23 13				23 43			
Wimbledon 6 ⊖173,179 🚊	d			21 49				22 19					22 49					23 17				23 49			
Wimbledon Chase 179	d			21 52				22 22					22 52					23 20				23 52			
South Merton 179	d			21 54				22 24					22 54					23 22				23 54			
Morden South 179	d			21 56				22 26					22 56					23 24				23 56			
St Helier 179	d			21 58				22 28					22 58					23 26				23 58			
Sutton Common 179	d			22 00				22 30					23 00					23 28				00 01			
West Sutton 179	d			22 03				22 33					23 03					23 31				00 04			
Sutton (Surrey) 4 179	a			22 09				22 39					23 09					23 35				00 09			
Denmark Hill 4 195	d		21 22			21 52					22 22				22 52						23 22				23 52
Peckham Rye 4 195	d		21 25			21 55					22 25				22 55						23 25				23 55
Nunhead 4 195	d		21 27			21 57					22 27				22 57						23 27				23 57
Crofton Park 195	d		21 30			22 00					22 30				23 00						23 30				23 59
Catford 195	d		21 33			22 03					22 33				23 03						23 33				00 03
Bellingham 195	d		21 35			22 05					22 35				23 05						23 35				00 05
Beckenham Hill 195	d		21 37			22 07					22 37				23 07						23 37				00 07
Ravensbourne 195	d		21 39			22 09					22 39				23 09						23 39				00 09
Shortlands 195	d		21 41			22 11					22 41				23 11						23 41				00 11
Bromley South 4 195	d		21 44			22 14					22 44				23 14						23 44				00 14
Bickley 4 195	d		21 47			22 17					22 47				23 17						23 47				00 17
St Mary Cray 195	d		21 51			22 21					22 51				23 21						23 51				00 21
Swanley 4 195	d		21 56			22 26					22 56				23 26						23 56				00 26
Eynsford 195	d		22 00			22 30					23 00				23 30						23 59				00 30
Shoreham (Kent) 195	d		22 04			22 34					23 04				23 34						00 04				00 34
Otford 4 195	d		22 07			22 37					23 07				23 37						00 07				00 37
Bat & Ball 195	d		22 10			22 40					23 10				23 40						00 10				00 40
Sevenoaks 4 195	a		22 13			22 43					23 13				23 43						00 13				00 43
East Croydon 🚊	d				21 55					22 25				22 55					23 25					23 57	
Redhill	d																								
Gatwick Airport 10 ✈	d				22 11					22 41				23 11					23 41					00 19	
Three Bridges 4	d				22 15					22 45				23 15					23 47					00a24	
Balcombe	d									22 53									23 53						
Haywards Heath 3	d				22 25					22 59				23 25					23 59						
Wivelsfield 4	d				22 29					23 03				23 29					00 03						
Burgess Hill 4	d				22 31					23 05				23 31					00 05						
Hassocks 4	d				22 34					23 08				23 34					00 08						
Preston Park	d				22 41					23 15				23 41					00 15						
Brighton 10	a				22 45					23 19				23 45					00 19						

A From Nottingham
B From Corby.
C until 27 December, from 10 February. From Corby.
D from 30 December until 7 February. From Corby.

The trains that operate to and from Sevenoaks, Orpington and Rochester (and a few other destinations at peak times) are operated jointly by First Capital Connect (north of Blackfriars) and Southeastern (south of Blackfriars)

Table 52 shows the complete service between Bedford and London, whilst services between London, Sevenoaks, Sutton and Brighton only show through Thameslink services. Other Tables should be consulted for additional journey opportunities.

Table 52

Mondays to Fridays

9 December to 16 May

Bedford, Luton, St Albans and City of London - South London, Gatwick Airport and Brighton

Network Diagram - refer to first Page of Table 52

Station			FC	FC 1	EM ◇1 A ⚮	FC 1	FC 1
Bedford 7		d		22 42	22 45	23 12	23 42
Flitwick		d		22 52		23 22	23 52
Harlington		d		22 56		23 26	23 56
Leagrave		d		23 02		23 32	00 02
Luton 10		d	22 50	23 06	23 02	23 36	00 06
Luton Airport Parkway 7	✈	d	22 52	23 09		23 39	00 09
Harpenden		d	22 58	23 15		23 45	00 15
St Albans City		d	23 04	23 21		23 51	00 21
Radlett		d	23 10	23 26		23 56	00 26
Elstree & Borehamwood		d	23 14	23 31		00 01	00 31
Mill Hill Broadway		d	23 18	23 35		00 05	00 35
Hendon		d	23 22	23 38		00 08	00 38
Cricklewood		d	23 25	23 42		00 12	00 42
West Hampstead Thameslink	⊖	d	23 29	23 45		00 15	00 45
Kentish Town	⊖	d	23 33	23 50		00 20	00 50
St Pancras International 15	⊖	a	23 37	23 53	23 40	00 23	00 53
		d	23 38	23 54		00 24	00 54
Farringdon 3	⊖	d	23 43	23 59		00 29	
City Thameslink 3		d					
London Blackfriars 3	⊖	d	23 48	00 05		00 35	01 05
Elephant & Castle	⊖173,179	d	23 51				
Loughborough Jn	173,179	d					
Herne Hill 4	173,179	d	23 58				
London Bridge 4		a		00 11		00 41	
		d		00 12		00 42	
Tulse Hill 3		d	00 02				
Streatham 4		d	00 06				
Mitcham Eastfields	173	d					
Mitcham Junction	173 🚋	d					
Hackbridge	173	d					
Carshalton	173	d					
Tooting	173	d	00 10				
Haydons Road	173	d	00 13				
Wimbledon 6	⊖173,179 🚋	d	00 19				
Wimbledon Chase	179	d	00 22				
South Merton	179	d	00 24				
Morden South	179	d	00 26				
St Helier	179	d	00 28				
Sutton Common	179	d	00 30				
West Sutton	179	d	00 33				
Sutton (Surrey) 4	179	a	00 39				
Denmark Hill 4	195	d					
Peckham Rye 4	195	d					
Nunhead 4	195	d					
Crofton Park	195	d					
Catford	195	d					
Bellingham	195	d					
Beckenham Hill	195	d					
Ravensbourne	195	d					
Shortlands	195	d					
Bromley South 4	195	d					
Bickley 4	195	d					
St Mary Cray	195	d					
Swanley 4	195	d					
Eynsford	195	d					
Shoreham (Kent)	195	d					
Otford 4	195	d					
Bat & Ball	195	d					
Sevenoaks 4	195	a					
East Croydon	🚋	d		00 29		00 57	01 36
Redhill		d					
Gatwick Airport 10	✈	d		00 49		01 19	01 56
Three Bridges 4		d		00a54		01a24	02a02
Balcombe		d					
Haywards Heath 3		d					
Wivelsfield 4		d					
Burgess Hill 4		d					
Hassocks 4		d					
Preston Park		d					
Brighton 10		a					

A From Nottingham

The trains that operate to and from Sevenoaks, Orpington and Rochester (and a few other destinations at peak times) are operated jointly by First Capital Connect (north of Blackfriars) and Southeastern (south of Blackfriars)

Table 52 shows the complete service between Bedford and London, whilst services between London, Sevenoaks, Sutton and Brighton only show through Thameslink services. Other Tables should be consulted for additional journey opportunities.

Table 52

Saturdays

14 December to 17 May

Bedford, Luton, St Albans and City of London - South London, Gatwick Airport and Brighton

Network Diagram - refer to first Page of Table 52

		FC	FC	FC	SE	SE	FC	FC	FC	FC	FC	FC	FC	FC	FC	FC	FC	FC	FC	SE	FC	FC	FC
				1			1	1	1	1	1	1	1	1	1	1	1		1				1
		A	A	B	C	C	B	B	B	B													
Bedford 7	d										00 42	01 42		02 42	03 12	03 42	04 22		04 52				05 22
Flitwick	d										00 52	01 52		02 52	03 22	03 52	04 32		05 02				05 32
Harlington	d										00 56	01 56		02 56	03 26	03 56	04 36		05 06				05 36
Leagrave	d									00 02	01 02	02 02		03 02	03 32	04 02	04 42		05 12				05 42
Luton 10	d									00 06	01 06	02 06		03 06	03 36	04 06	04 46		05 16			05 30	05 46
Luton Airport Parkway 7 ✈	d									00 09	01 09	02 09		03 09	03 39	04 09	04 49		05 19			05 32	05 49
Harpenden	d									00 15	01 15	02 15		03 15	03 45	04 15	04 55		05 25			05 38	05 55
St Albans City	d									00 21	01 21	02 21		03 21	03 51	04 21	05 01		05 31			05 44	06 01
Radlett	d									00 26	01 26	02 26		03 26	03 56	04 26	05 06					05 50	
Elstree & Borehamwood	d								00 01	00 31	01 31	02 31		03 31	04 01	04 31	05 11					05 54	
Mill Hill Broadway	d								00 05	00 35	01 35	02 35		03 35	04 05	04 35	05 15					05 58	
Hendon	d								00 08	00 38	01 38	02 38		03 38	04 08	04 38	05 18					06 02	
Cricklewood	d								00 12	00 42	01 42	02 42		03 42	04 12	04 42	05 22					06 05	
West Hampstead Thameslink ⊖	d								00 15	00 45	01 45	02 45		03 45	04 15	04 45	05 25	05 40	05 47			06 09	06 17
Kentish Town ⊖	d								00 20	00 50	01 50	02 50		03 50	04 20	04 50	05 30	05 44				06 14	
St Pancras International 15 ⊖	a								00 23	00 53	01 53	02 53		03 53	04 23	04 53	05 33	05 48	05 53			06 17	06 23
	d								00 24	00 54	01 54	02 54	03 25	03 54	04 24	04 54	05 34	05 48	05 53			06 18	06 24
Farringdon 3 ⊖	d								00 29							04 59	05 39	05 53	05 59			06 23	06 29
City Thameslink 3	d																						
London Blackfriars 3 ⊖	d							00 05	00 35	01 05	02 05	03 05	03 36	04 05	04 35	05 05	05 45	06 00	06 05	06 12	06 16	06 30	06 35
Elephant & Castle ⊖	173,179 d																	06 03		06 16	06 19	06 33	
Loughborough Jn	173,179 d																						
Herne Hill 4	173,179 d																	06 11			06 27	06 41	
London Bridge 4	a							00 11	00 41								05 51		06 11				06 41
	d							00 12	00 42								05 52		06 12				06 42
Tulse Hill 3	d		00 02															06 16			06 31	06 46	
Streatham 4	d		00 06															06 20			06 35	06 50	
Mitcham Eastfields	173 d																	06 24				06 54	
Mitcham Junction 🚋	173 d																	06 27				06 57	
Hackbridge	173 d																	06 30				07 00	
Carshalton	173 d																	06 33				07 03	
Tooting	173 d		00 10																		06 40		
Haydons Road	173 d		00 13																		06 43		
Wimbledon 6 ⊖ 🚋	173,179 d		00 19																		06 47		
Wimbledon Chase	179 d		00 22																		06 50		
South Merton	179 d		00 24																		06 52		
Morden South	179 d		00 26																		06 54		
St Helier	179 d		00 28																		06 56		
Sutton Common	179 d	00 01	00 30																		06 58		
West Sutton	179 d	00 04	00 33																		07 01		
Sutton (Surrey) 4	179 a	00 09	00 39															06 36			07 05	07 06	
Denmark Hill 4	195 d																			06 22			
Peckham Rye 4	195 d																			06 25			
Nunhead 4	195 d																			06 27			
Crofton Park	195 d																			06 30			
Catford	195 d					00 03														06 33			
Bellingham	195 d					00 05														06 35			
Beckenham Hill	195 d					00 07														06 37			
Ravensbourne	195 d					00 09														06 39			
Shortlands	195 d					00 11														06 41			
Bromley South 4	195 d					00 14														06 44			
Bickley 4	195 d					00 17														06 47			
St Mary Cray	195 d					00 21														06 51			
Swanley 4	195 d					00 26														06 56			
Eynsford	195 d					00 30														07 00			
Shoreham (Kent)	195 d				00 04	00 34														07 04			
Otford 4	195 d				00 07	00 37														07 07			
Bat & Ball	195 d				00 10	00 40														07 10			
Sevenoaks 4	195 a				00 13	00 43														07 13			
East Croydon 🚋	d							00 29	00 57	01 36	02 36	03 36	04 06	04 36	05 06	05 32	06 05		06 25				06 55
Redhill	d																						
Gatwick Airport 10 ✈	d						00 19	00 49	01 19	01 56	02 56	03 56	04 25	04 56	05 26	05 54	06 20		06 41				07 11
Three Bridges 4	d						00a24	00a54	01a24	02a02	03a02	04a02	04a32	05a02	05 32	06 00	06 25		06 45				07 15
Balcombe	d														05 38	06 06	06 31						07 21
Haywards Heath 3	d														05 44	06 11	06 37		06 55				07 27
Wivelsfield 4	d			00 03											05 48	06 15	06 41		06 59				07 31
Burgess Hill 4	d			00 05											05 50	06 17	06 43		07 01				07 33
Hassocks 4	d			00 08											05 53	06 21	06 46		07 04				07 36
Preston Park	d			00 15											06 00	06 27	06 53		07 11				07 43
Brighton 10	a			00 19											06 05	06 31	06 57		07 15				07 47

A From Luton
B From Bedford
C From London Blackfriars

The trains that operate to and from Sevenoaks, Orpington and Rochester (and a few other destinations at peak times) are operated jointly by First Capital Connect (north of Blackfriars) and Southeastern (south of Blackfriars)

Table 52 shows the complete service between Bedford and London, whilst services between London, Sevenoaks, Sutton and Brighton only show through Thameslink services. Other Tables should be consulted for additional journey opportunities.

Table 52

Saturdays

14 December to 17 May

Bedford, Luton, St Albans and City of London - South London, Gatwick Airport and Brighton

Network Diagram - refer to first Page of Table 52

		SE	EM	FC	FC	FC	FC	FC	SE	FC	FC	FC	FC	FC	SE	EM	FC	FC	FC	FC	FC	FC	SE
			◇1			1		1				1		1		◇1			1			1	
			A		B		C				B		C			D		B		C	B		
Bedford 7	d		05 37			05 40		05 54				06 10		06 24		06 40			06 40			06 54	
Flitwick	d					05 50		06 04				06 20		06 34					06 50			07 04	
Harlington	d					05 54		06 08				06 24		06 38					06 54			07 08	
Leagrave	d					05 59		06 13				06 29		06 43					06 59			07 13	
Luton 10	d				06 00	06 04		06 18			06 30	06 34		06 48		06 54		07 00	07 04		07 14	07 18	
Luton Airport Parkway 7 ✈	d		05 56		06 02	06 06		06 20			06 32	06 36		06 50				07 02	07 06		07 16	07 20	
Harpenden	d				06 08	06 12		06 26			06 38	06 42		06 56				07 08	07 12		07 22	07 26	
St Albans City	d				06 14	06 18		06 32			06 44	06 48		07 02				07 14	07 18		07 29	07 32	
Radlett	d				06 19						06 49							07 19			07 34		
Elstree & Borehamwood	d				06 23						06 53							07 23			07 38		
Mill Hill Broadway	d				06 28						06 58							07 28			07 43		
Hendon	d				06 31						07 01							07 31			07 46		
Cricklewood	d				06 35						07 05							07 35			07 50		
West Hampstead Thameslink ⊖	d			06 24	06 39			06 45		06 54	07 09			07 15			07 24	07 39			07 54	07 45	
Kentish Town ⊖	d			06 28	06 44		←			06 58	07 14		←				07 28	07 44		←	07 58		
St Pancras International 15 ⊖	a		06 20	06 32	06 47	06 39	06 47	06 52		07 02	07 17	07 09	07 17	07 23		07 19	07 32	07 47	07 39	07 47	08 02	07 52	
	d			06 34	06 48	06 40	06 48	06 54		07 04	07 18	07 10	07 18	07 24			07 34	07 48	07 40	07 48	08 04	07 54	
Farringdon 3 ⊖	d			06 39	→	06 45	06 53	06 59		07 09	→	07 15	07 23	07 29			07 39	→	07 45	07 53	→	07 59	
City Thameslink 3	d																						
London Blackfriars 3 ⊖	d	06 42		06 46		06 50	07 00	07 05	07 12	07 16		07 20	07 30	07 35	07 42		07 46		07 50	08 00		08 05	08 12
Elephant & Castle ⊖173,179	d	06 46		06 49			07 03		07 16	07 19			07 33		07 46		07 49			08 03			08 16
Loughborough Jn 173,179	d			06 53			07 07			07 23			07 37				07 53			08 07			
Herne Hill 4 173,179	d			06 57			07 11			07 27			07 41				07 57			08 11			
London Bridge 4	a					06 56		07 11				07 26		07 41					07 56			08 11	
	d					06 57		07 12				07 27		07 42					07 57			08 12	
Tulse Hill 3	d			07 01			07 16			07 31			07 46				08 01			08 16			
Streatham 4	d			07 05			07 20			07 35			07 50				08 05			08 20			
Mitcham Eastfields 173	d						07 24						07 54							08 24			
Mitcham Junction 173	d						07 27						07 57							08 27			
Hackbridge 173	d						07 30						08 00							08 30			
Carshalton 173	d						07 33						08 03							08 33			
Tooting 173	d			07 10						07 40							08 10						
Haydons Road 173	d			07 13						07 43							08 13						
Wimbledon 6 ⊖173,179	d			07 17						07 47							08 17						
Wimbledon Chase 179	d			07 20						07 50							08 20						
South Merton 179	d			07 22						07 52							08 22						
Morden South 179	d			07 24						07 54							08 24						
St Helier 179	d			07 26						07 56							08 26						
Sutton Common 179	d			07 28						07 58							08 28						
West Sutton 179	d			07 31						08 01							08 31						
Sutton (Surrey) 4 179	a			07 35			07 36			08 05			08 06				08 35			08 36			
Denmark Hill 4 195	d	06 52							07 22						07 52								08 22
Peckham Rye 4 195	d	06 55							07 25						07 55								08 25
Nunhead 4 195	d	06 57							07 27						07 57								08 27
Crofton Park 195	d	07 00							07 30						08 00								08 30
Catford 195	d	07 03							07 33						08 03								08 33
Bellingham 195	d	07 05							07 35						08 05								08 35
Beckenham Hill 195	d	07 07							07 37						08 07								08 37
Ravensbourne 195	d	07 09							07 39						08 09								08 39
Shortlands 195	d	07 11							07 41						08 11								08 41
Bromley South 4 195	d	07 14							07 44						08 14								08 44
Bickley 4 195	d	07 17							07 47						08 17								08 47
St Mary Cray 195	d	07 21							07 51						08 21								08 51
Swanley 4 195	d	07 26							07 56						08 26								08 56
Eynsford 195	d	07 30							08 00						08 30								09 00
Shoreham (Kent) 195	d	07 34							08 04						08 34								09 04
Otford 4 195	d	07 37							08 07						08 37								09 07
Bat & Ball 195	d	07 40							08 10						08 40								09 10
Sevenoaks 4 195	a	07 43							08 13						08 43								09 13
East Croydon	d					07 11		07 25				07 41		07 55					08 11			08 25	
Redhill	d																						
Gatwick Airport 10 ✈	d					07 27		07 41				07 57		08 11					08 27			08 41	
Three Bridges 4	d					07 32		07 45				08 02		08 15					08 32			08 45	
Balcombe	d													08 21									
Haywards Heath 3	d					07 41		07 55				08 11		08 27					08 41			08 55	
Wivelsfield 4	d							07 59						08 31								08 59	
Burgess Hill 4	d							08 01						08 33								09 01	
Hassocks 4	d							08 04						08 36								09 04	
Preston Park	d							08 11						08 43								09 11	
Brighton 10	a					07 55		08 15				08 25		08 47					08 55			09 15	

A From Leicester
B To Sutton (Surrey)
C From Luton
D From Derby

The trains that operate to and from Sevenoaks, Orpington and Rochester (and a few other destinations at peak times) are operated jointly by First Capital Connect (north of Blackfriars) and Southeastern (south of Blackfriars)

Table 52 shows the complete service between Bedford and London, whilst services between London, Sevenoaks, Sutton and Brighton only show through Thameslink services. Other Tables should be consulted for additional journey opportunities.

Table 52

Saturdays

14 December to 17 May

Bedford, Luton, St Albans and City of London - South London, Gatwick Airport and Brighton

Network Diagram - refer to first Page of Table 52

	FC A	FC ■ B	EM ◇■ C	FC D	FC ■ E	FC D	FC A	FC ■	SE	EM ◇■ F	FC D	FC A	FC ■	FC D	FC A	FC ■	SE	FC A	FC ■ B	EM ◇■ C	FC D	FC ■ E
Bedford [7] d		07 10	07 18					07 24		07 36			07 40			07 54			08 10	08 17		
Flitwick d		07 20						07 34					07 50			08 04			08 20			
Harlington d		07 24						07 38					07 54			08 08			08 24			
Leagrave d		07 29						07 43					07 59			08 13			08 29			
Luton [10] d	07 30	07 34					07 44	07 48		08 02		08 00	08 04		08 14	08 18			08 34			
Luton Airport Parkway [7] ✈ d	07 32	07 36	07 33				07 46	07 50				08 02	08 06		08 16	08 20			08 36	08 32		
Harpenden d	07 38	07 42					07 52	07 56				08 08	08 12		08 22	08 26			08 42			
St Albans City d	07 44	07 48					07 59	08 02				08 14	08 18		08 29	08 32		08 44	08 48			
Radlett d	07 49						08 04					08 19			08 34			08 49				
Elstree & Borehamwood d	07 53						08 08					08 23			08 38			08 53				
Mill Hill Broadway d	07 58						08 13					08 28			08 43			08 58				
Hendon d	08 01						08 16					08 31			08 46			09 01				
Cricklewood d	08 05						08 20					08 35			08 50			09 05				
West Hampstead Thameslink ⊖ d	08 09						08 24	08 15				08 39			08 54	08 45		09 09				
Kentish Town ⊖ d	08 14			←	←	←	08 28				←	08 44		←	08 58			09 14			←	←
St Pancras International [15] ⊖ a	08 17	08 09	07 57	08 02	08 09	08 17	08 32	08 22		08 26	08 32	08 47	08 39	08 47	09 02	08 52		09 17	09 09	08 57	09 02	09 09
d	08 18	08 10		08 04	08 10	08 18	08 34	08 24			08 34	08 48	08 40	08 48	09 04	08 54		09 18	09 10		09 04	09 10
Farringdon [3] ⊖ d	→	→		08 09	08 15	08 23	→	08 29			08 39	→	08 45	08 53	→	08 59		→	→		09 09	09 15
City Thameslink [3] d																09 03					09 13	09 18
London Blackfriars [3] ⊖ d				08 16	08 20	08 30		08 35	08 42		08 46		08 50	09 00		09 05	09 12				09 16	09 20
Elephant & Castle ⊖173,179 d				08 19		08 33			08 46		08 49			09 03			09 16				09 19	
Loughborough Jn 173,179 d				08 23		08 37					08 53			09 07							09 23	
Herne Hill [4] 173,179 d				08 27		08 41					08 57			09 11							09 27	
London Bridge [4] a					08 26			08 41					08 56			09 11						09 26
d					08 27			08 42					08 57			09 12						09 27
Tulse Hill [3] d				08 31		08 46					09 01			09 16							09 31	
Streatham [4] d				08 35		08 50					09 05			09 20							09 35	
Mitcham Eastfields 173 d						08 54								09 24								
Mitcham Junction 173 🚋 d						08 57								09 27								
Hackbridge 173 d						09 00								09 30								
Carshalton 173 d						09 03								09 33								
Tooting 173 d				08 40							09 10										09 40	
Haydons Road 173 d				08 43							09 13										09 43	
Wimbledon [6] ⊖173,179 🚋 d				08 47							09 17										09 47	
Wimbledon Chase 179 d				08 50							09 20										09 50	
South Merton 179 d				08 52							09 22										09 52	
Morden South 179 d				08 54							09 24										09 54	
St Helier 179 d				08 56							09 26										09 56	
Sutton Common 179 d				08 58							09 28										09 58	
West Sutton 179 d				09 01							09 31										10 01	
Sutton (Surrey) [4] 179 a				09 05		09 06					09 35			09 36							10 05	
Denmark Hill [4] 195 d									08 52								09 22					
Peckham Rye [4] 195 d									08 55								09 25					
Nunhead [4] 195 d									08 57								09 27					
Crofton Park 195 d									09 00								09 30					
Catford 195 d									09 03								09 33					
Bellingham 195 d									09 05								09 35					
Beckenham Hill 195 d									09 07								09 37					
Ravensbourne 195 d									09 09								09 39					
Shortlands 195 d									09 11								09 41					
Bromley South [4] 195 d									09 14								09 44					
Bickley [4] 195 d									09 17								09 47					
St Mary Cray 195 d									09 21								09 51					
Swanley [4] 195 d									09 26								09 56					
Eynsford 195 d									09 30								10 00					
Shoreham (Kent) 195 d									09 34								10 04					
Otford [4] 195 d									09 37								10 07					
Bat & Ball 195 d									09 40								10 10					
Sevenoaks [4] 195 a									09 43								10 13					
East Croydon 🚋 d					08 41			08 55					09 11			09 25						09 41
Redhill d																						
Gatwick Airport [10] ✈ d					08 57			09 11					09 27			09 41						09 57
Three Bridges [4] d					09 02			09 15					09 32			09 45						10 02
Balcombe d								09 21														
Haywards Heath [3] d					09 11			09 27					09 41			09 55						10 11
Wivelsfield [4] d								09 31								09 59						
Burgess Hill [4] d								09 33								10 01						
Hassocks [4] d								09 36								10 04						
Preston Park d								09 43								10 11						
Brighton [10] a					09 25			09 47					09 55			10 15						10 25

A To Sutton (Surrey)
B To Brighton
C From Nottingham
D From Luton
E From Bedford
F From Derby

The trains that operate to and from Sevenoaks, Orpington and Rochester (and a few other destinations at peak times) are operated jointly by First Capital Connect (north of Blackfriars) and Southeastern (south of Blackfriars)

Table 52 shows the complete service between Bedford and London, whilst services between London, Sevenoaks, Sutton and Brighton only show through Thameslink services. Other Tables should be consulted for additional journey opportunities.

Table 52

Saturdays

14 December to 17 May

Bedford, Luton, St Albans and City of London - South London, Gatwick Airport and Brighton

Network Diagram - refer to first Page of Table 52

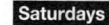

		FC	FC	FC	SE	FC	FC	EM	FC	FC	FC	FC	FC	SE	FC	FC	EM	FC	FC	FC	FC	FC	SE
				1			1	◇1		1			1			1	◇1		1			1	
		A	B			B	C	D	E	F	A	B			B	C	G	E	F	A	B		
Bedford 7	d			08 24			08 40	08 48					08 54			09 10	09 16					09 24	
Flitwick	d			08 34			08 50						09 04			09 20						09 34	
Harlington	d			08 38			08 54						09 08			09 24						09 38	
Leagrave	d			08 43			08 59						09 13			09 29						09 43	
Luton 10	d		08 44	08 48			09 04	09 02				09 14	09 18			09 34					09 44	09 48	
Luton Airport Parkway 7 ✈	d		08 46	08 50			09 06					09 16	09 20			09 36	09 31				09 46	09 50	
Harpenden	d		08 52	08 56			09 12					09 22	09 26			09 42					09 52	09 56	
St Albans City	d		08 59	09 02		09 14	09 18					09 29	09 32		09 44	09 48					09 59	10 02	
Radlett	d		09 04			09 19						09 34			09 49						10 04		
Elstree & Borehamwood	d		09 08			09 23						09 38			09 53						10 08		
Mill Hill Broadway	d		09 13			09 28						09 43			09 58						10 13		
Hendon	d		09 16			09 31						09 46			10 01						10 16		
Cricklewood	d		09 20			09 35						09 50			10 05						10 20		
West Hampstead Thameslink ⊖	d		09 24	09 15		09 39						09 54	09 45		10 09						10 24	10 15	
Kentish Town ⊖	d	←	09 28			09 44			←	←	←	09 58			10 14			←	←	←	10 28		
St Pancras International 15 ⊖	a	09 17	09 32	09 22		09 47	09 39	09 26	09 32	09 39	09 47	10 02	09 52		10 17	10 09	09 56	10 02	10 09	10 17	10 32	10 22	
	d	09 18	09 34	09 24		09 48	09 40		09 34	09 40	09 48	10 04	09 54		10 18	10 10		10 04	10 10	10 18	10 34	10 24	
Farringdon 3 ⊖	d	09 23	↪	09 29		↪	↪		09 39	09 45	09 53	↪	09 59		↪	↪		10 09	10 15	10 23	↪	10 29	
City Thameslink 3	d	09 27		09 33					09 43	09 48	09 57		10 03					10 13	10 18	10 27		10 33	
London Blackfriars 3 ⊖	d	09 30		09 35	09 42				09 46	09 50	10 00		10 05	10 12				10 16	10 20	10 30		10 35	10 42
Elephant & Castle ⊖173,179	d	09 33			09 46				09 49		10 03			10 16				10 19		10 33			10 46
Loughborough Jn 173,179	d	09 37							09 53		10 07							10 23		10 37			
Herne Hill 4 173,179	d	09 41							09 57		10 11							10 27		10 41			
London Bridge 4	a			09 41						09 56			10 11						10 26			10 41	
	d			09 42						09 57			10 12						10 27			10 42	
Tulse Hill 3	d	09 46							10 01		10 16							10 31		10 46			
Streatham 4	d	09 50							10 05		10 20							10 35		10 50			
Mitcham Eastfields 173	d	09 54									10 24									10 54			
Mitcham Junction 173 🚋	d	09 57									10 27									10 57			
Hackbridge 173	d	10 00									10 30									11 00			
Carshalton 173	d	10 03									10 33									11 03			
Tooting 173	d								10 10									10 40					
Haydons Road 173	d								10 13									10 43					
Wimbledon 6 ⊖173,179 🚋	d								10 17									10 47					
Wimbledon Chase 179	d								10 20									10 50					
South Merton 179	d								10 22									10 52					
Morden South 179	d								10 24									10 54					
St Helier 179	d								10 26									10 56					
Sutton Common 179	d								10 28									10 58					
West Sutton 179	d								10 31									11 01					
Sutton (Surrey) 4 179	a	10 06							10 35		10 36							11 05		11 06			
Denmark Hill 4 195	d				09 52									10 22									10 52
Peckham Rye 4 195	d				09 55									10 25									10 55
Nunhead 4 195	d				09 57									10 27									10 57
Crofton Park 195	d				10 00									10 30									11 00
Catford 195	d				10 03									10 33									11 03
Bellingham 195	d				10 05									10 35									11 05
Beckenham Hill 195	d				10 07									10 37									11 07
Ravensbourne 195	d				10 09									10 39									11 09
Shortlands 195	d				10 11									10 41									11 11
Bromley South 4 195	d				10 14									10 44									11 14
Bickley 4 195	d				10 17									10 47									11 17
St Mary Cray 195	d				10 21									10 51									11 21
Swanley 4 195	d				10 26									10 56									11 26
Eynsford 195	d				10 30									11 00									11 30
Shoreham (Kent) 195	d				10 34									11 04									11 34
Otford 4 195	d				10 37									11 07									11 37
Bat & Ball 195	d				10 40									11 10									11 40
Sevenoaks 4 195	a				10 43									11 13									11 43
East Croydon 🚋	d			09 55						10 11			10 25						10 41			10 55	
Redhill	d																						
Gatwick Airport 10 ✈	d			10 11						10 27			10 41						10 57			11 11	
Three Bridges 4	d			10 15						10 32			10 45						11 02			11 15	
Balcombe	d			10 21																		11 21	
Haywards Heath 3	d			10 27						10 41			10 55						11 11			11 27	
Wivelsfield 4	d			10 31									10 59									11 31	
Burgess Hill 4	d			10 33									11 01									11 33	
Hassocks 4	d			10 36									11 04									11 36	
Preston Park	d			10 43									11 11									11 43	
Brighton 10	a			10 47						10 55			11 15						11 25			11 47	

A From St Albans City
B To Sutton (Surrey)
C To Brighton
D From Corby.
E From Luton
F From Bedford
G From Lincoln

The trains that operate to and from Sevenoaks, Orpington and Rochester (and a few other destinations at peak times) are operated jointly by First Capital Connect (north of Blackfriars) and Southeastern (south of Blackfriars)

Table 52 shows the complete service between Bedford and London, whilst services between London, Sevenoaks, Sutton and Brighton only show through Thameslink services. Other Tables should be consulted for additional journey opportunities.

Table 52

Saturdays

14 December to 17 May

Bedford, Luton, St Albans and City of London - South London, Gatwick Airport and Brighton

Network Diagram - refer to first Page of Table 52

		FC	FC	EM	FC	FC	FC	FC	FC	SE	FC	FC	EM	FC	FC	FC	FC	FC	SE	FC	FC	EM	FC
			1	◇1		1			1			1	◇1		1			1			1	◇1	
		A	B	C	D	E	F	A			A	B	G	D	E	F	A			A	B	C	D
				🚲									🚲									🚲	
Bedford [7]	d		09 40	09 47					09 54			10 10	10 16					10 24			10 40	10 47	
Flitwick	d		09 50						10 04			10 20						10 34			10 50		
Harlington	d		09 54						10 08			10 24						10 38			10 54		
Leagrave	d		09 59						10 13			10 29						10 43			10 59		
Luton [10]	d		10 04	10 02				10 14	10 18			10 34					10 44	10 48			11 04	11 02	
Luton Airport Parkway [7] ✈	d		10 06					10 16	10 20			10 36	10 31				10 46	10 50			11 06		
Harpenden	d		10 12					10 22	10 26			10 42					10 52	10 56			11 12		
St Albans City	d	10 14	10 18					10 29	10 32		10 44	10 48					10 59	11 02		11 14	11 18		
Radlett	d	10 19						10 34			10 49						11 04			11 19			
Elstree & Borehamwood	d	10 23						10 38			10 53						11 08			11 23			
Mill Hill Broadway	d	10 28						10 43			10 58						11 13			11 28			
Hendon	d	10 31						10 46			11 01						11 16			11 31			
Cricklewood	d	10 35						10 50			11 05						11 20			11 35			
West Hampstead Thameslink ⊖	d	10 39						10 54	10 45		11 09						11 24	11 15		11 39			
Kentish Town ⊖	d	10 44			←	←	←	10 58			11 14			←	←	←	11 28			11 44			←
St Pancras International [15] ⊖	a	10 47	10 39	10 26	10 32	10 39	10 47	11 02	10 52		11 17	11 09	10 56	11 02	11 09	11 17	11 32	11 22		11 47	11 39	11 26	11 32
	d	10 48	10 40		10 34	10 40	10 48	11 04	10 54		11 18	11 10		11 04	11 10	11 18	11 34	11 24		11 48	11 40		11 34
Farringdon [3] ⊖	d	→	→		10 39	10 45	10 53	→	10 59		→	→		11 09	11 15	11 23	→	11 29		→	→		11 39
City Thameslink [3]	d				10 43	10 48	10 57		11 03					11 13	11 18	11 27		11 33					11 43
London Blackfriars [3] ⊖	d				10 46	10 50	11 00		11 05	11 12				11 16	11 20	11 30		11 35	11 42				11 46
Elephant & Castle ⊖173,179	d				10 49		11 03			11 16				11 19		11 33			11 46				11 49
Loughborough Jn 173,179	d				10 53		11 07							11 23		11 37							11 53
Herne Hill [4] 173,179	d				10 57		11 11							11 27		11 41							11 57
London Bridge [4]	a					10 56			11 11						11 26			11 41					
	d					10 57			11 12						11 27			11 42					
Tulse Hill [3]	d				11 01		11 16							11 31		11 46							12 01
Streatham [4]	d				11 05		11 20							11 35		11 50							12 05
Mitcham Eastfields 173	d						11 24									11 54							
Mitcham Junction 173 🚊	d						11 27									11 57							
Hackbridge 173	d						11 30									12 00							
Carshalton 173	d						11 33									12 03							
Tooting 173	d				11 10									11 40									12 10
Haydons Road 173	d				11 13									11 43									12 13
Wimbledon [6] ⊖173,179 🚊	d				11 17									11 47									12 17
Wimbledon Chase 179	d				11 20									11 50									12 20
South Merton 179	d				11 22									11 52									12 22
Morden South 179	d				11 24									11 54									12 24
St Helier 179	d				11 26									11 56									12 26
Sutton Common 179	d				11 28									11 58									12 28
West Sutton 179	d				11 31									12 01									12 31
Sutton (Surrey) [4] 179	a				11 35		11 36							12 05		12 06							12 35
Denmark Hill [4] 195	d									11 22									11 52				
Peckham Rye [4] 195	d									11 25									11 55				
Nunhead [4] 195	d									11 27									11 57				
Crofton Park 195	d									11 30									12 00				
Catford 195	d									11 33									12 03				
Bellingham 195	d									11 35									12 05				
Beckenham Hill 195	d									11 37									12 07				
Ravensbourne 195	d									11 39									12 09				
Shortlands 195	d									11 41									12 11				
Bromley South [4] 195	d									11 44									12 14				
Bickley [4] 195	d									11 47									12 17				
St Mary Cray 195	d									11 51									12 21				
Swanley [4] 195	d									11 56									12 26				
Eynsford 195	d									12 00									12 30				
Shoreham (Kent) 195	d									12 04									12 34				
Otford [4] 195	d									12 07									12 37				
Bat & Ball 195	d									12 10									12 40				
Sevenoaks [4] 195	a									12 13									12 43				
East Croydon 🚊	d					11 11			11 25						11 41			11 55					
Redhill	d																						
Gatwick Airport [10] ✈	d					11 27			11 41						11 57			12 11					
Three Bridges [4]	d					11 32			11 45						12 02			12 15					
Balcombe	d																	12 21					
Haywards Heath [3]	d					11 41			11 55						12 11			12 27					
Wivelsfield [4]	d								11 59									12 31					
Burgess Hill [4]	d								12 01									12 33					
Hassocks [4]	d								12 04									12 36					
Preston Park	d								12 11									12 43					
Brighton [10]	a					11 55			12 15						12 25			12 47					

A To Sutton (Surrey)
B To Brighton
C From Corby.
D From Luton
E From Bedford
F From St Albans City
G From Nottingham

The trains that operate to and from Sevenoaks, Orpington and Rochester (and a few other destinations at peak times) are operated jointly by First Capital Connect (north of Blackfriars) and Southeastern (south of Blackfriars)

Table 52 shows the complete service between Bedford and London, whilst services between London, Sevenoaks, Sutton and Brighton only show through Thameslink services. Other Tables should be consulted for additional journey opportunities.

Table 52

Saturdays

14 December to 17 May

Bedford, Luton, St Albans and City of London - South London, Gatwick Airport and Brighton

Network Diagram - refer to first Page of Table 52

		FC 1 A	FC B	FC C	FC 1	SE	FC C	FC 1 D	EM ◇1 E ⚹	FC F	FC 1 A	FC B	FC C	FC 1	SE	FC C	FC 1 D	EM ◇1 G ⚹	FC F	FC 1 A	FC B	FC C
Bedford 7	d				10 54			11 10	11 16					11 24			11 40	11 47				
Flitwick	d				11 04			11 20						11 34			11 50					
Harlington	d				11 08			11 24						11 38			11 54					
Leagrave	d				11 13			11 29						11 43			11 59					
Luton 10	d			11 14	11 18			11 34					11 44	11 48			12 04	12 02				12 14
Luton Airport Parkway 7 ✈	d			11 16	11 20			11 36	11 31				11 46	11 50			12 06					12 16
Harpenden	d			11 22	11 26			11 42					11 52	11 56			12 12					12 22
St Albans City	d			11 29	11 32		11 44	11 48					11 59	12 02		12 14	12 18					12 29
Radlett	d			11 34			11 49						12 04			12 19						12 34
Elstree & Borehamwood	d			11 38			11 53						12 08			12 23						12 38
Mill Hill Broadway	d			11 43			11 58						12 13			12 28						12 43
Hendon	d			11 46			12 01						12 16			12 31						12 46
Cricklewood	d			11 50			12 05						12 20			12 35						12 50
West Hampstead Thameslink ⊖	d			11 54	11 45		12 09						12 24	12 15		12 39						12 54
Kentish Town ⊖	d	←	←	11 58			12 14			←	←	←	12 28			12 44			←	←	←	12 58
St Pancras International 15 ⊖	a	11 39	11 47	12 02	11 52		12 17	12 09	11 56	12 02	12 09	12 17	12 32	12 22		12 47	12 39	12 26	12 32	12 39	12 47	13 02
	d	11 40	11 48	12 04	11 54		12 18	12 10		12 04	12 10	12 18	12 34	12 24		12 48	12 40		12 34	12 40	12 48	13 04
Farringdon 3 ⊖	d	11 45	11 53	→	11 59		→	→		12 09	12 15	12 23	→	12 29		→	→		12 39	12 45	12 53	→
City Thameslink 3	d	11 48	11 57		12 03					12 13	12 18	12 27		12 33					12 43	12 48	12 57	
London Blackfriars 3 ⊖	d	11 50	12 00		12 05	12 12				12 16	12 20	12 30		12 35	12 42				12 46	12 50	13 00	
Elephant & Castle ⊖173,179	d		12 03			12 16				12 19		12 33			12 46				12 49		13 03	
Loughborough Jn 173,179	d		12 07							12 23		12 37							12 53		13 07	
Herne Hill 4 173,179	d		12 11							12 27		12 41							12 57		13 11	
London Bridge 4	a	11 56			12 11						12 26			12 41						12 56		
	d	11 57			12 12						12 27			12 42						12 57		
Tulse Hill 3	d		12 16							12 31		12 46							13 01		13 16	
Streatham 4	d		12 20							12 35		12 50							13 05		13 20	
Mitcham Eastfields 173	d		12 24									12 54									13 24	
Mitcham Junction 173 ⛴	d		12 27									12 57									13 27	
Hackbridge 173	d		12 30									13 00									13 30	
Carshalton 173	d		12 33									13 03									13 33	
Tooting 173	d									12 40									13 10			
Haydons Road 173	d									12 43									13 13			
Wimbledon 6 ⊖173,179 ⛴	d									12 47									13 17			
Wimbledon Chase 179	d									12 50									13 20			
South Merton 179	d									12 52									13 22			
Morden South 179	d									12 54									13 24			
St Helier 179	d									12 56									13 26			
Sutton Common 179	d									12 58									13 28			
West Sutton 179	d									13 01									13 31			
Sutton (Surrey) 4 179	a		12 36							13 05		13 06							13 35		13 36	
Denmark Hill 4 195	d					12 22									12 52							
Peckham Rye 4 195	d					12 25									12 55							
Nunhead 4 195	d					12 27									12 57							
Crofton Park 195	d					12 30									13 00							
Catford 195	d					12 33									13 03							
Bellingham 195	d					12 35									13 05							
Beckenham Hill 195	d					12 37									13 07							
Ravensbourne 195	d					12 39									13 09							
Shortlands 195	d					12 41									13 11							
Bromley South 4 195	d					12 44									13 14							
Bickley 4 195	d					12 47									13 17							
St Mary Cray 195	d					12 51									13 21							
Swanley 4 195	d					12 56									13 26							
Eynsford 195	d					13 00									13 30							
Shoreham (Kent) 195	d					13 04									13 34							
Otford 4 195	d					13 07									13 37							
Bat & Ball 195	d					13 10									13 40							
Sevenoaks 4 195	a					13 13									13 43							
East Croydon ⛴	d	12 11			12 25						12 41			12 55						13 11		
Redhill	d																					
Gatwick Airport 10 ✈	d	12 27			12 41						12 57			13 11						13 27		
Three Bridges 4	d	12 32			12 45						13 02			13 15						13 32		
Balcombe	d													13 21								
Haywards Heath 3	d	12 41			12 55						13 11			13 27						13 41		
Wivelsfield 4	d				12 59									13 31								
Burgess Hill 4	d				13 01									13 33								
Hassocks 4	d				13 04									13 36								
Preston Park	d				13 11									13 43								
Brighton 10	a	12 55			13 15						13 25			13 47						13 55		

A From Bedford
B From St Albans City
C To Sutton (Surrey)
D To Brighton
E From Nottingham
F From Luton
G From Corby.

The trains that operate to and from Sevenoaks, Orpington and Rochester (and a few other destinations at peak times) are operated jointly by First Capital Connect (north of Blackfriars) and Southeastern (south of Blackfriars)

Table 52 shows the complete service between Bedford and London, whilst services between London, Sevenoaks, Sutton and Brighton only show through Thameslink services. Other Tables should be consulted for additional journey opportunities.

Table 52

Saturdays

14 December to 17 May

Bedford, Luton, St Albans and City of London - South London, Gatwick Airport and Brighton

Network Diagram - refer to first Page of Table 52

		FC [1]	SE	FC	FC [1]	EM ◇[1]	FC	FC [1]	FC	FC		FC [1]	SE	FC	FC [1]	EM ◇[1]	FC	FC [1]	FC	FC	FC [1]		SE	FC	FC [1]
				A	B	C ✠	D	E	F	A				A	B	G ✠	D	E	F	A				A	B
Bedford [7]	d	11 54			12 10	12 16						12 24			12 40	12 47					12 54				13 10
Flitwick	d	12 04			12 20							12 34			12 50						13 04				13 20
Harlington	d	12 08			12 24							12 38			12 54						13 08				13 24
Leagrave	d	12 13			12 29							12 43			12 59						13 13				13 29
Luton [10]	d	12 18			12 34					12 44		12 48			13 04	13 02				13 14	13 18				13 34
Luton Airport Parkway [7] ✈	d	12 20			12 36	12 31				12 46		12 50			13 06					13 16	13 20				13 36
Harpenden	d	12 26			12 42					12 52		12 56			13 12					13 22	13 26				13 42
St Albans City	d	12 32		12 44	12 48					12 59		13 02		13 14	13 18					13 29	13 32			13 44	13 48
Radlett	d			12 49						13 04				13 19						13 34				13 49	
Elstree & Borehamwood	d			12 53						13 08				13 23						13 38				13 53	
Mill Hill Broadway	d			12 58						13 13				13 28						13 43				13 58	
Hendon	d			13 01						13 16				13 31						13 46				14 01	
Cricklewood	d			13 05						13 20				13 35						13 50				14 05	
West Hampstead Thameslink ⊖	d	12 45		13 09						13 24		13 15		13 39						13 54	13 45			14 09	
Kentish Town ⊖	d			13 14			←	←	←	13 28				13 44			←	←	←	13 58				14 14	
St Pancras International [15] ⊖	a	12 52		13 17	13 09	12 56	13 02	13 09	13 17	13 32		13 22		13 47	13 39	13 26	13 32	13 39	13 47	14 02	13 52			14 17	14 09
	d	12 54		13 18	13 10		13 04	13 10	13 18	13 34		13 24		13 48	13 40		13 34	13 40	13 48	14 04	13 54			14 18	14 10
Farringdon [3] ⊖	d	12 59		↪	↪		13 09	13 15	13 23	↪		13 29		↪	↪		13 39	13 45	13 53	↪	13 59			↪	↪
City Thameslink [3]	d	13 03					13 13	13 18	13 27			13 33					13 43	13 48	13 57		14 03				
London Blackfriars [3] ⊖	d	13 05	13 12				13 16	13 20	13 30			13 35	13 42				13 46	13 50	14 00		14 05		14 12		
Elephant & Castle ⊖173,179	d		13 16				13 19		13 33				13 46				13 49		14 03				14 16		
Loughborough Jn 173,179	d						13 23		13 37								13 53		14 07						
Herne Hill [4] 173,179	d						13 27		13 41								13 57		14 11						
London Bridge [4]	a	13 11						13 26				13 41						13 56			14 11				
	d	13 12						13 27				13 42						13 57			14 12				
Tulse Hill [3]	d						13 31		13 46								14 01		14 16						
Streatham [4]	d						13 35		13 50								14 05		14 20						
Mitcham Eastfields 173	d								13 54										14 24						
Mitcham Junction 173 🚋	d								13 57										14 27						
Hackbridge 173	d								14 00										14 30						
Carshalton 173	d								14 03										14 33						
Tooting 173	d						13 40										14 10								
Haydons Road 173	d						13 43										14 13								
Wimbledon [6] ⊖173,179 🚋	d						13 47										14 17								
Wimbledon Chase 179	d						13 50										14 20								
South Merton 179	d						13 52										14 22								
Morden South 179	d						13 54										14 24								
St Helier 179	d						13 56										14 26								
Sutton Common 179	d						13 58										14 28								
West Sutton 179	d						14 01										14 31								
Sutton (Surrey) [4] 179	a						14 05		14 06								14 35		14 36						
Denmark Hill [4] 195	d		13 22										13 52										14 22		
Peckham Rye [4] 195	d		13 25										13 55										14 25		
Nunhead [4] 195	d		13 27										13 57										14 27		
Crofton Park 195	d		13 30										14 00										14 30		
Catford 195	d		13 33										14 03										14 33		
Bellingham 195	d		13 35										14 05										14 35		
Beckenham Hill 195	d		13 37										14 07										14 37		
Ravensbourne 195	d		13 39										14 09										14 39		
Shortlands 195	d		13 41										14 11										14 41		
Bromley South [4] 195	d		13 44										14 14										14 44		
Bickley [4] 195	d		13 47										14 17										14 47		
St Mary Cray 195	d		13 51										14 21										14 51		
Swanley [4] 195	d		13 56										14 26										14 56		
Eynsford 195	d		14 00										14 30										15 00		
Shoreham (Kent) 195	d		14 04										14 34										15 04		
Otford [4] 195	d		14 07										14 37										15 07		
Bat & Ball 195	d		14 10										14 40										15 10		
Sevenoaks [4] 195	a		14 13										14 43										15 13		
East Croydon 🚋	d	13 25						13 41				13 55						14 11			14 25				
Redhill	d																								
Gatwick Airport [10] ✈	d	13 41						13 57				14 11						14 27			14 41				
Three Bridges [4]	d	13 45						14 02				14 15						14 32			14 45				
Balcombe	d											14 21													
Haywards Heath [3]	d	13 55						14 11				14 27						14 41			14 55				
Wivelsfield [4]	d	13 59										14 31									14 59				
Burgess Hill [4]	d	14 01										14 33									15 01				
Hassocks [4]	d	14 04										14 36									15 04				
Preston Park	d	14 11										14 43									15 11				
Brighton [10]	a	14 15						14 25				14 47						14 55			15 15				

A To Sutton (Surrey)
B To Brighton
C From Nottingham
D From Luton
E From Bedford
F From St Albans City
G From Corby.

The trains that operate to and from Sevenoaks, Orpington and Rochester (and a few other destinations at peak times) are operated jointly by First Capital Connect (north of Blackfriars) and Southeastern (south of Blackfriars)

Table 52 shows the complete service between Bedford and London, whilst services between London, Sevenoaks, Sutton and Brighton only show through Thameslink services. Other Tables should be consulted for additional journey opportunities.

Table 52

Saturdays

14 December to 17 May

Bedford, Luton, St Albans and City of London - South London, Gatwick Airport and Brighton

Network Diagram - refer to first Page of Table 52

	EM	FC	FC	FC	FC	FC	SE	FC	FC	EM	FC	FC	FC	FC	FC	SE	FC	FC	EM	FC	FC	FC
	◇1		1			1			1	◇1		1			1			1	◇1		1	
	A	B	C	D	E			E	F	G	B	C	D	E			E	F	A	B	C	D
Bedford 7 d	13 16					13 24			13 40	13 47					13 54			14 10	14 16			
Flitwick d						13 34			13 50						14 04			14 20				
Harlington d						13 38			13 54						14 08			14 24				
Leagrave d						13 43			13 59						14 13			14 29				
Luton 10 d					13 44	13 48			14 04	14 02				14 14	14 18			14 34				
Luton Airport Parkway 7 ✈ d	13 31				13 46	13 50			14 06					14 16	14 20			14 36	14 31			
Harpenden d					13 52	13 56			14 12					14 22	14 26			14 42				
St Albans City d					13 59	14 02		14 14	14 18					14 29	14 32		14 44	14 48				
Radlett d					14 04			14 19						14 34			14 49					
Elstree & Borehamwood d					14 08			14 23						14 38			14 53					
Mill Hill Broadway d					14 13			14 28						14 43			14 58					
Hendon d					14 16			14 31						14 46			15 01					
Cricklewood d					14 20			14 35						14 50			15 05					
West Hampstead Thameslink ⊖ d					14 24	14 15		14 39						14 54	14 45		15 09					
Kentish Town ⊖ d		←	←	←	14 28			14 44			←	←	←	14 58			15 14			←	←	←
St Pancras International 15 ⊖ a	13 56	14 02	14 09	14 17	14 32	14 22		14 47	14 39	14 26	14 32	14 39	14 47	15 02	14 52		15 17	15 09	14 56	15 02	15 09	15 17
d		14 04	14 10	14 18	14 34	14 24		14 48	14 40		14 34	14 40	14 48	15 04	14 54		15 18	15 10		15 04	15 10	15 18
Farringdon 3 ⊖ d		14 09	14 15	14 23	→	14 29		→	→		14 39	14 45	14 53	→	14 59		→	→		15 09	15 15	15 23
City Thameslink 3 d		14 13	14 18	14 27		14 33					14 43	14 48	14 57		15 03					15 13	15 18	15 27
London Blackfriars 3 ⊖ d		14 16	14 20	14 30		14 35	14 42				14 46	14 50	15 00		15 05	15 12				15 16	15 20	15 30
Elephant & Castle ⊖173,179 d		14 19		14 33			14 46				14 49		15 03			15 16				15 19		15 33
Loughborough Jn 173,179 d		14 23		14 37							14 53		15 07							15 23		15 37
Herne Hill 4 173,179 d		14 27		14 41							14 57		15 11							15 27		15 41
London Bridge 4 a			14 26			14 41						14 56			15 11						15 26	
d			14 27			14 42						14 57			15 12						15 27	
Tulse Hill 3 d		14 31		14 46							15 01		15 16							15 31		15 46
Streatham 4 d		14 35		14 50							15 05		15 20							15 35		15 50
Mitcham Eastfields 173 d				14 54									15 24									15 54
Mitcham Junction 173 🚊 d				14 57									15 27									15 57
Hackbridge 173 d				15 00									15 30									16 00
Carshalton 173 d				15 03									15 33									16 03
Tooting 173 d		14 40									15 10									15 40		
Haydons Road 173 d		14 43									15 13									15 43		
Wimbledon 6 ⊖173,179 🚊 d		14 47									15 17									15 47		
Wimbledon Chase 179 d		14 50									15 20									15 50		
South Merton 179 d		14 52									15 22									15 52		
Morden South 179 d		14 54									15 24									15 54		
St Helier 179 d		14 56									15 26									15 56		
Sutton Common 179 d		14 58									15 28									15 58		
West Sutton 179 d		15 01									15 31									16 01		
Sutton (Surrey) 4 179 a		15 05		15 06							15 35		15 36							16 05		16 06
Denmark Hill 4 195 d							14 52									15 22						
Peckham Rye 4 195 d							14 55									15 25						
Nunhead 4 195 d							14 57									15 27						
Crofton Park 195 d							15 00									15 30						
Catford 195 d							15 03									15 33						
Bellingham 195 d							15 05									15 35						
Beckenham Hill 195 d							15 07									15 37						
Ravensbourne 195 d							15 09									15 39						
Shortlands 195 d							15 11									15 41						
Bromley South 4 195 d							15 14									15 44						
Bickley 4 195 d							15 17									15 47						
St Mary Cray 195 d							15 21									15 51						
Swanley 4 195 d							15 26									15 56						
Eynsford 195 d							15 30									16 00						
Shoreham (Kent) 195 d							15 34									16 04						
Otford 4 195 d							15 37									16 07						
Bat & Ball 195 d							15 40									16 10						
Sevenoaks 4 195 a							15 43									16 13						
East Croydon 🚊 d			14 41			14 55						15 11			15 25						15 41	
Redhill d																						
Gatwick Airport 10 ✈ d			14 57			15 11						15 27			15 41						15 57	
Three Bridges 4 d			15 02			15 15						15 32			15 45						16 02	
Balcombe d						15 21																
Haywards Heath 3 d			15 11			15 27						15 41			15 55						16 11	
Wivelsfield 4 d						15 31									15 59							
Burgess Hill 4 d						15 33									16 01							
Hassocks 4 d						15 36									16 04							
Preston Park d						15 43									16 11							
Brighton 10 a			15 25			15 47						15 55			16 15						16 25	

A From Nottingham
B From Luton
C From Bedford
D From St Albans City
E To Sutton (Surrey)
F To Brighton
G From Corby.

The trains that operate to and from Sevenoaks, Orpington and Rochester (and a few other destinations at peak times) are operated jointly by First Capital Connect (north of Blackfriars) and Southeastern (south of Blackfriars)

Table 52 shows the complete service between Bedford and London, whilst services between London, Sevenoaks, Sutton and Brighton only show through Thameslink services. Other Tables should be consulted for additional journey opportunities.

Table 52

Saturdays

14 December to 17 May

Bedford, Luton, St Albans and City of London - South London, Gatwick Airport and Brighton

Network Diagram - refer to first Page of Table 52

		FC	FC	SE	FC	FC	EM	FC	FC	FC	FC	FC	SE	FC	FC	EM	FC	FC	FC	FC	FC	SE	FC
			1			1	◇1		1			1			1	◇1		1			1		
		A			A	B	C	D	E	F	A			A	B	G	D	E	F	A			A
Bedford 7	d		14 24			14 40	14 47					14 54			15 10	15 16					15 24		
Flitwick	d		14 34			14 50						15 04			15 20						15 34		
Harlington	d		14 38			14 54						15 08			15 24						15 38		
Leagrave	d		14 43			14 59						15 13			15 29						15 43		
Luton 10	d	14 44	14 48			15 04	15 02				15 14	15 18			15 34					15 44	15 48		
Luton Airport Parkway 7 ✈	d	14 46	14 50			15 06					15 16	15 20			15 36	15 31				15 46	15 50		
Harpenden	d	14 52	14 56			15 12					15 22	15 26			15 42					15 52	15 56		
St Albans City	d	14 59	15 02		15 14	15 18					15 29	15 32		15 44	15 48					15 59	16 02		16 14
Radlett	d	15 04			15 19						15 34			15 49						16 04			16 19
Elstree & Borehamwood	d	15 08			15 23						15 38			15 53						16 08			16 23
Mill Hill Broadway	d	15 13			15 28						15 43			15 58						16 13			16 28
Hendon	d	15 16			15 31						15 46			16 01						16 16			16 31
Cricklewood	d	15 20			15 35						15 50			16 05						16 20			16 35
West Hampstead Thameslink ⊖	d	15 24	15 15		15 39						15 54	15 45		16 09						16 24	16 15		16 39
Kentish Town ⊖	d	15 28			15 44			←	←	←	15 58			16 14			←	←	←	16 28			16 44
St Pancras International 15 ⊖	a	15 32	15 22		15 47	15 39	15 26	15 32	15 39	15 47	16 02	15 52		16 17	16 09	15 56	16 02	16 09	16 17	16 32	16 22		16 47
	d	15 34	15 24		15 48	15 40		15 34	15 40	15 48	16 04	15 54		16 18	16 10		16 04	16 10	16 18	16 34	16 24		16 48
Farringdon 3 ⊖	d	→	15 29		→	→		15 39	15 45	15 53	→	15 59		→	→		16 09	16 15	16 23	→	16 29		→
City Thameslink 3	d		15 33					15 43	15 48	15 57		16 03					16 13	16 18	16 27		16 33		
London Blackfriars 3 ⊖	d		15 35	15 42				15 46	15 50	16 00		16 05	16 12				16 16	16 20	16 30		16 35	16 42	
Elephant & Castle ⊖173,179	d			15 46				15 49		16 03			16 16				16 19		16 33			16 46	
Loughborough Jn 173,179	d							15 53		16 07							16 23		16 37				
Herne Hill 4 173,179	d							15 57		16 11							16 27		16 41				
London Bridge 4	a		15 41						15 56			16 11						16 26			16 41		
	d		15 42						15 57			16 12						16 27			16 42		
Tulse Hill 3	d							16 01		16 16							16 31		16 46				
Streatham 4	d							16 05		16 20							16 35		16 50				
Mitcham Eastfields 173	d									16 24									16 54				
Mitcham Junction 173 ⛴	d									16 27									16 57				
Hackbridge 173	d									16 30									17 00				
Carshalton 173	d									16 33									17 03				
Tooting 173	d							16 10									16 40						
Haydons Road 173	d							16 13									16 43						
Wimbledon 6 ⊖173,179 ⛴	d							16 17									16 47						
Wimbledon Chase 179	d							16 20									16 50						
South Merton 179	d							16 22									16 52						
Morden South 179	d							16 24									16 54						
St Helier 179	d							16 26									16 56						
Sutton Common 179	d							16 28									16 58						
West Sutton 179	d							16 31									17 01						
Sutton (Surrey) 4 179	a							16 35		16 36							17 05		17 06				
Denmark Hill 4 195	d			15 52									16 22									16 52	
Peckham Rye 4 195	d			15 55									16 25									16 55	
Nunhead 4 195	d			15 57									16 27									16 57	
Crofton Park 195	d			16 00									16 30									17 00	
Catford 195	d			16 03									16 33									17 03	
Bellingham 195	d			16 05									16 35									17 05	
Beckenham Hill 195	d			16 07									16 37									17 07	
Ravensbourne 195	d			16 09									16 39									17 09	
Shortlands 195	d			16 11									16 41									17 11	
Bromley South 4 195	d			16 14									16 44									17 14	
Bickley 4 195	d			16 17									16 47									17 17	
St Mary Cray 195	d			16 21									16 51									17 21	
Swanley 4 195	d			16 26									16 56									17 26	
Eynsford 195	d			16 30									17 00									17 30	
Shoreham (Kent) 195	d			16 34									17 04									17 34	
Otford 4 195	d			16 37									17 07									17 37	
Bat & Ball 195	d			16 40									17 10									17 40	
Sevenoaks 4 195	a			16 43									17 13									17 43	
East Croydon ⛴	d		15 55						16 11			16 25						16 41			16 55		
Redhill	d																						
Gatwick Airport 10 ✈	d		16 11						16 27			16 41						16 57			17 11		
Three Bridges 4	d		16 15						16 32			16 45						17 02			17 15		
Balcombe	d		16 21																		17 21		
Haywards Heath 3	d		16 27						16 41			16 55						17 11			17 27		
Wivelsfield 4	d		16 31									16 59									17 31		
Burgess Hill 4	d		16 33									17 01									17 33		
Hassocks 4	d		16 36									17 04									17 36		
Preston Park	d		16 43									17 11									17 43		
Brighton 10	a		16 47						16 55			17 15						17 25			17 47		

A To Sutton (Surrey)
B To Brighton
C From Corby.
D From Luton
E From Bedford
F From St Albans City
G From Nottingham

The trains that operate to and from Sevenoaks, Orpington and Rochester (and a few other destinations at peak times) are operated jointly by First Capital Connect (north of Blackfriars) and Southeastern (south of Blackfriars)

Table 52 shows the complete service between Bedford and London, whilst services between London, Sevenoaks, Sutton and Brighton only show through Thameslink services. Other Tables should be consulted for additional journey opportunities.

Table 52

Saturdays

14 December to 17 May

Bedford, Luton, St Albans and City of London - South London, Gatwick Airport and Brighton

Network Diagram - refer to first Page of Table 52

		FC	EM	FC	FC	FC	FC	FC	SE	FC	FC	EM	FC	FC	FC	FC	FC	SE	FC	FC	EM	FC	FC
		1	◇1		1			1			1	◇1		1			1			1	◇1		1
		A	B	C	D	E	F			F	A	G	C	D	E	F			F	A	B	C	D
Bedford 7	d	15 40	15 47					15 54			16 10	16 16					16 24			16 40	16 47		
Flitwick	d	15 50						16 04			16 20						16 34			16 50			
Harlington	d	15 54						16 08			16 24						16 38			16 54			
Leagrave	d	15 59						16 13			16 29						16 43			16 59			
Luton 10	d	16 04	16 02				16 14	16 18			16 34					16 44	16 48			17 04	17 02		
Luton Airport Parkway 7 ✈	d	16 06					16 16	16 20			16 36	16 31				16 46	16 50			17 06			
Harpenden	d	16 12					16 22	16 26			16 42					16 52	16 56			17 12			
St Albans City	d	16 18					16 29	16 32		16 44	16 48					16 59	17 02		17 14	17 18			
Radlett	d						16 34			16 49						17 04			17 19				
Elstree & Borehamwood	d						16 38			16 53						17 08			17 23				
Mill Hill Broadway	d						16 43			16 58						17 13			17 28				
Hendon	d						16 46			17 01						17 16			17 31				
Cricklewood	d						16 50			17 05						17 20			17 35				
West Hampstead Thameslink ⊖	d						16 54	16 45		17 09						17 24	17 15		17 39				
Kentish Town ⊖	d			←	←	←	16 58			17 14			←	←	←	17 28			17 44			←	←
St Pancras International 15 ⊖	a	16 39	16 26	16 32	16 39	16 47	17 02	16 52		17 17	17 09	16 56	17 02	17 09	17 17	17 32	17 22		17 47	17 39	17 26	17 32	17 39
	d	16 40		16 34	16 40	16 48	17 04	16 54		17 18	17 10		17 04	17 10	17 18	17 34	17 24		17 48	17 40		17 34	17 40
Farringdon 3 ⊖	d	→		16 39	16 45	16 53	→	16 59		→	→		17 09	17 15	17 23	→	17 29		→	→		17 39	17 45
City Thameslink 3	d			16 43	16 48	16 57		17 03					17 13	17 18	17 27		17 33					17 43	17 48
London Blackfriars 3 ⊖	d			16 46	16 50	17 00		17 05	17 12				17 16	17 20	17 30		17 35	17 42				17 46	17 50
Elephant & Castle ⊖173,179	d			16 49		17 03			17 16				17 19		17 33			17 46				17 49	
Loughborough Jn 173,179	d			16 53		17 07							17 23		17 37							17 53	
Herne Hill 4 173,179	d			16 57		17 11							17 27		17 41							17 57	
London Bridge 4	a				16 56			17 11						17 26			17 41						17 56
	d				16 57			17 12						17 27			17 42						17 57
Tulse Hill 3	d			17 01		17 16							17 31		17 46							18 01	
Streatham 4	d			17 05		17 20							17 35		17 50							18 05	
Mitcham Eastfields 173	d					17 24									17 54								
Mitcham Junction 173 🚋	d					17 27									17 57								
Hackbridge 173	d					17 30									18 00								
Carshalton 173	d					17 33									18 03								
Tooting 173	d			17 10									17 40									18 10	
Haydons Road 173	d			17 13									17 43									18 13	
Wimbledon 6 ⊖173,179 🚋	d			17 17									17 47									18 17	
Wimbledon Chase 179	d			17 20									17 50									18 20	
South Merton 179	d			17 22									17 52									18 22	
Morden South 179	d			17 24									17 54									18 24	
St Helier 179	d			17 26									17 56									18 26	
Sutton Common 179	d			17 28									17 58									18 28	
West Sutton 179	d			17 31									18 01									18 31	
Sutton (Surrey) 4 179	a			17 35		17 36							18 05		18 06							18 35	
Denmark Hill 4 195	d								17 22									17 52					
Peckham Rye 4 195	d								17 25									17 55					
Nunhead 4 195	d								17 27									17 57					
Crofton Park 195	d								17 30									18 00					
Catford 195	d								17 33									18 03					
Bellingham 195	d								17 35									18 05					
Beckenham Hill 195	d								17 37									18 07					
Ravensbourne 195	d								17 39									18 09					
Shortlands 195	d								17 41									18 11					
Bromley South 4 195	d								17 44									18 14					
Bickley 4 195	d								17 47									18 17					
St Mary Cray 195	d								17 51									18 21					
Swanley 4 195	d								17 56									18 26					
Eynsford 195	d								18 00									18 30					
Shoreham (Kent) 195	d								18 04									18 34					
Otford 4 195	d								18 07									18 37					
Bat & Ball 195	d								18 10									18 40					
Sevenoaks 4 195	a								18 13									18 43					
East Croydon 🚋	d				17 11			17 25						17 41			17 55						18 11
Redhill	d																						
Gatwick Airport 10 ✈	d				17 27			17 41						17 57			18 11						18 27
Three Bridges 4	d				17 32			17 45						18 02			18 15						18 32
Balcombe	d																18 21						
Haywards Heath 3	d				17 41			17 55						18 11			18 27						18 41
Wivelsfield 4	d							17 59									18 31						
Burgess Hill 4	d							18 01									18 33						
Hassocks 4	d							18 04									18 36						
Preston Park	d							18 11									18 43						
Brighton 10	a				17 55			18 15						18 25			18 47						18 55

A To Brighton
B From Corby.
C From Luton
D From Bedford
E From St Albans City
F To Sutton (Surrey)
G From Nottingham

The trains that operate to and from Sevenoaks, Orpington and Rochester (and a few other destinations at peak times) are operated jointly by First Capital Connect (north of Blackfriars) and Southeastern (south of Blackfriars)

Table 52 shows the complete service between Bedford and London, whilst services between London, Sevenoaks, Sutton and Brighton only show through Thameslink services. Other Tables should be consulted for additional journey opportunities.

Table 52

Saturdays

14 December to 17 May

Bedford, Luton, St Albans and City of London - South London, Gatwick Airport and Brighton

Network Diagram - refer to first Page of Table 52

		FC	FC	FC 1	SE	FC	FC 1	EM ◇1	FC	FC 1	FC	FC	FC 1	SE	FC	FC 1	EM ◇1	FC	FC 1	FC	FC	FC 1
		A	B			B	C	D	E	F	A	B			B	C	G	E	F	A	B	
Bedford 7	d			16 54			17 10	17 16					17 24			17 40	17 47					17 54
Flitwick	d			17 04			17 20						17 34			17 50						18 04
Harlington	d			17 08			17 24						17 38			17 54						18 08
Leagrave	d			17 13			17 29						17 43			17 59						18 13
Luton 10	d		17 14	17 18			17 34					17 44	17 48			18 04	18 02				18 14	18 18
Luton Airport Parkway 7 ✈	d		17 16	17 20			17 36	17 31				17 46	17 50			18 06					18 16	18 20
Harpenden	d		17 22	17 26			17 42					17 52	17 56			18 12					18 22	18 26
St Albans City	d		17 29	17 32		17 44	17 48					17 59	18 02		18 14	18 18					18 29	18 32
Radlett	d		17 34			17 49						18 04			18 19						18 34	
Elstree & Borehamwood	d		17 38			17 53						18 08			18 23						18 38	
Mill Hill Broadway	d		17 43			17 58						18 13			18 28						18 43	
Hendon	d		17 46			18 01						18 16			18 31						18 46	
Cricklewood	d		17 50			18 05						18 20			18 35						18 50	
West Hampstead Thameslink ⊖	d		17 54	17 45		18 09						18 24	18 15		18 39						18 54	18 45
Kentish Town ⊖	d	←	17 58			18 14			←	←	←	18 28			18 44			←	←	←	18 58	
St Pancras International 15 ⊖	a	17 47	18 02	17 52		18 17	18 09	17 56	18 02	18 09	18 17	18 32	18 22		18 47	18 39	18 26	18 32	18 39	18 47	19 02	18 53
	d	17 48	18 04	17 54		18 18	18 10		18 04	18 10	18 18	18 34	18 24		18 48	18 40		18 34	18 40	18 48	19 04	18 54
Farringdon 3 ⊖	d	17 53	→	17 59		→	→		18 09	18 15	18 23	→	18 29		→	→		18 39	18 45	18 53	→	18 59
City Thameslink 3	d	17 57		18 03					18 13	18 18	18 27		18 33					18 43	18 48	18 57		19 03
London Blackfriars 3 ⊖	d	18 00		18 05	18 12				18 16	18 20	18 30		18 35	18 42				18 46	18 50	19 00		19 05
Elephant & Castle ⊖173,179	d	18 03			18 16				18 19		18 33			18 46				18 49		19 03		
Loughborough Jn 173,179	d	18 07							18 23		18 37							18 53		19 07		
Herne Hill 4 173,179	d	18 11							18 27		18 41							18 57		19 11		
London Bridge 4	a			18 11						18 26			18 41						18 56			19 11
	d			18 12						18 27			18 42						18 57			19 12
Tulse Hill 3	d	18 16							18 31		18 46							19 01		19 16		
Streatham 4	d	18 20							18 35		18 50							19 05		19 20		
Mitcham Eastfields 173	d	18 24									18 54									19 24		
Mitcham Junction 173 🚋	d	18 27									18 57									19 27		
Hackbridge 173	d	18 30									19 00									19 30		
Carshalton 173	d	18 33									19 03									19 33		
Tooting 173	d								18 40									19 10				
Haydons Road 173	d								18 43									19 13				
Wimbledon 6 ⊖173,179 🚋	d								18 47									19 17				
Wimbledon Chase 179	d								18 50									19 20				
South Merton 179	d								18 52									19 22				
Morden South 179	d								18 54									19 24				
St Helier 179	d								18 56									19 26				
Sutton Common 179	d								18 58									19 28				
West Sutton 179	d								19 01									19 31				
Sutton (Surrey) 4 179	a	18 36							19 05		19 06							19 35		19 36		
Denmark Hill 4 195	d				18 22									18 52								
Peckham Rye 4 195	d				18 25									18 55								
Nunhead 4 195	d				18 27									18 57								
Crofton Park 195	d				18 30									19 00								
Catford 195	d				18 33									19 03								
Bellingham 195	d				18 35									19 05								
Beckenham Hill 195	d				18 37									19 07								
Ravensbourne 195	d				18 39									19 09								
Shortlands 195	d				18 41									19 11								
Bromley South 4 195	d				18 44									19 14								
Bickley 4 195	d				18 47									19 17								
St Mary Cray 195	d				18 51									19 21								
Swanley 4 195	d				18 56									19 26								
Eynsford 195	d				19 00									19 30								
Shoreham (Kent) 195	d				19 04									19 34								
Otford 4 195	d				19 07									19 37								
Bat & Ball 195	d				19 10									19 40								
Sevenoaks 4 195	a				19 13									19 43								
East Croydon 🚋	d			18 25						18 41			18 55						19 11			19 25
Redhill	d																					
Gatwick Airport 10 ✈	d			18 41						18 57			19 11						19 27			19 41
Three Bridges 4	d			18 45						19 02			19 15						19 32			19 45
Balcombe	d												19 21									
Haywards Heath 3	d			18 55						19 11			19 27						19 41			19 55
Wivelsfield 4	d			18 59									19 31									19 59
Burgess Hill 4	d			19 01									19 33									20 01
Hassocks 4	d			19 04									19 36									20 04
Preston Park	d			19 11									19 43									20 11
Brighton 10	a			19 15						19 25			19 47						19 55			20 15

A From St Albans City
B To Sutton (Surrey)
C To Brighton
D From Nottingham
E From Luton
F From Bedford
G From Corby.

The trains that operate to and from Sevenoaks, Orpington and Rochester (and a few other destinations at peak times) are operated jointly by First Capital Connect (north of Blackfriars) and Southeastern (south of Blackfriars)

Table 52 shows the complete service between Bedford and London, whilst services between London, Sevenoaks, Sutton and Brighton only show through Thameslink services. Other Tables should be consulted for additional journey opportunities.

Table 52

Saturdays

14 December to 17 May

Bedford, Luton, St Albans and City of London - South London, Gatwick Airport and Brighton

Network Diagram - refer to first Page of Table 52

		SE	FC	FC	EM	FC	FC	FC	FC	FC	SE	FC	FC	EM	FC	FC	FC	FC	FC	SE	EM		FC	FC
				1	◇1		1			1			1	◇1		1			1		◇1			
			A	B	C	D	E	F	A			A	B	G	D	E	F	A			C		D	
Bedford 7	d			18 10	18 16					18 24			18 40	18 47					18 54		19 16			
Flitwick	d			18 20						18 34			18 50						19 04					
Harlington	d			18 24						18 38			18 54						19 08					
Leagrave	d			18 29						18 43			18 59						19 13					
Luton 10	d			18 34					18 44	18 48			19 04	19 02				19 14	19 18					
Luton Airport Parkway 7 ✈	d			18 36	18 31				18 46	18 50			19 06					19 16	19 20		19 31			
Harpenden	d			18 42					18 52	18 56			19 12					19 22	19 26					
St Albans City	d		18 44	18 48					18 59	19 02		19 14	19 18					19 29	19 32					19 44
Radlett	d		18 49						19 04			19 19						19 34						19 49
Elstree & Borehamwood	d		18 53						19 08			19 23						19 38						19 53
Mill Hill Broadway	d		18 58						19 13			19 28						19 43						19 58
Hendon	d		19 01						19 16			19 31						19 46						20 01
Cricklewood	d		19 05						19 20			19 35						19 50						20 05
West Hampstead Thameslink ⊖	d		19 09						19 24	19 15		19 39						19 54	19 45					20 09
Kentish Town ⊖	d		19 14			←	←	←	19 28			19 44			←	←	←	19 58					←	20 14
St Pancras International 15 ⊖	a		19 17	19 09	18 56	19 02	19 09	19 17	19 32	19 23		19 47	19 39	19 26	19 32	19 39	19 47	20 02	19 53		19 56		20 02	20 17
	d		19 18	19 10		19 04	19 10	19 18	19 34	19 24		19 48	19 40		19 34	19 40	19 48	20 04	19 54				20 04	20 18
Farringdon 3 ⊖	d		→	→		19 09	19 15	19 23	→	19 29		→	→		19 39	19 45	19 53	→	19 59				20 09	20 23
City Thameslink 3	d					19 13	19 18	19 27		19 33					19 43	19 48	19 57		20 03				20 13	20 27
London Blackfriars 3 ⊖	d	19 12				19 16	19 20	19 30		19 35	19 42				19 46	19 50	20 00		20 05	20 12			20 16	20 30
Elephant & Castle ⊖ 173,179	d	19 16				19 19		19 33			19 46				19 49		20 03			20 16			20 19	20 33
Loughborough Jn 173,179	d					19 23		19 37							19 53		20 07						20 23	20 37
Herne Hill 4 173,179	d					19 27		19 41							19 57		20 11						20 27	20 41
London Bridge 4	a						19 26			19 41						19 56			20 11					
	d						19 27			19 42						19 57			20 12					
Tulse Hill 3	d					19 31		19 46							20 01		20 16						20 31	20 46
Streatham 4	d					19 35		19 50							20 05		20 20						20 35	20 50
Mitcham Eastfields 173	d							19 54									20 24							20 54
Mitcham Junction 173 🚊	d							19 57									20 27							20 57
Hackbridge 173	d							20 00									20 30							21 00
Carshalton 173	d							20 03									20 33							21 03
Tooting 173	d					19 40									20 10								20 40	
Haydons Road 173	d					19 43									20 13								20 43	
Wimbledon 6 ⊖ 173,179 🚊	d					19 47									20 17								20 47	
Wimbledon Chase 179	d					19 50									20 20								20 50	
South Merton 179	d					19 52									20 22								20 52	
Morden South 179	d					19 54									20 24								20 54	
St Helier 179	d					19 56									20 26								20 56	
Sutton Common 179	d					19 58									20 28								20 58	
West Sutton 179	d					20 01									20 31								21 01	
Sutton (Surrey) 4 179	a					20 05		20 06							20 35		20 36						21 05	21 06
Denmark Hill 4 195	d	19 22									19 52									20 22				
Peckham Rye 4 195	d	19 25									19 55									20 25				
Nunhead 4 195	d	19 27									19 57									20 27				
Crofton Park 195	d	19 30									20 00									20 30				
Catford 195	d	19 33									20 03									20 33				
Bellingham 195	d	19 35									20 05									20 35				
Beckenham Hill 195	d	19 37									20 07									20 37				
Ravensbourne 195	d	19 39									20 09									20 39				
Shortlands 195	d	19 41									20 11									20 41				
Bromley South 4 195	d	19 44									20 14									20 44				
Bickley 4 195	d	19 47									20 17									20 47				
St Mary Cray 195	d	19 51									20 21									20 51				
Swanley 4 195	d	19 56									20 26									20 56				
Eynsford 195	d	20 00									20 30									21 00				
Shoreham (Kent) 195	d	20 04									20 34									21 04				
Otford 4 195	d	20 07									20 37									21 07				
Bat & Ball 195	d	20 10									20 40									21 10				
Sevenoaks 4 195	a	20 13									20 43									21 13				
East Croydon 🚊	d						19 41			19 55						20 11			20 25					
Redhill	d																							
Gatwick Airport 10 ✈	d						19 57			20 11						20 27			20 41					
Three Bridges 4	d						20 02			20 15						20 32			20 45					
Balcombe	d									20 21									20 51					
Haywards Heath 3	d						20 11			20 27						20 41			20 57					
Wivelsfield 4	d									20 31									21 01					
Burgess Hill 4	d									20 33									21 03					
Hassocks 4	d									20 36									21 06					
Preston Park	d									20 43									21 13					
Brighton 10	a						20 25			20 47						20 55			21 17					

A To Sutton (Surrey)
B To Brighton
C From Nottingham
D From Luton
E From Bedford
F From St Albans City
G From Corby.

The trains that operate to and from Sevenoaks, Orpington and Rochester (and a few other destinations at peak times) are operated jointly by First Capital Connect (north of Blackfriars) and Southeastern (south of Blackfriars)

Table 52 shows the complete service between Bedford and London, whilst services between London, Sevenoaks, Sutton and Brighton only show through Thameslink services. Other Tables should be consulted for additional journey opportunities.

Table 52

Saturdays

14 December to 17 May

Bedford, Luton, St Albans and City of London - South London, Gatwick Airport and Brighton

Network Diagram - refer to first Page of Table 52

		FC	SE	EM	FC	FC	FC	SE	EM	FC	FC	SE	EM	FC	FC	SE	EM	FC	FC	SE	EM	FC	FC
		1		◇1			1		◇1		1		◇1		1		◇1		1		◇1		1
				A					B				A				B				A		
Bedford 7	d	19 22		19 47			19 52		20 16		20 22		20 47		20 52		21 19		21 22		21 47		21 52
Flitwick	d	19 32					20 02				20 32				21 02				21 32				22 02
Harlington	d	19 36					20 06				20 36				21 06				21 36				22 06
Leagrave	d	19 41					20 11				20 41				21 11				21 41				22 11
Luton 10	d	19 46		20 02	19 50		20 16			20 20	20 46		21 02	20 50	21 16			21 20	21 46		22 02	21 50	22 16
Luton Airport Parkway 7 ✈	d	19 48			19 52		20 18		20 31	20 22	20 48			20 52	21 18		21 35	21 22	21 48			21 52	22 18
Harpenden	d	19 54			19 58		20 24			20 28	20 54			20 58	21 24			21 28	21 54			21 58	22 24
St Albans City	d	20 00			20 04	20 14	20 30			20 34	21 00			21 04	21 30			21 34	22 00			22 04	22 30
Radlett	d				20 09	20 19				20 39				21 09				21 39				22 09	
Elstree & Borehamwood	d				20 13	20 23				20 43				21 13				21 43				22 13	
Mill Hill Broadway	d				20 17	20 28				20 47				21 17				21 47				22 17	
Hendon	d				20 20	20 31				20 50				21 20				21 50				22 20	
Cricklewood	d				20 24	20 35				20 54				21 24				21 54				22 24	
West Hampstead Thameslink ⊖	d	20 15			20 26	20 39	20 45			20 56	21 15			21 26	21 45			21 56	22 15			22 26	22 45
Kentish Town ⊖	d				20 31	20 44				21 01				21 31				22 01				22 31	
St Pancras International 15 ⊖	a	20 22		20 26	20 35	20 47	20 52		20 56	21 05	21 22		21 26	21 35	21 52		21 59	22 05	22 22		22 26	22 35	22 52
	d	20 24			20 36	20 48	20 54			21 06	21 24			21 36	21 54			22 06	22 24			22 36	22 54
Farringdon 3 ⊖	d	20 29			20 40	20 53	20 59			21 10	21 29			21 40	21 59			22 10	22 29			22 40	22 59
City Thameslink 3	d	20 33			20 43	20 57	21 03																
London Blackfriars 3 ⊖	d	20 35	20 42		20 46	21 00	21 05	21 12		21 16	21 35	21 42		21 46	22 05	22 12		22 16	22 35	22 42		22 46	23 05
Elephant & Castle ⊖173,179	d		20 46		20 49	21 03		21 16		21 19		21 46		21 49		22 16		22 19		22 46		22 49	
Loughborough Jn 173,179	d				20 53	21 07				21 23				21 53				22 23				22 53	
Herne Hill 4 173,179	d				20 57	21 11				21 27				21 57				22 27				22 57	
London Bridge 4	a	20 41					21 11				21 41				22 11				22 41				23 11
	d	20 42					21 12				21 42				22 12				22 42				23 12
Tulse Hill 3	d				21 01	21 16				21 31				22 01				22 31				23 01	
Streatham 4	d				21 05	21 20				21 35				22 05				22 35				23 05	
Mitcham Eastfields 173	d					21 24																	
Mitcham Junction 173 ⇌	d					21 27																	
Hackbridge 173	d					21 30																	
Carshalton 173	d					21 33																	
Tooting 173	d				21 10					21 40				22 10				22 40				23 10	
Haydons Road 173	d				21 13					21 43				22 13				22 43				23 13	
Wimbledon 6 ⊖173,179 ⇌	d				21 17					21 47				22 17				22 47				23 17	
Wimbledon Chase 179	d				21 20					21 50				22 20				22 50				23 20	
South Merton 179	d				21 22					21 52				22 22				22 52				23 22	
Morden South 179	d				21 24					21 54				22 24				22 54				23 24	
St Helier 179	d				21 26					21 56				22 26				22 56				23 26	
Sutton Common 179	d				21 28					21 58				22 28				22 58				23 28	
West Sutton 179	d				21 31					22 01				22 31				23 01				23 31	
Sutton (Surrey) 4 179	a				21 35	21 42				22 05				22 35				23 05				23 35	
Denmark Hill 4 195	d		20 52					21 22				21 52				22 22				22 52			
Peckham Rye 4 195	d		20 55					21 25				21 55				22 25				22 55			
Nunhead 4 195	d		20 57					21 27				21 57				22 27				22 57			
Crofton Park 195	d		21 00					21 30				22 00				22 30				23 00			
Catford 195	d		21 03					21 33				22 03				22 33				23 03			
Bellingham 195	d		21 05					21 35				22 05				22 35				23 05			
Beckenham Hill 195	d		21 07					21 37				22 07				22 37				23 07			
Ravensbourne 195	d		21 09					21 39				22 09				22 39				23 09			
Shortlands 195	d		21 11					21 41				22 11				22 41				23 11			
Bromley South 4 195	d		21 14					21 44				22 14				22 44				23 14			
Bickley 4 195	d		21 17					21 47				22 17				22 47				23 17			
St Mary Cray 195	d		21 21					21 51				22 21				22 51				23 21			
Swanley 4 195	d		21 26					21 56				22 26				22 56				23 26			
Eynsford 195	d		21 30					22 00				22 30				23 00				23 30			
Shoreham (Kent) 195	d		21 34					22 04				22 34				23 04				23 34			
Otford 4 195	d		21 37					22 07				22 37				23 07				23 37			
Bat & Ball 195	d		21 40					22 10				22 40				23 10				23 40			
Sevenoaks 4 195	a		21 43					22 13				22 43				23 13				23 43			
East Croydon ⇌	d	20 55					21 25				21 55				22 25				22 55				23 25
Redhill	d																						
Gatwick Airport 10 ✈	d	21 11					21 41				22 11				22 41				23 11				23 41
Three Bridges 4	d	21 15					21 45				22 15				22 45				23 15				23 47
Balcombe	d						21 53								22 53								23 53
Haywards Heath 3	d	21 25					21 59				22 25				22 59				23 25				23 59
Wivelsfield 4	d	21 29					22 03				22 29				23 03				23 29				00 03
Burgess Hill 4	d	21 31					22 05				22 31				23 05				23 31				00 05
Hassocks 4	d	21 34					22 08				22 34				23 08				23 34				00 08
Preston Park	d	21 41					22 15				22 41				23 15				23 41				00 15
Brighton 10	a	21 45					22 19				22 45				23 19				23 45				00 19

A From Corby.

B From Nottingham

The trains that operate to and from Sevenoaks, Orpington and Rochester (and a few other destinations at peak times) are operated jointly by First Capital Connect (north of Blackfriars) and Southeastern (south of Blackfriars)

Table 52 shows the complete service between Bedford and London, whilst services between London, Sevenoaks, Sutton and Brighton only show through Thameslink services. Other Tables should be consulted for additional journey opportunities.

Table 52

Saturdays

14 December to 17 May

Bedford, Luton, St Albans and City of London - South London, Gatwick Airport and Brighton

Network Diagram - refer to first Page of Table 52

		SE	FC	FC	SE	EM	FC	FC	EM	FC	FC
				1		◇1		1	◇1	1	1
						A			A		
						⚮			⚮		
Bedford 7	d			22 18		22 22		22 42	22 44	23 12	23 42
Flitwick	d			22 28				22 52		23 22	23 52
Harlington	d			22 32				22 56		23 26	23 56
Leagrave	d			22 37				23 02		23 32	00 02
Luton 10	d		22 20	22 42		22 36	22 46	23 06	23 02	23 36	00 06
Luton Airport Parkway 7 ✈	d		22 22	22 44		22 39	22 49	23 09		23 39	00 09
Harpenden	d		22 28	22 50			22 55	23 15		23 45	00 15
St Albans City	d		22 34	22 56			23 01	23 21		23 51	00 21
Radlett	d		22 39				23 06	23 26		23 56	00 26
Elstree & Borehamwood	d		22 43				23 11	23 31		00 01	00 31
Mill Hill Broadway	d		22 47				23 15	23 35		00 05	00 35
Hendon	d		22 50				23 18	23 38		00 08	00 38
Cricklewood	d		22 54				23 22	23 42		00 12	00 42
West Hampstead Thameslink ⊖	d		22 56	23 13			23 24	23 45		00 15	00 45
Kentish Town ⊖	d		23 01				23 30	23 50		00 20	00 50
St Pancras International 15 ⊖	a		23 05	23 20		23 07	23 34	23 53	23 36	00 23	00 53
	d		23 06	23 24			23 38	23 54		00 24	00 54
Farringdon 3 ⊖	d		23 10	23 29			23 43	23 59		00 29	
City Thameslink 3	d										
London Blackfriars 3 ⊖	d	23 12	23 16	23 35	23 42		23 48	00 05		00 35	01 05
Elephant & Castle ⊖173,179	d	23 16	23 19		23 46		23 50				
Loughborough Jn 173,179	d		23 23								
Herne Hill 4 173,179	d		23 27				23 58				
London Bridge 4	a			23 41				00 11		00 41	
	d			23 42				00 12		00 42	
Tulse Hill 3	d		23 31				00 02				
Streatham 4	d		23 35				00 06				
Mitcham Eastfields 173	d										
Mitcham Junction 173 ⛴	d										
Hackbridge 173	d										
Carshalton 173	d										
Tooting 173	d		23 40				00 10				
Haydons Road 173	d		23 43				00 13				
Wimbledon 6 ⊖173,179 ⛴	d		23 47				00 17				
Wimbledon Chase 179	d		23 50				00 20				
South Merton 179	d		23 52				00 22				
Morden South 179	d		23 54				00 24				
St Helier 179	d		23 56				00 26				
Sutton Common 179	d		23 58				00 28				
West Sutton 179	d		00 01				00 31				
Sutton (Surrey) 4 179	a		00 05				00 35				
Denmark Hill 4 195	d	23 22			23 52						
Peckham Rye 4 195	d	23 25			23 55						
Nunhead 4 195	d	23 27			23 57						
Crofton Park 195	d	23 30			23 59						
Catford 195	d	23 33			00 03						
Bellingham 195	d	23 35			00 05						
Beckenham Hill 195	d	23 37			00 07						
Ravensbourne 195	d	23 39			00 09						
Shortlands 195	d	23 41			00 11						
Bromley South 4 195	d	23 44			00 14						
Bickley 4 195	d	23 47			00 17						
St Mary Cray 195	d	23 51			00 21						
Swanley 4 195	d	23 56			00 26						
Eynsford 195	d	23 59			00 30						
Shoreham (Kent) 195	d	00 04			00 34						
Otford 4 195	d	00 07			00 37						
Bat & Ball 195	d	00 10			00 40						
Sevenoaks 4 195	a	00 13			00 43						
East Croydon ⛴	d			23 57				00 29		00 57	01 36
Redhill	d										
Gatwick Airport 10 ✈	d			00 19				00 49		01 19	01 55
Three Bridges 4	d			00 24				00 54		01a24	02a02
Balcombe	d			00 30							
Haywards Heath 3	d			00 38				01 10			
Wivelsfield 4	d			00 43							
Burgess Hill 4	d			00 45				01 15			
Hassocks 4	d			00 48				01 18			
Preston Park	d			00 55							
Brighton 10	a			00 59				01 29			

A From Nottingham

The trains that operate to and from Sevenoaks, Orpington and Rochester (and a few other destinations at peak times) are operated jointly by First Capital Connect (north of Blackfriars) and Southeastern (south of Blackfriars)

Table 52 shows the complete service between Bedford and London, whilst services between London, Sevenoaks, Sutton and Brighton only show through Thameslink services. Other Tables should be consulted for additional journey opportunities.

Table 52

Sundays

8 December to 29 December

Bedford, Luton, St Albans and City of London - South London, Gatwick Airport and Brighton

Network Diagram - refer to first Page of Table 52

		FC	FC	FC	SE	SE	FC	FC	FC	FC	FC	FC	FC	SE	FC	SE	FC	SE	FC	FC	SE	FC	FC
				1			1	1	1	1	1	1	1		1		1			1			1
		A	A	B	C	C	B	B	B	B													
Bedford 7	d										05 40		06 10		06 38		07 12			07 50			08 06
Flitwick	d										05 50		06 20		06 48		07 22			08 00			08 16
Harlington	d										05 54		06 24		06 52		07 26			08 04			08 20
Leagrave	d									00 02	06 00		06 30		06 58		07 32			08 10			08 26
Luton 10	d									00 06	06 04		06 34		07 02		07 36			08 14		08 18	08 30
Luton Airport Parkway 7 ✈	d									00 09	06 07		06 37		07 05		07 39			08 17		08 21	08 33
Harpenden	d									00 15	06 13		06 43		07 11		07 45			08 23		08 27	08 39
St Albans City	d									00 21	06 19		06 49		07 17		07 51			08 29		08 33	08 45
Radlett	d									00 26	06 24		06 54		07 22		07 56					08 38	
Elstree & Borehamwood	d								00 01	00 31	06 29		06 59		07 27		08 01					08 42	
Mill Hill Broadway	d								00 05	00 35	06 33		07 03		07 31		08 05					08 46	
Hendon	d								00 08	00 38	06 36		07 06		07 34		08 08					08 50	
Cricklewood	d								00 12	00 42	06 40		07 10		07 38		08 12					08 53	
West Hampstead Thameslink ⊖	d								00 15	00 45	06 43		07 13		07 41		08 15			08 45		08 57	09 01
Kentish Town ⊖	d								00 20	00 50	06 48		07 18		07 46		08 20					09 01	
St Pancras International 15 ⊖	a								00 23	00 53	06 55		07 23		07 49		08 23			08 52		09 05	09 09
	d								00 24	00 54			07 24		07 50		08 24			08 54		09 06	09 10
Farringdon 3 ⊖	d								00 29				07 29		07 55		08 29			08 59		09 11	09 15
City Thameslink 3	d																						
London Blackfriars 3 ⊖	d							00 05	00 35	01 05		06 51	07 34	07 42	08 00	08 12	08 34	08 42	08 58	09 04	09 12	09 16	09 19
Elephant & Castle ⊖173,179	d													07 46		08 16		08 46	09 01		09 16	09 19	
Loughborough Jn 173,179	d																		09 05			09 23	
Herne Hill 4 173,179	d																		09 09			09 27	
London Bridge 4	a							00 11	00 41				07 40		08 06		08 40			09 10			09 25
	d							00 12	00 42				07 41		08 09		08 41			09 11			09 26
Tulse Hill 3	d		00 02																09 14			09 32	
Streatham 4	d		00 06																09 18			09 36	
Mitcham Eastfields 173	d																		09 22				
Mitcham Junction 173 🚊	d																		09 25				
Hackbridge 173	d																		09 29				
Carshalton 173	d																		09 31				
Tooting 173	d		00 10																			09 42	
Haydons Road 173	d		00 13																			09 45	
Wimbledon 6 ⊖173,179 🚊	d		00 17																			09 48	
Wimbledon Chase 179	d		00 20																			09 51	
South Merton 179	d		00 22																			09 53	
Morden South 179	d		00 24																			09 55	
St Helier 179	d		00 26																			09 57	
Sutton Common 179	d		00 28																			09 59	
West Sutton 179	d	00 01	00 31																			10 02	
Sutton (Surrey) 4 179	a	00 05	00 35																09 35			10 05	
Denmark Hill 4 195	d													07 52		08 22		08 52			09 22		
Peckham Rye 4 195	d													07 55		08 25		08 55			09 25		
Nunhead 4 195	d													07 57		08 27		08 57			09 27		
Crofton Park 195	d													08 00		08 30		09 00			09 30		
Catford 195	d					00 03								08 03		08 33		09 03			09 33		
Bellingham 195	d					00 05								08 05		08 35		09 05			09 35		
Beckenham Hill 195	d					00 07								08 07		08 37		09 07			09 37		
Ravensbourne 195	d					00 09								08 09		08 39		09 09			09 39		
Shortlands 195	d					00 11								08 11		08 41		09 11			09 41		
Bromley South 4 195	d					00 14								08 14		08 44		09 14			09 44		
Bickley 4 195	d					00 17								08 17		08 47		09 17			09 47		
St Mary Cray 195	d					00 21								08 21		08 51		09 21			09 51		
Swanley 4 195	d					00 26								08 26		08 56		09 26			09 56		
Eynsford 195	d					00 30								08 30		09 00		09 30			10 00		
Shoreham (Kent) 195	d				00 04	00 34								08 34		09 04		09 34			10 04		
Otford 4 195	d				00 07	00 37								08 37		09 07		09 37			10 07		
Bat & Ball 195	d				00 10	00 40								08 40		09 10		09 40			10 10		
Sevenoaks 4 195	a				00 13	00 43								08 43		09 13		09 43			10 13		
East Croydon 🚊	d							00 29	00 57	01 36		07 24	07 54		08 21		08 56			09 26			09 39
Redhill	d																						
Gatwick Airport 10 ✈	d						00 19	00 49	01 19	01 55		07 44	08 18		08 42		09 12			09 42			09 56
Three Bridges 4	d						00 24	00 54	01a24	02a02		07 49	08 23		08 47		09 17			09 47			10a01
Balcombe	d						00 30																
Haywards Heath 3	d						00 38	01 10				07 58	08 34		08 56		09 26			09 56			
Wivelsfield 4	d			00 03			00 43																
Burgess Hill 4	d			00 05			00 45	01 15				08 03	08 39		09 01		09 33			10 01			
Hassocks 4	d			00 08			00 48	01 18				08 07	08 43		09 05		09 37			10 05			
Preston Park	d			00 15			00 55																
Brighton 10	a			00 19			00 59	01 29				08 17	08 53		09 15		09 47			10 15			

A From Luton **B** From Bedford **C** From London Blackfriars

The trains that operate to and from Sevenoaks, Orpington and Rochester (and a few other destinations at peak times) are operated jointly by First Capital Connect (north of Blackfriars) and Southeastern (south of Blackfriars)

Table 52 shows the complete service between Bedford and London, whilst services between London, Sevenoaks, Sutton and Brighton only show through Thameslink services. Other Tables should be consulted for additional journey opportunities.

Table 52

Sundays

8 December to 29 December

Bedford, Luton, St Albans and City of London - South London, Gatwick Airport and Brighton

Network Diagram - refer to first Page of Table 52

		FC	EM ◇1 A 🍴	FC 1	SE	FC	FC 1	FC	EM ◇1 B 🍴		FC 1	SE	FC	FC 1	FC	EM ◇1 A 🍴	FC 1	SE	FC	FC 1		FC	EM ◇1 B 🍴	FC 1	SE
Bedford 7	d		08 15	08 20			08 36		08 45		08 50			09 06		09 15	09 20			09 36			09 45	09 50	
Flitwick	d			08 30			08 46				09 00			09 16			09 30			09 46				10 00	
Harlington	d			08 34			08 50				09 04			09 20			09 34			09 50				10 04	
Leagrave	d			08 40			08 56				09 10			09 26			09 40			09 56				10 10	
Luton 10	d		08 34	08 44		08 48	09 00				09 14		09 18	09 30		09 35	09 44		09 48	10 00				10 14	
Luton Airport Parkway 7 ✈	d			08 47		08 51	09 03		09 06		09 17		09 21	09 33			09 47		09 51	10 03			10 06	10 17	
Harpenden	d			08 53		08 57	09 09				09 23		09 27	09 39			09 53		09 57	10 09				10 23	
St Albans City	d			08 59		09 03	09 15				09 29		09 33	09 45			09 59		10 03	10 15				10 29	
Radlett	d					09 08							09 38						10 08						
Elstree & Borehamwood	d					09 12							09 42						10 12						
Mill Hill Broadway	d					09 16							09 46						10 16						
Hendon	d					09 20							09 50						10 20						
Cricklewood	d					09 23							09 53						10 23						
West Hampstead Thameslink ⊖	d			09 15		09 27	09 31				09 45		09 57	10 01			10 15		10 27	10 31				10 45	
Kentish Town ⊖	d					09 31							10 01						10 31						
St Pancras International 15 ⊖	a		09 13	09 22		09 35	09 39		09 44		09 52		10 05	10 09		10 13	10 22		10 35	10 39			10 48	10 52	
	d			09 24		09 36	09 40				09 54		10 06	10 10			10 24		10 36	10 40				10 54	
Farringdon 3 ⊖	d			09 29		09 41	09 45				09 59		10 11	10 15			10 29		10 41	10 45				10 59	
City Thameslink 3	d																								
London Blackfriars 3 ⊖	d	09 28		09 34	09 42	09 46	09 49	09 58			10 04	10 12	10 16	10 19	10 28		10 34	10 42	10 46	10 49		10 58		11 04	11 12
Elephant & Castle ⊖173,179	d	09 31			09 46	09 49		10 01				10 16	10 19		10 31			10 46	10 49			11 01			11 16
Loughborough Jn 173,179	d	09 35				09 53		10 05					10 23		10 35				10 53			11 05			
Herne Hill 4 173,179	d	09 39				09 57		10 09					10 27		10 39				10 57			11 09			
London Bridge 4	a			09 40			09 55				10 10			10 25			10 40			10 55				11 10	
	d			09 41			09 56				10 11			10 26			10 41			10 56				11 11	
Tulse Hill 3	d	09 44				10 02		10 14					10 32		10 44				11 02			11 14			
Streatham 4	d	09 48				10 06		10 18					10 36		10 48				11 06			11 18			
Mitcham Eastfields 173	d	09 52						10 22							10 52							11 22			
Mitcham Junction 173 🚋	d	09 55						10 25							10 55							11 25			
Hackbridge 173	d	09 59						10 29							10 59							11 29			
Carshalton 173	d	10 01						10 31							11 01							11 31			
Tooting 173	d					10 12							10 42						11 12						
Haydons Road 173	d					10 15							10 45						11 15						
Wimbledon 6 ⊖173,179 🚋	d					10 18							10 48						11 18						
Wimbledon Chase 179	d					10 21							10 51						11 21						
South Merton 179	d					10 23							10 53						11 23						
Morden South 179	d					10 25							10 55						11 25						
St Helier 179	d					10 27							10 57						11 27						
Sutton Common 179	d					10 29							10 59						11 29						
West Sutton 179	d					10 32							11 02						11 32						
Sutton (Surrey) 4 179	a	10 05				10 35		10 35					11 05		11 05				11 35			11 35			
Denmark Hill 4 195	d				09 52							10 22						10 52							11 22
Peckham Rye 4 195	d				09 55							10 25						10 55							11 25
Nunhead 4 195	d				09 57							10 27						10 57							11 27
Crofton Park 195	d				10 00							10 30						11 00							11 30
Catford 195	d				10 03							10 33						11 03							11 33
Bellingham 195	d				10 05							10 35						11 05							11 35
Beckenham Hill 195	d				10 07							10 37						11 07							11 37
Ravensbourne 195	d				10 09							10 39						11 09							11 39
Shortlands 195	d				10 11							10 41						11 11							11 41
Bromley South 4 195	d				10 14							10 44						11 14							11 44
Bickley 4 195	d				10 17							10 47						11 17							11 47
St Mary Cray 195	d				10 21							10 51						11 21							11 51
Swanley 4 195	d				10 26							10 56						11 26							11 56
Eynsford 195	d				10 30							11 00						11 30							12 00
Shoreham (Kent) 195	d				10 34							11 04						11 34							12 04
Otford 4 195	d				10 37							11 07						11 37							12 07
Bat & Ball 195	d				10 40							11 10						11 40							12 10
Sevenoaks 4 195	a				10 43							11 13						11 43							12 13
East Croydon 🚋	d			09 56			10 09				10 26			10 39			10 56			11 09				11 26	
Redhill	d																								
Gatwick Airport 10 ✈	d			10 12			10 26				10 42			10 56			11 12			11 26				11 42	
Three Bridges 4	d			10 17			10a33				10 47			11a01			11 17			11a33				11 47	
Balcombe	d																								
Haywards Heath 3	d			10 26							10 56						11 26							11 56	
Wivelsfield 4	d																								
Burgess Hill 4	d			10 33							11 01						11 33							12 01	
Hassocks 4	d			10 37							11 05						11 37							12 05	
Preston Park	d																								
Brighton 10	a			10 47							11 15						11 47							12 15	

A From Derby

B From Nottingham

The trains that operate to and from Sevenoaks, Orpington and Rochester (and a few other destinations at peak times) are operated jointly by First Capital Connect (north of Blackfriars) and Southeastern (south of Blackfriars)

Table 52 shows the complete service between Bedford and London, whilst services between London, Sevenoaks, Sutton and Brighton only show through Thameslink services. Other Tables should be consulted for additional journey opportunities.

Table 52

Sundays

8 December to 29 December

Bedford, Luton, St Albans and City of London - South London, Gatwick Airport and Brighton

Network Diagram - refer to first Page of Table 52

	FC	FC ■	FC	EM ◇■ A 🍴	FC ■	SE	FC	FC ■	FC	EM ◇■ B 🍴	FC ■	SE	FC	FC ■	FC	EM ◇■ A 🍴	FC ■	SE	FC	FC ■	FC	FC ■
Bedford ■ d		10 06		10 15	10 20			10 36		10 45	10 50			11 06		11 16	11 20			11 36		11 50
Flitwick d		10 16			10 30			10 46			11 00			11 16			11 30			11 46		12 00
Harlington d		10 20			10 34			10 50			11 04			11 20			11 34			11 50		12 04
Leagrave d		10 26			10 40			10 56			11 10			11 26			11 40			11 56		12 10
Luton ■ d	10 18	10 30		10 35	10 44		10 48	11 00			11 14		11 18	11 30		11 36	11 44		11 48	12 00		12 14
Luton Airport Parkway ■ ✈ d	10 21	10 33			10 47		10 51	11 03		11 06	11 17		11 21	11 33			11 47		11 51	12 03		12 17
Harpenden d	10 27	10 39			10 53		10 57	11 09			11 23		11 27	11 39			11 53		11 57	12 09		12 23
St Albans City d	10 33	10 45			10 59		11 03	11 15			11 29		11 33	11 45			11 59		12 03	12 15		12 29
Radlett d	10 38						11 08						11 38						12 08			
Elstree & Borehamwood d	10 42						11 12						11 42						12 12			
Mill Hill Broadway d	10 46						11 16						11 46						12 16			
Hendon d	10 50						11 20						11 50						12 20			
Cricklewood d	10 53						11 23						11 53						12 23			
West Hampstead Thameslink ⊖ d	10 57	11 01			11 15		11 27	11 31			11 45		11 57	12 01			12 15		12 27	12 31		12 45
Kentish Town ⊖ d	11 01						11 31						12 01						12 31			
St Pancras International ■ ⊖ a	11 05	11 09		11 17	11 22		11 35	11 39		11 48	11 52		12 05	12 09		12 14	12 22		12 35	12 39		12 52
d	11 06	11 10			11 24		11 36	11 40			11 54		12 06	12 10			12 24		12 36	12 40		12 54
Farringdon ■ ⊖ d	11 11	11 15			11 29		11 41	11 45			11 59		12 11	12 15			12 29		12 41	12 45		12 59
City Thameslink ■ d																						
London Blackfriars ■ ⊖ d	11 16	11 19	11 28		11 34	11 42	11 46	11 49	11 58		12 04	12 12	12 16	12 19	12 28		12 34	12 42	12 46	12 49	12 58	13 04
Elephant & Castle ⊖173,179 d	11 19		11 31			11 46	11 49		12 01			12 16	12 19		12 31			12 46	12 49		13 01	
Loughborough Jn 173,179 d	11 23		11 35				11 53		12 05				12 23		12 35				12 53		13 05	
Herne Hill ■ 173,179 d	11 27		11 39				11 57		12 09				12 27		12 39				12 57		13 09	
London Bridge ■ a		11 25			11 40			11 55			12 10			12 25			12 40			12 55		13 10
d		11 26			11 41			11 56			12 11			12 26			12 41			12 56		13 11
Tulse Hill ■ d	11 32		11 44				12 02		12 14				12 32		12 44				13 02		13 14	
Streatham ■ d	11 36		11 48				12 06		12 18				12 36		12 48				13 06		13 18	
Mitcham Eastfields 173 d			11 52						12 22						12 52						13 22	
Mitcham Junction 173 🚊 d			11 55						12 25						12 55						13 25	
Hackbridge 173 d			11 59						12 29						12 59						13 29	
Carshalton 173 d			12 01						12 31						13 01						13 31	
Tooting 173 d	11 42						12 12						12 42						13 12			
Haydons Road 173 d	11 45						12 15						12 45						13 15			
Wimbledon ■ ⊖173,179 🚊 d	11 48						12 18						12 48						13 18			
Wimbledon Chase 179 d	11 51						12 21						12 51						13 21			
South Merton 179 d	11 53						12 23						12 53						13 23			
Morden South 179 d	11 55						12 25						12 55						13 25			
St Helier 179 d	11 57						12 27						12 57						13 27			
Sutton Common 179 d	11 59						12 29						12 59						13 29			
West Sutton 179 d	12 02						12 32						13 02						13 32			
Sutton (Surrey) ■ 179 a	12 05		12 05				12 35		12 35				13 05		13 05				13 35		13 35	
Denmark Hill ■ 195 d						11 52						12 22						12 52				
Peckham Rye ■ 195 d						11 55						12 25						12 55				
Nunhead ■ 195 d						11 57						12 27						12 57				
Crofton Park 195 d						12 00						12 30						13 00				
Catford 195 d						12 03						12 33						13 03				
Bellingham 195 d						12 05						12 35						13 05				
Beckenham Hill 195 d						12 07						12 37						13 07				
Ravensbourne 195 d						12 09						12 39						13 09				
Shortlands 195 d						12 11						12 41						13 11				
Bromley South ■ 195 d						12 14						12 44						13 14				
Bickley ■ 195 d						12 17						12 47						13 17				
St Mary Cray 195 d						12 21						12 51						13 21				
Swanley ■ 195 d						12 26						12 56						13 26				
Eynsford 195 d						12 30						13 00						13 30				
Shoreham (Kent) 195 d						12 34						13 04						13 34				
Otford ■ 195 d						12 37						13 07						13 37				
Bat & Ball 195 d						12 40						13 10						13 40				
Sevenoaks ■ 195 a						12 43						13 13						13 43				
East Croydon 🚊 d		11 39			11 56			12 09			12 26			12 39			12 56			13 09		13 26
Redhill d																						
Gatwick Airport ■ ✈ d		11 56			12 12			12 26			12 42			12 56			13 12			13 26		13 42
Three Bridges ■ d		12a01			12 17			12a33			12 47			13a01			13 17			13a33		13 47
Balcombe d																						
Haywards Heath ■ d					12 26						12 56						13 26					13 56
Wivelsfield ■ d																						
Burgess Hill ■ d					12 33						13 01						13 33					14 01
Hassocks ■ d					12 37						13 05						13 37					14 05
Preston Park d																						
Brighton ■ a					12 47						13 15						13 47					14 15

A From Sheffield **B** From Nottingham

The trains that operate to and from Sevenoaks, Orpington and Rochester (and a few other destinations at peak times) are operated jointly by First Capital Connect (north of Blackfriars) and Southeastern (south of Blackfriars)

Table 52 shows the complete service between Bedford and London, whilst services between London, Sevenoaks, Sutton and Brighton only show through Thameslink services. Other Tables should be consulted for additional journey opportunities.

Table 52

Sundays

8 December to 29 December

Bedford, Luton, St Albans and City of London - South London, Gatwick Airport and Brighton

Network Diagram - refer to first Page of Table 52

Station		SE	EM ◇1 A ☕	FC	FC 1	FC	EM ◇1 B ☕	FC 1	SE	FC	FC 1	FC	FC 1	SE	EM ◇1 C ☕	FC	FC 1	FC	FC 1	SE	FC	FC 1	FC
Bedford 7	d		11 56		12 06		12 15	12 20			12 36		12 50		13 02		13 06		13 20			13 36	
Flitwick	d				12 16			12 30			12 46		13 00				13 16		13 30			13 46	
Harlington	d				12 20			12 34			12 50		13 04				13 20		13 34			13 50	
Leagrave	d				12 26			12 40			12 56		13 10				13 26		13 40			13 56	
Luton 10	d			12 18	12 30		12 32	12 44		12 48	13 00		13 14			13 18	13 30		13 44		13 48	14 00	
Luton Airport Parkway 7 ✈	d		12 13	12 21	12 33			12 47		12 51	13 03		13 17		13 18	13 21	13 33		13 47		13 51	14 03	
Harpenden	d			12 27	12 39			12 53		12 57	13 09		13 23			13 27	13 39		13 53		13 57	14 09	
St Albans City	d			12 33	12 45			12 59		13 03	13 15		13 29			13 33	13 45		13 59		14 03	14 15	
Radlett	d			12 38						13 08						13 38					14 08		
Elstree & Borehamwood	d			12 42						13 12						13 42					14 12		
Mill Hill Broadway	d			12 46						13 16						13 46					14 16		
Hendon	d			12 50						13 20						13 50					14 20		
Cricklewood	d			12 53						13 23						13 53					14 23		
West Hampstead Thameslink ⊖	d			12 57	13 01			13 15		13 27	13 31		13 45			13 57	14 01		14 15		14 27	14 31	
Kentish Town ⊖	d			13 01						13 31						14 01					14 31		
St Pancras International 15 ⊖	a		12 39	13 05	13 09		12 55	13 22		13 35	13 39		13 52		13 44	14 05	14 09		14 22		14 35	14 39	
	d			13 06	13 10			13 24		13 36	13 40		13 54			14 06	14 10		14 24		14 36	14 40	
Farringdon 3 ⊖	d			13 11	13 15			13 29		13 41	13 45		13 59			14 11	14 15		14 29		14 41	14 45	
City Thameslink 3	d																						
London Blackfriars 3 ⊖	d	13 12		13 16	13 19	13 28		13 34	13 42	13 46	13 49	13 58	14 04	14 12		14 16	14 19	14 28	14 34	14 42	14 46	14 49	14 58
Elephant & Castle ⊖173,179	d	13 16		13 19		13 31			13 46	13 49		14 01		14 16		14 19		14 31		14 46	14 49		15 01
Loughborough Jn 173,179	d			13 23		13 35				13 53		14 05				14 23		14 35			14 53		15 05
Herne Hill 4 173,179	d			13 27		13 39				13 57		14 09				14 27		14 39			14 57		15 09
London Bridge 4	a				13 25			13 40			13 55		14 10				14 25		14 40			14 55	
	d				13 26			13 41			13 56		14 11				14 26		14 41			14 56	
Tulse Hill 3	d			13 32		13 44				14 02		14 14				14 32		14 44			15 02		15 14
Streatham 4	d			13 36		13 48				14 06		14 18				14 36		14 48			15 06		15 18
Mitcham Eastfields 173	d					13 52						14 22						14 52					15 22
Mitcham Junction 173 🚋	d					13 55						14 25						14 55					15 25
Hackbridge 173	d					13 59						14 29						14 59					15 29
Carshalton 173	d					14 01						14 31						15 01					15 31
Tooting 173	d			13 42						14 12						14 42					15 12		
Haydons Road 173	d			13 45						14 15						14 45					15 15		
Wimbledon 5 ⊖173,179 🚋	d			13 48						14 18						14 48					15 18		
Wimbledon Chase 179	d			13 51						14 21						14 51					15 21		
South Merton 179	d			13 53						14 23						14 53					15 23		
Morden South 179	d			13 55						14 25						14 55					15 25		
St Helier 179	d			13 57						14 27						14 57					15 27		
Sutton Common 179	d			13 59						14 29						14 59					15 29		
West Sutton 179	d			14 02						14 32						15 02					15 32		
Sutton (Surrey) 4 179	a			14 05		14 05				14 35		14 35				15 05		15 05			15 35		15 35
Denmark Hill 4 195	d	13 22							13 52					14 22						14 52			
Peckham Rye 4 195	d	13 25							13 55					14 25						14 55			
Nunhead 4 195	d	13 27							13 57					14 27						14 57			
Crofton Park 195	d	13 30							14 00					14 30						15 00			
Catford 195	d	13 33							14 03					14 33						15 03			
Bellingham 195	d	13 35							14 05					14 35						15 05			
Beckenham Hill 195	d	13 37							14 07					14 37						15 07			
Ravensbourne 195	d	13 39							14 09					14 39						15 09			
Shortlands 195	d	13 41							14 11					14 41						15 11			
Bromley South 4 195	d	13 44							14 14					14 44						15 14			
Bickley 4 195	d	13 47							14 17					14 47						15 17			
St Mary Cray 195	d	13 51							14 21					14 51						15 21			
Swanley 4 195	d	13 56							14 26					14 56						15 26			
Eynsford 195	d	14 00							14 30					15 00						15 30			
Shoreham (Kent) 195	d	14 04							14 34					15 04						15 34			
Otford 4 195	d	14 07							14 37					15 07						15 37			
Bat & Ball 195	d	14 10							14 40					15 10						15 40			
Sevenoaks 4 195	a	14 13							14 43					15 13						15 43			
East Croydon 🚋	d				13 39			13 56			14 09		14 26				14 39		14 56			15 09	
Redhill	d																						
Gatwick Airport 10 ✈	d				13 56			14 12			14 26		14 42				14 56		15 12			15 26	
Three Bridges 4	d				14a01			14 17			14a33		14 47				15a01		15 17			15a33	
Balcombe	d																						
Haywards Heath 3	d							14 26					14 56						15 26				
Wivelsfield 4	d																						
Burgess Hill 4	d							14 33					15 01						15 33				
Hassocks 4	d							14 37					15 05						15 37				
Preston Park	d																						
Brighton 10	a							14 47					15 15						15 47				

A From Nottingham
B From Sheffield
C From Leeds

The trains that operate to and from Sevenoaks, Orpington and Rochester (and a few other destinations at peak times) are operated jointly by First Capital Connect (north of Blackfriars) and Southeastern (south of Blackfriars)

Table 52 shows the complete service between Bedford and London, whilst services between London, Sevenoaks, Sutton and Brighton only show through Thameslink services. Other Tables should be consulted for additional journey opportunities.

Table 52

Sundays

8 December to 29 December

Bedford, Luton, St Albans and City of London - South London, Gatwick Airport and Brighton

Network Diagram - refer to first Page of Table 52

	EM ◇1 A	FC 1	SE	FC	FC 1	FC	EM ◇1 B	FC 1	SE	FC	FC 1	FC	EM ◇1 C	FC 1	SE	FC	FC 1	FC	EM ◇1 B	FC 1	SE	FC
Bedford 7 d	13 43	13 50			14 06		14 15	14 20			14 36		14 39	14 50			15 06		15 15	15 20		
Flitwick d		14 00			14 16			14 30			14 46			15 00			15 16			15 30		
Harlington d		14 04			14 20			14 34			14 50			15 04			15 20			15 34		
Leagrave d		14 10			14 26			14 40			14 56			15 10			15 26			15 40		
Luton 10 d	14 01	14 14		14 18	14 30			14 44		14 48	15 00		14 54	15 14		15 18	15 30			15 44		15 48
Luton Airport Parkway 7 ✈ d		14 17		14 21	14 33		14 31	14 47		14 51	15 03			15 17		15 21	15 33		15 31	15 47		15 51
Harpenden d		14 23		14 27	14 39			14 53		14 57	15 09			15 23		15 27	15 39			15 53		15 57
St Albans City d		14 29		14 33	14 45			14 59		15 03	15 15			15 29		15 33	15 45			15 59		16 03
Radlett d				14 38						15 08						15 38						16 08
Elstree & Borehamwood d				14 42						15 12						15 42						16 12
Mill Hill Broadway d				14 46						15 16						15 46						16 16
Hendon d				14 50						15 20						15 50						16 20
Cricklewood d				14 53						15 23						15 53						16 23
West Hampstead Thameslink ⊖ d		14 45		14 57	15 01			15 15		15 27	15 31			15 45		15 57	16 01			16 15		16 27
Kentish Town ⊖ d				15 01						15 31						16 01						16 31
St Pancras International 15 ⊖ a	14 27	14 52		15 05	15 09		14 57	15 22		15 35	15 39		15 18	15 52		16 05	16 09		15 57	16 22		16 35
d		14 54		15 06	15 10			15 24		15 36	15 40			15 54		16 06	16 10			16 24		16 36
Farringdon 3 ⊖ d		14 59		15 11	15 15			15 29		15 41	15 45			15 59		16 11	16 15			16 29		16 41
City Thameslink 3 d																						
London Blackfriars 3 ⊖ d		15 04	15 12	15 16	15 19	15 28		15 34	15 42	15 46	15 49	15 58		16 04	16 12	16 16	16 19	16 28		16 34	16 42	16 46
Elephant & Castle ⊖173,179 d			15 16	15 19		15 31			15 46	15 49		16 01			16 16	16 19		16 31			16 46	16 49
Loughborough Jn 173,179 d				15 23		15 35				15 53		16 05				16 23		16 35				16 53
Herne Hill 4 173,179 d				15 27		15 39				15 57		16 09				16 27		16 39				16 57
London Bridge 4 a		15 10			15 25			15 40			15 55			16 10			16 25			16 40		
d		15 11			15 26			15 41			15 56			16 11			16 26			16 41		
Tulse Hill 3 d				15 32		15 44				16 02		16 14				16 32		16 44				17 02
Streatham 4 d				15 36		15 48				16 06		16 18				16 36		16 48				17 06
Mitcham Eastfields 173 d						15 52						16 22						16 52				
Mitcham Junction 173 🚊 d						15 55						16 25						16 55				
Hackbridge 173 d						15 59						16 29						16 59				
Carshalton 173 d						16 01						16 31						17 01				
Tooting 173 d				15 42						16 12						16 42						17 12
Haydons Road 173 d				15 45						16 15						16 45						17 15
Wimbledon 6 ⊖173,179 🚊 d				15 48						16 18						16 48						17 18
Wimbledon Chase 179 d				15 51						16 21						16 51						17 21
South Merton 179 d				15 53						16 23						16 53						17 23
Morden South 179 d				15 55						16 25						16 55						17 25
St Helier 179 d				15 57						16 27						16 57						17 27
Sutton Common 179 d				15 59						16 29						16 59						17 29
West Sutton 179 d				16 02						16 32						17 02						17 32
Sutton (Surrey) 4 179 a				16 05		16 05				16 35		16 35				17 05		17 05				17 35
Denmark Hill 4 195 d			15 22						15 52						16 22						16 52	
Peckham Rye 4 195 d			15 25						15 55						16 25						16 55	
Nunhead 4 195 d			15 27						15 57						16 27						16 57	
Crofton Park 195 d			15 30						16 00						16 30						17 00	
Catford 195 d			15 33						16 03						16 33						17 03	
Bellingham 195 d			15 35						16 05						16 35						17 05	
Beckenham Hill 195 d			15 37						16 07						16 37						17 07	
Ravensbourne 195 d			15 39						16 09						16 39						17 09	
Shortlands 195 d			15 41						16 11						16 41						17 11	
Bromley South 4 195 d			15 44						16 14						16 44						17 14	
Bickley 4 195 d			15 47						16 17						16 47						17 17	
St Mary Cray 195 d			15 51						16 21						16 51						17 21	
Swanley 4 195 d			15 56						16 26						16 56						17 26	
Eynsford 195 d			16 00						16 30						17 00						17 30	
Shoreham (Kent) 195 d			16 04						16 34						17 04						17 34	
Otford 4 195 d			16 07						16 37						17 07						17 37	
Bat & Ball 195 d			16 10						16 40						17 10						17 40	
Sevenoaks 4 195 a			16 13						16 43						17 13						17 43	
East Croydon 🚊 d		15 26			15 39			15 56			16 09			16 26			16 39			16 56		
Redhill d																						
Gatwick Airport 10 ✈ d		15 42			15 56			16 12			16 26			16 42			16 56			17 12		
Three Bridges 4 d		15 47			16a01			16 17			16a33			16 47			17a01			17 17		
Balcombe d																						
Haywards Heath 3 d		15 56						16 26						16 56						17 26		
Wivelsfield 4 d																						
Burgess Hill 4 d		16 01						16 33						17 01						17 33		
Hassocks 4 d		16 05						16 37						17 05						17 37		
Preston Park d																						
Brighton 10 a		16 15						16 47						17 15						17 47		

A From Leeds
B From Nottingham
C From Sheffield

The trains that operate to and from Sevenoaks, Orpington and Rochester (and a few other destinations at peak times) are operated jointly by First Capital Connect (north of Blackfriars) and Southeastern (south of Blackfriars)

Table 52 shows the complete service between Bedford and London, whilst services between London, Sevenoaks, Sutton and Brighton only show through Thameslink services. Other Tables should be consulted for additional journey opportunities.

Table 52

Sundays

8 December to 29 December

Bedford, Luton, St Albans and City of London - South London, Gatwick Airport and Brighton

Network Diagram - refer to first Page of Table 52

	FC	FC	EM	FC	SE	FC	FC	FC	EM	EM	FC	SE	FC	FC	FC	FC	SE	FC	FC	FC	EM
	1		◇1	1			1		◇1	◇1	1			1		1			1		◇1
			A						B	A											B
			☕						☕	☕											☕
Bedford 7 d	15 36		15 39	15 50			16 06		16 08		16 20			16 36		16 50			17 06		17 08
Flitwick d	15 46			16 00			16 16				16 30			16 46		17 00			17 16		
Harlington d	15 50			16 04			16 20				16 34			16 50		17 04			17 20		
Leagrave d	15 56			16 10			16 26				16 40			16 56		17 10			17 26		
Luton 10 d	16 00		15 54	16 14		16 18	16 30			16 42	16 44		16 48	17 00		17 14		17 18	17 30		
Luton Airport Parkway 7 ✈ d	16 03			16 17		16 21	16 33		16 23		16 47		16 51	17 03		17 17		17 21	17 33		17 24
Harpenden d	16 09			16 23		16 27	16 39				16 53		16 57	17 09		17 23		17 27	17 39		
St Albans City d	16 15			16 29		16 33	16 45				16 59		17 03	17 15		17 29		17 33	17 45		
Radlett d						16 38							17 08					17 38			
Elstree & Borehamwood d						16 42							17 12					17 42			
Mill Hill Broadway d						16 46							17 16					17 46			
Hendon d						16 50							17 20					17 50			
Cricklewood d						16 53							17 23					17 53			
West Hampstead Thameslink ⊖ d	16 31			16 45		16 57	17 01				17 15		17 27	17 31		17 45		17 57	18 01		
Kentish Town ⊖ d						17 01							17 31					18 01			
St Pancras International 15 ⊖ a	16 39		16 18	16 52		17 05	17 09		16 47	17 09	17 22		17 35	17 39		17 52		18 05	18 09		17 47
d	16 40			16 54		17 06	17 10				17 24		17 36	17 40		17 54		18 06	18 10		
Farringdon 3 ⊖ d	16 45			16 59		17 11	17 15				17 29		17 41	17 45		17 59		18 11	18 15		
City Thameslink 3 d																					
London Blackfriars 3 ⊖ d	16 49	16 58		17 04	17 12	17 16	17 19	17 28			17 34	17 42	17 46	17 49	17 58	18 04	18 12	18 16	18 19	18 28	
Elephant & Castle ⊖173,179 d		17 01			17 16	17 19		17 31				17 46	17 49		18 01		18 16	18 19		18 31	
Loughborough Jn 173,179 d		17 05				17 23		17 35					17 53		18 05			18 23		18 35	
Herne Hill 4 173,179 d		17 09				17 27		17 39					17 57		18 09			18 27		18 39	
London Bridge 4 a	16 55			17 10			17 25				17 40			17 55		18 10			18 25		
d	16 56			17 11			17 26				17 41			17 56		18 11			18 26		
Tulse Hill 3 d		17 14				17 32		17 44					18 02		18 14			18 32		18 44	
Streatham 4 d		17 18				17 36		17 48					18 06		18 18			18 36		18 48	
Mitcham Eastfields 173 d		17 22						17 52							18 22					18 52	
Mitcham Junction 173 🚆 d		17 25						17 55							18 25					18 55	
Hackbridge 173 d		17 29						17 59							18 29					18 59	
Carshalton 173 d		17 31						18 01							18 31					19 01	
Tooting 173 d						17 42							18 12					18 42			
Haydons Road 173 d						17 45							18 15					18 45			
Wimbledon 6 ⊖173,179 🚆 d						17 48							18 18					18 48			
Wimbledon Chase 179 d						17 51							18 21					18 51			
South Merton 179 d						17 53							18 23					18 53			
Morden South 179 d						17 55							18 25					18 55			
St Helier 179 d						17 57							18 27					18 57			
Sutton Common 179 d						17 59							18 29					18 59			
West Sutton 179 d						18 02							18 32					19 02			
Sutton (Surrey) 4 179 a		17 35				18 05		18 05					18 35		18 35			19 05		19 05	
Denmark Hill 4 195 d					17 22							17 52					18 22				
Peckham Rye 4 195 d					17 25							17 55					18 25				
Nunhead 4 195 d					17 27							17 57					18 27				
Crofton Park 195 d					17 30							18 00					18 30				
Catford 195 d					17 33							18 03					18 33				
Bellingham 195 d					17 35							18 05					18 35				
Beckenham Hill 195 d					17 37							18 07					18 37				
Ravensbourne 195 d					17 39							18 09					18 39				
Shortlands 195 d					17 41							18 11					18 41				
Bromley South 4 195 d					17 44							18 14					18 44				
Bickley 4 195 d					17 47							18 17					18 47				
St Mary Cray 195 d					17 51							18 21					18 51				
Swanley 4 195 d					17 56							18 26					18 56				
Eynsford 195 d					18 00							18 30					19 00				
Shoreham (Kent) 195 d					18 04							18 34					19 04				
Otford 4 195 d					18 07							18 37					19 07				
Bat & Ball 195 d					18 10							18 40					19 10				
Sevenoaks 4 195 a					18 13							18 43					19 13				
East Croydon 🚆 d	17 09			17 26			17 39				17 56			18 09		18 26			18 39		
Redhill d																					
Gatwick Airport 10 ✈ d	17 26			17 42			17 56				18 12			18 26		18 42			18 56		
Three Bridges 4 d	17a33			17 47			18a01				18 17			18a33		18 47			19a01		
Balcombe d																					
Haywards Heath 3 d				17 56							18 26					18 56					
Wivelsfield 4 d																					
Burgess Hill 4 d				18 01							18 33					19 01					
Hassocks 4 d				18 05							18 37					19 05					
Preston Park d																					
Brighton 10 a				18 15							18 47					19 15					

A From Sheffield

B From Nottingham

The trains that operate to and from Sevenoaks, Orpington and Rochester (and a few other destinations at peak times) are operated jointly by First Capital Connect (north of Blackfriars) and Southeastern (south of Blackfriars)

Table 52 shows the complete service between Bedford and London, whilst services between London, Sevenoaks, Sutton and Brighton only show through Thameslink services. Other Tables should be consulted for additional journey opportunities.

Table 52

Sundays

8 December to 29 December

Bedford, Luton, St Albans and City of London - South London, Gatwick Airport and Brighton

Network Diagram - refer to first Page of Table 52

Station		FC	SE	EM	FC	FC	FC	FC	SE	EM	EM	FC	FC	FC	SE	FC	FC	FC	SE	EM	FC	FC	FC
		1		◇1		1		1		◇1	◇1			1				1		◇1			1
				A						B	C									B			
				☕						☕	☕									☕			
Bedford 7	d	17 20		17 27		17 36		17 50		18 07	18 17			18 20				18 50		19 08			19 20
Flitwick	d	17 30				17 46		18 00						18 30				19 00					19 30
Harlington	d	17 34				17 50		18 04						18 34				19 04					19 34
Leagrave	d	17 40				17 56		18 10						18 40				19 10					19 40
Luton 10	d	17 44		17 44	17 48	18 00		18 14			18 32	18 18		18 44		18 48		19 14			19 18		19 44
Luton Airport Parkway 7 ✈	d	17 47			17 51	18 03		18 17		18 24		18 21		18 47		18 51		19 17		19 23	19 21		19 47
Harpenden	d	17 53			17 57	18 09		18 23				18 27		18 53		18 57		19 23			19 27		19 53
St Albans City	d	17 59			18 03	18 15		18 29				18 33		18 59		19 03		19 29			19 33		19 59
Radlett	d				18 08							18 38				19 08					19 38		
Elstree & Borehamwood	d				18 12							18 42				19 12					19 42		
Mill Hill Broadway	d				18 16							18 46				19 16					19 46		
Hendon	d				18 20							18 50				19 20					19 50		
Cricklewood	d				18 23							18 53				19 23					19 53		
West Hampstead Thameslink ⊖	d	18 15			18 27	18 31		18 45				18 57		19 15		19 27		19 45			19 57		20 15
Kentish Town ⊖	d				18 31							19 01				19 31					20 01		
St Pancras International 15 ⊖	a	18 22		18 09	18 35	18 39		18 52		18 47	18 56	19 05		19 22		19 35		19 52		19 48	20 05		20 22
	d	18 24			18 36	18 40		18 54				19 06		19 24		19 36		19 54			20 06		20 24
Farringdon 3 ⊖	d	18 29			18 41	18 45		18 59				19 11		19 29		19 41		19 59			20 11		20 29
City Thameslink 3	d																						
London Blackfriars 3 ⊖	d	18 34	18 42		18 46	18 49	18 58	19 04	19 12			19 16	19 28	19 34	19 42	19 46	19 58	20 04	20 12		20 16	20 28	20 34
Elephant & Castle ⊖173,179	d		18 46		18 49		19 01		19 16			19 19	19 31		19 46	19 49	20 01		20 16		20 19	20 31	
Loughborough Jn 173,179	d				18 53		19 05					19 23	19 35			19 53	20 05				20 23	20 35	
Herne Hill 4 173,179	d				18 57		19 09					19 27	19 39			19 57	20 09				20 27	20 39	
London Bridge 4	a	18 40				18 55		19 10						19 40				20 10					20 40
	d	18 41				18 56		19 11						19 41				20 11					20 41
Tulse Hill 3	d				19 02		19 14					19 32	19 44			20 02	20 14				20 32	20 44	
Streatham 4	d				19 06		19 18					19 36	19 48			20 06	20 18				20 36	20 48	
Mitcham Eastfields 173	d						19 22						19 52				20 22					20 52	
Mitcham Junction 173 🚋	d						19 25						19 55				20 25					20 55	
Hackbridge 173	d						19 29						19 59				20 29					20 59	
Carshalton 173	d						19 31						20 01				20 31					21 01	
Tooting 173	d				19 12							19 42				20 12					20 42		
Haydons Road 173	d				19 15							19 45				20 15					20 45		
Wimbledon 6 ⊖173,179 🚋	d				19 18							19 48				20 18					20 48		
Wimbledon Chase 179	d				19 21							19 51				20 21					20 51		
South Merton 179	d				19 23							19 53				20 23					20 53		
Morden South 179	d				19 25							19 55				20 25					20 55		
St Helier 179	d				19 27							19 57				20 27					20 57		
Sutton Common 179	d				19 29							19 59				20 29					20 59		
West Sutton 179	d				19 32							20 02				20 32					21 02		
Sutton (Surrey) 4 179	a				19 35		19 35					20 05	20 05			20 35	20 35				21 05	21 05	
Denmark Hill 4 195	d		18 52						19 22						19 52				20 22				
Peckham Rye 4 195	d		18 55						19 25						19 55				20 25				
Nunhead 4 195	d		18 57						19 27						19 57				20 27				
Crofton Park 195	d		19 00						19 30						20 00				20 30				
Catford 195	d		19 03						19 33						20 03				20 33				
Bellingham 195	d		19 05						19 35						20 05				20 35				
Beckenham Hill 195	d		19 07						19 37						20 07				20 37				
Ravensbourne 195	d		19 09						19 39						20 09				20 39				
Shortlands 195	d		19 11						19 41						20 11				20 41				
Bromley South 4 195	d		19 14						19 44						20 14				20 44				
Bickley 4 195	d		19 17						19 47						20 17				20 47				
St Mary Cray 195	d		19 21						19 51						20 21				20 51				
Swanley 4 195	d		19 26						19 56						20 26				20 56				
Eynsford 195	d		19 30						20 00						20 30				21 00				
Shoreham (Kent) 195	d		19 34						20 04						20 34				21 04				
Otford 4 195	d		19 37						20 07						20 37				21 07				
Bat & Ball 195	d		19 40						20 10						20 40				21 10				
Sevenoaks 4 195	a		19 43						20 13						20 43				21 13				
East Croydon 🚋	d	18 56				19 09		19 26						19 56				20 26					20 56
Redhill	d																						
Gatwick Airport 10 ✈	d	19 12				19 26		19 42						20 12				20 42					21 12
Three Bridges 4	d	19 17				19a33		19 47						20 17				20 47					21 17
Balcombe	d																						
Haywards Heath 3	d	19 26						19 56						20 26				20 56					21 26
Wivelsfield 4	d																						
Burgess Hill 4	d	19 33						20 01						20 33				21 01					21 33
Hassocks 4	d	19 37						20 05						20 37				21 05					21 37
Preston Park	d																						
Brighton 10	a	19 47						20 15						20 47				21 15					21 47

A From Leeds
B From Nottingham
C From Derby

The trains that operate to and from Sevenoaks, Orpington and Rochester (and a few other destinations at peak times) are operated jointly by First Capital Connect (north of Blackfriars) and Southeastern (south of Blackfriars)

Table 52 shows the complete service between Bedford and London, whilst services between London, Sevenoaks, Sutton and Brighton only show through Thameslink services. Other Tables should be consulted for additional journey opportunities.

Table 52

Sundays

8 December to 29 December

Bedford, Luton, St Albans and City of London - South London, Gatwick Airport and Brighton

Network Diagram - refer to first Page of Table 52

		SE	EM ◇1 A	FC	FC 1	SE	EM ◇1 B	EM ◇1 B		FC	FC 1	SE	EM ◇1 C	FC 1	SE	EM ◇1 B	FC 1	SE	EM ◇1 D		FC 1	SE	FC 1	SE	EM ◇1 D
Bedford 7	d		19 27		19 50		19 58	20 08			20 12		20 39	20 42		21 09	21 12		21 30		21 42		22 12		22 21
Flitwick	d				20 00						20 22			20 52			21 22				21 52		22 22		
Harlington	d				20 04						20 26			20 56			21 26				21 56		22 26		
Leagrave	d				20 10						20 32			21 02			21 32				22 02		22 32		
Luton 10	d		19 43	19 48	20 14		20 14			20 18	20 36			21 06		21 23	21 36		21 45		22 06		22 36		22 37
Luton Airport Parkway 7 ✈	d			19 51	20 17			20 23		20 21	20 39		20 54	21 09			21 39				22 09		22 39		
Harpenden	d			19 57	20 23					20 27	20 45			21 15			21 45				22 15		22 45		
St Albans City	d			20 03	20 29					20 33	20 51			21 21			21 51				22 21		22 51		
Radlett	d			20 08						20 38	20 56			21 26			21 56				22 26		22 56		
Elstree & Borehamwood	d			20 12						20 42	21 01			21 31			22 01				22 31		23 01		
Mill Hill Broadway	d			20 16						20 46	21 05			21 35			22 05				22 35		23 05		
Hendon	d			20 20						20 50	21 08			21 38			22 08				22 38		23 08		
Cricklewood	d			20 23						20 53	21 12			21 42			22 12				22 42		23 12		
West Hampstead Thameslink ⊖	d			20 27	20 45					20 57	21 15			21 45			22 15				22 45		23 15		
Kentish Town ⊖	d			20 31						21 01	21 20			21 50			22 20				22 50		23 20		
St Pancras International 15 ⊖	a		20 06	20 35	20 52		20 38	20 47		21 05	21 23		21 17	21 53		21 47	22 23		22 12		22 53		23 23		23 03
	d			20 36	20 54					21 06	21 24			21 54			22 24				22 54		23 24		
Farringdon 3 ⊖	d			20 41	20 59					21 11	21 29			21 59			22 29				22 59		23 29		
City Thameslink 3	d																								
London Blackfriars 3 ⊖	d	20 42		20 46	21 04	21 12				21 16	21 34	21 42		22 04	22 12		22 34	22 42			23 04	23 12	23 34	23 42	
Elephant & Castle ⊖173,179	d	20 46		20 49		21 16				21 19		21 46			22 16			22 46				23 16		23 46	
Loughborough Jn 173,179	d			20 53						21 23															
Herne Hill 4 173,179	d			20 57						21 27															
London Bridge 4	a				21 10						21 40			22 10			22 40				23 10		23 40		
	d				21 11						21 41			22 11			22 41				23 11		23 41		
Tulse Hill 3	d			21 02						21 32															
Streatham 4	d			21 06						21 36															
Mitcham Eastfields 173	d																								
Mitcham Junction 173 🚋	d																								
Hackbridge 173	d																								
Carshalton 173	d																								
Tooting 173	d			21 12						21 42															
Haydons Road 173	d			21 15						21 45															
Wimbledon 6 ⊖173,179 🚋	d			21 18						21 48															
Wimbledon Chase 179	d			21 21						21 51															
South Merton 179	d			21 23						21 53															
Morden South 179	d			21 25						21 55															
St Helier 179	d			21 27						21 57															
Sutton Common 179	d			21 29						21 59															
West Sutton 179	d			21 32						22 02															
Sutton (Surrey) 4 179	a			21 35						22 05															
Denmark Hill 4 195	d	20 52				21 22						21 52			22 22			22 52				23 22		23 52	
Peckham Rye 4 195	d	20 55				21 25						21 55			22 25			22 55				23 25		23 55	
Nunhead 4 195	d	20 57				21 27						21 57			22 27			22 57				23 27		23 57	
Crofton Park 195	d	21 00				21 30						22 00			22 30			23 00				23 30		23 59	
Catford 195	d	21 03				21 33						22 03			22 33			23 03				23 33		00 03	
Bellingham 195	d	21 05				21 35						22 05			22 35			23 05				23 35		00 05	
Beckenham Hill 195	d	21 07				21 37						22 07			22 37			23 07				23 37		00 07	
Ravensbourne 195	d	21 09				21 39						22 09			22 39			23 09				23 39		00 09	
Shortlands 195	d	21 11				21 41						22 11			22 41			23 11				23 41		00 11	
Bromley South 4 195	d	21 14				21 44						22 14			22 44			23 14				23 44		00 14	
Bickley 4 195	d	21 17				21 47						22 17			22 47			23 17				23 47		00 17	
St Mary Cray 195	d	21 21				21 51						22 21			22 51			23 21				23 51		00 21	
Swanley 4 195	d	21 26				21 56						22 26			22 56			23 26				23 56		00 26	
Eynsford 195	d	21 30				22 00						22 30			23 00			23 30				00 01		00 30	
Shoreham (Kent) 195	d	21 34				22 04						22 34			23 04			23 34				00 04		00 34	
Otford 4 195	d	21 37				22 07						22 37			23 07			23 37				00 07		00 37	
Bat & Ball 195	d	21 40				22 10						22 40			23 10			23 40				00 10		00 40	
Sevenoaks 4 195	a	21 43				22 13						22 43			23 13			23 43				00 13		00 43	
East Croydon 🚋	d				21 26						21 56			22 26			22 56				23 26		23 57		
Redhill	d																								
Gatwick Airport 10 ✈	d				21 42						22 12			22 42			23 12				23 42		00 20		
Three Bridges 4	d				21 47						22 17			22 47			23 17				23 47		00 25		
Balcombe	d																								
Haywards Heath 3	d				21 56						22 26			22 56			23 26				23 56		00 36		
Wivelsfield 4	d																								
Burgess Hill 4	d				22 01						22 33			23 01			23 33				00 02		00 42		
Hassocks 4	d				22 05						22 37			23 05			23 37				00 06		00 45		
Preston Park	d																								
Brighton 10	a				22 15						22 47			23 15			23 47				00 15		00 55		

A From Derby
B From Nottingham
C From York
D From Sheffield

The trains that operate to and from Sevenoaks, Orpington and Rochester (and a few other destinations at peak times) are operated jointly by First Capital Connect (north of Blackfriars) and Southeastern (south of Blackfriars)

Table 52 shows the complete service between Bedford and London, whilst services between London, Sevenoaks, Sutton and Brighton only show through Thameslink services. Other Tables should be consulted for additional journey opportunities.

Table 52

Sundays

8 December to 29 December

Bedford, Luton, St Albans and City of London - South London, Gatwick Airport and Brighton

Network Diagram - refer to first Page of Table 52

			EM	FC	FC	FC
			◇1 A ⊡	1	1	1
Bedford 7		d	22 39	22 42	23 12	23 42
Flitwick		d		22 52	23 22	23 52
Harlington		d		22 56	23 26	23 56
Leagrave		d		23 02	23 32	00 02
Luton 10		d	22 53	23 06	23 36	00 06
Luton Airport Parkway 7	✈	d		23 09	23 39	00 09
Harpenden		d		23 15	23 45	00 15
St Albans City		d		23 21	23 51	00 21
Radlett		d		23 26	23 56	00 26
Elstree & Borehamwood		d		23 31	00 01	00 31
Mill Hill Broadway		d		23 35	00 05	00 35
Hendon		d		23 38	00 08	00 38
Cricklewood		d		23 42	00 12	00 42
West Hampstead Thameslink	⊖	d		23 45	00 15	00 45
Kentish Town	⊖	d		23 50	00 20	00 50
St Pancras International 15	⊖	a	23 25	23 53	00 23	00 53
		d		23 54	00 24	00 54
Farringdon 3	⊖	d		23 59	00 29	
City Thameslink 3		d				
London Blackfriars 3	⊖	d		00 05	00 35	01 05
Elephant & Castle	⊖173,179	d				
Loughborough Jn	173,179	d				
Herne Hill 4	173,179	d				
London Bridge 4		a		00 11	00 41	
		d		00 12	00 42	
Tulse Hill 3		d				
Streatham 4		d				
Mitcham Eastfields	173	d				
Mitcham Junction	173 ⇌	d				
Hackbridge	173	d				
Carshalton	173	d				
Tooting	173	d				
Haydons Road	173	d				
Wimbledon 6	⊖173,179 ⇌	d				
Wimbledon Chase	179	d				
South Merton	179	d				
Morden South	179	d				
St Helier	179	d				
Sutton Common	179	d				
West Sutton	179	d				
Sutton (Surrey) 4	179	a				
Denmark Hill 4	195	d				
Peckham Rye 4	195	d				
Nunhead 4	195	d				
Crofton Park	195	d				
Catford	195	d				
Bellingham	195	d				
Beckenham Hill	195	d				
Ravensbourne	195	d				
Shortlands	195	d				
Bromley South 4	195	d				
Bickley 4	195	d				
St Mary Cray	195	d				
Swanley 4	195	d				
Eynsford	195	d				
Shoreham (Kent)	195	d				
Otford 4	195	d				
Bat & Ball	195	d				
Sevenoaks 4	195	a				
East Croydon	⇌	d		00 29	00 57	01 36
Redhill		d				
Gatwick Airport 10	✈	d		00 49	01 19	01 55
Three Bridges 4		d		00a54	01a24	02a02
Balcombe		d				
Haywards Heath 3		d				
Wivelsfield 4		d				
Burgess Hill 4		d				
Hassocks 4		d				
Preston Park		d				
Brighton 10		a				

A From Nottingham

The trains that operate to and from Sevenoaks, Orpington and Rochester (and a few other destinations at peak times) are operated jointly by First Capital Connect (north of Blackfriars) and Southeastern (south of Blackfriars)

Table 52 shows the complete service between Bedford and London, whilst services between London, Sevenoaks, Sutton and Brighton only show through Thameslink services. Other Tables should be consulted for additional journey opportunities.

Table 52

Sundays

5 January to 9 February

Bedford, Luton, St Albans and City of London - South London, Gatwick Airport and Brighton

Network Diagram - refer to first Page of Table 52

		FC	FC	FC	SE	SE	FC	FC	FC	FC	FC		FC	FC	FC	FC	FC	FC	FC	FC	FC	SE		FC	SE
				1			1	1	1	1	1			1	1	1		1	1	1				1	
		A	A	B	C	C	B	B	B	B															
													bus				bus				bus				
Bedford 7	d										05 40			05 58	06 28				06 58						
Flitwick	d										05 50			06 08	06 38				07 08						
Harlington	d										05 54			06 12	06 42				07 12						
Leagrave	d									00 02	06 00			06 18	06 48				07 18						
Luton 10	d									00 06	06 04			06 22	06 52				07 22						
Luton Airport Parkway 7 ✈	d									00 09	06 07			06 25	06 55				07 25						
Harpenden	d									00 15	06 13			06 31	07 01				07 31						
St Albans City	d									00 21	06a19		05 59	06a37	07a08		05 59		07a37		06 29				
Radlett	d									00 26															
Elstree & Borehamwood	d								00 01	00 31															
Mill Hill Broadway	d								00 05	00 35															
Hendon	d								00 08	00 38															
Cricklewood	d								00 12	00 42															
West Hampstead Thameslink ⊖	d								00 15	00 45						06 43				07 01				07 31	
Kentish Town ⊖	d								00 20	00 50						06 48				07 06				07 36	
St Pancras International 15 ⊖	a								00 23	00 53			07 51			06 55	06 59			07 09	07 29			07 39	
	d								00 24	00 54										07 10				07 40	
Farringdon 3 ⊖	d								00 29				↪							07 15				07 45	
City Thameslink 3	d																								
London Blackfriars 3 ⊖	d							00 05	00 35	01 05								06 51		07 21		07 42		07 51	08 12
Elephant & Castle ⊖173,179	d																			07 25		07 46		07 55	08 16
Loughborough Jn 173,179	d																								
Herne Hill 4 173,179	d																								
London Bridge 4	a							00 11	00 41																
	d							00 12	00 42																
Tulse Hill 3	d		00 02																						
Streatham 4	d		00 06																						
Mitcham Eastfields 173	d																								
Mitcham Junction 173 🚋	d																								
Hackbridge 173	d																								
Carshalton 173	d																								
Tooting 173	d		00 10																						
Haydons Road 173	d		00 13																						
Wimbledon 6 ⊖173,179 🚋	d		00 17																						
Wimbledon Chase 179	d		00 20																						
South Merton 179	d		00 22																						
Morden South 179	d		00 24																						
St Helier 179	d		00 26																						
Sutton Common 179	d		00 28																						
West Sutton 179	d	00 01	00 31																						
Sutton (Surrey) 4 179	a	00 05	00 35																						
Denmark Hill 4 195	d																					07 52			08 22
Peckham Rye 4 195	d																					07 55			08 25
Nunhead 4 195	d																					07 57			08 27
Crofton Park 195	d																					08 00			08 30
Catford 195	d					00 03																08 03			08 33
Bellingham 195	d					00 05																08 05			08 35
Beckenham Hill 195	d					00 07																08 07			08 37
Ravensbourne 195	d					00 09																08 09			08 39
Shortlands 195	d					00 11																08 11			08 41
Bromley South 4 195	d					00 14																08 14			08 44
Bickley 4 195	d					00 17																08 17			08 47
St Mary Cray 195	d					00 21																08 21			08 51
Swanley 4 195	d					00 26																08 26			08 56
Eynsford 195	d					00 30																08 30			09 00
Shoreham (Kent) 195	d				00 04	00 34																08 34			09 04
Otford 4 195	d				00 07	00 37																08 37			09 07
Bat & Ball 195	d				00 10	00 40																08 40			09 10
Sevenoaks 4 195	a				00 13	00 43																08 43			09 13
East Croydon 🚋	d							00 29	00 57	01 36								07 24		07 53				08 21	
Redhill	d																								
Gatwick Airport 10 ✈	d						00 19	00 49	01 19	01 55								07 44		08 18				08 42	
Three Bridges 4	d						00 24	00 54	01a24	02a02								07 49		08 23				08 47	
Balcombe	d						00 30																		
Haywards Heath 3	d						00 38	01 10										07 58		08 34				08 56	
Wivelsfield 4	d			00 03			00 43																		
Burgess Hill 4	d			00 05			00 45	01 15										08 03		08 39				09 01	
Hassocks 4	d			00 08			00 48	01 18										08 07		08 43				09 05	
Preston Park	d			00 15			00 55																		
Brighton 10	a			00 19			00 59	01 29										08 17		08 53				09 15	

A From Luton

B From Bedford

C From London Blackfriars

The trains that operate to and from Sevenoaks, Orpington and Rochester (and a few other destinations at peak times) are operated jointly by First Capital Connect (north of Blackfriars) and Southeastern (south of Blackfriars)

Table 52 shows the complete service between Bedford and London, whilst services between London, Sevenoaks, Sutton and Brighton only show through Thameslink services. Other Tables should be consulted for additional journey opportunities.

Table 52

Sundays

5 January to 9 February

Bedford, Luton, St Albans and City of London - South London, Gatwick Airport and Brighton

Network Diagram - refer to first Page of Table 52

		FC	FC	FC	FC	FC	FC	FC	SE		FC	FC	FC	SE	FC	FC	EM	FC	FC	SE		FC	FC	EM	FC
					1						1		1			1	◇1		1				1	◇1	
				A		A											B							C	
		🚌	🚌	🚌		🚌	🚌	🚌									☕							☕	
Bedford 7	d										07 28		07 50			08 06	08 14		08 20				08 36	08 46	
Flitwick	d										07 38		08 00			08 16			08 30				08 46		
Harlington	d										07 42		08 04			08 20			08 34				08 50		
Leagrave	d										07 48		08 10			08 26			08 40				08 56		
Luton 10	d										07 52		08 14		08 18	08 30	08 33		08 44			08 48	09 00		
Luton Airport Parkway 7 ✈	d										07 55		08 17		08 21	08 33			08 47			08 51	09 03	09 06	
Harpenden	d										08 01		08 23		08 27	08 39			08 53			08 57	09 09		
St Albans City	d	06 29	06 47				06 47	07 18			08 07		08 29		08 33	08 45			08 59			09 03	09 15		
Radlett	d	06 54					07 12	07 43			08 12				08 38							09 08			
Elstree & Borehamwood	d	07 06					07 24	07 55			08 17				08 42							09 12			
Mill Hill Broadway	d	07 21					07 39	08a10			08 21				08 46							09 16			
Hendon	d	07 31					07 49				08 24				08 50							09 20			
Cricklewood	d	07 41					07 59				08 28				08 53							09 23			
West Hampstead Thameslink ⊖	d	07 51			08 01		08 09				08 31		08 45		08 57	09 01			09 15			09 27	09 31		
Kentish Town ⊖	d	08 06		←	08 06	←	08a24				08 36				09 01							09 31			
St Pancras International 15 ⊖	a	08 21	07 47	07 51	08 09	08 21					08 39		08 52		09 05	09 09	09 14		09 22			09 35	09 39	09 44	
	d				08 10						08 40		08 54		09 06	09 10			09 24			09 36	09 40		
Farringdon 3 ⊖	d	→			08 15						08 45		08 59		09 11	09 15			09 29			09 41	09 45		
City Thameslink 3	d																								
London Blackfriars 3 ⊖	d				08 21				08 42		08 51	08 58	09 04	09 12	09 16	09 21		09 28	09 34	09 42		09 46	09 51		09 58
Elephant & Castle ⊖173,179	d				08 25				08 46		08 55	09 01	09 08	09 16	09 19	09 25		09 31	09 38	09 46		09 49	09 55		10 01
Loughborough Jn 173,179	d											09 05			09 23			09 35				09 53			10 05
Herne Hill 4 173,179	d											09 09			09 27			09 39				09 57			10 09
London Bridge 4	a																								
	d																								
Tulse Hill 3	d											09 14			09 32			09 44				10 02			10 14
Streatham 4	d											09 18			09 36			09 48				10 06			10 18
Mitcham Eastfields 173	d											09 22						09 52							10 22
Mitcham Junction 173 🚋	d											09 25						09 55							10 25
Hackbridge 173	d											09 29						09 59							10 29
Carshalton 173	d											09 31						10 01							10 31
Tooting 173	d														09 42							10 12			
Haydons Road 173	d														09 45							10 15			
Wimbledon 6 ⊖173,179 🚋	d														09 48							10 18			
Wimbledon Chase 179	d														09 51							10 21			
South Merton 179	d														09 53							10 23			
Morden South 179	d														09 55							10 25			
St Helier 179	d														09 57							10 27			
Sutton Common 179	d														09 59							10 29			
West Sutton 179	d														10 02							10 32			
Sutton (Surrey) 4 179	a											09 35			10 05			10 05				10 35			10 35
Denmark Hill 4 195	d								08 52					09 22						09 52					
Peckham Rye 4 195	d								08 55					09 25						09 55					
Nunhead 4 195	d								08 57					09 27						09 57					
Crofton Park 195	d								09 00					09 30						10 00					
Catford 195	d								09 03					09 33						10 03					
Bellingham 195	d								09 05					09 35						10 05					
Beckenham Hill 195	d								09 07					09 37						10 07					
Ravensbourne 195	d								09 09					09 39						10 09					
Shortlands 195	d								09 11					09 41						10 11					
Bromley South 4 195	d								09 14					09 44						10 14					
Bickley 4 195	d								09 17					09 47						10 17					
St Mary Cray 195	d								09 21					09 51						10 21					
Swanley 4 195	d								09 26					09 56						10 26					
Eynsford 195	d								09 30					10 00						10 30					
Shoreham (Kent) 195	d								09 34					10 04						10 34					
Otford 4 195	d								09 37					10 07						10 37					
Bat & Ball 195	d								09 40					10 10						10 40					
Sevenoaks 4 195	a								09 43					10 13						10 43					
East Croydon 🚋	d				08 56						09 26		09 39			09 56			10 09				10 26		
Redhill	d																								
Gatwick Airport 10 ✈	d				09 12						09 42		09 56			10 12			10 26				10 42		
Three Bridges 4	d				09 17						09 47		10a01			10 17			10a33				10 47		
Balcombe	d																								
Haywards Heath 3	d				09 26						09 56					10 26							10 56		
Wivelsfield 4	d																								
Burgess Hill 4	d				09 33						10 01					10 33							11 01		
Hassocks 4	d				09 37						10 05					10 37							11 05		
Preston Park	d																								
Brighton 10	a				09 47						10 15					10 47							11 15		

A From St Albans City **B** From Derby **C** From Nottingham

The trains that operate to and from Sevenoaks, Orpington and Rochester (and a few other destinations at peak times) are operated jointly by First Capital Connect (north of Blackfriars) and Southeastern (south of Blackfriars)

Table 52 shows the complete service between Bedford and London, whilst services between London, Sevenoaks, Sutton and Brighton only show through Thameslink services. Other Tables should be consulted for additional journey opportunities.

Table 52

Sundays

5 January to 9 February

Bedford, Luton, St Albans and City of London - South London, Gatwick Airport and Brighton

Network Diagram - refer to first Page of Table 52

		FC	SE	FC	FC	EM	FC	FC	SE	FC	FC	EM	FC	FC	SE	FC	FC	EM	FC	FC	SE	FC	FC
		1			1	◇1 A		1			1	◇1 B		1			1	◇1 C		1			1
Bedford 7	d	08 50			09 06	09 14		09 20			09 36	09 46		09 50			10 06	10 14		10 20			10 36
Flitwick	d	09 00			09 16			09 30			09 46			10 00			10 16			10 30			10 46
Harlington	d	09 04			09 20			09 34			09 50			10 04			10 20			10 34			10 50
Leagrave	d	09 10			09 26			09 40			09 56			10 10			10 26			10 40			10 56
Luton 10	d	09 14		09 18	09 30	09 35		09 44		09 48	10 00			10 14		10 18	10 30	10 35		10 44		10 48	11 00
Luton Airport Parkway 7 ✈	d	09 17		09 21	09 33			09 47		09 51	10 03	10 07		10 17		10 21	10 33			10 47		10 51	11 03
Harpenden	d	09 23		09 27	09 39			09 53		09 57	10 09			10 23		10 27	10 39			10 53		10 57	11 09
St Albans City	d	09 29		09 33	09 45			09 59		10 03	10 15			10 29		10 33	10 45			10 59		11 03	11 15
Radlett	d			09 38						10 08						10 38						11 08	
Elstree & Borehamwood	d			09 42						10 12						10 42						11 12	
Mill Hill Broadway	d			09 46						10 16						10 46						11 16	
Hendon	d			09 50						10 20						10 50						11 20	
Cricklewood	d			09 53						10 23						10 53						11 23	
West Hampstead Thameslink ⊖	d	09 45		09 57	10 01			10 15		10 27	10 31			10 45		10 57	11 01			11 15		11 27	11 31
Kentish Town ⊖	d			10 01						10 31						11 01						11 31	
St Pancras International 15 ⊖	a	09 52		10 05	10 09	10 14		10 22		10 35	10 39	10 48		10 52		11 05	11 09	11 18		11 22		11 35	11 39
	d	09 54		10 06	10 10			10 24		10 36	10 40			10 54		11 06	11 10			11 24		11 36	11 40
Farringdon 3 ⊖	d	09 59		10 11	10 15			10 29		10 41	10 45			10 59		11 11	11 15			11 29		11 41	11 45
City Thameslink 3	d																						
London Blackfriars 3 ⊖	d	10 04	10 12	10 16	10 21		10 28	10 34	10 42	10 46	10 51		10 58	11 04	11 12	11 16	11 21		11 28	11 34	11 42	11 46	11 51
Elephant & Castle ⊖173,179	d	10 08	10 16	10 19	10 25		10 31	10 38	10 46	10 49	10 55		11 01	11 08	11 16	11 19	11 25		11 31	11 38	11 46	11 49	11 55
Loughborough Jn 173,179	d			10 23			10 35			10 53			11 05			11 23			11 35			11 53	
Herne Hill 4 173,179	d			10 27			10 39			10 57			11 09			11 27			11 39			11 57	
London Bridge 4	a																						
	d																						
Tulse Hill 3	d			10 32			10 44			11 02			11 14			11 32			11 44			12 02	
Streatham 4	d			10 36			10 48			11 06			11 18			11 36			11 48			12 06	
Mitcham Eastfields 173	d						10 52						11 22						11 52				
Mitcham Junction 173 ↔	d						10 55						11 25						11 55				
Hackbridge 173	d						10 59						11 29						11 59				
Carshalton 173	d						11 01						11 31						12 01				
Tooting 173	d			10 42						11 12						11 42						12 12	
Haydons Road 173	d			10 45						11 15						11 45						12 15	
Wimbledon 6 ⊖173,179 ↔	d			10 48						11 18						11 48						12 18	
Wimbledon Chase 179	d			10 51						11 21						11 51						12 21	
South Merton 179	d			10 53						11 23						11 53						12 23	
Morden South 179	d			10 55						11 25						11 55						12 25	
St Helier 179	d			10 57						11 27						11 57						12 27	
Sutton Common 179	d			10 59						11 29						11 59						12 29	
West Sutton 179	d			11 02						11 32						12 02						12 32	
Sutton (Surrey) 4 179	a			11 05			11 05			11 35			11 35			12 05			12 05			12 35	
Denmark Hill 4 195	d		10 22						10 52						11 22						11 52		
Peckham Rye 4 195	d		10 25						10 55						11 25						11 55		
Nunhead 4 195	d		10 27						10 57						11 27						11 57		
Crofton Park 195	d		10 30						11 00						11 30						12 00		
Catford 195	d		10 33						11 03						11 33						12 03		
Bellingham 195	d		10 35						11 05						11 35						12 05		
Beckenham Hill 195	d		10 37						11 07						11 37						12 07		
Ravensbourne 195	d		10 39						11 09						11 39						12 09		
Shortlands 195	d		10 41						11 11						11 41						12 11		
Bromley South 4 195	d		10 44						11 14						11 44						12 14		
Bickley 4 195	d		10 47						11 17						11 47						12 17		
St Mary Cray 195	d		10 51						11 21						11 51						12 21		
Swanley 4 195	d		10 56						11 26						11 56						12 26		
Eynsford 195	d		11 00						11 30						12 00						12 30		
Shoreham (Kent) 195	d		11 04						11 34						12 04						12 34		
Otford 4 195	d		11 07						11 37						12 07						12 37		
Bat & Ball 195	d		11 10						11 40						12 10						12 40		
Sevenoaks 4 195	a		11 13						11 43						12 13						12 43		
East Croydon ↔	d	10 39			10 56			11 09			11 26			11 39			11 56			12 09			12 26
Redhill	d																						
Gatwick Airport 10 ✈	d	10 56			11 12			11 26			11 42			11 56			12 12			12 26			12 42
Three Bridges 4	d	11a01			11 17			11a33			11 47			12a01			12 17			12a33			12 47
Balcombe	d																						
Haywards Heath 3	d				11 26						11 56						12 26						12 56
Wivelsfield 4	d																						
Burgess Hill 4	d				11 33						12 01						12 33						13 01
Hassocks 4	d				11 37						12 05						12 37						13 05
Preston Park	d																						
Brighton 10	a				11 47						12 15						12 47						13 15

A From Derby   **B** From Nottingham   **C** From Sheffield

The trains that operate to and from Sevenoaks, Orpington and Rochester (and a few other destinations at peak times) are operated jointly by First Capital Connect (north of Blackfriars) and Southeastern (south of Blackfriars)

Table 52 shows the complete service between Bedford and London, whilst services between London, Sevenoaks, Sutton and Brighton only show through Thameslink services. Other Tables should be consulted for additional journey opportunities.

Table 52

Sundays

5 January to 9 February

Bedford, Luton, St Albans and City of London - South London, Gatwick Airport and Brighton

Network Diagram - refer to first Page of Table 52

Station		EM ◇1 A	FC	FC 1	SE	FC	FC 1	EM ◇1 B	FC	FC 1	SE	FC	FC 1	FC	FC 1	EM ◇1 A	SE	FC	FC 1	FC	FC 1	EM ◇1 B	SE
Bedford 7	d	10 45		10 50			11 06	11 15		11 20			11 36		11 50	11 57			12 06		12 20	12 23	
Flitwick	d			11 00			11 16			11 30			11 46		12 00				12 16		12 30		
Harlington	d			11 04			11 20			11 34			11 50		12 04				12 20		12 34		
Leagrave	d			11 10			11 26			11 40			11 56		12 10				12 26		12 40		
Luton 10	d			11 14		11 18	11 30	11 35		11 44		11 48	12 00		12 14			12 18	12 30		12 44	12 38	
Luton Airport Parkway 7 ✈	d	11 06		11 17		11 21	11 33			11 47		11 51	12 03		12 17	12 13		12 21	12 33		12 47		
Harpenden	d			11 23		11 27	11 39			11 53		11 57	12 09		12 23			12 27	12 39		12 53		
St Albans City	d			11 29		11 33	11 45			11 59		12 03	12 15		12 29			12 33	12 45		12 59		
Radlett	d					11 38						12 08						12 38					
Elstree & Borehamwood	d					11 42						12 12						12 42					
Mill Hill Broadway	d					11 46						12 16						12 46					
Hendon	d					11 50						12 20						12 50					
Cricklewood	d					11 53						12 23						12 53					
West Hampstead Thameslink ⊖	d			11 45		11 57	12 01			12 15		12 27	12 31		12 45			12 57	13 01		13 15		
Kentish Town ⊖	d					12 01						12 31						13 01					
St Pancras International 15 ⊖	a	11 48		11 52		12 05	12 09	12 13		12 22		12 35	12 39		12 52	12 40		13 05	13 09		13 22	13 03	
	d			11 54		12 06	12 10			12 24		12 36	12 40		12 54			13 06	13 10		13 24		
Farringdon 3 ⊖	d			11 59		12 11	12 15			12 29		12 41	12 45		12 59			13 11	13 15		13 29		
City Thameslink 3	d																						
London Blackfriars 3 ⊖	d		11 58	12 04	12 12	12 16	12 21		12 28	12 34	12 42	12 46	12 51	12 58	13 04		13 12	13 16	13 21	13 28	13 34		13 42
Elephant & Castle ⊖173,179	d		12 01	12 08	12 16	12 19	12 25		12 31	12 38	12 46	12 49	12 55	13 01	13 08		13 16	13 19	13 25	13 31	13 38		13 46
Loughborough Jn 173,179	d		12 05			12 23			12 35			12 53		13 05				13 23		13 35			
Herne Hill 4 173,179	d		12 09			12 27			12 39			12 57		13 09				13 27		13 39			
London Bridge 4	a																						
	d																						
Tulse Hill 3	d		12 14			12 32			12 44			13 02		13 14				13 32		13 44			
Streatham 4	d		12 18			12 36			12 48			13 06		13 18				13 36		13 48			
Mitcham Eastfields 173	d		12 22						12 52					13 22						13 52			
Mitcham Junction 173 🚊	d		12 25						12 55					13 25						13 55			
Hackbridge 173	d		12 29						12 59					13 29						13 59			
Carshalton 173	d		12 31						13 01					13 31						14 01			
Tooting 173	d					12 42						13 12						13 42					
Haydons Road 173	d					12 45						13 15						13 45					
Wimbledon 6 ⊖173,179 🚊	d					12 48						13 18						13 48					
Wimbledon Chase 179	d					12 51						13 21						13 51					
South Merton 179	d					12 53						13 23						13 53					
Morden South 179	d					12 55						13 25						13 55					
St Helier 179	d					12 57						13 27						13 57					
Sutton Common 179	d					12 59						13 29						13 59					
West Sutton 179	d					13 02						13 32						14 02					
Sutton (Surrey) 4 179	a		12 35			13 05			13 05			13 35		13 35				14 05		14 05			
Denmark Hill 4 195	d				12 22						12 52						13 22						13 52
Peckham Rye 4 195	d				12 25						12 55						13 25						13 55
Nunhead 4 195	d				12 27						12 57						13 27						13 57
Crofton Park 195	d				12 30						13 00						13 30						14 00
Catford 195	d				12 33						13 03						13 33						14 03
Bellingham 195	d				12 35						13 05						13 35						14 05
Beckenham Hill 195	d				12 37						13 07						13 37						14 07
Ravensbourne 195	d				12 39						13 09						13 39						14 09
Shortlands 195	d				12 41						13 11						13 41						14 11
Bromley South 4 195	d				12 44						13 14						13 44						14 14
Bickley 4 195	d				12 47						13 17						13 47						14 17
St Mary Cray 195	d				12 51						13 21						13 51						14 21
Swanley 4 195	d				12 56						13 26						13 56						14 26
Eynsford 195	d				13 00						13 30						14 00						14 30
Shoreham (Kent) 195	d				13 04						13 34						14 04						14 34
Otford 4 195	d				13 07						13 37						14 07						14 37
Bat & Ball 195	d				13 10						13 40						14 10						14 40
Sevenoaks 4 195	a				13 13						13 43						14 13						14 43
East Croydon 🚊	d			12 39			12 56			13 09			13 26		13 39				13 56		14 09		
Redhill	d																						
Gatwick Airport 10 ✈	d			12 56			13 12			13 26			13 42		13 56				14 12		14 26		
Three Bridges 4	d			13a01			13 17			13a33			13 47		14a01				14 17		14a33		
Balcombe	d																						
Haywards Heath 3	d						13 26						13 56						14 26				
Wivelsfield 4	d																						
Burgess Hill 4	d						13 33						14 01						14 33				
Hassocks 4	d						13 37						14 05						14 37				
Preston Park	d																						
Brighton 10	a						13 47						14 15						14 47				

A From Nottingham

B From Sheffield

The trains that operate to and from Sevenoaks, Orpington and Rochester (and a few other destinations at peak times) are operated jointly by First Capital Connect (north of Blackfriars) and Southeastern (south of Blackfriars)

Table 52 shows the complete service between Bedford and London, whilst services between London, Sevenoaks, Sutton and Brighton only show through Thameslink services. Other Tables should be consulted for additional journey opportunities.

Table 52

Sundays

5 January to 9 February

Bedford, Luton, St Albans and City of London - South London, Gatwick Airport and Brighton

Network Diagram - refer to first Page of Table 52

Station		FC	FC [1]		FC	FC [1]	EM ◇[1] A	SE	FC	FC [1]	FC	FC [1]	SE	FC		FC [1]	EM ◇[1] A	FC	FC [1]	SE	FC	FC [1]	EM ◇[1] B	FC	FC [1]
Bedford [7]	d		12 36			12 50	12 53			13 06		13 20				13 36	13 43		13 50			14 06	14 12		14 20
Flitwick	d		12 46			13 00				13 16		13 30				13 46			14 00			14 16			14 30
Harlington	d		12 50			13 04				13 20		13 34				13 50			14 04			14 20			14 34
Leagrave	d		12 56			13 10				13 26		13 40				13 56			14 10			14 26			14 40
Luton [10]	d	12 48	13 00			13 14			13 18	13 30		13 44		13 48		14 00	14 00		14 14		14 18	14 30			14 44
Luton Airport Parkway [7] ✈	d	12 51	13 03			13 17	13 09		13 21	13 33		13 47		13 51		14 03			14 17		14 21	14 33	14 28		14 47
Harpenden	d	12 57	13 09			13 23			13 27	13 39		13 53		13 57		14 09			14 23		14 27	14 39			14 53
St Albans City	d	13 03	13 15			13 29			13 33	13 45		13 59		14 03		14 15			14 29		14 33	14 45			14 59
Radlett	d	13 08							13 38					14 08							14 38				
Elstree & Borehamwood	d	13 12							13 42					14 12							14 42				
Mill Hill Broadway	d	13 16							13 46					14 16							14 46				
Hendon	d	13 20							13 50					14 20							14 50				
Cricklewood	d	13 23							13 53					14 23							14 53				
West Hampstead Thameslink ⊖	d	13 27	13 31			13 45			13 57	14 01		14 15		14 27		14 31			14 45		14 57	15 01			15 15
Kentish Town ⊖	d	13 31							14 01					14 31							15 01				
St Pancras International [15] ⊖	a	13 35	13 39			13 52	13 37		14 05	14 09		14 22		14 35		14 39	14 27		14 52		15 05	15 09	14 55		15 22
	d	13 36	13 40			13 54			14 06	14 10		14 24		14 36		14 40			14 54		15 06	15 10			15 24
Farringdon [3] ⊖	d	13 41	13 45			13 59			14 11	14 15		14 29		14 41		14 45			14 59		15 11	15 15			15 29
City Thameslink [3]	d																								
London Blackfriars [3] ⊖	d	13 46	13 51		13 58	14 04		14 12	14 16	14 21	14 28	14 34	14 42	14 46		14 51		14 58	15 04	15 12	15 16	15 21		15 28	15 34
Elephant & Castle ⊖173,179	d	13 49	13 55		14 01	14 08		14 16	14 19	14 25	14 31	14 38	14 46	14 49		14 55		15 01	15 08	15 16	15 19	15 25		15 31	15 38
Loughborough Jn 173,179	d	13 53			14 05				14 23		14 35			14 53				15 05			15 23			15 35	
Herne Hill [4] 173,179	d	13 57			14 09				14 27		14 39			14 57				15 09			15 27			15 39	
London Bridge [4]	a																								
	d																								
Tulse Hill [3]	d	14 02			14 14				14 32		14 44			15 02				15 14			15 32			15 44	
Streatham [4]	d	14 06			14 18				14 36		14 48			15 06				15 18			15 36			15 48	
Mitcham Eastfields 173	d				14 22						14 52							15 22						15 52	
Mitcham Junction 173 🚋	d				14 25						14 55							15 25						15 55	
Hackbridge 173	d				14 29						14 59							15 29						15 59	
Carshalton 173	d				14 31						15 01							15 31						16 01	
Tooting 173	d	14 12							14 42					15 12							15 42				
Haydons Road 173	d	14 15							14 45					15 15							15 45				
Wimbledon [6] ⊖173,179 🚋	d	14 18							14 48					15 18							15 48				
Wimbledon Chase 179	d	14 21							14 51					15 21							15 51				
South Merton 179	d	14 23							14 53					15 23							15 53				
Morden South 179	d	14 25							14 55					15 25							15 55				
St Helier 179	d	14 27							14 57					15 27							15 57				
Sutton Common 179	d	14 29							14 59					15 29							15 59				
West Sutton 179	d	14 32							15 02					15 32							16 02				
Sutton (Surrey) [4] 179	a	14 35			14 35				15 05		15 05			15 35				15 35			16 05			16 05	
Denmark Hill [4] 195	d							14 22					14 52							15 22					
Peckham Rye [4] 195	d							14 25					14 55							15 25					
Nunhead [4] 195	d							14 27					14 57							15 27					
Crofton Park 195	d							14 30					15 00							15 30					
Catford 195	d							14 33					15 03							15 33					
Bellingham 195	d							14 35					15 05							15 35					
Beckenham Hill 195	d							14 37					15 07							15 37					
Ravensbourne 195	d							14 39					15 09							15 39					
Shortlands 195	d							14 41					15 11							15 41					
Bromley South [4] 195	d							14 44					15 14							15 44					
Bickley [4] 195	d							14 47					15 17							15 47					
St Mary Cray 195	d							14 51					15 21							15 51					
Swanley [4] 195	d							14 56					15 26							15 56					
Eynsford 195	d							15 00					15 30							16 00					
Shoreham (Kent) 195	d							15 04					15 34							16 04					
Otford [4] 195	d							15 07					15 37							16 07					
Bat & Ball 195	d							15 10					15 40							16 10					
Sevenoaks [4] 195	a							15 13					15 43							16 13					
East Croydon 🚋	d		14 26			14 39				14 56		15 09				15 26			15 39			15 56			16 09
Redhill	d																								
Gatwick Airport [10] ✈	d		14 42			14 56				15 12		15 26				15 42			15 56			16 12			16 26
Three Bridges [4]	d		14 47			15a01				15 17		15a33				15 47			16a01			16 17			16a33
Balcombe	d																								
Haywards Heath [3]	d		14 56							15 26						15 56						16 26			
Wivelsfield [4]	d																								
Burgess Hill [4]	d		15 01							15 33						16 01						16 33			
Hassocks [4]	d		15 05							15 37						16 05						16 37			
Preston Park	d																								
Brighton [10]	a		15 15							15 47						16 15						16 47			

A From Leeds

B From Nottingham

The trains that operate to and from Sevenoaks, Orpington and Rochester (and a few other destinations at peak times) are operated jointly by First Capital Connect (north of Blackfriars) and Southeastern (south of Blackfriars)

Table 52 shows the complete service between Bedford and London, whilst services between London, Sevenoaks, Sutton and Brighton only show through Thameslink services. Other Tables should be consulted for additional journey opportunities.

Table 52

Sundays

5 January to 9 February

Bedford, Luton, St Albans and City of London - South London, Gatwick Airport and Brighton

Network Diagram - refer to first Page of Table 52

	SE	FC	FC ■1	EM ◇■1 A 🍴	FC	FC ■1	SE	FC	FC ■1	FC	FC ■1	EM ◇■1 B 🍴	SE	FC	FC ■1	EM ◇■1 A 🍴	FC	FC ■1	SE	FC	FC ■1
Bedford ■7 d			14 36	14 38		14 50			15 06		15 20	15 22			15 36	15 45		15 50			16 06
Flitwick d			14 46			15 00			15 16		15 30				15 46			16 00			16 16
Harlington d			14 50			15 04			15 20		15 34				15 50			16 04			16 20
Leagrave d			14 56			15 10			15 26		15 40				15 56			16 10			16 26
Luton ■10 d		14 48	15 00	14 54		15 14		15 18	15 30		15 44			15 48	16 00	16 01		16 14		16 18	16 30
Luton Airport Parkway ■7 ✈ d		14 51	15 03			15 17		15 21	15 33		15 47	15 38		15 51	16 03			16 17		16 21	16 33
Harpenden d		14 57	15 09			15 23		15 27	15 39		15 53			15 57	16 09			16 23		16 27	16 39
St Albans City d		15 03	15 15			15 29		15 33	15 45		15 59			16 03	16 15			16 29		16 33	16 45
Radlett d		15 08						15 38						16 08						16 38	
Elstree & Borehamwood d		15 12						15 42						16 12						16 42	
Mill Hill Broadway d		15 16						15 46						16 16						16 46	
Hendon d		15 20						15 50						16 20						16 50	
Cricklewood d		15 23						15 53						16 23						16 53	
West Hampstead Thameslink ⊖ d		15 27	15 31			15 45		15 57	16 01		16 15			16 27	16 31			16 45		16 57	17 01
Kentish Town ⊖ d		15 31						16 01						16 31						17 01	
St Pancras International ■15 ⊖ a		15 35	15 39	15 19		15 52		16 05	16 09		16 22	16 05		16 35	16 39	16 26		16 52		17 05	17 09
d		15 36	15 40			15 54		16 06	16 10		16 24			16 36	16 40			16 54		17 06	17 10
Farringdon ■3 ⊖ d		15 41	15 45			15 59		16 11	16 15		16 29			16 41	16 45			16 59		17 11	17 15
City Thameslink ■3 d																					
London Blackfriars ■3 ⊖ d	15 42	15 46	15 51		15 58	16 04	16 12	16 16	16 21	16 28	16 34		16 42	16 46	16 51		16 58	17 04	17 12	17 16	17 21
Elephant & Castle ⊖173,179 d	15 46	15 49	15 55		16 01	16 08	16 16	16 19	16 25	16 31	16 38		16 46	16 49	16 55		17 01	17 08	17 16	17 19	17 25
Loughborough Jn 173,179 d		15 53			16 05			16 23		16 35				16 53			17 05			17 23	
Herne Hill ■4 173,179 d		15 57			16 09			16 27		16 39				16 57			17 09			17 27	
London Bridge ■4 a																					
d																					
Tulse Hill ■3 d		16 02			16 14			16 32		16 44				17 02			17 14			17 32	
Streatham ■4 d		16 06			16 18			16 36		16 48				17 06			17 18			17 36	
Mitcham Eastfields 173 d					16 22					16 52							17 22				
Mitcham Junction 173 🚋 d					16 25					16 55							17 25				
Hackbridge 173 d					16 29					16 59							17 29				
Carshalton 173 d					16 31					17 01							17 31				
Tooting 173 d		16 12						16 42						17 12						17 42	
Haydons Road 173 d		16 15						16 45						17 15						17 45	
Wimbledon ■6 ⊖173,179 🚋 d		16 18						16 48						17 18						17 48	
Wimbledon Chase 179 d		16 21						16 51						17 21						17 51	
South Merton 179 d		16 23						16 53						17 23						17 53	
Morden South 179 d		16 25						16 55						17 25						17 55	
St Helier 179 d		16 27						16 57						17 27						17 57	
Sutton Common 179 d		16 29						16 59						17 29						17 59	
West Sutton 179 d		16 32						17 02						17 32						18 02	
Sutton (Surrey) ■4 179 a		16 35			16 35			17 05		17 05				17 35			17 35			18 05	
Denmark Hill ■4 195 d	15 52						16 22						16 52						17 22		
Peckham Rye ■4 195 d	15 55						16 25						16 55						17 25		
Nunhead ■4 195 d	15 57						16 27						16 57						17 27		
Crofton Park 195 d	16 00						16 30						17 00						17 30		
Catford 195 d	16 03						16 33						17 03						17 33		
Bellingham 195 d	16 05						16 35						17 05						17 35		
Beckenham Hill 195 d	16 07						16 37						17 07						17 37		
Ravensbourne 195 d	16 09						16 39						17 09						17 39		
Shortlands 195 d	16 11						16 41						17 11						17 41		
Bromley South ■4 195 d	16 14						16 44						17 14						17 44		
Bickley ■4 195 d	16 17						16 47						17 17						17 47		
St Mary Cray 195 d	16 21						16 51						17 21						17 51		
Swanley ■4 195 d	16 26						16 56						17 26						17 56		
Eynsford 195 d	16 30						17 00						17 30						18 00		
Shoreham (Kent) 195 d	16 34						17 04						17 34						18 04		
Otford ■4 195 d	16 37						17 07						17 37						18 07		
Bat & Ball 195 d	16 40						17 10						17 40						18 10		
Sevenoaks ■4 195 a	16 43						17 13						17 43						18 13		
East Croydon 🚋 d			16 26			16 39			16 56		17 09				17 26			17 39			17 56
Redhill d																					
Gatwick Airport ■10 ✈ d			16 42			16 56			17 12		17 26				17 42			17 56			18 12
Three Bridges ■4 d			16 47			17a01			17 17		17a33				17 47			18a01			18 17
Balcombe d																					
Haywards Heath ■3 d			16 56						17 26						17 56						18 26
Wivelsfield ■4 d																					
Burgess Hill ■4 d			17 01						17 33						18 01						18 33
Hassocks ■4 d			17 05						17 37						18 05						18 37
Preston Park d																					
Brighton ■10 a			17 15						17 47						18 15						18 47

A From Sheffield

B From Nottingham

The trains that operate to and from Sevenoaks, Orpington and Rochester (and a few other destinations at peak times) are operated jointly by First Capital Connect (north of Blackfriars) and Southeastern (south of Blackfriars)

Table 52 shows the complete service between Bedford and London, whilst services between London, Sevenoaks, Sutton and Brighton only show through Thameslink services. Other Tables should be consulted for additional journey opportunities.

Table 52

Sundays
5 January to 9 February

Bedford, Luton, St Albans and City of London - South London, Gatwick Airport and Brighton

Network Diagram - refer to first Page of Table 52

Station		EM ◇1 A 🍴	EM ◇1 B 🍴	FC	FC 1	SE	FC	FC 1	FC	FC 1		SE	FC
Bedford 7	d	16 11			16 20			16 36		16 50			
Flitwick	d				16 30			16 46		17 00			
Harlington	d				16 34			16 50		17 04			
Leagrave	d				16 40			16 56		17 10			
Luton 10	d		16 52		16 44		16 48	17 00		17 14			17 18
Luton Airport Parkway 7 ✈	d	16 26			16 47		16 51	17 03		17 17			17 21
Harpenden	d				16 53		16 57	17 09		17 23			17 27
St Albans City	d				16 59		17 03	17 15		17 29			17 33
Radlett	d						17 08						17 38
Elstree & Borehamwood	d						17 12						17 42
Mill Hill Broadway	d						17 16						17 46
Hendon	d						17 20						17 50
Cricklewood	d						17 23						17 53
West Hampstead Thameslink ⊖	d				17 15		17 27	17 31		17 45			17 57
Kentish Town ⊖	d						17 31						18 01
St Pancras International 15 ⊖	a	16 52	17 17		17 22		17 35	17 39		17 52			18 05
	d				17 24		17 36	17 40		17 54			18 06
Farringdon 3 ⊖	d				17 29		17 41	17 45		17 59			18 11
City Thameslink 3	d												
London Blackfriars 3 ⊖	d			17 28	17 34	17 42	17 46	17 51	17 58	18 04		18 12	18 16
Elephant & Castle ⊖173,179	d			17 31	17 38	17 46	17 49	17 55	18 01	18 08		18 16	18 19
Loughborough Jn 173,179	d			17 35			17 53		18 05				18 23
Herne Hill 4 173,179	d			17 39			17 57		18 09				18 27
London Bridge 4	a												
	d												
Tulse Hill 3	d			17 44			18 02		18 14				18 32
Streatham 4	d			17 48			18 06		18 18				18 36
Mitcham Eastfields 173	d			17 52					18 22				
Mitcham Junction 173 🚋	d			17 55					18 25				
Hackbridge 173	d			17 59					18 29				
Carshalton 173	d			18 01					18 31				
Tooting 173	d						18 12						18 42
Haydons Road 173	d						18 15						18 45
Wimbledon 6 ⊖173,179 🚋	d						18 18						18 48
Wimbledon Chase 179	d						18 21						18 51
South Merton 179	d						18 23						18 53
Morden South 179	d						18 25						18 55
St Helier 179	d						18 27						18 57
Sutton Common 179	d						18 29						18 59
West Sutton 179	d						18 32						19 02
Sutton (Surrey) 4 179	a			18 05			18 35		18 35				19 05
Denmark Hill 4 195	d					17 52						18 22	
Peckham Rye 4 195	d					17 55						18 25	
Nunhead 4 195	d					17 57						18 27	
Crofton Park 195	d					18 00						18 30	
Catford 195	d					18 03						18 33	
Bellingham 195	d					18 05						18 35	
Beckenham Hill 195	d					18 07						18 37	
Ravensbourne 195	d					18 09						18 39	
Shortlands 195	d					18 11						18 41	
Bromley South 4 195	d					18 14						18 44	
Bickley 4 195	d					18 17						18 47	
St Mary Cray 195	d					18 21						18 51	
Swanley 4 195	d					18 26						18 56	
Eynsford 195	d					18 30						19 00	
Shoreham (Kent) 195	d					18 34						19 04	
Otford 4 195	d					18 37						19 07	
Bat & Ball 195	d					18 40						19 10	
Sevenoaks 4 195	a					18 43						19 13	
East Croydon 🚋	d				18 09			18 26		18 39			
Redhill	d												
Gatwick Airport 10 ✈	d				18 26			18 42		18 56			
Three Bridges 4	d				18a33			18 47		19a01			
Balcombe	d												
Haywards Heath 3	d							18 56					
Wivelsfield 4	d												
Burgess Hill 4	d							19 01					
Hassocks 4	d							19 05					
Preston Park	d												
Brighton 10	a							19 15					

Station		FC 1	EM ◇1 A 🍴	FC	FC 1	SE	FC	FC 1	EM ◇1 C 🍴		FC	SE	FC
Bedford 7	d	17 06	17 11		17 20			17 36	17 38				
Flitwick	d	17 16			17 30			17 46					
Harlington	d	17 20			17 34			17 50					
Leagrave	d	17 26			17 40			17 56					
Luton 10	d	17 30			17 44		17 48	18 00	17 58				18 18
Luton Airport Parkway 7 ✈	d	17 33	17 27		17 47		17 51	18 03					18 21
Harpenden	d	17 39			17 53		17 57	18 09					18 27
St Albans City	d	17 45			17 59		18 03	18 15					18 33
Radlett	d						18 08						18 38
Elstree & Borehamwood	d						18 12						18 42
Mill Hill Broadway	d						18 16						18 46
Hendon	d						18 20						18 50
Cricklewood	d						18 23						18 53
West Hampstead Thameslink ⊖	d	18 01			18 15		18 27	18 31					18 57
Kentish Town ⊖	d						18 31						19 01
St Pancras International 15 ⊖	a	18 09	17 52		18 22		18 35	18 39	18 24				19 05
	d	18 10			18 24		18 36	18 40					19 06
Farringdon 3 ⊖	d	18 15			18 29		18 41	18 45					19 11
City Thameslink 3	d												
London Blackfriars 3 ⊖	d	18 21		18 28	18 34	18 42	18 46	18 51			18 58	19 12	19 16
Elephant & Castle ⊖173,179	d	18 25		18 31	18 38	18 46	18 49	18 55			19 01	19 16	19 19
Loughborough Jn 173,179	d			18 35			18 53				19 05		19 23
Herne Hill 4 173,179	d			18 39			18 57				19 09		19 27
London Bridge 4	a												
	d												
Tulse Hill 3	d			18 44			19 02				19 14		19 32
Streatham 4	d			18 48			19 06				19 18		19 36
Mitcham Eastfields 173	d			18 52							19 22		
Mitcham Junction 173 🚋	d			18 55							19 25		
Hackbridge 173	d			18 59							19 29		
Carshalton 173	d			19 01							19 31		
Tooting 173	d						19 12						19 42
Haydons Road 173	d						19 15						19 45
Wimbledon 6 ⊖173,179 🚋	d						19 18						19 48
Wimbledon Chase 179	d						19 21						19 51
South Merton 179	d						19 23						19 53
Morden South 179	d						19 25						19 55
St Helier 179	d						19 27						19 57
Sutton Common 179	d						19 29						19 59
West Sutton 179	d						19 32						20 02
Sutton (Surrey) 4 179	a			19 05			19 35				19 35		20 05
Denmark Hill 4 195	d					18 52						19 22	
Peckham Rye 4 195	d					18 55						19 25	
Nunhead 4 195	d					18 57						19 27	
Crofton Park 195	d					19 00						19 30	
Catford 195	d					19 03						19 33	
Bellingham 195	d					19 05						19 35	
Beckenham Hill 195	d					19 07						19 37	
Ravensbourne 195	d					19 09						19 39	
Shortlands 195	d					19 11						19 41	
Bromley South 4 195	d					19 14						19 44	
Bickley 4 195	d					19 17						19 47	
St Mary Cray 195	d					19 21						19 51	
Swanley 4 195	d					19 26						19 56	
Eynsford 195	d					19 30						20 00	
Shoreham (Kent) 195	d					19 34						20 04	
Otford 4 195	d					19 37						20 07	
Bat & Ball 195	d					19 40						20 10	
Sevenoaks 4 195	a					19 43						20 13	
East Croydon 🚋	d	18 56			19 09			19 26					
Redhill	d												
Gatwick Airport 10 ✈	d	19 12			19 26			19 42					
Three Bridges 4	d	19 17			19a33			19 47					
Balcombe	d												
Haywards Heath 3	d	19 26						19 56					
Wivelsfield 4	d												
Burgess Hill 4	d	19 33						20 01					
Hassocks 4	d	19 37						20 05					
Preston Park	d												
Brighton 10	a	19 47						20 15					

A From Nottingham
B From Sheffield
C From Leeds

The trains that operate to and from Sevenoaks, Orpington and Rochester (and a few other destinations at peak times) are operated jointly by First Capital Connect (north of Blackfriars) and Southeastern (south of Blackfriars)

Table 52 shows the complete service between Bedford and London, whilst services between London, Sevenoaks, Sutton and Brighton only show through Thameslink services. Other Tables should be consulted for additional journey opportunities.

Table 52

Sundays

5 January to 9 February

Bedford, Luton, St Albans and City of London - South London, Gatwick Airport and Brighton

Network Diagram - refer to first Page of Table 52

		FC	EM	FC	SE	FC	FC	EM	FC	SE	FC	FC	EM	FC	SE	FC	FC	EM	SE	FC	FC	EM	SE
		■1	◇■1				■1	◇■1				■1	◇■1				■1	◇■1			■1	◇■1	
			A					B					A					C				A	
Bedford ■7	d	18 06	18 08				18 36	18 43				19 06	19 08				19 36	19 46			20 06	20 08	
Flitwick	d	18 16					18 46					19 16					19 46				20 16		
Harlington	d	18 20					18 50					19 20					19 50				20 20		
Leagrave	d	18 26					18 56					19 26					19 56				20 26		
Luton ■10	d	18 30				18 48	19 00	18 58			19 18	19 30				19 48	20 00	20 01		20 18	20 30		
Luton Airport Parkway ■7 ✈	d	18 33	18 23			18 51	19 03				19 21	19 33	19 23			19 51	20 03			20 21	20 33	20 23	
Harpenden	d	18 39				18 57	19 09				19 27	19 39				19 57	20 09			20 27	20 39		
St Albans City	d	18 45				19 03	19 15				19 33	19 45				20 03	20 15			20 33	20 45		
Radlett	d					19 08					19 38					20 08				20 38			
Elstree & Borehamwood	d					19 12					19 42					20 12				20 42			
Mill Hill Broadway	d					19 16					19 46					20 16				20 46			
Hendon	d					19 20					19 50					20 20				20 50			
Cricklewood	d					19 23					19 53					20 23				20 53			
West Hampstead Thameslink ⊖	d	19 01				19 27	19 31				19 57	20 01				20 27	20 31			20 57	21 01		
Kentish Town ⊖	d					19 31					20 01					20 31				21 01			
St Pancras International ■15 ⊖	a	19 09	18 48			19 35	19 39	19 25			20 05	20 09	19 48			20 35	20 39	20 26		21 05	21 09	20 48	
	d	19 10				19 36	19 40				20 06	20 10				20 36	20 40			21 06	21 10		
Farringdon ■3 ⊖	d	19 15				19 41	19 45				20 11	20 15				20 41	20 45			21 11	21 15		
City Thameslink ■3	d																						
London Blackfriars ■3 ⊖	d	19 21		19 28	19 42	19 46	19 51		19 58	20 12	20 16	20 21		20 28	20 42	20 46	20 51		21 12	21 16	21 21		21 42
Elephant & Castle ⊖173,179	d	19 25		19 31	19 46	19 49	19 55		20 01	20 16	20 19	20 25		20 31	20 46	20 49	20 55		21 16	21 19	21 25		21 46
Loughborough Jn 173,179	d			19 35		19 53			20 05		20 23			20 35		20 53				21 23			
Herne Hill ■4 173,179	d			19 39		19 57			20 09		20 27			20 39		20 57				21 27			
London Bridge ■4	a																						
	d																						
Tulse Hill ■3	d			19 44		20 02			20 14		20 32			20 44		21 02				21 32			
Streatham ■4	d			19 48		20 06			20 18		20 36			20 48		21 06				21 36			
Mitcham Eastfields 173	d			19 52					20 22					20 52									
Mitcham Junction 173 🚋	d			19 55					20 25					20 55									
Hackbridge 173	d			19 59					20 29					20 59									
Carshalton 173	d			20 01					20 31					21 01									
Tooting 173	d					20 12					20 42					21 12				21 42			
Haydons Road 173	d					20 15					20 45					21 15				21 45			
Wimbledon ■6 ⊖173,179 🚋	d					20 18					20 48					21 18				21 48			
Wimbledon Chase 179	d					20 21					20 51					21 21				21 51			
South Merton 179	d					20 23					20 53					21 23				21 53			
Morden South 179	d					20 25					20 55					21 25				21 55			
St Helier 179	d					20 27					20 57					21 27				21 57			
Sutton Common 179	d					20 29					20 59					21 29				21 59			
West Sutton 179	d					20 32					21 02					21 32				22 02			
Sutton (Surrey) ■4 179	a			20 05		20 35			20 35		21 05			21 05		21 35				22 05			
Denmark Hill ■4 195	d				19 52					20 22					20 52				21 22				21 52
Peckham Rye ■4 195	d				19 55					20 25					20 55				21 25				21 55
Nunhead ■4 195	d				19 57					20 27					20 57				21 27				21 57
Crofton Park 195	d				20 00					20 30					21 00				21 30				22 00
Catford 195	d				20 03					20 33					21 03				21 33				22 03
Bellingham 195	d				20 05					20 35					21 05				21 35				22 05
Beckenham Hill 195	d				20 07					20 37					21 07				21 37				22 07
Ravensbourne 195	d				20 09					20 39					21 09				21 39				22 09
Shortlands 195	d				20 11					20 41					21 11				21 41				22 11
Bromley South ■4 195	d				20 14					20 44					21 14				21 44				22 14
Bickley ■4 195	d				20 17					20 47					21 17				21 47				22 17
St Mary Cray 195	d				20 21					20 51					21 21				21 51				22 21
Swanley ■4 195	d				20 26					20 56					21 26				21 56				22 26
Eynsford 195	d				20 30					21 00					21 30				22 00				22 30
Shoreham (Kent) 195	d				20 34					21 04					21 34				22 04				22 34
Otford ■4 195	d				20 37					21 07					21 37				22 07				22 37
Bat & Ball 195	d				20 40					21 10					21 40				22 10				22 40
Sevenoaks ■4 195	a				20 43					21 13					21 43				22 13				22 43
East Croydon 🚋	d	19 56					20 26					20 56					21 26				21 56		
Redhill	d																						
Gatwick Airport ■10 ✈	d	20 12					20 42					21 12					21 42				22 12		
Three Bridges ■4	d	20 17					20 47					21 17					21 47				22 17		
Balcombe	d																						
Haywards Heath ■3	d	20 26					20 56					21 26					21 56				22 26		
Wivelsfield ■4	d																						
Burgess Hill ■4	d	20 33					21 01					21 33					22 01				22 33		
Hassocks ■4	d	20 37					21 05					21 37					22 05				22 37		
Preston Park	d																						
Brighton ■10	a	20 47					21 15					21 47					22 15				22 47		

A From Nottingham B From Sheffield C From Derby

The trains that operate to and from Sevenoaks, Orpington and Rochester (and a few other destinations at peak times) are operated jointly by First Capital Connect (north of Blackfriars) and Southeastern (south of Blackfriars)

Table 52 shows the complete service between Bedford and London, whilst services between London, Sevenoaks, Sutton and Brighton only show through Thameslink services. Other Tables should be consulted for additional journey opportunities.

Table 52

Sundays

5 January to 9 February

Bedford, Luton, St Albans and City of London - South London, Gatwick Airport and Brighton

Network Diagram - refer to first Page of Table 52

		FC [1]	EM ◇[1] A ☕	SE	FC [1]	EM ◇[1] B ☕	SE	FC [1]	EM ◇[1] C ☕	SE	FC [1]	EM ◇[1] C ☕	SE	FC [1]	EM ◇[1] B ☕	FC [1]	FC [1]
Bedford [7]	d	20 28	20 35		20 58	21 09		21 28	21 34		21 58	22 21		22 28	22 39	23 02	23 42
Flitwick	d	20 38			21 08			21 38			22 08			22 38		23 12	23 52
Harlington	d	20 42			21 12			21 42			22 12			22 42		23 16	23 56
Leagrave	d	20 48			21 18			21 48			22 18			22 48		23 22	00 02
Luton [10]	d	20 52			21 22	21 24		21 52	21 49		22 22	22 37		22 52	22 53	23 26	00 06
Luton Airport Parkway [7] ✈	d	20 55	20 50		21 25			21 55			22 25			22 55		23 29	00 09
Harpenden	d	21 01			21 31			22 01			22 31			23 01		23 35	00 15
St Albans City	d	21 07			21 37			22 07			22 37			23 07		23 41	00 21
Radlett	d	21 12			21 42			22 12			22 42			23 12		23 46	00 26
Elstree & Borehamwood	d	21 17			21 47			22 17			22 47			23 17		23 51	00 31
Mill Hill Broadway	d	21 21			21 51			22 21			22 51			23 21		23 55	00 35
Hendon	d	21 24			21 54			22 24			22 54			23 24		23 58	00 38
Cricklewood	d	21 28			21 58			22 28			22 58			23 28		00 02	00 42
West Hampstead Thameslink ⊖	d	21 31			22 01			22 31			23 01			23 31		00 05	00 45
Kentish Town ⊖	d	21 36			22 06			22 36			23 06			23 36		00 10	00 50
St Pancras International [15] ⊖	a	21 39	21 15		22 09	21 49		22 39	22 17		23 09	23 04		23 39	23 28	00 13	00 53
	d	21 40			22 10			22 40			23 10			23 40		00 14	00 54
Farringdon [3] ⊖	d	21 45			22 15			22 45			23 15			23 45		00 19	
City Thameslink [3]	d																
London Blackfriars [3] ⊖	d	21 51		22 12	22 21		22 42	22 51		23 12	23 21		23 42	23 51		00 25	01 05
Elephant & Castle ⊖173,179	d	21 55		22 16	22 25		22 46	22 55		23 16	23 25		23 46				
Loughborough Jn 173,179	d																
Herne Hill [4] 173,179	d																
London Bridge [4]	a																
	d																
Tulse Hill [3]	d																
Streatham [4]	d																
Mitcham Eastfields 173	d																
Mitcham Junction 173 🚋	d																
Hackbridge 173	d																
Carshalton 173	d																
Tooting 173	d																
Haydons Road 173	d																
Wimbledon [6] ⊖173,179 🚋	d																
Wimbledon Chase 179	d																
South Merton 179	d																
Morden South 179	d																
St Helier 179	d																
Sutton Common 179	d																
West Sutton 179	d																
Sutton (Surrey) [4] 179	a																
Denmark Hill [4] 195	d			22 22			22 52			23 22			23 52				
Peckham Rye [4] 195	d			22 25			22 55			23 25			23 55				
Nunhead [4] 195	d			22 27			22 57			23 27			23 57				
Crofton Park 195	d			22 30			23 00			23 30			23 59				
Catford 195	d			22 33			23 03			23 33			00 03				
Bellingham 195	d			22 35			23 05			23 35			00 05				
Beckenham Hill 195	d			22 37			23 07			23 37			00 07				
Ravensbourne 195	d			22 39			23 09			23 39			00 09				
Shortlands 195	d			22 41			23 11			23 41			00 11				
Bromley South [4] 195	d			22 44			23 14			23 44			00 14				
Bickley [4] 195	d			22 47			23 17			23 47			00 17				
St Mary Cray 195	d			22 51			23 21			23 51			00 21				
Swanley [4] 195	d			22 56			23 26			23 56			00 26				
Eynsford 195	d			23 00			23 30			00 01			00 30				
Shoreham (Kent) 195	d			23 04			23 34			00 04			00 34				
Otford [4] 195	d			23 07			23 37			00 07			00 37				
Bat & Ball 195	d			23 10			23 40			00 10			00 40				
Sevenoaks [4] 195	a			23 13			23 43			00 13			00 43				
East Croydon 🚋	d	22 26			22 56			23 26			23 57			00 29		00 57	01 36
Redhill	d																
Gatwick Airport [10] ✈	d	22 42			23 12			23 42			00 20			00 49		01 19	01 55
Three Bridges [4]	d	22 47			23 17			23 47			00 25			00a54		01a24	02a02
Balcombe	d																
Haywards Heath [3]	d	22 56			23 26			23 56			00 36						
Wivelsfield [4]	d																
Burgess Hill [4]	d	23 01			23 33			00 02			00 42						
Hassocks [4]	d	23 05			23 37			00 06			00 45						
Preston Park	d																
Brighton [10]	a	23 15			23 47			00 15			00 55						

A From York **B** From Nottingham **C** From Sheffield

The trains that operate to and from Sevenoaks, Orpington and Rochester (and a few other destinations at peak times) are operated jointly by First Capital Connect (north of Blackfriars) and Southeastern (south of Blackfriars)

Table 52 shows the complete service between Bedford and London, whilst services between London, Sevenoaks, Sutton and Brighton only show through Thameslink services. Other Tables should be consulted for additional journey opportunities.

Table 52

Sundays

16 February to 23 March

Bedford, Luton, St Albans and City of London - South London, Gatwick Airport and Brighton

Network Diagram - refer to first Page of Table 52

	FC A	FC A	FC [1] B	SE C	SE C	FC [1] B	FC [1] B	FC [1] B	FC [1] B	FC [1]		FC (bus)	FC [1]	FC [1]	FC [1]	FC (bus)	FC [1]	FC [1]	FC [1]	FC (bus)	SE		FC [1]	SE
Bedford [7] d										05 40			05 58	06 28				06 58						
Flitwick d										05 50			06 08	06 38				07 08						
Harlington d										05 54			06 12	06 42				07 12						
Leagrave d									00 02	06 00			06 18	06 48				07 18						
Luton [10] d									00 06	06 04			06 22	06 52				07 22						
Luton Airport Parkway [7] ✈ d									00 09	06 07			06 25	06 55				07 25						
Harpenden d									00 15	06 13			06 31	07 01				07 31						
St Albans City d									00 21	06a19		05 59	06a37	07a08		05 59		07a37		06 29				
Radlett d									00 26															
Elstree & Borehamwood d								00 01	00 31															
Mill Hill Broadway d								00 05	00 35															
Hendon d								00 08	00 38															
Cricklewood d								00 12	00 42															
West Hampstead Thameslink ⊖ d								00 15	00 45						06 43				07 01				07 31	
Kentish Town ⊖ d								00 20	00 50						06 48				07 06				07 36	
St Pancras International [15] ⊖ a								00 23	00 53			07 51			06 55	06 59			07 09	07 29			07 39	
d								00 24	00 54										07 10				07 40	
Farringdon [3] ⊖ d								00 29				↪							07 15				07 45	
City Thameslink [3] d																								
London Blackfriars [3] ⊖ d							00 05	00 35	01 05								06 51		07 21		07 42		07 51	08 12
Elephant & Castle ⊖173,179 d																			07 25		07 46		07 55	08 16
Loughborough Jn 173,179 d																								
Herne Hill [4] 173,179 d																								
London Bridge [4] a							00 11	00 41																
d							00 12	00 42																
Tulse Hill [3] d		00 02																						
Streatham [4] d		00 06																						
Mitcham Eastfields 173 d																								
Mitcham Junction 173 🚋 d																								
Hackbridge 173 d																								
Carshalton 173 d																								
Tooting 173 d		00 10																						
Haydons Road 173 d		00 13																						
Wimbledon [6] ⊖173,179 🚋 d		00 17																						
Wimbledon Chase 179 d		00 20																						
South Merton 179 d		00 22																						
Morden South 179 d		00 24																						
St Helier 179 d		00 26																						
Sutton Common 179 d		00 28																						
West Sutton 179 d	00 01	00 31																						
Sutton (Surrey) [4] 179 a	00 05	00 35																						
Denmark Hill [4] 195 d																					07 52			08 22
Peckham Rye [4] 195 d																					07 55			08 25
Nunhead [4] 195 d																					07 57			08 27
Crofton Park 195 d																					08 00			08 30
Catford 195 d					00 03																08 03			08 33
Bellingham 195 d					00 05																08 05			08 35
Beckenham Hill 195 d					00 07																08 07			08 37
Ravensbourne 195 d					00 09																08 09			08 39
Shortlands 195 d					00 11																08 11			08 41
Bromley South [4] 195 d					00 14																08 14			08 44
Bickley [4] 195 d					00 17																08 17			08 47
St Mary Cray 195 d					00 21																08 21			08 51
Swanley [4] 195 d					00 26																08 26			08 56
Eynsford 195 d					00 30																08 30			09 00
Shoreham (Kent) 195 d				00 04	00 34																08 34			09 04
Otford [4] 195 d				00 07	00 37																08 37			09 07
Bat & Ball 195 d				00 10	00 40																08 40			09 10
Sevenoaks [4] 195 a				00 13	00 43																08 43			09 13
East Croydon 🚋 d							00 29	00 57	01 36								07 24		07 53				08 21	
Redhill d																								
Gatwick Airport [10] ✈ d						00 19	00 49	01 19	01 55								07 44		08 18				08 42	
Three Bridges [4] d						00 24	00 54	01a24	02a02								07 49		08 23				08 47	
Balcombe d						00 30																		
Haywards Heath [3] d						00 38	01 10										07 58		08 34				08 56	
Wivelsfield [4] d			00 03			00 43																		
Burgess Hill [4] d			00 05			00 45	01 15										08 03		08 39				09 01	
Hassocks [4] d			00 08			00 48	01 18										08 07		08 43				09 05	
Preston Park d			00 15			00 55																		
Brighton [10] a			00 19			00 59	01 29										08 17		08 53				09 15	

A From Luton

B From Bedford

C From London Blackfriars

The trains that operate to and from Sevenoaks, Orpington and Rochester (and a few other destinations at peak times) are operated jointly by First Capital Connect (north of Blackfriars) and Southeastern (south of Blackfriars)

Table 52 shows the complete service between Bedford and London, whilst services between London, Sevenoaks, Sutton and Brighton only show through Thameslink services. Other Tables should be consulted for additional journey opportunities.

Table 52

Sundays

16 February to 23 March

Bedford, Luton, St Albans and City of London - South London, Gatwick Airport and Brighton

Network Diagram - refer to first Page of Table 52

		FC	FC	FC	FC	FC	FC	FC	SE		FC	FC	FC	SE	FC	FC	EM	FC	FC	SE		FC	FC	EM	FC
					1						1		1			1	◇1		1				1	◇1	
				A		A											B							C	
		bus	bus	bus		bus	bus	bus									☕							☕	
Bedford 7	d										07 28		07 50			08 06	08 16		08 20				08 36	08 46	
Flitwick	d										07 38		08 00			08 16			08 30				08 46		
Harlington	d										07 42		08 04			08 20			08 34				08 50		
Leagrave	d										07 48		08 10			08 26			08 40				08 56		
Luton 10	d										07 52		08 14		08 18	08 30	08 34		08 44			08 48	09 00		
Luton Airport Parkway 7 ✈	d										07 55		08 17		08 21	08 33			08 47			08 51	09 03	09 06	
Harpenden	d										08 01		08 23		08 27	08 39			08 53			08 57	09 09		
St Albans City	d	06 29	06 47				06 47	07 18			08 07		08 29		08 33	08 45			08 59			09 03	09 15		
Radlett	d	06 54					07 12	07 43			08 12				08 38							09 08			
Elstree & Borehamwood	d	07 06					07 24	07 55			08 17				08 42							09 12			
Mill Hill Broadway	d	07 21					07 39	08a10			08 21				08 46							09 16			
Hendon	d	07 31					07 49				08 24				08 50							09 20			
Cricklewood	d	07 41					07 59				08 28				08 53							09 23			
West Hampstead Thameslink ⊖	d	07 51			08 01		08 09				08 31		08 45		08 57	09 01			09 15			09 27	09 31		
Kentish Town ⊖	d	08 06		←	08 06	←	08a24				08 36				09 01							09 31			
St Pancras International 15 ⊖	a	08 21	07 47	07 51	08 09	08 21					08 39		08 52		09 05	09 09	09 13		09 22			09 35	09 39	09 44	
	d				08 10						08 40		08 54		09 06	09 10			09 24			09 36	09 40		
Farringdon 3 ⊖	d	↪			08 15						08 45		08 59		09 11	09 15			09 29			09 41	09 45		
City Thameslink 3	d																								
London Blackfriars 3 ⊖	d				08 21				08 42		08 51	08 58	09 04	09 12	09 16	09 21		09 28	09 34	09 42		09 46	09 51		09 58
Elephant & Castle ⊖173,179	d				08 25				08 46		08 55	09 01	09 08	09 16	09 19	09 25		09 31	09 38	09 46		09 49	09 55		10 01
Loughborough Jn 173,179	d											09 05			09 23			09 35				09 53			10 05
Herne Hill 4 173,179	d											09 09			09 27			09 39				09 57			10 09
London Bridge 4	a																								
	d																								
Tulse Hill 3	d											09 14			09 32			09 44				10 02			10 14
Streatham 4	d											09 18			09 36			09 48				10 06			10 18
Mitcham Eastfields 173	d											09 22						09 52							10 22
Mitcham Junction 173 🚊	d											09 25						09 55							10 25
Hackbridge 173	d											09 29						09 59							10 29
Carshalton 173	d											09 31						10 01							10 31
Tooting 173	d														09 42							10 12			
Haydons Road 173	d														09 45							10 15			
Wimbledon 6 ⊖173,179 🚊	d														09 48							10 18			
Wimbledon Chase 179	d														09 51							10 21			
South Merton 179	d														09 53							10 23			
Morden South 179	d														09 55							10 25			
St Helier 179	d														09 57							10 27			
Sutton Common 179	d														09 59							10 29			
West Sutton 179	d														10 02							10 32			
Sutton (Surrey) 4 179	a											09 35			10 05			10 05				10 35			10 35
Denmark Hill 4 195	d								08 52					09 22						09 52					
Peckham Rye 4 195	d								08 55					09 25						09 55					
Nunhead 4 195	d								08 57					09 27						09 57					
Crofton Park 195	d								09 00					09 30						10 00					
Catford 195	d								09 03					09 33						10 03					
Bellingham 195	d								09 05					09 35						10 05					
Beckenham Hill 195	d								09 07					09 37						10 07					
Ravensbourne 195	d								09 09					09 39						10 09					
Shortlands 195	d								09 11					09 41						10 11					
Bromley South 4 195	d								09 14					09 44						10 14					
Bickley 4 195	d								09 17					09 47						10 17					
St Mary Cray 195	d								09 21					09 51						10 21					
Swanley 4 195	d								09 26					09 56						10 26					
Eynsford 195	d								09 30					10 00						10 30					
Shoreham (Kent) 195	d								09 34					10 04						10 34					
Otford 4 195	d								09 37					10 07						10 37					
Bat & Ball 195	d								09 40					10 10						10 40					
Sevenoaks 4 195	a								09 43					10 13						10 43					
East Croydon 🚊	d				08 56						09 26		09 39			09 56			10 09				10 26		
Redhill	d																								
Gatwick Airport 10 ✈	d				09 12						09 42		09 56			10 12			10 26				10 42		
Three Bridges 4	d				09 17						09 47		10a01			10 17			10a33				10 47		
Balcombe	d																								
Haywards Heath 3	d				09 26						09 56					10 26							10 56		
Wivelsfield 4	d																								
Burgess Hill 4	d				09 33						10 01					10 33							11 01		
Hassocks 4	d				09 37						10 05					10 37							11 05		
Preston Park	d																								
Brighton 10	a				09 47						10 15					10 47							11 15		

A From St Albans City
B From Derby
C From Nottingham

The trains that operate to and from Sevenoaks, Orpington and Rochester (and a few other destinations at peak times) are operated jointly by First Capital Connect (north of Blackfriars) and Southeastern (south of Blackfriars)

Table 52 shows the complete service between Bedford and London, whilst services between London, Sevenoaks, Sutton and Brighton only show through Thameslink services. Other Tables should be consulted for additional journey opportunities.

Table 52

Sundays

16 February to 23 March

Bedford, Luton, St Albans and City of London - South London, Gatwick Airport and Brighton

Network Diagram - refer to first Page of Table 52

		FC 1	SE	FC	FC 1	EM ◇1 A ⊡	FC		FC 1	SE	FC	FC 1	EM ◇1 B ⊡	FC	FC 1	SE	FC	FC 1		EM ◇1 C ⊡	FC	FC 1	SE	FC	FC 1
Bedford 7	d	08 50			09 06	09 16			09 20			09 36	09 46		09 50			10 06		10 16		10 20			10 36
Flitwick	d	09 00			09 16				09 30			09 46			10 00			10 16				10 30			10 46
Harlington	d	09 04			09 20				09 34			09 50			10 04			10 20				10 34			10 50
Leagrave	d	09 10			09 26				09 40			09 56			10 10			10 26				10 40			10 56
Luton 10	d	09 14		09 18	09 30	09 35			09 44		09 48	10 00			10 14		10 18	10 30		10 35		10 44		10 48	11 00
Luton Airport Parkway 7 ✈	d	09 17		09 21	09 33				09 47		09 51	10 03	10 06		10 17		10 21	10 33				10 47		10 51	11 03
Harpenden	d	09 23		09 27	09 39				09 53		09 57	10 09			10 23		10 27	10 39				10 53		10 57	11 09
St Albans City	d	09 29		09 33	09 45				09 59		10 03	10 15			10 29		10 33	10 45				10 59		11 03	11 15
Radlett	d			09 38							10 08						10 38							11 08	
Elstree & Borehamwood	d			09 42							10 12						10 42							11 12	
Mill Hill Broadway	d			09 46							10 16						10 46							11 16	
Hendon	d			09 50							10 20						10 50							11 20	
Cricklewood	d			09 53							10 23						10 53							11 23	
West Hampstead Thameslink ⊖	d	09 45		09 57	10 01				10 15		10 27	10 31			10 45		10 57	11 01				11 15		11 27	11 31
Kentish Town ⊖	d			10 01							10 31						11 01							11 31	
St Pancras International 15 ⊖	a	09 52		10 05	10 09	10 13			10 22		10 35	10 39	10 48		10 52		11 05	11 09		11 17		11 22		11 35	11 39
	d	09 54		10 06	10 10				10 24		10 36	10 40			10 54		11 06	11 10				11 24		11 36	11 40
Farringdon 3 ⊖	d	09 59		10 11	10 15				10 29		10 41	10 45			10 59		11 11	11 15				11 29		11 41	11 45
City Thameslink 3	d																								
London Blackfriars 3 ⊖	d	10 04	10 12	10 16	10 21		10 28		10 34	10 42	10 46	10 51		10 58	11 04	11 12	11 16	11 21			11 28	11 34	11 42	11 46	11 51
Elephant & Castle ⊖173,179	d	10 08	10 16	10 19	10 25		10 31		10 38	10 46	10 49	10 55		11 01	11 08	11 16	11 19	11 25			11 31	11 38	11 46	11 49	11 55
Loughborough Jn 173,179	d			10 23			10 35				10 53			11 05			11 23				11 35			11 53	
Herne Hill 4 173,179	d			10 27			10 39				10 57			11 09			11 27				11 39			11 57	
London Bridge 4	a																								
	d																								
Tulse Hill 3	d			10 32			10 44				11 02			11 14			11 32				11 44			12 02	
Streatham 4	d			10 36			10 48				11 06			11 18			11 36				11 48			12 06	
Mitcham Eastfields 173	d						10 52							11 22							11 52				
Mitcham Junction 173 🚋	d						10 55							11 25							11 55				
Hackbridge 173	d						10 59							11 29							11 59				
Carshalton 173	d						11 01							11 31							12 01				
Tooting 173	d			10 42							11 12						11 42							12 12	
Haydons Road 173	d			10 45							11 15						11 45							12 15	
Wimbledon 6 ⊖173,179 🚋	d			10 48							11 18						11 48							12 18	
Wimbledon Chase 179	d			10 51							11 21						11 51							12 21	
South Merton 179	d			10 53							11 23						11 53							12 23	
Morden South 179	d			10 55							11 25						11 55							12 25	
St Helier 179	d			10 57							11 27						11 57							12 27	
Sutton Common 179	d			10 59							11 29						11 59							12 29	
West Sutton 179	d			11 02							11 32						12 02							12 32	
Sutton (Surrey) 4 179	a			11 05			11 05				11 35			11 35			12 05				12 05			12 35	
Denmark Hill 4 195	d		10 22							10 52						11 22							11 52		
Peckham Rye 4 195	d		10 25							10 55						11 25							11 55		
Nunhead 4 195	d		10 27							10 57						11 27							11 57		
Crofton Park 195	d		10 30							11 00						11 30							12 00		
Catford 195	d		10 33							11 03						11 33							12 03		
Bellingham 195	d		10 35							11 05						11 35							12 05		
Beckenham Hill 195	d		10 37							11 07						11 37							12 07		
Ravensbourne 195	d		10 39							11 09						11 39							12 09		
Shortlands 195	d		10 41							11 11						11 41							12 11		
Bromley South 4 195	d		10 44							11 14						11 44							12 14		
Bickley 4 195	d		10 47							11 17						11 47							12 17		
St Mary Cray 195	d		10 51							11 21						11 51							12 21		
Swanley 4 195	d		10 56							11 26						11 56							12 26		
Eynsford 195	d		11 00							11 30						12 00							12 30		
Shoreham (Kent) 195	d		11 04							11 34						12 04							12 34		
Otford 4 195	d		11 07							11 37						12 07							12 37		
Bat & Ball 195	d		11 10							11 40						12 10							12 40		
Sevenoaks 4 195	a		11 13							11 43						12 13							12 43		
East Croydon 🚋	d	10 39			10 56				11 09			11 26			11 39			11 56				12 09			12 26
Redhill	d																								
Gatwick Airport 10 ✈	d	10 56			11 12				11 26			11 42			11 56			12 12				12 26			12 42
Three Bridges 4	d	11a01			11 17				11a33			11 47			12a01			12 17				12a33			12 47
Balcombe	d																								
Haywards Heath 3	d				11 26							11 56						12 26							12 56
Wivelsfield 4	d																								
Burgess Hill 4	d				11 33							12 01						12 33							13 01
Hassocks 4	d				11 37							12 05						12 37							13 05
Preston Park	d																								
Brighton 10	a				11 47							12 15						12 47							13 15

A From Derby **B** From Nottingham **C** From Sheffield

The trains that operate to and from Sevenoaks, Orpington and Rochester (and a few other destinations at peak times) are operated jointly by First Capital Connect (north of Blackfriars) and Southeastern (south of Blackfriars)

Table 52 shows the complete service between Bedford and London, whilst services between London, Sevenoaks, Sutton and Brighton only show through Thameslink services. Other Tables should be consulted for additional journey opportunities.

Table 52

Sundays

16 February to 23 March

Bedford, Luton, St Albans and City of London - South London, Gatwick Airport and Brighton

Network Diagram - refer to first Page of Table 52

Station		EM ◇1 A	FC	FC 1	SE	FC	FC 1	EM ◇1 B	FC	FC 1	SE	FC	FC 1	FC	FC 1	EM ◇1 A	SE	FC	FC 1	EM ◇1 B	FC	FC 1	SE
Bedford 7	d	10 46		10 50			11 06	11 15		11 20			11 36		11 50	11 56			12 06	12 15		12 20	
Flitwick	d			11 00			11 16			11 30			11 46		12 00				12 16			12 30	
Harlington	d			11 04			11 20			11 34			11 50		12 04				12 20			12 34	
Leagrave	d			11 10			11 26			11 40			11 56		12 10				12 26			12 40	
Luton 10	d			11 14		11 18	11 30	11 35		11 44		11 48	12 00		12 14			12 18	12 30	12 30		12 44	
Luton Airport Parkway 7 ✈	d	11 06		11 17		11 21	11 33			11 47		11 51	12 03		12 17	12 13		12 21	12 33			12 47	
Harpenden	d			11 23		11 27	11 39			11 53		11 57	12 09		12 23			12 27	12 39			12 53	
St Albans City	d			11 29		11 33	11 45			11 59		12 03	12 15		12 29			12 33	12 45			12 59	
Radlett	d					11 38						12 08						12 38					
Elstree & Borehamwood	d					11 42						12 12						12 42					
Mill Hill Broadway	d					11 46						12 16						12 46					
Hendon	d					11 50						12 20						12 50					
Cricklewood	d					11 53						12 23						12 53					
West Hampstead Thameslink ⊖	d			11 45		11 57	12 01			12 15		12 27	12 31		12 45			12 57	13 01			13 15	
Kentish Town ⊖	d					12 01						12 31						13 01					
St Pancras International 15 ⊖	a	11 48		11 52		12 05	12 09	12 13		12 22		12 35	12 39		12 52	12 39		13 05	13 09	12 54		13 22	
	d			11 54		12 06	12 10			12 24		12 36	12 40		12 54			13 06	13 10			13 24	
Farringdon 3 ⊖	d			11 59		12 11	12 15			12 29		12 41	12 45		12 59			13 11	13 15			13 29	
City Thameslink 3	d																						
London Blackfriars 3 ⊖	d		11 58	12 04	12 12	12 16	12 21		12 28	12 34	12 42	12 46	12 51	12 58	13 04		13 12	13 16	13 21		13 28	13 34	13 42
Elephant & Castle ⊖173,179	d		12 01	12 08	12 16	12 19	12 25		12 31	12 38	12 46	12 49	12 55	13 01	13 08		13 16	13 19	13 25		13 31	13 38	13 46
Loughborough Jn 173,179	d		12 05			12 23			12 35			12 53		13 05				13 23			13 35		
Herne Hill 4 173,179	d		12 09			12 27			12 39			12 57		13 09				13 27			13 39		
London Bridge 4	a																						
	d																						
Tulse Hill 3	d		12 14			12 32			12 44			13 02		13 14				13 32			13 44		
Streatham 4	d		12 18			12 36			12 48			13 06		13 18				13 36			13 48		
Mitcham Eastfields 173	d		12 22						12 52					13 22							13 52		
Mitcham Junction 173 🚋	d		12 25						12 55					13 25							13 55		
Hackbridge 173	d		12 29						12 59					13 29							13 59		
Carshalton 173	d		12 31						13 01					13 31							14 01		
Tooting 173	d					12 42						13 12						13 42					
Haydons Road 173	d					12 45						13 15						13 45					
Wimbledon 6 ⊖173,179 🚋	d					12 48						13 18						13 48					
Wimbledon Chase 179	d					12 51						13 21						13 51					
South Merton 179	d					12 53						13 23						13 53					
Morden South 179	d					12 55						13 25						13 55					
St Helier 179	d					12 57						13 27						13 57					
Sutton Common 179	d					12 59						13 29						13 59					
West Sutton 179	d					13 02						13 32						14 02					
Sutton (Surrey) 4 179	a		12 35			13 05			13 05			13 35		13 35				14 05			14 05		
Denmark Hill 4 195	d				12 22						12 52						13 22						13 52
Peckham Rye 4 195	d				12 25						12 55						13 25						13 55
Nunhead 4 195	d				12 27						12 57						13 27						13 57
Crofton Park 195	d				12 30						13 00						13 30						14 00
Catford 195	d				12 33						13 03						13 33						14 03
Bellingham 195	d				12 35						13 05						13 35						14 05
Beckenham Hill 195	d				12 37						13 07						13 37						14 07
Ravensbourne 195	d				12 39						13 09						13 39						14 09
Shortlands 195	d				12 41						13 11						13 41						14 11
Bromley South 4 195	d				12 44						13 14						13 44						14 14
Bickley 4 195	d				12 47						13 17						13 47						14 17
St Mary Cray 195	d				12 51						13 21						13 51						14 21
Swanley 4 195	d				12 56						13 26						13 56						14 26
Eynsford 195	d				13 00						13 30						14 00						14 30
Shoreham (Kent) 195	d				13 04						13 34						14 04						14 34
Otford 4 195	d				13 07						13 37						14 07						14 37
Bat & Ball 195	d				13 10						13 40						14 10						14 40
Sevenoaks 4 195	a				13 13						13 43						14 13						14 43
East Croydon 🚋	d			12 39			12 56			13 09			13 26		13 39				13 56			14 09	
Redhill	d																						
Gatwick Airport 10 ✈	d			12 56			13 12			13 26			13 42		13 56				14 12			14 26	
Three Bridges 4	d			13a01			13 17			13a33			13 47		14a01				14 17			14a33	
Balcombe	d																						
Haywards Heath 3	d						13 26						13 56						14 26				
Wivelsfield 4	d																						
Burgess Hill 4	d						13 33						14 01						14 33				
Hassocks 4	d						13 37						14 05						14 37				
Preston Park	d																						
Brighton 10	a						13 47						14 15						14 47				

A From Nottingham   **B** From Sheffield

The trains that operate to and from Sevenoaks, Orpington and Rochester (and a few other destinations at peak times) are operated jointly by First Capital Connect (north of Blackfriars) and Southeastern (south of Blackfriars)

Table 52 shows the complete service between Bedford and London, whilst services between London, Sevenoaks, Sutton and Brighton only show through Thameslink services. Other Tables should be consulted for additional journey opportunities.

Table 52

Sundays

16 February to 23 March

Bedford, Luton, St Albans and City of London - South London, Gatwick Airport and Brighton

Network Diagram - refer to first Page of Table 52

		FC	FC 1	FC	FC 1	EM ◇1 A	SE	FC	FC 1	FC	FC 1	SE	FC	FC 1	EM ◇1 A	FC	FC 1	SE	FC	FC 1	EM ◇1 B	FC	FC 1
Bedford 7	d		12 36		12 50	13 01			13 06		13 20			13 36	13 44		13 50			14 06	14 15		14 20
Flitwick	d		12 46		13 00				13 16		13 30			13 46			14 00			14 16			14 30
Harlington	d		12 50		13 04				13 20		13 34			13 50			14 04			14 20			14 34
Leagrave	d		12 56		13 10				13 26		13 40			13 56			14 10			14 26			14 40
Luton 10	d	12 48	13 00		13 14			13 18	13 30		13 44		13 48	14 00	14 01		14 14		14 18	14 30			14 44
Luton Airport Parkway 7 ✈	d	12 51	13 03		13 17	13 17		13 21	13 33		13 47		13 51	14 03			14 17		14 21	14 33	14 31		14 47
Harpenden	d	12 57	13 09		13 23			13 27	13 39		13 53		13 57	14 09			14 23		14 27	14 39			14 53
St Albans City	d	13 03	13 15		13 29			13 33	13 45		13 59		14 03	14 15			14 29		14 33	14 45			14 59
Radlett	d	13 08						13 38					14 08						14 38				
Elstree & Borehamwood	d	13 12						13 42					14 12						14 42				
Mill Hill Broadway	d	13 16						13 46					14 16						14 46				
Hendon	d	13 20						13 50					14 20						14 50				
Cricklewood	d	13 23						13 53					14 23						14 53				
West Hampstead Thameslink ⊖	d	13 27	13 31		13 45			13 57	14 01		14 15		14 27	14 31			14 45		14 57	15 01			15 15
Kentish Town ⊖	d	13 31						14 01					14 31						15 01				
St Pancras International 15 ⊖	a	13 35	13 39		13 52	13 44		14 05	14 09		14 22		14 35	14 39	14 27		14 52		15 05	15 09	14 57		15 22
	d	13 36	13 40		13 54			14 06	14 10		14 24		14 36	14 40			14 54		15 06	15 10			15 24
Farringdon 3 ⊖	d	13 41	13 45		13 59			14 11	14 15		14 29		14 41	14 45			14 59		15 11	15 15			15 29
City Thameslink 3	d																						
London Blackfriars 3 ⊖	d	13 46	13 51	13 58	14 04		14 12	14 16	14 21	14 28	14 34	14 42	14 46	14 51		14 58	15 04	15 12	15 16	15 21		15 28	15 34
Elephant & Castle ⊖173,179	d	13 49	13 55	14 01	14 08		14 16	14 19	14 25	14 31	14 38	14 46	14 49	14 55		15 01	15 08	15 16	15 19	15 25		15 31	15 38
Loughborough Jn 173,179	d	13 53		14 05				14 23		14 35			14 53			15 05			15 23			15 35	
Herne Hill 4 173,179	d	13 57		14 09				14 27		14 39			14 57			15 09			15 27			15 39	
London Bridge 4	a																						
	d																						
Tulse Hill 3	d	14 02		14 14				14 32		14 44			15 02			15 14			15 32			15 44	
Streatham 4	d	14 06		14 18				14 36		14 48			15 06			15 18			15 36			15 48	
Mitcham Eastfields 173	d			14 22						14 52						15 22						15 52	
Mitcham Junction 173 🚋	d			14 25						14 55						15 25						15 55	
Hackbridge 173	d			14 29						14 59						15 29						15 59	
Carshalton 173	d			14 31						15 01						15 31						16 01	
Tooting 173	d	14 12						14 42					15 12						15 42				
Haydons Road 173	d	14 15						14 45					15 15						15 45				
Wimbledon 6 ⊖173,179 🚋	d	14 18						14 48					15 18						15 48				
Wimbledon Chase 179	d	14 21						14 51					15 21						15 51				
South Merton 179	d	14 23						14 53					15 23						15 53				
Morden South 179	d	14 25						14 55					15 25						15 55				
St Helier 179	d	14 27						14 57					15 27						15 57				
Sutton Common 179	d	14 29						14 59					15 29						15 59				
West Sutton 179	d	14 32						15 02					15 32						16 02				
Sutton (Surrey) 4 179	a	14 35		14 35				15 05		15 05			15 35			15 35			16 05			16 05	
Denmark Hill 4 195	d						14 22					14 52						15 22					
Peckham Rye 4 195	d						14 25					14 55						15 25					
Nunhead 4 195	d						14 27					14 57						15 27					
Crofton Park 195	d						14 30					15 00						15 30					
Catford 195	d						14 33					15 03						15 33					
Bellingham 195	d						14 35					15 05						15 35					
Beckenham Hill 195	d						14 37					15 07						15 37					
Ravensbourne 195	d						14 39					15 09						15 39					
Shortlands 195	d						14 41					15 11						15 41					
Bromley South 4 195	d						14 44					15 14						15 44					
Bickley 4 195	d						14 47					15 17						15 47					
St Mary Cray 195	d						14 51					15 21						15 51					
Swanley 4 195	d						14 56					15 26						15 56					
Eynsford 195	d						15 00					15 30						16 00					
Shoreham (Kent) 195	d						15 04					15 34						16 04					
Otford 4 195	d						15 07					15 37						16 07					
Bat & Ball 195	d						15 10					15 40						16 10					
Sevenoaks 4 195	a						15 13					15 43						16 13					
East Croydon 🚋	d		14 26		14 39				14 56		15 09			15 26			15 39			15 56			16 09
Redhill	d																						
Gatwick Airport 10 ✈	d		14 42		14 56				15 12		15 26			15 42			15 56			16 12			16 26
Three Bridges 4	d		14 47		15a01				15 17		15a33			15 47			16a01			16 17			16a33
Balcombe	d																						
Haywards Heath 3	d		14 56						15 26					15 56						16 26			
Wivelsfield 4	d																						
Burgess Hill 4	d		15 01						15 33					16 01						16 33			
Hassocks 4	d		15 05						15 37					16 05						16 37			
Preston Park	d																						
Brighton 10	a		15 15						15 47					16 15						16 47			

A From Leeds

B From Nottingham

The trains that operate to and from Sevenoaks, Orpington and Rochester (and a few other destinations at peak times) are operated jointly by First Capital Connect (north of Blackfriars) and Southeastern (south of Blackfriars)

Table 52 shows the complete service between Bedford and London, whilst services between London, Sevenoaks, Sutton and Brighton only show through Thameslink services. Other Tables should be consulted for additional journey opportunities.

Table 52

Sundays

16 February to 23 March

Bedford, Luton, St Albans and City of London - South London, Gatwick Airport and Brighton

Network Diagram - refer to first Page of Table 52

	SE	FC	FC 1	EM ◇1 A ☕	FC	FC 1	SE	FC	FC 1	EM ◇1 B ☕	FC	FC 1	SE	FC	FC 1	EM ◇1 A ☕	FC	FC 1	SE	FC	FC 1
Bedford 7 d			14 36	14 39		14 50			15 06	15 15		15 20			15 36	15 40		15 50			16 06
Flitwick d			14 46			15 00			15 16			15 30			15 46			16 00			16 16
Harlington d			14 50			15 04			15 20			15 34			15 50			16 04			16 20
Leagrave d			14 56			15 10			15 26			15 40			15 56			16 10			16 26
Luton 10 d		14 48	15 00	14 54		15 14		15 18	15 30			15 44		15 48	16 00	15 55		16 14		16 18	16 30
Luton Airport Parkway 7 ✈ d		14 51	15 03			15 17		15 21	15 33	15 31		15 47		15 51	16 03			16 17		16 21	16 33
Harpenden d		14 57	15 09			15 23		15 27	15 39			15 53		15 57	16 09			16 23		16 27	16 39
St Albans City d		15 03	15 15			15 29		15 33	15 45			15 59		16 03	16 15			16 29		16 33	16 45
Radlett d		15 08						15 38						16 08						16 38	
Elstree & Borehamwood d		15 12						15 42						16 12						16 42	
Mill Hill Broadway d		15 16						15 46						16 16						16 46	
Hendon d		15 20						15 50						16 20						16 50	
Cricklewood d		15 23						15 53						16 23						16 53	
West Hampstead Thameslink ⊖ d		15 27	15 31			15 45		15 57	16 01			16 15		16 27	16 31			16 45		16 57	17 01
Kentish Town ⊖ d		15 31						16 01						16 31						17 01	
St Pancras International 15 ⊖ a		15 35	15 39	15 18		15 52		16 05	16 09	15 57		16 22		16 35	16 39	16 19		16 52		17 05	17 09
d		15 36	15 40			15 54		16 06	16 10			16 24		16 36	16 40			16 54		17 06	17 10
Farringdon 3 ⊖ d		15 41	15 45			15 59		16 11	16 15			16 29		16 41	16 45			16 59		17 11	17 15
City Thameslink 3 d																					
London Blackfriars 3 ⊖ d	15 42	15 46	15 51		15 58	16 04	16 12	16 16	16 21		16 28	16 34	16 42	16 46	16 51		16 58	17 04	17 12	17 16	17 21
Elephant & Castle ⊖173,179 d	15 46	15 49	15 55		16 01	16 08	16 16	16 19	16 25		16 31	16 38	16 46	16 49	16 55		17 01	17 08	17 16	17 19	17 25
Loughborough Jn 173,179 d		15 53			16 05			16 23			16 35			16 53			17 05			17 23	
Herne Hill 4 173,179 d		15 57			16 09			16 27			16 39			16 57			17 09			17 27	
London Bridge 4 a																					
d																					
Tulse Hill 3 d		16 02			16 14			16 32			16 44			17 02			17 14			17 32	
Streatham 4 d		16 06			16 18			16 36			16 48			17 06			17 18			17 36	
Mitcham Eastfields 173 d					16 22						16 52						17 22				
Mitcham Junction 173 ⛴ d					16 25						16 55						17 25				
Hackbridge 173 d					16 29						16 59						17 29				
Carshalton 173 d					16 31						17 01						17 31				
Tooting 173 d		16 12						16 42						17 12						17 42	
Haydons Road 173 d		16 15						16 45						17 15						17 45	
Wimbledon 6 ⊖173,179 ⛴ d		16 18						16 48						17 18						17 48	
Wimbledon Chase 179 d		16 21						16 51						17 21						17 51	
South Merton 179 d		16 23						16 53						17 23						17 53	
Morden South 179 d		16 25						16 55						17 25						17 55	
St Helier 179 d		16 27						16 57						17 27						17 57	
Sutton Common 179 d		16 29						16 59						17 29						17 59	
West Sutton 179 d		16 32						17 02						17 32						18 02	
Sutton (Surrey) 4 179 a		16 35			16 35			17 05			17 05			17 35			17 35			18 05	
Denmark Hill 4 195 d	15 52						16 22						16 52						17 22		
Peckham Rye 4 195 d	15 55						16 25						16 55						17 25		
Nunhead 4 195 d	15 57						16 27						16 57						17 27		
Crofton Park 195 d	16 00						16 30						17 00						17 30		
Catford 195 d	16 03						16 33						17 03						17 33		
Bellingham 195 d	16 05						16 35						17 05						17 35		
Beckenham Hill 195 d	16 07						16 37						17 07						17 37		
Ravensbourne 195 d	16 09						16 39						17 09						17 39		
Shortlands 195 d	16 11						16 41						17 11						17 41		
Bromley South 4 195 d	16 14						16 44						17 14						17 44		
Bickley 4 195 d	16 17						16 47						17 17						17 47		
St Mary Cray 195 d	16 21						16 51						17 21						17 51		
Swanley 4 195 d	16 26						16 56						17 26						17 56		
Eynsford 195 d	16 30						17 00						17 30						18 00		
Shoreham (Kent) 195 d	16 34						17 04						17 34						18 04		
Otford 4 195 d	16 37						17 07						17 37						18 07		
Bat & Ball 195 d	16 40						17 10						17 40						18 10		
Sevenoaks 4 195 a	16 43						17 13						17 43						18 13		
East Croydon ⛴ d			16 26			16 39			16 56			17 09			17 26			17 39			17 56
Redhill d																					
Gatwick Airport 10 ✈ d			16 42			16 56			17 12			17 26			17 42			17 56			18 12
Three Bridges 4 d			16 47			17a01			17 17			17a33			17 47			18a01			18 17
Balcombe d																					
Haywards Heath 3 d			16 56						17 26						17 56						18 26
Wivelsfield 4 d																					
Burgess Hill 4 d			17 01						17 33						18 01						18 33
Hassocks 4 d			17 05						17 37						18 05						18 37
Preston Park d																					
Brighton 10 a			17 15						17 47						18 15						18 47

A From Sheffield

B From Nottingham

The trains that operate to and from Sevenoaks, Orpington and Rochester (and a few other destinations at peak times) are operated jointly by First Capital Connect (north of Blackfriars) and Southeastern (south of Blackfriars)

Table 52 shows the complete service between Bedford and London, whilst services between London, Sevenoaks, Sutton and Brighton only show through Thameslink services. Other Tables should be consulted for additional journey opportunities.

Table 52

Sundays

16 February to 23 March

Bedford, Luton, St Albans and City of London - South London, Gatwick Airport and Brighton

Network Diagram - refer to first Page of Table 52

		EM ◇1 A 🍴	EM ◇1 B 🍴	FC	FC 1	SE	FC	FC 1	FC	FC 1		SE	FC	FC 1	EM ◇1 A 🍴	FC	FC 1	EM ◇1 C 🍴	SE	FC	FC 1		FC	SE	FC
Bedford 7	d	16 08			16 20			16 36		16 50				17 06	17 08		17 20	17 29			17 36				
Flitwick	d				16 30			16 46		17 00				17 16			17 30				17 46				
Harlington	d				16 34			16 50		17 04				17 20			17 34				17 50				
Leagrave	d				16 40			16 56		17 10				17 26			17 40				17 56				
Luton 10	d		16 40		16 44		16 48	17 00		17 14			17 18	17 30			17 44	17 45		17 48	18 00				18 18
Luton Airport Parkway 7 ✈	d	16 23			16 47		16 51	17 03		17 17			17 21	17 33	17 24		17 47			17 51	18 03				18 21
Harpenden	d				16 53		16 57	17 09		17 23			17 27	17 39			17 53			17 57	18 09				18 27
St Albans City	d				16 59		17 03	17 15		17 29			17 33	17 45			17 59			18 03	18 15				18 33
Radlett	d						17 08						17 38							18 08					18 38
Elstree & Borehamwood	d						17 12						17 42							18 12					18 42
Mill Hill Broadway	d						17 16						17 46							18 16					18 46
Hendon	d						17 20						17 50							18 20					18 50
Cricklewood	d						17 23						17 53							18 23					18 53
West Hampstead Thameslink ⊖	d				17 15		17 27	17 31		17 45			17 57	18 01			18 15			18 27	18 31				18 57
Kentish Town ⊖	d						17 31						18 01							18 31					19 01
St Pancras International 15 ⊖	a	16 47	17 03		17 22		17 35	17 39		17 52			18 05	18 09	17 47		18 22	18 11		18 35	18 39				19 05
	d				17 24		17 36	17 40		17 54			18 06	18 10			18 24			18 36	18 40				19 06
Farringdon 3 ⊖	d				17 29		17 41	17 45		17 59			18 11	18 15			18 29			18 41	18 45				19 11
City Thameslink 3	d																								
London Blackfriars 3 ⊖	d			17 28	17 34	17 42	17 46	17 51	17 58	18 04		18 12	18 16	18 21		18 28	18 34		18 42	18 46	18 51		18 58	19 12	19 16
Elephant & Castle ⊖173,179	d			17 31	17 38	17 46	17 49	17 55	18 01	18 08		18 16	18 19	18 25		18 31	18 38		18 46	18 49	18 55		19 01	19 16	19 19
Loughborough Jn 173,179	d			17 35			17 53		18 05				18 23			18 35				18 53			19 05		19 23
Herne Hill 4 173,179	d			17 39			17 57		18 09				18 27			18 39				18 57			19 09		19 27
London Bridge 4	a																								
	d																								
Tulse Hill 3	d			17 44			18 02		18 14				18 32			18 44				19 02			19 14		19 32
Streatham 4	d			17 48			18 06		18 18				18 36			18 48				19 06			19 18		19 36
Mitcham Eastfields 173	d			17 52					18 22							18 52							19 22		
Mitcham Junction 173 🚌	d			17 55					18 25							18 55							19 25		
Hackbridge 173	d			17 59					18 29							18 59							19 29		
Carshalton 173	d			18 01					18 31							19 01							19 31		
Tooting 173	d						18 12						18 42							19 12					19 42
Haydons Road 173	d						18 15						18 45							19 15					19 45
Wimbledon 6 ⊖173,179 🚌	d						18 18						18 48							19 18					19 48
Wimbledon Chase 179	d						18 21						18 51							19 21					19 51
South Merton 179	d						18 23						18 53							19 23					19 53
Morden South 179	d						18 25						18 55							19 25					19 55
St Helier 179	d						18 27						18 57							19 27					19 57
Sutton Common 179	d						18 29						18 59							19 29					19 59
West Sutton 179	d						18 32						19 02							19 32					20 02
Sutton (Surrey) 4 179	a			18 05			18 35		18 35				19 05			19 05				19 35			19 35		20 05
Denmark Hill 4 195	d					17 52						18 22							18 52					19 22	
Peckham Rye 4 195	d					17 55						18 25							18 55					19 25	
Nunhead 4 195	d					17 57						18 27							18 57					19 27	
Crofton Park 195	d					18 00						18 30							19 00					19 30	
Catford 195	d					18 03						18 33							19 03					19 33	
Bellingham 195	d					18 05						18 35							19 05					19 35	
Beckenham Hill 195	d					18 07						18 37							19 07					19 37	
Ravensbourne 195	d					18 09						18 39							19 09					19 39	
Shortlands 195	d					18 11						18 41							19 11					19 41	
Bromley South 4 195	d					18 14						18 44							19 14					19 44	
Bickley 4 195	d					18 17						18 47							19 17					19 47	
St Mary Cray 195	d					18 21						18 51							19 21					19 51	
Swanley 4 195	d					18 26						18 56							19 26					19 56	
Eynsford 195	d					18 30						19 00							19 30					20 00	
Shoreham (Kent) 195	d					18 34						19 04							19 34					20 04	
Otford 4 195	d					18 37						19 07							19 37					20 07	
Bat & Ball 195	d					18 40						19 10							19 40					20 10	
Sevenoaks 4 195	a					18 43						19 13							19 43					20 13	
East Croydon 🚌	d				18 09			18 26		18 39				18 56			19 09				19 26				
Redhill	d																								
Gatwick Airport 10 ✈	d				18 26			18 42		18 56				19 12			19 26				19 42				
Three Bridges 4	d				18a33			18 47		19a01				19 17			19a33				19 47				
Balcombe	d																								
Haywards Heath 3	d							18 56						19 26							19 56				
Wivelsfield 4	d																								
Burgess Hill 4	d							19 01						19 33							20 01				
Hassocks 4	d							19 05						19 37							20 05				
Preston Park	d																								
Brighton 10	a							19 15						19 47							20 15				

A From Nottingham **B** From Sheffield **C** From Leeds

The trains that operate to and from Sevenoaks, Orpington and Rochester (and a few other destinations at peak times) are operated jointly by First Capital Connect (north of Blackfriars) and Southeastern (south of Blackfriars)

Table 52 shows the complete service between Bedford and London, whilst services between London, Sevenoaks, Sutton and Brighton only show through Thameslink services. Other Tables should be consulted for additional journey opportunities.

Table 52

Sundays

16 February to 23 March

Bedford, Luton, St Albans and City of London - South London, Gatwick Airport and Brighton

Network Diagram - refer to first Page of Table 52

		FC 1	EM ◇1 A	EM ◇1 B	FC	SE	FC	FC 1	FC	SE	FC	FC 1	EM ◇1 A	EM ◇1 B	FC	SE	FC	FC 1	EM ◇1 A	SE	FC	FC 1	EM ◇1 A
Bedford 7	d	18 06	18 08	18 17				18 36				19 06	19 08	19 30				19 36	19 59			20 06	20 08
Flitwick	d	18 16						18 46				19 16						19 46				20 16	
Harlington	d	18 20						18 50				19 20						19 50				20 20	
Leagrave	d	18 26						18 56				19 26						19 56				20 26	
Luton 10	d	18 30		18 31			18 48	19 00			19 18	19 30		19 45			19 48	20 00	20 13		20 18	20 30	
Luton Airport Parkway 7 ✈	d	18 33	18 25				18 51	19 03			19 21	19 33	19 24				19 51	20 03			20 21	20 33	20 23
Harpenden	d	18 39					18 57	19 09			19 27	19 39					19 57	20 09			20 27	20 39	
St Albans City	d	18 45					19 03	19 15			19 33	19 45					20 03	20 15			20 33	20 45	
Radlett	d						19 08				19 38						20 08				20 38		
Elstree & Borehamwood	d						19 12				19 42						20 12				20 42		
Mill Hill Broadway	d						19 16				19 46						20 16				20 46		
Hendon	d						19 20				19 50						20 20				20 50		
Cricklewood	d						19 23				19 53						20 23				20 53		
West Hampstead Thameslink ⊖	d	19 01					19 27	19 31			19 57	20 01					20 27	20 31			20 57	21 01	
Kentish Town ⊖	d						19 31				20 01						20 31				21 01		
St Pancras International 15 ⊖	a	19 09	18 47	18 55			19 35	19 39			20 05	20 09	19 47	20 09			20 35	20 39	20 37		21 05	21 09	20 47
	d	19 10					19 36	19 40			20 06	20 10					20 36	20 40			21 06	21 10	
Farringdon 3 ⊖	d	19 15					19 41	19 45			20 11	20 15					20 41	20 45			21 11	21 15	
City Thameslink 3	d																						
London Blackfriars 3 ⊖	d	19 21			19 28	19 42	19 46	19 51	19 58	20 12	20 16	20 21			20 28	20 42	20 46	20 51		21 12	21 16	21 21	
Elephant & Castle ⊖173,179	d	19 25			19 31	19 46	19 49	19 55	20 01	20 16	20 19	20 25			20 31	20 46	20 49	20 55		21 16	21 19	21 25	
Loughborough Jn 173,179	d				19 35		19 53		20 05		20 23				20 35		20 53				21 23		
Herne Hill 4 173,179	d				19 39		19 57		20 09		20 27				20 39		20 57				21 27		
London Bridge 4	a																						
	d																						
Tulse Hill 3	d				19 44		20 02		20 14		20 32				20 44		21 02				21 32		
Streatham 4	d				19 48		20 06		20 18		20 36				20 48		21 06				21 36		
Mitcham Eastfields 173	d				19 52				20 22						20 52								
Mitcham Junction 173 🚋	d				19 55				20 25						20 55								
Hackbridge 173	d				19 59				20 29						20 59								
Carshalton 173	d				20 01				20 31						21 01								
Tooting 173	d						20 12				20 42						21 12				21 42		
Haydons Road 173	d						20 15				20 45						21 15				21 45		
Wimbledon 6 ⊖173,179 🚋	d						20 18				20 48						21 18				21 48		
Wimbledon Chase 179	d						20 21				20 51						21 21				21 51		
South Merton 179	d						20 23				20 53						21 23				21 53		
Morden South 179	d						20 25				20 55						21 25				21 55		
St Helier 179	d						20 27				20 57						21 27				21 57		
Sutton Common 179	d						20 29				20 59						21 29				21 59		
West Sutton 179	d						20 32				21 02						21 32				22 02		
Sutton (Surrey) 4 179	a				20 05		20 35		20 35		21 05				21 05		21 35				22 05		
Denmark Hill 4 195	d					19 52				20 22						20 52				21 22			
Peckham Rye 4 195	d					19 55				20 25						20 55				21 25			
Nunhead 4 195	d					19 57				20 27						20 57				21 27			
Crofton Park 195	d					20 00				20 30						21 00				21 30			
Catford 195	d					20 03				20 33						21 03				21 33			
Bellingham 195	d					20 05				20 35						21 05				21 35			
Beckenham Hill 195	d					20 07				20 37						21 07				21 37			
Ravensbourne 195	d					20 09				20 39						21 09				21 39			
Shortlands 195	d					20 11				20 41						21 11				21 41			
Bromley South 4 195	d					20 14				20 44						21 14				21 44			
Bickley 4 195	d					20 17				20 47						21 17				21 47			
St Mary Cray 195	d					20 21				20 51						21 21				21 51			
Swanley 4 195	d					20 26				20 56						21 26				21 56			
Eynsford 195	d					20 30				21 00						21 30				22 00			
Shoreham (Kent) 195	d					20 34				21 04						21 34				22 04			
Otford 4 195	d					20 37				21 07						21 37				22 07			
Bat & Ball 195	d					20 40				21 10						21 40				22 10			
Sevenoaks 4 195	a					20 43				21 13						21 43				22 13			
East Croydon 🚋	d	19 56						20 26				20 56						21 26				21 56	
Redhill	d																						
Gatwick Airport 10 ✈	d	20 12						20 42				21 12						21 42				22 12	
Three Bridges 4	d	20 17						20 47				21 17						21 47				22 17	
Balcombe	d																						
Haywards Heath 3	d	20 26						20 56				21 26						21 56				22 26	
Wivelsfield 4	d																						
Burgess Hill 4	d	20 33						21 01				21 33						22 01				22 33	
Hassocks 4	d	20 37						21 05				21 37						22 05				22 37	
Preston Park	d																						
Brighton 10	a	20 47						21 15				21 47						22 15				22 47	

A From Nottingham

B From Derby

The trains that operate to and from Sevenoaks, Orpington and Rochester (and a few other destinations at peak times) are operated jointly by First Capital Connect (north of Blackfriars) and Southeastern (south of Blackfriars)

Table 52 shows the complete service between Bedford and London, whilst services between London, Sevenoaks, Sutton and Brighton only show through Thameslink services. Other Tables should be consulted for additional journey opportunities.

Table 52

Sundays

16 February to 23 March

Bedford, Luton, St Albans and City of London - South London, Gatwick Airport and Brighton

Network Diagram - refer to first Page of Table 52

	SE	FC	EM	SE	FC		EM	EM	SE	FC	SE	FC	EM	SE	FC	EM		FC	FC
		1	◇1 A		1		◇1 B	◇1 C		1		1	◇1 C		1	◇1 B		1	1
Bedford 7 d		20 28	20 40		20 58		21 09	21 28		21 28		21 58	22 24		22 28	22 38		23 02	23 42
Flitwick d		20 38			21 08					21 38		22 08			22 38			23 12	23 52
Harlington d		20 42			21 12					21 42		22 12			22 42			23 16	23 56
Leagrave d		20 48			21 18					21 48		22 18			22 48			23 22	00 02
Luton 10 d		20 52			21 22		21 23	21 43		21 52		22 22	22 40		22 52	22 53		23 26	00 06
Luton Airport Parkway 7 ✈ d		20 55	20 55		21 25					21 55		22 25			22 55			23 29	00 09
Harpenden d		21 01			21 31					22 01		22 31			23 01			23 35	00 15
St Albans City d		21 07			21 37					22 07		22 37			23 07			23 41	00 21
Radlett d		21 12			21 42					22 12		22 42			23 12			23 46	00 26
Elstree & Borehamwood d		21 17			21 47					22 17		22 47			23 17			23 51	00 31
Mill Hill Broadway d		21 21			21 51					22 21		22 51			23 21			23 55	00 35
Hendon d		21 24			21 54					22 24		22 54			23 24			23 58	00 38
Cricklewood d		21 28			21 58					22 28		22 58			23 28			00 02	00 42
West Hampstead Thameslink ⊖ d		21 31			22 01					22 31		23 01			23 31			00 05	00 45
Kentish Town ⊖ d		21 36			22 06					22 36		23 06			23 36			00 10	00 50
St Pancras International 15 ⊖ a		21 39	21 19		22 09		21 47	22 10		22 39		23 09	23 06		23 39	23 25		00 13	00 53
d		21 40			22 10					22 40		23 10			23 40			00 14	00 54
Farringdon 3 ⊖ d		21 45			22 15					22 45		23 15			23 45			00 19	
City Thameslink 3 d																			
London Blackfriars 3 ⊖ d	21 42	21 51		22 12	22 21				22 42	22 51	23 12	23 21		23 42	23 51			00 25	01 05
Elephant & Castle ⊖173,179 d	21 46	21 55		22 16	22 25				22 46	22 55	23 16	23 25		23 46					
Loughborough Jn 173,179 d																			
Herne Hill 4 173,179 d																			
London Bridge 4 a																			
d																			
Tulse Hill 3 d																			
Streatham 4 d																			
Mitcham Eastfields 173 d																			
Mitcham Junction 173 🚊 d																			
Hackbridge 173 d																			
Carshalton 173 d																			
Tooting 173 d																			
Haydons Road 173 d																			
Wimbledon 6 ⊖173,179 🚊 d																			
Wimbledon Chase 179 d																			
South Merton 179 d																			
Morden South 179 d																			
St Helier 179 d																			
Sutton Common 179 d																			
West Sutton 179 d																			
Sutton (Surrey) 4 179 a																			
Denmark Hill 4 195 d	21 52			22 22					22 52		23 22			23 52					
Peckham Rye 4 195 d	21 55			22 25					22 55		23 25			23 55					
Nunhead 4 195 d	21 57			22 27					22 57		23 27			23 57					
Crofton Park 195 d	22 00			22 30					23 00		23 30			23 59					
Catford 195 d	22 03			22 33					23 03		23 33			00 03					
Bellingham 195 d	22 05			22 35					23 05		23 35			00 05					
Beckenham Hill 195 d	22 07			22 37					23 07		23 37			00 07					
Ravensbourne 195 d	22 09			22 39					23 09		23 39			00 09					
Shortlands 195 d	22 11			22 41					23 11		23 41			00 11					
Bromley South 4 195 d	22 14			22 44					23 14		23 44			00 14					
Bickley 4 195 d	22 17			22 47					23 17		23 47			00 17					
St Mary Cray 195 d	22 21			22 51					23 21		23 51			00 21					
Swanley 4 195 d	22 26			22 56					23 26		23 56			00 26					
Eynsford 195 d	22 30			23 00					23 30		00 01			00 30					
Shoreham (Kent) 195 d	22 34			23 04					23 34		00 04			00 34					
Otford 4 195 d	22 37			23 07					23 37		00 07			00 37					
Bat & Ball 195 d	22 40			23 10					23 40		00 10			00 40					
Sevenoaks 4 195 a	22 43			23 13					23 43		00 13			00 43					
East Croydon 🚊 d		22 26			22 56					23 26		23 57			00 29			00 57	01 36
Redhill d																			
Gatwick Airport 10 ✈ d		22 42			23 12					23 42		00 20			00 49			01 19	01 55
Three Bridges 4 d		22 47			23 17					23 47		00 25			00a54			01a24	02a02
Balcombe d																			
Haywards Heath 3 d		22 56			23 26					23 56		00 36							
Wivelsfield 4 d																			
Burgess Hill 4 d		23 01			23 33					00 02		00 42							
Hassocks 4 d		23 05			23 37					00 06		00 45							
Preston Park d																			
Brighton 10 a		23 15			23 47					00 15		00 55							

A From York B From Nottingham C From Sheffield

The trains that operate to and from Sevenoaks, Orpington and Rochester (and a few other destinations at peak times) are operated jointly by First Capital Connect (north of Blackfriars) and Southeastern (south of Blackfriars)

Table 52 shows the complete service between Bedford and London, whilst services between London, Sevenoaks, Sutton and Brighton only show through Thameslink services. Other Tables should be consulted for additional journey opportunities.

Table 52

Sundays

30 March to 11 May

Bedford, Luton, St Albans and City of London - South London, Gatwick Airport and Brighton

Network Diagram - refer to first Page of Table 52

	FC	FC	FC	SE	SE	FC	FC	FC	FC	FC	FC	FC	SE	FC	SE	FC	SE	FC	FC	FC	SE	FC
			1			1	1	1	1	1	1	1		1		1		1		1		
	A	A	B	C	C	B	B	B	B													
Bedford 7 d										05 40		05 58		06 28		06 58		07 28		07 50		
Flitwick d										05 50		06 08		06 38		07 08		07 38		08 00		
Harlington d										05 54		06 12		06 42		07 12		07 42		08 04		
Leagrave d									00 02	06 00		06 18		06 48		07 18		07 48		08 10		
Luton 10 d									00 06	06 04		06 22		06 52		07 22		07 52		08 14		08 18
Luton Airport Parkway 7 ✈ d									00 09	06 07		06 25		06 55		07 25		07 55		08 17		08 21
Harpenden d									00 15	06 13		06 31		07 01		07 31		08 01		08 23		08 27
St Albans City d									00 21	06 19		06 37		07 07		07 37		08 07		08 29		08 33
Radlett d									00 26	06 24		06 42		07 12		07 42		08 12				08 38
Elstree & Borehamwood d								00 01	00 31	06 29		06 47		07 17		07 47		08 17				08 42
Mill Hill Broadway d								00 05	00 35	06 33		06 51		07 21		07 51		08 21				08 46
Hendon d								00 08	00 38	06 36		06 54		07 24		07 54		08 24				08 50
Cricklewood d								00 12	00 42	06 40		06 58		07 28		07 58		08 28				08 53
West Hampstead Thameslink ⊖ d								00 15	00 45	06 43		07 01		07 31		08 01		08 31		08 45		08 57
Kentish Town ⊖ d								00 20	00 50	06 48		07 06		07 36		08 06		08 36				09 01
St Pancras International 15 ⊖ a								00 23	00 53	06 55		07 09		07 39		08 09		08 39		08 52		09 05
d								00 24	00 54			07 10		07 40		08 10		08 40		08 54		09 06
Farringdon 3 ⊖ d								00 29				07 15		07 45		08 15		08 45		08 59		09 11
City Thameslink 3 d																						
London Blackfriars 3 ⊖ d							00 05	00 35	01 05		06 51	07 21	07 42	07 51	08 12	08 21	08 42	08 51	08 58	09 04	09 12	09 16
Elephant & Castle ⊖173,179 d												07 25	07 46	07 55	08 16	08 25	08 46	08 55	09 01	09 08	09 16	09 19
Loughborough Jn 173,179 d																			09 05			09 23
Herne Hill 4 173,179 d																			09 09			09 27
London Bridge 4 a							00 11	00 41														
d							00 12	00 42														
Tulse Hill 3 d		00 02																	09 14			09 32
Streatham 4 d		00 06																	09 18			09 36
Mitcham Eastfields 173 d																			09 22			
Mitcham Junction 173 🚊 d																			09 25			
Hackbridge 173 d																			09 29			
Carshalton 173 d																			09 31			
Tooting 173 d		00 10																				09 42
Haydons Road 173 d		00 13																				09 45
Wimbledon 6 ⊖173,179 🚊 d		00 17																				09 48
Wimbledon Chase 179 d		00 20																				09 51
South Merton 179 d		00 22																				09 53
Morden South 179 d		00 24																				09 55
St Helier 179 d		00 26																				09 57
Sutton Common 179 d		00 28																				09 59
West Sutton 179 d	00 01	00 31																				10 02
Sutton (Surrey) 4 179 a	00 05	00 35																	09 35			10 05
Denmark Hill 4 195 d													07 52		08 22		08 52				09 22	
Peckham Rye 4 195 d													07 55		08 25		08 55				09 25	
Nunhead 4 195 d													07 57		08 27		08 57				09 27	
Crofton Park 195 d													08 00		08 30		09 00				09 30	
Catford 195 d					00 03								08 03		08 33		09 03				09 33	
Bellingham 195 d					00 05								08 05		08 35		09 05				09 35	
Beckenham Hill 195 d					00 07								08 07		08 37		09 07				09 37	
Ravensbourne 195 d					00 09								08 09		08 39		09 09				09 39	
Shortlands 195 d					00 11								08 11		08 41		09 11				09 41	
Bromley South 4 195 d					00 14								08 14		08 44		09 14				09 44	
Bickley 4 195 d					00 17								08 17		08 47		09 17				09 47	
St Mary Cray 195 d					00 21								08 21		08 51		09 21				09 51	
Swanley 4 195 d					00 26								08 26		08 56		09 26				09 56	
Eynsford 195 d					00 30								08 30		09 00		09 30				10 00	
Shoreham (Kent) 195 d				00 04	00 34								08 34		09 04		09 34				10 04	
Otford 4 195 d				00 07	00 37								08 37		09 07		09 37				10 07	
Bat & Ball 195 d				00 10	00 40								08 40		09 10		09 40				10 10	
Sevenoaks 4 195 a				00 13	00 43								08 43		09 13		09 43				10 13	
East Croydon 🚊 d							00 29	00 57	01 36		07 24	07 53		08 21		08 56		09 26		09 39		
Redhill d																						
Gatwick Airport 10 ✈ d						00 19	00 49	01 19	01 55		07 44	08 18		08 42		09 12		09 42		09 56		
Three Bridges 4 d						00 24	00 54	01a24	02a02		07 49	08 23		08 47		09 17		09 47		10a01		
Balcombe d						00 30																
Haywards Heath 3 d						00 38	01 10				07 58	08 34		08 56		09 26		09 56				
Wivelsfield 4 d			00 03			00 43																
Burgess Hill 4 d			00 05			00 45	01 15				08 03	08 39		09 01		09 33		10 01				
Hassocks 4 d			00 08			00 48	01 18				08 07	08 43		09 05		09 37		10 05				
Preston Park d			00 15			00 55																
Brighton 10 a			00 19			00 59	01 29				08 17	08 53		09 15		09 47		10 15				

A From Luton
B From Bedford
C From London Blackfriars

The trains that operate to and from Sevenoaks, Orpington and Rochester (and a few other destinations at peak times) are operated jointly by First Capital Connect (north of Blackfriars) and Southeastern (south of Blackfriars)

Table 52 shows the complete service between Bedford and London, whilst services between London, Sevenoaks, Sutton and Brighton only show through Thameslink services. Other Tables should be consulted for additional journey opportunities.

Table 52

Sundays

30 March to 11 May

Bedford, Luton, St Albans and City of London - South London, Gatwick Airport and Brighton

Network Diagram - refer to first Page of Table 52

	FC ■1	EM ◇■1 A ☕	FC	FC ■1	SE	FC	FC ■1	EM ◇■1 B ☕	FC	FC ■1	SE	FC	FC ■1	EM ◇■1 A ☕	FC	FC ■1	SE	FC	FC ■1	EM ◇■1 B ☕	FC	FC ■1
Bedford ■7 d	08 06	08 16		08 20			08 36	08 46		08 50			09 06	09 16		09 20			09 36	09 46		09 50
Flitwick d	08 16			08 30			08 46			09 00			09 16			09 30			09 46			10 00
Harlington d	08 20			08 34			08 50			09 04			09 20			09 34			09 50			10 04
Leagrave d	08 26			08 40			08 56			09 10			09 26			09 40			09 56			10 10
Luton ■10 d	08 30	08 34		08 44		08 48	09 00			09 14		09 18	09 30	09 35		09 44		09 48	10 00			10 14
Luton Airport Parkway ■7 ✈ d	08 33			08 47		08 51	09 03	09 06		09 17		09 21	09 33			09 47		09 51	10 03	10 06		10 17
Harpenden d	08 39			08 53		08 57	09 09			09 23		09 27	09 39			09 53		09 57	10 09			10 23
St Albans City d	08 45			08 59		09 03	09 15			09 29		09 33	09 45			09 59		10 03	10 15			10 29
Radlett d						09 08						09 38						10 08				
Elstree & Borehamwood d						09 12						09 42						10 12				
Mill Hill Broadway d						09 16						09 46						10 16				
Hendon d						09 20						09 50						10 20				
Cricklewood d						09 23						09 53						10 23				
West Hampstead Thameslink ⊖ d	09 01			09 15		09 27	09 31			09 45		09 57	10 01			10 15		10 27	10 31			10 45
Kentish Town ⊖ d						09 31						10 01						10 31				
St Pancras International ■15 ⊖ a	09 09	09 13		09 22		09 35	09 39	09 44		09 52		10 05	10 09	10 13		10 22		10 35	10 39	10 48		10 52
d	09 10			09 24		09 36	09 40			09 54		10 06	10 10			10 24		10 36	10 40			10 54
Farringdon ■3 ⊖ d	09 15			09 29		09 41	09 45			09 59		10 11	10 15			10 29		10 41	10 45			10 59
City Thameslink ■3 d																						
London Blackfriars ■3 ⊖ d	09 21		09 28	09 34	09 42	09 46	09 51		09 58	10 04	10 12	10 16	10 21		10 28	10 34	10 42	10 46	10 51		10 58	11 04
Elephant & Castle ⊖173,179 d	09 25		09 31	09 38	09 46	09 49	09 55		10 01	10 08	10 16	10 19	10 25		10 31	10 38	10 46	10 49	10 55		11 01	11 08
Loughborough Jn 173,179 d			09 35			09 53			10 05			10 23			10 35			10 53			11 05	
Herne Hill ■4 173,179 d			09 39			09 57			10 09			10 27			10 39			10 57			11 09	
London Bridge ■4 a																						
d																						
Tulse Hill ■3 d			09 44			10 02			10 14			10 32			10 44			11 02			11 14	
Streatham ■4 d			09 48			10 06			10 18			10 36			10 48			11 06			11 18	
Mitcham Eastfields 173 d			09 52						10 22						10 52						11 22	
Mitcham Junction 173 🚊 d			09 55						10 25						10 55						11 25	
Hackbridge 173 d			09 59						10 29						10 59						11 29	
Carshalton 173 d			10 01						10 31						11 01						11 31	
Tooting 173 d						10 12						10 42						11 12				
Haydons Road 173 d						10 15						10 45						11 15				
Wimbledon ■6 ⊖173,179 🚊 d						10 18						10 48						11 18				
Wimbledon Chase 179 d						10 21						10 51						11 21				
South Merton 179 d						10 23						10 53						11 23				
Morden South 179 d						10 25						10 55						11 25				
St Helier 179 d						10 27						10 57						11 27				
Sutton Common 179 d						10 29						10 59						11 29				
West Sutton 179 d						10 32						11 02						11 32				
Sutton (Surrey) ■4 179 a			10 05			10 35			10 35			11 05			11 05			11 35			11 35	
Denmark Hill ■4 195 d					09 52						10 22						10 52					
Peckham Rye ■4 195 d					09 55						10 25						10 55					
Nunhead ■4 195 d					09 57						10 27						10 57					
Crofton Park 195 d					10 00						10 30						11 00					
Catford 195 d					10 03						10 33						11 03					
Bellingham 195 d					10 05						10 35						11 05					
Beckenham Hill 195 d					10 07						10 37						11 07					
Ravensbourne 195 d					10 09						10 39						11 09					
Shortlands 195 d					10 11						10 41						11 11					
Bromley South ■4 195 d					10 14						10 44						11 14					
Bickley ■4 195 d					10 17						10 47						11 17					
St Mary Cray 195 d					10 21						10 51						11 21					
Swanley ■4 195 d					10 26						10 56						11 26					
Eynsford 195 d					10 30						11 00						11 30					
Shoreham (Kent) 195 d					10 34						11 04						11 34					
Otford ■4 195 d					10 37						11 07						11 37					
Bat & Ball 195 d					10 40						11 10						11 40					
Sevenoaks ■4 195 a					10 43						11 13						11 43					
East Croydon 🚊 d	09 56			10 09			10 26			10 39			10 56			11 09			11 26			11 39
Redhill d																						
Gatwick Airport ■10 ✈ d	10 12			10 26			10 42			10 56			11 12			11 26			11 42			11 56
Three Bridges ■4 d	10 17			10a33			10 47			11a01			11 17			11a33			11 47			12a01
Balcombe d																						
Haywards Heath ■3 d	10 26						10 56						11 26						11 56			
Wivelsfield ■4 d																						
Burgess Hill ■4 d	10 33						11 01						11 33						12 01			
Hassocks ■4 d	10 37						11 05						11 37						12 05			
Preston Park d																						
Brighton ■10 a	10 47						11 15						11 47						12 15			

A From Derby **B** From Nottingham

The trains that operate to and from Sevenoaks, Orpington and Rochester (and a few other destinations at peak times) are operated jointly by First Capital Connect (north of Blackfriars) and Southeastern (south of Blackfriars)

Table 52 shows the complete service between Bedford and London, whilst services between London, Sevenoaks, Sutton and Brighton only show through Thameslink services. Other Tables should be consulted for additional journey opportunities.

Table 52

Sundays

30 March to 11 May

Bedford, Luton, St Albans and City of London - South London, Gatwick Airport and Brighton

Network Diagram - refer to first Page of Table 52

		SE	FC	FC ■1	EM ◇■1 A ☕	FC	FC ■1		SE	FC	FC ■1	EM ◇■1 B ☕	FC	FC ■1	SE	FC	FC ■1	EM ◇■1 A ☕		FC	FC ■1	SE	FC	FC ■1	FC
Bedford ■7	d			10 06	10 16		10 20				10 36	10 46		10 50			11 06	11 15			11 20			11 36	
Flitwick	d			10 16			10 30				10 46			11 00			11 16				11 30			11 46	
Harlington	d			10 20			10 34				10 50			11 04			11 20				11 34			11 50	
Leagrave	d			10 26			10 40				10 56			11 10			11 26				11 40			11 56	
Luton ■10	d		10 18	10 30	10 35		10 44			10 48	11 00			11 14		11 18	11 30	11 35			11 44		11 48	12 00	
Luton Airport Parkway ■7 ✈	d		10 21	10 33			10 47			10 51	11 03	11 06		11 17		11 21	11 33				11 47		11 51	12 03	
Harpenden	d		10 27	10 39			10 53			10 57	11 09			11 23		11 27	11 39				11 53		11 57	12 09	
St Albans City	d		10 33	10 45			10 59			11 03	11 15			11 29		11 33	11 45				11 59		12 03	12 15	
Radlett	d		10 38							11 08						11 38							12 08		
Elstree & Borehamwood	d		10 42							11 12						11 42							12 12		
Mill Hill Broadway	d		10 46							11 16						11 46							12 16		
Hendon	d		10 50							11 20						11 50							12 20		
Cricklewood	d		10 53							11 23						11 53							12 23		
West Hampstead Thameslink ⊖	d		10 57	11 01			11 15			11 27	11 31			11 45		11 57	12 01				12 15		12 27	12 31	
Kentish Town ⊖	d		11 01							11 31						12 01							12 31		
St Pancras International ■15 ⊖	a		11 05	11 09	11 17		11 22			11 35	11 39	11 48		11 52		12 05	12 09	12 13			12 22		12 35	12 39	
	d		11 06	11 10			11 24			11 36	11 40			11 54		12 06	12 10				12 24		12 36	12 40	
Farringdon ■3 ⊖	d		11 11	11 15			11 29			11 41	11 45			11 59		12 11	12 15				12 29		12 41	12 45	
City Thameslink ■3	d																								
London Blackfriars ■3 ⊖	d	11 12	11 16	11 21		11 28	11 34		11 42	11 46	11 51		11 58	12 04	12 12	12 16	12 21			12 28	12 34	12 42	12 46	12 51	12 58
Elephant & Castle ⊖173,179	d	11 16	11 19	11 25		11 31	11 38		11 46	11 49	11 55		12 01	12 08	12 16	12 19	12 25			12 31	12 38	12 46	12 49	12 55	13 01
Loughborough Jn 173,179	d		11 23			11 35				11 53			12 05			12 23				12 35			12 53		13 05
Herne Hill ■4 173,179	d		11 27			11 39				11 57			12 09			12 27				12 39			12 57		13 09
London Bridge ■4	a																								
	d																								
Tulse Hill ■3	d		11 32			11 44				12 02			12 14			12 32				12 44			13 02		13 14
Streatham ■4	d		11 36			11 48				12 06			12 18			12 36				12 48			13 06		13 18
Mitcham Eastfields 173	d					11 52							12 22							12 52					13 22
Mitcham Junction 173 🚋	d					11 55							12 25							12 55					13 25
Hackbridge 173	d					11 59							12 29							12 59					13 29
Carshalton 173	d					12 01							12 31							13 01					13 31
Tooting 173	d		11 42							12 12						12 42							13 12		
Haydons Road 173	d		11 45							12 15						12 45							13 15		
Wimbledon ■6 ⊖173,179 🚋	d		11 48							12 18						12 48							13 18		
Wimbledon Chase 179	d		11 51							12 21						12 51							13 21		
South Merton 179	d		11 53							12 23						12 53							13 23		
Morden South 179	d		11 55							12 25						12 55							13 25		
St Helier 179	d		11 57							12 27						12 57							13 27		
Sutton Common 179	d		11 59							12 29						12 59							13 29		
West Sutton 179	d		12 02							12 32						13 02							13 32		
Sutton (Surrey) ■4 179	a		12 05			12 05				12 35			12 35			13 05				13 05			13 35		13 35
Denmark Hill ■4 195	d	11 22							11 52						12 22							12 52			
Peckham Rye ■4 195	d	11 25							11 55						12 25							12 55			
Nunhead ■4 195	d	11 27							11 57						12 27							12 57			
Crofton Park 195	d	11 30							12 00						12 30							13 00			
Catford 195	d	11 33							12 03						12 33							13 03			
Bellingham 195	d	11 35							12 05						12 35							13 05			
Beckenham Hill 195	d	11 37							12 07						12 37							13 07			
Ravensbourne 195	d	11 39							12 09						12 39							13 09			
Shortlands 195	d	11 41							12 11						12 41							13 11			
Bromley South ■4 195	d	11 44							12 14						12 44							13 14			
Bickley ■4 195	d	11 47							12 17						12 47							13 17			
St Mary Cray 195	d	11 51							12 21						12 51							13 21			
Swanley ■4 195	d	11 56							12 26						12 56							13 26			
Eynsford 195	d	12 00							12 30						13 00							13 30			
Shoreham (Kent) 195	d	12 04							12 34						13 04							13 34			
Otford ■4 195	d	12 07							12 37						13 07							13 37			
Bat & Ball 195	d	12 10							12 40						13 10							13 40			
Sevenoaks ■4 195	a	12 13							12 43						13 13							13 43			
East Croydon 🚋	d			11 56			12 09				12 26			12 39			12 56				13 09			13 26	
Redhill	d																								
Gatwick Airport ■10 ✈	d			12 12			12 26				12 42			12 56			13 12				13 26			13 42	
Three Bridges ■4	d			12 17			12a33				12 47			13a01			13 17				13a33			13 47	
Balcombe	d																								
Haywards Heath ■3	d			12 26							12 56						13 26							13 56	
Wivelsfield ■4	d																								
Burgess Hill ■4	d			12 33							13 01						13 33							14 01	
Hassocks ■4	d			12 37							13 05						13 37							14 05	
Preston Park	d																								
Brighton ■10	a			12 47							13 15						13 47							14 15	

A From Sheffield

B From Nottingham

The trains that operate to and from Sevenoaks, Orpington and Rochester (and a few other destinations at peak times) are operated jointly by First Capital Connect (north of Blackfriars) and Southeastern (south of Blackfriars)

Table 52 shows the complete service between Bedford and London, whilst services between London, Sevenoaks, Sutton and Brighton only show through Thameslink services. Other Tables should be consulted for additional journey opportunities.

Table 52

Sundays

30 March to 11 May

Bedford, Luton, St Albans and City of London - South London, Gatwick Airport and Brighton

Network Diagram - refer to first Page of Table 52

		FC ■1	EM ◇■1 A ☕	SE	FC	FC ■1	EM ◇■1 B ☕	FC	FC ■1	SE	FC	FC ■1	FC	FC ■1	EM ◇■1 C ☕	SE	FC	FC ■1	FC	FC ■1	SE	FC	FC ■1
Bedford ■7	d	11 50	11 56			12 06	12 15		12 20			12 36		12 50	13 01			13 06		13 20			13 36
Flitwick	d	12 00				12 16			12 30			12 46		13 00				13 16		13 30			13 46
Harlington	d	12 04				12 20			12 34			12 50		13 04				13 20		13 34			13 50
Leagrave	d	12 10				12 26			12 40			12 56		13 10				13 26		13 40			13 56
Luton ■10	d	12 14			12 18	12 30	12 30		12 44		12 48	13 00		13 14			13 18	13 30		13 44		13 48	14 00
Luton Airport Parkway ■7 ✈	d	12 17	12 13		12 21	12 33			12 47		12 51	13 03		13 17	13 17		13 21	13 33		13 47		13 51	14 03
Harpenden	d	12 23			12 27	12 39			12 53		12 57	13 09		13 23			13 27	13 39		13 53		13 57	14 09
St Albans City	d	12 29			12 33	12 45			12 59		13 03	13 15		13 29			13 33	13 45		13 59		14 03	14 15
Radlett	d				12 38						13 08						13 38					14 08	
Elstree & Borehamwood	d				12 42						13 12						13 42					14 12	
Mill Hill Broadway	d				12 46						13 16						13 46					14 16	
Hendon	d				12 50						13 20						13 50					14 20	
Cricklewood	d				12 53						13 23						13 53					14 23	
West Hampstead Thameslink ⊖	d	12 45			12 57	13 01			13 15		13 27	13 31		13 45			13 57	14 01		14 15		14 27	14 31
Kentish Town ⊖	d				13 01						13 31						14 01					14 31	
St Pancras International ■15 ⊖	a	12 52	12 39		13 05	13 09	12 54		13 22		13 35	13 39		13 52	13 44		14 05	14 09		14 22		14 35	14 39
	d	12 54			13 06	13 10			13 24		13 36	13 40		13 54			14 06	14 10		14 24		14 36	14 40
Farringdon ■3 ⊖	d	12 59			13 11	13 15			13 29		13 41	13 45		13 59			14 11	14 15		14 29		14 41	14 45
City Thameslink ■3	d																						
London Blackfriars ■3 ⊖	d	13 04		13 12	13 16	13 21		13 28	13 34	13 42	13 46	13 51	13 58	14 04		14 12	14 16	14 21	14 28	14 34	14 42	14 46	14 51
Elephant & Castle ⊖173,179	d	13 08		13 16	13 19	13 25		13 31	13 38	13 46	13 49	13 55	14 01	14 08		14 16	14 19	14 25	14 31	14 38	14 46	14 49	14 55
Loughborough Jn 173,179	d				13 23			13 35			13 53		14 05				14 23		14 35			14 53	
Herne Hill ■4 173,179	d				13 27			13 39			13 57		14 09				14 27		14 39			14 57	
London Bridge ■4	a																						
	d																						
Tulse Hill ■3	d				13 32			13 44			14 02		14 14				14 32		14 44			15 02	
Streatham ■4	d				13 36			13 48			14 06		14 18				14 36		14 48			15 06	
Mitcham Eastfields 173	d							13 52					14 22						14 52				
Mitcham Junction 173 🚊	d							13 55					14 25						14 55				
Hackbridge 173	d							13 59					14 29						14 59				
Carshalton 173	d							14 01					14 31						15 01				
Tooting 173	d				13 42						14 12						14 42					15 12	
Haydons Road 173	d				13 45						14 15						14 45					15 15	
Wimbledon ■6 ⊖173,179 🚊	d				13 48						14 18						14 48					15 18	
Wimbledon Chase 179	d				13 51						14 21						14 51					15 21	
South Merton 179	d				13 53						14 23						14 53					15 23	
Morden South 179	d				13 55						14 25						14 55					15 25	
St Helier 179	d				13 57						14 27						14 57					15 27	
Sutton Common 179	d				13 59						14 29						14 59					15 29	
West Sutton 179	d				14 02						14 32						15 02					15 32	
Sutton (Surrey) ■4 179	a				14 05			14 05			14 35		14 35				15 05		15 05			15 35	
Denmark Hill ■4 195	d			13 22						13 52						14 22					14 52		
Peckham Rye ■4 195	d			13 25						13 55						14 25					14 55		
Nunhead ■4 195	d			13 27						13 57						14 27					14 57		
Crofton Park 195	d			13 30						14 00						14 30					15 00		
Catford 195	d			13 33						14 03						14 33					15 03		
Bellingham 195	d			13 35						14 05						14 35					15 05		
Beckenham Hill 195	d			13 37						14 07						14 37					15 07		
Ravensbourne 195	d			13 39						14 09						14 39					15 09		
Shortlands 195	d			13 41						14 11						14 41					15 11		
Bromley South ■4 195	d			13 44						14 14						14 44					15 14		
Bickley ■4 195	d			13 47						14 17						14 47					15 17		
St Mary Cray 195	d			13 51						14 21						14 51					15 21		
Swanley ■4 195	d			13 56						14 26						14 56					15 26		
Eynsford 195	d			14 00						14 30						15 00					15 30		
Shoreham (Kent) 195	d			14 04						14 34						15 04					15 34		
Otford ■4 195	d			14 07						14 37						15 07					15 37		
Bat & Ball 195	d			14 10						14 40						15 10					15 40		
Sevenoaks ■4 195	a			14 13						14 43						15 13					15 43		
East Croydon 🚊	d	13 39				13 56			14 09			14 26		14 39				14 56		15 09			15 26
Redhill	d																						
Gatwick Airport ■10 ✈	d	13 56				14 12			14 26			14 42		14 56				15 12		15 26			15 42
Three Bridges ■4	d	14a01				14 17			14a33			14 47		15a01				15 17		15a33			15 47
Balcombe	d																						
Haywards Heath ■3	d					14 26						14 56						15 26					15 56
Wivelsfield ■4	d																						
Burgess Hill ■4	d					14 33						15 01						15 33					16 01
Hassocks ■4	d					14 37						15 05						15 37					16 05
Preston Park	d																						
Brighton ■10	a					14 47						15 15						15 47					16 15

A From Nottingham **B** From Sheffield **C** From Leeds

The trains that operate to and from Sevenoaks, Orpington and Rochester (and a few other destinations at peak times) are operated jointly by First Capital Connect (north of Blackfriars) and Southeastern (south of Blackfriars)

Table 52 shows the complete service between Bedford and London, whilst services between London, Sevenoaks, Sutton and Brighton only show through Thameslink services. Other Tables should be consulted for additional journey opportunities.

Table 52

Sundays
30 March to 11 May

Bedford, Luton, St Albans and City of London - South London, Gatwick Airport and Brighton

Network Diagram - refer to first Page of Table 52

		EM ◇1 A ⊡	FC	FC 1	SE	FC	FC 1	EM ◇1 B ⊡	FC	FC 1	SE	FC	FC 1	EM ◇1 C ⊡	FC	FC 1	SE	FC	FC 1	EM ◇1 B ⊡	FC	FC 1	SE
Bedford 7	d	13 44		13 50			14 06	14 15		14 20			14 36	14 39		14 50			15 06	15 15		15 20	
Flitwick	d			14 00			14 16			14 30			14 46			15 00			15 16			15 30	
Harlington	d			14 04			14 20			14 34			14 50			15 04			15 20			15 34	
Leagrave	d			14 10			14 26			14 40			14 56			15 10			15 26			15 40	
Luton 10	d	14 01		14 14		14 18	14 30			14 44		14 48	15 00	14 54		15 14		15 18	15 30			15 44	
Luton Airport Parkway 7 ✈	d			14 17		14 21	14 33	14 31		14 47		14 51	15 03			15 17		15 21	15 33	15 31		15 47	
Harpenden	d			14 23		14 27	14 39			14 53		14 57	15 09			15 23		15 27	15 39			15 53	
St Albans City	d			14 29		14 33	14 45			14 59		15 03	15 15			15 29		15 33	15 45			15 59	
Radlett	d					14 38						15 08						15 38					
Elstree & Borehamwood	d					14 42						15 12						15 42					
Mill Hill Broadway	d					14 46						15 16						15 46					
Hendon	d					14 50						15 20						15 50					
Cricklewood	d					14 53						15 23						15 53					
West Hampstead Thameslink ⊖	d			14 45		14 57	15 01			15 15		15 27	15 31			15 45		15 57	16 01			16 15	
Kentish Town ⊖	d					15 01						15 31						16 01					
St Pancras International 15 ⊖	a	14 27		14 52		15 05	15 09	14 57		15 22		15 35	15 39	15 18		15 52		16 05	16 09	15 57		16 22	
	d			14 54		15 06	15 10			15 24		15 36	15 40			15 54		16 06	16 10			16 24	
Farringdon 3 ⊖	d			14 59		15 11	15 15			15 29		15 41	15 45			15 59		16 11	16 15			16 29	
City Thameslink 3	d																						
London Blackfriars 3 ⊖	d		14 58	15 04	15 12	15 16	15 21		15 28	15 34	15 42	15 46	15 51		15 58	16 04	16 12	16 16	16 21		16 28	16 34	16 42
Elephant & Castle ⊖173,179	d		15 01	15 08	15 16	15 19	15 25		15 31	15 38	15 46	15 49	15 55		16 01	16 08	16 16	16 19	16 25		16 31	16 38	16 46
Loughborough Jn 173,179	d		15 05			15 23			15 35			15 53			16 05			16 23			16 35		
Herne Hill 4 173,179	d		15 09			15 27			15 39			15 57			16 09			16 27			16 39		
London Bridge 4	a																						
	d																						
Tulse Hill 3	d		15 14			15 32			15 44			16 02			16 14			16 32			16 44		
Streatham 4	d		15 18			15 36			15 48			16 06			16 18			16 36			16 48		
Mitcham Eastfields 173	d		15 22						15 52						16 22						16 52		
Mitcham Junction 173 🚋	d		15 25						15 55						16 25						16 55		
Hackbridge 173	d		15 29						15 59						16 29						16 59		
Carshalton 173	d		15 31						16 01						16 31						17 01		
Tooting 173	d					15 42						16 12						16 42					
Haydons Road 173	d					15 45						16 15						16 45					
Wimbledon 6 ⊖173,179 🚋	d					15 48						16 18						16 48					
Wimbledon Chase 179	d					15 51						16 21						16 51					
South Merton 179	d					15 53						16 23						16 53					
Morden South 179	d					15 55						16 25						16 55					
St Helier 179	d					15 57						16 27						16 57					
Sutton Common 179	d					15 59						16 29						16 59					
West Sutton 179	d					16 02						16 32						17 02					
Sutton (Surrey) 4 179	a		15 35			16 05			16 05			16 35			16 35			17 05			17 05		
Denmark Hill 4 195	d				15 22						15 52						16 22						16 52
Peckham Rye 4 195	d				15 25						15 55						16 25						16 55
Nunhead 4 195	d				15 27						15 57						16 27						16 57
Crofton Park 195	d				15 30						16 00						16 30						17 00
Catford 195	d				15 33						16 03						16 33						17 03
Bellingham 195	d				15 35						16 05						16 35						17 05
Beckenham Hill 195	d				15 37						16 07						16 37						17 07
Ravensbourne 195	d				15 39						16 09						16 39						17 09
Shortlands 195	d				15 41						16 11						16 41						17 11
Bromley South 4 195	d				15 44						16 14						16 44						17 14
Bickley 4 195	d				15 47						16 17						16 47						17 17
St Mary Cray 195	d				15 51						16 21						16 51						17 21
Swanley 4 195	d				15 56						16 26						16 56						17 26
Eynsford 195	d				16 00						16 30						17 00						17 30
Shoreham (Kent) 195	d				16 04						16 34						17 04						17 34
Otford 4 195	d				16 07						16 37						17 07						17 37
Bat & Ball 195	d				16 10						16 40						17 10						17 40
Sevenoaks 4 195	a				16 13						16 43						17 13						17 43
East Croydon 🚋	d			15 39			15 56			16 09			16 26			16 39			16 56			17 09	
Redhill	d																						
Gatwick Airport 10 ✈	d			15 56			16 12			16 26			16 42			16 56			17 12			17 26	
Three Bridges 4	d			16a01			16 17			16a33			16 47			17a01			17 17			17a33	
Balcombe	d																						
Haywards Heath 3	d						16 26						16 56						17 26				
Wivelsfield 4	d																						
Burgess Hill 4	d						16 33						17 01						17 33				
Hassocks 4	d						16 37						17 05						17 37				
Preston Park	d																						
Brighton 10	a						16 47						17 15						17 47				

A From Leeds **B** From Nottingham **C** From Sheffield

The trains that operate to and from Sevenoaks, Orpington and Rochester (and a few other destinations at peak times) are operated jointly by First Capital Connect (north of Blackfriars) and Southeastern (south of Blackfriars)

Table 52 shows the complete service between Bedford and London, whilst services between London, Sevenoaks, Sutton and Brighton only show through Thameslink services. Other Tables should be consulted for additional journey opportunities.

Table 52

Sundays

30 March to 11 May

Bedford, Luton, St Albans and City of London - South London, Gatwick Airport and Brighton

Network Diagram - refer to first Page of Table 52

		FC	FC ■1	EM ◇■1 A ⊡	FC	FC ■1	SE	FC	FC ■1	EM ◇■1 B ⊡	EM ◇■1 A ⊡	FC	FC ■1	SE	FC	FC ■1	FC	FC ■1	SE	FC	FC ■1	EM ◇■1 B ⊡
Bedford ■7	d		15 36	15 39		15 50			16 06	16 08			16 20			16 36		16 50			17 06	17 08
Flitwick	d		15 46			16 00			16 16				16 30			16 46		17 00			17 16	
Harlington	d		15 50			16 04			16 20				16 34			16 50		17 04			17 20	
Leagrave	d		15 56			16 10			16 26				16 40			16 56		17 10			17 26	
Luton ■10	d	15 48	16 00	15 54		16 14		16 18	16 30		16 42		16 44		16 48	17 00		17 14		17 18	17 30	
Luton Airport Parkway ■7 ✈	d	15 51	16 03			16 17		16 21	16 33	16 23			16 47		16 51	17 03		17 17		17 21	17 33	17 24
Harpenden	d	15 57	16 09			16 23		16 27	16 39				16 53		16 57	17 09		17 23		17 27	17 39	
St Albans City	d	16 03	16 15			16 29		16 33	16 45				16 59		17 03	17 15		17 29		17 33	17 45	
Radlett	d	16 08						16 38							17 08					17 38		
Elstree & Borehamwood	d	16 12						16 42							17 12					17 42		
Mill Hill Broadway	d	16 16						16 46							17 16					17 46		
Hendon	d	16 20						16 50							17 20					17 50		
Cricklewood	d	16 23						16 53							17 23					17 53		
West Hampstead Thameslink ⊖	d	16 27	16 31			16 45		16 57	17 01				17 15		17 27	17 31		17 45		17 57	18 01	
Kentish Town ⊖	d	16 31						17 01							17 31					18 01		
St Pancras International ■15 ⊖	a	16 35	16 39	16 18		16 52		17 05	17 09	16 47	17 06		17 22		17 35	17 39		17 52		18 05	18 09	17 47
	d	16 36	16 40			16 54		17 06	17 10				17 24		17 36	17 40		17 54		18 06	18 10	
Farringdon ■3 ⊖	d	16 41	16 45			16 59		17 11	17 15				17 29		17 41	17 45		17 59		18 11	18 15	
City Thameslink ■3	d																					
London Blackfriars ■3 ⊖	d	16 46	16 51		16 58	17 04	17 12	17 16	17 21			17 28	17 34	17 42	17 46	17 51	17 58	18 04	18 12	18 16	18 21	
Elephant & Castle ⊖173,179	d	16 49	16 55		17 01	17 08	17 16	17 19	17 25			17 31	17 38	17 46	17 49	17 55	18 01	18 08	18 16	18 19	18 25	
Loughborough Jn 173,179	d	16 53			17 05			17 23				17 35			17 53		18 05			18 23		
Herne Hill ■4 173,179	d	16 57			17 09			17 27				17 39			17 57		18 09			18 27		
London Bridge ■4	a																					
	d																					
Tulse Hill ■3	d	17 02			17 14			17 32				17 44			18 02		18 14			18 32		
Streatham ■4	d	17 06			17 18			17 36				17 48			18 06		18 18			18 36		
Mitcham Eastfields 173	d				17 22							17 52					18 22					
Mitcham Junction 173 🚋	d				17 25							17 55					18 25					
Hackbridge 173	d				17 29							17 59					18 29					
Carshalton 173	d				17 31							18 01					18 31					
Tooting 173	d	17 12						17 42							18 12					18 42		
Haydons Road 173	d	17 15						17 45							18 15					18 45		
Wimbledon ■6 ⊖173,179 🚋	d	17 18						17 48							18 18					18 48		
Wimbledon Chase 179	d	17 21						17 51							18 21					18 51		
South Merton 179	d	17 23						17 53							18 23					18 53		
Morden South 179	d	17 25						17 55							18 25					18 55		
St Helier 179	d	17 27						17 57							18 27					18 57		
Sutton Common 179	d	17 29						17 59							18 29					18 59		
West Sutton 179	d	17 32						18 02							18 32					19 02		
Sutton (Surrey) ■4 179	a	17 35			17 35			18 05				18 05			18 35		18 35			19 05		
Denmark Hill ■4 195	d						17 22							17 52					18 22			
Peckham Rye ■4 195	d						17 25							17 55					18 25			
Nunhead ■4 195	d						17 27							17 57					18 27			
Crofton Park 195	d						17 30							18 00					18 30			
Catford 195	d						17 33							18 03					18 33			
Bellingham 195	d						17 35							18 05					18 35			
Beckenham Hill 195	d						17 37							18 07					18 37			
Ravensbourne 195	d						17 39							18 09					18 39			
Shortlands 195	d						17 41							18 11					18 41			
Bromley South ■4 195	d						17 44							18 14					18 44			
Bickley ■4 195	d						17 47							18 17					18 47			
St Mary Cray 195	d						17 51							18 21					18 51			
Swanley ■4 195	d						17 56							18 26					18 56			
Eynsford 195	d						18 00							18 30					19 00			
Shoreham (Kent) 195	d						18 04							18 34					19 04			
Otford ■4 195	d						18 07							18 37					19 07			
Bat & Ball 195	d						18 10							18 40					19 10			
Sevenoaks ■4 195	a						18 13							18 43					19 13			
East Croydon 🚋	d		17 26			17 39			17 56				18 09			18 26		18 39			18 56	
Redhill	d																					
Gatwick Airport ■10 ✈	d		17 42			17 56			18 12				18 26			18 42		18 56			19 12	
Three Bridges ■4	d		17 47			18a01			18 17				18a33			18 47		19a01			19 17	
Balcombe	d																					
Haywards Heath ■3	d		17 56						18 26							18 56					19 26	
Wivelsfield ■4	d																					
Burgess Hill ■4	d		18 01						18 33							19 01					19 33	
Hassocks ■4	d		18 05						18 37							19 05					19 37	
Preston Park	d																					
Brighton ■10	a		18 15						18 47							19 15					19 47	

A From Sheffield **B** From Nottingham

The trains that operate to and from Sevenoaks, Orpington and Rochester (and a few other destinations at peak times) are operated jointly by First Capital Connect (north of Blackfriars) and Southeastern (south of Blackfriars)

Table 52 shows the complete service between Bedford and London, whilst services between London, Sevenoaks, Sutton and Brighton only show through Thameslink services. Other Tables should be consulted for additional journey opportunities.

Table 52

Sundays
30 March to 11 May

Bedford, Luton, St Albans and City of London - South London, Gatwick Airport and Brighton

Network Diagram - refer to first Page of Table 52

Station		FC	FC 1	EM ◇1 A ☕	SE	FC	FC 1	FC	SE	FC	FC 1	EM ◇1 B ☕	EM ◇1 C ☕	FC	SE	FC	FC 1	FC	SE	FC	FC 1	EM ◇1 B ☕	EM ◇1 C ☕
Bedford 7	d		17 20	17 27			17 36				18 06	18 08	18 17				18 36				19 06	19 08	19 27
Flitwick	d		17 30				17 46				18 16						18 46				19 16		
Harlington	d		17 34				17 50				18 20						18 50				19 20		
Leagrave	d		17 40				17 56				18 26						18 56				19 26		
Luton 10	d		17 44	17 43		17 48	18 00			18 18	18 30		18 31			18 48	19 00			19 18	19 30		19 43
Luton Airport Parkway 7 ✈	d		17 47			17 51	18 03			18 21	18 33	18 24				18 51	19 03			19 21	19 33	19 24	
Harpenden	d		17 53			17 57	18 09			18 27	18 39					18 57	19 09			19 27	19 39		
St Albans City	d		17 59			18 03	18 15			18 33	18 45					19 03	19 15			19 33	19 45		
Radlett	d					18 08				18 38						19 08				19 38			
Elstree & Borehamwood	d					18 12				18 42						19 12				19 42			
Mill Hill Broadway	d					18 16				18 46						19 16				19 46			
Hendon	d					18 20				18 50						19 20				19 50			
Cricklewood	d					18 23				18 53						19 23				19 53			
West Hampstead Thameslink ⊖	d		18 15			18 27	18 31			18 57	19 01					19 27	19 31			19 57	20 01		
Kentish Town ⊖	d					18 31				19 01						19 31				20 01			
St Pancras International 15 ⊖	a		18 22	18 09		18 35	18 39			19 05	19 09	18 47	18 55			19 35	19 39			20 05	20 09	19 47	20 07
	d		18 24			18 36	18 40			19 06	19 10					19 36	19 40			20 06	20 10		
Farringdon 3 ⊖	d		18 29			18 41	18 45			19 11	19 15					19 41	19 45			20 11	20 15		
City Thameslink 3	d																						
London Blackfriars 3 ⊖	d	18 28	18 34		18 42	18 46	18 51	18 58	19 12	19 16	19 21			19 28	19 42	19 46	19 51	19 58	20 12	20 16	20 21		
Elephant & Castle ⊖173,179	d	18 31	18 38		18 46	18 49	18 55	19 01	19 16	19 19	19 25			19 31	19 46	19 49	19 55	20 01	20 16	20 19	20 25		
Loughborough Jn 173,179	d	18 35				18 53		19 05		19 23				19 35		19 53		20 05		20 23			
Herne Hill 4 173,179	d	18 39				18 57		19 09		19 27				19 39		19 57		20 09		20 27			
London Bridge 4	a																						
	d																						
Tulse Hill 3	d	18 44				19 02		19 14		19 32				19 44		20 02		20 14		20 32			
Streatham 4	d	18 48				19 06		19 18		19 36				19 48		20 06		20 18		20 36			
Mitcham Eastfields 173	d	18 52						19 22						19 52				20 22					
Mitcham Junction 173 ⛴	d	18 55						19 25						19 55				20 25					
Hackbridge 173	d	18 59						19 29						19 59				20 29					
Carshalton 173	d	19 01						19 31						20 01				20 31					
Tooting 173	d					19 12				19 42						20 12				20 42			
Haydons Road 173	d					19 15				19 45						20 15				20 45			
Wimbledon 6 ⊖173,179 ⛴	d					19 18				19 48						20 18				20 48			
Wimbledon Chase 179	d					19 21				19 51						20 21				20 51			
South Merton 179	d					19 23				19 53						20 23				20 53			
Morden South 179	d					19 25				19 55						20 25				20 55			
St Helier 179	d					19 27				19 57						20 27				20 57			
Sutton Common 179	d					19 29				19 59						20 29				20 59			
West Sutton 179	d					19 32				20 02						20 32				21 02			
Sutton (Surrey) 4 179	a	19 05				19 35		19 35		20 05				20 05		20 35		20 35		21 05			
Denmark Hill 4 195	d				18 52				19 22						19 52				20 22				
Peckham Rye 4 195	d				18 55				19 25						19 55				20 25				
Nunhead 4 195	d				18 57				19 27						19 57				20 27				
Crofton Park 195	d				19 00				19 30						20 00				20 30				
Catford 195	d				19 03				19 33						20 03				20 33				
Bellingham 195	d				19 05				19 35						20 05				20 35				
Beckenham Hill 195	d				19 07				19 37						20 07				20 37				
Ravensbourne 195	d				19 09				19 39						20 09				20 39				
Shortlands 195	d				19 11				19 41						20 11				20 41				
Bromley South 4 195	d				19 14				19 44						20 14				20 44				
Bickley 4 195	d				19 17				19 47						20 17				20 47				
St Mary Cray 195	d				19 21				19 51						20 21				20 51				
Swanley 4 195	d				19 26				19 56						20 26				20 56				
Eynsford 195	d				19 30				20 00						20 30				21 00				
Shoreham (Kent) 195	d				19 34				20 04						20 34				21 04				
Otford 4 195	d				19 37				20 07						20 37				21 07				
Bat & Ball 195	d				19 40				20 10						20 40				21 10				
Sevenoaks 4 195	a				19 43				20 13						20 43				21 13				
East Croydon ⛴	d		19 09				19 26				19 56						20 26				20 56		
Redhill	d																						
Gatwick Airport 10 ✈	d		19 26				19 42				20 12						20 42				21 12		
Three Bridges 4	d		19a33				19 47				20 17						20 47				21 17		
Balcombe	d																						
Haywards Heath 3	d						19 56				20 26						20 56				21 26		
Wivelsfield 4	d																						
Burgess Hill 4	d						20 01				20 33						21 01				21 33		
Hassocks 4	d						20 05				20 37						21 05				21 37		
Preston Park	d																						
Brighton 10	a						20 15				20 47						21 15				21 47		

A From Leeds
B From Nottingham
C From Derby

The trains that operate to and from Sevenoaks, Orpington and Rochester (and a few other destinations at peak times) are operated jointly by First Capital Connect (north of Blackfriars) and Southeastern (south of Blackfriars)

Table 52 shows the complete service between Bedford and London, whilst services between London, Sevenoaks, Sutton and Brighton only show through Thameslink services. Other Tables should be consulted for additional journey opportunities.

Table 52

Sundays
30 March to 11 May

Bedford, Luton, St Albans and City of London - South London, Gatwick Airport and Brighton

Network Diagram - refer to first Page of Table 52

		FC	SE	FC	FC	EM	SE	FC	FC	EM	SE	FC	EM	SE	FC	EM	SE	FC	EM	SE	FC	EM	SE
					1	◇1			1	◇1		1	◇1		1	◇1		1	◇1		1	◇1	
						A				A			B			A			C			C	
						☕				☕			☕			☕			☕			☕	
Bedford 7	d				19 36	19 59			20 06	20 08		20 28	20 39		20 58	21 09		21 28	21 32		21 58	22 21	
Flitwick	d				19 46				20 16			20 38			21 08			21 38			22 08		
Harlington	d				19 50				20 20			20 42			21 12			21 42			22 12		
Leagrave	d				19 56				20 26			20 48			21 18			21 48			22 18		
Luton 10	d			19 48	20 00	20 13		20 18	20 30			20 52			21 22	21 23		21 52	21 47		22 22	22 37	
Luton Airport Parkway 7 ✈	d			19 51	20 03			20 21	20 33	20 23		20 55	20 54		21 25			21 55			22 25		
Harpenden	d			19 57	20 09			20 27	20 39			21 01			21 31			22 01			22 31		
St Albans City	d			20 03	20 15			20 33	20 45			21 07			21 37			22 07			22 37		
Radlett	d			20 08				20 38				21 12			21 42			22 12			22 42		
Elstree & Borehamwood	d			20 12				20 42				21 17			21 47			22 17			22 47		
Mill Hill Broadway	d			20 16				20 46				21 21			21 51			22 21			22 51		
Hendon	d			20 20				20 50				21 24			21 54			22 24			22 54		
Cricklewood	d			20 23				20 53				21 28			21 58			22 28			22 58		
West Hampstead Thameslink ⊖	d			20 27	20 31			20 57	21 01			21 31			22 01			22 31			23 01		
Kentish Town ⊖	d			20 31				21 01				21 36			22 06			22 36			23 06		
St Pancras International 15 ⊖	a			20 35	20 39	20 37		21 05	21 09	20 47		21 39	21 17		22 09	21 47		22 39	22 14		23 09	23 03	
	d			20 36	20 40			21 06	21 10			21 40			22 10			22 40			23 10		
Farringdon 3 ⊖	d			20 41	20 45			21 11	21 15			21 45			22 15			22 45			23 15		
City Thameslink 3	d																						
London Blackfriars 3 ⊖	d	20 28	20 42	20 46	20 51		21 12	21 16	21 21		21 42	21 51		22 12	22 21		22 42	22 51		23 12	23 21		23 42
Elephant & Castle ⊖173,179	d	20 31	20 46	20 49	20 55		21 16	21 19	21 25		21 46	21 55		22 16	22 25		22 46	22 55		23 16	23 25		23 46
Loughborough Jn 173,179	d	20 35		20 53				21 23															
Herne Hill 4 173,179	d	20 39		20 57				21 27															
London Bridge 4	a																						
	d																						
Tulse Hill 3	d	20 44		21 02				21 32															
Streatham 4	d	20 48		21 06				21 36															
Mitcham Eastfields 173	d	20 52																					
Mitcham Junction 173 🚌	d	20 55																					
Hackbridge 173	d	20 59																					
Carshalton 173	d	21 01																					
Tooting 173	d			21 12				21 42															
Haydons Road 173	d			21 15				21 45															
Wimbledon 6 ⊖173,179 🚌	d			21 18				21 48															
Wimbledon Chase 179	d			21 21				21 51															
South Merton 179	d			21 23				21 53															
Morden South 179	d			21 25				21 55															
St Helier 179	d			21 27				21 57															
Sutton Common 179	d			21 29				21 59															
West Sutton 179	d			21 32				22 02															
Sutton (Surrey) 4 179	a	21 05		21 35				22 05															
Denmark Hill 4 195	d		20 52				21 22				21 52			22 22			22 52			23 22			23 52
Peckham Rye 4 195	d		20 55				21 25				21 55			22 25			22 55			23 25			23 55
Nunhead 4 195	d		20 57				21 27				21 57			22 27			22 57			23 27			23 57
Crofton Park 195	d		21 00				21 30				22 00			22 30			23 00			23 30			23 59
Catford 195	d		21 03				21 33				22 03			22 33			23 03			23 33			00 03
Bellingham 195	d		21 05				21 35				22 05			22 35			23 05			23 35			00 05
Beckenham Hill 195	d		21 07				21 37				22 07			22 37			23 07			23 37			00 07
Ravensbourne 195	d		21 09				21 39				22 09			22 39			23 09			23 39			00 09
Shortlands 195	d		21 11				21 41				22 11			22 41			23 11			23 41			00 11
Bromley South 4 195	d		21 14				21 44				22 14			22 44			23 14			23 44			00 14
Bickley 4 195	d		21 17				21 47				22 17			22 47			23 17			23 47			00 17
St Mary Cray 195	d		21 21				21 51				22 21			22 51			23 21			23 51			00 21
Swanley 4 195	d		21 26				21 56				22 26			22 56			23 26			23 56			00 26
Eynsford 195	d		21 30				22 00				22 30			23 00			23 30			00 01			00 30
Shoreham (Kent) 195	d		21 34				22 04				22 34			23 04			23 34			00 04			00 34
Otford 4 195	d		21 37				22 07				22 37			23 07			23 37			00 07			00 37
Bat & Ball 195	d		21 40				22 10				22 40			23 10			23 40			00 10			00 40
Sevenoaks 4 195	a		21 43				22 13				22 43			23 13			23 43			00 13			00 43
East Croydon 🚌	d				21 26				21 56			22 26			22 56			23 26			23 57		
Redhill	d																						
Gatwick Airport 10 ✈	d				21 42				22 12			22 42			23 12			23 42			00 20		
Three Bridges 4	d				21 47				22 17			22 47			23 17			23 47			00 25		
Balcombe	d																						
Haywards Heath 3	d				21 56				22 26			22 56			23 26			23 56			00 36		
Wivelsfield 4	d																						
Burgess Hill 4	d				22 01				22 33			23 01			23 33			00 02			00 42		
Hassocks 4	d				22 05				22 37			23 05			23 37			00 06			00 45		
Preston Park	d																						
Brighton 10	a				22 15				22 47			23 15			23 47			00 15			00 55		

A From Nottingham
B From York
C From Sheffield

The trains that operate to and from Sevenoaks, Orpington and Rochester (and a few other destinations at peak times) are operated jointly by First Capital Connect (north of Blackfriars) and Southeastern (south of Blackfriars)

Table 52 shows the complete service between Bedford and London, whilst services between London, Sevenoaks, Sutton and Brighton only show through Thameslink services. Other Tables should be consulted for additional journey opportunities.

Table 52

Sundays
30 March to 11 May

Bedford, Luton, St Albans and City of London - South London, Gatwick Airport and Brighton

Network Diagram - refer to first Page of Table 52

			FC	EM	FC	FC
			1	◇1 A ⊡	1	1
Bedford 7		d	22 28	22 39	23 02	23 42
Flitwick		d	22 38		23 12	23 52
Harlington		d	22 42		23 16	23 56
Leagrave		d	22 48		23 22	00 02
Luton 10		d	22 52	22 53	23 26	00 06
Luton Airport Parkway 7	✈	d	22 55		23 29	00 09
Harpenden		d	23 01		23 35	00 15
St Albans City		d	23 07		23 41	00 21
Radlett		d	23 12		23 46	00 26
Elstree & Borehamwood		d	23 17		23 51	00 31
Mill Hill Broadway		d	23 21		23 55	00 35
Hendon		d	23 24		23 58	00 38
Cricklewood		d	23 28		00 02	00 42
West Hampstead Thameslink	⊖	d	23 31		00 05	00 45
Kentish Town	⊖	d	23 36		00 10	00 50
St Pancras International 15	⊖	a	23 39	23 25	00 13	00 53
		d	23 40		00 14	00 54
Farringdon 3	⊖	d	23 45		00 19	
City Thameslink 3		d				
London Blackfriars 3	⊖	d	23 51		00 25	01 05
Elephant & Castle	⊖173,179	d				
Loughborough Jn	173,179	d				
Herne Hill 4	173,179	d				
London Bridge 4		a				
		d				
Tulse Hill 3		d				
Streatham 4		d				
Mitcham Eastfields	173	d				
Mitcham Junction	173 🚋	d				
Hackbridge	173	d				
Carshalton	173	d				
Tooting	173	d				
Haydons Road	173	d				
Wimbledon 6	⊖173,179 🚋	d				
Wimbledon Chase	179	d				
South Merton	179	d				
Morden South	179	d				
St Helier	179	d				
Sutton Common	179	d				
West Sutton	179	d				
Sutton (Surrey) 4	179	a				
Denmark Hill 4	195	d				
Peckham Rye 4	195	d				
Nunhead 4	195	d				
Crofton Park	195	d				
Catford	195	d				
Bellingham	195	d				
Beckenham Hill	195	d				
Ravensbourne	195	d				
Shortlands	195	d				
Bromley South 4	195	d				
Bickley 4	195	d				
St Mary Cray	195	d				
Swanley 4	195	d				
Eynsford	195	d				
Shoreham (Kent)	195	d				
Otford 4	195	d				
Bat & Ball	195	d				
Sevenoaks 4	195	a				
East Croydon	🚋	d	00 29		00 57	01 36
Redhill		d				
Gatwick Airport 10	✈	d	00 49		01 19	01 55
Three Bridges 4		d	00a54		01a24	02a02
Balcombe		d				
Haywards Heath 3		d				
Wivelsfield 4		d				
Burgess Hill 4		d				
Hassocks 4		d				
Preston Park		d				
Brighton 10		a				

A From Nottingham

The trains that operate to and from Sevenoaks, Orpington and Rochester (and a few other destinations at peak times) are operated jointly by First Capital Connect (north of Blackfriars) and Southeastern (south of Blackfriars)

Table 52 shows the complete service between Bedford and London, whilst services between London, Sevenoaks, Sutton and Brighton only show through Thameslink services. Other Tables should be consulted for additional journey opportunities.

Table 52R

Mondays to Fridays

9 December to 16 May

Brighton, Gatwick Airport and South London - City of London, St Albans, Luton and Bedford

Network Diagram - refer to first Page of Table 52

Miles	Miles	Miles	Miles	Miles			FC	FC	FC	FC	FC	FC	FC	FC	FC	FC	FC	EM	FC	FC	FC	FC	FC	FC
							MO	MX	MX	MO	MX	MO	MX	MX	MO	MX	MO	MX	MO	MX	MX	MO	MO	MX
							1			1	1	1			1	1	1	◇1	1		1	1	1	1
							A	B	C	D	E	A	B	C	D	E	A	F	D		E	A	D	E
																		⚲						
0	—	—	—	—	**Brighton** 10	d																		
1½	—	—	—	—	Preston Park	d																		
7¼	—	—	—	—	Hassocks 4	d																		
9¼	—	—	—	—	Burgess Hill 4	d																		
10	—	—	—	—	Wivelsfield 4	d																		
13	—	—	—	—	**Haywards Heath** 3	d																		
17	—	—	—	—	Balcombe	d																		00 04
21½	—	—	—	—	Three Bridges 4	d																		00 10
24¼	—	—	—	—	**Gatwick Airport** 10 ✈	d																		00 15
30	—	—	—	—	Redhill	d																		00 24
40½	—	—	—	—	**East Croydon**	d															00 02	00 02	00 02	00 36
—	—	—	0	—	Sevenoaks 4	195 d																		
—	—	—	1¼	—	Bat & Ball	195 d																		
—	—	—	2¾	—	Otford 4	195 d																		
—	—	—	4¼	—	Shoreham (Kent)	195 d																		
—	—	—	6½	—	Eynsford	195 d																		
—	—	—	9½	—	Swanley 4	195 d																		
—	—	—	12	—	St Mary Cray 4	195 d																		
—	—	—	15	—	Bickley	195 d																		
—	—	—	16	—	Bromley South	195 d																		
—	—	—	16¾	—	Shortlands 4	195 d																		
—	—	—	17½	—	Ravensbourne	195 d																		
—	—	—	18¼	—	Beckenham Hill	195 d																		
—	—	—	19	—	Bellingham	195 d																		
—	—	—	20	—	Catford	195 d																		
—	—	—	20¾	—	Crofton Park	195 d																		
—	—	—	22	—	Nunhead 4	195 d																		
—	—	—	22¾	—	Peckham Rye 4	195 d																		
—	—	—	23¾	—	Denmark Hill 4	195 d																		
—	0	0	—	—	**Sutton (Surrey)** 4	179 d																		
—	1	—	—	—	West Sutton	179 d																		
—	2	—	—	—	Sutton Common	179 d																		
—	3	—	—	—	St Helier	179 d																		
—	3½	—	—	—	Morden South	179 d																		
—	4	—	—	—	South Merton	179 d																		
—	4½	—	—	—	Wimbledon Chase	179 d																		
—	5½	—	—	—	**Wimbledon** 6 ⊖173,179	d																		
—	6¾	—	—	—	Haydons Road	173 d																		
—	8	—	—	—	Tooting	173 d																		
—	—	1¼	—	—	Carshalton	173 d																		
—	—	2	—	—	Hackbridge	173 d																		
—	—	4	—	—	Mitcham Junction	173 d																		
—	—	5	—	—	Mitcham Eastfields	173 d																		
—	9½	6	—	—	Streatham 4	d																		
—	11	7½	—	—	Tulse Hill 3	d																		
50¾	—	—	—	—	**London Bridge** 4 ⊖	a															00 21	00 21		00 52
—	—	—	—	—		d															00 22	00 22		00 52
—	12	8½	—	—	Herne Hill 4	173,179 d																		
—	13	9½	—	—	Loughborough Jn	173,179 d																		
—	15	11¼	26¼	—	Elephant & Castle	173,179 d																		
51½	16	12½	27½	—	**London Blackfriars** 3 ⊖	d													00 08	00 09	00 28	00 29	00 30	00 58
52	—	—	—	—	City Thameslink 3	d																		
52¾	—	—	—	—	Farringdon 3 ⊖	d													00 14	00 14	00 34	00 34	00 36	
53¾	—	—	—	0	**St Pancras International** 15 ⊖	a													00 18	00 18	00 38	00 38	00 40	01 08
—	—	—	—	—		d										00 03	00 04	00 15	00 18	00 19	00 39	00 39	00 40	01 09
55½	—	—	—	—	Kentish Town ⊖	d											00 08		00 22	00 22	00 42	00 42	00 44	01 12
58	—	—	—	—	West Hampstead Thameslink ⊖	d										00 10	00 12		00 26	00 26	00 46	00 46	00 48	01 16
59	—	—	—	—	Cricklewood	d											00 15		00 29	00 29	00 49	00 49	00 51	01 19
61	—	—	—	—	Hendon	d							00 01	00 01	00 02		00 18		00 32	00 32	00 52	00 52	00 54	01 22
63¼	—	—	—	—	Mill Hill Broadway	d							00 05	00 05	00 06		00 22		00 36	00 36	00 56	00 56	00 58	01 26
66½	—	—	—	—	Elstree & Borehamwood	d							00 09	00 09	00 10		00 26		00 40	00 40	01 00	01 00	01 02	01 30
69½	—	—	—	—	Radlett	d						00 01	00 14	00 14	00 15		00 31		00 45	00 45	01 05	01 05	01 07	01 35
74	—	—	—	20	**St Albans City**	d						00 08	00 21	00 21	00 22	00 27	00 38		00 52	00 51	01 11	01 11	01 14	01 41
78¾	—	—	—	24¾	Harpenden	d					00 03	00 14	00 27	00 27	00 28	00 33	00 44		00 58	00 57	01 17	01 17	01 20	01 47
83¼	—	—	—	29¼	Luton Airport Parkway 7 ✈	d		00 03	00 03	00 04	00 09	00 20	00 33	00 33	00 34	00 39	00 50	00 43	01 04	01 03	01 23	01 23	01 26	01 53
84¼	30¼	—	—	30¼	**Luton** 10	d		00 06	00 06	00 07	00 12	00 23	00 36	00 36	00 37	00 42	00 53	00 47	01 07	01 06	01 26	01 26	01 29	01 56
86¾	—	—	—	32¾	Leagrave	d		00 10	00 10	00 11	00 16	00 27	00 40	00 40	00 41	00 46	00 57		01 11	01 10	01 30	01 30	01 33	02 00
91¾	—	—	—	37¾	Harlington	d	00 02	00 14	00 15	00 16	00 21	00 32	00 44	00 45	00 46	00 51	01 02		01 16	01 15	01 35	01 35	01 38	02 05
94¼	—	—	—	40¼	Flitwick	d	00 06	00 18	00 19	00 20	00 25	00 36	00 48	00 49	00 50	00 55	01 06		01 20	01 19	01 39	01 39	01 42	02 09
103¾	49¾	—	—	50	**Bedford** 7	a	00 19	00 32	00 32	00 33	00 38	00 49	01 02	01 02	01 03	01 08	01 19	01 11	01 33	01 32	01 52	01 52	01 55	02 22

A until 30 December. From Brighton
B from 31 December until 7 February. From Sutton (Surrey)
C until 27 December, from 11 February. From Sutton (Surrey)
D from 6 January. From Brighton
E From Brighton
F To Leicester

The trains that operate to and from Sevenoaks, Orpington and Rochester (and a few other destinations at peak times) are operated jointly by First Capital Connect (north of Blackfriars) and Southeastern (south of Blackfriars)

Table 52 shows the complete service between Bedford and London, whilst services between London, Sevenoaks, Sutton and Brighton only show through Thameslink services. Other Tables should be consulted for additional journey opportunities.

Table 52R

Mondays to Fridays

9 December to 16 May

Brighton, Gatwick Airport and South London - City of London, St Albans, Luton and Bedford

Network Diagram - refer to first Page of Table 52

		FC	FC	FC	FC	FC	FC	SE	SE	EM	FC	FC	FC	SE	EM	FC	FC	EM	EM	SE	FC
		MO	MO																		
		1	1	1	1	1	1			◇1	1		1		◇1	1		◇1	◇1		1
		A	B	C				I	I	J		L		I	J		L	M	M		
Brighton [10]	d															05 10					05 40
Preston Park	d															05 14					05 44
Hassocks [4]	d															05 20					05 50
Burgess Hill [4]	d															05 24					05 54
Wivelsfield [4]	d															05 26					05 56
Haywards Heath [3]	d	00 01	00 01													05 31					06 01
Balcombe	d															05 36					06 06
Three Bridges [4]	d	00 10	00 10	01 16	02 16	03 16	04 16				04 52					05 42					06 12
Gatwick Airport [10] ✈	d	00 15	00 15	01 21	02 21	03 21	04 21				04 57		05 27			05 47					06 17
Redhill	d	00 24	00 24										05 35								
East Croydon	d	00 36	00 36	01 40	02 40	03 40	04 40				05 16		05 48			06 02					06 32
Sevenoaks [4] 195	d																			05 40	
Bat & Ball 195	d																			05 43	
Otford [4] 195	d																			05 46	
Shoreham (Kent) 195	d																			05 49	
Eynsford 195	d																			05 53	
Swanley [4] 195	d																			05 58	
St Mary Cray [4] 195	d																			06 02	
Bickley 195	d							04 41	05 02					05 41						06 06	
Bromley South 195	d							04 44	05 05					05 44						06 10	
Shortlands [4] 195	d							04 47	05 08					05 47						06 13	
Ravensbourne 195	d							04 49						05 49						06 15	
Beckenham Hill 195	d							04 51						05 51						06 17	
Bellingham 195	d							04 53						05 53						06 19	
Catford 195	d							04 56						05 56						06 22	
Crofton Park 195	d							04 58						05 58						06 25	
Nunhead [4] 195	d							05 01						06 01						06 27	
Peckham Rye [4] 195	d							05 04						06 04						06 30	
Denmark Hill [4] 195	d							05 07						06 07						06 33	
Sutton (Surrey) [4] 179	d																				
West Sutton 179	d																				
Sutton Common 179	d																				
St Helier 179	d																				
Morden South 179	d																				
South Merton 179	d																				
Wimbledon Chase 179	d																				
Wimbledon [5] ⊖173,179	d																				
Haydons Road 173	d																				
Tooting 173	d																				
Carshalton 173	d																				
Hackbridge 173	d																				
Mitcham Junction 173	d																				
Mitcham Eastfields 173	d																				
Streatham [4]	d											05 46					06 09				
Tulse Hill [3]	d											05 51					06 13				
London Bridge [4] ⊖	a	00 51									05 34		06 02			06 15					06 46
	d	00 51									05 34		06 02			06 16					06 46
Herne Hill [4] 173,179	d								05 23			05 55					06 17				
Loughborough Jn. 173,179	d																06 20				
Elephant & Castle 173,179	d							05 13	05 29			06 00		06 13			06 24			06 40	
London Blackfriars [3] ⊖	d	00 58	01 04	02 09	03 09	04 09	05 09	05a17	05 33		05 42	06 04	06 12	06a17		06 24	06 30			06 48	06 52
City Thameslink [3]	d						05 11		05 35		05 44	06 07	06 14			06 26	06 32			06 50	06 54
Farringdon [3] ⊖	d								05 38		05 48	06 10	06 18			06 30	06 36			06 54	06 58
St Pancras International [15] ⊖	a	01 09	01 13	02 20	03 20	04 20	05 18		05 42		05 52	06 14	06 22			06 34	06 40			06 58	07 02
	d	01 10	01 15	02 21	03 21	04 21	05 20		05 43	05 45	05 52	06 15	06 22		06 32	06 34	06 40	06 52	06 55	06 58	07 02
Kentish Town ⊖	d	01 13	01 18	02 24	03 24	04 24	05 24		05a47		05 56	06 18					06 44			07 02	
West Hampstead Thameslink ⊖	d	01 17	01 22	02 28	03 28	04 28	05 28				06 00	06 22				06 42	06 48			07 06	07 10
Cricklewood	d	01 20	01 25	02 31	03 31	04 31	05 31				06 03	06 25					06 51			07 09	
Hendon	d	01 23	01 28	02 34	03 34	04 34	05 34				06 06	06 28					06 54			07 12	
Mill Hill Broadway	d	01 27	01 32	02 38	03 38	04 38	05 38				06 10	06 32					06 58			07 16	
Elstree & Borehamwood	d	01 31	01 36	02 42	03 42	04 42	05 42				06 14	06 36					07 02			07 20	
Radlett	d	01 36	01 41	02 47	03 47	04 47	05 47				06 18	06 42					07 06			07 24	
St Albans City	d	01 42	01 48	02 54	03 54	04 54	05 54				06 24	06 48	06 44			06 58	07 12			07a31	07 23
Harpenden	d	01 48	01 54	03 00	04 00	05 00	06 00				06 30	06 54	06 50			07 04	07 18				07 29
Luton Airport Parkway [7] ✈	d	01 54	02 00	03 06	04 06	05 06	06 06				06 36	07 00	06 56			07 10	07 24	07a12			07 34
Luton [10]	d	01 57	02 03	03 09	04 09	05 09	06 09			06 12	06 39	07a03	06 59		06 54	07 13	07 27		07 18		07 37
Leagrave	d	02 01	02 07	03 13	04 13	05 13	06 13				06 43		07 03			07 17	07 31				07 41
Harlington	d	02 06	02 12	03 18	04 18	05 18	06 18				06 48		07 08			07 22	07 36				07 46
Flitwick	d	02 10	02 16	03 22	04 22	05 22	06 22				06 52		07 12			07 26	07 40				07 50
Bedford [7]	a	02 23	02 29	03 35	04 35	05 35	06 37			06 26	07 04		07 24		07 08	07 40	07 52		07 33		08 03

A until 30 December. From Brighton
B from 6 January. From Brighton
C MO from 6 January
I From Orpington
J To Sheffield
L From Selhurst
M To Nottingham

The trains that operate to and from Sevenoaks, Orpington and Rochester (and a few other destinations at peak times) are operated jointly by First Capital Connect (north of Blackfriars) and Southeastern (south of Blackfriars)

Table 52 shows the complete service between Bedford and London, whilst services between London, Sevenoaks, Sutton and Brighton only show through Thameslink services. Other Tables should be consulted for additional journey opportunities.

Table 52R

Mondays to Fridays

9 December to 16 May

Brighton, Gatwick Airport and South London - City of London, St Albans, Luton and Bedford

Network Diagram - refer to first Page of Table 52

Station	Table		FC	FC	FC	SE	EM	SE	FC	FC	SE	SE	EM	FC	FC	SE	SE	FC	SE	EM	FC	SE	SE
				1			◇1	1	1				◇1	1		1				◇1	1	1	
							A	B			C		D			B	C			A		E	C
Brighton 10		d		05 50					06 08					06 24							07 02		
Preston Park		d		05 54					06 12					06 28							07 06		
Hassocks 4		d		06 00					06 19					06 35							07 13		
Burgess Hill 4		d		06 04					06 23					06 39							07 17		
Wivelsfield 4		d		06 06					06 25												07 20		
Haywards Heath 3		d		06 11					06 30					06 45							07 25		
Balcombe		d							06 36					06 51									
Three Bridges 4		d		06 20					06 42					06 57							07 34		
Gatwick Airport 10 ✈		d		06 25					06 47					07 02							07 39		
Redhill		d		06 33					06 56					07 11									
East Croydon		d		06 45					07 09					07 23							07 54		
Sevenoaks 4	195	d				06 13						06 42							07 11				
Bat & Ball	195	d				06 16						06 48							07 14				
Otford 4	195	d				06 19		06 37				06 51				07 23			07 18				
Shoreham (Kent)	195	d				06 22						06 54							07 21				
Eynsford	195	d				06 26						06 58							07 24				
Swanley 4	195	d				06 31		06 47				07 03				07 32			07 30				
St Mary Cray 4	195	d				06 35						07 07							07 34				
Bickley	195	d				06 39					07 05	07 11					07 35		07 39				07 55
Bromley South	195	d				06 42		06 57			07 08	07 14				07 40	07 38		07 42				07 58
Shortlands 4	195	d				06 45					07 11	07 17					07 41		07 44				08 00
Ravensbourne	195	d				06 47						07 19							07 47				
Beckenham Hill	195	d				06 49						07 21							07 49				
Bellingham	195	d				06 51						07 23							07 51				08 05
Catford	195	d				06 54						07 26							07 53				08 08
Crofton Park	195	d				06 57						07 29							07 56				08 10
Nunhead 4	195	d				06 59						07 31							07 58				08 14
Peckham Rye 4	195	d				07 02						07 34							08 01				08 16
Denmark Hill 4	195	d				07 05						07 37							08 04				08 19
Sutton (Surrey) 4	179	d	06 05		06 34					06 45					07 05			07 36					
West Sutton	179	d	06 08							06 48					07 08								
Sutton Common	179	d	06 10							06 50					07 10								
St Helier	179	d	06 13							06 53					07 13								
Morden South	179	d	06 15							06 55					07 15								
South Merton	179	d	06 17							06 57					07 17								
Wimbledon Chase	179	d	06 19							06 59					07 19								
Wimbledon 6	⊖173,179	d	06 28							07 06					07 26								
Haydons Road	173	d	06 30							07 08					07 28								
Tooting	173	d	06 33							07 11					07 31								
Carshalton	173	d			06 37													07 39					
Hackbridge	173	d			06 39													07 41					
Mitcham Junction	173	d			06 42													07 44					
Mitcham Eastfields	173	d			06 45													07 47					
Streatham 4		d	06 38		06 49					07 16					07 38			07 52					
Tulse Hill 3		d	06 42		06 53					07 20					07 43			07 57					
London Bridge 4 ⊖		a		06 58					07 23														
		d		06 58					07 24														
Herne Hill 4	173,179	d	06 46		06 57					07 24	07 31			07 41	07 47		07 57	08 01				08 13	
Loughborough Jn.	173,179	d	06 49		07 00					07 27	07 34				07 50		08 00	08 04				08 16	
Elephant & Castle	173,179	d	06 54		07 06	07 12		07 16		07 32	07 38	07 44		07 48	07 54	07 59	08 05	08 09	08 13			08 21	08 25
London Blackfriars 3 ⊖		d	06 58	07 06	07 12	07 18		07 24	07 30	07 36	07 42	07 48		07 54	07 58	08 04	08 09	08 13	08 17		08 21	08 25	08 29
City Thameslink 3		d	07 00	07 08	07 14	07 20		07 26	07 33	07 38	07 44	07 50		07 56	08 01	08 06	08 11	08 15	08 19		08 23	08 27	08 31
Farringdon 3 ⊖		d	07 04	07 12	07 18	07 24		07 30	07 36	07 42	07 48	07 54		08 00	08 04	08 10	08 15	08 19	08 23		08 27	08 31	08 35
St Pancras International 15 ⊖		a	07 08	07 16	07 22	07 28		07 34	07 40	07 46	07 52	07 58		08 04	08 08	08 14	08 19	08 23	08 27		08 31	08 35	08 39
		d	07 08	07 18	07 22	07 28	07 28	07 34	07 40	07 46	07 52	07 58	08 00	08 04	08 10	08 16	08 20	08 24	08 28	08 29	08 32	08 36	08 40
Kentish Town ⊖		d				07 32						08 02			08 14			08 29	08 32				
West Hampstead Thameslink ⊖		d	07 16	07 26	07 30	07 36				07 54	08 00	08 06		08 11	08 18		08 28	08 34	08a38			08 43	08 50
Cricklewood		d				07 39						08 09			08 21			08 37					
Hendon		d				07 42						08 12			08 24			08 40					
Mill Hill Broadway		d	07 23			07 46					08 07	08 16			08 28		08 35	08 44					08 57
Elstree & Borehamwood		d	07 28		07 40	07 50					08 11	08 20			08 32		08 39	08 48					09 01
Radlett		d	07 32		07 44	07 54					08 15	08 24			08 36		08 43	08 52					09 06
St Albans City		d	07 38	07 42	07a51	08a01		07 52		08 09	08a23	08 30		08 25	08a43	08 35	08 50	08a59			08 52	08 58	09 13
Harpenden		d	07 43	07 47				07 57		08 15		08 35		08 31		08 42	08 55					09 04	09 19
Luton Airport Parkway 7 ✈		d	07 49	07 53			07 49	08 03	08 06	08 21		08 41		08 37		08 48	09 01			08 50	09 02	09 10	09 25
Luton 10		d	07a53	07 57				08 06	08a10	08 24		08a45	08 22	08 40		08 51	09a04				09 05	09 13	09a29
Leagrave		d		08 00				08 10		08 27				08 44		08 54						09 17	
Harlington		d		08 05				08 15		08 32				08 49		08 59						09 22	
Flitwick		d		08 09				08 19		08 36				08 53		09 03					09 13	09 26	
Bedford 7		a		08 23			08 03	08 33		08 49			08 36	09 05		09 17				09 04	09 26	09 38	

A To Nottingham
B From Ashford International
C From Orpington
D To Corby.
E From Beckenham Junction

The trains that operate to and from Sevenoaks, Orpington and Rochester (and a few other destinations at peak times) are operated jointly by First Capital Connect (north of Blackfriars) and Southeastern (south of Blackfriars)

Table 52 shows the complete service between Bedford and London, whilst services between London, Sevenoaks, Sutton and Brighton only show through Thameslink services. Other Tables should be consulted for additional journey opportunities.

Table 52R

Mondays to Fridays

9 December to 16 May

Brighton, Gatwick Airport and South London - City of London, St Albans, Luton and Bedford

Network Diagram - refer to first Page of Table 52

Station		FC	SE	SE	FC	EM	SE	FC	SE	FC	SE	FC	FC	SE	EM	FC	SE	SE	FC	FC	SE	FC	EM
			1			◇1	1	1			1	1			◇1	1	1			1			◇1
			A			B 🚲					C				D 🚲			E					B 🚲
Brighton 10	d							07 24				07 50				08 02				08 16			
Preston Park	d							07 28				07 54				08 06				08 20			
Hassocks 4	d							07 35				08 01				08 13				08 27			
Burgess Hill 4	d							07 39								08 17				08 31			
Wivelsfield 4	d															08 20				08 34			
Haywards Heath 3	d							07 47				08 09				08 25				08 39			
Balcombe	d											08 15											
Three Bridges 4	d							07 56								08 34				08 48			
Gatwick Airport 10 ✈	d							08 01				08 24				08 39				08 53			
Redhill	d							08 09															
East Croydon	d							08 23				08 39				08 54				09 09			
Sevenoaks 4	195 d			07 36					07 53								08 24				08 43		
Bat & Ball	195 d			07 39					07 56								08 27				08 46		
Otford 4	195 d			07 43					08 00								08 31				08 49		
Shoreham (Kent)	195 d			07 46					08 03								08 34				08 52		
Eynsford	195 d			07 49					08 06								08 37				08 56		
Swanley 4	195 d		07 55	07 54					08 11								08 42				09 01		
St Mary Cray 4	195 d		08 00	07 59					08 16								08 46				09 05		
Bickley	195 d			08 03					08 20								08 51	08 55			09 09		
Bromley South	195 d		08 06	08 08			08 18		08 23					08 44			08 54	08 58			09 12		
Shortlands 4	195 d			08 10			08 20		08 26					08 46			08 56	09 00			09 15		
Ravensbourne	195 d			08 13			08 23							08 49				09 03			09 17		
Beckenham Hill	195 d			08 15			08 25							08 51				09 05			09 19		
Bellingham	195 d			08 17			08 27		08 30					08 53			09 01	09 07			09 21		
Catford	195 d			08 20			08 30		08 33					08 56			09 04	09 09			09 24		
Crofton Park	195 d								08 36					08 58				09 12			09 26		
Nunhead 4	195 d								08 38					09 01				09 14			09 29		
Peckham Rye 4	195 d						08 36		08 41					09 04			09 09	09 17			09 31		
Denmark Hill 4	195 d			08 26			08 39		08 45					09 07			09 12	09 19			09 34		
Sutton (Surrey) 4	179 d	07 40			08 08					08 08			08 39						08 41			09 13	
West Sutton	179 d	07 43								08 11									08 44				
Sutton Common	179 d	07 45								08 13									08 46				
St Helier	179 d	07 48								08 16									08 49				
Morden South	179 d	07 50								08 18									08 51				
South Merton	179 d	07 52								08 20									08 53				
Wimbledon Chase	179 d	07 54								08 22									08 55				
Wimbledon 6 ⊖173,179	d	08 00								08 28									08 58				
Haydons Road	173 d	08 02								08 30									09 00				
Tooting	173 d	08 06								08 33									09 03				
Carshalton	173 d				08 11								08 42									09 16	
Hackbridge	173 d				08 13								08 44									09 18	
Mitcham Junction	173 d				08 16								08 47									09 21	
Mitcham Eastfields	173 d				08 19								08 50									09 24	
Streatham 4	d	08 12			08 23					08 39			08 54						09 08			09 28	
Tulse Hill 3	d	08 16			08 28			08 37		08 43			08 58						09 16			09 32	
London Bridge 4 ⊖	a															09 08							
	d															09 09							
Herne Hill 4	173,179 d	08 20			08 32			08 41		08 47	08 52	08 57	09 02						09 20			09 36	
Loughborough Jn	173,179 d	08 24			08 36					08 50	08 57		09 05						09 23			09 40	
Elephant & Castle	173,179 d	08 29	08 31	08 35	08 40		08 45	08 50	08 54	08 58	09 02	09 06	09 10	09 14			09 20	09 26	09 30	09 34	09 42	09 45	
London Blackfriars 3 ⊖	d	08 33	08 37	08 42	08 46		08 50	08 54	08 58	09 02	09 06	09 10	09 14	09 18		09 22	09 26	09 30	09 34	09 38	09 46	09 50	
City Thameslink 3	d	08 35	08 39	08 44	08 48		08 52	08 56	09 00	09 04	09 08	09 12	09 16	09 20		09 24	09 28	09 32	09 36	09 40	09 48	09 52	
Farringdon 3 ⊖	d	08 39	08 43	08 48	08 52		08 56	09 00	09 04	09 08	09 12	09 16	09 20	09 24		09 28	09 32	09 36	09 40	09 44	09 52	09 56	
St Pancras International 15 ⊖	a	08 43	08 47	08 52	08 56		09 00	09 04	09 08	09 12	09 16	09 20	09 24	09 28		09 32	09 36	09 40	09 44	09 48	09 56	10 00	
	d	08 44	08 48	08 52	08 56	08 59	09 00	09 04	09 08	09 12	09 16	09 20	09 24	09 28	09 29	09 32	09 36	09 40	09 44	09 48	09 56	10 00	10 00
Kentish Town ⊖	d	08 48		08a57	09 00				09a13	09 16				09 34				09a45	09 48		10 00	10a05	
West Hampstead Thameslink ⊖	d	08 54			09 04			09 11		09 20			09 32	09 40			09 43		09 52		10 04		
Cricklewood	d	08 57			09 07					09 23				09 43					09 55		10 07		
Hendon	d	09 00			09 10					09 26				09 46					09 58		10 10		
Mill Hill Broadway	d	09 04			09 14					09 30				09 50					10 02		10 14		
Elstree & Borehamwood	d	09 08			09 18					09 34			09 42	09 54					10 06		10 18		
Radlett	d	09 12			09 22					09 38			09 46	09 58					10 10		10 22		
St Albans City	d	09 18	09 09		09a29		09 20	09 25		09 46		09 40	09a53	10 04		09 52	09 58		10 18	10 09	10a29		
Harpenden	d	09 24	09 15					09 32		09 51		09 46		10 09			10 04		10 23	10 15			
Luton Airport Parkway 7 ✈	d	09 30	09 21				09 29	09 38		09 57	09 44	09 52		10 15	09 50	10 01	10 10		10 29	10 21			
Luton 10	d	09a34	09 24			09 21	09 32	09 41		10a01	09 47	09 55		10a19		10 04	10 13		10a33	10 24			10 22
Leagrave	d		09 27					09 45			09 50	09 59					10 17			10 27			
Harlington	d		09 32					09 50				10 04					10 22			10 33			
Flitwick	d		09 36				09 43	09 55			09 58	10 08				10 12	10 26			10 37			
Bedford 7	a		09 49			09 35	09 55	10 07			10 11	10 20			10 04	10 23	10 38			10 49			10 36

A From Rochester
B To Corby.
C From Kent House
D To Nottingham
E From Orpington

The trains that operate to and from Sevenoaks, Orpington and Rochester (and a few other destinations at peak times) are operated jointly by First Capital Connect (north of Blackfriars) and Southeastern (south of Blackfriars)

Table 52 shows the complete service between Bedford and London, whilst services between London, Sevenoaks, Sutton and Brighton only show through Thameslink services. Other Tables should be consulted for additional journey opportunities.

Table 52R

Mondays to Fridays

9 December to 16 May

Brighton, Gatwick Airport and South London - City of London, St Albans, Luton and Bedford

Network Diagram - refer to first Page of Table 52

Station	Table		FC	FC	FC	FC	SE	EM	FC		FC	FC	FC	SE	EM	FC	FC	SE	FC	FC		EM	FC	FC	SE	FC
			[1]		[1]			◇[1]	[1]			[1]			◇[1]	[1]			[1]			◇[1]	[1]			[1]
								A							B							A				
Brighton [10]		d	08 34		09 00				09 07			09 34				09 37			10 04				10 07			10 34
Preston Park		d	08 38						09 11							09 41							10 11			
Hassocks [4]		d	08 44		09 09				09 17							09 47							10 17			
Burgess Hill [4]		d	08 48		09 12				09 21							09 51							10 21			
Wivelsfield [4]		d	08 50						09 23							09 53							10 23			
Haywards Heath [3]		d	09 00		09 18				09 31			09 48				10 01			10 18				10 31			10 48
Balcombe		d	09 06						09 37														10 37			
Three Bridges [4]		d	09 12		09 27				09 42			09 57				10 12			10 27				10 42			10 57
Gatwick Airport [10] ✈		d	09 17		09 32				09 47			10 02				10 17			10 32				10 47			11 02
Redhill		d																								
East Croydon		d	09 32		09 47				10 02			10 17				10 32			10 47				11 02			11 17
Sevenoaks [4]	195	d					09 13							09 42				10 02							10 32	
Bat & Ball	195	d					09 16							09 46				10 05							10 35	
Otford [4]	195	d					09 21							09 50				10 08							10 38	
Shoreham (Kent)	195	d					09 24							09 53				10 11							10 41	
Eynsford	195	d					09 28							09 56				10 15							10 45	
Swanley [4]	195	d					09 33							10 01				10 20							10 50	
St Mary Cray [4]	195	d					09 37							10 05				10 24							10 54	
Bickley	195	d					09 42							10 10				10 28							10 58	
Bromley South	195	d					09 45							10 15				10 31							11 01	
Shortlands [4]	195	d					09 48							10 18				10 34							11 04	
Ravensbourne	195	d					09 50							10 20				10 36							11 06	
Beckenham Hill	195	d					09 52							10 22				10 38							11 08	
Bellingham	195	d					09 54							10 24				10 40							11 10	
Catford	195	d					09 57							10 27				10 43							11 13	
Crofton Park	195	d					09 59							10 29				10 45							11 15	
Nunhead [4]	195	d					10 02							10 32				10 48							11 18	
Peckham Rye [4]	195	d					10 04							10 34				10 50							11 20	
Denmark Hill [4]	195	d					10 07							10 37				10 54							11 24	
Sutton (Surrey) [4]	179	d		09 11		09 38					09 37		10 08				10 07			10 38				10 37		
West Sutton	179	d		09 14							09 40						10 10							10 40		
Sutton Common	179	d		09 16							09 42						10 12							10 42		
St Helier	179	d		09 19							09 45						10 15							10 45		
Morden South	179	d		09 21							09 47						10 17							10 47		
South Merton	179	d		09 23							09 49						10 19							10 49		
Wimbledon Chase	179	d		09 25							09 51						10 21							10 51		
Wimbledon [6] ⊖	173,179	d		09 28							09 58						10 28							10 58		
Haydons Road	173	d		09 30							10 00						10 30							11 00		
Tooting	173	d		09 33							10 03						10 33							11 03		
Carshalton	173	d				09 41							10 11							10 41						
Hackbridge	173	d				09 43							10 13							10 43						
Mitcham Junction	173	d				09 46							10 16							10 46						
Mitcham Eastfields	173	d				09 49							10 19							10 49						
Streatham [4]		d		09 38		09 53					10 08		10 23				10 38			10 53				11 08		
Tulse Hill [3]		d		09 42		09 57					10 12		10 27				10 42			10 57				11 12		
London Bridge [4] ⊖		a	09 46		10 00				10 15			10 30				10 45			11 00				11 15			11 30
		d	09 46		10 00				10 16			10 30				10 45			11 00				11 15			11 30
Herne Hill [4]	173,179	d		09 46		10 01					10 16		10 31				10 46			11 01				11 16		
Loughborough Jn.	173,179	d		09 50		10 04					10 19		10 34				10 49			11 04				11 19		
Elephant & Castle	173,179	d		09 55		10 09	10 14				10 24		10 39	10 44			10 54	11 00		11 09				11 24	11 30	
London Blackfriars [3] ⊖		d	09 54	10 00	10 08	10 14	10 18		10 24		10 30	10 38	10 44	10 48		10 54	11 00	11 04	11 08	11 14			11 24	11 30	11 34	11 38
City Thameslink [3]		d	09 56	10 02	10 10	10 16	10 20		10 26		10 32	10 40	10 46	10 50		10 56	11 02	11 06	11 10	11 16			11 26	11 32	11 36	11 40
Farringdon [3] ⊖		d	10 00	10 06	10 14	10 19	10 24		10 29		10 36	10 44	10 49	10 54		10 59	11 06	11 10	11 14	11 19			11 29	11 36	11 40	11 44
St Pancras International [15] ⊖		a	10 04	10 10	10 18	10 23	10 28		10 33		10 40	10 48	10 53	10 58		11 03	11 10	11 14	11 18	11 23			11 33	11 40	11 44	11 48
		d	10 04	10 10	10 18	10 24	10 28	10 29	10 34		10 40	10 48	10 54	10 58	11 00	11 04	11 10	11 14	11 18	11 24		11 29	11 34	11 40	11 44	11 48
Kentish Town ⊖		d		10 14		10 27	10a33				10 44		10 57	11a03			11 14	11a19		11 27				11 44	11a49	
West Hampstead Thameslink ⊖		d	10 11	10 20		10 32			10 41		10 50		11 02			11 11	11 20			11 32			11 41	11 50		
Cricklewood		d		10 23		10 35					10 53		11 05				11 23			11 35				11 53		
Hendon		d		10 26		10 38					10 56		11 08				11 26			11 38				11 56		
Mill Hill Broadway		d		10 30		10 42					11 00		11 12				11 30			11 42				12 00		
Elstree & Borehamwood		d		10 34		10 46					11 04		11 16				11 34			11 46				12 04		
Radlett		d		10 38		10 50					11 08		11 20				11 38			11 50				12 08		
St Albans City		d	10 25	10 46	10 39	10a57			10 55		11 14	11 09	11a27			11 25	11 44		11 39	11a57			11 55	12 14		12 09
Harpenden		d	10 31	10 53	10 45				11 01		11 19	11 15				11 31	11 49		11 45				12 01	12 19		12 15
Luton Airport Parkway [7] ✈		d	10 37	10 59	10 51			10 50	11 07		11 25	11 21				11 37	11 55		11 51			11 50	12 07	12 25		12 21
Luton [10]		d	10 40	11a03	10 54				11 10		11a29	11 24			11 22	11 40	11a59		11 54				12 10	12a29		12 24
Leagrave		d	10 44		10 58				11 14			11 28				11 44			11 58				12 14			12 28
Harlington		d	10 49		11 03				11 19			11 33				11 49			12 03				12 19			12 33
Flitwick		d	10 53		11 07				11 23			11 37				11 53			12 07				12 23			12 37
Bedford [7]		a	11 05		11 19			11 04	11 35			11 49			11 36	12 05			12 19			12 04	12 35			12 49

A To Nottingham **B** To Corby.

The trains that operate to and from Sevenoaks, Orpington and Rochester (and a few other destinations at peak times) are operated jointly by First Capital Connect (north of Blackfriars) and Southeastern (south of Blackfriars)

Table 52 shows the complete service between Bedford and London, whilst services between London, Sevenoaks, Sutton and Brighton only show through Thameslink services. Other Tables should be consulted for additional journey opportunities.

Table 52R

Mondays to Fridays

9 December to 16 May

Brighton, Gatwick Airport and South London - City of London, St Albans, Luton and Bedford

Network Diagram - refer to first Page of Table 52

		FC	EM	FC	FC	SE	FC	FC	EM	FC	FC	SE	FC	FC	EM	FC	FC	SE	FC	FC	EM	FC	FC
			◇1	1			1		◇1	1			1		◇1	1			1		◇1	1	
			A						B						A						B		
Brighton 10	d			10 37			11 04			11 07			11 34			11 37			12 04			12 07	
Preston Park	d			10 41						11 11						11 41						12 11	
Hassocks 4	d			10 47						11 17						11 47						12 17	
Burgess Hill 4	d			10 51						11 21						11 51						12 21	
Wivelsfield 4	d			10 53						11 23						11 53						12 23	
Haywards Heath 3	d			11 01			11 18			11 31			11 48			12 01			12 18			12 31	
Balcombe	d									11 37												12 37	
Three Bridges 4	d			11 12			11 27			11 42			11 57			12 12			12 27			12 42	
Gatwick Airport 10 ✈	d			11 17			11 32			11 47			12 02			12 17			12 32			12 47	
Redhill	d																						
East Croydon	d			11 32			11 47			12 02			12 17			12 32			12 47			13 02	
Sevenoaks 4 195	d					11 02						11 32						12 02					
Bat & Ball 195	d					11 05						11 35						12 05					
Otford 4 195	d					11 08						11 38						12 08					
Shoreham (Kent) 195	d					11 11						11 41						12 11					
Eynsford 195	d					11 15						11 45						12 15					
Swanley 4 195	d					11 20						11 50						12 20					
St Mary Cray 4 195	d					11 24						11 54						12 24					
Bickley 195	d					11 28						11 58						12 28					
Bromley South 195	d					11 31						12 01						12 31					
Shortlands 4 195	d					11 34						12 04						12 34					
Ravensbourne 195	d					11 36						12 06						12 36					
Beckenham Hill 195	d					11 38						12 08						12 38					
Bellingham 195	d					11 40						12 10						12 40					
Catford 195	d					11 43						12 13						12 43					
Crofton Park 195	d					11 45						12 15						12 45					
Nunhead 4 195	d					11 48						12 18						12 48					
Peckham Rye 4 195	d					11 50						12 20						12 50					
Denmark Hill 4 195	d					11 54						12 24						12 54					
Sutton (Surrey) 4 179	d	11 08			11 07			11 38			11 37			12 08			12 07			12 38			12 37
West Sutton 179	d				11 10						11 40						12 10						12 40
Sutton Common 179	d				11 12						11 42						12 12						12 42
St Helier 179	d				11 15						11 45						12 15						12 45
Morden South 179	d				11 17						11 47						12 17						12 47
South Merton 179	d				11 19						11 49						12 19						12 49
Wimbledon Chase 179	d				11 21						11 51						12 21						12 51
Wimbledon 6 ⊖173,179	d				11 28						11 58						12 28						12 58
Haydons Road 173	d				11 30						12 00						12 30						13 00
Tooting 173	d				11 33						12 03						12 33						13 03
Carshalton 173	d	11 11						11 41						12 11						12 41			
Hackbridge 173	d	11 13						11 43						12 13						12 43			
Mitcham Junction 173	d	11 16						11 46						12 16						12 46			
Mitcham Eastfields 173	d	11 19						11 49						12 19						12 49			
Streatham 4	d	11 23			11 38			11 53			12 08			12 23			12 38			12 53			13 08
Tulse Hill 3	d	11 27			11 42			11 57			12 12			12 27			12 42			12 57			13 12
London Bridge 4 ⊖	a			11 45			12 00			12 15			12 30			12 45			13 00			13 15	
	d			11 45			12 00			12 15			12 30			12 45			13 00			13 15	
Herne Hill 4 173,179	d	11 31			11 46			12 01			12 16			12 31			12 46			13 01			13 16
Loughborough Jn. 173,179	d	11 34			11 49			12 04			12 19			12 34			12 49			13 04			13 19
Elephant & Castle 173,179	d	11 39			11 54	12 00		12 09			12 24	12 30		12 39			12 54	13 00		13 09			13 24
London Blackfriars 3 ⊖	d	11 44		11 54	12 00	12 04	12 08	12 14		12 24	12 30	12 34	12 38	12 44		12 54	13 00	13 04	13 08	13 14		13 24	13 30
City Thameslink 3	d	11 46		11 56	12 02	12 06	12 10	12 16		12 26	12 32	12 36	12 40	12 46		12 56	13 02	13 06	13 10	13 16		13 26	13 32
Farringdon 3 ⊖	d	11 49		11 59	12 06	12 10	12 14	12 19		12 29	12 36	12 40	12 44	12 49		12 59	13 06	13 10	13 14	13 19		13 29	13 36
St Pancras International 15 ⊖	a	11 53		12 03	12 10	12 14	12 18	12 23		12 33	12 40	12 44	12 48	12 53		13 03	13 10	13 14	13 18	13 23		13 33	13 40
	d	11 54	12 00	12 04	12 10	12 14	12 18	12 24	12 29	12 34	12 40	12 44	12 48	12 54	13 00	13 04	13 10	13 14	13 18	13 24	13 29	13 34	13 40
Kentish Town ⊖	d	11 57			12 14	12a19		12 27			12 44	12a49		12 57			13 14	13a19		13 27			13 44
West Hampstead Thameslink ⊖	d	12 02		12 11	12 20			12 32		12 41	12 50			13 02		13 11	13 20			13 32		13 41	13 50
Cricklewood	d	12 05			12 23			12 35			12 53			13 05			13 23			13 35			13 53
Hendon	d	12 08			12 26			12 38			12 56			13 08			13 26			13 38			13 56
Mill Hill Broadway	d	12 12			12 30			12 42			13 00			13 12			13 30			13 42			14 00
Elstree & Borehamwood	d	12 16			12 34			12 46			13 04			13 16			13 34			13 46			14 04
Radlett	d	12 20			12 38			12 50			13 08			13 20			13 38			13 50			14 08
St Albans City	d	12a27		12 25	12 44		12 39	12a57		12 55	13 14		13 09	13a27		13 25	13 44		13 39	13a57		13 55	14 14
Harpenden	d			12 31	12 49		12 45			13 01	13 19		13 15			13 31	13 49		13 45			14 01	14 19
Luton Airport Parkway 7 ✈	d			12 37	12 55		12 51		12 50	13 07	13 25		13 21			13 37	13 55		13 51		13 50	14 07	14 25
Luton 10	d		12 22	12 40	12 58		12 54			13 10	13a29		13 24		13 22	13 40	13a59		13 54			14 10	14a29
Leagrave	d			12 44			12 58			13 14			13 28			13 44			13 58			14 14	
Harlington	d			12 49			13 03			13 19			13 33			13 49			14 03			14 19	
Flitwick	d			12 53			13 07			13 23			13 37			13 53			14 07			14 23	
Bedford 7	a		12 36	13 05	13 24		13 19		13 04	13 35			13 49		13 36	14 05			14 19		14 04	14 35	

A To Corby.

B To Nottingham

The trains that operate to and from Sevenoaks, Orpington and Rochester (and a few other destinations at peak times) are operated jointly by First Capital Connect (north of Blackfriars) and Southeastern (south of Blackfriars)

Table 52 shows the complete service between Bedford and London, whilst services between London, Sevenoaks, Sutton and Brighton only show through Thameslink services. Other Tables should be consulted for additional journey opportunities.

Table 52R

Mondays to Fridays

9 December to 16 May

Brighton, Gatwick Airport and South London - City of London, St Albans, Luton and Bedford

Network Diagram - refer to first Page of Table 52

	SE	FC	FC		EM	FC	FC	SE	FC	FC	EM	FC	FC	SE		FC	FC	EM	FC	FC	SE	FC	FC	EM
		1			◇1	1			1		◇1	1				1		◇1	1			1		◇1
					A						B							A						B
Brighton 10 d		12 34				12 37			13 04			13 07				13 34			13 37			14 04		
Preston Park d						12 41						13 11							13 41					
Hassocks 4 d						12 47						13 17							13 47					
Burgess Hill 4 d						12 51						13 21							13 51					
Wivelsfield 4 d						12 53						13 23							13 53					
Haywards Heath 3 d		12 48				13 01			13 18			13 31				13 48			14 01			14 18		
Balcombe d												13 37												
Three Bridges 4 d		12 57				13 12			13 27			13 42				13 57			14 12			14 27		
Gatwick Airport 10 ✈ d		13 02				13 17			13 32			13 47				14 02			14 17			14 32		
Redhill d																								
East Croydon 🚋 d		13 17				13 32			13 47			14 02				14 17			14 32			14 47		
Sevenoaks 4 195 d	12 32							13 02						13 32							14 02			
Bat & Ball 195 d	12 35							13 05						13 35							14 05			
Otford 4 195 d	12 38							13 08						13 38							14 08			
Shoreham (Kent) 195 d	12 41							13 11						13 41							14 11			
Eynsford 195 d	12 45							13 15						13 45							14 15			
Swanley 4 195 d	12 50							13 20						13 50							14 20			
St Mary Cray 4 195 d	12 54							13 24						13 54							14 24			
Bickley 195 d	12 58							13 28						13 58							14 28			
Bromley South 195 d	13 01							13 31						14 01							14 31			
Shortlands 4 195 d	13 04							13 34						14 04							14 34			
Ravensbourne 195 d	13 06							13 36						14 06							14 36			
Beckenham Hill 195 d	13 08							13 38						14 08							14 38			
Bellingham 195 d	13 10							13 40						14 10							14 40			
Catford 195 d	13 13							13 43						14 13							14 43			
Crofton Park 195 d	13 15							13 45						14 15							14 45			
Nunhead 4 195 d	13 18							13 48						14 18							14 48			
Peckham Rye 4 195 d	13 20							13 50						14 20							14 50			
Denmark Hill 4 195 d	13 24							13 54						14 24							14 54			
Sutton (Surrey) 4 179 d			13 08				13 07			13 38			13 37				14 08			14 07			14 38	
West Sutton 179 d							13 10						13 40							14 10				
Sutton Common 179 d							13 12						13 42							14 12				
St Helier 179 d							13 15						13 45							14 15				
Morden South 179 d							13 17						13 47							14 17				
South Merton 179 d							13 19						13 49							14 19				
Wimbledon Chase 179 d							13 21						13 51							14 21				
Wimbledon 6 ⊖173,179 🚋 d							13 28						13 58							14 28				
Haydons Road 173 d							13 30						14 00							14 30				
Tooting 173 d							13 33						14 03							14 33				
Carshalton 173 d			13 11							13 41							14 11						14 41	
Hackbridge 173 d			13 13							13 43							14 13						14 43	
Mitcham Junction 173 🚋 d			13 16							13 46							14 16						14 46	
Mitcham Eastfields 173 d			13 19							13 49							14 19						14 49	
Streatham 4 d			13 23				13 38			13 53			14 08				14 23			14 38			14 53	
Tulse Hill 3 d			13 27				13 42			13 57			14 12				14 27			14 42			14 57	
London Bridge 4 ⊖ a		13 30				13 45			14 00			14 15				14 30			14 45			15 00		
d		13 30				13 45			14 00			14 15				14 30			14 45			15 00		
Herne Hill 4 173,179 d			13 31				13 46			14 01			14 16				14 31			14 46			15 01	
Loughborough Jn. 173,179 d			13 34				13 49			14 04			14 19				14 34			14 49			15 04	
Elephant & Castle 173,179 d	13 30		13 39				13 54	14 00		14 09			14 24	14 30			14 39			14 54	15 00		15 09	
London Blackfriars 3 ⊖ d	13 34	13 38	13 44			13 54	14 00	14 04	14 08	14 14		14 24	14 30	14 34		14 38	14 44		14 54	15 00	15 04	15 08	15 14	
City Thameslink 3 d	13 36	13 40	13 46			13 56	14 02	14 06	14 10	14 16		14 26	14 32	14 36		14 40	14 46		14 56	15 02	15 06	15 10	15 16	
Farringdon 3 ⊖ d	13 40	13 44	13 49			13 59	14 06	14 10	14 14	14 19		14 29	14 36	14 40		14 44	14 49		14 59	15 06	15 10	15 14	15 19	
St Pancras International 15 ⊖ a	13 44	13 48	13 53			14 03	14 10	14 14	14 18	14 23		14 33	14 40	14 44		14 48	14 53		15 03	15 10	15 14	15 18	15 23	
d	13 44	13 48	13 54		14 00	14 04	14 10	14 14	14 18	14 24	14 29	14 34	14 40	14 44		14 48	14 54	15 00	15 04	15 10	15 14	15 18	15 24	15 29
Kentish Town ⊖ d	13a49		13 57				14 14	14a19		14 27			14 44	14a49			14 57			15 14	15a19		15 27	
West Hampstead Thameslink ⊖ d			14 02			14 11	14 20			14 32		14 41	14 50				15 02		15 11	15 20			15 32	
Cricklewood d			14 05				14 23			14 35			14 53				15 05			15 23			15 35	
Hendon d			14 08				14 26			14 38			14 56				15 08			15 26			15 38	
Mill Hill Broadway d			14 12				14 30			14 42			15 00				15 12			15 30			15 42	
Elstree & Borehamwood d			14 16				14 34			14 46			15 04				15 16			15 34			15 46	
Radlett d			14 20				14 38			14 50			15 08				15 20			15 38			15 50	
St Albans City d		14 09	14a27			14 25	14 44		14 39	14a57		14 55	15 14			15 09	15a27		15 25	15 44		15 39	15a57	
Harpenden d		14 15				14 31	14 49		14 45			15 01	15 19			15 15			15 31	15 49		15 45		
Luton Airport Parkway 7 ✈ d		14 21				14 37	14 55		14 51		14 50	15 07	15 25			15 21			15 37	15 55		15 51		15 50
Luton 10 d		14 24			14 22	14 40	14a59		14 54			15 10	15a29			15 24		15 22	15 40	15a59		15 54		
Leagrave d		14 28				14 44			14 58			15 14				15 28			15 44			15 58		
Harlington d		14 33				14 49			15 03			15 19				15 33			15 49			16 03		
Flitwick d		14 37				14 53			15 07			15 23				15 37			15 53			16 07		
Bedford 7 a		14 49			14 36	15 05			15 19		15 04	15 35				15 49		15 36	16 05			16 19		16 04

A To Corby.

B To Nottingham

The trains that operate to and from Sevenoaks, Orpington and Rochester (and a few other destinations at peak times) are operated jointly by First Capital Connect (north of Blackfriars) and Southeastern (south of Blackfriars)

Table 52 shows the complete service between Bedford and London, whilst services between London, Sevenoaks, Sutton and Brighton only show through Thameslink services. Other Tables should be consulted for additional journey opportunities.

Table 52R

Mondays to Fridays

9 December to 16 May

Brighton, Gatwick Airport and South London - City of London, St Albans, Luton and Bedford

Network Diagram - refer to first Page of Table 52

Station			FC	FC	SE	FC	FC	EM	FC	FC	SE	FC	FC	EM	FC	FC	FC	SE	FC	EM	FC	FC	FC
			1			1		◇1 A	1			1		◇1 B	1	1		1		◇1 A	1	1	
Brighton 10		d	14 07			14 34			14 37			15 04				15 07					15 34	15 37	
Preston Park		d	14 11						14 41							15 11						15 41	
Hassocks 4		d	14 17						14 47							15 17						15 47	
Burgess Hill 4		d	14 21						14 51							15 21						15 51	
Wivelsfield 4		d	14 23						14 53							15 23						15 53	
Haywards Heath 3		d	14 31			14 48			15 01			15 18				15 31					15 48	15 58	
Balcombe		d	14 37													15 37							
Three Bridges 4		d	14 42			14 57			15 12			15 27				15 42					15 57	16 07	
Gatwick Airport 10	✈	d	14 47			15 02			15 17			15 32				15 47					16 02	16 12	
Redhill		d																					
East Croydon		d	15 02			15 17			15 32			15 47				16 02					16 17	16 28	
Sevenoaks 4	195	d			14 32						15 02							15 32					
Bat & Ball	195	d			14 35						15 05							15 35					
Otford 4	195	d			14 38						15 08							15 38					
Shoreham (Kent)	195	d			14 41						15 11							15 41					
Eynsford	195	d			14 45						15 15							15 45					
Swanley 4	195	d			14 50						15 20							15 50					
St Mary Cray 4	195	d			14 54						15 24							15 54					
Bickley	195	d			14 58						15 28							15 58					
Bromley South	195	d			15 01						15 31							16 01					
Shortlands 4	195	d			15 04						15 34							16 04					
Ravensbourne	195	d			15 06						15 36							16 06					
Beckenham Hill	195	d			15 08						15 38							16 08					
Bellingham	195	d			15 10						15 40							16 10					
Catford	195	d			15 13						15 43							16 13					
Crofton Park	195	d			15 15						15 45							16 15					
Nunhead 4	195	d			15 18						15 48							16 18					
Peckham Rye 4	195	d			15 20						15 50							16 20					
Denmark Hill 4	195	d			15 24						15 54							16 24					
Sutton (Surrey) 4	179	d		14 37			15 08			15 07			15 38				15 37		16 08				
West Sutton	179	d		14 40						15 10							15 40						
Sutton Common	179	d		14 42						15 12							15 42						
St Helier	179	d		14 45						15 15							15 45						
Morden South	179	d		14 47						15 17							15 47						
South Merton	179	d		14 49						15 19							15 49						
Wimbledon Chase	179	d		14 51						15 21							15 51						
Wimbledon 6	⊖173,179	d		14 58						15 28							15 58						
Haydons Road	173	d		15 00						15 30							16 00						
Tooting	173	d		15 03						15 33							16 03						
Carshalton	173	d					15 11						15 41						16 11				
Hackbridge	173	d					15 13						15 43						16 13				
Mitcham Junction	173	d					15 16						15 46						16 16				
Mitcham Eastfields	173	d					15 19						15 49						16 19				
Streatham 4		d		15 08			15 23			15 38			15 53				16 08		16 23				
Tulse Hill 3		d		15 12			15 27			15 42			15 57				16 12		16 27		16 32		
London Bridge 4	⊖	a	15 15			15 30			15 45			16 00				16 15							
		d	15 15			15 30			15 45			16 00				16 16							
Herne Hill 4	173,179	d		15 16			15 31			15 46			16 01				16 16		16 31				
Loughborough Jn	173,179	d		15 19			15 34			15 49			16 04				16 19		16 34				
Elephant & Castle	173,179	d		15 24	15 30		15 39			15 54	16 00		16 09		16 18		16 24	16 30	16 39		16 44		16 56
London Blackfriars 3	⊖	d	15 24	15 30	15 34	15 38	15 44		15 54	16 00	16 04	16 08	16 14		16 22	16 26	16 30	16 38	16 44		16 52	16 56	17 00
City Thameslink 3		d	15 26	15 32	15 36	15 40	15 46		15 56	16 02	16 06	16 10	16 16		16 24	16 28	16 32	16 40	16 46		16 54	16 58	17 02
Farringdon 3	⊖	d	15 29	15 36	15 40	15 44	15 49		15 59	16 06	16 10	16 13	16 19		16 27	16 31	16 35	16 43	16 49		16 57	17 01	17 05
St Pancras International 15	⊖	a	15 33	15 40	15 44	15 48	15 53		16 03	16 10	16 14	16 17	16 23		16 31	16 35	16 39	16 47	16 53		17 01	17 05	17 09
		d	15 34	15 40	15 44	15 48	15 54	16 00	16 04	16 10	16 14	16 18	16 24	16 29	16 32	16 36	16 40	16 48	16 54	17 00	17 02	17 06	17 10
Kentish Town	⊖	d		15 44	15a49		15 57			16 14	16a19		16 28				16 44		16 58				
West Hampstead Thameslink	⊖	d	15 41	15 50			16 02		16 11	16 20			16 32			16 43	16 50		17 02				17 18
Cricklewood		d		15 53			16 05			16 23			16 35				16 53		17 05				
Hendon		d		15 56			16 08			16 26			16 38				16 56		17 08				
Mill Hill Broadway		d		16 00			16 12			16 30			16 43				17 00		17 13				17 25
Elstree & Borehamwood		d		16 04			16 16			16 34			16 47				17 04		17 17				17 29
Radlett		d		16 08			16 20			16 38			16 51				17 08		17 21				17 33
St Albans City		d	15 55	16 14		16 09	16a27		16 25	16 44		16 39	16a59		16 52	16 57	17 14	17 09	17a29		17 20	17 26	17 39
Harpenden		d	16 01	16 19		16 15			16 31	16 50		16 46			16 58	17 02	17 19	17 15			17 26	17 32	17 47
Luton Airport Parkway 7	✈	d	16 07	16 25		16 21			16 37	16 56		16 52		16 50		17 08	17 25	17 21				17 38	17 52
Luton 10		d	16 10	16a29		16 24		16 23	16 40	17a00		16 55		16 53	17 04	17 11	17a29	17 24			17 32	17 41	17a56
Leagrave		d	16 14			16 28			16 44			16 58				17 15		17 27				17 45	
Harlington		d	16 19			16 33			16 49			17 03				17 20		17 32				17 50	
Flitwick		d	16 23			16 37			16 53			17 07			17 13	17 24		17 36			17 41	17 54	
Bedford 7		a	16 35			16 49		16 36	17 05			17 20		17 07	17 25	17 38		17 48		17 34	17 53	18 06	

A To Corby.
B To Nottingham

The trains that operate to and from Sevenoaks, Orpington and Rochester (and a few other destinations at peak times) are operated jointly by First Capital Connect (north of Blackfriars) and Southeastern (south of Blackfriars)

Table 52 shows the complete service between Bedford and London, whilst services between London, Sevenoaks, Sutton and Brighton only show through Thameslink services. Other Tables should be consulted for additional journey opportunities.

Table 52R

Mondays to Fridays

9 December to 16 May

Brighton, Gatwick Airport and South London - City of London, St Albans, Luton and Bedford

Network Diagram - refer to first Page of Table 52

		FC	EM	SE	FC	SE	EM	FC	FC	FC	EM		FC	SE	FC	EM	FC	SE	FC	SE	SE	FC		EM	FC
			◇1	1	1		◇1	1	1		◇1		1			◇1	1	1		1	1			◇1	
			A		B		A				C					D		E			F			G	
Brighton 10	d							16 04	16 07				16 24				16 30								
Preston Park	d								16 11								16 34								
Hassocks 4	d								16 17								16 40								
Burgess Hill 4	d								16 21								16 44								
Wivelsfield 4	d																16 46								
Haywards Heath 3	d							16 18	16 26				16 38				16 51								
Balcombe	d								16 32								16 56								
Three Bridges 4	d							16 27	16 37				16 47				17 02								
Gatwick Airport 10 ✈	d							16 32	16 42				16 53				17 08								
Redhill	d																								
East Croydon	d							16 47	16 58				17 09				17 23								
Sevenoaks 4	195 d			16 02		16 22								16 32						17 02					
Bat & Ball	195 d			16 05		16 25								16 35						17 05					
Otford 4	195 d			16 08		16 28								16 38						17 08					
Shoreham (Kent)	195 d			16 11										16 41						17 11					
Eynsford	195 d			16 15										16 45						17 15					
Swanley 4	195 d			16 20		16 37								16 50						17 20					
St Mary Cray 4	195 d			16 24		16 41								16 54						17 24					
Bickley	195 d			16 28										16 58						17 28	17 42				
Bromley South	195 d			16 31		16 47								17 01						17 31	17 45				
Shortlands 4	195 d			16 34										17 04						17 34					
Ravensbourne	195 d			16 36										17 06						17 36					
Beckenham Hill	195 d			16 38										17 08						17 38					
Bellingham	195 d			16 40		16 52								17 10						17 40					
Catford	195 d			16 43		16 55								17 13						17 43					
Crofton Park	195 d			16 45										17 15						17 45					
Nunhead 4	195 d			16 48		16 59								17 18						17 48					
Peckham Rye 4	195 d			16 50		17 02								17 20						17 50					
Denmark Hill 4	195 d			16 54		17 05								17 24						17 54					
Sutton (Surrey) 4	179 d	16 07			16 38					16 37					17 08				17 11						17 42
West Sutton	179 d	16 10								16 40									17 14						
Sutton Common	179 d	16 12								16 42									17 16						
St Helier	179 d	16 15								16 45									17 19						
Morden South	179 d	16 17								16 47									17 21						
South Merton	179 d	16 19								16 49									17 23						
Wimbledon Chase	179 d	16 21								16 51									17 25						
Wimbledon 6 ⊖173,179	d	16 30								17 00									17 30						
Haydons Road	173 d	16 32								17 02									17 32						
Tooting	173 d	16 35								17 05									17 35						
Carshalton	173 d				16 41										17 11										17 45
Hackbridge	173 d				16 43										17 13										17 47
Mitcham Junction	173 d				16 46										17 16										17 50
Mitcham Eastfields	173 d				16 49										17 19										17 53
Streatham 4	d	16 40			16 53					17 10					17 23				17 40						17 57
Tulse Hill 3	d	16 46			16 57				17 12	17 16					17 27				17 44						18 01
London Bridge 4 ⊖	a												17 27												
	d												17 27												
Herne Hill 4	173,179 d	16 50			17 01					17 21					17 31			17 44	17 48						18 06
Loughborough Jn	173,179 d	16 53								17 24					17 34			17 47	17 51						18 09
Elephant & Castle	173,179 d	17 00		17 04	17 08	17 12			17 22	17 28				17 34	17 39			17 52	17 56	18 01	18 05	18 09			18 14
London Blackfriars 3 ⊖	d	17 04		17 08	17 12	17 16		17 22	17 26	17 32			17 36	17 40	17 46		17 52	17 56	18 00	18 06	18 10	18 14			18 18
City Thameslink 3	d	17 06		17 10	17 14	17 18		17 24	17 28	17 34			17 38	17 42	17 48		17 54	17 58	18 02	18 08	18 12	18 16			18 20
Farringdon 3 ⊖	d	17 09		17 13	17 17	17 23		17 27	17 31	17 37			17 41	17 45	17 51		17 57	18 01	18 05	18 11	18 15	18 19			18 23
St Pancras International 15 ⊖	a	17 13		17 17	17 21	17 27		17 31	17 35	17 41			17 45	17 49	17 55		18 01	18 05	18 09	18 15	18 19	18 23			18 27
	d	17 14	17 15	17 18	17 22	17 28	17 30	17 32	17 36	17 42	17 45		17 46	17 50	17 56	18 00	18 02	18 06	18 10	18 16	18 20	18 24		18 25	18 28
Kentish Town ⊖	d	17 18				17 32				17 46					18 00				18 14						18 32
West Hampstead Thameslink ⊖	d	17 22				17 36				17 50				17 58	18 04				18 20			18 32			18 36
Cricklewood	d	17 25				17 39				17 53					18 07				18 23						18 39
Hendon	d	17 28				17 42				17 56					18 10				18 26						18 42
Mill Hill Broadway	d	17 33				17 47				18 01				18 05	18 15				18 31			18 40			18 47
Elstree & Borehamwood	d	17 37				17 51				18 05				18 10	18 19				18 35			18 44			18 51
Radlett	d	17 43				17 55				18 09				18 14	18 23				18 40			18 48			18 55
St Albans City	d	17a51		17 37	17 44	18a03		17 50	17 56	18 16			18 06	18 20	18a31		18 20	18 26	18 46	18 36	18 42	18 54			19a03
Harpenden	d				17 51			17 56	18 02	18 21			18 14	18 26			18 26	18 33	18 52		18 48	19 00			
Luton Airport Parkway 7 ✈	d			17 48	17 57				18 08	18 27	18a07		18 20	18 32				18 39	18 58	18 47	18 54	19 06			
Luton 10	d		17a39	17 51	18 00			18 02	18 11	18a31			18 23	18 35		18 23	18 32	18 42	19a01	18 50	18 57	19 09		18a49	
Leagrave	d				18 04				18 15				18 27	18 39				18 45			19 01	19 13			
Harlington	d				18 09				18 20				18 32	18 44				18 50			19 06	19 18			
Flitwick	d			18 01	18 13			18 11	18 24				18 36	18 48			18 43	18 54		19 00	19 10	19 22			
Bedford 7	a			18 13	18 26		18 03	18 23	18 36				18 48	19 02		18 37	18 55	19 06		19 12	19 26	19 34			

A To Nottingham
B 1 to Farringdon
C To Derby
D To Melton Mowbray
E From Beckenham Junction
F From Orpington
G To Sheffield

The trains that operate to and from Sevenoaks, Orpington and Rochester (and a few other destinations at peak times) are operated jointly by First Capital Connect (north of Blackfriars) and Southeastern (south of Blackfriars)

Table 52 shows the complete service between Bedford and London, whilst services between London, Sevenoaks, Sutton and Brighton only show through Thameslink services. Other Tables should be consulted for additional journey opportunities.

Table 52R

Mondays to Fridays

9 December to 16 May

Brighton, Gatwick Airport and South London - City of London, St Albans, Luton and Bedford

Network Diagram - refer to first Page of Table 52

			EM	FC	FC	FC	SE	FC	FC	EM		FC	FC	FC	SE	FC	FC	EM	FC	FC	SE		FC	FC	EM	FC
			◇1	1	1		1			◇1		1	1		1	1		◇1	1				1		◇1	1
			A							B					C			D							B	
Brighton 10		d		17 03	17 07							17 24	17 37			18 03			18 07				18 34			18 37
Preston Park		d			17 11							17 28	17 41						18 11							18 41
Hassocks 4		d			17 17							17 34	17 47						18 17							18 47
Burgess Hill 4		d		17 13	17 21							17 38	17 51			18 13			18 21							18 51
Wivelsfield 4		d										17 40	17 53						18 23							18 53
Haywards Heath 3		d		17 18	17 26							17 46	18 01			18 18			18 31				18 48			19 01
Balcombe		d											18 07						18 37							
Three Bridges 4		d		17 27								17 55	18 12			18 27			18 42				18 57			19 12
Gatwick Airport 10	✈	d		17 32	17 39							18 00	18 17			18 32			18 47				19 02			19 17
Redhill		d																								
East Croydon		d		17 47	17 58							18 16	18 32			18 47			19 02				19 17			19 32
Sevenoaks 4	195	d					17 32								18 02						18 32					
Bat & Ball	195	d					17 35								18 05						18 35					
Otford 4	195	d					17 38								18 08						18 38					
Shoreham (Kent)	195	d					17 41								18 11						18 41					
Eynsford	195	d					17 45								18 15						18 45					
Swanley 4	195	d					17 50								18 20						18 50					
St Mary Cray 4	195	d					17 54								18 24						18 54					
Bickley	195	d					17 58								18 28						18 58					
Bromley South	195	d					18 01								18 31						19 01					
Shortlands 4	195	d					18 04								18 34						19 04					
Ravensbourne	195	d					18 06								18 36						19 06					
Beckenham Hill	195	d					18 08								18 38						19 08					
Bellingham	195	d					18 10								18 40						19 10					
Catford	195	d					18 13								18 43						19 13					
Crofton Park	195	d					18 15								18 45						19 15					
Nunhead 4	195	d					18 18								18 48						19 18					
Peckham Rye 4	195	d					18 20								18 50						19 20					
Denmark Hill 4	195	d					18 23								18 54						19 24					
Sutton (Surrey) 4	179	d				17 41		18 08						18 11			18 38			18 43				19 08		
West Sutton	179	d				17 44								18 14						18 46						
Sutton Common	179	d				17 46								18 16						18 48						
St Helier	179	d				17 49								18 19						18 51						
Morden South	179	d				17 51								18 21						18 53						
South Merton	179	d				17 53								18 23						18 55						
Wimbledon Chase	179	d				17 55								18 25						18 57						
Wimbledon 6	⊖173,179	d				18 00								18 30						19 00						
Haydons Road	173	d				18 02								18 32						19 02						
Tooting	173	d				18 05								18 35						19 05						
Carshalton	173	d						18 11									18 41							19 11		
Hackbridge	173	d						18 13									18 43							19 13		
Mitcham Junction	173	d						18 16									18 46							19 16		
Mitcham Eastfields	173	d						18 19									18 49							19 19		
Streatham 4		d				18 10		18 23						18 40			18 53			19 10				19 23		
Tulse Hill 3		d			18 12	18 16		18 28				18 33		18 44			18 57			19 14				19 27		
London Bridge 4	⊖	a		18 13									18 46			19 00			19 15				19 30			19 45
		d		18 13									18 46			19 01			19 17				19 30			19 45
Herne Hill 4	173,179	d				18 20		18 32				18 41		18 48			19 02			19 17				19 31		
Loughborough Jn.	173,179	d				18 23		18 35						18 51			19 05			19 20				19 34		
Elephant & Castle	173,179	d			18 22	18 28	18 32	18 40	18 44			18 48		18 56	19 00		19 10			19 25	19 30			19 39		
London Blackfriars 3	⊖	d		18 22	18 26	18 32	18 36	18 44	18 48			18 52	18 56	19 00	19 06	19 10	19 18		19 24	19 30	19 34		19 38	19 46		19 54
City Thameslink 3		d		18 24	18 28	18 34	18 38	18 46	18 50			18 54	18 58	19 02	19 08	19 12	19 20		19 26	19 32	19 36		19 40	19 48		19 56
Farringdon 3	⊖	d		18 27	18 31	18 37	18 41	18 49	18 53			18 57	19 01	19 05	19 11	19 15	19 23		19 29	19 36	19 40		19 44	19 51		19 59
St Pancras International 15	⊖	a		18 31	18 35	18 41	18 45	18 53	18 57			19 01	19 05	19 09	19 15	19 19	19 27		19 33	19 40	19 44		19 48	19 55		20 03
		d	18 30	18 32	18 36	18 42	18 46	18 54	18 58	19 00		19 02	19 06	19 10	19 16	19 20	19 28	19 32	19 34	19 40	19 44		19 48	19 56	20 00	20 04
Kentish Town	⊖	d				18 46			19 02					19 14			19 32			19 44	19a49			19 59		
West Hampstead Thameslink	⊖	d			18 44	18 50		19 02	19 06				19 13	19 18		19 28	19 36		19 41	19 50				20 03		20 11
Cricklewood		d				18 53			19 09					19 21			19 39			19 53				20 06		
Hendon		d				18 56			19 12					19 24			19 42			19 56				20 09		
Mill Hill Broadway		d				19 01			19 17					19 28			19 46			20 00				20 13		
Elstree & Borehamwood		d				19 05		19 12	19 21					19 32		19 38	19 50			20 04				20 17		
Radlett		d				19 11		19 16	19 27					19 36			19 54			20 08				20 21		
St Albans City		d		18 50	18 58	19 18	19 06	19 22	19a33			19 20	19 28	19 42	19 36	19 46	20a01		19 55	20 14			20 09	20a29		20 25
Harpenden		d		18 56	19 04	19 24	19 12	19 28				19 26	19 34	19 48	19 44	19 52			20 01	20 19			20 15			20 32
Luton Airport Parkway 7	✈	d	18 52		19 10	19 30	19 18	19 34					19 40	19 54		19 58		19 55	20 07	20 25			20 21			20 38
Luton 10		d		19 02	19 13	19a33	19 23	19 37		19 23		19 32	19 43	19a57	19 50	20 01			20 10	20a29			20 24		20 22	20 41
Leagrave		d			19 17		19 27	19 41					19 46		19 54	20 04			20 14				20 28			20 45
Harlington		d			19 22		19 32	19 46					19 51			20 09			20 19				20 33			20 50
Flitwick		d		19 11	19 26		19 36	19 50				19 41	19 55			20 13			20 23				20 37			20 54
Bedford 7		a	19 07	19 23	19 38		19 48	20 02		19 38		19 55	20 08		20 12	20 26		20 10	20 35				20 49		20 36	21 06

A To Lincoln
B To Corby.
C 1 from London Blackfriars
D To Leeds

The trains that operate to and from Sevenoaks, Orpington and Rochester (and a few other destinations at peak times) are operated jointly by First Capital Connect (north of Blackfriars) and Southeastern (south of Blackfriars)

Table 52 shows the complete service between Bedford and London, whilst services between London, Sevenoaks, Sutton and Brighton only show through Thameslink services. Other Tables should be consulted for additional journey opportunities.

Table 52R

Mondays to Fridays

9 December to 16 May

Brighton, Gatwick Airport and South London - City of London, St Albans, Luton and Bedford

Network Diagram - refer to first Page of Table 52

Station	Table		FC	SE	FC ■1	FC	EM ◇■1 A 🚲	FC ■1	FC	SE	FC ■1	FC	EM ◇■1 B 🚲	FC ■1	FC	SE	FC ■1	FC	EM ◇■1 B 🚲	FC ■1	FC	SE	FC ■1
Brighton ■10		d						19 07			19 34			19 37			20 03			20 07			20 34
Preston Park		d						19 11						19 41						20 11			
Hassocks ■4		d						19 17						19 47						20 17			
Burgess Hill ■4		d						19 21						19 51			20 13			20 21			
Wivelsfield ■4		d						19 23						19 53						20 23			
Haywards Heath ■3		d						19 31			19 48			20 01			20 19			20 31			20 48
Balcombe		d						19 37												20 37			
Three Bridges ■4		d			19 27			19 42			19 57			20 12			20 27			20 42			20 57
Gatwick Airport ■10 ✈		d			19 32			19 47			20 02			20 17			20 32			20 47			21 02
Redhill		d																					
East Croydon 🚌		d			19 47			20 02			20 17			20 32			20 47			21 02			21 17
Sevenoaks ■4	195	d		19 02						19 32						20 02						20 32	
Bat & Ball	195	d		19 05						19 35						20 05						20 35	
Otford ■4	195	d		19 08						19 38						20 08						20 38	
Shoreham (Kent)	195	d		19 11						19 41						20 11						20 41	
Eynsford	195	d		19 15						19 45						20 15						20 45	
Swanley ■4	195	d		19 20						19 50						20 20						20 50	
St Mary Cray ■4	195	d		19 24						19 54						20 24						20 54	
Bickley	195	d		19 28						19 58						20 28						20 58	
Bromley South	195	d		19 31						20 01						20 31						21 01	
Shortlands ■4	195	d		19 34						20 04						20 34						21 04	
Ravensbourne	195	d		19 36						20 06						20 36						21 06	
Beckenham Hill	195	d		19 38						20 08						20 38						21 08	
Bellingham	195	d		19 40						20 10						20 40						21 10	
Catford	195	d		19 43						20 13						20 43						21 13	
Crofton Park	195	d		19 45						20 15						20 45						21 15	
Nunhead ■4	195	d		19 48						20 18						20 48						21 18	
Peckham Rye ■4	195	d		19 50						20 20						20 50						21 20	
Denmark Hill ■4	195	d		19 54						20 24						20 54						21 24	
Sutton (Surrey) ■4	179	d	19 13			19 42			19 37			20 12			20 07			20 42			20 37		
West Sutton	179	d	19 16						19 40						20 10						20 40		
Sutton Common	179	d	19 18						19 42						20 12						20 42		
St Helier	179	d	19 21						19 45						20 15						20 45		
Morden South	179	d	19 23						19 47						20 17						20 47		
South Merton	179	d	19 25						19 49						20 19						20 49		
Wimbledon Chase	179	d	19 27						19 51						20 21						20 51		
Wimbledon ■6 ⊖ 🚌	173,179	d	19 30						19 56						20 26						20 56		
Haydons Road	173	d	19 32						19 58						20 28						20 58		
Tooting	173	d	19 35						20 01						20 31						21 01		
Carshalton	173	d				19 45						20 15						20 45					
Hackbridge	173	d				19 47						20 17						20 47					
Mitcham Junction 🚌	173	d				19 50						20 20						20 50					
Mitcham Eastfields	173	d				19 53						20 23						20 53					
Streatham ■4		d	19 40			19 57			20 06			20 27			20 36			20 57			21 06		
Tulse Hill ■3		d	19 44			20 01			20 12			20 31			20 42			21 01			21 12		
London Bridge ■4 ⊖		a			20 00			20 15			20 30			20 45			21 00			21 15			21 30
		d			20 00			20 15			20 30			20 45			21 00			21 15			21 30
Herne Hill ■4	173,179	d	19 47			20 05			20 16			20 35			20 46			21 05			21 16		
Loughborough Jn.	173,179	d	19 50			20 08			20 19			20 38			20 49			21 08			21 19		
Elephant & Castle	173,179	d	19 55	20 00		20 13			20 24	20 30		20 43			20 54	21 00		21 13			21 24	21 30	
London Blackfriars ■3 ⊖		d	20 00	20 04	20 08	20 18		20 24	20 30	20 34	20 38	20 48		20 54	21 00	21 04	21 08	21 18		21 24	21 30	21a34	21 38
City Thameslink ■3		d	20 02	20 06	20 10	20 20		20 26	20 32	20 36	20 40	20 50		20 56	21 02	21 06	21 10	21 20		21 26	21 32		21 40
Farringdon ■3 ⊖		d	20 06	20 10	20 14	20 23		20 29	20 36	20 40	20 44	20 53		20 59	21 06	21 10	21 14	21 23		21 29	21 36		21 44
St Pancras International ■15 ⊖		a	20 10	20 14	20 18	20 27		20 33	20 40	20 44	20 48	20 57		21 03	21 10	21 14	21 18	21 27		21 33	21 40		21 48
		d	20 10	20 14	20 18	20 28	20 29	20 34	20 40	20 44	20 48	20 58	21 01	21 04	21 10	21 14	21 18	21 28	21 28	21 34	21 40		21 48
Kentish Town ⊖		d	20 14	20a19		20 31			20 44	20a49		21 01			21 14	21a19		21 31			21 44		
West Hampstead Thameslink ⊖		d	20 19			20 35		20 41	20 49			21 05		21 11	21 19			21 35		21 41	21 49		
Cricklewood		d	20 22			20 38			20 52			21 08			21 22			21 38			21 52		
Hendon		d	20 25			20 41			20 55			21 11			21 25			21 41			21 55		
Mill Hill Broadway		d	20 29			20 45			20 59			21 15			21 29			21 45			21 59		
Elstree & Borehamwood		d	20 33			20 49			21 03			21 19			21 33			21 49			22 03		
Radlett		d	20 38			20 53			21 08			21 23			21 37			21 53			22 07		
St Albans City		d	20 44		20 39	21a01		20 55	21 14		21 09	21a31		21 25	21 44		21 39	22a01		21 55	22 14		22 09
Harpenden		d	20 49		20 45			21 01	21 19		21 15			21 31	21 49		21 45			22 01	22 19		22 15
Luton Airport Parkway ■7 ✈		d	20 55		20 51		20 50	21 07	21 25		21 21			21 37	21 55		21 51		21 49	22 07	22 25		22 21
Luton ■10		d	20a59		20 54			21 10	21a29		21 24		21 23	21 40	21a59		21 54			22 10	22a29		22 24
Leagrave		d			20 58			21 14			21 28			21 44			21 58			22 14			22 28
Harlington		d			21 03			21 19			21 33			21 49			22 03			22 19			22 33
Flitwick		d			21 07			21 23			21 37			21 53			22 07			22 23			22 37
Bedford ■7		a			21 19		21 05	21 35			21 49		21 37	22 05			22 19		22 03	22 35			22 49

A To Nottingham

B To Derby

The trains that operate to and from Sevenoaks, Orpington and Rochester (and a few other destinations at peak times) are operated jointly by First Capital Connect (north of Blackfriars) and Southeastern (south of Blackfriars)

Table 52 shows the complete service between Bedford and London, whilst services between London, Sevenoaks, Sutton and Brighton only show through Thameslink services. Other Tables should be consulted for additional journey opportunities.

Table 52R

Mondays to Fridays

9 December to 16 May

Brighton, Gatwick Airport and South London - City of London, St Albans, Luton and Bedford

Network Diagram - refer to first Page of Table 52

Station			FC	EM	EM	FC	SE	FC	EM	EM	FC	SE	FC	FC	SE	EM	FC	FC	SE	FC
				◇1	◇1	1			◇1	◇1	1			1		◇1		1		
				A	B				E	F						G				
Brighton 10		d				20 37					21 11			21 37				22 07		
Preston Park		d				20 41								21 41				22 11		
Hassocks 4		d				20 47					21 20			21 47				22 17		
Burgess Hill 4		d				20 51					21 23			21 51				22 21		
Wivelsfield 4		d				20 53								21 53				22 23		
Haywards Heath 3		d				21 01					21 32			22 01				22 31		
Balcombe		d									21 37							22 37		
Three Bridges 4		d				21 12					21 43			22 12				22 42		
Gatwick Airport 10 ✈		d				21 17					21 47			22 17				22 47		
Redhill		d																		
East Croydon		d				21 32					22 02			22 32				23 02		
Sevenoaks 4	195	d					21 02					21 32			22 02				22 32	
Bat & Ball	195	d					21 05					21 35			22 05				22 35	
Otford 4	195	d					21 08					21 38			22 08				22 38	
Shoreham (Kent)	195	d					21 11					21 41			22 11				22 41	
Eynsford	195	d					21 15					21 45			22 15				22 45	
Swanley 4	195	d					21 20					21 50			22 20				22 50	
St Mary Cray 4	195	d					21 24					21 54			22 24				22 54	
Bickley	195	d					21 28					21 58			22 28				22 58	
Bromley South	195	d					21 31					22 01			22 31				23 01	
Shortlands 4	195	d					21 34					22 04			22 34				23 04	
Ravensbourne	195	d					21 36					22 06			22 36				23 06	
Beckenham Hill	195	d					21 38					22 08			22 38				23 08	
Bellingham	195	d					21 40					22 10			22 40				23 10	
Catford	195	d					21 43					22 13			22 43				23 13	
Crofton Park	195	d					21 45					22 15			22 45				23 15	
Nunhead 4	195	d					21 48					22 18			22 48				23 18	
Peckham Rye 4	195	d					21 50					22 20			22 50				23 20	
Denmark Hill 4	195	d					21 54					22 24			22 54				23 24	
Sutton (Surrey) 4	179	d	21 12					21 17					21 47				22 17			22 47
West Sutton	179	d						21 20					21 50				22 20			22 50
Sutton Common	179	d						21 22					21 52				22 22			22 52
St Helier	179	d						21 25					21 55				22 25			22 55
Morden South	179	d						21 27					21 57				22 27			22 57
South Merton	179	d						21 29					21 59				22 29			22 59
Wimbledon Chase	179	d						21 31					22 01				22 31			23 01
Wimbledon 6 ⊖	173,179	d						21 38					22 08				22 38			23 08
Haydons Road	173	d						21 40					22 10				22 40			23 10
Tooting	173	d						21 43					22 13				22 43			23 13
Carshalton	173	d	21 15																	
Hackbridge	173	d	21 17																	
Mitcham Junction	173	d	21 20																	
Mitcham Eastfields	173	d	21 23																	
Streatham 4		d	21 27					21 49					22 19				22 49			23 19
Tulse Hill 3		d	21 31					21 53					22 23				22 53			23 23
London Bridge 4 ⊖		a				21 45					22 15			22 45				23 15		
		d				21 45					22 15			22 45				23 15		
Herne Hill 4	173,179	d	21 35					21 57					22 27				22 57			23 27
Loughborough Jn.	173,179	d	21 38					22 00					22 30				23 00			
Elephant & Castle	173,179	d	21 43				22 00	22 04				22 30	22 34		23 00		23 04		23 30	23 34
London Blackfriars 3 ⊖		d	21 48			21 54	22a04	22 08			22 22	22a34	22 38	22 52	23a04		23 08	23 22	23a34	23 38
City Thameslink 3		d	21 50			21 56		22 10			22 24		22 40	22 54						
Farringdon 3 ⊖		d	21 53			21 59		22 13			22 28		22 43	22 58			23 13	23 28		23 43
St Pancras International 15 ⊖		a	21 57			22 03		22 17			22 31		22 47	23 02			23 17	23 32		23 47
		d	21 58	22 00	22 00	22 04		22 18	22 25	22 25	22 32		22 48	23 02		23 15	23 18	23 32		23 48
Kentish Town ⊖		d	22 01					22 21					22 51				23 21			23 51
West Hampstead Thameslink ⊖		d	22 05			22 11		22 25			22 40		22 55	23 10			23 25	23 40		23 55
Cricklewood		d	22 08					22 28					22 58				23 28			23 58
Hendon		d	22 11					22 31					23 01				23 31			00 01
Mill Hill Broadway		d	22 15					22 35					23 05				23 35			00 05
Elstree & Borehamwood		d	22 19					22 39					23 09				23 39			00 09
Radlett		d	22 23					22 43					23 14				23 44			00 14
St Albans City		d	22a31			22 25		22 50			22 57		23 21	23 27			23 51	23 57		00 21
Harpenden		d				22 31		22 56			23 03		23 27	23 33			23 57	00 03		00 27
Luton Airport Parkway 7 ✈		d				22 37		23 02	22 48	22 51	23 09		23 33	23 39			00 03	00 09		00 33
Luton 10		d		22 24	22 33	22 40		23 05			23 12		23 36	23 42		23 46	00 06	00 12		00 36
Leagrave		d				22 44		23 09			23 16		23 40	23 46			00 10	00 16		00 40
Harlington		d				22 49		23 14			23 21		23 44	23 51			00 14	00 21		00 44
Flitwick		d				22 53		23 18			23 25		23 48	23 55			00 18	00 25		00 48
Bedford 7		a		22 38	22 52	23 05		23 30	23 02	23 14	23 38		00 02	00 08		00 11	00 32	00 38		01 02

A until 27 December, from 10 February. To Nottingham
B from 30 December until 7 February. To Nottingham
E until 27 December, from 10 February. To Sheffield
F from 30 December until 7 February. To Sheffield
G To Derby

The trains that operate to and from Sevenoaks, Orpington and Rochester (and a few other destinations at peak times) are operated jointly by First Capital Connect (north of Blackfriars) and Southeastern (south of Blackfriars)

Table 52 shows the complete service between Bedford and London, whilst services between London, Sevenoaks, Sutton and Brighton only show through Thameslink services. Other Tables should be consulted for additional journey opportunities.

Table 52R

Mondays to Fridays

9 December to 16 May

Brighton, Gatwick Airport and South London - City of London, St Albans, Luton and Bedford

Network Diagram - refer to first Page of Table 52

			FC 1	FC 1	FC 1
Brighton 10		d	22 33	23 11	23 37
Preston Park		d	22 37		23 41
Hassocks 4		d	22 43	23 20	23 47
Burgess Hill 4		d	22 47	23 23	23 51
Wivelsfield 4		d	22 49		23 53
Haywards Heath 3		d	22 54	23 29	23 59
Balcombe		d	22 59		00 04
Three Bridges 4		d	23 12	23 38	00 10
Gatwick Airport 10	✈	d	23 17	23 43	00 15
Redhill		d			00 24
East Croydon	🚋	d	23 32	00 02	00 36
Sevenoaks 4	195	d			
Bat & Ball	195	d			
Otford 4	195	d			
Shoreham (Kent)	195	d			
Eynsford	195	d			
Swanley 4	195	d			
St Mary Cray 4	195	d			
Bickley	195	d			
Bromley South	195	d			
Shortlands 4	195	d			
Ravensbourne	195	d			
Beckenham Hill	195	d			
Bellingham	195	d			
Catford	195	d			
Crofton Park	195	d			
Nunhead 4	195	d			
Peckham Rye 4	195	d			
Denmark Hill 4	195	d			
Sutton (Surrey) 4	179	d			
West Sutton	179	d			
Sutton Common	179	d			
St Helier	179	d			
Morden South	179	d			
South Merton	179	d			
Wimbledon Chase	179	d			
Wimbledon 6	⊖173,179 🚋	d			
Haydons Road	173	d			
Tooting	173	d			
Carshalton	173	d			
Hackbridge	173	d			
Mitcham Junction	173 🚋	d			
Mitcham Eastfields	173	d			
Streatham 4		d			
Tulse Hill 3		d			
London Bridge 4	⊖	a	23 45	00 21	00 52
		d	23 45	00 22	00 52
Herne Hill 4	173,179	d			
Loughborough Jn.	173,179	d			
Elephant & Castle	173,179	d			
London Blackfriars 3	⊖	d	23 52	00 28	00 58
City Thameslink 3		d			
Farringdon 3	⊖	d	23 58	00 34	
St Pancras International 15	⊖	a	00 02	00 38	01 08
		d	00 03	00 39	01 09
Kentish Town	⊖	d		00 42	01 12
West Hampstead Thameslink	⊖	d	00 10	00 46	01 16
Cricklewood		d		00 49	01 19
Hendon		d		00 52	01 22
Mill Hill Broadway		d		00 56	01 26
Elstree & Borehamwood		d		01 00	01 30
Radlett		d		01 05	01 35
St Albans City		d	00 27	01 11	01 41
Harpenden		d	00 33	01 17	01 47
Luton Airport Parkway 7	✈	d	00 39	01 23	01 53
Luton 10		d	00 42	01 26	01 56
Leagrave		d	00 46	01 30	02 00
Harlington		d	00 51	01 35	02 05
Flitwick		d	00 55	01 39	02 09
Bedford 7		a	01 08	01 52	02 22

A until 27 December, from 10 February

The trains that operate to and from Sevenoaks, Orpington and Rochester (and a few other destinations at peak times) are operated jointly by First Capital Connect (north of Blackfriars) and Southeastern (south of Blackfriars)

Table 52 shows the complete service between Bedford and London, whilst services between London, Sevenoaks, Sutton and Brighton only show through Thameslink services. Other Tables should be consulted for additional journey opportunities.

Table 52R

Saturdays

14 December to 17 May

Brighton, Gatwick Airport and South London - City of London, St Albans, Luton and Bedford

Network Diagram - refer to first Page of Table 52

		FC A		FC 1 C	FC A		FC 1 C	EM ◇1 D	FC	FC 1 C	FC 1 C		FC 1	FC 1	FC 1	FC 1	EM ◇1 G	FC 1	FC 1	FC H	SE	EM ◇1 I		FC 1	EM ◇1 J
Brighton 10	d																							05 25	
Preston Park	d																							05 29	
Hassocks 4	d																							05 35	
Burgess Hill 4	d																							05 39	
Wivelsfield 4	d																							05 41	
Haywards Heath 3	d																							05 46	
Balcombe	d										00 04													05 51	
Three Bridges 4	d										00 10		01 16	02 16	03 16	04 16		04 52	05 22					05 57	
Gatwick Airport 10 ✈	d										00 15		01 21	02 21	03 21	04 21		04 57	05 27					06 02	
Redhill	d										00 24								05 36						
East Croydon	d									00 02	00 36		01 40	02 40	03 40	04 40		05 16	05 48					06 17	
Sevenoaks 4 195	d																				05 32				
Bat & Ball 195	d																				05 35				
Otford 4 195	d																				05 38				
Shoreham (Kent) 195	d																				05 41				
Eynsford 195	d																				05 45				
Swanley 4 195	d																				05 50				
St Mary Cray 4 195	d																				05 54				
Bickley 195	d																				05 58				
Bromley South 195	d																				06 01				
Shortlands 4 195	d																				06 04				
Ravensbourne 195	d																				06 06				
Beckenham Hill 195	d																				06 08				
Bellingham 195	d																				06 10				
Catford 195	d																				06 13				
Crofton Park 195	d																				06 15				
Nunhead 4 195	d																				06 18				
Peckham Rye 4 195	d																				06 20				
Denmark Hill 4 195	d																				06 24				
Sutton (Surrey) 4 179	d																								
West Sutton 179	d																								
Sutton Common 179	d																								
St Helier 179	d																								
Morden South 179	d																								
South Merton 179	d																								
Wimbledon Chase 179	d																								
Wimbledon 8 ⊖173,179	d																								
Haydons Road 173	d																								
Tooting 173	d																								
Carshalton 173	d																								
Hackbridge 173	d																								
Mitcham Junction 173	d																								
Mitcham Eastfields 173	d																								
Streatham 4	d																			05 49					
Tulse Hill 3	d																			05 56					
London Bridge 4 ⊖	a									00 21	00 52								06 02					06 30	
	d									00 22	00 52								06 02					06 30	
Herne Hill 4 173,179	d																			06 02					
Loughborough Jn. 173,179	d																								
Elephant & Castle 173,179	d																			06 09	06 30				
London Blackfriars 3 ⊖	d								00 09	00 28	00 58		02 09	03 09	04 09	05 09		05 44	06 08	06 14	06a34			06 38	
City Thameslink 3	d																								
Farringdon 3 ⊖	d								00 14	00 34						05 16		05 50	06 14	06 19				06 43	
St Pancras International 15 ⊖	a								00 18	00 38	01 08		02 20	03 20	04 20	05 20		05 54	06 18	06 23				06 47	
	d						00 03	00 15	00 19	00 39	01 09		02 21	03 21	04 21	05 24	05 45	05 54	06 18	06 24		06 37		06 48	06 52
Kentish Town ⊖	d								00 22	00 42	01 12		02 24	03 24	04 24	05 28		05 58		06 27					
West Hampstead Thameslink ⊖	d						00 10		00 26	00 46	01 16		02 28	03 28	04 28	05 32		06 02	06 25	06 32				06 55	
Cricklewood	d								00 29	00 49	01 19		02 31	03 31	04 31	05 35		06 05		06 35					
Hendon	d				00 01				00 32	00 52	01 22		02 34	03 34	04 34	05 38		06 08		06 38					
Mill Hill Broadway	d				00 05				00 36	00 56	01 26		02 38	03 38	04 38	05 42		06 12		06 42					
Elstree & Borehamwood	d				00 09				00 40	01 00	01 30		02 42	03 42	04 42	05 46		06 16		06 46					
Radlett	d				00 14				00 45	01 05	01 35		02 47	03 47	04 47	05 51		06 20		06 50					
St Albans City	d				00 21		00 27		00 51	01 11	01 41		02 54	03 54	04 54	05 58		06 26	06 41	06 56				07 10	
Harpenden	d			00 03	00 27		00 33		00 57	01 17	01 47		03 00	04 00	05 00	06 04		06 31	06 46	07 01				07 16	
Luton Airport Parkway 7 ✈	d	00 03		00 09	00 33		00 39	00 43	01 03	01 23	01 53		03 06	04 06	05 06	06 10		06 37	06 52	07 07				07 22	07a12
Luton 10	d	00 06		00 12	00 36		00 42	00 47	01 06	01 26	01 56		03 09	04 09	05 09	06 13	06 12	06 40	06 55	07a11		06a58		07 25	
Leagrave	d	00 10		00 16	00 40		00 46		01 10	01 30	02 00		03 13	04 13	05 13	06 17		06 44	06 59					07 29	
Harlington	d	00 14		00 21	00 44		00 51		01 15	01 35	02 05		03 18	04 18	05 18	06 22		06 49	07 04					07 34	
Flitwick	d	00 18		00 25	00 48		00 55		01 19	01 39	02 09		03 22	04 22	05 22	06 26		06 53	07 08					07 38	
Bedford 7	a	00 32		00 38	01 02		01 08	01 11	01 32	01 52	02 22		03 35	04 35	05 35	06 39	06 26	07 05	07 20					07 50	

A From Sutton (Surrey)
C From Brighton
D To Leicester
G To Sheffield
H From Selhurst
I To York
J To Nottingham

The trains that operate to and from Sevenoaks, Orpington and Rochester (and a few other destinations at peak times) are operated jointly by First Capital Connect (north of Blackfriars) and Southeastern (south of Blackfriars)

Table 52 shows the complete service between Bedford and London, whilst services between London, Sevenoaks, Sutton and Brighton only show through Thameslink services. Other Tables should be consulted for additional journey opportunities.

Table 52R

Saturdays

14 December to 17 May

Brighton, Gatwick Airport and South London - City of London, St Albans, Luton and Bedford

Network Diagram - refer to first Page of Table 52

Station			FC	SE	EM	FC	FC	EM	FC	SE		FC	FC	EM	FC	FC	SE	FC	FC	EM	FC		FC	SE	FC	FC
					◇1	1		◇1				1		◇1	1			1		◇1	1				1	
			A		B		A	B						C						B						
Brighton 10		d				06 02						06 25			06 37			07 04			07 07				07 34	
Preston Park		d										06 29			06 41						07 11					
Hassocks 4		d										06 35			06 47						07 17					
Burgess Hill 4		d				06 12						06 39			06 51						07 21					
Wivelsfield 4		d										06 41			06 53						07 23					
Haywards Heath 3		d				06 18						06 46			07 01			07 18			07 31				07 48	
Balcombe		d										06 51									07 37					
Three Bridges 4		d				06 27						06 57			07 12			07 27			07 42				07 57	
Gatwick Airport 10		d				06 32						07 02			07 17			07 32			07 47				08 02	
Redhill		d																								
East Croydon		d				06 47						07 17			07 32			07 47			08 02				08 17	
Sevenoaks 4	195	d		06 02						06 32							07 02							07 32		
Bat & Ball	195	d		06 05						06 35							07 05							07 35		
Otford 4	195	d		06 08						06 38							07 08							07 38		
Shoreham (Kent)	195	d		06 11						06 41							07 11							07 41		
Eynsford	195	d		06 15						06 45							07 15							07 45		
Swanley 4	195	d		06 20						06 50							07 20							07 50		
St Mary Cray 4	195	d		06 24						06 54							07 24							07 54		
Bickley	195	d		06 28						06 58							07 28							07 58		
Bromley South	195	d		06 31						07 01							07 31							08 01		
Shortlands 4	195	d		06 34						07 04							07 34							08 04		
Ravensbourne	195	d		06 36						07 06							07 36							08 06		
Beckenham Hill	195	d		06 38						07 08							07 38							08 08		
Bellingham	195	d		06 40						07 10							07 40							08 10		
Catford	195	d		06 43						07 13							07 43							08 13		
Crofton Park	195	d		06 45						07 15							07 45							08 15		
Nunhead 4	195	d		06 48						07 18							07 48							08 18		
Peckham Rye 4	195	d		06 50						07 20							07 50							08 20		
Denmark Hill 4	195	d		06 54						07 24							07 54							08 24		
Sutton (Surrey) 4	179	d							06 37				07 08			07 07			07 38				07 37			08 08
West Sutton	179	d							06 40							07 10							07 40			
Sutton Common	179	d							06 42							07 12							07 42			
St Helier	179	d							06 45							07 15							07 45			
Morden South	179	d							06 47							07 17							07 47			
South Merton	179	d							06 49							07 19							07 49			
Wimbledon Chase	179	d							06 51							07 21							07 51			
Wimbledon 5 ⊖	173,179	d							06 58							07 28							07 58			
Haydons Road	173	d							07 00							07 30							08 00			
Tooting	173	d							07 03							07 33							08 03			
Carshalton	173	d											07 11						07 41							08 11
Hackbridge	173	d											07 13						07 43							08 13
Mitcham Junction	173	d											07 16						07 46							08 16
Mitcham Eastfields	173	d											07 19						07 49							08 19
Streatham 4		d	06 19				06 49		07 08				07 23			07 38			07 53				08 08			08 23
Tulse Hill 3		d	06 26				06 56		07 12				07 27			07 42			07 57				08 12			08 27
London Bridge 4 ⊖		a				07 00						07 30			07 45			08 00			08 15				08 30	
		d				07 00						07 30			07 45			08 00			08 15				08 30	
Herne Hill 4	173,179	d	06 32				07 01		07 16				07 31			07 46			08 01				08 16			08 31
Loughborough Jn.	173,179	d	06 35				07 04		07 19				07 34			07 49			08 04				08 19			08 34
Elephant & Castle	173,179	d	06 39	07 00			07 09		07 24	07 30			07 39			07 54	08 00		08 09				08 24	08 30		08 39
London Blackfriars 3 ⊖		d	06 44	07a04		07 08	07 14		07 30	07a34		07 38	07 44		07 54	08 00	08a04	08 08	08 14		08 24		08 30	08a34	08 38	08 44
City Thameslink 3		d																								
Farringdon 3 ⊖		d	06 49			07 13	07 19		07 36			07 44	07 49		07 59	08 06		08 14	08 19		08 29		08 36		08 44	08 49
St Pancras International 15 ⊖		a	06 53			07 17	07 23		07 40			07 48	07 53		08 03	08 10		08 18	08 23		08 33		08 40		08 48	08 53
		d	06 54		06 58	07 18	07 24	07 28	07 40			07 48	07 54	08 00	08 04	08 10		08 18	08 24	08 29	08 34		08 40		08 48	08 54
Kentish Town ⊖		d	06 57				07 27		07 44				07 57			08 14			08 27				08 44			08 57
West Hampstead Thameslink ⊖		d	07 02			07 25	07 32		07 50				08 02		08 11	08 20			08 32		08 41		08 50			09 02
Cricklewood		d	07 05				07 35		07 53				08 05			08 23			08 35				08 53			09 05
Hendon		d	07 08				07 38		07 56				08 08			08 26			08 38				08 56			09 08
Mill Hill Broadway		d	07 12				07 42		08 00				08 12			08 30			08 42				09 00			09 12
Elstree & Borehamwood		d	07 16				07 46		08 04				08 16			08 34			08 46				09 04			09 16
Radlett		d	07 20				07 50		08 08				08 20			08 38			08 50				09 08			09 20
St Albans City		d	07 26			07 40	07 56		08 14			08 09	08a27		08 25	08 44		08 39	08a57		08 55		09 14		09 09	09a27
Harpenden		d	07 31			07 46	08 01		08 19			08 15			08 31	08 49		08 45			09 01		09 19		09 15	
Luton Airport Parkway 7		d	07 37			07 52	08 07	07 49	08 25			08 21			08 37	08 55		08 51		08 50	09 07		09 25		09 21	
Luton 10		d	07a41		07 19	07 55	08 10		08a29			08 24		08 22	08 40	08a59		08 54			09 10		09a29		09 24	
Leagrave		d				07 59	08 14					08 28			08 44			08 57			09 14				09 28	
Harlington		d				08 04	08 19					08 33			08 49			09 02			09 19				09 33	
Flitwick		d				08 08	08 23					08 37			08 53			09 06			09 23				09 37	
Bedford 7		a			07 33	08 20	08 35	08 03				08 49		08 36	09 05			09 19		09 04	09 35				09 49	

A From Selhurst
B To Nottingham
C To Corby.

The trains that operate to and from Sevenoaks, Orpington and Rochester (and a few other destinations at peak times) are operated jointly by First Capital Connect (north of Blackfriars) and Southeastern (south of Blackfriars)

Table 52 shows the complete service between Bedford and London, whilst services between London, Sevenoaks, Sutton and Brighton only show through Thameslink services. Other Tables should be consulted for additional journey opportunities.

Table 52R

Saturdays

14 December to 17 May

Brighton, Gatwick Airport and South London - City of London, St Albans, Luton and Bedford

Network Diagram - refer to first Page of Table 52

		EM ◇1 A	FC 1	FC	SE	FC 1	FC	EM ◇1 B	FC 1	FC	SE	FC 1	FC	EM ◇1 A	FC 1	FC	SE	FC 1	FC	EM ◇1 B	FC 1	FC	SE
Brighton 10	d		07 37			08 04			08 07			08 34			08 37			09 04			09 07		
Preston Park	d		07 41						08 11						08 41						09 11		
Hassocks 4	d		07 47						08 17						08 47						09 17		
Burgess Hill 4	d		07 51						08 21						08 51						09 21		
Wivelsfield 4	d		07 53						08 23						08 53						09 23		
Haywards Heath 3	d		08 01			08 18			08 31			08 48			09 01			09 18			09 31		
Balcombe	d								08 37												09 37		
Three Bridges 4	d		08 12			08 27			08 42			08 57			09 12			09 27			09 42		
Gatwick Airport 10 ✈	d		08 17			08 32			08 47			09 02			09 17			09 32			09 47		
Redhill	d																						
East Croydon	d		08 32			08 47			09 02			09 17			09 32			09 47			10 02		
Sevenoaks 4 195	d				08 02						08 32						09 02						09 32
Bat & Ball 195	d				08 05						08 35						09 05						09 35
Otford 4 195	d				08 08						08 38						09 08						09 38
Shoreham (Kent) 195	d				08 11						08 41						09 11						09 41
Eynsford 195	d				08 15						08 45						09 15						09 45
Swanley 4 195	d				08 20						08 50						09 20						09 50
St Mary Cray 4 195	d				08 24						08 54						09 24						09 54
Bickley 195	d				08 28						08 58						09 28						09 58
Bromley South 195	d				08 31						09 01						09 31						10 01
Shortlands 4 195	d				08 34						09 04						09 34						10 04
Ravensbourne 195	d				08 36						09 06						09 36						10 06
Beckenham Hill 195	d				08 38						09 08						09 38						10 08
Bellingham 195	d				08 40						09 10						09 40						10 10
Catford 195	d				08 43						09 13						09 43						10 13
Crofton Park 195	d				08 45						09 15						09 45						10 15
Nunhead 4 195	d				08 48						09 18						09 48						10 18
Peckham Rye 4 195	d				08 50						09 20						09 50						10 20
Denmark Hill 4 195	d				08 54						09 24						09 54						10 24
Sutton (Surrey) 4 179	d			08 07			08 38			08 37			09 08			09 07			09 38			09 37	
West Sutton 179	d			08 10						08 40						09 10						09 40	
Sutton Common 179	d			08 12						08 42						09 12						09 42	
St Helier 179	d			08 15						08 45						09 15						09 45	
Morden South 179	d			08 17						08 47						09 17						09 47	
South Merton 179	d			08 19						08 49						09 19						09 49	
Wimbledon Chase 179	d			08 21						08 51						09 21						09 51	
Wimbledon 5 ⊖173,179	d			08 28						08 58						09 28						09 58	
Haydons Road 173	d			08 30						09 00						09 30						10 00	
Tooting 173	d			08 33						09 03						09 33						10 03	
Carshalton 173	d						08 41						09 11						09 41				
Hackbridge 173	d						08 43						09 13						09 43				
Mitcham Junction 173	d						08 46						09 16						09 46				
Mitcham Eastfields 173	d						08 49						09 19						09 49				
Streatham 4	d			08 38			08 53			09 08			09 23			09 38			09 53			10 08	
Tulse Hill 3	d			08 42			08 57			09 12			09 27			09 42			09 57			10 12	
London Bridge 4 ⊖	a		08 45			09 00			09 15			09 30			09 45			10 00			10 15		
	d		08 45			09 00			09 15			09 30			09 45			10 00			10 15		
Herne Hill 4 173,179	d			08 46			09 01			09 16			09 31			09 46			10 01			10 16	
Loughborough Jn. 173,179	d			08 49			09 04			09 19			09 34			09 49			10 04			10 19	
Elephant & Castle 173,179	d			08 54	09 00		09 09			09 24	09 30		09 39			09 54	10 00		10 09			10 24	10 30
London Blackfriars 3 ⊖	d		08 54	09 00	09a04	09 08	09 14		09 24	09 30	09a34	09 38	09 44		09 54	10 00	10a04	10 08	10 14		10 24	10 30	10a34
City Thameslink 3	d			09 02		09 10	09 16		09 26	09 32		09 40	09 46		09 56	10 02		10 10	10 16		10 26	10 32	
Farringdon 3 ⊖	d		08 59	09 06		09 14	09 19		09 29	09 36		09 44	09 49		09 59	10 06		10 14	10 19		10 29	10 36	
St Pancras International 15 ⊖	a		09 03	09 10		09 18	09 23		09 33	09 40		09 48	09 53		10 03	10 10		10 18	10 23		10 33	10 40	
	d	09 00	09 04	09 10		09 18	09 24	09 29	09 34	09 40		09 48	09 54	10 00	10 04	10 10		10 18	10 24	10 29	10 34	10 40	
Kentish Town ⊖	d			09 14			09 27			09 44			09 57			10 14			10 27			10 44	
West Hampstead Thameslink ⊖	d		09 11	09 20			09 32		09 41	09 50			10 02		10 11	10 20			10 32		10 41	10 50	
Cricklewood	d			09 23			09 35			09 53			10 05			10 23			10 35			10 53	
Hendon	d			09 26			09 38			09 56			10 08			10 26			10 38			10 56	
Mill Hill Broadway	d			09 30			09 42			10 00			10 12			10 30			10 42			11 00	
Elstree & Borehamwood	d			09 34			09 46			10 04			10 16			10 34			10 46			11 04	
Radlett	d			09 38			09 50			10 08			10 20			10 38			10 50			11 08	
St Albans City	d		09 25	09 44		09 39	09a57		09 55	10 14		10 09	10a27		10 25	10 44		10 39	10a57		10 55	11 14	
Harpenden	d		09 31	09 49		09 45			10 01	10 19		10 15			10 31	10 49		10 45			11 01	11 19	
Luton Airport Parkway 7 ✈	d		09 37	09 55		09 51		09 50	10 07	10 25		10 21			10 37	10 55		10 51		10 50	11 07	11 25	
Luton 10	d	09 22	09 40	09a59		09 54			10 10	10a29		10 24		10 22	10 40	10a59		10 54			11 10	11a29	
Leagrave	d		09 44			09 58			10 14			10 28			10 44			10 58			11 14		
Harlington	d		09 49			10 03			10 19			10 33			10 49			11 03			11 19		
Flitwick	d		09 53			10 07			10 23			10 37			10 53			11 07			11 23		
Bedford 7	a	09 36	10 05			10 19		10 04	10 35			10 49		10 36	11 05			11 19		11 04	11 35		

A To Corby.

B To Nottingham

The trains that operate to and from Sevenoaks, Orpington and Rochester (and a few other destinations at peak times) are operated jointly by First Capital Connect (north of Blackfriars) and Southeastern (south of Blackfriars)

Table 52 shows the complete service between Bedford and London, whilst services between London, Sevenoaks, Sutton and Brighton only show through Thameslink services. Other Tables should be consulted for additional journey opportunities.

Table 52R

Saturdays

14 December to 17 May

Brighton, Gatwick Airport and South London - City of London, St Albans, Luton and Bedford

Network Diagram - refer to first Page of Table 52

		FC	FC	EM	FC		FC	SE	FC	FC	EM	FC	FC	SE	FC	FC		EM	FC	FC	SE	FC	FC	EM	FC
		1		◇1	1				1		◇1	1			1			◇1	1			1		◇1	1
				A							B							A						B	
Brighton 10	d	09 34			09 37				10 04			10 07			10 34				10 37			11 04			11 07
Preston Park	d				09 41							10 11							10 41						11 11
Hassocks 4	d				09 47							10 17							10 47						11 17
Burgess Hill 4	d				09 51							10 21							10 51						11 21
Wivelsfield 4	d				09 53							10 23							10 53						11 23
Haywards Heath 3	d	09 48			10 01				10 18			10 31			10 48				11 01			11 18			11 31
Balcombe	d											10 37													11 37
Three Bridges 4	d	09 57			10 12				10 27			10 41			10 57				11 12			11 27			11 42
Gatwick Airport 10 ✈	d	10 02			10 17				10 32			10 47			11 02				11 17			11 32			11 47
Redhill	d																								
East Croydon	d	10 17			10 32				10 47			11 02			11 17				11 32			11 47			12 02
Sevenoaks 4 195	d							10 02						10 32							11 02				
Bat & Ball 195	d							10 05						10 35							11 05				
Otford 4 195	d							10 08						10 38							11 08				
Shoreham (Kent) 195	d							10 11						10 41							11 11				
Eynsford 195	d							10 15						10 45							11 15				
Swanley 4 195	d							10 20						10 50							11 20				
St Mary Cray 4 195	d							10 24						10 54							11 24				
Bickley 195	d							10 28						10 58							11 28				
Bromley South 195	d							10 31						11 01							11 31				
Shortlands 4 195	d							10 34						11 04							11 34				
Ravensbourne 195	d							10 36						11 06							11 36				
Beckenham Hill 195	d							10 38						11 08							11 38				
Bellingham 195	d							10 40						11 10							11 40				
Catford 195	d							10 43						11 13							11 43				
Crofton Park 195	d							10 45						11 15							11 45				
Nunhead 4 195	d							10 48						11 18							11 48				
Peckham Rye 4 195	d							10 50						11 20							11 50				
Denmark Hill 4 195	d							10 54						11 24							11 54				
Sutton (Surrey) 4 179	d		10 08				10 07			10 38			10 37			11 08				11 07			11 38		
West Sutton 179	d						10 10						10 40							11 10					
Sutton Common 179	d						10 12						10 42							11 12					
St Helier 179	d						10 15						10 45							11 15					
Morden South 179	d						10 17						10 47							11 17					
South Merton 179	d						10 19						10 49							11 19					
Wimbledon Chase 179	d						10 21						10 51							11 21					
Wimbledon 6 ⊖173,179	d						10 28						10 58							11 28					
Haydons Road 173	d						10 30						11 00							11 30					
Tooting 173	d						10 33						11 03							11 33					
Carshalton 173	d		10 11							10 41						11 11							11 41		
Hackbridge 173	d		10 13							10 43						11 13							11 43		
Mitcham Junction 173	d		10 16							10 46						11 16							11 46		
Mitcham Eastfields 173	d		10 19							10 49						11 19							11 49		
Streatham 4	d		10 23				10 38			10 53			11 08			11 23				11 38			11 53		
Tulse Hill 3	d		10 27				10 42			10 57			11 12			11 27				11 42			11 57		
London Bridge 4 ⊖	a	10 30			10 45				11 00			11 15			11 30				11 45			12 00			12 15
	d	10 30			10 45				11 00			11 15			11 30				11 45			12 00			12 15
Herne Hill 4 173,179	d		10 31				10 46			11 01			11 16			11 31				11 46			12 01		
Loughborough Jn. 173,179	d		10 34				10 49			11 04			11 19			11 34				11 49			12 04		
Elephant & Castle 173,179	d		10 39				10 54	11 00		11 09			11 24	11 30		11 39				11 54	12 00		12 09		
London Blackfriars 3 ⊖	d	10 38	10 44		10 54		11 00	11a04	11 08	11 14		11 24	11 30	11a34	11 38	11 44			11 54	12 00	12a04	12 08	12 14		12 24
City Thameslink 3	d	10 40	10 46		10 56		11 02		11 10	11 16		11 26	11 32		11 40	11 46			11 56	12 02		12 10	12 16		12 26
Farringdon 3 ⊖	d	10 44	10 49		10 59		11 06		11 14	11 19		11 29	11 36		11 44	11 49			11 59	12 06		12 14	12 19		12 29
St Pancras International 15 ⊖	a	10 48	10 53		11 03		11 10		11 18	11 23		11 33	11 40		11 48	11 53			12 03	12 10		12 18	12 23		12 33
	d	10 48	10 54	11 00	11 04		11 10		11 18	11 24	11 29	11 34	11 40		11 48	11 54		12 00	12 04	12 10		12 18	12 24	12 29	12 34
Kentish Town ⊖	d		10 57				11 14			11 27			11 44			11 57				12 14			12 27		
West Hampstead Thameslink ⊖	d		11 02		11 11		11 20			11 32		11 41	11 50			12 02			12 11	12 20			12 32		12 41
Cricklewood	d		11 05				11 23			11 35			11 53			12 05				12 23			12 35		
Hendon	d		11 08				11 26			11 38			11 56			12 08				12 26			12 38		
Mill Hill Broadway	d		11 12				11 30			11 42			12 00			12 12				12 30			12 42		
Elstree & Borehamwood	d		11 16				11 34			11 46			12 04			12 16				12 34			12 46		
Radlett	d		11 20				11 38			11 50			12 08			12 20				12 38			12 50		
St Albans City	d	11 09	11a27		11 25		11 44		11 39	11a57		11 55	12 14		12 09	12a27			12 25	12 44		12 39	12a57		12 55
Harpenden	d	11 15			11 31		11 49		11 45			12 01	12 19		12 15				12 31	12 49		12 45			13 01
Luton Airport Parkway 7 ✈	d	11 21			11 37		11 55		11 51		11 50	12 07	12 25		12 21				12 37	12 55		12 51		12 50	13 07
Luton 10	d	11 24		11 22	11 40		11a59		11 54			12 10	12a29		12 24			12 22	12 40	12a59		12 54			13 10
Leagrave	d	11 28			11 44				11 58			12 14			12 28				12 44			12 58			13 14
Harlington	d	11 33			11 49				12 03			12 19			12 33				12 49			13 03			13 19
Flitwick	d	11 37			11 53				12 07			12 23			12 37				12 53			13 07			13 23
Bedford 7	a	11 49		11 36	12 05				12 19		12 04	12 35			12 49			12 36	13 05			13 19		13 04	13 35

A To Corby.

B To Nottingham

The trains that operate to and from Sevenoaks, Orpington and Rochester (and a few other destinations at peak times) are operated jointly by First Capital Connect (north of Blackfriars) and Southeastern (south of Blackfriars)

Table 52 shows the complete service between Bedford and London, whilst services between London, Sevenoaks, Sutton and Brighton only show through Thameslink services. Other Tables should be consulted for additional journey opportunities.

Table 52R

Saturdays

14 December to 17 May

Brighton, Gatwick Airport and South London - City of London, St Albans, Luton and Bedford

Network Diagram - refer to first Page of Table 52

Station		FC	SE	FC [1]	FC	EM ◇[1] A 🍴	FC [1]	FC	SE	FC [1]	FC	EM ◇[1] B 🍴	FC [1]	FC	SE	FC [1]	FC	EM ◇[1] A 🍴	FC [1]	FC	SE	FC [1]	FC
Brighton [10]	d			11 34			11 37			12 04			12 07			12 34			12 37			13 04	
Preston Park	d						11 41						12 11						12 41				
Hassocks [4]	d						11 47						12 17						12 47				
Burgess Hill [4]	d						11 51						12 21						12 51				
Wivelsfield [4]	d						11 53						12 23						12 53				
Haywards Heath [3]	d			11 48			12 01			12 18			12 31			12 48			13 01			13 18	
Balcombe	d												12 37										
Three Bridges [4]	d			11 57			12 12			12 27			12 42			12 57			13 12			13 27	
Gatwick Airport [10] ✈	d			12 02			12 17			12 32			12 47			13 02			13 17			13 32	
Redhill	d																						
East Croydon 🚋	d			12 17			12 32			12 47			13 02			13 17			13 32			13 47	
Sevenoaks [4]	195 d		11 32						12 02						12 32						13 02		
Bat & Ball	195 d		11 35						12 05						12 35						13 05		
Otford [4]	195 d		11 38						12 08						12 38						13 08		
Shoreham (Kent)	195 d		11 41						12 11						12 41						13 11		
Eynsford	195 d		11 45						12 15						12 45						13 15		
Swanley [4]	195 d		11 50						12 20						12 50						13 20		
St Mary Cray [4]	195 d		11 54						12 24						12 54						13 24		
Bickley	195 d		11 58						12 28						12 58						13 28		
Bromley South	195 d		12 01						12 31						13 01						13 31		
Shortlands [4]	195 d		12 04						12 34						13 04						13 34		
Ravensbourne	195 d		12 06						12 36						13 06						13 36		
Beckenham Hill	195 d		12 08						12 38						13 08						13 38		
Bellingham	195 d		12 10						12 40						13 10						13 40		
Catford	195 d		12 13						12 43						13 13						13 43		
Crofton Park	195 d		12 15						12 45						13 15						13 45		
Nunhead [4]	195 d		12 18						12 48						13 18						13 48		
Peckham Rye [4]	195 d		12 20						12 50						13 20						13 50		
Denmark Hill [4]	195 d		12 24						12 54						13 24						13 54		
Sutton (Surrey) [4]	179 d	11 37			12 08			12 07			12 38			12 37			13 08			13 07			13 38
West Sutton	179 d	11 40						12 10						12 40						13 10			
Sutton Common	179 d	11 42						12 12						12 42						13 12			
St Helier	179 d	11 45						12 15						12 45						13 15			
Morden South	179 d	11 47						12 17						12 47						13 17			
South Merton	179 d	11 49						12 19						12 49						13 19			
Wimbledon Chase	179 d	11 51						12 21						12 51						13 21			
Wimbledon [6] ⊖173,179 🚋	d	11 58						12 28						12 58						13 28			
Haydons Road	173 d	12 00						12 30						13 00						13 30			
Tooting	173 d	12 03						12 33						13 03						13 33			
Carshalton	173 d				12 11						12 41						13 11						13 41
Hackbridge	173 d				12 13						12 43						13 13						13 43
Mitcham Junction	173 🚋 d				12 16						12 46						13 16						13 46
Mitcham Eastfields	173 d				12 19						12 49						13 19						13 49
Streatham [4]	d	12 08			12 23			12 38			12 53			13 08			13 23			13 38			13 53
Tulse Hill [3]	d	12 12			12 27			12 42			12 57			13 12			13 27			13 42			13 57
London Bridge [4] ⊖	a			12 30			12 45			13 00			13 15			13 30			13 45			14 00	
	d			12 30			12 45			13 00			13 15			13 30			13 45			14 00	
Herne Hill [4]	173,179 d	12 16			12 31			12 46			13 01			13 16			13 31			13 46			14 01
Loughborough Jn.	173,179 d	12 19			12 34			12 49			13 04			13 19			13 34			13 49			14 04
Elephant & Castle	173,179 d	12 24	12 30		12 39			12 54	13 00		13 09			13 24	13 30		13 39			13 54	14 00		14 09
London Blackfriars [3] ⊖	d	12 30	12a34	12 38	12 44		12 54	13 00	13a04	13 08	13 14		13 24	13 30	13a34	13 38	13 44		13 54	14 00	14a04	14 08	14 14
City Thameslink [3]	d	12 32		12 40	12 46		12 56	13 02		13 10	13 16		13 26	13 32		13 40	13 46		13 56	14 02		14 10	14 16
Farringdon [3] ⊖	d	12 36		12 44	12 49		12 59	13 06		13 14	13 19		13 29	13 36		13 44	13 49		13 59	14 06		14 14	14 19
St Pancras International [15] ⊖	a	12 40		12 48	12 53		13 03	13 10		13 18	13 23		13 33	13 40		13 48	13 53		14 03	14 10		14 18	14 23
	d	12 40		12 48	12 54	13 00	13 04	13 10		13 18	13 24	13 29	13 34	13 40		13 48	13 54	14 00	14 04	14 10		14 18	14 24
Kentish Town ⊖	d	12 44			12 57			13 14			13 27			13 44			13 57			14 14			14 27
West Hampstead Thameslink ⊖	d	12 50			13 02		13 11	13 20			13 32		13 41	13 50			14 02		14 11	14 20			14 32
Cricklewood	d	12 53			13 05			13 23			13 35			13 53			14 05			14 23			14 35
Hendon	d	12 56			13 08			13 26			13 38			13 56			14 08			14 26			14 38
Mill Hill Broadway	d	13 00			13 12			13 30			13 42			14 00			14 12			14 30			14 42
Elstree & Borehamwood	d	13 04			13 16			13 34			13 46			14 04			14 16			14 34			14 46
Radlett	d	13 08			13 20			13 38			13 50			14 08			14 20			14 38			14 50
St Albans City	d	13 14		13 09	13a27		13 25	13 44		13 39	13a57		13 55	14 14		14 09	14a27		14 25	14 44		14 39	14a57
Harpenden	d	13 19		13 15			13 31	13 49		13 45			14 01	14 19		14 15			14 31	14 49		14 45	
Luton Airport Parkway [7] ✈	d	13 25		13 21			13 37	13 55		13 51		13 50	14 07	14 25		14 21			14 37	14 55		14 51	
Luton [10]	d	13a29		13 24		13 22	13 40	13a59		13 54			14 10	14a29		14 24		14 22	14 40	14a59		14 54	
Leagrave	d			13 28			13 44			13 58			14 14			14 28			14 44			14 58	
Harlington	d			13 33			13 49			14 03			14 19			14 33			14 49			15 03	
Flitwick	d			13 37			13 53			14 07			14 23			14 37			14 53			15 07	
Bedford [7]	a			13 49		13 36	14 05			14 19		14 04	14 35			14 49		14 36	15 05			15 19	

A To Corby.

B To Nottingham

The trains that operate to and from Sevenoaks, Orpington and Rochester (and a few other destinations at peak times) are operated jointly by First Capital Connect (north of Blackfriars) and Southeastern (south of Blackfriars)

Table 52 shows the complete service between Bedford and London, whilst services between London, Sevenoaks, Sutton and Brighton only show through Thameslink services. Other Tables should be consulted for additional journey opportunities.

Table 52R

Saturdays

14 December to 17 May

Brighton, Gatwick Airport and South London - City of London, St Albans, Luton and Bedford

Network Diagram - refer to first Page of Table 52

			EM	FC	FC	SE	FC	FC	EM	FC	FC	SE	FC	FC	EM	FC	FC	SE	FC	FC	EM	FC	FC
			◇1 A ⚲	1			1		◇1 B ⚲	1			1		◇1 A ⚲	1			1		◇1 B ⚲	1	
Brighton 10		d		13 07			13 34			13 37			14 04			14 07			14 34			14 37	
Preston Park		d		13 11						13 41						14 11						14 41	
Hassocks 4		d		13 17						13 47						14 17						14 47	
Burgess Hill 4		d		13 21						13 51						14 21						14 51	
Wivelsfield 4		d		13 23						13 53						14 23						14 53	
Haywards Heath 3		d		13 31			13 48			14 01			14 18			14 31			14 48			15 01	
Balcombe		d		13 37												14 37							
Three Bridges 4		d		13 42			13 57			14 12			14 27			14 42			14 57			15 12	
Gatwick Airport 10	✈	d		13 47			14 02			14 17			14 32			14 47			15 02			15 17	
Redhill		d																					
East Croydon	⇌	d		14 02			14 17			14 32			14 47			15 02			15 17			15 32	
Sevenoaks 4	195	d				13 32						14 02						14 32					
Bat & Ball	195	d				13 35						14 05						14 35					
Otford 4	195	d				13 38						14 08						14 38					
Shoreham (Kent)	195	d				13 41						14 11						14 41					
Eynsford	195	d				13 45						14 15						14 45					
Swanley 4	195	d				13 50						14 20						14 50					
St Mary Cray 4	195	d				13 54						14 24						14 54					
Bickley	195	d				13 58						14 28						14 58					
Bromley South	195	d				14 01						14 31						15 01					
Shortlands 4	195	d				14 04						14 34						15 04					
Ravensbourne	195	d				14 06						14 36						15 06					
Beckenham Hill	195	d				14 08						14 38						15 08					
Bellingham	195	d				14 10						14 40						15 10					
Catford	195	d				14 13						14 43						15 13					
Crofton Park	195	d				14 15						14 45						15 15					
Nunhead 4	195	d				14 18						14 48						15 18					
Peckham Rye 4	195	d				14 20						14 50						15 20					
Denmark Hill 4	195	d				14 24						14 54						15 24					
Sutton (Surrey) 4	179	d			13 37			14 08			14 07			14 38			14 37			15 08			15 07
West Sutton	179	d			13 40						14 10						14 40						15 10
Sutton Common	179	d			13 42						14 12						14 42						15 12
St Helier	179	d			13 45						14 15						14 45						15 15
Morden South	179	d			13 47						14 17						14 47						15 17
South Merton	179	d			13 49						14 19						14 49						15 19
Wimbledon Chase	179	d			13 51						14 21						14 51						15 21
Wimbledon 5	⊖173,179 ⇌	d			13 58						14 28						14 58						15 28
Haydons Road	173	d			14 00						14 30						15 00						15 30
Tooting	173	d			14 03						14 33						15 03						15 33
Carshalton	173	d						14 11						14 41						15 11			
Hackbridge	173	d						14 13						14 43						15 13			
Mitcham Junction	173 ⇌	d						14 16						14 46						15 16			
Mitcham Eastfields	173	d						14 19						14 49						15 19			
Streatham 4		d			14 08			14 23			14 38			14 53			15 08			15 23			15 38
Tulse Hill 3		d			14 12			14 27			14 42			14 57			15 12			15 27			15 42
London Bridge 4	⊖	a		14 15			14 30			14 45			15 00			15 15			15 30			15 45	
		d		14 15			14 30			14 45			15 00			15 15			15 30			15 45	
Herne Hill 4	173,179	d			14 16			14 31			14 46			15 01			15 16			15 31			15 46
Loughborough Jn.	173,179	d			14 19			14 34			14 49			15 04			15 19			15 34			15 49
Elephant & Castle	173,179	d			14 24	14 30		14 39			14 54	15 00		15 09			15 24	15 30		15 39			15 54
London Blackfriars 3	⊖	d		14 24	14 30	14a34	14 38	14 44		14 54	15 00	15a04	15 08	15 14		15 24	15 30	15a34	15 38	15 44		15 54	16 00
City Thameslink 3		d		14 26	14 32		14 40	14 46		14 56	15 02		15 10	15 16		15 26	15 32		15 40	15 46		15 56	16 02
Farringdon 3	⊖	d		14 29	14 36		14 44	14 49		14 59	15 06		15 14	15 19		15 29	15 36		15 44	15 49		15 59	16 06
St Pancras International 15	⊖	a		14 33	14 40		14 48	14 53		15 03	15 10		15 18	15 23		15 33	15 40		15 48	15 53		16 03	16 10
		d	14 29	14 34	14 40		14 48	14 54	15 00	15 04	15 10		15 18	15 24	15 29	15 34	15 40		15 48	15 54	16 00	16 04	16 10
Kentish Town	⊖	d			14 44			14 57			15 14			15 27			15 44			15 57			16 14
West Hampstead Thameslink	⊖	d		14 41	14 50			15 02		15 11	15 20			15 32		15 41	15 50			16 02		16 11	16 20
Cricklewood		d			14 53			15 05			15 23			15 35			15 53			16 05			16 23
Hendon		d			14 56			15 08			15 26			15 38			15 56			16 08			16 26
Mill Hill Broadway		d			15 00			15 12			15 30			15 42			16 00			16 12			16 30
Elstree & Borehamwood		d			15 04			15 16			15 34			15 46			16 04			16 16			16 34
Radlett		d			15 08			15 20			15 38			15 50			16 08			16 20			16 38
St Albans City		d		14 55	15 14		15 09	15a27		15 25	15 44		15 39	15a57		15 55	16 14		16 09	16a27		16 25	16 44
Harpenden		d		15 01	15 19		15 15			15 31	15 49		15 45			16 01	16 19		16 15			16 31	16 49
Luton Airport Parkway 7	✈	d	14 50	15 07	15 25		15 21			15 37	15 55		15 51		15 50	16 07	16 25		16 21			16 37	16 55
Luton 10		d		15 10	15a29		15 24		15 22	15 40	15a59		15 54			16 10	16a29		16 24		16 22	16 40	16a59
Leagrave		d		15 14			15 28			15 44			15 58			16 14			16 28			16 44	
Harlington		d		15 19			15 33			15 49			16 03			16 19			16 33			16 49	
Flitwick		d		15 23			15 37			15 53			16 07			16 23			16 37			16 53	
Bedford 7		a	15 04	15 35			15 49		15 36	16 05			16 19		16 04	16 35			16 49		16 36	17 05	

A To Nottingham

B To Corby.

The trains that operate to and from Sevenoaks, Orpington and Rochester (and a few other destinations at peak times) are operated jointly by First Capital Connect (north of Blackfriars) and Southeastern (south of Blackfriars)

Table 52 shows the complete service between Bedford and London, whilst services between London, Sevenoaks, Sutton and Brighton only show through Thameslink services. Other Tables should be consulted for additional journey opportunities.

Table 52R

Saturdays

14 December to 17 May

Brighton, Gatwick Airport and South London - City of London, St Albans, Luton and Bedford

Network Diagram - refer to first Page of Table 52

			SE	FC	FC	EM	FC	FC	SE	FC	FC		EM	FC	FC	SE	FC	FC	EM	FC	FC	SE		FC	FC	EM
				1		◇1 A 🚲	1			1			◇1 B 🚲	1			1		◇1 C 🚲	1				1		◇1 B 🚲
Brighton 10		d		15 04			15 07			15 34				15 37			16 04			16 07				16 34		
Preston Park		d					15 11							15 41						16 11						
Hassocks 4		d					15 17							15 47						16 17						
Burgess Hill 4		d					15 21							15 51						16 21						
Wivelsfield 4		d					15 23							15 53						16 23						
Haywards Heath 3		d		15 18			15 31			15 48				16 01			16 18			16 31				16 48		
Balcombe		d					15 37													16 37						
Three Bridges 4		d		15 27			15 41			15 57				16 12			16 27			16 42				16 57		
Gatwick Airport 10	✈	d		15 32			15 47			16 02				16 17			16 32			16 47				17 02		
Redhill		d																								
East Croydon	🚊	d		15 47			16 02			16 17				16 32			16 47			17 02				17 17		
Sevenoaks 4	195	d	15 02						15 32							16 02						16 32				
Bat & Ball	195	d	15 05						15 35							16 05						16 35				
Otford 4	195	d	15 08						15 38							16 08						16 38				
Shoreham (Kent)	195	d	15 11						15 41							16 11						16 41				
Eynsford	195	d	15 15						15 45							16 15						16 45				
Swanley 4	195	d	15 20						15 50							16 20						16 50				
St Mary Cray 4	195	d	15 24						15 54							16 24						16 54				
Bickley	195	d	15 28						15 58							16 28						16 58				
Bromley South	195	d	15 31						16 01							16 31						17 01				
Shortlands 4	195	d	15 34						16 04							16 34						17 04				
Ravensbourne	195	d	15 36						16 06							16 36						17 06				
Beckenham Hill	195	d	15 38						16 08							16 38						17 08				
Bellingham	195	d	15 40						16 10							16 40						17 10				
Catford	195	d	15 43						16 13							16 43						17 13				
Crofton Park	195	d	15 45						16 15							16 45						17 15				
Nunhead 4	195	d	15 48						16 18							16 48						17 18				
Peckham Rye 4	195	d	15 50						16 20							16 50						17 20				
Denmark Hill 4	195	d	15 54						16 24							16 54						17 24				
Sutton (Surrey) 4	179	d			15 38			15 37			16 08				16 07			16 38			16 37				17 08	
West Sutton	179	d						15 40							16 10						16 40					
Sutton Common	179	d						15 42							16 12						16 42					
St Helier	179	d						15 45							16 15						16 45					
Morden South	179	d						15 47							16 17						16 47					
South Merton	179	d						15 49							16 19						16 49					
Wimbledon Chase	179	d						15 51							16 21						16 51					
Wimbledon 6	⊖173,179 🚊	d						15 58							16 28						16 58					
Haydons Road	173	d						16 00							16 30						17 00					
Tooting	173	d						16 03							16 33						17 03					
Carshalton	173	d			15 41						16 11							16 41							17 11	
Hackbridge	173	d			15 43						16 13							16 43							17 13	
Mitcham Junction	173 🚊	d			15 46						16 16							16 46							17 16	
Mitcham Eastfields	173	d			15 49						16 19							16 49							17 19	
Streatham 4		d			15 53			16 08			16 23				16 38			16 53			17 08				17 23	
Tulse Hill 3		d			15 57			16 12			16 27				16 42			16 57			17 12				17 27	
London Bridge 4	⊖	a		16 00			16 15			16 30				16 45			17 00			17 15				17 30		
		d		16 00			16 15			16 30				16 45			17 00			17 15				17 30		
Herne Hill 4	173,179	d			16 01			16 16			16 31				16 46			17 01			17 16				17 31	
Loughborough Jn.	173,179	d			16 04			16 19			16 34				16 49			17 04			17 19				17 34	
Elephant & Castle	173,179	d	16 00		16 09			16 24	16 30		16 39				16 54	17 00		17 09			17 24	17 30			17 39	
London Blackfriars 3	⊖	d	16a04	16 08	16 14		16 24	16 30	16a34	16 38	16 44			16 54	17 00	17a04	17 08	17 14		17 24	17 30	17a34		17 38	17 44	
City Thameslink 3		d		16 10	16 16		16 26	16 32		16 40	16 46			16 56	17 02		17 10	17 16		17 26	17 32			17 40	17 46	
Farringdon 3	⊖	d		16 14	16 19		16 29	16 36		16 44	16 49			16 59	17 06		17 14	17 19		17 29	17 36			17 44	17 49	
St Pancras International 15	⊖	a		16 18	16 23		16 33	16 40		16 48	16 53			17 03	17 10		17 18	17 23		17 33	17 40			17 48	17 53	
		d		16 18	16 24	16 29	16 34	16 40		16 48	16 54		17 00	17 04	17 10		17 18	17 24	17 29	17 34	17 40			17 48	17 54	18 00
Kentish Town	⊖	d			16 27			16 44			16 57				17 14			17 27			17 44				17 57	
West Hampstead Thameslink	⊖	d			16 32		16 41	16 50			17 02			17 11	17 20			17 32		17 41	17 50				18 02	
Cricklewood		d			16 35			16 53			17 05				17 23			17 35			17 53				18 05	
Hendon		d			16 38			16 56			17 08				17 26			17 38			17 56				18 08	
Mill Hill Broadway		d			16 42			17 00			17 12				17 30			17 42			18 00				18 12	
Elstree & Borehamwood		d			16 46			17 04			17 16				17 34			17 46			18 04				18 16	
Radlett		d			16 50			17 08			17 20				17 38			17 50			18 08				18 20	
St Albans City		d		16 39	16a57		16 55	17 14		17 09	17a27			17 25	17 44		17 39	17a57		17 55	18 14			18 09	18a27	
Harpenden		d		16 45			17 01	17 19		17 15				17 31	17 49		17 45			18 01	18 19			18 15		
Luton Airport Parkway 7	✈	d		16 51		16 50	17 07	17 25		17 21				17 37	17 55		17 51		17 50	18 07	18 25			18 21		
Luton 10		d		16 54			17 10	17a29		17 24			17 22	17 40	17a59		17 54			18 10	18a29			18 24		18 22
Leagrave		d		16 58			17 14			17 28				17 44			17 58			18 14				18 28		
Harlington		d		17 03			17 19			17 33				17 49			18 03			18 19				18 33		
Flitwick		d		17 07			17 23			17 37				17 53			18 07			18 23				18 37		
Bedford 7		a		17 19		17 04	17 35			17 49			17 37	18 05			18 19		18 04	18 35				18 49		18 36

A To Nottingham B To Corby. C To Lincoln

The trains that operate to and from Sevenoaks, Orpington and Rochester (and a few other destinations at peak times) are operated jointly by First Capital Connect (north of Blackfriars) and Southeastern (south of Blackfriars)

Table 52 shows the complete service between Bedford and London, whilst services between London, Sevenoaks, Sutton and Brighton only show through Thameslink services. Other Tables should be consulted for additional journey opportunities.

Table 52R

Saturdays

14 December to 17 May

Brighton, Gatwick Airport and South London - City of London, St Albans, Luton and Bedford

Network Diagram - refer to first Page of Table 52

	FC	FC	SE	FC	FC	EM	FC		FC	SE	FC	FC	EM	FC	FC	SE	FC	FC		EM	FC	FC	SE	FC
	1			1		◇1	1				1		◇1	1			1			◇1	1			1
						A							B							A				
						✕							✕							✕				
Brighton 10 d	16 37			17 04			17 07				17 34			17 37			18 04				18 07			18 34
Preston Park d	16 41						17 11							17 41							18 11			
Hassocks 4 d	16 47						17 17							17 47							18 17			
Burgess Hill 4 d	16 51						17 21							17 51							18 21			
Wivelsfield 4 d	16 53						17 23							17 53							18 23			
Haywards Heath 3 d	17 01			17 18			17 31				17 48			18 01			18 18				18 31			18 48
Balcombe d							17 37														18 37			
Three Bridges 4 d	17 12			17 27			17 41				17 57			18 12			18 27				18 42			18 57
Gatwick Airport 10 ✈ d	17 17			17 32			17 47				18 02			18 17			18 32				18 47			19 02
Redhill d																								
East Croydon ⇌ d	17 32			17 47			18 02				18 17			18 32			18 47				19 02			19 17
Sevenoaks 4 195 d			17 02							17 32						18 02							18 32	
Bat & Ball 195 d			17 05							17 35						18 05							18 35	
Otford 4 195 d			17 08							17 38						18 08							18 38	
Shoreham (Kent) 195 d			17 11							17 41						18 11							18 41	
Eynsford 195 d			17 15							17 45						18 15							18 45	
Swanley 4 195 d			17 20							17 50						18 20							18 50	
St Mary Cray 4 195 d			17 24							17 54						18 24							18 54	
Bickley 195 d			17 28							17 58						18 28							18 58	
Bromley South 195 d			17 31							18 01						18 31							19 01	
Shortlands 4 195 d			17 34							18 04						18 34							19 04	
Ravensbourne 195 d			17 36							18 06						18 36							19 06	
Beckenham Hill 195 d			17 38							18 08						18 38							19 08	
Bellingham 195 d			17 40							18 10						18 40							19 10	
Catford 195 d			17 43							18 13						18 43							19 13	
Crofton Park 195 d			17 45							18 15						18 45							19 15	
Nunhead 4 195 d			17 48							18 18						18 48							19 18	
Peckham Rye 4 195 d			17 50							18 20						18 50							19 20	
Denmark Hill 4 195 d			17 54							18 24						18 54							19 24	
Sutton (Surrey) 4 179 d		17 07			17 38				17 37			18 08			18 07			18 38				18 37		
West Sutton 179 d		17 10							17 40						18 10							18 40		
Sutton Common 179 d		17 12							17 42						18 12							18 42		
St Helier 179 d		17 15							17 45						18 15							18 45		
Morden South 179 d		17 17							17 47						18 17							18 47		
South Merton 179 d		17 19							17 49						18 19							18 49		
Wimbledon Chase 179 d		17 21							17 51						18 21							18 51		
Wimbledon 6 ⊖173,179 ⇌ d		17 28							17 58						18 28							18 58		
Haydons Road 173 d		17 30							18 00						18 30							19 00		
Tooting 173 d		17 33							18 03						18 33							19 03		
Carshalton 173 d					17 41							18 11						18 41						
Hackbridge 173 d					17 43							18 13						18 43						
Mitcham Junction 173 ⇌ d					17 46							18 16						18 46						
Mitcham Eastfields 173 d					17 49							18 19						18 49						
Streatham 4 d		17 38			17 53				18 08			18 23			18 38			18 53				19 08		
Tulse Hill 3 d		17 42			17 57				18 12			18 27			18 42			18 57				19 12		
London Bridge 4 ⊖ a	17 45			18 00			18 15				18 30			18 45			19 00				19 15			19 30
d	17 45			18 00			18 15				18 30			18 45			19 00				19 15			19 30
Herne Hill 4 173,179 d		17 46			18 01				18 16			18 31			18 46			19 01				19 16		
Loughborough Jn. 173,179 d		17 49			18 04				18 19			18 34			18 49			19 04				19 19		
Elephant & Castle 173,179 d		17 54	18 00		18 09				18 24	18 30		18 39			18 54	19 00		19 09				19 24	19 30	
London Blackfriars 3 ⊖ d	17 54	18 00	18a04	18 08	18 14		18 24		18 30	18a34	18 38	18 44		18 54	19 00	19a04	19 08	19 14			19 24	19 30	19a34	19 38
City Thameslink 3 d	17 56	18 02		18 10	18 16		18 26		18 32		18 40	18 46		18 56	19 02		19 10	19 16			19 26	19 32		19 40
Farringdon 3 ⊖ d	17 59	18 06		18 14	18 19		18 29		18 36		18 44	18 49		18 59	19 06		19 14	19 19			19 29	19 36		19 44
St Pancras International 15 ⊖ a	18 03	18 10		18 18	18 23		18 33		18 40		18 48	18 53		19 03	19 10		19 18	19 23			19 33	19 40		19 48
d	18 04	18 10		18 18	18 24	18 29	18 34		18 40		18 48	18 54	19 00	19 04	19 10		19 18	19 24		19 29	19 34	19 40		19 48
Kentish Town ⊖ d		18 14			18 27				18 44			18 57			19 14			19 27				19 44		
West Hampstead Thameslink ⊖ d	18 11	18 20			18 32		18 41		18 50			19 02		19 11	19 20			19 32			19 41	19 50		
Cricklewood d		18 23			18 35				18 53			19 05			19 23			19 35				19 53		
Hendon d		18 26			18 38				18 56			19 08			19 26			19 38				19 56		
Mill Hill Broadway d		18 30			18 42				19 00			19 12			19 30			19 42				20 00		
Elstree & Borehamwood d		18 34			18 46				19 04			19 16			19 34			19 46				20 04		
Radlett d		18 38			18 50				19 08			19 20			19 38			19 50				20 08		
St Albans City d	18 25	18 44		18 39	18a57		18 55		19 14		19 09	19a27		19 25	19 44		19 39	19a57			19 55	20 14		20 09
Harpenden d	18 31	18 49		18 45			19 01		19 19		19 15			19 31	19 49		19 45				20 01	20 19		20 15
Luton Airport Parkway 7 ✈ d	18 37	18 55		18 51		18 50	19 07		19 25		19 21			19 37	19 55		19 51			19 50	20 07	20 25		20 21
Luton 10 d	18 40	18a59		18 54			19 10		19a29		19 24		19 22	19 40	19a59		19 54				20 10	20a29		20 24
Leagrave d	18 44			18 58			19 14				19 28			19 44			19 58				20 14			20 28
Harlington d	18 49			19 03			19 19				19 33			19 49			20 03				20 19			20 33
Flitwick d	18 53			19 07			19 23				19 37			19 53			20 07				20 23			20 37
Bedford 7 a	19 05			19 19		19 04	19 35				19 49		19 36	20 05			20 19			20 04	20 35			20 49

A To Nottingham **B** To Corby.

The trains that operate to and from Sevenoaks, Orpington and Rochester (and a few other destinations at peak times) are operated jointly by First Capital Connect (north of Blackfriars) and Southeastern (south of Blackfriars)

Table 52 shows the complete service between Bedford and London, whilst services between London, Sevenoaks, Sutton and Brighton only show through Thameslink services. Other Tables should be consulted for additional journey opportunities.

Table 52R

Saturdays

14 December to 17 May

Brighton, Gatwick Airport and South London - City of London, St Albans, Luton and Bedford

Network Diagram - refer to first Page of Table 52

			FC	EM	FC	FC	SE	FC	FC	EM	FC	FC	SE	FC	FC	EM	FC	FC	SE	FC	FC	EM	FC	FC
				◇1	1			1		◇1	1			1		◇1	1			1		◇1	1	
				A						B						C						C		
				✠						✠						✠						✠		
Brighton 10		d			18 37			19 04			19 07			19 34			19 37			20 04			20 07	
Preston Park		d			18 41						19 11						19 41						20 11	
Hassocks 4		d			18 47						19 17						19 47						20 17	
Burgess Hill 4		d			18 51						19 21						19 51						20 21	
Wivelsfield 4		d			18 53						19 23						19 53						20 23	
Haywards Heath 3		d			19 01			19 18			19 31			19 48			20 01			20 18			20 31	
Balcombe		d									19 37												20 37	
Three Bridges 4		d			19 12			19 27			19 42			19 57			20 12			20 27			20 42	
Gatwick Airport 10 ✈		d			19 17			19 32			19 47			20 02			20 17			20 32			20 47	
Redhill		d																						
East Croydon 🚋		d			19 32			19 47			20 02			20 17			20 32			20 47			21 02	
Sevenoaks 4	195	d					19 02						19 32						20 02					
Bat & Ball	195	d					19 05						19 35						20 05					
Otford 4	195	d					19 08						19 38						20 08					
Shoreham (Kent)	195	d					19 11						19 41						20 11					
Eynsford	195	d					19 15						19 45						20 15					
Swanley 4	195	d					19 20						19 50						20 20					
St Mary Cray 4	195	d					19 24						19 54						20 24					
Bickley	195	d					19 28						19 58						20 28					
Bromley South	195	d					19 31						20 01						20 31					
Shortlands 4	195	d					19 34						20 04						20 34					
Ravensbourne	195	d					19 36						20 06						20 36					
Beckenham Hill	195	d					19 38						20 08						20 38					
Bellingham	195	d					19 40						20 10						20 40					
Catford	195	d					19 43						20 13						20 43					
Crofton Park	195	d					19 45						20 15						20 45					
Nunhead 4	195	d					19 48						20 18						20 48					
Peckham Rye 4	195	d					19 50						20 20						20 50					
Denmark Hill 4	195	d					19 54						20 24						20 54					
Sutton (Surrey) 4	179	d	19 08			19 07			19 38			19 37			20 08			20 07			20 38			20 37
West Sutton	179	d				19 10						19 40						20 10						20 40
Sutton Common	179	d				19 12						19 42						20 12						20 42
St Helier	179	d				19 15						19 45						20 15						20 45
Morden South	179	d				19 17						19 47						20 17						20 47
South Merton	179	d				19 19						19 49						20 19						20 49
Wimbledon Chase	179	d				19 21						19 51						20 21						20 51
Wimbledon 6 ⊖	173,179 🚋	d				19 28						19 58						20 28						20 58
Haydons Road	173	d				19 30						20 00						20 30						21 00
Tooting	173	d				19 33						20 03						20 33						21 03
Carshalton	173	d	19 11						19 41						20 11						20 41			
Hackbridge	173	d	19 13						19 43						20 13						20 43			
Mitcham Junction	173 🚋	d	19 16						19 46						20 16						20 46			
Mitcham Eastfields	173	d	19 19						19 49						20 19						20 49			
Streatham 4		d	19 23			19 38			19 53			20 08			20 23			20 38			20 53			21 08
Tulse Hill 3		d	19 27			19 42			19 57			20 12			20 27			20 42			20 57			21 12
London Bridge 4 ⊖		a			19 45			20 00			20 15			20 30			20 45			21 00			21 15	
		d			19 45			20 00			20 15			20 30			20 45			21 00			21 15	
Herne Hill 4	173,179	d	19 31			19 46			20 01			20 16			20 31			20 46			21 01			21 16
Loughborough Jn.	173,179	d	19 34			19 49			20 04			20 19			20 34			20 49			21 04			21 19
Elephant & Castle	173,179	d	19 39			19 54	20 00		20 09			20 24	20 30		20 39			20 54	21 00		21 09			21 24
London Blackfriars 3 ⊖		d	19 44		19 54	20 00	20a04	20 08	20 14		20 24	20 30	20a34	20 38	20 44		20 54	21 00	21a04	21 08	21 14		21 24	21 30
City Thameslink 3		d	19 46		19 56	20 02		20 10	20 16		20 26	20 32		20 40	20 46		20 56							
Farringdon 3 ⊖		d	19 49		19 59	20 06		20 14	20 19		20 29	20 36		20 44	20 49		20 59	21 06		21 14	21 19		21 29	21 36
St Pancras International 15 ⊖		a	19 53		20 03	20 10		20 18	20 23		20 33	20 40		20 48	20 53		21 03	21 10		21 18	21 23		21 33	21 40
		d	19 54	20 02	20 04	20 10		20 18	20 24	20 29	20 34	20 40		20 48	20 54	21 00	21 04	21 10		21 18	21 24	21 30	21 34	21 40
Kentish Town ⊖		d	19 57			20 14			20 27			20 44			20 57			21 14			21 27			21 44
West Hampstead Thameslink ⊖		d	20 02		20 11	20 20			20 32		20 41	20 50			21 02		21 11	21 20			21 32		21 41	21 50
Cricklewood		d	20 05			20 23			20 35			20 53			21 05			21 23			21 35			21 53
Hendon		d	20 08			20 26			20 38			20 56			21 08			21 26			21 38			21 56
Mill Hill Broadway		d	20 12			20 30			20 42			21 00			21 12			21 30			21 42			22 00
Elstree & Borehamwood		d	20 16			20 34			20 46			21 04			21 16			21 34			21 46			22 04
Radlett		d	20 20			20 38			20 50			21 08			21 20			21 38			21 50			22 08
St Albans City		d	20 27		20 25	20 44		20 39	20 58		20 55	21 14		21 09	21a27		21 25	21 44		21 39	21a57		21 55	22 14
Harpenden		d	20 35		20 31	20 49		20 45	21 05		21 01	21 19		21 15			21 31	21 49		21 45			22 01	22 19
Luton Airport Parkway 7 ✈		d	20 41		20 37	20 55		20 51	21 11	20 50	21 07	21 25		21 21			21 37	21 55		21 51		21 51	22 07	22 25
Luton 10		d	20 44	20 25	20 40	20a59		20 54	21 14		21 10	21a29		21 24		21 23	21 40	21a59		21 54			22 10	22a29
Leagrave		d	20 48		20 44			20 58	21 18		21 14			21 28			21 44			21 58			22 14	
Harlington		d	20 53		20 49			21 03	21 23		21 19			21 33			21 49			22 03			22 19	
Flitwick		d	20 57		20 53			21 07	21 27		21 23			21 37			21 53			22 07			22 23	
Bedford 7		a	21 09	20 39	21 05			21 19	21 39	21 05	21 35			21 49		21 38	22 05			22 19		22 06	22 35	

A To Corby.
B To Nottingham
C To Derby

The trains that operate to and from Sevenoaks, Orpington and Rochester (and a few other destinations at peak times) are operated jointly by First Capital Connect (north of Blackfriars) and Southeastern (south of Blackfriars)

Table 52 shows the complete service between Bedford and London, whilst services between London, Sevenoaks, Sutton and Brighton only show through Thameslink services. Other Tables should be consulted for additional journey opportunities.

Table 52R

Saturdays

14 December to 17 May

Brighton, Gatwick Airport and South London - City of London, St Albans, Luton and Bedford

Network Diagram - refer to first Page of Table 52

		SE	FC 1	FC	EM ◇1 A 🚲	FC 1	SE	FC	EM ◇1 B 🚲	FC 1	SE	FC	FC 1	SE	FC	FC 1	SE	FC	FC 1	FC 1	FC 1
Brighton 10	d		20 34			20 37				21 07			21 37			22 07			22 33	23 11	23 37
Preston Park	d					20 41				21 11			21 41			22 11			22 37		23 41
Hassocks 4	d					20 47				21 17			21 47			22 17			22 43	23 20	23 47
Burgess Hill 4	d					20 51				21 21			21 51			22 21			22 47	23 23	23 51
Wivelsfield 4	d					20 53				21 23			21 53			22 23			22 49		23 53
Haywards Heath 3	d		20 48			21 01				21 31			22 01			22 31			22 54	23 29	23 59
Balcombe	d									21 37						22 37			22 59		00 05
Three Bridges 4	d		20 57			21 12				21 42			22 12			22 42			23 12	23 38	00 10
Gatwick Airport 10 ✈	d		21 02			21 17				21 47			22 17			22 47			23 17	23 43	00 15
Redhill	d																				00 24
East Croydon 🚌	d		21 17			21 32				22 02			22 32			23 02			23 32	00 02	00 36
Sevenoaks 4 195	d	20 32					21 02				21 32			22 02			22 32				
Bat & Ball 195	d	20 35					21 05				21 35			22 05			22 35				
Otford 4 195	d	20 38					21 08				21 38			22 08			22 38				
Shoreham (Kent) 195	d	20 41					21 11				21 41			22 11			22 41				
Eynsford 195	d	20 45					21 15				21 45			22 15			22 45				
Swanley 4 195	d	20 50					21 20				21 50			22 20			22 50				
St Mary Cray 4 195	d	20 54					21 24				21 54			22 24			22 54				
Bickley 195	d	20 58					21 28				21 58			22 28			22 58				
Bromley South 195	d	21 01					21 31				22 01			22 31			23 01				
Shortlands 4 195	d	21 04					21 34				22 04			22 34			23 04				
Ravensbourne 195	d	21 06					21 36				22 06			22 36			23 06				
Beckenham Hill 195	d	21 08					21 38				22 08			22 38			23 08				
Bellingham 195	d	21 10					21 40				22 10			22 40			23 10				
Catford 195	d	21 13					21 43				22 13			22 43			23 13				
Crofton Park 195	d	21 15					21 45				22 15			22 45			23 15				
Nunhead 4 195	d	21 18					21 48				22 18			22 48			23 18				
Peckham Rye 4 195	d	21 20					21 50				22 20			22 50			23 20				
Denmark Hill 4 195	d	21 24					21 54				22 24			22 54			23 24				
Sutton (Surrey) 4 179	d			21 08				21 15				21 45			22 15			22 45			
West Sutton 179	d							21 18				21 48			22 18			22 48			
Sutton Common 179	d							21 20				21 50			22 20			22 50			
St Helier 179	d							21 23				21 53			22 23			22 53			
Morden South 179	d							21 25				21 55			22 25			22 55			
South Merton 179	d							21 27				21 57			22 27			22 57			
Wimbledon Chase 179	d							21 29				21 59			22 29			22 59			
Wimbledon 8 ⊖173,179 🚌	d							21 38				22 08			22 38			23 08			
Haydons Road 173	d							21 40				22 10			22 40			23 10			
Tooting 173	d							21 43				22 13			22 43			23 13			
Carshalton 173	d			21 11																	
Hackbridge 173	d			21 13																	
Mitcham Junction 173 🚌	d			21 16																	
Mitcham Eastfields 173	d			21 19																	
Streatham 4	d			21 23				21 49				22 19			22 49			23 19			
Tulse Hill 3	d			21 27				21 53				22 23			22 53			23 23			
London Bridge 4 ⊖	a		21 30			21 45				22 15			22 45			23 15			23 44	00 21	00 51
	d		21 30			21 45				22 15			22 45			23 15			23 45	00 22	00 52
Herne Hill 4 173,179	d			21 31				21 57				22 27			22 57			23 27			
Loughborough Jn. 173,179	d			21 34				22 00				22 30			23 00						
Elephant & Castle 173,179	d	21 30		21 39			22 00	22 04			22 30	22 34		23 00	23 04		23 30	23 34			
London Blackfriars 3 ⊖	d	21a34	21 38	21 44		21 54	22a04	22 08		22 22	22a34	22 38	22 52	23a04	23 08	23 22	23a34	23 38	23 52	00 28	00 58
City Thameslink 3	d																				
Farringdon 3 ⊖	d		21 44	21 49		21 59		22 13		22 28		22 43	22 58		23 13	23 28		23 43	23 58	00 34	
St Pancras International 15 ⊖	a		21 48	21 53		22 03		22 17		22 32		22 47	23 02		23 17	23 32		23 47	00 02	00 38	01 08
	d		21 48	21 54	22 00	22 04		22 18	22 26	22 32		22 48	23 02		23 18	23 32		23 48	00 02	00 39	01 09
Kentish Town ⊖	d			21 57				22 21				22 51			23 21			23 51		00 42	01 12
West Hampstead Thameslink ⊖	d			22 02		22 11		22 25		22 40		22 55	23 10		23 25	23 40		23 55	00 10	00 46	01 16
Cricklewood	d			22 05				22 28				22 58			23 28			23 58		00 49	01 19
Hendon	d			22 08				22 31				23 01			23 31			00 01		00 52	01 22
Mill Hill Broadway	d			22 12				22 35				23 05			23 35			00 05		00 56	01 26
Elstree & Borehamwood	d			22 16				22 39				23 09			23 39			00 09		01 00	01 30
Radlett	d			22 20				22 43				23 14			23 44			00 14		01 05	01 35
St Albans City	d		22 09	22a27		22 25		22 50		22 57		23 21	23 27		23 51	23 57		00 21	00 27	01 11	01 41
Harpenden	d		22 15			22 31		22 56		23 03		23 27	23 33		23 57	00 03		00 27	00 33	01 17	01 47
Luton Airport Parkway 7 ✈	d		22 21			22 37		23 02	22 47	23 09		23 33	23 39		00 03	00 09		00 33	00 39	01 23	01 53
Luton 10	d		22 24		22 24	22 40		23 05		23 12		23 36	23 42		00 06	00 12		00 36	00 42	01 26	01 56
Leagrave	d		22 28			22 44		23 09		23 16		23 40	23 46		00 10	00 16		00 40	00 46	01 30	02 00
Harlington	d		22 33			22 49		23 14		23 21		23 45	23 51		00 15	00 21		00 45	00 51	01 35	02 05
Flitwick	d		22 37			22 53		23 18		23 25		23 49	23 55		00 19	00 25		00 49	00 55	01 39	02 09
Bedford 7	a		22 49		22 39	23 06		23 31	23 02	23 38		00 02	00 08		00 32	00 38		01 02	01 08	01 52	02 22

A To Nottingham

B To Derby

The trains that operate to and from Sevenoaks, Orpington and Rochester (and a few other destinations at peak times) are operated jointly by First Capital Connect (north of Blackfriars) and Southeastern (south of Blackfriars)

Table 52 shows the complete service between Bedford and London, whilst services between London, Sevenoaks, Sutton and Brighton only show through Thameslink services. Other Tables should be consulted for additional journey opportunities.

Table 52R

Sundays

8 December to 29 December

Brighton, Gatwick Airport and South London - City of London, St Albans, Luton and Bedford

Network Diagram - refer to first Page of Table 52

		FC	FC	FC	FC	FC	FC	FC	FC	FC	FC		FC	FC	FC	SE	FC	SE	FC	SE	EM	FC		SE	EM
			[1]		[1]		[1]	[1]							[1]		[1]		[1]		◇[1]	[1]			◇[1]
		A	B	A	B		B	B								C		C			D				E
																					☕				☕
Brighton [10]	d										05 36				06 06		06 36		07 04			07 36			
Preston Park	d																								
Hassocks [4]	d										05 45				06 15		06 45		07 13			07 45			
Burgess Hill [4]	d										05 48				06 18		06 48		07 16			07 48			
Wivelsfield [4]	d																								
Haywards Heath [3]	d										05 54				06 24		06 54		07 24			07 54			
Balcombe	d							00 05																	
Three Bridges [4]	d							00 10		05 13	06 02				06 32		07 02		07 32			08 02			
Gatwick Airport [10] ✈	d							00 15		05 18	06 08				06 38		07 08		07 38			08 08			
Redhill	d							00 24																	
East Croydon 🚊	d						00 02	00 36		05 37	06 27				06 57		07 27		07 57			08 27			
Sevenoaks [4]	195 d																			07 32				08 02	
Bat & Ball	195 d																			07 35				08 05	
Otford [4]	195 d																			07 38				08 08	
Shoreham (Kent)	195 d																			07 41				08 11	
Eynsford	195 d																			07 45				08 15	
Swanley [4]	195 d																			07 50				08 20	
St Mary Cray [4]	195 d																			07 54				08 24	
Bickley	195 d															06 58		07 28		07 58				08 28	
Bromley South	195 d															07 01		07 31		08 01				08 31	
Shortlands [4]	195 d															07 04		07 34		08 04				08 34	
Ravensbourne	195 d															07 06		07 36		08 06				08 36	
Beckenham Hill	195 d															07 08		07 38		08 08				08 38	
Bellingham	195 d															07 10		07 40		08 10				08 40	
Catford	195 d															07 13		07 43		08 13				08 43	
Crofton Park	195 d															07 15		07 45		08 15				08 45	
Nunhead [4]	195 d															07 18		07 48		08 18				08 48	
Peckham Rye [4]	195 d															07 20		07 50		08 20				08 50	
Denmark Hill [4]	195 d															07 24		07 54		08 24				08 54	
Sutton (Surrey) [4]	179 d																								
West Sutton	179 d																								
Sutton Common	179 d																								
St Helier	179 d																								
Morden South	179 d																								
South Merton	179 d																								
Wimbledon Chase	179 d																								
Wimbledon [6] ⊖173,179 🚊	d																								
Haydons Road	173 d																								
Tooting	173 d																								
Carshalton	173 d																								
Hackbridge	173 d																								
Mitcham Junction	173 🚊 d																								
Mitcham Eastfields	173 d																								
Streatham [4]	d																								
Tulse Hill [3]	d																								
London Bridge [4] ⊖	a						00 21	00 51							07 15		07 45		08 15			08 45			
	d						00 22	00 52							07 15		07 45		08 15			08 45			
Herne Hill [4]	173,179 d																								
Loughborough Jn	173,179 d																								
Elephant & Castle	173,179 d															07 30		08 00		08 30				09 00	
London Blackfriars [3] ⊖	d					00 08	00 28	00 58	01 29	06a04	06a54				07 24	07a34	07 54	08a04	08 24	08a34		08 54		09a04	
City Thameslink [3]	d																								
Farringdon [3] ⊖	d					00 13	00 34								07 30		08 00		08 30			09 00			
St Pancras International [15] ⊖	a					00 17	00 38	01 08	01 38						07 34		08 04		08 34			09 04			
	d				00 02	00 18	00 39	01 09	01 39				06 04	07 04	07 34		08 04		08 34		09 00	09 04			09 30
Kentish Town ⊖	d					00 21	00 42	01 12	01 42				06 08	07 08	07 38		08 08		08 38			09 08			
West Hampstead Thameslink ⊖	d				00 10	00 25	00 46	01 16	01 46				06 12	07 12	07 42		08 12		08 42			09 12			
Cricklewood	d					00 28	00 49	01 19	01 49				06 15	07 15	07 45		08 15		08 45			09 15			
Hendon	d			00 01		00 31	00 52	01 22	01 52				06 18	07 18	07 48		08 18		08 48			09 18			
Mill Hill Broadway	d			00 05		00 35	00 56	01 26	01 56				06 22	07 22	07 52		08 22		08 52			09 22			
Elstree & Borehamwood	d			00 09		00 39	01 00	01 30	02 00				06 26	07 26	07 56		08 26		08 56			09 26			
Radlett	d			00 14		00 44	01 05	01 35	02 05				06 31	07 31	08 01		08 31		09 01			09 31			
St Albans City	d			00 21	00 27	00 51	01 11	01 41	02 11				06 38	07 38	08 08		08 38		09 08			09 38			
Harpenden	d		00 03	00 27	00 33	00 57	01 17	01 47	02 17				06 44	07 44	08 14		08 44		09 14			09 44			
Luton Airport Parkway [7] ✈	d	00 03	00 09	00 33	00 39	01 03	01 23	01 53	02 23				06 50	07 50	08 20		08 50		09 20		09 28	09 50			
Luton [10]	d	00 06	00 12	00 36	00 42	01 06	01 26	01 56	02 26				06 53	07 53	08 23		08 53		09 23			09 53			09 59
Leagrave	d	00 10	00 16	00 40	00 46	01 10	01 30	02 00	02 30				06 57	07 57	08 27		08 57		09 27			09 57			
Harlington	d	00 15	00 21	00 45	00 51	01 15	01 35	02 05	02 35				07 02	08 02	08 32		09 02		09 32			10 02			
Flitwick	d	00 19	00 25	00 49	00 55	01 19	01 39	02 09	02 39				07 06	08 06	08 36		09 06		09 36			10 06			
Bedford [7]	a	00 32	00 38	01 02	01 08	01 32	01 52	02 22	02 52				07 19	08 19	08 49		09 19		09 49		09 50	10 19			10 19

A From Sutton (Surrey)
B From Brighton
C From Orpington
D To Nottingham
E To Sheffield

The trains that operate to and from Sevenoaks, Orpington and Rochester (and a few other destinations at peak times) are operated jointly by First Capital Connect (north of Blackfriars) and Southeastern (south of Blackfriars)

Table 52 shows the complete service between Bedford and London, whilst services between London, Sevenoaks, Sutton and Brighton only show through Thameslink services. Other Tables should be consulted for additional journey opportunities.

Table 52R

Sundays

8 December to 29 December

Brighton, Gatwick Airport and South London - City of London, St Albans, Luton and Bedford

Network Diagram - refer to first Page of Table 52

		FC	SE	EM	FC	SE	FC	EM	FC	FC	SE	FC	FC	EM	FC	FC	SE	FC	FC	EM	FC	FC	SE
		1		◇1	1		1	◇1	1			1		◇1	1			1		◇1	1		
				A				B						A						B			
Brighton 10	d	08 04			08 44				09 14						09 44						10 14		
Preston Park	d																						
Hassocks 4	d	08 13			08 53				09 23						09 53						10 23		
Burgess Hill 4	d	08 16			08 57				09 27						09 57						10 27		
Wivelsfield 4	d																						
Haywards Heath 3	d	08 24			09 03				09 33						10 03						10 33		
Balcombe	d																						
Three Bridges 4	d	08 32			09 12				09 42						10 12						10 42		
Gatwick Airport 10 ✈	d	08 38			09 17		09 27		09 47			09 57			10 17			10 27			10 47		
Redhill	d																						
East Croydon	d	08 56			09 33		09 47		10 03			10 17			10 33			10 47			11 03		
Sevenoaks 4	195 d		08 32			09 02					09 32						10 02						10 32
Bat & Ball	195 d		08 35			09 05					09 35						10 05						10 35
Otford 4	195 d		08 38			09 08					09 38						10 08						10 38
Shoreham (Kent)	195 d		08 41			09 11					09 41						10 11						10 41
Eynsford	195 d		08 45			09 15					09 45						10 15						10 45
Swanley 4	195 d		08 50			09 20					09 50						10 20						10 50
St Mary Cray 4	195 d		08 54			09 24					09 54						10 24						10 54
Bickley	195 d		08 58			09 28					09 58						10 28						10 58
Bromley South	195 d		09 01			09 31					10 01						10 31						11 01
Shortlands 4	195 d		09 04			09 34					10 04						10 34						11 04
Ravensbourne	195 d		09 06			09 36					10 06						10 36						11 06
Beckenham Hill	195 d		09 08			09 38					10 08						10 38						11 08
Bellingham	195 d		09 10			09 40					10 10						10 40						11 10
Catford	195 d		09 13			09 43					10 13						10 43						11 13
Crofton Park	195 d		09 15			09 45					10 15						10 45						11 15
Nunhead 4	195 d		09 18			09 48					10 18						10 48						11 18
Peckham Rye 4	195 d		09 20			09 50					10 20						10 50						11 20
Denmark Hill 4	195 d		09 24			09 54					10 24						10 54						11 24
Sutton (Surrey) 4	179 d									09 37			10 08			10 07			10 38			10 37	
West Sutton	179 d									09 40						10 10						10 40	
Sutton Common	179 d									09 42						10 12						10 42	
St Helier	179 d									09 45						10 15						10 45	
Morden South	179 d									09 47						10 17						10 47	
South Merton	179 d									09 49						10 19						10 49	
Wimbledon Chase	179 d									09 51						10 21						10 51	
Wimbledon 6 ⊖173,179	d									09 56						10 26						10 56	
Haydons Road	173 d									09 58						10 28						10 58	
Tooting	173 d									10 01						10 31						11 01	
Carshalton	173 d												10 11						10 41				
Hackbridge	173 d												10 13						10 43				
Mitcham Junction	173 d												10 16						10 46				
Mitcham Eastfields	173 d												10 19						10 49				
Streatham 4	d									10 06			10 23			10 36			10 53			11 06	
Tulse Hill 3	d									10 10			10 27			10 40			10 57			11 10	
London Bridge 4 ⊖	a	09 15			09 45		10 00		10 15			10 30			10 45			11 00			11 15		
	d	09 15			09 45		10 00		10 15			10 30			10 45			11 00			11 15		
Herne Hill 4	173,179 d									10 14			10 31			10 44			11 01			11 14	
Loughborough Jn.	173,179 d									10 17			10 34			10 47			11 04			11 17	
Elephant & Castle	173,179 d		09 30			10 00				10 22	10 30		10 39			10 52	11 00		11 09			11 22	11 30
London Blackfriars 3 ⊖	d	09 24	09a34		09 54	10a04	10 08		10 22	10 26	10a34	10 38	10a43		10 52	10 56	11a04	11 08	11a13		11 22	11 26	11a34
City Thameslink 3	d																						
Farringdon 3 ⊖	d	09 30			10 00		10 14		10 28	10 32		10 44			10 58	11 02		11 14			11 28	11 32	
St Pancras International 15 ⊖	a	09 34			10 04		10 18		10 32	10 36		10 48			11 02	11 06		11 18			11 32	11 36	
	d	09 34		10 00	10 04		10 18	10 30	10 32	10 36		10 48		11 00	11 02	11 06		11 18		11 30	11 32	11 36	
Kentish Town ⊖	d	09 38			10 08					10 40						11 10						11 40	
West Hampstead Thameslink ⊖	d	09 42			10 12		10 26		10 40	10 44		10 56			11 10	11 14		11 26			11 40	11 44	
Cricklewood	d	09 45			10 15					10 47						11 17						11 47	
Hendon	d	09 48			10 18					10 50						11 20						11 50	
Mill Hill Broadway	d	09 52			10 22					10 54						11 24						11 54	
Elstree & Borehamwood	d	09 56			10 26					10 58						11 28						11 58	
Radlett	d	10 01			10 31					11 02						11 32						12 02	
St Albans City	d	10 08			10 38		10 43		10 57	11 09		11 13			11 27	11 39		11 43			11 57	12 09	
Harpenden	d	10 14			10 44		10 49		11 03	11 15		11 19			11 33	11 45		11 49			12 03	12 15	
Luton Airport Parkway 7 ✈	d	10 20		10 29	10 50		10 55		11 09	11 20		11 25		11 29	11 39	11 50		11 55		11 59	12 09	12 20	
Luton 10	d	10 23			10 53		10a58	11 02	11 12	11a24		11 28		11 33	11 42	11a54		11 58		12 03	12 12	12a24	
Leagrave	d	10 27			10 57				11 16			11 32			11 46			12 02			12 16		
Harlington	d	10 32			11 02				11 21			11 37			11 51			12 07			12 21		
Flitwick	d	10 36			11 06				11 25			11 41			11 55			12 11			12 25		
Bedford 7	a	10 49		10 54	11 19			11 22	11 38			11 54		11 54	12 08			12 24		12 22	12 38		

A To Nottingham

B To Sheffield

The trains that operate to and from Sevenoaks, Orpington and Rochester (and a few other destinations at peak times) are operated jointly by First Capital Connect (north of Blackfriars) and Southeastern (south of Blackfriars)

Table 52 shows the complete service between Bedford and London, whilst services between London, Sevenoaks, Sutton and Brighton only show through Thameslink services. Other Tables should be consulted for additional journey opportunities.

Table 52R

Sundays

8 December to 29 December

Brighton, Gatwick Airport and South London - City of London, St Albans, Luton and Bedford

Network Diagram - refer to first Page of Table 52

		FC	FC	FC	FC	SE	EM		FC	FC	EM	FC	FC	SE	FC	FC	FC	FC		SE	EM	FC	FC	FC	FC
		1		1			◇1		1		◇1	1			1		1				◇1	1		1	
							A				B										A				
							☕				☕										☕				
Brighton [10]	d			10 44								11 14					11 44							12 14	
Preston Park	d																								
Hassocks [4]	d			10 53								11 23					11 53							12 23	
Burgess Hill [4]	d			10 57								11 27					11 57							12 27	
Wivelsfield [4]	d																								
Haywards Heath [3]	d			11 03								11 33					12 03							12 33	
Balcombe	d																								
Three Bridges [4]	d	10 52		11 12					11 22			11 42			11 52		12 12					12 22		12 42	
Gatwick Airport [10] ✈	d	10 57		11 17					11 27			11 47			11 57		12 17					12 27		12 47	
Redhill	d																								
East Croydon	d	11 17		11 33					11 47			12 03			12 17		12 33					12 47		13 03	
Sevenoaks [4] 195	d					11 02								11 32						12 02					
Bat & Ball 195	d					11 05								11 35						12 05					
Otford [4] 195	d					11 08								11 38						12 08					
Shoreham (Kent) 195	d					11 11								11 41						12 11					
Eynsford 195	d					11 15								11 45						12 15					
Swanley [4] 195	d					11 20								11 50						12 20					
St Mary Cray [4] 195	d					11 24								11 54						12 24					
Bickley 195	d					11 28								11 58						12 28					
Bromley South 195	d					11 31								12 01						12 31					
Shortlands [4] 195	d					11 34								12 04						12 34					
Ravensbourne 195	d					11 36								12 06						12 36					
Beckenham Hill 195	d					11 38								12 08						12 38					
Bellingham 195	d					11 40								12 10						12 40					
Catford 195	d					11 43								12 13						12 43					
Crofton Park 195	d					11 45								12 15						12 45					
Nunhead [4] 195	d					11 48								12 18						12 48					
Peckham Rye [4] 195	d					11 50								12 20						12 50					
Denmark Hill [4] 195	d					11 54								12 24						12 54					
Sutton (Surrey) [4] 179	d		11 08		11 07					11 38			11 37			12 08		12 07					12 38		12 37
West Sutton 179	d				11 10								11 40					12 10							12 40
Sutton Common 179	d				11 12								11 42					12 12							12 42
St Helier 179	d				11 15								11 45					12 15							12 45
Morden South 179	d				11 17								11 47					12 17							12 47
South Merton 179	d				11 19								11 49					12 19							12 49
Wimbledon Chase 179	d				11 21								11 51					12 21							12 51
Wimbledon [6] ⊖173,179	d				11 26								11 56					12 26							12 56
Haydons Road 173	d				11 28								11 58					12 28							12 58
Tooting 173	d				11 31								12 01					12 31							13 01
Carshalton 173	d		11 11							11 41						12 11							12 41		
Hackbridge 173	d		11 13							11 43						12 13							12 43		
Mitcham Junction 173	d		11 16							11 46						12 16							12 46		
Mitcham Eastfields 173	d		11 19							11 49						12 19							12 49		
Streatham [4]	d		11 23		11 36					11 53			12 06			12 23		12 36					12 53		13 06
Tulse Hill [3]	d		11 27		11 40					11 57			12 10			12 27		12 40					12 57		13 10
London Bridge [4] ⊖	a	11 30		11 45					12 00			12 15			12 30		12 45					13 00		13 15	
	d	11 30		11 45					12 00			12 15			12 30		12 45					13 00		13 15	
Herne Hill [4] 173,179	d		11 31		11 44					12 01			12 14			12 31		12 44					13 01		13 14
Loughborough Jn. 173,179	d		11 34		11 47					12 04			12 17			12 34		12 47					13 04		13 17
Elephant & Castle 173,179	d		11 39		11 52	12 00				12 09			12 22	12 30		12 39		12 52		13 00			13 09		13 22
London Blackfriars [3] ⊖	d	11 38	11a43	11 52	11 56	12a04			12 08	12a13		12 22	12 26	12a34	12 38	12a43	12 52	12 56		13a04		13 08	13a13	13 22	13 26
City Thameslink [3]	d																								
Farringdon [3] ⊖	d	11 44		11 58	12 02				12 14			12 28	12 32		12 44		12 58	13 02				13 14		13 28	13 32
St Pancras International [15] ⊖	a	11 48		12 02	12 06				12 18			12 32	12 36		12 48		13 02	13 06				13 18		13 32	13 36
	d	11 48		12 02	12 06		12 10		12 18		12 30	12 32	12 36		12 48		13 02	13 06			13 10	13 18		13 32	13 36
Kentish Town ⊖	d				12 10								12 40					13 10							13 40
West Hampstead Thameslink ⊖	d	11 56		12 10	12 14				12 26			12 40	12 44		12 56		13 10	13 14				13 26		13 40	13 44
Cricklewood	d				12 17								12 47					13 17							13 47
Hendon	d				12 20								12 50					13 20							13 50
Mill Hill Broadway	d				12 24								12 54					13 24							13 54
Elstree & Borehamwood	d				12 28								12 58					13 28							13 58
Radlett	d				12 32								13 02					13 32							14 02
St Albans City	d	12 13		12 27	12 39				12 43			12 57	13 09		13 13		13 27	13 39				13 43		13 57	14 09
Harpenden	d	12 19		12 33	12 45				12 49			13 03	13 15		13 19		13 33	13 45				13 49		14 03	14 15
Luton Airport Parkway [7] ✈	d	12 25		12 39	12 50		12 31		12 55		12 53	13 09	13 20		13 25		13 39	13 50			13 31	13 55		14 09	14 20
Luton [10]	d	12 28		12 42	12a54		12 34		12 58		12 57	13 12	13a24		13 28		13 42	13a54			13 34	13 58		14 12	14a24
Leagrave	d	12 32		12 46					13 02			13 16			13 32		13 46					14 02		14 16	
Harlington	d	12 37		12 51					13 07			13 21			13 37		13 51					14 07		14 21	
Flitwick	d	12 41		12 55					13 11			13 25			13 41		13 55					14 11		14 25	
Bedford [7]	a	12 54		13 08			12 49		13 24		13 12	13 38			13 54		14 08				13 49	14 24		14 38	

A To Nottingham

B To Sheffield

The trains that operate to and from Sevenoaks, Orpington and Rochester (and a few other destinations at peak times) are operated jointly by First Capital Connect (north of Blackfriars) and Southeastern (south of Blackfriars)

Table 52 shows the complete service between Bedford and London, whilst services between London, Sevenoaks, Sutton and Brighton only show through Thameslink services. Other Tables should be consulted for additional journey opportunities.

Table 52R

Sundays

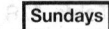

8 December to 29 December

Brighton, Gatwick Airport and South London - City of London, St Albans, Luton and Bedford

Network Diagram - refer to first Page of Table 52

Station	Table		SE	EM	FC	FC		FC	FC	SE	EM	FC	FC	FC	FC	SE	EM		FC	FC	FC	FC	SE	EM	FC	FC
				◇[1] A ☕	[1]			[1]			◇[1] B ☕	[1]		[1]			◇[1] C ☕		[1]		[1]			◇[1] B ☕	[1]	
Brighton [10]		d						12 44						13 14							13 44					
Preston Park		d																								
Hassocks [4]		d						12 53						13 23							13 53					
Burgess Hill [4]		d						12 57						13 27							13 57					
Wivelsfield [4]		d																								
Haywards Heath [3]		d						13 03						13 33							14 03					
Balcombe		d																								
Three Bridges [4]		d			12 52			13 12				13 22		13 42					13 52		14 12				14 22	
Gatwick Airport [10] ✈		d			12 57			13 17				13 27		13 47					13 57		14 17				14 27	
Redhill		d																								
East Croydon		d			13 17			13 33				13 47		14 03					14 17		14 33				14 47	
Sevenoaks [4]	195	d	12 32							13 02						13 32							14 02			
Bat & Ball	195	d	12 35							13 05						13 35							14 05			
Otford [4]	195	d	12 38							13 08						13 38							14 08			
Shoreham (Kent)	195	d	12 41							13 11						13 41							14 11			
Eynsford	195	d	12 45							13 15						13 45							14 15			
Swanley [4]	195	d	12 50							13 20						13 50							14 20			
St Mary Cray [4]	195	d	12 54							13 24						13 54							14 24			
Bickley	195	d	12 58							13 28						13 58							14 28			
Bromley South	195	d	13 01							13 31						14 01							14 31			
Shortlands [4]	195	d	13 04							13 34						14 04							14 34			
Ravensbourne	195	d	13 06							13 36						14 06							14 36			
Beckenham Hill	195	d	13 08							13 38						14 08							14 38			
Bellingham	195	d	13 10							13 40						14 10							14 40			
Catford	195	d	13 13							13 43						14 13							14 43			
Crofton Park	195	d	13 15							13 45						14 15							14 45			
Nunhead [4]	195	d	13 18							13 48						14 18							14 48			
Peckham Rye [4]	195	d	13 20							13 50						14 20							14 50			
Denmark Hill [4]	195	d	13 24							13 54						14 24							14 54			
Sutton (Surrey) [4]	179	d				13 08			13 07				13 38		13 37					14 08		14 07				14 38
West Sutton	179	d							13 10						13 40							14 10				
Sutton Common	179	d							13 12						13 42							14 12				
St Helier	179	d							13 15						13 45							14 15				
Morden South	179	d							13 17						13 47							14 17				
South Merton	179	d							13 19						13 49							14 19				
Wimbledon Chase	179	d							13 21						13 51							14 21				
Wimbledon [6] ⊖	173,179	d							13 26						13 56							14 26				
Haydons Road	173	d							13 28						13 58							14 28				
Tooting	173	d							13 31						14 01							14 31				
Carshalton	173	d				13 11							13 41							14 11						14 41
Hackbridge	173	d				13 13							13 43							14 13						14 43
Mitcham Junction	173	d				13 16							13 46							14 16						14 46
Mitcham Eastfields	173	d				13 19							13 49							14 19						14 49
Streatham [4]		d				13 23			13 36				13 53		14 06					14 23		14 36				14 53
Tulse Hill [3]		d				13 27			13 40				13 57		14 10					14 27		14 40				14 57
London Bridge [4] ⊖		a			13 30			13 45				14 00		14 15					14 30		14 45				15 00	
		d			13 30			13 45				14 00		14 15					14 30		14 45				15 00	
Herne Hill [4]	173,179	d				13 31			13 44				14 01		14 14					14 31		14 44				15 01
Loughborough Jn.	173,179	d				13 34			13 47				14 04		14 17					14 34		14 47				15 04
Elephant & Castle	173,179	d	13 30			13 39			13 52	14 00			14 09		14 22	14 30				14 39		14 52	15 00			15 09
London Blackfriars [3] ⊖		d	13a34		13 38	13a43		13 52	13 56	14a04		14 08	14a13	14 22	14 26	14a34			14 38	14a43	14 52	14 56	15a04		15 08	15a13
City Thameslink [3]		d																								
Farringdon [3] ⊖		d			13 44			13 58	14 02			14 14		14 28	14 32				14 44		14 58	15 02			15 14	
St Pancras International [15] ⊖		a			13 48			14 02	14 06			14 18		14 32	14 36				14 48		15 02	15 06			15 18	
		d		13 40	13 48			14 02	14 06		14 10	14 18		14 32	14 36		14 40		14 48		15 02	15 06		15 10	15 18	
Kentish Town ⊖		d							14 10						14 40							15 10				
West Hampstead Thameslink ⊖		d			13 56			14 10	14 14			14 26		14 40	14 44				14 56		15 10	15 14			15 26	
Cricklewood		d							14 17						14 47							15 17				
Hendon		d							14 20						14 50							15 20				
Mill Hill Broadway		d							14 24						14 54							15 24				
Elstree & Borehamwood		d							14 28						14 58							15 28				
Radlett		d							14 32						15 02							15 32				
St Albans City		d			14 13			14 27	14 39			14 43		14 57	15 09				15 13		15 27	15 39			15 43	
Harpenden		d			14 19			14 33	14 45			14 49		15 03	15 15				15 19		15 33	15 45			15 49	
Luton Airport Parkway [7] ✈		d		14 02	14 25			14 39	14 50		14 31	14 55		15 09	15 20				15 25		15 39	15 50		15 33	15 55	
Luton [10]		d		14 07	14 28			14 42	14a54			14 58		15 12	15a24		15 04		15 28		15 42	15a54			15 58	
Leagrave		d			14 32			14 46				15 02		15 16					15 32		15 46				16 02	
Harlington		d			14 37			14 51				15 07		15 21					15 37		15 51				16 07	
Flitwick		d			14 41			14 55				15 11		15 25					15 41		15 55				16 11	
Bedford [7]		a		14 22	14 54			15 08			14 46	15 24		15 38			15 19		15 54		16 08			15 48	16 24	

A To Sheffield
B To Nottingham
C To Leeds

The trains that operate to and from Sevenoaks, Orpington and Rochester (and a few other destinations at peak times) are operated jointly by First Capital Connect (north of Blackfriars) and Southeastern (south of Blackfriars)

Table 52 shows the complete service between Bedford and London, whilst services between London, Sevenoaks, Sutton and Brighton only show through Thameslink services. Other Tables should be consulted for additional journey opportunities.

Table 52R

Sundays

8 December to 29 December

Brighton, Gatwick Airport and South London - City of London, St Albans, Luton and Bedford

Network Diagram - refer to first Page of Table 52

	FC	FC		SE	EM	FC	FC	FC	FC	SE	EM	FC	FC		FC	FC	SE	EM	FC	FC	FC	FC	SE	EM
	1				◇1 A ☕	1		1			◇1 B ☕	1			1			◇1 C ☕	1		1			◇1 B ☕
Brighton 10 d	14 14							14 44							15 14						15 44			
Preston Park d																								
Hassocks 4 d	14 23							14 53							15 23						15 53			
Burgess Hill 4 d	14 27							14 57							15 27						15 57			
Wivelsfield 4 d																								
Haywards Heath 3 d	14 33							15 03							15 33						16 03			
Balcombe d																								
Three Bridges 4 d	14 42					14 52		15 12				15 22			15 42				15 52		16 12			
Gatwick Airport 10 ✈ d	14 47					14 57		15 17				15 27			15 47				15 57		16 17			
Redhill d																								
East Croydon ⇌ d	15 03					15 17		15 33				15 47			16 03				16 17		16 33			
Sevenoaks 4 195 d				14 32						15 02							15 32						16 02	
Bat & Ball 195 d				14 35						15 05							15 35						16 05	
Otford 4 195 d				14 38						15 08							15 38						16 08	
Shoreham (Kent) 195 d				14 41						15 11							15 41						16 11	
Eynsford 195 d				14 45						15 15							15 45						16 15	
Swanley 4 195 d				14 50						15 20							15 50						16 20	
St Mary Cray 4 195 d				14 54						15 24							15 54						16 24	
Bickley 195 d				14 58						15 28							15 58						16 28	
Bromley South 195 d				15 01						15 31							16 01						16 31	
Shortlands 4 195 d				15 04						15 34							16 04						16 34	
Ravensbourne 195 d				15 06						15 36							16 06						16 36	
Beckenham Hill 195 d				15 08						15 38							16 08						16 38	
Bellingham 195 d				15 10						15 40							16 10						16 40	
Catford 195 d				15 13						15 43							16 13						16 43	
Crofton Park 195 d				15 15						15 45							16 15						16 45	
Nunhead 4 195 d				15 18						15 48							16 18						16 48	
Peckham Rye 4 195 d				15 20						15 50							16 20						16 50	
Denmark Hill 4 195 d				15 24						15 54							16 24						16 54	
Sutton (Surrey) 4 179 d		14 37					15 08		15 07				15 38			15 37				16 08		16 07		
West Sutton 179 d		14 40							15 10							15 40						16 10		
Sutton Common 179 d		14 42							15 12							15 42						16 12		
St Helier 179 d		14 45							15 15							15 45						16 15		
Morden South 179 d		14 47							15 17							15 47						16 17		
South Merton 179 d		14 49							15 19							15 49						16 19		
Wimbledon Chase 179 d		14 51							15 21							15 51						16 21		
Wimbledon 6 ⊖173,179 ⇌ d		14 56							15 26							15 56						16 26		
Haydons Road 173 d		14 58							15 28							15 58						16 28		
Tooting 173 d		15 01							15 31							16 01						16 31		
Carshalton 173 d							15 11						15 41							16 11				
Hackbridge 173 d							15 13						15 43							16 13				
Mitcham Junction 173 ⇌ d							15 16						15 46							16 16				
Mitcham Eastfields 173 d							15 19						15 49							16 19				
Streatham 4 d		15 06					15 23		15 36				15 53			16 06				16 23		16 36		
Tulse Hill 3 d		15 10					15 27		15 40				15 57			16 10				16 27		16 40		
London Bridge 4 ⊖ a	15 15					15 30		15 45				16 00			16 15				16 30		16 45			
d	15 15					15 30		15 45				16 00			16 15				16 30		16 45			
Herne Hill 4 173,179 d		15 14					15 31		15 44				16 01			16 14				16 31		16 44		
Loughborough Jn. 173,179 d		15 17					15 34		15 47				16 04			16 17				16 34		16 47		
Elephant & Castle 173,179 d		15 22		15 30			15 39		15 52	16 00			16 09			16 22	16 30			16 39		16 52	17 00	
London Blackfriars 3 ⊖ d	15 22	15 26		15a34		15 38	15a43	15 52	15 56	16a04		16 08	16a13		16 22	16 26	16a34		16 38	16a43	16 52	16 56	17a04	
City Thameslink 3 d																								
Farringdon 3 ⊖ d	15 28	15 32				15 44		15 58	16 02			16 14			16 28	16 32			16 44		16 58	17 02		
St Pancras International 15 ⊖ a	15 32	15 36				15 48		16 02	16 06			16 18			16 32	16 36			16 48		17 02	17 06		
d	15 32	15 36			15 40	15 48		16 02	16 06		16 10	16 18			16 32	16 36		16 40	16 48		17 02	17 06		17 10
Kentish Town ⊖ d		15 40							16 10							16 40						17 10		
West Hampstead Thameslink ⊖ d	15 40	15 44				15 56		16 10	16 14			16 26			16 40	16 44			16 56		17 10	17 14		
Cricklewood d		15 47							16 17							16 47						17 17		
Hendon d		15 50							16 20							16 50						17 20		
Mill Hill Broadway d		15 54							16 24							16 54						17 24		
Elstree & Borehamwood d		15 58							16 28							16 58						17 28		
Radlett d		16 02							16 32							17 02						17 32		
St Albans City d	15 57	16 09				16 13		16 27	16 39			16 43			16 57	17 09			17 13		17 27	17 39		
Harpenden d	16 03	16 15				16 19		16 33	16 45			16 49			17 03	17 15			17 19		17 33	17 45		
Luton Airport Parkway 7 ✈ d	16 09	16 20				16 25		16 39	16 50		16 31	16 55			17 09	17 20			17 25		17 39	17 50		17 31
Luton 10 d	16 12	16a24			16 04	16 28		16 42	16a54			16 58			17 12	17a24		17 02	17 28		17 42	17a54		
Leagrave d	16 16					16 32		16 46				17 02			17 16				17 32		17 46			
Harlington d	16 21					16 37		16 51				17 07			17 21				17 37		17 51			
Flitwick d	16 25					16 41		16 55				17 11			17 25				17 41		17 55			
Bedford 7 a	16 38				16 19	16 54		17 08			16 46	17 24			17 38			17 16	17 54		18 08			17 46

A To Sheffield
B To Nottingham
C To Derby

The trains that operate to and from Sevenoaks, Orpington and Rochester (and a few other destinations at peak times) are operated jointly by First Capital Connect (north of Blackfriars) and Southeastern (south of Blackfriars)

Table 52 shows the complete service between Bedford and London, whilst services between London, Sevenoaks, Sutton and Brighton only show through Thameslink services. Other Tables should be consulted for additional journey opportunities.

Table 52R

Sundays

8 December to 29 December

Brighton, Gatwick Airport and South London - City of London, St Albans, Luton and Bedford

Network Diagram - refer to first Page of Table 52

		FC	FC	FC	FC	SE	EM	FC	FC	FC	FC	SE	EM	FC	FC	FC	FC	SE	EM	FC	FC	FC
		1		1			◇1	1		1			◇1	1		1			◇1	1		1
							A						B						A			
							☕						☕						☕			
Brighton 10	d			16 14						16 44						17 14						17 44
Preston Park	d																					
Hassocks 4	d			16 23						16 53						17 23						17 53
Burgess Hill 4	d			16 27						16 57						17 27						17 57
Wivelsfield 4	d																					
Haywards Heath 3	d			16 33						17 03						17 33						18 03
Balcombe	d																					
Three Bridges 4	d	16 22		16 42				16 52		17 12				17 22		17 42				17 52		18 12
Gatwick Airport 10 ✈	d	16 27		16 47				16 57		17 17				17 27		17 47				17 57		18 17
Redhill	d																					
East Croydon ⛴	d	16 47		17 03				17 17		17 33				17 47		18 03				18 17		18 33
Sevenoaks 4 195	d					16 32						17 02						17 32				
Bat & Ball 195	d					16 35						17 05						17 35				
Otford 4 195	d					16 38						17 08						17 38				
Shoreham (Kent) 195	d					16 41						17 11						17 41				
Eynsford 195	d					16 45						17 15						17 45				
Swanley 4 195	d					16 50						17 20						17 50				
St Mary Cray 4 195	d					16 54						17 24						17 54				
Bickley 195	d					16 58						17 28						17 58				
Bromley South 195	d					17 01						17 31						18 01				
Shortlands 4 195	d					17 04						17 34						18 04				
Ravensbourne 195	d					17 06						17 36						18 06				
Beckenham Hill 195	d					17 08						17 38						18 08				
Bellingham 195	d					17 10						17 40						18 10				
Catford 195	d					17 13						17 43						18 13				
Crofton Park 195	d					17 15						17 45						18 15				
Nunhead 4 195	d					17 18						17 48						18 18				
Peckham Rye 4 195	d					17 20						17 50						18 20				
Denmark Hill 4 195	d					17 24						17 54						18 24				
Sutton (Surrey) 4 179	d		16 38		16 37				17 08		17 07				17 38		17 37				18 08	
West Sutton 179	d				16 40						17 10						17 40					
Sutton Common 179	d				16 42						17 12						17 42					
St Helier 179	d				16 45						17 15						17 45					
Morden South 179	d				16 47						17 17						17 47					
South Merton 179	d				16 49						17 19						17 49					
Wimbledon Chase 179	d				16 51						17 21						17 51					
Wimbledon 6 ⊖173,179 ⛴	d				16 56						17 26						17 56					
Haydons Road 173	d				16 58						17 28						17 58					
Tooting 173	d				17 01						17 31						18 01					
Carshalton 173	d		16 41						17 11						17 41						18 11	
Hackbridge 173	d		16 43						17 13						17 43						18 13	
Mitcham Junction 173 ⛴	d		16 46						17 16						17 46						18 16	
Mitcham Eastfields 173	d		16 49						17 19						17 49						18 19	
Streatham 4	d		16 53		17 06				17 23		17 36				17 53		18 06				18 23	
Tulse Hill 3	d		16 57		17 10				17 27		17 40				17 57		18 10				18 27	
London Bridge 4 ⊖	a	17 00		17 15				17 30		17 45				18 00		18 15				18 30		18 45
	d	17 00		17 15				17 30		17 45				18 00		18 15				18 30		18 45
Herne Hill 4 173,179	d		17 01		17 14				17 31		17 44				18 01		18 14				18 31	
Loughborough Jn. 173,179	d		17 04		17 17				17 34		17 47				18 04		18 17				18 34	
Elephant & Castle 173,179	d		17 09		17 22	17 30			17 39		17 52	18 00			18 09		18 22	18 30			18 39	
London Blackfriars 3 ⊖	d	17 08	17a13	17 22	17 26	17a34		17 38	17a43	17 52	17 56	18a04		18 08	18a13	18 22	18 26	18a34		18 38	18a43	18 52
City Thameslink 3	d																					
Farringdon 3 ⊖	d	17 14		17 28	17 32			17 44		17 58	18 02			18 14		18 28	18 32			18 44		18 58
St Pancras International 15 ⊖	a	17 18		17 32	17 36			17 48		18 02	18 06			18 18		18 32	18 36			18 48		19 02
	d	17 18		17 32	17 36		17 40	17 48		18 02	18 06		18 10	18 18		18 32	18 36		18 40	18 48		19 02
Kentish Town ⊖	d				17 40						18 10						18 40					
West Hampstead Thameslink ⊖	d	17 26		17 40	17 44			17 56		18 10	18 14			18 26		18 40	18 44			18 56		19 10
Cricklewood	d				17 47						18 17						18 47					
Hendon	d				17 50						18 20						18 50					
Mill Hill Broadway	d				17 54						18 24						18 54					
Elstree & Borehamwood	d				17 58						18 28						18 58					
Radlett	d				18 02						18 32						19 02					
St Albans City	d	17 43		17 57	18 09			18 13		18 27	18 39			18 43		18 57	19 09			19 13		19 27
Harpenden	d	17 49		18 03	18 15			18 19		18 33	18 45			18 49		19 03	19 15			19 19		19 33
Luton Airport Parkway 7 ✈	d	17 55		18 09	18 20			18 25		18 39	18 50		18 31	18 55		19 09	19 20			19 25		19 39
Luton 10	d	17 58		18 12	18a24		18 02	18 28		18 42	18a54			18 58		19 12	19a24		19 02	19 28		19 42
Leagrave	d	18 02		18 16				18 32		18 46				19 02		19 16				19 32		19 46
Harlington	d	18 07		18 21				18 37		18 51				19 07		19 21				19 37		19 51
Flitwick	d	18 11		18 25				18 41		18 55				19 11		19 25				19 41		19 55
Bedford 7	a	18 24		18 38			18 16	18 54		19 08			18 46	19 24		19 38			19 16	19 54		20 08

A To Derby

B To Nottingham

The trains that operate to and from Sevenoaks, Orpington and Rochester (and a few other destinations at peak times) are operated jointly by First Capital Connect (north of Blackfriars) and Southeastern (south of Blackfriars)

Table 52 shows the complete service between Bedford and London, whilst services between London, Sevenoaks, Sutton and Brighton only show through Thameslink services. Other Tables should be consulted for additional journey opportunities.

Table 52R

Sundays

8 December to 29 December

Brighton, Gatwick Airport and South London - City of London, St Albans, Luton and Bedford

Network Diagram - refer to first Page of Table 52

	FC	SE	EM	FC	FC	FC	FC	SE	EM	FC	FC	FC	FC	SE	FC	EM	FC	FC	SE	FC	EM	FC
			◇1 A	1		1			◇1 B	1		1				◇1 A	1				◇1 C	1
Brighton 10 d						18 14						18 44					19 14					19 44
Preston Park d																						
Hassocks 4 d						18 23						18 53					19 23					19 53
Burgess Hill 4 d						18 27						18 57					19 27					19 57
Wivelsfield 4 d																						
Haywards Heath 3 d						18 33						19 03					19 33					20 03
Balcombe d																						
Three Bridges 4 d				18 22		18 42				18 52		19 12					19 42					20 12
Gatwick Airport 10 ✈ d				18 27		18 47				18 57		19 17					19 47					20 17
Redhill d																						
East Croydon d				18 47		19 03				19 17		19 33					20 03					20 33
Sevenoaks 4 195 d		18 02						18 32						19 02					19 32			
Bat & Ball 195 d		18 05						18 35						19 05					19 35			
Otford 4 195 d		18 08						18 38						19 08					19 38			
Shoreham (Kent) 195 d		18 11						18 41						19 11					19 41			
Eynsford 195 d		18 15						18 45						19 15					19 45			
Swanley 4 195 d		18 20						18 50						19 20					19 50			
St Mary Cray 4 195 d		18 24						18 54						19 24					19 54			
Bickley 195 d		18 28						18 58						19 28					19 58			
Bromley South 195 d		18 31						19 01						19 31					20 01			
Shortlands 4 195 d		18 34						19 04						19 34					20 04			
Ravensbourne 195 d		18 36						19 06						19 36					20 06			
Beckenham Hill 195 d		18 38						19 08						19 38					20 08			
Bellingham 195 d		18 40						19 10						19 40					20 10			
Catford 195 d		18 43						19 13						19 43					20 13			
Crofton Park 195 d		18 45						19 15						19 45					20 15			
Nunhead 4 195 d		18 48						19 18						19 48					20 18			
Peckham Rye 4 195 d		18 50						19 20						19 50					20 20			
Denmark Hill 4 195 d		18 54						19 24						19 54					20 24			
Sutton (Surrey) 4 179 d	18 07				18 38		18 37				19 08		19 07		19 38			19 37		20 08		
West Sutton 179 d	18 10						18 40						19 10					19 40				
Sutton Common 179 d	18 12						18 42						19 12					19 42				
St Helier 179 d	18 15						18 45						19 15					19 45				
Morden South 179 d	18 17						18 47						19 17					19 47				
South Merton 179 d	18 19						18 49						19 19					19 49				
Wimbledon Chase 179 d	18 21						18 51						19 21					19 51				
Wimbledon 6 ⊖173,179 d	18 26						18 56						19 26					19 56				
Haydons Road 173 d	18 28						18 58						19 28					19 58				
Tooting 173 d	18 31						19 01						19 31					20 01				
Carshalton 173 d					18 41						19 11				19 41					20 11		
Hackbridge 173 d					18 43						19 13				19 43					20 13		
Mitcham Junction 173 d					18 46						19 16				19 46					20 16		
Mitcham Eastfields 173 d					18 49						19 19				19 49					20 19		
Streatham 4 d	18 36				18 53		19 06				19 23		19 36		19 53			20 06		20 23		
Tulse Hill 3 d	18 40				18 57		19 10				19 27		19 40		19 57			20 10		20 27		
London Bridge 4 ⊖ a				19 00		19 15				19 30		19 45					20 15					20 45
d				19 00		19 15				19 30		19 45					20 15					20 45
Herne Hill 4 173,179 d	18 44				19 01		19 14				19 31		19 44		20 01			20 14		20 31		
Loughborough Jn. 173,179 d	18 47				19 04		19 17				19 34		19 47		20 04			20 17		20 34		
Elephant & Castle 173,179 d	18 52	19 00			19 09		19 22	19 30			19 39		19 52	20 00	20 09			20 22	20 30	20 39		
London Blackfriars 3 ⊖ d	18 56	19a04		19 08	19a13	19 22	19 26	19a34		19 38	19a43	19 52	19 56	20a04	20a13		20 22	20 26	20a34	20a43		20 52
City Thameslink 3 d																						
Farringdon 3 ⊖ d	19 02			19 14		19 28	19 32			19 44		19 58	20 02				20 28	20 32				20 58
St Pancras International 15 ⊖ a	19 06			19 18		19 32	19 36			19 48		20 02	20 06				20 32	20 36				21 02
d	19 06		19 10	19 18		19 32	19 36		19 40	19 48		20 02	20 06			20 10	20 32	20 36			20 40	21 02
Kentish Town ⊖ d	19 10						19 40						20 10					20 40				
West Hampstead Thameslink ⊖ d	19 14			19 26		19 40	19 44			19 56		20 10	20 14				20 40	20 44				21 10
Cricklewood d	19 17						19 47						20 17					20 47				
Hendon d	19 20						19 50						20 20					20 50				
Mill Hill Broadway d	19 24						19 54						20 24					20 54				
Elstree & Borehamwood d	19 28						19 58						20 28					20 58				
Radlett d	19 32						20 02						20 32					21 02				
St Albans City d	19 39			19 43		19 57	20 09			20 13		20 27	20 39				20 57	21 09				21 27
Harpenden d	19 45			19 49		20 03	20 15			20 19		20 33	20 45				21 03	21 15				21 33
Luton Airport Parkway 7 ✈ d	19 50		19 31	19 55		20 09	20 20			20 25		20 39	20 50			20 31	21 09	21 20				21 39
Luton 10 d	19a54			19 58		20 12	20 24		20 02	20 28		20 42	20 54				21 12	21 24			21 04	21 42
Leagrave d				20 02		20 16				20 32		20 46					21 16					21 46
Harlington d				20 07		20 21				20 37		20 51					21 21					21 51
Flitwick d				20 11		20 25				20 41		20 55					21 25					21 55
Bedford 7 a			19 46	20 24		20 38	20 46		20 16	20 54		21 08	21 16			20 46	21 38	21 46			21 19	22 08

A To Nottingham B To Derby C To Leeds

The trains that operate to and from Sevenoaks, Orpington and Rochester (and a few other destinations at peak times) are operated jointly by First Capital Connect (north of Blackfriars) and Southeastern (south of Blackfriars)

Table 52 shows the complete service between Bedford and London, whilst services between London, Sevenoaks, Sutton and Brighton only show through Thameslink services. Other Tables should be consulted for additional journey opportunities.

Table 52R

Sundays

8 December to 29 December

Brighton, Gatwick Airport and South London - City of London, St Albans, Luton and Bedford

Network Diagram - refer to first Page of Table 52

		FC	SE	FC	EM ◇[1] A	EM ◇[1] B	FC [1]	FC	SE	FC	FC [1]	FC	SE	FC	EM ◇[1] A	FC [1]	SE	FC	EM ◇[1] C	FC [1]	SE	FC [1]	SE
Brighton [10]	d						20 14				20 44					21 14				21 44		22 14	
Preston Park	d																						
Hassocks [4]	d						20 23				20 53					21 23				21 53		22 23	
Burgess Hill [4]	d						20 27				20 57					21 27				21 57		22 27	
Wivelsfield [4]	d																						
Haywards Heath [3]	d						20 33				21 03					21 33				22 03		22 33	
Balcombe	d																						
Three Bridges [4]	d						20 42				21 12					21 42				22 12		22 42	
Gatwick Airport [10] ✈	d						20 47				21 17					21 47				22 17		22 47	
Redhill	d																						
East Croydon	d						21 03				21 33					22 03				22 33		23 03	
Sevenoaks [4]	195 d		20 02						20 32				21 02				21 32				22 02		22 32
Bat & Ball	195 d		20 05						20 35				21 05				21 35				22 05		22 35
Otford [4]	195 d		20 08						20 38				21 08				21 38				22 08		22 38
Shoreham (Kent)	195 d		20 11						20 41				21 11				21 41				22 11		22 41
Eynsford	195 d		20 15						20 45				21 15				21 45				22 15		22 45
Swanley [4]	195 d		20 20						20 50				21 20				21 50				22 20		22 50
St Mary Cray [4]	195 d		20 24						20 54				21 24				21 54				22 24		22 54
Bickley	195 d		20 28						20 58				21 28				21 58				22 28		22 58
Bromley South	195 d		20 31						21 01				21 31				22 01				22 31		23 01
Shortlands [4]	195 d		20 34						21 04				21 34				22 04				22 34		23 04
Ravensbourne	195 d		20 36						21 06				21 36				22 06				22 36		23 06
Beckenham Hill	195 d		20 38						21 08				21 38				22 08				22 38		23 08
Bellingham	195 d		20 40						21 10				21 40				22 10				22 40		23 10
Catford	195 d		20 43						21 13				21 43				22 13				22 43		23 13
Crofton Park	195 d		20 45						21 15				21 45				22 15				22 45		23 15
Nunhead [4]	195 d		20 48						21 18				21 48				22 18				22 48		23 18
Peckham Rye [4]	195 d		20 50						21 20				21 50				22 20				22 50		23 20
Denmark Hill [4]	195 d		20 54						21 24				21 54				22 24				22 54		23 24
Sutton (Surrey) [4]	179 d	20 07		20 38				20 37		21 08		21 07		21 38				22 08					
West Sutton	179 d	20 10						20 40				21 10											
Sutton Common	179 d	20 12						20 42				21 12											
St Helier	179 d	20 15						20 45				21 15											
Morden South	179 d	20 17						20 47				21 17											
South Merton	179 d	20 19						20 49				21 19											
Wimbledon Chase	179 d	20 21						20 51				21 21											
Wimbledon [6] ⊖173,179	d	20 26						20 56				21 26											
Haydons Road	173 d	20 28						20 58				21 28											
Tooting	173 d	20 31						21 01				21 31											
Carshalton	173 d			20 41						21 11				21 41				22 11					
Hackbridge	173 d			20 43						21 13				21 43				22 13					
Mitcham Junction	173 d			20 46						21 16				21 46				22 16					
Mitcham Eastfields	173 d			20 49						21 19				21 49				22 19					
Streatham [4]	d	20 36		20 53				21 06		21 23		21 36		21 53				22 23					
Tulse Hill [3]	d	20 40		20 57				21 10		21 27		21 40		21 57				22 27					
London Bridge [4] ⊖	a						21 15				21 45					22 15				22 45		23 15	
	d						21 15				21 45					22 15				22 45		23 15	
Herne Hill [4]	173,179 d	20 44		21 01				21 14		21 31		21 44		22 01				22 31					
Loughborough Jn.	173,179 d	20 47		21 04				21 17		21 34		21 47		22 04				22 34					
Elephant & Castle	173,179 d	20 52	21 00	21 09				21 22	21 30	21 39		21 52	22 00	22 09			22 30	22 39			23 00		23 30
London Blackfriars [3] ⊖	d	20 56	21a04	21a13			21 22	21 26	21a34	21a43	21 52	21 56	22a04	22a13		22 24	22a34	22a43		22 54	23a04	23 24	23a34
City Thameslink [3]	d																						
Farringdon [3] ⊖	d	21 02					21 28	21 32			21 58	22 02				22 30				23 00		23 30	
St Pancras International [15] ⊖	a	21 06					21 32	21 36			22 02	22 06				22 34				23 04		23 34	
	d	21 06			21 10	21 30	21 32	21 36			22 02	22 06			22 30	22 34			23 00	23 04		23 34	
Kentish Town ⊖	d	21 10						21 40				22 10				22 38				23 08		23 38	
West Hampstead Thameslink ⊖	d	21 14					21 40	21 44			22 10	22 14				22 42				23 12		23 42	
Cricklewood	d	21 17						21 47				22 17				22 45				23 15		23 45	
Hendon	d	21 20						21 50				22 20				22 48				23 18		23 48	
Mill Hill Broadway	d	21 24						21 54				22 24				22 52				23 22		23 52	
Elstree & Borehamwood	d	21 28						21 58				22 28				22 56				23 26		23 56	
Radlett	d	21 32						22 02				22 32				23 01				23 31		00 01	
St Albans City	d	21 39					21 57	22 09			22 27	22 39				23 08				23 38		00 08	
Harpenden	d	21 45					22 03	22 15			22 33	22 45				23 14				23 44		00 14	
Luton Airport Parkway [7] ✈	d	21 50			21 31		22 09	22 20			22 39	22 50			22 51	23 20			23 30	23 50		00 20	
Luton [10]	d	21 54				21 52	22 12	22 24			22 42	22 54				23 23				23 53		00 23	
Leagrave	d						22 16				22 46					23 27				23 57		00 27	
Harlington	d						22 21				22 51					23 32				00 02		00 32	
Flitwick	d						22 25				22 55					23 36				00 06		00 36	
Bedford [7]	a	22 16			21 46	22 06	22 38	22 46			23 08	23 16			23 13	23 49			23 53	00 19		00 49	

A To Nottingham **B** To Sheffield **C** To Derby

The trains that operate to and from Sevenoaks, Orpington and Rochester (and a few other destinations at peak times) are operated jointly by First Capital Connect (north of Blackfriars) and Southeastern (south of Blackfriars)

Table 52 shows the complete service between Bedford and London, whilst services between London, Sevenoaks, Sutton and Brighton only show through Thameslink services. Other Tables should be consulted for additional journey opportunities.

Table 52R

Sundays

8 December to 29 December

Brighton, Gatwick Airport and South London - City of London, St Albans, Luton and Bedford

Network Diagram - refer to first Page of Table 52

Station			FC 1	FC 1	FC 1
Brighton 10		d	22 44	23 14	23 42
Preston Park		d			
Hassocks 4		d	22 53	23 23	23 51
Burgess Hill 4		d	22 57	23 27	23 55
Wivelsfield 4		d			
Haywards Heath 3		d	23 03	23 33	00 01
Balcombe		d			
Three Bridges 4		d	23 12	23 42	00 10
Gatwick Airport 10	✈	d	23 17	23 47	00 15
Redhill		d			00 24
East Croydon	🚋	d	23 33	00 02	00 36
Sevenoaks 4	195	d			
Bat & Ball	195	d			
Otford 4	195	d			
Shoreham (Kent)	195	d			
Eynsford	195	d			
Swanley 4	195	d			
St Mary Cray 4	195	d			
Bickley	195	d			
Bromley South	195	d			
Shortlands 4	195	d			
Ravensbourne	195	d			
Beckenham Hill	195	d			
Bellingham	195	d			
Catford	195	d			
Crofton Park	195	d			
Nunhead 4	195	d			
Peckham Rye 4	195	d			
Denmark Hill 4	195	d			
Sutton (Surrey) 4	179	d			
West Sutton	179	d			
Sutton Common	179	d			
St Helier	179	d			
Morden South	179	d			
South Merton	179	d			
Wimbledon Chase	179	d			
Wimbledon 6	⊖173,179 🚋	d			
Haydons Road	173	d			
Tooting	173	d			
Carshalton	173	d			
Hackbridge	173	d			
Mitcham Junction	173 🚋	d			
Mitcham Eastfields	173	d			
Streatham 4		d			
Tulse Hill 3		d			
London Bridge 4	⊖	a	23 45	00 21	00 51
		d	23 45	00 22	00 51
Herne Hill 4	173,179	d			
Loughborough Jn.	173,179	d			
Elephant & Castle	173,179	d			
London Blackfriars 3	⊖	d	23 54	00 29	00 58
City Thameslink 3		d			
Farringdon 3	⊖	d	23 59	00 34	
St Pancras International 15	⊖	a	00 03	00 38	01 09
		d	00 04	00 39	01 10
Kentish Town	⊖	d	00 08	00 42	01 13
West Hampstead Thameslink	⊖	d	00 12	00 46	01 17
Cricklewood		d	00 15	00 49	01 20
Hendon		d	00 18	00 52	01 23
Mill Hill Broadway		d	00 22	00 56	01 27
Elstree & Borehamwood		d	00 26	01 00	01 31
Radlett		d	00 31	01 05	01 36
St Albans City		d	00 38	01 11	01 42
Harpenden		d	00 44	01 17	01 48
Luton Airport Parkway 7	✈	d	00 50	01 23	01 54
Luton 10		d	00 53	01 26	01 57
Leagrave		d	00 57	01 30	02 01
Harlington		d	01 02	01 35	02 06
Flitwick		d	01 06	01 39	02 10
Bedford 7		a	01 19	01 52	02 23

The trains that operate to and from Sevenoaks, Orpington and Rochester (and a few other destinations at peak times) are operated jointly by First Capital Connect (north of Blackfriars) and Southeastern (south of Blackfriars)

Table 52 shows the complete service between Bedford and London, whilst services between London, Sevenoaks, Sutton and Brighton only show through Thameslink services. Other Tables should be consulted for additional journey opportunities.

Table 52R

Sundays

5 January to 9 February

Brighton, Gatwick Airport and South London - City of London, St Albans, Luton and Bedford

Network Diagram - refer to first Page of Table 52

		FC	FC	FC	FC	FC	FC	FC	FC	FC	FC	FC	FC	FC	FC	FC	FC	FC	FC	FC	FC	FC	FC
			1		1		1	1												1			1
		A	B	A	B		B	B															
												bus	bus	bus		bus	bus	bus			bus	bus	
Brighton [10]	d										05 36												06 06
Preston Park	d																						
Hassocks [4]	d										05 45												06 15
Burgess Hill [4]	d										05 48												06 18
Wivelsfield [4]	d																						
Haywards Heath [3]	d										05 54												06 24
Balcombe	d							00 05															
Three Bridges [4]	d							00 10		05 13	06 02												06 32
Gatwick Airport [10] ✈	d							00 15		05 18	06 08												06 38
Redhill	d							00 24															
East Croydon 🚋	d						00 02	00 36		05 37	06 27												06 57
Sevenoaks [4] 195	d																						
Bat & Ball 195	d																						
Otford [4] 195	d																						
Shoreham (Kent) 195	d																						
Eynsford 195	d																						
Swanley [4] 195	d																						
St Mary Cray [4] 195	d																						
Bickley 195	d																						
Bromley South 195	d																						
Shortlands [4] 195	d																						
Ravensbourne 195	d																						
Beckenham Hill 195	d																						
Bellingham 195	d																						
Catford 195	d																						
Crofton Park 195	d																						
Nunhead [4] 195	d																						
Peckham Rye [4] 195	d																						
Denmark Hill [4] 195	d																						
Sutton (Surrey) [4] 179	d																						
West Sutton 179	d																						
Sutton Common 179	d																						
St Helier 179	d																						
Morden South 179	d																						
South Merton 179	d																						
Wimbledon Chase 179	d																						
Wimbledon [3] ⊖173,179 🚋	d																						
Haydons Road 173	d																						
Tooting 173	d																						
Carshalton 173	d																						
Hackbridge 173	d																						
Mitcham Junction 173 🚋	d																						
Mitcham Eastfields 173	d																						
Streatham [4]	d																						
Tulse Hill [3]	d																						
London Bridge [4] ⊖	a						00 21	00 51															
	d						00 22	00 52															
Herne Hill [4] 173,179	d																						
Loughborough Jn. 173,179	d																						
Elephant & Castle 173,179	d																						
London Blackfriars [3] ⊖	d					00 08	00 28	00 58	01 29	06a04	06a54												07 24
City Thameslink [3]	d																						
Farringdon [3] ⊖	d					00 13	00 34																07 30
St Pancras International [15] ⊖	a					00 17	00 38	01 08	01 38														07 34
	d				00 02	00 18	00 39	01 09	01 39			04 30	04 39	05 30		05 36	06 06	06 30			06 36	07 06	07 34
Kentish Town ⊖	d					00 21	00 42	01 12	01 42				04 54			05 51	06 21				06 51	07 21	07 38
West Hampstead Thameslink ⊖	d				00 10	00 25	00 46	01 16	01 46				05 09			06 06	06 36				07 06	07 36	07a43
Cricklewood	d					00 28	00 49	01 19	01 49				05 19			06 16	06 46				07 16	07 46	
Hendon	d			00 01		00 31	00 52	01 22	01 52				05 29			06 26	06 56				07 26	07 56	
Mill Hill Broadway	d			00 05		00 35	00 56	01 26	01 56				05 39			06 36	07 06				07 36	08a06	
Elstree & Borehamwood	d			00 09		00 39	01 00	01 30	02 00				05 59			06 56	07 26				07 56		
Radlett	d			00 14		00 44	01 05	01 35	02 05				06 11			07 08	07 38				08 08		
St Albans City	d			00 21	00 27	00 51	01 11	01 41	02 11			05a30	06a31	06a30	06 41	07a28	07a58	07a30	07 38	08 08	08a28		
Harpenden	d		00 03	00 27	00 33	00 57	01 17	01 47	02 17						06 47				07 44	08 14			
Luton Airport Parkway [7] ✈	d	00 03	00 09	00 33	00 39	01 03	01 23	01 53	02 23						06 53				07 50	08 20			
Luton [10]	d	00 06	00 12	00 36	00 42	01 06	01 26	01 56	02 26						06 56				07 53	08 23			
Leagrave	d	00 10	00 16	00 40	00 46	01 10	01 30	02 00	02 30						07 00				07 57	08 27			
Harlington	d	00 15	00 21	00 45	00 51	01 15	01 35	02 05	02 35						07 05				08 02	08 32			
Flitwick	d	00 19	00 25	00 49	00 55	01 19	01 39	02 09	02 39						07 09				08 06	08 36			
Bedford [7]	a	00 32	00 38	01 02	01 08	01 32	01 52	02 22	02 52						07 22				08 19	08 49			

A From Sutton (Surrey) B From Brighton

The trains that operate to and from Sevenoaks, Orpington and Rochester (and a few other destinations at peak times) are operated jointly by First Capital Connect (north of Blackfriars) and Southeastern (south of Blackfriars)

Table 52 shows the complete service between Bedford and London, whilst services between London, Sevenoaks, Sutton and Brighton only show through Thameslink services. Other Tables should be consulted for additional journey opportunities.

Table 52R

Sundays

5 January to 9 February

Brighton, Gatwick Airport and South London - City of London, St Albans, Luton and Bedford

Network Diagram - refer to first Page of Table 52

		SE	FC	SE	FC	SE	EM	FC	SE	EM	FC	SE	EM	FC	SE	FC	EM	FC	FC	SE	FC	FC	EM
			1		1		◇1	1		◇1	1		◇1	1		1	◇1	1			1		◇1
		A		A			B			C			B				C						B
Brighton 10	d		06 36		07 04			07 36			08 04					08 44					09 14		
Preston Park	d																						
Hassocks 4	d		06 45		07 13			07 45			08 13					08 53					09 23		
Burgess Hill 4	d		06 48		07 16			07 48			08 16					08 57					09 27		
Wivelsfield 4	d																						
Haywards Heath 3	d		06 54		07 24			07 54			08 24					09 03					09 33		
Balcombe	d																						
Three Bridges 4	d		07 02		07 32			08 02			08 32					09 12					09 42		
Gatwick Airport 10 ✈	d		07 08		07 38			08 08			08 38			08 59		09 17		09 27			09 47		
Redhill	d																						
East Croydon	d		07 27		07 57			08 27			08 56			09 17		09 33		09 47			10 03		
Sevenoaks 4 195	d					07 32			08 02			08 32			09 02					09 32			
Bat & Ball 195	d					07 35			08 05			08 35			09 05					09 35			
Otford 4 195	d					07 38			08 08			08 38			09 08					09 38			
Shoreham (Kent) 195	d					07 41			08 11			08 41			09 11					09 41			
Eynsford 195	d					07 45			08 15			08 45			09 15					09 45			
Swanley 4 195	d					07 50			08 20			08 50			09 20					09 50			
St Mary Cray 4 195	d					07 54			08 24			08 54			09 24					09 54			
Bickley 195	d	06 58		07 28		07 58			08 28			08 58			09 28					09 58			
Bromley South 195	d	07 01		07 31		08 01			08 31			09 01			09 31					10 01			
Shortlands 4 195	d	07 04		07 34		08 04			08 34			09 04			09 34					10 04			
Ravensbourne 195	d	07 06		07 36		08 06			08 36			09 06			09 36					10 06			
Beckenham Hill 195	d	07 08		07 38		08 08			08 38			09 08			09 38					10 08			
Bellingham 195	d	07 10		07 40		08 10			08 40			09 10			09 40					10 10			
Catford 195	d	07 13		07 43		08 13			08 43			09 13			09 43					10 13			
Crofton Park 195	d	07 15		07 45		08 15			08 45			09 15			09 45					10 15			
Nunhead 4 195	d	07 18		07 48		08 18			08 48			09 18			09 48					10 18			
Peckham Rye 4 195	d	07 20		07 50		08 20			08 50			09 20			09 50					10 20			
Denmark Hill 4 195	d	07 24		07 54		08 24			08 54			09 24			09 54					10 24			
Sutton (Surrey) 4 179	d																		09 37			10 08	
West Sutton 179	d																		09 40				
Sutton Common 179	d																		09 42				
St Helier 179	d																		09 45				
Morden South 179	d																		09 47				
South Merton 179	d																		09 49				
Wimbledon Chase 179	d																		09 51				
Wimbledon 6 ⊖173,179	d																		09 56				
Haydons Road 173	d																		09 58				
Tooting 173	d																		10 01				
Carshalton 173	d																					10 11	
Hackbridge 173	d																					10 13	
Mitcham Junction 173	d																					10 16	
Mitcham Eastfields 173	d																					10 19	
Streatham 4	d																		10 06			10 23	
Tulse Hill 3	d																		10 10			10 27	
London Bridge 4 ⊖	a																						
	d																						
Herne Hill 4 173,179	d																		10 14			10 31	
Loughborough Jn. 173,179	d																		10 17			10 34	
Elephant & Castle 173,179	d	07 30	07 50	08 00	08 20	08 30		08 50	09 00		09 20	09 30		09 45	10 00	10 01		10 15	10 22	10 30	10 31	10 39	
London Blackfriars 3 ⊖	d	07a34	07 54	08a04	08 24	08a34		08 54	09a04		09 24	09a34		09 54	10a04	10 08		10 22	10 26	10a34	10 38	10a43	
City Thameslink 3	d																						
Farringdon 3 ⊖	d		08 00		08 30			09 00			09 30			10 00		10 14		10 28	10 32		10 44		
St Pancras International 15 ⊖	a		08 04		08 34			09 04			09 34			10 04		10 18		10 32	10 36		10 48		
	d		08 04		08 34		09 00	09 04		09 30	09 34		10 00	10 04		10 18	10 30	10 32	10 36		10 48		11 00
Kentish Town ⊖	d		08 08		08 38			09 08			09 38			10 08					10 40				
West Hampstead Thameslink ⊖	d		08 12		08 42			09 12			09 42			10 12		10 26		10 40	10 44		10 56		
Cricklewood	d		08 15		08 45			09 15			09 45			10 15					10 47				
Hendon	d		08 18		08 48			09 18			09 48			10 18					10 50				
Mill Hill Broadway	d		08 22		08 52			09 22			09 52			10 22					10 54				
Elstree & Borehamwood	d		08 26		08 56			09 26			09 56			10 26					10 58				
Radlett	d		08 31		09 01			09 31			10 01			10 31					11 02				
St Albans City	d		08 38		09 08			09 38			10 08			10 38		10 43		10 57	11 09		11 13		
Harpenden	d		08 44		09 14			09 44			10 14			10 44		10 49		11 03	11 15		11 19		
Luton Airport Parkway 7 ✈	d		08 50		09 20		09 28	09 50			10 20		10 29	10 50		10 55		11 09	11 20		11 25		11 29
Luton 10	d		08 53		09 23			09 53		09 59	10 23			10 53		10 58	11 02	11 12	11a24		11 28		11 33
Leagrave	d		08 57		09 27			09 57			10 27			10 57		11 02		11 16			11 32		
Harlington	d		09 02		09 32			10 02			10 32			11 02		11 07		11 21			11 37		
Flitwick	d		09 06		09 36			10 06			10 36			11 06		11 11		11 25			11 41		
Bedford 7	a		09 19		09 49		09 50	10 19		10 19	10 49		10 50	11 19		11 24	11 22	11 38			11 54		11 54

A From Orpington
B To Nottingham
C To Sheffield

The trains that operate to and from Sevenoaks, Orpington and Rochester (and a few other destinations at peak times) are operated jointly by First Capital Connect (north of Blackfriars) and Southeastern (south of Blackfriars)

Table 52 shows the complete service between Bedford and London, whilst services between London, Sevenoaks, Sutton and Brighton only show through Thameslink services. Other Tables should be consulted for additional journey opportunities.

Table 52R

Sundays

5 January to 9 February

Brighton, Gatwick Airport and South London - City of London, St Albans, Luton and Bedford

Network Diagram - refer to first Page of Table 52

			FC	FC	SE	FC	FC	EM	FC	FC	SE	FC	FC	FC	FC	SE	EM	FC	FC	FC	FC	SE	EM	FC
			1			1		◇1	1			1		1			◇1	1		1			◇1	1
								A									B						A	
								🍴									🍴						🍴	
Brighton 10		d				09 44						10 14						10 44						11 14
Preston Park		d																						
Hassocks 4		d				09 53						10 23						10 53						11 23
Burgess Hill 4		d				09 57						10 27						10 57						11 27
Wivelsfield 4		d																						
Haywards Heath 3		d				10 03						10 33						11 03						11 33
Balcombe		d																						
Three Bridges 4		d				10 12			10 22			10 42		10 52				11 12		11 22				11 42
Gatwick Airport 10	✈	d	09 57			10 17			10 27			10 47		10 57				11 17		11 27				11 47
Redhill		d																						
East Croydon	🚋	d	10 17			10 33			10 47			11 03		11 17				11 33		11 47				12 03
Sevenoaks 4	195	d			10 02						10 32					11 02						11 32		
Bat & Ball	195	d			10 05						10 35					11 05						11 35		
Otford 4	195	d			10 08						10 38					11 08						11 38		
Shoreham (Kent)	195	d			10 11						10 41					11 11						11 41		
Eynsford	195	d			10 15						10 45					11 15						11 45		
Swanley 4	195	d			10 20						10 50					11 20						11 50		
St Mary Cray 4	195	d			10 24						10 54					11 24						11 54		
Bickley	195	d			10 28						10 58					11 28						11 58		
Bromley South	195	d			10 31						11 01					11 31						12 01		
Shortlands 4	195	d			10 34						11 04					11 34						12 04		
Ravensbourne	195	d			10 36						11 06					11 36						12 06		
Beckenham Hill	195	d			10 38						11 08					11 38						12 08		
Bellingham	195	d			10 40						11 10					11 40						12 10		
Catford	195	d			10 43						11 13					11 43						12 13		
Crofton Park	195	d			10 45						11 15					11 45						12 15		
Nunhead 4	195	d			10 48						11 18					11 48						12 18		
Peckham Rye 4	195	d			10 50						11 20					11 50						12 20		
Denmark Hill 4	195	d			10 54						11 24					11 54						12 24		
Sutton (Surrey) 4	179	d		10 07			10 38			10 37			11 08		11 07				11 38		11 37			
West Sutton	179	d		10 10						10 40					11 10						11 40			
Sutton Common	179	d		10 12						10 42					11 12						11 42			
St Helier	179	d		10 15						10 45					11 15						11 45			
Morden South	179	d		10 17						10 47					11 17						11 47			
South Merton	179	d		10 19						10 49					11 19						11 49			
Wimbledon Chase	179	d		10 21						10 51					11 21						11 51			
Wimbledon 6	⊖173,179 🚋	d		10 26						10 56					11 26						11 56			
Haydons Road	173	d		10 28						10 58					11 28						11 58			
Tooting	173	d		10 31						11 01					11 31						12 01			
Carshalton	173	d					10 41						11 11						11 41					
Hackbridge	173	d					10 43						11 13						11 43					
Mitcham Junction	173 🚋	d					10 46						11 16						11 46					
Mitcham Eastfields	173	d					10 49						11 19						11 49					
Streatham 4		d		10 36			10 53			11 06			11 23		11 36				11 53		12 06			
Tulse Hill 3		d		10 40			10 57			11 10			11 27		11 40				11 57		12 10			
London Bridge 4	⊖	a																						
		d																						
Herne Hill 4	173,179	d		10 44			11 01			11 14			11 31		11 44				12 01		12 14			
Loughborough Jn.	173,179	d		10 47			11 04			11 17			11 34		11 47				12 04		12 17			
Elephant & Castle	173,179	d	10 45	10 52	11 00	11 01	11 09		11 15	11 22	11 30	11 31	11 39	11 45	11 52	12 00		12 01	12 09	12 15	12 22	12 30		12 31
London Blackfriars 3	⊖	d	10 52	10 56	11a04	11 08	11a13		11 22	11 26	11a34	11 38	11a43	11 52	11 56	12a04		12 08	12a13	12 22	12 26	12a34		12 38
City Thameslink 3		d																						
Farringdon 3	⊖	d	10 58	11 02		11 14			11 28	11 32		11 44		11 58	12 02			12 14		12 28	12 32			12 44
St Pancras International 15	⊖	a	11 02	11 06		11 18			11 32	11 36		11 48		12 02	12 06			12 18		12 32	12 36			12 48
		d	11 02	11 06		11 18		11 30	11 32	11 36		11 48		12 02	12 06		12 10	12 18		12 32	12 36		12 40	12 48
Kentish Town	⊖	d		11 10						11 40					12 10						12 40			
West Hampstead Thameslink	⊖	d	11 10	11 14		11 26			11 40	11 44		11 56		12 10	12 14			12 26		12 40	12 44			12 56
Cricklewood		d		11 17						11 47					12 17						12 47			
Hendon		d		11 20						11 50					12 20						12 50			
Mill Hill Broadway		d		11 24						11 54					12 24						12 54			
Elstree & Borehamwood		d		11 28						11 58					12 28						12 58			
Radlett		d		11 32						12 02					12 32						13 02			
St Albans City		d	11 27	11 39		11 43			11 57	12 09		12 13		12 27	12 39			12 43		12 57	13 09			13 13
Harpenden		d	11 33	11 45		11 49			12 03	12 15		12 19		12 33	12 45			12 49		13 03	13 15			13 19
Luton Airport Parkway 7	✈	d	11 39	11 50		11 55		12 00	12 09	12 20		12 25		12 39	12 50		12 31	12 55		13 09	13 20		13 03	13 25
Luton 10		d	11 42	11a54		11 58		12 03	12 12	12a24		12 28		12 42	12a54		12 34	12 58		13 12	13a24		13 07	13 28
Leagrave		d	11 46			12 02			12 16			12 32		12 46				13 02		13 16				13 32
Harlington		d	11 51			12 07			12 21			12 37		12 51				13 07		13 21				13 37
Flitwick		d	11 55			12 11			12 25			12 41		12 55				13 11		13 25				13 41
Bedford 7		a	12 08			12 24		12 21	12 38			12 54		13 08			12 49	13 24		13 38			13 22	13 54

A To Sheffield
B To Nottingham

The trains that operate to and from Sevenoaks, Orpington and Rochester (and a few other destinations at peak times) are operated jointly by First Capital Connect (north of Blackfriars) and Southeastern (south of Blackfriars)

Table 52 shows the complete service between Bedford and London, whilst services between London, Sevenoaks, Sutton and Brighton only show through Thameslink services. Other Tables should be consulted for additional journey opportunities.

Table 52R

Sundays

5 January to 9 February

Brighton, Gatwick Airport and South London - City of London, St Albans, Luton and Bedford

Network Diagram - refer to first Page of Table 52

Station		FC	FC 1	FC	SE	EM ◇1 A 🍴	FC 1	FC	FC 1	FC	SE	EM ◇1 B 🍴	FC 1	FC	FC 1	FC	SE	EM ◇1 A 🍴	FC 1	FC	FC 1	FC	SE
Brighton 10	d						11 44						12 14						12 44				
Preston Park	d																						
Hassocks 4	d						11 53						12 23						12 53				
Burgess Hill 4	d						11 57						12 27						12 57				
Wivelsfield 4	d																						
Haywards Heath 3	d						12 03						12 33						13 03				
Balcombe	d																						
Three Bridges 4	d		11 52				12 12		12 22				12 42		12 52				13 12		13 22		
Gatwick Airport 10 ✈	d		11 57				12 17		12 27				12 47		12 57				13 17		13 27		
Redhill	d																						
East Croydon 🚌	d		12 17				12 33		12 47				13 03		13 17				13 33		13 47		
Sevenoaks 4 195	d				12 02						12 32						13 02						13 32
Bat & Ball 195	d				12 05						12 35						13 05						13 35
Otford 4 195	d				12 08						12 38						13 08						13 38
Shoreham (Kent) 195	d				12 11						12 41						13 11						13 41
Eynsford 195	d				12 15						12 45						13 15						13 45
Swanley 4 195	d				12 20						12 50						13 20						13 50
St Mary Cray 4 195	d				12 24						12 54						13 24						13 54
Bickley 195	d				12 28						12 58						13 28						13 58
Bromley South 195	d				12 31						13 01						13 31						14 01
Shortlands 4 195	d				12 34						13 04						13 34						14 04
Ravensbourne 195	d				12 36						13 06						13 36						14 06
Beckenham Hill 195	d				12 38						13 08						13 38						14 08
Bellingham 195	d				12 40						13 10						13 40						14 10
Catford 195	d				12 43						13 13						13 43						14 13
Crofton Park 195	d				12 45						13 15						13 45						14 15
Nunhead 4 195	d				12 48						13 18						13 48						14 18
Peckham Rye 4 195	d				12 50						13 20						13 50						14 20
Denmark Hill 4 195	d				12 54						13 24						13 54						14 24
Sutton (Surrey) 4 179	d	12 08		12 07				12 38		12 37				13 08		13 07				13 38		13 37	
West Sutton 179	d			12 10						12 40						13 10						13 40	
Sutton Common 179	d			12 12						12 42						13 12						13 42	
St Helier 179	d			12 15						12 45						13 15						13 45	
Morden South 179	d			12 17						12 47						13 17						13 47	
South Merton 179	d			12 19						12 49						13 19						13 49	
Wimbledon Chase 179	d			12 21						12 51						13 21						13 51	
Wimbledon 6 ⊖173,179 🚌	d			12 26						12 56						13 26						13 56	
Haydons Road 173	d			12 28						12 58						13 28						13 58	
Tooting 173	d			12 31						13 01						13 31						14 01	
Carshalton 173	d	12 11						12 41						13 11						13 41			
Hackbridge 173	d	12 13						12 43						13 13						13 43			
Mitcham Junction 173 🚌	d	12 16						12 46						13 16						13 46			
Mitcham Eastfields 173	d	12 19						12 49						13 19						13 49			
Streatham 4	d	12 23		12 36				12 53		13 06				13 23		13 36				13 53		14 06	
Tulse Hill 3	d	12 27		12 40				12 57		13 10				13 27		13 40				13 57		14 10	
London Bridge 4 ⊖	a																						
	d																						
Herne Hill 4 173,179	d	12 31		12 44				13 01		13 14				13 31		13 44				14 01		14 14	
Loughborough Jn. 173,179	d	12 34		12 47				13 04		13 17				13 34		13 47				14 04		14 17	
Elephant & Castle 173,179	d	12 39	12 45	12 52	13 00		13 01	13 09	13 15	13 22	13 30		13 31	13 39	13 45	13 52	14 00		14 01	14 09	14 15	14 22	14 30
London Blackfriars 3 ⊖	d	12a43	12 52	12 56	13a04		13 08	13a13	13 22	13 26	13a34		13 38	13a43	13 52	13 56	14a04		14 08	14a13	14 22	14 26	14a34
City Thameslink 3	d																						
Farringdon 3 ⊖	d		12 58	13 02			13 14		13 28	13 32			13 44		13 58	14 02			14 14		14 28	14 32	
St Pancras International 15 ⊖	a		13 02	13 06			13 18		13 32	13 36			13 48		14 02	14 06			14 18		14 32	14 36	
	d		13 02	13 06		13 10	13 18		13 32	13 36		13 40	13 48		14 02	14 06		14 10	14 18		14 32	14 36	
Kentish Town ⊖	d			13 10						13 40						14 10						14 40	
West Hampstead Thameslink ⊖	d		13 10	13 14			13 26		13 40	13 44			13 56		14 10	14 14			14 26		14 40	14 44	
Cricklewood	d			13 17						13 47						14 17						14 47	
Hendon	d			13 20						13 50						14 20						14 50	
Mill Hill Broadway	d			13 24						13 54						14 24						14 54	
Elstree & Borehamwood	d			13 28						13 58						14 28						14 58	
Radlett	d			13 32						14 02						14 32						15 02	
St Albans City	d		13 27	13 39			13 43		13 57	14 09			14 13		14 27	14 39			14 43		14 57	15 09	
Harpenden	d		13 33	13 45			13 49		14 03	14 15			14 19		14 33	14 45			14 49		15 03	15 15	
Luton Airport Parkway 7 ✈	d		13 39	13 50		13 31	13 55		14 09	14 20		14 02	14 25		14 39	14 50		14 31	14 55		15 09	15 20	
Luton 10	d		13 42	13a54		13 34	13 58		14 12	14a24		14 07	14 28		14 42	14a54			14 58		15 12	15a24	
Leagrave	d		13 46				14 02		14 16				14 32		14 46				15 02		15 16		
Harlington	d		13 51				14 07		14 21				14 37		14 51				15 07		15 21		
Flitwick	d		13 55				14 11		14 25				14 41		14 55				15 11		15 25		
Bedford 7	a		14 08			13 49	14 24		14 38			14 22	14 54		15 08			14 46	15 24		15 38		

A To Nottingham

B To Sheffield

The trains that operate to and from Sevenoaks, Orpington and Rochester (and a few other destinations at peak times) are operated jointly by First Capital Connect (north of Blackfriars) and Southeastern (south of Blackfriars)

Table 52 shows the complete service between Bedford and London, whilst services between London, Sevenoaks, Sutton and Brighton only show through Thameslink services. Other Tables should be consulted for additional journey opportunities.

Table 52R

Sundays

5 January to 9 February

Brighton, Gatwick Airport and South London - City of London, St Albans, Luton and Bedford

Network Diagram - refer to first Page of Table 52

Station		EM ◇1 A ₽	FC 1		FC	FC 1	FC	SE	EM ◇1 B ₽	FC 1	FC	FC 1	FC	SE		EM ◇1 C ₽	FC 1	FC	FC 1	FC	SE	EM ◇1 B ₽	FC 1	FC	FC 1
Brighton 10	d		13 14							13 44							14 14						14 44		
Preston Park	d																								
Hassocks 4	d		13 23							13 53							14 23						14 53		
Burgess Hill 4	d		13 27							13 57							14 27						14 57		
Wivelsfield 4	d																								
Haywards Heath 3	d		13 33							14 03							14 33						15 03		
Balcombe	d																								
Three Bridges 4	d		13 42			13 52				14 12		14 22					14 42		14 52				15 12		15 22
Gatwick Airport 10 ✈	d		13 47			13 57				14 17		14 27					14 47		14 57				15 17		15 27
Redhill	d																								
East Croydon 🚋	d		14 03			14 17				14 33		14 47					15 03		15 17				15 33		15 47
Sevenoaks 4 195	d							14 02						14 32							15 02				
Bat & Ball 195	d							14 05						14 35							15 05				
Otford 4 195	d							14 08						14 38							15 08				
Shoreham (Kent) 195	d							14 11						14 41							15 11				
Eynsford 195	d							14 15						14 45							15 15				
Swanley 4 195	d							14 20						14 50							15 20				
St Mary Cray 4 195	d							14 24						14 54							15 24				
Bickley 195	d							14 28						14 58							15 28				
Bromley South 195	d							14 31						15 01							15 31				
Shortlands 4 195	d							14 34						15 04							15 34				
Ravensbourne 195	d							14 36						15 06							15 36				
Beckenham Hill 195	d							14 38						15 08							15 38				
Bellingham 195	d							14 40						15 10							15 40				
Catford 195	d							14 43						15 13							15 43				
Crofton Park 195	d							14 45						15 15							15 45				
Nunhead 4 195	d							14 48						15 18							15 48				
Peckham Rye 4 195	d							14 50						15 20							15 50				
Denmark Hill 4 195	d							14 54						15 24							15 54				
Sutton (Surrey) 4 179	d				14 08		14 07				14 38		14 37					15 08		15 07				15 38	
West Sutton 179	d						14 10						14 40							15 10					
Sutton Common 179	d						14 12						14 42							15 12					
St Helier 179	d						14 15						14 45							15 15					
Morden South 179	d						14 17						14 47							15 17					
South Merton 179	d						14 19						14 49							15 19					
Wimbledon Chase 179	d						14 21						14 51							15 21					
Wimbledon 5 ⊖173,179 🚋	d						14 26						14 56							15 26					
Haydons Road 173	d						14 28						14 58							15 28					
Tooting 173	d						14 31						15 01							15 31					
Carshalton 173	d				14 11						14 41							15 11						15 41	
Hackbridge 173	d				14 13						14 43							15 13						15 43	
Mitcham Junction 173 🚋	d				14 16						14 46							15 16						15 46	
Mitcham Eastfields 173	d				14 19						14 49							15 19						15 49	
Streatham 4	d				14 23		14 36				14 53		15 06					15 23		15 36				15 53	
Tulse Hill 3	d				14 27		14 40				14 57		15 10					15 27		15 40				15 57	
London Bridge 4 ⊖	a																								
	d																								
Herne Hill 4 173,179	d				14 31		14 44				15 01		15 14					15 31		15 44				16 01	
Loughborough Jn. 173,179	d				14 34		14 47				15 04		15 17					15 34		15 47				16 04	
Elephant & Castle 173,179	d		14 31		14 39	14 45	14 52	15 00		15 01	15 09	15 15	15 22	15 30			15 31	15 39	15 45	15 52	16 00		16 01	16 09	16 15
London Blackfriars 3 ⊖	d		14 38		14a43	14 52	14 56	15a04		15 08	15a13	15 22	15 26	15a34			15 38	15a43	15 52	15 56	16a04		16 08	16a13	16 22
City Thameslink 3	d																								
Farringdon 3 ⊖	d		14 44			14 58	15 02			15 14		15 28	15 32				15 44		15 58	16 02			16 14		16 28
St Pancras International 15 ⊖	a		14 48			15 02	15 06			15 18		15 32	15 36				15 48		16 02	16 06			16 18		16 32
	d	14 40	14 48			15 02	15 06		15 10	15 18		15 32	15 36			15 40	15 48		16 02	16 06		16 10	16 18		16 32
Kentish Town ⊖	d						15 10						15 40							16 10					
West Hampstead Thameslink ⊖	d		14 56			15 10	15 14			15 26		15 40	15 44				15 56		16 10	16 14			16 26		16 40
Cricklewood	d						15 17						15 47							16 17					
Hendon	d						15 20						15 50							16 20					
Mill Hill Broadway	d						15 24						15 54							16 24					
Elstree & Borehamwood	d						15 28						15 58							16 28					
Radlett	d						15 32						16 02							16 32					
St Albans City	d		15 13			15 27	15 39			15 43		15 57	16 09				16 13		16 27	16 39			16 43		16 57
Harpenden	d		15 19			15 33	15 45			15 49		16 03	16 15				16 19		16 33	16 45			16 49		17 03
Luton Airport Parkway 7 ✈	d		15 25			15 39	15 50		15 33	15 55		16 09	16 20				16 25		16 39	16 50		16 31	16 55		17 09
Luton 10	d	15 04	15 28			15 42	15a54			15 58		16 12	16a24			16 02	16 28		16 42	16a54			16 58		17 12
Leagrave	d		15 32			15 46				16 02		16 16					16 32		16 46				17 02		17 16
Harlington	d		15 37			15 51				16 07		16 21					16 37		16 51				17 07		17 21
Flitwick	d		15 41			15 55				16 11		16 25					16 41		16 55				17 11		17 25
Bedford 7	a	15 19	15 54			16 08			15 48	16 24		16 38				16 16	16 54		17 08			16 46	17 24		17 38

A To Leeds **B** To Nottingham **C** To Sheffield

The trains that operate to and from Sevenoaks, Orpington and Rochester (and a few other destinations at peak times) are operated jointly by First Capital Connect (north of Blackfriars) and Southeastern (south of Blackfriars)

Table 52 shows the complete service between Bedford and London, whilst services between London, Sevenoaks, Sutton and Brighton only show through Thameslink services. Other Tables should be consulted for additional journey opportunities.

Table 52R

Sundays
5 January to 9 February

Brighton, Gatwick Airport and South London - City of London, St Albans, Luton and Bedford

Network Diagram - refer to first Page of Table 52

	FC	SE	EM	FC	FC	FC	FC	SE	EM	FC	FC	FC	FC	SE	EM	FC	FC	FC	FC	SE	EM
			◇1	1		1			◇1	1		1			◇1	1		1			◇1
			A						B						A						B
			🍴						🍴						🍴						🍴
Brighton 10 d				15 14						15 44						16 14					
Preston Park d																					
Hassocks 4 d				15 23						15 53						16 23					
Burgess Hill 4 d				15 27						15 57						16 27					
Wivelsfield 4 d																					
Haywards Heath 3 d				15 33						16 03						16 33					
Balcombe d																					
Three Bridges 4 d				15 42		15 52				16 12		16 22				16 42		16 52			
Gatwick Airport 10 ✈ d				15 47		15 57				16 17		16 27				16 47		16 57			
Redhill d																					
East Croydon ⇌ d				16 03		16 17				16 33		16 47				17 03		17 17			
Sevenoaks 4 195 d		15 32						16 02						16 32						17 02	
Bat & Ball 195 d		15 35						16 05						16 35						17 05	
Otford 4 195 d		15 38						16 08						16 38						17 08	
Shoreham (Kent) 195 d		15 41						16 11						16 41						17 11	
Eynsford 195 d		15 45						16 15						16 45						17 15	
Swanley 4 195 d		15 50						16 20						16 50						17 20	
St Mary Cray 4 195 d		15 54						16 24						16 54						17 24	
Bickley 195 d		15 58						16 28						16 58						17 28	
Bromley South 195 d		16 01						16 31						17 01						17 31	
Shortlands 4 195 d		16 04						16 34						17 04						17 34	
Ravensbourne 195 d		16 06						16 36						17 06						17 36	
Beckenham Hill 195 d		16 08						16 38						17 08						17 38	
Bellingham 195 d		16 10						16 40						17 10						17 40	
Catford 195 d		16 13						16 43						17 13						17 43	
Crofton Park 195 d		16 15						16 45						17 15						17 45	
Nunhead 4 195 d		16 18						16 48						17 18						17 48	
Peckham Rye 4 195 d		16 20						16 50						17 20						17 50	
Denmark Hill 4 195 d		16 24						16 54						17 24						17 54	
Sutton (Surrey) 4 179 d	15 37				16 08		16 07				16 38		16 37				17 08		17 07		
West Sutton 179 d	15 40						16 10						16 40						17 10		
Sutton Common 179 d	15 42						16 12						16 42						17 12		
St Helier 179 d	15 45						16 15						16 45						17 15		
Morden South 179 d	15 47						16 17						16 47						17 17		
South Merton 179 d	15 49						16 19						16 49						17 19		
Wimbledon Chase 179 d	15 51						16 21						16 51						17 21		
Wimbledon 6 ⊖173,179 ⇌ d	15 56						16 26						16 56						17 26		
Haydons Road 173 d	15 58						16 28						16 58						17 28		
Tooting 173 d	16 01						16 31						17 01						17 31		
Carshalton 173 d					16 11						16 41						17 11				
Hackbridge 173 d					16 13						16 43						17 13				
Mitcham Junction 173 ⇌ d					16 16						16 46						17 16				
Mitcham Eastfields 173 d					16 19						16 49						17 19				
Streatham 4 d	16 06				16 23		16 36				16 53		17 06				17 23		17 36		
Tulse Hill 3 d	16 10				16 27		16 40				16 57		17 10				17 27		17 40		
London Bridge 4 ⊖ a																					
d																					
Herne Hill 4 173,179 d	16 14				16 31		16 44				17 01		17 14				17 31		17 44		
Loughborough Jn. 173,179 d	16 17				16 34		16 47				17 04		17 17				17 34		17 47		
Elephant & Castle 173,179 d	16 22	16 30		16 31	16 39	16 45	16 52	17 00		17 01	17 09	17 15	17 22	17 30		17 31	17 39	17 45	17 52	18 00	
London Blackfriars 3 ⊖ d	16 26	16a34		16 38	16a43	16 52	16 56	17a04		17 08	17a13	17 22	17 26	17a34		17 38	17a43	17 52	17 56	18a04	
City Thameslink 3 d																					
Farringdon 3 ⊖ d	16 32			16 44		16 58	17 02			17 14		17 28	17 32			17 44		17 58	18 02		
St Pancras International 15 ⊖ a	16 36			16 48		17 02	17 06			17 18		17 32	17 36			17 48		18 02	18 06		
d	16 36		16 40	16 48		17 02	17 06		17 10	17 18		17 32	17 36		17 40	17 48		18 02	18 06		18 10
Kentish Town ⊖ d	16 40						17 10						17 40						18 10		
West Hampstead Thameslink ⊖ d	16 44			16 56		17 10	17 14			17 26		17 40	17 44			17 56		18 10	18 14		
Cricklewood d	16 47						17 17						17 47						18 17		
Hendon d	16 50						17 20						17 50						18 20		
Mill Hill Broadway d	16 54						17 24						17 54						18 24		
Elstree & Borehamwood d	16 58						17 28						17 58						18 28		
Radlett d	17 02						17 32						18 02						18 32		
St Albans City d	17 09			17 13		17 27	17 39			17 43		17 57	18 09			18 13		18 27	18 39		
Harpenden d	17 15			17 19		17 33	17 45			17 49		18 03	18 15			18 19		18 33	18 45		
Luton Airport Parkway 7 ✈ d	17 20			17 25		17 39	17 50		17 31	17 55		18 09	18 20			18 25		18 39	18 50		18 31
Luton 10 d	17a24		17 04	17 28		17 42	17a54			17 58		18 12	18a24		18 02	18 28		18 42	18a54		
Leagrave d				17 32		17 46				18 02		18 16				18 32		18 46			
Harlington d				17 37		17 51				18 07		18 21				18 37		18 51			
Flitwick d				17 41		17 55				18 11		18 25				18 41		18 55			
Bedford 7 a			17 19	17 54		18 08			17 46	18 24		18 38			18 16	18 54		19 08			18 46

A To Sheffield
B To Nottingham

The trains that operate to and from Sevenoaks, Orpington and Rochester (and a few other destinations at peak times) are operated jointly by First Capital Connect (north of Blackfriars) and Southeastern (south of Blackfriars)

Table 52 shows the complete service between Bedford and London, whilst services between London, Sevenoaks, Sutton and Brighton only show through Thameslink services. Other Tables should be consulted for additional journey opportunities.

Table 52R

Sundays

5 January to 9 February

Brighton, Gatwick Airport and South London - City of London, St Albans, Luton and Bedford

Network Diagram - refer to first Page of Table 52

Station			FC [1]	FC	FC [1]	FC	SE	EM ◇[1] A ☕	FC [1]	FC	FC [1]		FC	SE	EM ◇[1] B ☕	FC [1]	FC	FC [1]	FC	SE	EM ◇[1] C ☕	FC [1]		FC	FC [1]	FC
Brighton [10]		d	16 44						17 14							17 44						18 14				
Preston Park		d																								
Hassocks [4]		d	16 53						17 23							17 53						18 23				
Burgess Hill [4]		d	16 57						17 27							17 57						18 27				
Wivelsfield [4]		d																								
Haywards Heath [3]		d	17 03						17 33							18 03						18 33				
Balcombe		d																								
Three Bridges [4]		d	17 12		17 22				17 42		17 52					18 12		18 22				18 42			18 52	
Gatwick Airport [10]	✈	d	17 17		17 27				17 47		17 57					18 17		18 27				18 47			18 57	
Redhill		d																								
East Croydon		d	17 33		17 47				18 03		18 17					18 33		18 47				19 03			19 17	
Sevenoaks [4]	195	d					17 32							18 02						18 32						
Bat & Ball	195	d					17 35							18 05						18 35						
Otford [4]	195	d					17 38							18 08						18 38						
Shoreham (Kent)	195	d					17 41							18 11						18 41						
Eynsford	195	d					17 45							18 15						18 45						
Swanley [4]	195	d					17 50							18 20						18 50						
St Mary Cray [4]	195	d					17 54							18 24						18 54						
Bickley	195	d					17 58							18 28						18 58						
Bromley South	195	d					18 01							18 31						19 01						
Shortlands [4]	195	d					18 04							18 34						19 04						
Ravensbourne	195	d					18 06							18 36						19 06						
Beckenham Hill	195	d					18 08							18 38						19 08						
Bellingham	195	d					18 10							18 40						19 10						
Catford	195	d					18 13							18 43						19 13						
Crofton Park	195	d					18 15							18 45						19 15						
Nunhead [4]	195	d					18 18							18 48						19 18						
Peckham Rye [4]	195	d					18 20							18 50						19 20						
Denmark Hill [4]	195	d					18 24							18 54						19 24						
Sutton (Surrey) [4]	179	d		17 38		17 37				18 08			18 07				18 38		18 37					19 08		19 07
West Sutton	179	d				17 40							18 10						18 40							19 10
Sutton Common	179	d				17 42							18 12						18 42							19 12
St Helier	179	d				17 45							18 15						18 45							19 15
Morden South	179	d				17 47							18 17						18 47							19 17
South Merton	179	d				17 49							18 19						18 49							19 19
Wimbledon Chase	179	d				17 51							18 21						18 51							19 21
Wimbledon [6]	⊖ 173,179	d				17 56							18 26						18 56							19 26
Haydons Road	173	d				17 58							18 28						18 58							19 28
Tooting	173	d				18 01							18 31						19 01							19 31
Carshalton	173	d		17 41						18 11							18 41							19 11		
Hackbridge	173	d		17 43						18 13							18 43							19 13		
Mitcham Junction	173	d		17 46						18 16							18 46							19 16		
Mitcham Eastfields	173	d		17 49						18 19							18 49							19 19		
Streatham [4]		d		17 53		18 06				18 23			18 36				18 53		19 06					19 23		19 36
Tulse Hill [3]		d		17 57		18 10				18 27			18 40				18 57		19 10					19 27		19 40
London Bridge [4]	⊖	a																								
		d																								
Herne Hill [4]	173,179	d		18 01		18 14				18 31			18 44				19 01		19 14					19 31		19 44
Loughborough Jn.	173,179	d		18 04		18 17				18 34			18 47				19 04		19 17					19 34		19 47
Elephant & Castle	173,179	d	18 01	18 09	18 15	18 22	18 30		18 31	18 39	18 45		18 52	19 00		19 01	19 09	19 15	19 22	19 30		19 31		19 39	19 45	19 52
London Blackfriars [3]	⊖	d	18 08	18a13	18 22	18 26	18a34		18 38	18a43	18 52		18 56	19a04		19 08	19a13	19 22	19 26	19a34		19 38		19a43	19 52	19 56
City Thameslink [3]		d																								
Farringdon [3]	⊖	d	18 14		18 28	18 32			18 44		18 58		19 02			19 14		19 28	19 32			19 44			19 58	20 02
St Pancras International [15]	⊖	a	18 18		18 32	18 36			18 48		19 02		19 06			19 18		19 32	19 36			19 48			20 02	20 06
		d	18 18		18 32	18 36		18 40	18 48		19 02		19 06		19 10	19 18		19 32	19 36		19 40	19 48			20 02	20 06
Kentish Town	⊖	d				18 40							19 10						19 40							20 10
West Hampstead Thameslink	⊖	d	18 26		18 40	18 44			18 56		19 10		19 14			19 26		19 40	19 44			19 56			20 10	20 14
Cricklewood		d				18 47							19 17						19 47							20 17
Hendon		d				18 50							19 20						19 50							20 20
Mill Hill Broadway		d				18 54							19 24						19 54							20 24
Elstree & Borehamwood		d				18 58							19 28						19 58							20 28
Radlett		d				19 02							19 32						20 02							20 32
St Albans City		d	18 43		18 57	19 09			19 13		19 27		19 39			19 43		19 57	20 09			20 13			20 27	20 39
Harpenden		d	18 49		19 03	19 15			19 19		19 33		19 45			19 49		20 03	20 15			20 19			20 33	20 45
Luton Airport Parkway [7]	✈	d	18 55		19 09	19 20			19 25		19 39		19 50		19 31	19 55		20 09	20 20			20 25			20 39	20 50
Luton [10]		d	18 58		19 12	19a24		19 04	19 28		19 42		19a54			19 58		20 12	20 24		20 02	20 28			20 42	20 54
Leagrave		d	19 02		19 16				19 32		19 46					20 02		20 16				20 32			20 46	
Harlington		d	19 07		19 21				19 37		19 51					20 07		20 21				20 37			20 51	
Flitwick		d	19 11		19 25				19 41		19 55					20 11		20 25				20 41			20 55	
Bedford [7]		a	19 24		19 38			19 19	19 54		20 08				19 46	20 24		20 38	20 46		20 16	20 54			21 08	21 16

A To Leeds B To Nottingham C To Sheffield

The trains that operate to and from Sevenoaks, Orpington and Rochester (and a few other destinations at peak times) are operated jointly by First Capital Connect (north of Blackfriars) and Southeastern (south of Blackfriars)

Table 52 shows the complete service between Bedford and London, whilst services between London, Sevenoaks, Sutton and Brighton only show through Thameslink services. Other Tables should be consulted for additional journey opportunities.

Table 52R

Sundays

5 January to 9 February

Brighton, Gatwick Airport and South London - City of London, St Albans, Luton and Bedford

Network Diagram - refer to first Page of Table 52

		SE	EM ◇1 A	FC 1	FC	FC 1	FC	SE	EM ◇1 B	FC 1	FC	FC 1	FC	SE	EM ◇1 A	FC 1	FC	EM ◇1 C	FC	SE	FC 1	FC	FC
Brighton 10	d			18 44						19 14						19 44					20 14		
Preston Park	d																						
Hassocks 4	d			18 53						19 23						19 53					20 23		
Burgess Hill 4	d			18 57						19 27						19 57					20 27		
Wivelsfield 4	d																						
Haywards Heath 3	d			19 03						19 33						20 03					20 33		
Balcombe	d																						
Three Bridges 4	d			19 12		19 22				19 42		19 52				20 12					20 42		
Gatwick Airport 10 ✈	d			19 17		19 27				19 47		19 57				20 17					20 47		
Redhill	d																						
East Croydon	d			19 33		19 47				20 03		20 17				20 33					21 03		
Sevenoaks 4	195 d	19 02						19 32						20 02						20 32			
Bat & Ball	195 d	19 05						19 35						20 05						20 35			
Otford 4	195 d	19 08						19 38						20 08						20 38			
Shoreham (Kent)	195 d	19 11						19 41						20 11						20 41			
Eynsford	195 d	19 15						19 45						20 15						20 45			
Swanley 4	195 d	19 20						19 50						20 20						20 50			
St Mary Cray 4	195 d	19 24						19 54						20 24						20 54			
Bickley	195 d	19 28						19 58						20 28						20 58			
Bromley South	195 d	19 31						20 01						20 31						21 01			
Shortlands 4	195 d	19 34						20 04						20 34						21 04			
Ravensbourne	195 d	19 36						20 06						20 36						21 06			
Beckenham Hill	195 d	19 38						20 08						20 38						21 08			
Bellingham	195 d	19 40						20 10						20 40						21 10			
Catford	195 d	19 43						20 13						20 43						21 13			
Crofton Park	195 d	19 45						20 15						20 45						21 15			
Nunhead 4	195 d	19 48						20 18						20 48						21 18			
Peckham Rye 4	195 d	19 50						20 20						20 50						21 20			
Denmark Hill 4	195 d	19 54						20 24						20 54						21 24			
Sutton (Surrey) 4	179 d				19 38		19 37				20 08		20 07				20 38		20 37			21 08	21 07
West Sutton	179 d						19 40						20 10						20 40				21 10
Sutton Common	179 d						19 42						20 12						20 42				21 12
St Helier	179 d						19 45						20 15						20 45				21 15
Morden South	179 d						19 47						20 17						20 47				21 17
South Merton	179 d						19 49						20 19						20 49				21 19
Wimbledon Chase	179 d						19 51						20 21						20 51				21 21
Wimbledon 6 ⊖ 173,179	d						19 56						20 26						20 56				21 26
Haydons Road	173 d						19 58						20 28						20 58				21 28
Tooting	173 d						20 01						20 31						21 01				21 31
Carshalton	173 d				19 41						20 11						20 41					21 11	
Hackbridge	173 d				19 43						20 13						20 43					21 13	
Mitcham Junction	173 d				19 46						20 16						20 46					21 16	
Mitcham Eastfields	173 d				19 49						20 19						20 49					21 19	
Streatham 4	d				19 53		20 06				20 23		20 36				20 53		21 06			21 23	21 36
Tulse Hill 3	d				19 57		20 10				20 27		20 40				20 57		21 10			21 27	21 40
London Bridge 4 ⊖	a																						
	d																						
Herne Hill 4	173,179 d				20 01		20 14				20 31		20 44				21 01		21 14			21 31	21 44
Loughborough Jn.	173,179 d				20 04		20 17				20 34		20 47				21 04		21 17			21 34	21 47
Elephant & Castle	173,179 d	20 00		20 01	20 09	20 15	20 22	20 30		20 31	20 39	20 45	20 52	21 00		21 01	21 09		21 22	21 30	21 31	21 39	21 52
London Blackfriars 3 ⊖	d	20a04		20 08	20a13	20 22	20 26	20a34		20 38	20a43	20 52	20 56	21a04		21 08	21a13		21 26	21a34	21 38	21a43	21 56
City Thameslink 3	d																						
Farringdon 3 ⊖	d			20 14		20 28	20 32			20 44		20 58	21 02			21 14			21 32		21 44		22 02
St Pancras International 15 ⊖	a			20 18		20 32	20 36			20 48		21 02	21 06			21 18			21 36		21 48		22 06
	d		20 10	20 18		20 32	20 36		20 40	20 48		21 02	21 06		21 10	21 18		21 30	21 36		21 48		22 06
Kentish Town ⊖	d						20 40						21 10						21 40				22 10
West Hampstead Thameslink ⊖	d			20 26		20 40	20 44			20 56		21 10	21 14			21 26			21 44		21 56		22 14
Cricklewood	d						20 47						21 17						21 47				22 17
Hendon	d						20 50						21 20						21 50				22 20
Mill Hill Broadway	d						20 54						21 24						21 54				22 24
Elstree & Borehamwood	d						20 58						21 28						21 58				22 28
Radlett	d						21 02						21 32						22 02				22 32
St Albans City	d			20 43		20 57	21 09			21 13		21 27	21 39			21 43			22 09		22 13		22 39
Harpenden	d			20 49		21 03	21 15			21 19		21 33	21 45			21 49			22 15		22 19		22 45
Luton Airport Parkway 7 ✈	d		20 31	20 55		21 09	21 20			21 25		21 39	21 50		21 31	21 55			22 20		22 25		22 50
Luton 10	d			20 58		21 12	21 24		21 04	21 28		21 42	21 54			21 58		21 52	22 24		22 28		22 54
Leagrave	d			21 02		21 16				21 32		21 46				22 02					22 32		
Harlington	d			21 07		21 21				21 37		21 51				22 07					22 37		
Flitwick	d			21 11		21 25				21 41		21 55				22 11					22 41		
Bedford 7	a		20 46	21 24		21 38	21 46		21 19	21 54		22 08	22 16		21 46	22 24		22 06	22 46		22 54		23 16

A To Nottingham B To Leeds C To Sheffield

The trains that operate to and from Sevenoaks, Orpington and Rochester (and a few other destinations at peak times) are operated jointly by First Capital Connect (north of Blackfriars) and Southeastern (south of Blackfriars)

Table 52 shows the complete service between Bedford and London, whilst services between London, Sevenoaks, Sutton and Brighton only show through Thameslink services. Other Tables should be consulted for additional journey opportunities.

Table 52R

Sundays

5 January to 9 February

Brighton, Gatwick Airport and South London - City of London, St Albans, Luton and Bedford

Network Diagram - refer to first Page of Table 52

Station			SE	FC	FC	SE	EM		FC	FC	SE	EM	FC	SE	FC	FC	FC	FC
				1			◇1 A ☕		1			◇1 B ☕	1		1	1	1	1
Brighton 10		d		20 44					21 14				21 44		22 14	22 44	23 14	23 42
Preston Park		d																
Hassocks 4		d		20 53					21 23				21 53		22 23	22 53	23 23	23 51
Burgess Hill 4		d		20 57					21 27				21 57		22 27	22 57	23 27	23 55
Wivelsfield 4		d																
Haywards Heath 3		d		21 03					21 33				22 03		22 33	23 03	23 33	00 01
Balcombe		d																
Three Bridges 4		d		21 12					21 42				22 12		22 42	23 12	23 42	00 10
Gatwick Airport 10 ✈		d		21 17					21 47				22 17		22 47	23 17	23 47	00 15
Redhill		d																00 24
East Croydon 🚋		d		21 33					22 03				22 33		23 03	23 33	00 02	00 36
Sevenoaks 4	195	d	21 02			21 32					22 02			22 32				
Bat & Ball	195	d	21 05			21 35					22 05			22 35				
Otford 4	195	d	21 08			21 38					22 08			22 38				
Shoreham (Kent)	195	d	21 11			21 41					22 11			22 41				
Eynsford	195	d	21 15			21 45					22 15			22 45				
Swanley 4	195	d	21 20			21 50					22 20			22 50				
St Mary Cray 4	195	d	21 24			21 54					22 24			22 54				
Bickley	195	d	21 28			21 58					22 28			22 58				
Bromley South	195	d	21 31			22 01					22 31			23 01				
Shortlands 4	195	d	21 34			22 04					22 34			23 04				
Ravensbourne	195	d	21 36			22 06					22 36			23 06				
Beckenham Hill	195	d	21 38			22 08					22 38			23 08				
Bellingham	195	d	21 40			22 10					22 40			23 10				
Catford	195	d	21 43			22 13					22 43			23 13				
Crofton Park	195	d	21 45			22 15					22 45			23 15				
Nunhead 4	195	d	21 48			22 18					22 48			23 18				
Peckham Rye 4	195	d	21 50			22 20					22 50			23 20				
Denmark Hill 4	195	d	21 54			22 24					22 54			23 24				
Sutton (Surrey) 4	179	d			21 38					22 08								
West Sutton	179	d																
Sutton Common	179	d																
St Helier	179	d																
Morden South	179	d																
South Merton	179	d																
Wimbledon Chase	179	d																
Wimbledon 6 ⊖	173,179 🚋	d																
Haydons Road	173	d																
Tooting	173	d																
Carshalton	173	d			21 41					22 11								
Hackbridge	173	d			21 43					22 13								
Mitcham Junction	173 🚋	d			21 46					22 16								
Mitcham Eastfields	173	d			21 49					22 19								
Streatham 4		d			21 53					22 23								
Tulse Hill 3		d			21 57					22 27								
London Bridge 4 ⊖		a																
		d																
Herne Hill 4	173,179	d			22 01					22 31								
Loughborough Jn.	173,179	d			22 04					22 34								
Elephant & Castle	173,179	d	22 00	22 01	22 09	22 30			22 31	22 39	23 00		23 01	23 30	23 31			
London Blackfriars 3 ⊖		d	22a04	22 08	22 14	22a34			22 38	22a43	23a04		23 08	23a34	23 38	00 08	00 30	01 04
City Thameslink 3		d																
Farringdon 3 ⊖		d		22 14	22 20				22 44				23 14		23 44	00 14	00 36	
St Pancras International 15 ⊖		a		22 18	22 24				22 48				23 18		23 48	00 18	00 40	01 13
		d		22 18	22 24		22 30		22 48			23 00	23 18		23 48	00 18	00 40	01 15
Kentish Town ⊖		d			22 28				22 52				23 22		23 52	00 22	00 44	01 18
West Hampstead Thameslink ⊖		d		22 26	22 32				22 56				23 26		23 56	00 26	00 48	01 22
Cricklewood		d			22 35				22 59				23 29		23 59	00 29	00 51	01 25
Hendon		d			22 38				23 02				23 32		00 02	00 32	00 54	01 28
Mill Hill Broadway		d			22 42				23 06				23 36		00 06	00 36	00 58	01 32
Elstree & Borehamwood		d			22 46				23 10				23 40		00 10	00 40	01 02	01 36
Radlett		d			22 51				23 15				23 45		00 15	00 45	01 07	01 41
St Albans City		d		22 43	22 58				23 22				23 52		00 22	00 52	01 14	01 48
Harpenden		d		22 49	23 04				23 28				23 58		00 28	00 58	01 20	01 54
Luton Airport Parkway 7 ✈		d		22 55	23 10		22 51		23 34			23 39	00 04		00 34	01 04	01 26	02 00
Luton 10		d		22 58	23 13				23 37				00 07		00 37	01 07	01 29	02 03
Leagrave		d		23 02	23 17				23 41				00 11		00 41	01 11	01 33	02 07
Harlington		d		23 07	23 22				23 46				00 16		00 46	01 16	01 38	02 12
Flitwick		d		23 11	23 26				23 50				00 20		00 50	01 20	01 42	02 16
Bedford 7		a		23 24	23 39		23 13		00 03			00 03	00 33		01 03	01 33	01 55	02 29

A To Nottingham

B To Derby

The trains that operate to and from Sevenoaks, Orpington and Rochester (and a few other destinations at peak times) are operated jointly by First Capital Connect (north of Blackfriars) and Southeastern (south of Blackfriars)

Table 52 shows the complete service between Bedford and London, whilst services between London, Sevenoaks, Sutton and Brighton only show through Thameslink services. Other Tables should be consulted for additional journey opportunities.

Table 52R

Sundays

16 February to 23 March

Brighton, Gatwick Airport and South London - City of London, St Albans, Luton and Bedford

Network Diagram - refer to first Page of Table 52

		FC	FC	FC	FC	FC	FC	FC	FC	FC	FC		FC	FC	FC	FC	FC	FC	FC	FC	FC	FC		FC	FC
			1		1		1	1													1				1
		A	B	A	B		B	B																	
													Bus	Bus	Bus		Bus	Bus	Bus			Bus		Bus	
Brighton 10	d										05 36														06 06
Preston Park	d																								
Hassocks 4	d										05 45														06 15
Burgess Hill 4	d										05 48														06 18
Wivelsfield 4	d																								
Haywards Heath 3	d										05 54														06 24
Balcombe	d							00 05																	
Three Bridges 4	d							00 10		05 13	06 02														06 32
Gatwick Airport 10 ✈	d							00 15		05 18	06 08														06 38
Redhill	d							00 24																	
East Croydon	d						00 02	00 36		05 37	06 27														06 57
Sevenoaks 4 195	d																								
Bat & Ball 195	d																								
Otford 4 195	d																								
Shoreham (Kent) 195	d																								
Eynsford 195	d																								
Swanley 4 195	d																								
St Mary Cray 4 195	d																								
Bickley 195	d																								
Bromley South 195	d																								
Shortlands 4 195	d																								
Ravensbourne 195	d																								
Beckenham Hill 195	d																								
Bellingham 195	d																								
Catford 195	d																								
Crofton Park 195	d																								
Nunhead 4 195	d																								
Peckham Rye 4 195	d																								
Denmark Hill 4 195	d																								
Sutton (Surrey) 4 179	d																								
West Sutton 179	d																								
Sutton Common 179	d																								
St Helier 179	d																								
Morden South 179	d																								
South Merton 179	d																								
Wimbledon Chase 179	d																								
Wimbledon 5 ⊖ 173,179	d																								
Haydons Road 173	d																								
Tooting 173	d																								
Carshalton 173	d																								
Hackbridge 173	d																								
Mitcham Junction 173	d																								
Mitcham Eastfields 173	d																								
Streatham 4	d																								
Tulse Hill 3	d																								
London Bridge 4 ⊖	a						00 21	00 51																	
	d						00 22	00 52																	
Herne Hill 4 173,179	d																								
Loughborough Jn. 173,179	d																								
Elephant & Castle 173,179	d																								
London Blackfriars 3 ⊖	d					00 08	00 28	00 58	01 29	06a04	06a54														07 24
City Thameslink 3	d																								
Farringdon 3 ⊖	d					00 13	00 34																		07 30
St Pancras International 15 ⊖	a					00 17	00 38	01 08	01 38																07 34
	d				00 02	00 18	00 39	01 09	01 39				04 30	04 39	05 30		05 36	06 06	06 30			06 36		07 06	07 34
Kentish Town ⊖	d					00 21	00 42	01 12	01 42					04 54			05 51	06 21				06 51		07 21	07 38
West Hampstead Thameslink ⊖	d				00 10	00 25	00 46	01 16	01 46					05 09			06 06	06 36				07 06		07 36	07a43
Cricklewood	d					00 28	00 49	01 19	01 49					05 19			06 16	06 46				07 16		07 46	
Hendon	d			00 01		00 31	00 52	01 22	01 52					05 29			06 26	06 56				07 26		07 56	
Mill Hill Broadway	d			00 05		00 35	00 56	01 26	01 56					05 39			06 36	07 06				07 36		08a06	
Elstree & Borehamwood	d			00 09		00 39	01 00	01 30	02 00					05 59			06 56	07 26				07 56			
Radlett	d			00 14		00 44	01 05	01 35	02 05					06 11			07 08	07 38				08 08			
St Albans City	d			00 21	00 27	00 51	01 11	01 41	02 11				05a30	06a31	06a30	06 41	07a28	07a58	07a30	07 38	08 08	08a28			
Harpenden	d		00 03	00 27	00 33	00 57	01 17	01 47	02 17							06 47				07 44	08 14				
Luton Airport Parkway 7 ✈	d	00 03	00 09	00 33	00 39	01 03	01 23	01 53	02 23							06 53				07 50	08 20				
Luton 10	d	00 06	00 12	00 36	00 42	01 06	01 26	01 56	02 26							06 56				07 53	08 23				
Leagrave	d	00 10	00 16	00 40	00 46	01 10	01 30	02 00	02 30							07 00				07 57	08 27				
Harlington	d	00 15	00 21	00 45	00 51	01 15	01 35	02 05	02 35							07 05				08 02	08 32				
Flitwick	d	00 19	00 25	00 49	00 55	01 19	01 39	02 09	02 39							07 09				08 06	08 36				
Bedford 7	a	00 32	00 38	01 02	01 08	01 32	01 52	02 22	02 52							07 22				08 19	08 49				

A From Sutton (Surrey) **B** From Brighton

The trains that operate to and from Sevenoaks, Orpington and Rochester (and a few other destinations at peak times) are operated jointly by First Capital Connect (north of Blackfriars) and Southeastern (south of Blackfriars)

Table 52 shows the complete service between Bedford and London, whilst services between London, Sevenoaks, Sutton and Brighton only show through Thameslink services. Other Tables should be consulted for additional journey opportunities.

Table 52R

Sundays

16 February to 23 March

Brighton, Gatwick Airport and South London - City of London, St Albans, Luton and Bedford

Network Diagram - refer to first Page of Table 52

			SE	FC	SE	FC	SE	EM	FC	SE	EM	FC	SE	EM	FC	SE	FC	EM	FC	FC	SE	FC	FC	EM
				1		1		◇1	1		◇1	1		◇1	1		1	◇1	1			1		◇1
			A		A			B			C			B				C						B
								☕			☕			☕				☕						☕
Brighton 10		d		06 36		07 04			07 36			08 04					08 44					09 14		
Preston Park		d																						
Hassocks 4		d		06 45		07 13			07 45			08 13					08 53					09 23		
Burgess Hill 4		d		06 48		07 16			07 48			08 16					08 57					09 27		
Wivelsfield 4		d																						
Haywards Heath 3		d		06 54		07 24			07 54			08 24					09 03					09 33		
Balcombe		d																						
Three Bridges 4		d		07 02		07 32			08 02			08 32					09 12					09 42		
Gatwick Airport 10	✈	d		07 08		07 38			08 08			08 38			08 59		09 17		09 29			09 47		
Redhill		d																						
East Croydon	🚋	d		07 27		07 57			08 27			08 56			09 17		09 33		09 47			10 03		
Sevenoaks 4	195	d					07 32			08 02			08 32			09 02					09 32			
Bat & Ball	195	d					07 35			08 05			08 35			09 05					09 35			
Otford 4	195	d					07 38			08 08			08 38			09 08					09 38			
Shoreham (Kent)	195	d					07 41			08 11			08 41			09 11					09 41			
Eynsford	195	d					07 45			08 15			08 45			09 15					09 45			
Swanley 4	195	d					07 50			08 20			08 50			09 20					09 50			
St Mary Cray 4	195	d					07 54			08 24			08 54			09 24					09 54			
Bickley	195	d	06 58		07 28		07 58			08 28			08 58			09 28					09 58			
Bromley South	195	d	07 01		07 31		08 01			08 31			09 01			09 31					10 01			
Shortlands 4	195	d	07 04		07 34		08 04			08 34			09 04			09 34					10 04			
Ravensbourne	195	d	07 06		07 36		08 06			08 36			09 06			09 36					10 06			
Beckenham Hill	195	d	07 08		07 38		08 08			08 38			09 08			09 38					10 08			
Bellingham	195	d	07 10		07 40		08 10			08 40			09 10			09 40					10 10			
Catford	195	d	07 13		07 43		08 13			08 43			09 13			09 43					10 13			
Crofton Park	195	d	07 15		07 45		08 15			08 45			09 15			09 45					10 15			
Nunhead 4	195	d	07 18		07 48		08 18			08 48			09 18			09 48					10 18			
Peckham Rye 4	195	d	07 20		07 50		08 20			08 50			09 20			09 50					10 20			
Denmark Hill 4	195	d	07 24		07 54		08 24			08 54			09 24			09 54					10 24			
Sutton (Surrey) 4	179	d																		09 37			10 08	
West Sutton	179	d																		09 40				
Sutton Common	179	d																		09 42				
St Helier	179	d																		09 45				
Morden South	179	d																		09 47				
South Merton	179	d																		09 49				
Wimbledon Chase	179	d																		09 51				
Wimbledon 5	⊖173,179 🚋	d																		09 56				
Haydons Road	173	d																		09 58				
Tooting	173	d																		10 01				
Carshalton	173	d																					10 11	
Hackbridge	173	d																					10 13	
Mitcham Junction	173 🚋	d																					10 16	
Mitcham Eastfields	173	d																					10 19	
Streatham 4		d																		10 06			10 23	
Tulse Hill 3		d																		10 10			10 27	
London Bridge 4	⊖	a																						
		d																						
Herne Hill 4	173,179	d																		10 14			10 31	
Loughborough Jn.	173,179	d																		10 17			10 34	
Elephant & Castle	173,179	d	07 30	07 50	08 00	08 20	08 30		08 50	09 00		09 20	09 30		09 45	10 00	10 01		10 15	10 22	10 30	10 31	10 39	
London Blackfriars 3	⊖	d	07a34	07 54	08a04	08 24	08a34		08 54	09a04		09 24	09a34		09 54	10a04	10 08		10 22	10 26	10a34	10 38	10a43	
City Thameslink 3		d																						
Farringdon 3	⊖	d		08 00		08 30			09 00			09 30			10 00		10 14		10 28	10 32		10 44		
St Pancras International 15	⊖	a		08 04		08 34			09 04			09 34			10 04		10 18		10 32	10 36		10 48		
		d		08 04		08 34		09 00	09 04		09 30	09 34		10 00	10 04		10 18	10 30	10 32	10 36		10 48		11 00
Kentish Town	⊖	d		08 08		08 38			09 08			09 38			10 08					10 40				
West Hampstead Thameslink	⊖	d		08 12		08 42			09 12			09 42			10 12		10 26		10 40	10 44		10 56		
Cricklewood		d		08 15		08 45			09 15			09 45			10 15					10 47				
Hendon		d		08 18		08 48			09 18			09 48			10 18					10 50				
Mill Hill Broadway		d		08 22		08 52			09 22			09 52			10 22					10 54				
Elstree & Borehamwood		d		08 26		08 56			09 26			09 56			10 26					10 58				
Radlett		d		08 31		09 01			09 31			10 01			10 31					11 02				
St Albans City		d		08 38		09 08			09 38			10 08			10 38		10 43		10 57	11 09		11 13		
Harpenden		d		08 44		09 14			09 44			10 14			10 44		10 49		11 03	11 15		11 19		
Luton Airport Parkway 7	✈	d		08 50		09 20		09 28	09 50			10 20		10 29	10 50		10 55		11 09	11 20		11 25		11 29
Luton 10		d		08 53		09 23			09 53		09 59	10 23			10 53		10 58	11 02	11 12	11a24		11 28		11 33
Leagrave		d		08 57		09 27			09 57			10 27			10 57		11 02		11 16			11 32		
Harlington		d		09 02		09 32			10 02			10 32			11 02		11 07		11 21			11 37		
Flitwick		d		09 06		09 36			10 06			10 36			11 06		11 11		11 25			11 41		
Bedford 7		a		09 19		09 49		09 50	10 19		10 18	10 49		10 50	11 19		11 24	11 24	11 38			11 54		11 54

A From Orpington
B To Nottingham
C To Sheffield

The trains that operate to and from Sevenoaks, Orpington and Rochester (and a few other destinations at peak times) are operated jointly by First Capital Connect (north of Blackfriars) and Southeastern (south of Blackfriars)

Table 52 shows the complete service between Bedford and London, whilst services between London, Sevenoaks, Sutton and Brighton only show through Thameslink services. Other Tables should be consulted for additional journey opportunities.

Table 52R

Sundays

16 February to 23 March

Brighton, Gatwick Airport and South London - City of London, St Albans, Luton and Bedford

Network Diagram - refer to first Page of Table 52

	FC [1]	FC	SE	FC [1]	FC	EM ◇[1] A ☕	FC [1]	FC	SE	FC [1]	FC	FC [1]	FC	SE	EM ◇[1] B ☕	FC [1]	FC	EM ◇[1] A ☕	FC [1]	FC	SE	FC [1]
Brighton [10] d				09 44						10 14						10 44						11 14
Preston Park d																						
Hassocks [4] d				09 53						10 23						10 53						11 23
Burgess Hill [4] d				09 57						10 27						10 57						11 27
Wivelsfield [4] d																						
Haywards Heath [3] d				10 03						10 33						11 03						11 33
Balcombe d																						
Three Bridges [4] d				10 12			10 24			10 42		10 54				11 12			11 24			11 42
Gatwick Airport [10] ✈ d	09 59			10 17			10 29			10 47		10 59				11 17			11 29			11 47
Redhill d																						
East Croydon 🚋 d	10 17			10 33			10 47			11 03		11 17				11 33			11 47			12 03
Sevenoaks [4] 195 d			10 02						10 32					11 02							11 32	
Bat & Ball 195 d			10 05						10 35					11 05							11 35	
Otford [4] 195 d			10 08						10 38					11 08							11 38	
Shoreham (Kent) 195 d			10 11						10 41					11 11							11 41	
Eynsford 195 d			10 15						10 45					11 15							11 45	
Swanley [4] 195 d			10 20						10 50					11 20							11 50	
St Mary Cray [4] 195 d			10 24						10 54					11 24							11 54	
Bickley 195 d			10 28						10 58					11 28							11 58	
Bromley South 195 d			10 31						11 01					11 31							12 01	
Shortlands [4] 195 d			10 34						11 04					11 34							12 04	
Ravensbourne 195 d			10 36						11 06					11 36							12 06	
Beckenham Hill 195 d			10 38						11 08					11 38							12 08	
Bellingham 195 d			10 40						11 10					11 40							12 10	
Catford 195 d			10 43						11 13					11 43							12 13	
Crofton Park 195 d			10 45						11 15					11 45							12 15	
Nunhead [4] 195 d			10 48						11 18					11 48							12 18	
Peckham Rye [4] 195 d			10 50						11 20					11 50							12 20	
Denmark Hill [4] 195 d			10 54						11 24					11 54							12 24	
Sutton (Surrey) [4] 179 d		10 07			10 38			10 37			11 08		11 07				11 38			11 37		
West Sutton 179 d		10 10						10 40					11 10							11 40		
Sutton Common 179 d		10 12						10 42					11 12							11 42		
St Helier 179 d		10 15						10 45					11 15							11 45		
Morden South 179 d		10 17						10 47					11 17							11 47		
South Merton 179 d		10 19						10 49					11 19							11 49		
Wimbledon Chase 179 d		10 21						10 51					11 21							11 51		
Wimbledon [6] ⊖173,179 🚋 d		10 26						10 56					11 26							11 56		
Haydons Road 173 d		10 28						10 58					11 28							11 58		
Tooting 173 d		10 31						11 01					11 31							12 01		
Carshalton 173 d					10 41						11 11						11 41					
Hackbridge 173 d					10 43						11 13						11 43					
Mitcham Junction 173 🚋 d					10 46						11 16						11 46					
Mitcham Eastfields 173 d					10 49						11 19						11 49					
Streatham [4] d		10 36			10 53			11 06			11 23		11 36				11 53			12 06		
Tulse Hill [3] d		10 40			10 57			11 10			11 27		11 40				11 57			12 10		
London Bridge [4] ⊖ a																						
d																						
Herne Hill [4] 173,179 d		10 44			11 01			11 14			11 31		11 44				12 01			12 14		
Loughborough Jn 173,179 d		10 47			11 04			11 17			11 34		11 47				12 04			12 17		
Elephant & Castle 173,179 d	10 45	10 52	11 00	11 01	11 09		11 15	11 22	11 30	11 31	11 39	11 45	11 52	12 00		12 01	12 09		12 15	12 22	12 30	12 31
London Blackfriars [3] ⊖ d	10 52	10 56	11a04	11 08	11a13		11 22	11 26	11a34	11 38	11a43	11 52	11 56	12a04		12 08	12a13		12 22	12 26	12a34	12 38
City Thameslink [3] d																						
Farringdon [3] ⊖ d	10 58	11 02		11 14			11 28	11 32		11 44		11 58	12 02			12 14			12 28	12 32		12 44
St Pancras International [15] ⊖ a	11 02	11 06		11 18			11 32	11 36		11 48		12 02	12 06			12 18			12 32	12 36		12 48
d	11 02	11 06		11 18		11 30	11 32	11 36		11 48		12 02	12 06		12 10	12 18		12 30	12 32	12 36		12 48
Kentish Town ⊖ d		11 10						11 40					12 10							12 40		
West Hampstead Thameslink ⊖ d	11 10	11 14		11 26			11 40	11 44		11 56		12 10	12 14			12 26			12 40	12 44		12 56
Cricklewood d		11 17						11 47					12 17							12 47		
Hendon d		11 20						11 50					12 20							12 50		
Mill Hill Broadway d		11 24						11 54					12 24							12 54		
Elstree & Borehamwood d		11 28						11 58					12 28							12 58		
Radlett d		11 32						12 02					12 32							13 02		
St Albans City d	11 27	11 39		11 43			11 57	12 09		12 13		12 27	12 39			12 43			12 57	13 09		13 13
Harpenden d	11 33	11 45		11 49			12 03	12 15		12 19		12 33	12 45			12 49			13 03	13 15		13 19
Luton Airport Parkway [7] ✈ d	11 39	11 50		11 55		11 59	12 09	12 20		12 25		12 39	12 50		12 31	12 55		12 53	13 09	13 20		13 25
Luton [10] d	11 42	11a54		11 58		12 03	12 12	12a24		12 28		12 42	12a54		12 34	12 58		12 57	13 12	13a24		13 28
Leagrave d	11 46			12 02			12 16			12 32		12 46				13 02			13 16			13 32
Harlington d	11 51			12 07			12 21			12 37		12 51				13 07			13 21			13 37
Flitwick d	11 55			12 11			12 25			12 41		12 55				13 11			13 25			13 41
Bedford [7] a	12 08			12 24		12 22	12 38			12 54		13 08			12 49	13 24		13 12	13 38			13 54

A To Sheffield

B To Nottingham

The trains that operate to and from Sevenoaks, Orpington and Rochester (and a few other destinations at peak times) are operated jointly by First Capital Connect (north of Blackfriars) and Southeastern (south of Blackfriars)

Table 52 shows the complete service between Bedford and London, whilst services between London, Sevenoaks, Sutton and Brighton only show through Thameslink services. Other Tables should be consulted for additional journey opportunities.

Table 52R

Sundays

16 February to 23 March

Brighton, Gatwick Airport and South London - City of London, St Albans, Luton and Bedford

Network Diagram - refer to first Page of Table 52

		FC	FC	FC	SE		EM	FC	FC	FC	FC	SE	EM	FC	FC	FC		FC	SE	EM	FC	FC	FC	FC	SE
			1				◇1	1		1			◇1	1		1				◇1	1		1		
							A						B							A					
Brighton 10	d							11 44						12 14							12 44				
Preston Park	d																								
Hassocks 4	d							11 53						12 23							12 53				
Burgess Hill 4	d							11 57						12 27							12 57				
Wivelsfield 4	d																								
Haywards Heath 3	d							12 03						12 33							13 03				
Balcombe	d																								
Three Bridges 4	d		11 54					12 12		12 24				12 42		12 54					13 12		13 24		
Gatwick Airport 10 ✈	d		11 59					12 17		12 29				12 47		12 59					13 17		13 29		
Redhill	d																								
East Croydon	d		12 17					12 33		12 47				13 03		13 17					13 33		13 47		
Sevenoaks 4 195	d				12 02							12 32							13 02						13 32
Bat & Ball 195	d				12 05							12 35							13 05						13 35
Otford 4 195	d				12 08							12 38							13 08						13 38
Shoreham (Kent) 195	d				12 11							12 41							13 11						13 41
Eynsford 195	d				12 15							12 45							13 15						13 45
Swanley 4 195	d				12 20							12 50							13 20						13 50
St Mary Cray 4 195	d				12 24							12 54							13 24						13 54
Bickley 195	d				12 28							12 58							13 28						13 58
Bromley South 195	d				12 31							13 01							13 31						14 01
Shortlands 4 195	d				12 34							13 04							13 34						14 04
Ravensbourne 195	d				12 36							13 06							13 36						14 06
Beckenham Hill 195	d				12 38							13 08							13 38						14 08
Bellingham 195	d				12 40							13 10							13 40						14 10
Catford 195	d				12 43							13 13							13 43						14 13
Crofton Park 195	d				12 45							13 15							13 45						14 15
Nunhead 4 195	d				12 48							13 18							13 48						14 18
Peckham Rye 4 195	d				12 50							13 20							13 50						14 20
Denmark Hill 4 195	d				12 54							13 24							13 54						14 24
Sutton (Surrey) 4 179	d	12 08		12 07					12 38		12 37				13 08			13 07				13 38		13 37	
West Sutton 179	d			12 10							12 40							13 10						13 40	
Sutton Common 179	d			12 12							12 42							13 12						13 42	
St Helier 179	d			12 15							12 45							13 15						13 45	
Morden South 179	d			12 17							12 47							13 17						13 47	
South Merton 179	d			12 19							12 49							13 19						13 49	
Wimbledon Chase 179	d			12 21							12 51							13 21						13 51	
Wimbledon 6 ⊖173,179	d			12 26							12 56							13 26						13 56	
Haydons Road 173	d			12 28							12 58							13 28						13 58	
Tooting 173	d			12 31							13 01							13 31						14 01	
Carshalton 173	d	12 11							12 41						13 11							13 41			
Hackbridge 173	d	12 13							12 43						13 13							13 43			
Mitcham Junction 173	d	12 16							12 46						13 16							13 46			
Mitcham Eastfields 173	d	12 19							12 49						13 19							13 49			
Streatham 4	d	12 23		12 36					12 53		13 06				13 23			13 36				13 53		14 06	
Tulse Hill 3	d	12 27		12 40					12 57		13 10				13 27			13 40				13 57		14 10	
London Bridge 4 ⊖	a																								
	d																								
Herne Hill 4 173,179	d	12 31		12 44					13 01		13 14				13 31			13 44				14 01		14 14	
Loughborough Jn. 173,179	d	12 34		12 47					13 04		13 17				13 34			13 47				14 04		14 17	
Elephant & Castle 173,179	d	12 39	12 45	12 52	13 00			13 01	13 09	13 15	13 22	13 30		13 31	13 39	13 45		13 52	14 00		14 01	14 09	14 15	14 22	14 30
London Blackfriars 3 ⊖	d	12a43	12 52	12 56	13a04			13 08	13a13	13 22	13 26	13a34		13 38	13a43	13 52		13 56	14a04		14 08	14a13	14 22	14 26	14a34
City Thameslink 3	d																								
Farringdon 3 ⊖	d		12 58	13 02				13 14		13 28	13 32			13 44		13 58		14 02			14 14		14 28	14 32	
St Pancras International 15 ⊖	a		13 02	13 06				13 18		13 32	13 36			13 48		14 02		14 06			14 18		14 32	14 36	
	d		13 02	13 06			13 10	13 18		13 32	13 36		13 40	13 48		14 02		14 06		14 10	14 18		14 32	14 36	
Kentish Town ⊖	d			13 10							13 40							14 10						14 40	
West Hampstead Thameslink ⊖	d		13 10	13 14				13 26		13 40	13 44			13 56		14 10		14 14			14 26		14 40	14 44	
Cricklewood	d			13 17							13 47							14 17						14 47	
Hendon	d			13 20							13 50							14 20						14 50	
Mill Hill Broadway	d			13 24							13 54							14 24						14 54	
Elstree & Borehamwood	d			13 28							13 58							14 28						14 58	
Radlett	d			13 32							14 02							14 32						15 02	
St Albans City	d		13 27	13 39				13 43		13 57	14 09			14 13		14 27		14 39			14 43		14 57	15 09	
Harpenden	d		13 33	13 45				13 49		14 03	14 15			14 19		14 33		14 45			14 49		15 03	15 15	
Luton Airport Parkway 7 ✈	d		13 39	13 50			13 31	13 55		14 09	14 20		14 02	14 25		14 39		14 50		14 31	14 55		15 09	15 20	
Luton 10	d		13 42	13a54			13 34	13 58		14 12	14a24		14 07	14 28		14 42		14a54			14 58		15 12	15a24	
Leagrave	d		13 46					14 02		14 16				14 32		14 46					15 02		15 16		
Harlington	d		13 51					14 07		14 21				14 37		14 51					15 07		15 21		
Flitwick	d		13 55					14 11		14 25				14 41		14 55					15 11		15 25		
Bedford 7	a		14 08				13 49	14 24		14 38			14 21	14 54		15 08				14 46	15 24		15 38		

A To Nottingham **B** To Sheffield

The trains that operate to and from Sevenoaks, Orpington and Rochester (and a few other destinations at peak times) are operated jointly by First Capital Connect (north of Blackfriars) and Southeastern (south of Blackfriars)

Table 52 shows the complete service between Bedford and London, whilst services between London, Sevenoaks, Sutton and Brighton only show through Thameslink services. Other Tables should be consulted for additional journey opportunities.

Table 52R

Sundays

16 February to 23 March

Brighton, Gatwick Airport and South London - City of London, St Albans, Luton and Bedford

Network Diagram - refer to first Page of Table 52

		EM	FC	FC	FC	FC	SE	EM	FC	FC	FC	FC	SE	EM	FC	FC	FC	FC	SE	EM	FC	FC	FC
		◇1	1		1			◇1	1		1			◇1	1		1			◇1	1		1
		A						B						C						B			
Brighton 10	d		13 14						13 44						14 14						14 44		
Preston Park	d																						
Hassocks 4	d		13 23						13 53						14 23						14 53		
Burgess Hill 4	d		13 27						13 57						14 27						14 57		
Wivelsfield 4	d																						
Haywards Heath 3	d		13 33						14 03						14 33						15 03		
Balcombe	d																						
Three Bridges 4	d		13 42		13 54				14 12		14 24				14 42		14 54				15 12		15 24
Gatwick Airport 10 ✈	d		13 47		13 59				14 17		14 29				14 47		14 59				15 17		15 29
Redhill	d																						
East Croydon	d		14 03		14 17				14 33		14 47				15 03		15 17				15 33		15 47
Sevenoaks 4 195	d						14 02						14 32						15 02				
Bat & Ball 195	d						14 05						14 35						15 05				
Otford 4 195	d						14 08						14 38						15 08				
Shoreham (Kent) 195	d						14 11						14 41						15 11				
Eynsford 195	d						14 15						14 45						15 15				
Swanley 4 195	d						14 20						14 50						15 20				
St Mary Cray 4 195	d						14 24						14 54						15 24				
Bickley 195	d						14 28						14 58						15 28				
Bromley South 195	d						14 31						15 01						15 31				
Shortlands 4 195	d						14 34						15 04						15 34				
Ravensbourne 195	d						14 36						15 06						15 36				
Beckenham Hill 195	d						14 38						15 08						15 38				
Bellingham 195	d						14 40						15 10						15 40				
Catford 195	d						14 43						15 13						15 43				
Crofton Park 195	d						14 45						15 15						15 45				
Nunhead 4 195	d						14 48						15 18						15 48				
Peckham Rye 4 195	d						14 50						15 20						15 50				
Denmark Hill 4 195	d						14 54						15 24						15 54				
Sutton (Surrey) 4 179	d			14 08		14 07				14 38		14 37				15 08		15 07				15 38	
West Sutton 179	d					14 10						14 40						15 10					
Sutton Common 179	d					14 12						14 42						15 12					
St Helier 179	d					14 15						14 45						15 15					
Morden South 179	d					14 17						14 47						15 17					
South Merton 179	d					14 19						14 49						15 19					
Wimbledon Chase 179	d					14 21						14 51						15 21					
Wimbledon 6 ⊖173,179	d					14 26						14 56						15 26					
Haydons Road 173	d					14 28						14 58						15 28					
Tooting 173	d					14 31						15 01						15 31					
Carshalton 173	d			14 11						14 41						15 11						15 41	
Hackbridge 173	d			14 13						14 43						15 13						15 43	
Mitcham Junction 173	d			14 16						14 46						15 16						15 46	
Mitcham Eastfields 173	d			14 19						14 49						15 19						15 49	
Streatham 4	d			14 23		14 36				14 53		15 06				15 23		15 36				15 53	
Tulse Hill 3	d			14 27		14 40				14 57		15 10				15 27		15 40				15 57	
London Bridge 4 ⊖	a																						
	d																						
Herne Hill 4 173,179	d			14 31		14 44				15 01		15 14				15 31		15 44				16 01	
Loughborough Jn. 173,179	d			14 34		14 47				15 04		15 17				15 34		15 47				16 04	
Elephant & Castle 173,179	d		14 31	14 39	14 45	14 52	15 00		15 01	15 09	15 15	15 22	15 30		15 31	15 39	15 45	15 52	16 00		16 01	16 09	16 15
London Blackfriars 3 ⊖	d		14 38	14a43	14 52	14 56	15a04		15 08	15a13	15 22	15 26	15a34		15 38	15a43	15 52	15 56	16a04		16 08	16a13	16 22
City Thameslink 3	d																						
Farringdon 3 ⊖	d		14 44		14 58	15 02			15 14		15 28	15 32			15 44		15 58	16 02			16 14		16 28
St Pancras International 15 ⊖	a		14 48		15 02	15 06			15 18		15 32	15 36			15 48		16 02	16 06			16 18		16 32
	d	14 40	14 48		15 02	15 06		15 10	15 18		15 32	15 36		15 40	15 48		16 02	16 06		16 10	16 18		16 32
Kentish Town ⊖	d					15 10						15 40						16 10					
West Hampstead Thameslink ⊖	d		14 56		15 10	15 14			15 26		15 40	15 44			15 56		16 10	16 14			16 26		16 40
Cricklewood	d					15 17						15 47						16 17					
Hendon	d					15 20						15 50						16 20					
Mill Hill Broadway	d					15 24						15 54						16 24					
Elstree & Borehamwood	d					15 28						15 58						16 28					
Radlett	d					15 32						16 02						16 32					
St Albans City	d		15 13		15 27	15 39			15 43		15 57	16 09			16 13		16 27	16 39			16 43		16 57
Harpenden	d		15 19		15 33	15 45			15 49		16 03	16 15			16 19		16 33	16 45			16 49		17 03
Luton Airport Parkway 7 ✈	d		15 25		15 39	15 50		15 33	15 55		16 09	16 20			16 25		16 39	16 50		16 31	16 55		17 09
Luton 10	d	15 04	15 28		15 42	15a54			15 58		16 12	16a24		16 04	16 28		16 42	16a54			16 58		17 12
Leagrave	d		15 32		15 46				16 02		16 16				16 32		16 46				17 02		17 16
Harlington	d		15 37		15 51				16 07		16 21				16 37		16 51				17 07		17 21
Flitwick	d		15 41		15 55				16 11		16 25				16 41		16 55				17 11		17 25
Bedford 7	a	15 19	15 54		16 08			15 48	16 24		16 38			16 19	16 54		17 08			16 46	17 24		17 38

A To Leeds
B To Nottingham
C To Sheffield

The trains that operate to and from Sevenoaks, Orpington and Rochester (and a few other destinations at peak times) are operated jointly by First Capital Connect (north of Blackfriars) and Southeastern (south of Blackfriars)

Table 52 shows the complete service between Bedford and London, whilst services between London, Sevenoaks, Sutton and Brighton only show through Thameslink services. Other Tables should be consulted for additional journey opportunities.

Table 52R

Sundays

16 February to 23 March

Brighton, Gatwick Airport and South London - City of London, St Albans, Luton and Bedford

Network Diagram - refer to first Page of Table 52

	FC	SE	EM	FC	FC	FC	FC	SE	EM	FC	FC	FC	FC	SE	EM	FC	FC	FC	FC	SE	EM
			◇[1]	[1]		[1]			◇[1]	[1]		[1]			◇[1]	[1]		[1]			◇[1]
			A						B						A						B
			☕						☕						☕						☕
Brighton [10] d				15 14						15 44						16 14					
Preston Park d																					
Hassocks [4] d				15 23						15 53						16 23					
Burgess Hill [4] d				15 27						15 57						16 27					
Wivelsfield [4] d																					
Haywards Heath [3] d				15 33						16 03						16 33					
Balcombe d																					
Three Bridges [4] d				15 42		15 54				16 12		16 24				16 42		16 54			
Gatwick Airport [10] ✈ d				15 47		15 59				16 17		16 29				16 47		16 59			
Redhill d																					
East Croydon 🚌 d				16 03		16 17				16 33		16 47				17 03		17 17			
Sevenoaks [4] 195 d		15 32						16 02						16 32						17 02	
Bat & Ball 195 d		15 35						16 05						16 35						17 05	
Otford [4] 195 d		15 38						16 08						16 38						17 08	
Shoreham (Kent) 195 d		15 41						16 11						16 41						17 11	
Eynsford 195 d		15 45						16 15						16 45						17 15	
Swanley [4] 195 d		15 50						16 20						16 50						17 20	
St Mary Cray [4] 195 d		15 54						16 24						16 54						17 24	
Bickley 195 d		15 58						16 28						16 58						17 28	
Bromley South 195 d		16 01						16 31						17 01						17 31	
Shortlands [4] 195 d		16 04						16 34						17 04						17 34	
Ravensbourne 195 d		16 06						16 36						17 06						17 36	
Beckenham Hill 195 d		16 08						16 38						17 08						17 38	
Bellingham 195 d		16 10						16 40						17 10						17 40	
Catford 195 d		16 13						16 43						17 13						17 43	
Crofton Park 195 d		16 15						16 45						17 15						17 45	
Nunhead [4] 195 d		16 18						16 48						17 18						17 48	
Peckham Rye [4] 195 d		16 20						16 50						17 20						17 50	
Denmark Hill [4] 195 d		16 24						16 54						17 24						17 54	
Sutton (Surrey) [4] 179 d	15 37				16 08		16 07				16 38		16 37				17 08		17 07		
West Sutton 179 d	15 40						16 10						16 40						17 10		
Sutton Common 179 d	15 42						16 12						16 42						17 12		
St Helier 179 d	15 45						16 15						16 45						17 15		
Morden South 179 d	15 47						16 17						16 47						17 17		
South Merton 179 d	15 49						16 19						16 49						17 19		
Wimbledon Chase 179 d	15 51						16 21						16 51						17 21		
Wimbledon [6] ⊖173,179 🚌 d	15 56						16 26						16 56						17 26		
Haydons Road 173 d	15 58						16 28						16 58						17 28		
Tooting 173 d	16 01						16 31						17 01						17 31		
Carshalton 173 d					16 11						16 41						17 11				
Hackbridge 173 d					16 13						16 43						17 13				
Mitcham Junction 173 🚌 d					16 16						16 46						17 16				
Mitcham Eastfields 173 d					16 19						16 49						17 19				
Streatham [4] d	16 06				16 23		16 36				16 53		17 06				17 23		17 36		
Tulse Hill [3] d	16 10				16 27		16 40				16 57		17 10				17 27		17 40		
London Bridge [4] ⊖ a																					
d																					
Herne Hill [4] 173,179 d	16 14				16 31		16 44				17 01		17 14				17 31		17 44		
Loughborough Jn. 173,179 d	16 17				16 34		16 47				17 04		17 17				17 34		17 47		
Elephant & Castle 173,179 d	16 22	16 30		16 31	16 39	16 45	16 52	17 00		17 01	17 09	17 15	17 22	17 30		17 31	17 39	17 45	17 52	18 00	
London Blackfriars [3] ⊖ d	16 26	16a34		16 38	16a43	16 52	16 56	17a04		17 08	17a13	17 22	17 26	17a34		17 38	17a43	17 52	17 56	18a04	
City Thameslink [3] d																					
Farringdon [3] ⊖ d	16 32			16 44		16 58	17 02			17 14		17 28	17 32			17 44		17 58	18 02		
St Pancras International [15] ⊖ a	16 36			16 48		17 02	17 06			17 18		17 32	17 36			17 48		18 02	18 06		
d	16 36		16 40	16 48		17 02	17 06		17 10	17 18		17 32	17 36		17 40	17 48		18 02	18 06		18 10
Kentish Town ⊖ d	16 40						17 10						17 40						18 10		
West Hampstead Thameslink ⊖ d	16 44			16 56		17 10	17 14			17 26		17 40	17 44			17 56		18 10	18 14		
Cricklewood d	16 47						17 17						17 47						18 17		
Hendon d	16 50						17 20						17 50						18 20		
Mill Hill Broadway d	16 54						17 24						17 54						18 24		
Elstree & Borehamwood d	16 58						17 28						17 58						18 28		
Radlett d	17 02						17 32						18 02						18 32		
St Albans City d	17 09			17 13		17 27	17 39			17 43		17 57	18 09			18 13		18 27	18 39		
Harpenden d	17 15			17 19		17 33	17 45			17 49		18 03	18 15			18 19		18 33	18 45		
Luton Airport Parkway [7] ✈ d	17 20			17 25		17 39	17 50		17 31	17 55		18 09	18 20			18 25		18 39	18 50		18 31
Luton [10] d	17a24		17 02	17 28		17 42	17a54			17 58		18 12	18a24		18 02	18 28		18 42	18a54		
Leagrave d				17 32		17 46				18 02		18 16				18 32		18 46			
Harlington d				17 37		17 51				18 07		18 21				18 37		18 51			
Flitwick d				17 41		17 55				18 11		18 25				18 41		18 55			
Bedford [7] a			17 16	17 54		18 08			17 46	18 24		18 38			18 16	18 54		19 08			18 46

A To Derby **B** To Nottingham

The trains that operate to and from Sevenoaks, Orpington and Rochester (and a few other destinations at peak times) are operated jointly by First Capital Connect (north of Blackfriars) and Southeastern (south of Blackfriars)

Table 52 shows the complete service between Bedford and London, whilst services between London, Sevenoaks, Sutton and Brighton only show through Thameslink services. Other Tables should be consulted for additional journey opportunities.

Table 52R

Sundays

16 February to 23 March

Brighton, Gatwick Airport and South London - City of London, St Albans, Luton and Bedford

Network Diagram - refer to first Page of Table 52

		FC	FC	FC	FC	SE	EM	FC	FC	FC		FC	SE	EM	FC	FC	FC	FC	SE	EM	FC		FC	FC	FC
		1		1			◇1	1		1				◇1	1		1			◇1	1			1	
							A							B						A					
Brighton	d	16 44						17 14							17 44						18 14				
Preston Park	d																								
Hassocks	d	16 53						17 23							17 53						18 23				
Burgess Hill	d	16 57						17 27							17 57						18 27				
Wivelsfield	d																								
Haywards Heath	d	17 03						17 33							18 03						18 33				
Balcombe	d																								
Three Bridges	d	17 12		17 24				17 42		17 54					18 12		18 24				18 42			18 54	
Gatwick Airport	d	17 17		17 29				17 47		17 59					18 17		18 29				18 47			18 59	
Redhill	d																								
East Croydon	d	17 33		17 47				18 03		18 17					18 33		18 47				19 03			19 17	
Sevenoaks 195	d					17 32							18 02						18 32						
Bat & Ball 195	d					17 35							18 05						18 35						
Otford 195	d					17 38							18 08						18 38						
Shoreham (Kent) 195	d					17 41							18 11						18 41						
Eynsford 195	d					17 45							18 15						18 45						
Swanley 195	d					17 50							18 20						18 50						
St Mary Cray 195	d					17 54							18 24						18 54						
Bickley 195	d					17 58							18 28						18 58						
Bromley South 195	d					18 01							18 31						19 01						
Shortlands 195	d					18 04							18 34						19 04						
Ravensbourne 195	d					18 06							18 36						19 06						
Beckenham Hill 195	d					18 08							18 38						19 08						
Bellingham 195	d					18 10							18 40						19 10						
Catford 195	d					18 13							18 43						19 13						
Crofton Park 195	d					18 15							18 45						19 15						
Nunhead 195	d					18 18							18 48						19 18						
Peckham Rye 195	d					18 20							18 50						19 20						
Denmark Hill 195	d					18 24							18 54						19 24						
Sutton (Surrey) 179	d		17 38		17 37				18 08			18 07				18 38		18 37					19 08		19 07
West Sutton 179	d				17 40							18 10						18 40							19 10
Sutton Common 179	d				17 42							18 12						18 42							19 12
St Helier 179	d				17 45							18 15						18 45							19 15
Morden South 179	d				17 47							18 17						18 47							19 17
South Merton 179	d				17 49							18 19						18 49							19 19
Wimbledon Chase 179	d				17 51							18 21						18 51							19 21
Wimbledon 173,179	d				17 56							18 26						18 56							19 26
Haydons Road 173	d				17 58							18 28						18 58							19 28
Tooting 173	d				18 01							18 31						19 01							19 31
Carshalton 173	d		17 41						18 11							18 41							19 11		
Hackbridge 173	d		17 43						18 13							18 43							19 13		
Mitcham Junction 173	d		17 46						18 16							18 46							19 16		
Mitcham Eastfields 173	d		17 49						18 19							18 49							19 19		
Streatham	d		17 53		18 06				18 23			18 36				18 53		19 06					19 23		19 36
Tulse Hill	d		17 57		18 10				18 27			18 40				18 57		19 10					19 27		19 40
London Bridge	a																								
	d																								
Herne Hill 173,179	d		18 01		18 14				18 31			18 44				19 01		19 14					19 31		19 44
Loughborough Jn. 173,179	d		18 04		18 17				18 34			18 47				19 04		19 17					19 34		19 47
Elephant & Castle 173,179	d	18 01	18 09	18 15	18 22	18 30		18 31	18 39	18 45		18 52	19 00		19 01	19 09	19 15	19 22	19 30		19 31		19 39	19 45	19 52
London Blackfriars	d	18 08	18a13	18 22	18 26	18a34		18 38	18a43	18 52		18 56	19a04		19 08	19a13	19 22	19 26	19a34		19 38		19a43	19 52	19 56
City Thameslink	d																								
Farringdon	d	18 14		18 28	18 32			18 44		18 58		19 02			19 14		19 28	19 32			19 44			19 58	20 02
St Pancras International	a	18 18		18 32	18 36			18 48		19 02		19 06			19 18		19 32	19 36			19 48			20 02	20 06
	d	18 18		18 32	18 36		18 40	18 48		19 02		19 06		19 10	19 18		19 32	19 36		19 40	19 48			20 02	20 06
Kentish Town	d				18 40							19 10						19 40							20 10
West Hampstead Thameslink	d	18 26		18 40	18 44			18 56		19 10		19 14			19 26		19 40	19 44			19 56			20 10	20 14
Cricklewood	d				18 47							19 17						19 47							20 17
Hendon	d				18 50							19 20						19 50							20 20
Mill Hill Broadway	d				18 54							19 24						19 54							20 24
Elstree & Borehamwood	d				18 58							19 28						19 58							20 28
Radlett	d				19 02							19 32						20 02							20 32
St Albans City	d	18 43		18 57	19 09			19 13		19 27		19 39			19 43		19 57	20 09			20 13			20 27	20 39
Harpenden	d	18 49		19 03	19 15			19 19		19 33		19 45			19 49		20 03	20 15			20 19			20 33	20 45
Luton Airport Parkway	d	18 55		19 09	19 20			19 25		19 39		19 50		19 31	19 55		20 09	20 20			20 25			20 39	20 50
Luton	d	18 58		19 12	19a24		19 02	19 28		19 42		19a54			19 58		20 12	20 24		20 02	20 28			20 42	20 54
Leagrave	d	19 02		19 16				19 32		19 46					20 02		20 16				20 32			20 46	
Harlington	d	19 07		19 21				19 37		19 51					20 07		20 21				20 37			20 51	
Flitwick	d	19 11		19 25				19 41		19 55					20 11		20 25				20 41			20 55	
Bedford	a	19 24		19 38			19 16	19 54		20 08				19 46	20 24		20 38	20 46		20 16	20 54			21 08	21 16

A To Derby

B To Nottingham

The trains that operate to and from Sevenoaks, Orpington and Rochester (and a few other destinations at peak times) are operated jointly by First Capital Connect (north of Blackfriars) and Southeastern (south of Blackfriars)

Table 52 shows the complete service between Bedford and London, whilst services between London, Sevenoaks, Sutton and Brighton only show through Thameslink services. Other Tables should be consulted for additional journey opportunities.

Table 52R

Sundays

16 February to 23 March

Brighton, Gatwick Airport and South London - City of London, St Albans, Luton and Bedford

Network Diagram - refer to first Page of Table 52

		SE	EM	FC	FC	FC	FC	SE	EM	FC	FC	FC	FC	SE	EM	FC	FC	EM	FC	SE	FC	FC	FC
			◇1	1		1			◇1	1		1			◇1	1		◇1			1		
			A						B						A			C					
			🍴						🍴						🍴			🍴					
Brighton 10	d			18 44						19 14						19 44					20 14		
Preston Park	d																						
Hassocks 4	d			18 53						19 23						19 53					20 23		
Burgess Hill 4	d			18 57						19 27						19 57					20 27		
Wivelsfield 4	d																						
Haywards Heath 3	d			19 03						19 33						20 03					20 33		
Balcombe	d																						
Three Bridges 4	d			19 12		19 24				19 42		19 54				20 12					20 42		
Gatwick Airport 10 ✈	d			19 17		19 29				19 47		19 59				20 17					20 47		
Redhill	d																						
East Croydon	d			19 33		19 47				20 03		20 17				20 33					21 03		
Sevenoaks 4	195 d	19 02						19 32						20 02						20 32			
Bat & Ball	195 d	19 05						19 35						20 05						20 35			
Otford 4	195 d	19 08						19 38						20 08						20 38			
Shoreham (Kent)	195 d	19 11						19 41						20 11						20 41			
Eynsford	195 d	19 15						19 45						20 15						20 45			
Swanley 4	195 d	19 20						19 50						20 20						20 50			
St Mary Cray 4	195 d	19 24						19 54						20 24						20 54			
Bickley	195 d	19 28						19 58						20 28						20 58			
Bromley South	195 d	19 31						20 01						20 31						21 01			
Shortlands 4	195 d	19 34						20 04						20 34						21 04			
Ravensbourne	195 d	19 36						20 06						20 36						21 06			
Beckenham Hill	195 d	19 38						20 08						20 38						21 08			
Bellingham	195 d	19 40						20 10						20 40						21 10			
Catford	195 d	19 43						20 13						20 43						21 13			
Crofton Park	195 d	19 45						20 15						20 45						21 15			
Nunhead 4	195 d	19 48						20 18						20 48						21 18			
Peckham Rye 4	195 d	19 50						20 20						20 50						21 20			
Denmark Hill 4	195 d	19 54						20 24						20 54						21 24			
Sutton (Surrey) 4	179 d				19 38		19 37				20 08		20 07				20 38		20 37			21 08	21 07
West Sutton	179 d						19 40						20 10						20 40				21 10
Sutton Common	179 d						19 42						20 12						20 42				21 12
St Helier	179 d						19 45						20 15						20 45				21 15
Morden South	179 d						19 47						20 17						20 47				21 17
South Merton	179 d						19 49						20 19						20 49				21 19
Wimbledon Chase	179 d						19 51						20 21						20 51				21 21
Wimbledon 6 ⊖173,179	d						19 56						20 26						20 56				21 26
Haydons Road	173 d						19 58						20 28						20 58				21 28
Tooting	173 d						20 01						20 31						21 01				21 31
Carshalton	173 d				19 41						20 11						20 41					21 11	
Hackbridge	173 d				19 43						20 13						20 43					21 13	
Mitcham Junction	173 d				19 46						20 16						20 46					21 16	
Mitcham Eastfields	173 d				19 49						20 19						20 49					21 19	
Streatham 4	d				19 53		20 06				20 23		20 36				20 53		21 06			21 23	21 36
Tulse Hill 3	d				19 57		20 10				20 27		20 40				20 57		21 10			21 27	21 40
London Bridge 4 ⊖	a																						
	d																						
Herne Hill 4	173,179 d				20 01		20 14				20 31		20 44				21 01		21 14			21 31	21 44
Loughborough Jn.	173,179 d				20 04		20 17				20 34		20 47				21 04		21 17			21 34	21 47
Elephant & Castle	173,179 d	20 00		20 01	20 09	20 15	20 22	20 30		20 31	20 39	20 45	20 52	21 00		21 01	21 09		21 22	21 30	21 31	21 39	21 52
London Blackfriars 3 ⊖	d	20a04		20 08	20a13	20 22	20 26	20a34		20 38	20a43	20 52	20 56	21a04		21 08	21a13		21 26	21a34	21 38	21a43	21 56
City Thameslink 3	d																						
Farringdon 3 ⊖	d			20 14		20 28	20 32			20 44		20 58	21 02			21 14			21 32		21 44		22 02
St Pancras International 15 ⊖	a			20 18		20 32	20 36			20 48		21 02	21 06			21 18			21 36		21 48		22 06
	d		20 10	20 18		20 32	20 36		20 40	20 48		21 02	21 06		21 10	21 18		21 30	21 36		21 48		22 06
Kentish Town ⊖	d						20 40						21 10						21 40				22 10
West Hampstead Thameslink ⊖	d			20 26		20 40	20 44			20 56		21 10	21 14			21 26			21 44		21 56		22 14
Cricklewood	d						20 47						21 17						21 47				22 17
Hendon	d						20 50						21 20						21 50				22 20
Mill Hill Broadway	d						20 54						21 24						21 54				22 24
Elstree & Borehamwood	d						20 58						21 28						21 58				22 28
Radlett	d						21 02						21 32						22 02				22 32
St Albans City	d			20 43		20 57	21 09			21 13		21 27	21 39			21 43			22 09		22 13		22 39
Harpenden	d			20 49		21 03	21 15			21 19		21 33	21 45			21 49			22 15		22 19		22 45
Luton Airport Parkway 7 ✈	d		20 31	20 55		21 09	21 20			21 25		21 39	21 50		21 31	21 55			22 20		22 25		22 50
Luton 10	d			20 58		21 12	21 24		21 04	21 28		21 42	21 54			21 58		21 52	22 24		22 28		22 54
Leagrave	d			21 02		21 16				21 32		21 46				22 02					22 32		
Harlington	d			21 07		21 21				21 37		21 51				22 07					22 37		
Flitwick	d			21 11		21 25				21 41		21 55				22 11					22 41		
Bedford 7	a		20 46	21 24		21 38	21 46		21 19	21 54		22 08	22 16		21 46	22 24		22 06	22 46		22 54		23 16

A To Nottingham **B** To Leeds **C** To Sheffield

The trains that operate to and from Sevenoaks, Orpington and Rochester (and a few other destinations at peak times) are operated jointly by First Capital Connect (north of Blackfriars) and Southeastern (south of Blackfriars)

Table 52 shows the complete service between Bedford and London, whilst services between London, Sevenoaks, Sutton and Brighton only show through Thameslink services. Other Tables should be consulted for additional journey opportunities.

Table 52R

Sundays

16 February to 23 March

Brighton, Gatwick Airport and South London - City of London, St Albans, Luton and Bedford

Network Diagram - refer to first Page of Table 52

		SE	FC	FC	SE	EM	FC	FC	SE	EM	FC	SE	FC	FC	FC	FC
			1			◇1	1			◇1	1		1	1	1	1
						A				B						
Brighton 10	d		20 44				21 14				21 44		22 14	22 44	23 14	23 42
Preston Park	d															
Hassocks 4	d		20 53				21 23				21 53		22 23	22 53	23 23	23 51
Burgess Hill 4	d		20 57				21 27				21 57		22 27	22 57	23 27	23 55
Wivelsfield 4	d															
Haywards Heath 3	d		21 03				21 33				22 03		22 33	23 03	23 33	00 01
Balcombe	d															
Three Bridges 4	d		21 12				21 42				22 12		22 42	23 12	23 42	00 10
Gatwick Airport 10 ✈	d		21 17				21 47				22 17		22 47	23 17	23 47	00 15
Redhill	d															00 24
East Croydon	d		21 33				22 03				22 33		23 03	23 33	00 02	00 36
Sevenoaks 4 195	d	21 02			21 32				22 02			22 32				
Bat & Ball 195	d	21 05			21 35				22 05			22 35				
Otford 4 195	d	21 08			21 38				22 08			22 38				
Shoreham (Kent) 195	d	21 11			21 41				22 11			22 41				
Eynsford 195	d	21 15			21 45				22 15			22 45				
Swanley 4 195	d	21 20			21 50				22 20			22 50				
St Mary Cray 4 195	d	21 24			21 54				22 24			22 54				
Bickley 195	d	21 28			21 58				22 28			22 58				
Bromley South 195	d	21 31			22 01				22 31			23 01				
Shortlands 4 195	d	21 34			22 04				22 34			23 04				
Ravensbourne 195	d	21 36			22 06				22 36			23 06				
Beckenham Hill 195	d	21 38			22 08				22 38			23 08				
Bellingham 195	d	21 40			22 10				22 40			23 10				
Catford 195	d	21 43			22 13				22 43			23 13				
Crofton Park 195	d	21 45			22 15				22 45			23 15				
Nunhead 4 195	d	21 48			22 18				22 48			23 18				
Peckham Rye 4 195	d	21 50			22 20				22 50			23 20				
Denmark Hill 4 195	d	21 54			22 24				22 54			23 24				
Sutton (Surrey) 4 179	d			21 38				22 08								
West Sutton 179	d															
Sutton Common 179	d															
St Helier 179	d															
Morden South 179	d															
South Merton 179	d															
Wimbledon Chase 179	d															
Wimbledon 6 ⊖173,179	d															
Haydons Road 173	d															
Tooting 173	d															
Carshalton 173	d			21 41				22 11								
Hackbridge 173	d			21 43				22 13								
Mitcham Junction 173	d			21 46				22 16								
Mitcham Eastfields 173	d			21 49				22 19								
Streatham 4	d			21 53				22 23								
Tulse Hill 3	d			21 57				22 27								
London Bridge 4 ⊖	a															
	d															
Herne Hill 4 173,179	d			22 01				22 31								
Loughborough Jn. 173,179	d			22 04				22 34								
Elephant & Castle 173,179	d	22 00	22 01	22 09	22 30		22 31	22 39	23 00		23 01	23 30	23 31			
London Blackfriars 3 ⊖	d	22a04	22 08	22 14	22a34		22 38	22a43	23a04		23 08	23a34	23 38	00 08	00 30	01 04
City Thameslink 3	d															
Farringdon 3 ⊖	d		22 14	22 20			22 44				23 14		23 44	00 14	00 36	
St Pancras International 15 ⊖	a		22 18	22 24			22 48				23 18		23 48	00 18	00 40	01 13
	d		22 18	22 24		22 30	22 48			23 00	23 18		23 48	00 18	00 40	01 15
Kentish Town ⊖	d			22 28			22 52				23 22		23 52	00 22	00 44	01 18
West Hampstead Thameslink ⊖	d		22 26	22 32			22 56				23 26		23 56	00 26	00 48	01 22
Cricklewood	d			22 35			22 59				23 29		23 59	00 29	00 51	01 25
Hendon	d			22 38			23 02				23 32		00 02	00 32	00 54	01 28
Mill Hill Broadway	d			22 42			23 06				23 36		00 06	00 36	00 58	01 32
Elstree & Borehamwood	d			22 46			23 10				23 40		00 10	00 40	01 02	01 36
Radlett	d			22 51			23 15				23 45		00 15	00 45	01 07	01 41
St Albans City	d		22 43	22 58			23 22				23 52		00 22	00 52	01 14	01 48
Harpenden	d		22 49	23 04			23 28				23 58		00 28	00 58	01 20	01 54
Luton Airport Parkway 7 ✈	d		22 55	23 10		22 51	23 34			23 39	00 04		00 34	01 04	01 26	02 00
Luton 10	d		22 58	23 13			23 37				00 07		00 37	01 07	01 29	02 03
Leagrave	d		23 02	23 17			23 41				00 11		00 41	01 11	01 33	02 07
Harlington	d		23 07	23 22			23 46				00 16		00 46	01 16	01 38	02 12
Flitwick	d		23 11	23 26			23 50				00 20		00 50	01 20	01 42	02 16
Bedford 7	a		23 24	23 39		23 13	00 03			00 03	00 33		01 03	01 33	01 55	02 29

A To Nottingham

B To Derby

The trains that operate to and from Sevenoaks, Orpington and Rochester (and a few other destinations at peak times) are operated jointly by First Capital Connect (north of Blackfriars) and Southeastern (south of Blackfriars)

Table 52 shows the complete service between Bedford and London, whilst services between London, Sevenoaks, Sutton and Brighton only show through Thameslink services. Other Tables should be consulted for additional journey opportunities.

Table 52R

Sundays

30 March to 11 May

Brighton, Gatwick Airport and South London - City of London, St Albans, Luton and Bedford

Network Diagram - refer to first Page of Table 52

		FC	FC	FC	FC	FC	FC	FC	FC	FC	FC		FC	FC	FC	SE	FC	SE	FC	SE	EM	FC		SE	EM
			1		1		1	1							1		1		1		◇1	1			◇1
		A	B	A	B		B	B								C		C			D				E
Brighton 10	d										05 36				06 06		06 36		07 04			07 36			
Preston Park	d																								
Hassocks 4	d										05 45				06 15		06 45		07 13			07 45			
Burgess Hill 4	d										05 48				06 18		06 48		07 16			07 48			
Wivelsfield 4	d																								
Haywards Heath 3	d										05 54				06 24		06 54		07 24			07 54			
Balcombe	d							00 05																	
Three Bridges 4	d							00 10		05 13	06 02				06 32		07 02		07 32			08 02			
Gatwick Airport 10 ✈	d							00 15		05 18	06 08				06 38		07 08		07 38			08 08			
Redhill	d							00 24																	
East Croydon	d						00 02	00 36		05 37	06 27				06 57		07 27		07 57			08 27			
Sevenoaks 4	195 d																			07 32				08 02	
Bat & Ball	195 d																			07 35				08 05	
Otford 4	195 d																			07 38				08 08	
Shoreham (Kent)	195 d																			07 41				08 11	
Eynsford	195 d																			07 45				08 15	
Swanley 4	195 d																			07 50				08 20	
St Mary Cray 4	195 d																			07 54				08 24	
Bickley	195 d															06 58		07 28		07 58				08 28	
Bromley South	195 d															07 01		07 31		08 01				08 31	
Shortlands 4	195 d															07 04		07 34		08 04				08 34	
Ravensbourne	195 d															07 06		07 36		08 06				08 36	
Beckenham Hill	195 d															07 08		07 38		08 08				08 38	
Bellingham	195 d															07 10		07 40		08 10				08 40	
Catford	195 d															07 13		07 43		08 13				08 43	
Crofton Park	195 d															07 15		07 45		08 15				08 45	
Nunhead 4	195 d															07 18		07 48		08 18				08 48	
Peckham Rye 4	195 d															07 20		07 50		08 20				08 50	
Denmark Hill 4	195 d															07 24		07 54		08 24				08 54	
Sutton (Surrey) 4	179 d																								
West Sutton	179 d																								
Sutton Common	179 d																								
St Helier	179 d																								
Morden South	179 d																								
South Merton	179 d																								
Wimbledon Chase	179 d																								
Wimbledon 5 ⊖	173,179 d																								
Haydons Road	173 d																								
Tooting	173 d																								
Carshalton	173 d																								
Hackbridge	173 d																								
Mitcham Junction	173 d																								
Mitcham Eastfields	173 d																								
Streatham 4	d																								
Tulse Hill 3	d																								
London Bridge 4 ⊖	a						00 21	00 51																	
	d						00 22	00 52																	
Herne Hill 4	173,179 d																								
Loughborough Jn.	173,179 d																								
Elephant & Castle	173,179 d															07 30	07 50	08 00	08 20	08 30		08 50		09 00	
London Blackfriars 3 ⊖	d					00 08	00 28	00 58	01 29	06a04	06a54				07 24	07a34	07 54	08a04	08 24	08a34		08 54		09a04	
City Thameslink 3	d																								
Farringdon 3 ⊖	d					00 13	00 34								07 30		08 00		08 30			09 00			
St Pancras International 15 ⊖	a					00 17	00 38	01 08	01 38						07 34		08 04		08 34			09 04			
	d				00 02	00 18	00 39	01 09	01 39				06 04	07 04	07 34		08 04		08 34		09 00	09 04			09 30
Kentish Town ⊖	d					00 21	00 42	01 12	01 42				06 08	07 08	07 38		08 08		08 38			09 08			
West Hampstead Thameslink ⊖	d				00 10	00 25	00 46	01 16	01 46				06 12	07 12	07 42		08 12		08 42			09 12			
Cricklewood	d					00 28	00 49	01 19	01 49				06 15	07 15	07 45		08 15		08 45			09 15			
Hendon	d			00 01		00 31	00 52	01 22	01 52				06 18	07 18	07 48		08 18		08 48			09 18			
Mill Hill Broadway	d			00 05		00 35	00 56	01 26	01 56				06 22	07 22	07 52		08 22		08 52			09 22			
Elstree & Borehamwood	d			00 09		00 39	01 00	01 30	02 00				06 26	07 26	07 56		08 26		08 56			09 26			
Radlett	d			00 14		00 44	01 05	01 35	02 05				06 31	07 31	08 01		08 31		09 01			09 31			
St Albans City	d			00 21	00 27	00 51	01 11	01 41	02 11				06 38	07 38	08 08		08 38		09 08			09 38			
Harpenden	d		00 03	00 27	00 33	00 57	01 17	01 47	02 17				06 44	07 44	08 14		08 44		09 14			09 44			
Luton Airport Parkway 7 ✈	d	00 03	00 09	00 33	00 39	01 03	01 23	01 53	02 23				06 50	07 50	08 20		08 50		09 20		09 28	09 50			
Luton 10	d	00 06	00 12	00 36	00 42	01 06	01 26	01 56	02 26				06 53	07 53	08 23		08 53		09 23			09 53			09 59
Leagrave	d	00 10	00 16	00 40	00 46	01 10	01 30	02 00	02 30				06 57	07 57	08 27		08 57		09 27			09 57			
Harlington	d	00 15	00 21	00 45	00 51	01 15	01 35	02 05	02 35				07 02	08 02	08 32		09 02		09 32			10 02			
Flitwick	d	00 19	00 25	00 49	00 55	01 19	01 39	02 09	02 39				07 06	08 06	08 36		09 06		09 36			10 06			
Bedford 7	a	00 32	00 38	01 02	01 08	01 32	01 52	02 22	02 52				07 19	08 19	08 49		09 19		09 49		09 50	10 19			10 18

A From Sutton (Surrey)
B From Brighton
C From Orpington
D To Nottingham
E To Sheffield

The trains that operate to and from Sevenoaks, Orpington and Rochester (and a few other destinations at peak times) are operated jointly by First Capital Connect (north of Blackfriars) and Southeastern (south of Blackfriars)

Table 52 shows the complete service between Bedford and London, whilst services between London, Sevenoaks, Sutton and Brighton only show through Thameslink services. Other Tables should be consulted for additional journey opportunities.

Table 52R

Sundays

30 March to 11 May

Brighton, Gatwick Airport and South London - City of London, St Albans, Luton and Bedford

Network Diagram - refer to first Page of Table 52

		FC 1	SE	EM ◇1 A	FC 1	SE	FC 1	EM ◇1 B	FC 1	FC	SE	FC 1	FC	EM ◇1 A	FC 1	FC	SE	FC 1	FC	EM ◇1 B	FC 1	FC	SE
Brighton 10	d	08 04					08 44					09 14						09 44					
Preston Park	d																						
Hassocks 4	d	08 13					08 53					09 23						09 53					
Burgess Hill 4	d	08 16					08 57					09 27						09 57					
Wivelsfield 4	d																						
Haywards Heath 3	d	08 24					09 03					09 33						10 03					
Balcombe	d																						
Three Bridges 4	d	08 32					09 12					09 42						10 12			10 24		
Gatwick Airport 10 ✈	d	08 38			08 59		09 17		09 29			09 47			09 59			10 17			10 29		
Redhill	d																						
East Croydon	d	08 56			09 17		09 33		09 47			10 03			10 17			10 33			10 47		
Sevenoaks 4 195	d		08 32			09 02					09 32						10 02						10 32
Bat & Ball 195	d		08 35			09 05					09 35						10 05						10 35
Otford 4 195	d		08 38			09 08					09 38						10 08						10 38
Shoreham (Kent) 195	d		08 41			09 11					09 41						10 11						10 41
Eynsford 195	d		08 45			09 15					09 45						10 15						10 45
Swanley 4 195	d		08 50			09 20					09 50						10 20						10 50
St Mary Cray 4 195	d		08 54			09 24					09 54						10 24						10 54
Bickley 195	d		08 58			09 28					09 58						10 28						10 58
Bromley South 195	d		09 01			09 31					10 01						10 31						11 01
Shortlands 4 195	d		09 04			09 34					10 04						10 34						11 04
Ravensbourne 195	d		09 06			09 36					10 06						10 36						11 06
Beckenham Hill 195	d		09 08			09 38					10 08						10 38						11 08
Bellingham 195	d		09 10			09 40					10 10						10 40						11 10
Catford 195	d		09 13			09 43					10 13						10 43						11 13
Crofton Park 195	d		09 15			09 45					10 15						10 45						11 15
Nunhead 4 195	d		09 18			09 48					10 18						10 48						11 18
Peckham Rye 4 195	d		09 20			09 50					10 20						10 50						11 20
Denmark Hill 4 195	d		09 24			09 54					10 24						10 54						11 24
Sutton (Surrey) 4 179	d									09 37			10 08			10 07			10 38			10 37	
West Sutton 179	d									09 40						10 10						10 40	
Sutton Common 179	d									09 42						10 12						10 42	
St Helier 179	d									09 45						10 15						10 45	
Morden South 179	d									09 47						10 17						10 47	
South Merton 179	d									09 49						10 19						10 49	
Wimbledon Chase 179	d									09 51						10 21						10 51	
Wimbledon 6 ⊖173,179	d									09 56						10 26						10 56	
Haydons Road 173	d									09 58						10 28						10 58	
Tooting 173	d									10 01						10 31						11 01	
Carshalton 173	d												10 11						10 41				
Hackbridge 173	d												10 13						10 43				
Mitcham Junction 173	d												10 16						10 46				
Mitcham Eastfields 173	d												10 19						10 49				
Streatham 4	d									10 06			10 23			10 36			10 53			11 06	
Tulse Hill 3	d									10 10			10 27			10 40			10 57			11 10	
London Bridge 4 ⊖	a																						
	d																						
Herne Hill 4 173,179	d									10 14			10 31			10 44			11 01			11 14	
Loughborough Jn. 173,179	d									10 17			10 34			10 47			11 04			11 17	
Elephant & Castle 173,179	d	09 20	09 30		09 45	10 00	10 01		10 15	10 22	10 30	10 31	10 39		10 45	10 52	11 00	11 01	11 09		11 15	11 22	11 30
London Blackfriars 3 ⊖	d	09 24	09a34		09 54	10a04	10 08		10 22	10 26	10a34	10 38	10a43		10 52	10 56	11a04	11 08	11a13		11 22	11 26	11a34
City Thameslink 3	d																						
Farringdon 3 ⊖	d	09 30			10 00		10 14		10 28	10 32		10 44			10 58	11 02		11 14			11 28	11 32	
St Pancras International 15 ⊖	a	09 34			10 04		10 18		10 32	10 36		10 48			11 02	11 06		11 18			11 32	11 36	
	d	09 34		10 00	10 04		10 18	10 30	10 32	10 36		10 48		11 00	11 02	11 06		11 18		11 30	11 32	11 36	
Kentish Town ⊖	d	09 38			10 08					10 40						11 10						11 40	
West Hampstead Thameslink ⊖	d	09 42			10 12		10 26		10 40	10 44		10 56			11 10	11 14		11 26			11 40	11 44	
Cricklewood	d	09 45			10 15					10 47						11 17						11 47	
Hendon	d	09 48			10 18					10 50						11 20						11 50	
Mill Hill Broadway	d	09 52			10 22					10 54						11 24						11 54	
Elstree & Borehamwood	d	09 56			10 26					10 58						11 28						11 58	
Radlett	d	10 01			10 31					11 02						11 32						12 02	
St Albans City	d	10 08			10 38		10 43		10 57	11 09		11 13			11 27	11 39		11 43			11 57	12 09	
Harpenden	d	10 14			10 44		10 49		11 03	11 15		11 19			11 33	11 45		11 49			12 03	12 15	
Luton Airport Parkway 7 ✈	d	10 20		10 29	10 50		10 55		11 09	11 20		11 25		11 29	11 39	11 50		11 55		11 59	12 09	12 20	
Luton 10	d	10 23			10 53		10 58	11 02	11 12	11a24		11 28		11 33	11 42	11a54		11 58		12 03	12 12	12a24	
Leagrave	d	10 27			10 57		11 02		11 16			11 32			11 46			12 02			12 16		
Harlington	d	10 32			11 02		11 07		11 21			11 37			11 51			12 07			12 21		
Flitwick	d	10 36			11 06		11 11		11 25			11 41			11 55			12 11			12 25		
Bedford 7	a	10 49		10 50	11 19		11 24	11 24	11 38			11 54		11 54	12 08			12 24		12 22	12 38		

A To Nottingham

B To Sheffield

The trains that operate to and from Sevenoaks, Orpington and Rochester (and a few other destinations at peak times) are operated jointly by First Capital Connect (north of Blackfriars) and Southeastern (south of Blackfriars)

Table 52 shows the complete service between Bedford and London, whilst services between London, Sevenoaks, Sutton and Brighton only show through Thameslink services. Other Tables should be consulted for additional journey opportunities.

Table 52R

Sundays

30 March to 11 May

Brighton, Gatwick Airport and South London - City of London, St Albans, Luton and Bedford

Network Diagram - refer to first Page of Table 52

		FC	FC	FC	FC	SE	EM	FC	FC	EM	FC	FC	SE	FC	FC	FC	FC	SE	EM	FC	FC	FC	FC
		1		1			◇1 A ☕	1		◇1 B ☕	1			1		1			◇1 A ☕	1		1	
Brighton 10	d	10 14						10 44						11 14						11 44			
Preston Park	d																						
Hassocks 4	d	10 23						10 53						11 23						11 53			
Burgess Hill 4	d	10 27						10 57						11 27						11 57			
Wivelsfield 4	d																						
Haywards Heath 3	d	10 33						11 03						11 33						12 03			
Balcombe	d																						
Three Bridges 4	d	10 42		10 54				11 12			11 24			11 42		11 54				12 12		12 24	
Gatwick Airport 10 ✈	d	10 47		10 59				11 17			11 29			11 47		11 59				12 17		12 29	
Redhill	d																						
East Croydon 🚋	d	11 03		11 17				11 33			11 47			12 03		12 17				12 33		12 47	
Sevenoaks 4 195	d					11 02							11 32					12 02					
Bat & Ball 195	d					11 05							11 35					12 05					
Otford 4 195	d					11 08							11 38					12 08					
Shoreham (Kent) 195	d					11 11							11 41					12 11					
Eynsford 195	d					11 15							11 45					12 15					
Swanley 4 195	d					11 20							11 50					12 20					
St Mary Cray 4 195	d					11 24							11 54					12 24					
Bickley 195	d					11 28							11 58					12 28					
Bromley South 195	d					11 31							12 01					12 31					
Shortlands 4 195	d					11 34							12 04					12 34					
Ravensbourne 195	d					11 36							12 06					12 36					
Beckenham Hill 195	d					11 38							12 08					12 38					
Bellingham 195	d					11 40							12 10					12 40					
Catford 195	d					11 43							12 13					12 43					
Crofton Park 195	d					11 45							12 15					12 45					
Nunhead 4 195	d					11 48							12 18					12 48					
Peckham Rye 4 195	d					11 50							12 20					12 50					
Denmark Hill 4 195	d					11 54							12 24					12 54					
Sutton (Surrey) 4 179	d		11 08		11 07				11 38			11 37			12 08		12 07				12 38		12 37
West Sutton 179	d				11 10							11 40					12 10						12 40
Sutton Common 179	d				11 12							11 42					12 12						12 42
St Helier 179	d				11 15							11 45					12 15						12 45
Morden South 179	d				11 17							11 47					12 17						12 47
South Merton 179	d				11 19							11 49					12 19						12 49
Wimbledon Chase 179	d				11 21							11 51					12 21						12 51
Wimbledon 6 ⊖173,179 🚋	d				11 26							11 56					12 26						12 56
Haydons Road 173	d				11 28							11 58					12 28						12 58
Tooting 173	d				11 31							12 01					12 31						13 01
Carshalton 173	d		11 11						11 41						12 11						12 41		
Hackbridge 173	d		11 13						11 43						12 13						12 43		
Mitcham Junction 173 🚋	d		11 16						11 46						12 16						12 46		
Mitcham Eastfields 173	d		11 19						11 49						12 19						12 49		
Streatham 4	d		11 23		11 36				11 53			12 06			12 23		12 36				12 53		13 06
Tulse Hill 3	d		11 27		11 40				11 57			12 10			12 27		12 40				12 57		13 10
London Bridge 4 ⊖	a																						
	d																						
Herne Hill 4 173,179	d		11 31		11 44				12 01			12 14			12 31		12 44				13 01		13 14
Loughborough Jn. 173,179	d		11 34		11 47				12 04			12 17			12 34		12 47				13 04		13 17
Elephant & Castle 173,179	d	11 31	11 39	11 45	11 52	12 00		12 01	12 09		12 15	12 22	12 30	12 31	12 39	12 45	12 52	13 00		13 01	13 09	13 15	13 22
London Blackfriars 3 ⊖	d	11 38	11a43	11 52	11 56	12a04		12 08	12a13		12 22	12 26	12a34	12 38	12a43	12 52	12 56	13a04		13 08	13a13	13 22	13 26
City Thameslink 3	d																						
Farringdon 3 ⊖	d	11 44		11 58	12 02			12 14			12 28	12 32		12 44		12 58	13 02			13 14		13 28	13 32
St Pancras International 15 ⊖	a	11 48		12 02	12 06			12 18			12 32	12 36		12 48		13 02	13 06			13 18		13 32	13 36
	d	11 48		12 02	12 06		12 10	12 18		12 30	12 32	12 36		12 48		13 02	13 06		13 10	13 18		13 32	13 36
Kentish Town ⊖	d				12 10							12 40					13 10						13 40
West Hampstead Thameslink ⊖	d	11 56		12 10	12 14			12 26			12 40	12 44		12 56		13 10	13 14			13 26		13 40	13 44
Cricklewood	d				12 17							12 47					13 17						13 47
Hendon	d				12 20							12 50					13 20						13 50
Mill Hill Broadway	d				12 24							12 54					13 24						13 54
Elstree & Borehamwood	d				12 28							12 58					13 28						13 58
Radlett	d				12 32							13 02					13 32						14 02
St Albans City	d	12 13		12 27	12 39			12 43			12 57	13 09		13 13		13 27	13 39			13 43		13 57	14 09
Harpenden	d	12 19		12 33	12 45			12 49			13 03	13 15		13 19		13 33	13 45			13 49		14 03	14 15
Luton Airport Parkway 7 ✈	d	12 25		12 39	12 50		12 31	12 55		12 53	13 09	13 20		13 25		13 39	13 50		13 31	13 55		14 09	14 20
Luton 10	d	12 28		12 42	12a54		12 34	12 58		12 57	13 12	13a24		13 28		13 42	13a54		13 34	13 58		14 12	14a24
Leagrave	d	12 32		12 46				13 02			13 16			13 32		13 46				14 02		14 16	
Harlington	d	12 37		12 51				13 07			13 21			13 37		13 51				14 07		14 21	
Flitwick	d	12 41		12 55				13 11			13 25			13 41		13 55				14 11		14 25	
Bedford 7	a	12 54		13 08			12 49	13 24		13 12	13 38			13 54		14 08			13 49	14 24		14 38	

A To Nottingham **B** To Sheffield

The trains that operate to and from Sevenoaks, Orpington and Rochester (and a few other destinations at peak times) are operated jointly by First Capital Connect (north of Blackfriars) and Southeastern (south of Blackfriars)

Table 52 shows the complete service between Bedford and London, whilst services between London, Sevenoaks, Sutton and Brighton only show through Thameslink services. Other Tables should be consulted for additional journey opportunities.

Table 52R

Sundays

30 March to 11 May

Brighton, Gatwick Airport and South London - City of London, St Albans, Luton and Bedford

Network Diagram - refer to first Page of Table 52

Station	Table		SE	EM	FC	FC	FC	FC	SE	EM	FC	FC	FC	FC	SE	EM	FC	FC	FC	FC	SE	EM	FC	FC
				◇[1]	[1]		[1]			◇[1]	[1]		[1]			◇[1]	[1]		[1]			◇[1]	[1]	
				A						B						C						B		
				⊡						⊡						⊡						⊡		
Brighton [10]		d			12 14						12 44						13 14						13 44	
Preston Park		d																						
Hassocks [4]		d			12 23						12 53						13 23						13 53	
Burgess Hill [4]		d			12 27						12 57						13 27						13 57	
Wivelsfield [4]		d																						
Haywards Heath [3]		d			12 33						13 03						13 33						14 03	
Balcombe		d																						
Three Bridges [4]		d			12 42		12 54				13 12		13 24				13 42		13 54				14 12	
Gatwick Airport [10] ✈		d			12 47		12 59				13 17		13 29				13 47		13 59				14 17	
Redhill		d																						
East Croydon 🚊		d			13 03		13 17				13 33		13 47				14 03		14 17				14 33	
Sevenoaks [4]	195	d	12 32						13 02						13 32						14 02			
Bat & Ball	195	d	12 35						13 05						13 35						14 05			
Otford [4]	195	d	12 38						13 08						13 38						14 08			
Shoreham (Kent)	195	d	12 41						13 11						13 41						14 11			
Eynsford	195	d	12 45						13 15						13 45						14 15			
Swanley [4]	195	d	12 50						13 20						13 50						14 20			
St Mary Cray [4]	195	d	12 54						13 24						13 54						14 24			
Bickley	195	d	12 58						13 28						13 58						14 28			
Bromley South	195	d	13 01						13 31						14 01						14 31			
Shortlands [4]	195	d	13 04						13 34						14 04						14 34			
Ravensbourne	195	d	13 06						13 36						14 06						14 36			
Beckenham Hill	195	d	13 08						13 38						14 08						14 38			
Bellingham	195	d	13 10						13 40						14 10						14 40			
Catford	195	d	13 13						13 43						14 13						14 43			
Crofton Park	195	d	13 15						13 45						14 15						14 45			
Nunhead [4]	195	d	13 18						13 48						14 18						14 48			
Peckham Rye [4]	195	d	13 20						13 50						14 20						14 50			
Denmark Hill [4]	195	d	13 24						13 54						14 24						14 54			
Sutton (Surrey) [4]	179	d				13 08		13 07				13 38		13 37				14 08		14 07				14 38
West Sutton	179	d						13 10						13 40						14 10				
Sutton Common	179	d						13 12						13 42						14 12				
St Helier	179	d						13 15						13 45						14 15				
Morden South	179	d						13 17						13 47						14 17				
South Merton	179	d						13 19						13 49						14 19				
Wimbledon Chase	179	d						13 21						13 51						14 21				
Wimbledon [6] ⊖	173,179 🚊	d						13 26						13 56						14 26				
Haydons Road	173	d						13 28						13 58						14 28				
Tooting	173	d						13 31						14 01						14 31				
Carshalton	173	d				13 11						13 41						14 11						14 41
Hackbridge	173	d				13 13						13 43						14 13						14 43
Mitcham Junction	173 🚊	d				13 16						13 46						14 16						14 46
Mitcham Eastfields	173	d				13 19						13 49						14 19						14 49
Streatham [4]		d				13 23		13 36				13 53		14 06				14 23		14 36				14 53
Tulse Hill [3]		d				13 27		13 40				13 57		14 10				14 27		14 40				14 57
London Bridge [4] ⊖		a																						
		d																						
Herne Hill [4]	173,179	d				13 31		13 44				14 01		14 14				14 31		14 44				15 01
Loughborough Jn	173,179	d				13 34		13 47				14 04		14 17				14 34		14 47				15 04
Elephant & Castle	173,179	d	13 30		13 31	13 39	13 45	13 52	14 00		14 01	14 09	14 15	14 22	14 30		14 31	14 39	14 45	14 52	15 00		15 01	15 09
London Blackfriars [3] ⊖		d	13a34		13 38	13a43	13 52	13 56	14a04		14 08	14a13	14 22	14 26	14a34		14 38	14a43	14 52	14 56	15a04		15 08	15a13
City Thameslink [3]		d																						
Farringdon [3] ⊖		d			13 44		13 58	14 02			14 14		14 28	14 32			14 44		14 58	15 02			15 14	
St Pancras International [15] ⊖		a			13 48		14 02	14 06			14 18		14 32	14 36			14 48		15 02	15 06			15 18	
		d		13 40	13 48		14 02	14 06		14 10	14 18		14 32	14 36		14 40	14 48		15 02	15 06		15 10	15 18	
Kentish Town ⊖		d						14 10						14 40						15 10				
West Hampstead Thameslink ⊖		d			13 56		14 10	14 14			14 26		14 40	14 44			14 56		15 10	15 14			15 26	
Cricklewood		d						14 17						14 47						15 17				
Hendon		d						14 20						14 50						15 20				
Mill Hill Broadway		d						14 24						14 54						15 24				
Elstree & Borehamwood		d						14 28						14 58						15 28				
Radlett		d						14 32						15 02						15 32				
St Albans City		d			14 13		14 27	14 39			14 43		14 57	15 09			15 13		15 27	15 39			15 43	
Harpenden		d			14 19		14 33	14 45			14 49		15 03	15 15			15 19		15 33	15 45			15 49	
Luton Airport Parkway [7] ✈		d		14 02	14 25		14 39	14 50		14 31	14 55		15 09	15 20			15 25		15 39	15 50		15 33	15 55	
Luton [10]		d		14 07	14 28		14 42	14a54			14 58		15 12	15a24		15 04	15 28		15 42	15a54			15 58	
Leagrave		d			14 32		14 46				15 02		15 16				15 32		15 46				16 02	
Harlington		d			14 37		14 51				15 07		15 21				15 37		15 51				16 07	
Flitwick		d			14 41		14 55				15 11		15 25				15 41		15 55				16 11	
Bedford [7]		a		14 21	14 54		15 08			14 46	15 24		15 38			15 19	15 54		16 08			15 48	16 24	

A To Sheffield

B To Nottingham

C To Leeds

The trains that operate to and from Sevenoaks, Orpington and Rochester (and a few other destinations at peak times) are operated jointly by First Capital Connect (north of Blackfriars) and Southeastern (south of Blackfriars)

Table 52 shows the complete service between Bedford and London, whilst services between London, Sevenoaks, Sutton and Brighton only show through Thameslink services. Other Tables should be consulted for additional journey opportunities.

Table 52R

Sundays

30 March to 11 May

Brighton, Gatwick Airport and South London - City of London, St Albans, Luton and Bedford

Network Diagram - refer to first Page of Table 52

	FC	FC		SE	EM	FC	FC	FC	FC	SE	EM	FC	FC		FC	FC	SE	EM	FC	FC	FC	FC	SE	EM
	1				◇1 A	1		1			◇1 B	1			1			◇1 C	1		1			◇1 B
Brighton 10 d						14 14						14 44							15 14					
Preston Park d																								
Hassocks 4 d						14 23						14 53							15 23					
Burgess Hill 4 d						14 27						14 57							15 27					
Wivelsfield 4 d																								
Haywards Heath 3 d						14 33						15 03							15 33					
Balcombe d																								
Three Bridges 4 d	14 24					14 42		14 54				15 12			15 24				15 42		15 54			
Gatwick Airport 10 ✈ d	14 29					14 47		14 59				15 17			15 29				15 47		15 59			
Redhill d																								
East Croydon ⇌ d	14 47					15 03		15 17				15 33			15 47				16 03		16 17			
Sevenoaks 4 195 d				14 32						15 02							15 32						16 02	
Bat & Ball 195 d				14 35						15 05							15 35						16 05	
Otford 4 195 d				14 38						15 08							15 38						16 08	
Shoreham (Kent) 195 d				14 41						15 11							15 41						16 11	
Eynsford 195 d				14 45						15 15							15 45						16 15	
Swanley 4 195 d				14 50						15 20							15 50						16 20	
St Mary Cray 4 195 d				14 54						15 24							15 54						16 24	
Bickley 195 d				14 58						15 28							15 58						16 28	
Bromley South 195 d				15 01						15 31							16 01						16 31	
Shortlands 4 195 d				15 04						15 34							16 04						16 34	
Ravensbourne 195 d				15 06						15 36							16 06						16 36	
Beckenham Hill 195 d				15 08						15 38							16 08						16 38	
Bellingham 195 d				15 10						15 40							16 10						16 40	
Catford 195 d				15 13						15 43							16 13						16 43	
Crofton Park 195 d				15 15						15 45							16 15						16 45	
Nunhead 4 195 d				15 18						15 48							16 18						16 48	
Peckham Rye 4 195 d				15 20						15 50							16 20						16 50	
Denmark Hill 4 195 d				15 24						15 54							16 24						16 54	
Sutton (Surrey) 4 179 d		14 37					15 08		15 07				15 38			15 37				16 08		16 07		
West Sutton 179 d		14 40							15 10							15 40						16 10		
Sutton Common 179 d		14 42							15 12							15 42						16 12		
St Helier 179 d		14 45							15 15							15 45						16 15		
Morden South 179 d		14 47							15 17							15 47						16 17		
South Merton 179 d		14 49							15 19							15 49						16 19		
Wimbledon Chase 179 d		14 51							15 21							15 51						16 21		
Wimbledon 6 ⊖173,179 ⇌ d		14 56							15 26							15 56						16 26		
Haydons Road 173 d		14 58							15 28							15 58						16 28		
Tooting 173 d		15 01							15 31							16 01						16 31		
Carshalton 173 d							15 11						15 41							16 11				
Hackbridge 173 d							15 13						15 43							16 13				
Mitcham Junction 173 ⇌ d							15 16						15 46							16 16				
Mitcham Eastfields 173 d							15 19						15 49							16 19				
Streatham 4 d		15 06					15 23		15 36				15 53			16 06				16 23		16 36		
Tulse Hill 3 d		15 10					15 27		15 40				15 57			16 10				16 27		16 40		
London Bridge 4 ⊖ a																								
d																								
Herne Hill 4 173,179 d		15 14					15 31		15 44				16 01			16 14				16 31		16 44		
Loughborough Jn. 173,179 d		15 17					15 34		15 47				16 04			16 17				16 34		16 47		
Elephant & Castle 173,179 d	15 15	15 22		15 30		15 31	15 39	15 45	15 52	16 00		16 01	16 09		16 15	16 22	16 30		16 31	16 39	16 45	16 52	17 00	
London Blackfriars 3 ⊖ d	15 22	15 26		15a34		15 38	15a43	15 52	15 56	16a04		16 08	16a13		16 22	16 26	16a34		16 38	16a43	16 52	16 56	17a04	
City Thameslink 3 d																								
Farringdon 3 ⊖ d	15 28	15 32				15 44		15 58	16 02			16 14			16 28	16 32			16 44		16 58	17 02		
St Pancras International 15 ⊖ a	15 32	15 36				15 48		16 02	16 06			16 18			16 32	16 36			16 48		17 02	17 06		
d	15 32	15 36			15 40	15 48		16 02	16 06		16 10	16 18			16 32	16 36		16 40	16 48		17 02	17 06		17 10
Kentish Town ⊖ d		15 40							16 10							16 40						17 10		
West Hampstead Thameslink ⊖ d	15 40	15 44				15 56		16 10	16 14			16 26			16 40	16 44			16 56		17 10	17 14		
Cricklewood d		15 47							16 17							16 47						17 17		
Hendon d		15 50							16 20							16 50						17 20		
Mill Hill Broadway d		15 54							16 24							16 54						17 24		
Elstree & Borehamwood d		15 58							16 28							16 58						17 28		
Radlett d		16 02							16 32							17 02						17 32		
St Albans City d	15 57	16 09				16 13		16 27	16 39			16 43			16 57	17 09			17 13		17 27	17 39		
Harpenden d	16 03	16 15				16 19		16 33	16 45			16 49			17 03	17 15			17 19		17 33	17 45		
Luton Airport Parkway 7 ✈ d	16 09	16 20				16 25		16 39	16 50		16 31	16 55			17 09	17 20			17 25		17 39	17 50		17 31
Luton 10 d	16 12	16a24			16 04	16 28		16 42	16a54			16 58			17 12	17a24		17 02	17 28		17 42	17a54		
Leagrave d	16 16					16 32		16 46				17 02			17 16				17 32		17 46			
Harlington d	16 21					16 37		16 51				17 07			17 21				17 37		17 51			
Flitwick d	16 25					16 41		16 55				17 11			17 25				17 41		17 55			
Bedford 7 a	16 38				16 19	16 54		17 08			16 46	17 24			17 38			17 16	17 54		18 08			17 46

A To Sheffield **B** To Nottingham **C** To Derby

The trains that operate to and from Sevenoaks, Orpington and Rochester (and a few other destinations at peak times) are operated jointly by First Capital Connect (north of Blackfriars) and Southeastern (south of Blackfriars)

Table 52 shows the complete service between Bedford and London, whilst services between London, Sevenoaks, Sutton and Brighton only show through Thameslink services. Other Tables should be consulted for additional journey opportunities.

Table 52R

Sundays
30 March to 11 May

Brighton, Gatwick Airport and South London - City of London, St Albans, Luton and Bedford

Network Diagram - refer to first Page of Table 52

		FC [1]	FC	FC [1]	FC	SE	EM ◇[1] A ☕	FC [1]	FC	FC [1]	FC	SE	EM ◇[1] B ☕	FC [1]	FC	FC [1]	FC	SE	EM ◇[1] A ☕	FC [1]	FC	FC [1]
Brighton [10]	d	15 44						16 14						16 44						17 14		
Preston Park	d																					
Hassocks [4]	d	15 53						16 23						16 53						17 23		
Burgess Hill [4]	d	15 57						16 27						16 57						17 27		
Wivelsfield [4]	d																					
Haywards Heath [3]	d	16 03						16 33						17 03						17 33		
Balcombe	d																					
Three Bridges [4]	d	16 12		16 24				16 42		16 54				17 12		17 24				17 42		17 54
Gatwick Airport [10] ✈	d	16 17		16 29				16 47		16 59				17 17		17 29				17 47		17 59
Redhill	d																					
East Croydon 🚋	d	16 33		16 47				17 03		17 17				17 33		17 47				18 03		18 17
Sevenoaks [4] 195	d					16 32						17 02						17 32				
Bat & Ball 195	d					16 35						17 05						17 35				
Otford [4] 195	d					16 38						17 08						17 38				
Shoreham (Kent) 195	d					16 41						17 11						17 41				
Eynsford 195	d					16 45						17 15						17 45				
Swanley [4] 195	d					16 50						17 20						17 50				
St Mary Cray [4] 195	d					16 54						17 24						17 54				
Bickley 195	d					16 58						17 28						17 58				
Bromley South 195	d					17 01						17 31						18 01				
Shortlands [4] 195	d					17 04						17 34						18 04				
Ravensbourne 195	d					17 06						17 36						18 06				
Beckenham Hill 195	d					17 08						17 38						18 08				
Bellingham 195	d					17 10						17 40						18 10				
Catford 195	d					17 13						17 43						18 13				
Crofton Park 195	d					17 15						17 45						18 15				
Nunhead [4] 195	d					17 18						17 48						18 18				
Peckham Rye [4] 195	d					17 20						17 50						18 20				
Denmark Hill [4] 195	d					17 24						17 54						18 24				
Sutton (Surrey) [4] 179	d		16 38		16 37				17 08		17 07				17 38		17 37				18 08	
West Sutton 179	d				16 40						17 10						17 40					
Sutton Common 179	d				16 42						17 12						17 42					
St Helier 179	d				16 45						17 15						17 45					
Morden South 179	d				16 47						17 17						17 47					
South Merton 179	d				16 49						17 19						17 49					
Wimbledon Chase 179	d				16 51						17 21						17 51					
Wimbledon [6] ⊖173,179 🚋	d				16 56						17 26						17 56					
Haydons Road 173	d				16 58						17 28						17 58					
Tooting 173	d				17 01						17 31						18 01					
Carshalton 173	d		16 41						17 11						17 41						18 11	
Hackbridge 173	d		16 43						17 13						17 43						18 13	
Mitcham Junction 173 🚋	d		16 46						17 16						17 46						18 16	
Mitcham Eastfields 173	d		16 49						17 19						17 49						18 19	
Streatham [4]	d		16 53		17 06				17 23		17 36				17 53		18 06				18 23	
Tulse Hill [3]	d		16 57		17 10				17 27		17 40				17 57		18 10				18 27	
London Bridge [4] ⊖	a																					
	d																					
Herne Hill [4] 173,179	d		17 01		17 14				17 31		17 44				18 01		18 14				18 31	
Loughborough Jn. 173,179	d		17 04		17 17				17 34		17 47				18 04		18 17				18 34	
Elephant & Castle 173,179	d	17 01	17 09	17 15	17 22	17 30		17 31	17 39	17 45	17 52	18 00		18 01	18 09	18 15	18 22	18 30		18 31	18 39	18 45
London Blackfriars [3] ⊖	d	17 08	17a13	17 22	17 26	17a34		17 38	17a43	17 52	17 56	18a04		18 08	18a13	18 22	18 26	18a34		18 38	18a43	18 52
City Thameslink [3]	d																					
Farringdon [3] ⊖	d	17 14		17 28	17 32			17 44		17 58	18 02			18 14		18 28	18 32			18 44		18 58
St Pancras International [15] ⊖	a	17 18		17 32	17 36			17 48		18 02	18 06			18 18		18 32	18 36			18 48		19 02
	d	17 18		17 32	17 36		17 40	17 48		18 02	18 06		18 10	18 18		18 32	18 36		18 40	18 48		19 02
Kentish Town ⊖	d				17 40						18 10						18 40					
West Hampstead Thameslink ⊖	d	17 26		17 40	17 44			17 56		18 10	18 14			18 26		18 40	18 44			18 56		19 10
Cricklewood	d				17 47						18 17						18 47					
Hendon	d				17 50						18 20						18 50					
Mill Hill Broadway	d				17 54						18 24						18 54					
Elstree & Borehamwood	d				17 58						18 28						18 58					
Radlett	d				18 02						18 32						19 02					
St Albans City	d	17 43		17 57	18 09			18 13		18 27	18 39			18 43		18 57	19 09			19 13		19 27
Harpenden	d	17 49		18 03	18 15			18 19		18 33	18 45			18 49		19 03	19 15			19 19		19 33
Luton Airport Parkway [7] ✈	d	17 55		18 09	18 20			18 25		18 39	18 50		18 31	18 55		19 09	19 20			19 25		19 39
Luton [10]	d	17 58		18 12	18a24		18 02	18 28		18 42	18a54			18 58		19 12	19a24		19 02	19 28		19 42
Leagrave	d	18 02		18 16				18 32		18 46				19 02		19 16				19 32		19 46
Harlington	d	18 07		18 21				18 37		18 51				19 07		19 21				19 37		19 51
Flitwick	d	18 11		18 25				18 41		18 55				19 11		19 25				19 41		19 55
Bedford [7]	a	18 24		18 38			18 16	18 54		19 08			18 46	19 24		19 38			19 16	19 54		20 08

A To Derby
B To Nottingham

The trains that operate to and from Sevenoaks, Orpington and Rochester (and a few other destinations at peak times) are operated jointly by First Capital Connect (north of Blackfriars) and Southeastern (south of Blackfriars)

Table 52 shows the complete service between Bedford and London, whilst services between London, Sevenoaks, Sutton and Brighton only show through Thameslink services. Other Tables should be consulted for additional journey opportunities.

Table 52R

Sundays

30 March to 11 May

Brighton, Gatwick Airport and South London - City of London, St Albans, Luton and Bedford

Network Diagram - refer to first Page of Table 52

	FC	SE	EM	FC	FC	FC	FC	SE	EM	FC	FC	FC	FC	SE	EM	FC	FC	FC	FC	SE	EM	FC
			◇[1]	[1]		[1]			◇[1]	[1]		[1]			◇[1]	[1]		[1]			◇[1]	[1]
			A						B						A						C	
			☕						☕						☕						☕	
Brighton [10] d				17 44						18 14						18 44						19 14
Preston Park d																						
Hassocks [4] d				17 53						18 23						18 53						19 23
Burgess Hill [4] d				17 57						18 27						18 57						19 27
Wivelsfield [4] d																						
Haywards Heath [3] d				18 03						18 33						19 03						19 33
Balcombe d																						
Three Bridges [4] d				18 12		18 24				18 42		18 54				19 12		19 24				19 42
Gatwick Airport [10] ✈ d				18 17		18 29				18 47		18 59				19 17		19 29				19 47
Redhill d																						
East Croydon 🚋 d				18 33		18 47				19 03		19 17				19 33		19 47				20 03
Sevenoaks [4] 195 d		18 02						18 32						19 02						19 32		
Bat & Ball 195 d		18 05						18 35						19 05						19 35		
Otford [4] 195 d		18 08						18 38						19 08						19 38		
Shoreham (Kent) 195 d		18 11						18 41						19 11						19 41		
Eynsford 195 d		18 15						18 45						19 15						19 45		
Swanley [4] 195 d		18 20						18 50						19 20						19 50		
St Mary Cray [4] 195 d		18 24						18 54						19 24						19 54		
Bickley 195 d		18 28						18 58						19 28						19 58		
Bromley South 195 d		18 31						19 01						19 31						20 01		
Shortlands [4] 195 d		18 34						19 04						19 34						20 04		
Ravensbourne 195 d		18 36						19 06						19 36						20 06		
Beckenham Hill 195 d		18 38						19 08						19 38						20 08		
Bellingham 195 d		18 40						19 10						19 40						20 10		
Catford 195 d		18 43						19 13						19 43						20 13		
Crofton Park 195 d		18 45						19 15						19 45						20 15		
Nunhead [4] 195 d		18 48						19 18						19 48						20 18		
Peckham Rye [4] 195 d		18 50						19 20						19 50						20 20		
Denmark Hill [4] 195 d		18 54						19 24						19 54						20 24		
Sutton (Surrey) [4] 179 d	18 07				18 38		18 37				19 08		19 07				19 38		19 37			
West Sutton 179 d	18 10						18 40						19 10						19 40			
Sutton Common 179 d	18 12						18 42						19 12						19 42			
St Helier 179 d	18 15						18 45						19 15						19 45			
Morden South 179 d	18 17						18 47						19 17						19 47			
South Merton 179 d	18 19						18 49						19 19						19 49			
Wimbledon Chase 179 d	18 21						18 51						19 21						19 51			
Wimbledon [6] ⊖173,179 🚋 d	18 26						18 56						19 26						19 56			
Haydons Road 173 d	18 28						18 58						19 28						19 58			
Tooting 173 d	18 31						19 01						19 31						20 01			
Carshalton 173 d					18 41						19 11						19 41					
Hackbridge 173 d					18 43						19 13						19 43					
Mitcham Junction 173 🚋 d					18 46						19 16						19 46					
Mitcham Eastfields 173 d					18 49						19 19						19 49					
Streatham [4] d	18 36				18 53		19 06				19 23		19 36				19 53		20 06			
Tulse Hill [3] d	18 40				18 57		19 10				19 27		19 40				19 57		20 10			
London Bridge [4] ⊖ a																						
d																						
Herne Hill [4] 173,179 d	18 44				19 01		19 14				19 31		19 44				20 01		20 14			
Loughborough Jn. 173,179 d	18 47				19 04		19 17				19 34		19 47				20 04		20 17			
Elephant & Castle 173,179 d	18 52	19 00		19 01	19 09	19 15	19 22	19 30		19 31	19 39	19 45	19 52	20 00		20 01	20 09	20 15	20 22	20 30		20 31
London Blackfriars [3] ⊖ d	18 56	19a04		19 08	19a13	19 22	19 26	19a34		19 38	19a43	19 52	19 56	20a04		20 08	20a13	20 22	20 26	20a34		20 38
City Thameslink [3] d																						
Farringdon [3] ⊖ d	19 02			19 14		19 28	19 32			19 44		19 58	20 02			20 14		20 28	20 32			20 44
St Pancras International [15] ⊖ a	19 06			19 18		19 32	19 36			19 48		20 02	20 06			20 18		20 32	20 36			20 48
d	19 06		19 10	19 18		19 32	19 36		19 40	19 48		20 02	20 06		20 10	20 18		20 32	20 36		20 40	20 48
Kentish Town ⊖ d	19 10						19 40						20 10						20 40			
West Hampstead Thameslink ⊖ d	19 14			19 26		19 40	19 44			19 56		20 10	20 14			20 26		20 40	20 44			20 56
Cricklewood d	19 17						19 47						20 17						20 47			
Hendon d	19 20						19 50						20 20						20 50			
Mill Hill Broadway d	19 24						19 54						20 24						20 54			
Elstree & Borehamwood d	19 28						19 58						20 28						20 58			
Radlett d	19 32						20 02						20 32						21 02			
St Albans City d	19 39			19 43		19 57	20 09			20 13		20 27	20 39			20 43		20 57	21 09			21 13
Harpenden d	19 45			19 49		20 03	20 15			20 19		20 33	20 45			20 49		21 03	21 15			21 19
Luton Airport Parkway [7] ✈ d	19 50		19 31	19 55		20 09	20 20			20 25		20 39	20 50		20 31	20 55		21 09	21 20			21 25
Luton [10] d	19a54			19 58		20 12	20 24		20 02	20 28		20 42	20 54			20 58		21 12	21 24		21 04	21 28
Leagrave d				20 02		20 16				20 32		20 46				21 02		21 16				21 32
Harlington d				20 07		20 21				20 37		20 51				21 07		21 21				21 37
Flitwick d				20 11		20 25				20 41		20 55				21 11		21 25				21 41
Bedford [7] a			19 46	20 24		20 38	20 46		20 16	20 54		21 08	21 16		20 46	21 24		21 38	21 46		21 19	21 54

A To Nottingham
B To Derby
C To Leeds

The trains that operate to and from Sevenoaks, Orpington and Rochester (and a few other destinations at peak times) are operated jointly by First Capital Connect (north of Blackfriars) and Southeastern (south of Blackfriars)

Table 52 shows the complete service between Bedford and London, whilst services between London, Sevenoaks, Sutton and Brighton only show through Thameslink services. Other Tables should be consulted for additional journey opportunities.

Table 52R

Sundays

30 March to 11 May

Brighton, Gatwick Airport and South London - City of London, St Albans, Luton and Bedford

Network Diagram - refer to first Page of Table 52

		FC	FC	FC	SE	EM	FC	FC	EM	FC	SE	FC	FC	FC	SE	FC	FC	SE	EM	FC	FC	SE	EM
			1			◇1 A	1		◇1 B			1				1			◇1 A	1			◇1 C
Brighton 10	d						19 44					20 14				20 44				21 14			
Preston Park	d																						
Hassocks 4	d						19 53					20 23				20 53				21 23			
Burgess Hill 4	d						19 57					20 27				20 57				21 27			
Wivelsfield 4	d																						
Haywards Heath 3	d						20 03					20 33				21 03				21 33			
Balcombe	d																						
Three Bridges 4	d		19 54				20 12					20 42				21 12				21 42			
Gatwick Airport 10 ✈	d		19 59				20 17					20 47				21 17				21 47			
Redhill	d																						
East Croydon 🚌	d		20 17				20 33					21 03				21 33				22 03			
Sevenoaks 4	195 d				20 02						20 32				21 02			21 32				22 02	
Bat & Ball	195 d				20 05						20 35				21 05			21 35				22 05	
Otford 4	195 d				20 08						20 38				21 08			21 38				22 08	
Shoreham (Kent)	195 d				20 11						20 41				21 11			21 41				22 11	
Eynsford	195 d				20 15						20 45				21 15			21 45				22 15	
Swanley 4	195 d				20 20						20 50				21 20			21 50				22 20	
St Mary Cray 4	195 d				20 24						20 54				21 24			21 54				22 24	
Bickley	195 d				20 28						20 58				21 28			21 58				22 28	
Bromley South	195 d				20 31						21 01				21 31			22 01				22 31	
Shortlands 4	195 d				20 34						21 04				21 34			22 04				22 34	
Ravensbourne	195 d				20 36						21 06				21 36			22 06				22 36	
Beckenham Hill	195 d				20 38						21 08				21 38			22 08				22 38	
Bellingham	195 d				20 40						21 10				21 40			22 10				22 40	
Catford	195 d				20 43						21 13				21 43			22 13				22 43	
Crofton Park	195 d				20 45						21 15				21 45			22 15				22 45	
Nunhead 4	195 d				20 48						21 18				21 48			22 18				22 48	
Peckham Rye 4	195 d				20 50						21 20				21 50			22 20				22 50	
Denmark Hill 4	195 d				20 54						21 24				21 54			22 24				22 54	
Sutton (Surrey) 4	179 d	20 08		20 07				20 38		20 37			21 08	21 07			21 38				22 08		
West Sutton	179 d			20 10						20 40				21 10									
Sutton Common	179 d			20 12						20 42				21 12									
St Helier	179 d			20 15						20 45				21 15									
Morden South	179 d			20 17						20 47				21 17									
South Merton	179 d			20 19						20 49				21 19									
Wimbledon Chase	179 d			20 21						20 51				21 21									
Wimbledon 6 ⊖173,179 🚌	d			20 26						20 56				21 26									
Haydons Road	173 d			20 28						20 58				21 28									
Tooting	173 d			20 31						21 01				21 31									
Carshalton	173 d	20 11						20 41					21 11				21 41				22 11		
Hackbridge	173 d	20 13						20 43					21 13				21 43				22 13		
Mitcham Junction	173 🚌 d	20 16						20 46					21 16				21 46				22 16		
Mitcham Eastfields	173 d	20 19						20 49					21 19				21 49				22 19		
Streatham 4	d	20 23		20 36				20 53		21 06			21 23	21 36			21 53				22 23		
Tulse Hill 3	d	20 27		20 40				20 57		21 10			21 27	21 40			21 57				22 27		
London Bridge 4 ⊖	a																						
	d																						
Herne Hill 4	173,179 d	20 31		20 44				21 01		21 14			21 31	21 44			22 01				22 31		
Loughborough Jn.	173,179 d	20 34		20 47				21 04		21 17			21 34	21 47			22 04				22 34		
Elephant & Castle	173,179 d	20 39	20 45	20 52	21 00		21 01	21 09		21 22	21 30	21 31	21 39	21 52	22 00	22 01	22 09	22 30		22 31	22 39	23 00	
London Blackfriars 3 ⊖	d	20a43	20 52	20 56	21a04		21 08	21a13		21 26	21a34	21 38	21a43	21 56	22a04	22 08	22 14	22a34		22 38	22a43	23a04	
City Thameslink 3	d																						
Farringdon 3 ⊖	d		20 58	21 02			21 14			21 32		21 44		22 02		22 14	22 20			22 44			
St Pancras International 15 ⊖	a		21 02	21 06			21 18			21 36		21 48		22 06		22 18	22 24			22 48			
	d		21 02	21 06		21 10	21 18		21 30	21 36		21 48		22 06		22 18	22 24		22 30	22 48			23 00
Kentish Town ⊖	d			21 10						21 40				22 10			22 28			22 52			
West Hampstead Thameslink ⊖	d		21 10	21 14			21 26			21 44		21 56		22 14		22 26	22 32			22 56			
Cricklewood	d			21 17						21 47				22 17			22 35			22 59			
Hendon	d			21 20						21 50				22 20			22 38			23 02			
Mill Hill Broadway	d			21 24						21 54				22 24			22 42			23 06			
Elstree & Borehamwood	d			21 28						21 58				22 28			22 46			23 10			
Radlett	d			21 32						22 02				22 32			22 51			23 15			
St Albans City	d		21 27	21 39			21 43			22 09		22 13		22 39		22 43	22 58			23 22			
Harpenden	d		21 33	21 45			21 49			22 15		22 19		22 45		22 49	23 04			23 28			
Luton Airport Parkway 7 ✈	d		21 39	21 50		21 31	21 55			22 20		22 25		22 50		22 55	23 10		22 51	23 34			23 39
Luton 10	d		21 42	21 54			21 58		21 52	22 24		22 28		22 54		22 58	23 13			23 37			
Leagrave	d		21 46				22 02					22 32				23 02	23 17			23 41			
Harlington	d		21 51				22 07					22 37				23 07	23 22			23 46			
Flitwick	d		21 55				22 11					22 41				23 11	23 26			23 50			
Bedford 7	a		22 08	22 16		21 46	22 24		22 06	22 46		22 54		23 16		23 24	23 39		23 13	00 03			00 03

A To Nottingham **B** To Sheffield **C** To Derby

The trains that operate to and from Sevenoaks, Orpington and Rochester (and a few other destinations at peak times) are operated jointly by First Capital Connect (north of Blackfriars) and Southeastern (south of Blackfriars)

Table 52 shows the complete service between Bedford and London, whilst services between London, Sevenoaks, Sutton and Brighton only show through Thameslink services. Other Tables should be consulted for additional journey opportunities.

Table 52R

Sundays

30 March to 11 May

Brighton, Gatwick Airport and South London - City of London, St Albans, Luton and Bedford

Network Diagram - refer to first Page of Table 52

Station			FC 1	SE	FC 1	FC 1	FC 1		FC 1
Brighton 10		d	21 44		22 14	22 44	23 14		23 42
Preston Park		d							
Hassocks 4		d	21 53		22 23	22 53	23 23		23 51
Burgess Hill 4		d	21 57		22 27	22 57	23 27		23 55
Wivelsfield 4		d							
Haywards Heath 3		d	22 03		22 33	23 03	23 33		00 01
Balcombe		d							
Three Bridges 4		d	22 12		22 42	23 12	23 42		00 10
Gatwick Airport 10	✈	d	22 17		22 47	23 17	23 47		00 15
Redhill		d							00 24
East Croydon		d	22 33		23 03	23 33	00 02		00 36
Sevenoaks 4	195	d		22 32					
Bat & Ball	195	d		22 35					
Otford 4	195	d		22 38					
Shoreham (Kent)	195	d		22 41					
Eynsford	195	d		22 45					
Swanley 4	195	d		22 50					
St Mary Cray 4	195	d		22 54					
Bickley	195	d		22 58					
Bromley South	195	d		23 01					
Shortlands 4	195	d		23 04					
Ravensbourne	195	d		23 06					
Beckenham Hill	195	d		23 08					
Bellingham	195	d		23 10					
Catford	195	d		23 13					
Crofton Park	195	d		23 15					
Nunhead 4	195	d		23 18					
Peckham Rye 4	195	d		23 20					
Denmark Hill 4	195	d		23 24					
Sutton (Surrey) 4	179	d							
West Sutton	179	d							
Sutton Common	179	d							
St Helier	179	d							
Morden South	179	d							
South Merton	179	d							
Wimbledon Chase	179	d							
Wimbledon 6	⊖173,179	d							
Haydons Road	173	d							
Tooting	173	d							
Carshalton	173	d							
Hackbridge	173	d							
Mitcham Junction	173	d							
Mitcham Eastfields	173	d							
Streatham 4		d							
Tulse Hill 3		d							
London Bridge 4	⊖	a							
		d							
Herne Hill 4	173,179	d							
Loughborough Jn.	173,179	d							
Elephant & Castle	173,179	d	23 01	23 30	23 31				
London Blackfriars 3	⊖	d	23 08	23a34	23 38	00 08	00 30		01 04
City Thameslink 3		d							
Farringdon 3	⊖	d	23 14		23 44	00 14	00 36		
St Pancras International 15	⊖	a	23 18		23 48	00 18	00 40		01 13
		d	23 18		23 48	00 18	00 40		01 15
Kentish Town	⊖	d	23 22		23 52	00 22	00 44		01 18
West Hampstead Thameslink	⊖	d	23 26		23 56	00 26	00 48		01 22
Cricklewood		d	23 29		23 59	00 29	00 51		01 25
Hendon		d	23 32		00 02	00 32	00 54		01 28
Mill Hill Broadway		d	23 36		00 06	00 36	00 58		01 32
Elstree & Borehamwood		d	23 40		00 10	00 40	01 02		01 36
Radlett		d	23 45		00 15	00 45	01 07		01 41
St Albans City		d	23 52		00 22	00 52	01 14		01 48
Harpenden		d	23 58		00 28	00 58	01 20		01 54
Luton Airport Parkway 7	✈	d	00 04		00 34	01 04	01 26		02 00
Luton 10		d	00 07		00 37	01 07	01 29		02 03
Leagrave		d	00 11		00 41	01 11	01 33		02 07
Harlington		d	00 16		00 46	01 16	01 38		02 12
Flitwick		d	00 20		00 50	01 20	01 42		02 16
Bedford 7		a	00 33		01 03	01 33	01 55		02 29

The trains that operate to and from Sevenoaks, Orpington and Rochester (and a few other destinations at peak times) are operated jointly by First Capital Connect (north of Blackfriars) and Southeastern (south of Blackfriars)

Table 52 shows the complete service between Bedford and London, whilst services between London, Sevenoaks, Sutton and Brighton only show through Thameslink services. Other Tables should be consulted for additional journey opportunities.

Route Diagram for Table 53

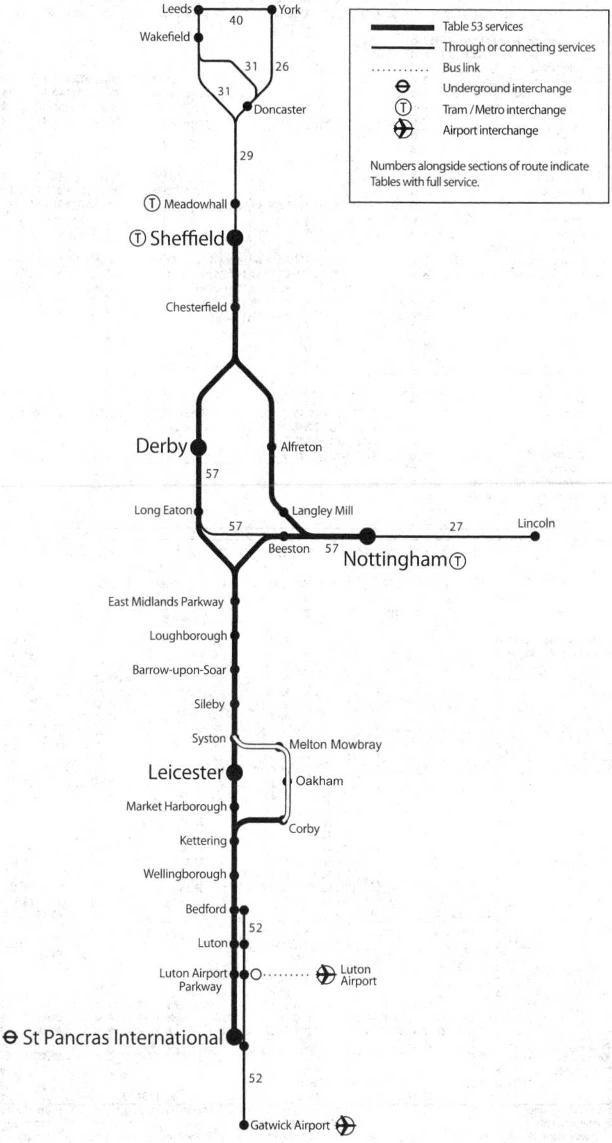

TOCs operating on this network - East Midlands Trains (EM), First Capital Connect (FC), Northern (NT), Cross Country (XC)

Table 53

Mondays to Fridays

9 December to 16 May

London - East Midlands - Sheffield

Route Diagram - see first Page of Table 53

Miles	Miles	Miles			EM MX ◇1 A	EM MO ◇1 B	EM MX ◇1 C	EM MX ◇1 A	EM MO ◇1 D	EM MO ◇1 E	EM MO ◇1 B	EM MO ◇1 F	EM MO ◇1 E	EM MO ◇1 G	EM MO ◇1 H	EM MX ◇1 I	EM MO ◇1 B	EM MX ◇1	EM ◇ J	XC ◇1 K	NT	EM ◇1	XC ◇1 L
0	0	—	**St Pancras International** ⊖52	d														00 15					
29¼	29¼	—	Luton Airport Parkway 7 52 ✈	d														00 43					
30¼	30¼	—	Luton 10 52	d														00 47					
49¾	49¾	—	Bedford 7 52	d									00 03	00 03	00 03	00 12		01 11					
65¼	65¼	—	Wellingborough	d								00 06	00 16	00 16	00 16	00 24		01 31					
72	72	0	Kettering 4	a								00 15	00 22	00 22	00 30	00 41		01 43					
—	—	—		d								00 16	00 23	00 23	00 31	00 42		01 43					
—	—	7½	Corby	d																			
—	—	21¾	Oakham	d																			
—	—	33¼	Melton Mowbray	d																			
83	83	—	Market Harborough	d								00 26	00 33	00 33		00 52	←	01 55					
99¼	99¼	48½	**Leicester**	a								00 46	00 51	00 51	01 23	01 05	01 23	02 10					
—	—	—		d				00 05	00 08	00 08	00 41	00 48	00 53	00 54	01 29	01 07	01 29						
103	103	—	Syston	d											↪								
105¾	105¾	—	Sileby	d																			
107¾	107¾	—	Barrow Upon Soar	d																			
111¾	111¾	—	Loughborough	d			00 04	00 17	00 18	00 18	00 51	00 58	01 03	01 04		01 17	01 40						
117½	117½	—	East Midlands Parkway ✈	a			00 16	00 29	00 30	00 34	01 02	01 09	01 15	01 15		01 28	01 52						
—	—	—		d	00 06		00 17	00 30	00 31	00 35	01 03	01 10	01 16	01 16		01 29	01 53						
123¼	—	—	Beeston	a	00 17				00 39	00 42	01 12					01 38							
126½	—	—	**Nottingham 8**	a	00 24				00 46	00 49	01 20					01 45							
—	—	—		d												01 51			05 21				
—	—	—	Newark Castle 27	a																			
—	—	—	Lincoln 27	a																			
138½	—	—	Langley Mill	d																			
144¾	—	—	Alfreton	d																			
—	120½	—	Long Eaton	a																			
—	128½	—	**Derby 6**	a		00 15	00 34	00 46				01 24	01 31	01 31		02 10	02 08						
—	—	—		d		00 25	00 35	00 47												05 56		06 27	06 35
155	152¾	—	Chesterfield	d		00 51	00 56	01 08											05 49	06 15	06 26	06 46	06 54
167¼	165	—	**Sheffield 7**	a		01 05	01 12	01 22											06 15	06 29	06 46	07 13	07 06
—	—	—	Doncaster 7 29	a																06 57			
—	—	—	Wakefield Kirkgate 4 31,34	a																	07 27		
—	—	—	Wakefield Westgate 7 31	a																			07 36
—	—	—	Leeds 10 31,34	a																	07 51		07 52
—	—	—	York 8 29	a																07 25			08 22

		NT	EM ◇ J	XC ◇1 M	EM ◇1	NT	EM	XC ◇1 N	EM ◇1	EM ◇ J	EM	XC FX ◇1 M	XC FO ◇1 M	EM ◇1	EM ◇1	NT	EM ◇1	XC ◇1 O	EM ◇ P	EM ◇1	EM Q	EM ◇1	EM R
St Pancras International ⊖52	d								05 45					06 32			06 52			06 55		07 24	
Luton Airport Parkway 7 52 ✈	d																07 13						
Luton 10 52	d								06 12					06 54						07 18			
Bedford 7 52	d								06 27					07 09						07 33			
Wellingborough	d								06 39					07 21						07 46			
Kettering 4	a								06 46					07 28						07 55			
	d								06 47					07 29	07 38					07 56			
Corby	d														07a47								
Oakham	d																						
Melton Mowbray	d																						
Market Harborough	d								06 57					07 39						08 07		08 16	
Leicester	a								07 10					07 51			07 57			08 22		08 29	
	d						06 26		07 12		07 28			07 52			07 58			08 23	08 26	08 30	
Syston	d						06 34				07 36										08 34		
Sileby	d						06 38				07 41										08 39		
Barrow Upon Soar	d						06 42				07 45										08 43		
Loughborough	d						06 47		07 22		07 50			08 02			08 08			08 34	08 48	08 40	←
East Midlands Parkway ✈	a						06 56		07 28		07 58						08 15			08 42	08 55	08 47	08 55
	d						06 56		07 29		07 59						08 16			08 43	08 56	08 48	08 56
Beeston	a						07 05				08 06						08 22				↪		09 03
Nottingham 8	a						07 15				08 15						08 31			08 55			09 14
	d	06 21	06 39			07 12				07 47						08 18			08 47				09 21
Newark Castle 27	a																						09 48
Lincoln 27	a																						10 14
Langley Mill	d	06 40				07 31										08 36							
Alfreton	d	06 48	07 00			07 39				08 08						08 44			09 08				
Long Eaton	a								07 33													08 51	
Derby 6	a								07 45					08 17								09 04	
	d			07 13	07 21			07 44	07 47			08 13	08 13	08 19				08 44				09 05	
Chesterfield	d	06 58	07 10	07 32	07 43	07 49		08 03	08 10	08 20		08 32	08 32	08 38		08 55		09 03	09 20			09 26	
Sheffield 7	a	07 18	07 28	07 45	08 00	08 04		08 16	08 26	08 37		08 45	08 45	08 55		09 15		09 17	09 37			09 41	
Doncaster 7 29	a			08 23								09 18	09 18										
Wakefield Kirkgate 4 31,34	a	07 57				08 57										09 57							
Wakefield Westgate 7 31	a							08 46										09 46					
Leeds 10 31,34	a	08 21				09 20		09 02								10 18		10 01					
York 8 29	a			08 47				09 26				09 42	09 43					10 27					

A from 31 December until 7 February. From St Pancras International
B from 6 January until 10 February. From St Pancras International
C until 27 December, from 11 February. From St Pancras International
D until 30 December, from 31 March. From St Pancras International
E from 17 February until 24 March. From St Pancras International
F until 30 December. From St Pancras International
G from 31 March. From St Pancras International
H from 6 January until 10 February. From St Pancras International to Derby
I From St Pancras International
J To Liverpool Lime Street
K To Newcastle
L From Birmingham New Street to Glasgow Central
M From Birmingham New Street to Newcastle
N From Birmingham New Street to Edinburgh
O From Bath Spa to Glasgow Central
P From Norwich to Liverpool Lime Street
Q To Lincoln
R From Leicester

For connections from Gatwick Airport see Table 52

Table 53

Mondays to Fridays

9 December to 16 May

London - East Midlands - Sheffield

Route Diagram - see first Page of Table 53

		EM	EM	XC	EM		EM	NT	XC	EM	EM	EM	EM	EM	EM		EM	XC	EM	EM	NT	XC	EM	EM	EM
		◇1	◇1	◇1	◇1		◇1		◇1	◇	◇1		◇1		◇1		◇	◇1	◇1	◇1		◇1	◇	◇1	
				A					B	C		D		E				F				G	C		D
St Pancras International ⊖52	d	07 28			07 57		08 00				08 13		08 26		08 29				08 56	08 59				09 15	
Luton Airport Parkway 7 52 ✈	d	07 49													08 50										
Luton 10 52	d						08 22													09 21					
Bedford 7 52	d	08 04					08 37								09 05					09 36					
Wellingborough	d	08 16					08 49								09 17					09 48					
Kettering 4	a	08 22					08 59								09 24					09 58					
	d	08 23	08 32				09 00								09 24					09 58					
Corby	d		08a42				09a10										09 26			10a07					
Oakham	d																09 48								
Melton Mowbray	d																10 01								
Market Harborough	d	08 33									09 10				09 34									10 10	
Leicester	a	08 46			08 59						09 24		09 30		09 47				09 59					10 24	
	d	08 48			09 00						09 26	09 26	09 30		09 47				10 00					10 26	10 26
Syston	d											09 34													10 34
Sileby	d											09 39													10 39
Barrow Upon Soar	d											09 43													10 43
Loughborough	d	08 58										09 48	09 40	←	09 58										10 48
East Midlands Parkway ✈	a										09 41	09 56	09 48	09 56			10 30							10 41	10 56
	d										09 42	09 56	09 48	09 56			10 30							10 42	10 56
Beeston	a	09 07										→		10 03	10 09										→
Nottingham 8	a	09 17									09 54			10 14	10 18									10 55	
	d							09 17		09 47				10 29							10 17		10 47		
Newark Castle 27	a													10 55											
Lincoln 27	a													11 32											
Langley Mill	d							09 36													10 36				
Alfreton	d							09 44		10 08											10 44		11 08		
Long Eaton	a												09 52												
Derby 6	a				09 23								10 04				10 45		10 23						
	d			09 16	09 25				09 44				10 05					10 16	10 25			10 44			
Chesterfield	d				09 44			09 55	10 03	10 20			10 26						10 44		10 55	11 03	11 20		
Sheffield 7	a			09 44	09 58			10 15	10 17	10 37			10 41					10 44	11 01		11 15	11 16	11 37		
Doncaster 7 29	a			10 18														11 18							
Wakefield Kirkgate 4 31,34	a							10 57													11 57				
Wakefield Westgate 7 31	a								10 46													11 46			
Leeds 10 31,34	a							11 18	11 01												12 18	12 01			
York 8 29	a			10 39					11 30									11 40				12 30			

			XC	EM	EM	EM	EM	EM	NT	XC	EM		EM	EM	EM	EM	EM	XC	EM	EM	NT		XC	EM	EM
			◇1	◇1		◇1	◇1	◇1		◇1	◇		◇1		◇1		◇1	◇1	◇1	◇1			◇1	◇	◇1
			H		E					B	C			D		E		F					I	C	
St Pancras International ⊖52	d			09 26		09 29	09 58	10 00					10 15		10 26		10 29		10 58	11 00					11 15
Luton Airport Parkway 7 52 ✈	d					09 50											10 50								
Luton 10 52	d							10 22												11 22					
Bedford 7 52	d					10 05		10 37									11 05			11 37					
Wellingborough	d					10 17		10 49									11 17			11 49					
Kettering 4	a					10 23		10 59									11 23			11 59					
	d					10 24		11 00									11 24			12 00					
Corby	d							11a10												12a10					
Oakham	d																								
Melton Mowbray	d																								
Market Harborough	d					10 34							11 10				11 34								12 10
Leicester	a			10 29		10 46	11 00						11 24		11 29		11 46		12 00						12 24
	d			10 29		10 47	11 00						11 26	11 26	11 29		11 47		12 00						12 26
Syston	d													11 33											
Sileby	d													11 39											
Barrow Upon Soar	d													11 43											
Loughborough	d			10 39	←	10 58								11 48	11 39	←	11 58								
East Midlands Parkway ✈	a			10 47	10 56								11 41	11 56	11 47	11 56									12 41
	d			10 47	10 56								11 42	11 56	11 47	11 56									12 42
Beeston	a				11 03	11 09								→		12 03	12 09								
Nottingham 8	a				11 14	11 18							11 55			12 14	12 18								12 55
	d				11 17				11 17		11 47					12 29					12 17			12 47	
Newark Castle 27	a				11 52											12 53									
Lincoln 27	a				12 20											13 20									
Langley Mill	d								11 36												12 36				
Alfreton	d								11 44		12 08										12 44			13 08	
Long Eaton	a			10 51											11 51										
Derby 6	a			11 04			11 23								12 04				12 23						
	d		11 11	11 14			11 25			11 44					12 05			12 16	12 25				12 44		
Chesterfield	d			11 34			11 44		11 55	12 03	12 20				12 28				12 44		12 55		13 03	13 20	
Sheffield 7	a		11 42	11 48			11 58		12 15	12 17	12 37				12 41			12 44	12 59		13 15		13 17	13 39	
Doncaster 7 29	a		12 18															13 18							
Wakefield Kirkgate 4 31,34	a								12 57												13 57				
Wakefield Westgate 7 31	a									12 46													13 46		
Leeds 10 31,34	a								13 18	13 02											14 18		14 01		
York 8 29	a		12 39							13 30								13 40					14 30		

A From Guildford to Newcastle
B From Plymouth to Edinburgh
C From Norwich to Liverpool Lime Street
D To Lincoln
E From Leicester
F From Reading to Newcastle
G From Plymouth to Glasgow Central
H From Winchester to Newcastle
I From Penzance to Glasgow Central

For connections from Gatwick Airport see Table 52

Table 53

Mondays to Fridays

9 December to 16 May

London - East Midlands - Sheffield

Route Diagram - see first Page of Table 53

		EM A	XC ◇1 B 🛒	EM ◇1 🛒	EM C	EM ◇1 🛒	EM ◇1 🛒	EM ◇1 🛒	NT	XC ◇1 D 🛒	EM ◇ E	EM ◇1 🛒	EM A	EM ◇1 🛒	EM C	EM ◇1 🛒	XC ◇1 F 🛒	EM ◇1 🛒	EM ◇1 🛒	NT	XC ◇1 G 🛒	EM ◇ E	EM ◇1 🛒
St Pancras International ⊖52	d			11 26		11 29	11 58	12 00				12 15		12 26		12 29		12 58	13 00				13 15
Luton Airport Parkway [7] 52 ✈	d					11 50										12 50							
Luton [10] 52	d							12 22											13 22				
Bedford [7] 52	d					12 05		12 37								13 05			13 37				
Wellingborough	d					12 17		12 49								13 17			13 49				
Kettering [4]	a					12 23		12 59								13 23			13 59				
	d					12 24		13 00								13 24			14 00				
Corby	d							13a10											14a10				
Oakham	d																						
Melton Mowbray	d																						
Market Harborough	d					12 34						13 10				13 34							14 10
Leicester	a			12 29		12 46	13 00					13 24		13 29		13 46		14 00					14 24
	d	12 26		12 29		12 47	13 00					13 26	13 26	13 29		13 47		14 00					14 26
Syston	d	12 34											13 33										
Sileby	d	12 39											13 39										
Barrow Upon Soar	d	12 43											13 43										
Loughborough	d	12 48		12 39	←	12 58							13 48	13 39	←	13 58							
East Midlands Parkway ✈	a	12 56		12 47	12 56							13 41	13 56	13 47	13 56								14 41
	d	12 56		12 47	12 56							13 42	13 56	13 47	13 56								14 42
Beeston	a	↪			13 03	13 08							↪		14 03	14 08							
Nottingham [8] 🚌	a				13 14	13 18						13 55			14 14	14 18							14 55
	d				13 16				13 17		13 47				14 29					14 17		14 47	
Newark Castle 27	a				13 51										14 53								
Lincoln 27	a				14 23										15 18								
Langley Mill	d								13 36											14 36			
Alfreton	d								13 44		14 08									14 44		15 08	
Long Eaton	a			12 51										13 51									
Derby [6]	a			13 04			13 23							14 04				14 23					
	d		13 11	13 14			13 25			13 44				14 05			14 16	14 25			14 44		
Chesterfield	d			13 34			13 44		13 55	14 03	14 20			14 27				14 44		14 55	15 03	15 21	
Sheffield [7] 🚌	a		13 42	13 48			14 01		14 15	14 17	14 37			14 41			14 44	14 59		15 15	15 17	15 37	
Doncaster [7] 29	a		14 18														15 18						
Wakefield Kirkgate [4] 31,34	a								14 57											15 57			
Wakefield Westgate [7] 31	a									14 46											15 46		
Leeds [10] 31,34	a								15 18	15 01										16 18	16 01		
York [8] 29	a		14 39							15 30							15 44				16 30		

		EM A	EM ◇1 🛒	EM C	EM ◇1 🛒	XC ◇1 B 🛒	EM ◇1 🛒	EM ◇1 🛒	NT	XC ◇1 H 🛒	EM ◇ E	EM ◇1 🛒	EM I	EM ◇1 🛒	EM J	EM ◇1 🛒	XC ◇1 F 🛒	EM ◇1 🛒	EM ◇1 🛒	NT	XC ◇1 K 🛒	EM ◇ E
St Pancras International ⊖52	d		13 26		13 29		13 58	14 00				14 15		14 26		14 29		14 58	15 00			
Luton Airport Parkway [7] 52 ✈	d				13 50											14 50						
Luton [10] 52	d							14 22											15 22			
Bedford [7] 52	d				14 05			14 37								15 05			15 37			
Wellingborough	d				14 17			14 49								15 17			15 49			
Kettering [4]	a				14 23			14 59								15 23			15 59			
	d				14 24			15 00								15 24			16 00			
Corby	d							15a10											16a10			
Oakham	d																					
Melton Mowbray	d																					
Market Harborough	d				14 34							15 10				15 34						
Leicester	a		14 29		14 46		15 00					15 24		15 29		15 46		16 00				
	d	14 26	14 29		14 47		15 00					15 26	15 26	15 29		15 47		16 00				
Syston	d	14 33											15 35									
Sileby	d	14 38											15 39									
Barrow Upon Soar	d	14 43											15 43									
Loughborough	d	14 48	14 39	←	14 58								15 48	15 39	←	15 58						
East Midlands Parkway ✈	a	14 56	14 47	14 56								15 41	15 57	15 47	15 57							
	d	14 56	14 47	14 56								15 42	15 57	15 47	15 57							
Beeston	a	↪		15 03	15 08								↪		16 04	16 08						
Nottingham [8] 🚌	a			15 14	15 18							15 55			16 14	16 18						
	d			15 29					15 17		15 47				16 15					16 17		16 47
Newark Castle 27	a			15 54											16 49							
Lincoln 27	a			16 25											17 17							
Langley Mill	d								15 36											16 38		
Alfreton	d								15 44		16 08									16 46		17 08
Long Eaton	a		14 51											15 51								
Derby [6]	a		15 04				15 23							16 04				16 23				
	d		15 05			15 16	15 25			15 44				16 05			16 16	16 25			16 43	
Chesterfield	d		15 28				15 44		15 55	16 03	16 21			16 28				16 44		16 57	17 04	17 18
Sheffield [7] 🚌	a		15 41			15 44	15 59		16 15	16 17	16 37			16 42			16 44	16 59		17 15	17 18	17 36
Doncaster [7] 29	a					16 18											17 18					
Wakefield Kirkgate [4] 31,34	a								16 57											17 57		
Wakefield Westgate [7] 31	a									16 49											17 47	
Leeds [10] 31,34	a								17 18	17 04										18 18	18 02	
York [8] 29	a					16 39				17 30							17 40				18 29	

A To Lincoln
B From Southampton Central to Newcastle
C From Leicester
D From Plymouth to Aberdeen
E From Norwich to Liverpool Lime Street
F From Reading to Newcastle
G From Penzance to Glasgow Central
H From Plymouth to Dundee
I To Sleaford
J From Leicester to Sleaford
K From Plymouth to Glasgow Central

For connections from Gatwick Airport see Table 52

Table 53

Mondays to Fridays

9 December to 16 May

London - East Midlands - Sheffield

Route Diagram - see first Page of Table 53

		EM ◇1 🍴	EM A	XC ◇1 B 🍴	EM ◇1 🍴	EM C	EM ◇1 🍴	EM ◇1 🍴	EM ◇1 🍴		NT	XC ◇1 D 🍴	EM ◇ E	EM ◇1 N 🍴	EM A	EM ◇1 🍴	EM C	EM ◇1 🍴	XC ◇1 F 🍴		EM ◇1 O 🍴	EM A	NT	XC ◇1 G 🍴	EM ◇ E
St Pancras International ⊖52	d	15 15			15 26		15 29	15 58	16 00					16 15		16 26		16 29			16 57				
Luton Airport Parkway 7 52 ✈	d						15 50											16 50							
Luton 10 52	d								16 23									16 53							
Bedford 7 52	d						16 05		16 37									17 08							
Wellingborough	d						16 17		16 49									17 20							
Kettering 4	a						16 23		16 59									17 26							
	d						16 24		17 00									17 27							
Corby	d								17a10																
Oakham	d																								
Melton Mowbray	d																								
Market Harborough	d	16 10					16 34							17 10				17 37							
Leicester	a	16 24			16 29		16 46	17 00						17 24		17 29		17 50			18 00				
	d	16 26	16 26		16 29		16 47	17 00						17 26	17 26	17 29		17 51			18 00	18 26			
Syston	d		16 35												17 35							18 35			
Sileby	d		16 39												17 40							18 40			
Barrow Upon Soar	d		16 43												17 45							18 44			
Loughborough	d		16 48		16 39	←	16 58								17 50	17 39	←	18 01				18 49			
East Midlands Parkway ✈	a	16 41	16 57		16 47	16 57								17 41	17 58	17 47	17 58					18 57			
	d	16 42	16 57		16 47	16 57								17 42	17 59	17 47	17 59					18 57			
Beeston	a		→			17 04	17 08								→		18 06	18 11				→			
Nottingham 8 🚊	a	16 55				17 14	17 18							17 55			18 16	18 21							
	d					17 18					17 17		17 45				18 18						18 17		18 47
Newark Castle 27	a					17 52											18 52								
Lincoln 27	a					18 26											19 24								
Langley Mill	d										17 36		18 01										18 36		
Alfreton	d										17 44		18 08										18 44		19 08
Long Eaton	a				16 51											17 51									
Derby 6	a				17 04			17 23								18 04					18 23				
	d			17 11	17 14			17 25				17 42				18 05			18 15		18 25			18 44	
Chesterfield	d				17 34			17 44			17 55	18 03	18 20			18 26					18 44		18 55	19 03	19 21
Sheffield 7 🚊	a			17 42	17 48			17 59			18 15	18 18	18 36			18 41			18 43		18 59		19 15	19 18	19 37
Doncaster 7 29	a																		19 16						
Wakefield Kirkgate 4 31,34	a										18 59												19 57		
Wakefield Westgate 7 31	a			18 13								18 47												19 50	
Leeds 10 31,34	a			18 32							19 23	19 03											20 18	20 05	
York 8 29	a			18 58								19 30							19 38					20 30	

		XC ◇1 H 🍴	EM ◇1 🍴		EM ◇1 🍴		EM ◇1 I 🍴	EM C	EM ◇1 🍴	EM ◇1 J 🍴	EM ◇1 P 🍴	EM ◇1 🍴	NT	XC ◇1 K 🍴	EM ◇ L		EM ◇1 I 🍴	XC ◇1 F	EM M	EM ◇1 🍴	EM C	EM ◇1 🍴	EM ◇1 🍴	EM ◇1 🍴	EM ◇1 🍴
St Pancras International ⊖52	d		17 00		17 15				17 30	17 45	17 57	18 00								18 15		18 25	18 30	18 57	19 00
Luton Airport Parkway 7 52 ✈	d									18 08													18 52		
Luton 10 52	d				17 40							18 23										18 50			19 23
Bedford 7 52	d		17 35						18 03			18 38											19 07		19 39
Wellingborough	d		17 51						18 15	18 32		18 51								19 00			19 19		19 53
Kettering 4	a		18 00						18 22	18 43		19 00								19 07			19 27		20 03
	d		18 06	18 14					18 22	18 44		19 06								19 08			19 27		20 04
Corby	d		18a15									19 16													20a14
Oakham	d											19 37													
Melton Mowbray	d											19a48													
Market Harborough	d				18 16		←		18 32	18 56							←					19 25		19 49	
Leicester	a			18 35	18 30		18 35		18 46	19 10	19 00						19 10			19 30		19 40	19 52	20 02	
	d			18 37	18 32		18 37		18 47	19 14	19 00						19 14		19 26	19 32		19 41	19 52	20 02	
Syston	d			→						→									19 35						
Sileby	d																		19 39						
Barrow Upon Soar	d																		19 43						
Loughborough	d						18 47	←	18 57								19 26		19 48	19 43	←	19 52		20 13	
East Midlands Parkway ✈	a				18 48		18 54	18 57	19 04								19 33		19 56	19 50	19 56		20 06	20 20	
	d				18 50		18 56	18 57	19 05								19 34		19 56	19 52	19 56		20 08	20 21	
Beeston	a				19 00			19 05	19 11										→		20 05		20 15		
Nottingham 8 🚊	a				19 08			19 12	19 20								19 47			20 08	20 13		20 23		
	d							19 20					19 17		19 41		20 06			20 34			20 30		
Newark Castle 27	a							19 53															20 54		
Lincoln 27	a							20 17															21 22		
Langley Mill	d												19 36							20 51					
Alfreton	d												19 44		20 02					20 59					
Long Eaton	a						18 59										20 18					20 01			
Derby 6	a						19 13				19 23						20 31					20 15		20 34	
	d	19 09					19 16				19 25			19 43				20 09				20 15		20 34	
Chesterfield	d	19 28					19 35				19 44		19 56	20 05	20 13					21 10		20 39		20 54	
Sheffield 7 🚊	a	19 41					19 52				19 59		20 15	20 19	20 27			20 39		21 25		20 54		21 08	
Doncaster 7 29	a	20 15																21 19							
Wakefield Kirkgate 4 31,34	a												20 58												
Wakefield Westgate 7 31	a													20 47						22 00					
Leeds 10 31,34	a												21 20	21 06						22 17					
York 8 29	a	20 38																21 44							

A To Lincoln
B From Southampton Central to Edinburgh
C From Leicester
D From Plymouth to Edinburgh
E From Norwich to Liverpool Lime Street
F From Reading to Newcastle
G From Plymouth to Edinburgh. 🍴 to Leeds
H From Southampton Central to Newcastle
I From St Pancras International
J To Derby
K From Plymouth
L From Norwich to Manchester Piccadilly
M To Nottingham
N The Robin Hood
O The Master Cutler
P The South Yorkshireman

For connections from Gatwick Airport see Table 52

Table 53

London - East Midlands - Sheffield

Mondays to Fridays

9 December to 16 May

Route Diagram - see first Page of Table 53

		XC	NT	EM	EM	EM	EM	XC	EM	EM	EM	NT	EM	EM	EM	EM	EM	XC	EM	EM	EM	EM
		◇1		◇1		◇1		◇1	◇1	◇1	◇1		◇1		◇1		◇1	◇1	◇1	◇1	◇1	◇1
		A			B		C	D						B		C		A				
				🍴		🍴			🍴	🍴	🍴		🍴		🍴		🍴		🍴	🍴	🍴	🍴
St Pancras International ⊖52	d			19 15		19 28			19 32	19 55	20 00		20 15		20 26		20 29		20 55	21 01		21 25
Luton Airport Parkway 7 52 ✈	d								19 55								20 50					
Luton 10 52	d										20 22									21 23		
Bedford 7 52	d								20 11		20 37						21 05			21 38		
Wellingborough	d								20 24		20 50						21 17			21 50		
Kettering 4	a					20 14					21 00						21 24			21 56		
	d					20 15					21 01						21 24			21 57	22 11	
Corby	d										21a11										22a20	
Oakham	d																					
Melton Mowbray	d																					
Market Harborough	d			20 11		20 25			20 39				21 09				21 34			22 07		22 18
Leicester	a			20 23		20 39			20 54	21 01			21 21		21 28		21 47		21 59	22 20		22 31
	d			20 25	20 28	20 41			20 54	21 02			21 21	21 27	21 29		21 48		22 01	22 22		22 33
Syston	d				20 36									21 34								
Sileby	d				20 40									21 38								
Barrow Upon Soar	d				20 44									21 42								
Loughborough	d				20 49	20 51	←		21 05					21 47	21 38	←	21 59			22 32		22 43
East Midlands Parkway ✈	a			20 37	20 58	20 57	20 58						21 34	21 56	21 45	21 56				22 38		22 49
	d			20 38	20 58	20 58	20 58						21 35	21 56	21 45	21 56				22 39		22 50
Beeston	a				↪		21 05		21 18					↪		22 05	22 10					
Nottingham 8 🚌	a			20 51			21 15		21 28				21 49			22 15	22 19					23 03
	d		20 47						21 33			21 15										
Newark Castle 27	a																					
Lincoln 27	a																					
Langley Mill	d								21 56			21 40										
Alfreton	d								22 04			21 48										
Long Eaton	a					21 02									21 49							
Derby 6	a		21 08			21 15				21 29					22 05				22 22	22 53		
	d	20 44	21 09					21 19		21 32								21 44	22 24			
Chesterfield	d	21 03	21 31					21 38	22 15	21 53		22 00						22 07	22 43			
Sheffield 7 🚌	a	21 15	21 55					21 50	22 34	22 08		22 19						22 24	22 57			
Doncaster 7 29	a							22 29														
Wakefield Kirkgate 4 31,34	a																					
Wakefield Westgate 7 31	a	21 47							23 21	22 46								22 59				
Leeds 10 31,34	a	22 02							23 41	23 05								23 15				
York 8 29	a							22 52														

		EM	EM	EM	EM	EM	EM	EM
		◇1	◇1	◇1	◇1	◇1	◇1	◇1
			E		F	E	F	
		🍴	🍴	🍴	🍴	🍴	🍴	🍴
St Pancras International ⊖52	d	21 28	22 00		22 00	22 25	22 25	23 15
Luton Airport Parkway 7 52 ✈	d	21 49				22 48	22 51	
Luton 10 52	d		22 24		22 33			23 46
Bedford 7 52	d	22 04	22 39		22 53	23 03	23 15	00 12
Wellingborough	d	22 16	22 52		23 06	23 17	23 28	00 24
Kettering 4	a	22 22	22 59		23 14	23 25	23 36	00 41
	d	22 23	23 00	23 11	23 15	23 26	23 37	00 42
Corby	d			23a20				
Oakham	d							
Melton Mowbray	d							
Market Harborough	d	22 33	23 11		23 26	23 37	23 48	00 52
Leicester	a	22 46	23 26		23 40	23 51	00 03	01 05
	d	22 48	23 27		23 42	23 53	00 05	01 07
Syston	d							
Sileby	d							
Barrow Upon Soar	d							
Loughborough	d	22 58	23 38		23 53	00 04	00 17	01 17
East Midlands Parkway ✈	a	23 09	23 51		00 05	00 16	00 29	01 28
	d	23 10	23 52		00 06	00 17	00 30	01 29
Beeston	a		00 02		00 17			01 38
Nottingham 8 🚌	a		00 09		00 24			01 45
	d							01 51
Newark Castle 27	a							
Lincoln 27	a							
Langley Mill	d							
Alfreton	d							
Long Eaton	a	23 17						
Derby 6	a	23 30				00 34	00 46	02 10
	d					00 35	00 47	
Chesterfield	d					00 56	01 08	
Sheffield 7 🚌	a					01 12	01 22	
Doncaster 7 29	a							
Wakefield Kirkgate 4 31,34	a							
Wakefield Westgate 7 31	a							
Leeds 10 31,34	a							
York 8 29	a							

A From Plymouth
B To Nottingham
C From Leicester
D From Southampton Central
E until 27 December, from 10 February
F from 30 December until 7 February

For connections from Gatwick Airport see Table 52

Table 53

London - East Midlands - Sheffield

Saturdays

14 December to 17 May

Route Diagram - see first Page of Table 53

		EM	EM	EM	EM	EM	EM	XC	EM	XC		EM	XC	EM	NT	EM	XC	EM	EM	EM		XC	EM	EM	NT
		◇1	◇1	◇1	◇1	◇1	◇	◇1	◇1	◇1		◇	◇1	◇1			◇1	◇1	◇			◇1	◇1	◇1	
		A	B	A	C		D	E		F		D	G				H		D			G			
		⚲	⚲	⚲	⚲	⚲			⚲	⚲			⚲	⚲			⚲	⚲				⚲	⚲	⚲	
St Pancras International ⊖52	d					00 15												05 45					06 37		
Luton Airport Parkway 7 52 ✈	d					00 43																			
Luton 10 52	d					00 47												06 12					06 59		
Bedford 7 52	d				00 12	01 11												06 27							
Wellingborough	d				00 24	01 31												06 39							
Kettering 4	a				00 41	01 43												06 46					07 26		
	d				00 42	01 43												06 47					07 27	07 35	
Corby	d																							07a44	
Oakham	d																								
Melton Mowbray	d																								
Market Harborough	d				00 52	01 55												06 57					07 37		
Leicester	a				01 05	02 10												07 10					07 51		
	d			00 05	01 07											06 26		07 12		07 27			07 52		
Syston	d															06 34				07 36					
Sileby	d															06 39				07 41					
Barrow Upon Soar	d															06 43				07 45					
Loughborough	d		00 04	00 17	01 17											06 48		07 23		07 50			08 02		
East Midlands Parkway ✈	a		00 16	00 29	01 28											06 56				07 58			08 09		
	d	00 06	00 17	00 30	01 29											06 56				07 59			08 10		
Beeston	a	00 17			01 38											07 05				08 05					
Nottingham 8 ⛴	a	00 24			01 45											07 15				08 15					
	d				01 51		05 20					06 40			07 11				07 47						08 17
Newark Castle 27	a																								
Lincoln 27	a																								
Langley Mill	d														07 30										08 36
Alfreton	d											07 01			07 38				08 09						08 44
Long Eaton	a																	07 31							
Derby 6	a		00 34	00 46	02 10													07 42					08 21		
	d		00 35	00 47				05 55	06 27	06 38			07 12	07 21			07 44	07 49				08 12	08 23		
Chesterfield	d		00 56	01 08			05 49	06 31	06 46	06 57		07 11	07 31	07 43	07 48		08 03	08 10	08 20			08 31	08 42		08 55
Sheffield 7 ⛴	a		01 12	01 22			06 15	06 43	07 10	07 09		07 28	07 48	07 59	08 11		08 16	08 26	08 37			08 45	08 57		09 15
Doncaster 7 29	a							07 16					08 23									09 18	09 53		
Wakefield Kirkgate 4 31,34	a														08 57										09 57
Wakefield Westgate 7 31	a									07 36							08 45								
Leeds 10 31,34	a									07 51					09 20		09 03								10 18
York 8 29	a							07 43		08 24			08 47				09 30					09 43	10 16		

		EM	XC	EM	EM	EM		EM	EM	EM	XC	EM	EM	NT	XC	EM		EM	EM	EM	EM	EM	XC	EM	EM
		◇1	◇1	◇	◇1			◇1		◇1	◇1	◇1	◇1		◇1	◇		◇1		◇1		◇1	◇1	◇1	◇1
			I	J		K			L		M				N	J			K		L		O		
		⚲	⚲		⚲			⚲		⚲	⚲	⚲	⚲		⚲			⚲		⚲		⚲	⚲	⚲	⚲
St Pancras International ⊖52	d	06 52			06 58					07 28		07 56	08 00					08 13		08 27		08 29		08 56	09 00
Luton Airport Parkway 7 52 ✈	d	07 13								07 49												08 50			
Luton 10 52	d				07 19								08 22												09 22
Bedford 7 52	d				07 33					08 03			08 37									09 05			09 37
Wellingborough	d				07 45					08 15			08 49									09 17			09 49
Kettering 4	a				07 54					08 22			08 59									09 24			09 59
	d				07 55					08 22			09 00									09 24			10 00
Corby	d												09a10												10a10
Oakham	d																								
Melton Mowbray	d																								
Market Harborough	d				08 05					08 32								09 10				09 34			
Leicester	a	07 59			08 21					08 46		08 59						09 24		09 30		09 46		10 00	
	d	08 00			08 23	08 26		08 29		08 47		09 00						09 26	09 26	09 30		09 47		10 00	
Syston	d					08 34													09 34						
Sileby	d					08 39													09 39						
Barrow Upon Soar	d					08 43													09 43						
Loughborough	d	08 10			08 33	08 48		08 39	←	08 57									09 48	09 40	←	09 58			
East Midlands Parkway ✈	a				08 39	08 56		08 46	08 56									09 41	09 56	09 47	09 56				
	d				08 40	08 56		08 47	08 56									09 42	09 56	09 47	09 56				
Beeston	a	08 20				↪			09 03	09 07									↪		10 03	10 09			
Nottingham 8 ⛴	a	08 30			08 53				09 12	09 17								09 54			10 14	10 18			
	d			08 48					09 22					09 17		09 47					10 29				
Newark Castle 27	a								09 49												10 55				
Lincoln 27	a								10 14												11 31				
Langley Mill	d													09 36											
Alfreton	d			09 10										09 44		10 10									
Long Eaton	a							08 50												09 51					
Derby 6	a							09 03				09 23								10 04				10 24	
	d		08 44					09 04			09 16	09 25			09 44					10 05			10 16	10 25	
Chesterfield	d		09 03	09 21				09 28				09 44		09 55	10 03	10 20				10 26				10 44	
Sheffield 7 ⛴	a		09 17	09 38				09 42			09 44	09 58		10 15	10 17	10 37				10 41			10 44	10 58	
Doncaster 7 29	a										10 17												11 15		
Wakefield Kirkgate 4 31,34	a													10 57											
Wakefield Westgate 7 31	a		09 46												10 46										
Leeds 10 31,34	a		10 01											11 18	11 01										
York 8 29	a		10 30								10 39				11 30								11 40		

A from 4 January until 8 February. From St Pancras International
B from 15 February. From St Pancras International
C From St Pancras International
D To Liverpool Lime Street
E To Newcastle
F From Birmingham New Street to Glasgow Central
G From Birmingham New Street to Newcastle
H From Birmingham New Street to Edinburgh
I From Bristol Temple Meads to Glasgow Central
J From Norwich to Liverpool Lime Street
K To Lincoln
L From Leicester
M From Guildford to Newcastle
N From Plymouth to Edinburgh
O From Bournemouth to Newcastle

For connections from Gatwick Airport see Table 52

Table 53

Saturdays

14 December to 17 May

London - East Midlands - Sheffield

Route Diagram - see first Page of Table 53

		NT		XC ◇1 A	EM ◇ B	EM ◇1	EM C	XC ◇1 D	EM ◇1	EM E	EM ◇1	EM ◇1		EM ◇1	NT	XC ◇1 F	EM ◇ B	EM ◇1	EM C	EM ◇1	EM E	EM ◇1		XC ◇1 G	EM ◇1
St Pancras International ⊖52	d					09 15			09 26		09 29	09 57		10 00				10 15		10 26		10 29			10 58
Luton Airport Parkway 7 52	d										09 50											10 50			
Luton 10 52	d													10 22											
Bedford 7 52	d										10 05			10 37								11 05			
Wellingborough	d										10 17			10 49								11 17			
Kettering 4	a										10 23			10 59								11 23			
	d										10 24			11 00								11 24			
Corby	d													11a10											
Oakham	d																								
Melton Mowbray	d																								
Market Harborough	d					10 10					10 34							11 10				11 34			
Leicester	a					10 24			10 29		10 46	11 00						11 24		11 29		11 46			11 59
	d					10 26	10 26		10 29		10 47	11 00						11 26	11 26	11 29		11 47			12 00
Syston	d						10 34												11 33						
Sileby	d						10 39												11 38						
Barrow Upon Soar	d						10 43												11 43						
Loughborough	d						10 48		10 39	←	10 58								11 48	11 39	←	11 58			
East Midlands Parkway	a					10 41	10 56		10 47	10 56								11 41	11 56	11 47	11 56				
	d					10 42	10 56		10 48	10 56								11 42	11 56	11 48	11 56				
Beeston	a						↪			11 03	11 09								↪		12 03	12 09			
Nottingham 8	a					10 55				11 14	11 18							11 55			12 14	12 18			
	d	10 17			10 47					11 17					11 17		11 47				12 27				
Newark Castle 27	a									11 52											12 50				
Lincoln 27	a									12 26											13 18				
Langley Mill	d	10 36													11 36										
Alfreton	d	10 44			11 10										11 44		12 10								
Long Eaton	a								10 51											11 51					
Derby 6	a								11 04			11 23								12 04					12 23
	d			10 44				11 11	11 15			11 25				11 44				12 05				12 16	12 25
Chesterfield	d	10 55		11 03	11 20				11 34			11 44			11 55	12 03	12 21			12 26					12 44
Sheffield 7	a	11 15		11 17	11 37			11 42	11 48			11 58			12 15	12 17	12 37			12 41				12 44	12 59
Doncaster 7 29	a							12 15																13 17	
Wakefield Kirkgate 4 31,34	a	11 58													12 57										
Wakefield Westgate 7 31	a			11 46												12 46									
Leeds 10 31,34	a	12 18		12 00											13 18	13 02									
York 8 29	a			12 30				12 39								13 30								13 39	

		EM ◇1	NT	XC ◇1 H	EM ◇ B	EM ◇1	EM C	XC ◇1 D		EM ◇1	EM E	EM ◇1	EM ◇1	EM ◇1	NT	XC ◇1 I	EM ◇ B	EM ◇1		EM C	EM ◇1	EM E	EM ◇1	XC ◇1 G	EM ◇1
St Pancras International ⊖52	d	11 00				11 15				11 26		11 29	11 58	12 00				12 15			12 26		12 29		12 58
Luton Airport Parkway 7 52	d											11 50											12 50		
Luton 10 52	d	11 22												12 22											
Bedford 7 52	d	11 37										12 05		12 37									13 05		
Wellingborough	d	11 49										12 17		12 49									13 17		
Kettering 4	a	11 59										12 23		12 59									13 23		
	d	12 00										12 24		13 00									13 24		
Corby	d	12a10												13a10											
Oakham	d																								
Melton Mowbray	d																								
Market Harborough	d					12 10						12 34						13 10					13 34		
Leicester	a					12 24				12 29		12 46	13 00					13 24			13 29		13 46		14 00
	d					12 26	12 26			12 29		12 47	13 00					13 26		13 26	13 29		13 47		14 00
Syston	d						12 34													13 34					
Sileby	d						12 39													13 39					
Barrow Upon Soar	d						12 43													13 43					
Loughborough	d						12 48			12 39	←	12 58								13 48	13 39	←	13 58		
East Midlands Parkway	a					12 41	12 56			12 47	12 56							13 41		13 56	13 47	13 56			
	d					12 42	12 56			12 48	12 56							13 42		13 56	13 48	13 56			
Beeston	a						↪				13 03	13 09								↪		14 03	14 09		
Nottingham 8	a					12 55					13 14	13 18						13 55				14 14	14 18		
	d		12 17		12 47						13 17				13 17		13 47					14 29			
Newark Castle 27	a										13 51											14 55			
Lincoln 27	a										14 23											15 22			
Langley Mill	d		12 36												13 36										
Alfreton	d		12 44		13 10										13 44		14 10								
Long Eaton	a									12 51											13 51				
Derby 6	a									13 04			13 23								14 04				14 24
	d			12 44				13 11		13 14			13 25			13 44					14 04			14 16	14 25
Chesterfield	d		12 55	13 03	13 20					13 34			13 44		13 55	14 03	14 20				14 28				14 45
Sheffield 7	a		13 15	13 17	13 37			13 43		13 48			14 01		14 15	14 17	14 37				14 41			14 44	14 59
Doncaster 7 29	a							14 18																15 17	
Wakefield Kirkgate 4 31,34	a		13 57												14 57										
Wakefield Westgate 7 31	a			13 46												14 46									
Leeds 10 31,34	a		14 18	14 01											15 18	15 01									
York 8 29	a			14 30				14 39								15 30								15 39	

A From Plymouth to Glasgow Central
B From Norwich to Liverpool Lime Street
C To Lincoln
D From Southampton Central to Newcastle
E From Leicester
F From Plymouth to Edinburgh
G From Reading to Newcastle
H From Penzance to Glasgow Central
I From Plymouth to Aberdeen

For connections from Gatwick Airport see Table 52

Table 53

Saturdays

14 December to 17 May

London - East Midlands - Sheffield

Route Diagram - see first Page of Table 53

		EM	NT	XC		EM	EM	EM	EM	EM	EM	XC	EM	EM		NT	XC	EM	EM	EM	EM	EM	EM	XC	
		◇1		◇1		◇	◇1		◇1		◇1	◇1	◇1	◇1			◇1	◇	◇1		◇1		◇1	◇1	
				A		B		C		D		E					F	B		C		D		G	
St Pancras International ⊖52	d	13 00					13 15		13 26		13 29		13 58	14 00					14 15		14 26		14 29		
Luton Airport Parkway 7 52	d										13 50												14 50		
Luton 10 52	d	13 22												14 22											
Bedford 7 52	d	13 37									14 05			14 37									15 05		
Wellingborough	d	13 49									14 17			14 49									15 17		
Kettering 4	a	13 59									14 23			14 59									15 23		
	d	14 00									14 24			15 00									15 24		
Corby	d	14a10												15a10											
Oakham	d																								
Melton Mowbray	d																								
Market Harborough	d						14 10				14 34								15 10				15 34		
Leicester	a						14 24		14 29		14 46		14 59						15 24		15 29		15 46		
	d						14 26	14 26	14 29		14 47		15 00						15 26	15 26	15 29		15 47		
Syston	d							14 34												15 34					
Sileby	d							14 39												15 38					
Barrow Upon Soar	d							14 43												15 43					
Loughborough	d							14 48	14 39	←	14 58									15 48	15 39	←	15 58		
East Midlands Parkway	a						14 41	14 56	14 47	14 56									15 41	15 56	15 47	15 56			
	d						14 42	14 56	14 48	14 56									15 42	15 56	15 47	15 56			
Beeston	a							→		15 03	15 09									→		16 03	16 09		
Nottingham 8	a						14 55			15 14	15 18								15 55			16 14	16 18		
	d		14 17			14 47				15 22						15 17		15 47				16 15			
Newark Castle 27	a									15 50												16 49			
Lincoln 27	a									16 21												17 16			
Langley Mill	d		14 36													15 36									
Alfreton	d		14 44			15 10										15 44		16 10							
Long Eaton	a								14 51												15 51				
Derby 6	a								15 04				15 23								16 04				
	d			14 44					15 05			15 15	15 25				15 44				16 05			16 16	
Chesterfield	d		14 55	15 03		15 20			15 28				15 44			15 55	16 03	16 20			16 28				
Sheffield 7	a		15 15	15 17		15 37			15 41			15 44	15 59			16 15	16 17	16 37			16 41			16 44	
Doncaster 7 29	a											16 18												17 16	
Wakefield Kirkgate 4 31,34	a		15 57													16 57									
Wakefield Westgate 7 31	a			15 46													16 46								
Leeds 10 31,34	a		16 18	16 01												17 18	17 01								
York 8 29	a			16 30								16 39					17 30							17 37	

		EM	EM	NT	XC	EM	EM	EM	EM	EM		EM	XC	EM	EM	NT	XC	EM	EM	EM		EM	EM	EM	XC
		◇1	◇1		◇1	◇	◇1		◇1			◇1	◇1	◇1	◇1		◇1	◇	◇1			◇1		◇1	◇1
					H	B		C		D			E				I	B		C			D		G
St Pancras International ⊖52	d	14 58	15 00				15 15		15 26			15 29		15 58	16 00				16 15			16 26		16 29	
Luton Airport Parkway 7 52	d											15 50												16 50	
Luton 10 52	d		15 22												16 22										
Bedford 7 52	d		15 37									16 05			16 37									17 05	
Wellingborough	d		15 49									16 17			16 49									17 17	
Kettering 4	a		15 59									16 23			16 59									17 23	
	d		16 00									16 24			17 00									17 24	
Corby	d		16a10												17a10										
Oakham	d																								
Melton Mowbray	d																								
Market Harborough	d						16 10					16 34							17 10					17 34	
Leicester	a	16 00					16 24		16 29			16 46		17 00					17 24			17 29		17 46	
	d	16 00					16 26	16 26	16 29			16 47		17 00					17 26	17 26		17 29		17 47	
Syston	d							16 34												17 34					
Sileby	d							16 39												17 39					
Barrow Upon Soar	d							16 43												17 44					
Loughborough	d							16 48	16 39	←		16 58								17 49		17 39	←	17 58	
East Midlands Parkway	a						16 41	16 56	16 47	16 56									17 41	17 57		17 47	17 57		
	d						16 42	16 57	16 48	16 57									17 42	17 58		17 47	17 58		
Beeston	a							→		17 04		17 09								→			18 05	18 09	
Nottingham 8	a						16 55			17 14		17 18							17 55				18 14	18 18	
	d			16 17		16 44				17 15						17 17		17 44					18 15		
Newark Castle 27	a									17 49													18 50		
Lincoln 27	a									18 22													19 25		
Langley Mill	d			16 36												17 36		18 00							
Alfreton	d			16 44		17 05										17 44		18 07							
Long Eaton	a								16 51													17 51			
Derby 6	a	16 23							17 04					17 23								18 04			
	d	16 25			16 43				17 05				17 16	17 25			17 44					18 05			18 13
Chesterfield	d	16 44		16 55	17 04	17 15			17 26					17 44		17 55	18 03	18 18				18 26			
Sheffield 7	a	16 59		17 15	17 18	17 34			17 41				17 44	17 59		18 15	18 18	18 33				18 41			18 43
Doncaster 7 29	a																								19 16
Wakefield Kirkgate 4 31,34	a			17 57												18 58									
Wakefield Westgate 7 31	a				17 47								18 12				18 46								
Leeds 10 31,34	a			18 18	18 02								18 31			19 23	19 00								
York 8 29	a				18 30								18 57				19 30								19 38

A From Penzance to Glasgow Central
B From Norwich to Liverpool Lime Street
C To Lincoln
D From Leicester
E From Southampton Central to Newcastle
F From Plymouth to Dundee
G From Reading to Newcastle
H From Plymouth to Glasgow Central
I From Plymouth to Edinburgh

For connections from Gatwick Airport see Table 52

Table 53

Saturdays

14 December to 17 May

London - East Midlands - Sheffield

Route Diagram - see first Page of Table 53

		EM	EM	NT	XC	EM		EM	EM	EM	EM	EM	XC	EM	EM	NT		XC	EM	EM	EM	EM	EM	EM	XC
		◇1	◇1		◇1	◇		◇1		◇1		◇1	◇1	◇1	◇1			◇1	◇	◇1		◇1		◇1	◇1
					A	B			C		D		E					F	G		H		D		I
		trolley	trolley		trolley			trolley		trolley		trolley	trolley	trolley	trolley			trolley		trolley		trolley		trolley	
St Pancras International ⊖52	d	16 57	17 00					17 15		17 26		17 29		17 57	18 00					18 15		18 26		18 29	
Luton Airport Parkway 7 52 ✈	d											17 50												18 50	
Luton 10 52	d		17 22												18 22										
Bedford 7 52	d		17 37									18 05			18 37									19 05	
Wellingborough	d		17 49									18 17			18 49									19 17	
Kettering 4	a		18 00									18 23			18 59									19 23	
	d		18 01									18 24			19 00									19 24	
Corby	d		18a11												19a09										
Oakham	d																								
Melton Mowbray	d																								
Market Harborough	d							18 10				18 34								19 10				19 34	
Leicester	a	18 00						18 24		18 29		18 46		19 00						19 24		19 29		19 46	
	d	18 00						18 26	18 26	18 29		18 47		19 00						19 26	19 26	19 29		19 47	
Syston	d								18 34												19 34				
Sileby	d								18 39												19 39				
Barrow Upon Soar	d								18 43												19 43				
Loughborough	d								18 48	18 39	←	18 58									19 48	19 39	←	19 58	
East Midlands Parkway ✈	a							18 41	18 56	18 47	18 56									19 41	19 56	19 47	19 56		
	d							18 42	18 56	18 48	18 56									19 42	19 56	19 48	19 56		
Beeston	a								↦		19 03	19 09									↦		20 03	20 09	
Nottingham 8 ⛴	a							18 55			19 15	19 18								19 55			20 12	20 18	
	d			18 17		18 47						19 29				19 17			19 39	20 16			20 30		
Newark Castle 27	a											19 52											20 55		
Lincoln 27	a											20 26											21 23		
Langley Mill	d			18 36												19 36				20 33					
Alfreton	d			18 44		19 10										19 44			20 00	20 41					
Long Eaton	a									18 51												19 51			
Derby 6	a	18 23								19 04				19 23								20 04			
	d	18 25			18 44					19 05			19 12	19 25				19 44				20 05			20 12
Chesterfield	d	18 44		18 55	19 03	19 21				19 26			19 31	19 44		19 55		20 05	20 10	20 52		20 26			20 31
Sheffield 7 ⛴	a	18 59		19 15	19 18	19 37				19 41			19 44	19 59		20 15		20 21	20 28	21 05		20 41			20 49
Doncaster 7 29	a												20 18												21 21
Wakefield Kirkgate 4 31,34	a			19 58												20 57									
Wakefield Westgate 7 31	a				19 49													20 48		21 59					
Leeds 10 31,34	a			20 20	20 04											21 20		21 02		22 18					
York 8 29	a				20 30								20 39					21 57							21 43

		EM		EM	XC	NT	EM	EM	EM	XC	NT	EM		EM	EM	EM	EM	EM	EM	EM	EM	EM		EM	XC
		◇1		◇1	◇1		◇1		◇1	◇1				◇1	◇1	◇1	◇1		◇1		◇1	◇1		◇1	◇1
					J			H		K		D						C		D	L	M		N	J
		trolley		trolley			trolley		trolley					trolley	trolley	trolley	trolley		trolley		trolley	trolley		trolley	
St Pancras International ⊖52	d	18 57		19 00			19 15		19 26					19 29	19 57	20 02	20 15		20 26		20 29	20 29		20 29	
Luton Airport Parkway 7 52 ✈	d													19 50							20 50	20 50		20 50	
Luton 10 52	d			19 22												20 25									
Bedford 7 52	d			19 37										20 05		20 39					21 05	21 05		21 05	
Wellingborough	d			19 49										20 17		20 51					21 17	21 17		21 17	
Kettering 4	a			19 59										20 23		21 01					21 24	21 24		21 24	
	d			20 00										20 24		21 02					21 24	21 24		21 24	
Corby	d			20a10												21a12									
Oakham	d																								
Melton Mowbray	d																								
Market Harborough	d						20 10							20 34			21 09				21 34	21 34		21 34	
Leicester	a	20 00					20 24		20 31					20 46	21 03		21 23		21 28		21 47	21 52		21 52	
	d	20 00					20 26	20 26	20 33					20 47	21 05		21 24	21 26	21 29		21 48	21 53		21 53	
Syston	d							20 34										21 34							
Sileby	d							20 39										21 39							
Barrow Upon Soar	d							20 43										21 43							
Loughborough	d							20 48	20 43			←		20 58				21 48	21 39	←	21 59	22 03		22 03	
East Midlands Parkway ✈	a						20 41	20 56	20 49			20 56					21 37	21 56	21 46	21 56	22 06	22 10		22 17	
	d						20 42	20 56	20 50			20 56					21 38	21 57	21 47	21 57	22 07	22 11		22 18	
Beeston	a							↦				21 03		21 09				↦		22 04	22 13	22 17		22 24	
Nottingham 8 ⛴	a						20 55					21 14		21 18			21 50			22 14	22 20	22 25		22 33	
	d					20 43					21 17	21 26													
Newark Castle 27	a											21 55													
Lincoln 27	a											22 40													
Langley Mill	d					21 08					21 36														
Alfreton	d					21 16					21 44														
Long Eaton	a								21 00										21 51						
Derby 6	a	20 23							21 12						21 31				22 05						
	d	20 25			20 44					21 27					21 37										21 44
Chesterfield	d	20 44			21 05	21 26				21 47	21 55				21 59										22 05
Sheffield 7 ⛴	a	20 59			21 19	21 43				22 05	22 14				22 16										22 22
Doncaster 7 29	a									22 30															22 51
Wakefield Kirkgate 4 31,34	a																								
Wakefield Westgate 7 31	a				21 48										22 44										23 09
Leeds 10 31,34	a				22 01										23 03										23 27
York 8 29	a									22 55															

A From Plymouth to Edinburgh. trolley to Leeds
B From Norwich to Liverpool Lime Street
C To Nottingham
D From Leicester
E From Southampton Central to Newcastle
F From Plymouth. trolley to Leeds
G From Norwich to Manchester Piccadilly
H To Lincoln
I From Reading to Newcastle
J From Plymouth
K From Southampton Central
L until 8 February
M from 29 March
N from 15 February until 22 March

For connections from Gatwick Airport see Table 52

Table 53

Saturdays

London - East Midlands - Sheffield

14 December to 17 May

Route Diagram - see first Page of Table 53

		EM	EM	EM	EM	EM	EM	EM	EM	EM	EM	EM	EM
		◇1	◇1	◇1	◇1	◇1	◇1	◇1	◇1	◇1	◇1	◇1	◇1
		A	B	A	B		A	B	B	A			
		🚲	🚲	🚲	🚲	☕	🚲	🚲	🚲	🚲	🚲	☕	🚲
St Pancras International ⊖52	d	20 56	20 56	21 00	21 00		21 25	21 25	21 30	21 30	22 00		22 26
Luton Airport Parkway 7 52 ✈	d								21 51	21 51			22 47
Luton 10 52	d			21 23	21 23						22 24		
Bedford 7 52	d			21 38	21 38				22 06	22 06	22 40		23 03
Wellingborough	d			21 51	21 51				22 18	22 18	22 53		23 15
Kettering 4	a			22 00	22 00				22 25	22 25	23 00		23 21
	d			22 01	22 01	22 06			22 25	22 25	23 01	23 06	23 22
Corby	d					22a15						23a15	
Oakham	d												
Melton Mowbray	d												
Market Harborough	d			22 12	22 12		22 19	22 19	22 35	22 35	23 12		23 32
Leicester	a	22 00	22 00	22 27	22 27		22 31	22 32	22 49	22 49	23 27		23 45
	d	22 00	22 00	22 28	22 28		22 33	22 33	22 50	22 50	23 28		23 47
Syston	d												
Sileby	d												
Barrow Upon Soar	d												
Loughborough	d			22 39	22 39		22 43	22 44	23 00	23 00	23 39		23 56
East Midlands Parkway ✈	a						22 49	22 57	23 12	23 12	23 50		00 07
	d						22 50	22 58	23 13	23 13	23 51		00 09
Beeston	a										00 01		
Nottingham 8	a						23 02	23 10			00 10		
	d												
Newark Castle 27	a												
Lincoln 27	a												
Langley Mill	d												
Alfreton	d												
Long Eaton	a								23 19	23 20			00 16
Derby 6	a	22 24	22 33	23 00	23 07				23 31	23 31			00 28
	d	22 26	22 35										
Chesterfield	d	22 48	22 56										
Sheffield 7	a	23 01	23 09										
Doncaster 7 29	a												
Wakefield Kirkgate 4 31,34	a												
Wakefield Westgate 7 31	a												
Leeds 10 31,34	a												
York 8 29	a												

Sundays

8 December to 29 December

		EM	XC	EM	EM	NT	XC	EM	EM	EM	NT	XC	EM	EM	EM	NT	EM	XC	EM	EM	EM	EM	XC
		◇1	◇1	◇	◇1		◇1	◇1	◇	◇1		◇1	◇1	◇1	◇		◇1	◇1	◇1	◇1	◇	◇1	◇1
		C	D	E			F		E			G			E			H			E		I
		🚲	🚲		☕		🚲	☕		☕		🚲	☕	☕			☕	🚲	☕	☕		☕	🚲
St Pancras International ⊖52	d									09 00			09 30				10 00		10 30			11 00	
Luton Airport Parkway 7 52 ✈	d									09 28							10 29					11 29	
Luton 10 52	d												09 59						11 02			11 33	
Bedford 7 52	d									09 50			10 19				10 54		11 23			11 54	
Wellingborough	d									10 03			10 31				11 08		11 34			12 07	
Kettering 4	a									10 09			10 38				11 15		11 41			12 14	
	d				09 55					10 10			10 38	10 55			11 16		11 41	11 55		12 15	
Corby	d				10a05									11a05						12a05			
Oakham	d																						
Melton Mowbray	d																						
Market Harborough	d									10 20			10 49				11 27		11 51			12 25	
Leicester	a									10 34			11 04				11 44		12 07			12 40	
	d							10 20		10 36			11 05				11 45		12 09			12 41	
Syston	d																						
Sileby	d																						
Barrow Upon Soar	d																						
Loughborough	d							10 30		10 46			11 15				11 56		12 19			12 51	
East Midlands Parkway ✈	a							10 36		10 52			11 22				12 04		12 25			12 58	
	d	00 09						10 37		10 53			11 23				12 05		12 26			12 59	
Beeston	a									10 59												13 04	
Nottingham 8	a									11 08							12 16					13 12	
	d			09 47		10 12			10 48		11 16				11 44	12 15					12 41		
Newark Castle 27	a																						
Lincoln 27	a																						
Langley Mill	d					10 36					11 35					12 34					12 57		
Alfreton	d			10 05		10 44			11 09		11 43				12 05	12 42					13 05		
Long Eaton	a	00 16						10 41					11 26						12 30				
Derby 6	a	00 28						10 54					11 39						12 42				
	d		09 44				10 44	10 55				11 44	11 50					12 44	12 51				13 11
Chesterfield	d		10 03	10 18		10 55	11 03	11 14	11 19		11 53	12 02	12 09		12 15	12 52		13 03	13 12		13 15		13 30
Sheffield 7	a		10 16	10 37		11 14	11 17	11 28	11 35		12 15	12 18	12 23		12 32	13 15		13 18	13 28		13 32		13 43
Doncaster 7 29	a							11 52															14 13
Wakefield Kirkgate 4 31,34	a					11 52					12 52					13 52							
Wakefield Westgate 7 31	a		10 44				11 44					12 44						13 45					
Leeds 10 31,34	a		11 02			12 18	12 01				13 18	13 02				14 18		14 02					
York 8 29	a		11 27				12 27	12 15				13 27						14 27					14 38

A until 8 February, from 29 March
B from 15 February until 22 March
C not 8 December. From St Pancras International
D From Birmingham New Street to Edinburgh
E To Liverpool Lime Street
F From Birmingham New Street to Glasgow Central
G From Bristol Temple Meads to Edinburgh
H From Bristol Temple Meads to Glasgow Central
I From Birmingham New Street to Newcastle

For connections from Gatwick Airport see Table 52

Table 53

Sundays

8 December to 29 December

London - East Midlands - Sheffield

Route Diagram - see first Page of Table 53

	NT	XC	EM	EM	EM	EM	XC	NT	XC	EM	EM	EM	EM	XC	NT	XC	EM	EM	EM	EM	XC	NT
		◇1	◇1	◇1	◇	◇1	◇1		◇1	◇1	◇1	◇	◇1	◇1		◇1	◇1	◇1	◇	◇1	◇1	
		A			B		C		D			E		F		G			H		I	
St Pancras International ⊖52 d			11 30			12 10				12 30			13 10				13 40			14 10		
Luton Airport Parkway 7 52 ✈ d			11 59			12 31				12 53			13 31				14 02			14 31		
Luton 10 52 d			12 03			12 34				12 57			13 34				14 07					
Bedford 7 52 d			12 23			12 49				13 12			13 49				14 22			14 46		
Wellingborough d			12 35			13 02				13 26			14 02				14 36			14 59		
Kettering 4 a			12 41			13 08				13 33			14 08				14 43			15 05		
d			12 42	12 55		13 09				13 34	13 55		14 09				14 43	14 55		15 06		
Corby d				13a05							14a05							15a05				
Oakham d																						
Melton Mowbray d																						
Market Harborough d			12 52			13 19				13 45			14 19				14 55			15 16		
Leicester a			13 07			13 34				14 02			14 34				15 12			15 31		
d			13 09			13 36				14 03			14 36				15 13			15 33		
Syston d																						
Sileby d																						
Barrow Upon Soar d																						
Loughborough d			13 19			13 46				14 14			14 46				15 24			15 43		
East Midlands Parkway ✈ a			13 25			13 52				14 22			14 52				15 32			15 49		
d			13 26			13 53				14 23			14 53				15 33			15 50		
Beeston a						13 59							14 59							15 58		
Nottingham 8 ⛴ a						14 07							15 07							16 05		
d	13 13				13 42			14 15				14 47			15 12				15 47			16 15
Newark Castle 27 a																						
Lincoln 27 a																						
Langley Mill d	13 34				13 58			14 34				15 03			15 36							16 34
Alfreton d	13 42				14 06			14 42				15 11			15 44				16 08			16 42
Long Eaton a			13 30							14 26							15 36					
Derby 6 a			13 43							14 42							15 49					
d		13 44	13 52				14 11		14 44	14 53				15 11		15 44	15 51				16 11	
Chesterfield d	13 52	14 03	14 11		14 16		14 30	14 53	15 03	15 14		15 21			15 56	16 03	16 12		16 18			16 52
Sheffield 7 ⛴ a	14 15	14 17	14 24		14 34		14 45	15 15	15 17	15 29		15 39		15 47	16 15	16 18	16 27		16 34		16 48	17 15
Doncaster 7 29 a							15 13							16 15							17 13	
Wakefield Kirkgate 4 31,34 a	14 52							15 52							16 52							17 52
Wakefield Westgate 7 31 a		14 44							15 44							16 44						
Leeds 10 31,34 a	15 18	15 02						16 18	16 02						17 16	17 02						18 18
York 8 29 a		15 27					15 42		16 27					16 38		17 27					17 40	

	XC	EM	EM	EM	EM	XC	NT	XC	EM	EM	EM	EM	XC	EM	EM	EM	NT	EM	XC	EM	EM
	◇1	◇1	◇1	◇	◇1	◇1		◇1	◇1	◇1	◇	◇1	◇1	◇1	◇1	◇1		◇1	◇1	◇	◇1
	D			B		I		J			B		K						J	L	
St Pancras International ⊖52 d		14 40			15 10				15 40			16 10		16 35	16 40			17 05			17 10
Luton Airport Parkway 7 52 ✈ d					15 33							16 31									17 31
Luton 10 52 d		15 04							16 04						17 02						
Bedford 7 52 d		15 19			15 48				16 19			16 46			17 16						17 46
Wellingborough d		15 33			16 02				16 33			16 59			17 29						17 58
Kettering 4 a		15 40			16 10				16 40			17 05			17 36						18 05
d		15 41	15 45		16 11				16 41	16 45		17 06			17 37	17 50					18 06
Corby d			15a55							16a55						18a00					
Oakham d																					
Melton Mowbray d																					
Market Harborough d		15 52			16 22				16 52			17 16			17 47						18 15
Leicester a		16 09			16 38				17 09			17 31		17 43	18 02			18 10			18 31
d		16 10			16 38				17 10			17 33		17 44	18 03			18 11			18 33
Syston d																					
Sileby d																					
Barrow Upon Soar d																					
Loughborough d		16 21			16 51				17 21			17 43			18 13						18 43
East Midlands Parkway ✈ a		16 29			16 58				17 29			17 49		18 00	18 20			18 24			18 49
d		16 30			16 59				17 30			17 50		18 00	18 21			18 25			18 50
Beeston a												17 58									18 58
Nottingham 8 ⛴ a					17 11							18 05						18 36			19 05
d				16 42			17 15				17 41						18 15			18 40	
Newark Castle 27 a																					
Lincoln 27 a																					
Langley Mill d				17 01			17 34				17 57						18 34			18 56	
Alfreton d				17 09			17 42				18 05						18 42			19 04	
Long Eaton a		16 33							17 33						18 24						
Derby 6 a		16 47							17 47					18 14	18 36						
d	16 44	16 52				17 11		17 43	17 50				18 11	18 14					18 43		
Chesterfield d	17 03	17 13		17 19			17 52	18 04	18 11		18 16			18 37			18 52		19 05	19 15	
Sheffield 7 ⛴ a	17 17	17 28		17 39		17 48	18 15	18 19	18 25		18 33		18 46	18 51			19 15		19 20	19 31	
Doncaster 7 29 a						18 13							19 15								
Wakefield Kirkgate 4 31,34 a							18 52										19 52				
Wakefield Westgate 7 31 a	17 44	18 05				18 33		18 47											19 48		
Leeds 10 31,34 a	18 02	18 24				18 51	19 18	19 04									20 18		20 05		
York 8 29 a	18 27					19 20		19 30					19 39						20 30		

A From Plymouth to Aberdeen
B From Norwich to Liverpool Lime Street
C From Birmingham New Street to Newcastle
D From Plymouth to Glasgow Central
E To Liverpool Lime Street
F From Guildford to Newcastle
G From Penzance to Edinburgh
H From Peterborough to Liverpool Lime Street
I From Reading to Newcastle
J From Plymouth to Edinburgh
K From Reading to Edinburgh
L From Norwich to Manchester Piccadilly

For connections from Gatwick Airport see Table 52

Table 53

Sundays

London - East Midlands - Sheffield

8 December to 29 December

Route Diagram - see first Page of Table 53

		XC	EM	EM	EM	NT	EM	XC		EM	EM	XC	EM	EM	EM	NT	EM	EM		XC	EM	EM	XC	EM	NT
		◇1	◇1	◇1	◇1		◇1	◇1		◇	◇1	◇1	◇1	◇1	◇1		◇1	◇1		◇1	◇1	◇1	◇1	◇1	
		A						B		C		D								E			F		
		🛒	☕	☕	☕		☕	🛒			☕	🛒	☕	☕	☕		☕	☕		🛒	☕	☕		☕	
St Pancras International ⊖52	d		17 35	17 40			18 05				18 10		18 35	18 40			19 05	19 10			19 35	19 40			
Luton Airport Parkway 7 52 ✈	d										18 31							19 31							
Luton 10 52	d			18 02										19 02								20 02			
Bedford 7 52	d			18 16							18 46			19 16				19 46				20 16			
Wellingborough	d			18 29							18 59			19 29				19 58				20 29			
Kettering 4	a			18 36							19 05			19 36				20 05				20 36			
	d			18 37	18 50						19 06			19 37	19 45			20 05				20 37		20 46	
Corby	d				19a00										19a55									20a56	
Oakham	d																								
Melton Mowbray	d																								
Market Harborough	d			18 47							19 16			19 47				20 15				20 47			
Leicester	a		18 40	19 02			19 09				19 31		19 43	20 02			20 16	20 31			20 43	21 02			
	d		18 41	19 03			19 10				19 33		19 45	20 03			20 21	20 33			20 45	21 03			
Syston	d																								
Sileby	d																								
Barrow Upon Soar	d																								
Loughborough	d			19 13							19 43			20 13				20 43				21 13			
East Midlands Parkway ✈	a		18 54	19 20			19 24				19 49		20 00	20 20			20 38	20 49			21 00	21 20			
	d		18 55	19 21			19 25				19 50		20 01	20 21			20 38	20 50			21 01	21 21			
Beeston	a										19 58							20 58							
Nottingham 8 🚌	a						19 36				20 05						20 50	21 05							
	d					19 15				19 43						20 15									21 33
Newark Castle 27	a																								
Lincoln 27	a																								
Langley Mill	d					19 34										20 34									21 57
Alfreton	d					19 42				20 04						20 42									22 05
Long Eaton	a			19 24										20 24								21 24			
Derby 6	a		19 07	19 37									20 14	20 37							21 14	21 36			
	d	19 05	19 16					19 42				20 08	20 16							20 44	21 16		21 44		
Chesterfield	d		19 34			19 52		20 03		20 14			20 37			20 52				21 03	21 37		22 03		22 16
Sheffield 7 🚌	a	19 39	19 50			20 15		20 18		20 31		20 40	20 51			21 14				21 16	21 53		22 18		22 36
Doncaster 7 29	a	20 16										21 19													
Wakefield Kirkgate 4 31,34	a					20 52																			23 26
Wakefield Westgate 7 31	a							20 49					21 27							21 47			22 43		
Leeds 10 31,34	a					21 16		21 06					21 44							22 04			23 01		00 05
York 8 29	a	20 38						21 31				21 42													

		EM	EM	EM		XC	EM	EM	EM	EM	EM	EM
		◇1	◇1	◇1		◇1	◇1	◇1	◇1	◇1	◇1	◇1
						E						
		☕	☕	☕			☕	☕	☕	☕	☕	☕
St Pancras International ⊖52	d	20 00	20 10	20 35			20 40		21 10	21 30	22 30	23 00
Luton Airport Parkway 7 52 ✈	d		20 31						21 31		22 51	23 30
Luton 10 52	d						21 04			21 52		
Bedford 7 52	d		20 47				21 20		21 46	22 06	23 13	23 53
Wellingborough	d		20 58				21 33		21 59	22 19	23 27	00 06
Kettering 4	a		21 05				21 40		22 05	22 26	23 36	00 15
	d		21 06				21 41	21 55	22 06	22 27	23 37	00 16
Corby	d							22a05				
Oakham	d											
Melton Mowbray	d											
Market Harborough	d		21 16				21 52		22 16	22 37	23 47	00 26
Leicester	a	21 08	21 31	21 40			22 09		22 31	22 52	00 07	00 46
	d	21 10	21 33	21 41			22 10		22 33	22 54	00 08	00 48
Syston	d											
Sileby	d											
Barrow Upon Soar	d											
Loughborough	d	21 21	21 43	21 51					22 47	23 04	00 18	00 58
East Midlands Parkway ✈	a	21 28	21 49	21 58			22 25		22 57	23 15	00 30	01 09
	d	21 29	21 50	21 59			22 26		22 58	23 16	00 31	01 10
Beeston	a		21 58						23 04		00 39	
Nottingham 8 🚌	a	21 45	22 05						23 11		00 46	
	d											
Newark Castle 27	a											
Lincoln 27	a											
Langley Mill	d											
Alfreton	d											
Long Eaton	a									23 23		
Derby 6	a			22 11			22 40			23 35		01 24
	d					22 44	22 49			23 36		
Chesterfield	d					23 05	23 10			23 55		
Sheffield 7 🚌	a					23 20	23 32			00 08		
Doncaster 7 29	a											
Wakefield Kirkgate 4 31,34	a											
Wakefield Westgate 7 31	a						00 06					
Leeds 10 31,34	a					00 16	00 23					
York 8 29	a											

A From Reading to Newcastle
B From Plymouth. 🛒 to Leeds
C From Norwich to Manchester Piccadilly
D From Reading to Newcastle. 🛒 to Sheffield
E From Plymouth
F From Penzance

For connections from Gatwick Airport see Table 52

Table 53

Sundays

5 January to 9 February

London - East Midlands - Sheffield

Route Diagram - see first Page of Table 53

	EM	XC	EM	NT	XC	EM	EM	NT	XC	EM	EM	NT	EM	XC	EM	EM	XC	NT	EM	XC	EM	EM
	◇1 A	◇1 B	◇ C		◇1 D	◇1	◇ C		◇1 E	◇ C	◇1		◇1	◇1 D	◇ C	◇1	◇1 F		◇1	◇1 G	◇ H	◇1
St Pancras International ⊖52 d											09 00		09 30			10 00			10 30			11 00
Luton Airport Parkway 7 52 ✈ d											09 28					10 29						11 29
Luton 10 52 d													09 59						11 02			11 33
Bedford 7 52 d											09 50		10 19			10 50			11 23			11 54
Wellingborough d											10 03		10 32			11 04			11 35			12 07
Kettering 4 a											10 17		10 46			11 18			11 49			12 21
d											10 18		10 54			11 20			12 02			12 31
Corby d											10 28		11 04			11 30						12 41
Oakham d																						
Melton Mowbray d																						
Market Harborough d																						
Leicester a											11 21		11 47			12 21			12 56			13 32
d						10 20					11 28		11 54			12 28			13 02			13 38
Syston d																						
Sileby d																						
Barrow Upon Soar d																						
Loughborough d						10 30					11 39		12 05			12 40			13 13			13 48
East Midlands Parkway ✈ a						10 36					11 45		12 11			12 47			13 20			13 55
d	00 09					10 37					11 46		12 12			12 48			13 21			13 56
Beeston a											11 59											14 01
Nottingham 8 a											12 07					13 06						14 09
d			09 47	10 12			10 48	11 16		11 44		12 15			12 41			13 13			13 42	
Newark Castle 27 a																						
Lincoln 27 a																						
Langley Mill d				10 36				11 35				12 34			12 57			13 34			13 58	
Alfreton d			10 05	10 44			11 09	11 43		12 05		12 42			13 05			13 42			14 06	
Long Eaton a	00 16					10 41							12 16						13 25			
Derby 6 a	00 28					10 54							12 27						13 35			
d		09 44			10 44	10 55			11 44				12 29	12 44			13 11		13 36	13 44		
Chesterfield d		10 03	10 18	10 55	11 03	11 14	11 19	11 53	12 03	12 15		12 52	12 55	13 03	13 15		13 30	13 52	13 58	14 03	14 16	
Sheffield 7 a		10 16	10 37	11 14	11 17	11 28	11 35	12 15	12 18	12 32		13 15	13 17	13 18	13 32		13 43	14 15	14 19	14 17	14 34	
Doncaster 7 29 a																						
Wakefield Kirkgate 4 31,34 a				11 52				12 52				13 52						14 52				
Wakefield Westgate 7 31 a		10 44			11 44				12 44					13 45						14 44		
Leeds 10 31,34 a		11 02		12 18	12 01			13 18	13 02			14 18		14 02				15 18		15 02		
York 8 29 a		11 27			12 27	12 20			13 27					14 27			14 38			15 27		

	XC	NT	XC	EM	EM	EM	XC	NT	XC	EM	EM	EM	XC	NT	XC	EM	EM	EM	XC	NT	XC	EM
	◇1 I		◇1 D	◇1	◇ C	◇1	◇1 I		◇1 J	◇1	◇ K	◇1	◇1 L		◇1 M	◇1	◇ H	◇1	◇1 N		◇1 O	◇1
St Pancras International ⊖52 d				11 30		12 10				12 40		13 10				13 40		14 10				14 40
Luton Airport Parkway 7 52 ✈ d				12 00		12 31				13 03		13 31				14 02		14 31				
Luton 10 52 d				12 03		12 34				13 07		13 34				14 07						15 04
Bedford 7 52 d				12 22		12 49				13 22		13 49				14 22		14 46				15 19
Wellingborough d				12 35		13 02				13 36		14 02				14 36		14 59				15 33
Kettering 4 a				12 50		13 16				13 50		14 16				14 50		15 13				15 47
d				12 52		13 22				13 51		14 18				14 52		15 24				15 50
Corby d				13 02		13 32						14 28						15 34				
Oakham d																						
Melton Mowbray d																						
Market Harborough d																						
Leicester a				13 58		14 15				14 58		15 11				15 55		16 19				16 56
d				14 04		14 22				15 04		15 18				16 01		16 29				17 02
Syston d																						
Sileby d																						
Barrow Upon Soar d																						
Loughborough d				14 16		14 33				15 16		15 29				16 13		16 39				17 14
East Midlands Parkway ✈ a				14 24		14 39				15 24		15 35				16 21		16 46				17 22
d				14 25		14 40				15 25		15 36				16 22		16 50				17 23
Beeston a						14 46						15 42						16 59				
Nottingham 8 a						14 55						15 51						17 08				
d		14 15			14 47			15 12			15 47			16 15			16 42			17 15		
Newark Castle 27 a																						
Lincoln 27 a																						
Langley Mill d		14 34			15 03			15 36						16 34			17 01			17 34		
Alfreton d		14 42			15 11			15 44			16 08			16 42			17 09			17 42		
Long Eaton a				14 28						15 28						16 27						17 26
Derby 6 a				14 42						15 42						16 40						17 40
d	14 11		14 44	14 47			15 11		15 44	15 48			16 11		16 44	16 53			17 11		17 43	17 49
Chesterfield d	14 30	14 53	15 03	15 08	15 21			15 56	16 03	16 09	16 18			16 52	17 03	17 14	17 19			17 52	18 04	18 10
Sheffield 7 a	14 45	15 15	15 17	15 22	15 39		15 42	16 15	16 18	16 25	16 34		16 41	17 15	17 17	17 28	17 39		17 42	18 15	18 19	18 26
Doncaster 7 29 a																						
Wakefield Kirkgate 4 31,34 a		15 52						16 52						17 52						18 52		
Wakefield Westgate 7 31 a			15 44						16 44						17 44				18 16		18 47	19 10
Leeds 10 31,34 a		16 18	16 02					17 16	17 02					18 18	18 02				18 34	19 18	19 04	19 27
York 8 29 a	15 42		16 27				16 38		17 27				17 44		18 27				19 20		19 31	

A From St Pancras International
B To Edinburgh
C To Liverpool Lime Street
D From Birmingham New Street to Glasgow Central
E From Birmingham New Street to Edinburgh
F From Bristol Temple Meads to Newcastle
G From Birmingham New Street to Aberdeen
H From Norwich to Liverpool Lime Street
I From Plymouth to Newcastle
J From Reading to Edinburgh
K From Peterborough to Liverpool Lime Street
L From Penzance to Newcastle
M From Reading to Glasgow Central
N From Exeter St Davids to Edinburgh
O From Reading to Newcastle

For connections from Gatwick Airport see Table 52

Table 53

Sundays

London - East Midlands - Sheffield

5 January to 9 February

Route Diagram - see first Page of Table 53

Station		EM	EM	XC	NT	XC	EM	EM	EM	XC	EM	NT	XC	EM	EM	XC	EM	NT	EM	XC	EM	NT
		◇	◇1	◇1		◇1	◇	◇1	◇1	◇1	◇1		◇1	◇	◇1	◇1	◇1		◇1	◇1	◇1	
		A		B		C	D			E			F	D		G				H		
			☕	🛒		🛒		☕	☕	🛒	☕		🛒		☕	🛒	☕		☕	🛒	☕	
St Pancras International ⊖52	d		15 10					15 40	16 10		16 40				17 10		17 40		18 10		18 40	
Luton Airport Parkway 7 52 ✈	d		15 33						16 31						17 31				18 31			
Luton 10 52	d							16 02			17 04						18 02				19 04	
Bedford 7 52	d		15 48					16 16	16 46		17 19				17 47		18 16		18 46		19 19	
Wellingborough	d		16 02					16 29	16 59		17 33				17 59		18 29		18 59		19 33	
Kettering 4	a		16 17					16 43	17 13		17 44				18 13		18 43		19 13		19 47	
	d		16 25					16 51	17 15		17 46				18 15		18 47		19 22		19 49	
Corby	d		16 35						17 25						18 25				19 32			
Oakham	d																					
Melton Mowbray	d																					
Market Harborough	d																					
Leicester	a		17 21					17 55	18 09		18 43				19 09		19 38		20 15		20 57	
	d		17 28					18 02	18 15		18 49				19 15		19 45		20 24		21 04	
Syston	d																					
Sileby	d																					
Barrow Upon Soar	d																					
Loughborough	d		17 40					18 13	18 29		19 01				19 29		19 56		20 35		21 16	
East Midlands Parkway ✈	a		17 47					18 19	18 36		19 09				19 36		20 02		20 42		21 23	
	d		17 48					18 20	18 37		19 10				19 37		20 03		20 43		21 24	
Beeston	a								18 42						19 42				20 48			
Nottingham 8 🚢	a		18 06						18 51						19 51				20 57			
	d	17 41			18 15		18 40					19 15		19 43				20 15				21 33
Newark Castle 27	a																					
Lincoln 27	a																					
Langley Mill	d	17 57			18 34		18 56					19 34						20 34				21 57
Alfreton	d	18 05			18 42		19 04					19 42		20 04				20 42				22 05
Long Eaton	a							18 27			19 13						20 07				21 28	
Derby 6	a							18 39			19 27						20 19				21 42	
	d			18 11		18 43		18 48		19 05	19 28		19 42			20 03	20 33			20 59	21 46	
Chesterfield	d	18 16			18 52	19 05	19 15	19 17			19 49	19 52	20 03	20 14			20 54	20 52		21 20	22 07	22 16
Sheffield 7 🚢	a	18 33		18 46	19 15	19 20	19 31	19 38		19 40	20 06	20 15	20 18	20 31		20 40	21 12	21 14		21 38	22 22	22 36
Doncaster 7 29	a																					
Wakefield Kirkgate 4 31,34	a				19 52							20 52										23 26
Wakefield Westgate 7 31	a					19 48							20 46							22 11	22 49	
Leeds 10 31,34	a				20 18	20 05						21 16	21 05							22 28	23 09	00 05
York 8 29	a			19 43		20 30				20 38			21 31			21 42						

Station		EM	XC	EM	EM	XC	EM	EM	EM	EM	EM
		◇1	◇1	◇1	◇1	◇1	◇1	◇1	◇1	◇1	◇1
			I			H					
		☕		☕	☕		☕	☕	☕	☕	☕
St Pancras International ⊖52	d	19 10		19 40	20 10		20 40	21 10	21 30	22 30	23 00
Luton Airport Parkway 7 52 ✈	d	19 31			20 31			21 31		22 51	23 39
Luton 10 52	d			20 02			21 04		21 52		
Bedford 7 52	d	19 46		20 16	20 47		21 20	21 46	22 06	23 13	00 03
Wellingborough	d	19 59		20 29	20 59		21 33	21 59	22 19	23 26	00 16
Kettering 4	a	20 11		20 43	21 13		21 47	22 13	22 33	23 40	00 30
	d	20 13		20 47	21 15		21 57	22 18	22 35	23 41	00 31
Corby	d	20 23			21 25			22 28		23 51	
Oakham	d										
Melton Mowbray	d										
Market Harborough	d										
Leicester	a	21 09		21 38	22 09		22 51	23 12	23 27	00 34	01 23
	d	21 15		21 45	22 15		22 57	23 18	23 34	00 41	01 29
Syston	d										
Sileby	d										
Barrow Upon Soar	d										
Loughborough	d	21 30		21 56	22 26			23 29	23 44	00 51	01 40
East Midlands Parkway ✈	a	21 37		22 02	22 33		23 13	23 40	23 56	01 02	01 52
	d	21 38		22 03	22 34		23 14	23 41	23 57	01 03	01 53
Beeston	a	21 43			22 42			23 49		01 12	
Nottingham 8 🚢	a	21 52			22 51			23 57		01 20	
	d										
Newark Castle 27	a										
Lincoln 27	a										
Langley Mill	d										
Alfreton	d										
Long Eaton	a			22 07					00 03		
Derby 6	a			22 20			23 32		00 15		02 08
	d		22 01	22 22		23 00	23 33		00 25		
Chesterfield	d		22 24	22 41		23 21	23 54		00 51		
Sheffield 7 🚢	a		22 38	22 54		23 36	00 09		01 05		
Doncaster 7 29	a										
Wakefield Kirkgate 4 31,34	a										
Wakefield Westgate 7 31	a		23 09				00 36				
Leeds 10 31,34	a		23 26			00 27	00 52				
York 8 29	a										

A From Norwich to Liverpool Lime Street
B From Plymouth to Edinburgh
C From Reading to Edinburgh
D From Norwich to Manchester Piccadilly
E From Plymouth to Newcastle
F From Reading
G From Plymouth to Newcastle. 🛒 to Sheffield
H From Plymouth
I From Penzance

For connections from Gatwick Airport see Table 52

Table 53

Sundays

16 February to 23 March

London - East Midlands - Sheffield

Route Diagram - see first Page of Table 53

		EM	EM	EM	NT	XC	EM	EM	EM	NT		XC	EM	EM	EM	NT	EM	XC	EM	EM		EM	XC	NT	EM
		◇1	◇	◇1		◇1	◇1	◇	◇1			◇1	◇1	◇1	◇		◇1	◇1	◇1	◇1		◇	◇1		◇1
		A	B			C		B				D			B			C				B	E		
		🚲		☕		🚲	☕		☕			🚲	☕	☕			☕	🚲	☕	☕			🚲		☕
St Pancras International ⊖52	d								09 00				09 30				10 00		10 30						11 00
Luton Airport Parkway 7 52 ✈	d								09 28								10 29								11 29
Luton 10	52 d												09 59						11 02						11 33
Bedford 7	52 d								09 50				10 18				10 50		11 25						11 54
Wellingborough	d								10 03				10 31				11 04		11 36						12 07
Kettering 4	a								10 09				10 38				11 11		11 43						12 14
	d			09 55					10 10				10 38	10 55			11 12		11 43	11 55					12 15
Corby	d			10a05										11a05						12a05					
Oakham	d																								
Melton Mowbray	d																								
Market Harborough	d								10 20				10 49				11 23		11 53						12 25
Leicester	a								10 34				11 04				11 40		12 09						12 40
	d						10 14		10 36				11 05				11 41		12 11						12 41
Syston	d																								
Sileby	d																								
Barrow Upon Soar	d																								
Loughborough	d						10 24		10 46				11 18				11 52		12 21						12 51
East Midlands Parkway ✈	a						10 35		10 57				11 29				12 03		12 32						13 02
	d	00 09					10 36		10 58				11 30				12 04		12 33						13 03
Beeston	a								11 04																13 10
Nottingham 8 🚊	a								11 11								12 17								13 18
	d		09 47		10 12			10 48		11 16					11 44	12 15						12 41		13 13	
Newark Castle	27 a																								
Lincoln	27 a																								
Langley Mill	d				10 36					11 35						12 34						12 57		13 34	
Alfreton	d		10 05		10 44			11 09		11 43					12 05	12 42						13 05		13 42	
Long Eaton	a	00 16					10 41						11 35						12 37						
Derby 6	a	00 28					10 54						11 47						12 50						
	d					10 44	10 55					11 44	11 50					12 44	12 50				13 11		
Chesterfield	d		10 18		10 55	11 03	11 14	11 19		11 53		12 03	12 09		12 15	12 52		13 03	13 11			13 15	13 30	13 52	
Sheffield 7 🚊	a		10 37		11 14	11 17	11 28	11 35		12 15		12 18	12 23		12 32	13 15		13 18	13 28			13 32	13 43	14 15	
Doncaster 7	29 a						11 52																14 13		
Wakefield Kirkgate 4	31,34 a				11 49					12 49						13 55								14 49	
Wakefield Westgate 7	31 a					11 44						12 44						13 45							
Leeds 10	31,34 a				12 15	12 01				13 15		13 02				14 23		14 02						15 15	
York 8	29 a					12 27	12 17					13 27						14 27					14 38		

		XC	EM	EM	EM	EM		XC	NT	XC	EM	EM	EM	EM	XC	NT		XC	EM	EM	EM	EM	XC	NT	XC
		◇1	◇1	◇1	◇	◇1		◇1		◇1	◇1	◇1	◇	◇1	◇1			◇1	◇1	◇1	◇	◇1	◇1		◇1
		F			G			H		C			B		H			I			J		H		K
		🚲	☕	☕		☕		🚲		🚲	☕	☕		☕	🚲			🚲	☕	☕		☕	🚲		🚲
St Pancras International ⊖52	d		11 30			12 10					12 30			13 10					13 40			14 10			
Luton Airport Parkway 7 52 ✈	d		11 59			12 31					12 53			13 31					14 02			14 31			
Luton 10	52 d		12 03			12 34					12 57			13 34					14 07						
Bedford 7	52 d		12 23			12 49					13 12			13 49					14 21			14 46			
Wellingborough	d		12 35			13 02					13 26			14 02					14 34			14 59			
Kettering 4	a		12 41			13 08					13 33			14 08					14 42			15 05			
	d		12 42	12 55		13 09					13 34	13 55		14 09					14 42	14 55		15 06			
Corby	d			13a05								14a05								15a05					
Oakham	d																								
Melton Mowbray	d																								
Market Harborough	d		12 52			13 19					13 45			14 19					14 53			15 16			
Leicester	a		13 07			13 34					14 02			14 34					15 10			15 31			
	d		13 09			13 36					14 03			14 36					15 11			15 33			
Syston	d																								
Sileby	d																								
Barrow Upon Soar	d																								
Loughborough	d		13 19			13 46					14 14			14 46					15 21			15 43			
East Midlands Parkway ✈	a		13 30			13 57					14 25			14 57					15 33			15 54			
	d		13 31			13 58					14 26			14 58					15 33			15 55			
Beeston	a					14 04								15 04								16 02			
Nottingham 8 🚊	a					14 12								15 12								16 09			
	d				13 42				14 15				14 47			15 12					15 47			16 15	
Newark Castle	27 a																								
Lincoln	27 a																								
Langley Mill	d				13 58				14 34				15 03			15 36								16 34	
Alfreton	d				14 06				14 42				15 11			15 44					16 08			16 42	
Long Eaton	a		13 35								14 31								15 39						
Derby 6	a		13 46								14 45								15 51						
	d	13 44	13 52					14 11		14 44	14 54				15 11			15 44	15 51				16 11		16 44
Chesterfield	d	14 03	14 11		14 16			14 30	14 52	15 03	15 15		15 21			15 56		16 03	16 12		16 18			16 52	17 03
Sheffield 7 🚊	a	14 17	14 24		14 34			14 45	15 15	15 17	15 29		15 39		15 47	16 15		16 18	16 31		16 34		16 48	17 15	17 17
Doncaster 7	29 a							15 15							16 15								17 13		
Wakefield Kirkgate 4	31,34 a								15 51							16 49								17 52	
Wakefield Westgate 7	31 a	14 44								15 44								16 44							17 44
Leeds 10	31,34 a	15 02							16 16	16 02						17 13		17 02						18 24	18 02
York 8	29 a	15 27						15 42		16 27					16 38			17 27					17 42		18 27

A From St Pancras International
B To Liverpool Lime Street
C From Birmingham New Street to Glasgow Central
D From Birmingham New Street to Edinburgh
E From Bristol Temple Meads to Newcastle
F From Birmingham New Street to Aberdeen
G From Norwich to Liverpool Lime Street
H From Exeter St Davids to Newcastle
I From Guildford to Edinburgh
J From Peterborough to Liverpool Lime Street
K From Reading to Glasgow Central

For connections from Gatwick Airport see Table 52

Table 53

Sundays

16 February to 23 March

London - East Midlands - Sheffield

Route Diagram - see first Page of Table 53

	EM ◇1 ☕		EM ◇1 ☕	EM ◇ A	XC ◇1 B 🛒	NT	EM ◇1 ☕	XC ◇1 C 🛒	EM ◇ A	EM ◇1 ☕	EM ◇1 ☕		EM ◇1 ☕	XC ◇1 B 🛒	EM ◇1 ☕	EM ◇1 ☕	EM ◇1 ☕	NT	XC ◇1 D 🛒	EM ◇ E	EM ◇1 ☕		EM ◇1 ☕	XC ◇1 F 🛒
St Pancras International ⊖52 d	14 40						15 10			15 40			16 10		16 35	16 40					17 05		17 10	
Luton Airport Parkway [7] 52 ✈ d							15 33						16 31										17 31	
Luton [10] 52 d	15 04									16 04						17 02								
Bedford [7] 52 d	15 19						15 48			16 19			16 46			17 16							17 46	
Wellingborough d	15 33						16 02			16 33			16 59			17 29							17 58	
Kettering [4] a	15 40						16 10			16 40			17 05			17 36							18 05	
d	15 41		15 45				16 11			16 41	16 45		17 06			17 37	17 50						18 06	
Corby d			15a55								16a55						18a00							
Oakham d																								
Melton Mowbray d																								
Market Harborough d	15 52						16 22			16 52			17 16			17 47							18 15	
Leicester a	16 09						16 38			17 09			17 31		17 43	18 02					18 10		18 31	
d	16 10						16 38			17 10			17 33		17 44	18 03					18 11		18 33	
Syston d																								
Sileby d																								
Barrow Upon Soar d																								
Loughborough d	16 21						16 51			17 21			17 45			18 13							18 43	
East Midlands Parkway ✈ a	16 32						17 02			17 32			17 56		18 05	18 24					18 31		18 54	
d	16 33						17 03			17 33			17 57		18 05	18 25					18 32		18 55	
Beeston a													18 05										19 01	
Nottingham [8] 🚊 a							17 16						18 12								18 44		19 08	
d				16 42		17 15			17 41									18 15		18 40				
Newark Castle 27 a																								
Lincoln 27 a																								
Langley Mill d				17 01		17 34			17 57									18 34		18 56				
Alfreton d				17 09		17 42			18 05									18 42		19 04				
Long Eaton a	16 38									17 40						18 30								
Derby [6] a	16 52									17 52					18 20	18 42								
d	16 53				17 11			17 43		17 54				18 11	18 20				18 43					19 05
Chesterfield d	17 14			17 19		17 52		18 04	18 16	18 21					18 43			18 52	19 05	19 15				
Sheffield [7] 🚊 a	17 29			17 39	17 48	18 15		18 19	18 33	18 37				18 46	18 58			19 15	19 20	19 31				19 39
Doncaster [7] 29 a					18 14									19 15										20 16
Wakefield Kirkgate [4] 31,34 a						18 49												19 49						
Wakefield Westgate [7] 31 a	18 05				18 33			18 47											19 48					
Leeds [10] 31,34 a	18 24				18 51	19 15		19 04										20 15	20 05					
York [8] 29 a					19 20			19 30						19 39					20 30					20 39

	EM ◇1 ☕	EM ◇1 ☕	EM ◇1 ☕	NT	XC ◇1 C 🛒	EM ◇ E	EM ◇1 ☕		EM ◇1 ☕	XC ◇1 G 🛒	EM ◇1 ☕	EM ◇1 ☕	EM ◇1 ☕	NT	EM ◇1 ☕	EM ◇1 ☕	XC ◇1 F 🛒		EM ◇1 ☕	EM ◇1 ☕	EM ◇1 ☕	NT	EM ◇1 ☕	EM ◇1 ☕
St Pancras International ⊖52 d	17 35	17 40					18 05		18 10		18 35	18 40			19 05	19 10			19 35	19 40			20 00	20 10
Luton Airport Parkway [7] 52 ✈ d									18 31							19 31								20 31
Luton [10] 52 d		18 02										19 02								20 02				
Bedford [7] 52 d		18 16							18 46			19 16				19 46				20 16				20 47
Wellingborough d		18 29							18 59			19 29				19 58				20 29				20 58
Kettering [4] a		18 36							19 05			19 36				20 05				20 36				21 05
d		18 37	18 50						19 06			19 37	19 45			20 05				20 37	20 46			21 06
Corby d			19a00										19a55								20a56			
Oakham d																								
Melton Mowbray d																								
Market Harborough d		18 47							19 16			19 47				20 15				20 47				21 16
Leicester a	18 40	19 02					19 10		19 31		19 43	20 02			20 13	20 31			20 43	21 02			21 08	21 31
d	18 41	19 03					19 11		19 33		19 45	20 03			20 14	20 33			20 45	21 03			21 10	21 33
Syston d																								
Sileby d																								
Barrow Upon Soar d																								
Loughborough d		19 13							19 43			20 13				20 43				21 13			21 21	21 43
East Midlands Parkway ✈ a	19 01	19 24					19 31		19 54		20 05	20 24			20 35	20 54			21 05	21 24			21 32	21 54
d	19 02	19 25					19 32		19 55		20 06	20 25			20 35	20 55			21 06	21 25			21 33	21 55
Beeston a									20 03							21 02								22 02
Nottingham [8] 🚊 a							19 44		20 10						20 49	21 09							21 46	22 09
d				19 15		19 43								20 15								21 33		
Newark Castle 27 a																								
Lincoln 27 a																								
Langley Mill d				19 34										20 34								21 57		
Alfreton d				19 42		20 04								20 42								22 05		
Long Eaton a		19 30										20 30								21 30				
Derby [6] a	19 15	19 43									20 21	20 42							21 20	21 42				
d	19 16				19 42					20 03	20 22						20 59		21 22					
Chesterfield d	19 34			19 52	20 03	20 14					20 43			20 52			21 20		21 43			22 16		
Sheffield [7] 🚊 a	19 50			20 15	20 18	20 31				20 40	20 58			21 14			21 38		21 59			22 36		
Doncaster [7] 29 a										21 19														
Wakefield Kirkgate [4] 31,34 a				20 49																		23 26		
Wakefield Westgate [7] 31 a					20 46						21 27						22 11							
Leeds [10] 31,34 a				21 13	21 05						21 44						22 28					00 05		
York [8] 29 a					21 31					21 42														

A From Norwich to Liverpool Lime Street
B From Exeter St Davids to Edinburgh
C From Reading to Newcastle
D From Reading to Edinburgh
E From Norwich to Manchester Piccadilly
F From Exeter St Davids
G From Exeter St Davids to Newcastle. 🛒 to Sheffield

For connections from Gatwick Airport see Table 52

Table 53

Sundays
16 February to 23 March

London - East Midlands - Sheffield

Route Diagram - see first Page of Table 53

		EM	XC	EM	EM	EM	XC	EM	EM	EM
		◇1	◇1	◇1	◇1	◇1	◇1	◇1	◇1	◇1
			A				B			
St Pancras International ⊖52	d	20 35		20 40		21 10		21 30	22 30	23 00
Luton Airport Parkway 7 52 ✈	d					21 31			22 51	23 39
Luton 10 52	d			21 04				21 52		
Bedford 7 52	d			21 20		21 46		22 06	23 13	00 03
Wellingborough	d			21 33		21 59		22 19	23 27	00 16
Kettering 4	a			21 40		22 05		22 26	23 36	00 22
	d			21 41	21 55	22 06		22 27	23 37	00 23
Corby	d				22a05					
Oakham	d									
Melton Mowbray	d									
Market Harborough	d			21 52		22 16		22 37	23 47	00 33
Leicester	a	21 40		22 09		22 31		22 52	00 07	00 51
	d	21 41		22 10		22 33		22 54	00 08	00 53
Syston	d									
Sileby	d									
Barrow Upon Soar	d									
Loughborough	d	21 51				22 47		23 04	00 18	01 03
East Midlands Parkway ✈	a	22 02		22 30		22 58		23 20	00 34	01 15
	d	22 03		22 31		22 59		23 21	00 35	01 16
Beeston	a					23 05			00 42	
Nottingham 8	a					23 12			00 49	
	d									
Newark Castle 27	a									
Lincoln 27	a									
Langley Mill	d									
Alfreton	d									
Long Eaton	a							23 25		
Derby 6	a	22 16		22 46				23 37		01 31
	d		22 01	22 49			23 00	23 39		
Chesterfield	d		22 20	23 10			23 21	23 58		
Sheffield 7	a		22 38	23 28			23 36	00 11		
Doncaster 7 29	a									
Wakefield Kirkgate 4 31,34	a									
Wakefield Westgate 7 31	a		23 09	00 01						
Leeds 10 31,34	a		23 26	00 17			00 27			
York 8 29	a									

Sundays
30 March to 11 May

		EM	XC	EM	EM	NT	XC	EM	EM	EM	NT	XC	EM	EM	EM	EM	NT	XC	EM	EM	EM	EM	XC
		◇1	◇1	◇	◇1		◇1	◇1	◇	◇1		◇1	◇1	◇1	◇	◇1		◇1	◇1	◇1	◇	◇1	◇1
		C	D	E			F		E			G			E			H			E		I
St Pancras International ⊖52	d									09 00			09 30			10 00			10 30			11 00	
Luton Airport Parkway 7 52 ✈	d									09 28						10 29						11 29	
Luton 10 52	d												09 59						11 02			11 33	
Bedford 7 52	d									09 50			10 18			10 50			11 25			11 54	
Wellingborough	d									10 03			10 31			11 04			11 36			12 07	
Kettering 4	a									10 09			10 38			11 11			11 43			12 14	
	d				09 55					10 10			10 38	10 55		11 12			11 43	11 55		12 15	
Corby	d				10a05									11a05						12a05			
Oakham	d																						
Melton Mowbray	d																						
Market Harborough	d									10 20			10 49			11 23			11 53			12 25	
Leicester	a									10 34			11 04			11 40			12 09			12 40	
	d							10 20		10 36			11 05			11 41			12 11			12 41	
Syston	d																						
Sileby	d																						
Barrow Upon Soar	d																						
Loughborough	d							10 30		10 46			11 15			11 52			12 21			12 51	
East Midlands Parkway ✈	a							10 36		10 52			11 22			12 00			12 27			12 58	
	d	00 09						10 37		10 53			11 23			12 01			12 28			12 59	
Beeston	a									10 59												13 04	
Nottingham 8	a									11 06						12 12						13 12	
	d			09 47		10 12			10 48		11 16				11 44		12 15				12 41		
Newark Castle 27	a																						
Lincoln 27	a																						
Langley Mill	d					10 36					11 35						12 34				12 57		
Alfreton	d			10 05		10 44			11 09		11 43				12 05		12 42				13 05		
Long Eaton	a	00 16						10 41					11 26						12 32				
Derby 6	a	00 28						10 54					11 39						12 44				
	d		09 44				10 44	10 55				11 44	11 50					12 44	12 51				13 11
Chesterfield	d		10 03	10 18		10 55	11 03	11 14	11 19		11 53	12 02	12 09		12 15		12 52	13 03	13 12		13 15		13 30
Sheffield 7	a		10 16	10 37		11 14	11 17	11 28	11 35		12 15	12 18	12 23		12 32		13 15	13 18	13 28		13 32		13 43
Doncaster 7 29	a							11 52															14 13
Wakefield Kirkgate 4 31,34	a					11 52					12 52						13 52						
Wakefield Westgate 7 31	a		10 44				11 44					12 44						13 45					
Leeds 10 31,34	a		11 02			12 18	12 01				13 18	13 02					14 18	14 02					
York 8 29	a		11 27				12 27	12 15				13 27						14 27					14 38

A From Exeter St Davids
B From Birmingham New Street
C From St Pancras International
D From Birmingham New Street to Edinburgh
E To Liverpool Lime Street
F From Birmingham New Street to Glasgow Central
G From Bristol Temple Meads to Edinburgh
H From Bristol Temple Meads to Glasgow Central
I From Birmingham New Street to Newcastle

For connections from Gatwick Airport see Table 52

Table 53

Sundays

30 March to 11 May

London - East Midlands - Sheffield

Route Diagram - see first Page of Table 53

		NT	XC	EM	EM	EM	EM	XC	NT	XC	EM	EM	EM	EM	XC	NT	XC	EM	EM	EM	EM	XC	NT
			◇1	◇1	◇1	◇	◇1	◇1		◇1	◇1	◇1	◇	◇1	◇1		◇1	◇1	◇1	◇	◇1	◇1	
			A			B		C		D			E		F		G			H		I	
			🛒	☕	☕		☕	🛒		🛒	☕	☕		☕	🛒		🛒	☕	☕		☕	🛒	
St Pancras International ⊖52	d			11 30			12 10				12 30			13 10				13 40			14 10		
Luton Airport Parkway 7 52 ✈	d			11 59			12 31				12 53			13 31				14 02			14 31		
Luton 10 52	d			12 03			12 34				12 57			13 34				14 07					
Bedford 7 52	d			12 23			12 49				13 12			13 49				14 21			14 46		
Wellingborough	d			12 35			13 02				13 26			14 02				14 35			14 59		
Kettering 4	a			12 41			13 08				13 33			14 08				14 42			15 05		
	d			12 42	12 55		13 09				13 34	13 55		14 09				14 42	14 55		15 06		
Corby	d				13a05							14a05							15a05				
Oakham	d																						
Melton Mowbray	d																						
Market Harborough	d			12 52			13 19				13 45			14 19				14 54			15 16		
Leicester	a			13 07			13 34				14 02			14 34				15 10			15 31		
	d			13 09			13 36				14 03			14 36				15 11			15 33		
Syston	d																						
Sileby	d																						
Barrow Upon Soar	d																						
Loughborough	d			13 19			13 46				14 14			14 46				15 22			15 43		
East Midlands Parkway ✈	a			13 25			13 52				14 22			14 52				15 30			15 49		
	d			13 26			13 53				14 23			14 53				15 31			15 50		
Beeston	a						13 59							14 59							15 58		
Nottingham 8 🚌	a						14 07							15 07							16 05		
	d	13 13				13 42			14 15				14 47			15 12				15 47			16 15
Newark Castle 27	a																						
Lincoln 27	a																						
Langley Mill	d	13 34				13 58			14 34				15 03			15 36							16 34
Alfreton	d	13 42				14 06			14 42				15 11			15 44				16 08			16 42
Long Eaton	a			13 30							14 26							15 34					
Derby 6	a			13 43							14 42							15 48					
	d		13 44	13 52				14 11		14 44	14 53				15 11		15 44	15 49				16 11	
Chesterfield	d	13 52	14 03	14 11		14 16		14 30	14 53	15 03	15 14		15 21			15 56	16 03	16 10		16 18			16 52
Sheffield 7 🚌	a	14 15	14 17	14 24		14 34		14 45	15 15	15 17	15 29		15 39		15 47	16 15	16 18	16 25		16 34		16 48	17 15
Doncaster 7 29	a							15 13							16 15							17 13	
Wakefield Kirkgate 4 31,34	a	14 52							15 52							16 52							17 52
Wakefield Westgate 7 31	a		14 44							15 44							16 44						
Leeds 10 31,34	a	15 18	15 02						16 18	16 02						17 16	17 02						18 18
York 8 29	a		15 27					15 42		16 27					16 38		17 27					17 40	

		XC	EM	EM	EM	EM	XC	NT	XC	EM	EM	EM	EM	XC	EM	EM	EM	NT	EM	XC	EM	EM
		◇1	◇1	◇1	◇	◇1	◇1		◇1	◇1	◇1	◇	◇1	◇1	◇1	◇1	◇1		◇1	◇1	◇	◇1
		D			B		I		J			B		K						J	L	
		🛒	☕	☕		☕	🛒		🛒	☕	☕		☕	🛒	☕	☕	☕		☕	🛒		☕
St Pancras International ⊖52	d		14 40			15 10				15 40			16 10		16 35	16 40			17 05			17 10
Luton Airport Parkway 7 52 ✈	d					15 33							16 31									17 31
Luton 10 52	d		15 04							16 04						17 02						
Bedford 7 52	d		15 19			15 48				16 19			16 46			17 16						17 46
Wellingborough	d		15 33			16 02				16 33			16 59			17 29						17 58
Kettering 4	a		15 40			16 10				16 40			17 05			17 36						18 05
	d		15 41	15 45		16 11				16 41	16 45		17 06			17 37	17 50					18 06
Corby	d			15a55							16a55						18a00					
Oakham	d																					
Melton Mowbray	d																					
Market Harborough	d		15 52			16 22				16 52			17 16			17 47						18 15
Leicester	a		16 09			16 38				17 09			17 31		17 43	18 02			18 10			18 31
	d		16 10			16 38				17 10			17 33		17 44	18 03			18 11			18 33
Syston	d																					
Sileby	d																					
Barrow Upon Soar	d																					
Loughborough	d		16 21			16 51				17 21			17 43			18 13						18 43
East Midlands Parkway ✈	a		16 29			16 58				17 29			17 49		18 00	18 20			18 24			18 49
	d		16 30			16 59				17 30			17 50		18 00	18 21			18 25			18 50
Beeston	a												17 58									18 58
Nottingham 8 🚌	a					17 11							18 05						18 36			19 05
	d				16 42			17 15				17 41						18 15			18 40	
Newark Castle 27	a																					
Lincoln 27	a																					
Langley Mill	d				17 01			17 34				17 57						18 34			18 56	
Alfreton	d				17 09			17 42				18 05						18 42			19 04	
Long Eaton	a		16 33							17 33						18 24						
Derby 6	a		16 47							17 47					18 14	18 36						
	d	16 44	16 52				17 11		17 43	17 50				18 11	18 14					18 43		
Chesterfield	d	17 03	17 13		17 19			17 52	18 04	18 11		18 16			18 37			18 52		19 05	19 15	
Sheffield 7 🚌	a	17 17	17 28		17 39		17 48	18 15	18 19	18 25		18 33		18 46	18 51			19 15		19 20	19 31	
Doncaster 7 29	a						18 13							19 15								
Wakefield Kirkgate 4 31,34	a							18 52										19 52				
Wakefield Westgate 7 31	a	17 44	18 05				18 33		18 47											19 48		
Leeds 10 31,34	a	18 02	18 24				18 51	19 18	19 04									20 18		20 05		
York 8 29	a	18 27					19 20		19 30					19 39						20 30		

A From Plymouth to Aberdeen
B From Norwich to Liverpool Lime Street
C From Birmingham New Street to Newcastle
D From Plymouth to Glasgow Central
E To Liverpool Lime Street
F From Guildford to Newcastle
G From Penzance to Edinburgh
H From Peterborough to Liverpool Lime Street
I From Reading to Newcastle
J From Plymouth to Edinburgh
K From Reading to Edinburgh
L From Norwich to Manchester Piccadilly

For connections from Gatwick Airport see Table 52

Table 53

Sundays

30 March to 11 May

London - East Midlands - Sheffield

Route Diagram - see first Page of Table 53

		XC	EM	EM	EM	NT	EM	XC	EM	EM	XC	EM	EM	EM	NT	EM	EM	XC	EM	EM	XC	EM	NT
		◇1	◇1	◇1	◇1		◇1	◇1	◇	◇1	◇1	◇1	◇1	◇1		◇1	◇1	◇1	◇1	◇1	◇1	◇1	
		A						B	C		D							B			E		
		🛒	☕	☕	☕		☕	🛒		☕	🛒	☕	☕	☕		☕	☕	🛒	☕	☕		☕	
St Pancras International ⊖52	d		17 35	17 40			18 05			18 10		18 35	18 40			19 05	19 10		19 35	19 40			
Luton Airport Parkway 7 52 ✈	d									18 31							19 31						
Luton 10 52	d			18 02									19 02							20 02			
Bedford 7 52	d			18 16						18 46			19 16				19 46			20 16			
Wellingborough	d			18 29						18 59			19 29				19 58			20 29			
Kettering 4	a			18 36						19 05			19 36				20 05			20 36			
	d			18 37	18 50					19 06			19 37	19 45			20 05			20 37		20 46	
Corby	d				19a00									19a55								20a56	
Oakham	d																						
Melton Mowbray	d																						
Market Harborough	d			18 47						19 16			19 47				20 15			20 47			
Leicester	a		18 40	19 02			19 10			19 31		19 43	20 02			20 17	20 31		20 43	21 02			
	d		18 41	19 03			19 11			19 33		19 45	20 03			20 21	20 33		20 45	21 03			
Syston	d																						
Sileby	d																						
Barrow Upon Soar	d																						
Loughborough	d			19 13						19 43			20 13				20 43			21 13			
East Midlands Parkway ✈	a		18 54	19 20			19 24			19 49		20 00	20 20			20 38	20 49		21 00	21 20			
	d		18 55	19 21			19 25			19 50		20 01	20 21			20 38	20 50		21 01	21 21			
Beeston	a									19 58							20 58						
Nottingham 8 ⛴	a						19 36			20 05						20 51	21 05						
	d					19 15			19 43						20 15								21 33
Newark Castle 27	a																						
Lincoln 27	a																						
Langley Mill	d					19 34									20 34								21 57
Alfreton	d					19 42			20 04						20 42								22 05
Long Eaton	a			19 24									20 24							21 24			
Derby 6	a		19 07	19 37								20 14	20 37						21 14	21 36			
	d	19 05	19 16					19 42			20 03	20 16						20 44	21 16		21 44		
Chesterfield	d		19 34			19 52		20 03	20 14			20 37			20 52			21 03	21 37		22 03		22 16
Sheffield 7 ⛴	a	19 39	19 50			20 15		20 18	20 31		20 40	20 51			21 14			21 16	21 53		22 18		22 36
Doncaster 7 29	a	20 16									21 19												
Wakefield Kirkgate 4 31,34	a					20 52																	23 26
Wakefield Westgate 7 31	a							20 49				21 27						21 47			22 43		
Leeds 10 31,34	a					21 16		21 06				21 44						22 04			23 01		00 05
York 8 29	a	20 38						21 31			21 42												

		EM	EM	EM	XC	EM	EM	EM	EM	EM	EM
		◇1	◇1	◇1	◇1	◇1	◇1	◇1	◇1	◇1	◇1
					B						
		☕	☕	☕		☕	☕	☕	☕	☕	☕
St Pancras International ⊖52	d	20 00	20 10	20 35		20 40		21 10	21 30	22 30	23 00
Luton Airport Parkway 7 52 ✈	d		20 31					21 31		22 51	23 39
Luton 10 52	d					21 04			21 52		
Bedford 7 52	d		20 47			21 20		21 46	22 06	23 13	00 03
Wellingborough	d		20 58			21 33		21 59	22 19	23 27	00 16
Kettering 4	a		21 05			21 40		22 05	22 26	23 36	00 22
	d		21 06			21 41	21 55	22 06	22 27	23 37	00 23
Corby	d						22a05				
Oakham	d										
Melton Mowbray	d										
Market Harborough	d		21 16			21 52		22 16	22 37	23 47	00 33
Leicester	a	21 08	21 31	21 40		22 09		22 31	22 52	00 07	00 51
	d	21 10	21 33	21 41		22 10		22 33	22 54	00 08	00 54
Syston	d										
Sileby	d										
Barrow Upon Soar	d										
Loughborough	d	21 21	21 43	21 51				22 47	23 04	00 18	01 04
East Midlands Parkway ✈	a	21 28	21 49	21 58		22 25		22 57	23 15	00 30	01 15
	d	21 29	21 50	21 59		22 26		22 58	23 16	00 31	01 16
Beeston	a		21 58					23 04		00 39	
Nottingham 8 ⛴	a	21 45	22 05					23 11		00 46	
	d										
Newark Castle 27	a										
Lincoln 27	a										
Langley Mill	d										
Alfreton	d										
Long Eaton	a								23 23		
Derby 6	a			22 11		22 40			23 35		01 31
	d				22 44	22 48			23 36		
Chesterfield	d				23 05	23 09			23 55		
Sheffield 7 ⛴	a				23 20	23 31			00 08		
Doncaster 7 29	a										
Wakefield Kirkgate 4 31,34	a										
Wakefield Westgate 7 31	a					00 03					
Leeds 10 31,34	a				00 16	00 20					
York 8 29	a										

A From Reading to Newcastle
B From Plymouth
C From Norwich to Manchester Piccadilly
D From Reading to Newcastle. 🛒 to Sheffield
E From Penzance

For connections from Gatwick Airport see Table 52

Table 53R

Mondays to Fridays

9 December to 16 May

Sheffield - East Midlands - London

Route Diagram - see first Page of Table 53

Miles	Miles	Miles			EM MX	EM	EM	EM	EM	EM	NT	EM	EM		EM	EM	EM	XC	EM	NT	EM	EM	EM		EM
					◇	◇1	◇1	◇1	◇1			◇1	◇1		◇1	◇1	◇1	◇1	◇1			◇1	◇1		◇1
					A													B							
						🛒	🛒	🛒	🛒			🛒	☒		🛒	🛒	☒		🛒			☒	☒		🛒
—	—	—	York [8] 29	d																					
—	—	—	Leeds [10] 31,34	d																		05 25			
—	—	—	Wakefield Westgate [7] 31	d																		05 38			
—	—	—	Wakefield Kirkgate [4] 31,34	d																					
—	—	—	Doncaster [7] 29	d																		05 57			
0	0	—	**Sheffield** [7] 🚊	d							05 05		05 30				05 59	06 01		06 03		06 29			
12¼	12¼	—	Chesterfield	d	00 02						05 20		05 42				06 12	06 26		06 19		06 40			
—	36½	—	**Derby** [6]	a									06 02				06 32	06 43				07 03			
—	—	—		d			05 00	05 19					06 04				06 33					07 05			
—	44	—	Long Eaton	d				05 28									06 44								
22½	—	—	Alfreton	d																06 30					
34½	—	—	Langley Mill	d																06 37					
—	—	—	Lincoln 27	d																					
—	—	—	Newark Castle 27	a																					
40¾	—	—	**Nottingham** [8] 🚊	a	00 39						06 11									07 02					
—	—	—		d					05 32	05 38						06 30			06 52				07 10		
44	—	—	Beeston	d												06 36			06 58				07 17		
—	—	—	East Midlands Parkway ✈	a			05 10		05 42				06 16			06 41			07 03				07 23		
—	—	—		d			05 11		05 43				06 17			06 42			07 04				07 25		
55½	53¼	—	Loughborough	d			05 18		05 52	05 58			06 26				06 53				07 00	07 22			
59½	57¼	—	Barrow Upon Soar	d						06 02											07 04				
61½	59¼	—	Sileby	d						06 07											07 09				
64¼	62	—	Syston	d						06 12											07 14				
68	65¾	0	**Leicester**	a			05 27	05 42	06 03	06 19			06 37			06 55	07 05		07 17		07 22	07 34	07 41		
—	—	—		d		04 45	05 29	05 43	06 04				06 39			06 57	07 06		07 19			07 36	07 42		
84¼	82	—	Market Harborough	d			05 43	05 58	06 20				06 54			07 11			07 33				07 57		
—	—	15¼	Melton Mowbray	d								06 00													
—	—	26¾	Oakham	d								06 12													
—	—	41	Corby	d								06 35			07 08										08 02
95¼	93	48½	Kettering [4]	a		05 04	05 52	06 07	06 30			06 44	07 04		07 17	07 20	07 28		07 42			07 57	08 07		08 11
—	—	—		d		05 05	05 54	06 08	06 31			06 45	07 06			07 21	07 29		07 43			07 59	08 09		
102¼	100	—	Wellingborough	d		05 17	06 02	06 16	06 40			06 54	07 14			07 29	07 38		07 51			08 07			
117½	115¼	—	Bedford [7] 52	d		05 37		06 30				07 09					07 54						08 29		
137	134¾	—	Luton [10] 52	d			06 25					07 24				07 59			08 15						
138	135¾	—	Luton Airport Parkway [7] 52 ✈	d		05 56			07 05				07 41				08 11								
167¼	165	—	**St Pancras International** ⊖52	a		06 19	06 49	07 08	07 31			07 48	08 07			08 23	08 39		08 42			08 56	09 06		

		EM	XC	EM	EM	EM	NT	XC	EM		EM	EM	EM	EM	XC	NT	XC	EM	EM		EM	EM	EM	EM	XC
																	R								
		◇1	◇1	◇1		◇1		◇1	◇1		◇1	◇1	◇1	◇1	◇1		1	◇1	◇1			◇1	◇	◇1	◇1
		N	C			L		D	M			E		F	G		H				I		J		K
		☒	🛒	🛒		🛒		🛒	☒		🛒	🛒	🛒	🛒	🛒		🛒	🛒	🛒			🛒		🛒	🛒
York [8] 29	d														06 32		07 23								07 45
Leeds [10] 31,34	d		06 00				06 05	06 16				06 34			07 05	07 05									08 11
Wakefield Westgate [7] 31	d		06 12					06 28				06 47			07 19										08 23
Wakefield Kirkgate [4] 31,34	d						06 21									07 25									
Doncaster [7] 29	d							06 46									07 56								
Sheffield [7] 🚊	d	06 49	06 52				07 03	07 18	07 29			07 37	07 46		07 53	08 08	08 20		08 29				08 38	08 49	08 56
Chesterfield	d	07 01	07 06				07 20	07 30	07 41			07 50	07 59		08 06	08 24	08 32		08 41				08 53	09 01	09 08
Derby [6]	a	07 19	07 25					07 48	08 00				08 18		08 25		08 50		08 59					09 19	09 25
	d	07 22		07 36					08 01				08 19						09 01					09 21	
Long Eaton	d			07 45									08 30											09 30	
Alfreton	d						07 31					08 01				08 34							09 03		
Langley Mill	d						07 39					08 09				08 42									
Lincoln 27	d										07 04										07 26				
Newark Castle 27	a										07 28										07 57				
Nottingham [8] 🚊	a						07 59				07 56	08 25				09 02					08 31		09 26		
	d				07 32	07 55					08 05	08 32									08 36	09 05			
Beeston	d				07 38						08 11			←							08 42	09 11			
East Midlands Parkway ✈	a	07 32			07 45	08 04						08 42	08 34	08 42							08 49			09 34	
	d	07 33			07 46	08 04						08 42	08 35	08 42							08 49			09 35	
Loughborough	d	07 41		07 54	07 54						08 21	↪	08 42								08 58	09 21		09 42	
Barrow Upon Soar	d				07 59																09 02				
Sileby	d				08 03																09 06				
Syston	d				08 08																09 12				
Leicester	a	07 52		08 04	08 20	08 18			08 24		08 31		08 53	08 58					09 22		09 25	09 31		09 52	
	d	07 56		08 05		08 18			08 24		08 32		08 54	08 59					09 24			09 32		09 52	
Market Harborough	d			08 19							08 46			09 13								09 46			
Melton Mowbray	d																								
Oakham	d																								
Corby	d																	09 16							
Kettering [4]	a	08 16		08 28							08 55							09 25				09 55			
	d	08 17		08 29							08 55							09 26				09 55			
Wellingborough	d	08 25		08 42							09 02							09 34				10 02			
Bedford [7] 52	d			09 05							09 16							09 47				10 16			
Luton [10] 52	d			09 19														10 02							
Luton Airport Parkway [7] 52 ✈	d										09 31											10 31			
St Pancras International ⊖52	a	09 10		09 45		09 26			09 33		09 56		10 06	10 15				10 26	10 30			10 56		10 59	

A From Liverpool Lime Street
B To Reading
C To Plymouth
D To Southampton Central
E To St Pancras International
F From Leeds
G **The South Yorshireman,** To Plymouth. 🛒 from Leeds
H From Newcastle to Reading
I From Sleaford
J From Liverpool Lime Street to Norwich
K From Newcastle to Plymouth
L **The Robin Rood**
M **The Master Cutler**
N **The Sheffield Continental**

For connections to Gatwick Airport see Table 52

Table 53R

Mondays to Fridays

9 December to 16 May

Sheffield - East Midlands - London

Route Diagram - see first Page of Table 53

		EM	NT	XC	EM		EM	EM	EM	EM	EM	XC	EM	NT	XC		EM	EM	EM	EM	EM	EM	XC	EM	NT
		◇1		◇1	◇1		◇1		◇1	◇	◇1	◇1	◇1		◇1		◇1	◇1		◇1	◇	◇1	◇1	◇1	
				A						B		C			D						B		E		
York [8] 29	d			08 26								08 45			09 35								09 45		
Leeds [10] 31,34	d		08 02									09 11		09 05									10 11		10 05
Wakefield Westgate [7] 31	d											09 24											10 23		
Wakefield Kirkgate [4] 31,34	d		08 23											09 23											10 23
Doncaster [7] 29	d			08 51											09 58										
Sheffield [7]	d		09 05	09 24			09 29			09 36	09 49	09 55		10 05	10 24			10 29			10 38	10 49	10 55		11 05
Chesterfield	d		09 21				09 41			09 52	10 01	10 06		10 21				10 41			10 52	11 01	11 07		11 21
Derby [6]	a			09 51			10 00				10 20	10 26			10 51			11 00				11 19	11 24		
	d						10 01				10 21							11 01				11 21			
Long Eaton	d										10 30											11 30			
Alfreton	d		09 32							10 02				10 31							11 03				11 31
Langley Mill	d		09 39											10 39											11 39
Lincoln 27	d							08 35											09 32						
Newark Castle 27	a							09 03											09 56						
Nottingham [8]	a		10 02					09 30		10 27				11 02					10 30		11 27				12 02
	d	09 32						09 36	10 05				10 32						10 36	11 05				11 32	
Beeston	d							09 42	10 11										10 42	11 11					
East Midlands Parkway	a	09 42						09 49			10 34		10 42						10 49			11 34		11 42	
	d	09 42						09 50			10 35		10 42						10 50			11 35		11 42	
Loughborough	d							09 58	10 21		10 42								10 58	11 21		11 42			
Barrow Upon Soar	d							10 03											11 03						
Sileby	d							10 07											11 07						
Syston	d							10 12											11 12						
Leicester	a	09 58					10 22	10 24	10 31		10 52		10 58					11 22	11 23	11 31		11 52		11 58	
	d	09 59					10 24		10 32		10 52		10 59					11 24		11 32		11 52		11 59	
Market Harborough	d	10 13							10 46				11 13							11 46				12 13	
Melton Mowbray	d																								
Oakham	d																								
Corby	d				10 16												11 16								
Kettering [4]	a				10 25				10 55								11 25			11 55					
	d				10 26				10 55								11 26			11 55					
Wellingborough	d				10 34				11 02								11 34			12 02					
Bedford [7] 52	d				10 47				11 16								11 47			12 16					
Luton [10] 52	d				11 02												12 02								
Luton Airport Parkway [7] 52	d								11 31											12 31					
St Pancras International ⊖52	a	11 14			11 26		11 30		11 56		11 59		12 14				12 26	12 30		12 56		12 59		13 14	

			XC	EM	EM	EM	EM	EM	EM	XC	EM		NT	XC	EM	EM	EM	EM	EM	EM	XC		EM	NT	XC
			◇1	◇1	◇1		◇1	◇	◇1	◇1	◇1			◇1	◇1	◇1		◇1	◇	◇1	◇1		◇1		◇1
			A					B		F				G					B		E				A
York [8] 29	d		10 35							10 45				11 34							11 45				12 35
Leeds [10] 31,34	d									11 11			11 05								12 11			12 05	
Wakefield Westgate [7] 31	d									11 24											12 23				
Wakefield Kirkgate [4] 31,34	d												11 23											12 23	
Doncaster [7] 29	d		10 59											11 58											12 59
Sheffield [7]	d		11 24		11 29			11 37	11 49	11 55			12 05	12 24		12 29			12 36	12 49	12 55			13 05	13 24
Chesterfield	d				11 41			11 52	12 01	12 06			12 21			12 41			12 52	13 01	13 07			13 21	
Derby [6]	a		11 51		12 00				12 19	12 26				12 51		13 00				13 20	13 24				13 51
	d				12 01				12 21							13 01				13 21					
Long Eaton	d								12 30											13 30					
Alfreton	d							12 02					12 31						13 02					13 33	
Langley Mill	d												12 39											13 40	
Lincoln 27	d					10 36											11 41								
Newark Castle 27	a					11 05											12 04								
Nottingham [8]	a					11 30		12 27					13 02				12 30		13 27					14 02	
	d					11 36	12 05				12 32						12 36	13 05					13 32		
Beeston	d					11 42	12 11										12 42	13 11							
East Midlands Parkway	a					11 49			12 34		12 42						12 49			13 34			13 42		
	d					11 50			12 35		12 42						12 50			13 35			13 42		
Loughborough	d					11 58	12 21		12 42								12 58	13 21		13 42					
Barrow Upon Soar	d					12 03											13 03								
Sileby	d					12 07											13 07								
Syston	d					12 12											13 12								
Leicester	a				12 22	12 23	12 31		12 52		12 58					13 22	13 24	13 31		13 52			13 58		
	d				12 24		12 32		12 52		12 59					13 24		13 32		13 52			13 59		
Market Harborough	d						12 45				13 13							13 46					14 13		
Melton Mowbray	d																								
Oakham	d																								
Corby	d			12 16											13 16										
Kettering [4]	a			12 25			12 55								13 25			13 55							
	d			12 26			12 55								13 26			13 55							
Wellingborough	d			12 34			13 02								13 34			14 02							
Bedford [7] 52	d			12 47			13 16								13 47			14 16							
Luton [10] 52	d			13 02											14 02										
Luton Airport Parkway [7] 52	d						13 31											14 31							
St Pancras International ⊖52	a			13 26	13 30		13 56		13 59		14 14				14 26	14 30		14 56		14 59			15 14		

A From Newcastle to Southampton Central
B From Liverpool Lime Street to Norwich
C From Edinburgh to Plymouth
D From Edinburgh to Reading
E From Glasgow Central to Plymouth
F From Dundee to Plymouth
G From Newcastle to Reading

For connections to Gatwick Airport see Table 52

Table 53R

Mondays to Fridays

9 December to 16 May

Sheffield - East Midlands - London

Route Diagram - see first Page of Table 53

Station			EM	EM	EM	EM	EM	EM	XC	EM	NT	XC	EM	EM	EM	EM	EM	EM	XC	EM	NT	XC	EM	EM
			◇1	◇1		◇1	◇	◇1	◇1	◇1		◇1	◇1	◇1		◇1	◇	◇1	◇1	◇1		◇1	◇1	◇1
							A		B			C					A		D			E		
			🛒	🛒		🛒		🛒	🛒	🛒		🛒	🛒	🛒		🛒		🛒	🛒	🛒		🛒	🛒	🛒
York 8	29	d							12 45			13 34							13 45			14 35		
Leeds 10	31,34	d							13 11		13 05								14 11		14 05			
Wakefield Westgate 7	31	d							13 23										14 23					
Wakefield Kirkgate 4	31,34	d									13 23										14 23			
Doncaster 7	29	d										13 58										14 59		
Sheffield 7		d		13 29			13 38	13 49	13 55		14 05	14 24		14 29			14 36	14 49	14 55		15 05	15 24		15 29
Chesterfield		d		13 41			13 54	14 01	14 07		14 22			14 41			14 52	15 01	15 07		15 21			15 41
Derby 6		a		14 00				14 19	14 24			14 51		15 00				15 20	15 24			15 51		16 00
		d		14 01				14 21						15 01				15 21						16 01
Long Eaton		d						14 30										15 30						
Alfreton		d					14 05				14 32						14 59				15 31			
Langley Mill		d									14 40										15 39			
Lincoln	27	d			12 30										13 40									
Newark Castle	27	a			12 58										14 04									
Nottingham 8		a			13 31		14 27				15 02				14 30		15 25				16 02			
		d			13 36	14 05				14 32					14 36	15 05				15 32				
Beeston		d			13 42	14 11									14 42	15 11								
East Midlands Parkway		a			13 49			14 34		14 42					14 49			15 34		15 42				
		d			13 50			14 35		14 42					14 50			15 35		15 42				
Loughborough		d			13 58	14 21		14 42							14 58	15 21		15 42						
Barrow Upon Soar		d			14 03										15 03									
Sileby		d			14 07										15 07									
Syston		d			14 12										15 12									
Leicester		a		14 22	14 24	14 31		14 52		14 59				15 22	15 24	15 31		15 52		15 58				16 23
		d		14 24		14 32		14 52		14 59				15 24		15 32		15 52		15 59				16 24
Market Harborough		d				14 46				15 13						15 46				16 13				
Melton Mowbray		d																						
Oakham		d																						
Corby		d	14 16										15 16										16 16	
Kettering 4		a	14 25			14 55							15 25			15 55							16 25	
		d	14 26			14 55							15 26			15 55							16 26	
Wellingborough		d	14 34			15 02							15 34			16 02							16 34	
Bedford 7	52	d	14 47			15 16							15 47			16 16							16 47	
Luton 10	52	d	15 02										16 02										17 02	
Luton Airport Parkway 7	52	d				15 31										16 31								
St Pancras International	⊖52	a	15 26	15 30		15 56		15 59		16 14			16 26	16 31		16 56		16 59		17 15			17 26	17 29

Station			EM	EM	EM	EM	XC	EM	NT	XC	EM	EM	EM	EM	EM	EM	EM	XC FO	XC FX	EM	NT	XC	EM
				◇1	◇	◇1	◇1	◇1		◇1	◇1	◇1	◇1		◇1	◇	◇1	◇1	◇1	◇1		◇1	◇1
					A		B			C						A		F	F			C	
				🛒		🛒	🛒	🛒		🛒	🛒	🛒	🛒		🛒		🛒	🛒	🛒	🛒		🛒	🛒
York 8	29	d					14 45			15 34								15 44	15 44			16 05	
Leeds 10	31,34	d					15 11		15 05									16 11	16 11		16 05	16 40	
Wakefield Westgate 7	31	d					15 24											16 23	16 23			16 52	
Wakefield Kirkgate 4	31,34	d							15 23												16 23		
Doncaster 7	29	d								15 58													
Sheffield 7		d			15 38	15 49	15 55		16 05	16 24		16 29				16 38	16 49	16 54	16 54		17 05	17 24	17 29
Chesterfield		d			15 52	16 01	16 07		16 21			16 41				16 53	17 01	17 05	17 07		17 21		17 41
Derby 6		a				16 19	16 24			16 51		17 00					17 19	17 25	17 25			17 51	18 00
		d				16 21						17 01	16 36				17 21						18 01
Long Eaton		d				16 30											17 30						
Alfreton		d			16 02				16 31							17 04					17 31		
Langley Mill		d							16 39												17 39		
Lincoln	27	d	14 33											15 30									
Newark Castle	27	a	14 58											15 58									
Nottingham 8		a	15 27		16 26				17 02					16 30		17 27					18 02		
		d	15 36	16 05				16 30						16 33	17 05					17 32			
Beeston		d	15 42	16 11										16 39	17 11								
East Midlands Parkway		a	15 49			16 34		16 40					16 47	16 49			17 34			17 42			
		d	15 50			16 35		16 40					16 47	16 49			17 35			17 42			
Loughborough		d	15 58	16 21		16 42								16 58	17 21		17 42						
Barrow Upon Soar		d	16 03											17 02									
Sileby		d	16 07											17 07									
Syston		d	16 12											17 11									
Leicester		a	16 24	16 31		16 52		16 56				17 23		17 23	17 31		17 52			17 58			18 24
		d		16 32		16 52		16 56				17 24			17 32		17 52			17 59			18 24
Market Harborough		d		16 46				17 10							17 46					18 13			
Melton Mowbray		d											17 14										
Oakham		d											17 27										
Corby		d									17 16		17 51										
Kettering 4		a		16 55		17 13					17 25		18 00		17 55		18 13						
		d		16 55		17 14					17 26		18 18		17 55		18 14						
Wellingborough		d		17 02							17 34		18 28		18 02								
Bedford 7	52	d		17 16							17 47		18 47		18 16								
Luton 10	52	d						17 49			18 02	18 11	19 02										
Luton Airport Parkway 7	52	d		17 31											18 31								
St Pancras International	⊖52	a		17 56		18 09		18 15			18 26	18 35	19 26		18 56		19 03			19 15			19 33

A From Liverpool Lime Street to Norwich
B From Glasgow Central to Penzance
C From Newcastle to Reading
D From Aberdeen to Penzance
E From Newcastle to Guildford
F From Edinburgh to Plymouth

For connections to Gatwick Airport see Table 52

Table 53R

Mondays to Fridays

9 December to 16 May

Sheffield - East Midlands - London

Route Diagram - see first Page of Table 53

Station			EM	EM	EM	EM	EM	XC	NT	XC		EM	EM	EM	EM	EM	EM	EM	EM	XC		NT	XC	EM	EM	EM
				◇1	◇1	◇	◇1	◇1		◇1		◇1	◇1		◇1	◇1	◇1		◇	◇1			◇1	◇1	◇1	◇1
						A		B		C									D	E			F			
				🛒	🛒		🛒	🛒		🛒		🛒	🛒		🛒	🛒	🛒			🛒			🛒	🛒	🛒	🛒
York [8]	29	d						16 45		17 35										17 45			18 34			
Leeds [10]	31,34	d						17 11	17 05											18 11		18 05				
Wakefield Westgate [7]	31	d						17 23												18 23						
Wakefield Kirkgate [4]	31,34	d							17 23													18 23				
Doncaster [7]	29	d								17 59													18 58			
Sheffield [7]		d			17 38	17 45		17 58	18 05	18 24			18 29			18 48			18 51	18 58		19 06	19 24		19 29	
Chesterfield		d			17 56	18 01		18 10	18 21				18 41			19 00			19 06	19 10		19 22			19 41	
Derby [6]		a			18 15			18 27		18 51			18 59			19 19				19 26			19 51		19 59	
		d			18 21								19 01			19 21									20 01	
Long Eaton		d			18 30											19 30										
Alfreton		d				18 11			18 31										19 16			19 32				
Langley Mill		d							18 39													19 40				
Lincoln	27	d	16 34											17 26				18 35								
Newark Castle	27	a	17 03											17 55				19 03								
Nottingham [8]		a	17 30			18 31			19 02					18 29				19 29	19 41			20 02				
		d	17 36	18 05			18 32							18 36	19 05		19 32	19 36								20 02
Beeston		d	17 41	18 11										18 42	19 11			19 42								20 08
East Midlands Parkway		a	17 51		18 34		18 42							18 49		19 34	19 42	19 49								20 14
		d	17 51		18 35		18 42							18 50		19 35	19 42	19 49								20 15
Loughborough		d	18 00	18 21	18 42									19 00	19 21	19 42		19 58								20 23
Barrow Upon Soar		d	18 04											19 04				20 02								
Sileby		d	18 09											19 09				20 06								
Syston		d	18 13											19 14				20 11								
Leicester		a	18 25	18 31	18 52		18 58						19 24	19 26	19 31	19 52	19 58	20 23							20 23	20 32
		d		18 32	18 52		18 59						19 24		19 32	19 52	19 59								20 24	20 34
Market Harborough		d		18 46			19 13								19 46		20 13									20 47
Melton Mowbray		d																								
Oakham		d																								
Corby		d										18 56												19 53		
Kettering [4]		a		18 55								19 05			19 55									20 02		20 56
		d		18 55								19 26			19 55									20 26		20 56
Wellingborough		d		19 02								19 34			20 02									20 34		21 05
Bedford [7]	52	d		19 16								19 47			20 16									20 47		21 18
Luton [10]	52	d										20 02												21 02		
Luton Airport Parkway [7]	52	d		19 31											20 31											21 34
St Pancras International ⊖	52	a		19 56	20 00		20 16					20 26	20 32		20 56	20 59	21 16							21 26	21 33	21 57

Station			EM	EM	XC	NT		XC	EM	EM	EM	EM	EM	EM	EM	XC		XC	EM	EM	EM	EM	XC	EM	EM	EM
			◇		◇1			◇1	◇1	◇1	◇1	◇1	◇	◇1	◇1	◇1		◇1	◇1		◇		◇1	◇1	◇1	◇1
			A		G			H	I	J			D	I	J	K		H			D		L			
					🛒			🛒	🛒	🛒	🛒	🛒		🛒	🛒	🛒			🛒				🛒	🛒	🛒	🛒
York [8]	29	d			18 45			19 35								19 45		20 35					20 45			
Leeds [10]	31,34	d			19 11	19 05										20 11							21 11			
Wakefield Westgate [7]	31	d			19 24											20 23							21 25			
Wakefield Kirkgate [4]	31,34	d				19 24																				
Doncaster [7]	29	d						19 59										21 02								
Sheffield [7]		d	19 37		19 54	20 05		20 24					20 41	20 49	20 49	20 57		21 29			21 39		22 00	22 01		23 21
Chesterfield		d	19 51		20 06	20 23							20 56	21 01	21 01	21 09		21 41			21 55		22 24	22 13		23 45
Derby [6]		a			20 23			20 51						21 20	21 20	21 27		22 00					22 42	22 34		00 05
		d												21 23	21 23											
Long Eaton		d																								
Alfreton		d	20 03			20 33							21 08								22 05					
Langley Mill		d				20 41															22 13					
Lincoln	27	d																								
Newark Castle	27	a																								
Nottingham [8]		a	20 29			21 02							21 33								22 35					
		d		20 36								21 02							21 31	21 35		23 10				
Beeston		d		20 42								21 08								21 41		23 15				
East Midlands Parkway		a		20 50								21 13		21 33	21 33					21 48		23 22				
		d		20 50								21 14		21 34	21 34					21 50		23 23				
Loughborough		d		20 58								21 22		21 41	21 41				21 46	21 58		23 31				
Barrow Upon Soar		d		21 03																22 03						
Sileby		d		21 07																22 07						
Syston		d		21 12																22 12						
Leicester		a		21 23								21 31		21 52	21 52				21 57	22 24		23 56				
		d										21 33		21 53	21 53				21 58							
Market Harborough		d										21 47							22 12							
Melton Mowbray		d																								
Oakham		d																								
Corby		d							20 51	20 51	21 43														22 43	
Kettering [4]		a							21 00	21 00	21 52	21 56							22 22						22 52	
		d							21 18	21 18		21 57							22 23							
Wellingborough		d							21 27	21 27		22 04							22 30							
Bedford [7]	52	d							21 42	21 42		22 19							22 45							
Luton [10]	52	d							21 59	21 59		22 36							23 02							
Luton Airport Parkway [7]	52	d										22 39														
St Pancras International ⊖	52	a							22 24	22 28		23 06		23 00	23 09				23 40							

A From Liverpool Lime Street to Norwich
B From Glasgow Central to Plymouth
C From Newcastle to Reading
D From Liverpool Lime Street
E From Edinburgh to Plymouth
F From Newcastle to Southampton Central
G From Glasgow Central to Bristol Temple Meads
H From Newcastle to Birmingham New Street
I until 27 December, from 10 February
J from 30 December until 7 February
K From Edinburgh to Bristol Temple Meads. 🛒 to Leeds
L From Glasgow Central to Birmingham New Street. 🛒 to Leeds

For connections to Gatwick Airport see Table 52

Table 53R

Sheffield - East Midlands - London

Mondays to Fridays

9 December to 16 May

Route Diagram - see first Page of Table 53

		EM
		◇
		A
York 8	29 d	
Leeds 10	31,34 d	
Wakefield Westgate 7	31 d	
Wakefield Kirkgate 4	31,34 d	
Doncaster 7	29 d	
Sheffield 7	d	23 37
Chesterfield	d	00 02
Derby 6	a	
	d	
Long Eaton	d	
Alfreton	d	
Langley Mill	d	
Lincoln	27 d	
Newark Castle	27 a	
Nottingham 8	a	00 39
	d	
Beeston	d	
East Midlands Parkway	a	
	d	
Loughborough	d	
Barrow Upon Soar	d	
Sileby	d	
Syston	d	
Leicester	a	
	d	
Market Harborough	d	
Melton Mowbray	d	
Oakham	d	
Corby	d	
Kettering 4	a	
	d	
Wellingborough	d	
Bedford 7	52 d	
Luton 10	52 d	
Luton Airport Parkway 7	52 d	
St Pancras International	⊖52 a	

Saturdays

14 December to 17 May

		EM	EM	EM	EM	EM	EM	EM	NT	EM		EM	EM	EM	EM	XC	EM	EM	NT	XC		EM	EM	EM	EM
		◇	◇1	◇1	◇1	◇1	◇1	◇1				◇1	◇1	◇1	◇1	◇1	◇1			◇1		◇1	◇1	◇1	◇1
		A														B			C	D					
			⊤	⊤	⊤	⊤	⊤	⊤				⊤	⊤	⊤	⊤	⊤	⊤			⊤		⊤	⊠	⊤	⊤
York 8	29 d																								
Leeds 10	31,34 d															06 00				06 16					
Wakefield Westgate 7	31 d															06 12				06 29					
Wakefield Kirkgate 4	31,34 d																								
Doncaster 7	29 d																			06 47					
Sheffield 7	d				05 29				05 54			06 29				06 50			07 03	07 18			07 29		
Chesterfield	d	00 02			05 41				06 20			06 41				07 03			07 19	07 30			07 41		
Derby 6	a				06 00							07 00				07 23				07 48			08 00		
	d			05 20	06 01		06 20					07 02			07 20								08 01		08 20
Long Eaton	d			05 29			06 29								07 29										08 29
Alfreton	d								06 30										07 29						
Langley Mill	d								06 38										07 37						
Lincoln	27 d																							07 04	
Newark Castle	27 a																							07 28	
Nottingham 8	a	00 39							07 02										08 00					07 57	
	d					06 06		06 32						07 06			07 30	07 34						08 05	
Beeston	d					06 12								07 12				07 39						08 11	
East Midlands Parkway	a			05 33			06 33	06 42							07 33		07 40	07 47							08 33
	d			05 35			06 35	06 43							07 34		07 41	07 50							08 35
Loughborough	d			05 42		06 22	06 42			06 59				07 22	07 42			07 58						08 21	08 42
Barrow Upon Soar	d									07 03								08 03							
Sileby	d									07 07								08 07							
Syston	d									07 12								08 12							
Leicester	a			05 52	06 23	06 32	06 52	06 58		07 21		07 23		07 32	07 51		07 56	08 21					08 24	08 31	08 52
	d		04 45	05 53	06 24	06 33	06 53	07 00				07 25		07 33	07 53		07 58						08 24	08 32	08 52
Market Harborough	d			06 07		06 47		07 15						07 47			08 13							08 46	
Melton Mowbray	d																								
Oakham	d																								
Corby	d												07 11									08 16			
Kettering 4	a		05 04	06 16		06 56	07 13						07 20	07 56								08 25		08 55	
	d		05 05	06 17		06 56	07 16							07 56								08 26		08 55	
Wellingborough	d		05 17	06 24		07 04	07 22							08 04								08 34		09 02	
Bedford 7	52 d		05 37	06 40		07 18	07 36							08 17								08 48		09 16	
Luton 10	52 d			06 54			08 02															09 02			
Luton Airport Parkway 7	52 d		05 56			07 33								08 32										09 31	
St Pancras International	⊖52 a		06 20	07 19	07 30	07 57	08 26	08 14				08 31		08 57	09 01		09 14					09 26	09 33	09 56	09 59

A From Liverpool Lime Street
B To Plymouth
C From Barnsley
D To Southampton Central

For connections to Gatwick Airport see Table 52

Table 53R

Saturdays

14 December to 17 May

Sheffield - East Midlands - London

Route Diagram - see first Page of Table 53

		EM	XC	NT	XC	EM		EM	EM	EM	EM	EM	EM	EM	XC	NT		XC	EM	EM	EM	EM	EM	EM	XC
		◇1	◇1		◇1	◇1		◇1		◇1	◇1	◇	◇1	◇1	◇1			◇1	◇1	◇1		◇1	◇	◇1	◇1
			A		B				C		D	E		F	G			H					E		I
		⊠	🛒		🛒	🛒		🛒		🛒	🛒		🛒	🛒	🛒			🛒	🛒	🛒		🛒		🛒	🛒
York 8 29	d		06 17		07 24										07 45			08 34							08 45
Leeds 10 31,34	d	06 34	07 10	07 05							07 34				08 11	08 05									09 11
Wakefield Westgate 7 31	d	06 46	07 22								07 46				08 24										09 24
Wakefield Kirkgate 4 31,34	d			07 25												08 23									
Doncaster 7 29	d				07 56													08 58							
Sheffield 7	d	07 37	07 56	08 08	08 20			08 29			08 34	08 38	08 49		08 54	09 05		09 23		09 29			09 37	09 48	09 54
Chesterfield	d	07 50	08 08	08 24	08 32			08 41			08 47	08 53	09 01		09 06	09 21				09 41			09 52	09 59	10 06
Derby 6	a		08 25		08 50			09 00					09 20		09 24			09 50		10 00				10 20	10 24
	d							09 01					09 21							10 01				10 21	
Long Eaton	d												09 30											10 30	
Alfreton	d	08 01		08 34							08 57	09 03				09 32							10 02		
Langley Mill	d	08 09		08 42												09 40									
Lincoln 27	d								07 26												08 35				
Newark Castle 27	a								07 54												09 04				
Nottingham 8	a	08 27		09 02					08 30		09 19	09 27				10 00					09 30		10 27		
	d	08 32							08 36	09 05	09 32										09 36	10 05			
Beeston	d								08 42	09 11				←							09 42	10 11			
East Midlands Parkway	a	08 42							08 49		09 42		09 35	09 42							09 49			10 35	
	d	08 42							08 49		09 42		09 35	09 42							09 50			10 35	
Loughborough	d								08 58	09 21	→		09 42								09 58	10 21		10 42	
Barrow Upon Soar	d								09 02												10 03				
Sileby	d								09 06												10 07				
Syston	d								09 12												10 12				
Leicester	a	08 58						09 22	09 25	09 31			09 52	09 58						10 22	10 24	10 31		10 52	
	d	08 59						09 24		09 32			09 52	09 59						10 24		10 32		10 52	
Market Harborough	d	09 13								09 46				10 13								10 46			
Melton Mowbray	d																								
Oakham	d																								
Corby	d					09 16													10 16						
Kettering 4	a					09 25				09 55									10 25			10 55			
	d					09 26				09 55									10 26			10 55			
Wellingborough	d					09 34				10 02									10 34			11 02			
Bedford 7 52	d					09 47				10 16									10 47			11 16			
Luton 10 52	d					10 02													11 02						
Luton Airport Parkway 7 52	d									10 31												11 31			
St Pancras International ⊖52	a	10 15				10 26		10 30		10 56			11 00	11 15					11 26	11 30		11 56		12 00	

		EM		NT	XC	EM	EM	EM	EM	EM	EM	XC		EM	EM	NT	XC	EM	EM	EM	EM	EM		XC	EM
		◇1			◇1	◇1	◇1		◇1	◇	◇1	◇1		◇1			◇1	◇1	◇1	◇1	◇	◇1		◇1	◇1
					J					E		K					H				E			L	
		🛒			🛒	🛒	🛒		🛒		🛒	🛒		🛒			🛒	🛒	🛒	🛒		🛒		🛒	🛒
York 8 29	d				09 35							09 45					10 35							10 45	
Leeds 10 31,34	d			09 05								10 11				10 05								11 11	
Wakefield Westgate 7 31	d											10 24												11 24	
Wakefield Kirkgate 4 31,34	d			09 23												10 23									
Doncaster 7 29	d				09 58												10 59								
Sheffield 7	d			10 05	10 24		10 29			10 38	10 49	10 54				11 05	11 23		11 29		11 37	11 49		11 54	
Chesterfield	d			10 21			10 41			10 53	11 01	11 06				11 21			11 41		11 52	12 01		12 07	
Derby 6	a				10 51		11 00				11 19	11 24					11 50		12 00			12 19		12 26	
	d						11 01				11 21								12 01			12 21			
Long Eaton	d										11 30											12 30			
Alfreton	d			10 31						11 03						11 31					12 02				
Langley Mill	d			10 39												11 39									
Lincoln 27	d							09 19							10 36										
Newark Castle 27	a							09 43							11 04										
Nottingham 8	a			11 00				10 25		11 27					11 30	12 00					12 28				
	d	10 32						10 36	11 05					11 32	11 36					12 05					12 32
Beeston	d							10 42	11 11						11 42					12 11					
East Midlands Parkway	a	10 42						10 49			11 34			11 42	11 49							12 34			12 42
	d	10 42						10 50			11 35			11 42	11 50							12 35			12 42
Loughborough	d							10 58	11 21		11 42				11 58					12 21		12 42			
Barrow Upon Soar	d							11 03							12 03										
Sileby	d							11 07							12 07										
Syston	d							11 12							12 12										
Leicester	a	10 58					11 22	11 23	11 31		11 52			11 58	12 22				12 22	12 31		12 52			12 58
	d	10 59					11 24		11 32		11 52			11 59					12 24	12 32		12 52			12 59
Market Harborough	d	11 13							11 46					12 13						12 46					13 13
Melton Mowbray	d																								
Oakham	d																								
Corby	d					11 16												12 16							
Kettering 4	a					11 25			11 55									12 25		12 55					
	d					11 26			11 55									12 26		12 55					
Wellingborough	d					11 34			12 02									12 34		13 02					
Bedford 7 52	d					11 47			12 16									12 47		13 16					
Luton 10 52	d					12 02												13 02							
Luton Airport Parkway 7 52	d								12 31											13 31					
St Pancras International ⊖52	a	12 14				12 26	12 30		12 56		13 00			13 14				13 26	13 30	13 56		14 00			14 14

A To Plymouth. 🛒 from Leeds
B From Newcastle to Reading
C From Sleaford
D To St Pancras International
E From Liverpool Lime Street to Norwich
F From Leeds
G From Newcastle to Plymouth. 🛒 from Leeds
H From Newcastle to Southampton Central
I From Edinburgh to Plymouth
J From Edinburgh to Reading
K From Glasgow Central to Plymouth
L From Dundee to Plymouth

For connections to Gatwick Airport see Table 52

Table 53R

Saturdays

14 December to 17 May

Sheffield - East Midlands - London

Route Diagram - see first Page of Table 53

		EM	NT	XC	EM	EM	EM	EM		EM	XC	EM	NT	XC	EM	EM	EM	EM		EM	EM	XC	EM	NT	XC
				◇1	◇1	◇1	◇1	◇		◇1	◇1	◇1		◇1	◇1	◇1		◇1		◇	◇1	◇1	◇1		◇1
				A				B			C			D						B		E			A
				T	T	T	T			T	T	T		T	T	T		T			T	T	T		T
York 8	29 d			11 35							11 45			12 35								12 45			13 34
Leeds 10	31,34 d		11 05								12 11		12 05									13 11		13 05	
Wakefield Westgate 7	31 d										12 24											13 23			
Wakefield Kirkgate 4	31,34 d		11 23										12 23											13 23	
Doncaster 7	29 d			11 59										12 59											13 58
Sheffield 7	d		12 05	12 23		12 29		12 37		12 49	12 54		13 05	13 23		13 29				13 37	13 49	13 54		14 05	14 23
Chesterfield	d		12 22			12 41		12 52		13 01	13 06		13 21			13 41				13 52	14 01	14 07		14 21	
Derby 6	a			12 50		13 00				13 19	13 24			13 50		14 00					14 19	14 27			14 50
	d					13 01				13 21						14 01					14 21				
Long Eaton	d									13 30											14 30				
Alfreton	d		12 32					13 02					13 31							14 02				14 31	
Langley Mill	d		12 40										13 40											14 39	
Lincoln	27 d	11 41															12 30								
Newark Castle	27 a	12 04															12 57								
Nottingham 8	a	12 31	13 00					13 27					14 00				13 30			14 27				15 00	
	d	12 36					13 05					13 32					13 36	14 05					14 32		
Beeston	d	12 42					13 11										13 42	14 11							
East Midlands Parkway	a	12 49								13 34		13 42					13 49				14 34		14 42		
	d	12 50								13 35		13 42					13 50				14 35		14 42		
Loughborough	d	12 58					13 21			13 42							13 58	14 21			14 42				
Barrow Upon Soar	d	13 03															14 03								
Sileby	d	13 07															14 07								
Syston	d	13 12															14 12								
Leicester	a	13 22				13 22	13 31			13 52		13 58				14 23	14 24	14 31			14 52		14 58		
	d					13 24	13 32			13 52		13 59				14 24		14 32			14 52		14 59		
Market Harborough	d						13 46					14 13						14 46					15 13		
Melton Mowbray	d																								
Oakham	d																								
Corby	d				13 16										14 16										
Kettering 4	a				13 25		13 55								14 25			14 55							
	d				13 26		13 55								14 26			14 55							
Wellingborough	d				13 34		14 02								14 34			15 02							
Bedford 7	52 d				13 47		14 16								14 47			15 16							
Luton 10	52 d				14 02										15 02										
Luton Airport Parkway 7	52 d						14 31											15 31							
St Pancras International	⊖52 a				14 26	14 30	14 56			14 59		15 14			15 26	15 30		15 56			15 59		16 14		

		EM	EM	EM		EM	EM	EM	XC	EM	NT	XC	EM	EM		EM	EM	EM	EM	XC	EM	EM	NT	XC	
		◇1	◇1			◇1	◇	◇1	◇1	◇1		◇1	◇1	◇1			◇1	◇	◇1	◇1	◇1			◇1	
							B		F			D						B		E				A	
		T	T			T		T	T	T		T	T	T			T		T	T	T			T	
York 8	29 d								13 45			14 35								14 45				15 35	
Leeds 10	31,34 d								14 11		14 05									15 11			15 05		
Wakefield Westgate 7	31 d								14 24											15 24					
Wakefield Kirkgate 4	31,34 d										14 23												15 23		
Doncaster 7	29 d											14 59												15 59	
Sheffield 7	d		14 29				14 37	14 49	14 54		15 05	15 23		15 29				15 37	15 49	15 54			16 05	16 23	
Chesterfield	d		14 41				14 52	15 01	15 06		15 21			15 41				15 52	16 01	16 07			16 21		
Derby 6	a		15 00					15 19	15 25			15 50		16 00					16 19	16 25				16 50	
	d		15 01					15 21						16 01					16 21						
Long Eaton	d							15 30											16 30						
Alfreton	d						15 02				15 32							16 03					16 31		
Langley Mill	d										15 39												16 39		
Lincoln	27 d			13 40												14 35						15 27			
Newark Castle	27 a			14 04												15 00						15 55			
Nottingham 8	a			14 30			15 27				16 00					15 30		16 27				16 30	17 00		
	d			14 36		15 05				15 32						15 36	16 05				16 30	16 34			
Beeston	d			14 42		15 11										15 42	16 11					16 40			
East Midlands Parkway	a			14 49				15 34		15 42						15 49			16 34		16 41	16 50			
	d			14 50				15 35		15 42						15 50			16 35		16 42	16 50			
Loughborough	d			14 58		15 21		15 42								15 58	16 21		16 42			16 59			
Barrow Upon Soar	d			15 03												16 03						17 03			
Sileby	d			15 07												16 07						17 08			
Syston	d			15 12												16 12						17 12			
Leicester	a		15 23	15 24		15 31		15 52		15 58				16 22		16 24	16 31		16 52		16 57	17 24			
	d		15 24			15 32		15 52		15 59				16 24			16 32		16 52		16 59				
Market Harborough	d					15 46				16 13							16 46				17 13				
Melton Mowbray	d																								
Oakham	d																								
Corby	d	15 16											16 16												
Kettering 4	a	15 25				15 55							16 25				16 55								
	d	15 26				15 55							16 26				16 55								
Wellingborough	d	15 34				16 02							16 34				17 02								
Bedford 7	52 d	15 47				16 16							16 47				17 16								
Luton 10	52 d	16 02											17 02												
Luton Airport Parkway 7	52 d					16 31											17 31								
St Pancras International	⊖52 a	16 26	16 31			16 56		17 00		17 14			17 26	17 30			17 56		18 00		18 14				

A From Newcastle to Reading
B From Liverpool Lime Street to Norwich
C From Glasgow Central to Plymouth
D From Newcastle to Southampton Central
E From Glasgow Central to Penzance
F From Aberdeen to Penzance

For connections to Gatwick Airport see Table 52

Table 53R

Saturdays

14 December to 17 May

Sheffield - East Midlands - London

Route Diagram - see first Page of Table 53

	EM	EM	EM	EM	EM	XC	EM	NT	XC		EM	EM	EM	EM	EM	EM	XC	EM	NT		XC	EM	EM	EM
	◇1	◇1	◇1	◇	◇1	◇1	◇1		◇1		◇1	◇1		◇1	◇	◇1	◇1	◇1			◇1	◇1	◇1	
				A		B			C						A		D				C			
	🍴	🍴	🍴		🍴	🍴	🍴		🍴		🍴	🍴		🍴		🍴	🍴	🍴			🍴	🍴	🍴	
York 8 29 d						15 45			16 05								16 45				17 35			
Leeds 10 31,34 d						16 11		16 05	16 40								17 11		17 05					
Wakefield Westgate 7 31 d						16 24			16 52								17 23							
Wakefield Kirkgate 4 31,34 d								16 23											17 23					
Doncaster 7 29 d																					17 59			
Sheffield 7 d		16 29		16 38	16 49	16 54		17 05	17 23			17 29			17 41	17 49	17 54		18 05		18 23		18 29	
Chesterfield d		16 41		16 53	17 01	17 06		17 21				17 41			17 59	18 01	18 07		18 21				18 41	
Derby 6 a		17 00			17 19	17 25			17 50			18 00				18 20	18 25				18 50		19 00	
d		17 01			17 21							18 01				18 21							19 01	
Long Eaton d					17 30											18 30								
Alfreton d				17 04				17 31							18 09				18 31					
Langley Mill d								17 39											18 39					
Lincoln 27 d													16 34											17 26
Newark Castle 27 a													17 03											17 55
Nottingham 8 a				17 27				18 00					17 30		18 31				19 00					18 29
d			17 05				17 32						17 36	18 05				18 32						18 36
Beeston d			17 11										17 42	18 11										18 42
East Midlands Parkway a					17 34		17 42						17 52			18 35		18 42						18 49
d					17 35		17 42						17 52			18 35		18 42						18 50
Loughborough d			17 21		17 42								18 00	18 21		18 42								18 58
Barrow Upon Soar d													18 05											19 03
Sileby d													18 09											19 07
Syston d													18 13											19 12
Leicester a		17 24	17 31		17 52		17 58					18 24	18 25	18 31		18 52		18 58					19 22	19 24
d		17 24	17 32		17 52		17 59					18 24		18 32		18 52		18 59					19 24	
Market Harborough d			17 46				18 13							18 46				19 13						
Melton Mowbray d																								
Oakham d																								
Corby d	17 16										18 16											19 16		
Kettering 4 a	17 25		17 55								18 25			18 55								19 25		
d	17 26		17 55								18 26			18 55								19 26		
Wellingborough d	17 34		18 02								18 34			19 02								19 34		
Bedford 7 52 d	17 47		18 16								18 47			19 16								19 47		
Luton 10 52 d	18 02										19 02											20 02		
Luton Airport Parkway 7 52 ✈ d			18 31											19 31										
St Pancras International ⊖52 a	18 26	18 32	18 56		19 00		19 14				19 26	19 32		19 56		20 00		20 14				20 26	20 30	

	EM	EM	EM	EM	EM		XC	NT	XC	EM	EM	EM	EM	EM	EM		XC	NT	XC	EM	EM	EM	EM	EM
	◇1	◇1	◇1	◇1	◇		◇1		◇1	◇1		◇1	◇1	◇			◇1		◇1	◇1	◇1	◇1	◇1	◇
					E		F		G					A			H		I					E
	🍴	🍴	🍴	🍴			🍴		🍴	🍴		🍴	🍴				🍴		🍴	🍴	🍽	🍴	🍴	
York 8 29 d			17 50				17 45		18 34								18 45		19 35					
Leeds 10 31,34 d							18 11	18 05									19 11	19 05						
Wakefield Westgate 7 31 d							18 23										19 24							
Wakefield Kirkgate 4 31,34 d								18 23										19 24						
Doncaster 7 29 d			18 18						18 59										19 59					
Sheffield 7 d			18 47		18 50		18 58	19 05	19 24	19 29				19 37			19 54	20 05	20 23	20 29				20 39
Chesterfield d			18 59		19 04		19 10	19 21		19 41				19 52			20 06	20 21		20 39				20 54
Derby 6 a			19 17				19 27		19 51	20 00							20 25		20 50	21 00				
d			19 21							20 01										21 01				
Long Eaton d			19 30																					
Alfreton d					19 15			19 32						20 03				20 31						21 05
Langley Mill d								19 39										20 39						
Lincoln 27 d											18 34													
Newark Castle 27 a											18 59													
Nottingham 8 a					19 39			20 00			19 28			20 31				21 00						21 33
d	19 05			19 32							19 36		20 05		20 32							21 05	21 31	
Beeston d	19 11										19 42		20 11		20 38							21 11		
East Midlands Parkway a			19 34	19 42							19 49		20 16		20 45					21 13		21 18		
d			19 35	19 42							19 50		20 17		20 46					21 14		21 19		
Loughborough d	19 21		19 42								19 58		20 25		20 54					21 22		21 27	21 46	
Barrow Upon Soar d											20 03				20 59									
Sileby d											20 07				21 03									
Syston d											20 12				21 08									
Leicester a	19 31		19 52	19 58						20 22	20 23		20 34		21 19					21 32		21 36	21 57	
d	19 32		19 52	19 59						20 24			20 36									21 38	21 58	
Market Harborough d	19 46			20 13									20 49									21 51	22 12	
Melton Mowbray d																								
Oakham d																								
Corby d		19 50										20 43									21 43			
Kettering 4 a	19 55	19 59	20 14									20 52	20 58								21 52	22 00	22 21	
d	19 55	20 26	20 15									21 26	20 58									22 00	22 22	
Wellingborough d	20 02	20 33										21 33	21 06									22 08	22 30	
Bedford 7 52 d	20 16	20 47										21 47	21 19									22 22	22 44	
Luton 10 52 d		21 02										22 02										22 36	23 02	
Luton Airport Parkway 7 52 ✈ d	20 31												21 35									22 39		
St Pancras International ⊖52 a	20 56	21 26	21 03	21 14						21 30		22 26	21 59									23 07	23 36	

A From Liverpool Lime Street to Norwich
B From Edinburgh to Plymouth
C From Newcastle to Reading
D From Glasgow Central to Plymouth
E From Liverpool Lime Street
F From Edinburgh to Exeter St Davids
G From Newcastle to Guildford
H From Glasgow Central to Bristol Temple Meads
I From Newcastle to Birmingham New Street

For connections to Gatwick Airport see Table 52

Table 53R

Saturdays

14 December to 17 May

Sheffield - East Midlands - London

Route Diagram - see first Page of Table 53

		EM		XC	XC	EM	EM	EM	XC	EM	EM	EM		EM	EM
				◇1	◇1	◇			◇1	◇	◇1	◇1		◇1	◇
				A	B	C	D	E	F	C		E		D	C
				🛒					🛒		☕	🛒		🛒	
York 8	29 d			19 45	20 35				20 45						
Leeds 10	31,34 d			20 11					21 11						
Wakefield Westgate 7	31 d			20 23					21 23						
Wakefield Kirkgate 4	31,34 d														
Doncaster 7	29 d				21 00										
Sheffield 7	d			20 54	21 23	21 38			21 54	22 35		23 20		23 28	23 38
Chesterfield	d			21 06	21 35	21 54			22 06	22 51		23 32		23 40	23 53
Derby 6	a			21 25	21 52				22 23			00 06		00 14	
	d														
Long Eaton	d														
Alfreton	d					22 04				23 02					
Langley Mill	d					22 11									
Lincoln	27 d														
Newark Castle	27 a														
Nottingham 8	a					22 33				23 32					00 30
	d	21 35					23 10	23 10							
Beeston	d	21 41					23 16	23 16							
East Midlands Parkway	a	21 48					23 23	23 24							
	d	21 50					23 24	23 25							
Loughborough	d	21 58					23 34	23 33							
Barrow Upon Soar	d	22 03													
Sileby	d	22 07													
Syston	d	22 12													
Leicester	a	22 24					23 53	23 52							
	d														
Market Harborough	d														
Melton Mowbray	d														
Oakham	d														
Corby	d										22 43				
Kettering 4	a										22 52				
	d														
Wellingborough	d														
Bedford 7	52 d														
Luton 10	52 d														
Luton Airport Parkway 7	52 d														
St Pancras International	⊖52 a														

Sundays

8 December to 29 December

		EM	EM	EM	EM	EM	EM	XC	EM	NT		EM	EM	XC	EM	NT	EM	EM	EM	XC		NT	EM	EM	XC
		◇1	◇1	◇1	◇1	◇1	◇1	◇1	◇1			◇1	◇1	◇1	◇1		◇1	◇1	◇1	◇1			◇1	◇1	◇1
								G						G						G					H
		☕	☕	☕	☕	☕	☕	🛒	☕			☕	☕	🛒	☕		☕	☕	☕	🛒			☕	☕	🛒
York 8	29 d																			09 33					10 33
Leeds 10	31,34 d							08 10						09 00		09 05			09 45	10 00		10 02		10 51	11 00
Wakefield Westgate 7	31 d							08 23						09 12					09 58	10 12				11 04	11 12
Wakefield Kirkgate 4	31,34 d															09 21						10 18			
Doncaster 7	29 d													09 32						10 30					11 30
Sheffield 7	d						08 18	08 54		09 05			09 25	09 57		10 07		10 25	10 31	10 57		11 03		11 45	11 57
Chesterfield	d						08 31	09 07		09 21			09 38	10 09		10 23		10 37	10 47	11 09		11 20		11 57	12 09
Derby 6	a						08 50	09 28					09 57	10 32				10 56		11 27				12 19	12 28
	d	06 51		07 55			08 52						09 59					10 58						12 21	
Long Eaton	d						09 01						10 09					11 07							
Alfreton	d									09 32						10 33						11 30			
Langley Mill	d									09 39						10 41						11 38			
Lincoln	27 d																								
Newark Castle	27 a																								
Nottingham 8	a									09 58						10 59			11 17			11 57			
	d		07 30		08 23				09 21						10 31				11 41						
Beeston	d				08 29										10 38										
East Midlands Parkway	a	07 02	07 39	08 05	08 35		09 05		09 31				10 12		10 44			11 11	11 50					12 33	
	d	07 03	07 40	08 06	08 36		09 06		09 32				10 13		10 45			11 12	11 51					12 34	
Loughborough	d			08 14	08 44		09 13		09 41				10 21		10 54			11 19	12 00					12 42	
Barrow Upon Soar	d																								
Sileby	d																								
Syston	d																								
Leicester	a	07 20	07 54	08 24	08 54		09 24		09 53				10 31		11 06			11 30	12 12					12 55	
	d	07 21	07 56	08 26	08 56		09 25		09 55				10 33		11 08			11 31	12 14					12 56	
Market Harborough	d	07 39	08 12	08 42	09 12		09 41		10 12				10 46		11 22			11 44	12 28					13 10	
Melton Mowbray	d																								
Oakham	d																								
Corby	d					09 30						10 25					11 25						12 30		
Kettering 4	a	07 49	08 21	08 51	09 21	09 39	09 50		10 22			10 34	10 55		11 32		11 34	11 53	12 38				12 39	13 20	
	d	07 50	08 22	08 52	09 22		09 51		10 23				10 56		11 33			11 54	12 39					13 21	
Wellingborough	d	08 02	08 33	09 03	09 33		10 03		10 31				11 03		11 41			12 02	12 47					13 29	
Bedford 7	52 d	08 15	08 45	09 15	09 45		10 15		10 45				11 16		11 56			12 15	13 02					13 43	
Luton 10	52 d	08 34		09 35			10 35						11 36					12 32						14 01	
Luton Airport Parkway 7	52 d		09 06		10 06				11 06						12 13				13 18						
St Pancras International	⊖52 a	09 13	09 44	10 13	10 48		11 17		11 48				12 14		12 39			12 55	13 44					14 27	

A From Edinburgh to Birmingham New Street. 🛒 to Leeds
B From Newcastle to Birmingham New Street
C From Liverpool Lime Street
D from 15 February until 22 March
E until 8 February, from 29 March
F From Glasgow Central to Birmingham New Street. 🛒 to Leeds
G To Plymouth
H From Newcastle to Plymouth

For connections to Gatwick Airport see Table 52

Table 53R

Sundays

8 December to 29 December

Sheffield - East Midlands - London

Route Diagram - see first Page of Table 53

		EM	EM	NT	NT	EM		EM	XC	EM	EM	NT	EM	EM	XC	XC		EM	EM	EM	EM	XC	EM	EM	EM
		◇1	◇1			◇		◇1	◇1	◇1	◇1		◇1	◇	◇1	◇1		◇1	◇1	◇	◇1	◇1	◇1	◇1	◇1
						A			B					C	D	E				F		B			
		☕	☕					☕	🛒	☕	☕		☕		🛒	🛒		☕	☕		☕	🛒	☕	☕	☕
York 8 29	d								11 40						12 40							13 40			
Leeds 10 31,34	d			10 57	11 29				12 10			12 29			13 10							14 10			
Wakefield Westgate 7 31	d								12 23						13 24							14 23			
Wakefield Kirkgate 4 31,34	d			11 13	11 46							12 49													
Doncaster 7 29	d																								
Sheffield 7 🚋	d			12 06	12 31	12 41		12 47	12 57			13 31	13 43	13 48	13 57	14 22				14 43	14 50	14 54			
Chesterfield	d			12 23	12 48	12 56		12 59	13 09			13 48	13 56	14 02	14 09	14 32				14 57	15 02	15 06			
Derby 6	a							13 19	13 31				14 16		14 27	14 50					15 21	15 24			
	d							13 21					14 17								15 23				
Long Eaton	d							13 30					14 27								15 32				
Alfreton	d			12 33	12 58	13 07						13 59		14 12						15 08					
Langley Mill	d			12 41	13 06							14 06								15 15					
Lincoln 27	d																								
Newark Castle 27	a																								
Nottingham 8 🚋	a			12 59	13 24	13 28						14 25		14 33						15 32					
	d		12 50								13 50								14 52				15 43		15 52
Beeston	d		12 57								13 57								14 58						15 58
East Midlands Parkway ✈	a		13 03					13 34			14 03		14 30						15 03		15 36		15 53		16 04
	d		13 04					13 35			14 04		14 31						15 04		15 37		15 53		16 05
Loughborough	d		13 13					13 42			14 13		14 39						15 12		15 44				16 12
Barrow Upon Soar	d																								
Sileby	d																								
Syston	d																								
Leicester	a		13 25					13 54			14 25		14 53						15 22		15 55		16 11		16 23
	d		13 27					13 55			14 27		14 55						15 24		15 56		16 12		16 24
Market Harborough	d		13 41					14 08			14 41		15 08						15 37						16 37
Melton Mowbray	d																								
Oakham	d																								
Corby	d	13 30								14 25								15 25						16 25	
Kettering 4	a	13 39	13 51					14 17		14 34	14 51		15 17					15 34	15 46					16 34	16 46
	d		13 52					14 18			14 52		15 18						15 47						16 47
Wellingborough	d		14 00					14 26			15 00		15 25						15 54						16 55
Bedford 7 52	d		14 15					14 39			15 15		15 39						16 08						17 08
Luton 10 52	d							14 54					15 54								16 42				
Luton Airport Parkway 7 52 ✈	d		14 31								15 31								16 23						17 24
St Pancras International ⊖52	a		14 57					15 18			15 57		16 18						16 47		17 09		17 23		17 47

		NT		XC	EM	EM	EM	XC	EM	EM	EM	NT		XC	EM	EM	EM	XC	EM	EM	EM	NT		XC	EM
				◇1	◇1	◇	◇1	◇1	◇1	◇1	◇1			◇1	◇1	◇	◇1	◇1	◇1	◇1	◇1			◇1	◇1
				G		F		H						G		F		I						J	
				🛒	☕		☕	🛒	☕	☕	☕			🛒	☕		☕	🛒	☕	☕	☕			🛒	☕
York 8 29	d			14 34				14 40						15 35				15 41						16 24	
Leeds 10 31,34	d	14 05			14 39			15 10				15 05						16 10				16 04			
Wakefield Westgate 7 31	d				14 53			15 23										16 22							
Wakefield Kirkgate 4 31,34	d	14 21										15 22										16 22			
Doncaster 7 29	d			14 59										15 59										16 52	
Sheffield 7 🚋	d	15 07		15 24	15 29	15 39	15 50	15 54				16 07		16 24		16 41	16 49	16 54				17 07		17 24	
Chesterfield	d	15 23			15 42	15 53	16 02	16 06				16 23				16 55	17 00	17 06				17 23			
Derby 6	a			15 52	16 02		16 21	16 24						16 53			17 19	17 26						17 52	
	d				16 02		16 26								16 59		17 23								18 07
Long Eaton	d														17 09										18 16
Alfreton	d	15 33				16 03						16 33				17 05						17 33			
Langley Mill	d	15 41				16 11						16 41				17 13						17 44			
Lincoln 27	d																								
Newark Castle 27	a																								
Nottingham 8 🚋	a	15 59				16 28						16 59				17 28						17 59			
	d								16 45		16 50								17 45		17 52				
Beeston	d										16 57										17 58				
East Midlands Parkway ✈	a				16 15		16 36		16 54		17 02				17 12		17 36		17 55		18 03				18 20
	d				16 16		16 37		16 55		17 03				17 13		17 36		17 55		18 04				18 21
Loughborough	d				16 25						17 11				17 21						18 12				18 28
Barrow Upon Soar	d																								
Sileby	d																								
Syston	d																								
Leicester	a				16 37		16 53		17 09		17 21				17 31		17 54		18 13		18 22				18 39
	d				16 39		16 55		17 10		17 24				17 33		17 54		18 14		18 25				18 40
Market Harborough	d				16 53						17 37				17 46						18 38				18 53
Melton Mowbray	d																								
Oakham	d																								
Corby	d									17 20										18 20					
Kettering 4	a				17 03					17 29	17 46				17 55					18 29	18 47				19 04
	d				17 03						17 47				17 56						18 48				19 05
Wellingborough	d				17 12						17 54				18 03						18 55				19 13
Bedford 7 52	d				17 27						18 07				18 17						19 08				19 27
Luton 10 52	d				17 44										18 32										19 43
Luton Airport Parkway 7 52 ✈	d										18 24										19 23				
St Pancras International ⊖52	a				18 09		18 02		18 17		18 47				18 56		19 10		19 25		19 48				20 06

A To Norwich
B From Edinburgh to Plymouth
C From Manchester Piccadilly to Norwich
D From Edinburgh to Penzance
E To Reading
F From Liverpool Lime Street to Norwich
G From Newcastle to Reading
H From Glasgow Central to Penzance
I From Glasgow Central to Plymouth
J From Edinburgh to Reading

For connections to Gatwick Airport see Table 52

Table 53R

Sundays

Sheffield - East Midlands - London

8 December to 29 December

Route Diagram - see first Page of Table 53

	EM	EM	XC	EM	EM	EM	NT	XC	EM	EM	XC	EM	EM	NT	XC	EM	EM	XC	NT	XC	EM	EM
	◇	◇1	◇1	◇1	◇1	◇1		◇1	◇	◇1	◇1	◇1	◇1		◇1	◇1	◇	◇1		◇1	◇1	◇1
	A		B					C	D		E			F	G		A	H		I		
		☕	🛒	☕	☕	☕		🛒		☕	🛒	☕	☕		🛒	☕		🛒		🛒	☕	☕
York [8] 29 d			16 40					17 34		17 49	17 40				18 35			18 40		19 24		
Leeds [10] 31,34 d			17 10				17 05				18 10			18 03				19 10	19 04			
Wakefield Westgate [7] 31 d			17 23								18 22							19 22				
Wakefield Kirkgate [4] 31,34 d							17 21							18 21					19 21			
Doncaster [7] 29 d								17 59		18 13					18 59					19 52		
Sheffield [7] d	17 40	17 50	17 54				18 07	18 24	18 40	18 47	18 54			19 07	19 24	19 28	19 40	19 54	20 07	20 20		20 26
Chesterfield d	17 54	18 03	18 06				18 23		18 55	18 59	19 06			19 23		19 41	19 54	20 06	20 23			20 39
Derby [6] a		18 21	18 25					18 53		19 19	19 25				19 52	20 01		20 25		20 49		20 59
d		18 26								19 20						20 03						21 01
Long Eaton d										19 30						20 13						
Alfreton d	18 05						18 33		19 05					19 33			20 05		20 33			
Langley Mill d	18 12						18 41		19 13					19 41			20 12		20 41			
Lincoln 27 d																						
Newark Castle 27 a																						
Nottingham [8] a	18 28						18 59		19 33					19 59			20 30		20 59			
d					18 45	18 51							19 51									
Beeston d						18 57							19 57									
East Midlands Parkway a		18 36			18 54	19 03				19 33			20 03			20 17						21 12
d		18 37			18 55	19 04				19 34			20 04			20 18						21 13
Loughborough d					19 02	19 11				19 42			20 11			20 27						
Barrow Upon Soar d																						
Sileby d																						
Syston d																						
Leicester a		18 53			19 13	19 22				19 52			20 22			20 39						21 30
d		18 54			19 14	19 24				19 54			20 24			20 41						21 32
Market Harborough d					19 27	19 37				20 07			20 37			20 55						21 46
Melton Mowbray d																						
Oakham d																						
Corby d				19 20								20 20									21 25	
Kettering [4] a				19 29	19 36	19 46				20 16		20 29	20 46			21 05					21 34	21 56
d					19 37	19 47				20 17			20 47			21 06						21 57
Wellingborough d					19 45	19 54				20 24			20 54			21 14						22 05
Bedford [7] 52 d					19 58	20 08				20 39			21 09			21 30						22 21
Luton [10] 52 d					20 14								21 23			21 45						22 37
Luton Airport Parkway [7] 52 d						20 23				20 54												
St Pancras International ⊖52 a		20 01			20 38	20 47				21 17			21 47			22 12						23 03

	EM	EM	XC	XC	EM	XC	EM	EM
	◇1	◇	◇1	◇1	◇	◇1	◇1	◇
		D	J	I	D	K		D
	☕		🛒			🛒	☕	
York [8] 29 d			19 40	20 24		20 40		
Leeds [10] 31,34 d			20 10			21 10		
Wakefield Westgate [7] 31 d			20 22			21 22		
Wakefield Kirkgate [4] 31,34 d								
Doncaster [7] 29 d				20 51				
Sheffield [7] d		20 40	20 54	21 20	21 40	21 54	22 36	23 27
Chesterfield d		20 54	21 06	21 32	21 56	22 06	22 49	23 42
Derby [6] a			21 25	21 51		22 24	23 26	
d								
Long Eaton d								
Alfreton d		21 05			22 06			23 52
Langley Mill d		21 12			22 14			23 59
Lincoln 27 d								
Newark Castle 27 a								
Nottingham [8] a		21 33			22 36			00 21
d	21 19							
Beeston d								
East Midlands Parkway a	21 30							
d	21 31							
Loughborough d	21 39							
Barrow Upon Soar d								
Sileby d								
Syston d								
Leicester a	21 53							
d	21 54							
Market Harborough d	22 08							
Melton Mowbray d								
Oakham d								
Corby d								
Kettering [4] a	22 17							
d	22 18							
Wellingborough d	22 25							
Bedford [7] 52 d	22 39							
Luton [10] 52 d	22 53							
Luton Airport Parkway [7] 52 d								
St Pancras International ⊖52 a	23 25							

A From Liverpool Lime Street to Norwich
B From Aberdeen to Plymouth
C From Newcastle to Reading
D From Liverpool Lime Street
E From Glasgow Central to Plymouth
F From Carlisle
G From Newcastle to Guildford
H From Glasgow Central to Bristol Temple Meads
I From Newcastle to Birmingham New Street
J From Edinburgh to Bristol Temple Meads. 🛒 to Leeds
K From Glasgow Central to Birmingham New Street. 🛒 to Leeds

For connections to Gatwick Airport see Table 52

Table 53R

Sundays

5 January to 9 February

Sheffield - East Midlands - London

Route Diagram - see first Page of Table 53

Station			EM	EM	EM	EM	EM	EM	EM	XC	EM	NT	EM	EM	EM	XC	NT	EM	XC	NT	EM	XC	EM	NT
			◇1	◇1	◇1	◇1	◇1	◇1	◇1	◇1	◇1		◇1	◇1	◇1	◇1		◇1	◇1		◇1	◇1	◇1	
										A			B		C	D			D			E		
			☕	☕	☕	☕	☕	☕	☕	🛒	☕		☕	☕	☕	🛒		☕	🛒		☕	🛒	☕	
York 8	29	d																	09 33			10 33		
Leeds 10	31,34	d								08 10			08 43			09 15	09 05	09 51	10 00	10 02		11 00		10 57
Wakefield Westgate 7	31	d								08 23			08 57			09 26		10 06	10 12			11 12		
Wakefield Kirkgate 4	31,34	d															09 21			10 18				11 13
Doncaster 7	29	d																						
Sheffield 7		d					07 40		08 44	08 54		09 05	09 41	09 51		09 57	10 07	10 52	10 57	11 03		11 57	12 01	12 06
Chesterfield		d					07 53		08 56	09 07		09 21	09 56	10 03		10 09	10 23	11 03	11 09	11 20		12 09	12 15	12 23
Derby 6		a					08 12		09 16	09 28				10 23		10 32		11 25	11 29			12 28	12 34	
		d	06 13		07 18		08 14		09 19					10 26				11 26					12 36	
Long Eaton		d					08 23		09 28					10 36									12 45	
Alfreton		d										09 32					10 33			11 30				12 33
Langley Mill		d										09 39					10 41			11 38				12 41
Lincoln	27	d																						
Newark Castle	27	a																						
Nottingham 8		a										09 58	10 25				10 59			11 57				12 59
		d		06 52		07 37		08 33			09 32		10 43								12 03			
Beeston		d				07 44					09 39				←						12 10			
East Midlands Parkway ✈		a	06 25	07 01	07 28	07 50	08 27	08 44	09 32		09 45		10 55	10 39	10 55			11 38			12 16		12 49	
		d	06 26	07 02	07 29	07 51	08 28	08 45	09 33		09 46		10 56	10 40	10 56			11 39			12 17		12 50	
Loughborough		d			07 36	08 00	08 35	08 54	09 40		09 55		→	10 48	11 05			11 47			12 26		12 57	
Barrow Upon Soar		d																						
Sileby		d																						
Syston		d																						
Leicester		a	06 42	07 16	07 47	08 12	08 46	09 06	09 53		10 07			10 58	11 17			12 00			12 38		13 08	
		d	06 48	07 22	07 53	08 19	08 52	09 13	09 59		10 14			11 05	11 24			12 06			12 45		13 14	
Market Harborough		d																						
Melton Mowbray		d																						
Oakham		d																						
Corby		d						10 04			11 08				12 19						13 38			
Kettering 4		a	07 48	08 19	08 50	09 18	09 50	10 15	10 53		11 19			12 01	12 30			13 13			13 48		14 13	
		d	07 49	08 20	08 51	09 19	09 51	10 16	10 54		11 32			12 02	12 31			13 21			13 49		14 18	
Wellingborough		d	08 01	08 33	09 03	09 31	10 02	10 26	11 02		11 40			12 10	12 39			13 29			13 57		14 25	
Bedford 7	52	d	08 14	08 46	09 14	09 46	10 14	10 45	11 15		11 57			12 23	12 53			13 43			14 12		14 38	
Luton 10	52	d	08 33		09 35		10 35		11 35					12 38				14 00					14 54	
Luton Airport Parkway 7	52 ✈	d		09 06		10 07		11 06			12 13				13 09						14 28			
St Pancras International	⊖52	a	09 14	09 44	10 14	10 48	11 18	11 48	12 13		12 40			13 03	13 37			14 27			14 55		15 19	

Station			EM	NT	EM	XC	EM	EM	NT	EM	XC	EM	XC	EM	EM	EM	XC	NT	EM	XC	EM	EM	XC	NT
			◇1		◇	◇1	◇1	◇1		◇	◇1	◇1	◇1	◇1	◇1	◇	◇1		◇1	◇1	◇	◇1	◇1	
					F	G				H	I		D			J	I			K	J		L	
			☕			🛒	☕	☕			🛒	☕	🛒	☕	☕		🛒		☕	🛒		☕	🛒	
York 8	29	d				11 40					12 40						13 40			14 34			14 40	
Leeds 10	31,34	d		11 29		12 10			12 29		13 10				13 41		14 10	14 05					15 10	15 05
Wakefield Westgate 7	31	d				12 23					13 24				13 55		14 23						15 23	
Wakefield Kirkgate 4	31,34	d		11 46					12 49									14 21						15 22
Doncaster 7	29	d																						
Sheffield 7		d		12 31	12 41	12 57	13 07		13 31	13 48	13 57	14 07	14 22		14 35	14 43	14 54	15 07		15 24	15 39	15 49	15 54	16 07
Chesterfield		d		12 48	12 56	13 09	13 19		13 48	14 02	14 09	14 19	14 32		14 57	14 57	15 06	15 23			15 53	16 02	16 06	16 23
Derby 6		a				13 31	13 38				14 27	14 38	14 50		15 18		15 24			15 52		16 21	16 24	
		d					13 44					14 49			15 25							16 22		
Long Eaton		d					13 53					14 58										16 33		
Alfreton		d		12 58	13 07				13 59	14 12						15 08		15 33			16 03			16 33
Langley Mill		d		13 06					14 06							15 15		15 41			16 11			16 41
Lincoln	27	d																						
Newark Castle	27	a																						
Nottingham 8		a		13 24	13 28				14 25	14 33						15 32		15 59			16 28			16 59
		d	13 02					14 04						15 05					16 03					
Beeston		d	13 09					14 10						15 11					16 09					
East Midlands Parkway ✈		a	13 19				13 57	14 22				15 02		15 22	15 39				16 15			16 37		
		d	13 20				13 58	14 23				15 03		15 23	15 40				16 16			16 38		
Loughborough		d	13 29				14 05	14 30				15 10		15 31	15 48				16 23			16 47		
Barrow Upon Soar		d																						
Sileby		d																						
Syston		d																						
Leicester		a	13 41				14 19	14 41				15 21		15 41	16 01				16 34			17 00		
		d	13 48				14 25	14 47				15 27		15 48	16 07				16 40			17 07		
Market Harborough		d																						
Melton Mowbray		d																						
Oakham		d																						
Corby		d	14 44					15 40						16 40					17 29					
Kettering 4		a	14 54				15 24	15 50				16 24		16 50	17 12				17 39			18 09		
		d	14 55				15 25	15 51				16 25		16 51	17 13				17 47			18 18		
Wellingborough		d	15 03				15 32	15 58						16 58	17 22				17 55			18 26		
Bedford 7	52	d	15 22				15 45	16 11						17 11	17 38				18 08			18 43		
Luton 10	52	d					16 01					16 52			17 58							18 58		
Luton Airport Parkway 7	52 ✈	d	15 38					16 26						17 27					18 23					
St Pancras International	⊖52	a	16 05				16 26	16 52				17 17		17 52	18 24				18 48			19 25		

A To Exeter St Davids
B To St Pancras International
C From Leeds
D To Plymouth
E From Newcastle to Reading
F To Norwich
G From Edinburgh to Plymouth
H From Manchester Piccadilly to Norwich
I From Edinburgh to Reading
J From Liverpool Lime Street to Norwich
K From Newcastle to Penzance
L From Glasgow Central to Reading

For connections to Gatwick Airport see Table 52

Table 53R

Sundays

5 January to 9 February

Sheffield - East Midlands - London

Route Diagram - see first Page of Table 53

Station			EM		XC	EM	XC	EM	NT	EM	XC	EM	EM		XC	NT	EM	XC	EM	EM	XC	NT	XC		EM	EM
			◇1		◇1	◇	◇1	◇1		◇1	◇1	◇	◇1		◇1		◇1	◇1	◇	◇1	◇1		◇1		◇	◇1
					A	B	C				D	B			E			A	F		G	H	I		B	
			☕		🛒		🛒	☕		☕	🛒		☕		🛒		☕	🛒		☕	🛒		🛒			☕
York 8	29	d			15 35		15 40				16 24		16 49		16 40			17 34			17 40		18 35			
Leeds 10	31,34	d					16 10		16 04						17 10	17 05					18 10	18 03				
Wakefield Westgate 7	31	d					16 22								17 23						18 22					
Wakefield Kirkgate 4	31,34	d							16 22							17 21						18 21				
Doncaster 7	29	d																								
Sheffield 7	🚆	d			16 25	16 41	16 54		17 07		17 24	17 40	17 50		17 54	18 07		18 24	18 40	18 41	18 54	19 07	19 24		19 40	19 47
Chesterfield		d				16 55	17 06		17 23			17 54	18 03		18 06	18 23			18 55	19 03	19 06	19 23			19 54	20 01
Derby 6		a			16 53		17 26				17 52		18 21		18 25			18 53		19 22	19 25		19 52			20 21
		d						17 44					18 29							19 24						20 22
Long Eaton		d						17 54					18 38							19 35						
Alfreton		d				17 05			17 33			18 05				18 33			19 05			19 33			20 05	
Langley Mill		d				17 13			17 44			18 12				18 41			19 13			19 41			20 12	
Lincoln	27	d																								
Newark Castle	27	a																								
Nottingham 8	🚆	a				17 28			17 59			18 28				18 59			19 33			19 59			20 30	
		d	17 01							18 03							19 14									
Beeston		d	17 07							18 10							19 20									
East Midlands Parkway	✈	a	17 13					17 58		18 16			18 42				19 25			19 39						20 34
		d	17 14					17 59		18 17			18 43				19 26			19 40						20 35
Loughborough		d	17 21					18 06		18 24			18 51				19 34			19 49						
Barrow Upon Soar		d																								
Sileby		d																								
Syston		d																								
Leicester		a	17 32					18 17		18 34			19 01				19 44			20 01						20 52
		d	17 38					18 24		18 41			19 08				19 51			20 10						21 00
Market Harborough		d																								
Melton Mowbray		d																								
Oakham		d																								
Corby		d	18 36							19 36							20 37									
Kettering 4		a	18 46					19 22		19 46			20 11				20 47			21 10						21 56
		d	18 47					19 24		19 47			20 14				20 48			21 11						21 58
Wellingborough		d	18 55					19 33		19 55			20 21				20 55			21 19						22 06
Bedford 7	52	d	19 08					19 46		20 08			20 35				21 09			21 34						22 21
Luton 10	52	d						20 01									21 24			21 49						22 37
Luton Airport Parkway 7	52 ✈	d	19 23							20 23			20 50													
St Pancras International	⊖52	a	19 48					20 26		20 48			21 15				21 49			22 17						23 04

Station			XC	EM	NT	XC	EM	XC	XC		EM	XC	EM	EM
			◇1	◇1		◇1	◇	◇1	◇1		◇	◇1	◇1	◇
			J			I	F	K	L		F	M		F
			🛒	☕		🛒		🛒				🛒	☕	
York 8	29	d	18 40			19 24		19 40	20 24			20 40		
Leeds 10	31,34	d	19 10		19 04			20 10				21 10		
Wakefield Westgate 7	31	d	19 22					20 22				21 22		
Wakefield Kirkgate 4	31,34	d			19 21									
Doncaster 7	29	d												
Sheffield 7	🚆	d	19 54		20 07	20 20	20 40	20 54	21 20		21 40	21 54	22 36	23 27
Chesterfield		d	20 06		20 23		20 54	21 06	21 32		21 56	22 06	22 49	23 42
Derby 6		a	20 25			20 49		21 25	21 51			22 24	23 26	
		d												
Long Eaton		d												
Alfreton		d			20 33		21 05				22 06			23 52
Langley Mill		d			20 41		21 12				22 14			23 59
Lincoln	27	d												
Newark Castle	27	a												
Nottingham 8	🚆	a			20 59		21 33				22 36			00 21
		d		20 34										
Beeston		d												
East Midlands Parkway	✈	a		20 43										
		d		20 44										
Loughborough		d		20 52										
Barrow Upon Soar		d												
Sileby		d												
Syston		d												
Leicester		a		21 02										
		d		21 09										
Market Harborough		d												
Melton Mowbray		d												
Oakham		d												
Corby		d												
Kettering 4		a		22 18										
		d		22 19										
Wellingborough		d		22 26										
Bedford 7	52	d		22 39										
Luton 10	52	d		22 53										
Luton Airport Parkway 7	52 ✈	d												
St Pancras International	⊖52	a		23 28										

A From Newcastle to Plymouth
B From Liverpool Lime Street to Norwich
C From Glasgow Central to Reading
D From Edinburgh to Plymouth
E From Aberdeen to Reading
F From Liverpool Lime Street
G From Glasgow Central to Guildford
H From Carlisle
I From Newcastle to Bristol Temple Meads
J From Glasgow Central to Birmingham New Street
K From Edinburgh to Birmingham New Street. 🛒 to Leeds
L From Newcastle to Birmingham New Street
M From Glasgow Central to Birmingham New Street. 🛒 to Leeds

For connections to Gatwick Airport see Table 52

Table 53R

Sundays

16 February to 23 March

Sheffield - East Midlands - London

Route Diagram - see first Page of Table 53

			EM	EM	EM	EM	EM	EM	XC	EM	NT		EM	EM	XC	EM	NT	EM	EM	EM	XC		NT	EM	EM	XC
			◇1	◇1	◇1	◇1	◇1	◇1	◇1	◇1			◇1	◇1	◇1	◇1		◇1	◇1	◇1	◇1			◇1	◇1	◇1
									A						A						A					B
			☕	☕	☕	☕	☕	☕	🛒	☕			☕	☕	🛒	☕		☕	☕	☕	🛒			☕	☕	🛒
York 8	29	d																			09 33					10 33
Leeds 10	31,34	d							08 10						09 00		09 05			09 45	10 00		10 02		10 15	11 00
Wakefield Westgate 7	31	d							08 23						09 12					09 58	10 12				10 28	11 12
Wakefield Kirkgate 4	31,34	d															09 21						10 18			
Doncaster 7	29	d													09 32						10 30					11 30
Sheffield 7		d						08 13	08 54		09 05			09 16	09 57		10 07		10 20	10 34	10 57		11 03		11 20	11 57
Chesterfield		d						08 26	09 07		09 21			09 28	10 09		10 23		10 32	10 47	11 10		11 20		11 31	12 10
Derby 6		a						08 46	09 28					09 48	10 32				10 52		11 31				11 53	12 28
		d	06 46		07 51			08 47						09 54					10 53						12 17	
Long Eaton		d						08 57						10 03					11 03							
Alfreton		d									09 32						10 33						11 30			
Langley Mill		d									09 39						10 41						11 38			
Lincoln	27	d																								
Newark Castle	27	a																								
Nottingham 8		a									09 58						10 59			11 17			11 57			
		d		07 25		08 19				09 17						10 26				11 35						
Beeston		d				08 25										10 33										
East Midlands Parkway		a	06 58	07 35	08 02	08 31		09 01		09 28				10 08		10 41			11 07	11 46					12 29	
		d	06 59	07 36	08 03	08 33		09 02		09 29				10 09		10 42			11 08	11 47					12 30	
Loughborough		d			08 14	08 44		09 13		09 41				10 20		10 54			11 19	11 59					12 42	
Barrow Upon Soar		d																								
Sileby		d																								
Syston		d																								
Leicester		a	07 20	07 54	08 24	08 54		09 24		09 53				10 30		11 06			11 30	12 12					12 55	
		d	07 21	07 56	08 26	08 56		09 25		09 55				10 32		11 08			11 31	12 13					12 56	
Market Harborough		d	07 39	08 12	08 42	09 12		09 41		10 12				10 45		11 22			11 44	12 27					13 10	
Melton Mowbray		d																								
Oakham		d																								
Corby		d					09 30						10 25					11 25						12 30		
Kettering 4		a	07 49	08 21	08 51	09 21	09 39	09 50		10 22			10 34	10 54		11 32		11 34	11 53	12 37				12 39	13 20	
		d	07 50	08 22	08 52	09 22		09 51		10 23				10 55		11 33			11 54	12 38					13 21	
Wellingborough		d	08 02	08 33	09 03	09 33		10 03		10 31				11 02		11 41			12 02	12 46					13 29	
Bedford 7	52	d	08 16	08 46	09 16	09 46		10 16		10 46				11 15		11 56			12 15	13 01					13 44	
Luton 10	52	d	08 34		09 35			10 35						11 35					12 30						14 01	
Luton Airport Parkway 7	52 ✈	d		09 06		10 06				11 06						12 13				13 17						
St Pancras International	⊖52	a	09 13	09 44	10 13	10 48		11 17		11 48				12 13		12 39			12 54	13 44					14 27	

			EM	EM	NT	NT	EM		EM	XC	EM	EM	NT	EM	EM	XC	XC		EM	EM	EM	EM	EM	XC	EM	EM
			◇1	◇1			◇1		◇	◇1	◇1	◇1		◇1	◇	◇1	◇1		◇1	◇1	◇1	◇	◇1	◇1	◇1	◇1
									C	D					E	F	A					G		F		
			☕	☕			☕			🛒	☕	☕		☕		🛒	🛒		☕	☕	☕		☕	🛒	☕	☕
York 8	29	d								11 40						12 40								13 40		
Leeds 10	31,34	d			10 57	11 29				12 10			12 29			13 10								14 10		
Wakefield Westgate 7	31	d								12 23						13 24								14 23		
Wakefield Kirkgate 4	31,34	d			11 13	11 46							12 49													
Doncaster 7	29	d																								
Sheffield 7		d			12 06	12 31	12 43		12 47	12 57			13 31	13 43	13 48	13 57	14 22				14 42	14 46		14 54		
Chesterfield		d			12 23	12 48	12 55		13 01	13 09			13 48	13 56	14 02	14 09	14 32				14 54	15 00		15 06		
Derby 6		a					13 15			13 31				14 16		14 27	14 50				15 14			15 24		
		d					13 16							14 18							15 15					
Long Eaton		d					13 26							14 27							15 25					
Alfreton		d			12 33	12 58			13 12				13 59		14 12							15 11				
Langley Mill		d			12 41	13 06							14 06									15 18				
Lincoln	27	d																								
Newark Castle	27	a																								
Nottingham 8		a			12 59	13 24			13 33				14 25		14 33							15 35				
		d		12 45								13 45								14 47			15 38			15 48
Beeston		d		12 52								13 52								14 53						15 54
East Midlands Parkway		a		13 00			13 30					14 00		14 32						15 00	15 29		15 49			16 00
		d		13 01			13 31					14 01		14 33						15 01	15 30		15 49			16 01
Loughborough		d		13 13			13 42					14 13		14 44						15 12	15 41					16 12
Barrow Upon Soar		d																								
Sileby		d																								
Syston		d																								
Leicester		a		13 25			13 53					14 25		14 54						15 22	15 52		16 11			16 23
		d		13 27			13 55					14 27		14 56						15 24	15 55		16 12			16 24
Market Harborough		d		13 41			14 08					14 41		15 09						15 37						16 37
Melton Mowbray		d																								
Oakham		d																								
Corby		d	13 30								14 25								15 25						16 25	
Kettering 4		a	13 39	13 51			14 17				14 34	14 51		15 18					15 34	15 46					16 34	16 46
		d		13 52			14 18					14 52		15 19						15 47						16 47
Wellingborough		d		14 00			14 25					15 00		15 26						15 54						16 55
Bedford 7	52	d		14 15			14 39					15 15		15 40						16 08						17 08
Luton 10	52	d					14 54							15 55							16 40					
Luton Airport Parkway 7	52 ✈	d		14 31								15 31								16 23						17 24
St Pancras International	⊖52	a		14 57			15 18					15 57		16 19						16 47	17 03		17 23			17 47

A To Exeter St Davids
B From Newcastle to Reading
C To Norwich
D From Edinburgh to Exeter St Davids
E From Manchester Piccadilly to Norwich
F From Edinburgh to Reading
G From Liverpool Lime Street to Norwich

For connections to Gatwick Airport see Table 52

Table 53R

Sundays

16 February to 23 March

Sheffield - East Midlands - London

Route Diagram - see first Page of Table 53

			EM		NT	XC	EM	EM	XC	EM	EM	EM	NT		XC	EM	EM	EM	XC	EM	EM	EM	NT		XC	EM
			◇1			◇1	◇	◇1	◇1	◇1	◇1	◇1			◇1	◇1	◇	◇1	◇1	◇1	◇1	◇1			◇1	◇1
						A	B		C						A		B		C						D	
			ᴅᴘ			⊥o		ᴅᴘ	⊥o	ᴅᴘ	ᴅᴘ	ᴅᴘ			⊥o	ᴅᴘ		ᴅᴘ	⊥o	ᴅᴘ	ᴅᴘ	ᴅᴘ			⊥o	ᴅᴘ
York 8	29	d				14 34			14 40						15 35				15 40						16 24	
Leeds 10	31,34	d	13 59		14 05				15 10				15 05						16 10				16 04			
Wakefield Westgate 7	31	d	14 13						15 23										16 22							
Wakefield Kirkgate 4	31,34	d			14 21								15 22										16 22			
Doncaster 7	29	d				14 59									15 59										16 52	
Sheffield 7		d	15 03		15 07	15 24	15 39	15 49	15 54				16 07		16 24		16 42	16 47	16 54				17 07		17 24	
Chesterfield		d	15 16		15 23		15 53	16 01	16 06				16 23				16 56	16 58	17 06				17 23			
Derby 6		a	15 35			15 52		16 21	16 24						16 53			17 19	17 26						17 52	
		d	15 55					16 22								16 54		17 19								18 02
Long Eaton		d														17 03										18 12
Alfreton		d			15 33		16 03						16 33				17 07						17 33			
Langley Mill		d			15 41		16 11						16 41				17 14						17 44			
Lincoln	27	d																								
Newark Castle	27	a																								
Nottingham 8		a			15 59		16 28						16 59				17 30						17 59			
		d								16 39		16 45								17 40		17 46				
Beeston		d										16 51										17 52				
East Midlands Parkway		a	16 10					16 33		16 49		16 58				17 08		17 33		17 51		17 59				18 16
		d	16 11					16 34		16 50		16 59				17 09		17 33		17 51		18 00				18 17
Loughborough		d	16 23									17 10				17 20						18 11				18 28
Barrow Upon Soar		d																								
Sileby		d																								
Syston		d																								
Leicester		a	16 35					16 53		17 09		17 20				17 30		17 54		18 13		18 21				18 39
		d	16 37					16 55		17 10		17 23				17 32		17 55		18 14		18 24				18 40
Market Harborough		d	16 51									17 36				17 45						18 37				18 53
Melton Mowbray		d																								
Oakham		d																								
Corby		d									17 20										18 20					
Kettering 4		a	17 01								17 29	17 45				17 54					18 29	18 46				19 04
		d	17 01									17 46				17 55						18 47				19 08
Wellingborough		d	17 10									17 53				18 02						18 54				19 17
Bedford 7	52	d	17 29									18 08				18 17						19 08				19 30
Luton 10	52	d	17 45													18 31										19 45
Luton Airport Parkway 7	52	d										18 25										19 24				
St Pancras International	⊖52	a	18 11					18 02		18 17		18 47				18 55		19 07		19 25		19 47				20 09

			EM	EM	XC	EM	EM	EM	NT		XC	EM	EM	XC	EM	EM	NT	EM	XC		EM	XC	NT	XC	EM	EM
			◇1	◇	◇1	◇1	◇1	◇1			◇1	◇1	◇	◇1	◇1	◇1		◇1	◇1		◇	◇1		◇1	◇1	◇1
				B	E						A		F	G			H		I		B	J		I		
			ᴅᴘ		⊥o	ᴅᴘ	ᴅᴘ	ᴅᴘ			⊥o	ᴅᴘ		⊥o	ᴅᴘ	ᴅᴘ		ᴅᴘ	⊥o			⊥o		⊥o	ᴅᴘ	ᴅᴘ
York 8	29	d			16 40						17 34	17 49		17 40					18 35			18 40		19 24		
Leeds 10	31,34	d			17 10				17 05					18 10			18 03					19 10	19 04			
Wakefield Westgate 7	31	d			17 23									18 22								19 22				
Wakefield Kirkgate 4	31,34	d							17 21								18 21						19 21			
Doncaster 7	29	d									17 59	18 13							18 59					19 52		
Sheffield 7		d	17 40	17 48	17 54				18 07		18 24	18 41	18 45	18 54			19 07	19 19	19 24		19 40	19 54	20 07	20 20		20 24
Chesterfield		d	17 53	18 02	18 06				18 23			18 55	19 00	19 06			19 23	19 32			19 54	20 06	20 23			20 38
Derby 6		a	18 12		18 25						18 53	19 15		19 25				19 50	19 53			20 25		20 49		20 58
		d	18 14									19 17						19 56								20 59
Long Eaton		d										19 27						20 07								
Alfreton		d		18 13					18 33				19 10				19 33				20 05		20 33			
Langley Mill		d		18 20					18 41				19 18				19 41				20 12		20 41			
Lincoln	27	d																								
Newark Castle	27	a																								
Nottingham 8		a		18 36					18 59				19 38				19 59				20 30		20 59			
		d					18 40	18 47								19 47										
Beeston		d						18 53								19 53										
East Midlands Parkway		a	18 25				18 50	18 59				19 31				19 59		20 12								21 12
		d	18 26				18 51	19 00				19 32				20 00		20 13								21 13
Loughborough		d					19 02	19 11				19 43				20 11		20 25								
Barrow Upon Soar		d																								
Sileby		d																								
Syston		d																								
Leicester		a	18 44				19 13	19 22				19 54				20 22		20 37								21 34
		d	18 45				19 14	19 24				19 55				20 24		20 39								21 35
Market Harborough		d					19 27	19 37				20 08				20 37		20 53								21 49
Melton Mowbray		d																								
Oakham		d																								
Corby		d				19 20									20 20										21 25	
Kettering 4		a				19 29	19 36	19 46				20 17			20 29	20 46		21 03							21 34	21 59
		d					19 37	19 47				20 18				20 47		21 04								22 00
Wellingborough		d					19 45	19 54				20 26				20 54		21 12								22 08
Bedford 7	52	d					19 59	20 08				20 40				21 09		21 28								22 24
Luton 10	52	d					20 13									21 23		21 43								22 40
Luton Airport Parkway 7	52	d						20 23				20 55														
St Pancras International	⊖52	a	19 55				20 37	20 47				21 19				21 47		22 10								23 06

- **A** From Newcastle to Exeter St Davids
- **B** From Liverpool Lime Street to Norwich
- **C** From Glasgow Central to Reading
- **D** From Edinburgh to Exeter St Davids
- **E** From Aberdeen to Reading
- **F** From Liverpool Lime Street
- **G** From Glasgow Central to Guildford
- **H** From Carlisle
- **I** From Newcastle to Bristol Temple Meads
- **J** From Glasgow Central to Birmingham New Street

For connections to Gatwick Airport see Table 52

Table 53R

Sundays

16 February to 23 March

Sheffield - East Midlands - London

Route Diagram - see first Page of Table 53

Station		EM	EM	XC	XC	EM	XC	EM	EM
		◇1	◇	◇1	◇1	◇	◇1	◇1	◇
			A	B	C	A	D		A
York 8 29	d			19 40	20 24		20 40		
Leeds 10 31,34	d			20 10			21 10		
Wakefield Westgate 7 31	d			20 22			21 22		
Wakefield Kirkgate 4 31,34	d								
Doncaster 7 29	d				20 51				
Sheffield 7	d		20 40	20 54	21 20	21 40	21 54	22 36	23 27
Chesterfield	d		20 54	21 06	21 32	21 56	22 06	22 49	23 42
Derby 6	a			21 25	21 51		22 24	23 26	
	d								
Long Eaton	d								
Alfreton	d		21 05			22 06			23 52
Langley Mill	d		21 12			22 14			23 59
Lincoln 27	d								
Newark Castle 27	a								
Nottingham 8	a		21 33			22 36			00 21
	d	21 17							
Beeston	d								
East Midlands Parkway	a	21 27							
	d	21 28							
Loughborough	d	21 39							
Barrow Upon Soar	d								
Sileby	d								
Syston	d								
Leicester	a	21 53							
	d	21 54							
Market Harborough	d	22 08							
Melton Mowbray	d								
Oakham	d								
Corby	d								
Kettering 4	a	22 17							
	d	22 18							
Wellingborough	d	22 25							
Bedford 7 52	d	22 38							
Luton 10 52	d	22 53							
Luton Airport Parkway 7 52	d								
St Pancras International ⊖52	a	23 25							

Sundays

30 March to 11 May

Station		EM	EM	EM	EM	EM	EM	XC	EM	NT	EM	EM	XC	EM	NT	EM	EM	EM	XC	NT	EM	EM	XC
		◇1	◇1	◇1	◇1	◇1	◇1	◇1	◇1		◇1	◇1	◇1	◇1		◇1	◇1	◇1	◇1		◇1	◇1	◇1
								E					E						E				F
York 8 29	d																		09 33				10 33
Leeds 10 31,34	d							08 10					09 00		09 05			09 45	10 00	10 02		10 51	11 00
Wakefield Westgate 7 31	d							08 23					09 12					09 58	10 12			11 04	11 12
Wakefield Kirkgate 4 31,34	d														09 21					10 18			
Doncaster 7 29	d												09 32						10 30				11 30
Sheffield 7	d						08 18	08 54		09 05		09 25	09 57		10 07		10 25	10 31	10 57	11 03		11 45	11 57
Chesterfield	d						08 31	09 07		09 21		09 38	10 09		10 23		10 37	10 47	11 09	11 20		11 57	12 09
Derby 6	a						08 50	09 28				09 57	10 32				10 56		11 27			12 19	12 28
	d	06 51		07 55			08 52					09 59					10 58					12 21	
Long Eaton	d						09 01					10 08					11 07						
Alfreton	d									09 32					10 33					11 30			
Langley Mill	d									09 39					10 41					11 38			
Lincoln 27	d																						
Newark Castle 27	a																						
Nottingham 8	a									09 58					10 59			11 17		11 57			
	d		07 30		08 23				09 21					10 31				11 40					
Beeston	d				08 29									10 38									
East Midlands Parkway	a	07 02	07 39	08 05	08 35		09 05		09 31			10 12		10 44			11 11	11 50				12 33	
	d	07 03	07 40	08 06	08 36		09 06		09 32			10 13		10 45			11 12	11 51				12 34	
Loughborough	d			08 14	08 44		09 13		09 41			10 20		10 54			11 19	11 59				12 42	
Barrow Upon Soar	d																						
Sileby	d																						
Syston	d																						
Leicester	a	07 20	07 54	08 24	08 54		09 24		09 53			10 30		11 06			11 30	12 12				12 55	
	d	07 21	07 56	08 26	08 56		09 25		09 55			10 32		11 08			11 31	12 13				12 56	
Market Harborough	d	07 39	08 12	08 42	09 12		09 41		10 12			10 45		11 22			11 44	12 27				13 10	
Melton Mowbray	d																						
Oakham	d																						
Corby	d					09 30					10 25					11 25					12 30		
Kettering 4	a	07 49	08 21	08 51	09 21	09 39	09 50		10 22		10 34	10 54		11 32		11 34	11 53	12 37			12 39	13 20	
	d	07 50	08 22	08 52	09 22		09 51		10 23			10 55		11 33			11 54	12 38				13 21	
Wellingborough	d	08 02	08 33	09 03	09 33		10 03		10 31			11 02		11 41			12 02	12 46				13 29	
Bedford 7 52	d	08 16	08 46	09 16	09 46		10 16		10 46			11 15		11 56			12 15	13 01				13 44	
Luton 10 52	d	08 34		09 35			10 35					11 35					12 30					14 01	
Luton Airport Parkway 7 52	d		09 06		10 06				11 06					12 13				13 17					
St Pancras International ⊖52	a	09 13	09 44	10 13	10 48		11 17		11 48			12 13		12 39			12 54	13 44				14 27	

A From Liverpool Lime Street
B From Edinburgh to Birmingham New Street. to Leeds
C From Newcastle to Birmingham New Street
D From Glasgow Central to Birmingham New Street. to Leeds
E To Plymouth
F From Newcastle to Plymouth

For connections to Gatwick Airport see Table 52

Table 53R

Sundays

30 March to 11 May

Sheffield - East Midlands - London

Route Diagram - see first Page of Table 53

	EM	EM	NT	NT	EM	EM	XC	EM	EM	NT	EM	EM	XC	XC	EM	EM	EM	EM	XC	EM	EM	EM
	◇1	◇1			◇	◇1	◇1	◇1	◇1		◇1	◇	◇1	◇1	◇1	◇1	◇	◇1	◇1	◇1	◇1	◇1
					A		B					C	D	E			F		B			
	☕	☕				☕	🛒	☕	☕		☕		🛒	🛒	☕	☕		☕	🛒	☕	☕	☕
York 8 29 d							11 40						12 40						13 40			
Leeds 10 31,34 d			10 57	11 29			12 10			12 29			13 10						14 10			
Wakefield Westgate 7 31 d							12 23						13 24						14 23			
Wakefield Kirkgate 4 31,34 d			11 13	11 46						12 49												
Doncaster 7 29 d																						
Sheffield 7 🚊 d			12 06	12 31	12 41	12 47	12 57			13 31	13 43	13 48	13 57	14 22			14 43	14 50	14 54			
Chesterfield d			12 23	12 48	12 56	12 59	13 09			13 48	13 56	14 02	14 09	14 32			14 57	15 02	15 06			
Derby 6 a						13 19	13 31				14 16		14 27	14 50				15 21	15 24			
d						13 21					14 20							15 23				
Long Eaton d						13 30					14 30							15 32				
Alfreton d			12 33	12 58	13 07					13 59		14 12					15 08					
Langley Mill d			12 41	13 06						14 06							15 15					
Lincoln 27 d																						
Newark Castle 27 a																						
Nottingham 8 🚊 a			12 59	13 24	13 28					14 25		14 33					15 32					
d		12 50							13 50							14 52				15 43		15 52
Beeston d		12 57							13 57							14 58						15 58
East Midlands Parkway ✈ a		13 03				13 34			14 03		14 33					15 03		15 36		15 53		16 04
d		13 04				13 35			14 04		14 34					15 04		15 37		15 53		16 05
Loughborough d		13 13				13 42			14 13		14 42					15 12		15 44				16 12
Barrow Upon Soar d																						
Sileby d																						
Syston d																						
Leicester a		13 25				13 54			14 25		14 53					15 22		15 55		16 11		16 23
d		13 27				13 55			14 27		14 55					15 24		15 56		16 12		16 24
Market Harborough d		13 41				14 08			14 41		15 08					15 37						16 37
Melton Mowbray d																						
Oakham d																						
Corby d	13 30							14 25							15 25						16 25	
Kettering 4 a	13 39	13 51				14 17		14 34	14 51		15 17				15 34	15 46					16 34	16 46
d		13 52				14 18			14 52		15 18					15 47						16 47
Wellingborough d		14 00				14 26			15 00		15 25					15 54						16 55
Bedford 7 52 d		14 15				14 39			15 15		15 39					16 08						17 08
Luton 10 52 d						14 54					15 54							16 42				
Luton Airport Parkway 7 52 ✈ d		14 31							15 31							16 23						17 24
St Pancras International ⊖52 a		14 57				15 18			15 57		16 18					16 47		17 06		17 23		17 47

	NT	XC	EM	EM	EM	XC	EM	EM	EM	NT	XC	EM	EM	EM	XC	EM	EM	EM	NT	XC	EM
		◇1	◇1	◇	◇1	◇1	◇1	◇1	◇1		◇1	◇1	◇	◇1	◇1	◇1	◇1	◇1		◇1	◇1
		G		F		H					G		F		I					J	
		🛒	☕		☕	🛒	☕	☕	☕		🛒	☕		☕	🛒	☕	☕	☕		🛒	☕
York 8 29 d		14 34				14 40					15 35				15 41					16 24	
Leeds 10 31,34 d	14 05		14 39			15 10				15 05					16 10				16 04		
Wakefield Westgate 7 31 d			14 53			15 23									16 22						
Wakefield Kirkgate 4 31,34 d	14 21									15 22									16 22		
Doncaster 7 29 d		14 59									15 59									16 52	
Sheffield 7 🚊 d	15 07	15 24	15 29	15 39	15 50	15 54				16 07	16 24		16 41	16 47	16 54				17 07	17 24	
Chesterfield d	15 23		15 42	15 53	16 02	16 06				16 23			16 55	16 59	17 06				17 23		
Derby 6 a		15 52	16 02		16 21	16 24					16 53			17 20	17 26					17 52	
d			16 02		16 26							16 58		17 23							18 07
Long Eaton d												17 08									18 16
Alfreton d	15 33			16 03						16 33			17 05						17 33		
Langley Mill d	15 41			16 11						16 41			17 13						17 44		
Lincoln 27 d																					
Newark Castle 27 a																					
Nottingham 8 🚊 a	15 59			16 28						16 59			17 28						17 59		
d							16 45		16 50							17 45		17 51			
Beeston d									16 56									17 57			
East Midlands Parkway ✈ a			16 15		16 36		16 54		17 02			17 11		17 36		17 55		18 02			18 20
d			16 16		16 37		16 55		17 03			17 12		17 36		17 55		18 03			18 21
Loughborough d			16 25						17 10			17 20						18 11			18 28
Barrow Upon Soar d																					
Sileby d																					
Syston d																					
Leicester a			16 37		16 53		17 09		17 21			17 30		17 54		18 13		18 21			18 39
d			16 39		16 55		17 10		17 23			17 32		17 54		18 14		18 24			18 40
Market Harborough d			16 53						17 36			17 45						18 37			18 53
Melton Mowbray d																					
Oakham d																					
Corby d								17 20									18 20				
Kettering 4 a			17 03					17 29	17 45			17 54					18 29	18 46			19 04
d			17 03						17 46			17 55						18 47			19 05
Wellingborough d			17 12						17 54			18 02						18 54			19 13
Bedford 7 52 d			17 27						18 08			18 17						19 08			19 27
Luton 10 52 d			17 43									18 31									19 43
Luton Airport Parkway 7 52 ✈ d									18 24									19 24			
St Pancras International ⊖52 a			18 09		18 02		18 17		18 47			18 55		19 07		19 25		19 47			20 07

A To Norwich
B From Edinburgh to Plymouth
C From Manchester Piccadilly to Norwich
D From Edinburgh to Penzance
E To Reading
F From Liverpool Lime Street to Norwich
G From Newcastle to Reading
H From Glasgow Central to Penzance
I From Glasgow Central to Plymouth
J From Edinburgh to Reading

For connections to Gatwick Airport see Table 52

Table 53R

Sundays

30 March to 11 May

Sheffield - East Midlands - London

Route Diagram - see first Page of Table 53

		EM	EM	XC	EM	EM	EM	NT	XC	EM	EM	XC	EM	EM	NT	XC	EM	EM	XC	NT	XC	EM	EM
		◇	◇1	◇1	◇1	◇1	◇1		◇1	◇	◇1	◇1	◇1	◇1		◇1	◇1	◇	◇1		◇1	◇1	◇1
		A		B					C	D		E			F	G		A	H		I		
			☕	🛒	☕	☕	☕		🛒		☕	🛒	☕	☕		🛒	☕		🛒		🛒	☕	☕
York	29 d			16 40					17 34		17 49	17 40				18 35			18 40		19 24		
Leeds	31,34 d			17 10				17 05				18 10			18 03				19 10	19 04			
Wakefield Westgate	31 d			17 23								18 22							19 22				
Wakefield Kirkgate	31,34 d							17 21							18 21					19 21			
Doncaster	29 d								17 59		18 13					18 59					19 52		
Sheffield	d	17 40	17 50	17 54				18 07	18 24	18 40	18 47	18 54			19 07	19 24	19 28	19 40	19 54	20 07	20 20		20 26
Chesterfield	d	17 54	18 03	18 06				18 23		18 55	18 59	19 06			19 23		19 41	19 54	20 06	20 23			20 39
Derby	a		18 22	18 25					18 53		19 19	19 25				19 52	20 01		20 25		20 49		20 59
	d		18 26								19 20						20 03						21 01
Long Eaton	d										19 30						20 13						
Alfreton	d	18 05						18 33		19 05					19 33			20 05		20 33			
Langley Mill	d	18 12						18 41		19 13					19 41			20 12		20 41			
Lincoln	27 d																						
Newark Castle	27 a																						
Nottingham	a	18 28						18 59		19 33					19 59			20 30		20 59			
	d					18 45	18 51							19 51									
Beeston	d						18 57							19 57									
East Midlands Parkway	a		18 36			18 54	19 03				19 33			20 03			20 17						21 12
	d		18 37			18 55	19 04				19 34			20 04			20 18						21 13
Loughborough	d					19 02	19 11				19 42			20 11			20 27						
Barrow Upon Soar	d																						
Sileby	d																						
Syston	d																						
Leicester	a		18 53			19 13	19 22				19 52			20 22			20 39						21 30
	d		18 54			19 14	19 24				19 54			20 24			20 41						21 32
Market Harborough	d					19 27	19 37				20 07			20 37			20 55						21 46
Melton Mowbray	d																						
Oakham	d																						
Corby	d				19 20								20 20									21 25	
Kettering	a				19 29	19 36	19 46				20 16		20 29	20 46			21 05					21 34	21 56
	d					19 37	19 47				20 17			20 47			21 06						21 57
Wellingborough	d					19 45	19 54				20 24			20 54			21 14						22 05
Bedford	52 d					19 59	20 08				20 39			21 09			21 32						22 21
Luton	52 d					20 13								21 23			21 47						22 37
Luton Airport Parkway	52 d						20 23				20 54												
St Pancras International	⊖52 a		20 01			20 37	20 47				21 17			21 47			22 14						23 03

		EM	EM	XC	XC	EM	XC	EM	EM
		◇1	◇	◇1	◇1	◇	◇1	◇1	◇
			D	J	I	D	K		D
		☕		🛒			🛒	☕	
York	29 d			19 40	20 24		20 40		
Leeds	31,34 d			20 10			21 10		
Wakefield Westgate	31 d			20 22			21 22		
Wakefield Kirkgate	31,34 d								
Doncaster	29 d				20 51				
Sheffield	d		20 40	20 54	21 20	21 40	21 54	22 36	23 27
Chesterfield	d		20 54	21 06	21 32	21 56	22 06	22 49	23 42
Derby	a			21 25	21 51		22 24	23 26	
	d								
Long Eaton	d								
Alfreton	d		21 05			22 06			23 52
Langley Mill	d		21 12			22 14			23 59
Lincoln	27 d								
Newark Castle	27 a								
Nottingham	a		21 33			22 36			00 21
	d	21 21							
Beeston	d								
East Midlands Parkway	a	21 30							
	d	21 31							
Loughborough	d	21 39							
Barrow Upon Soar	d								
Sileby	d								
Syston	d								
Leicester	a	21 53							
	d	21 54							
Market Harborough	d	22 08							
Melton Mowbray	d								
Oakham	d								
Corby	d								
Kettering	a	22 17							
	d	22 18							
Wellingborough	d	22 25							
Bedford	52 d	22 39							
Luton	52 d	22 53							
Luton Airport Parkway	52 d								
St Pancras International	⊖52 a	23 25							

A From Liverpool Lime Street to Norwich
B From Aberdeen to Plymouth
C From Newcastle to Reading
D From Liverpool Lime Street
E From Glasgow Central to Plymouth
F From Carlisle
G From Newcastle to Guildford
H From Glasgow Central to Bristol Temple Meads
I From Newcastle to Birmingham New Street
J From Edinburgh to Bristol Temple Meads. 🛒 to Leeds
K From Glasgow Central to Birmingham New Street. 🛒 to Leeds

For connections to Gatwick Airport see Table 52

Table 55

Nottingham - Mansfield - Worksop

Mondays to Fridays

9 December to 16 May

Network Diagram - refer to first Page of Table 50

Miles				EM	EM	EM	EM	EM	EM	EM	EM	EM	EM	EM	EM	EM	EM	EM	EM	EM	EM	EM	EM	EM
0	**Nottingham** 8	🚌	d	05 40	06 05	07 01	08 27	08 54	09 26	09 55	10 26	10 55	11 26	11 55	12 26	12 55	13 26	13 55	14 26	14 55	15 26	15 55	16 26	16 55
5½	Bulwell	🚌	d	05 49	06 14	07 10	08 36	09 03		10 06		11 06		12 06		13 06		14 06		15 06		16 06		17 06
8¼	Hucknall	🚌	d	05 54	06 19	07 16	08 41	09 08	09 39	10 11	10 39	11 11	11 39	12 11	12 39	13 11	13 39	14 11	14 39	15 11	15 39	16 11	16 39	17 12
10¾	Newstead		d	05 59	06 24	07 21	08 46	09 13	09 44		10 44		11 44		12 44		13 44		14 44		15 44		16 44	17 17
13¾	Kirkby In Ashfield		d	06 05	06 30	07 31	08 52	09 19	09 49	10 19	10 49	11 19	11 49	12 19	12 49	13 19	13 49	14 19	14 49	15 19	15 49	16 19	16 49	17 23
14½	Sutton Parkway		d	06 08	06 33	07 34	08 55	09 22	09 52	10 22	10 52	11 22	11 52	12 22	12 52	13 22	13 52	14 22	14 52	15 22	15 52	16 22	16 52	17 27
17¼	**Mansfield**		d	06 13	06 38	07 40	09 00	09 27	09 57	10 27	10 57	11 27	11 57	12 27	12 57	13 27	13 57	14 27	14 57	15 27	15 57	16 27	16 57	17 32
18¾	Mansfield Woodhouse		d	06 18	06 47	07 45	09 04	09a34	10 02	10a34	11 02	11a34	12 02	12a34	13 02	13a34	14 02	14a34	15 02	15a34	16 02	16a34	17 02	17a39
21½	Shirebrook		d	06 24	06 54	07 51	09 11		10 08		11 08		12 08		13 08		14 08		15 08		16 08		17 08	
22¼	Langwith - Whaley Thorns		d	06 28	06 58	07 55	09 15		10 12		11 12		12 12		13 12		14 12		15 12		16 12		17 12	
25½	Creswell (Derbys)		d	06 32	07 02	07 59	09 19		10 16		11 16		12 16		13 16		14 16		15 16		16 16		17 16	
26¾	Whitwell		d	06 36	07 05	08 03	09 22		10 20		11 20		12 20		13 20		14 20		15 20		16 20		17 20	
31½	**Worksop**		a	06 48	07 19	08 18	09 33		10 33		11 33		12 32		13 33		14 33		15 33		16 33		17 31	

			EM	EM	EM	EM	EM	EM
Nottingham 8	🚌	d	17 27	17 55	18 55	19 55	20 56	22 05
Bulwell	🚌	d	17 38	18 11	19 05	20 05	21 05	22 19
Hucknall	🚌	d	17 44	18 16	19 10	20 16	21 16	22 24
Newstead		d	17 49	18 21	19 15	20 21	21 21	22 29
Kirkby In Ashfield		d	17 55	18 27	19 21	20 27	21 27	22 34
Sutton Parkway		d	17 58	18 30	19 24	20 30	21 30	22 37
Mansfield		d	18 03	18 35	19 29	20 35	21 35	22 42
Mansfield Woodhouse		d	18 08	18 39	19 33	20 39	21 40	22 47
Shirebrook		d	18 14	18 46	19 40	20 46	21 46	22 53
Langwith - Whaley Thorns		d	18 18	18 50	19 44	20 50	21 50	22 57
Creswell (Derbys)		d	18 22	18 54	19 48	20 54	21 54	23 01
Whitwell		d	18 26	18 57	19 51	20 57	21 58	23 05
Worksop		a	18 37	19 08	20 03	21 09	22 08	23 14

Saturdays

14 December to 17 May

			EM	EM	EM	EM	EM	EM	EM	EM	EM	EM	EM	EM	EM	EM	EM	EM	EM	EM	EM	EM	EM	EM
Nottingham 8	🚌	d	05 40	06 05	06 59	08 27	08 53	09 26	09 56	10 26	10 56	11 26	11 56	12 26	12 56	13 26	13 56	14 26	14 56	15 26	15 56	16 26	16 56	17 27
Bulwell	🚌	d	05 49	06 14	07 09	08 36	09 02		10 06		11 07		12 06		13 06		14 06		15 06		16 06		17 06	17 39
Hucknall	🚌	d	05 54	06 19	07 14	08 41	09 07	09 39	10 11	10 39	11 12	11 39	12 11	12 39	13 11	13 39	14 11	14 39	15 11	15 39	16 11	16 39	17 12	17 44
Newstead		d	05 59	06 24	07 20	08 46	09 12	09 44		10 44		11 44		12 44		13 44		14 44		15 44		16 44	17 17	17 49
Kirkby In Ashfield		d	06 05	06 30	07 31	08 52	09 18	09 49	10 19	10 49	11 20	11 49	12 19	12 49	13 19	13 49	14 19	14 49	15 19	15 49	16 19	16 49	17 23	17 55
Sutton Parkway		d	06 08	06 33	07 34	08 55	09 21	09 52	10 22	10 52	11 23	11 52	12 22	12 52	13 22	13 52	14 22	14 52	15 22	15 52	16 22	16 52	17 27	17 58
Mansfield		d	06 13	06 38	07 40	09 00	09 26	09 57	10 27	10 57	11 28	11 57	12 27	12 57	13 27	13 57	14 27	14 57	15 27	15 57	16 27	16 57	17 32	18 03
Mansfield Woodhouse		d	06 18	06 47	07 45	09 04	09a33	10 02	10a34	11 02	11a35	12 02	12a34	13 02	13a34	14 02	14a34	15 02	15a34	16 02	16a34	17 02	17a39	18 08
Shirebrook		d	06 24	06 54	07 51	09 11		10 08		11 08		12 08		13 08		14 08		15 08		16 08		17 08		18 14
Langwith - Whaley Thorns		d	06 28	06 58	07 55	09 15		10 12		11 12		12 12		13 12		14 12		15 12		16 12		17 12		18 18
Creswell (Derbys)		d	06 32	07 02	07 59	09 19		10 16		11 16		12 16		13 16		14 16		15 16		16 16		17 16		18 22
Whitwell		d	06 36	07 05	08 03	09 22		10 20		11 20		12 20		13 20		14 20		15 20		16 20		17 20		18 26
Worksop		a	06 48	07 19	08 14	09 33		10 33		11 33		12 33		13 33		14 33		15 33		16 33		17 33		18 36

			EM	EM	EM	EM	EM	EM
Nottingham 8	🚌	d	17 56	18 56	19 56	20 52	22 05	23 05
Bulwell	🚌	d	18 11	19 05	20 05	21 01	22 19	23 15
Hucknall	🚌	d	18 16	19 10	20 16	21 12	22 24	23 20
Newstead		d	18 21	19 15	20 21	21 17	22 29	23 25
Kirkby In Ashfield		d	18 27	19 21	20 27	21 23	22 34	23 31
Sutton Parkway		d	18 30	19 24	20 30	21 26	22 37	23 34
Mansfield		d	18 35	19 29	20 35	21 31	22 42	23 40
Mansfield Woodhouse		d	18 39	19 33	20 39	21 36	22 47	23a45
Shirebrook		d	18 46	19 40	20 46	21 42	22 53	
Langwith - Whaley Thorns		d	18 50	19 44	20 50	21 46	22 57	
Creswell (Derbys)		d	18 54	19 48	20 54	21 50	23 01	
Whitwell		d	18 57	19 51	20 57	21 54	23 05	
Worksop		a	19 08	20 03	21 09	22 02	23 14	

Sundays

8 December to 11 May

			EM	EM	EM	EM	EM	EM	EM	EM
Nottingham 8	🚌	d	08 07	09 42	11 26	13 28	15 25	16 53	18 29	20 25
Bulwell	🚌	d	08 16	09 51	11 36	13 37	15 35	17 03	18 39	20 35
Hucknall	🚌	d	08 21	09 57	11 41	13 42	15 40	17 08	18 44	20 40
Newstead		d	08 26	10 02	11 46	13 47	15 45	17 13	18 49	20 45
Kirkby In Ashfield		d	08 32	10 07	11 52	13 52	15 50	17 18	18 54	20 50
Sutton Parkway		d	08 35	10 10	11 55	13 55	15 53	17 21	18 57	20 53
Mansfield		d	08 40	10 16	12 00	14 00	15 58	17 26	19 02	20 58
Mansfield Woodhouse		d	08a47	10a22	12a06	14a06	16a05	17a33	19a09	21a05
Shirebrook		d								
Langwith - Whaley Thorns		d								
Creswell (Derbys)		d								
Whitwell		d								
Worksop		a								

Table 55R

Worksop - Mansfield - Nottingham

Mondays to Fridays

9 December to 16 May

Network Diagram - refer to first Page of Table 50

Miles			EM	EM ◇	EM	EM	EM	EM	EM	EM	EM	EM	EM	EM	EM	EM	EM	EM	EM	EM	EM	EM	EM
0	**Worksop**	d	05 50		06 56		07 38	08 38		09 38		10 38		11 38		12 38		13 38		14 38		15 38	
4¾	Whitwell	d	05 58		07 05		07 47	08 47		09 47		10 47		11 47		12 47		13 47		14 47		15 47	
6	Creswell (Derbys)	d	06 02		07 08		07 50	08 50		09 50		10 50		11 50		12 50		13 50		14 50		15 50	
9¼	Langwith - Whaley Thorns	d	06 06		07 11		07 53	08 53		09 53		10 53		11 53		12 53		13 53		14 53		15 53	
10	Shirebrook	d	06 10		07 16		07 58	08 58		09 58		10 58		11 58		12 58		13 58		14 58		15 58	
12¾	Mansfield Woodhouse	d	06 17	07 07	07 24	07 39	08 06	09 06	09 37	10 06	10 37	11 06	11 37	12 06	12 37	13 06	13 37	14 06	14 37	15 06	15 37	16 06	16 37
14¼	**Mansfield**	d	06 21	07 11	07 29	07 43	08 10	09 10	09 40	10 10	10 40	11 10	11 40	12 10	12 40	13 10	13 40	14 10	14 40	15 10	15 40	16 10	16 40
17	Sutton Parkway	d	06 27	07 16	07 35	07 48	08 15	09 15	09 46	10 16	10 46	11 16	11 46	12 16	12 46	13 16	13 46	14 16	14 46	15 16	15 46	16 16	16 46
17¾	Kirkby In Ashfield	d	06 30	07 19	07 38	07 52	08 18	09 18	09 49	10 19	10 49	11 19	11 49	12 19	12 49	13 19	13 49	14 19	14 49	15 19	15 49	16 19	16 49
20¾	Newstead	d	06 35	07 26	07 43	07 57	08 23	09 23	09 54		10 54		11 54		12 54		13 54		14 54		15 54		16 54
23¼	Hucknall 🚊	d	06 40	07 31	07 48	08 02	08 28	09 27	09 58	10 26	10 58	11 26	11 58	12 26	12 58	13 26	13 58	14 26	14 58	15 26	15 58	16 26	16 58
26	Bulwell 🚊	d	06 44	07 35	07 53	08 06	08 32	09 31		10 30		11 30		12 30		13 30		14 30		15 30		16 30	
31½	**Nottingham** 8 🚊	a	06 57	07 48	08 04	08 19	08 45	09 43	10 15	10 43	11 15	11 43	12 15	12 43	13 15	13 43	14 15	14 43	15 15	15 44	16 15	16 43	17 15

		EM	EM	EM	EM	EM	EM	EM	EM
Worksop	d	16 42		17 46	18 41	19 22	20 15	21 20	22 23
Whitwell	d	16 51		17 54	18 50	19 30	20 23	21 29	22 32
Creswell (Derbys)	d	16 54		17 58	18 53	19 34	20 27	21 32	22 35
Langwith - Whaley Thorns	d	16 57		18 01	18 56	19 37	20 30	21 35	22 38
Shirebrook	d	17 02		18 06	19 01	19 41	20 35	21 40	22 43
Mansfield Woodhouse	d	17 10	17 43	18 14	19 09	19 49	20 43	21 48	22 51
Mansfield	d	17 14	17 46	18 18	19 13	19 53	20 50	21 53	22 55
Sutton Parkway	d	17 19	17 52	18 24	19 18	19 59	20 55	21 58	23 00
Kirkby In Ashfield	d	17 22	17 55	18 27	19 21	20 03	20 58	22 01	23 03
Newstead	d		17 59	18 31	19 26	20 07	21 03	22 06	23 08
Hucknall 🚊	d	17 29	18 04	18 36	19 30	20 12	21 07	22 10	23 12
Bulwell 🚊	d	17 33		18 40	19 34	20 16	21 14	22 14	23 16
Nottingham 8 🚊	a	17 46	18 19	18 52	19 47	20 30	21 24	22 25	23 28

Saturdays

14 December to 17 May

		EM	EM	EM	EM	EM	EM	EM	EM	EM	EM	EM	EM	EM	EM	EM	EM	EM	EM	EM	EM	EM	EM
Worksop	d	05 50	06 56	07 38	08 38		09 38		10 38		11 38		12 38		13 38		14 38		15 38		16 42		17 46
Whitwell	d	05 59	07 05	07 47	08 47		09 47		10 47		11 47		12 47		13 47		14 47		15 47		16 51		17 54
Creswell (Derbys)	d	06 02	07 08	07 50	08 50		09 50		10 50		11 50		12 50		13 50		14 50		15 50		16 54		17 58
Langwith - Whaley Thorns	d	06 06	07 13	07 53	08 53		09 53		10 53		11 53		12 53		13 53		14 53		15 53		16 57		18 01
Shirebrook	d	06 10	07 16	07 58	08 58		09 58		10 58		11 58		12 58		13 58		14 58		15 58		17 02		18 06
Mansfield Woodhouse	d	06 17	07 25	08 06	09 06	09 37	10 06	10 37	11 06	11 37	12 06	12 37	13 06	13 37	14 06	14 37	15 06	15 37	16 06	16 37	17 10	17 43	18 14
Mansfield	d	06 22	07 29	08 10	09 10	09 40	10 10	10 40	11 10	11 40	12 10	12 40	13 10	13 40	14 10	14 40	15 10	15 40	16 10	16 40	17 14	17 46	18 18
Sutton Parkway	d	06 27	07 35	08 15	09 15	09 46	10 16	10 46	11 16	11 46	12 16	12 46	13 16	13 46	14 16	14 46	15 16	15 46	16 16	16 46	17 19	17 52	18 24
Kirkby In Ashfield	d	06 30	07 38	08 18	09 18	09 49	10 19	10 49	11 19	11 49	12 19	12 49	13 19	13 49	14 19	14 49	15 19	15 49	16 19	16 49	17 22	17 55	18 27
Newstead	d	06 35	07 43	08 23	09 23	09 54		10 54		11 54		12 54		13 54		14 54		15 54		16 54		17 59	18 31
Hucknall 🚊	d	06 39	07 48	08 28	09 27	09 58	10 26	10 58	11 26	11 58	12 26	12 58	13 26	13 58	14 26	14 58	15 26	15 58	16 26	16 58	17 30	18 04	18 36
Bulwell 🚊	d	06 43	07 53	08 32	09 31		10 30		11 30		12 30		13 30		14 30		15 30		16 30		17 34		18 40
Nottingham 8 🚊	a	06 57	08 05	08 44	09 44	10 14	10 44	11 15	11 44	12 15	12 44	13 15	13 44	14 15	14 44	15 14	15 44	16 15	16 44	17 15	17 46	18 19	18 53

		EM	EM	EM	EM	EM
Worksop	d	18 41	19 22	20 15	21 19	22 19
Whitwell	d	18 50	19 30	20 23	21 28	22 27
Creswell (Derbys)	d	18 53	19 34	20 27	21 31	22 31
Langwith - Whaley Thorns	d	18 56	19 37	20 30	21 34	22 34
Shirebrook	d	19 01	19 41	20 35	21 39	22 38
Mansfield Woodhouse	d	19 09	19 49	20 43	21 47	22 46
Mansfield	d	19 13	19 53	20 48	21 52	22 50
Sutton Parkway	d	19 18	19 59	20 53	21 57	22 56
Kirkby In Ashfield	d	19 21	20 03	20 56	22 00	22 59
Newstead	d	19 26	20 07	21 01	22 05	23 03
Hucknall 🚊	d	19 30	20 12	21 05	22 09	23 08
Bulwell 🚊	d	19 34	20 16	21 14	22 13	23 12
Nottingham 8 🚊	a	19 48	20 30	21 25	22 25	23 24

Sundays

8 December to 11 May

		EM	EM	EM	EM	EM	EM	EM	EM
Worksop	d								
Whitwell	d								
Creswell (Derbys)	d								
Langwith - Whaley Thorns	d								
Shirebrook	d								
Mansfield Woodhouse	d	08 52	10 29	12 12	14 11	16 09	17 36	19 18	21 07
Mansfield	d	08 55	10 33	12 15	14 15	16 12	17 39	19 21	21 10
Sutton Parkway	d	09 01	10 38	12 21	14 20	16 18	17 45	19 27	21 16
Kirkby In Ashfield	d	09 04	10 41	12 24	14 23	16 21	17 48	19 30	21 19
Newstead	d	09 08	10 46	12 28	14 28	16 25	17 52	19 34	21 23
Hucknall 🚊	d	09 13	10 51	12 33	14 33	16 30	17 57	19 39	21 28
Bulwell 🚊	d	09 17	10 55	12 37	14 37	16 34	18 01	19 43	21 32
Nottingham 8 🚊	a	09 31	11 07	12 49	14 50	16 46	18 13	19 55	21 44

Table 56

Nottingham - Derby - Matlock

Mondays to Fridays

9 December to 16 May

Network Diagram - refer to first Page of Table 50

Miles			EM	EM	EM	XC	EM	EM	XC	EM	EM		XC	EM	EM	EM	EM	XC	EM	XC	EM		EM	EM	XC
			MO	MX																					
			◇1	◇1		◇1		◇1	◇1	◇1	◇1		◇1	◇1	◇1			1	◇1	◇1				◇1	1
			A	B		C		D	E	F	D		C	D	G		H	I	J	C			K	G	I
			🚌	🛒				🛒		🛒	🛒			⊠	🛒				🛒					🛒	
0	**Nottingham** 8	🚋 d		01 51		06 00	06 17	06 30	06 37		06 52		07 04	07 10		07 20	07 32	07 37	08 05	08 12	08 22		08 36		08 41
3¼	Beeston	d				06 06	06 24	06a35	06 43		06a57		07 09	07a16		07 25	07a37	07 42	08a10		08 28		08a42		08 47
4¾	Attenborough	d				06 09	06 27						07 13			07 29					08 31				
7¾	Long Eaton	d	00 04			06 18	06 36						07 21		07 34	07 38		07 52			08 40			08 52	08 56
13½	Spondon	d				06 25	06 43									07 45					08 47				09 02
16	**Derby** 6	a	00 15	02 10		06 31	06 50		06 59				07 31		07 45	07 50		08 02		08 33	08 53			09 04	09 07
—		d			05 40		06 52			07 21						07 52					08 55				
21¼	Duffield	d			05 47		06 59									07 59					09 02				
23¾	Belper	d			05 52		07 04			07a28						08 04					09 07				
26½	Ambergate	d			05 58		07 10									08 10					09 13				
28½	Whatstandwell	d			06 02		07 14									08 14					09 17				
31½	Cromford	d			06 08		07 20									08 20					09 23				
32¼	Matlock Bath	d			06 10		07 22									08 22					09 25				
33¼	**Matlock**	a			06 14		07 26									08 26					09 29				

		EM	XC	EM	EM	EM	XC		EM	XC	EM	EM	EM	XC	EM	XC	EM		EM	EM	XC	EM	XC	EM	EM
		◇1	◇1			◇1	1		◇1	◇1			◇1	1	◇1	◇1				◇1	1	◇1	◇1		
		D	C		L	G	I		D	C		L	G	I	D	C			L	G	I	D	C		L
		🛒	🛒			🛒			🛒	🛒			🛒		🛒	🛒				🛒		🛒	🛒		
Nottingham 8	🚋 d	09 05	09 10	09 20	09 36		09 41		10 05	10 10	10 20	10 36		10 41	11 05	11 10	11 20		11 36		11 41	12 05	12 10	12 20	12 36
Beeston	d	09a10		09 25	09a42		09 47		10a10		10 25	10a42		10 47	11a10		11 25		11a42		11 47	12a10		12 25	12a42
Attenborough	d			09 29							10 29						11 29							12 29	
Long Eaton	d			09 38		09 52	09 57				10 39		10 51	10 56			11 37			11 51	11 56			12 37	
Spondon	d																								
Derby 6	a		09 31	09 50		10 04	10 07			10 31	10 50		11 04	11 07		11 31	11 49			12 04	12 07		12 31	12 49	
	d			09 52							10 52						11 52							12 52	
Duffield	d			09 59							10 59						11 59							12 59	
Belper	d			10 04							11 04						12 04							13 04	
Ambergate	d			10 10							11 10						12 10							13 10	
Whatstandwell	d			10 14							11 14						12 14							13 14	
Cromford	d			10 20							11 20						12 20							13 20	
Matlock Bath	d			10 22							11 22						12 22							13 22	
Matlock	a			10 26							11 26						12 26							13 26	

		EM	XC		EM	XC	EM	EM	EM	XC	EM	XC	EM		EM	EM	XC	EM	XC	EM	EM	EM	XC		EM
		◇1	1		◇1	◇1			◇1	1	◇1	◇1				◇1	1	◇1	◇1			◇1	1		◇1
		G	I		D	C		L	G	I	D	C			L	G	I	D	C		L	G	I		D
		🛒			🛒	🛒			🛒	🛒	🛒	🛒				🛒		🛒	🛒			🛒	🛒		🛒
Nottingham 8	🚋 d		12 41		13 05	13 10	13 20	13 36		13 41	14 05	14 10	14 20		14 36		14 41	15 05	15 10	15 20	15 36		15 41		16 05
Beeston	d		12 47		13a10		13 25	13a42		13 47	14a10		14 25		14a42		14 47	15a10		15 25	15a42		15 47		16a10
Attenborough	d						13 29						14 29							15 29					
Long Eaton	d	12 51	12 56				13 37		13 51	13 56			14 37			14 51	14 56			15 37		15 51	15 56		
Spondon	d						13 45																		
Derby 6	a	13 04	13 07			13 31	13 50		14 04	14 07		14 31	14 48			15 04	15 07		15 31	15 49		16 04	16 07		
	d						13 52						14 52							15 52					
Duffield	d						13 59						14 59							15 59					
Belper	d						14 04						15 04							16 04					
Ambergate	d						14 10						15 10							16 10					
Whatstandwell	d						14 14						15 14							16 14					
Cromford	d						14 20						15 20							16 20					
Matlock Bath	d						14 22						15 22							16 22					
Matlock	a						14 26						15 26							16 26					

		XC	EM	EM	EM	XC	EM	EM	XC		EM	EM	EM	XC	EM	XC	EM	EM	XC		EM	EM	XC	EM	EM
		◇1			◇1	1		◇1	◇1				◇1	1	◇1	◇1			1		◇1	◇1	◇1		
		C		L	G	I		D	C			L	G	I	D	C		L	I		G	D	C		L
					🛒	🛒		🛒					🛒	🛒	🛒				🛒		🛒	🛒			
Nottingham 8	🚋 d	16 10	16 20	16 33		16 41	16 44	17 05	17 10		17 20	17 36		17 41	18 05	18 10	18 20	18 36	18 41			19 05	19 10	19 20	19 36
Beeston	d		16 25	16 39		16 47	16 50	17a10			17 25	17 41		17 47	18a10		18 25	18a42	18 47			19a10		19 25	19a42
Attenborough	d		16 29	16a42			16 53				17 29	17a44					18 29							19 29	
Long Eaton	d		16 37		16 51	16 57	17 02				17 37		17 51	17 56			18 37		18 56		19 00			19 36	
Spondon	d										17 45			18 02										19 44	
Derby 6	a	16 31	16 49		17 04	17 07	17 18		17 31		17 50		18 04	18 07		18 32	18 49		19 06		19 13		19 31	19 50	
	d		16 52								17 52						18 52							19 52	
Duffield	d		16 59								17 59						18 59							19 59	
Belper	d		17 04								18 04						19 04							20 04	
Ambergate	d		17 10								18 10						19 10							20 10	
Whatstandwell	d		17 14								18 14						19 14							20 14	
Cromford	d		17 20								18 20						19 20							20 20	
Matlock Bath	d		17 22								18 22						19 22							20 22	
Matlock	a		17 26								18 26						19 26							20 26	

A from 6 January until 10 February. From St Pancras International to Sheffield
B From St Pancras International
C To Cardiff Central
D To St Pancras International
E To Bournemouth
F To Sheffield
G From St Pancras International to Sheffield
H To Leicester
I To Birmingham New Street
J From Lincoln to St Pancras International
K From Sleaford to Leicester
L From Lincoln to Leicester

For connections from St Pancras International please see Table 53

Table 56

Nottingham - Derby - Matlock

Mondays to Fridays

9 December to 16 May

Network Diagram - refer to first Page of Table 50

		XC ■1 A 🛒	EM ◇■1 B 🛒	EM ◇■1 C 🛒		EM ◇■1 D 🛒	EM	EM E	XC ■1 A	NT F	EM ◇■1 C 🛒	EM ◇■1 D 🛒	EM	EM E		EM ◇■1 D 🛒	XC ■1 A	EM	EM	EM E	EM ◇■1 D 🛒	EM			
Nottingham 8	d	19 40		20 02		20 06	20 20	20 36	20 40	20 47	21 02		21 20	21 35			21 39		22 17	23 10		23 18			
Beeston	d	19 45		20a07			20 26	20a42	20 45		21a07		21 25	21a41			21 44		22 22	23a15		23 23			
Attenborough	d	19 49					20 30						21 29				21 48		22 26			23 27			
Long Eaton	d	19 56	20 02			20 19	20 39		20 54			21 03	21 37			21 49	21 56		22 33		23 18	23 35			
Spondon	d																22 02								
Derby 6	a	20 06	20 15			20 31	20 50		21 04	21 08		21 15	21 51			22 05	22 07		22 47		23 30	23 48			
	d						20 52											22 12							
Duffield	d						20 59											22 19							
Belper	d						21 04											22 24							
Ambergate	d						21 10											22 30							
Whatstandwell	d						21 14											22 34							
Cromford	d						21 20											22 40							
Matlock Bath	d						21 22											22 42							
Matlock	a						21 26											22 46							

Saturdays

14 December to 17 May

		EM ◇■1 D 🛒	EM	XC ◇■1 G	EM ◇■1 C 🛒	EM	XC ◇■1 H	EM ◇■1 F 🛒	XC ◇■1 G	EM ◇■1 C 🛒		EM ◇■1 B 🛒	EM	EM E	XC ■1 A	EM ◇■1 I 🛒	XC ◇■1 G	EM	EM J	EM ◇■1 K 🛒		XC ■1 A	EM ◇■1 C 🛒	XC ◇■1 G 🛒	EM
Nottingham 8	d	01 51		05 58	06 06	06 20	06 37		06 58	07 06			07 19	07 34	07 38	08 05	08 12	08 20	08 36			08 41	09 05	09 10	09 20
Beeston	d			06 03	06a11	06 25	06 43		07 03	07a11			07 25	07a39	07 44	08a10		08 25	08a42			08 47	09a10		09 25
Attenborough	d			06 07		06 28			07 07				07 28					08 29							09 29
Long Eaton	d			06 15		06 39			07 15			07 32	07 37		07 52			08 37		08 51		08 55			09 38
Spondon	d			06 22		06 47												08 45				09 01			
Derby 6	a	02 10		06 29		06 52	06 59		07 29			07 42	07 49		08 02		08 32	08 50		09 03		09 07		09 30	09 50
	d		05 40			06 54		07 21					07 52					08 52							09 52
Duffield	d		05 47			07 01							07 59					08 59							09 59
Belper	d		05 52			07 06		07a28					08 04					09 04							10 04
Ambergate	d		05 58			07 12							08 10					09 10							10 10
Whatstandwell	d		06 02			07 16							08 14					09 14							10 14
Cromford	d		06 08			07 22							08 20					09 20							10 20
Matlock Bath	d		06 10			07 24							08 22					09 22							10 22
Matlock	a		06 14			07 28							08 26					09 26							10 26

		EM L	EM ◇■1 B 🛒	XC ■1 A	EM ◇■1 C 🛒	XC ◇■1 G 🛒		EM	EM L	EM ◇■1 B 🛒	XC ■1 A	EM ◇■1 C 🛒	XC ◇■1 G 🛒	EM	EM L	EM ◇■1 B 🛒		XC ■1 A	EM ◇■1 C 🛒	XC ◇■1 G 🛒	EM	EM L	EM ◇■1 B 🛒	XC ■1 A	EM ◇■1 C 🛒
Nottingham 8	d	09 36		09 41	10 05	10 10		10 20	10 36		10 41	11 05	11 10	11 20	11 36			11 41	12 05	12 10	12 20	12 36		12 41	13 05
Beeston	d	09a42		09 47	10a10			10 25	10a42		10 47	11a10		11 25	11a42			11 47	12a10		12 25	12a42		12 47	13a10
Attenborough	d							10 29						11 29							12 29				
Long Eaton	d		09 51	09 57				10 38		10 52	10 56			11 37		11 51		11 56			12 37		12 52	12 56	
Spondon	d																								
Derby 6	a		10 04	10 07		10 31		10 49		11 04	11 07		11 29	11 49		12 04		12 07		12 30	12 49		13 04	13 07	
	d							10 52						11 52							12 52				
Duffield	d							10 59						11 59							12 59				
Belper	d							11 04						12 04							13 04				
Ambergate	d							11 10						12 10							13 10				
Whatstandwell	d							11 14						12 14							13 14				
Cromford	d							11 20						12 20							13 20				
Matlock Bath	d							11 22						12 22							13 22				
Matlock	a							11 26						12 26							13 26				

		XC ◇■1 G 🛒		EM	EM L	EM ◇■1 B 🛒	XC ■1 A 🛒	EM ◇■1 C 🛒	XC ◇■1 G 🛒	EM	EM L	EM ◇■1 B 🛒		XC ■1 A	EM ◇■1 C 🛒	XC ◇■1 G 🛒	EM	EM L	EM ◇■1 B 🛒	XC ■1 A 🛒	EM ◇■1 C 🛒	XC ◇■1 G		EM	EM L
Nottingham 8	d	13 10		13 20	13 36		13 41	14 05	14 10	14 20	14 36			14 41	15 05	15 10	15 20	15 36		15 41	16 05	16 10		16 20	16 34
Beeston	d			13 25	13a42		13 47	14a10		14 26	14a42			14 47	15a10		15 25	15a42		15 47	16a10			16 25	16 40
Attenborough	d			13 29						14 29							15 29							16 29	16a43
Long Eaton	d			13 37		13 52	13 56			14 38		14 52		14 56			15 37		15 51	15 56				16 37	
Spondon	d			13 45																					
Derby 6	a	13 30		13 50		14 04	14 07		14 30	14 50		15 04		15 07		15 30	15 49		16 04	16 07		16 30		16 49	
	d			13 52						14 53							15 52							16 52	
Duffield	d			13 59						15 00							15 59							16 59	
Belper	d			14 04						15 05							16 04							17 04	
Ambergate	d			14 10						15 11							16 10							17 10	
Whatstandwell	d			14 14						15 15							16 14							17 14	
Cromford	d			14 20						15 21							16 20							17 20	
Matlock Bath	d			14 22						15 23							16 22							17 22	
Matlock	a			14 26						15 27							16 26							17 26	

A To Birmingham New Street
B From St Pancras International to Sheffield
C To St Pancras International
D From St Pancras International
E To Leicester
F To Sheffield
G To Cardiff Central
H To Bournemouth
I From Lincoln to St Pancras International
J From Sleaford to Leicester
K From Leicester to Sheffield
L From Lincoln to Leicester

For connections from St Pancras International please see Table 53

Table 56

Nottingham - Derby - Matlock

Saturdays

14 December to 17 May

Network Diagram - refer to first Page of Table 50

		EM ◇1 A	XC 1 B	EM ◇1 C	XC ◇1 D	EM	EM E	EM ◇1 A	XC 1 B	EM ◇1 C	XC ◇1 D	EM	EM E	EM ◇1 A	XC 1 B	EM ◇1 C	XC ◇1 D	EM	EM E	EM ◇1 A	XC 1 B	EM ◇1 C
Nottingham 8	d		16 41	17 05	17 10	17 20	17 36		17 41	18 05	18 10	18 20	18 36		18 41	19 05	19 10	19 20	19 36		19 41	20 05
Beeston	d		16 47	17a10		17 25	17 42		17 47	18a10		18 25	18a42		18 47	19a10		19 25	19a42		19 47	20a10
Attenborough	d					17 29	17a45					18 29						19 29			19 50	
Long Eaton	d	16 52	16 56			17 37		17 52	17 56			18 37		18 52	18 56			19 37		19 52	19 57	
Spondon	d					17 45											19 27	19 45				
Derby 6	a	17 04	17 07		17 30	17 50		18 04	18 07		18 30	18 49		19 04	19 07		19 32	19 50		20 04	20 06	
	d					17 52						18 52						19 52				
Duffield	d					17 59						18 59						19 59				
Belper	d					18 04						19 04						20 04				
Ambergate	d					18 10						19 10						20 10				
Whatstandwell	d					18 14						19 14						20 14				
Cromford	d					18 20						19 20						20 20				
Matlock Bath	d					18 22						19 22						20 22				
Matlock	a					18 26						19 26						20 26				

		EM	EM F	XC 1 B	EM ◇1 G	EM ◇1 C	EM	EM F	EM ◇1 G	XC 1 B	EM	EM	EM F	EM ◇1 H	EM ◇1 I	EM
Nottingham 8	d	20 19	20 32	20 37		21 05	21 19	21 35		21 39		22 19	23 10			23 19
Beeston	d	20 25	20a38	20 43		21a10	21 25	21a41		21 45		22 25	23a16			23 24
Attenborough	d	20 28					21 28			21 48		22 28				23 28
Long Eaton	d	20 37		20 51	21 01		21 36		21 52	21 56		22 36		23 19	23 20	23 36
Spondon	d									22 02						
Derby 6	a	20 49		21 02	21 12		21 50		22 05	22 07		22 50		23 31	23 31	23 49
	d	20 52									22 16					
Duffield	d	20 59									22 23					
Belper	d	21 04									22 28					
Ambergate	d	21 10									22 35					
Whatstandwell	d	21 14									22 39					
Cromford	d	21 20									22 45					
Matlock Bath	d	21 22									22 47					
Matlock	a	21 26									22 50					

Sundays

8 December to 29 December

		EM ◇1 J	EM ◇1 C	EM	EM ◇1 C	EM ◇1 K	XC ◇1 D	EM ◇1 A	EM	XC ◇1 D	EM ◇1 A	EM ◇1 C	XC ◇1 D	EM ◇1 A	EM	EM ◇1 C	XC ◇1 D	EM ◇1 A	EM	EM ◇1 C	XC ◇1 D	EM ◇1 A	EM
Nottingham 8	d		08 23	09 26	10 31		11 11		11 27	12 10		12 50	13 10		13 23	13 50	14 10		14 22	14 52	15 10		15 22
Beeston	d		08a28	09 32	10a37				11 32			12a56			13 29	13a56			14 28	14a57			15 28
Attenborough	d			09 35					11 36						13 32				14 31				15 31
Long Eaton	d	00 17		09 43		10 41		11 27	11 43		12 31			13 31	13 40			14 27	14 39			15 37	15 42
Spondon	d																						
Derby 6	a	00 28		09 54		10 54	11 31	11 39	11 55	12 30	12 42		13 30	13 43	13 51		14 29	14 42	14 50		15 30	15 49	15 53
	d			09 56											13 56								15 56
Duffield	d			10 03					12 04						14 03								16 03
Belper	d			10 08					12 09						14 08								16 08
Ambergate	d			10 14					12 15						14 14								16 14
Whatstandwell	d			10 18					12 19						14 18								16 18
Cromford	d			10 24					12 24						14 24								16 24
Matlock Bath	d			10 26					12 27						14 26								16 26
Matlock	a			10 30					12 30						14 30								16 30

		EM ◇1 C	XC ◇1 D	EM ◇1 L	EM	EM ◇1 C	XC ◇1 D	EM ◇1 A	EM	EM ◇1 C	XC ◇1 D	EM ◇1 G	EM	EM ◇1 C	XC ◇1 B	EM ◇1 G	EM	EM ◇1 C	XC ◇1 B	EM ◇1 G	EM	XC ◇1 B	EM ◇1 G
Nottingham 8	d	15 52	16 10		16 23	16 50	17 10		17 22	17 52	18 10		18 22	18 51	19 10		19 22	19 51	20 10		20 20	21 10	
Beeston	d	15a57			16 29	16a56			17 28	17a57			18 28	18a56			19 28	19a56			20 26		
Attenborough	d				16 32				17 31				18 31				19 31				20 29		
Long Eaton	d			16 34	16 40			17 34	17 39			18 25	18 39			19 25	19 39			20 25	20 37		21 25
Spondon	d																						
Derby 6	a		16 30	16 47	16 51		17 29	17 47	17 50		18 30	18 36	18 50		19 30	19 37	19 50		20 29	20 37	20 49	21 30	21 36
	d								17 56								19 52						
Duffield	d								18 03								19 59						
Belper	d								18 08								20 04						
Ambergate	d								18 14								20 10						
Whatstandwell	d								18 18								20 14						
Cromford	d								18 24								20 20						
Matlock Bath	d								18 26								20 22						
Matlock	a								18 30								20 26						

- **A** From St Pancras International to Sheffield
- **B** To Birmingham New Street
- **C** To St Pancras International
- **D** To Cardiff Central
- **E** From Lincoln to Leicester
- **F** To Leicester
- **G** From St Pancras International
- **H** from 15 February until 22 March. From St Pancras International
- **I** until 8 February, from 29 March. From St Pancras International
- **J** not 8 December. From St Pancras International
- **K** From Leicester to York
- **L** From St Pancras International to Leeds

For connections from St Pancras International please see Table 53

Table 56

Sundays

8 December to 29 December

Nottingham - Derby - Matlock

Network Diagram - refer to first Page of Table 50

		EM	EM
			◇1
			A
			☕
Nottingham 8	d	21 22	
Beeston	d	21 28	
Attenborough	d	21 31	
Long Eaton	d	21 39	23 24
Spondon	d		
Derby 6	a	21 51	23 35
	d	21 53	
Duffield	d	22 00	
Belper	d	22 05	
Ambergate	d	22 11	
Whatstandwell	d	22 15	
Cromford	d	22 21	
Matlock Bath	d	22 23	
Matlock	a	22 27	

Sundays

5 January to 9 February

		EM	EM	EM	EM	EM	XC	EM	EM	EM		XC	EM	XC	EM	EM	EM	XC	EM	EM		EM	XC	EM	EM
		◇1	◇1		◇1	◇1	◇1		◇1	◇1		◇1	◇1	◇1	◇1		◇1	◇1	◇1			◇1	◇1	◇1	
		B	C		C	D			A	C			C		A		C		A			C		A	
		🚲	☕		☕	🚲			☕	☕			☕		☕		☕		☕			☕		☕	
Nottingham 8	d		07 37	09 26	09 32		11 11	11 27		12 03		12 10	13 02	13 10		13 23	14 04	14 10		14 22		15 05	15 10		15 22
Beeston	d		07a43	09 32	09a38			11 32		12a09			13a08			13 29	14a09			14 28		15a10			15 28
Attenborough	d			09 35				11 36								13 32				14 31					15 31
Long Eaton	d	00 17		09 43		10 41		11 43	12 17						13 26	13 40			14 29	14 39				15 29	15 39
Spondon	d																								
Derby 6	a	00 28		09 54		10 54	11 31		12 27			12 30		13 30	13 35	13 51		14 30	14 42	14 50			15 30	15 42	15 50
	d			09 56												13 56									15 56
Duffield	d			10 03				12 04								14 03									16 03
Belper	d			10 08				12 09								14 08									16 08
Ambergate	d			10 14				12 15								14 14									16 14
Whatstandwell	d			10 18				12 19								14 18									16 18
Cromford	d			10 24				12 24								14 24									16 24
Matlock Bath	d			10 26				12 27								14 26									16 26
Matlock	a			10 30				12 30								14 30									16 30

		EM	XC	EM	EM	EM		XC	EM	EM	EM	XC	EM	EM	EM	XC		EM	EM	EM	XC	EM	XC	EM	EM
		◇1	◇1	◇1		◇1		◇1	◇1		◇1	◇1	◇1		◇1	◇1		◇1		◇1	◇1		◇1	◇1	
		C		A		C			E		C		A		A			C		A				E	
		☕		☕		☕			☕		☕		☕		☕	🚲		☕		☕				☕	
Nottingham 8	d	16 03	16 10		16 23	17 01		17 10		17 22	18 03	18 10		18 22		19 10		19 14	19 22		20 10	20 20	21 10		21 22
Beeston	d	16a08			16 29	17a06				17 28	18a09			18 28				19a19	19 28			20 26			21 28
Attenborough	d				16 32					17 31				18 31					19 31			20 29			21 31
Long Eaton	d			16 28	16 40				17 27	17 39			18 28	18 39	19 14				19 39	20 08		20 37		21 29	21 39
Spondon	d																								
Derby 6	a		16 30	16 40	16 51			17 30	17 40	17 50		18 30	18 39	18 50	19 27	19 30			19 50	20 19	20 30	20 49	21 30	21 42	21 51
	d									17 56									19 52						21 53
Duffield	d									18 03									19 59						22 00
Belper	d									18 08									20 04						22 05
Ambergate	d									18 14									20 10						22 11
Whatstandwell	d									18 18									20 14						22 15
Cromford	d									18 24									20 20						22 21
Matlock Bath	d									18 26									20 22						22 23
Matlock	a									18 30									20 26						22 27

		EM
		◇1
		A
		☕
Nottingham 8	d	
Beeston	d	
Attenborough	d	
Long Eaton	d	22 08
Spondon	d	
Derby 6	a	22 20
	d	
Duffield	d	
Belper	d	
Ambergate	d	
Whatstandwell	d	
Cromford	d	
Matlock Bath	d	
Matlock	a	

A From St Pancras International to Sheffield
B From St Pancras International
C To St Pancras International
D From Leicester to York
E From St Pancras International to Leeds

For connections from St Pancras International please see Table 53

Table 56

Nottingham - Derby - Matlock

Sundays

16 February to 23 March

Network Diagram - refer to first Page of Table 50

		EM	EM	EM	EM	EM		XC	EM	EM	XC	EM	EM	XC	EM	EM		EM	XC	EM	EM	EM	XC	EM	EM
		◇1	◇1		◇1	◇1		◇1	◇1		◇1	◇1	◇1	◇1	◇1			◇1	◇1	◇1		◇1	◇1	◇1	
		A	B		B	C			D			D	B		D			B		D		B		D	
		🛒	☕		☕	☕			☕			☕	☕		☕			☕		☕		☕		☕	
Nottingham 8	d		08 19	09 26	10 26			11 11		11 27	12 10		12 45	13 10		13 23		13 45	14 10		14 22	14 47	15 10		15 28
Beeston	d		08a24	09 32	10a32					11 32			12a51			13 29		13a51			14 28	14a52			15 34
Attenborough	d			09 35						11 36						13 32					14 31				15 37
Long Eaton	d	00 17		09 43		10 41			11 36	11 43		12 38			13 36	13 40				14 32	14 39			15 39	15 45
Spondon	d																								
Derby 6	a	00 28		09 54		10 54		11 31	11 47		12 30	12 50		13 30	13 46	13 51			14 30	14 45	14 50		15 30	15 51	15 56
	d			09 56												13 56									16 00
Duffield	d			10 03						12 04						14 03									16 07
Belper	d			10 08						12 09						14 08									16 12
Ambergate	d			10 14						12 15						14 14									16 18
Whatstandwell	d			10 18						12 19						14 18									16 22
Cromford	d			10 24						12 24						14 24									16 28
Matlock Bath	d			10 26						12 27						14 26									16 30
Matlock	a			10 30						12 30						14 30									16 34

		EM		XC	EM	EM	EM	XC	EM	EM	EM	XC		EM	EM	EM	XC	EM	EM	EM	XC	EM		EM	XC
		◇1		◇1	◇1		◇1	◇1	◇1		◇1	◇1		◇1		◇1	◇1	◇1		◇1	◇1	◇1			◇1
		B			E		B		D		B			A		B		A		B		A			
		☕			☕		☕		☕		☕			☕		☕	🛒	☕		☕		☕			
Nottingham 8	d	15 48		16 10		16 28	16 45	17 10		17 27	17 46	18 10			18 22	18 47	19 10		19 22	19 47	20 10			20 20	21 10
Beeston	d	15a53				16 34	16a50			17 33	17a51				18 28	18a52			19 28	19a52				20 26	
Attenborough	d					16 37				17 36					18 31				19 31					20 29	
Long Eaton	d				16 39	16 45			17 41	17 44				18 31	18 39			19 31	19 39			20 31		20 37	
Spondon	d																								
Derby 6	a			16 30	16 52	16 58		17 30	17 52	17 55		18 30		18 42	18 50		19 30	19 43	19 50		20 30	20 42		20 49	21 30
	d									17 57									19 52						
Duffield	d									18 04									19 59						
Belper	d									18 09									20 04						
Ambergate	d									18 15									20 10						
Whatstandwell	d									18 19									20 14						
Cromford	d									18 25									20 20						
Matlock Bath	d									18 27									20 22						
Matlock	a									18 31									20 26						

		EM	EM	EM
		◇1		◇1
		A		D
		☕		☕
Nottingham 8	d		21 22	
Beeston	d		21 28	
Attenborough	d		21 31	
Long Eaton	d	21 31	21 39	23 26
Spondon	d			
Derby 6	a	21 42	21 51	23 37
	d		21 53	
Duffield	d		22 00	
Belper	d		22 05	
Ambergate	d		22 11	
Whatstandwell	d		22 15	
Cromford	d		22 21	
Matlock Bath	d		22 23	
Matlock	a		22 27	

Sundays

30 March to 11 May

		EM	EM	EM	EM	EM	XC	EM	EM	XC		EM	EM	XC	EM	EM	EM	XC	EM	EM		EM	XC	EM	EM
		◇1	◇1		◇1	◇1	◇1	◇1		◇1		◇1	◇1	◇1	◇1		◇1	◇1	◇1			◇1	◇1	◇1	
		A	B		B	C	F	D		F		D	B	F	D		B	F	D			B	F	D	
		🛒	☕		☕	☕		☕				☕	☕		☕		☕	🛒	☕			☕	🛒	☕	
Nottingham 8	d		08 23	09 26	10 31		11 11		11 27	12 10			12 50	13 10		13 23	13 50	14 10		14 22		14 52	15 10		15 22
Beeston	d		08a28	09 32	10a37				11 32				12a56			13 29	13a56			14 28		14a57			15 28
Attenborough	d			09 35					11 36							13 32				14 31					15 31
Long Eaton	d	00 17		09 43		10 41		11 27	11 43			12 33			13 31	13 40			14 27	14 39				15 35	15 39
Spondon	d																								
Derby 6	a	00 28		09 54		10 54	11 31	11 39		12 30		12 44		13 30	13 43	13 51		14 29	14 42	14 50			15 30	15 48	15 50
	d			09 56												13 56									15 56
Duffield	d			10 03					12 04							14 03									16 03
Belper	d			10 08					12 09							14 08									16 08
Ambergate	d			10 14					12 15							14 14									16 14
Whatstandwell	d			10 18					12 19							14 18									16 18
Cromford	d			10 24					12 24							14 24									16 24
Matlock Bath	d			10 26					12 27							14 26									16 26
Matlock	a			10 30					12 30							14 30									16 30

A From St Pancras International
B To St Pancras International
C From Leicester to York
D From St Pancras International to Sheffield
E From St Pancras International to Leeds
F To Cardiff Central

For connections from St Pancras International please see Table 53

Table 56

Sundays

30 March to 11 May

Nottingham - Derby - Matlock

Network Diagram - refer to first Page of Table 50

		EM		XC	EM	EM	EM	XC	EM	EM	EM	XC		EM	EM	EM	XC	EM	EM	EM	XC	EM		EM	XC
		◇1		◇1	◇1		◇1	◇1	◇1		◇1	◇1		◇1		◇1	◇1	◇1		◇1	◇1	◇1			◇1
		A		B	C		A	B	D		A	B		E		A	F	E		A	F	E			F
		🍴		🚲	🍴		🍴	🚲	🍴		🍴	🚲		🍴		🍴	🚲	🍴		🍴		🍴			
Nottingham 8 🚢	d	15 52		16 10		16 23	16 50	17 10		17 22	17 51	18 10			18 22	18 51	19 10		19 22	19 51	20 10			20 20	21 10
Beeston	d	15a57				16 29	16a55			17 28	17a56				18 28	18a56			19 28	19a56				20 26	
Attenborough	d					16 32				17 31					18 31				19 31					20 29	
Long Eaton	d				16 34	16 40			17 34	17 39				18 25	18 39			19 25	19 39			20 25		20 37	
Spondon	d																								
Derby 6	a			16 30	16 47	16 51		17 29	17 47	17 50		18 30		18 36	18 50		19 30	19 37	19 50		20 29	20 37		20 49	21 30
	d									17 56									19 52						
Duffield	d									18 03									19 59						
Belper	d									18 08									20 04						
Ambergate	d									18 14									20 10						
Whatstandwell	d									18 18									20 14						
Cromford	d									18 24									20 20						
Matlock Bath	d									18 26									20 22						
Matlock	a									18 30									20 26						

		EM	EM	EM
		◇1		◇1
		E		D
		🍴		🍴
Nottingham 8 🚢	d		21 26	
Beeston	d		21 31	
Attenborough	d		21 35	
Long Eaton	d	21 25	21 43	23 24
Spondon	d			
Derby 6	a	21 36	21 55	23 35
	d		21 57	
Duffield	d		22 04	
Belper	d		22 09	
Ambergate	d		22 15	
Whatstandwell	d		22 19	
Cromford	d		22 25	
Matlock Bath	d		22 27	
Matlock	a		22 31	

A To St Pancras International
B To Cardiff Central
C From St Pancras International to Leeds
D From St Pancras International to Sheffield
E From St Pancras International
F To Birmingham New Street

For connections from St Pancras International please see Table 53

Table 56R

Matlock - Derby - Nottingham

Mondays to Fridays

9 December to 16 May

Network Diagram - refer to first Page of Table 50

Miles	Station		EM	EM	EM	EM	EM	EM	EM	XC	EM	EM	EM	EM	EM	XC	EM	EM	EM	XC	EM	EM	EM
			MX	MX	MO	MO	MO	MX															
			◇1	◇1	◇1	◇1	◇1	◇1	◇1	◇		◇1			◇1	1			◇1	1			◇1
			A	B	C	D	E	F	G			H		I		J			G	J	I		K
			⊤	⊤	⊡	⊡	⊡	⊤	⊤			⊠			⊤				⊤				⊤
0	**Matlock**	d											06 20										
1	Matlock Bath	d											06 22										
1¾	Cromford	d											06 25										
4¾	Whatstandwell	d											06 30										
6¾	Ambergate	d											06 36				06 57						
9½	Belper	d											06 42				07 03						
12	Duffield	d											06 46				07 07						
17¼	**Derby** 6	a											06 54				07 15						
—		d							05 19	06 00	06 27	06 33			07 00	07 09		07 31	07 36	07 40		07 53	
19¾	Spondon	d									06 32					07 14				07 45			
25½	Long Eaton	d							05a27		06 39	06a43				07 21		07 41	07a44	07 50		08 03	
28½	Attenborough	d									06 47			07 02		07 28		07 49				08 10	
30	Beeston	d	00≀02	00≀18	00≀40	00≀43	01≀13	01 39		06 15	06 50			07 05		07 32		07 52		07 59	08 07	08 13	08 23
33¼	**Nottingham** 8	a	00≀09	00≀24	00≀46	00≀49	01≀20	01 45		06 22	06 59			07 15	07 19	07 38		08 02		08 09	08 15	08 22	08 31

Station		XC	EM	EM	XC	EM	EM	XC	EM	EM	XC	EM	EM	XC	EM	EM	XC	EM	EM	XC	EM	EM
		1		◇1	1		◇1	1		◇1	◇1		◇1	1		◇1	◇1		◇1	1		◇1
		J		H	J	L	K	J		H	M	L	K	J		H	M	L	K	J		H
		⊤		⊤			⊤	⊤		⊤			⊤	⊤		⊤			⊤	⊤		⊤
Matlock	d		07 37						08 37						09 37						10 37	
Matlock Bath	d		07 39						08 39						09 39						10 39	
Cromford	d		07 42						08 42						09 42						10 42	
Whatstandwell	d		07 47						08 47						09 47						10 47	
Ambergate	d		07 52						08 52						09 52						10 52	
Belper	d		07 59						08 59						09 59						10 59	
Duffield	d		08 03						09 03						10 03						11 03	
Derby 6	a		08 11						09 11						10 11						11 11	
	d	08 10	08 13	08 19	08 40			09 08	09 16	09 21	09 40			10 08	10 13	10 21	10 40			11 08	11 13	11 21
Spondon	d		08 18																			
Long Eaton	d	08 19	08 25	08a29	08 49				09 26	09a30	09 49				10 23	10a30	10 49				11 23	11a29
Attenborough	d		08 35		08 56				09 34						10 32						11 32	
Beeston	d	08 27	08 38		09 00	09 03	09 08		09 37		09 57	10 04	10 10		10 35		10 57	11 04	11 09		11 35	
Nottingham 8	a	08 34	08 46		09 06	09 14	09 17	09 28	09 46		10 03	10 14	10 18	10 28	10 41		11 03	11 14	11 18	11 28	11 41	

Station		XC	EM	EM	XC	EM	EM	XC	EM	EM	XC	EM	EM	XC	EM	EM	XC	EM	EM	XC	EM	EM	XC
		◇1		◇1	1		◇1	◇1		◇1	1		◇1	◇1		◇1	1		◇1	◇1		◇1	1
		M	L	K	J		H	M	L	K	J		H	M	L	K	J		H	M	L	K	J
				⊤	⊤		⊤	⊤		⊤			⊤			⊤	⊤		⊤	⊤		⊤	
Matlock	d					11 37						12 37						13 37					
Matlock Bath	d					11 39						12 39						13 39					
Cromford	d					11 42						12 42						13 42					
Whatstandwell	d					11 47						12 47						13 47					
Ambergate	d					11 52						12 52						13 52					
Belper	d					11 59						12 59						13 59					
Duffield	d					12 03						13 03						14 03					
Derby 6	a					12 11						13 11						14 11					
	d	11 40			12 08	12 13	12 21	12 40			13 08	13 13	13 21	13 40			14 08	14 13	14 21	14 40			15 08
Spondon	d											13 18											
Long Eaton	d	11 49				12 23	12a29	12 49				13 25	13a29	13 49				14 23	14a29	14 49			
Attenborough	d					12 32						13 33						14 32					
Beeston	d	11 57	12 04	12 10		12 35		12 57	13 04	13 09		13 36		13 57	14 04	14 09		14 35		14 57	15 04	15 09	
Nottingham 8	a	12 03	12 14	12 18	12 28	12 41		13 03	13 14	13 18	13 28	13 42		14 03	14 14	14 18	14 28	14 41		15 03	15 14	15 18	15 28

Station		EM	EM	XC	EM	EM	XC	EM	EM	XC	EM	EM	XC	EM	EM	XC	EM	EM	EM	XC	EM	EM	XC
			◇1	◇1		◇1	1		◇1	◇1		◇1	1		◇1	◇1		◇1		1		◇1	◇1
			H	M	N	K	J		H	M	L	K	J		H	M	L	K		J		H	M
			⊤	⊤		⊤			⊤	⊤		⊤			⊤	⊤		⊤				⊤	⊤
Matlock	d	14 37						15 37						16 37							17 37		
Matlock Bath	d	14 39						15 39						16 39							17 39		
Cromford	d	14 42						15 42						16 42							17 42		
Whatstandwell	d	14 47						15 47						16 47							17 47		
Ambergate	d	14 52						15 52						16 52							17 52		
Belper	d	14 59						15 59						16 59							17 59		
Duffield	d	15 03						16 03						17 03							18 03		
Derby 6	a	15 11						16 11						17 11							18 11		
	d	15 13	15 21	15 40			16 08	16 14	16 21	16 40			17 08	17 13	17 21	17 40			17 51	18 08	18 13	18 21	18 40
Spondon	d													17 18					17 57		18 19		
Long Eaton	d	15 23	15a29	15 49				16 24	16a29	16 49			17 17	17 25	17a30	17 49			18 04	18 17	18 26	18a29	18 49
Attenborough	d	15 32						16 32						17 34					18 15		18 34		
Beeston	d	15 35		15 57	16 04	16 09		16 35		16 57	17 04	17 09	17 25	17 37		17 57	18 06	18 12	18 18	18 25	18 38		18 57
Nottingham 8	a	15 41		16 03	16 14	16 18	16 28	16 41		17 03	17 14	17 18	17 31	17 44		18 03	18 16	18 21	18 25	18 31	18 46		19 03

A until 27 December, from 11 February. From St Pancras International
B from 31 December until 7 February. From St Pancras International
C until 30 December, from 31 March. From St Pancras International
D from 17 February until 24 March. From St Pancras International
E from 6 January until 10 February. From St Pancras International
F From St Pancras International to Derby
G To St Pancras International
H From Sheffield to St Pancras International
I From Leicester
J From Birmingham New Street
K From St Pancras International
L From Leicester to Lincoln
M From Cardiff Central
N From Leicester to Sleaford

For connections to St Pancras International please see Table 53

Table 56R

Mondays to Fridays

9 December to 16 May

Matlock - Derby - Nottingham

Network Diagram - refer to first Page of Table 50

		EM ◇1 A 🛒	EM B	EM ◇1 A 🛒	XC 1 C	EM	EM ◇1 D 🛒	XC ◇1 E		EM F	EM ◇1 G 🛒	XC 1 C	EM	XC ◇1 E	EM F	EM ◇1 H 🛒	EM	XC ◇1 E		EM	EM F	EM ◇1 A 🛒	XC 1 C	EM	XC 1 C
Matlock	d					18 37							19 37				20 37			21 41				22 55	
Matlock Bath	d					18 39							19 39				20 39			21 43				22 57	
Cromford	d					18 42							19 42				20 42			21 46				23 00	
Whatstandwell	d					18 47							19 47				20 47			21 51				23 05	
Ambergate	d					18 52							19 52				20 52			21 56				23 10	
Belper	d					18 59							19 59				20 59			22 03				23 17	
Duffield	d					19 03							20 03				21 03			22 07				23 21	
Derby 6	a					19 11							20 11				21 11			22 15				23 29	
	d				19 07	19 13	19 21	19 40				20 08	20 16	20 40			21 13	21 40					22 58	23 31	23 58
Spondon	d																	21 45					23 03		
Long Eaton	d				19 16	19 24	19a29	19 49					20 26	20 49			21 23	21 52					23 10	23 41	
Attenborough	d					19 31							20 34				21 31	21 58					23 17	23 49	
Beeston	d	19 01	19 05	19 12	19 23	19 34		19 57		20 05	20 16		20 37	20 57	21 05	21 19	21 34	22 01			22 05	22 10	23 20	23 52	
Nottingham 8	a	19 08	19 12	19 20	19 30	19 42		20 03		20 13	20 23	20 28	20 43	21 03	21 15	21 28	21 41	22 08			22 15	22 19	23 27	00 01	00 17

Saturdays

14 December to 17 May

		EM ◇1 I 🛒	EM ◇1 J 🛒	EM ◇1 K 🛒	EM ◇1 L 🛒	EM ◇1 L 🛒	EM	EM	EM F	XC 1 C		EM ◇1 L 🛒	EM	XC 1 C	EM F	EM ◇1 A 🛒	XC 1 C 🛒	EM	EM ◇1 L 🛒	XC 1 C		EM B	EM ◇1 A 🛒	XC 1 C 🛒	EM
Matlock	d							06 20										07 37							08 37
Matlock Bath	d							06 22										07 39							08 39
Cromford	d							06 25										07 42							08 42
Whatstandwell	d							06 30										07 47							08 47
Ambergate	d							06 36										07 52							08 52
Belper	d							06 42										07 59							08 59
Duffield	d							06 46										08 03							09 03
Derby 6	a							06 54										08 11							09 11
	d				05 20	06 20	06 24			07 10		07 20	07 32	07 39			08 10	08 13	08 20	08 40				09 08	09 13
Spondon	d						06 29			07 15				07 44				08 18							
Long Eaton	d				05a28	06a28	06 35			07 22		07a28	07 41	07 52			08 19	08 25	08a28	08 49					09 23
Attenborough	d						06 44		07 02	07 28			07 49					08 33		08 56					09 32
Beeston	d	00 02	00 18	01 39			06 47		07 05	07 32			07 52	07 59	08 05	08 20	08 27	08 36		09 00		09 04	09 08		09 35
Nottingham 8	a	00 09	00 24	01 45			06 57		07 15	07 38			08 03	08 08	08 15	08 30	08 34	08 43		09 06		09 12	09 17	09 28	09 41

		EM ◇1 D 🛒	XC ◇1 E	EM B	EM ◇1 A 🛒	XC 1 C 🛒		EM	EM ◇1 D 🛒	XC ◇1 E	EM B	EM ◇1 A 🛒	XC 1 C 🛒	EM	EM ◇1 D 🛒	XC ◇1 E		EM B	EM ◇1 A 🛒	XC 1 C 🛒	EM	EM ◇1 D 🛒	XC ◇1 E 🛒	EM B	EM ◇1 A 🛒
Matlock	d							09 37						10 37							11 37				
Matlock Bath	d							09 39						10 39							11 39				
Cromford	d							09 42						10 42							11 42				
Whatstandwell	d							09 47						10 47							11 47				
Ambergate	d							09 52						10 52							11 52				
Belper	d							09 59						10 59							11 59				
Duffield	d							10 03						11 03							12 03				
Derby 6	a							10 11						11 11							12 11				
	d	09 21	09 40			10 08		10 13	10 21	10 40			11 08	11 13	11 21	11 40				12 08	12 13	12 21	12 40		
Spondon	d																								
Long Eaton	d	09a30	09 49					10 23	10a30	10 51				11 23	11a29	11 49					12 23	12a29	12 49		
Attenborough	d							10 32						11 32							12 32				
Beeston	d		09 57	10 04	10 10			10 35		10 59	11 04	11 09		11 35		11 57		12 04	12 09		12 35		12 57	13 04	13 09
Nottingham 8	a		10 04	10 14	10 18	10 28		10 41		11 06	11 14	11 18	11 28	11 41		12 04		12 14	12 18	12 28	12 41		13 04	13 14	13 18

		XC 1 C		EM	EM ◇1 D 🛒	XC ◇1 E	EM B	EM ◇1 A 🛒	XC 1 C 🛒	EM	EM ◇1 D 🛒	XC ◇1 E 🛒		EM B	EM ◇1 A 🛒	XC 1 C	EM	EM ◇1 D 🛒	XC ◇1 E 🛒	EM B	EM ◇1 A 🛒	XC 1 C		EM	EM ◇1 D 🛒
Matlock	d			12 37						13 37							14 37							15 37	
Matlock Bath	d			12 39						13 39							14 39							15 39	
Cromford	d			12 42						13 42							14 42							15 42	
Whatstandwell	d			12 47						13 47							14 47							15 47	
Ambergate	d			12 52						13 52							14 52							15 52	
Belper	d			12 59						13 59							14 59							15 59	
Duffield	d			13 03						14 03							15 03							16 03	
Derby 6	a			13 11						14 11							15 11							16 11	
	d	13 08		13 13	13 21	13 40			14 08	14 13	14 21	14 40				15 08	15 13	15 21	15 40			16 08		16 13	16 21
Spondon	d			13 18																					
Long Eaton	d			13 25	13a29	13 49				14 23	14a29	14 49					15 23	15a29	15 49					16 23	16a29
Attenborough	d			13 33						14 32							15 32							16 32	
Beeston	d			13 36		13 57	14 04	14 09		14 35		14 57		15 04	15 09		15 35		15 57	16 04	16 09			16 35	
Nottingham 8	a	13 28		13 42		14 04	14 14	14 18	14 28	14 41		15 04		15 14	15 18	15 28	15 41		16 04	16 14	16 18	16 28		16 41	

A From St Pancras International
B From Leicester to Lincoln
C From Birmingham New Street
D From Sheffield to St Pancras International
E From Cardiff Central
F From Leicester
G From St Pancras International to Lincoln
H From St Pancras International to Leeds
I from 15 February. From St Pancras International
J from 4 January until 8 February. From St Pancras International
K From St Pancras International to Derby
L To St Pancras International

For connections to St Pancras International please see Table 53

Table 56R

Saturdays

Matlock - Derby - Nottingham

14 December to 17 May

Network Diagram - refer to first Page of Table 50

		XC ◇1 A	EM B	EM ◇1 C	XC 1 D	EM	EM ◇1 E	XC ◇1 A	EM B	EM ◇1 C	XC 1 D	EM	EM ◇1 E	XC ◇1 A	EM F	EM ◇1 G	XC 1 D	EM	EM ◇1 H	XC ◇1 A	EM B	EM ◇1 C
Matlock	d					16 37						17 37						18 37				
Matlock Bath	d					16 39						17 39						18 39				
Cromford	d					16 42						17 42						18 42				
Whatstandwell	d					16 47						17 47						18 47				
Ambergate	d					16 52						17 52						18 52				
Belper	d					16 59						17 59						18 59				
Duffield	d					17 03						18 03						19 03				
Derby 6	a					17 11						18 11						19 11				
	d	16 40			17 08	17 13	17 21	17 40			18 08	18 13	18 21	18 40			19 06	19 13	19 21	19 40		
Spondon	d					17 18																
Long Eaton	d	16 49			17 17	17 25	17a29	17 49			18 17	18 23	18a30	18 49			19 15	19 23	19a29	19 49		
Attenborough	d					17 33						18 32						19 32				
Beeston	d	16 57	17 04	17 09	17 25	17 36		17 57	18 05	18 09	18 25	18 35		18 57	19 04	19 09	19 25	19 35		19 57	20 04	20 09
Nottingham 8	a	17 04	17 14	17 18	17 31	17 42		18 04	18 14	18 18	18 31	18 41		19 04	19 15	19 18	19 34	19 41		20 04	20 12	20 18

		XC 1 D	EM	XC ◇1 A	EM B	EM ◇1 C	EM	XC ◇1 A	EM	EM F	EM ◇1 I	EM ◇1 J	EM ◇1 K	XC ◇1 A	EM
Matlock	d		19 37				20 37		21 41						22 55
Matlock Bath	d		19 39				20 39		21 43						22 57
Cromford	d		19 42				20 42		21 46						23 00
Whatstandwell	d		19 47				20 47		21 51						23 05
Ambergate	d		19 52				20 52		21 56						23 10
Belper	d		19 59				20 59		22 03						23 17
Duffield	d		20 03				21 03		22 07						23 21
Derby 6	a		20 11				21 11		22 15						23 29
	d	20 08	20 13	20 40			21 13	21 40						23 00	23 31
Spondon	d							21 45						23 05	
Long Eaton	d		20 23	20 49			21 23	21 52						23 12	23 41
Attenborough	d		20 32				21 32	21 58						23 18	23 49
Beeston	d		20 35	20 57	21 04	21 09	21 35	22 02		22 05	22 14	22 18	22 25	23 22	23 52
Nottingham 8	a	20 28	20 42	21 04	21 14	21 18	21 41	22 08		22 14	22 20	22 25	22 33	23 28	00 01

Sundays

8 December to 11 May

		EM ◇1 L	EM ◇1 M	EM ◇1 N	EM ◇1 O	EM	EM ◇1 M	EM ◇1 N	EM ◇1 O	EM ◇1 M	EM ◇1 N	EM ◇1 O	EM ◇1 P	EM ◇1 Q	EM ◇1 R	EM	XC ◇1 S	EM ◇1 T	EM ◇1 M	XC ◇1 U	XC ◇1 S	EM ◇1 V	EM ◇1 R
Matlock	d															10 38							
Matlock Bath	d															10 40							
Cromford	d															10 43							
Whatstandwell	d															10 48							
Ambergate	d															10 54							
Belper	d															11 00							
Duffield	d															11 05							
Derby 6	a															11 12							
	d		08 14	08 47	08 52	09 14	09 19	09 54	09 59	10 26	10 53	10 58				11 14	11 40		12 36	12 40	12 40		
Spondon	d																						
Long Eaton	d		08a22	08a56	09a00	09 24	09a27	10a02	10a07	10a35	11a02	11a06				11 24			12a44				
Attenborough	d					09 31										11 31							
Beeston	d	00 02				09 34							11 00	11 00	11 05	11 34		12 00				13 05	13 11
Nottingham 8	a	00 10				09 41							11 06	11 08	11 11	11 41	12 00	12 07		13 00	13 00	13 12	13 18

A From Cardiff Central
B From Leicester to Lincoln
C From St Pancras International
D From Birmingham New Street
E From Sheffield to St Pancras International
F From Leicester
G From St Pancras International to Lincoln
H From York to St Pancras International
I until 8 February. From St Pancras International
J from 29 March. From St Pancras International
K from 15 February until 22 March. From St Pancras International
L not 8 December. From St Pancras International
M from 5 January until 9 February. From Sheffield to St Pancras International
N from 16 February until 23 March. From Sheffield to St Pancras International
O until 29 December, from 30 March. From Sheffield to St Pancras International
P from 30 March. From St Pancras International
Q until 29 December. From St Pancras International
R from 16 February until 23 March. From St Pancras International
S from 5 January until 23 March
T from 5 January until 9 February. From St Pancras International
U until 29 December, from 30 March. From Birmingham New Street
V until 29 December, from 30 March. From St Pancras International

For connections to St Pancras International please see Table 53

Table 56R

Sundays

8 December to 11 May

Matlock - Derby - Nottingham

Network Diagram - refer to first Page of Table 50

		EM	EM	EM	EM	XC	XC	EM	EM	EM	EM	EM	EM	EM	EM	XC	XC	EM	EM	EM	EM	EM
			◇1	◇1		◇1	◇1	◇1	◇1	◇1	◇1	◇1	◇1	◇1	◇1	◇1	◇1	◇1	◇1	◇1	◇1	
		A	B	C	D	E	F	G	H	I	J	K	B	L	I	E	F	G	H	J	B	A
			☕	☕		🍴		☕	☕	☕	☕	☕	☕	☕	☕	🍴		☕	☕	☕	☕	
Matlock	d	12 38			12 51																	14 41
Matlock Bath	d	12 40			12 53																	14 43
Cromford	d	12 43			12 56																	14 46
Whatstandwell	d	12 48			13 01																	14 51
Ambergate	d	12 54			13 07																	14 56
Belper	d	13 00			13 13																	15 03
Duffield	d	13 05			13 18																	15 07
Derby 6	a	13 12			13 25																	15 15
	d	13 14	13 16	13 21	13 27	13 40	13 40	13 44				14 17	14 18	14 20		14 40	14 40	14 49			15 15	15 16
Spondon	d																					
Long Eaton	d	13 24	13a25	13a29	13 37			13a52				14a26	14a26	14a29				14a57			15a24	15 26
Attenborough	d	13 31			13 44																	15 34
Beeston	d	13 34			13 47				14 00	14 02	14 05				14 47				15 00	15 05		15 37
Nottingham 8	a	13 41			13 54	14 00	14 00		14 07	14 09	14 12				14 55	15 00	15 00		15 07	15 12		15 43

		EM	EM	EM	XC	XC	EM	EM	EM	EM	XC	XC	EM	EM	EM	EM	EM	XC	XC	EM	EM	EM	EM
		◇1		◇1	◇1	◇1	◇1	◇1		◇1	◇1	◇1	◇1	◇1	◇1	◇1		◇1	◇1	◇1	◇1	◇1	◇1
		C	D	I	E	F	H	J		G	E	F	M	N	O	I		E	F	P	H	M	J
		☕		☕	🍴		☕	☕		☕	🍴		☕	☕	☕	☕		🍴		☕	☕	☕	☕
Matlock	d		14 48														16 38						
Matlock Bath	d		14 50														16 40						
Cromford	d		14 53														16 43						
Whatstandwell	d		14 58														16 48						
Ambergate	d		15 03														16 54						
Belper	d		15 10														17 01						
Duffield	d		15 14														17 05						
Derby 6	a		15 21														17 12						
	d	15 23	15 23		15 40	15 40			16 14	16 22	16 40	16 40	16 54	16 58	16 59		17 14	17 40	17 40	17 44		18 02	
Spondon	d																						
Long Eaton	d	15a31	15 33						16 23	16a32			17a02	17a07	17a08		17 24			17a53		18a11	
Attenborough	d		15 41						16 31								17 31						
Beeston	d		15 44	15 43			15 59	16 03	16 34							17 00	17 34				17 58		18 05
Nottingham 8	a		15 50	15 51	16 00	16 00	16 05	16 09	16 43		17 00	17 00				17 08	17 44	18 00	18 00		18 05		18 12

		EM	EM	EM	EM	EM	XC	EM	EM	EM	EM	EM	EM	EM	EM	EM	XC	EM	EM	EM	EM	EM
		◇1		◇1		◇1	◇1	◇1	◇1				◇1	◇1	◇1	◇1	◇1	◇1	◇1	◇1	◇1	
		Q	A	I	D	R	S	H	J	D	T	U	V	W	G	I	S	B	H	C	J	
		☕		☕		☕		☕	☕				☕	☕	☕	☕		☕	☕	☕	☕	
Matlock	d									18 37	18 38	18 40										
Matlock Bath	d									18 39	18 40	18 42										
Cromford	d									18 42	18 43	18 45										
Whatstandwell	d									18 47	18 48	18 50										
Ambergate	d									18 53	18 54	18 56										
Belper	d									18 59	19 00	19 02										
Duffield	d									19 04	19 05	19 07										
Derby 6	a									19 11	19 12	19 14										
	d	18 07	18 14		18 25	18 29	18 40			19 13	19 14	19 16	19 17	19 20	19 24		19 40	19 56		20 03		20 14
Spondon	d																					
Long Eaton	d	18a15	18 24		18 35	18a37				19 23	19 24	19 26	19a26	19a29	19a34			20a06		20a12		20 23
Attenborough	d		18 34		18 42					19 30	19 34	19 33										20 31
Beeston	d		18 37	18 42	18 45			18 59	19 02	19 33	19 37	19 36				19 43			19 59		20 04	20 34
Nottingham 8	a		18 44	18 51	18 52		19 00	19 05	19 08	19 40	19 44	19 43				19 51	20 00		20 05		20 10	20 41

		EM	XC	EM	EM	EM	EM	XC	EM	EM	EM	EM	EM	EM	EM	EM
		◇1	◇1	◇1	◇1		◇1	◇1	◇1	◇1		◇1		◇1	◇1	◇1
		I	S	H	J		I	S	H	J		I		H	J	I
		☕		☕	☕		☕		☕	☕		☕		☕	☕	☕
Matlock	d					20 38							22 44			
Matlock Bath	d					20 40							22 46			
Cromford	d					20 43							22 49			
Whatstandwell	d					20 48							22 54			
Ambergate	d					20 54							23 00			
Belper	d					21 00							23 07			
Duffield	d					21 05							23 11			
Derby 6	a					21 12							23 18			
	d		20 40			21 14		21 40			22 18					
Spondon	d															
Long Eaton	d					21 24					22 28					
Attenborough	d					21 31					22 35					
Beeston	d	20 49		20 59	21 03	21 34	21 44		21 59	22 03	22 38	22 43		23 05	23 06	23 50
Nottingham 8	a	20 57	21 00	21 05	21 09	21 41	21 52	22 00	22 05	22 09	22 45	22 51		23 11	23 12	23 57

- **A** until 9 February, from 30 March
- **B** from 16 February until 23 March. From Sheffield to St Pancras International
- **C** until 29 December, from 30 March. From Sheffield to St Pancras International
- **D** from 16 February until 23 March
- **E** until 29 December, from 30 March. From Cardiff Central
- **F** from 5 January until 23 March
- **G** from 5 January until 9 February. From Sheffield to St Pancras International
- **H** until 29 December, from 30 March. From St Pancras International
- **I** from 5 January until 9 February. From St Pancras International
- **J** from 16 February until 23 March. From St Pancras International
- **K** until 29 December. From Sheffield to St Pancras International
- **L** from 30 March. From Sheffield to St Pancras International
- **M** from 16 February until 23 March. To St Pancras International
- **N** from 30 March. To St Pancras International
- **O** until 29 December. To St Pancras International
- **P** from 5 January until 9 February. To St Pancras International
- **Q** until 29 December, from 30 March. To St Pancras International
- **R** from 5 January until 9 February. From York to St Pancras International
- **S** From Cardiff Central
- **T** until 29 December
- **U** from 5 January until 9 February, from 30 March
- **V** from 16 February until 23 March. From York to St Pancras International
- **W** until 29 December, from 30 March. From York to St Pancras International

For connections to St Pancras International please see Table 53

Table 57

Mondays to Fridays

9 December to 16 May

Nottingham, Derby and Leicester
Birmingham - Cardiff and Bristol

Network Diagram - refer to first Page of Table 50

Miles	Miles	Miles			EM	AW	GW	XC	GW	GW	XC	GW	XC		GW	AW	XC	XC	XC	XC	XC	GW	EM		XC
					MX																				
					◇1		◇1	◇1		◇1	◇1	◇	◇1		◇1		◇1	1	◇1	◇1	◇1	◇1			1
					A	B	C		D	C		E	F		C	B	G		H	I	J	C	K		
					🛒		🍴			🍴			🛒		🍴		🛒		🛒		🛒	🍴			
0	—	—	**Nottingham 8**	56 🚊 d	01 51														06 00				06 17		
3¼	—	—	Beeston	56 d															06 06				06 24		
4¾	—	—	Attenborough	56 d															06 09				06 27		
7¾	—	—	Long Eaton	d															06 18				06 36		
16	—	—	**Derby 6**	a	02 10														06 31				06 50		
—	—	—		d													06 10		06 36	06 48					
22¼	—	—	Willington	d																					
27	—	—	Burton-on-Trent	d													06 20		06 48	06 58					
40	—	—	Tamworth	d													06 31		07 01	07 09					
41¾	—	—	Wilnecote	d															07 05						
—	0	—	**Leicester**	d														06 17							06 43
—	4	—	South Wigston	d														06 23							06 49
—	7	—	Narborough	d														06 28							06 54
—	15	—	Hinckley	d														06 36							07 02
—	18¾	—	Nuneaton	d														06 42							07 09
—	30¼	—	Coleshill Parkway	d														06 59							07 25
—	32½	—	Water Orton	d																					07 29
56¾	40	0	**Birmingham New Street 12**	a													06 52	07 14	07 25	07 27					07 44
—	—	—		d				05 00			05 37		06 42				07 12		07 30		07 42				
83¾	—	—	Worcester Shrub Hill 7	d			05 21					06 49			07 08										
98½	—	39¼	Ashchurch for Tewkesbury	d			05 40				06 27	07 05													
105¾	—	46½	Cheltenham Spa	d		05 37	05 53	06 02	06 24	06 30	06 43	07 16	07 23		07 29	07 46	07 52		08 14		08 25	08 31			
112¼	—	—	Gloucester 7	134 a		05 48	06 02	06 16	06 34	06 39	06 53	07 26			07 38	07 57			08 23			08 40			
—	—	87	Bristol Parkway 7	134 a					07 21			08 19	07 54				08 25				08 53				
—	—	92¾	**Bristol Temple Meads 10**	134 a					07 40			08 36	08 05				08 39				09 14				
157	—	—	Newport (South Wales)	132 a		06 41		07 08			07 52					08 50			09 12						
168¾	—	—	**Cardiff Central 7**	132 a		07 00		07 26			08 08					09 07			09 30						

		XC	XC	AW	XC	XC	XC	EM	XC		GW	XC	XC	XC	GW	XC	XC	XC	EM		XC	XC	XC	GW	XC
		◇1	◇1		◇1	1	◇1		◇1			◇1	◇1	1		◇1	1	◇1			1	◇1	◇1	◇1	1
		L	M	B	N			K	O		P	J	Q		R	S		T	K		U	Q	V	C	
					🛒				🛒			🛒				🛒		🛒			🛒		🛒	🍴	
Nottingham 8	56 🚊 d	06 37					07 04	07 20						07 37				08 12	08 22						08 41
Beeston	56 d	06 43					07 09	07 25						07 42					08 28						08 47
Attenborough	56 d						07 13	07 29											08 31						
Long Eaton	d						07 21	07 38						07 52					08 40						08 56
Derby 6	a	06 59					07 31	07 50						08 02				08 33	08 53						09 07
	d	07 06			07 27		07 36		07 50					08 06		08 28		08 37			08 53				09 11
Willington	d						07 44																		
Burton-on-Trent	d	07 17			07 38		07 50		08 00					08 18		08 38		08 49							09 22
Tamworth	d	07 30			07 50		08 03		08 11					08 30		08 50		09 02							09 34
Wilnecote	d						08 07							08 34											09 38
Leicester	d		07 10			07 24							07 51				08 16					08 48			
South Wigston	d												07 57												
Narborough	d					07 33							08 02				08 25								
Hinckley	d					07 42							08 10				08 34								
Nuneaton	d		07 29			07 50							08 17				08 41					09 10			
Coleshill Parkway	d		07 45			08 05							08 32				08 56					09 25			
Water Orton	d					08 09																			
Birmingham New Street 12	a	07 54	07 58		08 09	08 19	08 24		08 27				08 45	08 54		09 10	09 14	09 24			09 27	09 38			09 56
	d				08 12		08 30					08 42				09 20		09 30					09 42		
Worcester Shrub Hill 7	d														09 06										
Ashchurch for Tewkesbury	d														09 24										
Cheltenham Spa	d			08 46	08 51		09 10				09 20	09 26			09 33	10 00		10 10					10 25	10 31	
Gloucester 7	134 a			08 58			09 20				09 29				09 42			10 20						10 40	
Bristol Parkway 7	134 a				09 24							09 53			10 23	10 29							10 53		
Bristol Temple Meads 10	134 a				09 38							10 08			10 39	10 42							11 10		
Newport (South Wales)	132 a			09 51			10 11											11 11							
Cardiff Central 7	132 a			10 11			10 27											11 27							

A From St Pancras International
B To Maesteg
C To London Paddington
D To Westbury
E To Weymouth
F To Paignton
G To Plymouth. 🛒 from Birmingham New Street
H 🛒 from Birmingham New Street to Newport (South Wales)
I From Sheffield to Reading
J From Manchester Piccadilly
K To Matlock
L To Bournemouth
M From Cambridge
N From Leeds to Plymouth
O From Leeds to Southampton Central
P To Swindon
Q From Stansted Airport
R From Great Malvern to Westbury
S From York to Plymouth
T 🛒 from Birmingham New Street
U From Newcastle to Reading
V From Manchester Piccadilly to Paignton

Table 57

Mondays to Fridays

9 December to 16 May

Nottingham, Derby and Leicester
Birmingham - Cardiff and Bristol

Network Diagram - refer to first Page of Table 50

			AW	XC	XC	XC	EM	XC	XC	GW	XC		XC	GW	AW	XC	XC	XC	EM	XC	XC		GW	XC	XC
				◇1	1	◇1		◇1	◇1		◇1		1	■		◇1	1	◇1		◇1	◇1		◇1	◇1	1
			A	B			C	D	E	F	G			H		I			C	J	E		K	G	
				⊥		⊥		⊥	⊥		⊥					⊥		⊥		⊥	⊥		⊐	⊥	
Nottingham 8 56	d					09 10	09 20						09 41					10 10	10 20						10 41
Beeston 56	d						09 25						09 47						10 25						10 47
Attenborough 56	d						09 29												10 29						
Long Eaton	d						09 38						09 57						10 39						10 56
Derby 6	a					09 31	09 50						10 07					10 31	10 50						11 07
	d			09 28		09 36		09 53					10 11			10 28		10 36		10 53					11 11
Willington	d					09 44																			
Burton-on-Trent	d			09 38		09 50							10 22					10 49							11 22
Tamworth	d					10 02							10 34			10 48		11 02							11 34
Wilnecote	d												10 38												11 38
Leicester	d				09 18				09 48								10 18				10 48				
South Wigston	d																10 24								
Narborough	d				09 27												10 29								
Hinckley	d				09 36												10 37								
Nuneaton	d				09 43				10 10								10 44				11 10				
Coleshill Parkway	d				09 59				10 25								10 58				11 25				
Water Orton	d				10 02																				
Birmingham New Street 12	a			10 06	10 14	10 24		10 27	10 38				10 56			11 09	11 14	11 25		11 27	11 38				11 56
	d			10 20		10 30					10 42					11 20		11 30						11 42	
Worcester Shrub Hill 7	d													11 06											
Ashchurch for Tewkesbury	d													11 24											
Cheltenham Spa	d		10 45	11 02		11 10				11 20	11 26			11 33	11 45	12 02		12 10					12 20	12 26	
Gloucester 7 134	a		10 57			11 20				11 30				11 45	11 57			12 20					12 29		
Bristol Parkway 7 134	a			11 30							11 53			12 23		12 30								12 53	
Bristol Temple Meads 10 134	a			11 40							12 05			12 35		12 41								13 09	
Newport (South Wales) 132	a		11 50			12 10									12 50			13 11							
Cardiff Central 7 132	a		12 10			12 26									13 07			13 29							

		XC	XC	XC	EM	XC	XC		GW	XC	XC	GW	AW	XC	XC	XC	EM		XC	XC	GW	XC	XC	XC	XC
		◇1	1	◇1		◇1	◇1			◇1	1	◇		◇1	1	◇1			◇1	◇1	◇1	◇1	1	◇1	1
		L			C	D	E		F	G		M	A	N			C		O	E	P	Q		L	
		⊥		⊥		⊥	⊥			⊥				⊥		⊥			⊥	⊥	⊐	⊥		⊥	
Nottingham 8 56	d			11 10	11 20						11 41					12 10	12 20						12 41		
Beeston 56	d				11 25						11 47						12 25						12 47		
Attenborough 56	d				11 29												12 29								
Long Eaton	d				11 37						11 56						12 37						12 56		
Derby 6	a			11 31	11 49						12 07					12 31	12 49						13 07		
	d	11 28		11 37		11 53					12 11			12 28		12 37			12 53				13 11	13 28	
Willington	d																						13 19		
Burton-on-Trent	d			11 49							12 22					12 49							13 25	13 38	
Tamworth	d			12 02							12 34			12 48		13 02							13 36		
Wilnecote	d										12 38														
Leicester	d		11 18				11 48								12 18					12 48					13 18
South Wigston	d														12 24										
Narborough	d		11 27												12 29										13 27
Hinckley	d		11 36												12 37										13 36
Nuneaton	d		11 43				12 10								12 43					13 10					13 43
Coleshill Parkway	d		11 58				12 25								13 00					13 25					13 58
Water Orton	d		12 02																						14 02
Birmingham New Street 12	a	12 07	12 14	12 24		12 27	12 38				12 56			13 08	13 14	13 24			13 27	13 38			13 56	14 06	14 14
	d	12 20		12 30						12 42				13 20		13 30						13 42		14 20	
Worcester Shrub Hill 7	d											13 06													
Ashchurch for Tewkesbury	d											13 24													
Cheltenham Spa	d	13 02		13 10					13 20	13 26		13 33	13 45	14 01		14 10					14 20	14 26		15 02	
Gloucester 7 134	a			13 20					13 30			13 44	13 57			14 23					14 29				
Bristol Parkway 7 134	a	13 31								13 57		14 22		14 30								14 53		15 30	
Bristol Temple Meads 10 134	a	13 41								14 08		14 39		14 41								15 10		15 41	
Newport (South Wales) 132	a			14 10									14 50			15 10									
Cardiff Central 7 132	a			14 27									15 14			15 30									

A To Maesteg
B From Newcastle to Plymouth
C To Matlock
D From Newcastle to Southampton Central
E From Stansted Airport
F To Swindon
G From Manchester Piccadilly
H From Great Malvern to Brighton
I From Edinburgh to Plymouth
J From Edinburgh to Reading
K To London Paddington
L From Glasgow Central to Plymouth
M From Great Malvern to Weymouth
N From Dundee to Plymouth
O From Newcastle to Reading
P To London Paddington. The Cheltenham Spa Express
Q From Manchester Piccadilly to Exeter St Davids

Table 57

Mondays to Fridays

9 December to 16 May

Nottingham, Derby and Leicester
Birmingham - Cardiff and Bristol

Network Diagram - refer to first Page of Table 50

Station			XC	EM	XC	XC	GW	XC	XC	GW		XC	XC	XC	EM	XC	XC	GW	XC	AW		XC	XC	XC	XC	EM
			◇1		◇1	◇1		◇1	1	◇		◇1	1	◇1		◇1	◇1	◇1	◇1			1	◇1	1	◇1	
				A	B	C	D	E		F		G			A	H	C	I	J	K			L			A
			⊼		⊼	⊼		⊼	⊼			⊼		⊼		⊼	⊼	R	⊼				⊼		⊼	
Nottingham 8	56	d	13 10	13 20					13 41					14 10	14 20							14 41			15 10	15 20
Beeston	56	d		13 25					13 47						14 25							14 47				15 25
Attenborough	56	d		13 29											14 29											15 29
Long Eaton		d		13 37					13 56						14 37							14 56				15 37
Derby 6		a	13 31	13 50					14 07					14 31	14 48							15 07			15 31	15 49
		d	13 37		13 53				14 11			14 28		14 36		14 53						15 11	15 28		15 37	
Willington		d																				15 19				
Burton-on-Trent		d	13 49						14 22					14 50								15 25	15 38		15 49	
Tamworth		d	14 02						14 33			14 47		15 02								15 36			16 02	
Wilnecote		d							14 37																	
Leicester		d				13 48							14 18				14 48							15 18		
South Wigston		d											14 24													
Narborough		d											14 29											15 26		
Hinckley		d											14 37											15 36		
Nuneaton		d				14 10							14 43				15 10							15 43		
Coleshill Parkway		d				14 25							15 00				15 25							15 58		
Water Orton		d																						16 01		
Birmingham New Street 12		a	14 24		14 27	14 38			14 56			15 07	15 14	15 24		15 27	15 38					15 56	16 03	16 14	16 24	
		d	14 30					14 42				15 20		15 30					15 42				16 12		16 30	
Worcester Shrub Hill 7		d								15 06																
Ashchurch for Tewkesbury		d								15 24															17 05	
Cheltenham Spa		d	15 10				15 20	15 26		15 33		16 01		16 10				16 20	16 26	16 45			16 52		17 14	
Gloucester 7	134	a	15 20				15 30			15 44				16 20				16 30		16 56					17 23	
Bristol Parkway 7	134	a						15 55		16 22		16 33							16 53				17 25			
Bristol Temple Meads 10	134	a						16 10		16 38		16 44							17 10				17 39			
Newport (South Wales)	132	a	16 11											17 11						17 50					18 12	
Cardiff Central 7	132	a	16 29											17 28						18 10					18 28	

Station			XC	XC	XC	XC		GW	GW	AW	XC	XC	XC	EM	XC	XC		XC	GW	XC	EM	AW		XC	XC	XC
			◇1	◇1	◇1	1			◇		◇1	1	◇1		◇1	◇1		◇1	◇1	1				◇1	1	◇1
			M	C	E			N	O	K	G			A	H	C		E	I			K		P		
			⊼	⊼	⊼	⊼					⊼				⊼	⊼		⊼	R	⊼				⊼		
Nottingham 8	56	d				15 41							16 10	16 20						16 41	16 44					17 10
Beeston	56	d				15 47								16 25						16 47	16 50					
Attenborough	56	d												16 29							16 53					
Long Eaton		d				15 56								16 37						16 57	17 02					
Derby 6		a				16 07							16 31	16 49						17 07	17 18					17 31
		d	15 53			16 11					16 28		16 36		16 53					17 11				17 28		17 37
Willington		d																		17 19						
Burton-on-Trent		d				16 22							16 49							17 25				17 38		17 49
Tamworth		d				16 34					16 47		17 02							17 36						18 02
Wilnecote		d				16 38																				
Leicester		d		15 48								16 18				16 48									17 18	
South Wigston		d										16 24													17 24	
Narborough		d										16 29													17 29	
Hinckley		d										16 37													17 37	
Nuneaton		d		16 10								16 43				17 10									17 43	
Coleshill Parkway		d		16 25								17 00				17 25									18 00	
Water Orton		d																								
Birmingham New Street 12		a	16 27	16 38		16 56					17 09	17 14	17 24		17 28	17 38				17 56				18 05	18 13	18 26
		d			16 42						17 12		17 30					17 42						18 12		18 30
Worcester Shrub Hill 7		d						17 06																		
Ashchurch for Tewkesbury		d						17 24					18 09													
Cheltenham Spa		d			17 25			17 33	17 39	17 45	17 52		18 18					18 25	18 34			18 45		18 52		19 15
Gloucester 7	134	a						17 44	17 51	17 57			18 29						18 44			18 59				19 24
Bristol Parkway 7	134	a			17 54			18 23			18 28							18 53						19 26		
Bristol Temple Meads 10	134	a			18 07			18 38			18 41							19 05						19 38		
Newport (South Wales)	132	a								18 49			19 16									19 53				20 11
Cardiff Central 7	132	a								19 09			19 33									20 12				20 27

A To Matlock
B From Newcastle to Southampton Central
C From Stansted Airport
D To Swindon
E From Manchester Piccadilly
F From Great Malvern to Weymouth
G From Glasgow Central to Penzance
H From Newcastle to Reading
I To London Paddington
J From Manchester Piccadilly to Paignton
K To Maesteg
L From Aberdeen to Penzance
M From Newcastle to Guildford
N From Great Malvern to Westbury
O To Southampton Central
P From Edinburgh to Plymouth

Table 57

Mondays to Fridays

9 December to 16 May

Nottingham, Derby and Leicester
Birmingham - Cardiff and Bristol

Network Diagram - refer to first Page of Table 50

		EM	XC	XC	XC	XC	GW	AW	XC	GW	XC	XC	EM	XC	XC	XC	GW	XC	XC	GW	XC	XC	EM
			◇1	◇1	◇1	1			◇1		1	◇1		◇1	◇1	◇1	1	1	◇1		1	◇1	
		A	B	C	D		E	F	G	H			A	B	D	I			J	H			A
			🛒	🛒	🛒	🛒			🛒					🛒	🛒	🛒		🛒	🛒				
Nottingham 8	56 🚋 d	17 20				17 41						18 10	18 20					18 41				19 10	19 20
Beeston	56 d	17 25				17 47							18 25					18 47					19 25
Attenborough	56 d	17 29											18 29										19 29
Long Eaton	d	17 37				17 56							18 37					18 56					19 36
Derby 6	a	17 50				18 07						18 32	18 49					19 06				19 31	19 50
	d		17 53			18 11			18 29			18 37		18 53				19 10	19 29			19 36	
Willington	d					18 18																	
Burton-on-Trent	d					18 24						18 49						19 21	19 38			19 49	
Tamworth	d					18 36			18 48			19 02						19 33				20 03	
Wilnecote	d					18 39												19 37					
Leicester	d				17 48						18 18				18 48						19 18		
South Wigston	d				17 54						18 24										19 24		
Narborough	d				18 00						18 29										19 29		
Hinckley	d				18 08						18 37										19 37		
Nuneaton	d				18 17						18 44				19 10						19 44		
Coleshill Parkway	d				18 33						19 00				19 25						20 00		
Water Orton	d																						
Birmingham New Street 12	a		18 27		18 46	18 58			19 08		19 14	19 24		19 27	19 38			19 55	20 09		20 14	20 24	
	d			18 42					19 12			19 30				19 42			20 12			20 30	
Worcester Shrub Hill 7	d						19 07																
Ashchurch for Tewkesbury	d						19 24																
Cheltenham Spa	d			19 25			19 34	19 45	19 51	20 01		20 11				20 25	20 48		20 52	21 00		21 11	
Gloucester 7	134 a						19 42	19 56		20 11		20 20					20 58			21 10		21 20	
Bristol Parkway 7	134 a			19 58			20 23		20 28							20 55	21 50		21 25				
Bristol Temple Meads 10	134 a			20 09			20 39		20 42							21 05	22 11		21 36				
Newport (South Wales)	132 a			20 47				20 50				21 10										22 14	
Cardiff Central 7	132 a			21 02				21 10				21 28										22 35	

		XC	XC	XC	XC	XC	EM	XC	EM	XC	XC	XC	NT	GW	GW	XC	AW	XC	EM	XC	XC	GW
		◇1	◇1	◇1	1	◇1	◇1	1		◇1	◇1	1				◇1		1		◇1	◇1	
		K	D	L		M	N		A	O	D		P		E	Q				D	O	
		🛒	🛒		🛒	🛒	🛒			🛒												
Nottingham 8	56 🚋 d				19 40		20 06		20 20			20 40	20 47						21 20			
Beeston	56 d				19 45				20 26			20 45							21 25			
Attenborough	56 d				19 49				20 30										21 29			
Long Eaton	d				19 56		20 19		20 39			20 54							21 37			
Derby 6	a				20 06		20 31		20 50			21 04	21 08						21 51			
	d	19 54			20 10	20 28				20 54		21 10				21 29					22 02	
Willington	d											21 18										
Burton-on-Trent	d				20 21							21 24				21 40						
Tamworth	d				20 33	20 47						21 35				21 50						
Wilnecote	d				20 37							21 39										
Leicester	d		19 48					20 18			20 48							21 16		21 48		
South Wigston	d							20 24										21 22				
Narborough	d							20 29										21 27				
Hinckley	d							20 37										21 35				
Nuneaton	d		20 10					20 44			21 09							21 41		22 10		
Coleshill Parkway	d		20 25					21 00			21 24							21 58		22 25		
Water Orton	d																					
Birmingham New Street 12	a	20 27	20 38		20 56	21 07		21 15		21 29	21 37	21 58				22 09		22 11		22 38	22 51	
	d			20 42		21 12										22 12						
Worcester Shrub Hill 7	d														21 32							22 28
Ashchurch for Tewkesbury	d														21 52							22 51
Cheltenham Spa	d			21 27		21 52								22 01	22 07	22 53	23 00					23 05
Gloucester 7	134 a					22 01								22 11	22 21		23 12					23 17
Bristol Parkway 7	134 a			22 01		22 32									23 04	23 20						
Bristol Temple Meads 10	134 a			22 13		22 43									23 19	23 40						
Newport (South Wales)	132 a																00 06					
Cardiff Central 7	132 a																00 35					

- **A** To Matlock
- **B** From Newcastle to Reading
- **C** From Manchester Piccadilly. 🛒 to Bristol Temple Meads
- **D** From Stansted Airport
- **E** From Great Malvern
- **F** To Maesteg
- **G** From Glasgow Central to Plymouth
- **H** To Swindon
- **I** From Manchester Piccadilly to Plymouth
- **J** From Edinburgh to Plymouth
- **K** From Newcastle to Southampton Central
- **L** From Manchester Piccadilly
- **M** From Glasgow Central. 🛒 to Birmingham New Street
- **N** From St Pancras International
- **O** From Newcastle
- **P** To Sheffield
- **Q** From Edinburgh

Table 57

Mondays to Fridays

9 December to 16 May

Nottingham, Derby and Leicester
Birmingham - Cardiff and Bristol

Network Diagram - refer to first Page of Table 50

		LM FO	XC 1	XC 1	XC ◇1 A	EM	XC ◇1 B	EM
Nottingham 8 56 🚌	d		21 39			22 17		23 18
Beeston 56	d		21 44			22 22		23 23
Attenborough 56	d		21 48			22 26		23 27
Long Eaton	d		21 56			22 33		23 35
Derby 6	a		22 07			22 47		23 48
	d		22 11		22 45			
Willington	d							
Burton-on-Trent	d		22 22		22 55			
Tamworth	d		22 34		23 06			
Wilnecote	d		22 37					
Leicester	d			22 27			22 48	
South Wigston	d			22 33				
Narborough	d			22 38				
Hinckley	d			22 46				
Nuneaton	d			22 54			23 10	
Coleshill Parkway	d			23 10			23 25	
Water Orton	d							
Birmingham New Street 12	a		23 01	23 22	23 25		23 38	
	d	23 00						
Worcester Shrub Hill 7	d	23 46						
Ashchurch for Tewkesbury	d	00 01						
Cheltenham Spa	d	00 09						
Gloucester 7 134	a	00 20						
Bristol Parkway 7 134	a							
Bristol Temple Meads 10 134	a							
Newport (South Wales) 132	a							
Cardiff Central 7 132	a							

Saturdays

14 December to 17 May

		LM C	EM ◇1 D 🍴	GW E	XC ◇1	XC ◇1	GW F	GW ◇ G	XC ◇1 H 🍴	GW ◇1 E ☕	XC 1	AW I	XC ◇1 J 🍴	XC ◇1 K 🍴	XC ◇1 L	XC ◇1 M 🍴	AW I	EM N	XC 1	XC ◇1 O 🍴	XC ◇1 P	XC ◇1 Q 🍴	GW ◇1 R ☕
Nottingham 8 56 🚌	d		01 51											05 58				06 20		06 37			
Beeston 56	d													06 03				06 25		06 43			
Attenborough 56	d													06 07				06 28					
Long Eaton	d													06 15				06 39					
Derby 6	a		02 10											06 29				06 52		06 59			
	d												06 10	06 36	06 48					07 06		07 26	
Willington	d																						
Burton-on-Trent	d												06 20	06 48	06 59					07 17		07 37	
Tamworth	d												06 31	07 01	07 09					07 29		07 48	
Wilnecote	d													07 05									
Leicester	d										05 49								06 49		07 16		
South Wigston	d										05 55								06 55				
Narborough	d										06 00								07 00				
Hinckley	d										06 08								07 08				
Nuneaton	d										06 14								07 14		07 35		
Coleshill Parkway	d										06 30								07 30		07 50		
Water Orton	d																		07 35				
Birmingham New Street 12	a										06 43		06 50	07 24	07 27				07 47	07 52	08 02	08 08	
	d				05 00	05 42			06 42				07 12	07 30		07 42						08 12	
Worcester Shrub Hill 7	d							06 47															08 36
Ashchurch for Tewkesbury	d	00 01				06 33		07 03															
Cheltenham Spa	d	00 09		05 30	06 03	06 42	06 48	07 13	07 25	07 30		07 45	07 52	08 10		08 25	08 45					08 52	08 59
Gloucester 7 134	a	00 20		05 41	06 12	06 52	06 58	07 25		07 40		07 57		08 20			08 57						09 09
Bristol Parkway 7 134	a						07 39	08 18	07 53				08 24			08 53						09 24	
Bristol Temple Meads 10 134	a						07 55	08 34	08 05				08 38			09 06						09 38	
Newport (South Wales) 132	a				07 05	07 48						08 50		09 06			09 50						
Cardiff Central 7 132	a				07 21	08 04						09 10		09 22			10 07						

- **A** From Glasgow Central
- **B** From Stansted Airport
- **C** From Birmingham New Street
- **D** From St Pancras International
- **E** To Swindon
- **F** To Weston-super-Mare
- **G** To Weymouth
- **H** To Paignton
- **I** To Maesteg
- **J** To Plymouth. 🍴 from Birmingham New Street
- **K** 🍴 from Birmingham New Street to Newport (South Wales)
- **L** To Reading
- **M** From Manchester Piccadilly
- **N** To Matlock
- **O** To Bournemouth. 🍴 from Derby
- **P** From Cambridge
- **Q** From Leeds to Plymouth
- **R** To London Paddington

Table 57

Saturdays

14 December to 17 May

Nottingham, Derby and Leicester Birmingham - Cardiff and Bristol

Network Diagram - refer to first Page of Table 50

		XC		EM	XC	XC	XC	XC	GW	XC	GW	XC		XC	EM	XC	XC	XC	AW	XC	XC	GW		XC	XC
		◇1			◇1	◇1	◇1	1		◇1		1		◇1		◇1	◇1	◇1		1	◇1	◇1		1	◇1
				A	B	C	D		E	F	G			H	A	I	C	J	K		L	G			
					🛒		🛒			🛒				🛒		🛒		🛒			🛒	🍴			🛒
Nottingham [8] 56	d	06 58		07 19				07 38						08 12	08 20					08 41					09 10
Beeston 56	d	07 03		07 25				07 44							08 25					08 47					
Attenborough 56	d	07 07		07 28											08 29										
Long Eaton	d	07 15		07 37				07 52							08 37					08 55					
Derby [6]	a	07 29		07 49				08 02						08 32	08 50					09 07					09 30
	d	07 36			07 50			08 06		08 28				08 37		08 53				09 10	09 27				09 36
Willington	d	07 43																							09 44
Burton-on-Trent	d	07 50			08 00			08 18		08 38				08 49						09 21	09 37				09 50
Tamworth	d	08 02			08 11			08 30		08 49				09 02						09 33					10 02
Wilnecote	d	08 05						08 34												09 37					
Leicester	d					07 49						08 16					08 48							09 18	
South Wigston	d											08 22													
Narborough	d											08 27												09 27	
Hinckley	d											08 35												09 36	
Nuneaton	d					08 09						08 43					09 10							09 43	
Coleshill Parkway	d					08 24						09 01					09 25							09 58	
Water Orton	d																							10 02	
Birmingham New Street [12]	a	08 24			08 28	08 38		08 54		09 08		09 14		09 25		09 27	09 38			09 54	10 03			10 13	10 24
	d	08 30					08 42			09 12				09 30				09 42			10 12				10 30
Worcester Shrub Hill [7]	d								09 08																
Ashchurch for Tewkesbury	d								09 24																
Cheltenham Spa	d	09 10					09 25		09 34	09 52	10 01			10 10				10 25	10 45		10 52	11 00			11 10
Gloucester [7] 134	a	09 20							09 45		10 12			10 20					10 56			11 10			11 20
Bristol Parkway [7] 134	a						09 53		10 24	10 29								10 54			11 24				
Bristol Temple Meads [10] 134	a						10 04		10 39	10 42								11 09			11 38				
Newport (South Wales) 132	a	10 05												11 06					11 50						12 05
Cardiff Central [7] 132	a	10 21												11 24					12 06						12 23

		EM	XC	XC	XC	XC	GW	AW		XC	GW	XC	XC	EM	XC	XC	XC	XC		XC	GW	GW	XC	XC	EM
			◇1	◇1	◇1	1	R			◇1		1	◇1		◇1	◇1	◇1	1		◇1		◇1	1	◇1	
		A	M	C	D		N			O	G			A	P	C	D			Q	R	S			A
			🛒	🛒	🛒					🛒			🛒		🛒	🛒	🛒			🛒		🍴		🛒	
Nottingham [8] 56	d	09 20				09 41							10 10	10 20				10 41						11 10	11 20
Beeston 56	d	09 25				09 47								10 25				10 47							11 25
Attenborough 56	d	09 29												10 29											11 29
Long Eaton	d	09 38				09 57								10 38				10 56							11 37
Derby [6]	a	09 50				10 07							10 31	10 49				11 07						11 29	11 49
	d		09 52			10 11				10 27			10 37		10 52			11 11		11 26				11 36	
Willington	d																								
Burton-on-Trent	d					10 22							10 49					11 22		11 39				11 49	
Tamworth	d					10 34				10 48			11 02					11 34						12 02	
Wilnecote	d					10 38												11 38							
Leicester	d			09 48								10 18				10 48							11 18		
South Wigston	d											10 24													
Narborough	d											10 29											11 27		
Hinckley	d											10 37											11 36		
Nuneaton	d			10 10								10 44				11 10							11 43		
Coleshill Parkway	d			10 25								11 00				11 25							11 58		
Water Orton	d																						12 02		
Birmingham New Street [12]	a		10 27	10 38		10 55				11 04		11 12	11 24		11 27	11 38		11 56		12 08			12 13	12 24	
	d				10 42					11 12			11 30				11 42			12 12				12 30	
Worcester Shrub Hill [7]	d						11 06																		
Ashchurch for Tewkesbury	d						11 24																		
Cheltenham Spa	d				11 25		11 34	11 45		11 52	12 01		12 10				12 25			12 52	13 00	13 00		13 10	
Gloucester [7] 134	a						11 45	11 56			12 12		12 20								13 10	13 10		13 20	
Bristol Parkway [7] 134	a				11 53		12 24			12 29							12 53			13 24					
Bristol Temple Meads [10] 134	a				12 04		12 39			12 42							13 07			13 38					
Newport (South Wales) 132	a							12 49					13 05											14 06	
Cardiff Central [7] 132	a							13 06					13 21											14 22	

A To Matlock
B From Leeds to Southampton Central
C From Stansted Airport
D From Manchester Piccadilly
E To Westbury
F From York to Plymouth
G To Swindon
H 🛒 from Birmingham New Street
I From Newcastle to Reading
J From Manchester Piccadilly to Paignton
K To Maesteg
L From Newcastle to Plymouth
M From Newcastle to Southampton Central
N From Great Malvern to Brighton
O From Edinburgh to Plymouth
P From Edinburgh to Reading
Q From Glasgow Central to Plymouth
R from 4 January until 8 February. To Swindon
S from 15 February. To London Paddington

Table 57

Saturdays

14 December to 17 May

Nottingham, Derby and Leicester
Birmingham - Cardiff and Bristol

Network Diagram - refer to first Page of Table 50

Station			XC ◇1 A	XC ◇1 B	GW ◇ C	XC ◇1 D	AW E	XC 1	XC ◇1 F	GW 1 G	XC 1		GW H	XC ◇1	EM I	XC ◇1 J	XC ◇1 B	XC ◇1 K	XC 1	XC ◇1 L	GW M		GW ◇1 N	XC 1	XC ◇1	EM I
Nottingham 8	56	d						11 41						12 10	12 20				12 41						13 10	13 20
Beeston	56	d						11 47							12 25				12 47							13 25
Attenborough	56	d													12 29											13 29
Long Eaton		d						11 56							12 37				12 56							13 37
Derby 6		a						12 07						12 30	12 49				13 07						13 30	13 50
		d	11 52					12 11	12 29					12 36		12 52			13 11	13 27					13 36	
Willington		d																	13 19							
Burton-on-Trent		d						12 22						12 49					13 25	13 38					13 49	
Tamworth		d						12 34	12 49					13 02					13 36						14 02	
Wilnecote		d						12 38																		
Leicester		d		11 48							12 18						12 48							13 18		
South Wigston		d									12 24															
Narborough		d									12 29													13 27		
Hinckley		d									12 37													13 36		
Nuneaton		d		12 10							12 44						13 10							13 43		
Coleshill Parkway		d		12 25							13 00						13 25							13 58		
Water Orton		d																						14 02		
Birmingham New Street 12		a	12 27	12 38				12 56	13 08		13 13			13 23		13 26	13 38		13 55	14 04				14 13	14 23	
		d				12 42			13 12					13 30				13 42		14 12					14 30	
Worcester Shrub Hill 7		d			12 54																					
Ashchurch for Tewkesbury		d			13 10																					
Cheltenham Spa		d			13 20	13 26	13 45		13 52	14 01			14 01	14 10				14 25		14 52	15 00		15 00		15 10	
Gloucester 7	134	a			13 32		13 57			14 11			14 12	14 20							15 10		15 10		15 20	
Bristol Parkway 7	134	a			14 21	13 55			14 26									14 57		15 24						
Bristol Temple Meads 10	134	a			14 38	14 05			14 40									15 09		15 38						
Newport (South Wales)	132	a					14 50							15 10											16 06	
Cardiff Central 7	132	a					15 09							15 26											16 25	

Station			XC ◇1 A	XC ◇1 B	XC ◇1 D	XC 1	GW ◇ O		XC ◇1 P	GW Q	XC 1	XC ◇1	EM I	XC ◇1 J	XC ◇1 B	XC ◇1 R	AW E		XC 1	XC ◇1 S	GW ◇1 Q	XC 1	XC ◇1	EM I	XC ◇1 A	XC ◇1 B
Nottingham 8	56	d				13 41						14 10	14 20						14 41				15 10	15 20		
Beeston	56	d				13 47							14 26						14 47					15 25		
Attenborough	56	d											14 29											15 29		
Long Eaton		d				13 56							14 38						14 56					15 37		
Derby 6		a				14 07						14 30	14 50						15 07				15 30	15 49		
		d	13 52			14 11			14 30			14 36		14 53					15 11	15 27			15 37		15 52	
Willington		d																	15 19							
Burton-on-Trent		d				14 22						14 49							15 25	15 38			15 49			
Tamworth		d				14 34			14 49			15 02							15 34				16 02			
Wilnecote		d				14 38																				
Leicester		d		13 48							14 18				14 48							15 18				15 48
South Wigston		d									14 24															
Narborough		d									14 29											15 27				
Hinckley		d									14 37											15 36				
Nuneaton		d		14 10							14 44				15 10							15 43				16 10
Coleshill Parkway		d		14 25							15 00				15 25							15 58				16 25
Water Orton		d																				16 01				
Birmingham New Street 12		a	14 25	14 38		14 55			15 08		15 12	15 24		15 27	15 38				15 55	16 04		16 12	16 24		16 27	16 38
		d			14 42				15 12			15 30				15 42				16 12			16 30			
Worcester Shrub Hill 7		d					15 06																			
Ashchurch for Tewkesbury		d					15 24																			
Cheltenham Spa		d			15 25		15 34		15 52	16 01		16 10				16 25	16 45			16 52	17 00		17 10			
Gloucester 7	134	a					15 43			16 12		16 20					16 56				17 10		17 20			
Bristol Parkway 7	134	a			15 54		16 24		16 29							16 53				17 25						
Bristol Temple Meads 10	134	a			16 07		16 40		16 42							17 07				17 38						
Newport (South Wales)	132	a										17 08					17 50						18 06			
Cardiff Central 7	132	a										17 24					18 10						18 22			

A From Newcastle to Southampton Central
B From Stansted Airport
C From Worcester Foregate Street to Weymouth
D From Manchester Piccadilly
E To Maesteg
F From Dundee to Plymouth
G from 4 January until 8 February. To Swindon
H from 15 February. To Swindon
I To Matlock
J From Newcastle to Reading
K From Manchester Piccadilly to Exeter St Davids
L From Glasgow Central to Plymouth
M from 4 January until 8 February. To Westbury
N from 15 February. To London Paddington
O From Great Malvern to Weymouth
P From Glasgow Central to Penzance
Q To Swindon
R From Manchester Piccadilly to Paignton
S From Aberdeen to Penzance

Table 57

Saturdays

14 December to 17 May

Nottingham, Derby and Leicester
Birmingham - Cardiff and Bristol

Network Diagram - refer to first Page of Table 50

Station	Table		XC	XC	GW	AW	XC	GW	XC		XC	EM	XC	XC	XC	AW	XC	XC	GW		GW	XC	XC	EM	XC	XC
			◇1	1			◇1		1		◇1		◇1	◇1	◇1		1	◇1			◇1	1	◇1		◇1	◇1
			A		B	C	D	E				F	G	H	A	C		I	J		K			F	G	H
			trolley	trolley			trolley						trolley	trolley	trolley		trolley	trolley			restaurant				trolley	trolley
Nottingham 8	56	d		15 41							16 10	16 20					16 41						17 10	17 20		
Beeston	56	d		15 47								16 25					16 47							17 25		
Attenborough	56	d										16 29												17 29		
Long Eaton		d		15 56								16 37					16 56							17 37		
Derby 6		a		16 07							16 30	16 49					17 07						17 30	17 50		
		d		16 11			16 27				16 36		16 53				17 11	17 27					17 36		17 52	
Willington		d															17 19									
Burton-on-Trent		d		16 22							16 49						17 25	17 38					17 49			
Tamworth		d		16 34			16 48				17 02						17 36						18 02			
Wilnecote		d		16 38																						
Leicester		d							16 18					16 48								17 18				17 48
South Wigston		d							16 24													17 24				
Narborough		d							16 29													17 29				
Hinckley		d							16 37													17 37				
Nuneaton		d							16 44					17 10								17 43				18 10
Coleshill Parkway		d							17 00					17 25								17 58				18 25
Water Orton		d																								
Birmingham New Street 12		a		16 55			17 07		17 13		17 24		17 27	17 38			17 55	18 07				18 12	18 24		18 27	18 38
		d	16 42				17 12				17 30				17 42			18 12					18 30			
Worcester Shrub Hill 7		d			17 06																					
Ashchurch for Tewkesbury		d			17 24						18 07															
Cheltenham Spa		d	17 25		17 34	17 45	17 52	18 01			18 16				18 25	18 45		18 52	19 00		19 00		19 10			
Gloucester 7	134	a			17 45	17 56		18 12			18 26					18 56			19 10		19 10		19 20			
Bristol Parkway 7	134	a	17 53		18 24		18 29								18 53			19 25								
Bristol Temple Meads 10	134	a	18 07		18 39		18 42								19 04			19 38								
Newport (South Wales)	132	a				18 50					19 11					19 50							20 03			
Cardiff Central 7	132	a				19 10					19 30					20 11							20 20			

Station	Table		XC	XC	GW		AW	XC	GW	XC	GW		XC	EM	XC		XC	XC	XC	XC	GW	XC	XC	EM	XC	
			◇1	1				◇1	1	1			◇1		◇1		◇1	◇1	1	◇1		1	◇1		◇1	
			L		M		C	N	J		O			F	G		H	A		R				F	S	
			trolley	trolley				trolley							trolley		trolley	trolley	trolley	trolley					trolley	
Nottingham 8	56	d		17 41									18 10	18 20					18 41				19 10	19 20		
Beeston	56	d		17 47										18 25					18 47					19 25		
Attenborough	56	d												18 29										19 29		
Long Eaton		d		17 56										18 37					18 56					19 37		
Derby 6		a		18 07									18 30	18 49					19 07				19 32	19 50		
		d		18 11				18 27					18 36		18 52				19 11	19 29			19 36		19 53	
Willington		d		18 17																						
Burton-on-Trent		d		18 23									18 49						19 22	19 37			19 49			
Tamworth		d		18 35				18 46					19 02						19 34				20 02			
Wilnecote		d		18 38															19 38							
Leicester		d								18 18							18 48					19 18				
South Wigston		d								18 24												19 24				
Narborough		d								18 29												19 29				
Hinckley		d								18 37												19 37				
Nuneaton		d								18 44							19 10					19 44				
Coleshill Parkway		d								19 00							19 25					20 00				
Water Orton		d																								
Birmingham New Street 12		a		18 57				19 06		19 12			19 22		19 26		19 38		19 55	20 06		20 15	20 24		20 27	
		d	18 42					19 12					19 30					19 42		20 12			20 30			
Worcester Shrub Hill 7		d			19 06																					
Ashchurch for Tewkesbury		d			19 24																					
Cheltenham Spa		d	19 25		19 34		19 45	19 52	20 01		20 01		20 10					20 25		20 52	21 02		21 10			
Gloucester 7	134	a			19 45		19 56		20 11		20 12		20 20								21 12		21 20			
Bristol Parkway 7	134	a	19 55		20 24			20 29										20 53		21 20	21 53					
Bristol Temple Meads 10	134	a	20 05		20 39			20 42										21 04		21 35	22 05					
Newport (South Wales)	132	a	20 44				20 50						21 12										22 19			
Cardiff Central 7	132	a	21 00				21 09						21 29										22 45			

- **A** From Manchester Piccadilly
- **B** From Great Malvern to Westbury
- **C** To Maesteg
- **D** From Glasgow Central to Penzance
- **E** To Swindon
- **F** To Matlock
- **G** From Newcastle to Reading
- **H** From Stansted Airport
- **I** From Edinburgh to Plymouth
- **J** from 4 January until 8 February. To Swindon
- **K** from 15 February. To London Paddington
- **L** From Manchester Piccadilly. trolley to Bristol Temple Meads
- **M** From Great Malvern
- **N** From Glasgow Central to Plymouth
- **O** from 15 February. To Westbury
- **R** From Edinburgh to Exeter St Davids
- **S** From Newcastle to Guildford

Table 57

Nottingham, Derby and Leicester
Birmingham - Cardiff and Bristol

Saturdays

14 December to 17 May

Network Diagram - refer to first Page of Table 50

		XC	GW	XC	XC	XC	XC		EM	XC	XC	XC	XC	XC	EM	GW	XC		XC	XC	XC	XC	EM	EM
		◇1		◇1	1	◇1	1			◇1	◇1	1	◇1	1			◇1		◇1	1	◇1	1		
		A	B	C		D			E	F	A		G			H	A		F		I			
		🛒			🛒	🛒				🛒														
Nottingham [8] 56 (tram)	d				19 41				20 19			20 37			21 19					21 39			22 19	23 19
Beeston 56	d				19 47				20 25			20 43			21 25					21 45			22 25	23 24
Attenborough 56	d				19 50				20 28						21 28					21 48			22 28	23 28
Long Eaton	d				19 57				20 37			20 51			21 36					21 56			22 36	23 36
Derby [6]	a				20 06				20 49			21 02			21 50					22 07			22 50	23 49
	d				20 10	20 27				20 52		21 10	21 27						21 54	22 11	22 26			
Willington	d											21 18												
Burton-on-Trent	d				20 21							21 24	21 38							22 21	22 37			
Tamworth	d				20 33	20 46						21 35	21 49							22 33	22 47			
Wilnecote	d				20 37							21 39								22 37				
Leicester	d	19 48					20 18				20 48			21 18			21 48					22 16		
South Wigston	d						20 24							21 22								22 22		
Narborough	d						20 29							21 27								22 27		
Hinckley	d						20 37							21 35								22 35		
Nuneaton	d	20 10					20 44				21 10			21 42			22 10					22 42		
Coleshill Parkway	d	20 25					21 00				21 25			21 58			22 25					22 58		
Water Orton	d																							
Birmingham New Street [12]	a	20 38			20 56	21 03	21 13			21 25	21 38	21 57	22 06	22 13			22 38		22 43	23 02	23 06	23 13		
	d			20 42		21 12																		
Worcester Shrub Hill [7]	d															21 31								
Ashchurch for Tewkesbury	d															21 51								
Cheltenham Spa	d		21 20	21 25		21 50										22 01								
Gloucester [7] 134	a		21 30			21 59										22 11								
Bristol Parkway [7] 134	a			21 58		22 30																		
Bristol Temple Meads [10] 134	a			22 12		22 41																		
Newport (South Wales) 132	a																							
Cardiff Central [7] 132	a																							

Sundays

8 December to 29 December

		GW	XC	GW	GW	XC	XC	GW	EM	XC		GW	XC	AW	XC	GW	XC	XC	XC	GW		XC	XC	XC	AW
			◇1			◇1	◇1			◇1			◇1		◇1		1	◇1	◇1			1	◇1	◇1	
		B	J	K	B		L	B	E				L		M	B			N	B				A	
			🛒			🛒	🛒			🛒			🛒		🛒				🛒						
Nottingham [8] 56 (tram)	d								09 26									11 11					12 10		
Beeston 56	d								09 32																
Attenborough 56	d								09 35																
Long Eaton	d								09 43																
Derby [6]	a								09 54									11 31					12 30		
	d						09 28						10 33		11 29			11 36	12 29				12 36		
Willington	d																								
Burton-on-Trent	d														11 40			11 47					12 47		
Tamworth	d												10 53					12 00	12 48				13 00		
Wilnecote	d																								
Leicester	d																11 19					12 19		12 50	
South Wigston	d																					12 24			
Narborough	d																11 28					12 29			
Hinckley	d																11 36					12 38			
Nuneaton	d																11 42					12 45		13 10	
Coleshill Parkway	d																11 57					13 00		13 25	
Water Orton	d																								
Birmingham New Street [12]	a						10 19						11 21		12 05		12 15	12 22	13 06			13 15	13 21	13 38	
	d		09 12			10 12	10 30			11 12			11 30		12 12			12 30	13 12				13 30		
Worcester Shrub Hill [7]	d																								
Ashchurch for Tewkesbury	d																								
Cheltenham Spa	d	09 24	09 52	10 07	10 24	10 52	11 11	11 20		11 52		12 05	12 12	12 18	12 52	13 03		13 10	13 52	14 05			14 10		14 18
Gloucester [7] 134	a	09 35		10 17	10 34	11 02		11 30		12 02		12 16		12 28		13 13		13 21		14 15			14 20		14 29
Bristol Parkway [7] 134	a		10 20	10 53			11 39					12 58	12 40		13 20				14 20						
Bristol Temple Meads [10] 134	a		10 31	11 07			11 51					13 12	12 51		13 31				14 31						
Newport (South Wales) 132	a					11 48				12 52				13 33				14 06					15 08		15 31
Cardiff Central [7] 132	a					12 08				13 12				13 52				14 26					15 31		15 47

A From Stansted Airport
B To Swindon
C From Manchester Piccadilly
D From Glasgow Central. 🛒 to Birmingham New Street
E To Matlock
F From Newcastle
G From Edinburgh
H From Great Malvern
I From Glasgow Central
J To Penzance
K To Taunton
L From Leeds to Plymouth
M From York to Plymouth
N From Newcastle to Plymouth

Table 57

Sundays

8 December to 29 December

Nottingham, Derby and Leicester
Birmingham - Cardiff and Bristol

Network Diagram - refer to first Page of Table 50

Station			XC ◇1 trolley		XC ◇1 A trolley	XC 1	GW B	XC ◇1	EM C	XC ◇1 D trolley	XC ◇1 E	XC ◇1 F trolley	GW ◇1 G restaurant		XC ◇1 H trolley	XC 1	XC ◇1 trolley	EM	XC ◇1 I trolley	XC ◇1 E trolley	AW	XC ◇1 J trolley	GW K		XC ◇1 A trolley	XC 1
Nottingham 8	56 ⛴	d						13 10	13 23								14 10	14 22								
Beeston	56	d							13 29									14 28								
Attenborough	56	d							13 32									14 31								
Long Eaton		d							13 40									14 39								
Derby 6		a						13 30	13 51								14 29	14 50								
		d			13 32			13 36		13 55					14 29		14 35		14 53						15 26	
Willington		d																								
Burton-on-Trent		d			13 43			13 47									14 47								15 37	
Tamworth		d						14 00							14 48		15 00									
Wilnecote		d																								
Leicester		d				13 19					13 50					14 19				14 50						15 19
South Wigston		d														14 24										
Narborough		d				13 28										14 29										15 28
Hinckley		d				13 36										14 38										15 36
Nuneaton		d				13 43					14 09					14 45				15 09						15 43
Coleshill Parkway		d				13 59					14 25					15 00				15 25						15 58
Water Orton		d																								
Birmingham New Street 12		a			14 09	14 15		14 22		14 27	14 38				15 05	15 15	15 21		15 26	15 38					16 02	16 15
		d	13 42		14 12			14 30				14 42			15 12		15 30					15 42			16 12	
Worcester Shrub Hill 7		d					14 36																			
Ashchurch for Tewkesbury		d					14 51																			
Cheltenham Spa		d	14 25		14 52		15 01	15 10				15 26	15 46		15 52		16 10				16 18	16 26	16 32		16 51	
Gloucester 7	134	a					15 11	15 21					15 57				16 20				16 29		16 43			
Bristol Parkway 7	134	a	14 53		15 23		15 49					15 59			16 20							16 54			17 20	
Bristol Temple Meads 10	134	a	15 08		15 34		16 08					16 11			16 35							17 08			17 33	
Newport (South Wales)	132	a						16 06									17 06				17 37					
Cardiff Central 7	132	a						16 26									17 27				17 57					

Station			GW	XC ◇1 trolley	EM C	XC ◇1 L trolley	XC ◇1 E trolley	XC ◇1 J trolley	GW ◇1 G restaurant		XC ◇1 M trolley	XC 1	XC ◇1 N trolley	EM	XC ◇1 L trolley	XC ◇1 E trolley	XC ◇1 J trolley	AW	XC ◇1 O trolley		XC 1	GW	XC ◇1 N trolley	EM C	XC ◇1 P trolley	XC ◇1 E trolley
Nottingham 8	56 ⛴	d		15 10	15 22								16 10	16 23									17 10	17 22		
Beeston	56	d			15 28									16 29										17 28		
Attenborough	56	d			15 31									16 32										17 31		
Long Eaton		d			15 42									16 40										17 39		
Derby 6		a		15 30	15 53								16 30	16 51									17 29	17 50		
		d		15 35		15 53					16 27		16 35		16 54				17 26				17 36		17 54	
Willington		d																								
Burton-on-Trent		d		15 47									16 47						17 37				17 47			
Tamworth		d		16 00							16 48		17 00										18 00			
Wilnecote		d		16 03																						
Leicester		d					15 50					16 19				16 50					17 19					17 50
South Wigston		d										16 24									17 25					
Narborough		d										16 29									17 30					
Hinckley		d										16 38									17 38					
Nuneaton		d					16 09					16 45				17 09					17 45					18 10
Coleshill Parkway		d					16 25					17 00				17 25					18 00					18 26
Water Orton		d																								
Birmingham New Street 12		a		16 22		16 26	16 38				17 05	17 15	17 20		17 26	17 38			18 02		18 15		18 20		18 26	18 40
		d		16 30				16 42			17 12		17 30				17 42		18 12				18 30			
Worcester Shrub Hill 7		d	16 40																			18 40				
Ashchurch for Tewkesbury		d	16 56																			18 56				
Cheltenham Spa		d	17 06	17 11				17 26	17 46		17 52		18 10				18 26	18 35	18 52			19 06	19 12			
Gloucester 7	134	a	17 16	17 20					17 55				18 20					18 46				19 16	19 26			
Bristol Parkway 7	134	a	17 56					18 02			18 20						18 54		19 21			19 56				
Bristol Temple Meads 10	134	a	18 09					18 13			18 36						19 08		19 32			20 09				
Newport (South Wales)	132	a		18 06									19 06					19 51					20 11			
Cardiff Central 7	132	a		18 28									19 27					20 09					20 31			

A From Edinburgh to Plymouth
B To Weston-super-Mare
C To Matlock
D To Reading
E From Stansted Airport
F From Manchester Piccadilly to Paignton
G To London Paddington
H From Edinburgh to Penzance
I From Sheffield to Reading
J From Manchester Piccadilly
K To Swindon
L From Newcastle to Reading
M From Glasgow Central to Penzance
N trolley to Birmingham New Street
O From Glasgow Central to Plymouth
P From Edinburgh to Reading

Table 57

Sundays

8 December to 29 December

Nottingham, Derby and Leicester Birmingham - Cardiff and Bristol

Network Diagram - refer to first Page of Table 50

		XC	XC	GW	XC	XC	EM	XC	XC	AW		XC	XC	XC	XC	EM	XC	XC	GW	XC		GW	XC	XC	XC
		◇1	◇1	◇1	1	◇1		◇1	◇1			◇1	◇1	1	◇1		◇1	◇1		◇1			◇1	1	◇1
		A	B	C		D		E	F			G	H			I	J	F		G		K	L		
		trolley	trolley	restaurant		trolley		trolley	trolley			trolley	trolley		trolley		trolley						trolley		
Nottingham 8 56	d					18 10	18 22								19 10	19 22									20 10
Beeston 56	d						18 28									19 28									
Attenborough 56	d						18 31									19 31									
Long Eaton	d						18 39									19 39									
Derby 6	a					18 30	18 50								19 30	19 50									20 29
	d		18 26			18 35		18 54					19 27		19 36		19 56						20 27		20 36
Willington	d																								
Burton-on-Trent	d					18 47							19 38		19 47										20 48
Tamworth	d		18 45			19 00									20 00								20 45		21 00
Wilnecote	d														20 04										
Leicester	d				18 19				18 50					19 19				19 50						20 19	
South Wigston	d													19 24										20 24	
Narborough	d				18 28									19 29										20 29	
Hinckley	d				18 36									19 37										20 38	
Nuneaton	d				18 43				19 09					19 43				20 10						20 44	
Coleshill Parkway	d				18 59				19 25					19 59				20 25						21 00	
Water Orton	d																								
Birmingham New Street 12	a		19 04		19 14	19 21		19 28	19 38				20 05	20 15	20 23		20 27	20 38					21 03	21 16	21 20
	d	18 42	19 12			19 30						19 42	20 12							20 42			21 12		
Worcester Shrub Hill 7	d																		20 38						
Ashchurch for Tewkesbury	d																		20 54						
Cheltenham Spa	d	19 26	19 52	19 59		20 10				20 18		20 26	20 52						21 03	21 26		21 46	21 52		
Gloucester 7 134	a			20 08		20 21				20 28									21 13			21 56	22 03		
Bristol Parkway 7 134	a	20 03	20 20									20 56	21 20						21 53	21 59			22 33		
Bristol Temple Meads 10 134	a	20 14	20 31									21 06	21 29						22 07	22 10			22 44		
Newport (South Wales) 132	a					21 06				21 31															
Cardiff Central 7 132	a					21 26				21 49															

		EM	XC	XC	GW	XC		XC	XC	EM	XC	XC	XC	XC
			◇1	◇1		◇1		◇1	◇1		◇1	◇1	◇1	1
			M	F		G		N		I	M	F	O	
			trolley											
Nottingham 8 56	d	20 20							21 10	21 22				
Beeston 56	d	20 26								21 28				
Attenborough 56	d	20 29								21 31				
Long Eaton	d	20 37								21 39				
Derby 6	a	20 49							21 30	21 51				
	d		20 54					21 26	21 36		21 53		22 26	
Willington	d													
Burton-on-Trent	d							21 37	21 48		22 03		22 37	
Tamworth	d							21 47	21 59		22 14		22 47	
Wilnecote	d								22 03					
Leicester	d			20 50								21 50		22 19
South Wigston	d													22 24
Narborough	d													22 29
Hinckley	d													22 38
Nuneaton	d			21 10								22 10		22 45
Coleshill Parkway	d			21 25								22 25		23 00
Water Orton	d													
Birmingham New Street 12	a		21 25	21 38				22 05	22 23		22 30	22 38	23 04	23 15
	d					21 43		22 12						
Worcester Shrub Hill 7	d													
Ashchurch for Tewkesbury	d													
Cheltenham Spa	d				22 01	22 25		22 53						
Gloucester 7 134	a				22 12									
Bristol Parkway 7 134	a					22 52		23 22						
Bristol Temple Meads 10 134	a					23 06		23 33						
Newport (South Wales) 132	a													
Cardiff Central 7 132	a													

A From Manchester Piccadilly to Plymouth
B From Aberdeen to Plymouth
C To London Paddington
D trolley to Birmingham New Street
E From Newcastle to Reading
F From Stansted Airport
G From Manchester Piccadilly
H From Glasgow Central to Plymouth
I To Matlock
J From Newcastle to Guildford
K To Swindon
L From Glasgow Central. trolley to Birmingham New Street
M From Newcastle
N From Edinburgh
O From Glasgow Central

Table 57

Sundays

5 January to 23 March

Nottingham, Derby and Leicester
Birmingham - Cardiff and Bristol

Network Diagram - refer to first Page of Table 50

		GW	XC	GW	GW	GW		XC	XC	GW	EM	XC	GW	XC	GW	XC		XC	AW	XC	XC	GW	XC	XC	
			◇1					◇1	◇1			1		◇1		◇1		◇1		◇1	◇1		◇1	◇1	
		A	B	C	D	E			F	D	G		E			H		I			J	A	K	J	
			🛒					🛒	🛒					🛒		🛒		🛒			🛒		🛒	🛒	
Nottingham 8	56 🚢	d									09 26									11 11					
Beeston	56	d									09 32														
Attenborough	56	d									09 35														
Long Eaton		d									09 43														
Derby 6		a									09 54									11 31					
		d							09 28							10 33		10 33			11 31		11 33		
Willington		d																							
Burton-on-Trent		d																			11 41		11 44		
Tamworth		d																							
Wilnecote		d																							
Leicester		d										11 19													
South Wigston		d																							
Narborough		d										11 28													
Hinckley		d										11 36													
Nuneaton		d										11a42													
Coleshill Parkway		d																							
Water Orton		d																							
Birmingham New Street 12		a							10 19							11 24		11 26			12 27		12 24	12 27	
		d		09 12				10 12	10 30					11 12		11 30		11 30			12 30		12 30	12 30	
Worcester Shrub Hill 7		d																							
Ashchurch for Tewkesbury		d																							
Cheltenham Spa		d	09 24	09 52	10 07	10 18	10 24	10 52	11 11	11 18			11 20	11 52	12 05	12 12		12 12	12 18			13 03	13 09	13 09	
Gloucester 7	134	a	09 35		10 17	10 28	10 34	11 02		11 28			11 30	12 02	12 16				12 28			13 13			
Bristol Parkway 7	134	a		10 20	10 53				11 39						12 58	12 40		12 40					13 39	13 39	
Bristol Temple Meads 10	134	a		10 31	11 07				11 51						13 12	12 51		12 51					13 49	13 50	
Newport (South Wales)	132	a						11 48						12 52					13 33						
Cardiff Central 7	132	a						12 08						13 12					13 52						

		XC		XC	XC	GW	XC	XC		XC	XC	XC		AW	XC	XC	XC	GW	XC	XC	EM	XC		XC	XC
		◇1			◇1		1	◇1		◇1	◇1	◇1			◇1		◇1		◇1	◇1		◇1			◇1
					B	A											P	Q	R	S	G				T
				🚌												🚌								🚌	
					🛒			🛒							🛒				🛒	🛒					🛒
Nottingham 8	56 🚢	d									12 10	13 10									13 23				
Beeston	56	d																			13 29				
Attenborough	56	d																			13 32				
Long Eaton		d																			13 40				
Derby 6		a									12 30	13 30									13 51				
		d						12 29											13 32	13 32					
Willington		d																							
Burton-on-Trent		d						12 40											13 43	13 43					
Tamworth		d																							
Wilnecote		d																							
Leicester		d					12 19										12 50								
South Wigston		d					12 24										12 55								
Narborough		d					12 29										13 00								
Hinckley		d					12 38										13 09								
Nuneaton		d			11 50			12a44								12 50	13a15							13 20	
Coleshill Parkway		d			12 25											13 25								13 55	
Water Orton		d																							
Birmingham New Street 12		a			13 05				13 20							14 05			14 24	14 27				14 35	
		d	12 33			13 12					13 30				13 42				14 30	14 30		14 33			14 42
Worcester Shrub Hill 7		d																14 36							
Ashchurch for Tewkesbury		d																14 51							
Cheltenham Spa		d	13 13			13 52	14 05				14 10			14 18	14 25			15 01	15 10	15 10		15 16			15 26
Gloucester 7	134	a	13 23				14 15				14 20			14 29				15 12				15 25			
Bristol Parkway 7	134	a				14 20									14 53			15 52	15 39	15 39					15 59
Bristol Temple Meads 10	134	a				14 31									15 08			16 08	15 50	15 50					16 11
Newport (South Wales)	132	a	14 08								15 08			15 31								16 10			
Cardiff Central 7	132	a	14 28								15 31			15 47								16 30			

A To Swindon
B To Exeter St Davids
C To Taunton
D until 9 February. To Swindon
E from 16 February. To Swindon
F From Leeds to Exeter St Davids
G To Matlock
H from 16 February. From Leeds to Exeter St Davids
I until 9 February. From Leeds to Plymouth
J until 9 February. From York to Plymouth
K from 16 February. From York to Exeter St Davids
P From Stansted Airport
Q To Weston-super-Mare
R from 16 February. From Edinburgh to Exeter St Davids
S until 9 February. From Edinburgh to Plymouth
T From Manchester Piccadilly

Table 57

Sundays

5 January to 23 March

Nottingham, Derby and Leicester
Birmingham - Cardiff and Bristol

Network Diagram - refer to first Page of Table 50

		GW	XC	GW		XC	XC	XC	XC	XC	EM	XC		AW	XC		GW	XC	XC	XC	EM	GW	XC	XC	
		◇1	◇1	◇1		◇1	◇1	◇1	◇1			◇1			◇1			◇1	◇1	◇1			◇1		
		A	B	C		D	E					B			F			I	E		J				
										🚌														🚌	
		☕		☕		🛒	🛒	🛒				🛒			🛒			🛒	🛒				🛒		
Nottingham 8 56 🚊	d								14 10		14 22									15 10	15 22				
Beeston 56	d										14 28										15 28				
Attenborough 56	d										14 31										15 31				
Long Eaton	d										14 39										15 39				
Derby 6	a								14 30		14 50									15 30	15 50				
	d					13 55	14 29											14 53	15 25						
Willington	d																								
Burton-on-Trent	d						14 39												15 37						
Tamworth	d																								
Wilnecote	d																								
Leicester	d		13 50									14 50													
South Wigston	d		13 55									14 55													
Narborough	d		14 00									15 00													
Hinckley	d		14 09									15 09													
Nuneaton	d		14a15							14 20		15a15												15 20	
Coleshill Parkway	d									14 55														15 55	
Water Orton	d																								
Birmingham New Street 12	a					14 50	15 21			15 35								15 50	16 21					16 35	
	d					15 12		15 30							15 42			16 12					16 30		
Worcester Shrub Hill 7	d																					16 40			
Ashchurch for Tewkesbury	d																					16 56			
Cheltenham Spa	d	15 42		15 46		15 52		16 10						16 18	16 26		16 32	16 51				17 06	17 11		
Gloucester 7 134	a	15 51		15 57				16 20						16 29			16 43					17 16	17 20		
Bristol Parkway 7 134	a					16 20									16 54			17 20				17 56			
Bristol Temple Meads 10 134	a					16 35									17 08			17 33				18 09			
Newport (South Wales) 132	a							17 06						17 37									18 06		
Cardiff Central 7 132	a							17 27						17 57									18 28		

		XC	GW	XC	GW	XC	XC	EM	XC	XC		XC	XC	XC	AW	EM	XC	EM	XC	XC		XC	EM	GW	XC
		◇1	◇1	◇1	◇1	◇1	◇1		◇1	◇1		◇1		◇1			◇1		◇1	◇1		◇1			◇1
		F	A	B	C	K	L	M	N					F		O	P	Q	N	B			J		
													🚌												
		🛒	☕	🛒	☕	🛒	🛒		🛒	🛒				🛒			🛒		🛒	🛒					🛒
Nottingham 8 56 🚊	d							15 28				16 10				16 23		16 28				17 10	17 22		
Beeston 56	d							15 34								16 29		16 34					17 28		
Attenborough 56	d							15 37								16 32		16 37					17 31		
Long Eaton	d							15 45								16 40		16 45					17 39		
Derby 6	a							15 56				16 30				16 51		16 58				17 30	17 50		
	d					15 53	15 54		16 27								16 55		17 26						
Willington	d																								
Burton-on-Trent	d								16 37										17 37						
Tamworth	d																								
Wilnecote	d																								
Leicester	d			15 50																16 50					
South Wigston	d			15 55																16 55					
Narborough	d			16 00																17 00					
Hinckley	d			16 09																17 09					
Nuneaton	d			16a15									16 20							17a15					
Coleshill Parkway	d												16 55												
Water Orton	d																								
Birmingham New Street 12	a					16 49	16 49		17 17				17 35				17 50		18 21						
	d	16 42				17 12	17 12			17 30				17 42			18 12								18 30
Worcester Shrub Hill 7	d																							18 40	
Ashchurch for Tewkesbury	d																							18 56	
Cheltenham Spa	d	17 26	17 42		17 46	17 52	17 52			18 10				18 26	18 35		18 52							19 06	19 12
Gloucester 7 134	a		17 51		17 55					18 20					18 46									19 16	19 26
Bristol Parkway 7 134	a	18 02				18 20	18 20							18 54			19 21							19 56	
Bristol Temple Meads 10 134	a	18 13				18 36	18 36							19 08			19 32							20 09	
Newport (South Wales) 132	a									19 06					19 51										20 11
Cardiff Central 7 132	a									19 27					20 09										20 31

A until 9 February. To London Paddington
B From Stansted Airport
C from 16 February. To London Paddington
D To Exeter St Davids
E From Edinburgh to Reading
F From Manchester Piccadilly
I From Sheffield to Exeter St Davids
J until 9 February. To Matlock
K until 9 February. From Newcastle to Penzance
L from 16 February. From Newcastle to Exeter St Davids
M from 16 February. To Matlock
N From Glasgow Central to Reading
O until 9 February
P From Newcastle to Plymouth
Q from 16 February

Table 57

Sundays

5 January to 23 March

Nottingham, Derby and Leicester
Birmingham - Cardiff and Bristol

Network Diagram - refer to first Page of Table 50

		XC (bus)		XC ◇1 A (trolley)	XC ◇1 B (trolley)	XC ◇1 C (trolley)	GW ◇1 D (restaurant)	EM E	XC ◇1 (trolley)		XC ◇1 (trolley)	XC ◇1		XC (bus)	EM	XC ◇1 B (trolley)	AW	XC ◇1 A (trolley)	XC ◇1 H (trolley)	XC ◇1 I (trolley)	XC ◇1 (trolley)	XC (bus)		EM J	XC ◇1 B
Nottingham 8 56 (ferry)	d							17 27				18 10			18 22						19 10			19 22	
Beeston 56	d							17 33							18 28									19 28	
Attenborough 56	d							17 36							18 31									19 31	
Long Eaton	d							17 44							18 39									19 39	
Derby 6	a							17 55				18 30			18 50						19 30			19 50	
	d					17 54			18 26										18 55	19 27					
Willington	d																								
Burton-on-Trent	d								18 37											19 37					
Tamworth	d																								
Wilnecote	d																								
Leicester	d				17 50											18 50									19 50
South Wigston	d				17 55											18 55									19 56
Narborough	d				18 00											19 00									20 01
Hinckley	d				18 09											19 09									20 09
Nuneaton	d	17 20			18a15									18 20		19a15						19 20			20a15
Coleshill Parkway	d	17 55												18 55								19 55			
Water Orton	d																								
Birmingham New Street 12	a	18 35				18 50			19 21					19 35					19 50	20 21		20 35			
	d			18 42		19 12					19 30							19 42	20 12						
Worcester Shrub Hill 7	d																								
Ashchurch for Tewkesbury	d																								
Cheltenham Spa	d			19 26		19 52	19 59				20 10						20 18	20 26	20 52						
Gloucester 7 134	a						20 08				20 21						20 28								
Bristol Parkway 7 134	a			20 03		20 20												20 56	21 20						
Bristol Temple Meads 10 134	a			20 14		20 31												21 06	21 29						
Newport (South Wales) 132	a										21 06						21 31								
Cardiff Central 7 132	a										21 26						21 49								

		GW	XC ◇1 A	GW K	XC ◇1 L (trolley)	XC ◇1 M (trolley)	XC ◇1	EM		XC (bus)	XC ◇1 B	GW	XC ◇1 A		XC ◇1 O (trolley)	XC ◇1 P	XC ◇1	XC (bus)		EM J	XC ◇1 Q	XC ◇1 M	XC (bus)	XC 1	XC (bus)
Nottingham 8 56 (ferry)	d						20 10	20 20									21 10			21 22					
Beeston 56	d							20 26												21 28					
Attenborough 56	d							20 29												21 31					
Long Eaton	d							20 37												21 39					
Derby 6	a						20 30	20 49									21 30			21 51					
	d				19 56	20 27									20 54	21 27					21 52	22 26			
Willington	d																								
Burton-on-Trent	d					20 37										21 37					22 03	22 37			
Tamworth	d																								
Wilnecote	d																								
Leicester	d										20 50													22 19	
South Wigston	d										20 55													22 24	
Narborough	d										21 00													22 29	
Hinckley	d										21 09													22 38	
Nuneaton	d									20 20	21a15							21 20					22 20	22a44	22 50
Coleshill Parkway	d									20 55								21 55					22 55		23 25
Water Orton	d																								
Birmingham New Street 12	a				20 52	21 21				21 35					21 51	22 18		22 35			22 44	23 17	23 35		00 05
	d		20 42		21 12								21 43		22 12										
Worcester Shrub Hill 7	d	20 38																							
Ashchurch for Tewkesbury	d	20 54																							
Cheltenham Spa	d	21 03	21 26	21 46	21 52							22 01	22 25		22 53										
Gloucester 7 134	a	21 13		21 56	22 03							22 12													
Bristol Parkway 7 134	a	21 53	21 59		22 33								22 52		23 22										
Bristol Temple Meads 10 134	a	22 07	22 10		22 44								23 06		23 33										
Newport (South Wales) 132	a																								
Cardiff Central 7 132	a																								

A From Manchester Piccadilly
B From Stansted Airport
C From Edinburgh to Exeter St Davids
D To London Paddington
E from 16 February. To Matlock
H From Newcastle to Exeter St Davids
I From Glasgow Central to Guildford
J To Matlock
K To Swindon
L From Newcastle. (trolley) to Birmingham New Street
M From Glasgow Central
O (trolley) to Birmingham New Street
P From Edinburgh
Q From Newcastle

Table 57

Sundays

30 March to 11 May

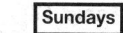

Nottingham, Derby and Leicester
Birmingham - Cardiff and Bristol

Network Diagram - refer to first Page of Table 50

		GW	XC	GW	GW	XC		XC	GW	EM	XC	GW	XC	AW	XC	GW		XC	XC	XC	GW	XC	XC	XC	AW
			◇1			◇1		◇1			◇1		◇1		◇1			1	◇1	◇1		1	◇1	◇1	
		A	B	C	A			D	A	E			D		F	A				G	A			H	
			🛒			🛒		🛒			🛒		🛒		🛒					🛒					
Nottingham 8	56 🚌 d									09 26									11 11				12 10		
Beeston	56 d									09 32															
Attenborough	56 d									09 35															
Long Eaton	d									09 43															
Derby 6	a									09 54									11 31				12 30		
	d							09 28					10 33		11 29				11 36	12 29			12 36		
Willington	d																								
Burton-on-Trent	d														11 40				11 47				12 47		
Tamworth	d												10 53						12 00	12 48			13 00		
Wilnecote	d																								
Leicester	d																	11 19				12 19		12 50	
South Wigston	d																					12 24			
Narborough	d																	11 28				12 29			
Hinckley	d																	11 36				12 38			
Nuneaton	d																	11 42				12 45		13 10	
Coleshill Parkway	d																	11 57				13 00		13 25	
Water Orton	d																								
Birmingham New Street 12	a							10 19					11 21		12 05			12 15	12 22	13 06		13 15	13 21	13 38	
	d		09 12			10 12		10 30			11 12		11 30		12 12				12 30	13 12			13 30		
Worcester Shrub Hill 7	d																								
Ashchurch for Tewkesbury	d																								
Cheltenham Spa	d	09 24	09 52	10 07	10 18	10 52		11 11	11 20		11 52	12 05	12 12	12 18	12 52	13 03			13 10	13 52	14 05		14 10		14 18
Gloucester 7	134 a	09 35		10 17	10 28	11 02			11 30		12 02	12 16		12 28		13 13			13 21		14 15		14 20		14 29
Bristol Parkway 7	134 a		10 20	10 53				11 39				12 58	12 40		13 20					14 20					
Bristol Temple Meads 10	134 a		10 31	11 07				11 51				13 12	12 51		13 31					14 31					
Newport (South Wales)	132 a					11 48					12 52			13 33					14 06				15 08		15 31
Cardiff Central 7	132 a					12 08					13 12			13 52					14 26				15 31		15 47

		XC		XC	XC	GW	XC	EM	XC	XC	XC	GW		XC	XC	XC	EM	XC	XC	AW	XC	GW		XC	XC
		◇1		◇1	1		◇1		◇1	◇1	◇1	◇1		◇1	1	◇1		◇1	◇1		◇1			◇1	1
				I		J		E	K	H	L	M		N				O	H		P	A		I	
		🛒		🛒					🛒		🛒	🍴		🛒		🛒		🛒	🛒		🛒			🛒	
Nottingham 8	56 🚌 d						13 10	13 23								14 10	14 22								
Beeston	56 d							13 29									14 28								
Attenborough	56 d							13 32									14 31								
Long Eaton	d							13 40									14 39								
Derby 6	a						13 30	13 51								14 29	14 50								
	d			13 32			13 36		13 55					14 29		14 35		14 53						15 25	
Willington	d																								
Burton-on-Trent	d			13 43			13 47									14 47								15 37	
Tamworth	d						14 00							14 48		15 00									
Wilnecote	d																								
Leicester	d				13 19					13 50					14 19				14 50						15 19
South Wigston	d														14 24										
Narborough	d				13 28										14 29										15 28
Hinckley	d				13 36										14 38										15 36
Nuneaton	d				13 43					14 09					14 45				15 09						15 43
Coleshill Parkway	d				13 59					14 25					15 00				15 25						15 58
Water Orton	d																								
Birmingham New Street 12	a			14 09	14 15		14 22		14 27	14 38				15 05	15 15	15 21		15 26	15 38					16 02	16 15
	d	13 42		14 12			14 30				14 42			15 12		15 30					15 42			16 12	
Worcester Shrub Hill 7	d					14 36																			
Ashchurch for Tewkesbury	d					14 51																			
Cheltenham Spa	d	14 25		14 52		15 01	15 10				15 26	15 42		15 52		16 10				16 18	16 26	16 32		16 51	
Gloucester 7	134 a					15 11	15 21					15 51				16 20				16 29		16 43			
Bristol Parkway 7	134 a	14 53		15 23		15 49					15 59			16 20							16 54			17 20	
Bristol Temple Meads 10	134 a	15 08		15 34		16 08					16 11			16 35							17 08			17 33	
Newport (South Wales)	132 a						16 06									17 06				17 37					
Cardiff Central 7	132 a						16 26									17 27				17 57					

- **A** To Swindon
- **B** To Penzance
- **C** To Taunton
- **D** From Leeds to Plymouth
- **E** To Matlock
- **F** From York to Plymouth
- **G** From Newcastle to Plymouth
- **H** From Stansted Airport
- **I** From Edinburgh to Plymouth
- **J** To Weston-super-Mare
- **K** To Reading
- **L** From Manchester Piccadilly to Paignton
- **M** To London Paddington
- **N** From Edinburgh to Penzance
- **O** From Sheffield to Reading
- **P** From Manchester Piccadilly

Table 57

Sundays

30 March to 11 May

Nottingham, Derby and Leicester Birmingham - Cardiff and Bristol

Network Diagram - refer to first Page of Table 50

		GW	XC	EM		XC	XC	XC	GW	XC	XC	XC	EM	XC		XC	XC	AW	XC	XC	GW	XC	EM	XC	
			◇1			◇1	◇1	◇1	◇1	◇1	1	◇1		◇1		◇1	◇1		◇1	1		◇1		◇1	
				A		B	C	D	E	F		G		B		C	D		H			G	A	I	
			☕			☕	☕	☕	🍽	☕		☕		☕		☕	☕		☕			☕		☕	
Nottingham 8 56	d		15 10	15 22								16 10	16 23									17 10	17 22		
Beeston 56	d			15 28									16 29										17 28		
Attenborough 56	d			15 31									16 32										17 31		
Long Eaton	d			15 39									16 40										17 39		
Derby 6	a		15 30	15 50								16 30	16 51									17 29	17 50		
	d		15 35			15 53				16 26		16 35		16 54					17 26			17 36		17 54	
Willington	d																								
Burton-on-Trent	d		15 47									16 47							17 37			17 47			
Tamworth	d		16 00							16 48		17 00										18 00			
Wilnecote	d		16 03																						
Leicester	d						15 50				16 19					16 50				17 19					
South Wigston	d										16 24									17 25					
Narborough	d										16 29									17 30					
Hinckley	d										16 38									17 38					
Nuneaton	d						16 09				16 45					17 09				17 45					
Coleshill Parkway	d						16 25				17 00					17 25				18 00					
Water Orton	d																								
Birmingham New Street 12	a		16 22			16 26	16 38			17 05	17 15	17 20		17 26		17 38			18 02	18 15		18 20		18 26	
	d		16 30					16 42		17 12		17 30					17 42		18 12			18 30			
Worcester Shrub Hill 7	d	16 40																			18 40				
Ashchurch for Tewkesbury	d	16 56																			18 56				
Cheltenham Spa	d	17 06	17 11					17 26	17 46	17 52		18 10					18 26	18 35	18 52		19 06	19 12			
Gloucester 7 134	a	17 16	17 20						17 55			18 20						18 46			19 16	19 26			
Bristol Parkway 7 134	a	17 56						18 02		18 20							18 54		19 21		19 56				
Bristol Temple Meads 10 134	a	18 09						18 13		18 36							19 08		19 32		20 09				
Newport (South Wales) 132	a		18 06									19 06						19 51				20 11			
Cardiff Central 7 132	a		18 28									19 27						20 09				20 31			

		XC	XC	XC	GW	XC	XC	EM	XC	XC		AW	XC	XC	XC	XC	EM	XC	XC	GW		XC	GW	XC	XC
		◇1	◇1	◇1	◇1	1	◇1		◇1	◇1			◇1	◇1	1	◇1		◇1	◇1			◇1		◇1	1
		C	J	K	E		G		B	C			D	H			A	L	C			D	M	N	
		☕	☕	☕	🍽		☕		☕	☕			☕	☕		☕		☕						☕	
Nottingham 8 56	d						18 10	18 22								19 10	19 22								
Beeston 56	d							18 28									19 28								
Attenborough 56	d							18 31									19 31								
Long Eaton	d							18 39									19 39								
Derby 6	a						18 30	18 50								19 30	19 50								
	d			18 25			18 35		18 54					19 27		19 36		19 56						20 26	
Willington	d																								
Burton-on-Trent	d						18 47							19 38		19 47									
Tamworth	d			18 45			19 00									20 00								20 45	
Wilnecote	d															20 04									
Leicester	d	17 50				18 19				18 50					19 19				19 50						20 19
South Wigston	d														19 24										20 24
Narborough	d					18 28									19 29										20 29
Hinckley	d					18 36									19 37										20 38
Nuneaton	d	18 10				18 43				19 09					19 43				20 10						20 44
Coleshill Parkway	d	18 26				18 59				19 25					19 59				20 25						21 00
Water Orton	d																								
Birmingham New Street 12	a	18 40		19 04		19 14	19 21		19 28	19 38				20 05	20 15	20 23		20 27	20 38					21 03	21 16
	d		18 42	19 12			19 30						19 42	20 12								20 42		21 12	
Worcester Shrub Hill 7	d																			20 38					
Ashchurch for Tewkesbury	d																			20 54					
Cheltenham Spa	d		19 26	19 52	19 59		20 10					20 18	20 26	20 52						21 03		21 26	21 46	21 52	
Gloucester 7 134	a				20 08		20 21					20 28								21 13			21 56	22 03	
Bristol Parkway 7 134	a		20 03	20 20									20 56	21 20						21 53		21 59		22 33	
Bristol Temple Meads 10 134	a		20 14	20 31									21 06	21 29						22 07		22 10		22 44	
Newport (South Wales) 132	a						21 06					21 31													
Cardiff Central 7 132	a						21 26					21 49													

A To Matlock
B From Newcastle to Reading
C From Stansted Airport
D From Manchester Piccadilly
E To London Paddington
F From Glasgow Central to Penzance
G ☕ to Birmingham New Street
H From Glasgow Central to Plymouth
I From Edinburgh to Reading
J From Manchester Piccadilly to Plymouth
K From Aberdeen to Plymouth
L From Newcastle to Guildford
M To Swindon
N From Glasgow Central. ☕ to Birmingham New Street

Table 57

Sundays

30 March to 11 May

Nottingham, Derby and Leicester
Birmingham - Cardiff and Bristol

Network Diagram - refer to first Page of Table 50

		XC		EM	XC	XC	GW	XC	XC	XC	XC	EM		XC	XC	XC
		◇1			◇1	◇1		◇1	◇1	◇1	◇1			◇1	◇1	1
					A	B		C	D		A	E		B	F	
					(trolley)											
Nottingham 8 56 (bus)	d	20 10		20 20						21 10		21 26				
Beeston 56	d			20 26								21 31				
Attenborough 56	d			20 29								21 35				
Long Eaton	d			20 37								21 43				
Derby 6	a	20 29		20 49						21 30		21 55				
	d	20 36			20 54				21 26	21 36	21 52				22 26	
Willington	d															
Burton-on-Trent	d	20 48							21 37	21 48	22 03				22 37	
Tamworth	d	21 00							21 47	21 59	22 14				22 47	
Wilnecote	d									22 03						
Leicester	d					20 50								21 50		22 19
South Wigston	d															22 24
Narborough	d															22 29
Hinckley	d															22 38
Nuneaton	d					21 10								22 10		22 45
Coleshill Parkway	d					21 25								22 25		23 00
Water Orton	d															
Birmingham New Street 12	a	21 20			21 25	21 38			22 05	22 23	22 30			22 38	23 04	23 15
	d							21 43	22 12							
Worcester Shrub Hill 7	d															
Ashchurch for Tewkesbury	d															
Cheltenham Spa	d						22 01	22 25	22 53							
Gloucester 7 134	a						22 12									
Bristol Parkway 7 134	a							22 52	23 22							
Bristol Temple Meads 10 134	a							23 06	23 33							
Newport (South Wales) 132	a															
Cardiff Central 7 132	a															

A From Newcastle
B From Stansted Airport
C From Manchester Piccadilly
D From Edinburgh
E To Matlock
F From Glasgow Central

Table 57R

Mondays to Fridays

9 December to 16 May

Bristol and Cardiff - Birmingham
Leicester, Derby and Nottingham

Network Diagram - refer to first Page of Table 50

Miles	Miles	Miles			AW	XC	XC	XC	GW	EM	XC	EM		XC	XC	XC	EM	XC	XC	XC	EM	XC		XC	XC
					MX	◇1	1	◇			◇1	◇1		1	◇1	◇1		1	1	◇1		1		◇1	◇1
					A	B					C 🚲	🚲			B 🚲	D 🚲				E 🚲		🚲		B 🚲	D 🚲
0	—	—	**Cardiff Central [7]** 132	d																					
11¾	—	—	Newport (South Wales) 132	d																					
—	—	0	**Bristol Temple Meads [10]** 134	d																					
—	—	5¾	Bristol Parkway [7] 134	d																					
56½	—	—	Gloucester [7] 134	d	00 41				06 00																
63	—	46¼	Cheltenham Spa	a	00 54				06 10																
—	—	—		d					06 11																
70¼	—	53½	Ashchurch for Tewkesbury	d					06 20																
85	—	—	Worcester Shrub Hill [7]	a					06 41																
112	0	92¾	**Birmingham New Street [12]**	a																					
—	—	—		d		05 22	05 52				06 00			06 19	06 22	06 30		06 49	06 52	07 03		07 19		07 22	07 30
119¾	7½	—	Water Orton	d																					
—	9¾	—	Coleshill Parkway	d		05 36	06 05								06 36				07 05					07 35	
—	21¼	—	Nuneaton	d		05 52	06 21								06 52				07 22					07 51	
—	25¼	—	Hinckley	d			06 28												07 29					07 58	
—	33	—	Narborough	d			06 37												07 37					08 06	
—	36	—	South Wigston	d			06 42												07 42					08 10	
—	40	—	**Leicester**	a		06 13	06 48								07 14				07 47					08 15	
127	—	—	Wilnecote	d										06 35								07 35			
128¾	—	—	Tamworth	d										06 39				07 07		07 19		07 39			
141¾	—	—	Burton-on-Trent	d										06 51				07 20		07 31		07 50			
146½	—	—	Willington	d														07 26							
152¾	—	—	**Derby [6]**	a							06 33			07 04		07 11		07 34		07 42		08 05			08 09
—	—	—		d				06 00		06 27		07 00		07 09			07 31	07 40			07 53	08 10			
161	—	—	Long Eaton	d						06 39				07 21			07 41	07 50			08 03	08 19			
164	—	—	Attenborough 56	d						06 47				07 28			07 49				08 10				
165½	—	—	Beeston 56	d				06 15		06 50				07 32			07 52	07 59			08 13	08 27			
168¾	—	—	**Nottingham [8]** 56 🚢	a				06 22		06 59		07 19		07 38			08 02	08 09			08 22	08 34			

		EM	XC	XC	XC	XC	XC	GW		AW	XC	XC	EM	XC	XC	GW	XC	XC		AW	XC	XC	XC	EM	XC
			1	1	◇1	1	◇1				◇1	◇1		◇1	1	◇1	◇1	1			◇1	◇1	◇1		◇1
		F			G 🚲	🚲	H 🚲	I			J 🚲	K 🚲	F			L ☕	M 🚲	🚲			B 🚲	N 🚲	O 🚲	F	
Cardiff Central [7] 132	d									06 12				06 40						07 06		07 00			07 45
Newport (South Wales) 132	d									06 28				06 55						07 23		07 15			08 02
Bristol Temple Meads [10] 134	d				06 27						07 00						07 30					08 00			
Bristol Parkway [7] 134	d				06 38						07 09						07 39					08 09			
Gloucester [7] 134	d						07 10	07 14		07 21				07 46		07 51				08 21					08 49
Cheltenham Spa	a				07 08		07 19	07 24		07 34	07 39			07 56		08 01	08 09			08 34		08 39			08 59
	d				07 10		07 21	07 25			07 40			07 57			08 11					08 40			09 01
Ashchurch for Tewkesbury	d						07 29	07 34						08 05											
Worcester Shrub Hill [7]	a							07 54																	
Birmingham New Street [12]	a				07 55		08 15				08 26			08 45			08 55					09 26			09 45
	d		07 49	07 52	08 03	08 19	08 22					08 30		08 49	08 52		09 03	09 19			09 22		09 30		09 49
Water Orton	d														09 03										
Coleshill Parkway	d			08 05			08 36								09 07						09 36				
Nuneaton	d			08 24			08 52								09 22						09 52				
Hinckley	d			08 31											09 30										
Narborough	d			08 39											09 39										
South Wigston	d			08 44																					
Leicester	a			08 50			09 13								09 51						10 16				
Wilnecote	d													09 05											
Tamworth	d		08 07		08 19	08 36								09 09				09 36							10 07
Burton-on-Trent	d		08 19		08 29	08 48								09 21			09 27	09 48							10 19
Willington	d		08 25																						10 25
Derby [6]	a		08 36		08 41	09 00						09 06		09 34			09 39	10 00					10 06		10 34
	d	08 13	08 40			09 08							09 16	09 40				10 08						10 13	10 40
Long Eaton	d	08 25	08 49										09 26	09 49										10 23	10 49
Attenborough 56	d	08 35	08 56										09 34											10 32	
Beeston 56	d	08 38	09 00										09 37	09 57										10 35	10 57
Nottingham [8] 56 🚢	a	08 46	09 06			09 28							09 46	10 03				10 28						10 41	11 03

A From Maesteg
B To Stansted Airport
C To Glasgow Central
D To Newcastle
E To Edinburgh
F From Matlock
G From Bath Spa to Glasgow Central
H To Stansted Airport. 🚲 from Birmingham New Street
I To Great Malvern
J To Manchester Piccadilly
K From Guildford to Newcastle
L From Swindon
M From Plymouth to Edinburgh
N To Manchester Piccadilly. 🚲 from Bristol Temple Meads
O From Reading to Newcastle

Table 57R

Mondays to Fridays

9 December to 16 May

Bristol and Cardiff - Birmingham
Leicester, Derby and Nottingham

Network Diagram - refer to first Page of Table 50

	XC	GW	XC	XC	XC	XC	XC	EM	GW		XC	XC	GW	XC	XC	AW	XC	XC	XC		EM	GW	XC	XC
	1		◇1	1	◇1	◇1	◇1				◇1	1	◇1	◇1	1		◇1	◇1	◇1				◇1	1
		A	B		C	D	E	F	G				H	I		J	C	K	L		F	M		
			🚲	🚲	🚲	🚲	🚲						⊡	🚲	🚲		🚲	🚲	🚲				🚲	
Cardiff Central 7 132 d											08 45					09 12							09 45	
Newport (South Wales) 132 d											09 00					09 27							10 00	
Bristol Temple Meads 10 134 d			08 30			09 00			08 41					09 30				10 00						
Bristol Parkway 7 134 d			08 39			09 09			08 52					09 39				10 09						
Gloucester 7 134 d		08 54							09 36		09 46		09 51			10 21						10 33	10 50	
Cheltenham Spa a		09 05	09 10			09 40			09 46		09 55		10 01	10 09		10 35		10 40				10 48	11 00	
d			09 12			09 42			09 48		09 56			10 11				10 41					11 01	
Ashchurch for Tewkesbury d									09 56															
Worcester Shrub Hill 7 a									10 14															
Birmingham New Street 12 a			09 56			10 25					10 45			10 55				11 26					11 45	
d	09 52		10 03	10 19	10 22		10 30				10 49	10 52		11 03	11 19		11 22		11 30				11 49	11 52
Water Orton d												11 03												
Coleshill Parkway d	10 07				10 36							11 07					11 36							12 07
Nuneaton d	10 23				10 52							11 23					11 52							12 23
Hinckley d	10 30											11 30												12 30
Narborough d	10 39											11 39												12 38
South Wigston d	10 44																							12 43
Leicester a	10 50				11 13							11 50					12 12							12 50
Wilnecote d											11 05													
Tamworth d			10 19	10 36							11 09				11 36								12 07	
Burton-on-Trent d				10 48							11 21			11 26	11 48								12 19	
Willington d																							12 25	
Derby 6 a			10 38	11 00			11 06				11 34			11 38	12 00				12 06				12 32	
d				11 08				11 13			11 40				12 08						12 13		12 40	
Long Eaton d								11 23			11 49										12 23		12 49	
Attenborough 56 d								11 32													12 32			
Beeston 56 d								11 35			11 57										12 35		12 57	
Nottingham 8 56 ⛴ a				11 28				11 41			12 03				12 28						12 41		13 03	

	XC	AW	XC	XC	XC		XC	EM	GW	GW	XC	XC	XC	XC	XC		XC	XC	EM	GW	XC	XC	XC	AW
	◇1		1	◇1	◇1		◇1		◇	◇1	◇1	1	◇1	1	◇1		◇1	◇1			◇1	1	◇1	
	N	J		C	K		O	F	P	H			Q		C		D	L	F	M			N	J
	🚲			🚲	🚲		🚲			⊡			🚲	🚲	🚲		🚲	🚲			🚲		🚲	
Cardiff Central 7 132 d		10 12									10 45										11 45			12 12
Newport (South Wales) 132 d		10 27									11 00										12 02			12 28
Bristol Temple Meads 10 134 d	10 30				11 00				10 41				11 30				12 00						12 30	
Bristol Parkway 7 134 d	10 39				11 09				10 55				11 39				12 09						12 39	
Gloucester 7 134 d		11 21							11 36	11 40	11 50									12 33	12 48			13 22
Cheltenham Spa a	11 09	11 35			11 40				11 46	11 52	12 00		12 09				12 39			12 46	12 58		13 09	13 36
d	11 11				11 42				11 48		12 01		12 11				12 40				12 58		13 11	
Ashchurch for Tewkesbury d									11 56												13 07			
Worcester Shrub Hill 7 a									12 13															
Birmingham New Street 12 a	11 58				12 26						12 45		12 55				13 26				13 45		13 56	
d	12 03		12 19	12 22			12 30				12 49	12 52	13 03	13 19	13 22			13 30			13 49	13 52	14 03	
Water Orton d												13 02												
Coleshill Parkway d				12 36								13 07			13 36							14 07		
Nuneaton d				12 52								13 22			13 52							14 23		
Hinckley d												13 29										14 30		
Narborough d												13 38										14 39		
South Wigston d																						14 43		
Leicester a				13 14								13 50			14 13							14 50		
Wilnecote d											13 05										14 05			
Tamworth d	12 19		12 35								13 09			13 36							14 09		14 19	
Burton-on-Trent d			12 47								13 19		13 28	13 48							14 21			
Willington d																								
Derby 6 a	12 38		13 00				13 06				13 34		13 40	14 00				14 06			14 34		14 40	
d			13 08					13 13			13 40			14 08					14 13		14 40			
Long Eaton d								13 25			13 49								14 23		14 49			
Attenborough 56 d								13 33											14 32					
Beeston 56 d								13 36			13 57								14 35		14 57			
Nottingham 8 56 ⛴ a			13 28					13 42			14 03			14 28					14 41		15 03			

A From Westbury
B From Plymouth to Glasgow Central
C To Stansted Airport
D From Paignton to Manchester Piccadilly
E From Winchester to Newcastle
F From Matlock
G From Warminster to Great Malvern
H From London Paddington
I From Plymouth to Edinburgh
J From Maesteg
K To Manchester Piccadilly
L From Reading to Newcastle
M From Swindon
N From Penzance to Glasgow Central
O From Southampton Central to Newcastle
P From Southampton Central to Great Malvern
Q From Plymouth to Aberdeen

Table 57R

Mondays to Fridays

9 December to 16 May

Bristol and Cardiff - Birmingham Leicester, Derby and Nottingham

Network Diagram - refer to first Page of Table 50

		XC 1	XC ◇1 A	XC ◇1 B	XC ◇1 C	EM D	GW ◇ E	GW ◇1 F	XC ◇1	XC 1	XC ◇1 G	XC 1	XC ◇1 A	XC ◇1 H	XC ◇1 I	EM D	GW J	XC ◇1	XC 1	XC ◇1 K	XC 1	XC 1	XC ◇1 A
Cardiff Central 7 132	d								12 45									13 45					
Newport (South Wales) 132	d								13 01									14 00					
Bristol Temple Meads 10 134	d			13 00			12 41				13 30			14 00						14 30			
Bristol Parkway 7 134	d			13 09			12 52				13 39			14 09						14 40			
Gloucester 7 134	d						13 37	13 40	13 50								14 33	14 50					
Cheltenham Spa	a			13 40			13 46	13 52	14 00		14 09			14 40			14 47	15 00		15 10			
	d			13 42			13 48		14 01		14 10			14 41				15 01		15 11			
Ashchurch for Tewkesbury	d						13 56																
Worcester Shrub Hill 7	a						14 13																
Birmingham New Street 12	a			14 25					14 45		14 55			15 23				15 45		15 56			
	d	14 19	14 22		14 30				14 49	14 52	15 03	15 19	15 22		15 30			15 49	15 52	16 03	16 09	16 19	16 22
Water Orton	d									15 03											16 19		
Coleshill Parkway	d		14 36							15 07			15 36						16 07		16 23		16 36
Nuneaton	d		14 52							15 23			15 52						16 23		16 39		16 52
Hinckley	d									15 30									16 30		16 46		
Narborough	d									15 38									16 39		16 55		
South Wigston	d																		16 43				
Leicester	a		15 13							15 50			16 13						16 50		17 04		17 14
Wilnecote	d								15 05									16 05					
Tamworth	d	14 36							15 09			15 36						16 09		16 19		16 36	
Burton-on-Trent	d	14 48							15 21		15 26	15 48						16 21				16 48	
Willington	d								15 26														
Derby 6	a	15 00			15 06				15 35		15 40	16 00			16 06			16 34		16 40		17 00	
	d	15 08				15 13			15 40			16 08				16 14		16 40				17 08	
Long Eaton	d					15 23			15 49							16 24		16 49				17 17	
Attenborough 56	d					15 32										16 32							
Beeston 56	d					15 35			15 57							16 35		16 57				17 25	
Nottingham 8 56	a	15 28				15 41			16 03			16 28				16 41		17 03				17 31	

		XC ◇1 B	XC ◇1 L	EM D	GW ◇ M	GW ◇1 N	XC ◇1	XC ◇1 O	XC ◇1 P	EM	AW Q	XC 1	XC 1	XC ◇1 A	XC ◇1 R	XC ◇1 I	EM D	GW J	XC 1	XC ◇1	XC 1	XC ◇1 P
Cardiff Central 7 132	d						14 45				15 12									15 45		
Newport (South Wales) 132	d						15 01				15 28									16 00		
Bristol Temple Meads 10 134	d	15 00			14 41				15 30						16 00							16 30
Bristol Parkway 7 134	d	15 09			14 52				15 40						16 09							16 39
Gloucester 7 134	d				15 36	15 40	15 50				16 22							16 33		16 50		
Cheltenham Spa	a	15 41			15 46	15 52	16 00		16 10		16 34				16 40			16 47		17 00		17 09
	d	15 42			15 48		16 01		16 11						16 41					17 01		17 11
Ashchurch for Tewkesbury	d				15 56																	
Worcester Shrub Hill 7	a				16 14																	
Birmingham New Street 12	a	16 26					16 45		16 56						17 23					17 45		17 55
	d		16 30				16 49	16 52	17 03			17 09	17 19	17 22		17 30			17 39	17 49	17 52	18 03
Water Orton	d											17 23							17 51		18 03	
Coleshill Parkway	d							17 06				17 27		17 36							18 07	
Nuneaton	d							17 20				17 44		17 52							18 23	
Hinckley	d							17 27				17 51		17 59							18 30	
Narborough	d							17 36						18 07							18 39	
South Wigston	d											18 02									18 44	
Leicester	a							17 48				18 07		18 16							18 50	
Wilnecote	d						17 05												17 59	18 05		
Tamworth	d						17 09						17 36						18 03	18 09		18 19
Burton-on-Trent	d						17 21		17 26				17 48						18 14	18 21		
Willington	d																		18 20			
Derby 6	a		17 06				17 34		17 39				18 00			18 06			18 29	18 34		18 38
	d			17 13			17 40			17 51			18 08				18 13			18 40		
Long Eaton	d			17 25			17 49			18 04			18 17				18 26			18 49		
Attenborough 56	d			17 34						18 15							18 34					
Beeston 56	d			17 37			17 57			18 18			18 25				18 38			18 57		
Nottingham 8 56	a			17 44			18 03			18 25			18 31				18 46			19 03		

A To Stansted Airport
B To Manchester Piccadilly
C From Southampton Central to Newcastle
D From Matlock
E From Brighton to Great Malvern
F From London Paddington. The Cheltenham Spa Express
G From Plymouth to Dundee
H From Penzance to Manchester Piccadilly
I From Reading to Newcastle
J From Swindon
K From Plymouth to Glasgow Central
L From Southampton Central to Edinburgh
M From Southampton Central to Great Malvern
N From London Paddington
O To Cambridge
P From Plymouth to Edinburgh
Q From Maesteg
R From Paignton to Manchester Piccadilly

Table 57R

Mondays to Fridays

9 December to 16 May

Bristol and Cardiff - Birmingham
Leicester, Derby and Nottingham

Network Diagram - refer to first Page of Table 50

Station	Table		AW	XC	XC	XC	XC		EM	GW	GW	XC	XC	XC	XC	AW	XC		XC	XC	EM	XC	XC	GW	XC
				1	◇1	◇1	◇1				◇1	◇1	1	◇1	1		◇1		◇1	◇1		◇1	1	◇	◇1
			A		B	C	D		E	F	G	H		I		A	B		J	K	E	H		L	M
						🛒	🛒				☕	🛒		🛒					🛒			🛒			🛒
Cardiff Central 7	132	d	16 10									16 45				17 12						17 45			
Newport (South Wales)	132	d	16 27									17 00				17 28						18 00			
Bristol Temple Meads 10	134	d				17 00				16 41				17 30					18 00						18 30
Bristol Parkway 7	134	d				17 09				16 52				17 40					18 09						18 39
Gloucester 7	134	d	17 23							17 36	17 40	17 50				18 22						18 46		18 53	
Cheltenham Spa		a	17 35			17 41				17 47	17 52	18 00		18 10		18 34			18 40			18 56		19 05	19 09
		d				17 42				17 48		18 01		18 11					18 41			18 57			19 11
Ashchurch for Tewkesbury		d								17 56												19 05			
Worcester Shrub Hill 7		a								18 16															
Birmingham New Street 12		a				18 24						18 45		18 55					19 23			19 45			19 56
		d		18 19	18 22		18 30					18 49	18 52	19 03	19 19		19 22			19 30		19 49	19 52		20 03
Water Orton		d																					20 03		
Coleshill Parkway		d			18 36								19 07				19 36						20 07		
Nuneaton		d			18 52								19 23				19 52						20 23		
Hinckley		d											19 30										20 30		
Narborough		d											19 39										20 39		
South Wigston		d											19 43										20 44		
Leicester		a			19 14								19 48				20 13						20 49		
Wilnecote		d										19 05										20 05			
Tamworth		d		18 36								19 09			19 36							20 09			20 19
Burton-on-Trent		d		18 48								19 21		19 25	19 48							20 21			
Willington		d																							
Derby 6		a		19 00			19 05					19 34		19 40	20 00					20 04		20 34			20 38
		d		19 07					19 13			19 40			20 08						20 16	20 40			
Long Eaton		d		19 16					19 24			19 49									20 26	20 49			
Attenborough	56	d							19 31												20 34				
Beeston	56	d		19 23					19 34			19 57									20 37	20 57			
Nottingham 8	56 🚋	a		19 30					19 42			20 03			20 28						20 43	21 03			

Station	Table		XC		AW	XC	XC	EM	GW	XC	XC	GW	XC		GW	XC	GW	XC	XC	XC	XC	GW	GW		GW
			◇1			◇1	◇1			◇1	1	◇1	◇1			◇1	◇1	◇1	1	◇1	1	◇			◇1
			O		A	C	P	E	F	H		G	M		Q		G			R		Q			G
						🛒				🛒		☕	🛒				☕								☕
Cardiff Central 7	132	d			18 12					18 45								19 50							
Newport (South Wales)	132	d			18 27					19 01								20 05							
Bristol Temple Meads 10	134	d				19 00			18 41				19 30		19 41	20 00				20 30			20 41		
Bristol Parkway 7	134	d				19 09			18 52				19 40		19 52	20 09				20 40			20 52		
Gloucester 7	134	d			19 21				19 38	19 46		19 51			20 36	20 46	20 51	20 58				21 23	21 33		21 52
Cheltenham Spa		a			19 34	19 39			19 49	19 56		20 02	20 10		20 48	20 54	21 02	21 09		21 15		21 33	21 44		22 02
		d				19 40			19 50	19 58			20 11			20 56		21 09		21 17			21 45		22 04
Ashchurch for Tewkesbury		d							19 59														21 54		
Worcester Shrub Hill 7		a							20 15														22 14		22 24
Birmingham New Street 12		a				20 23				20 41			20 52			21 40		21 51		22 04					
		d	20 22				20 30			20 49	20 52		21 03						22 03		22 22				
Water Orton		d																							
Coleshill Parkway		d	20 36								21 05										22 35				
Nuneaton		d	20 52								21 22										22 52				
Hinckley		d									21 29										22 59				
Narborough		d									21 38										23 08				
South Wigston		d									21 42										23 12				
Leicester		a	21 15								21 50										23 20				
Wilnecote		d								21 05															
Tamworth		d								21 09			21 19						22 27						
Burton-on-Trent		d								21 21			21 30						22 39						
Willington		d																							
Derby 6		a					21 09			21 33			21 43						22 52						
		d						21 13		21 40									22 58						
Long Eaton		d						21 23		21 52									23 10						
Attenborough	56	d						21 31		21 58									23 17						
Beeston	56	d						21 34		22 01									23 20						
Nottingham 8	56 🚋	a						21 41		22 08									23 27						

A From Maesteg
B To Stansted Airport
C To Manchester Piccadilly
D From Southampton Central to Newcastle
E From Matlock
F From Warminster to Great Malvern
G From London Paddington
H 🛒 to Birmingham New Street
I From Plymouth to Leeds
J From Exeter St Davids to Manchester Piccadilly
K From Reading to Newcastle
L From Swindon
M From Plymouth to Leeds. 🛒 to Birmingham New Street
O To Cambridge
P From Southampton Central to York
Q From Westbury
R From Plymouth

Table 57R

Mondays to Fridays

9 December to 16 May

Bristol and Cardiff - Birmingham Leicester, Derby and Nottingham

Network Diagram - refer to first Page of Table 50

		XC	AW	EM	XC	XC	XC	GW	AW
		◇1			1	◇1	◇1		
			A	B		C		D	A
Cardiff Central 7	132 d		21 12				21 50		23 20
Newport (South Wales)	132 d	21 05	21 27				22 05		23 40
Bristol Temple Meads 10	134 d	21 21				22 00			
Bristol Parkway 7	134 d					22 10			
Gloucester 7	134 d		22 23				22 47	22 57	00 41
Cheltenham Spa	a	22 04	22 37			22 39	22 56	23 10	00 54
	d	22 14				22 41	22 58		
Ashchurch for Tewkesbury	d	22 15							
Worcester Shrub Hill 7	a	22 23							
Birmingham New Street 12	a					23 43	23 59		
	d	23 05			23 09				
Water Orton	d								
Coleshill Parkway	d								
Nuneaton	d								
Hinckley	d								
Narborough	d								
South Wigston	d								
Leicester	a								
Wilnecote	d				23 24				
Tamworth	d				23 28				
Burton-on-Trent	d				23 40				
Willington	d				23 45				
Derby 6	a				23 54				
	d			23 31	23 58				
Long Eaton	d			23 41					
Attenborough	56 d			23 49					
Beeston	56 d			23 52					
Nottingham 8	56 ⛴ a			00 01	00 17				

Saturdays

14 December to 17 May

		AW	XC	GW	XC	EM	XC	XC	XC	XC	EM	XC	XC	XC	XC	XC	XC	EM	XC	XC	XC	XC	XC
			◇1		1		◇1	1	◇1	◇1		1	1	◇1	1	◇1	◇1		1	1	◇1	1	◇1
		A	E				F		E	G				H		E	G	B			F		I
							🚲		🚲	🚲				🚲	🚲	🚲	🚲				🚲	🚲	🚲
Cardiff Central 7	132 d																						
Newport (South Wales)	132 d																						
Bristol Temple Meads 10	134 d																				06 15		
Bristol Parkway 7	134 d																				06 24		
Gloucester 7	134 d	00 41		05 50																	07 00		07 07
Cheltenham Spa	a	00 54		05 59																	07 09		07 16
	d			06 00																	07 11		07 18
Ashchurch for Tewkesbury	d			06 09																			07 25
Worcester Shrub Hill 7	a			06 33																			
Birmingham New Street 12	a																				07 56		08 08
	d		05 22		05 52		05 57	06 19	06 22	06 30		06 49	06 52	07 03	07 19	07 22	07 30		07 49	07 52	08 03	08 19	08 22
Water Orton	d												07 02										
Coleshill Parkway	d		05 36		06 06				06 36				07 06			07 36				08 05			08 36
Nuneaton	d		05 52		06 21				06 52				07 22			07 52				08 22			08 52
Hinckley	d				06 28								07 29							08 29			
Narborough	d				06 36								07 37							08 37			
South Wigston	d				06 41								07 42							08 42			
Leicester	a		06 14		06 47				07 16				07 48			08 16				08 50			09 16
Wilnecote	d							06 35							07 35								
Tamworth	d						06 13	06 39		06 46		07 07		07 19	07 39		07 46		08 07		08 19	08 36	
Burton-on-Trent	d						06 24	06 51		06 56		07 19		07 29	07 50		07 56		08 19		08 29	08 48	
Willington	d											07 25							08 25				
Derby 6	a						06 35	07 05		07 09		07 34		07 42	08 05		08 09		08 34		08 42	09 00	
	d					06 24		07 10			07 32	07 39			08 10			08 13	08 40			09 08	
Long Eaton	d					06 35		07 22			07 41	07 52			08 19			08 25	08 49				
Attenborough	56 d					06 44		07 28			07 49							08 33	08 56				
Beeston	56 d					06 47		07 32			07 52	07 59			08 27			08 36	09 00				
Nottingham 8	56 ⛴ a					06 57		07 38			08 03	08 08			08 34			08 43	09 06			09 28	

A From Maesteg
B From Matlock
C From Paignton
D From Swindon
E To Stansted Airport
F To Glasgow Central
G To Newcastle
H To Edinburgh
I To Stansted Airport. 🚲 from Birmingham New Street

Table 57R

Saturdays

14 December to 17 May

Bristol and Cardiff - Birmingham Leicester, Derby and Nottingham

Network Diagram - refer to first Page of Table 50

Station			GW	AW	XC	XC	EM	XC	XC	XC	XC	GW	AW	XC	XC	XC	EM	XC	XC	XC	XC	XC	XC
					◇1	◇1		◇1	1	◇1	1			◇1	◇1	◇1		◇1	1	◇1	1	◇1	◇1
					A	B	C			D		E		F	G	H	C			I		F	J
					(trolley)	(trolley)				(trolley)	(trolley)			(trolley)	(trolley)	(trolley)				(trolley)	(trolley)	(trolley)	(trolley)
Cardiff Central [7]	132	d		06 12				06 40					07 12		07 00			07 45					
Newport (South Wales)	132	d		06 28				06 55					07 27		07 15			08 00					
Bristol Temple Meads [10]	134	d			07 00					07 30					08 00					08 30			09 00
Bristol Parkway [7]	134	d			07 09					07 39					08 09					08 39			09 09
Gloucester [7]	134	d	07 15	07 21				07 46				08 09	08 22					08 49					
Cheltenham Spa		a	07 24	07 34	07 39			07 55		08 11		08 24	08 35		08 40			08 59		09 09			09 39
		d	07 25		07 41			07 57		08 13					08 41			09 00		09 10			09 41
Ashchurch for Tewkesbury		d	07 34					08 04															
Worcester Shrub Hill [7]		a	07 52																				
Birmingham New Street [12]		a			08 25			08 45		08 56					09 26			09 45		09 55			10 25
		d				08 30		08 49	08 52	09 03	09 19			09 22		09 30		09 49	09 52	10 03	10 19	10 22	
Water Orton		d							09 03														
Coleshill Parkway		d							09 07					09 36					10 07			10 36	
Nuneaton		d							09 23					09 52					10 23			10 52	
Hinckley		d							09 30										10 30				
Narborough		d							09 39										10 39				
South Wigston		d																	10 43				
Leicester		a							09 51					10 16					10 50			11 17	
Wilnecote		d						09 05															
Tamworth		d						09 09			09 36							10 07		10 19	10 36		
Burton-on-Trent		d						09 21		09 28	09 48							10 19			10 48		
Willington		d																10 25					
Derby [6]		a				09 08		09 34		09 41	10 00					10 06		10 35		10 41	11 00		
		d					09 13	09 40			10 08						10 13	10 40			11 08		
Long Eaton		d					09 23	09 49									10 23	10 51					
Attenborough	56	d					09 32										10 32						
Beeston	56	d					09 35	09 57									10 35	10 59					
Nottingham [8]	56	a					09 41	10 04			10 28						10 41	11 06			11 28		

Station			XC	EM	GW	XC	XC	XC	XC	GW	AW	XC	XC	XC	EM	XC	XC	XC	GW	AW	XC	XC	XC	XC
			◇1			◇1	1	◇1	1	◇1		◇1	◇1	◇1		◇1	1	◇1			1	◇1	◇1	◇1
			K	C	L			D		M	N	F	A	O	C			P	E	N		F	A	K
			(trolley)					(trolley)	(trolley)	(restaurant)		(trolley)	(trolley)	(trolley)		(trolley)		(trolley)				(trolley)	(trolley)	(trolley)
Cardiff Central [7]	132	d				08 45					09 12					09 45				10 12				
Newport (South Wales)	132	d				09 00					09 26					10 00				10 27				
Bristol Temple Meads [10]	134	d			08 41			09 30					10 00					10 30					11 00	
Bristol Parkway [7]	134	d			08 52			09 39					10 09					10 39					11 09	
Gloucester [7]	134	d			09 37	09 50				10 12	10 21					10 50			11 11	11 22				
Cheltenham Spa		a			09 47	10 00		10 09		10 22	10 35		10 39			11 00		11 09	11 23	11 35			11 39	
		d			09 48	10 01		10 11					10 41			11 01		11 11					11 41	
Ashchurch for Tewkesbury		d			09 57																			
Worcester Shrub Hill [7]		a			10 14																			
Birmingham New Street [12]		a				10 45		10 56					11 26			11 45		11 55					12 26	
		d	10 30			10 49	10 52	11 03	11 19			11 22		11 30		11 49	11 52	12 03			12 19	12 22		12 30
Water Orton		d					11 03																	
Coleshill Parkway		d					11 07					11 36					12 07					12 36		
Nuneaton		d					11 23					11 52					12 23					12 52		
Hinckley		d					11 30										12 31							
Narborough		d					11 39										12 39							
South Wigston		d															12 43							
Leicester		a					11 50					12 16					12 49					13 16		
Wilnecote		d				11 05																		
Tamworth		d				11 09			11 36							12 07		12 19			12 36			
Burton-on-Trent		d				11 21		11 28	11 48							12 19					12 48			
Willington		d														12 25								
Derby [6]		a	11 09			11 34		11 41	12 00					12 06		12 35		12 41			13 00			13 06
		d		11 13		11 40			12 08						12 13	12 40					13 08			
Long Eaton		d		11 23		11 49									12 23	12 49								
Attenborough	56	d		11 32											12 32									
Beeston	56	d		11 35		11 57									12 35	12 57								
Nottingham [8]	56	a		11 41		12 04			12 28						12 41	13 04					13 28			

A To Manchester Piccadilly
B From Guildford to Newcastle
C From Matlock
D From Plymouth to Edinburgh
E From Swindon
F To Stansted Airport
G To Manchester Piccadilly. (trolley) from Bristol Temple Meads
H From Bournemouth to Newcastle
I From Plymouth to Glasgow Central
J From Paignton to Manchester Piccadilly
K From Southampton Central to Newcastle
L From Warminster to Great Malvern
M From London Paddington
N From Maesteg
O From Reading to Newcastle
P From Penzance to Glasgow Central

Table 57R

Saturdays

14 December to 17 May

Bristol and Cardiff - Birmingham Leicester, Derby and Nottingham

Network Diagram - refer to first Page of Table 50

		EM	GW	XC	XC	XC	XC	GW	GW	XC		XC	XC	EM	XC	XC	XC	GW	GW	AW		XC	XC	XC	XC
			◇	◇1	1	◇1	1		◇1	◇1		◇1	◇1		◇1	1	◇1	1				1	◇1	◇1	◇1
		A	B			C		D	E	F		G	H	A			I	D	J	K			F	L	M
						🛒	🛒		🍽	🛒		🛒	🛒		🛒		🛒						🛒	🛒	🛒
Cardiff Central 7 132	d			10 45											11 45					12 12					
Newport (South Wales) 132	d			11 00											12 00					12 27					
Bristol Temple Meads 10 134	d		10 41			11 30						12 00					12 30							13 00	
Bristol Parkway 7 134	d		10 52			11 39						12 09					12 39							13 09	
Gloucester 7 134	d		11 36	11 50				12⟆07	12⟆12						12 48			13⟆11	13⟆11	13 22					
Cheltenham Spa	a		11 47	12 00		12 09		12⟆18	12⟆22			12 39			12 58		13 09	13⟆23	13⟆24	13 35				13 39	
	d		11 48	12 01		12 11						12 41			12 59		13 11							13 41	
Ashchurch for Tewkesbury	d		11 57												13 07										
Worcester Shrub Hill 7	a		12 15																						
Birmingham New Street 12	a			12 45		12 55						13 26			13 45		13 55							14 26	
	d			12 49	12 52	13 03	13 19			13 22			13 30		13 49	13 52	14 03					14 19	14 22		14 30
Water Orton	d				13 03																				
Coleshill Parkway	d				13 07					13 36						14 07							14 36		
Nuneaton	d				13 23					13 52						14 23							14 52		
Hinckley	d				13 31											14 30									
Narborough	d				13 40											14 39									
South Wigston	d															14 43									
Leicester	a				13 50					14 16						14 50							15 16		
Wilnecote	d			13 05											14 05										
Tamworth	d			13 09			13 36								14 09		14 19					14 36			
Burton-on-Trent	d			13 21		13 27	13 48								14 21							14 47			
Willington	d																								
Derby 6	a			13 34		13 41	14 00						14 06		14 35		14 41					15 00			15 06
	d	13 13		13 40			14 08							14 13	14 40							15 08			
Long Eaton	d	13 25		13 49										14 23	14 49										
Attenborough 56	d	13 33												14 32											
Beeston 56	d	13 36		13 57										14 35	14 57										
Nottingham 8 56 ⛴	a	13 42		14 04			14 28							14 41	15 04							15 28			

		EM	GW	XC	XC	XC		XC	GW	GW	XC	XC	XC	EM	XC	XC		XC	GW	XC	XC	XC	XC	EM	GW
			◇	◇1	1	◇1		1	◇1		◇1	◇1	◇1		◇1	1		◇1		1	◇1	◇1	◇1		◇
		A	N			O			E	D	F	P	H	A				Q	R		F	L	M	A	S
				🛒		🛒			🍽		🛒	🛒	🛒		🛒			🛒			🛒	🛒	🛒		
Cardiff Central 7 132	d			12 45											13 45										
Newport (South Wales) 132	d			13 00											14 00										
Bristol Temple Meads 10 134	d		12 41			13 30						14 00						14 30				15 00			14 41
Bristol Parkway 7 134	d		12 52			13 39						14 09						14 40				15 09			14 52
Gloucester 7 134	d		13 37	13 50					14⟆12	14⟆12					14 50				15 13						15 37
Cheltenham Spa	a		13 47	14 00		14 09			14⟆22	14⟆22		14 39			15 00			15 09	15 25			15 39			15 47
	d		13 48	14 01		14 11						14 41			15 01			15 11				15 40			15 48
Ashchurch for Tewkesbury	d		13 57																						15 57
Worcester Shrub Hill 7	a		14 15																						16 14
Birmingham New Street 12	a			14 45		14 55						15 26			15 45			15 55				16 26			
	d			14 49	14 52	15 03		15 19			15 22		15 30		15 49	15 52		16 03		16 19	16 22		16 30		
Water Orton	d				15 03																				
Coleshill Parkway	d				15 07						15 36					16 07					16 36				
Nuneaton	d				15 23						15 52					16 23					16 52				
Hinckley	d				15 30											16 30									
Narborough	d				15 39											16 39									
South Wigston	d															16 43									
Leicester	a				15 50						16 16					16 50					17 16				
Wilnecote	d			15 05											16 05										
Tamworth	d			15 09				15 36							16 09			16 19		16 36					
Burton-on-Trent	d			15 21		15 27		15 48							16 21					16 48			16 54		
Willington	d			15 26																					
Derby 6	a			15 36		15 41		16 00					16 06		16 34			16 40		17 00			17 06		
	d	15 13		15 40				16 08						16 13	16 40					17 08				17 13	
Long Eaton	d	15 23		15 49										16 23	16 49					17 17				17 25	
Attenborough 56	d	15 32												16 32										17 33	
Beeston 56	d	15 35		15 57										16 35	16 57					17 25				17 36	
Nottingham 8 56 ⛴	a	15 41		16 04				16 28						16 41	17 04					17 31				17 42	

A From Matlock
B From Southampton Central to Worcester Foregate Street
C From Plymouth to Aberdeen
D from 4 January until 8 February. From Swindon
E from 15 February. From London Paddington
F To Stansted Airport
G From Paignton to Manchester Piccadilly
H From Reading to Newcastle
I From Penzance to Glasgow Central
J from 15 February. From Swindon
K From Maesteg
L To Manchester Piccadilly
M From Southampton Central to Newcastle
N From Brighton to Great Malvern
O From Plymouth to Dundee
P From Penzance to Manchester Piccadilly
Q From Plymouth to Glasgow Central
R From Swindon
S From Southampton Central to Great Malvern

Table 57R

Saturdays

14 December to 17 May

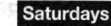

Bristol and Cardiff - Birmingham
Leicester, Derby and Nottingham

Network Diagram - refer to first Page of Table 50

Station	Table		XC	XC	XC	XC	GW	AW	XC		XC	XC	EM	XC	XC	XC	GW	AW	XC		XC	XC	XC	EM	GW	XC
			◇1	1	◇1	1	◇1		◇1		◇1	◇1		◇1	1	◇1			1		◇1	◇1	◇1			◇1
					A		B	C	D		E	F	G			A	H	C			D	I	J	G	K	L
			🛒		🛒		⊐				🛒	🛒		🛒		🛒						🛒	🛒			🛒
Cardiff Central 7	132	d	14 45					15 12						15 45				16 12								16 45
Newport (South Wales)	132	d	15 00					15 27						16 00				16 26								17 00
Bristol Temple Meads 10	134	d			15 30						16 00					16 30						17 00			16 41	
Bristol Parkway 7	134	d			15 39						16 09					16 39						17 09			16 52	
Gloucester 7	134	d	15 50				16 12	16 21						16 50			17 13	17 20							17 37	17 50
Cheltenham Spa		a	16 00		16 09		16 22	16 35			16 39			17 00		17 10	17 25	17 33				17 39			17 47	18 00
		d	16 01		16 11						16 40			17 01		17 11						17 41			17 48	18 01
Ashchurch for Tewkesbury		d																							17 57	
Worcester Shrub Hill 7		a																							18 16	
Birmingham New Street 12		a	16 45		16 55						17 26			17 45		17 55						18 26				18 45
		d	16 49	16 52	17 03	17 19			17 22			17 30		17 49	17 52	18 03			18 19		18 22		18 30			18 49
Water Orton		d		17 03																						
Coleshill Parkway		d		17 07					17 36						18 05						18 36					
Nuneaton		d		17 23					17 52						18 22						18 52					
Hinckley		d		17 30											18 29											
Narborough		d		17 39											18 38											
South Wigston		d													18 42											
Leicester		a		17 50					18 16						18 50						19 16					
Wilnecote		d	17 05											18 05												19 05
Tamworth		d	17 09			17 36								18 09		18 19			18 36							19 09
Burton-on-Trent		d	17 21		17 26	17 48								18 21					18 47							19 21
Willington		d												18 28												
Derby 6		a	17 34		17 41	18 00						18 06		18 36		18 41			19 00				19 05			19 35
		d	17 40			18 08							18 13	18 40					19 06					19 13		19 40
Long Eaton		d	17 49			18 17							18 23	18 49					19 15					19 23		19 49
Attenborough	56	d											18 32											19 32		
Beeston	56	d	17 57			18 25							18 35	18 57					19 25					19 35		19 57
Nottingham 8	56 ⛴	a	18 04			18 31							18 41	19 04					19 34					19 41		20 04

Station	Table		XC	XC	XC		GW	GW	AW	XC	XC	XC	EM	XC	XC		XC	EM	GW	GW	AW	XC	XC	XC	GW	
			1	◇1	1			◇1		◇1	◇1	◇1		◇1	1		◇1			1		◇1	◇1	◇1		
				M			N	O	C	D	P	F	G	L			Q	G	R	N	C	S	I	T	K	
				🛒				⊐			🛒			🛒			🛒						🛒			
Cardiff Central 7	132	d							17 12					17 45							18 12					
Newport (South Wales)	132	d							17 27					18 00							18 27					
Bristol Temple Meads 10	134	d		17 30							18 00						18 30						19 00		18 41	
Bristol Parkway 7	134	d		17 39							18 09						18 39						19 09		18 52	
Gloucester 7	134	d					18 08	18 12	18 23					18 46					19 13	19 13	19 21				19 37	
Cheltenham Spa		a		18 11			18 19	18 22	18 36		18 39			18 56			19 10		19 25	19 25	19 34		19 39		19 48	
		d		18 13							18 41			18 57			19 11						19 41		19 48	
Ashchurch for Tewkesbury		d												19 05											19 57	
Worcester Shrub Hill 7		a																							20 15	
Birmingham New Street 12		a		18 55							19 26			19 45			19 58						20 26			
		d	18 52	19 03	19 19					19 22		19 30		19 49	19 52		20 03					20 22		20 30		
Water Orton		d													20 03											
Coleshill Parkway		d	19 05							19 36					20 07							20 36				
Nuneaton		d	19 22							19 52					20 23							20 52				
Hinckley		d	19 29												20 30											
Narborough		d	19 38												20 39											
South Wigston		d	19 42												20 43											
Leicester		a	19 50							20 16					20 50							21 16				
Wilnecote		d												20 05												
Tamworth		d			19 36									20 09			20 19									
Burton-on-Trent		d		19 27	19 48									20 21												
Willington		d																								
Derby 6		a		19 39	20 00							20 06		20 34			20 42							21 24		
		d			20 08								20 13	20 40				21 13								
Long Eaton		d											20 23	20 49				21 23								
Attenborough	56	d											20 32					21 32								
Beeston	56	d											20 35	20 57				21 35								
Nottingham 8	56 ⛴	a			20 28								20 42	21 04				21 41								

A From Plymouth to Edinburgh
B From London Paddington
C From Maesteg
D To Stansted Airport
E From Paignton to Manchester Piccadilly
F From Reading to Newcastle
G From Matlock
H From Swindon
I To Manchester Piccadilly
J From Southampton Central to Newcastle
K From Warminster to Great Malvern
L 🛒 to Birmingham New Street
M From Plymouth to York
N from 4 January until 8 February. From Swindon
O from 15 February. From London Paddington
P From Exeter St Davids to Manchester Piccadilly
Q From Plymouth to Leeds. 🛒 to Birmingham New Street
R from 15 February. From Swindon
S To Cambridge
T From Southampton Central to York

Table 57R

Saturdays

14 December to 17 May

Bristol and Cardiff - Birmingham
Leicester, Derby and Nottingham

Network Diagram - refer to first Page of Table 50

			XC ◇1 A ⊥		XC 1	XC ◇1 B ⊥	GW C	GW ◇1 D ⊡	XC ◇1	GW E	GW F	GW C	XC ◇1 G		XC ◇1	XC 1	GW	XC ◇1	GW ◇1 H ⊡	EM I	XC 1
Cardiff Central 7	132	d	18 45												20 00			20 50			
Newport (South Wales)	132	d	19 00												20 15			21 05			
Bristol Temple Meads 10	134	d				19 30			20 00	19 41			20 30				20 43				
Bristol Parkway 7	134	d				19 40			20 09	19 52			20 39				20 52				
Gloucester 7	134	d	19 46				20∫08	20∫12		20 37	20∫53	20∫54			21 07		21 37	21 49	22 12		
Cheltenham Spa		a	19 56			20 09	20∫19	20∫22	20 39	20 49	21∫03	21∫04	21 09		21 16		21 48	21 58	22 21		
		d	19 57			20 11			20 41				21 11		21 18		21 48	22 00			
Ashchurch for Tewkesbury		d													21 25		21 57				
Worcester Shrub Hill 7		a															22 18				
Birmingham New Street 12		a	20 42			20 52			21 38				21 52		22 07			22 42			
		d	20 49		20 52	21 03									22 10	22 22					22 49
Water Orton		d																			
Coleshill Parkway		d			21 05											22 35					
Nuneaton		d			21 21											22 52					
Hinckley		d			21 29											22 59					
Narborough		d			21 38											23 08					
South Wigston		d			21 42											23 12					
Leicester		a			21 50											23 18					
Wilnecote		d	21 05																		23 04
Tamworth		d	21 09			21 19									22 27						23 08
Burton-on-Trent		d	21 21			21 30									22 39						23 20
Willington		d													22 45						
Derby 6		a	21 34			21 43									22 55						23 33
		d	21 40												23 00					23 31	
Long Eaton		d	21 52												23 12					23 41	
Attenborough	56	d	21 58												23 18					23 49	
Beeston	56	d	22 02												23 22					23 52	
Nottingham 8	56 ⛴	a	22 08												23 28					00 01	

Sundays

8 December to 29 December

			EM	XC ◇1 J ⊥	XC 1	XC ◇1 K ⊥	EM I	XC 1	XC ◇1 J ⊥	XC ◇1 L ⊥	GW		GW ◇1 M	XC ◇1 ⊥	XC 1	XC ◇1 K ⊥	XC ◇1 L ⊥	GW M	AW	XC ◇1 N ⊥	EM I		XC ◇1 O ⊥	XC 1	XC ◇1 P ⊥	XC ◇1 L ⊥
Cardiff Central 7	132	d																	10 23				10 45			
Newport (South Wales)	132	d																	10 38				10 59			
Bristol Temple Meads 10	134	d							09 15		09 41					10 30									11 30	
Bristol Parkway 7	134	d							09 24		09 52					10 39									11 39	
Gloucester 7	134	d							10 00		10 35		10 48					11 36	11 42				11 51			
Cheltenham Spa		a							10 09		10 45		10 57			11 09		11 45	11 54				12 01		12 09	
		d							10 12							11 10							12 03		12 10	
Ashchurch for Tewkesbury		d																								
Worcester Shrub Hill 7		a																								
Birmingham New Street 12		a							10 49							11 48							12 45		12 49	
		d		09 03	09 52	10 03		10 52	11 03	11 22				11 49	11 52	12 03	12 22			12 30			12 49	12 52	13 03	13 22
Water Orton		d																								
Coleshill Parkway		d			10 05			11 05		11 36					12 05		12 36							13 05		13 36
Nuneaton		d			10 22			11 22		11 52					12 22		12 52							13 22		13 52
Hinckley		d			10 29			11 29							12 29									13 29		
Narborough		d			10 37			11 37							12 37									13 37		
South Wigston		d			10 42										12 42											
Leicester		a			10 48			11 48		12 15					12 48		13 16							13 48		14 16
Wilnecote		d																								
Tamworth		d		09 19		10 18								12 07		12 19							13 07			
Burton-on-Trent		d		09 28		10 29			11 25					12 19									13 19		13 26	
Willington		d																								
Derby 6		a		09 41		10 40			11 37					12 34		12 41				13 01			13 33		13 37	
		d	09 14				11 14							12 40							13 14		13 40			
Long Eaton		d	09 24				11 24														13 24					
Attenborough	56	d	09 31				11 31														13 31					
Beeston	56	d	09 34				11 34														13 34					
Nottingham 8	56 ⛴	a	09 41				11 41							13 00							13 41		14 00			

- **A** ⊥ to Birmingham New Street
- **B** From Plymouth to Leeds. ⊥ to Birmingham New Street
- **C** from 4 January until 8 February. From Swindon
- **D** from 15 February. From London Paddington
- **E** From Westbury
- **F** from 15 February. From Swindon
- **G** From Plymouth
- **H** From London Paddington
- **I** From Matlock
- **J** To Edinburgh
- **K** To Glasgow Central
- **L** To Stansted Airport
- **M** From Swindon
- **N** To Newcastle
- **O** ⊥ from Newport (South Wales)
- **P** From Plymouth to Aberdeen

Table 57R

Sundays

8 December to 29 December

Bristol and Cardiff - Birmingham
Leicester, Derby and Nottingham

Network Diagram - refer to first Page of Table 50

	GW A		XC ◇1 B trolley	XC ◇1 C trolley	XC 1	XC ◇1 D trolley	XC ◇1 E trolley	GW	XC ◇1 F trolley	XC ◇1 G trolley	EM H		GW A	AW	XC ◇1 trolley	XC 1	XC ◇1 I trolley	XC ◇1 E trolley	XC ◇1 J trolley	XC ◇1 K trolley	EM		XC ◇1 C trolley	XC 1
Cardiff Central [7] 132 d				11 45										12 25	12 45								13 45	
Newport (South Wales) 132 d				11 59										12 40	12 59								13 59	
Bristol Temple Meads [10] 134 d						12 30		12 11	13 00								13 30		14 00					
Bristol Parkway [7] 134 d						12 39		12 21	13 09								13 39		14 09					
Gloucester [7] 134 d	12 42			12 47				13 05					13 35	13 42	13 49								14 47	
Cheltenham Spa a	12 51			12 56		13 09		13 16	13 39				13 45	13 51	13 58		14 09		14 39				14 56	
d				12 58		13 10		13 16	13 41						14 00		14 10		14 41				14 58	
Ashchurch for Tewkesbury d								13 25																
Worcester Shrub Hill [7] a								13 44																
Birmingham New Street [12] a				13 41		13 48			14 27						14 44		14 48		15 27				15 41	
d			13 30	13 49	13 52	14 03	14 22			14 30					14 49	14 52	15 03	15 22		15 30			15 49	15 52
Water Orton d																								
Coleshill Parkway d					14 05		14 36									15 05		15 36						16 05
Nuneaton d					14 22		14 52									15 22		15 52						16 22
Hinckley d					14 29											15 29								16 29
Narborough d					14 37											15 37								16 37
South Wigston d					14 42																			16 42
Leicester a					14 48		15 15									15 48		16 16						16 48
Wilnecote d															15 04									
Tamworth d				14 07		14 19									15 09								16 07	
Burton-on-Trent d				14 19											15 21		15 25						16 19	
Willington d																								
Derby [6] a			14 01	14 34		14 39				15 01					15 33		15 37			16 01			16 34	
d				14 40							15 16				15 40						16 14		16 40	
Long Eaton d											15 26										16 23			
Attenborough 56 d											15 34										16 31			
Beeston 56 d											15 37										16 34			
Nottingham [8] 56 a				15 00							15 43				16 00						16 43		17 00	

	XC ◇1 D trolley	XC ◇1 E	GW A	XC ◇1 J trolley	XC ◇1 K trolley	EM H	AW		XC ◇1 trolley	XC 1	GW	XC ◇1 L trolley	XC ◇1 E	XC ◇1 M trolley	XC ◇1 N trolley	EM	XC ◇1 O trolley		XC 1	GW A	XC ◇1 L trolley	XC ◇1 E	XC ◇1 P trolley	XC ◇1 K trolley
Cardiff Central [7] 132 d							14 25		14 45								15 45							
Newport (South Wales) 132 d							14 40		14 59								15 59							
Bristol Temple Meads [10] 134 d	14 30			15 00							14 41	15 30		16 00							16 30		17 00	
Bristol Parkway [7] 134 d	14 39			15 09							14 51	15 40		16 09							16 40		17 09	
Gloucester [7] 134 d			15 24				15 41		15 47		15 52						16 47			16 54				
Cheltenham Spa a	15 09		15 33	15 38			15 51		15 56		16 02	16 10		16 39			16 56			17 03	17 09		17 40	
d	15 10			15 41					15 58		16 03	16 11		16 40			16 58				17 12		17 41	
Ashchurch for Tewkesbury d											16 12													
Worcester Shrub Hill [7] a											16 32													
Birmingham New Street [12] a	15 48			16 26					16 41			16 49		17 26			17 41				17 48		18 28	
d	16 03	16 22			16 30				16 49	16 52		17 03	17 22		17 30		17 49		17 52		18 03	18 22		18 30
Water Orton d																								
Coleshill Parkway d		16 36								17 05			17 36						18 05			18 36		
Nuneaton d		16 52								17 22			17 52						18 22			18 52		
Hinckley d										17 29									18 29					
Narborough d										17 37									18 37					
South Wigston d										17 42									18 42					
Leicester a		17 16								17 48			18 13						18 48			19 16		
Wilnecote d																								
Tamworth d	16 19								17 07								18 07				18 19			
Burton-on-Trent d									17 19			17 28					18 19							
Willington d																								
Derby [6] a	16 38				17 01				17 34			17 40			18 01		18 33				18 39			19 02
d						17 14			17 40							18 14	18 40							
Long Eaton d						17 24										18 24								
Attenborough 56 d						17 31										18 34								
Beeston 56 d						17 34										18 37								
Nottingham [8] 56 a						17 44			18 00							18 44	19 00							

A From Swindon
B To Newcastle
C trolley from Birmingham New Street
D From Plymouth to Glasgow Central
E To Stansted Airport
F From Paignton to Manchester Piccadilly
G From Guildford to Newcastle
H From Matlock
I From Penzance to Edinburgh
J From Plymouth to Manchester Piccadilly
K From Reading to Newcastle
L From Plymouth to Edinburgh
M To Manchester Piccadilly
N From Reading to Edinburgh
O trolley to Birmingham New Street
P From Penzance to Manchester Piccadilly

Table 57R

Sundays

8 December to 29 December

Bristol and Cardiff - Birmingham
Leicester, Derby and Nottingham

Network Diagram - refer to first Page of Table 50

		EM	GW	AW	XC	XC	XC	XC	XC	XC		EM	GW	XC	XC	EM	XC	XC	GW	AW		XC	XC	XC	EM
					◇1	1	◇1	◇1	◇1	◇1			◇1	◇1	◇1		◇1	◇1				◇1	1	◇1	
		A			B		C	D	E	F			G	B	H	A	I	E				B		J	
					🛒		🛒		🛒	🛒			🍴	🛒	🛒			🛒				🛒		🛒	
Cardiff Central 7	132 d			16 23	16 45									17 45						18 23		18 45			
Newport (South Wales)	132 d			16 38	16 59									17 59						18 38		18 59			
Bristol Temple Meads 10	134 d		16 41				17 30		18 00						18 30			19 00	18 41					19 30	
Bristol Parkway 7	134 d		16 50				17 40		18 09						18 39			19 09	18 50					19 39	
Gloucester 7	134 d		17 35	17 40	17 47								18 33	18 47					19 37	19 42		19 52			
Cheltenham Spa	a		17 45	17 50	17 56		18 09		18 39				18 44	18 56	19 09			19 40	19 46	19 55		20 01		20 09	
	d		17 46		17 58		18 11		18 40					18 58	19 10			19 41	19 47			20 02		20 10	
Ashchurch for Tewkesbury	d		17 55																19 56						
Worcester Shrub Hill 7	a		18 15																20 22						
Birmingham New Street 12	a				18 41		18 48		19 26					19 41	19 48			20 27				20 44		20 49	
	d				18 49	18 52	19 03	19 22		19 30				19 49	20 03		20 22					20 49	20 52	21 03	
Water Orton	d																								
Coleshill Parkway	d					19 05		19 36									20 36						21 05		
Nuneaton	d					19 22		19 52									20 52						21 22		
Hinckley	d					19 29																	21 29		
Narborough	d					19 37																	21 37		
South Wigston	d					19 42																	21 42		
Leicester	a					19 48		20 16									21 16						21 48		
Wilnecote	d				19 04																				
Tamworth	d				19 09									20 07	20 19							21 06		21 19	
Burton-on-Trent	d				19 21		19 26							20 19								21 19		21 29	
Willington	d																								
Derby 6	a				19 33		19 40			20 01				20 34	20 38							21 33		21 41	
	d	19 14			19 40							20 14		20 40		21 14						21 40			22 18
Long Eaton	d	19 24										20 23				21 24									22 28
Attenborough	56 d	19 34										20 31				21 31									22 35
Beeston	56 d	19 37										20 34				21 34									22 38
Nottingham 8	56 ⛴ a	19 44			20 00							20 41		21 00		21 41						22 00			22 45

		XC	GW	XC	XC	GW		GW	XC	GW	XC	GW
		◇1	◇1	◇1	◇1				◇1	◇1	◇1	
		K	G		L	M				G		N
			🍴		🛒					🍴		
Cardiff Central 7	132 d			19 45					20 45			
Newport (South Wales)	132 d			20 00					20 59			
Bristol Temple Meads 10	134 d	20 00			20 30			20 41			22 10	
Bristol Parkway 7	134 d	20 09			20 40			20 50			22 20	
Gloucester 7	134 d		20 34	20 49		21 25		21 37	21 48	22 31		23 55
Cheltenham Spa	a	20 39	20 45	20 58	21 09	21 33		21 46	21 57	22 40	22 47	00 04
	d	20 40		21 00	21 11				21 59		22 49	
Ashchurch for Tewkesbury	d											
Worcester Shrub Hill 7	a											
Birmingham New Street 12	a	21 18		21 44	21 48				22 42		23 40	
	d			21 52	22 03							
Water Orton	d											
Coleshill Parkway	d			22 05								
Nuneaton	d			22 22								
Hinckley	d			22 29								
Narborough	d			22 37								
South Wigston	d			22 42								
Leicester	a			22 48								
Wilnecote	d											
Tamworth	d				22 19							
Burton-on-Trent	d											
Willington	d											
Derby 6	a				22 40							
	d											
Long Eaton	d											
Attenborough	56 d											
Beeston	56 d											
Nottingham 8	56 ⛴ a											

A From Matlock
B 🛒 to Birmingham New Street
C From Plymouth to York
D To Stansted Airport
E To Manchester Piccadilly
F From Reading to Newcastle
G From London Paddington
H From Plymouth to Leeds
I To Cambridge
J From Penzance to Leeds. 🛒 to Birmingham New Street
K From Paignton
L From Plymouth to Leeds. 🛒 to Birmingham New Street
M From Westbury
N From Swindon

Table 57R

Sundays

5 January to 23 March

Bristol and Cardiff - Birmingham
Leicester, Derby and Nottingham

Network Diagram - refer to first Page of Table 50

	EM	XC ◇1 A 🛒	EM B	XC 🚌	XC 1		XC 🚌	XC ◇1 C 🛒	XC ◇1 D 🛒	XC ◇1	XC ◇1 🛒	XC 🚌	XC ◇1 C 🛒	GW	GW ◇1 E		GW ◇1 F	XC ◇1 A 🛒	XC ◇1	XC ◇1 G 🛒	EM H	GW E	GW F	AW
Cardiff Central 7 132 d																								10 23
Newport (South Wales) 132 d																								10 38
Bristol Temple Meads 10 134 d											09 15			09 41						10 30				
Bristol Parkway 7 134 d											09 24			09 52						10 39				
Gloucester 7 134 d											10 00			10 35	10 48		10 50					11 36	11 37	11 42
Cheltenham Spa a											10 09			10 45	10 57		10 59			11 09		11 45	11 46	11 54
d											10 12									11 10				
Ashchurch for Tewkesbury d																								
Worcester Shrub Hill 7 a																								
Birmingham New Street 12 a											10 49									11 48				
d		09 30		09 52			10 22		10 30			11 22						11 30		12 03				
Water Orton d																								
Coleshill Parkway d				10 32			11 02					12 02												
Nuneaton d				11a07	11 22		11a37	11 52				12a37	12 52											
Hinckley d					11 29			11 59					12 59											
Narborough d					11 37			12 07					13 07											
South Wigston d					11 42			12 12					13 12											
Leicester a					11 48			12 16					13 16											
Wilnecote d																								
Tamworth d																								
Burton-on-Trent d		10 15							11 15									12 15						
Willington d																								
Derby 6 a		10 27							11 27									12 27		12 55				
d	09 14		11 14							11 40									12 40		13 14			
Long Eaton d	09 24		11 24																		13 24			
Attenborough 56 d	09 31		11 31																		13 31			
Beeston 56 d	09 34		11 34																		13 34			
Nottingham 8 56 🚢 a	09 41		11 41							12 00									13 00		13 41			

	XC 🚌		XC ◇1 C 🛒	XC ◇1 I 🛒	EM J	XC ◇1 K 🛒	XC ◇1	XC ◇1 L 🛒	XC 🚌	XC ◇1 C 🛒	GW E		GW F	XC ◇1 A 🛒	XC ◇1	XC ◇1	XC ◇1 L 🛒	EM H	GW	XC 🚌	XC ◇1 C 🛒		XC ◇1 M 🛒	GW N
Cardiff Central 7 132 d						10 45										11 45								
Newport (South Wales) 132 d						10 59										11 59								
Bristol Temple Meads 10 134 d								11 30									12 30		12 11				13 00	
Bristol Parkway 7 134 d								11 39									12 39		12 21				13 09	
Gloucester 7 134 d						11 51					12 34		12 42			12 47			13 05					13 35
Cheltenham Spa a						12 01		12 09			12 44		12 51			12 56	13 09		13 16				13 39	13 45
d						12 03		12 10								12 58	13 10		13 16				13 41	
Ashchurch for Tewkesbury d																			13 25					
Worcester Shrub Hill 7 a																			13 44					
Birmingham New Street 12 a						12 45		12 49								13 41	13 48						14 27	
d	12 22			12 30				13 03	13 22					13 30			14 03			14 22				
Water Orton d																								
Coleshill Parkway d	13 02								14 02											15 02				
Nuneaton d	13a37		13 52						14a37	14 52										15a37	15 52			
Hinckley d			13 59							14 59											15 59			
Narborough d			14 07							15 07											16 07			
South Wigston d			14 12							15 12											16 12			
Leicester a			14 16							15 16											16 16			
Wilnecote d																								
Tamworth d																								
Burton-on-Trent d				13 14										14 15										
Willington d																								
Derby 6 a				13 26				13 55						14 27			14 55							
d					13 27		13 40								14 40			15 16						
Long Eaton d					13 37													15 26						
Attenborough 56 d					13 44													15 34						
Beeston 56 d					13 47													15 37						
Nottingham 8 56 🚢 a					13 54		14 00								15 00			15 43						

A To Glasgow Central
B From Matlock
C To Stansted Airport
D To Edinburgh
E until 9 February. From Swindon
F from 16 February. From Swindon
G To Newcastle
H until 9 February. From Matlock
I To Aberdeen
J from 16 February. From Matlock
K 🛒 from Newport (South Wales)
L From Plymouth to Newcastle
M From Paignton to Manchester Piccadilly
N From Swindon

Table 57R

Sundays

5 January to 23 March

Bristol and Cardiff - Birmingham
Leicester, Derby and Nottingham

Network Diagram - refer to first Page of Table 50

Station			AW	EM A	XC ◇1 B 🚲		XC ◇1	XC ◇1 🚲	XC ◇1 C 🚲	EM	XC 🚌	XC ◇1 D	XC ◇1 E 🚲		XC ◇1 🚲		XC ◇1	XC ◇1	XC ◇1 H 🚲	EM I	GW J	XC 🚌	XC ◇1 D	XC ◇1 K 🚲	XC ◇1 L 🚲	
Cardiff Central 7	132	d	12 25					12 45										13 45								
Newport (South Wales)	132	d	12 40					12 59										13 59								
Bristol Temple Meads 10	134	d							13 30				14 00						14 30					15 00		
Bristol Parkway 7	134	d							13 39				14 09						14 39					15 09		
Gloucester 7	134	d	13 42					13 49										14 47			15 23					
Cheltenham Spa		a	13 51					13 58	14 09				14 39					14 56	15 09		15 33			15 38		
		d						14 00	14 10				14 41					14 58	15 10					15 41		
Ashchurch for Tewkesbury		d																								
Worcester Shrub Hill 7		a																								
Birmingham New Street 12		a						14 44	14 48				15 27					15 41	15 48					16 26		
		d			14 30				15 03		15 22				15 30				16 03			16 22			16 30	
Water Orton		d																								
Coleshill Parkway		d									16 02											17 02				
Nuneaton		d									16a37	16 52										17a37	17 52			
Hinckley		d										16 59											17 59			
Narborough		d										17 07											18 07			
South Wigston		d										17 12											18 12			
Leicester		a										17 16											18 16			
Wilnecote		d																								
Tamworth		d																								
Burton-on-Trent		d			15 15										16 15										17 16	
Willington		d																								
Derby 6		a			15 27				15 55						16 27				16 55						17 29	
		d		15 23			15 40			16 14							16 40			17 14						
Long Eaton		d		15 33						16 23										17 24						
Attenborough	56	d		15 41						16 31										17 31						
Beeston	56	d		15 44						16 34										17 34						
Nottingham 8	56 🚢	a		15 50			16 00			16 43							17 00			17 44						

Station			XC ◇1	AW	XC ◇1 🚲	GW	XC ◇1 M 🚲	XC ◇1 N 🚲	EM O	XC 🚌	XC ◇1 D		XC ◇1 P 🚲	EM Q	XC ◇1 R 🚲	XC ◇1	XC ◇1 🚲	GW J	XC ◇1 S 🚲	XC ◇1 T 🚲	EM A		XC 🚌	XC ◇1 D	XC ◇1 U 🚲	XC ◇1 V 🚲
Cardiff Central 7	132	d		14 25	14 45												15 45									
Newport (South Wales)	132	d		14 40	14 59												15 59									
Bristol Temple Meads 10	134	d				14 38	15 30	15 30					16 00						16 30	16 30					17 00	17 00
Bristol Parkway 7	134	d				14 48	15 40	15 40					16 09						16 40	16 40					17 09	17 09
Gloucester 7	134	d		15 41	15 47	15 52											16 47	16 54								
Cheltenham Spa		a		15 51	15 56	16 02	16 10	16 10					16 39				16 56	17 03	17 09	17 09					17 40	17 40
		d			15 58	16 03	16 11	16 11					16 40				16 58		17 12	17 12					17 41	17 41
Ashchurch for Tewkesbury		d				16 12																				
Worcester Shrub Hill 7		a				16 32																				
Birmingham New Street 12		a			16 41		16 49	16 49					17 26				17 41		17 48	17 48					18 27	18 28
		d					17 03	17 03		17 22					17 30				18 03	18 03			18 22			
Water Orton		d																								
Coleshill Parkway		d								18 02													19 02			
Nuneaton		d								18a37	18 52												19a37	19 52		
Hinckley		d									18 59													19 59		
Narborough		d									19 07													20 07		
South Wigston		d									19 12													20 12		
Leicester		a									19 16													20 16		
Wilnecote		d																								
Tamworth		d																								
Burton-on-Trent		d													18 16											
Willington		d																								
Derby 6		a					17 55	17 57							18 29				18 55	18 56						
		d	17 40						18 14					18 25		18 40					19 13					
Long Eaton		d							18 24					18 35							19 23					
Attenborough	56	d							18 34					18 42							19 30					
Beeston	56	d							18 37					18 45							19 33					
Nottingham 8	56 🚢	a	18 00						18 44					18 52		19 00					19 40					

A from 16 February. From Matlock
B From Guildford to Edinburgh
C From Penzance to Newcastle
D To Stansted Airport
E until 9 February. From Plymouth to Manchester Piccadilly
H From Exeter St Davids to Edinburgh
I From Matlock
J From Swindon
K From Plymouth to Manchester Piccadilly
L From Reading to Newcastle
M until 9 February. From Plymouth to Edinburgh
N from 16 February. From Exeter St Davids to Edinburgh
O until 9 February
P To Manchester Piccadilly
Q from 16 February
R From Reading to Edinburgh
S until 9 February. From Plymouth to Newcastle
T from 16 February. From Exeter St Davids to York
U from 16 February. To Manchester Piccadilly
V until 9 February. From Penzance to Manchester Piccadilly

Table 57R

Sundays

5 January to 23 March

Bristol and Cardiff - Birmingham Leicester, Derby and Nottingham

Network Diagram - refer to first Page of Table 50

		GW		GW	AW	EM	XC	XC	XC	XC	EM	XC		XC	XC	GW	XC	XC	XC	XC	XC	XC		EM	XC
							◇1	◇1	◇1	◇1				◇1	◇1	◇1	◇1		1	◇1	◇1	◇1			◇1
		A		B		C	D			E				F	G	H					I	J		K	G
												bus						bus							
							trolley		trolley	trolley					trolley	restaurant	trolley				trolley	trolley			trolley
Cardiff Central 7 132	d				16 23				16 45								17 45								
Newport (South Wales) 132	d				16 38				16 59								17 59								
Bristol Temple Meads 10 134	d	16 38		16 41						17 30					18 00						18 30	18 30			19 00
Bristol Parkway 7 134	d	16 48		16 50						17 40					18 09						18 40	18 40			19 09
Gloucester 7 134	d	17 35		17 35	17 40				17 47							18 33	18 47								
Cheltenham Spa	a	17 45		17 45	17 50				17 56	18 09					18 39	18 44	18 56				19 09	19 10			19 40
	d	17 46		17 46					17 58	18 11					18 40		18 58				19 11	19 11			19 41
Ashchurch for Tewkesbury	d	17 55		17 55																					
Worcester Shrub Hill 7	a	18 15		18 15																					
Birmingham New Street 12	a								18 41	18 48					19 26		19 41				19 49	19 49			20 27
	d						18 30			19 03		19 22						19 52			20 03	20 03			
Water Orton	d																								
Coleshill Parkway	d											20 02						20 32							
Nuneaton	d											20a37		20 52				21a07	21 22						
Hinckley	d													20 59					21 29						
Narborough	d													21 07					21 37						
South Wigston	d													21 12					21 42						
Leicester	a													21 16					21 48						
Wilnecote	d																								
Tamworth	d																								
Burton-on-Trent	d						19 16																		
Willington	d																								
Derby 6	a						19 29			19 55											20 57	20 57			
	d					19 16		19 40			20 14									20 40				21 14	
Long Eaton	d					19 26					20 23													21 24	
Attenborough 56	d					19 33					20 31													21 31	
Beeston 56	d					19 36					20 34													21 34	
Nottingham 8 56	a					19 43		20 00			20 41									21 00				21 41	

		GW	AW	XC	XC	XC	XC	XC		XC	EM	XC	GW	GW	XC	XC	XC	XC		GW	GW	XC	GW	XC	GW
				◇1		1	◇1	◇1		◇1		◇1	◇1	◇1	◇1	◇1	◇1	◇1				◇1	◇1	◇1	
								L		I		M	N	O		P	Q	R		S			H	T	U
					bus																				
				trolley				trolley		trolley			restaurant	restaurant			trolley	trolley					restaurant		
Cardiff Central 7 132	d		18 23	18 45											19 45							20 45			
Newport (South Wales) 132	d		18 38	18 59											20 00							20 59			
Bristol Temple Meads 10 134	d	18 41						19 30		19 30		20 00				20 30	20 30				20 41			22 10	
Bristol Parkway 7 134	d	18 50						19 39		19 39		20 09				20 40	20 40				20 50			22 20	
Gloucester 7 134	d	19 37	19 42	19 52									20 34	20 38	20 49					21 25	21 37	21 48	22 31		23 55
Cheltenham Spa	a	19 46	19 55	20 01				20 09		20 09		20 39	20 45	20 49	20 58	21 08	21 09			21 33	21 46	21 57	22 42	22 47	00 04
	d	19 47		20 02				20 10		20 10		20 40			21 00	21 11	21 11					21 59		22 49	
Ashchurch for Tewkesbury	d	19 56																							
Worcester Shrub Hill 7	a	20 22																							
Birmingham New Street 12	a			20 44				20 49		20 49		21 18			21 44	21 49	21 48					22 42		23 40	
	d				20 52			21 03		21 03							22 03	22 03							
Water Orton	d																								
Coleshill Parkway	d				21 32																				
Nuneaton	d				22a07	22 22																			
Hinckley	d					22 29																			
Narborough	d					22 37																			
South Wigston	d					22 42																			
Leicester	a					22 48																			
Wilnecote	d																								
Tamworth	d																								
Burton-on-Trent	d							21 47		21 47							22 46	22 46							
Willington	d																								
Derby 6	a							21 58		21 58							22 59	22 59							
	d						21 40				22 18														
Long Eaton	d										22 28														
Attenborough 56	d										22 35														
Beeston 56	d										22 38														
Nottingham 8 56	a						22 00				22 45														

A until 9 February
B from 16 February
C until 9 February. From Matlock
D From Reading to York
E From Plymouth to Newcastle
F To Cambridge
G To Manchester Piccadilly
H From London Paddington
I from 16 February. From Exeter St Davids to Leeds
J until 9 February. From Plymouth to Leeds
K From Matlock
L until 9 February. From Penzance to Leeds. trolley to Birmingham New Street
M From Paignton
N until 9 February. From London Paddington
O from 16 February. From London Paddington
P from 16 February. From Exeter St Davids
Q until 9 February. From Plymouth to Leeds. trolley to Birmingham New Street
R from 16 February. To Leeds
S From Westbury
T From Exeter St Davids
U From Swindon

Table 57R

Sundays

30 March to 11 May

Bristol and Cardiff - Birmingham Leicester, Derby and Nottingham

Network Diagram - refer to first Page of Table 50

		EM	XC	XC	XC	EM		XC	XC	XC	GW	GW	XC	XC	XC	XC		GW	AW	XC	EM	XC	XC	XC	XC
			◇1	1	◇1			1	◇1	◇1		◇1	◇1	1	◇1	◇1				◇1		◇1	1	◇1	◇1
			A		B	C			A	D		E			B	D		E		F	C	G		H	D
			[trolley]		[trolley]				[trolley]	[trolley]			[trolley]		[trolley]	[trolley]				[trolley]		[trolley]		[trolley]	[trolley]
Cardiff Central 7 . 132	d																		10 23			10 45			
Newport (South Wales) . 132	d																		10 38			10 59			
Bristol Temple Meads 10 134	d								09 15		09 41				10 30									11 30	
Bristol Parkway 7 . 134	d								09 24		09 52				10 39									11 39	
Gloucester 7 . 134	d								10 00		10 35	10 48						11 37	11 42			11 51			
Cheltenham Spa	a								10 09		10 45	10 57			11 09			11 46	11 54			12 01		12 09	
	d								10 12						11 10							12 03		12 10	
Ashchurch for Tewkesbury	d																								
Worcester Shrub Hill 7	a																								
Birmingham New Street 12	a								10 49						11 48							12 45		12 49	
	d		09 03	09 52	10 03			10 52	11 03	11 22			11 49	11 52	12 03	12 22				12 30		12 49	12 52	13 03	13 22
Water Orton	d																								
Coleshill Parkway	d			10 05				11 05		11 36				12 05		12 36							13 05		13 36
Nuneaton	d			10 22				11 22		11 52				12 22		12 52							13 22		13 52
Hinckley	d			10 29				11 29						12 29									13 29		
Narborough	d			10 37				11 37						12 37									13 37		
South Wigston	d			10 42										12 42											
Leicester	a			10 48				11 48		12 15				12 48		13 16							13 48		14 16
Wilnecote	d																								
Tamworth	d		09 19		10 18								12 07		12 19							13 07			
Burton-on-Trent	d		09 28		10 29				11 25				12 19									13 19		13 26	
Willington	d																								
Derby 6	a		09 41		10 40				11 37				12 34		12 41					13 01		13 33		13 37	
	d	09 14				11 14							12 40								13 14	13 40			
Long Eaton	d	09 24				11 24															13 24				
Attenborough . 56	d	09 31				11 31															13 31				
Beeston . 56	d	09 34				11 34															13 34				
Nottingham 8 . 56 ⇌	a	09 41				11 41							13 00								13 41	14 00			

		GW		XC	XC	XC	XC	XC	GW	XC	XC	EM		GW	AW	XC	XC	XC	XC	XC	XC	EM		XC	XC
				◇1	◇1	1	◇1	◇1		◇1	◇1					◇1	1	◇1	◇1	◇1	◇1			◇1	1
		E		F	I		J	D		K	L	C		E				M	D	N	O			I	
				[trolley]	[trolley]		[trolley]	[trolley]		[trolley]	[trolley]					[trolley]		[trolley]	[trolley]	[trolley]	[trolley]			[trolley]	
Cardiff Central 7 . 132	d				11 45										12 25	12 45								13 45	
Newport (South Wales) . 132	d				11 59										12 40	12 59								13 59	
Bristol Temple Meads 10 134	d						12 30		12 11	13 00								13 30		14 00					
Bristol Parkway 7 . 134	d						12 39		12 21	13 09								13 39		14 09					
Gloucester 7 . 134	d	12 42			12 47				13 05					13 35	13 42	13 49								14 47	
Cheltenham Spa	a	12 51			12 56		13 09		13 16	13 39				13 45	13 51	13 58		14 09		14 39				14 56	
	d				12 58		13 10		13 16	13 41						14 00		14 10		14 41				14 58	
Ashchurch for Tewkesbury	d								13 25																
Worcester Shrub Hill 7	a								13 44																
Birmingham New Street 12	a				13 41		13 48			14 27						14 44		14 48		15 27				15 41	
	d			13 30	13 49	13 52	14 03	14 22			14 30					14 49	14 52	15 03	15 22		15 30			15 49	15 52
Water Orton	d																								
Coleshill Parkway	d					14 05		14 36									15 05		15 36						16 05
Nuneaton	d					14 22		14 52									15 22		15 52						16 22
Hinckley	d					14 29											15 29								16 29
Narborough	d					14 37											15 37								16 37
South Wigston	d					14 42																			16 42
Leicester	a					14 48		15 15									15 48		16 16						16 48
Wilnecote	d															15 04									
Tamworth	d				14 07		14 19									15 09								16 07	
Burton-on-Trent	d				14 19											15 21		15 25						16 19	
Willington	d																								
Derby 6	a			14 01	14 34		14 39				15 01					15 33		15 37			16 01			16 34	
	d				14 40							15 16				15 40						16 14		16 40	
Long Eaton	d											15 26										16 23			
Attenborough . 56	d											15 34										16 31			
Beeston . 56	d											15 37										16 34			
Nottingham 8 . 56 ⇌	a				15 00							15 43				16 00						16 43		17 00	

A To Edinburgh
B To Glasgow Central
C From Matlock
D To Stansted Airport
E From Swindon
F To Newcastle
G [trolley] from Newport (South Wales)
H From Plymouth to Aberdeen
I [trolley] from Birmingham New Street
J From Plymouth to Glasgow Central
K From Paignton to Manchester Piccadilly
L From Guildford to Newcastle
M From Penzance to Edinburgh
N From Plymouth to Manchester Piccadilly
O From Reading to Newcastle

Table 57R

Sundays

30 March to 11 May

Bristol and Cardiff - Birmingham
Leicester, Derby and Nottingham

Network Diagram - refer to first Page of Table 50

			XC	XC	GW		XC	XC	EM	AW	XC	XC	GW	XC	XC		XC	XC	EM	XC	XC	GW	XC	XC	XC	
			◇1	◇1			◇1	◇1			◇1	1		◇1	◇1		◇1	◇1		◇1	1		◇1	◇1	◇1	
			A	B	C		D	E	F					G	B		H	I		J		C	G	B	K	
			🛒				🛒	🛒			🛒			🛒			🛒	🛒		🛒			🛒		🛒	
Cardiff Central [7]	132	d								14 25	14 45									15 45						
Newport (South Wales)	132	d								14 40	14 59									15 59						
Bristol Temple Meads [10]	134	d	14 30				15 00						14 38	15 30			16 00						16 30		17 00	
Bristol Parkway [7]	134	d	14 39				15 09						14 48	15 40			16 09						16 40		17 09	
Gloucester [7]	134	d			15 24					15 41	15 47		15 52							16 47		16 54				
Cheltenham Spa		a	15 09		15 33		15 38			15 51	15 56		16 02	16 10			16 39			16 56		17 03	17 09		17 40	
		d	15 10				15 41				15 58		16 03	16 11			16 40			16 58			17 12		17 41	
Ashchurch for Tewkesbury		d											16 12													
Worcester Shrub Hill [7]		a											16 32													
Birmingham New Street [12]		a	15 48				16 26				16 41			16 49			17 26			17 41			17 48		18 28	
		d	16 03	16 22				16 30			16 49	16 52		17 03	17 22			17 30		17 49	17 52		18 03	18 22		
Water Orton		d																								
Coleshill Parkway		d		16 36								17 05			17 36						18 05			18 36		
Nuneaton		d		16 52								17 22			17 52						18 22			18 52		
Hinckley		d										17 29									18 29					
Narborough		d										17 37									18 37					
South Wigston		d										17 42									18 42					
Leicester		a		17 16								17 48			18 17						18 48			19 17		
Wilnecote		d																								
Tamworth		d	16 19								17 07									18 07			18 19			
Burton-on-Trent		d									17 19			17 28						18 19						
Willington		d																								
Derby [6]		a	16 38					17 01			17 34			17 40				18 01		18 33			18 39			
		d							17 14		17 40								18 14	18 40						
Long Eaton		d							17 24										18 24							
Attenborough	56	d							17 31										18 34							
Beeston	56	d							17 34										18 37							
Nottingham [8]	56 ⛴	a							17 44		18 00								18 44	19 00						

			XC	EM	GW	AW	XC	XC	XC	XC	XC		XC	EM	GW	XC	XC	EM	XC	XC	GW		AW	XC	XC	XC
			◇1				◇1	1	◇1	◇1	◇1		◇1		◇1	◇1	◇1		◇1	◇1				◇1	1	◇1
			E	F			J		L	B	H		E		M	J	N	F	O	H				J		P
			🛒				🛒		🛒		🛒		🛒		🍽	🛒	🛒			🛒				🛒		🛒
Cardiff Central [7]	132	d				16 23	16 45									17 45							18 23	18 45		
Newport (South Wales)	132	d				16 38	16 59									17 59							18 38	18 59		
Bristol Temple Meads [10]	134	d			16 38				17 30		18 00						18 30			19 00	18 41					19 30
Bristol Parkway [7]	134	d			16 48				17 40		18 09						18 39			19 09	18 50					19 39
Gloucester [7]	134	d			17 35	17 40	17 47								18 33	18 47					19 37		19 42	19 52		
Cheltenham Spa		a			17 45	17 50	17 56		18 09		18 39				18 44	18 56	19 09			19 40	19 46		19 55	20 01		20 09
		d			17 46		17 58		18 11		18 40					18 58	19 10			19 41	19 47			20 02		20 10
Ashchurch for Tewkesbury		d			17 55																19 56					
Worcester Shrub Hill [7]		a			18 15																20 22					
Birmingham New Street [12]		a					18 41		18 48		19 26					19 41	19 48			20 27				20 44		20 49
		d	18 30				18 49	18 52	19 03	19 22			19 30			19 49	20 03		20 22					20 49	20 52	21 03
Water Orton		d																								
Coleshill Parkway		d						19 05		19 36									20 36						21 05	
Nuneaton		d						19 22		19 52									20 52						21 22	
Hinckley		d						19 29																	21 29	
Narborough		d						19 37																	21 37	
South Wigston		d						19 42																	21 42	
Leicester		a						19 48		20 16									21 16						21 48	
Wilnecote		d					19 04																			
Tamworth		d					19 09									20 07	20 19							21 06		21 19
Burton-on-Trent		d					19 21		19 26							20 19								21 19		21 29
Willington		d																								
Derby [6]		a	19 02				19 33		19 40				20 01			20 34	20 38							21 33		21 41
		d		19 16			19 40							20 14		20 40		21 14						21 40		
Long Eaton		d		19 26										20 23				21 24								
Attenborough	56	d		19 33										20 31				21 31								
Beeston	56	d		19 36										20 34				21 34								
Nottingham [8]	56 ⛴	a		19 43			20 00							20 41		21 00		21 41						22 00		

- **A** From Plymouth to Glasgow Central
- **B** To Stansted Airport
- **C** From Swindon
- **D** From Plymouth to Manchester Piccadilly
- **E** From Reading to Newcastle
- **F** From Matlock
- **G** From Plymouth to Edinburgh
- **H** To Manchester Piccadilly
- **I** From Reading to Edinburgh
- **J** 🛒 to Birmingham New Street
- **K** From Penzance to Manchester Piccadilly
- **L** From Plymouth to York
- **M** From London Paddington
- **N** From Plymouth to Leeds
- **O** To Cambridge
- **P** From Penzance to Leeds. 🛒 to Birmingham New Street

Table 57R

Sundays

30 March to 11 May

Bristol and Cardiff - Birmingham
Leicester, Derby and Nottingham

Network Diagram - refer to first Page of Table 50

			EM	XC	GW	XC	XC	GW	GW	XC	GW	XC	GW
				◇1	◇1	◇1	◇1			◇1	◇1	◇1	
				A	B		C	D			B		E
					☕		🍴				☕		
Cardiff Central 7	132	d				19 45				20 45			
Newport (South Wales)	132	d				20 00				20 59			
Bristol Temple Meads 10	134	d		20 00			20 30		20 41			22 10	
Bristol Parkway 7	134	d		20 09			20 40		20 50			22 20	
Gloucester 7	134	d			20 32	20 49		21 25	21 37	21 48	22 31		23 55
Cheltenham Spa		a		20 39	20 43	20 58	21 09	21 33	21 46	21 57	22 42	22 47	00 04
		d		20 40		21 00	21 11			21 59		22 49	
Ashchurch for Tewkesbury		d											
Worcester Shrub Hill 7		a											
Birmingham New Street 12		a		21 18		21 44	21 48			22 42		23 40	
		d				21 52	22 03						
Water Orton		d											
Coleshill Parkway		d				22 05							
Nuneaton		d				22 22							
Hinckley		d				22 29							
Narborough		d				22 37							
South Wigston		d				22 42							
Leicester		a				22 48							
Wilnecote		d											
Tamworth		d					22 19						
Burton-on-Trent		d											
Willington		d											
Derby 6		a					22 40						
		d	22 18										
Long Eaton		d	22 28										
Attenborough	56	d	22 35										
Beeston	56	d	22 38										
Nottingham 8	56 ⛴	a	22 45										

A From Paignton
B From London Paddington
C From Plymouth to Leeds. 🍴 to Birmingham New Street
D From Westbury
E From Swindon

Network Diagram for Tables 59, 60, 61, 62, 64, 66

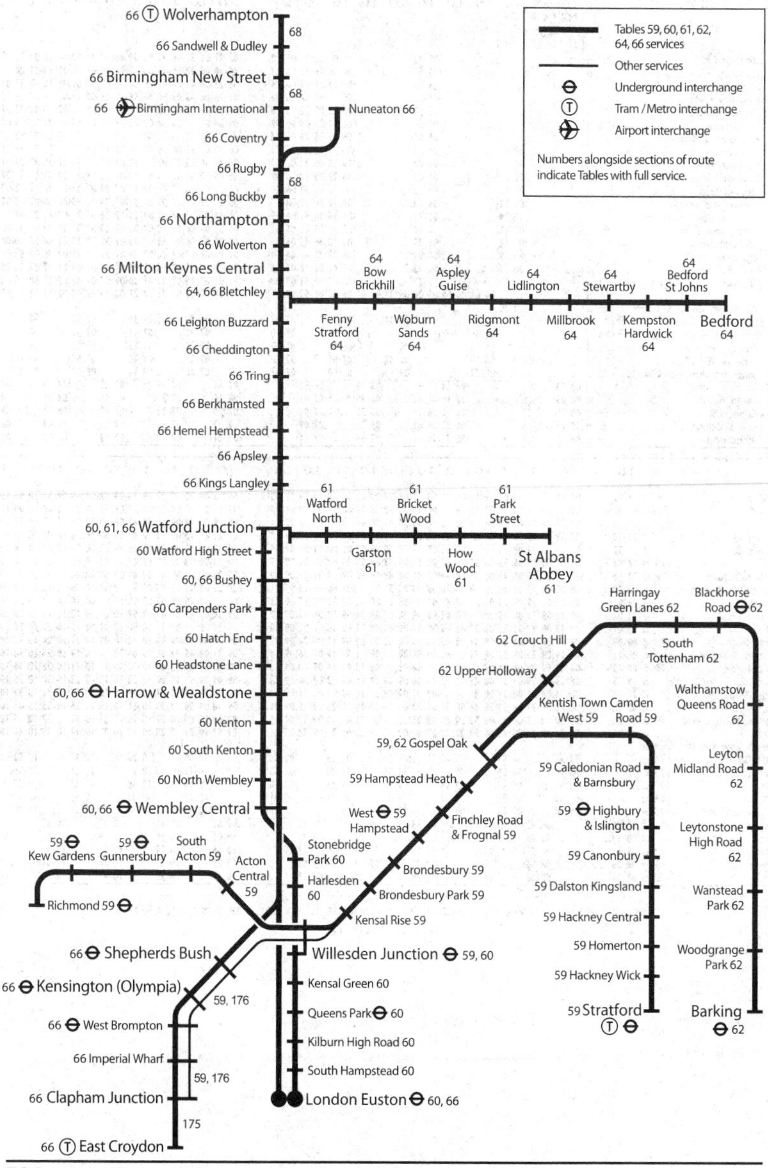
Tables 59, 60, 61, 62, 64, 66 services
Other services
Underground interchange
Tram / Metro interchange
Airport interchange
Numbers alongside sections of route indicate Tables with full service.
66 Wolverhampton
68
66 Sandwell & Dudley
66 Birmingham New Street
68
66 Birmingham International
Nuneaton 66
66 Coventry
66 Rugby
68
66 Long Buckby
66 Northampton
66 Wolverton
66 Milton Keynes Central
64, 66 Bletchley
64 Bow Brickhill
64 Aspley Guise
64 Lidlington
64 Stewartby
64 Bedford St Johns
Fenny Stratford 64
Woburn Sands 64
Ridgmont 64
Millbrook 64
Kempston Hardwick 64
Bedford 64
66 Leighton Buzzard
66 Cheddington
66 Tring
66 Berkhamsted
66 Hemel Hempstead
66 Apsley
66 Kings Langley
61 Watford North
61 Bricket Wood
61 Park Street
60, 61, 66 Watford Junction
Garston 61
How Wood 61
St Albans Abbey 61
60 Watford High Street
60, 66 Bushey
60 Carpenders Park
60 Hatch End
60 Headstone Lane
60, 66 Harrow & Wealdstone
60 Kenton
60 South Kenton
60 North Wembley
60, 66 Wembley Central
Harringay Green Lanes 62
Blackhorse Road 62
62 Crouch Hill
South Tottenham 62
62 Upper Holloway
Walthamstow Queens Road 62
Kentish Town West 59
Camden Road 59
59, 62 Gospel Oak
Leyton Midland Road 62
59 Caledonian Road & Barnsbury
59 Hampstead Heath
West Hampstead 59
Finchley Road & Frognal 59
59 Highbury & Islington
Leytonstone High Road 62
59 Kew Gardens
59 Gunnersbury
South Acton 59
Acton Central 59
Stonebridge Park 60
Harlesden 60
Brondesbury 59
59 Canonbury
59 Dalston Kingsland
Wanstead Park 62
Brondesbury Park 59
Richmond 59
Kensal Rise 59
59 Hackney Central
59 Homerton
Woodgrange Park 62
66 Shepherds Bush
Willesden Junction 59, 60
59 Hackney Wick
66 Kensington (Olympia)
Kensal Green 60
59, 176
59 Stratford
Barking 62
66 West Brompton
Queens Park 60
Kilburn High Road 60
66 Imperial Wharf
South Hampstead 60
59, 176
66 Clapham Junction
London Euston 60, 66
175
66 East Croydon

TOCs operating on this network - London Overground (LO), London Midland (LM), Southern (SN), Virgin Trains (VT)

Table 59

Mondays to Fridays

9 December to 16 May

Stratford - Highbury & Islington, West Hampstead, Willesden Junction, Clapham Junction and Richmond

Network Diagram - see first Page of Table 59

Miles	Miles		LO MX	SN MX 1	LO MX	LO	LO	LO	LO	LO	LO	LO	LO	LO	LO	LO	LO	LO	LO	LO	LO	LO	LO
0	—	**Stratford 7** ⊖ d						05 47			06 05	06 12	06 20	06 27	06 35	06 42	06 50	06 57	07 02	07 10	07 17	07 27	07 35
1	—	Hackney Wick d						05 50			06 08	06 15	06 23	06 30	06 38	06 45	06 53	07 00	07 06	07 13	07 20	07 30	07 38
1¾	—	Homerton d						05 53			06 11	06 18	06 26	06 33	06 41	06 48	06 56	07 03	07 09	07 16	07 23	07 33	07 41
2½	—	Hackney Central d						05 55			06 13	06 20	06 28	06 35	06 43	06 50	06 58	07 05	07 11	07 18	07 25	07 35	07 43
3¼	—	Dalston Kingsland d						05 57			06 15	06 22	06 30	06 37	06 45	06 52	07 00	07 07	07 13	07 20	07 27	07 37	07 45
4¼	—	Canonbury 178 d						05 59			06 17	06 24	06 32	06 39	06 47	06 54	07 02	07 09	07 15	07 22	07 29	07 39	07 47
4¾	—	**Highbury & Islington** ⊖178 d						06 01			06 19	06 26	06 34	06 41	06 49	06 56	07 04	07 11	07 17	07 25	07 32	07 42	07 49
5¼	—	Caledonian Rd & Barnsbury d			00 02			06 03			06 21	06 28	06 36	06 43	06 51	06 58	07 06	07 13	07 19	07 27	07 34	07 44	07 51
6¼	—	Camden Road d			00 05			06 07			06 25	06 32	06 40	06 47	06 55	07 02	07 10	07 17	07 23	07 30	07 37	07 47	07 55
6½	—	Kentish Town West d			00 07			06 09			06 27	06 34	06 42	06 49	06 57	07 04	07 12	07 19	07 25	07 33	07 40	07 50	07 57
7½	—	**Gospel Oak** d			00 10			06 12			06 30	06 37	06 45	06 52	07 00	07 07	07 15	07 22	07 27	07 36	07 43	07 53	08 00
8	—	Hampstead Heath d			00 12			06 14			06 32	06 39	06 47	06 54	07 02	07 09	07 17	07 24	07 29	07 38	07 45	07 55	08 02
9	—	Finchley Road & Frognal d			00 14			06 16			06 34	06 41	06 49	06 56	07 04	07 11	07 19	07 26	07 31	07 40	07 47	07 57	08 04
9½	—	West Hampstead ⊖ d			00 16			06 18			06 36	06 43	06 51	06 58	07 06	07 13	07 21	07 28	07 33	07 42	07 49	07 59	08 06
10	—	Brondesbury d			00 18			06 20			06 38	06 45	06 53	07 00	07 08	07 15	07 23	07 30	07 35	07 44	07 50	08 01	08 08
10¼	—	Brondesbury Park d			00 19			06 21			06 39	06 46	06 54	07 01	07 09	07 16	07 24	07 31	07 36	07 45	07 52	08 02	08 09
11	—	Kensal Rise d			00 21			06 23			06 41	06 48	06 56	07 03	07 11	07 18	07 26	07 33	07 38	07 47	07 54	08 04	08 11
12	0	**Willesden Jn. High Level** ⊖ a						06 27			06 45	06 51	07 00	07 07	07 15	07 22	07 30	07 37	07 42	07 51	08 00	08 07	08 15
—	—	d				06 01	06 09	06 28	06 33	06 41	06 46	06 52	07 01	07 08	07 16	07 23	07 31	07 38	07 43	07 52	08 01	08 08	08 16
12	—	**Willesden Jn Low Level** ⊖ a			00 30																		
—	2	**Shepherd's Bush** ⊖176 d				06 07			06 39		06 53		07 08		07 24		07 39		07 50		08 09		08 23
—	2¾	**Kensington (Olympia)** ⊖176 d				06 09			06 41		06 55		07 10		07 26		07 41		07 52		08 11		08 25
—	3½	West Brompton ⊖176 d		00 02		06 12			06 44		06 58		07 13		07 29		07 43		07 55		08 12		08 28
—	4½	Imperial Wharf 176 d		00a03		06 15			06 47		07 01		07 16		07 32		07 46		07 58		08 15		08 31
—	6	**Clapham Junction 10** 176 a				06 22			06 53		07 08		07 23		07 40		07 54		08 05		08 23		08 38
13½	—	Acton Central d	00 02				06 14	06 33		06 46		06 58		07 13		07 28		07 43		07 57		08 13	
14½	—	South Acton d	00 05				06 16	06 36		06 49		07 01		07 16		07 30		07 46		08 00		08 16	
15¼	—	Gunnersbury ⊖ d	00 10				06 20	06 39		06 53		07 04		07 20		07 33		07 49		08 04		08 19	
16¼	—	Kew Gardens ⊖ d	00 13				06 23	06 42		06 56		07 07		07 23		07 36		07 52		08 07		08 22	
17½	—	**Richmond** ⊖ a	00 18				06 31	06 46		07 04		07 11		07 27		07 44		07 59		08 12		08 29	

	LO	LO	LO	LO	LO	LO	LO	LO	LO	LO	LO	LO	LO	LO	LO	LO	LO	LO	LO	LO	LO	LO
Stratford 7 ⊖ d	07 42	07 50	07 57	08 03	08 12	08 20	08 27	08 35	08 42	08 50	08 57	09 05	09 12	09 20	09 27	09 35	09 42	09 50	09 57	10 05	10 15	
Hackney Wick d	07 45	07 53	08 00	08 06	08 15	08 23	08 30	08 38	08 45	08 53	09 00	09 08	09 15	09 23	09 30	09 38	09 45	09 53	10 00	10 09	10 18	
Homerton d	07 48	07 56	08 03	08 09	08 18	08 26	08 33	08 41	08 48	08 56	09 03	09 11	09 18	09 26	09 33	09 41	09 48	09 56	10 03	10 12	10 21	
Hackney Central d	07 50	07 58	08 05	08 11	08 20	08 28	08 35	08 43	08 50	08 58	09 05	09 13	09 20	09 28	09 35	09 43	09 50	09 58	10 05	10 14	10 23	
Dalston Kingsland d	07 52	08 00	08 07	08 13	08 22	08 30	08 37	08 45	08 52	09 00	09 07	09 15	09 22	09 30	09 37	09 45	09 52	10 00	10 07	10 16	10 25	
Canonbury 178 d	07 54	08 02	08 09	08 15	08 24	08 32	08 39	08 47	08 54	09 02	09 09	09 17	09 24	09 32	09 39	09 47	09 54	10 02	10 09	10 18	10 27	
Highbury & Islington ⊖178 d	07 56	08 04	08 11	08 18	08 26	08 34	08 41	08 49	08 56	09 04	09 11	09 19	09 26	09 34	09 41	09 49	09 56	10 04	10 11	10 20	10 29	
Caledonian Rd & Barnsbury d	07 58	08 06	08 13	08 20	08 28	08 36	08 43	08 51	08 58	09 06	09 13	09 21	09 28	09 36	09 43	09 51	09 58	10 06	10 13	10 22	10 31	
Camden Road d	08 02	08 10	08 17	08 23	08 32	08 40	08 47	08 55	09 02	09 10	09 17	09 25	09 32	09 40	09 47	09 55	10 02	10 10	10 17	10 26	10 35	
Kentish Town West d	08 04	08 12	08 19	08 25	08 34	08 42	08 49	08 57	09 04	09 12	09 19	09 27	09 34	09 42	09 49	09 57	10 04	10 12	10 19	10 28	10 37	
Gospel Oak d	08 07	08 15	08 22	08 28	08 37	08 45	08 52	09 00	09 07	09 15	09 22	09 30	09 37	09 45	09 52	10 00	10 07	10 15	10 22	10 30	10 39	
Hampstead Heath d	08 09	08 17	08 24	08 30	08 39	08 47	08 54	09 02	09 09	09 17	09 24	09 32	09 39	09 47	09 54	10 02	10 09	10 17	10 24	10 32	10 42	
Finchley Road & Frognal d	08 11	08 19	08 26	08 32	08 41	08 49	08 56	09 04	09 11	09 19	09 26	09 34	09 41	09 49	09 56	10 04	10 11	10 19	10 26	10 34	10 44	
West Hampstead ⊖ d	08 13	08 21	08 28	08 34	08 43	08 51	08 58	09 07	09 13	09 21	09 28	09 36	09 43	09 51	09 58	10 06	10 13	10 21	10 28	10 36	10 46	
Brondesbury d	08 15	08 23	08 30	08 35	08 45	08 53	09 00	09 08	09 15	09 23	09 30	09 38	09 45	09 53	10 00	10 08	10 15	10 23	10 30	10 38	10 47	
Brondesbury Park d	08 16	08 24	08 31	08 37	08 46	08 54	09 01	09 09	09 16	09 24	09 31	09 39	09 46	09 54	10 01	10 09	10 16	10 24	10 31	10 39	10 49	
Kensal Rise d	08 18	08 26	08 33	08 39	08 48	08 56	09 03	09 11	09 18	09 26	09 33	09 41	09 48	09 56	10 03	10 11	10 18	10 26	10 33	10 41	10 51	
Willesden Jn. High Level ⊖ a	08 22	08 30	08 37	08 41	08 52	09 00	09 07	09 15	09 21	09 30	09 37	09 45	09 52	10 00	10 07	10 16	10 21	10 31	10 37	10 45	10 54	
d	08 23	08 31	08 38	08 45	08 53	09 01	09 08	09 16	09 23	09 31	09 38	09 46	09 53	10 01	10 08	10 17	10 22	10 32	10 38	10 46	10 55	11 01
Willesden Jn Low Level ⊖ a																						
Shepherd's Bush ⊖176 d		08 38		08 53		09 09		09 24		09 38		09 54		10 09		10 26		10 39		10 53		11 09
Kensington (Olympia) ⊖176 d		08 40		08 55		09 11		09 26		09 40		09 56		10 12		10 29		10 41		10 55		11 11
West Brompton ⊖176 d		08 43		08 58		09 14		09 28		09 43		09 58		10 14		10 30		10 43		10 57		11 13
Imperial Wharf 176 d		08 46		09 01		09 17		09 31		09 46		10 01		10 17		10 33		10 46		11 00		11 16
Clapham Junction 10 176 a		08 54		09 08		09 24		09 38		09 53		10 08		10 24		10 40		10 54		11 08		11 23
Acton Central d	08 28		08 43		08 58		09 13		09 29		09 43		09 58		10 13		10 27		10 43		11 01	
South Acton d	08 30		08 46		09 00		09 16		09 32		09 46		10 01		10 16		10 30		10 45		11 04	
Gunnersbury ⊖ d	08 33		08 51		09 03		09 19		09 35		09 49		10 06		10 19		10 33		10 48		11 08	
Kew Gardens ⊖ d	08 36		08 54		09 06		09 22		09 38		09 52		10 09		10 22		10 36		10 51		11 11	
Richmond ⊖ a	08 43		08 58		09 12		09 28		09 44		09 57		10 14		10 28		10 41		10 56		11 16	

For full service between Willesden Jn, Shepherds Bush and Clapham Jn, please refer to Table 176

Table 59

Mondays to Fridays

9 December to 16 May

Stratford - Highbury & Islington, West Hampstead, Willesden Junction, Clapham Junction and Richmond

Network Diagram - see first Page of Table 59

Station			LO		LO	LO	LO	LO	LO	LO	LO	LO	LO	LO	LO		LO	LO	LO	LO	LO	LO	LO	LO	LO	LO
Stratford [7]	⊖	d	10 25		10 35	10 45		10 55	11 05	11 15		11 25	11 35	11 45			11 55	12 05	12 15		12 25	12 35	12 45		12 55	13 05
Hackney Wick		d	10 28		10 38	10 48		10 58	11 08	11 18		11 28	11 38	11 48			11 58	12 08	12 18		12 28	12 38	12 48		12 58	13 08
Homerton		d	10 31		10 41	10 51		11 01	11 11	11 21		11 31	11 41	11 51			12 01	12 11	12 21		12 31	12 41	12 51		13 01	13 11
Hackney Central		d	10 33		10 43	10 53		11 03	11 13	11 23		11 33	11 43	11 53			12 03	12 13	12 23		12 33	12 43	12 53		13 03	13 13
Dalston Kingsland		d	10 35		10 45	10 55		11 05	11 15	11 25		11 35	11 45	11 55			12 05	12 15	12 25		12 35	12 45	12 55		13 05	13 15
Canonbury	178	d	10 37		10 47	10 57		11 07	11 17	11 27		11 37	11 47	11 57			12 07	12 17	12 27		12 37	12 47	12 57		13 07	13 17
Highbury & Islington	⊖178	d	10 39		10 49	10 59		11 09	11 19	11 29		11 39	11 49	11 59			12 09	12 19	12 29		12 39	12 49	12 59		13 09	13 19
Caledonian Rd & Barnsbury		d	10 41		10 51	11 01		11 11	11 21	11 31		11 41	11 51	12 01			12 11	12 21	12 31		12 41	12 51	13 01		13 11	13 21
Camden Road		d	10 45		10 55	11 05		11 15	11 25	11 35		11 45	11 55	12 05			12 15	12 25	12 35		12 45	12 55	13 05		13 15	13 25
Kentish Town West		d	10 47		10 57	11 07		11 17	11 27	11 37		11 47	11 57	12 07			12 17	12 27	12 37		12 47	12 57	13 07		13 17	13 27
Gospel Oak		d	10 50		11 00	11 10		11 20	11 30	11 40		11 50	12 00	12 10			12 20	12 30	12 40		12 50	13 00	13 10		13 20	13 30
Hampstead Heath		d	10 52		11 02	11 12		11 22	11 32	11 42		11 52	12 02	12 12			12 22	12 32	12 42		12 52	13 02	13 12		13 22	13 32
Finchley Road & Frognal		d	10 54		11 04	11 14		11 24	11 34	11 44		11 54	12 04	12 14			12 24	12 34	12 44		12 54	13 04	13 14		13 24	13 34
West Hampstead	⊖	d	10 56		11 06	11 16		11 26	11 36	11 46		11 56	12 06	12 16			12 26	12 36	12 46		12 56	13 06	13 16		13 26	13 36
Brondesbury		d	10 58		11 08	11 18		11 28	11 38	11 48		11 58	12 08	12 18			12 28	12 38	12 48		12 58	13 08	13 18		13 28	13 38
Brondesbury Park		d	10 59		11 09	11 19		11 29	11 39	11 49		11 59	12 09	12 19			12 29	12 39	12 49		12 59	13 09	13 19		13 29	13 39
Kensal Rise		d	11 01		11 11	11 21		11 31	11 41	11 51		12 01	12 11	12 21			12 31	12 41	12 51		13 01	13 11	13 21		13 31	13 41
Willesden Jn. High Level	⊖	a	11 05		11 15	11 25		11 35	11 45	11 55		12 05	12 15	12 25			12 35	12 45	12 55		13 05	13 15	13 25		13 35	13 45
		d	11 06		11 16	11 26	11 31	11 36	11 46	11 56	12 01	12 06	12 16	12 26	12 31		12 36	12 46	12 56	13 01	13 06	13 16	13 26	13 31	13 36	13 46
Willesden Jn Low Level	⊖	a																								
Shepherd's Bush	⊖176	d			11 23		11 38		11 53		12 08		12 24		12 38			12 53		13 08		13 24		13 38		13 53
Kensington (Olympia)	⊖176	d			11 25		11 40		11 55		12 10		12 27		12 40			12 55		13 10		13 26		13 40		13 55
West Brompton	⊖176	d			11 27		11 42		11 57		12 12		12 29		12 42			12 57		13 12		13 28		13 42		13 58
Imperial Wharf	176	d			11 30		11 45		12 00		12 15		12 32		12 45			13 00		13 15		13 31		13 45		14 01
Clapham Junction [10]	176	a			11 38		11 52		12 08		12 22		12 39		12 52			13 08		13 22		13 39		13 52		14 08
Acton Central		d	11 11			11 31		11 41		12 01		12 11		12 31			12 41		13 01		13 11		13 31		13 41	
South Acton		d	11 14			11 34		11 44		12 04		12 14		12 34			12 44		13 04		13 14		13 34		13 44	
Gunnersbury	⊖	d	11 19			11 38		11 48		12 08		12 18		12 38			12 48		13 08		13 18		13 38		13 48	
Kew Gardens	⊖	d	11 22			11 41		11 51		12 11		12 21		12 41			12 51		13 11		13 21		13 41		13 51	
Richmond	⊖	a	11 26			11 46		11 56		12 16		12 26		12 46			12 56		13 16		13 26		13 46		13 56	

Station			LO		LO	LO	LO	LO	LO	LO	LO	LO	LO	LO	LO		LO	LO	LO	LO	LO	LO	LO	LO	LO	LO
Stratford [7]	⊖	d	13 15			13 25	13 35	13 45		13 55	14 05	14 15		14 25	14 35		14 45		14 55	15 05	15 15		15 25	15 35	15 42	15 50
Hackney Wick		d	13 18			13 28	13 38	13 48		13 58	14 08	14 18		14 28	14 38		14 48		14 58	15 08	15 18		15 28	15 38	15 45	15 53
Homerton		d	13 21			13 31	13 41	13 51		14 01	14 11	14 21		14 31	14 41		14 51		15 01	15 11	15 21		15 31	15 41	15 48	15 56
Hackney Central		d	13 23			13 33	13 43	13 53		14 03	14 13	14 23		14 33	14 43		14 53		15 03	15 13	15 23		15 33	15 43	15 50	15 58
Dalston Kingsland		d	13 25			13 35	13 45	13 55		14 05	14 15	14 25		14 35	14 45		14 55		15 05	15 15	15 25		15 35	15 45	15 52	16 00
Canonbury	178	d	13 27			13 37	13 47	13 57		14 07	14 17	14 27		14 37	14 47		14 57		15 07	15 17	15 27		15 37	15 47	15 54	16 02
Highbury & Islington	⊖178	d	13 29			13 39	13 49	13 59		14 09	14 19	14 29		14 39	14 49		14 59		15 09	15 19	15 29		15 39	15 49	15 56	16 04
Caledonian Rd & Barnsbury		d	13 31			13 41	13 51	14 01		14 11	14 21	14 31		14 41	14 51		15 01		15 11	15 21	15 31		15 41	15 51	15 58	16 06
Camden Road		d	13 35			13 45	13 55	14 05		14 15	14 25	14 35		14 45	14 55		15 05		15 15	15 25	15 35		15 45	15 55	16 03	16 10
Kentish Town West		d	13 37			13 47	13 57	14 07		14 17	14 27	14 37		14 47	14 57		15 07		15 17	15 27	15 37		15 47	15 57	16 06	16 12
Gospel Oak		d	13 40			13 50	14 00	14 10		14 20	14 30	14 40		14 50	15 00		15 10		15 20	15 30	15 40		15 50	16 00	16 08	16 15
Hampstead Heath		d	13 42			13 52	14 02	14 12		14 22	14 32	14 42		14 52	15 02		15 12		15 22	15 32	15 42		15 52	16 02	16 10	16 17
Finchley Road & Frognal		d	13 44			13 54	14 04	14 14		14 24	14 34	14 44		14 54	15 04		15 14		15 24	15 34	15 44		15 54	16 04	16 12	16 19
West Hampstead	⊖	d	13 46			13 56	14 06	14 16		14 26	14 36	14 46		14 56	15 06		15 16		15 26	15 36	15 46		15 56	16 06	16 14	16 21
Brondesbury		d	13 48			13 58	14 08	14 18		14 28	14 38	14 48		14 58	15 08		15 18		15 28	15 38	15 48		15 58	16 08	16 15	16 23
Brondesbury Park		d	13 49			13 59	14 09	14 19		14 29	14 39	14 49		14 59	15 09		15 19		15 29	15 39	15 49		15 59	16 09	16 17	16 24
Kensal Rise		d	13 51			14 01	14 11	14 21		14 31	14 41	14 51		15 01	15 11		15 21		15 31	15 41	15 51		16 01	16 11	16 19	16 26
Willesden Jn. High Level	⊖	a	13 54			14 05	14 15	14 25		14 35	14 45	14 54		15 05	15 15		15 25		15 35	15 45	15 55		16 05	16 15	16 22	16 30
		d	13 55		14 01	14 06	14 16	14 26	14 31	14 36	14 46	14 55	15 00	15 06	15 16		15 26	15 31	15 36	15 46	15 56	16 02	16 06	16 16	16 23	16 31
Willesden Jn Low Level	⊖	a																								
Shepherd's Bush	⊖176	d			14 08		14 24		14 38		14 53		15 07		15 25			15 38		15 53		16 07		16 24		16 38
Kensington (Olympia)	⊖176	d			14 10		14 27		14 40		14 55		15 09		15 27			15 40		15 55		16 09		16 27		16 40
West Brompton	⊖176	d			14 12		14 29		14 42		14 58		15 12		15 30			15 42		15 58		16 12		16 29		16 43
Imperial Wharf	176	d			14 15		14 32		14 45		15 01		15 15		15 33			15 45		16 01		16 15		16 32		16 46
Clapham Junction [10]	176	a			14 22		14 39		14 52		15 08		15 22		15 39			15 52		16 08		16 21		16 38		16 53
Acton Central		d	14 01			14 11		14 31		14 41		15 01		15 12			15 31		15 41		16 01		16 11		16 28	
South Acton		d	14 04			14 14		14 34		14 44		15 04		15 14			15 34		15 44		16 04		16 14		16 30	
Gunnersbury	⊖	d	14 08			14 18		14 38		14 48		15 08		15 18			15 38		15 48		16 08		16 18		16 33	
Kew Gardens	⊖	d	14 11			14 21		14 41		14 51		15 11		15 21			15 41		15 51		16 11		16 21		16 36	
Richmond	⊖	a	14 16			14 26		14 46		14 56		15 16		15 26			15 46		15 56		16 16		16 27		16 41	

For full service between Willesden Jn, Shepherds Bush and Clapham Jn, please refer to Table 176

Table 59

Mondays to Fridays

9 December to 16 May

Stratford - Highbury & Islington, West Hampstead, Willesden Junction, Clapham Junction and Richmond

Network Diagram - see first Page of Table 59

		LO		LO	LO	LO	LO	LO	LO	LO	LO	LO	LO	LO		LO	LO	LO	LO	LO	LO	LO	LO	LO	LO
Stratford 7 ⊖	d	15 59			16 12	16 20	16 27	16 35	16 42	16 50	16 57	17 05	17 12	17 20		17 27	17 35	17 42	17 50	17 57	18 05	18 12	18 20	18 27	18 35
Hackney Wick	d	16 02			16 15	16 23	16 30	16 38	16 45	16 53	17 00	17 08	17 15	17 23		17 30	17 38	17 45	17 53	18 00	18 08	18 15	18 23	18 30	18 38
Homerton	d	16 05			16 18	16 26	16 33	16 41	16 48	16 56	17 03	17 11	17 18	17 26		17 33	17 41	17 48	17 56	18 03	18 11	18 18	18 26	18 33	18 41
Hackney Central	d	16 07			16 20	16 28	16 35	16 43	16 50	16 58	17 05	17 13	17 20	17 28		17 35	17 43	17 50	17 58	18 05	18 13	18 20	18 28	18 35	18 43
Dalston Kingsland	d	16 09			16 22	16 30	16 37	16 45	16 52	17 00	17 07	17 15	17 22	17 30		17 37	17 45	17 52	18 00	18 07	18 15	18 22	18 31	18 37	18 45
Canonbury 178	d	16 11			16 24	16 32	16 39	16 47	16 54	17 02	17 09	17 17	17 24	17 32		17 39	17 47	17 54	18 02	18 09	18 17	18 24	18 32	18 39	18 47
Highbury & Islington ⊖178	d	16 13			16 26	16 34	16 41	16 49	16 56	17 04	17 11	17 19	17 26	17 35		17 41	17 49	17 56	18 04	18 11	18 19	18 26	18 34	18 41	18 50
Caledonian Rd & Barnsbury	d	16 15			16 28	16 36	16 43	16 51	16 58	17 06	17 13	17 21	17 28	17 37		17 43	17 51	17 58	18 06	18 13	18 21	18 28	18 36	18 43	18 52
Camden Road	d	16 19			16 32	16 40	16 47	16 55	17 02	17 10	17 17	17 25	17 32	17 40		17 47	17 55	18 02	18 10	18 17	18 25	18 32	18 40	18 47	18 56
Kentish Town West	d	16 21			16 34	16 42	16 49	16 58	17 04	17 13	17 19	17 27	17 34	17 42		17 49	17 58	18 05	18 13	18 19	18 27	18 34	18 42	18 49	18 57
Gospel Oak	d	16 24			16 37	16 45	16 52	17 03	17 08	17 17	17 23	17 30	17 37	17 45		17 52	18 02	18 08	18 16	18 22	18 30	18 37	18 45	18 52	19 01
Hampstead Heath	d	16 26			16 39	16 47	16 54	17 05	17 10	17 19	17 25	17 32	17 39	17 47		17 54	18 04	18 10	18 18	18 24	18 32	18 39	18 47	18 54	19 02
Finchley Road & Frognal	d	16 28			16 41	16 49	16 56	17 07	17 12	17 21	17 27	17 34	17 41	17 49		17 56	18 06	18 12	18 20	18 26	18 34	18 41	18 49	18 56	19 04
West Hampstead ⊖	d	16 30			16 43	16 51	16 58	17 09	17 14	17 23	17 29	17 36	17 43	17 51		17 58	18 08	18 14	18 22	18 28	18 36	18 43	18 51	18 58	19 06
Brondesbury	d	16 32			16 45	16 52	17 00	17 10	17 16	17 25	17 30	17 38	17 45	17 53		18 00	18 09	18 16	18 23	18 30	18 38	18 45	18 53	19 00	19 07
Brondesbury Park	d	16 33			16 46	16 54	17 01	17 12	17 17	17 26	17 32	17 39	17 46	17 54		18 01	18 11	18 17	18 25	18 31	18 39	18 46	18 54	19 01	19 09
Kensal Rise	d	16 35			16 48	16 56	17 03	17 14	17 19	17 28	17 34	17 41	17 48	17 56		18 03	18 13	18 19	18 27	18 33	18 41	18 48	18 56	19 03	19 11
Willesden Jn. High Level ⊖	a	16 39			16 52	16 59	17 07	17 18	17 23	17 31	17 38	17 45	17 52	18 00		18 07	18 17	18 23	18 30	18 37	18 45	18 52	19 00	19 07	19 15
	d	16 40		16 46	16 53	17 01	17 08	17 19	17 24	17 32	17 39	17 46	17 53	18 01		18 08	18 18	18 24	18 31	18 38	18 46	18 53	19 01	19 08	19 16
Willesden Jn Low Level ⊖	a																								
Shepherd's Bush ⊖176	d			16 53		17 08		17 26		17 39		17 54		18 09			18 24		18 39		18 53		19 08		19 24
Kensington (Olympia) ⊖176	d			16 55		17 11		17 28		17 41		17 56		18 11			18 26		18 41		18 55		19 10		19 26
West Brompton ⊖176	d			16 57		17 13		17 30		17 44		17 59		18 13			18 29		18 44		18 58		19 13		19 28
Imperial Wharf 176	d			17 00		17 16		17 33		17 47		18 02		18 16			18 32		18 47		19 01		19 16		19 31
Clapham Junction 10 176	a			17 07		17 23		17 40		17 53		18 08		18 24			18 39		18 53		19 08		19 23		19 37
Acton Central	d	16 45			16 58		17 13		17 29		17 44		17 58			18 13		18 29		18 43		18 58		19 13	
South Acton	d	16 48			17 00		17 16		17 34		17 46		18 00			18 16		18 32		18 46		19 01		19 16	
Gunnersbury ⊖	d	16 51			17 03		17 19		17 39		17 49		18 03			18 19		18 38		18 49		19 06		19 19	
Kew Gardens ⊖	d	16 54			17 06		17 22		17 42		17 52		18 06			18 22		18 41		18 52		19 09		19 22	
Richmond ⊖	a	16 58			17 11		17 26		17 46		17 58		18 13			18 28		18 45		18 58		19 14		19 29	

		LO		LO	LO	LO	LO	LO	LO	LO	LO	LO	LO	LO		LO	LO	LO	LO	LO	LO	LO	LO	LO	LO
Stratford 7 ⊖	d	18 42		18 48	18 57	19 05	19 15		19 25	19 35	19 45		19 55	20 05		20 15		20 23	20 35	20 45		21 00		21 15	
Hackney Wick	d	18 45		18 51	19 00	19 08	19 18		19 28	19 38	19 48		19 58	20 08		20 18		20 26	20 38	20 48		21 03		21 18	
Homerton	d	18 48		18 54	19 03	19 11	19 21		19 31	19 41	19 51		20 01	20 11		20 21		20 29	20 41	20 51		21 06		21 21	
Hackney Central	d	18 50		18 56	19 05	19 13	19 23		19 33	19 43	19 53		20 03	20 13		20 23		20 31	20 43	20 53		21 08		21 23	
Dalston Kingsland	d	18 52		18 58	19 07	19 15	19 25		19 35	19 45	19 55		20 05	20 15		20 25		20 33	20 45	20 55		21 10		21 25	
Canonbury 178	d	18 54		19 00	19 09	19 17	19 27		19 37	19 47	19 57		20 07	20 17		20 27		20 35	20 47	20 57		21 12		21 27	
Highbury & Islington ⊖178	d	18 56		19 02	19 12	19 19	19 29		19 39	19 49	19 59		20 09	20 19		20 29		20 37	20 49	20 59		21 15		21 29	
Caledonian Rd & Barnsbury	d	18 58		19 04	19 14	19 21	19 31		19 41	19 51	20 01		20 11	20 21		20 31		20 39	20 51	21 01		21 17		21 31	
Camden Road	d	19 02		19 08	19 17	19 25	19 34		19 45	19 55	20 05		20 15	20 25		20 35		20 42	20 55	21 05		21 20		21 35	
Kentish Town West	d	19 05		19 10	19 19	19 27	19 37		19 47	19 57	20 07		20 17	20 27		20 37		20 45	20 57	21 07		21 22		21 37	
Gospel Oak	d	19 09		19 13	19 24	19 30	19 40		19 50	20 00	20 10		20 20	20 30		20 40		20 50	21 00	21 10		21 24		21 40	
Hampstead Heath	d	19 11		19 15	19 26	19 32	19 42		19 52	20 02	20 12		20 22	20 32		20 42		20 52	21 02	21 12		21 27		21 42	
Finchley Road & Frognal	d	19 13		19 17	19 28	19 34	19 44		19 54	20 04	20 14		20 24	20 34		20 44		20 54	21 04	21 14		21 29		21 44	
West Hampstead ⊖	d	19 15		19 19	19 30	19 36	19 46		19 56	20 06	20 16		20 26	20 36		20 46		20 56	21 06	21 16		21 31		21 46	
Brondesbury	d	19 16		19 21	19 32	19 38	19 47		19 58	20 08	20 18		20 28	20 38		20 48		20 57	21 08	21 18		21 33		21 48	
Brondesbury Park	d	19 18		19 22	19 33	19 39	19 49		19 59	20 09	20 19		20 29	20 39		20 49		20 59	21 09	21 19		21 34		21 49	
Kensal Rise	d	19 20		19 24	19 35	19 41	19 51		20 01	20 11	20 21		20 31	20 41		20 51		21 01	21 11	21 21		21 36		21 51	
Willesden Jn. High Level ⊖	a	19 24		19 30	19 39	19 45	19 55		20 07	20 16	20 26		20 36	20 45		20 55		21 05	21 15	21 25		21 40		21 56	
	d	19 25		19 31	19 40	19 46	19 56	20 00	20 07	20 17	20 27	20 31	20 37	20 46		20 57	21 01	21 06	21 16	21 26	21 31	21 41	21 46	21 57	22 01
Willesden Jn Low Level ⊖	a																								
Shepherd's Bush ⊖176	d			19 38		19 53		20 06		20 26		20 38		20 53			21 07		21 24		21 38		21 53		22 07
Kensington (Olympia) ⊖176	d			19 40		19 56		20 08		20 28		20 40		20 55			21 09		21 26		21 40		21 55		22 09
West Brompton ⊖176	d			19 43		19 58		20 11		20 31		20 42		20 58			21 12		21 28		21 42		21 58		22 12
Imperial Wharf 176	d			19 46		20 01		20 14		20 34		20 45		21 01			21 15		21 31		21 45		22 01		22 15
Clapham Junction 10 176	a			19 53		20 09		20 21		20 40		20 52		21 08			21 22		21 37		21 52		22 08		22 22
Acton Central	d	19 30			19 45		20 01		20 12		20 32		20 42			21 03		21 11		21 31		21 46		22 02	
South Acton	d	19 32			19 48		20 03		20 15		20 34		20 44			21 05		21 13		21 34		21 49		22 04	
Gunnersbury ⊖	d	19 38			19 51		20 09		20 18		20 38		20 50			21 08		21 18		21 38		21 53		22 08	
Kew Gardens ⊖	d	19 41			19 54		20 12		20 21		20 41		20 53			21 11		21 21		21 41		21 56		22 11	
Richmond ⊖	a	19 46			19 59		20 16		20 26		20 46		20 57			21 16		21 26		21 46		22 00		22 16	

For full service between Willesden Jn, Shepherds Bush and Clapham Jn, please refer to Table 176

Table 59

Mondays to Fridays

9 December to 16 May

Stratford - Highbury & Islington, West Hampstead, Willesden Junction, Clapham Junction and Richmond

Network Diagram - see first Page of Table 59

		LO	LO	LO	LO	LO	LO	LO	LO	LO		LO	LO	LO	LO	LO
Stratford 7 ⊖	d	21 30		21 45		22 00	22 15		22 30	22 45			23 00	23 15	23 30	23 45
Hackney Wick	d	21 33		21 48		22 03	22 18		22 33	22 48			23 03	23 18	23 33	23 48
Homerton	d	21 36		21 51		22 06	22 21		22 36	22 51			23 06	23 21	23 36	23 51
Hackney Central	d	21 38		21 53		22 08	22 23		22 38	22 53			23 08	23 23	23 38	23 53
Dalston Kingsland	d	21 40		21 55		22 10	22 25		22 40	22 55			23 10	23 25	23 40	23 55
Canonbury 178	d	21 42		21 57		22 12	22 27		22 42	22 57			23 12	23 27	23 42	23 57
Highbury & Islington ⊖178	d	21 44		21 59		22 15	22 29		22 44	22 59			23 14	23 29	23 44	23 59
Caledonian Rd & Barnsbury	d	21 46		22 01		22 17	22 31		22 46	23 01			23 16	23 31	23 46	00 02
Camden Road	d	21 50		22 05		22 20	22 35		22 50	23 05			23 20	23 35	23a50	00 05
Kentish Town West	d	21 52		22 07		22 22	22 37		22 52	23 07			23 22	23 37		00 07
Gospel Oak	d	21 55		22 10		22 25	22 40		22 55	23 10			23 25	23 40		00 10
Hampstead Heath	d	21 57		22 12		22 27	22 42		22 57	23 12			23 27	23 42		00 12
Finchley Road & Frognal	d	21 59		22 14		22 29	22 44		22 59	23 14			23 29	23 44		00 14
West Hampstead ⊖	d	22 01		22 16		22 31	22 46		23 02	23 16			23 31	23 46		00 16
Brondesbury	d	22 03		22 18		22 33	22 48		23 04	23 18			23 33	23 48		00 18
Brondesbury Park	d	22 04		22 19		22 34	22 49		23 05	23 19			23 34	23 49		00 19
Kensal Rise	d	22 06		22 21		22 36	22 51		23 07	23 21			23 36	23 51		00 21
Willesden Jn. High Level ⊖	a	22 09		22 26		22 40	22 55		23 11	23 25			23 40	23 55		
	d	22 10	22 16	22 27	22 31	22 41	22 56	23 01	23 12	23 26		23 31	23 41	23 56		
Willesden Jn Low Level ⊖	a															00 30
Shepherd's Bush ⊖176	d		22 25		22 37			23 07				23 37				
Kensington (Olympia) ⊖176	d		22 27		22 39			23 09				23 39				
West Brompton ⊖176	d		22 29		22 42			23 12				23 42				
Imperial Wharf 176	d		22 32		22 45			23 15				23 45				
Clapham Junction 10 176	a		22 38		22 52			23 22				23 52				
Acton Central	d	22 16		22 32		22 46	23 01		23 17	23 31			23 46	00 02		
South Acton	d	22 19		22 34		22 49	23 04		23 20	23 34			23 49	00 05		
Gunnersbury ⊖	d	22 23		22 38		22 53	23 08		23 23	23 38			23 52	00 10		
Kew Gardens ⊖	d	22 26		22 41		22 56	23 11		23 26	23 41			23 55	00 13		
Richmond ⊖	a	22 30		22 46		23 00	23 16		23 30	23 46			23 59	00 18		

Saturdays

14 December to 17 May

		LO	SN 1	LO	LO	LO	LO	LO	LO	LO	LO	LO		LO	LO	LO	LO	LO	LO	LO	LO	LO	LO	LO
Stratford 7 ⊖	d						05 42		05 55	06 05	06 15			06 25	06 35	06 45		06 55	07 05	07 15		07 25	07 35	07 45
Hackney Wick	d						05 45		05 58	06 08	06 18			06 28	06 38	06 48		06 58	07 08	07 18		07 28	07 38	07 48
Homerton	d						05 48		06 01	06 11	06 21			06 31	06 41	06 51		07 01	07 11	07 21		07 31	07 41	07 51
Hackney Central	d						05 50		06 03	06 13	06 23			06 33	06 43	06 53		07 03	07 13	07 23		07 33	07 43	07 53
Dalston Kingsland	d						05 52		06 05	06 15	06 25			06 35	06 45	06 55		07 05	07 15	07 25		07 35	07 45	07 55
Canonbury 178	d						05 54		06 07	06 17	06 27			06 37	06 47	06 57		07 07	07 17	07 27		07 37	07 47	07 57
Highbury & Islington ⊖178	d						05 56		06 09	06 19	06 29			06 39	06 49	06 59		07 09	07 19	07 29		07 39	07 49	07 59
Caledonian Rd & Barnsbury	d			00 02			05 58		06 11	06 21	06 31			06 41	06 51	07 01		07 11	07 21	07 31		07 41	07 51	08 01
Camden Road	d			00 05			06 02		06 15	06 25	06 35			06 45	06 55	07 05		07 15	07 25	07 35		07 45	07 55	08 05
Kentish Town West	d			00 07			06 07		06 17	06 27	06 37			06 47	06 57	07 07		07 17	07 27	07 37		07 47	07 57	08 07
Gospel Oak	d			00 10			06 11		06 20	06 30	06 40			06 50	07 00	07 10		07 20	07 30	07 40		07 50	08 00	08 10
Hampstead Heath	d			00 12			06 13		06 22	06 32	06 42			06 52	07 02	07 12		07 22	07 32	07 42		07 52	08 02	08 12
Finchley Road & Frognal	d			00 14			06 15		06 24	06 34	06 44			06 54	07 04	07 14		07 24	07 34	07 44		07 54	08 04	08 14
West Hampstead ⊖	d			00 16			06 17		06 26	06 36	06 46			06 56	07 06	07 16		07 26	07 36	07 46		07 56	08 06	08 16
Brondesbury	d			00 18			06 19		06 28	06 38	06 48			06 58	07 08	07 18		07 28	07 38	07 48		07 58	08 08	08 18
Brondesbury Park	d			00 19			06 20		06 29	06 39	06 49			06 59	07 09	07 19		07 29	07 39	07 49		07 59	08 09	08 19
Kensal Rise	d			00 21			06 22		06 31	06 41	06 51			07 01	07 11	07 21		07 31	07 41	07 51		08 01	08 11	08 21
Willesden Jn. High Level ⊖	a						06 25		06 35	06 45	06 55			07 05	07 15	07 25		07 35	07 45	07 55		08 05	08 15	08 25
	d				06 02	06 06	06 26	06 31	06 36	06 46	06 56	07 01		07 06	07 16	07 26	07 31	07 36	07 46	07 56	08 01	08 06	08 16	08 26
Willesden Jn Low Level ⊖	a			00 30																				
Shepherd's Bush ⊖176	d				06 08			06 37		06 53		07 08			07 26		07 38		07 53		08 08		08 24	
Kensington (Olympia) ⊖176	d				06 10			06 39		06 56		07 10			07 29		07 40		07 56		08 10		08 26	
West Brompton ⊖176	d		00 02		06 13			06 42		06 58		07 12			07 32		07 42		07 58		08 12		08 29	
Imperial Wharf 176	d		00a03		06 16			06 45		07 01		07 15			07 35		07 45		08 01		08 15		08 32	
Clapham Junction 10 176	a				06 22			06 52		07 08		07 22			07 41		07 52		08 08		08 22		08 38	
Acton Central	d	00 02				06 11	06 31		06 41		07 01			07 11		07 31		07 41		08 01		08 11		08 31
South Acton	d	00 05				06 14	06 34		06 44		07 04			07 14		07 34		07 44		08 04		08 14		08 34
Gunnersbury ⊖	d	00 10				06 18	06 37		06 47		07 07			07 17		07 37		07 48		08 08		08 18		08 38
Kew Gardens ⊖	d	00 13				06 21	06 40		06 50		07 10			07 20		07 40		07 51		08 11		08 21		08 41
Richmond ⊖	a	00 18				06 29	06 44		06 54		07 15			07 24		07 46		07 56		08 16		08 26		08 46

For full service between Willesden Jn, Shepherds Bush and Clapham Jn, please refer to Table 176

Table 59

Saturdays

14 December to 17 May

Stratford - Highbury & Islington, West Hampstead, Willesden Junction, Clapham Junction and Richmond

Network Diagram - see first Page of Table 59

Station		LO	LO	LO	LO	LO	LO	LO	LO	LO	LO	LO
Stratford [7] ⊖	d		07 55	08 05	08 15		08 25	08 35	08 45		08 55	09 05
Hackney Wick	d		07 58	08 08	08 18		08 28	08 38	08 48		08 58	09 08
Homerton	d		08 01	08 11	08 21		08 31	08 41	08 51		09 01	09 11
Hackney Central	d		08 03	08 13	08 23		08 33	08 43	08 53		09 03	09 13
Dalston Kingsland	d		08 05	08 15	08 25		08 35	08 45	08 55		09 05	09 15
Canonbury 178	d		08 07	08 17	08 27		08 37	08 47	08 57		09 07	09 17
Highbury & Islington ⊖178	d		08 09	08 19	08 29		08 39	08 49	08 59		09 09	09 19
Caledonian Rd & Barnsbury	d		08 11	08 21	08 31		08 41	08 51	09 01		09 11	09 21
Camden Road	d		08 15	08 25	08 35		08 45	08 55	09 05		09 15	09 25
Kentish Town West	d		08 17	08 27	08 37		08 47	08 57	09 07		09 17	09 27
Gospel Oak	d		08 20	08 30	08 40		08 50	09 01	09 10		09 20	09 30
Hampstead Heath	d		08 22	08 32	08 42		08 52	09 03	09 12		09 22	09 32
Finchley Road & Frognal	d		08 24	08 34	08 44		08 54	09 05	09 14		09 24	09 34
West Hampstead ⊖	d		08 26	08 36	08 46		08 56	09 07	09 16		09 26	09 36
Brondesbury	d		08 28	08 38	08 48		08 58	09 08	09 18		09 28	09 38
Brondesbury Park	d		08 29	08 39	08 49		08 59	09 10	09 19		09 29	09 39
Kensal Rise	d		08 31	08 41	08 51		09 01	09 12	09 21		09 31	09 41
Willesden Jn. High Level ⊖	a		08 35	08 45	08 55		09 05	09 15	09 25		09 35	09 45
	d	08 31	08 36	08 46	08 56	09 01	09 06	09 16	09 26	09 31	09 36	09 46
Willesden Jn Low Level ⊖	a											
Shepherd's Bush ⊖176	d	08 38		08 53		09 07		09 24		09 37		09 53
Kensington (Olympia) ⊖176	d	08 40		08 56		09 09		09 27		09 39		09 55
West Brompton ⊖176	d	08 42		08 58		09 12		09 30		09 42		09 58
Imperial Wharf 176	d	08 45		09 01		09 15		09 33		09 45		10 01
Clapham Junction [10] 176	a	08 52		09 08		09 22		09 39		09 52		10 08
Acton Central	d		08 41		09 01		09 11		09 31		09 41	
South Acton	d		08 44		09 04		09 14		09 34		09 44	
Gunnersbury ⊖	d		08 48		09 08		09 18		09 38		09 48	
Kew Gardens ⊖	d		08 51		09 11		09 21		09 41		09 51	
Richmond ⊖	a		08 56		09 16		09 26		09 46		09 56	

Station		LO	LO	LO	LO	LO	LO	LO	LO	LO	LO	LO
Stratford [7] ⊖	d	09 15		09 25	09 35	09 45		09 55	10 05	10 15		10 25
Hackney Wick	d	09 18		09 28	09 38	09 48		09 58	10 08	10 18		10 28
Homerton	d	09 21		09 31	09 41	09 51		10 01	10 11	10 21		10 31
Hackney Central	d	09 23		09 33	09 43	09 53		10 03	10 13	10 23		10 33
Dalston Kingsland	d	09 25		09 35	09 45	09 55		10 05	10 15	10 25		10 35
Canonbury 178	d	09 27		09 37	09 47	09 57		10 07	10 17	10 27		10 37
Highbury & Islington ⊖178	d	09 29		09 39	09 49	09 59		10 09	10 19	10 29		10 39
Caledonian Rd & Barnsbury	d	09 31		09 41	09 51	10 01		10 11	10 21	10 31		10 41
Camden Road	d	09 35		09 45	09 55	10 05		10 15	10 25	10 35		10 45
Kentish Town West	d	09 37		09 47	09 57	10 07		10 17	10 27	10 37		10 47
Gospel Oak	d	09 40		09 50	10 00	10 10		10 20	10 30	10 39		10 50
Hampstead Heath	d	09 42		09 52	10 02	10 12		10 22	10 32	10 41		10 52
Finchley Road & Frognal	d	09 44		09 54	10 04	10 14		10 24	10 34	10 43		10 54
West Hampstead ⊖	d	09 46		09 56	10 06	10 16		10 26	10 36	10 45		10 56
Brondesbury	d	09 48		09 58	10 08	10 18		10 28	10 38	10 47		10 58
Brondesbury Park	d	09 49		09 59	10 09	10 19		10 29	10 39	10 48		10 59
Kensal Rise	d	09 51		10 01	10 11	10 21		10 31	10 41	10 50		11 01
Willesden Jn. High Level ⊖	a	09 55		10 05	10 15	10 25		10 35	10 45	10 53		11 05
	d	09 56	10 01	10 06	10 16	10 26	10 31	10 36	10 46	10 54	11 01	11 06
Willesden Jn Low Level ⊖	a											
Shepherd's Bush ⊖176	d		10 08		10 24		10 38		10 53		11 08	
Kensington (Olympia) ⊖176	d		10 10		10 27		10 40		10 56		11 10	
West Brompton ⊖176	d		10 12		10 30		10 42		10 58		11 12	
Imperial Wharf 176	d		10 15		10 33		10 45		11 01		11 15	
Clapham Junction [10] 176	a		10 22		10 39		10 52		11 08		11 22	
Acton Central	d	10 01		10 11		10 31		10 41		11 00		11 11
South Acton	d	10 04		10 14		10 34		10 44		11 04		11 14
Gunnersbury ⊖	d	10 08		10 18		10 38		10 48		11 08		11 18
Kew Gardens ⊖	d	10 11		10 21		10 41		10 51		11 11		11 21
Richmond ⊖	a	10 16		10 26		10 45		10 55		11 15		11 25

Station		LO	LO	LO	LO	LO	LO	LO	LO	LO	LO	LO
Stratford [7] ⊖	d	10 35	10 45		10 55	11 05	11 15		11 25	11 35	11 45	
Hackney Wick	d	10 38	10 48		10 58	11 08	11 18		11 28	11 38	11 48	
Homerton	d	10 41	10 51		11 01	11 11	11 21		11 31	11 41	11 51	
Hackney Central	d	10 43	10 53		11 03	11 13	11 23		11 33	11 43	11 53	
Dalston Kingsland	d	10 45	10 55		11 05	11 15	11 25		11 35	11 45	11 55	
Canonbury 178	d	10 47	10 57		11 07	11 17	11 27		11 37	11 47	11 57	
Highbury & Islington ⊖178	d	10 49	10 59		11 09	11 19	11 29		11 39	11 49	11 59	
Caledonian Rd & Barnsbury	d	10 51	11 01		11 11	11 21	11 31		11 41	11 51	12 01	
Camden Road	d	10 55	11 05		11 15	11 25	11 35		11 45	11 55	12 05	
Kentish Town West	d	10 57	11 07		11 17	11 27	11 37		11 47	11 57	12 07	
Gospel Oak	d	11 00	11 10		11 20	11 30	11 40		11 50	12 00	12 10	
Hampstead Heath	d	11 02	11 12		11 22	11 32	11 42		11 52	12 02	12 12	
Finchley Road & Frognal	d	11 04	11 14		11 24	11 34	11 44		11 54	12 04	12 14	
West Hampstead ⊖	d	11 06	11 16		11 26	11 36	11 46		11 56	12 06	12 16	
Brondesbury	d	11 08	11 18		11 28	11 38	11 48		11 58	12 08	12 18	
Brondesbury Park	d	11 09	11 19		11 29	11 39	11 49		11 59	12 09	12 19	
Kensal Rise	d	11 11	11 21		11 31	11 41	11 51		12 01	12 11	12 21	
Willesden Jn. High Level ⊖	a	11 15	11 25		11 35	11 45	11 55		12 05	12 15	12 25	
	d	11 16	11 26	11 31	11 36	11 46	11 56	12 01	12 06	12 16	12 26	12 31
Willesden Jn Low Level ⊖	a											
Shepherd's Bush ⊖176	d	11 24		11 37		11 53		12 08		12 23		12 38
Kensington (Olympia) ⊖176	d	11 27		11 39		11 56		12 10		12 26		12 40
West Brompton ⊖176	d	11 30		11 42		11 58		12 12		12 29		12 42
Imperial Wharf 176	d	11 33		11 45		12 01		12 15		12 32		12 45
Clapham Junction [10] 176	a	11 39		11 52		12 08		12 22		12 38		12 52
Acton Central	d		11 31		11 41		12 01		12 11		12 31	
South Acton	d		11 34		11 44		12 04		12 14		12 34	
Gunnersbury ⊖	d		11 38		11 48		12 08		12 18		12 38	
Kew Gardens ⊖	d		11 41		11 51		12 11		12 21		12 41	
Richmond ⊖	a		11 45		11 55		12 15		12 25		12 45	

Station		LO	LO	LO	LO	LO	LO	LO	LO	LO	LO	LO
Stratford [7] ⊖	d	11 55	12 05	12 15		12 25	12 35	12 45		12 55	13 05	13 15
Hackney Wick	d	11 58	12 08	12 18		12 28	12 38	12 48		12 58	13 08	13 18
Homerton	d	12 01	12 11	12 21		12 31	12 41	12 51		13 01	13 11	13 21
Hackney Central	d	12 03	12 13	12 23		12 33	12 43	12 53		13 03	13 13	13 23
Dalston Kingsland	d	12 05	12 15	12 25		12 35	12 45	12 55		13 05	13 15	13 25
Canonbury 178	d	12 07	12 17	12 27		12 37	12 47	12 57		13 07	13 17	13 27
Highbury & Islington ⊖178	d	12 09	12 19	12 29		12 39	12 49	12 59		13 09	13 19	13 29
Caledonian Rd & Barnsbury	d	12 11	12 21	12 31		12 41	12 51	13 01		13 11	13 21	13 31
Camden Road	d	12 15	12 25	12 35		12 45	12 55	13 05		13 15	13 25	13 35
Kentish Town West	d	12 17	12 27	12 37		12 47	12 57	13 07		13 17	13 27	13 37
Gospel Oak	d	12 20	12 30	12 40		12 50	13 00	13 10		13 20	13 30	13 40
Hampstead Heath	d	12 22	12 32	12 42		12 52	13 02	13 12		13 22	13 32	13 42
Finchley Road & Frognal	d	12 24	12 34	12 44		12 54	13 04	13 14		13 24	13 34	13 44
West Hampstead ⊖	d	12 26	12 36	12 46		12 56	13 06	13 16		13 26	13 36	13 46
Brondesbury	d	12 28	12 38	12 48		12 58	13 08	13 18		13 28	13 38	13 48
Brondesbury Park	d	12 29	12 39	12 49		12 59	13 09	13 19		13 29	13 39	13 49
Kensal Rise	d	12 31	12 41	12 51		13 01	13 11	13 21		13 31	13 41	13 51
Willesden Jn. High Level ⊖	a	12 35	12 45	12 55		13 05	13 15	13 25		13 35	13 45	13 55
	d	12 36	12 46	12 56	13 01	13 06	13 16	13 26	13 31	13 36	13 46	13 56
Willesden Jn Low Level ⊖	a											
Shepherd's Bush ⊖176	d		12 53		13 08		13 24		13 38		13 53	
Kensington (Olympia) ⊖176	d		12 56		13 10		13 26		13 40		13 56	
West Brompton ⊖176	d		12 58		13 12		13 29		13 42		13 58	
Imperial Wharf 176	d		13 01		13 15		13 32		13 45		14 01	
Clapham Junction [10] 176	a		13 08		13 22		13 38		13 52		14 08	
Acton Central	d	12 41		13 01		13 11		13 31		13 41		14 01
South Acton	d	12 44		13 04		13 14		13 34		13 44		14 04
Gunnersbury ⊖	d	12 48		13 08		13 18		13 38		13 48		14 08
Kew Gardens ⊖	d	12 51		13 11		13 21		13 41		13 51		14 11
Richmond ⊖	a	12 55		13 15		13 25		13 45		13 55		14 15

For full service between Willesden Jn, Shepherds Bush and Clapham Jn, please refer to Table 176

Table 59

Saturdays

14 December to 17 May

Stratford - Highbury & Islington, West Hampstead, Willesden Junction, Clapham Junction and Richmond

Network Diagram - see first Page of Table 59

Station		LO	LO	LO	LO	LO	LO	LO	LO	LO	LO	LO
Stratford 7 ⊖	d		13 25	13 35	13 45		13 55	14 05	14 15		14 25	14 35
Hackney Wick	d		13 28	13 38	13 48		13 58	14 08	14 18		14 28	14 38
Homerton	d		13 31	13 41	13 51		14 01	14 11	14 21		14 31	14 41
Hackney Central	d		13 33	13 43	13 53		14 03	14 13	14 23		14 33	14 43
Dalston Kingsland	d		13 35	13 45	13 55		14 05	14 15	14 25		14 35	14 45
Canonbury 178	d		13 37	13 47	13 57		14 07	14 17	14 27		14 37	14 47
Highbury & Islington ⊖178	d		13 39	13 49	13 59		14 09	14 19	14 29		14 39	14 49
Caledonian Rd & Barnsbury	d		13 41	13 51	14 01		14 11	14 21	14 31		14 41	14 51
Camden Road	d		13 45	13 55	14 05		14 15	14 25	14 35		14 45	14 55
Kentish Town West	d		13 47	13 57	14 07		14 17	14 27	14 37		14 47	14 57
Gospel Oak	d		13 50	14 00	14 10		14 20	14 30	14 40		14 50	15 00
Hampstead Heath	d		13 52	14 02	14 12		14 22	14 32	14 42		14 52	15 02
Finchley Road & Frognal	d		13 54	14 04	14 14		14 24	14 34	14 44		14 54	15 04
West Hampstead ⊖	d		13 56	14 06	14 16		14 26	14 36	14 46		14 56	15 06
Brondesbury	d		13 58	14 08	14 18		14 28	14 38	14 48		14 58	15 08
Brondesbury Park	d		13 59	14 09	14 19		14 29	14 39	14 49		14 59	15 09
Kensal Rise	d		14 01	14 11	14 21		14 31	14 41	14 51		15 01	15 11
Willesden Jn. High Level ⊖	a		14 05	14 15	14 25		14 35	14 45	14 55		15 05	15 15
	d	14 01	14 06	14 16	14 26	14 31	14 36	14 46	14 56	15 01	15 06	15 16
Willesden Jn Low Level ⊖	a											
Shepherd's Bush ⊖176	d	14 08		14 24		14 38		14 53		15 08		15 24
Kensington (Olympia) ⊖176	d	14 10		14 27		14 40		14 56		15 10		15 26
West Brompton ⊖176	d	14 12		14 30		14 42		14 58		15 12		15 29
Imperial Wharf 176	d	14 15		14 33		14 45		15 01		15 15		15 32
Clapham Junction 10 176	a	14 22		14 39		14 52		15 08		15 22		15 38
Acton Central	d		14 11		14 31		14 41		15 01		15 11	
South Acton	d		14 14		14 34		14 44		15 04		15 14	
Gunnersbury ⊖	d		14 18		14 38		14 48		15 08		15 18	
Kew Gardens ⊖	d		14 21		14 41		14 51		15 11		15 21	
Richmond ⊖	a		14 25		14 45		14 55		15 15		15 25	

Station		LO	LO	LO	LO	LO	LO	LO	LO	LO	LO	LO
Stratford 7 ⊖	d	14 45		14 55	15 05	15 15		15 25	15 35	15 45		15 55
Hackney Wick	d	14 48		14 58	15 08	15 18		15 28	15 38	15 48		15 58
Homerton	d	14 51		15 01	15 11	15 21		15 31	15 41	15 51		16 01
Hackney Central	d	14 53		15 03	15 13	15 23		15 33	15 43	15 53		16 03
Dalston Kingsland	d	14 55		15 05	15 15	15 25		15 35	15 45	15 55		16 05
Canonbury 178	d	14 57		15 07	15 17	15 27		15 37	15 47	15 57		16 07
Highbury & Islington ⊖178	d	14 59		15 09	15 19	15 29		15 39	15 49	15 59		16 09
Caledonian Rd & Barnsbury	d	15 01		15 11	15 21	15 31		15 41	15 51	16 01		16 11
Camden Road	d	15 05		15 15	15 25	15 35		15 45	15 55	16 05		16 15
Kentish Town West	d	15 07		15 17	15 27	15 37		15 47	15 57	16 07		16 17
Gospel Oak	d	15 10		15 20	15 30	15 40		15 50	16 00	16 10		16 20
Hampstead Heath	d	15 12		15 22	15 32	15 42		15 52	16 02	16 12		16 22
Finchley Road & Frognal	d	15 14		15 24	15 34	15 44		15 54	16 04	16 14		16 24
West Hampstead ⊖	d	15 16		15 26	15 36	15 46		15 56	16 06	16 16		16 26
Brondesbury	d	15 18		15 28	15 38	15 48		15 58	16 08	16 18		16 28
Brondesbury Park	d	15 19		15 29	15 39	15 49		15 59	16 09	16 19		16 29
Kensal Rise	d	15 21		15 31	15 41	15 51		16 01	16 11	16 21		16 31
Willesden Jn. High Level ⊖	a	15 25		15 35	15 45	15 55		16 05	16 15	16 25		16 35
	d	15 26	15 31	15 36	15 46	15 56	16 01	16 06	16 16	16 26	16 31	16 36
Willesden Jn Low Level ⊖	a											
Shepherd's Bush ⊖176	d		15 38		15 53		16 07		16 24		16 38	
Kensington (Olympia) ⊖176	d		15 40		15 56		16 09		16 26		16 40	
West Brompton ⊖176	d		15 42		15 58		16 12		16 29		16 42	
Imperial Wharf 176	d		15 45		16 01		16 15		16 32		16 45	
Clapham Junction 10 176	a		15 52		16 08		16 22		16 38		16 52	
Acton Central	d	15 31		15 41		16 01		16 11		16 31		16 41
South Acton	d	15 34		15 44		16 04		16 14		16 34		16 44
Gunnersbury ⊖	d	15 38		15 48		16 08		16 18		16 38		16 48
Kew Gardens ⊖	d	15 41		15 51		16 11		16 21		16 41		16 51
Richmond ⊖	a	15 45		15 55		16 15		16 25		16 45		16 55

Station		LO	LO	LO	LO	LO	LO	LO	LO	LO	LO	LO
Stratford 7 ⊖	d	16 05	16 15		16 25	16 35	16 45		16 55	17 05	17 15	
Hackney Wick	d	16 08	16 18		16 28	16 38	16 48		16 58	17 08	17 18	
Homerton	d	16 11	16 21		16 31	16 41	16 51		17 01	17 11	17 21	
Hackney Central	d	16 13	16 23		16 33	16 43	16 53		17 03	17 13	17 23	
Dalston Kingsland	d	16 15	16 25		16 35	16 45	16 55		17 05	17 15	17 25	
Canonbury 178	d	16 17	16 27		16 37	16 47	16 57		17 07	17 17	17 27	
Highbury & Islington ⊖178	d	16 19	16 29		16 39	16 49	16 59		17 09	17 19	17 29	
Caledonian Rd & Barnsbury	d	16 21	16 31		16 41	16 51	17 01		17 11	17 21	17 31	
Camden Road	d	16 25	16 35		16 45	16 55	17 05		17 15	17 25	17 35	
Kentish Town West	d	16 27	16 37		16 47	16 57	17 07		17 17	17 27	17 37	
Gospel Oak	d	16 30	16 40		16 50	17 00	17 10		17 20	17 30	17 40	
Hampstead Heath	d	16 32	16 42		16 52	17 02	17 12		17 22	17 32	17 42	
Finchley Road & Frognal	d	16 34	16 44		16 54	17 04	17 14		17 24	17 34	17 44	
West Hampstead ⊖	d	16 36	16 46		16 56	17 06	17 16		17 26	17 36	17 46	
Brondesbury	d	16 38	16 48		16 58	17 08	17 18		17 28	17 38	17 48	
Brondesbury Park	d	16 39	16 49		16 59	17 09	17 19		17 29	17 39	17 49	
Kensal Rise	d	16 41	16 51		17 01	17 11	17 21		17 31	17 41	17 51	
Willesden Jn. High Level ⊖	a	16 45	16 55		17 05	17 15	17 25		17 35	17 45	17 55	
	d	16 46	16 56	17 01	17 06	17 16	17 26	17 31	17 36	17 46	17 56	18 01
Willesden Jn Low Level ⊖	a											
Shepherd's Bush ⊖176	d	16 53		17 08		17 24		17 38		17 53		18 08
Kensington (Olympia) ⊖176	d	16 56		17 10		17 26		17 40		17 56		18 10
West Brompton ⊖176	d	16 58		17 12		17 29		17 42		17 58		18 13
Imperial Wharf 176	d	17 01		17 15		17 32		17 45		18 01		18 16
Clapham Junction 10 176	a	17 08		17 22		17 38		17 52		18 08		18 22
Acton Central	d		17 01		17 11		17 31		17 41		18 01	
South Acton	d		17 04		17 14		17 34		17 44		18 04	
Gunnersbury ⊖	d		17 08		17 18		17 38		17 48		18 08	
Kew Gardens ⊖	d		17 11		17 21		17 41		17 51		18 11	
Richmond ⊖	a		17 15		17 25		17 46		17 56		18 16	

Station		LO	LO	LO	LO	LO	LO	LO	LO	LO	LO	LO
Stratford 7 ⊖	d	17 25	17 35	17 45		17 55	18 05	18 15		18 25	18 35	18 45
Hackney Wick	d	17 28	17 38	17 48		17 58	18 08	18 18		18 28	18 38	18 48
Homerton	d	17 31	17 41	17 51		18 01	18 11	18 21		18 31	18 41	18 51
Hackney Central	d	17 33	17 43	17 53		18 03	18 13	18 23		18 33	18 43	18 53
Dalston Kingsland	d	17 35	17 45	17 55		18 05	18 15	18 25		18 35	18 45	18 55
Canonbury 178	d	17 37	17 47	17 57		18 07	18 17	18 27		18 37	18 47	18 57
Highbury & Islington ⊖178	d	17 39	17 49	17 59		18 09	18 19	18 29		18 39	18 49	18 59
Caledonian Rd & Barnsbury	d	17 41	17 51	18 01		18 11	18 21	18 31		18 41	18 51	19 01
Camden Road	d	17 45	17 55	18 05		18 15	18 25	18 35		18 45	18 55	19 05
Kentish Town West	d	17 47	17 57	18 07		18 17	18 27	18 37		18 47	18 57	19 07
Gospel Oak	d	17 50	18 00	18 10		18 20	18 30	18 40		18 50	19 00	19 10
Hampstead Heath	d	17 52	18 02	18 12		18 22	18 32	18 42		18 52	19 02	19 12
Finchley Road & Frognal	d	17 54	18 04	18 14		18 24	18 34	18 44		18 54	19 04	19 14
West Hampstead ⊖	d	17 56	18 06	18 16		18 26	18 36	18 46		18 56	19 06	19 16
Brondesbury	d	17 58	18 08	18 18		18 28	18 38	18 48		18 58	19 08	19 18
Brondesbury Park	d	17 59	18 09	18 19		18 29	18 39	18 49		18 59	19 09	19 19
Kensal Rise	d	18 01	18 11	18 21		18 31	18 41	18 51		19 01	19 11	19 21
Willesden Jn. High Level ⊖	a	18 05	18 15	18 25		18 35	18 45	18 55		19 05	19 15	19 25
	d	18 06	18 16	18 26	18 31	18 36	18 46	18 56	19 01	19 06	19 16	19 26
Willesden Jn Low Level ⊖	a											
Shepherd's Bush ⊖176	d		18 24		18 38		18 53		19 08		19 24	
Kensington (Olympia) ⊖176	d		18 26		18 40		18 56		19 10		19 26	
West Brompton ⊖176	d		18 29		18 42		18 58		19 12		19 29	
Imperial Wharf 176	d		18 32		18 45		19 01		19 15		19 32	
Clapham Junction 10 176	a		18 38		18 52		19 08		19 22		19 38	
Acton Central	d	18 11		18 31		18 41		19 01		19 11		19 31
South Acton	d	18 14		18 34		18 44		19 04		19 14		19 34
Gunnersbury ⊖	d	18 18		18 38		18 48		19 08		19 18		19 38
Kew Gardens ⊖	d	18 21		18 41		18 51		19 11		19 21		19 41
Richmond ⊖	a	18 26		18 46		18 56		19 17		19 26		19 46

For full service between Willesden Jn, Shepherds Bush and Clapham Jn, please refer to Table 176

Table 59

Saturdays

14 December to 17 May

Stratford - Highbury & Islington, West Hampstead, Willesden Junction, Clapham Junction and Richmond

Network Diagram - see first Page of Table 59

Station			LO	LO	LO	LO	LO	LO	LO	LO	LO	LO	LO	LO	LO	LO	LO	LO	LO	LO	LO	LO	LO	LO
Stratford 7	⊖	d		18 55	19 05	19 15		19 25	19 35	19 45		19 55	20 05	20 15		20 25	20 35	20 45		21 00		21 15		21 30
Hackney Wick		d		18 58	19 08	19 18		19 28	19 38	19 48		19 58	20 08	20 18		20 28	20 38	20 48		21 03		21 18		21 33
Homerton		d		19 01	19 11	19 21		19 31	19 41	19 51		20 01	20 11	20 21		20 31	20 41	20 51		21 06		21 21		21 36
Hackney Central		d		19 03	19 13	19 23		19 33	19 43	19 53		20 03	20 13	20 23		20 33	20 43	20 53		21 08		21 23		21 38
Dalston Kingsland		d		19 05	19 15	19 25		19 35	19 45	19 55		20 05	20 15	20 25		20 35	20 45	20 55		21 10		21 25		21 40
Canonbury	178	d		19 07	19 17	19 27		19 37	19 47	19 57		20 07	20 17	20 27		20 37	20 47	20 57		21 12		21 27		21 42
Highbury & Islington	⊖178	d		19 09	19 19	19 29		19 39	19 49	19 59		20 09	20 19	20 29		20 39	20 49	20 59		21 14		21 29		21 44
Caledonian Rd & Barnsbury		d		19 11	19 21	19 31		19 41	19 51	20 01		20 11	20 21	20 31		20 41	20 51	21 01		21 16		21 31		21 46
Camden Road		d		19 15	19 25	19 35		19 45	19 55	20 05		20 15	20 25	20 35		20 45	20 55	21 05		21 20		21 35		21 50
Kentish Town West		d		19 17	19 27	19 37		19 47	19 57	20 07		20 17	20 27	20 37		20 47	20 57	21 07		21 22		21 37		21 52
Gospel Oak		d		19 20	19 30	19 40		19 50	20 00	20 10		20 20	20 30	20 40		20 50	21 00	21 10		21 25		21 40		21 55
Hampstead Heath		d		19 22	19 32	19 42		19 52	20 02	20 12		20 22	20 32	20 42		20 52	21 02	21 12		21 27		21 42		21 57
Finchley Road & Frognal		d		19 24	19 34	19 44		19 54	20 04	20 14		20 24	20 34	20 44		20 54	21 04	21 14		21 29		21 44		21 59
West Hampstead	⊖	d		19 26	19 36	19 46		19 56	20 06	20 16		20 26	20 36	20 46		20 56	21 06	21 16		21 31		21 46		22 01
Brondesbury		d		19 28	19 38	19 48		19 58	20 08	20 18		20 28	20 38	20 48		20 58	21 08	21 18		21 33		21 48		22 03
Brondesbury Park		d		19 29	19 39	19 49		19 59	20 09	20 19		20 29	20 39	20 49		20 59	21 09	21 19		21 34		21 49		22 04
Kensal Rise		d		19 31	19 41	19 51		20 01	20 11	20 21		20 31	20 41	20 51		21 01	21 11	21 21		21 36		21 51		22 06
Willesden Jn. High Level	⊖	a		19 35	19 45	19 55		20 05	20 15	20 25		20 35	20 45	20 55		21 05	21 15	21 25		21 40		21 55		22 10
		d	19 31	19 36	19 46	19 56	20 01	20 06	20 16	20 26	20 31	20 36	20 46	20 56	21 01	21 06	21 16	21 26	21 31	21 41	21 46	21 56	22 01	22 11
Willesden Jn Low Level	⊖	a																						
Shepherd's Bush	⊖176	d	19 37		19 53		20 08		20 24		20 38		20 53		21 12		21 23		21 38		21 53		22 12	
Kensington (Olympia)	⊖176	d	19 39		19 56		20 10		20 27		20 40		20 56		21 14		21 25		21 40		21 55		22 14	
West Brompton	⊖176	d	19 42		19 58		20 12		20 29		20 42		20 58		21 17		21 27		21 42		21 57		22 17	
Imperial Wharf	176	d	19 45		20 01		20 15		20 32		20 45		21 01		21 20		21 30		21 45		22 00		22 20	
Clapham Junction 10	176	a	19 52		20 08		20 22		20 39		20 52		21 08		21 26		21 38		21 52		22 07		22 26	
Acton Central		d		19 41		20 01		20 11		20 31		20 41		21 01		21 11		21 31		21 46		22 01		22 16
South Acton		d		19 44		20 04		20 14		20 34		20 44		21 04		21 14		21 34		21 49		22 04		22 19
Gunnersbury	⊖	d		19 48		20 08		20 18		20 38		20 48		21 08		21 18		21 38		21 52		22 08		22 22
Kew Gardens	⊖	d		19 51		20 11		20 21		20 41		20 51		21 11		21 21		21 41		21 55		22 11		22 25
Richmond	⊖	a		19 55		20 15		20 25		20 45		20 55		21 15		21 25		21 45		22 00		22 15		22 29

Station			LO	LO	LO	LO	LO	LO	LO	LO	LO	LO	LO	LO	LO
Stratford 7	⊖	d		21 45		21 55	22 15		22 30	22 45		23 00	23 15	23 30	23 45
Hackney Wick		d		21 48		21 58	22 18		22 33	22 48		23 03	23 18	23 33	23 48
Homerton		d		21 51		22 01	22 21		22 36	22 51		23 06	23 21	23 36	23 51
Hackney Central		d		21 53		22 03	22 23		22 38	22 53		23 08	23 23	23 38	23 53
Dalston Kingsland		d		21 55		22 05	22 25		22 40	22 55		23 10	23 25	23 40	23 55
Canonbury	178	d		21 57		22 07	22 27		22 42	22 57		23 12	23 27	23 42	23 57
Highbury & Islington	⊖178	d		21 59		22 09	22 29		22 44	22 59		23 14	23 29	23 44	23 59
Caledonian Rd & Barnsbury		d		22 01		22 11	22 31		22 46	23 01		23 16	23 31	23 46	00 02
Camden Road		d		22 05		22 15	22 35		22a49	23 05		23 20	23 35	23a50	00 05
Kentish Town West		d		22 07		22 17	22 37			23 07		23 22	23 37		00 07
Gospel Oak		d		22 10		22 21	22 40			23 10		23 25	23 40		00 10
Hampstead Heath		d		22 12		22 23	22 42			23 12		23 27	23 42		00 12
Finchley Road & Frognal		d		22 14		22 25	22 44			23 14		23 29	23 44		00 14
West Hampstead	⊖	d		22 16		22 27	22 46			23 16		23 31	23 46		00 16
Brondesbury		d		22 18		22 29	22 48			23 18		23 33	23 48		00 18
Brondesbury Park		d		22 19		22 30	22 49			23 19		23 34	23 49		00 19
Kensal Rise		d		22 21		22 32	22 51			23 21		23 36	23 51		00 21
Willesden Jn. High Level	⊖	a		22 25		22 38	22 55			23 25		23 40	23 55		
		d	22 16	22 26	22 31	22 39	22 56	23 01		23 26	23 31	23 41	23 56		
Willesden Jn Low Level	⊖	a													00 30
Shepherd's Bush	⊖176	d	22 23		22 38			23 08			23 37				
Kensington (Olympia)	⊖176	d	22 25		22 40			23 10			23 39				
West Brompton	⊖176	d	22 27		22 42			23 12			23 42				
Imperial Wharf	176	d	22 30		22 45			23 15			23 45				
Clapham Junction 10	176	a	22 37		22 52			23 22			23 51				
Acton Central		d		22 31		22 44	23 01			23 31		23 46	00 02		
South Acton		d		22 34		22 47	23 04			23 34		23 49	00 04		
Gunnersbury	⊖	d		22 38		22 50	23 08			23 38		23 52	00 08		
Kew Gardens	⊖	d		22 41		22 53	23 11			23 41		23 55	00 11		
Richmond	⊖	a		22 45		22 56	23 16			23 46		00 01	00 18		

For full service between Willesden Jn, Shepherds Bush and Clapham Jn, please refer to Table 176

Table 59

Sundays

8 December to 11 May

Stratford - Highbury & Islington, West Hampstead, Willesden Junction, Clapham Junction and Richmond

Network Diagram - see first Page of Table 59

	LO A	LO A	LO	LO	LO	LO	LO	LO	LO	LO	LO	LO	LO	LO	LO	LO	LO	LO	LO	LO	LO	LO
Stratford 7 ⊖ d										09 15		09 27		09 45		09 57		10 20			10 35	10 45
Hackney Wick d										09 18		09 30		09 48		10 00		10 23			10 38	10 48
Homerton d										09 21		09 33		09 51		10 03		10 26			10 41	10 51
Hackney Central d										09 23		09 35		09 53		10 05		10 28			10 43	10 53
Dalston Kingsland d										09 25		09 37		09 55		10 07		10 30			10 45	10 55
Canonbury 178 d										09 27		09 39		09 57		10 09		10 32			10 47	10 57
Highbury & Islington ⊖178 d										09 29		09 41		09 59		10 11		10 34			10 49	10 59
Caledonian Rd & Barnsbury d		00 02								09 31		09 43		10 01		10 13		10 36			10 51	11 01
Camden Road d		00 05								09 35		09 47		10 05		10 17		10 40			10 55	11 05
Kentish Town West d		00 07								09 37		09 49		10 07		10 19		10 42			10 57	11 07
Gospel Oak d		00 10						09 28		09 40		09 52		10 10		10 22		10 45			11 00	11 10
Hampstead Heath d		00 12						09 29		09 42		09 54		10 12		10 24		10 47			11 02	11 12
Finchley Road & Frognal d		00 14						09 30		09 44		09 56		10 14		10 26		10 49			11 04	11 14
West Hampstead ⊖ d		00 16						09 31		09 46		09 58		10 16		10 28		10 51			11 06	11 16
Brondesbury d		00 18						09 33		09 48		10 00		10 18		10 30		10 53			11 08	11 18
Brondesbury Park d		00 19						09 34		09 49		10 01		10 19		10 31		10 54			11 09	11 19
Kensal Rise d		00 21						09 36		09 51		10 03		10 21		10 33		10 56			11 11	11 21
Willesden Jn. High Level ⊖ a								09 39		09 55		10 07		10 25		10 37		11 00			11 15	11 25
d			08 32	08 56	09 02	09 26	09 32	09 40	09 48	09 56	10 02	10 08	10 16	10 26	10 32	10 38	10 46	11 01	11 02	11 15	11 16	11 26
Willesden Jn Low Level ⊖ a		00 30																				
Shepherd's Bush ⊖176 d			08 39		09 08		09 39		09 54		10 08		10 24		10 38		10 54		11 10		11 23	
Kensington (Olympia) ⊖176 d			08 41		09 10		09 41		09 56		10 10		10 26		10 40		10 56		11 12		11 26	
West Brompton ⊖176 d			08 43		09 12		09 43		09 57		10 13		10 27		10 43		10 57		11 14		11 28	
Imperial Wharf 176 d			08 46		09 15		09 46		10 00		10 16		10 30		10 46		11 00		11 17		11 31	
Clapham Junction 10 176 a			08 53		09 23		09 54		10 08		10 26		10 37		10 54		11 07		11 26		11 40	
Acton Central d	00 02			09 01		09 31		09 45		10 01		10 13		10 31		10 43		11 06		11 21		11 31
South Acton d	00 04			09 03		09 34		09 47		10 04		10 16		10 34		10 46		11 09		11 24		11 34
Gunnersbury ⊖ d	00 08			09 08		09 38		09 50		10 08		10 19		10 38		10 49		11 12		11 28		11 38
Kew Gardens ⊖ d	00 11			09 11		09 41		09 53		10 11		10 22		10 41		10 52		11 15		11 31		11 41
Richmond ⊖ a	00 18			09 19		09 49		10 03		10 16		10 26		10 46		10 57		11 21		11 38		11 46

	LO	LO	LO	LO	LO	LO	LO	LO	LO	LO	LO	LO	LO	LO	LO	LO	LO	LO	LO	LO	LO	LO
Stratford 7 ⊖ d		10 55	11 05	11 15		11 25	11 35	11 45		11 55	12 05	12 15		12 25	12 35	12 45		12 55	13 05	13 15		13 25
Hackney Wick d		10 58	11 08	11 18		11 28	11 38	11 48		11 58	12 08	12 18		12 28	12 38	12 48		12 58	13 08	13 18		13 28
Homerton d		11 01	11 11	11 21		11 31	11 41	11 51		12 01	12 11	12 21		12 31	12 41	12 51		13 01	13 11	13 21		13 31
Hackney Central d		11 03	11 13	11 23		11 33	11 43	11 53		12 03	12 13	12 23		12 33	12 43	12 53		13 03	13 13	13 23		13 33
Dalston Kingsland d		11 05	11 15	11 25		11 35	11 45	11 55		12 05	12 15	12 25		12 35	12 45	12 55		13 05	13 15	13 25		13 35
Canonbury 178 d		11 07	11 17	11 27		11 37	11 47	11 57		12 07	12 17	12 27		12 37	12 47	12 57		13 07	13 17	13 27		13 37
Highbury & Islington ⊖178 d		11 09	11 19	11 29		11 39	11 49	11 59		12 09	12 19	12 29		12 39	12 49	12 59		13 09	13 19	13 29		13 39
Caledonian Rd & Barnsbury d		11 11	11 21	11 31		11 41	11 51	12 01		12 11	12 21	12 31		12 41	12 51	13 01		13 11	13 21	13 31		13 41
Camden Road d		11 15	11 25	11 35		11 45	11 55	12 05		12 15	12 25	12 35		12 45	12 55	13 05		13 15	13 25	13 35		13 45
Kentish Town West d		11 17	11 27	11 37		11 47	11 57	12 07		12 17	12 27	12 37		12 47	12 57	13 07		13 17	13 27	13 37		13 47
Gospel Oak d		11 20	11 30	11 40		11 50	12 00	12 10		12 20	12 30	12 40		12 50	13 00	13 10		13 20	13 30	13 40		13 50
Hampstead Heath d		11 22	11 32	11 42		11 52	12 02	12 12		12 22	12 32	12 42		12 52	13 02	13 12		13 22	13 32	13 42		13 52
Finchley Road & Frognal d		11 24	11 34	11 44		11 54	12 04	12 14		12 24	12 34	12 44		12 54	13 04	13 14		13 24	13 34	13 44		13 54
West Hampstead ⊖ d		11 26	11 36	11 46		11 56	12 06	12 16		12 26	12 36	12 46		12 56	13 06	13 16		13 26	13 36	13 46		13 56
Brondesbury d		11 28	11 38	11 48		11 58	12 08	12 18		12 28	12 38	12 48		12 58	13 08	13 18		13 28	13 38	13 48		13 58
Brondesbury Park d		11 29	11 39	11 49		11 59	12 09	12 19		12 29	12 39	12 49		12 59	13 09	13 19		13 29	13 39	13 49		13 59
Kensal Rise d		11 31	11 41	11 51		12 01	12 11	12 21		12 31	12 41	12 51		13 01	13 11	13 21		13 31	13 41	13 51		14 01
Willesden Jn. High Level ⊖ a		11 35	11 45	11 55		12 05	12 15	12 25		12 35	12 45	12 55		13 05	13 15	13 25		13 35	13 45	13 55		14 05
d	11 32	11 36	11 46	11 56	12 02	12 06	12 16	12 26	12 32	12 36	12 46	12 56	13 02	13 06	13 16	13 26	13 32	13 36	13 46	13 56	14 02	14 06
Willesden Jn Low Level ⊖ a																						
Shepherd's Bush ⊖176 d	11 39		11 53		12 09		12 23		12 39		12 53		13 09		13 23		13 39		13 53		14 09	
Kensington (Olympia) ⊖176 d	11 41		11 56		12 11		12 26		12 41		12 56		13 11		13 26		13 41		13 56		14 11	
West Brompton ⊖176 d	11 43		11 57		12 13		12 28		12 43		12 57		13 13		13 28		13 43		13 57		14 13	
Imperial Wharf 176 d	11 46		12 00		12 16		12 31		12 46		13 00		13 16		13 31		13 46		14 00		14 16	
Clapham Junction 10 176 a	11 54		12 08		12 23		12 38		12 53		13 08		13 23		13 38		13 53		14 08		14 23	
Acton Central d		11 41		12 01		12 11		12 31		12 41		13 01		13 11		13 31		13 41		14 01		14 11
South Acton d		11 44		12 04		12 14		12 34		12 44		13 04		13 14		13 34		13 44		14 04		14 14
Gunnersbury ⊖ d		11 48		12 08		12 18		12 38		12 48		13 08		13 18		13 38		13 48		14 08		14 18
Kew Gardens ⊖ d		11 51		12 11		12 21		12 41		12 51		13 11		13 21		13 41		13 51		14 11		14 21
Richmond ⊖ a		11 56		12 15		12 25		12 45		12 55		13 15		13 25		13 45		13 55		14 15		14 25

A not 8 December

For full service between Willesden Jn, Shepherds Bush and Clapham Jn, please refer to Table 176

Table 59

Sundays

8 December to 11 May

Stratford - Highbury & Islington, West Hampstead, Willesden Junction, Clapham Junction and Richmond

Network Diagram - see first Page of Table 59

		LO	LO	LO	LO	LO	LO	LO	LO	LO	LO	LO	LO	LO	LO	LO	LO	LO	LO	LO	LO	LO	LO
Stratford [7] ⊖	d	13 35	13 45		13 55	14 05	14 15		14 25	14 35	14 45		14 55	15 05	15 15		15 25	15 35	15 45		15 55	16 05	16 15
Hackney Wick	d	13 38	13 48		13 58	14 08	14 18		14 28	14 38	14 48		14 58	15 08	15 18		15 28	15 38	15 48		15 58	16 08	16 18
Homerton	d	13 41	13 51		14 01	14 11	14 21		14 31	14 41	14 51		15 01	15 11	15 21		15 31	15 41	15 51		16 01	16 11	16 21
Hackney Central	d	13 43	13 53		14 03	14 13	14 23		14 33	14 43	14 53		15 03	15 13	15 23		15 33	15 43	15 53		16 03	16 13	16 23
Dalston Kingsland	d	13 45	13 55		14 05	14 15	14 25		14 35	14 45	14 55		15 05	15 15	15 25		15 35	15 45	15 55		16 05	16 15	16 25
Canonbury 178	d	13 47	13 57		14 07	14 17	14 27		14 37	14 47	14 57		15 07	15 17	15 27		15 37	15 47	15 57		16 07	16 17	16 27
Highbury & Islington ⊖178	d	13 49	13 59		14 09	14 19	14 29		14 39	14 49	14 59		15 09	15 19	15 29		15 39	15 49	15 59		16 09	16 19	16 29
Caledonian Rd & Barnsbury	d	13 51	14 01		14 11	14 21	14 31		14 41	14 51	15 01		15 11	15 21	15 31		15 41	15 51	16 01		16 11	16 21	16 31
Camden Road	d	13 55	14 05		14 15	14 25	14 35		14 45	14 55	15 05		15 15	15 25	15 35		15 45	15 55	16 05		16 15	16 25	16 35
Kentish Town West	d	13 57	14 07		14 17	14 27	14 37		14 47	14 57	15 07		15 17	15 27	15 37		15 47	15 57	16 07		16 17	16 27	16 37
Gospel Oak	d	14 00	14 10		14 20	14 30	14 40		14 50	15 00	15 10		15 20	15 30	15 40		15 50	16 00	16 10		16 20	16 30	16 40
Hampstead Heath	d	14 02	14 12		14 22	14 32	14 42		14 52	15 02	15 12		15 22	15 32	15 42		15 52	16 02	16 12		16 22	16 32	16 42
Finchley Road & Frognal	d	14 04	14 14		14 24	14 34	14 44		14 54	15 04	15 14		15 24	15 34	15 44		15 54	16 04	16 14		16 24	16 34	16 44
West Hampstead ⊖	d	14 06	14 16		14 26	14 36	14 46		14 56	15 06	15 16		15 26	15 36	15 46		15 56	16 06	16 16		16 26	16 36	16 46
Brondesbury	d	14 08	14 18		14 28	14 38	14 48		14 58	15 08	15 18		15 28	15 38	15 48		15 58	16 08	16 18		16 28	16 38	16 48
Brondesbury Park	d	14 09	14 19		14 29	14 39	14 49		14 59	15 09	15 19		15 29	15 39	15 49		15 59	16 09	16 19		16 29	16 39	16 49
Kensal Rise	d	14 11	14 21		14 31	14 41	14 51		15 01	15 11	15 21		15 31	15 41	15 51		16 01	16 11	16 21		16 31	16 41	16 51
Willesden Jn. High Level ⊖	a	14 15	14 25		14 35	14 45	14 55		15 05	15 15	15 25		15 35	15 45	15 55		16 05	16 15	16 25		16 35	16 45	16 55
	d	14 16	14 26	14 32	14 36	14 46	14 56	15 02	15 06	15 16	15 26	15 32	15 36	15 46	15 56	16 02	16 06	16 16	16 26	16 32	16 36	16 46	16 56
Willesden Jn Low Level ⊖	a																						
Shepherd's Bush ⊖176	d	14 23		14 39		14 53		15 09		15 23		15 39		15 53		16 09		16 23		16 39		16 53	
Kensington (Olympia) ⊖176	d	14 26		14 41		14 56		15 11		15 26		15 41		15 56		16 11		16 26		16 41		16 56	
West Brompton ⊖176	d	14 28		14 43		14 57		15 13		15 28		15 43		15 57		16 13		16 28		16 43		16 57	
Imperial Wharf 176	d	14 31		14 46		15 00		15 16		15 31		15 46		16 00		16 16		16 31		16 46		17 00	
Clapham Junction [10] 176	a	14 38		14 53		15 08		15 22		15 38		15 53		16 08		16 23		16 38		16 53		17 08	
Acton Central	d		14 31		14 41		15 01		15 11		15 31		15 41		16 01		16 11		16 31		16 41		17 01
South Acton	d		14 34		14 44		15 04		15 14		15 34		15 44		16 04		16 14		16 34		16 44		17 04
Gunnersbury ⊖	d		14 38		14 48		15 08		15 18		15 38		15 48		16 08		16 18		16 38		16 48		17 08
Kew Gardens ⊖	d		14 41		14 51		15 11		15 21		15 41		15 51		16 11		16 21		16 41		16 51		17 11
Richmond ⊖	a		14 45		14 55		15 15		15 25		15 45		15 55		16 15		16 25		16 45		16 55		17 15

		LO	LO	LO	LO	LO	LO	LO	LO	LO	LO	LO	LO	LO	LO	LO	LO	LO	LO	LO	LO	LO	LO
Stratford [7] ⊖	d		16 25	16 35	16 45		16 55	17 05	17 15		17 25	17 35	17 45		17 55	18 05	18 15		18 25	18 35	18 45		18 55
Hackney Wick	d		16 28	16 38	16 48		16 58	17 08	17 18		17 28	17 38	17 48		17 58	18 08	18 18		18 28	18 38	18 48		18 58
Homerton	d		16 31	16 41	16 51		17 01	17 11	17 21		17 31	17 41	17 51		18 01	18 11	18 21		18 31	18 41	18 51		19 01
Hackney Central	d		16 33	16 43	16 53		17 03	17 13	17 23		17 33	17 43	17 53		18 03	18 13	18 23		18 33	18 43	18 53		19 03
Dalston Kingsland	d		16 35	16 45	16 55		17 05	17 15	17 25		17 35	17 45	17 55		18 05	18 15	18 25		18 35	18 45	18 55		19 05
Canonbury 178	d		16 37	16 47	16 57		17 07	17 17	17 27		17 37	17 47	17 57		18 07	18 17	18 27		18 37	18 47	18 57		19 07
Highbury & Islington ⊖178	d		16 39	16 49	16 59		17 09	17 19	17 29		17 39	17 49	17 59		18 09	18 19	18 29		18 39	18 49	18 59		19 09
Caledonian Rd & Barnsbury	d		16 41	16 51	17 01		17 11	17 21	17 31		17 41	17 51	18 01		18 11	18 21	18 31		18 41	18 51	19 01		19 11
Camden Road	d		16 45	16 55	17 05		17 15	17 25	17 35		17 45	17 55	18 05		18 15	18 25	18 35		18 45	18 55	19 05		19 15
Kentish Town West	d		16 47	16 57	17 07		17 17	17 27	17 37		17 47	17 57	18 07		18 17	18 27	18 37		18 47	18 57	19 07		19 17
Gospel Oak	d		16 50	17 00	17 10		17 20	17 30	17 40		17 50	18 00	18 10		18 20	18 30	18 40		18 50	19 00	19 10		19 20
Hampstead Heath	d		16 52	17 02	17 12		17 22	17 32	17 42		17 52	18 02	18 12		18 22	18 32	18 42		18 52	19 02	19 12		19 22
Finchley Road & Frognal	d		16 54	17 04	17 14		17 24	17 34	17 44		17 54	18 04	18 14		18 24	18 34	18 44		18 54	19 04	19 14		19 24
West Hampstead ⊖	d		16 56	17 06	17 16		17 26	17 36	17 46		17 56	18 06	18 16		18 26	18 36	18 46		18 56	19 06	19 16		19 26
Brondesbury	d		16 58	17 08	17 18		17 28	17 38	17 48		17 58	18 08	18 18		18 28	18 38	18 48		18 58	19 08	19 18		19 28
Brondesbury Park	d		16 59	17 09	17 19		17 29	17 39	17 49		17 59	18 09	18 19		18 29	18 39	18 49		18 59	19 09	19 19		19 29
Kensal Rise	d		17 01	17 11	17 21		17 31	17 41	17 51		18 01	18 11	18 21		18 31	18 41	18 51		19 01	19 11	19 21		19 31
Willesden Jn. High Level ⊖	a		17 05	17 15	17 25		17 35	17 45	17 55		18 05	18 15	18 25		18 35	18 45	18 55		19 05	19 15	19 25		19 35
	d	17 02	17 06	17 16	17 26	17 32	17 36	17 46	17 56	18 02	18 06	18 16	18 26	18 32	18 36	18 46	18 56	19 02	19 06	19 16	19 26	19 32	19 36
Willesden Jn Low Level ⊖	a																						
Shepherd's Bush ⊖176	d	17 09		17 23		17 39		17 53		18 09		18 23		18 39		18 53		19 09		19 23		19 39	
Kensington (Olympia) ⊖176	d	17 11		17 26		17 41		17 56		18 11		18 26		18 41		18 56		19 11		19 26		19 41	
West Brompton ⊖176	d	17 13		17 28		17 43		17 57		18 13		18 28		18 43		18 57		19 13		19 28		19 43	
Imperial Wharf 176	d	17 16		17 31		17 46		18 00		18 16		18 31		18 46		19 00		19 16		19 31		19 46	
Clapham Junction [10] 176	a	17 23		17 38		17 53		18 08		18 23		18 38		18 53		19 08		19 23		19 38		19 53	
Acton Central	d		17 11		17 31		17 41		18 01		18 11		18 31		18 41		19 01		19 11		19 31		19 41
South Acton	d		17 14		17 34		17 44		18 04		18 14		18 34		18 44		19 04		19 14		19 34		19 44
Gunnersbury ⊖	d		17 18		17 38		17 48		18 08		18 18		18 38		18 48		19 08		19 18		19 38		19 48
Kew Gardens ⊖	d		17 21		17 41		17 51		18 11		18 21		18 41		18 51		19 11		19 21		19 41		19 51
Richmond ⊖	a		17 25		17 46		17 56		18 16		18 26		18 46		18 56		19 16		19 26		19 46		19 55

For full service between Willesden Jn, Shepherds Bush and Clapham Jn, please refer to Table 176

Table 59

Sundays

8 December to 11 May

Stratford - Highbury & Islington, West Hampstead, Willesden Junction, Clapham Junction and Richmond

Network Diagram - see first Page of Table 59

Station		LO	LO	LO	LO	LO	LO	LO	LO	LO	LO	LO
Stratford 7 ⊖	d	19 05	19 15		19 25	19 35	19 45		19 55	20 05	20 15	
Hackney Wick	d	19 08	19 18		19 28	19 38	19 48		19 58	20 08	20 18	
Homerton	d	19 11	19 21		19 31	19 41	19 51		20 01	20 11	20 21	
Hackney Central	d	19 13	19 23		19 33	19 43	19 53		20 03	20 13	20 23	
Dalston Kingsland	d	19 15	19 25		19 35	19 45	19 55		20 05	20 15	20 25	
Canonbury 178	d	19 17	19 27		19 37	19 47	19 57		20 07	20 17	20 27	
Highbury & Islington ⊖178	d	19 19	19 29		19 39	19 49	19 59		20 09	20 19	20 29	
Caledonian Rd & Barnsbury	d	19 21	19 31		19 41	19 51	20 01		20 11	20 21	20 31	
Camden Road	d	19 25	19 35		19 45	19 55	20 05		20 15	20 25	20 35	
Kentish Town West	d	19 27	19 37		19 47	19 57	20 07		20 17	20 27	20 37	
Gospel Oak	d	19 30	19 40		19 50	20 00	20 10		20 20	20 30	20 40	
Hampstead Heath	d	19 32	19 42		19 52	20 02	20 12		20 22	20 32	20 42	
Finchley Road & Frognal	d	19 34	19 44		19 54	20 04	20 14		20 24	20 34	20 44	
West Hampstead ⊖	d	19 36	19 46		19 56	20 06	20 16		20 26	20 36	20 46	
Brondesbury	d	19 38	19 48		19 58	20 08	20 18		20 28	20 38	20 48	
Brondesbury Park	d	19 39	19 49		19 59	20 09	20 19		20 29	20 39	20 49	
Kensal Rise	d	19 41	19 51		20 01	20 11	20 21		20 31	20 41	20 51	
Willesden Jn. High Level ⊖	a	19 45	19 55		20 05	20 15	20 25		20 35	20 45	20 55	
	d	19 46	19 56	20 02	20 06	20 16	20 26	20 32	20 36	20 46	20 56	21 02
Willesden Jn Low Level ⊖	a											
Shepherd's Bush ⊖176	d	19 53		20 09		20 23		20 39		20 53		21 08
Kensington (Olympia) ⊖176	d	19 56		20 11		20 26		20 41		20 56		21 10
West Brompton ⊖176	d	19 57		20 13		20 28		20 43		20 58		21 12
Imperial Wharf 176	d	20 00		20 16		20 31		20 46		21 01		21 15
Clapham Junction 10 176	a	20 08		20 23		20 38		20 53		21 08		21 23
Acton Central	d		20 01		20 11		20 31		20 41		21 01	
South Acton	d		20 04		20 14		20 34		20 44		21 04	
Gunnersbury ⊖	d		20 08		20 18		20 38		20 48		21 08	
Kew Gardens ⊖	d		20 11		20 21		20 41		20 51		21 11	
Richmond ⊖	a		20 15		20 25		20 45		20 55		21 15	

Station		LO	LO	LO	LO	LO	LO	LO	LO	LO	LO	LO
Stratford 7 ⊖	d	20 25	20 35	20 45		20 55	21 05	21 15		21 30	21 45	
Hackney Wick	d	20 28	20 38	20 48		20 58	21 08	21 18		21 33	21 48	
Homerton	d	20 31	20 41	20 51		21 01	21 11	21 21		21 36	21 51	
Hackney Central	d	20 33	20 43	20 53		21 03	21 13	21 23		21 38	21 53	
Dalston Kingsland	d	20 35	20 45	20 55		21 05	21 15	21 25		21 40	21 55	
Canonbury 178	d	20 37	20 47	20 57		21 07	21 17	21 27		21 42	21 57	
Highbury & Islington ⊖178	d	20 39	20 49	20 59		21 09	21 19	21 29		21 44	21 59	
Caledonian Rd & Barnsbury	d	20 41	20 51	21 01		21 11	21 21	21 31		21 46	22 01	
Camden Road	d	20 45	20 55	21 05		21 15	21 25	21 35		21 50	22 05	
Kentish Town West	d	20 47	20 57	21 07		21 17	21 27	21 37		21 52	22 07	
Gospel Oak	d	20 50	21 00	21 10		21 20	21 30	21 40		21 55	22 10	
Hampstead Heath	d	20 52	21 02	21 12		21 22	21 32	21 42		21 57	22 12	
Finchley Road & Frognal	d	20 54	21 04	21 14		21 24	21 34	21 44		21 59	22 14	
West Hampstead ⊖	d	20 56	21 06	21 16		21 26	21 36	21 46		22 01	22 16	
Brondesbury	d	20 58	21 08	21 18		21 28	21 38	21 48		22 03	22 18	
Brondesbury Park	d	20 59	21 09	21 19		21 29	21 39	21 49		22 04	22 19	
Kensal Rise	d	21 01	21 11	21 21		21 31	21 41	21 51		22 06	22 21	
Willesden Jn. High Level ⊖	a	21 05	21 15	21 25		21 35	21 45	21 56		22 10	22 25	
	d	21 06	21 16	21 26	21 32	21 39	21 46	21 57	22 02	22 11	22 26	22 32
Willesden Jn Low Level ⊖	a											
Shepherd's Bush ⊖176	d		21 23		21 39		21 53		22 08			22 38
Kensington (Olympia) ⊖176	d		21 26		21 41		21 56		22 10			22 40
West Brompton ⊖176	d		21 28		21 44		21 58		22 12			22 43
Imperial Wharf 176	d		21 31		21 47		22 01		22 15			22 46
Clapham Junction 10 176	a		21 38		21 53		22 08		22 26			22 53
Acton Central	d	21 11		21 31		21 44		22 02		22 16	22 31	
South Acton	d	21 14		21 34		21 47		22 04		22 19	22 34	
Gunnersbury ⊖	d	21 18		21 38		21 51		22 08		22 22	22 38	
Kew Gardens ⊖	d	21 21		21 41		21 54		22 11		22 25	22 41	
Richmond ⊖	a	21 26		21 45		21 58		22 16		22 30	22 45	

Station		LO	LO	LO	LO	LO	LO	LO
Stratford 7 ⊖	d	22 00		22 15	22 30		22 45	23 05
Hackney Wick	d	22 03		22 18	22 33		22 48	23 08
Homerton	d	22 06		22 21	22 36		22 51	23 11
Hackney Central	d	22 08		22 23	22 38		22 53	23 13
Dalston Kingsland	d	22 10		22 25	22 40		22 55	23 15
Canonbury 178	d	22 12		22 27	22 42		22 57	23 17
Highbury & Islington ⊖178	d	22 14		22 29	22 44		22 59	23 19
Caledonian Rd & Barnsbury	d	22 16		22 31	22 46		23 01	23 21
Camden Road	d	22 20		22a34	22 50		23a04	23 25
Kentish Town West	d	22 22			22 52			23 27
Gospel Oak	d	22 25			22 55			23 30
Hampstead Heath	d	22 27			22 57			23 32
Finchley Road & Frognal	d	22 29			22 59			23 34
West Hampstead ⊖	d	22 31			23 01			23 36
Brondesbury	d	22 33			23 03			23 38
Brondesbury Park	d	22 34			23 04			23 39
Kensal Rise	d	22 36			23 06			23 41
Willesden Jn. High Level ⊖	a	22 40			23 10			
	d	22 41	22 46		23 11	23 18		
Willesden Jn Low Level ⊖	a							23 50
Shepherd's Bush ⊖176	d		22 53			23 23		
Kensington (Olympia) ⊖176	d		22 55			23 25		
West Brompton ⊖176	d		22 57			23 27		
Imperial Wharf 176	d		23 00			23a30		
Clapham Junction 10 176	a		23 09					
Acton Central	d	22 46			23 16			
South Acton	d	22 49			23 19			
Gunnersbury ⊖	d	22 52			23 22			
Kew Gardens ⊖	d	22 55			23 25			
Richmond ⊖	a	22 59			23 29			

For full service between Willesden Jn, Shepherds Bush and Clapham Jn, please refer to Table 176

Table 59R

Mondays to Fridays

9 December to 16 May

Richmond and Clapham Junction - Willesden Junction, West Hampstead, Highbury & Islington and Stratford

Network Diagram - see first Page of Table 59

Miles	Miles			LO MX	LO	LO	LO	LO	LO	LO	LO	LO	LO	LO	LO	LO	LO	LO	LO	LO	LO	LO	LO
0	—	**Richmond**	⊖ d					05 52	06 09		06 24		06 36		06 54		07 06		07 24		07 36		07 54
1½	—	Kew Gardens	⊖ d					05 55	06 12		06 27		06 39		06 57		07 09		07 27		07 39		07 57
2½	—	Gunnersbury	⊖ d					05 58	06 15		06 30		06 42		07 00		07 12		07 30		07 42		08 00
3¼	—	South Acton	d					06 03	06 18		06 33		06 45		07 03		07 15		07 33		07 45		08 03
4	—	Acton Central	d					06 06	06 21		06 36		06 48		07 06		07 19		07 36		07 51		08 06
—	0	**Clapham Junction 10**	176 d							06 15		06 30		06 45		07 00		07 15		07 30		07 45	
—	1½	Imperial Wharf	176 d		05 51					06 19		06 34		06 49		07 04		07 19		07 34		07 49	
—	2½	West Brompton	⊖176 d		05 54					06 22		06 37		06 52		07 07		07 22		07 37		07 52	
—	3¼	**Kensington (Olympia)**	⊖176 d		05 57					06 25		06 40		06 55		07 10		07 25		07 40		07 55	
—	4	**Shepherd's Bush**	⊖176 d		05 59					06 27		06 42		06 57		07 12		07 27		07 42		07 57	
5¾	—	**Willesden Jn Low Level**	⊖ d				05 58																
5¾	6	**Willesden Jn. High Level**	⊖ a		06 08			06 11	06 26	06 35	06 41	06 50	06 55	07 04	07 11	07 19	07 24	07 35	07 41	07 49	07 56	08 04	08 11
—	—		d					06 12	06 27	06 35	06 42	06 50	06 57	07 05	07 12	07 20	07 27	07 35	07 42	07 50	07 57	08 05	08 12
6¾	—	Kensal Rise	d				06 02	06 14	06 29	06 37	06 44	06 52	06 59	07 07	07 14	07 22	07 29	07 37	07 44	07 52	08 00	08 08	08 14
7½	—	Brondesbury Park	d				06 04	06 16	06 31	06 39	06 46	06 54	07 01	07 09	07 16	07 24	07 31	07 39	07 46	07 54	08 02	08 10	08 16
7¾	—	Brondesbury	d				06 06	06 18	06 33	06 41	06 48	06 56	07 03	07 11	07 18	07 26	07 33	07 41	07 48	07 56	08 03	08 11	08 18
8¼	—	West Hampstead	⊖ d				06 08	06 20	06 35	06 43	06 50	06 58	07 05	07 13	07 20	07 28	07 35	07 43	07 50	07 58	08 05	08 13	08 20
8¾	—	Finchley Road & Frognal	d				06 09	06 21	06 36	06 44	06 51	06 59	07 06	07 14	07 21	07 29	07 36	07 44	07 51	07 59	08 07	08 15	08 21
9¾	—	Hampstead Heath	d				06 12	06 24	06 39	06 47	06 54	07 02	07 09	07 17	07 24	07 32	07 39	07 47	07 54	08 02	08 09	08 17	08 24
10¼	—	**Gospel Oak**	d				06 14	06 26	06 41	06 49	06 56	07 04	07 11	07 19	07 26	07 34	07 41	07 51	07 56	08 04	08 12	08 20	08 26
11	—	Kentish Town West	d				06 16	06 28	06 43	06 51	06 58	07 06	07 13	07 21	07 28	07 36	07 43	07 53	07 58	08 06	08 14	08 22	08 28
11¼	—	Camden Road	d			06 12	06 20	06 32	06 47	06 55	07 02	07 10	07 17	07 25	07 32	07 40	07 47	07 56	08 02	08 10	08 17	08 25	08 32
12½	—	Caledonian Rd & Barnsbury	d			06 15	06 23	06 35	06 50	06 58	07 05	07 13	07 20	07 28	07 35	07 43	07 50	07 59	08 05	08 13	08 20	08 28	08 35
13	—	**Highbury & Islington**	⊖178 d			06 17	06 26	06 38	06 53	07 01	07 08	07 16	07 23	07 31	07 38	07 46	07 53	08 02	08 08	08 16	08 23	08 31	08 38
13½	—	Canonbury	⊖178 d			06 19	06 28	06 40	06 55	07 03	07 10	07 18	07 25	07 33	07 40	07 48	07 55	08 04	08 10	08 18	08 25	08 33	08 40
14½	—	Dalston Kingsland	d			06 21	06 30	06 42	06 57	07 05	07 12	07 20	07 27	07 35	07 42	07 50	07 57	08 06	08 12	08 20	08 27	08 35	08 42
15¼	—	Hackney Central	d			06 23	06 32	06 44	06 59	07 07	07 14	07 22	07 29	07 37	07 44	07 52	07 59	08 08	08 14	08 22	08 29	08 37	08 44
16	—	Homerton	d			06 25	06 34	06 46	07 01	07 09	07 16	07 24	07 31	07 39	07 46	07 54	08 01	08 10	08 16	08 24	08 31	08 39	08 46
16¾	—	Hackney Wick	d	00 02		06 27	06 36	06 48	07 03	07 11	07 18	07 26	07 33	07 41	07 48	07 56	08 03	08 12	08 18	08 26	08 33	08 41	08 48
17¾	—	**Stratford 7**	⊖ a	00 07		06 31	06 44	06 53	07 10	07 18	07 23	07 33	07 38	07 48	07 55	08 03	08 08	08 19	08 25	08 33	08 38	08 48	08 54

		LO	LO	LO	LO	LO	LO	LO	LO	LO	LO	LO	LO	LO	LO	LO	LO	LO	LO	LO	LO	LO	LO
Richmond	⊖ d		08 08		08 24		08 34		08 52		09 10		09 27		09 36		09 59		10 08		10 28		10 38
Kew Gardens	⊖ d		08 12		08 27		08 37		08 55		09 13		09 30		09 39		10 02		10 11		10 31		10 41
Gunnersbury	⊖ d		08 15		08 30		08 40		08 58		09 16		09 33		09 42		10 05		10 14		10 34		10 44
South Acton	d		08 18		08 33		08 43		09 01		09 19		09 36		09 45		10 08		10 17		10 37		10 47
Acton Central	d		08 21		08 36		08 47		09 05		09 22		09 40		09 50		10 11		10 20		10 40		10 50
Clapham Junction 10	176 d	08 00		08 10		08 30		08 45		09 01		09 16		09 31		09 46		10 01		10 16		10 31	
Imperial Wharf	176 d	08 04		08 14		08 34		08 49		09 05		09 20		09 35		09 50		10 05		10 20		10 35	
West Brompton	⊖176 d	08 07		08 17		08 37		08 52		09 08		09 23		09 38		09 53		10 08		10 23		10 38	
Kensington (Olympia)	⊖176 d	08 10		08 20		08 40		08 55		09 11		09 26		09 41		09 56		10 11		10 26		10 41	
Shepherd's Bush	⊖176 d	08 12		08 22		08 42		08 57		09 13		09 28		09 43		09 58		10 13		10 28		10 43	
Willesden Jn Low Level	⊖ d																						
Willesden Jn. High Level	⊖ a	08 19	08 26	08 30	08 41	08 49	08 54	09 04	09 10	09 19	09 26	09 35	09 45	09 51	09 55	10 05	10 16	10 21	10 25	10 36	10 46	10 51	10 55
	d	08 20	08 27	08 35	08 42	08 50	08 55	09 05	09 12	09 20	09 27	09 36	09 46		09 56	10 06	10 17		10 26	10 37	10 47		10 56
Kensal Rise	d	08 22	08 29	08 37	08 44	08 52	08 57	09 07	09 14	09 22	09 29	09 39	09 48		09 58	10 08	10 19		10 28	10 39	10 49		10 59
Brondesbury Park	d	08 24	08 31	08 39	08 46	08 54	08 59	09 09	09 16	09 24	09 31	09 41	09 50		10 00	10 10	10 21		10 30	10 41	10 51		11 01
Brondesbury	d	08 26	08 33	08 41	08 48	08 56	09 01	09 11	09 18	09 26	09 33	09 42	09 52		10 02	10 12	10 23		10 32	10 43	10 53		11 02
West Hampstead	⊖ d	08 28	08 35	08 43	08 50	08 58	09 03	09 13	09 20	09 28	09 35	09 44	09 54		10 04	10 14	10 25		10 34	10 45	10 55		11 04
Finchley Road & Frognal	d	08 29	08 36	08 44	08 51	08 59	09 04	09 14	09 21	09 29	09 36	09 46	09 55		10 05	10 15	10 26		10 35	10 46	10 56		11 06
Hampstead Heath	d	08 32	08 39	08 47	08 54	09 02	09 07	09 17	09 24	09 32	09 39	09 48	09 58		10 08	10 18	10 29		10 38	10 49	10 59		11 08
Gospel Oak	d	08 35	08 41	08 49	08 56	09 04	09 11	09 19	09 26	09 34	09 41	09 51	10 00		10 10	10 20	10 31		10 40	10 51	11 01		11 11
Kentish Town West	d	08 37	08 43	08 51	08 58	09 06	09 13	09 21	09 28	09 36	09 43	09 53	10 02		10 12	10 22	10 33		10 42	10 53	11 03		11 13
Camden Road	d	08 40	08 47	08 55	09 02	09 10	09 17	09 25	09 32	09 40	09 47	09 56	10 06		10 16	10 26	10 37		10 46	10 56	11 06		11 16
Caledonian Rd & Barnsbury	d	08 43	08 50	08 58	09 05	09 13	09 20	09 28	09 35	09 43	09 50	09 59	10 09		10 19	10 29	10 40		10 49	10 59	11 09		11 19
Highbury & Islington	⊖178 d	08 46	08 53	09 01	09 08	09 16	09 23	09 31	09 38	09 46	09 53	10 02	10 12		10 22	10 32	10 43		10 52	11 02	11 12		11 22
Canonbury	⊖178 d	08 48	08 55	09 03	09 10	09 18	09 25	09 33	09 40	09 48	09 55	10 04	10 14		10 24	10 34	10 45		10 54	11 04	11 14		11 24
Dalston Kingsland	d	08 50	08 57	09 05	09 12	09 20	09 27	09 35	09 42	09 50	09 57	10 06	10 16		10 26	10 36	10 47		10 56	11 06	11 16		11 26
Hackney Central	d	08 52	08 59	09 07	09 14	09 22	09 29	09 37	09 44	09 52	09 59	10 08	10 18		10 28	10 38	10 49		10 58	11 08	11 18		11 28
Homerton	d	08 54	09 01	09 09	09 16	09 24	09 31	09 40	09 46	09 54	10 01	10 10	10 20		10 30	10 40	10 51		11 00	11 10	11 20		11 30
Hackney Wick	d	08 56	09 03	09 11	09 18	09 26	09 33	09 42	09 48	09 56	10 03	10 12	10 22		10 32	10 42	10 53		11 02	11 12	11 22		11 32
Stratford 7	⊖ a	09 03	09 09	09 17	09 23	09 33	09 38	09 48	09 53	10 05	10 11	10 19	10 28		10 38	10 49	10 58		11 08	11 19	11 28		11 39

For full service between Willesden Jn, Shepherds Bush and Clapham Jn, please refer to Table 176

Table 59R

Mondays to Fridays

9 December to 16 May

Richmond and Clapham Junction - Willesden Junction, West Hampstead, Highbury & Islington and Stratford

Network Diagram - see first Page of Table 59

		LO	LO	LO	LO	LO	LO	LO	LO	LO	LO	LO	LO	LO	LO	LO	LO	LO	LO	LO	LO	LO	LO
Richmond	⊖ d		10 58		11 08		11 28		11 38		11 58		12 08		12 28		12 38		12 58		13 08		13 27
Kew Gardens	⊖ d		11 01		11 11		11 31		11 41		12 01		12 11		12 31		12 41		13 01		13 11		13 30
Gunnersbury	⊖ d		11 04		11 14		11 34		11 44		12 04		12 14		12 34		12 44		13 04		13 14		13 33
South Acton	d		11 07		11 17		11 37		11 47		12 07		12 17		12 37		12 47		13 07		13 17		13 36
Acton Central	d		11 10		11 20		11 40		11 50		12 10		12 20		12 40		12 50		13 10		13 20		13 39
Clapham Junction 10	176 d	10 46		11 01		11 16		11 31		11 46		12 01		12 16		12 31		12 46		13 01		13 16	
Imperial Wharf	176 d	10 50		11 05		11 20		11 35		11 50		12 05		12 20		12 35		12 50		13 05		13 20	
West Brompton	⊖176 d	10 53		11 08		11 23		11 38		11 53		12 08		12 23		12 38		12 53		13 08		13 23	
Kensington (Olympia)	⊖176 d	10 56		11 11		11 26		11 41		11 56		12 11		12 26		12 41		12 56		13 11		13 26	
Shepherd's Bush	⊖176 d	10 58		11 13		11 28		11 43		11 58		12 13		12 28		12 43		12 58		13 13		13 28	
Willesden Jn Low Level	⊖ d																						
Willesden Jn. High Level	⊖ a	11 05	11 15	11 21	11 25	11 35	11 45	11 51	11 55	12 05	12 15	12 22	12 25	12 35	12 45	12 51	12 55	13 05	13 15	13 21	13 25	13 35	13 44
	d	11 06	11 16		11 26	11 36	11 46		11 56	12 06	12 16		12 26	12 36	12 46		12 56	13 06	13 16		13 26	13 36	13 45
Kensal Rise	d	11 08	11 18		11 28	11 38	11 48		11 58	12 08	12 18		12 28	12 38	12 48		12 58	13 08	13 18		13 28	13 38	13 48
Brondesbury Park	d	11 10	11 20		11 30	11 40	11 50		12 00	12 10	12 20		12 30	12 40	12 50		13 00	13 10	13 20		13 30	13 40	13 50
Brondesbury	d	11 12	11 22		11 32	11 42	11 52		12 02	12 12	12 22		12 32	12 42	12 52		13 02	13 12	13 22		13 32	13 42	13 52
West Hampstead	⊖ d	11 14	11 24		11 34	11 44	11 54		12 04	12 14	12 24		12 34	12 44	12 54		13 04	13 14	13 24		13 34	13 44	13 54
Finchley Road & Frognal	d	11 15	11 25		11 35	11 45	11 55		12 05	12 15	12 25		12 35	12 45	12 55		13 05	13 15	13 25		13 35	13 45	13 55
Hampstead Heath	d	11 18	11 28		11 38	11 48	11 58		12 08	12 18	12 28		12 38	12 48	12 58		13 08	13 18	13 28		13 38	13 48	13 58
Gospel Oak	d	11 20	11 30		11 40	11 50	12 00		12 10	12 21	12 30		12 40	12 50	13 00		13 10	13 20	13 30		13 40	13 50	14 00
Kentish Town West	d	11 22	11 32		11 42	11 52	12 02		12 12	12 23	12 32		12 42	12 52	13 02		13 12	13 22	13 32		13 42	13 52	14 02
Camden Road	d	11 26	11 36		11 46	11 56	12 06		12 16	12 26	12 36		12 46	12 56	13 06		13 16	13 26	13 36		13 46	13 56	14 06
Caledonian Rd & Barnsbury	d	11 29	11 39		11 49	11 59	12 09		12 19	12 30	12 39		12 49	12 59	13 09		13 19	13 29	13 39		13 49	13 59	14 09
Highbury & Islington	⊖178 d	11 32	11 42		11 52	12 02	12 12		12 22	12 33	12 42		12 52	13 02	13 12		13 22	13 32	13 42		13 52	14 02	14 12
Canonbury	⊖178 d	11 34	11 44		11 54	12 04	12 14		12 24	12 35	12 44		12 54	13 04	13 14		13 24	13 34	13 45		13 54	14 04	14 14
Dalston Kingsland	d	11 36	11 46		11 56	12 06	12 16		12 26	12 37	12 46		12 56	13 06	13 16		13 26	13 36	13 47		13 56	14 06	14 16
Hackney Central	d	11 38	11 48		11 58	12 08	12 18		12 28	12 39	12 48		12 58	13 08	13 18		13 28	13 38	13 49		13 58	14 08	14 18
Homerton	d	11 40	11 50		12 00	12 10	12 20		12 30	12 41	12 50		13 00	13 10	13 20		13 30	13 40	13 51		14 00	14 10	14 20
Hackney Wick	d	11 42	11 52		12 02	12 12	12 22		12 32	12 43	12 52		13 02	13 12	13 22		13 32	13 42	13 53		14 02	14 12	14 22
Stratford 7	⊖ a	11 49	11 59		12 08	12 19	12 28		12 39	12 51	12 59		13 08	13 19	13 29		13 39	13 49	13 59		14 08	14 19	14 28

		LO	LO	LO	LO	LO	LO	LO	LO	LO	LO	LO	LO	LO	LO	LO	LO	LO	LO	LO	LO	LO	LO
Richmond	⊖ d		13 38		13 58		14 10		14 28		14 38		14 58		15 08		15 26		15 38		15 53		16 09
Kew Gardens	⊖ d		13 41		14 01		14 13		14 31		14 41		15 01		15 11		15 29		15 41		15 56		16 12
Gunnersbury	⊖ d		13 44		14 04		14 16		14 34		14 44		15 04		15 14		15 32		15 44		15 59		16 15
South Acton	d		13 47		14 07		14 19		14 37		14 47		15 07		15 17		15 35		15 47		16 02		16 18
Acton Central	d		13 50		14 10		14 22		14 40		14 50		15 10		15 20		15 38		15 50		16 06		16 21
Clapham Junction 10	176 d	13 31		13 46		14 01		14 16		14 31		14 46		15 01		15 16		15 30		15 46		16 00	
Imperial Wharf	176 d	13 35		13 50		14 05		14 20		14 35		14 55		15 05		15 20		15 34		15 50		16 04	
West Brompton	⊖176 d	13 38		13 53		14 08		14 23		14 38		14 58		15 08		15 23		15 37		15 53		16 07	
Kensington (Olympia)	⊖176 d	13 41		13 56		14 11		14 26		14 41		15 01		15 11		15 26		15 40		15 56		16 10	
Shepherd's Bush	⊖176 d	13 43		13 58		14 13		14 28		14 43		15 03		15 13		15 28		15 42		15 58		16 12	
Willesden Jn Low Level	⊖ d																						
Willesden Jn. High Level	⊖ a	13 52	13 55	14 05	14 15	14 20	14 26	14 35	14 45	14 51	14 56	15 09	15 15	15 20	15 25	15 35	15 44	15 50	15 55	16 04	16 11	16 20	16 26
	d		13 56	14 06	14 16		14 26	14 36	14 46		14 57	15 10	15 16		15 26	15 36	15 45	15 51	15 56	16 05	16 12	16 20	16 27
Kensal Rise	d		13 59	14 09	14 19		14 28	14 38	14 48		14 58	15 13	15 18		15 28	15 38	15 47	15 53	15 58	16 09	16 14	16 22	16 29
Brondesbury Park	d		14 01	14 11	14 21		14 30	14 40	14 50		15 00	15 15	15 20		15 30	15 40	15 49	15 55	16 00	16 11	16 16	16 24	16 31
Brondesbury	d		14 02	14 12	14 22		14 32	14 42	14 52		15 03	15 16	15 22		15 32	15 42	15 51	15 57	16 02	16 12	16 18	16 26	16 33
West Hampstead	⊖ d		14 04	14 14	14 24		14 34	14 44	14 54		15 05	15 18	15 24		15 34	15 44	15 53	15 59	16 04	16 14	16 20	16 28	16 35
Finchley Road & Frognal	d		14 06	14 16	14 26		14 35	14 45	14 55		15 06	15 20	15 25		15 35	15 45	15 54	16 00	16 05	16 16	16 21	16 29	16 36
Hampstead Heath	d		14 08	14 18	14 28		14 38	14 48	14 58		15 09	15 22	15 28		15 38	15 48	15 57	16 03	16 08	16 18	16 24	16 32	16 39
Gospel Oak	d		14 11	14 21	14 31		14 40	14 50	15 00		15 10	15 26	15 30		15 40	15 50	16 00	16 05	16 10	16 21	16 26	16 34	16 41
Kentish Town West	d		14 13	14 23	14 33		14 42	14 52	15 02		15 12	15 28	15 32		15 42	15 52	16 02	16 07	16 12	16 23	16 28	16 36	16 43
Camden Road	d		14 16	14 26	14 36		14 46	14 56	15 06		15 16	15 32	15 36		15 46	15 56	16 05	16 11	16 16	16 25	16 32	16 40	16 47
Caledonian Rd & Barnsbury	d		14 19	14 29	14 39		14 49	14 59	15 09		15 19	15 35	15 39		15 49	15 59	16 08	16 14	16 19	16 28	16 35	16 43	16 50
Highbury & Islington	⊖178 d		14 22	14 32	14 42		14 52	15 02	15 12		15 22	15 38	15 42		15 52	16 02	16 11	16 17	16 22	16 31	16 38	16 46	16 53
Canonbury	⊖178 d		14 24	14 34	14 44		14 54	15 04	15 14		15 24	15 40	15 44		15 54	16 04	16 13	16 19	16 24	16 33	16 40	16 48	16 55
Dalston Kingsland	d		14 26	14 36	14 46		14 56	15 06	15 16		15 26	15 42	15 46		15 56	16 06	16 15	16 21	16 26	16 35	16 42	16 50	16 57
Hackney Central	d		14 28	14 38	14 48		14 58	15 08	15 18		15 28	15 44	15 48		15 58	16 08	16 17	16 23	16 28	16 37	16 44	16 52	16 59
Homerton	d		14 30	14 40	14 50		15 00	15 10	15 20		15 30	15 46	15 50		16 00	16 10	16 19	16 25	16 30	16 39	16 46	16 54	17 01
Hackney Wick	d		14 32	14 42	14 52		15 02	15 12	15 22		15 32	15 49	15 52		16 02	16 12	16 21	16 27	16 32	16 42	16 48	16 56	17 03
Stratford 7	⊖ a		14 38	14 49	14 58		15 11	15 19	15 28		15 38	15 54	15 57		16 08	16 18	16 27	16 32	16 39	16 49	16 54	17 03	17 08

For full service between Willesden Jn, Shepherds Bush and Clapham Jn, please refer to Table 176

Table 59R

Mondays to Fridays

9 December to 16 May

Richmond and Clapham Junction - Willesden Junction, West Hampstead, Highbury & Islington and Stratford

Network Diagram - see first Page of Table 59

Station		LO	LO	LO	LO	LO	LO	LO	LO	LO	LO	LO	LO	LO	LO	LO	LO	LO	LO	LO	LO	LO	LO
Richmond ⊖	d		16 23		16 36		16 53		17 06		17 23		17 36		17 53		18 06		18 23		18 36		18 53
Kew Gardens ⊖	d		16 26		16 39		16 56		17 09		17 26		17 39		17 56		18 09		18 26		18 39		18 56
Gunnersbury ⊖	d		16 29		16 42		16 59		17 12		17 29		17 42		17 59		18 12		18 29		18 42		18 59
South Acton	d		16 32		16 45		17 02		17 15		17 32		17 45		18 02		18 15		18 32		18 45		19 02
Acton Central	d		16 36		16 49		17 06		17 20		17 36		17 51		18 06		18 21		18 35		18 51		19 06
Clapham Junction 10 176	d	16 15		16 30		16 45		17 00		17 15		17 30		17 45		18 00		18 15		18 30		18 45	
Imperial Wharf 176	d	16 19		16 34		16 49		17 04		17 19		17 34		17 49		18 04		18 19		18 34		18 49	
West Brompton ⊖176	d	16 22		16 37		16 52		17 07		17 22		17 37		17 52		18 07		18 22		18 37		18 52	
Kensington (Olympia) ⊖176	d	16 25		16 40		16 55		17 10		17 25		17 40		17 55		18 10		18 25		18 40		18 55	
Shepherd's Bush ⊖176	d	16 27		16 42		16 57		17 12		17 27		17 42		17 57		18 12		18 27		18 42		18 57	
Willesden Jn Low Level ⊖	d																						
Willesden Jn. High Level ⊖	a	16 35	16 41	16 49	16 56	17 04	17 11	17 19	17 25	17 34	17 41	17 49	17 56	18 04	18 11	18 19	18 26	18 34	18 40	18 49	18 56	19 03	19 11
	d	16 35	16 42	16 50	16 57	17 05	17 12	17 20	17 26	17 35	17 42	17 50	17 57	18 05	18 12	18 20	18 27	18 35	18 41	18 50	18 57	19 04	19 12
Kensal Rise	d	16 37	16 44	16 52	16 59	17 07	17 14	17 22	17 29	17 37	17 44	17 52	17 59	18 07	18 14	18 22	18 29	18 37	18 43	18 52	18 59	19 07	19 14
Brondesbury Park	d	16 39	16 46	16 54	17 01	17 09	17 16	17 24	17 31	17 39	17 46	17 54	18 01	18 09	18 16	18 24	18 31	18 39	18 45	18 54	19 01	19 09	19 16
Brondesbury	d	16 41	16 48	16 56	17 03	17 11	17 18	17 26	17 32	17 41	17 48	17 56	18 03	18 11	18 18	18 26	18 33	18 41	18 47	18 56	19 03	19 11	19 18
West Hampstead ⊖	d	16 43	16 50	16 58	17 05	17 13	17 20	17 28	17 34	17 43	17 50	17 58	18 05	18 13	18 20	18 28	18 35	18 43	18 49	18 58	19 05	19 13	19 20
Finchley Road & Frognal	d	16 44	16 51	16 59	17 06	17 14	17 21	17 29	17 36	17 44	17 51	17 59	18 06	18 14	18 21	18 29	18 36	18 44	18 50	18 59	19 06	19 14	19 21
Hampstead Heath	d	16 47	16 54	17 02	17 09	17 17	17 24	17 32	17 38	17 47	17 54	18 02	18 09	18 17	18 24	18 32	18 39	18 47	18 53	19 02	19 09	19 17	19 24
Gospel Oak	d	16 49	16 56	17 04	17 11	17 19	17 26	17 34	17 41	17 49	17 56	18 04	18 11	18 19	18 26	18 34	18 41	18 49	18 56	19 04	19 11	19 19	19 26
Kentish Town West	d	16 51	16 58	17 06	17 13	17 21	17 28	17 36	17 43	17 51	17 58	18 06	18 13	18 21	18 28	18 36	18 43	18 51	18 59	19 06	19 13	19 21	19 28
Camden Road	d	16 55	17 02	17 10	17 17	17 25	17 32	17 40	17 47	17 55	18 02	18 10	18 17	18 25	18 32	18 40	18 47	18 55	19 03	19 10	19 17	19 25	19 32
Caledonian Rd & Barnsbury	d	16 58	17 05	17 13	17 20	17 28	17 35	17 43	17 50	17 58	18 05	18 13	18 20	18 28	18 35	18 43	18 50	18 58	19 06	19 13	19 20	19 28	19 35
Highbury & Islington ⊖178	d	17 01	17 08	17 16	17 23	17 31	17 38	17 46	17 53	18 01	18 08	18 16	18 23	18 31	18 38	18 46	18 53	19 01	19 09	19 16	19 23	19 31	19 38
Canonbury ⊖178	d	17 03	17 10	17 18	17 25	17 33	17 40	17 48	17 55	18 03	18 10	18 18	18 25	18 33	18 40	18 48	18 55	19 03	19 11	19 18	19 25	19 33	19 40
Dalston Kingsland	d	17 05	17 12	17 20	17 27	17 35	17 42	17 50	17 57	18 05	18 12	18 20	18 27	18 35	18 42	18 50	18 57	19 05	19 13	19 20	19 27	19 35	19 42
Hackney Central	d	17 07	17 14	17 22	17 29	17 37	17 44	17 52	17 59	18 07	18 14	18 22	18 29	18 37	18 44	18 52	18 59	19 07	19 15	19 22	19 29	19 37	19 44
Homerton	d	17 09	17 16	17 24	17 31	17 39	17 46	17 54	18 01	18 09	18 16	18 24	18 31	18 39	18 46	18 54	19 01	19 09	19 17	19 24	19 31	19 39	19 46
Hackney Wick	d	17 11	17 18	17 26	17 33	17 41	17 48	17 56	18 03	18 11	18 18	18 26	18 33	18 41	18 48	18 56	19 03	19 11	19 19	19 26	19 33	19 41	19 48
Stratford 7 ⊖	a	17 18	17 24	17 33	17 39	17 50	17 54	18 05	18 08	18 20	18 24	18 35	18 39	18 50	18 54	19 05	19 08	19 18	19 25	19 33	19 40	19 47	19 54

Station		LO	LO	LO	LO	LO	LO	LO	LO	LO	LO	LO	LO	LO	LO	LO	LO	LO	LO	LO	LO	LO	LO
Richmond ⊖	d		19 11		19 26		19 41		19 56		20 07		20 21		20 36		20 51		21 08		21 21		21 38
Kew Gardens ⊖	d		19 14		19 29		19 44		19 59		20 10		20 24		20 39		20 54		21 11		21 24		21 41
Gunnersbury ⊖	d		19 17		19 32		19 47		20 02		20 13		20 27		20 42		20 57		21 14		21 27		21 44
South Acton	d		19 19		19 35		19 50		20 05		20 16		20 30		20 45		21 00		21 17		21 30		21 47
Acton Central	d		19 21		19 38		19 54		20 08		20 20		20 33		20 49		21 03		21 20		21 33		21 50
Clapham Junction 10 176	d	19 00		19 16		19 31		19 46		20 01		20 16		20 31		20 46		21 01		21 16		21 31	
Imperial Wharf 176	d	19 04		19 20		19 35		19 50		20 05		20 20		20 35		20 50		21 05		21 20		21 35	
West Brompton ⊖176	d	19 07		19 23		19 38		19 53		20 08		20 23		20 38		20 53		21 08		21 23		21 38	
Kensington (Olympia) ⊖176	d	19 10		19 26		19 41		19 56		20 11		20 26		20 41		20 56		21 11		21 26		21 41	
Shepherd's Bush ⊖176	d	19 12		19 28		19 43		19 58		20 13		20 28		20 43		20 58		21 13		21 28		21 43	
Willesden Jn Low Level ⊖	d																						
Willesden Jn. High Level ⊖	a	19 19	19 26	19 35	19 43	19 51	20 00	20 06	20 15	20 21	20 25	20 36	20 39	20 51	20 54	21 06	21 09	21 21	21 25	21 36	21 39	21 51	21 55
	d	19 20	19 27	19 35	19 44		20 01	20 06	20 16		20 26		20 40		20 55		21 10		21 26		21 40		21 56
Kensal Rise	d	19 22	19 29	19 37	19 46		20 03	20 07	20 18		20 28		20 43		20 58		21 13		21 28		21 43		21 58
Brondesbury Park	d	19 24	19 31	19 39	19 48		20 05	20 09	20 20		20 30		20 45		21 00		21 15		21 30		21 45		22 00
Brondesbury	d	19 26	19 33	19 41	19 50		20 07	20 11	20 22		20 32		20 46		21 01		21 16		21 32		21 46		22 02
West Hampstead ⊖	d	19 28	19 35	19 43	19 52		20 09	20 13	20 24		20 34		20 48		21 03		21 18		21 34		21 48		22 04
Finchley Road & Frognal	d	19 29	19 36	19 44	19 53		20 10	20 14	20 25		20 35		20 50		21 05		21 20		21 35		21 50		22 05
Hampstead Heath	d	19 32	19 39	19 47	19 56		20 13	20 17	20 28		20 38		20 52		21 07		21 22		21 38		21 52		22 08
Gospel Oak	d	19 34	19 41	19 49	20 00		20 15	20 19	20 30		20 42		20 55		21 10		21 25		21 40		21 55		22 10
Kentish Town West	d	19 36	19 43	19 51	20 02		20 17	20 21	20 32		20 45		20 57		21 12		21 27		21 42		21 57		22 12
Camden Road	d	19 40	19 47	19 55	20 06		20 20	20 25	20 36		20 50		21 00		21 16		21 30		21 46		22 00		22 16
Caledonian Rd & Barnsbury	d	19 43	19 50	19 58	20 09		20 23	20 28	20 39		20 53		21 03		21 19		21 33		21 49		22 03		22 19
Highbury & Islington ⊖178	d	19 46	19 53	20 01	20 12		20 26	20 31	20 42		20 56		21 06		21 22		21 36		21 52		22 06		22 22
Canonbury ⊖178	d	19 48	19 55	20 03	20 14		20 28	20 33	20 44		20 58		21 08		21 24		21 38		21 54		22 08		22 24
Dalston Kingsland	d	19 50	19 57	20 05	20 16		20 30	20 35	20 46		21 00		21 10		21 26		21 40		21 56		22 10		22 26
Hackney Central	d	19 52	19 59	20 07	20 18		20 32	20 37	20 48		21 02		21 12		21 28		21 42		21 58		22 12		22 28
Homerton	d	19 54	20 01	20 09	20 20		20 34	20 39	20 50		21 04		21 14		21 30		21 44		22 00		22 14		22 30
Hackney Wick	d	19 56	20 03	20 11	20 22		20 36	20 42	20 52		21 07		21 17		21 32		21 47		22 02		22 17		22 32
Stratford 7 ⊖	a	20 03	20 10	20 19	20 28		20 41	20 49	20 58		21 12		21 22		21 37		21 52		22 07		22 21		22 37

For full service between Willesden Jn, Shepherds Bush and Clapham Jn, please refer to Table 176

Table 59R

Mondays to Fridays

9 December to 16 May

Richmond and Clapham Junction - Willesden Junction, West Hampstead, Highbury & Islington and Stratford

Network Diagram - see first Page of Table 59

				LO	LO	LO	LO	LO	LO	LO	LO	LO	LO	LO		LO	LO	LO
Richmond	⊖	d			21 51		22 08		22 21		22 38		22 58			23 08	23 28	
Kew Gardens	⊖	d			21 54		22 11		22 24		22 41		23 01			23 11	23 31	
Gunnersbury	⊖	d			21 57		22 14		22 27		22 44		23 04			23 14	23 34	
South Acton		d			22 00		22 17		22 30		22 47		23 07			23 17	23 37	
Acton Central		d			22 03		22 20		22 34		22 50		23 10			23 20	23 40	
Clapham Junction 10	176	d		21 46		22 01		22 16		22 31		22 46		23 01				23 31
Imperial Wharf	176	d		21 50		22 05		22 20		22 35		22 50		23 05				23 35
West Brompton	⊖176	d		21 53		22 08		22 23		22 38		22 53		23 08				23 38
Kensington (Olympia)	⊖176	d		21 56		22 11		22 26		22 41		22 56		23 11				23 41
Shepherd's Bush	⊖176	d		21 58		22 13		22 28		22 43		22 58		23 13				23 43
Willesden Jn Low Level	⊖	d																
Willesden Jn. High Level	⊖	a		22 06	22 09	22 21	22 25	22 36	22 40	22 51	22 55	23 06	23 17	23 21		23 24	23 45	23 56
		d			22 10		22 26		22 41		22 56		23 18			23 25		
Kensal Rise		d			22 13		22 28		22 43		22 58		23 20			23 27		
Brondesbury Park		d			22 15		22 30		22 45		23 00		23 22			23 29		
Brondesbury		d			22 16		22 32		22 47		23 02		23 24			23 31		
West Hampstead	⊖	d			22 18		22 34		22 49		23 04		23 26			23 33		
Finchley Road & Frognal		d			22 20		22 35		22 50		23 05		23 27			23 34		
Hampstead Heath		d			22 22		22 38		22 53		23 08		23 30			23 37		
Gospel Oak		d			22 25		22 40		22 57		23 10		23 33			23 40		
Kentish Town West		d			22 27		22 42		22 59		23 12		23 35			23 42		
Camden Road		d			22 30		22 46		23 03		23 16		23 38			23 45		
Caledonian Rd & Barnsbury		d			22 33		22 49		23 06		23 19		23 42			23 48		
Highbury & Islington	⊖178	d			22 36		22 52		23 09		23 22		23 45			23 52		
Canonbury	⊖178	d			22 38		22 54		23 11		23 24		23 47			23 54		
Dalston Kingsland		d			22 40		22 56		23 13		23 26		23 49			23 56		
Hackney Central		d			22 42		22 58		23 15		23 28		23 51			23 58		
Homerton		d			22 44		23 00		23 17		23 30		23 53			23 59		
Hackney Wick		d			22 47		23 02		23 20		23 32		23 55			00 02		
Stratford 7	⊖	a			22 51		23 07		23 24		23 37		23 59			00 07		

Saturdays

14 December to 17 May

			LO	LO	LO	LO	LO	LO	LO	LO	LO	LO	LO		LO	LO	LO	LO	LO	LO	LO	LO	LO	LO	LO
Richmond	⊖	d				05 58	06 08		06 28		06 38		06 58			07 08		07 28		07 38		07 58		08 08	
Kew Gardens	⊖	d				06 01	06 11		06 31		06 41		07 01			07 11		07 31		07 41		08 01		08 11	
Gunnersbury	⊖	d				06 04	06 14		06 34		06 44		07 04			07 14		07 34		07 44		08 04		08 14	
South Acton		d				06 07	06 17		06 37		06 47		07 07			07 17		07 37		07 47		08 07		08 17	
Acton Central		d				06 10	06 20		06 40		06 50		07 10			07 20		07 40		07 50		08 10		08 20	
Clapham Junction 10	176	d						06 16		06 31		06 46			07 01		07 16		07 31		07 46		08 01		08 16
Imperial Wharf	176	d		05 52				06 20		06 35		06 50			07 05		07 20		07 35		07 50		08 05		08 20
West Brompton	⊖176	d		05 55				06 23		06 38		06 53			07 08		07 23		07 38		07 53		08 08		08 23
Kensington (Olympia)	⊖176	d		05 58				06 26		06 41		06 56			07 11		07 26		07 41		07 56		08 11		08 26
Shepherd's Bush	⊖176	d		06 00				06 28		06 43		06 58			07 13		07 28		07 43		07 58		08 13		08 28
Willesden Jn Low Level	⊖	d			05 57																				
Willesden Jn. High Level	⊖	a		06 08		06 16	06 25	06 35	06 45	06 50	06 55	07 05	07 15		07 20	07 25	07 35	07 45	07 51	07 55	08 05	08 15	08 21	08 25	08 35
		d				06 17	06 26	06 36	06 46		06 56	07 06	07 16			07 26	07 36	07 46		07 56	08 06	08 16		08 26	08 36
Kensal Rise		d			06 01	06 19	06 28	06 38	06 48		06 58	07 08	07 18			07 28	07 38	07 48		07 58	08 08	08 18		08 28	08 38
Brondesbury Park		d			06 03	06 21	06 30	06 40	06 50		07 00	07 10	07 20			07 30	07 40	07 50		08 00	08 10	08 20		08 30	08 40
Brondesbury		d			06 05	06 23	06 32	06 42	06 52		07 02	07 12	07 22			07 32	07 42	07 52		08 02	08 12	08 22		08 32	08 42
West Hampstead	⊖	d			06 07	06 25	06 34	06 44	06 54		07 04	07 14	07 24			07 34	07 44	07 54		08 04	08 14	08 24		08 34	08 44
Finchley Road & Frognal		d			06 08	06 26	06 35	06 45	06 55		07 05	07 15	07 25			07 35	07 45	07 55		08 05	08 15	08 25		08 35	08 45
Hampstead Heath		d			06 11	06 29	06 38	06 48	06 58		07 08	07 18	07 28			07 38	07 48	07 58		08 08	08 18	08 28		08 38	08 48
Gospel Oak		d			06 13	06 31	06 40	06 50	07 00		07 10	07 20	07 30			07 40	07 50	08 00		08 10	08 20	08 30		08 40	08 50
Kentish Town West		d			06 15	06 33	06 42	06 52	07 02		07 12	07 22	07 32			07 42	07 52	08 02		08 12	08 22	08 32		08 42	08 52
Camden Road		d			06 19	06 36	06 46	06 56	07 06		07 16	07 26	07 36			07 46	07 56	08 06		08 16	08 26	08 36		08 46	08 56
Caledonian Rd & Barnsbury		d			06 22	06 39	06 49	06 59	07 09		07 19	07 29	07 39			07 49	07 59	08 09		08 19	08 29	08 39		08 49	08 59
Highbury & Islington	⊖178	d			06 25	06 42	06 52	07 02	07 12		07 22	07 32	07 42			07 52	08 02	08 12		08 22	08 32	08 42		08 52	09 02
Canonbury	⊖178	d			06 27	06 44	06 54	07 04	07 14		07 24	07 34	07 44			07 54	08 04	08 14		08 24	08 34	08 44		08 54	09 04
Dalston Kingsland		d			06 29	06 46	06 56	07 06	07 16		07 26	07 36	07 46			07 56	08 06	08 16		08 26	08 36	08 46		08 56	09 06
Hackney Central		d			06 31	06 48	06 58	07 08	07 18		07 28	07 38	07 48			07 58	08 08	08 18		08 28	08 38	08 48		08 58	09 08
Homerton		d			06 33	06 50	07 00	07 10	07 20		07 30	07 40	07 50			08 00	08 10	08 20		08 30	08 40	08 50		09 00	09 10
Hackney Wick		d	00 02		06 35	06 52	07 02	07 12	07 22		07 32	07 42	07 52			08 02	08 12	08 22		08 32	08 42	08 52		09 02	09 12
Stratford 7	⊖	a	00 07		06 43	06 58	07 08	07 19	07 28		07 39	07 49	07 59			08 09	08 19	08 29		08 39	08 49	08 59		09 09	09 19

For full service between Willesden Jn, Shepherds Bush and Clapham Jn, please refer to Table 176

Table 59R

Saturdays
14 December to 17 May

Richmond and Clapham Junction - Willesden Junction, West Hampstead, Highbury & Islington and Stratford

Network Diagram - see first Page of Table 59

Station		LO	LO	LO	LO	LO	LO	LO	LO	LO	LO	LO
Richmond ⊖	d	08 28		08 38		08 58		09 08		09 28		09 38
Kew Gardens ⊖	d	08 31		08 41		09 01		09 11		09 31		09 41
Gunnersbury ⊖	d	08 34		08 44		09 04		09 14		09 34		09 44
South Acton	d	08 37		08 47		09 07		09 17		09 37		09 47
Acton Central	d	08 40		08 50		09 10		09 20		09 40		09 50
Clapham Junction 10 176	d		08 31		08 46		09 01		09 16		09 31	
Imperial Wharf 176	d		08 35		08 50		09 05		09 20		09 35	
West Brompton ⊖176	d		08 38		08 53		09 08		09 23		09 38	
Kensington (Olympia) ⊖176	d		08 41		08 56		09 11		09 26		09 41	
Shepherd's Bush ⊖176	d		08 43		08 58		09 13		09 28		09 43	
Willesden Jn Low Level ⊖	d											
Willesden Jn. High Level ⊖	a	08 45	08 51	08 55	09 05	09 15	09 21	09 25	09 35	09 45	09 51	09 55
	d	08 46		08 56	09 06	09 16		09 26	09 36	09 46		09 56
Kensal Rise	d	08 48		08 58	09 08	09 18		09 28	09 38	09 48		09 58
Brondesbury Park	d	08 50		09 00	09 10	09 20		09 30	09 40	09 50		10 00
Brondesbury	d	08 52		09 02	09 12	09 22		09 32	09 42	09 52		10 02
West Hampstead ⊖	d	08 54		09 04	09 14	09 24		09 34	09 44	09 54		10 04
Finchley Road & Frognal	d	08 55		09 05	09 15	09 25		09 35	09 45	09 55		10 05
Hampstead Heath	d	08 58		09 08	09 18	09 28		09 38	09 48	09 58		10 08
Gospel Oak	d	09 00		09 10	09 20	09 30		09 40	09 50	10 00		10 10
Kentish Town West	d	09 02		09 12	09 22	09 32		09 42	09 52	10 02		10 12
Camden Road	d	09 06		09 16	09 26	09 36		09 46	09 56	10 06		10 16
Caledonian Rd & Barnsbury	d	09 09		09 19	09 29	09 39		09 49	09 59	10 09		10 19
Highbury & Islington ⊖178	d	09 12		09 22	09 32	09 42		09 52	10 02	10 12		10 22
Canonbury ⊖178	d	09 14		09 24	09 34	09 44		09 54	10 04	10 14		10 24
Dalston Kingsland	d	09 16		09 26	09 36	09 46		09 56	10 06	10 16		10 26
Hackney Central	d	09 18		09 28	09 38	09 48		09 58	10 08	10 18		10 28
Homerton	d	09 20		09 30	09 40	09 50		10 00	10 10	10 20		10 30
Hackney Wick	d	09 22		09 32	09 42	09 52		10 02	10 12	10 22		10 32
Stratford 7 ⊖	a	09 29		09 39	09 49	09 59		10 09	10 19	10 29		10 38

Station		LO	LO	LO	LO	LO	LO	LO	LO	LO	LO	LO
Richmond ⊖	d		09 58		10 08		10 28		10 38		10 58	
Kew Gardens ⊖	d		10 01		10 11		10 31		10 41		11 01	
Gunnersbury ⊖	d		10 04		10 14		10 34		10 44		11 04	
South Acton	d		10 07		10 17		10 37		10 47		11 07	
Acton Central	d		10 10		10 20		10 40		10 50		11 10	
Clapham Junction 10 176	d	09 46		10 01		10 16		10 31		10 46		11 01
Imperial Wharf 176	d	09 50		10 05		10 20		10 35		10 50		11 05
West Brompton ⊖176	d	09 53		10 08		10 23		10 38		10 53		11 08
Kensington (Olympia) ⊖176	d	09 56		10 11		10 26		10 41		10 56		11 11
Shepherd's Bush ⊖176	d	09 58		10 13		10 28		10 43		10 58		11 13
Willesden Jn Low Level ⊖	d											
Willesden Jn. High Level ⊖	a	10 05	10 15	10 21	10 25	10 35	10 45	10 51	10 56	11 05	11 16	11 20
	d	10 06	10 16		10 26	10 36	10 46		10 56	11 06	11 17	
Kensal Rise	d	10 08	10 18		10 28	10 38	10 48		10 58	11 08	11 18	
Brondesbury Park	d	10 10	10 20		10 30	10 40	10 50		11 00	11 10	11 20	
Brondesbury	d	10 12	10 22		10 32	10 42	10 52		11 02	11 12	11 22	
West Hampstead ⊖	d	10 14	10 24		10 34	10 44	10 54		11 04	11 14	11 24	
Finchley Road & Frognal	d	10 15	10 25		10 35	10 45	10 55		11 05	11 15	11 25	
Hampstead Heath	d	10 18	10 28		10 38	10 48	10 58		11 08	11 18	11 28	
Gospel Oak	d	10 20	10 30		10 40	10 50	11 00		11 10	11 20	11 30	
Kentish Town West	d	10 22	10 32		10 42	10 52	11 02		11 12	11 22	11 32	
Camden Road	d	10 26	10 36		10 46	10 56	11 06		11 16	11 26	11 36	
Caledonian Rd & Barnsbury	d	10 29	10 39		10 49	10 59	11 09		11 19	11 29	11 39	
Highbury & Islington ⊖178	d	10 32	10 42		10 52	11 02	11 12		11 22	11 32	11 42	
Canonbury ⊖178	d	10 34	10 44		10 54	11 04	11 14		11 24	11 34	11 44	
Dalston Kingsland	d	10 36	10 46		10 56	11 06	11 16		11 26	11 36	11 46	
Hackney Central	d	10 38	10 48		10 58	11 08	11 18		11 28	11 38	11 48	
Homerton	d	10 40	10 50		11 00	11 10	11 20		11 30	11 40	11 50	
Hackney Wick	d	10 42	10 52		11 02	11 12	11 22		11 32	11 42	11 52	
Stratford 7 ⊖	a	10 49	10 58		11 08	11 19	11 28		11 40	11 49	11 58	

Station		LO	LO	LO	LO	LO	LO	LO	LO	LO	LO	LO
Richmond ⊖	d	11 08		11 28		11 38		11 58		12 08		12 28
Kew Gardens ⊖	d	11 11		11 31		11 41		12 01		12 11		12 31
Gunnersbury ⊖	d	11 14		11 34		11 44		12 04		12 14		12 34
South Acton	d	11 17		11 37		11 47		12 07		12 17		12 37
Acton Central	d	11 20		11 40		11 50		12 10		12 20		12 40
Clapham Junction 10 176	d		11 16		11 31		11 46		12 01		12 16	
Imperial Wharf 176	d		11 20		11 35		11 50		12 05		12 20	
West Brompton ⊖176	d		11 23		11 38		11 53		12 08		12 23	
Kensington (Olympia) ⊖176	d		11 26		11 41		11 56		12 11		12 26	
Shepherd's Bush ⊖176	d		11 28		11 43		11 58		12 13		12 28	
Willesden Jn Low Level ⊖	d											
Willesden Jn. High Level ⊖	a	11 25	11 35	11 45	11 51	11 55	12 05	12 15	12 21	12 25	12 35	12 45
	d	11 26	11 36	11 46		11 56	12 06	12 16		12 26	12 36	12 46
Kensal Rise	d	11 28	11 38	11 48		11 58	12 08	12 18		12 28	12 38	12 48
Brondesbury Park	d	11 30	11 40	11 50		12 00	12 10	12 20		12 30	12 40	12 50
Brondesbury	d	11 32	11 42	11 52		12 02	12 12	12 22		12 32	12 42	12 52
West Hampstead ⊖	d	11 34	11 44	11 54		12 04	12 14	12 24		12 34	12 44	12 54
Finchley Road & Frognal	d	11 35	11 45	11 55		12 05	12 15	12 25		12 35	12 45	12 55
Hampstead Heath	d	11 38	11 48	11 58		12 08	12 18	12 28		12 38	12 48	12 58
Gospel Oak	d	11 40	11 50	12 00		12 10	12 20	12 30		12 40	12 50	13 00
Kentish Town West	d	11 42	11 52	12 02		12 12	12 22	12 32		12 42	12 52	13 02
Camden Road	d	11 46	11 56	12 06		12 16	12 26	12 36		12 46	12 56	13 06
Caledonian Rd & Barnsbury	d	11 49	11 59	12 09		12 19	12 29	12 39		12 49	12 59	13 09
Highbury & Islington ⊖178	d	11 52	12 02	12 12		12 22	12 32	12 42		12 52	13 02	13 12
Canonbury ⊖178	d	11 54	12 04	12 14		12 24	12 34	12 44		12 54	13 04	13 14
Dalston Kingsland	d	11 56	12 06	12 16		12 26	12 36	12 46		12 56	13 06	13 16
Hackney Central	d	11 58	12 08	12 18		12 28	12 38	12 48		12 58	13 08	13 18
Homerton	d	12 00	12 10	12 20		12 30	12 40	12 50		13 00	13 10	13 20
Hackney Wick	d	12 02	12 12	12 22		12 32	12 42	12 52		13 02	13 12	13 22
Stratford 7 ⊖	a	12 08	12 19	12 28		12 38	12 49	12 58		13 08	13 19	13 28

Station		LO	LO	LO	LO	LO	LO	LO	LO	LO	LO	LO
Richmond ⊖	d		12 38		12 58		13 08		13 28		13 38	
Kew Gardens ⊖	d		12 41		13 01		13 11		13 31		13 41	
Gunnersbury ⊖	d		12 44		13 04		13 14		13 34		13 44	
South Acton	d		12 47		13 07		13 17		13 37		13 47	
Acton Central	d		12 50		13 10		13 20		13 40		13 50	
Clapham Junction 10 176	d	12 31		12 46		13 01		13 16		13 31		13 46
Imperial Wharf 176	d	12 35		12 50		13 05		13 20		13 35		13 50
West Brompton ⊖176	d	12 38		12 53		13 08		13 23		13 38		13 53
Kensington (Olympia) ⊖176	d	12 41		12 56		13 11		13 26		13 41		13 56
Shepherd's Bush ⊖176	d	12 43		12 58		13 13		13 28		13 43		13 58
Willesden Jn Low Level ⊖	d											
Willesden Jn. High Level ⊖	a	12 51	12 55	13 05	13 15	13 21	13 25	13 35	13 45	13 51	13 55	14 05
	d		12 56	13 06	13 16		13 26	13 36	13 46		13 56	14 06
Kensal Rise	d		12 58	13 08	13 18		13 28	13 38	13 48		13 58	14 09
Brondesbury Park	d		13 00	13 10	13 20		13 30	13 40	13 50		14 00	14 11
Brondesbury	d		13 02	13 12	13 22		13 32	13 42	13 52		14 02	14 13
West Hampstead ⊖	d		13 04	13 14	13 24		13 34	13 44	13 54		14 04	14 15
Finchley Road & Frognal	d		13 05	13 15	13 25		13 35	13 45	13 55		14 05	14 16
Hampstead Heath	d		13 08	13 18	13 28		13 38	13 48	13 58		14 08	14 19
Gospel Oak	d		13 10	13 20	13 30		13 40	13 50	14 00		14 10	14 21
Kentish Town West	d		13 12	13 22	13 32		13 42	13 52	14 02		14 12	14 23
Camden Road	d		13 16	13 26	13 36		13 46	13 56	14 06		14 16	14 26
Caledonian Rd & Barnsbury	d		13 19	13 29	13 39		13 49	13 59	14 09		14 19	14 29
Highbury & Islington ⊖178	d		13 22	13 32	13 42		13 52	14 02	14 12		14 22	14 32
Canonbury ⊖178	d		13 24	13 34	13 44		13 54	14 04	14 14		14 24	14 34
Dalston Kingsland	d		13 26	13 36	13 46		13 56	14 06	14 16		14 26	14 36
Hackney Central	d		13 28	13 38	13 48		13 58	14 08	14 18		14 28	14 38
Homerton	d		13 30	13 40	13 50		14 00	14 10	14 20		14 30	14 40
Hackney Wick	d		13 32	13 42	13 52		14 02	14 12	14 22		14 32	14 42
Stratford 7 ⊖	a		13 38	13 49	13 58		14 08	14 19	14 28		14 38	14 49

For full service between Willesden Jn, Shepherds Bush and Clapham Jn, please refer to Table 176

Table 59R

Saturdays

14 December to 17 May

Richmond and Clapham Junction - Willesden Junction, West Hampstead, Highbury & Islington and Stratford

Network Diagram - see first Page of Table 59

Station			LO	LO	LO	LO	LO	LO	LO	LO	LO	LO	LO	LO	LO	LO	LO	LO	LO	LO	LO	LO	LO	LO
Richmond	⊖	d	13 58		14 08		14 28		14 38		14 58		15 08		15 28		15 38		15 58		16 08		16 28	
Kew Gardens	⊖	d	14 01		14 11		14 31		14 41		15 01		15 11		15 31		15 41		16 01		16 11		16 31	
Gunnersbury	⊖	d	14 04		14 14		14 34		14 44		15 04		15 14		15 34		15 44		16 04		16 14		16 34	
South Acton		d	14 07		14 17		14 37		14 47		15 07		15 17		15 37		15 47		16 07		16 17		16 37	
Acton Central		d	14 10		14 20		14 40		14 50		15 10		15 20		15 40		15 50		16 10		16 20		16 40	
Clapham Junction 10	176	d		14 01		14 16		14 31		14 46		15 01		15 16		15 31		15 46		16 01		16 16		16 31
Imperial Wharf	176	d		14 05		14 20		14 35		14 50		15 05		15 20		15 35		15 50		16 05		16 20		16 35
West Brompton	⊖176	d		14 08		14 23		14 38		14 53		15 08		15 23		15 38		15 53		16 08		16 23		16 38
Kensington (Olympia)	⊖176	d		14 11		14 26		14 41		14 56		15 11		15 26		15 41		15 56		16 11		16 26		16 41
Shepherd's Bush	⊖176	d		14 13		14 28		14 43		14 58		15 13		15 28		15 43		15 58		16 13		16 28		16 43
Willesden Jn Low Level	⊖	d																						
Willesden Jn. High Level	⊖	a	14 15	14 21	14 25	14 35	14 45	14 51	14 55	15 05	15 15	15 21	15 25	15 35	15 45	15 51	15 55	16 05	16 15	16 21	16 25	16 35	16 45	16 50
		d	14 16		14 26	14 36	14 46		14 56	15 06	15 16		15 26	15 36	15 46		15 56	16 06	16 16		16 26	16 36	16 46	
Kensal Rise		d	14 19		14 28	14 38	14 48		14 58	15 08	15 18		15 28	15 38	15 48		15 58	16 08	16 18		16 28	16 38	16 48	
Brondesbury Park		d	14 21		14 30	14 40	14 50		15 00	15 10	15 20		15 30	15 40	15 50		16 00	16 10	16 20		16 30	16 40	16 50	
Brondesbury		d	14 23		14 32	14 42	14 52		15 02	15 12	15 22		15 32	15 42	15 52		16 02	16 12	16 22		16 32	16 42	16 52	
West Hampstead	⊖	d	14 25		14 34	14 44	14 54		15 04	15 14	15 24		15 34	15 44	15 54		16 04	16 14	16 24		16 34	16 44	16 54	
Finchley Road & Frognal		d	14 26		14 35	14 45	14 55		15 05	15 15	15 25		15 35	15 45	15 55		16 05	16 15	16 25		16 35	16 45	16 55	
Hampstead Heath		d	14 29		14 38	14 48	14 58		15 08	15 18	15 28		15 38	15 48	15 58		16 08	16 18	16 28		16 38	16 48	16 58	
Gospel Oak		d	14 31		14 40	14 50	15 00		15 10	15 20	15 30		15 40	15 50	16 00		16 10	16 20	16 30		16 40	16 50	17 00	
Kentish Town West		d	14 33		14 42	14 52	15 02		15 12	15 22	15 32		15 42	15 52	16 02		16 12	16 22	16 32		16 42	16 52	17 02	
Camden Road		d	14 36		14 46	14 56	15 06		15 16	15 26	15 36		15 46	15 56	16 06		16 16	16 26	16 36		16 46	16 56	17 06	
Caledonian Rd & Barnsbury		d	14 39		14 49	14 59	15 09		15 19	15 29	15 39		15 49	15 59	16 09		16 19	16 29	16 39		16 49	16 59	17 09	
Highbury & Islington	⊖178	d	14 42		14 52	15 02	15 12		15 22	15 32	15 42		15 52	16 02	16 12		16 22	16 32	16 42		16 52	17 02	17 12	
Canonbury	⊖178	d	14 44		14 54	15 04	15 14		15 24	15 34	15 44		15 54	16 04	16 14		16 24	16 34	16 44		16 54	17 04	17 14	
Dalston Kingsland		d	14 46		14 56	15 06	15 16		15 26	15 36	15 46		15 56	16 06	16 16		16 26	16 36	16 46		16 56	17 06	17 16	
Hackney Central		d	14 48		14 58	15 08	15 18		15 28	15 38	15 48		15 58	16 08	16 18		16 28	16 38	16 48		16 58	17 08	17 18	
Homerton		d	14 50		15 00	15 10	15 20		15 30	15 40	15 50		16 00	16 10	16 20		16 30	16 40	16 50		17 00	17 10	17 20	
Hackney Wick		d	14 52		15 02	15 12	15 22		15 32	15 42	15 52		16 02	16 12	16 22		16 32	16 42	16 52		17 02	17 12	17 22	
Stratford 7	⊖	a	14 58		15 08	15 19	15 28		15 38	15 49	15 58		16 08	16 21	16 28		16 38	16 51	16 58		17 08	17 21	17 28	

Station			LO	LO	LO	LO	LO	LO	LO	LO	LO	LO	LO	LO	LO	LO	LO	LO	LO	LO	LO	LO	LO	LO
Richmond	⊖	d	16 38		16 58		17 08		17 28		17 38		17 58		18 08		18 28		18 38		18 58		19 08	
Kew Gardens	⊖	d	16 41		17 01		17 11		17 31		17 41		18 01		18 11		18 31		18 41		19 01		19 11	
Gunnersbury	⊖	d	16 44		17 04		17 14		17 34		17 44		18 04		18 14		18 34		18 44		19 04		19 14	
South Acton		d	16 47		17 07		17 17		17 37		17 47		18 07		18 17		18 37		18 47		19 07		19 17	
Acton Central		d	16 50		17 10		17 20		17 40		17 50		18 10		18 20		18 40		18 50		19 10		19 20	
Clapham Junction 10	176	d		16 46		17 01		17 16		17 31		17 46		18 01		18 16		18 31		18 46		19 01		19 16
Imperial Wharf	176	d		16 50		17 05		17 20		17 35		17 50		18 05		18 20		18 35		18 50		19 05		19 20
West Brompton	⊖176	d		16 53		17 08		17 23		17 38		17 53		18 08		18 23		18 38		18 53		19 08		19 23
Kensington (Olympia)	⊖176	d		16 56		17 11		17 26		17 41		17 56		18 11		18 26		18 41		18 56		19 11		19 26
Shepherd's Bush	⊖176	d		16 58		17 13		17 28		17 43		17 58		18 13		18 28		18 43		18 58		19 13		19 28
Willesden Jn Low Level	⊖	d																						
Willesden Jn. High Level	⊖	a	16 55	17 05	17 15	17 21	17 25	17 35	17 45	17 51	17 55	18 05	18 15	18 21	18 25	18 35	18 45	18 51	18 55	19 05	19 15	19 21	19 25	19 35
		d	16 56	17 06	17 16		17 26	17 36	17 46		17 56	18 06	18 16		18 26	18 36	18 46		18 56	19 06	19 16		19 26	19 36
Kensal Rise		d	16 58	17 08	17 18		17 28	17 38	17 48		17 58	18 08	18 18		18 28	18 38	18 48		18 58	19 08	19 18		19 28	19 38
Brondesbury Park		d	17 00	17 10	17 20		17 30	17 40	17 50		18 00	18 10	18 20		18 30	18 40	18 50		19 00	19 10	19 20		19 30	19 40
Brondesbury		d	17 02	17 12	17 22		17 32	17 42	17 52		18 02	18 12	18 22		18 32	18 42	18 52		19 02	19 12	19 22		19 32	19 42
West Hampstead	⊖	d	17 04	17 14	17 24		17 34	17 44	17 54		18 04	18 14	18 24		18 34	18 44	18 54		19 04	19 14	19 24		19 34	19 44
Finchley Road & Frognal		d	17 05	17 15	17 25		17 35	17 45	17 55		18 05	18 15	18 25		18 35	18 45	18 55		19 05	19 15	19 25		19 35	19 45
Hampstead Heath		d	17 08	17 18	17 28		17 38	17 48	17 58		18 08	18 18	18 28		18 38	18 48	18 58		19 08	19 18	19 28		19 38	19 48
Gospel Oak		d	17 10	17 20	17 30		17 40	17 50	18 00		18 10	18 20	18 30		18 40	18 50	19 00		19 10	19 20	19 30		19 40	19 50
Kentish Town West		d	17 12	17 22	17 32		17 42	17 52	18 02		18 12	18 22	18 32		18 42	18 52	19 02		19 12	19 22	19 32		19 42	19 52
Camden Road		d	17 16	17 26	17 36		17 46	17 56	18 06		18 16	18 26	18 36		18 46	18 56	19 06		19 16	19 26	19 36		19 46	19 56
Caledonian Rd & Barnsbury		d	17 19	17 29	17 39		17 49	17 59	18 09		18 19	18 29	18 39		18 49	18 59	19 09		19 19	19 29	19 39		19 49	19 59
Highbury & Islington	⊖178	d	17 22	17 32	17 42		17 52	18 02	18 12		18 22	18 32	18 42		18 52	19 02	19 12		19 22	19 32	19 42		19 52	20 02
Canonbury	⊖178	d	17 24	17 34	17 44		17 54	18 04	18 14		18 24	18 34	18 44		18 54	19 04	19 14		19 24	19 34	19 44		19 54	20 04
Dalston Kingsland		d	17 26	17 36	17 46		17 56	18 06	18 16		18 26	18 36	18 46		18 56	19 06	19 16		19 26	19 36	19 46		19 56	20 06
Hackney Central		d	17 28	17 38	17 48		17 58	18 08	18 18		18 28	18 38	18 48		18 58	19 08	19 18		19 28	19 38	19 48		19 58	20 08
Homerton		d	17 30	17 40	17 50		18 00	18 10	18 20		18 30	18 40	18 50		19 00	19 10	19 20		19 30	19 40	19 50		20 00	20 10
Hackney Wick		d	17 32	17 42	17 52		18 02	18 12	18 22		18 32	18 42	18 52		19 02	19 12	19 22		19 32	19 42	19 52		20 02	20 12
Stratford 7	⊖	a	17 40	17 51	18 00		18 10	18 21	18 30		18 40	18 51	19 00		19 10	19 21	19 30		19 40	19 51	19 58		20 08	20 21

For full service between Willesden Jn, Shepherds Bush and Clapham Jn, please refer to Table 176

Table 59R

Saturdays

14 December to 17 May

Richmond and Clapham Junction - Willesden Junction, West Hampstead, Highbury & Islington and Stratford

Network Diagram - see first Page of Table 59

	LO	LO	LO	LO	LO	LO	LO	LO	LO	LO	LO
Richmond ⊖ d	19 28		19 38		19 58		20 08		20 20		20 38
Kew Gardens ⊖ d	19 31		19 41		20 01		20 11		20 23		20 41
Gunnersbury ⊖ d	19 34		19 44		20 04		20 14		20 26		20 44
South Acton d	19 37		19 47		20 07		20 17		20 29		20 47
Acton Central d	19 40		19 50		20 10		20 20		20 33		20 50
Clapham Junction 10 176 d		19 31		19 46		20 01		20 16		20 31	
Imperial Wharf 176 d		19 35		19 50		20 05		20 20		20 35	
West Brompton ⊖176 d		19 38		19 53		20 08		20 23		20 38	
Kensington (Olympia) ⊖176 d		19 41		19 56		20 11		20 26		20 41	
Shepherd's Bush ⊖176 d		19 43		19 58		20 13		20 28		20 43	
Willesden Jn Low Level ⊖ d											
Willesden Jn. High Level ⊖ a	19 45	19 51	19 55	20 05	20 15	20 21	20 25	20 36	20 40	20 51	20 55
d	19 46		19 56	20 06	20 16		20 26		20 41		20 56
Kensal Rise d	19 48		19 58	20 08	20 18		20 28		20 43		20 58
Brondesbury Park d	19 50		20 00	20 10	20 20		20 30		20 45		21 00
Brondesbury d	19 52		20 02	20 12	20 22		20 32		20 47		21 02
West Hampstead ⊖ d	19 54		20 04	20 14	20 24		20 34		20 49		21 04
Finchley Road & Frognal d	19 55		20 05	20 15	20 25		20 35		20 50		21 05
Hampstead Heath d	19 58		20 08	20 18	20 28		20 38		20 53		21 08
Gospel Oak d	20 00		20 10	20 20	20 30		20 40		20 55		21 10
Kentish Town West d	20 02		20 12	20 22	20 32		20 42		20 57		21 12
Camden Road d	20 06		20 16	20 26	20 36		20 46		21 01		21 16
Caledonian Rd & Barnsbury d	20 09		20 19	20 29	20 39		20 49		21 04		21 19
Highbury & Islington ⊖178 d	20 12		20 22	20 32	20 42		20 52		21 07		21 22
Canonbury ⊖178 d	20 14		20 24	20 34	20 44		20 54		21 09		21 24
Dalston Kingsland d	20 16		20 26	20 36	20 46		20 56		21 11		21 26
Hackney Central d	20 18		20 28	20 38	20 48		20 58		21 13		21 28
Homerton d	20 20		20 30	20 40	20 50		21 00		21 15		21 30
Hackney Wick d	20 22		20 32	20 42	20 52		21 02		21 17		21 32
Stratford 7 ⊖ a	20 28		20 38	20 49	20 57		21 07		21 22		21 37

	LO	LO	LO	LO	LO	LO	LO	LO	LO	LO	LO
Richmond ⊖ d		20 50		21 08		21 20		21 38		21 50	
Kew Gardens ⊖ d		20 53		21 11		21 23		21 41		21 53	
Gunnersbury ⊖ d		20 56		21 14		21 26		21 44		21 56	
South Acton d		20 59		21 17		21 29		21 47		21 59	
Acton Central d		21 03		21 20		21 33		21 50		22 03	
Clapham Junction 10 176 d	20 46		21 01		21 16		21 31		21 46		22 01
Imperial Wharf 176 d	20 50		21 05		21 20		21 35		21 50		22 05
West Brompton ⊖176 d	20 53		21 08		21 23		21 38		21 53		22 08
Kensington (Olympia) ⊖176 d	20 56		21 11		21 26		21 41		21 56		22 11
Shepherd's Bush ⊖176 d	20 58		21 13		21 28		21 43		21 58		22 13
Willesden Jn Low Level ⊖ d											
Willesden Jn. High Level ⊖ a	21 06	21 10	21 21	21 25	21 36	21 40	21 51	21 55	22 06	22 10	22 21
d		21 11		21 26		21 41		21 56		22 11	
Kensal Rise d		21 13		21 28		21 43		21 58		22 13	
Brondesbury Park d		21 15		21 30		21 45		22 00		22 15	
Brondesbury d		21 17		21 32		21 47		22 02		22 17	
West Hampstead ⊖ d		21 19		21 34		21 49		22 04		22 19	
Finchley Road & Frognal d		21 20		21 35		21 50		22 05		22 20	
Hampstead Heath d		21 23		21 38		21 53		22 08		22 23	
Gospel Oak d		21 25		21 40		21 55		22 10		22 25	
Kentish Town West d		21 27		21 42		21 57		22 12		22 27	
Camden Road d		21 31		21 46		22 01		22 16		22 31	
Caledonian Rd & Barnsbury d		21 34		21 49		22 04		22 19		22 34	
Highbury & Islington ⊖178 d		21 37		21 52		22 07		22 22		22 37	
Canonbury ⊖178 d		21 39		21 54		22 09		22 24		22 39	
Dalston Kingsland d		21 41		21 56		22 11		22 26		22 41	
Hackney Central d		21 43		21 58		22 13		22 28		22 43	
Homerton d		21 45		22 00		22 15		22 30		22 45	
Hackney Wick d		21 47		22 02		22 17		22 32		22 47	
Stratford 7 ⊖ a		21 52		22 07		22 22		22 37		22 52	

	LO	LO	LO	LO	LO	LO	LO	LO	LO	LO	LO
Richmond ⊖ d	22 08		22 20		22 38		22 50	23 02		23 28	
Kew Gardens ⊖ d	22 11		22 23		22 41		22 53	23 05		23 31	
Gunnersbury ⊖ d	22 14		22 26		22 44		22 56	23 08		23 34	
South Acton d	22 17		22 29		22 47		22 59	23 11		23 37	
Acton Central d	22 20		22 33		22 50		23 03	23 14		23 40	
Clapham Junction 10 176 d		22 16		22 31		22 46			23 01		23 31
Imperial Wharf 176 d		22 20		22 35		22 50			23 05		23 35
West Brompton ⊖176 d		22 23		22 38		22 53			23 08		23 38
Kensington (Olympia) ⊖176 d		22 26		22 41		22 56			23 11		23 41
Shepherd's Bush ⊖176 d		22 28		22 43		22 58			23 13		23 43
Willesden Jn Low Level ⊖ d											
Willesden Jn. High Level ⊖ a	22 25	22 36	22 40	22 51	22 55	23 06	23 10	23 19	23 24	23 46	23 51
d	22 26		22 41		22 56		23 11	23 20			
Kensal Rise d	22 28		22 43		22 58		23 13	23 22			
Brondesbury Park d	22 30		22 45		23 00		23 15	23 24			
Brondesbury d	22 32		22 47		23 02		23 17	23 26			
West Hampstead ⊖ d	22 34		22 49		23 04		23 19	23 28			
Finchley Road & Frognal d	22 35		22 50		23 05		23 20	23 29			
Hampstead Heath d	22 38		22 53		23 08		23 23	23 32			
Gospel Oak d	22 40		22 55		23 10		23 25	23 34			
Kentish Town West d	22 42		22 57		23 12		23 27	23 36			
Camden Road d	22 46		23 01		23 16		23 31	23 40			
Caledonian Rd & Barnsbury d	22 49		23 04		23 19		23 34	23 43			
Highbury & Islington ⊖178 d	22 52		23 07		23 22		23 37	23 46			
Canonbury ⊖178 d	22 54		23 09		23 24		23 39	23 48			
Dalston Kingsland d	22 56		23 11		23 26		23 41	23 50			
Hackney Central d	22 58		23 13		23 28		23 43	23 52			
Homerton d	23 00		23 15		23 30		23 45	23 54			
Hackney Wick d	23 02		23 17		23 32		23 47	23 56			
Stratford 7 ⊖ a	23 07		23 22		23 37		23 52	00 02			

For full service between Willesden Jn, Shepherds Bush and Clapham Jn, please refer to Table 176

Table 59R

Sundays

8 December to 11 May

Richmond and Clapham Junction - Willesden Junction, West Hampstead, Highbury & Islington and Stratford

Network Diagram - see first Page of Table 59

		LO	LO	LO	LO	LO	LO	LO	LO	LO	LO	LO
Richmond	⊖ d			08 59		09 17	09 29		09 47	09 58		10 10
Kew Gardens	⊖ d			09 02		09 20	09 32		09 50	10 02		10 13
Gunnersbury	⊖ d			09 05		09 23	09 35		09 53	10 05		10 16
South Acton	d			09 08		09 26	09 38		09 56	10 08		10 19
Acton Central	d			09 11		09 29	09 41		09 59	10 11		10 22
Clapham Junction 10	176 d	08 31			09 01			09 31			10 01	
Imperial Wharf	176 d	08 35			09 05			09 35			10 05	
West Brompton	⊖176 d	08 38			09 08			09 38			10 08	
Kensington (Olympia)	⊖176 d	08 41			09 11			09 41			10 11	
Shepherd's Bush	⊖176 d	08 43			09 13			09 43			10 13	
Willesden Jn Low Level	⊖ d		09 00									
Willesden Jn. High Level	⊖ a	08 51		09 16	09 21	09 34	09 46	09 51	10 04	10 16	10 21	10 27
	d			09 17		09 35	09 47		10 05	10 17		10 28
Kensal Rise	d		09 04	09 19		09 37	09 50		10 07	10 19		10 30
Brondesbury Park	d		09 06	09 21		09 39	09 52		10 09	10 21		10 32
Brondesbury	d		09 08	09 23		09 41	09 53		10 11	10 23		10 34
West Hampstead	⊖ d		09 10	09 25		09 43	09 55		10 13	10 25		10 36
Finchley Road & Frognal	d		09 11	09 26		09 44	09 57		10 14	10 26		10 37
Hampstead Heath	d		09 14	09 29		09 47	09 59		10 17	10 29		10 40
Gospel Oak	d		09 16	09 31		09 49	10 02		10 19	10 31		10 42
Kentish Town West	d		09 18	09 33		09 51	10 04		10 21	10 33		10 44
Camden Road	d		09 22	09 37		09 55	10 07		10 25	10 37		10 48
Caledonian Rd & Barnsbury	d		09 25	09 40		09 58	10 10		10 28	10 40		10 51
Highbury & Islington	⊖178 d		09 28	09 43		10 01	10 13		10 31	10 43		10 54
Canonbury	⊖178 d		09 30	09 45		10 03	10 15		10 33	10 45		10 56
Dalston Kingsland	d		09 32	09 47		10 05	10 17		10 35	10 47		10 58
Hackney Central	d		09 34	09 49		10 07	10 19		10 37	10 49		11 00
Homerton	d		09 36	09 51		10 09	10 21		10 39	10 51		11 02
Hackney Wick	d		09 38	09 53		10 11	10 23		10 41	10 53		11 04
Stratford 7	⊖ a		09 48	10 00		10 18	10 30		10 48	11 00		11 11

		LO	LO	LO	LO	LO	LO	LO	LO	LO	LO	LO
Richmond	⊖ d		10 29		10 40		10 59		11 10		11 29	
Kew Gardens	⊖ d		10 32		10 43		11 02		11 13		11 32	
Gunnersbury	⊖ d		10 35		10 46		11 05		11 16		11 35	
South Acton	d		10 38		10 49		11 08		11 19		11 38	
Acton Central	d		10 41		10 52		11 11		11 22		11 41	
Clapham Junction 10	176 d	10 21		10 31		10 46		11 01		11 21		11 31
Imperial Wharf	176 d	10 25		10 35		10 50		11 05		11 25		11 35
West Brompton	⊖176 d	10 28		10 38		10 53		11 08		11 28		11 38
Kensington (Olympia)	⊖176 d	10 31		10 41		10 56		11 11		11 31		11 41
Shepherd's Bush	⊖176 d	10 33		10 43		10 58		11 13		11 33		11 43
Willesden Jn Low Level	⊖ d											
Willesden Jn. High Level	⊖ a	10 40	10 46	10 51	10 57	11 05	11 16	11 21	11 27	11 40	11 46	11 51
	d	10 41	10 47		10 58	11 06	11 17		11 28	11 41	11 47	
Kensal Rise	d	10 43	10 49		11 00	11 08	11 19		11 30	11 43	11 49	
Brondesbury Park	d	10 45	10 51		11 02	11 10	11 21		11 32	11 45	11 51	
Brondesbury	d	10 47	10 53		11 04	11 12	11 23		11 34	11 47	11 53	
West Hampstead	⊖ d	10 49	10 55		11 06	11 14	11 25		11 36	11 49	11 55	
Finchley Road & Frognal	d	10 50	10 56		11 07	11 15	11 26		11 37	11 50	11 56	
Hampstead Heath	d	10 53	10 59		11 10	11 18	11 29		11 40	11 53	11 59	
Gospel Oak	d	10 55	11 01		11 12	11 20	11 31		11 42	11 55	12 01	
Kentish Town West	d	10 57	11 03		11 14	11 22	11 33		11 44	11 57	12 03	
Camden Road	d	11 01	11 07		11 18	11 26	11 37		11 48	12 01	12 07	
Caledonian Rd & Barnsbury	d	11 04	11 10		11 21	11 29	11 40		11 51	12 04	12 10	
Highbury & Islington	⊖178 d	11 07	11 13		11 24	11 32	11 43		11 54	12 07	12 13	
Canonbury	⊖178 d	11 09	11 15		11 26	11 34	11 45		11 56	12 09	12 15	
Dalston Kingsland	d	11 11	11 17		11 28	11 36	11 47		11 58	12 11	12 17	
Hackney Central	d	11 13	11 19		11 30	11 38	11 49		12 00	12 13	12 19	
Homerton	d	11 15	11 21		11 32	11 40	11 51		12 02	12 15	12 21	
Hackney Wick	d	11 17	11 23		11 34	11 42	11 53		12 04	12 17	12 23	
Stratford 7	⊖ a	11 24	11 30		11 41	11 49	12 00		12 09	12 24	12 28	

		LO	LO	LO	LO	LO	LO	LO	LO	LO	LO	LO
Richmond	⊖ d	11 40		11 59		12 10		12 29		12 40		12 59
Kew Gardens	⊖ d	11 43		12 02		12 13		12 32		12 43		13 02
Gunnersbury	⊖ d	11 46		12 05		12 16		12 35		12 46		13 05
South Acton	d	11 49		12 08		12 19		12 38		12 49		13 08
Acton Central	d	11 52		12 11		12 22		12 41		12 52		13 11
Clapham Junction 10	176 d		11 46		12 01		12 16		12 31		12 46	
Imperial Wharf	176 d		11 50		12 05		12 20		12 35		12 50	
West Brompton	⊖176 d		11 53		12 08		12 23		12 38		12 53	
Kensington (Olympia)	⊖176 d		11 56		12 11		12 26		12 41		12 56	
Shepherd's Bush	⊖176 d		11 58		12 13		12 28		12 43		12 58	
Willesden Jn Low Level	⊖ d											
Willesden Jn. High Level	⊖ a	11 57	12 05	12 16	12 21	12 27	12 35	12 46	12 51	12 57	13 05	13 16
	d	11 58	12 06	12 17		12 28	12 36	12 47		12 58	13 06	13 17
Kensal Rise	d	12 00	12 08	12 19		12 30	12 38	12 49		13 00	13 08	13 19
Brondesbury Park	d	12 02	12 10	12 21		12 32	12 40	12 51		13 02	13 10	13 21
Brondesbury	d	12 04	12 12	12 23		12 34	12 42	12 53		13 04	13 12	13 23
West Hampstead	⊖ d	12 06	12 14	12 25		12 36	12 44	12 55		13 06	13 14	13 25
Finchley Road & Frognal	d	12 07	12 15	12 26		12 37	12 45	12 56		13 07	13 15	13 26
Hampstead Heath	d	12 10	12 18	12 29		12 40	12 48	12 59		13 10	13 18	13 29
Gospel Oak	d	12 12	12 20	12 31		12 42	12 50	13 01		13 12	13 20	13 31
Kentish Town West	d	12 14	12 22	12 33		12 44	12 52	13 03		13 14	13 22	13 33
Camden Road	d	12 18	12 26	12 37		12 48	12 56	13 07		13 18	13 26	13 37
Caledonian Rd & Barnsbury	d	12 21	12 29	12 40		12 51	12 59	13 10		13 21	13 29	13 40
Highbury & Islington	⊖178 d	12 24	12 32	12 43		12 54	13 02	13 13		13 24	13 32	13 43
Canonbury	⊖178 d	12 26	12 34	12 45		12 56	13 04	13 15		13 26	13 34	13 45
Dalston Kingsland	d	12 28	12 36	12 47		12 58	13 06	13 17		13 28	13 36	13 47
Hackney Central	d	12 30	12 38	12 49		13 00	13 08	13 19		13 30	13 38	13 49
Homerton	d	12 32	12 40	12 51		13 02	13 10	13 21		13 32	13 40	13 51
Hackney Wick	d	12 34	12 42	12 53		13 04	13 12	13 23		13 34	13 42	13 53
Stratford 7	⊖ a	12 39	12 49	12 58		13 09	13 19	13 28		13 39	13 49	13 58

		LO	LO	LO	LO	LO	LO	LO	LO	LO	LO	LO
Richmond	⊖ d		13 10		13 29		13 40		13 59		14 10	
Kew Gardens	⊖ d		13 13		13 32		13 43		14 02		14 13	
Gunnersbury	⊖ d		13 16		13 35		13 46		14 05		14 16	
South Acton	d		13 19		13 38		13 49		14 08		14 19	
Acton Central	d		13 22		13 41		13 52		14 11		14 22	
Clapham Junction 10	176 d	13 01		13 16		13 31		13 46		14 01		14 16
Imperial Wharf	176 d	13 05		13 20		13 35		13 50		14 05		14 20
West Brompton	⊖176 d	13 08		13 23		13 38		13 53		14 08		14 23
Kensington (Olympia)	⊖176 d	13 11		13 26		13 41		13 56		14 11		14 26
Shepherd's Bush	⊖176 d	13 13		13 28		13 43		13 58		14 13		14 28
Willesden Jn Low Level	⊖ d											
Willesden Jn. High Level	⊖ a	13 21	13 27	13 35	13 46	13 51	13 57	14 05	14 16	14 22	14 27	14 35
	d		13 28	13 36	13 47		13 58	14 06	14 17		14 28	14 36
Kensal Rise	d		13 30	13 38	13 49		14 00	14 08	14 20		14 30	14 38
Brondesbury Park	d		13 32	13 40	13 51		14 02	14 10	14 22		14 32	14 40
Brondesbury	d		13 34	13 42	13 53		14 04	14 12	14 23		14 34	14 42
West Hampstead	⊖ d		13 36	13 44	13 55		14 06	14 14	14 25		14 36	14 44
Finchley Road & Frognal	d		13 37	13 45	13 56		14 07	14 15	14 27		14 37	14 45
Hampstead Heath	d		13 40	13 48	13 59		14 10	14 18	14 29		14 40	14 48
Gospel Oak	d		13 42	13 50	14 01		14 12	14 20	14 32		14 42	14 50
Kentish Town West	d		13 44	13 52	14 03		14 14	14 22	14 34		14 44	14 52
Camden Road	d		13 48	13 56	14 07		14 18	14 26	14 37		14 48	14 56
Caledonian Rd & Barnsbury	d		13 51	13 59	14 10		14 21	14 29	14 40		14 51	14 59
Highbury & Islington	⊖178 d		13 54	14 02	14 13		14 24	14 32	14 43		14 54	15 02
Canonbury	⊖178 d		13 56	14 04	14 15		14 26	14 34	14 45		14 56	15 04
Dalston Kingsland	d		13 58	14 06	14 17		14 28	14 36	14 47		14 58	15 06
Hackney Central	d		14 00	14 08	14 19		14 30	14 38	14 49		15 00	15 08
Homerton	d		14 02	14 10	14 21		14 32	14 40	14 51		15 02	15 10
Hackney Wick	d		14 04	14 12	14 23		14 34	14 42	14 53		15 04	15 12
Stratford 7	⊖ a		14 09	14 19	14 28		14 39	14 49	14 58		15 09	15 19

For full service between Willesden Jn, Shepherds Bush and Clapham Jn, please refer to Table 176

Table 59R

Sundays

8 December to 11 May

Richmond and Clapham Junction - Willesden Junction, West Hampstead, Highbury & Islington and Stratford

Network Diagram - see first Page of Table 59

		LO	LO	LO	LO	LO	LO	LO	LO	LO	LO	LO	LO	LO	LO	LO	LO	LO	LO	LO	LO	LO	LO
Richmond ⊖	d	14 29		14 40		14 59		15 10		15 29		15 40		15 59		16 10		16 29		16 40		16 59	
Kew Gardens ⊖	d	14 32		14 43		15 02		15 13		15 32		15 43		16 02		16 13		16 32		16 43		17 02	
Gunnersbury ⊖	d	14 35		14 46		15 05		15 16		15 35		15 46		16 05		16 16		16 35		16 46		17 05	
South Acton	d	14 38		14 49		15 08		15 19		15 38		15 49		16 08		16 19		16 38		16 49		17 08	
Acton Central	d	14 41		14 52		15 11		15 22		15 41		15 52		16 11		16 22		16 41		16 52		17 11	
Clapham Junction 10 176	d		14 31		14 46		15 01		15 16		15 31		15 46		16 01		16 16		16 31		16 46		17 01
Imperial Wharf 176	d		14 35		14 50		15 05		15 20		15 35		15 50		16 05		16 20		16 35		16 50		17 05
West Brompton ⊖176	d		14 38		14 53		15 08		15 23		15 38		15 53		16 08		16 23		16 38		16 53		17 08
Kensington (Olympia) ⊖176	d		14 41		14 56		15 11		15 26		15 41		15 56		16 11		16 26		16 41		16 56		17 11
Shepherd's Bush ⊖176	d		14 43		14 58		15 13		15 28		15 43		15 58		16 13		16 28		16 43		16 58		17 13
Willesden Jn Low Level ⊖	d																						
Willesden Jn. High Level ⊖	a	14 46	14 51	14 57	15 05	15 16	15 21	15 27	15 35	15 46	15 51	15 57	16 05	16 16	16 21	16 27	16 35	16 46	16 51	16 57	17 05	17 16	17 21
	d	14 47		14 58	15 06	15 17		15 28	15 36	15 47		15 58	16 06	16 17		16 28	16 36	16 47		16 58	17 06	17 17	
Kensal Rise	d	14 49		15 00	15 08	15 19		15 30	15 38	15 49		16 00	16 08	16 19		16 30	16 38	16 49		17 00	17 08	17 19	
Brondesbury Park	d	14 51		15 02	15 10	15 21		15 32	15 40	15 51		16 02	16 10	16 21		16 32	16 40	16 51		17 02	17 10	17 21	
Brondesbury	d	14 53		15 04	15 12	15 23		15 34	15 42	15 53		16 04	16 12	16 23		16 34	16 42	16 53		17 04	17 12	17 23	
West Hampstead ⊖	d	14 55		15 06	15 14	15 25		15 36	15 44	15 55		16 06	16 14	16 25		16 36	16 44	16 55		17 06	17 14	17 25	
Finchley Road & Frognal	d	14 56		15 07	15 15	15 26		15 37	15 45	15 56		16 07	16 15	16 26		16 37	16 45	16 56		17 07	17 15	17 26	
Hampstead Heath	d	14 59		15 10	15 18	15 29		15 40	15 48	15 59		16 10	16 18	16 29		16 40	16 48	16 59		17 10	17 18	17 29	
Gospel Oak	d	15 01		15 12	15 20	15 31		15 42	15 50	16 01		16 12	16 20	16 31		16 42	16 50	17 01		17 12	17 20	17 31	
Kentish Town West	d	15 03		15 14	15 22	15 33		15 44	15 52	16 03		16 14	16 22	16 33		16 44	16 52	17 03		17 14	17 22	17 33	
Camden Road	d	15 07		15 18	15 26	15 37		15 48	15 56	16 07		16 18	16 26	16 37		16 48	16 56	17 07		17 18	17 26	17 37	
Caledonian Rd & Barnsbury	d	15 10		15 21	15 29	15 40		15 51	15 59	16 10		16 21	16 29	16 40		16 51	16 59	17 10		17 21	17 29	17 40	
Highbury & Islington ⊖178	d	15 13		15 24	15 32	15 43		15 54	16 02	16 13		16 24	16 32	16 43		16 54	17 02	17 13		17 24	17 32	17 43	
Canonbury ⊖178	d	15 15		15 26	15 34	15 45		15 56	16 04	16 15		16 26	16 34	16 45		16 56	17 04	17 15		17 26	17 34	17 45	
Dalston Kingsland	d	15 17		15 28	15 36	15 47		15 58	16 06	16 17		16 28	16 36	16 47		16 58	17 06	17 17		17 28	17 36	17 47	
Hackney Central	d	15 19		15 30	15 38	15 49		16 00	16 08	16 19		16 30	16 38	16 49		17 00	17 08	17 19		17 30	17 38	17 49	
Homerton	d	15 21		15 32	15 40	15 51		16 02	16 10	16 21		16 32	16 40	16 51		17 02	17 10	17 21		17 32	17 40	17 51	
Hackney Wick	d	15 23		15 34	15 42	15 53		16 04	16 12	16 23		16 34	16 42	16 53		17 04	17 12	17 23		17 34	17 42	17 53	
Stratford 7 ⊖	a	15 28		15 39	15 49	15 58		16 09	16 19	16 28		16 39	16 49	16 58		17 09	17 19	17 28		17 39	17 49	18 00	

		LO	LO	LO	LO	LO	LO	LO	LO	LO	LO	LO	LO	LO	LO	LO	LO	LO	LO	LO	LO	LO	LO
Richmond ⊖	d	17 10		17 29		17 40		17 59		18 10		18 29		18 40		18 59		19 10		19 29		19 40	
Kew Gardens ⊖	d	17 13		17 32		17 43		18 02		18 13		18 32		18 43		19 02		19 13		19 32		19 43	
Gunnersbury ⊖	d	17 16		17 35		17 46		18 05		18 16		18 35		18 46		19 05		19 16		19 35		19 46	
South Acton	d	17 19		17 38		17 49		18 08		18 19		18 38		18 49		19 08		19 19		19 38		19 49	
Acton Central	d	17 22		17 41		17 52		18 11		18 22		18 41		18 52		19 11		19 22		19 41		19 52	
Clapham Junction 10 176	d		17 16		17 31		17 46		18 01		18 16		18 31		18 46		19 01		19 16		19 31		19 46
Imperial Wharf 176	d		17 20		17 35		17 50		18 05		18 20		18 35		18 50		19 05		19 20		19 35		19 50
West Brompton ⊖176	d		17 23		17 38		17 53		18 08		18 23		18 38		18 53		19 08		19 23		19 38		19 53
Kensington (Olympia) ⊖176	d		17 26		17 41		17 56		18 11		18 26		18 41		18 56		19 11		19 26		19 41		19 56
Shepherd's Bush ⊖176	d		17 28		17 43		17 58		18 13		18 28		18 43		18 58		19 13		19 28		19 43		19 58
Willesden Jn Low Level ⊖	d																						
Willesden Jn. High Level ⊖	a	17 27	17 35	17 46	17 51	17 57	18 05	18 16	18 21	18 27	18 35	18 46	18 51	18 57	19 05	19 16	19 21	19 27	19 35	19 46	19 51	19 57	20 05
	d	17 28	17 36	17 47		17 58	18 06	18 17		18 28	18 36	18 47		18 58	19 06	19 17		19 28	19 36	19 47		19 58	20 06
Kensal Rise	d	17 30	17 38	17 49		18 00	18 08	18 19		18 30	18 38	18 49		19 00	19 08	19 19		19 30	19 38	19 49		20 00	20 08
Brondesbury Park	d	17 32	17 40	17 51		18 02	18 10	18 21		18 32	18 40	18 51		19 02	19 10	19 21		19 32	19 40	19 51		20 02	20 10
Brondesbury	d	17 34	17 42	17 53		18 04	18 12	18 23		18 34	18 42	18 53		19 04	19 12	19 23		19 34	19 42	19 53		20 04	20 12
West Hampstead ⊖	d	17 36	17 44	17 55		18 06	18 14	18 25		18 36	18 44	18 55		19 06	19 14	19 25		19 36	19 44	19 55		20 06	20 14
Finchley Road & Frognal	d	17 37	17 45	17 56		18 07	18 15	18 26		18 37	18 45	18 56		19 07	19 15	19 26		19 37	19 45	19 56		20 07	20 15
Hampstead Heath	d	17 40	17 48	17 59		18 10	18 18	18 29		18 40	18 48	18 59		19 10	19 18	19 29		19 40	19 48	19 59		20 10	20 18
Gospel Oak	d	17 42	17 50	18 01		18 12	18 20	18 31		18 42	18 50	19 01		19 12	19 20	19 31		19 42	19 50	20 01		20 12	20 20
Kentish Town West	d	17 44	17 52	18 03		18 14	18 22	18 33		18 44	18 52	19 03		19 14	19 22	19 33		19 44	19 52	20 03		20 14	20 22
Camden Road	d	17 48	17 56	18 07		18 18	18 26	18 37		18 48	18 56	19 07		19 18	19 26	19 37		19 48	19 56	20 07		20 18	20 26
Caledonian Rd & Barnsbury	d	17 51	17 59	18 10		18 21	18 29	18 40		18 51	18 59	19 10		19 21	19 29	19 40		19 51	19 59	20 10		20 21	20 29
Highbury & Islington ⊖178	d	17 54	18 02	18 13		18 24	18 32	18 43		18 54	19 02	19 13		19 24	19 32	19 43		19 54	20 02	20 13		20 24	20 32
Canonbury ⊖178	d	17 56	18 04	18 15		18 26	18 34	18 45		18 56	19 04	19 15		19 26	19 34	19 45		19 56	20 04	20 15		20 26	20 34
Dalston Kingsland	d	17 58	18 06	18 17		18 28	18 36	18 47		18 58	19 06	19 17		19 28	19 36	19 47		19 58	20 06	20 17		20 28	20 36
Hackney Central	d	18 00	18 08	18 19		18 30	18 38	18 49		19 00	19 08	19 19		19 30	19 38	19 49		20 00	20 08	20 19		20 30	20 38
Homerton	d	18 02	18 10	18 21		18 32	18 40	18 51		19 02	19 10	19 21		19 32	19 40	19 51		20 02	20 10	20 21		20 32	20 40
Hackney Wick	d	18 04	18 12	18 23		18 34	18 42	18 53		19 04	19 12	19 23		19 34	19 42	19 53		20 04	20 12	20 23		20 34	20 42
Stratford 7 ⊖	a	18 11	18 19	18 30		18 41	18 49	19 00		19 11	19 19	19 30		19 41	19 49	19 58		20 09	20 19	20 28		20 39	20 49

For full service between Willesden Jn, Shepherds Bush and Clapham Jn, please refer to Table 176

Table 59R

Sundays

8 December to 11 May

Richmond and Clapham Junction - Willesden Junction, West Hampstead, Highbury & Islington and Stratford

Network Diagram - see first Page of Table 59

		LO	LO	LO	LO	LO	LO	LO	LO	LO	LO	LO
Richmond ⊖	d	19 59		20 10		20 29		20 40		20 59		21 17
Kew Gardens ⊖	d	20 02		20 13		20 32		20 43		21 02		21 20
Gunnersbury ⊖	d	20 05		20 16		20 35		20 46		21 05		21 23
South Acton	d	20 08		20 19		20 38		20 49		21 08		21 26
Acton Central	d	20 11		20 22		20 41		20 52		21 11		21 29
Clapham Junction 10 176	d		20 01		20 16		20 31		20 46		21 01	
Imperial Wharf 176	d		20 05		20 20		20 35		20 50		21 05	
West Brompton ⊖176	d		20 08		20 23		20 38		20 53		21 08	
Kensington (Olympia) ⊖176	d		20 11		20 26		20 41		20 56		21 11	
Shepherd's Bush ⊖176	d		20 13		20 28		20 43		20 58		21 13	
Willesden Jn Low Level ⊖	d											
Willesden Jn. High Level ⊖	a	20 16	20 21	20 27	20 36	20 46	20 51	20 57	21 08	21 16	21 21	21 34
	d	20 17		20 28		20 47		20 58		21 17		21 35
Kensal Rise	d	20 19		20 30		20 49		21 00		21 19		21 38
Brondesbury Park	d	20 21		20 32		20 51		21 02		21 21		21 40
Brondesbury	d	20 23		20 34		20 53		21 04		21 23		21 42
West Hampstead ⊖	d	20 25		20 36		20 55		21 06		21 25		21 44
Finchley Road & Frognal	d	20 26		20 37		20 56		21 07		21 26		21 45
Hampstead Heath	d	20 29		20 40		20 59		21 10		21 29		21 48
Gospel Oak	d	20 31		20 42		21 01		21 12		21 31		21 50
Kentish Town West	d	20 33		20 44		21 03		21 14		21 33		21 52
Camden Road	d	20 37		20 48		21 07		21 18		21 37		21 55
Caledonian Rd & Barnsbury	d	20 40		20 51		21 10		21 21		21 40		21 58
Highbury & Islington ⊖178	d	20 43		20 54		21 13		21 24		21 43		22 01
Canonbury ⊖178	d	20 45		20 56		21 15		21 26		21 45		22 03
Dalston Kingsland	d	20 47		20 58		21 17		21 28		21 47		22 05
Hackney Central	d	20 49		21 00		21 19		21 30		21 49		22 07
Homerton	d	20 51		21 02		21 21		21 32		21 51		22 09
Hackney Wick	d	20 53		21 04		21 23		21 34		21 53		22 11
Stratford 7 ⊖	a	20 58		21 09		21 28		21 39		21 58		22 16

		LO	LO	LO	LO	LO	LO	LO	LO	LO	LO	LO
Richmond ⊖	d		21 29		21 47		21 59			22 27		23 01
Kew Gardens ⊖	d		21 32		21 50		22 02			22 31		23 03
Gunnersbury ⊖	d		21 35		21 53		22 05			22 34		23 06
South Acton	d		21 38		21 56		22 08			22 37		23 09
Acton Central	d		21 41		21 59		22 11			22 40		23 12
Clapham Junction 10 176	d	21 16		21 31		21 46		22 01	22 21		22 46	
Imperial Wharf 176	d	21 20		21 35		21 50		22 05	22 25		22 50	
West Brompton ⊖176	d	21 23		21 38		21 53		22 08	22 28		22 53	
Kensington (Olympia) ⊖176	d	21 26		21 41		21 56		22 11	22 31		22 56	
Shepherd's Bush ⊖176	d	21 32		21 43		21 58		22 13	22 33		22 58	
Willesden Jn Low Level ⊖	d											
Willesden Jn. High Level ⊖	a	21 42	21 46	21 51	22 04	22 08	22 16	22 23	22 41	22 45	23 08	23 17
	d		21 47		22 05		22 17			22 46		23 18
Kensal Rise	d		21 49		22 07		22 19			22 49		23 20
Brondesbury Park	d		21 51		22 09		22 21			22 51		23 22
Brondesbury	d		21 53		22 11		22 23			22 52		23 24
West Hampstead ⊖	d		21 55		22 13		22 25			22 54		23 26
Finchley Road & Frognal	d		21 56		22 14		22 26			22 56		23 27
Hampstead Heath	d		21 59		22 17		22 29			22 58		23 30
Gospel Oak	d		22 01									
Kentish Town West	d		22 03		22 21		22 33			23 03		23 34
Camden Road	d		22 07		22 25		22 37			23 06		23 38
Caledonian Rd & Barnsbury	d		22 10		22 28		22 40			23 09		23 41
Highbury & Islington ⊖178	d		22 13		22 31		22 43			23 12		23 44
Canonbury ⊖178	d		22 15		22 33		22 45			23 14		23 46
Dalston Kingsland	d		22 17		22 35		22 47			23 16		23 48
Hackney Central	d		22 19		22 37		22 49			23 18		23 50
Homerton	d		22 21		22 39		22 51			23 20		23 52
Hackney Wick	d		22 23		22 41		22 53			23 22		23 54
Stratford 7 ⊖	a		22 28		22 46		23 00			23 27		23 59

		LO
Richmond ⊖	d	
Kew Gardens ⊖	d	
Gunnersbury ⊖	d	
South Acton	d	
Acton Central	d	
Clapham Junction 10 176	d	23 16
Imperial Wharf 176	d	23 20
West Brompton ⊖176	d	23 23
Kensington (Olympia) ⊖176	d	23 26
Shepherd's Bush ⊖176	d	23 28
Willesden Jn Low Level ⊖	d	
Willesden Jn. High Level ⊖	a	23 36
	d	
Kensal Rise	d	
Brondesbury Park	d	
Brondesbury	d	
West Hampstead ⊖	d	
Finchley Road & Frognal	d	
Hampstead Heath	d	
Gospel Oak	d	
Kentish Town West	d	
Camden Road	d	
Caledonian Rd & Barnsbury	d	
Highbury & Islington ⊖178	d	
Canonbury ⊖178	d	
Dalston Kingsland	d	
Hackney Central	d	
Homerton	d	
Hackney Wick	d	
Stratford 7 ⊖	a	

For full service between Willesden Jn, Shepherds Bush and Clapham Jn, please refer to Table 176

Table 60

Mondays to Fridays

9 December to 16 May

London, Queen's Park and Harrow & Wealdstone - Watford Junction

Network Diagram - see first Page of Table 59

Miles			LO MX	LO MO	LO MX	LO	LO	LO	LO	LO	LO	LO	LO	LO		LO	LO	LO		LO	LO	LO	LO	LO
0	**London Euston 15**	⊖66 d				05 37	06 07	06 37	06 57	07 17	07 37	07 57	08 17	08 37		14 57	15 17	15 37		15 57	16 17	16 37	16 57	17 17
2½	South Hampstead	d			00 03	05 43	06 13	06 43	07 03	07 23	07 43	08 03	08 23	08 43		15 03	15 23	15 43		16 03	16 23	16 43	17 03	17 23
3	Kilburn High Road	d			00 04	05 44	06 14	06 44	07 04	07 24	07 44	08 04	08 24	08 44		15 04	15 24	15 44		16 04	16 24	16 44	17 04	17 24
3¾	**Queen's Park (London)**	⊖ d			00 06	05 46	06 16	06 46	07 06	07 26	07 46	08 06	08 26	08 46		15 06	15 26	15 46		16 06	16 27	16 47	17 07	17 27
4½	Kensal Green	d			00 08	05 48	06 18	06 48	07 08	07 28	07 48	08 08	08 28	08 48		15 08	15 28	15 48		16 08	16 29	16 49	17 09	17 29
5½	**Willesden Jn Low Level**	d		00 01	00 11	05 51	06 21	06 51	07 11	07 31	07 51	08 11	08 31	08 51	and at	15 11	15 31	15 51		16 11	16 32	16 52	17 12	17 32
6	Harlesden	d		00 03	00 13	05 53	06 23	06 53	07 13	07 33	07 53	08 13	08 33	08 53	the same	15 13	15 33	15 53		16 13	16 34	16 54	17 14	17 34
7	Stonebridge Park	d		00 05	00 15	05 55	06 25	06 55	07 15	07 35	07 55	08 15	08 35	08 55	minutes	15 15	15 35	15 55		16 15	16 36	16 56	17 16	17 36
8	Wembley Central	66 d		00 08	00 18	05 58	06 28	06 58	07 18	07 38	07 58	08 18	08 38	08 58	past	15 18	15 38	15 58		16 18	16 39	16 59	17 19	17 39
9	North Wembley	d		00 10	00 20	06 00	06 30	07 00	07 20	07 40	08 00	08 20	08 40	09 00	each	15 20	15 40	16 00		16 20	16 41	17 01	17 21	17 41
9½	South Kenton	d		00 12	00 22	06 02	06 32	07 02	07 22	07 42	08 02	08 22	08 42	09 02	hour until	15 22	15 42	16 02		16 22	16 43	17 03	17 23	17 43
10¼	Kenton	d		00 14	00 24	06 04	06 34	07 04	07 24	07 44	08 04	08 24	08 44	09 04		15 24	15 44	16 04		16 24	16 45	17 05	17 25	17 45
11¼	**Harrow & Wealdstone**	66 d		00 16	00 26	06 06	06 36	07 06	07 26	07 46	08 06	08 26	08 46	09 06		15 26	15 46	16 06		16 26	16 48	17 08	17 28	17 48
12½	Headstone Lane	d		00 19	00 29	06 09	06 39	07 09	07 29	07 49	08 09	08 29	08 49	09 09		15 29	15 49	16 09		16 29	16 51	17 11	17 31	17 51
13¼	Hatch End	d	00 01	00 21	00 31	06 11	06 41	07 11	07 31	07 51	08 11	08 31	08 51	09 11		15 31	15 51	16 11		16 31	16 53	17 13	17 33	17 53
14¾	Carpenders Park	d	00 04	00 24	00 34	06 14	06 44	07 14	07 34	07 54	08 14	08 34	08 54	09 14		15 34	15 54	16 14		16 34	16 56	17 16	17 36	17 56
16	Bushey	66 d	00 07	00 27	00 37	06 17	06 47	07 17	07 37	07 57	08 17	08 37	08 57	09 17		15 37	15 57	16 17		16 37	16 59	17 19	17 39	17 59
16¾	Watford High Street	d	00 10	00 30	00 40	06 20	06 50	07 20	07 40	08 00	08 20	08 40	09 00	09 20		15 40	16 00	16 20		16 40	17 01	17 21	17 41	18 01
17¾	**Watford Junction**	66 a	00 14	00 35	00 44	06 24	06 54	07 24	07 46	08 04	08 28	08 44	09 04	09 24		15 44	16 04	16 24		16 44	17 08	17 28	17 48	18 08

		LO	LO	LO	LO		LO	LO	LO	LO	LO	LO	LO	LO	LO		LO	LO	LO	LO	LO
London Euston 15	⊖66 d	17 37	17 57	18 17	18 37		18 57	19 17	19 37	19 57	20 17	20 37	20 57	21 17	21 37		21 57	22 27	22 57	23 27	23 57
South Hampstead	d	17 43	18 03	18 23	18 43		19 03	19 23	19 43	20 03	20 23	20 43	21 03	21 23	21 43		22 03	22 33	23 03	23 33	00 03
Kilburn High Road	d	17 44	18 04	18 24	18 44		19 04	19 24	19 44	20 04	20 24	20 44	21 04	21 24	21 44		22 04	22 34	23 04	23 34	00 04
Queen's Park (London)	⊖ d	17 47	18 07	18 27	18 47		19 07	19 26	19 46	20 06	20 26	20 46	21 06	21 26	21 46		22 06	22 36	23 06	23 36	00 06
Kensal Green	d	17 49	18 09	18 29	18 49		19 09	19 28	19 48	20 08	20 28	20 48	21 08	21 28	21 48		22 08	22 38	23 08	23 38	00 08
Willesden Jn Low Level	d	17 52	18 12	18 32	18 52		19 12	19 31	19 51	20 11	20 31	20 51	21 11	21 31	21 51		22 11	22 41	23 11	23 41	00 11
Harlesden	d	17 54	18 14	18 34	18 54		19 14	19 33	19 53	20 13	20 33	20 53	21 13	21 33	21 53		22 13	22 43	23 13	23 43	00 13
Stonebridge Park	d	17 56	18 16	18 36	18 56		19 16	19 35	19 55	20 15	20 35	20 55	21 15	21 35	21 55		22 15	22 45	23 15	23 45	00 15
Wembley Central	66 d	17 59	18 19	18 39	18 59		19 19	19 38	19 58	20 18	20 38	20 58	21 18	21 38	21 58		22 18	22 48	23 18	23 48	00 18
North Wembley	d	18 01	18 21	18 41	19 01		19 21	19 40	20 00	20 20	20 40	21 00	21 20	21 40	22 00		22 20	22 50	23 20	23 50	00 20
South Kenton	d	18 03	18 23	18 43	19 03		19 23	19 42	20 02	20 22	20 42	21 02	21 22	21 42	22 02		22 22	22 52	23 22	23 52	00 22
Kenton	d	18 05	18 25	18 45	19 05		19 25	19 44	20 04	20 24	20 44	21 04	21 24	21 44	22 04		22 24	22 54	23 24	23 54	00 24
Harrow & Wealdstone	66 d	18 08	18 28	18 48	19 08		19 28	19 46	20 06	20 26	20 46	21 06	21 26	21 46	22 06		22 26	22 56	23 26	23 56	00 26
Headstone Lane	d	18 11	18 31	18 51	19 11		19 31	19 49	20 09	20 29	20 49	21 09	21 29	21 49	22 09		22 29	22 59	23 29	23 59	00 29
Hatch End	d	18 13	18 33	18 53	19 13		19 33	19 51	20 11	20 31	20 51	21 11	21 31	21 51	22 11		22 31	23 01	23 31	00 01	00 31
Carpenders Park	d	18 16	18 36	18 56	19 16		19 36	19 54	20 14	20 34	20 54	21 14	21 34	21 54	22 14		22 34	23 04	23 34	00 04	00 34
Bushey	66 d	18 19	18 39	18 59	19 19		19 39	19 57	20 17	20 37	20 57	21 17	21 37	21 57	22 17		22 37	23 07	23 37	00 07	00 37
Watford High Street	d	18 21	18 41	19 01	19 21		19 41	20 00	20 20	20 40	21 00	21 20	21 40	22 00	22 20		22 40	23 10	23 40	00 10	00 40
Watford Junction	66 a	18 28	18 48	19 08	19 28		19 48	20 04	20 28	20 44	21 08	21 28	21 44	22 04	22 25		22 44	23 14	23 44	00 14	00 44

Saturdays

14 December to 17 May

		LO	LO	LO	LO	LO	LO	LO	LO	LO		LO	LO	LO		LO	LO	LO	LO		LO	LO	LO
London Euston 15	⊖66 d			05 37	06 07	06 37	06 57	07 17	07 37	07 57		14 17	14 37	14 57		15 17	15 37	15 57	16 17		18 37	18 57	19 17
South Hampstead	d		00 03	05 43	06 13	06 43	07 03	07 23	07 43	08 03		14 23	14 43	15 03		15 23	15 43	16 03	16 23		18 43	19 03	19 23
Kilburn High Road	d		00 04	05 44	06 14	06 44	07 04	07 24	07 44	08 04		14 24	14 44	15 04		15 24	15 44	16 04	16 24		18 44	19 04	19 24
Queen's Park (London)	⊖ d		00 06	05 46	06 16	06 46	07 06	07 26	07 46	08 06		14 26	14 46	15 06		15 26	15 46	16 06	16 26		18 46	19 06	19 26
Kensal Green	d		00 08	05 48	06 18	06 48	07 08	07 28	07 48	08 08		14 28	14 48	15 08		15 28	15 48	16 08	16 28		18 48	19 08	19 28
Willesden Jn Low Level	d		00 11	05 51	06 21	06 51	07 11	07 31	07 51	08 11	and at	14 31	14 51	15 11		15 31	15 51	16 11	16 31	and at	18 51	19 11	19 31
Harlesden	d		00 13	05 53	06 23	06 53	07 13	07 33	07 53	08 13	the same	14 33	14 53	15 13		15 33	15 53	16 13	16 33	the same	18 53	19 13	19 33
Stonebridge Park	d		00 15	05 55	06 25	06 55	07 15	07 35	07 55	08 15	minutes	14 35	14 55	15 15		15 35	15 55	16 15	16 35	minutes	18 55	19 15	19 35
Wembley Central	66 d		00 18	05 58	06 28	06 58	07 18	07 38	07 58	08 18	past	14 38	14 58	15 18		15 38	15 58	16 18	16 38	past	18 58	19 18	19 38
North Wembley	d		00 20	06 00	06 30	07 00	07 20	07 40	08 00	08 20	each	14 40	15 00	15 20		15 40	16 00	16 20	16 40	each	19 00	19 20	19 40
South Kenton	d		00 22	06 02	06 32	07 02	07 22	07 42	08 02	08 22	hour until	14 42	15 02	15 22		15 42	16 02	16 22	16 42	hour until	19 02	19 22	19 42
Kenton	d		00 24	06 04	06 34	07 04	07 24	07 44	08 04	08 24		14 44	15 04	15 24		15 44	16 04	16 24	16 44		19 04	19 24	19 44
Harrow & Wealdstone	66 d		00 26	06 06	06 36	07 06	07 26	07 46	08 06	08 26		14 46	15 06	15 26		15 46	16 06	16 26	16 46		19 06	19 26	19 46
Headstone Lane	d		00 29	06 09	06 39	07 09	07 29	07 49	08 09	08 29		14 49	15 09	15 29		15 49	16 09	16 29	16 49		19 09	19 29	19 49
Hatch End	d	00 01	00 31	06 11	06 41	07 11	07 31	07 51	08 11	08 31		14 51	15 11	15 31		15 51	16 11	16 31	16 51		19 11	19 31	19 51
Carpenders Park	d	00 04	00 34	06 14	06 44	07 14	07 34	07 54	08 14	08 34		14 54	15 14	15 34		15 54	16 14	16 34	16 54		19 14	19 34	19 54
Bushey	66 d	00 07	00 37	06 17	06 47	07 17	07 37	07 57	08 17	08 37		14 57	15 17	15 37		15 57	16 17	16 37	16 57		19 17	19 37	19 57
Watford High Street	d	00 10	00 40	06 20	06 50	07 20	07 40	08 00	08 20	08 40		15 00	15 20	15 40		16 00	16 20	16 40	17 00		19 20	19 40	20 00
Watford Junction	66 a	00 14	00 44	06 24	06 55	07 24	07 46	08 04	08 24	08 44		15 04	15 24	15 44		16 04	16 28	16 48	17 08		19 28	19 48	20 08

		LO		LO	LO	LO	LO	LO	LO	LO	LO	LO		LO	LO
London Euston 15	⊖66 d	19 37		19 57	20 17	20 37	20 57	21 17	21 37	21 57	22 27	22 57		23 27	23 57
South Hampstead	d	19 43		20 03	20 23	20 43	21 03	21 23	21 43	22 03	22 33	23 03		23 33	00 03
Kilburn High Road	d	19 44		20 04	20 24	20 44	21 04	21 24	21 44	22 04	22 34	23 04		23 34	00 04
Queen's Park (London)	⊖ d	19 46		20 06	20 26	20 46	21 06	21 26	21 46	22 06	22 36	23 06		23 36	00 06
Kensal Green	d	19 48		20 08	20 28	20 48	21 08	21 28	21 48	22 08	22 38	23 08		23 38	00 08
Willesden Jn Low Level	d	19 51		20 11	20 31	20 51	21 11	21 31	21 51	22 11	22 41	23 11		23 41	00 11
Harlesden	d	19 53		20 13	20 33	20 53	21 13	21 33	21 53	22 13	22 43	23 13		23 43	00 13
Stonebridge Park	d	19 55		20 15	20 35	20 55	21 15	21 35	21 55	22 15	22 45	23 15		23 45	00 15
Wembley Central	66 d	19 58		20 18	20 38	20 58	21 18	21 38	21 58	22 18	22 48	23 18		23 48	00 18
North Wembley	d	20 00		20 20	20 40	21 00	21 20	21 40	22 00	22 20	22 50	23 20		23 50	00 20
South Kenton	d	20 02		20 22	20 42	21 02	21 22	21 42	22 02	22 22	22 52	23 22		23 52	00 22
Kenton	d	20 04		20 24	20 44	21 04	21 24	21 44	22 04	22 24	22 54	23 24		23 54	00 24
Harrow & Wealdstone	66 d	20 06		20 26	20 46	21 06	21 26	21 46	22 06	22 26	22 56	23 26		23 56	00 26
Headstone Lane	d	20 09		20 29	20 49	21 09	21 29	21 49	22 09	22 29	22 59	23 29		23 59	00 29
Hatch End	d	20 11		20 31	20 51	21 11	21 31	21 51	22 11	22 31	23 01	23 31		00 01	00 31
Carpenders Park	d	20 14		20 34	20 54	21 14	21 34	21 54	22 14	22 34	23 04	23 34		00 04	00 34
Bushey	66 d	20 17		20 37	20 57	21 17	21 37	21 57	22 17	22 37	23 07	23 37		00 07	00 37
Watford High Street	d	20 20		20 40	21 00	21 20	21 40	22 00	22 20	22 40	23 10	23 40		00 10	00 40
Watford Junction	66 a	20 28		20 48	21 04	21 24	21 44	22 08	22 24	22 44	23 14	23 44		00 14	00 44

Stations Queen's Park to Harrow & Wealdstone inclusive are also served by London Underground Bakerloo Line Services

Table 60

Sundays

8 December to 11 May

London, Queen's Park and Harrow & Wealdstone - Watford Junction

Network Diagram - see first Page of Table 59

		LO	LO	LO	LO	LO	LO	LO	LO	LO	LO	LO	LO	LO		LO	LO	LO	LO	LO	LO	LO
London Euston 15 ⊖66	d			06 47	07 17	07 47	08 17	08 47	09 17	09 37	09 57	10 17	10 37	10 57		14 17	14 37	14 57	15 17	15 37	15 57	16 17
South Hampstead	d		00 03	06 53	07 23	07 53	08 23	08 53	09 23	09 43	10 03	10 23	10 43	11 03		14 23	14 43	15 03	15 23	15 43	16 03	16 23
Kilburn High Road	d		00 04	06 54	07 24	07 54	08 24	08 54	09 24	09 44	10 04	10 24	10 44	11 04		14 24	14 44	15 04	15 24	15 44	16 04	16 24
Queen's Park (London) ⊖	d		00 06	06 56	07 26	07 56	08 26	08 56	09 26	09 46	10 06	10 26	10 46	11 06		14 26	14 46	15 06	15 26	15 46	16 06	16 26
Kensal Green	d		00 08	06 58	07 28	07 58	08 28	08 58	09 28	09 48	10 08	10 28	10 48	11 08		14 28	14 48	15 08	15 28	15 48	16 08	16 28
Willesden Jn Low Level	d		00 11	07 01	07 31	08 01	08 31	09 01	09 31	09 51	10 11	10 31	10 51	11 11	and at the same minutes past each hour until	14 31	14 51	15 11	15 31	15 51	16 11	16 31
Harlesden	d		00 13	07 03	07 33	08 03	08 33	09 03	09 33	09 53	10 13	10 33	10 53	11 13		14 33	14 53	15 13	15 33	15 53	16 13	16 33
Stonebridge Park	d		00 15	07 05	07 35	08 05	08 35	09 05	09 35	09 55	10 15	10 35	10 55	11 15		14 35	14 55	15 15	15 35	15 55	16 15	16 35
Wembley Central 66	d		00 18	07 08	07 38	08 08	08 38	09 08	09 38	09 58	10 18	10 38	10 58	11 18		14 38	14 58	15 18	15 38	15 58	16 18	16 38
North Wembley	d		00 20	07 10	07 40	08 10	08 40	09 10	09 40	10 00	10 20	10 40	11 00	11 20		14 40	15 00	15 20	15 40	16 00	16 20	16 40
South Kenton	d		00 22	07 12	07 42	08 12	08 42	09 12	09 42	10 02	10 22	10 42	11 02	11 22		14 42	15 02	15 22	15 42	16 02	16 22	16 42
Kenton	d		00 24	07 14	07 44	08 14	08 44	09 14	09 44	10 04	10 24	10 44	11 04	11 24		14 44	15 04	15 24	15 44	16 04	16 24	16 44
Harrow & Wealdstone 66	d		00 26	07 16	07 46	08 16	08 46	09 16	09 46	10 06	10 26	10 46	11 06	11 26		14 46	15 06	15 26	15 46	16 06	16 26	16 46
Headstone Lane	d		00 29	07 19	07 49	08 19	08 49	09 19	09 49	10 09	10 29	10 49	11 09	11 29		14 49	15 09	15 29	15 49	16 09	16 29	16 49
Hatch End	d	00 01	00 31	07 22	07 51	08 21	08 51	09 21	09 51	10 11	10 31	10 51	11 11	11 31		14 51	15 11	15 31	15 51	16 11	16 31	16 51
Carpenders Park	d	00 04	00 34	07 24	07 54	08 24	08 54	09 24	09 54	10 14	10 34	10 54	11 14	11 34		14 54	15 14	15 34	15 54	16 14	16 34	16 54
Bushey 66	d	00 07	00 37	07 27	07 57	08 27	08 57	09 27	09 57	10 17	10 37	10 57	11 17	11 37		14 57	15 17	15 37	15 57	16 17	16 37	16 57
Watford High Street	d	00 10	00 40	07 30	08 00	08 30	09 00	09 30	10 00	10 20	10 40	11 00	11 20	11 40		15 00	15 20	15 40	16 00	16 20	16 40	17 00
Watford Junction 66	a	00 14	00 44	07 36	08 06	08 34	09 04	09 35	10 04	10 24	10 45	11 04	11 24	11 44		15 04	15 24	15 44	16 04	16 28	16 48	17 08

		LO	LO	LO	LO	LO	LO	LO	LO	LO	LO	LO	LO	LO	LO	LO	LO	LO	LO	LO	LO	LO
London Euston 15 ⊖66	d	16 37	16 57	17 17	17 37	17 57	18 17	18 37	18 57	19 17	19 37	19 57	20 17	20 37	20 57	21 17	21 37	21 57	22 17	22 47	23 17	23 47
South Hampstead	d	16 43	17 03	17 23	17 43	18 03	18 23	18 43	19 03	19 23	19 43	20 03	20 23	20 43	21 03	21 23	21 43	22 03	22 23	22 53	23 23	23 53
Kilburn High Road	d	16 44	17 04	17 24	17 44	18 04	18 24	18 44	19 04	19 24	19 44	20 04	20 24	20 44	21 04	21 24	21 44	22 04	22 24	22 54	23 24	23 54
Queen's Park (London) ⊖	d	16 46	17 06	17 26	17 46	18 06	18 26	18 46	19 06	19 26	19 46	20 06	20 26	20 46	21 06	21 26	21 46	22 06	22 26	22 56	23 26	23 56
Kensal Green	d	16 48	17 08	17 28	17 48	18 08	18 28	18 48	19 08	19 28	19 48	20 08	20 28	20 48	21 08	21 28	21 48	22 08	22 28	22 58	23 28	23 58
Willesden Jn Low Level	d	16 51	17 11	17 31	17 51	18 11	18 31	18 51	19 11	19 31	19 51	20 11	20 31	20 51	21 11	21 31	21 51	22 11	22 31	23 01	23 31	00 01
Harlesden	d	16 53	17 13	17 33	17 53	18 13	18 33	18 53	19 13	19 33	19 53	20 13	20 33	20 53	21 13	21 33	21 53	22 13	22 33	23 03	23 33	00 03
Stonebridge Park	d	16 55	17 15	17 35	17 55	18 15	18 35	18 55	19 15	19 35	19 55	20 15	20 35	20 55	21 15	21 35	21 55	22 15	22 35	23 05	23 35	00 05
Wembley Central 66	d	16 58	17 18	17 38	17 58	18 18	18 38	18 58	19 18	19 38	19 58	20 18	20 38	20 58	21 18	21 38	21 58	22 18	22 38	23 08	23 38	00 08
North Wembley	d	17 00	17 20	17 40	18 00	18 20	18 40	19 00	19 20	19 40	20 00	20 20	20 40	21 00	21 20	21 40	22 00	22 20	22 40	23 10	23 40	00 10
South Kenton	d	17 02	17 22	17 42	18 02	18 22	18 42	19 02	19 22	19 42	20 02	20 22	20 42	21 02	21 22	21 42	22 02	22 22	22 42	23 12	23 42	00 12
Kenton	d	17 04	17 24	17 44	18 04	18 24	18 44	19 04	19 24	19 44	20 04	20 24	20 44	21 04	21 24	21 44	22 04	22 24	22 44	23 14	23 44	00 14
Harrow & Wealdstone 66	d	17 06	17 26	17 46	18 06	18 26	18 46	19 06	19 26	19 46	20 06	20 26	20 46	21 06	21 26	21 46	22 06	22 26	22 46	23 16	23 46	00 16
Headstone Lane	d	17 09	17 29	17 49	18 09	18 29	18 49	19 09	19 29	19 49	20 09	20 29	20 49	21 09	21 29	21 49	22 09	22 29	22 49	23 19	23 49	00 19
Hatch End	d	17 11	17 31	17 51	18 11	18 31	18 51	19 11	19 31	19 51	20 11	20 31	20 51	21 11	21 31	21 51	22 11	22 31	22 51	23 21	23 51	00 21
Carpenders Park	d	17 14	17 34	17 54	18 14	18 34	18 54	19 14	19 34	19 54	20 14	20 34	20 54	21 14	21 34	21 54	22 14	22 34	22 54	23 24	23 54	00 24
Bushey 66	d	17 17	17 37	17 57	18 17	18 37	18 57	19 17	19 37	19 57	20 17	20 37	20 57	21 17	21 37	21 57	22 17	22 37	22 57	23 27	23 57	00 27
Watford High Street	d	17 20	17 40	18 00	18 20	18 40	19 00	19 20	19 40	20 00	20 20	20 40	21 00	21 20	21 40	22 00	22 20	22 40	23 00	23 30	23 59	00 30
Watford Junction 66	a	17 24	17 44	18 08	18 28	18 48	19 08	19 28	19 48	20 04	20 28	20 48	21 04	21 24	21 45	22 04	22 24	22 44	23 04	23 34	00 04	00 35

Stations Queen's Park to Harrow & Wealdstone inclusive are also served by London Underground Bakerloo Line Services

Table 60R

Mondays to Fridays

9 December to 16 May

Watford Junction - Harrow & Wealdstone, Queen's Park and London

Network Diagram - see first Page of Table 59

Miles			LO	LO	LO	LO	LO	LO	LO	LO	LO	LO	LO	LO	LO	LO	LO	LO	LO	LO	
0	**Watford Junction**	66 d		05 11	05 41	06 11	06 40	07 00	07 20	07 40	08 00	08 20	08 40	09 00	09 21	09 41	10 01	10 21	10 41	11 01	
1	Watford High Street	d		05 14	05 44	06 14	06 43	07 03	07 23	07 43	08 03	08 23	08 43	09 03	09 24	09 44	10 04	10 24	10 44	11 04	
1¾	Bushey	66 d		05 16	05 46	06 16	06 45	07 05	07 25	07 45	08 05	08 25	08 45	09 05	09 26	09 46	10 06	10 26	10 46	11 06	
3	Carpenders Park	d		05 19	05 49	06 19	06 48	07 08	07 28	07 48	08 08	08 28	08 48	09 08	09 29	09 49	10 09	10 29	10 49	11 09	
4½	Hatch End	d		05 22	05 52	06 22	06 51	07 11	07 31	07 51	08 11	08 31	08 51	09 11	09 32	09 52	10 12	10 32	10 52	11 12	
5¼	Headstone Lane	d		05 24	05 54	06 24	06 53	07 13	07 33	07 53	08 13	08 33	08 53	09 13	09 34	09 54	10 14	10 34	10 54	11 14	and at the same minutes past each hour until
6½	**Harrow & Wealdstone**	66 d		05 27	05 57	06 27	06 56	07 16	07 36	07 56	08 16	08 36	08 56	09 16	09 37	09 57	10 17	10 37	10 57	11 17	
7½	Kenton	d		05 29	05 59	06 29	06 59	07 19	07 39	07 59	08 19	08 39	08 59	09 19	09 39	09 59	10 19	10 39	10 59	11 19	
8¼	South Kenton	d		05 31	06 01	06 31	07 01	07 21	07 41	08 01	08 21	08 41	09 01	09 21	09 41	10 01	10 21	10 41	11 01	11 21	
8¾	North Wembley	d		05 33	06 03	06 33	07 03	07 23	07 43	08 03	08 23	08 43	09 03	09 23	09 43	10 03	10 23	10 43	11 03	11 23	
9¾	Wembley Central	66 d		05 35	06 05	06 35	07 05	07 25	07 45	08 05	08 25	08 45	09 05	09 25	09 45	10 05	10 25	10 45	11 05	11 25	
10¾	Stonebridge Park	d		05 38	06 08	06 38	07 08	07 28	07 48	08 08	08 28	08 48	09 08	09 28	09 48	10 08	10 28	10 48	11 08	11 28	
11¾	Harlesden	d		05 40	06 10	06 40	07 10	07 30	07 50	08 10	08 30	08 50	09 10	09 30	09 50	10 10	10 30	10 50	11 10	11 30	
12¼	**Willesden Jn Low Level**	d		05 42	06 12	06 42	07 13	07 33	07 53	08 13	08 33	08 53	09 13	09 33	09 52	10 12	10 32	10 52	11 12	11 32	
13¼	Kensal Green	d		05 45	06 15	06 45	07 15	07 35	07 55	08 15	08 35	08 55	09 15	09 35	09 55	10 15	10 35	10 55	11 15	11 35	
14	**Queen's Park (London)**	⊖ d		05 47	06 17	06 47	07 18	07 38	07 58	08 18	08 38	08 58	09 18	09 38	09 57	10 17	10 37	10 57	11 17	11 37	
14¾	Kilburn High Road	d		05 49	06 19	06 49	07 20	07 40	08 00	08 20	08 40	09 00	09 20	09 40	09 59	10 19	10 39	10 59	11 19	11 39	
15¼	South Hampstead	d	00 01	05 51	06 21	06 51	07 22	07 42	08 02	08 22	08 42	09 02	09 22	09 42	10 01	10 21	10 41	11 01	11 21	11 41	
17¾	**London Euston** 15	⊖66 a	00 10	05 59	06 32	06 58	07 29	07 52	08 12	08 31	08 52	09 12	09 29	09 52	10 11	10 30	10 49	11 11	11 30	11 50	

		LO	LO	LO	LO	LO	LO	LO	LO	LO	LO	LO	LO	LO	LO	LO	LO	LO	LO	LO	LO	LO
Watford Junction	66 d	14 21	14 41	15 01	15 21	15 41	16 01	16 21	16 41	17 01	17 21	17 41	18 01	18 21	18 41	19 01	19 21	19 41	20 01	20 21	20 41	21 01
Watford High Street	d	14 24	14 44	15 04	15 24	15 44	16 04	16 24	16 44	17 04	17 24	17 44	18 04	18 24	18 44	19 04	19 24	19 44	20 04	20 24	20 44	21 04
Bushey	66 d	14 26	14 46	15 06	15 26	15 46	16 06	16 26	16 46	17 06	17 26	17 46	18 06	18 26	18 46	19 06	19 26	19 46	20 06	20 26	20 46	21 06
Carpenders Park	d	14 29	14 49	15 09	15 29	15 49	16 09	16 29	16 49	17 09	17 29	17 49	18 09	18 29	18 49	19 09	19 29	19 49	20 09	20 29	20 49	21 09
Hatch End	d	14 32	14 52	15 12	15 32	15 52	16 12	16 32	16 52	17 12	17 32	17 52	18 12	18 32	18 52	19 12	19 32	19 52	20 12	20 32	20 52	21 12
Headstone Lane	d	14 34	14 54	15 14	15 34	15 54	16 14	16 34	16 54	17 14	17 34	17 54	18 14	18 34	18 54	19 14	19 34	19 54	20 14	20 34	20 54	21 14
Harrow & Wealdstone	66 d	14 37	14 57	15 17	15 37	15 57	16 17	16 37	16 57	17 17	17 37	17 57	18 17	18 37	18 57	19 17	19 37	19 57	20 17	20 37	20 57	21 17
Kenton	d	14 39	14 59	15 19	15 39	15 59	16 19	16 39	16 59	17 19	17 39	17 59	18 19	18 39	18 59	19 19	19 39	19 59	20 19	20 39	20 59	21 19
South Kenton	d	14 41	15 01	15 21	15 41	16 01	16 21	16 41	17 01	17 21	17 41	18 01	18 21	18 41	19 01	19 21	19 41	20 01	20 21	20 41	21 01	21 21
North Wembley	d	14 43	15 03	15 23	15 43	16 03	16 23	16 43	17 03	17 23	17 43	18 03	18 23	18 43	19 03	19 23	19 43	20 03	20 23	20 43	21 03	21 23
Wembley Central	66 d	14 45	15 05	15 25	15 45	16 05	16 25	16 45	17 05	17 25	17 45	18 05	18 25	18 45	19 05	19 25	19 45	20 05	20 25	20 45	21 05	21 25
Stonebridge Park	d	14 48	15 08	15 28	15 48	16 08	16 28	16 48	17 08	17 28	17 48	18 08	18 28	18 48	19 08	19 28	19 48	20 08	20 28	20 48	21 08	21 28
Harlesden	d	14 50	15 10	15 30	15 50	16 10	16 30	16 50	17 10	17 30	17 50	18 10	18 30	18 50	19 10	19 30	19 50	20 10	20 30	20 50	21 10	21 30
Willesden Jn Low Level	d	14 52	15 12	15 32	15 52	16 12	16 32	16 52	17 12	17 32	17 52	18 12	18 32	18 52	19 12	19 32	19 52	20 12	20 32	20 52	21 12	21 32
Kensal Green	d	14 55	15 15	15 35	15 55	16 15	16 35	16 55	17 15	17 35	17 55	18 15	18 35	18 55	19 15	19 35	19 55	20 15	20 35	20 55	21 15	21 35
Queen's Park (London)	⊖ d	14 57	15 17	15 37	15 57	16 17	16 37	16 57	17 17	17 37	17 57	18 17	18 37	18 57	19 17	19 37	19 57	20 17	20 37	20 57	21 17	21 37
Kilburn High Road	d	14 59	15 19	15 39	15 59	16 19	16 39	16 59	17 19	17 39	17 59	18 19	18 39	18 59	19 19	19 39	19 59	20 19	20 39	20 59	21 19	21 39
South Hampstead	d	15 01	15 21	15 41	16 01	16 21	16 41	17 01	17 21	17 41	18 01	18 21	18 41	19 01	19 21	19 41	20 01	20 21	20 41	21 01	21 21	21 41
London Euston 15	⊖66 a	15 11	15 30	15 50	16 11	16 30	16 49	17 11	17 30	17 53	18 11	18 30	18 50	19 11	19 30	19 52	20 10	20 30	20 48	21 11	21 30	21 51

		LO	LO	LO	LO	LO	LO
Watford Junction	66 d	21 21	21 41	22 01	22 21	22 51	23 21
Watford High Street	d	21 24	21 44	22 04	22 24	22 54	23 24
Bushey	66 d	21 26	21 46	22 06	22 26	22 56	23 26
Carpenders Park	d	21 29	21 49	22 09	22 29	22 59	23 29
Hatch End	d	21 32	21 52	22 12	22 32	23 02	23 32
Headstone Lane	d	21 34	21 54	22 14	22 34	23 04	23 34
Harrow & Wealdstone	66 d	21 37	21 57	22 17	22 37	23 07	23 37
Kenton	d	21 39	21 59	22 19	22 39	23 09	23 39
South Kenton	d	21 41	22 01	22 21	22 41	23 11	23 41
North Wembley	d	21 43	22 03	22 23	22 43	23 13	23 43
Wembley Central	66 d	21 45	22 05	22 25	22 45	23 15	23 45
Stonebridge Park	d	21 48	22 08	22 28	22 48	23 18	23 48
Harlesden	d	21 50	22 10	22 30	22 50	23 20	23 50
Willesden Jn Low Level	d	21 52	22 12	22 32	22 52	23 22	23 52
Kensal Green	d	21 55	22 15	22 35	22 55	23 25	23 55
Queen's Park (London)	⊖ d	21 57	22 17	22 37	22 57	23 27	23 57
Kilburn High Road	d	21 59	22 19	22 39	22 59	23 29	23 59
South Hampstead	d	22 01	22 21	22 41	23 01	23 31	00 01
London Euston 15	⊖66 a	22 11	22 30	22 50	23 10	23 39	00 10

Saturdays

14 December to 17 May

		LO	LO	LO	LO	LO	LO	LO	LO	LO	LO	LO	LO	LO	LO	LO	LO	LO	LO		LO	LO	LO
Watford Junction	66 d		05 11	05 41	06 11	06 41	07 01	07 21	07 41	08 01	08 21	08 41	09 01	09 21	09 41	10 01	10 21	10 41	11 01		20 21	20 41	21 01
Watford High Street	d		05 14	05 44	06 14	06 44	07 04	07 24	07 44	08 04	08 24	08 44	09 04	09 24	09 44	10 04	10 24	10 44	11 04		20 24	20 44	21 04
Bushey	66 d		05 16	05 46	06 16	06 46	07 06	07 26	07 46	08 06	08 26	08 46	09 06	09 26	09 46	10 06	10 26	10 46	11 06		20 26	20 46	21 06
Carpenders Park	d		05 19	05 49	06 19	06 49	07 09	07 29	07 49	08 09	08 29	08 49	09 09	09 29	09 49	10 09	10 29	10 49	11 09		20 29	20 49	21 09
Hatch End	d		05 22	05 52	06 22	06 52	07 12	07 32	07 52	08 12	08 32	08 52	09 12	09 32	09 52	10 12	10 32	10 52	11 12		20 32	20 52	21 12
Headstone Lane	d		05 24	05 54	06 24	06 54	07 14	07 34	07 54	08 14	08 34	08 54	09 14	09 34	09 54	10 14	10 34	10 54	11 14	and at the same minutes past each hour until	20 34	20 54	21 14
Harrow & Wealdstone	66 d		05 27	05 57	06 27	06 57	07 17	07 37	07 57	08 17	08 37	08 57	09 17	09 37	09 57	10 17	10 37	10 57	11 17		20 37	20 57	21 17
Kenton	d		05 29	05 59	06 29	06 59	07 19	07 39	07 59	08 19	08 39	08 59	09 19	09 39	09 59	10 19	10 39	10 59	11 19		20 39	20 59	21 19
South Kenton	d		05 31	06 01	06 31	07 01	07 21	07 41	08 01	08 21	08 41	09 01	09 21	09 41	10 01	10 21	10 41	11 01	11 21		20 41	21 01	21 21
North Wembley	d		05 33	06 03	06 33	07 03	07 23	07 43	08 03	08 23	08 43	09 03	09 23	09 43	10 03	10 23	10 43	11 03	11 23		20 43	21 03	21 23
Wembley Central	66 d		05 35	06 05	06 35	07 05	07 25	07 45	08 05	08 25	08 45	09 05	09 25	09 45	10 05	10 25	10 45	11 05	11 25		20 45	21 05	21 25
Stonebridge Park	d		05 38	06 08	06 38	07 08	07 28	07 48	08 08	08 28	08 48	09 08	09 28	09 48	10 08	10 28	10 48	11 08	11 28		20 48	21 08	21 28
Harlesden	d		05 40	06 10	06 40	07 10	07 30	07 50	08 10	08 30	08 50	09 10	09 30	09 50	10 10	10 30	10 50	11 10	11 30		20 50	21 10	21 30
Willesden Jn Low Level	d		05 42	06 12	06 42	07 12	07 32	07 52	08 12	08 32	08 52	09 12	09 32	09 52	10 12	10 32	10 52	11 12	11 32		20 52	21 12	21 32
Kensal Green	d		05 45	06 15	06 45	07 15	07 35	07 55	08 15	08 35	08 55	09 15	09 35	09 55	10 15	10 35	10 55	11 15	11 35		20 55	21 15	21 35
Queen's Park (London)	⊖ d		05 47	06 17	06 47	07 17	07 37	07 57	08 17	08 37	08 57	09 17	09 37	09 57	10 17	10 37	10 57	11 17	11 37		20 57	21 17	21 37
Kilburn High Road	d		05 49	06 19	06 49	07 19	07 39	07 59	08 19	08 39	08 59	09 19	09 39	09 59	10 19	10 39	10 59	11 19	11 39		20 59	21 19	21 39
South Hampstead	d	00 01	05 51	06 21	06 51	07 21	07 41	08 01	08 21	08 41	09 01	09 21	09 41	10 01	10 21	10 41	11 01	11 21	11 41		21 01	21 21	21 41
London Euston 15	⊖66 a	00 10	06 00	06 30	06 59	07 30	07 49	08 13	08 30	08 50	09 12	09 30	09 50	10 13	10 30	10 49	11 13	11 30	11 50		21 13	21 30	21 50

Stations Harrow & Wealdstone to Queen's Park inclusive are also served by London Underground Bakerloo Line Services

Table 60R

Saturdays

14 December to 17 May

Watford Junction - Harrow & Wealdstone, Queen's Park and London

Network Diagram - see first Page of Table 59

			LO	LO	LO	LO	LO	LO
Watford Junction	66 d		21 21	21 41	22 01	22 21	22 51	23 21
Watford High Street	d		21 24	21 44	22 04	22 24	22 54	23 24
Bushey	66 d		21 26	21 46	22 06	22 26	22 56	23 26
Carpenders Park	d		21 29	21 49	22 09	22 29	22 59	23 29
Hatch End	d		21 32	21 52	22 12	22 32	23 02	23 32
Headstone Lane	d		21 34	21 54	22 14	22 34	23 04	23 34
Harrow & Wealdstone	66 d		21 37	21 57	22 17	22 37	23 07	23 37
Kenton	d		21 39	21 59	22 19	22 39	23 09	23 39
South Kenton	d		21 41	22 01	22 21	22 41	23 11	23 41
North Wembley	d		21 43	22 03	22 23	22 43	23 13	23 43
Wembley Central	66 d		21 45	22 05	22 25	22 45	23 15	23 45
Stonebridge Park	d		21 48	22 08	22 28	22 48	23 18	23 48
Harlesden	d		21 50	22 10	22 30	22 50	23 20	23 50
Willesden Jn Low Level	d		21 52	22 12	22 32	22 52	23 22	23 52
Kensal Green	d		21 55	22 15	22 35	22 55	23 25	23 55
Queen's Park (London)	⊖ d		21 57	22 17	22 37	22 57	23 27	23 57
Kilburn High Road	d		21 59	22 19	22 39	22 59	23 29	23 59
South Hampstead	d		22 01	22 21	22 41	23 01	23 31	00 01
London Euston 15	⊖66 a		22 10	22 30	22 53	23 11	23 38	00 10

Sundays

8 December to 11 May

		LO A	LO	LO	LO	LO	LO	LO	LO	LO		LO	LO	LO	LO	LO	LO	LO		LO	LO	LO		LO
Watford Junction	66 d		06 51	07 21	07 51	08 21	08 51	09 21	09 41	10 01		10 21	10 41	11 01	11 21	11 41	12 01	12 21		17 41	18 01	18 21		18 41
Watford High Street	d		06 54	07 24	07 54	08 24	08 54	09 24	09 44	10 04		10 24	10 44	11 04	11 24	11 44	12 04	12 24		17 44	18 04	18 24		18 44
Bushey	66 d		06 56	07 26	07 56	08 26	08 56	09 26	09 46	10 06		10 26	10 46	11 06	11 26	11 46	12 06	12 26		17 46	18 06	18 26		18 46
Carpenders Park	d		06 59	07 29	07 59	08 29	08 59	09 29	09 49	10 09		10 29	10 49	11 09	11 29	11 49	12 09	12 29		17 49	18 09	18 29		18 49
Hatch End	d		07 02	07 32	08 02	08 32	09 02	09 32	09 52	10 12		10 32	10 52	11 12	11 32	11 52	12 12	12 32		17 52	18 12	18 32		18 52
Headstone Lane	d		07 04	07 34	08 04	08 34	09 04	09 34	09 54	10 14		10 34	10 54	11 14	11 34	11 54	12 14	12 34	and at	17 54	18 14	18 34		18 54
Harrow & Wealdstone	66 d		07 07	07 37	08 07	08 37	09 07	09 37	09 57	10 17		10 37	10 57	11 17	11 37	11 57	12 17	12 37	the same	17 57	18 17	18 37		18 57
Kenton	d		07 09	07 39	08 09	08 39	09 09	09 39	09 59	10 19		10 39	10 59	11 19	11 39	11 59	12 19	12 39	minutes	17 59	18 19	18 39		18 59
South Kenton	d		07 11	07 41	08 11	08 41	09 11	09 41	10 01	10 21		10 41	11 01	11 21	11 41	12 01	12 21	12 41	past	18 01	18 21	18 41		19 01
North Wembley	d		07 13	07 43	08 13	08 43	09 13	09 43	10 03	10 23		10 43	11 03	11 23	11 43	12 03	12 23	12 43	each	18 03	18 23	18 43		19 03
Wembley Central	66 d		07 15	07 45	08 15	08 45	09 15	09 45	10 05	10 25		10 45	11 05	11 25	11 45	12 05	12 25	12 45	hour until	18 05	18 25	18 45		19 05
Stonebridge Park	d		07 18	07 48	08 18	08 48	09 18	09 48	10 08	10 28		10 48	11 08	11 28	11 48	12 08	12 28	12 48		18 08	18 28	18 48		19 08
Harlesden	d		07 20	07 50	08 20	08 50	09 20	09 50	10 10	10 30		10 50	11 10	11 30	11 50	12 10	12 30	12 50		18 10	18 30	18 50		19 10
Willesden Jn Low Level	d		07 22	07 52	08 22	08 52	09 22	09 52	10 12	10 32		10 52	11 12	11 32	11 52	12 12	12 32	12 52		18 12	18 32	18 52		19 12
Kensal Green	d		07 25	07 55	08 25	08 55	09 25	09 55	10 15	10 35		10 55	11 15	11 35	11 55	12 15	12 35	12 55		18 15	18 35	18 55		19 15
Queen's Park (London)	⊖ d		07 27	07 57	08 27	08 57	09 27	09 57	10 17	10 37		10 57	11 17	11 37	11 57	12 17	12 37	12 57		18 17	18 37	18 57		19 17
Kilburn High Road	d		07 29	07 59	08 29	08 59	09 29	09 59	10 19	10 39		10 59	11 19	11 39	11 59	12 19	12 39	12 59		18 19	18 39	18 59		19 19
South Hampstead	d	00 01	07 31	08 01	08 31	09 01	09 31	10 01	10 21	10 41		11 01	11 21	11 41	12 01	12 21	12 41	13 01		18 21	18 41	19 01		19 21
London Euston 15	⊖66 a	00 10	07 40	08 10	08 40	09 10	09 40	10 10	10 30	10 50		11 13	11 30	11 50	12 11	12 31	12 50	13 10		18 31	18 50	19 10		19 31

		LO	LO	LO	LO	LO	LO	LO	LO		LO	LO	LO	LO	LO
Watford Junction	66 d	19 01	19 21	19 41	20 01	20 21	20 41	21 01	21 21		21 41	22 01	22 21	22 51	23 21
Watford High Street	d	19 04	19 24	19 44	20 04	20 24	20 44	21 04	21 24		21 44	22 04	22 24	22 54	23 24
Bushey	66 d	19 06	19 26	19 46	20 06	20 26	20 46	21 06	21 26		21 46	22 06	22 26	22 56	23 26
Carpenders Park	d	19 09	19 29	19 49	20 09	20 29	20 49	21 09	21 29		21 49	22 09	22 29	22 59	23 29
Hatch End	d	19 12	19 32	19 52	20 12	20 32	20 52	21 12	21 32		21 52	22 12	22 32	23 02	23 32
Headstone Lane	d	19 14	19 34	19 54	20 14	20 34	20 54	21 14	21 34		21 54	22 14	22 34	23 04	23 34
Harrow & Wealdstone	66 d	19 17	19 37	19 57	20 17	20 37	20 57	21 17	21 37		21 57	22 17	22 37	23 07	23 37
Kenton	d	19 19	19 39	19 59	20 19	20 39	20 59	21 19	21 39		21 59	22 19	22 39	23 09	23 39
South Kenton	d	19 21	19 41	20 01	20 21	20 41	21 01	21 21	21 41		22 01	22 21	22 41	23 11	23 41
North Wembley	d	19 23	19 43	20 03	20 23	20 43	21 03	21 23	21 43		22 03	22 23	22 43	23 13	23 43
Wembley Central	66 d	19 25	19 45	20 05	20 25	20 45	21 05	21 25	21 45		22 05	22 25	22 45	23 15	23 45
Stonebridge Park	d	19 28	19 48	20 08	20 28	20 48	21 08	21 28	21 48		22 08	22 28	22 48	23 18	23 48
Harlesden	d	19 30	19 50	20 10	20 30	20 50	21 10	21 30	21 50		22 10	22 30	22 50	23 20	23 50
Willesden Jn Low Level	d	19 32	19 52	20 12	20 32	20 52	21 12	21 32	21 52		22 12	22 32	22 52	23 22	23 52
Kensal Green	d	19 35	19 55	20 15	20 35	20 55	21 15	21 35	21 55		22 15	22 35	22 55	23 25	23 55
Queen's Park (London)	⊖ d	19 37	19 57	20 17	20 37	20 57	21 17	21 37	21 57		22 17	22 37	22 57	23 27	23 57
Kilburn High Road	d	19 39	19 59	20 19	20 39	20 59	21 19	21 39	21 59		22 19	22 39	22 59	23 29	23 59
South Hampstead	d	19 41	20 01	20 21	20 41	21 01	21 21	21 41	22 01		22 21	22 41	23 01	23 31	00 01
London Euston 15	⊖66 a	19 49	20 10	20 31	20 49	21 13	21 30	21 51	22 10		22 30	22 49	23 10	23 40	00 10

A not 8 December

Stations Harrow & Wealdstone to Queen's Park inclusive are also served by London Underground Bakerloo Line Services

Table 61

Watford Junction - St. Albans Abbey

Mondays to Fridays

9 December to 16 May

Network Diagram - see first Page of Table 59

Miles			LM 1	LM 1	LM 1	LM 1	LM 1	LM 1	LM 1	LM 1	LM 1	LM 1	LM 1	LM 1	LM 1	LM 1	LM 1	LM 1	LM 1	LM 1	LM 1	LM 1	LM 1
0	**Watford Junction**	d	05 57	06 39	07 21	08 04	08 54	09 39	10 24	11 09	11 54	12 46	13 31	14 16	15 01	15 46	16 31	17 21	18 10	18 55	19 38	20 31	21 31
0¾	Watford North	d	05 59	06 41	07 23	08 06	08 56	09 41	10 26	11 11	11 56	12 48	13 33	14 18	15 03	15 48	16 33	17 23	18 12	18 57	19 40	20 33	21 33
1¾	Garston (Hertfordshire)	d	06 02	06 44	07 26	08 09	08 59	09 44	10 29	11 14	11 59	12 51	13 36	14 21	15 06	15 51	16 36	17 26	18 15	19 00	19 43	20 36	21 36
3¼	Bricket Wood	d	06 05	06 47	07 29	08 12	09 02	09 47	10 32	11 17	12 02	12 54	13 39	14 24	15 09	15 54	16 39	17 29	18 18	19 03	19 46	20 39	21 39
4½	How Wood	d	06 07	06 49	07 31	08 14	09 04	09 49	10 34	11 19	12 04	12 56	13 41	14 26	15 11	15 56	16 41	17 31	18 20	19 05	19 48	20 41	21 41
5	Park Street	d	06 09	06 51	07 33	08 16	09 06	09 51	10 36	11 21	12 06	12 58	13 43	14 28	15 13	15 58	16 43	17 33	18 22	19 07	19 50	20 43	21 43
6½	**St Albans Abbey**	a	06 13	06 55	07 37	08 20	09 10	09 55	10 40	11 25	12 10	13 02	13 47	14 32	15 17	16 02	16 47	17 37	18 26	19 11	19 54	20 47	21 47

Saturdays

14 December to 17 May

		LM 1	LM 1	LM 1	LM 1	LM 1	LM 1	LM 1	LM 1	LM 1	LM 1	LM 1	LM 1	LM 1	LM 1	LM 1	LM 1	LM 1	LM 1	LM 1	LM 1	LM 1
Watford Junction	d	06 01	06 45	07 31	08 15	09 01	09 46	10 31	11 14	11 56	12 46	13 31	14 16	15 01	15 46	16 31	17 16	18 01	18 46	19 31	20 31	21 31
Watford North	d	06 03	06 47	07 33	08 17	09 03	09 48	10 33	11 16	11 58	12 48	13 33	14 18	15 03	15 48	16 33	17 18	18 03	18 48	19 33	20 33	21 33
Garston (Hertfordshire)	d	06 06	06 50	07 36	08 20	09 06	09 51	10 36	11 19	12 01	12 51	13 36	14 21	15 06	15 51	16 36	17 21	18 06	18 51	19 36	20 36	21 36
Bricket Wood	d	06 09	06 53	07 39	08 23	09 09	09 54	10 39	11 22	12 04	12 54	13 39	14 24	15 09	15 54	16 39	17 24	18 09	18 54	19 39	20 39	21 39
How Wood	d	06 11	06 55	07 41	08 25	09 11	09 56	10 41	11 24	12 06	12 56	13 41	14 26	15 11	15 56	16 41	17 26	18 11	18 56	19 41	20 41	21 41
Park Street	d	06 13	06 57	07 43	08 27	09 13	09 58	10 43	11 26	12 08	12 58	13 43	14 28	15 13	15 58	16 43	17 28	18 13	18 58	19 43	20 43	21 43
St Albans Abbey	a	06 17	07 01	07 47	08 31	09 17	10 02	10 47	11 30	12 12	13 02	13 47	14 32	15 17	16 02	16 47	17 32	18 17	19 02	19 47	20 47	21 47

Sundays

8 December to 11 May

		LM 1	LM 1	LM 1	LM 1	LM 1		LM 1	LM 1	LM 1
Watford Junction	d	08 07	09 07	10 20	11 20	12 07	and	20 07	21 02	22 04
Watford North	d	08 09	09 09	10 22	11 22	12 09	hourly	20 09	21 04	22 06
Garston (Hertfordshire)	d	08 12	09 12	10 25	11 25	12 12	until	20 12	21 07	22 09
Bricket Wood	d	08 15	09 15	10 28	11 28	12 15		20 15	21 10	22 12
How Wood	d	08 17	09 17	10 30	11 30	12 17		20 17	21 12	22 14
Park Street	d	08 19	09 19	10 32	11 32	12 19		20 19	21 14	22 16
St Albans Abbey	a	08 23	09 23	10 36	11 36	12 23		20 23	21 18	22 20

For connections from London Euston please see Table 66

Table 61R

Mondays to Fridays

9 December to 16 May

St. Albans Abbey- Watford Junction

Network Diagram - refer to first Page of Table 39

Miles			LM	LM	LM	LM	LM	LM	LM	LM	LM	LM
			1	1	1	1	1	1	1	1	1	1
0	**St Albans Abbey**	d	06 18	07 00	07 42	08 25	09 15	10 00	10 45	11 30	12 15	13 07
1½	Park Street	d	06 21	07 03	07 45	08 28	09 18	10 03	10 48	11 33	12 18	13 10
2¼	How Wood	d	06 23	07 05	07 47	08 30	09 20	10 05	10 50	11 35	12 20	13 12
3	Bricket Wood	d	06 26	07 08	07 50	08 33	09 23	10 08	10 53	11 38	12 23	13 15
4¾	Garston (Hertfordshire)	d	06 29	07 11	07 53	08 36	09 26	10 11	10 56	11 41	12 26	13 18
5½	Watford North	d	06 31	07 13	07 55	08 38	09 28	10 13	10 58	11 43	12 28	13 20
6½	**Watford Junction**	a	06 34	07 16	07 58	08 41	09 31	10 16	11 01	11 46	12 31	13 23

Miles			LM	LM	LM	LM	LM	LM	LM	LM	LM	LM	LM
			1	1	1	1	1	1	1	1	1	1	1
0	**St Albans Abbey**	d	13 52	14 37	15 22	16 07	16 52	17 42	18 32	19 16	20 00	20 52	21 52
1½	Park Street	d	13 55	14 40	15 25	16 10	16 55	17 45	18 35	19 19	20 03	20 55	21 55
2¼	How Wood	d	13 57	14 42	15 27	16 12	16 57	17 47	18 37	19 21	20 05	20 57	21 57
3	Bricket Wood	d	14 00	14 45	15 30	16 15	17 00	17 50	18 40	19 24	20 08	21 00	22 00
4¾	Garston (Hertfordshire)	d	14 03	14 48	15 33	16 18	17 03	17 53	18 43	19 27	20 11	21 03	22 03
5½	Watford North	d	14 05	14 50	15 35	16 20	17 05	17 55	18 45	19 29	20 13	21 05	22 05
6½	**Watford Junction**	a	14 08	14 53	15 38	16 23	17 08	17 58	18 48	19 32	20 16	21 08	22 08

Saturdays

14 December to 17 May

		LM	LM	LM	LM	LM	LM	LM	LM	LM	LM
		1	1	1	1	1	1	1	1	1	1
St Albans Abbey	d	06 22	07 06	07 52	08 36	09 22	10 07	10 52	11 35	12 17	13 07
Park Street	d	06 25	07 09	07 55	08 39	09 25	10 10	10 55	11 38	12 20	13 10
How Wood	d	06 27	07 11	07 57	08 41	09 27	10 12	10 57	11 40	12 22	13 12
Bricket Wood	d	06 30	07 14	08 00	08 44	09 30	10 15	11 00	11 43	12 25	13 15
Garston (Hertfordshire)	d	06 33	07 17	08 03	08 47	09 33	10 18	11 03	11 46	12 28	13 18
Watford North	d	06 35	07 19	08 05	08 49	09 35	10 20	11 05	11 48	12 30	13 20
Watford Junction	a	06 38	07 22	08 08	08 52	09 38	10 23	11 08	11 51	12 33	13 23

		LM	LM	LM	LM	LM	LM	LM	LM	LM	LM	LM
		1	1	1	1	1	1	1	1	1	1	1
St Albans Abbey	d	13 52	14 37	15 22	16 07	16 52	17 37	18 22	19 07	19 52	20 52	21 52
Park Street	d	13 55	14 40	15 25	16 10	16 55	17 40	18 25	19 10	19 55	20 55	21 55
How Wood	d	13 57	14 42	15 27	16 12	16 57	17 42	18 27	19 12	19 57	20 57	21 57
Bricket Wood	d	14 00	14 45	15 30	16 15	17 00	17 45	18 30	19 15	20 00	21 00	22 00
Garston (Hertfordshire)	d	14 03	14 48	15 33	16 18	17 03	17 48	18 33	19 18	20 03	21 03	22 03
Watford North	d	14 05	14 50	15 35	16 20	17 05	17 50	18 35	19 20	20 05	21 05	22 05
Watford Junction	a	14 08	14 53	15 38	16 23	17 08	17 53	18 38	19 23	20 08	21 08	22 08

Sundays

8 December to 11 May

		LM	LM	LM	LM	LM		LM	LM	LM
		1	1	1	1	1		1	1	1
St Albans Abbey	d	08 28	09 28	10 42	11 42	12 28	and hourly until	20 28	21 23	22 25
Park Street	d	08 31	09 31	10 45	11 45	12 31		20 31	21 26	22 28
How Wood	d	08 33	09 33	10 47	11 47	12 33		20 33	21 28	22 30
Bricket Wood	d	08 36	09 36	10 50	11 50	12 36		20 36	21 31	22 33
Garston (Hertfordshire)	d	08 39	09 39	10 53	11 53	12 39		20 39	21 34	22 36
Watford North	d	08 41	09 41	10 55	11 55	12 41		20 41	21 36	22 38
Watford Junction	a	08 44	09 44	10 58	11 58	12 44		20 44	21 39	22 41

For connections to London Euston please see Table 66

Table 62

Gospel Oak - Barking

Mondays to Fridays

9 December to 16 May

Network Diagram - see first Page of Table 59

Miles			LO MX A	LO	LO	LO	LO	LO	LO	LO	LO	LO	LO	LO	LO	LO	LO	LO	LO	LO	LO	LO	LO
0	**Gospel Oak**	d		06 20	06 35	06 50	07 05	07 20	07 35	07 50	08 05	08 20	08 35	08 50	09 05	09 20	09 35	09 50	10 05	10 20	10 35	10 50	11 05
1¼	Upper Holloway	d		06 24	06 39	06 54	07 09	07 24	07 39	07 54	08 09	08 24	08 39	08 54	09 09	09 24	09 39	09 54	10 09	10 24	10 39	10 54	11 09
2	Crouch Hill	d		06 27	06 42	06 57	07 12	07 27	07 42	07 57	08 12	08 27	08 42	08 57	09 12	09 27	09 42	09 57	10 12	10 27	10 42	10 57	11 12
3	Harringay Green Lanes	d		06 30	06 45	07 00	07 15	07 30	07 45	08 00	08 15	08 30	08 45	09 00	09 15	09 30	09 45	10 00	10 15	10 30	10 45	11 00	11 15
4¼	South Tottenham	d		06 33	06 48	07 03	07 18	07 33	07 48	08 03	08 18	08 33	08 48	09 03	09 18	09 33	09 48	10 03	10 18	10 33	10 48	11 03	11 18
5¾	Blackhorse Road ⊖	d		06 36	06 51	07 06	07 21	07 36	07 51	08 06	08 21	08 36	08 51	09 06	09 21	09 36	09 51	10 06	10 21	10 36	10 51	11 06	11 21
6½	Walthamstow Queen's Road	d		06 39	06 54	07 09	07 24	07 39	07 54	08 09	08 24	08 39	08 54	09 09	09 24	09 39	09 54	10 09	10 24	10 39	10 54	11 09	11 24
7½	Leyton Midland Road	d		06 42	06 57	07 12	07 27	07 42	07 57	08 12	08 27	08 42	08 57	09 12	09 27	09 42	09 57	10 12	10 27	10 42	10 57	11 12	11 27
8¼	Leytonstone High Road	d		06 45	07 00	07 15	07 30	07 45	08 00	08 15	08 30	08 45	09 00	09 15	09 30	09 45	10 00	10 15	10 30	10 45	11 00	11 15	11 30
9½	Wanstead Park	d	00 03	06 48	07 03	07 18	07 33	07 48	08 03	08 18	08 33	08 48	09 03	09 18	09 33	09 48	10 03	10 18	10 33	10 48	11 03	11 18	11 33
10½	Woodgrange Park	d	00 05	06 50	07 05	07 20	07 35	07 50	08 05	08 20	08 35	08 50	09 05	09 20	09 35	09 50	10 05	10 20	10 35	10 50	11 05	11 20	11 35
12¼	**Barking** ⊖	a	00 10	06 58	07 10	07 25	07 40	07 55	08 10	08 25	08 40	08 55	09 10	09 25	09 40	09 55	10 10	10 25	10 40	10 56	11 11	11 25	11 40

		LO	LO	LO	LO	LO	LO		LO	LO	LO	LO	LO	LO	LO	LO	LO	LO	LO	LO	LO	LO
Gospel Oak	d	11 20	11 35	11 50	12 05	12 20	12 35	and at the same minutes past each hour until	17 50	18 05	18 20	18 35	18 50	19 05	19 20	19 35	19 50	20 05	20 20	20 35	20 50	21 05
Upper Holloway	d	11 24	11 39	11 54	12 09	12 24	12 39		17 54	18 09	18 24	18 39	18 54	19 09	19 24	19 39	19 54	20 09	20 24	20 39	20 54	21 09
Crouch Hill	d	11 27	11 42	11 57	12 12	12 27	12 42		17 57	18 12	18 27	18 42	18 57	19 12	19 27	19 42	19 57	20 12	20 27	20 42	20 57	21 12
Harringay Green Lanes	d	11 30	11 45	12 00	12 15	12 30	12 45		18 00	18 15	18 30	18 45	19 00	19 15	19 30	19 45	20 00	20 15	20 30	20 45	21 00	21 15
South Tottenham	d	11 33	11 48	12 03	12 18	12 33	12 48		18 03	18 18	18 33	18 48	19 03	19 18	19 33	19 48	20 03	20 18	20 33	20 48	21 03	21 18
Blackhorse Road ⊖	d	11 36	11 51	12 06	12 21	12 36	12 51		18 06	18 21	18 36	18 51	19 06	19 21	19 36	19 51	20 06	20 21	20 36	20 51	21 06	21 21
Walthamstow Queen's Road	d	11 39	11 54	12 09	12 24	12 39	12 54		18 09	18 24	18 39	18 54	19 09	19 24	19 39	19 54	20 09	20 24	20 39	20 54	21 09	21 24
Leyton Midland Road	d	11 42	11 57	12 12	12 27	12 42	12 57		18 12	18 27	18 42	18 57	19 12	19 27	19 42	19 57	20 12	20 27	20 42	20 57	21 12	21 27
Leytonstone High Road	d	11 45	12 00	12 15	12 30	12 45	13 00		18 15	18 30	18 45	19 00	19 15	19 30	19 45	20 00	20 15	20 30	20 45	21 00	21 15	21 30
Wanstead Park	d	11 48	12 03	12 18	12 33	12 48	13 03		18 18	18 33	18 48	19 03	19 18	19 33	19 48	20 03	20 18	20 33	20 48	21 03	21 18	21 33
Woodgrange Park	d	11 50	12 05	12 20	12 35	12 50	13 05		18 20	18 35	18 50	19 05	19 20	19 35	19 50	20 05	20 20	20 35	20 50	21 05	21 20	21 35
Barking ⊖	a	11 55	12 12	12 25	12 40	12 55	13 10		18 25	18 40	18 55	19 10	19 26	19 40	19 57	20 10	20 25	20 41	20 55	21 10	21 25	21 41

		LO	LO	LO	LO	LO	LO	LO
Gospel Oak	d	21 20	21 35	21 50	22 05	22 35	23 05	23 35
Upper Holloway	d	21 24	21 39	21 54	22 09	22 39	23 09	23 39
Crouch Hill	d	21 27	21 42	21 57	22 12	22 42	23 12	23 42
Harringay Green Lanes	d	21 30	21 45	22 00	22 15	22 45	23 15	23 45
South Tottenham	d	21 33	21 48	22 03	22 18	22 48	23 18	23 48
Blackhorse Road ⊖	d	21 36	21 51	22 06	22 21	22 51	23 21	23 51
Walthamstow Queen's Road	d	21 39	21 54	22 09	22 24	22 54	23 24	23 54
Leyton Midland Road	d	21 42	21 57	22 12	22 27	22 57	23 27	23 57
Leytonstone High Road	d	21 45	22 00	22 15	22 30	23 00	23 30	23 59
Wanstead Park	d	21 48	22 03	22 18	22 33	23 03	23 33	00 03
Woodgrange Park	d	21 50	22 05	22 20	22 35	23 05	23 35	00 05
Barking ⊖	a	21 55	22 10	22 25	22 42	23 10	23 40	00 10

Saturdays

14 December to 17 May

		LO A	LO	LO	LO	LO	LO	LO	LO	LO	LO	LO	LO	LO	LO	LO	LO	LO	LO	LO	LO	LO
Gospel Oak	d		06 20	06 35	06 50	07 05	07 20	07 35	07 50	08 05	08 20	08 35	08 50	09 05	09 20	09 35	09 50	10 05	10 20	10 35	10 50	11 05
Upper Holloway	d		06 24	06 39	06 54	07 09	07 24	07 39	07 54	08 09	08 24	08 39	08 54	09 09	09 24	09 39	09 54	10 09	10 24	10 39	10 54	11 09
Crouch Hill	d		06 27	06 42	06 57	07 12	07 27	07 42	07 57	08 12	08 27	08 42	08 57	09 12	09 27	09 42	09 57	10 12	10 27	10 42	10 57	11 12
Harringay Green Lanes	d		06 30	06 45	07 00	07 15	07 30	07 45	08 00	08 15	08 30	08 45	09 00	09 15	09 30	09 45	10 00	10 15	10 30	10 45	11 00	11 15
South Tottenham	d		06 33	06 48	07 03	07 18	07 33	07 48	08 03	08 18	08 33	08 48	09 03	09 18	09 33	09 48	10 03	10 18	10 33	10 48	11 03	11 18
Blackhorse Road ⊖	d		06 36	06 51	07 06	07 21	07 36	07 51	08 06	08 21	08 36	08 51	09 06	09 21	09 36	09 51	10 06	10 21	10 36	10 51	11 06	11 21
Walthamstow Queen's Road	d		06 39	06 54	07 09	07 24	07 39	07 54	08 09	08 24	08 39	08 54	09 09	09 24	09 39	09 54	10 09	10 24	10 39	10 54	11 09	11 24
Leyton Midland Road	d		06 42	06 57	07 12	07 27	07 42	07 57	08 12	08 27	08 42	08 57	09 12	09 27	09 42	09 57	10 12	10 27	10 42	10 57	11 12	11 27
Leytonstone High Road	d		06 45	07 00	07 15	07 30	07 45	08 00	08 15	08 30	08 45	09 00	09 15	09 30	09 45	10 00	10 15	10 30	10 45	11 00	11 15	11 30
Wanstead Park	d	00 03	06 48	07 03	07 18	07 33	07 48	08 03	08 18	08 33	08 48	09 03	09 18	09 33	09 48	10 03	10 18	10 33	10 48	11 03	11 18	11 33
Woodgrange Park	d	00 05	06 50	07 05	07 20	07 35	07 50	08 05	08 20	08 35	08 50	09 05	09 20	09 35	09 50	10 05	10 20	10 35	10 50	11 05	11 20	11 35
Barking ⊖	a	00 10	06 54	07 09	07 24	07 39	07 54	08 09	08 24	08 40	08 54	09 09	09 24	09 39	09 54	10 09	10 24	10 39	10 54	11 09	11 24	11 42

		LO	LO	LO	LO		LO	LO	LO	LO	LO	LO	LO	LO	LO	LO	LO	LO	LO	LO	LO	LO
Gospel Oak	d	11 20	11 35	11 50	12 05	and at the same minutes past each hour until	14 20	14 35	14 50	15 05	15 20	15 35	15 50	16 05	16 20	16 35	16 50	17 05	17 20	17 35	17 50	18 05
Upper Holloway	d	11 24	11 39	11 54	12 09		14 24	14 39	14 54	15 09	15 24	15 39	15 54	16 09	16 24	16 39	16 54	17 09	17 24	17 39	17 54	18 09
Crouch Hill	d	11 27	11 42	11 57	12 12		14 27	14 42	14 57	15 12	15 27	15 42	15 57	16 12	16 27	16 42	16 57	17 12	17 27	17 42	17 57	18 12
Harringay Green Lanes	d	11 30	11 45	12 00	12 15		14 30	14 45	15 00	15 15	15 30	15 45	16 00	16 15	16 30	16 45	17 00	17 15	17 30	17 45	18 00	18 15
South Tottenham	d	11 33	11 48	12 03	12 18		14 33	14 48	15 03	15 18	15 33	15 48	16 03	16 18	16 33	16 48	17 03	17 18	17 33	17 48	18 03	18 18
Blackhorse Road ⊖	d	11 36	11 51	12 06	12 21		14 36	14 51	15 06	15 21	15 36	15 51	16 06	16 21	16 36	16 51	17 06	17 21	17 36	17 51	18 06	18 21
Walthamstow Queen's Road	d	11 39	11 54	12 09	12 24		14 39	14 54	15 09	15 24	15 39	15 54	16 09	16 24	16 39	16 54	17 09	17 24	17 39	17 54	18 09	18 24
Leyton Midland Road	d	11 42	11 57	12 12	12 27		14 42	14 57	15 12	15 27	15 42	15 57	16 12	16 27	16 42	16 57	17 12	17 27	17 42	17 57	18 12	18 27
Leytonstone High Road	d	11 45	12 00	12 15	12 30		14 45	15 00	15 15	15 30	15 45	16 00	16 15	16 30	16 45	17 00	17 15	17 30	17 45	18 00	18 15	18 30
Wanstead Park	d	11 48	12 03	12 18	12 33		14 48	15 03	15 18	15 33	15 48	16 03	16 18	16 33	16 48	17 03	17 18	17 33	17 48	18 03	18 18	18 33
Woodgrange Park	d	11 50	12 05	12 20	12 35		14 50	15 05	15 20	15 35	15 50	16 05	16 20	16 35	16 50	17 05	17 20	17 35	17 50	18 05	18 20	18 35
Barking ⊖	a	11 54	12 09	12 24	12 39		14 54	15 09	15 24	15 39	15 54	16 09	16 24	16 42	16 57	17 12	17 27	17 42	17 54	18 09	18 24	18 39

		LO	LO	LO	LO	LO	LO	LO	LO	LO	LO	LO	LO	LO	LO	LO	LO	LO	LO	LO
Gospel Oak	d	18 20	18 35	18 50	19 05	19 20	19 35	19 50	20 05	20 20	20 35	20 50	21 05	21 20	21 35	21 50	22 05	22 35	23 05	23 35
Upper Holloway	d	18 24	18 39	18 54	19 09	19 24	19 39	19 54	20 09	20 24	20 39	20 54	21 09	21 24	21 39	21 54	22 09	22 39	23 09	23 39
Crouch Hill	d	18 27	18 42	18 57	19 12	19 27	19 42	19 57	20 12	20 27	20 42	20 57	21 12	21 27	21 42	21 57	22 12	22 42	23 12	23 42
Harringay Green Lanes	d	18 30	18 45	19 00	19 15	19 30	19 45	20 00	20 15	20 30	20 45	21 00	21 15	21 30	21 45	22 00	22 15	22 45	23 15	23 45
South Tottenham	d	18 33	18 48	19 03	19 18	19 33	19 48	20 03	20 18	20 33	20 48	21 03	21 18	21 33	21 48	22 03	22 18	22 48	23 18	23 48
Blackhorse Road ⊖	d	18 36	18 51	19 06	19 21	19 36	19 51	20 06	20 21	20 36	20 51	21 06	21 21	21 36	21 51	22 06	22 21	22 51	23 21	23 51
Walthamstow Queen's Road	d	18 39	18 54	19 09	19 24	19 39	19 54	20 09	20 24	20 39	20 54	21 09	21 24	21 39	21 54	22 09	22 24	22 54	23 24	23 54
Leyton Midland Road	d	18 42	18 57	19 12	19 27	19 42	19 57	20 12	20 27	20 42	20 57	21 12	21 27	21 42	21 57	22 12	22 27	22 57	23 27	23 57
Leytonstone High Road	d	18 45	19 00	19 15	19 30	19 45	20 00	20 15	20 30	20 45	21 00	21 15	21 30	21 45	22 00	22 15	22 30	23 00	23 30	23 59
Wanstead Park	d	18 48	19 03	19 18	19 33	19 48	20 03	20 18	20 33	20 48	21 03	21 18	21 33	21 48	22 03	22 18	22 33	23 03	23 33	00 03
Woodgrange Park	d	18 50	19 05	19 20	19 35	19 50	20 05	20 20	20 35	20 50	21 05	21 20	21 35	21 50	22 05	22 20	22 35	23 05	23 35	00 05
Barking ⊖	a	18 54	19 09	19 24	19 39	19 54	20 12	20 24	20 39	20 54	21 09	21 24	21 39	21 54	22 09	22 24	22 39	23 09	23 39	00 12

A From Gospel Oak

Table 62

Sundays

8 December to 11 May

Gospel Oak - Barking

Network Diagram - see first Page of Table 59

		LO A	LO	LO	LO	LO		LO	LO	LO	LO		LO	LO	LO	LO
Gospel Oak	d		08 55	09 10	09 25	09 40	and at the same minutes past each hour until	20 55	21 10	21 25	21 40		21 55	22 10	22 40	23 10
Upper Holloway	d		08 59	09 14	09 29	09 44		20 59	21 14	21 29	21 44		21 59	22 14	22 44	23 14
Crouch Hill	d		09 02	09 17	09 32	09 47		21 02	21 17	21 32	21 47		22 02	22 17	22 47	23 17
Harringay Green Lanes	d		09 05	09 20	09 35	09 50		21 05	21 20	21 35	21 50		22 05	22 20	22 50	23 20
South Tottenham	d		09 08	09 23	09 38	09 53		21 08	21 23	21 38	21 53		22 08	22 23	22 53	23 23
Blackhorse Road ⊖	d		09 11	09 26	09 41	09 56		21 11	21 26	21 41	21 56		22 11	22 26	22 56	23 26
Walthamstow Queen's Road	d		09 14	09 29	09 44	09 59		21 14	21 29	21 44	21 59		22 14	22 29	22 59	23 29
Leyton Midland Road	d		09 17	09 32	09 47	10 02		21 17	21 32	21 47	22 02		22 17	22 32	23 02	23 32
Leytonstone High Road	d		09 20	09 35	09 50	10 05		21 20	21 35	21 50	22 05		22 20	22 35	23 05	23 35
Wanstead Park	d	00 03	09 23	09 38	09 53	10 08		21 23	21 38	21 53	22 08		22 23	22 38	23 08	23 38
Woodgrange Park	d	00 05	09 25	09 40	09 55	10 10		21 25	21 40	21 55	22 10		22 25	22 40	23 10	23 40
Barking ⊖	a	00 12	09 29	09 44	09 59	10 14		21 29	21 44	21 59	22 14		22 29	22 44	23 14	23 44

A not 8 December. From Gospel Oak

Table 62R

Barking - Gospel Oak

Mondays to Fridays

9 December to 16 May

Network Diagram - see first Page of Table 59

Miles			LO MO A	LO MX A	LO	LO	LO	LO B		LO	LO	LO	LO	LO C	LO	LO	LO	LO		LO	LO	LO	LO	LO	LO
0	**Barking** ⊖	d			06 18	06 32	06 46	06 52		07 03	07 18	07 33	07 48		08 03	08 18	08 33	08 48		09 03	09 18	09 33	09 48	10 03	10 18
1¾	Woodgrange Park	d			06 21	06 36	06 51	06 57		07 06	07 21	07 36	07 51	07 59	08 06	08 21	08 36	08 51		09 06	09 21	09 36	09 51	10 06	10 21
2¾	Wanstead Park	d			06 24	06 39	06 54	07 00		07 09	07 24	07 39	07 54	08 02	08 09	08 24	08 39	08 54		09 09	09 24	09 39	09 54	10 09	10 24
4	Leytonstone High Road	d			06 28	06 43	06 58	07 04		07 13	07 28	07 43	07 58	08 05	08 13	08 28	08 43	08 58		09 13	09 28	09 43	09 58	10 13	10 28
4¾	Leyton Midland Road	d		00 01	06 30	06 45	07 00	07 07		07 15	07 30	07 45	08 00	08 08	08 15	08 30	08 45	09 00		09 15	09 30	09 45	10 00	10 15	10 30
5¾	Walthamstow Queen's Road	d		00 03	06 33	06 48	07 03	07 11		07 18	07 33	07 48	08 03	08 11	08 18	08 33	08 48	09 03		09 18	09 33	09 48	10 03	10 18	10 33
6½	Blackhorse Road ⊖	d		00 06	06 36	06 51	07 06	07 14		07 26	07 36	07 51	08 06	08 14	08 21	08 36	08 51	09 06		09 21	09 36	09 51	10 06	10 21	10 36
8¼	South Tottenham	d		00 10	06 40	06 55	07 10	07a18		07 30	07 40	07 55	08 10	08 18	08 25	08 40	08 55	09 10		09 25	09 40	09 55	10 10	10 25	10 40
9¼	Harringay Green Lanes	d	00 03	00 13	06 43	06 58	07 13			07 33	07 43	07 58	08 13	08 21	08 28	08 43	08 58	09 13		09 28	09 43	09 58	10 13	10 28	10 43
10¼	Crouch Hill	d	00 06	00 16	06 46	07 01	07 16			07 36	07 46	08 01	08 16	08 24	08 31	08 46	09 01	09 16		09 31	09 46	10 01	10 20	10 31	10 46
11	Upper Holloway	d	00 08	00 18	06 48	07 03	07 18			07 38	07 48	08 03	08 18	08a27	08 33	08 48	09 03	09 18		09 33	09 48	10 03	10 23	10 33	10 48
12¼	**Gospel Oak**	a	00 13	00 25	06 56	07 08	07 23			07 43	07 55	08 08	08 24		08 38	08 53	09 08	09 23		09 38	09 53	10 08	10 29	10 40	10 53

		LO	LO	LO		LO	LO	LO	LO	LO		LO	LO	LO	LO		LO	LO	LO	LO	LO	LO	LO	LO
Barking ⊖	d	10 33	10 48	11 03		11 18	11 33	11 48	12 03	12 18	and at the same minutes past each hour until	17 33	17 48	18 03	18 18		18 33	18 48	19 03	19 18	19 33	19 48	20 03	20 18
Woodgrange Park	d	10 36	10 51	11 06		11 21	11 36	11 51	12 06	12 21		17 36	17 51	18 06	18 21		18 36	18 51	19 06	19 21	19 36	19 51	20 06	20 21
Wanstead Park	d	10 39	10 54	11 09		11 24	11 39	11 54	12 09	12 24		17 39	17 54	18 09	18 24		18 39	18 54	19 09	19 24	19 39	19 54	20 09	20 24
Leytonstone High Road	d	10 43	10 58	11 13		11 28	11 43	11 58	12 13	12 28		17 43	17 58	18 13	18 28		18 43	18 58	19 13	19 28	19 43	19 58	20 13	20 28
Leyton Midland Road	d	10 45	11 00	11 15		11 30	11 45	12 00	12 15	12 30		17 45	18 00	18 15	18 30		18 45	19 00	19 15	19 30	19 45	20 00	20 15	20 30
Walthamstow Queen's Road	d	10 48	11 03	11 18		11 33	11 48	12 03	12 18	12 33		17 48	18 03	18 18	18 33		18 48	19 03	19 18	19 33	19 48	20 03	20 18	20 33
Blackhorse Road ⊖	d	10 51	11 06	11 21		11 36	11 51	12 06	12 21	12 36		17 51	18 06	18 21	18 36		18 51	19 06	19 21	19 36	19 51	20 06	20 21	20 36
South Tottenham	d	10 55	11 10	11 25		11 40	11 55	12 10	12 25	12 40		17 55	18 10	18 25	18 40		18 55	19 10	19 25	19 40	19 55	20 10	20 25	20 40
Harringay Green Lanes	d	10 58	11 13	11 28		11 43	11 58	12 13	12 28	12 43		17 58	18 13	18 28	18 43		18 58	19 13	19 28	19 43	19 58	20 13	20 28	20 43
Crouch Hill	d	11 01	11 16	11 31		11 46	12 01	12 16	12 31	12 46		18 01	18 16	18 31	18 46		19 01	19 16	19 31	19 46	20 01	20 16	20 31	20 46
Upper Holloway	d	11 03	11 18	11 33		11 48	12 03	12 18	12 33	12 48		18 03	18 18	18 33	18 48		19 03	19 18	19 33	19 48	20 03	20 18	20 33	20 48
Gospel Oak	a	11 08	11 23	11 41		11 55	12 08	12 23	12 38	12 53		18 08	18 23	18 38	18 53		19 08	19 27	19 38	19 53	20 10	20 23	20 38	20 53

		LO		LO	LO	LO	LO	LO	LO	LO	LO	LO		LO
Barking ⊖	d	20 33		20 48	21 02	21 18	21 33	21 48	22 03	22 18	22 48	23 18		23 48
Woodgrange Park	d	20 36		20 51	21 05	21 21	21 36	21 51	22 06	22 21	22 51	23 21		23 51
Wanstead Park	d	20 39		20 54	21 08	21 24	21 39	21 54	22 09	22 24	22 54	23 24		23 54
Leytonstone High Road	d	20 43		20 58	21 12	21 28	21 43	21 58	22 13	22 28	22 58	23 28		23 58
Leyton Midland Road	d	20 45		21 00	21 14	21 30	21 45	22 00	22 15	22 30	23 00	23 30		00 01
Walthamstow Queen's Road	d	20 48		21 03	21 17	21 33	21 48	22 03	22 18	22 33	23 03	23 33		00 03
Blackhorse Road ⊖	d	20 51		21 06	21 20	21 36	21 51	22 06	22 21	22 36	23 06	23 36		00 06
South Tottenham	d	20 55		21 10	21 24	21 40	21 55	22 10	22 25	22 40	23 10	23 40		00 10
Harringay Green Lanes	d	20 58		21 13	21 27	21 43	21 58	22 13	22 28	22 43	23 13	23 43		00 13
Crouch Hill	d	21 01		21 16	21 30	21 46	22 01	22 16	22 31	22 46	23 16	23 46		00 16
Upper Holloway	d	21 03		21 18	21 32	21 48	22 03	22 18	22 33	22 48	23 18	23 48		00 18
Gospel Oak	a	21 10		21 23	21 38	21 53	22 11	22 25	22 40	22 53	23 24	23 53		00 25

Saturdays

14 December to 17 May

		LO A	LO	LO	LO	LO	LO	LO	LO	LO		LO	LO	LO	LO	LO	LO	LO	LO	LO		LO
Barking ⊖	d		06 18	06 33	06 48	07 03	07 18	07 33	07 48	08 03		08 18	08 33	08 48	09 03	09 18	09 33	09 48	10 03	10 18		10 33
Woodgrange Park	d		06 21	06 36	06 51	07 06	07 21	07 36	07 51	08 06		08 21	08 36	08 51	09 06	09 21	09 36	09 51	10 06	10 21		10 36
Wanstead Park	d		06 24	06 39	06 54	07 09	07 24	07 39	07 54	08 09		08 24	08 39	08 54	09 09	09 24	09 39	09 54	10 09	10 24		10 39
Leytonstone High Road	d		06 28	06 43	06 58	07 13	07 28	07 43	07 58	08 13		08 28	08 43	08 58	09 13	09 28	09 43	09 58	10 13	10 28		10 43
Leyton Midland Road	d	00 01	06 30	06 45	07 00	07 15	07 30	07 45	08 00	08 15		08 30	08 45	09 00	09 15	09 30	09 45	10 00	10 15	10 30		10 45
Walthamstow Queen's Road	d	00 03	06 33	06 48	07 03	07 18	07 33	07 48	08 03	08 18		08 33	08 48	09 03	09 18	09 33	09 48	10 03	10 18	10 33		10 48
Blackhorse Road ⊖	d	00 06	06 36	06 51	07 06	07 21	07 36	07 51	08 06	08 21		08 36	08 51	09 06	09 21	09 36	09 51	10 06	10 21	10 36		10 51
South Tottenham	d	00 10	06 40	06 55	07 10	07 25	07 40	07 55	08 10	08 25		08 40	08 55	09 10	09 25	09 40	09 55	10 10	10 25	10 40		10 55
Harringay Green Lanes	d	00 13	06 43	06 58	07 13	07 28	07 43	07 58	08 13	08 28		08 43	08 58	09 13	09 28	09 43	09 58	10 13	10 28	10 43		10 58
Crouch Hill	d	00 16	06 46	07 01	07 16	07 31	07 46	08 01	08 16	08 31		08 46	09 01	09 16	09 31	09 46	10 01	10 16	10 31	10 46		11 01
Upper Holloway	d	00 18	06 48	07 03	07 18	07 33	07 48	08 03	08 18	08 33		08 48	09 03	09 18	09 33	09 48	10 03	10 18	10 33	10 48		11 03
Gospel Oak	a	00 25	06 53	07 08	07 23	07 38	07 53	08 09	08 23	08 38		08 53	09 08	09 23	09 38	09 53	10 08	10 23	10 38	10 53		11 11

		LO	LO	LO	LO		LO	LO	LO	LO		LO	LO	LO	LO	LO	LO	LO	LO	LO		LO	LO	LO
Barking ⊖	d	10 48	11 03	11 18	11 33	and at the same minutes past each hour until	17 48	18 03	18 18	18 33		18 48	19 03	19 18	19 33	19 48	20 03	20 18	20 33	20 48		21 03	21 18	21 33
Woodgrange Park	d	10 51	11 06	11 21	11 36		17 51	18 06	18 21	18 36		18 51	19 06	19 21	19 36	19 51	20 06	20 21	20 36	20 51		21 06	21 21	21 36
Wanstead Park	d	10 54	11 09	11 24	11 39		17 54	18 09	18 24	18 39		18 54	19 09	19 24	19 39	19 54	20 09	20 24	20 39	20 54		21 09	21 24	21 39
Leytonstone High Road	d	10 58	11 13	11 28	11 43		17 58	18 13	18 28	18 43		18 58	19 13	19 28	19 43	19 58	20 13	20 28	20 43	20 58		21 13	21 28	21 43
Leyton Midland Road	d	11 00	11 15	11 30	11 45		18 00	18 15	18 30	18 45		19 00	19 15	19 30	19 45	20 00	20 15	20 30	20 45	21 00		21 15	21 30	21 45
Walthamstow Queen's Road	d	11 03	11 18	11 33	11 48		18 03	18 18	18 33	18 48		19 03	19 18	19 33	19 48	20 03	20 18	20 33	20 48	21 03		21 18	21 33	21 48
Blackhorse Road ⊖	d	11 06	11 21	11 36	11 51		18 06	18 21	18 36	18 51		19 06	19 21	19 36	19 51	20 06	20 21	20 36	20 51	21 06		21 21	21 36	21 51
South Tottenham	d	11 10	11 25	11 40	11 55		18 10	18 25	18 40	18 55		19 10	19 25	19 40	19 55	20 10	20 25	20 40	20 55	21 10		21 25	21 40	21 55
Harringay Green Lanes	d	11 13	11 28	11 43	11 58		18 13	18 28	18 43	18 58		19 13	19 28	19 43	19 58	20 13	20 28	20 43	20 58	21 13		21 28	21 43	21 58
Crouch Hill	d	11 16	11 31	11 46	12 01		18 16	18 31	18 46	19 01		19 16	19 31	19 46	20 01	20 16	20 31	20 46	21 01	21 16		21 31	21 46	22 01
Upper Holloway	d	11 18	11 33	11 48	12 03		18 18	18 33	18 48	19 03		19 18	19 33	19 48	20 03	20 18	20 33	20 48	21 03	21 18		21 33	21 48	22 03
Gospel Oak	a	11 23	11 38	11 53	12 08		18 23	18 38	18 53	19 08		19 23	19 41	19 53	20 08	20 23	20 38	20 53	21 08	21 23		21 38	21 53	22 08

		LO	LO	LO	LO	LO	LO
Barking ⊖	d	21 48	22 03	22 18	22 48	23 18	23 48
Woodgrange Park	d	21 51	22 06	22 21	22 51	23 21	23 51
Wanstead Park	d	21 54	22 09	22 24	22 54	23 24	23 54
Leytonstone High Road	d	21 58	22 13	22 28	22 58	23 28	23 58
Leyton Midland Road	d	22 00	22 15	22 30	23 00	23 30	00 01
Walthamstow Queen's Road	d	22 03	22 18	22 33	23 03	23 33	00 03
Blackhorse Road ⊖	d	22 06	22 21	22 36	23 06	23 36	00 06
South Tottenham	d	22 10	22 25	22 40	23 10	23 40	00 10
Harringay Green Lanes	d	22 13	22 28	22 43	23 13	23 43	00 13
Crouch Hill	d	22 16	22 31	22 46	23 16	23 46	00 16
Upper Holloway	d	22 18	22 33	22 48	23 18	23 48	00 18
Gospel Oak	a	22 24	22 38	22 54	23 24	23 54	00 25

A From Barking

B not from 25 December until 1 January

C To Willesden Jn Low Level

Table 62R

Sundays

8 December to 11 May

Barking - Gospel Oak

Network Diagram - see first Page of Table 59

		LO A	LO	LO	LO	LO		LO	LO	LO	LO	LO	LO	LO	LO	LO
Barking ⊖	d		08 53	09 08	09 23	09 38	and at the same minutes past each hour until	20 53	21 08	21 23	21 38	21 53	22 08	22 38	23 08	23 38
Woodgrange Park	d		08 56	09 11	09 26	09 41		20 56	21 11	21 26	21 41	21 56	22 11	22 41	23 11	23 41
Wanstead Park	d		08 59	09 14	09 29	09 44		20 59	21 14	21 29	21 44	21 59	22 14	22 44	23 14	23 44
Leytonstone High Road	d		09 03	09 18	09 33	09 48		21 03	21 18	21 33	21 48	22 03	22 18	22 48	23 18	23 48
Leyton Midland Road	d	00 01	09 05	09 20	09 35	09 50		21 05	21 20	21 35	21 50	22 05	22 20	22 50	23 20	23 50
Walthamstow Queen's Road	d	00 03	09 08	09 23	09 38	09 53		21 08	21 23	21 38	21 53	22 08	22 23	22 53	23 23	23 53
Blackhorse Road ⊖	d	00 06	09 11	09 26	09 41	09 56		21 11	21 26	21 41	21 56	22 11	22 26	22 56	23 26	23 56
South Tottenham	d	00 10	09 15	09 30	09 45	10 00		21 15	21 30	21 45	22 00	22 15	22 30	23 00	23 30	23 59
Harringay Green Lanes	d	00 13	09 18	09 33	09 48	10 03		21 18	21 33	21 48	22 03	22 18	22 33	23 03	23 33	00 03
Crouch Hill	d	00 16	09 21	09 36	09 51	10 06		21 21	21 36	21 51	22 06	22 21	22 36	23 06	23 36	00 06
Upper Holloway	d	00 18	09 23	09 38	09 53	10 08		21 23	21 38	21 53	22 08	22 23	22 38	23 08	23 38	00 08
Gospel Oak	a	00 25	09 28	09 43	09 58	10 13		21 28	21 43	21 58	22 13	22 28	22 43	23 13	23 43	00 13

A not 8 December. From Barking

Table 64

Mondays to Saturdays

9 December to 17 May

Bletchley - Bedford

Network Diagram - see first Page of Table 59

Miles			LM SX	LM SO	LM SO	LM SX	LM	LM SX	LM SO	LM	LM	LM	LM	LM	LM	LM SO	LM SX	LM	LM	LM	LM	LM
0	**Bletchley**	d	05 31	05 41	06 37	06 41	07 32	08 22	08 39	10 05	11 05	12 01	13 01	14 01	15 01	15 47	15 49	16 47	17 31	18 31	20 01	21 01
1	Fenny Stratford	d	05 35	05 44	06 40	06 44	07 35	08 25	08 42	10 08	11 08	12 04	13 04	14 04	15 04	15 50	15 52	16 50	17 34	18 34	20 04	21 04
2	Bow Brickhill	d	05 38	05 48	06 44	06 48	07 39	08 29	08 46	10 12	11 12	12 08	13 08	14 08	15 08	15 54	15 56	16 54	17 38	18 38	20 08	21 08
4	Woburn Sands	d	05 42	05 52	06 48	06 52	07 43	08 33	08 50	10 16	11 16	12 12	13 12	14 12	15 12	15 58	16 00	16 58	17 42	18 42	20 12	21 12
5	Aspley Guise	d	05 45	05 55	06 51	06 55	07 46	08 36	08 53	10 19	11 19	12 15	13 15	14 15	15 15	16 01	16 03	17 01	17 45	18 45	20 15	21 15
6¾	Ridgmont	d	05 49	05 58	06 54	06 58	07 49	08 39	08 56	10 22	11 22	12 18	13 18	14 18	15 18	16 04	16 07	17 04	17 48	18 48	20 18	21 18
8½	Lidlington	d	05 53	06 02	06 58	07 02	07 53	08 43	09 00	10 26	11 26	12 22	13 22	14 22	15 22	16 08	16 11	17 08	17 52	18 52	20 22	21 22
10	Millbrook (Bedfordshire)	d	05 56	06 05	07 01	07 05	07 56	08 46	09 03	10 29	11 29	12 25	13 25	14 25	15 25	16 11	16 14	17 11	17 55	18 55	20 25	21 25
11¼	Stewartby	d	05 59	06 09	07 05	07 09	08 00	08 50	09 07	10 33	11 33	12 29	13 29	14 29	15 29	16 15	16 17	17 15	17 59	18 59	20 29	21 29
13	Kempston Hardwick	d	06 03	06 12	07 08	07 12	08 03	08 53	09 10	10 36	11 36	12 32	13 32	14 32	15 32	16 18	16 21	17 18	18 02	19 02	20 32	21 32
16	Bedford St Johns	d	06 09	06 19	07 15	07 20	08 10	09 00	09 17	10 43	11 43	12 39	13 39	14 39	15 39	16 25	16 27	17 25	18 09	19 09	20 39	21 39
16¾	**Bedford** 7	a	06 15	06 25	07 21	07 25	08 16	09 06	09 23	10 49	11 49	12 45	13 45	14 45	15 45	16 31	16 33	17 31	18 15	19 15	20 45	21 45

No Sunday Service

For connections from Milton Keynes Central please see Table 66

Table 64R

Mondays to Saturdays

9 December to 17 May

Bedford - Bletchley

Network Diagram - see first Page of Table 59

Miles			LM SX	LM SO	LM	LM	LM	LM	LM	LM	LM	LM	LM	LM SO	LM SX	LM	LM	LM	LM	LM
0	**Bedford** 7	d	06 25	06 31	07 31	08 31	09 33	10 55	11 55	12 55	13 55	14 55	15 55	16 37	16 39	17 37	18 21	19 21	20 55	21 56
0¾	Bedford St Johns	d	06 28	06 34	07 34	08 34	09 36	10 58	11 58	12 58	13 58	14 58	15 58	16 40	16 42	17 40	18 24	19 24	20 58	21 59
3¾	Kempston Hardwick	d	06 35	06 41	07 41	08 41	09 43	11 05	12 05	13 05	14 05	15 05	16 05	16 47	16 49	17 47	18 31	19 31	21 05	22 06
5½	Stewartby	d	06 38	06 44	07 44	08 44	09 46	11 08	12 08	13 08	14 08	15 08	16 08	16 50	16 52	17 50	18 34	19 34	21 08	22 09
6¾	Millbrook (Bedfordshire)	d	06 42	06 48	07 48	08 48	09 50	11 12	12 12	13 12	14 12	15 12	16 12	16 54	16 56	17 54	18 38	19 38	21 12	22 13
8¼	Lidlington	d	06 45	06 51	07 51	08 51	09 53	11 15	12 15	13 15	14 15	15 15	16 15	16 57	16 59	17 57	18 41	19 41	21 15	22 16
10	Ridgmont	d	06 50	06 56	07 56	08 56	09 58	11 20	12 20	13 20	14 20	15 20	16 20	17 02	17 04	18 02	18 46	19 46	21 20	22 21
11¾	Aspley Guise	d	06 53	06 59	07 59	08 59	10 01	11 23	12 23	13 23	14 23	15 23	16 23	17 05	17 07	18 05	18 49	19 49	21 23	22 24
12¾	Woburn Sands	d	06 56	07 02	08 02	09 02	10 04	11 26	12 26	13 26	14 26	15 26	16 26	17 08	17 10	18 08	18 52	19 52	21 26	22 27
14¾	Bow Brickhill	d	07 00	07 06	08 06	09 06	10 08	11 30	12 30	13 30	14 30	15 30	16 30	17 12	17 14	18 12	18 56	19 56	21 30	22 31
15¾	Fenny Stratford	d	07 03	07 09	08 09	09 09	10 11	11 33	12 33	13 33	14 33	15 33	16 33	17 15	17 17	18 15	18 59	19 59	21 33	22 34
16¾	**Bletchley**	a	07 08	07 14	08 14	09 14	10 16	11 38	12 38	13 38	14 38	15 38	16 38	17 20	17 22	18 20	19 04	20 04	21 38	22 39

No Sunday Service

For connections to Milton Keynes Central please see Table 66

Route Diagram for Table 65

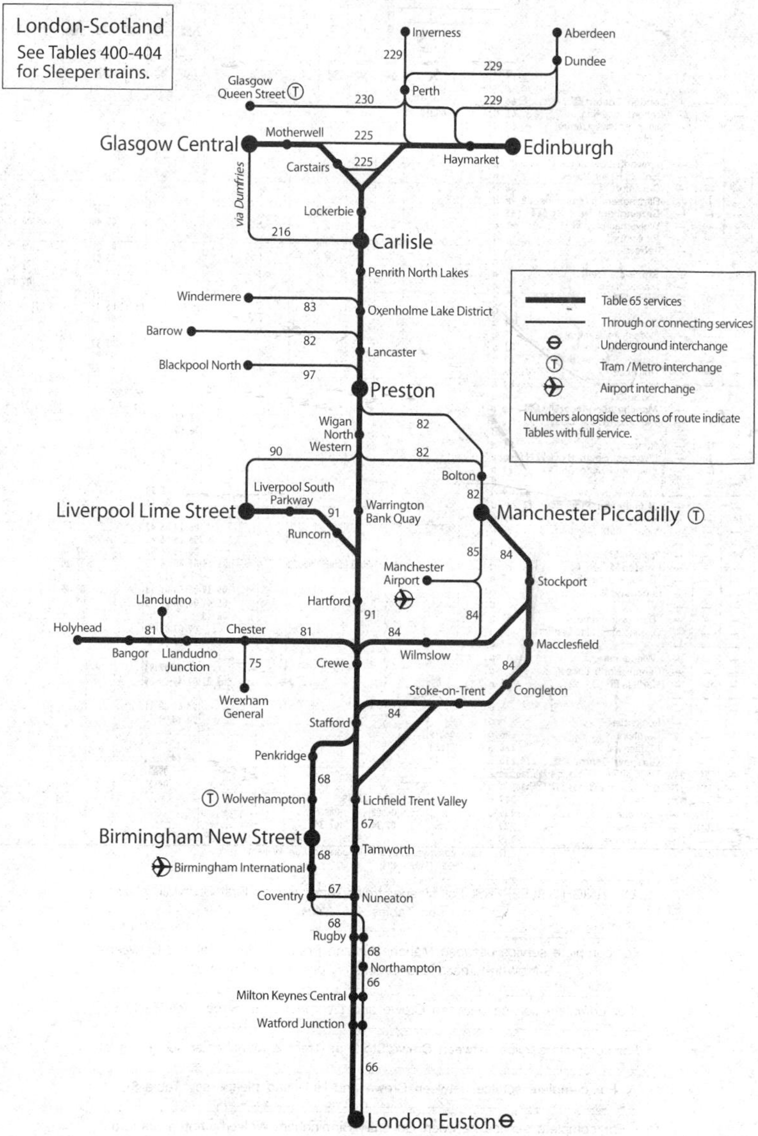

TOCs operating on this network - Virgin Trains (VT), Northern (NT), London Midlands (LM), First TransPennine Express (TP), Cross Country (XC), ScotRail (SR)

Table 65

Mondays to Fridays

9 December to 16 May

London and West Midlands - North West England and Scotland

Route Diagram - refer to first Page of Table 65

Miles	Miles	Miles	Miles	Miles			SR		SR	SR	SR	SR	NT	VT	TP	VT	VT	TP	AW	XC	LM
							MX		MO	MO	MX	MX									
							R		R	R	R	R									
									D	D	D	D		◇1	◇1	◇1	◇1	◇1		◇1	1
									A	A											
							🛏		🛏	🛏	🛏	🛏									
							✕		✕	✕	✕	✕		⊠	🛒		⊠				
0	—	—	—	—	**London Euston** 15 ⊖66	d															
17½	—	—	—	—	Watford Junction 66	d	00u10														
49¾	—	—	—	—	Milton Keynes Central 66	d															
82½	0	—	—	—	Rugby 66	d															
97	—	—	—	—	Nuneaton	d															
110	—	—	—	—	Tamworth Low Level	d															
116¼	—	0	—	—	Lichfield Trent Valley	d															
—	11½	—	—	—	Coventry 68	d															
—	22	—	—	—	Birmingham International 68 ✈	d															
—	30½	—	—	—	**Birmingham New St.** 12 68	d											05 30			05 57	06 01
—	43¼	—	—	—	Wolverhampton 7 ⇌	d											05 48			06 16	06 20
—	53¼	—	—	—	Penkridge	d															06 29
133½	59½	—	—	—	**Stafford**	a											06 01			06 29	06 35
—	—	—	—	—		d											06 02			06 30	06 36
—	75¾	30¼	—	—	**Stoke-on-Trent**	a														06 50	
—	95¼	50¼	—	—	Macclesfield	a														07 11	
158	—	—	0	—	**Crewe** 10	a											06 21				06 57
—	—	—	—	—		d								05 57		06 11	06 23		06 27		06 58
—	—	—	—	—	Chester 81	a											06 43				
—	—	—	—	—	Wrexham General 75	a															
—	—	—	—	—	Llandudno Junction 81	a											07 32				
—	—	—	—	—	Bangor (Gwynedd) 81	a											07 49				
—	—	—	—	—	Holyhead 81 ⛴	a											08 23				
—	—	—	—	—	Wilmslow 84	a										06 26			06 44		
—	107¼	62¼	—	—	Stockport 84	a										06 36			06 55	07 25	
—	113	68	—	—	**Manchester Piccadilly** 10 ⇌	a										06 48			07 07	07 34	
182	—	—	—	—	Warrington Bank Quay	a								06 13							
—	—	—	—	—		d								06 15							
—	—	—	22½	—	Runcorn 91	a															07 23
—	—	—	30	—	Liverpool South Pkwy 7 91 ✈	a															07 32
—	—	—	35½	—	**Liverpool Lime St.** 10 91	a															07 44
—	—	—	—	—		d															
—	—	—	—	—	Manchester Airport 82 ✈	d									05 58			06 18			
—	—	—	—	—	**Manchester Picc.** 10 82 ⇌	d									06 13			06 33			
—	—	79¼	—	—	Bolton 82	d												06 52			
193¾	—	—	—	—	Wigan North Western 90	a								06 24	06 42						
—	—	—	—	—		d								06 26	06 42						
209	—	99¼	—	—	**Preston** 8 90	a								06 38	06 56			07 18			
—	—	—	—	—	**Preston** 8 90	d			00u33	00u33	00u52	00u52	05 19	06 40	06 57			07 20			
—	—	—	—	—	Blackpool North 97	a															
230	—	—	—	—	**Lancaster** 6	a							05 39	06 54	07 13			07 35			
—	—	—	—	—		d							05 41	06 54	07 13			07 36			
—	—	—	—	—	Barrow-in-Furness 82	a							06 48					08 39			
249	—	—	—	—	Oxenholme Lake District	a								07 07	07 27						
—	—	—	—	—		d								07 09	07 28						
—	—	—	—	—	Windermere 83	a															
281¼	—	—	—	—	Penrith North Lakes	d								07 34	07 53						
299	—	—	—	—	**Carlisle** 8 216	a	05s10						09 21	07 49	08 09						
—	—	—	—	—																	
—	—	—	—	—		d								07 51	08 11						
324¼	—	—	0	—	Lockerbie	d								08 10	08 30						
372½	—	—	—	0	Carstairs 226	a	06s19														
388½	—	—	—	—	Motherwell 226	a	06s54														
401¼	—	—	—	—	**Glasgow Central** 15 216,226	a	07 18							09 14							
—	—	—	75	26¼	Haymarket 225,226,228,230,242	a									09s31						
—	—	—	76¼	27½	**Edinburgh** 10 225,226,228,230,242	a		07 22							09 37						
—	—	—	—	97¼	Perth 229	a				05s39		05s39									
—	—	—	135½	—	Dundee 229	a			06s08		06s08										
—	—	—	206¾	—	Aberdeen 229	a			07 34		07 34										
—	—	—	—	215¼	Inverness 229	a				08 36		08 36									

A until 10 February

D also conveys through sleepers to Fort William arr 0955. (Table 404)

OVERNIGHT SLEEPERS. For sleeper trains, operated by First ScotRail, please see Tables 400 - 404.

For complete service between Manchester and Preston, Blackpool and between Barrow-in-furness and Lancaster, please see Table 82.

For complete service between Crewe and Liverpool Lime Street, see Table 91

For complete service between Crewe/Stoke-on-Trent & Manchester see Table 84

For complete service between Crewe and Holyhead please see Table 81.

For complete service between Coventry-Birmingham-Wolverhampton-Stafford please see Table 68

For complete service between Windermere and Oxenholme Lake District, please see Table 83

Table 65

Mondays to Fridays

9 December to 16 May

London and West Midlands - North West England and Scotland

Route Diagram - refer to first Page of Table 65

		VT	XC	LM	VT	TP	VT	VT	LM	XC	LM	TP	NT	VT	LM	XC	TP	LM	XC	LM	LM	VT
		◇1	◇1	1	◇1	◇1	◇1	◇1	1	◇1	1	◇1		◇1	1	◇1	◇1	1	◇1	1	1	◇1
																	A					
		⊠	🛒		⊠	🛒	⊠	⊠		🛒		🛒		⊠		🛒	🛒		🛒			⊠
London Euston 15 ⊖66	d				05 27		05 39	06 16													06 24	06 36
Watford Junction 66	d				05u47		06u02														06 42	06u51
Milton Keynes Central 66	d				06 12		06 22	06 46													07 22	
Rugby 66	d			06 05			06 45								06 59						08 03	
Nuneaton	d			06 17	06 41										07 12						08 16	
Tamworth Low Level	d			06 32											07 29						08 30	
Lichfield Trent Valley	d			06 38											07 35						08 36	
Coventry 68	d																		07 27			
Birmingham International 68 ✈	d								06 17									07 17	07 38			
Birmingham New St. 12 68	d	06 15	06 22						06 36	06 57	07 01			07 15		07 31		07 36	07 57	08 01		
Wolverhampton 7 ⛴	d	06 37	06 41						06 52	07 15	07 20			07 37		07 49		07 54	08 15	08 20		
Penkridge	d								07 02		07 30							08 04		08 29		
Stafford	a		06 53	06 55	07 05				07 08	07 29	07 36				07 53	08 00		08 10	08 29	08 35	08 53	
	d		06 55	06 58	07 05				07 09	07 30	07 36				07 54	08 01		08 10	08 30	08 36	08 54	
Stoke-on-Trent	a		07 13	07 21				07 45							08 15	08 19			08 54		09 15	
Macclesfield	a		07 30					08 01								08 36			09 11			
Crewe 10	a	07 07		07 44	07 23		07 30		07 32	07 50	07 56			08 06	08 38			08 30		08 56	09 38	08 10
	d	07 09			07 25		07 32		07 34	07 52	07 58			08 09				08 32		08 58		08 11
Chester 81	a																	→		→		
Wrexham General 75	a																					
Llandudno Junction 81	a																					
Bangor (Gwynedd) 81	a																					
Holyhead 81 ⛴	a																					
Wilmslow 84	a									08 08												08 27
Stockport 84	a		07 45					08 16		08 20						08 50			09 27			08 36
Manchester Piccadilly 10 ⛴	a		07 59					08 28		08 34						08 59			09 38			08 49
Warrington Bank Quay	a	07 26					07 49							08 26								
	d	07 27					07 49							08 27								
Runcorn 91	a				07 42				08 00		08 22											
Liverpool South Pkwy 7 91 ✈	a								08 09		08 31											
Liverpool Lime St. 10 91	a				08 01				08 21		08 44											
	d																					
Manchester Airport 82 ✈	d					07 00						07 25										
Manchester Picc. 10 82 ⛴	d					07 15						07 45										
Bolton 82	d											07 59					08 52					
Wigan North Western 90	a	07 37				07 43	08 00							08 37								
	d	07 38				07 43	08 00							08 38								
Preston 8 90	a	07 51				07 57	08 13					08 22		08 51			09 22					
Preston 8 90	d	07 53				07 58	08 15					08 24		08 53			09 25					
Blackpool North 97	a																					
Lancaster 6	a	08 07				08 14	08 29					08 39		09 08			09 40					
	d	08 08				08 16	08 30					08 40	08 48	09 08			09 41					
Barrow-in-Furness 82	a												09 55				10 44					
Oxenholme Lake District	a	08 20					08 43					08 54										
	d	08 21					08 43					08 54										
Windermere 83	a																					
Penrith North Lakes	d					08 54						09 20		09 46								
Carlisle 8 216	a	08 59				09 10	09 21					09 36	12 38	10 00								
	d	09 01				09 11	09 22					09 36		10 02								
Lockerbie	d											09 56										
Carstairs 226	a																					
Motherwell 226	a																					
Glasgow Central 15 216,226	a					10 31	10 36							11 16								
Haymarket 225,226,228,230,242	a	10 16										10s57										
Edinburgh 10 225,226,228,230,242	a	10 21										11 04										
Perth 229	a																					
Dundee 229	a																					
Aberdeen 229	a																					
Inverness 229	a																					

A 🛒 to Preston

OVERNIGHT SLEEPERS. For sleeper trains, operated by First ScotRail, please see Tables 400 - 404.

For complete service between Manchester and Preston, Blackpool and between Barrow-in-furness and Lancaster, please see Table 82.

For complete service between Crewe and Liverpool Lime Street, see Table 91

For complete service between Crewe/Stoke-on-Trent & Manchester see Table 84

For complete service between Crewe and Holyhead please see Table 81.

For complete service between Coventry-Birmingham-Wolverhampton-Stafford please see Table 68

For complete service between Windermere and Oxenholme Lake District, please see Table 83

Table 65

Mondays to Fridays

9 December to 16 May

London and West Midlands - North West England and Scotland

Route Diagram - refer to first Page of Table 65

Station			LM	VT	VT	VT	VT	LM		VT	VT	VT	VT	XC	LM	XC	TP	LM		VT	LM	VT	VT	VT	LM	VT
			1	◇**1**	◇**1**	◇**1**	◇**1**	**1**		◇**1**	◇**1**	◇**1**	◇**1**	◇**1**	**1**	◇**1**	◇**1**	**1**		◇**1**	**1**	◇**1**	◇**1**	◇**1**	**1**	◇**1**
				⊠	⊠	⊠	⊠			⊠	⊠	⊠	⊠	⊤		⊤	⊤			⊠		⊠	⊠	⊠		⊠
London Euston **15**	⊖66	d		06 43	06 55	07 07	07 10			07 20	07 30		07 35							07 43	07 46	08 00	08 07	08 10		08 20
Watford Junction	66	d																								
Milton Keynes Central	66	d		07 13	07 27		07 41			07 50			08 06							08 13	08 19		08 38	08 43		08 50
Rugby	66	d																			08 42					
Nuneaton		d																			08 54					
Tamworth Low Level		d																			09 09					
Lichfield Trent Valley		d																			09 17					
Coventry	68	d		07 42												08 27				08 42						
Birmingham International	68 ✈	d		07 53												08 38				08 53						
Birmingham New St. **12**	68	d		08 15										08 31	08 36	08 57		09 01		09 15						
Wolverhampton **7**	🚌	d		08 37										08 49	08 54	09 15		09 20		09 37						
Penkridge		d													09 04											
Stafford		a				08 22								09 00	09 10	09 29		09 34			09 36		09 27			
		d				08 23								09 01	09 10	09 30		09 35			09 39		09 27			
Stoke-on-Trent		a			08 24					08 48				09 19		09 54					10 01	09 24				09 48
Macclesfield		a	←		08 41			←				←				10 11						09 41			←	
Crewe **10**		a	08 30	09 07		08 41	08 47	08 56				09 07	09 10		09 30			09 56		10 07	10 29			09 51	09 56	
		d	08 32	09 09		08 43	08 49	08 58				09 09	09 11		09 32			09 58		10 09				09 53	09 58	
Chester	81	a		→			09 13											→		→				10 13		
Wrexham General	75	a																								
Llandudno Junction	81	a																						11 04		
Bangor (Gwynedd)	81	a																						11 27		
Holyhead	81 ⛴	a																								
Wilmslow	84	a											09 27													
Stockport	84	a			08 55					09 16			09 36	09 49		10 27						09 55				10 16
Manchester Piccadilly **10**	🚌	a			09 07					09 28			09 49	09 59		10 38						10 07				10 28
Warrington Bank Quay		a									09 14	09 26														
		d									09 14	09 27														
Runcorn	91	a	08 50			09 02		09 21							09 50								10 00		10 24	
Liverpool South Pkwy **7**	91 ✈	a	08 59					09 30							09 59										10 33	
Liverpool Lime St. **10**	91	a	09 10			09 23		09 42							10 10								10 21		10 44	
		d																								
Manchester Airport	82 ✈	d															09 00									
Manchester Picc. **10**	82 🚌	d															09 16									
Bolton	82	d																								
Wigan North Western	90	a									09 25	09 37					09 43									
		d									09 25	09 38					09 43									
Preston **8**	90	a									09 38	09 51					09 57									
Preston **8**	90	d									09 41	09 53					09 59									
Blackpool North	97	a																								
Lancaster **6**		a									09 54	10 07					10 15									
		d									09 55	10 08					10 16									
Barrow-in-Furness	82	a																								
Oxenholme Lake District		a										10 21														
		d										10 22														
Windermere	83	a																								
Penrith North Lakes		d									10 31						10 53									
Carlisle **8**	216	a									10 46	10 59					11 08									
		d									10 47	11 01					11 11									
Lockerbie		d															11 30									
Carstairs	226	a																								
Motherwell	226	a																								
Glasgow Central **15**	216,226	a									12 01						12 30									
Haymarket	225,226,228,230,242	a										12 16														
Edinburgh **10**	225,226,228,230,242	a										12 21														
Perth	229	a																								
Dundee	229	a																								
Aberdeen	229	a																								
Inverness	229	a																								

OVERNIGHT SLEEPERS. For sleeper trains, operated by First ScotRail, please see Tables 400 - 404.

For complete service between Manchester and Preston, Blackpool and between Barrow-in-furness and Lancaster, please see Table 82.

For complete service between Crewe and Liverpool Lime Street, see Table 91

For complete service between Crewe/Stoke-on-Trent & Manchester see Table 84

For complete service between Crewe and Holyhead please see Table 81.

For complete service between Coventry-Birmingham-Wolverhampton-Stafford please see Table 68

For complete service between Windermere and Oxenholme Lake District, please see Table 83

Table 65

Mondays to Fridays

9 December to 16 May

London and West Midlands - North West England and Scotland

Route Diagram - refer to first Page of Table 65

		TP	VT		TP	VT	VT	XC	LM	XC	TP	NT	LM		VT	LM	VT	VT	VT	LM	VT	VT	VT		VT
		◇1	◇1		◇1	◇1	◇1	◇1	1	◇1	◇1		1		◇1	1	◇1	◇1	◇1	1	◇1	◇1	◇1		◇1
		☕	⊠			⊠	⊠	☕		☕	☕				⊡ A		⊠	⊠	⊠		⊠	⊠	⊡		⊠
London Euston 15 ⊖66	d		08 30				08 40								08 43	08 46	09 00	09 07	09 10		09 20	09 30			09 40
Watford Junction 66	d																								
Milton Keynes Central 66	d														09 13	09 19			09 41		09 50				
Rugby 66	d															09 42									
Nuneaton	d															09 54									
Tamworth Low Level	d															10 09									
Lichfield Trent Valley	d															10 17									
Coventry 68	d									09 27					09 42										
Birmingham International 68 ✈	d									09 38					09 53										
Birmingham New St. 12 68	d							09 31	09 36	09 57			10 01		10 15										
Wolverhampton 7 ⛴	d							09 49	09 54	10 15			10 20		10 37										
Penkridge	d								10 04																
Stafford	a							10 00	10 10	10 29			10 34			10 35		10 22							
	d							10 01	10 10	10 30			10 35			10 39		10 23							
Stoke-on-Trent	a							10 19		10 54						11 00	10 24				10 48				
Macclesfield	a					←				11 11							10 41			←			←		
Crewe 10	a					10 07	10 10		10 30				10 56		11 07	11 24		10 41	10 47	10 56			11 07		11 10
	d					10 09	10 11		10 32				10 57		11 09			10 43	10 49	10 57			11 09		11 11
Chester 81	a												↦		↦				11 13						
Wrexham General 75	a																								
Llandudno Junction 81	a																		12 00						
Bangor (Gwynedd) 81	a																		12 16						
Holyhead 81 ⛴	a																		12 50						
Wilmslow 84	a						10 27																		11 27
Stockport 84	a						10 36	10 49		11 27							10 55				11 16				11 36
Manchester Piccadilly 10 ⛴	a						10 49	10 59		11 38							11 07				11 28				11 49
Warrington Bank Quay	a		10 14			10 26																11 14	11 26		
	d		10 14			10 27																11 14	11 27		
Runcorn 91	a								10 50									11 00		11 21					
Liverpool South Pkwy 7 91 ✈	a								10 59											11 30					
Liverpool Lime St. 10 91	a								11 10									11 21		11 42					
	d																								
Manchester Airport 82 ✈	d	09 29									10 00														
Manchester Picc. 10 82 ⛴	d	09 46									10 16														
Bolton 82	d	10 07																							
Wigan North Western 90	a		10 25		←	10 37																11 25	11 37		
	d		10 25			10 38																11 25	11 38		
Preston 8 90	a	10 33	10 38		10 33	10 51					10 56											11 38	11 51		
Preston 8 90	d	10 45	10 41		10 45	10 53					10 57	11 05										11 41	11 53		
Blackpool North 97	a	↦																							
Lancaster 6	a		10 54		11 00	11 07					11 13	11 25										11 54	12 07		
	d		10 55		11 01	11 08					11 13											11 55	12 08		
Barrow-in-Furness 82	a																								
Oxenholme Lake District	a		11 08		11 17																		12 21		
	d		11 08		11 18																		12 22		
Windermere 83	a				11 39																				
Penrith North Lakes	d					11 45																12 30			
Carlisle 8 216	a		11 46			12 00					12 05											12 45	12 59		
	d		11 47			12 02					12 06											12 47	13 01		
Lockerbie	d																								
Carstairs 226	a																								
Motherwell 226	a																								
Glasgow Central 15 216,226	a		13 01			13 17																14 01			
Haymarket 225,226,228,230,242	a										13s19												14 15		
Edinburgh 10 225,226,228,230,242	a										13 27												14 22		
Perth 229	a																								
Dundee 229	a																								
Aberdeen 229	a																								
Inverness 229	a																								

A ⊠ available for passengers joining at Euston and Milton Keynes

OVERNIGHT SLEEPERS. For sleeper trains, operated by First ScotRail, please see Tables 400 - 404.

For complete service between Manchester and Preston, Blackpool and between Barrow-in-furness and Lancaster, please see Table 82.

For complete service between Crewe and Liverpool Lime Street, see Table 91

For complete service between Crewe/Stoke-on-Trent & Manchester see Table 84

For complete service between Crewe and Holyhead please see Table 81.

For complete service between Coventry-Birmingham-Wolverhampton-Stafford please see Table 68

For complete service between Windermere and Oxenholme Lake District, please see Table 83

Table 65

Mondays to Fridays

9 December to 16 May

London and West Midlands - North West England and Scotland

Route Diagram - refer to first Page of Table 65

	XC	LM	XC	TP	LM	VT	LM	VT	VT	VT	LM	VT	VT	TP	VT	VT	XC	LM	XC	TP	LM	VT
	◇1	1	◇1	◇1	1	◇1	1	◇1	◇1	◇1	1	◇1	◇1	◇1	◇1	◇1	◇1	1	R ◇1 B	◇1	1	◇1
	🛒		🛒	A 🛒		🍴 A		⊠	⊠	⊠		⊠	⊠		🍴	⊠	🛒		🛒	🛒		🍴
London Euston 15 ⊖66 d						09 43	09 46	10 00	10 07	10 10		10 20	10 30			10 40						10 43
Watford Junction 66 d																						
Milton Keynes Central 66 d						10 13	10 19			10 41		10 50										11 13
Rugby 66 d							10 42															
Nuneaton d							10 54															
Tamworth Low Level d							11 09															
Lichfield Trent Valley d							11 17															
Coventry 68 d			10 27			10 42													11 27			11 42
Birmingham International 68 ✈ d			10 38			10 53													11 38			11 53
Birmingham New St. 12 68 d	10 31	10 36	10 57		11 01	11 15											11 31	11 36	11 57		12 01	12 15
Wolverhampton 7 🚌 d	10 49	10 54	11 15		11 20	11 37											11 49	11 54	12 15		12 20	12 37
Penkridge d		11 04																12 04				
Stafford a	11 00	11 10	11 28		11 34		11 35		11 22								12 00	12 10	12 29		12 34	
d	11 01	11 10	11 30		11 35		11 39		11 23								12 01	12 10	12 30		12 35	
Stoke-on-Trent a	11 19		11 54				12 00	11 24				11 48					12 19		12 54			
Macclesfield a			12 11					11 41			←				←				13 11			
Crewe 10 a		11 30			11 56	12 07	12 24		11 41	11 47	11 56				12 07	12 10		12 30			12 57	13 07
d		11 32			11 57	12 09			11 43	11 49	11 57				12 09	12 11		12 32			12 58	13 09
Chester 81 a					→	→				12 13											→	→
Wrexham General 75 a																						
Llandudno Junction 81 a																						
Bangor (Gwynedd) 81 a																						
Holyhead 81 ⛴ a																						
Wilmslow 84 a																12 27						
Stockport 84 a	11 49		12 26					11 55				12 16				12 36	12 49		13 27			
Manchester Piccadilly 10 🚌 a	11 59		12 38					12 07				12 28				12 49	12 59		13 38			
Warrington Bank Quay a													12 14		12 26							
d													12 16		12 27							
Runcorn 91 a		11 50							12 00		12 24							12 50				
Liverpool South Pkwy 7 91 ✈ a		11 59									12 33							12 59				
Liverpool Lime St. 10 91 a		12 10							12 21		12 44							13 10				
d																						
Manchester Airport 82 ✈ d				11 00																12 00		
Manchester Picc. 10 82 🚌 d				11 16																12 16		
Bolton 82 d																						
Wigan North Western 90 a				11 43									12 24		12 37					12 43		
d				11 43									12 26		12 38					12 43		
Preston 8 90 a				11 57									12 38		12 51					12 57		
Preston 8 90 d				11 58									12 41	12 45	12 53					12 59		
Blackpool North 97 a																						
Lancaster 6 a				12 14										13 00	13 07					13 14		
d				12 15										13 01	13 08					13 15		
Barrow-in-Furness 82 a				13 09																		
Oxenholme Lake District a													13 05	13 17	13 21					13 29		
d													13 07	13 18	13 22					13 29		
Windermere 83 a														13 39								
Penrith North Lakes d																				13 55		
Carlisle 8 216 a													13 45		14 00					14 11		
d													13 47		14 03					14 11		
Lockerbie d																				14 29		
Carstairs 226 a																						
Motherwell 226 a																						
Glasgow Central 15 216,226 a													15 01		15 16							
Haymarket 225,226,228,230,242 a																				15s34		
Edinburgh 10 225,226,228,230,242 a																				15 39		
Perth 229 a																						
Dundee 229 a																						
Aberdeen 229 a																						
Inverness 229 a																						

A 🛒 to Preston

B ◇ from Birmingham New St. R to Birmingham New St.

A ⊠ available for passengers joining at Euston and Milton Keynes

OVERNIGHT SLEEPERS. For sleeper trains, operated by First ScotRail, please see Tables 400 - 404.

For complete service between Manchester and Preston, Blackpool and between Barrow-in-furness and Lancaster, please see Table 82.

For complete service between Crewe and Liverpool Lime Street, see Table 91

For complete service between Crewe/Stoke-on-Trent & Manchester see Table 84

For complete service between Crewe and Holyhead please see Table 81.

For complete service between Coventry-Birmingham-Wolverhampton-Stafford please see Table 68

For complete service between Windermere and Oxenholme Lake District, please see Table 83

Table 65

Mondays to Fridays

9 December to 16 May

London and West Midlands - North West England and Scotland

Route Diagram - refer to first Page of Table 65

		LM	VT	VT	VT		LM	VT	VT	VT	VT	XC	LM	XC	TP		LM	VT	LM	VT	VT	VT	LM	VT	VT
		1	◇1 ☕	◇1 ☕	◇1 ☕		1	◇1 ☕	R 1 ⊠	◇1 ☕	◇1 ☕	◇1 trolley	1	◇1 trolley	◇1 trolley		1	◇1 ☕	1	◇1 ☕	◇1 ☕	◇1 ☕	1	◇1 ☕	◇1 ⊠
London Euston 15	⊖66 d	10 46	11 00	11 07	11 10			11 20	11 30		11 40							11 43	11 46	12 00	12 07	12 10		12 20	12 30
Watford Junction	66 d																								
Milton Keynes Central	66 d	11 19			11 41			11 50										12 13	12 19			12 41		12 50	
Rugby	66 d	11 42																	12 42						
Nuneaton	d	11 54																	12 54						
Tamworth Low Level	d	12 09																	13 09						
Lichfield Trent Valley	d	12 17																	13 17						
Coventry	68 d													12 27				12 42							
Birmingham International	68 ✈ d													12 38				12 53							
Birmingham New St. 12	68 d											12 31	12 36	12 57			13 01	13 15							
Wolverhampton 7	⛴ d											12 49	12 54	13 15			13 20	13 37							
Penkridge	d												13 04												
Stafford	a	12 35		12 22								13 00	13 10	13 29			13 34		13 35		13 22				
	d	12 39		12 23								13 01	13 10	13 30			13 35		13 39		13 23				
Stoke-on-Trent	a	13 00	12 24					12 48				13 19		13 54					14 00	13 24				13 48	
Macclesfield	a		12 41				←			←				14 11						13 41			←		
Crewe 10	a	13 24		12 41	12 47		12 57			13 07	13 10		13 30				13 56	14 07	14 24		13 41	13 47	13 56		
	d			12 43	12 49		12 58			13 09	13 11		13 32				13 57	14 09			13 43	13 49	13 57		
Chester	81 a				13 13												↪	↪				14 13			
Wrexham General	75 a																								
Llandudno Junction	81 a																								
Bangor (Gwynedd)	81 a																								
Holyhead	81 ⛴ a																								
Wilmslow	84 a										13 27														
Stockport	84 a		12 55					13 16			13 36	13 49		14 27						13 55				14 16	
Manchester Piccadilly 10	⛴ a		13 07					13 28			13 49	13 59		14 38						14 07				14 28	
Warrington Bank Quay	a								13 14	13 26															14 14
	d								13 14	13 27															14 15
Runcorn	91 a			13 00			13 21						13 50								14 00		14 21		
Liverpool South Pkwy 7	91 ✈ a						13 30						13 59										14 30		
Liverpool Lime St. 10	91 a			13 21			13 42						14 10								14 21		14 42		
	d																								
Manchester Airport	82 ✈ d														13 00										
Manchester Picc. 10	82 ⛴ d														13 16										
Bolton	82 d																								
Wigan North Western	90 a								13 25	13 37					13 43										14 25
	d								13 25	13 38					13 43										14 26
Preston 8	90 a								13 38	13 51					13 57										14 39
Preston 8	90 d								13 41	13 53					13 58										14 41
Blackpool North	97 a																								
Lancaster 6	a								13 54	14 07					14 14										14 55
	d								13 55	14 08					14 15										14 56
Barrow-in-Furness	82 a																								
Oxenholme Lake District	a								14 08																
	d								14 08																
Windermere	83 a																								
Penrith North Lakes	d									14 43															15 30
Carlisle 8	216 a								14 46	14 58					15 06										15 45
	d								14 47	14 59					15 08										15 49
Lockerbie	d														15 27										
Carstairs	226 a																								
Motherwell	226 a																								
Glasgow Central 15	216,226 a								16 01						16 31										17 05
Haymarket	225,226,228,230,242 a									16 16															
Edinburgh 10	225,226,228,230,242 a									16 24															
Perth	229 a																								
Dundee	229 a																								
Aberdeen	229 a																								
Inverness	229 a																								

OVERNIGHT SLEEPERS. For sleeper trains, operated by First ScotRail, please see Tables 400 - 404.

For complete service between Manchester and Preston, Blackpool and between Barrow-in-furness and Lancaster, please see Table 82.

For complete service between Crewe and Liverpool Lime Street, see Table 91

For complete service between Crewe/Stoke-on-Trent & Manchester see Table 84

For complete service between Crewe and Holyhead please see Table 81.

For complete service between Coventry-Birmingham-Wolverhampton-Stafford please see Table 68

For complete service between Windermere and Oxenholme Lake District, please see Table 83

Table 65

Mondays to Fridays

9 December to 16 May

London and West Midlands - North West England and Scotland

Route Diagram - refer to first Page of Table 65

	VT	VT	XC	LM	XC	TP	LM	VT	LM	VT	VT	VT	LM	VT	TP	VT	NT	TP	VT	VT	XC
	◇1	◇1	◇1	1	◇1	◇1	1	◇1	1	◇1	◇1	◇1	1	◇1	◇1	◇1		◇1	◇1	◇1	◇1
															A			A			
	🍽	🍽	🛒		🛒	🛒		🍽		🍽	🍽	🍽		🍽	🛒	⊠			🍽	🍽	🛒
London Euston 15 ⊖66 d		12 40						12 43	12 46	13 00	13 07	13 10		13 20		13 30				13 40	
Watford Junction 66 d																					
Milton Keynes Central 66 d								13 13	13 19			13 41		13 50							
Rugby 66 d									13 42												
Nuneaton d									13 54												
Tamworth Low Level d									14 09												
Lichfield Trent Valley d									14 17												
Coventry 68 d					13 28			13 42													
Birmingham International 68 ✈ d					13 39			13 53													
Birmingham New St. 12 68 d			13 31	13 36	13 57		14 01	14 15													14 31
Wolverhampton 7 ⛴ d			13 49	13 54	14 15		14 20	14 37													14 49
Penkridge d				14 04																	
Stafford a			14 00	14 10	14 29		14 34		14 38		14 22										15 00
d			14 01	14 10	14 30		14 35		14 39		14 23										15 01
Stoke-on-Trent a			14 19		14 54				15 00	14 24				14 48							15 19
Macclesfield a	←				15 11					14 41			←						←		
Crewe 10 a	14 07	14 10		14 30			14 56	15 07	15 24		14 41	14 47	14 56						15 07	15 10	
d	14 09	14 11		14 32			14 57	15 09			14 43	14 49	14 57						15 09	15 11	
Chester 81 a							→	→				15 13									
Wrexham General 75 a																					
Llandudno Junction 81 a																					
Bangor (Gwynedd) 81 a																					
Holyhead 81 ⛴ a																					
Wilmslow 84 a		14 27																		15 27	
Stockport 84 a		14 36	14 49		15 27					14 55				15 16						15 36	15 49
Manchester Piccadilly 10 ⛴ a		14 49	14 59		15 38					15 07				15 28						15 49	15 59
Warrington Bank Quay a	14 26															15 14			15 26		
d	14 27															15 14			15 27		
Runcorn 91 a				14 50							15 00		15 21								
Liverpool South Pkwy 7 91 ✈ a				14 59									15 30								
Liverpool Lime St. 10 91 a				15 10							15 21		15 42								
d																					
Manchester Airport 82 ✈ d						14 00									14 29						
Manchester Picc. 10 82 ⛴ d						14 16									14 46						
Bolton 82 d															15 07						
Wigan North Western 90 a	14 37					14 43										15 25		←	15 37		
d	14 38					14 43										15 25			15 38		
Preston 8 90 a	14 51					14 57									15 33	15 38		15 33	15 52		
Preston 8 90 d	14 53					14 58									15 46	15 41		15 46	15 53		
Blackpool North 97 a															→						
Lancaster 6 a	15 08					15 14												16 01	16 08		
d	15 08					15 15											15 35	16 02	16 08		
Barrow-in-Furness 82 a																	16 39	17 04			
Oxenholme Lake District a	15 22					15 29										16 04					
d	15 23					15 29										16 06					
Windermere 83 a																					
Penrith North Lakes d						15 54										16 31			16 45		
Carlisle 8 216 a	16 00					16 11										16 46	19 08		17 00		
d	16 02					16 11										16 47			17 02		
Lockerbie d						16 30															
Carstairs 226 a																					
Motherwell 226 a																					
Glasgow Central 15 216,226 a	17 17															18 03					
Haymarket 225,226,228,230,242 a						17s30													18 17		
Edinburgh 10 225,226,228,230,242 a						17 38													18 26		
Perth 229 a																					
Dundee 229 a																					
Aberdeen 229 a																					
Inverness 229 a																					

A from 10 February

OVERNIGHT SLEEPERS. For sleeper trains, operated by First ScotRail, please see Tables 400 - 404.

For complete service between Manchester and Preston, Blackpool and between Barrow-in-furness and Lancaster, please see Table 82.

For complete service between Crewe and Liverpool Lime Street, see Table 91

For complete service between Crewe/Stoke-on-Trent & Manchester see Table 84

For complete service between Crewe and Holyhead please see Table 81.

For complete service between Coventry-Birmingham-Wolverhampton-Stafford please see Table 68

For complete service between Windermere and Oxenholme Lake District, please see Table 83

Table 65

Mondays to Fridays

9 December to 16 May

London and West Midlands - North West England and Scotland

Route Diagram - refer to first Page of Table 65

	LM	XC	TP	TP	LM	VT		LM	VT	VT	VT	LM	VT	VT	VT	VT		XC	LM	XC	TP FX		TP FO	TP
	1	◇1	◇1	◇1	1	◇1		1	◇1	◇1	◇1	1	◇1	R 1	◇1	◇1		◇1	1	◇1	◇1		◇1	◇1
			A	B																	C		D	E
		trolley	trolley	trolley		restaurant			restaurant	restaurant	restaurant		restaurant	⊠	restaurant	restaurant		trolley		trolley	trolley		trolley	trolley
London Euston 15 ⊖66 d						13 43		13 46	14 00	14 07	14 10		14 20	14 30		14 40								
Watford Junction 66 d																								
Milton Keynes Central 66 d						14 13		14 19			14 41		14 50											
Rugby 66 d								14 42																
Nuneaton d								14 54																
Tamworth Low Level d								15 09																
Lichfield Trent Valley d								15 17																
Coventry 68 d		14 27				14 42														15 27				
Birmingham International 68 ✈ d		14 38				14 53														15 38				
Birmingham New St. 12 68 d	14 36	14 57			15 01	15 15												15 31	15 36	15 57				
Wolverhampton 7 🚌 d	14 54	15 15			15 20	15 37												15 50	15 54	16 15				
Penkridge d	15 04																		16 04					
Stafford a	15 10	15 29			15 34			15 35		15 22								16 01	16 10	16 30				
d	15 10	15 30			15 35			15 39		15 23								16 02	16 10	16 31				
Stoke-on-Trent a		15 54						16 00	15 24				15 48					16 20		16 54				
Macclesfield a		16 11							15 41			←			←					17 11				
Crewe 10 a	15 30				15 56	16 07		16 24		15 41	15 47	15 56			16 07	16 10			16 30					
d	15 32				15 57	16 09				15 43	15 49	15 57			16 09	16 11			16 32					
Chester 81 a					→	→					16 13													
Wrexham General 75 a																								
Llandudno Junction 81 a																								
Bangor (Gwynedd) 81 a																								
Holyhead 81 ⛴ a																								
Wilmslow 84 a																16 27								
Stockport 84 a		16 27							15 55				16 16			16 36		16 49		17 27				
Manchester Piccadilly 10 🚌 a		16 38							16 07				16 28			16 49		16 59		17 38				
Warrington Bank Quay a														16 16	16 26									
d														16 17	16 27									
Runcorn 91 a	15 50									16 00		16 26							16 50					
Liverpool South Pkwy 7 91 ✈ a	15 59											16 35							16 59					
Liverpool Lime St. 10 91 a	16 10									16 21		16 45							17 10					
d																								
Manchester Airport 82 ✈ d			15§00	15§00																	16§00		16§00	16§00
Manchester Picc. 10 82 🚌 d			15§16	15§16																	16§16		16§16	16§16
Bolton 82 d																					16§33		16§33	16§33
Wigan North Western 90 a			15§43	15§43										16 28	16 37									
d			15§43	15§43										16 29	16 38									
Preston 8 90 a			15§57	15§57										16 42	16 51						16§56		16§58	16§58
Preston 8 90 d			15§58	15§58										16 43	16 53						16§58	17§05	16§58	16§58
Blackpool North 97 a																						→		
Lancaster 6 a			16§14	16§15										17 00	17 08						17§14		17§14	17§14
d			16§15											17 00	17 08						17§15		17§15	17§15
Barrow-in-Furness 82 a			17§18																					
Oxenholme Lake District a														17 15	17 21						17§29		17§28	17§29
d														17 16	17 22						17§29		17§29	17§29
Windermere 83 a																								
Penrith North Lakes d														17 42	17 47									
Carlisle 8 216 a														18 00	18 05						18§11		18§11	18§11
d														18 00	18 06						18§11		18§11	18§11
Lockerbie d																					18§30		18§30	18§30
Carstairs 226 a																								
Motherwell 226 a																								
Glasgow Central 15 216,226 a														19 15	19 23									
Haymarket 225,226,228,230,242 a																					19s34		19s34	19s34
Edinburgh 10 225,226,228,230,242 a																					19§39		19§39	19§39
Perth 229 a																								
Dundee 229 a																								
Aberdeen 229 a																								
Inverness 229 a																								

A until 7 February. trolley to Preston

B from 10 February. trolley to Preston

C until 6 February

D until 7 February

E from 10 February

OVERNIGHT SLEEPERS. For sleeper trains, operated by First ScotRail, please see Tables 400 - 404.

For complete service between Manchester and Preston, Blackpool and between Barrow-in-furness and Lancaster, please see Table 82.

For complete service between Crewe and Liverpool Lime Street, see Table 91

For complete service between Crewe/Stoke-on-Trent & Manchester see Table 84

For complete service between Crewe and Holyhead please see Table 81.

For complete service between Coventry-Birmingham-Wolverhampton-Stafford please see Table 68

For complete service between Windermere and Oxenholme Lake District, please see Table 83

Table 65

Mondays to Fridays

9 December to 16 May

London and West Midlands - North West England and Scotland

Route Diagram - refer to first Page of Table 65

		TP FX	LM		VT	LM	VT	VT	VT	LM	VT	VT	VT		VT	XC	LM	XC	TP	TP	TP FX	TP	LM		VT
					R								R												R
		◇1	1		1	1	◇1	◇1	◇1	1	◇1	◇1	1		◇1	◇1	1	◇1	◇1	◇1	◇1	◇1	1		1
		A																	B	C	A	D			
					⊠		☕	☕	☕		☕	⊠	⊠		☕	🍴		🍴	🍴	🍴		🍴			⊠
London Euston 15 ⊖66	d				14 43	14 46	15 00	15 07	15 10		15 20	15 30			15 40										15 43
Watford Junction 66	d																								
Milton Keynes Central 66	d				15 13	15 19			15 41		15 50														16 13
Rugby 66	d					15 42																			
Nuneaton	d					15 54																			
Tamworth Low Level	d					16 09																			
Lichfield Trent Valley	d					16 17																			
Coventry 68	d				15 42													16 27							16 42
Birmingham International 68 ✈	d				15 53													16 38							16 53
Birmingham New St. 12 68	d		16 01		16 15											16 31	16 36	16 57					17 01		17 15
Wolverhampton 7 ⛴	d		16 20		16 37											16 49	16 54	17 15					17 20		17 37
Penkridge	d		16 29														17 04						17 29		
Stafford	a		16 36			16 35		16 22								17 00	17 10	17 29					17 35		
	d		16 36			16 39		16 23								17 01	17 10	17 30					17 36		
Stoke-on-Trent	a					17 00	16 24				16 48					17 18		17 54							
Macclesfield	a						16 41			←			←					18 11							
Crewe 10	a		16 56		17 07	17 24		16 41	16 47	16 56			17 07		17 10		17 30						17 56		18 07
	d		16 58		17 09			16 43	16 49	16 58			17 09		17 11		17 32						17 57		18 09
Chester 81	a		→		→				17 13														→		→
Wrexham General 75	a																								
Llandudno Junction 81	a																								
Bangor (Gwynedd) 81	a																								
Holyhead 81 ⛴	a																								
Wilmslow 84	a														17 27										
Stockport 84	a						16 55				17 16				17 36	17 49		18 27							
Manchester Piccadilly 10 ⛴	a						17 07				17 28				17 49	17 58		18 38							
Warrington Bank Quay	a											17 14	17 26												
	d											17 14	17 27												
Runcorn 91	a							17 00		17 24							17 50								
Liverpool South Pkwy 7 91 ✈	a									17 33							17 59								
Liverpool Lime St. 10 91	a							17 21		17 45							18 10								
	d																								
Manchester Airport 82 ✈	d																		17 00	17 00					
Manchester Picc. 10 82 ⛴	d																		17 15	17 15					
Bolton 82	d																			17 32		17 32			
Wigan North Western 90	a	←										17 25	17 37												
	d											17 25	17 38												
Preston 8 90	a	16 56										17 38	17 51						17 55	17 57		18 01			
Preston 8 90	d	17 05										17 41	17 53						17 58	17 58	18 05	18 05			
Blackpool North 97	a																								
Lancaster 6	a	17 23										17 54	18 07						18 15	18 14	18 20	18 21			
	d	17 24										17 55	18 08						18 15	18 15	18 22	18 21			
Barrow-in-Furness 82	a																				19 25				
Oxenholme Lake District	a	17 41										18 08	18 21						18 29	18 29		18 37			
	d	17 42										18 08	18 22						18 30	18 29		18 37			
Windermere 83	a	18 01																				19 00			
Penrith North Lakes	d												18 47						18 54	18 54					
Carlisle 8 216	a											18 46	19 02						19 11	19 11					
	d											18 47	19 03						19 13	19 11					
Lockerbie	d																								
Carstairs 226	a																								
Motherwell 226	a																		20s15	20s15					
Glasgow Central 15 216,226	a											19 58							20 35	20 35					
Haymarket 225,226,228,230,242	a												20 20												
Edinburgh 10 225,226,228,230,242	a												20 27												
Perth 229	a																								
Dundee 229	a																								
Aberdeen 229	a																								
Inverness 229	a																								

A until 6 February
B from 10 February
C until 7 February
D from 10 February. 🍴 to Preston

OVERNIGHT SLEEPERS. For sleeper trains, operated by First ScotRail, please see Tables 400 - 404.

For complete service between Manchester and Preston, Blackpool and between Barrow-in-furness and Lancaster, please see Table 82.

For complete service between Crewe and Liverpool Lime Street, see Table 91

For complete service between Crewe/Stoke-on-Trent & Manchester see Table 84

For complete service between Crewe and Holyhead please see Table 81.

For complete service between Coventry-Birmingham-Wolverhampton-Stafford please see Table 68

For complete service between Windermere and Oxenholme Lake District, please see Table 83

Table 65

Mondays to Fridays

9 December to 16 May

London and West Midlands - North West England and Scotland

Route Diagram - refer to first Page of Table 65

		LM	VT	VT	VT	LM	VT	VT	TP	VT	TP	TP	TP		VT	VT	XC	TP	TP	TP	VT	TP	LM
											FO	FO	FO					FX	FO	FO		FO	
		1	◇1	◇1	◇1	1	◇1	◇1	◇1	R 1	◇1	◇1	◇1		◇1	◇1	◇1	◇1	◇1	◇1	◇1	◇1	1
									A		B	C	D						D	C		D	
			☕	☕	☕		☕	⊠	🛒	⊠	🛒	🛒	🛒		☕	☕	🛒	🛒	🛒	🛒	☕		
London Euston 15	⊖66 d	15 46	16 00	16 07	16 10		16 20	16 30							16 33	16 40							
Watford Junction	66 d																						
Milton Keynes Central	66 d	16 19			16u41		16 50																
Rugby	66 d	16 42													17 22								
Nuneaton	d	16 54																					
Tamworth Low Level	d	17 09																					
Lichfield Trent Valley	d	17 17																					
Coventry	68 d																						
Birmingham International	68 ✈ d																						
Birmingham New St. 12	68 d																17 31						17 36
Wolverhampton 7	⛴ d																17 50						17 54
Penkridge	d																						18 03
Stafford	a	17 35		17 22											17 52		18 01						18 09
	d	17 39		17 23											17 56		18 02						18 10
Stoke-on-Trent	a	18 00	17 24				17 48										18 20						
Macclesfield	a		17 41			←				←											←		
Crewe 10	a	18 24		17 41	17 47	17 56				18 07					18 16	18 10					18 16		18 30
	d			17 43	17 49	17 57				18 09					18 18	18 11					18 18		18 32
Chester	81 a				18 08										↪								
Wrexham General	75 a																						
Llandudno Junction	81 a				18 58																		
Bangor (Gwynedd)	81 a				19 21																		
Holyhead	81 ⛴ a																						
Wilmslow	84 a															18 27							
Stockport	84 a		17 55				18 16									18 36	18 49						
Manchester Piccadilly 10	⛴ a		18 07				18 28									18 49	18 59						
Warrington Bank Quay	a									18 26											18 35		
	d									18 27											18 36		
Runcorn	91 a			18 00		18 24																	18 56
Liverpool South Pkwy 7	91 ✈ a					18 33																	19 05
Liverpool Lime St. 10	91 a			18 21		18 45																	19 16
	d																						
Manchester Airport	82 ✈ d								17 29		18 00	18 00	18 00					18 00					
Manchester Picc. 10	82 ⛴ d								17 46		18 16	18 16	18 16					18 16					
Bolton	82 d								18 06														
Wigan North Western	90 a									18 37	18 42	18 42	18 42					18 43	←	←	18 46	←	
	d									18 38	18 42	18 43	18 43					18 43			18 47		
Preston 8	90 a							18 30	18 35	18 51	18 56	18 56	18 57					18 57	18 57	18 56	19 01	18 57	
Preston 8	90 d							18 30	18 43	18 53	18 58	18 59	18 59	19 05				18 58	18 59	18 59		19 05	
Blackpool North	97 a											↪	↪	↪									
Lancaster 6	a								18 58	19 07	19 16							19 14		19 16		19 21	
	d								18 59	19 08	19 16							19 15		19 17		19 22	
Barrow-in-Furness	82 a								20 02														
Oxenholme Lake District	a									19 21	19 30							19 29	19 28	19 31		19 38	
	d									19 23	19 31							19 29	19 29	19 31		19 39	
Windermere	83 a																					19 59	
Penrith North Lakes	d										19 55							19 54	19 53	19 56			
Carlisle 8	216 a									20 00	20 13							20 11	20 10	20 13			
	d									20 02	20 13							20 11	20 11	20 13			
Lockerbie	d																						
Carstairs	226 a																						
Motherwell	226 a																						
Glasgow Central 15	216,226 a							20 38		21 17													
Haymarket	225,226,228,230,242 a										21s31							21s31	21s31	21s31			
Edinburgh 10	225,226,228,230,242 a										21 40							21 40	21 40	21 40			
Perth	229 a																						
Dundee	229 a																						
Aberdeen	229 a																						
Inverness	229 a																						

A 🛒 to Preston
B from 14 February until 21 March
C from 28 March
D until 7 February

OVERNIGHT SLEEPERS. For sleeper trains, operated by First ScotRail, please see Tables 400 - 404.

For complete service between Manchester and Preston, Blackpool and between Barrow-in-furness and Lancaster, please see Table 82.

For complete service between Crewe and Liverpool Lime Street, see Table 91

For complete service between Crewe/Stoke-on-Trent & Manchester see Table 84

For complete service between Crewe and Holyhead please see Table 81.

For complete service between Coventry-Birmingham-Wolverhampton-Stafford please see Table 68

For complete service between Windermere and Oxenholme Lake District, please see Table 83

Table 65

Mondays to Fridays

9 December to 16 May

London and West Midlands - North West England and Scotland

Route Diagram - refer to first Page of Table 65

	XC	LM	VT	LM		VT	VT	VT		VT	LM	VT	VT	LM		VT	VT	TP	VT	VT	VT	XC	LM	XC
	◇1	1	◇1	1		◇1	◇1	◇1		◇1	1	◇1	◇1	1		◇1	◇1	◇1	◇1	◇1	◇1	◇1	1	◇1
	🛒		☒			☒	☒	☒		☒		☒	☒			☒	☒		☒	☒	☒	🛒		🛒
London Euston 15 ⊖66 d			16 43	16 46		16 57	17 00	17 07		17 10			17 20	17 24		17 30			17 33	17 40				
Watford Junction 66 d														17 44										
Milton Keynes Central 66 d			17 13	17 19						17u41			17u50	18 21										
Rugby 66 d				17 42										19 08					18 23					
Nuneaton d				18 00						18 12				19 24										
Tamworth Low Level d				18 15		18 00								19 39										
Lichfield Trent Valley d				18 22		18 07								19 45										
Coventry 68 d	17 28		17 42																					18 27
Birmingham International 68 ✈ d	17 39		17 53																					18 38
Birmingham New St. 12 68 d	17 57	18 01	18 15																			18 31	18 36	18 57
Wolverhampton 7 ⛴ d	18 15	18 20	18 37																			18 49	18 54	19 15
Penkridge d		18 29																					19 04	
Stafford a	18 29	18 35		18 39				18 22											18 52			19 00	19 10	19 27
d	18 30	18 36		18 44				18 23											18 55			19 01	19 10	19 29
Stoke-on-Trent a	18 54			19 04			18 24						18 49	20 13								19 19		19 54
Macclesfield a	19 11						18 41				←	←									←			20 11
Crewe 10 a		19 03	19 07	19 27				18 41		18 55	19 03	19 07		20 37					19 14	19 10	19 14		19 30	
d		19 04	19 09					18 43		18 57	19 04	19 09							19 16	19 11	19 16		19 32	
Chester 81 a		↪	↪							19 16									↪					
Wrexham General 75 a																								
Llandudno Junction 81 a										20 11														
Bangor (Gwynedd) 81 a										20 28														
Holyhead 81 ⛴ a										20 59														
Wilmslow 84 a																				19 27				
Stockport 84 a	19 27						18 55						19 16							19 36		19 48		20 27
Manchester Piccadilly 10 ⛴ a	19 38						19 07						19 28							19 49		19 59		20 37
Warrington Bank Quay a						18 49						19 26				19 14								
d						18 50						19 27				19 14								
Runcorn 91 a								19 00			19 25										19 33		19 56	
Liverpool South Pkwy 7 91 ✈ a											19 34												20 05	
Liverpool Lime St. 10 91 a								19 21			19 45										19 51		20 16	
d																								
Manchester Airport 82 ✈ d																		19 00						
Manchester Picc. 10 82 ⛴ d																		19 16						
Bolton 82 d																	←	19 33						
Wigan North Western 90 a						19 00						19 37				19 25	19 37							
d						19 01						19 38				19 25	19 38							
Preston 8 90 a						19 14						↪				19 38	19 51	19 57						
Preston 8 90 d						19 15										19 41	19 53	19 59						
Blackpool North 97 a																								
Lancaster 6 a						19 30										19 54	20 08	20 14						
d						19 30										19 55	20 08	20 15						
Barrow-in-Furness 82 a																		21 18						
Oxenholme Lake District a						19 43										20 08								
d						19 45										20 08								
Windermere 83 a																								
Penrith North Lakes d						20 10											20 45							
Carlisle 8 216 a						20 25										20 46	21 00							
d						20 25										20 47	21 02							
Lockerbie d						20 44																		
Carstairs 226 a																								
Motherwell 226 a						21 25										21 43								
Glasgow Central 15 216,226 a						21 48										22 02								
Haymarket 225,226,228,230,242 a																	22 13							
Edinburgh 10 225,226,228,230,242 a																	22 22							
Perth 229 a																								
Dundee 229 a																								
Aberdeen 229 a																								
Inverness 229 a																								

OVERNIGHT SLEEPERS. For sleeper trains, operated by First ScotRail, please see Tables 400 - 404.

For complete service between Manchester and Preston, Blackpool and between Barrow-in-furness and Lancaster, please see Table 82.

For complete service between Crewe and Liverpool Lime Street, see Table 91

For complete service between Crewe/Stoke-on-Trent & Manchester see Table 84

For complete service between Crewe and Holyhead please see Table 81.

For complete service between Coventry-Birmingham-Wolverhampton-Stafford please see Table 68

For complete service between Windermere and Oxenholme Lake District, please see Table 83

Table 65

Mondays to Fridays

9 December to 16 May

London and West Midlands - North West England and Scotland

Route Diagram - refer to first Page of Table 65

	LM	VT	VT	VT	LM	VT	VT	VT	VT	VT	TP	NT	VT	VT	VT	XC	LM	XC	VT	VT FO
	1	◇1	◇1	◇1	1	◇1	◇1 A	◇1	◇1	◇1	◇1		◇1	◇1	◇1	◇1	1	◇1	◇1	1
		☕	⊠	⊠		⊠	⊠	⊠	⊠	☕	🍴		⊠	⊠	⊠	🍴		🍴	⊠	⊠
London Euston 15 ⊖66 d		17 43	17 57	18 00	18 05	18 07	18 10	18 20	18 30				18 33	18 40					18 43	18 46
Watford Junction 66 d					18 26															
Milton Keynes Central 66 d		18u13			19 07		18u41	18u50											19 13	
Rugby 66 d					20 04								19 23							19 39
Nuneaton d					20 17		19 13													
Tamworth Low Level d			19 00		20 31															19s59
Lichfield Trent Valley d			19 08		20 37															20s08
Coventry 68 d		18 42																19 27	19 42	
Birmingham International 68 ✈ d		18 53																19 38	19 53	
Birmingham New St. 12 68 d	19 01	19 15														19 31	19 35	19 57	20 15	
Wolverhampton 7 🚌 d	19 20	19 37														19 49	19 53	20 16	20 37	
Penkridge d	19 29																20 04			
Stafford a	19 37				20 53	19 22							19 53			20 00	20 10	20 29	20 49	20s35
d	19 37				20 53	19 23							19 57			20 01	20 10	20 30	20 52	
Stoke-on-Trent a				19 24	21 14			19 48								20 19		20 54		
Macclesfield a				19 41						⟵					⟵			21 11		
Crewe 10 a	20 01	20 07			21 37	19 41	19 53			20 07			20 15	20 10	20 15		20 30		21 16	21s01
d		20 09				19 43	19 56			20 09			20 17	20 11	20 17		20 32			
Chester 81 a		⟶					20 15						⟶							⟶
Wrexham General 75 a							20 38													
Llandudno Junction 81 a							21 09													
Bangor (Gwynedd) 81 a							21 25													
Holyhead 81 ⛴ a							21 59													
Wilmslow 84 a														20 27						
Stockport 84 a				19 55				20 16						20 36		20 48		21 25		
Manchester Piccadilly 10 🚌 a				20 07				20 28						20 49		20 58		21 39		
Warrington Bank Quay a			19 49						20 14	20 26										
d			19 50						20 14	20 27										
Runcorn 91 a						20 00									20 34		20 56			
Liverpool South Pkwy 7 91 ✈ a																	21 05			
Liverpool Lime St. 10 91 a						20 21									20 53		21 16			
d																				
Manchester Airport 82 ✈ d											20 00									
Manchester Picc. 10 82 🚌 d											20 16									
Bolton 82 d																				
Wigan North Western 90 a			20 00						20 25	20 37	20 43									
d			20 01						20 25	20 38	20 43									
Preston 8 90 a			20 14						20 38	20 51	20 57									
Preston 8 90 d			20 15						20 41	20 53	20 58	21 14								
Blackpool North 97 a																				
Lancaster 6 a			20 33						20 54	21 07	21 14	21 34								
d									20 55	21 08	21 15									
Barrow-in-Furness 82 a																				
Oxenholme Lake District a									21 08	21 21	21 29									
d									21 09	21 23	21 29									
Windermere 83 a																				
Penrith North Lakes d									21 34		21 54									
Carlisle 8 216 a									21 49	22 00	22 11									
d									21 51	22 02	22 11									
Lockerbie d									22 10		22 30									
Carstairs 226 a																				
Motherwell 226 a									22 52											
Glasgow Central 15 216,226 a									23 11	23 18										
Haymarket 225,226,228,230,242 a											23s32									
Edinburgh 10 225,226,228,230,242 a											23 40									
Perth 229 a																				
Dundee 229 a																				
Aberdeen 229 a																				
Inverness 229 a																				

A ⊠ to Chester

OVERNIGHT SLEEPERS. For sleeper trains, operated by First ScotRail, please see Tables 400 - 404.

For complete service between Manchester and Preston, Blackpool and between Barrow-in-furness and Lancaster, please see Table 82.

For complete service between Crewe and Liverpool Lime Street, see Table 91

For complete service between Crewe/Stoke-on-Trent & Manchester see Table 84

For complete service between Crewe and Holyhead please see Table 81.

For complete service between Coventry-Birmingham-Wolverhampton-Stafford please see Table 68

For complete service between Windermere and Oxenholme Lake District, please see Table 83

Table 65

Mondays to Fridays

9 December to 16 May

London and West Midlands - North West England and Scotland

Route Diagram - refer to first Page of Table 65

			VT	VT	VT	VT	VT	VT		VT	VT	VT	TP	VT	XC	LM	XC	VT		VT	VT	VT	LM	XC	LM	VT
			ThFO	FX	FO							FO														
				R	R	R	R	R		R	R															
			◇	1	1	1	1	1		1	1	1	◇1	◇1	◇1	1	◇1	◇1		◇1	◇1	◇1	1	◇1	1	◇1
																	A									
			☕	☕	☕	☕	☕	☕		☕	☒	☒		☕	⚲		⚲	☕		☕	☕	☕				☕
London Euston [15]	⊖66	d	18 57	19 00	19 00	19 07	19 10	19 10		19 20	19 30			19 40				19 43		20 00	20 07	20 10			20 13	20 30
Watford Junction	66	d																								
Milton Keynes Central	66	d					19 41	19 41		19 50								20 13				20 41			20 55	
Rugby	66	d																							21 45	
Nuneaton		d				20 03															21 03				21 59	
Tamworth Low Level		d												20 43											22 15	21 35
Lichfield Trent Valley		d												20 50											22 21	21 42
Coventry	68	d															20 27	20 42						21 28		
Birmingham International	68 ✈	d															20 38	20 53						21 39		
Birmingham New St. [12]	68	d													20 31	20 36	20 57	21 15					21 36	21 57		
Wolverhampton [7]	⛴	d													20 49	20 54	21 16	21 37					21 54	22 16		
Penkridge		d														21 04							22 04			
Stafford		a				20 26								21 02		21 10	21 31	21 52			21 27		22 10	22 29	22 39	
		d				20 27								21 04		21 10	21 32	21 55			21 27		22 10	22 30	22 41	
Stoke-on-Trent		a		20 24	20 24					20 48					21 18		21 54			21 24				22 53		
Macclesfield		a		20 41	20 41							⟵					22 11			21 40				23 11		
Crewe [10]		a	20s33				20 47	20 48				21s01		21 21		21 30		22 16			21 46	21 47	22 30		23 04	
		d					20 49	20 50						21 23		21 32		22 18			21 48	21 49	22 32			
Chester	81	a					21 13	21 13										⟶				22 13	⟶			
Wrexham General	75	a																								
Llandudno Junction	81	a					22 06																			
Bangor (Gwynedd)	81	a					22 22																			
Holyhead	81 ⛴	a					22 56																			
Wilmslow	84	a												21 38												
Stockport	84	a		20 55	20 55					21 16					21 47		22 25			21 54				23 25		
Manchester Piccadilly [10]	⛴	a	21 09	21 07	21 10					21 28				21 57	21 59		22 34			22 07				23 34		
Warrington Bank Quay		a									21 16	21s20														22 23
		d									21 17															22 23
Runcorn	91	a				21 00										21 54					22 05					
Liverpool South Pkwy [7]	91 ✈	a														22 03										
Liverpool Lime St. [10]	91	a				21 21										22 15					22 25					
		d																								
Manchester Airport	82 ✈	d																								
Manchester Picc. [10]	82 ⛴	d																								
Bolton	82	d																								
Wigan North Western	90	a									21 27	21s31														22 34
		d									21 28															22 34
Preston [8]	90	a									21 40	21 46														22 53
Preston [8]	90	d									21 43		21 47													
Blackpool North	97	a																								
Lancaster [6]		a									21 56		22 02													
		d									21 58		22 03													
Barrow-in-Furness	82	a											23 06													
Oxenholme Lake District		a									22 10															
		d									22 11															
Windermere	83	a																								
Penrith North Lakes		d									22 36															
Carlisle [8]	216	a									22 51															
		d									22 52															
Lockerbie		d																								
Carstairs	226	a																								
Motherwell	226	a																								
Glasgow Central [15]	216,226	a									00 05															
Haymarket	225,226,228,230,242	a																								
Edinburgh [10]	225,226,228,230,242	a																								
Perth	229	a																								
Dundee	229	a																								
Aberdeen	229	a																								
Inverness	229	a																								

A ⚲ to Birmingham New St.

OVERNIGHT SLEEPERS. For sleeper trains, operated by First ScotRail, please see Tables 400 - 404.

For complete service between Manchester and Preston, Blackpool and between Barrow-in-furness and Lancaster, please see Table 82.

For complete service between Crewe and Liverpool Lime Street, see Table 91

For complete service between Crewe/Stoke-on-Trent & Manchester see Table 84

For complete service between Crewe and Holyhead please see Table 81.

For complete service between Coventry-Birmingham-Wolverhampton-Stafford please see Table 68

For complete service between Windermere and Oxenholme Lake District, please see Table 83

Table 65

London and West Midlands - North West England and Scotland

Mondays to Fridays

9 December to 16 May

Route Diagram - refer to first Page of Table 65

		VT	VT	LM	VT	VT	TP	TP FX	TP FX	VT	XC	LM	SR		VT	AW	VT	VT FO	VT TW ThO	VT MO	LM
													R								
		◇1	◇1	1	◇1	◇1	◇1	◇1	◇1	◇1	◇1	1			◇1	◇	◇1	◇1	◇1	◇1	1
							A	B	B				C								
		⊏P	⊏P		⊏P	⊏P				⊏P			🛏 ✕		⊏P		⊏P	⊏P	⊏P	⊏P	
London Euston 15 ⊖66	d	20 40			21 00	21 07				21 10			21 15		21 40		22 00	22 50	22 50	22 50	
Watford Junction 66	d									21u25			21u33					23u07	23u07	23u07	
Milton Keynes Central 66	d				21 31	21 38											22 32				
Rugby 66	d									22 04							22 55				
Nuneaton	d					22 08											23 07	00s04	00s39		
Tamworth Low Level	d																23s16				
Lichfield Trent Valley	d																23s23				
Coventry 68	d																				
Birmingham International 68 ✈	d																				
Birmingham New St. 12 68	d										22 30	22 38				22 55					23 09
Wolverhampton 7 ⛴	d										22 48	23 04				23 13					23 36
Penkridge	d											23 14									23 46
Stafford	a									22 34	23 00	23 20				23 30	23s40				23 52
	d									22 34	23 01	23 20				23 30					23 53
Stoke-on-Trent	a				22 28						23 20				23 06			00s45	01s20	01s20	
Macclesfield	a		←	←	22 44										23 23			01s12	01s37	01s37	
Crewe 10	a	22 12	22 16	22 30		22 46				22 53		23 47				23 55	00 06				00 16
	d	22 13	22 18	22 32		22 48				22 54			23u53			23 57					
Chester 81	a															00 18					
Wrexham General 75	a																				
Llandudno Junction 81	a															01 28					
Bangor (Gwynedd) 81	a															01 46					
Holyhead 81 ⛴	a															02 15					
Wilmslow 84	a	22 29																			
Stockport 84	a	22 38			22 58										23 37			01s45	01s58	01s58	
Manchester Piccadilly 10 ⛴	a	22 48			23 11						00 12				23 46			01 56	02 09	02 09	
Warrington Bank Quay	a		22 35							23 14											
	d		22 35							23 14											
Runcorn 91	a			22 56		23 05															
Liverpool South Pkwy 7 91 ✈	a			23 07																	
Liverpool Lime St. 10 91	a			23 21		23 24															
	d																				
Manchester Airport 82 ✈	d						22 00														
Manchester Picc. 10 82 ⛴	d						22 16	22 16	22 46												
Bolton 82	d						22 35	22 35	23 07												
Wigan North Western 90	a		22 46				22 48	22 48		23 25											
	d		22 46				22 50	22 50		23 25											
Preston 8 90	a		23 00				23 08	23 08	23 33	23 41											
Preston 8 90	d						23 11	23 11	23 35				00u52	00u52							
Blackpool North 97	a								00 01												
Lancaster 6	a						23 26	23 26													
	d						23 27	23 27													
Barrow-in-Furness 82	a						00 30	00 30													
Oxenholme Lake District	a																				
	d																				
Windermere 83	a																				
Penrith North Lakes	d																				
Carlisle 8 216	a																				
	d																				
Lockerbie	d																				
Carstairs 226	a																				
Motherwell 226	a																				
Glasgow Central 15 216,226	a																				
Haymarket 225,226,228,230,242	a																				
Edinburgh 10 225,226,228,230,242	a																				
Perth 229	a													05s39							
Dundee 229	a												06s08								
Aberdeen 229	a												07 34								
Inverness 229	a													08 36							

A until 27 December, FO from 3 January until 14 March, from 21 March

B from 30 December until 20 March

C also conveys through sleepers to Fort William arr 0955. (Table 404)

OVERNIGHT SLEEPERS. For sleeper trains, operated by First ScotRail, please see Tables 400 - 404.

For complete service between Manchester and Preston, Blackpool and between Barrow-in-furness and Lancaster, please see Table 82.

For complete service between Crewe and Liverpool Lime Street, see Table 91

For complete service between Crewe/Stoke-on-Trent & Manchester see Table 84

For complete service between Crewe and Holyhead please see Table 81.

For complete service between Coventry-Birmingham-Wolverhampton-Stafford please see Table 68

For complete service between Windermere and Oxenholme Lake District, please see Table 83

Table 65

London and West Midlands - North West England and Scotland

Mondays to Fridays

9 December to 16 May

Route Diagram - refer to first Page of Table 65

Station	Table		SR	
London Euston [15]	⊖66	d	23 50	
Watford Junction	66	d	00u10	
Milton Keynes Central	66	d		
Rugby	66	d		
Nuneaton		d		
Tamworth Low Level		d		
Lichfield Trent Valley		d		
Coventry	68	d		
Birmingham International	68 ✈	d		
Birmingham New St. [12]	68	d		
Wolverhampton [7]	⛴	d		
Penkridge		d		
Stafford		a		
		d		
Stoke-on-Trent		a		
Macclesfield		a		
Crewe [10]		a		
		d		
Chester	81	a		
Wrexham General	75	a		
Llandudno Junction	81	a		
Bangor (Gwynedd)	81	a		
Holyhead	81 ⛴	a		
Wilmslow	84	a		
Stockport	84	a		
Manchester Piccadilly [10]	⛴	a		
Warrington Bank Quay		a		
		d		
Runcorn	91	a		
Liverpool South Pkwy [7]	91 ✈	a		
Liverpool Lime St. [10]	91	a		
		d		
Manchester Airport	82 ✈	d		
Manchester Picc. [10]	82 ⛴	d		
Bolton	82	d		
Wigan North Western	90	a		
		d		
Preston [8]	90	a		
Preston [8]	90	d		
Blackpool North	97	a		
Lancaster [8]		a		
		d		
Barrow-in-Furness	82	a		
Oxenholme Lake District		a		
		d		
Windermere	83	a		
Penrith North Lakes		d		
Carlisle [8]	216	a	05s10	
		d		
Lockerbie		d		
Carstairs	226	a	06s19	
Motherwell	226	a	06s54	
Glasgow Central [15]	216,226	a	07 18	
Haymarket	225,226,228,230,242	a		
Edinburgh [10]	225,226,228,230,242	a		07 22
Perth	229	a		
Dundee	229	a		
Aberdeen	229	a		
Inverness	229	a		

Train SR: 1st class, sleeper, restaurant.

OVERNIGHT SLEEPERS. For sleeper trains, operated by First ScotRail, please see Tables 400 - 404.

For complete service between Manchester and Preston, Blackpool and between Barrow-in-furness and Lancaster, please see Table 82.

For complete service between Crewe and Liverpool Lime Street, see Table 91

For complete service between Crewe/Stoke-on-Trent & Manchester see Table 84

For complete service between Crewe and Holyhead please see Table 81.

For complete service between Coventry-Birmingham-Wolverhampton-Stafford please see Table 68

For complete service between Windermere and Oxenholme Lake District, please see Table 83

Table 65

Saturdays

14 December to 28 December

London and West Midlands - North West England and Scotland

Route Diagram - refer to first Page of Table 65

		SR		SR	SR	VT	VT	TP	TP	AW		XC	LM	VT	LM	XC	LM	XC	TP	TP		VT	NT	LM	VT
		R		R	R																				
						◇1	◇1	◇1	◇1			◇1	1	◇1	1	◇1	1	◇1	◇1	◇1		◇1		1	◇1
		🛏		🛏	🛏																				
		✕		✕	✕	☕	☕	🛒						☕		🛒		🛒	🛒	🛒		☕			☕
London Euston 15 ⊖66	d																					06 05			
Watford Junction 66	d	00u10																				06u20			
Milton Keynes Central 66	d																					06 41			
Rugby 66	d														06 02							07 03			
Nuneaton	d														06 14										
Tamworth Low Level	d														06 29										
Lichfield Trent Valley	d														06 35										
Coventry 68	d																								
Birmingham International 68 ✈	d																								
Birmingham New St. 12 68	d						05 30					05 57	06 01	06 15		06 31	06 36	06 57						07 01	07 15
Wolverhampton 7 🚌	d						05 48					06 16	06 20	06 37		06 49	06 52	07 15						07 20	07 37
Penkridge	d												06 29				07 02							07 29	
Stafford	a						06 00					06 29	06 35		06 53	07 00	07 09	07 29				07 33		07 35	
	d						06 01					06 30	06 36		06 54	07 01	07 09	07 30				07 34		07 38	
Stoke-on-Trent	a											06 50			07 14	07 18									
Macclesfield	a											07 11				07 36									
Crewe 10	a						06 20						06 56	07 07	07 37		07 33	07 50				07 53		07 58	08 06
	d					05 57	06 23			06 27			06 58	07 09			07 34	07 52				07 55		08 00	08 09
Chester 81	a						06 43																		
Wrexham General 75	a																								
Llandudno Junction 81	a						07 33																		
Bangor (Gwynedd) 81	a						07 49																		
Holyhead 81 ⛴	a						08 23																		
Wilmslow 84	a									06 44								08 08							
Stockport 84	a									06 55		07 25				07 49		08 20							
Manchester Piccadilly 10 🚌	a									07 07		07 34				07 59		08 34							
Warrington Bank Quay	a					06 13								07 26								08 11			08 26
	d					06 15								07 27								08 12			08 27
Runcorn 91	a												07 23				08 00							08 24	
Liverpool South Pkwy 7 91 ✈	a												07 32				08 09							08 33	
Liverpool Lime St. 10 91	a												07 44				08 21							08 46	
	d																								
Manchester Airport 82 ✈	d							05 58	06 18										07 00	07 25					
Manchester Picc. 10 82 🚌	d							06 13	06 33										07 15	07 45					
Bolton 82	d								06 52											07 59					
Wigan North Western 90	a					06 24		06 42						07 37					07 43			08 22			08 37
	d					06 26		06 42						07 38					07 43			08 23			08 38
Preston 8 90	a					06 38		06 56	07 18					07 51					07 57	08 22		08 36			08 51
Preston 8 90	d			00u52	00u52	06 40		06 57	07 20					07 53					07 58	08 24		08 37			08 53
Blackpool North 97	a																								
Lancaster 6	a					06 54		07 13	07 35					08 07					08 14	08 39		08 52			09 08
	d					06 54		07 13	07 36					08 08					08 16	08 40		08 52	09 02		09 08
Barrow-in-Furness 82	a								08 39														10 06		
Oxenholme Lake District	a					07 07		07 27						08 21								09 05			
	d					07 09		07 28						08 22								09 06			
Windermere 83	a																								
Penrith North Lakes	d					07 34		07 53											08 54			09 32			09 46
Carlisle 8 216	a	05s10				07 49		08 09						09 00					09 10	09 31		09 47	12 38		10 00
	d					07 51		08 11						09 00					09 11	09 31		09 48			10 02
Lockerbie	d					08 10		08 30												09 51					
Carstairs 226	a	06s19																							
Motherwell 226	a	06s54																							
Glasgow Central 15 216,226	a	07 18				09 13													10 31			11 03			11 16
Haymarket 225,226,228,230,242	a							09s29						10 16						10s49					
Edinburgh 10 225,226,228,230,242	a		07 22					09 34						10 25						10 57					
Perth 229	a				05s39																				
Dundee 229	a			06s08																					
Aberdeen 229	a			07 34																					
Inverness 229	a				08 36																				

OVERNIGHT SLEEPERS. For sleeper trains, operated by First ScotRail, please see Tables 400 - 404.

For complete service between Manchester and Preston, Blackpool and between Barrow-in-furness and Lancaster, please see Table 82.

For complete service between Crewe and Liverpool Lime Street, see Table 91

For complete service between Crewe/Stoke-on-Trent & Manchester see Table 84

For complete service between Crewe and Holyhead please see Table 81.

For complete service between Coventry-Birmingham-Wolverhampton-Stafford please see Table 68

For complete service between Windermere and Oxenholme Lake District, please see Table 83

Table 65

Saturdays

14 December to 28 December

London and West Midlands - North West England and Scotland

Route Diagram - refer to first Page of Table 65

Station	Table		LM 1	XC ◇1 ⊼	NT	TP ◇1	LM 1		LM 1	VT ◇1 ⊡	LM 1	VT ◇1 ⊡	VT ◇1 ⊡	VT ◇1 ⊡	XC ◇1 ⊼	VT ◇1 ⊡	LM 1		TP ◇1	VT ◇1 ⊡	VT ◇1 ⊡	XC ◇1 ⊼	LM 1	XC ◇1 ⊼	TP ◇1 ⊼	LM 1
London Euston 15	⊖66	d							06 24	06 36		06 55	07 07	07 20		07 30					07 35					
Watford Junction	66	d							06 41	06u51																
Milton Keynes Central	66	d							07 23			07 27		07 50							08 06					
Rugby	66	d	06 58						08 04																	
Nuneaton		d	07 12						08 16																	
Tamworth Low Level		d	07 29						08 30																	
Lichfield Trent Valley		d	07 35						08 36																	
Coventry	68	d													07 27									08 27		
Birmingham International	68 ✈	d													07 38									08 38		
Birmingham New St. 12	68	d		07 31			07 36								07 57		08 01			08 15		08 31	08 36	08 57		09 01
Wolverhampton 7	🚌	d		07 49			07 54								08 15		08 20			08 37		08 49	08 54	09 15		09 20
Penkridge		d					08 04										08 29						09 04			
Stafford		a	07 53	08 00			08 10		08 53				08 22		08 29		08 35					09 00	09 10	09 29		09 34
		d	07 54	08 01			08 10		08 54				08 23		08 30		08 36					09 01	09 10	09 30		09 35
Stoke-on-Trent		a	08 15	08 19					09 15			08 24		08 48	08 54							09 19		09 54		
Macclesfield		a		08 36							⟵	08 41			09 11									10 11		
Crewe 10		a	08 38				08 30		09 38	08 10	08 30		08 41				08 56			09 07	09 10		09 30			09 56
		d					08 32			08 11	08 32		08 43				08 58			09 09	09 11		09 32			09 57
Chester	81	a					⟶																			⟶
Wrexham General	75	a																								
Llandudno Junction	81	a																								
Bangor (Gwynedd)	81	a																								
Holyhead	81 ⛴	a																								
Wilmslow	84	a								08 27											09 27					
Stockport	84	a		08 49						08 36		08 55		09 16	09 27						09 36	09 49		10 27		
Manchester Piccadilly 10	🚌	a		08 59						08 49		09 07		09 28	09 38						09 49	09 59		10 38		
Warrington Bank Quay		a														09 14				09 26						
		d														09 14				09 27						
Runcorn	91	a									08 50		09 00				09 21						09 50			
Liverpool South Pkwy 7	91 ✈	a									08 59						09 30						09 59			
Liverpool Lime St. 10	91	a									09 10		09 21				09 42						10 10			
		d																								
Manchester Airport	82 ✈	d				08 25																			09 00	
Manchester Picc. 10	82 🚌	d				08 46																			09 16	
Bolton	82	d				09 07																			09 35	
Wigan North Western	90	a														09 25				09 37						
		d														09 25				09 38						
Preston 8	90	a				09 30										09 38				09 51					09 55	
Preston 8	90	d			09 07	09 32										09 41			09 45	09 53					09 59	
Blackpool North	97	a																								
Lancaster 6		a			09 27	09 47										09 54			10 00	10 07					10 14	
		d				09 48										09 55			10 01	10 08					10 15	
Barrow-in-Furness	82	a																	11 04							
Oxenholme Lake District		a				10 03														10 21						
		d				10 04														10 22						
Windermere	83	a				10 27																				
Penrith North Lakes		d														10 30									10 53	
Carlisle 8	216	a														10 46				10 59					11 07	
		d														10 47				11 01					11 10	
Lockerbie		d																							11 29	
Carstairs	226	a																								
Motherwell	226	a																								
Glasgow Central 15	216,226	a														12 02									12 29	
Haymarket	225,226,228,230,242	a																		12 16						
Edinburgh 10	225,226,228,230,242	a																		12 22						
Perth	229	a																								
Dundee	229	a																								
Aberdeen	229	a																								
Inverness	229	a																								

OVERNIGHT SLEEPERS. For sleeper trains, operated by First ScotRail, please see Tables 400 - 404.

For complete service between Manchester and Preston, Blackpool and between Barrow-in-furness and Lancaster, please see Table 82.

For complete service between Crewe and Liverpool Lime Street, see Table 91

For complete service between Crewe/Stoke-on-Trent & Manchester see Table 84

For complete service between Crewe and Holyhead please see Table 81.

For complete service between Coventry-Birmingham-Wolverhampton-Stafford please see Table 68

For complete service between Windermere and Oxenholme Lake District, please see Table 83

Table 65

Saturdays

14 December to 28 December

London and West Midlands - North West England and Scotland

Route Diagram - refer to first Page of Table 65

		VT		LM	VT	VT	VT	LM	VT	TP	VT	TP		VT	VT	XC	LM	XC	TP	NT	LM	VT		LM	VT
		◇1		1	◇1	◇1	◇1	1	◇1	◇1	◇1	◇1		◇1	◇1	◇1	1	◇1	◇1		1	◇1		1	◇1
London Euston 15 ⊖66	d	07 43		07 46	08 00	08 07	08 10		08 20		08 30				08 40							08 43		08 46	09 00
Watford Junction 66	d																								
Milton Keynes Central 66	d	08 13		08 19			08 41		08 50													09 13		09 19	
Rugby 66	d			08 42																				09 42	
Nuneaton	d			08 54																				09 54	
Tamworth Low Level	d			09 09																				10 09	
Lichfield Trent Valley	d			09 17																				10 17	
Coventry 68	d	08 42																09 27					09 42		
Birmingham International 68	d	08 53																09 38					09 53		
Birmingham New St. 12 68	d	09 15														09 31	09 36	09 57			10 01	10 15			
Wolverhampton 7	d	09 37														09 49	09 54	10 15			10 20	10 37			
Penkridge	d																10 04								
Stafford	a			09 35		09 22										10 00	10 10	10 29			10 35			10 35	
	d			09 39		09 23										10 01	10 10	10 30			10 35			10 39	
Stoke-on-Trent	a			10 00	09 24				09 48							10 19		10 54						11 00	10 24
Macclesfield	a				09 41			←						←				11 11							10 41
Crewe 10	a	10 07		10 24		09 41	09 47	09 56						10 07	10 10		10 30				10 56	11 07		11 24	
	d	10 09				09 43	09 49	09 57						10 09	10 11		10 32				10 57	11 09			
Chester 81	a	↪					10 13														→	→			
Wrexham General 75	a																								
Llandudno Junction 81	a																								
Bangor (Gwynedd) 81	a																								
Holyhead 81	a																								
Wilmslow 84	a														10 27										
Stockport 84	a				09 55				10 16						10 36	10 49		11 27							10 55
Manchester Piccadilly 10	a				10 07				10 28						10 49	10 59		11 38							11 07
Warrington Bank Quay	a										10 14			10 26											
	d										10 14			10 27											
Runcorn 91	a					10 00		10 23									10 50								
Liverpool South Pkwy 7 91	a							10 32									10 59								
Liverpool Lime St. 10 91	a					10 21		10 44									11 10								
	d																								
Manchester Airport 82	d									09 29									10 00						
Manchester Picc. 10 82	d									09 46									10 16						
Bolton 82	d									10 07															
Wigan North Western 90	a										10 25	←		10 37											
	d										10 25			10 38											
Preston 8 90	a									10 33	10 38	10 33		10 51					10 56						
Preston 8 90	d									10 45	10 41	10 45		10 53					10 57						
Blackpool North 97	a									↪															
Lancaster 6	a										10 54	11 00		11 07					11 13						
	d										10 55	11 01		11 08					11 13	11 28					
Barrow-in-Furness 82	a																			12 32					
Oxenholme Lake District	a										11 08	11 17													
	d										11 08	11 18													
Windermere 83	a											11 39													
Penrith North Lakes	d													11 45											
Carlisle 8 216	a										11 46			12 00					12 05	15 00					
	d										11 47			12 02					12 06						
Lockerbie	d																								
Carstairs 226	a																								
Motherwell 226	a																								
Glasgow Central 15 216,226	a										13 01			13 17											
Haymarket 225,226,228,230,242	a																		13s19						
Edinburgh 10 225,226,228,230,242	a																		13 27						
Perth 229	a																								
Dundee 229	a																								
Aberdeen 229	a																								
Inverness 229	a																								

OVERNIGHT SLEEPERS. For sleeper trains, operated by First ScotRail, please see Tables 400 - 404.

For complete service between Manchester and Preston, Blackpool and between Barrow-in-furness and Lancaster, please see Table 82.

For complete service between Crewe and Liverpool Lime Street, see Table 91

For complete service between Crewe/Stoke-on-Trent & Manchester see Table 84

For complete service between Crewe and Holyhead please see Table 81.

For complete service between Coventry-Birmingham-Wolverhampton-Stafford please see Table 68

For complete service between Windermere and Oxenholme Lake District, please see Table 83

Table 65

Saturdays

14 December to 28 December

London and West Midlands - North West England and Scotland

Route Diagram - refer to first Page of Table 65

			VT	VT	LM	VT	VT	VT	VT	XC	LM	XC	TP	LM	VT	LM	VT	VT	VT	LM	VT	TP	VT	TP
			◇1	◇1	1	◇1	◇1	◇1	◇1	◇1	1	◇1	◇1	1	◇1	1	◇1	◇1	◇1	1	◇1	◇1	◇1	◇1
			☕	☕		☕	☕	☕	☕	🛒		🛒			☕		☕	☕	☕		☕		☕	
London Euston [15] ⊖	66	d	09 07	09 10		09 20	09 30		09 40						09 43	09 46	10 00	10 07	10 10		10 20		10 30	
Watford Junction	66	d																						
Milton Keynes Central	66	d		09 41		09 50									10 13	10 19			10 41		10 50			
Rugby	66	d														10 42								
Nuneaton		d														10 54								
Tamworth Low Level		d														11 09								
Lichfield Trent Valley		d														11 17								
Coventry	68	d										10 27			10 42									
Birmingham International ✈	68	d										10 38			10 53									
Birmingham New St. [12]	68	d								10 31	10 36	10 57		11 01	11 15									
Wolverhampton [7] 🚋		d								10 49	10 54	11 15		11 20	11 37									
Penkridge		d									11 04													
Stafford		a	10 22							11 00	11 10	11 29		11 35		11 35		11 22						
		d	10 23							11 01	11 10	11 30		11 35		11 39		11 23						
Stoke-on-Trent		a				10 48				11 19		11 54				12 00	11 24				11 48			
Macclesfield		a			←			←				12 11					11 41			←				
Crewe [10]		a	10 41	10 47	10 56			11 07	11 10		11 30			11 56	12 07	12 24		11 41	11 47	11 56				
		d	10 43	10 49	10 57			11 09	11 11		11 32			11 57	12 09			11 43	11 49	11 57				
Chester	81	a		11 13										→	→				12 13					
Wrexham General	75	a																						
Llandudno Junction	81	a		12 00																				
Bangor (Gwynedd)	81	a		12 16																				
Holyhead ⛴	81	a		12 50																				
Wilmslow	84	a							11 27															
Stockport	84	a				11 16			11 36	11 49		12 26					11 55				12 16			
Manchester Piccadilly [10] 🚋		a				11 28			11 49	11 59		12 38					12 07				12 28			
Warrington Bank Quay		a					11 14	11 26															12 14	
		d					11 14	11 27															12 14	
Runcorn	91	a	11 00		11 21						11 51							12 00		12 24				
Liverpool South Pkwy [7] ✈	91	a			11 30						12 00									12 33				
Liverpool Lime St. [10]	91	a	11 21		11 42						12 11							12 21		12 44				
		d																						
Manchester Airport ✈	82	d											11 00									11 29		
Manchester Picc. [10] 🚋	82	d											11 16									11 46		
Bolton	82	d																				12 07		
Wigan North Western	90	a					11 25	11 37					11 43										12 25	←
		d					11 25	11 38					11 43										12 25	
Preston [8]	90	a					11 38	11 51					11 57									12 33	12 38	12 33
Preston [8]	90	d					11 41	11 52					11 58									12 45	12 41	12 45
Blackpool North	97	a																				→		
Lancaster [6]		a					11 54	12 07					12 14										12 54	13 00
		d					11 55	12 07					12 15										12 55	13 01
Barrow-in-Furness	82	a											13 09											
Oxenholme Lake District		a						12 20															13 08	13 17
		d						12 21															13 08	13 18
Windermere	83	a																						13 39
Penrith North Lakes		d					12 30																	
Carlisle [8]	216	a					12 46	12 59															13 46	
		d					12 47	13 01															13 47	
Lockerbie		d																						
Carstairs	226	a																						
Motherwell	226	a																						
Glasgow Central [15]	216,226	a					14 01																15 01	
Haymarket	225,226,228,230,242	a						14 15																
Edinburgh [10]	225,226,228,230,242	a						14 22																
Perth	229	a																						
Dundee	229	a																						
Aberdeen	229	a																						
Inverness	229	a																						

OVERNIGHT SLEEPERS. For sleeper trains, operated by First ScotRail, please see Tables 400 - 404.

For complete service between Manchester and Preston, Blackpool and between Barrow-in-furness and Lancaster, please see Table 82.

For complete service between Crewe and Liverpool Lime Street, see Table 91

For complete service between Crewe/Stoke-on-Trent & Manchester see Table 84

For complete service between Crewe and Holyhead please see Table 81.

For complete service between Coventry-Birmingham-Wolverhampton-Stafford please see Table 68

For complete service between Windermere and Oxenholme Lake District, please see Table 83

Table 65

Saturdays

14 December to 28 December

London and West Midlands - North West England and Scotland

Route Diagram - refer to first Page of Table 65

	VT	VT	XC		LM	XC	TP	NT	LM	VT	LM	VT	VT		VT	LM	VT	VT	VT	VT	XC	LM	XC	
	◇1	◇1	◇1		1	◇1	◇1		1	◇1	1	◇1	◇1		◇1	1	◇1	◇1	◇1	◇1	◇1	1	◇1	
London Euston 15 ⊖66 d		10 40								10 43	10 46	11 00	11 07		11 10		11 20	11 30		11 40				
Watford Junction 66 d																								
Milton Keynes Central 66 d										11 13	11 19				11 41		11 50							
Rugby 66 d											11 42													
Nuneaton d											11 54													
Tamworth Low Level d											12 09													
Lichfield Trent Valley d											12 17													
Coventry 68 d						11 27				11 42													12 27	
Birmingham International 68 ✈ d						11 38				11 53													12 38	
Birmingham New St. 12 68 d			11 31		11 36	11 57			12 01	12 15											12 31	12 36	12 57	
Wolverhampton 7 d			11 49		11 54	12 15			12 20	12 37											12 49	12 54	13 15	
Penkridge d					12 04																	13 04		
Stafford a			12 00		12 10	12 29			12 35		12 35		12 22								13 00	13 10	13 29	
d			12 01		12 10	12 30			12 35		12 39		12 23								13 01	13 10	13 30	
Stoke-on-Trent a			12 19			12 54					13 00	12 24					12 48				13 18		13 54	
Macclesfield a	←					13 11						12 41				←			←				14 11	
Crewe 10 a	12 07	12 10			12 30				12 56	13 07	13 24		12 41		12 47	12 56			13 07	13 10		13 30		
d	12 09	12 11			12 32				12 57	13 09			12 43		12 49	12 57			13 09	13 11		13 32		
Chester 81 a									↪	↪					13 13									
Wrexham General 75 a																								
Llandudno Junction 81 a																								
Bangor (Gwynedd) 81 a																								
Holyhead 81 ⛴ a																								
Wilmslow 84 a		12 27																		13 27				
Stockport 84 a		12 36	12 49			13 27						12 55					13 16			13 36	13 49		14 27	
Manchester Piccadilly 10 ⇌ a		12 49	12 59			13 38						13 07					13 28			13 49	13 59		14 38	
Warrington Bank Quay a	12 26																	13 14	13 26					
d	12 27																	13 14	13 27					
Runcorn 91 a					12 50								13 00			13 21						13 50		
Liverpool South Pkwy 7 91 ✈ a					12 59											13 30						13 59		
Liverpool Lime St. 10 91 a					13 10								13 21			13 42						14 10		
d																								
Manchester Airport 82 ✈ d							12 00																	
Manchester Picc. 10 82 ⇌ d							12 16																	
Bolton 82 d																								
Wigan North Western 90 a	12 37						12 43											13 25	13 37					
d	12 38						12 43											13 25	13 38					
Preston 8 90 a	12 51						12 57											13 38	13 51					
Preston 8 90 d	12 53						12 58											13 41	13 53					
Blackpool North 97 a																								
Lancaster 6 a	13 07						13 14											13 54	14 07					
d	13 08						13 15	13 32										13 55	14 08					
Barrow-in-Furness 82 a								14 36																
Oxenholme Lake District a	13 21						13 29											14 08						
d	13 22						13 29											14 08						
Windermere 83 a																								
Penrith North Lakes d							13 55												14 43					
Carlisle 8 216 a	14 00						14 11	17 21										14 46	14 58					
d	14 03						14 11											14 47	14 59					
Lockerbie d							14 30																	
Carstairs 226 a																								
Motherwell 226 a																								
Glasgow Central 15 216,226 a	15 17																	16 01						
Haymarket 225,226,228,230,242 a							15s33												16 17					
Edinburgh 10 225,226,228,230,242 a							15 38												16 22					
Perth 229 a																								
Dundee 229 a																								
Aberdeen 229 a																								
Inverness 229 a																								

OVERNIGHT SLEEPERS. For sleeper trains, operated by First ScotRail, please see Tables 400 - 404.

For complete service between Manchester and Preston, Blackpool and between Barrow-in-furness and Lancaster, please see Table 82.

For complete service between Crewe and Liverpool Lime Street, see Table 91

For complete service between Crewe/Stoke-on-Trent & Manchester see Table 84

For complete service between Crewe and Holyhead please see Table 81.

For complete service between Coventry-Birmingham-Wolverhampton-Stafford please see Table 68

For complete service between Windermere and Oxenholme Lake District, please see Table 83

Table 65

Saturdays

14 December to 28 December

London and West Midlands - North West England and Scotland

Route Diagram - refer to first Page of Table 65

		TP	TP	LM	VT	LM	VT	VT	VT	LM	VT	TP	VT	TP	VT	VT	XC	LM	XC	TP	LM	VT	LM
		◇1		1	◇1	1	◇1	◇1	◇1	1	◇1	◇1	◇1	◇1	◇1	◇1	◇1	1	◇1	◇1	1	◇1	1
		🛒			🍴		🍴	🍴	🍴		🍴		🍴		🍴	🍴	🛒		🛒	🛒		🍴	
London Euston 15 ⊖66	d				11 43	11 46	12 00	12 07	12 10		12 20		12 30			12 40						12 43	12 46
Watford Junction 66	d																						
Milton Keynes Central 66	d				12 13	12 19			12 41		12 50											13 13	13 19
Rugby 66	d					12 42																	13 42
Nuneaton	d					12 54																	13 54
Tamworth Low Level	d					13 09																	14 09
Lichfield Trent Valley	d					13 17																	14 17
Coventry 68	d				12 42														13 27			13 42	
Birmingham International 68 ✈	d				12 53														13 38			13 53	
Birmingham New St. 12 68	d			13 01	13 15												13 31	13 36	13 57		14 01	14 15	
Wolverhampton 7 🚌	d			13 20	13 37												13 49	13 54	14 15		14 20	14 37	
Penkridge	d																	14 04					
Stafford	a			13 35		13 35		13 22									14 00	14 10	14 29		14 35		14 35
	d			13 35		13 39		13 23									14 01	14 10	14 30		14 35		14 39
Stoke-on-Trent	a					14 00	13 24				13 48						14 19		14 54				15 00
Macclesfield	a						13 41			←					←				15 11				
Crewe 10	a			13 56	14 07	14 24		13 41	13 47	13 56					14 07	14 10		14 30			14 56	15 07	15 24
	d			13 57	14 09			13 43	13 49	13 57					14 09	14 11		14 32			14 57	15 09	
Chester 81	a			→	→				14 13												→	→	
Wrexham General 75	a																						
Llandudno Junction 81	a																						
Bangor (Gwynedd) 81	a																						
Holyhead 81 ⛴	a																						
Wilmslow 84	a															14 27							
Stockport 84	a						13 55				14 16					14 36	14 49		15 27				
Manchester Piccadilly 10 🚌	a						14 07				14 28					14 49	14 59		15 38				
Warrington Bank Quay	a												14 14		14 26								
	d												14 15		14 27								
Runcorn 91	a							14 00		14 21								14 50					
Liverpool South Pkwy 7 91 ✈	a									14 30								14 59					
Liverpool Lime St. 10 91	a							14 21		14 42								15 10					
	d																						
Manchester Airport 82 ✈	d	13 00										13 29								14 00			
Manchester Picc. 10 82 🚌	d	13 16										13 46								14 16			
Bolton 82	d											14 07											
Wigan North Western 90	a	13 43											14 25	←	14 37					14 43			
	d	13 43											14 26		14 38					14 43			
Preston 8 90	a	13 57										14 33	14 39	14 33	14 51					14 57			
Preston 8 90	d	13 58	14 06									14 45	14 41	14 45	14 53					14 58			
Blackpool North 97	a											→											
Lancaster 6	a	14 14	14 21										14 55	15 00	15 07					15 14			
	d	14 15	14 22										14 55	15 01	15 08					15 15			
Barrow-in-Furness 82	a		15 17																				
Oxenholme Lake District	a													15 17	15 21					15 29			
	d													15 18	15 22					15 29			
Windermere 83	a													15 39									
Penrith North Lakes	d												15 30							15 54			
Carlisle 8 216	a	15 06											15 46		15 59					16 11			
	d	15 08											15 46		16 02					16 11			
Lockerbie	d	15 27																		16 30			
Carstairs 226	a																						
Motherwell 226	a																						
Glasgow Central 15 216,226	a	16 29											17 01		17 17								
Haymarket 225,226,228,230,242	a																			17s30			
Edinburgh 10 225,226,228,230,242	a																			17 38			
Perth 229	a																						
Dundee 229	a																						
Aberdeen 229	a																						
Inverness 229	a																						

OVERNIGHT SLEEPERS. For sleeper trains, operated by First ScotRail, please see Tables 400 - 404.

For complete service between Manchester and Preston, Blackpool and between Barrow-in-furness and Lancaster, please see Table 82.

For complete service between Crewe and Liverpool Lime Street, see Table 91

For complete service between Crewe/Stoke-on-Trent & Manchester see Table 84

For complete service between Crewe and Holyhead please see Table 81.

For complete service between Coventry-Birmingham-Wolverhampton-Stafford please see Table 68

For complete service between Windermere and Oxenholme Lake District, please see Table 83

Table 65

Saturdays

14 December to 28 December

London and West Midlands - North West England and Scotland

Route Diagram - refer to first Page of Table 65

Station			VT	VT	VT	LM	VT		VT	VT	VT	XC	LM	XC	TP	LM	VT		LM	VT	VT	VT	LM	VT	VT	VT
			◇1	◇1	◇1	1	◇1		◇1	◇1	◇1	◇1	1	◇1	◇1	1	◇1		1	◇1	◇1	◇1	1	◇1	◇1	◇1
			☕	☕	☕		☕		☕	☕	☕	trolley		trolley			☕			☕	☕	☕		☕	☕	☕
London Euston 15	⊖66	d	13 00	13 07	13 10		13 20		13 30		13 40						13 43		13 46	14 00	14 07	14 10		14 20	14 30	
Watford Junction	66	d																								
Milton Keynes Central	66	d			13 41		13 50										14 13		14 19			14 41		14 50		
Rugby	66	d																	14 42							
Nuneaton		d																	14 54							
Tamworth Low Level		d																	15 09							
Lichfield Trent Valley		d																	15 17							
Coventry	68	d												14 27			14 42									
Birmingham International	68 ✈	d												14 38			14 53									
Birmingham New St. 12	68	d										14 31	14 36	14 57		15 01	15 15									
Wolverhampton 7	⛴	d										14 49	14 54	15 15		15 20	15 37									
Penkridge		d											15 04													
Stafford		a		14 22								15 00	15 10	15 29		15 35			15 35		15 22					
		d		14 23								15 01	15 10	15 30		15 35			15 39		15 23					
Stoke-on-Trent		a	14 24				14 48					15 19		15 54					16 00	15 24				15 48		
Macclesfield		a	14 41			←				←				16 11						15 41			←			←
Crewe 10		a		14 41	14 47	14 56				15 07	15 10		15 30			15 56	16 06		16 24		15 41	15 47	15 56			16 06
		d		14 43	14 49	14 57				15 09	15 11		15 32			15 57	16 09				15 43	15 49	15 57			16 09
Chester	81	a			15 13											→	→					16 10				
Wrexham General	75	a																								
Llandudno Junction	81	a																				17 01				
Bangor (Gwynedd)	81	a																				17 17				
Holyhead	81 ⛴	a																				17 51				
Wilmslow	84	a									15 27															
Stockport	84	a	14 55				15 16				15 36	15 49		16 27						15 55				16 16		
Manchester Piccadilly 10	⛴	a	15 07				15 28				15 49	15 59		16 38						16 07				16 28		
Warrington Bank Quay		a							15 14	15 26															16 14	16 27
		d							15 14	15 27															16 14	16 27
Runcorn	91	a		15 00		15 21							15 50								16 00		16 24			
Liverpool South Pkwy 7	91 ✈	a				15 30							15 59										16 33			
Liverpool Lime St. 10	91	a		15 21		15 42							16 10								16 21		16 45			
		d																								
Manchester Airport	82 ✈	d													15 00											
Manchester Picc. 10	82 ⛴	d													15 16											
Bolton	82	d																								
Wigan North Western	90	a							15 25	15 37					15 43										16 25	16 38
		d							15 25	15 37					15 43										16 25	16 38
Preston 8	90	a							15 38	15 51					15 57										16 38	16 51
Preston 8	90	d							15 41	15 53					15 58										16 41	16 53
Blackpool North	97	a																								
Lancaster 6		a							15 54	16 08					16 14										16 54	17 08
		d							15 55	16 08					16 15										16 55	17 08
Barrow-in-Furness	82	a													17 18											
Oxenholme Lake District		a							16 08																	17 21
		d							16 08																	17 22
Windermere	83	a																								
Penrith North Lakes		d								16 45															17 30	
Carlisle 8	216	a							16 46	17 00															17 46	18 00
		d							16 47	17 01															17 47	18 02
Lockerbie		d																								
Carstairs	226	a																								
Motherwell	226	a																								
Glasgow Central 15	216,226	a							18 03																19 01	19 16
Haymarket	225,226,228,230,242	a								18 16																
Edinburgh 10	225,226,228,230,242	a								18 24																
Perth	229	a																								
Dundee	229	a																								
Aberdeen	229	a																								
Inverness	229	a																								

OVERNIGHT SLEEPERS. For sleeper trains, operated by First ScotRail, please see Tables 400 - 404.

For complete service between Manchester and Preston, Blackpool and between Barrow-in-furness and Lancaster, please see Table 82.

For complete service between Crewe and Liverpool Lime Street, see Table 91

For complete service between Crewe/Stoke-on-Trent & Manchester see Table 84

For complete service between Crewe and Holyhead please see Table 81.

For complete service between Coventry-Birmingham-Wolverhampton-Stafford please see Table 68

For complete service between Windermere and Oxenholme Lake District, please see Table 83

Table 65

Saturdays

14 December to 28 December

London and West Midlands - North West England and Scotland

Route Diagram - refer to first Page of Table 65

	VT		XC	LM	XC	TP		LM	VT	LM	VT		VT	VT	LM	VT	TP	VT	TP	VT	VT		XC	LM
									R											R				
	◇1		◇1	1	◇1	◇1		1	1	1	◇1		◇1	◇1	1	◇1	◇1	◇1	◇1	1	◇1		◇1	1
	☕		☕		ℸ	ℸ			☕		☕		☕	☕		☕		☕		⊠	☕		ℸ	
London Euston 15 ⊖66 d	14 40								14 43	14 46	15 00		15 07	15 10		15 20		15 30			15 40			
Watford Junction 66 d																								
Milton Keynes Central 66 d									15 13	15 19				15 41		15 50								
Rugby 66 d										15 42														
Nuneaton d										15 54														
Tamworth Low Level d										16 09														
Lichfield Trent Valley d										16 17														
Coventry 68 d					15 27				15 42															
Birmingham International 68 ✈ d					15 38				15 53															
Birmingham New St. 12 68 d			15 31	15 36	15 57			16 01	16 15														16 31	16 36
Wolverhampton 7 ⛴ d			15 49	15 54	16 15			16 20	16 37														16 49	16 54
Penkridge d				16 04				16 29																17 04
Stafford a			16 00	16 10	16 29			16 35		16 35			16 22										17 00	17 10
d			16 01	16 10	16 30			16 36		16 39			16 23										17 01	17 10
Stoke-on-Trent a			16 19		16 54					17 00	16 24					16 48							17 19	
Macclesfield a					17 11						16 41				⟵					⟵				
Crewe 10 a	16 10			16 30				16 56	17 07	17 24			16 41	16 47	16 56					17 07	17 10			17 30
d	16 11			16 32				16 57	17 09				16 43	16 49	16 57					17 09	17 11			17 32
Chester 81 a								↦	↦					17 13										
Wrexham General 75 a																								
Llandudno Junction 81 a																								
Bangor (Gwynedd) 81 a																								
Holyhead 81 ⛴ a																								
Wilmslow 84 a	16 27																				17 27			
Stockport 84 a	16 36		16 49		17 27						16 55					17 16					17 36		17 49	
Manchester Piccadilly 10 ⛴ a	16 49		16 59		17 38						17 07					17 28					17 49		17 59	
Warrington Bank Quay a																		17 14		17 26				
d																		17 14		17 26				
Runcorn 91 a				16 50									17 00		17 24									17 50
Liverpool South Pkwy 7 91 ✈ a				16 59											17 33									17 59
Liverpool Lime St. 10 91 a				17 10									17 21		17 45									18 10
d																								
Manchester Airport 82 ✈ d						16 00											16 29							
Manchester Picc. 10 82 ⛴ d						16 16											16 46							
Bolton 82 d						16 33											17 07							
Wigan North Western 90 a																		17 25	⟵	17 37				
d																		17 25		17 37				
Preston 8 90 a						16 56											17 33	17 38	17 33	17 51				
Preston 8 90 d						16 58	17 05										17 45	17 41	17 45	17 52				
Blackpool North 97 a																	↦							
Lancaster 6 a						17 14	17 20											17 54	18 00	18 07				
d						17 15	17 21											17 55	18 01	18 07				
Barrow-in-Furness 82 a																			19 04					
Oxenholme Lake District a						17 29	17 37											18 08		18 21				
d						17 29	17 38											18 08		18 22				
Windermere 83 a							17 58																	
Penrith North Lakes d																				18 48				
Carlisle 8 216 a						18 11												18 46		19 02				
d						18 11												18 47		19 02				
Lockerbie d						18 30																		
Carstairs 226 a																								
Motherwell 226 a																								
Glasgow Central 15 216,226 a																		20 01						
Haymarket 225,226,228,230,242 a						19s34														20 14				
Edinburgh 10 225,226,228,230,242 a						19 39														20 20				
Perth 229 a																								
Dundee 229 a																								
Aberdeen 229 a																								
Inverness 229 a																								

OVERNIGHT SLEEPERS. For sleeper trains, operated by First ScotRail, please see Tables 400 - 404.

For complete service between Manchester and Preston, Blackpool and between Barrow-in-furness and Lancaster, please see Table 82.

For complete service between Crewe and Liverpool Lime Street, see Table 91

For complete service between Crewe/Stoke-on-Trent & Manchester see Table 84

For complete service between Crewe and Holyhead please see Table 81.

For complete service between Coventry-Birmingham-Wolverhampton-Stafford please see Table 68

For complete service between Windermere and Oxenholme Lake District, please see Table 83

Table 65

Saturdays

14 December to 28 December

London and West Midlands - North West England and Scotland

Route Diagram - refer to first Page of Table 65

Station		XC	TP	LM	VT	LM	VT	VT		VT	LM	VT	TP	VT	TP	VT	VT	VT		XC	LM	XC	TP	LM	VT
					R											R									
		◇1	◇1	1	1	1	◇1	◇1		◇1	1	◇1	◇1	◇1	◇1	1	◇1	◇1		◇1	1	◇1	◇1	1	◇1
		⊥	⊥		⊡		⊡	⊡		⊡		⊡		⊡		⊠	⊡	⊡		⊥		⊥	⊥		⊡
London Euston 15 ⊖66	d				15 43	15 46	16 00	16 07		16 10		16 20		16 30			16 33	16 40							16 43
Watford Junction 66	d																								
Milton Keynes Central 66	d				16 13	16 19				16 41		16 50													17 13
Rugby 66	d					16 42																			
Nuneaton	d					16 54																			
Tamworth Low Level	d					17 09											17 38								
Lichfield Trent Valley	d					17 17											17 45								
Coventry 68	d	16 27			16 42																	17 27			17 42
Birmingham International 68 ✈	d	16 38			16 53																	17 38			17 53
Birmingham New St. 12 68	d	16 57		17 01	17 15															17 31	17 36	17 57		18 01	18 15
Wolverhampton 7 🚌	d	17 15		17 20	17 37															17 49	17 54	18 15		18 20	18 37
Penkridge	d			17 29																	18 04			18 29	
Stafford	a	17 29		17 35		17 35		17 22									17 58			18 00	18 10	18 29		18 35	
	d	17 30		17 36		17 39		17 23									17 59			18 01	18 10	18 30		18 36	
Stoke-on-Trent	a	17 54				18 00	17 24					17 48								18 19		18 54			
Macclesfield	a	18 11					17 41				←					←						19 11			
Crewe 10	a			17 56	18 07	18 24		17 41		17 47	17 56					18 07		18 10			18 30			18 56	19 07
	d			17 57	18 09			17 43		17 49	17 57					18 09		18 11			18 33			18 59	19 09
Chester 81	a			→	→					18 09														→	→
Wrexham General 75	a																								
Llandudno Junction 81	a									19 05															
Bangor (Gwynedd) 81	a									19 21															
Holyhead 81 ⛴	a									19 55															
Wilmslow 84	a																	18 27							
Stockport 84	a	18 27					17 55					18 16						18 36		18 49		19 27			
Manchester Piccadilly 10 🚌	a	18 38					18 07					18 28						18 49		18 59		19 38			
Warrington Bank Quay	a													18 14		18 27									
	d													18 14		18 27									
Runcorn 91	a							18 00			18 24						18 31				18 52				
Liverpool South Pkwy 7 91 ✈	a										18 33										19 02				
Liverpool Lime St. 10 91	a							18 21			18 45						18 52				19 14				
	d																								
Manchester Airport 82 ✈	d		17 00										17 29										18 00		
Manchester Picc. 10 82 🚌	d		17 15										17 46										18 16		
Bolton 82	d		17 32										18 06												
Wigan North Western 90	a													18 25	←	18 38							18 43		
	d													18 25		18 38							18 43		
Preston 8 90	a		17 56										18 35	18 38	18 35	18 51							18 57		
Preston 8 90	d		18 00										18 45	18 41	18 45	18 53							18 58		
Blackpool North 97	a												→												
Lancaster 6	a		18 16											18 54	19 00	19 07							19 14		
	d		18 16											18 55	19 01	19 08							19 15		
Barrow-in-Furness 82	a														20 04										
Oxenholme Lake District	a		18 31											19 08		19 21							19 29		
	d		18 32											19 08		19 22							19 29		
Windermere 83	a																								
Penrith North Lakes	d		18 56											19 34									19 54		
Carlisle 8 216	a		19 12											19 49		20 00							20 11		
	d		19 14											19 51		20 02							20 11		
Lockerbie	d																						20 30		
Carstairs 226	a																								
Motherwell 226	a		20s14																						
Glasgow Central 15 216,226	a		20 35											21 01		21 19									
Haymarket 225,226,228,230,242	a																						21s34		
Edinburgh 10 225,226,228,230,242	a																						21 41		
Perth 229	a																								
Dundee 229	a																								
Aberdeen 229	a																								
Inverness 229	a																								

OVERNIGHT SLEEPERS. For sleeper trains, operated by First ScotRail, please see Tables 400 - 404.

For complete service between Manchester and Preston, Blackpool and between Barrow-in-furness and Lancaster, please see Table 82.

For complete service between Crewe and Liverpool Lime Street, see Table 91

For complete service between Crewe/Stoke-on-Trent & Manchester see Table 84

For complete service between Crewe and Holyhead please see Table 81.

For complete service between Coventry-Birmingham-Wolverhampton-Stafford please see Table 68

For complete service between Windermere and Oxenholme Lake District, please see Table 83

Table 65

Saturdays

14 December to 28 December

London and West Midlands - North West England and Scotland

Route Diagram - refer to first Page of Table 65

		LM	VT	VT		VT	VT	LM	VT	VT	VT	VT	XC	LM		XC	TP	LM	VT	LM	VT	VT	VT	LM	
		1	◇1	◇1		◇1	◇1	1	◇1	◇1	◇1	◇1	◇1	1		◇1	◇1	1	◇1	1	◇1	◇1	◇1	1	
			☕	☕		☕	☕		☕	☕	☕	☕	🍴			🍴			☕		☕	☕	☕		
London Euston 15 ⊖66	d	16 46	17 00	17 07		17 10	17 10		17 20	17 30		17 40							17 43	17 46	18 00	18 07	18 10		
Watford Junction 66	d																								
Milton Keynes Central 66	d	17 19				17u40	17 41		17 50										18 13	18 19			18 41		
Rugby 66	d	17 42																		18 42					
Nuneaton	d	17 54		18 03																18 54					
Tamworth Low Level	d	18 09																		19 09					
Lichfield Trent Valley	d	18 17																		19 17					
Coventry 68	d															18 27			18 42						
Birmingham International 68 ✈	d															18 38			18 53						
Birmingham New St. 12 68	d												18 31	18 36		18 57		19 01	19 15						
Wolverhampton 7 🚌	d												18 49	18 54		19 15		19 20	19 37						
Penkridge	d													19 04				19 29							
Stafford	a	18 38		18 26									19 00	19 10		19 29		19 35		19 35		19 22			
	d	18 39		18 27									19 01	19 10		19 30		19 36		19 39		19 23			
Stoke-on-Trent	a	19 00	18 24						18 48				19 19			19 54				20 00	19 24				
Macclesfield	a		18 41					←			←					20 11					19 41			←	
Crewe 10	a	19 25		18 45		18 49	18 49	18 56			19 07	19 10		19 30				19 56	20 07	20 24		19 41	19 47	19 56	
	d			18 47		18 52	18 52	18 59			19 09	19 11						19 58	20 09			19 43	19 49	19 58	
Chester 81	a					19 11	19 12											↪	↪				20 13		
Wrexham General 75	a																								
Llandudno Junction 81	a						20 07																		
Bangor (Gwynedd) 81	a						20 24																		
Holyhead 81 ⛴	a						20 58																		
Wilmslow 84	a											19 27													
Stockport 84	a		18 55						19 16			19 36	19 49			20 27					19 55				
Manchester Piccadilly 10 🚌	a		19 07						19 28			19 49	19 59			20 37					20 07				
Warrington Bank Quay	a									19 14	19 26														
	d									19 14	19 27														
Runcorn 91	a			19 04				19 22														20 00		20 24	
Liverpool South Pkwy 7 91 ✈	a							19 31																20 33	
Liverpool Lime St. 10 91	a			19 23				19 44														20 21		20 46	
	d																								
Manchester Airport 82 ✈	d																19 00								
Manchester Picc. 10 82 🚌	d																19 16								
Bolton 82	d																19 33								
Wigan North Western 90	a									19 25	19 37														
	d									19 25	19 38														
Preston 8 90	a									19 38	19 54						19 57								
Preston 8 90	d									19 41							19 59								
Blackpool North 97	a																								
Lancaster 6	a									19 54							20 14								
	d									19 55							20 15								
Barrow-in-Furness 82	a																21 18								
Oxenholme Lake District	a									20 08															
	d									20 08															
Windermere 83	a																								
Penrith North Lakes	d									20 34															
Carlisle 8 216	a									20 49															
	d									20 51															
Lockerbie	d																								
Carstairs 226	a																								
Motherwell 226	a																								
Glasgow Central 15 216,226	a									22 01															
Haymarket 225,226,228,230,242	a																								
Edinburgh 10 225,226,228,230,242	a																								
Perth 229	a																								
Dundee 229	a																								
Aberdeen 229	a																								
Inverness 229	a																								

OVERNIGHT SLEEPERS. For sleeper trains, operated by First ScotRail, please see Tables 400 - 404.

For complete service between Manchester and Preston, Blackpool and between Barrow-in-furness and Lancaster, please see Table 82.

For complete service between Crewe and Liverpool Lime Street, see Table 91

For complete service between Crewe/Stoke-on-Trent & Manchester see Table 84

For complete service between Crewe and Holyhead please see Table 81.

For complete service between Coventry-Birmingham-Wolverhampton-Stafford please see Table 68

For complete service between Windermere and Oxenholme Lake District, please see Table 83

Table 65

Saturdays

14 December to 28 December

London and West Midlands - North West England and Scotland

Route Diagram - refer to first Page of Table 65

		VT	VT	VT	NT	VT	VT	XC	XC	TP		TP	LM	VT	LM	VT	VT	LM	VT	VT		LM	VT	XC	LM
		◇1	◇1	◇1		◇1	◇1	◇1	◇1	◇1		◇1	1	◇1	1	◇1	◇1	1	◇1	◇1		1	◇1	◇1	1
									A																
		☕	☕	☕		☕	☕	🛒	🛒					☕		☕	☕		☕	☕			☕		
London Euston [15] ⊖66	d	18 20	18 30	18 33			18 40							18 43	18 46	19 00	19 07		19 20	19 30			19 40		
Watford Junction 66	d																								
Milton Keynes Central 66	d	18 50												19 13	19 19				19 50						
Rugby 66	d														19 42										
Nuneaton	d														19 58		20 03								
Tamworth Low Level	d			19 38											20 14										
Lichfield Trent Valley	d			19 45											20 21										
Coventry 68	d								19 27					19 42											
Birmingham International 68 ✈	d								19 38					19 53											
Birmingham New St. [12] 68	d							19 31	19 57				20 01	20 15										20 31	20 36
Wolverhampton [7] ⛴	d							19 49	20 15				20 22	20 37										20 49	20 54
Penkridge	d												20 31												21 04
Stafford	a			19 58				20 00	20 29				20 37	20 51	20 38		20 26							21 00	21 10
	d			19 59				20 01	20 30				20 38	20 52	20 42		20 27							21 01	21 10
Stoke-on-Trent	a	19 48						20 19	20 54						21 01	20 24			20 48					21 20	
Macclesfield	a					←		20 36	21 11							20 41		←				←		21 38	
Crewe [10]	a					20 07	20 10						20 58	21 10	21 24		20 45	20 58		21 04		20 58	21 18		21 30
	d					20 09	20 11						21 06				20 47	21 06		21 05		21 06	21 19		
Chester 81	a												→					→							
Wrexham General 75	a																								
Llandudno Junction 81	a																								
Bangor (Gwynedd) 81	a																								
Holyhead 81 ⛴	a																								
Wilmslow 84	a						20 27																21 34		
Stockport 84	a	20 16					20 36	20 49	21 25							20 55			21 16				21 44	21 53	
Manchester Piccadilly [10] ⛴	a	20 28					20 49	20 59	21 39							21 07			21 28				21 53	22 04	
Warrington Bank Quay	a		20 14			20 26														21 22					
	d		20 14			20 27														21 22					
Runcorn 91	a			20 31													21 05					21 29			
Liverpool South Pkwy [7] 91 ✈	a																					21 38			
Liverpool Lime St. [10] 91	a			20 52													21 25					21 50			
	d																								
Manchester Airport 82 ✈	d									20 00															
Manchester Picc. [10] 82 ⛴	d									20 16															
Bolton 82	d																								
Wigan North Western 90	a		20 25			20 37				20 43										21 33					
	d		20 25			20 38				20 43										21 33					
Preston [8] 90	a		20 38			20 59				20 57										21 49					
Preston [8] 90	d		20 41		20 45							21 47													
Blackpool North 97	a																								
Lancaster [6]	a		20 54		21 08							22 02													
	d		20 55		21 11							22 03													
Barrow-in-Furness 82	a				22 17							23 06													
Oxenholme Lake District	a		21 08																						
	d		21 09																						
Windermere 83	a																								
Penrith North Lakes	d		21 34																						
Carlisle [8] 216	a		21 49																						
	d		21 52																						
Lockerbie	d		22 10																						
Carstairs 226	a																								
Motherwell 226	a		22 52																						
Glasgow Central [15] 216,226	a		23 13																						
Haymarket 225,226,228,230,242	a																								
Edinburgh [10] 225,226,228,230,242	a																								
Perth 229	a																								
Dundee 229	a																								
Aberdeen 229	a																								
Inverness 229	a																								

A 🛒 to Birmingham New St.

OVERNIGHT SLEEPERS. For sleeper trains, operated by First ScotRail, please see Tables 400 - 404.

For complete service between Manchester and Preston, Blackpool and between Barrow-in-furness and Lancaster, please see Table 82.

For complete service between Crewe and Liverpool Lime Street, see Table 91

For complete service between Crewe/Stoke-on-Trent & Manchester see Table 84

For complete service between Crewe and Holyhead please see Table 81.

For complete service between Coventry-Birmingham-Wolverhampton-Stafford please see Table 68

For complete service between Windermere and Oxenholme Lake District, please see Table 83

Table 65

Saturdays

14 December to 28 December

London and West Midlands - North West England and Scotland

Route Diagram - refer to first Page of Table 65

Station		XC	VT	VT	TP	VT	LM	XC	VT	XC	LM
		◇1	◇1	◇1	◇1	◇1	1	◇1	◇1	◇1	1
		A									
London Euston 15 ⊖66	d		20 11	20 20		20 31			21 00		
Watford Junction 66	d					20u46					
Milton Keynes Central 66	d			21 05					21 45		
Rugby 66	d		21 15			21 36					
Nuneaton	d			21 33							
Tamworth Low Level	d					21 53					
Lichfield Trent Valley	d					22 00					
Coventry 68	d	20 27						21 27			
Birmingham International 68	d	20 38						21 38			
Birmingham New St. 12 68	d	20 57					21 36	21 57		22 31	22 38
Wolverhampton 7	d	21 15					21 59	22 15		22 49	23 05
Penkridge	d						22 09				23 15
Stafford	a	21 29	21 46				22 15	22 29	22 32	23 01	23 21
	d	21 30	21 46				22 16	22 30	22 34	23 02	23 22
Stoke-on-Trent	a	21 52		22 05				22 50		23 20	
Macclesfield	a	22 11		22 21				23 07		23 38	
Crewe 10	a		22 05			22 35	22 38		22 58		23 42
	d		22 06			22 37			22 59		
Chester 81	a										
Wrexham General 75	a										
Llandudno Junction 81	a										
Bangor (Gwynedd) 81	a										
Holyhead 81	a										
Wilmslow 84	a								23 14		
Stockport 84	a	22 25		22 35				23 20	23 24	23 53	
Manchester Piccadilly 10	a	22 34		22 51				23 30	23 38	00 10	
Warrington Bank Quay	a					22 53					
	d					22 54					
Runcorn 91	a		22 24								
Liverpool South Pkwy 7 91	a										
Liverpool Lime St. 10 91	a		22 46								
	d										
Manchester Airport 82	d				22 00						
Manchester Picc. 10 82	d				22 16						
Bolton 82	d				22 32						
Wigan North Western 90	a					23 04					
	d					23 05					
Preston 8 90	a				22 53	23 19					
Preston 8 90	d				22 55						
Blackpool North 97	a										
Lancaster 6	a				23 10						
	d				23 11						
Barrow-in-Furness 82	a				00 14						
Oxenholme Lake District	a										
	d										
Windermere 83	a										
Penrith North Lakes	d										
Carlisle 8 216	a										
	d										
Lockerbie	d										
Carstairs 226	a										
Motherwell 226	a										
Glasgow Central 15 216,226	a										
Haymarket 225,226,228,230,242	a										
Edinburgh 10 225,226,228,230,242	a										
Perth 229	a										
Dundee 229	a										
Aberdeen 229	a										
Inverness 229	a										

A to Birmingham New St.

OVERNIGHT SLEEPERS. For sleeper trains, operated by First ScotRail, please see Tables 400 - 404.

For complete service between Manchester and Preston, Blackpool and between Barrow-in-furness and Lancaster, please see Table 82.

For complete service between Crewe and Liverpool Lime Street, see Table 91

For complete service between Crewe/Stoke-on-Trent & Manchester see Table 84

For complete service between Crewe and Holyhead please see Table 81.

For complete service between Coventry-Birmingham-Wolverhampton-Stafford please see Table 68

For complete service between Windermere and Oxenholme Lake District, please see Table 83

Table 65

Saturdays

4 January to 8 February

London and West Midlands - North West England and Scotland

Route Diagram - refer to first Page of Table 65

	SR	SR	SR	SR	VT	VT	TP	TP	AW		XC	LM	VT	LM	XC	LM	XC	TP	TP		VT	NT	LM	VT
	B		B	B																				
					◇1	◇1	◇1	◇1			◇1	1	◇1	1	◇1	1	◇1	◇1	◇1		◇1		1	◇1
	🛏 ✕		🛏 ✕	🛏 ✕	☕	☕	🛒						☕		🛒		🛒	🛒	🛒		☕			⊠
London Euston 15 ⊖66 d																					06 05			
Watford Junction 66 d	00u10																				06u20			
Milton Keynes Central 66 d																					06 41			
Rugby 66 d														06 02							07 03			
Nuneaton d														06 14										
Tamworth Low Level d														06 29										
Lichfield Trent Valley d														06 35										
Coventry 68 d																								
Birmingham International 68 ✈ d																								
Birmingham New St. 12 68 d						05 30					05 57	06 01	06 15		06 31	06 36	06 57						07 01	07 15
Wolverhampton 7 🚌 d						05 48					06 16	06 20	06 37		06 49	06 52	07 15						07 20	07 37
Penkridge d												06 29				07 02							07 29	
Stafford a						06 00					06 29	06 35		06 53	07 00	07 09	07 29				07 33		07 35	
d						06 01					06 30	06 36		06 54	07 01	07 09	07 30				07 34		07 38	
Stoke-on-Trent a											06 50			07 14	07 18									
Macclesfield a											07 11				07 36									
Crewe 10 a						06 20						06 56	07 07	07 37		07 33	07 50				07 53		07 58	08 06
d					05 57	06 23			06 27			06 58	07 09			07 34	07 52				07 55		08 00	08 09
Chester 81 a						06 43																		
Wrexham General 75 a																								
Llandudno Junction 81 a						07 33																		
Bangor (Gwynedd) 81 a						07 49																		
Holyhead 81 ⛴ a						08 23																		
Wilmslow 84 a									06 44								08 08							
Stockport 84 a									06 55		07 25				07 49		08 20							
Manchester Piccadilly 10 🚌 a									07 07		07 34				07 59		08 34							
Warrington Bank Quay a					06 13								07 26								08 11			08 26
d					06 15								07 27								08 12			08 27
Runcorn 91 a												07 23				08 00							08 24	
Liverpool South Pkwy 7 91 ✈ a												07 32				08 09							08 33	
Liverpool Lime St. 10 91 a												07 44				08 21							08 46	
d																								
Manchester Airport 82 ✈ d							05 58	06 18										07 00	07 25					
Manchester Picc. 10 82 🚌 d							06 13	06 33										07 15	07 45					
Bolton 82 d								06 52											07 59					
Wigan North Western 90 a					06 24		06 42						07 37					07 43			08 22			08 37
d					06 26		06 42						07 38					07 43			08 23			08 38
Preston 8 90 a					06 38		06 56	07 18					07 51					07 57	08 22		08 36			08 51
Preston 8 90 d			00u52	00u52	06 40		06 57	07 20					07 53					07 58	08 24		08 37			08 53
Blackpool North 97 a																								
Lancaster 6 a					06 54		07 13	07 35					08 07					08 14	08 39		08 52			09 08
d					06 54		07 13	07 36					08 08					08 16	08 40		08 52	09 02		09 08
Barrow-in-Furness 82 a								08 39														10 06		
Oxenholme Lake District a					07 07		07 27						08 21								09 05			
d					07 09		07 28						08 22								09 06			
Windermere 83 a																								
Penrith North Lakes d					07 34		07 53											08 54			09 32			09 46
Carlisle 8 216 a	05s10				07 49		08 09						09 00					09 10	09 31		09 47	12 38		10 00
d					07 51		08 11						09 00					09 11	09 31		09 48			10 02
Lockerbie d					08 10		08 30												09 51					
Carstairs 226 a	06s19																							
Motherwell 226 a	06s54																							
Glasgow Central 15 216,226 a	07 18				09 13													10 31			11 03			11 16
Haymarket 225,226,228,230,242 a							09s29						10 16						10s49					
Edinburgh 10 225,226,228,230,242 a		07 22					09 34						10 25						10 57					
Perth 229 a				05s39																				
Dundee 229 a			06s08																					
Aberdeen 229 a			07 34																					
Inverness 229 a				08 36																				

OVERNIGHT SLEEPERS. For sleeper trains, operated by First ScotRail, please see Tables 400 - 404.

For complete service between Manchester and Preston, Blackpool and between Barrow-in-furness and Lancaster, please see Table 82.

For complete service between Crewe and Liverpool Lime Street, see Table 91

For complete service between Crewe/Stoke-on-Trent & Manchester see Table 84

For complete service between Crewe and Holyhead please see Table 81.

For complete service between Coventry-Birmingham-Wolverhampton-Stafford please see Table 68

For complete service between Windermere and Oxenholme Lake District, please see Table 83

Table 65

Saturdays

4 January to 8 February

London and West Midlands - North West England and Scotland

Route Diagram - refer to first Page of Table 65

		LM	XC	NT	TP	LM		LM	VT	LM	VT	VT	VT	XC	VT	LM		TP	VT	VT	XC	LM	XC	TP	LM
		1	◇1		◇1	1		1	◇1	1	◇1	◇1	◇1	◇1	◇1	1		◇1	◇1	◇1	◇1	1	◇1	◇1	1
			🛒						🍽		🍽	🍽	🍽	🛒	🍽				🍽	🍽	🛒		🛒	🛒	
London Euston 15 ⊖66	d							06 24	06 36		06 55	07 07	07 20		07 30					07 35					
Watford Junction 66	d							06 41	06u51																
Milton Keynes Central 66	d							07 23			07 27		07 50							08 06					
Rugby 66	d	06 58						08 04																	
Nuneaton	d	07 12						08 16																	
Tamworth Low Level	d	07 29						08 30																	
Lichfield Trent Valley	d	07 35						08 36																	
Coventry 68	d													07 27									08 27		
Birmingham International 68 ✈	d													07 38									08 38		
Birmingham New St. 12 68	d		07 31			07 36								07 57		08 01			08 15		08 31	08 36	08 57		09 01
Wolverhampton 7 ⛴	d		07 49			07 54								08 15		08 20			08 37		08 49	08 54	09 15		09 20
Penkridge	d					08 04										08 29						09 04			
Stafford	a	07 53	08 00			08 10		08 53				08 22		08 29		08 35					09 00	09 10	09 29		09 34
	d	07 54	08 01			08 10		08 54				08 23		08 30		08 36					09 01	09 10	09 30		09 35
Stoke-on-Trent	a	08 15	08 19					09 15			08 24		08 48	08 54							09 19		09 54		
Macclesfield	a		08 36							←	08 41			09 11									10 11		
Crewe 10	a	08 38				08 30		09 38	08 10	08 30		08 41				08 56			09 07	09 10		09 30			09 56
	d					08 32			08 11	08 32		08 43				08 58			09 09	09 11		09 32			09 57
Chester 81	a					→																			→
Wrexham General 75	a																								
Llandudno Junction 81	a																								
Bangor (Gwynedd) 81	a																								
Holyhead 81 ⛴	a																								
Wilmslow 84	a								08 27											09 27					
Stockport 84	a		08 49						08 36		08 55		09 16	09 27						09 36	09 49		10 27		
Manchester Piccadilly 10 ⛴	a		08 59						08 49		09 07		09 28	09 38						09 49	09 59		10 38		
Warrington Bank Quay	a														09 14				09 26						
	d														09 14				09 27						
Runcorn 91	a									08 50		09 00				09 21						09 50			
Liverpool South Pkwy 7 91 ✈	a									08 59						09 30						09 59			
Liverpool Lime St. 10 91	a									09 10		09 21				09 42						10 10			
	d																								
Manchester Airport 82 ✈	d				08 25																			09 00	
Manchester Picc. 10 82 ⛴	d				08 46																			09 16	
Bolton 82	d				09 07																			09 35	
Wigan North Western 90	a														09 25				09 37						
	d														09 25				09 38						
Preston 8 90	a				09 30										09 38				09 51					09 55	
Preston 8 90	d			09 07	09 32										09 41			09 45	09 53					09 59	
Blackpool North 97	a																								
Lancaster 6	a			09 27	09 47										09 54			10 00	10 08					10 14	
	d				09 48										09 55			10 01	10 08					10 15	
Barrow-in-Furness 82	a																	11 04							
Oxenholme Lake District	a				10 03														10 22						
	d				10 04														10 23						
Windermere 83	a				10 27																				
Penrith North Lakes	d														10 30									10 53	
Carlisle 8 216	a														10 46				11 00					11 07	
	d														10 47				11 02					11 10	
Lockerbie	d																							11 29	
Carstairs 226	a																								
Motherwell 226	a																								
Glasgow Central 15 216,226	a														12 02									12 29	
Haymarket 225,226,228,230,242	a																		12 16						
Edinburgh 10 225,226,228,230,242	a																		12 22						
Perth 229	a																								
Dundee 229	a																								
Aberdeen 229	a																								
Inverness 229	a																								

OVERNIGHT SLEEPERS. For sleeper trains, operated by First ScotRail, please see Tables 400 - 404.

For complete service between Manchester and Preston, Blackpool and between Barrow-in-furness and Lancaster, please see Table 82.

For complete service between Crewe and Liverpool Lime Street, see Table 91

For complete service between Crewe/Stoke-on-Trent & Manchester see Table 84

For complete service between Crewe and Holyhead please see Table 81.

For complete service between Coventry-Birmingham-Wolverhampton-Stafford please see Table 68

For complete service between Windermere and Oxenholme Lake District, please see Table 83

Table 65

Saturdays

4 January to 8 February

London and West Midlands - North West England and Scotland

Route Diagram - refer to first Page of Table 65

Station	Table		VT		LM	VT	VT	VT	LM	VT	TP	VT	TP		VT	VT	XC	LM	XC	TP	VT	NT	LM		VT	LM
			◇1 ☕		1	◇1 ☕	◇1 ☕	◇1 ☕	1	◇1 ☕	◇1	◇1 ☕	◇1		◇1 ⊠	◇1 ☕	◇1 🛒	1	◇1 🛒	◇1 🛒	◇1 ☕		1		◇1 ☕	1
London Euston 15	⊖66	d	07 43		07 46	08 00	08 07	08 10		08 20		08 30				08 40									08 43	08 46
Watford Junction	66	d																								
Milton Keynes Central	66	d	08 13		08 19			08 41		08 50															09 13	09 19
Rugby	66	d			08 42																					09 42
Nuneaton		d			08 54																					09 54
Tamworth Low Level		d			09 09																					10 09
Lichfield Trent Valley		d			09 17																					10 17
Coventry	68	d	08 42																09 27						09 42	
Birmingham International	68 ✈	d	08 53																09 38						09 53	
Birmingham New St. 12	68	d	09 15														09 31	09 36	09 57				10 01		10 15	
Wolverhampton 7	🚌	d	09 37														09 49	09 54	10 15				10 20		10 37	
Penkridge		d																10 04								
Stafford		a			09 35		09 22										10 00	10 10	10 29				10 35			10 35
		d			09 39		09 23										10 01	10 10	10 30				10 35			10 39
Stoke-on-Trent		a			10 00	09 24				09 48							10 19		10 54							11 00
Macclesfield		a				09 41			←						←				11 11							
Crewe 10		a	10 07		10 24		09 41	09 47	09 56						10 07	10 10		10 30					10 56		11 07	11 24
		d	10 09				09 43	09 49	09 57						10 09	10 11		10 32					10 57		11 09	
Chester	81	a	→					10 13															→		→	
Wrexham General	75	a																								
Llandudno Junction	81	a																								
Bangor (Gwynedd)	81	a																								
Holyhead	81 ⛴	a																								
Wilmslow	84	a														10 27										
Stockport	84	a				09 55				10 16						10 36	10 49		11 27							
Manchester Piccadilly 10	🚌	a				10 07				10 28						10 49	10 59		11 38							
Warrington Bank Quay		a										10 14			10 26											
		d										10 14			10 27											
Runcorn	91	a					10 00		10 23									10 50								
Liverpool South Pkwy 7	91 ✈	a							10 32									10 59								
Liverpool Lime St. 10	91	a					10 21		10 44									11 10								
		d																								
Manchester Airport	82 ✈	d									09 29									10 00						
Manchester Picc. 10	82 🚌	d									09 46									10 16						
Bolton	82	d									10 07															
Wigan North Western	90	a										10 25	←		10 37											
		d										10 25			10 38											
Preston 8	90	a									10 33	10 38	10 33		10 51					10 56						
Preston 8	90	d									10 45	10 41	10 45		10 53					10 57						
Blackpool North	97	a									→															
Lancaster 6		a										10 54	11 00		11 07					11 13						
		d										10 55	11 01		11 08					11 13		11 28				
Barrow-in-Furness	82	a																				12 32				
Oxenholme Lake District		a										11 08	11 17													
		d										11 08	11 18													
Windermere	83	a											11 39													
Penrith North Lakes		d													11 45											
Carlisle 8	216	a										11 46			12 00					12 05		15 00				
		d										11 47			12 02					12 06	13 01					
Lockerbie		d																			13 19					
Carstairs	226	a																								
Motherwell	226	a																								
Glasgow Central 15	216,226	a										13 01			13 17											
Haymarket	225,226,228,230,242	a																		13s19	14 15					
Edinburgh 10	225,226,228,230,242	a																		13 27	14 22					
Perth	229	a																								
Dundee	229	a																								
Aberdeen	229	a																								
Inverness	229	a																								

OVERNIGHT SLEEPERS. For sleeper trains, operated by First ScotRail, please see Tables 400 - 404.

For complete service between Manchester and Preston, Blackpool and between Barrow-in-furness and Lancaster, please see Table 82.

For complete service between Crewe and Liverpool Lime Street, see Table 91

For complete service between Crewe/Stoke-on-Trent & Manchester see Table 84

For complete service between Crewe and Holyhead please see Table 81.

For complete service between Coventry-Birmingham-Wolverhampton-Stafford please see Table 68

For complete service between Windermere and Oxenholme Lake District, please see Table 83

Table 65

Saturdays

4 January to 8 February

London and West Midlands - North West England and Scotland

Route Diagram - refer to first Page of Table 65

			VT	VT	VT	LM	VT	TP	VT	VT	VT	XC	LM	XC	TP	VT	VT	VT	LM	TP	VT	LM	VT	VT	VT	LM
			◇1	◇1	◇1	1	◇1		◇1	◇1	◇1	◇1	1	◇1	◇1			◇1	1		◇1	1	◇1	◇1	◇1	1
								▭								▭	▭			▭						
			⊡	⊡	⊡		⊡		⊡	⊡	⊡	⊤		⊤				⊡			⊡		⊡	⊡	⊡	
London Euston [15]	⊖66	d	09 00	09 07	09 10		09 20		09 30		09 40										09 43	09 46	10 00	10 07	10 10	
Watford Junction	66	d																								
Milton Keynes Central	66	d			09 41		09 50														10 13	10 19			10 41	
Rugby	66	d																				10 42				
Nuneaton		d																				10 54				
Tamworth Low Level		d																				11 09				
Lichfield Trent Valley		d																				11 17				
Coventry	68	d												10 27							10 42					
Birmingham International	68 ✈	d												10 38							10 53					
Birmingham New St. [12]	68	d										10 31	10 36	10 57					11 01		11 15					
Wolverhampton [7]	🚌	d										10 49	10 54	11 15					11 20		11 37					
Penkridge		d											11 04													
Stafford		a		10 22								11 00	11 10	11 29					11 35			11 35		11 22		
		d		10 23								11 01	11 10	11 30					11 35			11 39		11 23		
Stoke-on-Trent		a	10 24				10 48					11 19		11 54								12 00	11 24			
Macclesfield		a	10 41			←				←				12 11									11 41			←
Crewe [10]		a		10 41	10 47	10 56				11 07	11 10		11 30						11 56		12 07	12 24		11 41	11 47	11 56
		d		10 43	10 49	10 57				11 09	11 11		11 32						11 57		12 09			11 43	11 49	11 57
Chester	81	a			11 13														→		→				12 13	
Wrexham General	75	a																								
Llandudno Junction	81	a			12 00																					
Bangor (Gwynedd)	81	a			12 16																					
Holyhead	81 ⛴	a			12 50																					
Wilmslow	84	a									11 27															
Stockport	84	a	10 55				11 16				11 36	11 49		12 26									11 55			
Manchester Piccadilly [10]	🚌	a	11 07				11 28				11 49	11 59		12 38									12 07			
Warrington Bank Quay		a							11 14	11 26																
		d							11 14	11 27																
Runcorn	91	a		11 00		11 21							11 51											12 00		12 24
Liverpool South Pkwy [7]	91 ✈	a				11 30							12 00													12 33
Liverpool Lime St. [10]	91	a		11 21		11 42							12 11											12 21		12 44
		d																								
Manchester Airport	82 ✈	d													11 00											
Manchester Picc. [10]	82 🚌	d													11 16											
Bolton	82	d																								
Wigan North Western	90	a							11 25	11 37					11 43											
		d							11 25	11 38					11 43											
Preston [8]	90	a							11 38	11 51					11 57											
Preston [8]	90	d							11 41						11 58		12 09									
Blackpool North	97	a																								
Lancaster [6]		a							11 54						12 14											
		d							11 55						12 15	12 20				12 25						
Barrow-in-Furness	82	a													13 09											
Oxenholme Lake District		a														13 05										
		d						12 20								13 10										
Windermere	83	a						12 42												13 12						
Penrith North Lakes		d							12 30								13 54									
Carlisle [8]	216	a							12 46							14 25	14 29									
		d							12 47									14 59								
Lockerbie		d																15 17								
Carstairs	226	a																								
Motherwell	226	a																								
Glasgow Central [15]	216,226	a							14 01																	
Haymarket	225,226,228,230,242	a																16 16								
Edinburgh [10]	225,226,228,230,242	a																16 22								
Perth	229	a																								
Dundee	229	a																								
Aberdeen	229	a																								
Inverness	229	a																								

OVERNIGHT SLEEPERS. For sleeper trains, operated by First ScotRail, please see Tables 400 - 404.

For complete service between Manchester and Preston, Blackpool and between Barrow-in-furness and Lancaster, please see Table 82.

For complete service between Crewe and Liverpool Lime Street, see Table 91

For complete service between Crewe/Stoke-on-Trent & Manchester see Table 84

For complete service between Crewe and Holyhead please see Table 81.

For complete service between Coventry-Birmingham-Wolverhampton-Stafford please see Table 68

For complete service between Windermere and Oxenholme Lake District, please see Table 83

Table 65

Saturdays

4 January to 8 February

London and West Midlands - North West England and Scotland

Route Diagram - refer to first Page of Table 65

		VT	VT	VT		VT	XC	LM	XC	VT	TP	TP	VT	NT	TP	LM	VT	LM	VT	VT	VT	LM	VT	VT
		◇1	◇1	◇1		◇1	◇1	1	◇1		◇1	◇1				1	◇1	1	◇1	◇1	◇1	1	◇1	◇1
										🚌			🚌		🚌									
		☕	☕	☕		☕	🛒		🛒		🛒						☕		☕	☕	☕		☕	☕
London Euston 15 ⊖66	d	10 20	10 30			10 40											10 43	10 46	11 00	11 07	11 10		11 20	11 30
Watford Junction 66	d																							
Milton Keynes Central 66	d	10 50															11 13	11 19			11 41		11 50	
Rugby 66	d																	11 42						
Nuneaton	d																	11 54						
Tamworth Low Level	d																	12 09						
Lichfield Trent Valley	d																	12 17						
Coventry 68	d								11 27								11 42							
Birmingham International 68 ✈	d								11 38								11 53							
Birmingham New St. 12 68	d						11 31	11 36	11 57							12 01	12 15							
Wolverhampton 7 ⛴	d						11 49	11 54	12 15							12 20	12 37							
Penkridge	d							12 04																
Stafford	a						12 00	12 10	12 29							12 35		12 35		12 22				
	d						12 01	12 10	12 30							12 35		12 39		12 23				
Stoke-on-Trent	a	11 48					12 19		12 54									13 00	12 24				12 48	
Macclesfield	a			←					13 11										12 41			←		
Crewe 10	a			12 07		12 10		12 30								12 56	13 07	13 24		12 41	12 47	12 56		
	d			12 09		12 11		12 32								12 57	13 09			12 43	12 49	12 57		
Chester 81	a															→	→				13 13			
Wrexham General 75	a																							
Llandudno Junction 81	a																							
Bangor (Gwynedd) 81	a																							
Holyhead 81 ⛴	a																							
Wilmslow 84	a					12 27																		
Stockport 84	a	12 16				12 36	12 49		13 27										12 55				13 16	
Manchester Piccadilly 10 ⛴	a	12 28				12 49	12 59		13 38										13 07				13 28	
Warrington Bank Quay	a		12 14	12 26																				13 14
	d		12 14	12 27																				13 14
Runcorn 91	a							12 50												13 00		13 21		
Liverpool South Pkwy 7 91 ✈	a							12 59														13 30		
Liverpool Lime St. 10 91	a							13 10												13 21		13 42		
	d																							
Manchester Airport 82 ✈	d										12 00	12 06												
Manchester Picc. 10 82 ⛴	d										12 16	12 27												
Bolton 82	d																							
Wigan North Western 90	a		12 25	12 37							12 43													13 25
	d		12 25	12 38							12 43													13 25
Preston 8 90	a		12 38	12 51							12 57													13 38
Preston 8 90	d		12 41								12 58		13 09											13 41
Blackpool North 97	a																							
Lancaster 6	a		12 54								13 15													13 54
	d									13 05				13 32	13 25									
Barrow-in-Furness 82	a													14 36										
Oxenholme Lake District	a									13 50														
	d									13 55														
Windermere 83	a														14 12									
Penrith North Lakes	d									14 55			14 54											
Carlisle 8 216	a									15 30			15 29	17 21										
	d																							
Lockerbie	d																							
Carstairs 226	a																							
Motherwell 226	a																							
Glasgow Central 15 216,226	a																							
Haymarket 225,226,228,230,242	a																							
Edinburgh 10 225,226,228,230,242	a											16 40												
Perth 229	a																							
Dundee 229	a																							
Aberdeen 229	a																							
Inverness 229	a																							

OVERNIGHT SLEEPERS. For sleeper trains, operated by First ScotRail, please see Tables 400 - 404.

For complete service between Manchester and Preston, Blackpool and between Barrow-in-furness and Lancaster, please see Table 82.

For complete service between Crewe and Liverpool Lime Street, see Table 91

For complete service between Crewe/Stoke-on-Trent & Manchester see Table 84

For complete service between Crewe and Holyhead please see Table 81.

For complete service between Coventry-Birmingham-Wolverhampton-Stafford please see Table 68

For complete service between Windermere and Oxenholme Lake District, please see Table 83

Table 65

Saturdays

4 January to 8 February

London and West Midlands - North West England and Scotland

Route Diagram - refer to first Page of Table 65

		VT	VT	XC	LM	XC	VT	TP	TP	VT	TP	VT	LM	VT	LM	VT	VT	VT	LM	VT		VT	VT	VT	XC
		◇1	◇1	◇1	1	◇1		◇1				◇1	1	◇1	1	◇1	◇1	◇1	1	◇1		◇1	◇1	◇1	◇1
							🚌			🚌	🚌														
		☕	☕	🛒		🛒		🛒				☕		☕		☕	☕	☕		☕		☕	☕	☕	🛒
London Euston 15 ⊖66	d		11 40											11 43	11 46	12 00	12 07	12 10		12 20		12 30		12 40	
Watford Junction 66	d																								
Milton Keynes Central 66	d													12 13	12 19			12 41		12 50					
Rugby 66	d														12 42										
Nuneaton	d														12 54										
Tamworth Low Level	d														13 09										
Lichfield Trent Valley	d														13 17										
Coventry 68	d					12 27								12 42											
Birmingham International 68 ✈	d					12 38								12 53											
Birmingham New St. 12 68	d			12 31	12 36	12 57							13 01	13 15											13 31
Wolverhampton 7 ⛴	d			12 49	12 54	13 15							13 20	13 37											13 49
Penkridge	d				13 04																				
Stafford	a			13 00	13 10	13 29							13 35		13 35		13 22								14 00
	d			13 01	13 10	13 30							13 35		13 39		13 23								14 01
Stoke-on-Trent	a			13 18		13 54									14 00	13 24				13 48					14 19
Macclesfield	a	←				14 11										13 41			←				←		
Crewe 10	a	13 07	13 10		13 30								13 56	14 07	14 24		13 41	13 47	13 56				14 07	14 10	
	d	13 09	13 11		13 32								13 57	14 09			13 43	13 49	13 57				14 09	14 11	
Chester 81	a												↪	↪				14 13							
Wrexham General 75	a																								
Llandudno Junction 81	a																								
Bangor (Gwynedd) 81	a																								
Holyhead 81 ⛴	a																								
Wilmslow 84	a		13 27																					14 27	
Stockport 84	a		13 36	13 49		14 27										13 55				14 16				14 36	14 49
Manchester Piccadilly 10 ⛴	a		13 49	13 59		14 38										14 07				14 28				14 49	14 59
Warrington Bank Quay	a	13 26																				14 14	14 26		
	d	13 27																				14 15	14 27		
Runcorn 91	a				13 50												14 00		14 21						
Liverpool South Pkwy 7 91 ✈	a				13 59														14 30						
Liverpool Lime St. 10 91	a				14 10												14 21		14 42						
	d																								
Manchester Airport 82 ✈	d							13 00																	
Manchester Picc. 10 82 ⛴	d							13 16																	
Bolton 82	d																								
Wigan North Western 90	a	13 37						13 43														14 25	14 37		
	d	13 38						13 43														14 26	14 38		
Preston 8 90	a	13 51						13 57														14 39	14 51		
Preston 8 90	d							13 58	14 06	14 09												14 41			
Blackpool North 97	a																								
Lancaster 6	a							14 15	14 21													14 55			
	d						14 05		14 22		14 25														
Barrow-in-Furness 82	a								15 17																
Oxenholme Lake District	a						14 50																		
	d						14 55																		
Windermere 83	a										15 12														
Penrith North Lakes	d						15 55			15 54															
Carlisle 8 216	a						16 30			16 29															
	d											17 01													
Lockerbie	d											17 19													
Carstairs 226	a																								
Motherwell 226	a																								
Glasgow Central 15 216,226	a																								
Haymarket 225,226,228,230,242	a											18 16													
Edinburgh 10 225,226,228,230,242	a											18 24													
Perth 229	a																								
Dundee 229	a																								
Aberdeen 229	a																								
Inverness 229	a																								

OVERNIGHT SLEEPERS. For sleeper trains, operated by First ScotRail, please see Tables 400 - 404.

For complete service between Manchester and Preston, Blackpool and between Barrow-in-furness and Lancaster, please see Table 82.

For complete service between Crewe and Liverpool Lime Street, see Table 91

For complete service between Crewe/Stoke-on-Trent & Manchester see Table 84

For complete service between Crewe and Holyhead please see Table 81.

For complete service between Coventry-Birmingham-Wolverhampton-Stafford please see Table 68

For complete service between Windermere and Oxenholme Lake District, please see Table 83

Table 65

Saturdays

4 January to 8 February

London and West Midlands - North West England and Scotland

Route Diagram - refer to first Page of Table 65

Station	Table		LM	XC	VT	TP	TP	VT	TP	LM	VT	LM	VT	VT	VT	LM	VT		VT	VT	VT	XC	LM	XC	VT	TP
			1	◇1		◇1	◇1			1	◇1	1	◇1	◇1	◇1	1	◇1		◇1	◇1	◇1	◇1	1	◇1		◇1
					🚌			🚌	🚌																🚌	
				🛒		🛒					☕		☕	☕	☕		☕		☕	☕	☕	🛒		🛒		
London Euston 15	⊖66	d									12 43	12 46	13 00	13 07	13 10		13 20		13 30		13 40					
Watford Junction	66	d																								
Milton Keynes Central	66	d									13 13	13 19			13 41		13 50									
Rugby	66	d										13 42														
Nuneaton		d										13 54														
Tamworth Low Level		d										14 09														
Lichfield Trent Valley		d										14 17														
Coventry	68	d		13 27							13 42													14 27		
Birmingham International	68 ✈	d		13 38							13 53													14 38		
Birmingham New St. 12	68	d	13 36	13 57						14 01	14 15											14 31	14 36	14 57		
Wolverhampton 7	⛴	d	13 54	14 15						14 20	14 37											14 49	14 54	15 15		
Penkridge		d	14 04																				15 04			
Stafford		a	14 10	14 29						14 35		14 35		14 22								15 00	15 10	15 29		
		d	14 10	14 30						14 35		14 39		14 23								15 01	15 10	15 30		
Stoke-on-Trent		a		14 54								15 00	14 24				14 48					15 19		15 54		
Macclesfield		a		15 11									14 41			←				←				16 11		
Crewe 10		a	14 30							14 56	15 07	15 24		14 41	14 47	14 56				15 07	15 10		15 30			
		d	14 32							14 57	15 09			14 43	14 49	14 57				15 09	15 11		15 32			
Chester	81	a								→	→				15 13											
Wrexham General	75	a																								
Llandudno Junction	81	a																								
Bangor (Gwynedd)	81	a																								
Holyhead	81 ⛴	a																								
Wilmslow	84	a																			15 27					
Stockport	84	a		15 27									14 55				15 16				15 36	15 49		16 27		
Manchester Piccadilly 10	⛴	a		15 38									15 07				15 28				15 49	15 59		16 38		
Warrington Bank Quay		a																	15 14	15 26						
		d																	15 14	15 27						
Runcorn	91	a	14 50											15 00		15 21							15 50			
Liverpool South Pkwy 7	91 ✈	a	14 59													15 30							15 59			
Liverpool Lime St. 10	91	a	15 10											15 21		15 42							16 10			
		d																								
Manchester Airport	82 ✈	d				14 00	14 06																			15 00
Manchester Picc. 10	82 ⛴	d				14 16	14 27																			15 16
Bolton	82	d																								
Wigan North Western	90	a				14 43													15 25	15 37						15 43
		d				14 43													15 25	15 37						15 43
Preston 8	90	a				14 57													15 38	15 51						15 57
Preston 8	90	d				14 58		15 09											15 41							15 58
Blackpool North	97	a																								
Lancaster 6		a				15 15													15 54							16 14
		d			15 05				15 25																16 05	16 15
Barrow-in-Furness	82	a																								17 18
Oxenholme Lake District		a			15 50																				16 50	
		d			15 55																				16 55	
Windermere	83	a							16 12																	
Penrith North Lakes		d			16 55			16 54																	17 55	
Carlisle 8	216	a			17 30			17 29																	18 30	
		d																								
Lockerbie		d																								
Carstairs	226	a																								
Motherwell	226	a																								
Glasgow Central 15	216,226	a																								
Haymarket	225,226,228,230,242	a																								
Edinburgh 10	225,226,228,230,242	a					18 37																			
Perth	229	a																								
Dundee	229	a																								
Aberdeen	229	a																								
Inverness	229	a																								

OVERNIGHT SLEEPERS. For sleeper trains, operated by First ScotRail, please see Tables 400 - 404.

For complete service between Manchester and Preston, Blackpool and between Barrow-in-furness and Lancaster, please see Table 82.

For complete service between Crewe and Liverpool Lime Street, see Table 91

For complete service between Crewe/Stoke-on-Trent & Manchester see Table 84

For complete service between Crewe and Holyhead please see Table 81.

For complete service between Coventry-Birmingham-Wolverhampton-Stafford please see Table 68

For complete service between Windermere and Oxenholme Lake District, please see Table 83

Table 65

Saturdays

4 January to 8 February

London and West Midlands - North West England and Scotland

Route Diagram - refer to first Page of Table 65

Station		VT	TP	VT	LM	VT	LM	VT	VT	VT	LM	VT	VT	VT	VT	XC	LM	XC	VT	TP	TP	TP	VT	LM
				R																				
				1	1	◇1	1	◇1	◇1	◇1	1	◇1	◇1	◇1	◇1	◇1	1	◇1		◇1	◇1			1
		🚌	🚌																🚌			🚌	🚌	
				⊠		☕		☕	☕	☕		☕	☕	☕	☕	☕		🛒		🛒				
London Euston 15 ⊖66	d					13 43	13 46	14 00	14 07	14 10		14 20	14 30		14 40									
Watford Junction 66	d																							
Milton Keynes Central 66	d					14 13	14 19			14 41		14 50												
Rugby 66	d						14 42																	
Nuneaton	d						14 54																	
Tamworth Low Level	d						15 09																	
Lichfield Trent Valley	d						15 17																	
Coventry 68	d					14 42												15 27						
Birmingham International 68 ✈	d					14 53												15 38						
Birmingham New St. 12 68	d				15 01	15 15										15 31	15 36	15 57						16 01
Wolverhampton 7 ⛴	d				15 20	15 37										15 49	15 54	16 15						16 20
Penkridge	d																16 04							16 29
Stafford	a				15 35		15 35		15 22							16 00	16 10	16 29						16 35
	d				15 35		15 39		15 23							16 01	16 10	16 30						16 36
Stoke-on-Trent	a						16 00	15 24				15 48				16 19		16 54						
Macclesfield	a							15 41			←			←				17 11						
Crewe 10	a				15 56	16 06	16 24		15 41	15 47	15 56			16 06	16 10		16 30							16 56
	d				15 57	16 09			15 43	15 49	15 57			16 09	16 11		16 32							16 57
Chester 81	a				↪	↪				16 10														↪
Wrexham General 75	a																							
Llandudno Junction 81	a									17 01														
Bangor (Gwynedd) 81	a									17 17														
Holyhead 81 ⛴	a									17 51														
Wilmslow 84	a														16 27									
Stockport 84	a							15 55				16 16			16 36	16 49		17 27						
Manchester Piccadilly 10 ⛴	a							16 07				16 28			16 49	16 59		17 38						
Warrington Bank Quay	a												16 14	16 27										
	d												16 14	16 27										
Runcorn 91	a								16 00		16 24						16 50							
Liverpool South Pkwy 7 91 ✈	a										16 33						16 59							
Liverpool Lime St. 10 91	a								16 21		16 45						17 10							
	d																							
Manchester Airport 82 ✈	d																			16 00	16 06			
Manchester Picc. 10 82 ⛴	d																			16 16	16 27			
Bolton 82	d																			16 33				
Wigan North Western 90	a												16 25	16 38										
	d												16 25	16 38										
Preston 8 90	a												16 38	16 51						16 56				
Preston 8 90	d	16 09											16 41							16 58			17 09	
Blackpool North 97	a																							
Lancaster 6	a												16 54							17 15				
	d		16 25																17 05			17 25		
Barrow-in-Furness 82	a																							
Oxenholme Lake District	a																		17 50					
	d																		17 55					
Windermere 83	a		17 12																			18 12		
Penrith North Lakes	d	17 54																	18 55				18 54	
Carlisle 8 216	a	18 29																	19 30				19 29	
	d			18 56																				
Lockerbie	d			19 15																				
Carstairs 226	a																							
Motherwell 226	a																							
Glasgow Central 15 216,226	a																							
Haymarket 225,226,228,230,242	a			20 14																				
Edinburgh 10 225,226,228,230,242	a			20 20																	20 38			
Perth 229	a																							
Dundee 229	a																							
Aberdeen 229	a																							
Inverness 229	a																							

OVERNIGHT SLEEPERS. For sleeper trains, operated by First ScotRail, please see Tables 400 - 404.

For complete service between Manchester and Preston, Blackpool and between Barrow-in-furness and Lancaster, please see Table 82.

For complete service between Crewe and Liverpool Lime Street, see Table 91

For complete service between Crewe/Stoke-on-Trent & Manchester see Table 84

For complete service between Crewe and Holyhead please see Table 81.

For complete service between Coventry-Birmingham-Wolverhampton-Stafford please see Table 68

For complete service between Windermere and Oxenholme Lake District, please see Table 83

Table 65

Saturdays

4 January to 8 February

London and West Midlands - North West England and Scotland

Route Diagram - refer to first Page of Table 65

		VT	LM	VT	VT	VT	LM	VT		TP	VT	VT	TP	VT	XC	LM	XC	VT	TP	VT	TP	LM	VT	LM	VT
		R										R											R		
		1	1	◇1	◇1	◇1	1	◇1		◇1	◇1	1	◇1	◇1	◇1	1	◇1		◇1			1	1	1	◇1
																		🚌		🚌	🚌				
		🍴		🍴	🍴	🍴		🍴			🍴	☒		🍴	🛒		🛒		🛒				🍴		🍴
London Euston 15 ⊖66	d	14 43	14 46	15 00	15 07	15 10		15 20			15 30			15 40									15 43	15 46	16 00
Watford Junction 66	d																								
Milton Keynes Central 66	d	15 13	15 19			15 41		15 50															16 13	16 19	
Rugby 66	d		15 42																					16 42	
Nuneaton	d		15 54																					16 54	
Tamworth Low Level	d		16 09																					17 09	
Lichfield Trent Valley	d		16 17																					17 17	
Coventry 68	d	15 42															16 27						16 42		
Birmingham International 68 ✈	d	15 53															16 38						16 53		
Birmingham New St. 12 68	d	16 15													16 31	16 36	16 57					17 01	17 15		
Wolverhampton 7 ⛴	d	16 37													16 49	16 54	17 15					17 20	17 37		
Penkridge	d															17 04						17 29			
Stafford	a		16 35		16 22										17 00	17 10	17 29					17 35		17 35	
	d		16 39		16 23										17 01	17 10	17 30					17 36		17 39	
Stoke-on-Trent	a		17 00	16 24				16 48							17 19		17 54							18 00	17 24
Macclesfield	a			16 41			←					←					18 11								17 41
Crewe 10	a	17 07	17 24		16 41	16 47	16 56					17 07		17 10		17 30						17 56	18 07	18 24	
	d	17 09			16 43	16 49	16 57					17 09		17 11		17 32						17 57	18 09		
Chester 81	a	↪				17 13																↪	↪		
Wrexham General 75	a																								
Llandudno Junction 81	a																								
Bangor (Gwynedd) 81	a																								
Holyhead 81 ⛴	a																								
Wilmslow 84	a													17 27											
Stockport 84	a			16 55				17 16						17 36	17 49		18 27								17 55
Manchester Piccadilly 10 ⛴	a			17 07				17 28						17 49	17 59		18 38								18 07
Warrington Bank Quay	a										17 14	17 26													
	d										17 14	17 27													
Runcorn 91	a				17 00		17 24									17 50									
Liverpool South Pkwy 7 91 ✈	a						17 33									17 59									
Liverpool Lime St. 10 91	a				17 21		17 45									18 10									
	d																								
Manchester Airport 82 ✈	d									16 29									17 00						
Manchester Picc. 10 82 ⛴	d									16 46									17 15						
Bolton 82	d									17 07															
Wigan North Western 90	a										17 25	17 37	←												
	d										17 25	17 38													
Preston 8 90	a									17 33	17 38	17 51	17 33						17 56						
Preston 8 90	d									17 45	17 41		17 45						17 57	18 09					
Blackpool North 97	a									↪															
Lancaster 6	a										17 54		18 00						18 14						
	d												18 01					18 05			18 25				
Barrow-in-Furness 82	a												19 04												
Oxenholme Lake District	a																	18 50							
	d																	18 55							
Windermere 83	a																				19 12				
Penrith North Lakes	d																	19 55		19 54					
Carlisle 8 216	a																	20 30		20 29					
	d																								
Lockerbie	d																								
Carstairs 226	a																								
Motherwell 226	a																								
Glasgow Central 15 216,226	a																								
Haymarket 225,226,228,230,242	a																								
Edinburgh 10 225,226,228,230,242	a																								
Perth 229	a																								
Dundee 229	a																								
Aberdeen 229	a																								
Inverness 229	a																								

OVERNIGHT SLEEPERS. For sleeper trains, operated by First ScotRail, please see Tables 400 - 404.

For complete service between Manchester and Preston, Blackpool and between Barrow-in-furness and Lancaster, please see Table 82.

For complete service between Crewe and Liverpool Lime Street, see Table 91

For complete service between Crewe/Stoke-on-Trent & Manchester see Table 84

For complete service between Crewe and Holyhead please see Table 81.

For complete service between Coventry-Birmingham-Wolverhampton-Stafford please see Table 68

For complete service between Windermere and Oxenholme Lake District, please see Table 83

Table 65

Saturdays

4 January to 8 February

London and West Midlands - North West England and Scotland

Route Diagram - refer to first Page of Table 65

		VT	VT	LM		VT	TP	VT	VT	TP	VT	VT	XC	LM	XC	VT	TP	VT	VT	VT	LM	VT	LM	VT
									R															
		◇1	◇1	1		◇1	◇1	◇1	1	◇1	◇1	◇1	◇1	1	◇1		◇1				1	◇1	1	◇1
London Euston 15 ⊖66	d	16 07	16 10			16 20		16 30			16 33	16 40										16 43	16 46	17 00
Watford Junction 66	d																							
Milton Keynes Central 66	d		16 41			16 50																17 13	17 19	
Rugby 66	d																						17 42	
Nuneaton	d																						17 54	
Tamworth Low Level	d										17 38												18 09	
Lichfield Trent Valley	d										17 45												18 17	
Coventry 68	d														17 27							17 42		
Birmingham International 68 ✈	d														17 38							17 53		
Birmingham New St. 12 68	d												17 31	17 36	17 57						18 01	18 15		
Wolverhampton 7	d												17 49	17 54	18 15						18 20	18 37		
Penkridge	d													18 04							18 29			
Stafford	a	17 22									17 58		18 00	18 10	18 29						18 35		18 38	
	d	17 23									17 59		18 01	18 10	18 30						18 36		18 39	
Stoke-on-Trent	a					17 48							18 19		18 54								19 00	18 24
Macclesfield	a			⟵					⟵						19 11									18 41
Crewe 10	a	17 41	17 47	17 56					18 07			18 10		18 30							18 56	19 07	19 25	
	d	17 43	17 49	17 57					18 09			18 11		18 33							18 59	19 09		
Chester 81	a		18 09																		⟶	⟶		
Wrexham General 75	a																							
Llandudno Junction 81	a		19 05																					
Bangor (Gwynedd) 81	a		19 21																					
Holyhead 81	a		19 55																					
Wilmslow 84	a											18 27												
Stockport 84	a					18 16						18 36	18 49		19 27									18 55
Manchester Piccadilly 10	a					18 28						18 49	18 59		19 38									19 07
Warrington Bank Quay	a							18 14	18 26															
	d							18 14	18 27															
Runcorn 91	a	18 00		18 24							18 31			18 52										
Liverpool South Pkwy 7 91 ✈	a			18 33										19 02										
Liverpool Lime St. 10 91	a	18 21		18 45							18 52			19 14										
	d																							
Manchester Airport 82 ✈	d						17 29										18 00							
Manchester Picc. 10 82	d						17 46										18 16							
Bolton 82	d						18 06																	
Wigan North Western 90	a							18 25	18 37	⟵							18 43							
	d							18 25	18 38								18 43							
Preston 8 90	a						18 35	18 38	18 51	18 35							18 57							
Preston 8 90	d						18 45	18 41		18 45							18 58		19 05	19 09				
Blackpool North 97	a						⟶																	
Lancaster 6	a							18 54		19 00							19 15		19 55					
	d									19 01						19 05		19 25	20 00					
Barrow-in-Furness 82	a									20 04														
Oxenholme Lake District	a															19 50			20 45					
	d															19 55			20 50					
Windermere 83	a																	20 12						
Penrith North Lakes	d															20 55			21s45	20 54				
Carlisle 8 216	a															21 30			22 25	21 29				
	d																							
Lockerbie	d																							
Carstairs 226	a																							
Motherwell 226	a																							
Glasgow Central 15 216,226	a																							
Haymarket 225,226,228,230,242	a																							
Edinburgh 10 225,226,228,230,242	a																							
Perth 229	a																							
Dundee 229	a																							
Aberdeen 229	a																							
Inverness 229	a																							

OVERNIGHT SLEEPERS. For sleeper trains, operated by First ScotRail, please see Tables 400 - 404.

For complete service between Manchester and Preston, Blackpool and between Barrow-in-furness and Lancaster, please see Table 82.

For complete service between Crewe and Liverpool Lime Street, see Table 91

For complete service between Crewe/Stoke-on-Trent & Manchester see Table 84

For complete service between Crewe and Holyhead please see Table 81.

For complete service between Coventry-Birmingham-Wolverhampton-Stafford please see Table 68

For complete service between Windermere and Oxenholme Lake District, please see Table 83

Table 65

Saturdays

4 January to 8 February

London and West Midlands - North West England and Scotland

Route Diagram - refer to first Page of Table 65

		VT	VT	VT	LM	VT	VT	VT	XC	LM	XC	TP	TP	VT	VT	NT	TP	LM	VT	LM		VT	VT	VT	LM
		◇1	◇1	◇1	1	◇1	◇1	◇1	◇1	1	◇1	◇1						1	◇1	1		◇1	◇1	◇1	1
													🚌	🚌	🚌		🚌								
		☕	⊠	☕		☕	☕	☕	🛒		🛒								☕			☕	☕	☕	
London Euston 15 ⊖66	d	17 07	17 10	17 10			17 20	17 40											17 43	17 46		18 00	18 07	18 10	
Watford Junction 66	d																								
Milton Keynes Central 66	d		17u40	17 41			17 50												18 13	18 19				18 41	
Rugby 66	d																			18 42					
Nuneaton	d	18 03																		18 54					
Tamworth Low Level	d																			19 09					
Lichfield Trent Valley	d																			19 17					
Coventry 68	d										18 27								18 42						
Birmingham International 68 ✈	d										18 38								18 53						
Birmingham New St. 12 68	d								18 31	18 36	18 57							19 01	19 15						
Wolverhampton 7 ⛴	d								18 49	18 54	19 15							19 20	19 37						
Penkridge	d									19 04								19 29							
Stafford	a	18 26							19 00	19 10	19 29							19 35		19 35			19 22		
	d	18 27							19 01	19 10	19 30							19 36		19 39			19 23		
Stoke-on-Trent	a						18 48		19 19		19 54									20 00		19 24			
Macclesfield	a				←	←					20 11											19 41			←
Crewe 10	a	18 45	18 49	18 49	18 56	19 07		19 10		19 30								19 56	20 07	20 24			19 41	19 47	19 56
	d	18 47	18 52	18 52	18 59	19 09		19 11										19 58	20 09				19 43	19 49	19 58
Chester 81	a		19 11	19 12														→	→					20 13	
Wrexham General 75	a																								
Llandudno Junction 81	a			20 07																					
Bangor (Gwynedd) 81	a			20 24																					
Holyhead 81 ⛴	a			20 58																					
Wilmslow 84	a							19 27																	
Stockport 84	a						19 16	19 36	19 49		20 27											19 55			
Manchester Piccadilly 10 ⛴	a						19 28	19 49	19 59		20 37											20 07			
Warrington Bank Quay	a					19 26																			
	d					19 27																			
Runcorn 91	a	19 04			19 22																		20 00		20 24
Liverpool South Pkwy 7 91 ✈	a				19 31																				20 33
Liverpool Lime St. 10 91	a	19 23			19 44																		20 21		20 46
	d																								
Manchester Airport 82 ✈	d											19 00													
Manchester Picc. 10 82 ⛴	d											19 16													
Bolton 82	d											19 33					20 20								
Wigan North Western 90	a					19 37																			
	d					19 38																			
Preston 8 90	a					19 54						19 57					20 46								
Preston 8 90	d											19 59		20 05	20 10	20 45									
Blackpool North 97	a																								
Lancaster 6	a											20 14		20 55		21 08									
	d											20 15	20 25	21 00		21 11									
Barrow-in-Furness 82	a											21 18				22 17									
Oxenholme Lake District	a													21 45											
	d													21 50											
Windermere 83	a												21 12												
Penrith North Lakes	d													22s45											
Carlisle 8 216	a													23 25	22s10										
	d																								
Lockerbie	d																								
Carstairs 226	a																								
Motherwell 226	a																								
Glasgow Central 15 216,226	a														00 10										
Haymarket 225,226,228,230,242	a																								
Edinburgh 10 225,226,228,230,242	a																								
Perth 229	a																								
Dundee 229	a																								
Aberdeen 229	a																								
Inverness 229	a																								

OVERNIGHT SLEEPERS. For sleeper trains, operated by First ScotRail, please see Tables 400 - 404.

For complete service between Manchester and Preston, Blackpool and between Barrow-in-furness and Lancaster, please see Table 82.

For complete service between Crewe and Liverpool Lime Street, see Table 91

For complete service between Crewe/Stoke-on-Trent & Manchester see Table 84

For complete service between Crewe and Holyhead please see Table 81.

For complete service between Coventry-Birmingham-Wolverhampton-Stafford please see Table 68

For complete service between Windermere and Oxenholme Lake District, please see Table 83

Table 65

Saturdays

4 January to 8 February

London and West Midlands - North West England and Scotland

Route Diagram - refer to first Page of Table 65

		VT	VT	VT	VT	VT		VT	XC	XC	TP	TP	LM	VT	LM	VT		VT	LM	VT	VT	LM	VT	XC	LM
		◇1	◇1	◇1		◇1		◇1	◇1	◇1		◇1	1	◇1	1	◇1		◇1	1	◇1	◇1	1	◇1	◇1	1
										A															
					bus						bus														
		☕	☕	☕		☕		☕	trolley	trolley				☕		☕		☕		☕	☕		☕		
London Euston 15 ⊖66	d	18 20	18 30			18 33		18 40						18 43	18 46	19 00		19 07		19 20	19 30		19 40		
Watford Junction 66	d																								
Milton Keynes Central 66	d	18 50												19 13	19 19					19 50					
Rugby 66	d														19 42										
Nuneaton	d														19 58			20 03							
Tamworth Low Level	d					19 38									20 14										
Lichfield Trent Valley	d					19 45									20 21										
Coventry 68	d									19 27				19 42											
Birmingham International 68 ✈	d									19 38				19 53											
Birmingham New St. 12 68	d								19 31	19 57			20 01	20 15										20 31	20 36
Wolverhampton 7	d								19 49	20 15			20 22	20 37										20 49	20 54
Penkridge	d												20 31												21 04
Stafford	a					19 58			20 00	20 29			20 37	20 49	20 38			20 26						21 00	21 10
	d					19 59			20 01	20 30			20 38	20 50	20 42			20 27						21 01	21 10
Stoke-on-Trent	a	19 48							20 19	20 54					21 01	20 24				20 48				21 20	
Macclesfield	a			←					20 36	21 11						20 41			←			←		21 38	
Crewe 10	a		20 01	20 07				20 10					20 58	21 10	21 24			20 45	20 58		21 04	20 58	21 18		21 30
	d			20 09				20 11					21 06					20 47	21 06		21 05	21 06	21 19		
Chester 81	a												→						→						
Wrexham General 75	a																								
Llandudno Junction 81	a																								
Bangor (Gwynedd) 81	a																								
Holyhead 81 ⛴	a																								
Wilmslow 84	a							20 27															21 34		
Stockport 84	a	20 16						20 36	20 49	21 25						20 55				21 16			21 44	21 53	
Manchester Piccadilly 10	a	20 28						20 49	20 59	21 39						21 07				21 28			21 53	22 04	
Warrington Bank Quay	a			20 26																	21 22				
	d			20 27																	21 22				
Runcorn 91	a					20 31												21 05				21 29			
Liverpool South Pkwy 7 91 ✈	a																					21 38			
Liverpool Lime St. 10 91	a					20 52												21 25				21 50			
	d																								
Manchester Airport 82 ✈	d																								
Manchester Picc. 10 82	d																								
Bolton 82	d										21 20														
Wigan North Western 90	a			20 37																	21 33				
	d				20 50																				
Preston 8 90	a				21 35						21 46														
Preston 8 90	d											21 47													
Blackpool North 97	a																								
Lancaster 6	a											22 02													
	d											22 03													
Barrow-in-Furness 82	a											23 06													
Oxenholme Lake District	a																								
	d																								
Windermere 83	a																								
Penrith North Lakes	d																								
Carlisle 8 216	a																								
	d																								
Lockerbie	d																								
Carstairs 226	a																								
Motherwell 226	a																								
Glasgow Central 15 216,226	a																								
Haymarket 225,226,228,230,242	a																								
Edinburgh 10 225,226,228,230,242	a																								
Perth 229	a																								
Dundee 229	a																								
Aberdeen 229	a																								
Inverness 229	a																								

A trolley to Birmingham New St.

OVERNIGHT SLEEPERS. For sleeper trains, operated by First ScotRail, please see Tables 400 - 404.

For complete service between Manchester and Preston, Blackpool and between Barrow-in-furness and Lancaster, please see Table 82.

For complete service between Crewe and Liverpool Lime Street, see Table 91

For complete service between Crewe/Stoke-on-Trent & Manchester see Table 84

For complete service between Crewe and Holyhead please see Table 81.

For complete service between Coventry-Birmingham-Wolverhampton-Stafford please see Table 68

For complete service between Windermere and Oxenholme Lake District, please see Table 83

Table 65

Saturdays

4 January to 8 February

London and West Midlands - North West England and Scotland

Route Diagram - refer to first Page of Table 65

		XC	VT	VT	VT	LM	XC	VT	TP	TP	TP	VT	VT	VT	XC	LM
		◇1	◇1	◇1	◇1	1	◇1			◇1				◇1	◇1	1
		A														
								bus	bus		bus	bus	bus			
		trolley	buffet	buffet	buffet									buffet		
London Euston 15 ⊖66	d		20 11	20 20	20 31									21 00		
Watford Junction 66	d				20u46											
Milton Keynes Central 66	d			21 05										21 45		
Rugby 66	d		21 15		21 36											
Nuneaton	d			21 33												
Tamworth Low Level	d				21 53											
Lichfield Trent Valley	d				22 00											
Coventry 68	d	20 27					21 27									
Birmingham International 68 ✈	d	20 38					21 38									
Birmingham New St. 12 68	d	20 57				21 36	21 57								22 31	22 38
Wolverhampton 7 ⛴	d	21 15				21 59	22 15								22 49	23 05
Penkridge	d					22 09										23 15
Stafford	a	21 29	21 46			22 15	22 29							22 32	23 01	23 21
	d	21 30	21 46			22 16	22 30							22 34	23 02	23 22
Stoke-on-Trent	a	21 52		22 05			22 50								23 20	
Macclesfield	a	22 11		22 21			23 07								23 38	
Crewe 10	a		22 05		22 35	22 38								22 58		23 42
	d		22 06		22 36							22 50	22 50	22 59		
Chester 81	a															
Wrexham General 75	a															
Llandudno Junction 81	a															
Bangor (Gwynedd) 81	a															
Holyhead 81 ⛴	a															
Wilmslow 84	a													23 14		
Stockport 84	a	22 25		22 35			23 20							23 24	23 53	
Manchester Piccadilly 10 ⛴	a	22 34		22 51	23 05		23 30							23 38	00 10	
Warrington Bank Quay	a												23 40			
	d												23 45			
Runcorn 91	a		22 24													
Liverpool South Pkwy 7 91 ✈	a															
Liverpool Lime St. 10 91	a		22 46													
	d															
Manchester Airport 82 ✈	d															
Manchester Picc. 10 82 ⛴	d															
Bolton 82	d								22 20		23 20					
Wigan North Western 90	a												00s25			
	d							21 45								
Preston 8 90	a							22 30	22 46		23s45	00 15	01 15			
Preston 8 90	d									22 55						
Blackpool North 97	a										00 41					
Lancaster 6	a									23 10						
	d									23 11						
Barrow-in-Furness 82	a									00 14						
Oxenholme Lake District	a															
	d															
Windermere 83	a															
Penrith North Lakes	d															
Carlisle 8 216	a															
	d															
Lockerbie	d															
Carstairs 226	a															
Motherwell 226	a															
Glasgow Central 15 216,226	a															
Haymarket 225,226,228,230,242	a															
Edinburgh 10 225,226,228,230,242	a															
Perth 229	a															
Dundee 229	a															
Aberdeen 229	a															
Inverness 229	a															

A trolley to Birmingham New St.

OVERNIGHT SLEEPERS. For sleeper trains, operated by First ScotRail, please see Tables 400 - 404.

For complete service between Manchester and Preston, Blackpool and between Barrow-in-furness and Lancaster, please see Table 82.

For complete service between Crewe and Liverpool Lime Street, see Table 91

For complete service between Crewe/Stoke-on-Trent & Manchester see Table 84

For complete service between Crewe and Holyhead please see Table 81.

For complete service between Coventry-Birmingham-Wolverhampton-Stafford please see Table 68

For complete service between Windermere and Oxenholme Lake District, please see Table 83

Table 65

Saturdays

15 February to 17 May

London and West Midlands - North West England and Scotland

Route Diagram - refer to first Page of Table 65

	SR		SR	SR	VT	VT	TP	TP	AW		XC	LM	VT	LM	XC	LM	XC	TP	TP		VT	NT	LM	VT
	R		R	R																				
					◇1	◇1	◇1	◇1			◇1	1	◇1	1	◇1	1	◇1	◇1	◇1		◇1		1	◇1
	🛏✕		🛏✕	🛏✕	⊏P	⊏P	⊤						⊏P		⊤		⊤	⊤	⊤		⊏P			⊠
London Euston 15 ⊖66 d																					06 05			
Watford Junction 66 d	00u10																				06u20			
Milton Keynes Central 66 d																					06 41			
Rugby 66 d														06 02							07 03			
Nuneaton d														06 14										
Tamworth Low Level d														06 29										
Lichfield Trent Valley d														06 35										
Coventry 68 d																								
Birmingham International 68 ✈ d																								
Birmingham New St. 12 68 d						05 30					05 57	06 01	06 15		06 31	06 36	06 57						07 01	07 15
Wolverhampton 7 🚌 d						05 48					06 16	06 20	06 37		06 49	06 52	07 15						07 20	07 37
Penkridge d												06 29				07 02							07 29	
Stafford a						06 00					06 29	06 35		06 53	07 00	07 09	07 29				07 33		07 35	
d						06 01					06 30	06 36		06 54	07 01	07 09	07 30				07 34		07 38	
Stoke-on-Trent a											06 50			07 14	07 18									
Macclesfield a											07 11				07 36									
Crewe 10 a						06 20						06 56	07 07	07 37		07 33	07 50				07 53		07 58	08 06
d					05 57	06 23			06 27			06 58	07 09			07 34	07 52				07 55		08 00	08 09
Chester 81 a						06 43																		
Wrexham General 75 a																								
Llandudno Junction 81 a						07 33																		
Bangor (Gwynedd) 81 a						07 49																		
Holyhead 81 ⛴ a						08 23																		
Wilmslow 84 a									06 44								08 08							
Stockport 84 a									06 55		07 25				07 49		08 20							
Manchester Piccadilly 10 🚌 a									07 07		07 34				07 59		08 34							
Warrington Bank Quay a					06 13								07 26								08 11			08 26
d					06 15								07 27								08 12			08 27
Runcorn 91 a												07 23				08 00							08 24	
Liverpool South Pkwy 7 91 ✈ a												07 32				08 09							08 33	
Liverpool Lime St. 10 91 a												07 44				08 21							08 46	
d																								
Manchester Airport 82 ✈ d							05 58	06 18										07 00	07 25					
Manchester Picc. 10 82 🚌 d							06 13	06 33										07 15	07 45					
Bolton 82 d								06 52											07 59					
Wigan North Western 90 a					06 24		06 42						07 37					07 43			08 22			08 37
d					06 26		06 42						07 38					07 43			08 23			08 38
Preston 8 90 a					06 38		06 56	07 18					07 51					07 57	08 22		08 36			08 51
Preston 8 90 d			00u52	00u52	06 40		06 57	07 20					07 53					07 58	08 24		08 37			08 53
Blackpool North 97 a																								
Lancaster 6 a					06 54		07 13	07 35					08 07					08 14	08 39		08 52			09 08
d					06 54		07 13	07 36					08 08					08 16	08 40		08 52	09 02		09 08
Barrow-in-Furness 82 a								08 39														10 06		
Oxenholme Lake District a					07 07		07 27						08 21								09 05			
d					07 09		07 28						08 22								09 06			
Windermere 83 a																								
Penrith North Lakes d					07 34		07 53											08 54			09 32			09 46
Carlisle 8 216 a	05s10				07 49		08 09						09 00					09 10	09 31		09 47	12 38		10 00
d					07 51		08 11						09 00					09 11	09 31		09 48			10 02
Lockerbie d					08 10		08 30												09 51					
Carstairs 226 a	06s19																							
Motherwell 226 a	06s54																							
Glasgow Central 15 216,226 a	07 18				09 13													10 31			11 03			11 16
Haymarket 225,226,228,230,242 a							09s29						10 16						10s49					
Edinburgh 10 225,226,228,230,242 a		07 22					09 34						10 25						10 57					
Perth 229 a				05s39																				
Dundee 229 a			06s08																					
Aberdeen 229 a			07 34																					
Inverness 229 a				08 36																				

OVERNIGHT SLEEPERS. For sleeper trains, operated by First ScotRail, please see Tables 400 - 404.

For complete service between Manchester and Preston, Blackpool and between Barrow-in-furness and Lancaster, please see Table 82.

For complete service between Crewe and Liverpool Lime Street, see Table 91

For complete service between Crewe/Stoke-on-Trent & Manchester see Table 84

For complete service between Crewe and Holyhead please see Table 81.

For complete service between Coventry-Birmingham-Wolverhampton-Stafford please see Table 68

For complete service between Windermere and Oxenholme Lake District, please see Table 83

Table 65

Saturdays

15 February to 17 May

London and West Midlands - North West England and Scotland

Route Diagram - refer to first Page of Table 65

		LM	XC	NT	TP	LM		LM	VT	LM	VT	VT	VT	XC	VT	LM		TP	VT	VT	XC	LM	XC	TP	TP
		1	◇1		◇1	1		1	◇1	1	◇1	◇1	◇1	◇1	◇1	1		◇1	◇1	◇1	◇1	1	◇1	◇1	◇1
London Euston 15 ⊖66	d							06 24	06 36		06 55	07 07	07 20		07 30					07 35					
Watford Junction 66	d							06 41	06u51																
Milton Keynes Central 66	d							07 23			07 27		07 50							08 06					
Rugby 66	d	06 58						08 04																	
Nuneaton	d	07 12						08 16																	
Tamworth Low Level	d	07 29						08 30																	
Lichfield Trent Valley	d	07 35						08 36																	
Coventry 68	d													07 27									08 27		
Birmingham International 68 ✈	d													07 38									08 38		
Birmingham New St. 12 68	d		07 31			07 36								07 57		08 01			08 15		08 31	08 36	08 57		
Wolverhampton 7	d		07 49			07 54								08 15		08 20			08 37		08 49	08 54	09 15		
Penkridge	d					08 04										08 29						09 04			
Stafford	a	07 53	08 00			08 10		08 53				08 22		08 29		08 35					09 00	09 10	09 29		
	d	07 54	08 01			08 10		08 54				08 23		08 30		08 36					09 01	09 10	09 30		
Stoke-on-Trent	a	08 15	08 19					09 15			08 24		08 48	08 54							09 19		09 54		
Macclesfield	a		08 36							←	08 41			09 11									10 11		
Crewe 10	a	08 38				08 30		09 38	08 10	08 30		08 41				08 56			09 07	09 10		09 30			
	d					08 32			08 11	08 32		08 43				08 58			09 09	09 11		09 32			
Chester 81	a					→																			
Wrexham General 75	a																								
Llandudno Junction 81	a																								
Bangor (Gwynedd) 81	a																								
Holyhead 81 ⛴	a																								
Wilmslow 84	a								08 27											09 27					
Stockport 84	a		08 49						08 36		08 55		09 16	09 27						09 36	09 49		10 27		
Manchester Piccadilly 10	a		08 59						08 49		09 07		09 28	09 38						09 49	09 59		10 38		
Warrington Bank Quay	a														09 14				09 26						
	d														09 14				09 27						
Runcorn 91	a									08 50		09 00				09 21						09 50			
Liverpool South Pkwy 7 91 ✈	a									08 59						09 30						09 59			
Liverpool Lime St. 10 91	a									09 10		09 21				09 42						10 10			
	d																								
Manchester Airport 82 ✈	d				08 25																			09 00	
Manchester Picc. 10 82	d				08 46																			09 16	
Bolton 82	d				09 07																				09 35
Wigan North Western 90	a														09 25				09 37					09 43	
	d														09 25				09 38					09 43	
Preston 8 90	a				09 30										09 38				09 51					09 57	10 03
Preston 8 90	d			09 07	09 32										09 41			09 45	09 53					09 59	10 09
Blackpool North 97	a																								10 33
Lancaster 6	a			09 27	09 47										09 54			10 00	10 07					10 15	
	d				09 48										09 55			10 01	10 08					10 16	
Barrow-in-Furness 82	a																	11 04							
Oxenholme Lake District	a				10 03														10 21						
	d				10 04														10 22						
Windermere 83	a				10 27																				
Penrith North Lakes	d														10 30									10 53	
Carlisle 8 216	a														10 46				10 59					11 08	
	d														10 47				11 01					11 11	
Lockerbie	d																							11 30	
Carstairs 226	a																								
Motherwell 226	a																								
Glasgow Central 15 216,226	a														12 02									12 30	
Haymarket 225,226,228,230,242	a																		12 16						
Edinburgh 10 225,226,228,230,242	a																		12 22						
Perth 229	a																								
Dundee 229	a																								
Aberdeen 229	a																								
Inverness 229	a																								

OVERNIGHT SLEEPERS. For sleeper trains, operated by First ScotRail, please see Tables 400 - 404.

For complete service between Manchester and Preston, Blackpool and between Barrow-in-furness and Lancaster, please see Table 82.

For complete service between Crewe and Liverpool Lime Street, see Table 91

For complete service between Crewe/Stoke-on-Trent & Manchester see Table 84

For complete service between Crewe and Holyhead please see Table 81.

For complete service between Coventry-Birmingham-Wolverhampton-Stafford please see Table 68

For complete service between Windermere and Oxenholme Lake District, please see Table 83

Table 65

Saturdays

15 February to 17 May

London and West Midlands - North West England and Scotland

Route Diagram - refer to first Page of Table 65

		LM		VT	LM	VT	VT	VT	LM	VT	TP	VT		TP	VT	VT	XC	LM	XC	TP	NT	LM		VT	LM
		1		◇1	1	◇1	◇1	◇1	1	◇1	◇1	◇1		◇1	◇1	◇1	◇1	1	◇1	◇1		1		◇1	1
				⊡P		⊡P	⊡P	⊡P		⊡P		⊡P			☒	⊡P	⊼		⊼	⊼				⊡P	
London Euston 15 ⊖66	d			07 43	07 46	08 00	08 07	08 10		08 20		08 30				08 40								08 43	08 46
Watford Junction 66	d																								
Milton Keynes Central 66	d			08 13	08 19			08 41		08 50														09 13	09 19
Rugby 66	d				08 42																				09 42
Nuneaton	d				08 54																				09 54
Tamworth Low Level	d				09 09																				10 09
Lichfield Trent Valley	d				09 17																				10 17
Coventry 68	d			08 42															09 27					09 42	
Birmingham International 68 ✈	d			08 53															09 38					09 53	
Birmingham New St. 12 68	d	09 01		09 15													09 31	09 36	09 57			10 01		10 15	
Wolverhampton 7 ⛴	d	09 20		09 37													09 49	09 54	10 15			10 20		10 37	
Penkridge	d																	10 04							
Stafford	a	09 34			09 35		09 22										10 00	10 10	10 29			10 35			10 35
	d	09 35			09 39		09 23										10 01	10 10	10 30			10 35			10 39
Stoke-on-Trent	a				10 00	09 24				09 48							10 19		10 54						11 00
Macclesfield	a					09 41			←						←				11 11						
Crewe 10	a	09 56		10 07	10 24		09 41	09 47	09 56						10 07	10 10		10 30				10 56		11 07	11 24
	d	09 57		10 09			09 43	09 49	09 57						10 09	10 11		10 32				10 57		11 09	
Chester 81	a	→		→				10 13														→		→	
Wrexham General 75	a																								
Llandudno Junction 81	a																								
Bangor (Gwynedd) 81	a																								
Holyhead 81 ⛴	a																								
Wilmslow 84	a															10 27									
Stockport 84	a					09 55				10 16						10 36	10 49		11 27						
Manchester Piccadilly 10 ⛴	a					10 07				10 28						10 49	10 59		11 38						
Warrington Bank Quay	a											10 14			10 26										
	d											10 14			10 27										
Runcorn 91	a						10 00		10 23									10 50							
Liverpool South Pkwy 7 91 ✈	a								10 32									10 59							
Liverpool Lime St. 10 91	a						10 21		10 44									11 10							
	d																								
Manchester Airport 82 ✈	d										09 29									10 00					
Manchester Picc. 10 82 ⛴	d										09 46									10 16					
Bolton 82	d										10 07														
Wigan North Western 90	a											10 25		←	10 37										
	d											10 25			10 38										
Preston 8 90	a										10 33	10 38		10 33	10 51					10 56					
Preston 8 90	d										10 45	10 41		10 45	10 53					10 57					
Blackpool North 97	a										→														
Lancaster 6	a											10 54		11 00	11 07					11 13					
	d											10 55		11 01	11 08					11 13	11 28				
Barrow-in-Furness 82	a																				12 32				
Oxenholme Lake District	a											11 08		11 17											
	d											11 08		11 18											
Windermere 83	a													11 39											
Penrith North Lakes	d														11 45										
Carlisle 8 216	a											11 46			12 00					12 05	15 00				
	d											11 47			12 02					12 06					
Lockerbie	d																								
Carstairs 226	a																								
Motherwell 226	a																								
Glasgow Central 15 216,226	a											13 01			13 17										
Haymarket 225,226,228,230,242	a																			13s19					
Edinburgh 10 225,226,228,230,242	a																			13 27					
Perth 229	a																								
Dundee 229	a																								
Aberdeen 229	a																								
Inverness 229	a																								

OVERNIGHT SLEEPERS. For sleeper trains, operated by First ScotRail, please see Tables 400 - 404.

For complete service between Manchester and Preston, Blackpool and between Barrow-in-furness and Lancaster, please see Table 82.

For complete service between Crewe and Liverpool Lime Street, see Table 91

For complete service between Crewe/Stoke-on-Trent & Manchester see Table 84

For complete service between Crewe and Holyhead please see Table 81.

For complete service between Coventry-Birmingham-Wolverhampton-Stafford please see Table 68

For complete service between Windermere and Oxenholme Lake District, please see Table 83

Table 65

Saturdays

15 February to 17 May

London and West Midlands - North West England and Scotland

Route Diagram - refer to first Page of Table 65

Station	VT	VT	VT	LM	VT	VT	VT		VT	XC	LM	XC	TP	LM	VT	LM	VT		VT	VT	LM	VT	TP	VT
	◇1 🍴	◇1 🍴	◇1 🍴	1	◇1 🍴	◇1 🍴	◇1 🍴		◇1 🍴	◇1 trolley	1	◇1 trolley	◇1	1	◇1 🍴	1	◇1 🍴		◇1 🍴	◇1 🍴	1	◇1 🍴	◇1	◇1 🍴
London Euston 15 ⊖66 d	09 00	09 07	09 10		09 20	09 30			09 40						09 43	09 46	10 00		10 07	10 10		10 20		10 30
Watford Junction 66 d																								
Milton Keynes Central 66 d			09 41		09 50										10 13	10 19				10 41		10 50		
Rugby 66 d																10 42								
Nuneaton d																10 54								
Tamworth Low Level d																11 09								
Lichfield Trent Valley d																11 17								
Coventry 68 d												10 27			10 42									
Birmingham International 68 ✈ d												10 38			10 53									
Birmingham New St. 12 68 d										10 31	10 36	10 57		11 01	11 15									
Wolverhampton 7 🚌 d										10 49	10 54	11 15		11 20	11 37									
Penkridge d											11 04													
Stafford a		10 22								11 00	11 10	11 29		11 35		11 35			11 22					
d		10 23								11 01	11 10	11 30		11 35		11 39			11 23					
Stoke-on-Trent a	10 24				10 48					11 19		11 54				12 00	11 24					11 48		
Macclesfield a	10 41			←			←					12 11					11 41				←			
Crewe 10 a		10 41	10 47	10 56			11 07		11 10		11 30			11 56	12 07	12 24			11 41	11 47	11 56			
d		10 43	10 49	10 57			11 09		11 11		11 32			11 57	12 09				11 43	11 49	11 57			
Chester 81 a			11 13											→	→					12 13				
Wrexham General 75 a																								
Llandudno Junction 81 a			12 00																					
Bangor (Gwynedd) 81 a			12 16																					
Holyhead 81 ⛴ a			12 50																					
Wilmslow 84 a									11 27															
Stockport 84 a	10 55				11 16				11 36	11 49		12 26					11 55					12 16		
Manchester Piccadilly 10 🚌 a	11 07				11 28				11 49	11 59		12 38					12 07					12 28		
Warrington Bank Quay a						11 14	11 26																	12 14
d						11 14	11 27																	12 14
Runcorn 91 a		11 00		11 21							11 51								12 00		12 24			
Liverpool South Pkwy 7 91 ✈ a				11 30							12 00										12 33			
Liverpool Lime St. 10 91 a		11 21		11 42							12 11								12 21		12 44			
d																								
Manchester Airport 82 ✈ d													11 00										11 29	
Manchester Picc. 10 82 🚌 d													11 16										11 46	
Bolton 82 d																							12 07	
Wigan North Western 90 a						11 25	11 37						11 43											12 25
d						11 25	11 38						11 43											12 25
Preston 8 90 a						11 38	11 51						11 57										12 33	12 38
Preston 8 90 d						11 41	11 53						11 58										12 45	12 41
Blackpool North 97 a																							→	
Lancaster 6 a						11 54	12 07						12 14											12 54
d						11 55	12 07						12 15											12 55
Barrow-in-Furness 82 a													13 09											
Oxenholme Lake District a							12 20																	13 08
d							12 21																	13 08
Windermere 83 a																								
Penrith North Lakes d						12 30																		
Carlisle 8 216 a						12 46	12 59																	13 46
d						12 47	13 01																	13 47
Lockerbie d																								
Carstairs 226 a																								
Motherwell 226 a																								
Glasgow Central 15 216,226 a						14 01																		15 01
Haymarket 225,226,228,230,242 a							14 15																	
Edinburgh 10 225,226,228,230,242 a							14 22																	
Perth 229 a																								
Dundee 229 a																								
Aberdeen 229 a																								
Inverness 229 a																								

OVERNIGHT SLEEPERS. For sleeper trains, operated by First ScotRail, please see Tables 400 - 404.

For complete service between Manchester and Preston, Blackpool and between Barrow-in-furness and Lancaster, please see Table 82.

For complete service between Crewe and Liverpool Lime Street, see Table 91

For complete service between Crewe/Stoke-on-Trent & Manchester see Table 84

For complete service between Crewe and Holyhead please see Table 81.

For complete service between Coventry-Birmingham-Wolverhampton-Stafford please see Table 68

For complete service between Windermere and Oxenholme Lake District, please see Table 83

Table 65

Saturdays

15 February to 17 May

London and West Midlands - North West England and Scotland

Route Diagram - refer to first Page of Table 65

Station	Table		TP	VT	VT		XC	LM	XC	TP	NT	LM	VT	LM	VT		VT	VT	LM	VT	VT	VT	VT	XC	LM	
			◇1	◇1	◇1		◇1	1	◇1	◇1		1	◇1	1	◇1		◇1	◇1	1	◇1	◇1	◇1	◇1	◇1	1	
London Euston 15	⊖66	d			10 40								10 43	10 46	11 00		11 07	11 10		11 20	11 30		11 40			
Watford Junction	66	d																								
Milton Keynes Central	66	d											11 13	11 19				11 41		11 50						
Rugby	66	d												11 42												
Nuneaton		d												11 54												
Tamworth Low Level		d												12 09												
Lichfield Trent Valley		d												12 17												
Coventry	68	d							11 27				11 42													
Birmingham International	68 ✈	d							11 38				11 53													
Birmingham New St. 12	68	d					11 31	11 36	11 57			12 01	12 15											12 31	12 36	
Wolverhampton 7	⛴	d					11 49	11 54	12 15			12 20	12 37											12 49	12 54	
Penkridge		d						12 04																	13 04	
Stafford		a					12 00	12 10	12 29			12 35		12 35			12 22							13 00	13 10	
		d					12 01	12 10	12 30			12 35		12 39			12 23							13 01	13 10	
Stoke-on-Trent		a					12 19		12 54					13 00	12 24					12 48				13 18		
Macclesfield		a		←					13 11						12 41				←			←				
Crewe 10		a		12 07	12 10			12 30				12 56	13 07	13 24			12 41	12 47	12 56			13 07	13 10		13 30	
		d		12 09	12 11			12 32				12 57	13 09				12 43	12 49	12 57			13 09	13 11		13 32	
Chester	81	a										→	→					13 13								
Wrexham General	75	a																								
Llandudno Junction	81	a																								
Bangor (Gwynedd)	81	a																								
Holyhead	81 ⛴	a																								
Wilmslow	84	a			12 27																		13 27			
Stockport	84	a			12 36		12 49		13 27						12 55					13 16			13 36	13 49		
Manchester Piccadilly 10	⛴	a			12 49		12 59		13 38						13 07					13 28			13 49	13 59		
Warrington Bank Quay		a		12 26																	13 14	13 26				
		d		12 27																	13 14	13 27				
Runcorn	91	a						12 50									13 00		13 21						13 50	
Liverpool South Pkwy 7	91 ✈	a						12 59											13 30						13 59	
Liverpool Lime St. 10	91	a						13 10									13 21		13 42						14 10	
		d																								
Manchester Airport	82 ✈	d								12 00																
Manchester Picc. 10	82 ⛴	d								12 16																
Bolton	82	d																								
Wigan North Western	90	a	←	12 37						12 43											13 25	13 37				
		d		12 38						12 43											13 25	13 38				
Preston 8	90	a	12 33	12 51						12 57											13 38	13 51				
Preston 8	90	d	12 45	12 53						12 58											13 41	13 53				
Blackpool North	97	a																								
Lancaster 6		a	13 00	13 07						13 14											13 54	14 07				
		d	13 01	13 08						13 15	13 32										13 55	14 08				
Barrow-in-Furness	82	a									14 36															
Oxenholme Lake District		a	13 17	13 21						13 29											14 08					
		d	13 18	13 22						13 29											14 08					
Windermere	83	a	13 39																							
Penrith North Lakes		d								13 55												14 43				
Carlisle 8	216	a		14 00						14 11	17 21										14 46	14 58				
		d		14 03						14 11											14 47	14 59				
Lockerbie		d								14 30																
Carstairs	226	a																								
Motherwell	226	a																								
Glasgow Central 15	216,226	a		15 17																	16 01					
Haymarket	225,226,228,230,242	a								15s33												16 17				
Edinburgh 10	225,226,228,230,242	a								15 38												16 22				
Perth	229	a																								
Dundee	229	a																								
Aberdeen	229	a																								
Inverness	229	a																								

OVERNIGHT SLEEPERS. For sleeper trains, operated by First ScotRail, please see Tables 400 - 404.

For complete service between Manchester and Preston, Blackpool and between Barrow-in-furness and Lancaster, please see Table 82.

For complete service between Crewe and Liverpool Lime Street, see Table 91

For complete service between Crewe/Stoke-on-Trent & Manchester see Table 84

For complete service between Crewe and Holyhead please see Table 81.

For complete service between Coventry-Birmingham-Wolverhampton-Stafford please see Table 68

For complete service between Windermere and Oxenholme Lake District, please see Table 83

Table 65

Saturdays

15 February to 17 May

London and West Midlands - North West England and Scotland

Route Diagram - refer to first Page of Table 65

		XC	TP	TP	LM	VT	LM	VT	VT	VT		LM	VT	VT	TP	VT	VT	XC	LM	XC		TP	LM	VT	LM
		◇1	◇1		1	◇1	1	◇1	◇1	◇1		1	◇1	◇1	◇1	◇1	◇1	◇1	1	◇1		◇1	1	◇1	1
London Euston 15 ⊖66	d					11 43	11 46	12 00	12 07	12 10			12 20	12 30			12 40							12 43	12 46
Watford Junction 66	d																								
Milton Keynes Central 66	d					12 13	12 19			12 41			12 50											13 13	13 19
Rugby 66	d						12 42																		13 42
Nuneaton	d						12 54																		13 54
Tamworth Low Level	d						13 09																		14 09
Lichfield Trent Valley	d						13 17																		14 17
Coventry 68	d	12 27				12 42														13 27				13 42	
Birmingham International 68 ✈	d	12 38				12 53														13 38				13 53	
Birmingham New St. 12 68	d	12 57			13 01	13 15												13 31	13 36	13 57			14 01	14 15	
Wolverhampton 7	d	13 15			13 20	13 37												13 49	13 54	14 15			14 20	14 37	
Penkridge	d																		14 04						
Stafford	a	13 29			13 35		13 35		13 22									14 00	14 10	14 29			14 35		14 35
	d	13 30			13 35		13 39		13 23									14 01	14 10	14 30			14 35		14 39
Stoke-on-Trent	a	13 54					14 00	13 24					13 48					14 19		14 54					15 00
Macclesfield	a	14 11						13 41				←				←				15 11					
Crewe 10	a				13 56	14 07	14 24		13 41	13 47		13 56				14 07	14 10		14 30				14 56	15 07	15 24
	d				13 57	14 09			13 43	13 49		13 57				14 09	14 11		14 32				14 57	15 09	
Chester 81	a				↪	↪				14 13													↪	↪	
Wrexham General 75	a																								
Llandudno Junction 81	a																								
Bangor (Gwynedd) 81	a																								
Holyhead 81 ⛴	a																								
Wilmslow 84	a																14 27								
Stockport 84	a	14 27						13 55					14 16				14 36	14 49		15 27					
Manchester Piccadilly 10 ⛴	a	14 38						14 07					14 28				14 49	14 59		15 38					
Warrington Bank Quay	a													14 14		14 26									
	d													14 15		14 27									
Runcorn 91	a								14 00			14 21							14 50						
Liverpool South Pkwy 7 91 ✈	a											14 30							14 59						
Liverpool Lime St. 10 91	a								14 21			14 42							15 10						
	d																								
Manchester Airport 82 ✈	d		13 00																			14 00			
Manchester Picc. 10 82 ⛴	d		13 16																			14 16			
Bolton 82	d																								
Wigan North Western 90	a		13 43											14 25		14 37						14 43			
	d		13 43											14 26		14 38						14 43			
Preston 8 90	a		13 57											14 39		14 51						14 57			
Preston 8 90	d		13 58	14 06										14 41	14 45	14 53						14 58			
Blackpool North 97	a																								
Lancaster 6	a		14 14	14 21										14 55	15 00	15 07						15 14			
	d		14 15	14 22										14 55	15 01	15 08						15 15			
Barrow-in-Furness 82	a			15 17																					
Oxenholme Lake District	a														15 17	15 21						15 29			
	d														15 18	15 22						15 29			
Windermere 83	a														15 39										
Penrith North Lakes	d													15 30								15 54			
Carlisle 8 216	a		15 06											15 46		15 59						16 11			
	d		15 08											15 46		16 02						16 11			
Lockerbie	d		15 27																			16 30			
Carstairs 226	a																								
Motherwell 226	a																								
Glasgow Central 15 216,226	a		16 29											17 01		17 17									
Haymarket 225,226,228,230,242	a																					17s30			
Edinburgh 10 225,226,228,230,242	a																					17 38			
Perth 229	a																								
Dundee 229	a																								
Aberdeen 229	a																								
Inverness 229	a																								

OVERNIGHT SLEEPERS. For sleeper trains, operated by First ScotRail, please see Tables 400 - 404.

For complete service between Manchester and Preston, Blackpool and between Barrow-in-furness and Lancaster, please see Table 82.

For complete service between Crewe and Liverpool Lime Street, see Table 91

For complete service between Crewe/Stoke-on-Trent & Manchester see Table 84

For complete service between Crewe and Holyhead please see Table 81.

For complete service between Coventry-Birmingham-Wolverhampton-Stafford please see Table 68

For complete service between Windermere and Oxenholme Lake District, please see Table 83

Table 65

Saturdays

15 February to 17 May

London and West Midlands - North West England and Scotland

Route Diagram - refer to first Page of Table 65

		VT	VT	VT	LM	VT		TP	VT	TP	VT	VT	XC	LM	XC	TP		LM	VT	LM	VT	VT	VT	LM	VT
		◇[1]	◇[1]	◇[1]	[1]	◇[1]		◇[1]	◇[1]	◇[1]	◇[1]	◇[1]	◇[1]	[1]	◇[1]	◇[1]		[1]	◇[1]	[1]	◇[1]	◇[1]	◇[1]	[1]	◇[1]
																A									
		☕	☕	☕		☕			☕		☕	☕	⍑		⍑	⍑			☕		☕	☕	☕		☕
London Euston [15] ⊖66	d	13 00	13 07	13 10		13 20			13 30			13 40							13 43	13 46	14 00	14 07	14 10		14 20
Watford Junction 66	d																								
Milton Keynes Central 66	d			13 41		13 50													14 13	14 19			14 41		14 50
Rugby 66	d																			14 42					
Nuneaton	d																			14 54					
Tamworth Low Level	d																			15 09					
Lichfield Trent Valley	d																			15 17					
Coventry 68	d														14 27				14 42						
Birmingham International 68 ✈	d														14 38				14 53						
Birmingham New St. [12] 68	d												14 31	14 36	14 57			15 01	15 15						
Wolverhampton [7] 🚊	d												14 49	14 54	15 15			15 20	15 37						
Penkridge	d													15 04											
Stafford	a		14 22										15 00	15 10	15 29			15 35		15 35		15 22			
	d		14 23										15 01	15 10	15 30			15 35		15 39		15 23			
Stoke-on-Trent	a	14 24				14 48							15 19		15 54					16 00	15 24				15 48
Macclesfield	a	14 41			←						←				16 11						15 41			←	
Crewe [10]	a		14 41	14 47	14 56						15 07	15 10		15 30				15 56	16 06	16 24		15 41	15 47	15 56	
	d		14 43	14 49	14 57						15 09	15 11		15 32				15 57	16 09			15 43	15 49	15 57	
Chester 81	a			15 13														↦	↦				16 10		
Wrexham General 75	a																								
Llandudno Junction 81	a																						17 01		
Bangor (Gwynedd) 81	a																						17 17		
Holyhead 81 ⛴	a																						17 51		
Wilmslow 84	a											15 27													
Stockport 84	a	14 55				15 16						15 36	15 49		16 27						15 55				16 16
Manchester Piccadilly [10] 🚊	a	15 07				15 28						15 49	15 59		16 38						16 07				16 28
Warrington Bank Quay	a								15 14		15 26														
	d								15 14		15 27														
Runcorn 91	a		15 00		15 21									15 50								16 00		16 24	
Liverpool South Pkwy [7] 91 ✈	a				15 30									15 59										16 33	
Liverpool Lime St. [10] 91	a		15 21		15 42									16 10								16 21		16 45	
	d																								
Manchester Airport 82 ✈	d							14 29								15 00									
Manchester Picc. [10] 82 🚊	d							14 46								15 16									
Bolton 82	d							15 07																	
Wigan North Western 90	a								15 25	←	15 37					15 43									
	d								15 25		15 37					15 43									
Preston [8] 90	a							15 33	15 38	15 33	15 51					15 57									
Preston [8] 90	d							15 46	15 41	15 46	15 53					15 58									
Blackpool North 97	a							↦																	
Lancaster [6]	a								15 54	16 01	16 08					16 15									
	d								15 55	16 02	16 08														
Barrow-in-Furness 82	a									17 04															
Oxenholme Lake District	a								16 08																
	d								16 08																
Windermere 83	a																								
Penrith North Lakes	d										16 45														
Carlisle [8] 216	a								16 46		17 00														
	d								16 47		17 01														
Lockerbie	d																								
Carstairs 226	a																								
Motherwell 226	a																								
Glasgow Central [15] 216,226	a								18 03																
Haymarket 225,226,228,230,242	a										18 16														
Edinburgh [10] 225,226,228,230,242	a										18 24														
Perth 229	a																								
Dundee 229	a																								
Aberdeen 229	a																								
Inverness 229	a																								

A ⍑ to Preston

OVERNIGHT SLEEPERS. For sleeper trains, operated by First ScotRail, please see Tables 400 - 404.

For complete service between Manchester and Preston, Blackpool and between Barrow-in-furness and Lancaster, please see Table 82.

For complete service between Crewe and Liverpool Lime Street, see Table 91

For complete service between Crewe/Stoke-on-Trent & Manchester see Table 84

For complete service between Crewe and Holyhead please see Table 81.

For complete service between Coventry-Birmingham-Wolverhampton-Stafford please see Table 68

For complete service between Windermere and Oxenholme Lake District, please see Table 83

Table 65

Saturdays

15 February to 17 May

London and West Midlands - North West England and Scotland

Route Diagram - refer to first Page of Table 65

		VT		VT	VT	XC	LM	XC	TP		LM	VT		LM	VT	VT	VT	LM	VT	TP	VT	TP		VT	VT
												R												R	
		◇1		◇1	◇1	◇1	1	◇1	◇1		1	1		1	◇1	◇1	◇1	1	◇1	◇1	◇1	◇1		1	◇1
		ꟾP		ꟾP	ꟾP	ꟾP		Ŧ	Ŧ			ꟾP			ꟾP	ꟾP	ꟾP		ꟾP		ꟾP			⊠	ꟾP
London Euston [15] ⊖66	d	14 30			14 40							14 43		14 46	15 00	15 07	15 10		15 20		15 30				15 40
Watford Junction 66	d																								
Milton Keynes Central 66	d											15 13		15 19			15 41		15 50						
Rugby 66	d													15 42											
Nuneaton	d													15 54											
Tamworth Low Level	d													16 09											
Lichfield Trent Valley	d													16 17											
Coventry 68	d							15 27				15 42													
Birmingham International 68 ✈	d							15 38				15 53													
Birmingham New St. [12] 68	d					15 31	15 36	15 57			16 01	16 15													
Wolverhampton [7] ⛴	d					15 49	15 54	16 15			16 20	16 37													
Penkridge	d						16 04				16 29														
Stafford	a					16 00	16 10	16 29			16 35			16 35		16 22									
	d					16 01	16 10	16 30			16 36			16 39		16 23									
Stoke-on-Trent	a					16 19		16 54						17 00	16 24				16 48						
Macclesfield	a			←				17 11							16 41			←						←	
Crewe [10]	a			16 06	16 10		16 30				16 56	17 07		17 24		16 41	16 47	16 56						17 07	17 10
	d			16 09	16 11		16 32				16 57	17 09				16 43	16 49	16 57						17 09	17 11
Chester 81	a										↦	↦					17 13								
Wrexham General 75	a																								
Llandudno Junction 81	a																								
Bangor (Gwynedd) 81	a																								
Holyhead 81 ⛴	a																								
Wilmslow 84	a				16 27																				17 27
Stockport 84	a				16 36	16 49		17 27							16 55				17 16						17 36
Manchester Piccadilly [10] ⛴	a				16 49	16 59		17 38							17 07				17 28						17 49
Warrington Bank Quay	a	16 14		16 27																	17 14			17 26	
	d	16 14		16 27																	17 14			17 26	
Runcorn 91	a						16 50									17 00		17 24							
Liverpool South Pkwy [7] 91 ✈	a						16 59											17 33							
Liverpool Lime St. [10] 91	a						17 10									17 21		17 45							
	d																								
Manchester Airport 82 ✈	d								16 00											16 29					
Manchester Picc. [10] 82 ⛴	d								16 16											16 46					
Bolton 82	d								16 33											17 07					
Wigan North Western 90	a	16 25		16 38																	17 25	←		17 37	
	d	16 25		16 38																	17 25			17 37	
Preston [8] 90	a	16 38		16 51					16 58											17 33	17 38	17 33		17 51	
Preston [8] 90	d	16 41		16 53					16 58	17 05										17 45	17 41	17 45		17 52	
Blackpool North 97	a																			↦					
Lancaster [6]	a	16 54		17 08					17 14	17 20											17 54	18 00		18 07	
	d	16 55		17 08					17 15	17 21											17 55	18 01		18 07	
Barrow-in-Furness 82	a																					19 04			
Oxenholme Lake District	a			17 21					17 29	17 37											18 08			18 21	
	d			17 22					17 29	17 38											18 08			18 22	
Windermere 83	a									17 58															
Penrith North Lakes	d	17 30																						18 48	
Carlisle [8] 216	a	17 46		18 00					18 11												18 46			19 02	
	d	17 47		18 02					18 11												18 47			19 02	
Lockerbie	d								18 30																
Carstairs 226	a																								
Motherwell 226	a																								
Glasgow Central [15] 216,226	a	19 01		19 16																	20 01				
Haymarket 225,226,228,230,242	a								19s34															20 14	
Edinburgh [10] 225,226,228,230,242	a								19 39															20 20	
Perth 229	a																								
Dundee 229	a																								
Aberdeen 229	a																								
Inverness 229	a																								

OVERNIGHT SLEEPERS. For sleeper trains, operated by First ScotRail, please see Tables 400 - 404.

For complete service between Manchester and Preston, Blackpool and between Barrow-in-furness and Lancaster, please see Table 82.

For complete service between Crewe and Liverpool Lime Street, see Table 91

For complete service between Crewe/Stoke-on-Trent & Manchester see Table 84

For complete service between Crewe and Holyhead please see Table 81.

For complete service between Coventry-Birmingham-Wolverhampton-Stafford please see Table 68

For complete service between Windermere and Oxenholme Lake District, please see Table 83

Table 65

Saturdays

15 February to 17 May

London and West Midlands - North West England and Scotland

Route Diagram - refer to first Page of Table 65

	XC	LM	XC	TP	LM	VT	LM	VT	VT	VT	LM	VT	TP	VT	TP	VT	VT	VT	XC	LM	XC	TP
						R										R						
	◇1	1	◇1	◇1	1	1	1	◇1	◇1	◇1	1	◇1	◇1	◇1	◇1	1	◇1	◇1	◇1	1	◇1	◇1
	T		T	T		☕		☕	☕	☕		☕		☕		⊠	☕	☕	T		T	T
London Euston 15 ⊖66 d						15 43	15 46	16 00	16 07	16 10		16 20		16 30			16 33	16 40				
Watford Junction 66 d																						
Milton Keynes Central 66 d						16 13	16 19			16 41		16 50										
Rugby 66 d							16 42															
Nuneaton d							16 54															
Tamworth Low Level d							17 09										17 38					
Lichfield Trent Valley d							17 17										17 45					
Coventry 68 d			16 27			16 42															17 27	
Birmingham International 68 ✈ d			16 38			16 53															17 38	
Birmingham New St. 12 68 d	16 31	16 36	16 57		17 01	17 15													17 31	17 36	17 57	
Wolverhampton 7 🚌 d	16 49	16 54	17 15		17 20	17 37													17 49	17 54	18 15	
Penkridge d		17 04			17 29															18 04		
Stafford a	17 00	17 10	17 29		17 35		17 35		17 22								17 58		18 00	18 10	18 29	
d	17 01	17 10	17 30		17 36		17 39		17 23								17 59		18 01	18 10	18 30	
Stoke-on-Trent a	17 19		17 54				18 00	17 24				17 48							18 19		18 54	
Macclesfield a			18 11					17 41			⟵					⟵					19 11	
Crewe 10 a		17 30			17 56	18 07	18 24		17 41	17 47	17 56					18 07		18 10		18 30		
d		17 32			17 57	18 09			17 43	17 49	17 57					18 09		18 11		18 33		
Chester 81 a					⟶	⟶				18 09												
Wrexham General 75 a																						
Llandudno Junction 81 a										19 05												
Bangor (Gwynedd) 81 a										19 21												
Holyhead 81 ⛴ a										19 55												
Wilmslow 84 a																		18 27				
Stockport 84 a	17 49		18 27					17 55				18 16						18 36	18 49		19 27	
Manchester Piccadilly 10 🚌 a	17 59		18 38					18 07				18 28						18 49	18 59		19 38	
Warrington Bank Quay a														18 14		18 27						
d														18 14		18 27						
Runcorn 91 a		17 50							18 00		18 24						18 31			18 52		
Liverpool South Pkwy 7 91 ✈ a		17 59									18 33									19 02		
Liverpool Lime St. 10 91 a		18 10							18 21		18 45						18 52			19 14		
d																						
Manchester Airport 82 ✈ d				17 00									17 29									18 00
Manchester Picc. 10 82 🚌 d				17 15									17 46									18 16
Bolton 82 d				17 32									18 06									
Wigan North Western 90 a														18 25	⟵	18 38						18 43
d														18 25		18 38						18 43
Preston 8 90 a				17 56									18 35	18 38	18 35	18 51						18 57
Preston 8 90 d				18 00									18 45	18 41	18 45	18 53						18 58
Blackpool North 97 a													⟶									
Lancaster 6 a				18 16										18 54	19 00	19 07						19 14
d				18 16										18 55	19 01	19 08						19 15
Barrow-in-Furness 82 a															20 04							
Oxenholme Lake District a				18 31										19 08		19 21						19 29
d				18 32										19 08		19 22						19 29
Windermere 83 a																						
Penrith North Lakes d				18 56										19 34								19 54
Carlisle 8 216 a				19 12										19 49		20 00						20 11
d				19 14										19 51		20 02						20 11
Lockerbie d																						20 30
Carstairs 226 a																						
Motherwell 226 a				20s14																		
Glasgow Central 15 216,226 a				20 35										21 01		21 19						
Haymarket 225,226,228,230,242 a																						21s34
Edinburgh 10 225,226,228,230,242 a																						21 41
Perth 229 a																						
Dundee 229 a																						
Aberdeen 229 a																						
Inverness 229 a																						

OVERNIGHT SLEEPERS. For sleeper trains, operated by First ScotRail, please see Tables 400 - 404.

For complete service between Manchester and Preston, Blackpool and between Barrow-in-furness and Lancaster, please see Table 82.

For complete service between Crewe and Liverpool Lime Street, see Table 91

For complete service between Crewe/Stoke-on-Trent & Manchester see Table 84

For complete service between Crewe and Holyhead please see Table 81.

For complete service between Coventry-Birmingham-Wolverhampton-Stafford please see Table 68

For complete service between Windermere and Oxenholme Lake District, please see Table 83

Table 65

Saturdays

15 February to 17 May

London and West Midlands - North West England and Scotland

Route Diagram - refer to first Page of Table 65

	LM	VT	LM		VT	VT	VT	VT	LM	VT	VT	VT	VT		XC	LM	XC	TP	LM	VT	LM	VT	VT	
	1	◇1	1		◇1	◇1	◇1	◇1	1	◇1	◇1	◇1	◇1		◇1	1	◇1	◇1	1	◇1	1	◇1	◇1	
		⊡			⊡	⊡	⊠	⊡		⊡	⊡	⊡	⊡		🛒		🛒			⊡		⊡	⊡	
London Euston 15 ⊖66 d		16 43	16 46		17 00	17 07	17 10	17 10		17 20	17 30		17 40							17 43	17 46	18 00	18 07	
Watford Junction 66 d																								
Milton Keynes Central 66 d		17 13	17 19				17u40	17 41		17 50										18 13	18 19			
Rugby 66 d			17 42																		18 42			
Nuneaton d			17 54			18 03															18 54			
Tamworth Low Level d			18 09																		19 09			
Lichfield Trent Valley d			18 17																		19 17			
Coventry 68 d		17 42															18 27			18 42				
Birmingham International 68 ✈ d		17 53															18 38			18 53				
Birmingham New St. 12 68 d	18 01	18 15													18 31	18 36	18 57		19 01	19 15				
Wolverhampton 7 🚌 d	18 20	18 37													18 49	18 54	19 15		19 20	19 37				
Penkridge d	18 29															19 04			19 29					
Stafford a	18 35		18 38			18 26									19 00	19 10	19 29		19 35		19 35		19 22	
d	18 36		18 39			18 27									19 01	19 10	19 30		19 36		19 39		19 23	
Stoke-on-Trent a			19 00		18 24					18 48					19 19		19 54				20 00	19 24		
Macclesfield a					18 41				←			←					20 11					19 41		
Crewe 10 a	18 56	19 07	19 25			18 45	18 49	18 49	18 56			19 07	19 10			19 30			19 56	20 07	20 24		19 41	
d	18 59	19 09				18 47	18 52	18 52	18 59			19 09	19 11						19 58	20 09			19 43	
Chester 81 a	→	→					19 11	19 12											→	→				
Wrexham General 75 a																								
Llandudno Junction 81 a								20 07																
Bangor (Gwynedd) 81 a								20 24																
Holyhead 81 ⛴ a								20 58																
Wilmslow 84 a													19 27											
Stockport 84 a					18 55					19 16			19 36		19 49		20 27					19 55		
Manchester Piccadilly 10 🚌 a					19 07					19 28			19 49		19 59		20 37					20 07		
Warrington Bank Quay a											19 14	19 26												
d											19 14	19 27												
Runcorn 91 a						19 04			19 22														20 00	
Liverpool South Pkwy 7 91 ✈ a									19 31															
Liverpool Lime St. 10 91 a						19 23			19 44														20 21	
d																								
Manchester Airport 82 ✈ d																		19 00						
Manchester Picc. 10 82 🚌 d																		19 16						
Bolton 82 d																		19 33						
Wigan North Western 90 a											19 25	19 37												
d											19 25	19 38												
Preston 8 90 a											19 38	19 54						19 57						
Preston 8 90 d											19 41							19 59						
Blackpool North 97 a																								
Lancaster 6 a											19 54							20 14						
d											19 55							20 15						
Barrow-in-Furness 82 a																		21 18						
Oxenholme Lake District a											20 08													
d											20 08													
Windermere 83 a																								
Penrith North Lakes d											20 34													
Carlisle 8 216 a											20 49													
d											20 51													
Lockerbie d																								
Carstairs 226 a																								
Motherwell 226 a																								
Glasgow Central 15 216,226 a											22 01													
Haymarket 225,226,228,230,242 a																								
Edinburgh 10 225,226,228,230,242 a																								
Perth 229 a																								
Dundee 229 a																								
Aberdeen 229 a																								
Inverness 229 a																								

OVERNIGHT SLEEPERS. For sleeper trains, operated by First ScotRail, please see Tables 400 - 404.

For complete service between Manchester and Preston, Blackpool and between Barrow-in-furness and Lancaster, please see Table 82.

For complete service between Crewe and Liverpool Lime Street, see Table 91

For complete service between Crewe/Stoke-on-Trent & Manchester see Table 84

For complete service between Crewe and Holyhead please see Table 81.

For complete service between Coventry-Birmingham-Wolverhampton-Stafford please see Table 68

For complete service between Windermere and Oxenholme Lake District, please see Table 83

Table 65

Saturdays

15 February to 17 May

London and West Midlands - North West England and Scotland

Route Diagram - refer to first Page of Table 65

		VT	LM	VT	VT	VT	NT	VT	VT	XC		XC	TP	TP	LM	VT	LM	VT	VT	LM		VT	VT	LM	VT
		◇[1]	[1]	◇[1]	◇[1]	◇[1]		◇[1]	◇[1]	◇[1]		◇[1]	◇[1]		[1]	◇[1]	[1]	◇[1]	◇[1]	[1]		◇[1]	◇[1]	[1]	◇[1]
												A		B 🚌											
		☕		☕	☕	☕		☕	☕	🛒		🛒				☕		☕	☕			☕	☕		☕
London Euston [15] ⊖66	d	18 10		18 20	18 30	18 33			18 40							18 43	18 46	19 00	19 07			19 20	19 30		19 40
Watford Junction 66	d																								
Milton Keynes Central 66	d	18 41		18 50												19 13	19 19					19 50			
Rugby 66	d																19 42								
Nuneaton	d																19 58		20 03						
Tamworth Low Level	d					19 38											20 14								
Lichfield Trent Valley	d					19 45											20 21								
Coventry 68	d											19 27				19 42									
Birmingham International 68 ✈	d											19 38				19 53									
Birmingham New St. [12] 68	d									19 31		19 57			20 01	20 15									
Wolverhampton [7] 🚌	d									19 49		20 15			20 22	20 37									
Penkridge	d														20 31										
Stafford	a					19 58				20 00		20 29			20 37	20 51	20 38		20 26						
	d					19 59				20 01		20 30			20 38	20 52	20 42		20 27						
Stoke-on-Trent	a			19 48						20 19		20 54					21 01	20 24				20 48			
Macclesfield	a		←					←		20 36		21 11						20 41		←				←	
Crewe [10]	a	19 47	19 56					20 07	20 10						20 58	21 10	21 24		20 45	20 58			21 04	20 58	21 18
	d	19 49	19 58					20 09	20 11						21 06				20 47	21 06			21 05	21 06	21 19
Chester 81	a	20 13													↪					↪					
Wrexham General 75	a																								
Llandudno Junction 81	a																								
Bangor (Gwynedd) 81	a																								
Holyhead 81 ⛴	a																								
Wilmslow 84	a								20 27																21 34
Stockport 84	a			20 16					20 36	20 49		21 25						20 55				21 16			21 44
Manchester Piccadilly [10] 🚌	a			20 28					20 49	20 59		21 39						21 07				21 28			21 53
Warrington Bank Quay	a				20 14			20 26															21 22		
	d				20 14			20 27															21 22		
Runcorn 91	a		20 24			20 31													21 05					21 29	
Liverpool South Pkwy [7] 91 ✈	a		20 33																					21 38	
Liverpool Lime St. [10] 91	a		20 46			20 52													21 25					21 50	
	d																								
Manchester Airport 82 ✈	d												20 00												
Manchester Picc. [10] 82 🚌	d												20 16												
Bolton 82	d																								
Wigan North Western 90	a				20 25			20 37					20 43										21 33		
	d				20 25			20 38					20 43										21 33		
Preston [8] 90	a				20 38			20 59					20 57										21 49		
Preston [8] 90	d				20 41		20 45							21 25											
Blackpool North 97	a																								
Lancaster [6]	a				20 54		21 08							22 15											
	d				20 55		21 11																		
Barrow-in-Furness 82	a						22 17																		
Oxenholme Lake District	a				21 08																				
	d				21 09																				
Windermere 83	a																								
Penrith North Lakes	d				21 34																				
Carlisle [8] 216	a				21 49																				
	d				21 52																				
Lockerbie	d				22 10																				
Carstairs 226	a																								
Motherwell 226	a				22 52																				
Glasgow Central [15] 216,226	a				23 13																				
Haymarket 225,226,228,230,242	a																								
Edinburgh [10] 225,226,228,230,242	a																								
Perth 229	a																								
Dundee 229	a																								
Aberdeen 229	a																								
Inverness 229	a																								

A 🛒 to Birmingham New St.

B until 22 March

OVERNIGHT SLEEPERS. For sleeper trains, operated by First ScotRail, please see Tables 400 - 404.

For complete service between Manchester and Preston, Blackpool and between Barrow-in-furness and Lancaster, please see Table 82.

For complete service between Crewe and Liverpool Lime Street, see Table 91

For complete service between Crewe/Stoke-on-Trent & Manchester see Table 84

For complete service between Crewe and Holyhead please see Table 81.

For complete service between Coventry-Birmingham-Wolverhampton-Stafford please see Table 68

For complete service between Windermere and Oxenholme Lake District, please see Table 83

Table 65

Saturdays
15 February to 17 May

London and West Midlands - North West England and Scotland

Route Diagram - refer to first Page of Table 65

		XC	LM	XC	VT	VT		TP	TP	TP	TP	VT	LM	XC	VT	XC		LM
		◇1	1	◇1	◇1	◇1			◇1	◇1		◇1	1	◇1	◇1	◇1		1
				A				B	C	B								
				trolley	restaurant	restaurant		bus			bus	restaurant			restaurant			
London Euston 15 ⊖66	d				20 11	20 20						20 31			21 00			
Watford Junction 66	d											20u46						
Milton Keynes Central 66	d					21 05									21 45			
Rugby 66	d				21 15							21 36						
Nuneaton	d					21 33												
Tamworth Low Level	d											21 53						
Lichfield Trent Valley	d											22 00						
Coventry 68	d			20 27										21 27				
Birmingham International 68 ✈	d			20 38										21 38				
Birmingham New St. 12 68	d	20 31	20 36	20 57									21 36	21 57		22 31		22 38
Wolverhampton 7 🚌	d	20 49	20 54	21 15									21 59	22 15		22 49		23 05
Penkridge	d		21 04										22 09					23 15
Stafford	a	21 00	21 10	21 29	21 46								22 15	22 29	22 32	23 01		23 21
	d	21 01	21 10	21 30	21 46								22 16	22 30	22 34	23 02		23 22
Stoke-on-Trent	a	21 20		21 52		22 05								22 50		23 20		
Macclesfield	a	21 38		22 11		22 21								23 07		23 38		
Crewe 10	a		21 30		22 05							22 35	22 38		22 58			23 42
	d				22 06							22 37			22 59			
Chester 81	a																	
Wrexham General 75	a																	
Llandudno Junction 81	a																	
Bangor (Gwynedd) 81	a																	
Holyhead 81 ⛴	a																	
Wilmslow 84	a														23 14			
Stockport 84	a	21 53		22 25		22 35								23 20	23 24	23 53		
Manchester Piccadilly 10 🚌	a	22 04		22 34		22 51								23 30	23 38	00 10		
Warrington Bank Quay	a											22 53						
	d											22 54						
Runcorn 91	a				22 24													
Liverpool South Pkwy 7 91 ✈	a																	
Liverpool Lime St. 10 91	a				22 46													
	d																	
Manchester Airport 82 ✈	d								22 00	22 00								
Manchester Picc. 10 82 🚌	d								22 16	22 16								
Bolton 82	d								22 32	22 32								
Wigan North Western 90	a											23 04						
	d											23 05						
Preston 8 90	a								22 53	22 55		23 19						
Preston 8 90	d							22 10			23 05							
Blackpool North 97	a																	
Lancaster 6	a							23 00			23 55							
	d																	
Barrow-in-Furness 82	a																	
Oxenholme Lake District	a																	
	d																	
Windermere 83	a																	
Penrith North Lakes	d																	
Carlisle 8 216	a																	
	d																	
Lockerbie	d																	
Carstairs 226	a																	
Motherwell 226	a																	
Glasgow Central 15 216,226	a																	
Haymarket 225,226,228,230,242	a																	
Edinburgh 10 225,226,228,230,242	a																	
Perth 229	a																	
Dundee 229	a																	
Aberdeen 229	a																	
Inverness 229	a																	

A trolley to Birmingham New St. B until 22 March C from 29 March

OVERNIGHT SLEEPERS. For sleeper trains, operated by First ScotRail, please see Tables 400 - 404.

For complete service between Manchester and Preston, Blackpool and between Barrow-in-furness and Lancaster, please see Table 82.

For complete service between Crewe and Liverpool Lime Street, see Table 91

For complete service between Crewe/Stoke-on-Trent & Manchester see Table 84

For complete service between Crewe and Holyhead please see Table 81.

For complete service between Coventry-Birmingham-Wolverhampton-Stafford please see Table 68

For complete service between Windermere and Oxenholme Lake District, please see Table 83

Table 65

Sundays

8 December to 29 December

London and West Midlands - North West England and Scotland

Route Diagram - refer to first Page of Table 65

		AW	TP	AW	VT	XC	VT	VT	TP	VT	VT	VT	LM	XC	TP	VT	VT	LM	VT	VT	LM	VT	XC
			◇1		◇1	◇1	◇1	◇1	◇1	◇1	◇1	◇1	1	◇1	◇1	◇1	◇1	1	◇1	◇1	1	◇1	◇1
			⛟		⊡	⛟	⊡	⊡	⛟	⊡	⊡	⊡		⛟		⊡	⊡		⊡	⊡		⊡	⛟
London Euston 15	⊖66 d							08 10			08 15	08 20				08 45			09 15	09 20		09 45	
Watford Junction	66 d																						
Milton Keynes Central	66 d							08 56				09 06				09 32				10 07		10 33	
Rugby	66 d															10 09		10 00				11 09	
Nuneaton	d										09 44							10 14	10 45				
Tamworth Low Level	d																	10 29					
Lichfield Trent Valley	d																	10 35					
Coventry	68 d																						10 28
Birmingham International 68	✈ d																						10 40
Birmingham New St. 12	68 d				08 45	09 01	09 20						09 42	10 01			10 20				10 42		11 01
Wolverhampton 7	⛴ d				09 04	09 19	09 38						10 00	10 19			10 38				11 00		11 19
Penkridge	d												10 10								11 10		
Stafford	a				09 17	09 32					10 08		10 16	10 32				10 56	11 09		11 16		11 32
	d				09 17	09 33					10 08		10 17	10 33				10 57	11 09		11 17		11 33
Stoke-on-Trent	a											10 19		10 51				11 15		11 20			11 51
Macclesfield	a											10 36		11 08						11 37			12 09
Crewe 10	a				09 35	09 54	10 08	10 17			10 28		10 37			10 55	11 07	11 43	11 30		11 37	11 55	
	d	08 28		09 28	09 37	09 56	10 08	10 19		10 21	10 30		10 38			10 57	11 09		11 32		11 38	11 57	
Chester	81 a																						
Wrexham General	75 a																						
Llandudno Junction	81 a																						
Bangor (Gwynedd)	81 a																						
Holyhead	81 ⛴ a																						
Wilmslow	84 a	08 47		09 46		10 12		10 33															
Stockport	84 a					10 21		10 43				10 50		11 22						11 51			12 22
Manchester Piccadilly 10	⛴ a	09 11		10 11		10 37		10 55				11 03		11 31						12 04			12 40
Warrington Bank Quay	a				09 54		10 27			10 37						11 14	11 26					12 14	
	d				09 54		10 27			10 37						11 14	11 27					12 14	
Runcorn	91 a										10 47		11 00						11 49		12 01		
Liverpool South Pkwy 7 91	✈ a												11 09								12 10		
Liverpool Lime St. 10	91 a										11 09		11 21						12 10		12 21		
	d																						
Manchester Airport	82 ✈ d		09 00						10 00														
Manchester Picc. 10	82 ⛴ d		09 16						10 15														
Bolton	82 d								10 32														
Wigan North Western	90 a		09 42		10 05		10 38			10 48						11 25	11 37					12 25	
	d		09 43		10 05		10 38			10 48						11 25	11 38					12 25	
Preston 8	90 a		09 57		10 22		10 51		10 54	11 02						11 38	11 51					12 38	
Preston 8	90 d		09 58				10 53		10 57	11 08					11 14	11 40	11 53					12 40	
Blackpool North	97 a																						
Lancaster 6	a		10 14				11 07		11 14	11 24					11 31	11 54	12 08					12 54	
	d		10 15				11 09		11 14						11 32	11 55	12 08					12 55	
Barrow-in-Furness	82 a														12 30								
Oxenholme Lake District	a		10 29				11 21		11 28							12 08	12 22					13 08	
	d		10 29				11 23		11 29							12 08	12 24					13 08	
Windermere	83 a																						
Penrith North Lakes	d		10 54						11 54							12 34						13 34	
Carlisle 8	216 a		11 11				11 59		12 11							12 49	13 01					13 49	
	d		11 11				12 01		12 11							12 50	13 03					13 50	
Lockerbie	d		11 30						12 30														
Carstairs	226 a																						
Motherwell	226 a																						
Glasgow Central 15	216,226 a						13 20		13 34							14 02						15 02	
Haymarket	225,226,228,230,242 a		12s30														14 14						
Edinburgh 10	225,226,228,230,242 a		12 38														14 22						
Perth	229 a																						
Dundee	229 a																						
Aberdeen	229 a																						
Inverness	229 a																						

OVERNIGHT SLEEPERS. For sleeper trains, operated by First ScotRail, please see Tables 400 - 404.

For complete service between Manchester and Preston, Blackpool and between Barrow-in-furness and Lancaster, please see Table 82.

For complete service between Crewe and Liverpool Lime Street, see Table 91

For complete service between Crewe/Stoke-on-Trent & Manchester see Table 84

For complete service between Crewe and Holyhead please see Table 81.

For complete service between Coventry-Birmingham-Wolverhampton-Stafford please see Table 68

For complete service between Windermere and Oxenholme Lake District, please see Table 83

Table 65

Sundays

8 December to 29 December

London and West Midlands - North West England and Scotland

Route Diagram - refer to first Page of Table 65

Station		TP ◇1	VT ◇1	LM 1	VT ◇1	VT ◇1	LM 1	XC ◇1	LM 1	TP ◇1	VT ◇1	VT ◇1	VT ◇1	VT ◇1	LM 1	LM 1	VT ◇1	VT ◇1	XC ◇1	TP ◇1	VT ◇1	VT ◇1	VT ◇1
London Euston 15 ⊖66	d			09 54	10 15	10 20			10 24		10 45		11 15	11 20		11 24	12 05	12 17			12 28		12 37
Watford Junction 66	d			10 10					10 40							11 42							
Milton Keynes Central 66	d			10 50		11 07			11 20		11 33		12 04	12 08		12 28		12 50					
Rugby 66	d			11 30					12 03		12 09					13 26							
Nuneaton	d			11 43	11 47				12 17							13 40							
Tamworth Low Level	d			11 57					12 32							13 55							
Lichfield Trent Valley	d			12 04					12 38							14 01							
Coventry 68	d							11 29											12 28				
Birmingham International 68 ✈	d							11 40											12 40				
Birmingham New St. 12 68	d		11 20				11 42	12 01				12 20			12 35				13 01			13 20	
Wolverhampton 7	d		11 38				12 00	12 19				12 37			12 53				13 19			13 37	
Penkridge	d						12 10								13 03								
Stafford	a			12 21	12 13		12 16	12 32	12 59				12 53		13 09	14 18	13 24		13 33				
	d			12 21	12 14		12 17	12 33	13 00				12 53		13 09	14 19	13 25		13 34				
Stoke-on-Trent	a			12 39		12 24		12 52	13 18					13 09		14 37		13 50	13 56				
Macclesfield	a					12 40		13 10						13 26					14 14				
Crewe 10	a		12 07	13 02	12 32		12 37		13 43		12 56	13 07	13 13		13 30	15 00	13 43					14 07	14 12
	d		12 09		12 34		12 38				12 58	13 09	13 15		13 31		13 45					14 09	14 13
Chester 81	a																						
Wrexham General 75	a																						
Llandudno Junction 81	a																						
Bangor (Gwynedd) 81	a																						
Holyhead 81 ⛴	a																						
Wilmslow 84	a																						14 29
Stockport 84	a					12 55		13 28						13 41				14 18	14 28				14 38
Manchester Piccadilly 10 ⛴	a					13 08		13 40						13 53				14 29	14 40				14 50
Warrington Bank Quay	a		12 26								13 15	13 26									14 16	14 26	
	d		12 27								13 15	13 27									14 16	14 27	
Runcorn 91	a				12 51		13 01						13 32		13 54		14 02						
Liverpool South Pkwy 7 91 ✈	a						13 10								14 03								
Liverpool Lime St. 10 91	a				13 12		13 21						13 54		14 14		14 24						
	d																						
Manchester Airport 82 ✈	d									12 00										13 00			
Manchester Picc. 10 82 ⛴	d									12 14										13 16			
Bolton 82	d																						
Wigan North Western 90	a		12 37							12 42	13 26	13 37								13 43	14 27	14 37	
	d		12 38							12 43	13 26	13 38								13 43	14 27	14 38	
Preston 8 90	a		12 51							12 57	13 40	13 51								13 57	14 40	14 50	
Preston 8 90	d	12 48	12 53							12 57	13 42	13 53								13 58	14 42	14 53	
Blackpool North 97	a																						
Lancaster 6	a	13 03	13 07							13 14	13 56	14 08								14 14	14 56	15 08	
	d	13 04	13 08							13 14	13 57	14 08								14 15	14 58	15 09	
Barrow-in-Furness 82	a	14 07																					
Oxenholme Lake District	a		13 21							13 28	14 10									14 29		15 22	
	d		13 22							13 29	14 10									14 29		15 24	
Windermere 83	a																						
Penrith North Lakes	d									13 54	14 36	14 45								14 55	15 32		
Carlisle 8 216	a		14 00							14 11	14 51	15 00								15 11	15 47	16 01	
	d		14 02							14 11	14 52	15 03								15 17	15 48	16 03	
Lockerbie	d									14 30													
Carstairs 226	a																						
Motherwell 226	a																						
Glasgow Central 15 216,226	a		15 16								16 05									16 34	17 00	17 17	
Haymarket 225,226,228,230,242	a									15s29		16 14											
Edinburgh 10 225,226,228,230,242	a									15 36		16 23											
Perth 229	a																						
Dundee 229	a																						
Aberdeen 229	a																						
Inverness 229	a																						

OVERNIGHT SLEEPERS. For sleeper trains, operated by First ScotRail, please see Tables 400 - 404.

For complete service between Manchester and Preston, Blackpool and between Barrow-in-furness and Lancaster, please see Table 82.

For complete service between Crewe and Liverpool Lime Street, see Table 91

For complete service between Crewe/Stoke-on-Trent & Manchester see Table 84

For complete service between Crewe and Holyhead please see Table 81.

For complete service between Coventry-Birmingham-Wolverhampton-Stafford please see Table 68

For complete service between Windermere and Oxenholme Lake District, please see Table 83

Table 65

Sundays

8 December to 29 December

London and West Midlands - North West England and Scotland

Route Diagram - refer to first Page of Table 65

	XC		LM	XC	TP	VT	LM	VT	VT	VT	VT		VT	VT	XC	LM	XC	TP	VT	LM	VT		VT	VT
	◇1		1	◇1	◇1	◇1	1	◇1	◇1	◇1	◇1		◇1	◇1	◇1	1	◇1	◇1	◇1	1	◇1		◇1	◇1
London Euston 15 ⊖66 d						12 40	12 50	12 57	13 05	13 17	13 28			13 37					13 40	13 50	13 57		14 05	14 17
Watford Junction 66 d							13 06													14 06				
Milton Keynes Central 66 d						13 13	13 37			13 50									14 13	14 37				14 50
Rugby 66 d							14 26													15 26				
Nuneaton d							14 40													15 40				
Tamworth Low Level d							14 55													15 55				
Lichfield Trent Valley d							15 01													16 01				
Coventry 68 d				13 26		13 42											14 26		14 44					
Birmingham International 68 ✈ d				13 38		13 53											14 38		14 54					
Birmingham New St. 12 68 d	13 31		13 35	14 01		14 16									14 31	14 35	15 01		15 17					
Wolverhampton 7 d	13 49		13 53	14 19		14 37									14 49	14 53	15 19		15 38					
Penkridge d			14 03													15 03								
Stafford a			14 09	14 33			15 18		14 23							15 09	15 33			16 18			15 24	
d			14 09	14 34			15 20		14 24							15 09	15 34			16 20			15 25	
Stoke-on-Trent a	14 19			14 56			15 39	14 26		14 50					15 19		15 56			16 38	15 25			15 50
Macclesfield a				15 14				14 42					←				16 14				15 42			
Crewe 10 a			14 29			15 07	16 03		14 43				15 07	15 12		15 29			16 07	17 03			15 43	
d			14 31			15 09			14 45				15 09	15 13		15 31			16 09				15 45	
Chester 81 a						→													→					
Wrexham General 75 a																								
Llandudno Junction 81 a																								
Bangor (Gwynedd) 81 a																								
Holyhead 81 ⛴ a																								
Wilmslow 84 a														15 29										
Stockport 84 a				15 28				14 56		15 18				15 38			16 28				15 56			16 18
Manchester Piccadilly 10 ⇌ a	14 57			15 40				15 09		15 29				15 50	15 59		16 40				16 09			16 29
Warrington Bank Quay a											15 16		15 26											
d											15 16		15 27											
Runcorn 91 a			14 53						15 02							15 53							16 02	
Liverpool South Pkwy 7 91 ✈ a			15 02													16 02								
Liverpool Lime St. 10 91 a			15 14						15 24							16 14							16 24	
d																								
Manchester Airport 82 ✈ d					14 00													15 00						
Manchester Picc. 10 82 ⇌ d					14 14													15 14						
Bolton 82 d																								
Wigan North Western 90 a					14 42						15 27		15 37					15 42						
d					14 43						15 27		15 38					15 43						
Preston 8 90 a					14 57						15 40		15 51					15 57						
Preston 8 90 d					14 57						15 42		15 53					15 57						
Blackpool North 97 a																								
Lancaster 6 a					15 14						15 56		16 08					16 14						
d					15 14						15 58		16 08					16 14						
Barrow-in-Furness 82 a																		17 18						
Oxenholme Lake District a					15 28						16 10													
d					15 29						16 11													
Windermere 83 a																								
Penrith North Lakes d					15 54								16 45											
Carlisle 8 216 a					16 11						16 48		17 00											
d					16 11						16 49		17 02											
Lockerbie d					16 30																			
Carstairs 226 a																								
Motherwell 226 a																								
Glasgow Central 15 216,226 a											18 01													
Haymarket 225,226,228,230,242 a					17s30								18 13											
Edinburgh 10 225,226,228,230,242 a					17 38								18 22											
Perth 229 a																								
Dundee 229 a																								
Aberdeen 229 a																								
Inverness 229 a																								

OVERNIGHT SLEEPERS. For sleeper trains, operated by First ScotRail, please see Tables 400 - 404.

For complete service between Manchester and Preston, Blackpool and between Barrow-in-furness and Lancaster, please see Table 82.

For complete service between Crewe and Liverpool Lime Street, see Table 91

For complete service between Crewe/Stoke-on-Trent & Manchester see Table 84

For complete service between Crewe and Holyhead please see Table 81.

For complete service between Coventry-Birmingham-Wolverhampton-Stafford please see Table 68

For complete service between Windermere and Oxenholme Lake District, please see Table 83

Table 65

Sundays

8 December to 29 December

London and West Midlands - North West England and Scotland

Route Diagram - refer to first Page of Table 65

Station		VT	VT	VT	XC	LM	XC	TP		VT	LM	VT	VT	VT	VT	VT	VT	VT		XC	LM	XC	TP	VT	LM
		◇1	◇1	◇1	◇1	1	◇1	◇1		◇1	1	◇1	◇1	◇1	◇1	◇1	◇1	◇1		◇1	1	◇1	◇1	◇1	1
London Euston 15 ⊖66	d	14 28		14 37						14 40	14 50	14 57	15 05	15 08	15 17	15 28		15 37						15 40	15 50
Watford Junction 66	d										15 06														16 06
Milton Keynes Central 66	d									15 13	15 37			15 42	15 50									16 13	16 37
Rugby 66	d										16 26														17 26
Nuneaton	d										16 40														17 40
Tamworth Low Level	d										16 55														17 55
Lichfield Trent Valley	d										17 01														18 01
Coventry 68	d						15 26			15 42												16 26		16 42	
Birmingham International 68 ✈	d						15 38			15 53												16 38		16 53	
Birmingham New St. 12 68	d				15 31	15 35	16 01			16 16										16 31	16 35	17 01		17 16	
Wolverhampton 7	d				15 49	15 53	16 19			16 37										16 49	16 53	17 19		17 37	
Penkridge	d					16 03															17 03				
Stafford	a					16 09	16 34				17 18		16 24								17 09	17 35			18 18
	d					16 09	16 34				17 20		16 25								17 09	17 36			18 20
Stoke-on-Trent	a				16 19		16 56				17 38	16 24			16 50					17 19		17 56			18 39
Macclesfield	a		←				17 14					16 42					←					18 14			
Crewe 10	a		16 07	16 12		16 30				17 07	18 03		16 43	16 50			17 07	17 12			17 30			18 07	19 07
	d		16 09	16 13		16 31				17 09			16 45	16 52			17 09	17 13			17 31			18 09	
Chester 81	a									→				17 14										→	
Wrexham General 75	a																								
Llandudno Junction 81	a																								
Bangor (Gwynedd) 81	a																								
Holyhead 81 ⛴	a																								
Wilmslow 84	a			16 29														17 29							
Stockport 84	a			16 38			17 28					16 56			17 18			17 38				18 28			
Manchester Piccadilly 10 ⛴	a			16 50	16 59		17 40					17 09			17 29			17 50		17 56		18 40			
Warrington Bank Quay	a	16 16	16 26													17 16	17 26								
	d	16 16	16 27													17 16	17 27								
Runcorn 91	a					16 54							17 02								17 54				
Liverpool South Pkwy 7 91 ✈	a					17 03															18 03				
Liverpool Lime St. 10 91	a					17 14							17 22								18 14				
	d																								
Manchester Airport 82 ✈	d							16 00															17 00		
Manchester Picc. 10 82 ⛴	d							16 14															17 14		
Bolton 82	d																								
Wigan North Western 90	a	16 27	16 37					16 42								17 27	17 37						17 42		
	d	16 27	16 37					16 43								17 27	17 38						17 43		
Preston 8 90	a	16 40	16 51					16 57								17 40	17 51						17 57		
Preston 8 90	d	16 42	16 53					16 57								17 42	17 53						17 57		
Blackpool North 97	a																								
Lancaster 6	a	16 56	17 08					17 14								17 56	18 07						18 14		
	d	16 57	17 08					17 14								17 57	18 08						18 14		
Barrow-in-Furness 82	a																								
Oxenholme Lake District	a		17 22					17 28								18 10	18 21						18 28		
	d		17 23					17 29								18 10	18 22						18 29		
Windermere 83	a																								
Penrith North Lakes	d	17 32						17 54									18 48						18 54		
Carlisle 8 216	a	17 47	18 01					18 11								18 48	19 03						19 11		
	d	17 48	18 03					18 11								18 49	19 04						19 17		
Lockerbie	d																						19 36		
Carstairs 226	a																								
Motherwell 226	a																						20s22		
Glasgow Central 15 216,226	a	19 00	19 17													20 01							20 40		
Haymarket 225,226,228,230,242	a							19s27									20 16								
Edinburgh 10 225,226,228,230,242	a							19 34									20 21								
Perth 229	a																								
Dundee 229	a																								
Aberdeen 229	a																								
Inverness 229	a																								

OVERNIGHT SLEEPERS. For sleeper trains, operated by First ScotRail, please see Tables 400 - 404.

For complete service between Manchester and Preston, Blackpool and between Barrow-in-furness and Lancaster, please see Table 82.

For complete service between Crewe and Liverpool Lime Street, see Table 91

For complete service between Crewe/Stoke-on-Trent & Manchester see Table 84

For complete service between Crewe and Holyhead please see Table 81.

For complete service between Coventry-Birmingham-Wolverhampton-Stafford please see Table 68

For complete service between Windermere and Oxenholme Lake District, please see Table 83

Table 65

Sundays

8 December to 29 December

London and West Midlands - North West England and Scotland

Route Diagram - refer to first Page of Table 65

		VT	VT	VT	VT	TP	VT	VT	VT	XC	LM	XC	TP	TP		VT	LM	VT	VT	VT	VT	VT
		◇1	◇1	◇1	◇1	◇1	◇1	◇1	◇1	◇1	1	◇1	◇1	◇1		◇1	1	◇1	◇1	◇1	◇1	◇1
London Euston 15 ⊖66	d	15 57	16 05	16 08	16 17		16 28		16 37							16 40	16 50	16 57	17 05	17 08	17 08	17 17
Watford Junction 66	d																17 06					
Milton Keynes Central 66	d			16 42	16 50											17 13	17 37			17 42	17 42	17 50
Rugby 66	d																18 26					
Nuneaton	d																18 40		18 04			
Tamworth Low Level	d																18 55					
Lichfield Trent Valley	d																19 01					
Coventry 68	d											17 26				17 44						
Birmingham International 68 ✈	d											17 38				17 54						
Birmingham New St. 12 68	d									17 31	17 35	18 01				18 16						
Wolverhampton 7 ⛴	d									17 49	17 53	18 19				18 37						
Penkridge	d										18 03											
Stafford	a		17 24								18 09	18 35					19 18			18 34	18 34	
	d		17 25								18 09	18 36					19 20			18 35	18 35	
Stoke-on-Trent	a	17 25			17 50					18 19		18 56					19 40	18 25				18 50
Macclesfield	a	17 42						⟵				19 15						18 42				
Crewe 10	a		17 43	17 50				18 07	18 12		18 30					19 06	20 07		18 44	18 53	18 53	
	d		17 45	17 52				18 09	18 13		18 31					19 09			18 46	18 56	18 56	
Chester 81	a			18 15												⟶				19 14	19 14	
Wrexham General 75	a																					
Llandudno Junction 81	a																				20 11	
Bangor (Gwynedd) 81	a																				20 27	
Holyhead 81 ⛴	a																				20 59	
Wilmslow 84	a								18 29													
Stockport 84	a	17 56			18 18				18 38			19 28						18 56				19 18
Manchester Piccadilly 10 ⛴	a	18 09			18 29				18 50	18 56		19 40						19 09				19 29
Warrington Bank Quay	a						18 16	18 26														
	d						18 17	18 27														
Runcorn 91	a		18 02								18 54								19 02			
Liverpool South Pkwy 7 91 ✈	a										19 03											
Liverpool Lime St. 10 91	a		18 22								19 14								19 25			
	d																					
Manchester Airport 82 ✈	d					17 30								18 00								
Manchester Picc. 10 82 ⛴	d					17 46								18 14								
Bolton 82	d					18 05								18 31								
Wigan North Western 90	a						18 27	18 37					⟵									
	d						18 28	18 38														
Preston 8 90	a					18 33	18 40	18 51					18 33	18 54								
Preston 8 90	d					19 06	18 42	18 53					19 06	18 57	19 06							
Blackpool North 97	a					⟶																
Lancaster 6	a						18 56	19 07					19 22	19 14	19 22							
	d						18 58	19 08					19 22	19 14	19 22							
Barrow-in-Furness 82	a												20 26		20 26							
Oxenholme Lake District	a						19 10	19 21						19 28								
	d						19 11	19 22						19 29								
Windermere 83	a																					
Penrith North Lakes	d						19 36							19 54								
Carlisle 8 216	a						19 51	20 00						20 11								
	d						19 53	20 01						20 11								
Lockerbie	d													20 30								
Carstairs 226	a																					
Motherwell 226	a																					
Glasgow Central 15 216,226	a						21 09	21 15														
Haymarket 225,226,228,230,242	a													21s29								
Edinburgh 10 225,226,228,230,242	a													21 36								
Perth 229	a																					
Dundee 229	a																					
Aberdeen 229	a																					
Inverness 229	a																					

OVERNIGHT SLEEPERS. For sleeper trains, operated by First ScotRail, please see Tables 400 - 404.

For complete service between Manchester and Preston, Blackpool and between Barrow-in-furness and Lancaster, please see Table 82.

For complete service between Crewe and Liverpool Lime Street, see Table 91

For complete service between Crewe/Stoke-on-Trent & Manchester see Table 84

For complete service between Crewe and Holyhead please see Table 81.

For complete service between Coventry-Birmingham-Wolverhampton-Stafford please see Table 68

For complete service between Windermere and Oxenholme Lake District, please see Table 83

Table 65

Sundays

8 December to 29 December

London and West Midlands - North West England and Scotland

Route Diagram - refer to first Page of Table 65

Station		VT	VT	VT	XC	LM	XC	TP	VT	LM		VT	VT	VT	VT	VT	VT	VT	VT	XC		LM	XC	VT	LM
									R									R							
		◇1	◇1	◇1	◇1	1	◇1	◇1	1	1		◇1	◇1	◇1	◇1	◇1	◇1	1	◇1	◇1		1	◇1	◇1	1
London Euston 15 ⊖66	d	17 28		17 37					17 40	17 50		17 57	18 05	18 08	18 08	18 17	18 28		18 37					18 40	18 50
Watford Junction 66	d									18 06															19 06
Milton Keynes Central 66	d								18 13	18 37				18 42	18 42	18 50								19 13	19 37
Rugby 66	d									19 26															20 26
Nuneaton	d									19 40															20 40
Tamworth Low Level	d									19 55															20 55
Lichfield Trent Valley	d									20 01															21 01
Coventry 68	d						18 26		18 44														19 26	19 42	
Birmingham International 68 ✈	d						18 38		18 54														19 38	19 53	
Birmingham New St. 12 68	d				18 31	18 35	19 01		19 16											19 31		19 35	20 01	20 16	
Wolverhampton 7 ⛴	d				18 49	18 53	19 19		19 37											19 49		19 53	20 19	20 38	
Penkridge	d					19 03																20 03			
Stafford	a					19 09	19 37			20 18			19 24									20 09	20 36	20 52	21 18
	d					19 09	19 38			20 20			19 25									20 09	20 37	20 53	21 20
Stoke-on-Trent	a				19 19		19 56			20 39		19 25				19 50				20 19			20 56		21 38
Macclesfield	a		←				20 14					19 42						←					21 15		
Crewe 10	a		19 06	19 12		19 29			20 07	21 07			19 43	19 50	19 50			20 07	20 12			20 30		21 10	22 07
	d		19 09	19 13		19 31			20 09				19 45	19 52	19 52			20 09	20 13			20 31			
Chester 81	a								→					20 11	20 11										
Wrexham General 75	a																								
Llandudno Junction 81	a														21 07										
Bangor (Gwynedd) 81	a														21 23										
Holyhead 81 ⛴	a														21 54										
Wilmslow 84	a			19 29															20 29						
Stockport 84	a			19 38			20 28					19 56				20 18			20 38				21 28		
Manchester Piccadilly 10 ⛴	a			19 50	19 58		20 40					20 09				20 29			20 50	21 00			21 40		
Warrington Bank Quay	a	19 16	19 25														20 16	20 26							
	d	19 16	19 27														20 16	20 27							
Runcorn 91	a					19 53							20 02									20 54			
Liverpool South Pkwy 7 91 ✈	a					20 02																21 03			
Liverpool Lime St. 10 91	a					20 14							20 21									21 14			
	d																								
Manchester Airport 82 ✈	d							19 00																	
Manchester Picc. 10 82 ⛴	d							19 14																	
Bolton 82	d							19 33																	
Wigan North Western 90	a	19 27	19 36														20 27	20 37							
	d	19 27	19 38														20 27	20 38							
Preston 8 90	a	19 40	19 51					19 57									20 40	20 51							
Preston 8 90	d	19 42	19 53					20 06									20 42	20 53							
Blackpool North 97	a																								
Lancaster 6	a	19 56	20 07					20 23									20 56	21 08							
	d	19 57	20 08					20 24									20 57	21 08							
Barrow-in-Furness 82	a							21 27																	
Oxenholme Lake District	a	20 10															21 10	21 22							
	d	20 10															21 11	21 23							
Windermere 83	a																								
Penrith North Lakes	d	20 36	20 45														21 36								
Carlisle 8 216	a	20 51	20 59														21 51	22 01							
	d	20 52	21 02														21 52	22 02							
Lockerbie	d																	22 21							
Carstairs 226	a																								
Motherwell 226	a																22 48	23 03							
Glasgow Central 15 216,226	a	22 07															23 09	23 20							
Haymarket 225,226,228,230,242	a		22 14																						
Edinburgh 10 225,226,228,230,242	a		22 20																						
Perth 229	a																								
Dundee 229	a																								
Aberdeen 229	a																								
Inverness 229	a																								

OVERNIGHT SLEEPERS. For sleeper trains, operated by First ScotRail, please see Tables 400 - 404.

For complete service between Manchester and Preston, Blackpool and between Barrow-in-furness and Lancaster, please see Table 82.

For complete service between Crewe and Liverpool Lime Street, see Table 91

For complete service between Crewe/Stoke-on-Trent & Manchester see Table 84

For complete service between Crewe and Holyhead please see Table 81.

For complete service between Coventry-Birmingham-Wolverhampton-Stafford please see Table 68

For complete service between Windermere and Oxenholme Lake District, please see Table 83

Table 65

Sundays

8 December to 29 December

London and West Midlands - North West England and Scotland

Route Diagram - refer to first Page of Table 65

			VT	VT	VT	VT	VT	VT	XC	XC	VT	LM	VT	VT	VT	VT	VT	VT	VT	LM	VT	SR		XC
			◇1	◇1	◇1	◇1	◇1	◇1	◇1	◇1	◇1	1	◇1	◇1	◇1	◇1	◇1	◇1	◇1	1	◇1			◇1
										A												B		A
London Euston 15	⊖66	d	18 57	19 05	19 08	19 17	19 28	19 37			19 40	19 50	19 57	20 05	20 08	20 15	20 25		20 35		20 50	20 57		
Watford Junction	66	d										20 06										21u17		
Milton Keynes Central	66	d			19 42	19 50					20 13	20 37			20 41	20 48					21 37			
Rugby	66	d										21 30									22 01			
Nuneaton		d		20 04								21 43		21 04										
Tamworth Low Level		d										21 58					21 32							
Lichfield Trent Valley		d										22 04					21 39							
Coventry	68	d								20 26	20 44													21 26
Birmingham International	68 ✈	d								20 38	20 54													21 38
Birmingham New St. 12	68	d							20 31	21 01	21 16									21 35				22 01
Wolverhampton 7	⛴	d							20 53	21 19	21 37									21 59				22 20
Penkridge		d																		22 09				
Stafford		a		20 28						21 36	21 55	22 25			21 31				21 59	22 15				22 36
		d		20 29						21 37	21 57	22 26			21 33				22 00	22 16				22 37
Stoke-on-Trent		a	20 25			20 50			21 20	21 56		22 44	21 25			21 50								22 55
Macclesfield		a	20 42							22 14			21 42					←						23 12
Crewe 10		a		20 47	20 50			21 13			22 16	23 07		21 44	21 53		22 10	22 16	22 20	22 38	22 49			
		d		20 49	20 55			21 14			22 17			21 46	21 55		22 13	22 17	22 21		22 51	23u34		
Chester	81	a			21 14						→													
Wrexham General	75	a																						
Llandudno Junction	81	a			22 06																			
Bangor (Gwynedd)	81	a			22 22																			
Holyhead	81 ⛴	a			22 56																			
Wilmslow	84	a						21 30											22 36					
Stockport	84	a	20 56			21 18		21 39		22 27			21 56			22 18			22 45					23 27
Manchester Piccadilly 10	⛴	a	21 09			21 29		21 50	21 57	22 39			22 09			22 29			22 57					23 41
Warrington Bank Quay		a					21 16										22 29	22 35			23 08			
		d					21 16										22 30	22 35			23 08			
Runcorn	91	a		21 06										22 03	22 12									
Liverpool South Pkwy 7	91 ✈	a																						
Liverpool Lime St. 10	91	a		21 27										22 23	22 33									
		d																						
Manchester Airport	82 ✈	d																						
Manchester Picc. 10	82 ⛴	d																						
Bolton	82	d																						
Wigan North Western	90	a					21 27										22 40	22 46			23 19			
		d					21 27										22 41	22 46			23 19			
Preston 8	90	a					21 40										22 58	23 05			23 39			
Preston 8	90	d					21 42															00u33	00u33	
Blackpool North	97	a																						
Lancaster 6		a					21 56																	
		d					21 57																	
Barrow-in-Furness	82	a																						
Oxenholme Lake District		a					22 10																	
		d					22 11																	
Windermere	83	a																						
Penrith North Lakes		d					22 36																	
Carlisle 8	216	a					22 51																	
		d					22 53																	
Lockerbie		d																						
Carstairs	226	a																						
Motherwell	226	a																						
Glasgow Central 15	216,226	a					00 02																	
Haymarket	225,226,228,230,242	a																						
Edinburgh 10	225,226,228,230,242	a																						
Perth	229	a																					05s39	
Dundee	229	a																				06s08		
Aberdeen	229	a																				07 34		
Inverness	229	a																					08 36	

A to Birmingham New St.

B also conveys through sleepers to Fort William arr 0955. (Table 404)

OVERNIGHT SLEEPERS. For sleeper trains, operated by First ScotRail, please see Tables 400 - 404.

For complete service between Manchester and Preston, Blackpool and between Barrow-in-furness and Lancaster, please see Table 82.

For complete service between Crewe and Liverpool Lime Street, see Table 91

For complete service between Crewe/Stoke-on-Trent & Manchester see Table 84

For complete service between Crewe and Holyhead please see Table 81.

For complete service between Coventry-Birmingham-Wolverhampton-Stafford please see Table 68

For complete service between Windermere and Oxenholme Lake District, please see Table 83

Table 65

Sundays

8 December to 29 December

London and West Midlands - North West England and Scotland

Route Diagram - refer to first Page of Table 65

Station	Table		VT	VT	AW	VT	SR
							R
			◇1	◇1	◇	◇1	
							🛏
			☕	☕		☕	☕ ✕
London Euston 15	⊖66	d	21 21	21 25		21 51	23 27
Watford Junction	66	d					23u47
Milton Keynes Central	66	d		22 14		22 39	
Rugby	66	d				23 19	
Nuneaton		d	22 52			23 30	
Tamworth Low Level		d					
Lichfield Trent Valley		d					
Coventry	68	d					
Birmingham International	68 ✈	d			22 43		
Birmingham New St. 12	68	d			22 55		
Wolverhampton 7	⛴	d			23 15		
Penkridge		d					
Stafford		a	23 16		23 30	23s55	
		d	23 17		23 31		
Stoke-on-Trent		a		23 29			
Macclesfield		a		23 45			
Crewe 10		a	23 43		23 57	00s21	
		d	23 45		00 01		
Chester	81	a			00 22		
Wrexham General	75	a					
Llandudno Junction	81	a			01 27		
Bangor (Gwynedd)	81	a			01 45		
Holyhead	81 ⛴	a			02 20		
Wilmslow	84	a					
Stockport	84	a		23 59		00s50	
Manchester Piccadilly 10	⛴	a		00 12		01 00	
Warrington Bank Quay		a					
		d					
Runcorn	91	a	00 07				
Liverpool South Pkwy 7	91 ✈	a					
Liverpool Lime St. 10	91	a	00 30				
		d					
Manchester Airport	82 ✈	d					
Manchester Picc. 10	82 ⛴	d					
Bolton	82	d					
Wigan North Western	90	a					
		d					
Preston 8	90	a					
Preston 8	90	d					
Blackpool North	97	a					
Lancaster 6		a					
		d					
Barrow-in-Furness	82	a					
Oxenholme Lake District		a					
		d					
Windermere	83	a					
Penrith North Lakes		d					
Carlisle 8	216	a					05s10
		d					
Lockerbie		d					
Carstairs	226	a					06s19
Motherwell	226	a					06s54
Glasgow Central 15	216,226	a					07 18
Haymarket	225,226,228,230,242	a					
Edinburgh 10	225,226,228,230,242	a					07 22
Perth	229	a					
Dundee	229	a					
Aberdeen	229	a					
Inverness	229	a					

OVERNIGHT SLEEPERS. For sleeper trains, operated by First ScotRail, please see Tables 400 - 404.

For complete service between Manchester and Preston, Blackpool and between Barrow-in-furness and Lancaster, please see Table 82.

For complete service between Crewe and Liverpool Lime Street, see Table 91

For complete service between Crewe/Stoke-on-Trent & Manchester see Table 84

For complete service between Crewe and Holyhead please see Table 81.

For complete service between Coventry-Birmingham-Wolverhampton-Stafford please see Table 68

For complete service between Windermere and Oxenholme Lake District, please see Table 83

Table 65

Sundays

5 January to 9 February

London and West Midlands - North West England and Scotland

Route Diagram - refer to first Page of Table 65

	AW	TP	AW	VT	XC	VT	VT	TP	VT		VT	VT	VT	TP	VT	VT	VT	VT	VT		VT	LM	VT	XC
		◇1		◇1	◇1			◇1			◇1			◇1	◇1			◇1	◇1		◇1	1	◇1	◇1
						🚌	🚌		🚌			🚌	🚌			🚌	🚌							
				🍽	🛒						🍽				🍽			🍽	🍽		🍽		🍽	🛒
London Euston 15 ⊖66 d																		08 10	08 15		08 20		08 45	
Watford Junction 66 d																								
Milton Keynes Central 66 d																		08 56			09 06		09 32	
Rugby 66 d																							10 09	
Nuneaton d																			09 44					
Tamworth Low Level d																								
Lichfield Trent Valley d																								
Coventry 68 d																								
Birmingham International 68 ✈ d																								
Birmingham New St. 12 68 d				08 45	09 01										09 20							09 42		10 01
Wolverhampton 7 🚌 d				09 04	09 19										09 38							10 00		10 19
Penkridge d																						10 10		
Stafford a				09 17	09 32														10 08			10 16		10 32
d				09 17	09 33														10 08			10 17		10 33
Stoke-on-Trent a																					10 19			10 51
Macclesfield a																					10 36			11 08
Crewe 10 a				09 35	09 54										10 08			10 17	10 28			10 37	10 55	
d	08 28		09 28	09 37	09 56										10 08			10 19	10 30			10 38		
Chester 81 a																								
Wrexham General 75 a																								
Llandudno Junction 81 a																								
Bangor (Gwynedd) 81 a																								
Holyhead 81 ⛴ a																								
Wilmslow 84 a	08 47		09 46		10 12													10 33						
Stockport 84 a					10 21													10 43			10 50			11 22
Manchester Piccadilly 10 🚌 a	09 11		10 11		10 37													10 55			11 03			11 31
Warrington Bank Quay a				09 54											10 27									
d				09 54											10 27									
Runcorn 91 a																			10 47			11 00		
Liverpool South Pkwy 7 91 ✈ a																						11 09		
Liverpool Lime St. 10 91 a																			11 09			11 21		
d																								
Manchester Airport 82 ✈ d		09 22																						
Manchester Picc. 10 82 🚌 d		09 41																						
Bolton 82 d																								
Wigan North Western 90 a				10 05											10 38									
d													10 15			10 50								
Preston 8 90 a													11 00			11 35								
Preston 8 90 d								10 20	10 40				11 05	11 14			11 40							
Blackpool North 97 a																								
Lancaster 6 a								10 35						11 29										
d							10 15					11 15		11 30										
Barrow-in-Furness 82 a														12 29										
Oxenholme Lake District a							11 00					12 00	12 20											
d						10 35	11 05					12 05	12 25											
Windermere 83 a																								
Penrith North Lakes d							12 05					13 05												
Carlisle 8 216 a						11 50	12 40		12 40			13 40	13 40				13 40							
d											12 59													
Lockerbie d											13 17													
Carstairs 226 a																								
Motherwell 226 a																								
Glasgow Central 15 216,226 a																								
Haymarket 225,226,228,230,242 a											14 14													
Edinburgh 10 225,226,228,230,242 a		13 32									14 22													
Perth 229 a																								
Dundee 229 a																								
Aberdeen 229 a																								
Inverness 229 a																								

OVERNIGHT SLEEPERS. For sleeper trains, operated by First ScotRail, please see Tables 400 - 404.

For complete service between Manchester and Preston, Blackpool and between Barrow-in-furness and Lancaster, please see Table 82.

For complete service between Crewe and Liverpool Lime Street, see Table 91

For complete service between Crewe/Stoke-on-Trent & Manchester see Table 84

For complete service between Crewe and Holyhead please see Table 81.

For complete service between Coventry-Birmingham-Wolverhampton-Stafford please see Table 68

For complete service between Windermere and Oxenholme Lake District, please see Table 83

Table 65

Sundays

5 January to 9 February

London and West Midlands - North West England and Scotland

Route Diagram - refer to first Page of Table 65

		VT	LM	VT	VT	LM		XC	VT	TP	TP	TP	VT	VT	VT	VT		LM	VT	VT	LM	XC	TP	VT	VT
		◇1	1	◇1	◇1	1		◇1		◇1	◇1	◇1		◇1		◇1		1	◇1	◇1	1	◇1	◇1		
									🚌				🚌		🚌									🚌	🚌
		☕		☕	☕			🛒		🛒				☕		☕			☕	☕		🛒			
London Euston 15 ⊖66	d			09 15	09 20													09 54	10 15	10 20					
Watford Junction 66	d																	10 10							
Milton Keynes Central 66	d				10 07													10 50		11 07					
Rugby 66	d		10 00															11 30							
Nuneaton	d		10 14	10 45														11 43	11 47						
Tamworth Low Level	d		10 29															11 57							
Lichfield Trent Valley	d		10 35															12 04							
Coventry 68	d							10 28														11 29			
Birmingham International 68 ✈	d							10 40														11 40			
Birmingham New St. 12 68	d	10 20				10 42		11 01								11 20					11 42	12 01			
Wolverhampton 7	d	10 38				11 00		11 19								11 38					12 00	12 19			
Penkridge	d					11 10															12 10				
Stafford	a		10 56	11 09		11 16		11 32										12 21	12 13		12 16	12 32			
	d		10 57	11 09		11 17		11 33										12 21	12 14		12 17	12 33			
Stoke-on-Trent	a		11 15		11 20			11 51										12 39		12 24		12 52			
Macclesfield	a				11 37			12 09												12 40		13 10			
Crewe 10	a	11 07	11 43	11 30		11 37										12 07		13 02	12 32		12 37				
	d	11 09		11 32		11 38										12 09			12 34		12 38				
Chester 81	a																								
Wrexham General 75	a																								
Llandudno Junction 81	a																								
Bangor (Gwynedd) 81	a																								
Holyhead 81 ⛴	a																								
Wilmslow 84	a																								
Stockport 84	a				11 51			12 22												12 55		13 28			
Manchester Piccadilly 10 ⛴	a				12 04			12 40												13 08		13 40			
Warrington Bank Quay	a	11 26														12 26									
	d	11 27														12 27									
Runcorn 91	a			11 49		12 01													12 51		13 01				
Liverpool South Pkwy 7 91 ✈	a					12 10															13 10				
Liverpool Lime St. 10 91	a			12 10		12 21													13 12		13 21				
	d																								
Manchester Airport 82 ✈	d										11 20														
Manchester Picc. 10 82 ⛴	d										11 42														
Bolton 82	d																								
Wigan North Western 90	a	11 37														12 37									
	d												11 50		11 50										12 47
Preston 8 90	a														12 35										
Preston 8 90	d											12 05	12u40		12 40								12 48		13u37
Blackpool North 97	a																								
Lancaster 6	a											12 20			13 30								13 03		
	d								11 45						13 35								13 04	13 10	
Barrow-in-Furness 82	a																						14 07		
Oxenholme Lake District	a								12 30						14 20									13 55	
	d								12 35						14 25									14 00	
Windermere 83	a																								
Penrith North Lakes	d								13 35						15 25									15 00	
Carlisle 8 216	a								14 10				14 40		16 00									15 35	15 37
	d									14 11				15 03											
Lockerbie	d									14 30															
Carstairs 226	a																								
Motherwell 226	a																								
Glasgow Central 15 216,226	a																								
Haymarket 225,226,228,230,242	a									15s29				16 14											
Edinburgh 10 225,226,228,230,242	a									15 38	15 42			16 23											
Perth 229	a																								
Dundee 229	a																								
Aberdeen 229	a																								
Inverness 229	a																								

OVERNIGHT SLEEPERS. For sleeper trains, operated by First ScotRail, please see Tables 400 - 404.

For complete service between Manchester and Preston, Blackpool and between Barrow-in-furness and Lancaster, please see Table 82.

For complete service between Crewe and Liverpool Lime Street, see Table 91

For complete service between Crewe/Stoke-on-Trent & Manchester see Table 84

For complete service between Crewe and Holyhead please see Table 81.

For complete service between Coventry-Birmingham-Wolverhampton-Stafford please see Table 68

For complete service between Windermere and Oxenholme Lake District, please see Table 83

Table 65

Sundays

5 January to 9 February

London and West Midlands - North West England and Scotland

Route Diagram - refer to first Page of Table 65

		VT		VT	LM	VT	VT	LM	LM	VT	VT	XC		TP	VT	VT	VT	VT	XC	LM	XC	TP		VT	LM
				◇1	1	◇1	◇1	1	1	◇1	◇1	◇1		◇1		◇1	◇1	◇1	◇1	1	◇1	◇1		◇1	1
		🚌													🚌										
				☕		☕	☕			☕	☕	🛒				☕	☕	☕	🛒		🛒	🛒		☕	
London Euston [15] ⊖66	d				10 24	11 15	11 20		11 24	12 05	12 17					12 28		12 37						12 40	12 50
Watford Junction 66	d				10 40				11 42																13 06
Milton Keynes Central 66	d				11 20	12 04	12 08		12 28		12 50													13 13	13 37
Rugby 66	d				12 03				13 26																14 26
Nuneaton	d				12 17				13 40																14 40
Tamworth Low Level	d				12 32				13 55																14 55
Lichfield Trent Valley	d				12 38				14 01																15 01
Coventry 68	d											12 28									13 26			13 42	
Birmingham International 68 ✈	d											12 40									13 38			13 53	
Birmingham New St. [12] 68	d			12 20				12 35				13 01					13 20		13 31	13 35	14 01			14 16	
Wolverhampton [7]	d			12 38				12 53				13 19					13 38		13 49	13 53	14 19			14 37	
Penkridge	d							13 03												14 03					
Stafford	a				12 59	12 53		13 09	14 18	13 24		13 33								14 09	14 33				15 18
	d				13 00	12 53		13 09	14 19	13 25		13 34								14 09	14 34				15 20
Stoke-on-Trent	a				13 18		13 09		14 37		13 50	13 56							14 19		14 56				15 39
Macclesfield	a						13 26					14 14									15 14				
Crewe [10]	a			13 07	13 43	13 13		13 30	15 00	13 43							14 07	14 12		14 29				15 07	16 03
	d			13 09		13 15		13 31		13 45							14 09	14 13		14 31				15 09	
Chester 81	a																							↪	
Wrexham General 75	a																								
Llandudno Junction 81	a																								
Bangor (Gwynedd) 81	a																								
Holyhead 81 ⛴	a																								
Wilmslow 84	a																	14 29							
Stockport 84	a						13 41				14 18	14 28						14 38			15 28				
Manchester Piccadilly [10]	a						13 53				14 29	14 40						14 50	14 57		15 40				
Warrington Bank Quay	a			13 26												14 16	14 27								
	d			13 27												14 16	14 27								
Runcorn 91	a					13 32		13 54		14 02										14 53					
Liverpool South Pkwy [7] 91 ✈	a							14 03												15 02					
Liverpool Lime St. [10] 91	a					13 54		14 14		14 24										15 14					
	d																								
Manchester Airport 82 ✈	d																					14 00			
Manchester Picc. [10] 82	d																					14 14			
Bolton 82	d																								
Wigan North Western 90	a			13 37												14 27	14 38					14 42			
	d	12 50													13 50	14 27	14 38					14 43			
Preston [8] 90	a	13 35													14 35	14 40	14 51					14 57			
Preston [8] 90	d	13 40												13 48		14 42						14 57			
Blackpool North 97	a																								
Lancaster [6]	a	14 30												14 03		14 56						15 14			
	d	14 35																				15 14			
Barrow-in-Furness 82	a																								
Oxenholme Lake District	a	15 20																				15 28			
	d																					15 29			
Windermere 83	a																								
Penrith North Lakes	d																					15 54			
Carlisle [8] 216	a																					16 11			
	d																					16 11			
Lockerbie	d																					16 30			
Carstairs 226	a																								
Motherwell 226	a																								
Glasgow Central [15] 216,226	a																								
Haymarket 225,226,228,230,242	a																					17s30			
Edinburgh [10] 225,226,228,230,242	a																					17 38			
Perth 229	a																								
Dundee 229	a																								
Aberdeen 229	a																								
Inverness 229	a																								

OVERNIGHT SLEEPERS. For sleeper trains, operated by First ScotRail, please see Tables 400 - 404.

For complete service between Manchester and Preston, Blackpool and between Barrow-in-furness and Lancaster, please see Table 82.

For complete service between Crewe and Liverpool Lime Street, see Table 91

For complete service between Crewe/Stoke-on-Trent & Manchester see Table 84

For complete service between Crewe and Holyhead please see Table 81.

For complete service between Coventry-Birmingham-Wolverhampton-Stafford please see Table 68

For complete service between Windermere and Oxenholme Lake District, please see Table 83

Table 65

Sundays

5 January to 9 February

London and West Midlands - North West England and Scotland

Route Diagram - refer to first Page of Table 65

		VT	VT	VT	VT	VT	VT	XC		LM	XC	TP	VT	LM	VT	VT	VT	VT		VT	VT	XC	LM	XC	TP
		◇1	◇1	◇1	◇1	◇1	◇1	◇1		1	◇1	◇1	◇1	1	◇1	◇1	◇1	◇1		◇1	◇1	◇1	1	◇1	◇1
London Euston 15 ⊖66	d	12 57	13 05	13 17	13 28		13 37						13 40	13 50	13 57	14 05	14 17	14 28			14 37				
Watford Junction 66	d													14 06											
Milton Keynes Central 66	d			13 50									14 13	14 37			14 50								
Rugby 66	d													15 26											
Nuneaton	d													15 40											
Tamworth Low Level	d													15 55											
Lichfield Trent Valley	d													16 01											
Coventry 68	d										14 26		14 44											15 26	
Birmingham International 68 ✈	d										14 38		14 54											15 38	
Birmingham New St. 12 68	d							14 31		14 35	15 01		15 17									15 31	15 35	16 01	
Wolverhampton 7	d							14 49		14 53	15 19		15 38									15 49	15 53	16 19	
Penkridge	d									15 03													16 03		
Stafford	a		14 23							15 09	15 33			16 18		15 24							16 09	16 34	
	d		14 24							15 09	15 34			16 20		15 25							16 09	16 34	
Stoke-on-Trent	a	14 26		14 50				15 19			15 56			16 38	15 25		15 50					16 19		16 56	
Macclesfield	a	14 42				←					16 14				15 42					←				17 14	
Crewe 10	a		14 43			15 07	15 12			15 29			16 07	17 03		15 43				16 07	16 12		16 30		
	d		14 45			15 09	15 13			15 31			16 09			15 45				16 09	16 13		16 31		
Chester 81	a												→												
Wrexham General 75	a																								
Llandudno Junction 81	a																								
Bangor (Gwynedd) 81	a																								
Holyhead 81 ⛴	a																								
Wilmslow 84	a						15 29														16 29				
Stockport 84	a	14 56		15 18			15 38				16 28				15 56		16 18				16 38			17 28	
Manchester Piccadilly 10	a	15 09		15 29			15 50	15 59			16 40				16 09		16 29				16 50	16 59		17 40	
Warrington Bank Quay	a				15 16	15 26												16 16		16 26					
	d				15 16	15 27												16 16		16 27					
Runcorn 91	a		15 02							15 53						16 02							16 54		
Liverpool South Pkwy 7 91 ✈	a									16 02													17 03		
Liverpool Lime St. 10 91	a		15 24							16 14						16 24							17 14		
	d																								
Manchester Airport 82 ✈	d											15 00													16 00
Manchester Picc. 10 82	d											15 14													16 14
Bolton 82	d																								
Wigan North Western 90	a				15 27	15 37						15 42						16 27		16 37					16 42
	d				15 27	15 38						15 43						16 27		16 37					16 43
Preston 8 90	a				15 40	15 51						15 57						16 40		16 51					16 57
Preston 8 90	d				15 42	15 53						15 57						16 42		16 53					16 57
Blackpool North 97	a																								
Lancaster 6	a				15 56	16 08						16 14						16 56		17 08					17 14
	d				15 58	16 08						16 14						16 57		17 08					17 14
Barrow-in-Furness 82	a											17 18													
Oxenholme Lake District	a				16 10															17 22					17 28
	d				16 11															17 23					17 29
Windermere 83	a																								
Penrith North Lakes	d					16 45												17 32							17 54
Carlisle 8 216	a				16 48	17 00												17 47		18 01					18 11
	d				16 49	17 02												17 48		18 03					18 11
Lockerbie	d																								
Carstairs 226	a																								
Motherwell 226	a																								
Glasgow Central 15 216,226	a				18 01													19 00		19 17					
Haymarket 225,226,228,230,242	a					18 13																			19s27
Edinburgh 10 225,226,228,230,242	a					18 22																			19 34
Perth 229	a																								
Dundee 229	a																								
Aberdeen 229	a																								
Inverness 229	a																								

OVERNIGHT SLEEPERS. For sleeper trains, operated by First ScotRail, please see Tables 400 - 404.

For complete service between Manchester and Preston, Blackpool and between Barrow-in-furness and Lancaster, please see Table 82.

For complete service between Crewe and Liverpool Lime Street, see Table 91

For complete service between Crewe/Stoke-on-Trent & Manchester see Table 84

For complete service between Crewe and Holyhead please see Table 81.

For complete service between Coventry-Birmingham-Wolverhampton-Stafford please see Table 68

For complete service between Windermere and Oxenholme Lake District, please see Table 83

Table 65

Sundays

5 January to 9 February

London and West Midlands - North West England and Scotland

Route Diagram - refer to first Page of Table 65

Station		VT	LM	VT		VT	VT	VT	VT	VT	VT	XC	LM	XC		TP	VT	LM	VT	VT	VT	VT	TP	VT	
		◇1	1	◇1		◇1	◇1	◇1	◇1	◇1	◇1	◇1	1	◇1		◇1	◇1	1	◇1	◇1	◇1	◇1	◇1	◇1	
London Euston 15 ⊖ 66	d	14 40	14 50	14 57		15 05	15 08	15 17	15 28		15 37						15 40	15 50	15 57	16 05	16 08	16 17		16 28	
Watford Junction 66	d		15 06															16 06							
Milton Keynes Central 66	d	15 13	15 37				15 42	15 50									16 13	16 37			16 42	16 50			
Rugby 66	d		16 26															17 26							
Nuneaton	d		16 40															17 40							
Tamworth Low Level	d		16 55															17 55							
Lichfield Trent Valley	d		17 01															18 01							
Coventry 68	d	15 42												16 26			16 42								
Birmingham International 68 ✈	d	15 53												16 38			16 53								
Birmingham New St. 12 68	d	16 16										16 31	16 35	17 01			17 16								
Wolverhampton 7 ⛴	d	16 37										16 49	16 53	17 19			17 37								
Penkridge	d												17 03												
Stafford	a		17 18			16 24							17 09	17 35				18 18		17 24					
	d		17 20			16 25							17 09	17 36				18 20		17 25					
Stoke-on-Trent	a		17 38	16 24				16 50				17 19		17 56				18 39	17 25			17 50			
Macclesfield	a			16 42						←				18 14					17 42						
Crewe 10	a	17 07	18 03			16 43	16 50			17 07	17 12		17 30				18 07	19 07		17 43	17 50				
	d	17 09				16 45	16 52			17 09	17 13		17 31				18 09			17 45	17 52				
Chester 81	a	→					17 14										→				18 15				
Wrexham General 75	a																								
Llandudno Junction 81	a																								
Bangor (Gwynedd) 81	a																								
Holyhead 81 ⛴	a																								
Wilmslow 84	a										17 29														
Stockport 84	a			16 56				17 18			17 38			18 28					17 56			18 18			
Manchester Piccadilly 10 ⛴	a			17 09				17 29			17 50	17 56		18 40					18 09			18 29			
Warrington Bank Quay	a								17 16	17 26														18 16	
	d								17 16	17 27														18 17	
Runcorn 91	a					17 02							17 54							18 02					
Liverpool South Pkwy 7 91 ✈	a												18 03												
Liverpool Lime St. 10 91	a					17 22							18 14							18 22					
	d																								
Manchester Airport 82 ✈	d															17 00							17 30		
Manchester Picc. 10 82 ⛴	d															17 14							17 46		
Bolton 82	d																						18 05		
Wigan North Western 90	a								17 27	17 37						17 42								18 27	
	d								17 27	17 38						17 43								18 28	
Preston 8 90	a								17 40	17 51						17 57							18 33	18 40	
Preston 8 90	d								17 42	17 53						17 57							19 06	18 42	
Blackpool North 97	a																						→		
Lancaster 6	a								17 56	18 07						18 14								18 56	
	d								17 57	18 08						18 14								18 58	
Barrow-in-Furness 82	a																								
Oxenholme Lake District	a								18 10	18 21						18 28								19 10	
	d								18 10	18 22						18 29								19 11	
Windermere 83	a																								
Penrith North Lakes	d									18 48						18 54								19 36	
Carlisle 8 216	a								18 48	19 03						19 11								19 51	
	d								18 49	19 04						19 17								19 53	
Lockerbie	d															19 36									
Carstairs 226	a																								
Motherwell 226	a															20s22									
Glasgow Central 15 216,226	a								20 01							20 40								21 09	
Haymarket 225,226,228,230,242	a									20 16															
Edinburgh 10 225,226,228,230,242	a									20 21															
Perth 229	a																								
Dundee 229	a																								
Aberdeen 229	a																								
Inverness 229	a																								

OVERNIGHT SLEEPERS. For sleeper trains, operated by First ScotRail, please see Tables 400 - 404.

For complete service between Manchester and Preston, Blackpool and between Barrow-in-furness and Lancaster, please see Table 82.

For complete service between Crewe and Liverpool Lime Street, see Table 91

For complete service between Crewe/Stoke-on-Trent & Manchester see Table 84

For complete service between Crewe and Holyhead please see Table 81.

For complete service between Coventry-Birmingham-Wolverhampton-Stafford please see Table 68

For complete service between Windermere and Oxenholme Lake District, please see Table 83

Table 65

Sundays

5 January to 9 February

London and West Midlands - North West England and Scotland

Route Diagram - refer to first Page of Table 65

		VT	VT	XC	LM	XC	TP	TP		VT		LM	VT	VT	VT	VT	VT	VT	VT	VT		XC	LM	XC	TP
		◇1	◇1	◇1	1	◇1	◇1	◇1		◇1		1	◇1	◇1	◇1	◇1	◇1	◇1	◇1	◇1		◇1	1	◇1	◇1
		🍴	🍴	🛒		🛒		🛒		🍴			🍴	🍴	🍴	🍴	🍴	🍴	🍴	🍴		🛒		🛒	
London Euston [15] ⊖66	d		16 37							16 40		16 50	16 57	17 05	17 08	17 08	17 17	17 28		17 37					
Watford Junction 66	d											17 06													
Milton Keynes Central 66	d									17 14		17 37			17 42	17 42	17 50								
Rugby 66	d											18 26													
Nuneaton	d											18 40		18 04											
Tamworth Low Level	d											18 55													
Lichfield Trent Valley	d											19 01													
Coventry 68	d					17 26				17 43														18 26	
Birmingham International 68 ✈	d					17 38				17 54														18 38	
Birmingham New St. [12] 68	d			17 31	17 35	18 01				18 16												18 31	18 35	19 01	
Wolverhampton [7] 🚊	d			17 49	17 53	18 19				18 38												18 49	18 53	19 19	
Penkridge	d				18 03																		19 03		
Stafford	a				18 09	18 35						19 18			18 34	18 34							19 09	19 37	
	d				18 09	18 36						19 20			18 35	18 35							19 09	19 38	
Stoke-on-Trent	a			18 19		18 56						19 40	18 25				18 50					19 19		19 56	
Macclesfield	a	←				19 15							18 42						←					20 14	
Crewe [10]	a	18 07	18 12		18 30					19 06		20 07		18 44	18 53	18 53			19 06	19 12			19 29		
	d	18 09	18 13		18 31					19 09				18 46	18 56	18 56			19 09	19 13			19 31		
Chester 81	a									→					19 14	19 14									
Wrexham General 75	a																								
Llandudno Junction 81	a															20 11									
Bangor (Gwynedd) 81	a															20 27									
Holyhead 81 ⛴	a															20 59									
Wilmslow 84	a		18 29																	19 29					
Stockport 84	a		18 38			19 28							18 56				19 18			19 38				20 28	
Manchester Piccadilly [10] 🚊	a		18 50	18 56		19 40							19 09				19 29			19 50		19 58		20 40	
Warrington Bank Quay	a	18 26																19 16	19 26						
	d	18 27																19 16	19 27						
Runcorn 91	a				18 54									19 02									19 53		
Liverpool South Pkwy [7] 91 ✈	a				19 03																		20 02		
Liverpool Lime St. [10] 91	a				19 14									19 25									20 14		
	d																								
Manchester Airport 82 ✈	d							18 00																	19 00
Manchester Picc. [10] 82 🚊	d							18 14																	19 14
Bolton 82	d							18 31																	19 33
Wigan North Western 90	a	18 37					←											19 27	19 37						
	d	18 38																19 27	19 38						
Preston [8] 90	a	18 51					18 33	18 54										19 40	19 51						19 57
Preston [8] 90	d	18 53					19 06	18 57	19 06									19 42	19 53						20 06
Blackpool North 97	a																								
Lancaster [6]	a	19 07					19 22	19 14	19 22									19 56	20 07						20 23
	d	19 08					19 22	19 14	19 22									19 57	20 08						20 24
Barrow-in-Furness 82	a						20 26		20 26																21 27
Oxenholme Lake District	a	19 21						19 28										20 10							
	d	19 22						19 29										20 10							
Windermere 83	a																								
Penrith North Lakes	d							19 54										20 36	20 45						
Carlisle [8] 216	a	20 00						20 11										20 51	20 59						
	d	20 01						20 11										20 52	21 02						
Lockerbie	d							20 30																	
Carstairs 226	a																								
Motherwell 226	a																								
Glasgow Central [15] 216,226	a	21 15																22 07							
Haymarket 225,226,228,230,242	a							21s29											22 14						
Edinburgh [10] 225,226,228,230,242	a							21 36											22 20						
Perth 229	a																								
Dundee 229	a																								
Aberdeen 229	a																								
Inverness 229	a																								

OVERNIGHT SLEEPERS. For sleeper trains, operated by First ScotRail, please see Tables 400 - 404.

For complete service between Manchester and Preston, Blackpool and between Barrow-in-furness and Lancaster, please see Table 82.

For complete service between Crewe and Liverpool Lime Street, see Table 91

For complete service between Crewe/Stoke-on-Trent & Manchester see Table 84

For complete service between Crewe and Holyhead please see Table 81.

For complete service between Coventry-Birmingham-Wolverhampton-Stafford please see Table 68

For complete service between Windermere and Oxenholme Lake District, please see Table 83

Table 65

Sundays

5 January to 9 February

London and West Midlands - North West England and Scotland

Route Diagram - refer to first Page of Table 65

		VT	LM	VT	VT	VT		VT	VT	VT	VT	VT	XC	LM	XC	VT		LM	VT	VT	VT	VT	VT	VT	XC
		R									R														
		1	1	◇1	◇1	◇1		◇1	◇1	◇1	1	◇1	◇1	1	◇1	◇1		1	◇1	◇1	◇1	◇1	◇1	◇1	◇1
		☕		☕	☕	☕		☕	☕	☕	☕	☕	🛒		🛒	☕			☕	☕	☕	☕	☕	☕	
London Euston 15 ⊖66	d	17 40	17 50	17 57	18 05	18 08		18 08	18 17	18 28		18 37				18 40		18 50	18 57	19 05	19 08	19 17	19 28	19 37	
Watford Junction 66	d		18 06															19 06							
Milton Keynes Central 66	d	18 13	18 37			18 42		18 42	18 50							19 13		19 37			19 42	19 50			
Rugby 66	d		19 26															20 26							
Nuneaton	d		19 40															20 40		20 04					
Tamworth Low Level	d		19 55															20 55							
Lichfield Trent Valley	d		20 01															21 01							
Coventry 68	d	18 44													19 26	19 42									
Birmingham International 68 ✈	d	18 54													19 38	19 53									
Birmingham New St. 12 68	d	19 16											19 31	19 35	20 01	20 16									20 31
Wolverhampton 7 🚌	d	19 37											19 49	19 53	20 19	20 38									20 53
Penkridge	d													20 03											
Stafford	a		20 18		19 24									20 09	20 36	20 52		21 18		20 28					
	d		20 20		19 25									20 09	20 37	20 53		21 20		20 29					
Stoke-on-Trent	a		20 39	19 25					19 50				20 19		20 56			21 38	20 25			20 50			21 20
Macclesfield	a			19 42							←				21 15				20 42						
Crewe 10	a	20 07	21 07		19 43	19 50		19 50			20 07	20 12		20 30		21 10		22 07		20 47	20 50			21 13	
	d	20 09			19 45	19 52		19 52			20 09	20 13		20 31						20 49	20 55			21 14	
Chester 81	a	→				20 11		20 11													21 14				
Wrexham General 75	a																								
Llandudno Junction 81	a							21 07													22 06				
Bangor (Gwynedd) 81	a							21 23													22 22				
Holyhead 81 ⛴	a							21 54													22 56				
Wilmslow 84	a											20 29												21 30	
Stockport 84	a			19 56					20 18			20 38			21 28				20 56			21 18		21 39	
Manchester Piccadilly 10 🚌	a			20 09					20 29			20 50	21 00		21 40				21 09			21 29		21 50	21 57
Warrington Bank Quay	a									20 16	20 26												21 16		
	d									20 16	20 27												21 16		
Runcorn 91	a				20 02									20 54						21 06					
Liverpool South Pkwy 7 91 ✈	a													21 03											
Liverpool Lime St. 10 91	a				20 21									21 14						21 27					
	d																								
Manchester Airport 82 ✈	d																								
Manchester Picc. 10 82 🚌	d																								
Bolton 82	d																								
Wigan North Western 90	a									20 27	20 37												21 27		
	d									20 27	20 38												21 27		
Preston 8 90	a									20 40	20 51												21 40		
Preston 8 90	d									20 42	20 53												21 42		
Blackpool North 97	a																								
Lancaster 6	a									20 56	21 08												21 56		
	d									20 57	21 08												21 57		
Barrow-in-Furness 82	a																								
Oxenholme Lake District	a									21 10	21 22												22 10		
	d									21 11	21 23												22 11		
Windermere 83	a																								
Penrith North Lakes	d									21 36													22 36		
Carlisle 8 216	a									21 51	22 01												22 51		
	d									21 52	22 02												22 53		
Lockerbie	d										22 21														
Carstairs 226	a																								
Motherwell 226	a									22 48	23 03														
Glasgow Central 15 216,226	a									23 09	23 20												00 02		
Haymarket 225,226,228,230,242	a																								
Edinburgh 10 225,226,228,230,242	a																								
Perth 229	a																								
Dundee 229	a																								
Aberdeen 229	a																								
Inverness 229	a																								

OVERNIGHT SLEEPERS. For sleeper trains, operated by First ScotRail, please see Tables 400 - 404.

For complete service between Manchester and Preston, Blackpool and between Barrow-in-furness and Lancaster, please see Table 82.

For complete service between Crewe and Liverpool Lime Street, see Table 91

For complete service between Crewe/Stoke-on-Trent & Manchester see Table 84

For complete service between Crewe and Holyhead please see Table 81.

For complete service between Coventry-Birmingham-Wolverhampton-Stafford please see Table 68

For complete service between Windermere and Oxenholme Lake District, please see Table 83

Table 65

Sundays

5 January to 9 February

London and West Midlands - North West England and Scotland

Route Diagram - refer to first Page of Table 65

	XC		TP	VT	LM	VT	VT	VT	VT	VT	VT		VT	LM	VT	SR		XC	VT	VT	AW	VT	SR	
																R							R	
	◇1			◇1	1	◇1	◇1	◇1	◇1	◇1	◇1		◇1	1	◇1			◇1	◇1	◇1	◇	◇1		
	A															B		A						
London Euston 15 ⊖66 d				19 40	19 50	19 57	20 05	20 08	20 15	20 25			20 35		20 50	20 57			21 21	21 25		21 51	23 27	
Watford Junction 66 d					20 06											21u17							23u47	
Milton Keynes Central 66 d				20 13	20 37			20 41	20 48						21 37					22 14		22 39		
Rugby 66 d					21 30										22 01							23 19		
Nuneaton d					21 43		21 04												22 52			23 30		
Tamworth Low Level d					21 58					21 32														
Lichfield Trent Valley d					22 04					21 39														
Coventry 68 d	20 26			20 42														21 26						
Birmingham International 68 ✈ d	20 38			20 53														21 38			22 43			
Birmingham New St. 12 68 d	21 01			21 16										21 35				22 01			22 55			
Wolverhampton 7 d	21 19			21 37										21 59				22 20			23 15			
Penkridge d														22 09										
Stafford a	21 36			21 56	22 25			21 31					21 59	22 15				22 36	23 16		23 30	23s55		
d	21 37			21 57	22 26			21 33					22 00	22 16				22 37	23 17		23 31			
Stoke-on-Trent a	21 56				22 44	21 25			21 50									22 55		23 29				
Macclesfield a	22 14					21 42					←							23 12		23 45				
Crewe 10 a				22 16	23 07		21 44	21 53		22 10	22 16		22 20	22 38	22 49				23 43		23 57	00s21		
d				22 17			21 46	21 55		22 13	22 17		22 21		22 51	23u34			23 45		00 01			
Chester 81 a				→																	00 22			
Wrexham General 75 a																								
Llandudno Junction 81 a																					01 27			
Bangor (Gwynedd) 81 a																					01 45			
Holyhead 81 ⛴ a																					02 20			
Wilmslow 84 a													22 36											
Stockport 84 a	22 27					21 56			22 18				22 45					23 27		23 59		00s50		
Manchester Piccadilly 10 a	22 39					22 09			22 29				22 57					23 41		00 12		01 00		
Warrington Bank Quay a										22 29	22 35				23 08									
d										22 30	22 35				23 08									
Runcorn 91 a							22 03	22 12											00 07					
Liverpool South Pkwy 7 91 ✈ a																								
Liverpool Lime St. 10 91 a							22 23	22 33											00 30					
d																								
Manchester Airport 82 ✈ d																								
Manchester Picc. 10 82 d																								
Bolton 82 d			22 15																					
Wigan North Western 90 a										22 40	22 46				23 19									
d										22 41	22 46				23 19									
Preston 8 90 a			22 41							22 58	23 05				23 39									
Preston 8 90 d																00u33	00u33							
Blackpool North 97 a																								
Lancaster 6 a																								
d																								
Barrow-in-Furness 82 a																								
Oxenholme Lake District a																								
d																								
Windermere 83 a																								
Penrith North Lakes d																								
Carlisle 8 216 a																							05s10	
d																								
Lockerbie d																								
Carstairs 226 a																							06s19	
Motherwell 226 a																								06s54
Glasgow Central 15 216,226 a																								07 18
Haymarket 225,226,228,230,242 a																								
Edinburgh 10 225,226,228,230,242 a																							07 22	
Perth 229 a																	05s39							
Dundee 229 a																06s08								
Aberdeen 229 a																07 34								
Inverness 229 a																	08 36							

A to Birmingham New St.

B also conveys through sleepers to Fort William arr 0955. (Table 404)

OVERNIGHT SLEEPERS. For sleeper trains, operated by First ScotRail, please see Tables 400 - 404.

For complete service between Manchester and Preston, Blackpool and between Barrow-in-furness and Lancaster, please see Table 82.

For complete service between Crewe and Liverpool Lime Street, see Table 91

For complete service between Crewe/Stoke-on-Trent & Manchester see Table 84

For complete service between Crewe and Holyhead please see Table 81.

For complete service between Coventry-Birmingham-Wolverhampton-Stafford please see Table 68

For complete service between Windermere and Oxenholme Lake District, please see Table 83

Table 65

Sundays

16 February to 23 March

London and West Midlands - North West England and Scotland

Route Diagram - refer to first Page of Table 65

			TP	AW	AW	VT	XC	VT	VT	TP	TP		VT	VT	VT	LM	VT	XC	VT	LM	VT		VT	LM	XC	TP
			◇1			◇1	◇1	◇1	◇1	◇1	◇1		◇1	◇1	◇1	1	◇1	◇1	◇1	1	◇1		◇1	1	◇1	◇1
						□P	⊼	□P	□P	⊼			□P	□P	□P		□P	⊼	□P		□P		□P		⊼	⊼
London Euston 15	⊖66	d							08 10					08 15	08 20		08 45				09 15		09 20			
Watford Junction	66	d																								
Milton Keynes Central	66	d							08 56						09 06		09 32						10 07			
Rugby	66	d															10 09			10 00						
Nuneaton		d												09 44						10 14	10 45					
Tamworth Low Level		d																		10 29						
Lichfield Trent Valley		d																		10 35						
Coventry	68	d																							10 28	
Birmingham International	68 ✈	d																							10 40	
Birmingham New St. 12	68	d				08 45	09 01	09 20								09 42		10 01	10 20					10 42	11 01	
Wolverhampton 7	⛴	d				09 04	09 19	09 38								10 00		10 19	10 38					11 00	11 19	
Penkridge		d														10 10								11 10		
Stafford		a				09 17	09 32							10 08		10 16		10 32		10 56	11 09			11 16	11 32	
		d				09 17	09 33							10 08		10 17		10 33		10 57	11 09			11 17	11 33	
Stoke-on-Trent		a													10 19			10 51		11 15			11 20		11 51	
Macclesfield		a													10 36			11 08					11 37		12 09	
Crewe 10		a				09 35	09 54	10 08	10 17					10 28		10 37	10 55		11 07	11 43	11 30			11 37		
		d		08 28	09 28	09 37	09 56	10 08	10 19				10 21	10 30		10 38	10 57		11 09		11 32			11 38		
Chester	81	a																								
Wrexham General	75	a																								
Llandudno Junction	81	a																								
Bangor (Gwynedd)	81	a																								
Holyhead	81 ⛴	a																								
Wilmslow	84	a		08 47	09 46		10 12		10 33																	
Stockport	84	a					10 21		10 43						10 50			11 22					11 51		12 22	
Manchester Piccadilly 10	⛴	a		09 11	10 11		10 37		10 55						11 03			11 31					12 04		12 40	
Warrington Bank Quay		a				09 54		10 27					10 37				11 14		11 26							
		d				09 54		10 27					10 37				11 14		11 27							
Runcorn	91	a												10 47		11 00					11 49			12 01		
Liverpool South Pkwy 7	91 ✈	a														11 09								12 10		
Liverpool Lime St. 10	91	a												11 09		11 21					12 10			12 21		
		d																								
Manchester Airport	82 ✈	d								10 00																11 00
Manchester Picc. 10	82 ⛴	d	08 16							10 14																11 14
Bolton	82	d	08 35																							
Wigan North Western	90	a				10 05		10 38		10 41			10 48				11 25		11 37							
		d				10 05		10 38		10 42			10 48				11 25		11 38							
Preston 8	90	a	09 05			10 25		10 54		11 00			11 05				11 40		11 52							11 59
Preston 8	90	d	09 06					11 04		11 09	11 14		11 17				11 42		11 54							11 59
Blackpool North	97	a	09 32																							
Lancaster 6		a						11 18		11 25	11 29		11 35				11 56		12 08							12 16
		d						11 20		11 25	11 30						11 57		12 09							12 16
Barrow-in-Furness	82	a									12 29															
Oxenholme Lake District		a						11 32		11 42							12 10		12 22							12 30
		d						11 34		11 43							12 10		12 24							12 31
Windermere	83	a																								
Penrith North Lakes		d								12 08							12 36									
Carlisle 8	216	a						12 10		12 24							12 50		13 01							13 10
		d						12 12		12 25							12 51		13 03							13 17
Lockerbie		d								12 45																13 37
Carstairs	226	a																								
Motherwell	226	a																								
Glasgow Central 15	216,226	a						13 29									14 02									14 40
Haymarket	225,226,228,230,242	a								13s44									14 14							
Edinburgh 10	225,226,228,230,242	a								13 51									14 22							
Perth	229	a																								
Dundee	229	a																								
Aberdeen	229	a																								
Inverness	229	a																								

OVERNIGHT SLEEPERS. For sleeper trains, operated by First ScotRail, please see Tables 400 - 404.

For complete service between Manchester and Preston, Blackpool and between Barrow-in-furness and Lancaster, please see Table 82.

For complete service between Crewe and Liverpool Lime Street, see Table 91

For complete service between Crewe/Stoke-on-Trent & Manchester see Table 84

For complete service between Crewe and Holyhead please see Table 81.

For complete service between Coventry-Birmingham-Wolverhampton-Stafford please see Table 68

For complete service between Windermere and Oxenholme Lake District, please see Table 83

Table 65

Sundays

16 February to 23 March

London and West Midlands - North West England and Scotland

Route Diagram - refer to first Page of Table 65

			VT	TP	VT	LM	VT		VT	LM	XC	LM	TP	VT	VT	VT	VT		LM	LM	VT	VT	XC	TP	VT	VT
			◇1	◇1	◇1	1	◇1		◇1	1	◇1	1	◇1	◇1	◇1	◇1	◇1		1	1	◇1	◇1	◇1	◇1	◇1	◇1
			☕		☕		☕		☕		🛒		🛒	☕	☕	☕	☕				☕	☕	🛒	🛒	☕	☕
London Euston 15	⊖66	d	09 45			09 54	10 15		10 20			10 24		10 45		11 15	11 20			11 24	12 05	12 17			12 28	
Watford Junction	66	d				10 10						10 40								11 42						
Milton Keynes Central	66	d	10 33			10 50			11 07			11 20		11 33		12 04	12 08			12 28		12 50				
Rugby	66	d	11 09			11 30						12 03		12 09						13 26						
Nuneaton		d				11 43	11 47					12 17								13 40						
Tamworth Low Level		d				11 57						12 32								13 55						
Lichfield Trent Valley		d				12 04						12 38								14 01						
Coventry	68	d									11 29												12 28			
Birmingham International	68 ✈	d									11 40												12 39			
Birmingham New St. 12	68	d			11 20					11 42	12 01				12 20				12 35				13 00			13 20
Wolverhampton 7	🚌	d			11 38					12 00	12 19				12 37				12 53				13 18			13 37
Penkridge		d								12 10									13 03							
Stafford		a				12 21	12 13			12 16	12 32	12 59				12 53			13 09	14 18	13 24		13 32			
		d				12 21	12 14			12 17	12 33	13 00				12 53			13 09	14 19	13 25		13 33			
Stoke-on-Trent		a				12 39			12 24		12 52	13 18					13 09			14 37		13 50	13 55			
Macclesfield		a							12 40		13 10						13 26						14 13			
Crewe 10		a	11 55		12 07	13 02	12 32			12 37		13 43		12 56	13 07	13 13			13 30	15 00	13 43					14 07
		d	11 57		12 09		12 34			12 38				12 58	13 09	13 15			13 31		13 45					14 09
Chester	81	a																								
Wrexham General	75	a																								
Llandudno Junction	81	a																								
Bangor (Gwynedd)	81	a																								
Holyhead	81 ⛴	a																								
Wilmslow	84	a																								
Stockport	84	a							12 55		13 28						13 41					14 18	14 27			
Manchester Piccadilly 10	🚌	a							13 08		13 40						13 53					14 29	14 39			
Warrington Bank Quay		a	12 14		12 26									13 15	13 26										14 16	14 26
		d	12 14		12 27									13 15	13 27										14 16	14 27
Runcorn	91	a					12 51			13 01						13 32			13 54		14 02					
Liverpool South Pkwy 7	91 ✈	a								13 10									14 03							
Liverpool Lime St. 10	91	a					13 12			13 21						13 54			14 14		14 24					
		d																								
Manchester Airport	82 ✈	d											12 00											13 00		
Manchester Picc. 10	82 🚌	d											12 14											13 14		
Bolton	82	d																								
Wigan North Western	90	a	12 25		12 37								12 42	13 26	13 37									13 42	14 27	14 37
		d	12 25		12 38								12 43	13 26	13 38									13 43	14 27	14 38
Preston 8	90	a	12 38		12 51								12 57	13 40	13 51									13 57	14 40	14 50
Preston 8	90	d	12 40	12 48	12 53								12 57	13 42	13 53									13 57	14 42	14 53
Blackpool North	97	a																								
Lancaster 6		a	12 54	13 03	13 07								13 14	13 56	14 08									14 14	14 56	15 08
		d	12 55	13 04	13 08								13 14	13 57	14 08									14 14	14 58	15 09
Barrow-in-Furness	82	a		14 07																						
Oxenholme Lake District		a	13 08		13 21								13 28	14 10										14 28		15 22
		d	13 08		13 22								13 29	14 10										14 29		15 24
Windermere	83	a																								
Penrith North Lakes		d	13 34										13 54	14 36	14 45									14 54	15 32	
Carlisle 8	216	a	13 49		14 00								14 11	14 51	15 00									15 11	15 47	16 01
		d	13 50		14 02								14 11	14 52	15 03									15 17	15 48	16 03
Lockerbie		d											14 30													
Carstairs	226	a																								
Motherwell	226	a																								
Glasgow Central 15	216,226	a	15 02		15 16									16 05										16 34	17 00	17 17
Haymarket	225,226,228,230,242	a											15s29		16 14											
Edinburgh 10	225,226,228,230,242	a											15 36		16 23											
Perth	229	a																								
Dundee	229	a																								
Aberdeen	229	a																								
Inverness	229	a																								

OVERNIGHT SLEEPERS. For sleeper trains, operated by First ScotRail, please see Tables 400 - 404.

For complete service between Manchester and Preston, Blackpool and between Barrow-in-furness and Lancaster, please see Table 82.

For complete service between Crewe and Liverpool Lime Street, see Table 91

For complete service between Crewe/Stoke-on-Trent & Manchester see Table 84

For complete service between Crewe and Holyhead please see Table 81.

For complete service between Coventry-Birmingham-Wolverhampton-Stafford please see Table 68

For complete service between Windermere and Oxenholme Lake District, please see Table 83

Table 65

Sundays

16 February to 23 March

London and West Midlands - North West England and Scotland

Route Diagram - refer to first Page of Table 65

Station			VT		XC	LM	XC	TP	VT	LM	VT	VT	VT		VT	VT	VT	XC	LM	XC	TP	VT	LM		VT	VT
			◇1		◇1	1	◇1	◇1	◇1	1	◇1	◇1	◇1		◇1	◇1	◇1	◇1	1	◇1	◇1	◇1	1		◇1	◇1
London Euston 15	⊖66	d	12 37						12 40	12 50	12 57	13 05	13 17		13 28		13 37					13 40	13 50		13 57	14 05
Watford Junction	66	d								13 06													14 06			
Milton Keynes Central	66	d							13 13	13 37			13 50									14 13	14 37			
Rugby	66	d								14 26													15 26			
Nuneaton		d								14 40													15 40			
Tamworth Low Level		d								14 55													15 55			
Lichfield Trent Valley		d								15 01													16 01			
Coventry	68	d					13 28		13 42											14 28		14 44				
Birmingham International	68 ✈	d					13 39		13 53											14 38		14 54				
Birmingham New St. 12	68	d			13 31	13 35	14 01		14 16									14 31	14 35	15 00		15 17				
Wolverhampton 7	⛴	d			13 49	13 53	14 19		14 37									14 49	14 53	15 18		15 38				
Penkridge		d				14 03													15 03							
Stafford		a				14 09	14 33			15 18		14 23							15 09	15 32			16 18			15 24
		d				14 09	14 34			15 20		14 24							15 09	15 33			16 20			15 25
Stoke-on-Trent		a			14 19		14 56			15 39	14 26		14 50					15 19		15 55			16 38		15 25	
Macclesfield		a					15 14				14 42					←				16 13					15 42	
Crewe 10		a	14 12			14 29			15 07	16 03		14 43				15 07	15 12		15 29			16 07	17 03			15 43
		d	14 13			14 31			15 09			14 45				15 09	15 13		15 31			16 09				15 45
Chester	81	a							→													→				
Wrexham General	75	a																								
Llandudno Junction	81	a																								
Bangor (Gwynedd)	81	a																								
Holyhead	81 ⛴	a																								
Wilmslow	84	a	14 29														15 29									
Stockport	84	a	14 38				15 28				14 56		15 18				15 38			16 27					15 56	
Manchester Piccadilly 10	⛴	a	14 50		14 57		15 40				15 09		15 29				15 50	15 59		16 39					16 09	
Warrington Bank Quay		a													15 16	15 26										
		d													15 16	15 27										
Runcorn	91	a				14 53						15 02							15 53							16 02
Liverpool South Pkwy 7	91 ✈	a				15 02													16 02							
Liverpool Lime St. 10	91	a				15 14						15 24							16 14							16 24
		d																								
Manchester Airport	82 ✈	d						14 00													15 00					
Manchester Picc. 10	82 ⛴	d						14 14													15 14					
Bolton	82	d																								
Wigan North Western	90	a						14 42							15 27	15 37					15 42					
		d						14 43							15 27	15 38					15 43					
Preston 8	90	a						14 57							15 40	15 51					15 57					
Preston 8	90	d						14 57							15 42	15 53					15 57					
Blackpool North	97	a																								
Lancaster 6		a						15 14							15 56	16 08					16 14					
		d						15 14							15 58	16 08					16 14					
Barrow-in-Furness	82	a																			17 18					
Oxenholme Lake District		a						15 28							16 10											
		d						15 29							16 11											
Windermere	83	a																								
Penrith North Lakes		d						15 54								16 45										
Carlisle 8	216	a						16 11							16 48	17 00										
		d						16 11							16 49	17 02										
Lockerbie		d						16 30																		
Carstairs	226	a																								
Motherwell	226	a																								
Glasgow Central 15	216,226	a													18 01											
Haymarket	225,226,228,230,242	a						17s30								18 13										
Edinburgh 10	225,226,228,230,242	a						17 38								18 22										
Perth	229	a																								
Dundee	229	a																								
Aberdeen	229	a																								
Inverness	229	a																								

OVERNIGHT SLEEPERS. For sleeper trains, operated by First ScotRail, please see Tables 400 - 404.

For complete service between Manchester and Preston, Blackpool and between Barrow-in-furness and Lancaster, please see Table 82.

For complete service between Crewe and Liverpool Lime Street, see Table 91

For complete service between Crewe/Stoke-on-Trent & Manchester see Table 84

For complete service between Crewe and Holyhead please see Table 81.

For complete service between Coventry-Birmingham-Wolverhampton-Stafford please see Table 68

For complete service between Windermere and Oxenholme Lake District, please see Table 83

Table 65

Sundays

16 February to 23 March

London and West Midlands - North West England and Scotland

Route Diagram - refer to first Page of Table 65

		VT	VT	VT	VT	XC	LM	XC		TP	VT	LM	VT	VT	VT	VT	VT	VT		VT	XC	LM	XC	TP	VT
		◇1	◇1	◇1	◇1	◇1	1	◇1		◇1	◇1	1	◇1	◇1	◇1	◇1	◇1	◇1		◇1	◇1	1	◇1	◇1	◇1
London Euston 15 ⊖66	d	14 17	14 28		14 37						14 40	14 50	14 57	15 05	15 08	15 17	15 28			15 37					15 40
Watford Junction 66	d											15 06													
Milton Keynes Central 66	d	14 50									15 13	15 37			15 42	15 50									16 13
Rugby 66	d											16 26													
Nuneaton	d											16 40													
Tamworth Low Level	d											16 55													
Lichfield Trent Valley	d											17 01													
Coventry 68	d							15 27			15 42												16 28		16 42
Birmingham International 68 ✈	d							15 39			15 53												16 39		16 53
Birmingham New St. 12 68	d					15 31	15 35	16 01			16 16										16 31	16 35	17 01		17 16
Wolverhampton 7	d					15 49	15 53	16 19			16 37										16 49	16 53	17 19		17 37
Penkridge	d						16 03															17 03			
Stafford	a						16 09	16 34				17 18		16 24								17 09	17 35		
	d						16 09	16 34				17 20		16 25								17 09	17 36		
Stoke-on-Trent	a	15 50				16 19		16 56				17 38	16 24			16 50					17 19		17 56		
Macclesfield	a			←				17 14					16 42					←					18 14		
Crewe 10	a			16 07	16 12		16 30				17 07	18 03		16 43	16 50			17 07		17 12		17 30			18 07
	d			16 09	16 13		16 31				17 09			16 45	16 52			17 09		17 13		17 31			18 09
Chester 81	a										→				17 14										→
Wrexham General 75	a																								
Llandudno Junction 81	a																								
Bangor (Gwynedd) 81	a																								
Holyhead 81 ⛴	a																								
Wilmslow 84	a				16 29															17 29					
Stockport 84	a	16 18			16 38			17 28					16 56			17 18				17 38			18 28		
Manchester Piccadilly 10 ⛴	a	16 29			16 50	16 59		17 40					17 09			17 29				17 50	17 56		18 40		
Warrington Bank Quay	a		16 16	16 26													17 16	17 26							
	d		16 16	16 27													17 16	17 27							
Runcorn 91	a						16 54							17 02								17 54			
Liverpool South Pkwy 7 91 ✈	a						17 03															18 03			
Liverpool Lime St. 10 91	a						17 14							17 22								18 14			
	d																								
Manchester Airport 82 ✈	d									16 00														17 00	
Manchester Picc. 10 82 ⛴	d									16 14														17 14	
Bolton 82	d																								
Wigan North Western 90	a		16 27	16 37						16 42							17 27	17 37						17 42	
	d		16 27	16 37						16 43							17 27	17 38						17 43	
Preston 8 90	a		16 40	16 51						16 57							17 40	17 51						17 57	
Preston 8 90	d		16 42	16 53						16 57							17 42	17 53						17 57	
Blackpool North 97	a																								
Lancaster 6	a		16 56	17 08						17 14							17 56	18 07						18 14	
	d		16 57	17 08						17 14							17 57	18 08						18 14	
Barrow-in-Furness 82	a																								
Oxenholme Lake District	a			17 22						17 28							18 10	18 21						18 28	
	d			17 23						17 29							18 10	18 22						18 29	
Windermere 83	a																								
Penrith North Lakes	d		17 32							17 54								18 48						18 54	
Carlisle 8 216	a		17 47	18 01						18 11							18 48	19 03						19 11	
	d		17 48	18 03						18 11							18 49	19 04						19 17	
Lockerbie	d																							19 36	
Carstairs 226	a																								
Motherwell 226	a																							20s22	
Glasgow Central 15 216,226	a		19 00	19 17													20 01							20 40	
Haymarket 225,226,228,230,242	a									19s27								20 16							
Edinburgh 10 225,226,228,230,242	a									19 34								20 21							
Perth 229	a																								
Dundee 229	a																								
Aberdeen 229	a																								
Inverness 229	a																								

OVERNIGHT SLEEPERS. For sleeper trains, operated by First ScotRail, please see Tables 400 - 404.

For complete service between Manchester and Preston, Blackpool and between Barrow-in-furness and Lancaster, please see Table 82.

For complete service between Crewe and Liverpool Lime Street, see Table 91

For complete service between Crewe/Stoke-on-Trent & Manchester see Table 84

For complete service between Crewe and Holyhead please see Table 81.

For complete service between Coventry-Birmingham-Wolverhampton-Stafford please see Table 68

For complete service between Windermere and Oxenholme Lake District, please see Table 83

Table 65

Sundays

16 February to 23 March

London and West Midlands - North West England and Scotland

Route Diagram - refer to first Page of Table 65

Station	Table		LM	VT	VT		VT	VT	TP	VT	VT	VT	XC	LM	XC		TP	TP (a)	TP (b)	VT	LM	VT	VT	VT	VT
			[1]	◇[1]	◇[1]		◇[1]	◇[1]	◇[1]	◇[1]	◇[1]	◇[1]	◇[1]	[1]	◇[1]		◇[1]	◇[1]		◇[1]	[1]	◇[1]	◇[1]	◇[1]	◇[1]
				☕	☕		☕	☕		☕	☕	☕	🛒		🛒			🛒		☕		☕	☕	☕	☕
London Euston [15]	⊖66	d	15 50	15 57	16 05		16 08	16 17		16 28		16 37								16 40	16 50	16 57	17 05	17 08	17 08
Watford Junction	66	d	16 06																		17 06				
Milton Keynes Central	66	d	16 37				16 42	16 50												17 13	17 37			17 42	17 42
Rugby	66	d	17 26																		18 26				
Nuneaton		d	17 40																		18 40		18 04		
Tamworth Low Level		d	17 55																		18 55				
Lichfield Trent Valley		d	18 01																		19 01				
Coventry	68	d													17 28					17 44					
Birmingham International	68 ✈	d													17 39					17 54					
Birmingham New St. [12]	68	d											17 31	17 35	18 01					18 16					
Wolverhampton [7]	⛴	d											17 49	17 53	18 19					18 37					
Penkridge		d												18 03											
Stafford		a	18 18		17 24									18 09	18 35						19 18			18 34	18 34
		d	18 20		17 25									18 09	18 36						19 20			18 35	18 35
Stoke-on-Trent		a	18 39	17 25				17 50					18 19		18 56						19 40	18 25			
Macclesfield		a		17 42							←				19 15							18 42			
Crewe [10]		a	19 07		17 43		17 50				18 07	18 12		18 30						19 06	20 07		18 44	18 53	18 53
		d			17 45		17 52				18 09	18 13		18 31						19 09			18 46	18 56	18 56
Chester	81	a					18 15													→				19 14	19 14
Wrexham General	75	a																							
Llandudno Junction	81	a																							20 11
Bangor (Gwynedd)	81	a																							20 27
Holyhead	81 ⛴	a																							20 59
Wilmslow	84	a										18 29													
Stockport	84	a		17 56				18 18				18 38			19 28							18 56			
Manchester Piccadilly [10]	⛴	a		18 09				18 29				18 50	18 56		19 40							19 09			
Warrington Bank Quay		a								18 16	18 26														
		d								18 17	18 27														
Runcorn	91	a			18 02									18 54									19 02		
Liverpool South Pkwy [7]	91 ✈	a												19 03											
Liverpool Lime St. [10]	91	a			18 22									19 14									19 25		
		d																							
Manchester Airport	82 ✈	d							17 30									18 00							
Manchester Picc. [10]	82 ⛴	d							17 46									18 14							
Bolton	82	d							18 05									18 31							
Wigan North Western	90	a								18 27	18 37						←								
		d								18 28	18 38														
Preston [8]	90	a							18 33	18 40	18 51						18 33	18 54							
Preston [8]	90	d							19 06	18 42	18 53						19 06	18 57	19 06						
Blackpool North	97	a							→																
Lancaster [6]		a								18 56	19 07						19 22	19 14	19 22						
		d								18 58	19 08						19 22	19 14	19 22						
Barrow-in-Furness	82	a															20 26		20 26						
Oxenholme Lake District		a								19 10	19 21							19 28							
		d								19 11	19 22							19 29							
Windermere	83	a																							
Penrith North Lakes		d								19 36								19 54							
Carlisle [8]	216	a								19 51	20 00							20 11							
		d								19 53	20 01							20 11							
Lockerbie		d																20 30							
Carstairs	226	a																							
Motherwell	226	a																							
Glasgow Central [15]	216,226	a								21 09	21 15														
Haymarket	225,226,228,230,242	a																21s29							
Edinburgh [10]	225,226,228,230,242	a																21 36							
Perth	229	a																							
Dundee	229	a																							
Aberdeen	229	a																							
Inverness	229	a																							

OVERNIGHT SLEEPERS. For sleeper trains, operated by First ScotRail, please see Tables 400 - 404.

For complete service between Manchester and Preston, Blackpool and between Barrow-in-furness and Lancaster, please see Table 82.

For complete service between Crewe and Liverpool Lime Street, see Table 91

For complete service between Crewe/Stoke-on-Trent & Manchester see Table 84

For complete service between Crewe and Holyhead please see Table 81.

For complete service between Coventry-Birmingham-Wolverhampton-Stafford please see Table 68

For complete service between Windermere and Oxenholme Lake District, please see Table 83

Table 65

Sundays

16 February to 23 March

London and West Midlands - North West England and Scotland

Route Diagram - refer to first Page of Table 65

Station			VT	VT	VT	VT	XC	LM	XC	TP	VT		LM	VT	VT	VT	VT	VT	VT	VT	VT		XC	LM	XC	VT
											R									R						
			◇1	◇1	◇1	◇1	◇1	1	◇1	◇1	1		1	◇1	◇1	◇1	◇1	◇1	◇1	1	◇1		◇1	1	◇1	◇1
			🍽	🍽	🍽	🍽	🛒		🛒		🍽			🍽	🍽	🍽	🍽	🍽	🍽	🍽	🍽		🛒		🛒	🍽
London Euston 15	⊖66	d	17 17	17 28		17 37					17 40		17 50	17 57	18 05	18 08	18 08	18 17	18 28		18 37					18 40
Watford Junction	66	d											18 06													
Milton Keynes Central	66	d	17 50								18 13		18 37			18 42	18 42	18 50								19 13
Rugby	66	d											19 26													
Nuneaton		d											19 40													
Tamworth Low Level		d											19 55													
Lichfield Trent Valley		d											20 01													
Coventry	68	d							18 28		18 44														19 28	19 42
Birmingham International	68 ✈	d							18 39		18 54														19 40	19 53
Birmingham New St. 12	68	d					18 31	18 35	19 01		19 16												19 31	19 35	20 01	20 16
Wolverhampton 7	⛴	d					18 49	18 53	19 19		19 37												19 49	19 53	20 19	20 38
Penkridge		d						19 03																20 03		
Stafford		a						19 09	19 37				20 18		19 24									20 09	20 36	20 52
		d						19 09	19 38				20 20		19 25									20 09	20 37	20 53
Stoke-on-Trent		a	18 50				19 19		19 56				20 39	19 25				19 50					20 19		20 56	
Macclesfield		a			←				20 14					19 42						←					21 15	
Crewe 10		a			19 06	19 12		19 29			20 07		21 07		19 43	19 50	19 50			20 07	20 12			20 30		21 10
		d			19 09	19 13		19 31			20 09				19 45	19 52	19 52			20 09	20 13			20 31		
Chester	81	a									↪					20 11	20 11									
Wrexham General	75	a																								
Llandudno Junction	81	a															21 07									
Bangor (Gwynedd)	81	a															21 23									
Holyhead	81 ⛴	a															21 54									
Wilmslow	84	a				19 29															20 29					
Stockport	84	a	19 18			19 38			20 28					19 56				20 18			20 38				21 28	
Manchester Piccadilly 10	⛴	a	19 29			19 50	19 58		20 40					20 09				20 29			20 50		21 00		21 40	
Warrington Bank Quay		a		19 16	19 25														20 16	20 26						
		d		19 16	19 27														20 16	20 27						
Runcorn	91	a						19 53							20 02									20 54		
Liverpool South Pkwy 7	91 ✈	a						20 02																21 03		
Liverpool Lime St. 10	91	a						20 14							20 21									21 14		
		d																								
Manchester Airport	82 ✈	d								19 00																
Manchester Picc. 10	82 ⛴	d								19 14																
Bolton	82	d								19 33																
Wigan North Western	90	a		19 27	19 36														20 27	20 37						
		d		19 27	19 38														20 27	20 38						
Preston 8	90	a		19 40	19 51					19 57									20 40	20 51						
Preston 8	90	d		19 42	19 53					20 06									20 42	20 53						
Blackpool North	97	a																								
Lancaster 6		a		19 56	20 07					20 23									20 56	21 08						
		d		19 57	20 08					20 24									20 57	21 08						
Barrow-in-Furness	82	a								21 27																
Oxenholme Lake District		a		20 10															21 10	21 22						
		d		20 10															21 11	21 23						
Windermere	83	a																								
Penrith North Lakes		d		20 36	20 45														21 36							
Carlisle 8	216	a		20 51	20 59														21 51	22 01						
		d		20 52	21 02														21 52	22 02						
Lockerbie		d																		22 21						
Carstairs	226	a																								
Motherwell	226	a																	22 48	23 03						
Glasgow Central 15	216,226	a		22 07															23 09	23 20						
Haymarket	225,226,228,230,242	a			22 14																					
Edinburgh 10	225,226,228,230,242	a			22 20																					
Perth	229	a																								
Dundee	229	a																								
Aberdeen	229	a																								
Inverness	229	a																								

OVERNIGHT SLEEPERS. For sleeper trains, operated by First ScotRail, please see Tables 400 - 404.

For complete service between Manchester and Preston, Blackpool and between Barrow-in-furness and Lancaster, please see Table 82.

For complete service between Crewe and Liverpool Lime Street, see Table 91

For complete service between Crewe/Stoke-on-Trent & Manchester see Table 84

For complete service between Crewe and Holyhead please see Table 81.

For complete service between Coventry-Birmingham-Wolverhampton-Stafford please see Table 68

For complete service between Windermere and Oxenholme Lake District, please see Table 83

Table 65

Sundays

16 February to 23 March

London and West Midlands - North West England and Scotland

Route Diagram - refer to first Page of Table 65

		LM	VT	VT	VT	VT	VT	VT	XC	XC	VT	LM	VT	VT	VT	VT	VT	VT	SR	VT	LM	VT
		1	◇1	◇1	◇1	◇1	◇1	◇1	◇1	◇1	◇1	1	◇1	◇1	◇1	◇1	◇1	◇1	R ✕	◇1	1	◇1
										A									B			
London Euston 15 ⊖66	d	18 50	18 57	19 05	19 08	19 17	19 28	19 37			19 40	19 50	19 57	20 05	20 08	20 15	20 25		20 28	20 35		20 50
Watford Junction 66	d	19 06										20 06										
Milton Keynes Central 66	d	19 37			19 42	19 50					20 13	20 37			20 41	20 48						21 37
Rugby 66	d	20 26										21 30										22 01
Nuneaton	d	20 40		20 04								21 43		21 04								
Tamworth Low Level	d	20 55										21 58					21 32					
Lichfield Trent Valley	d	21 01										22 04					21 39					
Coventry 68	d									20 28	20 44											
Birmingham International 68 ✈	d									20 40	20 54											
Birmingham New St. 12 68	d								20 31	21 01	21 16										21 35	
Wolverhampton 7	d								20 53	21 19	21 37										21 59	
Penkridge	d																				22 09	
Stafford	a	21 18		20 28						21 36	21 55	22 25			21 31					21 59	22 15	
	d	21 20		20 29						21 37	21 57	22 26			21 33					22 00	22 16	
Stoke-on-Trent	a	21 38	20 25			20 50			21 20	21 56		22 44	21 25			21 50						
Macclesfield	a		20 42							22 14			21 42					←				
Crewe 10	a	22 07		20 47	20 50			21 13			22 16	23 07		21 44	21 53		22 10	22 16		22 20	22 38	22 49
	d			20 49	20 55			21 14			22 17			21 46	21 55		22 13	22 17		22 21		22 51
Chester 81	a				21 14						↦											
Wrexham General 75	a																					
Llandudno Junction 81	a				22 06																	
Bangor (Gwynedd) 81	a				22 22																	
Holyhead 81 ⛴	a				22 56																	
Wilmslow 84	a							21 30												22 36		
Stockport 84	a		20 56			21 18		21 39		22 27			21 56			22 18				22 45		
Manchester Piccadilly 10	a		21 09			21 29		21 50	21 57	22 39			22 09			22 29				22 57		
Warrington Bank Quay	a						21 16										22 29	22 35				23 08
	d						21 16										22 30	22 35				23 08
Runcorn 91	a			21 06										22 03	22 12							
Liverpool South Pkwy 7 91 ✈	a																					
Liverpool Lime St. 10 91	a			21 27										22 23	22 33							
	d																					
Manchester Airport 82 ✈	d																					
Manchester Picc. 10 82	d																					
Bolton 82	d																					
Wigan North Western 90	a						21 27										22 40	22 46				23 19
	d						21 27										22 41	22 46				23 19
Preston 8 90	a						21 40										22 58	23 05				23 39
Preston 8 90	d						21 42															
Blackpool North 97	a																					
Lancaster 6	a						21 56															
	d						21 57															
Barrow-in-Furness 82	a																					
Oxenholme Lake District	a						22 10															
	d						22 11															
Windermere 83	a																					
Penrith North Lakes	d						22 36															
Carlisle 8 216	a						22 51															
	d						22 53															
Lockerbie	d																					
Carstairs 226	a																					
Motherwell 226	a																					
Glasgow Central 15 216,226	a						00 02															
Haymarket 225,226,228,230,242	a																					
Edinburgh 10 225,226,228,230,242	a																					
Perth 229	a																		05s39			
Dundee 229	a																		06s08			
Aberdeen 229	a																		07 34			
Inverness 229	a																		08 36			

A to Birmingham New St.

B also conveys through sleepers to Fort William arr 0955. (Table 404)

OVERNIGHT SLEEPERS. For sleeper trains, operated by First ScotRail, please see Tables 400 - 404.

For complete service between Manchester and Preston, Blackpool and between Barrow-in-furness and Lancaster, please see Table 82.

For complete service between Crewe and Liverpool Lime Street, see Table 91

For complete service between Crewe/Stoke-on-Trent & Manchester see Table 84

For complete service between Crewe and Holyhead please see Table 81.

For complete service between Coventry-Birmingham-Wolverhampton-Stafford please see Table 68

For complete service between Windermere and Oxenholme Lake District, please see Table 83

Table 65

Sundays

16 February to 23 March

London and West Midlands - North West England and Scotland

Route Diagram - refer to first Page of Table 65

		XC	VT	VT	SR	AW	VT
		◇1	◇1	◇1	R	◇	◇1
		A					
		🚲	☕	☕	🛏 ☕ ✕		☕
London Euston 15 ⊖66	d		21 21	21 25	21 45		21 51
Watford Junction 66	d						
Milton Keynes Central 66	d			22 14			22 39
Rugby 66	d						23 19
Nuneaton	d		22 52				23 30
Tamworth Low Level	d						
Lichfield Trent Valley	d						
Coventry 68	d	21 29					
Birmingham International 68 ✈	d	21 40				22 43	
Birmingham New St. 12 68	d	22 01				22 55	
Wolverhampton 7 🚌	d	22 20				23 15	
Penkridge	d						
Stafford	a	22 36	23 16			23 30	23s55
	d	22 37	23 17			23 31	
Stoke-on-Trent	a	22 55		23 29			
Macclesfield	a	23 12		23 45			
Crewe 10	a		23 43			23 57	00s21
	d		23 45			00 01	
Chester 81	a					00 22	
Wrexham General 75	a						
Llandudno Junction 81	a					01 27	
Bangor (Gwynedd) 81	a					01 45	
Holyhead 81 ⛴	a					02 20	
Wilmslow 84	a						
Stockport 84	a	23 27		23 59			00s50
Manchester Piccadilly 10 🚌	a	23 41		00 12			01 00
Warrington Bank Quay	a						
	d						
Runcorn 91	a		00 07				
Liverpool South Pkwy 7 91 ✈	a						
Liverpool Lime St. 10 91	a		00 30				
	d						
Manchester Airport 82 ✈	d						
Manchester Picc. 10 82 🚌	d						
Bolton 82	d						
Wigan North Western 90	a						
	d						
Preston 8 90	a						
Preston 8 90	d						
Blackpool North 97	a						
Lancaster 6	a						
	d						
Barrow-in-Furness 82	a						
Oxenholme Lake District	a						
	d						
Windermere 83	a						
Penrith North Lakes	d						
Carlisle 8 216	a						
	d						
Lockerbie	d						
Carstairs 226	a				07 00		
Motherwell 226	a				07 27		
Glasgow Central 15 216,226	a				07s59		
Haymarket 225,226,228,230,242	a						
Edinburgh 10 225,226,228,230,242	a				05s50		
Perth 229	a						
Dundee 229	a						
Aberdeen 229	a						
Inverness 229	a						

A 🚲 to Birmingham New St.

OVERNIGHT SLEEPERS. For sleeper trains, operated by First ScotRail, please see Tables 400 - 404.

For complete service between Manchester and Preston, Blackpool and between Barrow-in-furness and Lancaster, please see Table 82.

For complete service between Crewe and Liverpool Lime Street, see Table 91

For complete service between Crewe/Stoke-on-Trent & Manchester see Table 84

For complete service between Crewe and Holyhead please see Table 81.

For complete service between Coventry-Birmingham-Wolverhampton-Stafford please see Table 68

For complete service between Windermere and Oxenholme Lake District, please see Table 83

Table 65

Sundays

30 March to 11 May

London and West Midlands - North West England and Scotland

Route Diagram - refer to first Page of Table 65

		AW	AW	VT	XC	VT	VT	TP	TP	VT		VT	VT	LM	VT	XC	VT	LM	VT	VT		LM	XC	TP	VT
				◇1	◇1	◇1	◇1	◇1	◇1	◇1		◇1	◇1	1	◇1	◇1	◇1	1	◇1	◇1		1	◇1	◇1	◇1
				🍴	🛒	🍴	🍴	🛒		🍴		🍴	🍴		🍴	🛒	🍴		🍴	🍴			🛒	🛒	🍴
London Euston 15 ⊖66	d						08 10					08 15	08 20		08 45				09 15	09 20					09 45
Watford Junction 66	d																								
Milton Keynes Central 66	d						08 56						09 06		09 32					10 07					10 33
Rugby 66	d														10 09			10 00							11 09
Nuneaton	d											09 44						10 14	10 45						
Tamworth Low Level	d																	10 29							
Lichfield Trent Valley	d																	10 35							
Coventry 68	d																						10 28		
Birmingham International 68 ✈	d																						10 40		
Birmingham New St. 12 68	d			08 45	09 01	09 20								09 42		10 01	10 20					10 42	11 01		
Wolverhampton 7 🚌	d			09 04	09 19	09 38								10 00		10 19	10 38					11 00	11 19		
Penkridge	d													10 10								11 10			
Stafford	a			09 17	09 32							10 08		10 16		10 32		10 56	11 09			11 16	11 32		
	d			09 17	09 33							10 08		10 17		10 33		10 57	11 09			11 17	11 33		
Stoke-on-Trent	a												10 19			10 51		11 15		11 20			11 51		
Macclesfield	a												10 36			11 08				11 37			12 09		
Crewe 10	a			09 35	09 54	10 08	10 17					10 28		10 37	10 55		11 07	11 43	11 30			11 37			11 55
	d	08 28	09 28	09 37	09 56	10 08	10 19			10 21		10 30		10 38	10 57		11 09		11 32			11 38			11 57
Chester 81	a																								
Wrexham General 75	a																								
Llandudno Junction 81	a																								
Bangor (Gwynedd) 81	a																								
Holyhead 81 ⛴	a																								
Wilmslow 84	a	08 47	09 46		10 12		10 33																		
Stockport 84	a				10 21		10 43						10 50			11 22				11 51			12 22		
Manchester Piccadilly 10 🚌	a	09 11	10 11		10 37		10 55						11 03			11 31				12 04			12 40		
Warrington Bank Quay	a			09 54		10 27				10 37					11 14		11 26								12 14
	d			09 54		10 27				10 37					11 14		11 27								12 14
Runcorn 91	a											10 47		11 00					11 49			12 01			
Liverpool South Pkwy 7 91 ✈	a													11 09								12 10			
Liverpool Lime St. 10 91	a											11 09		11 21					12 10			12 21			
	d																								
Manchester Airport 82 ✈	d							10 00																11 00	
Manchester Picc. 10 82 🚌	d							10 15																11 14	
Bolton 82	d																								
Wigan North Western 90	a			10 05		10 38		10 42		10 48					11 25		11 37							11 42	12 25
	d			10 05		10 38		10 43		10 48					11 25		11 38							11 43	12 25
Preston 8 90	a			10 22		10 51		10 57		11 04					11 38		11 51							11 57	12 38
Preston 8 90	d					11 04		11 10	11 14	11 17					11 40		11 53							11 57	12 40
Blackpool North 97	a																								
Lancaster 6	a					11 18		11 25	11 29	11 35					11 54		12 08							12 14	12 54
	d					11 20		11 26	11 30						11 55		12 08							12 14	12 55
Barrow-in-Furness 82	a								12 29																
Oxenholme Lake District	a					11 32		11 41							12 08		12 22							12 28	13 08
	d					11 34		11 41							12 08		12 24							12 29	13 08
Windermere 83	a																								
Penrith North Lakes	d							12 06							12 34										13 34
Carlisle 8 216	a					12 10		12 24							12 49		13 01							13 08	13 49
	d					12 12		12 24							12 50		13 03							13 09	13 50
Lockerbie	d							12 43																13 28	
Carstairs 226	a																								
Motherwell 226	a																								
Glasgow Central 15 216,226	a					13 29									14 02									14 34	15 02
Haymarket 225,226,228,230,242	a							13s44									14 14								
Edinburgh 10 225,226,228,230,242	a							13 51									14 22								
Perth 229	a																								
Dundee 229	a																								
Aberdeen 229	a																								
Inverness 229	a																								

OVERNIGHT SLEEPERS. For sleeper trains, operated by First ScotRail, please see Tables 400 - 404.

For complete service between Manchester and Preston, Blackpool and between Barrow-in-furness and Lancaster, please see Table 82.

For complete service between Crewe and Liverpool Lime Street, see Table 91

For complete service between Crewe/Stoke-on-Trent & Manchester see Table 84

For complete service between Crewe and Holyhead please see Table 81.

For complete service between Coventry-Birmingham-Wolverhampton-Stafford please see Table 68

For complete service between Windermere and Oxenholme Lake District, please see Table 83

Table 65

Sundays

30 March to 11 May

London and West Midlands - North West England and Scotland

Route Diagram - refer to first Page of Table 65

Station		TP	VT	LM	VT	VT	LM	XC	LM	TP	VT	VT	VT	VT	LM	LM	VT	VT	XC	TP	VT	VT	VT
		◇1	◇1	1	◇1	◇1	1	◇1	1	◇1	◇1	◇1	◇1	◇1	1	1	◇1	◇1	◇1	◇1	◇1	◇1	◇1
London Euston 15 ⊖66	d			09 54	10 15	10 20			10 24		10 45		11 15	11 20		11 24	12 05	12 17			12 28		12 37
Watford Junction 66	d			10 10					10 40							11 42							
Milton Keynes Central 66	d			10 50		11 07			11 20		11 33		12 04	12 08		12 28		12 50					
Rugby 66	d			11 30					12 03		12 09					13 26							
Nuneaton	d			11 43	11 47				12 17							13 40							
Tamworth Low Level	d			11 57					12 32							13 55							
Lichfield Trent Valley	d			12 04					12 38							14 01							
Coventry 68	d							11 29											12 28				
Birmingham International 68 ✈	d							11 40											12 40				
Birmingham New St. 12 68	d		11 20				11 42	12 01				12 20			12 35				13 01			13 20	
Wolverhampton 7	d		11 38				12 00	12 19				12 37			12 53				13 19			13 37	
Penkridge	d						12 10								13 03								
Stafford	a			12 21	12 13		12 16	12 32	12 59				12 53		13 09	14 18	13 24		13 33				
	d			12 21	12 14		12 17	12 33	13 00				12 53		13 09	14 19	13 25		13 34				
Stoke-on-Trent	a			12 39		12 24		12 52	13 18					13 09		14 37		13 50	13 56				
Macclesfield	a					12 40		13 10						13 26					14 14				
Crewe 10	a		12 07	13 02	12 32		12 37		13 43		12 56	13 07	13 13		13 30	15 00	13 43					14 07	14 12
	d		12 09		12 34		12 38				12 58	13 09	13 15		13 31		13 45					14 09	14 13
Chester 81	a																						
Wrexham General 75	a																						
Llandudno Junction 81	a																						
Bangor (Gwynedd) 81	a																						
Holyhead 81 ⛴	a																						
Wilmslow 84	a																						14 29
Stockport 84	a					12 55		13 28						13 41				14 18	14 28				14 38
Manchester Piccadilly 10 ⛴	a					13 08		13 40						13 53				14 29	14 40				14 50
Warrington Bank Quay	a		12 26								13 15	13 26									14 16	14 26	
	d		12 27								13 15	13 27									14 16	14 27	
Runcorn 91	a				12 51		13 01						13 32		13 54		14 02						
Liverpool South Pkwy 7 91 ✈	a						13 10								14 03								
Liverpool Lime St. 10 91	a				13 12		13 21						13 54		14 14		14 24						
	d																						
Manchester Airport 82 ✈	d									12 00										13 00			
Manchester Picc. 10 82 ⛴	d									12 14										13 14			
Bolton 82	d																						
Wigan North Western 90	a		12 37							12 42	13 26	13 37								13 42	14 27	14 37	
	d		12 38							12 43	13 26	13 38								13 43	14 27	14 38	
Preston 8 90	a		12 51							12 57	13 40	13 51								13 57	14 40	14 50	
Preston 8 90	d	12 48	12 53							12 57	13 42	13 53								13 57	14 42	14 53	
Blackpool North 97	a																						
Lancaster 6	a	13 03	13 07							13 14	13 56	14 08								14 14	14 56	15 08	
	d	13 04	13 08							13 14	13 57	14 08								14 14	14 58	15 09	
Barrow-in-Furness 82	a	14 07																					
Oxenholme Lake District	a		13 21							13 28	14 10									14 28		15 22	
	d		13 22							13 29	14 10									14 29		15 24	
Windermere 83	a																						
Penrith North Lakes	d									13 54	14 36	14 45								14 54	15 32		
Carlisle 8 216	a		14 00							14 11	14 51	15 00								15 11	15 47	16 01	
	d		14 02							14 11	14 52	15 03								15 17	15 48	16 03	
Lockerbie	d									14 30													
Carstairs 226	a																						
Motherwell 226	a																						
Glasgow Central 15 216,226	a		15 16								16 05									16 34	17 00	17 17	
Haymarket 225,226,228,230,242	a									15s29		16 14											
Edinburgh 10 225,226,228,230,242	a									15 36		16 23											
Perth 229	a																						
Dundee 229	a																						
Aberdeen 229	a																						
Inverness 229	a																						

OVERNIGHT SLEEPERS. For sleeper trains, operated by First ScotRail, please see Tables 400 - 404.

For complete service between Manchester and Preston, Blackpool and between Barrow-in-furness and Lancaster, please see Table 82.

For complete service between Crewe and Liverpool Lime Street, see Table 91

For complete service between Crewe/Stoke-on-Trent & Manchester see Table 84

For complete service between Crewe and Holyhead please see Table 81.

For complete service between Coventry-Birmingham-Wolverhampton-Stafford please see Table 68

For complete service between Windermere and Oxenholme Lake District, please see Table 83

Table 65

Sundays
30 March to 11 May

London and West Midlands - North West England and Scotland

Route Diagram - refer to first Page of Table 65

		XC		LM	XC	TP	VT	LM	VT	VT	VT	VT		VT	VT	XC	LM	XC	TP	VT	LM	VT		VT	VT
		◇1		1	◇1	◇1	◇1	1	◇1	◇1	◇1	◇1		◇1	◇1	◇1	1	◇1	◇1	◇1	1	◇1		◇1	◇1
		🛒			🛒	🛒	⊡		⊡	⊡	⊡	⊡		⊡	⊡	🛒		🛒		⊡		⊡		⊡	⊡
London Euston 15 ⊖66	d						12 40	12 50	12 57	13 05	13 17	13 28			13 37					13 40	13 50	13 57		14 05	14 17
Watford Junction 66	d							13 06													14 06				
Milton Keynes Central 66	d						13 13	13 37			13 50									14 13	14 37				14 50
Rugby 66	d							14 26													15 26				
Nuneaton	d							14 40													15 40				
Tamworth Low Level	d							14 55													15 55				
Lichfield Trent Valley	d							15 01													16 01				
Coventry 68	d				13 26		13 42											14 26		14 44					
Birmingham International 68 ✈	d				13 38		13 53											14 38		14 54					
Birmingham New St. 12 68	d	13 31		13 35	14 01		14 16									14 31	14 35	15 01		15 17					
Wolverhampton 7 ⛴	d	13 49		13 53	14 19		14 37									14 49	14 53	15 19		15 38					
Penkridge	d			14 03													15 03								
Stafford	a			14 09	14 33			15 18		14 23							15 09	15 33			16 18			15 24	
	d			14 09	14 34			15 20		14 24							15 09	15 34			16 20			15 25	
Stoke-on-Trent	a	14 19			14 56			15 39	14 26		14 50					15 19		15 56			16 38	15 25			15 50
Macclesfield	a				15 14				14 42					←				16 14				15 42			
Crewe 10	a			14 29			15 07	16 03		14 43				15 07	15 12		15 29			16 07	17 03			15 43	
	d			14 31			15 09			14 45				15 09	15 13		15 31			16 09				15 45	
Chester 81	a						→													→					
Wrexham General 75	a																								
Llandudno Junction 81	a																								
Bangor (Gwynedd) 81	a																								
Holyhead 81 ⛴	a																								
Wilmslow 84	a														15 29										
Stockport 84	a				15 28				14 56		15 18				15 38			16 28				15 56			16 18
Manchester Piccadilly 10 ⛴	a	14 57			15 40				15 09		15 29				15 50	15 59		16 40				16 09			16 29
Warrington Bank Quay	a											15 16		15 26											
	d											15 16		15 27											
Runcorn 91	a			14 53						15 02							15 53							16 02	
Liverpool South Pkwy 7 91 ✈	a			15 02													16 02								
Liverpool Lime St. 10 91	a			15 14						15 24							16 14							16 24	
	d																								
Manchester Airport 82 ✈	d					14 00													15 00						
Manchester Picc. 10 82 ⛴	d					14 14													15 14						
Bolton 82	d																								
Wigan North Western 90	a					14 42						15 27		15 37					15 42						
	d					14 43						15 27		15 38					15 43						
Preston 8 90	a					14 57						15 40		15 51					15 57						
Preston 8 90	d					14 57						15 42		15 53					15 57						
Blackpool North 97	a																								
Lancaster 6	a					15 14						15 56		16 08					16 14						
	d					15 14						15 58		16 08					16 14						
Barrow-in-Furness 82	a																		17 18						
Oxenholme Lake District	a					15 28						16 10													
	d					15 29						16 11													
Windermere 83	a																								
Penrith North Lakes	d					15 54								16 45											
Carlisle 8 216	a					16 11						16 48		17 00											
	d					16 11						16 49		17 02											
Lockerbie	d					16 30																			
Carstairs 226	a																								
Motherwell 226	a																								
Glasgow Central 15 216,226	a											18 01													
Haymarket 225,226,228,230,242	a					17s30								18 13											
Edinburgh 10 225,226,228,230,242	a					17 38								18 22											
Perth 229	a																								
Dundee 229	a																								
Aberdeen 229	a																								
Inverness 229	a																								

OVERNIGHT SLEEPERS. For sleeper trains, operated by First ScotRail, please see Tables 400 - 404.

For complete service between Manchester and Preston, Blackpool and between Barrow-in-furness and Lancaster, please see Table 82.

For complete service between Crewe and Liverpool Lime Street, see Table 91

For complete service between Crewe/Stoke-on-Trent & Manchester see Table 84

For complete service between Crewe and Holyhead please see Table 81.

For complete service between Coventry-Birmingham-Wolverhampton-Stafford please see Table 68

For complete service between Windermere and Oxenholme Lake District, please see Table 83

Table 65

Sundays

30 March to 11 May

London and West Midlands - North West England and Scotland

Route Diagram - refer to first Page of Table 65

	VT ◇1	VT ◇1	VT ◇1	XC ◇1	LM 1	XC ◇1	TP ◇1		VT ◇1	LM 1	VT ◇1	VT ◇1	VT ◇1	VT ◇1	VT ◇1	VT ◇1	VT ◇1		XC ◇1	LM 1	XC ◇1	TP ◇1	VT ◇1	LM 1
London Euston 15 ⊖66 d	14 28		14 37						14 40	14 50	14 57	15 05	15 08	15 17	15 28		15 37						15 40	15 50
Watford Junction 66 d										15 06														16 06
Milton Keynes Central 66 d									15 13	15 37			15 42	15 50									16 13	16 37
Rugby 66 d										16 26														17 26
Nuneaton d										16 40														17 40
Tamworth Low Level d										16 55														17 55
Lichfield Trent Valley d										17 01														18 01
Coventry 68 d						15 26			15 42												16 26		16 42	
Birmingham International 68 ✈ d						15 38			15 53												16 38		16 53	
Birmingham New St. 12 68 d				15 31	15 35	16 01			16 16										16 31	16 35	17 01		17 16	
Wolverhampton 7 ⛴ d				15 49	15 53	16 19			16 37										16 49	16 53	17 19		17 37	
Penkridge d					16 03															17 03				
Stafford a					16 09	16 34				17 18		16 24								17 09	17 35			18 18
d					16 09	16 34				17 20		16 25								17 09	17 36			18 20
Stoke-on-Trent a				16 19		16 56				17 38	16 24			16 50					17 19		17 56			18 39
Macclesfield a		←				17 14					16 42					←					18 14			
Crewe 10 a		16 07	16 12		16 30				17 07	18 03		16 43	16 50			17 07	17 12			17 30			18 07	19 07
d		16 09	16 13		16 31				17 09			16 45	16 52			17 09	17 13			17 31			18 09	
Chester 81 a									↪				17 14										↪	
Wrexham General 75 a																								
Llandudno Junction 81 a																								
Bangor (Gwynedd) 81 a																								
Holyhead 81 ⛴ a																								
Wilmslow 84 a			16 29														17 29							
Stockport 84 a			16 38			17 28					16 56			17 18			17 38				18 28			
Manchester Piccadilly 10 ⛴ a			16 50	16 59		17 40					17 09			17 29			17 50		17 56		18 40			
Warrington Bank Quay a	16 16	16 26													17 16	17 26								
d	16 16	16 27													17 16	17 27								
Runcorn 91 a					16 54							17 02								17 54				
Liverpool South Pkwy 7 91 ✈ a					17 03															18 03				
Liverpool Lime St. 10 91 a					17 14							17 22								18 14				
d																								
Manchester Airport 82 ✈ d							16 00															17 00		
Manchester Picc. 10 82 ⛴ d							16 14															17 14		
Bolton 82 d																								
Wigan North Western 90 a	16 27	16 37					16 42								17 27	17 37						17 42		
d	16 27	16 37					16 43								17 27	17 38						17 43		
Preston 8 90 a	16 40	16 51					16 57								17 40	17 51						17 57		
Preston 8 90 d	16 42	16 53					16 57								17 42	17 53						17 57		
Blackpool North 97 a																								
Lancaster 6 a	16 56	17 08					17 14								17 56	18 07						18 14		
d	16 57	17 08					17 14								17 57	18 08						18 14		
Barrow-in-Furness 82 a																								
Oxenholme Lake District a		17 22					17 28								18 10	18 21						18 28		
d		17 23					17 29								18 10	18 22						18 29		
Windermere 83 a																								
Penrith North Lakes d	17 32						17 54									18 48						18 54		
Carlisle 8 216 a	17 47	18 01					18 11								18 48	19 03						19 11		
d	17 48	18 03					18 11								18 49	19 04						19 17		
Lockerbie d																						19 36		
Carstairs 226 a																								
Motherwell 226 a																						20s22		
Glasgow Central 15 216,226 a	19 00	19 17													20 01							20 40		
Haymarket 225,226,228,230,242 a							19s27									20 16								
Edinburgh 10 225,226,228,230,242 a							19 34									20 21								
Perth 229 a																								
Dundee 229 a																								
Aberdeen 229 a																								
Inverness 229 a																								

OVERNIGHT SLEEPERS. For sleeper trains, operated by First ScotRail, please see Tables 400 - 404.

For complete service between Manchester and Preston, Blackpool and between Barrow-in-furness and Lancaster, please see Table 82.

For complete service between Crewe and Liverpool Lime Street, see Table 91

For complete service between Crewe/Stoke-on-Trent & Manchester see Table 84

For complete service between Crewe and Holyhead please see Table 81.

For complete service between Coventry-Birmingham-Wolverhampton-Stafford please see Table 68

For complete service between Windermere and Oxenholme Lake District, please see Table 83

Table 65

Sundays

30 March to 11 May

London and West Midlands - North West England and Scotland

Route Diagram - refer to first Page of Table 65

		VT	VT	VT		VT	VT	VT	VT	XC	LM	XC	TP	TP		VT	LM	VT	VT	VT	VT	VT	VT	VT	
		◇1	◇1	◇1		◇1	◇1	◇1	◇1	◇1	1	◇1	◇1	◇1		◇1	1	◇1	◇1	◇1	◇1	◇1	◇1	◇1	
London Euston 15 ⊖66	d	15 57	16 05	16 08		16 17	16 28		16 37							16 40	16 50	16 57	17 05	17 08	17 08	17 17	17 28		
Watford Junction 66	d																17 06								
Milton Keynes Central 66	d			16 42		16 50										17 13	17 37			17 42	17 42	17 50			
Rugby 66	d																18 26								
Nuneaton	d																18 40		18 04						
Tamworth Low Level	d																18 55								
Lichfield Trent Valley	d																19 01								
Coventry 68	d											17 26				17 44									
Birmingham International 68 ✈	d											17 38				17 54									
Birmingham New St. 12 68	d									17 31	17 35	18 01				18 16									
Wolverhampton 7	d									17 49	17 53	18 19				18 37									
Penkridge	d										18 03														
Stafford	a		17 24								18 09	18 35					19 18			18 34	18 34				
	d		17 25								18 09	18 36					19 20			18 35	18 35				
Stoke-on-Trent	a	17 25				17 50				18 19		18 56					19 40	18 25				18 50			
Macclesfield	a	17 42						←				19 15						18 42						←	
Crewe 10	a		17 43	17 50				18 07	18 12		18 30					19 06	20 07		18 44	18 53	18 53			19 06	
	d		17 45	17 52				18 09	18 13		18 31					19 09			18 46	18 56	18 56			19 09	
Chester 81	a			18 15												→				19 14	19 14				
Wrexham General 75	a																								
Llandudno Junction 81	a																				20 11				
Bangor (Gwynedd) 81	a																				20 27				
Holyhead 81 ⛴	a																				20 59				
Wilmslow 84	a								18 29																
Stockport 84	a	17 56				18 18			18 38			19 28						18 56				19 18			
Manchester Piccadilly 10 ⛴	a	18 09				18 29			18 50	18 56		19 40						19 09				19 29			
Warrington Bank Quay	a						18 16	18 26															19 16	19 25	
	d						18 17	18 27															19 16	19 27	
Runcorn 91	a		18 02								18 54								19 02						
Liverpool South Pkwy 7 91 ✈	a										19 03														
Liverpool Lime St. 10 91	a		18 22								19 14								19 25						
	d																								
Manchester Airport 82 ✈	d												18 00												
Manchester Picc. 10 82 ⛴	d												18 14												
Bolton 82	d																								
Wigan North Western 90	a						18 27	18 37					18 42										19 27	19 36	
	d						18 28	18 38					18 43										19 27	19 38	
Preston 8 90	a						18 40	18 51					18 57										19 40	19 51	
Preston 8 90	d						18 42	18 53					18 57	19 06									19 42	19 53	
Blackpool North 97	a																								
Lancaster 6	a						18 56	19 07					19 14	19 22									19 56	20 07	
	d						18 58	19 08					19 14	19 22									19 57	20 08	
Barrow-in-Furness 82	a													20 26											
Oxenholme Lake District	a						19 10	19 21					19 28										20 10		
	d						19 11	19 22					19 29										20 10		
Windermere 83	a																								
Penrith North Lakes	d						19 36						19 54										20 36	20 45	
Carlisle 8 216	a						19 51	20 00					20 11										20 51	20 59	
	d						19 53	20 01					20 11										20 52	21 02	
Lockerbie	d												20 30												
Carstairs 226	a																								
Motherwell 226	a																								
Glasgow Central 15 216,226	a						21 09	21 15															22 07		
Haymarket 225,226,228,230,242	a												21s29											22 14	
Edinburgh 10 225,226,228,230,242	a												21 36											22 20	
Perth 229	a																								
Dundee 229	a																								
Aberdeen 229	a																								
Inverness 229	a																								

OVERNIGHT SLEEPERS. For sleeper trains, operated by First ScotRail, please see Tables 400 - 404.

For complete service between Manchester and Preston, Blackpool and between Barrow-in-furness and Lancaster, please see Table 82.

For complete service between Crewe and Liverpool Lime Street, see Table 91

For complete service between Crewe/Stoke-on-Trent & Manchester see Table 84

For complete service between Crewe and Holyhead please see Table 81.

For complete service between Coventry-Birmingham-Wolverhampton-Stafford please see Table 68

For complete service between Windermere and Oxenholme Lake District, please see Table 83

Table 65

Sundays

30 March to 11 May

London and West Midlands - North West England and Scotland

Route Diagram - refer to first Page of Table 65

		VT	XC	LM	XC	TP	VT	LM	VT	VT	VT	VT	VT	VT	VT	VT	XC	LM	XC	VT	LM	VT	VT
		◇1	◇1	1	◇1	◇1	R 1	1	◇1	◇1	◇1	◇1	◇1	◇1	R 1	◇1	◇1	1	◇1	◇1	1	◇1	◇1
London Euston 15 ⊖66	d	17 37					17 40	17 50	17 57	18 05	18 08	18 08	18 17	18 28		18 37				18 40	18 50	18 57	19 05
Watford Junction 66	d							18 06													19 06		
Milton Keynes Central 66	d						18 13	18 37			18 42	18 42	18 50							19 13	19 37		
Rugby 66	d							19 26													20 26		
Nuneaton	d							19 40													20 40		20 04
Tamworth Low Level	d							19 55													20 55		
Lichfield Trent Valley	d							20 01													21 01		
Coventry 68	d				18 26		18 44												19 26	19 42			
Birmingham International 68 ✈	d				18 38		18 54												19 38	19 53			
Birmingham New St. 12 68	d		18 31	18 35	19 01		19 16										19 31	19 35	20 01	20 16			
Wolverhampton 7	d		18 49	18 53	19 19		19 37										19 49	19 53	20 19	20 38			
Penkridge	d			19 03														20 03					
Stafford	a			19 09	19 37			20 18		19 24								20 09	20 36	20 52	21 18		20 28
	d			19 09	19 38			20 20		19 25								20 09	20 37	20 53	21 20		20 29
Stoke-on-Trent	a		19 19		19 56			20 39	19 25				19 50				20 19		20 56		21 38	20 25	
Macclesfield	a				20 14				19 42						↤				21 15			20 42	
Crewe 10	a	19 12		19 29			20 07	21 07		19 43	19 50	19 50			20 07	20 12		20 30		21 10	22 07		20 47
	d	19 13		19 31			20 09			19 45	19 52	19 52			20 09	20 13		20 31					20 49
Chester 81	a						↦				20 11	20 11											
Wrexham General 75	a																						
Llandudno Junction 81	a											21 07											
Bangor (Gwynedd) 81	a											21 23											
Holyhead 81 ⛴	a											21 54											
Wilmslow 84	a	19 29														20 29							
Stockport 84	a	19 38			20 28				19 56				20 18			20 38			21 28			20 56	
Manchester Piccadilly 10	a	19 50	19 58		20 40				20 09				20 29			20 50	21 00		21 40			21 09	
Warrington Bank Quay	a													20 16	20 26								
	d													20 16	20 27								
Runcorn 91	a			19 53						20 02								20 54					21 06
Liverpool South Pkwy 7 91 ✈	a			20 02														21 03					
Liverpool Lime St. 10 91	a			20 14						20 21								21 14					21 27
	d																						
Manchester Airport 82 ✈	d					19 00																	
Manchester Picc. 10 82	d					19 14																	
Bolton 82	d					19 33																	
Wigan North Western 90	a													20 27	20 37								
	d													20 27	20 38								
Preston 8 90	a					19 57								20 40	20 51								
Preston 8 90	d					20 06								20 42	20 53								
Blackpool North 97	a																						
Lancaster 6	a					20 23								20 56	21 08								
	d					20 24								20 57	21 08								
Barrow-in-Furness 82	a					21 27																	
Oxenholme Lake District	a													21 10	21 22								
	d													21 11	21 23								
Windermere 83	a																						
Penrith North Lakes	d													21 36									
Carlisle 8 216	a													21 51	22 01								
	d													21 52	22 02								
Lockerbie	d														22 21								
Carstairs 226	a																						
Motherwell 226	a													22 48	23 03								
Glasgow Central 15 216,226	a													23 09	23 20								
Haymarket 225,226,228,230,242	a																						
Edinburgh 10 225,226,228,230,242	a																						
Perth 229	a																						
Dundee 229	a																						
Aberdeen 229	a																						
Inverness 229	a																						

OVERNIGHT SLEEPERS. For sleeper trains, operated by First ScotRail, please see Tables 400 - 404.

For complete service between Manchester and Preston, Blackpool and between Barrow-in-furness and Lancaster, please see Table 82.

For complete service between Crewe and Liverpool Lime Street, see Table 91

For complete service between Crewe/Stoke-on-Trent & Manchester see Table 84

For complete service between Crewe and Holyhead please see Table 81.

For complete service between Coventry-Birmingham-Wolverhampton-Stafford please see Table 68

For complete service between Windermere and Oxenholme Lake District, please see Table 83

Table 65

Sundays

30 March to 11 May

London and West Midlands - North West England and Scotland

Route Diagram - refer to first Page of Table 65

		VT	VT	VT	VT	XC	XC	VT	LM	VT	VT	VT	VT	VT	VT	VT	LM	SR	VT	XC	VT	VT	SR
																		R					R
		◇1	◇1	◇1	◇1	◇1	◇1	◇1	1	◇1	◇1	◇1	◇1	◇1	◇1	◇1	1	✕	◇1	◇1	◇1	◇1	
							A											B		A			
																		🛏					🛏
		☕	☕	☕	☕		🛒	☕		☕	☕	☕	☕	☕	☕	☕		☕	☕	🛒	☕	☕	☕ ✕
London Euston 15 ⊖66	d	19 08	19 17	19 28	19 37			19 40	19 50	19 57	20 05	20 08	20 15	20 25		20 35		20 28	20 50		21 21	21 25	21 45
Watford Junction 66	d								20 06														
Milton Keynes Central 66	d	19 42	19 50					20 13	20 37			20 41	20 48						21 37			22 14	
Rugby 66	d								21 30										22 01				
Nuneaton	d								21 43		21 04										22 52		
Tamworth Low Level	d								21 58					21 32									
Lichfield Trent Valley	d								22 04					21 39									
Coventry 68	d						20 26	20 44												21 26			
Birmingham International 68 ✈	d						20 38	20 54												21 38			
Birmingham New St. 12 68	d					20 31	21 01	21 16									21 35			22 01			
Wolverhampton 7 🚌	d					20 53	21 19	21 37									21 59			22 20			
Penkridge	d																22 09						
Stafford	a						21 36	21 55	22 25			21 31				21 59	22 15			22 36	23 16		
	d						21 37	21 57	22 26			21 33				22 00	22 16			22 37	23 17		
Stoke-on-Trent	a		20 50			21 20	21 56		22 44	21 25			21 50							22 55		23 29	
Macclesfield	a						22 14			21 42					←					23 12		23 45	
Crewe 10	a	20 50			21 13			22 16	23 07		21 44	21 53		22 10	22 16	22 20	22 38		22 49		23 43		
	d	20 55			21 14			22 17			21 46	21 55		22 13	22 17	22 21			22 51		23 45		
Chester 81	a	21 14						→															
Wrexham General 75	a																						
Llandudno Junction 81	a	22 06																					
Bangor (Gwynedd) 81	a	22 22																					
Holyhead 81 ⛴	a	22 56																					
Wilmslow 84	a				21 30											22 36							
Stockport 84	a		21 18		21 39		22 27			21 56			22 18			22 45				23 27		23 59	
Manchester Piccadilly 10 🚌	a		21 29		21 50	21 57	22 39			22 09			22 29			22 57				23 41		00 12	
Warrington Bank Quay	a			21 16										22 29	22 35				23 08				
	d			21 16										22 30	22 35				23 08				
Runcorn 91	a										22 03	22 12									00 07		
Liverpool South Pkwy 7 91 ✈	a																						
Liverpool Lime St. 10 91	a										22 23	22 33									00 30		
	d																						
Manchester Airport 82 ✈	d																						
Manchester Picc. 10 82 🚌	d																						
Bolton 82	d																						
Wigan North Western 90	a			21 27										22 40	22 46				23 19				
	d			21 27										22 41	22 46				23 19				
Preston 8 90	a			21 40										22 58	23 05				23 39				
Preston 8 90	d			21 42																			
Blackpool North 97	a																						
Lancaster 6	a			21 56																			
	d			21 57																			
Barrow-in-Furness 82	a																						
Oxenholme Lake District	a			22 10																			
	d			22 11																			
Windermere 83	a																						
Penrith North Lakes	d			22 36																			
Carlisle 8 216	a			22 51																			
	d			22 53																			
Lockerbie	d																						
Carstairs 226	a																						07 00
Motherwell 226	a																						07 27
Glasgow Central 15 216,226	a			00 02																			07s59
Haymarket 225,226,228,230,242	a																						
Edinburgh 10 225,226,228,230,242	a																						05s50
Perth 229	a																	05s44					
Dundee 229	a																	06s08					
Aberdeen 229	a																	07 34					
Inverness 229	a																	08 37					

A 🛒 to Birmingham New St.

B also conveys through sleepers to Fort William arr 0955. (Table 404)

OVERNIGHT SLEEPERS. For sleeper trains, operated by First ScotRail, please see Tables 400 - 404.

For complete service between Manchester and Preston, Blackpool and between Barrow-in-furness and Lancaster, please see Table 82.

For complete service between Crewe and Liverpool Lime Street, see Table 91

For complete service between Crewe/Stoke-on-Trent & Manchester see Table 84

For complete service between Crewe and Holyhead please see Table 81.

For complete service between Coventry-Birmingham-Wolverhampton-Stafford please see Table 68

For complete service between Windermere and Oxenholme Lake District, please see Table 83

Table 65

Sundays

30 March to 11 May

London and West Midlands - North West England and Scotland

Route Diagram - refer to first Page of Table 65

			AW	VT
			◇	◇1 ☕
London Euston 15	⊖66	d		21 51
Watford Junction	66	d		
Milton Keynes Central	66	d		22 39
Rugby	66	d		23 19
Nuneaton		d		23 30
Tamworth Low Level		d		
Lichfield Trent Valley		d		
Coventry	68	d		
Birmingham International	68 ✈	d	22 43	
Birmingham New St. 12	68	d	22 55	
Wolverhampton 7	🚌	d	23 15	
Penkridge		d		
Stafford		a	23 30	23s55
		d	23 31	
Stoke-on-Trent		a		
Macclesfield		a		
Crewe 10		a	23 57	00s21
		d	00 01	
Chester	81	a	00 22	
Wrexham General	75	a		
Llandudno Junction	81	a	01 27	
Bangor (Gwynedd)	81	a	01 45	
Holyhead	81 ⛴	a	02 20	
Wilmslow	84	a		
Stockport	84	a		00s50
Manchester Piccadilly 10	🚌	a		01 00
Warrington Bank Quay		a		
		d		
Runcorn	91	a		
Liverpool South Pkwy 7	91 ✈	a		
Liverpool Lime St. 10	91	a		
		d		
Manchester Airport	82 ✈	d		
Manchester Picc. 10	82 🚌	d		
Bolton	82	d		
Wigan North Western	90	a		
		d		
Preston 8	90	a		
Preston 8	90	d		
Blackpool North	97	a		
Lancaster 6		a		
		d		
Barrow-in-Furness	82	a		
Oxenholme Lake District		a		
		d		
Windermere	83	a		
Penrith North Lakes		d		
Carlisle 8	216	a		
		d		
Lockerbie		d		
Carstairs	226	a		
Motherwell	226	a		
Glasgow Central 15	216,226	a		
Haymarket	225,226,228,230,242	a		
Edinburgh 10	225,226,228,230,242	a		
Perth	229	a		
Dundee	229	a		
Aberdeen	229	a		
Inverness	229	a		

OVERNIGHT SLEEPERS. For sleeper trains, operated by First ScotRail, please see Tables 400 - 404.

For complete service between Manchester and Preston, Blackpool and between Barrow-in-furness and Lancaster, please see Table 82.

For complete service between Crewe and Liverpool Lime Street, see Table 91

For complete service between Crewe/Stoke-on-Trent & Manchester see Table 84

For complete service between Crewe and Holyhead please see Table 81.

For complete service between Coventry-Birmingham-Wolverhampton-Stafford please see Table 68

For complete service between Windermere and Oxenholme Lake District, please see Table 83

Table 65R

Mondays to Fridays

9 December to 16 May

Scotland and North West England - West Midlands and London

Route Diagram - refer to first Page of Table 65

Miles	Miles	Miles	Miles	Miles			NT MX	AW	SR MO	SR MX		LM	VT	XC	VT	XC		VT		LM	VT	VT	XC	NT	
								◇	🅁	🅁															
												■1	◇■1	◇■1	◇■1	◇■1		◇■1		■1	◇■1	◇■1	◇■1		
									A 🛏 ✕	🛏 ✕			⊠	trolley	⊠	trolley		⊠			⊠	⊠	trolley		
—	0	—	—	—	Inverness 229	d																			
—	—	0	—	—	Aberdeen 229	d																			
—	—	71¼	—	—	Dundee 229	d																			
—	118	—	—	—	Perth 229	d																			
—	130¼	187¼	—	—	**Edinburgh** ■10 225,226,228,230,242	d																			
—	131½	188½	—	—	Haymarket 225,226,228,230,242	d																			
0	—	—	—	—	**Glasgow Central** ■15 226,216	d																			
12¾	—	—	—	—	Motherwell 226	d				00u01															
28¾	158	—	—	—	Carstairs 226	d				00u16															
77	—	263½	—	—	Lockerbie	d																			
102¼	—	—	—	—	**Carlisle** ■8 216	a																			
—	—	—	—	—		d			01u12	01u40															
120	—	—	—	—	Penrith North Lakes	d																			
—	—	—	—	—	Windermere 83	d																			
152¼	—	—	—	—	Oxenholme Lake District	a																			
—	—	—	—	—		d																			
—	—	—	—	—	Barrow-in-Furness 82	d																			
171¼	—	—	—	—	Lancaster ■6	a																			
—	—	—	—	—		d																			
—	—	—	—	—	Blackpool North 97	d																			
192¼	—	—	—	—	**Preston** ■8 90	a																			
—	—	—	0	—	**Preston** ■8 90	d												05 33							
207½	—	—	—	—	Wigan North Western 90	a												05 43							
—	—	—	—	—		d												05 45							
—	—	—	20	—	Bolton 82	a																			
—	—	—	31¼	—	**Manchester Picc.** ■10 82 ⛴	a																			
—	—	—	—	—	Manchester Airport ✈	a																			
—	0	—	—	—	**Liverpool Lime Street** ■10 91	a																			
—	—	—	—	—		d									05 27							06 05			
—	5½	—	—	—	Liverpool South Parkway 91 ✈	d																			
—	13	—	—	—	Runcorn 91	d									05 43							06 21			
219¼	—	—	—	—	Warrington Bank Quay	a												05 55							
—	—	—	—	—		d												05 56							
—	—	—	—	0	**Manchester Picc.** ■10 84 ⛴	d							05 05	05 11							05 55		06 00	06 06	
—	—	—	37	5¾	Stockport 84	d							05 13								06 03		06 08	06 19	
—	—	—	—	—	Wilmslow 84	d	00 01														06 11		06 16	06 34	
—	—	—	—	—	Holyhead 81 ⛴	d																			
—	—	—	—	—	Bangor (Gwynedd) 81	d																			
—	—	—	—	—	Llandudno Junction 81	d																			
—	—	—	—	—	Wrexham General 75	d																			
—	—	—	—	—	Chester 81	d		04 22																	
243½	35½	—	—	—	**Crewe** ■10	a	00 30	04 44					05 34	05 44	06 00						06 27		06 33	07 04	
—	—	—	—	—		d		04 59				05 18	05 36	05 47	06 02					06 20	06 29		06 38		
—	—	—	49	17¾	Macclesfield	d																			
—	—	—	68¾	37¼	**Stoke-on-Trent**	d								06 07		←									
267¾	—	—	—	53½	**Stafford**	a		05 24					05 54	06 24	06 20	06 24				06 40		06 52	06 57		
—	—	—	—	—		d		05 25					05 55	06 25	06 22	06 25				06 41		06 54	06 58		
—	—	—	—	59¼	Penkridge	a								→						06 46					
—	—	—	—	69¾	Wolverhampton ■7 ⛴	a		05 39								06 39				06 57			07 13		
—	—	—	—	82½	**Birmingham New St.** ■12 68	a		05 59								06 57				07 20			07 33		
—	—	—	—	91	Birmingham International 68 ✈	a										07 13									
—	—	—	—	101½	Coventry 68	a										07 24									
285	—	—	99¼	—	Lichfield Trent Valley	a						06 04						06 40				07 08			
291¼	—	—	—	—	Tamworth Low Level	a						06 11						06 47				07 15			
304¼	—	—	—	—	Nuneaton	a						06 27	06 17								07 06				
318¾	—	—	—	113	Rugby 66	a						06 43	06 31		06 52			07 07							
351½	—	—	—	—	Milton Keynes Central 66	a						07 30	06 51		07 13										
383½	—	—	—	—	Watford Junction 66	a			06s22	06s22															
401¼	—	—	—	—	**London Euston** ■15 ⊖66	a			06 47	06 48		08 11	07 29		07 51			07 58			08 08	08 23			

A until 10 February

OVERNIGHT SLEEPERS. For sleeper trains, operated by First ScotRail, please see Tables 400 - 404.

For complete service between Manchester and Preston, Blackpool and between Barrow-in-furness and Lancaster, please see Table 82.

For complete service between Crewe and Liverpool Lime Street, see Table 91

For complete service between Crewe/Stoke-on-Trent & Manchester see Table 84

For complete service between Crewe and Holyhead please see Table 81.

For complete service between Coventry-Birmingham-Wolverhampton-Stafford please see Table 68

For complete service between Windermere and Oxenholme Lake District, please see Table 83

Table 65R

Mondays to Fridays

9 December to 16 May

Scotland and North West England - West Midlands and London

Route Diagram - refer to first Page of Table 65

		LM	VT	LM	VT	VT	LM	VT	TP	VT	VT		LM	VT	NT	VT	VT	VT	LM	LM			XC	LM	VT
		1	◇1 ⊠	1	◇1 ⊠	◇1 ⊠		◇1 ⊠	◇1	◇1 ⊠	◇1 ⊠		1	◇1 ⊠		◇1 ⊠	◇1 ⊠	◇1 ⊠	1	1			◇1	1	◇1 ⊠
Inverness 229	d																								
Aberdeen 229	d																								
Dundee 229	d																								
Perth 229	d																								
Edinburgh 10 225,226,228,230,242	d																								
Haymarket 225,226,228,230,242	d																								
Glasgow Central 15 226,216	d																	04 28							
Motherwell 226	d																								
Carstairs 226	d																								
Lockerbie	d																								
Carlisle 8 216	a																	05 42							
	d																	05 43							
Penrith North Lakes	d																	05 58							
Windermere 83	d																								
Oxenholme Lake District	a																	06 20							
	d																	06 21							
Barrow-in-Furness 82	d								05 32																
Lancaster 6	a								06 24									06 35							
	d				05 35				06 24									06 36							
Blackpool North 97	d																								
Preston 8 90	a				05 52				06 43									06 54							
Preston 8 90	d				06 00			06 16	06 44									06 56							
Wigan North Western 90	a				06 11			06 27										07 07							
	d				06 11			06 27										07 08							
Bolton 82	a								07 07																
Manchester Picc. 10 82 ⛴	a								07 27																
Manchester Airport ✈	a								07 46																
Liverpool Lime Street 10 91	a																								
	d												06 30				07 00							07 04	
Liverpool South Parkway 91 ✈	d												06 40											07 14	
Runcorn 91	d												06 48				07u15							07 22	
Warrington Bank Quay	a				06 22			06 38										07 18							
	d				06 22			06 38										07 18							
Manchester Picc. 10 84 ⛴	d		06 10							06 27	06 35			06 43	06 46	07 00							07 07		07 15
Stockport 84	d		06 18							06 35	06 43			06 51		07u07							07 16		07 23
Wilmslow 84	d													06 59	07 21										
Holyhead 81 ⛴	d					04 48																			
Bangor (Gwynedd) 81	d					05 14																			
Llandudno Junction 81	d					05 32																			
Wrexham General 75	d																								
Chester 81	d					06 26																			
Crewe 10	a				06 42	06 47		06 58					07 14	07 15	07 46									07 48	
	d	06 47		06 52	06 53		06 56	07 01					07 16	07 17										07 49	
Macclesfield	d		06 31							06 48	06 56														
Stoke-on-Trent	d		06 48	07 17						07 06	07 12								←	←			07 44		07 50
Stafford	a	07 10		07 39			07 17			07 27			07 40	07 35					07 39	07 40			08 01	08 10	
	d	07 12		07 40			07 18			07 28			07 41	07 36					07 40	07 41			08 02	08 10	
Penkridge	a	07 17		↪									↪							07 46				08 16	
Wolverhampton 7 ⛴	a	07 28					07 31	07 36		07 43										07 57			08 15	08 26	
Birmingham New St. 12 68	a	07 49					08 03	08 01		08 05										08 17			08 34	08 47	
Birmingham International 68 ✈	a									08 19															
Coventry 68	a									08 30															
Lichfield Trent Valley	a																		07 56						
Tamworth Low Level	a																		08 02						
Nuneaton	a				07 32														08 18						
Rugby 66	a		07 28								07 52								08 33						
Milton Keynes Central 66	a																		08 55						08 46
Watford Junction 66	a									09s16															
London Euston 15 ⊖66	a		08 23		08 34					09 34	08 46			08 53		09 00	09 04	09 07	09 37						09 24

OVERNIGHT SLEEPERS. For sleeper trains, operated by First ScotRail, please see Tables 400 - 404.

For complete service between Manchester and Preston, Blackpool and between Barrow-in-furness and Lancaster, please see Table 82.

For complete service between Crewe and Liverpool Lime Street, see Table 91

For complete service between Crewe/Stoke-on-Trent & Manchester see Table 84

For complete service between Crewe and Holyhead please see Table 81.

For complete service between Coventry-Birmingham-Wolverhampton-Stafford please see Table 68

For complete service between Windermere and Oxenholme Lake District, please see Table 83

Table 65R

Mondays to Fridays

9 December to 16 May

Scotland and North West England - West Midlands and London

Route Diagram - refer to first Page of Table 65

	XC	LM	VT	VT	VT	VT	TP	TP	TP	LM	VT	LM	VT	VT	TP	XC	LM	VT	VT	XC
	◇1 A	1	◇1	◇1 B	◇1	◇1	◇1 C	◇1 D	◇1 E	1	◇1	1	◇1	◇1	◇1 F	◇1	1	◇1	◇1	◇1
			⊠	⊠	⊠	⊠					⊠		⊠	⊠				⊠	⊠	
Inverness 229 d																				
Aberdeen 229 d																				
Dundee 229 d																				
Perth 229 d																				
Edinburgh 10 225,226,228,230,242 d																				
Haymarket 225,226,228,230,242 d																				
Glasgow Central 15 226,216 d														05 40						
Motherwell 226 d																				
Carstairs 226 d																				
Lockerbie d																				
Carlisle 8 216 a														06 47						
d														06 49						
Penrith North Lakes d																				
Windermere 83 d																				
Oxenholme Lake District a														07 22						
d														07 24						
Barrow-in-Furness 82 d							06 15	06 15							06 48					
Lancaster 6 a							07 15	07 15						07 37	07 48					
d						06 58	07 15	07 23	07 23					07 38	07 48					
Blackpool North 97 d																				
Preston 8 90 a						07 15	07 34	07 41	07 41					07 56	08 07					
Preston 8 90 d						07 17		07 43	07 43					07 58	08 12					
Wigan North Western 90 a						07 28		07 55	07 55					08 09						
d						07 28		07 56	07 56					08 09						
Bolton 82 a															08 34					
Manchester Picc. 10 82 a								08 26	08 26						08 56					
Manchester Airport a								08 47	08 47						09 17					
Liverpool Lime Street 10 91 a																				
d										07 34	07 47						08 04			
Liverpool South Parkway 91 d										07 45							08 15			
Runcorn 91 d										07 53	08 03						08 24			
Warrington Bank Quay a						07 39								08 20						
d						07 39								08 20						
Manchester Picc. 10 84 d	07 27				07 35								07 55			08 07		08 15		08 27
Stockport 84 d	07 35				07 43								08 04			08 16		08 23		08 35
Wilmslow 84 d													08 11							
Holyhead 81 d			05 51																06 55	
Bangor (Gwynedd) 81 d			06 18																07 22	
Llandudno Junction 81 d			06 36																07 40	
Wrexham General 75 d				07 00																
Chester 81 d			07 35																08 35	
Crewe 10 a			07 54			07 57				08 16	08 21		08 27				08 47		08 54	
d		07 55	07 57			08 01				08 18	08 22		08 29				08 49		08 56	
Macclesfield d	07 49				07 56															08 49
Stoke-on-Trent d	08 07	08 18			08 12							←				08 44		08 50		09 07
Stafford a	08 24	08 37								08 44	08 40	08 44				09 02	09 09			09 24
d	08 25	08 37								08 44	08 42	08 44				09 03	09 10			09 25
Penkridge a										↪		08 50					09 15			
Wolverhampton 7 a	08 39					08 33						09 00				09 15	09 27			09 39
Birmingham New St. 12 68 a	08 58					09 05						09 18				09 32	09 47			09 58
Birmingham International 68 a	09 13					09 19														10 13
Coventry 68 a	09 24					09 30														10 24
Lichfield Trent Valley a		09 03																		
Tamworth Low Level a		09 10																		
Nuneaton a		09 27			08 44															
Rugby 66 a		09 44	08 45																	
Milton Keynes Central 66 a		10 14				09 58												09 46	10 02	
Watford Junction 66 a					09s32															
London Euston 15 ⊖66 a		10 50	09 41		09 52	10 32					10 01		10 06	10 13				10 24	10 39	

A ◇ from Birmingham New St. to Birmingham New St.

B ⊠ from Chester

C from 10 February

D until 7 February. from Preston

E from 10 February. from Preston

F from Preston

OVERNIGHT SLEEPERS. For sleeper trains, operated by First ScotRail, please see Tables 400 - 404.

For complete service between Manchester and Preston, Blackpool and between Barrow-in-furness and Lancaster, please see Table 82.

For complete service between Crewe and Liverpool Lime Street, see Table 91

For complete service between Crewe/Stoke-on-Trent & Manchester see Table 84

For complete service between Crewe and Holyhead please see Table 81.

For complete service between Coventry-Birmingham-Wolverhampton-Stafford please see Table 68

For complete service between Windermere and Oxenholme Lake District, please see Table 83

Table 65R

Mondays to Fridays

9 December to 16 May

Scotland and North West England - West Midlands and London

Route Diagram - refer to first Page of Table 65

		VT	VT	LM	TP	TP	LM	VT	LM	VT	VT	LM	XC	LM	VT	XC	VT	VT	VT
						FO													
		◇1	◇1	1	◇1	◇1	1	◇1	1	◇1	◇1	1	◇1	1	◇1	◇1	◇1	◇1	◇1
					A	B													
		⊠	⊠		🍴	🍴		⊠		⊠	⊠		🍴		⊠	🍴	⊠	⊠	⊠
Inverness 229	d																		
Aberdeen 229	d																		
Dundee 229	d																		
Perth 229	d																		
Edinburgh 10 225,226,228,230,242	d				06 15	06 15													06 52
Haymarket 225,226,228,230,242	d				06u19	06u19													06 56
Glasgow Central 15 226,216	d		05 50								06 30								
Motherwell 226	d		06 04								06 44								
Carstairs 226	d																		
Lockerbie	d										07 25								
Carlisle 8 216	a		07 00		07 33	07 33					07 43								08 05
	d		07 02		07 33	07 33					07 46								08 06
Penrith North Lakes	d		07 18								08 00								08 21
Windermere 83	d																		
Oxenholme Lake District	a		07 41		08 09	08 09					08 22								
	d		07 41		08 10	08 10					08 23								
Barrow-in-Furness 82	d																		
Lancaster 6	a		07 56		08 25	08 25					08 37								08 56
	d		07 56		08 26	08 26					08 38								08 57
Blackpool North 97	d																		
Preston 8 90	a		08 14		08 44	08 44					08 56								09 14
Preston 8 90	d		08 17		08 45	08 45					08 58								09 17
Wigan North Western 90	a		08 28		08 58	08 58					09 09								09 28
	d		08 28		08 58	08 58					09 09								09 29
Bolton 82	a																		
Manchester Picc. 10 82	a				09 27	09 27													
Manchester Airport ✈	a				09 47	09 51													
Liverpool Lime Street 10 91	a																		
	d						08 34	08 47						09 04					
Liverpool South Parkway 91 ✈	d						08 44							09 15					
Runcorn 91	d						08 52	09 03						09 25					
Warrington Bank Quay	a		08 39								09 20								09 39
	d		08 39								09 20								09 39
Manchester Picc. 10 84	d	08 35								08 55			09 07		09 15	09 27		09 35	
Stockport 84	d	08 43								09 04			09 16		09 23	09 35		09 43	
Wilmslow 84	d									09 11									
Holyhead 81 ⛴	d																		
Bangor (Gwynedd) 81	d																		
Llandudno Junction 81	d																		
Wrexham General 75	d																		
Chester 81	d																09 35		
Crewe 10	a		08 57				09 19	09 23		09 29				09 45			09 54		09 58
	d		09 01	09 02			09 19	09 25		09 30				09 49			09 56		10 01
Macclesfield	d	08 56														09 49		09 56	
Stoke-on-Trent	d	09 12		09 28					←			←	09 44		09 50	10 07		10 12	
Stafford	a			09 51			09 45	09 43	09 45			09 51	10 02	10 09		10 24			
	d			09 56			09 45	09 44	09 45			09 56	10 03	10 10		10 25			
Penkridge	a			→			→							10 15					
Wolverhampton 7	a		09 31						09 58				10 15	10 27		10 39			10 33
Birmingham New St. 12 68	a		10 05						10 17				10 33	10 47		10 58			11 05
Birmingham International 68 ✈	a		10 19													11 13			11 19
Coventry 68	a		10 30													11 24			11 30
Lichfield Trent Valley	a											10 12							
Tamworth Low Level	a											10 20							
Nuneaton	a											10 36							
Rugby 66	a											10 52							
Milton Keynes Central 66	a		10 58									11 14			10 46		11 02		11 58
Watford Junction 66	a																		
London Euston 15 ⊖66	a	10 43	11 34					11 05		11 08	11 14	11 50			11 24		11 39	11 43	12 34

A FX until 6 February, from 10 February **B** until 7 February

OVERNIGHT SLEEPERS. For sleeper trains, operated by First ScotRail, please see Tables 400 - 404.

For complete service between Manchester and Preston, Blackpool and between Barrow-in-furness and Lancaster, please see Table 82.

For complete service between Crewe and Liverpool Lime Street, see Table 91

For complete service between Crewe/Stoke-on-Trent & Manchester see Table 84

For complete service between Crewe and Holyhead please see Table 81.

For complete service between Coventry-Birmingham-Wolverhampton-Stafford please see Table 68

For complete service between Windermere and Oxenholme Lake District, please see Table 83

Table 65R

Mondays to Fridays

9 December to 16 May

Scotland and North West England - West Midlands and London

Route Diagram - refer to first Page of Table 65

		LM	TP	LM	VT	LM	VT	VT	VT	LM	TP	TP	XC	LM	VT	VT	XC	VT	VT	LM	TP
								FO				FX									
		1	◇1	1	◇1	1	◇1	◇	◇1	1	◇1	◇1	◇1	1	◇1	◇1	◇1	◇1	◇1	1	◇1
												A									
			⊥		⊠		⊠	⊡	⊠			⊥	⊥		⊠	⊠	⊥	⊠	⊠		⊥
Inverness 229	d																				
Aberdeen 229	d																				
Dundee 229	d																				
Perth 229	d																				
Edinburgh [10] 225,226,228,230,242	d																				08 12
Haymarket 225,226,228,230,242	d																				08u15
Glasgow Central [15] 226,216	d		07 09						07 37										08 00		
Motherwell 226	d								07 52												
Carstairs 226	d																				
Lockerbie	d		08 08																		
Carlisle [8] 216	a		08 29						08 47										09 08		09 29
	d		08 30						08 49										09 10		09 30
Penrith North Lakes	d		08 45																		09 46
Windermere 83	d																				
Oxenholme Lake District	a		09 09						09 22												10 09
	d		09 11						09 23												10 10
Barrow-in-Furness 82	d										08 50	08 50									
Lancaster [6]	a		09 26						09 37		09 46	09 46							09 56		10 24
	d		09 26						09 38		09 47	09 47							09 56		10 25
Blackpool North 97	d																				
Preston [8] 90	a		09 45						09 56		10 07	10 07							10 14		10 44
Preston [8] 90	d		09 45					09 49	09 58			10 12							10 17		10 45
Wigan North Western 90	a		09 58					10 01	10 09										10 28		10 58
	d		09 58					10 01	10 09										10 28		10 58
Bolton 82	a											10 34									
Manchester Picc. [10] 82 (tram)	a		10 27									10 56									11 27
Manchester Airport ✈	a		10 47									11 15									11 47
Liverpool Lime Street [10] 91	a																				
	d			09 34	09 47									10 04							
Liverpool South Parkway 91 ✈	d			09 44										10 15							
Runcorn 91	d			09 52	10 03									10 25							
Warrington Bank Quay	a							10 12	10 20										10 39		
	d							10 13	10 20										10 39		
Manchester Picc. [10] 84 (tram)	d						09 55						10 07		10 15		10 27	10 35			
Stockport 84	d						10 04						10 16		10 23		10 35	10 43			
Wilmslow 84	d						10 11														
Holyhead 81 ⛴	d															08 55					
Bangor (Gwynedd) 81	d															09 22					
Llandudno Junction 81	d															09 40					
Wrexham General 75	d																				
Chester 81	d															10 35					
Crewe [10]	a			10 16	10 21		10 27	10 34						10 45		10 54			10 58		
	d	10 02		10 19	10 22		10 29	10 40						10 49		10 56			11 01	11 02	
Macclesfield	d																10 49	10 56			
Stoke-on-Trent	d	10 28				←				←			10 44		10 50		11 07	11 12		11 28	
Stafford	a	10 51		10 42	10 40	10 42				10 51			11 01	11 09			11 24			11 51	
	d	10 56		10 43	10 42	10 43				10 56			11 02	11 10			11 25			11 56	
Penkridge	a	→		→										11 15						→	
Wolverhampton [7] (tram)	a					10 56							11 15	11 27			11 39		11 34		
Birmingham New St. [12] 68	a					11 17							11 33	11 47			11 58		12 05		
Birmingham International 68 ✈	a																12 13		12 19		
Coventry 68	a																12 24		12 30		
Lichfield Trent Valley	a									11 12											
Tamworth Low Level	a									11 19											
Nuneaton	a									11 35											
Rugby 66	a									11 52											
Milton Keynes Central 66	a									12 14					11 46	12 02			12 58		
Watford Junction 66	a																				
London Euston [15] ⊖66	a				11 59		12 05	12 30	12 13	12 50					12 24	12 39		12 43	13 33		

A until 6 February. ⊥ from Preston

OVERNIGHT SLEEPERS. For sleeper trains, operated by First ScotRail, please see Tables 400 - 404.

For complete service between Manchester and Preston, Blackpool and between Barrow-in-furness and Lancaster, please see Table 82.

For complete service between Crewe and Liverpool Lime Street, see Table 91

For complete service between Crewe/Stoke-on-Trent & Manchester see Table 84

For complete service between Crewe and Holyhead please see Table 81.

For complete service between Coventry-Birmingham-Wolverhampton-Stafford please see Table 68

For complete service between Windermere and Oxenholme Lake District, please see Table 83

Table 65R

Mondays to Fridays

9 December to 16 May

Scotland and North West England - West Midlands and London

Route Diagram - refer to first Page of Table 65

	LM	VT	LM	VT	LM	NT	XC	LM	VT	XC	VT	VT	VT	LM	TP	NT	LM	VT	LM	VT
	1	◇1	1	◇1	1		◇1	1	◇1	◇1	◇1	◇1	◇1	1	◇1		1	◇1	1	◇1
															A					
		⊠		⊠			⊥		☕	⊥	☕	☕	⊠		⊥			☕		☕
Inverness 229 d																				
Aberdeen 229 d																				
Dundee 229 d																				
Perth 229 d																				
Edinburgh 10 225,226,228,230,242 d													08 52							
Haymarket 225,226,228,230,242 d													08 57							
Glasgow Central 15 226,216 d				08 40																
Motherwell 226 d																				
Carstairs 226 d																				
Lockerbie d																				
Carlisle 8 216 a				09 47									10 07							
d				09 49									10 08							
Penrith North Lakes d				10 03																
Windermere 83 d															10 51					
Oxenholme Lake District a													10 43		11 08					
d													10 43		11 08					
Barrow-in-Furness 82 d																				
Lancaster 6 a				10 37									10 57		11 25					
d				10 38									10 57		11 25					
Blackpool North 97 d																				
Preston 8 90 a				10 56									11 15		11 44					
Preston 8 90 d				10 58									11 17		11 45					
Wigan North Western 90 a				11 09									11 28		11 57					
d				11 09									11 28		11 57					
Bolton 82 a																				
Manchester Picc. 10 82 ⛴ a															12 26					
Manchester Airport ✈ a															12 47					
Liverpool Lime Street 10 91 a																				
d	10 34	10 47						11 04									11 34	11 47		
Liverpool South Parkway 91 ✈ d	10 44							11 15									11 44			
Runcorn 91 d	10 52	11 03						11 25									11 52	12 03		
Warrington Bank Quay a				11 20									11 39							
d				11 20									11 39							
Manchester Picc. 10 84 ⛴ d						11 04	11 07		11 15	11 27		11 35				11 46				11 55
Stockport 84 d						11 17	11 16		11 23	11 35		11 43								12 04
Wilmslow 84 d						11 31										12 20				12 11
Holyhead 81 ⛴ d																				
Bangor (Gwynedd) 81 d																				
Llandudno Junction 81 d																				
Wrexham General 75 d																				
Chester 81 d											11 35									
Crewe 10 a	11 16	11 21				12 01		11 45			11 54		11 58			12 45	12 16	12 21		12 27
d	11 17	11 22						11 49			11 56		12 01	12 02			12 19	12 22		12 29
Macclesfield d										11 49		11 56								
Stoke-on-Trent d			←		←		11 44		11 50	12 07		12 12		12 28					←	
Stafford a	11 42	11 40	11 42		11 51		12 02	12 09		12 24				12 51			12 43	12 40	12 43	
d	11 42	11 42	11 42		11 56		12 03	12 10		12 25				12 56			12 44	12 42	12 44	
Penkridge a	→							12 15						→			→			
Wolverhampton 7 ⛴ a			11 57				12 15	12 27		12 39			12 32						12 57	
Birmingham New St. 12 68 a			12 17				12 33	12 47		12 58			13 05						13 17	
Birmingham International 68 ✈ a										13 13			13 19							
Coventry 68 a										13 24			13 30							
Lichfield Trent Valley a					12 12															
Tamworth Low Level a					12 19															
Nuneaton a					12 35															
Rugby 66 a					12 52															
Milton Keynes Central 66 a					13 14				12 46		13 02		13 58							
Watford Junction 66 a																				
London Euston 15 ⊖66 a		12 59		13 13	13 50				13 24		13 39	13 43	14 33					14 00		14 05

A ⊥ from Preston

OVERNIGHT SLEEPERS. For sleeper trains, operated by First ScotRail, please see Tables 400 - 404.

For complete service between Manchester and Preston, Blackpool and between Barrow-in-furness and Lancaster, please see Table 82.

For complete service between Crewe and Liverpool Lime Street, see Table 91

For complete service between Crewe/Stoke-on-Trent & Manchester see Table 84

For complete service between Crewe and Holyhead please see Table 81.

For complete service between Coventry-Birmingham-Wolverhampton-Stafford please see Table 68

For complete service between Windermere and Oxenholme Lake District, please see Table 83

Table 65R

Mondays to Fridays

9 December to 16 May

Scotland and North West England - West Midlands and London

Route Diagram - refer to first Page of Table 65

			VT ◇1 ⊠	LM 1	TP ◇1	XC ◇1 🛒	LM 1	VT ◇1 ☕	XC ◇1 🛒	VT ◇1 ☕	VT ◇1 ☕	VT ◇1 ⊠	LM 1	TP ◇1 🛒	NT	LM 1	VT ◇1 ☕	LM 1	VT ◇1 ☕	VT ◇1 ⊠	LM 1
Inverness	229	d																			
Aberdeen	229	d																			
Dundee	229	d																			
Perth	229	d																			
Edinburgh 10	225,226,228,230,242	d												10 08							
Haymarket	225,226,228,230,242	d												10u12							
Glasgow Central 15	226,216	d	09 40									10 00								10 40	
Motherwell	226	d																			
Carstairs	226	d																			
Lockerbie		d												11 06							
Carlisle 8	216	a	10 47									11 09		11 27						11 47	
		d	10 49									11 10		11 31						11 49	
Penrith North Lakes		d										11 25		11 47							
Windermere	83	d																			
Oxenholme Lake District		a	11 22											12 09						12 22	
		d	11 23											12 10						12 23	
Barrow-in-Furness	82	d			11 20																
Lancaster 6		a	11 37		12 17									12 25						12 37	
		d	11 38		12 17									12 26						12 38	
Blackpool North	97	d																			
Preston 8	90	a	11 56		12 37							12 14		12 44						12 56	
Preston 8	90	d	11 58									12 17		12 45						12 58	
Wigan North Western	90	a	12 09									12 28		12 58						13 09	
		d	12 09									12 28		12 58						13 09	
Bolton	82	a																			
Manchester Picc. 10	82 ⛴	a												13 27							
Manchester Airport	✈	a												13 46							
Liverpool Lime Street 10	91	a																			
		d					12 04									12 34	12 47				
Liverpool South Parkway	91 ✈	d					12 15									12 44					
Runcorn	91	d					12 25									12 52	13 03				
Warrington Bank Quay		a	12 20									12 39								13 20	
		d	12 20									12 39								13 20	
Manchester Picc. 10	84 ⛴	d				12 07		12 15	12 27		12 35				12 46				12 55		
Stockport	84	d				12 16		12 23	12 35		12 43								13 04		
Wilmslow	84	d													13 21				13 11		
Holyhead	81 ⛴	d																			
Bangor (Gwynedd)	81	d																			
Llandudno Junction	81	d																			
Wrexham General	75	d																			
Chester	81	d								12 35											
Crewe 10		a					12 45			12 54		12 57			13 46	13 19	13 23		13 29		
		d					12 49			12 56		13 01	13 02			13 19	13 25		13 30		
Macclesfield		d							12 49		12 56										
Stoke-on-Trent		d		←		12 44		12 50	13 07		13 12		13 28					←			←
Stafford		a		12 51		13 01	13 09		13 24				13 56			13 46	13 43	13 46			13 56
		d		12 56		13 02	13 10		13 25				13 56			13 46	13 44	13 46			13 56
Penkridge		a					13 15						→			→					
Wolverhampton 7	⛴	a				13 16	13 27		13 39			13 33						14 03			
Birmingham New St. 12	68	a				13 33	13 47		13 58			14 05						14 21			
Birmingham International	68 ✈	a							14 13			14 19									
Coventry	68	a							14 23			14 29									
Lichfield Trent Valley		a		13 12																	14 12
Tamworth Low Level		a		13 19																	14 19
Nuneaton		a		13 35																	14 35
Rugby	66	a		13 51																	14 51
Milton Keynes Central	66	a		14 14				13 46		14 02		14 58									15 14
Watford Junction	66	a																			
London Euston 15	⊖66	a	14 13	14 50				14 24		14 39	14 43	15 33					15 05		15 09	15 16	15 50

OVERNIGHT SLEEPERS. For sleeper trains, operated by First ScotRail, please see Tables 400 - 404.

For complete service between Manchester and Preston, Blackpool and between Barrow-in-furness and Lancaster, please see Table 82.

For complete service between Crewe and Liverpool Lime Street, see Table 91

For complete service between Crewe/Stoke-on-Trent & Manchester see Table 84

For complete service between Crewe and Holyhead please see Table 81.

For complete service between Coventry-Birmingham-Wolverhampton-Stafford please see Table 68

For complete service between Windermere and Oxenholme Lake District, please see Table 83

Table 65R

Mondays to Fridays

9 December to 16 May

Scotland and North West England - West Midlands and London

Route Diagram - refer to first Page of Table 65

		XC	LM	VT	VT	XC	VT	VT	LM	TP	LM	VT	LM	VT	VT	LM	NT	XC	LM	VT	XC	VT
		◇1	1	◇1	◇1	◇1	◇1	◇1	1	◇1	1	◇1	1	◇1	◇1	1		◇1	1	◇1	◇1	◇1
		🛒		🍽	🍽	🛒	🍽	🍽		🛒		🍽		🍽	☒			🛒		🍽	🛒	🍽
Inverness 229	d																					
Aberdeen 229	d																					
Dundee 229	d																					
Perth 229	d																					
Edinburgh 10 225,226,228,230,242	d							10 51														
Haymarket 225,226,228,230,242	d							10 57														
Glasgow Central 15 226,216	d									11 09					11 40							
Motherwell 226	d																					
Carstairs 226	d																					
Lockerbie	d									12 08												
Carlisle 8 216	a							12 06		12 30					12 47							
	d							12 08		12 31					12 49							
Penrith North Lakes	d									12 46					13 03							
Windermere 83	d																					
Oxenholme Lake District	a							12 41		13 10												
	d							12 43		13 10												
Barrow-in-Furness 82	d																					
Lancaster 6	a							12 56		13 25					13 37							
	d							12 57		13 25					13 39							
Blackpool North 97	d																					
Preston 8 90	a							13 15		13 44					13 56							
Preston 8 90	d							13 17		13 44					13 58							
Wigan North Western 90	a							13 28		13 57					14 09							
	d							13 28		13 58					14 09							
Bolton 82	a																					
Manchester Picc. 10 82 🚊	a									14 26												
Manchester Airport ✈	a									14 46												
Liverpool Lime Street 10 91	a																					
	d		13 04								13 34	13 47							14 04			
Liverpool South Parkway 91 ✈	d		13 15								13 44								14 15			
Runcorn 91	d		13 25								13 52	14 03							14 25			
Warrington Bank Quay	a							13 39							14 20							
	d							13 39							14 20							
Manchester Picc. 10 84 🚊	d	13 07		13 15		13 27	13 35							13 55			14 04	14 07		14 15	14 27	
Stockport 84	d	13 16		13 23		13 35	13 43							14 04			14 17	14 16		14 23	14 35	
Wilmslow 84	d													14 11			14 31					
Holyhead 81 ⛴	d																					
Bangor (Gwynedd) 81	d				12 24																	
Llandudno Junction 81	d				12 42																	
Wrexham General 75	d																					
Chester 81	d				13 35																	14 35
Crewe 10	a		13 45		13 54			13 57			14 16	14 21		14 27			15 01		14 45			14 54
	d		13 49		13 56			14 01	14 02		14 19	14 22		14 29					14 49			14 56
Macclesfield	d					13 49	13 56														14 49	
Stoke-on-Trent	d	13 44		13 50		14 07	14 12		14 28				←			←		14 44		14 50	15 08	
Stafford	a	14 01	14 09			14 24			14 50		14 42	14 40	14 42			14 50		15 02	15 09		15 24	
	d	14 02	14 10			14 25			14 56		14 43	14 42	14 43			14 56		15 03	15 10		15 25	
Penkridge	a		14 15						↪		↪								15 15			
Wolverhampton 7 🚊	a	14 15	14 27			14 39		14 33					14 58					15 15	15 27		15 39	
Birmingham New St. 12 68	a	14 33	14 51			14 58		15 05					15 18					15 33	15 47		15 58	
Birmingham International 68 ✈	a					15 13		15 19													16 13	
Coventry 68	a					15 23		15 30													16 23	
Lichfield Trent Valley	a															15 12						
Tamworth Low Level	a															15 19						
Nuneaton	a															15 35						
Rugby 66	a															15 51						
Milton Keynes Central 66	a			14 46	15 02			15 58								16 14				15 46		16 02
Watford Junction 66	a																					
London Euston 15 ⊖66	a			15 24	15 39		15 43	16 32				15 59		16 05	16 12	16 50				16 24		16 39

OVERNIGHT SLEEPERS. For sleeper trains, operated by First ScotRail, please see Tables 400 - 404.

For complete service between Manchester and Preston, Blackpool and between Barrow-in-furness and Lancaster, please see Table 82.

For complete service between Crewe and Liverpool Lime Street, see Table 91

For complete service between Crewe/Stoke-on-Trent & Manchester see Table 84

For complete service between Crewe and Holyhead please see Table 81.

For complete service between Coventry-Birmingham-Wolverhampton-Stafford please see Table 68

For complete service between Windermere and Oxenholme Lake District, please see Table 83

Table 65R **Mondays to Fridays**

9 December to 16 May

Scotland and North West England - West Midlands and London

Route Diagram - refer to first Page of Table 65

			VT	VT	LM	TP	TP	NT	TP	TP	TP	TP	LM	VT	LM	VT	VT	LM	XC	LM	VT	VT
						FO	FO		FX	FX	FO	FO										
			◇1	◇1	1	◇1	◇1		◇1	◇1	◇1	◇1	1	◇1	1	◇1	◇1	1	◇1	1	◇1	◇1
						A			A													
			☕	☕		🛒	🛒		🛒	🛒	🛒	🛒		☕		☕	⊠		🛒		☕	☕
Inverness	229	d																				
Aberdeen	229	d																				
Dundee	229	d																				
Perth	229	d																				
Edinburgh 10	225,226,228,230,242	d					12 12			12 12												
Haymarket	225,226,228,230,242	d					12u16			12u16												
Glasgow Central 15	226,216	d		12 00													12 40					
Motherwell	226	d																				
Carstairs	226	d																				
Lockerbie		d					13 11			13 11												
Carlisle 8	216	a		13 09			13 33			13 33							13 47					
		d		13 11			13 33			13 33							13 49					
Penrith North Lakes		d																				
Windermere	83	d																				
Oxenholme Lake District		a								14 09							14 22					
		d								14 10							14 24					
Barrow-in-Furness	82	d				13 20			13 20													
Lancaster 6		a		13 57		14 17	14 23		14 17	14 24							14 37					
		d		13 57		14 17	14 24		14 17	14 25							14 39					
Blackpool North	97	d																				
Preston 8	90	a		14 15		14 37	14 42		14 37	14 45							14 56					
Preston 8	90	d		14 17			14 47			14 45							14 58					
Wigan North Western	90	a		14 28							←	←					15 09					
		d		14 28													15 10					
Bolton	82	a					15 08			15 07	15 08	15 08										
Manchester Picc. 10	82 ⛴	a					→			15 28	15 29	15 29										
Manchester Airport	✈	a								15 47	15 47	15 47										
Liverpool Lime Street 10	91	a																				
		d											14 34	14 47						15 04		
Liverpool South Parkway	91 ✈	d											14 44							15 15		
Runcorn	91	d											14 52	15 03						15 25		
Warrington Bank Quay		a		14 39													15 20					
		d		14 39													15 21					
Manchester Picc. 10	84 ⛴	d	14 35					14 46								14 55			15 07		15 15	
Stockport	84	d	14 43													15 04			15 16		15 23	
Wilmslow	84	d						15 20								15 11						
Holyhead	81 ⛴	d																				13 58
Bangor (Gwynedd)	81	d																				14 25
Llandudno Junction	81	d																				14 43
Wrexham General	75	d																				
Chester	81	d																				15 35
Crewe 10		a		14 59				15 45					15 16	15 21		15 27				15 45		15 54
		d		15 01	15 02								15 19	15 22		15 29				15 49		15 56
Macclesfield		d	14 56																			
Stoke-on-Trent		d	15 12		15 28										←			←	15 44		15 50	
Stafford		a			15 50								15 42	15 40	15 42			15 50	16 02	16 09		
		d			15 56								15 43	15 42	15 43			15 56	16 03	16 10		
Penkridge		a			↪								↪							16 15		
Wolverhampton 7	⛴	a		15 32											15 56				16 15	16 26		
Birmingham New St. 12	68	a		16 05											16 17				16 33	16 48		
Birmingham International	68 ✈	a		16 19																		
Coventry	68	a		16 30																		
Lichfield Trent Valley		a																16 12				
Tamworth Low Level		a																16 19				
Nuneaton		a																16 35				
Rugby	66	a																16 51				
Milton Keynes Central	66	a		16 58														17 14			16 46	17 02
Watford Junction	66	a																				
London Euston 15	⊖66	a	16 43	17 34										17 00		17 05	17 13	17 50			17 24	17 39

A 🛒 from Preston

OVERNIGHT SLEEPERS. For sleeper trains, operated by First ScotRail, please see Tables 400 - 404.

For complete service between Manchester and Preston, Blackpool and between Barrow-in-furness and Lancaster, please see Table 82.

For complete service between Crewe and Liverpool Lime Street, see Table 91

For complete service between Crewe/Stoke-on-Trent & Manchester see Table 84

For complete service between Crewe and Holyhead please see Table 81.

For complete service between Coventry-Birmingham-Wolverhampton-Stafford please see Table 68

For complete service between Windermere and Oxenholme Lake District, please see Table 83

Table 65R

Mondays to Fridays

9 December to 16 May

Scotland and North West England - West Midlands and London

Route Diagram - refer to first Page of Table 65

		XC	VT	VT	LM	TP	TP	TP	TP	LM	VT	LM	VT	VT	LM	NT	XC	LM	VT	XC	VT	VT
						FX	FO															
		◇1	◇1	◇1	1	◇1	◇1	◇1	◇1	1	◇1	1	◇1	◇1	1		◇1	1	◇1	◇1	◇1	◇1
						A	B	C	D													
		[trolley]	[IP]	[IP]		[trolley]	[trolley]	[trolley]	[trolley]		[IP]		[IP]	[⊠]			[trolley]		[IP]	[trolley]	[IP]	[IP]
Inverness 229	d																					
Aberdeen 229	d																					
Dundee 229	d																					
Perth 229	d																					
Edinburgh 10 225,226,228,230,242	d			12 51																		
Haymarket 225,226,228,230,242	d			12 57																		
Glasgow Central 15 226,216	d					13 09	13 09	13 09						13 40								
Motherwell 226	d																					
Carstairs 226	d																					
Lockerbie	d					14 07	14 07	14 07														
Carlisle 8 216	a			14 05		14 29	14 29	14 29						14 46								
	d			14 08		14 30	14 30	14 30						14 49								
Penrith North Lakes	d			14 22		14 45	14 45	14 45														
Windermere 83	d																					
Oxenholme Lake District	a						15 08	15 08						15 22								
	d						15 09	15 09						15 24								
Barrow-in-Furness 82	d								14 40													
Lancaster 6	a			14 56		15 21	15 23	15 23	15 32					15 37								
	d			14 57		15 22	15 24	15 24	15 32					15 39								
Blackpool North 97	d																					
Preston 8 90	a			15 15		15 40	15 42	15 43	15 51					15 56								
Preston 8 90	d			15 17		15 45	15 45	15 45	16 10					15 59								
Wigan North Western 90	a			15 28		15 58	15 58	15 58						16 09								
	d			15 28		15 58	15 58	15 58						16 09								
Bolton 82	a								16 34													
Manchester Picc. 10 82 ⛴	a					16 27	16 27	16 27	16 56													
Manchester Airport ✈	a					16 47	16 47	16 47	17 17													
Liverpool Lime Street 10 91	a																					
	d									15 34	15 47							16 04				
Liverpool South Parkway 91 ✈	d									15 44								16 15				
Runcorn 91	d									15 52	16 03							16 25				
Warrington Bank Quay	a			15 39										16 20								
	d			15 39										16 20								
Manchester Picc. 10 84 ⛴	d	15 27	15 35										15 55			16 04	16 07		16 15	16 27		16 35
Stockport 84	d	15 35	15 43										16 04			16 17	16 16		16 23	16 35		16 43
Wilmslow 84	d												16 11			16 31						
Holyhead 81 ⛴	d																					
Bangor (Gwynedd) 81	d																					
Llandudno Junction 81	d																					
Wrexham General 75	d																					
Chester 81	d																				16 35	
Crewe 10	a			15 58						16 16	16 21		16 27			17 01		16 45			16 54	
	d			16 01	16 02					16 19	16 22		16 29					16 49			16 56	
Macclesfield	d	15 49	15 56																	16 49		16 56
Stoke-on-Trent	d	16 07	16 12		16 28							←			←		16 44		16 50	17 07		17 12
Stafford	a	16 24			16 50					16 42	16 40	16 42			16 50		17 02	17 10		17 24		
	d	16 25			16 56					16 43	16 42	16 43			16 56		17 03	17 10		17 25		
Penkridge	a				→					→								17 16				
Wolverhampton 7 ⛴	a	16 39		16 32								16 57					17 15	17 26		17 39		
Birmingham New St. 12 68	a	16 58		17 05								17 17					17 33	17 47		17 58		
Birmingham International 68 ✈	a	17 13		17 19																18 13		
Coventry 68	a	17 23		17 30																18 23		
Lichfield Trent Valley	a														17 12							
Tamworth Low Level	a														17 19							
Nuneaton	a														17 35							
Rugby 66	a														17 52							
Milton Keynes Central 66	a			17 58											18 15				17 46		18 02	
Watford Junction 66	a																					
London Euston 15 ⊖66	a		17 43	18 34							17 59		18 05	18 10	18 51				18 24		18 39	18 43

A until 6 February

B until 7 February

C from 10 February

D [trolley] from Preston

OVERNIGHT SLEEPERS. For sleeper trains, operated by First ScotRail, please see Tables 400 - 404.

For complete service between Manchester and Preston, Blackpool and between Barrow-in-furness and Lancaster, please see Table 82.

For complete service between Crewe and Liverpool Lime Street, see Table 91

For complete service between Crewe/Stoke-on-Trent & Manchester see Table 84

For complete service between Crewe and Holyhead please see Table 81.

For complete service between Coventry-Birmingham-Wolverhampton-Stafford please see Table 68

For complete service between Windermere and Oxenholme Lake District, please see Table 83

Table 65R

Mondays to Fridays

9 December to 16 May

Scotland and North West England - West Midlands and London

Route Diagram - refer to first Page of Table 65

		VT	LM	TP			LM	VT	LM	VT	VT	LM	NT	XC	LM		VT	VT	VT	LM	XC	VT			LM
																			■						
		◇1	1	◇1			1	◇1	1	◇1	◇1	1		◇1	1		◇1	◇1	1	1	◇1	◇1			1
		⊡		⊤				⊡		⊡	⊠			⊤			⊠	⊠	⊡		⊤	⊠			
Inverness 229	d																								
Aberdeen 229	d																								
Dundee 229	d																								
Perth 229	d																								
Edinburgh 10 225,226,228,230,242	d			14 16															14 51						
Haymarket 225,226,228,230,242	d			14u21															14 57						
Glasgow Central 15 226,216	d	14 00									14 40														
Motherwell 226	d																								
Carstairs 226	d																								
Lockerbie	d			15 15																					
Carlisle 8 216	a	15 07		15 36							15 46								16 06						
	d	15 10		15 38							15 49								16 08						
Penrith North Lakes	d																		16 21						
Windermere 83	d																								
Oxenholme Lake District	a	15 43		16 14							16 22														
	d	15 44		16 14							16 24														
Barrow-in-Furness 82	d																								
Lancaster 6	a			16 29							16 37								16 56						
	d			16 29							16 38								16 57						
Blackpool North 97	d																								
Preston 8 90	a	16 13		16 48							16 56								17 15						
Preston 8 90	d	16 17		16 49							16 58								17 17						
Wigan North Western 90	a	16 28									17 09								17 28						
	d	16 28									17 09								17 28						
Bolton 82	a																								
Manchester Picc. 10 82	a			17 30																					
Manchester Airport	a			17 47																					
Liverpool Lime Street 10 91	a																								
	d						16 34	16 47							17 04										17 34
Liverpool South Parkway 91	d						16 44								17 15										17 44
Runcorn 91	d						16 52	17 03							17 25										17 52
Warrington Bank Quay	a	16 39									17 20								17 39						
	d	16 39									17 20								17 39						
Manchester Picc. 10 84	d									16 55			17 03	17 05			17 15				17 27	17 35			
Stockport 84	d									17 04			17 16	17 13			17 23				17 35	17 43			
Wilmslow 84	d									17 11			17 31								17 44				
Holyhead 81	d																								
Bangor (Gwynedd) 81	d																								
Llandudno Junction 81	d																								
Wrexham General 75	d																								
Chester 81	d																	17 35							
Crewe 10	a	16 58					17 20			17 27			18 01		17 47			17 54	17 59		18 04				18 18
	d	17 01	17 02				17 21			17 29					17 49			17 56	18 01	18 02	18 07				18 19
Macclesfield	d													17 27								17 56			
Stoke-on-Trent	d		17 28						←			←		17 44			17 50			18 28		18 12			
Stafford	a		17 50				17 41	17 34	17 41			17 50		18 03	18 09					18 50	18 27				18 44
	d		17 56				17 42	17 36	17 42			17 56		18 04	18 10					18 56	18 28				18 44
Penkridge	a		→				→								18 15					→					→
Wolverhampton 7	a	17 33							17 55					18 14	18 27				18 33		18 39				
Birmingham New St. 12 68	a	18 05							18 16					18 32	18 48				19 05		18 58				
Birmingham International 68	a	18 19																	19 19		19 13				
Coventry 68	a	18 30																	19 30		19 23				
Lichfield Trent Valley	a											18 12													
Tamworth Low Level	a											18 19													
Nuneaton	a											18 35													
Rugby 66	a											18 51													
Milton Keynes Central 66	a	18 58						18 23				19 14					18 49	19 02	19 58						
Watford Junction 66	a									18s48															
London Euston 15 ⊖66	a	19 32						19 02		19 09	19 14	19 50					19 26	19 39	20 34			19 43			

OVERNIGHT SLEEPERS. For sleeper trains, operated by First ScotRail, please see Tables 400 - 404.

For complete service between Manchester and Preston, Blackpool and between Barrow-in-furness and Lancaster, please see Table 82.

For complete service between Crewe and Liverpool Lime Street, see Table 91

For complete service between Crewe/Stoke-on-Trent & Manchester see Table 84

For complete service between Crewe and Holyhead please see Table 81.

For complete service between Coventry-Birmingham-Wolverhampton-Stafford please see Table 68

For complete service between Windermere and Oxenholme Lake District, please see Table 83

Table 65R

Mondays to Fridays

9 December to 16 May

Scotland and North West England - West Midlands and London

Route Diagram - refer to first Page of Table 65

Station		VT	LM	VT	VT	LM	TP	TP FX	XC	LM	VT	XC	VT	VT	LM	TP	TP	TP FX	TP	LM	VT
		◇1	1	◇1	◇1	1	◇1	◇1	◇1	1	◇1	◇1	◇1	◇1	1	◇1	◇1	◇1	◇1	1	◇1
							A	B									C	D	E		
		⊠		⊠	⊠		(trolley)	(trolley)	(trolley)		⊠	(trolley)	⊠	⊠		(trolley)					⊠
Inverness 229	d																				
Aberdeen 229	d																				
Dundee 229	d																				
Perth 229	d																				
Edinburgh 10 225,226,228,230,242	d															16 12					
Haymarket 225,226,228,230,242	d															16u16					
Glasgow Central 15 226,216	d				15 40									16 00							
Motherwell 226	d																				
Carstairs 226	d																				
Lockerbie	d															17 10					
Carlisle 8 216	a				16 46									17 08		17 32					
	d				16 48									17 09		17 33					
Penrith North Lakes	d				17 03											17 48					
Windermere 83	d							17 06									18 02	18 05	18 02		
Oxenholme Lake District	a							17 25						17 44			18 21	18 22	18 21		
	d							17 30						17 44			18 22	18 22	18 22		
Barrow-in-Furness 82	d																				
Lancaster 6	a				17 37			17 47								18 24	18 39	18 39	18 39		
	d				17 37		17 45	17 48								18 25	18 40	18 40	18 40		
Blackpool North 97	d																				
Preston 8 90	a				17 55		18 03	18 06						18 12		18 45	18 58	18 58	18 58		
Preston 8 90	d				17 58		18 05	18 08						18 17		18 45	19 10	19 10	20 10		
Wigan North Western 90	a				18 08		18 17							18 27		18 58					
	d				18 09		18 17							18 28		18 59					
Bolton 82	a							18 34									19 35	19 35	20 34		
Manchester Picc. 10 82 (ferry)	a						18 52	18 56								19 29	19 57	19 57	20 56		
Manchester Airport (air)	a						19 13	19 17								19 47	20 17	20 17	21 17		
Liverpool Lime Street 10 91	a																				
	d	17 47								18 04										18 34	18 47
Liverpool South Parkway 91 (air)	d									18 15										18 44	
Runcorn 91	d	18 03								18 24										18 52	19 03
Warrington Bank Quay	a				18 19									18 38							
	d				18 20									18 39							
Manchester Picc. 10 84 (ferry)	d			17 55					18 05		18 15	18 27	18 35								
Stockport 84	d			18 04					18 13		18 23	18 35	18 43								
Wilmslow 84	d			18 11																	
Holyhead 81 (ferry)	d																				
Bangor (Gwynedd) 81	d																				
Llandudno Junction 81	d																				
Wrexham General 75	d																				
Chester 81	d																				
Crewe 10	a	18 22		18 28						18 47				18 58						19 16	19 21
	d	18 24		18 30						18 49				19 01	19 02					19 19	19 22
Macclesfield	d								18 26				18 56								
Stoke-on-Trent	d		←			←			18 44		18 50	19 07	19 12		19 28						
Stafford	a	18 42	18 44			18 50			19 01	19 09		19 24			19 50					19 42	19 40
	d	18 43	18 44			18 56			19 02	19 10		19 25			19 51					19 43	19 42
Penkridge	a									19 15					→					→	
Wolverhampton 7 (ferry)	a		18 57						19 15	19 27		19 39		19 32							
Birmingham New St. 12 68	a		19 17						19 33	19 48		19 58		20 05							
Birmingham International 68 (air)	a											20 13		20 19							
Coventry 68	a											20 23		20 30							
Lichfield Trent Valley	a					19 12															
Tamworth Low Level	a					19 19															
Nuneaton	a					19 35															
Rugby 66	a					19 49															
Milton Keynes Central 66	a			19 33		20 14					19 46			20 58							
Watford Junction 66	a	19s47												21s19							20s45
London Euston 15 ⊖66	a	20 07		20 08	20 12	20 50					20 24		20 42	21 39							21 04

A from 10 February. (trolley) from Preston
B until 6 February. (trolley) from Preston
C from 10 February until 21 March
D until 6 February
E from 10 February

OVERNIGHT SLEEPERS. For sleeper trains, operated by First ScotRail, please see Tables 400 - 404.

For complete service between Manchester and Preston, Blackpool and between Barrow-in-furness and Lancaster, please see Table 82.

For complete service between Crewe and Liverpool Lime Street, see Table 91

For complete service between Crewe/Stoke-on-Trent & Manchester see Table 84

For complete service between Crewe and Holyhead please see Table 81.

For complete service between Coventry-Birmingham-Wolverhampton-Stafford please see Table 68

For complete service between Windermere and Oxenholme Lake District, please see Table 83

Table 65R

Mondays to Fridays

9 December to 16 May

Scotland and North West England - West Midlands and London

Route Diagram - refer to first Page of Table 65

	LM	LM	VT	VT	XC	LM	VT	XC	VT	VT	LM	TP	TP FO	TP	LM	VT	VT	LM	VT	XC
										R										
	1	1	◇1	◇1	◇1	1	◇1	◇1	◇1	1	1	◇1	◇1	◇1	1	◇1	◇1	1	◇1	◇1
													A	B						
			⊠	⊠	🛒		☕	🛒	☕	⊠		🛒				☕	☕		☕	
Inverness 229 d																				
Aberdeen 229 d																				
Dundee 229 d																				
Perth 229 d																				
Edinburgh 10 225,226,228,230,242 d										16 52										
Haymarket 225,226,228,230,242 d										16 57										
Glasgow Central 15 226,216 d				16 40								17 06							17 30	
Motherwell 226 d				16 54																
Carstairs 226 d																				
Lockerbie d												18 04								
Carlisle 8 216 a				17 50						18 05		18 28							18 44	
d				17 52						18 08		18 30							18 46	
Penrith North Lakes d				18 06								18 45							19 00	
Windermere 83 d													18 56	18 56						
Oxenholme Lake District a				18 28						18 41		19 09	19 15	19 15					19 22	
d				18 30						18 42		19 09	19 16	19 16					19 23	
Barrow-in-Furness 82 d																				
Lancaster 6 a				18 43						18 56		19 24	19 32	19 32					19 37	
d				18 44						18 57		19 24	19 32	19 32					19 37	
Blackpool North 97 d																				
Preston 8 90 a				19 02						19 15		19 44	19 51	19 51					19 55	
Preston 8 90 d				19 05						19 16		19 45		20 10					19 58	
Wigan North Western 90 a				19 16						19 28		19 58							20 09	
d				19 16						19 29		19 59							20 09	
Bolton 82 a														20 34						
Manchester Picc. 10 82 a												20 27		20 56						
Manchester Airport a												20 46		21 17						
Liverpool Lime Street 10 91 a																				
d						19 11									19 34	19 48				
Liverpool South Parkway 91 d						19 21									19 44					
Runcorn 91 d						19 29									19 52	20 04				
Warrington Bank Quay a				19 27						19 39									20 20	
d				19 27						19 39									20 20	
Manchester Picc. 10 84 d			18 55		19 07		19 15	19 27									19 55			20 07
Stockport 84 d			19 04		19 16		19 23	19 35									20 04			20 16
Wilmslow 84 d			19 11														20 11			
Holyhead 81 d																				
Bangor (Gwynedd) 81 d																				
Llandudno Junction 81 d																				
Wrexham General 75 d																				
Chester 81 d									19 35											
Crewe 10 a			19 27			19 53			19 54	19 59					20 16	20 21	20 27		20 39	
d			19 29			19 55			19 56	20 01	20 15				20 18	20 23	20 29		20 41	
Macclesfield d							19 36	19 49												
Stoke-on-Trent d	←	←			19 44		19 52	20 07			20 37							←		20 44
Stafford a	19 42	19 50			20 03	20 15		20 26			20 55				20 38		20 47	20 55		21 02
d	19 43	19 51			20 04	20 16		20 28			21 04				20 42		20 49	21 04		21 03
Penkridge a	19 48										↦				20 47			↦		
Wolverhampton 7 a	19 58				20 16	20 29		20 42		20 39					20 57					21 15
Birmingham New St. 12 68 a	20 19				20 33	20 47		21 00		21 05					21 17					21 33
Birmingham International 68 a								21 13		21 19										
Coventry 68 a								21 23		21 30										
Lichfield Trent Valley a		20 08																		
Tamworth Low Level a		20 14																		
Nuneaton a		20 30														21 02				
Rugby 66 a		20 46																	21 27	
Milton Keynes Central 66 a			20 31	20 45			20 48		21 04	21 58							21 35		21 48	
Watford Junction 66 a										22s20						21s49				
London Euston 15 ⊖66 a			21 06	21 25			21 26		21 43	22 43						22 09	22 13		22 23	

A until 7 February

B 13 December, 20 December, 27 December

OVERNIGHT SLEEPERS. For sleeper trains, operated by First ScotRail, please see Tables 400 - 404.

For complete service between Manchester and Preston, Blackpool and between Barrow-in-furness and Lancaster, please see Table 82.

For complete service between Crewe and Liverpool Lime Street, see Table 91

For complete service between Crewe/Stoke-on-Trent & Manchester see Table 84

For complete service between Crewe and Holyhead please see Table 81.

For complete service between Coventry-Birmingham-Wolverhampton-Stafford please see Table 68

For complete service between Windermere and Oxenholme Lake District, please see Table 83

Table 65R

Mondays to Fridays

9 December to 16 May

Scotland and North West England - West Midlands and London

Route Diagram - refer to first Page of Table 65

	LM	LM	VT	TP FX	TP	TP	VT	VT	XC	LM	VT	VT	VT	VT	TP	VT	TP	TP FX	XC	LM
	1	1	◇1	◇1	◇1	◇1	◇1	◇1	◇1	1	◇1	◇1	◇1	◇1	◇1	◇1	◇1	◇1	◇1	1
				A	B	C											D	A		
			☒	⚲	⚲	⚲	☕	☒			☕	☕	☕	☒		☕	⚲	⚲		
Inverness 229 d																				
Aberdeen 229 d																				
Dundee 229 d																				
Perth 229 d																				
Edinburgh 10 225,226,228,230,242 d				18 12	18 12	18 12								18 52			20 12	20 12		
Haymarket 225,226,228,230,242 d				18u16	18u16	18u16								18 56			20u16	20u16		
Glasgow Central 15 226,216 d			17 40					18 40								20 10				
Motherwell 226 d																				
Carstairs 226 d																				
Lockerbie d			18 35	19 14	19 14	19 14										21 05	21 11	21 11		
Carlisle 8 216 a			18 56	19 36	19 36	19 36		19 47						20 05		21 24	21 32	21 32		
d			18 57	19 36	19 36	19 36		19 49						20 06		21 26	21 33	21 33		
Penrith North Lakes d				19 51	19 51	19 51										21 39				
Windermere 83 d																				
Oxenholme Lake District a			19 32	20 16	20 16	20 16		20 22						20 41		22 03	22 09	22 09		
d			19 32	20 16	20 16	20 16		20 24						20 41		22 03	22 10	22 10		
Barrow-in-Furness 82 d															20 10					
Lancaster 6 a			19 47	20 31	20 31	20 31		20 37						20 56	21 10	22 18	22 24	22 24		
d			19 47	20 31	20 31	20 31		20 38						20 56	21 11	22 18	22 25	22 25		
Blackpool North 97 d																				
Preston 8 90 a			20 05	20 50	20 50	20 50		20 56						21 14	21 30	22 36	22 44	22 44		
Preston 8 90 d			20 07	20 51	20 51	20 51		20 58						21 16		22 40	22 45	22 45		
Wigan North Western 90 a			20 19					21 09						21 27		22 50	22 58	22 58		
d			20 19					21 09						21 28		22 52	22 58	22 58		
Bolton 82 a																				
Manchester Picc. 10 82 a				21 30	21 30	21 30											23 27	23 28		
Manchester Airport ✈ a					21 47	21 49											23 46			
Liverpool Lime Street 10 91 a																				
d		20 04								20 34		20 48								21 34
Liverpool South Parkway 91 ✈ d		20 15								20 44										21 44
Runcorn 91 d		20 24								20 52		21 04								21 52
Warrington Bank Quay a			20 30					21 20						21 39		23 01				
d			20 31					21 20						21 39		23 03				
Manchester Picc. 10 84 d							20 15		20 27		21 15								21 27	
Stockport 84 d							20 23		20 35		21 23								21 35	
Wilmslow 84 d																				
Holyhead 81 ⛴ d																				
Bangor (Gwynedd) 81 d													20 20							
Llandudno Junction 81 d													20 38							
Wrexham General 75 d																				
Chester 81 d													21 35							
Crewe 10 a		20 45	20 50							21 16		21 21	21 54	21 59		23 24				22 18
d		20 47	20 53							21 18		21 24	21 56	22 01						22 20
Macclesfield d							20 36		20 49		21 36								21 49	
Stoke-on-Trent d	←						20 53		21 07		21 53								22 08	
Stafford a	20 55	21 08	21 12						21 24	21 38		21 43							22 25	22 40
d	21 04	21 10	21 13						21 25	21 41		21 44							22 26	22 41
Penkridge a		21 15								21 46										22 46
Wolverhampton 7 a		21 26	21 30						21 39	21 57			22 27	22 32					22 39	23 00
Birmingham New St. 12 68 a		21 47	21 50						22 00	22 17			22 50	22 58					22 58	23 27
Birmingham International 68 ✈ a																				
Coventry 68 a																				
Lichfield Trent Valley a	21 20											21 57								
Tamworth Low Level a	21 26											22 04								
Nuneaton a	21 42											22 17								
Rugby 66 a	21 57											22 31								
Milton Keynes Central 66 a							21 52	22 40			22 52	22 58								
Watford Junction 66 a							22s13	23s15			23s25	23s33								
London Euston 15 ⊖66 a							22 33	23 39			23 48	23 57								

A from 30 December until 20 March

B until 27 December, FO from 3 January until 21 March

C from 24 March

D until 27 December, FO from 3 January until 14 March, from 21 March

OVERNIGHT SLEEPERS. For sleeper trains, operated by First ScotRail, please see Tables 400 - 404.

For complete service between Manchester and Preston, Blackpool and between Barrow-in-furness and Lancaster, please see Table 82.

For complete service between Crewe and Liverpool Lime Street, see Table 91

For complete service between Crewe/Stoke-on-Trent & Manchester see Table 84

For complete service between Crewe and Holyhead please see Table 81.

For complete service between Coventry-Birmingham-Wolverhampton-Stafford please see Table 68

For complete service between Windermere and Oxenholme Lake District, please see Table 83

Table 65R

Mondays to Fridays

9 December to 16 May

Scotland and North West England - West Midlands and London

Route Diagram - refer to first Page of Table 65

		NT	NT	XC	LM	NT	TP	LM		SR	SR	SR	SR
										B	B	B	B
												A	
				◇1	1		◇1	1					
										sleeper, ✕	sleeper, ✕	sleeper, ✕	sleeper, ✕
Inverness 229	d											20 44	
Aberdeen 229	d												21 43
Dundee 229	d												23u06
Perth 229	d											23u21	
Edinburgh 10 225,226,228,230,242	d									23 40			
Haymarket 225,226,228,230,242	d												
Glasgow Central 15 226,216	d										23 40		
Motherwell 226	d										00u01		
Carstairs 226	d										00u16		
Lockerbie	d												
Carlisle 8 216	a												
	d									01u40			
Penrith North Lakes	d												
Windermere 83	d						22 45						
Oxenholme Lake District	a						23 04						
	d						23 05						
Barrow-in-Furness 82	d	21 43											
Lancaster 6	a	22 45					23 22						
	d	22 46				23 02	23 22						
Blackpool North 97	d												
Preston 8 90	a	23 11				23 23	23 42					04s40	04s40
Preston 8 90	d												
Wigan North Western 90	a												
	d												
Bolton 82	a												
Manchester Picc. 10 82	a												
Manchester Airport	a												
Liverpool Lime Street 10 91	a												
	d				22 34			23 34					
Liverpool South Parkway 91	d				22 45			23 45					
Runcorn 91	d				22 54			23 53					
Warrington Bank Quay	a												
	d												
Manchester Picc. 10 84	d		22 04	22 07									
Stockport 84	d		22 17	22 16									
Wilmslow 84	d		22 31										
Holyhead 81	d												
Bangor (Gwynedd) 81	d												
Llandudno Junction 81	d												
Wrexham General 75	d												
Chester 81	d												
Crewe 10	a		23 01		23 21			00 22				05s36	
	d												
Macclesfield	d			22 29									
Stoke-on-Trent	d			22 47									
Stafford	a			23 06									
	d			23 07									
Penkridge	a												
Wolverhampton 7	a			23 19									
Birmingham New St. 12 68	a			23 39									
Birmingham International 68	a												
Coventry 68	a												
Lichfield Trent Valley	a												
Tamworth Low Level	a												
Nuneaton	a												
Rugby 66	a												
Milton Keynes Central 66	a												
Watford Junction 66	a									06s23			
London Euston 15 ⊖66	a									06 48		07 47	

A also conveys through sleepers from Fort William dep 1950. (Table 404)

OVERNIGHT SLEEPERS. For sleeper trains, operated by First ScotRail, please see Tables 400 - 404.

For complete service between Manchester and Preston, Blackpool and between Barrow-in-furness and Lancaster, please see Table 82.

For complete service between Crewe and Liverpool Lime Street, see Table 91

For complete service between Crewe/Stoke-on-Trent & Manchester see Table 84

For complete service between Crewe and Holyhead please see Table 81.

For complete service between Coventry-Birmingham-Wolverhampton-Stafford please see Table 68

For complete service between Windermere and Oxenholme Lake District, please see Table 83

Table 65R

Saturdays

14 December to 28 December

Scotland and North West England - West Midlands and London

Route Diagram - refer to first Page of Table 65

		NT	SR	XC	VT	XC	LM	VT	VT	VT	XC	LM	VT	VT	NT	LM	VT	TP	LM	VT
			R	◇1	◇1	◇1	1	◇1	◇1	◇1	◇1	1	◇1	◇1		1	◇1	◇1	1	◇1
			✕																	
Inverness 229	d																			
Aberdeen 229	d																			
Dundee 229	d																			
Perth 229	d																			
Edinburgh 10 225,226,228,230,242	d																			
Haymarket 225,226,228,230,242	d																			
Glasgow Central 15 226,216	d																			
Motherwell 226	d		00u01																	
Carstairs 226	d		00u16																	
Lockerbie	d																			
Carlisle 8 216	a																			
	d		01u40																	
Penrith North Lakes	d																			
Windermere 83	d																			
Oxenholme Lake District	a																			
	d																			
Barrow-in-Furness 82	d																	05 32		
Lancaster 6	a																	06 24		
	d									05 38								06 24		
Blackpool North 97	d																			
Preston 8 90	a									05 55								06 43		
Preston 8 90	d									05 58							06 17	06 44		
Wigan North Western 90	a									06 09							06 28			
	d									06 09							06 28			
Bolton 82	a																	07 07		
Manchester Picc. 10 82	a																	07 27		
Manchester Airport	a																	07 47		
Liverpool Lime Street 10 91	a																			
	d							05 47											06 32	06 45
Liverpool South Parkway 91	d																		06 42	
Runcorn 91	d							06 03											06 50	07 01
Warrington Bank Quay	a									06 20							06 39			
	d									06 20							06 39			
Manchester Picc. 10 84	d			05 11	05 25				05 55		06 00		06 10	06 35	06 46					
Stockport 84	d				05 34				06 03		06 08		06 18	06 43						
Wilmslow 84	d	00 01			05 41				06 11						07 21					
Holyhead 81	d																			
Bangor (Gwynedd) 81	d																			
Llandudno Junction 81	d																			
Wrexham General 75	d																			
Chester 81	d																			
Crewe 10	a	00 30		05 41	05 57				06 27						07 46		06 58		07 14	07 18
	d			05 47	06 00		06 11		06 29			06 47				06 59	07 01		07 16	07 20
Macclesfield	d										06 21		06 31	06 56						
Stoke-on-Trent	d			06 08		←					06 39		06 48	07 12		07 20				
Stafford	a			06 25	06 18	06 25	06 34	06 34			06 57	07 10				07 43			07 37	07 38
	d			06 26	06 19	06 26	06 35	06 36			06 58	07 12				07 48			07 41	07 39
Penkridge	a			→			06 40					07 17				→			→	
Wolverhampton 7	a					06 39	06 51				07 12	07 28					07 31			
Birmingham New St. 12 68	a					06 57	07 18				07 33	07 47					08 05			
Birmingham International 68	a					07 13											08 19			
Coventry 68	a					07 24											08 29			
Lichfield Trent Valley	a												07 11							
Tamworth Low Level	a												07 17							
Nuneaton	a							06 58												
Rugby 66	a				06 50									07 52						
Milton Keynes Central 66	a				07 11				07 31	07 38							08 58			
Watford Junction 66	a		06s23		07s32			07s45												
London Euston 15 ⊖66	a		06 48		07 53			08 05	08 10	08 17			08 28	08 46			09 34			09 00

OVERNIGHT SLEEPERS. For sleeper trains, operated by First ScotRail, please see Tables 400 - 404.

For complete service between Manchester and Preston, Blackpool and between Barrow-in-furness and Lancaster, please see Table 82.

For complete service between Crewe and Liverpool Lime Street, see Table 91

For complete service between Crewe/Stoke-on-Trent & Manchester see Table 84

For complete service between Crewe and Holyhead please see Table 81.

For complete service between Coventry-Birmingham-Wolverhampton-Stafford please see Table 68

For complete service between Windermere and Oxenholme Lake District, please see Table 83

Table 65R

Saturdays

14 December to 28 December

Scotland and North West England - West Midlands and London

Route Diagram - refer to first Page of Table 65

		LM	VT	VT	LM			XC	VT	VT	LM	VT	XC	VT	VT	LM		TP		LM	VT	LM	VT	VT	LM
		1	◇1	◇1	1			◇1	◇1	◇1	1	◇1	◇1	◇1	◇1	1		◇1		1	◇1	1	◇1	◇1	1
			☕	☕				🛒	☕	☕		☕	🛒	☕	☕						☕		☕	☕	
Inverness 229	d																								
Aberdeen 229	d																								
Dundee 229	d																								
Perth 229	d																								
Edinburgh 10 225,226,228,230,242	d																								
Haymarket 225,226,228,230,242	d																								
Glasgow Central 15 226,216	d			04 26																				05 40	
Motherwell 226	d																								
Carstairs 226	d																								
Lockerbie	d																								
Carlisle 8 216	a			05 42																				06 47	
	d			05 44																				06 49	
Penrith North Lakes	d			05 58																					
Windermere 83	d																								
Oxenholme Lake District	a			06 21																				07 22	
	d			06 21																				07 24	
Barrow-in-Furness 82	d																	06 15							
Lancaster 6	a			06 36														07 15						07 37	
	d			06 36											06 58			07 23						07 38	
Blackpool North 97	d																								
Preston 8 90	a			06 54											07 15			07 41						07 56	
Preston 8 90	d			06 57											07 17			07 43						07 58	
Wigan North Western 90	a			07 07											07 28			07 55						08 09	
	d			07 09											07 28			07 56						08 09	
Bolton 82	a																								
Manchester Picc. 10 82	a																	08 26							
Manchester Airport	a																	08 47							
Liverpool Lime Street 10 91	a																								
	d										07 04	07 19								07 34	07 47				
Liverpool South Parkway 91	d										07 14									07 44					
Runcorn 91	d										07 22	07 36								07 52	08 03				
Warrington Bank Quay	a			07 18											07 39									08 20	
	d			07 19											07 39									08 20	
Manchester Picc. 10 84	d		06 55					07 07	07 15				07 27	07 35									07 55		
Stockport 84	d		07 04					07 16	07 23				07 35	07 43									08 04		
Wilmslow 84	d		07 11																				08 11		
Holyhead 81	d																								
Bangor (Gwynedd) 81	d																								
Llandudno Junction 81	d																								
Wrexham General 75	d																								
Chester 81	d									07 17															
Crewe 10	a		07 27							07 36	07 47	07 52			07 58					08 16	08 21		08 27		
	d		07 29							07 41	07 49	07 55			08 01	08 02				08 19	08 22		08 29		
Macclesfield	d												07 49	07 56											
Stoke-on-Trent	d	←			←			07 44	07 50				08 07	08 12		08 28						←			←
Stafford	a	07 37			07 43			08 02			08 09	08 15	08 25			08 50				08 42	08 40	08 42			08 50
	d	07 41			07 48			08 03			08 10	08 16	08 26			08 56				08 43	08 42	08 43			08 56
Penkridge	a	07 46									08 15					→				→		08 48			
Wolverhampton 7	a	07 57						08 15			08 26		08 39		08 32							08 58			
Birmingham New St. 12 68	a	08 17						08 34			08 48		08 58		09 05							09 17			
Birmingham International 68	a												09 13		09 19										
Coventry 68	a												09 24		09 30										
Lichfield Trent Valley	a				08 04							08 30													09 12
Tamworth Low Level	a				08 11							08 37													09 19
Nuneaton	a				08 26																09 04				09 35
Rugby 66	a				08 42																				09 51
Milton Keynes Central 66	a				09 05				08 46						09 58										10 14
Watford Junction 66	a																								
London Euston 15 ⊖66	a		09 05	09 13	09 50				09 24	09 30		09 47		09 43	10 35						10 06		10 11	10 16	10 50

OVERNIGHT SLEEPERS. For sleeper trains, operated by First ScotRail, please see Tables 400 - 404.

For complete service between Manchester and Preston, Blackpool and between Barrow-in-furness and Lancaster, please see Table 82.

For complete service between Crewe and Liverpool Lime Street, see Table 91

For complete service between Crewe/Stoke-on-Trent & Manchester see Table 84

For complete service between Crewe and Holyhead please see Table 81.

For complete service between Coventry-Birmingham-Wolverhampton-Stafford please see Table 68

For complete service between Windermere and Oxenholme Lake District, please see Table 83

Table 65R

Saturdays

14 December to 28 December

Scotland and North West England - West Midlands and London

Route Diagram - refer to first Page of Table 65

Station		XC ◇1	LM 1	VT ◇1	VT ◇1	XC ◇1	VT ◇1	VT ◇1	LM 1	TP ◇1		TP ◇1		LM 1	VT ◇1	LM 1	VT ◇1	VT ◇1	LM 1	NT		XC ◇1	LM 1
Inverness	229 d																						
Aberdeen	229 d																						
Dundee	229 d																						
Perth	229 d																						
Edinburgh 10	225,226,228,230,242 d									06 15													
Haymarket	225,226,228,230,242 d									06u19													
Glasgow Central 15	226,216 d							05 50										06 30					
Motherwell	226 d							06 04										06 44					
Carstairs	226 d																						
Lockerbie	d																	07 25					
Carlisle 8	216 a							07 01		07 33								07 43					
	d							07 02		07 33								07 46					
Penrith North Lakes	d							07 18										08 00					
Windermere	83 d																						
Oxenholme Lake District	a							07 41		08 09								08 22					
	d							07 42		08 10								08 23					
Barrow-in-Furness	82 d											07 33											
Lancaster 6	a							07 56		08 25		08 33						08 37					
	d							07 57		08 26		08 33						08 38					
Blackpool North	97 d																						
Preston 8	90 a							08 15		08 44		08 52						08 56					
Preston 8	90 d							08 17		08 45		09 10						08 58					
Wigan North Western	90 a							08 28		08 58								09 09					
	d							08 28		08 58								09 09					
Bolton	82 a											09 34											
Manchester Picc. 10	82 a									09 27		09 56											
Manchester Airport	a									09 47		10 17											
Liverpool Lime Street 10	91 a																						
	d		08 04											08 34	08 47								09 04
Liverpool South Parkway	91 d		08 15											08 44									09 15
Runcorn	91 d		08 24											08 52	09 03								09 25
Warrington Bank Quay	a							08 39										09 20					
	d							08 39										09 20					
Manchester Picc. 10	84 d	08 07		08 15		08 27	08 35										08 55			09 04		09 07	
Stockport	84 d	08 16		08 23		08 35	08 43										09 04			09 17		09 16	
Wilmslow	84 d																09 11			09 31			
Holyhead	81 d				06 52																		
Bangor (Gwynedd)	81 d				07 20																		
Llandudno Junction	81 d				07 38																		
Wrexham General	75 d																						
Chester	81 d				08 35																		
Crewe 10	a		08 47		08 54			08 58						09 19	09 23		09 29			10 01			09 45
	d		08 49		08 56			09 01	09 02					09 19	09 25		09 30						09 49
Macclesfield	d					08 49	08 56																
Stoke-on-Trent	d	08 44		08 50		09 07	09 12		09 28							←			←			09 44	
Stafford	a	09 02	09 09			09 25			09 51					09 45	09 43	09 45			09 51			10 02	10 10
	d	09 03	09 10			09 26			09 56					09 45	09 44	09 45			09 56			10 03	10 10
Penkridge	a		09 15						→					→									10 16
Wolverhampton 7	a	09 15	09 26			09 39		09 33								09 58						10 15	10 27
Birmingham New St. 12	68 a	09 33	09 47			09 58		10 05								10 17						10 33	10 47
Birmingham International	68 a					10 13		10 19															
Coventry	68 a					10 24		10 30															
Lichfield Trent Valley	a																		10 12				
Tamworth Low Level	a																		10 19				
Nuneaton	a																		10 35				
Rugby	66 a																		10 51				
Milton Keynes Central	66 a			09 46	10 02			10 58											11 14				
Watford Junction	66 a																						
London Euston 15	⊖66 a			10 24	10 39		10 43	11 33							11 05		11 08	11 16	11 50				

OVERNIGHT SLEEPERS. For sleeper trains, operated by First ScotRail, please see Tables 400 - 404.

For complete service between Manchester and Preston, Blackpool and between Barrow-in-furness and Lancaster, please see Table 82.

For complete service between Crewe and Liverpool Lime Street, see Table 91

For complete service between Crewe/Stoke-on-Trent & Manchester see Table 84

For complete service between Crewe and Holyhead please see Table 81.

For complete service between Coventry-Birmingham-Wolverhampton-Stafford please see Table 68

For complete service between Windermere and Oxenholme Lake District, please see Table 83

Table 65R

Saturdays

14 December to 28 December

Scotland and North West England - West Midlands and London

Route Diagram - refer to first Page of Table 65

Station	Table		VT	VT	XC	VT	VT	LM	TP	LM	VT	LM	VT	VT	LM	TP	XC	LM	VT	VT	XC	VT
			◇1	◇1	◇1	◇1	◇1	1	◇1	1	◇1	1	◇1	◇1	1	◇1	◇1	1	◇1	◇1	◇1	◇1
Inverness	229	d																				
Aberdeen	229	d																				
Dundee	229	d																				
Perth	229	d																				
Edinburgh 10	225,226,228,230,242	d					06 52															
Haymarket	225,226,228,230,242	d					06 56															
Glasgow Central 15	226,216	d							07 09					07 35								
Motherwell	226	d												07 52								
Carstairs	226	d																				
Lockerbie		d							08 08													
Carlisle 8	216	a					08 06		08 29					08 47								
		d					08 07		08 29					08 49								
Penrith North Lakes		d					08 22		08 45													
Windermere	83	d																				
Oxenholme Lake District		a							09 09					09 22								
		d							09 10					09 23								
Barrow-in-Furness	82	d														08 50						
Lancaster 6		a					08 57		09 25					09 37		09 46						
		d					08 57		09 25					09 38		09 47						
Blackpool North	97	d																				
Preston 8	90	a					09 15		09 44					09 56		10 07						
Preston 8	90	d					09 17		09 44					09 58								
Wigan North Western	90	a					09 28		09 57					10 09								
		d					09 28		09 58					10 09								
Bolton	82	a																				
Manchester Picc. 10	82	a							10 26													
Manchester Airport		a							10 46													
Liverpool Lime Street 10	91	a																				
		d								09 34	09 47							10 04				
Liverpool South Parkway	91	d								09 44								10 15				
Runcorn	91	d								09 52	10 03							10 25				
Warrington Bank Quay		a					09 39							10 20								
		d					09 39							10 20								
Manchester Picc. 10	84	d	09 15		09 27	09 35							09 55				10 07		10 15		10 27	10 35
Stockport	84	d	09 23		09 35	09 43							10 04				10 16		10 23		10 35	10 43
Wilmslow	84	d											10 11									
Holyhead	81	d		07 55																08 55		
Bangor (Gwynedd)	81	d		08 22																09 22		
Llandudno Junction	81	d		08 40																09 40		
Wrexham General	75	d																				
Chester	81	d		09 35																10 35		
Crewe 10		a		09 54			09 58			10 16	10 21		10 27					10 45		10 54		
		d		09 56			10 01	10 02		10 19	10 22		10 29					10 49		10 56		
Macclesfield		d			09 49	09 56															10 49	10 56
Stoke-on-Trent		d	09 50		10 07	10 12		10 28				←			←		10 44		10 50		11 07	11 12
Stafford		a			10 25			10 50		10 42	10 40	10 42			10 50		11 02	11 09			11 25	
		d			10 26			10 56		10 43	10 42	10 43			10 56		11 03	11 10			11 26	
Penkridge		a						→		→								11 15				
Wolverhampton 7		a			10 39		10 32					10 56					11 15	11 27			11 39	
Birmingham New St. 12	68	a			10 58		11 05					11 17					11 33	11 47			11 59	
Birmingham International	68	a			11 13		11 19														12 13	
Coventry	68	a			11 24		11 30														12 24	
Lichfield Trent Valley		a													11 12							
Tamworth Low Level		a													11 19							
Nuneaton		a													11 35							
Rugby	66	a													11 51							
Milton Keynes Central	66	a	10 46	11 02			11 58								12 14				11 46	12 02		
Watford Junction	66	a																				
London Euston 15	⊖66	a	11 24	11 39		11 43	12 33				11 59		12 05	12 13	12 50				12 24	12 39		12 43

OVERNIGHT SLEEPERS. For sleeper trains, operated by First ScotRail, please see Tables 400 - 404.

For complete service between Manchester and Preston, Blackpool and between Barrow-in-furness and Lancaster, please see Table 82.

For complete service between Crewe and Liverpool Lime Street, see Table 91

For complete service between Crewe/Stoke-on-Trent & Manchester see Table 84

For complete service between Crewe and Holyhead please see Table 81.

For complete service between Coventry-Birmingham-Wolverhampton-Stafford please see Table 68

For complete service between Windermere and Oxenholme Lake District, please see Table 83

Table 65R

Saturdays

14 December to 28 December

Scotland and North West England - West Midlands and London

Route Diagram - refer to first Page of Table 65

		VT	LM	TP		TP		LM	VT	LM	VT	VT	LM			XC	LM	VT	XC	VT	VT	VT	LM	TP
		◇1	1	◇1		◇1		1	◇1	1	◇1	◇1	1			◇1	1	◇1	◇1	◇1	◇1	◇1	1	◇1
Inverness 229	d																							
Aberdeen 229	d																							
Dundee 229	d																							
Perth 229	d																							
Edinburgh 10 225,226,228,230,242	d					08 10																08 52		
Haymarket 225,226,228,230,242	d					08u14																08 57		
Glasgow Central 15 226,216	d	08 00										08 40												
Motherwell 226	d																							
Carstairs 226	d																							
Lockerbie	d																							
Carlisle 8 216	a	09 08				09 29						09 47										10 07		
	d	09 09				09 30						09 49										10 08		
Penrith North Lakes	d					09 46						10 03												
Windermere 83	d			09 37																				10 48
Oxenholme Lake District	a			09 56		10 09																10 42		11 08
	d			09 57		10 10																10 42		11 08
Barrow-in-Furness 82	d																							
Lancaster 6	a	09 56		10 13		10 24						10 37										10 57		11 26
	d	09 56		10 14		10 25						10 38										10 57		11 26
Blackpool North 97	d																							
Preston 8 90	a	10 14		10 33		10 43						10 56										11 15		11 45
Preston 8 90	d	10 17				10 45						10 58										11 18		11 46
Wigan North Western 90	a	10 28				10 58						11 09										11 28		11 58
	d	10 28				10 58						11 09										11 28		11 58
Bolton 82	a																							
Manchester Picc. 10 82	a					11 27																		12 27
Manchester Airport	a					11 47																		12 47
Liverpool Lime Street 10 91	a																							
	d							10 34	10 47								11 04							
Liverpool South Parkway 91	d							10 44									11 15							
Runcorn 91	d							10 52	11 03								11 25							
Warrington Bank Quay	a	10 39										11 20										11 39		
	d	10 39										11 20										11 40		
Manchester Picc. 10 84	d										10 55					11 07		11 15	11 27		11 35			
Stockport 84	d										11 04					11 16		11 23	11 35		11 43			
Wilmslow 84	d										11 11													
Holyhead 81	d																							
Bangor (Gwynedd) 81	d																							
Llandudno Junction 81	d																							
Wrexham General 75	d																							
Chester 81	d																			11 35				
Crewe 10	a	10 58						11 16	11 21		11 27						11 45			11 54		11 58		
	d	11 01	11 02					11 19	11 22		11 29						11 49			11 56		12 01	12 02	
Macclesfield	d																		11 49		11 56			
Stoke-on-Trent	d		11 28							←			←			11 44		11 50	12 07		12 12		12 28	
Stafford	a		11 50					11 42	11 40	11 42			11 50			12 02	12 09		12 24				12 50	
	d		11 56					11 43	11 42	11 43			11 56			12 03	12 10		12 25				12 56	
Penkridge	a		↪					↪									12 15						↪	
Wolverhampton 7	a	11 31								11 56						12 15	12 27		12 39			12 33		
Birmingham New St. 12 68	a	12 05								12 17						12 33	12 47		12 58			13 05		
Birmingham International 68	a	12 19																	13 13			13 19		
Coventry 68	a	12 30																	13 24			13 30		
Lichfield Trent Valley	a												12 12											
Tamworth Low Level	a												12 19											
Nuneaton	a												12 35											
Rugby 66	a												12 51											
Milton Keynes Central 66	a	12 58											13 14					12 46		13 02		13 58		
Watford Junction 66	a																							
London Euston 15 ⊖66	a	13 35							12 59		13 05	13 13	13 50					13 24		13 39	13 43	14 33		

OVERNIGHT SLEEPERS. For sleeper trains, operated by First ScotRail, please see Tables 400 - 404.

For complete service between Manchester and Preston, Blackpool and between Barrow-in-furness and Lancaster, please see Table 82.

For complete service between Crewe and Liverpool Lime Street, see Table 91

For complete service between Crewe/Stoke-on-Trent & Manchester see Table 84

For complete service between Crewe and Holyhead please see Table 81.

For complete service between Coventry-Birmingham-Wolverhampton-Stafford please see Table 68

For complete service between Windermere and Oxenholme Lake District, please see Table 83

Table 65R

Saturdays

14 December to 28 December

Scotland and North West England - West Midlands and London

Route Diagram - refer to first Page of Table 65

		LM	VT	LM	VT	VT	LM	TP	XC	LM	VT	XC	VT	VT	VT	LM	TP	LM	VT	LM
		1	◇1	1	◇1	◇1	1	◇1	◇1	1	◇1	◇1	◇1	◇1	◇1	1	◇1	1	◇1	1
Inverness 229	d																			
Aberdeen 229	d																			
Dundee 229	d																			
Perth 229	d																			
Edinburgh 10 225,226,228,230,242	d																10 08			
Haymarket 225,226,228,230,242	d																10 12			
Glasgow Central 15 226,216	d					09 40									10 00					
Motherwell 226	d																			
Carstairs 226	d																			
Lockerbie	d																11 07			
Carlisle 8 216	a					10 47									11 09		11 28			
	d					10 49									11 11		11 31			
Penrith North Lakes	d														11 25		11 47			
Windermere 83	d																			
Oxenholme Lake District	a					11 22											12 09			
	d					11 23											12 10			
Barrow-in-Furness 82	d							11 20												
Lancaster 6	a					11 37		12 17									12 25			
	d					11 38		12 17									12 26			
Blackpool North 97	d																			
Preston 8 90	a					11 56		12 37							12 14		12 44			
Preston 8 90	d					11 58									12 17		12 45			
Wigan North Western 90	a					12 09									12 27		12 58			
	d					12 09									12 28		12 58			
Bolton 82	a																			
Manchester Picc. 10 82	a																13 27			
Manchester Airport	a																13 47			
Liverpool Lime Street 10 91	a																			
	d	11 34	11 47							12 04								12 34	12 47	
Liverpool South Parkway 91	d	11 44								12 15								12 44		
Runcorn 91	d	11 52	12 03							12 25								12 52	13 03	
Warrington Bank Quay	a					12 20									12 38					
	d					12 20									12 39					
Manchester Picc. 10 84	d				11 55				12 07		12 15	12 27		12 35						
Stockport 84	d				12 04				12 16		12 23	12 35		12 43						
Wilmslow 84	d				12 11															
Holyhead 81	d																			
Bangor (Gwynedd) 81	d																			
Llandudno Junction 81	d																			
Wrexham General 75	d																			
Chester 81	d												12 35							
Crewe 10	a	12 16	12 21		12 27					12 45			12 54		12 58			13 19	13 23	
	d	12 19	12 22		12 29					12 49			12 56		13 01	13 02		13 19	13 25	
Macclesfield	d											12 49		12 56						
Stoke-on-Trent	d			←			←		12 44		12 50	13 07		13 12		13 28				←
Stafford	a	12 42	12 40	12 42			12 50		13 02	13 09		13 25				13 50		13 45	13 43	13 45
	d	12 43	12 42	12 43			12 56		13 03	13 10		13 26				13 56		13 45	13 44	13 45
Penkridge	a	↪								13 15						↪		↪		
Wolverhampton 7	a			12 56					13 14	13 27		13 39			13 33					13 58
Birmingham New St. 12 68	a			13 17					13 32	13 47		13 58			14 05					14 17
Birmingham International 68	a											14 13			14 19					
Coventry 68	a											14 24			14 30					
Lichfield Trent Valley	a						13 12													
Tamworth Low Level	a						13 19													
Nuneaton	a						13 35													
Rugby 66	a						13 51													
Milton Keynes Central 66	a						14 14				13 46		14 02		14 58					
Watford Junction 66	a																			
London Euston 15 ⊖66	a		14 00		14 05	14 13	14 50				14 24		14 39	14 43	15 34				15 05	

OVERNIGHT SLEEPERS. For sleeper trains, operated by First ScotRail, please see Tables 400 - 404.

For complete service between Manchester and Preston, Blackpool and between Barrow-in-furness and Lancaster, please see Table 82.

For complete service between Crewe and Liverpool Lime Street, see Table 91

For complete service between Crewe/Stoke-on-Trent & Manchester see Table 84

For complete service between Crewe and Holyhead please see Table 81.

For complete service between Coventry-Birmingham-Wolverhampton-Stafford please see Table 68

For complete service between Windermere and Oxenholme Lake District, please see Table 83

Table 65R

Saturdays

14 December to 28 December

Scotland and North West England - West Midlands and London

Route Diagram - refer to first Page of Table 65

	VT ◇1	VT ◇1	LM 1		XC ◇1		LM 1	VT ◇1	XC ◇1	VT ◇1	VT ◇1	VT ◇1	LM 1	TP ◇1	TP ◇1			LM 1	VT ◇1	LM 1	VT ◇1	VT ◇1	LM 1
Inverness 229 d																							
Aberdeen 229 d																							
Dundee 229 d																							
Perth 229 d																							
Edinburgh 10 225,226,228,230,242 d												10 52											
Haymarket 225,226,228,230,242 d												10 57											
Glasgow Central 15 226,216 d		10 40												11 09								11 40	
Motherwell 226 d																							
Carstairs 226 d																							
Lockerbie d														12 09									
Carlisle 8 216 a		11 47										12 04		12 31								12 47	
d		11 49										12 08		12 31								12 49	
Penrith North Lakes d														12 46								13 03	
Windermere 83 d															12 52								
Oxenholme Lake District a		12 22										12 41		13 10	13 12								
d		12 23										12 43		13 10	13 13								
Barrow-in-Furness 82 d																							
Lancaster 6 a		12 37										12 56		13 25	13 29							13 37	
d		12 38										12 57		13 25	13 29							13 38	
Blackpool North 97 d																							
Preston 8 90 a		12 56										13 15		13 44	13 49							13 56	
Preston 8 90 d		12 58										13 17		13 44								13 58	
Wigan North Western 90 a		13 09										13 28		13 57								14 09	
d		13 09										13 28		13 58								14 09	
Bolton 82 a																							
Manchester Picc. 10 82 a														14 26									
Manchester Airport a														14 45									
Liverpool Lime Street 10 91 a																							
d							13 04											13 34	13 47				
Liverpool South Parkway 91 d							13 15											13 44					
Runcorn 91 d							13 25											13 52	14 03				
Warrington Bank Quay a		13 20										13 39										14 20	
d		13 20										13 39										14 20	
Manchester Picc. 10 84 d	12 55				13 07			13 15	13 27		13 35										13 55		
Stockport 84 d	13 04				13 16			13 23	13 35		13 43										14 04		
Wilmslow 84 d	13 11																				14 11		
Holyhead 81 d																							
Bangor (Gwynedd) 81 d																							
Llandudno Junction 81 d																							
Wrexham General 75 d																							
Chester 81 d										13 35													
Crewe 10 a	13 29						13 45			13 54		13 58						14 16	14 21		14 27		
d	13 30						13 49			13 56		14 01	14 02					14 19	14 22		14 29		
Macclesfield d									13 49		13 56												
Stoke-on-Trent d			←		13 44			13 50	14 07		14 12		14 28							←			←
Stafford a			13 50		14 02		14 09		14 25				14 50					14 42	14 40	14 42			14 50
d			13 56		14 03		14 10		14 26				14 56					14 43	14 42	14 43			14 56
Penkridge a							14 15						→					→					
Wolverhampton 7 a					14 15		14 27		14 39			14 33								14 56			
Birmingham New St. 12 68 a					14 33		14 47		14 58			15 05								15 17			
Birmingham International 68 a									15 13			15 19											
Coventry 68 a									15 24			15 30											
Lichfield Trent Valley a			14 12																				15 12
Tamworth Low Level a			14 19																				15 19
Nuneaton a			14 35																				15 35
Rugby 66 a			14 51																				15 51
Milton Keynes Central 66 a			15 14					14 46		15 02		15 58											16 14
Watford Junction 66 a																							
London Euston 15 ⊖66 a	15 09	15 13	15 50					15 24		15 39	15 43	16 34							15 59		16 05	16 13	16 50

OVERNIGHT SLEEPERS. For sleeper trains, operated by First ScotRail, please see Tables 400 - 404.

For complete service between Manchester and Preston, Blackpool and between Barrow-in-furness and Lancaster, please see Table 82.

For complete service between Crewe and Liverpool Lime Street, see Table 91

For complete service between Crewe/Stoke-on-Trent & Manchester see Table 84

For complete service between Crewe and Holyhead please see Table 81.

For complete service between Coventry-Birmingham-Wolverhampton-Stafford please see Table 68

For complete service between Windermere and Oxenholme Lake District, please see Table 83

Table 65R

Saturdays

14 December to 28 December

Scotland and North West England - West Midlands and London

Route Diagram - refer to first Page of Table 65

		XC		LM	VT	XC	VT	VT	VT	LM	TP	TP			LM	VT	LM	VT	VT	LM		XC		LM	VT
		◇1		1	◇1	◇1	◇1	◇1	◇1	1	◇1	◇1			1	◇1	1	◇1	◇1	1		◇1		1	◇1
											A														
		⊤			⊏P	⊤	⊏P	⊏P	⊏P		⊤	⊤				⊏P		⊏P	⊏P			⊤			⊏P
Inverness 229	d																								
Aberdeen 229	d																								
Dundee 229	d																								
Perth 229	d																								
Edinburgh 10 225,226,228,230,242	d											12 12													
Haymarket 225,226,228,230,242	d											12u16													
Glasgow Central 15 226,216	d								12 00										12 40						
Motherwell 226	d																								
Carstairs 226	d																								
Lockerbie	d											13 11													
Carlisle 8 216	a								13 09			13 33							13 47						
	d								13 11			13 33							13 49						
Penrith North Lakes	d																								
Windermere 83	d																								
Oxenholme Lake District	a											14 09							14 22						
	d											14 10							14 24						
Barrow-in-Furness 82	d										13 20														
Lancaster 6	a								13 57		14 17	14 24							14 37						
	d								13 58		14 17	14 25							14 39						
Blackpool North 97	d																								
Preston 8 90	a								14 15		14 37	14 45							14 56						
Preston 8 90	d								14 17		14 45								14 58						
Wigan North Western 90	a								14 28										15 09						
	d								14 28										15 10						
Bolton 82	a										15 07														
Manchester Picc. 10 82	a										15 28														
Manchester Airport ✈	a										15 47														
Liverpool Lime Street 10 91	a																								
	d			14 04											14 34	14 47								15 04	
Liverpool South Parkway 91 ✈	d			14 15											14 44									15 15	
Runcorn 91	d			14 25											14 52	15 03								15 25	
Warrington Bank Quay	a								14 39										15 20						
	d								14 39										15 21						
Manchester Picc. 10 84	d	14 07			14 15	14 27		14 35										14 55				15 07			15 15
Stockport 84	d	14 16			14 23	14 35		14 43										15 04				15 16			15 23
Wilmslow 84	d																	15 11							
Holyhead 81	d																								
Bangor (Gwynedd) 81	d																								
Llandudno Junction 81	d																								
Wrexham General 75	d																								
Chester 81	d						14 35																		
Crewe 10	a			14 45			14 54		14 58						15 16	15 21		15 27						15 45	
	d			14 49			14 56		15 01	15 02					15 19	15 22		15 29						15 49	
Macclesfield	d					14 49		14 56																	
Stoke-on-Trent	d	14 44			14 50	15 07		15 12		15 28							←			←		15 44			15 50
Stafford	a	15 02		15 09		15 25				15 50					15 42	15 40	15 42			15 50		16 02		16 09	
	d	15 03		15 10		15 26				15 56					15 43	15 42	15 43			15 56		16 03		16 10	
Penkridge	a			15 15						→					→									16 15	
Wolverhampton 7	a	15 16		15 27		15 39			15 31								15 56					16 16		16 27	
Birmingham New St. 12 68	a	15 33		15 47		15 58			16 05								16 17					16 33		16 47	
Birmingham International 68 ✈	a					16 13			16 19																
Coventry 68	a					16 24			16 30																
Lichfield Trent Valley	a																			16 12					
Tamworth Low Level	a																			16 19					
Nuneaton	a																			16 35					
Rugby 66	a																			16 51					
Milton Keynes Central 66	a				15 46		16 02		16 58											17 14					16 46
Watford Junction 66	a																								
London Euston 15 ⊖66	a				16 24		16 39	16 43	17 33							16 59		17 05	17 13	17 50					17 24

A ⊤ from Preston

OVERNIGHT SLEEPERS. For sleeper trains, operated by First ScotRail, please see Tables 400 - 404.

For complete service between Manchester and Preston, Blackpool and between Barrow-in-furness and Lancaster, please see Table 82.

For complete service between Crewe and Liverpool Lime Street, see Table 91

For complete service between Crewe/Stoke-on-Trent & Manchester see Table 84

For complete service between Crewe and Holyhead please see Table 81.

For complete service between Coventry-Birmingham-Wolverhampton-Stafford please see Table 68

For complete service between Windermere and Oxenholme Lake District, please see Table 83

Table 65R

Saturdays

14 December to 28 December

Scotland and North West England - West Midlands and London

Route Diagram - refer to first Page of Table 65

	VT	XC	VT	VT	LM	TP	TP			LM	VT	LM	VT	VT	LM	TP			XC	LM	VT	XC	VT	VT
	◇1	◇1	◇1	◇1	1	◇1	◇1			1	◇1	1	◇1	◇1	1	◇1			◇1	1	◇1	◇1	◇1	◇1
Inverness 229 d																								
Aberdeen 229 d																								
Dundee 229 d																								
Perth 229 d																								
Edinburgh 10 225,226,228,230,242 d				12 52																				
Haymarket 225,226,228,230,242 d				12 57																				
Glasgow Central 15 226,216 d						13 09								13 40										
Motherwell 226 d																								
Carstairs 226 d																								
Lockerbie d						14 07																		
Carlisle 8 216 a				14 05		14 29								14 46										
d				14 08		14 30								14 49										
Penrith North Lakes d				14 22		14 45																		
Windermere 83 d							14 52																	
Oxenholme Lake District a						15 08	15 11							15 22										
d						15 09	15 12							15 23										
Barrow-in-Furness 82 d																15 25								
Lancaster 6 a				14 56		15 23	15 28							15 37		16 17								
d				14 56		15 24	15 28							15 38		16 17								
Blackpool North 97 d																								
Preston 8 90 a				15 15		15 42	15 48							15 56		16 37								
Preston 8 90 d				15 17		15 45	16 10							15 58										
Wigan North Western 90 a				15 28		15 58								16 09										
d				15 28		15 58								16 09										
Bolton 82 a							16 34																	
Manchester Picc. 10 82 ⛴ a						16 27	16 56																	
Manchester Airport ✈ a						16 47	17 17																	
Liverpool Lime Street 10 91 a																								
d										15 34	15 47									16 04				
Liverpool South Parkway 91 ✈ d										15 44										16 15				
Runcorn 91 d										15 52	16 03									16 25				
Warrington Bank Quay a				15 39										16 20										
d				15 39										16 20										
Manchester Picc. 10 84 ⛴ d		15 27	15 35										15 55						16 07		16 15	16 27		16 35
Stockport 84 d		15 35	15 43										16 04						16 16		16 23	16 35		16 43
Wilmslow 84 d													16 11											
Holyhead 81 ⛴ d	13 58																							
Bangor (Gwynedd) 81 d	14 25																							
Llandudno Junction 81 d	14 43																							
Wrexham General 75 d																								
Chester 81 d	15 35																						16 35	
Crewe 10 a	15 54			15 58						16 16	16 21		16 27							16 45			16 54	
d	15 56			16 01	16 02					16 19	16 22		16 29							16 49			16 56	
Macclesfield d		15 49	15 56																			16 49		16 56
Stoke-on-Trent d		16 07	16 12		16 28							←			←				16 44		16 50	17 07		17 12
Stafford a		16 24			16 50					16 44	16 40	16 44			16 50				17 02	17 09		17 25		
d		16 25			16 56					16 45	16 42	16 45			16 56				17 03	17 10		17 26		
Penkridge a					→					→										17 15				
Wolverhampton 7 ⛴ a		16 39		16 33								16 58							17 16	17 27		17 39		
Birmingham New St. 12 68 a		16 58		17 05								17 17							17 33	17 47		17 58		
Birmingham International 68 ✈ a		17 13		17 19																		18 13		
Coventry 68 a		17 24		17 30																		18 24		
Lichfield Trent Valley a															17 12									
Tamworth Low Level a															17 19									
Nuneaton a															17 35									
Rugby 66 a															17 51									
Milton Keynes Central 66 a	17 02			17 58											18 14						17 46		18 02	
Watford Junction 66 a																								
London Euston 15 ⊖66 a	17 39		17 43	18 34							17 59		18 05	18 13	18 50						18 24		18 39	18 43

OVERNIGHT SLEEPERS. For sleeper trains, operated by First ScotRail, please see Tables 400 - 404.

For complete service between Manchester and Preston, Blackpool and between Barrow-in-furness and Lancaster, please see Table 82.

For complete service between Crewe and Liverpool Lime Street, see Table 91

For complete service between Crewe/Stoke-on-Trent & Manchester see Table 84

For complete service between Crewe and Holyhead please see Table 81.

For complete service between Coventry-Birmingham-Wolverhampton-Stafford please see Table 68

For complete service between Windermere and Oxenholme Lake District, please see Table 83

Table 65R

Saturdays

14 December to 28 December

Scotland and North West England - West Midlands and London

Route Diagram - refer to first Page of Table 65

Station		VT ◇1	LM 1	TP ◇1			VT ◇1	VT ◇	LM 1	VT ◇1	LM 1	VT ◇1	VT ◇1	LM 1			XC ◇1	LM 1	VT ◇1	XC ◇1	VT ◇1	VT ◇1	LM 1		
Inverness 229	d																								
Aberdeen 229	d																								
Dundee 229	d																								
Perth 229	d																								
Edinburgh 225,226,228,230,242	d			14 16																		14 52			
Haymarket 225,226,228,230,242	d			14u21																		14 57			
Glasgow Central 226,216	d	14 00											14 40												
Motherwell 226	d																								
Carstairs 226	d																								
Lockerbie	d			15 15																					
Carlisle 216	a	15 07		15 36									15 46									16 06			
	d	15 10		15 38									15 49									16 08			
Penrith North Lakes	d																					16 22			
Windermere 83	d																								
Oxenholme Lake District	a	15 43		16 14									16 22												
	d	15 44		16 14									16 24												
Barrow-in-Furness 82	d																								
Lancaster	a			16 29									16 37									16 56			
	d			16 29									16 38									16 57			
Blackpool North 97	d																								
Preston 90	a	16 12		16 48									16 56									17 15			
Preston 90	d	16 17		16 49									16 58									17 17			
Wigan North Western 90	a	16 28											17 09									17 28			
	d	16 28											17 09									17 28			
Bolton 82	a																								
Manchester Picc. 82	a			17 30																					
Manchester Airport	a			17 47																					
Liverpool Lime Street 91	a																								
	d								16 34	16 47								17 04							
Liverpool South Parkway 91	d								16 44									17 15							
Runcorn 91	d								16 52	17 03								17 25							
Warrington Bank Quay	a	16 39											17 20									17 39			
	d	16 39											17 20									17 39			
Manchester Picc. 84	d											16 55					17 06		17 15	17 27	17 35				
Stockport 84	d											17 04					17 15		17 23	17 36	17 43				
Wilmslow 84	d											17 11													
Holyhead 81	d																								
Bangor (Gwynedd) 81	d																								
Llandudno Junction 81	d																								
Wrexham General 75	d																								
Chester 81	d						17 35	20 35																	
Crewe	a	16 58					17 54	20 54	17 17	17 22		17 27						17 47				17 59			
	d	17 01	17 02						17 19	17 23		17 29						17 49				18 01	18 02		
Macclesfield	d																17 27				17 56				
Stoke-on-Trent	d		17 28								←			←			17 45		17 50	18 07	18 12		18 28		
Stafford	a		17 49						17 43	17 41	17 43			17 49			18 03	18 09		18 25			18 50		
	d		17 56						17 44	17 43	17 44			17 56			18 04	18 10		18 26			18 56		
Penkridge	a		→						→									18 15					→		
Wolverhampton	a	17 33									17 57						18 15	18 27		18 40		18 32			
Birmingham New St. 68	a	18 05									18 17						18 33	18 47		18 58		19 05			
Birmingham International 68	a	18 19																		19 13		19 19			
Coventry 68	a	18 30																		19 24		19 30			
Lichfield Trent Valley	a													18 12											
Tamworth Low Level	a													18 19											
Nuneaton	a													18 35											
Rugby 66	a													18 51								19 42			
Milton Keynes Central 66	a	18 58												19 14					18 46			20 05			
Watford Junction 66	a																					20s34			
London Euston ⊖66	a	19 34								19 01		19 09	19 14	19 50					19 24		19 43	20 55			

OVERNIGHT SLEEPERS. For sleeper trains, operated by First ScotRail, please see Tables 400 - 404.

For complete service between Manchester and Preston, Blackpool and between Barrow-in-furness and Lancaster, please see Table 82.

For complete service between Crewe and Liverpool Lime Street, see Table 91

For complete service between Crewe/Stoke-on-Trent & Manchester see Table 84

For complete service between Crewe and Holyhead please see Table 81.

For complete service between Coventry-Birmingham-Wolverhampton-Stafford please see Table 68

For complete service between Windermere and Oxenholme Lake District, please see Table 83

Table 65R

Saturdays

14 December to 28 December

Scotland and North West England - West Midlands and London

Route Diagram - refer to first Page of Table 65

		LM	VT	LM	LM	VT	VT	TP	TP	XC	LM	VT	XC	VT	VT	LM	TP	LM	VT	LM	LM	VT
		1	◇1	1	1	◇1	◇1	◇1	◇1	◇1	1	◇1	◇1	◇1	◇1	1	◇1	1	◇1	1	1	◇1
Inverness 229	d																					
Aberdeen 229	d																					
Dundee 229	d																					
Perth 229	d																					
Edinburgh 10 225,226,228,230,242	d																16 12					
Haymarket 225,226,228,230,242	d																16u16					
Glasgow Central 15 226,216	d						15 40								16 00							
Motherwell 226	d																					
Carstairs 226	d																					
Lockerbie	d																17 10					
Carlisle 8 216	a						16 46								17 08		17 32					
	d						16 49								17 09		17 33					
Penrith North Lakes	d						17 03										17 48					
Windermere 83	d							17 06														
Oxenholme Lake District	a							17 25							17 44							
	d							17 30							17 44							
Barrow-in-Furness 82	d								17 21													
Lancaster 6	a						17 37	17 47	18 17								18 24					
	d						17 38	17 48	18 17								18 25					
Blackpool North 97	d																					
Preston 8 90	a						17 56	18 06	18 37						18 12		18 45					
Preston 8 90	d						17 58	18 08							18 17		18 45					
Wigan North Western 90	a						18 09								18 27		18 58					
	d						18 09								18 28		18 59					
Bolton 82	a							18 34														
Manchester Picc. 10 82	a							18 56									19 29					
Manchester Airport	a							19 17									19 46					
Liverpool Lime Street 10 91	a																					
	d	17 34	17 47								18 04							18 34	18 47			
Liverpool South Parkway 91	d	17 44									18 15							18 44				
Runcorn 91	d	17 52	18 03								18 24							18 52	19 03			
Warrington Bank Quay	a						18 20								18 38							
	d						18 20								18 39							
Manchester Picc. 10 84	d					17 55				18 05		18 15	18 27	18 35								18 55
Stockport 84	d					18 04				18 13		18 23	18 35	18 43								19 04
Wilmslow 84	d					18 11																19 11
Holyhead 81	d																					
Bangor (Gwynedd) 81	d																					
Llandudno Junction 81	d																					
Wrexham General 75	d																					
Chester 81	d																					
Crewe 10	a	18 20				18 27					18 46				18 58			19 19				19 27
	d	18 22				18 29					18 49				19 01	19 02		19 21				19 29
Macclesfield	d									18 26				18 56								
Stoke-on-Trent	d			←	←					18 44		18 49	19 07	19 12		19 28				←	←	
Stafford	a	18 42	18 36	18 42	18 50					19 02	19 09		19 25			19 50		19 45	19 35	19 45	19 50	
	d	18 43	18 36	18 43	18 56					19 03	19 10		19 25			19 51		19 45	19 36	19 45	19 51	
Penkridge	a	→									19 15					→		→		19 51		
Wolverhampton 7	a			18 56						19 15	19 27		19 39		19 32					20 01		
Birmingham New St. 12 68	a			19 17						19 33	19 47		19 59		20 05					20 19		
Birmingham International 68	a												20 13		20 19							
Coventry 68	a												20 24		20 30							
Lichfield Trent Valley	a				19 12																20 07	
Tamworth Low Level	a				19 19																20 14	
Nuneaton	a				19 35																20 30	
Rugby 66	a				19 51										20 42						20 46	
Milton Keynes Central 66	a											19 45			21 04							
Watford Junction 66	a														21s35							
London Euston 15 ⊖66	a		19 59			20 05	20 16					20 26		20 59	21 56				21 15			21 20

OVERNIGHT SLEEPERS. For sleeper trains, operated by First ScotRail, please see Tables 400 - 404.

For complete service between Manchester and Preston, Blackpool and between Barrow-in-furness and Lancaster, please see Table 82.

For complete service between Crewe and Liverpool Lime Street, see Table 91

For complete service between Crewe/Stoke-on-Trent & Manchester see Table 84

For complete service between Crewe and Holyhead please see Table 81.

For complete service between Coventry-Birmingham-Wolverhampton-Stafford please see Table 68

For complete service between Windermere and Oxenholme Lake District, please see Table 83

Table 65R

Saturdays

14 December to 28 December

Scotland and North West England - West Midlands and London

Route Diagram - refer to first Page of Table 65

		VT		XC	LM	XC		VT	VT	TP	LM	VT	VT	NT	XC	VT		TP	TP	XC	LM	VT		XC	VT
		◇1		◇1	1	◇1		◇1	◇1	◇1	1	◇1	◇1		◇1	◇1		◇1	◇1	◇1	1	◇1		◇1	◇1
						A																			
		☕		🛒		🛒		☕	☕	🛒		☕	☕			☕			🛒			☕			☕
Inverness 229	d																								
Aberdeen 229	d																								
Dundee 229	d																								
Perth 229	d																								
Edinburgh 225,226,228,230,242	d								16 52										18 12						
Haymarket 225,226,228,230,242	d								16 57										18u16						
Glasgow Central 226,216	d	16 40								17 06			17 40			18 00									18 40
Motherwell 226	d	16 54																							
Carstairs 226	d																								
Lockerbie	d									18 06			18 32						19 11						
Carlisle 216	a	17 49							18 06	18 30			18 50			19 07			19 32						19 46
	d	17 52							18 07	18 30			18 52			19 09			19 33						19 48
Penrith North Lakes	d									18 45			19 06						19 48						20 02
Windermere 83	d																								
Oxenholme Lake District	a	18 25							18 42	19 09			19 28						20 12						20 24
	d	18 26							18 43	19 09			19 29						20 13						20 25
Barrow-in-Furness 82	d																	19 17							
Lancaster	a	18 40							18 57	19 24			19 43			19 55		20 17	20 27						20 39
	d	18 41							18 58	19 24			19 44			19 57		20 18	20 28						20 40
Blackpool North 97	d																								
Preston 90	a	18 59							19 15	19 44			20 02			20 15		20 37	20 46						20 58
Preston 90	d	19 01							19 17	19 45			20 04			20 17			20 48						21 00
Wigan North Western 90	a	19 12							19 29				20 15			20 28									21 11
	d	19 12							19 29				20 15			20 28									21 11
Bolton 82	a									20 08															
Manchester Picc. 82	a									20 27									21 27						
Manchester Airport	a									20 46									21 46						
Liverpool Lime Street 91	a																								
	d				19 04						19 34	19 48									20 34				
Liverpool South Parkway 91	d				19 14						19 44										20 44				
Runcorn 91	d				19 23						19 52	20 04									20 52				
Warrington Bank Quay	a	19 23							19 39				20 26			20 39									21 22
	d	19 23							19 40				20 26			20 39									21 22
Manchester Picc. 84	d			19 07		19 27		19 35						20 04	20 07					20 27		20 35		21 07	
Stockport 84	d			19 16		19 35		19 43						20 17	20 16					20 35		20 43			
Wilmslow 84	d													20 31											
Holyhead 81	d																								
Bangor (Gwynedd) 81	d																								
Llandudno Junction 81	d																								
Wrexham General 75	d																								
Chester 81	d																								
Crewe	a				19 49				19 59		20 16	20 21	20 45	21 01		20 59					21 16				21 41
	d				19 51				20 01		20 18	20 23	20 47			21 01					21 17				21 43
Macclesfield	d					19 49		19 56												20 49		20 56			
Stoke-on-Trent	d			19 44		20 07		20 12							20 44					21 07		21 12		21 45	
Stafford	a			20 02	20 11	20 25					20 40	20 41			21 02					21 26	21 42			22 02	22 07
	d			20 03	20 12	20 26					20 40	20 43			21 03					21 27	21 42			22 03	22 08
Penkridge	a										20 49										21 48				
Wolverhampton	a			20 15	20 28	20 39			20 32		20 59				21 15	21 32				21 39	21 59			22 14	22 22
Birmingham New St. 68	a			20 33	20 48	20 58			21 05		21 17				21 32	21 55				21 58	22 20			22 32	22 46
Birmingham International 68	a					21 13			21 19																
Coventry 68	a					21 24			21 30																
Lichfield Trent Valley	a																								
Tamworth Low Level	a																								
Nuneaton	a																								
Rugby 66	a								21 42																
Milton Keynes Central 66	a	20 42						21 10	22 04				21 51									22 10			
Watford Junction 66	a	21s15							22s34													22s40			
London Euston 66	a	21 38						22 00	22 55			22 15	22 45									23 02			

A 🛒 to Birmingham New St.

OVERNIGHT SLEEPERS. For sleeper trains, operated by First ScotRail, please see Tables 400 - 404.

For complete service between Manchester and Preston, Blackpool and between Barrow-in-furness and Lancaster, please see Table 82.

For complete service between Crewe and Liverpool Lime Street, see Table 91

For complete service between Crewe/Stoke-on-Trent & Manchester see Table 84

For complete service between Crewe and Holyhead please see Table 81.

For complete service between Coventry-Birmingham-Wolverhampton-Stafford please see Table 68

For complete service between Windermere and Oxenholme Lake District, please see Table 83

Table 65R

Saturdays

14 December to 28 December

Scotland and North West England - West Midlands and London

Route Diagram - refer to first Page of Table 65

Station	Table		VT	XC	LM	TP	NT	LM
			◇1	◇1	1	◇1		1
			🍴					
Inverness	229	d						
Aberdeen	229	d						
Dundee	229	d						
Perth	229	d						
Edinburgh 10	225,226,228,230,242	d	18 52					
Haymarket	225,226,228,230,242	d	18 56					
Glasgow Central 15	226,216	d						
Motherwell	226	d						
Carstairs	226	d						
Lockerbie		d						
Carlisle 8	216	a	20 05					
		d	20 08					
Penrith North Lakes		d	20 22					
Windermere	83	d				21 40		
Oxenholme Lake District		a	20 45			21 59		
		d	20 45			22 00		
Barrow-in-Furness	82	d					21 43	
Lancaster 6		a	21 00			22 17	22 45	
		d	21 00			22 17	22 46	
Blackpool North	97	d						
Preston 8	90	a	21 18			22 38	23 11	
Preston 8	90	d	21 21					
Wigan North Western	90	a	21 31					
		d	21 32					
Bolton	82	a						
Manchester Picc. 10	82 ⛴	a						
Manchester Airport	✈	a						
Liverpool Lime Street 10	91	a						
		d			21 34			22 04
Liverpool South Parkway	91 ✈	d			21 44			22 14
Runcorn	91	d			21 52			22 23
Warrington Bank Quay		a	21 42					
		d	21 43					
Manchester Picc. 10	84 ⛴	d		21 27				
Stockport	84	d		21 35				
Wilmslow	84	d						
Holyhead	81 ⛴	d						
Bangor (Gwynedd)	81	d						
Llandudno Junction	81	d						
Wrexham General	75	d						
Chester	81	d						
Crewe 10		a	22 02		22 16			22 48
		d	22 04		22 24			
Macclesfield		d		21 49				
Stoke-on-Trent		d		22 07				
Stafford		a	22 22	22 28	22 44			
		d	22 23	22 29	22 45			
Penkridge		a			22 50			
Wolverhampton 7	⛴	a	22 40	22 43	23 01			
Birmingham New St. 12	68	a	22 59	23 01	23 20			
Birmingham International	68 ✈	a						
Coventry	68	a						
Lichfield Trent Valley		a						
Tamworth Low Level		a						
Nuneaton		a						
Rugby	66	a						
Milton Keynes Central	66	a						
Watford Junction	66	a						
London Euston 15	⊖66	a						

OVERNIGHT SLEEPERS. For sleeper trains, operated by First ScotRail, please see Tables 400 - 404.

For complete service between Manchester and Preston, Blackpool and between Barrow-in-furness and Lancaster, please see Table 82.

For complete service between Crewe and Liverpool Lime Street, see Table 91

For complete service between Crewe/Stoke-on-Trent & Manchester see Table 84

For complete service between Crewe and Holyhead please see Table 81.

For complete service between Coventry-Birmingham-Wolverhampton-Stafford please see Table 68

For complete service between Windermere and Oxenholme Lake District, please see Table 83

Table 65R

Saturdays

4 January to 8 February

Scotland and North West England - West Midlands and London

Route Diagram - refer to first Page of Table 65

	NT	SR	XC	VT	XC	NT	LM	VT	VT	VT	XC	LM	VT	VT	NT	LM	VT	TP	LM	VT
		B	◇1	◇1	◇1		1	◇1	◇1	◇1	◇1	1	◇1	◇1		1	◇1	◇1	1	◇1
		🛏 ✕	🛒	☕	🛒			☕	☕	☕	🛒		☕	☕			☕			☕
Inverness 229 d																				
Aberdeen 229 d																				
Dundee 229 d																				
Perth 229 d																				
Edinburgh 10 225,226,228,230,242 d																				
Haymarket 225,226,228,230,242 d																				
Glasgow Central 15 226,216 d																				
Motherwell 226 d		00u01																		
Carstairs 226 d		00u16																		
Lockerbie d																				
Carlisle 8 216 a																				
d		01u40																		
Penrith North Lakes d																				
Windermere 83 d																				
Oxenholme Lake District a																				
d																				
Barrow-in-Furness 82 d																		05 32		
Lancaster 6 a																		06 24		
d										05 38								06 24		
Blackpool North 97 d																				
Preston 8 90 a										05 55								06 43		
Preston 8 90 d										05 58							06 17	06 44		
Wigan North Western 90 a										06 09							06 27			
d										06 09							06 28			
Bolton 82 a																		07 07		
Manchester Picc. 10 82 a																		07 27		
Manchester Airport a																		07 47		
Liverpool Lime Street 10 91 a																				
d								05 47											06 32	06 45
Liverpool South Parkway 91 d																			06 42	
Runcorn 91 d								06 03											06 50	07 01
Warrington Bank Quay a										06 20							06 39			
d										06 20							06 39			
Manchester Picc. 10 84 d			05 11	05 25		05 35			05 55		06 00		06 10	06 35	06 46					
Stockport 84 d				05 34					06 03		06 08		06 18	06 43						
Wilmslow 84 d	00 01			05 41		06 14			06 11						07 21					
Holyhead 81 d																				
Bangor (Gwynedd) 81 d																				
Llandudno Junction 81 d																				
Wrexham General 75 d																				
Chester 81 d																				
Crewe 10 a	00 30		05 41	05 57		06 43			06 27						07 46		06 58		07 14	07 18
d			05 47	06 00			06 11		06 29			06 47				06 59	07 01		07 16	07 20
Macclesfield d											06 21		06 31	06 56						
Stoke-on-Trent d			06 08		←						06 39		06 48	07 12		07 20				
Stafford a			06 25	06 18	06 25		06 34	06 34			06 57	07 10				07 43			07 37	07 38
d			06 26	06 19	06 26		06 35	06 36			06 58	07 12				07 48			07 41	07 39
Penkridge a			→				06 40					07 17				→			→	
Wolverhampton 7 a					06 39		06 51				07 12	07 28					07 32			
Birmingham New St. 12 68 a					06 57		07 18				07 33	07 47					08 05			
Birmingham International 68 a					07 13												08 19			
Coventry 68 a					07 24												08 29			
Lichfield Trent Valley a													07 11							
Tamworth Low Level a													07 17							
Nuneaton a								06 58												
Rugby 66 a				06 50										07 52						
Milton Keynes Central 66 a				07 11					07 31	07 38							08 58			
Watford Junction 66 a		06s23		07s32				07s45												
London Euston 15 ⊖66 a		06 48		07 53				08 05	08 10	08 17			08 28	08 46			09 34			09 00

OVERNIGHT SLEEPERS. For sleeper trains, operated by First ScotRail, please see Tables 400 - 404.

For complete service between Manchester and Preston, Blackpool and between Barrow-in-furness and Lancaster, please see Table 82.

For complete service between Crewe and Liverpool Lime Street, see Table 91

For complete service between Crewe/Stoke-on-Trent & Manchester see Table 84

For complete service between Crewe and Holyhead please see Table 81.

For complete service between Coventry-Birmingham-Wolverhampton-Stafford please see Table 68

For complete service between Windermere and Oxenholme Lake District, please see Table 83

Table 65R

Saturdays

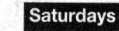

4 January to 8 February

Scotland and North West England - West Midlands and London

Route Diagram - refer to first Page of Table 65

Station			LM	VT	VT	LM			XC	VT	VT	LM	VT	XC	VT	VT	LM		TP		LM	VT	LM	VT	VT	LM
			1	◇1	◇1	1			◇1	◇1	◇1	1	◇1	◇1	◇1	◇1	1		◇1		1	◇1	1	◇1	◇1	1
				☕	☕				🛒	☕	☕		☕	🛒	☕	☕						☕		☕	☕	
Inverness	229	d																								
Aberdeen	229	d																								
Dundee	229	d																								
Perth	229	d																								
Edinburgh [10]	225,226,228,230,242	d																								
Haymarket	225,226,228,230,242	d																								
Glasgow Central [15]	226,216	d			04 26																				05 40	
Motherwell	226	d																								
Carstairs	226	d																								
Lockerbie		d																								
Carlisle [8]	216	a			05 42																				06 47	
		d			05 44																				06 49	
Penrith North Lakes		d			05 58																					
Windermere	83	d																								
Oxenholme Lake District		a			06 21																				07 22	
		d			06 21																				07 24	
Barrow-in-Furness	82	d																	06 15							
Lancaster [6]		a			06 36														07 15						07 37	
		d			06 36											06 58			07 23						07 38	
Blackpool North	97	d																								
Preston [8]	90	a			06 54											07 15			07 41						07 56	
Preston [8]	90	d			06 57											07 17			07 43						07 58	
Wigan North Western	90	a			07 07											07 28			07 55						08 09	
		d			07 09											07 28			07 56						08 09	
Bolton	82	a																								
Manchester Picc. [10]	82 🚊	a																	08 26							
Manchester Airport	✈	a																	08 47							
Liverpool Lime Street [10]	91	a																								
		d										07 04	07 19								07 34	07 47				
Liverpool South Parkway	91 ✈	d										07 14									07 44					
Runcorn	91	d										07 22	07 36								07 52	08 03				
Warrington Bank Quay		a			07 18											07 39									08 20	
		d			07 19											07 39									08 20	
Manchester Picc. [10]	84 🚊	d		06 55					07 07	07 15				07 27	07 35									07 55		
Stockport	84	d		07 04					07 16	07 23				07 35	07 43									08 04		
Wilmslow	84	d		07 11																				08 11		
Holyhead	81 ⛴	d																								
Bangor (Gwynedd)	81	d																								
Llandudno Junction	81	d																								
Wrexham General	75	d																								
Chester	81	d									07 17															
Crewe [10]		a		07 27							07 36	07 47	07 52			07 58					08 16	08 21		08 27		
		d		07 29							07 41	07 49	07 55			08 01	08 02				08 19	08 22		08 29		
Macclesfield		d												07 49	07 56											
Stoke-on-Trent		d	←			←			07 44	07 50				08 07	08 12		08 28						←			←
Stafford		a	07 37			07 43			08 02			08 09	08 15	08 25			08 50				08 42	08 40	08 42			08 50
		d	07 41			07 48			08 03			08 10	08 16	08 26			08 56				08 43	08 42	08 43			08 56
Penkridge		a	07 46									08 15					↪				↪		08 48			
Wolverhampton [7]	🚊	a	07 57						08 15			08 26		08 39		08 32							08 58			
Birmingham New St. [12]	68	a	08 17						08 34			08 48		08 58		09 05							09 17			
Birmingham International	68 ✈	a												09 13		09 19										
Coventry	68	a												09 24		09 30										
Lichfield Trent Valley		a				08 04							08 30													09 12
Tamworth Low Level		a				08 11							08 37													09 19
Nuneaton		a				08 26																09 04				09 35
Rugby	66	a				08 42																				09 51
Milton Keynes Central	66	a				09 05				08 46						09 58										10 14
Watford Junction	66	a																								
London Euston [15]	⊖66	a		09 05	09 13	09 50				09 24	09 30		09 47		09 43	10 35						10 06		10 11	10 16	10 50

OVERNIGHT SLEEPERS. For sleeper trains, operated by First ScotRail, please see Tables 400 - 404.

For complete service between Manchester and Preston, Blackpool and between Barrow-in-furness and Lancaster, please see Table 82.

For complete service between Crewe and Liverpool Lime Street, see Table 91

For complete service between Crewe/Stoke-on-Trent & Manchester see Table 84

For complete service between Crewe and Holyhead please see Table 81.

For complete service between Coventry-Birmingham-Wolverhampton-Stafford please see Table 68

For complete service between Windermere and Oxenholme Lake District, please see Table 83

Table 65R

Saturdays

4 January to 8 February

Scotland and North West England - West Midlands and London

Route Diagram - refer to first Page of Table 65

Station	Table		XC	LM	VT	VT	XC	VT	VT	LM	TP	TP	NT	LM	VT	LM	VT	VT	LM	XC	LM
			◇1	1	◇1	◇1	◇1	◇1	◇1	1	◇1	◇1		1	◇1	1	◇1	◇1	1	◇1	1
			⊼		⊏P	⊏P	⊼	⊏P	⊏P		⊼				⊏P		⊏P	⊏P		⊼	
Inverness	229	d																			
Aberdeen	229	d																			
Dundee	229	d																			
Perth	229	d																			
Edinburgh 10	225,226,228,230,242	d									06 15										
Haymarket	225,226,228,230,242	d									06u19										
Glasgow Central 15	226,216	d							05 50									06 30			
Motherwell	226	d							06 04									06 44			
Carstairs	226	d																			
Lockerbie		d																07 25			
Carlisle 8	216	a							07 01		07 33							07 43			
		d							07 02		07 33							07 46			
Penrith North Lakes		d							07 18									08 00			
Windermere	83	d																			
Oxenholme Lake District		a							07 41		08 09							08 22			
		d							07 42		08 10							08 23			
Barrow-in-Furness	82	d										07 33									
Lancaster 6		a							07 56		08 25	08 33						08 37			
		d							07 57		08 26	08 33						08 38			
Blackpool North	97	d																			
Preston 8	90	a							08 15		08 44	08 52						08 56			
Preston 8	90	d							08 17		08 45	09 10						08 58			
Wigan North Western	90	a							08 28		08 58							09 09			
		d							08 28		08 58							09 09			
Bolton	82	a										09 34									
Manchester Picc. 10	82 ⛴	a									09 27	09 56									
Manchester Airport	✈	a									09 47	10 17									
Liverpool Lime Street 10	91	a																			
		d		08 04										08 34	08 47						09 04
Liverpool South Parkway	91 ✈	d		08 15										08 44							09 15
Runcorn	91	d		08 24										08 52	09 03						09 25
Warrington Bank Quay		a							08 39									09 20			
		d							08 39									09 20			
Manchester Picc. 10	84 ⛴	d	08 07		08 15		08 27	08 35					08 46				08 55			09 07	
Stockport	84	d	08 16		08 23		08 35	08 43									09 04			09 16	
Wilmslow	84	d											09 18				09 11				
Holyhead	81 ⛴	d				06 52															
Bangor (Gwynedd)	81	d				07 20															
Llandudno Junction	81	d				07 38															
Wrexham General	75	d																			
Chester	81	d				08 35															
Crewe 10		a		08 47		08 54			08 58				09 44	09 19	09 23		09 29				09 45
		d		08 49		08 56			09 01	09 02				09 19	09 25		09 30				09 49
Macclesfield		d					08 49	08 56													
Stoke-on-Trent		d	08 44		08 50		09 07	09 12		09 28						←			←	09 44	
Stafford		a	09 02	09 09			09 25			09 51				09 45	09 43	09 45			09 51	10 02	10 10
		d	09 03	09 10			09 26			09 56				09 45	09 44	09 45			09 56	10 03	10 10
Penkridge		a		09 15						→				→							10 16
Wolverhampton 7	⛴	a	09 15	09 26			09 39		09 33							09 58				10 15	10 27
Birmingham New St. 12	68	a	09 33	09 47			09 58		10 05							10 17				10 33	10 47
Birmingham International	68 ✈	a					10 13		10 19												
Coventry	68	a					10 24		10 30												
Lichfield Trent Valley		a																	10 12		
Tamworth Low Level		a																	10 19		
Nuneaton		a																	10 35		
Rugby	66	a																	10 51		
Milton Keynes Central	66	a			09 46	10 02			10 58										11 14		
Watford Junction	66	a																			
London Euston 15	⊖66	a			10 24	10 39		10 43	11 33						11 05		11 08	11 16	11 50		

OVERNIGHT SLEEPERS. For sleeper trains, operated by First ScotRail, please see Tables 400 - 404.

For complete service between Manchester and Preston, Blackpool and between Barrow-in-furness and Lancaster, please see Table 82.

For complete service between Crewe and Liverpool Lime Street, see Table 91

For complete service between Crewe/Stoke-on-Trent & Manchester see Table 84

For complete service between Crewe and Holyhead please see Table 81.

For complete service between Coventry-Birmingham-Wolverhampton-Stafford please see Table 68

For complete service between Windermere and Oxenholme Lake District, please see Table 83

Table 65R

Saturdays

4 January to 8 February

Scotland and North West England - West Midlands and London

Route Diagram - refer to first Page of Table 65

		VT	VT	XC	VT	VT	LM	TP			LM	VT	LM	VT	VT	LM	TP			XC	LM	VT	VT	XC	VT
		◇1	◇1	◇1	◇1	◇1	1	◇1			1	◇1	1	◇1	◇1	1	◇1			◇1	1	◇1	◇1	◇1	◇1
Inverness 229	d																								
Aberdeen 229	d																								
Dundee 229	d																								
Perth 229	d																								
Edinburgh 10 225,226,228,230,242	d					06 52																			
Haymarket 225,226,228,230,242	d					06 56																			
Glasgow Central 15 226,216	d							07 09							07 35										
Motherwell 226	d														07 52										
Carstairs 226	d																								
Lockerbie	d							08 08																	
Carlisle 8 216	a					08 06		08 29							08 47										
	d					08 07		08 29							08 49										
Penrith North Lakes	d					08 22		08 45																	
Windermere 83	d																								
Oxenholme Lake District	a							09 09							09 22										
	d							09 10							09 23										
Barrow-in-Furness 82	d																08 50								
Lancaster 6	a					08 57		09 25							09 37		09 46								
	d					08 57		09 25							09 38		09 47								
Blackpool North 97	d																								
Preston 8 90	a					09 15		09 44							09 56		10 07								
Preston 8 90	d					09 17		09 44							09 58										
Wigan North Western 90	a					09 28		09 57							10 09										
	d					09 28		09 58							10 09										
Bolton 82	a																								
Manchester Picc. 10 82	a							10 26																	
Manchester Airport	a							10 46																	
Liverpool Lime Street 10 91	a																								
	d										09 34	09 47									10 04				
Liverpool South Parkway 91	d										09 44										10 15				
Runcorn 91	d										09 52	10 03									10 25				
Warrington Bank Quay	a					09 39									10 20										
	d					09 39									10 20										
Manchester Picc. 10 84	d	09 15		09 27	09 35									09 55						10 07		10 15		10 27	10 35
Stockport 84	d	09 23		09 35	09 43									10 04						10 16		10 23		10 35	10 43
Wilmslow 84	d													10 11											
Holyhead 81	d		07 55																				08 55		
Bangor (Gwynedd) 81	d		08 22																				09 22		
Llandudno Junction 81	d		08 40																				09 40		
Wrexham General 75	d																								
Chester 81	d		09 35																				10 35		
Crewe 10	a		09 54			09 58					10 16	10 21		10 27							10 45		10 54		
	d		09 56			10 01	10 02				10 19	10 22		10 29							10 49		10 56		
Macclesfield	d			09 49	09 56																			10 49	10 56
Stoke-on-Trent	d	09 50		10 07	10 12		10 28						←			←				10 44		10 50		11 07	11 12
Stafford	a			10 25			10 50				10 42	10 40	10 42			10 50				11 02	11 09			11 25	
	d			10 26			10 56				10 43	10 42	10 43			10 56				11 03	11 10			11 26	
Penkridge	a						→				→										11 15				
Wolverhampton 7	a			10 39		10 32							10 56							11 15	11 27			11 39	
Birmingham New St. 12 68	a			10 58		11 05							11 17							11 33	11 47			11 59	
Birmingham International 68	a			11 13		11 19																		12 13	
Coventry 68	a			11 24		11 30																		12 24	
Lichfield Trent Valley	a															11 12									
Tamworth Low Level	a															11 19									
Nuneaton	a															11 35									
Rugby 66	a															11 51									
Milton Keynes Central 66	a	10 46	11 02			11 58										12 14						11 46	12 02		
Watford Junction 66	a																								
London Euston 15 ⊖66	a	11 24	11 39		11 43	12 33						11 59		12 05	12 13	12 50						12 24	12 39		12 43

OVERNIGHT SLEEPERS. For sleeper trains, operated by First ScotRail, please see Tables 400 - 404.

For complete service between Manchester and Preston, Blackpool and between Barrow-in-furness and Lancaster, please see Table 82.

For complete service between Crewe and Liverpool Lime Street, see Table 91

For complete service between Crewe/Stoke-on-Trent & Manchester see Table 84

For complete service between Crewe and Holyhead please see Table 81.

For complete service between Coventry-Birmingham-Wolverhampton-Stafford please see Table 68

For complete service between Windermere and Oxenholme Lake District, please see Table 83

Table 65R

Saturdays

4 January to 8 February

Scotland and North West England - West Midlands and London

Route Diagram - refer to first Page of Table 65

	VT	LM	TP		TP		LM	VT	LM	VT	VT	LM			XC	LM	VT	XC	VT	VT	VT	LM	TP	
	◇1	1	◇1		◇1		1	◇1	1	◇1	◇1	1			◇1	1	◇1	◇1	◇1	◇1	◇1	1	◇1	
	☕				🛒			☕		☕	☕				🛒		☕	🛒	☕	☕	☕			
Inverness 229 d																								
Aberdeen 229 d																								
Dundee 229 d																								
Perth 229 d																								
Edinburgh 10 225,226,228,230,242 d					08 10																08 52			
Haymarket 225,226,228,230,242 d					08u14																08 57			
Glasgow Central 15 226,216 d	08 00										08 40													
Motherwell 226 d																								
Carstairs 226 d																								
Lockerbie d																								
Carlisle 8 216 a	09 08				09 29						09 47										10 07			
d	09 09				09 30						09 49										10 08			
Penrith North Lakes d					09 46						10 03													
Windermere 83 d			09 37																				10 48	
Oxenholme Lake District a			09 56		10 09																10 42		11 08	
d			09 57		10 10																10 42		11 08	
Barrow-in-Furness 82 d																								
Lancaster 6 a	09 56		10 13		10 24						10 37										10 57		11 26	
d	09 56		10 14		10 25						10 38										10 57		11 26	
Blackpool North 97 d																								
Preston 8 90 a	10 14		10 33		10 43						10 56										11 15		11 45	
Preston 8 90 d	10 17				10 45						10 58										11 18		11 46	
Wigan North Western 90 a	10 28				10 58						11 09										11 28		11 58	
d	10 28				10 58						11 09										11 28		11 58	
Bolton 82 a																								
Manchester Picc. 10 82 ⛴ a					11 27																		12 27	
Manchester Airport ✈ a					11 47																		12 47	
Liverpool Lime Street 10 91 a																								
d							10 34	10 47								11 04								
Liverpool South Parkway 91 ✈ d							10 44									11 15								
Runcorn 91 d							10 52	11 03								11 25								
Warrington Bank Quay a	10 39										11 20										11 39			
d	10 39										11 20										11 40			
Manchester Picc. 10 84 ⛴ d										10 55					11 07		11 15	11 27		11 35				
Stockport 84 d										11 04					11 16		11 23	11 35		11 43				
Wilmslow 84 d										11 11														
Holyhead 81 ⛴ d																								
Bangor (Gwynedd) 81 d																								
Llandudno Junction 81 d																								
Wrexham General 75 d																								
Chester 81 d																			11 35					
Crewe 10 a	10 58						11 16	11 21		11 27						11 45			11 54		11 58			
d	11 01	11 02					11 19	11 22		11 29						11 49			11 56		12 01	12 02		
Macclesfield d																		11 49		11 56				
Stoke-on-Trent d		11 28							←			←			11 44		11 50	12 07		12 12		12 28		
Stafford a		11 50					11 42	11 40	11 42			11 50			12 02	12 09		12 24				12 50		
d		11 56					11 43	11 42	11 43			11 56			12 03	12 10		12 25				12 56		
Penkridge a		↦					↦									12 15						↦		
Wolverhampton 7 ⛴ a	11 31								11 56						12 15	12 27		12 39			12 33			
Birmingham New St. 12 68 a	12 05								12 17						12 33	12 47		12 58			13 05			
Birmingham International 68 ✈ a	12 19																	13 13			13 19			
Coventry 68 a	12 30																	13 24			13 30			
Lichfield Trent Valley a												12 12												
Tamworth Low Level a												12 19												
Nuneaton a												12 35												
Rugby 66 a												12 51												
Milton Keynes Central 66 a	12 58											13 14					12 46		13 02		13 58			
Watford Junction 66 a																								
London Euston 15 ⊖66 a	13 35							12 59		13 05	13 13	13 50					13 24		13 39	13 43	14 33			

OVERNIGHT SLEEPERS. For sleeper trains, operated by First ScotRail, please see Tables 400 - 404.

For complete service between Manchester and Preston, Blackpool and between Barrow-in-furness and Lancaster, please see Table 82.

For complete service between Crewe and Liverpool Lime Street, see Table 91

For complete service between Crewe/Stoke-on-Trent & Manchester see Table 84

For complete service between Crewe and Holyhead please see Table 81.

For complete service between Coventry-Birmingham-Wolverhampton-Stafford please see Table 68

For complete service between Windermere and Oxenholme Lake District, please see Table 83

Table 65R

Saturdays

4 January to 8 February

Scotland and North West England - West Midlands and London

Route Diagram - refer to first Page of Table 65

				LM	VT	LM	VT	VT	LM	TP			XC	LM	VT	XC	VT	VT	VT	LM	TP	TP	NT	LM	VT	LM
				1	◇1	1	◇1	◇1	1	◇1			◇1	1	◇1	◇1	◇1	◇1	◇1	1	◇1			1	◇1	1
					🍴		🍴	🍴					🛒		🍴	🛒	🍴	🍴	🍴		🛒	🚌			🍴	
Inverness	229	d																								
Aberdeen	229	d																								
Dundee	229	d																								
Perth	229	d																								
Edinburgh 10	225,226,228,230,242	d																			10 08					
Haymarket	225,226,228,230,242	d																			10 12					
Glasgow Central 15	226,216	d						09 40											10 00							
Motherwell	226	d																								
Carstairs	226	d																								
Lockerbie		d																			11 07					
Carlisle 8	216	a						10 47											11 09		11 28					
		d						10 49											11 11		11 31					
Penrith North Lakes		d																	11 25		11 47					
Windermere	83	d																				12 45				
Oxenholme Lake District		a						11 22													12 09					
		d						11 23													12 10					
Barrow-in-Furness	82	d								11 20																
Lancaster 6		a						11 37		12 17											12 25	13 24				
		d						11 38		12 17											12 26					
Blackpool North	97	d																								
Preston 8	90	a						11 56		12 37									12 14		12 44					
Preston 8	90	d						11 58											12 17		12 45					
Wigan North Western	90	a						12 09											12 27		12 58					
		d						12 09											12 28		12 58					
Bolton	82	a																								
Manchester Picc. 10	82 ⛴	a																			13 27					
Manchester Airport	✈	a																			13 47					
Liverpool Lime Street 10	91	a																								
		d		11 34	11 47									12 04										12 34	12 47	
Liverpool South Parkway	91 ✈	d		11 44										12 15										12 44		
Runcorn	91	d		11 52	12 03									12 25										12 52	13 03	
Warrington Bank Quay		a						12 20											12 38							
		d						12 20											12 39							
Manchester Picc. 10	84 ⛴	d					11 55						12 07		12 15	12 27		12 35					12 46			
Stockport	84	d					12 04						12 16		12 23	12 35		12 43								
Wilmslow	84	d					12 11																13 21			
Holyhead	81 ⛴	d																								
Bangor (Gwynedd)	81	d																								
Llandudno Junction	81	d																								
Wrexham General	75	d																								
Chester	81	d															12 35									
Crewe 10		a		12 16	12 21		12 27							12 45			12 54		12 58				13 46	13 19	13 23	
		d		12 19	12 22		12 29							12 49			12 56		13 01	13 02				13 19	13 25	
Macclesfield		d														12 49		12 56								
Stoke-on-Trent		d				←			←				12 44		12 50	13 07		13 12		13 28						←
Stafford		a		12 42	12 40	12 42			12 50				13 02	13 09		13 25				13 50				13 45	13 43	13 45
		d		12 43	12 42	12 43			12 56				13 03	13 10		13 26				13 56				13 45	13 44	13 45
Penkridge		a		→										13 15						→				→		
Wolverhampton 7	⛴	a				12 56							13 14	13 27		13 39			13 33							13 58
Birmingham New St. 12	68	a				13 17							13 32	13 47		13 58			14 05							14 17
Birmingham International	68 ✈	a														14 13			14 19							
Coventry	68	a														14 24			14 30							
Lichfield Trent Valley		a							13 12																	
Tamworth Low Level		a							13 19																	
Nuneaton		a							13 35																	
Rugby	66	a							13 51																	
Milton Keynes Central	66	a							14 14						13 46		14 02		14 58							
Watford Junction	66	a																								
London Euston 15	⊖66	a			14 00		14 05	14 13	14 50						14 24		14 39	14 43	15 34						15 05	

OVERNIGHT SLEEPERS. For sleeper trains, operated by First ScotRail, please see Tables 400 - 404.

For complete service between Manchester and Preston, Blackpool and between Barrow-in-furness and Lancaster, please see Table 82.

For complete service between Crewe and Liverpool Lime Street, see Table 91

For complete service between Crewe/Stoke-on-Trent & Manchester see Table 84

For complete service between Crewe and Holyhead please see Table 81.

For complete service between Coventry-Birmingham-Wolverhampton-Stafford please see Table 68

For complete service between Windermere and Oxenholme Lake District, please see Table 83

Table 65R

Saturdays

4 January to 8 February

Scotland and North West England - West Midlands and London

Route Diagram - refer to first Page of Table 65

	VT	TP		TP	TP	VT	LM	NT	XC	LM	VT	XC	VT	VT	VT	LM	TP	LM	VT	LM	VT	VT	LM
	◇1					◇1	1		◇1	1	◇1	◇1	◇1	◇1	◇1	1	◇1	1	◇1	1	◇1	◇1	1
	⊏P	🚌		🚌	🚌	⊏P			⊤o		⊏P	⊤o	⊏P	⊏P	⊏P		⊤o		⊏P		⊏P	⊏P	
					A																		
Inverness 229 d																							
Aberdeen 229 d																							
Dundee 229 d																							
Perth 229 d																							
Edinburgh 10 225,226,228,230,242 d																							
Haymarket 225,226,228,230,242 d																							
Glasgow Central 15 226,216 d						10 40																	
Motherwell 226 d																							
Carstairs 226 d																							
Lockerbie d																							
Carlisle 8 216 a						11 47																	
d						11 49																	
Penrith North Lakes d																							
Windermere 83 d		13 45		17 45	18 55																		
Oxenholme Lake District a						12 22																	
d						12 23																	
Barrow-in-Furness 82 d																							
Lancaster 6 a		14 24		18 24	19 34	12 37																	
d						12 38											13 25					13 38	
Blackpool North 97 d																							
Preston 8 90 a						12 56											13 43					13 56	
Preston 8 90 d						12 58									13 17		13 44					13 58	
Wigan North Western 90 a						13 09									13 28		13 57					14 09	
d						13 09									13 28		13 57					14 09	
Bolton 82 a																							
Manchester Picc. 10 82 🚊 a			and														14 26						
Manchester Airport ✈ a			hourly														14 47						
Liverpool Lime Street 10 91 a			until																				
d										13 04								13 34	13 47				
Liverpool South Parkway 91 ✈ d										13 15								13 44					
Runcorn 91 d										13 25								13 52	14 03				
Warrington Bank Quay a						13 20									13 39							14 20	
d						13 20									13 39							14 20	
Manchester Picc. 10 84 🚊 d	12 55							13 04	13 07		13 15	13 27		13 35							13 55		
Stockport 84 d	13 04							13 17	13 16		13 23	13 35		13 43							14 04		
Wilmslow 84 d	13 11							13 31													14 11		
Holyhead 81 ⛴ d																							
Bangor (Gwynedd) 81 d																							
Llandudno Junction 81 d																							
Wrexham General 75 d																							
Chester 81 d													13 35										
Crewe 10 a	13 29							14 01		13 45			13 54		13 58			14 16	14 21		14 27		
d	13 30									13 49			13 56		14 01	14 02		14 19	14 22		14 29		
Macclesfield d												13 49		13 56									
Stoke-on-Trent d							←		13 44		13 50	14 07		14 12		14 28				←			←
Stafford a							13 50		14 02	14 09		14 25				14 50		14 42	14 40	14 42			14 50
d							13 56		14 03	14 10		14 26				14 56		14 43	14 42	14 43			14 56
Penkridge a										14 15						→		→					
Wolverhampton 7 🚊 a									14 15	14 27		14 39			14 33					14 56			
Birmingham New St. 12 68 a									14 33	14 47		14 58			15 05					15 17			
Birmingham International 68 ✈ a												15 13			15 19								
Coventry 68 a												15 24			15 30								
Lichfield Trent Valley a							14 12																15 12
Tamworth Low Level a							14 19																15 19
Nuneaton a							14 35																15 35
Rugby 66 a							14 51																15 51
Milton Keynes Central 66 a							15 14				14 46		15 02		15 58								16 14
Watford Junction 66 a																							
London Euston 15 ⊖66 a	15 09					15 13	15 50				15 24		15 39	15 43	16 34				15 59		16 05	16 13	16 50

A also see last page of this date set for 2055

OVERNIGHT SLEEPERS. For sleeper trains, operated by First ScotRail, please see Tables 400 - 404.

For complete service between Manchester and Preston, Blackpool and between Barrow-in-furness and Lancaster, please see Table 82.

For complete service between Crewe and Liverpool Lime Street, see Table 91

For complete service between Crewe/Stoke-on-Trent & Manchester see Table 84

For complete service between Crewe and Holyhead please see Table 81.

For complete service between Coventry-Birmingham-Wolverhampton-Stafford please see Table 68

For complete service between Windermere and Oxenholme Lake District, please see Table 83

Table 65R

Saturdays

4 January to 8 February

Scotland and North West England - West Midlands and London

Route Diagram - refer to first Page of Table 65

	XC	LM	VT	XC	VT	VT	VT	LM		TP	TP		TP	LM	VT	LM	VT	VT	LM	NT	XC		LM	VT
	◇1 🛒	1	◇1 ☕	◇1 🛒	◇1 ☕	◇1 ☕	◇1 ☕	1		◇1 A 🛒	◇1 🛒		◇1 🛒	1	◇1 ☕	1	◇1 ☕	◇1 ☕	1		◇1 🛒		1	◇1 ☕
Inverness 229 d																								
Aberdeen 229 d																								
Dundee 229 d																								
Perth 229 d																								
Edinburgh 10 225,226,228,230,242 d																								
Haymarket 225,226,228,230,242 d																								
Glasgow Central 15 226,216 d																								
Motherwell 226 d																								
Carstairs 226 d																								
Lockerbie d																								
Carlisle 8 216 a																								
d																								
Penrith North Lakes d																								
Windermere 83 d																								
Oxenholme Lake District a																								
d																								
Barrow-in-Furness 82 d										13 20														
Lancaster 6 a										14 17														
d										14 17	14 25							14 39						
Blackpool North 97 d																								
Preston 8 90 a										14 37	14 44							14 56						
Preston 8 90 d							14 17			14 45	14 45							14 58						
Wigan North Western 90 a							14 28						←					15 09						
d							14 28											15 10						
Bolton 82 a										15 07	15 06		15 07											
Manchester Picc. 10 82 ⛴ a										↪	15 27		15 28											
Manchester Airport ✈ a											15 47		15 47											
Liverpool Lime Street 10 91 a																								
d		14 04												14 34	14 47								15 04	
Liverpool South Parkway 91 ✈ d		14 15												14 44									15 15	
Runcorn 91 d		14 25												14 52	15 03								15 25	
Warrington Bank Quay a							14 39											15 20						
d							14 39											15 21						
Manchester Picc. 10 84 ⛴ d	14 07		14 15	14 27		14 35											14 55			15 04	15 07			15 15
Stockport 84 d	14 16		14 23	14 35		14 43											15 04			15 17	15 16			15 23
Wilmslow 84 d																	15 11			15 31				
Holyhead 81 ⛴ d																								
Bangor (Gwynedd) 81 d																								
Llandudno Junction 81 d																								
Wrexham General 75 d																								
Chester 81 d					14 35																			
Crewe 10 a		14 45			14 54		14 58							15 16	15 21		15 27			16 01			15 45	
d		14 49			14 56		15 01	15 02						15 19	15 22		15 29						15 49	
Macclesfield d				14 49		14 56																		
Stoke-on-Trent d	14 44		14 50	15 07		15 12		15 28								←			←		15 44			15 50
Stafford a	15 02	15 09		15 25				15 50						15 42	15 40	15 42			15 50		16 02		16 09	
d	15 03	15 10		15 26				15 56						15 43	15 42	15 43			15 56		16 03		16 10	
Penkridge a		15 15						↪						↪									16 15	
Wolverhampton 7 ⛴ a	15 16	15 27		15 39			15 33									15 56					16 16		16 27	
Birmingham New St. 12 68 a	15 33	15 47		15 58			16 05									16 17					16 33		16 47	
Birmingham International 68 ✈ a				16 13			16 19																	
Coventry 68 a				16 24			16 30																	
Lichfield Trent Valley a																			16 12					
Tamworth Low Level a																			16 19					
Nuneaton a																			16 35					
Rugby 66 a																			16 51					
Milton Keynes Central 66 a			15 46		16 02		16 58												17 14					16 46
Watford Junction 66 a																								
London Euston 15 ⊖66 a			16 24		16 39	16 43	17 33								16 59		17 05	17 13	17 50					17 24

A 🛒 from Preston

OVERNIGHT SLEEPERS. For sleeper trains, operated by First ScotRail, please see Tables 400 - 404.

For complete service between Manchester and Preston, Blackpool and between Barrow-in-furness and Lancaster, please see Table 82.

For complete service between Crewe and Liverpool Lime Street, see Table 91

For complete service between Crewe/Stoke-on-Trent & Manchester see Table 84

For complete service between Crewe and Holyhead please see Table 81.

For complete service between Coventry-Birmingham-Wolverhampton-Stafford please see Table 68

For complete service between Windermere and Oxenholme Lake District, please see Table 83

Table 65R

Saturdays

4 January to 8 February

Scotland and North West England - West Midlands and London

Route Diagram - refer to first Page of Table 65

Station	Table		VT	XC	VT	VT	LM	TP	NT		LM	VT	LM	VT	VT	LM	NT	XC	LM		VT	XC	VT	VT	VT	LM
			◇1	◇1	◇1	◇1	1	◇1			1	◇1	1	◇1	◇1	1		◇1	1		◇1	◇1	◇1	◇1	◇1	1
			☕	🛒	☕	☕		🛒				☕		☕	☕			🛒			☕	🛒	☕	☕	☕	
Inverness	229	d																								
Aberdeen	229	d																								
Dundee	229	d																								
Perth	229	d																								
Edinburgh 10	225,226,228,230,242	d																								
Haymarket	225,226,228,230,242	d																								
Glasgow Central 15	226,216	d																								
Motherwell	226	d																								
Carstairs	226	d																								
Lockerbie		d																								
Carlisle 8	216	a																								
		d																								
Penrith North Lakes		d																								
Windermere	83	d																								
Oxenholme Lake District		a																								
		d																								
Barrow-in-Furness	82	d																								
Lancaster 6		a																								
		d						15 24							15 38											
Blackpool North	97	d																								
Preston 8	90	a						15 42							15 56											
Preston 8	90	d				15 17		15 44							15 58										16 17	
Wigan North Western	90	a				15 28		15 57							16 09										16 28	
		d				15 28		15 58							16 09										16 28	
Bolton	82	a																								
Manchester Picc. 10	82	a						16 26																		
Manchester Airport	✈	a						16 47																		
Liverpool Lime Street 10	91	a																								
		d									15 34	15 47							16 04							
Liverpool South Parkway	91 ✈	d									15 44								16 15							
Runcorn	91	d									15 52	16 03							16 25							
Warrington Bank Quay		a				15 39									16 20										16 39	
		d				15 39									16 20										16 39	
Manchester Picc. 10	84	d		15 27	15 35				15 46					15 55			16 04	16 07			16 15	16 27		16 35		
Stockport	84	d		15 35	15 43									16 04			16 17	16 16			16 23	16 35		16 43		
Wilmslow	84	d							16 19					16 11			16 31									
Holyhead	81	d	13 58																							
Bangor (Gwynedd)	81	d	14 25																							
Llandudno Junction	81	d	14 43																							
Wrexham General	75	d																								
Chester	81	d	15 35																				16 35			
Crewe 10		a	15 54			15 58			16 44		16 16	16 21		16 27			17 01		16 45				16 54		16 58	
		d	15 56			16 01	16 02				16 19	16 22		16 29					16 49				16 56		17 01	17 02
Macclesfield		d		15 49	15 56																	16 49		16 56		
Stoke-on-Trent		d		16 07	16 12		16 28						←			←		16 44			16 50	17 07		17 12		17 28
Stafford		a		16 24			16 50				16 44	16 40	16 44			16 50		17 02	17 09			17 25				17 49
		d		16 25			16 56				16 45	16 42	16 45			16 56		17 03	17 10			17 26				17 56
Penkridge		a					→				→								17 15							→
Wolverhampton 7		a		16 39		16 33							16 58					17 16	17 27			17 39			17 33	
Birmingham New St. 12	68	a		16 58		17 05							17 17					17 33	17 47			17 58			18 05	
Birmingham International	68 ✈	a		17 13		17 19																18 13			18 19	
Coventry	68	a		17 24		17 30																18 24			18 30	
Lichfield Trent Valley		a														17 12										
Tamworth Low Level		a														17 19										
Nuneaton		a														17 35										
Rugby	66	a														17 51										
Milton Keynes Central	66	a	17 02			17 58										18 14					17 46		18 02		18 58	
Watford Junction	66	a																								
London Euston 15	⊖66	a	17 39		17 43	18 34						17 59		18 05	18 13	18 50					18 24		18 39	18 43	19 34	

OVERNIGHT SLEEPERS. For sleeper trains, operated by First ScotRail, please see Tables 400 - 404.

For complete service between Manchester and Preston, Blackpool and between Barrow-in-furness and Lancaster, please see Table 82.

For complete service between Crewe and Liverpool Lime Street, see Table 91

For complete service between Crewe/Stoke-on-Trent & Manchester see Table 84

For complete service between Crewe and Holyhead please see Table 81.

For complete service between Coventry-Birmingham-Wolverhampton-Stafford please see Table 68

For complete service between Windermere and Oxenholme Lake District, please see Table 83

Table 65R

Saturdays

4 January to 8 February

Scotland and North West England - West Midlands and London

Route Diagram - refer to first Page of Table 65

	TP	NT	VT		VT	LM	VT	LM	VT	VT	LM		XC		LM	VT	XC	VT	VT	LM	NT	LM	VT
	1		◇1		◇	1	◇1	1	◇1	◇1	1		◇1		1	◇1	◇1	◇1	◇1	1		1	◇1
Inverness 229 d																							
Aberdeen 229 d																							
Dundee 229 d																							
Perth 229 d																							
Edinburgh 10 225,226,228,230,242 d																							
Haymarket 225,226,228,230,242 d																							
Glasgow Central 15 226,216 d																							
Motherwell 226 d																							
Carstairs 226 d																							
Lockerbie d																							
Carlisle 8 216 a																							
d																							
Penrith North Lakes d																							
Windermere 83 d																							
Oxenholme Lake District a																							
d																							
Barrow-in-Furness 82 d	15 25																						
Lancaster 6 a	16 17																						
d	16 29									16 38													
Blackpool North 97 d																							
Preston 8 90 a	16 47									16 56													
Preston 8 90 d	16 49									16 58									17 17				
Wigan North Western 90 a										17 09									17 28				
d										17 09									17 28				
Bolton 82 a																							
Manchester Picc. 10 82 a	17 28																						
Manchester Airport a	17 47																						
Liverpool Lime Street 10 91 a																							
d						16 34	16 47								17 04							17 34	17 47
Liverpool South Parkway 91 d						16 44									17 15							17 44	
Runcorn 91 d						16 52	17 03								17 25							17 52	18 03
Warrington Bank Quay a										17 20									17 39				
d										17 20									17 39				
Manchester Picc. 10 84 d		16 46							16 55				17 06			17 15	17 27	17 35			17 46		
Stockport 84 d									17 04				17 15			17 23	17 36	17 43					
Holyhead 81 d		[illegible]							17 11												18 21		
Bangor (Gwynedd) 81 d																							
Llandudno Junction 81 d																							
Wrexham General 75 d																							
Chester 81 d			17 35		20 35																		
Crewe 10 a		17 46	17 54		20 54	17 17	17 22		17 27						17 47				17 59		18 46	18 20	
d						17 19	17 23		17 29						17 49				18 01	18 02		18 22	
Macclesfield d													17 27					17 56					
Stoke-on-Trent d								←			←		17 45			17 50	18 07	18 12		18 28			
Stafford a						17 43	17 41	17 43			17 49		18 03		18 09		18 25			18 50		18 42	18 36
d						17 44	17 43	17 44			17 56		18 04		18 10		18 26			18 56		18 43	18 36
Penkridge a						→									18 15					→		→	
Wolverhampton 7 a								17 57					18 15		18 27		18 40		18 32				
Birmingham New St. 12 68 a								18 17					18 33		18 47		18 58		19 05				
Birmingham International 68 a																	19 13		19 19				
Coventry 68 a																	19 24		19 30				
Lichfield Trent Valley a											18 12												
Tamworth Low Level a											18 19												
Nuneaton a											18 35												
Rugby 66 a											18 51								19 42				
Milton Keynes Central 66 a											19 14					18 46			20 05				
Watford Junction 66 a																			20s34				
London Euston 15 ⊖66 a							19 01		19 09	19 14	19 50					19 24		19 43	20 55				19 59

OVERNIGHT SLEEPERS. For sleeper trains, operated by First ScotRail, please see Tables 400 - 404.

For complete service between Manchester and Preston, Blackpool and between Barrow-in-furness and Lancaster, please see Table 82.

For complete service between Crewe and Liverpool Lime Street, see Table 91

For complete service between Crewe/Stoke-on-Trent & Manchester see Table 84

For complete service between Crewe and Holyhead please see Table 81.

For complete service between Coventry-Birmingham-Wolverhampton-Stafford please see Table 68

For complete service between Windermere and Oxenholme Lake District, please see Table 83

Table 65R

Saturdays

4 January to 8 February

Scotland and North West England - West Midlands and London

Route Diagram - refer to first Page of Table 65

Station	Table		LM	LM	VT	VT	TP	XC	LM	NT	VT		XC	VT	VT	LM	LM	VT	LM	LM	VT		VT		XC	LM
			1	1	◇1	◇1	◇1	◇1	1		◇1		◇1	◇1	◇1	1	1	◇1	1	1	◇1		◇1		◇1	1
					⊏P	⊏P		⊥			⊏P		⊥	⊏P	⊏P			⊏P			⊏P		⊏P		⊥	
Inverness	229	d																								
Aberdeen	229	d																								
Dundee	229	d																								
Perth	229	d																								
Edinburgh 10	225,226,228,230,242	d																								
Haymarket	225,226,228,230,242	d																								
Glasgow Central 15	226,216	d																								
Motherwell	226	d																								
Carstairs	226	d																								
Lockerbie		d																								
Carlisle 8	216	a																								
		d																								
Penrith North Lakes		d																								
Windermere	83	d																								
Oxenholme Lake District		a																								
		d																								
Barrow-in-Furness	82	d																								
Lancaster 6		a																								
		d				17 38	17 48																18 41			
Blackpool North	97	d																								
Preston 8	90	a				17 56	18 06																18 59			
Preston 8	90	d				17 58	18 08								18 17								19 01			
Wigan North Western	90	a				18 09									18 27								19 12			
		d				18 09									18 28								19 12			
Bolton	82	a					18 34																			
Manchester Picc. 10	82	a					18 56																			
Manchester Airport		a					19 17																			
Liverpool Lime Street 10	91	a																								
		d							18 04								18 34	18 47								19 04
Liverpool South Parkway	91	d							18 15								18 44									19 14
Runcorn	91	d							18 24								18 52	19 03								19 23
Warrington Bank Quay		a				18 20									18 38								19 23			
		d				18 20									18 39								19 23			
Manchester Picc. 10	84	d			17 55			18 05		18 08	18 15		18 27	18 35							18 55				19 07	
Stockport	84	d			18 04			18 13		18 22	18 23		18 35	18 43							19 04				19 16	
Wilmslow	84	d			18 11					18 37											19 11					
Holyhead	81	d																								
Bangor (Gwynedd)	81	d																								
Llandudno Junction	81	d																								
Wrexham General	75	d																								
Chester	81	d																								
Crewe 10		a			18 27				18 46	19 06					18 58		19 19				19 27					19 49
		d			18 29				18 49						19 01	19 02	19 21				19 29					19 51
Macclesfield		d						18 26						18 56												
Stoke-on-Trent		d	←	←				18 44			18 49		19 07	19 12		19 28			←	←					19 44	
Stafford		a	18 42	18 50				19 02	19 09				19 25			19 50	19 45	19 35	19 45	19 50					20 02	20 11
		d	18 43	18 56				19 03	19 10				19 25			19 51	19 45	19 36	19 45	19 51					20 03	20 12
Penkridge		a							19 15							→	→		19 51							
Wolverhampton 7		a	18 56					19 15	19 27				19 39		19 32				20 01						20 15	20 28
Birmingham New St. 12	68	a	19 17					19 33	19 47				19 59		20 05				20 19						20 33	20 48
Birmingham International	68	a											20 13		20 19											
Coventry	68	a											20 24		20 30											
Lichfield Trent Valley		a		19 12																20 07						
Tamworth Low Level		a		19 19																20 14						
Nuneaton		a		19 35																20 30						
Rugby	66	a		19 51											20 42					20 46						
Milton Keynes Central	66	a									19 45				21 04								20 42			
Watford Junction	66	a													21s35								21s15			
London Euston 15	⊖66	a			20 05	20 16					20 26			20 59	21 56			21 15			21 20		21 38			

OVERNIGHT SLEEPERS. For sleeper trains, operated by First ScotRail, please see Tables 400 - 404.

For complete service between Manchester and Preston, Blackpool and between Barrow-in-furness and Lancaster, please see Table 82.

For complete service between Crewe and Liverpool Lime Street, see Table 91

For complete service between Crewe/Stoke-on-Trent & Manchester see Table 84

For complete service between Crewe and Holyhead please see Table 81.

For complete service between Coventry-Birmingham-Wolverhampton-Stafford please see Table 68

For complete service between Windermere and Oxenholme Lake District, please see Table 83

Table 65R

Saturdays

4 January to 8 February

Scotland and North West England - West Midlands and London

Route Diagram - refer to first Page of Table 65

		XC	VT	VT	TP	LM	VT	XC	VT	VT	TP	VT	XC	LM	VT	XC	VT	VT	VT	XC	LM
		◇1	◇1	◇1	◇1	1	◇1	◇1	◇1		◇1	◇1	◇1	1	◇1	◇1	◇1			◇1	1
		A																			
		trolley	buffet	buffet	trolley		buffet		buffet	bus		buffet			buffet		buffet	bus	bus		
Inverness 229	d																				
Aberdeen 229	d																				
Dundee 229	d																				
Perth 229	d																				
Edinburgh 10 225,226,228,230,242	d																				
Haymarket 225,226,228,230,242	d																				
Glasgow Central 15 226,216	d																				
Motherwell 226	d																				
Carstairs 226	d																				
Lockerbie	d																				
Carlisle 8 216	a																				
	d									17 00								18 25	19 00		
Penrith North Lakes	d									17 40								19 05	19 40		
Windermere 83	d																				
Oxenholme Lake District	a									18 35								20 00	20 35		
	d									18 40								20 05	20 40		
Barrow-in-Furness 82	d										19 17										
Lancaster 6	a									19 25	20 17							20 50	21 25		
	d				19 22					19 30	20 18							20 55	21 30		
Blackpool North 97	d																				
Preston 8 90	a				19 41					20 20	20 37							21 45	22 20		
Preston 8 90	d			19 17	19 45					20 25								21 50	22 25		
Wigan North Western 90	a			19 29						21 10								22 35	23 10		
	d			19 29					20 15								21 32				
Bolton 82	a				20 08																
Manchester Picc. 10 82	a				20 27																
Manchester Airport ✈	a				20 46																
Liverpool Lime Street 10 91	a																				
	d					19 34	19 48							20 34							21 34
Liverpool South Parkway 91 ✈	d					19 44								20 44							21 44
Runcorn 91	d					19 52	20 04							20 52							21 52
Warrington Bank Quay	a			19 39					20 26								21 42				
	d			19 40					20 26			20 39					21 43				
Manchester Picc. 10 84	d	19 27	19 35					20 07					20 27		20 35	21 07				21 27	
Stockport 84	d	19 35	19 43					20 16					20 35		20 43					21 35	
Wilmslow 84	d																				
Holyhead 81 ⛴	d																				
Bangor (Gwynedd) 81	d																				
Llandudno Junction 81	d																				
Wrexham General 75	d																				
Chester 81	d																				
Crewe 10	a			19 59		20 16	20 21		20 45			20 59		21 16			22 02				22 16
	d			20 01		20 18	20 23		20 47			21 01		21 17			22 04				22 24
Macclesfield	d	19 49	19 56										20 49		20 56					21 49	
Stoke-on-Trent	d	20 07	20 12					20 44					21 07		21 12	21 45				22 07	
Stafford	a	20 25				20 40	20 41	21 02					21 26	21 42		22 02	22 22			22 28	22 44
	d	20 26				20 40	20 43	21 03					21 27	21 42		22 03	22 23			22 29	22 45
Penkridge	a					20 49								21 48							22 50
Wolverhampton 7	a	20 39		20 32		20 59		21 15				21 32	21 39	21 59		22 14	22 40			22 43	23 01
Birmingham New St. 12 68	a	20 58		21 05		21 17		21 32				21 55	21 58	22 20		22 32	22 59			23 01	23 20
Birmingham International 68 ✈	a	21 13		21 19																	
Coventry 68	a	21 24		21 30																	
Lichfield Trent Valley	a																				
Tamworth Low Level	a																				
Nuneaton	a																				
Rugby 66	a			21 42																	
Milton Keynes Central 66	a		21 10	22 04					21 51						22 10						
Watford Junction 66	a			22s34											22s40						
London Euston 15 ⊖66	a		22 00	22 55			22 15		22 45						23 02						

A trolley to Birmingham New St.

OVERNIGHT SLEEPERS. For sleeper trains, operated by First ScotRail, please see Tables 400 - 404.

For complete service between Manchester and Preston, Blackpool and between Barrow-in-furness and Lancaster, please see Table 82.

For complete service between Crewe and Liverpool Lime Street, see Table 91

For complete service between Crewe/Stoke-on-Trent & Manchester see Table 84

For complete service between Crewe and Holyhead please see Table 81.

For complete service between Coventry-Birmingham-Wolverhampton-Stafford please see Table 68

For complete service between Windermere and Oxenholme Lake District, please see Table 83

Table 65R

Saturdays

4 January to 8 February

Scotland and North West England - West Midlands and London

Route Diagram - refer to first Page of Table 65

		TP	LM			TP	NT	VT
			1			◇1		
Inverness 229	d							
Aberdeen 229	d							
Dundee 229	d							
Perth 229	d							
Edinburgh 10 225,226,228,230,242	d							
Haymarket 225,226,228,230,242	d							
Glasgow Central 15 226,216	d							
Motherwell 226	d							
Carstairs 226	d							
Lockerbie	d							
Carlisle 8 216	a							
	d							20 25
Penrith North Lakes	d							21 05
Windermere 83	d	20 55						
Oxenholme Lake District	a							22 00
	d							22 05
Barrow-in-Furness 82	d						21 43	
Lancaster 6	a	21 34					22 45	22 50
	d					22 17	22 46	22 55
Blackpool North 97	d							
Preston 8 90	a					22 38	23 11	23 45
Preston 8 90	d							
Wigan North Western 90	a							
	d							
Bolton 82	a							
Manchester Picc. 10 82	a							
Manchester Airport ✈	a							
Liverpool Lime Street 10 91	a							
	d		22 04					
Liverpool South Parkway 91 ✈	d		22 14					
Runcorn 91	d		22 23					
Warrington Bank Quay	a							
	d							
Manchester Picc. 10 84	d							
Stockport 84	d							
Wilmslow 84	d							
Holyhead 81	d							
Bangor (Gwynedd) 81	d							
Llandudno Junction 81	d							
Wrexham General 75	d							
Chester 81	d							
Crewe 10	a		22 48					
	d							
Macclesfield	d							
Stoke-on-Trent	d							
Stafford	a							
	d							
Penkridge	a							
Wolverhampton 7	a							
Birmingham New St. 12 68	a							
Birmingham International 68 ✈	a							
Coventry 68	a							
Lichfield Trent Valley	a							
Tamworth Low Level	a							
Nuneaton	a							
Rugby 66	a							
Milton Keynes Central 66	a							
Watford Junction 66	a							
London Euston 15 ⊖66	a							

OVERNIGHT SLEEPERS. For sleeper trains, operated by First ScotRail, please see Tables 400 - 404.

For complete service between Manchester and Preston, Blackpool and between Barrow-in-furness and Lancaster, please see Table 82.

For complete service between Crewe and Liverpool Lime Street, see Table 91

For complete service between Crewe/Stoke-on-Trent & Manchester see Table 84

For complete service between Crewe and Holyhead please see Table 81.

For complete service between Coventry-Birmingham-Wolverhampton-Stafford please see Table 68

For complete service between Windermere and Oxenholme Lake District, please see Table 83

Table 65R

Saturdays

15 February to 17 May

Scotland and North West England - West Midlands and London

Route Diagram - refer to first Page of Table 65

	NT	SR		XC	VT	XC		LM	VT		VT	VT	XC	NT	LM	VT	VT		LM		VT	TP	LM	VT
		B																						
				◇1	◇1	◇1		1	◇1		◇1	◇1	◇1		1	◇1	◇1		1		◇1	◇1	1	◇1
		🛏																						
		X		🛒	☕	🛒			☕		☕	☕	🛒			☕	☕				☕			☕
Inverness 229 d																								
Aberdeen 229 d																								
Dundee 229 d																								
Perth 229 d																								
Edinburgh 10 225,226,228,230,242 d																								
Haymarket 225,226,228,230,242 d																								
Glasgow Central 15 226,216 d																								
Motherwell 226 d		00u01																						
Carstairs 226 d		00u16																						
Lockerbie d																								
Carlisle 8 216 a																								
d		01u40																						
Penrith North Lakes d																								
Windermere 83 d																								
Oxenholme Lake District a																								
d																								
Barrow-in-Furness 82 d																						05 32		
Lancaster 6 a																						06 24		
d												05 38										06 24		
Blackpool North 97 d																								
Preston 8 90 a												05 55										06 43		
Preston 8 90 d												05 58									06 17	06 44		
Wigan North Western 90 a												06 09									06 28			
d												06 09									06 28			
Bolton 82 a																						07 07		
Manchester Picc. 10 82 a																						07 27		
Manchester Airport a																						07 45		
Liverpool Lime Street 10 91 a																								
d									05 47														06 32	06 45
Liverpool South Parkway 91 d																							06 42	
Runcorn 91 d									06 03														06 50	07 01
Warrington Bank Quay a												06 20									06 39			
d												06 20									06 39			
Manchester Picc. 10 84 d				05 11	05 25						05 55		06 00	06 06		06 10	06 35							
Stockport 84 d					05 34						06 03		06 08	06 19		06 18	06 43							
Wilmslow 84 d	00 01				05 41						06 11			06 33										
Holyhead 81 d																								
Bangor (Gwynedd) 81 d																								
Llandudno Junction 81 d																								
Wrexham General 75 d																								
Chester 81 d																								
Crewe 10 a	00 30			05 41	05 57						06 27			06 59							06 58		07 14	07 18
d				05 47	06 00			06 11			06 29				06 47				06 59		07 01		07 16	07 20
Macclesfield d													06 21			06 31	06 56							
Stoke-on-Trent d				06 08		←							06 39			06 48	07 12		07 20					
Stafford a				06 25	06 18	06 25		06 34	06 34				06 57		07 10				07 43				07 37	07 38
d				06 26	06 19	06 26		06 35	06 36				06 58		07 12				07 48				07 41	07 39
Penkridge a				↪				06 40							07 17				↪				↪	
Wolverhampton 7 a						06 39		06 51					07 12		07 28						07 31			
Birmingham New St. 12 68 a						06 57		07 18					07 33		07 47						08 05			
Birmingham International 68 a						07 13															08 19			
Coventry 68 a						07 24															08 29			
Lichfield Trent Valley a																07 11								
Tamworth Low Level a																07 17								
Nuneaton a									06 58															
Rugby 66 a					06 50												07 52							
Milton Keynes Central 66 a					07 11						07 31	07 38									08 58			
Watford Junction 66 a		06s23			07s32				07s45															
London Euston 15 ⊖66 a		06 48			07 53				08 05		08 10	08 17				08 28	08 46				09 34			09 00

OVERNIGHT SLEEPERS. For sleeper trains, operated by First ScotRail, please see Tables 400 - 404.

For complete service between Manchester and Preston, Blackpool and between Barrow-in-furness and Lancaster, please see Table 82.

For complete service between Crewe and Liverpool Lime Street, see Table 91

For complete service between Crewe/Stoke-on-Trent & Manchester see Table 84

For complete service between Crewe and Holyhead please see Table 81.

For complete service between Coventry-Birmingham-Wolverhampton-Stafford please see Table 68

For complete service between Windermere and Oxenholme Lake District, please see Table 83

Table 65R

Saturdays

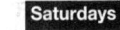

15 February to 17 May

Scotland and North West England - West Midlands and London

Route Diagram - refer to first Page of Table 65

	LM	VT	VT	LM			XC	VT	VT	LM	VT	XC	VT	VT	LM		TP	TP	NT	LM	VT	LM	VT	VT
	1	◇1 🍴	◇1 🍴	1			◇1 🛒	◇1 🍴	◇1 🍴	1	◇1 🍴	◇1 🛒	◇1 🍴	◇1 🍴	1		◇1	◇1		1	◇1 🍴	1	◇1 🍴	◇1 🍴
Inverness 229 d																								
Aberdeen 229 d																								
Dundee 229 d																								
Perth 229 d																								
Edinburgh 10 225,226,228,230,242 d																								
Haymarket 225,226,228,230,242 d																								
Glasgow Central 15 226,216 d			04 26																					05 40
Motherwell 226 d																								
Carstairs 226 d																								
Lockerbie d																								
Carlisle 8 216 a			05 42																					06 47
d			05 44																					06 49
Penrith North Lakes d			05 58																					
Windermere 83 d																								
Oxenholme Lake District a			06 21																					07 22
d			06 21																					07 24
Barrow-in-Furness 82 d																	06 15							
Lancaster 6 a			06 36														07 15							07 37
d			06 36											06 58			07 15	07 23						07 38
Blackpool North 97 d																								
Preston 8 90 a			06 54											07 15			07 34	07 41						07 56
Preston 8 90 d			06 57											07 17				07 43						07 58
Wigan North Western 90 a			07 07											07 28				07 55						08 09
d			07 09											07 28				07 56						08 09
Bolton 82 a																								
Manchester Picc. 10 82 ⛴ a																		08 26						
Manchester Airport ✈ a																		08 47						
Liverpool Lime Street 10 91 a																								
d										07 04	07 19									07 34	07 47			
Liverpool South Parkway 91 ✈ d										07 14										07 44				
Runcorn 91 d										07 22	07 36									07 52	08 03			
Warrington Bank Quay a			07 18											07 39										08 20
d			07 19											07 39										08 20
Manchester Picc. 10 84 ⛴ d		06 55					07 07	07 15				07 27	07 35						07 46				07 55	
Stockport 84 d		07 04					07 16	07 23				07 35	07 43										08 04	
Wilmslow 84 d		07 11																	08 21				08 11	
Holyhead 81 ⛴ d																								
Bangor (Gwynedd) 81 d																								
Llandudno Junction 81 d																								
Wrexham General 75 d																								
Chester 81 d									07 17															
Crewe 10 a		07 27							07 36	07 47	07 52			07 58					08 46	08 16	08 21		08 27	
d		07 29							07 41	07 49	07 55			08 01	08 02					08 19	08 22		08 29	
Macclesfield d												07 49	07 56											
Stoke-on-Trent d	←			←			07 44	07 50				08 07	08 12		08 28							←		
Stafford a	07 37			07 43			08 02			08 09	08 15	08 25			08 50					08 42	08 40	08 42		
d	07 41			07 48			08 03			08 10	08 16	08 26			08 56					08 43	08 42	08 43		
Penkridge a	07 46									08 15					→					→		08 48		
Wolverhampton 7 ⛴ a	07 57						08 15			08 26		08 39		08 32								08 58		
Birmingham New St. 12 68 a	08 17						08 34			08 48		08 58		09 05								09 17		
Birmingham International 68 ✈ a												09 13		09 19										
Coventry 68 a												09 24		09 30										
Lichfield Trent Valley a				08 04							08 30													
Tamworth Low Level a				08 11							08 37													
Nuneaton a				08 26																	09 04			
Rugby 66 a				08 42																				
Milton Keynes Central 66 a				09 05				08 46						09 58										
Watford Junction 66 a																								
London Euston 15 ⊖66 a		09 05	09 13	09 50				09 24	09 30		09 47		09 43	10 35							10 06		10 11	10 16

OVERNIGHT SLEEPERS. For sleeper trains, operated by First ScotRail, please see Tables 400 - 404.

For complete service between Manchester and Preston, Blackpool and between Barrow-in-furness and Lancaster, please see Table 82.

For complete service between Crewe and Liverpool Lime Street, see Table 91

For complete service between Crewe/Stoke-on-Trent & Manchester see Table 84

For complete service between Crewe and Holyhead please see Table 81.

For complete service between Coventry-Birmingham-Wolverhampton-Stafford please see Table 68

For complete service between Windermere and Oxenholme Lake District, please see Table 83

Table 65R

Saturdays

15 February to 17 May

Scotland and North West England - West Midlands and London

Route Diagram - refer to first Page of Table 65

		LM			XC	LM	VT	VT	XC	VT	VT	LM		TP	TP	NT	LM	VT	LM	VT	VT	LM		NT	XC
		1			◇1 ✕	1	◇1 ⊡	◇1 ⊡	◇1 ✕	◇1 ⊡	◇1 ⊡	1		◇1 ✕	◇1		1	◇1 ⊡	1	◇1 ⊡	◇1 ⊡	1			◇1 ✕
Inverness 229	d																								
Aberdeen 229	d																								
Dundee 229	d																								
Perth 229	d																								
Edinburgh 10 225,226,228,230,242	d													06 15											
Haymarket 225,226,228,230,242	d													06u19											
Glasgow Central 15 226,216	d										05 50										06 30				
Motherwell 226	d										06 04										06 44				
Carstairs 226	d																								
Lockerbie	d																				07 25				
Carlisle 8 216	a										07 01			07 33							07 43				
	d										07 02			07 33							07 46				
Penrith North Lakes	d										07 18										08 00				
Windermere 83	d																								
Oxenholme Lake District	a										07 41			08 09							08 22				
	d										07 42			08 10							08 23				
Barrow-in-Furness 82	d														07 33										
Lancaster 6	a										07 56			08 25	08 33						08 37				
	d										07 57			08 26	08 33						08 38				
Blackpool North 97	d																								
Preston 8 90	a										08 15			08 44	08 52						08 56				
Preston 8 90	d										08 17			08 45	09 10						08 58				
Wigan North Western 90	a										08 28			08 58							09 09				
	d										08 28			08 58							09 09				
Bolton 82	a														09 34										
Manchester Picc. 10 82 ⇌	a													09 27	09 56										
Manchester Airport ✈	a													09 47	10 17										
Liverpool Lime Street 10 91	a																								
	d					08 04											08 34	08 47							
Liverpool South Parkway 91 ✈	d					08 15											08 44								
Runcorn 91	d					08 24											08 52	09 03							
Warrington Bank Quay	a										08 39										09 20				
	d										08 39										09 20				
Manchester Picc. 10 84 ⇌	d				08 07		08 15		08 27	08 35						08 46				08 55				09 04	09 07
Stockport 84	d				08 16		08 23		08 35	08 43										09 04				09 17	09 16
Wilmslow 84	d															09 18				09 11				09 31	
Holyhead 81 ⛴	d							06 52																	
Bangor (Gwynedd) 81	d							07 20																	
Llandudno Junction 81	d							07 38																	
Wrexham General 75	d																								
Chester 81	d							08 35																	
Crewe 10	a					08 47		08 54			08 58					09 44	09 19	09 23		09 29				10 01	
	d					08 49		08 56			09 01	09 02					09 19	09 25		09 30					
Macclesfield	d								08 49	08 56															
Stoke-on-Trent	d	←			08 44		08 50		09 07	09 12		09 28							←			←			09 44
Stafford	a	08 50			09 02	09 09			09 25			09 51					09 45	09 43	09 45			09 51			10 02
	d	08 56			09 03	09 10			09 26			09 56					09 45	09 44	09 45			09 56			10 03
Penkridge	a					09 15						↦					↦								
Wolverhampton 7 ⇌	a				09 15	09 26			09 39		09 33								09 58						10 15
Birmingham New St. 12 68	a				09 33	09 47			09 58		10 05								10 17						10 33
Birmingham International 68 ✈	a								10 13		10 19														
Coventry 68	a								10 24		10 30														
Lichfield Trent Valley	a	09 12																				10 12			
Tamworth Low Level	a	09 19																				10 19			
Nuneaton	a	09 35																				10 35			
Rugby 66	a	09 51																				10 51			
Milton Keynes Central 66	a	10 14					09 46	10 02			10 58											11 14			
Watford Junction 66	a																								
London Euston 15 ⊖66	a	10 50					10 24	10 39		10 43	11 33							11 05		11 08	11 16	11 50			

OVERNIGHT SLEEPERS. For sleeper trains, operated by First ScotRail, please see Tables 400 - 404.

For complete service between Manchester and Preston, Blackpool and between Barrow-in-furness and Lancaster, please see Table 82.

For complete service between Crewe and Liverpool Lime Street, see Table 91

For complete service between Crewe/Stoke-on-Trent & Manchester see Table 84

For complete service between Crewe and Holyhead please see Table 81.

For complete service between Coventry-Birmingham-Wolverhampton-Stafford please see Table 68

For complete service between Windermere and Oxenholme Lake District, please see Table 83

Table 65R

Saturdays

15 February to 17 May

Scotland and North West England - West Midlands and London

Route Diagram - refer to first Page of Table 65

		LM	VT	VT	XC	VT	VT	LM		TP		LM	VT	LM	VT	VT	LM	TP		NT	XC	LM	VT	VT	XC
		1	◇1	◇1	◇1	◇1	◇1	1		◇1		1	◇1	1	◇1	◇1	1	◇1			◇1	1	◇1	◇1	◇1
Inverness 229	d																								
Aberdeen 229	d																								
Dundee 229	d																								
Perth 229	d																								
Edinburgh 10 225,226,228,230,242	d						06 52																		
Haymarket 225,226,228,230,242	d						06 56																		
Glasgow Central 15 226,216	d									07 09						07 35									
Motherwell 226	d															07 52									
Carstairs 226	d																								
Lockerbie	d									08 08															
Carlisle 8 216	a						08 06			08 29						08 47									
	d						08 07			08 29						08 49									
Penrith North Lakes	d						08 22			08 45															
Windermere 83	d																								
Oxenholme Lake District	a									09 09						09 22									
	d									09 10						09 23									
Barrow-in-Furness 82	d																	08 50							
Lancaster 6	a						08 57			09 25						09 37		09 46							
	d						08 57			09 25						09 38		09 47							
Blackpool North 97	d																								
Preston 8 90	a						09 15			09 44						09 56		10 07							
Preston 8 90	d						09 17			09 44						09 58									
Wigan North Western 90	a						09 28			09 57						10 09									
	d						09 28			09 58						10 09									
Bolton 82	a																								
Manchester Picc. 10 82	a									10 26															
Manchester Airport	a									10 46															
Liverpool Lime Street 10 91	a																								
	d	09 04										09 34	09 47									10 04			
Liverpool South Parkway 91	d	09 15										09 44										10 15			
Runcorn 91	d	09 25										09 52	10 03									10 25			
Warrington Bank Quay	a						09 39									10 20									
	d						09 39									10 20									
Manchester Picc. 10 84	d		09 15		09 27	09 35									09 55					10 04	10 07		10 15		10 27
Stockport 84	d		09 23		09 35	09 43									10 04					10 17	10 16		10 23		10 35
Wilmslow 84	d														10 11					10 31					
Holyhead 81	d			07 55																				08 55	
Bangor (Gwynedd) 81	d			08 22																				09 22	
Llandudno Junction 81	d			08 40																				09 40	
Wrexham General 75	d																								
Chester 81	d			09 35																				10 35	
Crewe 10	a	09 45		09 54			09 58					10 16	10 21		10 27					11 01		10 45		10 54	
	d	09 49		09 56			10 01	10 02				10 19	10 22		10 29							10 49		10 56	
Macclesfield	d				09 49	09 56																			10 49
Stoke-on-Trent	d		09 50		10 07	10 12		10 28						←			←				10 44		10 50		11 07
Stafford	a	10 10			10 25			10 50				10 42	10 40	10 42			10 50				11 02	11 09			11 25
	d	10 10			10 26			10 56				10 43	10 42	10 43			10 56				11 03	11 10			11 26
Penkridge	a	10 16						→				→										11 15			
Wolverhampton 7	a	10 27			10 39		10 32							10 56							11 15	11 27			11 39
Birmingham New St. 12 68	a	10 47			10 58		11 05							11 17							11 33	11 47			11 59
Birmingham International 68	a				11 13		11 19																		12 13
Coventry 68	a				11 24		11 30																		12 24
Lichfield Trent Valley	a																11 12								
Tamworth Low Level	a																11 19								
Nuneaton	a																11 35								
Rugby 66	a																11 51								
Milton Keynes Central 66	a		10 46	11 02			11 58										12 14						11 46	12 02	
Watford Junction 66	a																								
London Euston 15 ⊖66	a		11 24	11 39		11 43	12 33						11 59		12 05	12 13	12 50						12 24	12 39	

OVERNIGHT SLEEPERS. For sleeper trains, operated by First ScotRail, please see Tables 400 - 404.

For complete service between Manchester and Preston, Blackpool and between Barrow-in-furness and Lancaster, please see Table 82.

For complete service between Crewe and Liverpool Lime Street, see Table 91

For complete service between Crewe/Stoke-on-Trent & Manchester see Table 84

For complete service between Crewe and Holyhead please see Table 81.

For complete service between Coventry-Birmingham-Wolverhampton-Stafford please see Table 68

For complete service between Windermere and Oxenholme Lake District, please see Table 83

Table 65R

Saturdays

15 February to 17 May

Scotland and North West England - West Midlands and London

Route Diagram - refer to first Page of Table 65

		VT	VT	LM		TP	TP		LM	VT	LM	VT	VT	LM		NT	XC	LM	VT	XC	VT	VT	VT	LM	
		◇1	◇1	1		◇1	◇1		1	◇1	1	◇1	◇1	1			◇1	1	◇1	◇1	◇1	◇1	◇1	1	
		☕	☕				🍴			☕		☕	☕				🍴		☕	🍴	☕	☕	☕		
Inverness 229	d																								
Aberdeen 229	d																								
Dundee 229	d																								
Perth 229	d																								
Edinburgh [10] 225,226,228,230,242	d						08 10																08 52		
Haymarket 225,226,228,230,242	d						08u14																08 57		
Glasgow Central [15] 226,216	d		08 00										08 40												
Motherwell 226	d																								
Carstairs 226	d																								
Lockerbie	d																								
Carlisle [8] 216	a		09 08				09 29						09 47										10 07		
	d		09 09				09 30						09 49										10 08		
Penrith North Lakes	d						09 46						10 03												
Windermere 83	d					09 37																			
Oxenholme Lake District	a					09 56	10 09																10 42		
	d					09 57	10 10																10 42		
Barrow-in-Furness 82	d																								
Lancaster [6]	a		09 56			10 13	10 24						10 37										10 57		
	d		09 56			10 14	10 25						10 38										10 57		
Blackpool North 97	d																								
Preston [8] 90	a		10 14			10 33	10 43						10 56										11 15		
Preston [8] 90	d		10 17				10 45						10 58										11 18		
Wigan North Western 90	a		10 28				10 58						11 09										11 28		
	d		10 28				10 58						11 09										11 28		
Bolton 82	a																								
Manchester Picc. [10] 82 ⛴	a						11 27																		
Manchester Airport ✈	a						11 47																		
Liverpool Lime Street [10] 91	a																								
	d								10 34	10 47								11 04							
Liverpool South Parkway 91 ✈	d								10 44									11 15							
Runcorn 91	d								10 52	11 03								11 25							
Warrington Bank Quay	a		10 39										11 20										11 39		
	d		10 39										11 20										11 40		
Manchester Picc. [10] 84 ⛴	d	10 35										10 55				11 04	11 07		11 15	11 27		11 35			
Stockport 84	d	10 43										11 04				11 17	11 16		11 23	11 35		11 43			
Wilmslow 84	d											11 11				11 31									
Holyhead 81 ⛴	d																								
Bangor (Gwynedd) 81	d																								
Llandudno Junction 81	d																								
Wrexham General 75	d																								
Chester 81	d																				11 35				
Crewe [10]	a		10 58						11 16	11 21		11 27				12 01		11 45			11 54		11 58		
	d		11 01	11 02					11 19	11 22		11 29						11 49			11 56		12 01	12 02	
Macclesfield	d	10 56																		11 49		11 56			
Stoke-on-Trent	d	11 12		11 28							←			←			11 44		11 50	12 07		12 12		12 28	
Stafford	a			11 50					11 42	11 40	11 42			11 50			12 02	12 09		12 24				12 50	
	d			11 56					11 43	11 42	11 43			11 56			12 03	12 10		12 25				12 56	
Penkridge	a			↪					↪									12 15						↪	
Wolverhampton [7] ⛴	a		11 31								11 56						12 15	12 27		12 39			12 33		
Birmingham New St. [12] 68	a		12 05								12 17						12 33	12 47		12 58			13 05		
Birmingham International 68 ✈	a		12 19																	13 13			13 19		
Coventry 68	a		12 30																	13 24			13 30		
Lichfield Trent Valley	a													12 12											
Tamworth Low Level	a													12 19											
Nuneaton	a													12 35											
Rugby 66	a													12 51											
Milton Keynes Central 66	a		12 58											13 14					12 46		13 02		13 58		
Watford Junction 66	a																								
London Euston [15] ⊖66	a	12 43	13 35							12 59		13 05	13 13	13 50					13 24		13 39	13 43	14 33		

OVERNIGHT SLEEPERS. For sleeper trains, operated by First ScotRail, please see Tables 400 - 404.

For complete service between Manchester and Preston, Blackpool and between Barrow-in-furness and Lancaster, please see Table 82.

For complete service between Crewe and Liverpool Lime Street, see Table 91

For complete service between Crewe/Stoke-on-Trent & Manchester see Table 84

For complete service between Crewe and Holyhead please see Table 81.

For complete service between Coventry-Birmingham-Wolverhampton-Stafford please see Table 68

For complete service between Windermere and Oxenholme Lake District, please see Table 83

Table 65R

Saturdays

15 February to 17 May

Scotland and North West England - West Midlands and London

Route Diagram - refer to first Page of Table 65

	TP		LM	VT	LM	VT	VT	LM	TP		NT	XC	LM	VT	XC	VT	VT	VT	LM		TP	NT	LM	VT
	◇1		1	◇1	1	◇1	◇1	1	◇1			◇1	1	◇1	◇1	◇1	◇1	◇1	1		◇1		1	◇1
				⊥P		⊥P	⊥P					⊥o		⊥P	⊥o	⊥P	⊥P	⊥P			⊥o			⊥P
Inverness 229 d																								
Aberdeen 229 d																								
Dundee 229 d																								
Perth 229 d																								
Edinburgh 10 225,226,228,230,242 d																					10 08			
Haymarket 225,226,228,230,242 d																					10 12			
Glasgow Central 15 226,216 d							09 40											10 00						
Motherwell 226 d																								
Carstairs 226 d																								
Lockerbie d																					11 07			
Carlisle 8 216 a							10 47											11 09			11 28			
d							10 49											11 11			11 31			
Penrith North Lakes d																		11 25			11 47			
Windermere 83 d	10 48																							
Oxenholme Lake District a	11 08						11 22														12 09			
d	11 08						11 23														12 10			
Barrow-in-Furness 82 d									11 20															
Lancaster 6 a	11 26						11 37		12 17												12 25			
d	11 26						11 38		12 17												12 26			
Blackpool North 97 d																								
Preston 8 90 a	11 45						11 56		12 37									12 14			12 44			
Preston 8 90 d	11 46						11 58											12 17			12 45			
Wigan North Western 90 a	11 58						12 09											12 27			12 58			
d	11 58						12 09											12 28			12 58			
Bolton 82 a																								
Manchester Picc. 10 82 a	12 27																				13 27			
Manchester Airport a	12 47																				13 47			
Liverpool Lime Street 10 91 a																								
d			11 34	11 47									12 04										12 34	12 47
Liverpool South Parkway 91 d			11 44										12 15										12 44	
Runcorn 91 d			11 52	12 03									12 25										12 52	13 03
Warrington Bank Quay a							12 20											12 38						
d							12 20											12 39						
Manchester Picc. 10 84 d						11 55					12 04	12 07		12 15	12 27		12 35					12 46		
Stockport 84 d						12 04					12 17	12 16		12 23	12 35		12 43							
Wilmslow 84 d						12 11					12 31											13 21		
Holyhead 81 d																								
Bangor (Gwynedd) 81 d																								
Llandudno Junction 81 d																								
Wrexham General 75 d																								
Chester 81 d																12 35								
Crewe 10 a			12 16	12 21		12 27					13 01		12 45			12 54		12 58				13 46	13 19	13 23
d			12 19	12 22		12 29							12 49			12 56		13 01	13 02				13 19	13 25
Macclesfield d															12 49		12 56							
Stoke-on-Trent d					←			←				12 44		12 50	13 07		13 12		13 28					
Stafford a			12 42	12 40	12 42			12 50				13 02	13 09		13 25				13 50				13 45	13 43
d			12 43	12 42	12 43			12 56				13 03	13 10		13 26				13 56				13 45	13 44
Penkridge a			↦										13 15						↦				↦	
Wolverhampton 7 a					12 56							13 14	13 27		13 39			13 33						
Birmingham New St. 12 68 a					13 17							13 32	13 47		13 58			14 05						
Birmingham International 68 a															14 13			14 19						
Coventry 68 a															14 24			14 30						
Lichfield Trent Valley a								13 12																
Tamworth Low Level a								13 19																
Nuneaton a								13 35																
Rugby 66 a								13 51																
Milton Keynes Central 66 a								14 14						13 46		14 02		14 58						
Watford Junction 66 a																								
London Euston 15 ⊖66 a				14 00		14 05	14 13	14 50						14 24		14 39	14 43	15 34						15 05

OVERNIGHT SLEEPERS. For sleeper trains, operated by First ScotRail, please see Tables 400 - 404.

For complete service between Manchester and Preston, Blackpool and between Barrow-in-furness and Lancaster, please see Table 82.

For complete service between Crewe and Liverpool Lime Street, see Table 91

For complete service between Crewe/Stoke-on-Trent & Manchester see Table 84

For complete service between Crewe and Holyhead please see Table 81.

For complete service between Coventry-Birmingham-Wolverhampton-Stafford please see Table 68

For complete service between Windermere and Oxenholme Lake District, please see Table 83

Table 65R

Saturdays

15 February to 17 May

Scotland and North West England - West Midlands and London

Route Diagram - refer to first Page of Table 65

		LM	VT	VT	LM			XC	LM	VT	XC	VT	VT	VT	LM	TP		TP	NT	LM	VT	LM	VT	VT	LM
		1	◇1	◇1	1			◇1	1	◇1	◇1	◇1	◇1	◇1	1	◇1		◇1		1	◇1	1	◇1	◇1	1
			☕	☕				🛒		☕	🛒	☕	☕	☕		🛒					☕		☕	☕	
Inverness 229	d																								
Aberdeen 229	d																								
Dundee 229	d																								
Perth 229	d																								
Edinburgh 10 225,226,228,230,242	d													10 52											
Haymarket 225,226,228,230,242	d													10 57											
Glasgow Central 15 226,216	d			10 40												11 09								11 40	
Motherwell 226	d																								
Carstairs 226	d																								
Lockerbie	d															12 09									
Carlisle 8 216	a			11 47										12 04		12 31								12 47	
	d			11 49										12 08		12 31								12 49	
Penrith North Lakes	d															12 46								13 03	
Windermere 83	d																	12 52							
Oxenholme Lake District	a			12 22										12 41		13 10		13 12							
	d			12 23										12 43		13 10		13 13							
Barrow-in-Furness 82	d																								
Lancaster 6	a			12 37										12 56		13 25		13 29						13 37	
	d			12 38										12 57		13 25		13 29						13 38	
Blackpool North 97	d																								
Preston 8 90	a			12 56										13 15		13 44		13 49						13 56	
Preston 8 90	d			12 58										13 17		13 44								13 58	
Wigan North Western 90	a			13 09										13 28		13 57								14 09	
	d			13 09										13 28		13 58								14 09	
Bolton 82	a																								
Manchester Picc. 10 82 [metro]	a															14 26									
Manchester Airport [airport]	a															14 45									
Liverpool Lime Street 10 91	a																								
	d								13 04											13 34	13 47				
Liverpool South Parkway 91 [airport]	d								13 15											13 44					
Runcorn 91	d								13 25											13 52	14 03				
Warrington Bank Quay	a			13 20										13 39										14 20	
	d			13 20										13 39										14 20	
Manchester Picc. 10 84 [metro]	d		12 55					13 07		13 15	13 27		13 35						13 46				13 55		
Stockport 84	d		13 04					13 16		13 23	13 35		13 43										14 04		
Wilmslow 84	d		13 11																14 20				14 11		
Holyhead 81 [ferry]	d																								
Bangor (Gwynedd) 81	d																								
Llandudno Junction 81	d																								
Wrexham General 75	d																								
Chester 81	d											13 35													
Crewe 10	a		13 29						13 45			13 54		13 58					14 45	14 16	14 21		14 27		
	d		13 30						13 49			13 56		14 01	14 02					14 19	14 22		14 29		
Macclesfield	d										13 49		13 56												
Stoke-on-Trent	d	←			←			13 44		13 50	14 07		14 12		14 28							←			←
Stafford	a	13 45			13 50			14 02	14 09		14 25				14 50					14 42	14 40	14 42			14 50
	d	13 45			13 56			14 03	14 10		14 26				14 56					14 43	14 42	14 43			14 56
Penkridge	a								14 15						↦					↦					
Wolverhampton 7 [metro]	a	13 58						14 15	14 27		14 39			14 33								14 56			
Birmingham New St. 12 68	a	14 17						14 33	14 47		14 58			15 05								15 17			
Birmingham International 68 [airport]	a										15 13			15 19											
Coventry 68	a										15 24			15 30											
Lichfield Trent Valley	a				14 12																				15 12
Tamworth Low Level	a				14 19																				15 19
Nuneaton	a				14 35																				15 35
Rugby 66	a				14 51																				15 51
Milton Keynes Central 66	a				15 14					14 46		15 02		15 58											16 14
Watford Junction 66	a																								
London Euston 15 [underground] 66	a		15 09	15 13	15 50					15 24		15 39	15 43	16 34							15 59		16 05	16 13	16 50

OVERNIGHT SLEEPERS. For sleeper trains, operated by First ScotRail, please see Tables 400 - 404.

For complete service between Manchester and Preston, Blackpool and between Barrow-in-furness and Lancaster, please see Table 82.

For complete service between Crewe and Liverpool Lime Street, see Table 91

For complete service between Crewe/Stoke-on-Trent & Manchester see Table 84

For complete service between Crewe and Holyhead please see Table 81.

For complete service between Coventry-Birmingham-Wolverhampton-Stafford please see Table 68

For complete service between Windermere and Oxenholme Lake District, please see Table 83

Table 65R

Saturdays

15 February to 17 May

Scotland and North West England - West Midlands and London

Route Diagram - refer to first Page of Table 65

		XC	LM	VT	XC	VT	VT	VT	LM	TP	TP	NT	LM	VT	LM	VT	VT	LM	NT	XC	LM
		◇1	1	◇1	◇1	◇1	◇1	◇1	1	◇1	◇1		1	◇1	1	◇1	◇1	1		◇1	1
										A											
		🍴		☕	🍴	☕	☕	☕		🍴	🍴			☕		☕	☕			🍴	
Inverness 229	d																				
Aberdeen 229	d																				
Dundee 229	d																				
Perth 229	d																				
Edinburgh 10 225,226,228,230,242	d										12 12										
Haymarket 225,226,228,230,242	d										12u16										
Glasgow Central 15 226,216	d							12 00									12 40				
Motherwell 226	d																				
Carstairs 226	d																				
Lockerbie	d										13 11										
Carlisle 8 216	a							13 09			13 33						13 47				
	d							13 11			13 33						13 49				
Penrith North Lakes	d																				
Windermere 83	d																				
Oxenholme Lake District	a										14 09						14 22				
	d										14 10						14 24				
Barrow-in-Furness 82	d									13 20											
Lancaster 6	a							13 57		14 17	14 24						14 37				
	d							13 58		14 17	14 25						14 39				
Blackpool North 97	d																				
Preston 8 90	a							14 15		14 37	14 45						14 56				
Preston 8 90	d							14 17		14 45							14 58				
Wigan North Western 90	a							14 28									15 09				
	d							14 28									15 10				
Bolton 82	a									15 07											
Manchester Picc. 10 82 🚊	a									15 28											
Manchester Airport ✈	a									15 47											
Liverpool Lime Street 10 91	a																				
	d		14 04										14 34	14 47							15 04
Liverpool South Parkway 91 ✈	d		14 15										14 44								15 15
Runcorn 91	d		14 25										14 52	15 03							15 25
Warrington Bank Quay	a							14 39									15 20				
	d							14 39									15 21				
Manchester Picc. 10 84 🚊	d	14 07		14 15	14 27		14 35					14 46				14 55			15 04	15 07	
Stockport 84	d	14 16		14 23	14 35		14 43									15 04			15 17	15 16	
Wilmslow 84	d											15 20				15 11			15 31		
Holyhead 81 ⛴	d																				
Bangor (Gwynedd) 81	d																				
Llandudno Junction 81	d																				
Wrexham General 75	d																				
Chester 81	d					14 35															
Crewe 10	a		14 45			14 54		14 58				15 45	15 16	15 21		15 27			16 01		15 45
	d		14 49			14 56		15 01	15 02				15 19	15 22		15 29					15 49
Macclesfield	d				14 49		14 56														
Stoke-on-Trent	d	14 44		14 50	15 07		15 12		15 28						←			←		15 44	
Stafford	a	15 02	15 09		15 25				15 50				15 42	15 40	15 42			15 50		16 02	16 09
	d	15 03	15 10		15 26				15 56				15 43	15 42	15 43			15 56		16 03	16 10
Penkridge	a		15 15						↦				↦								16 15
Wolverhampton 7 🚊	a	15 16	15 27		15 39			15 31							15 56					16 16	16 27
Birmingham New St. 12 68	a	15 33	15 47		15 58			16 05							16 17					16 33	16 47
Birmingham International 68 ✈	a				16 13			16 19													
Coventry 68	a				16 24			16 30													
Lichfield Trent Valley	a																	16 12			
Tamworth Low Level	a																	16 19			
Nuneaton	a																	16 35			
Rugby 66	a																	16 51			
Milton Keynes Central 66	a			15 46		16 02		16 58										17 14			
Watford Junction 66	a																				
London Euston 15 ⊖66	a			16 24		16 39	16 43	17 33						16 59		17 05	17 13	17 50			

A 🍴 from Preston

OVERNIGHT SLEEPERS. For sleeper trains, operated by First ScotRail, please see Tables 400 - 404.

For complete service between Manchester and Preston, Blackpool and between Barrow-in-furness and Lancaster, please see Table 82.

For complete service between Crewe and Liverpool Lime Street, see Table 91

For complete service between Crewe/Stoke-on-Trent & Manchester see Table 84

For complete service between Crewe and Holyhead please see Table 81.

For complete service between Coventry-Birmingham-Wolverhampton-Stafford please see Table 68

For complete service between Windermere and Oxenholme Lake District, please see Table 83

Table 65R

Saturdays

15 February to 17 May

Scotland and North West England - West Midlands and London

Route Diagram - refer to first Page of Table 65

Station		VT	VT	XC	VT	VT	LM	TP	TP	LM	VT	LM	VT	VT	LM	TP	NT	XC	LM	VT	XC	VT
		◇1	◇1	◇1	◇1	◇1	1	◇1	◇1	1	◇1	1	◇1	◇1	1	◇1		◇1	1	◇1	◇1	◇1
		☕	☕	🛒	☕	☕		🛒			☕		☕	☕				🛒		☕	🛒	☕
Inverness 229	d																					
Aberdeen 229	d																					
Dundee 229	d																					
Perth 229	d																					
Edinburgh 10 225,226,228,230,242	d					12 52																
Haymarket 225,226,228,230,242	d					12 57																
Glasgow Central 15 226,216	d							13 09						13 40								
Motherwell 226	d																					
Carstairs 226	d																					
Lockerbie	d							14 07														
Carlisle 8 216	a					14 05		14 29						14 46								
	d					14 08		14 30						14 49								
Penrith North Lakes	d					14 22		14 45														
Windermere 83	d								14 52													
Oxenholme Lake District	a							15 08	15 11					15 22								
	d							15 09	15 12					15 23								
Barrow-in-Furness 82	d															15 25						
Lancaster 6	a					14 56		15 23	15 28					15 37		16 17						
	d					14 56		15 24	15 28					15 38		16 17						
Blackpool North 97	d																					
Preston 8 90	a					15 15		15 42	15 48					15 56		16 37						
Preston 8 90	d					15 17		15 45	16 10					15 58								
Wigan North Western 90	a					15 28		15 58						16 09								
	d					15 28		15 58						16 09								
Bolton 82	a								16 34													
Manchester Picc. 10 82 ⛴	a							16 27	16 56													
Manchester Airport ✈	a							16 47	17 17													
Liverpool Lime Street 10 91	a																					
	d									15 34	15 47								16 04			
Liverpool South Parkway 91 ✈	d									15 44									16 15			
Runcorn 91	d									15 52	16 03								16 25			
Warrington Bank Quay	a					15 39								16 20								
	d					15 39								16 20								
Manchester Picc. 10 84 ⛴	d	15 15		15 27	15 35								15 55					16 07		16 15	16 27	
Stockport 84	d	15 23		15 35	15 43								16 04					16 16		16 23	16 35	
Wilmslow 84	d												16 11									
Holyhead 81 ⛴	d		13 58																			
Bangor (Gwynedd) 81	d		14 25																			
Llandudno Junction 81	d		14 43																			
Wrexham General 75	d																					
Chester 81	d		15 35																			16 35
Crewe 10	a		15 54			15 58				16 16	16 21		16 27						16 45			16 54
	d		15 56			16 01	16 02			16 19	16 22		16 29						16 49			16 56
Macclesfield	d			15 49	15 56																16 49	
Stoke-on-Trent	d	15 50		16 07	16 12		16 28					←			←			16 44		16 50	17 07	
Stafford	a			16 24			16 50			16 44	16 40	16 44			16 50			17 02	17 09		17 25	
	d			16 25			16 56			16 45	16 42	16 45			16 56			17 03	17 10		17 26	
Penkridge	a						→			→									17 15			
Wolverhampton 7 ⛴	a			16 39		16 33						16 58						17 16	17 27		17 39	
Birmingham New St. 12 68	a			16 58		17 05						17 17						17 33	17 47		17 58	
Birmingham International 68 ✈	a			17 13		17 19															18 13	
Coventry 68	a			17 24		17 30															18 24	
Lichfield Trent Valley	a														17 12							
Tamworth Low Level	a														17 19							
Nuneaton	a														17 35							
Rugby 66	a														17 51							
Milton Keynes Central 66	a	16 46	17 02			17 58									18 14					17 46		18 02
Watford Junction 66	a																					
London Euston 15 ⊖66	a	17 24	17 39		17 43	18 34					17 59		18 05	18 13	18 50					18 24		18 39

OVERNIGHT SLEEPERS. For sleeper trains, operated by First ScotRail, please see Tables 400 - 404.

For complete service between Manchester and Preston, Blackpool and between Barrow-in-furness and Lancaster, please see Table 82.

For complete service between Crewe and Liverpool Lime Street, see Table 91

For complete service between Crewe/Stoke-on-Trent & Manchester see Table 84

For complete service between Crewe and Holyhead please see Table 81.

For complete service between Coventry-Birmingham-Wolverhampton-Stafford please see Table 68

For complete service between Windermere and Oxenholme Lake District, please see Table 83

Table 65R

Saturdays

15 February to 17 May

Scotland and North West England - West Midlands and London

Route Diagram - refer to first Page of Table 65

	VT	VT	LM	TP	TP	VT	VT	LM	VT	LM	VT	VT	LM	XC	LM	VT	XC	VT	VT	LM
	◇1	◇1	1	◇1	◇1	◇1	◇	1	◇1	1	◇1	◇1	1	◇1	1	◇1	◇1	◇1	◇1	1
				A	B															
	⊡	⊡		⊤	⊤	⊡	⊡		⊡		⊡	⊡		⊤		⊡	⊤	⊡	⊡	
Inverness 229 d																				
Aberdeen 229 d																				
Dundee 229 d																				
Perth 229 d																				
Edinburgh 10 225,226,228,230,242 d				14 16	14 16														14 52	
Haymarket 225,226,228,230,242 d				14u21	14u21														14 57	
Glasgow Central 15 226,216 d		14 00										14 40								
Motherwell 226 d																				
Carstairs 226 d																				
Lockerbie d				15 15	15 15															
Carlisle 8 216 a		15 07		15 36	15 36							15 46							16 06	
d		15 10		15 38	15 38							15 49							16 08	
Penrith North Lakes d																			16 22	
Windermere 83 d																				
Oxenholme Lake District a		15 43		16 14	16 14							16 22								
d		15 44		16 14	16 14							16 24								
Barrow-in-Furness 82 d																				
Lancaster 6 a				16 29	16 29							16 37							16 56	
d				16 29	16 29							16 38							16 57	
Blackpool North 97 d																				
Preston 8 90 a		16 12		16 48	16 48							16 56							17 15	
Preston 8 90 d		16 17		16 49	16 49							16 58							17 17	
Wigan North Western 90 a		16 28										17 09							17 28	
d		16 28										17 09							17 28	
Bolton 82 a																				
Manchester Picc. 10 82 ⛴ a				17 30	17 30															
Manchester Airport ✈ a				17 46	17 50															
Liverpool Lime Street 10 91 a																				
d								16 34	16 47						17 04					
Liverpool South Parkway 91 ✈ d								16 44							17 15					
Runcorn 91 d								16 52	17 03						17 25					
Warrington Bank Quay a		16 39										17 20							17 39	
d		16 39										17 20							17 39	
Manchester Picc. 10 84 ⛴ d	16 35										16 55			17 06		17 15	17 27	17 35		
Stockport 84 d	16 43										17 04			17 15		17 23	17 36	17 43		
Wilmslow 84 d											17 11									
Holyhead 81 ⛴ d																				
Bangor (Gwynedd) 81 d																				
Llandudno Junction 81 d																				
Wrexham General 75 d																				
Chester 81 d						17 35	20 35													
Crewe 10 a		16 58				17 54	20 54	17 17	17 22		17 27				17 47				17 59	
d		17 01	17 02					17 19	17 23		17 29				17 49				18 01	18 02
Macclesfield d	16 56													17 27				17 56		
Stoke-on-Trent d	17 12		17 28							←			←	17 45		17 50	18 07	18 12		18 28
Stafford a			17 49					17 43	17 41	17 43			17 49	18 03	18 09		18 25			18 50
d			17 56					17 44	17 43	17 44			17 56	18 04	18 10		18 26			18 56
Penkridge a			→					→							18 15					→
Wolverhampton 7 ⛴ a		17 33								17 57				18 15	18 27		18 40		18 32	
Birmingham New St. 12 68 a		18 05								18 17				18 33	18 47		18 58		19 05	
Birmingham International 68 ✈ a		18 19															19 13		19 19	
Coventry 68 a		18 30															19 24		19 30	
Lichfield Trent Valley a													18 12							
Tamworth Low Level a													18 19							
Nuneaton a													18 35							
Rugby 66 a													18 51						19 42	
Milton Keynes Central 66 a		18 58											19 14			18 46			20 05	
Watford Junction 66 a																			20s34	
London Euston 15 ⊖66 a	18 43	19 34							19 01		19 09	19 14	19 50			19 24		19 43	20 55	

A from 29 March

B until 22 March

OVERNIGHT SLEEPERS. For sleeper trains, operated by First ScotRail, please see Tables 400 - 404.

For complete service between Manchester and Preston, Blackpool and between Barrow-in-furness and Lancaster, please see Table 82.

For complete service between Crewe and Liverpool Lime Street, see Table 91

For complete service between Crewe/Stoke-on-Trent & Manchester see Table 84

For complete service between Crewe and Holyhead please see Table 81.

For complete service between Coventry-Birmingham-Wolverhampton-Stafford please see Table 68

For complete service between Windermere and Oxenholme Lake District, please see Table 83

Table 65R

Saturdays

15 February to 17 May

Scotland and North West England - West Midlands and London

Route Diagram - refer to first Page of Table 65

			LM	VT	LM	LM	VT	VT	TP	TP		XC	LM	NT	VT	XC	VT	VT	LM	TP		LM	VT	LM
			1	◇1	1	1	◇1	◇1	◇1	◇1		◇1	1		◇1	◇1	◇1	◇1	1	◇1		1	◇1	1
Inverness 229 d																								
Aberdeen 229 d																								
Dundee 229 d																								
Perth 229 d																								
Edinburgh 10 225,226,228,230,242 d																				16 12				
Haymarket 225,226,228,230,242 d																				16u16				
Glasgow Central 15 226,216 d								15 40										16 00						
Motherwell 226 d																								
Carstairs 226 d																								
Lockerbie d																				17 10				
Carlisle 8 216 a								16 46										17 08		17 32				
d								16 49										17 09		17 33				
Penrith North Lakes d								17 03												17 48				
Windermere 83 d									17 06															
Oxenholme Lake District a									17 25									17 44						
d									17 30									17 44						
Barrow-in-Furness 82 d										17 21														
Lancaster 6 a								17 37	17 47	18 17										18 24				
d								17 38	17 48	18 17										18 25				
Blackpool North 97 d																								
Preston 8 90 a								17 56	18 06	18 37								18 12		18 45				
Preston 8 90 d								17 58	18 08									18 17		18 45				
Wigan North Western 90 a								18 09										18 27		18 58				
d								18 09										18 28		18 59				
Bolton 82 a									18 34															
Manchester Picc. 10 82 ⛴ a									18 56											19 29				
Manchester Airport ✈ a									19 17											19 47				
Liverpool Lime Street 10 91 a																								
d			17 34	17 47									18 04									18 34	18 47	
Liverpool South Parkway 91 ✈ d			17 44										18 15									18 44		
Runcorn 91 d			17 52	18 03									18 24									18 52	19 03	
Warrington Bank Quay a								18 20										18 38						
d								18 20										18 39						
Manchester Picc. 10 84 ⛴ d							17 55					18 05		18 08	18 15	18 27	18 35							
Stockport 84 d							18 04					18 13		18 22	18 23	18 35	18 43							
Wilmslow 84 d							18 11							18 37										
Holyhead 81 ⛴ d																								
Bangor (Gwynedd) 81 d																								
Llandudno Junction 81 d																								
Wrexham General 75 d																								
Chester 81 d																								
Crewe 10 a			18 20				18 27						18 46	19 06				18 58				19 19		
d			18 22				18 29						18 49					19 01	19 02			19 21		
Macclesfield d												18 26					18 56							
Stoke-on-Trent d					←	←						18 44			18 49	19 07	19 12		19 28					←
Stafford a			18 42	18 36	18 42	18 50						19 02	19 09			19 25			19 50			19 45	19 35	19 45
d			18 43	18 36	18 43	18 56						19 03	19 10			19 25			19 51			19 45	19 36	19 45
Penkridge a			↪										19 15						↪			↪		19 51
Wolverhampton 7 ⛴ a					18 56							19 15	19 27			19 39		19 32						20 01
Birmingham New St. 12 68 a					19 17							19 33	19 47			19 59		20 05						20 19
Birmingham International 68 ✈ a																20 13		20 19						
Coventry 68 a																20 24		20 30						
Lichfield Trent Valley a						19 12																		
Tamworth Low Level a						19 19																		
Nuneaton a						19 35																		
Rugby 66 a						19 51												20 42						
Milton Keynes Central 66 a															19 45			21 04						
Watford Junction 66 a																		21s35						
London Euston 15 ⊖66 a				19 59			20 05	20 16							20 26		20 59	21 56					21 15	

OVERNIGHT SLEEPERS. For sleeper trains, operated by First ScotRail, please see Tables 400 - 404.

For complete service between Manchester and Preston, Blackpool and between Barrow-in-furness and Lancaster, please see Table 82.

For complete service between Crewe and Liverpool Lime Street, see Table 91

For complete service between Crewe/Stoke-on-Trent & Manchester see Table 84

For complete service between Crewe and Holyhead please see Table 81.

For complete service between Coventry-Birmingham-Wolverhampton-Stafford please see Table 68

For complete service between Windermere and Oxenholme Lake District, please see Table 83

Table 65R

Saturdays

15 February to 17 May

Scotland and North West England - West Midlands and London

Route Diagram - refer to first Page of Table 65

	LM	VT	VT		XC	LM		XC	VT	VT	TP	LM	VT	VT		XC		VT	TP	TP	XC	LM	VT	
	■1	◇■1	◇■1		◇■1	■1		◇■1	◇■1	◇■1	◇■1	■1	◇■1	◇■1		◇■1		◇■1	◇■1	◇■1	◇■1	■1	◇■1	
								A																
		🍴	🍴		🛒			🛒	🍴	🍴	🛒		🍴	🍴				🍴		🛒			🍴	
Inverness 229 d																								
Aberdeen 229 d																								
Dundee 229 d																								
Perth 229 d																								
Edinburgh ■10 225,226,228,230,242 d										16 52										18 12				
Haymarket 225,226,228,230,242 d										16 57										18u16				
Glasgow Central ■15 226,216 d			16 40								17 06			17 40				18 00						
Motherwell 226 d			16 54																					
Carstairs 226 d																								
Lockerbie d											18 06			18 32						19 11				
Carlisle ■8 216 a			17 49							18 06	18 30			18 50				19 07		19 32				
d			17 52							18 07	18 30			18 52				19 09		19 33				
Penrith North Lakes d											18 45			19 06						19 48				
Windermere 83 d																								
Oxenholme Lake District a			18 25							18 42	19 09			19 28						20 12				
d			18 26							18 43	19 09			19 29						20 13				
Barrow-in-Furness 82 d																			19 17					
Lancaster ■6 a			18 40							18 57	19 24			19 43				19 55	20 17	20 27				
d			18 41							18 58	19 24			19 44				19 57	20 18	20 28				
Blackpool North 97 d																								
Preston ■8 90 a			18 59							19 15	19 44			20 02				20 15	20 37	20 46				
Preston ■8 90 d			19 01							19 17	19 45			20 04				20 17		20 48				
Wigan North Western 90 a			19 12							19 29	19 58			20 15				20 28						
d			19 12							19 29	19 59			20 15				20 28						
Bolton 82 a																								
Manchester Picc. ■10 82 ⛴ a											20 27									21 27				
Manchester Airport ✈ a											20 47									21 46				
Liverpool Lime Street ■10 91 a																								
d						19 04						19 34	19 48									20 34		
Liverpool South Parkway 91 ✈ d						19 14						19 44										20 44		
Runcorn 91 d						19 23						19 52	20 04									20 52		
Warrington Bank Quay a			19 23							19 39				20 26				20 39						
d			19 23							19 40				20 26				20 39						
Manchester Picc. ■10 84 ⛴ d		18 55			19 07			19 27	19 35							20 07					20 27		20 35	
Stockport 84 d		19 04			19 16			19 35	19 43							20 16					20 35		20 43	
Wilmslow 84 d		19 11																						
Holyhead 81 ⛴ d																								
Bangor (Gwynedd) 81 d																								
Llandudno Junction 81 d																								
Wrexham General 75 d																								
Chester 81 d																								
Crewe ■10 a		19 27				19 49				19 59		20 16	20 21	20 45				20 59				21 16		
d		19 29				19 51				20 01		20 18	20 23	20 47				21 01				21 17		
Macclesfield d								19 49	19 56												20 49		20 56	
Stoke-on-Trent d	←				19 44			20 07	20 12							20 44					21 07		21 12	
Stafford a	19 50				20 02	20 11		20 25				20 40	20 41			21 02					21 26	21 42		
d	19 51				20 03	20 12		20 26				20 40	20 43			21 03					21 27	21 42		
Penkridge a												20 49										21 48		
Wolverhampton ■7 ⛴ a					20 15	20 28		20 39		20 32		20 59				21 15		21 32			21 39	21 59		
Birmingham New St. ■12 68 a					20 33	20 48		20 58		21 05		21 17				21 32		21 55			21 58	22 20		
Birmingham International 68 ✈ a								21 13		21 19														
Coventry 68 a								21 24		21 30														
Lichfield Trent Valley a	20 07																							
Tamworth Low Level a	20 14																							
Nuneaton a	20 30																							
Rugby 66 a	20 46									21 42														
Milton Keynes Central 66 a			20 42						21 10	22 04				21 51									22 10	
Watford Junction 66 a			21s15							22s34													22s40	
London Euston ■15 ⊖66 a		21 20	21 38						22 00	22 55			22 15	22 45									23 02	

A 🛒 to Birmingham New St.

OVERNIGHT SLEEPERS. For sleeper trains, operated by First ScotRail, please see Tables 400 - 404.

For complete service between Manchester and Preston, Blackpool and between Barrow-in-furness and Lancaster, please see Table 82.

For complete service between Crewe and Liverpool Lime Street, see Table 91

For complete service between Crewe/Stoke-on-Trent & Manchester see Table 84

For complete service between Crewe and Holyhead please see Table 81.

For complete service between Coventry-Birmingham-Wolverhampton-Stafford please see Table 68

For complete service between Windermere and Oxenholme Lake District, please see Table 83

Table 65R

Saturdays
15 February to 17 May

Scotland and North West England - West Midlands and London

Route Diagram - refer to first Page of Table 65

		XC	VT	VT	XC	LM	LM	NT
		◇1	◇1	◇1	◇1	1	1	A
			⊡	⊡				🚌
Inverness 229	d							
Aberdeen 229	d							
Dundee 229	d							
Perth 229	d							
Edinburgh 10 225,226,228,230,242	d			18 52				
Haymarket 225,226,228,230,242	d			18 56				
Glasgow Central 15 226,216	d		18 40					
Motherwell 226	d							
Carstairs 226	d							
Lockerbie	d							
Carlisle 8 216	a		19 46	20 05				
	d		19 48	20 08				
Penrith North Lakes	d		20 02	20 22				
Windermere 83	d							
Oxenholme Lake District	a		20 24	20 45				
	d		20 25	20 45				
Barrow-in-Furness 82	d							
Lancaster 6	a		20 39	21 00				
	d		20 40	21 00				23 10
Blackpool North 97	d							
Preston 8 90	a		20 58	21 18				23 50
Preston 8 90	d		21 00	21 21				
Wigan North Western 90	a		21 11	21 31				
	d		21 11	21 32				
Bolton 82	a							
Manchester Picc. 10 82 ⇌	a							
Manchester Airport ✈	a							
Liverpool Lime Street 10 91	a							
	d					21 34	22 04	
Liverpool South Parkway 91 ✈	d					21 44	22 14	
Runcorn 91	d					21 52	22 23	
Warrington Bank Quay	a		21 22	21 42				
	d		21 22	21 43				
Manchester Picc. 10 84 ⇌	d	21 07			21 27			
Stockport 84	d				21 35			
Wilmslow 84	d							
Holyhead 81 ⛴	d							
Bangor (Gwynedd) 81	d							
Llandudno Junction 81	d							
Wrexham General 75	d							
Chester 81	d							
Crewe 10	a		21 41	22 02		22 16	22 48	
	d		21 43	22 04		22 24		
Macclesfield	d				21 49			
Stoke-on-Trent	d	21 45			22 07			
Stafford	a	22 02	22 07	22 22	22 28	22 44		
	d	22 03	22 08	22 23	22 29	22 45		
Penkridge	a					22 50		
Wolverhampton 7 ⇌	a	22 14	22 22	22 40	22 43	23 01		
Birmingham New St. 12 68	a	22 32	22 46	22 59	23 01	23 20		
Birmingham International 68 ✈	a							
Coventry 68	a							
Lichfield Trent Valley	a							
Tamworth Low Level	a							
Nuneaton	a							
Rugby 66	a							
Milton Keynes Central 66	a							
Watford Junction 66	a							
London Euston 15 ⊖66	a							

A from 29 March

OVERNIGHT SLEEPERS. For sleeper trains, operated by First ScotRail, please see Tables 400 - 404.

For complete service between Manchester and Preston, Blackpool and between Barrow-in-furness and Lancaster, please see Table 82.

For complete service between Crewe and Liverpool Lime Street, see Table 91

For complete service between Crewe/Stoke-on-Trent & Manchester see Table 84

For complete service between Crewe and Holyhead please see Table 81.

For complete service between Coventry-Birmingham-Wolverhampton-Stafford please see Table 68

For complete service between Windermere and Oxenholme Lake District, please see Table 83

Table 65R

Sundays

8 December to 29 December

Scotland and North West England - West Midlands and London

Route Diagram - refer to first Page of Table 65

	VT	VT	VT	XC	VT	LM	VT	VT	XC	VT	LM	LM	VT	VT	VT	TP	XC	VT	VT	VT
	◇1	◇1	◇1	◇1	◇1	1	◇1	◇1	◇1	◇1	1	1	◇1	◇1	◇1	◇1	◇1	◇1	◇1	◇1
				A					A											
	☕	☕	☕	☕🛒	☕		☕	☕	☕🛒	☕			☕	☕	☕		🛒	☕	☕	☕
Inverness 229 d																				
Aberdeen 229 d																				
Dundee 229 d																				
Perth 229 d																				
Edinburgh 10 225,226,228,230,242 d																				
Haymarket 225,226,228,230,242 d																				
Glasgow Central 15 226,216 d																				
Motherwell 226 d																				
Carstairs 226 d																				
Lockerbie d																				
Carlisle 8 216 a																				
d																				
Penrith North Lakes d																				
Windermere 83 d																				
Oxenholme Lake District a																				
d																				
Barrow-in-Furness 82 d																09 17				
Lancaster 6 a																10 17				
d																10 24				
Blackpool North 97 d																				
Preston 8 90 a																10 42				
Preston 8 90 d							09 00						10 00		10 17	10 47				10 58
Wigan North Western 90 a							09 10						10 10		10 28					11 09
d							09 11						10 11		10 28					11 09
Bolton 82 a																11 08				
Manchester Picc. 10 82 a																11 27				
Manchester Airport a																11 47				
Liverpool Lime Street 10 91 a																				
d			08 15		08 38					09 38									10 38	
Liverpool South Parkway 91 d																				
Runcorn 91 d			08 35		08 54					09 54									10 54	
Warrington Bank Quay a							09 21						10 21		10 39					11 20
d							09 22						10 22		10 39					11 20
Manchester Picc. 10 84 d	08 05	08 20		08 27				09 20	09 27					10 20			10 27	10 35		
Stockport 84 d	08 14	08 28		08 36				09 27	09 36					10 29			10 36	10 43		
Wilmslow 84 d	08 22			08 43										10 36						
Holyhead 81 d																				
Bangor (Gwynedd) 81 d																				
Llandudno Junction 81 d																				
Wrexham General 75 d																				
Chester 81 d																				
Crewe 10 a	08 39		08 52	09 01	09 11		09 41			10 12			10 41	10 53	10 59				11 12	
d	08 43		08 53	09 05	09 13	09 30	09 43			10 14	10 20	10 37	10 43	10 55	11 01				11 14	
Macclesfield d		08 42						09 40	09 49								10 49	10 55		
Stoke-on-Trent d		08 59				09 51		09 57	10 07			10 59					11 07	11 13		
Stafford a	09 01			09 25	09 31	10 14			10 26	10 32	10 41	11 17					11 27		11 35	
d	09 03			09 26	09 33	10 18			10 27	10 34	10 42	11 18					11 28		11 36	
Penkridge a											10 49									
Wolverhampton 7 a				09 40					10 42		11 00				11 31		11 41			
Birmingham New St. 12 68 a				09 58					10 59		11 18				11 55		11 59			
Birmingham International 68 a				10 13					11 13								12 13			
Coventry 68 a				10 24					11 24								12 24			
Lichfield Trent Valley a						10 34						11 35								
Tamworth Low Level a						10 41						11 41								
Nuneaton a					09 55	10 57				10 56		11 57							11 58	
Rugby 66 a						11 17	10 32					12 13	11 32							
Milton Keynes Central 66 a			10 18			12 02	11 07	11 16		11 46		13 04	12 07					12 21		
Watford Junction 66 a	10s35	10s41			11s16	12 32	11s44					13 34		12s36					12s52	
London Euston 15 ⊖66 a	10 58	11 02	11 06		11 37	12 51	12 06	12 09		12 32		13 53	12 46	12 57				13 00	13 13	13 22

A ☕ from Birmingham New St. 🛒 to Birmingham New St.

OVERNIGHT SLEEPERS. For sleeper trains, operated by First ScotRail, please see Tables 400 - 404.

For complete service between Manchester and Preston, Blackpool and between Barrow-in-furness and Lancaster, please see Table 82.

For complete service between Crewe and Liverpool Lime Street, see Table 91

For complete service between Crewe/Stoke-on-Trent & Manchester see Table 84

For complete service between Crewe and Holyhead please see Table 81.

For complete service between Coventry-Birmingham-Wolverhampton-Stafford please see Table 68

For complete service between Windermere and Oxenholme Lake District, please see Table 83

Table 65R

Sundays

8 December to 29 December

Scotland and North West England - West Midlands and London

Route Diagram - refer to first Page of Table 65

Station	Table		VT	LM	VT	VT	TP		XC	LM	VT	VT	VT	VT	VT	LM	VT		XC	VT	VT	TP	LM	VT	VT	VT
			◇1	1	◇1	◇1	◇1		◇1	1	◇1	◇1	◇1	◇1	◇1	1	◇1		◇1	◇1	◇1	◇1	1	◇1	◇1	◇1
									A										A							
			⊏P		⊏P	⊏P			⊏P⊼		⊏P	⊏P	⊏P	⊏P	⊏P		⊏P		⊏P⊼	⊏P	⊏P	⊼		⊏P	⊏P	⊏P
Inverness	229	d																								
Aberdeen	229	d																								
Dundee	229	d																								
Perth	229	d																								
Edinburgh 10	225,226,228,230,242	d																				10 10				
Haymarket	225,226,228,230,242	d																				10u14				
Glasgow Central 15	226,216	d												09 37												10 34
Motherwell	226	d																								10 49
Carstairs	226	d																								
Lockerbie		d																				11 08				
Carlisle 8	216	a												10 44								11 29				11 44
		d												10 46								11 30				11 46
Penrith North Lakes		d												11 00								11 45				12 00
Windermere	83	d																								
Oxenholme Lake District		a												11 22								12 09				12 22
		d												11 23								12 10				12 24
Barrow-in-Furness	82	d					10 25																			
Lancaster 6		a					11 25							11 37								12 24				12 37
		d					11 25							11 38							11 58	12 25				12 38
Blackpool North	97	d																								
Preston 8	90	a					11 44							11 56							12 15	12 43				12 56
Preston 8	90	d				11 17	11 49							11 58							12 17	12 45				12 58
Wigan North Western	90	a				11 28								12 09							12 28	12 58				13 09
		d				11 28								12 09							12 28	12 58				13 09
Bolton	82	a					12 09																			
Manchester Picc. 10	82 ⇌	a					12 28															13 27				
Manchester Airport	✈	a					12 46															13 47				
Liverpool Lime Street 10	91	a																								
		d								11 34		11 47											12 34	12 47		
Liverpool South Parkway	91 ✈	d								11 44													12 44			
Runcorn	91	d								11 52		12 03											12 52	13 03		
Warrington Bank Quay		a				11 39								12 20							12 39					13 20
		d				11 39								12 20							12 39					13 20
Manchester Picc. 10	84 ⇌	d	11 15						11 27		11 35		11 55		12 15				12 26	12 35					12 55	
Stockport	84	d	11 23						11 36		11 43		12 05		12 23				12 35	12 44					13 05	
Wilmslow	84	d											12 12												13 12	
Holyhead	81 ⛴	d															10 55									
Bangor (Gwynedd)	81	d															11 22									
Llandudno Junction	81	d															11 40									
Wrexham General	75	d																								
Chester	81	d			11 28												12 32									
Crewe 10		a			11 47	11 59				12 18		12 21	12 28				12 53				12 59		13 17	13 21	13 28	
		d		11 37	11 49	12 01				12 19		12 23	12 30			12 37	12 55				13 01		13 19	13 23	13 30	
Macclesfield		d							11 49		11 56								12 49	12 57						
Stoke-on-Trent		d	11 51	11 59					12 07		12 13				12 51	12 59			13 07	13 14						
Stafford		a		12 17					12 24	12 40		12 42				13 18			13 24				13 40	13 42		
		d		12 18					12 25	12 40		12 44				13 18			13 25				13 40	13 44		
Penkridge		a								12 46													13 46			
Wolverhampton 7	⇌	a				12 32			12 40	12 56									13 40		13 32		13 56			
Birmingham New St. 12	68	a				12 54			12 58	13 15									13 58		14 06		14 15			
Birmingham International	68 ✈	a							13 13										14 13		14 19					
Coventry	68	a							13 24										14 24		14 30					
Lichfield Trent Valley		a		12 35												13 35										
Tamworth Low Level		a		12 41												13 41										
Nuneaton		a		12 57	12 31											13 57										
Rugby	66	a		13 13												14 13										
Milton Keynes Central	66	a	12 50	14 04	13 04										13 47	15 04	14 03				14 58					
Watford Junction	66	a		14 34												15 34										
London Euston 15	⊖66	a	13 28	14 53	13 46						13 48	14 04	14 10	14 17	14 27	15 53	14 44			14 48	15 39			15 04	15 08	15 13

A ⊏P from Birmingham New St. ⊼ to Birmingham New St.

OVERNIGHT SLEEPERS. For sleeper trains, operated by First ScotRail, please see Tables 400 - 404.

For complete service between Manchester and Preston, Blackpool and between Barrow-in-furness and Lancaster, please see Table 82.

For complete service between Crewe and Liverpool Lime Street, see Table 91

For complete service between Crewe/Stoke-on-Trent & Manchester see Table 84

For complete service between Crewe and Holyhead please see Table 81.

For complete service between Coventry-Birmingham-Wolverhampton-Stafford please see Table 68

For complete service between Windermere and Oxenholme Lake District, please see Table 83

Table 65R

Sundays

8 December to 29 December

Scotland and North West England - West Midlands and London

Route Diagram - refer to first Page of Table 65

		XC	VT	LM	VT	VT	XC	VT	VT	TP	LM	VT	VT	VT	XC	VT	LM	VT	XC	VT	VT
		◇1	◇1	1	◇1	◇1	◇1	◇1	◇1	◇1	1	◇1	◇1	◇1	◇1	◇1	1	◇1	◇1	◇1	◇1
							A												A		
		⊼	⊡		⊡	⊡	⊡⊼	⊡	⊡			⊡	⊡	⊡	⊼	⊡		⊡	⊡⊼	⊡	⊡
Inverness 229	d																				
Aberdeen 229	d																				
Dundee 229	d																				
Perth 229	d																				
Edinburgh 10 225,226,228,230,242	d								10 51												
Haymarket 225,226,228,230,242	d								10 55												
Glasgow Central 15 226,216	d													11 36							
Motherwell 226	d																				
Carstairs 226	d																				
Lockerbie	d																				
Carlisle 8 216	a								12 05					12 47							
	d								12 07					12 49							
Penrith North Lakes	d																				
Windermere 83	d																				
Oxenholme Lake District	a								12 41					13 22							
	d								12 43					13 23							
Barrow-in-Furness 82	d									12 33											
Lancaster 6	a								12 56	13 25				13 37							
	d								12 57	13 25				13 38							
Blackpool North 97	d																				
Preston 8 90	a								13 15	13 44				13 56							
Preston 8 90	d								13 17	13 45				13 58							
Wigan North Western 90	a								13 28	13 58				14 09							
	d								13 28	13 58				14 09							
Bolton 82	a																				
Manchester Picc. 10 82	a									14 27											
Manchester Airport	a									14 47											
Liverpool Lime Street 10 91	a																				
	d										13 34	13 47									
Liverpool South Parkway 91	d										13 44										
Runcorn 91	d										13 52	14 03									
Warrington Bank Quay	a								13 39					14 20							
	d								13 39					14 20							
Manchester Picc. 10 84	d	13 07	13 15				13 27	13 35					13 55		14 07	14 15			14 27		14 35
Stockport 84	d		13 22				13 36	13 42					14 04			14 22			14 36		14 42
Wilmslow 84	d												14 11								
Holyhead 81	d				11 50													12 50			
Bangor (Gwynedd) 81	d				12 17													13 18			
Llandudno Junction 81	d				12 35													13 36			
Wrexham General 75	d																				
Chester 81	d				13 30	13 30												14 33		14 33	
Crewe 10	a				13 50	13 50			13 59		14 17	14 21	14 27					14 53		14 52	
	d			13 37	13 52	13 52			14 01		14 19	14 23	14 29				14 33	14 54		14 55	
Macclesfield	d						13 49	13 55											14 49		14 55
Stoke-on-Trent	d	13 43	13 50	13 59			14 07	14 12							14 43	14 50	14 55		15 07		15 12
Stafford	a			14 17			14 24				14 40	14 42					15 12		15 24		
	d			14 18			14 25				14 40	14 44					15 18		15 25		
Penkridge	a										14 46										
Wolverhampton 7	a	14 13					14 40		14 31		14 56				15 13				15 40		
Birmingham New St. 12 68	a	14 31					14 58		15 06		15 15				15 31				15 58		
Birmingham International 68	a						15 13		15 19										16 13		
Coventry 68	a						15 24		15 30										16 24		
Lichfield Trent Valley	a			14 35													15 35				
Tamworth Low Level	a			14 41													15 41				
Nuneaton	a			14 57	14 32	14 32											15 57				
Rugby 66	a			15 13													16 13				
Milton Keynes Central 66	a		14 48	16 04	15 03	15 03			15 58							15 48	17 04	16 03		16 03	
Watford Junction 66	a			16 34													17 34				
London Euston 15 ⊖66	a		15 26	16 53	15 45	15 45		15 48	16 39			16 04	16 07	16 13		16 26	17 53	16 44		16 41	16 48

A ⊡ from Birmingham New St. ⊼ to Birmingham New St.

OVERNIGHT SLEEPERS. For sleeper trains, operated by First ScotRail, please see Tables 400 - 404.

For complete service between Manchester and Preston, Blackpool and between Barrow-in-furness and Lancaster, please see Table 82.

For complete service between Crewe and Liverpool Lime Street, see Table 91

For complete service between Crewe/Stoke-on-Trent & Manchester see Table 84

For complete service between Crewe and Holyhead please see Table 81.

For complete service between Coventry-Birmingham-Wolverhampton-Stafford please see Table 68

For complete service between Windermere and Oxenholme Lake District, please see Table 83

Table 65R

Sundays

8 December to 29 December

Scotland and North West England - West Midlands and London

Route Diagram - refer to first Page of Table 65

	VT	TP	LM	VT	VT	VT			XC	VT	LM	VT	XC	VT	VT	TP	LM		VT	VT	VT	XC	VT	LM
	◇1	◇1	1	◇1	◇1	◇1			◇1	◇1	1	◇1	◇1	◇1	◇1	◇1	1		◇1	◇1	◇1	◇1	◇1	1
													A											
Inverness 229 d																								
Aberdeen 229 d																								
Dundee 229 d																								
Perth 229 d																								
Edinburgh 10 225,226,228,230,242 d		12 10													12 51									
Haymarket 225,226,228,230,242 d		12u14													12 55									
Glasgow Central 15 226,216 d	11 58					12 42															13 36			
Motherwell 226 d																								
Carstairs 226 d																								
Lockerbie d		13 08																						
Carlisle 8 216 a	13 09	13 29				13 52									14 05						14 46			
d	13 10	13 30				13 54									14 07						14 49			
Penrith North Lakes d		13 45													14 22									
Windermere 83 d																								
Oxenholme Lake District a		14 09				14 27															15 22			
d		14 10				14 28															15 23			
Barrow-in-Furness 82 d																14 25								
Lancaster 6 a	13 56	14 24				14 42									14 56	15 25					15 37			
d	13 58	14 25				14 43									14 57	15 25					15 38			
Blackpool North 97 d																								
Preston 8 90 a	14 15	14 43				15 01									15 15	15 44					15 56			
Preston 8 90 d	14 17	14 45				15 03									15 17	15 45					15 58			
Wigan North Western 90 a	14 28	14 58				15 14									15 28	15 58					16 09			
d	14 28	14 58				15 14									15 28	15 58					16 09			
Bolton 82 a																								
Manchester Picc. 10 82 a		15 27														16 27								
Manchester Airport a		15 47														16 47								
Liverpool Lime Street 10 91 a																								
d			14 34	14 47													15 34		15 47					
Liverpool South Parkway 91 d			14 44														15 44							
Runcorn 91 d			14 52	15 03													15 52		16 03					
Warrington Bank Quay a	14 39					15 25									15 39						16 20			
d	14 39					15 25									15 39						16 20			
Manchester Picc. 10 84 d					14 55				15 07	15 15			15 27	15 35						15 55		16 07	16 15	
Stockport 84 d					15 04					15 22			15 36	15 42						16 04			16 23	
Wilmslow 84 d					15 11															16 11				
Holyhead 81 d												13 55												
Bangor (Gwynedd) 81 d												14 22												
Llandudno Junction 81 d												14 40												
Wrexham General 75 d																								
Chester 81 d												15 33												
Crewe 10 a	14 58		15 17	15 21	15 27							15 52			15 59		16 17		16 21	16 27				
d	15 01		15 19	15 23	15 29						15 37	15 54			16 01		16 19		16 23	16 29				16 33
Macclesfield d													15 49	15 55										
Stoke-on-Trent d									15 43	15 50	15 59		16 07	16 12								16 43	16 50	16 55
Stafford a			15 40	15 42							16 17		16 24				16 40		16 42					17 17
d			15 40	15 44							16 18		16 25				16 40		16 44					17 18
Penkridge a			15 46														16 46							
Wolverhampton 7 a	15 34		15 56						16 13				16 40		16 32		16 56					17 13		
Birmingham New St. 12 68 a	16 07		16 15						16 31				16 58		17 06		17 15					17 31		
Birmingham International 68 a	16 19												17 13		17 19									
Coventry 68 a	16 31												17 24		17 29									
Lichfield Trent Valley a											16 35													17 35
Tamworth Low Level a											16 41													17 41
Nuneaton a											16 57													17 57
Rugby 66 a											17 13													18 13
Milton Keynes Central 66 a	16 58									16 50	18 04	17 03			17 58								17 49	19 04
Watford Junction 66 a											18 34													19 34
London Euston 15 ⊖66 a	17 38			17 04	17 09	17 21				17 27	18 53	17 44		17 46	18 38				18 03	18 09	18 14		18 27	19 53

A [catering symbol] from Birmingham New St. [catering symbol] to Birmingham New St.

OVERNIGHT SLEEPERS. For sleeper trains, operated by First ScotRail, please see Tables 400 - 404.

For complete service between Manchester and Preston, Blackpool and between Barrow-in-furness and Lancaster, please see Table 82.

For complete service between Crewe and Liverpool Lime Street, see Table 91

For complete service between Crewe/Stoke-on-Trent & Manchester see Table 84

For complete service between Crewe and Holyhead please see Table 81.

For complete service between Coventry-Birmingham-Wolverhampton-Stafford please see Table 68

For complete service between Windermere and Oxenholme Lake District, please see Table 83

Table 65R

Sundays

8 December to 29 December

Scotland and North West England - West Midlands and London

Route Diagram - refer to first Page of Table 65

Station			VT	XC	VT	VT	TP	LM	VT	VT	VT	XC	VT	LM	XC	VT	VT	VT	TP	LM	VT	VT
			◇1	◇1	◇1	◇1	◇1	1	◇1	◇1	◇1	◇1	◇1	1	◇1	◇1	◇1	◇1	◇1	1	◇1	◇1
				A											A							
			🍴	🍴🛒	🍴	🍴	🛒		🍴	🍴	🍴	🛒	🍴		🍴🛒	🍴	🍴	🍴	🛒		🍴	🍴
Inverness	229	d																				
Aberdeen	229	d																				
Dundee	229	d																				
Perth	229	d																				
Edinburgh 10	225,226,228,230,242	d					14 10											14 51				
Haymarket	225,226,228,230,242	d					14u14											14 56				
Glasgow Central 15	226,216	d				13 55					14 36								15 06			
Motherwell	226	d																				
Carstairs	226	d																				
Lockerbie		d					15 08												16 05			
Carlisle 8	216	a				15 09	15 29				15 46							16 05	16 26			
		d				15 12	15 30				15 49							16 07	16 30			
Penrith North Lakes		d					15 46											16 22	16 45			
Windermere	83	d																				
Oxenholme Lake District		a				15 46	16 09				16 22								17 08			
		d				15 47	16 10				16 23								17 09			
Barrow-in-Furness	82	d																				
Lancaster 6		a					16 24				16 37							16 57	17 23			
		d					16 25				16 38							16 57	17 24			
Blackpool North	97	d																				
Preston 8	90	a				16 15	16 43				16 56							17 15	17 42			
Preston 8	90	d				16 17	16 45				16 58							17 18	17 45			
Wigan North Western	90	a				16 28	16 58				17 09							17 28	17 58			
		d				16 29	16 58				17 09							17 29	17 58			
Bolton	82	a																				
Manchester Picc. 10	82 ⛴	a					17 27												18 27			
Manchester Airport	✈	a					17 47												18 47			
Liverpool Lime Street 10	91	a																				
		d	16 18					16 34	16 47											17 34	17 47	
Liverpool South Parkway	91 ✈	d						16 44												17 44		
Runcorn	91	d	16 34					16 52	17 03											17 52	18 03	
Warrington Bank Quay		a				16 39					17 20							17 39				
		d				16 40					17 20							17 40				
Manchester Picc. 10	84 ⛴	d		16 27	16 35					16 55		17 07	17 15		17 27		17 35					17 55
Stockport	84	d		16 36	16 42					17 04			17 22		17 36		17 42					18 04
Wilmslow	84	d								17 11												18 11
Holyhead	81 ⛴	d																				
Bangor (Gwynedd)	81	d																				
Llandudno Junction	81	d																				
Wrexham General	75	d																				
Chester	81	d														17 35						
Crewe 10		a	16 51			16 58		17 17	17 21	17 27						17 53		17 59		18 17	18 21	18 27
		d	16 54			17 00		17 19	17 23	17 29				17 37		17 55		18 01		18 19	18 23	18 29
Macclesfield		d		16 49	16 55										17 49		17 55					
Stoke-on-Trent		d		17 08	17 12							17 43	17 50	17 59	18 08		18 12					
Stafford		a		17 25				17 40	17 42					18 17	18 26					18 40	18 42	
		d		17 26				17 40	17 44					18 18	18 27					18 40	18 44	
Penkridge		a						17 46												18 46		
Wolverhampton 7	⛴	a		17 40		17 32		17 56				18 13			18 40			18 33		18 56		
Birmingham New St. 12	68	a		17 58		18 07		18 15				18 31			18 58			19 06		19 15		
Birmingham International	68 ✈	a		18 13		18 19									19 13			19 19				
Coventry	68	a		18 24		18 31									19 24			19 30				
Lichfield Trent Valley		a	17 25											18 35								
Tamworth Low Level		a												18 41								
Nuneaton		a												18 57								
Rugby	66	a												19 13								
Milton Keynes Central	66	a	18 03			18 58							18 49	20 06		19 03		19 58				
Watford Junction	66	a												20 34								
London Euston 15	⊖66	a	18 44		18 48	19 38			19 04	19 07	19 11		19 27	20 53		19 45	19 48	20 39			20 05	20 08

A 🍴 from Birmingham New St. 🛒 to Birmingham New St.

OVERNIGHT SLEEPERS. For sleeper trains, operated by First ScotRail, please see Tables 400 - 404.

For complete service between Manchester and Preston, Blackpool and between Barrow-in-furness and Lancaster, please see Table 82.

For complete service between Crewe and Liverpool Lime Street, see Table 91

For complete service between Crewe/Stoke-on-Trent & Manchester see Table 84

For complete service between Crewe and Holyhead please see Table 81.

For complete service between Coventry-Birmingham-Wolverhampton-Stafford please see Table 68

For complete service between Windermere and Oxenholme Lake District, please see Table 83

Table 65R

Sundays

8 December to 29 December

Scotland and North West England - West Midlands and London

Route Diagram - refer to first Page of Table 65

Station		VT	XC	VT	LM	XC	VT	VT	VT	TP		LM	VT	VT	VT		XC	VT	VT	LM		VT	TP	TP	XC
		◇1	◇1	◇1	1	◇1	◇1	◇1	◇1	◇1		1	◇1	◇1	◇1		◇1	◇1	◇	1		◇1	◇1	◇1	◇1
						A																			
		☕	🛒	☕		☕🛒	☕	☕	☕	🛒			☕	☕	☕		🛒	☕	☕			☕		🛒	🛒
Inverness 229	d																								
Aberdeen 229	d																								
Dundee 229	d																								
Perth 229	d																								
Edinburgh 10 225,226,228,230,242	d									16 10												16 51			
Haymarket 225,226,228,230,242	d									16u14												16 55			
Glasgow Central 15 226,216	d	15 36							15 57						16 40									17 06	
Motherwell 226	d														16 54										
Carstairs 226	d																								
Lockerbie	d									17 08														18 07	
Carlisle 8 216	a	16 46							17 07	17 29					17 49							18 05		18 26	
	d	16 49							17 09	17 30					17 51							18 07		18 30	
Penrith North Lakes	d	17 03								17 45					18 05									18 45	
Windermere 83	d																								
Oxenholme Lake District	a								17 44	18 09					18 27							18 41		19 09	
	d								17 44	18 10					18 28							18 42		19 09	
Barrow-in-Furness 82	d																						18 17		
Lancaster 6	a	17 37								18 24					18 42							18 56	19 17	19 24	
	d	17 38								18 25					18 43							18 57	19 17	19 24	
Blackpool North 97	d																								
Preston 8 90	a	17 56							18 13	18 43					19 01							19 15	19 37	19 44	
Preston 8 90	d	17 58							18 17	18 45					19 03							19 17		19 45	
Wigan North Western 90	a	18 09							18 28	18 58					19 14							19 28		19 58	
	d	18 09							18 28	18 58					19 14							19 28		19 59	
Bolton 82	a																								
Manchester Picc. 10 82 ⛴	a									19 27														20 27	
Manchester Airport ✈	a									19 47														20 45	
Liverpool Lime Street 10 91	a																								
	d											18 34	18 47												
Liverpool South Parkway 91 ✈	d											18 44													
Runcorn 91	d											18 52	19 03												
Warrington Bank Quay	a	18 20							18 39						19 25							19 39			
	d	18 20							18 39						19 25							19 39			
Manchester Picc. 10 84 ⛴	d		18 07	18 15		18 27		18 35						18 55			19 07	19 15							19 27
Stockport 84	d			18 22		18 36		18 42						19 04				19 22							19 36
Wilmslow 84	d													19 11											
Holyhead 81 ⛴	d																								
Bangor (Gwynedd) 81	d																								
Llandudno Junction 81	d																								
Wrexham General 75	d																								
Chester 81	d						18 35												19 35						
Crewe 10	a						18 53		18 58			19 17	19 21	19 27					19 56			19 59			
	d				18 37		18 55		19 01			19 19	19 23	19 29						19 37		20 01			
Macclesfield	d					18 49		18 55																	19 49
Stoke-on-Trent	d		18 43	18 50	18 59	19 07		19 12									19 43	19 50		19 59					20 07
Stafford	a				19 18	19 24						19 40	19 42							20 17					20 26
	d				19 18	19 25						19 40	19 44							20 18					20 27
Penkridge	a											19 46													
Wolverhampton 7 ⛴	a		19 13			19 40			19 34			19 56					20 13					20 33			20 39
Birmingham New St. 12 68	a		19 31			19 58			20 06			20 15					20 31					20 51			20 58
Birmingham International 68 ✈	a					20 13			20 19																21 13
Coventry 68	a					20 24			20 30																21 23
Lichfield Trent Valley	a				19 35															20 35					
Tamworth Low Level	a				19 41															20 41					
Nuneaton	a				19 57															20 57					
Rugby 66	a				20 13															21 13					
Milton Keynes Central 66	a			19 48	21 07		20 03		20 59									20 46		22 10					
Watford Junction 66	a				21 35															22 52					
London Euston 15 ⊖66	a	20 13		20 27	21 55		20 46	20 48	21 48				21 04	21 10	21 22			21 31		23 15					

A ☕ from Birmingham New St. 🛒 to Birmingham New St.

OVERNIGHT SLEEPERS. For sleeper trains, operated by First ScotRail, please see Tables 400 - 404.

For complete service between Manchester and Preston, Blackpool and between Barrow-in-furness and Lancaster, please see Table 82.

For complete service between Crewe and Liverpool Lime Street, see Table 91

For complete service between Crewe/Stoke-on-Trent & Manchester see Table 84

For complete service between Crewe and Holyhead please see Table 81.

For complete service between Coventry-Birmingham-Wolverhampton-Stafford please see Table 68

For complete service between Windermere and Oxenholme Lake District, please see Table 83

Table 65R

Sundays

8 December to 29 December

Scotland and North West England - West Midlands and London

Route Diagram - refer to first Page of Table 65

		LM	VT	VT	XC	VT	LM	VT	TP	VT	LM	VT	VT	VT	XC	VT	TP	VT	LM	XC	SR	SR
																					R	R
		■1	◇■1	◇■1	◇■1	◇	■1	◇■1	◇■1	◇■1	■1	◇■1	◇■1	◇■1	◇■1	◇■1	◇■1	◇■1	■1	◇■1	🛏	🛏
			☕	☕		☕		☕	🛒	☕		☕	☕	☕		☕	🛒	☕			✕	✕
Inverness 229	d																					
Aberdeen 229	d																					
Dundee 229	d																					
Perth 229	d																					
Edinburgh 10 225,226,228,230,242	d								18 10							18 51	19 57					23 15
Haymarket 225,226,228,230,242	d								18u14							18 56	20u01					
Glasgow Central 15 226,216	d							17 36						18 30				20 08			23 15	
Motherwell 226	d																				23u30	
Carstairs 226	d																				23u47	
Lockerbie	d							18 32	19 08									21 03				
Carlisle 8 216	a							18 50	19 29					19 43		20 05	21 13	21 21				
	d							18 52	19 30					19 44		20 07	21 14	21 24				01u12
Penrith North Lakes	d							19 06	19 45							20 22		21 39				
Windermere 83	d																					
Oxenholme Lake District	a							19 28	20 09					20 19			21 51	22 02				
	d							19 29	20 10					20 19			21 51	22 03				
Barrow-in-Furness 82	d																					
Lancaster 6	a							19 43	20 24					20 34		20 56	22 06	22 17				
	d							19 44	20 25					20 34		20 57	22 06	22 18				
Blackpool North 97	d																					
Preston 8 90	a							20 02	20 43					20 52		21 15	22 25	22 35				
Preston 8 90	d							20 04	20 46					20 55		21 17	22 26	22 38				
Wigan North Western 90	a							20 15						21 06		21 28	22 39	22 48				
	d							20 15						21 07		21 29	22 39	22 50				
Bolton 82	a																					
Manchester Picc. 10 82 ⛴	a								21 25								23 08					
Manchester Airport ✈	a								21 45								23 24					
Liverpool Lime Street 10 91	a																					
	d	19 34		19 47							20 34		20 47						21 34			
Liverpool South Parkway 91 ✈	d	19 44									20 44								21 44			
Runcorn 91	d	19 52		20 03							20 52		21 03						21 52			
Warrington Bank Quay	a							20 26						21 18		21 39		22 59				
	d							20 26						21 18		21 39		23 01				
Manchester Picc. 10 84 ⛴	d		19 35		20 07					20 21		20 55			21 07					22 07		
Stockport 84	d		19 41		20 16					20 27		21 03			21 16					22 16		
Wilmslow 84	d																					
Holyhead 81 ⛴	d																					
Bangor (Gwynedd) 81	d																					
Llandudno Junction 81	d																					
Wrexham General 75	d																					
Chester 81	d					20 37																
Crewe 10	a	20 16		20 22		20 56		20 45			21 16		21 21	21 38		21 59		23 22	22 18			
	d	20 18		20 24			20 44	20 47			21 18		21 23	21 40		22 01			22 22			
Macclesfield	d		19 54		20 29					20 40		21 15			21 29					22 29		
Stoke-on-Trent	d		20 11		20 47		21 06			20 57		21 33			21 47					22 47		
Stafford	a	20 38		20 42	21 08		21 25				21 39		21 42	22 01	22 06				22 42	23 04		
	d	20 39		20 43	21 09		21 25				21 39		21 44	22 02	22 06				22 43	23 05		
Penkridge	a	20 44									21 45								22 48			
Wolverhampton 7 ⛴	a	20 55			21 21						21 55			22 17	22 20	22 34			22 59	23 18		
Birmingham New St. 12 68	a	21 16			21 39						22 17			22 38	22 40	22 55			23 16	23 36		
Birmingham International 68 ✈	a																					
Coventry 68	a																					
Lichfield Trent Valley	a						21 41						21 59									
Tamworth Low Level	a						21 48						22 06									
Nuneaton	a						22 04						22 17									
Rugby 66	a						22 20						22 31									
Milton Keynes Central 66	a			21 36				21 52		22 03		22 46	23 04									
Watford Junction 66	a							22s31				23s28	23s34									06s22
London Euston 15 ⊖66	a		21 58	22 28				22 55		22 57		23 49	23 54									06 47

OVERNIGHT SLEEPERS. For sleeper trains, operated by First ScotRail, please see Tables 400 - 404.

For complete service between Manchester and Preston, Blackpool and between Barrow-in-furness and Lancaster, please see Table 82.

For complete service between Crewe and Liverpool Lime Street, see Table 91

For complete service between Crewe/Stoke-on-Trent & Manchester see Table 84

For complete service between Crewe and Holyhead please see Table 81.

For complete service between Coventry-Birmingham-Wolverhampton-Stafford please see Table 68

For complete service between Windermere and Oxenholme Lake District, please see Table 83

Table 65R

Sundays

8 December to 29 December

Scotland and North West England - West Midlands and London

Route Diagram - refer to first Page of Table 65

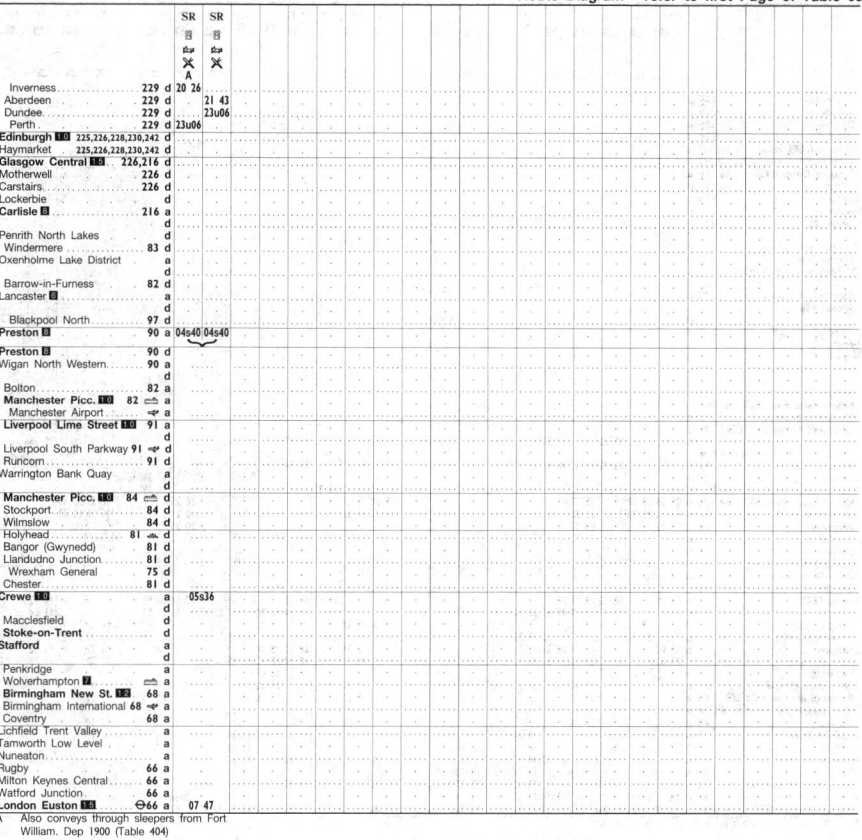

Station	Table		SR	SR
			R	R
			🛏	🛏
			✕	✕
			A	
Inverness	229	d	20 26	
Aberdeen	229	d		21 43
Dundee	229	d		23u06
Perth	229	d	23u06	
Edinburgh 10	225,226,228,230,242	d		
Haymarket	225,226,228,230,242	d		
Glasgow Central 15	226,216	d		
Motherwell	226	d		
Carstairs	226	d		
Lockerbie		d		
Carlisle 8	216	a		
		d		
Penrith North Lakes		d		
Windermere	83	d		
Oxenholme Lake District		a		
		d		
Barrow-in-Furness	82	d		
Lancaster 6		a		
		d		
Blackpool North	97	d		
Preston 8	90	a	04s40	04s40
Preston 8	90	d		
Wigan North Western	90	a		
		d		
Bolton	82	a		
Manchester Picc. 10	82 ⛴	a		
Manchester Airport	✈	a		
Liverpool Lime Street 10	91	a		
		d		
Liverpool South Parkway	91 ✈	d		
Runcorn	91	d		
Warrington Bank Quay		a		
		d		
Manchester Picc. 10	84 ⛴	d		
Stockport	84	d		
Wilmslow	84	d		
Holyhead	81 ⛴	d		
Bangor (Gwynedd)	81	d		
Llandudno Junction	81	d		
Wrexham General	75	d		
Chester	81	d		
Crewe 10		a	05s36	
		d		
Macclesfield		d		
Stoke-on-Trent		d		
Stafford		a		
		d		
Penkridge		a		
Wolverhampton 7	⛴	a		
Birmingham New St. 12	68	a		
Birmingham International	68 ✈	a		
Coventry	68	a		
Lichfield Trent Valley		a		
Tamworth Low Level		a		
Nuneaton		a		
Rugby	66	a		
Milton Keynes Central	66	a		
Watford Junction	66	a		
London Euston 15	⊖66	a	07 47	

A Also conveys through sleepers from Fort William. Dep 1900 (Table 404)

OVERNIGHT SLEEPERS. For sleeper trains, operated by First ScotRail, please see Tables 400 - 404.

For complete service between Manchester and Preston, Blackpool and between Barrow-in-furness and Lancaster, please see Table 82.

For complete service between Crewe and Liverpool Lime Street, see Table 91

For complete service between Crewe/Stoke-on-Trent & Manchester see Table 84

For complete service between Crewe and Holyhead please see Table 81.

For complete service between Coventry-Birmingham-Wolverhampton-Stafford please see Table 68

For complete service between Windermere and Oxenholme Lake District, please see Table 83

Table 65R

Sundays

5 January to 9 February

Scotland and North West England - West Midlands and London

Route Diagram - refer to first Page of Table 65

			VT	VT	VT	XC	VT	LM		VT	TP		VT	XC	VT	VT	LM	LM	VT	VT	VT		XC	VT	VT	TP
			◇1	◇1	◇1	◇1	◇1	1		◇1	◇1		◇1	◇1		◇1	1	1	◇1	◇1	◇1		◇1	◇1	◇1	◇1
						A								A												
			🍴	🍴	🍴	🍴🛒	🍴			🍴			🍴	🍴🛒		🍴			🍴	🍴	🍴		🛒	🍴	🍴	
Inverness	229	d																								
Aberdeen	229	d																								
Dundee	229	d																								
Perth	229	d																								
Edinburgh 10	225,226,228,230,242	d																								
Haymarket	225,226,228,230,242	d																								
Glasgow Central 15	226,216	d																								
Motherwell	226	d																								
Carstairs	226	d																								
Lockerbie		d																								
Carlisle 8	216	a																								
		d																								
Penrith North Lakes		d																								
Windermere	83	d																								
Oxenholme Lake District		a																								
		d																								
Barrow-in-Furness	82	d									09 17															
Lancaster 6		a									10 17															
		d									10 24															10 53
Blackpool North	97	d																								
Preston 8	90	a									10 42															11 11
Preston 8	90	d																								
Wigan North Western	90	a																								
		d																			10 28					
Bolton	82	a																								
Manchester Picc. 10	82 ⛴	a																								
Manchester Airport	✈	a																								
Liverpool Lime Street 10	91	a																								
		d			08 15		08 38									09 38									10 38	
Liverpool South Parkway	91 ✈	d																								
Runcorn	91	d			08 35		08 54									09 54									10 54	
Warrington Bank Quay		a																			10 39					
		d													09 35						10 39					
Manchester Picc. 10	84 ⛴	d	08 05	08 20		08 27							09 20	09 27						10 20			10 27	10 35		
Stockport	84	d	08 14	08 28		08 36							09 27	09 36						10 29			10 36	10 43		
Wilmslow	84	d	08 22			08 43														10 36						
Holyhead	81 ⛴	d																								
Bangor (Gwynedd)	81	d																								
Llandudno Junction	81	d																								
Wrexham General	75	d																								
Chester	81	d																								
Crewe 10		a	08 39		08 52	09 01	09 11								10 30	10 12				10 53	10 59				11 12	
		d	08 43		08 53	09 05	09 13	09 30		09 43						10 14	10 20	10 37	10 43	10 55	11 01				11 14	
Macclesfield		d		08 42									09 40	09 49									10 49	10 55		
Stoke-on-Trent		d		08 59				09 51					09 57	10 07				10 59					11 07	11 13		
Stafford		a	09 01			09 25	09 31	10 14						10 26		10 32	10 41	11 17					11 27		11 35	
		d	09 03			09 26	09 33	10 18						10 27		10 34	10 42	11 18					11 28		11 36	
Penkridge		a															10 49									
Wolverhampton 7	⛴	a				09 40								10 42			11 00				11 31		11 41			
Birmingham New St. 12	68	a				09 58								10 59			11 18				11 55		11 59			
Birmingham International	68 ✈	a				10 13								11 13									12 13			
Coventry	68	a				10 24								11 24									12 24			
Lichfield Trent Valley		a						10 34										11 35								
Tamworth Low Level		a						10 41										11 41								
Nuneaton		a					09 55	10 57								10 56		11 57							11 58	
Rugby	66	a						11 17		10 32								12 13	11 33							
Milton Keynes Central	66	a			10 18			12 02		11 07			11 16			11 46		13 04	12 07					12 21		
Watford Junction	66	a	10s35	10s41			11s16	12 32		11s44								13 34		12s36					12s52	
London Euston 15	⊖66	a	10 58	11 02	11 06		11 37	12 51		12 06			12 09			12 32		13 53	12 48	12 57				13 00	13 13	

A 🍴 from Birmingham New St. 🛒 to Birmingham New St.

OVERNIGHT SLEEPERS. For sleeper trains, operated by First ScotRail, please see Tables 400 - 404.

For complete service between Manchester and Preston, Blackpool and between Barrow-in-furness and Lancaster, please see Table 82.

For complete service between Crewe and Liverpool Lime Street, see Table 91

For complete service between Crewe/Stoke-on-Trent & Manchester see Table 84

For complete service between Crewe and Holyhead please see Table 81.

For complete service between Coventry-Birmingham-Wolverhampton-Stafford please see Table 68

For complete service between Windermere and Oxenholme Lake District, please see Table 83

Table 65R

Sundays

5 January to 9 February

Scotland and North West England - West Midlands and London

Route Diagram - refer to first Page of Table 65

		TP	NT	VT	VT	LM		VT	VT	XC	LM	VT	VT	VT	VT	LM		VT	XC	VT	VT	VT	TP	LM	VT
		◇1		◇1	◇1	1		◇1	◇1	◇1	1	◇1	◇1	◇1	◇1	1		◇1	◇1	◇1	◇1		◇1	1	◇1
										A									A						
Inverness 229	d																								
Aberdeen 229	d																								
Dundee 229	d																								
Perth 229	d																								
Edinburgh 10 225,226,228,230,242	d																								
Haymarket 225,226,228,230,242	d																								
Glasgow Central 15 226,216	d																								
Motherwell 226	d																								
Carstairs 226	d																								
Lockerbie	d																								
Carlisle 8 216	a																								
	d																								
Penrith North Lakes	d																								
Windermere 83	d																								
Oxenholme Lake District	a																								
	d																								
Barrow-in-Furness 82	d	10 25																							
Lancaster 6	a	11 25																							
	d	11 25																				11 35	12 26		
Blackpool North 97	d																								
Preston 8 90	a	11 44																				12 25	12 42		
Preston 8 90	d																					12 30			
Wigan North Western 90	a																					13 15			
	d								11 28												12 28				
Bolton 82	a																								
Manchester Picc. 10 82	a																								
Manchester Airport	a																								
Liverpool Lime Street 10 91	a																								
	d										11 34		11 47											12 34	12 47
Liverpool South Parkway 91	d										11 44													12 44	
Runcorn 91	d										11 52		12 03											12 52	13 03
Warrington Bank Quay	a								11 39												12 39				
	d								11 40												12 40				
Manchester Picc. 10 84	d				11 15					11 27		11 35		11 55	12 15				12 26	12 35					
Stockport 84	d				11 23					11 36		11 43		12 05	12 23				12 35	12 44					
Wilmslow 84	d													12 12											
Holyhead 81	d																	10 55							
Bangor (Gwynedd) 81	d																	11 22							
Llandudno Junction 81	d																	11 40							
Wrexham General 75	d																								
Chester 81	d							11 28										12 32							
Crewe 10	a							11 47	11 59		12 18		12 21	12 28				12 53			12 59			13 17	13 21
	d			11 35		11 37		11 49	12 01		12 19		12 23	12 30		12 37		12 55			13 01			13 19	13 23
Macclesfield	d									11 49		11 56							12 49	12 57					
Stoke-on-Trent	d				11 51	11 59				12 07		12 13			12 51	12 59			13 07	13 14					
Stafford	a					12 17				12 24	12 40		12 42			13 18			13 24					13 40	13 42
	d					12 18				12 25	12 40		12 44			13 18			13 25					13 40	13 44
Penkridge	a										12 46													13 46	
Wolverhampton 7	a								12 34	12 40	12 56								13 40		13 34			13 56	
Birmingham New St. 12 68	a								12 56	12 58	13 15								13 58		14 06			14 15	
Birmingham International 68	a									13 13									14 13		14 19				
Coventry 68	a									13 24									14 24		14 30				
Lichfield Trent Valley	a					12 35										13 35									
Tamworth Low Level	a					12 41										13 41									
Nuneaton	a					12 57		12 31								13 57									
Rugby 66	a					13 13										14 13									
Milton Keynes Central 66	a				12 50	14 04		13 04							13 47	15 04		14 03			14 58				
Watford Junction 66	a					14 34										15 34									
London Euston 15 ⊖66	a			13 22	13 28	14 53		13 46				13 48	14 04	14 10	14 27	15 53		14 44		14 48	15 39				15 04

A from Birmingham New St. to Birmingham New St.

OVERNIGHT SLEEPERS. For sleeper trains, operated by First ScotRail, please see Tables 400 - 404.

For complete service between Manchester and Preston, Blackpool and between Barrow-in-furness and Lancaster, please see Table 82.

For complete service between Crewe and Liverpool Lime Street, see Table 91

For complete service between Crewe/Stoke-on-Trent & Manchester see Table 84

For complete service between Crewe and Holyhead please see Table 81.

For complete service between Coventry-Birmingham-Wolverhampton-Stafford please see Table 68

For complete service between Windermere and Oxenholme Lake District, please see Table 83

Table 65R

Sundays

5 January to 9 February

Scotland and North West England - West Midlands and London

Route Diagram - refer to first Page of Table 65

		VT			XC	VT	LM	VT	VT	XC	VT	VT		VT	TP	LM	VT	VT	XC	VT	LM	VT		XC	VT
		◇1			◇1	◇1	1	◇1	◇1	◇1	◇1	◇1			◇1	1	◇1	◇1	◇1	◇1	1	◇1		◇1	◇1
										A														A	
														🚌											
		ᴿ			✠	ᴿ		ᴿ	ᴿ	ᴿ✠	ᴿ	ᴿ					ᴿ	ᴿ	✠	ᴿ		ᴿ		ᴿ✠	ᴿ
Inverness 229	d																								
Aberdeen 229	d																								
Dundee 229	d																								
Perth 229	d																								
Edinburgh 10 225,226,228,230,242	d																								
Haymarket 225,226,228,230,242	d																								
Glasgow Central 15 226,216	d																								
Motherwell 226	d																								
Carstairs 226	d																								
Lockerbie	d																								
Carlisle 8 216	a																								
	d																								
Penrith North Lakes	d													11 20											
Windermere 83	d																								
Oxenholme Lake District	a																								
	d																								
Barrow-in-Furness 82	d														12 33										
Lancaster 6	a													12 30	13 25										
	d													12 35	13 25										
Blackpool North 97	d																								
Preston 8 90	a													13 25	13 44										
Preston 8 90	d													13 30											
Wigan North Western 90	a													14 15											
	d											13 28													
Bolton 82	a																								
Manchester Picc. 10 82 ⛴	a																								
Manchester Airport ✈	a																								
Liverpool Lime Street 10 91	a																								
	d															13 34	13 47								
Liverpool South Parkway 91 ✈	d															13 44									
Runcorn 91	d															13 52	14 03								
Warrington Bank Quay	a											13 39													
	d											13 39													
Manchester Picc. 10 84 ⛴	d	12 55			13 07	13 15				13 27	13 35							13 55	14 07	14 15				14 27	
Stockport 84	d	13 05				13 22				13 36	13 42							14 04		14 22				14 36	
Wilmslow 84	d	13 12																14 11							
Holyhead 81 ⛴	d							11 50														12 50			
Bangor (Gwynedd) 81	d							12 17														13 18			
Llandudno Junction 81	d							12 35														13 36			
Wrexham General 75	d																								
Chester 81	d							13 30	13 30													14 33			14 33
Crewe 10	a	13 28						13 50	13 50			13 59				14 17	14 21	14 27				14 53			14 52
	d	13 30					13 37	13 52	13 52			14 01				14 19	14 23	14 29			14 33	14 54			14 55
Macclesfield	d									13 49	13 55													14 49	
Stoke-on-Trent	d				13 43	13 50	13 59			14 07	14 12								14 43	14 50	14 55			15 07	
Stafford	a						14 17			14 24						14 40	14 42				15 12			15 24	
	d						14 18			14 25						14 40	14 44				15 18			15 25	
Penkridge	a															14 46									
Wolverhampton 7 ⛴	a				14 13					14 40		14 31				14 56			15 13					15 40	
Birmingham New St. 12 68	a				14 31					14 58		15 06				15 15			15 31					15 58	
Birmingham International 68 ✈	a									15 13		15 19												16 13	
Coventry 68	a									15 24		15 30												16 24	
Lichfield Trent Valley	a						14 35														15 35				
Tamworth Low Level	a						14 41														15 41				
Nuneaton	a						14 57	14 32	14 32												15 57				
Rugby 66	a						15 13														16 13				
Milton Keynes Central 66	a					14 48	16 04	15 03	15 03			15 58								15 48	17 04	16 03			16 03
Watford Junction 66	a						16 34														17 34				
London Euston 15 ⊖66	a	15 08				15 26	16 53	15 45	15 45		15 48	16 39					16 04	16 07		16 26	17 53	16 44			16 41

A ᴿ from Birmingham New St. ✠ to Birmingham New St.

OVERNIGHT SLEEPERS. For sleeper trains, operated by First ScotRail, please see Tables 400 - 404.

For complete service between Manchester and Preston, Blackpool and between Barrow-in-furness and Lancaster, please see Table 82.

For complete service between Crewe and Liverpool Lime Street, see Table 91

For complete service between Crewe/Stoke-on-Trent & Manchester see Table 84

For complete service between Crewe and Holyhead please see Table 81.

For complete service between Coventry-Birmingham-Wolverhampton-Stafford please see Table 68

For complete service between Windermere and Oxenholme Lake District, please see Table 83

Table 65R

Sundays

5 January to 9 February

Scotland and North West England - West Midlands and London

Route Diagram - refer to first Page of Table 65

		VT	VT	TP	LM	VT	VT	VT	XC	VT	LM	VT	XC	VT	VT	TP	LM	VT	VT	VT	XC	VT
		◇1	◇1	◇1	1	◇1	◇1	◇1	◇1	◇1	1	◇1	◇1	◇1	◇1	◇1	1	◇1	◇1	◇1	◇1	◇1
													A									
		🍽	🍽	🛒		🍽	🍽	🍽	🛒	🍽		🍽	🍽🛒	🍽	🍽			🍽	🍽	🍽	🛒	🍽
Inverness 229	d																					
Aberdeen 229	d																					
Dundee 229	d																					
Perth 229	d																					
Edinburgh 10 225,226,228,230,242	d																					
Haymarket 225,226,228,230,242	d																					
Glasgow Central 15 226,216	d																					
Motherwell 226	d																					
Carstairs 226	d																					
Lockerbie	d																					
Carlisle 8 216	a																					
	d																					
Penrith North Lakes	d																					
Windermere 83	d																					
Oxenholme Lake District	a																					
	d																					
Barrow-in-Furness 82	d															14 25						
Lancaster 6	a															15 25						
	d			14 24												15 25				15 38		
Blackpool North 97	d																					
Preston 8 90	a			14 43												15 44				15 56		
Preston 8 90	d			14 46				15 03							15 17	15 45				15 58		
Wigan North Western 90	a			14 59				15 14							15 28	15 58				16 09		
	d		14 28	15 00				15 14							15 29	15 58				16 09		
Bolton 82	a																					
Manchester Picc. 10 82 ⛴	a			15 28												16 27						
Manchester Airport ✈	a			15 47												16 47						
Liverpool Lime Street 10 91	a																					
	d				14 34	14 47											15 34	15 47				
Liverpool South Parkway 91 ✈	d				14 44												15 44					
Runcorn 91	d				14 52	15 03											15 52	16 03				
Warrington Bank Quay	a		14 39					15 25							15 39					16 20		
	d		14 39					15 25							15 40					16 20		
Manchester Picc. 10 84 ⛴	d	14 35					14 55		15 07	15 15			15 27	15 35					15 55		16 07	16 15
Stockport 84	d	14 42					15 04			15 22			15 36	15 42					16 04			16 23
Wilmslow 84	d						15 11												16 11			
Holyhead 81 ⛴	d											13 55										
Bangor (Gwynedd) 81	d											14 22										
Llandudno Junction 81	d											14 40										
Wrexham General 75	d																					
Chester 81	d											15 33										
Crewe 10	a		14 58		15 17	15 21	15 27					15 52			15 58		16 17	16 21	16 27			
	d		15 01		15 19	15 23	15 29				15 37	15 54			16 01		16 19	16 23	16 29			
Macclesfield	d	14 55											15 49	15 55								
Stoke-on-Trent	d	15 12							15 43	15 50	15 59		16 07	16 12							16 43	16 50
Stafford	a				15 40	15 42					16 17		16 24				16 40	16 42				
	d				15 40	15 44					16 18		16 25				16 40	16 44				
Penkridge	a				15 46												16 46					
Wolverhampton 7 ⛴	a		15 34		15 56				16 13				16 40		16 32		16 56				17 13	
Birmingham New St. 12 68	a		16 07		16 15				16 31				16 58		17 06		17 15				17 31	
Birmingham International 68 ✈	a		16 19										17 13		17 19							
Coventry 68	a		16 31										17 24		17 30							
Lichfield Trent Valley	a										16 35											
Tamworth Low Level	a										16 41											
Nuneaton	a										16 57											
Rugby 66	a										17 13											
Milton Keynes Central 66	a		16 58							16 50	18 04	17 03			17 58							17 49
Watford Junction 66	a										18 34											
London Euston 15 ⊖66	a	16 48	17 38			17 04	17 09	17 21		17 27	18 53	17 44		17 46	18 38			18 03	18 09	18 14		18 27

A 🍽 from Birmingham New St. 🛒 to Birmingham New St.

OVERNIGHT SLEEPERS. For sleeper trains, operated by First ScotRail, please see Tables 400 - 404.

For complete service between Manchester and Preston, Blackpool and between Barrow-in-furness and Lancaster, please see Table 82.

For complete service between Crewe and Liverpool Lime Street, see Table 91

For complete service between Crewe/Stoke-on-Trent & Manchester see Table 84

For complete service between Crewe and Holyhead please see Table 81.

For complete service between Coventry-Birmingham-Wolverhampton-Stafford please see Table 68

For complete service between Windermere and Oxenholme Lake District, please see Table 83

Table 65R

Sundays

5 January to 9 February

Scotland and North West England - West Midlands and London

Route Diagram - refer to first Page of Table 65

		LM	VT	XC	VT	VT	TP	LM	VT	VT	XC	LM	VT	VT	VT	XC	VT	VT	VT	TP	LM
		1	◇1	◇1	◇1	◇1	◇1	1	◇1	◇1	◇1	1	◇1	◇1	◇1	◇1	◇1	◇1	◇1	◇1	1
				A												A					
			☕	☕🍴	☕	☕	🍴		☕	☕	🍴		☕	☕	☕	☕🍴	☕	☕	☕	🍴	
Inverness 229	d																				
Aberdeen 229	d																				
Dundee 229	d																				
Perth 229	d																				
Edinburgh 10 225,226,228,230,242	d						14 10												14 51		
Haymarket 225,226,228,230,242	d						14u14												14 56		
Glasgow Central 15 226,216	d												13 55	14 36						15 06	
Motherwell 226	d																				
Carstairs 226	d																				
Lockerbie	d						15 08													16 05	
Carlisle 8 216	a						15 29						15 09	15 46					16 05	16 26	
	d						15 30						15 35	15 49					16 07	16 30	
Penrith North Lakes	d						15 46						15 52						16 22	16 45	
Windermere 83	d																				
Oxenholme Lake District	a						16 09						16 15	16 22						17 08	
	d						16 10						16 15	16 23						17 09	
Barrow-in-Furness 82	d																				
Lancaster 6	a						16 24						16 30	16 37					16 57	17 23	
	d						16 25						16 31	16 38					16 57	17 24	
Blackpool North 97	d																				
Preston 8 90	a						16 43						16 48	16 56					17 15	17 42	
Preston 8 90	d					16 17	16 45						16 51	16 58					17 18	17 45	
Wigan North Western 90	a					16 28	16 58						17 02	17 09					17 28	17 58	
	d					16 29	16 58						17 03	17 09					17 29	17 58	
Bolton 82	a																				
Manchester Picc. 10 82	a						17 27													18 27	
Manchester Airport ✈	a						17 47													18 47	
Liverpool Lime Street 10 91	a																				
	d		16 18					16 34	16 47												17 34
Liverpool South Parkway 91 ✈	d							16 44													17 44
Runcorn 91	d		16 34					16 52	17 03												17 52
Warrington Bank Quay	a					16 39							17 13	17 20					17 39		
	d					16 40							17 15	17 20					17 40		
Manchester Picc. 10 84	d			16 27	16 35					16 55	17 07				17 15	17 27		17 35			
Stockport 84	d			16 36	16 42					17 04					17 22	17 36		17 42			
Wilmslow 84	d									17 11											
Holyhead 81 ⛴	d																				
Bangor (Gwynedd) 81	d																				
Llandudno Junction 81	d																				
Wrexham General 75	d																				
Chester 81	d																17 35				
Crewe 10	a		16 51			16 58		17 17	17 21	17 27			17 33				17 53		17 59		18 17
	d	16 33	16 54			17 00		17 19	17 23	17 29		17 37	17 42				17 55		18 01		18 19
Macclesfield	d			16 49	16 55											17 49		17 55			
Stoke-on-Trent	d	16 55		17 08	17 12						17 43	17 59			17 50	18 08		18 12			
Stafford	a	17 17		17 25				17 40	17 42			18 17				18 26					18 40
	d	17 18		17 26				17 40	17 44			18 18				18 27					18 40
Penkridge	a							17 46													18 46
Wolverhampton 7	a			17 40		17 32		17 56			18 13					18 40			18 33		18 56
Birmingham New St. 12 68	a			17 58		18 07		18 15			18 31					18 58			19 06		19 15
Birmingham International 68 ✈	a			18 13		18 19										19 13			19 19		
Coventry 68	a			18 24		18 31										19 24			19 30		
Lichfield Trent Valley	a	17 35	17 25									18 35									
Tamworth Low Level	a	17 41										18 41									
Nuneaton	a	17 57										18 57									
Rugby 66	a	18 13										19 13									
Milton Keynes Central 66	a	19 04	18 03			18 58						20 06			18 49		19 03		19 58		
Watford Junction 66	a	19 34										20 34									
London Euston 15 ⊖66	a	19 53	18 44		18 48	19 38			19 04	19 07		20 53	19 32	19 11	19 27		19 45	19 48	20 39		

A ☕ from Birmingham New St. 🍴 to Birmingham New St.

OVERNIGHT SLEEPERS. For sleeper trains, operated by First ScotRail, please see Tables 400 - 404.

For complete service between Manchester and Preston, Blackpool and between Barrow-in-furness and Lancaster, please see Table 82.

For complete service between Crewe and Liverpool Lime Street, see Table 91

For complete service between Crewe/Stoke-on-Trent & Manchester see Table 84

For complete service between Crewe and Holyhead please see Table 81.

For complete service between Coventry-Birmingham-Wolverhampton-Stafford please see Table 68

For complete service between Windermere and Oxenholme Lake District, please see Table 83

Table 65R

Sundays

5 January to 9 February

Scotland and North West England - West Midlands and London

Route Diagram - refer to first Page of Table 65

		VT	VT	VT	XC	VT	LM	XC	VT	VT	VT	TP	LM	VT	VT	VT	XC	VT	VT	LM	VT	TP
		◇1	◇1	◇1	◇1	◇1	1	◇1	◇1	◇1	◇1	◇1	1	◇1	◇1	◇1	◇1	◇1	◇	1	◇1	◇1
								A														
		☕	☕	☕	🛒	☕		☕🛒	☕	☕	☕	🛒		☕	☕	☕	🛒	☕	☕		☕	
Inverness 229	d																					
Aberdeen 229	d																					
Dundee 229	d																					
Perth 229	d																					
Edinburgh 10 225,226,228,230,242	d											16 10									16 51	
Haymarket 225,226,228,230,242	d											16u14									16 55	
Glasgow Central 15 226,216	d			15 36							15 57					16 40						
Motherwell 226	d															16 54						
Carstairs 226	d																					
Lockerbie	d											17 08										
Carlisle 8 216	a			16 46							17 07	17 29				17 49					18 05	
	d			16 49							17 09	17 30				17 51					18 07	
Penrith North Lakes	d			17 03								17 45				18 05						
Windermere 83	d																					
Oxenholme Lake District	a										17 44	18 09				18 27					18 41	
	d										17 44	18 10				18 28					18 42	
Barrow-in-Furness 82	d																					18 17
Lancaster 6	a			17 37								18 24				18 42					18 56	19 17
	d			17 38								18 25				18 43					18 57	19 17
Blackpool North 97	d																					
Preston 8 90	a			17 56							18 13	18 43				19 01					19 15	19 37
Preston 8 90	d			17 58							18 17	18 45				19 03					19 17	
Wigan North Western 90	a			18 09							18 28	18 58				19 14					19 28	
	d			18 09							18 28	18 58				19 14					19 28	
Bolton 82	a																					
Manchester Picc. 10 82 ⛴	a											19 27										
Manchester Airport ✈	a											19 47										
Liverpool Lime Street 10 91	a																					
	d	17 47											18 34	18 47								
Liverpool South Parkway 91 ✈	d												18 44									
Runcorn 91	d	18 03											18 52	19 03								
Warrington Bank Quay	a			18 20							18 39					19 25					19 39	
	d			18 20							18 39					19 25					19 39	
Manchester Picc. 10 84 ⛴	d		17 55		18 07	18 15		18 27		18 35					18 55		19 07	19 15				
Stockport 84	d		18 04			18 22		18 36		18 42					19 04			19 22				
Wilmslow 84	d		18 11												19 11							
Holyhead 81 ⛴	d																					
Bangor (Gwynedd) 81	d																					
Llandudno Junction 81	d																					
Wrexham General 75	d																					
Chester 81	d								18 35										19 35			
Crewe 10	a	18 21	18 27						18 53		18 58		19 17	19 21	19 27				19 56		19 59	
	d	18 23	18 29				18 37		18 55		19 01		19 19	19 23	19 29					19 37	20 01	
Macclesfield	d							18 49		18 55												
Stoke-on-Trent	d				18 43	18 50	18 59	19 07		19 12							19 43	19 50		19 59		
Stafford	a	18 42					19 18	19 24					19 40	19 42						20 17		
	d	18 44					19 18	19 25					19 40	19 44						20 18		
Penkridge	a												19 46									
Wolverhampton 7 ⛴	a				19 13			19 40			19 34		19 56				20 13				20 33	
Birmingham New St. 12 68	a				19 31			19 58			20 06		20 15				20 31				20 51	
Birmingham International 68 ✈	a							20 13			20 19											
Coventry 68	a							20 24			20 30											
Lichfield Trent Valley	a						19 35													20 35		
Tamworth Low Level	a						19 41													20 41		
Nuneaton	a						19 57													20 57		
Rugby 66	a						20 13													21 13		
Milton Keynes Central 66	a					19 48	21 07		20 03		20 59							20 46		22 10		
Watford Junction 66	a						21 35													22 52		
London Euston 15 ⊖66	a	20 05	20 08	20 13		20 27	21 55		20 46	20 48	21 48			21 04	21 10	21 22		21 31		23 15		

A ☕ from Birmingham New St. 🛒 to Birmingham New St.

OVERNIGHT SLEEPERS. For sleeper trains, operated by First ScotRail, please see Tables 400 - 404.

For complete service between Manchester and Preston, Blackpool and between Barrow-in-furness and Lancaster, please see Table 82.

For complete service between Crewe and Liverpool Lime Street, see Table 91

For complete service between Crewe/Stoke-on-Trent & Manchester see Table 84

For complete service between Crewe and Holyhead please see Table 81.

For complete service between Coventry-Birmingham-Wolverhampton-Stafford please see Table 68

For complete service between Windermere and Oxenholme Lake District, please see Table 83

Table 65R

Sundays

5 January to 9 February

Scotland and North West England - West Midlands and London

Route Diagram - refer to first Page of Table 65

	TP	XC	LM	VT	VT		XC	VT	LM	VT	TP	VT	LM	VT	VT		VT		XC	VT	TP	VT	LM	XC
	◇1	◇1	1	◇1	◇1		◇1	◇	1	◇1	◇1	◇1	1	◇1	◇1		◇1		◇1	◇1	◇1	◇1	1	◇1
	🛒	🛒		🍴	🍴			🍴		🍴	🛒	🍴		🍴	🍴		🍴			🍴	🛒	🍴		
Inverness 229 d																								
Aberdeen 229 d																								
Dundee 229 d																								
Perth 229 d																								
Edinburgh 10 225,226,228,230,242 d											18 10									18 51	19 57			
Haymarket 225,226,228,230,242 d											18u14									18 56	20u01			
Glasgow Central 15 226,216 d	17 06									17 36							18 30					20 08		
Motherwell 226 d																								
Carstairs 226 d																								
Lockerbie d	18 07									18 32	19 08											21 03		
Carlisle 8 216 a	18 26									18 50	19 29						19 43			20 05	21 13	21 21		
d	18 30									18 52	19 30						19 44			20 07	21 14	21 24		
Penrith North Lakes d	18 45									19 06	19 45									20 22		21 39		
Windermere 83 d																								
Oxenholme Lake District a	19 09									19 28	20 09						20 19				21 51	22 02		
d	19 09									19 29	20 10						20 19				21 51	22 03		
Barrow-in-Furness 82 d																								
Lancaster 6 a	19 24									19 43	20 24						20 34			20 56	22 06	22 17		
d	19 24									19 44	20 25						20 34			20 57	22 06	22 18		
Blackpool North 97 d																								
Preston 8 90 a	19 44									20 02	20 43						20 52			21 15	22 25	22 35		
Preston 8 90 d	19 45									20 04	20 46						20 55			21 17	22 33	22 38		
Wigan North Western 90 a	19 58									20 15							21 06			21 28	22 46	22 48		
d	19 59									20 15							21 07			21 29	22 46	22 50		
Bolton 82 a																								
Manchester Picc. 10 82 ⛴ a	20 27										21 25										23 24			
Manchester Airport ✈ a	20 45										21 45										23 40			
Liverpool Lime Street 10 91 a																								
d			19 34		19 47								20 34		20 47								21 34	
Liverpool South Parkway 91 ✈ d			19 44										20 44										21 44	
Runcorn 91 d			19 52		20 03								20 52		21 03								21 52	
Warrington Bank Quay a										20 26							21 18			21 39		22 59		
d										20 26							21 18			21 39		23 01		
Manchester Picc. 10 84 ⛴ d		19 27		19 35			20 07					20 21		20 55					21 07					22 07
Stockport 84 d		19 36		19 41			20 16					20 27		21 03					21 16					22 16
Wilmslow 84 d																								
Holyhead 81 ⛴ d																								
Bangor (Gwynedd) 81 d																								
Llandudno Junction 81 d																								
Wrexham General 75 d																								
Chester 81 d								20 37																
Crewe 10 a			20 16		20 22			20 56		20 45			21 16		21 21		21 38			21 59		23 22	22 18	
d			20 18		20 24				20 44	20 47			21 18		21 23		21 40			22 01			22 22	
Macclesfield d		19 49		19 54			20 29					20 40		21 15					21 29					22 29
Stoke-on-Trent d		20 07		20 11			20 47		21 06			20 57		21 33					21 47					22 47
Stafford a		20 26	20 38		20 42		21 08		21 25				21 39		21 42		22 01		22 06				22 42	23 04
d		20 27	20 39		20 43		21 09		21 25				21 39		21 44		22 02		22 06				22 43	23 05
Penkridge a			20 44										21 45										22 48	
Wolverhampton 7 ⛴ a		20 39	20 55				21 21						21 55				22 17		22 20	22 34			22 59	23 18
Birmingham New St. 12 68 a		20 58	21 16				21 39						22 17				22 38		22 40	22 55			23 16	23 36
Birmingham International 68 ✈ a		21 13																						
Coventry 68 a		21 23																						
Lichfield Trent Valley a									21 41						21 59									
Tamworth Low Level a									21 48						22 06									
Nuneaton a									22 04						22 17									
Rugby 66 a									22 20						22 31									
Milton Keynes Central 66 a					21 36					21 52		22 03		22 46	23 04									
Watford Junction 66 a										22s31				23s28	23s34									
London Euston 15 ⊖66 a				21 58	22 28					22 55		22 57		23 49	23 54									

OVERNIGHT SLEEPERS. For sleeper trains, operated by First ScotRail, please see Tables 400 - 404.

For complete service between Manchester and Preston, Blackpool and between Barrow-in-furness and Lancaster, please see Table 82.

For complete service between Crewe and Liverpool Lime Street, see Table 91

For complete service between Crewe/Stoke-on-Trent & Manchester see Table 84

For complete service between Crewe and Holyhead please see Table 81.

For complete service between Coventry-Birmingham-Wolverhampton-Stafford please see Table 68

For complete service between Windermere and Oxenholme Lake District, please see Table 83

Table 65R

Sundays

5 January to 9 February

Scotland and North West England - West Midlands and London

Route Diagram - refer to first Page of Table 65

Station	Table		SR	SR		SR	SR
			R	R		R	R
			sleeper	sleeper		sleeper	sleeper
			✕	✕		✕	✕
						A	
Inverness	229	d				20 26	
Aberdeen	229	d					21 43
Dundee	229	d					23u06
Perth	229	d				23u06	
Edinburgh 10	225,226,228,230,242	d		23 15			
Haymarket	225,226,228,230,242	d					
Glasgow Central 15	226,216	d	23 15				
Motherwell	226	d	23u30				
Carstairs	226	d	23u47				
Lockerbie		d					
Carlisle 8	216	a					
		d	01u12				
Penrith North Lakes		d					
Windermere	83	d					
Oxenholme Lake District		a					
		d					
Barrow-in-Furness	82	d					
Lancaster 6		a					
		d					
Blackpool North	97	d					
Preston 8	90	a				04s40	04s40
Preston 8	90	d					
Wigan North Western	90	a					
		d					
Bolton	82	a					
Manchester Picc. 10	82	a					
Manchester Airport		a					
Liverpool Lime Street 10	91	a					
		d					
Liverpool South Parkway	91	d					
Runcorn	91	d					
Warrington Bank Quay		a					
		d					
Manchester Picc. 10	84	d					
Stockport	84	d					
Wilmslow	84	d					
Holyhead	81	d					
Bangor (Gwynedd)	81	d					
Llandudno Junction	81	d					
Wrexham General	75	d					
Chester	81	d					
Crewe 10		a				05s36	
		d					
Macclesfield		d					
Stoke-on-Trent		d					
Stafford		a					
		d					
Penkridge		a					
Wolverhampton 7		a					
Birmingham New St. 12	68	a					
Birmingham International	68	a					
Coventry	68	a					
Lichfield Trent Valley		a					
Tamworth Low Level		a					
Nuneaton		a					
Rugby	66	a					
Milton Keynes Central	66	a					
Watford Junction	66	a	06s22				
London Euston 15	⊖66	a	06 47			07 47	

A also conveys through sleepers from Fort William. Dep 1900 (Table 404)

OVERNIGHT SLEEPERS. For sleeper trains, operated by First ScotRail, please see Tables 400 - 404.

For complete service between Manchester and Preston, Blackpool and between Barrow-in-furness and Lancaster, please see Table 82.

For complete service between Crewe and Liverpool Lime Street, see Table 91

For complete service between Crewe/Stoke-on-Trent & Manchester see Table 84

For complete service between Crewe and Holyhead please see Table 81.

For complete service between Coventry-Birmingham-Wolverhampton-Stafford please see Table 68

For complete service between Windermere and Oxenholme Lake District, please see Table 83

Table 65R

Sundays

16 February to 23 March

Scotland and North West England - West Midlands and London

Route Diagram - refer to first Page of Table 65

		VT	VT	VT	XC	VT	LM	VT		VT		XC	VT	LM	LM	VT	VT	VT	TP	XC		VT	VT	VT	
		◇1	◇1	◇1	◇1	◇1	1	◇1		◇1		◇1	◇1	1	1	◇1	◇1	◇1	◇1	◇1		◇1	◇1	◇1	
					A							A													
		🍴	🍴	🍴	🍴🛒	🍴		🍴		🍴		🍴🛒	🍴			🍴	🍴	🍴		🛒		🍴	🍴	🍴	
Inverness 229	d																								
Aberdeen 229	d																								
Dundee 229	d																								
Perth 229	d																								
Edinburgh 10 225,226,228,230,242	d																								
Haymarket 225,226,228,230,242	d																								
Glasgow Central 15 226,216	d																								
Motherwell 226	d																								
Carstairs 226	d																								
Lockerbie	d																								
Carlisle 8 216	a																								
	d																								
Penrith North Lakes	d																								
Windermere 83	d																								
Oxenholme Lake District	a																								
	d																								
Barrow-in-Furness 82	d																		09 17						
Lancaster 6	a																		10 17						
	d																		10 22						
Blackpool North 97	d																								
Preston 8 90	a																		10 40						
Preston 8 90	d							09 00								09 56		10 14	10 42					10 58	
Wigan North Western 90	a							09 14								10 10		10 28						11 13	
	d							09 15								10 11		10 28						11 13	
Bolton 82	a																								
Manchester Picc. 10 82 ⛴	a																		11 25						
Manchester Airport ✈	a																		11 45						
Liverpool Lime Street 10 91	a																								
	d			08 15		08 38							09 38										10 38		
Liverpool South Parkway 91 ✈	d																								
Runcorn 91	d			08 35		08 54							09 54										10 54		
Warrington Bank Quay	a							09 25								10 21		10 39						11 24	
	d							09 26								10 22		10 39						11 24	
Manchester Picc. 10 84 ⛴	d	08 05	08 20		08 27					09 20		09 27					10 20			10 27		10 35			
Stockport 84	d	08 14	08 28		08 36					09 27		09 36					10 29			10 36		10 43			
Wilmslow 84	d	08 22			08 43												10 36								
Holyhead 81 ⛴	d																								
Bangor (Gwynedd) 81	d																								
Llandudno Junction 81	d																								
Wrexham General 75	d																								
Chester 81	d																								
Crewe 10	a	08 39		08 52	09 01	09 11		09 45					10 12			10 41	10 53	10 59					11 12		
	d	08 43		08 53	09 05	09 13	09 30	09 47					10 14	10 20	10 37	10 43	10 55	11 01					11 14		
Macclesfield	d		08 42							09 40		09 49								10 49		10 55			
Stoke-on-Trent	d		08 59				09 51			09 57		10 07			10 59					11 07		11 13			
Stafford	a	09 01			09 25	09 31	10 14					10 26	10 32	10 41	11 17					11 27			11 35		
	d	09 03			09 26	09 33	10 18					10 27	10 34	10 42	11 18					11 28			11 36		
Penkridge	a													10 49											
Wolverhampton 7 ⛴	a				09 40							10 42		11 00				11 31		11 41					
Birmingham New St. 12 68	a				09 58							10 59		11 18				11 55		11 59					
Birmingham International 68 ✈	a				10 13							11 13								12 13					
Coventry 68	a				10 24							11 24								12 24					
Lichfield Trent Valley	a						10 34								11 35										
Tamworth Low Level	a						10 41								11 41										
Nuneaton	a					09 55	10 57						10 56		11 57								11 58		
Rugby 66	a						11 17	10 36							12 13	11 32									
Milton Keynes Central 66	a			10 18			12 02	11 11		11 16			11 46		13 04	12 07						12 21			
Watford Junction 66	a	10s35	10s41			11s16	12 32	11s43							13 34		12s36						12s52		
London Euston 15 ⊖66	a	10 58	11 02	11 06		11 37	12 51	12 06		12 09			12 32		13 53	12 46	12 57					13 00	13 13	13 22	

A 🍴 from Birmingham New St. 🛒 to Birmingham New St.

OVERNIGHT SLEEPERS. For sleeper trains, operated by First ScotRail, please see Tables 400 - 404.

For complete service between Manchester and Preston, Blackpool and between Barrow-in-furness and Lancaster, please see Table 82.

For complete service between Crewe and Liverpool Lime Street, see Table 91

For complete service between Crewe/Stoke-on-Trent & Manchester see Table 84

For complete service between Crewe and Holyhead please see Table 81.

For complete service between Coventry-Birmingham-Wolverhampton-Stafford please see Table 68

For complete service between Windermere and Oxenholme Lake District, please see Table 83

Table 65R

Sundays

16 February to 23 March

Scotland and North West England - West Midlands and London

Route Diagram - refer to first Page of Table 65

	VT	LM	VT	VT	TP	XC	LM	VT	VT	VT	VT	VT	LM	VT	XC	VT	VT	TP	LM	VT	VT	VT
	◇1	1	◇1	◇1	◇1	◇1	1	◇1	◇1	◇1	◇1	◇1	1	◇1	◇1	◇1	◇1	◇1	1	◇1	◇1	◇1
						A									A							
	🍴		🍴	🍴		🍴🛒		🍴	🍴	🍴	🍴	🍴		🍴	🍴🛒	🍴	🍴	🛒		🍴	🍴	🍴
Inverness 229 d																						
Aberdeen 229 d																						
Dundee 229 d																						
Perth 229 d																						
Edinburgh 10 225,226,228,230,242 d																		10 10				
Haymarket 225,226,228,230,242 d																		10u14				
Glasgow Central 15 226,216 d											09 37											10 34
Motherwell 226 d																						10 49
Carstairs 226 d																						
Lockerbie d																		11 08				
Carlisle 8 216 a											10 44							11 29				11 44
d											10 56							11 30				11 46
Penrith North Lakes d											11 10							11 45				12 00
Windermere 83 d																						
Oxenholme Lake District a											11 32							12 09				12 22
d											11 33							12 10				12 24
Barrow-in-Furness 82 d					10 25																	
Lancaster 6 a					11 25						11 47							12 24				12 37
d					11 25						11 48						11 58	12 25				12 38
Blackpool North 97 d																						
Preston 8 90 a					11 44						12 06						12 15	12 43				12 56
Preston 8 90 d				11 14	11 45						12 08						12 17	12 45				12 58
Wigan North Western 90 a				11 28	11 59						12 19						12 28	12 58				13 09
d				11 28	12 00						12 19						12 28	12 58				13 09
Bolton 82 a																						
Manchester Picc. 10 82 ⛴ a					12 29													13 27				
Manchester Airport ✈ a					12 46													13 47				
Liverpool Lime Street 10 91 a																						
d							11 34		11 47										12 34	12 47		
Liverpool South Parkway 91 ✈ d							11 44												12 44			
Runcorn 91 d							11 52		12 03										12 52	13 03		
Warrington Bank Quay a				11 39							12 30						12 39					13 20
d				11 39							12 30						12 39					13 20
Manchester Picc. 10 84 ⛴ d	11 15					11 27		11 35		11 55		12 15			12 26	12 35					12 55	
Stockport 84 d	11 23					11 36		11 43		12 05		12 23			12 35	12 44					13 05	
Wilmslow 84 d										12 12											13 12	
Holyhead 81 ⛴ d														10 55								
Bangor (Gwynedd) 81 d														11 22								
Llandudno Junction 81 d														11 40								
Wrexham General 75 d																						
Chester 81 d			11 28											12 32								
Crewe 10 a			11 47	11 59			12 18		12 21	12 28				12 53			12 59		13 17	13 21	13 28	
d		11 37	11 49	12 01			12 19		12 23	12 30			12 37	12 55			13 01		13 19	13 23	13 30	
Macclesfield d						11 49		11 56							12 49	12 57						
Stoke-on-Trent d	11 51	11 59				12 07		12 13				12 51	12 59		13 07	13 14						
Stafford a		12 17				12 24	12 40		12 42				13 18		13 24				13 40	13 42		
d		12 18				12 25	12 40		12 44				13 18		13 25				13 40	13 44		
Penkridge a							12 46												13 46			
Wolverhampton 7 ⛴ a				12 32		12 40	12 56								13 40		13 32		13 56			
Birmingham New St. 12 68 a				12 54		12 58	13 15								13 58		14 06		14 15			
Birmingham International 68 ✈ a						13 13									14 13		14 19					
Coventry 68 a						13 24									14 24		14 30					
Lichfield Trent Valley a		12 35											13 35									
Tamworth Low Level a		12 41											13 41									
Nuneaton a		12 57	12 31										13 57									
Rugby 66 a		13 13											14 13									
Milton Keynes Central 66 a	12 50	14 04	13 04									13 50	15 04	14 03			14 58					
Watford Junction 66 a		14 34											15 34									
London Euston 15 ⊖66 a	13 28	14 53	13 46					13 48	14 04	14 10	14 25	14 28	15 53	14 44		14 48	15 39			15 04	15 08	15 13

A 🍴 from Birmingham New St. 🛒 to Birmingham New St.

OVERNIGHT SLEEPERS. For sleeper trains, operated by First ScotRail, please see Tables 400 - 404.

For complete service between Manchester and Preston, Blackpool and between Barrow-in-furness and Lancaster, please see Table 82.

For complete service between Crewe and Liverpool Lime Street, see Table 91

For complete service between Crewe/Stoke-on-Trent & Manchester see Table 84

For complete service between Crewe and Holyhead please see Table 81.

For complete service between Coventry-Birmingham-Wolverhampton-Stafford please see Table 68

For complete service between Windermere and Oxenholme Lake District, please see Table 83

Table 65R

Sundays

16 February to 23 March

Scotland and North West England - West Midlands and London

Route Diagram - refer to first Page of Table 65

				XC	VT	LM	VT	VT	XC	VT	VT	TP		LM	VT	VT	VT	XC	VT	LM	VT	XC		VT	VT
				◇1	◇1	1	◇1	◇1	◇1	◇1	◇1	◇1		1	◇1	◇1	◇1	◇1	◇1	1	◇1	◇1		◇1	◇1
									A													A			
				🛒	☕		☕	☕	☕🛒	☕	☕				☕	☕	☕	🛒	☕		☕	☕🛒		☕	☕
Inverness 229	d																								
Aberdeen 229	d																								
Dundee 229	d																								
Perth 229	d																								
Edinburgh 10 225,226,228,230,242	d										10 51														
Haymarket 225,226,228,230,242	d										10 55														
Glasgow Central 15 226,216	d																11 36								
Motherwell 226	d																								
Carstairs 226	d																								
Lockerbie	d																								
Carlisle 8 216	a										12 05						12 47								
	d										12 07						12 49								
Penrith North Lakes	d																								
Windermere 83	d																								
Oxenholme Lake District	a										12 41						13 22								
	d										12 43						13 23								
Barrow-in-Furness 82	d											12 33													
Lancaster 6	a										12 56	13 25					13 37								
	d										12 57	13 25					13 38								
Blackpool North 97	d																								
Preston 8 90	a										13 15	13 44					13 56								
Preston 8 90	d										13 17	13 45					13 58								
Wigan North Western 90	a										13 28	13 58					14 09								
	d										13 28	13 58					14 09								
Bolton 82	a																								
Manchester Picc. 10 82 ⛴	a											14 27													
Manchester Airport ✈	a											14 47													
Liverpool Lime Street 10 91	a																								
	d													13 34	13 47										
Liverpool South Parkway 91 ✈	d													13 44											
Runcorn 91	d													13 52	14 03										
Warrington Bank Quay	a										13 39						14 20								
	d										13 39						14 20								
Manchester Picc. 10 84 ⛴	d			13 07	13 15				13 27	13 35						13 55		14 07	14 15			14 27			14 35
Stockport 84	d				13 22				13 36	13 42						14 04			14 22			14 36			14 42
Wilmslow 84	d															14 11									
Holyhead 81 ⛴	d						11 50														12 50				
Bangor (Gwynedd) 81	d						12 17														13 18				
Llandudno Junction 81	d						12 35														13 36				
Wrexham General 75	d																								
Chester 81	d						13 30	13 30													14 33			14 33	
Crewe 10	a						13 50	13 50			13 59			14 17	14 21	14 27					14 53			14 52	
	d					13 37	13 52	13 52			14 01			14 19	14 23	14 29				14 33	14 54			14 55	
Macclesfield	d								13 49	13 55												14 49			14 55
Stoke-on-Trent	d			13 43	13 50	13 59			14 07	14 12								14 43	14 50	14 55		15 07			15 12
Stafford	a					14 17			14 24					14 40	14 42					15 12		15 24			
	d					14 18			14 25					14 40	14 44					15 18		15 25			
Penkridge	a													14 46											
Wolverhampton 7 ⛴	a			14 13					14 40		14 31			14 56				15 13				15 40			
Birmingham New St. 12 68	a			14 31					14 58		15 06			15 15				15 31				15 58			
Birmingham International 68 ✈	a								15 13		15 19											16 13			
Coventry 68	a								15 24		15 30											16 24			
Lichfield Trent Valley	a					14 35														15 35					
Tamworth Low Level	a					14 41														15 41					
Nuneaton	a					14 57	14 32	14 32												15 57					
Rugby 66	a					15 13														16 13					
Milton Keynes Central 66	a				14 48	16 04	15 03	15 03			15 58								15 48	17 04	16 03			16 03	
Watford Junction 66	a					16 34														17 34					
London Euston 15 ⊖66	a				15 26	16 53	15 45	15 45		15 48	16 39				16 04	16 07	16 13		16 26	17 53	16 44			16 41	16 48

A ☕ from Birmingham New St. 🛒 to Birmingham New St.

OVERNIGHT SLEEPERS. For sleeper trains, operated by First ScotRail, please see Tables 400 - 404.

For complete service between Manchester and Preston, Blackpool and between Barrow-in-furness and Lancaster, please see Table 82.

For complete service between Crewe and Liverpool Lime Street, see Table 91

For complete service between Crewe/Stoke-on-Trent & Manchester see Table 84

For complete service between Crewe and Holyhead please see Table 81.

For complete service between Coventry-Birmingham-Wolverhampton-Stafford please see Table 68

For complete service between Windermere and Oxenholme Lake District, please see Table 83

Table 65R

Sundays

16 February to 23 March

Scotland and North West England - West Midlands and London

Route Diagram - refer to first Page of Table 65

	VT	TP	LM	VT	VT	VT	XC	VT	LM	VT	XC	VT	VT	TP	LM	VT	VT	VT	XC	VT	LM
	◇[1]	◇[1]	[1]	◇[1]	◇[1]	◇[1]	◇[1]	◇[1]	[1]	◇[1]	◇[1]	◇[1]	◇[1]	◇[1]	[1]	◇[1]	◇[1]	◇[1]	◇[1]	◇[1]	[1]
											A										
	⊡	🛒		⊡	⊡	⊡	🛒	⊡		⊡	⊡🛒	⊡	⊡			⊡	⊡	⊡	🛒	⊡	
Inverness 229 d																					
Aberdeen 229 d																					
Dundee 229 d																					
Perth 229 d																					
Edinburgh [10] 225,226,228,230,242 d		12 10											12 51								
Haymarket 225,226,228,230,242 d		12u14											12 55								
Glasgow Central [15] 226,216 d	11 58					12 42												13 36			
Motherwell 226 d																					
Carstairs 226 d																					
Lockerbie d		13 08																			
Carlisle [8] 216 a	13 09	13 29				13 52							14 05					14 46			
d	13 10	13 30				13 54							14 07					14 49			
Penrith North Lakes d		13 45											14 22								
Windermere 83 d																					
Oxenholme Lake District a		14 09				14 27												15 22			
d		14 10				14 28												15 23			
Barrow-in-Furness 82 d														14 25							
Lancaster [6] a	13 56	14 24				14 42							14 56	15 25				15 37			
d	13 58	14 25				14 43							14 57	15 25				15 38			
Blackpool North 97 d																					
Preston [8] 90 a	14 15	14 43				15 01							15 15	15 44				15 56			
Preston [8] 90 d	14 17	14 45				15 03							15 17	15 45				15 58			
Wigan North Western 90 a	14 28	14 58				15 14							15 28	15 58				16 09			
d	14 28	14 58				15 14							15 28	15 58				16 09			
Bolton 82 a																					
Manchester Picc. [10] 82 ⛴ a		15 27												16 27							
Manchester Airport ✈ a		15 47												16 47							
Liverpool Lime Street [10] 91 a																					
d			14 34	14 47											15 34	15 47					
Liverpool South Parkway 91 ✈ d			14 44												15 44						
Runcorn 91 d			14 52	15 03											15 52	16 03					
Warrington Bank Quay a	14 39					15 25							15 39					16 20			
d	14 39					15 25							15 39					16 20			
Manchester Picc. [10] 84 ⛴ d					14 55		15 07	15 15			15 27	15 35					15 55		16 07	16 15	
Stockport 84 d					15 04			15 22			15 36	15 42					16 04			16 23	
Wilmslow 84 d					15 11												16 11				
Holyhead 81 ⛴ d										13 55											
Bangor (Gwynedd) 81 d										14 22											
Llandudno Junction 81 d										14 40											
Wrexham General 75 d																					
Chester 81 d										15 33											
Crewe [10] a	14 58		15 17	15 21	15 27					15 52			15 59		16 17	16 21	16 27				
d	15 01		15 19	15 23	15 29				15 37	15 54			16 01		16 19	16 23	16 29				16 33
Macclesfield d											15 49	15 55									
Stoke-on-Trent d							15 43	15 50	15 59		16 07	16 12							16 43	16 50	16 55
Stafford a			15 40	15 42					16 17		16 24				16 40	16 42					17 17
d			15 40	15 44					16 18		16 25				16 40	16 44					17 18
Penkridge a			15 46												16 46						
Wolverhampton [7] ⛴ a	15 34		15 56				16 13				16 40		16 32		16 56				17 13		
Birmingham New St. [12] 68 a	16 07		16 15				16 31				16 58		17 06		17 15				17 31		
Birmingham International 68 ✈ a	16 19										17 13		17 19								
Coventry 68 a	16 31										17 24		17 29								
Lichfield Trent Valley a									16 35												17 35
Tamworth Low Level a									16 41												17 41
Nuneaton a									16 57												17 57
Rugby 66 a									17 13												18 13
Milton Keynes Central 66 a	16 58							16 50	18 04	17 03			17 58							17 49	19 04
Watford Junction 66 a									18 34												19 34
London Euston [15] ⊖66 a	17 38			17 04	17 09	17 21		17 27	18 53	17 44		17 46	18 38			18 03	18 09	18 14		18 27	19 53

A ⊡ from Birmingham New St. 🛒 to Birmingham New St.

OVERNIGHT SLEEPERS. For sleeper trains, operated by First ScotRail, please see Tables 400 - 404.

For complete service between Manchester and Preston, Blackpool and between Barrow-in-furness and Lancaster, please see Table 82.

For complete service between Crewe and Liverpool Lime Street, see Table 91

For complete service between Crewe/Stoke-on-Trent & Manchester see Table 84

For complete service between Crewe and Holyhead please see Table 81.

For complete service between Coventry-Birmingham-Wolverhampton-Stafford please see Table 68

For complete service between Windermere and Oxenholme Lake District, please see Table 83

Table 65R

Sundays

16 February to 23 March

Scotland and North West England - West Midlands and London

Route Diagram - refer to first Page of Table 65

	VT	XC	VT	VT	TP	LM	VT	VT	VT	XC	VT	LM	XC	VT	VT	VT	TP	LM	VT	VT
	◇1	◇1	◇1	◇1	◇1	1	◇1	◇1	◇1	◇1	◇1	1	◇1	◇1	◇1	◇1	◇1	1	◇1	◇1
		A											A							
Inverness 229 d																				
Aberdeen 229 d																				
Dundee 229 d																				
Perth 229 d																				
Edinburgh 10 225,226,228,230,242 d					14 10											14 51				
Haymarket 225,226,228,230,242 d					14u14											14 56				
Glasgow Central 15 226,216 d				13 55					14 36								15 06			
Motherwell 226 d																				
Carstairs 226 d																				
Lockerbie d					15 08												16 05			
Carlisle 8 216 a				15 09	15 29				15 46							16 05	16 26			
d				15 12	15 30				15 49							16 07	16 30			
Penrith North Lakes d					15 46											16 22	16 45			
Windermere 83 d																				
Oxenholme Lake District a				15 46	16 09				16 22								17 08			
d				15 47	16 10				16 23								17 09			
Barrow-in-Furness 82 d																				
Lancaster 6 a					16 24				16 37							16 57	17 23			
d					16 25				16 38							16 57	17 24			
Blackpool North 97 d																				
Preston 8 90 a				16 15	16 43				16 56							17 15	17 42			
Preston 8 90 d				16 17	16 45				16 58							17 18	17 45			
Wigan North Western 90 a				16 28	16 58				17 09							17 28	17 58			
d				16 29	16 58				17 09							17 29	17 58			
Bolton 82 a																				
Manchester Picc. 10 82 a					17 27												18 27			
Manchester Airport a					17 47												18 47			
Liverpool Lime Street 10 91 a																				
d	16 18					16 34	16 47											17 34	17 47	
Liverpool South Parkway 91 d						16 44												17 44		
Runcorn 91 d	16 34					16 52	17 03											17 52	18 03	
Warrington Bank Quay a				16 39					17 20							17 39				
d				16 40					17 20							17 40				
Manchester Picc. 10 84 d		16 27	16 35					16 55		17 07	17 15		17 27		17 35					17 55
Stockport 84 d		16 36	16 42					17 04			17 22		17 36		17 42					18 04
Wilmslow 84 d								17 11												18 11
Holyhead 81 d																				
Bangor (Gwynedd) 81 d																				
Llandudno Junction 81 d																				
Wrexham General 75 d																				
Chester 81 d														17 35						
Crewe 10 a	16 51			16 58		17 17	17 21	17 27						17 53		17 59		18 17	18 21	18 27
d	16 54			17 00		17 19	17 23	17 29				17 37		17 55		18 01		18 19	18 23	18 29
Macclesfield d		16 49	16 55										17 49		17 55					
Stoke-on-Trent d		17 08	17 12							17 43	17 50	17 59	18 08		18 12					
Stafford a		17 25				17 40	17 42					18 17	18 26					18 40	18 42	
d		17 26				17 40	17 44					18 18	18 27					18 40	18 44	
Penkridge a						17 46												18 46		
Wolverhampton 7 a		17 40		17 32		17 56				18 13			18 40			18 33		18 56		
Birmingham New St. 12 68 a		17 58		18 07		18 15				18 31			18 58			19 06		19 15		
Birmingham International 68 a		18 13		18 19									19 13			19 19				
Coventry 68 a		18 24		18 31									19 24			19 30				
Lichfield Trent Valley a	17 25											18 35								
Tamworth Low Level a												18 41								
Nuneaton a												18 57								
Rugby 66 a												19 13								
Milton Keynes Central 66 a	18 03			18 58							18 49	20 06		19 03		19 58				
Watford Junction 66 a												20 34								
London Euston 15 ⊖66 a	18 44		18 48	19 38			19 04	19 07	19 11		19 27	20 53		19 45	19 48	20 39			20 05	20 08

A from Birmingham New St. to Birmingham New St.

OVERNIGHT SLEEPERS. For sleeper trains, operated by First ScotRail, please see Tables 400 - 404.

For complete service between Manchester and Preston, Blackpool and between Barrow-in-furness and Lancaster, please see Table 82.

For complete service between Crewe and Liverpool Lime Street, see Table 91

For complete service between Crewe/Stoke-on-Trent & Manchester see Table 84

For complete service between Crewe and Holyhead please see Table 81.

For complete service between Coventry-Birmingham-Wolverhampton-Stafford please see Table 68

For complete service between Windermere and Oxenholme Lake District, please see Table 83

Table 65R

Sundays

16 February to 23 March

Scotland and North West England - West Midlands and London

Route Diagram - refer to first Page of Table 65

		VT	XC	VT	LM	XC	VT	VT	VT	TP	LM	VT	VT	VT	XC	VT	VT	LM	VT	TP	TP	XC
		◇1	◇1	◇1	1	◇1	◇1	◇1	◇1	◇1	1	◇1	◇1	◇1	◇1	◇1	◇	1	◇1	◇1	◇1	◇1
						A																
		⊡	🛒	⊡		⊡🛒	⊡	⊡	⊡	🛒		⊡	⊡	⊡	🛒	⊡	⊡		⊡		🛒	🛒
Inverness 229	d																					
Aberdeen 229	d																					
Dundee 229	d																					
Perth 229	d																					
Edinburgh 10 225,226,228,230,242	d									16 10									16 51			
Haymarket 225,226,228,230,242	d									16u14									16 55			
Glasgow Central 15 226,216	d	15 36							15 57					16 40							17 06	
Motherwell 226	d													16 54								
Carstairs 226	d																					
Lockerbie	d									17 08											18 07	
Carlisle 8 216	a	16 46							17 07	17 29				17 49					18 05		18 26	
	d	16 49							17 09	17 30				17 51					18 07		18 30	
Penrith North Lakes	d	17 03								17 45				18 05							18 45	
Windermere 83	d																					
Oxenholme Lake District	a								17 44	18 09				18 27					18 41		19 09	
	d								17 44	18 10				18 28					18 42		19 09	
Barrow-in-Furness 82	d																			18 17		
Lancaster 6	a	17 37								18 24				18 42					18 56	19 17	19 24	
	d	17 38								18 25				18 43					18 57	19 17	19 24	
Blackpool North 97	d																					
Preston 8 90	a	17 56							18 13	18 43				19 01					19 15	19 37	19 44	
Preston 8 90	d	17 58							18 17	18 45				19 03					19 17		19 45	
Wigan North Western 90	a	18 09							18 28	18 58				19 14					19 28		19 58	
	d	18 09							18 28	18 58				19 14					19 28		19 59	
Bolton 82	a																					
Manchester Picc. 10 82	a									19 27											20 27	
Manchester Airport ✈	a									19 47											20 45	
Liverpool Lime Street 10 91	a																					
	d										18 34	18 47										
Liverpool South Parkway 91 ✈	d										18 44											
Runcorn 91	d										18 52	19 03										
Warrington Bank Quay	a	18 20							18 39					19 25					19 39			
	d	18 20							18 39					19 25					19 39			
Manchester Picc. 10 84	d		18 07	18 15		18 27		18 35					18 55		19 07	19 15						19 27
Stockport 84	d			18 22		18 36		18 42					19 04			19 22						19 36
Wilmslow 84	d												19 11									
Holyhead 81 ⛴	d																					
Bangor (Gwynedd) 81	d																					
Llandudno Junction 81	d																					
Wrexham General 75	d																					
Chester 81	d						18 35										19 35					
Crewe 10	a						18 53		18 58		19 17	19 21	19 27				19 56		19 59			
	d				18 37		18 55		19 01		19 19	19 23	19 29					19 37	20 01			
Macclesfield	d					18 49		18 55														19 49
Stoke-on-Trent	d		18 43	18 50	18 59	19 07		19 12							19 43	19 50		19 59				20 07
Stafford	a				19 18	19 24					19 40	19 42						20 17				20 26
	d				19 18	19 25					19 40	19 44						20 18				20 27
Penkridge	a										19 46											
Wolverhampton 7	a		19 13			19 40			19 34		19 56				20 13				20 33			20 39
Birmingham New St. 12 68	a		19 31			19 58			20 06		20 15				20 31				20 51			20 58
Birmingham International 68 ✈	a					20 13			20 19													21 13
Coventry 68	a					20 24			20 30													21 23
Lichfield Trent Valley	a				19 35													20 35				
Tamworth Low Level	a				19 41													20 41				
Nuneaton	a				19 57													20 57				
Rugby 66	a				20 13													21 13				
Milton Keynes Central 66	a			19 48	21 07		20 03		20 59							20 46		22 10				
Watford Junction 66	a				21 35													22 52				
London Euston 15 ⊖66	a	20 13		20 27	21 55		20 46	20 48	21 48			21 04	21 10	21 22		21 31		23 15				

A ⊡ from Birmingham New St. 🛒 to Birmingham New St.

OVERNIGHT SLEEPERS. For sleeper trains, operated by First ScotRail, please see Tables 400 - 404.

For complete service between Manchester and Preston, Blackpool and between Barrow-in-furness and Lancaster, please see Table 82.

For complete service between Crewe and Liverpool Lime Street, see Table 91

For complete service between Crewe/Stoke-on-Trent & Manchester see Table 84

For complete service between Crewe and Holyhead please see Table 81.

For complete service between Coventry-Birmingham-Wolverhampton-Stafford please see Table 68

For complete service between Windermere and Oxenholme Lake District, please see Table 83

Table 65R

Sundays

16 February to 23 March

Scotland and North West England - West Midlands and London

Route Diagram - refer to first Page of Table 65

	LM	VT	VT	XC	VT		LM	VT	TP	VT	LM	VT	VT	VT			XC	VT	TP	VT	LM	SR	SR	SR
																						B	B	B
	1	◇1	◇1	◇1	◇		1	◇1	◇1	◇1	1	◇1	◇1	◇1			◇1	◇1	◇1	◇1	1			
																							A	
Inverness 229 d																							20 26	
Aberdeen 229 d																								21 43
Dundee 229 d																								23u06
Perth 229 d																							23u06	
Edinburgh 10 225,226,228,230,242 d									18 10									18 51	19 57			23c21		
Haymarket 225,226,228,230,242 d									18u14									18 56	20u01					
Glasgow Central 15 226,216 d								17 36						18 30						20 08		21 46		
Motherwell 226 d																						22u07		
Carstairs 226 d																						22u24		
Lockerbie d								18 32	19 08											21 03				
Carlisle 8 216 a								18 50	19 29					19 43				20 05	21 13	21 21				
d								18 52	19 30					19 44				20 07	21 14	21 24				
Penrith North Lakes d								19 06	19 45									20 22		21 39				
Windermere 83 d																								
Oxenholme Lake District a								19 28	20 09					20 19					21 51	22 02				
d								19 29	20 10					20 19					21 51	22 03				
Barrow-in-Furness 82 d																								
Lancaster 6 a								19 43	20 24					20 34				20 56	22 06	22 17				
d								19 44	20 25					20 34				20 57	22 06	22 18				
Blackpool North 97 d																								
Preston 8 90 a								20 02	20 43					20 52				21 15	22 25	22 35				
Preston 8 90 d								20 04	20 46					20 55				21 17	22 26	22 38				
Wigan North Western 90 a								20 15						21 06				21 28	22 39	22 48				
d								20 15						21 07				21 29	22 39	22 50				
Bolton 82 a																								
Manchester Picc. 10 82 a									21 25										23 08					
Manchester Airport a									21 45										23 24					
Liverpool Lime Street 10 91 a																								
d	19 34		19 47								20 34		20 47								21 34			
Liverpool South Parkway 91 d	19 44										20 44										21 44			
Runcorn 91 d	19 52		20 03								20 52		21 03								21 52			
Warrington Bank Quay a								20 26						21 18				21 39		22 59				
d								20 26						21 18				21 39		23 01				
Manchester Picc. 10 84 d		19 35		20 07						20 21		20 55					21 07							
Stockport 84 d		19 41		20 16						20 27		21 03					21 16							
Wilmslow 84 d																								
Holyhead 81 d																								
Bangor (Gwynedd) 81 d																								
Llandudno Junction 81 d																								
Wrexham General 75 d																								
Chester 81 d					20 37																			
Crewe 10 a	20 16		20 22		20 56			20 45			21 16		21 21	21 38				21 59		23 22	22 18			
d	20 18		20 24				20 44	20 47			21 18		21 23	21 40				22 01			22 22			
Macclesfield d		19 54		20 29						20 40		21 15					21 29							
Stoke-on-Trent d		20 11		20 47			21 06			20 57		21 33					21 47							
Stafford a	20 38		20 42	21 08			21 25				21 39		21 42	22 01			22 06				22 42			
d	20 39		20 43	21 09			21 25				21 39		21 44	22 02			22 06				22 43			
Penkridge a	20 44										21 45										22 48			
Wolverhampton 7 a	20 55			21 21							21 55			22 17			22 20	22 34			22 59			
Birmingham New St. 12 68 a	21 16			21 39							22 17			22 38			22 40	22 55			23 16			
Birmingham International 68 a																								
Coventry 68 a																								
Lichfield Trent Valley a							21 41						21 59											
Tamworth Low Level a							21 48						22 06											
Nuneaton a							22 04						22 17											
Rugby 66 a							22 20						22 31											
Milton Keynes Central 66 a			21 36					21 52		22 03		22 46	23 04											
Watford Junction 66 a								22s31				23s28	23s34											
London Euston 15 ⊖66 a		21 58	22 28					22 55		22 57		23 49	23 54									07 06		08 57

A also conveys through sleepers from Fort William. Dep 1900 (Table 404)

c calls after Carstairs

OVERNIGHT SLEEPERS. For sleeper trains, operated by First ScotRail, please see Tables 400 - 404.

For complete service between Manchester and Preston, Blackpool and between Barrow-in-furness and Lancaster, please see Table 82.

For complete service between Crewe and Liverpool Lime Street, see Table 91

For complete service between Crewe/Stoke-on-Trent & Manchester see Table 84

For complete service between Crewe and Holyhead please see Table 81.

For complete service between Coventry-Birmingham-Wolverhampton-Stafford please see Table 68

For complete service between Windermere and Oxenholme Lake District, please see Table 83

Table 65R

Sundays

16 February to 23 March

Scotland and North West England - West Midlands and London

Route Diagram - refer to first Page of Table 65

Station	Table		XC ◇[1]
Inverness	229	d	
Aberdeen	229	d	
Dundee	229	d	
Perth	229	d	
Edinburgh [10]	225,226,228,230,242	d	
Haymarket	225,226,228,230,242	d	
Glasgow Central [15]	226,216	d	
Motherwell	226	d	
Carstairs	226	d	
Lockerbie		d	
Carlisle [8]	216	a	
		d	
Penrith North Lakes		d	
Windermere	83	d	
Oxenholme Lake District		a	
		d	
Barrow-in-Furness	82	d	
Lancaster [6]		a	
		d	
Blackpool North	97	d	
Preston [8]	90	a	
Preston [8]	90	d	
Wigan North Western	90	a	
		d	
Bolton	82	a	
Manchester Picc. [10]	82 ⇌	a	
Manchester Airport	✈	a	
Liverpool Lime Street [10]	91	a	
		d	
Liverpool South Parkway	91 ✈	d	
Runcorn	91	d	
Warrington Bank Quay		a	
		d	
Manchester Picc. [10]	84 ⇌	d	22 07
Stockport	84	d	22 16
Wilmslow	84	d	
Holyhead	81 ⛴	d	
Bangor (Gwynedd)	81	d	
Llandudno Junction	81	d	
Wrexham General	75	d	
Chester	81	d	
Crewe [10]		a	
		d	
Macclesfield		d	22 29
Stoke-on-Trent		d	22 47
Stafford		a	23 04
		d	23 05
Penkridge		a	
Wolverhampton [7]	⇌	a	23 18
Birmingham New St. [12]	68	a	23 36
Birmingham International	68 ✈	a	
Coventry	68	a	
Lichfield Trent Valley		a	
Tamworth Low Level		a	
Nuneaton		a	
Rugby	66	a	
Milton Keynes Central	66	a	
Watford Junction	66	a	
London Euston [15]	⊖66	a	

OVERNIGHT SLEEPERS. For sleeper trains, operated by First ScotRail, please see Tables 400 - 404.

For complete service between Manchester and Preston, Blackpool and between Barrow-in-furness and Lancaster, please see Table 82.

For complete service between Crewe and Liverpool Lime Street, see Table 91

For complete service between Crewe/Stoke-on-Trent & Manchester see Table 84

For complete service between Crewe and Holyhead please see Table 81.

For complete service between Coventry-Birmingham-Wolverhampton-Stafford please see Table 68

For complete service between Windermere and Oxenholme Lake District, please see Table 83

Table 65R

Sundays

30 March to 11 May

Scotland and North West England - West Midlands and London

Route Diagram - refer to first Page of Table 65

Station	Table		VT	VT	VT	XC	VT	LM	VT		VT		XC	VT	LM	LM	VT	VT	VT	XC	VT		VT	VT		VT
			◇1	◇1	◇1	◇1	◇1	1	◇1		◇1		◇1	◇1	1	1	◇1	◇1	◇1	◇1	◇1		◇1	◇1		◇1
						A							A													
			☕	☕	☕	☕🛒	☕		☕		☕		☕🛒	☕			☕	☕	☕	🛒	☕		☕	☕		☕
Inverness	229	d																								
Aberdeen	229	d																								
Dundee	229	d																								
Perth	229	d																								
Edinburgh 10	225,226,228,230,242	d																								
Haymarket	225,226,228,230,242	d																								
Glasgow Central 15	226,216	d																								
Motherwell	226	d																								
Carstairs	226	d																								
Lockerbie		d																								
Carlisle 8	216	a																								
		d																								
Penrith North Lakes		d																								
Windermere	83	d																								
Oxenholme Lake District		a																								
		d																								
Barrow-in-Furness	82	d																								
Lancaster 6		a																								
		d																								
Blackpool North	97	d																								
Preston 8	90	a																								
Preston 8	90	d							09 00								10 00		10 17					10 58		
Wigan North Western	90	a							09 10								10 10		10 28					11 11		
		d							09 11								10 11		10 28					11 11		
Bolton	82	a																								
Manchester Picc. 10	82	a																								
Manchester Airport		a																								
Liverpool Lime Street 10	91	a																								
		d			08 15		08 38							09 38									10 38			
Liverpool South Parkway	91	d																								
Runcorn	91	d			08 35		08 54							09 54									10 54			
Warrington Bank Quay		a							09 21								10 21		10 39					11 22		
		d							09 22								10 22		10 39					11 22		
Manchester Picc. 10	84	d	08 05	08 20		08 27					09 20		09 27					10 20		10 27	10 35					11 15
Stockport	84	d	08 14	08 28		08 36					09 27		09 36					10 29		10 37	10 43					11 23
Wilmslow	84	d	08 22			08 43												10 37								
Holyhead	81	d																								
Bangor (Gwynedd)	81	d																								
Llandudno Junction	81	d																								
Wrexham General	75	d																								
Chester	81	d																								
Crewe 10		a	08 39		08 52	09 01	09 11		09 41					10 12			10 41	10 53	10 59				11 12			
		d	08 43		08 53	09 05	09 13	09 30	09 43					10 14	10 20	10 37	10 43	10 55	11 01				11 14			
Macclesfield		d		08 42							09 40		09 49							10 50	10 56					
Stoke-on-Trent		d		08 59				09 51			09 57		10 07			10 59				11 08	11 13					11 51
Stafford		a	09 01			09 25	09 31	10 14					10 26	10 32	10 41	11 17				11 27			11 35			
		d	09 03			09 26	09 33	10 18					10 27	10 34	10 42	11 18				11 28			11 36			
Penkridge		a													10 49											
Wolverhampton 7		a				09 40							10 42		11 00				11 31	11 41						
Birmingham New St. 12	68	a				09 58							10 59		11 18				11 55	11 59						
Birmingham International	68	a				10 13							11 13							12 13						
Coventry	68	a				10 24							11 24							12 24						
Lichfield Trent Valley		a						10 34								11 35										
Tamworth Low Level		a						10 41								11 41										
Nuneaton		a					09 55	10 57						10 56		11 57							11 58			
Rugby	66	a						11 17	10 32							12 13	11 32									
Milton Keynes Central	66	a			10 18			12 02	11 07		11 16			11 46		13 04	12 07				12 21					12 50
Watford Junction	66	a	10s35	10s41			11s16	12 32	11s43							13 34		12s36					12s52			
London Euston 15	⊖66	a	10 58	11 02	11 06		11 37	12 51	12 06		12 09			12 32		13 53	12 46	12 57			13 00		13 13	13 22		13 28

A ☕ from Birmingham New St. 🛒 to Birmingham New St.

OVERNIGHT SLEEPERS. For sleeper trains, operated by First ScotRail, please see Tables 400 - 404.

For complete service between Manchester and Preston, Blackpool and between Barrow-in-furness and Lancaster, please see Table 82.

For complete service between Crewe and Liverpool Lime Street, see Table 91

For complete service between Crewe/Stoke-on-Trent & Manchester see Table 84

For complete service between Crewe and Holyhead please see Table 81.

For complete service between Coventry-Birmingham-Wolverhampton-Stafford please see Table 68

For complete service between Windermere and Oxenholme Lake District, please see Table 83

Table 65R

Sundays

30 March to 11 May

Scotland and North West England - West Midlands and London

Route Diagram - refer to first Page of Table 65

		LM	VT	VT	TP	XC	LM	VT	VT	VT	VT	VT	LM	VT	XC	VT	VT	TP	LM	VT	VT	VT
		1	◇1	◇1	◇1	◇1	1	◇1	◇1	◇1	◇1	◇1	1	◇1	◇1	◇1	◇1	◇1	1	◇1	◇1	◇1
						A									A							
			🍴	🍴		🍴🛒		🍴	🍴	🍴	🍴	🍴		🍴	🍴🛒	🍴	🍴	🛒		🍴	🍴	🍴
Inverness 229	d																					
Aberdeen 229	d																					
Dundee 229	d																					
Perth 229	d																					
Edinburgh 10 225,226,228,230,242	d																	10 10				
Haymarket 225,226,228,230,242	d																	10u14				
Glasgow Central 15 226,216	d										09 37											10 34
Motherwell 226	d																					10 49
Carstairs 226	d																					
Lockerbie	d																	11 08				
Carlisle 8 216	a										10 44							11 29				11 44
	d										10 56							11 30				11 46
Penrith North Lakes	d										11 10							11 45				12 00
Windermere 83	d																					
Oxenholme Lake District	a										11 32							12 09				12 22
	d										11 33							12 10				12 24
Barrow-in-Furness 82	d				10 25																	
Lancaster 6	a				11 25						11 47							12 24				12 37
	d				11 25						11 48						11 58	12 25				12 38
Blackpool North 97	d																					
Preston 8 90	a				11 44						12 06						12 15	12 43				12 56
Preston 8 90	d			11 17	11 47						12 08						12 17	12 45				12 58
Wigan North Western 90	a			11 28							12 19						12 28	12 58				13 09
	d			11 28							12 19						12 28	12 58				13 09
Bolton 82	a				12 08																	
Manchester Picc. 10 82 ⛴	a				12 27													13 27				
Manchester Airport ✈	a				12 42													13 47				
Liverpool Lime Street 10 91	a																					
	d						11 34		11 47										12 34	12 47		
Liverpool South Parkway 91 ✈	d						11 44												12 44			
Runcorn 91	d						11 52		12 03										12 52	13 03		
Warrington Bank Quay	a			11 39							12 30						12 39					13 20
	d			11 39							12 30						12 39					13 20
Manchester Picc. 10 84 ⛴	d					11 27		11 35		11 55		12 15			12 26	12 35					12 55	
Stockport 84	d					11 36		11 43		12 05		12 23			12 35	12 44					13 05	
Wilmslow 84	d									12 12											13 12	
Holyhead 81 ⛴	d													10 55								
Bangor (Gwynedd) 81	d													11 22								
Llandudno Junction 81	d													11 40								
Wrexham General 75	d																					
Chester 81	d		11 28											12 32								
Crewe 10	a		11 47	11 59			12 18		12 21	12 28				12 53			12 59		13 17	13 21	13 28	
	d	11 37	11 49	12 01			12 19		12 23	12 30			12 37	12 55			13 01		13 19	13 23	13 30	
Macclesfield	d					11 49		11 56							12 49	12 57						
Stoke-on-Trent	d	11 59				12 07		12 13				12 51	12 59		13 07	13 14						
Stafford	a	12 17				12 24	12 40		12 42				13 18		13 24				13 40	13 42		
	d	12 18				12 25	12 40		12 44				13 18		13 25				13 40	13 44		
Penkridge	a						12 46												13 46			
Wolverhampton 7 ⛴	a			12 32		12 40	12 56								13 40		13 32		13 56			
Birmingham New St. 12 68	a			12 54		12 58	13 15								13 58		14 06		14 15			
Birmingham International 68 ✈	a					13 13									14 13		14 19					
Coventry 68	a					13 24									14 24		14 30					
Lichfield Trent Valley	a	12 35											13 35									
Tamworth Low Level	a	12 41											13 41									
Nuneaton	a	12 57	12 31										13 57									
Rugby 66	a	13 13											14 13									
Milton Keynes Central 66	a	14 04	13 04									13 50	15 04	14 03			14 58					
Watford Junction 66	a	14 34											15 34									
London Euston 15 ⊖66	a	14 53	13 46					13 48	14 04	14 10	14 25	14 28	15 53	14 44		14 48	15 39			15 04	15 08	15 13

A 🍴 from Birmingham New St. 🛒 to Birmingham New St.

OVERNIGHT SLEEPERS. For sleeper trains, operated by First ScotRail, please see Tables 400 - 404.

For complete service between Manchester and Preston, Blackpool and between Barrow-in-furness and Lancaster, please see Table 82.

For complete service between Crewe and Liverpool Lime Street, see Table 91

For complete service between Crewe/Stoke-on-Trent & Manchester see Table 84

For complete service between Crewe and Holyhead please see Table 81.

For complete service between Coventry-Birmingham-Wolverhampton-Stafford please see Table 68

For complete service between Windermere and Oxenholme Lake District, please see Table 83

Table 65R

Sundays
30 March to 11 May

Scotland and North West England - West Midlands and London

Route Diagram - refer to first Page of Table 65

		XC	VT	LM	VT	VT	XC	VT	VT	TP	LM	VT	VT	VT	XC	VT	LM	VT	XC	VT	VT	VT
		◇1	◇1	1	◇1	◇1	◇1	◇1	◇1	◇1	1	◇1	◇1	◇1	◇1	◇1	1	◇1	◇1	◇1	◇1	◇1
							A												A			
Inverness	229 d																					
Aberdeen	229 d																					
Dundee	229 d																					
Perth	229 d																					
Edinburgh 10 225,226,228,230,242	d								10 51													
Haymarket 225,226,228,230,242	d								10 55													
Glasgow Central 15 226,216	d													11 36								11 58
Motherwell	226 d																					
Carstairs	226 d																					
Lockerbie	d																					
Carlisle 8	216 a								12 05					12 47								13 09
	d								12 07					12 49								13 10
Penrith North Lakes	d																					
Windermere	83 d																					
Oxenholme Lake District	a								12 41					13 22								
	d								12 43					13 23								
Barrow-in-Furness	82 d									12 33												
Lancaster 6	a								12 56	13 25				13 37								13 56
	d								12 57	13 25				13 38								13 58
Blackpool North	97 d																					
Preston 8	90 a								13 15	13 44				13 56								14 15
Preston 8	90 d								13 17	13 45				13 58								14 17
Wigan North Western	90 a								13 28	13 58				14 09								14 28
	d								13 28	13 58				14 09								14 28
Bolton	82 a																					
Manchester Picc. 10	82 a									14 27												
Manchester Airport	✈ a									14 47												
Liverpool Lime Street 10	91 a																					
	d										13 34	13 47										
Liverpool South Parkway 91	✈ d										13 44											
Runcorn	91 d										13 52	14 03										
Warrington Bank Quay	a								13 39					14 20								14 39
	d								13 39					14 20								14 39
Manchester Picc. 10	84 d	13 07	13 15				13 27	13 35					13 55		14 07	14 15			14 27		14 35	
Stockport	84 d		13 22				13 36	13 42					14 04			14 22			14 36		14 42	
Wilmslow	84 d												14 11									
Holyhead	81 d				11 50													12 50				
Bangor (Gwynedd)	81 d				12 17													13 18				
Llandudno Junction	81 d				12 35													13 36				
Wrexham General	75 d																					
Chester	81 d				13 30	13 30												14 33		14 33		
Crewe 10	a				13 50	13 50			13 59		14 17	14 21	14 27					14 53		14 52		14 58
	d			13 37	13 52	13 52			14 01		14 19	14 23	14 29				14 33	14 54		14 55		15 01
Macclesfield	d						13 49	13 55											14 49		14 55	
Stoke-on-Trent	d	13 43	13 50	13 59			14 07	14 12							14 43	14 50	14 55		15 07		15 12	
Stafford	a			14 17			14 24				14 40	14 42					15 12		15 24			
	d			14 18			14 25				14 40	14 44					15 18		15 25			
Penkridge	a										14 46											
Wolverhampton 7	a	14 13					14 40		14 31		14 56				15 13				15 40			15 34
Birmingham New St. 12	68 a	14 31					14 58		15 06		15 15				15 31				15 58			16 07
Birmingham International 68	✈ a						15 13		15 19										16 13			16 19
Coventry	68 a						15 24		15 30										16 24			16 31
Lichfield Trent Valley	a			14 35													15 35					
Tamworth Low Level	a			14 41													15 41					
Nuneaton	a			14 57	14 32	14 32											15 57					
Rugby	66 a			15 13													16 13					
Milton Keynes Central	66 a		14 48	16 04	15 03	15 03			15 58							15 48	17 04	16 03		16 03		16 58
Watford Junction	66 a			16 34													17 34					
London Euston 15	⊖66 a		15 26	16 53	15 45	15 45		15 48	16 39			16 04	16 07	16 13		16 26	17 53	16 44		16 41	16 48	17 38

A — from Birmingham New St. — to Birmingham New St.

OVERNIGHT SLEEPERS. For sleeper trains, operated by First ScotRail, please see Tables 400 - 404.

For complete service between Manchester and Preston, Blackpool and between Barrow-in-furness and Lancaster, please see Table 82.

For complete service between Crewe and Liverpool Lime Street, see Table 91

For complete service between Crewe/Stoke-on-Trent & Manchester see Table 84

For complete service between Crewe and Holyhead please see Table 81.

For complete service between Coventry-Birmingham-Wolverhampton-Stafford please see Table 68

For complete service between Windermere and Oxenholme Lake District, please see Table 83

Table 65R

Sundays

30 March to 11 May

Scotland and North West England - West Midlands and London

Route Diagram - refer to first Page of Table 65

		TP	LM	VT	VT	VT		XC		VT	LM	VT	XC	VT	VT	TP	LM	VT		VT	VT	XC	VT	LM	VT
		◇1	1	◇1	◇1	◇1		◇1		◇1	1	◇1	◇1	◇1	◇1	◇1	1	◇1		◇1	◇1	◇1	◇1	1	◇1
													A												
		🛒		🍽	🍽	🍽		🛒		🍽		🍽	🍽🛒	🍽	🍽			🍽		🍽	🍽	🛒	🍽		🍽
Inverness 229	d																								
Aberdeen 229	d																								
Dundee 229	d																								
Perth 229	d																								
Edinburgh 10 225,226,228,230,242	d	12 10													12 51										
Haymarket 225,226,228,230,242	d	12u14													12 55										
Glasgow Central 15 226,216	d					12 42															13 36				
Motherwell 226	d																								
Carstairs 226	d																								
Lockerbie	d	13 08																							
Carlisle 8 216	a	13 29				13 52									14 05						14 46				
	d	13 30				13 54									14 07						14 49				
Penrith North Lakes	d	13 45													14 22										
Windermere 83	d																								
Oxenholme Lake District	a	14 09				14 27															15 22				
	d	14 10				14 28															15 23				
Barrow-in-Furness 82	d															14 25									
Lancaster 6	a	14 24				14 42									14 56	15 25					15 37				
	d	14 25				14 43									14 57	15 25					15 38				
Blackpool North 97	d																								
Preston 8 90	a	14 43				15 01									15 15	15 44					15 56				
Preston 8 90	d	14 45				15 03									15 17	15 45					15 58				
Wigan North Western 90	a	14 58				15 14									15 28	15 58					16 09				
	d	14 58				15 14									15 28	15 58					16 09				
Bolton 82	a																								
Manchester Picc. 10 82 ⛴	a	15 27														16 27									
Manchester Airport ✈	a	15 47														16 47									
Liverpool Lime Street 10 91	a																								
	d		14 34	14 47													15 34	15 47							16 18
Liverpool South Parkway 91 ✈	d		14 44														15 44								
Runcorn 91	d		14 52	15 03													15 52	16 03							16 34
Warrington Bank Quay	a					15 25									15 39						16 20				
	d					15 25									15 39						16 20				
Manchester Picc. 10 84 ⛴	d				14 55			15 07		15 15			15 27	15 35						15 55		16 07	16 15		
Stockport 84	d				15 04					15 22			15 36	15 42						16 04			16 23		
Wilmslow 84	d				15 11															16 11					
Holyhead 81 ⛴	d											13 55													
Bangor (Gwynedd) 81	d											14 22													
Llandudno Junction 81	d											14 40													
Wrexham General 75	d																								
Chester 81	d											15 33													
Crewe 10	a		15 17	15 21	15 27							15 52			15 59		16 17	16 21		16 27					16 51
	d		15 19	15 23	15 29						15 37	15 54			16 01		16 19	16 23		16 29				16 33	16 54
Macclesfield	d												15 49	15 55											
Stoke-on-Trent	d							15 43		15 50	15 59		16 07	16 12								16 43	16 50	16 55	
Stafford	a		15 40	15 42							16 17		16 24				16 40	16 42						17 17	
	d		15 40	15 44							16 18		16 25				16 40	16 44						17 18	
Penkridge	a		15 46														16 46								
Wolverhampton 7 ⛴	a		15 56					16 13					16 40		16 32		16 56					17 13			
Birmingham New St. 12 68	a		16 15					16 31					16 58		17 06		17 15					17 31			
Birmingham International 68 ✈	a												17 13		17 19										
Coventry 68	a												17 24		17 29										
Lichfield Trent Valley	a										16 35													17 35	17 25
Tamworth Low Level	a										16 41													17 41	
Nuneaton	a										16 57													17 57	
Rugby 66	a										17 13													18 13	
Milton Keynes Central 66	a									16 50	18 04	17 03			17 58								17 49	19 04	18 03
Watford Junction 66	a										18 34													19 34	
London Euston 15 ⊖66	a			17 04	17 09	17 21				17 27	18 53	17 44		17 46	18 38			18 03		18 09	18 14		18 27	19 53	18 44

A 🍽 from Birmingham New St. 🛒 to Birmingham New St.

OVERNIGHT SLEEPERS. For sleeper trains, operated by First ScotRail, please see Tables 400 - 404.

For complete service between Manchester and Preston, Blackpool and between Barrow-in-furness and Lancaster, please see Table 82.

For complete service between Crewe and Liverpool Lime Street, see Table 91

For complete service between Crewe/Stoke-on-Trent & Manchester see Table 84

For complete service between Crewe and Holyhead please see Table 81.

For complete service between Coventry-Birmingham-Wolverhampton-Stafford please see Table 68

For complete service between Windermere and Oxenholme Lake District, please see Table 83

Table 65R

Sundays

30 March to 11 May

Scotland and North West England - West Midlands and London

Route Diagram - refer to first Page of Table 65

	XC	VT	VT	TP	LM	VT	VT	VT	XC	VT	LM	XC	VT	VT	VT	TP	LM	VT	VT	VT
	◇1	◇1	◇1	◇1	1	◇1	◇1	◇1	◇1	◇1	1	◇1	◇1	◇1	◇1	◇1	1	◇1	◇1	◇1
	A											A								
Inverness 229 d																				
Aberdeen 229 d																				
Dundee 229 d																				
Perth 229 d																				
Edinburgh 10 225,226,228,230,242 d				14 10											14 51					
Haymarket 225,226,228,230,242 d				14u14											14 56					
Glasgow Central 15 226,216 d			13 55					14 36								15 06				15 36
Motherwell 226 d																				
Carstairs 226 d																				
Lockerbie d				15 08												16 05				
Carlisle 8 216 a			15 09	15 29				15 46							16 05	16 26				16 46
d			15 12	15 30				15 49							16 07	16 30				16 49
Penrith North Lakes d				15 46											16 22	16 45				17 03
Windermere 83 d																				
Oxenholme Lake District a			15 46	16 09				16 22								17 08				
d			15 47	16 10				16 23								17 09				
Barrow-in-Furness 82 d																				
Lancaster 6 a				16 24				16 37							16 57	17 23				17 37
d				16 25				16 38							16 57	17 24				17 38
Blackpool North 97 d																				
Preston 8 90 a			16 15	16 43				16 56							17 15	17 42				17 56
Preston 8 90 d			16 17	16 45				16 58							17 18	17 45				17 58
Wigan North Western 90 a			16 28	16 58				17 09							17 28	17 58				18 09
d			16 29	16 58				17 09							17 29	17 58				18 09
Bolton 82 a																				
Manchester Picc. 10 82 a				17 27												18 27				
Manchester Airport a				17 47												18 47				
Liverpool Lime Street 10 91 a																				
d					16 34	16 47											17 34	17 47		
Liverpool South Parkway 91 d					16 44												17 44			
Runcorn 91 d					16 52	17 03											17 52	18 03		
Warrington Bank Quay a			16 39					17 20							17 39					18 20
d			16 40					17 20							17 40					18 20
Manchester Picc. 10 84 d	16 27	16 35					16 55		17 07	17 15		17 27		17 35					17 55	
Stockport 84 d	16 36	16 42					17 04			17 22		17 36		17 42					18 04	
Wilmslow 84 d							17 11												18 11	
Holyhead 81 d																				
Bangor (Gwynedd) 81 d																				
Llandudno Junction 81 d																				
Wrexham General 75 d																				
Chester 81 d													17 35							
Crewe 10 a			16 58		17 17	17 21	17 27						17 53		17 59		18 17	18 21	18 27	
d			17 00		17 19	17 23	17 29				17 37		17 55		18 01		18 19	18 23	18 29	
Macclesfield d	16 49	16 55										17 49		17 55						
Stoke-on-Trent d	17 08	17 12							17 43	17 50	17 59	18 08		18 12						
Stafford a	17 25				17 40	17 42					18 17	18 26					18 40	18 42		
d	17 26				17 40	17 44					18 18	18 27					18 40	18 44		
Penkridge a					17 46												18 46			
Wolverhampton 7 a	17 40		17 32		17 56				18 13			18 40			18 33		18 56			
Birmingham New St. 12 68 a	17 58		18 07		18 15				18 31			18 58			19 06		19 15			
Birmingham International 68 a	18 13		18 19									19 13			19 19					
Coventry 68 a	18 24		18 31									19 24			19 30					
Lichfield Trent Valley a											18 35									
Tamworth Low Level a											18 41									
Nuneaton a											18 57									
Rugby 66 a											19 13									
Milton Keynes Central 66 a			18 58							18 49	20 06		19 03		19 58					
Watford Junction 66 a											20 34									
London Euston 15 ⊖66 a		18 48	19 38			19 04	19 07	19 11		19 27	20 53		19 45	19 48	20 39			20 05	20 08	20 13

A from Birmingham New St. to Birmingham New St.

OVERNIGHT SLEEPERS. For sleeper trains, operated by First ScotRail, please see Tables 400 - 404.

For complete service between Manchester and Preston, Blackpool and between Barrow-in-furness and Lancaster, please see Table 82.

For complete service between Crewe and Liverpool Lime Street, see Table 91

For complete service between Crewe/Stoke-on-Trent & Manchester see Table 84

For complete service between Crewe and Holyhead please see Table 81.

For complete service between Coventry-Birmingham-Wolverhampton-Stafford please see Table 68

For complete service between Windermere and Oxenholme Lake District, please see Table 83

Table 65R

Sundays

30 March to 11 May

Scotland and North West England - West Midlands and London

Route Diagram - refer to first Page of Table 65

	XC	VT	LM	XC	VT	VT	VT	TP	LM		VT	VT	VT		XC	VT	VT	LM	VT		TP	TP	XC	LM
	◇[1]	◇[1]	[1]	◇[1]	◇[1]	◇[1]	◇[1]	◇[1]	[1]		◇[1]	◇[1]	◇[1]		◇[1]	◇[1]	◇	[1]	◇[1]		◇[1]	◇[1]	◇[1]	[1]
				A																				
	[trolley]	[buffet]		[buffet][trolley]	[buffet]	[buffet]	[buffet]	[trolley]			[buffet]	[buffet]	[buffet]		[trolley]	[buffet]	[buffet]		[buffet]			[trolley]	[trolley]	
Inverness 229 d																								
Aberdeen 229 d																								
Dundee 229 d																								
Perth 229 d																								
Edinburgh [10] 225,226,228,230,242 d								16 10											16 51					
Haymarket 225,226,228,230,242 d								16u14											16 55					
Glasgow Central [15] 226,216 d							15 57						16 40									17 06		
Motherwell 226 d													16 54											
Carstairs 226 d																								
Lockerbie d								17 08														18 07		
Carlisle [8] 216 a							17 07	17 29					17 49						18 05			18 26		
d							17 09	17 30					17 51						18 07			18 30		
Penrith North Lakes d								17 45					18 05									18 45		
Windermere 83 d																								
Oxenholme Lake District a							17 44	18 09					18 27						18 41			19 09		
d							17 44	18 10					18 28						18 42			19 09		
Barrow-in-Furness 82 d																					18 17			
Lancaster [6] a								18 24					18 42						18 56		19 17	19 24		
d								18 25					18 43						18 57		19 17	19 24		
Blackpool North 97 d																								
Preston [8] 90 a							18 13	18 43					19 01						19 15		19 37	19 44		
Preston [8] 90 d							18 17	18 45					19 03						19 17			19 45		
Wigan North Western 90 a							18 28	18 58					19 14						19 28			19 58		
d							18 28	18 58					19 14						19 28			19 59		
Bolton 82 a																								
Manchester Picc. [10] 82 a								19 27														20 27		
Manchester Airport a								19 47														20 45		
Liverpool Lime Street [10] 91 a																								
d									18 34		18 47													19 34
Liverpool South Parkway 91 d									18 44															19 44
Runcorn 91 d									18 52		19 03													19 52
Warrington Bank Quay a							18 39						19 25						19 39					
d							18 39						19 25						19 39					
Manchester Picc. [10] 84 d	18 07	18 15		18 27		18 35						18 55			19 07	19 15							19 27	
Stockport 84 d		18 22		18 36		18 42						19 04				19 22							19 36	
Wilmslow 84 d												19 11												
Holyhead 81 d																								
Bangor (Gwynedd) 81 d																								
Llandudno Junction 81 d																								
Wrexham General 75 d																								
Chester 81 d					18 35												19 35							
Crewe [10] a					18 53		18 58		19 17		19 21	19 27					19 56		19 59					20 16
d			18 37		18 55		19 01		19 19		19 23	19 29						19 37	20 01					20 18
Macclesfield d				18 49		18 55																	19 49	
Stoke-on-Trent d	18 43	18 50	18 59	19 07		19 12									19 43	19 50		19 59					20 07	
Stafford a			19 18	19 24					19 40		19 42							20 17					20 26	20 38
d			19 18	19 25					19 40		19 44							20 18					20 27	20 39
Penkridge a									19 46															20 44
Wolverhampton [7] a	19 13			19 40			19 34		19 56						20 13				20 33				20 39	20 55
Birmingham New St. [12] 68 a	19 31			19 58			20 06		20 15						20 31				20 51				20 58	21 16
Birmingham International 68 a				20 13			20 19																21 13	
Coventry 68 a				20 24			20 30																21 23	
Lichfield Trent Valley a			19 35															20 35						
Tamworth Low Level a			19 41															20 41						
Nuneaton a			19 57															20 57						
Rugby 66 a			20 13															21 13						
Milton Keynes Central 66 a		19 48	21 07		20 03		20 59									20 46		22 10						
Watford Junction 66 a			21 35															22 52						
London Euston [15] ⊖66 a		20 27	21 55		20 46	20 48	21 48				21 04	21 10	21 22			21 31		23 15						

A [buffet] from Birmingham New St. [trolley] to Birmingham New St.

OVERNIGHT SLEEPERS. For sleeper trains, operated by First ScotRail, please see Tables 400 - 404.

For complete service between Manchester and Preston, Blackpool and between Barrow-in-furness and Lancaster, please see Table 82.

For complete service between Crewe and Liverpool Lime Street, see Table 91

For complete service between Crewe/Stoke-on-Trent & Manchester see Table 84

For complete service between Crewe and Holyhead please see Table 81.

For complete service between Coventry-Birmingham-Wolverhampton-Stafford please see Table 68

For complete service between Windermere and Oxenholme Lake District, please see Table 83

Table 65R

Sundays

30 March to 11 May

Scotland and North West England - West Midlands and London

Route Diagram - refer to first Page of Table 65

	VT	VT	XC	VT	LM		VT	TP	VT	LM	VT	VT	VT		XC		VT	TP	VT	LM	SR	SR	SR	XC
																					B	B	B	
	◇1	◇1	◇1	◇	1		◇1	◇1	◇1	1	◇1	◇1	◇1		◇1		◇1	◇1	◇1	1				◇1
																					🛏	🛏	🛏	
	☕	☕		☕			☕	🍴	☕		☕	☕	☕				☕	🍴	☕		✕	✕	✕	
																						A		
Inverness 229 d																						20 26		
Aberdeen 229 d																							21 43	
Dundee 229 d																							23u06	
Perth 229 d																						23u06		
Edinburgh 10 225,226,228,230,242 d								18 10									18 51	19 57			23c21			
Haymarket 225,226,228,230,242 d								18u14									18 56	20u01						
Glasgow Central 15 226,216 d							17 36						18 30						20 08		21 46			
Motherwell 226 d																					22u07			
Carstairs 226 d																					22u24			
Lockerbie d							18 32	19 08											21 03					
Carlisle 8 216 a							18 50	19 29					19 43				20 05	21 13	21 21					
d							18 52	19 30					19 44				20 07	21 14	21 24					
Penrith North Lakes d							19 06	19 45									20 22		21 39					
Windermere 83 d																								
Oxenholme Lake District a							19 28	20 09					20 19					21 51	22 02					
d							19 29	20 10					20 19					21 51	22 03					
Barrow-in-Furness 82 d																								
Lancaster 6 a							19 43	20 24					20 34				20 56	22 06	22 17					
d							19 44	20 25					20 34				20 57	22 06	22 18					
Blackpool North 97 d																								
Preston 8 90 a							20 02	20 43					20 52				21 15	22 25	22 35					
Preston 8 90 d							20 04	20 46					20 55				21 17	22 26	22 38					
Wigan North Western 90 a							20 15						21 06				21 28	22 39	22 48					
d							20 15						21 07				21 29	22 39	22 50					
Bolton 82 a																								
Manchester Picc. 10 82 a								21 25										23 08						
Manchester Airport ✈ a								21 45										23 24						
Liverpool Lime Street 10 91 a																								
d		19 47								20 34		20 47								21 34				
Liverpool South Parkway 91 ✈ d										20 44										21 44				
Runcorn 91 d		20 03								20 52		21 03								21 52				
Warrington Bank Quay a							20 26						21 18				21 39		22 59					
d							20 26						21 18				21 39		23 01					
Manchester Picc. 10 84 d	19 35		20 07						20 21		20 55				21 07									22 07
Stockport 84 d	19 41		20 16						20 27		21 03				21 16									22 16
Wilmslow 84 d																								
Holyhead 81 ⛴ d																								
Bangor (Gwynedd) 81 d																								
Llandudno Junction 81 d																								
Wrexham General 75 d																								
Chester 81 d				20 37																				
Crewe 10 a		20 22		20 56			20 45			21 16		21 21	21 38				21 59		23 22	22 18				
d		20 24			20 44		20 47			21 18		21 23	21 40				22 01			22 22				
Macclesfield d	19 54		20 29						20 40		21 15				21 29									22 29
Stoke-on-Trent d	20 11		20 47		21 06				20 57		21 33				21 47									22 47
Stafford a		20 42	21 08		21 25					21 39		21 42	22 01		22 06					22 42				23 04
d		20 43	21 09		21 25					21 39		21 44	22 02		22 06					22 43				23 05
Penkridge a										21 45										22 48				
Wolverhampton 7 a			21 21							21 55			22 17		22 20		22 34			22 59				23 18
Birmingham New St. 12 68 a			21 39							22 17			22 38		22 40		22 55			23 16				23 36
Birmingham International 68 ✈ a																								
Coventry 68 a																								
Lichfield Trent Valley a					21 41							21 59												
Tamworth Low Level a					21 48							22 06												
Nuneaton a					22 04							22 17												
Rugby 66 a					22 20							22 31												
Milton Keynes Central 66 a		21 36					21 52		22 03		22 46	23 04												
Watford Junction 66 a							22s31				23s28	23s34												
London Euston 15 ⊖66 a	21 58	22 28					22 55		22 57		23 49	23 54									07 06	08 57	08 57	

A also conveys through sleepers from Fort William. Dep 1900 (Table 404) ccalls after Carstairs

c calls after Carstairs

OVERNIGHT SLEEPERS. For sleeper trains, operated by First ScotRail, please see Tables 400 - 404.

For complete service between Manchester and Preston, Blackpool and between Barrow-in-furness and Lancaster, please see Table 82.

For complete service between Crewe and Liverpool Lime Street, see Table 91

For complete service between Crewe/Stoke-on-Trent & Manchester see Table 84

For complete service between Crewe and Holyhead please see Table 81.

For complete service between Coventry-Birmingham-Wolverhampton-Stafford please see Table 68

For complete service between Windermere and Oxenholme Lake District, please see Table 83

Table 66

Mondays to Fridays

9 December to 16 May

London - Watford Junction, Milton Keynes Central, Northampton and West Midlands

Network Diagram - see first Page of Table 59

Miles	Miles	Miles		LM MX [1] A	LM MO [1] A	VT MO ◇[1] A ☕	LM MX [1] A	VT MX ◇[1] A ☕	LM MX [1] A	LM MO [1] A	LM [1]	LM MO [1]		LM MX [1]	LM [1]	LM [1]	SN [1]	VT ◇[1] B ⊠	VT ◇[1] C ⊠	VT ◇[1] ⊠	LM [1]	VT ◇[1] D ⊠		SN [1] E
0	0	—	**London Euston** [15] ⊖60 d								00 04	00 34		00 34	01 34			05 27	05 39	06 20	05 32	06 16		
—	—	0	East Croydon 176 ⛴ d																					
—	—	7¾	Clapham Junction 176 d														05 01							05 30
—	—	8¾	Imperial Wharf 176 d														05 05							05 39
—	—	9¼	West Brompton ⊖176 d														05 08							05 41
—	—	11¼	Kensington (Olympia) ⊖176 d														05 12							05 44
—	—	12½	Shepherd's Bush ⊖176 d														05 15							05 47
8	—	16¾	Wembley Central ⊖60,176 d									00 43		00 45	01 45									06 03
11½	—	—	Harrow & Wealdstone ⊖60 d								00 16	00 48		00 50	01 50		05 33				05 44			06 08
16	—	—	Bushey 60 d									00s53		00 55										
17½	17½	—	**Watford Junction** 60 a								00 22	00 57		00 57	01 56		05 40				05 52			06 15
—	—	—	d								00 23	00 58		00 58	01 57			05u47	06u02	06u34	05 53			06 15
21	—	—	Kings Langley d									01 02		01 02							05 57			
23	—	—	Apsley d						00 02	00 03		01 06		01 06							06 01			
24½	—	—	Hemel Hempstead d						00 05	00 06	00 30	01 09		01 09	02 04						06 04			06 23
28	—	—	Berkhamsted d						00 09	00 11	00 35	01 14		01 14	02 09						06 09			06 27
31¾	—	—	Tring d						00 15	00 15	00 41	01 18		01 18	02 13						06 14			06 33
36	—	—	Cheddington d						00 20	00 21		01 24		01 24							06 20			
40¼	—	—	Leighton Buzzard d				00 05		00 26	00 27	00 50	01 30		01 30	02 22						06 24			06 42
46¾	—	—	Bletchley d				00 13		00 33	00 34	00 57	01 37		01 37	02 29						06 31			06 49
49¾	49¾	—	**Milton Keynes Central** [10] a				00 21		00 41	00 42	01 05	01 45		01 45	02 37			06 11	06 22		06 36	06 46		06 56
—	—	—	d		00 05	00 12	00 21	00 28		00 43	01 05	01 46		01 46		05 37		06 12	06 22		06 37			
52½	52½	—	Wolverton d	00 01	00 08		00 25			00 46	01 09	01 49		01 49		05 40					06 40			
65¾	—	—	**Northampton** 68 a	00 15	00 22		00 38			01 00	01 23	02 03		02 03		05 53					06 53			
—	—	—	d													05 55					06 55			
75¼	—	—	Long Buckby 68 a													06 06					07 06			
84½	82½	—	**Rugby** 68 a			00s46		01 00								06 17			06 44	07 12	07 17			
—	—	—	Nuneaton 65 a															06 40						
96	—	—	Coventry 68 a			00s58		01 13								06 29				07 22	07 29			
106¾	—	—	Birmingham International 68 ✈ a			01s09		01 24								06 45				07 33	07 45			
115¼	—	—	**Birmingham New Street** [12] 68 a			01s22		01 36								07 01				07 45	08 03			
120½	—	—	Sandwell & Dudley 68 a																					
128	—	—	Wolverhampton [7] 68 ⛴ a			01 44		02 07																

	LM [1]	SN [1]	VT ◇[1] F ⊠	VT ◇[1] ⊠	LM [1] G	VT ◇[1] D ⊠	LM [1]	SN [1]		VT ◇[1] H ⊠	LM [1]	VT ◇[1] D ⊠	LM [1]	SN [1]	LM [1]	VT ◇[1] ⊠	VT ◇[1] D ⊠	VT ◇[1] C ⊠		LM [1] G	LM [1]	LM [1]	VT ◇[1] ⊠	LM [1]
London Euston [15] ⊖60 d	06 04		06 43	07 03	06 24	06 55	06 34			07 10	06 53	07 20	07 13		07 04	07 23	07 35	07 43		07 46	07 24	07 34	08 03	07 49
East Croydon 176 ⛴ d																								
Clapham Junction 176 d		05 55						06 20						06 38										
Imperial Wharf 176 d		06 00						06 24						06 42										
West Brompton ⊖176 d		06 03						06 27						06 45										
Kensington (Olympia) ⊖176 d		06 07						06 30						06 49										
Shepherd's Bush ⊖176 d		06 10						06 33						06 52										
Wembley Central ⊖60,176 d		06 25						06 49						07 07										
Harrow & Wealdstone ⊖60 d	06 17	06 30					06 47							07 12	07 17							07 46		
Bushey 60 d																								
Watford Junction 60 a	06 24	06 37			06 41		06 53	06 59			07 08			07 19	07 24						07 42	07 52		08 03
d	06 24				06 42		06 54				07 10			07 20	07 25	07u37					07 42	07 53		08 03
Kings Langley d	06 29						06 58								07 29							07 58		
Apsley d	06 33						07 02								07 33							08 01		
Hemel Hempstead d	06 35				06 49		07 05				07 17			07 27	07 36						07 50	08 04		
Berkhamsted d	06 40				06 54		07 10				07 22			07 32	07 40						07 54	08 09		
Tring d	06a47				06 59		07 15							07 39	07a48						08 00	08a16		
Cheddington d					07 05		07 20														08 05			
Leighton Buzzard d					07 10		07 25				07 35		07 42	07 50							08 10			
Bletchley d					07 17		07 32				07 43		07 50	07 57							08 17			
Milton Keynes Central [10] a			07 13		07 22	07 25	07 37			07 40	07 48	07 50	07 54	08 03			08 05	08 13		08 18	08 22			08 25
d			07 13		07 22		07 37						07 54					08 13		08 19				08 26
Wolverton d					07 26		07 41						07 58											
Northampton 68 a					07 38		07 53						08 11											08 41
d					07 43		07 55						08 13											08 55
Long Buckby 68 a							08 06						08 24											09 06
Rugby 68 a				07 51	08 02		08 17						08 35							08 41			08 51	09 17
Nuneaton 65 a					08 15															08 53				
Coventry 68 a			07 42	08 02			08 28						08 46			08 22		08 42					09 02	09 29
Birmingham International 68 ✈ a			07 53	08 13			08 44						09 05			08 33		08 53					09 13	09 45
Birmingham New Street [12] 68 a			08 08	08 27			09 01						09 17			08 45		09 08					09 27	10 01
Sandwell & Dudley 68 a			08 24															09 24						
Wolverhampton [7] 68 ⛴ a			08 37															09 37						

A From London Euston
B To Liverpool Lime Street
C To Glasgow Central
D To Manchester Piccadilly
E From Balham
F To Edinburgh
G To Crewe
H To Chester

Table 66

Mondays to Fridays

9 December to 16 May

London - Watford Junction, Milton Keynes Central, Northampton and West Midlands

Network Diagram - see first Page of Table 59

		VT	VT	LM	VT		LM	SN	LM	VT	VT	LM	LM	LM	SN		VT	LM	VT	LM	VT	LM	SN	LM	VT
		◇1	◇1	1	◇1		1	1	1	◇1	◇1	1	1	1	1		◇1	1	◇1	1	◇1	1	1	1	◇1
		A	B		C						D	E			F				G		C				
		⊠	⊠		⊠					⊠	☕						⊠		⊠		⊠				⊠
London Euston [15] ⊖60	d	08 07	08 10	07 54	08 20		08 13		08 07	08 23	08 43	08 46	08 24	08 34			09 03	08 49	09 10	08 54	09 20	09 13		09 05	09 23
East Croydon 176 🚌	d														07 50								08 07		
Clapham Junction 176	d							07 39							08 19								08 39		
Imperial Wharf 176	d							07 44							08 24								08 44		
West Brompton ⊖176	d							07 47							08 27								08 47		
Kensington (Olympia) ⊖176	d							07 50							08 31								08 50		
Shepherd's Bush ⊖176	d							07 53							08 34								08 53		
Wembley Central ⊖60,176	d							08 09							08 50								09 09		
Harrow & Wealdstone ⊖60	d							08 14	08 22				08 36	08 46	08 56								09 14	09 18	
Bushey 60	d								08 27					08 51										09 23	
Watford Junction 60	a			08 11				08 21	08 30				08 43	08 54	09 03			09 03		09 11			09 21	09 26	
	d			08 12				08 21	08 30	08u37			08 44	08 55				09 03		09 11			09 21	09 27	09u37
Kings Langley	d								08 35					08 59										09 31	
Apsley	d								08 39					09 03										09 35	
Hemel Hempstead	d			08 19				08 29	08 41				08 51	09 06						09 18			09 29	09 38	
Berkhamsted	d			08 24				08 33	08 46				08 56	09 10						09 23			09 33	09 42	
Tring	d							08 39	08a53				09 02	09a17									09 39	09a49	
Cheddington	d												09 07												
Leighton Buzzard	d			08 37			08 42	08 48					09 12							09 36		09 42	09 48		
Bletchley	d			08 44			08 50	08 55					09 20							09 43		09 50	09 55		
Milton Keynes Central [10]	a	08 37	08 42	08 49	08 50		08 54	09 01			09 13	09 18	09 26					09 25	09 40	09 48	09 50	09 54	10 01		
	d			08 50			08 54				09 13	09 19						09 26		09 49		09 54			
Wolverton	d			08 53			08 58													09 52		09 58			
Northampton 68	a			09 07			09 10											09 41		10 05		10 11			
	d			09 16														09 55				10 16			
Long Buckby 68	a			09 27														10 06				10 27			
Rugby 68	a			09 38								09 41					09 51	10 17				10 38			
Nuneaton 65	a											09 53													
Coventry 68	a			09 49						09 22	09 42						10 02	10 29				10 49			10 22
Birmingham International 68 ✈	a			10 04						09 33	09 53						10 13	10 45				11 04			10 33
Birmingham New Street [12] 68	a			10 17						09 45	10 08						10 27	11 01				11 17			10 45
Sandwell & Dudley 68	a										10 24														
Wolverhampton [7] 68 🚌	a										10 37														

			VT	LM	LM	LM	VT	LM	VT	LM	VT		LM	SN	LM	VT	VT	LM	LM	LM	VT		LM	VT	LM
			◇1	1	1	1	◇1	1	◇1	1	◇1		1	1	1	◇1	◇1	1	1	1	◇1		1	◇1	1
			H	E					I		C						D	E						I	
			☕				⊠		⊠		⊠					⊠	☕				☕			☕	
London Euston [15] ⊖60	d		09 43	09 46	09 24	09 34	10 03	09 49	10 10	09 54	10 20		10 13		10 05	10 23	10 43	10 46	10 24	10 34	11 03		10 49	11 10	10 54
East Croydon 176 🚌	d													09 08											
Clapham Junction 176	d													09 39											
Imperial Wharf 176	d													09 44											
West Brompton ⊖176	d													09 47											
Kensington (Olympia) ⊖176	d													09 50											
Shepherd's Bush ⊖176	d													09 53											
Wembley Central ⊖60,176	d													10 09											
Harrow & Wealdstone ⊖60	d					09 46								10 14	10 18					10 46					
Bushey 60	d					09 51									10 23					10 51					
Watford Junction 60	a				09 39	09 54		10 03		10 09				10 21	10 26				10 40	10 54			11 03		11 10
	d				09 41	09 55		10 03		10 11				10 21	10 26	10u37			10 41	10 55			11 03		11 11
Kings Langley	d					09 59									10 31					10 59					
Apsley	d					10 03									10 35					11 03					
Hemel Hempstead	d				09 48	10 06				10 18				10 29	10 37				10 48	11 06					11 18
Berkhamsted	d				09 53	10 11				10 23				10 33	10 42				10 53	11 11					11 23
Tring	d				09 59	10a17								10 39	10a49				11 00	11a17					
Cheddington	d				10 04														11 05						
Leighton Buzzard	d				10 09					10 36			10 42	10 48					11 10						11 36
Bletchley	d				10 16					10 43			10 50	10 55					11 17						11 43
Milton Keynes Central [10]	a		10 13	10 18	10 21			10 25	10 40	10 48	10 50		10 54	11 01			11 13	11 18	11 23				11 25	11 40	11 48
	d		10 13	10 19				10 26		10 49			10 54				11 13	11 19					11 26		11 49
Wolverton	d									10 52			10 58												11 52
Northampton 68	a							10 41		11 08			11 12										11 41		12 06
	d							10 55					11 16										11 55		
Long Buckby 68	a							11 06					11 27										12 06		
Rugby 68	a			10 41			10 51	11 17					11 38					11 41			11 51		12 17		
Nuneaton 65	a			10 53														11 53							
Coventry 68	a		10 42				11 02	11 29					11 49			11 22	11 42				12 02		12 29		
Birmingham International 68 ✈	a		10 53				11 13	11 45					12 04			11 33	11 53				12 13		12 45		
Birmingham New Street [12] 68	a		11 10				11 28	12 01					12 17			11 45	12 08				12 27		13 01		
Sandwell & Dudley 68	a		11 24														12 24								
Wolverhampton [7] 68 🚌	a		11 37														12 37								

A To Liverpool Lime Street
B To Bangor (Gwynedd)
C To Manchester Piccadilly
D To Edinburgh
E To Crewe
F From Coulsdon Town
G To Holyhead
H To Glasgow Central
I To Chester

Table 66

Mondays to Fridays

9 December to 16 May

London - Watford Junction, Milton Keynes Central, Northampton and West Midlands

Network Diagram - see first Page of Table 59

		VT	LM	SN	LM	VT	VT	LM	LM	LM	VT	LM	VT	LM	VT	LM	SN	LM	VT	VT	LM	LM	LM
		◇1	1	1	1	◇1	◇1	1	1	1	◇1	1	◇1	1	◇1	1	1	1	◇1	◇1	1	1	1
		A		B			C	D					E		A		B			F	D		
		☕				☕	☕				☕		☕		☕				☕	☕			
London Euston 15 ⊖60	d	11 20	11 13		11 05	11 23	11 43	11 46	11 24	11 34	12 03	11 49	12 10	11 54	12 20	12 13		12 05	12 23	12 43	12 46	12 24	12 34
East Croydon 176 ⛴	d			10 10													11 11						
Clapham Junction 176	d			10 39													11 39						
Imperial Wharf 176	d			10 44													11 44						
West Brompton ⊖176	d			10 47													11 47						
Kensington (Olympia) ⊖176	d			10 50													11 50						
Shepherd's Bush ⊖176	d			10 53													11 53						
Wembley Central ⊖60,176	d			11 09													12 09						
Harrow & Wealdstone ⊖60	d			11 14	11 18					11 46							12 14	12 18					12 46
Bushey 60	d				11 23					11 51								12 23					12 51
Watford Junction 60	a			11 21	11 26				11 40	11 54		12 03		12 09			12 21	12 26				12 40	12 54
	d			11 21	11 27	11u37			11 41	11 55		12 03		12 11			12 21	12 27	12u37			12 41	12 55
Kings Langley	d				11 31					11 59								12 31					12 59
Apsley	d				11 35					12 03								12 35					13 03
Hemel Hempstead	d			11 29	11 38				11 48	12 06				12 18			12 29	12 38				12 48	13 06
Berkhamsted	d			11 33	11 42				11 54	12 11				12 23			12 33	12 43				12 53	13 11
Tring	d			11 39	11a49				12 00	12a17							12 39	12a49				12 59	13a17
Cheddington	d								12 05													13 04	
Leighton Buzzard	d		11 42	11 48					12 10					12 36		12 42	12 48					13 09	
Bletchley	d		11 50	11 55					12 17					12 43		12 50	12 55					13 16	
Milton Keynes Central 10	a	11 50	11 54	12 01			12 13	12 18	12 23			12 25	12 40	12 48	12 50	12 54	13 01			13 13	13 18	13 21	
	d		11 54				12 13	12 19				12 27		12 49		12 54				13 13	13 19		
Wolverton	d		11 58											12 52		12 58							
Northampton 68	a		12 11									12 42		13 05		13 11							
	d		12 16									12 55				13 16							
Long Buckby 68	a		12 27									13 06				13 27							
Rugby 68	a		12 38					12 41			12 51	13 17				13 38					13 41		
Nuneaton 65	a							12 53													13 53		
Coventry 68	a		12 49			12 22	12 42				13 02	13 29				13 49			13 24	13 42			
Birmingham International 68 ✈	a		13 04			12 33	12 53				13 13	13 46				14 04			13 33	13 53			
Birmingham New Street 12 68	a		13 17			12 45	13 08				13 27	14 02				14 17			13 45	14 08			
Sandwell & Dudley 68	a						13 24													14 24			
Wolverhampton 7 68 ⛴	a						13 37													14 37			

		VT	LM	VT	LM	VT	LM	SN	LM	VT	VT	LM	LM	LM	VT	LM	VT	LM	VT	LM	SN	LM
		◇1	1	◇1	1	◇1	1	1	1	◇1	◇1	1	1	1	◇1	1	◇1	1	◇1	1	1	1
				E		A		B			C	D					E		A		B	
		☕		☕		☕				☕	☕				☕		☕		☕			
London Euston 15 ⊖60	d	13 03	12 49	13 10	12 54	13 20	13 13		13 05	13 23	13 43	13 46	13 24	13 34	14 03	13 49	14 10	13 54	14 20	14 13		14 05
East Croydon 176 ⛴	d							12 10													13 10	
Clapham Junction 176	d							12 39													13 39	
Imperial Wharf 176	d							12 44													13 44	
West Brompton ⊖176	d							12 47													13 47	
Kensington (Olympia) ⊖176	d							12 50													13 50	
Shepherd's Bush ⊖176	d							12 53													13 53	
Wembley Central ⊖60,176	d							13 09													14 09	
Harrow & Wealdstone ⊖60	d							13 14	13 18					13 46							14 14	14 18
Bushey 60	d								13 23					13 51								14 23
Watford Junction 60	a		13 03		13 09			13 21	13 26				13 43	13 54		14 03		14 10			14 21	14 26
	d		13 03		13 11			13 21	13 27	13u37			13 44	13 55		14 03		14 11			14 21	14 27
Kings Langley	d								13 31					13 59								14 31
Apsley	d								13 35					14 03								14 35
Hemel Hempstead	d				13 18			13 29	13 38				13 51	14 06				14 18			14 29	14 38
Berkhamsted	d				13 23			13 33	13 42				13 56	14 11				14 23			14 33	14 42
Tring	d							13 39	13a49				14 01	14a17							14 39	14a49
Cheddington	d												14 06									
Leighton Buzzard	d				13 36		13 42	13 48					14 11					14 36		14 42	14 48	
Bletchley	d				13 43		13 50	13 55					14 18					14 43		14 50	14 55	
Milton Keynes Central 10	a		13 25	13 40	13 48	13 50	13 54	14 01			14 13	14 18	14 23			14 25	14 40	14 48	14 50	14 54	15 01	
	d		13 26		13 49		13 54				14 13	14 19				14 26		14 49		14 54		
Wolverton	d				13 52		13 58											14 52		14 58		
Northampton 68	a		13 41		14 05		14 11									14 41		15 05		15 10		
	d		13 55				14 16									14 55				15 16		
Long Buckby 68	a		14 06				14 27									15 06				15 27		
Rugby 68	a	13 51	14 17				14 38					14 41			14 51	15 17				15 38		
Nuneaton 65	a											14 53										
Coventry 68	a	14 02	14 29				14 49			14 22	14 42				15 02	15 29				15 49		
Birmingham International 68 ✈	a	14 13	14 45				15 04			14 33	14 53				15 13	15 45				16 04		
Birmingham New Street 12 68	a	14 27	15 01				15 16			14 45	15 08				15 27	16 01				16 17		
Sandwell & Dudley 68	a										15 24											
Wolverhampton 7 68 ⛴	a										15 37											

A To Manchester Piccadilly
B From South Croydon
C To Glasgow Central
D To Crewe
E To Chester
F To Edinburgh

Table 66

Mondays to Fridays

9 December to 16 May

London - Watford Junction, Milton Keynes Central, Northampton and West Midlands

Network Diagram - see first Page of Table 59

		VT	VT	LM	LM	LM	VT	LM	VT	LM	VT	LM	SN	LM	VT	VT	LM	LM	LM	VT	LM	VT	LM
		◇1	R 1	1	1	1	◇1	1	◇1	1	◇1	1	1	1	◇1	R 1	1	1	1	◇1	1	◇1	1
			A	B					C		D		E			F	B					G	
		☕	⊠				☕		☕		☕				☕	⊠				☕		☕	
London Euston [15] ⊖60	d	14 23	14 43	14 46	14 24	14 34	15 03	14 49	15 10	14 54	15 20	15 13		15 05	15 23	15 43	15 46	15 24	15 34	16 03	15 49	16 33	15 54
East Croydon 176 🚌	d												14 10										
Clapham Junction 176	d												14 39										
Imperial Wharf 176	d												14 44										
West Brompton ⊖176	d												14 47										
Kensington (Olympia) ⊖176	d												14 50										
Shepherd's Bush ⊖176	d												14 53										
Wembley Central ⊖60,176	d												15 09										
Harrow & Wealdstone ⊖60	d					14 46							15 14	15 18					15 46				
Bushey 60	d					14 51								15 23					15 51				
Watford Junction 60	a				14 40	14 54		15 03		15 09			15 21	15 26				15 40	15 54		16 03		16 09
	d	14u37			14 41	14 55		15 03		15 11			15 21	15 27	15u37			15 41	15 55		16 03		16 11
Kings Langley	d					14 59								15 31					15 59				
Apsley	d					15 03								15 35					16 03				
Hemel Hempstead	d				14 48	15 06				15 18			15 29	15 38				15 48	16 06				16 18
Berkhamsted	d				14 53	15 11				15 23			15 33	15 42				15 53	16 11				16 23
Tring	d				14 59	15a17							15 39	15a49				15 59	16a17				
Cheddington	d				15 04													16 04					
Leighton Buzzard	d				15 09					15 36		15 42	15 48					16 09					16 36
Bletchley	d				15 16					15 43		15 50	15 55					16 16					16 43
Milton Keynes Central [10]	a		15 13	15 18	15 22			15 25	15 40	15 48	15 50	15 54	16 01			16 13	16 18	16 23			16 25		16 48
	d		15 13	15 19				15 26		15 49		15 54				16 13	16 19				16 26		16 49
Wolverton	d									15 52		15 58											16 52
Northampton 68	a							15 41		16 05		16 11									16 41		17 05
	d							15 55				16 16									16 55		17 16
Long Buckby 68	a							16 06				16 27									17 06		17 27
Rugby 68	a			15 41			15 51	16 17				16 38					16 41			16 51	17 17	17 21	17 38
Nuneaton 65	a			15 53													16 53						
Coventry 68	a	15 22	15 42				16 02	16 29				16 49			16 21	16 42				17 02	17 29		17 49
Birmingham International 68 ✈	a	15 33	15 53				16 13	16 45				17 04			16 33	16 53				17 13	17 45		18 04
Birmingham New Street [12] 68	a	15 45	16 08				16 27	17 01				17 16			16 46	17 08				17 27	18 01		18 17
Sandwell & Dudley 68	a		16 24													17 24							
Wolverhampton [7] 68 🚌	a		16 37													17 37							

		VT	LM	SN	LM	VT	VT	LM	LM	LM	VT	LM	LM	VT	VT	LM	SN	LM	LM	VT	VT	VT
		◇1	1	1	1	◇1	◇1	1	1	1	◇1	1	1	◇1	◇1	1	1	1	1	◇1	◇1	◇1
		D		E			A	B						C	H		E				F	
		☕				☕	⊠				⊠			⊠	⊠					⊠	☕	⊠
London Euston [15] ⊖60	d	16 20	16 13		16 05	16 23	16 43	16 46	16 24	16 34	17 03	16 50	16 54	17 10	17 33	17 13		17 05	17 12	17 23	17 43	18 03
East Croydon 176 🚌	d			15 10													16 10					
Clapham Junction 176	d			15 39													16 39					
Imperial Wharf 176	d			15 44													16 44					
West Brompton ⊖176	d			15 47													16 47					
Kensington (Olympia) ⊖176	d			15 50													16 50					
Shepherd's Bush ⊖176	d			15 53													16 53					
Wembley Central ⊖60,176	d			16 09													17 09					
Harrow & Wealdstone ⊖60	d			16 14	16 18					16 46			17 06				17 14	17 19	17 25			
Bushey 60	d				16 23					16 51			17 11						17 30			
Watford Junction 60	a			16 21	16 26				16 46	16 54			17 14				17 21	17 26	17 33			
	d			16 21	16 26	16u37			16 47	16 55			17 14				17 21	17 27	17 33	17u37		
Kings Langley	d				16 31					16 59								17 31	17 38			
Apsley	d				16 35					17 03			17 20						17 41			
Hemel Hempstead	d			16 29	16 37				16 54	17 06			17 23				17 29	17 36				
Berkhamsted	d			16 33	16 42				16 59	17 11			17 28				17 33	17 41				
Tring	d			16 39	16a50				17 06	17a19			17a36				17 39	17 46	17a52			
Cheddington	d								17 11									17 51				
Leighton Buzzard	d		16 43	16 48					17 16			17 20				17 42	17 48					
Bletchley	d		16 50	16 55					17 23			17 27					17 55	18 01				
Milton Keynes Central [10]	a	16 50	16 55	17 01			17 13	17 18	17 30			17 32				17 51	18 01	18 06				
	d		16 55				17 13	17 19				17 32		17u41		17 52					18u13	
Wolverton	d		16 59									17 36				17 56						
Northampton 68	a		17 13									17 48				18 11						
	d											17 55				18 20						
Long Buckby 68	a											18 06				18 31						
Rugby 68	a							17 41			17 51	18 17			18 21	18 42						18 52
Nuneaton 65	a							17 59						18 11								
Coventry 68	a					17 22	17 42				18 02	18 30				18 53				18 22	18 42	19 03
Birmingham International 68 ✈	a					17 33	17 53				18 13	18 46				19 08				18 33	18 53	19 14
Birmingham New Street [12] 68	a					17 45	18 08				18 27	19 01				19 21				18 45	19 08	19 27
Sandwell & Dudley 68	a						18 24														19 24	
Wolverhampton [7] 68 🚌	a						18 37														19 37	20 13

A To Edinburgh
B To Crewe
C To Chester
D To Manchester Piccadilly
E From South Croydon
F To Glasgow Central
G To Preston
H To Liverpool Lime Street

Table 66

Mondays to Fridays

9 December to 16 May

London - Watford Junction, Milton Keynes Central, Northampton and West Midlands

Network Diagram - see first Page of Table 59

		VT	LM	LM	LM	LM	LM	VT	LM	VT	LM	SN	LM	LM	VT	LM	LM	LM	LM	LM	VT	VT	VT
																					R	R	R
		◇1	1	1	1	1	1	◇1	1	◇1	1	1	1	1	◇1	1	1	1	1	1	1	1	1
			A					B		C		D	A		A							E	F
		⊠						⊠		⊠					⊠						☕	☕	☕
London Euston 15 ⊖60	d	18 23	17 24	17 30	17 34	17 41	17 46	18 10	17 51	18 33	18 13		18 05	18 12	18 43	18 21	18 29	18 34	18 40	18 49	19 03	19 10	19 20
East Croydon 176	d											17 10											
Clapham Junction 176	d											17 39											
Imperial Wharf 176	d											17 44											
West Brompton ⊖176	d											17 47											
Kensington (Olympia) ⊖176	d											17 50											
Shepherd's Bush ⊖176	d											17 53											
Wembley Central ⊖60,176	d											18 09											
Harrow & Wealdstone ⊖60	d				17 46				18 03			18 14	18 19			18 34		18 46					
Bushey 60	d				17 52	17 56								18 28				18 52	18 57				
Watford Junction 60	a		17 43	17 48	17 55	18 00			18 09			18 21	18 26	18 31		18 40	18 46	18 54	19 00				
	d	18u37	17 44	17 49		18 01			18 11			18 21	18 26	18 32		18 41	18 47	18 56	19 01				
Kings Langley	d					18 05							18 31			18 46			19 05				
Apsley	d			17 55									18 35				18 53		19 09				
Hemel Hempstead	d		17 51	17 58		18 10			18 18			18 29		18 40		18 51		19 03	19 12				
Berkhamsted	d		17 57			18 15			18 23			18 33		18 45			18 59		19 16				
Tring	d			18 05		18a22						18 39	18 44	18a54		18 59		19 12	19a26				
Cheddington	d			18 10									18 49				19 08	19 17					
Leighton Buzzard	d		18 09				18 19				18 42	18 48	18 54			19 07		19 24		19 20			
Bletchley	d		18 16	18 22					18 41			18 55	19 01				19 18	19a32		19 26			
Milton Keynes Central 10	a		18 21	18 28			18 31		18 45		18 52	19 00	19 06		19 13	19 19	19 23			19 31		19 40	19 50
	d		18 21				18 31	18u41	18 46		18 54		19 07		19 13		19 23			19 32			
Wolverton	d		18 25				18 35		18 49		18 57		19 11				19 27			19 36			
Northampton 68	a		18 37				18 48		19 03		19 11		19 23				19 39			19 50			
	d		18 46				18 57				19 20		19 45							19 55			
Long Buckby 68	a		18 57				19 08				19 31									20 06			
Rugby 68	a		19 08				19 19			19 22	19 42		20 04							20 17	19 51		
Nuneaton 65	a		19 23					19 12					20 16										
Coventry 68	a	19 22					19 31				19 53				19 42					20 29	20 02		
Birmingham International 68 ✈	a	19 33					19 47				20 08				19 53					20 45	20 13		
Birmingham New Street 12 68	a	19 45					20 03				20 21				20 08					21 01	20 27		
Sandwell & Dudley 68	a	19 58													20 24								
Wolverhampton 7 68	a	20 11													20 37								

		LM	LM	SN	LM	VT	VT	VT	LM	LM	VT	LM	VT	LM	LM	SN	LM	VT	VT	VT	LM	LM	LM
						R	R																
		1	1	1	1	1	1	◇1	1	1	◇1	1	◇1	1	1	1	1	◇1	◇1	◇1	1	1	1
						C		G					E		A			C					H
						☕	☕	☕			☕		☕					☕	☕	☕			
London Euston 15 ⊖60	d	18 52	19 13		19 05	19 07	19 23	19 43	19 24	19 34	20 03	19 46	20 10	19 54	20 13		20 05	20 07	20 23	20 43	20 24	20 34	20 46
East Croydon 176	d			18 10												19 10							
Clapham Junction 176	d			18 39												19 39							
Imperial Wharf 176	d			18 44												19 44							
West Brompton ⊖176	d			18 47												19 47							
Kensington (Olympia) ⊖176	d			18 50												19 50							
Shepherd's Bush ⊖176	d			18 53												19 53							
Wembley Central ⊖60,176	d			19 09												20 09							
Harrow & Wealdstone ⊖60	d	19 04		19 14	19 18					19 46						20 14	20 18					20 46	
Bushey 60	d				19 23					19 51							20 23					20 51	
Watford Junction 60	a	19 11		19 21	19 26				19 40	19 54				20 09		20 21	20 27				20 42	20 54	
	d	19 11		19 21	19 27		19u37		19 43	19 55				20 11		20 21	20 27		20u37		20 43	20 55	
Kings Langley	d				19 31					19 59							20 31					20 59	
Apsley	d				19 35					20 03							20 35					21 03	
Hemel Hempstead	d	19 19		19 29	19 38				19 50	20 06				20 18		20 29	20 38				20 51	21 06	
Berkhamsted	d	19 23		19 33	19 43				19 55	20 11				20 23		20 33	20 42				20 57	21 11	
Tring	d	19 29		19 39	19a50				20 02	20a17						20 39	20a50				21 02	21a19	
Cheddington	d								20 07												21 07		
Leighton Buzzard	d	19 37	19 42	19 48					20 12			20 18		20 36	20 42	20 48					21 12		21 18
Bletchley	d	19 45		19 55					20 19					20 43	20 50	20 55					21 18		
Milton Keynes Central 10	a	19 51	19 55	20 01				20 13	20 24			20 28	20 40	20 48	20 54	21 01				21 13	21 23		21 27
	d		19 56					20 13				20 29		20 49	20 55					21 13			21 29
Wolverton	d		19 59									20 33		20 52	20 59								21 32
Northampton 68	a		20 11									20 46		21 06	21 13								21 46
	d		20 20									20 55		21 16	21 26								21 55
Long Buckby 68	a		20 31									21 06		21 27									↦
Rugby 68	a		20 42								20 51	21 17		21 38	21 45								
Nuneaton 65	a					20 02									21 57			21 02					
Coventry 68	a		20 53				20 22	20 42			21 02	21 30		21 49					21 24	21 42			
Birmingham International 68 ✈	a		21 08				20 33	20 53			21 13	21 46		22 04					21 34	21 53			
Birmingham New Street 12 68	a		21 20				20 45	21 08			21 27	22 02		22 17					21 46	22 04			
Sandwell & Dudley 68	a						20 58	21 24											21 59	22 15			
Wolverhampton 7 68	a						21 12	21 37			21 56								22 12	22 30			

A To Crewe
B To Wrexham General
C To Liverpool Lime Street
D From South Croydon
E To Chester
F To Manchester Piccadilly
G To Preston
H To Birmingham New Street

Table 66

Mondays to Fridays

9 December to 16 May

London - Watford Junction, Milton Keynes Central, Northampton and West Midlands

Network Diagram - see first Page of Table 59

		VT ◇1 A	VT ◇1	VT ◇1 B	LM 1	VT ◇1 C	LM 1 D	LM 1	SN 1	LM 1	VT ◇1	LM 1	LM 1	VT ◇1 E	LM 1	LM 1	SN 1	LM 1	LM 1	VT ◇1	LM 1	VT MX ◇1 F
London Euston 15 ⊖60	d	21 00	21 03	21 07	20 54	21 10		21 13		21 05	21 43	21 24	21 34	22 00	21 46	21 54		22 04	22 24	22 30	22 34	22 50
East Croydon 176	d																					
Clapham Junction 176	d								20 39								21 39					
Imperial Wharf 176	d								20 44								21 44					
West Brompton ⊖176	d								20 47								21 47					
Kensington (Olympia) ⊖176	d								20 50								21 50					
Shepherd's Bush ⊖176	d								20 53								21 53					
Wembley Central ⊖60,176	d								21 09													
Harrow & Wealdstone ⊖60	d								21 14	21 18			21 46				22 15	22 17			22 49	
Bushey 60	d									21 23			21 51					22s22			22 54	
Watford Junction 60	a				21 10				21 21	21 26		21 39	21 53			22 09	22 22	22 25	22 40		22 57	
	d				21 11	21u25			21 21	21 26	21u58	21 41	21 54			22 11		22 26	22 41	22u45	22 58	23u07
Kings Langley	d									21 31			21 58					22 30			23 02	
Apsley	d									21 34			22 02					22 34			23 06	
Hemel Hempstead	d				21 18				21 29	21 37		21 48	22 05			22 18		22 37	22 48		23 09	
Berkhamsted	d				21 23				21 33	21 42		21 53	22 10			22 23		22 42	22 53		23 14	
Tring	d								21 39	21 48			22 16			22 27		22 47			23 18	
Cheddington	d									21 53			22 22								23 24	
Leighton Buzzard	d				21 36			21 44	21 49	21 57		22 06	22 26		22 18	22 37		22 57	23 06		23 30	
Bletchley	d				21 43			21 52	21 57	22a04		22 14	22a32			22 46		23 07	23 14		23 37	
Milton Keynes Central 10	a	21 30	21 33	21 37	21 49			21 56	22 05		22 17	22 19		22 30	22 32	22 53		23 13	23 22	23 28	23 45	
	d		21 34	21 38	21 49			21 57			22 17			22 32	22 32	22 54			23 23	23 29		
Wolverton	d				21 53		←	22 00							22 36	22 57			23 26			
Northampton 68	a				22 06		21 46	22 15							22 50	23 11			23 42			
	d						21 55	22 18							22 55							
Long Buckby 68	a						22 06	22 29							23 06							
Rugby 68	a		21 56			22 02	22 17	22 40						22 54	23 17					23 58		
Nuneaton 65	a			22 07										23 05								00s39
Coventry 68	a		22 06				22 29	22 52			22 46				23 29					00 10		
Birmingham International 68 ✈	a		22 18				22 45	23 10			23 00				23 47					00 21		
Birmingham New Street 12 68	a		22 29				23 02	23 22			23 16				00 04					00 32		
Sandwell & Dudley 68	a		22 41								23 33											
Wolverhampton 7 68	a		22 56								23 47									01 03		

		LM 1	SN 1	LM 1	VT FX ◇1	VT FO ◇1	LM 1
London Euston 15 ⊖60	d	22 54		23 24	23 30	23 30	23 34
East Croydon 176	d						
Clapham Junction 176	d		22 39				
Imperial Wharf 176	d		22 44				
West Brompton ⊖176	d		22 47				
Kensington (Olympia) ⊖176	d		22 50				
Shepherd's Bush ⊖176	d		22 53				
Wembley Central ⊖60,176	d						
Harrow & Wealdstone ⊖60	d	23 06	23 16				23 46
Bushey 60	d						23 51
Watford Junction 60	a	23 12	23 23	23 39			23 54
	d	23 13		23 40			23 54
Kings Langley	d	23 17					23 59
Apsley	d	23 21					00 02
Hemel Hempstead	d	23 24		23 47			00 05
Berkhamsted	d	23 29		23 52			00 09
Tring	d	23 35					00 15
Cheddington	d						00 20
Leighton Buzzard	d	23 42		00 05			00 26
Bletchley	d	23 51		00 13			00 33
Milton Keynes Central 10	a	23 57		00 21	00 27	00 27	00 41
	d	23 58		00 21	00 28	00 28	
Wolverton	d	00 01		00 25			
Northampton 68	a	00 15		00 38			
	d						
Long Buckby 68	a						
Rugby 68	a				01 00	01 05	
Nuneaton 65	a						
Coventry 68	a				01 13	01 18	
Birmingham International 68 ✈	a				01 24	01 29	
Birmingham New Street 12 68	a				01 36	01 41	
Sandwell & Dudley 68	a						
Wolverhampton 7 68	a				02 07	02 10	

A To Manchester Piccadilly
B To Liverpool Lime Street
C To Preston
D From London Euston
E To Crewe
F not 25 December, 26 December, 1 January. To Manchester Piccadilly

Table 66

Saturdays

14 December to 28 December

London - Watford Junction, Milton Keynes Central, Northampton and West Midlands

Network Diagram - see first Page of Table 59

	LM	LM	VT	LM	LM	LM	LM	SN	LM		LM	VT	SN	VT	VT	LM	SN	VT	VT		SN	VT	LM	VT
	1	1	◇1	1	1	1	1	1	1		1	◇1	1	◇1	◇1	1	1	◇1	◇1		1	◇1	1	◇1
	A	A	A	A								B	C			D		E	E			E	F	
			☕									☕		☕	☕			☕	☕			☕		☕
London Euston 15 ⊖60 d					00 04	00 34	01 34				05 34	06 05		06 23	07 03	06 24		06 55	07 20			07 35	07 05	07 23
East Croydon 176 d																					06 10			
Clapham Junction 176 d								05 08					05 38				06 09				06 36			
Imperial Wharf 176 d								05 12					05 42				06 13				06 41			
West Brompton ⊖176 d								05 15					05 45				06 16				06 44			
Kensington (Olympia) ⊖176 d								05 19					05 49				06 20				06 47			
Shepherd's Bush ⊖176 d								05 22					05 52				06 23				06 50			
Wembley Central ⊖60,176 d						00 45	01 45						06 07				06 38				07 09			
Harrow & Wealdstone ⊖60 d					00 16	00 50	01 50	05 40			05 46		06 12				06 43				07 14		07 18	
Bushey 60 d						00 55																	07 23	
Watford Junction 60 a					00 22	00 57	01 56	05 47			05 52		06 19			06 39	06 50				07 21		07 26	
d					00 23	00 58	01 57				05 52	06u20	06 20	06u37		06 41					07 21		07 26	07u37
Kings Langley d						01 02					05 57												07 31	
Apsley d				00 02		01 06					06 01												07 34	
Hemel Hempstead d				00 05	00 30	01 09	02 04				06 03		06 27			06 48					07 29		07 37	
Berkhamsted d				00 09	00 35	01 14	02 09				06 08		06 32			06 53					07 33		07 42	
Tring d				00 15	00 41	01 18	02 13				06 13		06 38			06 59					07 39		07 48	
Cheddington d				00 20		01 24					06 18					07 05							07 53	
Leighton Buzzard d		00 05		00 26	00 50	01 30	02 22				06 25		06 47			07 10					07 48		07 58	
Bletchley d		00 13		00 33	00 57	01 37	02 29		05 31		06 32		06 55			07 17					07 55		08 04	
Milton Keynes Central 10 a		00 21		00 41	01 05	01 45	02 37		05 36		06 37	06 39	07 00			07 22		07 25	07 50		08 00	08 05	08 09	
d		00 21	00 28		01 05	01 46			05 37		06 37	06 41				07 23							08 10	
Wolverton d	00 01	00 25			01 09	01 49			05 40		06 41					07 26							08 13	
Northampton 68 a	00 15	00 38			01 23	02 03			05 53		06 53					07 39							08 26	
d									05 55		06 55					07 45							08 35	
Long Buckby 68 a									06 06		07 06												↪	
Rugby 68 a			01 05						06 17		07 17	07 02			07 51	08 04								
Nuneaton 65 a																08 16								
Coventry 68 a			01 18						06 29		07 29			07 22	08 02									08 22
Birmingham International 68 ✈ a			01 29						06 45		07 45			07 33	08 13									08 33
Birmingham New Street 12 68 a			01 41						07 01		08 01			07 47	08 27									08 45
Sandwell & Dudley 68 a																								
Wolverhampton 7 68 a			02 10																					

	VT	LM	LM	LM	VT		LM	LM	VT	LM	VT	SN	LM	VT	VT		LM	LM	LM	VT	LM	VT	LM	VT
	◇1	1	1	1	◇1		1	1	◇1	1	◇1	1	1	◇1	◇1		1	1	1	◇1	1	◇1	1	◇1
	B	D					A		G		E	H			I		D					J		E
	⊠				☕				☕		☕			☕	☕					☕		☕		☕
London Euston 15 ⊖60 d	07 43	07 46	07 24	07 35	08 03			07 49	08 10	07 54	08 20		08 05	08 23	08 43		08 46	08 24	08 34	09 03	08 49	09 10	08 54	09 20
East Croydon 176 d												07 10												
Clapham Junction 176 d												07 39												
Imperial Wharf 176 d												07 44												
West Brompton ⊖176 d												07 47												
Kensington (Olympia) ⊖176 d												07 50												
Shepherd's Bush ⊖176 d												07 53												
Wembley Central ⊖60,176 d												08 09												
Harrow & Wealdstone ⊖60 d				07 47								08 14	08 18						08 46					
Bushey 60 d													08 23						08 51					
Watford Junction 60 a			07 39	07 53				08 03		08 09		08 21	08 26					08 39	08 54		09 03		09 09	
d			07 42	07 54				08 03		08 11		08 21	08 26	08u37				08 41	08 55		09 03		09 11	
Kings Langley d				07 59									08 31						08 59					
Apsley d				08 02									08 35						09 03					
Hemel Hempstead d			07 49	08 05						08 18		08 29	08 37					08 48	09 06				09 18	
Berkhamsted d			07 54	08 10						08 23		08 33	08 42					08 53	09 11				09 23	
Tring d			08 01	08a17								08 39	08a49					08 59	09a17					
Cheddington d			08 06															09 04						
Leighton Buzzard d			08 11							08 36		08 48						09 09					09 36	
Bletchley d			08 18							08 43		08 55						09 16					09 43	
Milton Keynes Central 10 a	08 13	08 18	08 23					08 25	08 40	08 48	08 50	09 00			09 13		09 18	09 21			09 26	09 40	09 48	09 50
d	08 13	08 19						08 26		08 49					09 13		09 19				09 26		09 49	
Wolverton d							↩			08 52													09 52	
Northampton 68 a							08 26	08 41		09 05											09 42		10 05	
d							08 35	08 55		09 16											09 55			
Long Buckby 68 a							08 46	09 06		09 27											10 06			
Rugby 68 a		08 41			08 51		08 57	09 17		09 38							09 41			09 51	10 17			
Nuneaton 65 a		08 53															09 53							
Coventry 68 a	08 42				09 02		09 08	09 29		09 49				09 22	09 42					10 02	10 29			
Birmingham International 68 ✈ a	08 53				09 13		09 28	09 45		10 04				09 33	09 53					10 13	10 45			
Birmingham New Street 12 68 a	09 08				09 27		09 42	10 01		10 16				09 45	10 08					10 27	11 01			
Sandwell & Dudley 68 a	09 24														10 24									
Wolverhampton 7 68 a	09 37														10 37									

A From London Euston
B To Glasgow Central
C From Balham
D To Crewe
E To Manchester Piccadilly
F To Birmingham New Street
G To Chester
H From South Croydon
I To Edinburgh
J To Holyhead

Table 66

Saturdays

14 December to 28 December

London - Watford Junction, Milton Keynes Central, Northampton and West Midlands

Network Diagram - see first Page of Table 59

		LM		SN	LM	VT	VT	LM	LM	LM	VT	LM		VT	LM	VT	LM	SN	LM	VT	VT	LM		LM	LM
		1		1	1	◇1	◇1	1	1	1	◇1	1		◇1	1	◇1	1	1	1	◇1	◇1	1		1	1
				A			B	C						D		E		A			F	C			
						☕	☕				☕			☕		☕				☕	☕				
London Euston 15 ⊖60	d	09 13			09 05	09 23	09 43	09 46	09 24	09 34	10 03	09 49		10 10	09 54	10 20	10 13		10 05	10 23	10 43	10 46		10 24	10 34
East Croydon 176 ⛴	d			08 10														09 10							
Clapham Junction 176	d			08 39														09 39							
Imperial Wharf 176	d			08 44														09 44							
West Brompton ⊖176	d			08 47														09 47							
Kensington (Olympia) ⊖176	d			08 50														09 50							
Shepherd's Bush ⊖176	d			08 53														09 53							
Wembley Central ⊖60,176	d			09 09														10 09							
Harrow & Wealdstone ⊖60	d			09 14	09 18					09 46								10 14	10 18						10 46
Bushey 60	d				09 23					09 51									10 23						10 51
Watford Junction 60	a			09 21	09 26				09 39	09 54		10 03			10 09			10 21	10 26					10 39	10 54
	d			09 21	09 26	09u37			09 41	09 55		10 03			10 11			10 21	10 26	10u37				10 41	10 55
Kings Langley	d				09 31					09 59									10 31						10 59
Apsley	d				09 35					10 03									10 35						11 03
Hemel Hempstead	d			09 29	09 37				09 48	10 06					10 18			10 29	10 37					10 48	11 06
Berkhamsted	d			09 33	09 42				09 53	10 11					10 23			10 33	10 42					10 53	11 11
Tring	d			09 39	09a49				09 59	10a17								10 39	10a49					10 59	11a17
Cheddington	d								10 04															11 04	
Leighton Buzzard	d	09 42		09 48					10 09						10 36		10 42	10 48						11 09	
Bletchley	d	09 50		09 55					10 16						10 43		10 50	10 55						11 16	
Milton Keynes Central 10	a	09 54		10 00			10 13	10 18	10 21			10 26		10 40	10 48	10 50	10 54	11 00			11 13	11 18		11 21	
	d	09 54					10 13	10 19				10 26			10 49		10 54				11 13	11 19			
Wolverton	d	09 58													10 52		10 58								
Northampton 68	a	10 12										10 42			11 05		11 12								
	d	10 16										10 55					11 16								
Long Buckby 68	a	10 27										11 06					11 27								
Rugby 68	a	10 37						10 41			10 51	11 17					11 37					11 41			
Nuneaton 65	a							10 53														11 53			
Coventry 68	a	10 49				10 22	10 42				11 03	11 29					11 49			11 22	11 42				
Birmingham International 68 ✈	a	11 04				10 33	10 53				11 13	11 45					12 04			11 33	11 53				
Birmingham New Street 12 68	a	11 16				10 45	11 08				11 27	12 01					12 16			11 45	12 08				
Sandwell & Dudley 68	a						11 24														12 24				
Wolverhampton 7 68 ⛴	a						11 37														12 37				

		VT	LM	VT	LM	VT	LM	SN		LM	VT	VT	LM	LM	LM	VT	LM	VT		LM	VT	LM	SN	LM	VT
		◇1	1	◇1	1	◇1	1	1		1	◇1	◇1	1	1	1	◇1	1	◇1		1	◇1	1	1	1	◇1
				D		E		A				B	C					D			E		A		
		☕		☕		☕					☕	☕				☕		☕			☕				☕
London Euston 15 ⊖60	d	11 03	10 49	11 10	10 54	11 20	11 13			11 05	11 23	11 43	11 46	11 24	11 34	12 03	11 49	12 10		11 54	12 20	12 13		12 05	12 23
East Croydon 176 ⛴	d							10 10															11 10		
Clapham Junction 176	d							10 39															11 39		
Imperial Wharf 176	d							10 44															11 44		
West Brompton ⊖176	d							10 47															11 47		
Kensington (Olympia) ⊖176	d							10 50															11 50		
Shepherd's Bush ⊖176	d							10 53															11 53		
Wembley Central ⊖60,176	d							11 09															12 09		
Harrow & Wealdstone ⊖60	d							11 14		11 18					11 46								12 14	12 18	
Bushey 60	d									11 23					11 51									12 23	
Watford Junction 60	a		11 03		11 10			11 21		11 26				11 40	11 54		12 03			12 09			12 21	12 26	
	d		11 03		11 11			11 21		11 26	11u37			11 41	11 55		12 03			12 11			12 21	12 26	12u37
Kings Langley	d									11 31					11 59									12 31	
Apsley	d									11 35					12 03									12 35	
Hemel Hempstead	d				11 18			11 29		11 37				11 48	12 06					12 18			12 29	12 37	
Berkhamsted	d				11 23			11 33		11 42				11 53	12 11					12 23			12 33	12 42	
Tring	d							11 39		11a49				11 59	12a17								12 39	12a49	
Cheddington	d													12 04											
Leighton Buzzard	d				11 36		11 42	11 48						12 09						12 36		12 42	12 48		
Bletchley	d				11 43		11 50	11 55						12 16						12 43		12 50	12 55		
Milton Keynes Central 10	a		11 25	11 40	11 48	11 50	11 54	12 00				12 13	12 18	12 21			12 25	12 40		12 48	12 50	12 54	13 00		
	d		11 26		11 49		11 54					12 13	12 19				12 26			12 49		12 54			
Wolverton	d				11 52		11 58													12 52		12 58			
Northampton 68	a		11 41		12 05		12 12										12 41			13 05		13 12			
	d		11 55				12 16										12 55					13 16			
Long Buckby 68	a		12 06				12 27										13 06					13 27			
Rugby 68	a	11 51	12 17				12 37						12 41			12 51	13 17					13 37			
Nuneaton 65	a												12 53												
Coventry 68	a	12 02	12 29				12 49				12 22	12 42				13 02	13 29					13 49			13 22
Birmingham International 68 ✈	a	12 13	12 45				13 04				12 33	12 53				13 13	13 45					14 04			13 33
Birmingham New Street 12 68	a	12 27	13 01				13 16				12 45	13 08				13 27	14 01					14 16			13 45
Sandwell & Dudley 68	a											13 24													
Wolverhampton 7 68 ⛴	a											13 37													

A From South Croydon
B To Glasgow Central
C To Crewe
D To Chester
E To Manchester Piccadilly
F To Edinburgh

Table 66

Saturdays

14 December to 28 December

London - Watford Junction, Milton Keynes Central, Northampton and West Midlands

Network Diagram - see first Page of Table 59

	VT ◇1 A ☕	LM 1 B	LM 1		LM 1	VT ◇1 ☕	LM 1	VT ◇1 C ☕	LM 1	VT ◇1 D ☕	LM 1	SN 1 E	LM 1
London Euston 15 ⊖60 d	12 43	12 46	12 24		12 34	13 03	12 49	13 10	12 54	13 20	13 13		13 05
East Croydon 176 🚊 d												12 10	
Clapham Junction 176 d												12 39	
Imperial Wharf 176 d												12 44	
West Brompton ⊖176 d												12 47	
Kensington (Olympia) ⊖176 d												12 50	
Shepherd's Bush ⊖176 d												12 53	
Wembley Central ⊖60,176 d												13 09	
Harrow & Wealdstone ⊖60 d					12 46							13 14	13 18
Bushey 60 d					12 51								13 23
Watford Junction 60 a			12 39		12 54		13 03		13 09			13 21	13 26
d			12 41		12 55		13 03		13 11			13 21	13 26
Kings Langley d					12 59								13 31
Apsley d					13 03								13 35
Hemel Hempstead d			12 48		13 06				13 18			13 29	13 37
Berkhamsted d			12 53		13 11				13 23			13 33	13 42
Tring d			12 59		13a17							13 39	13a49
Cheddington d			13 04										
Leighton Buzzard d			13 09						13 36		13 42	13 48	
Bletchley d			13 16						13 43		13 50	13 55	
Milton Keynes Central 10 a	13 13	13 18	13 21				13 25	13 40	13 48	13 50	13 54	14 00	
d	13 13	13 19					13 26		13 49		13 54		
Wolverton d									13 52		13 58		
Northampton 68 a							13 41		14 05		14 12		
d							13 55				14 16		
Long Buckby 68 a							14 06				14 27		
Rugby 68 a		13 41				13 51	14 17				14 37		
Nuneaton 65 a		13 53											
Coventry 68 a	13 42					14 02	14 29				14 49		
Birmingham International 68 ✈ a	13 53					14 13	14 45				15 04		
Birmingham New Street 12 68 a	14 08					14 27	15 01				15 17		
Sandwell & Dudley 68 a	14 24												
Wolverhampton 7 68 🚊 a	14 37												

		VT ◇1 ☕	VT ◇1 F ☕	LM 1 B	LM 1	LM 1	VT ◇1 ☕	LM 1	VT ◇1 G ☕	LM 1	
London Euston 15 ⊖60 d		13 23	13 43	13 46	13 24	13 34	14 03	13 49	14 10	13 54	
East Croydon 176 🚊 d											
Clapham Junction 176 d											
Imperial Wharf 176 d											
West Brompton ⊖176 d											
Kensington (Olympia) ⊖176 d											
Shepherd's Bush ⊖176 d											
Wembley Central ⊖60,176 d											
Harrow & Wealdstone ⊖60 d						13 46					
Bushey 60 d						13 51					
Watford Junction 60 a					13 40	13 54		14 03		14 09	
d		13u37			13 41	13 55		14 03		14 11	
Kings Langley d						13 59					
Apsley d						14 03					
Hemel Hempstead d					13 48	14 06				14 18	
Berkhamsted d					13 53	14 11				14 23	
Tring d					13 59	14a17					
Cheddington d					14 04						
Leighton Buzzard d					14 09					14 36	
Bletchley d					14 16					14 43	
Milton Keynes Central 10 a			14 13	14 18	14 21			14 25	14 40	14 48	
d			14 13	14 19				14 26		14 49	
Wolverton d										14 52	
Northampton 68 a								14 41		15 05	
d								14 55			
Long Buckby 68 a								15 06			
Rugby 68 a				14 41			14 51	15 17			
Nuneaton 65 a				14 53							
Coventry 68 a		14 22	14 42				15 02	15 29			
Birmingham International 68 ✈ a		14 33	14 53				15 13	15 45			
Birmingham New Street 12 68 a		14 45	15 08				15 27	16 01			
Sandwell & Dudley 68 a			15 24								
Wolverhampton 7 68 🚊 a			15 37								

	VT ◇1 D ☕	LM 1	SN 1 E	LM 1	VT ◇1 ☕	VT R 1 A ⊠	LM 1 B	LM 1	LM 1		VT ◇1 ☕	LM 1
London Euston 15 ⊖60 d	14 20	14 13		14 05	14 23	14 43	14 46	14 24	14 34		15 03	14 49
East Croydon 176 🚊 d			13 10									
Clapham Junction 176 d			13 39									
Imperial Wharf 176 d			13 44									
West Brompton ⊖176 d			13 47									
Kensington (Olympia) ⊖176 d			13 50									
Shepherd's Bush ⊖176 d			13 53									
Wembley Central ⊖60,176 d			14 09									
Harrow & Wealdstone ⊖60 d			14 14	14 18					14 46			
Bushey 60 d				14 23					14 51			
Watford Junction 60 a			14 21	14 26				14 39	14 54			15 03
d			14 21	14 26	14u37			14 41	14 55			15 03
Kings Langley d				14 31					14 59			
Apsley d				14 35					15 03			
Hemel Hempstead d			14 29	14 37				14 48	15 06			
Berkhamsted d			14 33	14 42				14 53	15 11			
Tring d			14 39	14a49				14 59	15a17			
Cheddington d								15 04				
Leighton Buzzard d		14 42	14 48					15 09				
Bletchley d		14 50	14 55					15 16				
Milton Keynes Central 10 a	14 50	14 54	15 00			15 13	15 18	15 21				15 25
d		14 54				15 13	15 19					15 26
Wolverton d		14 58										
Northampton 68 a		15 12										15 41
d		15 16										15 55
Long Buckby 68 a		15 27										16 06
Rugby 68 a		15 37					15 41				15 51	16 17
Nuneaton 65 a							15 53					
Coventry 68 a		15 49			15 22	15 42					16 02	16 29
Birmingham International 68 ✈ a		16 04			15 33	15 53					16 13	16 45
Birmingham New Street 12 68 a		16 16			15 45	16 08					16 27	17 01
Sandwell & Dudley 68 a						16 24						
Wolverhampton 7 68 🚊 a						16 37						

	VT ◇1 C ☕	LM 1	VT ◇1 D ☕	LM 1	SN 1 E	LM 1	VT ◇1 ☕		VT R 1 F ⊠	LM 1 B	LM 1	LM 1
London Euston 15 ⊖60 d	15 10	14 54	15 20	15 13		15 05	15 23		15 43	15 46	15 24	15 34
East Croydon 176 🚊 d					14 10							
Clapham Junction 176 d					14 39							
Imperial Wharf 176 d					14 44							
West Brompton ⊖176 d					14 47							
Kensington (Olympia) ⊖176 d					14 50							
Shepherd's Bush ⊖176 d					14 53							
Wembley Central ⊖60,176 d					15 09							
Harrow & Wealdstone ⊖60 d					15 14	15 18						15 46
Bushey 60 d						15 23						15 51
Watford Junction 60 a		15 09			15 21	15 26					15 39	15 54
d		15 11			15 21	15 26	15u37				15 41	15 55
Kings Langley d						15 31						15 59
Apsley d						15 35						16 03
Hemel Hempstead d		15 18			15 29	15 37					15 48	16 06
Berkhamsted d		15 23			15 33	15 42					15 53	16 11
Tring d					15 39	15a49					15 59	16a17
Cheddington d											16 04	
Leighton Buzzard d		15 36		15 42	15 48						16 09	
Bletchley d		15 43		15 50	15 55						16 16	
Milton Keynes Central 10 a	15 40	15 48	15 50	15 54	16 00				16 13	16 18	16 21	
d		15 49		15 54					16 13	16 19		
Wolverton d		15 52		15 58								
Northampton 68 a		16 05		16 12								
d				16 16								
Long Buckby 68 a				16 27								
Rugby 68 a				16 37						16 41		
Nuneaton 65 a										16 53		
Coventry 68 a				16 49			16 22		16 42			
Birmingham International 68 ✈ a				17 04			16 33		16 53			
Birmingham New Street 12 68 a				17 16			16 45		17 08			
Sandwell & Dudley 68 a									17 24			
Wolverhampton 7 68 🚊 a									17 37			

A To Edinburgh
B To Crewe
C To Chester
D To Manchester Piccadilly
E From South Croydon
F To Glasgow Central
G To Holyhead

Table 66

Saturdays

14 December to 28 December

London - Watford Junction, Milton Keynes Central, Northampton and West Midlands

Network Diagram - see first Page of Table 59

Station		VT	LM	VT	LM	VT	LM	SN	LM	VT	VT	LM	LM	LM	VT	LM	VT	LM	VT	LM	SN	LM	VT
		◇1	1	◇1	1	◇1	1	1	1	◇1	◇1	1	1	1	◇1	1	◇1	1	◇1	1	1	1	◇1
				A		B		C			D	E					A		B		C		F
		☕		☕		☕				☕	☕				☕		☕		☕				☕
London Euston 15	⊖60 d	16 03	15 49	16 10	15 54	16 20	16 13		16 05	16 23	16 43	16 46	16 24	16 34	17 03	16 49	17 10	16 54	17 20	17 13		17 05	17 07
East Croydon	176 d							15 10													16 10		
Clapham Junction	176 d							15 39													16 39		
Imperial Wharf	176 d							15 44													16 44		
West Brompton	⊖176 d							15 47													16 47		
Kensington (Olympia)	⊖176 d							15 50													16 50		
Shepherd's Bush	⊖176 d							15 53													16 53		
Wembley Central	⊖60,176 d							16 09													17 09		
Harrow & Wealdstone	⊖60 d							16 14	16 18					16 46							17 14	17 18	
Bushey	60 d								16 23					16 51								17 23	
Watford Junction	60 a		16 03		16 09			16 21	16 26				16 39	16 54		17 03		17 09			17 21	17 26	
	d		16 03		16 11			16 21	16 26	16u37			16 41	16 55		17 03		17 11			17 21	17 26	
Kings Langley	d								16 31					16 59								17 31	
Apsley	d								16 35					17 03								17 35	
Hemel Hempstead	d				16 18			16 29	16 37				16 48	17 06				17 18			17 29	17 37	
Berkhamsted	d				16 23			16 33	16 42				16 53	17 11				17 23			17 33	17 42	
Tring	d							16 39	16a49				16 59	17a17							17 39	17a49	
Cheddington	d												17 04										
Leighton Buzzard	d				16 36		16 42	16 48					17 09					17 36		17 42	17 48		
Bletchley	d				16 43		16 50	16 55					17 16					17 43		17 50	17 55		
Milton Keynes Central 10	a		16 25	16 40	16 48	16 50	16 54	17 00			17 13	17 18	17 21			17 25	17 40	17 48	17 50	17 54	18 00		
	d		16 26		16 49		16 54				17 13	17 19				17 26		17 49		17 54			
Wolverton	d				16 52		16 58											17 52		17 58			
Northampton	68 a		16 41		17 05		17 12									17 41		18 05		18 12			
	d		16 55				17 16									17 55				18 16			
Long Buckby	68 a		17 06				17 27									18 06				18 27			
Rugby	68 a	16 51	17 17				17 37					17 41			17 51	18 17				18 37			
Nuneaton	65 a											17 53											18 02
Coventry	68 a	17 02	17 29				17 49			17 22	17 42				18 02	18 29				18 49			
Birmingham International	68 ✈ a	17 13	17 45				18 04			17 33	17 53				18 13	18 45				19 04			
Birmingham New Street 12	68 a	17 27	18 01				18 16			17 45	18 08				18 27	19 01				19 17			
Sandwell & Dudley	68 a										18 24												
Wolverhampton 7	68 a										18 37												

Station		VT	VT	LM	LM	LM	VT	LM	VT	LM	VT	LM	SN	LM	VT	VT	LM	LM	LM	VT	LM	LM
		◇1	◇1	1	1	1	◇1	1	◇1	1	◇1	1	1	1	◇1	◇1	1	1	1	◇1	1	1
			D	E					G		B		C			E	E					
		☕	☕				☕		☕		☕				☕	☕				☕		
London Euston 15	⊖60 d	17 23	17 43	17 46	17 24	17 34	18 03	17 49	18 10	17 54	18 20	18 13		18 05	18 23	18 43	18 46	18 24	18 34	19 03	18 49	18 54
East Croydon	176 d												17 10									
Clapham Junction	176 d												17 39									
Imperial Wharf	176 d												17 44									
West Brompton	⊖176 d												17 47									
Kensington (Olympia)	⊖176 d												17 50									
Shepherd's Bush	⊖176 d												17 53									
Wembley Central	⊖60,176 d												18 09									
Harrow & Wealdstone	⊖60 d					17 46							18 14	18 18					18 46			
Bushey	60 d					17 51								18 23					18 51			
Watford Junction	60 a				17 39	17 54		18 03		18 09			18 21	18 26				18 42	18 54		19 03	19 09
	d	17u37			17 41	17 55		18 03		18 11			18 21	18 26	18u37			18 44	18 55		19 03	19 11
Kings Langley	d					17 59								18 31					18 59			
Apsley	d					18 03								18 35					19 03			
Hemel Hempstead	d				17 48	18 06				18 18			18 29	18 37				18 51	19 06			19 18
Berkhamsted	d				17 53	18 11				18 23			18 33	18 42				18 56	19 11			19 23
Tring	d				17 59	18a17							18 39	18a49				19 02	19a17			
Cheddington	d				18 04													19 07				
Leighton Buzzard	d				18 09					18 36		18 42	18 48					19 12				19 36
Bletchley	d				18 16					18 43		18 50	18 55					19 19				19 43
Milton Keynes Central 10	a		18 13	18 18	18 21			18 25	18 40	18 48	18 50	18 54	19 00			19 13	19 18	19 24			19 25	19 48
	d		18 13	18 19				18 26		18 49		18 54				19 13	19 19				19 26	19 49
Wolverton	d									18 52		18 58										19 52
Northampton	68 a							18 41		19 05		19 12									19 44	20 05
	d							18 55				19 16									19 55	
Long Buckby	68 a							19 06				19 27									20 06	
Rugby	68 a			18 41			18 51	19 17				19 37					19 41			19 51	20 17	
Nuneaton	65 a			18 53													19 53					
Coventry	68 a	18 22	18 42				19 02	19 29				19 49			19 22	19 42				20 02	20 29	
Birmingham International	68 ✈ a	18 33	18 53				19 13	19 45				20 04			19 33	19 53				20 13	20 45	
Birmingham New Street 12	68 a	18 45	19 08				19 27	20 01				20 18			19 45	20 08				20 27	21 01	
Sandwell & Dudley	68 a	18 58	19 24				19 43								19 58	20 24				20 52		
Wolverhampton 7	68 a	19 11	19 37				19 58								20 11	20 37				21 07		

A To Holyhead
B To Manchester Piccadilly
C From South Croydon
D To Preston
E To Crewe
F To Liverpool Lime Street
G To Chester

Table 66

Saturdays

14 December to 28 December

London - Watford Junction, Milton Keynes Central, Northampton and West Midlands

Network Diagram - see first Page of Table 59

	SN	LM	VT	VT	LM	LM	VT		VT	LM	VT	VT	LM	SN	LM	VT	VT		LM	LM	SN	VT	VT	LM
	1	1	◇1	◇1	1	1	◇1		◇1	1	◇1	◇1	1	1	1	◇1	◇1		1	1	1	◇1	◇1	1
	A		B	C							B	D		A		C			E			C		F
			⊡	⊡			⊡		⊡		⊡	⊡				⊡	⊡					⊡	⊡	
London Euston (15) ⊖60 d		19 05	19 07	19 20	19 13	19 14	19 23		19 43	19 30	20 11	20 31	19 46		20 02	20 20	20 25		20 34	20 40		21 00	21 03	
East Croydon 176 ⇌ d	18 10													19 10										
Clapham Junction 176 d	18 39													19 38							20 25			
Imperial Wharf 176 d	18 44													19 42							20 29			
West Brompton ⊖176 d	18 47													19 45							20 32			
Kensington (Olympia) ⊖176 d	18 50													19 48							20 36			
Shepherd's Bush ⊖176 d	18 53													19 50							20 39			
Wembley Central ⊖60,176 d	19 09																							
Harrow & Wealdstone ⊖60 d	19 14	19 18								19 42				20 08						20 52	21 02			
Bushey 60 d		19 23								19 47										20s57				
Watford Junction 60 a	19 21	19 26				19 31				19 50			20 01	20 15	20 18				20 49	21 00	21 09			
d		19 26				19 33	19u37			19 53		20u46	20 02		20 19		20u40		20 50	21 01			21u18	
Kings Langley d		19 31								19 57			20 06							21 05				
Apsley d		19 35								20 01			20 10							21 09				
Hemel Hempstead d						19 41				20 04			20 13		20 26				20 57					
Berkhamsted d		19 40				19 46				20 09			20 18		20 31				21 02					
Tring d		19a47				19 51				20 13			20 23							21 19				
Cheddington d						19 56							20 28						21 10					
Leighton Buzzard d					19 42	20 01				20 22			20 35		20 42				21 15					
Bletchley d					19 50	20 07				20 29			20 42		20 49				21 22	21 31				
Milton Keynes Central (10) a				19 50	19 54	20 13			20 21	20 34			20 49		20 54	21 03			21 30	21 39		21 43	21 50	
d					19 54				20 21				20 49			21 05			21 30				21 50	
Wolverton d					19 58								20 53						21 34					←
Northampton 68 a					20 12								21 07						21 50					21 50
d					20 22								21 16						21 59					21 59
Long Buckby 68 a					20 33								21 27						↪					22 10
Rugby 68 a					20 44						21 15	21 34	21 38										22 11	22 21
Nuneaton 65 a			20 02													21 32								
Coventry 68 a					20 55		20 22		20 50				21 49				21 36						22 22	22 32
Birmingham International 68 ✈ a					21 13		20 33		21 01				22 04				21 50						22 33	22 48
Birmingham New Street (12) 68 a					21 25		20 45		21 13				22 16				22 04						22 45	23 04
Sandwell & Dudley 68 a							20 58										22 24						22 56	
Wolverhampton (7) 68 ⇌ a							21 11		21 38								22 38						23 10	

	LM	LM	VT		LM	LM	SN	LM	SN	LM	LM
	1	1	◇1		1	1	1	1	1	1	1
		E			F						
			⊡								
London Euston (15) ⊖60 d	21 08	21 28	21 43			21 54		22 34		23 04	23 44
East Croydon 176 ⇌ d											
Clapham Junction 176 d							21 39		22 39		
Imperial Wharf 176 d							21 44		22 44		
West Brompton ⊖176 d							21 47		22 47		
Kensington (Olympia) ⊖176 d							21 50		22 50		
Shepherd's Bush ⊖176 d							21 53		22 53		
Wembley Central ⊖60,176 d											
Harrow & Wealdstone ⊖60 d						22 06	22 13		23 12	23 16	23 56
Bushey 60 d						22s11					
Watford Junction 60 a	21 24	21 43				22 14	22 20	22 49	23 19	23 23	00 02
d	21 25	21 44	21u58			22 15		22 50		23 24	00 02
Kings Langley d						22 19				23 28	00 07
Apsley d						22 23				23 32	00 11
Hemel Hempstead d	21 32	21 51				22 26		22 57		23 35	00 13
Berkhamsted d	21 37	21 56				22 31		23 02		23 40	00 18
Tring d						22 35				23 44	00 24
Cheddington d						22 41				23 49	00 29
Leighton Buzzard d	21 50	22 07				22 47		23 13		23 56	00 34
Bletchley d	21 57	22 14				22 54		23 20		00 03	00 41
Milton Keynes Central (10) a	22 05	22 22	22 29			23 02		23 28		00 11	00 48
d	22 06	22 22	22 30			23 03		23 28		00 11	00 48
Wolverton d	22 09	22 26			←	23 06		23 32		00 15	00 52
Northampton 68 a	22 27	22 43			22 43	23 20		23 49		00 28	01 10
d		22 55			22 55						
Long Buckby 68 a		↪			23 06						
Rugby 68 a			22 51		23 17						
Nuneaton 65 a											
Coventry 68 a			23 02		23 28						
Birmingham International 68 ✈ a			23 13		23 46						
Birmingham New Street (12) 68 a			23 25		00 04						
Sandwell & Dudley 68 a			23 36								
Wolverhampton (7) 68 ⇌ a			23 50								

A From South Croydon
B To Liverpool Lime Street
C To Manchester Piccadilly
D To Preston
E To Birmingham New Street
F From London Euston

Table 66

Saturdays

4 January to 8 February

London - Watford Junction, Milton Keynes Central, Northampton and West Midlands

Network Diagram - see first Page of Table 59

		LM	LM	VT	LM	LM	LM	LM	SN	LM	LM	VT	SN	VT	VT	LM	SN	VT	VT	SN	VT	LM	VT
		1	1	◇1	1	1	1	1	1	1	1	◇1	1	◇1	◇1	1	1	◇1	◇1	1	◇1	1	◇1
		A	A	A	A							B	C			D		E	E		E	F	
				☕								☕		☕	☕			☕	☕		☕		☕
London Euston 15 ⊖60	d					00 04	00 34	01 34			05 34	06 05		06 23	07 03	06 24		06 55	07 20		07 35	07 05	07 23
East Croydon 176	d																			06 10			
Clapham Junction 176	d								05 08				05 38				06 09			06 36			
Imperial Wharf 176	d								05 12				05 42				06 13			06 41			
West Brompton ⊖176	d								05 15				05 45				06 16			06 44			
Kensington (Olympia) ⊖176	d								05 19				05 49				06 20			06 47			
Shepherd's Bush ⊖176	d								05 22				05 52				06 23			06 50			
Wembley Central ⊖60,176	d						00 45	01 45					06 07				06 38			07 09			
Harrow & Wealdstone ⊖60	d					00 16	00 50	01 50	05 40		05 46		06 12				06 43			07 14		07 18	
Bushey 60	d						00 55															07 23	
Watford Junction 60	a					00 22	00 57	01 56	05 47		05 52		06 19			06 39	06 50			07 21		07 26	
	d					00 23	00 58	01 57			05 52	06u20	06 20	06u37		06 41				07 21		07 26	07u37
Kings Langley	d						01 02				05 57											07 31	
Apsley	d				00 02		01 06				06 01											07 34	
Hemel Hempstead	d				00 05	00 30	01 09	02 04			06 03		06 27			06 48				07 29		07 37	
Berkhamsted	d				00 09	00 35	01 14	02 09			06 08		06 32			06 53				07 33		07 42	
Tring	d				00 15	00 41	01 18	02 13			06 13		06 38			06 59				07 39		07 48	
Cheddington	d				00 20		01 24				06 18					07 05						07 53	
Leighton Buzzard	d		00 05		00 26	00 50	01 30	02 22			06 25		06 47			07 10				07 48		07 58	
Bletchley	d		00 13		00 33	00 57	01 37	02 29		05 31	06 32		06 55			07 17				07 55		08 04	
Milton Keynes Central 10	a		00 21		00 41	01 05	01 45	02 37		05 36	06 37	06 39	07 00			07 22		07 25	07 50	08 00	08 05	08 09	
	d		00 21	00 28		01 05	01 46			05 37	06 37	06 41				07 23						08 10	
Wolverton	d	00 01	00 25			01 09	01 49			05 40	06 41					07 26						08 13	
Northampton 68	a	00 15	00 38			01 23	02 03			05 53	06 53					07 39						08 26	
	d									05 55	06 55					07 45						08 35	
Long Buckby 68	a									06 06	07 06											↪	
Rugby 68	a			01 05						06 17	07 17	07 02			07 51	08 04							
Nuneaton 65	a															08 16							
Coventry 68	a			01 18						06 29	07 29			07 22	08 02								08 22
Birmingham International 68 ✈	a			01 29						06 45	07 45			07 33	08 13								08 33
Birmingham New Street 12 68	a			01 41						07 01	08 01			07 47	08 27								08 45
Sandwell & Dudley 68	a																						
Wolverhampton 7 68	a			02 10																			

		VT	LM	LM	LM	VT	LM	LM	VT	LM	VT	SN	LM	VT	VT	LM	LM	LM	VT	LM	VT	LM	VT
		◇1	1	1	1	◇1	1	1	◇1	1	◇1	1	1	◇1	◇1	1	1	1	◇1	1	◇1	1	◇1
		B	D				A		G		E	H			I	D					J		E
		☒				☕			☕		☕			☕	☕				☕		☕		☕
London Euston 15 ⊖60	d	07 43	07 46	07 24	07 35	08 03		07 49	08 10	07 54	08 20		08 05	08 23	08 43	08 46	08 24	08 34	09 03	08 49	09 10	08 54	09 20
East Croydon 176	d											07 10											
Clapham Junction 176	d											07 39											
Imperial Wharf 176	d											07 44											
West Brompton ⊖176	d											07 47											
Kensington (Olympia) ⊖176	d											07 50											
Shepherd's Bush ⊖176	d											07 53											
Wembley Central ⊖60,176	d											08 09											
Harrow & Wealdstone ⊖60	d				07 47							08 14	08 18					08 46					
Bushey 60	d												08 23					08 51					
Watford Junction 60	a			07 39	07 53			08 03		08 09		08 21	08 26				08 39	08 54		09 03		09 09	
	d			07 42	07 54			08 03		08 11		08 21	08 26	08u37			08 41	08 55		09 03		09 11	
Kings Langley	d				07 59								08 31					08 59					
Apsley	d				08 02								08 35					09 03					
Hemel Hempstead	d			07 49	08 05					08 18		08 29	08 37				08 48	09 06				09 18	
Berkhamsted	d			07 54	08 10					08 23		08 33	08 42				08 53	09 11				09 23	
Tring	d			08 01	08a17							08 39	08a49				08 59	09a17					
Cheddington	d			08 06													09 04						
Leighton Buzzard	d			08 11						08 36		08 48					09 09					09 36	
Bletchley	d			08 18						08 43		08 55					09 16					09 43	
Milton Keynes Central 10	a	08 13	08 18	08 23				08 25	08 40	08 48	08 50	09 00			09 13	09 18	09 21			09 26	09 40	09 48	09 50
	d	08 13	08 19					08 26		08 49					09 13	09 19				09 26		09 49	
Wolverton	d						←			08 52												09 52	
Northampton 68	a						08 26	08 41		09 05										09 42		10 05	
	d						08 35	08 55		09 16										09 55			
Long Buckby 68	a						08 46	09 06		09 27										10 06			
Rugby 68	a		08 41			08 51	08 57	09 17		09 38						09 41			09 51	10 17			
Nuneaton 65	a		08 53													09 53							
Coventry 68	a	08 42				09 02	09 08	09 29		09 49				09 22	09 42				10 02	10 29			
Birmingham International 68 ✈	a	08 53				09 13	09 28	09 45		10 04				09 33	09 53				10 13	10 45			
Birmingham New Street 12 68	a	09 08				09 27	09 42	10 01		10 16				09 45	10 08				10 27	11 01			
Sandwell & Dudley 68	a	09 24													10 24								
Wolverhampton 7 68	a	09 37													10 37								

A From London Euston
B To Glasgow Central
C From Balham
D To Crewe
E To Manchester Piccadilly
F To Birmingham New Street
G To Chester
H From South Croydon
I To Preston
J To Holyhead

Table 66

Saturdays

4 January to 8 February

London - Watford Junction, Milton Keynes Central, Northampton and West Midlands

Network Diagram - see first Page of Table 59

	LM		SN	LM	VT	VT	LM	LM	LM	VT	LM		VT	LM	VT	LM	SN	LM	VT	VT	LM		LM	LM
	1		1	1	◇1	◇1	1	1	1	◇1	1		◇1	1	◇1	1	1	1	◇1	◇1	1		1	1
			A			B	C						D		E		A			B	C			
					☕	☕				☕			☕		☕				☕	☕				
London Euston 15 ⊖60 d	09 13			09 05	09 23	09 43	09 46	09 24	09 34	10 03	09 49		10 10	09 54	10 20	10 13		10 05	10 23	10 43	10 46		10 24	10 34
East Croydon 176 ⇌ d			08 10														09 10							
Clapham Junction 176 d			08 39														09 39							
Imperial Wharf 176 d			08 44														09 44							
West Brompton ⊖176 d			08 47														09 47							
Kensington (Olympia) ⊖176 d			08 50														09 50							
Shepherd's Bush ⊖176 d			08 53														09 53							
Wembley Central ⊖60,176 d			09 09														10 09							
Harrow & Wealdstone ⊖60 d			09 14	09 18					09 46								10 14	10 18						10 46
Bushey 60 d				09 23					09 51									10 23						10 51
Watford Junction 60 a			09 21	09 26				09 39	09 54		10 03			10 09			10 21	10 26					10 39	10 54
d			09 21	09 26	09u37			09 41	09 55		10 03			10 11			10 21	10 26	10u37				10 41	10 55
Kings Langley d				09 31					09 59									10 31						10 59
Apsley d				09 35					10 03									10 35						11 03
Hemel Hempstead d			09 29	09 37				09 48	10 06					10 18			10 29	10 37					10 48	11 06
Berkhamsted d			09 33	09 42				09 53	10 11					10 23			10 33	10 42					10 53	11 11
Tring d			09 39	09a49				09 59	10a17								10 39	10a49					10 59	11a17
Cheddington d								10 04															11 04	
Leighton Buzzard d	09 42		09 48					10 09						10 36		10 42	10 48						11 09	
Bletchley d	09 50		09 55					10 16						10 43		10 50	10 55						11 16	
Milton Keynes Central 10 a	09 54		10 00			10 13	10 18	10 21			10 26		10 40	10 48	10 50	10 54	11 00			11 13	11 18		11 21	
d	09 54					10 13	10 19				10 26			10 49		10 54				11 13	11 19			
Wolverton d	09 58													10 52		10 58								
Northampton 68 a	10 12										10 42			11 05		11 12								
d	10 16										10 55					11 16								
Long Buckby 68 a	10 27										11 06					11 27								
Rugby 68 a	10 37						10 41			10 51	11 17					11 37					11 41			
Nuneaton 65 a							10 53														11 53			
Coventry 68 a	10 49				10 22	10 42				11 02	11 29					11 49			11 22	11 42				
Birmingham International 68 ✈ a	11 04				10 33	10 53				11 13	11 45					12 04			11 33	11 53				
Birmingham New Street 12 68 a	11 16				10 45	11 08				11 27	12 01					12 16			11 45	12 08				
Sandwell & Dudley 68 a						11 24														12 24				
Wolverhampton 7 68 ⇌ a						11 37														12 37				

	VT	LM	VT	LM	VT	LM	SN		LM	VT	VT	LM	LM	LM	VT	LM	VT		LM	VT	LM	SN	LM	VT
	◇1	1	◇1	1	◇1	1	1		1	◇1	◇1	1	1	1	◇1	1	◇1		1	◇1	1	1	1	◇1
			D		E		A				B	C					D			E		A		
	☕		☕		☕					☕	☕				☕		☕			☕				☕
London Euston 15 ⊖60 d	11 03	10 49	11 10	10 54	11 20	11 13			11 05	11 23	11 43	11 46	11 24	11 34	12 03	11 49	12 10		11 54	12 20	12 13		12 05	12 23
East Croydon 176 ⇌ d							10 10															11 10		
Clapham Junction 176 d							10 39															11 39		
Imperial Wharf 176 d							10 44															11 44		
West Brompton ⊖176 d							10 47															11 47		
Kensington (Olympia) ⊖176 d							10 50															11 50		
Shepherd's Bush ⊖176 d							10 53															11 53		
Wembley Central ⊖60,176 d							11 09															12 09		
Harrow & Wealdstone ⊖60 d							11 14		11 18					11 46								12 14	12 18	
Bushey 60 d									11 23					11 51									12 23	
Watford Junction 60 a		11 03		11 10			11 21		11 26				11 40	11 54		12 03			12 09			12 21	12 26	
d		11 03		11 11			11 21		11 26	11u37			11 41	11 55		12 03			12 11			12 21	12 26	12u37
Kings Langley d									11 31					11 59									12 31	
Apsley d									11 35					12 03									12 35	
Hemel Hempstead d				11 18			11 29		11 37				11 48	12 06					12 18			12 29	12 37	
Berkhamsted d				11 23			11 33		11 42				11 53	12 11					12 23			12 33	12 42	
Tring d							11 39		11a49				11 59	12a17								12 39	12a49	
Cheddington d													12 04											
Leighton Buzzard d				11 36		11 42	11 48						12 09						12 36		12 42	12 48		
Bletchley d				11 43		11 50	11 55						12 16						12 43		12 50	12 55		
Milton Keynes Central 10 a		11 25	11 40	11 48	11 50	11 54	12 00				12 13	12 18	12 21			12 25	12 40		12 48	12 50	12 54	13 00		
d		11 26		11 49		11 54					12 13	12 19				12 26			12 49		12 54			
Wolverton d				11 52		11 58													12 52		12 58			
Northampton 68 a		11 41		12 05		12 12										12 41			13 05		13 12			
d		11 55				12 16										12 55					13 16			
Long Buckby 68 a		12 06				12 27										13 06					13 27			
Rugby 68 a	11 51	12 17				12 37						12 41			12 51	13 17					13 37			
Nuneaton 65 a												12 53												
Coventry 68 a	12 02	12 29				12 49				12 22	12 42				13 02	13 29					13 49			13 22
Birmingham International 68 ✈ a	12 13	12 45				13 04				12 33	12 53				13 13	13 45					14 04			13 33
Birmingham New Street 12 68 a	12 27	13 01				13 16				12 45	13 08				13 27	14 01					14 16			13 45
Sandwell & Dudley 68 a											13 24													
Wolverhampton 7 68 ⇌ a											13 37													

A From South Croydon
B To Preston
C To Crewe
D To Chester
E To Manchester Piccadilly

Table 66

Saturdays

4 January to 8 February

London - Watford Junction, Milton Keynes Central, Northampton and West Midlands

Network Diagram - see first Page of Table 59

	VT	LM	LM	LM	VT	LM	VT	LM	VT	LM	SN	LM	VT	VT	LM	LM	LM	VT	LM	VT	LM
	◇1	1	1	1	◇1	1	◇1	1	◇1	1	1	1	◇1	◇1	1	1	1	◇1	1	◇1	1
	A	B					C		D		E			A	B					F	
	☕				☕		☕		☕				☕	☕				☕		☕	
London Euston 15 ⊖60 d	12 43	12 46	12 24	12 34	13 03	12 49	13 10	12 54	13 20	13 13		13 05	13 23	13 43	13 46	13 24	13 34	14 03	13 49	14 10	13 54
East Croydon 176 ⛴ d											12 10										
Clapham Junction 176 d											12 39										
Imperial Wharf 176 d											12 44										
West Brompton ⊖176 d											12 47										
Kensington (Olympia) ⊖176 d											12 50										
Shepherd's Bush ⊖176 d											12 53										
Wembley Central ⊖60,176 d											13 09										
Harrow & Wealdstone ⊖60 d				12 46							13 14	13 18					13 46				
Bushey 60 d				12 51								13 23					13 51				
Watford Junction 60 a			12 39	12 54		13 03		13 09			13 21	13 26				13 40	13 54		14 03		14 09
d			12 41	12 55		13 03		13 11			13 21	13 26	13u37			13 41	13 55		14 03		14 11
Kings Langley d				12 59								13 31					13 59				
Apsley d				13 03								13 35					14 03				
Hemel Hempstead d			12 48	13 06				13 18			13 29	13 37				13 48	14 06				14 18
Berkhamsted d			12 53	13 11				13 23			13 33	13 42				13 53	14 11				14 23
Tring d			12 59	13a17							13 39	13a49				13 59	14a17				
Cheddington d			13 04													14 04					
Leighton Buzzard d			13 09					13 36		13 42	13 48					14 09					14 36
Bletchley d			13 16					13 43		13 50	13 55					14 16					14 43
Milton Keynes Central 10 a	13 13	13 18	13 21			13 25	13 40	13 48	13 50	13 54	14 00			14 13	14 18	14 21			14 25	14 40	14 48
d	13 13	13 19				13 26		13 49		13 54				14 13	14 19				14 26		14 49
Wolverton d								13 52		13 58											14 52
Northampton 68 a						13 41		14 05		14 12									14 41		15 05
d						13 55				14 16									14 55		
Long Buckby 68 a						14 06				14 27									15 06		
Rugby 68 a		13 41			13 51	14 17				14 37					14 41			14 51	15 17		
Nuneaton 65 a		13 53													14 53						
Coventry 68 a	13 42				14 02	14 29				14 49			14 22	14 42				15 02	15 29		
Birmingham International 68 ✈ a	13 53				14 13	14 45				15 04			14 33	14 53				15 13	15 45		
Birmingham New Street 12 68 a	14 08				14 27	15 01				15 17			14 45	15 08				15 27	16 01		
Sandwell & Dudley 68 a	14 24													15 24							
Wolverhampton 7 68 ⛴ a	14 37													15 37							

	VT	LM	SN	LM	VT	VT	LM	LM	LM	VT	LM	VT	LM	VT	LM	SN	LM	VT	VT	LM	LM	LM
						R													R			
	◇1	1	1	1	◇1	1	1	1	1	◇1	1	◇1	1	◇1	1	1	1	◇1	1	1	1	1
	D		E			A	B					C		D		E			A	B		
	☕				☕	⊠				☕		☕		☕				☕	⊠			
London Euston 15 ⊖60 d	14 20	14 13		14 05	14 23	14 43	14 46	14 24	14 34	15 03	14 49	15 10	14 54	15 20	15 13		15 05	15 23	15 43	15 46	15 24	15 34
East Croydon 176 ⛴ d			13 10													14 10						
Clapham Junction 176 d			13 39													14 39						
Imperial Wharf 176 d			13 44													14 44						
West Brompton ⊖176 d			13 47													14 47						
Kensington (Olympia) ⊖176 d			13 50													14 50						
Shepherd's Bush ⊖176 d			13 53													14 53						
Wembley Central ⊖60,176 d			14 09													15 09						
Harrow & Wealdstone ⊖60 d			14 14	14 18					14 46							15 14	15 18					15 46
Bushey 60 d				14 23					14 51								15 23					15 51
Watford Junction 60 a			14 21	14 26				14 39	14 54		15 03		15 09			15 21	15 26				15 39	15 54
d			14 21	14 26	14u37			14 41	14 55		15 03		15 11			15 21	15 26	15u37			15 41	15 55
Kings Langley d				14 31					14 59								15 31					15 59
Apsley d				14 35					15 03								15 35					16 03
Hemel Hempstead d			14 29	14 37				14 48	15 06				15 18			15 29	15 37				15 48	16 06
Berkhamsted d			14 33	14 42				14 53	15 11				15 23			15 33	15 42				15 53	16 11
Tring d			14 39	14a49				14 59	15a17							15 39	15a49				15 59	16a17
Cheddington d								15 04													16 04	
Leighton Buzzard d		14 42	14 48					15 09					15 36		15 42	15 48					16 09	
Bletchley d		14 50	14 55					15 16					15 43		15 50	15 55					16 16	
Milton Keynes Central 10 a	14 50	14 54	15 00			15 13	15 18	15 21			15 25	15 40	15 48	15 50	15 54	16 00			16 13	16 18	16 21	
d		14 54				15 13	15 19				15 26		15 49		15 54				16 13	16 19		
Wolverton d		14 58											15 52		15 58							
Northampton 68 a		15 12									15 41		16 05		16 12							
d		15 16									15 55				16 16							
Long Buckby 68 a		15 27									16 06				16 27							
Rugby 68 a		15 37					15 41			15 51	16 17				16 37					16 41		
Nuneaton 65 a							15 53													16 53		
Coventry 68 a		15 49			15 22	15 42				16 02	16 29				16 49			16 22	16 42			
Birmingham International 68 ✈ a		16 04			15 33	15 53				16 13	16 45				17 04			16 33	16 53			
Birmingham New Street 12 68 a		16 16			15 45	16 08				16 27	17 01				17 16			16 45	17 08			
Sandwell & Dudley 68 a						16 24													17 24			
Wolverhampton 7 68 ⛴ a						16 37													17 37			

A To Preston
B To Crewe
C To Chester
D To Manchester Piccadilly
E From South Croydon
F To Holyhead

Table 66

Saturdays

4 January to 8 February

London - Watford Junction, Milton Keynes Central, Northampton and West Midlands

Network Diagram - see first Page of Table 59

			VT	LM	VT	LM	VT		LM	SN	LM	VT	VT	LM	LM	LM	VT		LM	VT	LM	VT	LM	SN	LM	VT
			◇1	1	◇1	1	◇1		1	1	1	◇1	◇1	1	1	1	◇1		1	◇1	1	◇1	1	1	1	◇1
					A		B			C			D	E						A		B		C		F
London Euston 15	⊖60	d	16 03	15 49	16 10	15 54	16 20		16 13		16 05	16 23	16 43	16 46	16 24	16 34	17 03		16 49	17 10	16 54	17 20	17 13		17 05	17 07
East Croydon	176	d								15 10														16 10		
Clapham Junction	176	d								15 39														16 39		
Imperial Wharf	176	d								15 44														16 44		
West Brompton	⊖176	d								15 47														16 47		
Kensington (Olympia)	⊖176	d								15 50														16 50		
Shepherd's Bush	⊖176	d								15 53														16 53		
Wembley Central	⊖60,176	d								16 09														17 09		
Harrow & Wealdstone	⊖60	d								16 14	16 18					16 46								17 14	17 18	
Bushey	60	d									16 23					16 51									17 23	
Watford Junction	60	a		16 03		16 09				16 21	16 26				16 39	16 54			17 03		17 09			17 21	17 26	
		d		16 03		16 11				16 21	16 26	16u37			16 41	16 55			17 03		17 11			17 21	17 26	
Kings Langley		d									16 31					16 59									17 31	
Apsley		d									16 35					17 03									17 35	
Hemel Hempstead		d				16 18				16 29	16 37				16 48	17 06					17 18			17 29	17 37	
Berkhamsted		d				16 23				16 33	16 42				16 53	17 11					17 23			17 33	17 42	
Tring		d								16 39	16a49				16 59	17a17								17 39	17a49	
Cheddington		d													17 04											
Leighton Buzzard		d				16 36			16 42	16 48					17 09						17 36		17 42	17 48		
Bletchley		d				16 43			16 50	16 55					17 16						17 43		17 50	17 55		
Milton Keynes Central 10		a		16 25	16 40	16 48	16 50		16 54	17 00			17 13	17 18	17 21				17 25	17 40	17 48	17 50	17 54	18 00		
		d		16 26		16 49			16 54				17 13	17 19					17 26		17 49		17 54			
Wolverton		d				16 52			16 58												17 52		17 58			
Northampton	68	a		16 41		17 05			17 12										17 41		18 05		18 12			
		d		16 55					17 16										17 55				18 16			
Long Buckby	68	a		17 06					17 27										18 06				18 27			
Rugby	68	a	16 51	17 17					17 37					17 41			17 51		18 17				18 37			
Nuneaton	65	a												17 53												18 02
Coventry	68	a	17 02	17 29					17 49			17 22	17 42				18 02		18 29				18 49			
Birmingham International	68 ✈	a	17 13	17 45					18 04			17 33	17 53				18 13		18 45				19 04			
Birmingham New Street 12	68	a	17 27	18 01					18 16			17 45	18 08				18 27		19 01				19 17			
Sandwell & Dudley	68	a											18 24													
Wolverhampton 7	68	a											18 37													

			VT		VT	LM	LM	LM	VT	LM	VT	LM	VT		LM	SN	LM	VT	VT	LM	LM	LM	VT		LM	LM
			◇1		◇1	1	1	1	◇1	1	◇1	1	◇1		1	1	1	◇1	◇1	1	1	1	◇1		1	1
					G	E					H		B			C			E	E						
London Euston 15	⊖60	d	17 23		17 43	17 46	17 24	17 34	18 03	17 49	18 10	17 54	18 20		18 13		18 05	18 23	18 43	18 46	18 24	18 34	19 03		18 49	18 54
East Croydon	176	d														17 10										
Clapham Junction	176	d														17 39										
Imperial Wharf	176	d														17 44										
West Brompton	⊖176	d														17 47										
Kensington (Olympia)	⊖176	d														17 50										
Shepherd's Bush	⊖176	d														17 53										
Wembley Central	⊖60,176	d														18 09										
Harrow & Wealdstone	⊖60	d						17 46								18 14	18 18					18 46				
Bushey	60	d						17 51									18 23					18 51				
Watford Junction	60	a					17 39	17 54		18 03		18 09				18 21	18 26				18 42	18 54			19 03	19 09
		d	17u37				17 41	17 55		18 03		18 11				18 21	18 26	18u37			18 44	18 55			19 03	19 11
Kings Langley		d						17 59									18 31					18 59				
Apsley		d						18 03									18 35					19 03				
Hemel Hempstead		d					17 48	18 06				18 18				18 29	18 37				18 51	19 06				19 18
Berkhamsted		d					17 53	18 11				18 23				18 33	18 42				18 56	19 11				19 23
Tring		d					17 59	18a17								18 39	18a49				19 02	19a17				
Cheddington		d					18 04														19 07					
Leighton Buzzard		d					18 09					18 36			18 42	18 48					19 12					19 36
Bletchley		d					18 16					18 43			18 50	18 55					19 19					19 43
Milton Keynes Central 10		a			18 13	18 18	18 21			18 25	18 40	18 48	18 50		18 54	19 00			19 13	19 18	19 24				19 25	19 48
		d			18 13	18 19				18 26		18 49			18 54				19 13	19 19					19 26	19 49
Wolverton		d										18 52			18 58											19 52
Northampton	68	a								18 41		19 05			19 12										19 44	20 05
		d								18 55					19 16										19 55	
Long Buckby	68	a								19 06					19 27										20 06	
Rugby	68	a				18 41			18 51	19 17					19 37					19 41			19 51		20 17	
Nuneaton	65	a				18 53														19 53						
Coventry	68	a	18 24		18 42				19 02	19 29					19 49			19 22	19 42				20 02		20 29	
Birmingham International	68 ✈	a	18 34		18 53				19 13	19 45					20 04			19 33	19 53				20 13		20 45	
Birmingham New Street 12	68	a	18 45		19 08				19 27	20 01					20 18			19 45	20 08				20 27		21 01	
Sandwell & Dudley	68	a	18 58		19 24				19 43									19 58	20 24				20 52			
Wolverhampton 7	68	a	19 11		19 37				19 58									20 11	20 37				21 07			

A To Holyhead
B To Manchester Piccadilly
C From South Croydon
D To Preston
E To Crewe
F To Liverpool Lime Street
G To Wigan North Western
H To Chester

Table 66

Saturdays

4 January to 8 February

London - Watford Junction, Milton Keynes Central, Northampton and West Midlands

Network Diagram - see first Page of Table 59

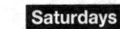

Station		SN 1 A	LM 1	VT ◇1 B	VT ◇1 C	LM 1	LM 1	VT ◇1		VT ◇1	LM 1	VT ◇1 B	VT ◇1 C	LM 1	SN 1 A	LM 1	VT ◇1 C	VT ◇1		LM 1 D	LM 1	SN 1	VT ◇1 C	VT ◇1	LM 1 E
London Euston 15 ⊖60	d		19 05	19 07	19 20	19 13	19 14	19 23		19 43	19 30	20 11	20 31	19 46		20 02	20 20	20 25		20 34	20 40		21 00	21 03	
East Croydon 176	d	18 10													19 10										
Clapham Junction 176	d	18 39													19 38							20 25			
Imperial Wharf 176	d	18 44													19 42							20 29			
West Brompton ⊖176	d	18 47													19 45							20 32			
Kensington (Olympia) ⊖176	d	18 50													19 48							20 36			
Shepherd's Bush ⊖176	d	18 53													19 50							20 39			
Wembley Central ⊖60,176	d	19 09																							
Harrow & Wealdstone ⊖60	d	19 14	19 18								19 42				20 08						20 52	21 02			
Bushey 60	d		19 23								19 47										20s57				
Watford Junction 60	a	19 21	19 26				19 31				19 50			20 01	20 15	20 18				20 49	21 00	21 09			
	d		19 26				19 33	19u37			19 53		20u46	20 02		20 19		20u40		20 50	21 01			21u18	
Kings Langley	d		19 31								19 57			20 06							21 05				
Apsley	d		19 35								20 01			20 10							21 09				
Hemel Hempstead	d						19 41				20 04			20 13		20 26				20 57					
Berkhamsted	d		19 40				19 46				20 09			20 18		20 31				21 02					
Tring	d		19a47				19 51				20 13			20 23							21 19				
Cheddington	d						19 56							20 28						21 10					
Leighton Buzzard	d					19 42	20 01				20 22			20 35		20 42				21 15					
Bletchley	d					19 50	20 07				20 29			20 42		20 49				21 22	21 31				
Milton Keynes Central 10	a				19 50	19 54	20 13			20 21	20 34			20 49		20 54	21 03			21 30	21 39		21 43	21 50	
	d					19 54				20 21				20 49			21 05			21 30				21 50	
Wolverton	d					19 58								20 53						21 34					←
Northampton 68	a					20 12								21 07						21 50					21 50
	d					20 22								21 16						21 59					21 59
Long Buckby 68	a					20 33								21 27						↦					22 10
Rugby 68	a					20 44						21 15	21 34	21 38										22 11	22 21
Nuneaton 65	a			20 02													21 32								
Coventry 68	a					20 55		20 22		20 50				21 49				21 36						22 22	22 32
Birmingham International 68 ✈	a					21 13		20 33		21 01				22 04				21 50						22 33	22 48
Birmingham New Street 12 68	a					21 25		20 45		21 13				22 16				22 04						22 45	23 04
Sandwell & Dudley 68	a							20 58										22 24						22 56	
Wolverhampton 7 68	a							21 11		21 38								22 38						23 10	

Station		LM 1	LM 1 D	VT ◇1		LM 1 E	LM 1	SN 1	LM 1	SN 1	LM 1	LM 1
London Euston 15 ⊖60	d	21 08	21 28	21 43			21 54		22 34		23 04	23 44
East Croydon 176	d											
Clapham Junction 176	d							21 39		22 39		
Imperial Wharf 176	d							21 44		22 44		
West Brompton ⊖176	d							21 47		22 47		
Kensington (Olympia) ⊖176	d							21 50		22 50		
Shepherd's Bush ⊖176	d							21 53		22 53		
Wembley Central ⊖60,176	d											
Harrow & Wealdstone ⊖60	d						22 06	22 13		23 12	23 16	23 56
Bushey 60	d						22s11					
Watford Junction 60	a	21 24	21 43				22 14	22 20	22 49	23 19	23 23	00 02
	d	21 25	21 44	21u58			22 15		22 50		23 24	00 02
Kings Langley	d						22 19				23 28	00 07
Apsley	d						22 23				23 32	00 11
Hemel Hempstead	d	21 32	21 51				22 26		22 57		23 35	00 13
Berkhamsted	d	21 37	21 56				22 31		23 02		23 40	00 18
Tring	d						22 35				23 44	00 24
Cheddington	d						22 41				23 49	00 29
Leighton Buzzard	d	21 50	22 07				22 47		23 13		23 56	00 34
Bletchley	d	21 57	22 14				22 54		23 20		00 03	00 41
Milton Keynes Central 10	a	22 05	22 22	22 29			23 02		23 28		00 11	00 48
	d	22 06	22 22	22 30			23 03		23 28		00 11	00 48
Wolverton	d	22 09	22 26			←	23 06		23 32		00 15	00 52
Northampton 68	a	22 27	22 43			22 43	23 20		23 49		00 28	01 10
	d		22 55			22 55						
Long Buckby 68	a		↦			23 06						
Rugby 68	a			22 51		23 17						
Nuneaton 65	a											
Coventry 68	a			23 02		23 28						
Birmingham International 68 ✈	a			23 13		23 46						
Birmingham New Street 12 68	a			23 25		00 04						
Sandwell & Dudley 68	a			23 36								
Wolverhampton 7 68	a			23 50								

A From South Croydon
B To Liverpool Lime Street
C To Manchester Piccadilly
D To Birmingham New Street
E From London Euston

Table 66

Saturdays

15 February to 17 May

London - Watford Junction, Milton Keynes Central, Northampton and West Midlands

Network Diagram - see first Page of Table 59

		LM	LM	VT	LM	LM	LM	LM	SN	LM		LM	VT	SN	VT	VT	LM	SN	VT	VT		SN	VT	LM	VT
		1	1	◇1	1	1	1	1	1	1		1	◇1	1	◇1	◇1	1	1	◇1	◇1		1	◇1	1	◇1
		A	A	A	A								B	C			D		E	E			E	F	
				☕									☕		☕	☕			☕	☕			☕		☕
London Euston 15 ⊖60	d					00 04	00 34	01 34				05 34	06 05		06 23	07 03	06 24		06 55	07 20			07 35	07 05	07 23
East Croydon 176 🚊	d																					06 10			
Clapham Junction 176	d								05 08					05 38				06 09				06 36			
Imperial Wharf 176	d								05 12					05 42				06 13				06 41			
West Brompton ⊖176	d								05 15					05 45				06 16				06 44			
Kensington (Olympia) ⊖176	d								05 19					05 49				06 20				06 47			
Shepherd's Bush ⊖176	d								05 22					05 52				06 23				06 50			
Wembley Central ⊖60,176	d						00 45	01 45						06 07				06 38				07 09			
Harrow & Wealdstone ⊖60	d					00 16	00 50	01 50	05 40			05 46		06 12				06 43				07 14		07 18	
Bushey 60	d						00 55																	07 23	
Watford Junction 60	a					00 22	00 57	01 56	05 47			05 52		06 19			06 39	06 50				07 21		07 26	
	d					00 23	00 58	01 57				05 52	06u20	06 20	06u37		06 41					07 21		07 26	07u37
Kings Langley	d						01 02					05 57												07 31	
Apsley	d				00 02		01 06					06 01												07 34	
Hemel Hempstead	d				00 05	00 30	01 09	02 04				06 03		06 27			06 48					07 29		07 37	
Berkhamsted	d				00 09	00 35	01 14	02 09				06 08		06 32			06 53					07 33		07 42	
Tring	d				00 15	00 41	01 18	02 13				06 13		06 38			06 59					07 39		07 48	
Cheddington	d				00 20		01 24					06 18					07 05							07 53	
Leighton Buzzard	d		00 05		00 26	00 50	01 30	02 22				06 25		06 47			07 10					07 48		07 58	
Bletchley	d		00 13		00 33	00 57	01 37	02 29		05 31		06 32		06 55			07 17					07 55		08 04	
Milton Keynes Central 10	a		00 21		00 41	01 05	01 45	02 37		05 36		06 37	06 39	07 00			07 22		07 25	07 50		08 00	08 05	08 09	
	d		00 21	00 28		01 05	01 46			05 37		06 37	06 41				07 23							08 10	
Wolverton	d	00 01	00 25			01 09	01 49			05 40		06 41					07 26							08 13	
Northampton 68	a	00 15	00 38			01 23	02 03			05 53		06 53					07 39							08 26	
	d									05 55		06 55					07 45							08 35	
Long Buckby 68	a									06 06		07 06												→	
Rugby 68	a			01 05						06 17		07 17	07 02			07 51	08 04								
Nuneaton 65	a																08 16								
Coventry 68	a			01 18						06 29		07 29			07 22	08 02									08 22
Birmingham International 68 ✈	a			01 29						06 45		07 45			07 33	08 13									08 33
Birmingham New Street 12 68	a			01 41						07 01		08 01			07 47	08 27									08 45
Sandwell & Dudley 68	a																								
Wolverhampton 7 68 🚊	a			02 10																					

		VT	LM	LM	LM	VT		LM	LM	VT	LM	VT	SN	LM	VT	VT		LM	LM	LM	VT	LM	VT	LM	VT
		◇1	1	1	1	◇1		1	1	◇1	1	◇1	1	1	◇1	◇1		1	1	1	◇1	1	◇1	1	◇1
		B	D					A		G		E	H			I		D					J		E
		⊠				☕				☕		☕			☕	☕					☕		☕		☕
London Euston 15 ⊖60	d	07 43	07 46	07 24	07 35	08 03			07 49	08 10	07 54	08 20		08 05	08 23	08 43		08 46	08 24	08 34	09 03	08 49	09 10	08 54	09 20
East Croydon 176 🚊	d												07 10												
Clapham Junction 176	d												07 39												
Imperial Wharf 176	d												07 44												
West Brompton ⊖176	d												07 47												
Kensington (Olympia) ⊖176	d												07 50												
Shepherd's Bush ⊖176	d												07 53												
Wembley Central ⊖60,176	d												08 09												
Harrow & Wealdstone ⊖60	d				07 47								08 14	08 18						08 46					
Bushey 60	d													08 23						08 51					
Watford Junction 60	a			07 39	07 53				08 03		08 09		08 21	08 26					08 39	08 54		09 03		09 09	
	d			07 42	07 54				08 03		08 11		08 21	08 26	08u37				08 41	08 55		09 03		09 11	
Kings Langley	d				07 59									08 31						08 59					
Apsley	d				08 02									08 35						09 03					
Hemel Hempstead	d			07 49	08 05						08 18		08 29	08 37					08 48	09 06				09 18	
Berkhamsted	d			07 54	08 10						08 23		08 33	08 42					08 53	09 11				09 23	
Tring	d			08 01	08a17								08 39	08a49					08 59	09a17					
Cheddington	d			08 06															09 04						
Leighton Buzzard	d			08 11							08 36		08 48						09 09					09 36	
Bletchley	d			08 18							08 43		08 55						09 16					09 43	
Milton Keynes Central 10	a	08 13	08 18	08 23					08 25	08 40	08 48	08 50	09 00			09 13		09 18	09 21			09 26	09 40	09 48	09 50
	d	08 13	08 19						08 26		08 49					09 13		09 19				09 26		09 49	
Wolverton	d							←			08 52													09 52	
Northampton 68	a							08 26	08 41		09 05											09 42		10 05	
	d							08 35	08 55		09 16											09 55			
Long Buckby 68	a							08 46	09 06		09 27											10 06			
Rugby 68	a		08 41			08 51		08 57	09 17		09 38							09 41			09 51	10 17			
Nuneaton 65	a		08 53															09 53							
Coventry 68	a	08 42				09 02		09 08	09 29		09 49				09 22	09 42					10 02	10 29			
Birmingham International 68 ✈	a	08 53				09 13		09 28	09 45		10 04				09 33	09 53					10 13	10 45			
Birmingham New Street 12 68	a	09 08				09 27		09 42	10 01		10 16				09 45	10 08					10 27	11 01			
Sandwell & Dudley 68	a	09 24														10 24									
Wolverhampton 7 68 🚊	a	09 37														10 37									

A From London Euston
B To Glasgow Central
C From Balham
D To Crewe
E To Manchester Piccadilly
F To Birmingham New Street
G To Chester
H From South Croydon
I To Edinburgh
J To Holyhead

Table 66

Saturdays

15 February to 17 May

London - Watford Junction, Milton Keynes Central, Northampton and West Midlands

Network Diagram - see first Page of Table 59

Station		LM 1	SN 1 A	LM 1	VT ◇1	VT ◇1 B	LM 1 C	LM 1	LM 1	VT ◇1	LM 1	VT ◇1 D	LM 1	VT ◇1 E	LM 1	SN 1 A	LM 1	VT ◇1	VT ◇1 F	LM 1 C	LM 1	LM 1
London Euston 15 ⊖60	d	09 13		09 05	09 23	09 43	09 46	09 24	09 34	10 03	09 49	10 10	09 54	10 20	10 13		10 05	10 23	10 43	10 46	10 24	10 34
East Croydon 176	d		08 10													09 10						
Clapham Junction 176	d		08 39													09 39						
Imperial Wharf 176	d		08 44													09 44						
West Brompton ⊖176	d		08 47													09 47						
Kensington (Olympia) ⊖176	d		08 50													09 50						
Shepherd's Bush ⊖176	d		08 53													09 53						
Wembley Central ⊖60,176	d		09 09													10 09						
Harrow & Wealdstone ⊖60	d		09 14	09 18					09 46							10 14	10 18					10 46
Bushey 60	d			09 23					09 51								10 23					10 51
Watford Junction 60	a		09 21	09 26				09 39	09 54		10 03		10 09			10 21	10 26				10 39	10 54
	d		09 21	09 26	09u37			09 41	09 55		10 03		10 11			10 21	10 26	10u37			10 41	10 55
Kings Langley	d			09 31					09 59								10 31					10 59
Apsley	d			09 35					10 03								10 35					11 03
Hemel Hempstead	d		09 29	09 37				09 48	10 06				10 18			10 29	10 37				10 48	11 06
Berkhamsted	d		09 33	09 42				09 53	10 11				10 23			10 33	10 42				10 53	11 11
Tring	d		09 39	09a49				09 59	10a17							10 39	10a49				10 59	11a17
Cheddington	d							10 04													11 04	
Leighton Buzzard	d	09 42	09 48					10 09					10 36		10 42	10 48					11 09	
Bletchley	d	09 50	09 55					10 16					10 43		10 50	10 55					11 16	
Milton Keynes Central 10	a	09 54	10 00			10 13	10 18	10 21			10 26	10 40	10 48	10 50	10 54	11 00			11 13	11 18	11 21	
	d	09 54				10 13	10 19				10 26		10 49		10 54				11 13	11 19		
Wolverton	d	09 58											10 52		10 58							
Northampton 68	a	10 12									10 42		11 05		11 12							
	d	10 16									10 55				11 16							
Long Buckby 68	a	10 27									11 06				11 27							
Rugby 68	a	10 37					10 41			10 51	11 17				11 37					11 41		
Nuneaton 65	a						10 53													11 53		
Coventry 68	a	10 49			10 22	10 42				11 03	11 29				11 49			11 22	11 42			
Birmingham International 68 ✈	a	11 04			10 33	10 53				11 13	11 45				12 04			11 33	11 53			
Birmingham New Street 12 68	a	11 16			10 45	11 08				11 27	12 01				12 16			11 45	12 08			
Sandwell & Dudley 68	a					11 24													12 24			
Wolverhampton 7 68	a					11 37													12 37			

Station		VT ◇1	LM 1	VT ◇1 D	LM 1	VT ◇1 E	LM 1	SN 1 A	LM 1	VT ◇1	VT ◇1 B	LM 1 C	LM 1	LM 1	VT ◇1	LM 1	VT ◇1 D	LM 1	VT ◇1 E	LM 1	SN 1 A	LM 1	VT ◇1
London Euston 15 ⊖60	d	11 03	10 49	11 10	10 54	11 20	11 13		11 05	11 23	11 43	11 46	11 24	11 34	12 03	11 49	12 10	11 54	12 20	12 13		12 05	12 23
East Croydon 176	d							10 10													11 10		
Clapham Junction 176	d							10 39													11 39		
Imperial Wharf 176	d							10 44													11 44		
West Brompton ⊖176	d							10 47													11 47		
Kensington (Olympia) ⊖176	d							10 50													11 50		
Shepherd's Bush ⊖176	d							10 53													11 53		
Wembley Central ⊖60,176	d							11 09													12 09		
Harrow & Wealdstone ⊖60	d							11 14	11 18					11 46							12 14	12 18	
Bushey 60	d								11 23					11 51								12 23	
Watford Junction 60	a		11 03		11 10			11 21	11 26				11 40	11 54		12 03		12 09			12 21	12 26	
	d		11 03		11 11			11 21	11 26	11u37			11 41	11 55		12 03		12 11			12 21	12 26	12u37
Kings Langley	d								11 31					11 59								12 31	
Apsley	d								11 35					12 03								12 35	
Hemel Hempstead	d				11 18			11 29	11 37				11 48	12 06				12 18			12 29	12 37	
Berkhamsted	d				11 23			11 33	11 42				11 53	12 11				12 23			12 33	12 42	
Tring	d							11 39	11a49				11 59	12a17							12 39	12a49	
Cheddington	d												12 04										
Leighton Buzzard	d				11 36		11 42	11 48					12 09					12 36		12 42	12 48		
Bletchley	d				11 43		11 50	11 55					12 16					12 43		12 50	12 55		
Milton Keynes Central 10	a		11 25	11 40	11 48	11 50	11 54	12 00			12 13	12 18	12 21			12 25	12 40	12 48	12 50	12 54	13 00		
	d		11 26		11 49		11 54				12 13	12 19				12 26		12 49		12 54			
Wolverton	d				11 52		11 58											12 52		12 58			
Northampton 68	a		11 41		12 05		12 12									12 41		13 05		13 12			
	d		11 55				12 16									12 55				13 16			
Long Buckby 68	a		12 06				12 27									13 06				13 27			
Rugby 68	a	11 51	12 17				12 37					12 41			12 51	13 17				13 37			
Nuneaton 65	a											12 53											
Coventry 68	a	12 02	12 29				12 49			12 22	12 42				13 02	13 29				13 49			13 22
Birmingham International 68 ✈	a	12 13	12 45				13 04			12 33	12 53				13 13	13 45				14 04			13 33
Birmingham New Street 12 68	a	12 27	13 01				13 16			12 45	13 08				13 27	14 01				14 16			13 45
Sandwell & Dudley 68	a										13 24												
Wolverhampton 7 68	a										13 37												

A From South Croydon
B To Glasgow Central
C To Crewe
D To Chester
E To Manchester Piccadilly
F To Edinburgh

Table 66

Saturdays

15 February to 17 May

London - Watford Junction, Milton Keynes Central, Northampton and West Midlands

Network Diagram - see first Page of Table 59

	VT	LM	LM	LM	VT	LM	VT	LM	VT	LM	SN	LM	VT	VT	LM	LM	LM	VT	LM	VT	LM
	◇1	1	1	1	◇1	1	◇1	1	◇1	1	1	1	◇1	◇1	1	1	1	◇1	1	◇1	1
	A	B					C		D		E			F	B					G	
	☕				☕		☕		☕				☕	☕				☕		☕	
London Euston [15] ⊖60 d	12 43	12 46	12 24	12 34	13 03	12 49	13 10	12 54	13 20	13 13		13 05	13 23	13 43	13 46	13 24	13 34	14 03	13 49	14 10	13 54
East Croydon 176 ⛴ d											12 10										
Clapham Junction 176 d											12 39										
Imperial Wharf 176 d											12 44										
West Brompton ⊖176 d											12 47										
Kensington (Olympia) ⊖176 d											12 50										
Shepherd's Bush ⊖176 d											12 53										
Wembley Central ⊖60,176 d											13 09										
Harrow & Wealdstone ⊖60 d				12 46							13 14	13 18					13 46				
Bushey 60 d				12 51								13 23					13 51				
Watford Junction 60 a			12 39	12 54		13 03		13 09			13 21	13 26				13 40	13 54		14 03		14 09
d			12 41	12 55		13 03		13 11			13 21	13 26	13u37			13 41	13 55		14 03		14 11
Kings Langley d				12 59								13 31					13 59				
Apsley d				13 03								13 35					14 03				
Hemel Hempstead d			12 48	13 06				13 18			13 29	13 37				13 48	14 06				14 18
Berkhamsted d			12 53	13 11				13 23			13 33	13 42				13 53	14 11				14 23
Tring d			12 59	13a17							13 39	13a49				13 59	14a17				
Cheddington d			13 04													14 04					
Leighton Buzzard d			13 09					13 36		13 42	13 48					14 09					14 36
Bletchley d			13 16					13 43		13 50	13 55					14 16					14 43
Milton Keynes Central [10] a	13 13	13 18	13 21			13 25	13 40	13 48	13 50	13 54	14 00			14 13	14 18	14 21			14 25	14 40	14 48
d	13 13	13 19				13 26		13 49		13 54				14 13	14 19				14 26		14 49
Wolverton d								13 52		13 58											14 52
Northampton 68 a						13 41		14 05		14 12									14 41		15 05
d						13 55				14 16									14 55		
Long Buckby 68 a						14 06				14 27									15 06		
Rugby 68 a		13 41			13 51	14 17				14 37					14 41			14 51	15 17		
Nuneaton 65 a		13 53													14 53						
Coventry 68 a	13 42				14 02	14 29				14 49			14 22	14 42				15 02	15 29		
Birmingham International 68 ✈ a	13 53				14 13	14 45				15 04			14 33	14 53				15 13	15 45		
Birmingham New Street [12] 68 a	14 08				14 27	15 01				15 17			14 45	15 08				15 27	16 01		
Sandwell & Dudley 68 a	14 24													15 24							
Wolverhampton [7] 68 ⛴ a	14 37													15 37							

	VT	LM	SN	LM	VT	VT	LM	LM	LM	VT	LM	VT	LM	VT	LM	SN	LM	VT	VT	LM	LM	LM
						R													R			
	◇1	1	1	1	◇1	1	1	1	1	◇1	1	◇1	1	◇1	1	1	1	◇1	1	1	1	1
	D		E			A	B					C		D		E			F	B		
	☕				☕	⊠				☕		☕		☕				☕	⊠			
London Euston [15] ⊖60 d	14 20	14 13		14 05	14 23	14 43	14 46	14 24	14 34	15 03	14 49	15 10	14 54	15 20	15 13		15 05	15 23	15 43	15 46	15 24	15 34
East Croydon 176 ⛴ d			13 10													14 10						
Clapham Junction 176 d			13 39													14 39						
Imperial Wharf 176 d			13 44													14 44						
West Brompton ⊖176 d			13 47													14 47						
Kensington (Olympia) ⊖176 d			13 50													14 50						
Shepherd's Bush ⊖176 d			13 53													14 53						
Wembley Central ⊖60,176 d			14 09													15 09						
Harrow & Wealdstone ⊖60 d			14 14	14 18					14 46							15 14	15 18					15 46
Bushey 60 d				14 23					14 51								15 23					15 51
Watford Junction 60 a			14 21	14 26				14 39	14 54		15 03		15 09			15 21	15 26				15 39	15 54
d			14 21	14 26	14u37			14 41	14 55		15 03		15 11			15 21	15 26	15u37			15 41	15 55
Kings Langley d				14 31					14 59								15 31					15 59
Apsley d				14 35					15 03								15 35					16 03
Hemel Hempstead d			14 29	14 37				14 48	15 06				15 18			15 29	15 37				15 48	16 06
Berkhamsted d			14 33	14 42				14 53	15 11				15 23			15 33	15 42				15 53	16 11
Tring d			14 39	14a49				14 59	15a17							15 39	15a49				15 59	16a17
Cheddington d								15 04													16 04	
Leighton Buzzard d		14 42	14 48					15 09					15 36		15 42	15 48					16 09	
Bletchley d		14 50	14 55					15 16					15 43		15 50	15 55					16 16	
Milton Keynes Central [10] a	14 50	14 54	15 00			15 13	15 18	15 21			15 25	15 40	15 48	15 50	15 54	16 00			16 13	16 18	16 21	
d		14 54				15 13	15 19				15 26		15 49		15 54				16 13	16 19		
Wolverton d		14 58											15 52		15 58							
Northampton 68 a		15 12									15 41		16 05		16 12							
d		15 16									15 55				16 16							
Long Buckby 68 a		15 27									16 06				16 27							
Rugby 68 a		15 37					15 41			15 51	16 17				16 37					16 41		
Nuneaton 65 a							15 53													16 53		
Coventry 68 a		15 49			15 22	15 42				16 02	16 29				16 49			16 22	16 42			
Birmingham International 68 ✈ a		16 04			15 33	15 53				16 13	16 45				17 04			16 33	16 53			
Birmingham New Street [12] 68 a		16 16			15 45	16 08				16 27	17 01				17 16			16 45	17 08			
Sandwell & Dudley 68 a						16 24													17 24			
Wolverhampton [7] 68 ⛴ a						16 37													17 37			

A To Edinburgh
B To Crewe
C To Chester
D To Manchester Piccadilly
E From South Croydon
F To Glasgow Central
G To Holyhead

Table 66

Saturdays

15 February to 17 May

London - Watford Junction, Milton Keynes Central, Northampton and West Midlands

Network Diagram - see first Page of Table 59

Station			VT	LM	VT	LM	VT		LM	SN	LM	VT	VT	LM	LM	LM	VT		LM	VT	LM	VT	LM	SN	LM	VT
			◇1	1	◇1	1	◇1		1	1	1	◇1	◇1	1	1	1	◇1		1	◇1	1	◇1	1	1	1	◇1
					A		B			C			D	E						A		B		C		F
			⊡		⊡		⊡					⊡	⊡				⊡			⊡		⊡				⊡
London Euston 15	⊖60	d	16 03	15 49	16 10	15 54	16 20		16 13		16 05	16 23	16 43	16 46	16 24	16 34	17 03		16 49	17 10	16 54	17 20	17 13		17 05	17 07
East Croydon	176 🚌	d								15 10														16 10		
Clapham Junction	176	d								15 39														16 39		
Imperial Wharf	176	d								15 44														16 44		
West Brompton	⊖176	d								15 47														16 47		
Kensington (Olympia)	⊖176	d								15 50														16 50		
Shepherd's Bush	⊖176	d								15 53														16 53		
Wembley Central	⊖60,176	d								16 09														17 09		
Harrow & Wealdstone	⊖60	d								16 14	16 18					16 46								17 14	17 18	
Bushey	60	d									16 23					16 51									17 23	
Watford Junction	60	a		16 03		16 09				16 21	16 26				16 39	16 54			17 03		17 09			17 21	17 26	
		d		16 03		16 11				16 21	16 26	16u37			16 41	16 55			17 03		17 11			17 21	17 26	
Kings Langley		d									16 31					16 59									17 31	
Apsley		d									16 35					17 03									17 35	
Hemel Hempstead		d				16 18				16 29	16 37				16 48	17 06					17 18			17 29	17 37	
Berkhamsted		d				16 23				16 33	16 42				16 53	17 11					17 23			17 33	17 42	
Tring		d								16 39	16a49				16 59	17a17								17 39	17a49	
Cheddington		d													17 04											
Leighton Buzzard		d				16 36			16 42	16 48					17 09						17 36		17 42	17 48		
Bletchley		d				16 43			16 50	16 55					17 16						17 43		17 50	17 55		
Milton Keynes Central 10		a		16 25	16 40	16 48	16 50		16 54	17 00			17 13	17 18	17 21				17 25	17 40	17 48	17 50	17 54	18 00		
		d		16 26		16 49			16 54				17 13	17 19					17 26		17 49		17 54			
Wolverton		d				16 52			16 58												17 52		17 58			
Northampton	68	a		16 41		17 05			17 12										17 41		18 05		18 12			
		d		16 55					17 16										17 55				18 16			
Long Buckby	68	a		17 06					17 27										18 06				18 27			
Rugby	68	a	16 51	17 17					17 37					17 41			17 51		18 17				18 37			
Nuneaton	65	a												17 53												18 02
Coventry	68	a	17 02	17 29					17 49			17 22	17 42				18 02		18 29				18 49			
Birmingham International	68 ✈	a	17 13	17 45					18 04			17 33	17 53				18 13		18 45				19 04			
Birmingham New Street 12	68	a	17 27	18 01					18 16			17 45	18 08				18 27		19 01				19 17			
Sandwell & Dudley	68	a											18 24													
Wolverhampton 7	68 🚌	a											18 37													

Station			VT		VT	LM	LM	LM	VT	LM	VT	LM	VT		LM	SN	LM	VT	VT	LM	LM	LM	VT		LM	LM
			◇1		◇1	1	1	1	◇1	1	◇1	1	◇1		1	1	1	◇1	◇1	1	1	1	◇1		1	1
					D	E					G		B			C			E	E						
			⊡		⊡				⊡		⊡		⊡					⊡	⊡				⊡			
London Euston 15	⊖60	d	17 23		17 43	17 46	17 24	17 34	18 03	17 49	18 10	17 54	18 20		18 13		18 05	18 23	18 43	18 46	18 24	18 34	19 03		18 49	18 54
East Croydon	176 🚌	d														17 10										
Clapham Junction	176	d														17 39										
Imperial Wharf	176	d														17 44										
West Brompton	⊖176	d														17 47										
Kensington (Olympia)	⊖176	d														17 50										
Shepherd's Bush	⊖176	d														17 53										
Wembley Central	⊖60,176	d														18 09										
Harrow & Wealdstone	⊖60	d						17 46								18 14	18 18					18 46				
Bushey	60	d						17 51									18 23					18 51				
Watford Junction	60	a					17 39	17 54		18 03		18 09				18 21	18 26				18 42	18 54			19 03	19 09
		d	17u37				17 41	17 55		18 03		18 11				18 21	18 26	18u37			18 44	18 55			19 03	19 11
Kings Langley		d						17 59									18 31					18 59				
Apsley		d						18 03									18 35					19 03				
Hemel Hempstead		d					17 48	18 06				18 18				18 29	18 37				18 51	19 06				19 18
Berkhamsted		d					17 53	18 11				18 23				18 33	18 42				18 56	19 11				19 23
Tring		d					17 59	18a17								18 39	18a49				19 02	19a17				
Cheddington		d					18 04														19 07					
Leighton Buzzard		d					18 09					18 36			18 42	18 48					19 12					19 36
Bletchley		d					18 16					18 43			18 50	18 55					19 19					19 43
Milton Keynes Central 10		a			18 13	18 18	18 21			18 25	18 40	18 48	18 50		18 54	19 00			19 13	19 18	19 24				19 25	19 48
		d			18 13	18 19				18 26		18 49			18 54				19 13	19 19					19 26	19 49
Wolverton		d										18 52			18 58											19 52
Northampton	68	a								18 41		19 05			19 12										19 44	20 05
		d								18 55					19 16										19 55	
Long Buckby	68	a								19 06					19 27										20 06	
Rugby	68	a				18 41			18 51	19 17					19 37					19 41			19 51		20 17	
Nuneaton	65	a				18 53														19 53						
Coventry	68	a	18 22		18 42				19 02	19 29					19 49			19 22	19 42				20 02		20 29	
Birmingham International	68 ✈	a	18 33		18 53				19 13	19 45					20 04			19 33	19 53				20 13		20 45	
Birmingham New Street 12	68	a	18 45		19 08				19 27	20 01					20 18			19 45	20 08				20 27		21 01	
Sandwell & Dudley	68	a	18 58		19 24				19 43									19 58	20 24				20 52			
Wolverhampton 7	68 🚌	a	19 11		19 37				19 58									20 11	20 37				21 07			

A To Holyhead
B To Manchester Piccadilly
C From South Croydon
D To Preston
E To Crewe
F To Liverpool Lime Street
G To Chester

Table 66

Saturdays
15 February to 17 May

London - Watford Junction, Milton Keynes Central, Northampton and West Midlands

Network Diagram - see first Page of Table 59

		SN	LM	VT	VT	LM	LM	VT		VT	LM	VT	VT	LM	SN	LM	VT	VT		LM	LM	SN	VT	VT	LM
		■1	■1	◇■1	◇■1	■1	■1	◇■1		◇■1	■1	◇■1	◇■1	■1	■1	■1	◇■1	◇■1		■1	■1	■1	◇■1	◇■1	■1
		A		B	C							B	D		A		C			E			C		F
				🍴	🍴			🍴		🍴		🍴	🍴				🍴	🍴					🍴	🍴	
London Euston ■15 ⊖60	d		19 05	19 07	19 20	19 13	19 14	19 23		19 43	19 30	20 11	20 31	19 46		20 02	20 20	20 25		20 34	20 40		21 00	21 03	
East Croydon 176 ⛴	d	18 10													19 10										
Clapham Junction 176	d	18 39													19 38							20 25			
Imperial Wharf 176	d	18 44													19 42							20 29			
West Brompton ⊖176	d	18 47													19 45							20 32			
Kensington (Olympia) ⊖176	d	18 50													19 48							20 36			
Shepherd's Bush ⊖176	d	18 53													19 50							20 39			
Wembley Central ⊖60,176	d	19 09																							
Harrow & Wealdstone ⊖60	d	19 14	19 18								19 42				20 08						20 52	21 02			
Bushey 60	d		19 23								19 47										20s57				
Watford Junction 60	a	19 21	19 26				19 31				19 50			20 01	20 15	20 18				20 49	21 00	21 09			
	d		19 26				19 33	19u37			19 53		20u46	20 02		20 19		20u40		20 50	21 01			21u18	
Kings Langley	d		19 31								19 57			20 06							21 05				
Apsley	d		19 35								20 01			20 10							21 09				
Hemel Hempstead	d						19 41				20 04			20 13		20 26				20 57					
Berkhamsted	d		19 40				19 46				20 09			20 18		20 31				21 02					
Tring	d		19a47				19 51				20 13			20 23							21 19				
Cheddington	d						19 56							20 28						21 10					
Leighton Buzzard	d					19 42	20 01				20 22			20 35		20 42				21 15					
Bletchley	d					19 50	20 07				20 29			20 42		20 49				21 22	21 31				
Milton Keynes Central ■10	a				19 50	19 54	20 13			20 21	20 34			20 49		20 54	21 03			21 30	21 39		21 43	21 50	
	d					19 54				20 21				20 49			21 05			21 30				21 50	
Wolverton	d					19 58								20 53						21 34					←
Northampton 68	a					20 12								21 07						21 50					21 50
	d					20 22								21 16						21 59					21 59
Long Buckby 68	a					20 33								21 27						→					22 10
Rugby 68	a					20 44						21 15	21 34	21 38										22 11	22 21
Nuneaton 65	a			20 02													21 32								
Coventry 68	a					20 55		20 22		20 50				21 49				21 36						22 22	22 32
Birmingham International 68 ✈	a					21 13		20 33		21 01				22 04				21 50						22 33	22 48
Birmingham New Street ■12 68	a					21 25		20 45		21 13				22 16				22 04						22 45	23 04
Sandwell & Dudley 68	a							20 58										22 24						22 56	
Wolverhampton ■7 68 ⛴	a							21 11		21 38								22 38						23 10	

		LM	LM	VT		LM	LM	SN	LM	SN	LM	LM
		■1	■1	◇■1		■1	■1	■1	■1	■1	■1	■1
			E			F						
				🍴								
London Euston ■15 ⊖60	d	21 08	21 28	21 43			21 54		22 34		23 04	23 44
East Croydon 176 ⛴	d											
Clapham Junction 176	d							21 39		22 39		
Imperial Wharf 176	d							21 44		22 44		
West Brompton ⊖176	d							21 47		22 47		
Kensington (Olympia) ⊖176	d							21 50		22 50		
Shepherd's Bush ⊖176	d							21 53		22 53		
Wembley Central ⊖60,176	d											
Harrow & Wealdstone ⊖60	d						22 06	22 13		23 12	23 16	23 56
Bushey 60	d						22s11					
Watford Junction 60	a	21 24	21 43				22 14	22 20	22 49	23 19	23 23	00 02
	d	21 25	21 44	21u58			22 15		22 50		23 24	00 02
Kings Langley	d						22 19				23 28	00 07
Apsley	d						22 23				23 32	00 11
Hemel Hempstead	d	21 32	21 51				22 26		22 57		23 35	00 13
Berkhamsted	d	21 37	21 56				22 31		23 02		23 40	00 18
Tring	d						22 35				23 44	00 24
Cheddington	d						22 41				23 49	00 29
Leighton Buzzard	d	21 50	22 07				22 47		23 13		23 56	00 34
Bletchley	d	21 57	22 14				22 54		23 20		00 03	00 41
Milton Keynes Central ■10	a	22 05	22 22	22 29			23 02		23 28		00 11	00 48
	d	22 06	22 22	22 30			23 03		23 28		00 11	00 48
Wolverton	d	22 09	22 26			←	23 06		23 32		00 15	00 52
Northampton 68	a	22 27	22 43			22 43	23 20		23 49		00 28	01 10
	d		22 55			22 55						
Long Buckby 68	a		→			23 06						
Rugby 68	a			22 51		23 17						
Nuneaton 65	a											
Coventry 68	a			23 02		23 28						
Birmingham International 68 ✈	a			23 13		23 46						
Birmingham New Street ■12 68	a			23 25		00 04						
Sandwell & Dudley 68	a			23 36								
Wolverhampton ■7 68 ⛴	a			23 50								

A From South Croydon
B To Liverpool Lime Street
C To Manchester Piccadilly
D To Preston
E To Birmingham New Street
F From London Euston

Table 66

Sundays

8 December to 29 December

London - Watford Junction, Milton Keynes Central, Northampton and West Midlands

Network Diagram - see first Page of Table 59

		LM 1 A	LM 1 A	LM 1	LM 🚌	LM 🚌	LM 1	LM 1	LM 1	VT ◇1 B ☕		VT ◇1 C ☕	VT ◇1 B ☕	LM 1 D	SN 1	VT ◇1 E ☕	VT ◇1 ☕	LM 1 F	LM 1	VT ◇1 C ☕		VT ◇1 B ☕	LM 1 D	SN 1	VT ◇1 E ☕
London Euston 15 ⊖60	d			00 15			06 53	07 23	07 52	08 10		08 15	08 20	08 23		08 45	08 50		08 54	09 15		09 20	09 24		09 45
East Croydon 176	d																								
Clapham Junction 176	d														08 15									09 15	
Imperial Wharf 176	d														08 19									09 19	
West Brompton ⊖176	d														08 22									09 22	
Kensington (Olympia) ⊖176	d														08 26									09 26	
Shepherd's Bush ⊖176	d														08 29									09 29	
Wembley Central ⊖60,176	d			00 24																					
Harrow & Wealdstone ⊖60	d			00 29			07 05	07 35	08 04					08 35	08 49				09 06				09 36	09 48	
Bushey 60	d							07s40						08s40									09s41		
Watford Junction 60	a			00 35			07 11	07 43	08 10					08 43	08 56				09 12				09 43	09 58	
	d		00 02	00 35	02 50	02 55	07 12	07 44	08 10					08 43			09u04		09 12				09 44		
Kings Langley	d		00 07	00 40		03 11		07 48						08 48									09 48		
Apsley	d		00 11	00 44		03 22		07 52						08 52									09 52		
Hemel Hempstead	d		00 13	00 46	03 16	03 28	07 19	07 55	08 17					08 54					09 19				09 54		
Berkhamsted	d		00 18	00 51		03 39	07 24	08 00	08 22					08 59					09 24				09 59		
Tring	d		00 24	00 56		03 55	07 28		08 27										09 29						
Cheddington	d		00 29	01 01		04 16	07 34		08 32										09 34						
Leighton Buzzard	d		00 34	01 06	03 53	04 37	07 40	08 13	08 39					09 12					09 40				10 12		
Bletchley	d	00 03	00 41	01 13	04 19	05 03	07 47	08 20	08 45					09 19					09 47				10 19		
Milton Keynes Central 10	a	00 11	00 48	01 19	04 34	05 18	07 55	08 28	08 50	08 55			09 05	09 24		09 31	09 37		09 55			10 06	10 27		10 32
	d	00 11	00 48	01 19			07 56	08 28	08 51					09 24		09 32	09 38		09 56				10 27		10 33
Wolverton	d	00 15	00 52	01 23			07 59	08 32	08 54					09 28				←	09 59				10 31		
Northampton 68	a	00 28	01 10	01 36			08 13	08 45	09 09					09 44				09 44	10 13				10 44		
	d								09 26					10 00				10 00					11 00		
Long Buckby 68	a								09 37					→				10 11					→		
Rugby 68	a								09 48							10 07	10 12	10 22							11 07
Nuneaton 65	a											09 43								10 44					
Coventry 68	a								09 59								10 23	10 33							
Birmingham International 68 ✈	a								10 09								10 34	10 51							
Birmingham New Street 12 68	a								10 26								10 47	11 03							
Sandwell & Dudley 68	a																10 59								
Wolverhampton 7 68	a																11 13								

		VT ◇1 ☕	LM 1 F	LM 1 G	LM 1	VT ◇1 C ☕		VT ◇1 B ☕	LM 1 G	LM 1 D	SN 1	VT ◇1 E ☕	VT ◇1 ☕	LM 1 F	LM 1	VT ◇1 C ☕		VT ◇1 B ☕	LM 1 D		SN 1	VT ◇1 ☕	LM 1 F	LM 1 H	VT ◇1 B ☕
London Euston 15 ⊖60	d	09 50		09 54	10 01	10 15		10 20	10 24	10 28		10 45	10 49		10 53	11 15		11 20	11 24			11 50			12 17
East Croydon 176	d																								
Clapham Junction 176	d										10 15										11 15				
Imperial Wharf 176	d										10 19										11 19				
West Brompton ⊖176	d										10 22										11 22				
Kensington (Olympia) ⊖176	d										10 26										11 26				
Shepherd's Bush ⊖176	d										10 29										11 29				
Wembley Central ⊖60,176	d																								
Harrow & Wealdstone ⊖60	d				10 13					10 40	10 48				11 05				11 36		11 48				
Bushey 60	d														11s10										
Watford Junction 60	a			10 09	10 19				10 39	10 46	10 56				11 13				11 42		11 56				
	d	10u06		10 10	10 19				10 40	10 46			11u03		11 14				11 42			12u05			
Kings Langley	d									10 51									11 47						
Apsley	d									10 55									11 51						
Hemel Hempstead	d			10 17	10 26				10 47	10 57					11 21				11 53						
Berkhamsted	d			10 22	10 31				10 52	11 02					11 26				11 58						
Tring	d				10 36										11 30										
Cheddington	d				10 41										11 36										
Leighton Buzzard	d			10 35	10 47				11 05	11 15					11 42				12 12						
Bletchley	d			10 42					11 12						11 49				12 19						
Milton Keynes Central 10	a	10 37		10 50	10 59			11 06	11 20	11 27		11 32	11 37		11 57	12 02		12 08	12 27			12 28			12 50
	d	10 39		10 50	10 59				11 20	11 28		11 33	11 39		11 58				12 28			12 30			
Wolverton	d		←		11 03					11 32				←	12 01				12 32				←	←	
Northampton 68	a		10 44	11 06	11 16				11 36	11 45				11 45	12 15				12 45				12 45	12 45	
	d		11 00	11 08					11 40	11 58				11 58					12 55	13 02			12 55	13 02	
Long Buckby 68	a		11 11	11 19					11 51	→				12 09					→	→			13 06	13 13	
Rugby 68	a	11 13	11 22	11 30					12 02			12 07	12 13	12 20								12 49	13 17	13 24	
Nuneaton 65	a			11 42		11 46			12 16															13 40	
Coventry 68	a	11 24	11 33										12 23	12 31								12 59	13 29		
Birmingham International 68 ✈	a	11 35	11 51										12 34	12 49								13 10	13 47		
Birmingham New Street 12 68	a	11 47	12 03										12 46	13 01								13 24	13 59		
Sandwell & Dudley 68	a	11 59											12 58												
Wolverhampton 7 68	a	12 13											13 12												

A not 8 December. From London Euston
B To Manchester Piccadilly
C To Liverpool Lime Street
D To Birmingham New Street
E To Glasgow Central
F From London Euston
G To Crewe
H From London Euston to Crewe

Table 66

Sundays

8 December to 29 December

London - Watford Junction, Milton Keynes Central, Northampton and West Midlands

Network Diagram - see first Page of Table 59

	LM 1		LM 1	SN 1	VT ◇1 ☕	VT ◇1 A ☕	VT ◇1 ☕	LM 1	LM 1 B	VT ◇1 C ☕	LM 1		LM 1	SN 1	VT ◇1 ☕	VT ◇1 D ☕	VT ◇1 ☕	LM 1	LM 1 B	VT ◇1 C ☕	LM 1		LM 1	SN 1
London Euston 15 ⊖60 d	11 53		12 14		12 20	12 40	13 00	12 34	12 50	13 17	12 54		13 14		13 20	13 40	14 00	13 34	13 50	14 17	13 54		14 14	
East Croydon 176 d																								
Clapham Junction 176 d				12 05										13 05										14 05
Imperial Wharf 176 d				12 09										13 09										14 09
West Brompton ⊖176 d				12 12										13 12										14 12
Kensington (Olympia) ⊖176 d				12 16										13 16										14 16
Shepherd's Bush ⊖176 d				12 19										13 19										14 19
Wembley Central ⊖60,176 d																								
Harrow & Wealdstone ⊖60 d	12 06		12 26	12 37							13 06		13 26	13 37							14 06		14 26	14 37
Bushey 60 d	12s11		12 31										13 31										14 31	
Watford Junction 60 a	12 14		12 34	12 44				12 49	13 06		13 12		13 34	13 44				13 49	14 06		14 12		14 34	14 44
d	12 14		12 34		12u34			12 50	13 06		13 13		13 34		13u34			13 50	14 06		14 13		14 34	
Kings Langley d			12 39										13 39										14 39	
Apsley d			12 43										13 43										14 43	
Hemel Hempstead d	12 21		12 45					12 57			13 20		13 45					13 57			14 20		14 45	
Berkhamsted d	12 26		12 50					13 02			13 25		13 50					14 02			14 25		14 50	
Tring d	12 31		12a57								13 29		13a57								14 29		14a57	
Cheddington d	12 36										13 35										14 35			
Leighton Buzzard d	12 43							13 15	13 27		13 41							14 15	14 27		14 41			
Bletchley d	12 50							13 22			13 48							14 22			14 48			
Milton Keynes Central 10 a	12 58					13 13		13 27	13 36	13 50	13 54					14 13		14 27	14 37	14 50	14 54			
d	12 58					13 13		13 28	13 37							14 13		14 28	14 37					
Wolverton d	13 02							13 31										14 31						
Northampton 68 a	13 15							13 44	13 51									14 44	14 52					
d								13 55	14 02									14 55	15 02					
Long Buckby 68 a								14 06	14 13									15 06	15 13					
Rugby 68 a							13 51	14 17	14 24								14 51	15 17	15 24					
Nuneaton 65 a									14 39										15 39					
Coventry 68 a					13 21	13 42	14 02	14 29							14 21	14 44	15 02	15 29						
Birmingham International 68 ✈ a					13 32	13 53	14 13	14 47							14 32	14 54	15 13	15 47						
Birmingham New Street 12 68 a					13 44	14 05	14 25	14 59							14 44	15 06	15 25	15 59						
Sandwell & Dudley 68 a					13 56	14 24										15 25								
Wolverhampton 7 68 a					14 10	14 37										15 37								

	VT ◇1 ☕	VT ◇1 A ☕	VT ◇1 ☕	LM 1	LM 1 B	VT ◇1 E ☕	VT ◇1 C ☕		LM 1	LM 1	SN 1	VT ◇1 ☕	VT ◇1 D ☕	VT ◇1 ☕	LM 1	LM 1 B	VT ◇1 E ☕		VT ◇1 C ☕	LM 1	LM 1	SN 1	VT ◇1 ☕	VT ◇1 A ☕
London Euston 15 ⊖60 d	14 20	14 40	15 00	14 34	14 50	15 08	15 17		14 54	15 14		15 20	15 40	16 00	15 34	15 50	16 08		16 17	15 54	16 14		16 20	16 40
East Croydon 176 d																								
Clapham Junction 176 d											15 05											16 05		
Imperial Wharf 176 d											15 09											16 09		
West Brompton ⊖176 d											15 12											16 12		
Kensington (Olympia) ⊖176 d											15 16											16 16		
Shepherd's Bush ⊖176 d											15 19											16 19		
Wembley Central ⊖60,176 d																								
Harrow & Wealdstone ⊖60 d									15 06	15 26	15 37									16 06	16 26	16 37		
Bushey 60 d										15 31											16 31			
Watford Junction 60 a				14 49	15 06				15 12	15 34	15 44				15 49	16 06				16 12	16 34	16 44		
d	14u34			14 50	15 06				15 13	15 34		15u34			15 50	16 06				16 13	16 34		16u34	
Kings Langley d										15 39											16 39			
Apsley d										15 43											16 43			
Hemel Hempstead d				14 57					15 20	15 45					15 57					16 20	16 45			
Berkhamsted d				15 02					15 25	15 50					16 02					16 25	16 50			
Tring d									15 29	15a57										16 29	16a57			
Cheddington d									15 35											16 35				
Leighton Buzzard d				15 15	15 27				15 41						16 15	16 27				16 41				
Bletchley d				15 22					15 48						16 22					16 48				
Milton Keynes Central 10 a		15 13		15 27	15 37	15 41	15 50		15 54				16 13		16 27	16 37	16 41		16 50	16 54				17 13
d		15 13		15 28	15 37								16 13		16 28	16 37								17 13
Wolverton d				15 31											16 31									
Northampton 68 a				15 44	15 52										16 44	16 53								
d				15 55	16 02										16 55	17 02								
Long Buckby 68 a				16 06	16 13										17 06	17 13								
Rugby 68 a			15 52	16 17	16 24									16 51	17 17	17 24								
Nuneaton 65 a					16 39											17 39								
Coventry 68 a	15 21	15 42	16 03	16 29								16 21	16 42	17 02	17 29								17 21	17 44
Birmingham International 68 ✈ a	15 32	15 53	16 13	16 47								16 32	16 53	17 13	17 47								17 32	17 54
Birmingham New Street 12 68 a	15 44	16 05	16 25	16 59								16 44	17 05	17 25	17 59								17 44	18 06
Sandwell & Dudley 68 a		16 24											17 24											18 24
Wolverhampton 7 68 a		16 37											17 37											18 37

A To Edinburgh
B To Crewe
C To Manchester Piccadilly
D To Glasgow Central
E To Chester

Table 66

Sundays

8 December to 29 December

London - Watford Junction, Milton Keynes Central, Northampton and West Midlands

Network Diagram - see first Page of Table 59

	VT	LM	LM		VT	VT	LM	VT	LM	SN	VT	VT	VT		LM	LM	VT	VT	LM	LM	SN	VT	VT	
	◇1	1	1		◇1	◇1	1	◇1	1	1	◇1	R 1	◇1		1	1	◇1	◇1	1	1	1	◇1	◇1	
			A		B	C		D				E				A	B	C					A	
	🛒				🛒	🛒		🛒			🛒	🛒	🛒				🛒	🛒				🛒	🛒	
London Euston 15 ⊖60 d	17 00	16 34	16 50		17 08	17 17	16 54	17 05	17 14		17 20	17 40	18 00		17 34	17 50	18 08	18 17	17 54	18 14		18 20	18 40	
East Croydon 176 ⇌ d																								
Clapham Junction 176 d										17 05											18 05			
Imperial Wharf 176 d										17 09											18 09			
West Brompton ⊖176 d										17 12											18 12			
Kensington (Olympia) ⊖176 d										17 16											18 16			
Shepherd's Bush ⊖176 d										17 19											18 19			
Wembley Central ⊖60,176 d																								
Harrow & Wealdstone ⊖60 d							17 06		17 26	17 37									18 06	18 26	18 37			
Bushey 60 d									17 31											18 31				
Watford Junction 60 a		16 49	17 06				17 12		17 34	17 44					17 49	18 06			18 12	18 34	18 44			
d		16 50	17 06				17 13		17 34		17u34				17 50	18 06			18 13	18 34		18u34		
Kings Langley d									17 39											18 39				
Apsley d									17 43											18 43				
Hemel Hempstead d		16 57					17 20		17 45						17 57				18 20	18 45				
Berkhamsted d		17 02					17 25		17 50						18 02				18 25	18 50				
Tring d							17 29		17a57										18 29	18a57				
Cheddington d							17 35												18 35					
Leighton Buzzard d		17 15	17 27				17 41								18 15	18 27			18 41					
Bletchley d		17 22					17 48								18 22				18 48					
Milton Keynes Central 10 a		17 27	17 37		17 41	17 50	17 54					18 13			18 27	18 37	18 41	18 50	18 54				19 13	
d		17 28	17 37									18 13			18 28	18 37							19 13	
Wolverton d		17 31													18 31									
Northampton 68 a		17 44	17 52												18 44	18 54								
d		17 55	18 02												18 55	19 02								
Long Buckby 68 a		18 06	18 13												19 06	19 13								
Rugby 68 a	17 51	18 17	18 24										18 51		19 17	19 24								
Nuneaton 65 a			18 39					18 03								19 39								
Coventry 68 a	18 02	18 29									18 21	18 44	19 02		19 28							19 22	19 42	
Birmingham International 68 ✈ a	18 13	18 47									18 32	18 54	19 13		19 47							19 32	19 53	
Birmingham New Street 12 68 a	18 25	18 59									18 44	19 06	19 24		19 59							19 44	20 05	
Sandwell & Dudley 68 a												19 24	19 48										20 24	
Wolverhampton 7 68 ⇌ a												19 37	20 02										20 36	

	VT	LM	LM	VT	VT	LM	VT	LM	SN		VT	VT	VT	LM	LM	VT	VT	LM	VT		LM	SN	VT	VT
	◇1	1	1	◇1	◇1	1	◇1	1	1		◇1	◇1	◇1	1	1	◇1	◇1	1	◇1		1	1	◇1	◇1
			A	F	C		D					G			A	D	C		D					
	🛒			🛒	🛒		🛒				🛒	🛒	🛒			🛒	🛒		🛒				🛒	🛒
London Euston 15 ⊖60 d	19 00	18 34	18 50	19 08	19 17	18 54	19 05	19 14			19 20	19 40	20 00	19 34	19 50	20 08	20 15	19 54	20 05		20 14		20 18	20 38
East Croydon 176 ⇌ d																								
Clapham Junction 176 d									19 05													20 05		
Imperial Wharf 176 d									19 09													20 09		
West Brompton ⊖176 d									19 12													20 12		
Kensington (Olympia) ⊖176 d									19 16													20 16		
Shepherd's Bush ⊖176 d									19 19													20 19		
Wembley Central ⊖60,176 d																								
Harrow & Wealdstone ⊖60 d						19 06		19 26	19 36									20 06			20 26	20 37		
Bushey 60 d								19 31													20 31			
Watford Junction 60 a		18 49	19 05			19 12		19 34	19 43					19 49	20 06			20 12			20 34	20 44		
d		18 50	19 06			19 13		19 34			19u34			19 50	20 06			20 13			20 34		20u32	
Kings Langley d								19 39													20 39			
Apsley d								19 43													20 43			
Hemel Hempstead d		18 57				19 20		19 45						19 57				20 20			20 45			
Berkhamsted d		19 02				19 25		19 50						20 02				20 25			20 50			
Tring d						19 29		19a57										20 29			20a57			
Cheddington d						19 35												20 35						
Leighton Buzzard d		19 15	19 27			19 41								20 15	20 27			20 41						
Bletchley d		19 22				19 48								20 22				20 48						
Milton Keynes Central 10 a		19 27	19 37	19 41	19 50	19 54						20 13		20 27	20 37	20 41	20 48	20 54						21 16
d		19 28	19 37									20 13		20 28	20 37									21 16
Wolverton d		19 31												20 31										
Northampton 68 a		19 44	19 53											20 44	20 54									
d		19 55	20 02											20 55	21 06									
Long Buckby 68 a		20 06	20 13											21 06	21 17									
Rugby 68 a	19 52	20 17	20 24										20 51	21 17	21 28									
Nuneaton 65 a			20 39				20 03								21 42				21 03					
Coventry 68 a	20 03	20 29									20 22	20 41	21 02	21 29									21 20	21 46
Birmingham International 68 ✈ a	20 13	20 47									20 32	20 52	21 13	21 47									21 31	21 57
Birmingham New Street 12 68 a	20 24	20 59									20 44	21 03	21 24	21 59									21 44	22 09
Sandwell & Dudley 68 a	20 34										20 56	21 25	21 36										21 56	22 24
Wolverhampton 7 68 ⇌ a	20 46										21 10	21 37	21 51										22 10	22 38

A To Crewe
B To Chester
C To Manchester Piccadilly
D To Liverpool Lime Street
E To Glasgow Central
F To Holyhead
G To Preston

Table 66

Sundays

8 December to 29 December

London - Watford Junction, Milton Keynes Central, Northampton and West Midlands

Network Diagram - see first Page of Table 59

Station			LM 1 A	VT ◇1 B ☕	VT ◇1 ☕	LM 1 C	LM 1	VT ◇1 D ☕	VT ◇1 E ☕	LM 1	SN 1	VT ◇1 E ☕	VT ◇1 ☕	LM 1 F	VT ◇1 ☕	LM 1 C	LM 1	SN 1	LM 1	VT ◇1 ☕	LM 1
London Euston 15	⊖60	d	20 34	20 50	20 54		21 06	21 21	21 25	21 30		21 51	21 55	22 00	22 25		22 28		22 58	23 25	23 34
East Croydon	176	d																			
Clapham Junction	176	d									21 15							22 15			
Imperial Wharf	176	d									21 19							22 19			
West Brompton	⊖176	d									21 22							22 22			
Kensington (Olympia)	⊖176	d									21 25							22 26			
Shepherd's Bush	⊖176	d									21 28							22 29			
Wembley Central	⊖60,176	d																			
Harrow & Wealdstone	⊖60	d								21 42	21 46			22 12			22 40	22 49	23 10		23 46
Bushey	60	d								21s47							22s45				23s51
Watford Junction	60	a	20 49				21 22			21 49	21 53			22 18			22 48	22 56	23 16		23 54
		d	20 50		21u10		21 23			21 50			22u09	22 19	22u39		22 49		23 17	23u39	23 55
Kings Langley		d								21 54							22 53		23 21		23 59
Apsley		d								21 58							22 57		23 25		00 03
Hemel Hempstead		d	20 57				21 30			22 01				22 26			23 00		23 28		00 06
Berkhamsted		d	21 03				21 35			22 06				22 31			23 05		23 33		00 11
Tring		d					21 39							22 35					23 37		00 15
Cheddington		d					21 45							22 41					23 43		00 21
Leighton Buzzard		d	21 16				21 49			22 19				22 47			23 18		23 49		00 27
Bletchley		d	21 23				21 56			22 26				22 54			23 25		23 56		00 34
Milton Keynes Central 10		a	21 28	21 35	21 41		22 04		22 13	22 34		22 37	22 43	23 02	23 11		23 33		00 04	00 11	00 42
		d	21 29	21 37	21 43		22 05			22 34		22 39	22 45	23 03	23 12		23 33		00 05	00 12	00 43
Wolverton		d	21 32			←	22 08			22 38				23 06		←	23 37		00 08		00 46
Northampton	68	a	21 45			21 45	22 22			22 50				23 20		23 20	23 50		00 22		01 00
		d	21 55			21 55				22 52				23 32		23 32					
Long Buckby	68	a	↪			22 06				23 03				↪		23 43					
Rugby	68	a		21 59	22 05	22 17				23 14		23 18	23 22		23 46	23 54				00s46	
Nuneaton	65	a						22 51				23 29									
Coventry	68	a			22 16	22 29				23 25			23 33		23 57	00 05				00s58	
Birmingham International	68 ✈	a			22 27	22 47				23 55			23 44		00 08					01s09	
Birmingham New Street 12	68	a			22 39	22 59				00 07			23 55		00 21					01s22	
Sandwell & Dudley	68	a			22 51																
Wolverhampton 7	68	a			23 06								00 17		00 43					01 44	

Sundays

5 January to 9 February

Station			LM 1 C	LM 1 C	LM 1	LM 🚌	LM 🚌	LM 1	LM 1	LM 1	VT ◇1 E ☕	VT ◇1 D ☕	VT ◇1 E ☕	LM 1 A	SN 1	VT ◇1 G ☕	VT ◇1 ☕	LM 1 C	LM 1	VT ◇1 D ☕	VT ◇1 E ☕	LM 1 A	SN 1	VT ◇1 ☕
London Euston 15	⊖60	d			00 15			06 53	07 23	07 52	08 10	08 15	08 20	08 23		08 45	08 50		08 54	09 15	09 20	09 24		09 50
East Croydon	176	d																						
Clapham Junction	176	d													08 15								09 15	
Imperial Wharf	176	d													08 19								09 19	
West Brompton	⊖176	d													08 22								09 22	
Kensington (Olympia)	⊖176	d													08 26								09 26	
Shepherd's Bush	⊖176	d													08 29								09 29	
Wembley Central	⊖60,176	d			00 24																			
Harrow & Wealdstone	⊖60	d			00 29			07 05	07 35	08 04				08 35	08 49				09 06			09 36	09 48	
Bushey	60	d							07s40					08s40								09s41		
Watford Junction	60	a			00 35			07 11	07 43	08 10				08 43	08 56				09 12			09 43	09 58	
		d		00 02	00 35	02 50	02 55	07 12	07 44	08 10				08 43			09u04		09 12			09 44		10u06
Kings Langley		d		00 07	00 40		03 11		07 48					08 48								09 48		
Apsley		d		00 11	00 44		03 22		07 52					08 52								09 52		
Hemel Hempstead		d		00 13	00 46	03 16	03 28	07 19	07 55	08 17				08 54					09 19			09 54		
Berkhamsted		d		00 18	00 51		03 39	07 24	08 00	08 22				08 59					09 24			09 59		
Tring		d		00 24	00 56		03 55	07 28		08 27									09 29					
Cheddington		d		00 29	01 01		04 16	07 34		08 32									09 34					
Leighton Buzzard		d		00 34	01 06	03 53	04 37	07 40	08 13	08 39				09 12					09 40			10 12		
Bletchley		d	00 03	00 41	01 13	04 19	05 03	07 47	08 20	08 45				09 19					09 47			10 19		
Milton Keynes Central 10		a	00 11	00 48	01 19	04 34	05 18	07 55	08 28	08 50	08 55		09 05	09 24		09 31	09 37		09 55		10 06	10 27		10 37
		d	00 11	00 48	01 19			07 56	08 28	08 51				09 24		09 32	09 38		09 56			10 27		10 39
Wolverton		d	00 15	00 52	01 23			07 59	08 32	08 54				09 28				←	09 59			10 31		
Northampton	68	a	00 28	01 10	01 36			08 13	08 45	09 09				09 44				09 44	10 13			10 44		
		d								09 26				10 00				10 00				11 00		
Long Buckby	68	a								09 37				↪				10 11				↪		
Rugby	68	a								09 48						10 07	10 12	10 22						11 13
Nuneaton	65	a										09 43								10 44				
Coventry	68	a								09 59							10 23	10 33						11 24
Birmingham International	68 ✈	a								10 09							10 34	10 51						11 35
Birmingham New Street 12	68	a								10 26							10 47	11 03						11 47
Sandwell & Dudley	68	a															10 59							11 59
Wolverhampton 7	68	a															11 13							12 13

A To Birmingham New Street
B To Preston
C From London Euston
D To Liverpool Lime Street
E To Manchester Piccadilly
F To Coventry
G To Crewe

Table 66

Sundays

5 January to 9 February

London - Watford Junction, Milton Keynes Central, Northampton and West Midlands

Network Diagram - see first Page of Table 59

			LM	LM	LM	VT	VT	LM	LM	SN	VT	LM	LM	VT	VT	LM	SN	VT	LM	LM	VT	LM	LM
			1	1	1	◇1	◇1	1	1	1	◇1	1	1	◇1	◇1	1	1	◇1	1	1	◇1	1	1
			A	B		C	D	B	E			A		C	D	E			A	F	D		
						☕	☕				☕			☕	☕			☕			☕		
London Euston 15	⊖60	d		09 54	10 01	10 15	10 20	10 24	10 28		10 49		10 53	11 15	11 20	11 24		11 50			12 17	11 53	12 14
East Croydon	176	d																					
Clapham Junction	176	d								10 15							11 15						
Imperial Wharf	176	d								10 19							11 19						
West Brompton	⊖176	d								10 22							11 22						
Kensington (Olympia)	⊖176	d								10 26							11 26						
Shepherd's Bush	⊖176	d								10 29							11 29						
Wembley Central	⊖60,176	d																					
Harrow & Wealdstone	⊖60	d			10 13				10 40	10 48			11 05			11 36	11 48					12 06	12 26
Bushey	60	d											11s10									12s11	12 31
Watford Junction	60	a		10 09	10 19			10 39	10 46	10 56			11 13			11 42	11 56					12 14	12 34
		d		10 10	10 19			10 40	10 46		11u03		11 14			11 42		12u05				12 14	12 34
Kings Langley		d							10 51							11 47							12 39
Apsley		d							10 55							11 51							12 43
Hemel Hempstead		d		10 17	10 26			10 47	10 57				11 21			11 53						12 21	12 45
Berkhamsted		d		10 22	10 31			10 52	11 02				11 26			11 58						12 26	12 50
Tring		d			10 36								11 30									12 31	12a57
Cheddington		d			10 41								11 36									12 36	
Leighton Buzzard		d		10 35	10 47			11 05	11 15				11 42			12 12						12 43	
Bletchley		d		10 42				11 12					11 49			12 19						12 50	
Milton Keynes Central 10		a		10 50	10 59		11 06	11 20	11 27		11 37		11 57	12 02	12 08	12 27		12 28			12 50	12 58	
		d		10 50	10 59			11 20	11 28		11 39		11 58			12 28		12 30				12 58	
Wolverton		d	←		11 03				11 32			←	12 01			12 32			←	←		13 02	
Northampton	68	a	10 44	11 06	11 16			11 36	11 45			11 45	12 15			12 45			12 45	12 45		13 15	
		d	11 00	11 08				11 40	11 58			11 58				12 55 → / 13 02 →			12 55	13 02			
Long Buckby	68	a	11 11	11 19				11 51	→			12 09							13 06	13 13			
Rugby	68	a	11 22	11 30				12 02			12 13	12 20						12 49	13 17	13 24			
Nuneaton	65	a		11 42		11 46		12 16												13 40			
Coventry	68	a	11 33								12 23	12 31						12 59	13 29				
Birmingham International	68 ✈	a	11 51								12 34	12 49						13 10	13 47				
Birmingham New Street 12	68	a	12 03								12 46	13 01						13 24	13 59				
Sandwell & Dudley	68	a									12 58												
Wolverhampton 7	68 🚊	a									13 12												

			SN	VT	VT	VT	LM	LM	VT	LM	LM	SN	VT	VT	VT	LM	LM	VT	LM	LM	SN	VT	VT
			1	◇1	◇1	◇1	1	1	◇1	1	1	1	◇1	◇1	◇1	1	1	◇1	1	1	1	◇1	◇1
					G			B	D					H			B	D					G
				☕	☕	☕			☕				☕	☕	☕			☕				☕	☕
London Euston 15	⊖60	d		12 20	12 40	13 00	12 34	12 50	13 17	12 54	13 14		13 20	13 40	14 00	13 34	13 50	14 17	13 54	14 14		14 20	14 40
East Croydon	176	d																					
Clapham Junction	176	d	12 05									13 05									14 05		
Imperial Wharf	176	d	12 09									13 09									14 09		
West Brompton	⊖176	d	12 12									13 12									14 12		
Kensington (Olympia)	⊖176	d	12 16									13 16									14 16		
Shepherd's Bush	⊖176	d	12 19									13 19									14 19		
Wembley Central	⊖60,176	d																					
Harrow & Wealdstone	⊖60	d	12 37							13 06	13 26	13 37							14 06	14 26	14 37		
Bushey	60	d									13 31									14 31			
Watford Junction	60	a	12 44				12 49	13 06		13 12	13 34	13 44				13 49	14 06		14 12	14 34	14 44		
		d		12u34			12 50	13 06		13 13	13 34		13u34			13 50	14 06		14 13	14 34		14u34	
Kings Langley		d									13 39									14 39			
Apsley		d									13 43									14 43			
Hemel Hempstead		d					12 57			13 20	13 45					13 57			14 20	14 45			
Berkhamsted		d					13 02			13 25	13 50					14 02			14 25	14 50			
Tring		d								13 29	13a57								14 29	14a57			
Cheddington		d								13 35									14 35				
Leighton Buzzard		d					13 15	13 27		13 41						14 15	14 27		14 41				
Bletchley		d					13 22			13 48						14 22			14 48				
Milton Keynes Central 10		a			13 13		13 27	13 36	13 50	13 54				14 13		14 27	14 37	14 50	14 54				15 13
		d			13 13		13 28	13 37						14 13		14 28	14 37						15 13
Wolverton		d					13 31									14 31							
Northampton	68	a					13 44	13 51								14 44	14 52						
		d					13 55	14 02								14 55	15 02						
Long Buckby	68	a					14 06	14 13								15 06	15 13						
Rugby	68	a				13 51	14 17	14 24							14 51	15 17	15 24						
Nuneaton	65	a						14 39									15 39						
Coventry	68	a		13 21	13 42	14 02	14 29						14 21	14 44	15 02	15 29						15 21	15 42
Birmingham International	68 ✈	a		13 32	13 53	14 13	14 47						14 32	14 54	15 13	15 47						15 32	15 53
Birmingham New Street 12	68	a		13 44	14 05	14 25	14 59						14 44	15 06	15 25	15 59						15 44	16 05
Sandwell & Dudley	68	a		13 56	14 24									15 25									16 24
Wolverhampton 7	68 🚊	a		14 10	14 37									15 37									16 37

A From London Euston
B To Crewe
C To Liverpool Lime Street
D To Manchester Piccadilly
E To Birmingham New Street
F From London Euston to Crewe
G To Edinburgh
H To Glasgow Central

Table 66

Sundays

5 January to 9 February

London - Watford Junction, Milton Keynes Central, Northampton and West Midlands

Network Diagram - see first Page of Table 59

	VT ◇1 ☕	LM 1	LM 1 A	VT ◇1 B ☕	VT ◇1 C ☕	LM 1	LM 1	SN 1	VT ◇1 ☕	VT ◇1 D ☕	VT ◇1 ☕	LM 1	LM 1 A	VT ◇1 B ☕	VT ◇1 C ☕	LM 1	LM 1	SN 1	VT ◇1 ☕	VT ◇1 E ☕	VT ◇1 ☕	LM 1
London Euston 15 ⊖60 d	15 00	14 34	14 50	15 08	15 17	14 54	15 14		15 20	15 40	16 00	15 34	15 50	16 08	16 17	15 54	16 14		16 20	16 40	17 00	16 34
East Croydon 176 d																						
Clapham Junction 176 d								15 05										16 05				
Imperial Wharf 176 d								15 09										16 09				
West Brompton ⊖176 d								15 12										16 12				
Kensington (Olympia) ⊖176 d								15 16										16 16				
Shepherd's Bush ⊖176 d								15 19										16 19				
Wembley Central ⊖60,176 d																						
Harrow & Wealdstone ⊖60 d						15 06	15 26	15 37								16 06	16 26	16 37				
Bushey 60 d							15 31										16 31					
Watford Junction 60 a		14 49	15 06			15 12	15 34	15 44				15 49	16 06			16 12	16 34	16 44				16 49
d		14 50	15 06			15 13	15 34		15u34			15 50	16 06			16 13	16 34		16u34			16 50
Kings Langley d							15 39										16 39					
Apsley d							15 43										16 43					
Hemel Hempstead d		14 57				15 20	15 45					15 57				16 20	16 45					16 57
Berkhamsted d		15 02				15 25	15 50					16 02				16 25	16 50					17 02
Tring d						15 29	15a57									16 29	16a57					
Cheddington d						15 35										16 35						
Leighton Buzzard d		15 15	15 27			15 41						16 15	16 27			16 41						17 15
Bletchley d		15 22				15 48						16 22				16 48						17 22
Milton Keynes Central 10 a		15 27	15 37	15 41	15 50	15 54				16 13		16 27	16 37	16 41	16 50	16 54				17 13		17 27
d		15 28	15 37							16 13		16 28	16 37							17 14		17 28
Wolverton d		15 31										16 31										17 31
Northampton 68 a		15 44	15 52									16 44	16 53									17 44
d		15 55	16 02									16 55	17 02									17 55
Long Buckby 68 a		16 06	16 13									17 06	17 13									18 06
Rugby 68 a	15 52	16 17	16 24								16 51	17 17	17 24								17 51	18 17
Nuneaton 65 a			16 39										17 39									
Coventry 68 a	16 03	16 29							16 21	16 42	17 02	17 29							17 21	17 42	18 02	18 29
Birmingham International 68 ✈ a	16 13	16 47							16 32	16 53	17 13	17 47							17 32	17 53	18 13	18 47
Birmingham New Street 12 68 a	16 25	16 59							16 44	17 05	17 25	17 59							17 44	18 06	18 25	18 59
Sandwell & Dudley 68 a										17 24										18 25		
Wolverhampton 7 68 a										17 37										18 37		

	LM 1 A	VT ◇1 B ☕	VT ◇1 C ☕	LM 1	VT ◇1 F ☕	LM 1	SN 1	VT ◇1 ☕	VT R 1 D ☕	VT ◇1 ☕	LM 1	LM 1 A	VT ◇1 B ☕	VT ◇1 C ☕	LM 1	LM 1	SN 1	VT ◇1 ☕	VT ◇1 A ☕	VT ◇1 ☕	LM 1	LM 1 A
London Euston 15 ⊖60 d	16 50	17 08	17 17	16 54	17 05	17 14		17 20	17 40	18 00	17 34	17 50	18 08	18 17	17 54	18 14		18 20	18 40	19 00	18 34	18 50
East Croydon 176 d																						
Clapham Junction 176 d							17 05										18 05					
Imperial Wharf 176 d							17 09										18 09					
West Brompton ⊖176 d							17 12										18 12					
Kensington (Olympia) ⊖176 d							17 16										18 16					
Shepherd's Bush ⊖176 d							17 19										18 19					
Wembley Central ⊖60,176 d																						
Harrow & Wealdstone ⊖60 d				17 06		17 26	17 37								18 06	18 26	18 37					
Bushey 60 d						17 31										18 31						
Watford Junction 60 a	17 06			17 12		17 34	17 44				17 49	18 06			18 12	18 34	18 44				18 49	19 05
d	17 06			17 13		17 34		17u34			17 50	18 06			18 13	18 34		18u34			18 50	19 06
Kings Langley d						17 39										18 39						
Apsley d						17 43										18 43						
Hemel Hempstead d				17 20		17 45					17 57				18 20	18 45					18 57	
Berkhamsted d				17 25		17 50					18 02				18 25	18 50					19 02	
Tring d				17 29		17a57									18 29	18a57						
Cheddington d				17 35											18 35							
Leighton Buzzard d	17 27			17 41							18 15	18 27			18 41						19 15	19 27
Bletchley d				17 48							18 22				18 48						19 22	
Milton Keynes Central 10 a	17 37	17 41	17 50	17 54					18 13		18 27	18 37	18 41	18 50	18 54				19 13		19 27	19 37
d	17 37								18 13		18 28	18 37							19 13		19 28	19 37
Wolverton d											18 31										19 31	
Northampton 68 a	17 52										18 44	18 54									19 44	19 53
d	18 02										18 55	19 02									19 55	20 02
Long Buckby 68 a	18 13										19 06	19 13									20 06	20 13
Rugby 68 a	18 24									18 51	19 17	19 24								19 52	20 17	20 24
Nuneaton 65 a	18 39				18 03							19 39										20 39
Coventry 68 a								18 21	18 44	19 02	19 28							19 22	19 42	20 03	20 29	
Birmingham International 68 ✈ a								18 32	18 54	19 13	19 47							19 32	19 53	20 13	20 47	
Birmingham New Street 12 68 a								18 44	19 06	19 24	19 59							19 44	20 05	20 24	20 59	
Sandwell & Dudley 68 a									19 24	19 48									20 24	20 34		
Wolverhampton 7 68 a									19 37	20 02									20 36	20 46		

A To Crewe
B To Chester
C To Manchester Piccadilly
D To Glasgow Central
E To Edinburgh
F To Liverpool Lime Street

Table 66

Sundays

5 January to 9 February

London - Watford Junction, Milton Keynes Central, Northampton and West Midlands

Network Diagram - see first Page of Table 59

	VT	VT	LM	VT	LM	SN	VT	VT	VT	LM	LM	VT	VT	LM	VT	LM	SN	VT	VT	LM	VT
	◇1	◇1	1	◇1	1	1	◇1	◇1	◇1	1	1	◇1	◇1	1	◇1	1	1	◇1	◇1	1	◇1
	A	B		C				D			E	C	B		C					F	D
	🍴	🍴		🍴			🍴	🍴	🍴			🍴	🍴		🍴			🍴	🍴		🍴
London Euston 15 ⊖60 d	19 08	19 17	18 54	19 05	19 14		19 20	19 40	20 00	19 34	19 50	20 08	20 15	19 54	20 05	20 14		20 18	20 38	20 34	20 50
East Croydon 176 🚌 d																					
Clapham Junction 176 d						19 05											20 05				
Imperial Wharf 176 d						19 09											20 09				
West Brompton ⊖176 d						19 12											20 12				
Kensington (Olympia) ⊖176 d						19 16											20 16				
Shepherd's Bush ⊖176 d						19 19											20 19				
Wembley Central ⊖60,176 d																					
Harrow & Wealdstone ⊖60 d			19 06		19 26	19 36								20 06		20 26	20 37				
Bushey 60 d					19 31											20 31					
Watford Junction 60 a			19 12		19 34	19 43				19 49	20 06			20 12		20 34	20 44			20 49	
d			19 13		19 34		19u34			19 50	20 06			20 13		20 34		20u32		20 50	
Kings Langley d					19 39											20 39					
Apsley d					19 43											20 43					
Hemel Hempstead d			19 20		19 45					19 57				20 20		20 45				20 57	
Berkhamsted d			19 25		19 50					20 02				20 25		20 50				21 03	
Tring d			19 29		19a57									20 29		20a57					
Cheddington d			19 35											20 35							
Leighton Buzzard d			19 41							20 15	20 27			20 41						21 16	
Bletchley d			19 48							20 22				20 48						21 23	
Milton Keynes Central 10 a	19 41	19 50	19 54					20 13		20 27	20 37	20 41	20 48	20 54					21 16	21 28	21 35
d								20 13		20 28	20 37								21 16	21 29	21 37
Wolverton d										20 31										21 32	
Northampton 68 a										20 44	20 54									21 45	
d										20 55	21 06									21 55	
Long Buckby 68 a										21 06	21 17									↦	
Rugby 68 a									20 51	21 17	21 28										21 59
Nuneaton 65 a				20 03							21 42				21 03						
Coventry 68 a							20 22	20 42	21 02	21 29								21 20	21 46		
Birmingham International 68 ✈ a							20 32	20 53	21 13	21 47								21 31	21 57		
Birmingham New Street 12 68 a							20 44	21 04	21 24	21 59								21 44	22 09		
Sandwell & Dudley 68 a							20 56	21 24	21 36									21 56	22 24		
Wolverhampton 7 68 🚌 a							21 10	21 37	21 51									22 10	22 38		

	VT	LM	LM	VT	VT	LM	SN	VT	VT	LM	VT	LM	LM	SN	LM	VT	LM
	◇1	1	1	◇1	◇1	1	1	◇1	◇1	1	◇1	1	1	1	1	◇1	1
		G		C	B			B		H		G					
	🍴			🍴	🍴			🍴	🍴		🍴					🍴	
London Euston 15 ⊖60 d	20 54		21 06	21 21	21 25	21 30		21 51	21 55	22 00	22 25		22 28		22 58	23 25	23 34
East Croydon 176 🚌 d																	
Clapham Junction 176 d							21 15							22 15			
Imperial Wharf 176 d							21 19							22 19			
West Brompton ⊖176 d							21 22							22 22			
Kensington (Olympia) ⊖176 d							21 25							22 26			
Shepherd's Bush ⊖176 d							21 28							22 29			
Wembley Central ⊖60,176 d																	
Harrow & Wealdstone ⊖60 d						21 42	21 46			22 12			22 40	22 49	23 10		23 46
Bushey 60 d						21s47							22s45				23s51
Watford Junction 60 a			21 22			21 49	21 53			22 18			22 48	22 56	23 16		23 54
d	21u10		21 23			21 50			22u09	22 19	22u39		22 49		23 17	23u39	23 55
Kings Langley d						21 54							22 53		23 21		23 59
Apsley d						21 58							22 57		23 25		00 03
Hemel Hempstead d			21 30			22 01				22 26			23 00		23 28		00 06
Berkhamsted d			21 35			22 06				22 31			23 05		23 33		00 11
Tring d			21 39							22 35					23 37		00 15
Cheddington d			21 45							22 41					23 43		00 21
Leighton Buzzard d			21 49			22 19				22 47			23 18		23 49		00 27
Bletchley d			21 56			22 26				22 54			23 25		23 56		00 34
Milton Keynes Central 10 a	21 41		22 04		22 13	22 34		22 37	22 43	23 02	23 11		23 33		00 04	00 11	00 42
d	21 43		22 05			22 34		22 39	22 45	23 03	23 12		23 33		00 05	00 12	00 43
Wolverton d		↤	22 08			22 38				23 06		↤	23 37		00 08		00 46
Northampton 68 a		21 45	22 22			22 50				23 20		23 20	23 50		00 22		01 00
d		21 55				22 52				23 32		23 32					
Long Buckby 68 a		22 06				23 03				↦		23 43					
Rugby 68 a	22 05	22 17				23 14		23 18	23 22		23 46	23 54				00s46	
Nuneaton 65 a				22 51				23 29									
Coventry 68 a	22 16	22 29				23 25			23 33		23 57	00 05				00s58	
Birmingham International 68 ✈ a	22 27	22 47				23 55			23 44		00 08					01s09	
Birmingham New Street 12 68 a	22 39	22 59				00 07			23 55		00 21					01s22	
Sandwell & Dudley 68 a	22 51																
Wolverhampton 7 68 🚌 a	23 06								00 17		00 43					01 44	

A To Holyhead
B To Manchester Piccadilly
C To Liverpool Lime Street
D To Preston
E To Crewe
F To Birmingham New Street
G From London Euston
H To Coventry

Table 66

Sundays

16 February to 23 March

London - Watford Junction, Milton Keynes Central, Northampton and West Midlands

Network Diagram - see first Page of Table 59

	LM	LM	LM	LM	LM	LM	LM	LM	VT		VT	VT	LM	SN	VT	LM	LM	VT	VT		LM	SN	VT	VT
	1	1	1			1	1	1	◇1		◇1	◇1	1	1	◇1	1	1	◇1	◇1		1	1	◇1	◇1
	A	A							B		C	B	D			A		C	B		D		E	
				🚌	🚌				☕		☕	☕			☕			☕	☕				☕	☕
London Euston 15 ⊖60 d			00 15			06 53	07 23	07 52	08 10		08 15	08 20	08 23		08 50		08 54	09 15	09 20		09 24		09 45	09 50
East Croydon 176 🚊 d																								
Clapham Junction 176 d														08 15								09 15		
Imperial Wharf 176 d														08 19								09 19		
West Brompton ⊖176 d														08 22								09 22		
Kensington (Olympia) ⊖176 d														08 26								09 26		
Shepherd's Bush ⊖176 d														08 29								09 29		
Wembley Central ⊖60,176 d			00 24																					
Harrow & Wealdstone ⊖60 d			00 29			07 05	07 35	08 04					08 35	08 49			09 06				09 36	09 48		
Bushey 60 d							07s40						08s40								09s41			
Watford Junction 60 a			00 35			07 11	07 43	08 10					08 43	08 56			09 12				09 43	09 58		
d		00 02	00 35	02 50	02 55	07 12	07 44	08 10					08 43		09u04		09 12				09 44			10u06
Kings Langley d		00 07	00 40		03 11		07 48						08 48								09 48			
Apsley d		00 11	00 44		03 22		07 52						08 52								09 52			
Hemel Hempstead d		00 13	00 46	03 16	03 28	07 19	07 55	08 17					08 54				09 19				09 54			
Berkhamsted d		00 18	00 51		03 39	07 24	08 00	08 22					08 59				09 24				09 59			
Tring d		00 24	00 56		03 55	07 28		08 27									09 29							
Cheddington d		00 29	01 01		04 16	07 34		08 32									09 34							
Leighton Buzzard d		00 34	01 06	03 53	04 37	07 40	08 13	08 39					09 12				09 40				10 12			
Bletchley d	00 03	00 41	01 13	04 19	05 03	07 47	08 20	08 45					09 19				09 47				10 19			
Milton Keynes Central 10 a	00 11	00 48	01 19	04 34	05 18	07 55	08 28	08 50	08 55			09 05	09 24		09 37		09 55		10 06		10 27		10 32	10 37
d	00 11	00 48	01 19			07 56	08 28	08 51					09 24		09 38		09 56				10 27		10 33	10 39
Wolverton d	00 15	00 52	01 23			07 59	08 32	08 54					09 28			←	09 59				10 31			
Northampton 68 a	00 28	01 10	01 36			08 13	08 45	09 09					09 44			09 44	10 13				10 44			
d								09 26					10 00			10 00					11 00			
Long Buckby 68 a								09 37					→			10 11					→			
Rugby 68 a								09 48							10 12	10 22							11 07	11 13
Nuneaton 65 a											09 43							10 44						
Coventry 68 a								09 59							10 23	10 33								11 24
Birmingham International 68 ✈ a								10 09							10 34	10 51								11 35
Birmingham New Street 12 68 a								10 26							10 47	11 03								11 47
Sandwell & Dudley 68 a															10 59									11 59
Wolverhampton 7 68 🚊 a															11 13									12 13

	LM	LM	LM	VT	VT		LM	LM	SN	VT	VT	LM	LM	VT	VT		LM	SN	VT	LM	LM	VT	LM
	1	1	1	◇1	◇1		1	1	1	◇1	◇1	1	1	◇1	◇1		1	1	◇1	1	1	◇1	1
	A	F		C	B		F	D		E		A		C	B		D			A	G	B	
				☕	☕					☕	☕			☕	☕				☕			☕	
London Euston 15 ⊖60 d		09 54	10 01	10 15	10 20		10 24	10 28		10 45	10 49		10 53	11 15	11 20		11 24		11 50			12 17	11 53
East Croydon 176 🚊 d																							
Clapham Junction 176 d									10 15									11 15					
Imperial Wharf 176 d									10 19									11 19					
West Brompton ⊖176 d									10 22									11 22					
Kensington (Olympia) ⊖176 d									10 26									11 26					
Shepherd's Bush ⊖176 d									10 29									11 29					
Wembley Central ⊖60,176 d																							
Harrow & Wealdstone ⊖60 d			10 13					10 40	10 48				11 05				11 36	11 48					12 06
Bushey 60 d													11s10										12s11
Watford Junction 60 a		10 09	10 19				10 39	10 46	10 56				11 13				11 42	11 56					12 14
d		10 10	10 19				10 40	10 46			11u03		11 14				11 42		12u05				12 14
Kings Langley d								10 51									11 47						
Apsley d								10 55									11 51						
Hemel Hempstead d		10 17	10 26				10 47	10 57					11 21				11 53						12 21
Berkhamsted d		10 22	10 31				10 52	11 02					11 26				11 58						12 26
Tring d			10 36										11 30										12 31
Cheddington d			10 41										11 36										12 36
Leighton Buzzard d		10 35	10 47				11 05	11 15					11 42				12 12						12 43
Bletchley d		10 42					11 12						11 49				12 19						12 50
Milton Keynes Central 10 a		10 50	10 59		11 06		11 20	11 27		11 32	11 37		11 57	12 02	12 08		12 27		12 28			12 50	12 58
d		10 50	10 59				11 20	11 28		11 33	11 39		11 58				12 28		12 30				12 58
Wolverton d	←		11 03					11 32				←	12 01				12 32			←	←		13 02
Northampton 68 a	10 44	11 06	11 16				11 36	11 45				11 45	12 15				12 45			12 45	12 45		13 15
d	11 00	11 08					11 40	11 58				11 58					12 55 13 02			12 55	13 02		
Long Buckby 68 a	11 11	11 19					11 51	→				12 09					→ →			13 06	13 13		
Rugby 68 a	11 22	11 30					12 02			12 07	12 13	12 20							12 49	13 17	13 24		
Nuneaton 65 a		11 42		11 46			12 16														13 40		
Coventry 68 a	11 33										12 23	12 31							12 59	13 29			
Birmingham International 68 ✈ a	11 51										12 34	12 49							13 10	13 47			
Birmingham New Street 12 68 a	12 03										12 46	13 01							13 24	13 59			
Sandwell & Dudley 68 a											12 58												
Wolverhampton 7 68 🚊 a											13 12												

A From London Euston
B To Manchester Piccadilly
C To Liverpool Lime Street
D To Birmingham New Street
E To Glasgow Central
F To Crewe
G From London Euston to Crewe

Table 66

Sundays

16 February to 23 March

London - Watford Junction, Milton Keynes Central, Northampton and West Midlands

Network Diagram - see first Page of Table 59

	LM	SN	VT	VT	VT	LM	LM	VT	LM	LM	SN	VT	VT	VT	LM	LM	VT	LM	LM	SN	VT
	1	1	◇1	◇1	◇1	1	1	◇1	1	1	1	◇1	◇1	◇1	1	1	◇1	1	1	1	◇1
				A			B	C					D			B	C				
			☕	☕	☕			☕				☕	☕	☕			☕				☕
London Euston [15] ⊖60 d	12 14		12 20	12 40	13 00	12 34	12 50	13 17	12 54	13 14		13 20	13 40	14 00	13 34	13 50	14 17	13 54	14 14		14 20
East Croydon 176 d																					
Clapham Junction 176 d		12 05									13 05									14 05	
Imperial Wharf 176 d		12 09									13 09									14 09	
West Brompton ⊖176 d		12 12									13 12									14 12	
Kensington (Olympia) ⊖176 d		12 16									13 16									14 16	
Shepherd's Bush ⊖176 d		12 19									13 19									14 19	
Wembley Central ⊖60,176 d																					
Harrow & Wealdstone ⊖60 d	12 26	12 37							13 06	13 26	13 37							14 06	14 26	14 37	
Bushey 60 d	12 31									13 31									14 31		
Watford Junction 60 a	12 34	12 44				12 49	13 06		13 12	13 34	13 44				13 49	14 06		14 12	14 34	14 44	
d	12 34		12u34			12 50	13 06		13 13	13 34		13u34			13 50	14 06		14 13	14 34		14u34
Kings Langley d	12 39									13 39									14 39		
Apsley d	12 43									13 43									14 43		
Hemel Hempstead d	12 45					12 57			13 20	13 45					13 57			14 20	14 45		
Berkhamsted d	12 50					13 02			13 25	13 50					14 02			14 25	14 50		
Tring d	12a57								13 29	13a57								14 29	14a57		
Cheddington d									13 35									14 35			
Leighton Buzzard d						13 15	13 27		13 41						14 15	14 27		14 41			
Bletchley d						13 22			13 48						14 22			14 48			
Milton Keynes Central [10] a				13 13		13 27	13 36	13 50	13 54				14 13		14 27	14 37	14 50	14 54			
d				13 13		13 28	13 37						14 13		14 28	14 37					
Wolverton d						13 31									14 31						
Northampton 68 a						13 44	13 51								14 44	14 52					
d						13 55	14 02								14 55	15 02					
Long Buckby 68 a						14 06	14 13								15 06	15 13					
Rugby 68 a					13 51	14 17	14 24							14 51	15 17	15 24					
Nuneaton 65 a							14 39									15 39					
Coventry 68 a			13 21	13 42	14 02	14 28						14 21	14 44	15 02	15 28						15 21
Birmingham International 68 ✈ a			13 32	13 53	14 13	14 47						14 32	14 54	15 13	15 47						15 32
Birmingham New Street [12] 68 a			13 44	14 05	14 25	14 59						14 44	15 06	15 25	15 59						15 44
Sandwell & Dudley 68 a			13 56	14 24									15 25								
Wolverhampton [7] 68 a			14 10	14 37									15 37								

	VT	VT	LM	LM	VT	VT	LM	LM	SN	VT	VT	VT	LM	LM	VT	VT	LM	LM	SN	VT	VT	VT
	◇1	◇1	1	1	◇1	◇1	1	1	1	◇1	◇1	◇1	1	1	◇1	◇1	1	1	1	◇1	◇1	◇1
	A			B	E	C					D			B	E	C					A	
	☕	☕			☕	☕				☕	☕	☕			☕	☕				☕	☕	☕
London Euston [15] ⊖60 d	14 40	15 00	14 34	14 50	15 08	15 17	14 54	15 14		15 20	15 40	16 00	15 34	15 50	16 08	16 17	15 54	16 14		16 20	16 40	17 00
East Croydon 176 d																						
Clapham Junction 176 d									15 05										16 05			
Imperial Wharf 176 d									15 09										16 09			
West Brompton ⊖176 d									15 12										16 12			
Kensington (Olympia) ⊖176 d									15 16										16 16			
Shepherd's Bush ⊖176 d									15 19										16 19			
Wembley Central ⊖60,176 d																						
Harrow & Wealdstone ⊖60 d							15 06	15 26	15 37								16 06	16 26	16 37			
Bushey 60 d								15 31										16 31				
Watford Junction 60 a			14 49	15 06			15 12	15 34	15 44				15 49	16 06			16 12	16 34	16 44			
d			14 50	15 06			15 13	15 34		15u34			15 50	16 06			16 13	16 34		16u34		
Kings Langley d								15 39										16 39				
Apsley d								15 43										16 43				
Hemel Hempstead d			14 57				15 20	15 45					15 57				16 20	16 45				
Berkhamsted d			15 02				15 25	15 50					16 02				16 25	16 50				
Tring d							15 29	15a57									16 29	16a57				
Cheddington d							15 35										16 35					
Leighton Buzzard d			15 15	15 27			15 41						16 15	16 27			16 41					
Bletchley d			15 22				15 48						16 22				16 48					
Milton Keynes Central [10] a	15 13		15 27	15 37	15 41	15 50	15 54				16 13		16 27	16 37	16 41	16 50	16 54				17 13	
d	15 13		15 28	15 37							16 13		16 28	16 37							17 13	
Wolverton d			15 31										16 31									
Northampton 68 a			15 44	15 52									16 44	16 53								
d			15 55	16 02									16 55	17 02								
Long Buckby 68 a			16 06	16 13									17 06	17 13								
Rugby 68 a		15 52	16 17	16 24								16 51	17 17	17 24								17 51
Nuneaton 65 a				16 39										17 39								
Coventry 68 a	15 42	16 03	16 28							16 21	16 42	17 02	17 28							17 21	17 44	18 02
Birmingham International 68 ✈ a	15 53	16 13	16 47							16 32	16 53	17 13	17 47							17 32	17 54	18 13
Birmingham New Street [12] 68 a	16 05	16 25	16 59							16 44	17 05	17 25	17 59							17 44	18 06	18 25
Sandwell & Dudley 68 a	16 24										17 24										18 24	
Wolverhampton [7] 68 a	16 37										17 37										18 37	

A To Edinburgh
B To Crewe
C To Manchester Piccadilly
D To Glasgow Central
E To Chester

Table 66

Sundays

16 February to 23 March

London - Watford Junction, Milton Keynes Central, Northampton and West Midlands

Network Diagram - see first Page of Table 59

	LM 1	LM 1 A	VT ◇1 B ☕	VT ◇1 C ☕	LM 1	VT ◇1 D ☕	LM 1	SN 1	VT ◇1 ☕	VT R 1 E ☕	VT ◇1 ☕	LM 1	LM 1 A	VT ◇1 B ☕	VT ◇1 C ☕	LM 1	LM 1	SN 1	VT ◇1 ☕	VT ◇1 A ☕	VT ◇1 ☕
London Euston 15 ⊖60 d	16 34	16 50	17 08	17 17	16 54	17 05	17 14		17 20	17 40	18 00	17 34	17 50	18 08	18 17	17 54	18 14		18 20	18 40	19 00
East Croydon 176 🚊 d																					
Clapham Junction 176 d								17 05										18 05			
Imperial Wharf 176 d								17 09										18 09			
West Brompton ⊖176 d								17 12										18 12			
Kensington (Olympia) ⊖176 d								17 16										18 16			
Shepherd's Bush ⊖176 d								17 19										18 19			
Wembley Central ⊖60,176 d																					
Harrow & Wealdstone ⊖60 d					17 06		17 26	17 37								18 06	18 26	18 37			
Bushey 60 d							17 31										18 31				
Watford Junction 60 a	16 49	17 06			17 12		17 34	17 44				17 49	18 06			18 12	18 34	18 44			
d	16 50	17 06			17 13		17 34		17u34			17 50	18 06			18 13	18 34		18u34		
Kings Langley d							17 39										18 39				
Apsley d							17 43										18 43				
Hemel Hempstead d	16 57				17 20		17 45					17 57				18 20	18 45				
Berkhamsted d	17 02				17 25		17 50					18 02				18 25	18 50				
Tring d					17 29		17a57									18 29	18a57				
Cheddington d					17 35											18 35					
Leighton Buzzard d	17 15	17 27			17 41							18 15	18 27			18 41					
Bletchley d	17 22				17 48							18 22				18 48					
Milton Keynes Central 10 a	17 27	17 37	17 41	17 50	17 54					18 13		18 27	18 37	18 41	18 50	18 54				19 13	
d	17 28	17 37								18 13		18 28	18 37							19 13	
Wolverton d	17 31											18 31									
Northampton 68 a	17 44	17 52										18 44	18 54								
d	17 55	18 02										18 55	19 02								
Long Buckby 68 a	18 06	18 13										19 06	19 13								
Rugby 68 a	18 17	18 24									18 51	19 17	19 24								19 52
Nuneaton 65 a		18 39				18 03							19 39								
Coventry 68 a	18 28								18 21	18 44	19 02	19 28							19 22	19 42	20 03
Birmingham International 68 ✈ a	18 47								18 32	18 54	19 13	19 47							19 32	19 53	20 13
Birmingham New Street 12 68 a	18 59								18 44	19 06	19 24	19 59							19 44	20 05	20 24
Sandwell & Dudley 68 a										19 24	19 48									20 24	20 34
Wolverhampton 7 68 🚊 a										19 37	20 02									20 36	20 46

	LM 1	LM 1 A	VT ◇1 F ☕	VT ◇1 C ☕	LM 1	VT ◇1 D ☕	LM 1	SN 1	VT ◇1 ☕	VT ◇1 G ☕	VT ◇1 ☕	LM 1	LM 1 A	VT ◇1 D ☕	VT ◇1 C ☕	LM 1	VT ◇1 D ☕	LM 1	SN 1	VT ◇1 ☕	VT ◇1 ☕	LM 1 H
London Euston 15 ⊖60 d	18 34	18 50	19 08	19 17	18 54	19 05	19 14		19 20	19 40	20 00	19 34	19 50	20 08	20 15	19 54	20 05	20 14		20 18	20 38	20 34
East Croydon 176 🚊 d																						
Clapham Junction 176 d								19 05											20 05			
Imperial Wharf 176 d								19 09											20 09			
West Brompton ⊖176 d								19 12											20 12			
Kensington (Olympia) ⊖176 d								19 16											20 16			
Shepherd's Bush ⊖176 d								19 19											20 19			
Wembley Central ⊖60,176 d																						
Harrow & Wealdstone ⊖60 d					19 06		19 26	19 36								20 06		20 26	20 37			
Bushey 60 d							19 31											20 31				
Watford Junction 60 a	18 49	19 05			19 12		19 34	19 43				19 49	20 06			20 12		20 34	20 44			20 49
d	18 50	19 06			19 13		19 34		19u34			19 50	20 06			20 13		20 34		20u32		20 50
Kings Langley d							19 39											20 39				
Apsley d							19 43											20 43				
Hemel Hempstead d	18 57				19 20		19 45					19 57				20 20		20 45				20 57
Berkhamsted d	19 02				19 25		19 50					20 02				20 25		20 50				21 03
Tring d					19 29		19a57									20 29		20a57				
Cheddington d					19 35											20 35						
Leighton Buzzard d	19 15	19 27			19 41							20 15	20 27			20 41						21 16
Bletchley d	19 22				19 48							20 22				20 48						21 23
Milton Keynes Central 10 a	19 27	19 37	19 41	19 50	19 54					20 13		20 27	20 37	20 41	20 48	20 54					21 16	21 28
d	19 28	19 37								20 13		20 28	20 37								21 16	21 29
Wolverton d	19 31											20 31										21 32
Northampton 68 a	19 44	19 53										20 44	20 54									21 45
d	19 55	20 02										20 55	21 06									21 55
Long Buckby 68 a	20 06	20 13										21 06	21 17									↦
Rugby 68 a	20 17	20 24									20 51	21 17	21 28									
Nuneaton 65 a		20 39				20 03							21 42				21 03					
Coventry 68 a	20 28								20 22	20 41	21 02	21 28								21 20	21 46	
Birmingham International 68 ✈ a	20 47								20 32	20 52	21 13	21 47								21 31	21 57	
Birmingham New Street 12 68 a	20 59								20 44	21 03	21 24	21 59								21 44	22 09	
Sandwell & Dudley 68 a									20 56	21 25	21 36									21 56	22 24	
Wolverhampton 7 68 🚊 a									21 10	21 37	21 51									22 10	22 38	

A To Crewe
B To Chester
C To Manchester Piccadilly
D To Liverpool Lime Street
E To Glasgow Central
F To Holyhead
G To Preston
H To Birmingham New Street

Table 66

Sundays

16 February to 23 March

London - Watford Junction, Milton Keynes Central, Northampton and West Midlands

Network Diagram - see first Page of Table 59

		VT	VT	LM	LM	VT		VT	LM	SN	VT	VT	LM	VT	LM	LM		SN	LM	VT	LM				
		◇1	◇1	1	1	◇1		◇1	1	1	◇1	◇1	1	◇1	1	1		1	1	◇1	1				
		A		B		C		D			D		E		B										
		☕	☕			☕		☕			☕	☕		☕						☕					
London Euston 15 ⊖60	d	20 50	20 54		21 06	21 21		21 25	21 30		21 51	21 55	22 00	22 25		22 28			22 58	23 25	23 34				
East Croydon 176	d																								
Clapham Junction 176	d									21 15								22 15							
Imperial Wharf 176	d									21 19								22 19							
West Brompton ⊖176	d									21 22								22 22							
Kensington (Olympia) ⊖176	d									21 25								22 26							
Shepherd's Bush ⊖176	d									21 28								22 29							
Wembley Central ⊖60,176	d																								
Harrow & Wealdstone ⊖60	d								21 42	21 46			22 12			22 40		22 49	23 10		23 46				
Bushey 60	d								21s47							22s45					23s51				
Watford Junction 60	a				21 22				21 49	21 53			22 18			22 48		22 56	23 16		23 54				
	d		21u10		21 23				21 50			22u09	22 19	22u39		22 49			23 17	23u39	23 55				
Kings Langley	d								21 54							22 53			23 21		23 59				
Apsley	d								21 58							22 57			23 25		00 03				
Hemel Hempstead	d				21 30				22 01				22 26			23 00			23 28		00 06				
Berkhamsted	d				21 35				22 06				22 31			23 05			23 33		00 11				
Tring	d				21 39								22 35						23 37		00 15				
Cheddington	d				21 45								22 41						23 43		00 21				
Leighton Buzzard	d				21 49				22 19				22 47			23 18			23 49		00 27				
Bletchley	d				21 56				22 26				22 54			23 25			23 56		00 34				
Milton Keynes Central 10	a	21 35	21 41		22 04			22 13	22 34		22 37	22 43	23 02	23 11		23 33			00 04	00 11	00 42				
	d	21 37	21 43		22 05				22 34		22 39	22 45	23 03	23 12		23 33			00 05	00 12	00 43				
Wolverton	d			←	22 08				22 38				23 06		←	23 37			00 08		00 46				
Northampton 68	a			21 45	22 22				22 50				23 20		23 20	23 50			00 22		01 00				
	d			21 55					22 52				23 32		23 32										
Long Buckby 68	a			22 06					23 03				→		23 43										
Rugby 68	a	21 59	22 05	22 17					23 14		23 18	23 22		23 46	23 54					00s46					
Nuneaton 65	a					22 51					23 29														
Coventry 68	a		22 16	22 28					23 25			23 33		23 57	00 05					00s58					
Birmingham International 68 ✈	a		22 27	22 47					23 55			23 44		00 08						01s09					
Birmingham New Street 12 68	a		22 39	22 59					00 07			23 55		00 21						01s22					
Sandwell & Dudley 68	a		22 51																						
Wolverhampton 7 68	a		23 06									00 17		00 43						01 44					

Sundays

30 March to 11 May

		LM	LM	LM	LM	LM	LM	LM	LM	VT		VT	VT	LM	SN	VT	VT	LM	LM	VT		VT	LM	SN	VT
		1	1	1			1	1	1	◇1		◇1	◇1	1	1	◇1	◇1	1	1	◇1		◇1	1	1	◇1
		B	B							D		C	D	F		G		B		C		D	F		G
					🚌	🚌																			
										☕		☕	☕			☕	☕			☕		☕			☕
London Euston 15 ⊖60	d			00 15			06 53	07 23	07 52	08 10		08 15	08 20	08 23		08 45	08 50		08 54	09 15		09 20	09 24		09 45
East Croydon 176	d																								
Clapham Junction 176	d														08 15									09 15	
Imperial Wharf 176	d														08 19									09 19	
West Brompton ⊖176	d														08 22									09 22	
Kensington (Olympia) ⊖176	d														08 26									09 26	
Shepherd's Bush ⊖176	d														08 29									09 29	
Wembley Central ⊖60,176	d			00 24																					
Harrow & Wealdstone ⊖60	d			00 29			07 05	07 35	08 04					08 35	08 49				09 06				09 36	09 48	
Bushey 60	d							07s40						08s40									09s41		
Watford Junction 60	a			00 35			07 11	07 43	08 10					08 43	08 56				09 12				09 43	09 58	
	d		00 02	00 35	02 50	02 55	07 12	07 44	08 10					08 43			09u04		09 12				09 44		
Kings Langley	d		00 07	00 40		03 11		07 48						08 48									09 48		
Apsley	d		00 11	00 44		03 22		07 52						08 52									09 52		
Hemel Hempstead	d		00 13	00 46	03 16	03 28	07 19	07 55	08 17					08 54					09 19				09 54		
Berkhamsted	d		00 18	00 51		03 39	07 24	08 00	08 22					08 59					09 24				09 59		
Tring	d		00 24	00 56		03 55	07 28		08 27										09 29						
Cheddington	d		00 29	01 01		04 16	07 34		08 32										09 34						
Leighton Buzzard	d		00 34	01 06	03 53	04 37	07 40	08 13	08 39					09 12					09 40				10 12		
Bletchley	d	00 03	00 41	01 13	04 19	05 03	07 47	08 20	08 45					09 19					09 47				10 19		
Milton Keynes Central 10	a	00 11	00 48	01 19	04 34	05 18	07 55	08 28	08 50	08 55			09 05	09 24		09 31	09 37		09 55			10 06	10 27		10 32
	d	00 11	00 48	01 19			07 56	08 28	08 51					09 24		09 32	09 38		09 56				10 27		10 33
Wolverton	d	00 15	00 52	01 23			07 59	08 32	08 54					09 28				←	09 59				10 31		
Northampton 68	a	00 28	01 10	01 36			08 13	08 45	09 09					09 44				09 44	10 13				10 44		
	d								09 26					10 00				10 00					11 00		
Long Buckby 68	a								09 37					→				10 11					→		
Rugby 68	a								09 48							10 07	10 12	10 22							11 07
Nuneaton 65	a											09 43								10 44					
Coventry 68	a								09 59								10 23	10 33							
Birmingham International 68 ✈	a								10 09								10 34	10 51							
Birmingham New Street 12 68	a								10 26								10 47	11 03							
Sandwell & Dudley 68	a																10 59								
Wolverhampton 7 68	a																11 13								

A To Preston
B From London Euston
C To Liverpool Lime Street
D To Manchester Piccadilly
E To Coventry
F To Birmingham New Street
G To Glasgow Central

Table 66

Sundays

30 March to 11 May

London - Watford Junction, Milton Keynes Central, Northampton and West Midlands

Network Diagram - see first Page of Table 59

		VT ◇1 ☕	LM 1 A	LM 1 B	LM 1	VT ◇1 C ☕		VT ◇1 D ☕	LM 1 B	LM 1 E	SN 1	VT ◇1 F ☕	VT ◇1 ☕	LM 1 A	LM 1	VT ◇1 C ☕		VT ◇1 D ☕	LM 1 E		SN 1	VT ◇1 ☕	LM 1 A	LM 1 G	VT ◇1 D ☕
London Euston 15 ⊖60	d	09 50		09 54	10 01	10 15		10 20	10 24	10 28		10 45	10 49		10 53	11 15		11 20	11 24			11 50			12 17
East Croydon 176	d																								
Clapham Junction 176	d										10 15										11 15				
Imperial Wharf 176	d										10 19										11 19				
West Brompton ⊖176	d										10 22										11 22				
Kensington (Olympia) ⊖176	d										10 26										11 26				
Shepherd's Bush ⊖176	d										10 29										11 29				
Wembley Central ⊖60,176	d																								
Harrow & Wealdstone ⊖60	d				10 13					10 40	10 48				11 05				11 36		11 48				
Bushey 60	d														11s10										
Watford Junction 60	a			10 09	10 19				10 39	10 46	10 56				11 13				11 42		11 56				
	d	10u06		10 10	10 19				10 40	10 46			11u03		11 14				11 42			12u05			
Kings Langley	d									10 51									11 47						
Apsley	d									10 55									11 51						
Hemel Hempstead	d			10 17	10 26				10 47	10 57					11 21				11 53						
Berkhamsted	d			10 22	10 31				10 52	11 02					11 26				11 58						
Tring	d				10 36										11 30										
Cheddington	d				10 41										11 36										
Leighton Buzzard	d			10 35	10 47				11 05	11 15					11 42				12 12						
Bletchley	d			10 42					11 12						11 49				12 19						
Milton Keynes Central 10	a	10 37		10 50	10 59			11 06	11 20	11 27		11 32	11 37		11 57	12 02		12 08	12 27			12 28			12 50
	d	10 39		10 50	10 59				11 20	11 28		11 33	11 39		11 58				12 28			12 30			
Wolverton	d		←		11 03					11 32				←	12 01				12 32				←	←	
Northampton 68	a		10 44	11 06	11 16				11 36	11 45				11 45	12 15				12 45				12 45	12 45	
	d		11 00	11 08					11 40	11 58				11 58					12 55	13 02			12 55	13 02	
Long Buckby 68	a		11 11	11 19					11 51	→				12 09					→	→			13 06	13 13	
Rugby 68	a	11 13	11 22	11 30					12 02			12 07	12 13	12 20								12 49	13 17	13 24	
Nuneaton 65	a			11 42		11 46			12 16															13 40	
Coventry 68	a	11 24	11 33										12 23	12 31								12 59	13 29		
Birmingham International 68 ✈	a	11 35	11 51										12 34	12 49								13 10	13 47		
Birmingham New Street 12 68	a	11 47	12 03										12 46	13 01								13 24	13 59		
Sandwell & Dudley 68	a	11 59											12 58												
Wolverhampton 7 68	a	12 13											13 12												

		LM 1		LM 1	SN 1	VT ◇1 ☕	VT ◇1 H ☕	VT ◇1 ☕	LM 1	LM 1 B	VT ◇1 D ☕	LM 1		LM 1	SN 1	VT ◇1 ☕	VT ◇1 F ☕	VT ◇1 ☕	LM 1	LM 1 B	VT ◇1 D ☕	LM 1		LM 1	SN 1
London Euston 15 ⊖60	d	11 53		12 14		12 20	12 40	13 00	12 34	12 50	13 17	12 54		13 14		13 20	13 40	14 00	13 34	13 50	14 17	13 54		14 14	
East Croydon 176	d																								
Clapham Junction 176	d				12 05										13 05										14 05
Imperial Wharf 176	d				12 09										13 09										14 09
West Brompton ⊖176	d				12 12										13 12										14 12
Kensington (Olympia) ⊖176	d				12 16										13 16										14 16
Shepherd's Bush ⊖176	d				12 19										13 19										14 19
Wembley Central ⊖60,176	d																								
Harrow & Wealdstone ⊖60	d	12 06		12 26	12 37							13 06		13 26	13 37							14 06		14 26	14 37
Bushey 60	d	12s11		12 31										13 31										14 31	
Watford Junction 60	a	12 14		12 34	12 44				12 49	13 06		13 12		13 34	13 44				13 49	14 06		14 12		14 34	14 44
	d	12 14		12 34		12u34			12 50	13 06		13 13		13 34		13u34			13 50	14 06		14 13		14 34	
Kings Langley	d			12 39										13 39										14 39	
Apsley	d			12 43										13 43										14 43	
Hemel Hempstead	d	12 21		12 45					12 57			13 20		13 45					13 57			14 20		14 45	
Berkhamsted	d	12 26		12 50					13 02			13 25		13 50					14 02			14 25		14 50	
Tring	d	12 31		12a57								13 29		13a57								14 29		14a57	
Cheddington	d	12 36										13 35										14 35			
Leighton Buzzard	d	12 43							13 15	13 27		13 41							14 15	14 27		14 41			
Bletchley	d	12 50							13 22			13 48							14 22			14 48			
Milton Keynes Central 10	a	12 58					13 13		13 27	13 36	13 50	13 54					14 13		14 27	14 37	14 50	14 54			
	d	12 58					13 13		13 28	13 37							14 13		14 28	14 37					
Wolverton	d	13 02							13 31										14 31						
Northampton 68	a	13 15							13 44	13 51									14 44	14 52					
	d								13 55	14 02									14 55	15 02					
Long Buckby 68	a								14 06	14 13									15 06	15 13					
Rugby 68	a							13 51	14 17	14 24								14 51	15 17	15 24					
Nuneaton 65	a									14 39										15 39					
Coventry 68	a					13 21	13 42	14 02	14 29							14 21	14 44	15 02	15 29						
Birmingham International 68 ✈	a					13 32	13 53	14 13	14 47							14 32	14 54	15 13	15 47						
Birmingham New Street 12 68	a					13 44	14 05	14 25	14 59							14 44	15 06	15 25	15 59						
Sandwell & Dudley 68	a					13 56	14 24										15 25								
Wolverhampton 7 68	a					14 10	14 37										15 37								

A From London Euston
B To Crewe
C To Liverpool Lime Street
D To Manchester Piccadilly
E To Birmingham New Street
F To Glasgow Central
G From London Euston to Crewe
H To Edinburgh

Table 66

Sundays

30 March to 11 May

London - Watford Junction, Milton Keynes Central, Northampton and West Midlands

Network Diagram - see first Page of Table 59

		VT	VT	VT	LM	LM	VT	VT		LM	LM	SN	VT	VT	VT	LM	LM	VT		VT	LM	LM	SN	VT	VT
		◇1	◇1	◇1	1	1	◇1	◇1		1	1	1	◇1	◇1	◇1	1	1	◇1		◇1	1	1	1	◇1	◇1
			A			B	C	D						E			B	C		D					A
		🍴	🍴	🍴			🍴	🍴					🍴	🍴	🍴			🍴		🍴				🍴	🍴
London Euston 15 ⊖60	d	14 20	14 40	15 00	14 34	14 50	15 08	15 17		14 54	15 14		15 20	15 40	16 00	15 34	15 50	16 08		16 17	15 54	16 14		16 20	16 40
East Croydon 176 🚊	d																								
Clapham Junction 176	d											15 05											16 05		
Imperial Wharf 176	d											15 09											16 09		
West Brompton ⊖176	d											15 12											16 12		
Kensington (Olympia) ⊖176	d											15 16											16 16		
Shepherd's Bush ⊖176	d											15 19											16 19		
Wembley Central ⊖60,176	d																								
Harrow & Wealdstone ⊖60	d									15 06	15 26	15 37									16 06	16 26	16 37		
Bushey 60	d										15 31											16 31			
Watford Junction 60	a				14 49	15 06				15 12	15 34	15 44				15 49	16 06				16 12	16 34	16 44		
	d	14u34			14 50	15 06				15 13	15 34		15u34			15 50	16 06				16 13	16 34		16u34	
Kings Langley	d										15 39											16 39			
Apsley	d										15 43											16 43			
Hemel Hempstead	d				14 57					15 20	15 45					15 57					16 20	16 45			
Berkhamsted	d				15 02					15 25	15 50					16 02					16 25	16 50			
Tring	d									15 29	15a57										16 29	16a57			
Cheddington	d									15 35											16 35				
Leighton Buzzard	d				15 15	15 27				15 41						16 15	16 27				16 41				
Bletchley	d				15 22					15 48						16 22					16 48				
Milton Keynes Central 10	a		15 13		15 27	15 37	15 41	15 50		15 54				16 13		16 27	16 37	16 41		16 50	16 54				17 13
	d		15 13		15 28	15 37								16 13		16 28	16 37								17 13
Wolverton	d				15 31											16 31									
Northampton 68	a				15 44	15 52										16 44	16 53								
	d				15 55	16 02										16 55	17 02								
Long Buckby 68	a				16 06	16 13										17 06	17 13								
Rugby 68	a			15 52	16 17	16 24									16 51	17 17	17 24								
Nuneaton 65	a					16 39											17 39								
Coventry 68	a	15 21	15 42	16 03	16 29								16 21	16 42	17 02	17 29								17 21	17 44
Birmingham International 68 ✈	a	15 32	15 53	16 13	16 47								16 32	16 53	17 13	17 47								17 32	17 54
Birmingham New Street 12 68	a	15 44	16 05	16 25	16 59								16 44	17 05	17 25	17 59								17 44	18 06
Sandwell & Dudley 68	a		16 24											17 24											18 24
Wolverhampton 7 68 🚊	a		16 37											17 37											18 37

		VT	LM	LM		VT	VT	LM	VT	LM	SN	VT	VT	VT		LM	LM	VT	VT	LM	LM	SN	VT	VT	
													R												
		◇1	1	1		◇1	◇1	1	◇1	1	1	◇1	1	◇1		1	1	◇1	◇1	1	1	1	◇1	◇1	
				B		C	D		F				E				B	C	D					B	
		🍴				🍴	🍴		🍴			🍴	🍴	🍴				🍴	🍴				🍴	🍴	
London Euston 15 ⊖60	d	17 00	16 34	16 50		17 08	17 17	16 54	17 05	17 14		17 20	17 40	18 00		17 34	17 50	18 08	18 17	17 54	18 14		18 20	18 40	
East Croydon 176 🚊	d																								
Clapham Junction 176	d										17 05											18 05			
Imperial Wharf 176	d										17 09											18 09			
West Brompton ⊖176	d										17 12											18 12			
Kensington (Olympia) ⊖176	d										17 16											18 16			
Shepherd's Bush ⊖176	d										17 19											18 19			
Wembley Central ⊖60,176	d																								
Harrow & Wealdstone ⊖60	d							17 06		17 26	17 37									18 06	18 26	18 37			
Bushey 60	d									17 31											18 31				
Watford Junction 60	a		16 49	17 06				17 12		17 34	17 44					17 49	18 06			18 12	18 34	18 44			
	d		16 50	17 06				17 13		17 34		17u34				17 50	18 06			18 13	18 34		18u34		
Kings Langley	d									17 39											18 39				
Apsley	d									17 43											18 43				
Hemel Hempstead	d		16 57					17 20		17 45						17 57				18 20	18 45				
Berkhamsted	d		17 02					17 25		17 50						18 02				18 25	18 50				
Tring	d							17 29		17a57										18 29	18a57				
Cheddington	d							17 35												18 35					
Leighton Buzzard	d		17 15	17 27				17 41								18 15	18 27			18 41					
Bletchley	d		17 22					17 48								18 22				18 48					
Milton Keynes Central 10	a		17 27	17 37		17 41	17 50	17 54					18 13			18 27	18 37	18 41	18 50	18 54				19 13	
	d		17 28	17 37									18 13			18 28	18 37							19 13	
Wolverton	d		17 31													18 31									
Northampton 68	a		17 44	17 52												18 44	18 54								
	d		17 55	18 02												18 55	19 02								
Long Buckby 68	a		18 06	18 13												19 06	19 13								
Rugby 68	a	17 51	18 17	18 24										18 51		19 17	19 24								
Nuneaton 65	a			18 39					18 03								19 39								
Coventry 68	a	18 02	18 29									18 21	18 44	19 02		19 28							19 22	19 42	
Birmingham International 68 ✈	a	18 13	18 47									18 32	18 54	19 13		19 47							19 32	19 53	
Birmingham New Street 12 68	a	18 25	18 59									18 44	19 06	19 24		19 59							19 44	20 05	
Sandwell & Dudley 68	a												19 24	19 48										20 24	
Wolverhampton 7 68 🚊	a												19 37	20 02										20 36	

A To Edinburgh
B To Crewe
C To Chester
D To Manchester Piccadilly
E To Glasgow Central
F To Liverpool Lime Street

Table 66

Sundays
30 March to 11 May

London - Watford Junction, Milton Keynes Central, Northampton and West Midlands

Network Diagram - see first Page of Table 59

		VT	LM	LM	VT	VT	LM	VT	LM	SN		VT	VT	VT	LM	LM	VT	VT	LM	VT		LM	SN	VT	VT
		◇1	1	1	◇1	◇1	1	◇1	1	1		◇1	◇1	◇1	1	1	◇1	◇1	1	◇1		1	1	◇1	◇1
				A	B	C		D					E			A	D	C		D					
		☕			☕	☕		☕				☕	☕	☕			☕	☕		☕				☕	☕
London Euston 15 ⊖60	d	19 00	18 34	18 50	19 08	19 17	18 54	19 05	19 14			19 20	19 40	20 00	19 34	19 50	20 08	20 15	19 54	20 05		20 14		20 18	20 38
East Croydon 176	d																								
Clapham Junction 176	d									19 05													20 05		
Imperial Wharf 176	d									19 09													20 09		
West Brompton ⊖176	d									19 12													20 12		
Kensington (Olympia) ⊖176	d									19 16													20 16		
Shepherd's Bush ⊖176	d									19 19													20 19		
Wembley Central ⊖60,176	d																								
Harrow & Wealdstone ⊖60	d						19 06		19 26	19 36									20 06			20 26	20 37		
Bushey 60	d								19 31													20 31			
Watford Junction 60	a		18 49	19 05			19 12		19 34	19 43					19 49	20 06			20 12			20 34	20 44		
	d		18 50	19 06			19 13		19 34			19u34			19 50	20 06			20 13			20 34		20u32	
Kings Langley	d								19 39													20 39			
Apsley	d								19 43													20 43			
Hemel Hempstead	d		18 57				19 20		19 45						19 57				20 20			20 45			
Berkhamsted	d		19 02				19 25		19 50						20 02				20 25			20 50			
Tring	d						19 29		19a57										20 29			20a57			
Cheddington	d						19 35												20 35						
Leighton Buzzard	d		19 15	19 27			19 41								20 15	20 27			20 41						
Bletchley	d		19 22				19 48								20 22				20 48						
Milton Keynes Central 10	a		19 27	19 37	19 41	19 50	19 54						20 13		20 27	20 37	20 41	20 48	20 54						21 16
	d		19 28	19 37									20 13		20 28	20 37									21 16
Wolverton	d		19 31												20 31										
Northampton 68	a		19 44	19 53											20 44	20 54									
	d		19 55	20 02											20 55	21 06									
Long Buckby 68	a		20 06	20 13											21 06	21 17									
Rugby 68	a	19 52	20 17	20 24										20 51	21 17	21 28									
Nuneaton 65	a			20 39				20 03								21 42				21 03					
Coventry 68	a	20 03	20 29									20 22	20 41	21 02	21 29									21 20	21 46
Birmingham International 68 ✈	a	20 13	20 47									20 32	20 52	21 13	21 47									21 31	21 57
Birmingham New Street 12 68	a	20 24	20 59									20 44	21 03	21 24	21 59									21 44	22 09
Sandwell & Dudley 68	a	20 34										20 56	21 25	21 36										21 56	22 24
Wolverhampton 7 68	a	20 46										21 10	21 37	21 51										22 10	22 38

		LM	VT	VT	LM	LM		VT	VT	LM	SN	VT	VT	LM	VT	LM		LM	SN	LM	VT	LM			
		1	◇1	◇1	1	1		◇1	◇1	1	1	◇1	◇1	1	◇1	1		1	1	1	◇1	1			
		F	E		G			D	C			C		H		G									
			☕	☕				☕	☕			☕	☕		☕						☕				
London Euston 15 ⊖60	d	20 34	20 50	20 54		21 06		21 21	21 25	21 30		21 51	21 55	22 00	22 25			22 28		22 58	23 25	23 34			
East Croydon 176	d																								
Clapham Junction 176	d										21 15								22 15						
Imperial Wharf 176	d										21 19								22 19						
West Brompton ⊖176	d										21 22								22 22						
Kensington (Olympia) ⊖176	d										21 25								22 26						
Shepherd's Bush ⊖176	d										21 28								22 29						
Wembley Central ⊖60,176	d																								
Harrow & Wealdstone ⊖60	d									21 42	21 46			22 12				22 40	22 49	23 10		23 46			
Bushey 60	d									21s47								22s45				23s51			
Watford Junction 60	a	20 49				21 22				21 49	21 53			22 18				22 48	22 56	23 16		23 54			
	d	20 50		21u10		21 23				21 50			22u09	22 19	22u39			22 49		23 17	23u39	23 55			
Kings Langley	d									21 54								22 53		23 21		23 59			
Apsley	d									21 58								22 57		23 25		00 03			
Hemel Hempstead	d	20 57				21 30				22 01				22 26				23 00		23 28		00 06			
Berkhamsted	d	21 03				21 35				22 06				22 31				23 05		23 33		00 11			
Tring	d					21 39								22 35						23 37		00 15			
Cheddington	d					21 45								22 41						23 43		00 21			
Leighton Buzzard	d	21 16				21 49				22 19				22 47				23 18		23 49		00 27			
Bletchley	d	21 23				21 56				22 26				22 54				23 25		23 56		00 34			
Milton Keynes Central 10	a	21 28	21 35	21 41		22 04			22 13	22 34		22 37	22 43	23 02	23 11			23 33		00 04	00 11	00 42			
	d	21 29	21 37	21 43		22 05				22 34		22 39	22 45	23 03	23 12			23 33		00 05	00 12	00 43			
Wolverton	d	21 32			←	22 08				22 38				23 06		←		23 37		00 08		00 46			
Northampton 68	a	21 45			21 45	22 22				22 50				23 20		23 20		23 50		00 22		01 00			
	d	21 55			21 55					22 52				23 32		23 32									
Long Buckby 68	a	→			22 06					23 03				→		23 43									
Rugby 68	a		21 59	22 05	22 17					23 14		23 18	23 22		23 46	23 54					00s46				
Nuneaton 65	a							22 51				23 29													
Coventry 68	a			22 16	22 29					23 25			23 33		23 57	00 05					00s58				
Birmingham International 68 ✈	a			22 27	22 47					23 55			23 44		00 08						01s09				
Birmingham New Street 12 68	a			22 39	22 59					00 07			23 55		00 21						01s22				
Sandwell & Dudley 68	a			22 51																					
Wolverhampton 7 68	a			23 06									00 17		00 43						01 44				

A To Crewe
B To Holyhead
C To Manchester Piccadilly
D To Liverpool Lime Street
E To Preston
F To Birmingham New Street
G From London Euston
H To Coventry

Table 66R

Mondays to Fridays

9 December to 16 May

West Midlands, Northampton, Milton Keynes Central and Watford Junction - London

Network Diagram - see first Page of Table 59

Miles	Miles	Miles			LM	LM	VT	LM	LM	LM	SN	LM	LM		LM	LM	LM	VT	LM	SN	LM	LM	VT		LM
						MX	MX																		
					[1]	[1]	◇[1]	[1]	[1]	[1]	[1]	[1]	[1]		[1]	[1]	[1]	◇[1]	[1]	[1]	[1]		◇[1]		[1]
					A	B	C										D				E				
							🚌											⊠					⊠		
0	—	—	Wolverhampton [7] 68 🚊	d														05 00					05 24		
7½	—	—	Sandwell & Dudley 68	d																			05 34		
12¾	—	—	**Birmingham New Street** [12] 68	d														05 29					05 50		
21¼	—	—	Birmingham International 68 ✈	d														05 40					06 00		
32	—	—	Coventry 68	d														05 51					06 11		
—	—	—	Nuneaton 65	d																					
43½	0	—	**Rugby** 68	d												05 16		06 03							
53	—	—	Long Buckby 68	a												05 25									
62¼	—	—	**Northampton** 68	a												05 37									
—	—	—		d					04 15	04 49		05 05				05 46						06 18			
75¼	30	—	Wolverton	d					04 27	05 01		05 17				05 58						06 30			
78¼	32¾	—	**Milton Keynes Central** [10]	a					04 30	05 04		05 20				06 01		06 22				06 34	06 38		
—	—	—		d			00 24	03 30	04 31	05 05		05 21			05 54	06 02	06 19	06 23				06 35	06 38		
81¼	—	—	Bletchley	d				03 35	04 36	05 09		05 26	05 38		05 59	06 07	06 24					06 40			06 34
87¾	—	—	Leighton Buzzard	d		00 04		03 41	04 42	05 16		05 33	05 45		06 05	06 14	06 31					06 47			06 41
92	—	—	Cheddington	d		00 11				05 21			05 50				06 37								
96¼	—	—	Tring	d		00 16		03 53	04 54	05 30			05 56				06 42		06 24						06 52
100	—	—	Berkhamsted	d		00 21		03 58	04 59	05 34		05 47	06 01		06 17		06 47		06 28						06 56
103½	—	—	Hemel Hempstead	d		00 25		04 02	05 03	05 39		05 52	06 05		06 22		06 52		06 33						07 01
105	—	—	Apsley	d						05 42			06 08						06 36						07 04
107	—	—	Kings Langley	d						05 45			06 11						06 39		←				07 07
110½	65	—	**Watford Junction** 60	a		00 32	00s52	04 09	05 10	05 49		05 59	06 16		06 29	06 31	06 59	06s43	06 44		06 59	07 04			07 12
—	—	—		d		00 32		04 10	05 11	05 50	05 54	06 01	06 17		06 29	06 33	07 00		06 45	06 53	07 00	07 05			07 12
112	—	—	Bushey 60	d	00 01												→		06 48						07 15
116½	—	—	Harrow & Wealdstone ⊖60	d	00 07	00 38		04 16	05 17	05 56	06 00		06 23						06 53	06 59	07 06				07 20
119¾	—	0	Wembley Central ⊖60,176	d		00 42		04 20	05 21		06 05									07 04					
—	—	4¼	Shepherd's Bush ⊖176	a							06 21									07 20					
—	—	5½	Kensington (Olympia) ⊖176	a							06 23									07 22					
—	—	7½	West Brompton ⊖176	a							06 26									07 25					
—	—	8	Imperial Wharf 176	a							06 29									07 28					
—	—	9	Clapham Junction 176	a							06 34									07 33					
—	—	16¾	East Croydon 176 🚊	a																					
128	82½	—	**London Euston** [15] ⊖60	a	00 21	00 55	01 15	04 35	05 35	06 12		06 19	06 40		06 49	06 51		07 02	07 07		07 20	07 22	07 13		07 34

		LM	SN	LM	LM	VT	VT	LM	VT		SN	LM	VT	VT	VT	LM	LM	VT	LM		LM	LM	VT	VT	VT
		[1]	[1]	[1]	[1]	◇[1]	◇[1]	[1]	◇[1]		[1]	[1]	◇[1]	◇[1]	◇[1]	[1]	[1]	◇[1]	[1]		[1]	[1]	◇[1]	◇[1]	◇[1]
					D		F	G				H	I		J			F				K		F	
						⊠	⊠		⊠				⊠	⊠	⊠			⊠					⊠	⊠	⊠
Wolverhampton [7] 68 🚊	d								05 45					06 04									06 27		06 45
Sandwell & Dudley 68	d								05 55					06 15									06 38		06 56
Birmingham New Street [12] 68	d								06 10					06 30									06 50		07 10
Birmingham International 68 ✈	d								06 20					06 40									07 00		07 20
Coventry 68	d				05 57				06 31					06 51									07 11		07 31
Nuneaton 65	d						06 18					06 28						07 08							
Rugby 68	d				06 13	06 20	06 32					06 43	06 54		07 08									07 29	
Long Buckby 68	a				06 22							06 53													
Northampton 68	a				06 34	06 40						07 05													
	d				06 38	06 41						07 14				07 00									
Wolverton	d				06 50			←				07 26				07 12						←			
Milton Keynes Central [10]	a				06 53		06 51	06 53	06 59			07 30	07 13			07 15						07 30	07s40		
	d			06 48	06 55		06 53	06 55	06 59		07 01	07 32	07 14			07 17					07 21	07 32			
Bletchley	d			06 53	→			07 00			07 05	→					07 13				07 26				
Leighton Buzzard	d			06 59				07 07			07 12					07 26					07 33	07 41			
Cheddington	d			07 05																	07 39				
Tring	d	07 00		07 11							07 21						07 28				07 45				
Berkhamsted	d	07 05		07 16							07 26						07 32				07 50				
Hemel Hempstead	d	07 10		07 20							07 30						07 37				07 55				
Apsley	d			07 24																	07 58				
Kings Langley	d			07 27																	08 02				
Watford Junction 60	a	07 17		07 31							07 37			07s37			07 44				08 06				
	d	07 18	07 23	07 32							07 38						07 45		07 55		08 07				
Bushey 60	d	07 21		07 34															07 59						
Harrow & Wealdstone ⊖60	d		07 30	07 40							07 44								08 05						
Wembley Central ⊖60,176	d		07 35								07 49														
Shepherd's Bush ⊖176	a		07 54								08 05														
Kensington (Olympia) ⊖176	a		07 56								08 07														
West Brompton ⊖176	a		07 59								08 10														
Imperial Wharf 176	a		08 02								08 13														
Clapham Junction 176	a		08 07								08 18														
East Croydon 176 🚊	a										09 04														
London Euston [15] ⊖60	a	07 42		07 54		07 31	07 29	07 39	07 34				07 51	07 53	07 58	08 02	08 05	08 08	08 18		08 26	08 11	08 15	08 23	08 31

A From Birmingham New Street
B From Northampton
C From Wolverhampton
D To London Euston
E From Milton Keynes Central
F From Manchester Piccadilly
G From Coventry
H From Crewe to London Euston
I From Liverpool Lime Street
J From Preston
K From Crewe

Table 66R

Mondays to Fridays

9 December to 16 May

West Midlands, Northampton, Milton Keynes Central and Watford Junction - London

Network Diagram - see first Page of Table 59

	LM	VT	LM	LM		LM	LM	VT	LM	LM	SN	LM
	1	◇1	1	1		1	1	◇1	1	1	1	1
		A									B	
		⊠						⊠				
Wolverhampton 7 68 d								07 05				
Sandwell & Dudley 68 d								07 15				
Birmingham New Street 12 68 d								07 30				06 54
Birmingham International 68 ✈ d												07 05
Coventry 68 d												07 21
Nuneaton 65 d		07 34										
Rugby 68 d												07 32
Long Buckby 68 a												07 42
Northampton 68 a												07 54
d						07 32	07 39					08 05
Wolverton d							07 51					08 17
Milton Keynes Central 10 a						07 46	07 54					08 21
d						07 46	07 55		07 59		08 13	08 21
Bletchley d	07 39					07 51			08 04		08 17	08 27
Leighton Buzzard d	07 46					07 57	08 06		08 11		08 24	08 34
Cheddington d						08 03						
Tring d				08 04		08 09				08 25	08 35	
Berkhamsted d	07 59					08 14				08 30	08 40	
Hemel Hempstead d	08 03					08 19			08 28	08 34	08 44	
Apsley d				08 13						08 37		
Kings Langley d				08 16						08 41		
Watford Junction 60 a	08 10			08 21		08 26			08 35	08 45	08 51	
d	08 11		08 15	08 22		08 28			08 36	08 46	08 52	
Bushey 60 d			08 19							08 48		
Harrow & Wealdstone ⊖60 d	08 17		08 24	08 29		08 34				08 54	08 58	
Wembley Central ⊖60,176 d											09 03	
Shepherd's Bush ⊖176 a											09 19	
Kensington (Olympia) ⊖176 a											09 21	
West Brompton ⊖176 a											09 24	
Imperial Wharf 176 a											09 27	
Clapham Junction 176 a											09 31	
East Croydon 176 a											09 56	
London Euston 15 ⊖60 a	08 33	08 34	08 38	08 42		08 49	08 39	08 43	08 54	09 08		09 10

	LM	VT		VT	VT	LM	SN	LM	LM	VT	VT	LM
	1	◇1		◇1	◇1	1	1	1	1	◇1	◇1	1
		C			C			D	D		C	E
		⊠		⊠	⊠					⊠	⊠	
Wolverhampton 7 68 d										07 25	07 45	
Sandwell & Dudley 68 d											07 57	
Birmingham New Street 12 68 d	07 14								07 33	07 50	08 10	
Birmingham International 68 ✈ d	07 30			07 41					07 45	08 00	08 20	
Coventry 68 d	07 42			07 52					08 04	08 11	08 31	
Nuneaton 65 d												08 18
Rugby 68 d	07 53	07 55							08 15	08 23		08 34
Long Buckby 68 a	08 02								08 25			
Northampton 68 a	08 20								08 37			
d	08 25								08 47			
Wolverton d	08 37								08 59			
Milton Keynes Central 10 a	08 41								09 03			08 55
d	08 41				08 47			08 47	09 04			09 00
Bletchley d	08 46							08 52	↪			
Leighton Buzzard d	08 53							08 58				
Cheddington d								09 04				
Tring d						08 49		09 10				
Berkhamsted d						08 53		09 15				
Hemel Hempstead d						08 57		09 19				
Apsley d												
Kings Langley d												
Watford Junction 60 a						09 04		09 26			09s16	
d						09 05	09 15	09 27				
Bushey 60 d						09 08		↪				
Harrow & Wealdstone ⊖60 d						09 13	09 22					
Wembley Central ⊖60,176 d							09 27					
Shepherd's Bush ⊖176 a							09 44					
Kensington (Olympia) ⊖176 a							09 46					
West Brompton ⊖176 a							09 49					
Imperial Wharf 176 a							09 52					
Clapham Junction 176 a							09 57					
East Croydon 176 a												
London Euston 15 ⊖60 a	09 27	08 46		08 50	09 24	09 27				09 13	09 34	09 37

		LM	LM	LM	VT	LM	SN	VT	LM	VT		LM
		1	1	1	◇1	1	1	◇1	1	◇1		1
			F	G	C		B			A		
					⊠			⊠		⊠		
Wolverhampton 7 68 d												
Sandwell & Dudley 68 d												
Birmingham New Street 12 68 d								08 30	07 54			
Birmingham International 68 ✈ d								08 40	08 05			
Coventry 68 d								08 51	08 21			
Nuneaton 65 d					08 46							
Rugby 68 d									08 39	08 47		
Long Buckby 68 a									08 48			
Northampton 68 a									09 00			
d									09 05			09 25
Wolverton d			↩						09 17			09 37
Milton Keynes Central 10 a			09 03					09 18	09 20			09 41
d			09 04				09 13	09 20	09 22			09 41
Bletchley d							09 17		09 27			09 46
Leighton Buzzard d							09 24		09 33			09 53
Cheddington d												
Tring d		09 02				09 26	09 34					
Berkhamsted d		09 06				09 31	09 39		09 46			
Hemel Hempstead d		09 11				09 35	09 43		09 51			
Apsley d		09 14				09 38						
Kings Langley d		09 17		↩		09 42						
Watford Junction 60 a		09 21		09 26	09s32	09 46	09 52		09 58			
d		09 22		09 27		09 47	09 53		09 59			
Bushey 60 d		09 24				09 50						
Harrow & Wealdstone ⊖60 d		09 29		09 34		09 55	09 59					
Wembley Central ⊖60,176 d							10 05					
Shepherd's Bush ⊖176 a							10 21					
Kensington (Olympia) ⊖176 a							10 23					
West Brompton ⊖176 a							10 26					
Imperial Wharf 176 a							10 29					
Clapham Junction 176 a							10 34					
East Croydon 176 a							10 56					
London Euston 15 ⊖60 a		09 43	09 45	09 48	09 52	10 08		09 55	10 18	09 41		10 27

	VT	LM	LM	VT	VT	LM	VT	VT		LM	SN	LM
	◇1	1	1	◇1	◇1	1	◇1	◇1		1	1	1
	C			H	A						B	D
	⊠			⊠	⊠		⊠	⊠				
Wolverhampton 7 68 d				08 45								
Sandwell & Dudley 68 d				08 55								
Birmingham New Street 12 68 d				09 10		08 33	08 50	09 30				08 54
Birmingham International 68 ✈ d				09 20		08 45	09 00	09 40				09 05
Coventry 68 d				09 31		09 00	09 11	09 51				09 21
Nuneaton 65 d												
Rugby 68 d						09 12	09 23					09 32
Long Buckby 68 a						09 21						09 41
Northampton 68 a						09 34						09 54
d						09 50						10 05
Wolverton d												10 17
Milton Keynes Central 10 a				09 58		10 04						10 20
d	09 47		09 47	10 00	10 03	10 06					10 13	10 22
Bletchley d			09 52								10 17	↪
Leighton Buzzard d			09 58								10 24	
Cheddington d			10 04									
Tring d		09 56	10 10							10 26	10 34	
Berkhamsted d		10 00	10 15							10 31	10 39	
Hemel Hempstead d		10 05	10 19							10 35	10 43	
Apsley d		10 08								10 38		
Kings Langley d		10 11								10 41		
Watford Junction 60 a		10 16	10 26			10 30		10s39		10 46	10 51	
d		10 16	10 27			10 30				10 46	10 51	
Bushey 60 d		10 19								10 49		
Harrow & Wealdstone ⊖60 d		10 24								10 54	10 59	
Wembley Central ⊖60,176 d											11 03	
Shepherd's Bush ⊖176 a											11 19	
Kensington (Olympia) ⊖176 a											11 21	
West Brompton ⊖176 a											11 24	
Imperial Wharf 176 a											11 26	
Clapham Junction 176 a											11 31	
East Croydon 176 a											11 56	
London Euston 15 ⊖60 a	10 24	10 38	10 45	10 32	10 39	10 46	10 15	10 55		11 08		

A From Holyhead
B To South Croydon
C From Manchester Piccadilly
D To London Euston
E From Crewe
F From Birmingham New Street
G From Milton Keynes Central
H From Lancaster

Table 66R

Mondays to Fridays

9 December to 16 May

West Midlands, Northampton, Milton Keynes Central and Watford Junction - London

Network Diagram - see first Page of Table 59

			LM	LM	LM	VT	LM	LM	VT	VT	LM	VT	VT	LM	SN	LM	LM	LM	LM	VT	LM	LM	VT
			1	1	1	◇1	1	1	◇1	◇1	1	◇1	◇1	1	1	1	1	1	1	◇1	1	1	◇1
			A	B		C			D	E					F	G	A	B		C			H
						⊠			⊠	⊠		⊠	⊠							⊠			⊠
Wolverhampton 7	68 ⛴	d							09 45														10 45
Sandwell & Dudley	68	d							09 55														10 55
Birmingham New Street 12	68	d			09 14				10 10		09 33	09 50	10 30			09 54			10 14				11 10
Birmingham International	68 ✈	d			09 30				10 20		09 45	10 00	10 40			10 05			10 30				11 20
Coventry	68	d			09 48				10 31		10 00	10 11	10 51			10 21			10 48				11 31
Nuneaton	65	d	09 28														10 36						
Rugby	68	d	09 53		09 59						10 12	10 23				10 32	10 53		10 59				
Long Buckby	68	a			10 08						10 21					10 41			11 08				
Northampton	68	a			10 20						10 34					10 53			11 20				
		d			10 25						10 50					11 05			11 25				
Wolverton		d		←	10 37											11 17		←	11 37				
Milton Keynes Central 10		a	10 14	10 20	10 41				10 58		11 04					11 20	11 14	11 20	11 41				11 58
		d	10 15	10 22	10 41	10 47		10 47	11 00	11 03	11 06				11 13	11 22	11 15	11 22	11 41	11 47		11 47	12 00
Bletchley		d		10 27	10 46			10 52							11 17	→		11 27	11 46			11 52	
Leighton Buzzard		d		10 33	10 53			10 58							11 24			11 33	11 53			11 58	
Cheddington		d						11 04														12 04	
Tring		d					10 56	11 10						11 26	11 34						11 56	12 10	
Berkhamsted		d		10 46			11 01	11 15						11 31	11 39			11 46			12 00	12 15	
Hemel Hempstead		d		10 51			11 05	11 19						11 35	11 43			11 51			12 05	12 19	
Apsley		d					11 08							11 38							12 08		
Kings Langley		d					11 11							11 41							12 11		
Watford Junction	60	a		10 58			11 16	11 26			11 30		11s39	11 45	11 52			11 58			12 16	12 26	
		d		10 59			11 16	11 27			11 30			11 46	11 53			11 59			12 16	12 27	
Bushey	60	d					11 19							11 49							12 19		
Harrow & Wealdstone	⊖60	d					11 24							11 54	11 59						12 24		
Wembley Central	⊖60,176	d													12 04								
Shepherd's Bush	⊖176	a													12 20								
Kensington (Olympia)	⊖176	a													12 22								
West Brompton	⊖176	a													12 25								
Imperial Wharf	176	a													12 28								
Clapham Junction	176	a													12 33								
East Croydon	176 ⛴	a													12 57								
London Euston 15	⊖60	a	10 50	11 17	11 27	11 24	11 38	11 46	11 34	11 39	11 46	11 15	11 55	12 08			11 50	12 17	12 27	12 24	12 38	12 46	12 34

			VT	LM	VT	VT	LM	SN	LM	LM	LM	LM	VT	LM	LM	VT	VT	LM	VT	VT	LM	SN	LM
			◇1	1	◇1	◇1	1	1	1	1	1	1	◇1	1	1	◇1	◇1	1	◇1	◇1	1	1	1
			I					F	G	A	B		C			D	E					F	G
			⊠		⊠	⊐P							⊐P			⊠	⊐P		⊐P	⊐P			
Wolverhampton 7	68 ⛴	d														11 45							
Sandwell & Dudley	68	d														11 55							
Birmingham New Street 12	68	d		10 33	10 50	11 30			10 54			11 14				12 10		11 33	11 50	12 30			11 54
Birmingham International	68 ✈	d		10 45	11 00	11 40			11 05			11 30				12 20		11 45	12 00	12 40			12 05
Coventry	68	d		11 00	11 11	11 51			11 21			11 48				12 31		12 00	12 11	12 51			12 21
Nuneaton	65	d								11 36													
Rugby	68	d		11 12	11 23				11 32	11 53		11 59						12 18	12 23				12 32
Long Buckby	68	a		11 21					11 41			12 08						12 27					12 41
Northampton	68	a		11 34					11 53			12 20						12 44					12 53
		d		11 50					12 05			12 25						12 50					13 05
Wolverton		d							12 17		←	12 37											13 17
Milton Keynes Central 10		a		12 04					12 20	12 14	12 20	12 41				12 58		13 04					13 20
		d	12 03	12 06				12 13	12 22	12 15	12 22	12 41	12 47		12 47	13 00	13 03	13 06				13 13	13 22
Bletchley		d						12 17	→		12 27	12 46			12 52							13 17	→
Leighton Buzzard		d						12 24			12 33	12 53			12 58							13 24	
Cheddington		d													13 04								
Tring		d					12 26	12 33						12 56	13 10						13 26	13 34	
Berkhamsted		d					12 31	12 38			12 46			13 01	13 15						13 31	13 39	
Hemel Hempstead		d					12 35	12 42			12 51			13 05	13 19						13 35	13 43	
Apsley		d					12 38							13 08							13 38		
Kings Langley		d					12 41							13 11							13 41		
Watford Junction	60	a		12 30		12s39	12 46	12 51			12 58			13 16	13 26			13 30		13s39	13 46	13 51	
		d		12 30			12 46	12 51			12 59			13 16	13 27			13 30			13 46	13 52	
Bushey	60	d					12 49							13 19							13 49		
Harrow & Wealdstone	⊖60	d					12 54	12 59						13 24							13 54	13 59	
Wembley Central	⊖60,176	d						13 03														14 04	
Shepherd's Bush	⊖176	a						13 19														14 20	
Kensington (Olympia)	⊖176	a						13 22														14 22	
West Brompton	⊖176	a						13 25														14 25	
Imperial Wharf	176	a						13 28														14 28	
Clapham Junction	176	a						13 33														14 33	
East Croydon	176 ⛴	a						13 56														14 55	
London Euston 15	⊖60	a	12 39	12 46	12 15	12 55	13 08			12 50	13 17	13 27	13 24	13 38	13 46	13 33	13 39	13 46	13 15	13 55	14 08		

A From Crewe
B From Birmingham New Street
C From Manchester Piccadilly
D From Glasgow Central
E From Chester
F To South Croydon
G To London Euston
H From Edinburgh
I From Holyhead

Table 66R

Mondays to Fridays

9 December to 16 May

West Midlands, Northampton, Milton Keynes Central and Watford Junction - London

Network Diagram - see first Page of Table 59

Station	LM 1 A	LM 1 B	LM 1	VT ◇1 C ☕	LM 1	LM 1	VT ◇1 D ⊠	VT ◇1 E ☕	LM 1	VT ◇1 ☕	VT ◇1 ☕	LM 1	SN 1 F	LM 1 G	LM 1 A	LM 1 B	LM 1	VT ◇1 C ☕	LM 1	LM 1	VT ◇1 H ⊠	VT ◇1 I ☕
Wolverhampton 7 68 d							12 45														13 45	
Sandwell & Dudley 68 d							12 55														13 56	
Birmingham New Street 12 68 d			12 14				13 10		12 33	12 50	13 30			12 54			13 14				14 10	
Birmingham International 68 ✈ d			12 30				13 20		12 45	13 00	13 40			13 05			13 30				14 20	
Coventry 68 d			12 48				13 31		13 00	13 11	13 51			13 21			13 48				14 30	
Nuneaton 65 d	12 36														13 36							
Rugby 68 d	12 53		12 59						13 12	13 23				13 32	13 53		13 59					
Long Buckby 68 a			13 08						13 21					13 41			14 08					
Northampton 68 a			13 20						13 34					13 53			14 20					
d			13 25						13 50					14 05			14 25					
Wolverton d		←	13 37											14 17		←	14 37					
Milton Keynes Central 10 a	13 14	13 20	13 41				13 58		14 04					14 20	14 14	14 20	14 41				14 58	
d	13 15	13 22	13 41	13 47		13 47	14 00	14 03	14 06				14 13	14 22	14 15	14 22	14 41	14 47		14 47	14 59	15 03
Bletchley d		13 27	13 46			13 52							14 17	→		14 27	14 46			14 52		
Leighton Buzzard d		13 33	13 53			13 58							14 24			14 33	14 53			14 58		
Cheddington d						14 04														15 04		
Tring d					13 56	14 10						14 26	14 34						14 56	15 10		
Berkhamsted d		13 46			14 00	14 15						14 31	14 39			14 46			15 00	15 15		
Hemel Hempstead d		13 51			14 05	14 19						14 35	14 43			14 51			15 05	15 19		
Apsley d					14 08							14 38							15 08			
Kings Langley d					14 11							14 41							15 11			
Watford Junction 60 a		13 58			14 16	14 26			14 31		14s39	14 46	14 52			14 58			15 16	15 26		
d		13 59			14 16	14 27			14 31			14 46	14 52			14 59			15 16	15 27		
Bushey 60 d					14 19							14 49							15 19			
Harrow & Wealdstone ⊖60 d					14 24							14 54	14 59						15 24			
Wembley Central ⊖60,176 d													15 03									
Shepherd's Bush ⊖176 a													15 22									
Kensington (Olympia) ⊖176 a													15 24									
West Brompton ⊖176 a													15 26									
Imperial Wharf 176 a													15 29									
Clapham Junction 176 a													15 33									
East Croydon 176 a													15 56									
London Euston 15 ⊖60 a	13 50	14 17	14 26	14 24	14 38	14 45	14 33	14 39	14 47	14 15	14 55	15 08			14 50	15 17	15 27	15 24	15 38	15 45	15 33	15 39

Station	LM 1	VT ◇1 ☕	VT ◇1 ☕	LM 1	SN 1 F	LM 1 G	LM 1 A	LM 1 B	LM 1	VT ◇1 C ☕	LM 1	LM 1	VT ◇1 D ☕	VT ◇1 E ☕	LM 1	VT ◇1 ☕	VT ◇1 ☕	LM 1	SN 1	LM 1 G	LM 1 A	LM 1 B
Wolverhampton 7 68 d													14 45									
Sandwell & Dudley 68 d													14 55									
Birmingham New Street 12 68 d	13 33	13 50	14 30			13 54			14 14				15 10		14 33	14 50	15 30			14 54		
Birmingham International 68 ✈ d	13 45	14 00	14 40			14 05			14 30				15 20		14 45	15 00	15 40			15 05		
Coventry 68 d	14 00	14 11	14 51			14 21			14 48				15 31		15 00	15 11	15 51			15 21		
Nuneaton 65 d							14 36														15 36	
Rugby 68 d	14 12	14 23				14 32	14 53		14 59						15 12	15 23				15 32	15 53	
Long Buckby 68 a	14 21					14 41			15 08						15 21					15 41		
Northampton 68 a	14 34					14 54			15 20						15 33					15 56		
d	14 50					15 05			15 25						15 50					16 05		
Wolverton d						15 17		←	15 37											16 17		←
Milton Keynes Central 10 a	15 04					15 22	15 14	15 22	15 41				15 58		16 04					16 20	16 14	16 20
d	15 06				15 13	15 22	15 15	15 22	15 41	15 47		15 47	16 00	16 03	16 06				16 13	16 22	16 15	16 22
Bletchley d					15 17	→		15 27	15 46			15 52							16 17	→		16 27
Leighton Buzzard d					15 24			15 33	15 53			15 58							16 24			16 33
Cheddington d												16 04										
Tring d				15 26	15 34						15 56	16 10						16 26	16 34			
Berkhamsted d				15 31	15 39			15 46			16 00	16 15						16 31	16 39			16 46
Hemel Hempstead d				15 35	15 43			15 51			16 05	16 19						16 35	16 43			16 51
Apsley d				15 38							16 08							16 38				
Kings Langley d				15 41							16 11							16 41				
Watford Junction 60 a	15 30		15s39	15 46	15 51			15 59			16 16	16 26			16 30		16s37	16 46	16 51			16 58
d	15 30			15 46	15 52			15 59			16 16	16 27			16 30			16 46	16 52			16 59
Bushey 60 d				15 49							16 19							16 49				
Harrow & Wealdstone ⊖60 d				15 54	15 59						16 24							16 54	16 59			
Wembley Central ⊖60,176 d					16 04														17 04			
Shepherd's Bush ⊖176 a					16 20														17 20			
Kensington (Olympia) ⊖176 a					16 22														17 22			
West Brompton ⊖176 a					16 25														17 25			
Imperial Wharf 176 a					16 28														17 28			
Clapham Junction 176 a					16 33														17 33			
East Croydon 176 a					16 58														18 00			
London Euston 15 ⊖60 a	15 46	15 15	15 55	16 08			15 50	16 18	16 27	16 24	16 38	16 45	16 32	16 39	16 46	16 15	16 57	17 08			16 50	17 18

A From Crewe
B From Birmingham New Street
C From Manchester Piccadilly
D From Edinburgh
E From Chester
F To South Croydon
G To London Euston
H From Glasgow Central
I From Bangor (Gwynedd)

Table 66R

Mondays to Fridays

9 December to 16 May

West Midlands, Northampton, Milton Keynes Central and Watford Junction - London

Network Diagram - see first Page of Table 59

Station			LM 1	VT ◇1 A ☕	LM 1	LM 1	VT ◇1 B ☕	VT ◇1 C ☕	LM 1	VT ◇1 ☕	VT ◇1 ☕	LM 1	SN 1	LM 1 D	LM 1 E	LM 1 F	LM 1	VT ◇1 A ☕	LM 1	LM 1	VT ◇1 G ☕	VT ◇1 H ☕	LM 1
Wolverhampton 7	68	d					15 45														16 45		
Sandwell & Dudley	68	d					15 55														16 55		
Birmingham New Street 12	68	d	15 14				16 10		15 33	15 50	16 30			15 54							17 10		16 33
Birmingham International	68 ✈	d	15 30				16 20		15 45	16 00	16 40			16 05							17 20		16 45
Coventry	68	d	15 48				16 31		16 00	16 11	16 51			16 21							17 31		17 00
Nuneaton	65	d													16 36								
Rugby	68	d	15 59						16 12	16 23				16 32	16 53								17 16
Long Buckby	68	a	16 08						16 21					16 41									17 25
Northampton	68	a	16 20						16 39					16 57									17 37
		d	16 25						16 50					17 05			17 25						17 50
Wolverton		d	16 37											17 17		←	17 37						
Milton Keynes Central 10		a	16 41				16 58		17 04					17 21	17 14	17 21	17 41				17 58		18 04
		d	16 41	16 47		16 47	16 58	17 03	17 06				17 13	17 22	17 15	17 22	17 41	17 47		17 47	18 00	18 03	18 06
Bletchley		d	16 46			16 52							17 17	→		17 27	17 46			17 52			
Leighton Buzzard		d	16 53			16 58							17 24			17 33	17 53			17 58			
Cheddington		d				17 04														18 04			
Tring		d			16 56	17 10						17 26	17 34						17 59	18 10			
Berkhamsted		d			17 01	17 15						17 31	17 39			17 46			18 04	18 15			
Hemel Hempstead		d			17 05	17 19						17 35	17 43			17 51			18 08	18 19			
Apsley		d			17 08							17 38							18 11				
Kings Langley		d			17 11							17 41							18 15				
Watford Junction	60	a			17 16	17 26			17 30		17s39	17 46	17 51			17 59			18 19	18 26			18 30
		d			17 16	17 27			17 30			17 46	17 51			17 59			18 20	18 27			18 30
Bushey	60	d			17 19							17 49							18 23				
Harrow & Wealdstone	⊖60	d			17 24							17 54	17 59						18 28				
Wembley Central	⊖60,176	d											18 03										
Shepherd's Bush	⊖176	a											18 19										
Kensington (Olympia)	⊖176	a											18 22										
West Brompton	⊖176	a											18 25										
Imperial Wharf	176	a											18 28										
Clapham Junction	176	a											18 33										
East Croydon	176	a											19 02										
London Euston 15	⊖60	a	17 27	17 24	17 38	17 47	17 34	17 39	17 46	17 15	17 55	18 08			17 50	18 18	18 27	18 24	18 41	18 46	18 34	18 39	18 46

Station			VT ◇1 ☕	VT ◇1 ⊠	LM 1	SN 1 I	LM 1 D	LM 1 E	LM 1 F	VT ◇1 J ☕	LM 1	LM 1	LM 1	VT ◇1 A ⊠	VT ◇1 B ☕	VT ◇1 H ⊠	LM 1	VT ◇1 ⊠	VT ◇1 ⊠	LM 1	SN 1	LM 1 D	LM 1 E	LM 1 F
Wolverhampton 7	68	d													17 45									
Sandwell & Dudley	68	d													17 55									
Birmingham New Street 12	68	d	16 50	17 30			16 54				17 13				18 10		17 33	17 50	18 30			17 54		
Birmingham International	68 ✈	d	17 00	17 40			17 05				17 25				18 20		17 45	18 00	18 40			18 05		
Coventry	68	d	17 11	17 51			17 21				17 40				18 31		18 00	18 11	18 51			18 21		
Nuneaton	65	d						17 36															18 36	
Rugby	68	d	17 23				17 32	17 53			17 56						18 12	18 23				18 32	18 53	
Long Buckby	68	a					17 41				18 05						18 21					18 41		
Northampton	68	a					17 56				18 17						18 34					18 53		
		d					18 05				18 25						18 50					19 05		
Wolverton		d					18 17		←		18 37											19 17		←
Milton Keynes Central 10		a					18 20	18 15	18 20		18 41				18 58		19 04					19 20	19 14	19 20
		d				18 13	18 22	18 15	18 22	18 24	18 41		18 47	18 50	19 00	19 03	19 06				19 15	19 22	19 15	19 22
Bletchley		d				18 17	→		18 27		18 46		18 54								19 20	→		19 27
Leighton Buzzard		d				18 24			18 33		18 53		19 00								19 27			19 33
Cheddington		d											19 06											
Tring		d			18 27	18 34						19 00	19 12							19 29	19 36			
Berkhamsted		d			18 32	18 39			18 46			19 05	19 17							19 34	19 41			19 46
Hemel Hempstead		d			18 36	18 43			18 51			19 09	19 21							19 38	19 45			19 51
Apsley		d			18 39							19 12								19 41				
Kings Langley		d			18 42							19 15								19 44				
Watford Junction	60	a		18s39	18 46	18 51			18 58			19 19	19 28				19 30		19s39	19 49	19 54			19 59
		d			18 47	18 52			18 59			19 20	19 29				19 31			19 49	19 54			19 59
Bushey	60	d			18 49							19 23								19 52				
Harrow & Wealdstone	⊖60	d			18 54	18 59						19 28								19 57	20 02			
Wembley Central	⊖60,176	d				19 04															20 06			
Shepherd's Bush	⊖176	a				19 20															20 22			
Kensington (Olympia)	⊖176	a				19 22															20 24			
West Brompton	⊖176	a				19 25															20 27			
Imperial Wharf	176	a				19 27															20 29			
Clapham Junction	176	a				19 32															20 34			
East Croydon	176	a																						
London Euston 15	⊖60	a	18 15	18 55	19 09			18 51	19 18	19 02	19 29	19 42	19 47	19 26	19 32	19 39	19 46	19 15	19 55	20 11			19 50	20 19

A From Manchester Piccadilly
B From Glasgow Central
C From Holyhead
D To London Euston
E From Crewe
F From Birmingham New Street
G From Edinburgh
H From Chester
I To Selhurst
J From Liverpool Lime Street

Table 66R

West Midlands, Northampton, Milton Keynes Central and Watford Junction - London

Mondays to Fridays

9 December to 16 May

Network Diagram - see first Page of Table 59

		VT	LM		VT	LM	LM	VT	LM	SN	VT	LM	LM		VT	LM	SN	LM	VT	LM	VT	LM	LM		VT
								R																	
		◇1	1		◇1	1	1	1	1	1	◇1	1	1		◇1	1	1	1	◇1	1	◇1	1	1		◇1
		A			A			B		C		D	E				F	G	A		H		D		A
		⊠			⊠			☕			⊠				☕				⊠		⊠				☕
Wolverhampton 7 68 🚌	d							18 45																	
Sandwell & Dudley 68	d							18 55																	
Birmingham New Street 12 68	d							19 10	18 33		18 50	18 54			19 30										
Birmingham International 68 ✈	d							19 20	18 45		19 00	19 05			19 40										
Coventry 68	d							19 31	19 00		19 11	19 21			19 51										
Nuneaton 65	d												19 36												
Rugby 68	d								19 18		19 23	19 32	19 53		20 03										
Long Buckby 68	a								19 27			19 41													
Northampton 68	a								19 45			19 54													
	d		19 25						19 50			20 05								20 25					
Wolverton	d		19 37									20 17						←		20 37					
Milton Keynes Central 10	a		19 41					19 58	20 04			20 20	20 14					20 20		20 41					
	d	19 34	19 41		19 47		19 47	20 00	20 06	20 13		20 22	20 15					20 22	20 33	20 41	20 47		20 47		20 50
Bletchley	d		19 46				19 52			20 17		→						20 27		20 46			20 52		
Leighton Buzzard	d		19 53				19 58			20 24								20 33		20 53			20 58		
Cheddington	d						20 04																21 06		
Tring	d					19 56	20 10			20 34						20 26						20 56	21 11		
Berkhamsted	d					20 01	20 15			20 39						20 31		20 46				21 01	21 16		
Hemel Hempstead	d					20 05	20 19			20 43						20 35		20 51				21 05	21 20		
Apsley	d					20 08										20 38						21 08			
Kings Langley	d					20 11										20 41	←					21 12			
Watford Junction 60	a					20 15	20 26		20 29	20 51					20s41	20 46	20 51	20 58				21 16	21 27		
	d					20 16	20 27		20 30	20 51						20 46	20 51	20 59				21 17	21 27		
Bushey 60	d					20 19				→						20 49						21 19	→		
Harrow & Wealdstone ⊖60	d					20 24										20 54	20 59					21 25			
Wembley Central ⊖60,176	d																21 04								
Shepherd's Bush ⊖176	a																21 20								
Kensington (Olympia) ⊖176	a																21 22								
West Brompton ⊖176	a																21 24								
Imperial Wharf 176	a																21 27								
Clapham Junction 176	a																21 32								
East Croydon 176 🚌	a																								
London Euston 15 ⊖60	a	20 08	20 27		20 24	20 39	20 45	20 34	20 45		20 15		20 50		20 58	21 08		21 17	21 06	21 29	21 25	21 38			21 26

		VT	VT	LM	LM	VT	SN	LM	VT		LM	VT	VT	VT	LM	VT	VT	SN	LM		LM	SN	LM	VT	VT
													FX	FO											
																	R								
		◇1	◇1	1	1	◇1	1	1	◇1		1	◇1	◇1	◇1	1	◇1	1	1	1		1	1	1	◇1	◇1
		H	I	F		J			A		D		H	H	K	A	B		G					H	A
		⊠	☕			☕			☕			☕	☕	☕		☕	⊠							⊠	☕
Wolverhampton 7 68 🚌	d	19 45															20 47								
Sandwell & Dudley 68	d	19 55															20 57								
Birmingham New Street 12 68	d	20 10						19 54			20 33	20 50					21 10						20 54		
Birmingham International 68 ✈	d	20 20						20 05			20 45	21 00					21 20						21 05		
Coventry 68	d	20 31						20 21			21 00	21 11					21 31						21 21		
Nuneaton 65	d					21 03																			
Rugby 68	d							20 32			21 14	21 23	21 29	21 29									21 32		
Long Buckby 68	a							20 41			21 23												21 41		
Northampton 68	a							20 53			21 35												21 53		
	d							21 05			21 37												22 05		
Wolverton	d							21 17			21 49				←								22 17		
Milton Keynes Central 10	a	20 58						21 20			21 52		21 48	21 48	21 52		21 58						22 20		
	d	21 00	21 05				21 13	21 22	21 37		21 53		21 49	21 50	21 53	21 54	21 59				22 05	22 11	22 22	22 41	22 53
Bletchley	d						21 17	21 27			→				21 58						22 10	22 15	22 27		
Leighton Buzzard	d						21 24	21 33							22 04						22 17	22 22	22 33		
Cheddington	d														22 10						22 23				
Tring	d				21 26		21 34								22 16						22 28	22 34			
Berkhamsted	d				21 31		21 39	21 46							22 20						22 33	22 39	22 48		
Hemel Hempstead	d				21 35		21 43	21 51							22 25						22 37	22 44	22 53		
Apsley	d				21 38																22 41				
Kings Langley	d			←	21 41														←		22 44				
Watford Junction 60	a	21s19		21 27	21 46	21s49	21 51	21 58							22 32	22s13	22s20		22 32		22 48	22 53	23 00	23s15	23s25
	d			21 27	21 46		21 52	21 59							22 33			22 27	22 33		22 49	22 54	23 01		
Bushey 60	d				21 49										→						22 51				
Harrow & Wealdstone ⊖60	d				21 54		21 59											22 33			22 57	23 01			
Wembley Central ⊖60,176	d																								
Shepherd's Bush ⊖176	a						22 18											22 52				23 21			
Kensington (Olympia) ⊖176	a						22 21											22 54				23 23			
West Brompton ⊖176	a						22 24											22 57				23 27			
Imperial Wharf 176	a						22 27											22 59				23 30			
Clapham Junction 176	a						22 31											23 05				23 35			
East Croydon 176 🚌	a																					23 59			
London Euston 15 ⊖60	a	21 39	21 43	21 46	22 08	22 09		22 20	22 13			22 13	22 23	22 23		22 33	22 43		22 52		23 12		23 21	23 39	23 48

- **A** From Manchester Piccadilly
- **B** From Edinburgh
- **C** To Clapham Junction
- **D** To London Euston
- **E** From Crewe
- **F** From Milton Keynes Central
- **G** From Birmingham New Street
- **H** From Glasgow Central
- **I** From Chester
- **J** From Liverpool Lime Street
- **K** From Birmingham New Street to London Euston

Table 66R

Mondays to Fridays

9 December to 16 May

West Midlands, Northampton, Milton Keynes Central and Watford Junction - London

Network Diagram - see first Page of Table 59

		SN	LM	VT	VT	LM	LM	VT
		1	1	◇1	◇1	1	1	◇1
			A	B		C		
				🍴	🍴			🍴
Wolverhampton 7	68 🚊 d				21 45			22 45
Sandwell & Dudley	68 d				21 56			22 55
Birmingham New Street 12	68 d		21 54		22 10			23 10
Birmingham International	68 ✈ d		22 05		22 20			23 20
Coventry	68 d		22 21		22 31			23 31
Nuneaton	65 d			22 18				
Rugby	68 d		22 32	22 34	22 43			23 44
Long Buckby	68 a		22 41					
Northampton	68 a		22 53					00s05
	d		22 55				23 35	
Wolverton	d		23 08			←	23 49	
Milton Keynes Central 10	a		23 12	22 58	23 05	23 12	23 52	00 23
	d		23 13	23 00	23 06	23 13	23 53	00 24
Bletchley	d		↪			23 18	23 58	
Leighton Buzzard	d					23 24	00 04	
Cheddington	d					23 29	00 11	
Tring	d					23 38	00 16	
Berkhamsted	d					23 43	00 21	
Hemel Hempstead	d					23 47	00 25	
Apsley	d					23 50		
Kings Langley	d					23 53		
Watford Junction	60 a			23s33	23s37	23 58	00 32	00s52
	d	23 29				23 59	00 32	
Bushey	60 d					00 01		
Harrow & Wealdstone	⊖60 d	23 35				00 07	00 38	
Wembley Central	⊖60,176 d						00 42	
Shepherd's Bush	⊖176 a	23 54						
Kensington (Olympia)	⊖176 a	23 57						
West Brompton	⊖176 a	00 01						
Imperial Wharf	176 a	00 03						
Clapham Junction	176 a	00 07						
East Croydon	176 🚊 a							
London Euston 15	⊖60 a			23 57	00 06	00 21	00 55	01 15

Saturdays

14 December to 28 December

		LM	LM	VT	LM	LM	SN	LM	LM	VT	SN	LM	LM	LM	VT	LM	VT	VT	VT	LM	SN	LM	VT
		1	1	◇1	1	1	1	1	1	◇1	1	1	1	1	◇1	1	◇1	◇1	◇1	1	1	1	◇1
		C	D	E			F				F			A		G	H		B		F		H
				🍴						🍴					🍴		🍴	🍴	🍴				🍴
Wolverhampton 7	68 🚊 d														05 45			06 06					
Sandwell & Dudley	68 d														05 56			06 17					
Birmingham New Street 12	68 d									05 50					06 10			06 30					
Birmingham International	68 ✈ d									06 00					06 20			06 40					
Coventry	68 d									06 10					06 31			06 51					
Nuneaton	65 d																		06 59				
Rugby	68 d									06 24							06 51						
Long Buckby	68 a																						
Northampton	68 a																						
	d							05 16				06 05										07 05	
Wolverton	d							05 28				06 17										07 17	
Milton Keynes Central 10	a							05 31				06 20			06 59		07 11					07 20	
	d			00 24	03 40	04 35		05 32				06 22		06 47	06 59		07 13				07 13	07 22	07 33
Bletchley	d				03 45	04 40		05 37	06 10			06 27	06 40	06 52						07 10	07 17	07 26	
Leighton Buzzard	d		00 04		03 51	04 46		05 43	06 16			06 33	06 47	06 58						07 16	07 24	07 33	
Cheddington	d		00 11					05 49						07 04									
Tring	d		00 16		04 03	04 58		05 55	06 25			06 43	06 56	07 10						07 25	07 33		
Berkhamsted	d		00 21		04 08	05 03		06 00	06 30			06 47	07 01	07 15						07 30	07 38	07 46	
Hemel Hempstead	d		00 25		04 12	05 07		06 04	06 34			06 52	07 05	07 19						07 34	07 42	07 50	
Apsley	d							06 07	06 37				07 08							07 37			
Kings Langley	d							06 10	06 40				07 11			←				07 40			
Watford Junction	60 a		00 32	00s52	04 19	05 14		06 15	06 45			06 59	07 16	07 26	07s19	07 26	07s32	07s36	07s45	07 45	07 50	07 57	
	d		00 32		04 20	05 15	05 52	06 16	06 46		06 55	07 01	07 17	07 27		07 27				07 45	07 51	07 59	
Bushey	60 d	00 01						06 18	06 48				07 20	↪						07 48			
Harrow & Wealdstone	⊖60 d	00 07	00 38		04 26	05 21	05 58	06 24	06 54		07 01		07 25							07 53	07 58		
Wembley Central	⊖60,176 d		00 42		04 34	05 25					07 06										08 03		
Shepherd's Bush	⊖176 a						06 20				07 22										08 19		
Kensington (Olympia)	⊖176 a						06 22				07 24										08 21		
West Brompton	⊖176 a						06 25				07 27										08 24		
Imperial Wharf	176 a						06 28				07 30										08 27		
Clapham Junction	176 a						06 33				07 35										08 33		
East Croydon	176 🚊 a						06 56				07 57										08 56		
London Euston 15	⊖60 a	00 21	00 55	01 15	04 46	05 41		06 38	07 09	07 17		07 20	07 39		07 38	07 45	07 53	07 55	08 05	08 09		08 18	08 10

A To London Euston
B From Liverpool Lime Street
C From Birmingham New Street
D From Northampton
E From Wolverhampton
F To South Croydon
G From Milton Keynes Central
H From Manchester Piccadilly

Table 66R

Saturdays

14 December to 28 December

West Midlands, Northampton, Milton Keynes Central and Watford Junction - London

Network Diagram - see first Page of Table 59

			VT ◇1 A ☕	LM 1	LM 1 B	LM 1	VT ◇1 ☕		VT ◇1 ☕	LM 1 C	VT ◇1 ☕	LM 1	SN 1 D	LM 1	VT ◇1 E ☕	LM 1	VT ◇1 E ☕		LM 1	LM 1	VT ◇1 F ☕	LM 1	VT ◇1 ☕	VT ◇1 ☕	LM 1	SN 1 D
Wolverhampton 7	68 🚊	d					06 27		06 45		07 05										07 45					
Sandwell & Dudley	68	d					06 37		06 56		07 14										07 55					
Birmingham New Street 12	68	d				06 14	06 50		07 10		07 30			06 54		07 14					08 10	07 33	07 50	08 30		
Birmingham International	68 ✈	d				06 30	07 00		07 20		07 40			07 05		07 30					08 20	07 45	08 00	08 40		
Coventry	68	d				06 48	07 11		07 31		07 51			07 21		07 48					08 30	08 00	08 11	08 51		
Nuneaton	65	d																								
Rugby	68	d				06 59	07 23							07 32	07 54	07 59						08 12	08 23			
Long Buckby	68	a				07 08								07 41		08 08						08 21				
Northampton	68	a				07 21								07 53		08 20						08 34				
		d				07 33								08 05		08 25						08 50				
Wolverton		d				07 45								08 17		08 37										
Milton Keynes Central 10		a				07 49			07 58					08 20		08 41					08 58	09 04				
		d	07 39		07 44	07 49			07 59				08 13	08 22		08 41	08 47			08 47	08 59	09 06				09 13
Bletchley		d			07 49	07 54							08 17	08 27		08 46				08 52						09 17
Leighton Buzzard		d			07 55	08 01							08 24	08 33		08 53				08 58						09 24
Cheddington		d			08 01															09 04						
Tring		d		07 56	08 07							08 26	08 34						08 56	09 10					09 26	09 34
Berkhamsted		d		08 01	08 11							08 31	08 39	08 46					09 01	09 15					09 31	09 39
Hemel Hempstead		d		08 05	08 16							08 35	08 43	08 51					09 05	09 19					09 35	09 43
Apsley		d		08 08								08 38							09 08						09 38	
Kings Langley		d		08 11						←		08 41							09 11						09 41	
Watford Junction	60	a		08 16	08 23	08 22				08 23	08s35	08 46	08 51	08 58					09 16	09 26				09s39	09 46	09 51
		d		08 16	08 24	08 23				08 24		08 46	08 52	08 59					09 16	09 27					09 46	09 52
Bushey	60	d		08 19	→							08 49							09 19						09 49	
Harrow & Wealdstone	⊖60	d		08 24								08 54	08 59						09 24						09 54	09 59
Wembley Central	⊖60,176	d											09 04													10 04
Shepherd's Bush	⊖176	a											09 20													10 20
Kensington (Olympia)	⊖176	a											09 22													10 22
West Brompton	⊖176	a											09 25													10 25
Imperial Wharf	176	a											09 28													10 28
Clapham Junction	176	a											09 33													10 33
East Croydon	176 🚊	a											09 56													10 56
London Euston 15	⊖60	a	08 17	08 38		08 40	08 17		08 35	08 42	08 54	09 08		09 17	08 46	09 27	09 24		09 38	09 45	09 34	09 47	09 15	09 59	10 08	

			LM 1 B		LM 1 G	VT ◇1 H ☕	LM 1 I	LM 1	LM 1	LM 1	VT ◇1 E ☕	VT ◇1 A ☕	VT ◇1 J ☕		LM 1	VT ◇1 ☕	VT ◇1 ☕	LM 1	SN 1 D	LM 1 B	LM 1 G	LM 1 I	LM 1		VT ◇1 E ☕	LM 1
Wolverhampton 7	68 🚊	d										08 45														
Sandwell & Dudley	68	d										08 55														
Birmingham New Street 12	68	d	07 54					08 14				09 10			08 33	08 50	09 30			08 54			09 14			
Birmingham International	68 ✈	d	08 05					08 30				09 20			08 45	09 00	09 40			09 05			09 30			
Coventry	68	d	08 21					08 48				09 31			09 00	09 11	09 51			09 21			09 48			
Nuneaton	65	d			08 27	09 05															09 36					
Rugby	68	d	08 32		08 43			08 59							09 12	09 23				09 32	09 53		09 59			
Long Buckby	68	a	08 41					09 08							09 21					09 41			10 08			
Northampton	68	a	08 56					09 20							09 34					09 55			10 20			
		d	09 05					09 25							09 50					10 05			10 25			
Wolverton		d	09 17				←	09 37												10 17		←	10 37			
Milton Keynes Central 10		a	09 20		09 05		09 20	09 41				09 58			10 04					10 20	10 14	10 20	10 41			
		d	09 22		09 15		09 22	09 41		09 47	09 48	09 59	10 03		10 07				10 13	10 22	10 15	10 22	10 41		10 47	
Bletchley		d	→				09 27	09 46		09 52									10 17	→		10 27	10 46			
Leighton Buzzard		d					09 33	09 53		09 58									10 24			10 33	10 53			
Cheddington		d								10 04																
Tring		d							09 56	10 10								10 26	10 34							10 56
Berkhamsted		d					09 46		10 01	10 15								10 31	10 39			10 46				11 01
Hemel Hempstead		d					09 51		10 05	10 19								10 35	10 43			10 51				11 05
Apsley		d							10 08									10 38								11 08
Kings Langley		d							10 11									10 41								11 11
Watford Junction	60	a					09 58		10 16	10 26					10 30		10s39	10 46	10 51			10 58				11 16
		d					09 59		10 16	10 27					10 31			10 46	10 52			10 59				11 16
Bushey	60	d							10 19									10 49								11 19
Harrow & Wealdstone	⊖60	d							10 24									10 54	10 59							11 24
Wembley Central	⊖60,176	d																	11 04							
Shepherd's Bush	⊖176	a																	11 20							
Kensington (Olympia)	⊖176	a																	11 22							
West Brompton	⊖176	a																	11 25							
Imperial Wharf	176	a																	11 28							
Clapham Junction	176	a																	11 33							
East Croydon	176 🚊	a																	11 56							
London Euston 15	⊖60	a			09 50	10 06	10 17	10 27	10 38	10 45	10 24	10 35	10 39		10 46	10 15	10 55	11 08			10 50	11 17	11 27		11 24	11 38

A From Lancaster
B To London Euston
C From Milton Keynes Central
D To South Croydon
E From Manchester Piccadilly
F From Preston
G From Crewe
H From Liverpool Lime Street
I From Birmingham New Street
J From Holyhead

Table 66R

Saturdays

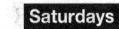

14 December to 28 December

West Midlands, Northampton, Milton Keynes Central and Watford Junction - London

Network Diagram - see first Page of Table 59

Station	Table		LM	VT	VT	LM	VT	VT	LM		SN	LM	LM	LM	LM	VT	LM	LM	VT		VT	LM	VT	VT	LM	SN
			[1]	◇[1]	◇[1]	[1]	◇[1]	◇[1]	[1]		[1]	[1]	[1]	[1]	[1]	◇[1]	[1]	[1]	◇[1]		◇[1]	[1]	◇[1]	◇[1]	[1]	[1]
				A	B						C	D	E	F		G			H		B					C
				☕	☕		☕	☕								☕			☕		☕		☕	☕		
Wolverhampton [7]	68 ⛴	d		09 45															10 45							
Sandwell & Dudley	68	d		09 55															10 55							
Birmingham New Street [12]	68	d		10 10		09 33	09 50	10 30				09 54			10 14				11 10			10 33	10 50	11 30		
Birmingham International	68 ✈	d		10 20		09 45	10 00	10 40				10 05			10 30				11 20			10 45	11 00	11 40		
Coventry	68	d		10 31		10 00	10 11	10 51				10 21			10 48				11 31			11 00	11 11	11 51		
Nuneaton	65	d											10 36													
Rugby	68	d				10 12	10 23					10 32	10 53		10 59							11 12	11 23			
Long Buckby	68	a				10 21						10 41			11 08							11 21				
Northampton	68	a				10 34						10 53			11 20							11 34				
		d				10 50						11 05			11 25							11 50				
Wolverton		d										11 17		←	11 37											
Milton Keynes Central [10]		a		10 58		11 04						11 20	11 14	11 20	11 41				11 58			12 04				
		d	10 47	10 59	11 03	11 07					11 13	11 22	11 15	11 22	11 41	11 47		11 47	11 59		12 03	12 07				12 13
Bletchley		d	10 52								11 17	↪		11 27	11 46			11 52								12 17
Leighton Buzzard		d	10 58								11 24			11 33	11 53			11 58								12 24
Cheddington		d	11 04															12 04								
Tring		d	11 10						11 26		11 34						11 56	12 10							12 26	12 34
Berkhamsted		d	11 15						11 31		11 39			11 46			12 01	12 15							12 31	12 39
Hemel Hempstead		d	11 19						11 35		11 43			11 51			12 05	12 19							12 35	12 43
Apsley		d							11 38								12 08								12 38	
Kings Langley		d							11 41								12 11								12 41	
Watford Junction	60	a	11 26			11 30		11s39	11 46		11 51			11 58			12 16	12 26				12 30		12s39	12 46	12 51
		d	11 27			11 31			11 46		11 52			11 59			12 16	12 27				12 31			12 46	12 52
Bushey	60	d							11 49								12 19								12 49	
Harrow & Wealdstone	⊖60	d							11 54		11 58						12 24								12 54	12 58
Wembley Central	⊖60,176	d									12 03															13 03
Shepherd's Bush	⊖176	a									12 19															13 19
Kensington (Olympia)	⊖176	a									12 21															13 21
West Brompton	⊖176	a									12 24															13 24
Imperial Wharf	176	a									12 27															13 27
Clapham Junction	176	a									12 32															13 33
East Croydon	176 ⛴	a									12 56															13 56
London Euston [15]	⊖60	a	11 45	11 33	11 39	11 46	11 15	11 55	12 08				11 50	12 17	12 27	12 24	12 38	12 45	12 33		12 39	12 46	12 15	12 55	13 08	

Station	Table		LM	LM	LM		LM	VT	LM	LM	VT	VT	LM	VT	VT		LM	SN	LM	LM	LM	LM	VT	LM	LM	
			[1]	[1]	[1]		[1]	◇[1]	[1]	[1]	◇[1]	◇[1]	[1]	◇[1]	◇[1]		[1]	[1]	[1]	[1]	[1]	[1]	◇[1]	[1]	[1]	
			D	E	F			G			A	I						C	D	E	F		G			
								☕			☕	☕		☕	☕								☕			
Wolverhampton [7]	68 ⛴	d									11 45															
Sandwell & Dudley	68	d									11 55															
Birmingham New Street [12]	68	d	10 54				11 14				12 10		11 33	11 50	12 30				11 54			12 14				
Birmingham International	68 ✈	d	11 05				11 30				12 20		11 45	12 00	12 40				12 05			12 30				
Coventry	68	d	11 21				11 48				12 30		12 00	12 11	12 51				12 21			12 48				
Nuneaton	65	d		11 36																12 36						
Rugby	68	d	11 32	11 53			11 59						12 12	12 23					12 32	12 53		12 59				
Long Buckby	68	a	11 41				12 08						12 21						12 41			13 08				
Northampton	68	a	11 53				12 20						12 34						12 53			13 20				
		d	12 05				12 25						12 50						13 05			13 25				
Wolverton		d	12 17		←		12 37												13 17		←	13 37				
Milton Keynes Central [10]		a	12 20	12 14	12 20		12 41				12 58		13 04						13 20	13 14	13 20	13 41				
		d	12 22	12 15	12 22		12 41	12 47		12 47	12 59	13 03	13 07					13 13	13 22	13 15	13 22	13 41	13 47		13 47	
Bletchley		d	↪		12 27		12 46			12 52								13 17	↪		13 27	13 46			13 52	
Leighton Buzzard		d			12 33		12 53			12 58								13 24			13 33	13 53			13 58	
Cheddington		d								13 04															14 04	
Tring		d							12 56	13 10							13 26	13 34						13 56	14 10	
Berkhamsted		d			12 46				13 01	13 15							13 31	13 39			13 46			14 01	14 15	
Hemel Hempstead		d			12 51				13 05	13 19							13 35	13 43			13 51			14 05	14 19	
Apsley		d							13 08								13 38							14 08		
Kings Langley		d							13 11								13 41							14 11		
Watford Junction	60	a			12 58				13 16	13 26			13 30		13s39		13 46	13 52			13 58			14 16	14 26	
		d			12 59				13 16	13 27			13 31				13 46	13 53			13 59			14 16	14 27	
Bushey	60	d							13 19								13 49							14 19		
Harrow & Wealdstone	⊖60	d							13 24								13 54	13 59						14 24		
Wembley Central	⊖60,176	d																14 04								
Shepherd's Bush	⊖176	a																14 20								
Kensington (Olympia)	⊖176	a																14 22								
West Brompton	⊖176	a																14 25								
Imperial Wharf	176	a																14 28								
Clapham Junction	176	a																14 33								
East Croydon	176 ⛴	a																14 56								
London Euston [15]	⊖60	a		12 50	13 17		13 27	13 24	13 38	13 47	13 35	13 39	13 46	13 15	13 55		14 08			13 50	14 17	14 27	14 24	14 38	14 45	

A From Glasgow Central
B From Holyhead
C To South Croydon
D To London Euston
E From Crewe
F From Birmingham New Street
G From Manchester Piccadilly
H From Edinburgh
I From Chester

Table 66R

Saturdays

14 December to 28 December

West Midlands, Northampton, Milton Keynes Central and Watford Junction - London

Network Diagram - see first Page of Table 59

	VT	VT	LM	VT	VT	LM	SN	LM	LM	LM	LM	VT	LM	LM	VT	VT	LM	VT	VT	LM	SN	LM
	◇[1]	◇[1]	[1]	◇[1]	◇[1]	[1]	[1]	[1]	[1]	[1]	[1]	◇[1]	[1]	[1]	◇[1]	◇[1]	[1]	◇[1]	◇[1]	[1]	[1]	[1]
	A	B					C	D	E	F		G			H	B					C	D
	☕	☕		☕	☕							☕			☕	☕		☕	☕			
Wolverhampton [7] 68 d	12 45														13 45							
Sandwell & Dudley 68 d	12 55														13 55							
Birmingham New Street [12] 68 d	13 10		12 33	12 50	13 30			12 54			13 14				14 10		13 33	13 50	14 30			13 54
Birmingham International 68 d	13 20		12 45	13 00	13 40			13 05			13 30				14 20		13 45	14 00	14 40			14 05
Coventry 68 d	13 31		13 00	13 11	13 51			13 21			13 48				14 31		14 00	14 11	14 51			14 21
Nuneaton 65 d									13 36													
Rugby 68 d			13 12	13 23				13 32	13 53		13 59						14 12	14 23				14 32
Long Buckby 68 a			13 21					13 41			14 08						14 21					14 41
Northampton 68 a			13 34					13 53			14 20						14 34					14 53
d			13 50					14 05			14 25						14 50					15 05
Wolverton d								14 17		←	14 37											15 17
Milton Keynes Central [10] a	13 58		14 04					14 20	14 14	14 20	14 41				14 58		15 04					15 20
d	14 00	14 03	14 07				14 13	14 22	14 15	14 22	14 41	14 47		14 47	14 59	15 03	15 07				15 13	15 22
Bletchley d							14 17	→		14 27	14 46			14 52							15 17	→
Leighton Buzzard d							14 24			14 33	14 53			14 58							15 24	
Cheddington d														15 04								
Tring d						14 26	14 34						14 56	15 10						15 26	15 34	
Berkhamsted d						14 31	14 39			14 46			15 01	15 15						15 31	15 39	
Hemel Hempstead d						14 35	14 43			14 51			15 05	15 19						15 35	15 43	
Apsley d						14 38							15 08							15 38		
Kings Langley d						14 41							15 11							15 41		
Watford Junction 60 a			14 30		14s39	14 46	14 51			14 58			15 16	15 26			15 30		15s39	15 46	15 51	
d			14 31			14 46	14 51			14 59			15 16	15 27			15 31			15 46	15 51	
Bushey 60 d						14 49							15 19							15 49		
Harrow & Wealdstone ⊖60 d						14 54	14 59						15 24							15 54	15 59	
Wembley Central ⊖60,176 d							15 03														16 03	
Shepherd's Bush ⊖176 a							15 19														16 19	
Kensington (Olympia) ⊖176 a							15 22														16 22	
West Brompton ⊖176 a							15 25														16 25	
Imperial Wharf 176 a							15 28														16 28	
Clapham Junction 176 a							15 33														16 33	
East Croydon 176 a							15 56														16 56	
London Euston [15] ⊖60 a	14 33	14 39	14 46	14 15	14 55	15 08			14 50	15 18	15 27	15 24	15 38	15 45	15 34	15 39	15 46	15 15	15 55	16 08		

	LM	LM	LM	VT	LM	LM	VT	VT	LM	VT	VT	LM	SN	LM	LM	LM	LM	VT	LM	LM	VT	VT
	[1]	[1]	[1]	◇[1]	[1]	[1]	◇[1]	◇[1]	[1]	◇[1]	◇[1]	[1]	[1]	[1]	[1]	[1]	[1]	◇[1]	[1]	[1]	◇[1]	◇[1]
	E	F		G			A	B					C	D	E	F		G			H	I
				☕			☕	☕		☕	☕							☕			☕	☕
Wolverhampton [7] 68 d							14 45														15 45	
Sandwell & Dudley 68 d							14 55														15 55	
Birmingham New Street [12] 68 d			14 14				15 10		14 33	14 50	15 30			14 54			15 14				16 10	
Birmingham International 68 d			14 30				15 20		14 45	15 00	15 40			15 05			15 30				16 20	
Coventry 68 d			14 48				15 31		15 00	15 11	15 51			15 21			15 48				16 31	
Nuneaton 65 d	14 36														15 36							
Rugby 68 d	14 53		14 59						15 12	15 23				15 32	15 53		15 59					
Long Buckby 68 a			15 08						15 21					15 41			16 08					
Northampton 68 a			15 20						15 34					15 53			16 20					
d			15 25						15 50					16 05			16 25					
Wolverton d		←	15 37											16 17		←	16 37					
Milton Keynes Central [10] a	15 14	15 20	15 41				15 58		16 04					16 20	16 14	16 20	16 41				16 58	
d	15 15	15 22	15 41	15 47		15 47	15 59	16 03	16 07				16 13	16 22	16 15	16 22	16 41	16 47		16 47	16 59	17 03
Bletchley d		15 27	15 46			15 52							16 17	→		16 27	16 46			16 52		
Leighton Buzzard d		15 33	15 53			15 58							16 24			16 33	16 53			16 58		
Cheddington d						16 04														17 04		
Tring d					15 56	16 10						16 26	16 34						16 55	17 10		
Berkhamsted d		15 46			16 01	16 15						16 31	16 39			16 46			16 59	17 15		
Hemel Hempstead d		15 51			16 05	16 19						16 35	16 43			16 51			17 04	17 19		
Apsley d					16 08							16 38							17 07			
Kings Langley d					16 11							16 41							17 10			
Watford Junction 60 a		15 58			16 16	16 26			16 30		16s39	16 46	16 51			16 58			17 15	17 26		
d		15 59			16 16	16 27			16 31			16 46	16 52			16 59			17 15	17 27		
Bushey 60 d					16 19							16 49							17 18			
Harrow & Wealdstone ⊖60 d					16 24							16 54	16 59						17 23			
Wembley Central ⊖60,176 d													17 03									
Shepherd's Bush ⊖176 a													17 19									
Kensington (Olympia) ⊖176 a													17 22									
West Brompton ⊖176 a													17 25									
Imperial Wharf 176 a													17 28									
Clapham Junction 176 a													17 32									
East Croydon 176 a													17 56									
London Euston [15] ⊖60 a	15 50	16 18	16 27	16 24	16 38	16 45	16 34	16 39	16 46	16 15	16 57	17 08			16 50	17 17	17 27	17 24	17 37	17 45	17 33	17 39

A From Edinburgh
B From Chester
C To South Croydon
D To London Euston
E From Crewe
F From Birmingham New Street
G From Manchester Piccadilly
H From Glasgow Central
I From Holyhead

Table 66R

Saturdays

14 December to 28 December

West Midlands, Northampton, Milton Keynes Central and Watford Junction - London

Network Diagram - see first Page of Table 59

	LM		VT	VT	LM	SN	LM	LM	LM	LM	VT		LM	LM	VT	VT	LM	VT	VT	LM	SN		LM	LM
	1		◇1	◇1	1	1	1	1	1	1	◇1		1	1	◇1	◇1	1	◇1	◇1	1	1		1	1
						A	B	C	D		E				F	G							B	C
			🍴	🍴							🍴				🍴	🍴		🍴	🍴					
Wolverhampton 7 68 🚌 d															16 45									
Sandwell & Dudley 68 d															16 55									
Birmingham New Street 12 68 d	15 33		15 50	16 30			15 54			16 14					17 10		16 33	16 50	17 30				16 54	
Birmingham International 68 ✈ d	15 45		16 00	16 40			16 05			16 30					17 20		16 45	17 00	17 40				17 05	
Coventry 68 d	16 00		16 11	16 51			16 21			16 48					17 31		17 00	17 11	17 51				17 21	
Nuneaton 65 d								16 36																17 36
Rugby 68 d	16 12		16 23				16 32	16 53		16 59							17 12	17 23					17 32	17 53
Long Buckby 68 a	16 21						16 41			17 08							17 21						17 41	
Northampton 68 a	16 34						16 53			17 21							17 34						17 53	
d	16 50						17 05			17 25							17 50						18 05	
Wolverton d							17 17		←	17 37													18 17	
Milton Keynes Central 10 a	17 04						17 20	17 14	17 20	17 41					17 58		18 04						18 20	18 14
d	17 07					17 13	17 22	17 15	17 22	17 41	17 47			17 47	17 59	18 03	18 07				18 13		18 22	18 15
Bletchley d						17 17	→		17 27	17 46				17 52							18 17		→	
Leighton Buzzard d						17 24			17 33	17 53				17 58							18 24			
Cheddington d														18 04										
Tring d					17 26	17 34							17 56	18 10						18 26	18 34			
Berkhamsted d					17 30	17 39			17 46				18 01	18 15						18 31	18 39			
Hemel Hempstead d					17 35	17 43			17 51				18 05	18 19						18 35	18 43			
Apsley d					17 38								18 08							18 38				
Kings Langley d					17 41								18 11							18 41				
Watford Junction 60 a	17 30			17s39	17 46	17 51			17 58				18 16	18 26			18 30		18s39	18 46	18 51			
d	17 31				17 46	17 51			17 59				18 16	18 27			18 31			18 46	18 51			
Bushey 60 d					17 49								18 19							18 49				
Harrow & Wealdstone ⊖60 d					17 54	17 59							18 24							18 54	18 59			
Wembley Central ⊖60,176 d						18 03															19 03			
Shepherd's Bush ⊖176 a						18 19															19 19			
Kensington (Olympia) ⊖176 a						18 22															19 22			
West Brompton ⊖176 a						18 25															19 25			
Imperial Wharf 176 a						18 27															19 27			
Clapham Junction 176 a						18 32															19 32			
East Croydon 176 🚌 a						18 56															19 57			
London Euston 15 ⊖60 a	17 46		17 15	17 55	18 08			17 50	18 17	18 27	18 24		18 38	18 45	18 34	18 39	18 46	18 15	18 55	19 08				18 50

	LM	VT	LM	LM	VT	LM	SN		VT	VT	LM	SN	LM	LM	LM	VT	LM		LM	VT	LM	VT	SN	LM
	1	◇1	1	1	◇1	1	1		◇1	◇1	1	1	1	1	1	◇1	1		1	◇1	1	◇1	1	1
	D	E			H								B	C	D	E					B	F		D
		🍴			🍴				🍴	🍴						🍴				🍴		🍴		
Wolverhampton 7 68 🚌 d					17 45																	18 45		
Sandwell & Dudley 68 d					17 55																	18 55		
Birmingham New Street 12 68 d				17 13	18 10	17 33			17 50	18 30			17 54						18 14	18 50	18 54	19 10		
Birmingham International 68 ✈ d				17 30	18 20	17 45			18 00	18 40			18 05						18 30	19 00	19 05	19 20		
Coventry 68 d				17 48	18 31	18 00			18 11	18 51			18 21						18 48	19 11	19 21	19 31		
Nuneaton 65 d														18 36										
Rugby 68 d				17 59		18 12			18 23				18 32	18 53					18 59	19 23	19 32	19 44		
Long Buckby 68 a				18 08		18 21							18 41						19 08		19 41			
Northampton 68 a				18 20		18 34							18 53						19 20		19 53			
d				18 31		18 50							19 05						19 31		20 00			
Wolverton d	←			18 43									19 17		←				19 43		20 12			←
Milton Keynes Central 10 a	18 20			18 46	18 58	19 04							19 20	19 14	19 20				19 46		20 15	20 05		20 15
d	18 22	18 47		18 47	18 59	19 06						19 14	19 22	19 15	19 22	19 46			19 47		20 16	20 07		20 16
Bletchley d	18 27			18 52								19 18	→		19 27				19 52		→			20 21
Leighton Buzzard d	18 33			18 58								19 25			19 33				19 58					20 27
Cheddington d				19 04															20 04					
Tring d			18 56	19 10							19 24	19 34					19 58		20 10					
Berkhamsted d	18 46		19 01	19 15							19 29	19 39			19 46		20 03		20 15					
Hemel Hempstead d	18 51		19 05	19 19							19 33	19 43			19 51		20 07		20 19					
Apsley d			19 08								19 36						20 10							
Kings Langley d			19 11								19 39						20 13							
Watford Junction 60 a	18 58		19 16	19 26		19 29				19s39	19 44	19 50			19 58		20 18		20 26			20s34		20 50
d	18 59		19 16	19 27		19 30	19 31				19 44	19 51			20 00		20 19		20 27				20 43	20 51
Bushey 60 d			19 19								19 47													
Harrow & Wealdstone ⊖60 d			19 24				19 37				19 52	20 01					20 25						20 49	
Wembley Central ⊖60,176 d							19 42																	
Shepherd's Bush ⊖176 a							19 58					20 20											21 08	
Kensington (Olympia) ⊖176 a							20 00					20 22											21 11	
West Brompton ⊖176 a							20 03					20 25											21 14	
Imperial Wharf 176 a							20 06					20 28											21 16	
Clapham Junction 176 a							20 10					20 33											21 21	
East Croydon 176 🚌 a												20 59												
London Euston 15 ⊖60 a	19 17	19 24	19 38	19 45	19 34	19 45			19 15	19 55	20 06			19 50	20 18	20 26	20 39		20 45	20 22		20 55		21 09

A To South Croydon
B To London Euston
C From Crewe
D From Birmingham New Street
E From Manchester Piccadilly
F From Edinburgh
G From Chester
H From Glasgow Central

Table 66R

Saturdays

14 December to 28 December

West Midlands, Northampton, Milton Keynes Central and Watford Junction - London

Network Diagram - see first Page of Table 59

	VT	LM	LM		LM	VT	SN	VT	LM	LM	VT	LM	VT		VT	SN	LM	VT	SN	LM	LM			
	◇1	1	1		1	◇1	1	◇1	1	1	◇1	1	◇1		◇1	1	1	◇1	1	1	1			
	A				B	A		C	D		A	B	E		C	F	D							
	☕					☕		☕			☕		☕		☕			☕						
Wolverhampton 7 68 🚊 d						19 45							20 45					21 07						
Sandwell & Dudley 68 d						19 55							20 55					21 17						
Birmingham New Street 12 68 d		19 14			19 54	20 10						20 54	21 10					21 30		21 34	22 14			
Birmingham International 68 ✈ d		19 30			20 05	20 20						21 05	21 20					21 40		21 45	22 30			
Coventry 68 d		19 48			20 21	20 31						21 21	21 31					21 51		22 00	22 48			
Nuneaton 65 d																								
Rugby 68 d		19 59			20 32	20 43						21 32	21 43					22 03		22 12	22 59			
Long Buckby 68 a		20 08			20 41							21 41								22 21	23 08			
Northampton 68 a		20 20			20 53							21 53								22 34	23 21			
d		20 32			21 02					21 20		22 05								22 43	23 30			
Wolverton d					21 14				←			22 17					←			22 55	23 42			
Milton Keynes Central 10 a		20 47			21 17	21 04			21 17	21 34		22 20	22 04				22 20	22 25		22 58	23 45			
d	20 43	20 47	20 50		21 18	21 05		21 11	21 18	21 34	21 52	22 21	22 05		22 11		22 21	22 26		22 59	23 46			
Bletchley d			20 55		→					21 39		→					22 26			23 04	23 51			
Leighton Buzzard d		20 56								21 46							22 32			23 10	23 57			
Cheddington d		21 03								21 51							22 37			23 15				
Tring d		21 08	21 12							21 58							22 44			23 24				
Berkhamsted d			21 17						21 40	22 02							22 49			23 29				
Hemel Hempstead d		21 15	21 21						21 44	22 07							22 53			23 33				
Apsley d		21 18								22 10							22 56			23 37				
Kings Langley d		21 21								22 13							23 00			23 40				
Watford Junction 60 a	21s15	21 26	21 30			21s35			21 51	22 18			22s34		22s40		23 06	23s11		23 44	00 19			
d		21 26	21 31				21 44		21 52	22 19						22 48	23 07		23 25	23 45	00 20			
Bushey 60 d			21 33																					
Harrow & Wealdstone ⊖60 d			21 39				21 50									22 55	23 13		23 31	23 51				
Wembley Central ⊖60,176 d																								
Shepherd's Bush ⊖176 a							22 09									23 14			23 50					
Kensington (Olympia) ⊖176 a							22 12									23 16			23 53					
West Brompton ⊖176 a							22 14									23 19			23 55					
Imperial Wharf 176 a							22 17									23 21			23 58					
Clapham Junction 176 a							22 21									23 26			00 02					
East Croydon 176 🚊 a																								
London Euston 15 ⊖60 a	21 38	21 45	21 52			21 56		22 00	22 11	22 37	22 45		22 55		23 02		23 27	23 30		00 05	00 40			

Saturdays

4 January to 8 February

	LM	LM	VT	LM	LM	SN	LM	LM	VT		SN	LM	LM	LM	VT	LM	VT	VT	VT		LM	SN	LM	VT
	1	1	◇1	1	1	1	1	1	◇1		1	1	1	1	◇1	1	◇1	◇1	◇1		1	1	1	◇1
	D	G	H			I					I			B		J	C		K			I		C
			☕						☕						☕		☕	☕	☕					☕
Wolverhampton 7 68 🚊 d															05 45			06 06						
Sandwell & Dudley 68 d															05 56			06 17						
Birmingham New Street 12 68 d									05 50						06 10			06 30						
Birmingham International 68 ✈ d									06 00						06 20			06 40						
Coventry 68 d									06 10						06 31			06 51						
Nuneaton 65 d																			06 59					
Rugby 68 d									06 24								06 51							
Long Buckby 68 a																								
Northampton 68 a																								
d							05 16					06 05											07 05	
Wolverton d							05 28					06 17											07 17	
Milton Keynes Central 10 a							05 31					06 20			06 59		07 11						07 20	
d			00 24	03 40	04 35		05 32					06 22		06 47	06 59		07 13					07 13	07 22	07 33
Bletchley d				03 45	04 40		05 37	06 10				06 27	06 40	06 52							07 10	07 17	07 26	
Leighton Buzzard d		00 04		03 51	04 46		05 43	06 16				06 33	06 47	06 58							07 16	07 24	07 33	
Cheddington d		00 11					05 49							07 04										
Tring d		00 16		04 03	04 58		05 55	06 25				06 43	06 56	07 10							07 25	07 33		
Berkhamsted d		00 21		04 08	05 03		06 00	06 30				06 47	07 01	07 15							07 30	07 38	07 46	
Hemel Hempstead d		00 25		04 12	05 07		06 04	06 34				06 52	07 05	07 19							07 34	07 42	07 50	
Apsley d							06 07	06 37					07 08								07 37			
Kings Langley d							06 10	06 40					07 11			←					07 40			
Watford Junction 60 a		00 32	00s52	04 19	05 14		06 15	06 45				06 59	07 16	07 26	07s19	07 26	07s32	07s36	07s45		07 45	07 50	07 57	
d		00 32		04 20	05 15	05 52	06 16	06 46			06 55	07 01	07 17	07 27		07 27					07 45	07 51	07 59	
Bushey 60 d	00 01						06 18	06 48					07 20	→							07 48			
Harrow & Wealdstone ⊖60 d	00 07	00 38		04 26	05 21	05 58	06 24	06 54			07 01		07 25								07 53	07 58		
Wembley Central ⊖60,176 d		00 42		04 34	05 25						07 06											08 03		
Shepherd's Bush ⊖176 a						06 20					07 22											08 19		
Kensington (Olympia) ⊖176 a						06 22					07 24											08 21		
West Brompton ⊖176 a						06 25					07 27											08 24		
Imperial Wharf 176 a						06 28					07 30											08 27		
Clapham Junction 176 a						06 33					07 35											08 33		
East Croydon 176 🚊 a						06 56					07 57											08 56		
London Euston 15 ⊖60 a	00 21	00 55	01 15	04 46	05 41		06 38	07 09	07 17			07 20	07 39		07 38	07 45	07 53	07 55	08 05		08 09		08 18	08 10

A From Glasgow Central
B To London Euston
C From Manchester Piccadilly
D From Birmingham New Street
E From Edinburgh
F To Selhurst
G From Northampton
H From Wolverhampton
I To South Croydon
J From Milton Keynes Central
K From Liverpool Lime Street

Table 66R

Saturdays

4 January to 8 February

West Midlands, Northampton, Milton Keynes Central and Watford Junction - London

Network Diagram - see first Page of Table 59

		VT	LM	LM	LM	VT		VT	LM	VT	LM	SN	LM	VT	LM	VT		LM	LM	VT	LM	VT	VT	LM	SN
		◇1	1	1	1	◇1		◇1	1	◇1	1	1	1	◇1	1	◇1		1	1	◇1	1	◇1	◇1	1	1
		A		B					C			D		E		E				F					D
		☕				☕		☕		☕				☕		☕				☕		☕	☕		
Wolverhampton 7 . . . 68 🚌	d					06 27		06 45		07 05										07 45					
Sandwell & Dudley . 68	d					06 37		06 56		07 14										07 55					
Birmingham New Street 12 68	d				06 14	06 50		07 10		07 30			06 54		07 14					08 10	07 33	07 50	08 30		
Birmingham International 68 ✈	d				06 30	07 00		07 20		07 40			07 05		07 30					08 20	07 45	08 00	08 40		
Coventry . . . 68	d				06 48	07 11		07 31		07 51			07 21		07 48					08 30	08 00	08 11	08 51		
Nuneaton . . . 65	d																								
Rugby . . . 68	d				06 59	07 23							07 32	07 54	07 59						08 12	08 23			
Long Buckby . . . 68	a				07 08								07 41		08 08						08 21				
Northampton . . . 68	a				07 21								07 53		08 20						08 34				
	d				07 33								08 05		08 25						08 50				
Wolverton . . .	d				07 45								08 17		08 37										
Milton Keynes Central 10	a				07 49			07 58					08 20		08 41					08 58	09 04				
	d	07 39		07 44	07 49			07 59				08 13	08 22		08 41	08 47			08 47	08 59	09 06				09 13
Bletchley . . .	d			07 49	07 54							08 17	08 27		08 46				08 52						09 17
Leighton Buzzard . . .	d			07 55	08 01							08 24	08 33		08 53				08 58						09 24
Cheddington . . .	d			08 01															09 04						
Tring . . .	d		07 56	08 07							08 26	08 34						08 56	09 10					09 26	09 34
Berkhamsted . . .	d		08 01	08 11							08 31	08 39	08 46					09 01	09 15					09 31	09 39
Hemel Hempstead . . .	d		08 05	08 16							08 35	08 43	08 51					09 05	09 19					09 35	09 43
Apsley . . .	d		08 08								08 38							09 08						09 38	
Kings Langley . . .	d		08 11						←		08 41							09 11						09 41	
Watford Junction . . . 60	a		08 16	08 23	08 22				08 23	08s35	08 46	08 51	08 58					09 16	09 26				09s39	09 46	09 51
	d		08 16	08 24	08 23				08 24		08 46	08 52	08 59					09 16	09 27					09 46	09 52
Bushey . . . 60	d		08 19	→							08 49							09 19						09 49	
Harrow & Wealdstone . . . ⊖60	d		08 24								08 54	08 59						09 24						09 54	09 59
Wembley Central . . . ⊖60,176	d											09 04													10 04
Shepherd's Bush . . . ⊖176	a											09 20													10 20
Kensington (Olympia) . ⊖176	a											09 22													10 22
West Brompton . . . ⊖176	a											09 25													10 25
Imperial Wharf . . . 176	a											09 28													10 28
Clapham Junction . . . 176	a											09 33													10 33
East Croydon . . . 176 🚌	a											09 56													10 56
London Euston 15 . . . ⊖60	a	08 17	08 38		08 40	08 17		08 35	08 42	08 54	09 08		09 17	08 46	09 27	09 24		09 38	09 45	09 34	09 47	09 15	09 59	10 08	

		LM		LM	VT	LM	LM	LM	LM	VT	VT	VT		LM	VT	VT	LM	SN	LM	LM	LM	LM		VT	LM
		1		1	◇1	1	1	1	1	◇1	◇1	◇1		1	◇1	◇1	1	1	1	1	1	1		◇1	1
		B		G	H	I				E	A	J						D	B	G	I			E	
					☕					☕	☕	☕			☕	☕								☕	
Wolverhampton 7 . . . 68 🚌	d										08 45														
Sandwell & Dudley . 68	d										08 55														
Birmingham New Street 12 68	d	07 54					08 14				09 10			08 33	08 50	09 30			08 54			09 14			
Birmingham International 68 ✈	d	08 05					08 30				09 20			08 45	09 00	09 40			09 05			09 30			
Coventry . . . 68	d	08 21					08 48				09 31			09 00	09 11	09 51			09 21			09 48			
Nuneaton . . . 65	d			08 27	09 05															09 36					
Rugby . . . 68	d	08 32		08 43			08 59							09 12	09 23				09 32	09 53		09 59			
Long Buckby . . . 68	a	08 41					09 08							09 21					09 41			10 08			
Northampton . . . 68	a	08 56					09 20							09 34					09 55			10 20			
	d	09 05					09 25							09 50					10 05			10 25			
Wolverton . . .	d	09 17				←	09 37												10 17		←	10 37			
Milton Keynes Central 10	a	09 20		09 05		09 20	09 41				09 58			10 04					10 20	10 14	10 20	10 41			
	d	09 22		09 15		09 22	09 41		09 47	09 48	09 59	10 03		10 07				10 13	10 22	10 15	10 22	10 41		10 47	
Bletchley . . .	d	→				09 27	09 46		09 52									10 17	→		10 27	10 46			
Leighton Buzzard . . .	d					09 33	09 53		09 58									10 24			10 33	10 53			
Cheddington . . .	d								10 04																
Tring . . .	d							09 56	10 10								10 26	10 34							10 56
Berkhamsted . . .	d					09 46		10 01	10 15								10 31	10 39			10 46				11 01
Hemel Hempstead . . .	d					09 51		10 05	10 19								10 35	10 43			10 51				11 05
Apsley . . .	d							10 08									10 38								11 08
Kings Langley . . .	d							10 11									10 41								11 11
Watford Junction . . . 60	a					09 58		10 16	10 26					10 30		10s39	10 46	10 51			10 58				11 16
	d					09 59		10 16	10 27					10 31			10 46	10 52			10 59				11 16
Bushey . . . 60	d							10 19									10 49								11 19
Harrow & Wealdstone . . . ⊖60	d							10 24									10 54	10 59							11 24
Wembley Central . . . ⊖60,176	d																	11 04							
Shepherd's Bush . . . ⊖176	a																	11 20							
Kensington (Olympia) . ⊖176	a																	11 22							
West Brompton . . . ⊖176	a																	11 25							
Imperial Wharf . . . 176	a																	11 28							
Clapham Junction . . . 176	a																	11 33							
East Croydon . . . 176 🚌	a																	11 56							
London Euston 15 . . . ⊖60	a			09 50	10 06	10 17	10 27	10 38	10 45	10 24	10 35	10 39		10 46	10 15	10 55	11 08			10 50	11 17	11 27		11 24	11 38

A From Lancaster
B To London Euston
C From Milton Keynes Central
D To South Croydon
E From Manchester Piccadilly
F From Preston
G From Crewe
H From Liverpool Lime Street
I From Birmingham New Street
J From Holyhead

Table 66R

Saturdays

4 January to 8 February

West Midlands, Northampton, Milton Keynes Central and Watford Junction - London

Network Diagram - see first Page of Table 59

	LM	VT	VT	LM	VT	VT	LM		SN	LM	LM	LM	LM	VT	LM	LM	VT		VT	LM	VT	VT	LM	SN
	1	◇1	◇1	1	◇1	◇1	1		1	1	1	1	1	◇1	1	1	◇1		◇1	1	◇1	◇1	1	1
		A	B						C	D	E	F		G			H		B					C
		☕	☕		☕	☕								☕			☕		☕		☕	☕		
Wolverhampton 7 68 d		09 45															10 45							
Sandwell & Dudley 68 d		09 55															10 55							
Birmingham New Street 12 68 d		10 10		09 33	09 50	10 30				09 54			10 14				11 10			10 33	10 50	11 30		
Birmingham International 68 d		10 20		09 45	10 00	10 40				10 05			10 30				11 20			10 45	11 00	11 40		
Coventry 68 d		10 31		10 00	10 11	10 51				10 21			10 48				11 31			11 00	11 11	11 51		
Nuneaton 65 d											10 36													
Rugby 68 d				10 12	10 23					10 32	10 53		10 59							11 12	11 23			
Long Buckby 68 a				10 21						10 41			11 08							11 21				
Northampton 68 a				10 34						10 53			11 20							11 34				
d				10 50						11 05			11 25							11 50				
Wolverton d										11 17		←	11 37											
Milton Keynes Central 10 a		10 58		11 04						11 20	11 14	11 20	11 41				11 58			12 04				
d	10 47	10 59	11 03	11 07					11 13	11 22	11 15	11 22	11 41	11 47		11 47	11 59		12 03	12 07				12 13
Bletchley d	10 52								11 17	→		11 27	11 46			11 52								12 17
Leighton Buzzard d	10 58								11 24			11 33	11 53			11 58								12 24
Cheddington d	11 04															12 04								
Tring d	11 10						11 26		11 34						11 56	12 10							12 26	12 34
Berkhamsted d	11 15						11 31		11 39			11 46			12 01	12 15							12 31	12 39
Hemel Hempstead d	11 19						11 35		11 43			11 51			12 05	12 19							12 35	12 43
Apsley d							11 38								12 08								12 38	
Kings Langley d							11 41								12 11								12 41	
Watford Junction 60 a	11 26			11 30		11s39	11 46		11 51			11 58			12 16	12 26				12 30		12s39	12 46	12 51
d	11 27			11 31			11 46		11 52			11 59			12 16	12 27				12 31			12 46	12 52
Bushey 60 d							11 49								12 19								12 49	
Harrow & Wealdstone ⊖60 d							11 54		11 58						12 24								12 54	12 58
Wembley Central ⊖60,176 d									12 03															13 03
Shepherd's Bush ⊖176 a									12 19															13 19
Kensington (Olympia) ⊖176 a									12 21															13 21
West Brompton ⊖176 a									12 24															13 24
Imperial Wharf 176 a									12 27															13 27
Clapham Junction 176 a									12 32															13 33
East Croydon 176 a									12 56															13 56
London Euston 15 ⊖60 a	11 45	11 33	11 39	11 46	11 15	11 55	12 08				11 50	12 17	12 27	12 24	12 38	12 45	12 33		12 39	12 46	12 15	12 55	13 08	

	LM	LM	LM		LM	VT	LM	LM	VT	VT	LM	VT	VT		LM	SN	LM	LM	LM	LM	VT	LM	LM	
	1	1	1		1	◇1	1	1	◇1	◇1	1	◇1	◇1		1	1	1	1	1	1	◇1	1	1	
	D	E	F			G			A	I						C	D	E	F		G			
						☕			☕	☕		☕	☕								☕			
Wolverhampton 7 68 d									11 45															
Sandwell & Dudley 68 d									11 55															
Birmingham New Street 12 68 d	10 54				11 14				12 10		11 33	11 50	12 30				11 54			12 14				
Birmingham International 68 d	11 05				11 30				12 20		11 45	12 00	12 40				12 05			12 30				
Coventry 68 d	11 21				11 48				12 30		12 00	12 11	12 51				12 21			12 48				
Nuneaton 65 d		11 36																12 36						
Rugby 68 d	11 32	11 53			11 59						12 12	12 23					12 32	12 53		12 59				
Long Buckby 68 a	11 41				12 08						12 21						12 41			13 08				
Northampton 68 a	11 53				12 20						12 34						12 53			13 20				
d	12 05				12 25						12 50						13 05			13 25				
Wolverton d	12 17		←		12 37												13 17		←	13 37				
Milton Keynes Central 10 a	12 20	12 14	12 20		12 41				12 58		13 04						13 20	13 14	13 20	13 41				
d	12 22	12 15	12 22		12 41	12 47		12 47	12 59	13 03	13 07					13 13	13 22	13 15	13 22	13 41	13 47		13 47	
Bletchley d	→		12 27		12 46			12 52								13 17	→		13 27	13 46			13 52	
Leighton Buzzard d			12 33		12 53			12 58								13 24			13 33	13 53			13 58	
Cheddington d								13 04															14 04	
Tring d							12 56	13 10							13 26	13 34						13 56	14 10	
Berkhamsted d			12 46				13 01	13 15							13 31	13 39			13 46			14 01	14 15	
Hemel Hempstead d			12 51				13 05	13 19							13 35	13 43			13 51			14 05	14 19	
Apsley d							13 08								13 38							14 08		
Kings Langley d							13 11								13 41							14 11		
Watford Junction 60 a			12 58				13 16	13 26			13 30		13s39		13 46	13 52			13 58			14 16	14 26	
d			12 59				13 16	13 27			13 31				13 46	13 53			13 59			14 16	14 27	
Bushey 60 d							13 19								13 49							14 19		
Harrow & Wealdstone ⊖60 d							13 24								13 54	13 59						14 24		
Wembley Central ⊖60,176 d																14 04								
Shepherd's Bush ⊖176 a																14 20								
Kensington (Olympia) ⊖176 a																14 22								
West Brompton ⊖176 a																14 25								
Imperial Wharf 176 a																14 28								
Clapham Junction 176 a																14 33								
East Croydon 176 a																14 56								
London Euston 15 ⊖60 a		12 50	13 17		13 27	13 24	13 38	13 47	13 35	13 39	13 46	13 15	13 55		14 08			13 50	14 17	14 27	14 24	14 38	14 45	

A From Glasgow Central
B From Holyhead
C To South Croydon
D To London Euston
E From Crewe
F From Birmingham New Street
G From Manchester Piccadilly
H From Edinburgh
I From Chester

Table 66R

Saturdays

4 January to 8 February

West Midlands, Northampton, Milton Keynes Central and Watford Junction - London

Network Diagram - see first Page of Table 59

			VT	VT	LM	VT	VT	LM	SN	LM	LM		LM	LM	VT	LM	LM	VT	VT	LM	VT		VT	LM	SN	LM
			◇1	◇1	1	◇1	◇1	1	1	1	1		1	1	◇1	1	1	◇1	◇1	1	◇1		◇1	1	1	1
			A	B					C	D	E		F		G			H	B						C	D
			☕	☕		☕	☕								☕			☕	☕		☕		☕			
Wolverhampton 7	68 🚊	d	12 45															13 45								
Sandwell & Dudley	68	d	12 55															13 55								
Birmingham New Street 12	68	d	13 10		12 33	12 50	13 30			12 54				13 14				14 10		13 33	13 50		14 30			13 54
Birmingham International	68 ✈	d	13 20		12 45	13 00	13 40			13 05				13 30				14 20		13 45	14 00		14 40			14 05
Coventry	68	d	13 31		13 00	13 11	13 51			13 21				13 48				14 31		14 00	14 11		14 51			14 21
Nuneaton	65	d									13 36															
Rugby	68	d			13 12	13 23				13 32	13 53			13 59						14 12	14 23					14 32
Long Buckby	68	a			13 21					13 41				14 08						14 21						14 41
Northampton	68	a			13 34					13 53				14 20						14 34						14 53
		d			13 50					14 05				14 25						14 50						15 05
Wolverton		d								14 17			←	14 37												15 17
Milton Keynes Central 10		a	13 58		14 04					14 20	14 14		14 20	14 41				14 58		15 04						15 20
		d	14 00	14 03	14 07				14 13	14 22	14 15		14 22	14 41	14 47		14 47	14 59	15 03	15 07					15 13	15 22
Bletchley		d							14 17	→			14 27	14 46			14 52								15 17	→
Leighton Buzzard		d							14 24				14 33	14 53			14 58								15 24	
Cheddington		d															15 04									
Tring		d						14 26	14 34							14 56	15 10							15 26	15 34	
Berkhamsted		d						14 31	14 39				14 46			15 01	15 15							15 31	15 39	
Hemel Hempstead		d						14 35	14 43				14 51			15 05	15 19							15 35	15 43	
Apsley		d						14 38								15 08								15 38		
Kings Langley		d						14 41								15 11								15 41		
Watford Junction	60	a			14 30		14s39	14 46	14 51				14 58			15 16	15 26			15 30			15s39	15 46	15 51	
		d			14 31			14 46	14 51				14 59			15 16	15 27			15 31				15 46	15 51	
Bushey	60	d						14 49								15 19								15 49		
Harrow & Wealdstone	⊖60	d						14 54	14 59							15 24								15 54	15 59	
Wembley Central	⊖60,176	d							15 03																16 03	
Shepherd's Bush	⊖176	a							15 19																16 19	
Kensington (Olympia)	⊖176	a							15 22																16 22	
West Brompton	⊖176	a							15 25																16 25	
Imperial Wharf	176	a							15 28																16 28	
Clapham Junction	176	a							15 33																16 33	
East Croydon	176 🚊	a							15 56																16 56	
London Euston 15	⊖60	a	14 33	14 39	14 46	14 15	14 55	15 08			14 50		15 18	15 27	15 24	15 38	15 45	15 34	15 39	15 46	15 15		15 55	16 08		

			LM	LM	LM	VT	LM		LM	VT	VT	LM	VT	VT	LM	SN	LM		LM	LM	LM	VT	LM	LM	VT	VT
			1	1	1	◇1	1		1	◇1	◇1	1	◇1	◇1	1	1	1		1	1	1	◇1	1	1	◇1	◇1
			E	F		G				I	B					C	D		E	F		G			I	J
						☕				☕	☕		☕	☕								☕			☕	☕
Wolverhampton 7	68 🚊	d								14 45															15 45	
Sandwell & Dudley	68	d								14 55															15 55	
Birmingham New Street 12	68	d			14 14					15 10		14 33	14 50	15 30			14 54				15 14				16 10	
Birmingham International	68 ✈	d			14 30					15 20		14 45	15 00	15 40			15 05				15 30				16 20	
Coventry	68	d			14 48					15 31		15 00	15 10	15 51			15 21				15 48				16 31	
Nuneaton	65	d	14 36																15 36							
Rugby	68	d	14 53		14 59							15 12	15 23				15 32		15 53		15 59					
Long Buckby	68	a			15 08							15 21					15 41				16 08					
Northampton	68	a			15 20							15 34					15 53				16 20					
		d			15 25							15 50					16 05				16 25					
Wolverton		d		←	15 37												16 17			←	16 37					
Milton Keynes Central 10		a	15 14	15 20	15 41					15 58		16 04					16 20		16 14	16 20	16 41				16 58	
		d	15 15	15 22	15 41	15 47			15 47	15 59	16 03	16 07				16 13	16 22		16 15	16 22	16 41	16 47		16 47	16 59	17 03
Bletchley		d		15 27	15 46				15 52							16 17	→			16 27	16 46			16 52		
Leighton Buzzard		d		15 33	15 53				15 58							16 24				16 33	16 53			16 58		
Cheddington		d							16 04															17 04		
Tring		d					15 56		16 10						16 26	16 34							16 55	17 10		
Berkhamsted		d		15 46			16 01		16 15						16 31	16 39				16 46			16 59	17 15		
Hemel Hempstead		d		15 51			16 05		16 19						16 35	16 43				16 51			17 04	17 19		
Apsley		d					16 08								16 38								17 07			
Kings Langley		d					16 11								16 41								17 10			
Watford Junction	60	a		15 58			16 16		16 26			16 30		16s39	16 46	16 51				16 58			17 15	17 26		
		d		15 59			16 16		16 27			16 31			16 46	16 52				16 59			17 15	17 27		
Bushey	60	d					16 19								16 49								17 18			
Harrow & Wealdstone	⊖60	d					16 24								16 54	16 59							17 23			
Wembley Central	⊖60,176	d														17 03										
Shepherd's Bush	⊖176	a														17 19										
Kensington (Olympia)	⊖176	a														17 22										
West Brompton	⊖176	a														17 25										
Imperial Wharf	176	a														17 28										
Clapham Junction	176	a														17 32										
East Croydon	176 🚊	a														17 56										
London Euston 15	⊖60	a	15 50	16 18	16 27	16 24	16 38		16 45	16 34	16 39	16 46	16 15	16 57	17 08				16 50	17 17	17 27	17 24	17 37	17 45	17 33	17 39

A From Edinburgh
B From Chester
C To South Croydon
D To London Euston
E From Crewe
F From Birmingham New Street
G From Manchester Piccadilly
H From Glasgow Central
I From Preston
J From Holyhead

Table 66R

Saturdays

4 January to 8 February

West Midlands, Northampton, Milton Keynes Central and Watford Junction - London

Network Diagram - see first Page of Table 59

		LM		VT	VT	LM	SN	LM	LM	LM	LM	VT		LM	LM	VT	VT	LM	VT	VT	LM	SN		LM	LM
		1		◇1	◇1	1	1	1	1	1	1	◇1		1	1	◇1	◇1	1	◇1	◇1	1	1		1	1
							A	B	C	D		E				F	G							B	C
				☕	☕							☕				☕	☕		☕	☕					
Wolverhampton 7 68	d															16 45									
Sandwell & Dudley 68	d															16 55									
Birmingham New Street 12 68	d	15 33		15 50	16 30			15 54			16 14					17 10		16 33	16 50	17 30				16 54	
Birmingham International 68	d	15 45		16 00	16 40			16 05			16 30					17 20		16 45	17 00	17 40				17 05	
Coventry 68	d	16 00		16 11	16 51			16 21			16 48					17 31		17 00	17 11	17 51				17 21	
Nuneaton 65	d								16 36																17 36
Rugby 68	d	16 12		16 23				16 32	16 53		16 59							17 12	17 23					17 32	17 53
Long Buckby 68	a	16 21						16 41			17 08							17 21						17 41	
Northampton 68	a	16 34						16 53			17 21							17 34						17 53	
	d	16 50						17 05			17 25							17 50						18 05	
Wolverton	d							17 17		←	17 37													18 17	
Milton Keynes Central 10	a	17 04						17 20	17 14	17 20	17 41					17 58		18 04						18 20	18 14
	d	17 07					17 13	17 22	17 15	17 22	17 41	17 47			17 47	17 59	18 03	18 07				18 13		18 22	18 15
Bletchley	d						17 17	→		17 27	17 46				17 52							18 17		→	
Leighton Buzzard	d						17 24			17 33	17 53				17 58							18 24			
Cheddington	d														18 04										
Tring	d					17 26	17 34							17 56	18 10						18 26	18 34			
Berkhamsted	d					17 30	17 39			17 46				18 01	18 15						18 31	18 39			
Hemel Hempstead	d					17 35	17 43			17 51				18 05	18 19						18 35	18 43			
Apsley	d					17 38								18 08							18 38				
Kings Langley	d					17 41								18 11							18 41				
Watford Junction 60	a	17 30			17s39	17 46	17 51			17 58				18 16	18 26			18 30		18s39	18 46	18 51			
	d	17 31				17 46	17 51			17 59				18 16	18 27			18 31			18 46	18 51			
Bushey 60	d					17 49								18 19							18 49				
Harrow & Wealdstone ⊖60	d					17 54	17 59							18 24							18 54	18 59			
Wembley Central ⊖60,176	d						18 03															19 03			
Shepherd's Bush ⊖176	a						18 19															19 19			
Kensington (Olympia) ⊖176	a						18 22															19 22			
West Brompton ⊖176	a						18 25															19 25			
Imperial Wharf 176	a						18 27															19 27			
Clapham Junction 176	a						18 32															19 32			
East Croydon 176	a						18 56															19 57			
London Euston 15 ⊖60	a	17 46		17 15	17 55	18 08			17 50	18 17	18 27	18 24		18 38	18 45	18 34	18 39	18 46	18 15	18 55	19 08				18 50

		LM	VT	LM	LM	VT	LM	SN		VT	VT	LM	SN	LM	LM	LM	VT	LM		LM	VT	LM	VT	SN	LM
		1	◇1	1	1	◇1	1	1		◇1	◇1	1	1	1	1	1	◇1	1		1	◇1	1	◇1	1	1
		D	E			F								B	C	D	E					B	F		D
			☕			☕				☕	☕						☕				☕		☕		
Wolverhampton 7 68	d					17 45																	18 45		
Sandwell & Dudley 68	d					17 55																	18 55		
Birmingham New Street 12 68	d				17 13	18 10	17 33			17 50	18 30			17 54						18 14	18 50	18 54	19 10		
Birmingham International 68	d				17 30	18 20	17 45			18 00	18 40			18 05						18 30	19 00	19 05	19 20		
Coventry 68	d				17 48	18 31	18 00			18 11	18 51			18 21						18 48	19 11	19 21	19 31		
Nuneaton 65	d														18 36										
Rugby 68	d				17 59		18 12			18 23				18 32	18 53					18 59	19 23	19 32	19 44		
Long Buckby 68	a				18 08		18 21							18 41						19 08		19 41			
Northampton 68	a				18 20		18 34							18 53						19 20		19 53			
	d				18 31		18 50							19 05						19 31		20 00			
Wolverton	d	←			18 43									19 17		←				19 43		20 12			←
Milton Keynes Central 10	a	18 20			18 46	18 58	19 04							19 20	19 14	19 20				19 46		20 15	20 05		20 15
	d	18 22	18 47		18 47	18 59	19 06						19 14	19 22	19 15	19 22	19 46			19 47		20 16	20 07		20 16
Bletchley	d	18 27			18 52								19 18	→		19 27				19 52		→			20 21
Leighton Buzzard	d	18 33			18 58								19 25			19 33				19 58					20 27
Cheddington	d				19 04															20 04					
Tring	d			18 56	19 10							19 24	19 34					19 58		20 10					
Berkhamsted	d	18 46		19 01	19 15							19 29	19 39			19 46		20 03		20 15					
Hemel Hempstead	d	18 51		19 05	19 19							19 33	19 43			19 51		20 07		20 19					
Apsley	d			19 08								19 36						20 10							
Kings Langley	d			19 11								19 39						20 13							
Watford Junction 60	a	18 58		19 16	19 26		19 29				19s39	19 44	19 50			19 58		20 18		20 26			20s34		20 50
	d	18 59		19 16	19 27		19 30	19 31				19 44	19 51			20 00		20 19		20 27				20 43	20 51
Bushey 60	d			19 19								19 47													
Harrow & Wealdstone ⊖60	d			19 24				19 37				19 52	20 01					20 25						20 49	
Wembley Central ⊖60,176	d							19 42																	
Shepherd's Bush ⊖176	a							19 58					20 20											21 08	
Kensington (Olympia) ⊖176	a							20 00					20 22											21 11	
West Brompton ⊖176	a							20 03					20 25											21 14	
Imperial Wharf 176	a							20 06					20 28											21 16	
Clapham Junction 176	a							20 10					20 33											21 21	
East Croydon 176	a												20 59												
London Euston 15 ⊖60	a	19 17	19 24	19 38	19 45	19 34	19 45			19 15	19 55	20 06			19 50	20 18	20 26	20 39		20 45	20 22		20 55		21 09

A To South Croydon
B To London Euston
C From Crewe
D From Birmingham New Street
E From Manchester Piccadilly
F From Preston
G From Chester

Table 66R

Saturdays

4 January to 8 February

West Midlands, Northampton, Milton Keynes Central and Watford Junction - London

Network Diagram - see first Page of Table 59

		VT	LM	LM		LM	VT	SN	VT	LM	LM	VT	LM	VT		VT	SN	LM	VT	SN	LM	LM			
		◇1	1	1		1	◇1	1	◇1	1	1	◇1	1	◇1		◇1	1	1	◇1	1	1	1			
		A				B	C		D	E		F	B	C		D	G	E							
		🛒					🛒		🛒			🛒		🛒		🛒			🛒						
Wolverhampton [7] 68 🚋	d						19 45							20 45					21 07						
Sandwell & Dudley 68	d						19 55							20 55					21 17						
Birmingham New Street [12] 68	d		19 14			19 54	20 10						20 54	21 10					21 30		21 34	22 14			
Birmingham International 68 ✈	d		19 30			20 05	20 20						21 05	21 20					21 40		21 45	22 30			
Coventry 68	d		19 48			20 21	20 31						21 21	21 31					21 51		22 00	22 48			
Nuneaton 65	d																								
Rugby 68	d		19 59			20 32	20 43						21 32	21 43					22 03		22 12	22 59			
Long Buckby 68	a		20 08			20 41							21 41								22 21	23 08			
Northampton 68	a		20 20			20 53							21 53								22 34	23 21			
	d		20 32			21 02					21 20		22 05								22 43	23 30			
Wolverton	d					21 14				←			22 17					←			22 55	23 42			
Milton Keynes Central [10]	a		20 47			21 17	21 04			21 17	21 34		22 20	22 04				22 20	22 25		22 58	23 45			
	d	20 43	20 47	20 50		21 18	21 05		21 11	21 18	21 34	21 52	22 21	22 05		22 11		22 21	22 26		22 59	23 46			
Bletchley	d			20 55		↪					21 39		↪					22 26			23 04	23 51			
Leighton Buzzard	d		20 56								21 46							22 32			23 10	23 57			
Cheddington	d		21 03								21 51							22 37			23 15				
Tring	d		21 08	21 12							21 58							22 44			23 24				
Berkhamsted	d			21 17						21 40	22 02							22 49			23 29				
Hemel Hempstead	d		21 15	21 21						21 44	22 07							22 53			23 33				
Apsley	d		21 18								22 10							22 56			23 37				
Kings Langley	d		21 21								22 13							23 00			23 40				
Watford Junction 60	a	21s15	21 26	21 30			21s35			21 51	22 18			22s34		22s40		23 06	23s11		23 44	00 19			
	d		21 26	21 31				21 44		21 52	22 19						22 48	23 07		23 25	23 45	00 20			
Bushey 60	d			21 33																					
Harrow & Wealdstone ⊖60	d			21 39				21 50									22 55	23 13		23 31	23 51				
Wembley Central ⊖60,176	d																								
Shepherd's Bush ⊖176	a							22 09									23 14			23 50					
Kensington (Olympia) ⊖176	a							22 12									23 16			23 53					
West Brompton ⊖176	a							22 14									23 19			23 55					
Imperial Wharf 176	a							22 17									23 21			23 58					
Clapham Junction 176	a							22 21									23 26			00 02					
East Croydon 176 🚋	a																								
London Euston [15] ⊖60	a	21 38	21 45	21 52			21 56		22 00	22 11	22 37	22 45		22 55		23 02		23 27	23 30		00 05	00 40			

Saturdays

15 February to 17 May

		LM	LM	VT	LM	LM	SN	LM	LM	VT		SN	LM	LM	LM	VT	LM	VT	VT	VT		LM	SN	LM	VT
		1	1	◇1	1	1	1	1	1	◇1		1	1	1	1	◇1	1	◇1	◇1	◇1		1	1	1	◇1
		E	H	I			J					J			B		K	D		L			J		D
				🛒						🛒						🛒		🛒	🛒	🛒					🛒
Wolverhampton [7] 68 🚋	d															05 45			06 06						
Sandwell & Dudley 68	d															05 56			06 17						
Birmingham New Street [12] 68	d									05 50						06 10			06 30						
Birmingham International 68 ✈	d									06 00						06 20			06 40						
Coventry 68	d									06 10						06 31			06 51						
Nuneaton 65	d																			06 59					
Rugby 68	d									06 24								06 51							
Long Buckby 68	a																								
Northampton 68	a																								
	d							05 16					06 05											07 05	
Wolverton	d							05 28					06 17											07 17	
Milton Keynes Central [10]	a							05 31					06 20			06 59		07 11						07 20	
	d			00 24	03 40	04 35		05 32					06 22		06 47	06 59		07 13					07 13	07 22	07 33
Bletchley	d				03 45	04 40		05 37	06 10				06 27	06 40	06 52							07 10	07 17	07 26	
Leighton Buzzard	d		00 04		03 51	04 46		05 43	06 16				06 33	06 47	06 58							07 16	07 24	07 33	
Cheddington	d		00 11					05 49							07 04										
Tring	d		00 16		04 03	04 58		05 55	06 25				06 43	06 56	07 10							07 25	07 33		
Berkhamsted	d		00 21		04 08	05 03		06 00	06 30				06 47	07 01	07 15							07 30	07 38	07 46	
Hemel Hempstead	d		00 25		04 12	05 07		06 04	06 34				06 52	07 05	07 19							07 34	07 42	07 50	
Apsley	d							06 07	06 37					07 08								07 37			
Kings Langley	d							06 10	06 40					07 11			←					07 40			
Watford Junction 60	a		00 32	00s52	04 19	05 14		06 15	06 45				06 59	07 16	07 26	07s19	07 26	07s32	07s36	07s45		07 45	07 50	07 57	
	d		00 32		04 20	05 15	05 52	06 16	06 46			06 55	07 01	07 17	07 27		07 27					07 45	07 51	07 59	
Bushey 60	d	00 01						06 18	06 48					07 20	↪							07 48			
Harrow & Wealdstone ⊖60	d	00 07	00 38		04 26	05 21	05 58	06 24	06 54			07 01		07 25								07 53	07 58		
Wembley Central ⊖60,176	d		00 42		04 34	05 25						07 06											08 03		
Shepherd's Bush ⊖176	a						06 20					07 22											08 19		
Kensington (Olympia) ⊖176	a						06 22					07 24											08 21		
West Brompton ⊖176	a						06 25					07 27											08 24		
Imperial Wharf 176	a						06 28					07 30											08 27		
Clapham Junction 176	a						06 33					07 35											08 33		
East Croydon 176 🚋	a						06 56					07 57											08 56		
London Euston [15] ⊖60	a	00 21	00 55	01 15	04 46	05 41		06 38	07 09	07 17			07 20	07 39		07 38	07 45	07 53	07 55	08 05		08 09		08 18	08 10

A From Lancaster
B To London Euston
C From Preston
D From Manchester Piccadilly
E From Birmingham New Street
F From Wigan North Western
G To Selhurst
H From Northampton
I From Wolverhampton
J To South Croydon
K From Milton Keynes Central
L From Liverpool Lime Street

Table 66R

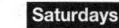

Saturdays
15 February to 17 May

West Midlands, Northampton, Milton Keynes Central and Watford Junction - London

Network Diagram - see first Page of Table 59

Station			VT	LM	LM	LM	VT	VT	LM	VT	LM	SN	LM	VT	LM	VT	LM	LM	VT	LM	VT	VT	LM	SN
			◇1	1	1	1	◇1	◇1	1	◇1	1	1	1	◇1	1	◇1	1	1	◇1	1	◇1	◇1	1	1
			A		B				C			D		E		E			F					D
			☕				☕	☕		☕				☕		☕			☕		☕	☕		
Wolverhampton 7	68 ⛴	d					06 27	06 45		07 05									07 45					
Sandwell & Dudley	68	d					06 37	06 56		07 14									07 55					
Birmingham New Street 12	68	d				06 14	06 50	07 10		07 30			06 54		07 14				08 10	07 33	07 50	08 30		
Birmingham International	68 ✈	d				06 30	07 00	07 20		07 40			07 05		07 30				08 20	07 45	08 00	08 40		
Coventry	68	d				06 48	07 11	07 31		07 51			07 21		07 48				08 30	08 00	08 11	08 51		
Nuneaton	65	d																						
Rugby	68	d				06 59	07 23						07 32	07 54	07 59					08 12	08 23			
Long Buckby	68	a				07 08							07 41		08 08					08 21				
Northampton	68	a				07 21							07 53		08 20					08 34				
		d				07 33							08 05		08 25					08 50				
Wolverton		d				07 45							08 17		08 37									
Milton Keynes Central 10		a				07 49		07 58					08 20		08 41				08 58	09 04				
		d	07 39		07 44	07 49		07 59				08 13	08 22		08 41	08 47		08 47	08 59	09 06				09 13
Bletchley		d			07 49	07 54						08 17	08 27		08 46			08 52						09 17
Leighton Buzzard		d			07 55	08 01						08 24	08 33		08 53			08 58						09 24
Cheddington		d			08 01													09 04						
Tring		d		07 56	08 07						08 26	08 34					08 56	09 10					09 26	09 34
Berkhamsted		d		08 01	08 11						08 31	08 39	08 46				09 01	09 15					09 31	09 39
Hemel Hempstead		d		08 05	08 16						08 35	08 43	08 51				09 05	09 19					09 35	09 43
Apsley		d		08 08							08 38						09 08						09 38	
Kings Langley		d		08 11					←		08 41						09 11						09 41	
Watford Junction	60	a		08 16	08 23	08 22			08 23	08s35	08 46	08 51	08 58				09 16	09 26				09s39	09 46	09 51
		d		08 16	08 24	08 23			08 24		08 46	08 52	08 59				09 16	09 27					09 46	09 52
Bushey	60	d		08 19	→						08 49						09 19						09 49	
Harrow & Wealdstone	⊖60	d		08 24							08 54	08 59					09 24						09 54	09 59
Wembley Central	⊖60,176	d										09 04												10 04
Shepherd's Bush	⊖176	a										09 20												10 20
Kensington (Olympia)	⊖176	a										09 22												10 22
West Brompton	⊖176	a										09 25												10 25
Imperial Wharf	176	a										09 28												10 28
Clapham Junction	176	a										09 33												10 33
East Croydon	176 ⛴	a										09 56												10 56
London Euston 15	⊖60	a	08 17	08 38		08 40	08 17	08 35	08 42	08 54	09 08		09 17	08 46	09 27	09 24	09 38	09 45	09 34	09 47	09 15	09 59	10 08	

Station			LM	LM	VT	LM	LM	LM	LM	VT	VT	VT	LM	VT	VT	LM	SN	LM	LM	LM	LM	VT	LM
			1	1	◇1	1	1	1	1	◇1	◇1	◇1	1	◇1	◇1	1	1	1	1	1	1	◇1	1
			B	G	H	I				E	A	J					D	B	G	I		E	
					☕					☕	☕	☕		☕	☕							☕	
Wolverhampton 7	68 ⛴	d									08 45												
Sandwell & Dudley	68	d									08 55												
Birmingham New Street 12	68	d	07 54				08 14				09 10		08 33	08 50	09 30			08 54			09 14		
Birmingham International	68 ✈	d	08 05				08 30				09 20		08 45	09 00	09 40			09 05			09 30		
Coventry	68	d	08 21				08 48				09 31		09 00	09 11	09 51			09 21			09 48		
Nuneaton	65	d		08 27	09 05														09 36				
Rugby	68	d	08 32	08 43			08 59						09 12	09 23				09 32	09 53		09 59		
Long Buckby	68	a	08 41				09 08						09 21					09 41			10 08		
Northampton	68	a	08 56				09 20						09 34					09 55			10 20		
		d	09 05				09 25						09 50					10 05			10 25		
Wolverton		d	09 17			←	09 37											10 17		←	10 37		
Milton Keynes Central 10		a	09 20	09 05		09 20	09 41				09 58		10 04					10 20	10 14	10 20	10 41		
		d	09 22	09 15		09 22	09 41		09 47	09 48	09 59	10 03	10 07				10 13	10 22	10 15	10 22	10 41	10 47	
Bletchley		d	→			09 27	09 46		09 52								10 17	→		10 27	10 46		
Leighton Buzzard		d				09 33	09 53		09 58								10 24			10 33	10 53		
Cheddington		d							10 04														
Tring		d						09 56	10 10							10 26	10 34						10 56
Berkhamsted		d				09 46		10 01	10 15							10 31	10 39			10 46			11 01
Hemel Hempstead		d				09 51		10 05	10 19							10 35	10 43			10 51			11 05
Apsley		d						10 08								10 38							11 08
Kings Langley		d						10 11								10 41							11 11
Watford Junction	60	a				09 58		10 16	10 26				10 30		10s39	10 46	10 51			10 58			11 16
		d				09 59		10 16	10 27				10 31			10 46	10 52			10 59			11 16
Bushey	60	d						10 19								10 49							11 19
Harrow & Wealdstone	⊖60	d						10 24								10 54	10 59						11 24
Wembley Central	⊖60,176	d															11 04						
Shepherd's Bush	⊖176	a															11 20						
Kensington (Olympia)	⊖176	a															11 22						
West Brompton	⊖176	a															11 25						
Imperial Wharf	176	a															11 28						
Clapham Junction	176	a															11 33						
East Croydon	176 ⛴	a															11 56						
London Euston 15	⊖60	a		09 50	10 06	10 17	10 27	10 38	10 45	10 24	10 35	10 39	10 46	10 15	10 55	11 08			10 50	11 17	11 27	11 24	11 38

A From Lancaster
B To London Euston
C From Milton Keynes Central
D To South Croydon
E From Manchester Piccadilly
F From Preston
G From Crewe
H From Liverpool Lime Street
I From Birmingham New Street
J From Holyhead

Table 66R

Saturdays

15 February to 17 May

West Midlands, Northampton, Milton Keynes Central and Watford Junction - London

Network Diagram - see first Page of Table 59

Station		LM	VT	VT	LM	VT	VT	LM		SN	LM	LM	LM	LM	VT	LM	LM	VT		VT	LM	VT	VT	LM	SN
		1	◇1	◇1	1	◇1	◇1	1		1	1	1	1	1	◇1	1	1	◇1		◇1	1	◇1	◇1	1	1
			A	B						C	D	E	F		G			H		B					C
			☕	☕		☕	☕								☕			☕		☕		☕	☕		
Wolverhampton 7 68 🚌	d		09 45															10 45							
Sandwell & Dudley 68	d		09 55															10 55							
Birmingham New Street 12 68	d		10 10		09 33	09 50	10 30				09 54			10 14				11 10			10 33	10 50	11 30		
Birmingham International 68 ✈	d		10 20		09 45	10 00	10 40				10 05			10 30				11 20			10 45	11 00	11 40		
Coventry 68	d		10 31		10 00	10 11	10 51				10 21			10 48				11 31			11 00	11 11	11 51		
Nuneaton 65	d											10 36													
Rugby 68	d				10 12	10 23					10 32	10 53		10 59							11 12	11 23			
Long Buckby 68	a				10 21						10 41			11 08							11 21				
Northampton 68	a				10 34						10 53			11 20							11 34				
	d				10 50						11 05			11 25							11 50				
Wolverton	d										11 17		←	11 37											
Milton Keynes Central 10	a		10 58		11 04						11 20	11 14	11 20	11 41				11 58			12 04				
	d	10 47	10 59	11 03	11 07					11 13	11 22	11 15	11 22	11 41	11 47		11 47	11 59		12 03	12 07				12 13
Bletchley	d	10 52								11 17	→		11 27	11 46			11 52								12 17
Leighton Buzzard	d	10 58								11 24			11 33	11 53			11 58								12 24
Cheddington	d	11 04															12 04								
Tring	d	11 10						11 26		11 34						11 56	12 10							12 26	12 34
Berkhamsted	d	11 15						11 31		11 39			11 46			12 01	12 15							12 31	12 39
Hemel Hempstead	d	11 19						11 35		11 43			11 51			12 05	12 19							12 35	12 43
Apsley	d							11 38								12 08								12 38	
Kings Langley	d							11 41								12 11								12 41	
Watford Junction 60	a	11 26			11 30		11s39	11 46		11 51			11 58			12 16	12 26				12 30		12s39	12 46	12 51
	d	11 27			11 31			11 46		11 52			11 59			12 16	12 27				12 31			12 46	12 52
Bushey 60	d							11 49								12 19								12 49	
Harrow & Wealdstone ⊖60	d							11 54		11 58						12 24								12 54	12 58
Wembley Central ⊖60,176	d									12 03															13 03
Shepherd's Bush ⊖176	a									12 19															13 19
Kensington (Olympia) ⊖176	a									12 21															13 21
West Brompton ⊖176	a									12 24															13 24
Imperial Wharf 176	a									12 27															13 27
Clapham Junction 176	a									12 32															13 33
East Croydon 176 🚌	a									12 56															13 56
London Euston 15 ⊖60	a	11 45	11 33	11 39	11 46	11 15	11 55	12 08				11 50	12 17	12 27	12 24	12 38	12 45	12 33		12 39	12 46	12 15	12 55	13 08	

Station		LM	LM	LM		LM	VT	LM	LM	VT	VT	LM	VT	VT		LM	SN	LM	LM	LM	LM	VT	LM	LM	
		1	1	1		1	◇1	1	1	◇1	◇1	1	◇1	◇1		1	1	1	1	1	1	◇1	1	1	
		D	E	F			G			A	I						C	D	E	F		G			
							☕			☕	☕		☕	☕								☕			
Wolverhampton 7 68 🚌	d									11 45															
Sandwell & Dudley 68	d									11 55															
Birmingham New Street 12 68	d	10 54				11 14				12 10		11 33	11 50	12 30				11 54			12 14				
Birmingham International 68 ✈	d	11 05				11 30				12 20		11 45	12 00	12 40				12 05			12 30				
Coventry 68	d	11 21				11 48				12 30		12 00	12 11	12 51				12 21			12 48				
Nuneaton 65	d		11 36																12 36						
Rugby 68	d	11 32	11 53			11 59						12 12	12 23					12 32	12 53		12 59				
Long Buckby 68	a	11 41				12 08						12 21						12 41			13 08				
Northampton 68	a	11 53				12 20						12 34						12 53			13 20				
	d	12 05				12 25						12 50						13 05			13 25				
Wolverton	d	12 17		←		12 37												13 17		←	13 37				
Milton Keynes Central 10	a	12 20	12 14	12 20		12 41				12 58		13 04						13 20	13 14	13 20	13 41				
	d	12 22	12 15	12 22		12 41	12 47		12 47	12 59	13 03	13 07					13 13	13 22	13 15	13 22	13 41	13 47		13 47	
Bletchley	d	→		12 27		12 46			12 52								13 17	→		13 27	13 46			13 52	
Leighton Buzzard	d			12 33		12 53			12 58								13 24			13 33	13 53			13 58	
Cheddington	d								13 04															14 04	
Tring	d							12 56	13 10							13 26	13 34						13 56	14 10	
Berkhamsted	d			12 46				13 01	13 15							13 31	13 39			13 46			14 01	14 15	
Hemel Hempstead	d			12 51				13 05	13 19							13 35	13 43			13 51			14 05	14 19	
Apsley	d							13 08								13 38							14 08		
Kings Langley	d							13 11								13 41							14 11		
Watford Junction 60	a			12 58				13 16	13 26			13 30		13s39		13 46	13 52			13 58			14 16	14 26	
	d			12 59				13 16	13 27			13 31				13 46	13 53			13 59			14 16	14 27	
Bushey 60	d							13 19								13 49							14 19		
Harrow & Wealdstone ⊖60	d							13 24								13 54	13 59						14 24		
Wembley Central ⊖60,176	d																14 04								
Shepherd's Bush ⊖176	a																14 20								
Kensington (Olympia) ⊖176	a																14 22								
West Brompton ⊖176	a																14 25								
Imperial Wharf 176	a																14 28								
Clapham Junction 176	a																14 33								
East Croydon 176 🚌	a																14 56								
London Euston 15 ⊖60	a		12 50	13 17		13 27	13 24	13 38	13 47	13 35	13 39	13 46	13 15	13 55		14 08			13 50	14 17	14 27	14 24	14 38	14 45	

A From Glasgow Central
B From Holyhead
C To South Croydon
D To London Euston
E From Crewe
F From Birmingham New Street
G From Manchester Piccadilly
H From Edinburgh
I From Chester

Table 66R

Saturdays

15 February to 17 May

West Midlands, Northampton, Milton Keynes Central and Watford Junction - London

Network Diagram - see first Page of Table 59

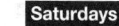

		VT	VT	LM	VT	VT	LM	SN	LM	LM		LM	LM	VT	LM	LM	VT	VT	LM	VT		VT	LM	SN	LM
		◇1	◇1	1	◇1	◇1	1	1	1	1		1	1	◇1	1	1	◇1	◇1	1	◇1		◇1	1	1	1
		A	B					C	D	E		F		G			H	B						C	D
		☕	☕		☕	☕								☕			☕	☕		☕		☕			
Wolverhampton 7 68 🚌	d	12 45															13 45								
Sandwell & Dudley 68	d	12 55															13 55								
Birmingham New Street 12 68	d	13 10		12 33	12 50	13 30			12 54				13 14				14 10		13 33	13 50		14 30			13 54
Birmingham International 68 ✈	d	13 20		12 45	13 00	13 40			13 05				13 30				14 20		13 45	14 00		14 40			14 05
Coventry 68	d	13 31		13 00	13 11	13 51			13 21				13 48				14 31		14 00	14 11		14 51			14 21
Nuneaton 65	d									13 36															
Rugby 68	d			13 12	13 23				13 32	13 53			13 59						14 12	14 23					14 32
Long Buckby 68	a			13 21					13 41				14 08						14 21						14 41
Northampton 68	a			13 34					13 53				14 20						14 34						14 53
	d			13 50					14 05				14 25						14 50						15 05
Wolverton	d								14 17			←	14 37												15 17
Milton Keynes Central 10	a	13 58		14 04					14 20	14 14		14 20	14 41				14 58		15 04						15 20
	d	14 00	14 03	14 07				14 13	14 22	14 15		14 22	14 41	14 47		14 47	14 59	15 03	15 07					15 13	15 22
Bletchley	d							14 17	→			14 27	14 46			14 52								15 17	→
Leighton Buzzard	d							14 24				14 33	14 53			14 58								15 24	
Cheddington	d															15 04									
Tring	d						14 26	14 34							14 56	15 10							15 26	15 34	
Berkhamsted	d						14 31	14 39				14 46			15 01	15 15							15 31	15 39	
Hemel Hempstead	d						14 35	14 43				14 51			15 05	15 19							15 35	15 43	
Apsley	d						14 38								15 08								15 38		
Kings Langley	d						14 41								15 11								15 41		
Watford Junction 60	a			14 30		14s39	14 46	14 51				14 58			15 16	15 26			15 30			15s39	15 46	15 51	
	d			14 31			14 46	14 51				14 59			15 16	15 27			15 31				15 46	15 51	
Bushey 60	d						14 49								15 19								15 49		
Harrow & Wealdstone ⊖60	d						14 54	14 59							15 24								15 54	15 59	
Wembley Central ⊖60,176	d							15 03																16 03	
Shepherd's Bush ⊖176	a							15 19																16 19	
Kensington (Olympia) ⊖176	a							15 22																16 22	
West Brompton ⊖176	a							15 25																16 25	
Imperial Wharf 176	a							15 28																16 28	
Clapham Junction 176	a							15 33																16 33	
East Croydon 176 🚌	a							15 56																16 56	
London Euston 15 ⊖60	a	14 33	14 39	14 46	14 15	14 55	15 08			14 50		15 18	15 27	15 24	15 38	15 45	15 34	15 39	15 46	15 15		15 55	16 08		

		LM	LM	LM	VT	LM		LM	VT	VT	LM	VT	VT	LM	SN	LM		LM	LM	LM	VT	LM	LM	VT	VT
		1	1	1	◇1	1		1	◇1	◇1	1	◇1	◇1	1	1	1		1	1	1	◇1	1	1	◇1	◇1
		E	F		G				A	B					C	D		E	F		G			H	I
					☕				☕	☕		☕	☕								☕			☕	☕
Wolverhampton 7 68 🚌	d								14 45															15 45	
Sandwell & Dudley 68	d								14 55															15 55	
Birmingham New Street 12 68	d			14 14					15 10		14 33	14 50	15 30			14 54				15 14				16 10	
Birmingham International 68 ✈	d			14 30					15 20		14 45	15 00	15 40			15 05				15 30				16 20	
Coventry 68	d			14 48					15 31		15 00	15 11	15 51			15 21				15 48				16 31	
Nuneaton 65	d	14 36																15 36							
Rugby 68	d	14 53		14 59							15 12	15 23				15 32		15 53		15 59					
Long Buckby 68	a			15 08							15 21					15 41				16 08					
Northampton 68	a			15 20							15 34					15 53				16 20					
	d			15 25							15 50					16 05				16 25					
Wolverton	d		←	15 37												16 17			←	16 37					
Milton Keynes Central 10	a	15 14	15 20	15 41					15 58		16 04					16 20		16 14	16 20	16 41				16 58	
	d	15 15	15 22	15 41	15 47			15 47	15 59	16 03	16 07				16 13	16 22		16 15	16 22	16 41	16 47		16 47	16 59	17 03
Bletchley	d		15 27	15 46				15 52							16 17	→			16 27	16 46			16 52		
Leighton Buzzard	d		15 33	15 53				15 58							16 24				16 33	16 53			16 58		
Cheddington	d							16 04															17 04		
Tring	d					15 56		16 10						16 26	16 34							16 55	17 10		
Berkhamsted	d		15 46			16 01		16 15						16 31	16 39				16 46			16 59	17 15		
Hemel Hempstead	d		15 51			16 05		16 19						16 35	16 43				16 51			17 04	17 19		
Apsley	d					16 08								16 38								17 07			
Kings Langley	d					16 11								16 41								17 10			
Watford Junction 60	a		15 58			16 16		16 26			16 30		16s39	16 46	16 51				16 58			17 15	17 26		
	d		15 59			16 16		16 27			16 31			16 46	16 52				16 59			17 15	17 27		
Bushey 60	d					16 19								16 49								17 18			
Harrow & Wealdstone ⊖60	d					16 24								16 54	16 59							17 23			
Wembley Central ⊖60,176	d														17 03										
Shepherd's Bush ⊖176	a														17 19										
Kensington (Olympia) ⊖176	a														17 22										
West Brompton ⊖176	a														17 25										
Imperial Wharf 176	a														17 28										
Clapham Junction 176	a														17 32										
East Croydon 176 🚌	a														17 56										
London Euston 15 ⊖60	a	15 50	16 18	16 27	16 24	16 38		16 45	16 34	16 39	16 46	16 15	16 57	17 08				16 50	17 17	17 27	17 24	17 37	17 45	17 33	17 39

A From Edinburgh
B From Chester
C To South Croydon
D To London Euston
E From Crewe
F From Birmingham New Street
G From Manchester Piccadilly
H From Glasgow Central
I From Holyhead

Table 66R

Saturdays

15 February to 17 May

West Midlands, Northampton, Milton Keynes Central and Watford Junction - London

Network Diagram - see first Page of Table 59

Station	Table		LM		VT	VT	LM	SN	LM	LM	LM	LM	VT		LM	LM	VT	VT	LM	VT	VT	LM	SN		LM	LM
			1		◇1	◇1	1	1	1	1	1	1	◇1		1	1	◇1	◇1	1	◇1	◇1	1	1		1	1
								A	B	C	D		E				F	G							B	C
					☕	☕							☕				☕	☕		☕	☕					
Wolverhampton 7	68 ⇌	d															16 45									
Sandwell & Dudley	68	d															16 55									
Birmingham New Street 12	68	d	15 33		15 50	16 30			15 54			16 14					17 10		16 33	16 50	17 30				16 54	
Birmingham International	68 ✈	d	15 45		16 00	16 40			16 05			16 30					17 20		16 45	17 00	17 40				17 05	
Coventry	68	d	16 00		16 11	16 51			16 21			16 48					17 31		17 00	17 11	17 51				17 21	
Nuneaton	65	d								16 36																17 36
Rugby	68	d	16 12		16 23				16 32	16 53		16 59							17 12	17 23					17 32	17 53
Long Buckby	68	a	16 21						16 41			17 08							17 21						17 41	
Northampton	68	a	16 34						16 53			17 21							17 34						17 53	
		d	16 50						17 05			17 25							17 50						18 05	
Wolverton		d							17 17		←	17 37													18 17	
Milton Keynes Central 10		a	17 04						17 20	17 14	17 20	17 41					17 58		18 04						18 20	18 14
		d	17 07					17 13	17 22	17 15	17 22	17 41	17 47			17 47	17 59	18 03	18 07				18 13		18 22	18 15
Bletchley		d						17 17	→		17 27	17 46				17 52							18 17		→	
Leighton Buzzard		d						17 24			17 33	17 53				17 58							18 24			
Cheddington		d														18 04										
Tring		d					17 26	17 34							17 56	18 10						18 26	18 34			
Berkhamsted		d					17 30	17 39			17 46				18 01	18 15						18 31	18 39			
Hemel Hempstead		d					17 35	17 43			17 51				18 05	18 19						18 35	18 43			
Apsley		d					17 38								18 08							18 38				
Kings Langley		d					17 41								18 11							18 41				
Watford Junction	60	a	17 30			17s39	17 46	17 51			17 58				18 16	18 26			18 30		18s39	18 46	18 51			
		d	17 31				17 46	17 51			17 59				18 16	18 27			18 31			18 46	18 51			
Bushey	60	d					17 49								18 19							18 49				
Harrow & Wealdstone	⊖60	d					17 54	17 59							18 24							18 54	18 59			
Wembley Central	⊖60,176	d						18 03															19 03			
Shepherd's Bush	⊖176	a						18 19															19 19			
Kensington (Olympia)	⊖176	a						18 22															19 22			
West Brompton	⊖176	a						18 25															19 25			
Imperial Wharf	176	a						18 27															19 27			
Clapham Junction	176	a						18 32															19 32			
East Croydon	176 ⇌	a						18 56															19 57			
London Euston 15	⊖60	a	17 46		17 15	17 55	18 08			17 50	18 17	18 27	18 24		18 38	18 45	18 34	18 39	18 46	18 15	18 55	19 08				18 50

Station	Table		LM	VT	LM	LM	VT	LM	SN		VT	VT	LM	SN	LM	LM	LM	VT	LM		LM	VT	LM	VT	SN	LM
			1	◇1	1	1	◇1	1	1		◇1	◇1	1	1	1	1	1	◇1	1		1	◇1	1	◇1	1	1
			D	E			H								B	C	D	E					B	F		D
				☕			☕				☕	☕						☕				☕		☕		
Wolverhampton 7	68 ⇌	d					17 45																	18 45		
Sandwell & Dudley	68	d					17 55																	18 55		
Birmingham New Street 12	68	d				17 13	18 10	17 33			17 50	18 30			17 54						18 14	18 50	18 54	19 10		
Birmingham International	68 ✈	d				17 30	18 20	17 45			18 00	18 40			18 05						18 30	19 00	19 05	19 20		
Coventry	68	d				17 48	18 31	18 00			18 11	18 51			18 21						18 48	19 11	19 21	19 31		
Nuneaton	65	d														18 36										
Rugby	68	d				17 59		18 12			18 23				18 32	18 53					18 59	19 23	19 32	19 44		
Long Buckby	68	a				18 08		18 21							18 41						19 08		19 41			
Northampton	68	a				18 20		18 34							18 53						19 20		19 53			
		d				18 31		18 50							19 05						19 31		20 00			
Wolverton		d	←			18 43									19 17		←				19 43		20 12			←
Milton Keynes Central 10		a	18 20			18 46	18 58	19 04							19 20	19 14	19 20				19 46		20 15	20 05		20 15
		d	18 22	18 47		18 47	18 59	19 06						19 14	19 22	19 15	19 22	19 46			19 47		20 16	20 07		20 16
Bletchley		d	18 27			18 52								19 18	→		19 27				19 52		→			20 21
Leighton Buzzard		d	18 33			18 58								19 25			19 33				19 58					20 27
Cheddington		d				19 04															20 04					
Tring		d			18 56	19 10							19 24	19 34					19 58		20 10					
Berkhamsted		d	18 46		19 01	19 15							19 29	19 39			19 46		20 03		20 15					
Hemel Hempstead		d	18 51		19 05	19 19							19 33	19 43			19 51		20 07		20 19					
Apsley		d			19 08								19 36						20 10							
Kings Langley		d			19 11								19 39						20 13							
Watford Junction	60	a	18 58		19 16	19 26		19 29				19s39	19 44	19 50			19 58		20 18		20 26			20s34		20 50
		d	18 59		19 16	19 27		19 30	19 31				19 44	19 51			20 00		20 19		20 27				20 43	20 51
Bushey	60	d			19 19								19 47													
Harrow & Wealdstone	⊖60	d			19 24				19 37				19 52	20 01					20 25						20 49	
Wembley Central	⊖60,176	d							19 42																	
Shepherd's Bush	⊖176	a							19 58					20 20											21 08	
Kensington (Olympia)	⊖176	a							20 00					20 22											21 11	
West Brompton	⊖176	a							20 03					20 25											21 14	
Imperial Wharf	176	a							20 06					20 28											21 16	
Clapham Junction	176	a							20 10					20 33											21 21	
East Croydon	176 ⇌	a												20 59												
London Euston 15	⊖60	a	19 17	19 24	19 38	19 45	19 34	19 45			19 15	19 55	20 06			19 50	20 18	20 26	20 39		20 45	20 22		20 55		21 09

A To South Croydon
B To London Euston
C From Crewe
D From Birmingham New Street
E From Manchester Piccadilly
F From Edinburgh
G From Chester
H From Glasgow Central

Table 66R

Saturdays

15 February to 17 May

West Midlands, Northampton, Milton Keynes Central and Watford Junction - London

Network Diagram - see first Page of Table 59

	VT	LM	LM		LM	VT	SN	VT	LM	LM	VT	LM	VT		VT	SN	LM	VT	SN	LM	LM			
	◇1	1	1		1	◇1	1	◇1	1	1	◇1	1	◇1		◇1	1	1	◇1	1	1	1			
	A				B	A		C	D		A	B	E		C	F	D							
	☕					☕		☕			☕		☕		☕			☕						
Wolverhampton [7] 68 🚊 d						19 45							20 45					21 07						
Sandwell & Dudley 68 d						19 55							20 55					21 17						
Birmingham New Street [12] 68 d		19 14			19 54	20 10						20 54	21 10					21 30		21 34	22 14			
Birmingham International 68 ✈ d		19 30			20 05	20 20						21 05	21 20					21 40		21 45	22 30			
Coventry 68 d		19 48			20 21	20 31						21 21	21 31					21 51		22 00	22 48			
Nuneaton 65 d																								
Rugby 68 d		19 59			20 32	20 43						21 32	21 43					22 03		22 12	22 59			
Long Buckby 68 a		20 08			20 41							21 41								22 21	23 08			
Northampton 68 a		20 20			20 53							21 53								22 34	23 21			
d		20 32			21 02					21 20		22 05								22 43	23 30			
Wolverton d					21 14				←			22 17					←			22 55	23 42			
Milton Keynes Central [10] a		20 47			21 17	21 04			21 17	21 34		22 20	22 04				22 20	22 25		22 58	23 45			
d	20 43	20 47	20 50		21 18	21 05		21 11	21 18	21 34	21 52	22 21	22 05		22 11		22 21	22 26		22 59	23 46			
Bletchley d			20 55		→					21 39		→					22 26			23 04	23 51			
Leighton Buzzard d		20 56								21 46							22 32			23 10	23 57			
Cheddington d		21 03								21 51							22 37			23 15				
Tring d		21 08	21 12							21 58							22 44			23 24				
Berkhamsted d			21 17						21 40	22 02							22 49			23 29				
Hemel Hempstead d		21 15	21 21						21 44	22 07							22 53			23 33				
Apsley d		21 18								22 10							22 56			23 37				
Kings Langley d		21 21								22 13							23 00			23 40				
Watford Junction 60 a	21s15	21 26	21 30			21s35			21 51	22 18			22s34		22s40		23 06	23s11		23 44	00 19			
d		21 26	21 31				21 44		21 52	22 19						22 48	23 07		23 25	23 45	00 20			
Bushey 60 d			21 33																					
Harrow & Wealdstone ⊖60 d			21 39				21 50									22 55	23 13		23 31	23 51				
Wembley Central ⊖60,176 d																								
Shepherd's Bush ⊖176 a							22 09									23 14			23 50					
Kensington (Olympia) ⊖176 a							22 12									23 16			23 53					
West Brompton ⊖176 a							22 14									23 19			23 55					
Imperial Wharf 176 a							22 17									23 21			23 58					
Clapham Junction 176 a							22 21									23 26			00 02					
East Croydon 176 🚊 a																								
London Euston [15] ⊖60 a	21 38	21 45	21 52			21 56		22 00	22 11	22 37	22 45		22 55		23 02		23 27	23 30		00 05	00 40			

Sundays

8 December to 29 December

	LM	LM	LM	LM	LM	LM	SN	LM	LM		VT	SN	LM	VT	LM	LM	VT	VT	SN		LM	VT	VT	LM
	1	1		1	1	1	1	1	1		◇1	1	1	◇1	1	1	◇1	◇1	1		1	◇1	◇1	1
	G													H		B		H			D	I	C	
			🚌								☕			☕			☕	☕				☕	☕	
Wolverhampton [7] 68 🚊 d											08 05						09 05							
Sandwell & Dudley 68 d											08 15						09 15							
Birmingham New Street [12] 68 d											08 30					09 14	09 30							
Birmingham International 68 ✈ d											08 40					09 25	09 40							
Coventry 68 d											08 51					09 44	09 51							
Nuneaton 65 d																		09 56						
Rugby 68 d											09 04					09 55	10 04					10 33		
Long Buckby 68 a																10 05								
Northampton 68 a																10 17								
d			06 20			07 53		08 23	08 53				09 31		10 08	10 37								11 08
Wolverton d			06 52			08 05		08 37	09 05				09 43		10 20	10 51					←			11 20
Milton Keynes Central [10] a			07 00			08 08		08 40	09 08		09 37		09 46		10 23	10 54	10 37				10 54	11 07		11 23
d		06 42		07 11	07 40	08 09		08 41	09 09		09 39		09 47	10 19	10 24	10 55	10 39				10 55	11 08	11 17	11 24
Bletchley d		06 47		07 16	07 45	08 14		08 46	09 14				09 52		10 29	→					11 00			11 29
Leighton Buzzard d		06 53		07 22	07 51	08 20		08 52	09 20				09 58		10 35						11 06			11 35
Cheddington d				07 27		08 25			09 25						10 44									11 40
Tring d				07 36		08 34			09 34						10 49									11 49
Berkhamsted d		07 08		07 41	08 06	08 39		09 07	09 38				10 13		10 54						11 21			11 53
Hemel Hempstead d		07 13		07 45	08 11	08 43		09 12	09 42				10 18		10 58						11 26			11 58
Apsley d		07 16			08 14			09 15					10 21								11 29			
Kings Langley d		07 19			08 17			09 18					10 24								11 32			
Watford Junction 60 a		07 24		07 52	08 22	08 50		09 23	09 49		10s07		10 29		11 05		11s11	11s16			11 37	11s44		12 06
d	00 20	07 24		07 53	08 22	08 53	09 17	09 23	09 53			10 17	10 29		11 05				11 22		11 37			12 06
Bushey 60 d					08 25			09 26					10 32								11 40			
Harrow & Wealdstone ⊖60 d		07 30		07 59	08 30	08 59	09 23	09 31	09 59			10 23	10 37		11 11				11 28		11 45			12 12
Wembley Central ⊖60,176 d																								
Shepherd's Bush ⊖176 a							09 44					10 44							11 48					
Kensington (Olympia) ⊖176 a							09 47					10 46							11 50					
West Brompton ⊖176 a							09 50					10 49							11 53					
Imperial Wharf 176 a							09 53					10 52							11 56					
Clapham Junction 176 a							09 58					10 56							12 00					
East Croydon 176 🚊 a																								
London Euston [15] ⊖60 a	00 40	07 44		08 13	08 44	09 13		09 45	10 13		10 28		10 51	11 06	11 25		11 31	11 37			11 59	12 06	12 09	12 25

A From Glasgow Central
B To London Euston
C From Manchester Piccadilly
D From Birmingham New Street
E From Edinburgh
F To Selhurst
G not 8 December. From Birmingham New Street
H From Liverpool Lime Street
I From Preston

Table 66R

Sundays

8 December to 29 December

West Midlands, Northampton, Milton Keynes Central and Watford Junction - London

Network Diagram - see first Page of Table 59

Station	Table		LM	VT	LM	VT	SN		LM	VT	LM	LM	VT	LM	VT	VT	LM		VT	VT	VT	SN	LM	VT	LM	VT
			1	◇1	1	◇1	1		1	◇1	1	1	◇1	1	◇1	◇1	1		◇1	◇1	◇1	1	1	◇1	1	◇1
			A		B	C			D	E			F	A		C	B		F		G		D			
				☕		☕				☕			☕		☕	☕			☕	☕	☕			☕		☕
Wolverhampton 7	68 🚌	d		10 05											11 05					11 45						
Sandwell & Dudley	68	d		10 15											11 15					11 57						
Birmingham New Street 12	68	d	10 14	10 30										11 14	11 30					12 10				11 50		12 30
Birmingham International	68 ✈	d	10 25	10 40										11 25	11 40					12 20				12 00		12 40
Coventry	68	d	10 44	10 51										11 44	11 51					12 31				12 11		12 51
Nuneaton	65	d				10 57			10 58							11 59					12 32		11 58			
Rugby	68	d	10 55	11 04					11 20	11 33				11 55	12 05								12 20	12 25		
Long Buckby	68	a	11 05						11 29					12 05									12 30			
Northampton	68	a	11 17						11 41					12 17									12 42			
		d	11 25						11 48					12 26									12 50			
Wolverton		d	11 37		←									12 38			←									
Milton Keynes Central 10		a	11 42	11 37	11 42	11 46			12 02	12 07				12 41	12 26		12 41			13 00	13 04		13 04			
		d	11 43	11 39	11 43	11 48			12 03	12 08		12 12	12 22	12 42	12 27		12 42		12 52	13 01	13 05		13 07			
Bletchley		d	→		11 47						11 57	12 17		→			12 46									
Leighton Buzzard		d			11 54				12 11		12 03	12 23					12 53						13 16			
Cheddington		d									12 09	12 29														
Tring		d									12 15	12 35													13 15	
Berkhamsted		d			12 06						12 20	12 39					13 06								13 20	
Hemel Hempstead		d			12 10						12 24	12 44					13 10								13 24	
Apsley		d									12 27														13 27	
Kings Langley		d									12 30														13 30	
Watford Junction	60	a		12s08	12 17				12 32		12 35	12 52				12s52	13 17						13 34		13 35	13s38
		d			12 18		12 22		12 33		12 35	12 52					13 18					13 22	13 35		13 35	
Bushey	60	d									12 38														13 38	
Harrow & Wealdstone	⊖60	d			12 24		12 29				12 43	12 58					13 24					13 28			13 43	
Wembley Central	⊖60,176	d																								
Shepherd's Bush	⊖176	a					12 48															13 48				
Kensington (Olympia)	⊖176	a					12 50															13 50				
West Brompton	⊖176	a					12 53															13 53				
Imperial Wharf	176	a					12 56															13 56				
Clapham Junction	176	a					13 00															14 00				
East Croydon	176 🚌	a																								
London Euston 15	⊖60	a		12 27	12 37	12 32			12 51	12 46	12 57	13 11	13 00		13 06	13 13	13 38		13 28	13 38	13 46		13 53	13 20	13 57	13 57

Station	Table		LM		LM	VT	VT	VT	SN	LM	VT	LM	VT		LM	LM	VT	VT	VT	SN	LM	VT	LM		VT	LM
			1		1	◇1	◇1	◇1	1	1	◇1	1	◇1		1	1	◇1	◇1	◇1	1	1	◇1	1		◇1	1
						F		H		D							F	I	H		D					
						☕	☕	☕			☕		☕				☕	☕	☕			☕			☕	
Wolverhampton 7	68 🚌	d					12 45											13 45								
Sandwell & Dudley	68	d					12 55											13 56								
Birmingham New Street 12	68	d			12 14		13 10				12 50		13 30			13 14		14 10				13 50			14 30	
Birmingham International	68 ✈	d			12 25		13 20				13 00		13 40			13 25		14 20				14 01			14 40	
Coventry	68	d			12 44		13 31				13 10		13 51			13 44		14 31				14 14			14 51	
Nuneaton	65	d								12 58									14 33		13 58					
Rugby	68	d			12 55					13 20	13 25					13 55					14 20	14 26				
Long Buckby	68	a			13 05					13 29						14 05					14 30					
Northampton	68	a			13 17					13 41						14 17					14 42					
		d			13 25					13 50						14 25					14 50					
Wolverton		d			13 37											14 37										
Milton Keynes Central 10		a			13 40		13 58			14 04						14 40		14 58	15 03		15 04					
		d	13 12		13 41	13 49	13 59	14 04		14 07					14 12	14 41	14 50	14 59	15 04		15 07					15 12
Bletchley		d	13 17		13 46										14 17	14 46										15 17
Leighton Buzzard		d	13 23		13 52					14 16					14 23	14 52					15 16					15 23
Cheddington		d	13 29												14 29											15 29
Tring		d	13 35									14 15			14 35								15 15			15 35
Berkhamsted		d	13 39		14 05							14 20			14 39	15 05							15 20			15 39
Hemel Hempstead		d	13 44		14 10							14 24			14 44	15 10							15 24			15 44
Apsley		d										14 27											15 27			
Kings Langley		d										14 30											15 30			
Watford Junction	60	a	13 52		14 17					14 34		14 35	14s38		14 52	15 17					15 34		15 35		15s38	15 52
		d	13 52		14 17				14 22	14 35		14 35			14 52	15 17				15 22	15 35		15 35			15 52
Bushey	60	d										14 38											15 38			
Harrow & Wealdstone	⊖60	d	13 58		14 23				14 28			14 43			14 58	15 23				15 28			15 43			15 58
Wembley Central	⊖60,176	d																								
Shepherd's Bush	⊖176	a							14 48											15 48						
Kensington (Olympia)	⊖176	a							14 50											15 50						
West Brompton	⊖176	a							14 53											15 53						
Imperial Wharf	176	a							14 56											15 56						
Clapham Junction	176	a							15 00											16 00						
East Croydon	176 🚌	a																								
London Euston 15	⊖60	a	14 11		14 37	14 27	14 38	14 44		14 53	14 18	14 57	14 57		15 11	15 37	15 26	15 39	15 45		15 53	15 18	15 57		15 57	16 11

A To London Euston
B From Birmingham New Street
C From Liverpool Lime Street
D From Crewe
E From Preston
F From Manchester Piccadilly
G From Chester
H From Holyhead
I From Lancaster

Table 66R

Sundays

8 December to 29 December

West Midlands, Northampton, Milton Keynes Central and Watford Junction - London

Network Diagram - see first Page of Table 59

		LM	VT	VT	VT	VT	SN	LM	VT	LM	VT	LM	LM	VT	VT	VT	SN	LM	VT	LM	VT	LM	LM
		1	◇1	◇1	◇1	◇1	1	1	◇1	1	◇1	1	1	◇1	◇1	◇1	1	1	◇1	1	◇1	1	1
			A	B	C	D		E						A	F	D		E					
Wolverhampton 7 ... 68	d			14 45											15 45								
Sandwell & Dudley 68	d			14 56											15 56								
Birmingham New Street 12 68	d	14 14		15 10					14 50		15 30		15 14		16 10				15 50		16 30		16 14
Birmingham International 68 ✈	d	14 25		15 20					15 01		15 40		15 25		16 21				16 01		16 40		16 25
Coventry 68	d	14 44		15 31					15 14		15 51		15 44		16 31				16 11		16 51		16 44
Nuneaton 65	d							14 58										15 58					
Rugby 68	d	14 55						15 20	15 26				15 55					16 20	16 24				16 55
Long Buckby 68	a	15 05						15 30					16 05					16 29					17 05
Northampton 68	a	15 17						15 42					16 17					16 41					17 17
	d	15 26						15 50					16 26					16 50					17 25
Wolverton	d	15 38											16 38										17 37
Milton Keynes Central 10	a	15 41		15 58				16 04					16 41		16 58			17 04					17 40
	d	15 42	15 50	15 59	16 04	16 04		16 07				16 12	16 42	16 51	17 00	17 04		17 07				17 12	17 41
Bletchley	d	15 46										16 17	16 46									17 17	17 46
Leighton Buzzard	d	15 53						16 16				16 23	16 53					17 16				17 23	17 52
Cheddington	d											16 29										17 29	
Tring	d									16 15		16 35								17 15		17 35	
Berkhamsted	d	16 06								16 20		16 39	17 06							17 20		17 39	18 05
Hemel Hempstead	d	16 10								16 24		16 44	17 10							17 24		17 44	18 10
Apsley	d									16 27										17 27			
Kings Langley	d									16 30										17 30			
Watford Junction 60	a	16 17						16 34		16 35	16s38	16 52	17 17					17 34		17 35	17s38	17 52	18 17
	d	16 18					16 22	16 35		16 35		16 52	17 18				17 22	17 35		17 35		17 52	18 17
Bushey 60	d									16 38										17 38			
Harrow & Wealdstone ⊖60	d	16 24					16 28			16 43		16 58	17 24				17 28			17 43		17 58	18 23
Wembley Central ⊖60,176	d																						
Shepherd's Bush ⊖176	a						16 47										17 47						
Kensington (Olympia) ⊖176	a						16 50										17 50						
West Brompton ⊖176	a						16 53										17 53						
Imperial Wharf 176	a						16 56										17 56						
Clapham Junction 176	a						17 00										18 00						
East Croydon 176 ⛴	a																						
London Euston 15 ⊖60	a	16 38	16 26	16 39	16 41	16 44		16 53	16 18	16 57	16 57	17 11	17 38	17 27	17 38	17 44		17 53	17 17	17 57	17 57	18 11	18 37

		VT	VT	VT	SN	LM	VT	LM	VT	LM	LM	VT	VT	VT	SN	LM	VT	LM	VT	LM	LM	VT
		◇1	◇1	◇1	1	1	◇1	1	◇1	1	1	◇1	◇1	◇1	1	1	◇1	1	◇1	1	1	◇1
		A	B	G		E						A	F	C		E						A
Wolverhampton 7 ... 68	d		16 45										17 45									
Sandwell & Dudley 68	d		16 56										17 56									
Birmingham New Street 12 68	d		17 10				16 50		17 30		17 14		18 10				17 50		18 30		18 14	
Birmingham International 68 ✈	d		17 20				17 00		17 40		17 25		18 21				18 00		18 40		18 25	
Coventry 68	d		17 29				17 11		17 51		17 44		18 31				18 11		18 51		18 44	
Nuneaton 65	d					16 58										17 58						
Rugby 68	d					17 20	17 25				17 55					18 20	18 26				18 55	
Long Buckby 68	a					17 30					18 05					18 30					19 05	
Northampton 68	a					17 42					18 17					18 42					19 17	
	d					17 50					18 25					18 50					19 26	
Wolverton	d										18 37										19 38	
Milton Keynes Central 10	a		17 58			18 04					18 40		18 58			19 04					19 41	
	d	17 50	17 59	18 04		18 07				18 12	18 41	18 50	19 00	19 04		19 07				19 12	19 42	19 50
Bletchley	d									18 17	18 46									19 17	19 46	
Leighton Buzzard	d					18 16				18 23	18 52					19 16				19 23	19 53	
Cheddington	d									18 29										19 29		
Tring	d							18 15		18 35								19 15		19 35		
Berkhamsted	d							18 20		18 39	19 05							19 20		19 39	20 06	
Hemel Hempstead	d							18 24		18 44	19 10							19 24		19 44	20 10	
Apsley	d							18 27										19 27				
Kings Langley	d							18 30										19 30				
Watford Junction 60	a					18 34		18 35	18s38	18 52	19 17					19 34		19 35	19s38	19 52	20 17	
	d				18 22	18 35		18 35		18 52	19 17				19 22	19 35		19 35		19 52	20 18	
Bushey 60	d							18 38										19 38				
Harrow & Wealdstone ⊖60	d				18 28			18 43		18 58	19 23				19 28			19 43		19 58	20 24	
Wembley Central ⊖60,176	d																					
Shepherd's Bush ⊖176	a				18 47										19 48							
Kensington (Olympia) ⊖176	a				18 50										19 50							
West Brompton ⊖176	a				18 53										19 53							
Imperial Wharf 176	a				18 55										19 56							
Clapham Junction 176	a				19 00										20 00							
East Croydon 176 ⛴	a																					
London Euston 15 ⊖60	a	18 27	18 38	18 44		18 53	18 18	18 57	18 57	19 11	19 37	19 27	19 38	19 45		19 53	19 18	19 57	19 57	20 11	20 38	20 27

A From Manchester Piccadilly
B From Edinburgh
C From Chester
D From Holyhead
E From Crewe
F From Glasgow Central
G From Liverpool Lime Street

Table 66R

Sundays

8 December to 29 December

West Midlands, Northampton, Milton Keynes Central and Watford Junction - London

Network Diagram - see first Page of Table 59

Station	Table		VT ◇1 A	VT ◇1 B	SN 1	LM 1 C	VT ◇1	LM 1	VT ◇1	LM 1	SN 1		LM 1	VT ◇1 D	VT ◇1 E	LM 1 C	LM 1	LM 1 F	VT ◇1	SN 1	VT ◇1 G		LM 1 H	VT ◇1 E	VT ◇1 D	LM 1 C
Wolverhampton 7	68	d	18 45												19 42											
Sandwell & Dudley	68	d	18 56												19 56											
Birmingham New Street 12	68	d	19 10				18 50		19 30				19 14		20 10			20 14	20 30							
Birmingham International	68	d	19 20				19 01		19 40				19 25		20 20			20 25	20 40							
Coventry	68	d	19 32				19 14		19 51				19 44		20 31			20 44	20 51							
Nuneaton	65	d				18 58										19 58										20 58
Rugby	68	d				19 20	19 26						19 55			20 14		20 55	21 05							21 20
Long Buckby	68	a				19 30							20 05			20 24		21 05								21 30
Northampton	68	a				19 42							20 17			20 36		21 17								21 42
		d				19 50							20 25			20 50		21 25								21 54
Wolverton		d				20 03							20 37			21 02		21 38					←			22 06
Milton Keynes Central 10		a	19 58			20 06							20 40		20 59	21 07		21 42	21 26				21 42			22 10
		d	20 00	20 04		20 07				20 12			20 41	20 48	21 01	21 07	21 15	21 42	21 28		21 37		21 42	21 53	22 04	22 10
Bletchley		d								20 17			20 46				21 20	→					21 47			22 15
Leighton Buzzard		d				20 16				20 23			20 52			21 16	21 26						21 54			22 22
Cheddington		d								20 28							21 35									22 27
Tring		d						20 15		20 37							21 40									22 36
Berkhamsted		d						20 20		20 42			21 07				21 44						22 09			22 40
Hemel Hempstead		d						20 24		20 46			21 11				21 49						22 13			22 45
Apsley		d						20 27					21 14										22 16			
Kings Langley		d						20 30					21 17										22 19			
Watford Junction	60	a				20 34		20 35	20s38	20 53			21 22			21 35	21 56		22s02				22 23	22s31		22 52
		d			20 22	20 35		20 35		20 54	21 17		21 22			21 35	21 56			22 17			22 24			22 52
Bushey	60	d						20 38									21 59									22 55
Harrow & Wealdstone	⊖60	d			20 28			20 43		21 00	21 23		21 28				22 04			22 23			22 30			23 00
Wembley Central	⊖60,176	d																								
Shepherd's Bush	⊖176	a			20 47						21 45									22 45						
Kensington (Olympia)	⊖176	a			20 50						21 47									22 48						
West Brompton	⊖176	a			20 53						21 50									22 51						
Imperial Wharf	176	a			20 56						21 53									22 53						
Clapham Junction	176	a			21 00						21 58									22 58						
East Croydon	176	a																								
London Euston 15	⊖60	a	20 39	20 46		20 53	20 18	20 59	20 57	21 14			21 42	21 31	21 48	21 55	22 19		22 23		22 28		22 44	22 55	22 57	23 15

Station	Table		LM 1 F	VT ◇1	SN 1	LM 1 H	VT ◇1 D		VT ◇1 G	LM 1	VT ◇1	VT ◇1
Wolverhampton 7	68	d		21 05							22 05	22 37
Sandwell & Dudley	68	d		21 17							22 16	22 48
Birmingham New Street 12	68	d	21 14	21 30							22 30	23 01
Birmingham International	68	d	21 25	21 40							22 40	23 11
Coventry	68	d	21 44	21 51							22 51	23 22
Nuneaton	65	d							22 18			
Rugby	68	d	21 55	22 04					22 33		23 04	23 35
Long Buckby	68	a	22 05									
Northampton	68	a	22 17									23s54
		d	22 25							23 00		
Wolverton		d	22 37			←				23 12		
Milton Keynes Central 10		a	22 40	22 35		22 40			23 04	23 15	23 36	00s13
		d	22 41	22 37		22 41	22 48		23 06	23 16	23 37	
Bletchley		d	→			22 46				23 21		
Leighton Buzzard		d				22 52				23 27		
Cheddington		d								23 32		
Tring		d								23 41		
Berkhamsted		d				23 07				23 45		
Hemel Hempstead		d				23 12				23 50		
Apsley		d				23 15						
Kings Langley		d				23 18						
Watford Junction	60	a		23s05		23 22	23s28		23s34	23 57	00s06	00s43
		d			23 17	23 23				23 59		
Bushey	60	d								00 01		
Harrow & Wealdstone	⊖60	d			23 23	23 29				00 07		
Wembley Central	⊖60,176	d										
Shepherd's Bush	⊖176	a			23 42							
Kensington (Olympia)	⊖176	a			23 44							
West Brompton	⊖176	a			23 47							
Imperial Wharf	176	a			23 49							
Clapham Junction	176	a			23 54							
East Croydon	176	a			00 15							
London Euston 15	⊖60	a		23 25		23 43	23 49		23 54	00 21	00 27	01 05

A From Edinburgh
B From Chester
C From Crewe
D From Manchester Piccadilly
E From Glasgow Central
F To London Euston
G From Liverpool Lime Street
H From Birmingham New Street

Table 66R

Sundays
5 January to 9 February

West Midlands, Northampton, Milton Keynes Central and Watford Junction - London

Network Diagram - see first Page of Table 59

Station	LM 1 A	LM 1	LM (bus)	LM 1	LM 1	LM 1	SN 1	LM 1	LM 1	VT ◇1 ☕	SN 1	LM 1	VT ◇1 B ☕	LM 1	LM 1 C	VT ◇1 ☕	VT ◇1 B ☕	SN 1	LM 1 A	VT ◇1 D ☕	VT ◇1 E ☕	LM 1
Wolverhampton 7 68 d										08 05						09 05						
Sandwell & Dudley 68 d										08 15						09 15						
Birmingham New Street 12 68 d										08 30					09 14	09 30						
Birmingham International 68 d										08 40					09 25	09 40						
Coventry 68 d										08 51					09 44	09 51						
Nuneaton 65 d																	09 56					
Rugby 68 d										09 04					09 55	10 04				10 33		
Long Buckby 68 a															10 05							
Northampton 68 a															10 17							
d			06 20			07 53		08 23	08 53			09 31		10 08	10 37							11 08
Wolverton d			06 52			08 05		08 37	09 05			09 43		10 20	10 51				←			11 20
Milton Keynes Central 10 a			07 00			08 08		08 40	09 08	09 37		09 46		10 23	10 54	10 37			10 54	11 07		11 23
d		06 42		07 11	07 40	08 09		08 41	09 09	09 39		09 47	10 19	10 24	10 55	10 39			10 55	11 08	11 17	11 24
Bletchley d		06 47		07 16	07 45	08 14		08 46	09 14			09 52		10 29	→				11 00			11 29
Leighton Buzzard d		06 53		07 22	07 51	08 20		08 52	09 20			09 58		10 35					11 06			11 35
Cheddington d				07 27		08 25			09 25					10 44								11 40
Tring d				07 36		08 34			09 34					10 49								11 49
Berkhamsted d		07 08		07 41	08 06	08 39		09 07	09 38			10 13		10 54					11 21			11 53
Hemel Hempstead d		07 13		07 45	08 11	08 43		09 12	09 42			10 18		10 58					11 26			11 58
Apsley d		07 16			08 14			09 15				10 21							11 29			
Kings Langley d		07 19			08 17			09 18				10 24							11 32			
Watford Junction 60 a		07 24		07 52	08 22	08 50		09 23	09 49	10s07		10 29		11 05		11s11	11s16		11 37	11s44		12 06
d	00 20	07 24		07 53	08 22	08 53	09 17	09 23	09 53		10 17	10 29		11 05				11 22	11 37			12 06
Bushey 60 d					08 25			09 26				10 32							11 40			
Harrow & Wealdstone ⊖60 d		07 30		07 59	08 30	08 59	09 23	09 31	09 59		10 23	10 37		11 11				11 28	11 45			12 12
Wembley Central ⊖60,176 d																						
Shepherd's Bush ⊖176 a							09 44				10 44							11 48				
Kensington (Olympia) ⊖176 a							09 47				10 46							11 50				
West Brompton ⊖176 a							09 50				10 49							11 53				
Imperial Wharf 176 a							09 53				10 52							11 56				
Clapham Junction 176 a							09 58				10 56							12 00				
East Croydon 176 a																						
London Euston 15 ⊖60 a	00 40	07 44		08 13	08 44	09 13		09 45	10 13	10 28		10 51	11 06	11 25		11 31	11 37		11 59	12 06	12 09	12 25

Station	LM 1 C	VT ◇1 ☕	LM 1 A	VT ◇1 B ☕	SN 1	LM 1 D	VT ◇1 D ☕	LM 1	LM 1	VT ◇1 E ☕	LM 1 C	VT ◇1 ☕	VT ◇1 B ☕	LM 1 A	VT ◇1 E ☕	VT ◇1 ☕	VT ◇1 F ☕	SN 1	LM 1 D	VT ◇1 ☕	LM 1	VT ◇1 ☕
Wolverhampton 7 68 d		10 05										11 05				11 45						
Sandwell & Dudley 68 d		10 15										11 15				11 57						
Birmingham New Street 12 68 d	10 14	10 30									11 14	11 30				12 10				11 50		12 30
Birmingham International 68 d	10 25	10 40									11 25	11 40				12 20				12 00		12 40
Coventry 68 d	10 44	10 51									11 44	11 51				12 31				12 11		12 51
Nuneaton 65 d				10 57		10 58							11 59				12 32		11 58			
Rugby 68 d	10 55	11 04				11 20	11 34				11 55	12 05							12 20	12 25		
Long Buckby 68 a	11 05					11 29					12 05								12 30			
Northampton 68 a	11 17					11 41					12 17								12 42			
d	11 25					11 48					12 26								12 50			
Wolverton d	11 37		←								12 38			←								
Milton Keynes Central 10 a	11 42	11 37	11 42	11 46		12 02	12 07				12 41	12 26		12 41		13 00	13 04		13 04			
d	11 43	11 39	11 43	11 48		12 03	12 08		12 12	12 22	12 42	12 27		12 42	12 52	13 01	13 05		13 07			
Bletchley d	→		11 47					11 57	12 17		→			12 46								
Leighton Buzzard d			11 54			12 11		12 03	12 23					12 53					13 16			
Cheddington d								12 09	12 29													
Tring d								12 15	12 35												13 15	
Berkhamsted d			12 06					12 20	12 39					13 06							13 20	
Hemel Hempstead d			12 10					12 24	12 44					13 10							13 24	
Apsley d								12 27													13 27	
Kings Langley d								12 30													13 30	
Watford Junction 60 a		12s08	12 17			12 32		12 35	12 52				12s52	13 17					13 34		13 35	13s38
d			12 18		12 22	12 33		12 35	12 52					13 18				13 22	13 35		13 35	
Bushey 60 d								12 38													13 38	
Harrow & Wealdstone ⊖60 d			12 24		12 29			12 43	12 58					13 24				13 28			13 43	
Wembley Central ⊖60,176 d																						
Shepherd's Bush ⊖176 a					12 48													13 48				
Kensington (Olympia) ⊖176 a					12 50													13 50				
West Brompton ⊖176 a					12 53													13 53				
Imperial Wharf 176 a					12 56													13 56				
Clapham Junction 176 a					13 00													14 00				
East Croydon 176 a																						
London Euston 15 ⊖60 a		12 27	12 37	12 32		12 51	12 48	12 57	13 11	13 00		13 06	13 13	13 38	13 28	13 38	13 46		13 53	13 20	13 57	13 57

A From Birmingham New Street
B From Liverpool Lime Street
C To London Euston
D From Crewe
E From Manchester Piccadilly
F From Chester

Table 66R

Sundays

5 January to 9 February

West Midlands, Northampton, Milton Keynes Central and Watford Junction - London

Network Diagram - see first Page of Table 59

	LM		LM	VT	VT	VT	SN	LM	VT	LM	VT		LM	LM	VT	VT	VT	SN	LM	VT	LM		VT	LM
	1		1	◇1	◇1	◇1	1	1	◇1	1	◇1		1	1	◇1	◇1	◇1	1	1	◇1	1		◇1	1
				A		B		C							A	D	B		C					
				☕	☕	☕			☕		☕				☕	☕	☕			☕			☕	
Wolverhampton 7 . . . 68 ⇌ d					12 45											13 45								
Sandwell & Dudley 68 d					12 55											13 56								
Birmingham New Street 12 68 d			12 14		13 10				12 50		13 30			13 14		14 10				13 50			14 30	
Birmingham International 68 ✈ d			12 25		13 20				13 00		13 40			13 25		14 20				14 01			14 40	
Coventry 68 d			12 44		13 31				13 10		13 51			13 44		14 32				14 14			14 51	
Nuneaton 65 d								12 58									14 33		13 58					
Rugby 68 d			12 55					13 20	13 25					13 55					14 20	14 26				
Long Buckby 68 a			13 05					13 29						14 05					14 30					
Northampton 68 a			13 17					13 41						14 17					14 42					
d			13 25					13 50						14 25					14 50					
Wolverton d			13 37											14 37										
Milton Keynes Central 10 a			13 40		13 58			14 04						14 40		14 58	15 03		15 04					
d	13 12		13 41	13 49	13 59	14 04		14 07					14 12	14 41	14 50	15 00	15 04		15 07					15 12
Bletchley d	13 17		13 46										14 17	14 46										15 17
Leighton Buzzard d	13 23		13 52					14 16					14 23	14 52					15 16					15 23
Cheddington d	13 29												14 29											15 29
Tring d	13 35									14 15			14 35								15 15			15 35
Berkhamsted d	13 39		14 05							14 20			14 39	15 05							15 20			15 39
Hemel Hempstead d	13 44		14 10							14 24			14 44	15 10							15 24			15 44
Apsley d										14 27											15 27			
Kings Langley d										14 30											15 30			
Watford Junction 60 a	13 52		14 17					14 34		14 35	14s38		14 52	15 17					15 34		15 35		15s38	15 52
d	13 52		14 17				14 22	14 35		14 35			14 52	15 17				15 22	15 35		15 35			15 52
Bushey 60 d										14 38											15 38			
Harrow & Wealdstone ⊖60 d	13 58		14 23				14 28			14 43			14 58	15 23				15 28			15 43			15 58
Wembley Central ⊖60,176 d																								
Shepherd's Bush ⊖176 a							14 48											15 48						
Kensington (Olympia) ⊖176 a							14 50											15 50						
West Brompton ⊖176 a							14 53											15 53						
Imperial Wharf 176 a							14 56											15 56						
Clapham Junction 176 a							15 00											16 00						
East Croydon 176 ⇌ a																								
London Euston 15 ⊖60 a	14 11		14 37	14 27	14 38	14 44		14 53	14 18	14 57	14 57		15 11	15 37	15 26	15 39	15 45		15 53	15 18	15 57		15 57	16 11

	LM	VT	VT	VT	VT	SN	LM		VT	LM	VT	LM	LM	VT	VT	VT	SN		LM	VT	LM	VT	LM	LM
	1	◇1	◇1	◇1	◇1	1	1		◇1	1	◇1	1	1	◇1	◇1	◇1	1		1	◇1	1	◇1	1	1
		A	D	E	B		C							A	D	B			C					
		☕	☕	☕	☕				☕		☕			☕	☕	☕				☕		☕		
Wolverhampton 7 . . . 68 ⇌ d			14 45												15 45									
Sandwell & Dudley 68 d			14 56												15 56									
Birmingham New Street 12 68 d	14 14		15 10						14 50		15 30		15 14		16 10					15 50		16 30		16 14
Birmingham International 68 ✈ d	14 25		15 20						15 01		15 40		15 25		16 21					16 01		16 40		16 25
Coventry 68 d	14 44		15 31						15 14		15 51		15 44		16 31					16 11		16 51		16 44
Nuneaton 65 d							14 58												15 58					
Rugby 68 d	14 55						15 20		15 26				15 55						16 20	16 24				16 55
Long Buckby 68 a	15 05						15 30						16 05						16 29					17 05
Northampton 68 a	15 17						15 42						16 17						16 41					17 17
d	15 26						15 50						16 26						16 50					17 25
Wolverton d	15 38												16 38											17 37
Milton Keynes Central 10 a	15 41		15 58				16 04						16 41		16 58				17 04					17 40
d	15 42	15 50	15 59	16 04	16 04		16 07					16 12	16 42	16 51	17 00	17 04			17 07				17 12	17 41
Bletchley d	15 46											16 17	16 46										17 17	17 46
Leighton Buzzard d	15 53						16 16					16 23	16 53						17 16				17 23	17 52
Cheddington d												16 29											17 29	
Tring d										16 15		16 35									17 15		17 35	
Berkhamsted d	16 06									16 20		16 39	17 06								17 20		17 39	18 05
Hemel Hempstead d	16 10									16 24		16 44	17 10								17 24		17 44	18 10
Apsley d										16 27											17 27			
Kings Langley d										16 30											17 30			
Watford Junction 60 a	16 17						16 34			16 35	16s38	16 52	17 17						17 34		17 35	17s38	17 52	18 17
d	16 18					16 22	16 35			16 35		16 52	17 18				17 22		17 35		17 35		17 52	18 17
Bushey 60 d										16 38											17 38			
Harrow & Wealdstone ⊖60 d	16 24					16 28				16 43		16 58	17 24				17 28				17 43		17 58	18 23
Wembley Central ⊖60,176 d																								
Shepherd's Bush ⊖176 a						16 47											17 47							
Kensington (Olympia) ⊖176 a						16 50											17 50							
West Brompton ⊖176 a						16 53											17 53							
Imperial Wharf 176 a						16 56											17 56							
Clapham Junction 176 a						17 00											18 00							
East Croydon 176 ⇌ a																								
London Euston 15 ⊖60 a	16 38	16 26	16 39	16 41	16 44		16 53		16 18	16 57	16 57	17 11	17 38	17 27	17 38	17 44			17 53	17 17	17 57	17 57	18 11	18 37

A From Manchester Piccadilly
B From Holyhead
C From Crewe
D From Wigan North Western
E From Chester

Table 66R

Sundays

5 January to 9 February

West Midlands, Northampton, Milton Keynes Central and Watford Junction - London

Network Diagram - see first Page of Table 59

		VT	VT	VT		SN	LM	VT	LM	VT	LM	LM	VT	VT		VT	SN	LM	VT	LM	VT	LM	LM	VT	
		◇1	◇1	◇1		1	1	◇1	1	◇1	1	1	◇1	◇1		◇1	1	1	◇1	1	◇1	1	1	◇1	
		A	B	C			D						A	B		E		D						A	
		☕	☕	☕				☕		☕			☕	☕		☕			☕		☕			☕	
Wolverhampton 7 . . . 68 🚊	d		16 45											17 45											
Sandwell & Dudley 68	d		16 56											17 56											
Birmingham New Street 12 68	d		17 10					16 50		17 30		17 14		18 10					17 50		18 30		18 14		
Birmingham International 68 ✈	d		17 20					17 00		17 40		17 25		18 21					18 00		18 40		18 25		
Coventry . . . 68	d		17 31					17 11		17 51		17 44		18 31					18 11		18 51		18 44		
Nuneaton 65	d						16 58											17 58							
Rugby . . . 68	d						17 20	17 25				17 55						18 20	18 26				18 55		
Long Buckby 68	a						17 30					18 05						18 30					19 05		
Northampton . . . 68	a						17 42					18 17						18 42					19 17		
	d						17 50					18 25						18 50					19 26		
Wolverton . . .	d											18 37											19 38		
Milton Keynes Central 10	a		17 58				18 04					18 40		18 58				19 04					19 41		
	d	17 50	17 59	18 04			18 07				18 12	18 41	18 50	19 00		19 04		19 07				19 12	19 42	19 50	
Bletchley	d										18 17	18 46										19 17	19 46		
Leighton Buzzard . . .	d						18 16				18 23	18 52						19 16				19 23	19 53		
Cheddington	d										18 29											19 29			
Tring . . .	d								18 15		18 35									19 15		19 35			
Berkhamsted	d								18 20		18 39	19 05								19 20		19 39	20 06		
Hemel Hempstead . . .	d								18 24		18 44	19 10								19 24		19 44	20 10		
Apsley	d								18 27											19 27					
Kings Langley . . .	d								18 30											19 30					
Watford Junction 60	a						18 34		18 35	18s38	18 52	19 17						19 34		19 35	19s38	19 52	20 17		
	d					18 22	18 35		18 35		18 52	19 17					19 22	19 35		19 35		19 52	20 18		
Bushey 60	d								18 38											19 38					
Harrow & Wealdstone . . . ⊖60	d					18 28			18 43		18 58	19 23					19 28			19 43		19 58	20 24		
Wembley Central ⊖60,176	d																								
Shepherd's Bush . . . ⊖176	a					18 47											19 48								
Kensington (Olympia) ⊖176	a					18 50											19 50								
West Brompton . . . ⊖176	a					18 53											19 53								
Imperial Wharf 176	a					18 55											19 56								
Clapham Junction . . . 176	a					19 00											20 00								
East Croydon 176 🚊	a																								
London Euston 15 . . . ⊖60	a	18 27	18 38	18 44			18 53	18 18	18 57	18 57	19 11	19 37	19 27	19 38		19 45		19 53	19 18	19 57	19 57	20 11	20 38	20 27	

		VT	VT	SN	LM	VT	LM	VT	LM	SN		LM	VT	VT	LM	LM	LM	VT	SN	VT		LM	VT	VT	LM
		◇1	◇1	1	1	◇1	1	◇1	1	1		1	◇1	◇1	1	1	1	◇1	1	◇1		1	◇1	◇1	1
		F	E		D								A	G	D		H			C		I	G	A	D
		☕	☕			☕		☕					☕	☕				☕		☕			☕	☕	
Wolverhampton 7 . . . 68 🚊	d	18 45												19 42											
Sandwell & Dudley 68	d	18 56												19 56											
Birmingham New Street 12 68	d	19 10				18 50		19 30				19 14		20 10			20 14	20 30							
Birmingham International 68 ✈	d	19 20				19 01		19 40				19 25		20 20			20 25	20 40							
Coventry . . . 68	d	19 32				19 14		19 51				19 44		20 31			20 44	20 51							
Nuneaton 65	d				18 58										19 58										20 58
Rugby . . . 68	d				19 20	19 26						19 55			20 14		20 55	21 05							21 20
Long Buckby 68	a				19 30							20 05			20 24		21 05								21 30
Northampton . . . 68	a				19 42							20 17			20 36		21 17								21 42
	d				19 50							20 25			20 50		21 25								21 54
Wolverton . . .	d				20 03							20 37			21 02		21 38					←			22 06
Milton Keynes Central 10	a	19 58			20 06							20 40		20 59	21 07		21 42	21 26				21 42			22 10
	d	20 00	20 04		20 07				20 12			20 41	20 48	21 01	21 07	21 15	21 42	21 28		21 37		21 42	21 53	22 04	22 10
Bletchley	d								20 17			20 46				21 20	↦					21 47			22 15
Leighton Buzzard . . .	d				20 16				20 23			20 52			21 16	21 26						21 54			22 22
Cheddington	d								20 28							21 35									22 27
Tring . . .	d						20 15		20 37							21 40									22 36
Berkhamsted	d						20 20		20 42			21 07				21 44						22 09			22 40
Hemel Hempstead . . .	d						20 24		20 46			21 11				21 49						22 13			22 45
Apsley	d						20 27					21 14										22 16			
Kings Langley . . .	d						20 30					21 17										22 19			
Watford Junction 60	a				20 34		20 35	20s38	20 53			21 22			21 35	21 56		22s02				22 23	22s31		22 52
	d			20 22	20 35		20 35		20 54	21 17		21 22			21 35	21 56			22 17			22 24			22 52
Bushey 60	d						20 38									21 59									22 55
Harrow & Wealdstone . . . ⊖60	d			20 28			20 43		21 00	21 23		21 28				22 04			22 23			22 30			23 00
Wembley Central ⊖60,176	d																								
Shepherd's Bush . . . ⊖176	a			20 47						21 45									22 45						
Kensington (Olympia) ⊖176	a			20 50						21 47									22 48						
West Brompton . . . ⊖176	a			20 53						21 50									22 51						
Imperial Wharf 176	a			20 56						21 53									22 53						
Clapham Junction . . . 176	a			21 00						21 58									22 58						
East Croydon 176 🚊	a																								
London Euston 15 . . . ⊖60	a	20 39	20 46		20 53	20 18	20 59	20 57	21 14			21 42	21 31	21 48	21 55	22 19		22 23		22 28		22 44	22 55	22 57	23 15

A From Manchester Piccadilly
B From Preston
C From Liverpool Lime Street
D From Crewe
E From Chester
F From Edinburgh
G From Glasgow Central
H To London Euston
I From Birmingham New Street

Table 66R

Sundays

5 January to 9 February

West Midlands, Northampton, Milton Keynes Central and Watford Junction - London

Network Diagram - see first Page of Table 59

Station			LM	VT	SN	LM	VT	VT	LM	VT	VT
			■1	◇■1	■1	■1	◇■1	◇■1	■1	◇■1	◇■1
			A			B	C	D			
				☕			☕	☕		☕	☕
Wolverhampton 7	68	d		21 05						22 05	22 37
Sandwell & Dudley	68	d		21 17						22 16	22 48
Birmingham New Street 12	68	d	21 14	21 30						22 30	23 01
Birmingham International	68 ✈	d	21 25	21 40						22 40	23 11
Coventry	68	d	21 44	21 51						22 51	23 22
Nuneaton	65	d						22 18			
Rugby	68	d	21 55	22 04				22 33		23 04	23 35
Long Buckby	68	a	22 05								
Northampton	68	a	22 17								23s54
		d	22 25						23 00		
Wolverton		d	22 37			⟵			23 12		
Milton Keynes Central 10		a	22 40	22 35		22 40		23 04	23 15	23 36	00s13
		d	22 41	22 37		22 41	22 48	23 06	23 16	23 37	
Bletchley		d	⟶			22 46			23 21		
Leighton Buzzard		d				22 52			23 27		
Cheddington		d							23 32		
Tring		d							23 41		
Berkhamsted		d				23 07			23 45		
Hemel Hempstead		d				23 12			23 50		
Apsley		d				23 15					
Kings Langley		d				23 18					
Watford Junction	60	a		23s05		23 22	23s28	23s34	23 57	00s06	00s43
		d			23 17	23 23			23 59		
Bushey	60	d							00 01		
Harrow & Wealdstone	⊖60	d			23 23	23 29			00 07		
Wembley Central	⊖60,176	d									
Shepherd's Bush	⊖176	a			23 42						
Kensington (Olympia)	⊖176	a			23 44						
West Brompton	⊖176	a			23 47						
Imperial Wharf	176	a			23 49						
Clapham Junction	176	a			23 54						
East Croydon	176	a			00 15						
London Euston 15	⊖60	a		23 25		23 43	23 49	23 54	00 21	00 27	01 05

Sundays

16 February to 23 March

Station			LM	LM	LM	LM	LM	LM	SN	LM	LM	VT	SN	LM	VT	LM	LM	VT	VT	SN	LM	VT	VT	LM
			■1	■1		■1	■1	■1	■1	■1	■1	◇■1	■1	■1	◇■1	■1	■1	◇■1	◇■1	■1	■1	◇■1	◇■1	■1
			B												D		A		D		B	E	C	
					🚌							☕			☕			☕	☕			☕	☕	
Wolverhampton 7	68	d										08 05						09 05						
Sandwell & Dudley	68	d										08 15						09 15						
Birmingham New Street 12	68	d										08 30					09 14	09 30						
Birmingham International	68 ✈	d										08 40					09 25	09 40						
Coventry	68	d										08 51					09 44	09 51						
Nuneaton	65	d																	09 56					
Rugby	68	d										09 04					09 55	10 04				10 37		
Long Buckby	68	a															10 05							
Northampton	68	a															10 17							
		d			06 20			07 53		08 23	08 53			09 31		10 08	10 37							11 08
Wolverton		d			06 52			08 05		08 37	09 05			09 43		10 20	10 51				⟵			11 20
Milton Keynes Central 10		a			07 00			08 08		08 40	09 08	09 37		09 46		10 23	10 54	10 37			10 54	11 11		11 23
		d		06 42		07 11	07 40	08 09		08 41	09 09	09 39		09 47	10 19	10 24	10 55	10 39			10 55	11 12	11 17	11 24
Bletchley		d		06 47		07 16	07 45	08 14		08 46	09 14			09 52		10 29	⟶				11 00			11 29
Leighton Buzzard		d		06 53		07 22	07 51	08 20		08 52	09 20			09 58		10 35					11 06			11 35
Cheddington		d				07 27		08 25			09 25					10 44								11 40
Tring		d				07 36		08 34			09 34					10 49								11 49
Berkhamsted		d		07 08		07 41	08 06	08 39		09 07	09 38			10 13		10 54					11 21			11 53
Hemel Hempstead		d		07 13		07 45	08 11	08 43		09 12	09 42			10 18		10 58					11 26			11 58
Apsley		d		07 16			08 14			09 15				10 21							11 29			
Kings Langley		d		07 19			08 17			09 18				10 24							11 32			
Watford Junction	60	a		07 24		07 52	08 22	08 50		09 23	09 49	10s07		10 29		11 05		11s11	11s16		11 37	11s43		12 06
		d	00 20	07 24		07 53	08 22	08 53	09 17	09 23	09 53		10 17	10 29		11 05				11 22	11 37			12 06
Bushey	60	d					08 25			09 26				10 32							11 40			
Harrow & Wealdstone	⊖60	d		07 30		07 59	08 30	08 59	09 23	09 31	09 59		10 23	10 37		11 11				11 28	11 45			12 12
Wembley Central	⊖60,176	d																						
Shepherd's Bush	⊖176	a							09 44				10 44							11 48				
Kensington (Olympia)	⊖176	a							09 47				10 46							11 50				
West Brompton	⊖176	a							09 50				10 49							11 53				
Imperial Wharf	176	a							09 53				10 52							11 56				
Clapham Junction	176	a							09 58				10 56							12 00				
East Croydon	176	a																						
London Euston 15	⊖60	a	00 40	07 44		08 13	08 44	09 13		09 45	10 13	10 28		10 51	11 06	11 25		11 31	11 37		11 59	12 06	12 09	12 25

A To London Euston
B From Birmingham New Street
C From Manchester Piccadilly
D From Liverpool Lime Street
E From Preston

Table 66R

Sundays

16 February to 23 March

West Midlands, Northampton, Milton Keynes Central and Watford Junction - London

Network Diagram - see first Page of Table 59

	LM	VT	LM	VT	SN		LM	VT	LM	LM	VT	LM	VT	VT	LM		VT	VT	VT	SN	LM	VT	LM	VT
	1	◇1	1	◇1	1		1	◇1	1	1	◇1	1	◇1	◇1	1		◇1	◇1	◇1	1	1	◇1	1	◇1
	A		B	C			D	E			F	A		C	B		F		G		D			
		☕		☕				☕			☕		☕	☕			☕	☕	☕			☕		☕
Wolverhampton 7 68 d		10 05											11 05					11 45						
Sandwell & Dudley 68 d		10 15											11 15					11 57						
Birmingham New Street 12 68 d	10 14	10 30										11 14	11 30					12 10				11 50		12 30
Birmingham International 68 ✈ d	10 25	10 40										11 25	11 40					12 20				12 00		12 40
Coventry 68 d	10 44	10 51										11 44	11 51					12 31				12 11		12 51
Nuneaton 65 d				10 57			10 58							11 59					12 32		11 58			
Rugby 68 d	10 55	11 04					11 20	11 33				11 55	12 05								12 20	12 25		
Long Buckby 68 a	11 05						11 29					12 05									12 30			
Northampton 68 a	11 17						11 41					12 17									12 42			
d	11 25						11 48					12 26									12 50			
Wolverton d	11 37		←									12 38			←									
Milton Keynes Central 10 a	11 42	11 37	11 42	11 46			12 02	12 07				12 41	12 26		12 41			13 00	13 04		13 04			
d	11 43	11 39	11 43	11 48			12 03	12 08		12 12	12 22	12 42	12 27		12 42		12 52	13 01	13 05		13 07			
Bletchley d	→		11 47						11 57	12 17		→			12 46									
Leighton Buzzard d			11 54				12 11		12 03	12 23					12 53						13 16			
Cheddington d									12 09	12 29														
Tring d									12 15	12 35													13 15	
Berkhamsted d			12 06						12 20	12 39					13 06								13 20	
Hemel Hempstead d			12 10						12 24	12 44					13 10								13 24	
Apsley d									12 27														13 27	
Kings Langley d									12 30														13 30	
Watford Junction 60 a		12s08	12 17				12 32		12 35	12 52				12s52	13 17						13 34		13 35	13s38
d			12 18		12 22		12 33		12 35	12 52					13 18					13 22	13 35		13 35	
Bushey 60 d									12 38														13 38	
Harrow & Wealdstone Θ60 d			12 24		12 29				12 43	12 58					13 24					13 28			13 43	
Wembley Central Θ60,176 d																								
Shepherd's Bush Θ176 a					12 48															13 48				
Kensington (Olympia) Θ176 a					12 50															13 50				
West Brompton Θ176 a					12 53															13 53				
Imperial Wharf 176 a					12 56															13 56				
Clapham Junction 176 a					13 00															14 00				
East Croydon 176 a																								
London Euston 15 Θ60 a		12 27	12 37	12 32			12 51	12 46	12 57	13 11	13 00		13 06	13 13	13 38		13 28	13 38	13 46		13 53	13 20	13 57	13 57

	LM		LM	VT	VT	VT	SN	LM	VT	LM	VT		LM	LM	VT	VT	VT	SN	LM	VT	LM		VT	LM
	1		1	◇1	◇1	◇1	1	1	◇1	1	◇1		1	1	◇1	◇1	◇1	1	1	◇1	1		◇1	1
				F		H		D							F	I	H		D					
				☕	☕	☕			☕		☕				☕	☕	☕			☕			☕	
Wolverhampton 7 68 d					12 45											13 45								
Sandwell & Dudley 68 d					12 55											13 56								
Birmingham New Street 12 68 d			12 14		13 10				12 50		13 30			13 14		14 10				13 50			14 30	
Birmingham International 68 ✈ d			12 25		13 20				13 00		13 40			13 25		14 20				14 01			14 40	
Coventry 68 d			12 44		13 31				13 10		13 51			13 44		14 31				14 14			14 51	
Nuneaton 65 d								12 58									14 33		13 58					
Rugby 68 d			12 55					13 20	13 25					13 55					14 20	14 26				
Long Buckby 68 a			13 05					13 29						14 05					14 30					
Northampton 68 a			13 17					13 41						14 17					14 42					
d			13 25					13 50						14 25					14 50					
Wolverton d			13 37											14 37										
Milton Keynes Central 10 a			13 40		13 58			14 04						14 40		14 58	15 03		15 04					
d	13 12		13 41	13 52	13 59	14 04		14 07					14 12	14 41	14 50	14 59	15 04		15 07					15 12
Bletchley d	13 17		13 46										14 17	14 46										15 17
Leighton Buzzard d	13 23		13 52					14 16					14 23	14 52					15 16					15 23
Cheddington d	13 29												14 29											15 29
Tring d	13 35									14 15			14 35								15 15			15 35
Berkhamsted d	13 39		14 05							14 20			14 39	15 05							15 20			15 39
Hemel Hempstead d	13 44		14 10							14 24			14 44	15 10							15 24			15 44
Apsley d										14 27											15 27			
Kings Langley d										14 30											15 30			
Watford Junction 60 a	13 52		14 17					14 34		14 35	14s38		14 52	15 17					15 34		15 35		15s38	15 52
d	13 52		14 17				14 22	14 35		14 35			14 52	15 17				15 22	15 35		15 35			15 52
Bushey 60 d										14 38											15 38			
Harrow & Wealdstone Θ60 d	13 58		14 23				14 28			14 43			14 58	15 23				15 28			15 43			15 58
Wembley Central Θ60,176 d																								
Shepherd's Bush Θ176 a							14 48											15 48						
Kensington (Olympia) Θ176 a							14 50											15 50						
West Brompton Θ176 a							14 53											15 53						
Imperial Wharf 176 a							14 56											15 56						
Clapham Junction 176 a							15 00											16 00						
East Croydon 176 a																								
London Euston 15 Θ60 a	14 11		14 37	14 28	14 38	14 44		14 53	14 18	14 57	14 57		15 11	15 37	15 26	15 39	15 45		15 53	15 18	15 57		15 57	16 11

A To London Euston
B From Birmingham New Street
C From Liverpool Lime Street
D From Crewe
E From Preston
F From Manchester Piccadilly
G From Chester
H From Holyhead
I From Lancaster

Table 66R

Sundays

16 February to 23 March

West Midlands, Northampton, Milton Keynes Central and Watford Junction - London

Network Diagram - see first Page of Table 59

Station	Table		LM 1	VT ◇1 A ☕	VT ◇1 B ☕	VT ◇1 C ☕	VT ◇1 D ☕	SN 1	LM 1 E		VT ◇1 ☕	LM 1	VT ◇1 ☕	LM 1	LM 1	VT ◇1 A ☕	VT ◇1 F ☕	VT ◇1 D ☕	SN 1		LM 1 E	VT ◇1 ☕	LM 1	VT ◇1 ☕	LM 1	LM 1
Wolverhampton 7	68	d			14 45												15 45									
Sandwell & Dudley	68	d			14 56												15 56									
Birmingham New Street 12	68	d	14 14		15 10						14 50		15 30		15 14		16 10					15 50		16 30		16 14
Birmingham International	68 ✈	d	14 25		15 20						15 01		15 40		15 25		16 21					16 01		16 40		16 25
Coventry	68	d	14 44		15 31						15 14		15 51		15 44		16 31					16 11		16 51		16 44
Nuneaton	65	d							14 58												15 58					
Rugby	68	d	14 55						15 20		15 26				15 55						16 20	16 24				16 55
Long Buckby	68	a	15 05						15 30						16 05						16 29					17 05
Northampton	68	a	15 17						15 42						16 17						16 41					17 17
		d	15 26						15 50						16 26						16 50					17 25
Wolverton		d	15 38												16 38											17 37
Milton Keynes Central 10		a	15 41		15 58				16 04						16 41		16 58				17 04					17 40
		d	15 42	15 50	15 59	16 04	16 04		16 07					16 12	16 42	16 51	17 00	17 04			17 07				17 12	17 41
Bletchley		d	15 46											16 17	16 46										17 17	17 46
Leighton Buzzard		d	15 53						16 16					16 23	16 53						17 16				17 23	17 52
Cheddington		d												16 29											17 29	
Tring		d										16 15		16 35									17 15		17 35	
Berkhamsted		d	16 06									16 20		16 39	17 06								17 20		17 39	18 05
Hemel Hempstead		d	16 10									16 24		16 44	17 10								17 24		17 44	18 10
Apsley		d										16 27											17 27			
Kings Langley		d										16 30											17 30			
Watford Junction	60	a	16 17						16 34			16 35	16s38	16 52	17 17						17 34		17 35	17s38	17 52	18 17
		d	16 18					16 22	16 35			16 35		16 52	17 18				17 22		17 35		17 35		17 52	18 17
Bushey	60	d										16 38											17 38			
Harrow & Wealdstone	⊖60	d	16 24					16 28				16 43		16 58	17 24				17 28				17 43		17 58	18 23
Wembley Central	⊖60,176	d																								
Shepherd's Bush	⊖176	a						16 47											17 47							
Kensington (Olympia)	⊖176	a						16 50											17 50							
West Brompton	⊖176	a						16 53											17 53							
Imperial Wharf	176	a						16 56											17 56							
Clapham Junction	176	a						17 00											18 00							
East Croydon	176	a																								
London Euston 15	⊖60	a	16 38	16 26	16 39	16 41	16 44		16 53		16 18	16 57	16 57	17 11	17 38	17 27	17 38	17 44			17 53	17 17	17 57	17 57	18 11	18 37

Station	Table		VT ◇1 A ☕	VT ◇1 B ☕	VT ◇1 G ☕		SN 1	LM 1 E	VT ◇1 ☕	LM 1	VT ◇1 ☕	LM 1	LM 1	VT ◇1 A ☕	VT ◇1 F ☕		VT ◇1 C ☕	SN 1	LM 1 E	VT ◇1 ☕	LM 1	VT ◇1 ☕	LM 1	LM 1	VT ◇1 A ☕	
Wolverhampton 7	68	d		16 45											17 45											
Sandwell & Dudley	68	d		16 56											17 56											
Birmingham New Street 12	68	d		17 10					16 50		17 30		17 14		18 10					17 50		18 30		18 14		
Birmingham International	68 ✈	d		17 20					17 00		17 40		17 25		18 21					18 00		18 40		18 25		
Coventry	68	d		17 29					17 11		17 51		17 44		18 31					18 11		18 51		18 44		
Nuneaton	65	d						16 58											17 58							
Rugby	68	d						17 20	17 25				17 55						18 20	18 26				18 55		
Long Buckby	68	a						17 30					18 05						18 30					19 05		
Northampton	68	a						17 42					18 17						18 42					19 17		
		d						17 50					18 25						18 50					19 26		
Wolverton		d											18 37											19 38		
Milton Keynes Central 10		a		17 58				18 04					18 40		18 58				19 04					19 41		
		d	17 50	17 59	18 04			18 07				18 12	18 41	18 50	19 00		19 04		19 07				19 12	19 42	19 50	
Bletchley		d										18 17	18 46										19 17	19 46		
Leighton Buzzard		d						18 16				18 23	18 52						19 16				19 23	19 53		
Cheddington		d										18 29											19 29			
Tring		d								18 15		18 35									19 15		19 35			
Berkhamsted		d								18 20		18 39	19 05								19 20		19 39	20 06		
Hemel Hempstead		d								18 24		18 44	19 10								19 24		19 44	20 10		
Apsley		d								18 27											19 27					
Kings Langley		d								18 30											19 30					
Watford Junction	60	a						18 34		18 35	18s38	18 52	19 17						19 34		19 35	19s38	19 52	20 17		
		d					18 22	18 35		18 35		18 52	19 17					19 22	19 35		19 35		19 52	20 18		
Bushey	60	d								18 38											19 38					
Harrow & Wealdstone	⊖60	d					18 28			18 43		18 58	19 23					19 28			19 43		19 58	20 24		
Wembley Central	⊖60,176	d																								
Shepherd's Bush	⊖176	a					18 47											19 48								
Kensington (Olympia)	⊖176	a					18 50											19 50								
West Brompton	⊖176	a					18 53											19 53								
Imperial Wharf	176	a					18 55											19 56								
Clapham Junction	176	a					19 00											20 00								
East Croydon	176	a																								
London Euston 15	⊖60	a	18 27	18 38	18 44			18 53	18 18	18 57	18 57	19 11	19 37	19 27	19 38		19 45		19 53	19 18	19 57	19 57	20 11	20 38	20 27	

A From Manchester Piccadilly
B From Edinburgh
C From Chester
D From Holyhead
E From Crewe
F From Glasgow Central
G From Liverpool Lime Street

Table 66R

Sundays

16 February to 23 March

West Midlands, Northampton, Milton Keynes Central and Watford Junction - London

Network Diagram - see first Page of Table 59

		VT	VT	SN	LM	VT	LM	VT	LM	SN		LM	VT	VT	LM	LM	LM	VT	SN	VT		LM	VT	VT	LM
		◇1	◇1	1	1	◇1	1	◇1	1	1		1	◇1	◇1	1	1	1	◇1	1	◇1		1	◇1	◇1	1
		A	B		C								D	E	C		F			G		H	E	D	C
		☕	☕			☕		☕					☕	☕				☕		☕			☕	☕	
Wolverhampton [7] 68	d	18 45												19 42											
Sandwell & Dudley 68	d	18 56												19 56											
Birmingham New Street [12] 68	d	19 10				18 50		19 30				19 14		20 10			20 14	20 30							
Birmingham International 68 ✈	d	19 20				19 01		19 40				19 25		20 20			20 25	20 40							
Coventry 68	d	19 32				19 14		19 51				19 44		20 31			20 44	20 51							
Nuneaton 65	d				18 58										19 58										20 58
Rugby 68	d				19 20	19 26						19 55			20 14		20 55	21 05							21 20
Long Buckby 68	a				19 30							20 05			20 24		21 05								21 30
Northampton 68	a				19 42							20 17			20 36		21 17								21 42
	d				19 50							20 25			20 50		21 25								21 54
Wolverton	d				20 03							20 37			21 02		21 38					←			22 06
Milton Keynes Central [10]	a	19 58			20 06							20 40		20 59	21 07		21 42	21 26				21 42			22 10
	d	20 00	20 04		20 07				20 12			20 41	20 48	21 01	21 07	21 15	21 42	21 28		21 37		21 42	21 53	22 04	22 10
Bletchley	d								20 17			20 46				21 20	→					21 47			22 15
Leighton Buzzard	d				20 16				20 23			20 52			21 16	21 26						21 54			22 22
Cheddington	d								20 28							21 35									22 27
Tring	d						20 15		20 37							21 40									22 36
Berkhamsted	d						20 20		20 42			21 07				21 44						22 09			22 40
Hemel Hempstead	d						20 24		20 46			21 11				21 49						22 13			22 45
Apsley	d						20 27					21 14										22 16			
Kings Langley	d						20 30					21 17										22 19			
Watford Junction 60	a				20 34		20 35	20s38	20 53			21 22			21 35	21 56		22s02				22 23	22s31		22 52
	d			20 22	20 35		20 35		20 54	21 17		21 22			21 35	21 56			22 17			22 24			22 52
Bushey 60	d						20 38									21 59									22 55
Harrow & Wealdstone ⊖60	d			20 28			20 43		21 00	21 23		21 28				22 04			22 23			22 30			23 00
Wembley Central ⊖60,176	d																								
Shepherd's Bush ⊖176	a			20 47						21 45									22 45						
Kensington (Olympia) ⊖176	a			20 50						21 47									22 48						
West Brompton ⊖176	a			20 53						21 50									22 51						
Imperial Wharf 176	a			20 56						21 53									22 53						
Clapham Junction 176	a			21 00						21 58									22 58						
East Croydon 176 🚋	a																								
London Euston [15] ⊖60	a	20 39	20 46		20 53	20 18	20 59	20 57	21 14			21 42	21 31	21 48	21 55	22 19		22 23		22 28		22 44	22 55	22 57	23 15

		LM	VT	SN	LM	VT		VT	LM	VT	VT
		1	◇1	1	1	◇1		◇1	1	◇1	◇1
		F			H	D		G			
			☕			☕		☕		☕	☕
Wolverhampton [7] 68 🚋	d		21 05							22 05	22 37
Sandwell & Dudley 68	d		21 17							22 16	22 48
Birmingham New Street [12] 68	d	21 14	21 30							22 30	23 01
Birmingham International 68 ✈	d	21 25	21 40							22 40	23 11
Coventry 68	d	21 44	21 51							22 51	23 22
Nuneaton 65	d							22 18			
Rugby 68	d	21 55	22 04					22 33		23 04	23 35
Long Buckby 68	a	22 05									
Northampton 68	a	22 17									23s54
	d	22 25							23 00		
Wolverton	d	22 37			←				23 12		
Milton Keynes Central [10]	a	22 40	22 35		22 40			23 04	23 15	23 36	00s13
	d	22 41	22 37		22 41	22 48		23 06	23 16	23 37	
Bletchley	d	→			22 46				23 21		
Leighton Buzzard	d				22 52				23 27		
Cheddington	d								23 32		
Tring	d								23 41		
Berkhamsted	d				23 07				23 45		
Hemel Hempstead	d				23 12				23 50		
Apsley	d				23 15						
Kings Langley	d				23 18						
Watford Junction 60	a		23s05		23 22	23s28		23s34	23 57	00s06	00s43
	d			23 17	23 23				23 59		
Bushey 60	d								00 01		
Harrow & Wealdstone ⊖60	d			23 23	23 29				00 07		
Wembley Central ⊖60,176	d										
Shepherd's Bush ⊖176	a			23 42							
Kensington (Olympia) ⊖176	a			23 44							
West Brompton ⊖176	a			23 47							
Imperial Wharf 176	a			23 49							
Clapham Junction 176	a			23 54							
East Croydon 176 🚋	a			00 15							
London Euston [15] ⊖60	a		23 25		23 43	23 49		23 54	00 21	00 27	01 05

A From Edinburgh
B From Chester
C From Crewe
D From Manchester Piccadilly
E From Glasgow Central
F To London Euston
G From Liverpool Lime Street
H From Birmingham New Street

Table 66R

Sundays
30 March to 11 May

West Midlands, Northampton, Milton Keynes Central and Watford Junction - London

Network Diagram - see first Page of Table 59

		LM	LM	LM	LM	LM	LM	SN	LM	LM		VT	SN	LM	VT	LM	LM	VT	VT	SN		LM	VT	VT	LM
		1	1		1	1	1	1	1	1		◇1	1	1	◇1	1	1	◇1	◇1	1		1	◇1	◇1	1
		A													B		C		B			A	D	E	
Wolverhampton 7 68	d											08 05						09 05							
Sandwell & Dudley 68	d											08 15						09 15							
Birmingham New Street 12 68	d											08 30					09 14	09 30							
Birmingham International 68	d											08 40					09 25	09 40							
Coventry 68	d											08 51					09 44	09 51							
Nuneaton 65	d																		09 56						
Rugby 68	d											09 04					09 55	10 04					10 33		
Long Buckby 68	a																10 05								
Northampton 68	a																10 17								
	d			06 20			07 53		08 23	08 53				09 31		10 08	10 37								11 08
Wolverton	d			06 52			08 05		08 37	09 05				09 43		10 20	10 51					←			11 20
Milton Keynes Central 10	a			07 00			08 08		08 40	09 08		09 37		09 46		10 23	10 54	10 37				10 54	11 07		11 23
	d		06 42		07 11	07 40	08 09		08 41	09 09		09 39		09 47	10 19	10 24	10 55	10 39				10 55	11 08	11 17	11 24
Bletchley	d		06 47		07 16	07 45	08 14		08 46	09 14				09 52		10 29	↪					11 00			11 29
Leighton Buzzard	d		06 53		07 22	07 51	08 20		08 52	09 20				09 58		10 35						11 06			11 35
Cheddington	d				07 27		08 25			09 25						10 44									11 40
Tring	d				07 36		08 34			09 34						10 49									11 49
Berkhamsted	d		07 08		07 41	08 06	08 39		09 07	09 38				10 13		10 54						11 21			11 53
Hemel Hempstead	d		07 13		07 45	08 11	08 43		09 12	09 42				10 18		10 58						11 26			11 58
Apsley	d		07 16			08 14			09 15					10 21								11 29			
Kings Langley	d		07 19			08 17			09 18					10 24								11 32			
Watford Junction 60	a		07 24		07 52	08 22	08 50		09 23	09 49		10s07		10 29		11 05		11s11	11s16			11 37	11s43		12 06
	d	00 20	07 24		07 53	08 22	08 53	09 17	09 23	09 53			10 17	10 29		11 05				11 22		11 37			12 06
Bushey 60	d					08 25			09 26					10 32								11 40			
Harrow & Wealdstone ⊖60	d		07 30		07 59	08 30	08 59	09 23	09 31	09 59			10 23	10 37		11 11				11 28		11 45			12 12
Wembley Central ⊖60,176	d																								
Shepherd's Bush ⊖176	a							09 44					10 44							11 48					
Kensington (Olympia) ⊖176	a							09 47					10 46							11 50					
West Brompton ⊖176	a							09 50					10 49							11 53					
Imperial Wharf 176	a							09 53					10 52							11 56					
Clapham Junction 176	a							09 58					10 56							12 00					
East Croydon 176	a																								
London Euston 15 ⊖60	a	00 40	07 44		08 13	08 44	09 13		09 45	10 13		10 28		10 51	11 06	11 25		11 31	11 37			11 59	12 06	12 09	12 25

		LM	VT	LM	VT	SN		LM	VT	LM	LM	VT	LM	VT	VT	LM		VT	VT	VT	SN	LM	VT	LM	VT
		1	◇1	1	◇1	1		1	◇1	1	1	◇1	1	◇1	◇1	1		◇1	◇1	◇1	1	1	◇1	1	◇1
		C		A	B			F	D			E	C		B	A		E		G		F			
Wolverhampton 7 68	d		10 05											11 05					11 45						
Sandwell & Dudley 68	d		10 15											11 15					11 57						
Birmingham New Street 12 68	d	10 14	10 30										11 14	11 30					12 10				11 50		12 30
Birmingham International 68	d	10 25	10 40										11 25	11 40					12 20				12 00		12 40
Coventry 68	d	10 44	10 51										11 44	11 51					12 31				12 11		12 51
Nuneaton 65	d				10 57			10 58							11 59					12 32		11 58			
Rugby 68	d	10 55	11 04					11 20	11 33				11 55	12 05								12 20	12 25		
Long Buckby 68	a	11 05						11 29					12 05									12 30			
Northampton 68	a	11 17						11 41					12 17									12 42			
	d	11 25						11 48					12 26									12 50			
Wolverton	d	11 37		←									12 38			←									
Milton Keynes Central 10	a	11 42	11 37	11 42	11 46			12 02	12 07				12 41	12 26		12 41			13 00	13 04		13 04			
	d	11 43	11 39	11 43	11 48			12 03	12 08		12 12	12 22	12 42	12 27		12 42		12 52	13 01	13 05		13 07			
Bletchley	d	↪		11 47						11 57	12 17		↪			12 46									
Leighton Buzzard	d			11 54				12 11		12 03	12 23					12 53						13 16			
Cheddington	d									12 09	12 29														
Tring	d									12 15	12 35													13 15	
Berkhamsted	d			12 06						12 20	12 39					13 06								13 20	
Hemel Hempstead	d			12 10						12 24	12 44					13 10								13 24	
Apsley	d									12 27														13 27	
Kings Langley	d									12 30														13 30	
Watford Junction 60	a		12s08	12 17				12 32		12 35	12 52				12s52	13 17						13 34		13 35	13s38
	d			12 18		12 22		12 33		12 35	12 52					13 18					13 22	13 35		13 35	
Bushey 60	d									12 38														13 38	
Harrow & Wealdstone ⊖60	d			12 24		12 29				12 43	12 58					13 24					13 28			13 43	
Wembley Central ⊖60,176	d																								
Shepherd's Bush ⊖176	a					12 48															13 48				
Kensington (Olympia) ⊖176	a					12 50															13 50				
West Brompton ⊖176	a					12 53															13 53				
Imperial Wharf 176	a					12 56															13 56				
Clapham Junction 176	a					13 00															14 00				
East Croydon 176	a																								
London Euston 15 ⊖60	a		12 27	12 37	12 32			12 51	12 46	12 57	13 11	13 00		13 06	13 13	13 38		13 28	13 38	13 46		13 53	13 20	13 57	13 57

A From Birmingham New Street
B From Liverpool Lime Street
C To London Euston
D From Preston
E From Manchester Piccadilly
F From Crewe
G From Chester

Table 66R

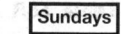

Sundays
30 March to 11 May

West Midlands, Northampton, Milton Keynes Central and Watford Junction - London

Network Diagram - see first Page of Table 59

Station		LM 1		LM 1	VT ◇1 A	VT ◇1	VT ◇1 B	SN 1	LM 1 C	VT ◇1	LM 1	VT ◇1		LM 1	LM 1	VT ◇1 A	VT ◇1 D	VT ◇1 B	SN 1	LM 1 C	VT ◇1	LM 1		VT ◇1	LM 1
Wolverhampton 7 68	d					12 45											13 45								
Sandwell & Dudley 68	d					12 55											13 56								
Birmingham New Street 12 68	d			12 14		13 10				12 50		13 30			13 14		14 10				13 50			14 30	
Birmingham International 68	d			12 25		13 20				13 00		13 40			13 25		14 20				14 01			14 40	
Coventry 68	d			12 44		13 31				13 10		13 51			13 44		14 31				14 14			14 51	
Nuneaton 65	d								12 58									14 33		13 58					
Rugby 68	d			12 55					13 20	13 25					13 55					14 20	14 26				
Long Buckby 68	a			13 05					13 29						14 05					14 30					
Northampton 68	a			13 17					13 41						14 17					14 42					
	d			13 25					13 50						14 25					14 50					
Wolverton	d			13 37											14 37										
Milton Keynes Central 10	a			13 40		13 58			14 04						14 40		14 58	15 03		15 04					
	d	13 12		13 41	13 52	13 59	14 04		14 07					14 12	14 41	14 50	14 59	15 04		15 07					15 12
Bletchley	d	13 17		13 46										14 17	14 46										15 17
Leighton Buzzard	d	13 23		13 52					14 16					14 23	14 52					15 16					15 23
Cheddington	d	13 29												14 29											15 29
Tring	d	13 35									14 15			14 35								15 15			15 35
Berkhamsted	d	13 39		14 05							14 20			14 39	15 05							15 20			15 39
Hemel Hempstead	d	13 44		14 10							14 24			14 44	15 10							15 24			15 44
Apsley	d										14 27											15 27			
Kings Langley	d										14 30											15 30			
Watford Junction 60	a	13 52		14 17					14 34		14 35	14s38		14 52	15 17					15 34		15 35		15s38	15 52
	d	13 52		14 17				14 22	14 35		14 35			14 52	15 17				15 22	15 35		15 35			15 52
Bushey 60	d										14 38											15 38			
Harrow & Wealdstone ⊖60	d	13 58		14 23				14 28			14 43			14 58	15 23				15 28			15 43			15 58
Wembley Central ⊖60,176	d																								
Shepherd's Bush ⊖176	a							14 48											15 48						
Kensington (Olympia) ⊖176	a							14 50											15 50						
West Brompton ⊖176	a							14 53											15 53						
Imperial Wharf 176	a							14 56											15 56						
Clapham Junction 176	a							15 00											16 00						
East Croydon 176	a																								
London Euston 15 ⊖60	a	14 11		14 37	14 28	14 38	14 44		14 53	14 18	14 57	14 57		15 11	15 37	15 26	15 39	15 45		15 53	15 18	15 57		15 57	16 11

Station		LM 1	VT ◇1 A	VT ◇1 E	VT ◇1 F	VT ◇1 B	SN 1	LM 1 C		VT ◇1	LM 1	VT ◇1	LM 1	LM 1	VT ◇1 A	VT ◇1 G	VT ◇1 B	SN 1		LM 1 C	VT ◇1	LM 1	VT ◇1	LM 1	LM 1
Wolverhampton 7 68	d			14 45												15 45									
Sandwell & Dudley 68	d			14 56												15 56									
Birmingham New Street 12 68	d	14 14		15 10						14 50		15 30		15 14		16 10					15 50		16 30		16 14
Birmingham International 68	d	14 25		15 20						15 01		15 40		15 25		16 21					16 01		16 40		16 25
Coventry 68	d	14 44		15 31						15 14		15 51		15 44		16 31					16 11		16 51		16 44
Nuneaton 65	d							14 58												15 58					
Rugby 68	d	14 55						15 20		15 26				15 55						16 20	16 24				16 55
Long Buckby 68	a	15 05						15 30						16 05						16 29					17 05
Northampton 68	a	15 17						15 42						16 17						16 41					17 17
	d	15 26						15 50						16 26						16 50					17 25
Wolverton	d	15 38												16 38											17 37
Milton Keynes Central 10	a	15 41		15 58				16 04						16 41		16 58				17 04					17 40
	d	15 42	15 50	15 59	16 04	16 04		16 07					16 12	16 42	16 51	17 00	17 04			17 07				17 12	17 41
Bletchley	d	15 46											16 17	16 46										17 17	17 46
Leighton Buzzard	d	15 53						16 16					16 23	16 53						17 16				17 23	17 52
Cheddington	d												16 29											17 29	
Tring	d										16 15		16 35									17 15		17 35	
Berkhamsted	d	16 06									16 20		16 39	17 06								17 20		17 39	18 05
Hemel Hempstead	d	16 10									16 24		16 44	17 10								17 24		17 44	18 10
Apsley	d										16 27											17 27			
Kings Langley	d										16 30											17 30			
Watford Junction 60	a	16 17						16 34			16 35	16s38	16 52	17 17						17 34		17 35	17s38	17 52	18 17
	d	16 18					16 22	16 35			16 35		16 52	17 18				17 22		17 35		17 35		17 52	18 17
Bushey 60	d										16 38											17 38			
Harrow & Wealdstone ⊖60	d	16 24					16 28				16 43		16 58	17 24				17 28				17 43		17 58	18 23
Wembley Central ⊖60,176	d																								
Shepherd's Bush ⊖176	a						16 47											17 47							
Kensington (Olympia) ⊖176	a						16 50											17 50							
West Brompton ⊖176	a						16 53											17 53							
Imperial Wharf 176	a						16 56											17 56							
Clapham Junction 176	a						17 00											18 00							
East Croydon 176	a																								
London Euston 15 ⊖60	a	16 38	16 26	16 39	16 41	16 44		16 53		16 18	16 57	16 57	17 11	17 38	17 27	17 38	17 44			17 53	17 17	17 57	17 57	18 11	18 37

A From Manchester Piccadilly
B From Holyhead
C From Crewe
D From Lancaster
E From Edinburgh
F From Chester
G From Glasgow Central

Table 66R

Sundays

30 March to 11 May

West Midlands, Northampton, Milton Keynes Central and Watford Junction - London

Network Diagram - see first Page of Table 59

		VT	VT	VT		SN	LM	VT	LM	VT	LM	LM	VT	VT		VT	SN	LM	VT	LM	VT	LM	LM	VT	
		◇1	◇1	◇1		1	1	◇1	1	◇1	1	1	◇1	◇1		◇1	1	1	◇1	1	◇1	1	1	◇1	
		A	B	C			D						A	E		F		D						A	
		☕	☕	☕				☕		☕			☕	☕		☕			☕		☕			☕	
Wolverhampton 7 68 ⛴	d		16 45											17 45											
Sandwell & Dudley 68	d		16 56											17 56											
Birmingham New Street 12 68	d		17 10					16 50		17 30		17 14		18 10					17 50		18 30		18 14		
Birmingham International 68 ✈	d		17 20					17 00		17 40		17 25		18 21					18 00		18 40		18 25		
Coventry 68	d		17 29					17 11		17 51		17 44		18 31					18 11		18 51		18 44		
Nuneaton 65	d						16 58											17 58							
Rugby 68	d						17 20	17 25				17 55						18 20	18 26				18 55		
Long Buckby 68	a						17 30					18 05						18 30					19 05		
Northampton 68	a						17 42					18 17						18 42					19 17		
	d						17 50					18 25						18 50					19 26		
Wolverton	d											18 37											19 38		
Milton Keynes Central 10	a		17 58				18 04					18 40		18 58				19 04					19 41		
	d	17 50	17 59	18 04			18 07				18 12	18 41	18 50	19 00		19 04		19 07				19 12	19 42	19 50	
Bletchley	d										18 17	18 46										19 17	19 46		
Leighton Buzzard	d						18 16				18 23	18 52						19 16				19 23	19 53		
Cheddington	d										18 29											19 29			
Tring	d								18 15		18 35									19 15		19 35			
Berkhamsted	d								18 20		18 39	19 05								19 20		19 39	20 06		
Hemel Hempstead	d								18 24		18 44	19 10								19 24		19 44	20 10		
Apsley	d								18 27											19 27					
Kings Langley	d								18 30											19 30					
Watford Junction 60	a						18 34		18 35	18s38	18 52	19 17						19 34		19 35	19s38	19 52	20 17		
	d					18 22	18 35		18 35		18 52	19 17					19 22	19 35		19 35		19 52	20 18		
Bushey 60	d								18 38											19 38					
Harrow & Wealdstone ⊖60	d					18 28			18 43		18 58	19 23					19 28			19 43		19 58	20 24		
Wembley Central ⊖60,176	d																								
Shepherd's Bush ⊖176	a					18 47											19 48								
Kensington (Olympia) ⊖176	a					18 50											19 50								
West Brompton ⊖176	a					18 53											19 53								
Imperial Wharf 176	a					18 55											19 56								
Clapham Junction 176	a					19 00											20 00								
East Croydon 176 ⛴	a																								
London Euston 15 ⊖60	a	18 27	18 38	18 44			18 53	18 18	18 57	18 57	19 11	19 37	19 27	19 38		19 45		19 53	19 18	19 57	19 57	20 11	20 38	20 27	

		VT	VT	SN	LM	VT	LM	VT	LM	SN		LM	VT	VT	LM	LM	LM	VT	SN	VT		LM	VT	VT	LM
		◇1	◇1	1	1	◇1	1	◇1	1	1		1	◇1	◇1	1	1	1	◇1	1	◇1		1	◇1	◇1	1
		B	F		D								A	E	D		G			C		H	E	A	D
		☕	☕			☕		☕					☕	☕				☕		☕			☕	☕	
Wolverhampton 7 68 ⛴	d	18 45												19 42											
Sandwell & Dudley 68	d	18 56												19 56											
Birmingham New Street 12 68	d	19 10				18 50		19 30				19 14		20 10			20 14	20 30							
Birmingham International 68 ✈	d	19 20				19 01		19 40				19 25		20 20			20 25	20 40							
Coventry 68	d	19 32				19 14		19 51				19 44		20 31			20 44	20 51							
Nuneaton 65	d				18 58										19 58										20 58
Rugby 68	d				19 20	19 26						19 55			20 14		20 55	21 05							21 20
Long Buckby 68	a				19 30							20 05			20 24		21 05								21 30
Northampton 68	a				19 42							20 17			20 36		21 17								21 42
	d				19 50							20 25			20 50		21 25								21 54
Wolverton	d				20 03							20 37			21 02		21 38					←			22 06
Milton Keynes Central 10	a	19 58			20 06							20 40		20 59	21 07		21 42	21 26				21 42			22 10
	d	20 00	20 04		20 07				20 12			20 41	20 48	21 01	21 07	21 15	21 42	21 28		21 37		21 42	21 53	22 04	22 10
Bletchley	d								20 17			20 46				21 20	→					21 47			22 15
Leighton Buzzard	d				20 16				20 23			20 52			21 16	21 26						21 54			22 22
Cheddington	d								20 28							21 35									22 27
Tring	d						20 15		20 37							21 40									22 36
Berkhamsted	d						20 20		20 42			21 07				21 44						22 09			22 40
Hemel Hempstead	d						20 24		20 46			21 11				21 49						22 13			22 45
Apsley	d						20 27					21 14										22 16			
Kings Langley	d						20 30					21 17										22 19			
Watford Junction 60	a				20 34		20 35	20s38	20 53			21 22			21 35	21 56		22s02				22 23	22s31		22 52
	d			20 22	20 35		20 35		20 54	21 17		21 22			21 35	21 56			22 17			22 24			22 52
Bushey 60	d						20 38									21 59									22 55
Harrow & Wealdstone ⊖60	d			20 28			20 43		21 00	21 23		21 28				22 04			22 23			22 30			23 00
Wembley Central ⊖60,176	d																								
Shepherd's Bush ⊖176	a			20 47						21 45									22 45						
Kensington (Olympia) ⊖176	a			20 50						21 47									22 48						
West Brompton ⊖176	a			20 53						21 50									22 51						
Imperial Wharf 176	a			20 56						21 53									22 53						
Clapham Junction 176	a			21 00						21 58									22 58						
East Croydon 176 ⛴	a																								
London Euston 15 ⊖60	a	20 39	20 46		20 53	20 18	20 59	20 57	21 14			21 42	21 31	21 48	21 55	22 19		22 23		22 28		22 44	22 55	22 57	23 15

A From Manchester Piccadilly
B From Edinburgh
C From Liverpool Lime Street
D From Crewe
E From Glasgow Central
F From Chester
G To London Euston
H From Birmingham New Street

Table 66R

Sundays
30 March to 11 May

West Midlands, Northampton, Milton Keynes Central and Watford Junction - London

Network Diagram - see first Page of Table 59

		LM	VT	SN	LM	VT	VT	LM	VT	VT
		1	◇1	1	1	◇1	◇1	1	◇1	◇1
		A			B	C	D			
			🍴			🍴	🍴		🍴	🍴
Wolverhampton 7	68 🚌 d		21 05						22 05	22 37
Sandwell & Dudley	68 d		21 17						22 16	22 48
Birmingham New Street 12	68 d	21 14	21 30						22 30	23 01
Birmingham International	68 ✈ d	21 25	21 40						22 40	23 11
Coventry	68 d	21 44	21 51						22 51	23 22
Nuneaton	65 d						22 18			
Rugby	68 d	21 55	22 04				22 33		23 04	23 35
Long Buckby	68 a	22 05								
Northampton	68 a	22 17								23s54
	d	22 25						23 00		
Wolverton	d	22 37			←			23 12		
Milton Keynes Central 10	a	22 40	22 35		22 40		23 04	23 15	23 36	00s13
	d	22 41	22 37		22 41	22 48	23 06	23 16	23 37	
Bletchley	d	↦			22 46			23 21		
Leighton Buzzard	d				22 52			23 27		
Cheddington	d							23 32		
Tring	d							23 41		
Berkhamsted	d				23 07			23 45		
Hemel Hempstead	d				23 12			23 50		
Apsley	d				23 15					
Kings Langley	d				23 18					
Watford Junction	60 a		23s05		23 22	23s28	23s34	23 57	00s06	00s43
	d			23 17	23 23			23 59		
Bushey	60 d							00 01		
Harrow & Wealdstone	⊖60 d			23 23	23 29			00 07		
Wembley Central	⊖60,176 d									
Shepherd's Bush	⊖176 a			23 42						
Kensington (Olympia)	⊖176 a			23 44						
West Brompton	⊖176 a			23 47						
Imperial Wharf	176 a			23 49						
Clapham Junction	176 a			23 54						
East Croydon	176 🚌 a			00 15						
London Euston 15	⊖60 a		23 25		23 43	23 49	23 54	00 21	00 27	01 05

A To London Euston
B From Birmingham New Street
C From Manchester Piccadilly
D From Liverpool Lime Street

Network Diagram for Tables 67, 68, 69, 70

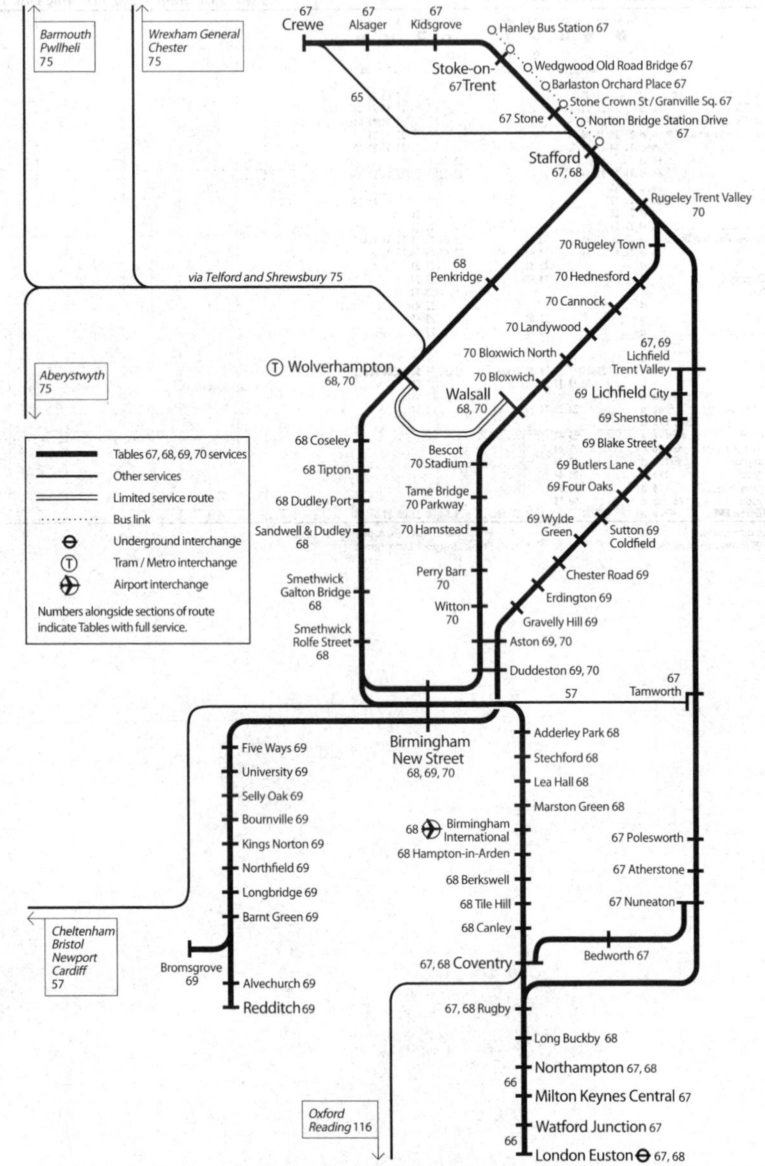

TOCs operating on this network - Virgin Trains (VT), Cross Country (XC), London Midlands (LM), Arriva Trains Wales (AW)

Table 67

Mondays to Fridays

9 December to 16 May

London - Stoke-on-Trent and Crewe
Coventry - Nuneaton

Network Diagram - refer to first Page of Table 67

Miles	Miles	Miles				VT	XC	LM	XC	LM	LM	VT	VT	LM		XC	LM	LM	LM	LM	XC	LM	VT	LM		VT
						◇1	◇1	1	◇1	1		◇1	◇1	1		◇1		1	1		◇1	1	◇1	1		◇1
						☒			🛒			☒	☒			🛒	🚌				🛒		☒			☒
0	—	—	**London Euston** 15	⊖66	d							05 27	05 39									06 24	06 36			06 43
17½	—	—	Watford Junction	66	d							05u47	06u02									06 42	06u51			
49¾	—	—	Milton Keynes Central	66	d							06 12	06 22									07 22				07 13
65¾	—	—	Northampton	68	d					05 42									06 35			07 43				
84½	—	—	Rugby		d					06 05			06 45						06 59			08 03				
—	—	0	**Coventry**		d						06 12									07 06						07 42
—	—	6¼	Bedworth		d						06 23									07 17						
99	—	10	Nuneaton		a					06 16	06 30	06 40							07 11	07 27		08 15				
—	—	—			d					06 17		06 41							07 12			08 16				
104	—	—	Atherstone		d					06 23									07 18			08 22				
108	—	—	Polesworth		d														07 23							
111½	—	—	Tamworth		d					06 32									07 29			08 30				
117¾	—	—	Lichfield Trent Valley		d					06 38									07 35			08 36				
125¾	—	—	Rugeley Trent Valley		d					06 46									07 43			08 43				
135½	0	—	**Stafford**		d	06 02	06 30	06 36	06 55	06 58		07 05		07 09		07 30		07 36	07 54		08 01	08 54		08 10		
—	—	—	Norton Bridge Station Drv		d																	→				
144½	—	—	Stone		d					07 10									08 05							
—	—	—	Stone Crown Street		d												07 34									
—	—	—	Stone Granville Square		a																					
—	—	—	Barlaston Orchard Place		d												07 46									
—	—	—	Wedgwood Old Road Bridge		d												07 50									
151¾	—	—	**Stoke-on-Trent**	50	d		06a50		07a13	07 21							08 00		08 15		08a19					
—	—	—	Hanley Bus Station		a												08 07									
159	—	—	Kidsgrove	50	d					07 30									08 23							
161¼	—	—	Alsager	50	d					07 34									08 28							
167¾	24½	—	**Crewe**	65,50	a	06 21		06 57		07 44		07 23	07 30	07 32		07 50		07 56	08 38				08 10	08 30		09 07

			VT	LM	VT	XC	LM	LM	VT	LM		XC	LM	VT	LM	VT	VT	XC	LM	LM		LM	VT	LM	XC	LM
			◇1		◇1	◇1		1	◇1	1		◇1	1	◇1	1	◇1	◇1	◇1				1	◇1	1	◇1	1
			☒	🚌	☒	🛒			☒			🛒		☒		☒	☒	🛒		🚌			☒		🛒	
London Euston 15	⊖66	d	07 07		07 10				07 35					07 43	07 46	08 07	08 10						08 40			
Watford Junction	66	d																								
Milton Keynes Central	66	d			07 41				08 06					08 13	08 19	08 38	08 43									
Northampton	68	d																								
Rugby		d													08 42											
Coventry		d				07 27	08 04							08 42				08 27	09 06							
Bedworth		d					08 15												09 17							
Nuneaton		a					08 23								08 53				09 25							
		d													08 54											
Atherstone		d													09 00											
Polesworth		d																								
Tamworth		d													09 09											
Lichfield Trent Valley		d													09 17											
Rugeley Trent Valley		d								←					09 25									←		
Stafford		d	08 23	08 25		08 30		08 36		08 54		09 01	09 10		09 39	09a27		09 30				09 35		09 39	10 01	10 10
Norton Bridge Station Drv		d		08 40											→											
Stone		d								09 05														09 50		
Stone Crown Street		d																		09 34						
Stone Granville Square		a		09 02																						
Barlaston Orchard Place		d																		09 46						
Wedgwood Old Road Bridge		d																		09 50						
Stoke-on-Trent	50	d				08a54				09 15		09a19						09a54		10 00				10 03	10a19	
Hanley Bus Station		a																		10 07						
Kidsgrove	50	d								09 24														10 11		
Alsager	50	d								09 28														10 15		
Crewe	65,50	a	08 41		08 47			08 56	09 10	09 38			09 30	10 07			09 51					09 56	10 10	10 29		10 30

			VT	LM	VT	LM		VT	XC	LM	VT	LM	XC	LM	VT	LM		LM	VT	VT	XC	LM	LM	VT	LM	XC
			◇1	1	◇1			◇1	◇1	1	◇1	1	◇1	1	◇1			1	◇1	◇1	◇1		1	◇1	1	◇1
			☕		☒	🚌		☒	🛒		☒		🛒		☕	🚌			☒	☒	🛒			☒		🛒
London Euston 15	⊖66	d	08 43	08 46	09 07			09 10			09 40				09 43			09 46	10 07	10 10				10 40		
Watford Junction	66	d																								
Milton Keynes Central	66	d	09 13	09 19				09 41							10 13			10 19		10 41						
Northampton	68	d																								
Rugby		d		09 42														10 42								
Coventry		d	09 42						09 27						10 42						10 27	10 42				
Bedworth		d																				10 53				
Nuneaton		a		09 53														10 53				11 00				
		d		09 54														10 54								
Atherstone		d		10 00														11 00								
Polesworth		d																								
Tamworth		d		10 09														11 09								
Lichfield Trent Valley		d		10 17														11 17								
Rugeley Trent Valley		d		10 25								←						11 25							←	
Stafford		d		10 39	10 23	10 25			10 30	10 35		10 39	11 01	11 10				11 39	11 23		11 30		11 35		11 39	12 01
Norton Bridge Station Drv		d		→		10 40												→								
Stone		d										10 50													11 50	
Stone Crown Street		d														11 24										
Stone Granville Square		a				11 02																				
Barlaston Orchard Place		d														11 37										
Wedgwood Old Road Bridge		d														11 41										
Stoke-on-Trent	50	d							10a54			11 02	11a19			11 51					11a54				12 02	12a19
Hanley Bus Station		a														11 57										
Kidsgrove	50	d										11 10													12 10	
Alsager	50	d										11 14													12 14	
Crewe	65,50	a	11 07		10 41			10 47		10 56	11 10	11 24		11 30	12 07				11 41	11 47			11 56	12 10	12 24	

Table 67

Mondays to Fridays

9 December to 16 May

London - Stoke-on-Trent and Crewe
Coventry - Nuneaton

Network Diagram - refer to first Page of Table 67

Station			LM 1	VT ◇1 ☕	LM 1	VT ◇1 ☕	VT ◇1 ☕	XC ◇1 A 🛒	LM 🚌	LM	LM 1		VT ◇1 ☕	LM 1	XC ◇1 🛒	LM 1	VT ◇1 ☕	LM 🚌	LM 1	VT ◇1 ☕	VT ◇1 ☕		XC ◇1 🛒	LM	LM 1
London Euston 15 ⊖66	d			10 43	10 46	11 07	11 10						11 40				11 43		11 46	12 07	12 10				
Watford Junction 66	d																								
Milton Keynes Central 66	d			11 13	11 19		11 41										12 13		12 19		12 41				
Northampton 68	d																								
Rugby	d				11 42														12 42						
Coventry	d			11 42				11 27		11 42							12 42						12 27	12 42	
Bedworth	d									11 53														12 53	
Nuneaton	a				11 53					12 00									12 53					13 00	
	d				11 54														12 54						
Atherstone	d				12 00														13 00						
Polesworth	d																								
Tamworth	d				12 09														13 09						
Lichfield Trent Valley	d				12 17														13 17						
Rugeley Trent Valley	d				12 25									←					13 25						
Stafford	d		12 10		12 39	12 23		12 30	12 35		12 35			12 39	13 01	13 10			13 39	13 23			13 30		13 35
Norton Bridge Station Drv	d				→				12 59										→						
Stone	d													12 50											
Stone Crown Street	d																	13 24							
Stone Granville Square	a								13 39																
Barlaston Orchard Place	d																	13 37							
Wedgwood Old Road Bridge	d																	13 41							
Stoke-on-Trent 50	d							12a54						13 02	13a19			13 51					13a54		
Hanley Bus Station	a																	13 57							
Kidsgrove 50	d													13 10											
Alsager 50	d													13 14											
Crewe 65,50	a		12 30	13 07		12 41	12 47				12 57		13 10	13 24		13 30	14 07			13 41	13 47				13 56

Station		VT ◇1 ☕	LM 1	XC ◇1 🛒	LM 1	VT ◇1 ☕	LM 🚌		LM 1	VT ◇1 ☕	VT ◇1 ☕	XC ◇1 🛒	LM	LM 1	VT ◇1 ☕	LM 1	XC ◇1 🛒		LM 1	VT ◇1 ☕	LM 🚌	LM 1	VT ◇1 ☕	VT ◇1 ☕	XC ◇1 🛒
London Euston 15 ⊖66	d	12 40				12 43			12 46	13 07	13 10				13 40					13 43		13 46	14 07	14 10	
Watford Junction 66	d																								
Milton Keynes Central 66	d					13 13			13 19		13 41									14 13		14 19		14 41	
Northampton 68	d																								
Rugby	d								13 42													14 42			
Coventry	d					13 42						13 28	13 42							14 42					14 27
Bedworth	d												13 53												
Nuneaton	a								13 53				14 00									14 53			
	d								13 54													14 54			
Atherstone	d								14 00													15 00			
Polesworth	d																								
Tamworth	d								14 09													15 09			
Lichfield Trent Valley	d								14 17													15 17			
Rugeley Trent Valley	d		←						14 25							←						15 25			
Stafford	d		13 39	14 01	14 10		14 18		14 39	14 23		14 30		14 35		14 39	15 01		15 10			15 39	15 23		15 30
Norton Bridge Station Drv	d						14 42		→													→			
Stone	d		13 50													14 50									
Stone Crown Street	d																				15 24				
Stone Granville Square	a						14 54																		
Barlaston Orchard Place	d																				15 37				
Wedgwood Old Road Bridge	d																				15 41				
Stoke-on-Trent 50	d		14 02	14a19								14a54				15 02	15a19				15 51				15a54
Hanley Bus Station	a																				15 57				
Kidsgrove 50	d		14 10													15 10									
Alsager 50	d		14 14													15 14									
Crewe 65,50	a	14 10	14 24		14 30	15 07				14 41	14 47			14 56	15 10	15 24			15 30	16 07			15 41	15 47	

A ◇ from Stafford

Table 67

Mondays to Fridays

9 December to 16 May

London - Stoke-on-Trent and Crewe
Coventry - Nuneaton

Network Diagram - refer to first Page of Table 67

	LM	LM	VT	LM	XC	LM	VT	LM		LM	VT	VT	XC	LM	LM	VT	LM	XC		LM	VT	LM	LM	VT
		1	◇1	1	◇1	1	R 1			1	◇1	◇1	◇1		1	◇1	1	◇1		1	R 1		1	◇1
			☕		🛒		⊠	🚌			☕	☕	🛒			☕		🛒			⊠	🚌		☕
London Euston 15 ⊖66 d			14 40				14 43			14 46	15 07	15 10				15 40					15 43		15 46	16 07
Watford Junction 66 d																								
Milton Keynes Central 66 d							15 13			15 19		15 41									16 13		16 19	
Northampton 68 d																								
Rugby d										15 42													16 42	
Coventry d	14 42						15 42						15 27	15 42							16 42			
Bedworth d	14 53													15 53										
Nuneaton a	15 00									15 53				16 00									16 53	
Nuneaton d										15 54													16 54	
Atherstone d										16 00													17 00	
Polesworth d																								
Tamworth d										16 09													17 09	
Lichfield Trent Valley d										16 17													17 17	
Rugeley Trent Valley d				←						16 25							←						17 25	
Stafford d		15 35		15 39	16 02	16 10		16 18		16 39	16 23		16 31		16 36		16 39	17 01		17 10			17 39	17 23
Norton Bridge Station Drv d								16a42		↪													↪	
Stone d				15 50													16 50							
Stone Crown Street d																						17 24		
Stone Granville Square a																								
Barlaston Orchard Place d																						17 37		
Wedgwood Old Road Bridge d																						17 41		
Stoke-on-Trent 50 d				16 02	16a20								16a54				17 02	17a18				17a51		
Hanley Bus Station a																								
Kidsgrove 50 d				16 10													17 10							
Alsager 50 d				16 14													17 14							
Crewe 65,50 a		15 56	16 10	16 24		16 30	17 07				16 41	16 47			16 56	17 10	17 24			17 30	18 07			17 41

	VT	XC	LM	LM		LM	LM	VT	XC	VT	LM	VT	LM	VT		XC	LM	VT	LM	LM	LM	LM	VT	XC
	◇1	◇1		1		1		◇1	◇1	◇1	1	◇1	1	◇1		◇1		◇1	1	1		1	◇1	◇1
	☕	🛒					🚌	☕	🛒	☕		⊠		⊠		🛒		⊠					⊠	🛒
London Euston 15 ⊖66 d	16 10							16 33		16 40		16 43	16 46	17 07				17 10				17 24	17 33	
Watford Junction 66 d																						17 44		
Milton Keynes Central 66 d	16u41											17 13	17 19					17u41				18 21		
Northampton 68 d																						18 46		
Rugby d								17 22					17 42									19 08	18 23	
Coventry d		16 27	16 42									17 42				17 28	17 42				18 42			
Bedworth d			16 53														17 53				18 53			
Nuneaton a			17 00										17 59				18 00	18 11			19 00	19 23		
Nuneaton d													18 00					18 12				19 24		
Atherstone d													18 06									19 30		
Polesworth d																								
Tamworth d													18 15									19 39		
Lichfield Trent Valley d													18 22									19 45		
Rugeley Trent Valley d						←							18 29							←		19 53		
Stafford d		17 30		17 36		17 39	17 40	17 56	18 02		18 10		18 44	18 23		18 30			18 36	18 44			18 55	19 01
Norton Bridge Station Drv d							18a04						↪											
Stone d						17 50														18 57				
Stone Crown Street d																								
Stone Granville Square a																								
Barlaston Orchard Place d																								
Wedgwood Old Road Bridge d																								
Stoke-on-Trent 50 d		17a54				18 02			18a20							18a54				19 05		20 14		19a19
Hanley Bus Station a																								
Kidsgrove 50 d						18 10														19 13		20 22		
Alsager 50 d						18 14														19 17		20 26		
Crewe 65,50 a	17 47			17 56		18 24		18 16		18 10	18 30	19 07		18 41				18 55	19 03	19 27		20 37	19 14	

Table 67

Mondays to Fridays

9 December to 16 May

London - Stoke-on-Trent and Crewe
Coventry - Nuneaton

Network Diagram - refer to first Page of Table 67

			VT	LM	VT	LM	VT	VT		XC	LM	VT	XC	VT	LM	VT	LM	VT ThFO		VT	VT	VT	XC	VT	LM	VT
			◇1 ⊠	1	◇1 ☕	1	◇1 ⊠	◇1 ⊠		◇1 🛒	1	◇1 ⊠	◇1 🛒	◇1 ⊠	1	◇1 ⊠		◇ ☕		R 1 ☕	R 1 ☕	R 1 ☕	◇1 🛒	◇1 ⊠	1	◇1 ☕
London Euston 15	⊖66	d	17 40		17 43	18 05	18 07	18 10				18 33		18 40		18 43		18 57		19 07	19 10	19 10				19 40
Watford Junction	66	d				18 26																				
Milton Keynes Central	66	d			18u13	19 07		18u41								19 13					19 41	19 41				
Northampton	68	d				19 45																				
Rugby		d				20 04						19 23														
Coventry		d			18 42					18 27						19 42	19 43						19 27			
Bedworth		d															19 54									
Nuneaton		a				20 16		19 12									20 01			20 02						
		d				20 17		19 13												20 03						
Atherstone		d				20 23																				
Polesworth		d																								
Tamworth		d				20 31																				20 43
Lichfield Trent Valley		d				20 37																				20 50
Rugeley Trent Valley		d				20 43																		←	←	
Stafford		d		19 10		20 53	19 23			19 29	19 37	19 57	20 01		20 10	20 52				20a26			20 30	20 52	20 53	21 04
Norton Bridge Station Drv		d				↪										↪										
Stone		d																							21 04	
Stone Crown Street		d																								
Stone Granville Square		a																								
Barlaston Orchard Place		d																								
Wedgwood Old Road Bridge		d																								
Stoke-on-Trent	50	d								19a54			20a19										20a54		21 14	
Hanley Bus Station		a																								
Kidsgrove	50	d																							21 23	
Alsager	50	d																							21 27	
Crewe	65,50	a	19 10	19 30	20 07		19 41	19 53			20 01	20 15		20 10	20 30			20s33			20 47	20 48		21 16	21 37	21 21

			LM	LM		VT	VT	VT	XC	LM	VT	VT	LM	XC		LM	VT	VT	LM	XC	LM	AW	VT	VT MX		LM
				1		◇1 ☕	◇1 ☕	◇1 ☕	◇1	1	◇1 ☕	◇1 ☕	1	◇1			◇1 ☕	◇1 ☕	1	◇1	1	◇	◇1 ☕	◇1 A ☕		1
London Euston 15	⊖66	d				19 43	20 07	20 10		20 13	20 40						21 07	21 10					22 00	22 50		
Watford Junction	66	d																21u25						23u07		
Milton Keynes Central	66	d				20 13		20 41		20 55							21 38						22 32	⌇		
Northampton	68	d								21 26														⌇		
Rugby		d								21 45								22 04					22 55	⌇		
Coventry		d	20 42			20 42			20 27					21 28		21 42								⌇		
Bedworth		d	20 53													21 53								⌇		
Nuneaton		a	21 00				21 02			21 57						22 02	22 07						23 05	00s39		
		d					21 03			21 59							22 08						23 07	⌇		
Atherstone		d								22 05														⌇		
Polesworth		d																						⌇		
Tamworth		d								22 15													23s16	⌇		
Lichfield Trent Valley		d								22 21													23s23	⌇		
Rugeley Trent Valley		d								22 29		←							←					⌇		
Stafford		d		21 10		21 55	21 27		21 32	22 41		21 55	22 10	22 30				22 34	22 41	23 01	23 20	23 30	23s40	⌇		23 53
Norton Bridge Station Drv		d				↪				↪														⌇		
Stone		d																						⌇		
Stone Crown Street		d																						⌇		
Stone Granville Square		a																						⌇		
Barlaston Orchard Place		d																						⌇		
Wedgwood Old Road Bridge		d																						⌇		
Stoke-on-Trent	50	d							21a54					22a53						23a20				01s20		
Hanley Bus Station		a																								
Kidsgrove	50	d																								
Alsager	50	d																								
Crewe	65,50	a		21 30			21 46	21 47			22 12	22 16	22 30				22 46	22 53	23 04		23 47	23 55	00 06			00 16

A not 25 December, 26 December, 1 January

Table 67

Saturdays

14 December to 28 December

London - Stoke-on-Trent and Crewe
Coventry - Nuneaton

Network Diagram - refer to first Page of Table 67

		VT ◇1	XC ◇1	LM 1	LM 1	LM		XC ◇1	LM 1	LM	XC ◇1	VT ◇1	LM 1	LM 1	LM	XC ◇1		LM 1	VT ◇1	LM 1	VT ◇1	LM	XC ◇1	LM 1	VT ◇1
London Euston 15 ⊖66	d											06 05						06 24	06 36		07 07				07 35
Watford Junction 66	d											06u20						06 41	06u51						
Milton Keynes Central 66	d											06 41						07 23							08 06
Northampton 68	d				05 42									06 38				07 45							
Rugby	d				06 02							07 03		06 58				08 04							
Coventry	d					06 16									07 16								07 27		
Bedworth	d					06 27									07 27										
Nuneaton	a				06 13	06 34								07 09	07 35			08 16							
	d				06 14									07 12				08 16							
Atherstone	d				06 20									07 18				08 22							
Polesworth	d													07 23											
Tamworth	d				06 29									07 29				08 30							
Lichfield Trent Valley	d				06 35									07 35				08 36							
Rugeley Trent Valley	d				06 43									07 43				08 43							
Stafford	d	06 01	06 30	06 36	06 54			07 01	07 09		07 30	07 34	07 38	07 54		08 01		08 54		08 10	08 23	08 25	08 30	08 36	
Norton Bridge Station Drv	d																	→				08 40			
Stone	d				07 04									08 05											
Stone Crown Street	d									07 29															
Stone Granville Square	a																					09 02			
Barlaston Orchard Place	d									07 42															
Wedgwood Old Road Bridge	d									07 46															
Stoke-on-Trent 50	d		06a50		07 14			07a18		07 58				08 15		08a19							08a54		
Hanley Bus Station	a									08 04															
Kidsgrove 50	d				07 23									08 23											
Alsager 50	d				07 27									08 28											
Crewe 65,50	a	06 20		06 56	07 37				07 33		07 50	07 53	07 58	08 38					08 10	08 30	08 41			08 56	09 10

		LM 1		XC ◇1	LM 1	VT ◇1	LM 1	VT ◇1	VT ◇1	XC ◇1	LM	LM		LM 1	VT ◇1	LM 1	XC ◇1	LM 1	VT ◇1	LM 1	VT ◇1	LM		VT ◇1	XC ◇1
London Euston 15 ⊖66	d					07 43	07 46	08 07	08 10						08 40				08 43	08 46	09 07			09 10	
Watford Junction 66	d																								
Milton Keynes Central 66	d					08 13	08 19		08 41										09 13	09 19				09 41	
Northampton 68	d																								
Rugby	d						08 42													09 42					
Coventry	d					08 42				08 27	08 42								09 42						09 27
Bedworth	d										08 53														
Nuneaton	a						08 53				09 00									09 53					
	d						08 54													09 54					
Atherstone	d						09 00													10 00					
Polesworth	d																								
Tamworth	d						09 09													10 09					
Lichfield Trent Valley	d						09 17													10 17					
Rugeley Trent Valley	d	←					09 25									←				10 25					
Stafford	d	08 54		09 01	09 10		09 39	09 23		09 30				09 35		09 39	10 01	10 10		10 39	10 23	10 25			10 30
Norton Bridge Station Drv	d						→													→		10 40			
Stone	d	09 05														09 50									
Stone Crown Street	d											09 29													
Stone Granville Square	a																					11 02			
Barlaston Orchard Place	d											09 42													
Wedgwood Old Road Bridge	d											09 46													
Stoke-on-Trent 50	d	09 15		09a19						09a54		09 58				10 02	10a19								10a54
Hanley Bus Station	a											10 04													
Kidsgrove 50	d	09 23														10 10									
Alsager 50	d	09 28														10 14									
Crewe 65,50	a	09 38			09 30	10 07		09 41	09 47					09 56	10 10	10 24		10 30	11 07		10 41			10 47	

		LM	LM 1	VT ◇1	LM 1	XC ◇1	LM 1	VT ◇1		LM	LM 1	VT ◇1	VT ◇1	XC ◇1	LM	LM 1	VT ◇1	LM 1		XC ◇1	LM 1	VT ◇1	LM 1	VT ◇1	VT ◇1
London Euston 15 ⊖66	d			09 40				09 43			09 46	10 07	10 10				10 40					10 43	10 46	11 07	11 10
Watford Junction 66	d																								
Milton Keynes Central 66	d							10 13			10 19		10 41									11 13	11 19		11 41
Northampton 68	d																								
Rugby	d										10 42												11 42		
Coventry	d	09 42						10 42						10 27	10 42							11 42			
Bedworth	d	09 53													10 53										
Nuneaton	a	10 00									10 53				11 00								11 53		
	d										10 54												11 54		
Atherstone	d										11 00												12 00		
Polesworth	d																								
Tamworth	d										11 09												12 09		
Lichfield Trent Valley	d										11 17												12 17		
Rugeley Trent Valley	d				←						11 25							←					12 25		
Stafford	d		10 35		10 39	11 01	11 10				11 39	11 23		11 30		11 35		11 39		12 01	12 10		12 39	12 23	
Norton Bridge Station Drv	d										→												→		
Stone	d				10 50													11 50							
Stone Crown Street	d									11 19															
Stone Granville Square	a																								
Barlaston Orchard Place	d									11 32															
Wedgwood Old Road Bridge	d									11 36															
Stoke-on-Trent 50	d				11 02	11a19				11 48				11a54				12 02		12a19					
Hanley Bus Station	a									11 54															
Kidsgrove 50	d				11 10													12 10							
Alsager 50	d				11 14													12 14							
Crewe 65,50	a		10 56	11 10	11 24		11 30	12 07				11 41	11 47			11 56	12 10	12 24			12 30	13 07		12 41	12 47

Table 67

Saturdays

14 December to 28 December

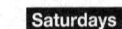

London - Stoke-on-Trent and Crewe
Coventry - Nuneaton

Network Diagram - refer to first Page of Table 67

		XC	LM	LM		LM	VT	LM	XC	LM	VT	LM	LM	VT		VT	XC	LM	LM	VT	LM	XC	LM	VT
		◇1				1	◇1	1	◇1	1	◇1		1	◇1		◇1	◇1		1	◇1	1	◇1	1	◇1
			🚌									🚌												
		trolley					restaurant		trolley		restaurant			restaurant		restaurant	trolley			restaurant		trolley		restaurant
London Euston 15 ⊖66	d						11 40				11 43		11 46	12 07		12 10				12 40				12 43
Watford Junction 66	d																							
Milton Keynes Central 66	d										12 13		12 19			12 41								13 13
Northampton 68	d																							
Rugby	d												12 42											
Coventry	d	11 27		11 42							12 42						12 27	12 42						13 42
Bedworth	d			11 53														12 53						
Nuneaton	a			12 00									12 53					13 00						
	d												12 54											
Atherstone	d												13 00											
Polesworth	d																							
Tamworth	d												13 09											
Lichfield Trent Valley	d												13 17											
Rugeley Trent Valley	d							←					13 25								←			
Stafford	d	12 30	12 35			12 35		12 39	13 01	13 10			13 39	13 23			13 30		13 35		13 39	14 01	14 10	
Norton Bridge Station Drv	d		12 59										→											
Stone	d							12 50													13 50			
Stone Crown Street	d											13 19												
Stone Granville Square	a		13 39																					
Barlaston Orchard Place	d											13 32												
Wedgwood Old Road Bridge	d											13 36												
Stoke-on-Trent 50	d	12a54						13 02	13a18			13 48					13a54				14 02	14a19		
Hanley Bus Station	a											13 54												
Kidsgrove 50	d							13 10													14 10			
Alsager 50	d							13 14													14 14			
Crewe 65,50	a					12 56	13 10	13 24		13 30	14 07			13 41		13 47			13 56	14 10	14 24		14 30	15 07

		LM	LM	VT	VT	XC	LM	LM	VT	LM		XC	LM	VT	LM	VT	VT	XC	LM	LM		VT	LM	XC	LM
			1	◇1	◇1	◇1		1	◇1	1		◇1	1	◇1	1	◇1	◇1	◇1		1		◇1	1	◇1	1
		🚌																							
				restaurant	restaurant	trolley			restaurant			trolley		restaurant		restaurant	restaurant	trolley				restaurant		restaurant	
London Euston 15 ⊖66	d		12 46	13 07	13 10				13 40					13 43	13 46	14 07	14 10					14 40			
Watford Junction 66	d																								
Milton Keynes Central 66	d		13 19		13 41									14 13	14 19		14 41								
Northampton 68	d																								
Rugby	d		13 42												14 42										
Coventry	d					13 27	13 42							14 42				14 27	14 42						
Bedworth	d						13 53												14 53						
Nuneaton	a		13 53				14 00								14 53				15 00						
	d		13 54												14 54										
Atherstone	d		14 00												15 00										
Polesworth	d																								
Tamworth	d		14 09												15 09										
Lichfield Trent Valley	d		14 17												15 17										
Rugeley Trent Valley	d		14 25							←					15 25								←		
Stafford	d	14 18	14 39	14 23		14 30		14 35		14 39		15 01	15 10		15 39	15 23		15 30		15 35			15 39	16 01	16 10
Norton Bridge Station Drv	d	14 42	→												→										
Stone	d									14 50													15 50		
Stone Crown Street	d																								
Stone Granville Square	a	14 54																							
Barlaston Orchard Place	d																								
Wedgwood Old Road Bridge	d																								
Stoke-on-Trent 50	d					14a54				15 02		15a19						15a54					16 02	16a19	
Hanley Bus Station	a																								
Kidsgrove 50	d									15 10													16 10		
Alsager 50	d									15 14													16 14		
Crewe 65,50	a			14 41	14 47			14 56	15 10	15 24			15 30	16 06		15 41	15 47			15 56		16 10	16 24		16 30

Table 67

Saturdays

14 December to 28 December

London - Stoke-on-Trent and Crewe
Coventry - Nuneaton

Network Diagram - refer to first Page of Table 67

		VT		LM	LM	LM	VT	VT	XC	LM	LM	VT		LM	XC	LM	VT	LM	LM	VT	VT	XC		LM	LM
		R 1				1	◇1	◇1	◇1		1	◇1		1	◇1	1	R 1		1	◇1	◇1	◇1			1
		⊠		🚌	🚌		☕	☕	🛒			☕			🛒		⊠	🚌		☕	☕	🛒			
London Euston 15 ⊖66	d	14 43				14 46	15 07	15 10				15 40					15 43		15 46	16 07	16 10				
Watford Junction 66	d																								
Milton Keynes Central 66	d	15 13				15 19		15 41									16 13		16 19		16 41				
Northampton 68	d																								
Rugby	d					15 42													16 42						
Coventry	d	15 42							15 27	15 42							16 42					16 27		16 42	
Bedworth	d									15 53														16 53	
Nuneaton	a					15 53				16 00									16 53					17 00	
	d					15 54													16 54						
Atherstone	d					16 00													17 00						
Polesworth	d																								
Tamworth	d					16 09													17 09						
Lichfield Trent Valley	d					16 17													17 17						
Rugeley Trent Valley	d					16 25								←					17 25						
Stafford	d			16 18		16 39	16 23		16 30		16 36			16 39	17 01	17 10			17 39	17 23		17 30			17 36
Norton Bridge Station Drv	d			16a42		↦													↦						
Stone	d													16 50											
Stone Crown Street	d				16 18													17 18							
Stone Granville Square	a																								
Barlaston Orchard Place	d				16 29													17 29							
Wedgwood Old Road Bridge	d				16 33													17 33							
Stoke-on-Trent 50	d				16a45				16a54					17 02	17a19			17a45				17a54			
Hanley Bus Station	a																								
Kidsgrove 50	d													17 10											
Alsager 50	d													17 14											
Crewe 65,50	a	17 07					16 41	16 47			16 56	17 10		17 24		17 30	18 07			17 41	17 47				17 56

		LM	LM	VT	XC	VT	LM	VT		LM	LM	VT	VT	VT	XC	LM	VT	LM		XC	LM	VT	LM	VT	VT
		1		◇1	◇1	◇1	1	◇1		1		◇1	◇1	◇1	◇1	1	◇1	1		◇1	1	◇1	1	◇1	◇1
			🚌	☕	🛒	☕		☕				☕	⊠	☕	🛒		☕			🛒		☕		☕	☕
London Euston 15 ⊖66	d			16 33		16 40		16 43		16 46		17 07	17 10	17 10			17 40					17 43	17 46	18 07	18 10
Watford Junction 66	d																								
Milton Keynes Central 66	d							17 13		17 19			17u40	17 41								18 13	18 19		18 41
Northampton 68	d																								
Rugby	d									17 42													18 42		
Coventry	d							17 42			17 42				17 27							18 42			
Bedworth	d										17 53														
Nuneaton	a									17 53	18 00	18 02											18 53		
	d									17 54		18 03											18 54		
Atherstone	d									18 00													19 00		
Polesworth	d																								
Tamworth	d			17 38						18 09													19 09		
Lichfield Trent Valley	d			17 45						18 17													19 17		
Rugeley Trent Valley	d	←								18 25								←					19 25		
Stafford	d	17 39	17 40	17a58	18 01		18 10			18 39		18 27			18 30	18 36		18 39		19 01	19 10		19 39	19 23	
Norton Bridge Station Drv	d		18a04							↦													↦		
Stone	d	17 50																18 50							
Stone Crown Street	d																								
Stone Granville Square	a																								
Barlaston Orchard Place	d																								
Wedgwood Old Road Bridge	d																								
Stoke-on-Trent 50	d	18 02			18a19										18a54			19 02		19a19					
Hanley Bus Station	a																								
Kidsgrove 50	d	18 10																19 10							
Alsager 50	d	18 14																19 14							
Crewe 65,50	a	18 24				18 10	18 30	19 07				18 45	18 49	18 49		18 56	19 10	19 24			19 30	20 07		19 41	19 47

		XC	LM	LM		LM	VT	XC	VT	VT	LM	VT	XC	LM		LM	VT	LM	VT	VT	XC	LM	XC	VT	
		◇1		1		1	◇1	◇1	◇1	◇1	1	◇1	◇1			1	◇1	1	◇1	◇1	◇1	1	◇1	◇1	
		🛒					☕	🛒	☕	☕		☕					☕		☕	☕				☕	
London Euston 15 ⊖66	d						18 33		18 40	18 43	18 46	19 07					19 30			19 40				20 11	
Watford Junction 66	d																								
Milton Keynes Central 66	d									19 13	19 19														
Northampton 68	d																								
Rugby	d										19 42													21 15	
Coventry	d	18 27	18 42							19 42			19 27	20 15									20 27		
Bedworth	d		18 53											20 26											
Nuneaton	a		19 00								19 53	20 02		20 34											
	d										19 58	20 03													
Atherstone	d										20 04														
Polesworth	d																								
Tamworth	d						19 38				20 14														
Lichfield Trent Valley	d						19 45				20 21														
Rugeley Trent Valley	d					←					20 29							←	←						
Stafford	d	19 30		19 36		19 39	19a58	20 01		20 52	20 42	20 27	20 30			20 38		20 42	20 52		21 01	21 10	21 30	21 46	
Norton Bridge Station Drv	d									↦	↦														
Stone	d					19 50												20 52							
Stone Crown Street	d																								
Stone Granville Square	a																								
Barlaston Orchard Place	d																								
Wedgwood Old Road Bridge	d																								
Stoke-on-Trent 50	d	19a54				20 02		20a19					20a54					21 02			21a20		21a52		
Hanley Bus Station	a																								
Kidsgrove 50	d					20 10												21 10							
Alsager 50	d					20 14												21 14							
Crewe 65,50	a			19 56		20 24			20 10			20 45				20 58	21 04	21 24	21 10	21 18		21 30		22 05	

Table 67

Saturdays

14 December to 28 December

London - Stoke-on-Trent and Crewe
Coventry - Nuneaton

Network Diagram - refer to first Page of Table 67

			VT	VT	LM	XC	VT	XC	LM	LM
			◇1	◇1	1	◇1	◇1	◇1		1
			☕	☕			☕			
London Euston 15	⊖66	d	20 20	20 31			21 00			
Watford Junction	66	d		20u46						
Milton Keynes Central	66	d	21 05				21 45			
Northampton	68	d								
Rugby		d		21 36						
Coventry		d				21 27			21 45	
Bedworth		d							21 56	
Nuneaton		a	21 32						22 03	
		d	21 33							
Atherstone		d								
Polesworth		d								
Tamworth		d		21 53						
Lichfield Trent Valley		d		22 00						
Rugeley Trent Valley		d								
Stafford		d			22 16	22 30	22 34	23 02		23 22
Norton Bridge Station Drv		d								
Stone		d								
Stone Crown Street		d								
Stone Granville Square		a								
Barlaston Orchard Place		d								
Wedgwood Old Road Bridge		d								
Stoke-on-Trent	50	d	22a05			22a50		23a20		
Hanley Bus Station		a								
Kidsgrove	50	d								
Alsager	50	d								
Crewe	65,50	a		22 35	22 38		22 58			23 42

Saturdays

4 January to 8 February

			VT	XC	LM	LM	LM	XC	LM	LM	XC		VT	LM	LM	LM	XC	LM	VT	LM	VT		LM	XC	LM	VT
			◇1	◇1	1	1		◇1	1		◇1		◇1	1	1		◇1	1	◇1	1	◇1			◇1	1	◇1
										🚌													🚌			
			☕					🛒			🛒		☕				🛒		☕		☕			🛒		☕
London Euston 15	⊖66	d											06 05					06 24	06 36		07 07					07 35
Watford Junction	66	d											06u20					06 41	06u51							
Milton Keynes Central	66	d											06 41					07 23								08 06
Northampton	68	d				05 42									06 38			07 45								
Rugby		d				06 02							07 03		06 58			08 04								
Coventry		d					06 16									07 16								07 27		
Bedworth		d					06 27									07 27										
Nuneaton		a				06 13	06 34								07 09	07 35		08 16								
		d				06 14									07 12			08 16								
Atherstone		d				06 20									07 18			08 22								
Polesworth		d													07 23											
Tamworth		d				06 29									07 29			08 30								
Lichfield Trent Valley		d				06 35									07 35			08 36								
Rugeley Trent Valley		d				06 43									07 43			08 43								
Stafford		d	06 01	06 30	06 36	06 54		07 01	07 09		07 30		07 34	07 38	07 54		08 01	08 54		08 10	08 23		08 25	08 30	08 36	
Norton Bridge Station Drv		d																⟶					08 40			
Stone		d				07 04									08 05											
Stone Crown Street		d								07 29																
Stone Granville Square		a																					09 02			
Barlaston Orchard Place		d								07 42																
Wedgwood Old Road Bridge		d								07 46																
Stoke-on-Trent	50	d		06a50		07 14		07a18		07 58					08 15		08a19							08a54		
Hanley Bus Station		a								08 04																
Kidsgrove	50	d				07 23									08 23											
Alsager	50	d				07 27									08 28											
Crewe	65,50	a	06 20		06 56	07 37			07 33		07 50		07 53	07 58	08 38				08 10	08 30	08 41				08 56	09 10

Table 67

Saturdays

4 January to 8 February

London - Stoke-on-Trent and Crewe
Coventry - Nuneaton

Network Diagram - refer to first Page of Table 67

	LM	XC	LM	VT	LM	VT	VT	XC	LM	LM	LM	VT	LM	XC	LM	VT	LM	VT	LM	VT	XC
	1	◇1	1	◇1	1	◇1	◇1	◇1		Bus	1	◇1	1	◇1	1	◇1	1	◇1	Bus	◇1	◇1
		trolley		⊠		☕	☕	trolley				☕		trolley		☕		☕		☕	trolley
London Euston 15 ⊖66 d				07 43	07 46	08 07	08 10					08 40				08 43	08 46	09 07		09 10	
Watford Junction 66 d																					
Milton Keynes Central 66 d				08 13	08 19		08 41									09 13	09 19			09 41	
Northampton 68 d																					
Rugby d					08 42												09 42				
Coventry d				08 42				08 27	08 42							09 42					09 27
Bedworth d									08 53												
Nuneaton a					08 53				09 00								09 53				
d					08 54												09 54				
Atherstone d					09 00												10 00				
Polesworth d																					
Tamworth d					09 09												10 09				
Lichfield Trent Valley d					09 17												10 17				
Rugeley Trent Valley d	←				09 25								←				10 25				
Stafford d	08 54	09 01	09 10		09 39	09 23		09 30			09 35		09 39	10 01	10 10		10 39	10 23	10 25		10 30
Norton Bridge Station Drv d					→												→		10 40		
Stone d	09 05												09 50								
Stone Crown Street d										09 29											
Stone Granville Square a																			11 02		
Barlaston Orchard Place d										09 42											
Wedgwood Old Road Bridge d										09 46											
Stoke-on-Trent 50 d	09 15	09a19						09a54		09 58			10 02	10a19							10a54
Hanley Bus Station a										10 04											
Kidsgrove 50 d	09 23												10 10								
Alsager 50 d	09 28												10 14								
Crewe 65,50 a	09 38		09 30	10 07		09 41	09 47				09 56	10 10	10 24		10 30	11 07		10 41		10 47	

	LM	LM	VT	LM	XC	LM	VT	LM	LM	VT	VT	XC	LM	LM	VT	LM	XC	LM	VT	LM	VT	VT
		1	◇1	1	◇1	1	◇1	Bus	1	◇1	◇1	◇1		1	◇1	1	◇1	1	◇1	1	◇1	◇1
			☕		trolley		☕			☕	☕	trolley			☕		trolley		☕		☕	☕
London Euston 15 ⊖66 d			09 40				09 43		09 46	10 07	10 10				10 40				10 43	10 46	11 07	11 10
Watford Junction 66 d																						
Milton Keynes Central 66 d							10 13		10 19		10 41								11 13	11 19		11 41
Northampton 68 d																						
Rugby d									10 42											11 42		
Coventry d	09 42						10 42					10 27	10 42						11 42			
Bedworth d	09 53												10 53									
Nuneaton a	10 00								10 53				11 00							11 53		
d									10 54											11 54		
Atherstone d									11 00											12 00		
Polesworth d																						
Tamworth d									11 09											12 09		
Lichfield Trent Valley d									11 17											12 17		
Rugeley Trent Valley d				←					11 25							←				12 25		
Stafford d		10 35		10 39	11 01	11 10			11 39	11 23		11 30		11 35		11 39	12 01	12 10		12 39	12 23	
Norton Bridge Station Drv d									→											→		
Stone d				10 50												11 50						
Stone Crown Street d								11 19														
Stone Granville Square a																						
Barlaston Orchard Place d								11 32														
Wedgwood Old Road Bridge d								11 36														
Stoke-on-Trent 50 d				11 02	11a19			11 48				11a54				12 02	12a19					
Hanley Bus Station a								11 54														
Kidsgrove 50 d				11 10												12 10						
Alsager 50 d				11 14												12 14						
Crewe 65,50 a		10 56	11 10	11 24		11 30	12 07			11 41	11 47			11 56	12 10	12 24		12 30	13 07		12 41	12 47

	XC	LM	LM	LM	VT	LM	XC	LM	VT	LM	LM	VT	VT	XC	LM	LM	VT	LM	XC	LM	VT
	◇1	Bus		1	◇1	1	◇1	1	◇1	Bus	1	◇1	◇1	◇1		1	◇1	1	◇1	1	◇1
	trolley				☕		trolley		☕			☕	☕	trolley			☕		trolley		☕
London Euston 15 ⊖66 d					11 40				11 43		11 46	12 07	12 10				12 40				12 43
Watford Junction 66 d																					
Milton Keynes Central 66 d									12 13		12 19		12 41								13 13
Northampton 68 d																					
Rugby d											12 42										
Coventry d	11 27		11 42						12 42					12 27	12 42						13 42
Bedworth d			11 53												12 53						
Nuneaton a			12 00								12 53				13 00						
d											12 54										
Atherstone d											13 00										
Polesworth d																					
Tamworth d											13 09										
Lichfield Trent Valley d											13 17										
Rugeley Trent Valley d						←					13 25							←			
Stafford d	12 30	12 35		12 35		12 39	13 01	13 10			13 39	13 23		13 30		13 35		13 39	14 01	14 10	
Norton Bridge Station Drv d		12 59									→										
Stone d						12 50												13 50			
Stone Crown Street d										13 19											
Stone Granville Square a		13 39																			
Barlaston Orchard Place d										13 32											
Wedgwood Old Road Bridge d										13 36											
Stoke-on-Trent 50 d	12a54					13 02	13a18			13 48				13a54				14 02	14a19		
Hanley Bus Station a										13 54											
Kidsgrove 50 d						13 10												14 10			
Alsager 50 d						13 14												14 14			
Crewe 65,50 a				12 56	13 10	13 24		13 30	14 07			13 41	13 47			13 56	14 10	14 24		14 30	15 07

Table 67

Saturdays

4 January to 8 February

London - Stoke-on-Trent and Crewe
Coventry - Nuneaton

Network Diagram - refer to first Page of Table 67

		LM	LM	VT	VT	XC	LM	LM	VT	LM		XC	LM	VT	LM	VT	VT	XC	LM	LM		VT	LM	XC	LM
			1	◇1	◇1	◇1		1	◇1	1		◇1	1	◇1	1	◇1	◇1	◇1		1		◇1	1	◇1	1
		🚌		☕	☕	🛒			☕			🛒		☕		☕	☕	🛒				☕		☕	
London Euston 15	⊖66 d		12 46	13 07	13 10				13 40					13 43	13 46	14 07	14 10					14 40			
Watford Junction	66 d																								
Milton Keynes Central	66 d		13 19		13 41									14 13	14 19		14 41								
Northampton	68 d																								
Rugby	d		13 42												14 42										
Coventry	d					13 27	13 42							14 42				14 27	14 42						
Bedworth	d						13 53												14 53						
Nuneaton	a		13 53				14 00								14 53				15 00						
	d		13 54												14 54										
Atherstone	d		14 00												15 00										
Polesworth	d																								
Tamworth	d		14 09												15 09										
Lichfield Trent Valley	d		14 17												15 17										
Rugeley Trent Valley	d		14 25							←					15 25								←		
Stafford	d	14 18	14 39	14 23		14 30		14 35		14 39		15 01	15 10		15 39	15 23		15 30		15 35			15 39	16 01	16 10
Norton Bridge Station Drv	d	14 42	→												→										
Stone	d									14 50													15 50		
Stone Crown Street	d																								
Stone Granville Square	a	14 54																							
Barlaston Orchard Place	d																								
Wedgwood Old Road Bridge	d																								
Stoke-on-Trent	50 d					14a54				15 02		15a19						15a54					16 02	16a19	
Hanley Bus Station	a																								
Kidsgrove	50 d									15 10													16 10		
Alsager	50 d									15 14													16 14		
Crewe	65,50 a			14 41	14 47			14 56	15 10	15 24			15 30	16 06		15 41	15 47			15 56		16 10	16 24		16 30

		VT	LM	LM	LM	VT		VT	XC	LM	LM	VT	LM	XC	LM	VT		LM	LM	VT	VT	XC	LM	LM	LM
		R 1			1	◇1		◇1	◇1		1	◇1	1	◇1	1	R 1			1	◇1	◇1	◇1		1	1
		⊠	🚌	🚌		☕		☕	🛒			☕		🛒		⊠		🚌		☕	☕	🛒			
London Euston 15	⊖66 d	14 43			14 46	15 07		15 10				15 40				15 43			15 46	16 07	16 10				
Watford Junction	66 d																								
Milton Keynes Central	66 d	15 13			15 19			15 41								16 13			16 19		16 41				
Northampton	68 d																								
Rugby	d				15 42														16 42						
Coventry	d	15 42							15 27	15 42						16 42						16 27	16 42		
Bedworth	d									15 53													16 53		
Nuneaton	a				15 53					16 00									16 53				17 00		
	d				15 54														16 54						
Atherstone	d				16 00														17 00						
Polesworth	d																								
Tamworth	d				16 09														17 09						
Lichfield Trent Valley	d				16 17														17 17						
Rugeley Trent Valley	d				16 25								←						17 25						←
Stafford	d		16 18		16 39	16 23			16 30		16 36		16 39	17 01	17 10				17 39	17 23		17 30		17 36	17 39
Norton Bridge Station Drv	d		16a42		→														→						
Stone	d												16 50												17 50
Stone Crown Street	d			16 18														17 18							
Stone Granville Square	a																								
Barlaston Orchard Place	d			16 29														17 29							
Wedgwood Old Road Bridge	d			16 33														17 33							
Stoke-on-Trent	50 d			16a45					16a54				17 02	17a19				17a45				17a54			18 02
Hanley Bus Station	a																								
Kidsgrove	50 d												17 10												18 10
Alsager	50 d												17 14												18 14
Crewe	65,50 a	17 07				16 41		16 47			16 56	17 10	17 24		17 30	18 07				17 41	17 47			17 56	18 24

Table 67

Saturdays

4 January to 8 February

London - Stoke-on-Trent and Crewe
Coventry - Nuneaton

Network Diagram - refer to first Page of Table 67

Station			LM	VT	XC	VT	LM	VT	LM		LM	VT	VT	VT	XC	LM	VT	LM	XC		LM	VT	LM	VT	VT	XC
				◇1	◇1	◇1	1	◇1	1			◇1	◇1	◇1	◇1	1	◇1	1	◇1		1	◇1	1	◇1	◇1	◇1
			🚌																							
				☕	🛒	☕		☕				☕	☒	☕	🛒		☕		🛒			☕		☕	☕	🛒
London Euston 15	⊖66	d		16 33		16 40		16 43	16 46			17 07	17 10	17 10			17 40					17 43	17 46	18 07	18 10	
Watford Junction	66	d																								
Milton Keynes Central	66	d						17 13	17 19				17u40	17 41								18 13	18 19		18 41	
Northampton	68	d																								
Rugby		d							17 42														18 42			
Coventry		d						17 42			17 42				17 27							18 42				18 27
Bedworth		d									17 53															
Nuneaton		a							17 53		18 00	18 02											18 53			
		d							17 54			18 03											18 54			
Atherstone		d							18 00														19 00			
Polesworth		d																								
Tamworth		d		17 38					18 09														19 09			
Lichfield Trent Valley		d		17 45					18 17														19 17			
Rugeley Trent Valley		d							18 25									←					19 25			
Stafford		d	17 40	17a58	18 01		18 10		18 39			18 27			18 30	18 36		18 39	19 01		19 10		19 39	19 23		19 30
Norton Bridge Station Drv		d	18a04						→														→			
Stone		d																18 50								
Stone Crown Street		d																								
Stone Granville Square		a																								
Barlaston Orchard Place		d																								
Wedgwood Old Road Bridge		d																								
Stoke-on-Trent	50	d			18a19										18a54			19 02	19a19							19a54
Hanley Bus Station		a																								
Kidsgrove	50	d																19 10								
Alsager	50	d																19 14								
Crewe	65,50	a				18 10	18 30	19 07				18 45	18 49	18 49		18 56	19 10	19 24			19 30	20 07		19 41	19 47	

Station			LM	LM	VT		LM	VT	XC	VT	VT	LM	VT	XC	LM		LM	VT	LM	VT	VT	XC	LM	XC	VT	
				1	◇1		1	◇1	◇1	◇1	◇1	1	◇1	◇1			1	◇1	1	◇1	◇1	◇1	1	◇1	◇1	
					☕			☕	🛒	☕	☕		☕					☕		☕	☕				☕	
London Euston 15	⊖66	d			18 30			18 33		18 40	18 43	18 46	19 07					19 30			19 40				20 11	
Watford Junction	66	d																								
Milton Keynes Central	66	d									19 13	19 19														
Northampton	68	d																								
Rugby		d										19 42													21 15	
Coventry		d	18 42								19 42			19 27	20 15									20 27		
Bedworth		d	18 53												20 26											
Nuneaton		a	19 00									19 53	20 02		20 34											
		d										19 58	20 03													
Atherstone		d										20 04														
Polesworth		d																								
Tamworth		d						19 38				20 14														
Lichfield Trent Valley		d						19 45				20 21														
Rugeley Trent Valley		d					←					20 29							←	←						
Stafford		d		19 36			19 39	19a58	20 01		20 50	20 42	20 27	20 30			20 38		20 42	20 50		21 01	21 10	21 30	21 46	
Norton Bridge Station Drv		d									→	→														
Stone		d					19 50												20 52							
Stone Crown Street		d																								
Stone Granville Square		a																								
Barlaston Orchard Place		d																								
Wedgwood Old Road Bridge		d																								
Stoke-on-Trent	50	d					20 02		20a19					20a54					21 02			21a20		21a52		
Hanley Bus Station		a																								
Kidsgrove	50	d					20 10												21 10							
Alsager	50	d					20 14												21 14							
Crewe	65,50	a		19 56	20 01		20 24			20 10			20 45				20 58	21 04	21 24	21 10	21 18		21 30		22 05	

Station			VT	VT	LM	XC	VT	XC	LM	LM
			◇1	◇1	1	◇1	◇1	◇1		1
			☕	☕			☕			
London Euston 15	⊖66	d	20 20	20 31			21 00			
Watford Junction	66	d		20u46						
Milton Keynes Central	66	d	21 05				21 45			
Northampton	68	d								
Rugby		d		21 36						
Coventry		d				21 27			21 45	
Bedworth		d							21 56	
Nuneaton		a	21 32						22 03	
		d	21 33							
Atherstone		d								
Polesworth		d								
Tamworth		d		21 53						
Lichfield Trent Valley		d		22 00						
Rugeley Trent Valley		d								
Stafford		d			22 16	22 30	22 34	23 02		23 22
Norton Bridge Station Drv		d								
Stone		d								
Stone Crown Street		d								
Stone Granville Square		a								
Barlaston Orchard Place		d								
Wedgwood Old Road Bridge		d								
Stoke-on-Trent	50	d	22a05			22a50		23a20		
Hanley Bus Station		a								
Kidsgrove	50	d								
Alsager	50	d								
Crewe	65,50	a		22 35	22 38		22 58			23 42

Table 67

Saturdays

15 February to 17 May

London - Stoke-on-Trent and Crewe
Coventry - Nuneaton

Network Diagram - refer to first Page of Table 67

	VT	XC	LM	LM	LM	XC	LM	LM	XC		VT	LM	LM	LM	XC	LM	VT	LM	VT		LM	XC	LM	VT
	◇1	◇1	1	1		◇1	1	🚌	◇1		◇1	1	1		◇1	1	◇1	1	◇1		🚌	◇1	1	◇1
	☕					🛒			🛒		☕				🛒		☕		☕			🛒		☕
London Euston 15 ⊖66 d											06 05					06 24	06 36		07 07					07 35
Watford Junction 66 d											06u20					06 41	06u51							
Milton Keynes Central 66 d											06 41					07 23								08 06
Northampton 68 d				05 42									06 38			07 45								
Rugby d				06 02							07 03		06 58			08 04								
Coventry d					06 16									07 16								07 27		
Bedworth d					06 27									07 27										
Nuneaton a				06 13	06 34								07 09	07 35		08 16								
d				06 14									07 12			08 16								
Atherstone d				06 20									07 18			08 22								
Polesworth d													07 23											
Tamworth d				06 29									07 29			08 30								
Lichfield Trent Valley d				06 35									07 35			08 36								
Rugeley Trent Valley d				06 43									07 43			08 43								
Stafford d	06 01	06 30	06 36	06 54		07 01	07 09		07 30		07 34	07 38	07 54		08 01	08 54		08 10	08 23		08 25	08 30	08 36	
Norton Bridge Station Drv d																→					08 40			
Stone d				07 04									08 05											
Stone Crown Street d								07 29																
Stone Granville Square a																					09 02			
Barlaston Orchard Place d								07 42																
Wedgwood Old Road Bridge d								07 46																
Stoke-on-Trent 50 d		06a50		07 14		07a18		07 58					08 15		08a19							08a54		
Hanley Bus Station a								08 04																
Kidsgrove 50 d				07 23									08 23											
Alsager 50 d				07 27									08 28											
Crewe 65,50 a	06 20		06 56	07 37			07 33		07 50		07 53	07 58	08 38				08 10	08 30	08 41				08 56	09 10

	LM	XC	LM	VT	LM		VT	VT	XC	LM	LM	LM	VT	LM	XC		LM	VT	LM	VT	LM	VT	XC	LM
	1	◇1	1	◇1	1		◇1	◇1	◇1		🚌	1	◇1	1	◇1		1	◇1	1	◇1	🚌	◇1	◇1	
		🛒		⊠			☕	☕	🛒				☕		🛒			☕		☕		☕	🛒	
London Euston 15 ⊖66 d				07 43	07 46		08 07	08 10					08 40					08 43	08 46	09 07		09 10		
Watford Junction 66 d																								
Milton Keynes Central 66 d				08 13	08 19			08 41										09 13	09 19			09 41		
Northampton 68 d																								
Rugby d					08 42														09 42					
Coventry d				08 42					08 27	08 42								09 42					09 27	09 42
Bedworth d										08 53														09 53
Nuneaton a					08 53					09 00									09 53					10 00
d					08 54														09 54					
Atherstone d					09 00														10 00					
Polesworth d																								
Tamworth d					09 09														10 09					
Lichfield Trent Valley d					09 17														10 17					
Rugeley Trent Valley d	←				09 25									←					10 25					
Stafford d	08 54	09 01	09 10		09 39		09 23		09 30			09 35		09 39	10 01		10 10		10 39	10 23	10 25		10 30	
Norton Bridge Station Drv d					→														→		10 40			
Stone d	09 05													09 50										
Stone Crown Street d											09 29													
Stone Granville Square a																					11 02			
Barlaston Orchard Place d											09 42													
Wedgwood Old Road Bridge d											09 46													
Stoke-on-Trent 50 d	09 15	09a19							09a54		09 58			10 02	10a19								10a54	
Hanley Bus Station a											10 04													
Kidsgrove 50 d	09 23													10 10										
Alsager 50 d	09 28													10 14										
Crewe 65,50 a	09 38		09 30	10 07			09 41	09 47				09 56	10 10	10 24			10 30	11 07		10 41		10 47		

	LM		VT	LM	XC	LM	VT	LM	LM	VT	VT		XC	LM	LM	VT	LM	XC	LM	VT	LM		VT	VT
	1		◇1	1	◇1	1	◇1	🚌	1	◇1	◇1		◇1		1	◇1	1	◇1	1	◇1	1		◇1	◇1
			☕		🛒		☕			☕	☕		🛒			☕		🛒		☕			☕	☕
London Euston 15 ⊖66 d			09 40				09 43		09 46	10 07	10 10					10 40				10 43	10 46		11 07	11 10
Watford Junction 66 d																								
Milton Keynes Central 66 d							10 13		10 19		10 41									11 13	11 19			11 41
Northampton 68 d																								
Rugby d									10 42												11 42			
Coventry d							10 42						10 27	10 42						11 42				
Bedworth d														10 53										
Nuneaton a									10 53					11 00							11 53			
d									10 54												11 54			
Atherstone d									11 00												12 00			
Polesworth d																								
Tamworth d									11 09												12 09			
Lichfield Trent Valley d									11 17												12 17			
Rugeley Trent Valley d				←					11 25								←				12 25			
Stafford d	10 35			10 39	11 01	11 10			11 39	11 23			11 30		11 35		11 39	12 01	12 10		12 39		12 23	
Norton Bridge Station Drv d									→												→			
Stone d				10 50													11 50							
Stone Crown Street d								11 19																
Stone Granville Square a																								
Barlaston Orchard Place d								11 32																
Wedgwood Old Road Bridge d								11 36																
Stoke-on-Trent 50 d				11 02	11a19			11 48					11a54				12 02	12a19						
Hanley Bus Station a								11 54																
Kidsgrove 50 d				11 10													12 10							
Alsager 50 d				11 14													12 14							
Crewe 65,50 a	10 56		11 10	11 24		11 30	12 07			11 41	11 47				11 56	12 10	12 24		12 30	13 07			12 41	12 47

Table 67

Saturdays

15 February to 17 May

London - Stoke-on-Trent and Crewe
Coventry - Nuneaton

Network Diagram - refer to first Page of Table 67

	XC	LM	LM	LM	VT	LM	XC		LM	VT	LM	LM	VT	VT	XC	LM	LM		VT	LM	XC	LM	VT	LM
	◇1			1	◇1	1	◇1		1	◇1		1	◇1	◇1	◇1		1		◇1	1	◇1	1	◇1	
	🛒	🚌			☕		🛒			☕	🚌		☕	☕	🛒				☕		🛒		☕	🚌
London Euston 15 ⊖66 d					11 40					11 43		11 46	12 07	12 10					12 40				12 43	
Watford Junction 66 d																								
Milton Keynes Central 66 d										12 13		12 19		12 41									13 13	
Northampton 68 d																								
Rugby d												12 42												
Coventry d	11 27		11 42							12 42					12 27	12 42							13 42	
Bedworth d			11 53													12 53								
Nuneaton a			12 00									12 53				13 00								
d												12 54												
Atherstone d												13 00												
Polesworth d																								
Tamworth d												13 09												
Lichfield Trent Valley d												13 17												
Rugeley Trent Valley d						←						13 25								←				
Stafford d	12 30	12 35		12 35		12 39	13 01		13 10			13 39	13 23		13 30		13 35			13 39	14 01	14 10		14 18
Norton Bridge Station Drv d		12 59										↪												14 42
Stone d						12 50														13 50				
Stone Crown Street d											13 19													
Stone Granville Square a		13 39																						14 54
Barlaston Orchard Place d											13 32													
Wedgwood Old Road Bridge d											13 36													
Stoke-on-Trent 50 d	12a54					13 02	13a18				13 48				13a54					14 02	14a19			
Hanley Bus Station a											13 54													
Kidsgrove 50 d						13 10														14 10				
Alsager 50 d						13 14														14 14				
Crewe 65,50 a				12 56	13 10	13 24			13 30	14 07			13 41	13 47			13 56		14 10	14 24		14 30	15 07	

	LM	VT	VT		XC	LM	LM	VT	LM	XC	LM	VT	LM		VT	VT	XC	LM	LM	VT	LM	XC	LM	
	1	◇1	◇1		◇1		1	◇1	1	◇1	1	◇1	1		◇1	◇1	◇1		1	◇1	1	◇1	1	
		☕	☕		🛒			☕		🛒		☕			☕	☕	🛒			☕		☕		
London Euston 15 ⊖66 d	12 46	13 07	13 10					13 40				13 43	13 46		14 07	14 10				14 40				
Watford Junction 66 d																								
Milton Keynes Central 66 d	13 19		13 41									14 13	14 19			14 41								
Northampton 68 d																								
Rugby d	13 42												14 42											
Coventry d					13 27	13 42						14 42					14 27	14 42						
Bedworth d						13 53												14 53						
Nuneaton a	13 53					14 00							14 53					15 00						
d	13 54												14 54											
Atherstone d	14 00												15 00											
Polesworth d																								
Tamworth d	14 09												15 09											
Lichfield Trent Valley d	14 17												15 17											
Rugeley Trent Valley d	14 25								←				15 25								←			
Stafford d	14 39	14 23			14 30		14 35		14 39	15 01	15 10		15 39		15 23		15 30		15 35		15 39	16 01	16 10	
Norton Bridge Station Drv d	↪												↪											
Stone d									14 50												15 50			
Stone Crown Street d																								
Stone Granville Square a																								
Barlaston Orchard Place d																								
Wedgwood Old Road Bridge d																								
Stoke-on-Trent 50 d					14a54				15 02	15a19							15a54				16 02	16a19		
Hanley Bus Station a																								
Kidsgrove 50 d									15 10												16 10			
Alsager 50 d									15 14												16 14			
Crewe 65,50 a		14 41	14 47				14 56	15 10	15 24		15 30	16 06			15 41	15 47			15 56	16 10	16 24		16 30	

	VT	LM	LM	LM	VT	VT	XC	LM	LM		VT	LM	XC	LM	VT	LM	LM	VT	VT		XC	LM	LM	LM
	R 1			1	◇1	◇1	◇1		1		◇1	1	◇1	1	R 1		1	◇1	◇1		◇1		1	1
	☒	🚌	🚌		☕	☕	🛒				☕		🛒		☒	🚌		☕	☕		🛒			
London Euston 15 ⊖66 d	14 43			14 46	15 07	15 10					15 40				15 43		15 46	16 07	16 10					
Watford Junction 66 d																								
Milton Keynes Central 66 d	15 13			15 19		15 41									16 13		16 19		16 41					
Northampton 68 d																								
Rugby d				15 42													16 42							
Coventry d	15 42						15 27	15 42							16 42						16 27	16 42		
Bedworth d								15 53														16 53		
Nuneaton a				15 53				16 00									16 53					17 00		
d				15 54													16 54							
Atherstone d				16 00													17 00							
Polesworth d																								
Tamworth d				16 09													17 09							
Lichfield Trent Valley d				16 17													17 17							
Rugeley Trent Valley d				16 25								←					17 25							←
Stafford d		16 18		16 39	16 23		16 30		16 36			16 39	17 01	17 10			17 39	17 23			17 30		17 36	17 39
Norton Bridge Station Drv d		16a42		↪													↪							
Stone d												16 50												17 50
Stone Crown Street d			16 18													17 18								
Stone Granville Square a																								
Barlaston Orchard Place d			16 29													17 29								
Wedgwood Old Road Bridge d			16 33													17 33								
Stoke-on-Trent 50 d			16a45				16a54					17 02	17a19			17a45					17a54			18 02
Hanley Bus Station a																								
Kidsgrove 50 d												17 10												18 10
Alsager 50 d												17 14												18 14
Crewe 65,50 a	17 07				16 41	16 47			16 56		17 10	17 24		17 30	18 07			17 41	17 47				17 56	18 24

Table 67

Saturdays

15 February to 17 May

London - Stoke-on-Trent and Crewe
Coventry - Nuneaton

Network Diagram - refer to first Page of Table 67

		LM	VT	XC	VT	LM		VT	LM	LM	VT	VT	VT	XC	LM	VT		LM	XC	LM	VT	LM	VT	VT	XC
			◇1	◇1	◇1	1		◇1	1		◇1	◇1	◇1	◇1	1	◇1		1	◇1	1	◇1	1	◇1	◇1	◇1
		🚌	☕	🛒	☕			☕			☕	⊠	☕	🛒		☕			🛒		☕		☕	☕	🛒
London Euston 15 ⊖66	d		16 33		16 40			16 43	16 46		17 07	17 10	17 10			17 40					17 43	17 46	18 07	18 10	
Watford Junction 66	d																								
Milton Keynes Central 66	d							17 13	17 19			17u40	17 41								18 13	18 19		18 41	
Northampton 68	d																								
Rugby	d								17 42													18 42			
Coventry	d							17 42		17 42				17 27							18 42				18 27
Bedworth	d									17 53															
Nuneaton	a								17 53	18 00	18 02											18 53			
	d								17 54		18 03											18 54			
Atherstone	d								18 00													19 00			
Polesworth	d																								
Tamworth	d		17 38						18 09													19 09			
Lichfield Trent Valley	d		17 45						18 17													19 17			
Rugeley Trent Valley	d								18 25									←				19 25			
Stafford	d	17 40	17a58	18 01		18 10			18 39		18 27			18 30	18 36			18 39	19 01	19 10		19 39	19 23		19 30
Norton Bridge Station Drv	d	18a04							→													→			
Stone	d																	18 50							
Stone Crown Street	d																								
Stone Granville Square	a																								
Barlaston Orchard Place	d																								
Wedgwood Old Road Bridge	d																								
Stoke-on-Trent 50	d			18a19										18a54				19 02	19a19						19a54
Hanley Bus Station	a																								
Kidsgrove 50	d																	19 10							
Alsager 50	d																	19 14							
Crewe 65,50	a				18 10	18 30		19 07			18 45	18 49	18 49		18 56	19 10		19 24		19 30	20 07		19 41	19 47	

		LM		LM	LM	VT	XC	VT	VT	LM	VT	XC		LM	LM	VT	LM	VT	VT	XC	LM	XC		VT	VT
				1	1	◇1	◇1	◇1	◇1	1	◇1	◇1			1	◇1	1	◇1	◇1	◇1	1	◇1		◇1	◇1
						☕	🛒	☕	☕		☕					☕		☕	☕					☕	☕
London Euston 15 ⊖66	d					18 33		18 40	18 43	18 46	19 07					19 30			19 40					20 11	20 20
Watford Junction 66	d																								
Milton Keynes Central 66	d								19 13	19 19															21 05
Northampton 68	d																								
Rugby	d									19 42														21 15	
Coventry	d	18 42							19 42			19 27		20 15								20 27			
Bedworth	d	18 53												20 26											
Nuneaton	a	19 00								19 53	20 02			20 34											21 32
	d									19 58	20 03														21 33
Atherstone	d									20 04															
Polesworth	d																								
Tamworth	d					19 38				20 14															
Lichfield Trent Valley	d					19 45				20 21															
Rugeley Trent Valley	d				←					20 29							←	←							
Stafford	d			19 36	19 39	19a58	20 01		20 52	20 42	20 27	20 30			20 38		20 42	20 52		21 01	21 10	21 30		21 46	
Norton Bridge Station Drv	d								→	→															
Stone	d				19 50												20 52								
Stone Crown Street	d																								
Stone Granville Square	a																								
Barlaston Orchard Place	d																								
Wedgwood Old Road Bridge	d																								
Stoke-on-Trent 50	d				20 02		20a19					20a54					21 02			21a20		21a52			22a05
Hanley Bus Station	a																								
Kidsgrove 50	d				20 10												21 10								
Alsager 50	d				20 14												21 14								
Crewe 65,50	a			19 56	20 24			20 10			20 45				20 58	21 04	21 24	21 10	21 18		21 30			22 05	

		VT	LM	XC	VT	XC	LM	LM
		◇1	1	◇1	◇1	◇1		1
		☕			☕			
London Euston 15 ⊖66	d	20 31			21 00			
Watford Junction 66	d	20u46						
Milton Keynes Central 66	d				21 45			
Northampton 68	d							
Rugby	d	21 36						
Coventry	d			21 27			21 45	
Bedworth	d						21 56	
Nuneaton	a						22 03	
	d							
Atherstone	d							
Polesworth	d							
Tamworth	d	21 53						
Lichfield Trent Valley	d	22 00						
Rugeley Trent Valley	d							
Stafford	d		22 16	22 30	22 34	23 02		23 22
Norton Bridge Station Drv	d							
Stone	d							
Stone Crown Street	d							
Stone Granville Square	a							
Barlaston Orchard Place	d							
Wedgwood Old Road Bridge	d							
Stoke-on-Trent 50	d			22a50		23a20		
Hanley Bus Station	a							
Kidsgrove 50	d							
Alsager 50	d							
Crewe 65,50	a	22 35	22 38		22 58			23 42

Table 67

Sundays

8 December to 29 December

London - Stoke-on-Trent and Crewe
Coventry - Nuneaton

Network Diagram - refer to first Page of Table 67

		VT	XC	VT	VT	LM	VT	XC	LM	VT		LM	VT	XC	LM	VT	LM	LM	LM	VT		LM	XC	VT	LM
		◇1	◇1	◇1	◇1	1	◇1	◇1	1	◇1		1	◇1	◇1	1	◇1		1	1	◇1		1	◇1	◇1	1
		☕	🛒	☕	☕		☕	🛒		☕			☕	🛒		☕				☕			🛒	☕	
London Euston 15 ⊖66	d			08 10	08 15		08 45			09 15			09 45		09 54	10 15			10 24	10 45				11 15	
Watford Junction 66	d														10 10				10 40						
Milton Keynes Central 66	d			08 56			09 32						10 33		10 50				11 20	11 33				12 04	
Northampton 68	d								09 38						11 08				11 40						
Rugby	d						10 09		10 00				11 09		11 30				12 03	12 09					
Coventry	d													10 28			11 55						11 29		
Bedworth	d																12 06								
Nuneaton	a				09 43				10 13	10 44					11 42	11 46	12 13		12 16						
	d				09 44				10 14	10 45					11 43	11 47			12 17						
Atherstone	d								10 20						11 49				12 23						
Polesworth	d																								
Tamworth	d								10 29						11 57				12 32						
Lichfield Trent Valley	d								10 35						12 04				12 38						
Rugeley Trent Valley	d								10 43						12 11				12 46			←			←
Stafford	d	09 17	09 33		10 08	10 17		10 33	10 57	11 09		11 17		11 33	12 21	12 14		12 17	13 00			12 21	12 33	12 53	13 00
Norton Bridge Station Drv	d														→				→						
Stone	d								11 07													12 31			13 10
Stone Crown Street	d																								
Stone Granville Square	a																								
Barlaston Orchard Place	d																								
Wedgwood Old Road Bridge	d																								
Stoke-on-Trent 50	d							10a51	11 16					11a51								12 40	12a52		13 20
Hanley Bus Station	a																								
Kidsgrove 50	d								11 24													12 48			13 28
Alsager 50	d								11 28													12 52			13 32
Crewe 65,50	a	09 35	09 54	10 17	10 28	10 37	10 55		11 43	11 30		11 37	11 55			12 32		12 37		12 56		13 02		13 13	13 43

		LM	LM	VT	XC	VT		LM	LM	VT	LM	LM	VT	XC	VT	LM		LM	VT	LM	LM	VT	XC	VT	LM
		1	1	◇1	◇1	◇1		1	1	◇1		1	◇1	◇1	◇1	1		1	◇1		1	◇1	◇1	◇1	1
				☕	🛒	☕				☕			☕	🛒	☕				☕			☕	🛒	☕	
London Euston 15 ⊖66	d		11 24	12 05		12 37				12 40		12 50	13 05		13 37				13 40		13 50	14 05		14 37	
Watford Junction 66	d		11 42									13 06									14 06				
Milton Keynes Central 66	d		12 28							13 13		13 37							14 13		14 37				
Northampton 68	d		13 02									14 02									15 02				
Rugby	d		13 26									14 26									15 26				
Coventry	d				12 28					13 42	13 46			13 26					14 44	14 46			14 26		
Bedworth	d										13 57									14 57					
Nuneaton	a		13 40								14 04	14 39								15 04	15 39				
	d		13 40									14 40									15 40				
Atherstone	d		13 46									14 46									15 46				
Polesworth	d																								
Tamworth	d		13 55									14 55									15 55				
Lichfield Trent Valley	d		14 01									15 01									16 01				
Rugeley Trent Valley	d		14 09						←			15 09						←			16 09				
Stafford	d	13 09	14 19	13 25	13 34			14 09	14 19			15 20	14 24	14 34		15 09		15 20			16 20	15 25	15 34		16 09
Norton Bridge Station Drv	d		→									→									→				
Stone	d								14 29									15 30							
Stone Crown Street	d																								
Stone Granville Square	a																								
Barlaston Orchard Place	d																								
Wedgwood Old Road Bridge	d																								
Stoke-on-Trent 50	d				13a56				14 37					14a56				15 41					15a56		
Hanley Bus Station	a																								
Kidsgrove 50	d								14 45									15 49							
Alsager 50	d								14 50									15 53							
Crewe 65,50	a	13 30		13 43		14 12		14 29	15 00	15 07			14 43		15 12	15 29		16 03	16 07			15 43		16 12	16 30

		LM		VT	LM	LM	VT	VT	XC	VT	LM	LM		VT	LM	LM	VT	VT	XC	VT	LM	VT		LM	VT
		1		◇1		1	◇1	◇1	◇1	◇1	1	1		◇1		1	◇1	◇1	◇1	◇1	1	◇1		1	◇1
				☕			☕	☕	🛒	☕				☕			☕	☕	🛒	☕		☕			☕
London Euston 15 ⊖66	d			14 40		14 50	15 05	15 08		15 37				15 40		15 50	16 05	16 08		16 37		16 40		16 50	17 05
Watford Junction 66	d					15 06										16 06								17 06	
Milton Keynes Central 66	d			15 13		15 37		15 42						16 13		16 37		16 42				17 13		17 37	
Northampton 68	d					16 02										17 02								18 02	
Rugby	d					16 26										17 26								18 26	
Coventry	d			15 42	15 46				15 26					16 42	16 46				16 26			17 44			
Bedworth	d				15 57										16 57										
Nuneaton	a				16 04	16 39									17 04	17 39								18 39	18 03
	d					16 40										17 40								18 40	18 04
Atherstone	d					16 46										17 46								18 46	
Polesworth	d																								
Tamworth	d					16 55										17 55								18 55	
Lichfield Trent Valley	d					17 01										18 01								19 01	
Rugeley Trent Valley	d	←				17 09						←				18 09								19 09	
Stafford	d	16 20				17 20	16 25		16 34		17 09	17 20				18 20	17 25		17 36		18 09			19 20	
Norton Bridge Station Drv	d					→										→								→	
Stone	d	16 30										17 30													
Stone Crown Street	d																								
Stone Granville Square	a																								
Barlaston Orchard Place	d																								
Wedgwood Old Road Bridge	d																								
Stoke-on-Trent 50	d	16 41							16a56			17 41							17a56						
Hanley Bus Station	a																								
Kidsgrove 50	d	16 49										17 49													
Alsager 50	d	16 53										17 53													
Crewe 65,50	a	17 03		17 07			16 43	16 50		17 12	17 30	18 03		18 07			17 43	17 50		18 12	18 30	19 06			18 44

Table 67

Sundays

8 December to 29 December

London - Stoke-on-Trent and Crewe
Coventry - Nuneaton

Network Diagram - refer to first Page of Table 67

	LM	VT	XC	VT	LM	LM	LM		VT	LM	VT	VT	XC	VT	LM	LM	VT		LM	VT	VT	XC	VT	VT
									R															
	1	◇1	◇1	◇1		1	1		1	1	◇1	◇1	◇1	◇1	1	1	◇1		1	◇1	◇1	◇1	◇1	◇1
		⊐P	⊤	⊐P					⊐P		⊐P	⊐P	⊤	⊐P			⊐P			⊐P	⊐P	⊤	⊐P	⊐P
London Euston 15 ⊖66 d		17 08		17 37					17 40	17 50	18 05	18 08		18 37			18 40		18 50	19 05	19 08			19 37
Watford Junction 66 d										18 06									19 06					
Milton Keynes Central 66 d		17 42							18 13	18 37		18 42					19 13		19 37		19 42			
Northampton 68 d										19 02									20 02					
Rugby d										19 26									20 26					
Coventry d			17 26		17 46				18 44				18 26				19 42					19 26		
Bedworth d					17 57																			
Nuneaton a					18 04					19 39									20 39	20 03				
d										19 40									20 40	20 04				
Atherstone d										19 46									20 46					
Polesworth d																								
Tamworth d										19 55									20 55					
Lichfield Trent Valley d										20 01									21 01					
Rugeley Trent Valley d	←						←			20 09						←			21 09				←	
Stafford d	18 20	18 35	18 36			19 09	19 20			20 20	19 25		19 38		20 09	20 20	20 53		21 20	20 29		20 37	20 53	
Norton Bridge Station Drv d										↦							↦		↦					
Stone d	18 30						19 30									20 30								
Stone Crown Street d																								
Stone Granville Square a																								
Barlaston Orchard Place d																								
Wedgwood Old Road Bridge d																								
Stoke-on-Trent 50 d	18 45		18a56				19 45						19a56			20 45						20a56		
Hanley Bus Station a																								
Kidsgrove 50 d	18 53						19 53									20 53								
Alsager 50 d	18 57						19 57									20 57								
Crewe 65,50 a	19 07	18 53		19 12		19 29	20 07		20 07		19 43	19 50		20 12	20 30	21 07				20 47	20 50		21 10	21 13

	LM	VT	LM		VT	LM	VT	VT	XC	VT	VT	LM	VT		LM	XC	LM	VT	AW	VT
		◇1	1		◇1	1	◇1	◇1	◇1	◇1	◇1	1	◇1		1	◇1		◇1	◇	◇1
		⊐P			⊐P		⊐P	⊐P		⊐P	⊐P		⊐P					⊐P		⊐P
London Euston 15 ⊖66 d		19 40	19 50		20 05		20 08	20 25			20 35		20 50					21 21		21 51
Watford Junction 66 d			20 06																	
Milton Keynes Central 66 d		20 13	20 37				20 41						21 37							22 39
Northampton 68 d			21 06																	
Rugby d			21 30										22 01							23 19
Coventry d	19 46	20 41							20 26							21 26	21 35			
Bedworth d	19 57																21 46			
Nuneaton a	20 04		21 42		21 03												21 53	22 51		23 29
d			21 43		21 04													22 52		23 30
Atherstone d			21 49																	
Polesworth d															←					
Tamworth d			21 58					21 32							21 58					
Lichfield Trent Valley d			↦					21 39							22 04					
Rugeley Trent Valley d						←				←					22 12					
Stafford d		21 56				21 20	21 33		21 37	21 56	22 00	22 16			22 26	22 37		23 17	23 31	23s55
Norton Bridge Station Drv d		↦																		
Stone d						21 30									22 36					
Stone Crown Street d																				
Stone Granville Square a																				
Barlaston Orchard Place d																				
Wedgwood Old Road Bridge d																				
Stoke-on-Trent 50 d						21 45			21a56						22 45	22a55				
Hanley Bus Station a																				
Kidsgrove 50 d						21 53									22 53					
Alsager 50 d						21 57									22 57					
Crewe 65,50 a					21 44	22 07	21 53	22 10		22 15	22 20	22 38	22 49		23 07			23 43	23 57	00s21

Table 67

Sundays

5 January to 9 February

London - Stoke-on-Trent and Crewe
Coventry - Nuneaton

Network Diagram - refer to first Page of Table 67

	VT	XC	VT	VT	LM		VT	XC	LM	VT	LM	XC	LM	VT	LM		LM	XC	LM	LM	VT	LM	LM	LM
	◇1	◇1	◇1	◇1	1		◇1	◇1	1	◇1	1	◇1	1	◇1	1		1	◇1		1	◇1	1	1	1
	☕	🛒	☕	☕			☕	🛒		☕		🛒		☕				🛒			☕			
London Euston 15 ⊖66 d			08 10	08 15			08 45			09 15			09 54	10 15						10 24	11 15			11 24
Watford Junction 66 d													10 10							10 40				11 42
Milton Keynes Central 66 d			08 56				09 32						10 50							11 20	12 04			12 28
Northampton 68 d									09 38				11 08							11 40				13 02
Rugby d							10 09		10 00				11 30							12 03				13 26
Coventry d												10 28						11 29	11 55					
Bedworth d																			12 06					
Nuneaton a				09 43					10 13	10 44			11 42	11 46					12 13	12 16				13 40
d				09 44					10 14	10 45			11 43	11 47						12 17				13 40
Atherstone d									10 20				11 49							12 23				13 46
Polesworth d																								
Tamworth d									10 29				11 57							12 32				13 55
Lichfield Trent Valley d									10 35				12 04							12 38				14 01
Rugeley Trent Valley d									10 43				12 11				←			12 46		←		14 09
Stafford d	09 17	09 33		10 08	10 17			10 33	10 57	11 09	11 17	11 33	12 21	12 14	12 17		12 21	12 33		13 00	12 53	13 00	13 09	14 19
Norton Bridge Station Drv d													↪							↪				↪
Stone d									11 07								12 31					13 10		
Stone Crown Street d																								
Stone Granville Square a																								
Barlaston Orchard Place d																								
Wedgwood Old Road Bridge d																								
Stoke-on-Trent 50 d								10a51	11 16			11a51					12 40	12a52				13 20		
Hanley Bus Station a																								
Kidsgrove 50 d									11 24								12 48					13 28		
Alsager 50 d									11 28								12 52					13 32		
Crewe 65,50 a	09 35	09 54	10 17	10 28	10 37		10 55		11 43	11 30	11 37			12 32	12 37		13 02				13 13	13 43	13 30	

	VT		XC	VT	LM	LM	VT	LM	LM	VT	XC		VT	LM	LM	VT	LM	LM	VT	XC	VT		LM	LM
	◇1		◇1	◇1	1	1	◇1		1	◇1	◇1		◇1	1	1	◇1		1	◇1	◇1	◇1		1	1
	☕		🛒	☕			☕			☕	🛒		☕			☕			☕	🛒	☕			
London Euston 15 ⊖66 d	12 05			12 37			12 40		12 50	13 05			13 37			13 40		13 50	14 05		14 37			
Watford Junction 66 d									13 06									14 06						
Milton Keynes Central 66 d							13 13		13 37							14 13		14 37						
Northampton 68 d									14 02									15 02						
Rugby d									14 26									15 26						
Coventry d			12 28				13 42	13 46			13 26					14 44	14 46			14 26				
Bedworth d								13 57									14 57							
Nuneaton a								14 04	14 39								15 04	15 39						
d									14 40									15 40						
Atherstone d									14 46									15 46						
Polesworth d																								
Tamworth d									14 55									15 55						
Lichfield Trent Valley d									15 01									16 01						
Rugeley Trent Valley d						←			15 09						←			16 09						←
Stafford d	13 25		13 34		14 09	14 19			15 20	14 24	14 34			15 09	15 20			16 20	15 25	15 34			16 09	16 20
Norton Bridge Station Drv d									↪									↪						
Stone d						14 29									15 30									16 30
Stone Crown Street d																								
Stone Granville Square a																								
Barlaston Orchard Place d																								
Wedgwood Old Road Bridge d																								
Stoke-on-Trent 50 d			13a56			14 37					14a56				15 41					15a56				16 41
Hanley Bus Station a																								
Kidsgrove 50 d						14 45									15 49									16 49
Alsager 50 d						14 50									15 53									16 53
Crewe 65,50 a	13 43			14 12	14 29	15 00	15 07			14 43			15 12	15 29	16 03	16 07			15 43		16 12		16 30	17 03

	VT	LM	LM	VT	VT	XC	VT		LM	LM	VT	LM	LM	VT	VT	XC	VT		LM	VT	LM	VT	LM	VT
	◇1		1	◇1	◇1	◇1	◇1		1	1	◇1		1	◇1	◇1	◇1	◇1		1	◇1	1	◇1	1	◇1
	☕			☕	☕	🛒	☕				☕			☕	☕	🛒	☕			☕		☕		☕
London Euston 15 ⊖66 d	14 40		14 50	15 05	15 08		15 37				15 40		15 50	16 05	16 08		16 37			16 40	16 50	17 05		17 08
Watford Junction 66 d			15 06										16 06								17 06			
Milton Keynes Central 66 d	15 13		15 37		15 42						16 13		16 37		16 42					17 14	17 37			17 42
Northampton 68 d			16 02										17 02								18 02			
Rugby d			16 26										17 26								18 26			
Coventry d	15 42	15 46				15 26					16 42	16 46				16 26				17 43				
Bedworth d		15 57										16 57												
Nuneaton a		16 04	16 39									17 04	17 39								18 39	18 03		
d			16 40										17 40								18 40	18 04		
Atherstone d			16 46										17 46								18 46			
Polesworth d																								
Tamworth d			16 55										17 55								18 55			
Lichfield Trent Valley d			17 01										18 01								19 01			
Rugeley Trent Valley d			17 09							←			18 09								19 09		←	
Stafford d			17 20	16 25		16 34			17 09	17 20			18 20	17 25		17 36			18 09		19 20		18 20	18 35
Norton Bridge Station Drv d			↪										↪								↪			
Stone d										17 30													18 30	
Stone Crown Street d																								
Stone Granville Square a																								
Barlaston Orchard Place d																								
Wedgwood Old Road Bridge d																								
Stoke-on-Trent 50 d						16a56				17 41						17a56							18 45	
Hanley Bus Station a																								
Kidsgrove 50 d										17 49													18 53	
Alsager 50 d										17 53													18 57	
Crewe 65,50 a	17 07			16 43	16 50		17 12		17 30	18 03	18 07			17 43	17 50		18 12		18 30	19 06		18 44	19 07	18 53

Table 67

Sundays

5 January to 9 February

London - Stoke-on-Trent and Crewe
Coventry - Nuneaton

Network Diagram - refer to first Page of Table 67

	XC	VT	LM		LM	LM	VT	LM	VT	VT	XC	VT	LM		LM	VT	LM	VT	VT	XC	VT	VT	LM
	◇1	◇1			1	1	R 1	1	◇1	◇1	◇1	◇1	1		1	◇1	1	◇1	◇1	◇1	◇1	◇1	
	🛒	☕					☕		☕	☕	🛒	☕				☕		☕	☕	🛒	☕	☕	
London Euston 15 ⊖66 d		17 37					17 40	17 50	18 05	18 08		18 37				18 40	18 50	19 05	19 08			19 37	
Watford Junction 66 d								18 06									19 06						
Milton Keynes Central 66 d							18 13	18 37		18 42						19 13	19 37		19 42				
Northampton 68 d								19 02									20 02						
Rugby d								19 26									20 26						
Coventry d	17 26		17 46				18 44				18 26					19 42				19 26			19 46
Bedworth d			17 57																				19 57
Nuneaton a			18 04					19 39									20 39	20 03					20 04
d								19 40									20 40	20 04					
Atherstone d								19 46									20 46						
Polesworth d																							
Tamworth d								19 55									20 55						
Lichfield Trent Valley d								20 01									21 01						
Rugeley Trent Valley d						←		20 09							←		21 09				←		
Stafford d	18 36				19 09	19 20		20 20	19 25		19 38		20 09		20 20	20 53	21 20	20 29		20 37	20 53		
Norton Bridge Station Drv d								→								→	→						
Stone d						19 30									20 30								
Stone Crown Street d																							
Stone Granville Square a																							
Barlaston Orchard Place d																							
Wedgwood Old Road Bridge d																							
Stoke-on-Trent 50 d	18a56					19 45					19a56				20 45					20a56			
Hanley Bus Station a																							
Kidsgrove 50 d						19 53									20 53								
Alsager 50 d						19 57									20 57								
Crewe 65,50 a		19 12			19 29	20 07	20 07		19 43	19 50		20 12	20 30		21 07			20 47	20 50		21 10	21 13	

	VT	LM	VT	LM	VT	VT	XC	VT	VT		LM	VT	LM	XC	LM	VT	AW	VT
	◇1	1	◇1	1	◇1	◇1	◇1	◇1	◇1		1	◇1	1	◇1		◇1	◇	◇1
	☕		☕		☕	☕		☕	☕			☕				☕		☕
London Euston 15 ⊖66 d	19 40	19 50	20 05		20 08	20 25			20 35			20 50				21 21		21 51
Watford Junction 66 d		20 06																
Milton Keynes Central 66 d	20 13	20 37			20 41							21 37						22 39
Northampton 68 d		21 06																
Rugby d		21 30										22 01						23 19
Coventry d	20 42						20 26							21 26	21 35			
Bedworth d															21 46			
Nuneaton a		21 42	21 03												21 53	22 51		23 29
d		21 43	21 04													22 52		23 30
Atherstone d		21 49																
Polesworth d													←					
Tamworth d		21 58				21 32							21 58					
Lichfield Trent Valley d		→				21 39							22 04					
Rugeley Trent Valley d				←				←					22 12					
Stafford d	21 57			21 20	21 33		21 37	21 57	22 00		22 16		22 26	22 37		23 17	23 31	23s55
Norton Bridge Station Drv d	→																	
Stone d				21 30									22 36					
Stone Crown Street d																		
Stone Granville Square a																		
Barlaston Orchard Place d																		
Wedgwood Old Road Bridge d																		
Stoke-on-Trent 50 d				21 45			21a56						22 45	22a55				
Hanley Bus Station a																		
Kidsgrove 50 d				21 53									22 53					
Alsager 50 d				21 57									22 57					
Crewe 65,50 a			21 44	22 07	21 53	22 10		22 16	22 20		22 38	22 49	23 07			23 43	23 57	00s21

Table 67

Sundays

16 February to 23 March

London - Stoke-on-Trent and Crewe
Coventry - Nuneaton

Network Diagram - refer to first Page of Table 67

	VT	XC	VT	VT	LM		XC	LM	VT	LM	VT	XC	LM	VT	LM		LM	LM	VT	LM	XC	VT	LM	LM
	◇1	◇1	◇1	◇1	1		◇1	1	◇1	1	◇1	◇1	1	◇1			1	1	◇1	1	◇1	◇1	1	1
	☕	🛒	☕	☕			🛒		☕		☕	🛒		☕					☕		🛒	☕		
London Euston 15 ⊖66 d			08 10	08 15					09 15		09 45		09 54	10 15				10 24	10 45			11 15		
Watford Junction 66 d													10 10					10 40						
Milton Keynes Central 66 d			08 56								10 33		10 50					11 20	11 33			12 04		
Northampton 68 d								09 38					11 08					11 40						
Rugby d								10 00			11 09		11 30					12 03	12 09					
Coventry d												10 28			11 55						11 29			
Bedworth d															12 06									
Nuneaton a				09 43				10 13	10 44				11 42	11 46	12 13			12 16						
d				09 44				10 14	10 45				11 43	11 47				12 17						
Atherstone d								10 20					11 49					12 23						
Polesworth d																								
Tamworth d								10 29					11 57					12 32						
Lichfield Trent Valley d								10 35					12 04					12 38						
Rugeley Trent Valley d								10 43					12 11					12 46		←			←	
Stafford d	09 17	09 33		10 08	10 17		10 33	10 57	11 09	11 17		11 33	12 21	12 14			12 17	13 00		12 21	12 33	12 53	13 00	13 09
Norton Bridge Station Drv d													→					→						
Stone d								11 07												12 31			13 10	
Stone Crown Street d																								
Stone Granville Square a																								
Barlaston Orchard Place d																								
Wedgwood Old Road Bridge d																								
Stoke-on-Trent 50 d							10a51	11 16				11a51								12 40	12a52		13 20	
Hanley Bus Station a																								
Kidsgrove 50 d								11 24												12 48			13 28	
Alsager 50 d								11 28												12 52			13 32	
Crewe 65,50 a	09 35	09 54	10 17	10 28	10 37			11 43	11 30	11 37	11 55			12 32			12 37		12 56	13 02		13 13	13 43	13 30

	LM		VT	XC	VT	LM	LM	VT	LM	LM	VT		XC	VT	LM	LM	VT	LM	LM	VT	XC		VT	LM
	1		◇1	◇1	◇1	1	1	◇1		1	◇1		◇1	◇1	1	1	◇1		1	◇1	◇1		◇1	1
			☕	🛒	☕			☕			☕		🛒	☕			☕			☕	🛒		☕	
London Euston 15 ⊖66 d	11 24		12 05		12 37			12 40		12 50	13 05			13 37			13 40		13 50	14 05			14 37	
Watford Junction 66 d	11 42									13 06									14 06					
Milton Keynes Central 66 d	12 28							13 13		13 37							14 13		14 37					
Northampton 68 d	13 02									14 02									15 02					
Rugby d	13 26									14 26									15 26					
Coventry d				12 28				13 42	13 46				13 28				14 44	14 46			14 28			
Bedworth d									13 57									14 57						
Nuneaton a	13 40								14 04	14 39								15 04	15 39					
d	13 40									14 40									15 40					
Atherstone d	13 46									14 46									15 46					
Polesworth d																								
Tamworth d	13 55									14 55									15 55					
Lichfield Trent Valley d	14 01									15 01									16 01					
Rugeley Trent Valley d	14 09						←			15 09						←			16 09					
Stafford d	14 19		13 25	13 33		14 09	14 19			15 20	14 24		14 34		15 09	15 20			16 20	15 25	15 33			16 09
Norton Bridge Station Drv d	→									→									→					
Stone d							14 29									15 30								
Stone Crown Street d																								
Stone Granville Square a																								
Barlaston Orchard Place d																								
Wedgwood Old Road Bridge d																								
Stoke-on-Trent 50 d				13a55			14 37						14a56			15 41					15a55			
Hanley Bus Station a																								
Kidsgrove 50 d							14 45									15 49								
Alsager 50 d							14 50									15 53								
Crewe 65,50 a			13 43		14 12	14 29	15 00	15 07			14 43			15 12	15 29	16 03	16 07			15 43			16 12	16 30

	LM	VT	LM	LM	VT	VT	XC		VT	LM	LM	VT	LM	LM	VT	VT	XC		VT	LM	VT	LM	VT	LM
	1	◇1		1	◇1	◇1	◇1		◇1	1	1	◇1		1	◇1	◇1	◇1		◇1	1	◇1	1	◇1	1
		☕			☕	☕	🛒		☕			☕			☕	☕	🛒		☕		☕		☕	
London Euston 15 ⊖66 d		14 40		14 50	15 05	15 08			15 37			15 40		15 50	16 05	16 08			16 37		16 40	16 50	17 05	
Watford Junction 66 d				15 06										16 06								17 06		
Milton Keynes Central 66 d		15 13		15 37		15 42						16 13		16 37		16 42					17 13	17 37		
Northampton 68 d				16 02										17 02								18 02		
Rugby d				16 26										17 26								18 26		
Coventry d		15 42	15 46				15 27					16 42	16 46				16 28				17 44			
Bedworth d			15 57										16 57											
Nuneaton a			16 04	16 39									17 04	17 39								18 39	18 03	
d				16 40										17 40								18 40	18 04	
Atherstone d				16 46										17 46								18 46		
Polesworth d																								
Tamworth d				16 55										17 55								18 55		
Lichfield Trent Valley d				17 01										18 01								19 01		
Rugeley Trent Valley d	←			17 09							←			18 09								19 09		←
Stafford d	16 20			17 20	16 25		16 34			17 09	17 20			18 20	17 25		17 36			18 09		19 20		18 20
Norton Bridge Station Drv d				→										→								→		
Stone d	16 30										17 30													18 30
Stone Crown Street d																								
Stone Granville Square a																								
Barlaston Orchard Place d																								
Wedgwood Old Road Bridge d																								
Stoke-on-Trent 50 d	16 41						16a56				17 41						17a56							18 45
Hanley Bus Station a																								
Kidsgrove 50 d	16 49										17 49													18 53
Alsager 50 d	16 53										17 53													18 57
Crewe 65,50 a	17 03	17 07			16 43	16 50			17 12	17 30	18 03	18 07			17 43	17 50			18 12	18 30	19 06		18 44	19 07

Table 67

Sundays

16 February to 23 March

London - Stoke-on-Trent and Crewe
Coventry - Nuneaton

Network Diagram - refer to first Page of Table 67

Station			VT	XC	VT		LM	LM	LM	VT	LM	VT	VT	XC	VT		LM	LM	VT	LM	VT	VT	XC	VT	VT	
			◇1	◇1	◇1			1	1	R 1	1	◇1	◇1	◇1	◇1		1	1	◇1	1	◇1	◇1	◇1	◇1	◇1	
			☕	🍴	☕					☕		☕	☕	🍴	☕				☕		☕	☕	🍴	☕	☕	
London Euston 15	⊖66	d	17 08		17 37					17 40	17 50	18 05	18 08		18 37				18 40	18 50	19 05	19 08			19 37	
Watford Junction	66	d									18 06									19 06						
Milton Keynes Central	66	d	17 42							18 13	18 37		18 42						19 13	19 37		19 42				
Northampton	68	d									19 02									20 02						
Rugby		d									19 26									20 26						
Coventry		d		17 28			17 46			18 44				18 28					19 42				19 28			
Bedworth		d					17 57																			
Nuneaton		a					18 04				19 39									20 39	20 03					
		d									19 40									20 40	20 04					
Atherstone		d									19 46									20 46						
Polesworth		d																								
Tamworth		d									19 55									20 55						
Lichfield Trent Valley		d									20 01									21 01						
Rugeley Trent Valley		d							←		20 09							←		21 09				←		
Stafford		d	18 35	18 36				19 09	19 20		20 20	19 25		19 38			20 09	20 20	20 53	21 20	20 29		20 37	20 53		
Norton Bridge Station Drv		d									→								→	→						
Stone		d							19 30									20 30								
Stone Crown Street		d																								
Stone Granville Square		a																								
Barlaston Orchard Place		d																								
Wedgwood Old Road Bridge		d																								
Stoke-on-Trent	50	d		18a56					19 45					19a56				20 45					20a56			
Hanley Bus Station		a																								
Kidsgrove	50	d							19 53									20 53								
Alsager	50	d							19 57									20 57								
Crewe	65,50	a	18 53		19 12			19 29	20 07	20 07		19 43	19 50		20 12		20 30	21 07			20 47	20 50		21 10	21 13	

Station			LM	VT	LM	VT	LM	VT	VT	XC	VT		VT	LM	VT	LM	XC	LM	VT	AW	VT
				◇1	1	◇1	1	◇1	◇1	◇1	◇1		◇1	1	◇1	1	◇1		◇1	◇	◇1
				☕		☕		☕	☕		☕		☕		☕				☕		☕
London Euston 15	⊖66	d		19 40	19 50	20 05		20 08	20 25				20 35		20 50				21 21		21 51
Watford Junction	66	d			20 06																
Milton Keynes Central	66	d		20 13	20 37			20 41							21 37						22 39
Northampton	68	d			21 06																
Rugby		d			21 30										22 01						23 19
Coventry		d	19 46	20 41						20 28							21 29	21 35			
Bedworth		d	19 57															21 46			
Nuneaton		a	20 04		21 42	21 03												21 53	22 51		23 29
		d			21 43	21 04													22 52		23 30
Atherstone		d			21 49																
Polesworth		d														←					
Tamworth		d			21 58				21 32							21 58					
Lichfield Trent Valley		d			→				21 39							22 04					
Rugeley Trent Valley		d					←				←					22 12					
Stafford		d		21 56			21 20	21 33		21 37	21 56		22 00	22 16		22 26	22 37		23 17	23 31	23s55
Norton Bridge Station Drv		d		→																	
Stone		d					21 30									22 36					
Stone Crown Street		d																			
Stone Granville Square		a																			
Barlaston Orchard Place		d																			
Wedgwood Old Road Bridge		d																			
Stoke-on-Trent	50	d					21 45			21a56						22 45	22a55				
Hanley Bus Station		a																			
Kidsgrove	50	d					21 53									22 53					
Alsager	50	d					21 57									22 57					
Crewe	65,50	a				21 44	22 07	21 53	22 10		22 15		22 20	22 38	22 49	23 07			23 43	23 57	00s21

Table 67

Sundays
30 March to 11 May

London - Stoke-on-Trent and Crewe Coventry - Nuneaton

Network Diagram - refer to first Page of Table 67

	VT	XC	VT	VT	LM		VT	XC	LM	VT	LM	VT	XC	LM	VT		LM	LM	LM	VT	LM	XC	VT	LM
	◇1	◇1	◇1	◇1	1		◇1	◇1	1	◇1	1	◇1	◇1	1	◇1			1	1	◇1	1	◇1	◇1	1
London Euston 15 ⊖66 d			08 10	08 15			08 45			09 15		09 45		09 54	10 15				10 24	10 45			11 15	
Watford Junction 66 d														10 10					10 40					
Milton Keynes Central 66 d			08 56				09 32					10 33		10 50					11 20	11 33			12 04	
Northampton 68 d									09 38					11 08					11 40					
Rugby d							10 09		10 00			11 09		11 30					12 03	12 09				
Coventry d													10 28				11 55					11 29		
Bedworth d																	12 06							
Nuneaton a				09 43					10 13	10 44				11 42	11 46		12 13		12 16					
d				09 44					10 14	10 45				11 43	11 47				12 17					
Atherstone d									10 20					11 49					12 23					
Polesworth d																								
Tamworth d									10 29					11 57					12 32					
Lichfield Trent Valley d									10 35					12 04					12 38					
Rugeley Trent Valley d									10 43					12 11					12 46		←			←
Stafford d	09 17	09 33		10 08	10 17			10 33	10 57	11 09	11 17		11 33	12 21	12 14			12 17	13 00		12 21	12 33	12 53	13 00
Norton Bridge Station Drv d														↳					↳					
Stone d									11 07												12 31			13 10
Stone Crown Street d																								
Stone Granville Square a																								
Barlaston Orchard Place d																								
Wedgwood Old Road Bridge d																								
Stoke-on-Trent 50 d								10a51	11 16				11a51								12 40	12a52		13 20
Hanley Bus Station a																								
Kidsgrove 50 d									11 24												12 48			13 28
Alsager 50 d									11 28												12 52			13 32
Crewe 65,50 a	09 35	09 54	10 17	10 28	10 37		10 55		11 43	11 30	11 37	11 55			12 32			12 37		12 56	13 02		13 13	13 43

	LM		LM	VT	XC	VT	LM	LM	VT	LM	LM		VT	XC	VT	LM	LM	VT	LM	LM	VT		XC	VT
	1		1	◇1	◇1	◇1	1	1	◇1		1		◇1	◇1	◇1	1	1	◇1		1	◇1		◇1	◇1
London Euston 15 ⊖66 d			11 24	12 05		12 37			12 40		12 50		13 05		13 37			13 40		13 50	14 05			14 37
Watford Junction 66 d			11 42								13 06									14 06				
Milton Keynes Central 66 d			12 28						13 13		13 37							14 13		14 37				
Northampton 68 d			13 02								14 02									15 02				
Rugby d			13 26								14 26									15 26				
Coventry d					12 28				13 42	13 46				13 26				14 44	14 46				14 26	
Bedworth d										13 57									14 57					
Nuneaton a			13 40							14 04	14 39								15 04	15 39				
d			13 40								14 40									15 40				
Atherstone d			13 46								14 46									15 46				
Polesworth d																								
Tamworth d			13 55								14 55									15 55				
Lichfield Trent Valley d			14 01								15 01									16 01				
Rugeley Trent Valley d			14 09					←			15 09						←			16 09				
Stafford d	13 09		14 19	13 25	13 34		14 09	14 19			15 20		14 24	14 34		15 09	15 20			16 20	15 25		15 34	
Norton Bridge Station Drv d			↳								↳									↳				
Stone d								14 29									15 30							
Stone Crown Street d																								
Stone Granville Square a																								
Barlaston Orchard Place d																								
Wedgwood Old Road Bridge d																								
Stoke-on-Trent 50 d					13a56			14 37						14a56			15 41						15a56	
Hanley Bus Station a																								
Kidsgrove 50 d								14 45									15 49							
Alsager 50 d								14 50									15 53							
Crewe 65,50 a	13 30			13 43		14 12	14 29	15 00	15 07				14 43		15 12	15 29	16 03	16 07			15 43			16 12

	LM	LM	VT	LM	LM	VT	VT		XC	VT	LM	LM	VT	LM	LM	VT	VT		XC	VT	LM	VT	LM	VT
	1	1	◇1		1	◇1	◇1		◇1	◇1	1	1	◇1		1	◇1	◇1		◇1	◇1	1	◇1	1	◇1
London Euston 15 ⊖66 d			14 40		14 50	15 05	15 08			15 37			15 40		15 50	16 05	16 08			16 37		16 40	16 50	17 05
Watford Junction 66 d					15 06										16 06								17 06	
Milton Keynes Central 66 d			15 13		15 37		15 42						16 13		16 37		16 42					17 13	17 37	
Northampton 68 d					16 02										17 02								18 02	
Rugby d					16 26										17 26								18 26	
Coventry d			15 42	15 46					15 26				16 42	16 46					16 26			17 44		
Bedworth d				15 57										16 57										
Nuneaton a				16 04	16 39									17 04	17 39								18 39	18 03
d					16 40										17 40								18 40	18 04
Atherstone d					16 46										17 46								18 46	
Polesworth d																								
Tamworth d					16 55										17 55								18 55	
Lichfield Trent Valley d					17 01										18 01								19 01	
Rugeley Trent Valley d		←			17 09							←			18 09								19 09	
Stafford d	16 09	16 20			17 20	16 25			16 34		17 09	17 20			18 20	17 25			17 36		18 09		19 20	
Norton Bridge Station Drv d					↳										↳								↳	
Stone d		16 30										17 30												
Stone Crown Street d																								
Stone Granville Square a																								
Barlaston Orchard Place d																								
Wedgwood Old Road Bridge d																								
Stoke-on-Trent 50 d		16 41							16a56			17 41							17a56					
Hanley Bus Station a																								
Kidsgrove 50 d		16 49										17 49												
Alsager 50 d		16 53										17 53												
Crewe 65,50 a	16 30	17 03	17 07			16 43	16 50			17 12	17 30	18 03	18 07			17 43	17 50			18 12	18 30	19 06		18 44

Table 67

Sundays

30 March to 11 May

London - Stoke-on-Trent and Crewe
Coventry - Nuneaton

Network Diagram - refer to first Page of Table 67

	LM	VT	XC		VT	LM	LM	LM	VT	LM	VT	VT	XC		VT	LM	LM	VT	LM	VT	VT	XC	VT	
	1	◇1	◇1		◇1		1	1	R 1	1	◇1	◇1	◇1		◇1	1	1	◇1	1	◇1	◇1	◇1	◇1	
		☕	🛒		☕				☕		☕	☕	🛒		☕			☕		☕	☕	🛒	☕	
London Euston 15 ⊖66 d		17 08			17 37				17 40	17 50	18 05	18 08			18 37			18 40	18 50	19 05	19 08			
Watford Junction 66 d										18 06									19 06					
Milton Keynes Central 66 d		17 42							18 13	18 37		18 42						19 13	19 37		19 42			
Northampton 68 d										19 02									20 02					
Rugby d										19 26									20 26					
Coventry d			17 26			17 46			18 44				18 26					19 42				19 26		
Bedworth d						17 57																		
Nuneaton a						18 04				19 39									20 39	20 03				
d										19 40									20 40	20 04				
Atherstone d										19 46									20 46					
Polesworth d																								
Tamworth d										19 55									20 55					
Lichfield Trent Valley d										20 01									21 01					
Rugeley Trent Valley d	←							←		20 09							←		21 09				←	
Stafford d	18 20	18 35	18 36				19 09	19 20		20 20	19 25		19 38			20 09	20 20	20 53	21 20	20 29		20 37	20 53	
Norton Bridge Station Drv d										→								→	→					
Stone d	18 30							19 30									20 30							
Stone Crown Street d																								
Stone Granville Square a																								
Barlaston Orchard Place d																								
Wedgwood Old Road Bridge d																								
Stoke-on-Trent 50 d	18 45		18a56					19 45					19a56				20 45					20a56		
Hanley Bus Station a																								
Kidsgrove 50 d	18 53							19 53									20 53							
Alsager 50 d	18 57							19 57									20 57							
Crewe 65,50 a	19 07	18 53			19 12		19 29	20 07	20 07		19 43	19 50			20 12	20 30	21 07			20 47	20 50		21 10	

	VT	LM	VT	LM	VT	LM	VT	VT	XC		VT	VT	LM	VT	LM	XC	LM	VT	AW		VT			
	◇1		◇1	1	◇1	1	◇1	◇1	◇1		◇1	◇1	1	◇1	1	◇1		◇1	◇		◇1			
	☕		☕		☕		☕	☕			☕	☕		☕				☕			☕			
London Euston 15 ⊖66 d	19 37		19 40	19 50	20 05		20 08	20 25				20 35		20 50				21 21			21 51			
Watford Junction 66 d				20 06																				
Milton Keynes Central 66 d			20 13	20 37			20 41							21 37							22 39			
Northampton 68 d				21 06																				
Rugby d				21 30										22 01							23 19			
Coventry d		19 46	20 41						20 26							21 26	21 35							
Bedworth d		19 57															21 46							
Nuneaton a		20 04		21 42	21 03												21 53	22 51			23 29			
d				21 43	21 04													22 52			23 30			
Atherstone d				21 49																				
Polesworth d															←									
Tamworth d				21 58				21 32							21 58									
Lichfield Trent Valley d				→				21 39							22 04									
Rugeley Trent Valley d						←					←				22 12									
Stafford d			21 56			21 20	21 33		21 37		21 56	22 00	22 16		22 26	22 37		23 17	23 31		23s55			
Norton Bridge Station Drv d			→																					
Stone d						21 30									22 36									
Stone Crown Street d																								
Stone Granville Square a																								
Barlaston Orchard Place d																								
Wedgwood Old Road Bridge d																								
Stoke-on-Trent 50 d						21 45			21a56						22 45	22a55								
Hanley Bus Station a																								
Kidsgrove 50 d						21 53									22 53									
Alsager 50 d						21 57									22 57									
Crewe 65,50 a	21 13				21 44	22 07	21 53	22 10			22 15	22 20	22 38	22 49	23 07			23 43	23 57		00s21			

Table 67R

Mondays to Fridays

9 December to 16 May

Crewe and Stoke-on-Trent - London
Nuneaton - Coventry

Network Diagram - refer to first Page of Table 67

Miles	Miles	Miles				AW	LM	VT	LM	XC	VT	XC	LM	LM	VT	LM	VT	XC	LM	VT	LM	VT	LM	LM
							1	◇1 ⊠		◇1 🛒	◇1 ⊠	◇1 🛒	1	🚌	◇1 ⊠	1	◇1 ⊠	◇1 🛒	1	◇1 ⊠	1	◇1 ⊠		
0	0	—	**Crewe**	65,50	d	04 59	05 18	05 36		05 47	06 02		06 20		06 29			06 38	06 47		06 52	06 53		06 56
6¼	—	—	Alsager	50	d																07 01			
8½	—	—	Kidsgrove	50	d																07 08			
—	—	—	Hanley Bus Station		d									06 21										
15	—	—	**Stoke-on-Trent**	50	d					06 07				06 27						07 06	07 17			
—	—	—	Wedgwood Old Road Bridge		d									06 39										
—	—	—	Barlaston Orchard Place		d									06 43										
—	—	—	Stone Granville Square		d									06a56										
23¼	—	—	Stone		d																07 25			
—	—	—	Norton Bridge Station Drv		d							←												
32¼	24½	—	**Stafford**		d	05a24		05 55		06 25	06 22	06 25	06a40				06 54	06a57	07a10	07 28	07 40			07a17
42	—	—	Rugeley Trent Valley		d		05 56			↪											↪			
50	—	—	Lichfield Trent Valley		d		06 05										07 08							
56¼	—	—	Tamworth		d		06 12										07 15							
59¾	—	—	Polesworth		d																			
63¾	—	—	Atherstone		d		06 20																	
68¾	—	0	Nuneaton		a		06 27	06 17							07 06							07 32		
—	—	—			d		06 28	06 18	06 37						07 08							07 34	07 37	
—	—	3¾	Bedworth		d				06 44														07 44	
—	—	10	**Coventry**		a				06 56			07 24								08 30			07 57	
83¼	—	—	Rugby		a		06 43	06 31			06 52													
102	—	—	Northampton	68	a		07 05									←								
118	—	—	Milton Keynes Central	66	a		07 30	06 51			07 13					07 30								
150¼	—	—	Watford Junction	66	a		↪													09s16				
167¾	—	—	**London Euston** 15	⊖66	a			07 29			07 51				08 08	08 11	08 23			09 34		08 34		

			LM	VT	LM	LM	XC	LM	LM	XC	VT	LM	VT	VT	LM	VT	VT	LM	XC	LM	VT	LM	XC	VT
			1	◇1 ⊠	1		◇1 🛒	1	🚌	R 1 A 🛒	◇1 ⊠	1	◇1 ⊠	◇1 ⊠	1	◇1 ⊠	◇1 ⊠	🚌	◇1 🛒	1	◇1 ⊠	1	◇1 🛒	◇1 ⊠
Crewe	65,50	d	07 16	07 17				07 49				07 55	07 57	08 01	08 18	08 22	08 29			08 49	08 56			09 01
Alsager	50	d										08 05												
Kidsgrove	50	d										08 09												
Hanley Bus Station		d																08 31						
Stoke-on-Trent	50	d					07 44			08 07	08 12	08 18						08 37	08 44				09 07	
Wedgwood Old Road Bridge		d																08 49						
Barlaston Orchard Place		d																08 53						
Stone Granville Square		d																09a06						
Stone		d										08 26												
Norton Bridge Station Drv		d			←				07 52															
Stafford		d	07a40	07 36	07 40		08a01	08a10	08a22	08 25		08 37			08a44	08 42			09a02	09a09			09 25	
Rugeley Trent Valley		d			07 48							08 55												
Lichfield Trent Valley		d			07 56							09 04												
Tamworth		d			08 03							09 12												
Polesworth		d																						
Atherstone		d			08 11							09 21												
Nuneaton		a			08 18						08 44	09 27												
		d			08 18	08 28					08 46	09 28												
Bedworth		d				08 35																		
Coventry		a				08 47				09 24				09 30									10 24	10 30
Rugby		a			08 33							09 44	08 45											
Northampton	68	a																				←		
Milton Keynes Central	66	a			08 55							10 14		09 58							10 02	10 14		10 58
Watford Junction	66	a									09s32	↪												
London Euston 15	⊖66	a		08 53	09 37						09 52		09 41	10 32		10 01	10 06				10 39	10 50		11 34

A R to Stafford

Table 67R

Mondays to Fridays

9 December to 16 May

Crewe and Stoke-on-Trent - London
Nuneaton - Coventry

Network Diagram - refer to first Page of Table 67

		LM	LM	LM	VT	LM	VT	XC	LM	LM		VT	LM	XC	VT	LM	LM	LM	VT	LM		VT	LM	VT	XC
																								FO	
			1	1	◇1	1	◇1	◇1	1			◇1	1	◇1	◇1		1	1	◇1	1		◇1		◇	◇1
										🚌													🚌		
					⊠		⊠	⊥				⊠		⊥	⊠				⊠			⊠		⊏	⊥
Crewe	65,50 d		09 02	09 19	09 25		09 30		09 49			09 56			10 01		10 02	10 19	10 22			10 29		10 40	
Alsager	50 d		09 11														10 11								
Kidsgrove	50 d		09 15														10 15								
Hanley Bus Station	d																						10 31		
Stoke-on-Trent	50 d		09 28					09 44						10 07			10 28						10 37		10 44
Wedgwood Old Road Bridge	d																						10 49		
Barlaston Orchard Place	d																						10 53		
Stone Granville Square	d																						11a06		
Stone	d		09 36														10 36								
Norton Bridge Station Drv	d					←				09 52										←					
Stafford	d		09 56	09a45	09 44	09 56		10a02	10a09	10a22				10 25			10 56	10a42	10 42	10 56					11a01
Rugeley Trent Valley	d		↪			10 05											↪			11 05					
Lichfield Trent Valley	d					10 13														11 13					
Tamworth	d					10 20														11 20					
Polesworth	d																								
Atherstone	d					10 28														11 28					
Nuneaton	a					10 36														11 35					
	d	10 15				10 36										11 17				11 36					
Bedworth	d	10 22														11 24									
Coventry	a	10 34												11 24	11 30	11 36									
Rugby	a					10 52														11 52					
Northampton	68 a												←												
Milton Keynes Central	66 a					11 14						11 02	11 14		11 58					12 14					
Watford Junction	66 a					↪														↪					
London Euston 15	⊖66 a				11 05		11 08					11 39	11 50		12 34				11 59			12 05		12 30	

		LM	VT	LM	XC	VT		LM	LM	LM	VT	LM	VT	XC	LM	VT		LM	XC	LM	VT	LM	LM	LM	VT
		1	◇1	1	◇1	◇1			1	1	◇1	1	◇1	◇1	1	◇1		1	◇1		◇1		1	1	◇1
																				🚌					
			⊠		⊥	⊠					⊠		⊠	⊥		⊏			⊥		⊠				⊏
Crewe	65,50 d	10 49	10 56			11 01			11 02	11 17	11 22		11 29		11 49	11 56					12 01		12 02	12 19	12 22
Alsager	50 d								11 11														12 11		
Kidsgrove	50 d								11 15														12 15		
Hanley Bus Station	d																								
Stoke-on-Trent	50 d				11 07				11 28					11 44					12 07				12 28		
Wedgwood Old Road Bridge	d																								
Barlaston Orchard Place	d																								
Stone Granville Square	d																			11 39					
Stone	d								11 36														12 36		
Norton Bridge Station Drv	d											←								12 02					
Stafford	d	11a09			11 25				11 56	11a42	11 42	11 56		12a02	12a09				12 25	12a32			12 56	12a43	12 42
Rugeley Trent Valley	d								↪			12 05											↪		
Lichfield Trent Valley	d											12 13													
Tamworth	d											12 20													
Polesworth	d																								
Atherstone	d											12 28													
Nuneaton	a											12 35													
	d							12 15				12 36										13 15			
Bedworth	d							12 22														13 22			
Coventry	a				12 24	12 30		12 34											13 24		13 30	13 34			
Rugby	a											12 52													
Northampton	68 a			←														←							
Milton Keynes Central	66 a		12 02	12 14		12 58						13 14				13 02		13 14			13 58				
Watford Junction	66 a											↪													
London Euston 15	⊖66 a		12 39	12 50		13 33					12 59		13 05			13 39		13 50			14 33				14 00

		LM		VT	LM	XC	LM	VT	LM	XC	VT	LM		LM	LM	VT	LM	VT	XC	LM	LM	VT		LM	XC
		1		◇1		◇1	1	◇1	1	◇1	◇1			1	1	◇1	1	◇1	◇1	1		◇1		1	◇1
					🚌																🚌				
				⊏		⊥		⊏		⊥	⊠					⊏		⊏	⊥			⊏			⊥
Crewe	65,50 d			12 29			12 49	12 56			13 01			13 02	13 19	13 25		13 30		13 49		13 56			
Alsager	50 d													13 11											
Kidsgrove	50 d													13 15											
Hanley Bus Station	d				12 31																				
Stoke-on-Trent	50 d				12 37	12 44				13 07				13 28					13 44						14 07
Wedgwood Old Road Bridge	d				12 49																				
Barlaston Orchard Place	d				12 53																				
Stone Granville Square	d				13a06																13 39				
Stone	d													13 36											
Norton Bridge Station Drv	d	←															←				13 54				
Stafford	d	12 56				13a01	13a09			13 25				13 56	13a46	13 44	13 56		14a01	14a09	14a15				14 25
Rugeley Trent Valley	d	13 05												↪			14 05								
Lichfield Trent Valley	d	13 13															14 13								
Tamworth	d	13 20															14 20								
Polesworth	d																								
Atherstone	d	13 28															14 28								
Nuneaton	a	13 35															14 35								
	d	13 36										14 15					14 36								
Bedworth	d											14 22													
Coventry	a									14 23	14 29	14 34													15 23
Rugby	a	13 51															14 51								
Northampton	68 a								←															←	
Milton Keynes Central	66 a	14 14						14 02	14 14		14 58						15 14					15 02		15 14	
Watford Junction	66 a	↪															↪								
London Euston 15	⊖66 a			14 05				14 39	14 50		15 33					15 05		15 09				15 39		15 50	

Table 67R

Mondays to Fridays

9 December to 16 May

Crewe and Stoke-on-Trent - London
Nuneaton - Coventry

Network Diagram - refer to first Page of Table 67

		VT	LM	LM	LM	VT	LM	VT		LM	XC	LM	VT	LM	XC	VT	LM	LM		LM	VT	LM	VT	XC	LM
		◇1		1	1	◇1	1	◇1			◇1	1	◇1	1	◇1	◇1		1		1	◇1	1	◇1	◇1	1
		☕				☕		☕		🚌	🛒		☕		🛒	☕					☕		☕	🛒	
Crewe 65,50	d	14 01		14 02	14 19	14 22		14 29				14 49	14 56			15 01		15 02		15 19	15 22		15 29		15 49
Alsager 50	d			14 11														15 11							
Kidsgrove 50	d			14 15														15 15							
Hanley Bus Station	d									14 31															
Stoke-on-Trent 50	d			14 28						14 37	14 44				15 08			15 28						15 44	
Wedgwood Old Road Bridge	d									14 49															
Barlaston Orchard Place	d									14 53															
Stone Granville Square	d									15a06															
Stone	d			14 36														15 36							
Norton Bridge Station Drv	d						←															←			
Stafford	d			14 56	14a42	14 42	14 56				15a02	15a09			15 25			15 56		15a42	15 42	15 56		16a02	16a09
Rugeley Trent Valley	d			→			15 05											→				16 05			
Lichfield Trent Valley	d						15 13															16 13			
Tamworth	d						15 20															16 20			
Polesworth	d																								
Atherstone	d						15 28															16 28			
Nuneaton	a						15 35															16 35			
	d		15 15				15 36										16 13					16 36			
Bedworth	d		15 22														16 20								
Coventry	a	15 30	15 34												16 23	16 30	16 34								
Rugby	a						15 51															16 51			
Northampton 68	a													←											
Milton Keynes Central 66	a	15 58					16 14						16 02	16 14		16 58						17 14			
Watford Junction 66	a						→															→			
London Euston 15 ⊖66	a	16 32				15 59		16 05					16 39	16 50		17 34					17 00		17 05		

		LM	VT	LM		XC	VT	LM	LM	LM	VT	LM	VT	LM		XC	LM	VT	LM	XC	VT	VT	LM	LM	
			◇1	1		◇1	◇1		1	1	◇1	1	◇1			◇1	1	◇1	1	◇1	◇1	◇1		1	
		🚌	☕			🛒	☕				☕		☕	🚌		🛒		☕		🛒	☕	☕			
Crewe 65,50	d		15 56				16 01		16 02	16 19	16 22		16 29				16 49	16 56				17 01		17 02	
Alsager 50	d								16 11															17 11	
Kidsgrove 50	d								16 15															17 15	
Hanley Bus Station	d													16 31											
Stoke-on-Trent 50	d					16 07			16 28					16 37		16 44				17 07				17 28	
Wedgwood Old Road Bridge	d													16 49											
Barlaston Orchard Place	d													16 53											
Stone Granville Square	d	15 29												17a06											
Stone	d								16 36															17 36	
Norton Bridge Station Drv	d	15 52										←													
Stafford	d	16a13				16 25			16 56	16a42	16 42	16 56				17a02	17a10			17 25	17 36			17 56	
Rugeley Trent Valley	d								→			17 05												18 05	
Lichfield Trent Valley	d											17 13												18 13	
Tamworth	d											17 20												18 20	
Polesworth	d																								
Atherstone	d											17 28												18 28	
Nuneaton	a											17 35												18 35	
	d							17 15				17 36											18 10	18 36	
Bedworth	d							17 22															18 17		
Coventry	a					17 23	17 30	17 34												18 23		18 30	18 34		
Rugby	a											17 52												18 51	
Northampton 68	a			←															←						
Milton Keynes Central 66	a		17 02	17 14			17 58					18 15						18 02	18 15		18 23	18 58		19 14	
Watford Junction 66	a											→												→	
London Euston 15 ⊖66	a		17 39	17 50			18 34				17 59		18 05					18 39	18 51		19 02	19 32			

		LM	VT	XC	LM	LM	VT	LM	VT	LM		XC	LM	VT	VT	VT	LM	LM	XC	LM		XC	VT	LM	LM
									R							R									
		1	◇1	◇1	1		◇1	1	1	1		◇1	1	◇1	◇1	1		1	◇1	1		◇1	◇1		1
			☕	🛒		🚌	⊠		☕			🛒		⊠	⊠	☕			🛒			🛒	⊠		
Crewe 65,50	d	17 21	17 29		17 49		17 56		18 01	18 02		18 07	18 19	18 24	18 30					18 49			19 01		19 02
Alsager 50	d									18 11															19 11
Kidsgrove 50	d									18 15															19 15
Hanley Bus Station	d																								
Stoke-on-Trent 50	d			17 44		17 53				18 28									18 44			19 07			19 28
Wedgwood Old Road Bridge	d					18 05																			
Barlaston Orchard Place	d					18 09																			
Stone Granville Square	d					18a22																			
Stone	d									18 36															19 36
Norton Bridge Station Drv	d																	←							
Stafford	d	17a41		18a03	18a09					18 56		18 28	18a44	18 43				18 56	19a01	19a09		19 25			19 51
Rugeley Trent Valley	d									→								19 05							→
Lichfield Trent Valley	d																	19 13							
Tamworth	d																	19 20							
Polesworth	d																								
Atherstone	d																	19 28							
Nuneaton	a																	19 35							
	d																19 15	19 36						20 15	
Bedworth	d																19 22							20 22	
Coventry	a								19 30			19 23					19 38					20 23	20 30	20 34	
Rugby	a																	19 49							
Northampton 68	a							←								←									
Milton Keynes Central 66	a						19 02	19 14	19 58						19 33	19 58		20 14					20 58		
Watford Junction 66	a		18s48						→					19s47									→		
London Euston 15 ⊖66	a		19 09				19 39	19 50						20 07	20 08	20 34		20 50							

Table 67R

Mondays to Fridays

9 December to 16 May

Crewe and Stoke-on-Trent - London
Nuneaton - Coventry

Network Diagram - refer to first Page of Table 67

		LM	VT	LM	VT	VT		XC	LM	VT	XC	VT	LM	LM	VT	LM		VT	VT	VT	XC	LM	LM	VT	XC
												R								R					
		1	◇1	1	◇1	◇1		◇1	1	◇1	◇1	1	1	1	◇1			◇1	◇1	1	◇1	1	1	◇1	◇1
			⊠		⊠	⊠		🛒		☕	🛒	⊠			☕			☕	☕	⊠				⊠	
Crewe	65,50 d	19 19	19 22		19 29				19 55	19 56		20 01	20 15	20 18	20 23			20 29	20 41				20 47	20 53	
Alsager	50 d												20 24												
Kidsgrove	50 d												20 28												
Hanley Bus Station	d																								
Stoke-on-Trent	50 d							19 44			20 07		20 37								20 44				21 07
Wedgwood Old Road Bridge	d																								
Barlaston Orchard Place	d																								
Stone Granville Square	d																								
Stone	d												20 45												
Norton Bridge Station Drv	d			←																		←			
Stafford	d	19a42	19 42	19 51				20a03	20a15		20 28		21 04	20a38				20 49			21a02	21 04	21a08	21a12	21a24
Rugeley Trent Valley	d			20 00									→									21 12			
Lichfield Trent Valley	d			20 08																		21 20			
Tamworth	d			20 15																		21 27			
Polesworth	d																								
Atherstone	d			20 23																		21 35			
Nuneaton	a			20 30											21 02							21 42			
	d			20 31											21 03	21 15						21 42			
Bedworth	d															21 22									
Coventry	a										21 23	21 30				21 34									
Rugby	a			20 46															21 27			21 57			
Northampton	68 a			21 07		←														←		22 17			
Milton Keynes Central	66 a				20 31	20 58				21 04		21 58						21 35	21 48	21 58					
Watford Junction	66 a		20s45			21s19						→			21s49					22s20					
London Euston 15	⊖66 a		21 04		21 06	21 39				21 43					22 09			22 13	22 23	22 43					

		LM		VT	LM	XC	LM	XC
		1		◇1		◇1	1	◇1
				☕				
Crewe	65,50 d	21 18		21 24			22 20	
Alsager	50 d							
Kidsgrove	50 d							
Hanley Bus Station	d							
Stoke-on-Trent	50 d					22 08		22 47
Wedgwood Old Road Bridge	d							
Barlaston Orchard Place	d							
Stone Granville Square	d							
Stone	d							
Norton Bridge Station Drv	d							
Stafford	d	21a38		21 44		22a25	22a40	23a06
Rugeley Trent Valley	d							
Lichfield Trent Valley	d			21 58				
Tamworth	d			22 05				
Polesworth	d							
Atherstone	d							
Nuneaton	a			22 17				
	d			22 18	22 20			
Bedworth	d				22 27			
Coventry	a				22 39			
Rugby	a			22 31				
Northampton	68 a							
Milton Keynes Central	66 a			22 58				
Watford Junction	66 a			23s33				
London Euston 15	⊖66 a			23 57				

Saturdays

14 December to 28 December

		AW	LM	XC	VT	XC	LM	VT	VT	XC		LM	LM	VT	LM	VT	VT	VT	LM	LM		XC	LM	VT	LM
				◇1	◇1	◇1	1	◇1	◇1	◇1		1	1	◇1	1	◇1	◇1	◇1		1		◇1	1	◇1	
				🛒	☕	🛒		☕	☕	🛒				☕		☕	☕	☕				🛒		☕	🚌
Crewe	65,50 d	04 59		05 47	06 00		06 11		06 29			06 47	06 59	07 01	07 16	07 20	07 29	07 41					07 49	07 55	
Alsager	50 d												07 07												
Kidsgrove	50 d												07 12												
Hanley Bus Station	d																								
Stoke-on-Trent	50 d			06 08						06 39			07 20									07 44			
Wedgwood Old Road Bridge	d																								
Barlaston Orchard Place	d																								
Stone Granville Square	d																								
Stone	d												07 29												
Norton Bridge Station Drv	d					←														←					07 52
Stafford	d	05a24		06 26	06 19	06 26	06a34	06 36		06a57		07a10	07 48		07a37	07 39				07 48		08a02	08a09	08 16	08a22
Rugeley Trent Valley	d			→									→							07 57					
Lichfield Trent Valley	d																			08 05				08 31	
Tamworth	d																			08 11				08 38	
Polesworth	d																								
Atherstone	d																			08 20					
Nuneaton	a							06 58												08 26					
	d		06 47					06 59											08 14	08 27					
Bedworth	d		06 54																08 21						
Coventry	a		07 06			07 24								08 29					08 33						
Rugby	a				06 50															08 42					
Northampton	68 a																								
Milton Keynes Central	66 a				07 11				07 31					08 58						09 05					
Watford Junction	66 a				07s32			07s45																	
London Euston 15	⊖66 a				07 53			08 05	08 10					09 34		09 00	09 05	09 30		09 50				09 47	

Table 67R

Saturdays

14 December to 28 December

Crewe and Stoke-on-Trent - London
Nuneaton - Coventry

Network Diagram - refer to first Page of Table 67

	XC	VT	LM	LM	VT		LM	LM	VT	LM	XC	LM	VT	LM	XC		VT	LM	LM	LM	VT	LM	VT	XC
	◇1	◇1	1	1	◇1			1	◇1		◇1	1	◇1	1	◇1		◇1		1	1	◇1	1	◇1	◇1
	🛒	☕			☕				☕	🚌	🛒		☕		🛒		☕				☕		☕	🛒
Crewe 65,50 d		08 01	08 02	08 19	08 22				08 29			08 49	08 56				09 01		09 02	09 19	09 25		09 30	
Alsager 50 d			08 11																09 11					
Kidsgrove 50 d			08 15																09 15					
Hanley Bus Station d										08 35														
Stoke-on-Trent 50 d	08 07		08 28							08 41	08 44				09 07				09 28					09 44
Wedgwood Old Road Bridge d										08 53														
Barlaston Orchard Place d										08 57														
Stone Granville Square d										09a10														
Stone d			08 36																09 36					
Norton Bridge Station Drv d								←														←		
Stafford d	08 26		08 56	08a42	08 42			08 56			09a02	09a09			09 26				09 56	09a45	09 44	09 56		10a02
Rugeley Trent Valley d			→					09 05											→			10 05		
Lichfield Trent Valley d								09 13														10 13		
Tamworth d								09 20														10 20		
Polesworth d																								
Atherstone d								09 28														10 28		
Nuneaton a					09 04			09 35														10 35		
d					09 05		09 15	09 36										10 15				10 36		
Bedworth d							09 22											10 22						
Coventry a	09 24	09 30					09 34								10 24		10 30	10 34						
Rugby a								09 51														10 51		
Northampton 68 a														←										
Milton Keynes Central 66 a		09 58						10 14					10 02	10 14			10 58					11 14		
Watford Junction 66 a								→														→		
London Euston 15 ⊖66 a		10 35			10 06				10 11				10 39	10 50			11 33				11 05		11 08	

	LM		LM	VT	LM	XC	VT	LM	LM	LM	VT		LM	VT	LM	XC	LM	VT	LM	XC	VT		LM	LM
	1			◇1	1	◇1	◇1		1	1	◇1		1	◇1		◇1	1	◇1	1	◇1	◇1			1
			🚌	☕		🛒	☕				☕			☕	🚌	🛒		☕		🛒	☕			
Crewe 65,50 d	09 49			09 56			10 01		10 02	10 19	10 22			10 29			10 49	10 56			11 01			11 02
Alsager 50 d									10 11															11 11
Kidsgrove 50 d									10 15															11 15
Hanley Bus Station d															10 35									
Stoke-on-Trent 50 d						10 07			10 28						10 41	10 44				11 07				11 28
Wedgwood Old Road Bridge d															10 53									
Barlaston Orchard Place d															10 57									
Stone Granville Square d															11a10									
Stone d									10 36															11 36
Norton Bridge Station Drv d			09 52										←											
Stafford d	10a10		10a22			10 26			10 56	10a42	10 42		10 56			11a02	11a09			11 26				11 56
Rugeley Trent Valley d									→				11 05											→
Lichfield Trent Valley d													11 13											
Tamworth d													11 20											
Polesworth d																								
Atherstone d													11 28											
Nuneaton a													11 35											
d								11 15					11 36										12 15	
Bedworth d								11 22															12 22	
Coventry a						11 24	11 30	11 34												12 24	12 30		12 34	
Rugby a													11 51											
Northampton 68 a					←														←					
Milton Keynes Central 66 a				11 02	11 14		11 58						12 14					12 02	12 14		12 58			
Watford Junction 66 a													→											
London Euston 15 ⊖66 a				11 39	11 50		12 33				11 59			12 05				12 39	12 50		13 35			

	LM	VT	LM	VT	XC	LM	VT		LM	XC	LM	VT	LM	LM	LM	VT	LM		VT	LM	XC	LM	VT	LM
	1	◇1	1	◇1	◇1	1	◇1		1	◇1		◇1		1	1	◇1	1		◇1		◇1	1	◇1	1
		☕		☕	🛒		☕			🛒	🚌	☕				☕			☕	🚌	🛒		☕	
Crewe 65,50 d	11 19	11 22		11 29		11 49	11 56					12 01		12 02	12 19	12 22			12 29			12 49	12 56	
Alsager 50 d														12 11										
Kidsgrove 50 d														12 15										
Hanley Bus Station d																				12 35				
Stoke-on-Trent 50 d					11 44					12 07				12 28						12 41	12 44			
Wedgwood Old Road Bridge d																				12 53				
Barlaston Orchard Place d																				12 57				
Stone Granville Square d											11 39									13a10				
Stone d														12 36										
Norton Bridge Station Drv d			←								12 02						←							
Stafford d	11a42	11 42	11 56		12a02	12a09				12 25	12a32			12 56	12a42	12 42	12 56				13a02	13a09		
Rugeley Trent Valley d			12 05											→			13 05							
Lichfield Trent Valley d			12 13														13 13							
Tamworth d			12 20														13 20							
Polesworth d																								
Atherstone d			12 28														13 28							
Nuneaton a			12 35														13 35							
d			12 36										13 15				13 36							
Bedworth d													13 22											
Coventry a										13 24		13 30	13 34											
Rugby a			12 51														13 51							
Northampton 68 a									←															←
Milton Keynes Central 66 a			13 14				13 02		13 14			13 58					14 14						14 02	14 14
Watford Junction 66 a			→														→							
London Euston 15 ⊖66 a		12 59		13 05			13 39		13 50			14 33				14 00			14 05				14 39	14 50

Table 67R

Saturdays

14 December to 28 December

Crewe and Stoke-on-Trent - London
Nuneaton - Coventry

Network Diagram - refer to first Page of Table 67

	XC	VT	LM		LM	LM	VT	LM	VT	XC	LM	LM	VT		LM	XC	VT	LM	LM	LM	VT	LM	VT	
	◇1	◇1			1	1	◇1	1	◇1	◇1	1		◇1		1	◇1	◇1		1	1	◇1	1	◇1	
	🛒	☕					☕		☕	🛒		🚌	☕			🛒	☕				☕		☕	
Crewe 65,50 d		13 01			13 02	13 19	13 25		13 30		13 49		13 56				14 01		14 02	14 19	14 22		14 29	
Alsager 50 d					13 11														14 11					
Kidsgrove 50 d					13 15														14 15					
Hanley Bus Station d																								
Stoke-on-Trent 50 d	13 07				13 28					13 44						14 07			14 28					
Wedgwood Old Road Bridge d																								
Barlaston Orchard Place d																								
Stone Granville Square d												13 39												
Stone d					13 36														14 36					
Norton Bridge Station Drv d								←				13 54										←		
Stafford d	13 26				13 56	13a45	13 44	13 56		14a02	14a09	14a15				14 26			14 56	14a42	14 42	14 56		
Rugeley Trent Valley d					→			14 05											→			15 05		
Lichfield Trent Valley d								14 13														15 13		
Tamworth d								14 20														15 20		
Polesworth d																								
Atherstone d								14 28														15 28		
Nuneaton a								14 35														15 35		
d			14 15					14 36										15 15				15 36		
Bedworth d			14 22															15 22						
Coventry a	14 24	14 30	14 34													15 24	15 30	15 34						
Rugby a								14 51														15 51		
Northampton 68 a															←									
Milton Keynes Central 66 a		14 58						15 14					15 02		15 14		15 58					16 14		
Watford Junction 66 a								→														→		
London Euston 15 ⊖66 a		15 34					15 05		15 09				15 39		15 50		16 34				15 59		16 05	

	LM	XC	LM	VT	LM	XC	VT	LM	LM		LM	VT	LM	VT	XC	LM	LM	VT	LM		XC	VT	LM	LM
		◇1	1	◇1	1	◇1	◇1		1		1	◇1	1	◇1	◇1	1		◇1	1		◇1	◇1		1
	🚌	🛒		☕		🛒	☕					☕		☕	🛒		🚌	☕			🛒	☕		
Crewe 65,50 d			14 49	14 56			15 01		15 02		15 19	15 22		15 29		15 49		15 56				16 01		16 02
Alsager 50 d									15 11															16 11
Kidsgrove 50 d									15 15															16 15
Hanley Bus Station d	14 35																							
Stoke-on-Trent 50 d	14 41	14 44				15 07			15 28						15 44						16 07			16 28
Wedgwood Old Road Bridge d	14 53																							
Barlaston Orchard Place d	14 57																							
Stone Granville Square d	15a10																15 29							
Stone d									15 36															16 36
Norton Bridge Station Drv d													←				15 52							
Stafford d		15a02	15a09			15 26			15 56		15a42	15 42	15 56		16a02	16a09	16a13				16 25			16 56
Rugeley Trent Valley d									→				16 05											→
Lichfield Trent Valley d													16 13											
Tamworth d													16 20											
Polesworth d																								
Atherstone d													16 28											
Nuneaton a													16 35											
d								16 15					16 36										17 15	
Bedworth d								16 22															17 22	
Coventry a						16 24	16 30	16 34													17 24	17 30	17 34	
Rugby a													16 51											
Northampton 68 a					←														←					
Milton Keynes Central 66 a				16 02	16 14		16 58						17 14					17 02	17 14			17 58		
Watford Junction 66 a													→											
London Euston 15 ⊖66 a				16 39	16 50		17 33					16 59		17 05				17 39	17 50			18 34		

	LM	VT	LM	VT	XC		LM	LM	VT	LM	XC	VT	LM	LM	LM		VT	VT	LM	XC	LM	LM	XC	VT
	1	◇1	1	◇1	◇1			1	◇1	1	◇1	◇1		1	1		◇1	◇1	1	◇1		1	◇1	◇1
		☕		☕	🛒		🚌		☕		🛒	☕					☕	☕		🛒	🚌		🛒	☕
Crewe 65,50 d	16 19	16 22		16 29				16 49	16 56			17 01		17 02	17 19		17 23	17 29				17 49		
Alsager 50 d														17 11										
Kidsgrove 50 d														17 15										
Hanley Bus Station d																								
Stoke-on-Trent 50 d					16 44		16 47				17 07			17 28						17 45	17 47		18 07	
Wedgwood Old Road Bridge d							16 59														17 59			
Barlaston Orchard Place d							17 03														18 03			
Stone Granville Square d							17a16														18a16			
Stone d														17 36										
Norton Bridge Station Drv d			←																←					
Stafford d	16a44	16 42	16 56		17a02			17a09			17 26			17 56	17a43		17 43		17 56	18a03		18a09	18 26	18 36
Rugeley Trent Valley d			17 05											→					18 05					
Lichfield Trent Valley d			17 13																18 13					
Tamworth d			17 20																18 20					
Polesworth d																								
Atherstone d			17 28																18 28					
Nuneaton a			17 35																18 35					
d			17 36										18 15						18 36					
Bedworth d													18 22											
Coventry a											18 24	18 30	18 34										19 24	
Rugby a			17 51																18 51					
Northampton 68 a										←														
Milton Keynes Central 66 a			18 14						18 02	18 14		18 58							19 14					
Watford Junction 66 a			→																					
London Euston 15 ⊖66 a		17 59		18 05					18 39	18 50		19 34					19 01	19 09	19 50					19 59

Table 67R

Saturdays

14 December to 28 December

Crewe and Stoke-on-Trent - London
Nuneaton - Coventry

Network Diagram - refer to first Page of Table 67

	VT ◇1 🍽		LM 1	LM	LM 1	VT ◇1 🍽	XC ◇1 🛒	LM 1	XC ◇1 🛒	VT ◇1 🍽	VT ◇1 🍽		LM 1	LM 1	VT ◇1 🍽	XC ◇1 🛒	LM 1	XC ◇1 A 🛒	VT ◇1 🍽	LM 1	VT ◇1 🍽		XC ◇1	VT ◇1 🍽
Crewe 65,50 d	18 01		18 02		18 22	18 29		18 49			19 01		19 02	19 21	19 29		19 51		20 01	20 18	20 23			20 47
Alsager 50 d			18 11										19 11											
Kidsgrove 50 d			18 15										19 15											
Hanley Bus Station d																								
Stoke-on-Trent 50 d			18 28				18 44		19 07				19 28			19 44		20 07					20 44	
Wedgwood Old Road Bridge d																								
Barlaston Orchard Place d																								
Stone Granville Square d																								
Stone d			18 36										19 36											
Norton Bridge Station Drv d																								
Stafford d			18 56		18a42		19a02	19a09	19 25	19 36			19 51	19a45		20a02	20a11	20 26		20a40	20 43		21a02	
Rugeley Trent Valley d			19 05										20 00											
Lichfield Trent Valley d			19 13										20 08											
Tamworth d			19 20										20 15											
Polesworth d																								
Atherstone d			19 28										20 23											
Nuneaton a			19 35										20 30											
d			19 36	19 46									20 31											
Bedworth d				19 53																				
Coventry a	19 30			20 05					20 24		20 30							21 24	21 30					
Rugby a	19 42		19 51								20 42		20 46						21 42					
Northampton 68 a			20 12										21 07											
Milton Keynes Central 66 a	20 05										21 04								22 04					21 51
Watford Junction 66 a	20s34										21s35								→					
London Euston 15 ⊖66 a	20 55					20 05				21 15	21 56				21 20						22 15			22 45

	VT ◇1 🍽	XC ◇1	LM	LM 1	XC ◇1	VT ◇1 🍽	VT ◇1 🍽		XC ◇1	LM	LM 1
Crewe 65,50 d				21 17		21 43	22 04				22 24
Alsager 50 d											
Kidsgrove 50 d											
Hanley Bus Station d											
Stoke-on-Trent 50 d		21 07			21 45				22 07		
Wedgwood Old Road Bridge d											
Barlaston Orchard Place d											
Stone Granville Square d											
Stone d											
Norton Bridge Station Drv d											
Stafford d		21a26		21a42	22a02	22a07	22a22		22a28		22a44
Rugeley Trent Valley d											
Lichfield Trent Valley d											
Tamworth d											
Polesworth d											
Atherstone d											
Nuneaton a											
d			21 15							22 15	
Bedworth d			21 22							22 22	
Coventry a			21 34							22 34	
Rugby a											
Northampton 68 a	←										
Milton Keynes Central 66 a	22 04										
Watford Junction 66 a	22s34										
London Euston 15 ⊖66 a	22 55										

Saturdays

4 January to 8 February

	AW	LM	XC ◇1 🛒	VT ◇1 🍽	XC ◇1 🛒	LM 1	VT ◇1 🍽	VT ◇1 🍽	XC ◇1 🛒		LM 1	LM 1	VT ◇1 🍽	LM 1	VT ◇1 🍽	VT ◇1 🍽	VT ◇1 🍽	LM	LM 1		XC ◇1 🛒	LM 1	VT ◇1 🍽	LM 🚌
Crewe 65,50 d	04 59		05 47	06 00		06 11		06 29			06 47	06 59	07 01	07 16	07 20	07 29	07 41					07 49	07 55	
Alsager 50 d												07 07												
Kidsgrove 50 d												07 12												
Hanley Bus Station d																								
Stoke-on-Trent 50 d			06 08						06 39			07 20									07 44			
Wedgwood Old Road Bridge d																								
Barlaston Orchard Place d																								
Stone Granville Square d																								
Stone d												07 29												
Norton Bridge Station Drv d					←														←					07 52
Stafford d	05a24		06 26	06 19	06 26	06a34	06 36		06a57		07a10	07 48		07a37	07 39				07 48		08a02	08a09	08 16	08a22
Rugeley Trent Valley d			→									→							07 57					
Lichfield Trent Valley d																			08 05				08 31	
Tamworth d																			08 11				08 38	
Polesworth d																								
Atherstone d																			08 20					
Nuneaton a							06 58												08 26					
d		06 47					06 59											08 14	08 27					
Bedworth d		06 54																08 21						
Coventry a		07 06			07 24								08 29					08 33						
Rugby a				06 50															08 42					
Northampton 68 a																								
Milton Keynes Central 66 a				07 11				07 31					08 58						09 05					
Watford Junction 66 a				07s32			07s45																	
London Euston 15 ⊖66 a				07 53			08 05	08 10					09 34		09 00	09 05	09 30		09 50				09 47	

A 🛒 to Stafford

Table 67R

Saturdays

4 January to 8 February

Crewe and Stoke-on-Trent - London
Nuneaton - Coventry

Network Diagram - refer to first Page of Table 67

			XC	VT	LM	LM	VT		LM	LM	VT	LM	XC	LM	VT	LM	XC		VT	LM	LM	LM	VT	LM	VT	XC
			◇1	◇1	1	1	◇1			1	◇1		◇1	1	◇1	1	◇1		◇1		1	1	◇1	1	◇1	◇1
												🚌														
			⊼	☕			☕				☕		⊼		☕		⊼		☕				☕		☕	⊼
Crewe	65,50	d		08 01	08 02	08 19	08 22				08 29			08 49	08 56				09 01		09 02	09 19	09 25		09 30	
Alsager	50	d			08 11																09 11					
Kidsgrove	50	d			08 15																09 15					
Hanley Bus Station		d										08 35														
Stoke-on-Trent	50	d	08 07		08 28							08 41	08 44				09 07				09 28					09 44
Wedgwood Old Road Bridge		d										08 53														
Barlaston Orchard Place		d										08 57														
Stone Granville Square		d										09a10														
Stone		d			08 36																09 36					
Norton Bridge Station Drv		d								←														←		
Stafford		d	08 26		08 56	08a42	08 42			08 56			09a02	09a09			09 26				09 56	09a45	09 44	09 56		10a02
Rugeley Trent Valley		d			→					09 05											→			10 05		
Lichfield Trent Valley		d								09 13														10 13		
Tamworth		d								09 20														10 20		
Polesworth		d																								
Atherstone		d								09 28														10 28		
Nuneaton		a					09 04			09 35														10 35		
		d					09 05		09 15	09 36										10 15				10 36		
Bedworth		d							09 22											10 22						
Coventry		a	09 24	09 30					09 34								10 24		10 30	10 34						
Rugby		a								09 51														10 51		
Northampton	68	a														←										
Milton Keynes Central	66	a		09 58						10 14					10 02	10 14			10 58					11 14		
Watford Junction	66	a								→														→		
London Euston 15	⊖66	a		10 35			10 06				10 11				10 39	10 50			11 33				11 05		11 08	

			LM		LM	VT	LM	XC	VT	LM	LM	LM	VT		LM	VT	LM	XC	LM	VT	LM	XC	VT		LM	LM
			1			◇1	1	◇1	◇1		1	1	◇1		1	◇1		◇1	1	◇1	1	◇1	◇1			1
					🚌												🚌									
						☕		⊼	☕				☕			☕		⊼		☕		⊼	☕			
Crewe	65,50	d	09 49			09 56			10 01		10 02	10 19	10 22			10 29			10 49	10 56			11 01			11 02
Alsager	50	d									10 11															11 11
Kidsgrove	50	d									10 15															11 15
Hanley Bus Station		d															10 35									
Stoke-on-Trent	50	d						10 07			10 28						10 41	10 44				11 07				11 28
Wedgwood Old Road Bridge		d															10 53									
Barlaston Orchard Place		d															10 57									
Stone Granville Square		d															11a10									
Stone		d									10 36															11 36
Norton Bridge Station Drv		d			09 52										←											
Stafford		d	10a10		10a22			10 26			10 56	10a42	10 42		10 56			11a02	11a09			11 26				11 56
Rugeley Trent Valley		d									→				11 05											→
Lichfield Trent Valley		d													11 13											
Tamworth		d													11 20											
Polesworth		d																								
Atherstone		d													11 28											
Nuneaton		a													11 35											
		d								11 15					11 36										12 15	
Bedworth		d								11 22															12 22	
Coventry		a						11 24	11 30	11 34												12 24	12 30		12 34	
Rugby		a													11 51											
Northampton	68	a					←														←					
Milton Keynes Central	66	a				11 02	11 14		11 58						12 14					12 02	12 14		12 58			
Watford Junction	66	a													→											
London Euston 15	⊖66	a				11 39	11 50		12 33				11 59			12 05				12 39	12 50		13 35			

			LM	VT	LM	VT	XC	LM	VT		LM	XC	LM	VT	LM	LM	LM	VT	LM		VT	LM	XC	LM	VT	LM
			1	◇1	1	◇1	◇1	1	◇1		1	◇1		◇1		1	1	◇1	1		◇1		◇1	1	◇1	1
													🚌									🚌				
				☕		☕	⊼		☕			⊼		☕				☕			☕		⊼		☕	
Crewe	65,50	d	11 19	11 22		11 29		11 49	11 56					12 01		12 02	12 19	12 22			12 29			12 49	12 56	
Alsager	50	d														12 11										
Kidsgrove	50	d														12 15										
Hanley Bus Station		d																				12 35				
Stoke-on-Trent	50	d					11 44					12 07				12 28						12 41	12 44			
Wedgwood Old Road Bridge		d																				12 53				
Barlaston Orchard Place		d																				12 57				
Stone Granville Square		d											11 39									13a10				
Stone		d														12 36										
Norton Bridge Station Drv		d			←								12 02						←							
Stafford		d	11a42	11 42	11 56		12a02	12a09				12 25	12a32			12 56	12a42	12 42	12 56				13a02	13a09		
Rugeley Trent Valley		d			12 05											→			13 05							
Lichfield Trent Valley		d			12 13														13 13							
Tamworth		d			12 20														13 20							
Polesworth		d																								
Atherstone		d			12 28														13 28							
Nuneaton		a			12 35														13 35							
		d			12 36										13 15				13 36							
Bedworth		d													13 22											
Coventry		a										13 24		13 30	13 34											
Rugby		a			12 51														13 51							
Northampton	68	a									←															←
Milton Keynes Central	66	a			13 14				13 02		13 14			13 58					14 14						14 02	14 14
Watford Junction	66	a			→														→							
London Euston 15	⊖66	a		12 59		13 05			13 39		13 50			14 33				14 00			14 05				14 39	14 50

Table 67R

Saturdays

4 January to 8 February

Crewe and Stoke-on-Trent - London
Nuneaton - Coventry

Network Diagram - refer to first Page of Table 67

		XC	VT	LM		LM	LM	VT	LM	VT	XC	LM	LM	VT		LM	XC	VT	LM	LM	LM	VT	LM	VT	
		◇1	◇1			1	1	◇1	1	◇1	◇1	1		◇1		1	◇1	◇1		1	1	◇1	1	◇1	
Crewe	65,50 d		13 01			13 02	13 19	13 25		13 30		13 49		13 56				14 01		14 02	14 19	14 22		14 29	
Alsager	50 d					13 11														14 11					
Kidsgrove	50 d					13 15														14 15					
Hanley Bus Station	d																								
Stoke-on-Trent	50 d	13 07				13 28					13 44						14 07			14 28					
Wedgwood Old Road Bridge	d																								
Barlaston Orchard Place	d																								
Stone Granville Square	d												13 39												
Stone	d					13 36														14 36					
Norton Bridge Station Drv	d								←				13 54										←		
Stafford	d	13 26				13 56	13a45	13 44	13 56		14a02	14a09	14a15				14 26			14 56	14a42	14 42	14 56		
Rugeley Trent Valley	d					→			14 05											→			15 05		
Lichfield Trent Valley	d								14 13														15 13		
Tamworth	d								14 20														15 20		
Polesworth	d																								
Atherstone	d								14 28														15 28		
Nuneaton	a								14 35														15 35		
	d			14 15					14 36										15 15				15 36		
Bedworth	d			14 22															15 22						
Coventry	a	14 24	14 30	14 34													15 24	15 30	15 34						
Rugby	a								14 51														15 51		
Northampton	68 a															←									
Milton Keynes Central	66 a		14 58						15 14					15 02		15 14		15 58					16 14		
Watford Junction	66 a								→														→		
London Euston 15	⊖66 a		15 34					15 05		15 09				15 39		15 50		16 34				15 59		16 05	

		LM	XC	LM	VT	LM	XC	VT	LM	LM		LM	VT	LM	VT	XC	LM	LM	VT	LM		XC	VT	LM	LM
			◇1	1	◇1	1	◇1	◇1		1		1	◇1	1	◇1	◇1	1		◇1	1		◇1	◇1		1
Crewe	65,50 d			14 49	14 56			15 01		15 02		15 19	15 22		15 29		15 49		15 56				16 01		16 02
Alsager	50 d									15 11															16 11
Kidsgrove	50 d									15 15															16 15
Hanley Bus Station	d	14 35																							
Stoke-on-Trent	50 d	14 41	14 44				15 07			15 28						15 44						16 07			16 28
Wedgwood Old Road Bridge	d	14 53																							
Barlaston Orchard Place	d	14 57																							
Stone Granville Square	d	15a10																15 29							
Stone	d									15 36															16 36
Norton Bridge Station Drv	d													←				15 52							
Stafford	d		15a02	15a09			15 26			15 56		15a42	15 42	15 56		16a02	16a09	16a13				16 25			16 56
Rugeley Trent Valley	d									→				16 05											→
Lichfield Trent Valley	d													16 13											
Tamworth	d													16 20											
Polesworth	d																								
Atherstone	d													16 28											
Nuneaton	a													16 35											
	d								16 15					16 36										17 15	
Bedworth	d								16 22															17 22	
Coventry	a						16 24	16 30	16 34													17 24	17 30	17 34	
Rugby	a													16 51											
Northampton	68 a					←														←					
Milton Keynes Central	66 a				16 02	16 14		16 58						17 14					17 02	17 14			17 58		
Watford Junction	66 a													→											
London Euston 15	⊖66 a				16 39	16 50		17 33					16 59		17 05				17 39	17 50			18 34		

		LM	VT	LM	VT	XC		LM	LM	VT	LM	XC	VT	LM	LM	LM		VT	VT	LM	XC	LM	LM	XC	VT
		1	◇1	1	◇1	◇1			1	◇1	1	◇1	◇1		1	1		◇1	◇1	1	◇1		1	◇1	◇1
Crewe	65,50 d	16 19	16 22		16 29				16 49	16 56			17 01		17 02	17 19		17 23	17 29				17 49		
Alsager	50 d														17 11										
Kidsgrove	50 d														17 15										
Hanley Bus Station	d																								
Stoke-on-Trent	50 d					16 44		16 47				17 07			17 28						17 45	17 47		18 07	
Wedgwood Old Road Bridge	d							16 59														17 59			
Barlaston Orchard Place	d							17 03														18 03			
Stone Granville Square	d							17a16														18a16			
Stone	d														17 36										
Norton Bridge Station Drv	d			←																←					
Stafford	d	16a44	16 42	16 56		17a02			17a09			17 26			17 56	17a43		17 43		17 56	18a03		18a09	18 26	18 36
Rugeley Trent Valley	d			17 05											→					18 05					
Lichfield Trent Valley	d			17 13																18 13					
Tamworth	d			17 20																18 20					
Polesworth	d																								
Atherstone	d			17 28																18 28					
Nuneaton	a			17 35																18 35					
	d			17 36										18 15						18 36					
Bedworth	d													18 22											
Coventry	a											18 24	18 30	18 34										19 24	
Rugby	a			17 51																18 51					
Northampton	68 a										←														
Milton Keynes Central	66 a			18 14						18 02	18 14		18 58							19 14					
Watford Junction	66 a			→																					
London Euston 15	⊖66 a		17 59		18 05					18 39	18 50		19 34					19 01	19 09	19 50					19 59

Table 67R

Saturdays

4 January to 8 February

Crewe and Stoke-on-Trent - London
Nuneaton - Coventry

Network Diagram - refer to first Page of Table 67

	VT		LM	LM	LM	VT	XC	LM	XC	VT	VT		LM	LM	VT	XC	LM	XC	VT	LM	VT		XC	VT
	◇1		1		1	◇1	◇1	1	◇1	◇1	◇1		1	1	◇1	◇1	1	◇1	◇1	1	◇1		◇1	◇1
																		A						
	⊡					⊡	⊥		⊥	⊡	⊡				⊡	⊥		⊥	⊡		⊡			⊡
Crewe 65,50 d	18 01		18 02		18 22	18 29		18 49			19 01		19 02	19 21	19 29		19 51		20 01	20 18	20 23			20 47
Alsager 50 d			18 11										19 11											
Kidsgrove 50 d			18 15										19 15											
Hanley Bus Station d																								
Stoke-on-Trent 50 d			18 28				18 44		19 07				19 28			19 44		20 07					20 44	
Wedgwood Old Road Bridge d																								
Barlaston Orchard Place d																								
Stone Granville Square d																								
Stone d			18 36										19 36											
Norton Bridge Station Drv d																								
Stafford d			18 56		18a42		19a02	19a09	19 25	19 36			19 51	19a45		20a02	20a11	20 26		20a40	20 43		21a02	
Rugeley Trent Valley d			19 05										20 00											
Lichfield Trent Valley d			19 13										20 08											
Tamworth d			19 20										20 15											
Polesworth d																								
Atherstone d			19 28										20 23											
Nuneaton a			19 35										20 30											
d			19 36	19 46									20 31											
Bedworth d				19 53																				
Coventry a	19 30			20 05					20 24		20 30							21 24	21 30					
Rugby a	19 42		19 51								20 42		20 46						21 42					
Northampton 68 a			20 12										21 07											
Milton Keynes Central 66 a	20 05										21 04								22 04					21 51
Watford Junction 66 a	20s34										21s35								↦					
London Euston 15 ⊖66 a	20 55					20 05				21 15	21 56				21 20						22 15			22 45

	VT	XC	LM	LM	XC	VT	XC		LM	LM
	◇1	◇1		1	◇1	◇1	◇1			1
	⊡					⊡				
Crewe 65,50 d				21 17		22 04				22 24
Alsager 50 d										
Kidsgrove 50 d										
Hanley Bus Station d										
Stoke-on-Trent 50 d		21 07			21 45		22 07			
Wedgwood Old Road Bridge d										
Barlaston Orchard Place d										
Stone Granville Square d										
Stone d										
Norton Bridge Station Drv d										
Stafford d		21a26		21a42	22a02	22a22	22a28			22a44
Rugeley Trent Valley d										
Lichfield Trent Valley d										
Tamworth d										
Polesworth d										
Atherstone d										
Nuneaton a										
d			21 15						22 15	
Bedworth d			21 22						22 22	
Coventry a			21 34						22 34	
Rugby a										
Northampton 68 a	↤									
Milton Keynes Central 66 a	22 04									
Watford Junction 66 a	22s34									
London Euston 15 ⊖66 a	22 55									

Saturdays

15 February to 17 May

	AW	LM	XC	VT	XC	LM	VT	VT	XC		LM	LM	VT	LM	VT	VT	VT	LM	LM		XC	LM	VT	LM
			◇1	◇1	◇1	1	◇1	◇1	◇1		1	1	◇1	1	◇1	◇1	◇1		1		◇1	1	◇1	
			⊥	⊡	⊥		⊡	⊡	⊥				⊡		⊡	⊡	⊡				⊥		⊡	🚌
Crewe 65,50 d	04 59		05 47	06 00		06 11		06 29			06 47	06 59	07 01	07 16	07 20	07 29	07 41					07 49	07 55	
Alsager 50 d												07 07												
Kidsgrove 50 d												07 12												
Hanley Bus Station d																								
Stoke-on-Trent 50 d			06 08						06 39			07 20									07 44			
Wedgwood Old Road Bridge d																								
Barlaston Orchard Place d																								
Stone Granville Square d																								
Stone d												07 29												
Norton Bridge Station Drv d					↤														↤					07 52
Stafford d	05a24		06 26	06 19	06 26	06a34	06 36		06a57		07a10	07 48		07a37	07 39				07 48		08a02	08a09	08 16	08a22
Rugeley Trent Valley d			↦									↦							07 57					
Lichfield Trent Valley d																			08 05				08 31	
Tamworth d																			08 11				08 38	
Polesworth d																								
Atherstone d																			08 20					
Nuneaton a							06 58												08 26					
d		06 47					06 59											08 14	08 27					
Bedworth d		06 54																08 21						
Coventry a		07 06			07 24								08 29					08 33						
Rugby a				06 50															08 42					
Northampton 68 a																								
Milton Keynes Central 66 a				07 11				07 31					08 58						09 05					
Watford Junction 66 a				07s32			07s45																	
London Euston 15 ⊖66 a				07 53			08 05	08 10					09 34		09 00	09 05	09 30		09 50				09 47	

A ⊥ to Stafford

Table 67R

Saturdays

15 February to 17 May

Crewe and Stoke-on-Trent - London
Nuneaton - Coventry

Network Diagram - refer to first Page of Table 67

	XC ◇1	VT ◇1	LM 1	LM 1	VT ◇1		LM	LM 1	VT ◇1	LM	XC ◇1	LM 1	VT ◇1	LM 1	XC ◇1		VT ◇1	LM	LM 1	LM 1	VT ◇1	LM 1	VT ◇1	XC ◇1
Crewe 65,50 d		08 01	08 02	08 19	08 22				08 29			08 49	08 56				09 01		09 02	09 19	09 25		09 30	
Alsager 50 d			08 11																09 11					
Kidsgrove 50 d			08 15																09 15					
Hanley Bus Station d										08 35														
Stoke-on-Trent 50 d	08 07		08 28							08 41	08 44				09 07				09 28					09 44
Wedgwood Old Road Bridge d										08 53														
Barlaston Orchard Place d										08 57														
Stone Granville Square d										09a10														
Stone d			08 36																09 36					
Norton Bridge Station Drv d								←														←		
Stafford d	08 26		08 56	08a42	08 42			08 56			09a02	09a09			09 26				09 56	09a45	09 44	09 56		10a02
Rugeley Trent Valley d			↪					09 05											↪			10 05		
Lichfield Trent Valley d								09 13														10 13		
Tamworth d								09 20														10 20		
Polesworth d																								
Atherstone d								09 28														10 28		
Nuneaton a					09 04			09 35														10 35		
d					09 05		09 15	09 36										10 15				10 36		
Bedworth d							09 22											10 22						
Coventry a	09 24	09 30					09 34								10 24		10 30	10 34						
Rugby a								09 51														10 51		
Northampton 68 a														←										
Milton Keynes Central 66 a		09 58						10 14					10 02	10 14			10 58					11 14		
Watford Junction 66 a								↪														↪		
London Euston 15 ⊖66 a		10 35			10 06				10 11				10 39	10 50			11 33				11 05		11 08	

	LM 1		LM	VT ◇1	LM 1	XC ◇1	VT ◇1	LM	LM 1	LM 1	VT ◇1		LM 1	VT ◇1	LM	XC ◇1	LM 1	VT ◇1	LM 1	XC ◇1	VT ◇1		LM	LM 1
Crewe 65,50 d	09 49			09 56			10 01		10 02	10 19	10 22			10 29			10 49	10 56			11 01			11 02
Alsager 50 d									10 11															11 11
Kidsgrove 50 d									10 15															11 15
Hanley Bus Station d															10 35									
Stoke-on-Trent 50 d						10 07			10 28						10 41	10 44				11 07				11 28
Wedgwood Old Road Bridge d															10 53									
Barlaston Orchard Place d															10 57									
Stone Granville Square d															11a10									
Stone d									10 36															11 36
Norton Bridge Station Drv d			09 52										←											
Stafford d	10a10		10a22			10 26			10 56	10a42	10 42		10 56			11a02	11a09			11 26				11 56
Rugeley Trent Valley d									↪				11 05											↪
Lichfield Trent Valley d													11 13											
Tamworth d													11 20											
Polesworth d																								
Atherstone d													11 28											
Nuneaton a													11 35											
d								11 15					11 36										12 15	
Bedworth d								11 22															12 22	
Coventry a						11 24	11 30	11 34												12 24	12 30		12 34	
Rugby a													11 51											
Northampton 68 a					←														←					
Milton Keynes Central 66 a				11 02	11 14		11 58						12 14					12 02	12 14		12 58			
Watford Junction 66 a													↪											
London Euston 15 ⊖66 a				11 39	11 50		12 33				11 59			12 05				12 39	12 50		13 35			

	LM 1	VT ◇1	LM 1	VT ◇1	XC ◇1	LM 1	VT ◇1		LM 1	XC ◇1	LM	VT ◇1	LM	LM 1	LM 1	VT ◇1	LM 1		VT ◇1	LM	XC ◇1	LM 1	VT ◇1	LM 1
Crewe 65,50 d	11 19	11 22		11 29		11 49	11 56					12 01		12 02	12 19	12 22			12 29			12 49	12 56	
Alsager 50 d														12 11										
Kidsgrove 50 d														12 15										
Hanley Bus Station d																				12 35				
Stoke-on-Trent 50 d					11 44					12 07				12 28						12 41	12 44			
Wedgwood Old Road Bridge d																				12 53				
Barlaston Orchard Place d																				12 57				
Stone Granville Square d											11 39									13a10				
Stone d														12 36										
Norton Bridge Station Drv d			←								12 02						←							
Stafford d	11a42	11 42	11 56		12a02	12a09				12 25	12a32			12 56	12a42	12 42	12 56				13a02	13a09		
Rugeley Trent Valley d			12 05											↪			13 05							
Lichfield Trent Valley d			12 13														13 13							
Tamworth d			12 20														13 20							
Polesworth d																								
Atherstone d			12 28														13 28							
Nuneaton a			12 35														13 35							
d			12 36										13 15				13 36							
Bedworth d													13 22											
Coventry a										13 24		13 30	13 34											
Rugby a			12 51														13 51							
Northampton 68 a									←															←
Milton Keynes Central 66 a			13 14				13 02		13 14			13 58					14 14						14 02	14 14
Watford Junction 66 a			↪														↪							
London Euston 15 ⊖66 a		12 59		13 05			13 39		13 50			14 33				14 00			14 05				14 39	14 50

Table 67R

Saturdays

15 February to 17 May

Crewe and Stoke-on-Trent - London
Nuneaton - Coventry

Network Diagram - refer to first Page of Table 67

	XC	VT	LM		LM	LM	VT	LM	VT	XC	LM	LM	VT		LM	XC	VT	LM	LM	LM	VT	LM	VT	
	◇1	◇1			1	1	◇1	1	◇1	◇1	1		◇1		1	◇1	◇1		1	1	◇1	1	◇1	
	🛒	☕					☕		☕	🛒		🚌	☕			🛒	☕				☕		☕	
Crewe 65,50 d		13 01			13 02	13 19	13 25		13 30		13 49		13 56				14 01		14 02	14 19	14 22		14 29	
Alsager 50 d					13 11														14 11					
Kidsgrove 50 d					13 15														14 15					
Hanley Bus Station d																								
Stoke-on-Trent 50 d	13 07				13 28					13 44						14 07			14 28					
Wedgwood Old Road Bridge d																								
Barlaston Orchard Place d																								
Stone Granville Square d												13 39												
Stone d					13 36														14 36					
Norton Bridge Station Drv d								←				13 54										←		
Stafford d	13 26				13 56	13a45	13 44	13 56		14a02	14a09	14a15				14 26			14 56	14a42	14 42	14 56		
Rugeley Trent Valley d					→			14 05											→			15 05		
Lichfield Trent Valley d								14 13														15 13		
Tamworth d								14 20														15 20		
Polesworth d																								
Atherstone d								14 28														15 28		
Nuneaton a								14 35														15 35		
d			14 15					14 36										15 15				15 36		
Bedworth d			14 22															15 22						
Coventry a	14 24	14 30	14 34													15 24	15 30	15 34						
Rugby a								14 51														15 51		
Northampton 68 a															←									
Milton Keynes Central 66 a		14 58						15 14					15 02		15 14		15 58					16 14		
Watford Junction 66 a								→														→		
London Euston 15 ⊖66 a		15 34					15 05		15 09				15 39		15 50		16 34				15 59		16 05	

	LM	XC	LM	VT	LM	XC	VT	LM	LM		LM	VT	LM	VT	XC	LM	LM	VT	LM		XC	VT	LM	LM
		◇1	1	◇1	1	◇1	◇1		1		1	◇1	1	◇1	◇1	1		◇1	1		◇1	◇1		1
	🚌	🛒		☕		🛒	☕					☕		☕	🛒		🚌	☕			🛒	☕		
Crewe 65,50 d			14 49	14 56			15 01		15 02		15 19	15 22		15 29		15 49		15 56				16 01		16 02
Alsager 50 d									15 11															16 11
Kidsgrove 50 d									15 15															16 15
Hanley Bus Station d	14 35																							
Stoke-on-Trent 50 d	14 41	14 44				15 07			15 28						15 44						16 07			16 28
Wedgwood Old Road Bridge d	14 53																							
Barlaston Orchard Place d	14 57																							
Stone Granville Square d	15a10																15 29							
Stone d									15 36															16 36
Norton Bridge Station Drv d													←				15 52							
Stafford d		15a02	15a09			15 26			15 56		15a42	15 42	15 56		16a02	16a09	16a13				16 25			16 56
Rugeley Trent Valley d									→				16 05											→
Lichfield Trent Valley d													16 13											
Tamworth d													16 20											
Polesworth d																								
Atherstone d													16 28											
Nuneaton a													16 35											
d								16 15					16 36										17 15	
Bedworth d								16 22															17 22	
Coventry a						16 24	16 30	16 34													17 24	17 30	17 34	
Rugby a													16 51											
Northampton 68 a					←														←					
Milton Keynes Central 66 a				16 02	16 14		16 58						17 14					17 02	17 14			17 58		
Watford Junction 66 a													→											
London Euston 15 ⊖66 a				16 39	16 50		17 33					16 59		17 05				17 39	17 50			18 34		

	LM	VT	LM	VT	XC		LM	LM	VT	LM	XC	VT	LM	LM	LM		VT	VT	LM	XC	LM	LM	XC	VT
	1	◇1	1	◇1	◇1			1	◇1	1	◇1	◇1		1	1		◇1	◇1	1	◇1		1	◇1	◇1
		☕		☕	🛒		🚌		☕		🛒	☕					☕	☕		🛒	🚌		🛒	☕
Crewe 65,50 d	16 19	16 22		16 29				16 49	16 56			17 01		17 02	17 19		17 23	17 29				17 49		
Alsager 50 d														17 11										
Kidsgrove 50 d														17 15										
Hanley Bus Station d																								
Stoke-on-Trent 50 d					16 44		16 47				17 07			17 28						17 45	17 47		18 07	
Wedgwood Old Road Bridge d							16 59														17 59			
Barlaston Orchard Place d							17 03														18 03			
Stone Granville Square d							17a16														18a16			
Stone d														17 36										
Norton Bridge Station Drv d			←																←					
Stafford d	16a44	16 42	16 56		17a02			17a09			17 26			17 56	17a43		17 43		17 56	18a03		18a09	18 26	18 36
Rugeley Trent Valley d			17 05											→					18 05					
Lichfield Trent Valley d			17 13																18 13					
Tamworth d			17 20																18 20					
Polesworth d																								
Atherstone d			17 28																18 28					
Nuneaton a			17 35																18 35					
d			17 36										18 15						18 36					
Bedworth d													18 22											
Coventry a											18 24	18 30	18 34										19 24	
Rugby a			17 51																18 51					
Northampton 68 a										←														
Milton Keynes Central 66 a			18 14						18 02	18 14		18 58							19 14					
Watford Junction 66 a			→																					
London Euston 15 ⊖66 a		17 59		18 05					18 39	18 50		19 34					19 01	19 09	19 50					19 59

Table 67R

Saturdays

15 February to 17 May

Crewe and Stoke-on-Trent - London
Nuneaton - Coventry

Network Diagram - refer to first Page of Table 67

			VT		LM	LM	LM	VT	XC	LM	XC	VT	VT		LM	LM	VT	XC	LM	XC	VT	LM	VT		XC	VT
			◇1		1		1	◇1	◇1	1	◇1	◇1	◇1		1	1	◇1	◇1	1	◇1	◇1	1	◇1		◇1	◇1
																				A						
			☕					☕	🛒		🛒	☕	☕				☕	🛒		🛒	☕		☕			☕
Crewe	65,50	d	18 01		18 02		18 22	18 29		18 49			19 01		19 02	19 21	19 29		19 51		20 01	20 18	20 23			20 47
Alsager	50	d			18 11										19 11											
Kidsgrove	50	d			18 15										19 15											
Hanley Bus Station		d																								
Stoke-on-Trent	50	d			18 28				18 44		19 07				19 28			19 44		20 07					20 44	
Wedgwood Old Road Bridge		d																								
Barlaston Orchard Place		d																								
Stone Granville Square		d																								
Stone		d			18 36										19 36											
Norton Bridge Station Drv		d																								
Stafford		d			18 56		18a42		19a02	19a09	19 25	19 36			19 51	19a45		20a02	20a11	20 26		20a40	20 43		21a02	
Rugeley Trent Valley		d			19 05										20 00											
Lichfield Trent Valley		d			19 13										20 08											
Tamworth		d			19 20										20 15											
Polesworth		d																								
Atherstone		d			19 28										20 23											
Nuneaton		a			19 35										20 30											
		d			19 36	19 46									20 31											
Bedworth		d				19 53																				
Coventry		a	19 30			20 05					20 24		20 30							21 24	21 30					
Rugby		a	19 42		19 51								20 42		20 46						21 42					
Northampton	68	a			20 12										21 07											
Milton Keynes Central	66	a	20 05										21 04								22 04					21 51
Watford Junction	66	a	20s34										21s35								↪					
London Euston 15	⊖66	a	20 55					20 05				21 15	21 56				21 20						22 15			22 45

			VT	XC	LM	LM	XC	VT	VT		XC	LM	LM
			◇1	◇1		1	◇1	◇1	◇1		◇1		1
			☕					☕	☕				
Crewe	65,50	d				21 17		21 43	22 04				22 24
Alsager	50	d											
Kidsgrove	50	d											
Hanley Bus Station		d											
Stoke-on-Trent	50	d		21 07			21 45				22 07		
Wedgwood Old Road Bridge		d											
Barlaston Orchard Place		d											
Stone Granville Square		d											
Stone		d											
Norton Bridge Station Drv		d											
Stafford		d		21a26		21a42	22a02	22a07	22a22		22a28		22a44
Rugeley Trent Valley		d											
Lichfield Trent Valley		d											
Tamworth		d											
Polesworth		d											
Atherstone		d											
Nuneaton		a											
		d			21 15							22 15	
Bedworth		d			21 22							22 22	
Coventry		a			21 34							22 34	
Rugby		a											
Northampton	68	a	↤										
Milton Keynes Central	66	a	22 04										
Watford Junction	66	a	22s34										
London Euston 15	⊖66	a	22 55										

Sundays

8 December to 29 December

			VT	VT	XC	VT	LM	VT	XC	VT	LM		LM	LM	VT	VT	XC	VT	LM	LM	VT		LM	XC	LM	VT
			◇1	◇1	◇1	◇1	1	◇1	◇1	◇1	1		1	1	◇1	◇1	◇1	◇1		1	◇1		1	◇1	1	◇1
					A				A															A		
			☕	☕	🛒	☕		☕	🛒	☕					☕	☕	🛒	☕			☕			🛒		☕
Crewe	65,50	d	08 43	08 53	09 05	09 13	09 30	09 43		10 14			10 20	10 37	10 43	10 55		11 14		11 37	11 49				12 19	12 23
Alsager	50	d					09 38							10 46						11 46						
Kidsgrove	50	d					09 43							10 50						11 50						
Hanley Bus Station		d																								
Stoke-on-Trent	50	d					09 51		10 07					10 59			11 07			11 59				12 07		
Wedgwood Old Road Bridge		d																								
Barlaston Orchard Place		d																								
Stone Granville Square		d																								
Stone		d					10 00							11 07						12 07						
Norton Bridge Station Drv		d																								
Stafford		d	09 03		09 26	09 33	10 18		10 27	10 34			10a41	11 18			11 28	11 36		12 18				12 25	12a40	12 44
Rugeley Trent Valley		d					10 27							11 27						12 27						
Lichfield Trent Valley		d					10 35							11 35						12 35						
Tamworth		d					10 42							11 42						12 42						
Polesworth		d																								
Atherstone		d					10 51							11 51						12 51						
Nuneaton		a				09 55	10 57			10 56				11 57				11 58		12 57	12 31					
		d				09 56	10 58			10 57				11 58				11 59	12 30	12 58	12 32					
Bedworth		d																	12 36							
Coventry		a			10 24				11 24								12 24		12 54					13 24		
Rugby		a					11 17	10 32						12 13	11 32					13 13						
Northampton	68	a					11 41				↤			12 42						13 41			↤			
Milton Keynes Central	66	a		10 18			12 02	11 07		11 46	12 02			13 04	12 07					14 04	13 04		13 04			
Watford Junction	66	a	10s35			11s16	↪	11s44			12 32			↪		12s36		12s52		↪			13 34			
London Euston 15	⊖66	a	10 58	11 06		11 37		12 06		12 32	12 51				12 46	12 57		13 13			13 46		13 53			14 04

A 🛒 to Stafford

Table 67R

Sundays

8 December to 29 December

Crewe and Stoke-on-Trent - London
Nuneaton - Coventry

Network Diagram - refer to first Page of Table 67

			VT	LM	VT	LM	XC		VT	LM	VT	VT	LM	LM	VT	LM	XC		VT	LM	VT	VT	LM	LM	VT	VT
			◇1	1	◇1	1	◇1		◇1	1	◇1	◇1		1	◇1	1	◇1		◇1	1	◇1	◇1		1	◇1	◇1
							A										A									
			☕		☕		🛒		☕		☕	☕			☕		🛒		☕		☕	☕			☕	☕
Crewe	65,50	d	12 30	12 37	12 55				13 01	13 19	13 23	13 30		13 37	13 52				14 01	14 19	14 23	14 29		14 33	14 54	14 55
Alsager	50	d		12 46										13 46										14 42		
Kidsgrove	50	d		12 50										13 50										14 46		
Hanley Bus Station		d																								
Stoke-on-Trent	50	d		12 59			13 07							13 59			14 07							14 55		
Wedgwood Old Road Bridge		d																								
Barlaston Orchard Place		d																								
Stone Granville Square		d																								
Stone		d		13 07										14 07										15 03		
Norton Bridge Station Drv		d																								
Stafford		d		13 18			13 25			13a40	13 44			14 18			14 25			14a40	14 44			15 18		
Rugeley Trent Valley		d		13 27										14 27										15 27		
Lichfield Trent Valley		d		13 35										14 35										15 35		
Tamworth		d		13 42										14 42										15 42		
Polesworth		d																								
Atherstone		d		13 51										14 51										15 51		
Nuneaton		a		13 57										14 57	14 32									15 57		
		d		13 58									14 11	14 58	14 33								15 11	15 58		
Bedworth		d											14 17										15 17			
Coventry		a					14 24		14 30				14 34				15 24		15 30				15 34			
Rugby		a		14 13										15 13										16 13		
Northampton	68	a		14 42		←								15 42		←								16 41		
Milton Keynes Central	66	a		15 04	14 03	14 04			14 58					16 04	15 03	15 04			15 58					17 04	16 03	16 03
Watford Junction	66	a		→		14 34								→		15 34								→		
London Euston 15	⊖66	a	14 10		14 44	14 53			15 39		15 04	15 08			15 45	15 53			16 39		16 04	16 07			16 44	16 41

			LM		XC	VT	LM	VT	VT	LM	LM	VT	LM		XC	VT	LM	VT	VT	LM	LM	VT	LM		XC	VT
			1		◇1	◇1	1	◇1	◇1		1	◇1	1		◇1	◇1	1	◇1	◇1		1	◇1	1		◇1	◇1
					A										A										A	
					🛒	☕		☕	☕			☕			🛒	☕		☕	☕			☕			🛒	☕
Crewe	65,50	d				15 01	15 19	15 23	15 29		15 37	15 54				16 01	16 19	16 23	16 29		16 33	16 54				17 00
Alsager	50	d									15 46										16 42					
Kidsgrove	50	d									15 50										16 46					
Hanley Bus Station		d																								
Stoke-on-Trent	50	d			15 07						15 59				16 07						16 55				17 08	
Wedgwood Old Road Bridge		d																								
Barlaston Orchard Place		d																								
Stone Granville Square		d																								
Stone		d									16 07										17 03					
Norton Bridge Station Drv		d																								
Stafford		d			15 25		15a40	15 44			16 18				16 25		16a40	16 44			17 18				17 26	
Rugeley Trent Valley		d									16 27										17 27					
Lichfield Trent Valley		d									16 35										17 35	17 26				
Tamworth		d									16 42										17 42					
Polesworth		d																								
Atherstone		d									16 51										17 51					
Nuneaton		a									16 57										17 57					
		d								16 11	16 58									17 11	17 58					
Bedworth		d								16 17										17 17						
Coventry		a			16 24	16 31				16 34					17 24	17 29				17 34					18 24	18 31
Rugby		a									17 13										18 13					
Northampton	68	a	←								17 42		←								18 42		←			
Milton Keynes Central	66	a	16 04			16 58					18 04	17 03	17 04			17 58					19 04	18 03	18 04			18 58
Watford Junction	66	a	16 34								→		17 34								→		18 34			
London Euston 15	⊖66	a	16 53			17 38		17 04	17 09			17 44	17 53			18 38		18 03	18 09			18 44	18 53			19 38

			LM	VT	VT	LM	LM	VT	LM		XC	VT	LM	VT	VT	LM	VT	LM	XC		VT	LM	VT	VT	LM	LM
			1	◇1	◇1		1	◇1	1		◇1	◇1	1	◇1	◇1	1	◇1	1	◇1		◇1	1	◇1	◇1	1	
											A								A							
				☕	☕			☕			🛒	☕		☕	☕		☕		🛒		☕		☕	☕		
Crewe	65,50	d	17 19	17 23	17 29		17 37	17 55				18 01	18 19	18 23	18 29	18 37	18 55				19 01	19 19	19 23	19 29		
Alsager	50	d					17 46									18 46										
Kidsgrove	50	d					17 50									18 50										
Hanley Bus Station		d																								
Stoke-on-Trent	50	d					17 59				18 08					18 59			19 07							
Wedgwood Old Road Bridge		d																								
Barlaston Orchard Place		d																								
Stone Granville Square		d																								
Stone		d					18 07									19 07										
Norton Bridge Station Drv		d																								
Stafford		d	17a40	17 44			18 18				18 27		18a40	18 44		19 18			19 25			19a40	19 44			
Rugeley Trent Valley		d					18 27									19 27										
Lichfield Trent Valley		d					18 35									19 35										
Tamworth		d					18 42									19 42										
Polesworth		d																								
Atherstone		d					18 51									19 51										
Nuneaton		a					18 57									19 57										
		d				18 11	18 58									19 58										20 11
Bedworth		d				18 17																				20 17
Coventry		a				18 34					19 24	19 30							20 24		20 30					20 34
Rugby		a					19 13									20 13										
Northampton	68	a					19 42		←							20 36		←							←	
Milton Keynes Central	66	a					20 06	19 03	19 04			19 58				21 07	20 03	20 06			20 59				21 07	
Watford Junction	66	a					→		19 34							→		20 34							21 35	
London Euston 15	⊖66	a		19 04	19 07			19 45	19 53			20 39		20 05	20 08		20 46	20 53			21 48		21 04	21 10	21 55	

A 🛒 to Stafford

Table 67R

Sundays

8 December to 29 December

Crewe and Stoke-on-Trent - London
Nuneaton - Coventry

Network Diagram - refer to first Page of Table 67

	LM	XC	LM		VT	XC	LM	LM	VT	LM	AW	LM	VT		VT	XC	LM	XC						
	1	◇1	1		◇1	◇1		1	◇1	1	◇	1	◇1		◇1	◇1	1	◇1						
		🛒			☕				☕		🛒		☕		☕									
Crewe 65,50 d	19 37		20 18		20 24			20 44	20 47		20 52	21 18	21 23		21 40		22 22							
Alsager 50 d	19 46							20 53																
Kidsgrove 50 d	19 50							20 59																
Hanley Bus Station d																								
Stoke-on-Trent 50 d	19 59	20 07				20 47		21 06								21 47		22 47						
Wedgwood Old Road Bridge d																								
Barlaston Orchard Place d																								
Stone Granville Square d																								
Stone d	20 07							21 14																
Norton Bridge Station Drv d																								
Stafford d	20 18	20 27	20a38		20 43	21a08		21 25			21a16	21a39	21 44		22a01	22a06	22a42	23a04						
Rugeley Trent Valley d	20 27							21 34																
Lichfield Trent Valley d	20 35							21 42					22 00											
Tamworth d	20 42							21 49					22 07											
Polesworth d																								
Atherstone d	20 51							21 57																
Nuneaton a	20 57							22 04					22 17											
d	20 58						22 00	22 05					22 18											
Bedworth d							22 06																	
Coventry a		21 23					22 21																	
Rugby a	21 13							22 20					22 31											
Northampton 68 a	21 42							22 43		←														
Milton Keynes Central 66 a	22 10				21 36				21 52	22 10			23 04											
Watford Junction 66 a	↪								22s31	22 52			23s34											
London Euston 15 ⊖66 a					22 28				22 55	23 15			23 54											

Sundays

5 January to 9 February

	VT	VT	XC	VT	LM	VT	XC	VT	LM		LM	LM	VT	VT	XC	VT	LM	VT	LM		VT	LM	XC	LM
	◇1	◇1	◇1	◇1	1	◇1	◇1	◇1	1		1	1	◇1	◇1	◇1	◇1		◇1	1		◇1	1	◇1	1
			A				A																A	
	☕	☕	🛒	☕		☕	🛒	☕					☕	☕	🛒	☕		☕			☕		🛒	
Crewe 65,50 d	08 43	08 53	09 05	09 13	09 30	09 43		10 14			10 20	10 37	10 43	10 55		11 14		11 35	11 37		11 49			12 19
Alsager 50 d					09 38							10 46							11 46					
Kidsgrove 50 d					09 43							10 50							11 50					
Hanley Bus Station d																								
Stoke-on-Trent 50 d					09 51		10 07					10 59			11 07				11 59				12 07	
Wedgwood Old Road Bridge d																								
Barlaston Orchard Place d																								
Stone Granville Square d																								
Stone d					10 00							11 07							12 07					
Norton Bridge Station Drv d																								
Stafford d	09 03		09 26	09 33	10 18		10 27	10 34			10a41	11 18			11 28	11 36			12 18				12 25	12a40
Rugeley Trent Valley d					10 27							11 27							12 27					
Lichfield Trent Valley d					10 35							11 35							12 35					
Tamworth d					10 42							11 42							12 42					
Polesworth d																								
Atherstone d					10 51							11 51							12 51					
Nuneaton a				09 55	10 57			10 56				11 57				11 58			12 57		12 31			
d				09 56	10 58			10 57				11 58				11 59	12 30		12 58		12 32			
Bedworth d																	12 36							
Coventry a			10 24				11 24								12 24		12 54						13 24	
Rugby a					11 17	10 32						12 13	11 33						13 13					
Northampton 68 a					11 41				←			12 42							13 41			←		
Milton Keynes Central 66 a		10 18			12 02	11 07		11 46	12 02			13 04	12 07						14 04		13 04	13 04		
Watford Junction 66 a	10s35			11s16	↪	11s44			12 32			↪		12s36		12s52			↪			13 34		
London Euston 15 ⊖66 a	10 58	11 06		11 37		12 06		12 32	12 51				12 48	12 57		13 13		13 22			13 46	13 53		

	VT	VT	LM	VT	LM		XC	VT	LM	VT	VT	LM	LM	VT	LM		XC	VT	LM	VT	VT	LM	LM	VT
	◇1	◇1	1	◇1	1		◇1	◇1	1	◇1	◇1		1	◇1	1		◇1	◇1	1	◇1	◇1		1	◇1
							A										A							
	☕	☕		☕			🛒	☕		☕	☕			☕			🛒	☕		☕	☕			☕
Crewe 65,50 d	12 23	12 30	12 37	12 55				13 01	13 19	13 23	13 30		13 37	13 52				14 01	14 19	14 23	14 29		14 33	14 54
Alsager 50 d			12 46										13 46										14 42	
Kidsgrove 50 d			12 50										13 50										14 46	
Hanley Bus Station d																								
Stoke-on-Trent 50 d			12 59				13 07						13 59				14 07						14 55	
Wedgwood Old Road Bridge d																								
Barlaston Orchard Place d																								
Stone Granville Square d																								
Stone d			13 07										14 07										15 03	
Norton Bridge Station Drv d																								
Stafford d	12 44		13 18				13 25		13a40	13 44			14 18				14 25		14a40	14 44			15 18	
Rugeley Trent Valley d			13 27										14 27										15 27	
Lichfield Trent Valley d			13 35										14 35										15 35	
Tamworth d			13 42										14 42										15 42	
Polesworth d																								
Atherstone d			13 51										14 51										15 51	
Nuneaton a			13 57										14 57	14 32									15 57	
d			13 58									14 11	14 58	14 33								15 11	15 58	
Bedworth d												14 17										15 17		
Coventry a							14 24	14 30				14 34					15 24	15 30				15 34		
Rugby a			14 13										15 13										16 13	
Northampton 68 a			14 42		←								15 42		←								16 41	
Milton Keynes Central 66 a			15 04	14 03	14 04			14 58					16 04	15 03	15 04			15 58					17 04	16 03
Watford Junction 66 a			↪		14 34								↪		15 34								↪	
London Euston 15 ⊖66 a	14 04	14 10		14 44	14 53			15 39		15 04	15 08			15 45	15 53			16 39		16 04	16 07			16 44

A 🛒 to Stafford

Table 67R

Sundays

5 January to 9 February

Crewe and Stoke-on-Trent - London
Nuneaton - Coventry

Network Diagram - refer to first Page of Table 67

	VT		LM	XC	VT	LM	VT	VT	LM	LM	VT		LM	XC	VT	LM	VT	VT	LM	LM	VT		LM	XC
	◇1		1	◇1	◇1	1	◇1	◇1		1	◇1		1	◇1	◇1	1	◇1	◇1		1	◇1		1	◇1
				A										A										A
	🍴			🚲	🍴		🍴	🍴			🍴			🚲	🍴		🍴	🍴			🍴			🚲
Crewe 65,50 d	14 55				15 01	15 19	15 23	15 29		15 37	15 54				16 01	16 19	16 23	16 29		16 33	16 54			
Alsager 50 d										15 46										16 42				
Kidsgrove 50 d										15 50										16 46				
Hanley Bus Station d																								
Stoke-on-Trent 50 d				15 07						15 59				16 07						16 55				17 08
Wedgwood Old Road Bridge d																								
Barlaston Orchard Place d																								
Stone Granville Square d																								
Stone d										16 07										17 03				
Norton Bridge Station Drv d																								
Stafford d				15 25		15a40	15 44			16 18				16 25		16a40	16 44			17 18				17 26
Rugeley Trent Valley d										16 27										17 27				
Lichfield Trent Valley d										16 35										17 35	17 26			
Tamworth d										16 42										17 42				
Polesworth d																								
Atherstone d										16 51										17 51				
Nuneaton a										16 57										17 57				
d									16 11	16 58									17 11	17 58				
Bedworth d									16 17										17 17					
Coventry a				16 24	16 31				16 34					17 24	17 30				17 34					18 24
Rugby a										17 13										18 13				
Northampton 68 a			←							17 42			←							18 42			←	
Milton Keynes Central 66 a	16 03		16 04		16 58					18 04	17 03		17 04		17 58					19 04	18 03		18 04	
Watford Junction 66 a			16 34							→			17 34							→			18 34	
London Euston 15 ⊖66 a	16 41		16 53		17 38		17 04	17 09			17 44		17 53		18 38		18 03	18 09			18 44		18 53	

	VT	LM	VT	VT	LM	LM	VT		VT	LM	XC	VT	LM	VT	VT	LM	VT		LM	XC	VT	LM	VT	VT
	◇1	1	◇1	◇1		1	◇1		◇1	1	◇1	◇1	1	◇1	◇1	1	◇1		1	◇1	◇1	1	◇1	◇1
											A									A				
	🍴		🍴	🍴			🍴		🍴		🚲	🍴		🍴	🍴		🍴			🚲	🍴		🍴	🍴
Crewe 65,50 d	17 00	17 19	17 23	17 29		17 37	17 42		17 55			18 01	18 19	18 23	18 29	18 37	18 55				19 01	19 19	19 23	19 29
Alsager 50 d						17 46										18 46								
Kidsgrove 50 d						17 50										18 50								
Hanley Bus Station d																								
Stoke-on-Trent 50 d						17 59					18 08					18 59				19 07				
Wedgwood Old Road Bridge d																								
Barlaston Orchard Place d																								
Stone Granville Square d																								
Stone d						18 07										19 07								
Norton Bridge Station Drv d																								
Stafford d		17a40	17 44			18 18					18 27		18a40	18 44		19 18				19 25		19a40	19 44	
Rugeley Trent Valley d						18 27										19 27								
Lichfield Trent Valley d						18 35										19 35								
Tamworth d						18 42										19 42								
Polesworth d																								
Atherstone d						18 51										19 51								
Nuneaton a						18 57										19 57								
d					18 11	18 58										19 58								
Bedworth d					18 17																			
Coventry a	18 31				18 34						19 24	19 30								20 24	20 30			
Rugby a						19 13										20 13								
Northampton 68 a						19 42				←						20 36			←					
Milton Keynes Central 66 a	18 58					20 06			19 03	19 04		19 58				21 07	20 03		20 06		20 59			
Watford Junction 66 a						→				19 34						→			20 34					
London Euston 15 ⊖66 a	19 38		19 04	19 07			19 32		19 45	19 53		20 39		20 05	20 08		20 46		20 53		21 48		21 04	21 10

	LM	LM	LM		XC	LM	VT	XC	LM	LM	VT	LM	AW		LM	VT	VT	XC	LM	XC				
	1		1		◇1	1	◇1	◇1		1	◇1	1	◇		1	◇1	◇1	◇1	1	◇1				
					🚲		🍴				🍴		🚲			🍴	🍴							
Crewe 65,50 d			19 37			20 18	20 24			20 44	20 47		20 52		21 18	21 23	21 40		22 22					
Alsager 50 d			19 46							20 53														
Kidsgrove 50 d			19 50							20 59														
Hanley Bus Station d																								
Stoke-on-Trent 50 d			19 59		20 07			20 47		21 06								21 47		22 47				
Wedgwood Old Road Bridge d																								
Barlaston Orchard Place d																								
Stone Granville Square d																								
Stone d			20 07							21 14														
Norton Bridge Station Drv d																								
Stafford d			20 18		20 27	20a38	20 43	21a08		21 25			21a16		21a39	21 44	22a01	22a06	22a42	23a04				
Rugeley Trent Valley d			20 27							21 34														
Lichfield Trent Valley d			20 35							21 42						22 00								
Tamworth d			20 42							21 49						22 07								
Polesworth d																								
Atherstone d			20 51							21 57														
Nuneaton a			20 57							22 04						22 17								
d		20 11	20 58						22 00	22 05						22 18								
Bedworth d		20 17							22 06															
Coventry a		20 34			21 23				22 21															
Rugby a			21 13							22 20						22 31								
Northampton 68 a	←		21 42							22 43		←												
Milton Keynes Central 66 a	21 07		22 10				21 36				21 52	22 10				23 04								
Watford Junction 66 a	21 35		→								22s31	22 52				23s34								
London Euston 15 ⊖66 a	21 55						22 28				22 55	23 15				23 54								

A 🚲 to Stafford

Table 67R

Sundays

16 February to 23 March

Crewe and Stoke-on-Trent - London
Nuneaton - Coventry

Network Diagram - refer to first Page of Table 67

	VT	VT	XC	VT	LM	VT	XC	VT	LM		LM	LM	VT	VT	XC	VT	LM	LM	VT		LM	XC	LM	VT
	◇1	◇1	◇1	◇1	1	◇1	◇1	◇1	1		1	1	◇1	◇1	◇1	◇1		1	◇1		1	◇1	1	◇1
			A				A															A		
	☕	☕	🛒	☕		☕	🛒	☕					☕	☕	🛒	☕			☕			🛒		☕
Crewe 65,50 d	08 43	08 53	09 05	09 13	09 30	09 47		10 14			10 20	10 37	10 43	10 55		11 14		11 37	11 49				12 19	12 23
Alsager 50 d					09 38							10 46						11 46						
Kidsgrove 50 d					09 43							10 50						11 50						
Hanley Bus Station d																								
Stoke-on-Trent 50 d					09 51		10 07					10 59			11 07			11 59				12 07		
Wedgwood Old Road Bridge d																								
Barlaston Orchard Place d																								
Stone Granville Square d																								
Stone d					10 00							11 07						12 07						
Norton Bridge Station Drv d																								
Stafford d	09 03		09 26	09 33	10 18		10 27	10 34			10a41	11 18			11 28	11 36		12 18				12 25	12a40	12 44
Rugeley Trent Valley d					10 27							11 27						12 27						
Lichfield Trent Valley d					10 35							11 35						12 35						
Tamworth d					10 42							11 42						12 42						
Polesworth d																								
Atherstone d					10 51							11 51						12 51						
Nuneaton a				09 55	10 57			10 56				11 57				11 58		12 57	12 31					
d				09 56	10 58			10 57				11 58				11 59	12 30	12 58	12 32					
Bedworth d																	12 36							
Coventry a			10 24				11 24								12 24		12 54					13 24		
Rugby a					11 17	10 36						12 13	11 32					13 13						
Northampton 68 a					11 41				←			12 42						13 41			←			
Milton Keynes Central 66 a		10 18			12 02	11 11		11 46	12 02			13 04	12 07					14 04	13 04		13 04			
Watford Junction 66 a	10s35			11s16	↪	11s43			12 32			↪		12s36		12s52		↪			13 34			
London Euston 15 ⊖66 a	10 58	11 06		11 37		12 06		12 32	12 51				12 46	12 57		13 13			13 46		13 53			14 04

	VT	LM	VT	LM	XC		VT	LM	VT	VT	LM	LM	VT	LM	XC		VT	LM	VT	VT	LM	LM	VT	VT
	◇1	1	◇1	1	◇1		◇1	1	◇1	◇1		1	◇1	1	◇1		◇1	1	◇1	◇1		1	◇1	◇1
					A										A									
	☕		☕		🛒		☕		☕	☕			☕		🛒		☕		☕	☕			☕	☕
Crewe 65,50 d	12 30	12 37	12 55				13 01	13 19	13 23	13 30		13 37	13 52				14 01	14 19	14 23	14 29		14 33	14 54	14 55
Alsager 50 d		12 46										13 46										14 42		
Kidsgrove 50 d		12 50										13 50										14 46		
Hanley Bus Station d																								
Stoke-on-Trent 50 d		12 59			13 07							13 59			14 07							14 55		
Wedgwood Old Road Bridge d																								
Barlaston Orchard Place d																								
Stone Granville Square d																								
Stone d		13 07										14 07										15 03		
Norton Bridge Station Drv d																								
Stafford d		13 18			13 25			13a40	13 44			14 18			14 25			14a40	14 44			15 18		
Rugeley Trent Valley d		13 27										14 27										15 27		
Lichfield Trent Valley d		13 35										14 35										15 35		
Tamworth d		13 42										14 42										15 42		
Polesworth d																								
Atherstone d		13 51										14 51										15 51		
Nuneaton a		13 57										14 57	14 32									15 57		
d		13 58									14 11	14 58	14 33								15 11	15 58		
Bedworth d											14 17										15 17			
Coventry a					14 24		14 30				14 34				15 24		15 30				15 34			
Rugby a		14 13										15 13										16 13		
Northampton 68 a		14 42		←								15 42		←								16 41		
Milton Keynes Central 66 a		15 04	14 03	14 04			14 58					16 04	15 03	15 04			15 58					17 04	16 03	16 03
Watford Junction 66 a		↪		14 34								↪		15 34								↪		
London Euston 15 ⊖66 a	14 10		14 44	14 53			15 39		15 04	15 08			15 45	15 53			16 39		16 04	16 07			16 44	16 41

	LM		XC	VT	LM	VT	VT	LM	LM	VT	LM		XC	VT	LM	VT	VT	LM	LM	VT	LM		XC	VT
	1		◇1	◇1	1	◇1	◇1		1	◇1	1		◇1	◇1	1	◇1	◇1		1	◇1	1		◇1	◇1
			A										A										A	
			🛒	☕		☕	☕			☕			🛒	☕		☕	☕			☕			🛒	☕
Crewe 65,50 d				15 01	15 19	15 23	15 29		15 37	15 54				16 01	16 19	16 23	16 29		16 33	16 54				17 00
Alsager 50 d									15 46										16 42					
Kidsgrove 50 d									15 50										16 46					
Hanley Bus Station d																								
Stoke-on-Trent 50 d			15 07						15 59				16 07						16 55				17 08	
Wedgwood Old Road Bridge d																								
Barlaston Orchard Place d																								
Stone Granville Square d																								
Stone d									16 07										17 03					
Norton Bridge Station Drv d																								
Stafford d			15 25		15a40	15 44			16 18				16 25		16a40	16 44			17 18				17 26	
Rugeley Trent Valley d									16 27										17 27					
Lichfield Trent Valley d									16 35										17 35	17 26				
Tamworth d									16 42										17 42					
Polesworth d																								
Atherstone d									16 51										17 51					
Nuneaton a									16 57										17 57					
d								16 11	16 58									17 11	17 58					
Bedworth d								16 17										17 17						
Coventry a			16 24	16 31				16 34					17 24	17 29				17 34					18 24	18 31
Rugby a									17 13										18 13					
Northampton 68 a	←								17 42		←								18 42		←			
Milton Keynes Central 66 a	16 04			16 58					18 04	17 03	17 04			17 58					19 04	18 03	18 04			18 58
Watford Junction 66 a	16 34								↪		17 34								↪		18 34			
London Euston 15 ⊖66 a	16 53			17 38		17 04	17 09			17 44	17 53			18 38		18 03	18 09			18 44	18 53			19 38

A 🛒 to Stafford

Table 67R

Sundays

16 February to 23 March

Crewe and Stoke-on-Trent - London
Nuneaton - Coventry

Network Diagram - refer to first Page of Table 67

	LM 1	VT ◇1 🍴	VT ◇1 🍴	LM	LM 1	VT ◇1 🍴	LM 1		XC ◇1 A 🛒	VT ◇1 🍴	LM 1	VT ◇1 🍴	VT ◇1 🍴	LM 1	VT ◇1 🍴	LM 1	XC ◇1 A 🛒		VT ◇1 🍴	LM 1	VT ◇1 🍴	VT ◇1 🍴	LM 1	LM
Crewe 65,50 d	17 19	17 23	17 29		17 37	17 55				18 01	18 19	18 23	18 29	18 37	18 55				19 01	19 19	19 23	19 29		
Alsager 50 d					17 46									18 46										
Kidsgrove 50 d					17 50									18 50										
Hanley Bus Station d																								
Stoke-on-Trent 50 d					17 59				18 08					18 59			19 07							
Wedgwood Old Road Bridge d																								
Barlaston Orchard Place d																								
Stone Granville Square d																								
Stone d					18 07									19 07										
Norton Bridge Station Drv d																								
Stafford d	17a40	17 44			18 18				18 27		18a40	18 44		19 18			19 25			19a40	19 44			
Rugeley Trent Valley d					18 27									19 27										
Lichfield Trent Valley d					18 35									19 35										
Tamworth d					18 42									19 42										
Polesworth d																								
Atherstone d					18 51									19 51										
Nuneaton a					18 57									19 57										
d				18 11	18 58									19 58										20 11
Bedworth d				18 17																				20 17
Coventry a				18 34					19 24	19 30							20 24		20 30					20 34
Rugby a					19 13									20 13										
Northampton 68 a					19 42		←							20 36		←							←	
Milton Keynes Central 66 a					20 06	19 03	19 04			19 58				21 07	20 03	20 06			20 59				21 07	
Watford Junction 66 a					→		19 34							→		20 34							21 35	
London Euston 15 ⊖66 a		19 04	19 07			19 45	19 53			20 39		20 05	20 08		20 46	20 53			21 48		21 04	21 10	21 55	

	LM 1	XC ◇1 🛒	LM 1		VT ◇1 🍴	XC ◇1	LM	LM 1	VT ◇1 🍴	LM 1	AW ◇ 🛒	LM 1	VT ◇1 🍴		VT ◇1 🍴	XC ◇1	LM 1	XC ◇1						
Crewe 65,50 d	19 37		20 18		20 24			20 44	20 47		20 52	21 18	21 23		21 40		22 22							
Alsager 50 d	19 46							20 53																
Kidsgrove 50 d	19 50							20 59																
Hanley Bus Station d																								
Stoke-on-Trent 50 d	19 59	20 07				20 47		21 06								21 47		22 47						
Wedgwood Old Road Bridge d																								
Barlaston Orchard Place d																								
Stone Granville Square d																								
Stone d	20 07							21 14																
Norton Bridge Station Drv d																								
Stafford d	20 18	20 27	20a38		20 43	21a08		21 25			21a16	21a39	21 44		22a01	22a06	22a42	23a04						
Rugeley Trent Valley d	20 27							21 34																
Lichfield Trent Valley d	20 35							21 42					22 00											
Tamworth d	20 42							21 49					22 07											
Polesworth d																								
Atherstone d	20 51							21 57																
Nuneaton a	20 57							22 04					22 17											
d	20 58						22 00	22 05					22 18											
Bedworth d							22 06																	
Coventry a		21 23					22 21																	
Rugby a	21 13							22 20					22 31											
Northampton 68 a	21 42							22 43		←														
Milton Keynes Central 66 a	22 10				21 36				21 52	22 10			23 04											
Watford Junction 66 a	→								22s31	22 52			23s34											
London Euston 15 ⊖66 a					22 28				22 55	23 15			23 54											

Sundays

30 March to 11 May

	VT ◇1 🍴	VT ◇1 🍴	XC ◇1 A 🛒	VT ◇1 🍴	LM 1	VT ◇1 🍴	XC ◇1 A 🛒	VT ◇1 🍴	LM 1		LM 1	LM 1	VT ◇1 🍴	VT ◇1 🍴	XC ◇1 🛒	VT ◇1 🍴	LM	LM 1	VT ◇1 🍴		LM 1	XC ◇1 A 🛒	LM 1	VT ◇1 🍴
Crewe 65,50 d	08 43	08 53	09 05	09 13	09 30	09 43		10 14			10 20	10 37	10 43	10 55		11 14		11 37	11 49				12 19	12 23
Alsager 50 d					09 38							10 46						11 46						
Kidsgrove 50 d					09 43							10 50						11 50						
Hanley Bus Station d																								
Stoke-on-Trent 50 d					09 51		10 07					10 59			11 08			11 59				12 07		
Wedgwood Old Road Bridge d																								
Barlaston Orchard Place d																								
Stone Granville Square d																								
Stone d					10 00							11 07						12 07						
Norton Bridge Station Drv d																								
Stafford d	09 03		09 26	09 33	10 18		10 27	10 34			10a41	11 18			11 28	11 36		12 18				12 25	12a40	12 44
Rugeley Trent Valley d					10 27							11 27						12 27						
Lichfield Trent Valley d					10 35							11 35						12 35						
Tamworth d					10 42							11 42						12 42						
Polesworth d																								
Atherstone d					10 51							11 51						12 51						
Nuneaton a				09 55	10 57			10 56				11 57				11 58		12 57	12 31					
d				09 56	10 58			10 57				11 58				11 59	12 30	12 58	12 32					
Bedworth d																	12 36							
Coventry a			10 24				11 24								12 24		12 54					13 24		
Rugby a					11 17	10 32						12 13	11 32					13 13						
Northampton 68 a					11 41				←			12 42						13 41			←			
Milton Keynes Central 66 a		10 18			12 02	11 07		11 46	12 02			13 04	12 07					14 04	13 04		13 04			
Watford Junction 66 a	10s35			11s16	→	11s43			12 32			→		12s36		12s52		→			13 34			
London Euston 15 ⊖66 a	10 58	11 06		11 37		12 06		12 32	12 51				12 46	12 57		13 13			13 46		13 53			14 04

A 🛒 to Stafford

Table 67R

Sundays

30 March to 11 May

Crewe and Stoke-on-Trent - London
Nuneaton - Coventry

Network Diagram - refer to first Page of Table 67

			VT	LM	VT	LM	XC		VT	LM	VT	VT	LM	LM	VT	LM	XC		VT	LM	VT	VT	LM	LM	VT	VT
			◇1	1	◇1	1	◇1		◇1	1	◇1	◇1		1	◇1	1	◇1		◇1	1	◇1	◇1		1	◇1	◇1
							A										A									
			☕		☕		🛒		☕		☕	☕			☕		🛒		☕		☕	☕			☕	☕
Crewe	65,50	d	12 30	12 37	12 55				13 01	13 19	13 23	13 30		13 37	13 52				14 01	14 19	14 23	14 29		14 33	14 54	14 55
Alsager	50	d		12 46										13 46										14 42		
Kidsgrove	50	d		12 50										13 50										14 46		
Hanley Bus Station		d																								
Stoke-on-Trent	50	d		12 59			13 07							13 59			14 07							14 55		
Wedgwood Old Road Bridge		d																								
Barlaston Orchard Place		d																								
Stone Granville Square		d																								
Stone		d		13 07										14 07										15 03		
Norton Bridge Station Drv		d																								
Stafford		d		13 18			13 25			13a40	13 44			14 18			14 25			14a40	14 44			15 18		
Rugeley Trent Valley		d		13 27										14 27										15 27		
Lichfield Trent Valley		d		13 35										14 35										15 35		
Tamworth		d		13 42										14 42										15 42		
Polesworth		d																								
Atherstone		d		13 51										14 51										15 51		
Nuneaton		a		13 57										14 57	14 32									15 57		
		d		13 58									14 11	14 58	14 33								15 11	15 58		
Bedworth		d											14 17										15 17			
Coventry		a					14 24		14 30				14 34				15 24		15 30				15 34			
Rugby		a		14 13										15 13										16 13		
Northampton	68	a		14 42		←								15 42		←								16 41		
Milton Keynes Central	66	a		15 04	14 03	14 04			14 58					16 04	15 03	15 04			15 58					17 04	16 03	16 03
Watford Junction	66	a		→		14 34								→		15 34								→		
London Euston 15	⊖66	a	14 10		14 44	14 53			15 39		15 04	15 08			15 45	15 53			16 39		16 04	16 07			16 44	16 41

			LM		XC	VT	LM	VT	VT	LM	LM	VT	LM		XC	VT	LM	VT	VT	LM	LM	VT	LM		XC	VT
			1		◇1	◇1	1	◇1	◇1		1	◇1	1		◇1	◇1	1	◇1	◇1		1	◇1	1		◇1	◇1
					A										A										A	
					🛒	☕		☕	☕			☕			🛒	☕		☕	☕			☕			🛒	☕
Crewe	65,50	d				15 01	15 19	15 23	15 29		15 37	15 54				16 01	16 19	16 23	16 29		16 33	16 54				17 00
Alsager	50	d									15 46										16 42					
Kidsgrove	50	d									15 50										16 46					
Hanley Bus Station		d																								
Stoke-on-Trent	50	d			15 07						15 59				16 07						16 55				17 08	
Wedgwood Old Road Bridge		d																								
Barlaston Orchard Place		d																								
Stone Granville Square		d																								
Stone		d									16 07										17 03					
Norton Bridge Station Drv		d																								
Stafford		d			15 25		15a40	15 44			16 18				16 25		16a40	16 44			17 18				17 26	
Rugeley Trent Valley		d									16 27										17 27					
Lichfield Trent Valley		d									16 35										17 35	17 26				
Tamworth		d									16 42										17 42					
Polesworth		d																								
Atherstone		d									16 51										17 51					
Nuneaton		a									16 57										17 57					
		d								16 11	16 58									17 11	17 58					
Bedworth		d								16 17										17 17						
Coventry		a			16 24	16 31				16 34					17 24	17 29				17 34					18 24	18 31
Rugby		a									17 13										18 13					
Northampton	68	a	←								17 42		←								18 42		←			
Milton Keynes Central	66	a	16 04			16 58					18 04	17 03	17 04			17 58					19 04	18 03	18 04			18 58
Watford Junction	66	a	16 34								→		17 34								→		18 34			
London Euston 15	⊖66	a	16 53			17 38		17 04	17 09			17 44	17 53			18 38		18 03	18 09			18 44	18 53			19 38

			LM	VT	VT	LM	LM	VT	LM		XC	VT	LM	VT	VT	LM	VT	LM	XC		VT	LM	VT	VT	LM	LM
			1	◇1	◇1		1	◇1	1		◇1	◇1	1	◇1	◇1	1	◇1	1	◇1		◇1	1	◇1	◇1	1	
											A								A							
				☕	☕			☕			🛒	☕		☕	☕		☕		🛒		☕		☕	☕		
Crewe	65,50	d	17 19	17 23	17 29		17 37	17 55				18 01	18 19	18 23	18 29	18 37	18 55				19 01	19 19	19 23	19 29		
Alsager	50	d					17 46									18 46										
Kidsgrove	50	d					17 50									18 50										
Hanley Bus Station		d																								
Stoke-on-Trent	50	d					17 59				18 08					18 59			19 07							
Wedgwood Old Road Bridge		d																								
Barlaston Orchard Place		d																								
Stone Granville Square		d																								
Stone		d					18 07									19 07										
Norton Bridge Station Drv		d																								
Stafford		d	17a40	17 44			18 18				18 27		18a40	18 44		19 18			19 25			19a40	19 44			
Rugeley Trent Valley		d					18 27									19 27										
Lichfield Trent Valley		d					18 35									19 35										
Tamworth		d					18 42									19 42										
Polesworth		d																								
Atherstone		d					18 51									19 51										
Nuneaton		a					18 57									19 57										
		d				18 11	18 58									19 58										20 11
Bedworth		d				18 17																				20 17
Coventry		a				18 34					19 24	19 30							20 24		20 30					20 34
Rugby		a					19 13									20 13										
Northampton	68	a					19 42		←							20 36		←							←	
Milton Keynes Central	66	a					20 06	19 03	19 04			19 58				21 07	20 03	20 06			20 59				21 07	
Watford Junction	66	a					→		19 34							→		20 34							21 35	
London Euston 15	⊖66	a		19 04	19 07			19 45	19 53			20 39		20 05	20 08		20 46	20 53			21 48		21 04	21 10	21 55	

A 🛒 to Stafford

Table 67R

Sundays
30 March to 11 May

Crewe and Stoke-on-Trent - London
Nuneaton - Coventry

Network Diagram - refer to first Page of Table 67

		LM	XC	LM		VT	XC	LM	LM	VT	LM	AW	LM	VT		VT	XC	LM	XC
		1	◇1	1		◇1	◇1		1	◇1	1	◇	1	◇1		◇1	◇1	1	◇1
			🛒			☕				☕		🛒		☕		☕			
Crewe	65,50 d	19 37		20 18		20 24			20 44	20 47		20 52	21 18	21 23		21 40		22 22	
Alsager	50 d	19 46							20 53										
Kidsgrove	50 d	19 50							20 59										
Hanley Bus Station	d																		
Stoke-on-Trent	50 d	19 59	20 07				20 47		21 06								21 47		22 47
Wedgwood Old Road Bridge	d																		
Barlaston Orchard Place	d																		
Stone Granville Square	d																		
Stone	d	20 07							21 14										
Norton Bridge Station Drv	d																		
Stafford	d	20 18	20 27	20a38		20 43	21a08		21 25			21a16	21a39	21 44		22a01	22a06	22a42	23a04
Rugeley Trent Valley	d	20 27							21 34										
Lichfield Trent Valley	d	20 35							21 42					22 00					
Tamworth	d	20 42							21 49					22 07					
Polesworth	d																		
Atherstone	d	20 51							21 57										
Nuneaton	a	20 57							22 04					22 17					
	d	20 58						22 00	22 05					22 18					
Bedworth	d							22 06											
Coventry	a		21 23					22 21											
Rugby	a	21 13							22 20					22 31					
Northampton	68 a	21 42							22 43		←								
Milton Keynes Central	66 a	22 10				21 36				21 52	22 10			23 04					
Watford Junction	66 a	↪								22s31	22 52			23s34					
London Euston 15	⊖66 a					22 28				22 55	23 15			23 54					

Table 68

Mondays to Fridays

9 December to 16 May

Northampton - Coventry - Birmingham - Wolverhampton - Stafford

Network Diagram - refer to first Page of Table 67

Miles			VT MO ◇1 A	VT MX ◇1 A	VT MX ◇1 A	VT ◇1 B ⊠	LM C	XC ◇1 D	LM 1 E	LM	VT ◇1 F ⊠		LM 1	XC ◇1 D	LM 1 G	AW ◇ H	LM 1 E	LM I	LM 1	XC ◇1 D	LM 1 J		LM 1 E	LM	VT ◇1 K ⊠
—	London Euston 15 ⊖66	d																							
0	**Northampton**	d											05 16		05 42						05 55				
9½	Long Buckby	d											05 27								06 06				
18¾	Rugby	d		00 01	01 00								05 38		06 05						06 17				
32¼	**Coventry**	a		00 10	01 13								05 49								06 29				
—		d		00 10	01 13								05 50						06 11		06 30				
34	Canley	d																	06 14		06 33				
36	Tile Hill	d											05 55						06 18		06 37				
38	Berkswell	d																	06 21		06 40				
41¼	Hampton-in-Arden	d											06 01						06 25						
43	**Birmingham International** ✈	a		00 21	01 24								06 04						06 28		06 45				
—		d	00 09	00 21	01 24								06 05				06 17		06 29		06 46				
45	Marston Green	d											06 08						06 32		06 49				
46½	Lea Hall	d															06 22				06 52				
47¾	Stechford	d															06 25				06 55				
49½	Adderley Park	d															06 28								
51½	**Birmingham New Street** 12	a	00 21	00 32	01 36								06 16				06 34		06 42		07 01				
—		d	00 24	00 35	01 37	05 30	05 51	05 57	06 01	06 04	06 15			06 22		06 25	06 36	06 38		06 57			07 01	07 08	07 15
54¾	Smethwick Rolfe Street	d								06 10								06 44						07 14	
55½	Smethwick Galton Bridge 7	d							06 08	06 12						06 30		06 46					07 08	07 16	
56¾	Sandwell & Dudley	d					05 59			06 15	06 24							06 49						07 19	07 24
57¾	Dudley Port	d								06 19								06 52						07 22	
58½	Tipton	d								06 21								06 54						07 24	
60	Coseley	d								06 25								06 57						07 27	
64¼	**Wolverhampton** 7	a	00 43	01 03	02 07	05 47	06 09	06 14	06 19	06 31	06 37			06 40		06 42	06 51	07 03		07 14			07 19	07 33	07 37
—		d				05 48		06 16	06 20					06 41			06 52			07 15			07 20		
74¼	Penkridge	d							06 29								07 02						07 30		
79½	**Stafford**	a				06 01		06 29	06 35					06 53	06 55		07 08			07 29			07 36		

		LM 1	LM 1 G	AW ◇ L	LM C	XC ◇1 D	LM 1 E		LM	VT ◇1 ⊠	XC ◇1 M	LM 1 N	LM 1	LM C	LM 1 G	LM	VT ◇1 F ⊠		LM 1	AW ◇ H	VT ◇1 ⊠	XC ◇1 O	LM	LM 1 E	LM I
London Euston 15 ⊖66	d									06 20			05 32		06 24		06 43				07 03				
Northampton	d	06 16	06 35										06 55		07 43				07 16						
Long Buckby	d	06 27											07 06						07 27						
Rugby	d	06 38	06 59							07 13			07 17		08 03				07 38		07 51				
Coventry	a	06 49								07 22			07 29				07 42		07 49		08 02				
	d	06 50							07 06	07 22	07 27		07 30				07 42		07 50		08 02				
Canley	d								07 08				07 33												
Tile Hill	d	06 55							07 12				07 37						07 55						
Berkswell	d								07 15				07 40												
Hampton-in-Arden	d	07 01							07 19										08 01						
Birmingham International ✈	a	07 04							07 22	07 33	07 37		07 45				07 53		08 04		08 13				
	d	07 05		07 08			07 17		07 22	07 33	07 38		07 46				07 53		08 05	08 08	08 13		08 17		
Marston Green	d	07 08							07 26				07 49						08 08				08 20		
Lea Hall	d						07 22						07 52										08 23		
Stechford	d						07 25						07 55										08 26		
Adderley Park	d						07 28						07 58										08 29		
Birmingham New Street 12	a	07 17		07 20			07 32		07 36	07 45	07 48		08 03				08 08		08 17	08 20	08 27		08 33		
	d			07 23	07 26	07 31	07 36		07 38		07 57	08 01		08 05		08 08	08 15			08 23		08 31		08 36	08 38
Smethwick Rolfe Street	d								07 44							08 14									08 44
Smethwick Galton Bridge 7	d			07 29					07 46			08 08				08 16				08 29					08 46
Sandwell & Dudley	d								07 49					08 13		08 19	08 24								08 49
Dudley Port	d								07 52							08 22									08 52
Tipton	d								07 54							08 24									08 54
Coseley	d						07 47		07 57							08 27								08 47	08 57
Wolverhampton 7	a			07 40	07 44	07 48	07 53		08 03		08 14	08 19		08 24		08 33	08 37			08 41		08 48		08 53	09 03
	d					07 49	07 54				08 15	08 20										08 49		08 54	
Penkridge	d						08 04					08 29												09 04	
Stafford	a		07 53			08 00	08 10				08 29	08 35			08 53							09 00		09 10	

A From London Euston
B To Holyhead
C To Shrewsbury
D To Manchester Piccadilly
E To Liverpool Lime Street
F To Edinburgh
G To Crewe
H To Aberystwyth
I From Walsall
J From Milton Keynes Central
K To Glasgow Central
L To Llandudno
M From Southampton Central to Manchester Piccadilly
N From Walsall to Liverpool Lime Street
O From Bristol Temple Meads to Manchester Piccadilly

Table 68

Mondays to Fridays

9 December to 16 May

Northampton - Coventry - Birmingham - Wolverhampton - Stafford

Network Diagram - refer to first Page of Table 67

		LM	VT	XC	LM	LM	LM	LM	VT		LM	AW	VT	XC	LM	LM	LM	LM	VT		XC	LM	LM	LM	LM
		1	◇1	◇1	1	1			◇1		1	◇	◇1	◇1		1		1	◇1		◇1	1	1		
				A	B		C		D			E		F		B	G				H	B		C	G
			⊠	⊥					⊠			⊥	⊠	⊥					⊠		⊥				
London Euston [15] ⊖66	d		07 23			06 34			07 43		07 13		08 03						08 23				07 49		
Northampton	d					07 55					08 13												08 55		
Long Buckby	d					08 06					08 24												09 06		
Rugby	d					08 17					08 35		08 51										09 17		
Coventry	a		08 22			08 28			08 42		08 46		09 02						09 22				09 29		
	d	08 11	08 22	08 27		08 29			08 42		08 51		09 02					09 11	09 22		09 27		09 30		
Canley	d	08 14				08 32												09 14					09 33		
Tile Hill	d	08 18				08 36					08 56							09 18					09 37		
Berkswell	d	08 21				08 39												09 21					09 40		
Hampton-in-Arden	d	08 25									09 02							09 25							
Birmingham International ✈	a	08 28	08 33	08 37		08 44			08 53		09 05		09 13					09 28	09 33		09 37		09 45		
	d	08 29	08 33	08 38		08 45			08 53		09 06	09 09	09 13		09 17			09 29	09 33		09 38		09 46		
Marston Green	d	08 32				08 48					09 09							09 32					09 49		
Lea Hall	d					08 51									09 21								09 52		
Stechford	d					08 54									09 24								09 55		
Adderley Park	d														09 27										
Birmingham New Street [12]	a	08 42	08 45	08 48		09 01			09 08		09 17	09 20	09 27		09 33			09 42	09 45		09 48		10 01		
	d			08 57	09 01		09 05	09 08	09 15			09 23		09 31		09 36	09 38				09 57	10 01		10 05	10 08
Smethwick Rolfe Street	d							09 14									09 44								10 14
Smethwick Galton Bridge [7]	d				09 08			09 16				09 29					09 46					10 08			10 16
Sandwell & Dudley	d						09 13	09 19	09 24								09 49							10 13	10 19
Dudley Port	d							09 22									09 52								10 22
Tipton	d							09 24									09 54								10 24
Coseley	d							09 27								09 47	09 57								10 27
Wolverhampton [7]	a			09 14	09 19		09 24	09 33	09 37			09 42		09 48		09 53	10 03				10 14	10 19		10 24	10 33
	d			09 15	09 20									09 49		09 54					10 15	10 20			
Penkridge	d															10 04									
Stafford	a			09 29	09 34									10 00		10 10					10 29	10 34			

		VT	LM	AW	LM		VT	XC	LM	LM	LM	LM	VT	XC	LM		LM	LM	LM	VT	LM	AW	LM	VT	XC
		◇1	1	◇	1		◇1	◇1		1		1	◇1	◇1	1		1			◇1	1	◇	1	◇1	◇1
		I		J	K			L		B	G	M		H	B			C	G	D		E	K		N
		🛏		⊥			⊠	⊥					⊠	⊥						🛏		⊥		⊠	⊥
London Euston [15] ⊖66	d	08 43	07 54				09 03						09 23				08 49			09 43	09 13			10 03	
Northampton	d		09 16		09 25												09 55				10 16		10 25		
Long Buckby	d		09 27		09 36												10 06				10 27		10 36		
Rugby	d		09 38		09 47		09 51					←					10 17				10 38		10 47	10 51	
Coventry	a	09 42	09 49		09 58		10 02					09 58	10 22				10 29			10 42	10 49		10 58	11 02	
	d	09 42	09 50		10 11		10 02					10 11	10 22	10 27			10 30			10 42	10 50		11 11	11 02	
Canley	d				→							10 14					10 33						→		
Tile Hill	d		09 55									10 18					10 37				10 55				
Berkswell	d											10 21					10 40								
Hampton-in-Arden	d		10 01									10 25									11 01				
Birmingham International ✈	a	09 53	10 04				10 13					10 28	10 33	10 37			10 45			10 53	11 04			11 13	
	d	09 53	10 05	10 08			10 13		10 17			10 29	10 33	10 38			10 46			10 53	11 05	11 08		11 13	
Marston Green	d		10 08									10 32					10 49				11 08				
Lea Hall	d								10 21								10 52								
Stechford	d								10 24								10 55								
Adderley Park	d								10 27																
Birmingham New Street [12]	a	10 08	10 17	10 20			10 27		10 33			10 42	10 45	10 48			11 01			11 10	11 17	11 20		11 28	
	d	10 15		10 23				10 31		10 36	10 38			10 57	11 01			11 05	11 08	11 15		11 23			11 31
Smethwick Rolfe Street	d										10 44								11 14						
Smethwick Galton Bridge [7]	d			10 29							10 46				11 08				11 16			11 29			
Sandwell & Dudley	d	10 24									10 49							11 14	11 19	11 24					
Dudley Port	d										10 52								11 22						
Tipton	d										10 54								11 24						
Coseley	d									10 47	10 57								11 27						
Wolverhampton [7]	a	10 37		10 42				10 48		10 53	11 04			11 14	11 19			11 24	11 34	11 37		11 41			11 48
	d							10 49		10 54				11 15	11 20										11 49
Penkridge	d									11 04															
Stafford	a							11 00		11 10				11 28	11 34										12 00

A From Southampton Central to Manchester Piccadilly
B To Liverpool Lime Street
C To Shrewsbury
D To Glasgow Central
E To Holyhead
F From Cardiff Central to Manchester Piccadilly
G From Walsall
H From Bournemouth to Manchester Piccadilly
I To Edinburgh
J To Aberystwyth
K To Birmingham New Street
L From Paignton to Manchester Piccadilly
M From Northampton
N From Bristol Temple Meads to Manchester Piccadilly

Table 68

Mondays to Fridays

9 December to 16 May

Northampton - Coventry - Birmingham - Wolverhampton - Stafford

Network Diagram - refer to first Page of Table 67

Station		LM	LM	LM	LM	VT	XC		LM	LM	LM	LM	VT	LM	AW	LM	VT		XC	LM	LM	LM	LM	VT	XC
			1		1	◇1	R ◇1		1	1			◇1	1	◇	1	◇1		◇1		1		1	◇1	◇1
			A	B	C		D		A		E	B	F		G	H			I		A	B	C		J
						⊠	(trolley)						(catering)		(trolley)		(catering)		(trolley)					(catering)	(trolley)
London Euston 15 ⊖66	d					10 23				09 49			10 43	10 13			11 03							11 23	
Northampton	d									10 55				11 16		11 25									
Long Buckby	d									11 06				11 27		11 36									
Rugby	d				←					11 17				11 38		11 47	11 51						←		
Coventry	a				10 58	11 22				11 29			11 42	11 49		11 58	12 02						11 58	12 22	
	d				11 11	11 22	11 27			11 30			11 42	11 50		12 11	12 02						12 11	12 22	12 27
Canley	d				11 14					11 33						↦							12 14		
Tile Hill	d				11 18					11 37				11 55									12 18		
Berkswell	d				11 21					11 40													12 21		
Hampton-in-Arden	d				11 25									12 01									12 25		
Birmingham International ✈	a				11 28	11 33	11 37			11 45			11 53	12 04			12 13						12 28	12 33	12 37
	d	11 17			11 29	11 33	11 38			11 46			11 53	12 05	12 08		12 13			12 17			12 29	12 33	12 38
Marston Green	d				11 32					11 49				12 08									12 32		
Lea Hall	d	11 21								11 52										12 21					
Stechford	d	11 24								11 55										12 24					
Adderley Park	d	11 27																		12 27					
Birmingham New Street 12	a	11 33			11 42	11 45	11 48			12 01			12 08	12 17	12 20		12 27			12 33			12 42	12 45	12 48
	d		11 36	11 38			11 57		12 01		12 05	12 08	12 15		12 23				12 31		12 36	12 38			12 57
Smethwick Rolfe Street	d			11 44								12 14										12 44			
Smethwick Galton Bridge 7	d			11 46					12 08			12 16			12 29							12 46			
Sandwell & Dudley	d			11 49							12 13	12 19	12 24									12 49			
Dudley Port	d			11 52								12 22										12 52			
Tipton	d			11 54								12 24										12 54			
Coseley	d		11 47	11 57								12 27									12 47	12 57			
Wolverhampton 7 🚌	a		11 53	12 03			12 14		12 19		12 24	12 33	12 37		12 41				12 48		12 53	13 03			13 14
	d		11 54				12 15		12 20										12 49		12 54				13 15
Penkridge	d		12 04																		13 04				
Stafford	a		12 10				12 29		12 34										13 00		13 10				13 29

Station		LM	LM		LM	LM	VT	LM	AW	LM	VT	XC	LM		LM	LM	LM	VT	XC	LM	LM	LM	LM		VT
		1	1				◇1	1	◇	1	◇1	◇1			1		1	◇1	◇1	1	1				◇1
		A			E	B	K		L	H		M			A	B	C		J	A		E	B		F
							(catering)		(trolley)		(catering)	(trolley)						(catering)	(trolley)						(catering)
London Euston 15 ⊖66	d		10 49				11 43	11 13			12 03							12 23			11 49				12 43
Northampton	d		11 55					12 16		12 25											12 55				
Long Buckby	d		12 06					12 27		12 36											13 06				
Rugby	d		12 17					12 38		12 47	12 51						←				13 17				
Coventry	a		12 29				12 42	12 49		12 58	13 02						12 58	13 24			13 29				13 42
	d		12 30				12 42	12 50		13 11	13 02						13 11	13 25	13 28		13 31				13 42
Canley	d		12 33							↦							13 14				13 34				
Tile Hill	d		12 37					12 55									13 18				13 38				
Berkswell	d		12 40														13 21				13 41				
Hampton-in-Arden	d							13 01									13 25								
Birmingham International ✈	a		12 45				12 53	13 04			13 13						13 28	13 33	13 37		13 46				13 53
	d		12 46				12 53	13 05	13 08		13 13		13 17				13 29	13 33	13 39		13 47				13 53
Marston Green	d		12 49					13 08									13 32				13 50				
Lea Hall	d		12 52										13 21								13 53				
Stechford	d		12 55										13 24								13 56				
Adderley Park	d												13 27												
Birmingham New Street 12	a		13 01				13 08	13 17	13 22		13 27		13 33				13 42	13 45	13 49		14 02				14 08
	d	13 01			13 05	13 08	13 15		13 23			13 31			13 36	13 38			13 57	14 01		14 05	14 08		14 15
Smethwick Rolfe Street	d					13 14										13 44							14 14		
Smethwick Galton Bridge 7	d	13 08				13 16			13 29							13 46				14 08			14 16		
Sandwell & Dudley	d				13 13	13 19	13 24									13 49						14 13	14 19		14 24
Dudley Port	d					13 22										13 52							14 22		
Tipton	d					13 24										13 54							14 24		
Coseley	d					13 27									13 47	13 57							14 27		
Wolverhampton 7 🚌	a	13 19			13 24	13 34	13 37		13 41			13 48			13 53	14 04			14 14	14 19		14 24	14 33		14 37
	d	13 20										13 49			13 54				14 15	14 20					
Penkridge	d														14 04										
Stafford	a	13 34										14 00			14 10				14 29	14 34					

A To Liverpool Lime Street
B From Walsall
C From Northampton
D From Bournemouth to Manchester Piccadilly. ◇ from Birmingham New Street R to Birmingham New Street
E To Shrewsbury
F To Edinburgh
G To Aberystwyth
H To Birmingham New Street
I From Bristol Temple Meads to Manchester Piccadilly
J From Bournemouth to Manchester Piccadilly
K To Glasgow Central
L To Holyhead
M From Paignton to Manchester Piccadilly

Table 68

Mondays to Fridays

9 December to 16 May

Northampton - Coventry - Birmingham - Wolverhampton - Stafford

Network Diagram - refer to first Page of Table 67

		LM	AW	LM	VT		XC	LM	LM	LM	LM	VT	XC	LM	LM		LM	LM	VT	LM	AW	LM	VT	XC	LM
		■1	◇	■1	◇■1		◇■1		■1		■1	◇■1	◇■1	■1	■1				◇■1	■1	◇	■1	◇■1	◇■1	
			A	B			C		D	E	F		G	D			H	E	I		J	B		K	
			🛒		☕		🛒					☕	🛒						☕		🛒		☕	🛒	
London Euston 15 ⊖66	d	12 13			13 03							13 23			12 49				13 43	13 13			14 03		
Northampton	d	13 16		13 25											13 55					14 16		14 25			
Long Buckby	d	13 27		13 36											14 06					14 27		14 36			
Rugby	d	13 38		13 47	13 51						←				14 17					14 38		14 47	14 51		
Coventry	a	13 49		13 58	14 02						13 58	14 22			14 29				14 42	14 49		14 58	15 02		
	d	13 50		14 11	14 02						14 11	14 22	14 27		14 30				14 42	14 50		15 11	15 02		
Canley	d			→							14 14				14 33							→			
Tile Hill	d	13 55									14 18				14 37					14 55					
Berkswell	d										14 21				14 40										
Hampton-in-Arden	d	14 01									14 25									15 01					
Birmingham International ✈	a	14 04			14 13						14 28	14 33	14 37		14 45				14 53	15 04			15 13		
	d	14 05	14 08		14 13			14 17			14 29	14 33	14 38		14 46				14 53	15 05	15 08		15 13		15 17
Marston Green	d	14 08									14 32				14 49					15 08					
Lea Hall	d							14 21							14 52										15 21
Stechford	d							14 24							14 55										15 24
Adderley Park	d							14 27																	15 27
Birmingham New Street 12	a	14 17	14 20		14 27			14 33			14 42	14 45	14 48		15 01				15 08	15 16	15 20		15 27		15 33
	d		14 23				14 31		14 36	14 38			14 57	15 01			15 05	15 08	15 15		15 23			15 31	
Smethwick Rolfe Street	d									14 44								15 14							
Smethwick Galton Bridge 7	d		14 29							14 46				15 08				15 16			15 27				
Sandwell & Dudley	d									14 49							15 13	15 19	15 24						
Dudley Port	d									14 52								15 22							
Tipton	d									14 54								15 24							
Coseley	d								14 47	14 57								15 27							
Wolverhampton 7 ⛴	a		14 41				14 48		14 53	15 03			15 14	15 19			15 24	15 33	15 37		15 40			15 49	
	d						14 49		14 54				15 15	15 20										15 50	
Penkridge	d								15 04																
Stafford	a						15 00		15 10				15 29	15 34										16 01	

			LM	LM	LM	VT	XC	LM	LM	LM	LM		VT	LM	AW	VT	XC	LM	LM	LM	LM		VT	XC	LM
													R		R										
			■1		■1	◇■1	◇■1	■1	■1				■1	■1		◇■1	◇■1		■1		■1		◇■1	◇■1	■1
			D	E	F		G	D		H	E		L		A		C		D	E				G	D
						☕	🛒						⊠		🛒	☕	🛒						☕	🛒	
London Euston 15 ⊖66	d					14 23			13 49				14 43	14 13		15 03							15 23		
Northampton	d								14 55					15 16							15 37				
Long Buckby	d								15 06					15 27							15 48				
Rugby	d				←				15 17					15 38		15 51					15 59				
Coventry	a				14 58	15 22			15 29				15 42	15 49		16 02					16 10		16 21		
	d				15 11	15 22	15 27		15 30				15 42	15 50		16 02					16 11		16 22	16 27	
Canley	d				15 14				15 33												16 14				
Tile Hill	d				15 18				15 37					15 55							16 18				
Berkswell	d				15 21				15 40												16 21				
Hampton-in-Arden	d				15 25									16 01							16 25				
Birmingham International ✈	a				15 28	15 33	15 37		15 45				15 53	16 04		16 13					16 28		16 33	16 37	
	d				15 29	15 33	15 38		15 46				15 53	16 05	16 09	16 13		16 17			16 29		16 33	16 38	
Marston Green	d				15 32				15 49					16 08							16 32				
Lea Hall	d								15 52									16 21							
Stechford	d								15 55									16 24							
Adderley Park	d																	16 27							
Birmingham New Street 12	a				15 42	15 45	15 48		16 01				16 08	16 17	16 20	16 27		16 33			16 42		16 46	16 48	
	d		15 36	15 38			15 57	16 01		16 05	16 08		16 15		16 23		16 31		16 36	16 38				16 57	17 01
Smethwick Rolfe Street	d			15 44							16 14									16 44					
Smethwick Galton Bridge 7	d			15 46				16 08			16 16				16 29					16 46					17 08
Sandwell & Dudley	d			15 49						16 13	16 19		16 24							16 49					
Dudley Port	d			15 52							16 22									16 53					
Tipton	d			15 54							16 24									16 56					
Coseley	d		15 47	15 57							16 27								16 47	16 58					
Wolverhampton 7 ⛴	a		15 53	16 04			16 14	16 19		16 24	16 33		16 37		16 42		16 48		16 53	17 04				17 14	17 19
	d		15 54				16 15	16 20									16 49		16 54					17 15	17 20
Penkridge	d		16 04					16 29											17 04						17 29
Stafford	a		16 10				16 30	16 36									17 00		17 10					17 29	17 35

- **A** To Aberystwyth
- **B** To Birmingham New Street
- **C** From Bristol Temple Meads to Manchester Piccadilly
- **D** To Liverpool Lime Street
- **E** From Walsall
- **F** From Northampton
- **G** From Bournemouth to Manchester Piccadilly
- **H** To Shrewsbury
- **I** To Glasgow Central
- **J** To Holyhead
- **K** From Penzance to Manchester Piccadilly
- **L** To Edinburgh

Table 68

Mondays to Fridays

9 December to 16 May

Northampton - Coventry - Birmingham - Wolverhampton - Stafford

Network Diagram - refer to first Page of Table 67

		LM	LM		LM	VT	LM	AW	VT	XC	LM	LM	LM		LM	VT	LM	XC	LM	LM	LM	LM	VT		LM
		1				R 1	1	◇	◇1	◇1		1			1	◇1		◇1	1	1			◇1		1
			A		B	C		D		E		F	B				A	G	F		A	B	H		
						⊠		🛒	☕	🛒						☕		🛒					⊠		
London Euston 15 ⊖66	d	14 49				15 43	15 13		16 03							16 23				15 49			16 43		15 54
Northampton	d	15 55					16 16													16 55					17 16
Long Buckby	d	16 06					16 27													17 06					17 27
Rugby	d	16 17					16 38		16 51											17 17					17 38
Coventry	a	16 29				16 42	16 49		17 02							17 22				17 29			17 42		17 49
	d	16 30				16 42	16 50		17 02						17 12	17 24		17 28		17 30			17 42		17 50
Canley	d	16 33													17 15					17 33					
Tile Hill	d	16 37					16 55								17 19					17 37					17 55
Berkswell	d	16 40													17 22					17 40					
Hampton-in-Arden	d						17 01								17 26										18 01
Birmingham International ✈	a	16 45				16 53	17 04		17 13						17 29	17 33		17 37		17 45			17 53		18 04
	d	16 46				16 53	17 05	17 08	17 13		17 18				17 30	17 35		17 39		17 46			17 53		18 05
Marston Green	d	16 49					17 08								17 33					17 49					18 08
Lea Hall	d	16 52									17 22									17 52					
Stechford	d	16 55									17 25									17 55					
Adderley Park	d										17 28														
Birmingham New Street 12	a	17 01				17 08	17 16	17 20	17 27		17 33				17 42	17 45		17 49		18 01			18 08		18 17
	d		17 05		17 08	17 15		17 23		17 31		17 36	17 38				17 46	17 57	18 01		18 05	18 08	18 15		
Smethwick Rolfe Street	d				17 14								17 44									18 14			
Smethwick Galton Bridge 7	d				17 16			17 29					17 46						18 08			18 16			
Sandwell & Dudley	d		17 13		17 19	17 24							17 49								18 13	18 19	18 24		
Dudley Port	d				17 22								17 52				17 56					18 22			
Tipton	d				17 24								17 54				17 59					18 24			
Coseley	d				17 27							17 47	17 57									18 27			
Wolverhampton 7 🚌	a		17 24		17 33	17 37		17 42		17 49		17 53	18 03				18 06	18 14	18 19		18 24	18 33	18 37		
	d									17 50		17 54						18 15	18 20						
Penkridge	d											18 03							18 29						
Stafford	a									18 01		18 09						18 29	18 35						

		AW	VT	XC	LM	LM	LM	LM	VT		XC	LM	LM	LM	LM	VT	AW	LM	XC		LM	VT	LM	LM	LM
		◇	◇1	◇1		1		1	◇1		◇1	1	1			◇1	◇	1	◇1		1	◇1		1	
		I		J		F	B				G	K		A	B	C	L		M		K	N		F	B
		🛒	⊠	🛒					⊠		🛒					☕	🛒		🛒			⊠			
London Euston 15 ⊖66	d		17 03						17 23				16 50			17 43		17 13			17 24	18 03			
Northampton	d												17 55					18 20			18 46				
Long Buckby	d												18 06					18 31			18 57				
Rugby	d		17 51										18 17					18 42			19a08	18 52			
Coventry	a		18 02						18 22				18 30			18 42		18 53				19 03			
	d		18 02					18 11	18 22		18 27		18 30			18 42		18 54				19 04			
Canley	d							18 14					18 33												
Tile Hill	d							18 18					18 37					18 59							
Berkswell	d							18 21					18 40												
Hampton-in-Arden	d							18 25										19 05							
Birmingham International ✈	a		18 13					18 28	18 33		18 37		18 46			18 53		19 08				19 14			
	d	18 09	18 13		18 17			18 29	18 33		18 38		18 46			18 53	19 04	19 09				19 14	19 17		
Marston Green	d							18 32					18 49					19 12							
Lea Hall	d				18 21								18 52										19 21		
Stechford	d				18 24								18 55										19 24		
Adderley Park	d				18 27																		19 27		
Birmingham New Street 12	a	18 20	18 27		18 34			18 42	18 45		18 49		19 01			19 08	19 17	19 21				19 27	19 33		
	d	18 23		18 31		18 36	18 38				18 57	19 01		19 05	19 08	19 15	19 23		19 31					19 35	19 38
Smethwick Rolfe Street	d						18 44								19 14							↪			19 44
Smethwick Galton Bridge 7	d	18 29					18 46					19 08			19 16		19 29								19 46
Sandwell & Dudley	d						18 49							19 13	19 19	19 24									19 49
Dudley Port	d						18 52								19 22										19 52
Tipton	d						18 54								19 24										19 54
Coseley	d					18 47	18 57								19 27									19 45	19 57
Wolverhampton 7 🚌	a	18 41		18 48		18 53	19 03				19 14	19 19		19 24	19 33	19 37	19 42		19 48					19 51	20 04
	d			18 49		18 54					19 15	19 20							19 49					19 53	
Penkridge	d					19 04						19 29												20 04	
Stafford	a			19 00		19 10					19 27	19 37							20 00					20 10	

- **A** To Shrewsbury
- **B** From Walsall
- **C** To Glasgow Central
- **D** To Llandudno
- **E** From Paignton to Manchester Piccadilly
- **F** To Liverpool Lime Street
- **G** From Bournemouth to Manchester Piccadilly
- **H** To Edinburgh
- **I** To Aberystwyth
- **J** From Bristol Temple Meads to Manchester Piccadilly
- **K** To Crewe
- **L** To Chester
- **M** From Exeter St Davids to Manchester Piccadilly
- **N** To Wolverhampton

Table 68

Mondays to Fridays

9 December to 16 May

Northampton - Coventry - Birmingham - Wolverhampton - Stafford

Network Diagram - refer to first Page of Table 67

			VT	LM	VT	XC	LM	LM	LM	VT	LM		AW	LM	VT	XC	LM	LM	LM	LM	VT		XC	LM	LM
			◇1	1	◇1	◇1	1			◇1	1		◇	1	R 1	◇1		1		1	R 1		◇1	1	
			A			B		C	D	E	E		F			G		H					I		C
			⊠		⊠	🛒				⊠					☕	🛒					☕		🛒		
London Euston 15 ⊖66	d				18 23		17 46			18 43	18 05			18 13	19 03						19 23			18 49	
Northampton	d						18 57				19 45			19 20										19 55	
Long Buckby	d						19 08							19 31										20 06	
Rugby	d						19 19				20 04			19 42	19 51									20 17	
Coventry	a				19 22		19 31			19 42				19 53	20 02						20 22			20 29	
	d			19 11	19 22	19 27	19 32			19 42				19 54	20 02					20 11	20 22		20 27	20 30	
Canley	d			19 14			19 35													20 14				20 33	
Tile Hill	d			19 18			19 39							19 59						20 18				20 37	
Berkswell	d			19 21			19 42													20 21				20 40	
Hampton-in-Arden	d			19 25										20 05						20 25					
Birmingham International ✈	a			19 28	19 33	19 37	19 47			19 53				20 08	20 13					20 28	20 33		20 37	20 45	
	d			19 29	19 33	19 38	19 48			19 53			20 04	20 09	20 13		20 17			20 29	20 33		20 38	20 46	
Marston Green	d			19 32			19 51							20 12						20 32				20 49	
Lea Hall	d						19 54										20 21							20 52	
Stechford	d						19 57										20 24							20 55	
Adderley Park	d		←														20 27								
Birmingham New Street 12	a		19 27	19 42	19 45	19 48	20 03			20 08			20 16	20 21	20 27		20 34			20 42	20 45		20 48	21 01	
	d				19 50	19 57		20 05	20 08	20 15			20 23			20 31		20 36	20 38		20 50		20 57		21 05
Smethwick Rolfe Street	d								20 14										20 44						
Smethwick Galton Bridge 7	d								20 16				20 29						20 46						
Sandwell & Dudley	d				19 59			20 13	20 19	20 24									20 49		20 59				21 13
Dudley Port	d								20 22										20 52						
Tipton	d								20 24										20 54						
Coseley	d								20 27									20 47	20 57						
Wolverhampton 7 🚌	a		20 13		20 11	20 14		20 24	20 33	20 37			20 41			20 48		20 53	21 04		21 12		21 14		21 24
	d					20 16				20 37								20 54					21 16		
Penkridge	d																	21 04							
Stafford	a					20 29				20 49	20 53							21 10					21 31		

		LM	VT	AW	LM	VT	LM		LM	LM	LM	VT	XC	LM	VT	LM	LM		LM	XC	VT	LM	LM	LM	XC
			◇1	◇	1	◇1			1		1	◇1	◇1	1	◇1		1		1	◇1	◇1	1		1	◇1
			J	K					H				B			C			E	K		E			L
			☕			☕						☕			☕						☕				
London Euston 15 ⊖66	d		19 43		19 13	20 03						20 23		19 46	20 43		19 54		20 13		21 03				
Northampton	d				20 20									20 55			21 16		21 26						
Long Buckby	d				20 31									21 06			21 27								
Rugby	d				20 42	20 51								21 17			21 38		21 45		21 57				
Coventry	a		20 42		20 53	21 02						21 24		21 30	21 42		21 49				22 06				
	d		20 42		20 54	21 02					21 11	21 25	21 28	21 31	21 42		21 50				22 07			22 11	22 24
Canley	d										21 14			21 34										22 14	
Tile Hill	d				20 59						21 18			21 38			21 55							22 18	
Berkswell	d										21 21			21 41										22 21	
Hampton-in-Arden	d				21 05						21 25						22 01							22 25	
Birmingham International ✈	a		20 53		21 08	21 13					21 28	21 34	21 37	21 46	21 53		22 04				22 18			22 28	22 33
	d		20 53	21 04	21 09	21 13	21 17				21 29	21 35	21 39	21 47	21 53		22 05				22 18		22 23	22 29	22 34
Marston Green	d				21 12						21 32			21 50			22 08							22 32	
Lea Hall	d						21 21							21 53									22 27		
Stechford	d						21 24							21 56									22 30		
Adderley Park	d						21 27																22 33		
Birmingham New Street 12	a		21 08	21 16	21 20	21 27	21 33				21 42	21 46	21 49	22 02	22 04		22 17				22 29		22 38	22 42	22 45
	d	21 08	21 15	21 23		21 28			21 36	21 38		21 50	21 57		22 06	22 12				22 30	22 32	22 38			
Smethwick Rolfe Street	d	21 14								21 44						22 18						22 44			
Smethwick Galton Bridge 7	d	21 16		21 29						21 46						22 20						22 46			
Sandwell & Dudley	d	21 19	21 24							21 49		22 00			22 16	22 23					22 42	22 49			
Dudley Port	d	21 22								21 52						22 27						22 53			
Tipton	d	21 24								21 54						22 29						22 55			
Coseley	d	21 27							21 47	21 57						22 33						22 58			
Wolverhampton 7 🚌	a	21 33	21 37	21 41		21 56			21 53	22 03		22 12	22 14		22 30	22 41				22 47	22 56	23 03			
	d		21 37						21 54				22 16							22 48		23 04			
Penkridge	d								22 04													23 14			
Stafford	a		21 52						22 10				22 29						22 39	23 00		23 20			

- **A** From London Euston
- **B** From Bournemouth to Manchester Piccadilly
- **C** To Shrewsbury
- **D** From Walsall
- **E** To Crewe
- **F** To Aberystwyth
- **G** From Bristol Temple Meads to Manchester Piccadilly
- **H** To Liverpool Lime Street
- **I** From Bournemouth to Manchester Piccadilly. 🛒 to Birmingham New Street
- **J** To Preston
- **K** To Manchester Piccadilly
- **L** From Bournemouth

Table 68

Mondays to Fridays

9 December to 16 May

Northampton - Coventry - Birmingham - Wolverhampton - Stafford

Network Diagram - refer to first Page of Table 67

		AW	LM	LM	VT	LM	AW	AW	XC		LM	VT	VT	VT
							MW FO	TThO					FX	FO
		◇	1	1	◇1	1			◇1		1	◇1	◇1	◇1
		A		B			C	C	D					
					⊡							⊡	⊡	⊡
London Euston 15 ⊖66	d		20 46		21 43	21 13					21 46	22 30	23 30	23 30
Northampton	d		21 55			22 18					22 55			
Long Buckby	d		22 06			22 29					23 06			
Rugby	d		22 17			22 41					23 17	00 01	01 00	01 05
Coventry	a		22 29		22 46	22 52					23 29	00 10	01 13	01 18
	d		22 30		22 46	22 52			23 25		23 30	00 10	01 13	01 18
Canley	d		22 33			22 55					23 33			
Tile Hill	d		22 37			22 59					23 37			
Berkswell	d		22 40			23 02					23 40			
Hampton-in-Arden	d					23 07					23 44			
Birmingham International ✈	a		22 45		23 00	23 10			23 34		23 47	00 21	01 24	01 29
	d		22 46		23 01	23 10			23 36		23 48	00 21	01 24	01 29
Marston Green	d		22 49			23 13					23 51			
Lea Hall	d		22 52								23 54			
Stechford	d		22 55								23 57			
Adderley Park	d													
Birmingham New Street 12	a		23 02		23 16	23 22			00 02		00 04	00 32	01 36	01 41
	d	22 55		23 09	23 20		23 32	23 32				00 35	01 37	01 42
Smethwick Rolfe Street	d			23 15										
Smethwick Galton Bridge 7	d			23 17										
Sandwell & Dudley	d			23 20	23 34									
Dudley Port	d			23 24										
Tipton	d			23 26										
Coseley	d			23 29										
Wolverhampton 7 🚌	a	23 11		23 35	23 47		00 01	00 02				01 03	02 07	02 10
	d	23 13		23 36										
Penkridge	d			23 46										
Stafford	a	23 30		23 52										

Saturdays

14 December to 28 December

		VT	VT	VT	XC	LM	LM	LM	VT	AW		XC	LM	LM	LM	LM	XC	LM	LM	LM		LM	VT	LM	LM
		◇1	◇1	◇1	◇1	1	1		◇1	◇		◇1		1		1	◇1	1	1				◇1	1	1
		E	E	A	F	G	B		H	I		F		G			F	J	G	C		K	L		B
		⊡	⊡	⊡					⊡	🚲		🚲					🚲						⊠		
London Euston 15 ⊖66	d																								
Northampton	d						05 42											05 55						06 16	06 38
Long Buckby	d																	06 06						06 27	
Rugby	d	00 01	01 05				06 02											06 17						06 38	06 58
Coventry	a	00 10	01 18															06 29						06 49	
	d	00 10	01 18													06 11		06 30						06 50	
Canley	d															06 14		06 33							
Tile Hill	d															06 18		06 37						06 55	
Berkswell	d															06 21		06 40							
Hampton-in-Arden	d															06 25								07 01	
Birmingham International ✈	a	00 21	01 29													06 28		06 45						07 04	
	d	00 21	01 29										06 17			06 29		06 46						07 05	
Marston Green	d															06 32		06 49						07 08	
Lea Hall	d												06 21					06 52							
Stechford	d												06 24					06 55							
Adderley Park	d												06 27												
Birmingham New Street 12	a	00 32	01 41										06 32			06 40		07 01						07 16	
	d	00 35	01 42	05 30	05 57	06 01		06 08	06 15	06 23		06 31		06 36	06 38		06 57		07 01	07 05		07 08	07 15		
Smethwick Rolfe Street	d							06 14							06 44							07 14			
Smethwick Galton Bridge 7	d					06 08		06 16		06 29					06 46				07 08			07 16			
Sandwell & Dudley	d							06 19	06 24						06 49					07 13		07 19	07 24		
Dudley Port	d							06 22							06 52							07 22			
Tipton	d							06 24							06 54							07 24			
Coseley	d							06 27							06 57							07 27			
Wolverhampton 7 🚌	a	01 03	02 10	05 47	06 14	06 19		06 32	06 37	06 42		06 48		06 52	07 03		07 14		07 19	07 24		07 33	07 37		
	d			05 48	06 16	06 20						06 49		06 52			07 15		07 20						
Penkridge	d					06 29								07 02					07 29						
Stafford	a			06 00	06 29	06 35	06 53					07 00		07 09			07 29		07 35						07 53

A To Holyhead
B To Crewe
C To Shrewsbury
D From Reading
E From London Euston
F To Manchester Piccadilly
G To Liverpool Lime Street
H To Edinburgh
I To Aberystwyth
J From Bletchley
K From Walsall
L To Glasgow Central

Table 68

Saturdays

14 December to 28 December

Northampton - Coventry - Birmingham - Wolverhampton - Stafford

Network Diagram - refer to first Page of Table 67

		AW		XC	LM	LM	LM	LM	VT	XC	LM	LM		LM	LM	VT	LM	LM	AW	VT	XC	LM		LM	LM
		◇ A		◇1 B		1 C		1	◇1	◇1 D	1 C	1		E	F	◇1 G	1	1 H	◇ I	◇1	◇1 J			1 C	F
London Euston 15 ⊖66	d								06 23			05 34						06 24		07 03					
Northampton	d											06 55					07 16	07 45							
Long Buckby	d											07 06					07 27								
Rugby	d											07 17					07 38	08 04		07 51					
Coventry	a								07 22			07 29					07 49			08 02					
	d							07 11	07 22	07 27		07 30					07 50			08 02					
Canley	d							07 14				07 33													
Tile Hill	d							07 18				07 37					07 55								
Berkswell	d							07 21				07 40													
Hampton-in-Arden	d							07 25									08 01								
Birmingham International ✈	a							07 28	07 33	07 37		07 45					08 04			08 13					
	d	07 09			07 17			07 29	07 33	07 38		07 46					08 05		08 09	08 13		08 17			
Marston Green	d							07 32				07 49					08 08								
Lea Hall	d				07 21							07 52										08 21			
Stechford	d				07 24							07 55										08 24			
Adderley Park	d				07 27																	08 27			
Birmingham New Street 12	a	07 19			07 32			07 42	07 47	07 48		08 01					08 16		08 20	08 27		08 32			
	d	07 22		07 31		07 36	07 38			07 57	08 01			08 05	08 08	08 15			08 23		08 31			08 36	08 38
Smethwick Rolfe Street	d						07 44								08 14										08 44
Smethwick Galton Bridge 7	d	07 28					07 46				08 08				08 16				08 29						08 46
Sandwell & Dudley	d						07 49							08 13	08 19	08 24									08 49
Dudley Port	d						07 52								08 22										08 52
Tipton	d						07 54								08 24										08 54
Coseley	d					07 47	07 57								08 27									08 47	08 57
Wolverhampton 7	a	07 39		07 48		07 53	08 03			08 14	08 19			08 24	08 33	08 37			08 42		08 48			08 53	09 03
	d			07 49		07 54				08 15	08 20										08 49			08 54	
Penkridge	d					08 04					08 29													09 04	
Stafford	a			08 00		08 10				08 29	08 35							08 53			09 00			09 10	

		LM	VT	XC	LM	LM	LM	LM		VT	LM	AW	VT	XC	LM	LM	LM	LM		VT	XC	LM	LM	LM	LM
		1	◇1	◇1 D	1 C	1	E	F		◇1 K	1	◇ A	◇1	◇1 L		1 C	F	1		◇1	◇1 M	1 C	1	E	F
London Euston 15 ⊖66	d		07 23							07 43			08 03					07 05		08 23			07 49		
Northampton	d	07 37				07 55					08 16							08 35					08 55		
Long Buckby	d	07 48				08 06					08 27							08 46					09 06		
Rugby	d	07 59				08 17					08 38		08 51					08 57					09 17		
Coventry	a	08 10	08 22			08 29				08 42	08 49		09 02					09 08		09 22			09 29		
	d	08 11	08 22	08 27		08 30				08 42	08 50		09 02					09 11		09 22	09 27		09 30		
Canley	d	08 14				08 33												09 14					09 33		
Tile Hill	d	08 18				08 37					08 55							09 18					09 37		
Berkswell	d	08 21				08 40												09 21					09 40		
Hampton-in-Arden	d	08 25									09 01							09 25							
Birmingham International ✈	a	08 28	08 33	08 37		08 45				08 53	09 04		09 13					09 28		09 33	09 37		09 45		
	d	08 29	08 33	08 38		08 46				08 53	09 05	09 09	09 13		09 17			09 29		09 33	09 38		09 46		
Marston Green	d	08 32				08 49					09 08							09 32					09 49		
Lea Hall	d					08 52									09 21								09 52		
Stechford	d					08 55									09 24								09 55		
Adderley Park	d														09 27										
Birmingham New Street 12	a	08 42	08 45	08 48		09 01				09 08	09 16	09 20	09 27		09 32			09 42		09 45	09 48		10 01		
	d			08 57	09 01		09 05	09 08		09 15		09 23		09 31		09 36	09 38				09 57	10 01		10 05	10 08
Smethwick Rolfe Street	d							09 14									09 44								10 14
Smethwick Galton Bridge 7	d				09 08			09 16				09 29					09 46					10 08			10 16
Sandwell & Dudley	d						09 13	09 19		09 24							09 49							10 13	10 19
Dudley Port	d							09 22									09 52								10 22
Tipton	d							09 24									09 54								10 24
Coseley	d							09 27								09 47	09 57								10 27
Wolverhampton 7	a			09 14	09 19		09 24	09 33		09 37		09 42		09 48		09 53	10 03				10 14	10 19		10 24	10 33
	d			09 15	09 20									09 49		09 54					10 15	10 20			
Penkridge	d															10 04									
Stafford	a			09 29	09 34									10 00		10 10					10 29	10 35			

A To Holyhead
B To Manchester Piccadilly
C To Liverpool Lime Street
D From Southampton Central to Manchester Piccadilly
E To Shrewsbury
F From Walsall
G To Edinburgh
H To Crewe
I To Aberystwyth
J From Bristol Temple Meads to Manchester Piccadilly
K To Glasgow Central
L From Cardiff Central to Manchester Piccadilly
M From Bournemouth to Manchester Piccadilly

Table 68

Saturdays

14 December to 28 December

Northampton - Coventry - Birmingham - Wolverhampton - Stafford

Network Diagram - refer to first Page of Table 67

	VT ◇1 A	LM 1	AW ◇ B	VT ◇1	XC ◇1 C	LM	LM 1 D	LM E	LM 1		VT ◇1	XC ◇1 F	LM 1 D	LM 1	LM G	LM E	VT ◇1 H	LM 1	AW ◇ I		LM 1 J	VT ◇1	XC ◇1 K	LM
London Euston 15 ⊖66 d	08 43	07 54		09 03							09 23			08 49			09 43	09 13				10 03		
Northampton d		09 16							09 35					09 55				10 16			10 25			
Long Buckby d		09 27							09 46					10 06				10 27			10 36			
Rugby d		09 38		09 51					09 57					10 17				10 38			10 47	10 51		
Coventry a	09 42	09 49		10 02					10 08		10 22			10 29			10 42	10 49			10 58	11 03		
d	09 42	09 50		10 02					10 11		10 22	10 27		10 30			10 42	10 50			11 11	11 03		
Canley d									10 14					10 33							↦			
Tile Hill d		09 55							10 18					10 37				10 55						
Berkswell d									10 21					10 40										
Hampton-in-Arden d		10 01							10 25									11 01						
Birmingham International ✈ a	09 53	10 04		10 13					10 28		10 33	10 37		10 45			10 53	11 04				11 13		
d	09 53	10 05	10 09	10 13		10 17			10 29		10 33	10 38		10 46			10 53	11 05	11 09			11 13		11 17
Marston Green d		10 08							10 32					10 49				11 08						
Lea Hall d						10 21								10 52										11 21
Stechford d						10 24								10 55										11 24
Adderley Park d						10 27																		11 27
Birmingham New Street 12 a	10 08	10 16	10 20	10 27		10 32			10 42		10 45	10 48		11 01			11 08	11 16	11 20			11 27		11 32
d	10 15		10 23		10 31		10 36	10 38				10 57	11 01		11 05	11 08	11 15		11 23				11 31	
Smethwick Rolfe Street d								10 44								11 14								
Smethwick Galton Bridge 7 d			10 30					10 46					11 08			11 16			11 29					
Sandwell & Dudley d	10 24							10 49							11 13	11 19	11 24							
Dudley Port d								10 52								11 22								
Tipton d								10 54								11 24								
Coseley d							10 47	10 57								11 27								
Wolverhampton 7 ⛴ a	10 37		10 42		10 48		10 53	11 03				11 14	11 19		11 24	11 33	11 37		11 41				11 48	
d					10 49		10 54					11 15	11 20										11 49	
Penkridge d							11 04																	
Stafford a					11 00		11 10					11 29	11 35										12 00	

	LM 1 D	LM E	LM 1 L	VT ◇1	XC ◇1 F		LM 1 D	LM 1	LM G	LM E	VT ◇1 A	LM 1	AW ◇ B	LM 1 J	VT ◇1		XC ◇1 K	LM	LM 1 D	LM E	LM 1 L	VT ◇1	XC ◇1 F	LM 1 D
London Euston 15 ⊖66 d				10 23				09 49			10 43	10 13			11 03							11 23		
Northampton d								10 55				11 16		11 25										
Long Buckby d								11 06				11 27		11 36										
Rugby d			↤					11 17				11 38		11 47	11 51						↤			
Coventry a			10 58	11 22				11 29			11 42	11 49		11 58	12 02						11 58	12 22		
d			11 11	11 22	11 27			11 30			11 42	11 50		12 11	12 02						12 11	12 22	12 27	
Canley d			11 14					11 33						↦							12 14			
Tile Hill d			11 18					11 37				11 55									12 18			
Berkswell d			11 21					11 40													12 21			
Hampton-in-Arden d			11 25									12 01									12 25			
Birmingham International ✈ a			11 28	11 33	11 37			11 45			11 53	12 04			12 13						12 28	12 33	12 37	
d			11 29	11 33	11 38			11 46			11 53	12 05	12 09		12 13			12 17			12 29	12 33	12 38	
Marston Green d			11 32					11 49				12 08									12 32			
Lea Hall d								11 52										12 21						
Stechford d								11 55										12 24						
Adderley Park d																		12 27						
Birmingham New Street 12 a			11 42	11 45	11 48			12 01			12 08	12 16	12 21		12 27			12 32			12 42	12 45	12 48	
d	11 36	11 38			11 57		12 01		12 05	12 08	12 15		12 23				12 31		12 36	12 38			12 57	13 01
Smethwick Rolfe Street d		11 44								12 14										12 44				
Smethwick Galton Bridge 7 d		11 46					12 08			12 16			12 29							12 46				13 08
Sandwell & Dudley d		11 49							12 13	12 19	12 24									12 49				
Dudley Port d		11 52								12 22										12 52				
Tipton d		11 54								12 24										12 54				
Coseley d	11 47	11 57								12 27									12 47	12 57				
Wolverhampton 7 ⛴ a	11 53	12 03			12 14		12 19		12 24	12 33	12 37		12 42				12 48		12 53	13 03			13 14	13 19
d	11 54				12 15		12 20										12 49		12 54				13 15	13 20
Penkridge d	12 04																		13 04					
Stafford a	12 10				12 29		12 35										13 00		13 10				13 29	13 35

- **A** To Edinburgh
- **B** To Aberystwyth
- **C** From Paignton to Manchester Piccadilly
- **D** To Liverpool Lime Street
- **E** From Walsall
- **F** From Bournemouth to Manchester Piccadilly
- **G** To Shrewsbury
- **H** To Glasgow Central
- **I** To Holyhead
- **J** To Birmingham New Street
- **K** From Bristol Temple Meads to Manchester Piccadilly
- **L** From Northampton

Table 68

Saturdays

14 December to 28 December

Northampton - Coventry - Birmingham - Wolverhampton - Stafford

Network Diagram - refer to first Page of Table 67

		LM 1	LM A	LM B	VT ◇1 C	LM 1	AW ◇ D	LM 1 E		VT ◇1	XC ◇1 F	LM	LM 1 G	LM B	LM 1 H	VT ◇1	XC ◇1 I	LM 1 G		LM 1	LM A	LM B	VT ◇1 J	LM 1	AW ◇ K
London Euston 15 ⊖66	d	10 49			11 43	11 13				12 03						12 23				11 49			12 43	12 13	
Northampton	d	11 55				12 16		12 25												12 55				13 16	
Long Buckby	d	12 06				12 27		12 36												13 06				13 27	
Rugby	d	12 17				12 38		12 47		12 51					←					13 17				13 38	
Coventry	a	12 29			12 42	12 49		12 58		13 02					12 58	13 22				13 29			13 42	13 49	
	d	12 30			12 42	12 50		13 11		13 02					13 11	13 22	13 27			13 30			13 42	13 50	
Canley	d	12 33						↦							13 14					13 33					
Tile Hill	d	12 37				12 55									13 18					13 37				13 55	
Berkswell	d	12 40													13 21					13 40					
Hampton-in-Arden	d					13 01									13 25									14 01	
Birmingham International ✈	a	12 45			12 53	13 04				13 13					13 28	13 33	13 37			13 45			13 53	14 04	
	d	12 46			12 53	13 05	13 09			13 13		13 17			13 29	13 33	13 38			13 46			13 53	14 05	14 09
Marston Green	d	12 49				13 08									13 32					13 49				14 08	
Lea Hall	d	12 52										13 21								13 52					
Stechford	d	12 55										13 24								13 55					
Adderley Park	d											13 27													
Birmingham New Street 12	a	13 01			13 08	13 16	13 21			13 27		13 32			13 42	13 45	13 48			14 01			14 08	14 16	14 20
	d		13 05	13 08	13 15		13 23				13 31		13 36	13 38			13 57	14 01			14 05	14 08	14 15		14 23
Smethwick Rolfe Street	d			13 14										13 44								14 14			
Smethwick Galton Bridge 7	d			13 16			13 29							13 46				14 08				14 16			14 29
Sandwell & Dudley	d		13 13	13 19	13 24									13 49							14 13	14 19	14 24		
Dudley Port	d			13 22										13 52								14 22			
Tipton	d			13 24										13 54								14 24			
Coseley	d			13 27									13 47	13 57								14 27			
Wolverhampton 7	a		13 24	13 33	13 37		13 41				13 48		13 53	14 03			14 14	14 19			14 24	14 33	14 37		14 41
	d										13 49		13 54				14 15	14 20							
Penkridge	d												14 04												
Stafford	a										14 00		14 10				14 29	14 35							

		LM 1 E	VT ◇1	XC ◇1 L		LM	LM 1 G	LM B	LM 1 H	VT ◇1	XC ◇1 I	LM 1 G	LM 1	LM A		LM B	VT ◇1 C	LM 1	AW ◇ D	LM 1 E	VT ◇1	XC ◇1 M	LM	LM 1 G	
London Euston 15 ⊖66	d		13 03							13 23			12 49				13 43	13 13			14 03				
Northampton	d	13 25											13 55					14 16		14 25					
Long Buckby	d	13 36											14 06					14 27		14 36					
Rugby	d	13 47	13 51						←				14 17					14 38		14 47	14 51				
Coventry	a	13 58	14 02						13 58	14 22			14 29				14 42	14 49		14 58	15 02				
	d	14 11	14 02						14 11	14 22	14 27		14 30				14 42	14 50		15 11	15 02				
Canley	d	↦							14 14				14 33							↦					
Tile Hill	d								14 18				14 37					14 55							
Berkswell	d								14 21				14 40												
Hampton-in-Arden	d								14 25									15 01							
Birmingham International ✈	a		14 13						14 28	14 33	14 37		14 45				14 53	15 04			15 13				
	d		14 13			14 17			14 29	14 33	14 38		14 46				14 53	15 05	15 09		15 13		15 17		
Marston Green	d								14 32				14 49					15 08							
Lea Hall	d					14 21							14 52										15 21		
Stechford	d					14 24							14 55										15 24		
Adderley Park	d					14 27																	15 27		
Birmingham New Street 12	a		14 27			14 32			14 42	14 45	14 48		15 01				15 08	15 17	15 20		15 27		15 32		
	d			14 31			14 36	14 38			14 57	15 01		15 05		15 08	15 15		15 23			15 31		15 36	
Smethwick Rolfe Street	d							14 44								15 14									
Smethwick Galton Bridge 7	d							14 46				15 08				15 16			15 29						
Sandwell & Dudley	d							14 49						15 13		15 19	15 24								
Dudley Port	d							14 52								15 22									
Tipton	d							14 54								15 24									
Coseley	d						14 47	14 57								15 27								15 47	
Wolverhampton 7	a			14 48			14 53	15 03			15 14	15 19		15 24		15 33	15 37		15 42			15 48		15 53	
	d			14 49			14 54				15 15	15 20										15 49		15 54	
Penkridge	d						15 04																	16 04	
Stafford	a			15 00			15 10				15 29	15 35										16 00		16 10	

A To Shrewsbury
B From Walsall
C To Glasgow Central
D To Holyhead
E To Birmingham New Street
F From Paignton to Manchester Piccadilly
G To Liverpool Lime Street
H From Northampton
I From Bournemouth to Manchester Piccadilly
J To Edinburgh
K To Aberystwyth
L From Bristol Temple Meads to Manchester Piccadilly
M From Penzance to Manchester Piccadilly

Table 68

Saturdays

14 December to 28 December

Northampton - Coventry - Birmingham - Wolverhampton - Stafford

Network Diagram - refer to first Page of Table 67

		LM	LM	VT	XC	LM		LM	LM	LM	VT	LM	AW	LM	VT	XC		LM	LM	LM	LM	VT	XC	LM	LM
											R		R												
			1	◇1	◇1	1		1			1	1		1	◇1	◇1			1		1	◇1	◇1	1	1
		A	B		C	D			E	A	F		G	H		I			D	A	B		C	D	
				[buffet]	[trolley]						⊠		[trolley]		[buffet]	[trolley]						[buffet]	[trolley]		
London Euston 15 ⊖66	d			14 23				13 49			14 43	14 13			15 03							15 23			14 49
Northampton	d							14 55				15 16		15 25											15 55
Long Buckby	d							15 06				15 27		15 36											16 06
Rugby	d		←					15 17				15 38		15 47	15 51						←				16 17
Coventry	a		14 58	15 22				15 29			15 42	15 49		15 58	16 02						15 58	16 22			16 29
	d		15 11	15 22	15 27			15 30			15 42	15 50		16 11	16 02						16 11	16 22	16 27		16 30
Canley	d		15 14					15 33						→							16 14				16 33
Tile Hill	d		15 18					15 37				15 55									16 18				16 37
Berkswell	d		15 21					15 40													16 21				16 40
Hampton-in-Arden	d		15 25									16 01									16 25				
Birmingham International ✈	a		15 28	15 33	15 37			15 45			15 53	16 04			16 13						16 28	16 33	16 37		16 45
	d		15 29	15 33	15 38			15 46			15 53	16 05	16 09		16 13			16 17			16 29	16 33	16 38		16 46
Marston Green	d		15 32					15 49				16 08									16 32				16 49
Lea Hall	d							15 52										16 21							16 52
Stechford	d							15 55										16 24							16 55
Adderley Park	d																	16 27							
Birmingham New Street 12	a		15 42	15 45	15 48			16 01			16 08	16 16	16 20		16 27			16 32			16 42	16 45	16 48		17 01
	d	15 38			15 57	16 01			16 05	16 08	16 15		16 23			16 31			16 36	16 38			16 57	17 01	
Smethwick Rolfe Street	d	15 44								16 14										16 44					
Smethwick Galton Bridge 7	d	15 46				16 08				16 16			16 29							16 46				17 08	
Sandwell & Dudley	d	15 49							16 13	16 19	16 24									16 49					
Dudley Port	d	15 52								16 22										16 52					
Tipton	d	15 54								16 24										16 54					
Coseley	d	15 57								16 27									16 47	16 57					
Wolverhampton 7 🚌	a	16 03			16 14	16 19			16 24	16 33	16 37		16 41			16 48			16 53	17 04			17 14	17 19	
	d				16 15	16 20										16 49			16 54				17 15	17 20	
Penkridge	d					16 29													17 04					17 29	
Stafford	a				16 29	16 35										17 00			17 10				17 29	17 35	

		LM		LM	VT	LM	AW	LM	VT	XC	LM	LM		LM	LM	VT	XC	LM	LM	LM	LM	VT		LM	AW
					R																				
					1	1	◇	1	◇1	◇1		1			1	◇1	◇1	1	1			◇1		1	◇
		E		A	J		K	H		L		D		A	B		C	D		E	A	M			G
					⊠		[trolley]		[buffet]	[trolley]						[buffet]	[trolley]					[buffet]			[trolley]
London Euston 15 ⊖66	d				15 43	15 13			16 03							16 23			15 49			16 43		16 13	
Northampton	d					16 16		16 25											16 55					17 16	
Long Buckby	d					16 27		16 36											17 06					17 27	
Rugby	d					16 38		16 47	16 51						←				17 17					17 38	
Coventry	a				16 42	16 49		16 58	17 02						16 58	17 22			17 29			17 42		17 49	
	d				16 42	16 50		17 11	17 02						17 11	17 22	17 27		17 30			17 42		17 50	
Canley	d							→							17 14				17 33						
Tile Hill	d					16 55									17 18				17 37					17 55	
Berkswell	d														17 21				17 40						
Hampton-in-Arden	d					17 01									17 25									18 01	
Birmingham International ✈	a				16 53	17 04			17 13						17 28	17 33	17 37		17 45			17 53		18 04	
	d				16 53	17 05	17 09		17 13		17 17				17 29	17 33	17 38		17 46			17 53		18 05	18 09
Marston Green	d					17 08									17 32				17 49					18 08	
Lea Hall	d										17 21								17 52						
Stechford	d										17 24								17 55						
Adderley Park	d										17 27														
Birmingham New Street 12	a				17 08	17 16	17 20		17 27		17 32				17 42	17 45	17 48		18 01			18 08		18 16	18 20
	d	17 05		17 08	17 15		17 23			17 31		17 36		17 38			17 57	18 01		18 05	18 08	18 15			18 23
Smethwick Rolfe Street	d			17 14										17 44							18 14				
Smethwick Galton Bridge 7	d			17 16			17 30							17 46				18 08			18 16				18 29
Sandwell & Dudley	d	17 13		17 19	17 24									17 49						18 13	18 19	18 24			
Dudley Port	d			17 22										17 52							18 22				
Tipton	d			17 24										17 54							18 24				
Coseley	d			17 27								17 47		17 57							18 27				
Wolverhampton 7 🚌	a	17 24		17 33	17 37		17 41			17 48		17 53		18 03			18 14	18 19		18 24	18 33	18 37			18 41
	d									17 49		17 54					18 15	18 20							
Penkridge	d											18 04						18 29							
Stafford	a									18 00		18 10					18 29	18 35							

A From Walsall
B From Northampton
C From Bournemouth to Manchester Piccadilly
D To Liverpool Lime Street
E To Shrewsbury
F To Edinburgh
G To Aberystwyth
H To Birmingham New Street
I From Bristol Temple Meads to Manchester Piccadilly
J To Glasgow Central
K To Holyhead
L From Paignton to Manchester Piccadilly
M To Preston

Table 68

Saturdays

14 December to 28 December

Northampton - Coventry - Birmingham - Wolverhampton - Stafford

Network Diagram - refer to first Page of Table 67

		LM	VT	XC		LM	LM	LM	LM	VT	XC	LM	LM	LM		LM	VT	LM	AW	XC	LM	VT	LM	LM	
		1	◇1	◇1			1		1	◇1	◇1	1	1				◇1	1	◇	◇1	1	◇1			
		A		B			C	D	E		F	G		H		D	I		J	K	A			D	
			ꟾP	🛒						ꟾP	🛒						ꟾP		🛒	🛒		ꟾP			
London Euston 15 ⊖66	d		17 03							17 23			16 49				17 43	17 13				18 03			
Northampton	d	17 25											17 55					18 16			18 25				
Long Buckby	d	17 36											18 06					18 27			18 36				
Rugby	d	17 47	17 51						←				18 17					18 38			18 47	18 51			
Coventry	a	17 58	18 02						17 58	18 22			18 29				18 42	18 49			18 58	19 02			
	d	18 11	18 02						18 11	18 22	18 27		18 30				18 42	18 50			19 11	19 02			
Canley	d	↪							18 14				18 33								↪				
Tile Hill	d								18 18				18 37					18 55							
Berkswell	d								18 21				18 40												
Hampton-in-Arden	d								18 25									19 01							
Birmingham International ✈	a		18 13						18 28	18 33	18 37		18 45				18 53	19 04				19 13			
	d		18 13			18 17			18 29	18 33	18 38		18 46				18 53	19 05	19 09			19 13	19 17		
Marston Green	d								18 32				18 49					19 08							
Lea Hall	d					18 21							18 52										19 21		
Stechford	d					18 24							18 55										19 24		
Adderley Park	d					18 27																	19 27		
Birmingham New Street 12	a		18 27			18 32			18 42	18 45	18 48		19 01				19 08	19 17	19 20			19 27	19 32		
	d			18 31			18 36	18 38		18 50	18 57	19 01		19 05		19 08	19 15		19 23	19 31		19 35		19 38	
Smethwick Rolfe Street	d							18 44								19 14								19 44	
Smethwick Galton Bridge 7	d							18 46				19 08				19 16			19 29					19 46	
Sandwell & Dudley	d							18 49		18 59				19 13		19 19	19 24					19 44		19 49	
Dudley Port	d							18 52								19 22								19 52	
Tipton	d							18 54								19 24								19 54	
Coseley	d						18 47	18 57								19 27								19 57	
Wolverhampton 7 🚢	a			18 48			18 53	19 03		19 11	19 14	19 19		19 24		19 33	19 37		19 42	19 48		19 58		20 03	
	d			18 49			18 54				19 15	19 20								19 49					
Penkridge	d						19 04					19 29													
Stafford	a			19 00			19 10				19 29	19 35								20 00					

		LM	VT	XC	LM	LM	LM	LM	VT	LM		AW	XC	VT	LM	LM	LM	VT	LM	VT		XC	LM	LM	LM
		1	◇1	◇1	1	1			◇1	1		◇	◇1	◇1		1		◇1	1	◇1		◇1	1		
		E		L	G		H		C			M	B	N		C		O				L		H	D
			ꟾP	🛒					ꟾP					ꟾP				ꟾP		ꟾP		🛒			
London Euston 15 ⊖66	d		18 23			17 49			18 43	18 13				19 03						19 23			18 49		
Northampton	d					18 55				19 16									19 35				19 55		
Long Buckby	d					19 06				19 27									19 46				20 06		
Rugby	d	←				19 17				19 38				19 51					19 57				20 17		
Coventry	a	18 58	19 22			19 29			19 42	19 49				20 02					20 08	20 22			20 29		
	d	19 11	19 22	19 27		19 30			19 42	19 50				20 02					20 11	20 22		20 27	20 30		
Canley	d	19 14				19 33													20 14				20 33		
Tile Hill	d	19 18				19 37				19 55									20 18				20 37		
Berkswell	d	19 21				19 40													20 21				20 40		
Hampton-in-Arden	d	19 25								20 01									20 25						
Birmingham International ✈	a	19 28	19 33	19 37		19 45			19 53	20 04				20 13					20 28	20 33		20 37	20 45		
	d	19 29	19 33	19 38		19 46			19 53	20 05		20 09		20 13	20 17				20 29	20 33		20 38	20 46		
Marston Green	d	19 32				19 49				20 08									20 32				20 49		
Lea Hall	d					19 52									20 21								20 52		
Stechford	d					19 55									20 24								20 55		
Adderley Park	d														20 27			←							
Birmingham New Street 12	a	19 42	19 45	19 48		20 01			20 08	20 18		20 21		20 27	20 32			20 27	20 42	20 45		20 48	21 01		
	d		19 50	19 57	20 01		20 05	20 08	20 15			20 23	20 31	20 42		20 36	20 38	20 42		20 50		20 57		21 05	21 08
Smethwick Rolfe Street	d							20 14						↪			20 44								21 14
Smethwick Galton Bridge 7	d				20 08			20 16				20 29					20 46								21 16
Sandwell & Dudley	d		19 59				20 13	20 19	20 24								20 49	20 53		20 59				21 13	21 19
Dudley Port	d							20 22									20 52								21 22
Tipton	d							20 24									20 54								21 24
Coseley	d							20 27								20 47	20 57								21 27
Wolverhampton 7 🚢	a		20 11	20 14	20 20		20 24	20 33	20 37			20 41	20 48			20 53	21 03	21 07		21 11		21 14		21 24	21 33
	d			20 15	20 22				20 37				20 49			20 54						21 15			
Penkridge	d				20 31											21 04									
Stafford	a			20 29	20 37				20 51				21 00			21 10						21 29			

A To Birmingham New Street
B From Bristol Temple Meads to Manchester Piccadilly
C To Crewe
D From Walsall
E From Northampton
F From Bournemouth to Manchester Piccadilly
G To Liverpool Lime Street
H To Shrewsbury
I To Preston
J To Chester
K From Exeter St Davids to Manchester Piccadilly
L From Bournemouth to Manchester Piccadilly. 🛒 to Birmingham New Street
M To Aberystwyth
N To Wolverhampton
O From London Euston

Table 68

Saturdays

14 December to 28 December

Northampton - Coventry - Birmingham - Wolverhampton - Stafford

Network Diagram - refer to first Page of Table 67

		VT ◇1 ᴾ		AW ◇ A	LM 1	LM	LM 1 B	LM	LM 1	XC ◇1 C	LM 1	LM D		LM E	VT ◇1 ᴾ	LM 1	XC ◇1 F	XC ◇1 G	LM	LM 1 B	LM 1	VT ◇1 ᴾ		XC ◇1 H	AW B
London Euston 15 ⊖66	d	19 43			19 13										20 25	19 46						21 03			
Northampton	d				20 22						20 55					21 16									
Long Buckby	d				20 33						21 06					21 27									
Rugby	d				20 44						21 17					21 38						22 12			
Coventry	a	20 50			20 55						21 29				21 36	21 49						22 22			
	d	20 50			20 56				21 11	21 27	21 30				21 36	21 50	21 56				22 11	22 23		22 27	
Canley	d				20 59				21 14		21 33										22 14				
Tile Hill	d				21 03				21 18		21 37					21 55					22 18				
Berkswell	d				21 06				21 21		21 40										22 21				
Hampton-in-Arden	d				21 10				21 25							22 01					22 25				
Birmingham International ✈	a	21 01			21 13				21 28	21 37	21 45				21 50	22 04	22 10				22 28	22 33		22 36	
	d	21 01		21 09	21 14	21 17			21 29	21 38	21 46				21 50	22 05	22 11		22 22		22 29	22 34		22 38	
Marston Green	d				21 17				21 32		21 49					22 08					22 32				
Lea Hall	d					21 21					21 52								22 26						
Stechford	d					21 24					21 55								22 29						
Adderley Park	d					21 27													22 32						
Birmingham New Street 12	a	21 13		21 20	21 25	21 32			21 42	21 48	22 01				22 04	22 16	22 21		22 36		22 42	22 45		22 48	
	d	21 17		21 23			21 36	21 38		21 57		22 05		22 08	22 16			22 31		22 38		22 48			22 55
Smethwick Rolfe Street	d							21 44						22 14						22 44					
Smethwick Galton Bridge 7	d			21 29				21 46						22 16						22 46					
Sandwell & Dudley	d							21 49				22 13		22 19	22 25					22 49		22 57			
Dudley Port	d							21 52						22 22						22 53					
Tipton	d							21 54						22 24						22 55					
Coseley	d						21 47	21 57						22 27						22 58					
Wolverhampton 7 ⛴	a	21 38		21 41			21 53	22 03		22 14		22 24		22 33	22 38			22 48		23 04		23 10			23 12
	d						21 59			22 15								22 49		23 05					
Penkridge	d						22 09													23 15					
Stafford	a						22 15			22 29								23 01		23 21					

		LM 1	LM D	LM 1	VT ◇1 ᴾ	AW D	LM 1
London Euston 15 ⊖66	d	20 34			21 43		21 28
Northampton	d	21 59		22 16			22 55
Long Buckby	d	22 10		22 27			23 06
Rugby	d	22 21		22 38	22 53		23 17
Coventry	a	22 32		22 49	23 02		23 28
	d	22 33		22 50	23 02		23 29
Canley	d	22 36					23 32
Tile Hill	d	22 40		22 55			23 36
Berkswell	d	22 43					23 39
Hampton-in-Arden	d			23 01			23 43
Birmingham International ✈	a	22 48		23 04	23 13		23 46
	d	22 49		23 05	23 13		23 47
Marston Green	d	22 52		23 08			23 50
Lea Hall	d	22 55					23 53
Stechford	d	22 58					23 56
Adderley Park	d						
Birmingham New Street 12	a	23 04		23 16	23 25		00 04
	d		23 08		23 27	23 35	
Smethwick Rolfe Street	d		23 14				
Smethwick Galton Bridge 7	d		23 16				
Sandwell & Dudley	d		23 19		23 37		
Dudley Port	d		23 22				
Tipton	d		23 24				
Coseley	d		23 27				
Wolverhampton 7 ⛴	a		23 35		23 50	23 53	
	d						
Penkridge	d						
Stafford	a						

A To Chester
B To Crewe
C From Bournemouth to Manchester Piccadilly
D To Shrewsbury
E From Walsall
F From Reading
G To Manchester Piccadilly
H From Bournemouth

Table 68

Saturdays

4 January to 8 February

Northampton - Coventry - Birmingham - Wolverhampton - Stafford

Network Diagram - refer to first Page of Table 67

	VT	VT	VT	XC	LM		LM	LM	VT	AW	XC	LM	LM	LM	LM		XC	LM	LM	LM	LM	VT	LM	LM
	◇1	◇1	◇1	◇1	1		1		◇1	◇	◇1		1		1		◇1	1	1			◇1	1	1
	A	A	B	C	D		E		F	G	C		D				C	H	D	I	J	K		E
	☕	☕	☕						☕	🛒	🛒						🛒					⊠		
London Euston 15 ⊖66 d																								
Northampton d							05 42											05 55					06 16	06 38
Long Buckby d																		06 06					06 27	
Rugby d	00 01	01 05					06 02											06 17					06 38	06 58
Coventry a	00 10	01 18																06 29					06 49	
d	00 10	01 18													06 11			06 30					06 50	
Canley d															06 14			06 33						
Tile Hill d															06 18			06 37					06 55	
Berkswell d															06 21			06 40						
Hampton-in-Arden d															06 25								07 01	
Birmingham International ✈ a	00 21	01 29													06 28			06 45					07 04	
d	00 21	01 29										06 17			06 29			06 46					07 05	
Marston Green d															06 32			06 49					07 08	
Lea Hall d												06 21						06 52						
Stechford d												06 24						06 55						
Adderley Park d												06 27												
Birmingham New Street 12 a	00 32	01 41										06 32			06 40			07 01					07 16	
d	00 35	01 42	05 30	05 57	06 01			06 08	06 15	06 23	06 31		06 36	06 38			06 57		07 01	07 05	07 08	07 15		
Smethwick Rolfe Street d								06 14						06 44							07 14			
Smethwick Galton Bridge 7 d					06 08			06 16		06 29				06 46					07 08		07 16			
Sandwell & Dudley d								06 19	06 24					06 49						07 13	07 19	07 24		
Dudley Port d								06 22						06 52							07 22			
Tipton d								06 24						06 54							07 24			
Coseley d								06 27						06 57							07 27			
Wolverhampton 7 🚌 a	01 03	02 10	05 47	06 14	06 19			06 32	06 37	06 42	06 48		06 52	07 03			07 14		07 19	07 24	07 33	07 37		
d			05 48	06 16	06 20						06 49		06 52				07 15		07 20					
Penkridge d					06 29								07 02						07 29					
Stafford a			06 00	06 29	06 35		06 53				07 00		07 09				07 29		07 35					07 53

	AW		XC	LM	LM	LM	LM	VT	XC	LM	LM		LM	LM	VT	LM	LM	AW	VT	XC	LM		LM	LM
	◇		◇1		1		1	◇1	◇1	1	1				◇1	1	1	◇	◇1	◇1			1	
	B		C		D				L	D			I	J	F		E	G		M			D	J
	🛒		🛒					☕	🛒						☕			🛒	☕	🛒				
London Euston 15 ⊖66 d								06 23			05 34						06 24		07 03					
Northampton d											06 55					07 16	07 45							
Long Buckby d											07 06					07 27								
Rugby d											07 17					07 38	08 04		07 51					
Coventry a								07 22			07 29					07 49			08 02					
d							07 11	07 22	07 27		07 30					07 50			08 02					
Canley d							07 14				07 33													
Tile Hill d							07 18				07 37					07 55								
Berkswell d							07 21				07 40													
Hampton-in-Arden d							07 25									08 01								
Birmingham International ✈ a							07 28	07 33	07 37		07 45					08 04			08 13					
d	07 09			07 17			07 29	07 33	07 38		07 46					08 05		08 09	08 13		08 17			
Marston Green d							07 32				07 49					08 08								
Lea Hall d				07 21							07 52										08 21			
Stechford d				07 24							07 55										08 24			
Adderley Park d				07 27																	08 27			
Birmingham New Street 12 a	07 19			07 32			07 42	07 47	07 48		08 01					08 16		08 20	08 27		08 32			
d	07 22		07 31		07 36	07 38			07 57	08 01			08 05	08 08	08 15			08 23		08 31			08 36	08 38
Smethwick Rolfe Street d						07 44								08 14										08 44
Smethwick Galton Bridge 7 d	07 28					07 46				08 08				08 16				08 29						08 46
Sandwell & Dudley d						07 49							08 13	08 19	08 24									08 49
Dudley Port d						07 52								08 22										08 52
Tipton d						07 54								08 24										08 54
Coseley d					07 47	07 57								08 27									08 47	08 57
Wolverhampton 7 🚌 a	07 39		07 48		07 53	08 03			08 14	08 19			08 24	08 33	08 37			08 42		08 48			08 53	09 03
d			07 49		07 54				08 15	08 20										08 49			08 54	
Penkridge d					08 04					08 29													09 04	
Stafford a			08 00		08 10				08 29	08 35							08 53			09 00			09 10	

A From London Euston
B To Holyhead
C To Manchester Piccadilly
D To Liverpool Lime Street
E To Crewe
F To Edinburgh
G To Aberystwyth
H From Bletchley
I To Shrewsbury
J From Walsall
K To Glasgow Central
L From Southampton Central to Manchester Piccadilly
M From Bristol Temple Meads to Manchester Piccadilly

Table 68

Saturdays

4 January to 8 February

Northampton - Coventry - Birmingham - Wolverhampton - Stafford

Network Diagram - refer to first Page of Table 67

		LM	VT	XC		LM	LM	LM	LM	VT	LM	AW	VT	XC		LM	LM	LM	LM	VT	XC	LM	LM	LM	
		1	◇1	◇1		1	1			◇1	1	◇	◇1	◇1			1		1	◇1	◇1	1	1		
				A		B		C	D	E		F		G			B	D			H	B		C	
			🍴	☕						⊠		☕	🍴	☕						🍴	☕				
London Euston 15 ⊖66	d		07 23							07 43			08 03						07 05	08 23			07 49		
Northampton	d	07 37					07 55				08 16								08 35				08 55		
Long Buckby	d	07 48					08 06				08 27								08 46				09 06		
Rugby	d	07 59					08 17				08 38		08 51						08 57				09 17		
Coventry	a	08 10	08 22				08 29			08 42	08 49		09 02						09 08	09 22			09 29		
	d	08 11	08 22	08 27			08 30			08 42	08 50		09 02						09 11	09 22	09 27		09 30		
Canley	d	08 14					08 33												09 14				09 33		
Tile Hill	d	08 18					08 37				08 55								09 18				09 37		
Berkswell	d	08 21					08 40												09 21				09 40		
Hampton-in-Arden	d	08 25									09 01								09 25						
Birmingham International ✈	a	08 28	08 33	08 37			08 45			08 53	09 04		09 13						09 28	09 33	09 37		09 45		
	d	08 29	08 33	08 38			08 46			08 53	09 05	09 09	09 13			09 17			09 29	09 33	09 38		09 46		
Marston Green	d	08 32					08 49				09 08								09 32				09 49		
Lea Hall	d						08 52									09 21							09 52		
Stechford	d						08 55									09 24							09 55		
Adderley Park	d															09 27									
Birmingham New Street 12	a	08 42	08 45	08 48			09 01			09 08	09 16	09 20	09 27			09 32			09 42	09 45	09 48		10 01		
	d			08 57		09 01		09 05	09 08	09 15		09 23		09 31			09 36	09 38			09 57	10 01		10 05	
Smethwick Rolfe Street	d								09 14									09 44							
Smethwick Galton Bridge 7	d					09 08			09 16			09 29						09 46				10 08			
Sandwell & Dudley	d							09 13	09 19	09 24								09 49						10 13	
Dudley Port	d								09 22									09 52							
Tipton	d								09 24									09 54							
Coseley	d								09 27								09 47	09 57							
Wolverhampton 7 🚊	a			09 14		09 19		09 24	09 33	09 37		09 42		09 48			09 53	10 03			10 14	10 19		10 24	
	d			09 15		09 20								09 49			09 54				10 15	10 20			
Penkridge	d																10 04								
Stafford	a			09 29		09 34								10 00			10 10				10 29	10 35			

		LM	VT	LM	AW	VT	XC	LM	LM	LM		LM	VT	XC	LM	LM	LM	LM	VT	LM		AW	LM	VT	XC
			◇1	1	◇	◇1	◇1		1			1	◇1	◇1	1	1			◇1	1		◇	1	◇1	◇1
		D	I		J		K		B	D				H	B		C	D	I			F	L		M
			🍴		☕	🍴	☕						🍴	☕					🍴			☕		🍴	☕
London Euston 15 ⊖66	d		08 43	07 54		09 03							09 23			08 49			09 43	09 13				10 03	
Northampton	d			09 16								09 35				09 55				10 16			10 25		
Long Buckby	d			09 27								09 46				10 06				10 27			10 36		
Rugby	d			09 38		09 51						09 57				10 17				10 38			10 47	10 51	
Coventry	a		09 42	09 49		10 02						10 08	10 22			10 29			10 42	10 49			10 58	11 02	
	d		09 42	09 50		10 02						10 11	10 22	10 27		10 30			10 42	10 50			11 11	11 02	
Canley	d											10 14				10 33							↪		
Tile Hill	d			09 55								10 18				10 37				10 55					
Berkswell	d											10 21				10 40									
Hampton-in-Arden	d			10 01								10 25								11 01					
Birmingham International ✈	a		09 53	10 04		10 13						10 28	10 33	10 37		10 45			10 53	11 04				11 13	
	d		09 53	10 05	10 09	10 13		10 17				10 29	10 33	10 38		10 46			10 53	11 05		11 09		11 13	
Marston Green	d			10 08								10 32				10 49				11 08					
Lea Hall	d							10 21								10 52									
Stechford	d							10 24								10 55									
Adderley Park	d							10 27																	
Birmingham New Street 12	a		10 08	10 16	10 20	10 27		10 32				10 42	10 45	10 48		11 01			11 08	11 16		11 20		11 27	
	d	10 08	10 15		10 23		10 31		10 36	10 38				10 57	11 01		11 05	11 08	11 15			11 23			11 31
Smethwick Rolfe Street	d	10 14								10 44								11 14							
Smethwick Galton Bridge 7	d	10 16			10 30					10 46					11 08			11 16				11 29			
Sandwell & Dudley	d	10 19	10 24							10 49							11 13	11 19	11 24						
Dudley Port	d	10 22								10 52								11 22							
Tipton	d	10 24								10 54								11 24							
Coseley	d	10 27							10 47	10 57								11 27							
Wolverhampton 7 🚊	a	10 33	10 37		10 42		10 48		10 53	11 03				11 14	11 19		11 24	11 33	11 37			11 41			11 48
	d						10 49		10 54					11 15	11 20										11 49
Penkridge	d								11 04																
Stafford	a						11 00		11 10					11 29	11 35										12 00

A From Southampton Central to Manchester Piccadilly
B To Liverpool Lime Street
C To Shrewsbury
D From Walsall
E To Glasgow Central
F To Holyhead
G From Cardiff Central to Manchester Piccadilly
H From Bournemouth to Manchester Piccadilly
I To Preston
J To Aberystwyth
K From Paignton to Manchester Piccadilly
L To Birmingham New Street
M From Bristol Temple Meads to Manchester Piccadilly

Table 68

Saturdays

4 January to 8 February

Northampton - Coventry - Birmingham - Wolverhampton - Stafford

Network Diagram - refer to first Page of Table 67

		LM		LM 1 A	LM B	LM 1 C	VT ◇1	XC ◇1 D	LM 1 A	LM 1	LM E	LM B		VT ◇1 F	LM 1	AW ◇ G	LM 1 H	VT ◇1	XC ◇1 I	LM	LM 1 A	LM B		LM 1 C	VT ◇1
London Euston 15 ⊖66	d						10 23			09 49				10 43	10 13			11 03							11 23
Northampton	d									10 55					11 16		11 25								
Long Buckby	d									11 06					11 27		11 36								
Rugby	d					←				11 17					11 38		11 47	11 51						←	
Coventry	a					10 58	11 22			11 29				11 42	11 49		11 58	12 02						11 58	12 22
	d					11 11	11 22	11 27		11 30				11 42	11 50		12 11	12 02						12 11	12 22
Canley	d					11 14				11 33							↦							12 14	
Tile Hill	d					11 18				11 37					11 55									12 18	
Berkswell	d					11 21				11 40														12 21	
Hampton-in-Arden	d					11 25									12 01									12 25	
Birmingham International ✈	a					11 28	11 33	11 37		11 45				11 53	12 04			12 13						12 28	12 33
	d	11 17				11 29	11 33	11 38		11 46				11 53	12 05	12 09		12 13		12 17				12 29	12 33
Marston Green	d					11 32				11 49					12 08									12 32	
Lea Hall	d	11 21								11 52										12 21					
Stechford	d	11 24								11 55										12 24					
Adderley Park	d	11 27																		12 27					
Birmingham New Street 12	a	11 32				11 42	11 45	11 48		12 01				12 08	12 16	12 21		12 27		12 32				12 42	12 45
	d			11 36	11 38			11 57	12 01		12 05	12 08		12 15		12 23			12 31		12 36	12 38			
Smethwick Rolfe Street	d				11 44							12 14										12 44			
Smethwick Galton Bridge 7	d				11 46				12 08			12 16				12 29						12 46			
Sandwell & Dudley	d				11 49						12 13	12 19		12 24								12 49			
Dudley Port	d				11 52							12 22										12 52			
Tipton	d				11 54							12 24										12 54			
Coseley	d			11 47	11 57							12 27									12 47	12 57			
Wolverhampton 7 🚌	a			11 53	12 03			12 14	12 19		12 24	12 33		12 37		12 42			12 48		12 53	13 03			
	d			11 54				12 15	12 20										12 49		12 54				
Penkridge	d			12 04																	13 04				
Stafford	a			12 10				12 29	12 35										13 00		13 10				

		XC ◇1 D	LM 1 A	LM 1	LM E	LM B	VT ◇1 F	LM 1		AW ◇ J	LM 1 H	VT ◇1	XC ◇1 K	LM	LM 1 A	LM B	LM 1 C	VT ◇1		XC ◇1 D	LM 1 A	LM 1	LM E	LM B	VT ◇1 F
London Euston 15 ⊖66	d			10 49			11 43	11 13				12 03						12 23				11 49			12 43
Northampton	d			11 55				12 16			12 25											12 55			
Long Buckby	d			12 06				12 27			12 36											13 06			
Rugby	d			12 17				12 38			12 47	12 51					←					13 17			
Coventry	a			12 29			12 42	12 49			12 58	13 02					12 58	13 22				13 29			13 42
	d	12 27		12 30			12 42	12 50			13 11	13 02					13 11	13 22		13 27		13 30			13 42
Canley	d			12 33							↦						13 14					13 33			
Tile Hill	d			12 37				12 55									13 18					13 37			
Berkswell	d			12 40													13 21					13 40			
Hampton-in-Arden	d							13 01									13 25								
Birmingham International ✈	a	12 37		12 45			12 53	13 04				13 13					13 28	13 33		13 37		13 45			13 53
	d	12 38		12 46			12 53	13 05		13 09		13 13		13 17			13 29	13 33		13 38		13 46			13 53
Marston Green	d			12 49				13 08									13 32					13 49			
Lea Hall	d			12 52										13 21								13 52			
Stechford	d			12 55										13 24								13 55			
Adderley Park	d													13 27											
Birmingham New Street 12	a	12 48		13 01			13 08	13 16		13 21		13 27		13 32			13 42	13 45		13 48		14 01			14 08
	d	12 57	13 01		13 05	13 08	13 15			13 23			13 31		13 36	13 38				13 57	14 01		14 05	14 08	14 15
Smethwick Rolfe Street	d					13 14										13 44								14 14	
Smethwick Galton Bridge 7	d		13 08			13 16				13 29						13 46					14 08			14 16	
Sandwell & Dudley	d				13 13	13 19	13 24									13 49							14 13	14 19	14 24
Dudley Port	d					13 22										13 52								14 22	
Tipton	d					13 24										13 54								14 24	
Coseley	d					13 27									13 47	13 57								14 27	
Wolverhampton 7 🚌	a	13 14	13 19		13 24	13 33	13 37			13 41			13 48		13 53	14 03				14 14	14 19		14 24	14 33	14 37
	d	13 15	13 20										13 49		13 54					14 15	14 20				
Penkridge	d														14 04										
Stafford	a	13 29	13 35										14 00		14 10					14 29	14 35				

A To Liverpool Lime Street
B From Walsall
C From Northampton
D From Bournemouth to Manchester Piccadilly
E To Shrewsbury
F To Preston
G To Aberystwyth
H To Birmingham New Street
I From Bristol Temple Meads to Manchester Piccadilly
J To Holyhead
K From Paignton to Manchester Piccadilly

Table 68

Saturdays

4 January to 8 February

Northampton - Coventry - Birmingham - Wolverhampton - Stafford

Network Diagram - refer to first Page of Table 67

		LM	AW	LM	VT	XC	LM	LM	LM	LM		VT	XC	LM	LM	LM	LM	VT	LM	AW		LM	VT	XC	LM
		1	◇	1	◇1	◇1		1		1		◇1	◇1	1	1			◇1	1	◇		1	◇1	◇1	
			A	B		C		D	E	F			G	D		H	E	I		J		B		K	
London Euston 15 ⊖66	d	12 13			13 03							13 23			12 49			13 43	13 13				14 03		
Northampton	d	13 16		13 25											13 55				14 16			14 25			
Long Buckby	d	13 27		13 36											14 06				14 27			14 36			
Rugby	d	13 38		13 47	13 51					←					14 17				14 38			14 47	14 51		
Coventry	a	13 49		13 58	14 02					13 58		14 22			14 29			14 42	14 49			14 58	15 02		
	d	13 50		14 11	14 02					14 11		14 22	14 27		14 30			14 42	14 50			15 11	15 02		
Canley	d			→						14 14					14 33							→			
Tile Hill	d	13 55								14 18					14 37				14 55						
Berkswell	d									14 21					14 40										
Hampton-in-Arden	d	14 01								14 25									15 01						
Birmingham International ✈	a	14 04			14 13					14 28		14 33	14 37		14 45			14 53	15 04				15 13		
	d	14 05	14 09		14 13		14 17			14 29		14 33	14 38		14 46			14 53	15 05	15 09			15 13		15 17
Marston Green	d	14 08								14 32					14 49				15 08						
Lea Hall	d						14 21								14 52										15 21
Stechford	d						14 24								14 55										15 24
Adderley Park	d						14 27																		15 27
Birmingham New Street 12	a	14 16	14 20		14 27		14 32			14 42		14 45	14 48		15 01			15 08	15 17	15 20			15 27		15 32
	d		14 23			14 31		14 36	14 38				14 57	15 01		15 05	15 08	15 15		15 23				15 31	
Smethwick Rolfe Street	d								14 44								15 14								
Smethwick Galton Bridge 7	d		14 29						14 46					15 08			15 16			15 29					
Sandwell & Dudley	d								14 49							15 13	15 19	15 24							
Dudley Port	d								14 52								15 22								
Tipton	d								14 54								15 24								
Coseley	d							14 47	14 57								15 27								
Wolverhampton 7	a		14 41			14 48		14 53	15 03				15 14	15 19		15 24	15 33	15 37		15 42				15 48	
	d					14 49		14 54					15 15	15 20										15 49	
Penkridge	d							15 04																	
Stafford	a					15 00		15 10					15 29	15 35										16 00	

		LM	LM	LM	VT	XC		LM	LM	LM	LM	VT	LM	AW	LM	VT		XC	LM	LM	LM	LM	VT	XC	LM
												R		R											
		1		1	◇1	◇1		1	1			1	1		1	◇1		◇1		1		1	◇1	◇1	1
		D	E	F		G		D		H	E	I		A	B			C		D	E	F		G	D
London Euston 15 ⊖66	d				14 23				13 49			14 43	14 13			15 03							15 23		
Northampton	d								14 55				15 16		15 25										
Long Buckby	d								15 06				15 27		15 36										
Rugby	d			←					15 17				15 38		15 47	15 51						←			
Coventry	a			14 58	15 22				15 29			15 42	15 49		15 58	16 02						15 58	16 22		
	d			15 11	15 22	15 27			15 30			15 42	15 50		16 11	16 02						16 11	16 22	16 27	
Canley	d			15 14					15 33						→							16 14			
Tile Hill	d			15 18					15 37				15 55									16 18			
Berkswell	d			15 21					15 40													16 21			
Hampton-in-Arden	d			15 25									16 01									16 25			
Birmingham International ✈	a			15 28	15 33	15 37			15 45			15 53	16 04			16 13						16 28	16 33	16 37	
	d			15 29	15 33	15 38			15 46			15 53	16 05	16 09		16 13			16 17			16 29	16 33	16 38	
Marston Green	d			15 32					15 49				16 08									16 32			
Lea Hall	d								15 52										16 21						
Stechford	d								15 55										16 24						
Adderley Park	d																		16 27						
Birmingham New Street 12	a			15 42	15 45	15 48			16 01			16 08	16 16	16 20		16 27			16 32			16 42	16 45	16 48	
	d	15 36	15 38			15 57		16 01		16 05	16 08	16 15		16 23				16 31		16 36	16 38			16 57	17 01
Smethwick Rolfe Street	d		15 44								16 14										16 44				
Smethwick Galton Bridge 7	d		15 46					16 08			16 16			16 29							16 46				17 08
Sandwell & Dudley	d		15 49							16 13	16 19	16 24									16 49				
Dudley Port	d		15 52								16 22										16 52				
Tipton	d		15 54								16 24										16 54				
Coseley	d	15 47	15 57								16 27									16 47	16 57				
Wolverhampton 7	a	15 53	16 03			16 14		16 19		16 24	16 33	16 37		16 41				16 48		16 53	17 04			17 14	17 19
	d	15 54				16 15		16 20										16 49		16 54				17 15	17 20
Penkridge	d	16 04						16 29												17 04					17 29
Stafford	a	16 10				16 29		16 35										17 00		17 10				17 29	17 35

A To Aberystwyth
B To Birmingham New Street
C From Bristol Temple Meads to Manchester Piccadilly
D To Liverpool Lime Street
E From Walsall
F From Northampton
G From Bournemouth to Manchester Piccadilly
H To Shrewsbury
I To Preston
J To Holyhead
K From Penzance to Manchester Piccadilly

Table 68

Saturdays

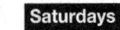

4 January to 8 February

Northampton - Coventry - Birmingham - Wolverhampton - Stafford

Network Diagram - refer to first Page of Table 67

		LM 1	LM A	LM B	VT R 1 C ⊠	LM 1	AW ◇ D	LM 1 E		VT ◇1	XC ◇1 F	LM	LM 1 G	LM B	LM 1 H	VT ◇1	XC ◇1 I	LM 1 G		LM 1	LM A	LM B	VT ◇1 C	LM 1	AW ◇ J
London Euston 15 ⊖66	d	14 49			15 43	15 13				16 03						16 23				15 49			16 43	16 13	
Northampton	d	15 55				16 16		16 25												16 55				17 16	
Long Buckby	d	16 06				16 27		16 36												17 06				17 27	
Rugby	d	16 17				16 38		16 47		16 51					←					17 17				17 38	
Coventry	a	16 29			16 42	16 49		16 58		17 02					16 58	17 22				17 29			17 42	17 49	
	d	16 30			16 42	16 50		17 11		17 02					17 11	17 22	17 27			17 30			17 42	17 50	
Canley	d	16 33						↪							17 14					17 33					
Tile Hill	d	16 37				16 55									17 18					17 37				17 55	
Berkswell	d	16 40													17 21					17 40					
Hampton-in-Arden	d					17 01									17 25									18 01	
Birmingham International	a	16 45			16 53	17 04				17 13					17 28	17 33	17 37			17 45			17 53	18 04	
	d	16 46			16 53	17 05	17 09			17 13		17 17			17 29	17 33	17 38			17 46			17 53	18 05	18 09
Marston Green	d	16 49				17 08									17 32					17 49				18 08	
Lea Hall	d	16 52										17 21								17 52					
Stechford	d	16 55										17 24								17 55					
Adderley Park	d											17 27													
Birmingham New Street 12	a	17 01			17 08	17 16	17 20			17 27		17 32			17 42	17 45	17 48			18 01			18 08	18 16	18 20
	d		17 05	17 08	17 15		17 23				17 31		17 36	17 38			17 57	18 01			18 05	18 08	18 15		18 23
Smethwick Rolfe Street	d			17 14										17 44								18 14			
Smethwick Galton Bridge 7	d			17 16			17 30							17 46				18 08				18 16			18 29
Sandwell & Dudley	d		17 13	17 19	17 24									17 49							18 13	18 19	18 24		
Dudley Port	d			17 22										17 52								18 22			
Tipton	d			17 24										17 54								18 24			
Coseley	d			17 27									17 47	17 57								18 27			
Wolverhampton 7	a		17 24	17 33	17 37		17 41				17 48		17 53	18 03			18 14	18 19			18 24	18 33	18 37		18 41
	d										17 49		17 54				18 15	18 20							
Penkridge	d												18 04					18 29							
Stafford	a										18 00		18 10				18 29	18 35							

		LM 1 E	VT ◇1	XC ◇1 K		LM	LM 1 L	LM B	LM 1 H	VT ◇1	XC ◇1 I	LM 1 G	LM 1	LM A		LM B	VT ◇1 M	LM 1	AW ◇ N	XC ◇1 O	LM 1 E	VT ◇1	LM	LM B	
London Euston 15 ⊖66	d		17 03							17 23			16 49				17 43	17 13				18 03			
Northampton	d	17 25											17 55					18 16			18 25				
Long Buckby	d	17 36											18 06					18 27			18 36				
Rugby	d	17 47	17 51						←				18 17					18 38			18 47	18 51			
Coventry	a	17 58	18 02						17 58	18 24			18 29				18 42	18 49			18 58	19 02			
	d	18 11	18 02						18 11	18 24	18 27		18 30				18 42	18 50			19 11	19 02			
Canley	d	↪							18 14				18 33								↪				
Tile Hill	d								18 18				18 37					18 55							
Berkswell	d								18 21				18 40												
Hampton-in-Arden	d								18 25									19 01							
Birmingham International	a		18 13						18 28	18 34	18 37		18 45				18 53	19 04				19 13			
	d		18 13			18 17			18 29	18 34	18 38		18 46				18 53	19 05	19 09			19 13	19 17		
Marston Green	d								18 32				18 49					19 08							
Lea Hall	d					18 21							18 52										19 21		
Stechford	d					18 24							18 55										19 24		
Adderley Park	d					18 27																	19 27		
Birmingham New Street 12	a		18 27			18 32			18 42	18 45	18 48		19 01				19 08	19 17	19 20			19 27	19 32		
	d			18 31			18 36	18 38		18 50	18 57	19 01		19 05		19 08	19 15		19 23	19 31		19 35		19 38	
Smethwick Rolfe Street	d							18 44								19 14								19 44	
Smethwick Galton Bridge 7	d							18 46				19 08				19 16			19 29					19 46	
Sandwell & Dudley	d							18 49		18 59				19 13		19 19	19 24					19 44		19 49	
Dudley Port	d							18 52								19 22								19 52	
Tipton	d							18 54								19 24								19 54	
Coseley	d						18 47	18 57								19 27								19 57	
Wolverhampton 7	a			18 48			18 53	19 03		19 11	19 14	19 19		19 24		19 33	19 37		19 42	19 48		19 58		20 03	
	d			18 49			18 54				19 15	19 20								19 49					
Penkridge	d						19 04					19 29													
Stafford	a			19 00			19 10				19 29	19 35								20 00					

A To Shrewsbury
B From Walsall
C To Preston
D To Holyhead
E To Birmingham New Street
F From Paignton to Manchester Piccadilly
G To Liverpool Lime Street
H From Northampton
I From Bournemouth to Manchester Piccadilly
J To Aberystwyth
K From Bristol Temple Meads to Manchester Piccadilly
L To Crewe
M To Wigan North Western
N To Chester
O From Exeter St Davids to Manchester Piccadilly

Table 68

Saturdays

4 January to 8 February

Northampton - Coventry - Birmingham - Wolverhampton - Stafford

Network Diagram - refer to first Page of Table 67

		LM ■1 A	VT ◇■1 🍴	XC ◇■1 B 🛒	LM ■1 C	LM ■1		LM D	LM	VT ◇■1 E 🍴	LM ■1	AW ◇ F	XC ◇■1 G	VT ◇■1 H 🍴	LM	LM ■1 E		LM	VT ◇■1 I 🍴	LM ■1	VT ◇■1 🍴	XC ◇■1 B 🛒	LM ■1	LM D	LM J
London Euston 15 ⊖66	d		18 23			17 49				18 43	18 13			19 03							19 23		18 49		
Northampton	d					18 55					19 16									19 35			19 55		
Long Buckby	d					19 06					19 27									19 46			20 06		
Rugby	d	←				19 17					19 38			19 51						19 57			20 17		
Coventry	a	18 58	19 22			19 29				19 42	19 49			20 02						20 08	20 22		20 29		
	d	19 11	19 22	19 27		19 30				19 42	19 50			20 02						20 11	20 22	20 27	20 30		
Canley	d	19 14				19 33														20 14			20 33		
Tile Hill	d	19 18				19 37					19 55									20 18			20 37		
Berkswell	d	19 21				19 40														20 21			20 40		
Hampton-in-Arden	d	19 25									20 01									20 25					
Birmingham International ✈	a	19 28	19 33	19 37		19 45				19 53	20 04			20 13						20 28	20 33	20 37	20 45		
	d	19 29	19 33	19 38		19 46				19 53	20 05	20 09		20 13	20 17					20 29	20 33	20 38	20 46		
Marston Green	d	19 32				19 49					20 08									20 32			20 49		
Lea Hall	d					19 52									20 21								20 52		
Stechford	d					19 55									20 24								20 55		
Adderley Park	d														20 27				←						
Birmingham New Street 12	a	19 42	19 45	19 48		20 01				20 08	20 18	20 21		20 27	20 32				20 27	20 42	20 45	20 48	21 01		
	d		19 50	19 57	20 01			20 05	20 08	20 15		20 23	20 31	20 42		20 36		20 38	20 42		20 50	20 57		21 05	21 08
Smethwick Rolfe Street	d								20 14					→				20 44							21 14
Smethwick Galton Bridge 7	d				20 08				20 16			20 29						20 46							21 16
Sandwell & Dudley	d		19 59					20 13	20 19	20 24								20 49	20 53		20 59			21 13	21 19
Dudley Port	d								20 22									20 52							21 22
Tipton	d								20 24									20 54							21 24
Coseley	d								20 27							20 47		20 57							21 27
Wolverhampton 7	a		20 11	20 14	20 20			20 24	20 33	20 37		20 41	20 48			20 53		21 03	21 07		21 11	21 14		21 24	21 33
	d			20 15	20 22					20 37			20 49			20 54						21 15			
Penkridge	d				20 31											21 04									
Stafford	a			20 29	20 37					20 49			21 00			21 10						21 29			

		VT ◇■1 🍴		AW ◇ K	LM ■1	LM	LM ■1 E	LM	LM ■1	XC ◇■1 L	LM ■1	LM D		LM J	VT ◇■1 🍴	LM ■1	XC ◇■1 M	XC ◇■1 N	LM	LM ■1 E	LM ■1	VT ◇■1 🍴		XC ◇■1 O	AW E
London Euston 15 ⊖66	d	19 43			19 13										20 25	19 46						21 03			
Northampton	d				20 22						20 55					21 16									
Long Buckby	d				20 33						21 06					21 27									
Rugby	d				20 44						21 17					21 38						22 12			
Coventry	a	20 50			20 55						21 29				21 36	21 49						22 22			
	d	20 50			20 56				21 11	21 27	21 30				21 36	21 50	21 56				22 11	22 23		22 27	
Canley	d				20 59				21 14		21 33										22 14				
Tile Hill	d				21 03				21 18		21 37					21 55					22 18				
Berkswell	d				21 06				21 21		21 40										22 21				
Hampton-in-Arden	d				21 10				21 25							22 01					22 25				
Birmingham International ✈	a	21 01			21 13				21 28	21 37	21 45				21 50	22 04	22 10				22 28	22 33		22 36	
	d	21 01		21 09	21 14	21 17			21 29	21 38	21 46				21 50	22 05	22 11		22 22		22 29	22 34		22 38	
Marston Green	d				21 17				21 32		21 49					22 08					22 32				
Lea Hall	d					21 21					21 52								22 26						
Stechford	d					21 24					21 55								22 29						
Adderley Park	d					21 27													22 32						
Birmingham New Street 12	a	21 13		21 20	21 25	21 32			21 42	21 48	22 01				22 04	22 16	22 21		22 36		22 42	22 45		22 48	
	d	21 17		21 23			21 36	21 38		21 57		22 05		22 08	22 16			22 31		22 38		22 48			22 55
Smethwick Rolfe Street	d							21 44						22 14						22 44					
Smethwick Galton Bridge 7	d			21 29				21 46						22 16						22 46					
Sandwell & Dudley	d							21 49				22 13		22 19	22 25					22 49		22 57			
Dudley Port	d							21 52						22 22						22 53					
Tipton	d							21 54						22 24						22 55					
Coseley	d						21 47	21 57						22 27						22 58					
Wolverhampton 7	a	21 38		21 41			21 53	22 03		22 14		22 24		22 33	22 38			22 48		23 04		23 10			23 12
	d						21 59			22 15								22 49		23 05					
Penkridge	d						22 09													23 15					
Stafford	a						22 15			22 29								23 01		23 21					

A From Northampton
B From Bournemouth to Manchester Piccadilly. 🛒 to Birmingham New Street
C To Liverpool Lime Street
D To Shrewsbury
E To Crewe
F To Aberystwyth
G From Bristol Temple Meads to Manchester Piccadilly
H To Wolverhampton
I From London Euston
J From Walsall
K To Chester
L From Bournemouth to Manchester Piccadilly
M From Reading
N To Manchester Piccadilly
O From Bournemouth

Table 68

Saturdays
4 January to 8 February

Northampton - Coventry - Birmingham - Wolverhampton - Stafford

Network Diagram - refer to first Page of Table 67

		LM 1	LM A	LM 1	VT ◇1	AW A	LM 1
London Euston 15 ⊖66	d	20 34			21 43		21 28
Northampton	d	21 59		22 16			22 55
Long Buckby	d	22 10		22 27			23 06
Rugby	d	22 21		22 38	22 53		23 17
Coventry	a	22 32		22 49	23 02		23 28
	d	22 33		22 50	23 02		23 29
Canley	d	22 36					23 32
Tile Hill	d	22 40		22 55			23 36
Berkswell	d	22 43					23 39
Hampton-in-Arden	d			23 01			23 43
Birmingham International ✈	a	22 48		23 04	23 13		23 46
	d	22 49		23 05	23 13		23 47
Marston Green	d	22 52		23 08			23 50
Lea Hall	d	22 55					23 53
Stechford	d	22 58					23 56
Adderley Park	d						
Birmingham New Street 12	a	23 04		23 16	23 25		00 04
	d		23 08		23 27	23 35	
Smethwick Rolfe Street	d		23 14				
Smethwick Galton Bridge 7	d		23 16				
Sandwell & Dudley	d		23 19		23 37		
Dudley Port	d		23 22				
Tipton	d		23 24				
Coseley	d		23 27				
Wolverhampton 7	a		23 35		23 50	23 53	
	d						
Penkridge	d						
Stafford	a						

Saturdays
15 February to 17 May

		VT ◇1 B	VT ◇1 B	VT ◇1 C	XC ◇1 D	LM 1 E	LM 1 F	LM	VT ◇1 G	AW ◇ H	XC ◇1 D	LM	LM 1 E	LM	LM 1	XC ◇1 D	LM 1 I	LM 1 E	LM A	LM J	VT ◇1 K	LM 1	LM 1 F
London Euston 15 ⊖66	d																						
Northampton	d						05 42										05 55					06 16	06 38
Long Buckby	d																06 06					06 27	
Rugby	d	00 01	01 05				06 02										06 17					06 38	06 58
Coventry	a	00 10	01 18														06 29					06 49	
	d	00 10	01 18												06 11		06 30					06 50	
Canley	d														06 14		06 33						
Tile Hill	d														06 18		06 37					06 55	
Berkswell	d														06 21		06 40						
Hampton-in-Arden	d														06 25							07 01	
Birmingham International ✈	a	00 21	01 29												06 28		06 45					07 04	
	d	00 21	01 29									06 17			06 29		06 46					07 05	
Marston Green	d														06 32		06 49					07 08	
Lea Hall	d											06 21					06 52						
Stechford	d											06 24					06 55						
Adderley Park	d											06 27											
Birmingham New Street 12	a	00 32	01 41									06 32			06 40		07 01					07 16	
	d	00 35	01 42	05 30	05 57	06 01		06 08	06 15	06 23	06 31		06 36	06 38		06 57		07 01	07 05	07 08	07 15		
Smethwick Rolfe Street	d							06 14						06 44						07 14			
Smethwick Galton Bridge 7	d					06 08		06 16		06 29				06 46				07 08		07 16			
Sandwell & Dudley	d							06 19	06 24					06 49					07 13	07 19	07 24		
Dudley Port	d							06 22						06 52						07 22			
Tipton	d							06 24						06 54						07 24			
Coseley	d							06 27						06 57						07 27			
Wolverhampton 7	a	01 03	02 10	05 47	06 14	06 19		06 32	06 37	06 42	06 48		06 52	07 03		07 14		07 19	07 24	07 33	07 37		
	d			05 48	06 16	06 20					06 49		06 52			07 15		07 20					
Penkridge	d					06 29							07 02					07 29					
Stafford	a			06 00	06 29	06 35	06 53				07 00		07 09			07 29		07 35					07 53

A To Shrewsbury
B From London Euston
C To Holyhead
D To Manchester Piccadilly
E To Liverpool Lime Street
F To Crewe
G To Edinburgh
H To Aberystwyth
I From Bletchley
J From Walsall
K To Glasgow Central

Table 68

Saturdays

15 February to 17 May

Northampton - Coventry - Birmingham - Wolverhampton - Stafford

Network Diagram - refer to first Page of Table 67

		AW		XC	LM	LM	LM	LM	VT	XC	LM	LM		LM	LM	VT	LM	LM	AW	VT	XC	LM		LM	LM
		◇		◇1		1		1	◇1	◇1	1	1				◇1	1	1	◇	◇1	◇1			1	
		A		B		C				D	C			E	F	G		H	I		J			C	F
London Euston 15 ⊖66	d								06 23			05 34						06 24		07 03					
Northampton	d											06 55					07 16	07 45							
Long Buckby	d											07 06					07 27								
Rugby	d											07 17					07 38	08 04		07 51					
Coventry	a								07 22			07 29					07 49			08 02					
	d							07 11	07 22	07 27		07 30					07 50			08 02					
Canley	d							07 14				07 33													
Tile Hill	d							07 18				07 37					07 55								
Berkswell	d							07 21				07 40													
Hampton-in-Arden	d							07 25									08 01								
Birmingham International ✈	a							07 28	07 33	07 37		07 45					08 04			08 13					
	d	07 09			07 17			07 29	07 33	07 38		07 46					08 05		08 09	08 13		08 17			
Marston Green	d							07 32				07 49					08 08								
Lea Hall	d				07 21							07 52										08 21			
Stechford	d				07 24							07 55										08 24			
Adderley Park	d				07 27																	08 27			
Birmingham New Street 12	a	07 19			07 32			07 42	07 47	07 48		08 01					08 16		08 20	08 27		08 32			
	d	07 22		07 31		07 36	07 38			07 57	08 01			08 05	08 08	08 15			08 23		08 31			08 36	08 38
Smethwick Rolfe Street	d						07 44								08 14										08 44
Smethwick Galton Bridge 7	d	07 28					07 46				08 08				08 16				08 29						08 46
Sandwell & Dudley	d						07 49							08 13	08 19	08 24									08 49
Dudley Port	d						07 52								08 22										08 52
Tipton	d						07 54								08 24										08 54
Coseley	d					07 47	07 57								08 27									08 47	08 57
Wolverhampton 7	a	07 39		07 48		07 53	08 03			08 14	08 19			08 24	08 33	08 37			08 42		08 48			08 53	09 03
	d			07 49		07 54				08 15	08 20										08 49			08 54	
Penkridge	d					08 04					08 29													09 04	
Stafford	a			08 00		08 10				08 29	08 35							08 53			09 00			09 10	

		LM	VT	XC	LM	LM	LM	LM		VT	LM	AW	VT	XC	LM	LM	LM	LM		VT	XC	LM	LM	LM	LM
		1	◇1	◇1	1	1				◇1	1	◇	◇1	◇1		1		1		◇1	◇1	1	1		
				D	C		E	F		K		A		L		C	F				M	C		E	F
London Euston 15 ⊖66	d		07 23							07 43			08 03					07 05		08 23			07 49		
Northampton	d	07 37				07 55					08 16							08 35					08 55		
Long Buckby	d	07 48				08 06					08 27							08 46					09 06		
Rugby	d	07 59				08 17					08 38		08 51					08 57					09 17		
Coventry	a	08 10	08 22			08 29				08 42	08 49		09 02					09 08		09 22			09 29		
	d	08 11	08 22	08 27		08 30				08 42	08 50		09 02					09 11		09 22	09 27		09 30		
Canley	d	08 14				08 33												09 14					09 33		
Tile Hill	d	08 18				08 37					08 55							09 18					09 37		
Berkswell	d	08 21				08 40												09 21					09 40		
Hampton-in-Arden	d	08 25									09 01							09 25							
Birmingham International ✈	a	08 28	08 33	08 37		08 45				08 53	09 04		09 13					09 28		09 33	09 37		09 45		
	d	08 29	08 33	08 38		08 46				08 53	09 05	09 09	09 13		09 17			09 29		09 33	09 38		09 46		
Marston Green	d	08 32				08 49					09 08							09 32					09 49		
Lea Hall	d					08 52									09 21								09 52		
Stechford	d					08 55									09 24								09 55		
Adderley Park	d														09 27										
Birmingham New Street 12	a	08 42	08 45	08 48		09 01				09 08	09 16	09 20	09 27		09 32			09 42		09 45	09 48		10 01		
	d			08 57	09 01		09 05	09 08		09 15		09 23		09 31		09 36	09 38				09 57	10 01		10 05	10 08
Smethwick Rolfe Street	d							09 14									09 44								10 14
Smethwick Galton Bridge 7	d				09 08			09 16				09 29					09 46					10 08			10 16
Sandwell & Dudley	d						09 13	09 19		09 24							09 49							10 13	10 19
Dudley Port	d							09 22									09 52								10 22
Tipton	d							09 24									09 54								10 24
Coseley	d							09 27								09 47	09 57								10 27
Wolverhampton 7	a			09 14	09 19		09 24	09 33		09 37		09 42		09 48		09 53	10 03				10 14	10 19		10 24	10 33
	d			09 15	09 20									09 49		09 54					10 15	10 20			
Penkridge	d															10 04									
Stafford	a			09 29	09 34									10 00		10 10					10 29	10 35			

A To Holyhead
B To Manchester Piccadilly
C To Liverpool Lime Street
D From Southampton Central to Manchester Piccadilly
E To Shrewsbury
F From Walsall
G To Edinburgh
H To Crewe
I To Aberystwyth
J From Bristol Temple Meads to Manchester Piccadilly
K To Glasgow Central
L From Cardiff Central to Manchester Piccadilly
M From Bournemouth to Manchester Piccadilly

Table 68

Saturdays

15 February to 17 May

Northampton - Coventry - Birmingham - Wolverhampton - Stafford

Network Diagram - refer to first Page of Table 67

		VT	LM	AW	VT	XC	LM	LM	LM	LM		VT	XC	LM	LM	LM	LM	VT	LM	AW		LM	VT	XC	LM
		◇1	1	◇	◇1	◇1		1		1		◇1	◇1	1	1			◇1	1	◇		1	◇1	◇1	
		A		B		C		D	E				F	D		G	E	H		I		J		K	
		☕		🛒	☕	🛒						☕	🛒					☕		🛒			☕	🛒	
London Euston 15 ⊖66	d	08 43	07 54		09 03							09 23			08 49			09 43	09 13				10 03		
Northampton	d		09 16							09 35					09 55				10 16			10 25			
Long Buckby	d		09 27							09 46					10 06				10 27			10 36			
Rugby	d		09 38		09 51					09 57					10 17				10 38			10 47	10 51		
Coventry	a	09 42	09 49		10 02					10 08		10 22			10 29			10 42	10 49			10 58	11 03		
	d	09 42	09 50		10 02					10 11		10 22	10 27		10 30			10 42	10 50			11 11	11 03		
Canley	d									10 14					10 33							→			
Tile Hill	d		09 55							10 18					10 37				10 55						
Berkswell	d									10 21					10 40										
Hampton-in-Arden	d		10 01							10 25									11 01						
Birmingham International ✈	a	09 53	10 04		10 13					10 28		10 33	10 37		10 45			10 53	11 04				11 13		
	d	09 53	10 05	10 09	10 13		10 17			10 29		10 33	10 38		10 46			10 53	11 05	11 09			11 13		11 17
Marston Green	d		10 08							10 32					10 49				11 08						
Lea Hall	d						10 21								10 52										11 21
Stechford	d						10 24								10 55										11 24
Adderley Park	d						10 27																		11 27
Birmingham New Street 12	a	10 08	10 16	10 20	10 27		10 32			10 42		10 45	10 48		11 01			11 08	11 16	11 20			11 27		11 32
	d	10 15		10 23		10 31		10 36	10 38				10 57	11 01		11 05	11 08	11 15		11 23				11 31	
Smethwick Rolfe Street	d								10 44								11 14								
Smethwick Galton Bridge 7	d			10 30					10 46					11 08			11 16			11 29					
Sandwell & Dudley	d	10 24							10 49							11 13	11 19	11 24							
Dudley Port	d								10 52								11 22								
Tipton	d								10 54								11 24								
Coseley	d							10 47	10 57								11 27								
Wolverhampton 7	a	10 37		10 42		10 48		10 53	11 03				11 14	11 19		11 24	11 33	11 37		11 41				11 48	
	d					10 49		10 54					11 15	11 20										11 49	
Penkridge	d							11 04																	
Stafford	a					11 00		11 10					11 29	11 35										12 00	

		LM	LM	LM	VT	XC		LM	LM	LM	LM	VT	LM	AW	LM	VT		XC	LM	LM	LM	LM	VT	XC	LM
		1		1	◇1	◇1		1	1			◇1	1	◇	1	◇1		◇1		1		1	◇1	◇1	1
		D	E	L		F		D		G	E	A		B	J			K		D	E	L		F	D
					☕	🛒						☕		🛒		☕		🛒					☕	🛒	
London Euston 15 ⊖66	d				10 23				09 49			10 43	10 13			11 03							11 23		
Northampton	d								10 55				11 16		11 25										
Long Buckby	d								11 06				11 27		11 36										
Rugby	d			←					11 17				11 38		11 47	11 51						←			
Coventry	a			10 58	11 22				11 29			11 42	11 49		11 58	12 02						11 58	12 22		
	d			11 11	11 22	11 27			11 30			11 42	11 50		12 11	12 02						12 11	12 22	12 27	
Canley	d			11 14					11 33						→							12 14			
Tile Hill	d			11 18					11 37				11 55									12 18			
Berkswell	d			11 21					11 40													12 21			
Hampton-in-Arden	d			11 25									12 01									12 25			
Birmingham International ✈	a			11 28	11 33	11 37			11 45			11 53	12 04			12 13						12 28	12 33	12 37	
	d			11 29	11 33	11 38			11 46			11 53	12 05	12 09		12 13			12 17			12 29	12 33	12 38	
Marston Green	d			11 32					11 49				12 08									12 32			
Lea Hall	d								11 52										12 21						
Stechford	d								11 55										12 24						
Adderley Park	d																		12 27						
Birmingham New Street 12	a			11 42	11 45	11 48			12 01			12 08	12 16	12 21		12 27			12 32			12 42	12 45	12 48	
	d	11 36	11 38			11 57		12 01		12 05	12 08	12 15		12 23				12 31		12 36	12 38			12 57	13 01
Smethwick Rolfe Street	d		11 44								12 14										12 44				
Smethwick Galton Bridge 7	d		11 46					12 08			12 16			12 29							12 46				13 08
Sandwell & Dudley	d		11 49							12 13	12 19	12 24									12 49				
Dudley Port	d		11 52								12 22										12 52				
Tipton	d		11 54								12 24										12 54				
Coseley	d	11 47	11 57								12 27									12 47	12 57				
Wolverhampton 7	a	11 53	12 03			12 14		12 19		12 24	12 33	12 37		12 42				12 48		12 53	13 03			13 14	13 19
	d	11 54				12 15		12 20										12 49		12 54				13 15	13 20
Penkridge	d	12 04																		13 04					
Stafford	a	12 10				12 29		12 35										13 00		13 10				13 29	13 35

A To Edinburgh
B To Aberystwyth
C From Paignton to Manchester Piccadilly
D To Liverpool Lime Street
E From Walsall
F From Bournemouth to Manchester Piccadilly
G To Shrewsbury
H To Glasgow Central
I To Holyhead
J To Birmingham New Street
K From Bristol Temple Meads to Manchester Piccadilly
L From Northampton

Table 68

Saturdays

15 February to 17 May

Northampton - Coventry - Birmingham - Wolverhampton - Stafford

Network Diagram - refer to first Page of Table 67

		LM	LM	LM	VT	LM	AW	LM		VT	XC	LM	LM	LM	LM	VT	XC	LM		LM	LM	LM	VT	LM	AW
		1			◇1	1	◇	1		◇1	◇1		1		1	◇1	◇1	1		1			◇1	1	◇
			A	B	C		D	E			F		G	B	H		I	G			A	B	J		K
London Euston 15 ⊖66	d	10 49			11 43	11 13				12 03						12 23				11 49			12 43	12 13	
Northampton	d	11 55				12 16		12 25												12 55				13 16	
Long Buckby	d	12 06				12 27		12 36												13 06				13 27	
Rugby	d	12 17				12 38		12 47		12 51					←					13 17				13 38	
Coventry	a	12 29			12 42	12 49		12 58		13 02					12 58	13 22				13 29			13 42	13 49	
	d	12 30			12 42	12 50		13 11		13 02					13 11	13 22	13 27			13 30			13 42	13 50	
Canley	d	12 33						→							13 14					13 33					
Tile Hill	d	12 37				12 55									13 18					13 37				13 55	
Berkswell	d	12 40													13 21					13 40					
Hampton-in-Arden	d					13 01									13 25									14 01	
Birmingham International ✈	a	12 45			12 53	13 04				13 13					13 28	13 33	13 37			13 45			13 53	14 04	
	d	12 46			12 53	13 05	13 09			13 13		13 17			13 29	13 33	13 38			13 46			13 53	14 05	14 09
Marston Green	d	12 49				13 08									13 32					13 49				14 08	
Lea Hall	d	12 52										13 21								13 52					
Stechford	d	12 55										13 24								13 55					
Adderley Park	d											13 27													
Birmingham New Street 12	a	13 01			13 08	13 16	13 21			13 27		13 32			13 42	13 45	13 48			14 01			14 08	14 16	14 20
	d		13 05	13 08	13 15		13 23				13 31		13 36	13 38			13 57	14 01			14 05	14 08	14 15		14 23
Smethwick Rolfe Street	d			13 14										13 44								14 14			
Smethwick Galton Bridge 7	d			13 16			13 29							13 46				14 08				14 16			14 29
Sandwell & Dudley	d		13 13	13 19	13 24									13 49							14 13	14 19	14 24		
Dudley Port	d			13 22										13 52								14 22			
Tipton	d			13 24										13 54								14 24			
Coseley	d			13 27									13 47	13 57								14 27			
Wolverhampton 7	a		13 24	13 33	13 37		13 41				13 48		13 53	14 03			14 14	14 19			14 24	14 33	14 37		14 41
	d										13 49		13 54				14 15	14 20							
Penkridge	d												14 04												
Stafford	a										14 00		14 10				14 29	14 35							

		LM	VT	XC		LM	LM	LM	LM	VT	XC	LM	LM	LM		LM	VT	LM	AW	LM	VT	XC	LM	LM	
		1	◇1	◇1			1		1	◇1	◇1	1	1				◇1	1	◇	1	◇1	◇1		1	
		E		L			G	B	H		I	G		A		B	C		D	E		M		G	
London Euston 15 ⊖66	d		13 03							13 23			12 49				13 43	13 13			14 03				
Northampton	d	13 25											13 55					14 16		14 25					
Long Buckby	d	13 36											14 06					14 27		14 36					
Rugby	d	13 47	13 51						←				14 17					14 38		14 47	14 51				
Coventry	a	13 58	14 02						13 58	14 22			14 29				14 42	14 49		14 58	15 02				
	d	14 11	14 02						14 11	14 22	14 27		14 30				14 42	14 50		15 11	15 02				
Canley	d	→							14 14				14 33							→					
Tile Hill	d								14 18				14 37					14 55							
Berkswell	d								14 21				14 40												
Hampton-in-Arden	d								14 25									15 01							
Birmingham International ✈	a		14 13						14 28	14 33	14 37		14 45				14 53	15 04			15 13				
	d		14 13			14 17			14 29	14 33	14 38		14 46				14 53	15 05	15 09		15 13		15 17		
Marston Green	d								14 32				14 49					15 08							
Lea Hall	d					14 21							14 52										15 21		
Stechford	d					14 24							14 55										15 24		
Adderley Park	d					14 27																	15 27		
Birmingham New Street 12	a		14 27			14 32			14 42	14 45	14 48		15 01				15 08	15 17	15 20		15 27		15 32		
	d			14 31			14 36	14 38			14 57	15 01		15 05		15 08	15 15		15 23			15 31		15 36	
Smethwick Rolfe Street	d							14 44								15 14									
Smethwick Galton Bridge 7	d							14 46				15 08				15 16			15 29						
Sandwell & Dudley	d							14 49						15 13		15 19	15 24								
Dudley Port	d							14 52								15 22									
Tipton	d							14 54								15 24									
Coseley	d						14 47	14 57								15 27								15 47	
Wolverhampton 7	a			14 48			14 53	15 03			15 14	15 19		15 24		15 33	15 37		15 42			15 48		15 53	
	d			14 49			14 54				15 15	15 20										15 49		15 54	
Penkridge	d						15 04																	16 04	
Stafford	a			15 00			15 10				15 29	15 35										16 00		16 10	

A To Shrewsbury
B From Walsall
C To Glasgow Central
D To Holyhead
E To Birmingham New Street
F From Paignton to Manchester Piccadilly
G To Liverpool Lime Street
H From Northampton
I From Bournemouth to Manchester Piccadilly
J To Edinburgh
K To Aberystwyth
L From Bristol Temple Meads to Manchester Piccadilly
M From Penzance to Manchester Piccadilly

Table 68

Saturdays

15 February to 17 May

Northampton - Coventry - Birmingham - Wolverhampton - Stafford

Network Diagram - refer to first Page of Table 67

		LM	LM	VT	XC	LM		LM	LM	LM	VT	LM	AW	LM	VT	XC		LM	LM	LM	LM	VT	XC	LM	LM
											R		R												
			1	◇1	◇1	1		1			1	1		1	◇1	◇1			1		1	◇1	◇1	1	1
		A	B		C	D			E	A	F ☒		G	H		I			D	A	B		C	D	
London Euston 15 ⊖66	d			14 23				13 49			14 43	14 13			15 03							15 23			14 49
Northampton	d							14 55				15 16		15 25											15 55
Long Buckby	d							15 06				15 27		15 36											16 06
Rugby	d		←					15 17				15 38		15 47	15 51						←				16 17
Coventry	a		14 58	15 22				15 29			15 42	15 49		15 58	16 02						15 58	16 22			16 29
	d		15 11	15 22	15 27			15 30			15 42	15 50		16 11	16 02						16 11	16 22	16 27		16 30
Canley	d		15 14					15 33						→							16 14				16 33
Tile Hill	d		15 18					15 37				15 55									16 18				16 37
Berkswell	d		15 21					15 40													16 21				16 40
Hampton-in-Arden	d		15 25									16 01									16 25				
Birmingham International ✈	a		15 28	15 33	15 37			15 45			15 53	16 04			16 13						16 28	16 33	16 37		16 45
	d		15 29	15 33	15 38			15 46			15 53	16 05	16 09		16 13			16 17			16 29	16 33	16 38		16 46
Marston Green	d		15 32					15 49				16 08									16 32				16 49
Lea Hall	d							15 52										16 21							16 52
Stechford	d							15 55										16 24							16 55
Adderley Park	d																	16 27							
Birmingham New Street 12	a		15 42	15 45	15 48			16 01			16 08	16 16	16 20		16 27			16 32			16 42	16 45	16 48		17 01
	d	15 38			15 57	16 01			16 05	16 08	16 15		16 23			16 31			16 36	16 38			16 57	17 01	
Smethwick Rolfe Street	d	15 44								16 14										16 44					
Smethwick Galton Bridge 7	d	15 46				16 08				16 16			16 29							16 46				17 08	
Sandwell & Dudley	d	15 49							16 13	16 19	16 24									16 49					
Dudley Port	d	15 52								16 22										16 52					
Tipton	d	15 54								16 24										16 54					
Coseley	d	15 57								16 27									16 47	16 57					
Wolverhampton 7	a	16 03			16 14	16 19			16 24	16 33	16 37		16 41			16 48			16 53	17 04			17 14	17 19	
	d				16 15	16 20										16 49			16 54				17 15	17 20	
Penkridge	d					16 29													17 04					17 29	
Stafford	a				16 29	16 35										17 00			17 10				17 29	17 35	

		LM		LM	VT	LM	AW	LM	VT	XC	LM	LM		LM	LM	VT	XC	LM	LM	LM	LM	VT		LM	AW
					R																				
					1	1	◇	1	◇1	◇1		1			1	◇1	◇1	1	1			◇1		1	◇
		E		A	J ☒		K	H		L		D		A	B		C	D		E	A	M			G
London Euston 15 ⊖66	d				15 43	15 13			16 03							16 23			15 49			16 43		16 13	
Northampton	d					16 16		16 25											16 55					17 16	
Long Buckby	d					16 27		16 36											17 06					17 27	
Rugby	d					16 38		16 47	16 51						←				17 17					17 38	
Coventry	a				16 42	16 49		16 58	17 02						16 58	17 22			17 29			17 42		17 49	
	d				16 42	16 50		17 11	17 02						17 11	17 22	17 27		17 30			17 42		17 50	
Canley	d							→							17 14				17 33						
Tile Hill	d					16 55									17 18				17 37					17 55	
Berkswell	d														17 21				17 40						
Hampton-in-Arden	d					17 01									17 25									18 01	
Birmingham International ✈	a				16 53	17 04			17 13						17 28	17 33	17 37		17 45			17 53		18 04	
	d				16 53	17 05	17 09		17 13		17 17				17 29	17 33	17 38		17 46			17 53		18 05	18 09
Marston Green	d					17 08									17 32				17 49					18 08	
Lea Hall	d										17 21								17 52						
Stechford	d										17 24								17 55						
Adderley Park	d										17 27														
Birmingham New Street 12	a				17 08	17 16	17 20		17 27		17 32				17 42	17 45	17 48		18 01			18 08		18 16	18 20
	d	17 05		17 08	17 15		17 23			17 31		17 36		17 38			17 57	18 01		18 05	18 08	18 15			18 23
Smethwick Rolfe Street	d			17 14										17 44							18 14				
Smethwick Galton Bridge 7	d			17 16			17 30							17 46				18 08			18 16				18 29
Sandwell & Dudley	d	17 13		17 19	17 24									17 49						18 13	18 19	18 24			
Dudley Port	d			17 22										17 52							18 22				
Tipton	d			17 24										17 54							18 24				
Coseley	d			17 27								17 47		17 57							18 27				
Wolverhampton 7	a	17 24		17 33	17 37		17 41			17 48		17 53		18 03			18 14	18 19		18 24	18 33	18 37			18 41
	d									17 49		17 54					18 15	18 20							
Penkridge	d											18 04						18 29							
Stafford	a									18 00		18 10					18 29	18 35							

A From Walsall
B From Northampton
C From Bournemouth to Manchester Piccadilly
D To Liverpool Lime Street
E To Shrewsbury
F To Edinburgh
G To Aberystwyth
H To Birmingham New Street
I From Bristol Temple Meads to Manchester Piccadilly
J To Glasgow Central
K To Holyhead
L From Paignton to Manchester Piccadilly
M To Preston

Table 68

Saturdays

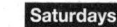

15 February to 17 May

Northampton - Coventry - Birmingham - Wolverhampton - Stafford

Network Diagram - refer to first Page of Table 67

		LM	VT	XC		LM	LM	LM	LM	VT	XC	LM	LM	LM		LM	VT	LM	AW	XC	LM	VT	LM	LM
		1	◇1	◇1			1		1	◇1	◇1	1	1				◇1	1	◇	◇1	1	◇1		
		A		B			C	D	E		F	G		H		D	I		J	K	A			D
			🍴	🛒						🍴	🛒						🍴		🛒	🛒		🍴		
London Euston [15] ⊖66	d		17 03							17 23			16 49				17 43	17 13				18 03		
Northampton	d	17 25											17 55					18 16			18 25			
Long Buckby	d	17 36											18 06					18 27			18 36			
Rugby	d	17 47	17 51						←				18 17					18 38			18 47	18 51		
Coventry	a	17 58	18 02						17 58	18 22			18 29				18 42	18 49			18 58	19 02		
	d	18 11	18 02						18 11	18 22	18 27		18 30				18 42	18 50			19 11	19 02		
Canley	d	↦							18 14				18 33								↦			
Tile Hill	d								18 18				18 37					18 55						
Berkswell	d								18 21				18 40											
Hampton-in-Arden	d								18 25									19 01						
Birmingham International ✈	a		18 13						18 28	18 33	18 37		18 45				18 53	19 04				19 13		
	d		18 13			18 17			18 29	18 33	18 38		18 46				18 53	19 05	19 09			19 13	19 17	
Marston Green	d								18 32				18 49					19 08						
Lea Hall	d					18 21							18 52										19 21	
Stechford	d					18 24							18 55										19 24	
Adderley Park	d					18 27																	19 27	
Birmingham New Street [12]	a		18 27			18 32			18 42	18 45	18 48		19 01				19 08	19 17	19 20			19 27	19 32	
	d			18 31			18 36	18 38		18 50	18 57	19 01		19 05		19 08	19 15		19 23	19 31		19 35		19 38
Smethwick Rolfe Street	d							18 44								19 14								19 44
Smethwick Galton Bridge [7]	d							18 46				19 08				19 16			19 29					19 46
Sandwell & Dudley	d							18 49		18 59				19 13		19 19	19 24					19 44		19 49
Dudley Port	d							18 52								19 22								19 52
Tipton	d							18 54								19 24								19 54
Coseley	d						18 47	18 57								19 27								19 57
Wolverhampton [7] 🚌	a			18 48			18 53	19 03		19 11	19 14	19 19		19 24		19 33	19 37		19 42	19 48		19 58		20 03
	d			18 49			18 54				19 15	19 20								19 49				
Penkridge	d						19 04					19 29												
Stafford	a			19 00			19 10				19 29	19 35								20 00				

		LM	VT	XC	LM	LM	LM	LM	VT	LM		AW	XC	VT	LM	LM	LM	VT	LM	VT		XC	LM	LM	LM
		1	◇1	◇1	1	1			◇1	1		◇	◇1	◇1		1		◇1	1	◇1		◇1	1		
		E		L	G		H		C			M	B	N		C		O				L		H	D
			🍴	🛒					🍴					🍴				🍴		🍴		🛒			
London Euston [15] ⊖66	d		18 23			17 49			18 43	18 13				19 03						19 23			18 49		
Northampton	d					18 55				19 16									19 35				19 55		
Long Buckby	d					19 06				19 27									19 46				20 06		
Rugby	d	←				19 17				19 38				19 51					19 57				20 17		
Coventry	a	18 58	19 22			19 29			19 42	19 49				20 02					20 08	20 22			20 29		
	d	19 11	19 22	19 27		19 30			19 42	19 50				20 02					20 11	20 22		20 27	20 30		
Canley	d	19 14				19 33													20 14				20 33		
Tile Hill	d	19 18				19 37				19 55									20 18				20 37		
Berkswell	d	19 21				19 40													20 21				20 40		
Hampton-in-Arden	d	19 25								20 01									20 25						
Birmingham International ✈	a	19 28	19 33	19 37		19 45			19 53	20 04				20 13					20 28	20 33		20 37	20 45		
	d	19 29	19 33	19 38		19 46			19 53	20 05		20 09		20 13	20 17				20 29	20 33		20 38	20 46		
Marston Green	d	19 32				19 49				20 08									20 32				20 49		
Lea Hall	d					19 52									20 21								20 52		
Stechford	d					19 55									20 24								20 55		
Adderley Park	d														20 27			←							
Birmingham New Street [12]	a	19 42	19 45	19 48		20 01			20 08	20 18		20 21		20 27	20 32			20 27	20 42	20 45		20 48	21 01		
	d		19 50	19 57	20 01		20 05	20 08	20 15			20 23	20 31	20 42		20 36	20 38	20 42		20 50		20 57		21 05	21 08
Smethwick Rolfe Street	d							20 14						↦			20 44								21 14
Smethwick Galton Bridge [7]	d				20 08			20 16				20 29					20 46								21 16
Sandwell & Dudley	d		19 59				20 13	20 19	20 24								20 49	20 53		20 59				21 13	21 19
Dudley Port	d							20 22									20 52								21 22
Tipton	d							20 24									20 54								21 24
Coseley	d							20 27								20 47	20 57								21 27
Wolverhampton [7] 🚌	a		20 11	20 14	20 20		20 24	20 33	20 37			20 41	20 48			20 53	21 03	21 07		21 11		21 14		21 24	21 33
	d			20 15	20 22				20 37				20 49			20 54						21 15			
Penkridge	d				20 31											21 04									
Stafford	a			20 29	20 37				20 51				21 00			21 10						21 29			

- **A** To Birmingham New Street
- **B** From Bristol Temple Meads to Manchester Piccadilly
- **C** To Crewe
- **D** From Walsall
- **E** From Northampton
- **F** From Bournemouth to Manchester Piccadilly
- **G** To Liverpool Lime Street
- **H** To Shrewsbury
- **I** To Preston
- **J** To Chester
- **K** From Exeter St Davids to Manchester Piccadilly
- **L** From Bournemouth to Manchester Piccadilly. 🛒 to Birmingham New Street
- **M** To Aberystwyth
- **N** To Wolverhampton
- **O** From London Euston

Table 68

Saturdays

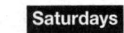

15 February to 17 May

Northampton - Coventry - Birmingham - Wolverhampton - Stafford

Network Diagram - refer to first Page of Table 67

		VT		AW	LM	LM	LM	LM	LM	XC	LM	LM		LM	VT	LM	XC	XC	LM	LM	LM	VT		XC	AW
		◇1		◇	1		1		1	◇1	1				◇1	1	◇1	◇1		1	1	◇1		◇1	
				A			B			C		D		E			F	G		B				H	B
		🍴													🍴							🍴			
London Euston 15 ⊖66	d	19 43			19 13										20 25	19 46						21 03			
Northampton	d				20 22						20 55					21 16									
Long Buckby	d				20 33						21 06					21 27									
Rugby	d				20 44						21 17					21 38						22 12			
Coventry	a	20 50			20 55						21 29				21 36	21 49						22 22			
	d	20 50			20 56				21 11	21 27	21 30				21 36	21 50	21 56				22 11	22 23		22 27	
Canley	d				20 59				21 14		21 33										22 14				
Tile Hill	d				21 03				21 18		21 37					21 55					22 18				
Berkswell	d				21 06				21 21		21 40										22 21				
Hampton-in-Arden	d				21 10				21 25							22 01					22 25				
Birmingham International ✈	a	21 01			21 13				21 28	21 37	21 45				21 50	22 04	22 10				22 28	22 33		22 36	
	d	21 01		21 09	21 14	21 17			21 29	21 38	21 46				21 50	22 05	22 11		22 22		22 29	22 34		22 38	
Marston Green	d				21 17				21 32		21 49					22 08					22 32				
Lea Hall	d					21 21					21 52								22 26						
Stechford	d					21 24					21 55								22 29						
Adderley Park	d					21 27													22 32						
Birmingham New Street 12	a	21 13		21 20	21 25	21 32			21 42	21 48	22 01				22 04	22 16	22 21		22 36		22 42	22 45		22 48	
	d	21 17		21 23			21 36	21 38		21 57		22 05		22 08	22 16			22 31		22 38		22 48			22 55
Smethwick Rolfe Street	d							21 44						22 14						22 44					
Smethwick Galton Bridge 7	d			21 29				21 46						22 16						22 46					
Sandwell & Dudley	d							21 49				22 13		22 19	22 25					22 49		22 57			
Dudley Port	d							21 52						22 22						22 53					
Tipton	d							21 54						22 24						22 55					
Coseley	d						21 47	21 57						22 27						22 58					
Wolverhampton 7 ⛴	a	21 38		21 41			21 53	22 03		22 14		22 24		22 33	22 38			22 48		23 04		23 10			23 12
	d						21 59			22 15								22 49		23 05					
Penkridge	d						22 09													23 15					
Stafford	a						22 15			22 29								23 01		23 21					

		LM	LM	LM	VT	AW	LM
		1		1	◇1		1
			D			D	
					🍴		
London Euston 15 ⊖66	d	20 34			21 43		21 28
Northampton	d	21 59		22 16			22 55
Long Buckby	d	22 10		22 27			23 06
Rugby	d	22 21		22 38	22 53		23 17
Coventry	a	22 32		22 49	23 02		23 28
	d	22 33		22 50	23 02		23 29
Canley	d	22 36					23 32
Tile Hill	d	22 40		22 55			23 36
Berkswell	d	22 43					23 39
Hampton-in-Arden	d			23 01			23 43
Birmingham International ✈	a	22 48		23 04	23 13		23 46
	d	22 49		23 05	23 13		23 47
Marston Green	d	22 52		23 08			23 50
Lea Hall	d	22 55					23 53
Stechford	d	22 58					23 56
Adderley Park	d						
Birmingham New Street 12	a	23 04		23 16	23 25		00 04
	d		23 08		23 27	23 35	
Smethwick Rolfe Street	d		23 14				
Smethwick Galton Bridge 7	d		23 16				
Sandwell & Dudley	d		23 19		23 37		
Dudley Port	d		23 22				
Tipton	d		23 24				
Coseley	d		23 27				
Wolverhampton 7 ⛴	a		23 35		23 50	23 53	
	d						
Penkridge	d						
Stafford	a						

A To Chester
B To Crewe
C From Bournemouth to Manchester Piccadilly
D To Shrewsbury
E From Walsall
F From Reading
G To Manchester Piccadilly
H From Bournemouth

Table 68

Sundays

8 December to 29 December

Northampton - Coventry - Birmingham - Wolverhampton - Stafford

Network Diagram - refer to first Page of Table 67

		VT ◇1 A 🍽	XC ◇1 B 🛒	LM 1	LM	LM 1		VT ◇1 C 🍽	LM 1	LM 1 D	XC ◇1 B 🛒	AW E	LM	VT ◇1 F 🍽	LM 1	LM 1		LM 1 G	LM 1 D	VT ◇1 🍽	XC ◇1 H 🛒	AW ◇ I	LM 1	LM	VT ◇1 C
London Euston 15 ⊖66	d														07 52					08 50			08 23		
Northampton	d														09 26			09 38					10 00		
Long Buckby	d														09 37			09 49					10 11		
Rugby	d														09 48			10 00		10 14			10 22		
Coventry	a														09 59					10 23			10 33		
	d			08 37					09 11						10 00	10 11				10 24	10 28		10 34		
Canley	d			08 40					09 14							10 14							10 37		
Tile Hill	d			08 44					09 18							10 18							10 41		
Berkswell	d			08 47					09 21							10 21							10 44		
Hampton-in-Arden	d			08 51					09 25							10 25							10 48		
Birmingham International ✈	a			08 54					09 28						10 09	10 28				10 34	10 38		10 51		
	d			08 55		09 03			09 29			09 51			10 09	10 29				10 35	10 40	10 48	10 52		
Marston Green	d			08 58		09 06			09 32						10 12	10 32							10 55		
Lea Hall	d					09 09									10 16										
Stechford	d					09 12									10 18										
Adderley Park	d					09 15									10 22										
Birmingham New Street 12	a			09 06		09 20			09 40			10 01			10 26	10 40				10 47	10 50	10 58	11 03		
	d	08 45	09 01		09 09			09 20		09 42	10 01	10 04	10 09	10 20					10 42	10 51	11 01	11 05		11 09	11 20
Smethwick Rolfe Street	d				09 15								10 15											11 15	
Smethwick Galton Bridge 7	d				09 17								10 17											11 17	
Sandwell & Dudley	d				09 19								10 19							11 00				11 19	
Dudley Port	d				09 22								10 22											11 22	
Tipton	d				09 24								10 24											11 24	
Coseley	d				09 27								10 27											11 27	
Wolverhampton 7 🚌	a	09 03	09 18		09 32			09 37		09 59	10 18	10 21	10 32	10 37					10 59	11 13	11 18	11 26		11 32	11 37
	d	09 04	09 19							10 00	10 19								11 00		11 19				
Penkridge	d									10 10									11 10						
Stafford	a	09 17	09 32							10 16	10 32							10 56	11 16		11 32				

		LM 1		LM 1 D	VT ◇1 🍽		XC ◇1 J 🛒	LM 1	LM 1 G	LM	LM 1 G	VT ◇1 F 🍽	AW ◇ K 🛒		LM 1 D	LM 1	VT ◇1 🍽	XC ◇1 L 🛒	LM 1	LM	VT ◇1 C 🍽	AW ◇ I 🛒	VT ◇1 🍽	XC ◇1 B 🛒	LM 1 D
London Euston 15 ⊖66	d				09 50			09 24	09 54		10 24						10 49		10 28				11 50		
Northampton	d							11 00	11 08		11 40								11 58						
Long Buckby	d							11 11	11 19		11 51								12 09						
Rugby	d				11 14			11 22	11 30		12 03						12 14		12 20				12 50		
Coventry	a				11 24			11 33									12 23		12 31				12 59		
	d	11 11			11 24		11 29	11 34								12 11	12 24	12 28	12 32				12 59		
Canley	d							11 37											12 35						
Tile Hill	d							11 41											12 39						
Berkswell	d							11 44											12 42						
Hampton-in-Arden	d							11 48											12 46						
Birmingham International ✈	a	11 20			11 35		11 38	11 51								12 20	12 34	12 38	12 49				13 10		
	d	11 20			11 35		11 40	11 52					12 08			12 20	12 34	12 40	12 50			13 07	13 10		
Marston Green	d	11 23						11 55								12 23			12 53						
Lea Hall	d	11 27														12 27									
Stechford	d	11 29														12 29									
Adderley Park	d	11 32														12 32									
Birmingham New Street 12	a	11 38			11 47		11 51	12 03					12 18			12 38	12 46	12 50	13 01			13 17	13 24		
	d			11 42	11 51		12 01			12 09		12 20	12 24		12 35		12 50	13 01		13 09	13 20	13 24		13 31	13 35
Smethwick Rolfe Street	d									12 15										13 15					
Smethwick Galton Bridge 7	d									12 17										13 17					
Sandwell & Dudley	d				12 00					12 19							12 59			13 19					
Dudley Port	d									12 22										13 22					
Tipton	d									12 24										13 24					
Coseley	d									12 27										13 27					
Wolverhampton 7 🚌	a			11 59	12 13		12 19			12 32		12 37	12 42		12 52		13 12	13 18		13 32	13 37	13 41		13 48	13 52
	d			12 00			12 19								12 53			13 19							13 53
Penkridge	d			12 10											13 03										14 03
Stafford	a			12 16			12 32		12 21		12 59				13 09			13 33							14 09

A To Preston
B To Manchester Piccadilly
C To Glasgow Central
D To Liverpool Lime Street
E To Shrewsbury
F To Edinburgh
G To Crewe
H From Reading to Manchester Piccadilly
I To Chester
J From Southampton Central to Manchester Piccadilly
K To Aberystwyth
L From Bournemouth to Manchester Piccadilly

Table 68

Sundays

8 December to 29 December

Northampton - Coventry - Birmingham - Wolverhampton - Stafford

Network Diagram - refer to first Page of Table 67

		LM	VT	XC		LM		LM	VT	AW	VT	XC	LM	LM		LM	VT	XC	LM	LM	VT	AW	VT	XC	
		1	◇1	◇1		1			◇1	◇	◇1	◇1	1	1		1	◇1	◇1	1		◇1	◇	◇1	◇1	
				A		B			C	D		E	F	B				A			G	H		I	
			☕	🍴					☕	🍴	☕	🍴					☕	🍴			☕	🍴	☕	🍴	
London Euston 15 ⊖66	d		12 20			11 24			12 40		13 00			12 50			13 20		12 34		13 40		14 00		
Northampton	d					12 55	13 02							14 02					13 55						
Long Buckby	d					13 06	13 13							14 13					14 06						
Rugby	d					13 17	13 26				13 51			14 26					14 17				14 51		
Coventry	a		13 21			13 29			13 42		14 02						14 21		14 29		14 44		15 02		
	d	13 11	13 22	13 26		13 30			13 42		14 02					14 11	14 22	14 26	14 30		14 44		15 02		
Canley	d					13 33													14 33						
Tile Hill	d	13 16				13 37										14 16			14 37						
Berkswell	d					13 40													14 40						
Hampton-in-Arden	d					13 44													14 44						
Birmingham International ✈	a	13 23	13 32	13 37		13 47			13 53		14 13					14 23	14 32	14 37	14 47		14 54		15 13		
	d	13 23	13 33	13 38		13 48			13 53	14 07	14 13					14 23	14 33	14 38	14 48		14 54	15 07	15 13		
Marston Green	d	13 26				13 51										14 26			14 51						
Lea Hall	d	13 30														14 30									
Stechford	d	13 32														14 32									
Adderley Park	d	13 35														14 35									
Birmingham New Street 12	a	13 41	13 44	13 48		13 59			14 05	14 18	14 25					14 41	14 44	14 48	14 59		15 06	15 18	15 25		
	d		13 48	14 01				14 09	14 16	14 24		14 31	14 35					15 01		15 09	15 17	15 24		15 31	
Smethwick Rolfe Street	d							14 15												15 15					
Smethwick Galton Bridge 7	d							14 17												15 17					
Sandwell & Dudley	d		13 57					14 19	14 26											15 19	15 26				
Dudley Port	d							14 22												15 22					
Tipton	d							14 24												15 24					
Coseley	d							14 27												15 27					
Wolverhampton 7 🚌	a		14 10	14 18				14 32	14 37	14 42		14 48	14 52					15 18		15 32	15 37	15 42		15 48	
	d			14 19									14 53					15 19							
Penkridge	d												15 03												
Stafford	a			14 33			14 18						15 09	15 18				15 33							

		LM	LM	LM	VT	XC	LM	LM	VT	AW		VT	XC	LM	LM	LM	VT	XC	LM	LM		VT	AW	VT	XC
		1	1	1	◇1	◇1	1		◇1	◇		◇1	◇1	1	1	1	◇1	◇1	1			◇1	◇	◇1	◇1
		F	B			A			C	D			I	F	B			A				G	J		K
					☕	🍴			☕	🍴		☕	🍴				☕	🍴				☕	🍴	☕	🍴
London Euston 15 ⊖66	d		13 50		14 20		13 34		14 40			15 00			14 50		15 20		14 34			15 40		16 00	
Northampton	d		15 02				14 55								16 02				15 55						
Long Buckby	d		15 13				15 06								16 13				16 06						
Rugby	d		15 26				15 17					15 53			16 26				16 17					16 51	
Coventry	a				15 21		15 29		15 42			16 03					16 21		16 29			16 42		17 02	
	d			15 11	15 22	15 26	15 30		15 42			16 04				16 11	16 22	16 26	16 30			16 42		17 02	
Canley	d						15 33												16 33						
Tile Hill	d			15 16			15 37									16 16			16 37						
Berkswell	d						15 40												16 40						
Hampton-in-Arden	d						15 44												16 44						
Birmingham International ✈	a			15 23	15 32	15 35	15 47		15 53			16 13				16 23	16 32	16 35	16 47			16 53		17 13	
	d			15 23	15 33	15 38	15 48		15 53	16 07		16 14				16 23	16 33	16 38	16 48			16 53	17 07	17 13	
Marston Green	d			15 26			15 51									16 26			16 51						
Lea Hall	d			15 30												16 30									
Stechford	d			15 32												16 32									
Adderley Park	d			15 35												16 35									
Birmingham New Street 12	a			15 41	15 44	15 48	15 59		16 05	16 18		16 25				16 41	16 44	16 48	16 59			17 05	17 18	17 25	
	d	15 35				16 01		16 09	16 16	16 24			16 31	16 35				17 01		17 09		17 16	17 24		17 31
Smethwick Rolfe Street	d							16 15												17 15					
Smethwick Galton Bridge 7	d							16 17												17 17					
Sandwell & Dudley	d							16 19	16 26											17 19		17 26			
Dudley Port	d							16 22												17 22					
Tipton	d							16 24												17 24					
Coseley	d							16 27												17 27					
Wolverhampton 7 🚌	a	15 52				16 18		16 32	16 37	16 42			16 48	16 52				17 18		17 32		17 37	17 42		17 48
	d	15 53				16 19								16 53				17 19							
Penkridge	d	16 03												17 03											
Stafford	a	16 09	16 18			16 34								17 09	17 18			17 35							

A From Bournemouth to Manchester Piccadilly
B To Crewe
C To Edinburgh
D To Aberystwyth
E From Paignton to Manchester Piccadilly
F To Liverpool Lime Street
G To Glasgow Central
H To Chester
I From Plymouth to Manchester Piccadilly
J To Holyhead
K From Bristol Temple Meads to Manchester Piccadilly

Table 68

Sundays

8 December to 29 December

Northampton - Coventry - Birmingham - Wolverhampton - Stafford

Network Diagram - refer to first Page of Table 67

		LM		LM	LM	VT	XC	LM	LM	VT	AW	VT		XC	LM	LM	LM	VT	XC	LM	LM	VT		AW	XC
																						R			
		1		1	1	◇1	◇1	1		◇1	◇	◇1		◇1	1	1	1	◇1	◇1	1		1		◇	◇1
		A		B			C			D	E			F	A	B			C			G		H	I
						☕	🛒			☕	🛒	☕		🛒				☕	🛒			☕		🛒	🛒
London Euston 15 ⊖66	d			15 50		16 20		15 34		16 40		17 00				16 50		17 20		16 34		17 40			
Northampton	d			17 02				16 55								18 02				17 55					
Long Buckby	d			17 13				17 06								18 13				18 06					
Rugby	d			17 26				17 17				17 51				18 26				18 17					
Coventry	a					17 21		17 29		17 44		18 02						18 21		18 29		18 44			
	d				17 11	17 22	17 26	17 30		17 44		18 02					18 11	18 22	18 26	18 30		18 44			
Canley	d							17 33												18 33					
Tile Hill	d				17 16			17 37									18 16			18 37					
Berkswell	d							17 40												18 40					
Hampton-in-Arden	d							17 44												18 44					
Birmingham International ✈	a				17 23	17 32	17 35	17 47		17 54		18 13					18 23	18 32	18 35	18 47		18 54			
	d				17 23	17 33	17 38	17 48		17 54	18 07	18 13					18 23	18 33	18 38	18 48		18 54		19 07	
Marston Green	d				17 26			17 51									18 26			18 51					
Lea Hall	d				17 30												18 30								
Stechford	d				17 32												18 32								
Adderley Park	d				17 35												18 35								
Birmingham New Street 12	a				17 41	17 44	17 48	17 59		18 06	18 18	18 25					18 41	18 44	18 48	18 59		19 06		19 18	
	d	17 35					18 01		18 09	18 16	18 24			18 31	18 35				19 01		19 09	19 16		19 24	19 31
Smethwick Rolfe Street	d								18 15												19 15				
Smethwick Galton Bridge 7	d								18 17												19 17				
Sandwell & Dudley	d								18 19	18 26											19 19	19 26			
Dudley Port	d								18 22												19 22				
Tipton	d								18 24												19 24				
Coseley	d								18 27												19 27				
Wolverhampton 7 🚌	a	17 52					18 18		18 32	18 37	18 42			18 48	18 52				19 18		19 32	19 37		19 42	19 48
	d	17 53					18 19								18 53				19 19						
Penkridge	d	18 03													19 03										
Stafford	a	18 09		18 18			18 35								19 09	19 18			19 37						

		LM	LM	VT	LM	VT	XC	LM	LM	VT	XC	AW	VT	LM	XC	LM	VT		XC	LM	LM	VT	XC	AW
		1	1	◇1	1	◇1	◇1	1		◇1	◇1	◇	◇1	1	◇1	1	◇1		◇1	1		◇1	◇1	◇
		A	B				C			B	J	E		B	I				K			L	J	H
				☕		☕	🛒			☕	🛒		☕				☕		🛒			☕	🛒	
London Euston 15 ⊖66	d		17 50	18 00		18 20		17 34		18 40			19 00	18 50			19 20			18 34		19 40		
Northampton	d		19 02					18 55						20 02						19 55				
Long Buckby	d		19 13					19 06						20 13						20 06				
Rugby	d		19 26	18 51				19 17					19 52	20 26						20 17				
Coventry	a			19 02		19 22		19 28		19 42			20 03				20 22			20 29		20 41		
	d			19 02	19 11	19 22	19 26	19 30		19 42	19 54		20 03			20 11	20 22		20 26	20 30		20 41	20 54	
Canley	d							19 33												20 33				
Tile Hill	d				19 16			19 37								20 16				20 37				
Berkswell	d							19 40												20 40				
Hampton-in-Arden	d							19 44												20 44				
Birmingham International ✈	a			19 13	19 23	19 32	19 37	19 47		19 53	20 03		20 13			20 23	20 32		20 35	20 47		20 52	21 03	
	d			19 13	19 23	19 33	19 38	19 48		19 53	20 04	20 07	20 13			20 23	20 33		20 38	20 48		20 52	21 04	21 08
Marston Green	d				19 26			19 51								20 26				20 51				
Lea Hall	d				19 30											20 30								
Stechford	d				19 32											20 32								
Adderley Park	d				19 35											20 35								
Birmingham New Street 12	a			19 24	19 41	19 44	19 48	19 59		20 05	20 15	20 18	20 24			20 41	20 44		20 48	20 59		21 03	21 15	21 18
	d	19 35		19 39			20 01		20 09	20 16		20 24	20 25		20 31		20 48		21 01		21 09	21 13		21 24
Smethwick Rolfe Street	d								20 15												21 15			
Smethwick Galton Bridge 7	d								20 17												21 17			
Sandwell & Dudley	d			19 49					20 19	20 26			20 34				20 57				21 19	21 26		
Dudley Port	d								20 22												21 22			
Tipton	d								20 24												21 24			
Coseley	d								20 27												21 27			
Wolverhampton 7 🚌	a	19 52		20 02			20 18		20 32	20 36		20 42	20 46		20 51		21 10		21 18		21 33	21 37		21 42
	d	19 53					20 19			20 38									21 19			21 38		
Penkridge	d	20 03																						
Stafford	a	20 09	20 18				20 36			20 52				21 18					21 36			21 55		

A To Liverpool Lime Street
B To Crewe
C From Bournemouth to Manchester Piccadilly
D To Edinburgh
E To Aberystwyth
F From Penzance to Manchester Piccadilly
G To Glasgow Central
H To Chester
I From Bristol Temple Meads to Manchester Piccadilly
J From Reading
K From Bournemouth to Manchester Piccadilly. 🛒 to Birmingham New Street
L To Preston

Table 68

Sundays

8 December to 29 December

Northampton - Coventry - Birmingham - Wolverhampton - Stafford

Network Diagram - refer to first Page of Table 67

		VT	LM	LM	LM	VT	XC	LM	LM	VT		XC	AW	LM	VT	XC	AW	LM	LM	XC		AW	LM	LM	VT
		◇1	1	1	1	◇1	◇1	1		◇1		◇1		1	◇1	◇1	◇	1		◇1			1	1	◇1
			A	A			B					C	D			E	F			C		D		G	
		☕				☕	🛒			☕					☕										☕
London Euston 15 ⊖66	d	20 00		19 50		20 18		19 34		20 38					20 54			20 34						21 30	21 55
Northampton	d			21 06				20 55										21 55						22 52	
Long Buckby	d			21 17				21 06										22 06						23 03	
Rugby	d	20 51		21 30				21 17							22 07			22 17						23 14	23 23
Coventry	a	21 02				21 20		21 29		21 46					22 16			22 29						23 25	23 33
	d	21 02			21 10	21 20	21 26	21 30		21 46		21 53		22 08	22 16	22 23		22 30		22 53			23 06	23 38	23 33
Canley	d							21 33										22 33						↪	
Tile Hill	d				21 15			21 37										22 37							
Berkswell	d							21 40										22 40							
Hampton-in-Arden	d							21 44										22 44							
Birmingham International ✈	a	21 13			21 22	21 31	21 35	21 47		21 57		22 02		22 17	22 27	22 32		22 47		23 02			23 15		23 44
	d	21 13			21 22	21 31	21 38	21 48		21 57		22 03	22 11	22 18	22 27	22 33	22 43	22 48		23 03		23 08	23 15		23 44
Marston Green	d				21 25			21 51						22 21				22 51					23 18		
Lea Hall	d				21 29									22 24									23 22		
Stechford	d				21 31									22 27									23 24		
Adderley Park	d				21 35									22 30									23 28		
Birmingham New Street 12	a	21 24			21 40	21 44	21 48	21 59		22 09		22 14	22 21	22 36	22 39	22 43	22 53	22 59		23 13		23 19	23 33		23 55
	d	21 28	21 35			21 48	22 01		22 09	22 16			22 24		22 43		22 55		23 09			23 24			23 58
Smethwick Rolfe Street	d								22 15										23 15						
Smethwick Galton Bridge 7	d								22 17										23 17						
Sandwell & Dudley	d	21 37				21 57			22 19	22 25					22 52				23 19						
Dudley Port	d								22 22										23 22						
Tipton	d								22 24										23 24						
Coseley	d								22 27										23 27						
Wolverhampton 7	a	21 51	21 56			22 10	22 19		22 32	22 38			22 41		23 06		23 13		23 32			23 40			00 17
	d		21 59				22 20										23 15								
Penkridge	d		22 09																						
Stafford	a		22 15	22 25			22 36										23 30								

		LM	VT	LM	VT
		1	◇1	1	◇1
		H			
			☕		☕
London Euston 15 ⊖66	d		22 25	22 00	23 25
Northampton	d			23 32	
Long Buckby	d			23 43	
Rugby	d	↩	23 48	23 54	00s46
Coventry	a	23 25	23 57	00 05	00s58
	d	23 38	23 58		
Canley	d	23 41			
Tile Hill	d	23 45			
Berkswell	d	23 48			
Hampton-in-Arden	d	23 52			
Birmingham International ✈	a	23 55	00 08		01s09
	d	23 56	00 09		
Marston Green	d	23 59			
Lea Hall	d				
Stechford	d				
Adderley Park	d				
Birmingham New Street 12	a	00 07	00 21		01s22
	d		00 24		
Smethwick Rolfe Street	d				
Smethwick Galton Bridge 7	d				
Sandwell & Dudley	d				
Dudley Port	d				
Tipton	d				
Coseley	d				
Wolverhampton 7	a		00 43		01 44
	d				
Penkridge	d				
Stafford	a				

A To Crewe
B From Bournemouth to Manchester Piccadilly. 🛒 to Birmingham New Street
C From Reading
D To Shrewsbury
E From Bournemouth
F To Holyhead
G To Birmingham New Street
H From London Euston

Table 68

Sundays

5 January to 9 February

Northampton - Coventry - Birmingham - Wolverhampton - Stafford

Network Diagram - refer to first Page of Table 67

		VT	XC	LM	LM	LM		VT	LM	LM	XC	AW	LM	VT	LM	LM		LM	LM	VT	XC	AW	LM	LM	VT
		◇1	◇1	1		1		◇1	1	1	◇1			◇1	1	1		1	1	◇1	◇1	◇	1		◇1
		A	B					A		C	B	D		A				E	C		F	G			A
London Euston 15 ⊖66	d														07 52					08 50			08 23		
Northampton	d														09 26			09 38					10 00		
Long Buckby	d														09 37			09 49					10 11		
Rugby	d														09 48			10 00		10 14			10 22		
Coventry	a														09 59					10 23			10 33		
	d			08 37					09 11						10 00	10 11				10 24	10 28		10 34		
Canley	d			08 40					09 14							10 14							10 37		
Tile Hill	d			08 44					09 18							10 18							10 41		
Berkswell	d			08 47					09 21							10 21							10 44		
Hampton-in-Arden	d			08 51					09 25							10 25							10 48		
Birmingham International ✈	a			08 54					09 28						10 09	10 28				10 34	10 38		10 51		
	d			08 55		09 03			09 29			09 51			10 09	10 29				10 35	10 40	10 48	10 52		
Marston Green	d			08 58		09 06			09 32						10 12	10 32							10 55		
Lea Hall	d					09 09									10 16										
Stechford	d					09 12									10 18										
Adderley Park	d					09 15									10 22										
Birmingham New Street 12	a			09 06		09 20			09 40			10 01			10 26	10 40				10 47	10 50	10 58	11 03		
	d	08 45	09 01		09 09			09 20		09 42	10 01	10 04	10 09	10 20					10 42	10 51	11 01	11 05		11 09	11 20
Smethwick Rolfe Street	d				09 15								10 15											11 15	
Smethwick Galton Bridge 7	d				09 17								10 17											11 17	
Sandwell & Dudley	d				09 19								10 19							11 00				11 19	
Dudley Port	d				09 22								10 22											11 22	
Tipton	d				09 24								10 24											11 24	
Coseley	d				09 27								10 27											11 27	
Wolverhampton 7	a	09 03	09 18		09 32			09 37		09 59	10 18	10 21	10 32	10 37					10 59	11 13	11 18	11 26		11 32	11 37
	d	09 04	09 19							10 00	10 19								11 00		11 19				
Penkridge	d									10 10									11 10						
Stafford	a	09 17	09 32							10 16	10 32							10 56	11 16		11 32				

		LM		LM	VT		XC	LM	LM	LM	LM	VT	AW		LM	LM	VT	XC	LM	LM	VT	AW	VT	XC	LM
		1		1	◇1		◇1	1	1		1	◇1	◇		1	1	◇1	◇1	1		◇1	◇	◇1	◇1	1
				C			H		E		E	A	I		C			J			K	G		B	C
London Euston 15 ⊖66	d				09 50			09 24	09 54		10 24						10 49		10 28				11 50		
Northampton	d							11 00	11 08		11 40								11 58						
Long Buckby	d							11 11	11 19		11 51								12 09						
Rugby	d				11 14			11 22	11 30		12 03						12 14		12 20				12 50		
Coventry	a				11 24			11 33									12 23		12 31				12 59		
	d	11 11			11 24		11 29	11 34								12 11	12 24	12 28	12 32				12 59		
Canley	d							11 37											12 35						
Tile Hill	d							11 41											12 39						
Berkswell	d							11 44											12 42						
Hampton-in-Arden	d							11 48											12 46						
Birmingham International ✈	a	11 20			11 35		11 38	11 51								12 20	12 34	12 38	12 49				13 10		
	d	11 20			11 35		11 40	11 52					12 08			12 20	12 34	12 40	12 50			13 07	13 10		
Marston Green	d	11 23						11 55								12 23			12 53						
Lea Hall	d	11 27														12 27									
Stechford	d	11 29														12 29									
Adderley Park	d	11 32														12 32									
Birmingham New Street 12	a	11 38			11 47		11 51	12 03					12 18			12 38	12 46	12 50	13 01			13 17	13 24		
	d			11 42	11 51		12 01			12 09		12 20	12 24		12 35		12 50	13 01		13 09	13 20	13 24		13 31	13 35
Smethwick Rolfe Street	d									12 15										13 15					
Smethwick Galton Bridge 7	d									12 17										13 17					
Sandwell & Dudley	d				12 00					12 19							12 59			13 19					
Dudley Port	d									12 22										13 22					
Tipton	d									12 24										13 24					
Coseley	d									12 27										13 27					
Wolverhampton 7	a			11 59	12 13		12 19			12 32		12 37	12 42		12 52		13 12	13 18		13 32	13 37	13 41		13 48	13 52
	d			12 00			12 19								12 53			13 19							13 53
Penkridge	d			12 10											13 03										14 03
Stafford	a			12 16			12 32		12 21		12 59				13 09			13 33							14 09

A To Wigan North Western
B To Manchester Piccadilly
C To Liverpool Lime Street
D To Shrewsbury
E To Crewe
F From Reading to Manchester Piccadilly
G To Chester
H From Southampton Central to Manchester Piccadilly
I To Aberystwyth
J From Bournemouth to Manchester Piccadilly
K To Preston

Table 68

Sundays

5 January to 9 February

Northampton - Coventry - Birmingham - Wolverhampton - Stafford

Network Diagram - refer to first Page of Table 67

		LM 1	VT ◇1 ☕	XC ◇1 A 🛒		LM 1 B		LM	VT ◇1 C ☕	AW ◇ D 🛒	VT ◇1 ☕	XC ◇1 E 🛒	LM 1 F	LM 1 B		LM 1	VT ◇1 ☕	XC ◇1 A 🛒	LM 1	LM	VT ◇1 G ☕	AW ◇ H 🛒	VT ◇1 ☕	XC ◇1 I 🛒	
London Euston 15 ⊖66	d		12 20			11 24			12 40		13 00			12 50			13 20		12 34		13 40		14 00		
Northampton	d					12 55	13 02							14 02					13 55						
Long Buckby	d					13 06	13 13							14 13					14 06						
Rugby	d					13 17	13 26				13 51			14 26					14 17				14 51		
Coventry	a		13 21			13 29			13 42		14 02						14 21		14 29		14 44		15 02		
	d	13 11	13 22	13 26		13 30			13 42		14 02					14 11	14 22	14 26	14 30		14 44		15 02		
Canley	d					13 33													14 33						
Tile Hill	d	13 16				13 37										14 16			14 37						
Berkswell	d					13 40													14 40						
Hampton-in-Arden	d					13 44													14 44						
Birmingham International ✈	a	13 23	13 32	13 37		13 47			13 53		14 13					14 23	14 32	14 37	14 47		14 54		15 13		
	d	13 23	13 33	13 38		13 48			13 53	14 07	14 13					14 23	14 33	14 38	14 48		14 54	15 07	15 13		
Marston Green	d	13 26				13 51										14 26			14 51						
Lea Hall	d	13 30														14 30									
Stechford	d	13 32														14 32									
Adderley Park	d	13 35														14 35									
Birmingham New Street 12	a	13 41	13 44	13 48		13 59			14 05	14 18	14 25					14 41	14 44	14 48	14 59		15 06	15 18	15 25		
	d		13 48	14 01				14 09	14 16	14 24		14 31	14 35					15 01		15 09	15 17	15 24		15 31	
Smethwick Rolfe Street	d							14 15												15 15					
Smethwick Galton Bridge 7	d							14 17												15 17					
Sandwell & Dudley	d		13 57					14 19	14 26											15 19	15 26				
Dudley Port	d							14 22												15 22					
Tipton	d							14 24												15 24					
Coseley	d							14 27												15 27					
Wolverhampton 7	a		14 10	14 18				14 32	14 37	14 42		14 48	14 52					15 18		15 32	15 37	15 42		15 48	
	d			14 19									14 53					15 19							
Penkridge	d												15 03												
Stafford	a			14 33			14 18						15 09	15 18				15 33							

		LM 1 F	LM 1 B	LM 1	VT ◇1 ☕	XC ◇1 A 🛒	LM 1	LM	VT ◇1 C ☕	AW ◇ D 🛒		VT ◇1 ☕	XC ◇1 I 🛒	LM 1 F	LM 1 B	LM 1	VT ◇1 ☕	XC ◇1 A 🛒	LM 1	LM		VT ◇1 G ☕	AW ◇ J 🛒	VT ◇1 ☕	XC ◇1 K 🛒
London Euston 15 ⊖66	d		13 50		14 20		13 34		14 40			15 00			14 50		15 20		14 34			15 40		16 00	
Northampton	d		15 02				14 55								16 02				15 55						
Long Buckby	d		15 13				15 06								16 13				16 06						
Rugby	d		15 26				15 17					15 53			16 26				16 17					16 51	
Coventry	a				15 21		15 29		15 42			16 03					16 21		16 29			16 42		17 02	
	d			15 11	15 22	15 26	15 30		15 42			16 04				16 11	16 22	16 26	16 30			16 42		17 02	
Canley	d						15 33												16 33						
Tile Hill	d			15 16			15 37									16 16			16 37						
Berkswell	d						15 40												16 40						
Hampton-in-Arden	d						15 44												16 44						
Birmingham International ✈	a			15 23	15 32	15 35	15 47		15 53			16 13				16 23	16 32	16 35	16 47			16 53		17 13	
	d			15 23	15 33	15 38	15 48		15 53	16 07		16 14				16 23	16 33	16 38	16 48			16 53	17 07	17 13	
Marston Green	d			15 26			15 51									16 26			16 51						
Lea Hall	d			15 30												16 30									
Stechford	d			15 32												16 32									
Adderley Park	d			15 35												16 35									
Birmingham New Street 12	a			15 41	15 44	15 48	15 59		16 05	16 18		16 25				16 41	16 44	16 48	16 59			17 05	17 18	17 25	
	d	15 35				16 01		16 09	16 16	16 24			16 31	16 35				17 01		17 09		17 16	17 24		17 31
Smethwick Rolfe Street	d							16 15												17 15					
Smethwick Galton Bridge 7	d							16 17												17 17					
Sandwell & Dudley	d							16 19	16 26											17 19		17 26			
Dudley Port	d							16 22												17 22					
Tipton	d							16 24												17 24					
Coseley	d							16 27												17 27					
Wolverhampton 7	a	15 52				16 18		16 32	16 37	16 42			16 48	16 52				17 18		17 32		17 37	17 42		17 48
	d	15 53				16 19								16 53				17 19							
Penkridge	d	16 03												17 03											
Stafford	a	16 09	16 18			16 34								17 09	17 18			17 35							

A From Bournemouth to Manchester Piccadilly
B To Crewe
C To Edinburgh
D To Aberystwyth
E From Paignton to Manchester Piccadilly
F To Liverpool Lime Street
G To Glasgow Central
H To Chester
I From Plymouth to Manchester Piccadilly
J To Holyhead
K From Bristol Temple Meads to Manchester Piccadilly

Table 68

Sundays

5 January to 9 February

Northampton - Coventry - Birmingham - Wolverhampton - Stafford

Network Diagram - refer to first Page of Table 67

		LM		LM	LM	VT	XC	LM	LM	VT	AW	VT		XC	LM	LM	LM	VT	XC	LM	LM	VT		AW	XC
		1		1	1	◇1	◇1	1		◇1	◇	◇1		◇1	1	1	1	◇1	◇1	1		R 1		◇	◇1
		A		B			C			D	E			F	A	B			C			G		H	I
						☕	🛒			☕	🛒	☕		🛒				☕	🛒			☕		🛒	🛒
London Euston 15 ⊖66	d			15 50		16 20		15 34		16 40		17 00				16 50		17 20		16 34		17 40			
Northampton	d			17 02				16 55								18 02				17 55					
Long Buckby	d			17 13				17 06								18 13				18 06					
Rugby	d			17 26				17 17				17 51				18 26				18 17					
Coventry	a					17 21		17 29		17 42		18 02						18 21		18 29		18 44			
	d				17 11	17 22	17 26	17 30		17 43		18 02					18 11	18 22	18 26	18 30		18 44			
Canley	d							17 33												18 33					
Tile Hill	d				17 16			17 37									18 16			18 37					
Berkswell	d							17 40												18 40					
Hampton-in-Arden	d							17 44												18 44					
Birmingham International ✈	a				17 23	17 32	17 35	17 47		17 53		18 13					18 23	18 32	18 35	18 47		18 54			
	d				17 23	17 33	17 38	17 48		17 54	18 07	18 13					18 23	18 33	18 38	18 48		18 54		19 07	
Marston Green	d				17 26			17 51									18 26			18 51					
Lea Hall	d				17 30												18 30								
Stechford	d				17 32												18 32								
Adderley Park	d				17 35												18 35								
Birmingham New Street 12	a				17 41	17 44	17 48	17 59		18 06	18 18	18 25					18 41	18 44	18 48	18 59		19 06		19 18	
	d	17 35					18 01		18 09	18 16	18 24			18 31	18 35				19 01		19 09	19 16		19 24	19 31
Smethwick Rolfe Street	d								18 15												19 15				
Smethwick Galton Bridge 7	d								18 17												19 17				
Sandwell & Dudley	d								18 19	18 26											19 19	19 26			
Dudley Port	d								18 22												19 22				
Tipton	d								18 24												19 24				
Coseley	d								18 27												19 27				
Wolverhampton 7 ⛴	a	17 52					18 18		18 32	18 37	18 42			18 48	18 52				19 18		19 32	19 37		19 42	19 48
	d	17 53					18 19								18 53				19 19						
Penkridge	d	18 03													19 03										
Stafford	a	18 09		18 18			18 35								19 09	19 18			19 37						

		LM	LM	VT	LM	VT	XC	LM	LM	VT		XC	AW	VT	LM	XC	LM	VT		XC	LM	LM	VT	XC	AW
		1	1	◇1	1	◇1	◇1	1		◇1		◇1	◇	◇1	1	◇1	1	◇1		◇1	1		◇1	◇1	◇
		A	B				C			B		J	E		B	I				K			L	J	H
				☕		☕	🛒			☕		🛒		☕				☕		🛒			☕	🛒	
London Euston 15 ⊖66	d		17 50	18 00		18 20		17 34		18 40				19 00	18 50			19 20			18 34		19 40		
Northampton	d		19 02					18 55							20 02						19 55				
Long Buckby	d		19 13					19 06							20 13						20 06				
Rugby	d		19 26	18 51				19 17						19 52	20 26						20 17				
Coventry	a			19 02		19 22		19 28		19 42				20 03				20 22			20 29		20 42		
	d			19 02	19 11	19 22	19 26	19 30		19 42		19 54		20 03			20 11	20 22		20 26	20 30		20 42	20 54	
Canley	d							19 33													20 33				
Tile Hill	d				19 16			19 37									20 16				20 37				
Berkswell	d							19 40													20 40				
Hampton-in-Arden	d							19 44													20 44				
Birmingham International ✈	a			19 13	19 23	19 32	19 37	19 47		19 53		20 03		20 13			20 23	20 32		20 35	20 47		20 53	21 03	
	d			19 13	19 23	19 33	19 38	19 48		19 53		20 04	20 07	20 13			20 23	20 33		20 38	20 48		20 53	21 04	21 08
Marston Green	d				19 26			19 51									20 26				20 51				
Lea Hall	d				19 30												20 30								
Stechford	d				19 32												20 32								
Adderley Park	d				19 35												20 35								
Birmingham New Street 12	a			19 24	19 41	19 44	19 48	19 59		20 05		20 15	20 18	20 24			20 41	20 44		20 48	20 59		21 04	21 15	21 18
	d	19 35		19 39			20 01		20 09	20 16			20 24	20 25		20 31		20 48		21 01		21 09	21 16		21 24
Smethwick Rolfe Street	d								20 15													21 15			
Smethwick Galton Bridge 7	d								20 17													21 17			
Sandwell & Dudley	d			19 49					20 19	20 26				20 34				20 57				21 19	21 26		
Dudley Port	d								20 22													21 22			
Tipton	d								20 24													21 24			
Coseley	d								20 27													21 27			
Wolverhampton 7 ⛴	a	19 52		20 02			20 18		20 32	20 36			20 42	20 46		20 51		21 10		21 18		21 33	21 37		21 42
	d	19 53					20 19			20 38										21 19			21 37		
Penkridge	d	20 03																							
Stafford	a	20 09	20 18				20 36			20 52					21 18					21 36			21 56		

A To Liverpool Lime Street
B To Crewe
C From Bournemouth to Manchester Piccadilly
D To Edinburgh
E To Aberystwyth
F From Penzance to Manchester Piccadilly
G To Glasgow Central
H To Chester
I From Bristol Temple Meads to Manchester Piccadilly
J From Reading
K From Bournemouth to Manchester Piccadilly. 🛒 to Birmingham New Street
L To Preston

Table 68

Sundays

5 January to 9 February

Northampton - Coventry - Birmingham - Wolverhampton - Stafford

Network Diagram - refer to first Page of Table 67

	VT	LM	LM	LM	VT	XC	LM	LM	VT		XC	AW	LM	VT	XC	AW	LM	LM	XC		AW	LM	LM	VT
	◇1	1	1	1	◇1	◇1	1		◇1		◇1		1	◇1	◇1	◇	1		◇1			1	1	◇1
		A	A			B					C	D			E	F			C		D		G	
	⊏P				⊏P	⊼			⊏P					⊏P										⊏P
London Euston 15 ⊖66 d	20 00		19 50		20 18		19 34		20 38					20 54			20 34						21 30	21 55
Northampton d			21 06				20 55										21 55						22 52	
Long Buckby d			21 17				21 06										22 06						23 03	
Rugby d	20 51		21 30				21 17							22 07			22 17						23 14	23 23
Coventry a	21 02				21 20		21 29		21 46					22 16			22 29						23 25	23 33
d	21 02			21 10	21 20	21 26	21 30		21 46		21 53		22 08	22 16	22 23		22 30		22 53			23 06	23 38	23 33
Canley d							21 33										22 33						↳	
Tile Hill d				21 15			21 37										22 37							
Berkswell d							21 40										22 40							
Hampton-in-Arden d							21 44										22 44							
Birmingham International ✈ a	21 13			21 22	21 31	21 35	21 47		21 57		22 02		22 17	22 27	22 32		22 47		23 02			23 15		23 44
d	21 13			21 22	21 31	21 38	21 48		21 57		22 03	22 11	22 18	22 27	22 33	22 43	22 48		23 03		23 08	23 15		23 44
Marston Green d				21 25			21 51						22 21				22 51					23 18		
Lea Hall d				21 29									22 24									23 22		
Stechford d				21 31									22 27									23 24		
Adderley Park d				21 35									22 30									23 28		
Birmingham New Street 12 a	21 24			21 40	21 44	21 48	21 59		22 09		22 14	22 21	22 36	22 39	22 43	22 53	22 59		23 13		23 19	23 33		23 55
d	21 28	21 35			21 48	22 01		22 09	22 16			22 24		22 43		22 55		23 09			23 24			23 58
Smethwick Rolfe Street d								22 15										23 15						
Smethwick Galton Bridge 7 d								22 17										23 17						
Sandwell & Dudley d	21 37				21 57			22 19	22 25					22 52				23 19						
Dudley Port d								22 22										23 22						
Tipton d								22 24										23 24						
Coseley d								22 27										23 27						
Wolverhampton 7 🚌 a	21 51	21 56			22 10	22 19		22 32	22 38			22 41		23 06		23 13		23 32			23 40			00 17
d		21 59				22 20										23 15								
Penkridge d		22 09																						
Stafford a		22 15	22 25			22 36										23 30								

	LM	VT	LM	VT
	1	◇1	1	◇1
	H			
		⊏P		⊏P
London Euston 15 ⊖66 d		22 25	22 00	23 25
Northampton d			23 32	
Long Buckby d			23 43	
Rugby d	↤	23 48	23 54	00s46
Coventry a	23 25	23 57	00 05	00s58
d	23 38	23 58		
Canley d	23 41			
Tile Hill d	23 45			
Berkswell d	23 48			
Hampton-in-Arden d	23 52			
Birmingham International ✈ a	23 55	00 08		01s09
d	23 56	00 09		
Marston Green d	23 59			
Lea Hall d				
Stechford d				
Adderley Park d				
Birmingham New Street 12 a	00 07	00 21		01s22
d		00 24		
Smethwick Rolfe Street d				
Smethwick Galton Bridge 7 d				
Sandwell & Dudley d				
Dudley Port d				
Tipton d				
Coseley d				
Wolverhampton 7 🚌 a		00 43		01 44
d				
Penkridge d				
Stafford a				

A To Crewe
B From Bournemouth to Manchester Piccadilly. ⊼ to Birmingham New Street
C From Reading
D To Shrewsbury
E From Bournemouth
F To Holyhead
G To Birmingham New Street
H From London Euston

Table 68

Sundays

16 February to 23 March

Northampton - Coventry - Birmingham - Wolverhampton - Stafford

Network Diagram - refer to first Page of Table 67

		VT	XC	LM	LM	LM		VT	LM	LM	XC	AW	LM	VT	LM	LM		LM	LM	VT	XC	AW	LM	LM	VT
		◇1	◇1	1		1		◇1	1	1	◇1			◇1	1	1		1	1	◇1	◇1	◇	1		◇1
		A	B					C		D	B	E		F				G	D		H	I			C
		☕	🛒					☕			🛒			☕						☕	🛒				☕
London Euston 15 ⊖66	d														07 52					08 50			08 23		
Northampton	d														09 26			09 38					10 00		
Long Buckby	d														09 37			09 49					10 11		
Rugby	d														09 48			10 00		10 14			10 22		
Coventry	a														09 59					10 23			10 33		
	d			08 37					09 11						10 00	10 11				10 24	10 28		10 34		
Canley	d			08 40					09 14							10 14							10 37		
Tile Hill	d			08 44					09 18							10 18							10 41		
Berkswell	d			08 47					09 21							10 21							10 44		
Hampton-in-Arden	d			08 51					09 25							10 25							10 48		
Birmingham International ✈	a			08 54					09 28						10 09	10 28				10 34	10 38		10 51		
	d			08 55		09 03			09 29			09 51			10 09	10 29				10 35	10 40	10 48	10 52		
Marston Green	d			08 58		09 06			09 32						10 12	10 32							10 55		
Lea Hall	d					09 09									10 16										
Stechford	d					09 12									10 18										
Adderley Park	d					09 15									10 22										
Birmingham New Street 12	a			09 06		09 20			09 40			10 01			10 26	10 40				10 47	10 50	10 58	11 03		
	d	08 45	09 01		09 09			09 20		09 42	10 01	10 04	10 09	10 20					10 42	10 51	11 01	11 05		11 09	11 20
Smethwick Rolfe Street	d				09 15								10 15											11 15	
Smethwick Galton Bridge 7	d				09 17								10 17											11 17	
Sandwell & Dudley	d				09 19								10 19							11 00				11 19	
Dudley Port	d				09 22								10 22											11 22	
Tipton	d				09 24								10 24											11 24	
Coseley	d				09 27								10 27											11 27	
Wolverhampton 7 🚌	a	09 03	09 18		09 32			09 37		09 59	10 18	10 21	10 32	10 37					10 59	11 13	11 18	11 26		11 32	11 37
	d	09 04	09 19							10 00	10 19								11 00		11 19				
Penkridge	d									10 10									11 10						
Stafford	a	09 17	09 32							10 16	10 32							10 56	11 16		11 32				

		LM		LM	VT		XC	LM	LM	LM	LM	VT	AW		LM	LM	VT	XC	LM	LM	VT	AW	VT	XC	LM
		1		1	◇1		◇1	1	1		1	◇1	◇		1	1	◇1	◇1	1		◇1	◇	◇1	◇1	1
				D			J		G		G	F	K		D			L			C	I		B	D
					☕		🛒					☕	🛒				☕	🛒			☕	🛒	☕	🛒	
London Euston 15 ⊖66	d				09 50			09 24	09 54		10 24						10 49		10 28				11 50		
Northampton	d							11 00	11 08		11 40								11 58						
Long Buckby	d							11 11	11 19		11 51								12 09						
Rugby	d				11 14			11 22	11 30		12 03						12 14		12 20				12 50		
Coventry	a				11 24			11 33									12 23		12 31				12 59		
	d	11 11			11 24		11 29	11 34								12 11	12 24	12 28	12 32				12 59		
Canley	d							11 37											12 35						
Tile Hill	d							11 41											12 39						
Berkswell	d							11 44											12 42						
Hampton-in-Arden	d							11 48											12 46						
Birmingham International ✈	a	11 20			11 35		11 38	11 51								12 20	12 34	12 37	12 49				13 10		
	d	11 20			11 35		11 40	11 52					12 08			12 20	12 34	12 39	12 50			13 07	13 10		
Marston Green	d	11 23						11 55								12 23			12 53						
Lea Hall	d	11 27														12 27									
Stechford	d	11 29														12 29									
Adderley Park	d	11 32														12 32									
Birmingham New Street 12	a	11 38			11 47		11 51	12 03					12 18			12 38	12 46	12 49	13 01			13 17	13 24		
	d			11 42	11 51		12 01			12 09		12 20	12 24		12 35		12 50	13 00		13 09	13 20	13 24		13 31	13 35
Smethwick Rolfe Street	d									12 15										13 15					
Smethwick Galton Bridge 7	d									12 17										13 17					
Sandwell & Dudley	d				12 00					12 19							12 59			13 19					
Dudley Port	d									12 22										13 22					
Tipton	d									12 24										13 24					
Coseley	d									12 27										13 27					
Wolverhampton 7 🚌	a			11 59	12 13		12 19			12 32		12 37	12 42		12 52		13 12	13 17		13 32	13 37	13 41		13 48	13 52
	d			12 00			12 19								12 53			13 18							13 53
Penkridge	d			12 10											13 03										14 03
Stafford	a			12 16			12 32		12 21		12 59				13 09			13 32							14 09

A To Preston
B To Manchester Piccadilly
C To Glasgow Central
D To Liverpool Lime Street
E To Shrewsbury
F To Edinburgh
G To Crewe
H From Reading to Manchester Piccadilly
I To Chester
J From Southampton Central to Manchester Piccadilly
K To Aberystwyth
L From Bournemouth to Manchester Piccadilly

Table 68

Sundays

16 February to 23 March

Northampton - Coventry - Birmingham - Wolverhampton - Stafford

Network Diagram - refer to first Page of Table 67

		LM 1	VT ◇1	XC ◇1 A		LM 1 B		LM	VT ◇1 C	AW ◇ D	VT ◇1	XC ◇1 E	LM 1 F		LM 1	VT ◇1	XC ◇1 A	LM 1	LM 1 B	LM	VT ◇1 G	AW ◇ H	VT ◇1	XC ◇1 I	
London Euston 15 ⊖66	d		12 20			11 24			12 40		13 00					13 20		12 34	12 50		13 40		14 00		
Northampton	d					12 55	13 02											13 55	14 02						
Long Buckby	d					13 06	13 13											14 06	14 13						
Rugby	d					13 17	13 26				13 51							14 17	14 26				14 51		
Coventry	a		13 21			13 29			13 42		14 02					14 21		14 28			14 44		15 02		
	d	13 11	13 22	13 28		13 30			13 42		14 02				14 11	14 22	14 28	14 30			14 44		15 02		
Canley	d					13 33												14 33							
Tile Hill	d	13 16				13 37									14 16			14 37							
Berkswell	d					13 40												14 40							
Hampton-in-Arden	d					13 44												14 44							
Birmingham International ✈	a	13 23	13 32	13 37		13 47			13 53		14 13				14 23	14 32	14 37	14 47			14 54		15 13		
	d	13 23	13 33	13 39		13 48			13 53	14 07	14 13				14 23	14 33	14 38	14 48			14 54	15 07	15 13		
Marston Green	d	13 26				13 51									14 26			14 51							
Lea Hall	d	13 30													14 30										
Stechford	d	13 32													14 32										
Adderley Park	d	13 35													14 35										
Birmingham New Street 12	a	13 41	13 44	13 50		13 59			14 05	14 18	14 25				14 41	14 44	14 48	14 59			15 06	15 18	15 25		
	d		13 48	14 01				14 09	14 16	14 24		14 31	14 35				15 00			15 09	15 17	15 24		15 31	
Smethwick Rolfe Street	d							14 15												15 15					
Smethwick Galton Bridge 7	d							14 17												15 17					
Sandwell & Dudley	d		13 57					14 19	14 26											15 19	15 26				
Dudley Port	d							14 22												15 22					
Tipton	d							14 24												15 24					
Coseley	d							14 27												15 27					
Wolverhampton 7	a		14 10	14 18				14 32	14 37	14 42		14 48	14 52				15 17			15 32	15 37	15 42		15 48	
	d			14 19									14 53				15 18								
Penkridge	d												15 03												
Stafford	a			14 33			14 18						15 09				15 32		15 18						

		LM 1 F	LM 1	VT ◇1	XC ◇1 A	LM 1	LM 1 B	LM	VT ◇1 C	AW ◇ D		VT ◇1	XC ◇1 E	LM 1 F		LM 1	VT ◇1	XC ◇1 A	LM 1	LM 1 B	LM	VT ◇1 G	AW ◇ J	VT ◇1	XC ◇1 E
London Euston 15 ⊖66	d			14 20		13 34	13 50		14 40			15 00					15 20		14 34	14 50		15 40		16 00	
Northampton	d					14 55	15 02												15 55	16 02					
Long Buckby	d					15 06	15 13												16 06	16 13					
Rugby	d					15 17	15 26					15 53							16 17	16 26				16 51	
Coventry	a			15 21		15 28			15 42			16 03					16 21		16 28			16 42		17 02	
	d		15 11	15 22	15 27	15 30			15 42			16 04				16 11	16 22	16 28	16 30			16 42		17 02	
Canley	d					15 33													16 33						
Tile Hill	d		15 16			15 37										16 16			16 37						
Berkswell	d					15 40													16 40						
Hampton-in-Arden	d					15 44													16 44						
Birmingham International ✈	a		15 23	15 32	15 37	15 47			15 53			16 13				16 23	16 32	16 37	16 47			16 53		17 13	
	d		15 23	15 33	15 39	15 48			15 53	16 07		16 14				16 23	16 33	16 39	16 48			16 53	17 07	17 13	
Marston Green	d		15 26			15 51										16 26			16 51						
Lea Hall	d		15 30													16 30									
Stechford	d		15 32													16 32									
Adderley Park	d		15 35													16 35									
Birmingham New Street 12	a		15 41	15 44	15 50	15 59			16 05	16 18		16 25				16 41	16 44	16 50	16 59			17 05	17 18	17 25	
	d	15 35			16 01			16 09	16 16	16 24			16 31	16 35				17 01			17 09	17 16	17 24		17 31
Smethwick Rolfe Street	d							16 15													17 15				
Smethwick Galton Bridge 7	d							16 17													17 17				
Sandwell & Dudley	d							16 19	16 26												17 19	17 26			
Dudley Port	d							16 22													17 22				
Tipton	d							16 24													17 24				
Coseley	d							16 27													17 27				
Wolverhampton 7	a	15 52			16 18			16 32	16 37	16 42			16 48	16 52				17 18			17 32	17 37	17 42		17 48
	d	15 53			16 19									16 53				17 19							
Penkridge	d	16 03												17 03											
Stafford	a	16 09			16 34		16 18							17 09				17 35		17 18					

A From Bournemouth to Manchester Piccadilly
B To Crewe
C To Edinburgh
D To Aberystwyth
E From Bristol Temple Meads to Manchester Piccadilly
F To Liverpool Lime Street
G To Glasgow Central
H To Chester
I To Manchester Piccadilly
J To Holyhead

Table 68

Sundays

16 February to 23 March

Northampton - Coventry - Birmingham - Wolverhampton - Stafford

Network Diagram - refer to first Page of Table 67

Station		LM		LM	VT	XC	LM	LM	LM	VT	AW	VT		XC	LM		LM	VT	XC	LM	LM	LM	VT	AW	XC
		1		1	◇1	◇1	1	1		◇1	◇	◇1		◇1	1		1	◇1	◇1	1	1		R 1	◇	◇1
		A				C		B		D	E			F	A				C		B		G	H	F
					☕	🛒				☕	🛒	☕		🛒				☕	🛒				☕	🛒	🛒
London Euston 15 ⊖66	d				16 20		15 34	15 50		16 40		17 00						17 20		16 34	16 50		17 40		
Northampton	d						16 55	17 02												17 55	18 02				
Long Buckby	d						17 06	17 13												18 06	18 13				
Rugby	d						17 17	17 26				17 51								18 17	18 26				
Coventry	a				17 21		17 28			17 44		18 02						18 21		18 28			18 44		
	d			17 11	17 22	17 28	17 30			17 44		18 02					18 11	18 22	18 28	18 30			18 44		
Canley	d						17 33													18 33					
Tile Hill	d			17 16			17 37										18 16			18 37					
Berkswell	d						17 40													18 40					
Hampton-in-Arden	d						17 44													18 44					
Birmingham International ✈	a			17 23	17 32	17 37	17 47			17 54		18 13					18 23	18 32	18 37	18 47			18 54		
	d			17 23	17 33	17 39	17 48			17 54	18 07	18 13					18 23	18 33	18 39	18 48			18 54	19 07	
Marston Green	d			17 26			17 51										18 26			18 51					
Lea Hall	d			17 30													18 30								
Stechford	d			17 32													18 32								
Adderley Park	d			17 35													18 35								
Birmingham New Street 12	a			17 41	17 44	17 50	17 59			18 06	18 18	18 25					18 41	18 44	18 50	18 59			19 06	19 18	
	d	17 35				18 01			18 09	18 16	18 24			18 31	18 35				19 01			19 09	19 16	19 24	19 31
Smethwick Rolfe Street	d								18 15													19 15			
Smethwick Galton Bridge 7	d								18 17													19 17			
Sandwell & Dudley	d								18 19	18 26												19 19	19 26		
Dudley Port	d								18 22													19 22			
Tipton	d								18 24													19 24			
Coseley	d								18 27													19 27			
Wolverhampton 7 🚌	a	17 52				18 18			18 32	18 37	18 42			18 48	18 52				19 18			19 32	19 37	19 42	19 48
	d	17 53				18 19									18 53				19 19						
Penkridge	d	18 03													19 03										
Stafford	a	18 09				18 35		18 18							19 09				19 37		19 18				

Station		LM	VT	LM	VT	XC	LM	LM	LM	VT		XC	AW	VT	XC	LM	VT		XC	LM	LM	LM	VT	XC	AW
		1	◇1	1	◇1	◇1	1	1		◇1		◇1	◇	◇1	◇1	1	◇1		◇1	1	1		◇1	◇1	◇
		A				C		B		B		I	E		F				J		B		K	I	H
			☕		☕	🛒				☕		🛒		☕			☕		🛒				☕	🛒	
London Euston 15 ⊖66	d		18 00		18 20		17 34	17 50		18 40				19 00			19 20			18 34	18 50		19 40		
Northampton	d						18 55	19 02												19 55	20 02				
Long Buckby	d						19 06	19 13												20 06	20 13				
Rugby	d		18 51				19 17	19 26						19 52						20 17	20 26				
Coventry	a		19 02		19 22		19 28			19 42				20 03			20 22			20 28			20 41		
	d		19 02	19 11	19 22	19 28	19 30			19 42		19 54		20 03		20 11	20 22		20 28	20 30			20 41	20 55	
Canley	d						19 33													20 33					
Tile Hill	d			19 16			19 37									20 16				20 37					
Berkswell	d						19 40													20 40					
Hampton-in-Arden	d						19 44													20 44					
Birmingham International ✈	a		19 13	19 23	19 32	19 38	19 47			19 53		20 03		20 13		20 23	20 32		20 38	20 47			20 52	21 04	
	d		19 13	19 23	19 33	19 40	19 48			19 53		20 04	20 07	20 13		20 23	20 33		20 40	20 48			20 52	21 05	21 08
Marston Green	d			19 26			19 51									20 26				20 51					
Lea Hall	d			19 30												20 30									
Stechford	d			19 32												20 32									
Adderley Park	d			19 35												20 35									
Birmingham New Street 12	a		19 24	19 41	19 44	19 50	19 59			20 05		20 15	20 18	20 24		20 41	20 44		20 50	20 59			21 03	21 16	21 18
	d	19 35	19 39			20 01			20 09	20 16			20 24	20 25	20 31		20 48		21 01			21 09	21 14		21 24
Smethwick Rolfe Street	d								20 15													21 15			
Smethwick Galton Bridge 7	d								20 17													21 17			
Sandwell & Dudley	d		19 49						20 19	20 26				20 34			20 57					21 19	21 26		
Dudley Port	d								20 22													21 22			
Tipton	d								20 24													21 24			
Coseley	d								20 27													21 27			
Wolverhampton 7 🚌	a	19 52	20 02			20 18			20 32	20 36			20 42	20 46	20 51		21 10		21 18			21 33	21 37		21 42
	d	19 53				20 19				20 38									21 19				21 38		
Penkridge	d	20 03																							
Stafford	a	20 09				20 36		20 18		20 52									21 36		21 18		21 55		

- **A** To Liverpool Lime Street
- **B** To Crewe
- **C** From Bournemouth to Manchester Piccadilly
- **D** To Edinburgh
- **E** To Aberystwyth
- **F** From Bristol Temple Meads to Manchester Piccadilly
- **G** To Glasgow Central
- **H** To Chester
- **I** From Reading
- **J** From Bournemouth to Manchester Piccadilly. 🛒 to Birmingham New Street
- **K** To Preston

Table 68

Sundays

16 February to 23 March

Northampton - Coventry - Birmingham - Wolverhampton - Stafford

Network Diagram - refer to first Page of Table 67

		VT	LM		LM	VT	XC	LM	LM	LM	VT		XC	AW	LM	VT	XC	AW	LM	LM	XC	AW	LM	LM	VT
		◇1	1		1	◇1	◇1	1	1		◇1		◇1		1	◇1	◇1	◇	1		◇1		1	1	◇1
			A				B		A				C	D			E	F			C	D		G	
		☕				☕	🍴				☕					☕									☕
London Euston 15 ⊖66	d	20 00				20 18		19 34	19 50		20 38					20 54			20 34					21 30	21 55
Northampton	d							20 55	21 06										21 55					22 52	
Long Buckby	d							21 06	21 17										22 06					23 03	
Rugby	d	20 51						21 17	21 30							22 07			22 17					23 14	23 23
Coventry	a	21 02				21 20		21 28			21 46					22 16			22 28					23 25	23 33
	d	21 02			21 10	21 20	21 29	21 30			21 46		21 53		22 08	22 16	22 29		22 30		22 53		23 06	23 38	23 33
Canley	d							21 33											22 33					→	
Tile Hill	d				21 15			21 37											22 37						
Berkswell	d							21 40											22 40						
Hampton-in-Arden	d							21 44											22 44						
Birmingham International ✈	a	21 13			21 22	21 31	21 38	21 47			21 57		22 02		22 17	22 27	22 38		22 47		23 02		23 15		23 44
	d	21 13			21 22	21 31	21 40	21 48			21 57		22 03	22 11	22 18	22 27	22 39	22 43	22 48		23 03	23 08	23 15		23 44
Marston Green	d				21 25			21 51							22 21				22 51				23 18		
Lea Hall	d				21 29										22 24								23 22		
Stechford	d				21 31										22 27								23 24		
Adderley Park	d				21 35										22 30								23 28		
Birmingham New Street 12	a	21 24			21 40	21 44	21 50	21 59			22 09		22 14	22 21	22 36	22 39	22 49	22 53	22 59		23 13	23 19	23 33		23 55
	d	21 28	21 35			21 48	22 01			22 09	22 16			22 24		22 43		22 55		23 09		23 24			23 58
Smethwick Rolfe Street	d									22 15										23 15					
Smethwick Galton Bridge 7	d									22 17										23 17					
Sandwell & Dudley	d	21 37				21 57				22 19	22 25					22 52				23 19					
Dudley Port	d									22 22										23 22					
Tipton	d									22 24										23 24					
Coseley	d									22 27										23 27					
Wolverhampton 7 ⛴	a	21 51	21 56			22 10	22 19			22 32	22 38			22 41		23 06		23 13		23 32		23 40			00 17
	d		21 59				22 20											23 15							
Penkridge	d		22 09																						
Stafford	a		22 15				22 36		22 25									23 30							

		LM	VT	LM	VT
		1	◇1	1	◇1
		H			
			☕		☕
London Euston 15 ⊖66	d		22 25	22 00	23 25
Northampton	d			23 32	
Long Buckby	d			23 43	
Rugby	d	←	23 48	23 54	00s46
Coventry	a	23 25	23 57	00 05	00s58
	d	23 38	23 58		
Canley	d	23 41			
Tile Hill	d	23 45			
Berkswell	d	23 48			
Hampton-in-Arden	d	23 52			
Birmingham International ✈	a	23 55	00 08		01s09
	d	23 56	00 09		
Marston Green	d	23 59			
Lea Hall	d				
Stechford	d				
Adderley Park	d				
Birmingham New Street 12	a	00 07	00 21		01s22
	d		00 24		
Smethwick Rolfe Street	d				
Smethwick Galton Bridge 7	d				
Sandwell & Dudley	d				
Dudley Port	d				
Tipton	d				
Coseley	d				
Wolverhampton 7 ⛴	a		00 43		01 44
	d				
Penkridge	d				
Stafford	a				

A To Crewe
B From Bournemouth to Manchester Piccadilly. 🍴 to Birmingham New Street
C From Reading
D To Shrewsbury
E From Bournemouth
F To Holyhead
G To Birmingham New Street
H From London Euston

Table 68

Sundays

30 March to 11 May

Northampton - Coventry - Birmingham - Wolverhampton - Stafford

Network Diagram - refer to first Page of Table 67

		VT	XC	LM	LM	LM		VT	LM	LM	XC	AW	LM	VT	LM	LM		LM	LM	VT	XC	AW	LM	LM	VT
		◇1	◇1	1		1		◇1	1	1	◇1			◇1	1	1		1	1	◇1	◇1	◇	1		◇1
		A	B					C		D	B	E		F				G	D		H	I			C
		🍴	🛒					🍴			🛒			🍴						🍴	🛒				🍴
London Euston [15] ⊖66	d														07 52					08 50			08 23		
Northampton	d														09 26			09 38					10 00		
Long Buckby	d														09 37			09 49					10 11		
Rugby	d														09 48			10 00		10 14			10 22		
Coventry	a														09 59					10 23			10 33		
	d			08 37					09 11						10 00	10 11				10 24	10 28		10 34		
Canley	d			08 40					09 14							10 14							10 37		
Tile Hill	d			08 44					09 18							10 18							10 41		
Berkswell	d			08 47					09 21							10 21							10 44		
Hampton-in-Arden	d			08 51					09 25							10 25							10 48		
Birmingham International ✈	a			08 54					09 28						10 09	10 28				10 34	10 38		10 51		
	d			08 55		09 03			09 29			09 51			10 09	10 29				10 35	10 40	10 48	10 52		
Marston Green	d			08 58		09 06			09 32						10 12	10 32							10 55		
Lea Hall	d					09 09									10 16										
Stechford	d					09 12									10 18										
Adderley Park	d					09 15									10 22										
Birmingham New Street [12]	a			09 06		09 20			09 40			10 01			10 26	10 40				10 47	10 50	10 58	11 03		
	d	08 45	09 01		09 09			09 20		09 42	10 01	10 04	10 09	10 20					10 42	10 51	11 01	11 05		11 09	11 20
Smethwick Rolfe Street	d				09 15								10 15											11 15	
Smethwick Galton Bridge [7]	d				09 17								10 17											11 17	
Sandwell & Dudley	d				09 19								10 19							11 00				11 19	
Dudley Port	d				09 22								10 22											11 22	
Tipton	d				09 24								10 24											11 24	
Coseley	d				09 27								10 27											11 27	
Wolverhampton [7]	a	09 03	09 18		09 32			09 37		09 59	10 18	10 21	10 32	10 37					10 59	11 13	11 18	11 26		11 32	11 37
	d	09 04	09 19							10 00	10 19								11 00		11 19				
Penkridge	d									10 10									11 10						
Stafford	a	09 17	09 32							10 16	10 32							10 56	11 16		11 32				

		LM		LM	VT		XC	LM	LM	LM	LM	VT	AW		LM	LM	VT	XC	LM	LM	VT	AW	VT	XC	LM
		1		1	◇1		◇1	1	1		1	◇1	◇		1	1	◇1	◇1	1		◇1	◇	◇1	◇1	1
				D			J		G		G	F	K		D			L			C	I		B	D
					🍴		🛒					🍴	🛒				🍴	🛒			🍴	🛒	🍴	🛒	
London Euston [15] ⊖66	d				09 50			09 24	09 54		10 24						10 49		10 28				11 50		
Northampton	d							11 00	11 08		11 40								11 58						
Long Buckby	d							11 11	11 19		11 51								12 09						
Rugby	d				11 14			11 22	11 30		12 03						12 14		12 20				12 50		
Coventry	a				11 24			11 33									12 23		12 31				12 59		
	d	11 11			11 24		11 29	11 34								12 11	12 24	12 28	12 32				12 59		
Canley	d							11 37											12 35						
Tile Hill	d							11 41											12 39						
Berkswell	d							11 44											12 42						
Hampton-in-Arden	d							11 48											12 46						
Birmingham International ✈	a	11 20			11 35		11 38	11 51								12 20	12 34	12 38	12 49				13 10		
	d	11 20			11 35		11 40	11 52					12 08			12 20	12 34	12 40	12 50			13 07	13 10		
Marston Green	d	11 23						11 55								12 23			12 53						
Lea Hall	d	11 27														12 27									
Stechford	d	11 29														12 29									
Adderley Park	d	11 32														12 32									
Birmingham New Street [12]	a	11 38			11 47		11 51	12 03					12 18			12 38	12 46	12 50	13 01			13 17	13 24		
	d			11 42	11 51		12 01			12 09		12 20	12 24		12 35		12 50	13 01		13 09	13 20	13 24		13 31	13 35
Smethwick Rolfe Street	d									12 15										13 15					
Smethwick Galton Bridge [7]	d									12 17										13 17					
Sandwell & Dudley	d				12 00					12 19							12 59			13 19					
Dudley Port	d									12 22										13 22					
Tipton	d									12 24										13 24					
Coseley	d									12 27										13 27					
Wolverhampton [7]	a			11 59	12 13		12 19			12 32		12 37	12 42		12 52		13 12	13 18		13 32	13 37	13 41		13 48	13 52
	d			12 00			12 19								12 53			13 19							13 53
Penkridge	d			12 10											13 03										14 03
Stafford	a			12 16			12 32		12 21		12 59				13 09			13 33							14 09

A To Preston
B To Manchester Piccadilly
C To Glasgow Central
D To Liverpool Lime Street
E To Shrewsbury
F To Edinburgh
G To Crewe
H From Reading to Manchester Piccadilly
I To Chester
J From Southampton Central to Manchester Piccadilly
K To Aberystwyth
L From Bournemouth to Manchester Piccadilly

Table 68

Sundays

30 March to 11 May

Northampton - Coventry - Birmingham - Wolverhampton - Stafford

Network Diagram - refer to first Page of Table 67

		LM	VT	XC		LM		LM	VT	AW	VT	XC	LM
		■1	◇■1	◇■1		■1			◇■1	◇	◇■1	◇■1	■1
				A		B			C	D		E	F
			⊏P	⊥					⊏P	⊥	⊏P	⊥	
London Euston 15 ⊖66	d		12 20			11 24			12 40		13 00		
Northampton	d					12 55	13 02						
Long Buckby	d					13 06	13 13						
Rugby	d					13 17	13 26				13 51		
Coventry	a		13 21			13 29			13 42		14 02		
	d	13 11	13 22	13 26		13 30			13 42		14 02		
Canley	d					13 33							
Tile Hill	d	13 16				13 37							
Berkswell	d					13 40							
Hampton-in-Arden	d					13 44							
Birmingham International ✈	a	13 23	13 32	13 37		13 47			13 53		14 13		
	d	13 23	13 33	13 38		13 48			13 53	14 07	14 13		
Marston Green	d	13 26				13 51							
Lea Hall	d	13 30											
Stechford	d	13 32											
Adderley Park	d	13 35											
Birmingham New Street 12	a	13 41	13 44	13 48		13 59			14 05	14 18	14 25		
	d		13 48	14 01				14 09	14 16	14 24		14 31	14 35
Smethwick Rolfe Street	d							14 15					
Smethwick Galton Bridge 7	d							14 17					
Sandwell & Dudley	d		13 57					14 19	14 26				
Dudley Port	d							14 22					
Tipton	d							14 24					
Coseley	d							14 27					
Wolverhampton 7	a		14 10	14 18				14 32	14 37	14 42		14 48	14 52
	d			14 19									14 53
Penkridge	d												15 03
Stafford	a			14 33			14 18						15 09

			LM	VT	XC	LM	LM	LM	VT	AW	VT	XC	
			■1	◇■1	◇■1	■1	■1		◇■1	◇	◇■1	◇■1	
					A		B		G	H		I	
				⊏P	⊥				⊏P	⊥	⊏P	⊥	
London Euston 15 ⊖66	d			13 20		12 34	12 50		13 40		14 00		
Northampton	d					13 55	14 02						
Long Buckby	d					14 06	14 13						
Rugby	d					14 17	14 26				14 51		
Coventry	a			14 21		14 29			14 44		15 02		
	d		14 11	14 22	14 26	14 30			14 44		15 02		
Canley	d					14 33							
Tile Hill	d		14 16			14 37							
Berkswell	d					14 40							
Hampton-in-Arden	d					14 44							
Birmingham International ✈	a		14 23	14 32	14 37	14 47			14 54		15 13		
	d		14 23	14 33	14 38	14 48			14 54	15 07	15 13		
Marston Green	d		14 26			14 51							
Lea Hall	d		14 30										
Stechford	d		14 32										
Adderley Park	d		14 35										
Birmingham New Street 12	a		14 41	14 44	14 48	14 59			15 06	15 18	15 25		
	d				15 01			15 09	15 17	15 24		15 31	
Smethwick Rolfe Street	d							15 15					
Smethwick Galton Bridge 7	d							15 17					
Sandwell & Dudley	d							15 19	15 26				
Dudley Port	d							15 22					
Tipton	d							15 24					
Coseley	d							15 27					
Wolverhampton 7	a				15 18			15 32	15 37	15 42		15 48	
	d				15 19								
Penkridge	d												
Stafford	a				15 33		15 18						

		LM		LM	VT	XC	LM	LM	LM	VT	AW	VT	XC	LM
		■1		■1	◇■1	◇■1	■1	■1		◇■1	◇	◇■1	◇■1	■1
		F				A		B		C	D		I	F
					⊏P	⊥				⊏P	⊥	⊏P	⊥	
London Euston 15 ⊖66	d				14 20		13 34	13 50		14 40		15 00		
Northampton	d						14 55	15 02						
Long Buckby	d						15 06	15 13						
Rugby	d						15 17	15 26				15 53		
Coventry	a				15 21		15 29			15 42		16 03		
	d			15 11	15 22	15 26	15 30			15 42		16 04		
Canley	d						15 33							
Tile Hill	d			15 16			15 37							
Berkswell	d						15 40							
Hampton-in-Arden	d						15 44							
Birmingham International ✈	a			15 23	15 32	15 35	15 47			15 53		16 13		
	d			15 23	15 33	15 38	15 48			15 53	16 07	16 14		
Marston Green	d			15 26			15 51							
Lea Hall	d			15 30										
Stechford	d			15 32										
Adderley Park	d			15 35										
Birmingham New Street 12	a			15 41	15 44	15 48	15 59			16 05	16 18	16 25		
	d	15 35				16 01			16 09	16 16	16 24		16 31	16 35
Smethwick Rolfe Street	d								16 15					
Smethwick Galton Bridge 7	d								16 17					
Sandwell & Dudley	d								16 19	16 26				
Dudley Port	d								16 22					
Tipton	d								16 24					
Coseley	d								16 27					
Wolverhampton 7	a	15 52				16 18			16 32	16 37	16 42		16 48	16 52
	d	15 53				16 19								16 53
Penkridge	d	16 03												17 03
Stafford	a	16 09				16 34		16 18						17 09

			LM	VT	XC	LM	LM	LM	VT	AW	VT	XC
			■1	◇■1	◇■1	■1	■1		◇■1	◇	◇■1	◇■1
					A		B		G	J		K
				⊏P	⊥				⊏P	⊥	⊏P	⊥
London Euston 15 ⊖66	d			15 20		14 34	14 50		15 40		16 00	
Northampton	d					15 55	16 02					
Long Buckby	d					16 06	16 13					
Rugby	d					16 17	16 26				16 51	
Coventry	a			16 21		16 29			16 42		17 02	
	d		16 11	16 22	16 26	16 30			16 42		17 02	
Canley	d					16 33						
Tile Hill	d		16 16			16 37						
Berkswell	d					16 40						
Hampton-in-Arden	d					16 44						
Birmingham International ✈	a		16 23	16 32	16 35	16 47			16 53		17 13	
	d		16 23	16 33	16 38	16 48			16 53	17 07	17 13	
Marston Green	d		16 26			16 51						
Lea Hall	d		16 30									
Stechford	d		16 32									
Adderley Park	d		16 35									
Birmingham New Street 12	a		16 41	16 44	16 48	16 59			17 05	17 18	17 25	
	d				17 01			17 09	17 16	17 24		17 31
Smethwick Rolfe Street	d							17 15				
Smethwick Galton Bridge 7	d							17 17				
Sandwell & Dudley	d							17 19	17 26			
Dudley Port	d							17 22				
Tipton	d							17 24				
Coseley	d							17 27				
Wolverhampton 7	a				17 18			17 32	17 37	17 42		17 48
	d				17 19							
Penkridge	d											
Stafford	a				17 35		17 18					

A From Bournemouth to Manchester Piccadilly
B To Crewe
C To Edinburgh
D To Aberystwyth
E From Paignton to Manchester Piccadilly
F To Liverpool Lime Street
G To Glasgow Central
H To Chester
I From Plymouth to Manchester Piccadilly
J To Holyhead
K From Bristol Temple Meads to Manchester Piccadilly

Table 68

Sundays

30 March to 11 May

Northampton - Coventry - Birmingham - Wolverhampton - Stafford

Network Diagram - refer to first Page of Table 67

		LM	LM	LM	VT	XC	LM	LM	LM	VT	AW	VT	XC	LM		LM	VT	XC	LM	LM	LM	VT		AW	XC
		1	1	1	◇1	◇1	1	1		◇1	◇	◇1	◇1	1		1	◇1	◇1	1	1		R 1		◇	◇1
		A	B			C		B		D	E		F	A				C		B		G		H	I
London Euston 15 ⊖66	d		15 50		16 20		15 34	15 50		16 40		17 00					17 20		16 34	16 50		17 40			
Northampton	d		17 02				16 55	17 02											17 55	18 02					
Long Buckby	d		17 13				17 06	17 13											18 06	18 13					
Rugby	d		17 26				17 17	17 26				17 51							18 17	18 26					
Coventry	a				17 21		17 29			17 44		18 02					18 21		18 29			18 44			
	d			17 11	17 22	17 26	17 30			17 44		18 02				18 11	18 22	18 26	18 30			18 44			
Canley	d						17 33												18 33						
Tile Hill	d			17 16			17 37									18 16			18 37						
Berkswell	d						17 40												18 40						
Hampton-in-Arden	d						17 44												18 44						
Birmingham International ✈	a			17 23	17 32	17 35	17 47			17 54		18 13				18 23	18 32	18 35	18 47			18 54			
	d			17 23	17 33	17 38	17 48			17 54	18 07	18 13				18 23	18 33	18 38	18 48			18 54		19 07	
Marston Green	d			17 26			17 51									18 26			18 51						
Lea Hall	d			17 30												18 30									
Stechford	d			17 32												18 32									
Adderley Park	d			17 35												18 35									
Birmingham New Street 12	a			17 41	17 44	17 48	17 59			18 06	18 18	18 25				18 41	18 44	18 48	18 59			19 06		19 18	
	d	17 35				18 01			18 09	18 16	18 24		18 31	18 35				19 01			19 09	19 16		19 24	19 31
Smethwick Rolfe Street	d								18 15												19 15				
Smethwick Galton Bridge 7	d								18 17												19 17				
Sandwell & Dudley	d								18 19	18 26											19 19	19 26			
Dudley Port	d								18 22												19 22				
Tipton	d								18 24												19 24				
Coseley	d								18 27												19 27				
Wolverhampton 7 ⛴	a	17 52				18 18			18 32	18 37	18 42		18 48	18 52				19 18			19 32	19 37		19 42	19 48
	d	17 53				18 19								18 53				19 19							
Penkridge	d	18 03												19 03											
Stafford	a	18 09	18 18			18 35		18 18						19 09				19 37		19 18					

		LM	VT	LM	VT	XC	LM	LM	LM	VT		XC	AW	VT	LM	XC	LM	VT		XC		LM	VT	XC	AW
		1	◇1	1	◇1	◇1	1	1		◇1		◇1	◇	◇1	1	◇1	1	◇1		◇1			◇1	◇1	◇
		A				C		B		B		J	E		B	I				K			L	J	H
London Euston 15 ⊖66	d		18 00		18 20		17 34	17 50		18 40				19 00	18 50			19 20					19 40		
Northampton	d						18 55	19 02							20 02										
Long Buckby	d						19 06	19 13							20 13										
Rugby	d		18 51				19 17	19 26						19 52	20 26										
Coventry	a		19 02		19 22		19 28			19 42				20 03				20 22					20 41		
	d		19 02	19 11	19 22	19 26	19 30			19 42		19 54		20 03			20 11	20 22		20 26			20 41	20 54	
Canley	d						19 33																		
Tile Hill	d			19 16			19 37										20 16								
Berkswell	d						19 40																		
Hampton-in-Arden	d						19 44																		
Birmingham International ✈	a		19 13	19 23	19 32	19 37	19 47			19 53		20 03		20 13			20 23	20 32		20 35			20 52	21 03	
	d		19 13	19 23	19 33	19 38	19 48			19 53		20 04	20 07	20 13			20 23	20 33		20 38			20 52	21 04	21 08
Marston Green	d			19 26			19 51										20 26								
Lea Hall	d			19 30													20 30								
Stechford	d			19 32													20 32								
Adderley Park	d			19 35													20 35								
Birmingham New Street 12	a		19 24	19 41	19 44	19 48	19 59			20 05		20 15	20 18	20 24			20 41	20 44		20 48			21 03	21 15	21 18
	d	19 35	19 39			20 01			20 09	20 16			20 24	20 25		20 31		20 48		21 01		21 09	21 14		21 24
Smethwick Rolfe Street	d								20 15													21 15			
Smethwick Galton Bridge 7	d								20 17													21 17			
Sandwell & Dudley	d		19 49						20 19	20 26				20 34				20 57				21 19	21 26		
Dudley Port	d								20 22													21 22			
Tipton	d								20 24													21 24			
Coseley	d								20 27													21 27			
Wolverhampton 7 ⛴	a	19 52	20 02			20 18			20 32	20 36			20 42	20 46		20 51		21 10		21 18		21 33	21 37		21 42
	d	19 53				20 19				20 38										21 19			21 38		
Penkridge	d	20 03																							
Stafford	a	20 09				20 36		20 18		20 52					21 18					21 36			21 55		

A To Liverpool Lime Street
B To Crewe
C From Bournemouth to Manchester Piccadilly
D To Edinburgh
E To Aberystwyth
F From Penzance to Manchester Piccadilly
G To Glasgow Central
H To Chester
I From Bristol Temple Meads to Manchester Piccadilly
J From Reading
K From Bournemouth to Manchester Piccadilly. to Birmingham New Street
L To Preston

Table 68

Sundays

30 March to 11 May

Northampton - Coventry - Birmingham - Wolverhampton - Stafford

Network Diagram - refer to first Page of Table 67

		VT	LM	LM	LM	VT	XC	LM	LM	VT		XC	AW	LM	VT	XC	AW	LM	LM	XC		AW	LM	LM	VT
		◇1	1	1	1	◇1	◇1	1		◇1		◇1		1	◇1	◇1	◇	1		◇1			1	1	◇1
			A	A			B					C	D			E	F			C		D		G	
		🍴				🍴	🛒			🍴					🍴										🍴
London Euston 15 ⊖66	d	20 00		19 50		20 18		19 34		20 38					20 54			20 34						21 30	21 55
Northampton	d			21 06				20 55										21 55						22 52	
Long Buckby	d			21 17				21 06										22 06						23 03	
Rugby	d	20 51		21 30				21 17							22 07			22 17						23 14	23 23
Coventry	a	21 02				21 20		21 29		21 46					22 16			22 29						23 25	23 33
	d	21 02			21 10	21 20	21 26	21 30		21 46		21 53		22 08	22 16	22 23		22 30		22 53			23 06	23 38	23 33
Canley	d							21 33										22 33						→	
Tile Hill	d				21 15			21 37										22 37							
Berkswell	d							21 40										22 40							
Hampton-in-Arden	d							21 44										22 44							
Birmingham International ✈	a	21 13			21 22	21 31	21 35	21 47		21 57		22 02		22 17	22 27	22 32		22 47		23 02			23 15		23 44
	d	21 13			21 22	21 31	21 38	21 48		21 57		22 03	22 11	22 18	22 27	22 33	22 43	22 48		23 03		23 08	23 15		23 44
Marston Green	d				21 25			21 51						22 21				22 51					23 18		
Lea Hall	d				21 29									22 24									23 22		
Stechford	d				21 31									22 27									23 24		
Adderley Park	d				21 35									22 30									23 28		
Birmingham New Street 12	a	21 24			21 40	21 44	21 48	21 59		22 09		22 14	22 21	22 36	22 39	22 43	22 53	22 59		23 13		23 19	23 33		23 55
	d	21 28	21 35			21 48	22 01		22 09	22 16			22 24		22 43		22 55		23 09			23 24			23 58
Smethwick Rolfe Street	d								22 15										23 15						
Smethwick Galton Bridge 7	d								22 17										23 17						
Sandwell & Dudley	d	21 37				21 57			22 19	22 25					22 52				23 19						
Dudley Port	d								22 22										23 22						
Tipton	d								22 24										23 24						
Coseley	d								22 27										23 27						
Wolverhampton 7 ⛴	a	21 51	21 56			22 10	22 19		22 32	22 38			22 41		23 06		23 13		23 32			23 40			00 17
	d		21 59				22 20										23 15								
Penkridge	d		22 09																						
Stafford	a		22 15	22 25			22 36										23 30								

		LM	VT	LM	VT
		1	◇1	1	◇1
		H			
			🍴		🍴
London Euston 15 ⊖66	d		22 25	22 00	23 25
Northampton	d			23 32	
Long Buckby	d			23 43	
Rugby	d	←	23 48	23 54	00s46
Coventry	a	23 25	23 57	00 05	00s58
	d	23 38	23 58		
Canley	d	23 41			
Tile Hill	d	23 45			
Berkswell	d	23 48			
Hampton-in-Arden	d	23 52			
Birmingham International ✈	a	23 55	00 08		01s09
	d	23 56	00 09		
Marston Green	d	23 59			
Lea Hall	d				
Stechford	d				
Adderley Park	d				
Birmingham New Street 12	a	00 07	00 21		01s22
	d		00 24		
Smethwick Rolfe Street	d				
Smethwick Galton Bridge 7	d				
Sandwell & Dudley	d				
Dudley Port	d				
Tipton	d				
Coseley	d				
Wolverhampton 7 ⛴	a		00 43		01 44
	d				
Penkridge	d				
Stafford	a				

A To Crewe
B From Bournemouth to Manchester Piccadilly. 🛒 to Birmingham New Street
C From Reading
D To Shrewsbury
E From Bournemouth
F To Holyhead
G To Birmingham New Street
H From London Euston

Table 68R

Mondays to Fridays

9 December to 16 May

Stafford - Wolverhampton - Birmingham - Coventry - Northampton

Network Diagram - refer to first Page of Table 67

Miles			LM MX 1 A	LM 1	VT ◇1 ⊠	VT ◇1 ⊠	LM 1	VT ◇1 ⊠	LM 1	AW B	XC ◇1 C ⌶	VT ◇1 ⊠	LM 1 D	LM 1	AW E	VT ◇1 ⊠	LM 1	AW F	LM G	LM	VT ◇1 ⊠	LM 1	XC ◇1 H ⌶
—	**Stafford**	d								05 25													06 25
0	Penkridge	d																					
9½	**Wolverhampton 7**	a								05 39													06 39
—		d			05 00	05 24				05 40		05 45			05 59	06 04			06 14		06 27		06 41
18¾	Coseley	d																	06 20				
32¼	Tipton	d																	06 23				
34	Dudley Port	d																	06 25				
36	Sandwell & Dudley	d				05 34						05 55				06 15			06 28		06 38		
38	Smethwick Galton Bridge 7	d													06 10				06 31				
41¼	Smethwick Rolfe Street	d																←	06 33				
43	**Birmingham New Street 12**	a			05 26	05 43				05 59		06 04			06 15	06 24		06 15	06 39		06 47		06 57
—		d			05 29	05 50			05 53		06 04	06 10		06 14	06 36	06 30	06 33	06 36		06 39	06 50	06 54	07 04
45	Adderley Park	d													→					06 44			
46½	Stechford	d												06 20						06 47			
47¾	Lea Hall	d												06 23						06 50			
49½	Marston Green	d	00 02						06 00					06 26			06 42					07 02	
51½	**Birmingham International** ✈	a	00 05		05 38	05 59			06 04		06 13	06 19		06 29		06 39	06 45	06 50		06 55	06 59	07 05	07 13
—		d	00 06		05 40	06 00			06 05		06 14	06 20		06 30		06 40	06 45				07 00	07 05	07 14
54¾	Hampton-in-Arden	d												06 33			06 48					07 08	
55½	Berkswell	d							06 10					06 38								07 13	
56¾	Tile Hill	d							06 14					06 41			06 55						
57¾	Canley	d							06 17					06 44								07 18	
58½	**Coventry**	a	00 15		05 50	06 10			06 20		06 24	06 30		06 47		06 50	07 01				07 10	07 21	07 24
—		d			05 51	06 11	05 57		06 20			06 31		06 47		06 51					07 11	07 21	
60	Rugby	d		05 16	06 03		06 13	06 20	06 32				06 43	06 58								07 32	
64¼	Long Buckby	d		05 25			06 22		06 42				06 53	07 11								07 42	
74¼	**Northampton**	a		05 37			06 34	06 40	06 54				07 05	07 24								07 54	
79½	London Euston 15 ⊖66	a		06 51	07 02	07 13	07 39	07 31				07 34	08 11			07 53					08 15	09 10	

		VT ◇1 ⊠	LM 1	LM F	LM 1 I	VT ◇1 ⊠	VT ◇1 ⊠	LM 1	AW ◇ B	XC ◇1 J ⌶	LM	LM K	VT ◇1 ⊠	LM 1 D	LM F	LM 1	VT ◇1 L ⊠	LM D	XC ◇1 M ⌶	VT ◇1 N ⊠	LM 1	LM O
Stafford	d				06 41					06 58				07 12				07 18		07 28		
Penkridge	d				06 47									07 18								
Wolverhampton 7	a				06 57					07 13				07 28				07 31		07 43		
	d	06 45		06 49	06 59	07 05			07 12	07 16		07 19	07 25	07 29	07 34		07 37	07 39		07 45		07 49
Coseley	d			06 55	07 04							07 24						07 45				07 54
Tipton	d			06 58								07 26						07 48				07 57
Dudley Port	d			07 01								07 28						07 50				07 59
Sandwell & Dudley	d	06 56		07 05		07 15						07 32		07 39	07 43					07 57		08 02
Smethwick Galton Bridge 7	d			07 08					07 23			07 34		07 43				07 54				08 05
Smethwick Rolfe Street	d			07 11								07 36						07 57				08 07
Birmingham New Street 12	a	07 05		07 17	07 20	07 25			07 30	07 33		07 43	07 46	07 49	07 52		08 01	08 03		08 05		08 14
	d	07 10	07 14			07 30		07 33	07 36		07 39		07 50			07 54			08 04	08 10	08 14	
Adderley Park	d										07 44											
Stechford	d		07 20								07 47										08 20	
Lea Hall	d		07 23								07 50										08 23	
Marston Green	d		07 26					07 42								08 02					08 26	
Birmingham International ✈	a	07 19	07 29					07 45	07 50		07 55		07 59			08 05			08 13	08 19	08 29	
	d	07 20	07 30				07 41	07 45					08 00			08 05			08 14	08 20	08 30	
Hampton-in-Arden	d							07 48													08 33	
Berkswell	d							07 53								08 11					08 38	
Tile Hill	d		07 37					07 56								08 14					08 41	
Canley	d							08 00								08 17					08 44	
Coventry	a	07 31	07 41				07 51	08 04					08 10			08 20			08 24	08 30	08 47	
	d	07 31	07 42				07 52	08 04					08 11			08 21				08 31	08 48	
Rugby	d		07 53					08 15					08 23			08 39					08 59	
Long Buckby	d		08 03					08 25								08 48						
Northampton	a		08 20					08 37								09 00					09 18	
London Euston 15 ⊖66	a	08 31	09 27			08 43	08 50	09 45					09 13			10 18				09 34		

A From Birmingham New Street
B From Chester
C To Bournemouth
D From Crewe
E From Shrewsbury to Birmingham International
F From Shrewsbury
G From Shrewsbury to Rugeley Trent Valley
H From Manchester Piccadilly to Bournemouth
I From Crewe to Walsall
J From Manchester Piccadilly to Bristol Temple Meads
K To Four Oaks
L From Preston
M From Nottingham to Bournemouth
N From Manchester Piccadilly
O To Walsall

Table 68R

Mondays to Fridays

9 December to 16 May

Stafford - Wolverhampton - Birmingham - Coventry - Northampton

Network Diagram - refer to first Page of Table 67

		LM	LM	VT	LM	AW		XC	LM	LM	LM	VT	LM	LM	XC	VT		LM	LM	LM	VT	AW	XC	LM	AW BHX
															[R]										
		[1]		◇[1]	[1]	◇		◇[1]			[1]	◇[1]	[1]		◇[1]	◇[1]		[1]		[1]	◇[1]	◇	◇[1]	[1]	◇
		A	B			C		D		E	A			B	F	G			E	A		H	I		J
				☒		🛒		🛒				☒			🛒	☒					☒	🛒	🛒		🛒
Stafford	d	07 41						08 02			08 10				08 25					08 44			09 03		
Penkridge	d	07 47									08 16									08 50					
Wolverhampton [7] 🚉	a	07 57						08 15			08 26				08 39					09 00			09 15		
	d	07 59	08 07			08 11		08 16		08 20	08 29			08 37	08 41	08 45			08 49	09 00		09 11	09 16		
Coseley	d	08 04								08 24									08 54	09 06					
Tipton	d									08 26									08 56						
Dudley Port	d									08 28									08 58						
Sandwell & Dudley	d									08 32				08 46		08 55			09 02						
Smethwick Galton Bridge [7]	d					08 23				08 34	08 40								09 04			09 22			
Smethwick Rolfe Street	d									08 36									09 08						←
Birmingham New Street [12]	a	08 17	08 23			08 29		08 34		08 45	08 47			08 55	08 58	09 05			09 14	09 18		09 29	09 32		09 29
	d			08 30	08 33	08 36			08 39			08 50	08 54		09 04	09 10		09 14			09 30	09 36		09 33	09 36
Adderley Park	d								08 44													→			
Stechford	d								08 47									09 20							
Lea Hall	d								08 50									09 23							
Marston Green	d				08 42								09 02					09 26						09 42	
Birmingham International ✈	a			08 39	08 45	08 50			08 55			08 59	09 05		09 13	09 19		09 29			09 39			09 45	09 49
	d			08 40	08 45							09 00	09 05		09 14	09 20		09 30			09 40			09 45	
Hampton-in-Arden	d				08 48													09 33						09 48	
Berkswell	d												09 11					09 38							
Tile Hill	d				08 55								09 14					09 41						09 55	
Canley	d												09 17					09 44							
Coventry	a			08 50	09 00							09 10	09 20		09 24	09 30		09 47			09 50			10 00	
	d			08 51	09 00							09 11	09 21			09 31		09 48			09 51			10 00	
Rugby	d				09 12							09 23	09 32					09 59						10 12	
Long Buckby	d				09 21								09 41					10 08						10 21	
Northampton	a				09 34								09 54					10 20						10 34	
London Euston [15] ⊖66	a			09 55	10 46							10 15	11 17			10 32		11 27			10 55			11 46	

		LM		LM	LM	VT	LM	LM	XC	VT		LM		LM	LM	VT	LM	AW	XC	LM	LM	LM		VT	LM
					[1]	◇[1]	[1]		◇[1]	◇[1]				[1]	[1]	◇[1]	[1]	◇	◇[1]			[1]		◇[1]	[1]
				E	A			B	K	L		E			A			M	D		E	A			
						☒			🛒	☒						☒		🛒	🛒					☒	
Stafford	d				09 10				09 25						09 45				10 03			10 10			
Penkridge	d				09 16																	10 16			
Wolverhampton [7] 🚉	a				09 27				09 39						09 58				10 15			10 27			
	d			09 19	09 29			09 37	09 41	09 45		09 49			09 59			10 10	10 17		10 19	10 29			
Coseley	d			09 24								09 54			10 04						10 24				
Tipton	d			09 26								09 56									10 26				
Dudley Port	d			09 28								09 58									10 28				
Sandwell & Dudley	d			09 32				09 46		09 55		10 02									10 32				
Smethwick Galton Bridge [7]	d			09 34	09 40							10 04						10 21			10 34	10 40			
Smethwick Rolfe Street	d			09 36								10 06									10 36				
Birmingham New Street [12]	a			09 45	09 47			09 55	09 58	10 05		10 13			10 17			10 30	10 33		10 45	10 47			
	d	09 39				09 50	09 54		10 04	10 10				10 14		10 30	10 33	10 36		10 39				10 50	10 54
Adderley Park	d	09 44																		10 44					
Stechford	d	09 47												10 20						10 47					
Lea Hall	d	09 50												10 23						10 50					
Marston Green	d						10 02							10 26			10 42								11 02
Birmingham International ✈	a	09 55				09 59	10 05		10 13	10 19				10 29		10 39	10 45	10 49		10 55				10 59	11 05
	d					10 00	10 05		10 14	10 20				10 30		10 40	10 45							11 00	11 05
Hampton-in-Arden	d													10 33			10 48								
Berkswell	d						10 11							10 38											11 11
Tile Hill	d						10 14							10 41			10 55								11 14
Canley	d						10 17							10 44											11 17
Coventry	a					10 10	10 20		10 24	10 30				10 47		10 50	11 00							11 10	11 20
	d					10 11	10 21			10 31				10 48		10 51	11 00							11 11	11 21
Rugby	d					10 23	10 32							10 59			11 12							11 23	11 32
Long Buckby	d						10 41							11 08			11 21								11 41
Northampton	a						10 53							11 20			11 34								11 53
London Euston [15] ⊖66	a					11 15	12 17			11 34				12 27		11 55	12 46							12 15	13 17

A From Liverpool Lime Street
B From Shrewsbury
C From Aberystwyth
D From Manchester Piccadilly to Bristol Temple Meads
E To Walsall
F From Manchester Piccadilly to Bournemouth. ◇ from Birmingham New Street [R] to Birmingham New Street
G From Lancaster
H From Holyhead to Birmingham International
I From Manchester Piccadilly to Paignton
J From Holyhead
K From Manchester Piccadilly to Bournemouth
L From Glasgow Central
M From Barmouth

Table 68R

Mondays to Fridays

9 December to 16 May

Stafford - Wolverhampton - Birmingham - Coventry - Northampton

Network Diagram - refer to first Page of Table 67

		LM	XC	VT	LM	LM	LM	VT	LM	AW	XC	LM	LM	LM	VT	LM	LM	XC	VT	LM	LM	LM
			◇1	◇1	1		1	◇1	1	◇	◇1			1	◇1	1		◇1	◇1	1		1
		A	B	C		D	E			F	G		D	E			A	B	H		D	E
Stafford	d		10 25				10 43				11 02			11 10				11 25				11 42
Penkridge	d													11 16								
Wolverhampton 7	a		10 39				10 56				11 15			11 27				11 39				11 57
	d	10 37	10 41	10 45		10 49	10 59			11 09	11 16		11 19	11 29			11 37	11 41	11 45		11 49	11 59
Coseley	d					10 54	11 04						11 24								11 54	12 04
Tipton	d					10 56							11 26								11 56	
Dudley Port	d					10 58							11 28								11 58	
Sandwell & Dudley	d	10 46		10 55		11 02							11 32				11 46		11 55		12 02	
Smethwick Galton Bridge 7	d					11 04				11 20			11 34	11 40							12 04	
Smethwick Rolfe Street	d					11 06							11 36								12 08	
Birmingham New Street 12	a	10 55	10 58	11 05		11 14	11 17			11 30	11 33		11 45	11 47			11 55	11 58	12 05		12 14	12 17
	d		11 04	11 10	11 14			11 30	11 33	11 36		11 39			11 50	11 54		12 04	12 10	12 14		
Adderley Park	d											11 44										
Stechford	d				11 20							11 47								12 20		
Lea Hall	d				11 23							11 50								12 23		
Marston Green	d				11 26				11 42							12 02				12 26		
Birmingham International	a		11 13	11 19	11 29			11 39	11 45	11 49		11 55			11 59	12 05		12 13	12 19	12 29		
	d		11 14	11 20	11 30			11 40	11 45						12 00	12 05		12 14	12 20	12 30		
Hampton-in-Arden	d				11 33				11 48											12 33		
Berkswell	d				11 38											12 11				12 38		
Tile Hill	d				11 41				11 55							12 14				12 41		
Canley	d				11 44											12 17				12 44		
Coventry	a		11 24	11 30	11 47			11 50	12 00						12 10	12 20		12 24	12 30	12 47		
	d			11 31	11 48			11 51	12 00						12 11	12 21			12 31	12 48		
Rugby	d				11 59				12 18						12 23	12 32				12 59		
Long Buckby	d				12 08				12 27							12 41				13 08		
Northampton	a				12 20				12 44							12 53				13 20		
London Euston 15 ⊖66	a			12 34	13 27			12 55	13 46						13 15	14 17			13 33	14 26		

		VT	LM	AW	XC	LM	LM	LM	VT	LM	LM	XC	VT	LM	LM	LM	VT	LM	AW	XC	LM	LM	LM
		◇1	1	◇	◇1			1	◇1	1		◇1	◇1	1		1	◇1	1	◇	◇1			1
				I	G		D	E			A	B	C		D	E			F	J		D	E
Stafford	d				12 03			12 10				12 25				12 44				13 02			13 10
Penkridge	d							12 16															13 16
Wolverhampton 7	a				12 15			12 27				12 39				12 57				13 16			13 27
	d			12 11	12 16		12 19	12 29			12 37	12 41	12 45		12 49	12 59			13 10	13 17		13 19	13 29
Coseley	d						12 24								12 54	13 04						13 24	
Tipton	d						12 26								12 56							13 26	
Dudley Port	d						12 28								12 58							13 28	
Sandwell & Dudley	d						12 32				12 46		12 55		13 02							13 32	
Smethwick Galton Bridge 7	d			12 22			12 34	12 40							13 04				13 22			13 34	13 40
Smethwick Rolfe Street	d						12 36								13 06							13 36	
Birmingham New Street 12	a			12 30	12 33		12 45	12 47			12 55	12 58	13 05		13 14	13 17			13 29	13 33		13 45	13 47
	d	12 30	12 33	12 36		12 39			12 50	12 54		13 04	13 10	13 14			13 30	13 33	13 36		13 39		
Adderley Park	d					12 44															13 44		
Stechford	d					12 47								13 20							13 47		
Lea Hall	d					12 50								13 23							13 50		
Marston Green	d		12 42							13 02				13 26				13 42					
Birmingham International	a	12 39	12 45	12 49		12 55			12 59	13 05		13 13	13 19	13 29			13 39	13 45	13 49		13 55		
	d	12 40	12 45						13 00	13 05		13 14	13 20	13 30			13 40	13 45					
Hampton-in-Arden	d		12 48											13 33				13 48					
Berkswell	d									13 11				13 38									
Tile Hill	d		12 55							13 14				13 41				13 55					
Canley	d									13 17				13 44									
Coventry	a	12 50	13 00						13 10	13 20		13 24	13 30	13 47			13 50	14 00					
	d	12 51	13 00						13 11	13 21			13 31	13 48			13 51	14 00					
Rugby	d		13 12						13 23	13 32				13 59				14 12					
Long Buckby	d		13 21							13 41				14 08				14 21					
Northampton	a		13 34							13 53				14 20				14 34					
London Euston 15 ⊖66	a	13 55	14 47						14 15	15 17			14 33	15 27			14 55	15 46					

A From Shrewsbury
B From Manchester Piccadilly to Bournemouth
C From Edinburgh
D To Walsall
E From Liverpool Lime Street
F From Holyhead
G From Manchester Piccadilly to Bristol Temple Meads
H From Glasgow Central
I From Pwllheli
J From Manchester Piccadilly to Exeter St Davids

Table 68R

Mondays to Fridays

9 December to 16 May

Stafford - Wolverhampton - Birmingham - Coventry - Northampton

Network Diagram - refer to first Page of Table 67

		VT		LM	LM	XC	VT	LM	LM	LM	VT	LM		AW	XC	LM	LM	VT	LM	LM	LM	XC		VT	LM
		◇1		1		◇1	◇1	1		1	◇1	1		◇	◇1			◇1	1	1		◇1		◇1	
					A	B	C		D	E				F	G				E		A	B		H	D
		☕				🛒	⊠				☕			🛒	🛒			☕				🛒		☕	
Stafford	d					13 25				13 46					14 02				14 10			14 25			
Penkridge	d																		14 16						
Wolverhampton 7 🚌	a					13 39				13 59					14 15				14 27			14 39			
	d				13 37	13 41	13 45		13 49	14 01				14 10	14 16		14 19		14 27		14 37	14 41		14 45	14 49
Coseley	d								13 54	14 06							14 24								14 54
Tipton	d								13 56								14 26								14 56
Dudley Port	d								13 58								14 28								14 58
Sandwell & Dudley	d				13 46		13 56		14 02								14 32				14 46			14 55	15 02
Smethwick Galton Bridge 7	d								14 04					14 22			14 34		14 43						15 04
Smethwick Rolfe Street	d								14 06								14 36								15 06
Birmingham New Street 12	a				13 56	13 58	14 05		14 14	14 18				14 30	14 33		14 45		14 51		14 55	14 58		15 05	15 13
	d	13 50		13 54		14 04	14 10	14 14			14 30	14 33		14 36		14 39		14 50		14 54		15 04		15 10	
Adderley Park	d															14 44									
Stechford	d							14 20								14 47									
Lea Hall	d							14 23								14 50									
Marston Green	d			14 02				14 26				14 42								15 02					
Birmingham International ✈	a	13 59		14 05		14 13	14 19	14 29			14 39	14 45		14 49		14 55		14 59		15 05		15 13		15 19	
	d	14 00		14 05		14 14	14 20	14 30			14 40	14 45						15 00		15 05		15 14		15 20	
Hampton-in-Arden	d							14 33				14 48													
Berkswell	d			14 11				14 38												15 11					
Tile Hill	d			14 14				14 41				14 55								15 14					
Canley	d			14 17				14 44												15 17					
Coventry	a	14 10		14 20		14 23	14 29	14 47			14 50	15 00						15 10		15 20		15 23		15 30	
	d	14 11		14 21			14 30	14 48			14 51	15 00						15 11		15 21				15 31	
Rugby	d	14 23		14 32				14 59				15 12						15 23		15 32					
Long Buckby	d			14 41				15 08				15 21								15 41					
Northampton	a			14 54				15 20				15 33								15 56					
London Euston 15 ⊖66	a	15 15		16 18			15 33	16 27			15 55	16 46						16 15		17 18				16 32	

		LM	LM	VT	LM	AW	XC	LM		LM	LM	VT	LM	LM	XC	VT	LM	LM		LM	VT	LM	AW	XC	LM
		1	1	◇1	1	◇	◇1				1	◇1	1		◇1	◇1	1			1	◇1	1	◇	◇1	
			E			I	J			D	E			A	B	C		D		E			F	G	
				☕		🛒	🛒					☕			🛒	☕					☕		🛒	🛒	
Stafford	d		14 43				15 03				15 10				15 25					15 43				16 03	
Penkridge	d										15 16														
Wolverhampton 7 🚌	a		14 58				15 15				15 27				15 39					15 56				16 15	
	d		14 59			15 11	15 17			15 19	15 29			15 37	15 41	15 45		15 49		15 59			16 11	16 16	
Coseley	d		15 04							15 24								15 54		16 04					
Tipton	d									15 26								15 56							
Dudley Port	d									15 28								15 58							
Sandwell & Dudley	d									15 32				15 46		15 55		16 02							
Smethwick Galton Bridge 7	d					15 22				15 34	15 40							16 04					16 22		
Smethwick Rolfe Street	d									15 36								16 06							
Birmingham New Street 12	a		15 18			15 30	15 33			15 45	15 47			15 55	15 58	16 05		16 14		16 17			16 30	16 33	
	d	15 14		15 30	15 33	15 36		15 39				15 50	15 54		16 04	16 10	16 14				16 30	16 33	16 36		16 39
Adderley Park	d							15 44																	16 44
Stechford	d	15 20						15 47									16 20								16 47
Lea Hall	d	15 23						15 50									16 23								16 50
Marston Green	d	15 26			15 42								16 02				16 26					16 42			
Birmingham International ✈	a	15 29		15 39	15 45	15 49		15 55				15 59	16 05		16 13	16 19	16 29				16 39	16 45	16 49		16 55
	d	15 30		15 40	15 45							16 00	16 05		16 14	16 20	16 30				16 40	16 45			
Hampton-in-Arden	d	15 33			15 48												16 33					16 48			
Berkswell	d	15 38											16 11				16 38								
Tile Hill	d	15 41			15 55								16 14				16 41					16 55			
Canley	d	15 44											16 17				16 44								
Coventry	a	15 47		15 50	16 00							16 10	16 20		16 23	16 30	16 47				16 50	17 00			
	d	15 48		15 51	16 00							16 11	16 21			16 31					16 51	17 00			
Rugby	d	15 59			16 12							16 23	16 32									17 16			
Long Buckby	d	16 08			16 21								16 41									17 25			
Northampton	a	16 20			16 39								16 57									17 37			
London Euston 15 ⊖66	a	17 27		16 57	17 46							17 15	18 18			17 34					17 55	18 46			

A From Shrewsbury
B From Manchester Piccadilly to Bournemouth
C From Glasgow Central
D To Walsall
E From Liverpool Lime Street
F From Pwllheli
G From Manchester Piccadilly to Bristol Temple Meads
H From Edinburgh
I From Holyhead
J From Manchester Piccadilly to Paignton

Table 68R

Mondays to Fridays

9 December to 16 May

Stafford - Wolverhampton - Birmingham - Coventry - Northampton

Network Diagram - refer to first Page of Table 67

		LM	LM	VT	LM	LM	XC	VT	LM	LM		LM	LM	VT	LM	AW	XC	LM	LM	LM		VT	LM	LM	XC
			■1	◇■1	■1		◇■1	◇■1	■1			■1	■1	◇■1	■1	◇	◇■1			■1		◇■1	■1		◇■1
			A			B	C	D		E			A			F	G		E	A				B	C
				⊡			🛒	⊡						⊠		🛒	🛒					⊠			🛒
Stafford	d		16 10				16 25						16 43				17 03			17 10					17 25
Penkridge	d		16 16																	17 16					
Wolverhampton ■7 🚌	a		16 26				16 39						16 57				17 15			17 26					17 39
	d	16 19	16 29			16 37	16 41	16 45		16 49			16 59			17 09	17 16		17 19	17 29				17 37	17 41
Coseley	d	16 24								16 54			17 04						17 24						
Tipton	d	16 26								16 56									17 26						
Dudley Port	d	16 28								16 58									17 28						
Sandwell & Dudley	d	16 32				16 46		16 55		17 02									17 32					17 46	
Smethwick Galton Bridge ■7	d	16 34	16 41							17 04						17 22			17 34	17 40					
Smethwick Rolfe Street	d	16 36								17 06									17 36						
Birmingham New Street ■12	a	16 45	16 48			16 55	16 58	17 05		17 14			17 17			17 30	17 33		17 45	17 47				17 55	17 58
	d			16 50	16 54		17 04	17 10	17 13			17 16		17 30	17 33	17 36		17 39				17 50	17 54		18 04
Adderley Park	d											17 21						17 44							
Stechford	d								17 20									17 47							
Lea Hall	d											17 25						17 50							
Marston Green	d				17 02							17 28			17 42								18 02		
Birmingham International ✈	a			16 59	17 05		17 13	17 19	17 25			17 32		17 39	17 45	17 49		17 55				17 59	18 05		18 13
	d			17 00	17 05		17 14	17 20	17 25			17 32		17 40	17 45							18 00	18 05		18 14
Hampton-in-Arden	d											17 35			17 48										
Berkswell	d				17 11							17 40											18 11		
Tile Hill	d				17 14				17 32						17 55								18 14		
Canley	d				17 17				17 36														18 17		
Coventry	a			17 10	17 20		17 23	17 30	17 40			17 47		17 50	18 00							18 10	18 20		18 23
	d			17 11	17 21			17 31	17 40					17 51	18 00							18 11	18 21		
Rugby	d			17 23	17 32				17 56						18 12							18 23	18 32		
Long Buckby	d				17 41				18 05						18 21								18 41		
Northampton	a				17 56				18 17						18 34								18 53		
London Euston ■15 ⊖66	a			18 15	19 18			18 34	19 29					18 55	19 46							19 15	20 19		

		VT	LM	LM	LM	VT		AW	XC	LM	AW	LM	LM	LM	VT	LM		LM	XC	VT	LM	LM	LM	VT	LM
																				R					
		◇■1	■1		■1	◇■1		◇	◇■1	■1	◇			■1	◇■1	■1			◇■1	■1	■1		■1	◇■1	■1
		H		E	A			I	J		K		E	A				B	C	D			A		
		⊡				⊠		🛒	🛒		🛒				⊠				🛒	⊡				⊡	
Stafford	d				17 42				18 04					18 10					18 28				18 44		
Penkridge	d													18 16											
Wolverhampton ■7 🚌	a				17 55				18 14					18 27					18 39				18 57		
	d	17 45		17 49	17 57			18 11	18 15				18 19	18 29				18 37	18 41	18 45		18 49	18 59		
Coseley	d			17 54	18 02								18 24									18 54	19 04		
Tipton	d			17 56									18 26									18 56			
Dudley Port	d			17 58									18 28									18 58			
Sandwell & Dudley	d	17 55		18 02									18 32					18 46		18 55		19 02			
Smethwick Galton Bridge ■7	d			18 04				18 22					18 34	18 40								19 04			
Smethwick Rolfe Street	d			18 06							←		18 36									19 06			
Birmingham New Street ■12	a	18 05		18 14	18 16			18 30	18 32		18 30		18 45	18 48				18 55	18 58	19 05		19 14	19 17		
	d	18 10	18 14			18 30		18 36		18 33	18 36	18 39			18 50	18 54			19 04	19 10	19 14			19 30	19 33
Adderley Park	d							↪				18 44													
Stechford	d		18 20									18 47									19 20				
Lea Hall	d		18 23									18 50									19 23				
Marston Green	d		18 26							18 42						19 02					19 26				19 42
Birmingham International ✈	a	18 19	18 29			18 39				18 45	18 49	18 55			18 59	19 05			19 13	19 19	19 29			19 39	19 45
	d	18 20	18 30			18 40				18 45					19 00	19 05			19 14	19 20	19 30			19 40	19 45
Hampton-in-Arden	d		18 33							18 48											19 33				19 48
Berkswell	d		18 38													19 11					19 38				
Tile Hill	d		18 41							18 55						19 14					19 41				19 55
Canley	d		18 44													19 17					19 44				
Coventry	a	18 30	18 47			18 50				19 00					19 10	19 20			19 23	19 30	19 47			19 50	20 00
	d	18 31				18 51				19 00					19 11	19 21				19 31				19 51	20 00
Rugby	d									19 18					19 23	19 32								20 03	20 12
Long Buckby	d									19 27						19 41									20 21
Northampton	a									19 45						19 54									20 38
London Euston ■15 ⊖66	a	19 32				19 55				20 45					20 15	21 17				20 34				20 58	

- **A** From Liverpool Lime Street
- **B** From Shrewsbury
- **C** From Manchester Piccadilly to Bournemouth
- **D** From Edinburgh
- **E** To Walsall
- **F** From Holyhead
- **G** From Manchester Piccadilly to Bristol Temple Meads
- **H** From Glasgow Central
- **I** From Pwllheli to Birmingham International
- **J** From Manchester Piccadilly to Cardiff Central
- **K** From Pwllheli

Table 68R

Mondays to Fridays

9 December to 16 May

Stafford - Wolverhampton - Birmingham - Coventry - Northampton

Network Diagram - refer to first Page of Table 67

		AW ◇ A	XC ◇1 B	LM	LM C	LM 1 D	LM 1	LM E	XC ◇1 F	VT ◇1 G	LM 1	LM	LM 1 D	LM 1 H	LM 1	AW ◇ I	XC ◇1 J	LM	LM	LM 1 D	VT ◇1	LM 1	LM E
Stafford	d		19 02			19 10			19 25				19 43	19 51			20 04			20 16			
Penkridge	d					19 16							19 48										
Wolverhampton 7	a		19 15			19 27			19 39				19 58				20 16			20 29			
	d	19 11	19 16		19 19	19 29		19 37	19 41	19 45		19 49	20 00			20 11	20 17		20 19	20 30			20 39
Coseley	d				19 24							19 54	20 05						20 24				
Tipton	d				19 26							19 56							20 26				
Dudley Port	d				19 28							19 58							20 28				
Sandwell & Dudley	d				19 32			19 46		19 55		20 02							20 32				20 47
Smethwick Galton Bridge 7	d	19 22			19 34	19 40						20 04				20 22			20 34	20 40			
Smethwick Rolfe Street	d				19 36							20 06							20 36				
Birmingham New Street 12	a	19 30	19 33		19 44	19 48		19 55	19 58	20 05		20 14	20 19			20 29	20 33		20 44	20 47			20 56
	d	19 36		19 39			19 54		20 04	20 10	20 14				20 33	20 36		20 39			20 50	20 54	
Adderley Park	d			19 44														20 44					
Stechford	d			19 47							20 20							20 47					
Lea Hall	d			19 50							20 23							20 50					
Marston Green	d						20 02				20 26				20 42							21 02	
Birmingham International	a	19 50		19 55			20 05		20 13	20 19	20 29				20 45	20 49		20 55			20 59	21 05	
	d						20 05		20 14	20 20	20 30				20 45						21 00	21 05	
Hampton-in-Arden	d										20 33				20 48								
Berkswell	d						20 11				20 38											21 11	
Tile Hill	d						20 14				20 41				20 55							21 14	
Canley	d						20 17				20 44											21 17	
Coventry	a						20 20		20 23	20 30	20 47				21 00						21 10	21 20	
	d						20 21			20 31					21 00						21 11	21 21	
Rugby	d						20 32							20 47	21 14						21 23	21 32	
Long Buckby	d						20 41								21 23							21 41	
Northampton	a						20 53							21 07	21 35							21 53	
London Euston 15 ⊖66	a						22 20			21 39					22 52						22 13	23 21	

		XC ◇1 K	VT R 1 L	LM 1	LM	LM 1 D	XC ◇1 M	LM 1 H	LM 1	LM	LM C	LM 1 D	VT ◇1 G	LM 1	LM E	XC ◇1 M	XC ◇1 N	VT ◇1	LM 1	LM	LM 1 D	AW ◇ I
Stafford	d	20 28				20 42	21 03	21 04				21 10	21 13			21 25					21 41	
Penkridge	d					20 47						21 16									21 47	
Wolverhampton 7	a	20 42				20 57	21 15					21 26	21 30			21 39					21 57	
	d	20 44	20 47		20 49	20 59	21 16				21 19	21 29	21 32		21 37	21 41		21 45		21 49	21 59	22 09
Coseley	d				20 54	21 04					21 24									21 54	22 04	
Tipton	d				20 56						21 26									21 56		
Dudley Port	d				20 58						21 28									21 58		
Sandwell & Dudley	d		20 57		21 02						21 32				21 46			21 56		22 02		
Smethwick Galton Bridge 7	d				21 04						21 34	21 40								22 04		22 20
Smethwick Rolfe Street	d				21 06						21 36									22 06		
Birmingham New Street 12	a	21 00	21 05		21 14	21 17	21 33				21 43	21 47	21 50		21 55	22 00		22 06		22 14	22 17	22 33
	d	21 04	21 10	21 14					21 34	21 39				21 54			22 04	22 10	22 14			
Adderley Park	d									21 44												
Stechford	d			21 20						21 47									22 20			
Lea Hall	d			21 23						21 50									22 23			
Marston Green	d			21 26					21 42					22 02					22 26			
Birmingham International	a	21 13	21 19	21 29					21 45	21 55				22 05			22 13	22 19	22 29			
	d	21 14	21 20	21 30					21 45					22 05			22 14	22 20	22 30			
Hampton-in-Arden	d			21 33					21 48										22 33			
Berkswell	d			21 38										22 11					22 38			
Tile Hill	d			21 41					21 55					22 14					22 41			
Canley	d			21 44										22 17					22 44			
Coventry	a	21 23	21 30	21 47					22 00					22 20			22 24	22 30	22 47			
	d		21 31						22 00					22 21				22 31				
Rugby	d							21 58	22 12					22 32				22 43				
Long Buckby	d								22 21					22 41								
Northampton	a							22 17	22 34					22 53								
London Euston 15 ⊖66	a		22 43											00 21				00 06				

- **A** From Holyhead
- **B** From Manchester Piccadilly to Plymouth
- **C** To Walsall
- **D** From Liverpool Lime Street
- **E** From Shrewsbury
- **F** From Manchester Piccadilly to Bournemouth
- **G** From Glasgow Central
- **H** From Crewe
- **I** From Aberystwyth
- **J** From Manchester Piccadilly to Bristol Temple Meads
- **K** From Manchester Piccadilly to Southampton Central
- **L** From Edinburgh
- **M** From Manchester Piccadilly
- **N** To Reading

Table 68R

Mondays to Fridays

9 December to 16 May

Stafford - Wolverhampton - Birmingham - Coventry - Northampton

Network Diagram - refer to first Page of Table 67

		LM	LM	VT	LM		VT	LM	XC	VT	LM	AW	AW	LM	XC		LM
												MW FO	TThO				
		1		◇1	1		◇1		◇1	◇1	1	◇	◇	1	◇1		1
				A			B	C	D			E	E	F	D		
				☕			✕			☕							
Stafford	d								22 26					22 41	23 07		
Penkridge	d													22 47			
Wolverhampton 7	a								22 39					23 00	23 19		
	d		22 19	22 28			22 33	22 37	22 41	22 45		22 55	22 55	23 01	23 21		
Coseley	d		22 24											23 06			
Tipton	d		22 26											23 09			
Dudley Port	d		22 28											23 11			
Sandwell & Dudley	d		22 32					22 47		22 55				23 15			
Smethwick Galton Bridge 7	d		22 34											23 18			
Smethwick Rolfe Street	d		22 36											23 20			
Birmingham New Street 12	a		22 44	22 50			22 58	22 55	22 58	23 06		23 27	23 28	23 27	23 39		
	d	22 34			22 54					23 10	23 14						23 54
Adderley Park	d										23 19						
Stechford	d										23 22						
Lea Hall	d										23 25						
Marston Green	d	22 42			23 02						23 27						00 02
Birmingham International ✈	a	22 45			23 05					23 19	23 30						00 05
	d	22 45			23 05					23 20	23 31						00 06
Hampton-in-Arden	d	22 48									23 34						
Berkswell	d				23 11						23 38						
Tile Hill	d	22 55			23 14						23 41						
Canley	d				23 17						23 45						
Coventry	a	23 00			23 20					23 30	23 48						00 15
	d				23 21					23 31							
Rugby	d				23 32					23 44							
Long Buckby	d				23 41												
Northampton	a				23 54					00s05							
London Euston 15 ⊖66	a									01 15							

Saturdays

14 December to 28 December

		LM	VT	AW	XC	VT	LM	AW	VT	LM		AW	LM	LM	VT	LM	XC	VT	LM	LM		VT	LM	AW	XC
		1	◇1		◇1	◇1	1		◇1	1					◇1	1	◇1	◇1	1	1		◇1	1		◇1
		G		H	I			J				C		C			K			L				C	M
			☕		🛒	☕			☕						☕		🛒	☕				☕			🛒
Stafford	d			05 25													06 26			06 35					06 58
Penkridge	d																			06 41					
Wolverhampton 7	a			05 39													06 39			06 51					07 12
	d			05 40		05 45		06 02	06 06					06 19	06 27		06 41	06 45		06 53		07 05		07 12	07 16
Coseley	d													06 24						06 58					
Tipton	d													06 27						07 01					
Dudley Port	d													06 29						07 03					
Sandwell & Dudley	d					05 56			06 17					06 32	06 37			06 56		07 07		07 14			
Smethwick Galton Bridge 7	d							06 13						06 35						07 10				07 23	
Smethwick Rolfe Street	d											←		06 37						07 12					
Birmingham New Street 12	a			05 58		06 06		06 20	06 26			06 20		06 45	06 47		06 57	07 06		07 18		07 25		07 28	07 33
	d		05 50		06 04	06 10	06 14	06 36	06 30	06 33		06 36	06 39		06 50	06 54	07 04	07 10	07 14			07 30	07 33	07 36	
Adderley Park	d							→					06 44												
Stechford	d						06 20						06 47						07 20						
Lea Hall	d						06 23						06 50						07 23						
Marston Green	d	00 02					06 26			06 42						07 02			07 26				07 42		
Birmingham International ✈	a	00 05	05 59		06 13	06 19	06 29		06 39	06 45		06 49	06 54		06 59	07 05	07 13	07 19	07 29			07 39	07 45	07 50	
	d	00 06	06 00		06 14	06 20	06 30		06 40	06 45					07 00	07 05	07 14	07 20	07 30			07 40	07 45		
Hampton-in-Arden	d						06 33			06 48									07 33				07 48		
Berkswell	d						06 38									07 11			07 38						
Tile Hill	d						06 41			06 55						07 14			07 41				07 55		
Canley	d						06 44									07 17			07 44						
Coventry	a	00 15	06 10		06 24	06 30	06 47		06 49	07 00					07 10	07 20	07 24	07 30	07 47			07 50	08 00		
	d		06 10			06 31	06 48		06 51	07 00					07 11	07 21		07 31	07 48			07 51	08 00		
Rugby	d		06 24				06 59			07 12					07 23	07 32			07 59				08 12		
Long Buckby	d						07 08			07 21						07 41			08 08				08 21		
Northampton	a						07 21			07 34						07 53			08 20				08 34		
London Euston 15 ⊖66	a		07 17			07 38	08 40		07 55						08 17	09 17		08 35	09 27			08 54	09 47		

A From Bangor (Gwynedd)
B From Edinburgh
C From Shrewsbury
D From Manchester Piccadilly
E From Holyhead
F From Liverpool Lime Street
G From Birmingham New Street
H From Chester
I To Bournemouth
J From Shrewsbury to Birmingham International
K From Manchester Piccadilly to Bournemouth
L From Crewe to Walsall
M From Manchester Piccadilly to Bristol Temple Meads

Table 68R

Saturdays

14 December to 28 December

Stafford - Wolverhampton - Birmingham - Coventry - Northampton

Network Diagram - refer to first Page of Table 67

		LM		LM	LM	VT	LM	LM	XC	VT	LM	LM		LM	VT	LM	AW	XC	LM	LM	LM	VT		LM	LM
					■1	◇■1	■1		◇■1	◇■1		■1		■1	◇■1	■1	◇	◇■1			■1	◇■1		■1	
				A	B			C	D	E	A			F			G	H		A	F				C
						☕			🛒	☕					☕		🛒	🛒				☕			
Stafford	d				07 12									07 41				08 03			08 10				
Penkridge	d				07 18									07 47							08 16				
Wolverhampton ■7	a				07 28									07 57				08 15			08 26				
	d			07 19	07 29			07 37		07 45	07 49			07 59			08 09	08 16		08 19	08 29				08 37
Coseley	d			07 24							07 54			08 04						08 24					
Tipton	d			07 26							07 56									08 26					
Dudley Port	d			07 28							07 58									08 28					
Sandwell & Dudley	d			07 32				07 46		07 55	08 02									08 32					08 46
Smethwick Galton Bridge ■7	d			07 34	07 40						08 04						08 21			08 34	08 40				
Smethwick Rolfe Street	d			07 36							08 06									08 36					
Birmingham New Street ■12	a			07 44	07 47			07 55		08 05	08 13			08 17			08 26	08 34		08 44	08 48				08 55
	d	07 39				07 50	07 54		08 04	08 10		08 14			08 30	08 33	08 36		08 39			08 50		08 54	
Adderley Park	d	07 44																	08 44						
Stechford	d	07 47										08 20							08 47						
Lea Hall	d	07 50										08 23							08 50						
Marston Green	d						08 02					08 26				08 42								09 02	
Birmingham International ✈	a	07 54				07 59	08 05		08 13	08 19		08 29			08 39	08 45	08 50		08 54			08 59		09 05	
	d					08 00	08 05		08 14	08 20		08 30			08 40	08 45						09 00		09 05	
Hampton-in-Arden	d											08 33				08 48									
Berkswell	d						08 11					08 38												09 11	
Tile Hill	d						08 14					08 41				08 55								09 14	
Canley	d						08 17					08 44												09 17	
Coventry	a					08 10	08 20		08 24	08 29		08 47			08 50	09 00						09 10		09 20	
	d					08 11	08 21			08 30		08 48			08 51	09 00						09 11		09 21	
Rugby	d					08 23	08 32					08 59				09 12						09 23		09 32	
Long Buckby	d						08 41					09 08				09 21								09 41	
Northampton	a						08 56					09 20				09 34								09 55	
London Euston ■15 ⊖66	a					09 15	10 17			09 34		10 27			09 59	10 46						10 15		11 17	

		XC	VT	LM	LM	LM	VT	LM		AW	XC	LM	LM	LM	VT	LM	LM	XC		VT	LM	LM	LM	VT	LM
		◇■1	◇■1		■1	■1	◇■1	■1		◇	◇■1			■1	◇■1	■1		◇■1		◇■1		■1	■1	◇■1	■1
		I	J	A		F				K	L			F			C	I		M	A		F		
		🛒	☕				☕			🛒	🛒				☕			🛒		☕				☕	
Stafford	d	08 26				08 43					09 03			09 10				09 26					09 45		
Penkridge	d					08 48								09 16											
Wolverhampton ■7	a	08 39				08 58					09 15			09 26				09 39					09 58		
	d	08 41	08 45	08 49		08 59				09 12	09 16		09 19	09 29			09 37	09 41		09 45	09 49		09 59		
Coseley	d			08 54		09 04							09 24								09 54		10 04		
Tipton	d			08 56									09 26								09 56				
Dudley Port	d			08 58									09 28								09 58				
Sandwell & Dudley	d		08 55	09 02									09 32				09 46			09 55	10 02				
Smethwick Galton Bridge ■7	d			09 04						09 23			09 34	09 40							10 04				
Smethwick Rolfe Street	d			09 06									09 36								10 06				
Birmingham New Street ■12	a	08 58	09 05	09 13		09 17				09 27	09 33		09 44	09 47			09 55	09 58		10 05	10 13		10 17		
	d	09 04	09 10		09 14		09 30	09 33		09 36		09 39			09 50	09 54		10 04		10 10		10 14		10 30	10 33
Adderley Park	d											09 44													
Stechford	d				09 20							09 47										10 20			
Lea Hall	d				09 23							09 50										10 23			
Marston Green	d				09 26			09 42								10 02						10 26			10 42
Birmingham International ✈	a	09 13	09 19		09 29		09 39	09 45		09 49		09 54			09 59	10 05		10 13		10 19		10 29		10 39	10 45
	d	09 14	09 20		09 30		09 40	09 45							10 00	10 05		10 14		10 20		10 30		10 40	10 45
Hampton-in-Arden	d				09 33			09 48														10 33			10 48
Berkswell	d				09 38											10 11						10 38			
Tile Hill	d				09 41			09 55								10 14						10 41			10 55
Canley	d				09 44											10 17						10 44			
Coventry	a	09 24	09 30		09 47		09 50	10 00							10 10	10 20		10 24		10 30		10 47		10 50	11 00
	d		09 31		09 48		09 51	10 00							10 11	10 21				10 31		10 48		10 51	11 00
Rugby	d				09 59			10 12							10 23	10 32						10 59			11 12
Long Buckby	d				10 08			10 21								10 41						11 08			11 21
Northampton	a				10 20			10 34								10 53						11 20			11 34
London Euston ■15 ⊖66	a		10 35		11 27		10 55	11 46							11 15	12 17				11 33		12 27		11 55	12 46

A To Walsall
B From Crewe
C From Shrewsbury
D From Nottingham to Bournemouth
E From Preston
F From Liverpool Lime Street
G From Aberystwyth
H From Manchester Piccadilly to Bristol Temple Meads
I From Manchester Piccadilly to Bournemouth
J From Lancaster
K From Holyhead
L From Manchester Piccadilly to Paignton
M From Glasgow Central

Table 68R

Saturdays

14 December to 28 December

Stafford - Wolverhampton - Birmingham - Coventry - Northampton

Network Diagram - refer to first Page of Table 67

		AW	XC	LM	LM	LM	VT	LM	LM	XC		VT	LM	LM	LM	VT	LM	AW	XC	LM		LM	LM	VT	LM
		◇	◇1			1	◇1	1		◇1		◇1		1	1	◇1	1	◇	◇1				1	◇1	1
		A	B		C	D			E	F		G	C		D			H	B			C	D		
Stafford	d		10 03			10 10				10 26					10 43				11 03				11 10		
Penkridge	d					10 16																	11 16		
Wolverhampton 7	a		10 15			10 27				10 39					10 56				11 15				11 27		
	d	10 11	10 17		10 19	10 29			10 37	10 41		10 45	10 49		10 59			11 11	11 16			11 19	11 29		
Coseley	d				10 24								10 54		11 04							11 24			
Tipton	d				10 26								10 56									11 26			
Dudley Port	d				10 28								10 58									11 28			
Sandwell & Dudley	d				10 32				10 46			10 55	11 02									11 32			
Smethwick Galton Bridge 7	d	10 22			10 34	10 40							11 04					11 22				11 34	11 40		
Smethwick Rolfe Street	d				10 36								11 06									11 36			
Birmingham New Street 12	a	10 28	10 33		10 44	10 47			10 55	10 58		11 05	11 13		11 17			11 28	11 33			11 44	11 47		
	d	10 36		10 39			10 50	10 54		11 04		11 10		11 14		11 30	11 33	11 36		11 39				11 50	11 54
Adderley Park	d			10 44																11 44					
Stechford	d			10 47										11 20						11 47					
Lea Hall	d			10 50										11 23						11 50					
Marston Green	d							11 02						11 26			11 42								12 02
Birmingham International ✈	a	10 50		10 54			10 59	11 05		11 13		11 19		11 29		11 39	11 45	11 50		11 54				11 59	12 05
	d						11 00	11 05		11 14		11 20		11 30		11 40	11 45							12 00	12 05
Hampton-in-Arden	d													11 33			11 48								
Berkswell	d							11 11						11 38											12 11
Tile Hill	d							11 14						11 41			11 55								12 14
Canley	d							11 17						11 44											12 17
Coventry	a						11 10	11 20		11 24		11 30		11 47		11 49	12 00							12 10	12 20
	d						11 11	11 21				11 31		11 48		11 51	12 00							12 11	12 21
Rugby	d						11 23	11 32						11 59			12 12							12 23	12 32
Long Buckby	d							11 41						12 08			12 21								12 41
Northampton	a							11 53						12 20			12 34								12 53
London Euston 15 ⊖66	a						12 15	13 17				12 33		13 27		12 55	13 46							13 15	14 17

		LM	XC	VT	LM	LM		LM	VT	LM	AW	XC	LM	LM	LM	VT		LM	LM	XC	VT	LM	LM	LM	VT
			◇1	◇1		1		1	◇1	1	◇	◇1			1	◇1		1		◇1	◇1		1	1	◇1
		E	F	I	C			D			J	B		C	D				E	F	G	C		D	
Stafford	d		11 26					11 43				12 03			12 10					12 25				12 43	
Penkridge	d														12 16										
Wolverhampton 7	a		11 39					11 56				12 15			12 27					12 39				12 56	
	d	11 37	11 41	11 45	11 49			11 59			12 11	12 16		12 19	12 29				12 37	12 41	12 45	12 49		12 59	
Coseley	d				11 54			12 04						12 24								12 54		13 04	
Tipton	d				11 56									12 26								12 56			
Dudley Port	d				11 58									12 28								12 58			
Sandwell & Dudley	d	11 47		11 55	12 02									12 32					12 46		12 55	13 02			
Smethwick Galton Bridge 7	d				12 04						12 22			12 34	12 40							13 04			
Smethwick Rolfe Street	d				12 06									12 36								13 06			
Birmingham New Street 12	a	11 56	11 59	12 05	12 13			12 17			12 28	12 33		12 44	12 47				12 55	12 58	13 05	13 13		13 17	
	d		12 04	12 10		12 14			12 30	12 33	12 36		12 39			12 50		12 54		13 04	13 10		13 14		13 30
Adderley Park	d												12 44												
Stechford	d					12 20							12 47										13 20		
Lea Hall	d					12 23							12 50										13 23		
Marston Green	d					12 26				12 42								13 02					13 26		
Birmingham International ✈	a		12 13	12 19		12 29			12 39	12 45	12 50		12 54			12 59		13 05		13 13	13 19		13 29		13 39
	d		12 14	12 20		12 30			12 40	12 45						13 00		13 05		13 14	13 20		13 30		13 40
Hampton-in-Arden	d					12 33				12 48													13 33		
Berkswell	d					12 38												13 11					13 38		
Tile Hill	d					12 41				12 55								13 14					13 41		
Canley	d					12 44												13 17					13 44		
Coventry	a		12 24	12 30		12 47			12 49	13 00						13 10		13 20		13 24	13 30		13 47		13 50
	d			12 30		12 48			12 51	13 00						13 11		13 21			13 31		13 48		13 51
Rugby	d					12 59				13 12						13 23		13 32					13 59		
Long Buckby	d					13 08				13 21								13 41					14 08		
Northampton	a					13 20				13 34								13 53					14 20		
London Euston 15 ⊖66	a			13 35		14 27			13 55	14 46						14 15		15 18			14 33		15 27		14 55

A From Barmouth
B From Manchester Piccadilly to Bristol Temple Meads
C To Walsall
D From Liverpool Lime Street
E From Shrewsbury
F From Manchester Piccadilly to Bournemouth
G From Edinburgh
H From Holyhead
I From Glasgow Central
J From Pwllheli

Table 68R

Saturdays

14 December to 28 December

Stafford - Wolverhampton - Birmingham - Coventry - Northampton

Network Diagram - refer to first Page of Table 67

		AW	XC	LM	AW	LM	LM	LM		VT	LM	LM	XC	VT	LM	LM	LM	VT		LM	AW	XC	LM	LM	LM
		◇	◇■1	■1	◇			■1		◇■1	■1		◇■1	◇■1		■1	■1	◇■1		■1	◇	◇■1			■1
		A	B		C		D	E				F	G	H	D		E				I	J		D	E
		🛒	🛒		🛒					☕			🛒	☕				☕			🛒	🛒			
Stafford	d		13 03					13 10					13 26				13 45					14 03			14 10
Penkridge	d							13 16																	14 16
Wolverhampton ■7 🚢	a		13 14					13 27					13 39				13 58					14 15			14 27
	d	13 10	13 16				13 19	13 29				13 37	13 41	13 45	13 49		13 59				14 11	14 16		14 19	14 29
Coseley	d						13 24								13 54		14 04							14 24	
Tipton	d						13 26								13 56									14 26	
Dudley Port	d						13 28								13 58									14 28	
Sandwell & Dudley	d						13 32					13 46		13 55	14 02									14 32	
Smethwick Galton Bridge ■7	d	13 22					13 34	13 40							14 04						14 22			14 34	14 40
Smethwick Rolfe Street	d				←		13 36								14 06									14 36	
Birmingham New Street ■12	a	13 28	13 32		13 28		13 44	13 47				13 55	13 58	14 05	14 13		14 17				14 28	14 33		14 44	14 47
	d	13 36		13 33	13 36	13 39				13 50	13 54		14 04	14 10		14 14		14 30		14 33	14 36		14 39		
Adderley Park	d	→				13 44																	14 44		
Stechford	d					13 47										14 20							14 47		
Lea Hall	d					13 50										14 23							14 50		
Marston Green	d			13 42							14 02					14 26				14 42					
Birmingham International ✈	a			13 45	13 50	13 54				13 59	14 05		14 13	14 19		14 29		14 39		14 45	14 50		14 54		
	d			13 45						14 00	14 05		14 14	14 20		14 30		14 40		14 45					
Hampton-in-Arden	d			13 48												14 33				14 48					
Berkswell	d										14 11					14 38									
Tile Hill	d			13 55							14 14					14 41				14 55					
Canley	d										14 17					14 44									
Coventry	a			14 00						14 10	14 20		14 24	14 30		14 47		14 49		15 00					
	d			14 00						14 11	14 21			14 31		14 48		14 51		15 00					
Rugby	d			14 12						14 23	14 32					14 59				15 12					
Long Buckby	d			14 21							14 41					15 08				15 21					
Northampton	a			14 34							14 53					15 20				15 34					
London Euston ■15 ⊖66	a			15 46						15 15	16 18			15 34		16 27		15 55		16 46					

		VT	LM	LM		XC	VT	LM	LM	LM	VT	LM	AW	XC		LM	LM	LM	VT	LM	LM	XC	VT	LM	
		◇■1	■1			◇■1	◇■1		■1	■1	◇■1	■1	◇	◇■1				■1	◇■1	■1		◇■1	◇■1		
				F		G	K	D		E			C	L			D	E			F	G	H	D	
		☕				🛒	☕				☕		🛒	🛒					☕			🛒	☕		
Stafford	d					14 26				14 43				15 03				15 10				15 26			
Penkridge	d																	15 16							
Wolverhampton ■7 🚢	a					14 39				14 56				15 16				15 27				15 39			
	d			14 37		14 41	14 45	14 49		14 59			15 11	15 17			15 19	15 29			15 37	15 41	15 45	15 49	
Coseley	d							14 54		15 04							15 24							15 54	
Tipton	d							14 56									15 26							15 56	
Dudley Port	d							14 58									15 28							15 58	
Sandwell & Dudley	d			14 46			14 55	15 02									15 32				15 46		15 55	16 02	
Smethwick Galton Bridge ■7	d							15 04					15 22				15 34	15 40						16 04	
Smethwick Rolfe Street	d							15 06									15 36							16 06	
Birmingham New Street ■12	a			14 55		14 58	15 05	15 13		15 17			15 28	15 33			15 44	15 47			15 55	15 58	16 05	16 13	
	d	14 50	14 54			15 04	15 10		15 14		15 30	15 33	15 36			15 39			15 50	15 54		16 04	16 10		
Adderley Park	d															15 44									
Stechford	d								15 20							15 47									
Lea Hall	d								15 23							15 50									
Marston Green	d		15 02						15 26			15 42								16 02					
Birmingham International ✈	a	14 59	15 05			15 13	15 19		15 29		15 39	15 45	15 49			15 54			15 59	16 05		16 13	16 19		
	d	15 00	15 05			15 14	15 20		15 30		15 40	15 45							16 00	16 05		16 14	16 20		
Hampton-in-Arden	d								15 33			15 48													
Berkswell	d		15 11						15 38											16 11					
Tile Hill	d		15 14						15 41			15 55								16 14					
Canley	d		15 17						15 44											16 17					
Coventry	a	15 10	15 20			15 24	15 30		15 47		15 50	16 00							16 10	16 20		16 24	16 30		
	d	15 11	15 21				15 31		15 48		15 51	16 00							16 11	16 21			16 31		
Rugby	d	15 23	15 32						15 59			16 12							16 23	16 32					
Long Buckby	d		15 41						16 08			16 21								16 41					
Northampton	a		15 53						16 20			16 34								16 53					
London Euston ■15 ⊖66	a	16 15	17 17				16 34		17 27		16 57	17 46							17 15	18 17			17 33		

A From Holyhead to Birmingham International
B From Manchester Piccadilly to Exeter St Davids
C From Holyhead
D To Walsall
E From Liverpool Lime Street
F From Shrewsbury
G From Manchester Piccadilly to Bournemouth
H From Glasgow Central
I From Pwllheli
J From Manchester Piccadilly to Bristol Temple Meads
K From Edinburgh
L From Manchester Piccadilly to Paignton

Table 68R

Saturdays

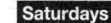

14 December to 28 December

Stafford - Wolverhampton - Birmingham - Coventry - Northampton

Network Diagram - refer to first Page of Table 67

Station		LM 1	LM 1 A	VT ◇1	LM 1	AW ◇ B	XC ◇1 C	LM	LM D	LM 1 A	VT ◇1	LM 1	LM E	XC ◇1 F	VT ◇1 G	LM 1	LM D	LM 1 A	VT ◇1	LM 1	AW ◇ H	XC ◇1 C	LM
Stafford	d		15 43				16 03			16 10				16 25				16 45				17 03	
Penkridge	d									16 16													
Wolverhampton 7	a		15 56				16 16			16 27				16 39				16 58				17 16	
	d		15 59			16 11	16 17		16 19	16 29			16 37	16 41	16 45		16 49	16 59			17 07	17 17	
Coseley	d		16 04						16 24								16 54	17 04					
Tipton	d								16 26								16 56						
Dudley Port	d								16 28								16 58						
Sandwell & Dudley	d								16 32				16 46		16 55		17 02						
Smethwick Galton Bridge 7	d					16 22			16 34	16 40							17 04				17 20		
Smethwick Rolfe Street	d								16 36								17 06						
Birmingham New Street 12	a		16 17			16 28	16 33		16 44	16 47			16 55	16 58	17 05		17 13	17 17			17 26	17 33	
	d	16 14		16 30	16 33	16 36		16 39			16 50	16 54		17 04	17 10	17 13			17 30	17 33	17 36		17 39
Adderley Park	d							16 44								17 17							17 44
Stechford	d	16 20						16 47								17 21							17 47
Lea Hall	d	16 23						16 50								17 23							17 50
Marston Green	d	16 26			16 42							17 02				17 26				17 42			
Birmingham International ✈	a	16 29		16 39	16 45	16 50		16 54			16 59	17 05		17 13	17 19	17 29			17 39	17 45	17 49		17 54
	d	16 30		16 40	16 45						17 00	17 05		17 14	17 20	17 30			17 40	17 45			
Hampton-in-Arden	d	16 33			16 48											17 33				17 48			
Berkswell	d	16 38										17 11				17 38							
Tile Hill	d	16 41			16 55							17 14				17 41				17 55			
Canley	d	16 44										17 17				17 44							
Coventry	a	16 47		16 50	17 00						17 10	17 20		17 24	17 30	17 47			17 49	18 00			
	d	16 48		16 51	17 00						17 11	17 21			17 31	17 48			17 51	18 00			
Rugby	d	16 59			17 12						17 23	17 32				17 59				18 12			
Long Buckby	d	17 08			17 21							17 41				18 08				18 21			
Northampton	a	17 21			17 34							17 53				18 20				18 34			
London Euston 15 ⊖66	a	18 27		17 55	18 46						18 15	19 17			18 34	19 45			18 55	19 45			

Station		LM D	LM 1 A	VT ◇1	LM 1	LM E	XC ◇1 F	VT ◇1 I	LM D	LM 1	LM 1 A	VT ◇1	LM 1	AW ◇ B	XC ◇1 J	LM	LM D	LM 1 A	VT ◇1	LM 1	LM E	XC ◇1 F
Stafford	d		17 10				17 26				17 44				18 04			18 10				18 26
Penkridge	d		17 16															18 16				
Wolverhampton 7	a		17 27				17 39				17 57				18 15			18 27				18 40
	d	17 19	17 29			17 37	17 41	17 45	17 49		17 59			18 11	18 16		18 19	18 29			18 37	18 41
Coseley	d	17 24							17 54		18 04						18 24					
Tipton	d	17 26							17 56								18 26					
Dudley Port	d	17 28							17 58								18 28					
Sandwell & Dudley	d	17 32				17 46		17 55	18 02								18 32				18 46	
Smethwick Galton Bridge 7	d	17 34	17 40						18 04					18 22			18 34	18 40				
Smethwick Rolfe Street	d	17 36							18 06								18 36					
Birmingham New Street 12	a	17 44	17 47			17 55	17 58	18 05	18 13		18 17			18 28	18 33		18 44	18 47			18 55	18 58
	d			17 50	17 54		18 04	18 10		18 14		18 30	18 33	18 36		18 39			18 50	18 54		19 04
Adderley Park	d															18 44						
Stechford	d									18 20						18 47						
Lea Hall	d									18 23						18 50						
Marston Green	d				18 02					18 26			18 42							19 02		
Birmingham International ✈	a			17 59	18 05		18 13	18 19		18 29		18 39	18 45	18 50		18 54			18 59	19 05		19 13
	d			18 00	18 05		18 14	18 20		18 30		18 40	18 45						19 00	19 05		19 14
Hampton-in-Arden	d									18 33			18 48									
Berkswell	d				18 11					18 38										19 11		
Tile Hill	d				18 14					18 41			18 55							19 14		
Canley	d				18 17					18 44										19 17		
Coventry	a			18 10	18 20		18 24	18 30		18 47		18 49	19 00						19 10	19 20		19 24
	d			18 11	18 21			18 31		18 48		18 51	19 00						19 11	19 21		
Rugby	d			18 23	18 32					18 59			19 12						19 23	19 32		
Long Buckby	d				18 41					19 08			19 21							19 41		
Northampton	a				18 53					19 20			19 34							19 53		
London Euston 15 ⊖66	a			19 15	20 18			19 34		20 45		19 55							20 22	21 09		

A From Liverpool Lime Street
B From Pwllheli
C From Manchester Piccadilly to Bristol Temple Meads
D To Walsall
E From Shrewsbury
F From Manchester Piccadilly to Bournemouth
G From Edinburgh
H From Holyhead
I From Glasgow Central
J From Manchester Piccadilly to Cardiff Central

Table 68R

Saturdays

14 December to 28 December

Stafford - Wolverhampton - Birmingham - Coventry - Northampton

Network Diagram - refer to first Page of Table 67

		VT ◇1 A 🍽	LM 1	LM	LM 1 B	LM 1 C	LM 1	AW ◇ D 🛒	XC ◇1 E 🛒	LM	LM F	LM 1 B	LM 1	LM G	XC ◇1 H 🛒	VT ◇1 I 🍽	LM 1	LM	LM 1 B	LM 1 C	LM 1	AW ◇ J 🛒
Stafford	d				18 43	18 56			19 03			19 10			19 25				19 45	19 51		
Penkridge	d											19 16							19 51			
Wolverhampton 7	a				18 56				19 15			19 27			19 39				20 01			
	d	18 45		18 49	18 59			19 11	19 16		19 19	19 29		19 37	19 41	19 45		19 49	20 02			20 10
Coseley	d			18 54	19 04						19 24							19 54	20 07			
Tipton	d			18 56							19 26							19 56				
Dudley Port	d			18 58							19 28							19 58				
Sandwell & Dudley	d	18 55		19 02							19 32			19 46		19 55		20 02				
Smethwick Galton Bridge 7	d			19 04				19 22			19 34	19 40						20 04				20 21
Smethwick Rolfe Street	d			19 06							19 36							20 06				
Birmingham New Street 12	a	19 05		19 14	19 17			19 28	19 33		19 44	19 47		19 55	19 59	20 05		20 14	20 19			20 26
	d	19 10	19 14				19 33	19 36		19 39			19 54		20 04	20 10	20 14				20 33	20 36
Adderley Park	d									19 44												
Stechford	d		19 20							19 47							20 20					
Lea Hall	d		19 23							19 50							20 23					
Marston Green	d		19 26				19 42						20 02				20 26				20 42	
Birmingham International ✈	a	19 19	19 29				19 45	19 50		19 54			20 05		20 13	20 19	20 29				20 45	20 50
	d	19 20	19 30				19 45						20 05		20 14	20 20	20 30				20 45	
Hampton-in-Arden	d		19 33				19 48										20 33				20 48	
Berkswell	d		19 38										20 11				20 38					
Tile Hill	d		19 41				19 55						20 14				20 41				20 55	
Canley	d		19 44										20 17				20 44					
Coventry	a	19 30	19 47				20 00						20 20		20 24	20 30	20 47				21 00	
	d	19 31	19 48				20 00						20 21			20 31					21 00	
Rugby	d	19 44	19 59			19 52	20 12						20 32			20 43				20 47	21 12	
Long Buckby	d		20 08				20 21						20 41								21 21	
Northampton	a		20 20			20 12	20 35						20 53							21 07	21 34	
London Euston 15 ⊖66	a	20 55	21 45										22 11			21 56						

		XC ◇1 K 🛒	LM	LM F	LM 1 B	LM 1	LM G	XC ◇1 L 🛒	VT ◇1 A 🍽	LM 1	LM	LM 1 B	VT ◇1 🍽	XC ◇1 M	LM 1	LM	LM F	LM 1	VT ◇1 I 🍽	LM G	XC ◇1 M	LM 1	LM
Stafford	d	20 03			20 12			20 26				20 40		21 03							21 27		
Penkridge	d											20 49											
Wolverhampton 7	a	20 15			20 28			20 39				20 59		21 15							21 39		
	d	20 16		20 19	20 29		20 37	20 41	20 45		20 49	20 59	21 07	21 16			21 19		21 34	21 37	21 41		21 49
Coseley	d			20 24							20 54	21 04					21 24						21 54
Tipton	d			20 26							20 56						21 26						21 56
Dudley Port	d			20 28							20 58						21 28						21 58
Sandwell & Dudley	d			20 32			20 46		20 55		21 02		21 17				21 32			21 47			22 02
Smethwick Galton Bridge 7	d			20 34	20 40						21 04						21 34						22 04
Smethwick Rolfe Street	d			20 36							21 06						21 36						22 06
Birmingham New Street 12	a	20 33		20 44	20 48		20 55	20 58	21 05		21 14	21 17	21 26	21 32			21 43		21 55	21 55	21 58		22 14
	d		20 39			20 54		21 04	21 10	21 14			21 30		21 34	21 39		21 54				22 14	
Adderley Park	d		20 44													21 44							
Stechford	d		20 47							21 20						21 47						22 20	
Lea Hall	d		20 50							21 23						21 50						22 23	
Marston Green	d					21 02				21 26					21 42			22 02				22 26	
Birmingham International ✈	a		20 54			21 05		21 13	21 19	21 29			21 39		21 45	21 54		22 05				22 29	
	d					21 05		21 14	21 20	21 30			21 40		21 45			22 05				22 30	
Hampton-in-Arden	d									21 33					21 48							22 33	
Berkswell	d					21 11				21 38								22 11				22 38	
Tile Hill	d					21 14				21 41					21 55			22 14				22 41	
Canley	d					21 17				21 44								22 17				22 44	
Coventry	a					21 20		21 24	21 30	21 47			21 50		22 00			22 20				22 47	
	d					21 21			21 31				21 51		22 00			22 21				22 48	
Rugby	d					21 32			21 43				22 03		22 12			22 32				22 59	
Long Buckby	d					21 41									22 21			22 41				23 09	
Northampton	a					21 53									22 34			22 53				23 21	
London Euston 15 ⊖66	a					23 27			22 55				23 30		00 05							00 40	

A From Edinburgh
B From Liverpool Lime Street
C From Crewe
D From Holyhead
E From Manchester Piccadilly to Plymouth
F To Walsall
G From Shrewsbury
H From Manchester Piccadilly to Bournemouth
I From Glasgow Central
J From Aberystwyth
K From Manchester Piccadilly to Bristol Temple Meads
L From Manchester Piccadilly to Southampton Central. 🛒 to Birmingham New Street
M From Manchester Piccadilly

Table 68R

Saturdays

14 December to 28 December

Stafford - Wolverhampton - Birmingham - Coventry - Northampton

Network Diagram - refer to first Page of Table 67

		LM	AW	XC	LM	LM	VT	LM	LM	VT	XC	LM	LM	LM	AW
		[1]	◇	◇[1]	[1]		◇[1]	[1]		◇[1]	◇[1]	[1]		[1]	◇
		A	B	C		D	E		F	G	C			A	H
							☕			☕					
Stafford	d	21 42		22 03			22 08			22 23	22 29			22 45	
Penkridge	d	21 48												22 51	
Wolverhampton [7]	a	21 59		22 14			22 22			22 40	22 43			23 01	
	d	22 02	22 08	22 16		22 19	22 23		22 37	22 40	22 44		22 49	23 03	23 08
Coseley	d	22 07				22 24							22 54	23 08	
Tipton	d					22 26							22 56		
Dudley Port	d					22 28							22 58		
Sandwell & Dudley	d					22 32			22 46				23 02		
Smethwick Galton Bridge [7]	d		22 19			22 34							23 04		
Smethwick Rolfe Street	d					22 36							23 06		
Birmingham New Street [12]	a	22 20	22 32	22 32		22 43	22 46		22 55	22 59	23 01		23 14	23 20	23 29
	d				22 34			22 54				23 14			
Adderley Park	d											23 18			
Stechford	d											23 22			
Lea Hall	d											23 24			
Marston Green	d				22 42			23 02				23 27			
Birmingham International ✈	a				22 45			23 05				23 30			
	d				22 45			23 05				23 31			
Hampton-in-Arden	d				22 48							23 34			
Berkswell	d							23 11				23 39			
Tile Hill	d				22 55			23 14				23 42			
Canley	d							23 17				23 45			
Coventry	a				23 00			23 20				23 48			
	d							23 21							
Rugby	d							23 32							
Long Buckby	d							23 41							
Northampton	a							23 55							
London Euston [15] ⊖66	a														

Saturdays

4 January to 8 February

		LM	VT	AW	XC	VT	LM	AW	VT	LM	AW	LM	LM	VT	LM	XC	VT	LM	LM	VT	LM	AW	XC
		[1]	◇[1]		◇[1]	◇[1]	[1]		◇[1]	[1]				◇[1]	[1]	◇[1]	◇[1]	[1]	[1]	◇[1]	[1]		◇[1]
		I		J	K			L			F		F			M			N			F	O
			☕		🛒	☕			☕					☕		🛒	☕			☕			🛒
Stafford	d			05 25												06 26			06 35				06 58
Penkridge	d																		06 41				
Wolverhampton [7]	a			05 39												06 39			06 51				07 12
	d			05 40		05 45		06 02	06 06				06 19	06 27		06 41	06 45		06 53	07 05		07 12	07 16
Coseley	d												06 24						06 58				
Tipton	d												06 27						07 01				
Dudley Port	d												06 29						07 03				
Sandwell & Dudley	d					05 56			06 17				06 32	06 37			06 56		07 07	07 14			
Smethwick Galton Bridge [7]	d							06 13					06 35						07 10			07 23	
Smethwick Rolfe Street	d										←		06 37						07 12				
Birmingham New Street [12]	a			05 58		06 06		06 20	06 26		06 20		06 45	06 47		06 57	07 06		07 18	07 25		07 28	07 33
	d		05 50		06 04	06 10	06 14	06 36	06 30	06 33	06 36	06 39		06 50	06 54	07 04	07 10	07 14		07 30	07 33	07 36	
Adderley Park	d							→				06 44											
Stechford	d						06 20					06 47						07 20					
Lea Hall	d						06 23					06 50						07 23					
Marston Green	d	00 02					06 26			06 42					07 02			07 26			07 42		
Birmingham International ✈	a	00 05	05 59		06 13	06 19	06 29		06 39	06 45	06 49	06 54		06 59	07 05	07 13	07 19	07 29		07 39	07 45	07 50	
	d	00 06	06 00		06 14	06 20	06 30		06 40	06 45				07 00	07 05	07 14	07 20	07 30		07 40	07 45		
Hampton-in-Arden	d						06 33			06 48								07 33			07 48		
Berkswell	d						06 38								07 11			07 38					
Tile Hill	d						06 41			06 55					07 14			07 41			07 55		
Canley	d						06 44								07 17			07 44					
Coventry	a	00 15	06 10		06 24	06 30	06 47		06 49	07 00				07 10	07 20	07 24	07 30	07 47		07 50	08 00		
	d		06 10			06 31	06 48		06 51	07 00				07 11	07 21		07 31	07 48		07 51	08 00		
Rugby	d		06 24				06 59			07 12				07 23	07 32			07 59			08 12		
Long Buckby	d						07 08			07 21					07 41			08 08			08 21		
Northampton	a						07 21			07 34					07 53			08 20			08 34		
London Euston [15] ⊖66	a		07 17			07 38	08 40		07 55					08 17	09 17		08 35	09 27		08 54	09 47		

- **A** From Liverpool Lime Street
- **B** From Aberystwyth
- **C** From Manchester Piccadilly
- **D** To Walsall
- **E** From Glasgow Central
- **F** From Shrewsbury
- **G** From Edinburgh
- **H** From Holyhead
- **I** From Birmingham New Street
- **J** From Chester
- **K** To Bournemouth
- **L** From Shrewsbury to Birmingham International
- **M** From Manchester Piccadilly to Bournemouth
- **N** From Crewe to Walsall
- **O** From Manchester Piccadilly to Bristol Temple Meads

Table 68R

Saturdays

4 January to 8 February

Stafford - Wolverhampton - Birmingham - Coventry - Northampton

Network Diagram - refer to first Page of Table 67

		LM		LM A	LM 1 B	VT ◇1 🍴	LM 1	LM C	XC ◇1 D 🛒	VT ◇1 E 🍴	LM A	LM 1		LM 1 F	VT ◇1 🍴	LM 1	AW ◇ G 🛒	XC ◇1 H 🛒	LM	LM A	LM 1 F	VT ◇1 🍴		LM 1	LM C
Stafford	d				07 12									07 41				08 03			08 10				
Penkridge	d				07 18									07 47							08 16				
Wolverhampton 7	a				07 28									07 57				08 15			08 26				
	d			07 19	07 29			07 37		07 45	07 49			07 59			08 09	08 16		08 19	08 29				08 37
Coseley	d			07 24							07 54			08 04						08 24					
Tipton	d			07 26							07 56									08 26					
Dudley Port	d			07 28							07 58									08 28					
Sandwell & Dudley	d			07 32				07 46		07 55	08 02									08 32					08 46
Smethwick Galton Bridge 7	d			07 34	07 40						08 04						08 21			08 34	08 40				
Smethwick Rolfe Street	d			07 36							08 06									08 36					
Birmingham New Street 12	a			07 44	07 47			07 55		08 05	08 13			08 17			08 26	08 34		08 44	08 48				08 55
	d	07 39				07 50	07 54		08 04	08 10		08 14			08 30	08 33	08 36		08 39			08 50		08 54	
Adderley Park	d	07 44																	08 44						
Stechford	d	07 47										08 20							08 47						
Lea Hall	d	07 50										08 23							08 50						
Marston Green	d						08 02					08 26				08 42								09 02	
Birmingham International ✈	a	07 54				07 59	08 05		08 13	08 19		08 29			08 39	08 45	08 50		08 54			08 59		09 05	
	d					08 00	08 05		08 14	08 20		08 30			08 40	08 45						09 00		09 05	
Hampton-in-Arden	d											08 33				08 48									
Berkswell	d						08 11					08 38												09 11	
Tile Hill	d						08 14					08 41				08 55								09 14	
Canley	d						08 17					08 44												09 17	
Coventry	a					08 10	08 20		08 24	08 29		08 47			08 50	09 00						09 10		09 20	
	d					08 11	08 21			08 30		08 48			08 51	09 00						09 11		09 21	
Rugby	d					08 23	08 32					08 59				09 12						09 23		09 32	
Long Buckby	d						08 41					09 08				09 21								09 41	
Northampton	a						08 56					09 20				09 34								09 55	
London Euston 15 ⊖66	a					09 15	10 17			09 34		10 27			09 59	10 46						10 15		11 17	

		XC ◇1 I 🛒	VT ◇1 J 🍴	LM A	LM 1	LM 1 F	VT ◇1 🍴	LM 1		AW ◇ K 🛒	XC ◇1 L 🛒	LM	LM	LM 1 F	VT ◇1 🍴	LM 1	LM C	XC ◇1 I 🛒		VT ◇1 M 🍴	LM A	LM 1	LM 1 F	VT ◇1 🍴	LM 1
Stafford	d	08 26				08 43					09 03			09 10				09 26					09 45		
Penkridge	d					08 48								09 16											
Wolverhampton 7	a	08 39				08 58					09 15			09 26				09 39					09 58		
	d	08 41	08 45	08 49		08 59				09 12	09 16		09 19	09 29			09 37	09 41		09 45	09 49		09 59		
Coseley	d			08 54		09 04							09 24								09 54		10 04		
Tipton	d			08 56									09 26								09 56				
Dudley Port	d			08 58									09 28								09 58				
Sandwell & Dudley	d		08 55	09 02									09 32				09 46			09 55	10 02				
Smethwick Galton Bridge 7	d			09 04						09 23			09 34	09 40							10 04				
Smethwick Rolfe Street	d			09 06									09 36								10 06				
Birmingham New Street 12	a	08 58	09 05	09 13		09 17				09 27	09 33		09 44	09 47			09 55	09 58		10 05	10 13		10 17		
	d	09 04	09 10		09 14		09 30	09 33		09 36		09 39			09 50	09 54		10 04		10 10		10 14		10 30	10 33
Adderley Park	d											09 44													
Stechford	d				09 20							09 47										10 20			
Lea Hall	d				09 23							09 50										10 23			
Marston Green	d				09 26			09 42								10 02						10 26			10 42
Birmingham International ✈	a	09 13	09 19		09 29		09 39	09 45		09 49		09 54			09 59	10 05		10 13		10 19		10 29		10 39	10 45
	d	09 14	09 20		09 30		09 40	09 45							10 00	10 05		10 14		10 20		10 30		10 40	10 45
Hampton-in-Arden	d				09 33			09 48														10 33			10 48
Berkswell	d				09 38											10 11						10 38			
Tile Hill	d				09 41			09 55								10 14						10 41			10 55
Canley	d				09 44											10 17						10 44			
Coventry	a	09 24	09 30		09 47		09 50	10 00							10 10	10 20		10 24		10 30		10 47		10 50	11 00
	d		09 31		09 48		09 51	10 00							10 11	10 21				10 31		10 48		10 51	11 00
Rugby	d				09 59			10 12							10 23	10 32						10 59			11 12
Long Buckby	d				10 08			10 21								10 41						11 08			11 21
Northampton	a				10 20			10 34								10 53						11 20			11 34
London Euston 15 ⊖66	a		10 35		11 27		10 55	11 46							11 15	12 17				11 33		12 27		11 55	12 46

- **A** To Walsall
- **B** From Crewe
- **C** From Shrewsbury
- **D** From Nottingham to Bournemouth
- **E** From Preston
- **F** From Liverpool Lime Street
- **G** From Aberystwyth
- **H** From Manchester Piccadilly to Bristol Temple Meads
- **I** From Manchester Piccadilly to Bournemouth
- **J** From Lancaster
- **K** From Holyhead
- **L** From Manchester Piccadilly to Paignton
- **M** From Glasgow Central

Table 68R

Saturdays

4 January to 8 February

Stafford - Wolverhampton - Birmingham - Coventry - Northampton

Network Diagram - refer to first Page of Table 67

		AW ◇ A	XC ◇1 B	LM	LM C	LM 1 D	VT ◇1	LM 1	LM E	XC ◇1 F	VT ◇1 G	LM C	LM 1	LM 1 D	VT ◇1	LM 1	AW ◇ H	XC ◇1 B	LM	LM C	LM 1 D	VT ◇1	LM 1
Stafford	d		10 03			10 10				10 26				10 43				11 03			11 10		
Penkridge	d					10 16															11 16		
Wolverhampton 7	a		10 15			10 27				10 39				10 56				11 15			11 27		
	d	10 11	10 17		10 19	10 29			10 37	10 41	10 45	10 49		10 59			11 11	11 16		11 19	11 29		
Coseley	d				10 24							10 54		11 04						11 24			
Tipton	d				10 26							10 56								11 26			
Dudley Port	d				10 28							10 58								11 28			
Sandwell & Dudley	d				10 32				10 46		10 55	11 02								11 32			
Smethwick Galton Bridge 7	d	10 22			10 34	10 40						11 04					11 22			11 34	11 40		
Smethwick Rolfe Street	d				10 36							11 06								11 36			
Birmingham New Street 12	a	10 28	10 33		10 44	10 47			10 55	10 58	11 05	11 13		11 17			11 28	11 33		11 44	11 47		
	d	10 36		10 39			10 50	10 54		11 04	11 10		11 14		11 30	11 33	11 36		11 39			11 50	11 54
Adderley Park	d			10 44															11 44				
Stechford	d			10 47									11 20						11 47				
Lea Hall	d			10 50									11 23						11 50				
Marston Green	d							11 02					11 26			11 42							12 02
Birmingham International ✈	a	10 50		10 54			10 59	11 05		11 13	11 19		11 29		11 39	11 45	11 50		11 54			11 59	12 05
	d						11 00	11 05		11 14	11 20		11 30		11 40	11 45						12 00	12 05
Hampton-in-Arden	d												11 33			11 48							
Berkswell	d							11 11					11 38										12 11
Tile Hill	d							11 14					11 41			11 55							12 14
Canley	d							11 17					11 44										12 17
Coventry	a						11 10	11 20		11 24	11 30		11 47		11 49	12 00						12 10	12 20
	d						11 11	11 21			11 31		11 48		11 51	12 00						12 11	12 21
Rugby	d						11 23	11 32					11 59			12 12						12 23	12 32
Long Buckby	d							11 41					12 08			12 21							12 41
Northampton	a							11 53					12 20			12 34							12 53
London Euston 15 ⊖66	a						12 15	13 17			12 33		13 27		12 55	13 46						13 15	14 17

		LM E	XC ◇1 F	VT ◇1 I	LM C	LM 1	LM 1 D	VT ◇1	LM 1	AW ◇ J	XC ◇1 B	LM	LM C	LM 1 D	VT ◇1	LM 1	LM E	XC ◇1 F	VT ◇1 G	LM C	LM 1	LM 1 D	VT ◇1
Stafford	d		11 26				11 43				12 03			12 10				12 25				12 43	
Penkridge	d													12 16									
Wolverhampton 7	a		11 39				11 56				12 15			12 27				12 39				12 56	
	d	11 37	11 41	11 45	11 49		11 59			12 11	12 16		12 19	12 29			12 37	12 41	12 45	12 49		12 59	
Coseley	d				11 54		12 04						12 24							12 54		13 04	
Tipton	d				11 56								12 26							12 56			
Dudley Port	d				11 58								12 28							12 58			
Sandwell & Dudley	d	11 47		11 55	12 02								12 32				12 46		12 55	13 02			
Smethwick Galton Bridge 7	d				12 04					12 22			12 34	12 40						13 04			
Smethwick Rolfe Street	d				12 06								12 36							13 06			
Birmingham New Street 12	a	11 56	11 59	12 05	12 13		12 17			12 28	12 33		12 44	12 47			12 55	12 58	13 05	13 13		13 17	
	d		12 04	12 10		12 14		12 30	12 33	12 36		12 39			12 50	12 54		13 04	13 10		13 14		13 30
Adderley Park	d											12 44											
Stechford	d					12 20						12 47									13 20		
Lea Hall	d					12 23						12 50									13 23		
Marston Green	d					12 26			12 42							13 02					13 26		
Birmingham International ✈	a		12 13	12 19		12 29		12 39	12 45	12 50		12 54			12 59	13 05		13 13	13 19		13 29		13 39
	d		12 14	12 20		12 30		12 40	12 45						13 00	13 05		13 14	13 20		13 30		13 40
Hampton-in-Arden	d					12 33			12 48												13 33		
Berkswell	d					12 38										13 11					13 38		
Tile Hill	d					12 41			12 55							13 14					13 41		
Canley	d					12 44										13 17					13 44		
Coventry	a		12 24	12 30		12 47		12 49	13 00						13 10	13 20		13 24	13 30		13 47		13 50
	d			12 30		12 48		12 51	13 00						13 11	13 21			13 31		13 48		13 51
Rugby	d					12 59			13 12						13 23	13 32					13 59		
Long Buckby	d					13 08			13 21							13 41					14 08		
Northampton	a					13 20			13 34							13 53					14 20		
London Euston 15 ⊖66	a			13 35		14 27		13 55	14 46						14 15	15 18			14 33		15 27		14 55

A From Barmouth
B From Manchester Piccadilly to Bristol Temple Meads
C To Walsall
D From Liverpool Lime Street
E From Shrewsbury
F From Manchester Piccadilly to Bournemouth
G From Edinburgh
H From Holyhead
I From Glasgow Central
J From Pwllheli

Table 68R

Saturdays

4 January to 8 February

Stafford - Wolverhampton - Birmingham - Coventry - Northampton

Network Diagram - refer to first Page of Table 67

		AW	XC	LM	AW	LM	LM	LM		VT	LM	LM	XC	VT	LM	LM	LM	VT		LM	AW	XC	LM	LM	LM
		◇	◇1	1	◇			1		◇1	1		◇1	◇1		1	1	◇1		1	◇	◇1			1
		A	B		C		D	E				F	G	H	D		E				I	J		D	E
		🍴	🍴		🍴					☕			🍴	☕				☕			🍴	🍴			
Stafford	d		13 03					13 10					13 26				13 45					14 03			14 10
Penkridge	d							13 16																	14 16
Wolverhampton 7 ⛴	a		13 14					13 27					13 39				13 58					14 15			14 27
	d	13 10	13 16				13 19	13 29				13 37	13 41	13 45	13 49		13 59				14 11	14 16		14 19	14 29
Coseley	d						13 24								13 54		14 04							14 24	
Tipton	d						13 26								13 56									14 26	
Dudley Port	d						13 28								13 58									14 28	
Sandwell & Dudley	d						13 32					13 46		13 55	14 02									14 32	
Smethwick Galton Bridge 7	d	13 22					13 34	13 40							14 04						14 22			14 34	14 40
Smethwick Rolfe Street	d				←		13 36								14 06									14 36	
Birmingham New Street 12	a	13 28	13 32		13 28		13 44	13 47				13 55	13 58	14 05	14 13		14 17				14 28	14 33		14 44	14 47
	d	13 36		13 33	13 36	13 39				13 50	13 54		14 04	14 10		14 14		14 30		14 33	14 36		14 39		
Adderley Park	d	→				13 44																	14 44		
Stechford	d					13 47										14 20							14 47		
Lea Hall	d					13 50										14 23							14 50		
Marston Green	d			13 42							14 02					14 26				14 42					
Birmingham International ✈	a			13 45	13 50	13 54				13 59	14 05		14 13	14 19		14 29		14 39		14 45	14 50		14 54		
	d			13 45						14 00	14 05		14 14	14 20		14 30		14 40		14 45					
Hampton-in-Arden	d			13 48												14 33				14 48					
Berkswell	d										14 11					14 38									
Tile Hill	d			13 55							14 14					14 41				14 55					
Canley	d										14 17					14 44									
Coventry	a			14 00						14 10	14 20		14 24	14 30		14 47		14 49		15 00					
	d			14 00						14 11	14 21			14 31		14 48		14 51		15 00					
Rugby	d			14 12						14 23	14 32					14 59				15 12					
Long Buckby	d			14 21							14 41					15 08				15 21					
Northampton	a			14 34							14 53					15 20				15 34					
London Euston 15 ⊖66	a			15 46						15 15	16 18			15 34		16 27		15 55		16 46					

		VT	LM	LM		XC	VT	LM	LM	LM	VT	LM	AW	XC		LM	LM	LM	VT	LM	LM	XC	VT	LM	
		◇1	1			◇1	◇1		1	1	◇1	1	◇	◇1				1	◇1	1		◇1	◇1		
				F		G	K	D		E			C	L			D	E			F	G	K	D	
		☕				🍴	☕				☕		🍴	🍴					☕			🍴	☕		
Stafford	d					14 26				14 43				15 03				15 10				15 26			
Penkridge	d																	15 16							
Wolverhampton 7 ⛴	a					14 39				14 56				15 16				15 27				15 39			
	d			14 37		14 41	14 45	14 49		14 59			15 11	15 17			15 19	15 29			15 37	15 41	15 45	15 49	
Coseley	d							14 54		15 04							15 24							15 54	
Tipton	d							14 56									15 26							15 56	
Dudley Port	d							14 58									15 28							15 58	
Sandwell & Dudley	d			14 46			14 55	15 02									15 32				15 46		15 55	16 02	
Smethwick Galton Bridge 7	d							15 04					15 22				15 34	15 40						16 04	
Smethwick Rolfe Street	d							15 06									15 36							16 06	
Birmingham New Street 12	a			14 55		14 58	15 05	15 13		15 17			15 28	15 33			15 44	15 47			15 55	15 58	16 05	16 13	
	d	14 50	14 54			15 04	15 10		15 14		15 30	15 33	15 36			15 39			15 50	15 54		16 04	16 10		
Adderley Park	d															15 44									
Stechford	d								15 20							15 47									
Lea Hall	d								15 23							15 50									
Marston Green	d		15 02						15 26			15 42								16 02					
Birmingham International ✈	a	14 59	15 05			15 13	15 19		15 29		15 39	15 45	15 49			15 54			15 59	16 05		16 13	16 19		
	d	15 00	15 05			15 14	15 20		15 30		15 40	15 45							16 00	16 05		16 14	16 20		
Hampton-in-Arden	d								15 33			15 48													
Berkswell	d		15 11						15 38											16 11					
Tile Hill	d		15 14						15 41			15 55								16 14					
Canley	d		15 17						15 44											16 17					
Coventry	a	15 09	15 20			15 24	15 30		15 47		15 50	16 00							16 10	16 20		16 24	16 30		
	d	15 10	15 21				15 31		15 48		15 51	16 00							16 11	16 21			16 31		
Rugby	d	15 23	15 32						15 59			16 12							16 23	16 32					
Long Buckby	d		15 41						16 08			16 21								16 41					
Northampton	a		15 53						16 20			16 34								16 53					
London Euston 15 ⊖66	a	16 15	17 17				16 34		17 27		16 57	17 46							17 15	18 17			17 33		

A From Holyhead to Birmingham International
B From Manchester Piccadilly to Exeter St Davids
C From Holyhead
D To Walsall
E From Liverpool Lime Street
F From Shrewsbury
G From Manchester Piccadilly to Bournemouth
H From Glasgow Central
I From Pwllheli
J From Manchester Piccadilly to Bristol Temple Meads
K From Preston
L From Manchester Piccadilly to Paignton

Table 68R

Saturdays

4 January to 8 February

Stafford - Wolverhampton - Birmingham - Coventry - Northampton

Network Diagram - refer to first Page of Table 67

		LM 1	LM 1 A	VT ◇1 ☕	LM 1	AW ◇ B 🍴		XC ◇1 C 🍴	LM	LM D	LM 1 A	VT ◇1 ☕	LM 1	LM E	XC ◇1 F 🍴	VT ◇1 G ☕		LM 1	LM D	LM 1 A	VT ◇1 ☕	LM 1	AW ◇ H 🍴	XC ◇1 C 🍴	LM
Stafford	d		15 43					16 03			16 10				16 25					16 45				17 03	
Penkridge	d										16 16														
Wolverhampton 7	a		15 56					16 16			16 27				16 39					16 58				17 16	
	d		15 59			16 11		16 17		16 19	16 29			16 37	16 41	16 45			16 49	16 59			17 07	17 17	
Coseley	d		16 04							16 24									16 54	17 04					
Tipton	d									16 26									16 56						
Dudley Port	d									16 28									16 58						
Sandwell & Dudley	d									16 32				16 46		16 55			17 02						
Smethwick Galton Bridge 7	d					16 22				16 34	16 40								17 04				17 20		
Smethwick Rolfe Street	d									16 36									17 06						
Birmingham New Street 12	a		16 17			16 28		16 33		16 44	16 47			16 55	16 58	17 05			17 13	17 17			17 26	17 33	
	d	16 14		16 30	16 33	16 36			16 39			16 50	16 54		17 04	17 10		17 13			17 30	17 33	17 36		17 39
Adderley Park	d								16 44									17 17							17 44
Stechford	d	16 20							16 47									17 21							17 47
Lea Hall	d	16 23							16 50									17 23							17 50
Marston Green	d	16 26			16 42								17 02					17 26				17 42			
Birmingham International ✈	a	16 29		16 39	16 45	16 50			16 54			16 59	17 05		17 13	17 19		17 29			17 39	17 45	17 49		17 54
	d	16 30		16 40	16 45							17 00	17 05		17 14	17 20		17 30			17 40	17 45			
Hampton-in-Arden	d	16 33			16 48													17 33				17 48			
Berkswell	d	16 38											17 11					17 38							
Tile Hill	d	16 41			16 55								17 14					17 41				17 55			
Canley	d	16 44											17 17					17 44							
Coventry	a	16 47		16 50	17 00							17 10	17 20		17 24	17 30		17 47			17 49	18 00			
	d	16 48		16 51	17 00							17 11	17 21			17 31		17 48			17 51	18 00			
Rugby	d	16 59			17 12							17 23	17 32					17 59				18 12			
Long Buckby	d	17 08			17 21								17 41					18 08				18 21			
Northampton	a	17 21			17 34								17 53					18 20				18 34			
London Euston 15 ⊖66	a	18 27		17 55	18 46							18 15	19 17			18 34		19 45			18 55	19 45			

		LM D		LM 1 A	VT ◇1 ☕	LM 1	LM E	XC ◇1 F 🍴	VT ◇1 G ☕	LM D	LM 1	LM 1 A		VT ◇1 ☕	LM 1	AW ◇ B 🍴	XC ◇1 I 🍴	LM	LM D	LM 1 A	VT ◇1 ☕	LM 1		LM E	XC ◇1 F 🍴
Stafford	d			17 10				17 26				17 44					18 04			18 10					18 26
Penkridge	d			17 16																18 16					
Wolverhampton 7	a			17 27				17 39				17 57					18 15			18 27					18 40
	d	17 19		17 29			17 37	17 41	17 45	17 49		17 59				18 11	18 16		18 19	18 29				18 37	18 41
Coseley	d	17 24								17 54		18 04							18 24						
Tipton	d	17 26								17 56									18 26						
Dudley Port	d	17 28								17 58									18 28						
Sandwell & Dudley	d	17 32					17 46		17 55	18 02									18 32					18 46	
Smethwick Galton Bridge 7	d	17 34		17 40						18 04						18 22			18 34	18 40					
Smethwick Rolfe Street	d	17 36								18 06									18 36						
Birmingham New Street 12	a	17 44		17 47			17 55	17 58	18 05	18 13		18 17				18 28	18 33		18 44	18 47				18 55	18 58
	d				17 50	17 54		18 04	18 10		18 14			18 30	18 33	18 36		18 39			18 50	18 54			19 04
Adderley Park	d																	18 44							
Stechford	d										18 20							18 47							
Lea Hall	d										18 23							18 50							
Marston Green	d					18 02					18 26				18 42							19 02			
Birmingham International ✈	a				17 59	18 05		18 13	18 19		18 29			18 39	18 45	18 50		18 54			18 59	19 05			19 13
	d				18 00	18 05		18 14	18 20		18 30			18 40	18 45						19 00	19 05			19 14
Hampton-in-Arden	d										18 33				18 48										
Berkswell	d					18 11					18 38											19 11			
Tile Hill	d					18 14					18 41				18 55							19 14			
Canley	d					18 17					18 44											19 17			
Coventry	a				18 10	18 20		18 24	18 30		18 47			18 49	19 00						19 10	19 20			19 24
	d				18 11	18 21			18 31		18 48			18 51	19 00						19 11	19 21			
Rugby	d				18 23	18 32					18 59				19 12						19 23	19 32			
Long Buckby	d					18 41					19 08				19 21							19 41			
Northampton	a					18 53					19 20				19 34							19 53			
London Euston 15 ⊖66	a				19 15	20 18			19 34		20 45			19 55							20 22	21 09			

A From Liverpool Lime Street
B From Pwllheli
C From Manchester Piccadilly to Bristol Temple Meads
D To Walsall
E From Shrewsbury
F From Manchester Piccadilly to Bournemouth
G From Preston
H From Holyhead
I From Manchester Piccadilly to Cardiff Central

Table 68R

Saturdays

4 January to 8 February

Stafford - Wolverhampton - Birmingham - Coventry - Northampton

Network Diagram - refer to first Page of Table 67

		VT	LM	LM		LM	LM	LM	AW	XC	LM	LM	LM	LM		LM	XC	VT	LM	LM	LM	LM	LM	AW	
		◇1	1			1	1	1	◇	◇1			1	1			◇1	◇1	1		1	1	1	◇	
		A				B	C		D	E		F	B			G	H	A			B	C		I	
Stafford	d					18 43	18 56			19 03			19 10				19 25				19 45	19 51			
Penkridge	d												19 16								19 51				
Wolverhampton 7	a					18 56				19 15			19 27				19 39				20 01				
	d	18 45		18 49		18 59			19 11	19 16		19 19	19 29			19 37	19 41	19 45		19 49	20 02			20 10	
Coseley	d			18 54		19 04						19 24								19 54	20 07				
Tipton	d			18 56								19 26								19 56					
Dudley Port	d			18 58								19 28								19 58					
Sandwell & Dudley	d	18 55		19 02								19 32				19 46		19 55		20 02					
Smethwick Galton Bridge 7	d			19 04					19 22			19 34	19 40							20 04				20 21	
Smethwick Rolfe Street	d			19 06								19 36								20 06					
Birmingham New Street 12	a	19 05		19 14		19 17			19 28	19 33		19 44	19 47			19 55	19 59	20 05		20 14	20 19			20 26	
	d	19 10	19 14					19 33	19 36		19 39			19 54			20 04	20 10	20 14				20 33	20 36	
Adderley Park	d										19 44														
Stechford	d		19 20								19 47								20 20						
Lea Hall	d		19 23								19 50								20 23						
Marston Green	d		19 26					19 42						20 02					20 26				20 42		
Birmingham International	a	19 19	19 29					19 45	19 50		19 54			20 05			20 13	20 19	20 29				20 45	20 50	
	d	19 20	19 30					19 45						20 05			20 14	20 20	20 30				20 45		
Hampton-in-Arden	d		19 33					19 48											20 33				20 48		
Berkswell	d		19 38											20 11					20 38						
Tile Hill	d		19 41					19 55						20 14					20 41				20 55		
Canley	d		19 44											20 17					20 44						
Coventry	a	19 30	19 47					20 00						20 20			20 24	20 30	20 47				21 00		
	d	19 31	19 48					20 00						20 21				20 31					21 00		
Rugby	d	19 44	19 59				19 52	20 12						20 32				20 43				20 47	21 12		
Long Buckby	d		20 08					20 21						20 41									21 21		
Northampton	a		20 20				20 12	20 35						20 53								21 07	21 34		
London Euston 15 ⊖66	a	20 55	21 45											22 11				21 56							

		XC	LM	LM	LM	LM	LM	XC	VT	LM		LM	LM	VT	XC	LM	LM	LM	LM	VT		LM	XC	LM	LM
		◇1			1	1		◇1	◇1	1			1	◇1	◇1	1			1	◇1			◇1	1	
		J		F	B		G	K	A				B		L			F		M		G	L		
Stafford	d	20 03			20 12			20 26					20 40		21 03								21 27		
Penkridge	d												20 49												
Wolverhampton 7	a	20 15			20 28			20 39					20 59		21 15								21 39		
	d	20 16		20 19	20 29		20 37	20 41	20 45			20 49	20 59	21 07	21 16			21 19		21 34		21 37	21 41		21 49
Coseley	d			20 24								20 54	21 04					21 24							21 54
Tipton	d			20 26								20 56						21 26							21 56
Dudley Port	d			20 28								20 58						21 28							21 58
Sandwell & Dudley	d			20 32			20 46		20 55			21 02		21 17				21 32				21 47			22 02
Smethwick Galton Bridge 7	d			20 34	20 40							21 04						21 34							22 04
Smethwick Rolfe Street	d			20 36								21 06						21 36							22 06
Birmingham New Street 12	a	20 33		20 44	20 48		20 55	20 58	21 05			21 14	21 17	21 26	21 32			21 43		21 55		21 55	21 58		22 14
	d		20 39			20 54		21 04	21 10	21 14				21 30		21 34	21 39		21 54					22 14	
Adderley Park	d		20 44														21 44								
Stechford	d		20 47							21 20							21 47							22 20	
Lea Hall	d		20 50							21 23							21 50							22 23	
Marston Green	d					21 02				21 26						21 42			22 02					22 26	
Birmingham International	a		20 54			21 05		21 13	21 19	21 29				21 39		21 45	21 54		22 05					22 29	
	d					21 05		21 14	21 20	21 30				21 40		21 45			22 05					22 30	
Hampton-in-Arden	d									21 33						21 48								22 33	
Berkswell	d					21 11				21 38									22 11					22 38	
Tile Hill	d					21 14				21 41						21 55			22 14					22 41	
Canley	d					21 17				21 44									22 17					22 44	
Coventry	a					21 20		21 24	21 30	21 47				21 50		22 00			22 20					22 47	
	d					21 21			21 31					21 51		22 00			22 21					22 48	
Rugby	d					21 32			21 43					22 03		22 12			22 32					22 59	
Long Buckby	d					21 41										22 21			22 41					23 09	
Northampton	a					21 53										22 34			22 53					23 21	
London Euston 15 ⊖66	a					23 27			22 55					23 30		00 05								00 40	

A From Preston
B From Liverpool Lime Street
C From Crewe
D From Holyhead
E From Manchester Piccadilly to Plymouth
F To Walsall
G From Shrewsbury
H From Manchester Piccadilly to Bournemouth
I From Aberystwyth
J From Manchester Piccadilly to Bristol Temple Meads
K From Manchester Piccadilly to Southampton Central. Trolley to Birmingham New Street
L From Manchester Piccadilly
M From Warrington Bank Quay

Table 68R

Saturdays
4 January to 8 February

Stafford - Wolverhampton - Birmingham - Coventry - Northampton

Network Diagram - refer to first Page of Table 67

		LM		AW	XC	LM	LM	LM	LM	VT	XC	LM		LM	LM	AW
		1		◇	◇1	1		1		◇1	◇1	1			1	◇
		A		B	C		D		E	F	C				A	G
										☕						
Stafford	d	21 42			22 03					22 23	22 29				22 45	
Penkridge	d	21 48													22 51	
Wolverhampton 7	a	21 59			22 14					22 40	22 43				23 01	
	d	22 02		22 08	22 16		22 19		22 37	22 40	22 44			22 49	23 03	23 08
Coseley	d	22 07					22 24							22 54	23 08	
Tipton	d						22 26							22 56		
Dudley Port	d						22 28							22 58		
Sandwell & Dudley	d						22 32		22 46					23 02		
Smethwick Galton Bridge 7	d			22 19			22 34							23 04		
Smethwick Rolfe Street	d						22 36							23 06		
Birmingham New Street 12	a	22 20		22 32	22 32		22 43		22 55	22 59	23 01			23 14	23 20	23 29
	d					22 34		22 54				23 14				
Adderley Park	d											23 18				
Stechford	d											23 22				
Lea Hall	d											23 24				
Marston Green	d					22 42		23 02				23 27				
Birmingham International ✈	a					22 45		23 05				23 30				
	d					22 45		23 05				23 31				
Hampton-in-Arden	d					22 48						23 34				
Berkswell	d							23 11				23 39				
Tile Hill	d					22 55		23 14				23 42				
Canley	d							23 17				23 45				
Coventry	a					23 00		23 20				23 48				
	d							23 21								
Rugby	d							23 32								
Long Buckby	d							23 41								
Northampton	a							23 55								
London Euston 15 ⊖66	a															

Saturdays
15 February to 17 May

		LM	VT	AW	XC	VT	LM	AW	VT	LM		AW	LM	LM	VT	LM	XC	VT	LM	LM		VT	LM	AW	XC
		1	◇1		◇1	◇1	1		◇1	1					◇1	1	◇1	◇1	1	1		◇1	1		◇1
		H		I	J			K				E		E			L			M				E	N
			☕		🛒	☕			☕						☕		🛒	☕				☕			🛒
Stafford	d			05 25													06 26			06 35					06 58
Penkridge	d																			06 41					
Wolverhampton 7	a			05 39													06 39			06 51					07 12
	d			05 40		05 45		06 02	06 06					06 19	06 27		06 41	06 45		06 53		07 05		07 12	07 16
Coseley	d													06 24						06 58					
Tipton	d													06 27						07 01					
Dudley Port	d													06 29						07 03					
Sandwell & Dudley	d					05 56			06 17					06 32	06 37			06 56		07 07		07 14			
Smethwick Galton Bridge 7	d							06 13						06 35						07 10				07 23	
Smethwick Rolfe Street	d											⟵		06 37						07 12					
Birmingham New Street 12	a			05 58		06 06		06 20	06 26			06 20		06 45	06 47		06 57	07 06		07 18		07 25		07 28	07 33
	d		05 50		06 04	06 10	06 14	06 36	06 30	06 33		06 36	06 39		06 50	06 54	07 04	07 10	07 14			07 30	07 33	07 36	
Adderley Park	d							⟶					06 44												
Stechford	d						06 20						06 47						07 20						
Lea Hall	d						06 23						06 50						07 23						
Marston Green	d	00 02					06 26			06 42						07 02			07 26				07 42		
Birmingham International ✈	a	00 05	05 59		06 13	06 19	06 29		06 39	06 45		06 49	06 54		06 59	07 05	07 13	07 19	07 29			07 39	07 45	07 50	
	d	00 06	06 00		06 14	06 20	06 30		06 40	06 45					07 00	07 05	07 14	07 20	07 30			07 40	07 45		
Hampton-in-Arden	d						06 33			06 48									07 33				07 48		
Berkswell	d						06 38									07 11			07 38						
Tile Hill	d						06 41			06 55						07 14			07 41				07 55		
Canley	d						06 44									07 17			07 44						
Coventry	a	00 15	06 10		06 24	06 30	06 47		06 49	07 00					07 10	07 20	07 24	07 30	07 47			07 50	08 00		
	d		06 10			06 31	06 48		06 51	07 00					07 11	07 21		07 31	07 48			07 51	08 00		
Rugby	d		06 24				06 59			07 12					07 23	07 32			07 59				08 12		
Long Buckby	d						07 08			07 21						07 41			08 08				08 21		
Northampton	a						07 21			07 34						07 53			08 20				08 34		
London Euston 15 ⊖66	a		07 17			07 38	08 40		07 55						08 17	09 17		08 35	09 27			08 54	09 47		

A From Liverpool Lime Street
B From Aberystwyth
C From Manchester Piccadilly
D To Walsall
E From Shrewsbury
F From Wigan North Western
G From Holyhead
H From Birmingham New Street
I From Chester
J To Bournemouth
K From Shrewsbury to Birmingham International
L From Manchester Piccadilly to Bournemouth
M From Crewe to Walsall
N From Manchester Piccadilly to Bristol Temple Meads

Table 68R

Saturdays

15 February to 17 May

Stafford - Wolverhampton - Birmingham - Coventry - Northampton

Network Diagram - refer to first Page of Table 67

		LM		LM	LM	VT	LM	LM	XC	VT	LM	LM		LM	VT	LM	AW	XC	LM	LM	LM	VT		LM	LM
					1	◇1	1		◇1	◇1		1		1	◇1	1	◇	◇1			1	◇1		1	
				A	B			C	D	E	A			F			G	H		A	F				C
						🍴			🛒	🍴					🍴		🛒	🛒				🍴			
Stafford	d				07 12									07 41				08 03			08 10				
Penkridge	d				07 18									07 47							08 16				
Wolverhampton 7	a				07 28									07 57				08 15			08 26				
	d			07 19	07 29			07 37		07 45	07 49			07 59			08 09	08 16		08 19	08 29				08 37
Coseley	d			07 24							07 54			08 04						08 24					
Tipton	d			07 26							07 56									08 26					
Dudley Port	d			07 28							07 58									08 28					
Sandwell & Dudley	d			07 32				07 46		07 55	08 02									08 32					08 46
Smethwick Galton Bridge 7	d			07 34	07 40						08 04						08 21			08 34	08 40				
Smethwick Rolfe Street	d			07 36							08 06									08 36					
Birmingham New Street 12	a			07 44	07 47			07 55		08 05	08 13			08 17			08 26	08 34		08 44	08 48				08 55
	d	07 39				07 50	07 54		08 04	08 10		08 14			08 30	08 33	08 36		08 39			08 50		08 54	
Adderley Park	d	07 44																	08 44						
Stechford	d	07 47										08 20							08 47						
Lea Hall	d	07 50										08 23							08 50						
Marston Green	d						08 02					08 26				08 42								09 02	
Birmingham International ✈	a	07 54				07 59	08 05		08 13	08 19		08 29			08 39	08 45	08 50		08 54			08 59		09 05	
	d					08 00	08 05		08 14	08 20		08 30			08 40	08 45						09 00		09 05	
Hampton-in-Arden	d											08 33				08 48									
Berkswell	d						08 11					08 38												09 11	
Tile Hill	d						08 14					08 41				08 55								09 14	
Canley	d						08 17					08 44												09 17	
Coventry	a					08 10	08 20		08 24	08 29		08 47			08 50	09 00						09 10		09 20	
	d					08 11	08 21			08 30		08 48			08 51	09 00						09 11		09 21	
Rugby	d					08 23	08 32					08 59				09 12						09 23		09 32	
Long Buckby	d						08 41					09 08				09 21								09 41	
Northampton	a						08 56					09 20				09 34								09 55	
London Euston 15 ⊖66	a					09 15	10 17			09 34		10 27			09 59	10 46						10 15		11 17	

		XC	VT	LM	LM	LM	VT	LM		AW	XC	LM	LM	LM	VT	LM	LM	XC		VT	LM	LM	LM	VT	LM
		◇1	◇1		1	1	◇1	1		◇	◇1			1	◇1	1		◇1		◇1		1	1	◇1	1
		I	J	A		F				K	L			F			C	I		M	A		F		
		🛒	🍴				🍴			🛒	🛒				🍴			🛒		🍴				🍴	
Stafford	d	08 26				08 43					09 03			09 10				09 26					09 45		
Penkridge	d					08 48								09 16											
Wolverhampton 7	a	08 39				08 58					09 15			09 26				09 39					09 58		
	d	08 41	08 45	08 49		08 59				09 12	09 16		09 19	09 29			09 37	09 41		09 45	09 49		09 59		
Coseley	d			08 54		09 04							09 24								09 54		10 04		
Tipton	d			08 56									09 26								09 56				
Dudley Port	d			08 58									09 28								09 58				
Sandwell & Dudley	d		08 55	09 02									09 32				09 46			09 55	10 02				
Smethwick Galton Bridge 7	d			09 04						09 23			09 34	09 40							10 04				
Smethwick Rolfe Street	d			09 06									09 36								10 06				
Birmingham New Street 12	a	08 58	09 05	09 13		09 17				09 27	09 33		09 44	09 47			09 55	09 58		10 05	10 13		10 17		
	d	09 04	09 10		09 14		09 30	09 33		09 36		09 39			09 50	09 54		10 04		10 10		10 14		10 30	10 33
Adderley Park	d											09 44													
Stechford	d				09 20							09 47										10 20			
Lea Hall	d				09 23							09 50										10 23			
Marston Green	d				09 26			09 42								10 02						10 26			10 42
Birmingham International ✈	a	09 13	09 19		09 29		09 39	09 45		09 49		09 54			09 59	10 05		10 13		10 19		10 29		10 39	10 45
	d	09 14	09 20		09 30		09 40	09 45							10 00	10 05		10 14		10 20		10 30		10 40	10 45
Hampton-in-Arden	d				09 33			09 48														10 33			10 48
Berkswell	d				09 38											10 11						10 38			
Tile Hill	d				09 41			09 55								10 14						10 41			10 55
Canley	d				09 44											10 17						10 44			
Coventry	a	09 24	09 30		09 47		09 50	10 00							10 10	10 20		10 24		10 30		10 47		10 50	11 00
	d		09 31		09 48		09 51	10 00							10 11	10 21				10 31		10 48		10 51	11 00
Rugby	d				09 59			10 12							10 23	10 32						10 59			11 12
Long Buckby	d				10 08			10 21								10 41						11 08			11 21
Northampton	a				10 20			10 34								10 53						11 20			11 34
London Euston 15 ⊖66	a		10 35		11 27		10 55	11 46							11 15	12 17				11 33		12 27		11 55	12 46

A To Walsall
B From Crewe
C From Shrewsbury
D From Nottingham to Bournemouth
E From Preston
F From Liverpool Lime Street
G From Aberystwyth
H From Manchester Piccadilly to Bristol Temple Meads
I From Manchester Piccadilly to Bournemouth
J From Lancaster
K From Holyhead
L From Manchester Piccadilly to Paignton
M From Glasgow Central

Table 68R

Saturdays

15 February to 17 May

Stafford - Wolverhampton - Birmingham - Coventry - Northampton

Network Diagram - refer to first Page of Table 67

		AW	XC	LM	LM	LM	VT	LM	LM	XC		VT	LM	LM	LM	VT	LM	AW	XC	LM		LM	LM	VT	LM
		◇	◇[1]			[1]	◇[1]	[1]		◇[1]		◇[1]		[1]	[1]	◇[1]	[1]	◇	◇[1]				[1]	◇[1]	[1]
		A	B		C	D			E	F		G	C		D			H	B			C	D		
		🛒	🛒				☕			🛒		☕				☕		🛒	🛒					☕	
Stafford	d		10 03			10 10				10 26					10 43				11 03				11 10		
Penkridge	d					10 16																	11 16		
Wolverhampton [7] 🚢	a		10 15			10 27				10 39					10 56				11 15				11 27		
	d	10 11	10 17		10 19	10 29			10 37	10 41		10 45	10 49		10 59			11 11	11 16			11 19	11 29		
Coseley	d				10 24								10 54		11 04							11 24			
Tipton	d				10 26								10 56									11 26			
Dudley Port	d				10 28								10 58									11 28			
Sandwell & Dudley	d				10 32				10 46			10 55	11 02									11 32			
Smethwick Galton Bridge [7]	d	10 22			10 34	10 40							11 04					11 22				11 34	11 40		
Smethwick Rolfe Street	d				10 36								11 06									11 36			
Birmingham New Street [12]	a	10 28	10 33		10 44	10 47			10 55	10 58		11 05	11 13		11 17			11 28	11 33			11 44	11 47		
	d	10 36		10 39			10 50	10 54		11 04		11 10		11 14		11 30	11 33	11 36		11 39				11 50	11 54
Adderley Park	d			10 44																11 44					
Stechford	d			10 47										11 20						11 47					
Lea Hall	d			10 50										11 23						11 50					
Marston Green	d							11 02						11 26			11 42								12 02
Birmingham International ✈	a	10 50		10 54			10 59	11 05		11 13		11 19		11 29		11 39	11 45	11 50		11 54				11 59	12 05
	d						11 00	11 05		11 14		11 20		11 30		11 40	11 45							12 00	12 05
Hampton-in-Arden	d													11 33			11 48								
Berkswell	d							11 11						11 38											12 11
Tile Hill	d							11 14						11 41			11 55								12 14
Canley	d							11 17						11 44											12 17
Coventry	a						11 10	11 20		11 24		11 30		11 47		11 49	12 00							12 10	12 20
	d						11 11	11 21				11 31		11 48		11 51	12 00							12 11	12 21
Rugby	d						11 23	11 32						11 59			12 12							12 23	12 32
Long Buckby	d							11 41						12 08			12 21								12 41
Northampton	a							11 53						12 20			12 34								12 53
London Euston [15] ⊖66	a						12 15	13 17				12 33		13 27		12 55	13 46							13 15	14 17

		LM	XC	VT	LM	LM		LM	VT	LM	AW	XC	LM	LM	LM	VT		LM	LM	XC	VT	LM	LM	LM	VT
			◇[1]	◇[1]		[1]		[1]	◇[1]	[1]	◇	◇[1]			[1]	◇[1]		[1]		◇[1]	◇[1]		[1]	[1]	◇[1]
		E	F	I	C			D			J	B		C	D				E	F	G	C		D	
			🛒	☕					☕		🛒	🛒				☕				🛒	☕				☕
Stafford	d		11 26					11 43				12 03			12 10					12 25				12 43	
Penkridge	d														12 16										
Wolverhampton [7] 🚢	a		11 39					11 56				12 15			12 27					12 39				12 56	
	d	11 37	11 41	11 45	11 49			11 59			12 11	12 16		12 19	12 29				12 37	12 41	12 45	12 49		12 59	
Coseley	d				11 54			12 04						12 24								12 54		13 04	
Tipton	d				11 56									12 26								12 56			
Dudley Port	d				11 58									12 28								12 58			
Sandwell & Dudley	d	11 47		11 55	12 02									12 32					12 46		12 55	13 02			
Smethwick Galton Bridge [7]	d				12 04						12 22			12 34	12 40							13 04			
Smethwick Rolfe Street	d				12 06									12 36								13 06			
Birmingham New Street [12]	a	11 56	11 59	12 05	12 13			12 17			12 28	12 33		12 44	12 47				12 55	12 58	13 05	13 13		13 17	
	d		12 04	12 10		12 14			12 30	12 33	12 36		12 39			12 50		12 54		13 04	13 10		13 14		13 30
Adderley Park	d												12 44												
Stechford	d					12 20							12 47										13 20		
Lea Hall	d					12 23							12 50										13 23		
Marston Green	d					12 26				12 42								13 02					13 26		
Birmingham International ✈	a		12 13	12 19		12 29			12 39	12 45	12 50		12 54			12 59		13 05		13 13	13 19		13 29		13 39
	d		12 14	12 20		12 30			12 40	12 45						13 00		13 05		13 14	13 20		13 30		13 40
Hampton-in-Arden	d					12 33				12 48													13 33		
Berkswell	d					12 38												13 11					13 38		
Tile Hill	d					12 41				12 55								13 14					13 41		
Canley	d					12 44												13 17					13 44		
Coventry	a		12 24	12 30		12 47			12 49	13 00						13 10		13 20		13 24	13 30		13 47		13 50
	d			12 30		12 48			12 51	13 00						13 11		13 21			13 31		13 48		13 51
Rugby	d					12 59				13 12						13 23		13 32					13 59		
Long Buckby	d					13 08				13 21								13 41					14 08		
Northampton	a					13 20				13 34								13 53					14 20		
London Euston [15] ⊖66	a			13 35		14 27			13 55	14 46						14 15		15 18			14 33		15 27		14 55

A From Barmouth
B From Manchester Piccadilly to Bristol Temple Meads
C To Walsall
D From Liverpool Lime Street
E From Shrewsbury
F From Manchester Piccadilly to Bournemouth
G From Edinburgh
H From Holyhead
I From Glasgow Central
J From Pwllheli

Table 68R

Saturdays

15 February to 17 May

Stafford - Wolverhampton - Birmingham - Coventry - Northampton

Network Diagram - refer to first Page of Table 67

		AW	XC	LM	AW	LM	LM	LM		VT	LM	LM	XC	VT	LM	LM	LM	VT		LM	AW	XC	LM	LM	LM
		◇	◇[1]	[1]	◇			[1]		◇[1]	[1]		◇[1]	◇[1]		[1]	[1]	◇[1]		[1]	◇	◇[1]			[1]
		A	B		C		D	E				F	G	H	D		E				I	J		D	E
		🛒	🛒		🛒					☕			🛒	☕				☕			🛒	🛒			
Stafford	d		13 03					13 10					13 26				13 45					14 03			14 10
Penkridge	d							13 16																	14 16
Wolverhampton [7] 🚋	a		13 14					13 27					13 39				13 58					14 15			14 27
	d	13 10	13 16				13 19	13 29				13 37	13 41	13 45	13 49		13 59				14 11	14 16		14 19	14 29
Coseley	d						13 24								13 54		14 04							14 24	
Tipton	d						13 26								13 56									14 26	
Dudley Port	d						13 28								13 58									14 28	
Sandwell & Dudley	d						13 32					13 46		13 55	14 02									14 32	
Smethwick Galton Bridge [7]	d	13 22					13 34	13 40							14 04						14 22			14 34	14 40
Smethwick Rolfe Street	d				←		13 36								14 06									14 36	
Birmingham New Street [12]	a	13 28	13 32		13 28		13 44	13 47				13 55	13 58	14 05	14 13		14 17				14 28	14 33		14 44	14 47
	d	13 36		13 33	13 36	13 39				13 50	13 54		14 04	14 10		14 14		14 30		14 33	14 36		14 39		
Adderley Park	d	↦				13 44																	14 44		
Stechford	d					13 47										14 20							14 47		
Lea Hall	d					13 50										14 23							14 50		
Marston Green	d			13 42							14 02					14 26				14 42					
Birmingham International ✈	a			13 45	13 50	13 54				13 59	14 05		14 13	14 19		14 29		14 39		14 45	14 50		14 54		
	d			13 45						14 00	14 05		14 14	14 20		14 30		14 40		14 45					
Hampton-in-Arden	d			13 48												14 33				14 48					
Berkswell	d										14 11					14 38									
Tile Hill	d			13 55							14 14					14 41				14 55					
Canley	d										14 17					14 44									
Coventry	a			14 00						14 10	14 20		14 24	14 30		14 47		14 49		15 00					
	d			14 00						14 11	14 21			14 31		14 48		14 51		15 00					
Rugby	d			14 12						14 23	14 32					14 59				15 12					
Long Buckby	d			14 21							14 41					15 08				15 21					
Northampton	a			14 34							14 53					15 20				15 34					
London Euston [15] ⊖66	a			15 46						15 15	16 18			15 34		16 27		15 55		16 46					

		VT	LM	LM		XC	VT	LM	LM	LM	VT	LM	AW	XC		LM	LM	LM	VT	LM	LM	XC	VT	LM	
		◇[1]	[1]			◇[1]	◇[1]		[1]	[1]	◇[1]	[1]	◇	◇[1]				[1]	◇[1]	[1]		◇[1]	◇[1]		
				F		G	K	D		E			C	L			D	E			F	G	H	D	
		☕				🛒	☕				☕		🛒	🛒					☕			🛒	☕		
Stafford	d					14 26				14 43				15 03				15 10				15 26			
Penkridge	d																	15 16							
Wolverhampton [7] 🚋	a					14 39				14 56				15 16				15 27				15 39			
	d			14 37		14 41	14 45	14 49		14 59			15 11	15 17			15 19	15 29			15 37	15 41	15 45	15 49	
Coseley	d							14 54		15 04							15 24							15 54	
Tipton	d							14 56									15 26							15 56	
Dudley Port	d							14 58									15 28							15 58	
Sandwell & Dudley	d			14 46			14 55	15 02									15 32				15 46		15 55	16 02	
Smethwick Galton Bridge [7]	d							15 04					15 22				15 34	15 40						16 04	
Smethwick Rolfe Street	d							15 06									15 36							16 06	
Birmingham New Street [12]	a			14 55		14 58	15 05	15 13		15 17			15 28	15 33			15 44	15 47			15 55	15 58	16 05	16 13	
	d	14 50	14 54			15 04	15 10		15 14		15 30	15 33	15 36			15 39			15 50	15 54		16 04	16 10		
Adderley Park	d															15 44									
Stechford	d								15 20							15 47									
Lea Hall	d								15 23							15 50									
Marston Green	d		15 02						15 26			15 42								16 02					
Birmingham International ✈	a	14 59	15 05			15 13	15 19		15 29		15 39	15 45	15 49			15 54			15 59	16 05		16 13	16 19		
	d	15 00	15 05			15 14	15 20		15 30		15 40	15 45							16 00	16 05		16 14	16 20		
Hampton-in-Arden	d								15 33			15 48													
Berkswell	d		15 11						15 38											16 11					
Tile Hill	d		15 14						15 41			15 55								16 14					
Canley	d		15 17						15 44											16 17					
Coventry	a	15 10	15 20			15 24	15 30		15 47		15 50	16 00							16 10	16 20		16 24	16 30		
	d	15 11	15 21				15 31		15 48		15 51	16 00							16 11	16 21			16 31		
Rugby	d	15 23	15 32						15 59			16 12							16 23	16 32					
Long Buckby	d		15 41						16 08			16 21								16 41					
Northampton	a		15 53						16 20			16 34								16 53					
London Euston [15] ⊖66	a	16 15	17 17				16 34		17 27		16 57	17 46							17 15	18 17			17 33		

A From Holyhead to Birmingham International
B From Manchester Piccadilly to Exeter St Davids
C From Holyhead
D To Walsall
E From Liverpool Lime Street
F From Shrewsbury
G From Manchester Piccadilly to Bournemouth
H From Glasgow Central
I From Pwllheli
J From Manchester Piccadilly to Bristol Temple Meads
K From Edinburgh
L From Manchester Piccadilly to Paignton

Table 68R

Saturdays

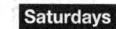

15 February to 17 May

Stafford - Wolverhampton - Birmingham - Coventry - Northampton

Network Diagram - refer to first Page of Table 67

		LM	LM	VT	LM	AW		XC	LM	LM	LM	VT	LM	LM	XC	VT		LM	LM	LM	VT	LM	AW	XC	LM
		1	1	◇1	1	◇		◇1			1	◇1	1		◇1	◇1		1		1	◇1	1	◇	◇1	
			A			B		C		D	A			E	F	G			D	A			H	C	
				⊥P		⊥o		⊥o				⊥P			⊥o	⊥P					⊥P		⊥o	⊥o	
Stafford	d		15 43					16 03			16 10				16 25					16 45				17 03	
Penkridge	d										16 16														
Wolverhampton 7	a		15 56					16 16			16 27				16 39					16 58				17 16	
	d		15 59			16 11		16 17		16 19	16 29			16 37	16 41	16 45			16 49	16 59			17 07	17 17	
Coseley	d		16 04							16 24									16 54	17 04					
Tipton	d									16 26									16 56						
Dudley Port	d									16 28									16 58						
Sandwell & Dudley	d									16 32				16 46		16 55			17 02						
Smethwick Galton Bridge 7	d					16 22				16 34	16 40								17 04				17 20		
Smethwick Rolfe Street	d									16 36									17 06						
Birmingham New Street 12	a		16 17			16 28		16 33		16 44	16 47			16 55	16 58	17 05			17 13	17 17			17 26	17 33	
	d	16 14		16 30	16 33	16 36			16 39			16 50	16 54		17 04	17 10		17 13			17 30	17 33	17 36		17 39
Adderley Park	d								16 44									17 17							17 44
Stechford	d	16 20							16 47									17 21							17 47
Lea Hall	d	16 23							16 50									17 23							17 50
Marston Green	d	16 26			16 42								17 02					17 26				17 42			
Birmingham International ✈	a	16 29		16 39	16 45	16 50			16 54			16 59	17 05		17 13	17 19		17 29			17 39	17 45	17 49		17 54
	d	16 30		16 40	16 45							17 00	17 05		17 14	17 20		17 30			17 40	17 45			
Hampton-in-Arden	d	16 33			16 48													17 33				17 48			
Berkswell	d	16 38											17 11					17 38							
Tile Hill	d	16 41			16 55								17 14					17 41				17 55			
Canley	d	16 44											17 17					17 44							
Coventry	a	16 47		16 50	17 00							17 10	17 20		17 24	17 30		17 47			17 49	18 00			
	d	16 48		16 51	17 00							17 11	17 21			17 31		17 48			17 51	18 00			
Rugby	d	16 59			17 12							17 23	17 32					17 59				18 12			
Long Buckby	d	17 08			17 21								17 41					18 08				18 21			
Northampton	a	17 21			17 34								17 53					18 20				18 34			
London Euston 15 ⊖66	a	18 27		17 55	18 46							18 15	19 17			18 34		19 45			18 55	19 45			

		LM		LM	VT	LM	LM	XC	VT	LM	LM	LM		VT	LM	AW	XC	LM	LM	LM	VT	LM		LM	XC
				1	◇1	1		◇1	◇1		1	1		◇1	1	◇	◇1			1	◇1	1			◇1
		D		A			E	F	I	D		A				B	J		D	A				E	F
					⊥P			⊥o	⊥P					⊥P		⊥o	⊥o				⊥P				⊥o
Stafford	d			17 10				17 26				17 44					18 04			18 10					18 26
Penkridge	d			17 16																18 16					
Wolverhampton 7	a			17 27				17 39				17 57					18 15			18 27					18 40
	d	17 19		17 29			17 37	17 41	17 45	17 49		17 59				18 11	18 16		18 19	18 29				18 37	18 41
Coseley	d	17 24								17 54		18 04							18 24						
Tipton	d	17 26								17 56									18 26						
Dudley Port	d	17 28								17 58									18 28						
Sandwell & Dudley	d	17 32					17 46		17 55	18 02									18 32					18 46	
Smethwick Galton Bridge 7	d	17 34		17 40						18 04						18 22			18 34	18 40					
Smethwick Rolfe Street	d	17 36								18 06									18 36						
Birmingham New Street 12	a	17 44		17 47			17 55	17 58	18 05	18 13		18 17				18 28	18 33		18 44	18 47				18 55	18 58
	d				17 50	17 54		18 04	18 10		18 14			18 30	18 33	18 36		18 39			18 50	18 54			19 04
Adderley Park	d																	18 44							
Stechford	d										18 20							18 47							
Lea Hall	d										18 23							18 50							
Marston Green	d					18 02					18 26				18 42							19 02			
Birmingham International ✈	a				17 59	18 05		18 13	18 19		18 29			18 39	18 45	18 50		18 54			18 59	19 05			19 13
	d				18 00	18 05		18 14	18 20		18 30			18 40	18 45						19 00	19 05			19 14
Hampton-in-Arden	d										18 33				18 48										
Berkswell	d					18 11					18 38											19 11			
Tile Hill	d					18 14					18 41				18 55							19 14			
Canley	d					18 17					18 44											19 17			
Coventry	a				18 10	18 20		18 24	18 30		18 47			18 49	19 00						19 10	19 20			19 24
	d				18 11	18 21			18 31		18 48			18 51	19 00						19 11	19 21			
Rugby	d				18 23	18 32					18 59										19 23	19 32			
Long Buckby	d					18 41					19 08											19 41			
Northampton	a					18 53					19 20											19 53			
London Euston 15 ⊖66	a				19 15	20 18			19 34		20 45			19 55							20 22	21 09			

A From Liverpool Lime Street
B From Pwllheli
C From Manchester Piccadilly to Bristol Temple Meads
D To Walsall
E From Shrewsbury
F From Manchester Piccadilly to Bournemouth
G From Edinburgh
H From Holyhead
I From Glasgow Central
J From Manchester Piccadilly to Cardiff Central

Table 68R

Saturdays

15 February to 17 May

Stafford - Wolverhampton - Birmingham - Coventry - Northampton

Network Diagram - refer to first Page of Table 67

Station		VT ◇1 A 🍴	LM 1	LM		LM 1 B	LM 1 C	LM 1	AW ◇ D 🛒	XC ◇1 E 🛒	LM	LM F	LM 1 B	LM 1		LM G	XC ◇1 H 🛒	VT ◇1 I 🍴	LM 1	LM	LM 1 B	LM 1 C	LM 1	AW ◇ J 🛒	
Stafford	d					18 43	18 56			19 03			19 10				19 25				19 45	19 51			
Penkridge	d												19 16								19 51				
Wolverhampton 7 🚌	a					18 56				19 15			19 27				19 39				20 01				
	d	18 45		18 49		18 59			19 11	19 16		19 19	19 29			19 37	19 41	19 45		19 49	20 02			20 10	
Coseley	d			18 54		19 04						19 24								19 54	20 07				
Tipton	d			18 56								19 26								19 56					
Dudley Port	d			18 58								19 28								19 58					
Sandwell & Dudley	d	18 55		19 02								19 32				19 46		19 55		20 02					
Smethwick Galton Bridge 7	d			19 04					19 22			19 34	19 40							20 04				20 21	
Smethwick Rolfe Street	d			19 06								19 36								20 06					
Birmingham New Street 12	a	19 05		19 14		19 17			19 28	19 33		19 44	19 47			19 55	19 59	20 05		20 14	20 19			20 26	
	d	19 10	19 14					19 33	19 36		19 39			19 54			20 04	20 10	20 14				20 33	20 36	
Adderley Park	d										19 44														
Stechford	d		19 20								19 47								20 20						
Lea Hall	d		19 23								19 50								20 23						
Marston Green	d		19 26					19 42						20 02					20 26				20 42		
Birmingham International ✈	a	19 19	19 29					19 45	19 50		19 54			20 05			20 13	20 19	20 29				20 45	20 50	
	d	19 20	19 30					19 45						20 05			20 14	20 20	20 30				20 45		
Hampton-in-Arden	d		19 33					19 48											20 33				20 48		
Berkswell	d		19 38											20 11					20 38						
Tile Hill	d		19 41					19 55						20 14					20 41				20 55		
Canley	d		19 44											20 17					20 44						
Coventry	a	19 30	19 47					20 00						20 20			20 24	20 30	20 47				21 00		
	d	19 31	19 48					20 00						20 21				20 31					21 00		
Rugby	d	19 44	19 59				19 52	20 12						20 32				20 43				20 47	21 12		
Long Buckby	d		20 08					20 21						20 41									21 21		
Northampton	a		20 20				20 12	20 35						20 53								21 07	21 34		
London Euston 15 ⊖66	a	20 55	21 45											22 11				21 56							

Station		XC ◇1 E 🛒	LM	LM F	LM 1 B	LM 1	LM G	XC ◇1 K 🛒	VT ◇1 A 🍴	LM 1		LM	LM 1 B	VT ◇1 🍴	XC ◇1 L	LM 1	LM	LM F	LM 1	VT ◇1 I 🍴		LM G	XC ◇1 L	LM 1	LM
Stafford	d	20 03			20 12			20 26					20 40		21 03								21 27		
Penkridge	d												20 49												
Wolverhampton 7 🚌	a	20 15			20 28			20 39					20 59		21 15								21 39		
	d	20 16		20 19	20 29		20 37	20 41	20 45			20 49	20 59	21 07	21 16			21 19		21 34		21 37	21 41		21 49
Coseley	d			20 24								20 54	21 04					21 24							21 54
Tipton	d			20 26								20 56						21 26							21 56
Dudley Port	d			20 28								20 58						21 28							21 58
Sandwell & Dudley	d			20 32			20 46		20 55			21 02		21 17				21 32				21 47			22 02
Smethwick Galton Bridge 7	d			20 34	20 40							21 04						21 34							22 04
Smethwick Rolfe Street	d			20 36								21 06						21 36							22 06
Birmingham New Street 12	a	20 33		20 44	20 48		20 55	20 58	21 05			21 14	21 17	21 26	21 32			21 43		21 55		21 55	21 58		22 14
	d		20 39			20 54		21 04	21 10	21 14				21 30		21 34	21 39		21 54					22 14	
Adderley Park	d		20 44														21 44								
Stechford	d		20 47							21 20							21 47							22 20	
Lea Hall	d		20 50							21 23							21 50							22 23	
Marston Green	d					21 02				21 26						21 42			22 02					22 26	
Birmingham International ✈	a		20 54			21 05		21 13	21 19	21 29				21 39		21 45	21 54		22 05					22 29	
	d					21 05		21 14	21 20	21 30				21 40		21 45			22 05					22 30	
Hampton-in-Arden	d									21 33						21 48								22 33	
Berkswell	d					21 11				21 38									22 11					22 38	
Tile Hill	d					21 14				21 41						21 55			22 14					22 41	
Canley	d					21 17				21 44									22 17					22 44	
Coventry	a					21 20		21 24	21 30	21 47				21 50		22 00			22 20					22 47	
	d					21 21			21 31					21 51		22 00			22 21					22 48	
Rugby	d					21 32			21 43					22 03		22 12			22 32					22 59	
Long Buckby	d					21 41										22 21			22 41					23 09	
Northampton	a					21 53										22 34			22 53					23 21	
London Euston 15 ⊖66	a					23 27			22 55					23 30		00 05								00 40	

A From Edinburgh
B From Liverpool Lime Street
C From Crewe
D From Holyhead
E From Manchester Piccadilly to Bristol Temple Meads
F To Walsall
G From Shrewsbury
H From Manchester Piccadilly to Bournemouth
I From Glasgow Central
J From Aberystwyth
K From Manchester Piccadilly to Southampton Central. 🛒 to Birmingham New Street
L From Manchester Piccadilly

Table 68R

Saturdays

15 February to 17 May

Stafford - Wolverhampton - Birmingham - Coventry - Northampton

Network Diagram - refer to first Page of Table 67

		LM	AW	XC	LM	LM	VT	LM	LM	VT	XC	LM	LM	LM	AW
		1	◇	◇1	1		◇1	1		◇1	◇1	1		1	◇
		A	B	C		D	E		F	G	C			A	H
Stafford	d	21 42		22 03			22 08			22 23	22 29			22 45	
Penkridge	d	21 48												22 51	
Wolverhampton 7	a	21 59		22 14			22 22			22 40	22 43			23 01	
	d	22 02	22 08	22 16		22 19	22 23		22 37	22 40	22 44		22 49	23 03	23 08
Coseley	d	22 07				22 24							22 54	23 08	
Tipton	d					22 26							22 56		
Dudley Port	d					22 28							22 58		
Sandwell & Dudley	d					22 32			22 46				23 02		
Smethwick Galton Bridge 7	d		22 19			22 34							23 04		
Smethwick Rolfe Street	d					22 36							23 06		
Birmingham New Street 12	a	22 20	22 32	22 32		22 43	22 46		22 55	22 59	23 01		23 14	23 20	23 29
	d				22 34			22 54				23 14			
Adderley Park	d											23 18			
Stechford	d											23 22			
Lea Hall	d											23 24			
Marston Green	d				22 42			23 02				23 27			
Birmingham International	a				22 45			23 05				23 30			
	d				22 45			23 05				23 31			
Hampton-in-Arden	d				22 48							23 34			
Berkswell	d							23 11				23 39			
Tile Hill	d				22 55			23 14				23 42			
Canley	d							23 17				23 45			
Coventry	a				23 00			23 20				23 48			
	d							23 21							
Rugby	d							23 32							
Long Buckby	d							23 41							
Northampton	a							23 55							
London Euston 15 ⊖66	a														

Sundays

8 December to 29 December

		VT	LM	LM	LM	XC	LM	AW	VT	LM	LM	XC	LM	AW	VT	LM	LM	LM	XC	LM	AW	LM	VT
		◇1	1	1		◇1	1		◇1	1		◇1	1		◇1	1	1		◇1	1	◇	1	◇1
						I		F				J		F			K		J		L	K	
Stafford	d											09 26					10 18		10 27			10 42	
Penkridge	d																					10 49	
Wolverhampton 7	a											09 40							10 42			11 00	
	d	08 05			08 22			09 00	09 05		09 22	09 41		09 59	10 05			10 22	10 43		10 57	11 00	11 05
Coseley	d				08 27						09 27							10 27					
Tipton	d				08 29						09 29							10 29					
Dudley Port	d				08 31						09 31							10 31					
Sandwell & Dudley	d	08 15			08 35				09 15		09 35				10 15			10 35					11 15
Smethwick Galton Bridge 7	d				08 37						09 37							10 37					
Smethwick Rolfe Street	d				08 39						09 39							10 39					
Birmingham New Street 12	a	08 24			08 46			09 15	09 24		09 46	09 58		10 14	10 24			10 46	10 59		11 13	11 18	11 26
	d	08 30	08 34	08 38		09 04	09 14	09 20	09 30	09 34		10 04	10 14	10 20	10 30	10 34			11 04	11 14	11 19		11 30
Adderley Park	d			08 42						09 38						10 38							
Stechford	d			08 46						09 42						10 42							
Lea Hall	d			08 48						09 44						10 44							
Marston Green	d		08 42	08 52			09 22			09 48			10 22			10 48				11 22			
Birmingham International	a	08 39	08 45	08 55		09 13	09 25	09 31	09 39	09 51		10 13	10 25	10 32	10 39	10 51			11 13	11 25	11 31		11 39
	d	08 40	08 45			09 14	09 25		09 40	09 51		10 14	10 25		10 40	10 51			11 14	11 25			11 40
Hampton-in-Arden	d						09 28						10 28							11 28			
Berkswell	d		08 51				09 33						10 33							11 33			
Tile Hill	d		08 54				09 36						10 36							11 36			
Canley	d		08 57				09 40						10 40							11 40			
Coventry	a	08 50	09 00			09 24	09 44		09 50	10 04		10 24	10 44		10 50	11 01			11 24	11 44			11 50
	d	08 51					09 44		09 51				10 44		10 51					11 44			11 51
Rugby	d	09 04					09 55		10 04				10 55		11 04		11 20			11 55			12 05
Long Buckby	d						10 05						11 05				11 29			12 05			
Northampton	a						10 17						11 17				11 41			12 17			
London Euston 15 ⊖66	a	10 28					11 59		11 31				12 37		12 27		12 51			13 38			13 06

A From Liverpool Lime Street
B From Aberystwyth
C From Manchester Piccadilly
D To Walsall
E From Glasgow Central
F From Shrewsbury
G From Edinburgh
H From Holyhead
I To Bournemouth
J From Manchester Piccadilly to Bournemouth. from Birmingham New Street to Birmingham New Street
K From Crewe
L From Chester

Table 68R

Sundays

8 December to 29 December

Stafford - Wolverhampton - Birmingham - Coventry - Northampton

Network Diagram - refer to first Page of Table 67

		LM		LM	LM	VT	VT	XC	VT	LM	VT	LM		LM	AW	LM	VT	VT	XC	VT	LM	LM		VT	LM
		1		1		◇1	◇1	◇1	◇1	1	◇1	1		1	◇		◇1	◇1	◇1	◇1	1	1		◇1	1
				A			B	C				A			D			B	E			F			A
						☕	☕	🛒	☕		☕				🛒		☕	☕	☕🛒	☕				☕	
Stafford	d			11 18				11 28				12 18							12 25			12 40			13 18
Penkridge	d																					12 46			
Wolverhampton 7	a							11 41											12 40			12 56			
	d				11 22		11 32	11 42	11 45						12 17	12 22		12 32	12 41	12 45		12 59			
Coseley	d				11 27											12 27									
Tipton	d				11 29											12 29									
Dudley Port	d				11 31											12 31									
Sandwell & Dudley	d				11 35				11 57							12 35				12 55					
Smethwick Galton Bridge 7	d				11 37											12 37									
Smethwick Rolfe Street	d				11 39											12 39									
Birmingham New Street 12	a				11 46		11 55	11 59	12 06						12 32	12 46		12 54	12 58	13 06		13 15			
	d	11 34				11 50		12 04	12 10	12 14	12 30			12 34	12 37		12 50		13 04	13 10	13 14			13 30	
Adderley Park	d	11 38												12 38											
Stechford	d	11 42												12 42											
Lea Hall	d	11 44												12 44											
Marston Green	d	11 48								12 22				12 48							13 22				
Birmingham International ✈	a	11 51				11 59		12 13	12 19	12 25	12 39			12 51	12 56		12 59		13 13	13 19	13 25			13 39	
	d	11 51				12 00		12 14	12 20	12 25	12 40			12 51			13 00		13 14	13 20	13 25			13 40	
Hampton-in-Arden	d									12 28											13 28				
Berkswell	d									12 33											13 33				
Tile Hill	d									12 36				12 58							13 36				
Canley	d									12 40											13 40				
Coventry	a	12 01				12 10		12 24	12 30	12 44	12 50			13 04			13 10		13 24	13 30	13 44			13 50	
	d					12 11			12 31	12 44	12 51						13 10			13 31	13 44			13 51	
Rugby	d			12 20		12 25				12 55		13 20					13 25				13 55				14 20
Long Buckby	d			12 30						13 05		13 29									14 05				14 30
Northampton	a			12 42						13 17		13 41									14 17				14 42
London Euston 15 ⊖66	a			13 53		13 20			13 38	14 37	13 57	14 53					14 18			14 38	15 37			14 57	15 53

		LM	AW	LM	VT	XC	VT	LM		LM	VT	LM	AW	XC	LM	AW	LM	VT		XC	VT	LM	LM	VT	LM
		1	◇		◇1	◇1	◇1	1		1	◇1	1	◇	◇1	1	◇		◇1		◇1	◇1	1	1	◇1	1
			G			E	H			F		A	I	J		D				E	K		F		A
			🛒		☕	☕🛒	☕				☕		🛒	🛒		🛒		☕		☕🛒	☕			☕	
Stafford	d					13 25				13 40		14 18								14 25			14 40		15 18
Penkridge	d									13 46													14 46		
Wolverhampton 7	a					13 40				13 56										14 40			14 56		
	d		13 08	13 22		13 41	13 45			13 59			14 08	14 15			14 22			14 41	14 45		14 59		
Coseley	d			13 27													14 27								
Tipton	d			13 29													14 29								
Dudley Port	d			13 31													14 31								
Sandwell & Dudley	d			13 35			13 56										14 35				14 56				
Smethwick Galton Bridge 7	d			13 37													14 37								
Smethwick Rolfe Street	d			13 39												←	14 39								
Birmingham New Street 12	a		13 23	13 46		13 58	14 06			14 15			14 23	14 31		14 23	14 46			14 58	15 06		15 15		
	d	13 34	13 36		13 50	14 04	14 10	14 14			14 30		14 36		14 34	14 36		14 50		15 04	15 10	15 14		15 30	
Adderley Park	d	13 38											→		14 38										
Stechford	d	13 42													14 42										
Lea Hall	d	13 44													14 44										
Marston Green	d	13 48						14 22							14 48							15 22			
Birmingham International ✈	a	13 51	13 55		13 59	14 13	14 19	14 25			14 39				14 51	14 55		14 59		15 13	15 19	15 25		15 39	
	d	13 51			14 01	14 14	14 20	14 25			14 40				14 51			15 01		15 14	15 20	15 25		15 40	
Hampton-in-Arden	d							14 28														15 28			
Berkswell	d							14 33														15 33			
Tile Hill	d	13 58						14 36							14 58							15 36			
Canley	d							14 40														15 40			
Coventry	a	14 04			14 13	14 24	14 30	14 44			14 50				15 04			15 13		15 24	15 30	15 44		15 50	
	d				14 14		14 31	14 44			14 51							15 14			15 31	15 44		15 51	
Rugby	d				14 26			14 55				15 20						15 26				15 55			16 20
Long Buckby	d							15 05				15 30										16 05			16 29
Northampton	a							15 17				15 42										16 17			16 41
London Euston 15 ⊖66	a				15 18		15 39	16 38			15 57	16 53						16 18			16 39	17 38		16 57	17 53

- **A** From Crewe
- **B** From Preston
- **C** From Manchester Piccadilly to Bournemouth
- **D** From Aberystwyth
- **E** From Manchester Piccadilly to Bournemouth. ☕ from Birmingham New Street 🛒 to Birmingham New Street
- **F** From Liverpool Lime Street
- **G** From Chester
- **H** From Lancaster
- **I** From Aberystwyth to Birmingham International
- **J** From Manchester Piccadilly to Paignton
- **K** From Edinburgh

Table 68R

Sundays

8 December to 29 December

Stafford - Wolverhampton - Birmingham - Coventry - Northampton

Network Diagram - refer to first Page of Table 67

		AW	XC	LM	AW	LM	VT	XC	VT	LM		LM	VT	LM	AW	XC	LM	AW	LM	VT		XC	VT	LM	LM
		◇	◇1	1	◇		◇1	◇1	◇1	1		1	◇1	1	◇	◇1	1	◇		◇1		◇1	◇1	1	1
		A	B		C			D	E			F		G	H	B		I				D	J		F
			🛒				☕	☕🛒	☕				☕		🛒	🛒		🛒		☕		☕🛒	☕		
Stafford	d							15 25				15 40		16 18								16 25			16 40
Penkridge	d											15 46													16 46
Wolverhampton 7	a							15 40				15 56										16 40			16 56
	d	15 09	15 15			15 22		15 41	15 45			15 59			16 09	16 15			16 22			16 41	16 45		16 59
Coseley	d					15 27													16 27						
Tipton	d					15 29													16 29						
Dudley Port	d					15 31													16 31						
Sandwell & Dudley	d					15 35			15 56										16 35				16 56		
Smethwick Galton Bridge 7	d					15 37													16 37						
Smethwick Rolfe Street	d				←	15 39												←	16 39						
Birmingham New Street 12	a	15 24	15 31		15 24	15 46		15 58	16 07			16 15			16 24	16 31		16 24	16 46			16 58	17 06		17 15
	d	15 39		15 34	15 39		15 50	16 04	16 10	16 14			16 30		16 36		16 34	16 36		16 50		17 04	17 10	17 14	
Adderley Park	d	↪		15 38											↪		16 38								
Stechford	d			15 42													16 42								
Lea Hall	d			15 44													16 44								
Marston Green	d			15 48						16 22							16 48							17 22	
Birmingham International ✈	a			15 51	15 58		15 59	16 13	16 19	16 25			16 39				16 51	16 55		16 59		17 13	17 19	17 25	
	d			15 51			16 01	16 14	16 21	16 25			16 40				16 51			17 00		17 14	17 20	17 25	
Hampton-in-Arden	d									16 28														17 28	
Berkswell	d									16 33														17 33	
Tile Hill	d			15 58						16 36							16 58							17 36	
Canley	d									16 40														17 40	
Coventry	a			16 04			16 11	16 24	16 31	16 44			16 50				17 05			17 10		17 24	17 29	17 44	
	d						16 11		16 31	16 44			16 51							17 11			17 29	17 44	
Rugby	d						16 24			16 55				17 20						17 25				17 55	
Long Buckby	d									17 05				17 30										18 05	
Northampton	a									17 17				17 42										18 17	
London Euston 15 ⊖66	a						17 17		17 38	18 37			17 57	18 53						18 18			18 38	19 37	

		VT	XC	LM	LM	AW		LM	VT	XC	VT	LM	LM	VT	LM	AW		XC	LM	AW	LM	VT	XC	VT	LM
		◇1	◇1	1	1	◇			◇1	◇1	◇1	1	1	◇1	1	◇		◇1	1	◇		◇1	◇1	◇1	1
			B		G	C				D	E		F		G	K		L		M			D	J	
		☕	🛒			🛒			☕	☕🛒	☕			☕		🛒		🛒		🛒		☕	☕🛒	☕	
Stafford	d				17 18					17 26			17 40		18 18								18 27		
Penkridge	d												17 46												
Wolverhampton 7	a									17 40			17 56										18 40		
	d		17 15			17 19		17 22		17 41	17 45		17 59			18 09		18 15			18 22		18 41	18 45	
Coseley	d							17 27													18 27				
Tipton	d							17 29													18 29				
Dudley Port	d							17 31													18 31				
Sandwell & Dudley	d							17 35			17 56										18 35			18 56	
Smethwick Galton Bridge 7	d							17 37													18 37				
Smethwick Rolfe Street	d							17 39												←	18 39				
Birmingham New Street 12	a		17 31			17 35		17 46		17 58	18 07		18 15			18 27		18 31		18 27	18 46		18 58	19 06	
	d	17 30		17 34		17 38			17 50	18 04	18 10	18 14		18 30		18 36			18 34	18 36		18 50	19 04	19 10	19 14
Adderley Park	d			17 38												↪			18 38						
Stechford	d			17 42															18 42						
Lea Hall	d			17 44															18 44						
Marston Green	d			17 48								18 22							18 48						19 22
Birmingham International ✈	a	17 39		17 51		17 56			17 59	18 13	18 19	18 25		18 39					18 51	18 55		18 59	19 13	19 19	19 25
	d	17 40		17 51					18 00	18 14	18 21	18 25		18 40					18 51			19 01	19 14	19 20	19 25
Hampton-in-Arden	d											18 28													19 28
Berkswell	d											18 33													19 33
Tile Hill	d			17 58								18 36							18 58						19 36
Canley	d											18 40													19 40
Coventry	a	17 50		18 05					18 10	18 24	18 31	18 44		18 50					19 05			19 13	19 24	19 30	19 44
	d	17 51							18 11		18 31	18 44		18 51								19 14		19 32	19 44
Rugby	d				18 20				18 26			18 55			19 20							19 26			19 55
Long Buckby	d				18 30							19 05			19 30										20 05
Northampton	a				18 42							19 17			19 42										20 17
London Euston 15 ⊖66	a	18 57			19 53				19 18		19 38	20 38		19 57	20 53							20 18		20 39	21 42

A From Chester to Birmingham International
B From Manchester Piccadilly to Bristol Temple Meads
C From Chester
D From Manchester Piccadilly to Bournemouth. ☕ from Birmingham New Street 🛒 to Birmingham New Street
E From Glasgow Central
F From Liverpool Lime Street
G From Crewe
H From Aberystwyth to Birmingham International
I From Aberystwyth
J From Edinburgh
K From Pwllheli to Birmingham International
L From Manchester Piccadilly to Plymouth
M From Pwllheli

Table 68R

Sundays

8 December to 29 December

Stafford - Wolverhampton - Birmingham - Coventry - Northampton

Network Diagram - refer to first Page of Table 67

		LM	VT	LM	AW	XC	LM	AW		LM	XC	VT	LM	LM	VT	LM	AW	XC		LM	AW	LM	VT	XC	LM
		1	◇1	1	◇	◇1	1	◇			◇1	◇1	1	1	◇1	1	◇	◇1		1	◇		◇1	◇1	1
		A		B	C	D		E			F	G		A		B	H	D			I		J	K	
			🍴			🛒					🍴🛒	🍴			🍴		🛒	🛒			🛒		🍴	🛒	
Stafford	d	18 40		19 18							19 25			19 40		20 18								20 27	
Penkridge	d	18 46												19 46											
Wolverhampton 7	a	18 56									19 40			19 56										20 39	
	d	18 59			19 08	19 15				19 22	19 41	19 42		19 59			20 08	20 15				20 22	20 33	20 41	
Coseley	d									19 27												20 27			
Tipton	d									19 29												20 29			
Dudley Port	d									19 31												20 31			
Sandwell & Dudley	d									19 35		19 56										20 35			
Smethwick Galton Bridge 7	d									19 37												20 37			
Smethwick Rolfe Street	d							←		19 39											←	20 39			
Birmingham New Street 12	a	19 15			19 25	19 31		19 25		19 46	19 58	20 06		20 15			20 23	20 31			20 23	20 46	20 51	20 58	
	d		19 30		19 36		19 34	19 36			20 04	20 10	20 14		20 30		20 37			20 34	20 37			21 04	21 14
Adderley Park	d				↪		19 38										↪			20 38					
Stechford	d						19 42													20 42					
Lea Hall	d						19 44													20 44					
Marston Green	d						19 48						20 22							20 48					21 22
Birmingham International ✈	a		19 39				19 51	19 55			20 13	20 19	20 25		20 39					20 51	20 58			21 13	21 25
	d		19 40				19 51				20 14	20 20	20 25		20 40					20 51				21 14	21 25
Hampton-in-Arden	d												20 28												21 28
Berkswell	d												20 33												21 33
Tile Hill	d						19 58						20 36							20 58					21 36
Canley	d												20 40												21 40
Coventry	a		19 50				20 05				20 24	20 30	20 44		20 50					21 04				21 23	21 44
	d		19 51									20 31	20 44		20 51										21 44
Rugby	d			20 14									20 55		21 05	21 20									21 55
Long Buckby	d			20 24									21 05			21 30									22 05
Northampton	a			20 36									21 17			21 42									22 17
London Euston 15 ⊖66	a		20 57	21 55								21 48	22 44		22 23	23 15									23 43

		LM	VT	LM		AW	XC	LM	AW	LM	LM	LM	VT	LM		AW	VT	XC	LM	VT	VT	LM	LM	XC	
		1	◇1	1			◇1		◇	1	1	1	◇1	1		◇	◇1	◇1		◇1	◇1	1	1	◇1	
		A				E	D		L	B		A				I	G	M		J			A	M	
			🍴						🛒				🍴				🍴			🍴	🍴				
Stafford	d	20 39					21 09		21 16	21 25		21 39					22 02	22 06					22 43	23 05	
Penkridge	d	20 45										21 45											22 49		
Wolverhampton 7	a	20 55					21 21		21 34			21 55					22 17	22 20					22 59	23 18	
	d	21 00	21 05			21 12	21 22	21 25	21 35			22 00	22 05			22 09	22 18	22 22	22 25	22 34	22 37		23 00	23 19	
Coseley	d							21 30											22 30						
Tipton	d							21 32											22 32						
Dudley Port	d							21 34											22 34						
Sandwell & Dudley	d		21 17					21 38					22 16						22 38		22 48				
Smethwick Galton Bridge 7	d							21 40											22 40						
Smethwick Rolfe Street	d							21 42											22 42						
Birmingham New Street 12	a	21 16	21 26			21 29	21 39	21 49	21 52			22 17	22 24			22 28	22 38	22 40	22 49	22 55	22 57		23 16	23 36	
	d		21 30	21 34		21 37			21 55		22 14		22 30	22 34		22 37					23 01	23 14			
Adderley Park	d			21 38										22 38								23 19			
Stechford	d			21 42										22 42								23 22			
Lea Hall	d			21 44										22 45								23 25			
Marston Green	d			21 48							22 22			22 48								23 28			
Birmingham International ✈	a		21 39	21 51		21 56			22 08		22 25		22 39	22 51		22 58					23 10	23 31			
	d		21 40	21 51							22 25		22 40	22 52							23 11	23 32			
Hampton-in-Arden	d										22 28											23 35			
Berkswell	d										22 33											23 40			
Tile Hill	d										22 36											23 43			
Canley	d										22 40											23 46			
Coventry	a		21 50	22 01							22 44		22 50	23 01							23 21	23 50			
	d		21 51								22 44		22 51								23 22				
Rugby	d		22 04							22 20	22 55		23 04								23 35				
Long Buckby	d									22 30	23 05														
Northampton	a									22 43	23 17										23s54				
London Euston 15 ⊖66	a		23 25										00 27								01 05				

A From Liverpool Lime Street
B From Crewe
C From Chester to Birmingham International
D From Manchester Piccadilly to Bristol Temple Meads
E From Chester
F From Manchester Piccadilly to Southampton Central. 🍴 from Birmingham New Street 🛒 to Birmingham New Street
G From Glasgow Central
H From Aberystwyth to Birmingham International
I From Aberystwyth
J From Edinburgh
K From Manchester Piccadilly to Reading
L From Holyhead
M From Manchester Piccadilly

Table 68R

Sundays

5 January to 9 February

Stafford - Wolverhampton - Birmingham - Coventry - Northampton

Network Diagram - refer to first Page of Table 67

		VT	LM	LM	LM	XC		LM	AW	VT	LM	LM	XC	LM	AW	VT		LM	LM	LM	XC	LM	AW	LM	VT
		◇**1**	**1**	**1**		◇**1**		**1**		◇**1**	**1**		◇**1**	**1**		◇**1**		**1**	**1**		◇**1**	**1**	◇	**1**	◇**1**
						A			B				C		B				D		C		E	D	
		🍴				☕				🍴			🍴☕			🍴					🍴☕				🍴
Stafford	d												09 26						10 18		10 27			10 42	
Penkridge	d																							10 49	
Wolverhampton 7 🚌	a												09 40								10 42			11 00	
	d	08 05			08 22				09 00	09 05		09 22	09 41		09 59	10 05				10 22	10 43		10 57	11 00	11 05
Coseley	d				08 27							09 27								10 27					
Tipton	d				08 29							09 29								10 29					
Dudley Port	d				08 31							09 31								10 31					
Sandwell & Dudley	d	08 15			08 35					09 15		09 35				10 15				10 35					11 15
Smethwick Galton Bridge 7	d				08 37							09 37								10 37					
Smethwick Rolfe Street	d				08 39							09 39								10 39					
Birmingham New Street 12	a	08 24			08 46				09 15	09 24		09 46	09 58		10 14	10 24				10 46	10 59		11 13	11 18	11 26
	d	08 30	08 34	08 38		09 04		09 14	09 20	09 30	09 34		10 04	10 14	10 20	10 30		10 34			11 04	11 14	11 19		11 30
Adderley Park	d			08 42							09 38							10 38							
Stechford	d			08 46							09 42							10 42							
Lea Hall	d			08 48							09 44							10 44							
Marston Green	d		08 42	08 52				09 22			09 48			10 22				10 48				11 22			
Birmingham International ✈	a	08 39	08 45	08 55		09 13		09 25	09 31	09 39	09 51		10 13	10 25	10 32	10 39		10 51			11 13	11 25	11 31		11 39
	d	08 40	08 45			09 14		09 25		09 40	09 51		10 14	10 25		10 40		10 51			11 14	11 25			11 40
Hampton-in-Arden	d							09 28						10 28								11 28			
Berkswell	d		08 51					09 33						10 33								11 33			
Tile Hill	d		08 54					09 36						10 36								11 36			
Canley	d		08 57					09 40						10 40								11 40			
Coventry	a	08 50	09 00			09 24		09 44		09 50	10 04		10 24	10 44		10 50		11 01			11 24	11 44			11 50
	d	08 51						09 44		09 51				10 44		10 51						11 44			11 51
Rugby	d	09 04						09 55		10 04				10 55		11 04			11 20			11 55			12 05
Long Buckby	d							10 05						11 05					11 29			12 05			
Northampton	a							10 17						11 17					11 41			12 17			
London Euston 15 ⊖66	a	10 28						11 59		11 31				12 37		12 27			12 51			13 38			13 06

		LM		LM	LM	VT	VT	XC	VT	LM	VT	LM		LM	AW	LM	VT	VT	XC	VT	LM	LM		VT	LM
		1		**1**		◇**1**	◇**1**	◇**1**	◇**1**	**1**	◇**1**	**1**		**1**	◇		◇**1**	◇**1**	◇**1**	◇**1**	**1**	**1**		◇**1**	**1**
				D			F	G				D			H			F	C			I			D
						🍴	🍴	☕	🍴		🍴				☕		🍴	🍴	🍴☕	🍴				🍴	
Stafford	d			11 18				11 28				12 18							12 25			12 40			13 18
Penkridge	d																					12 46			
Wolverhampton 7 🚌	a							11 41											12 40			12 56			
	d				11 22		11 32	11 42	11 45						12 17	12 22		12 34	12 41	12 45		12 59			
Coseley	d				11 27											12 27									
Tipton	d				11 29											12 29									
Dudley Port	d				11 31											12 31									
Sandwell & Dudley	d				11 35				11 57							12 35				12 55					
Smethwick Galton Bridge 7	d				11 37											12 37									
Smethwick Rolfe Street	d				11 39											12 39									
Birmingham New Street 12	a				11 46		11 55	11 59	12 06						12 32	12 46		12 56	12 58	13 06		13 15			
	d	11 34				11 50		12 04	12 10	12 14	12 30			12 34	12 37		12 50		13 04	13 10	13 14			13 30	
Adderley Park	d	11 38												12 38											
Stechford	d	11 42												12 42											
Lea Hall	d	11 44												12 44											
Marston Green	d	11 48								12 22				12 48							13 22				
Birmingham International ✈	a	11 51				11 59		12 13	12 19	12 25	12 39			12 51	12 56		12 59		13 13	13 19	13 25			13 39	
	d	11 51				12 00		12 14	12 20	12 25	12 40			12 51			13 00		13 14	13 20	13 25			13 40	
Hampton-in-Arden	d									12 28											13 28				
Berkswell	d									12 33											13 33				
Tile Hill	d									12 36				12 58							13 36				
Canley	d									12 40											13 40				
Coventry	a	12 01				12 10		12 24	12 30	12 44	12 50			13 04			13 10		13 24	13 30	13 44			13 50	
	d					12 11			12 31	12 44	12 51						13 10			13 31	13 44			13 51	
Rugby	d			12 20		12 25				12 55		13 20					13 25				13 55				14 20
Long Buckby	d			12 30						13 05		13 29									14 05				14 30
Northampton	a			12 42						13 17		13 41									14 17				14 42
London Euston 15 ⊖66	a			13 53		13 20			13 38	14 37	13 57	14 53					14 18			14 38	15 37			14 57	15 53

A To Bournemouth
B From Shrewsbury
C From Manchester Piccadilly to Bournemouth. 🍴 from Birmingham New Street ☕ to Birmingham New Street
D From Crewe
E From Chester
F From Wigan North Western
G From Manchester Piccadilly to Bournemouth
H From Aberystwyth
I From Liverpool Lime Street

Table 68R

Sundays

5 January to 9 February

Stafford - Wolverhampton - Birmingham - Coventry - Northampton

Network Diagram - refer to first Page of Table 67

	LM	AW	LM	VT	XC	VT	LM	LM	VT	LM	AW	XC	LM	AW	LM	VT	XC	VT	LM	LM	VT
	1	◇ A 🛒		◇1 ☕	◇1 B ☕🛒	◇1 C ☕	1	1 D	◇1 ☕	1 E	◇ F 🛒	◇1 G 🛒	1	◇ H 🛒		◇1 ☕	◇1 B ☕🛒	◇1 C ☕	1	1 D	◇1 ☕
Stafford d					13 25			13 40		14 18							14 25			14 40	
Penkridge d								13 46												14 46	
Wolverhampton 7 a					13 40			13 56									14 40			14 56	
d		13 08	13 22		13 41	13 45		13 59			14 08	14 15			14 22		14 41	14 45		14 59	
Coseley d			13 27												14 27						
Tipton d			13 29												14 29						
Dudley Port d			13 31												14 31						
Sandwell & Dudley d			13 35			13 56									14 35			14 56			
Smethwick Galton Bridge 7 d			13 37												14 37						
Smethwick Rolfe Street d			13 39											←	14 39						
Birmingham New Street 12 a		13 23	13 46		13 58	14 06		14 15			14 23	14 31		14 23	14 46		14 58	15 06		15 15	
d	13 34	13 36		13 50	14 04	14 10	14 14		14 30		14 36		14 34	14 36		14 50	15 04	15 10	15 14		15 30
Adderley Park d	13 38										→		14 38								
Stechford d	13 42												14 42								
Lea Hall d	13 44												14 44								
Marston Green d	13 48						14 22						14 48						15 22		
Birmingham International ✈ a	13 51	13 55		13 59	14 13	14 19	14 25		14 39				14 51	14 55		14 59	15 13	15 19	15 25		15 39
d	13 51			14 01	14 14	14 20	14 25		14 40				14 51			15 01	15 14	15 20	15 25		15 40
Hampton-in-Arden d							14 28												15 28		
Berkswell d							14 33												15 33		
Tile Hill d	13 58						14 36						14 58						15 36		
Canley d							14 40												15 40		
Coventry a	14 04			14 13	14 24	14 30	14 44		14 50				15 04			15 13	15 24	15 30	15 44		15 50
d				14 14		14 32	14 44		14 51							15 14		15 31	15 44		15 51
Rugby d				14 26			14 55			15 20						15 26			15 55		
Long Buckby d							15 05			15 30									16 05		
Northampton a							15 17			15 42									16 17		
London Euston 15 ⊖66 a				15 18		15 39	16 38		15 57	16 53						16 18		16 39	17 38		16 57

	LM	AW	XC	LM	AW	LM	VT	XC	VT	LM	LM	VT	LM	AW	XC	LM	AW	LM	VT	XC	VT	LM
	1 E	◇ I	◇1 J 🛒	1	◇ A		◇1 ☕	◇1 B ☕🛒	◇1 C ☕	1	1 D	◇1 ☕	1 E	◇ F 🛒	◇1 J 🛒	1	◇ H 🛒		◇1 ☕	◇1 B ☕🛒	◇1 K ☕	1
Stafford d	15 18							15 25			15 40		16 18							16 25		
Penkridge d											15 46											
Wolverhampton 7 a								15 40			15 56									16 40		
d		15 09	15 15			15 22		15 41	15 45		15 59			16 09	16 15			16 22		16 41	16 45	
Coseley d						15 27												16 27				
Tipton d						15 29												16 29				
Dudley Port d						15 31												16 31				
Sandwell & Dudley d						15 35			15 56									16 35			16 56	
Smethwick Galton Bridge 7 d						15 37												16 37				
Smethwick Rolfe Street d					←	15 39											←	16 39				
Birmingham New Street 12 a		15 24	15 31		15 24	15 46		15 58	16 07		16 15			16 24	16 31		16 24	16 46		16 58	17 06	
d		15 39		15 34	15 39		15 50	16 04	16 10	16 14		16 30		16 36		16 34	16 36		16 50	17 04	17 10	17 14
Adderley Park d		→		15 38										→		16 38						
Stechford d				15 42												16 42						
Lea Hall d				15 44												16 44						
Marston Green d				15 48						16 22						16 48						17 22
Birmingham International ✈ a				15 51	15 58		15 59	16 13	16 19	16 25		16 39				16 51	16 55		16 59	17 13	17 19	17 25
d				15 51			16 01	16 14	16 21	16 25		16 40				16 51			17 00	17 14	17 20	17 25
Hampton-in-Arden d										16 28												17 28
Berkswell d										16 33												17 33
Tile Hill d				15 58						16 36						16 58						17 36
Canley d										16 40												17 40
Coventry a				16 04			16 11	16 24	16 31	16 44		16 50				17 05			17 10	17 24	17 30	17 44
d							16 11		16 31	16 44		16 51							17 11		17 31	17 44
Rugby d	16 20						16 24			16 55			17 20						17 25			17 55
Long Buckby d	16 29									17 05			17 30									18 05
Northampton a	16 41									17 17			17 42									18 17
London Euston 15 ⊖66 a	17 53						17 17		17 38	18 37		17 57	18 53						18 18		18 38	19 37

A From Chester
B From Manchester Piccadilly to Bournemouth. ☕ from Birmingham New Street 🛒 to Birmingham New Street
C From Wigan North Western
D From Liverpool Lime Street
E From Crewe
F From Aberystwyth to Birmingham International
G From Manchester Piccadilly to Paignton
H From Aberystwyth
I From Chester to Birmingham International
J From Manchester Piccadilly to Bristol Temple Meads
K From Preston

Table 68R

Sundays

5 January to 9 February

Stafford - Wolverhampton - Birmingham - Coventry - Northampton

Network Diagram - refer to first Page of Table 67

		LM	VT	XC	LM	LM	AW	LM	VT	XC	VT	LM	LM	VT	LM	AW	XC	LM	AW	LM	VT	XC
		1	◇1	◇1	1	1	◇		◇1	◇1	◇1	1	1	◇1	1	◇	◇1	1	◇		◇1	◇1
		A		B		C	D			E	F		A		C	G	H		I			E
			☕	🛒			🛒		☕	☕🛒	☕			☕		🛒	🛒		🛒		☕	☕🛒
Stafford	d	16 40				17 18				17 26			17 40		18 18							18 27
Penkridge	d	16 46											17 46									
Wolverhampton 7 ⛴	a	16 56								17 40			17 56									18 40
	d	16 59		17 15			17 19	17 22		17 41	17 45		17 59			18 09	18 15			18 22		18 41
Coseley	d							17 27												18 27		
Tipton	d							17 29												18 29		
Dudley Port	d							17 31												18 31		
Sandwell & Dudley	d							17 35			17 56									18 35		
Smethwick Galton Bridge 7	d							17 37												18 37		
Smethwick Rolfe Street	d							17 39											←	18 39		
Birmingham New Street 12	a	17 15		17 31			17 35	17 46		17 58	18 07		18 15			18 27	18 31		18 27	18 46		18 58
	d		17 30		17 34		17 38		17 50	18 04	18 10	18 14		18 30		18 36		18 34	18 36		18 50	19 04
Adderley Park	d				17 38											↦		18 38				
Stechford	d				17 42													18 42				
Lea Hall	d				17 44													18 44				
Marston Green	d				17 48							18 22						18 48				
Birmingham International ✈	a		17 39		17 51		17 56		17 59	18 13	18 19	18 25		18 39				18 51	18 55		18 59	19 13
	d		17 40		17 51				18 00	18 14	18 21	18 25		18 40				18 51			19 01	19 14
Hampton-in-Arden	d											18 28										
Berkswell	d											18 33										
Tile Hill	d				17 58							18 36						18 58				
Canley	d											18 40										
Coventry	a		17 50		18 05				18 10	18 24	18 31	18 44		18 50				19 05			19 13	19 24
	d		17 51						18 11		18 31	18 44		18 51							19 14	
Rugby	d					18 20			18 26			18 55			19 20						19 26	
Long Buckby	d					18 30						19 05			19 30							
Northampton	a					18 42						19 17			19 42							
London Euston 15 ⊖66	a		18 57			19 53			19 18		19 38	20 38		19 57	20 53						20 18	

		VT	LM	LM	VT	LM	AW	XC	LM	AW	LM	XC	VT	LM	LM	VT	LM	AW	XC	LM	AW	LM	VT
		◇1	1	1	◇1	1	◇	◇1	1	◇		◇1	◇1	1	1	◇1	1	◇	◇1	1	◇		◇1
		J		A		C	K	B		D		L	M		A		C	N	B		O		J
		☕			☕			🛒				☕🛒	☕			☕		🛒	🛒		🛒		☕
Stafford	d			18 40		19 18						19 25			19 40		20 18						
Penkridge	d			18 46											19 46								
Wolverhampton 7 ⛴	a			18 56								19 40			19 56								
	d	18 45		18 59			19 08	19 15			19 22	19 41	19 42		19 59			20 08	20 15			20 22	20 33
Coseley	d										19 27											20 27	
Tipton	d										19 29											20 29	
Dudley Port	d										19 31											20 31	
Sandwell & Dudley	d	18 56									19 35		19 56									20 35	
Smethwick Galton Bridge 7	d										19 37											20 37	
Smethwick Rolfe Street	d									←	19 39										←	20 39	
Birmingham New Street 12	a	19 06		19 15			19 25	19 31		19 25	19 46	19 58	20 06		20 15			20 23	20 31		20 23	20 46	20 51
	d	19 10	19 14		19 30		19 36		19 34	19 36		20 04	20 10	20 14		20 30		20 37		20 34	20 37		
Adderley Park	d						↦		19 38									↦		20 38			
Stechford	d								19 42											20 42			
Lea Hall	d								19 44											20 44			
Marston Green	d		19 22						19 48					20 22						20 48			
Birmingham International ✈	a	19 19	19 25		19 39				19 51	19 55		20 13	20 19	20 25		20 39				20 51	20 58		
	d	19 20	19 25		19 40				19 51			20 14	20 20	20 25		20 40				20 51			
Hampton-in-Arden	d		19 28											20 28									
Berkswell	d		19 33											20 33									
Tile Hill	d		19 36						19 58					20 36						20 58			
Canley	d		19 40											20 40									
Coventry	a	19 30	19 44		19 50				20 05			20 24	20 30	20 44		20 50				21 04			
	d	19 32	19 44		19 51								20 31	20 44		20 51							
Rugby	d		19 55			20 14								20 55		21 05	21 20						
Long Buckby	d		20 05			20 24								21 05			21 30						
Northampton	a		20 17			20 36								21 17			21 42						
London Euston 15 ⊖66	a	20 39	21 42		20 57	21 55							21 48	22 44		22 23	23 15						

A From Liverpool Lime Street
B From Manchester Piccadilly to Bristol Temple Meads
C From Crewe
D From Chester
E From Manchester Piccadilly to Bournemouth. ☕ from Birmingham New Street 🛒 to Birmingham New Street
F From Preston
G From Pwllheli to Birmingham International
H From Manchester Piccadilly to Plymouth
I From Pwllheli
J From Edinburgh
K From Chester to Birmingham International
L From Manchester Piccadilly to Southampton Central. ☕ from Birmingham New Street 🛒 to Birmingham New Street
M From Glasgow Central
N From Aberystwyth to Birmingham International
O From Aberystwyth

Table 68R

Sundays

5 January to 9 February

Stafford - Wolverhampton - Birmingham - Coventry - Northampton

Network Diagram - refer to first Page of Table 67

		XC	LM	LM	VT	LM	AW	XC	LM	AW		LM	LM	LM	VT	LM	AW	VT	XC	LM		VT	VT	LM	LM
		◇1	1	1	◇1	1		◇1		◇		1	1	1	◇1	1	◇	◇1	◇1			◇1	◇1	1	1
		A		B			C	D		E		F		B			G	H	I			J			B
		🛒			☕					🛒					☕			☕				☕	☕		
Stafford	d	20 27		20 39				21 09		21 16		21 25		21 39				22 02	22 06						22 43
Penkridge	d			20 45										21 45											22 49
Wolverhampton 7	a	20 39		20 55				21 21		21 34				21 55				22 17	22 20						22 59
	d	20 41		21 00	21 05		21 12	21 22	21 25	21 35				22 00	22 05		22 09	22 18	22 22	22 25		22 34	22 37		23 00
Coseley	d								21 30											22 30					
Tipton	d								21 32											22 32					
Dudley Port	d								21 34											22 34					
Sandwell & Dudley	d				21 17				21 38						22 16					22 38			22 48		
Smethwick Galton Bridge 7	d								21 40											22 40					
Smethwick Rolfe Street	d								21 42											22 42					
Birmingham New Street 12	a	20 58		21 16	21 26		21 29	21 39	21 49	21 52				22 17	22 24		22 28	22 38	22 40	22 49		22 55	22 57		23 16
	d	21 04	21 14		21 30	21 34	21 37			21 55			22 14		22 30	22 34	22 37						23 01	23 14	
Adderley Park	d					21 38										22 38								23 19	
Stechford	d					21 42										22 42								23 22	
Lea Hall	d					21 44										22 45								23 25	
Marston Green	d		21 22			21 48							22 22			22 48								23 28	
Birmingham International ✈	a	21 13	21 25		21 39	21 51	21 56			22 08			22 25		22 39	22 51	22 58						23 10	23 31	
	d	21 14	21 25		21 40	21 51							22 25		22 40	22 52							23 11	23 32	
Hampton-in-Arden	d		21 28										22 28											23 35	
Berkswell	d		21 33										22 33											23 40	
Tile Hill	d		21 36										22 36											23 43	
Canley	d		21 40										22 40											23 46	
Coventry	a	21 23	21 44		21 50	22 01							22 44		22 50	23 01							23 21	23 50	
	d		21 44		21 51								22 44		22 51								23 22		
Rugby	d		21 55		22 04							22 20	22 55		23 04								23 35		
Long Buckby	d		22 05									22 30	23 05												
Northampton	a		22 17									22 43	23 17										23s54		
London Euston 15 ⊖66	a		23 43		23 25										00 27								01 05		

		XC
		◇1
		I
Stafford	d	23 05
Penkridge	d	
Wolverhampton 7	a	23 18
	d	23 19
Coseley	d	
Tipton	d	
Dudley Port	d	
Sandwell & Dudley	d	
Smethwick Galton Bridge 7	d	
Smethwick Rolfe Street	d	
Birmingham New Street 12	a	23 36
	d	
Adderley Park	d	
Stechford	d	
Lea Hall	d	
Marston Green	d	
Birmingham International ✈	a	
	d	
Hampton-in-Arden	d	
Berkswell	d	
Tile Hill	d	
Canley	d	
Coventry	a	
	d	
Rugby	d	
Long Buckby	d	
Northampton	a	
London Euston 15 ⊖66	a	

A From Manchester Piccadilly to Reading
B From Liverpool Lime Street
C From Chester
D From Manchester Piccadilly to Bristol Temple Meads
E From Holyhead
F From Crewe
G From Aberystwyth
H From Glasgow Central
I From Manchester Piccadilly
J From Edinburgh

Table 68R

Sundays

16 February to 23 March

Stafford - Wolverhampton - Birmingham - Coventry - Northampton

Network Diagram - refer to first Page of Table 67

		VT ◇1 ☕	LM 1	LM 1	LM	XC ◇1 A 🛒		LM 1	AW B	VT ◇1 ☕	LM 1	LM	XC ◇1 C ☕🛒	LM 1	AW B	VT ◇1 ☕		LM 1	LM 1 D	LM	XC ◇1 C ☕🛒	LM 1	AW ◇ E	LM 1 D	VT ◇1 ☕
Stafford	d												09 26						10 18		10 27			10 42	
Penkridge	d																							10 49	
Wolverhampton 7	a												09 40								10 42			11 00	
	d	08 05			08 22				09 00	09 05		09 22	09 41		09 59	10 05				10 22	10 43		10 57	11 00	11 05
Coseley	d				08 27							09 27								10 27					
Tipton	d				08 29							09 29								10 29					
Dudley Port	d				08 31							09 31								10 31					
Sandwell & Dudley	d	08 15			08 35					09 15		09 35				10 15				10 35					11 15
Smethwick Galton Bridge 7	d				08 37							09 37								10 37					
Smethwick Rolfe Street	d				08 39							09 39								10 39					
Birmingham New Street 12	a	08 24			08 46				09 15	09 24		09 46	09 58		10 14	10 24				10 46	10 59		11 13	11 18	11 26
	d	08 30	08 34	08 38		09 04		09 14	09 20	09 30	09 34		10 04	10 14	10 20	10 30		10 34			11 04	11 14	11 19		11 30
Adderley Park	d			08 42							09 38							10 38							
Stechford	d			08 46							09 42							10 42							
Lea Hall	d			08 48							09 44							10 44							
Marston Green	d		08 42	08 52				09 22			09 48			10 22				10 48				11 22			
Birmingham International ✈	a	08 39	08 45	08 55		09 13		09 25	09 31	09 39	09 51		10 13	10 25	10 32	10 39		10 51			11 13	11 25	11 31		11 39
	d	08 40	08 45			09 14		09 25		09 40	09 51		10 14	10 25		10 40		10 51			11 14	11 25			11 40
Hampton-in-Arden	d							09 28						10 28								11 28			
Berkswell	d		08 51					09 33						10 33								11 33			
Tile Hill	d		08 54					09 36						10 36								11 36			
Canley	d		08 57					09 40						10 40								11 40			
Coventry	a	08 50	09 00			09 24		09 44		09 50	10 04		10 24	10 44		10 50		11 01			11 24	11 44			11 50
	d	08 51						09 44		09 51				10 44		10 51						11 44			11 51
Rugby	d	09 04						09 55		10 04				10 55		11 04			11 20			11 55			12 05
Long Buckby	d							10 05						11 05					11 29			12 05			
Northampton	a							10 17						11 17					11 41			12 17			
London Euston 15 ⊖66	a	10 28						11 59		11 31				12 37		12 27			12 51			13 38			13 06

		LM 1		LM 1 D	LM	VT ◇1 ☕	VT ◇1 F ☕	XC ◇1 G 🛒	VT ◇1 ☕	LM 1	VT ◇1 ☕	LM 1 D		LM 1	AW ◇ H 🛒	LM	VT ◇1 ☕	VT ◇1 F ☕	XC ◇1 C ☕🛒	VT ◇1 ☕	LM 1	LM 1 I		VT ◇1 ☕	LM 1 D
Stafford	d			11 18				11 28				12 18							12 25			12 40			13 18
Penkridge	d																					12 46			
Wolverhampton 7	a							11 41											12 40			12 56			
	d				11 22		11 32	11 42	11 45						12 17	12 22		12 32	12 41	12 45		12 59			
Coseley	d				11 27											12 27									
Tipton	d				11 29											12 29									
Dudley Port	d				11 31											12 31									
Sandwell & Dudley	d				11 35				11 57							12 35				12 55					
Smethwick Galton Bridge 7	d				11 37											12 37									
Smethwick Rolfe Street	d				11 39											12 39									
Birmingham New Street 12	a				11 46		11 55	11 59	12 06						12 32	12 46		12 54	12 58	13 06		13 15			
	d	11 34				11 50		12 04	12 10	12 14	12 30			12 34	12 37		12 50		13 04	13 10	13 14			13 30	
Adderley Park	d	11 38												12 38											
Stechford	d	11 42												12 42											
Lea Hall	d	11 44												12 44											
Marston Green	d	11 48								12 22				12 48							13 22				
Birmingham International ✈	a	11 51				11 59		12 13	12 19	12 25	12 39			12 51	12 56		12 59		13 13	13 19	13 25			13 39	
	d	11 51				12 00		12 14	12 20	12 25	12 40			12 51			13 00		13 14	13 20	13 25			13 40	
Hampton-in-Arden	d									12 28											13 28				
Berkswell	d									12 33											13 33				
Tile Hill	d									12 36				12 58							13 36				
Canley	d									12 40											13 40				
Coventry	a	12 01				12 10		12 24	12 30	12 44	12 50			13 04			13 10		13 24	13 30	13 44			13 50	
	d					12 11			12 31	12 44	12 51						13 10			13 31	13 44			13 51	
Rugby	d			12 20		12 25				12 55		13 20					13 25				13 55				14 20
Long Buckby	d			12 30						13 05		13 29									14 05				14 30
Northampton	a			12 42						13 17		13 41									14 17				14 42
London Euston 15 ⊖66	a			13 53		13 20			13 38	14 37	13 57	14 53					14 18			14 38	15 37			14 57	15 53

A To Bournemouth
B From Shrewsbury
C From Manchester Piccadilly to Bournemouth. ☕ from Birmingham New Street 🛒 to Birmingham New Street
D From Crewe
E From Chester
F From Preston
G From Manchester Piccadilly to Bournemouth
H From Aberystwyth
I From Liverpool Lime Street

Table 68R

Sundays

16 February to 23 March

Stafford - Wolverhampton - Birmingham - Coventry - Northampton

Network Diagram - refer to first Page of Table 67

		LM	AW	LM		VT	XC	VT	LM	LM	VT	LM	AW	XC		LM	AW	LM	VT	XC	VT	LM	LM	VT	
		■1	◇			◇■1	◇■1	◇■1	■1	■1	◇■1	■1	◇	◇■1		■1	◇		◇■1	◇■1	◇■1	■1	■1	◇■1	
			A				B	C		D		E	F	G			H			B	I		D		
			🛒			☕	☕🛒	☕			☕		🛒	🛒			🛒		☕	☕🛒	☕			☕	
Stafford	d						13 25			13 40		14 18								14 25			14 40		
Penkridge	d									13 46													14 46		
Wolverhampton ■7 🚊	a						13 40			13 56										14 40			14 56		
	d		13 08	13 22			13 41	13 45		13 59			14 08	14 15				14 22		14 41	14 45		14 59		
Coseley	d			13 27														14 27							
Tipton	d			13 29														14 29							
Dudley Port	d			13 31														14 31							
Sandwell & Dudley	d			13 35				13 56										14 35			14 56				
Smethwick Galton Bridge ■7	d			13 37														14 37							
Smethwick Rolfe Street	d			13 39													←	14 39							
Birmingham New Street ■12	a		13 23	13 46			13 58	14 06		14 15			14 23	14 31			14 23	14 46		14 58	15 06		15 15		
	d	13 34	13 36			13 50	14 04	14 10	14 14		14 30		14 36			14 34	14 36		14 50	15 04	15 10	15 14		15 30	
Adderley Park	d	13 38											→			14 38									
Stechford	d	13 42														14 42									
Lea Hall	d	13 44														14 44									
Marston Green	d	13 48							14 22							14 48						15 22			
Birmingham International ✈	a	13 51	13 55			13 59	14 13	14 19	14 25		14 39					14 51	14 55		14 59	15 13	15 19	15 25		15 39	
	d	13 51				14 01	14 14	14 20	14 25		14 40					14 51			15 01	15 14	15 20	15 25		15 40	
Hampton-in-Arden	d								14 28													15 28			
Berkswell	d								14 33													15 33			
Tile Hill	d	13 58							14 36							14 58						15 36			
Canley	d								14 40													15 40			
Coventry	a	14 04				14 13	14 24	14 30	14 44		14 50					15 04			15 13	15 24	15 30	15 44		15 50	
	d					14 14		14 31	14 44		14 51								15 14		15 31	15 44		15 51	
Rugby	d					14 26			14 55			15 20							15 26			15 55			
Long Buckby	d								15 05			15 30										16 05			
Northampton	a								15 17			15 42										16 17			
London Euston ■15 ⊖66	a					15 18		15 39	16 38		15 57	16 53							16 18		16 39	17 38		16 57	

		LM	AW	XC	LM	AW	LM	VT	XC	VT		LM	LM	VT	LM	AW	XC	LM	AW	LM		VT	XC	VT	LM
		■1	◇	◇■1	■1	◇		◇■1	◇■1	◇■1		■1	■1	◇■1	■1	◇	◇■1	■1	◇			◇■1	◇■1	◇■1	■1
		E	J	G		A			B	K			D		E	F	G		H				B	I	
				🛒				☕	☕🛒	☕				☕		🛒	🛒		🛒			☕	☕🛒	☕	
Stafford	d	15 18							15 25				15 40		16 18								16 25		
Penkridge	d												15 46												
Wolverhampton ■7 🚊	a								15 40				15 56										16 40		
	d		15 09	15 15			15 22		15 41	15 45			15 59			16 09	16 15			16 22			16 41	16 45	
Coseley	d						15 27													16 27					
Tipton	d						15 29													16 29					
Dudley Port	d						15 31													16 31					
Sandwell & Dudley	d						15 35			15 56										16 35				16 56	
Smethwick Galton Bridge ■7	d						15 37													16 37					
Smethwick Rolfe Street	d					←	15 39												←	16 39					
Birmingham New Street ■12	a		15 24	15 31		15 24	15 46		15 58	16 07			16 15			16 24	16 31		16 24	16 46			16 58	17 06	
	d		15 39		15 34	15 39		15 50	16 04	16 10		16 14		16 30		16 36		16 34	16 36			16 50	17 04	17 10	17 14
Adderley Park	d		→		15 38											→		16 38							
Stechford	d				15 42													16 42							
Lea Hall	d				15 44													16 44							
Marston Green	d				15 48							16 22						16 48							17 22
Birmingham International ✈	a				15 51	15 58		15 59	16 13	16 19		16 25		16 39				16 51	16 55			16 59	17 13	17 19	17 25
	d				15 51			16 01	16 14	16 21		16 25		16 40				16 51				17 00	17 14	17 20	17 25
Hampton-in-Arden	d											16 28													17 28
Berkswell	d											16 33													17 33
Tile Hill	d				15 58							16 36						16 58							17 36
Canley	d											16 40													17 40
Coventry	a				16 04			16 11	16 24	16 31		16 44		16 50				17 05				17 10	17 24	17 29	17 44
	d							16 11		16 31		16 44		16 51								17 11		17 29	17 44
Rugby	d	16 20						16 24				16 55			17 20							17 25			17 55
Long Buckby	d	16 29										17 05			17 30										18 05
Northampton	a	16 41										17 17			17 42										18 17
London Euston ■15 ⊖66	a	17 53						17 17		17 38		18 37		17 57	18 53							18 18		18 38	19 37

A From Chester
B From Manchester Piccadilly to Bournemouth. ☕ from Birmingham New Street 🛒 to Birmingham New Street
C From Lancaster
D From Liverpool Lime Street
E From Crewe
F From Aberystwyth to Birmingham International
G From Manchester Piccadilly to Bristol Temple Meads
H From Aberystwyth
I From Edinburgh
J From Chester to Birmingham International
K From Glasgow Central

Table 68R

Sundays

16 February to 23 March

Stafford - Wolverhampton - Birmingham - Coventry - Northampton

Network Diagram - refer to first Page of Table 67

Station		LM 1 A		VT ◇1	XC ◇1 B	LM 1	LM 1 C	AW ◇ D	LM	VT ◇1	XC ◇1 E	VT ◇1 F		LM 1	LM 1 A	VT ◇1	LM 1 C	AW ◇ G	XC ◇1 B	LM 1	AW ◇ H	LM		VT ◇1	XC ◇1 E
Stafford	d	16 40					17 18				17 26				17 40		18 18								18 27
Penkridge	d	16 46													17 46										
Wolverhampton 7	a	16 56									17 40				17 56										18 40
	d	16 59			17 15			17 19	17 22		17 41	17 45			17 59			18 09	18 15			18 22			18 41
Coseley	d								17 27													18 27			
Tipton	d								17 29													18 29			
Dudley Port	d								17 31													18 31			
Sandwell & Dudley	d								17 35			17 56										18 35			
Smethwick Galton Bridge 7	d								17 37													18 37			
Smethwick Rolfe Street	d								17 39												←	18 39			
Birmingham New Street 12	a	17 15			17 31			17 35	17 46		17 58	18 07			18 15			18 27	18 31		18 27	18 46			18 58
	d			17 30		17 34		17 38		17 50	18 04	18 10		18 14		18 30		18 36		18 34	18 36			18 50	19 04
Adderley Park	d					17 38												↪		18 38					
Stechford	d					17 42														18 42					
Lea Hall	d					17 44														18 44					
Marston Green	d					17 48								18 22						18 48					
Birmingham International ✈	a			17 39		17 51		17 56		17 59	18 13	18 19		18 25		18 39				18 51	18 55			18 59	19 13
	d			17 40		17 51				18 00	18 14	18 21		18 25		18 40				18 51				19 01	19 14
Hampton-in-Arden	d													18 28											
Berkswell	d													18 33											
Tile Hill	d					17 58								18 36						18 58					
Canley	d													18 40											
Coventry	a			17 50		18 05				18 10	18 24	18 31		18 44		18 50				19 05				19 13	19 24
	d			17 51						18 11		18 31		18 44		18 51								19 14	
Rugby	d						18 20			18 26				18 55			19 20							19 26	
Long Buckby	d						18 30							19 05			19 30								
Northampton	a						18 42							19 17			19 42								
London Euston 15 ⊖66	a			18 57			19 53			19 18		19 38		20 38		19 57	20 53							20 18	

Station		VT ◇1 I	LM 1	LM 1 A	VT ◇1	LM 1 C	AW ◇ J	XC ◇1 B		LM 1	AW ◇ D	LM	XC ◇1 K	VT ◇1 F	LM 1	LM 1 A	VT ◇1	LM 1 C		AW ◇ L	XC ◇1 B	LM 1	AW ◇ M	LM	VT ◇1 I
Stafford	d			18 40		19 18							19 25			19 40		20 18							
Penkridge	d			18 46												19 46									
Wolverhampton 7	a			18 56									19 40			19 56									
	d	18 45		18 59			19 08	19 15				19 22	19 41	19 42		19 59				20 08	20 15			20 22	20 33
Coseley	d											19 27												20 27	
Tipton	d											19 29												20 29	
Dudley Port	d											19 31												20 31	
Sandwell & Dudley	d	18 56										19 35		19 56										20 35	
Smethwick Galton Bridge 7	d											19 37												20 37	
Smethwick Rolfe Street	d										←	19 39											←	20 39	
Birmingham New Street 12	a	19 06		19 15			19 25	19 31			19 25	19 46	19 58	20 06		20 15				20 23	20 31		20 23	20 46	20 51
	d	19 10	19 14		19 30		19 36			19 34	19 36		20 04	20 10	20 14		20 30			20 37		20 34	20 37		
Adderley Park	d						↪			19 38										↪		20 38			
Stechford	d									19 42												20 42			
Lea Hall	d									19 44												20 44			
Marston Green	d		19 22							19 48					20 22							20 48			
Birmingham International ✈	a	19 19	19 25		19 39					19 51	19 55		20 13	20 19	20 25		20 39					20 51	20 58		
	d	19 20	19 25		19 40					19 51			20 14	20 20	20 25		20 40					20 51			
Hampton-in-Arden	d		19 28												20 28										
Berkswell	d		19 33												20 33										
Tile Hill	d		19 36							19 58					20 36							20 58			
Canley	d		19 40												20 40										
Coventry	a	19 30	19 44		19 50					20 05			20 24	20 30	20 44		20 50					21 04			
	d	19 32	19 44		19 51									20 31	20 44		20 51								
Rugby	d		19 55			20 14									20 55		21 05	21 20							
Long Buckby	d		20 05			20 24									21 05			21 30							
Northampton	a		20 17			20 36									21 17			21 42							
London Euston 15 ⊖66	a	20 39	21 42		20 57	21 55								21 48	22 44		22 23	23 15							

A From Liverpool Lime Street
B From Manchester Piccadilly to Bristol Temple Meads
C From Crewe
D From Chester
E From Manchester Piccadilly to Bournemouth. ☕ from Birmingham New Street trolley to Birmingham New Street
F From Glasgow Central
G From Pwllheli to Birmingham International
H From Pwllheli
I From Edinburgh
J From Chester to Birmingham International
K From Manchester Piccadilly to Southampton Central. ☕ from Birmingham New Street trolley to Birmingham New Street
L From Aberystwyth to Birmingham International
M From Aberystwyth

Table 68R

Sundays

16 February to 23 March

Stafford - Wolverhampton - Birmingham - Coventry - Northampton

Network Diagram - refer to first Page of Table 67

		XC	LM	LM	VT	LM	AW	XC	LM	AW		LM	LM	LM	VT	LM	AW	VT	XC	LM		VT	VT	LM	LM
		◇1	1	1	◇1	1		◇1		◇		1	1	1	◇1	1	◇	◇1	◇1			◇1	◇1	1	1
		A		B			C	D		E		F		B			G	H	I			J			B
Stafford	d	20 27		20 39				21 09		21 16		21 25		21 39				22 02	22 06						22 43
Penkridge	d			20 45										21 45											22 49
Wolverhampton 7	a	20 39		20 55				21 21		21 34				21 55				22 17	22 20						22 59
	d	20 41		21 00	21 05		21 12	21 22	21 25	21 35				22 00	22 05		22 09	22 18	22 22	22 25		22 34	22 37		23 00
Coseley	d								21 30											22 30					
Tipton	d								21 32											22 32					
Dudley Port	d								21 34											22 34					
Sandwell & Dudley	d				21 17				21 38						22 16					22 38			22 48		
Smethwick Galton Bridge 7	d								21 40											22 40					
Smethwick Rolfe Street	d								21 42											22 42					
Birmingham New Street 12	a	20 58		21 16	21 26		21 29	21 39	21 49	21 52				22 17	22 24		22 28	22 38	22 40	22 49		22 55	22 57		23 16
	d	21 04	21 14		21 30	21 34	21 37			21 55			22 14		22 30	22 34	22 37						23 01	23 14	
Adderley Park	d					21 38										22 38								23 19	
Stechford	d					21 42										22 42								23 22	
Lea Hall	d					21 44										22 45								23 25	
Marston Green	d		21 22			21 48							22 22			22 48								23 28	
Birmingham International	a	21 13	21 25		21 39	21 51	21 56			22 08			22 25		22 39	22 51	22 58						23 10	23 31	
	d	21 14	21 25		21 40	21 51							22 25		22 40	22 52							23 11	23 32	
Hampton-in-Arden	d		21 28										22 28											23 35	
Berkswell	d		21 33										22 33											23 40	
Tile Hill	d		21 36										22 36											23 43	
Canley	d		21 40										22 40											23 46	
Coventry	a	21 23	21 44		21 50	22 01							22 44		22 50	23 01							23 21	23 50	
	d		21 44		21 51								22 44		22 51								23 22		
Rugby	d		21 55		22 04							22 20	22 55		23 04								23 35		
Long Buckby	d		22 05									22 30	23 05												
Northampton	a		22 17									22 43	23 17										23s54		
London Euston 15 ⊖66	a		23 43		23 25										00 27								01 05		

		XC
		◇1
		I
Stafford	d	23 05
Penkridge	d	
Wolverhampton 7	a	23 18
	d	23 19
Coseley	d	
Tipton	d	
Dudley Port	d	
Sandwell & Dudley	d	
Smethwick Galton Bridge 7	d	
Smethwick Rolfe Street	d	
Birmingham New Street 12	a	23 36
	d	
Adderley Park	d	
Stechford	d	
Lea Hall	d	
Marston Green	d	
Birmingham International	a	
	d	
Hampton-in-Arden	d	
Berkswell	d	
Tile Hill	d	
Canley	d	
Coventry	a	
	d	
Rugby	d	
Long Buckby	d	
Northampton	a	
London Euston 15 ⊖66	a	

A From Manchester Piccadilly to Reading
B From Liverpool Lime Street
C From Chester
D From Manchester Piccadilly to Bristol Temple Meads
E From Holyhead
F From Crewe
G From Aberystwyth
H From Glasgow Central
I From Manchester Piccadilly
J From Edinburgh

Table 68R

Sundays

30 March to 11 May

Stafford - Wolverhampton - Birmingham - Coventry - Northampton

Network Diagram - refer to first Page of Table 67

		VT	LM	LM	LM	XC		LM	AW	VT	LM	LM	XC	LM	AW	VT		LM	LM	LM	XC	LM	AW	LM	VT
		◇1	1	1		◇1		1		◇1	1		◇1	1		◇1		1	1		◇1	1	◇	1	◇1
						A			B				C		B				D		C		E	D	
		☕				🛒				☕			☕🛒			☕					☕🛒				☕
Stafford	d												09 26						10 18		10 27			10 42	
Penkridge	d																							10 49	
Wolverhampton [7]	a												09 40								10 42			11 00	
	d	08 05			08 22				09 00	09 05		09 22	09 41		09 59	10 05				10 22	10 43		10 57	11 00	11 05
Coseley	d				08 27							09 27								10 27					
Tipton	d				08 29							09 29								10 29					
Dudley Port	d				08 31							09 31								10 31					
Sandwell & Dudley	d	08 15			08 35					09 15		09 35				10 15				10 35					11 15
Smethwick Galton Bridge [7]	d				08 37							09 37								10 37					
Smethwick Rolfe Street	d				08 39							09 39								10 39					
Birmingham New Street [12]	a	08 24			08 46				09 15	09 24		09 46	09 58		10 14	10 24				10 46	10 59		11 13	11 18	11 26
	d	08 30	08 34	08 38		09 04		09 14	09 20	09 30	09 34		10 04	10 14	10 20	10 30		10 34			11 04	11 14	11 19		11 30
Adderley Park	d			08 42							09 38							10 38							
Stechford	d			08 46							09 42							10 42							
Lea Hall	d			08 48							09 44							10 44							
Marston Green	d		08 42	08 52				09 22			09 48			10 22				10 48				11 22			
Birmingham International ✈	a	08 39	08 45	08 55		09 13		09 25	09 31	09 39	09 51		10 13	10 25	10 32	10 39		10 51			11 13	11 25	11 31		11 39
	d	08 40	08 45			09 14		09 25		09 40	09 51		10 14	10 25		10 40		10 51			11 14	11 25			11 40
Hampton-in-Arden	d							09 28						10 28								11 28			
Berkswell	d		08 51					09 33						10 33								11 33			
Tile Hill	d		08 54					09 36						10 36								11 36			
Canley	d		08 57					09 40						10 40								11 40			
Coventry	a	08 50	09 00			09 24		09 44		09 50	10 04		10 24	10 44		10 50		11 01			11 24	11 44			11 50
	d	08 51						09 44		09 51				10 44		10 51						11 44			11 51
Rugby	d	09 04						09 55		10 04				10 55		11 04			11 20			11 55			12 05
Long Buckby	d							10 05						11 05					11 29			12 05			
Northampton	a							10 17						11 17					11 41			12 17			
London Euston [15] ⊖66	a	10 28						11 59		11 31				12 37		12 27			12 51			13 38			13 06

		LM		LM	LM	VT	VT	XC	VT	LM	VT	LM		LM	AW	LM	VT	VT	XC	VT	LM	LM		VT	LM
		1		1		◇1	◇1	◇1	◇1	1	◇1	1		1	◇		◇1	◇1	◇1	◇1	1	1		◇1	1
				D			F	G				D			H			F	C			I			D
						☕	☕	🛒	☕		☕				🛒		☕	☕	☕🛒	☕				☕	
Stafford	d			11 18				11 28				12 18							12 25			12 40			13 18
Penkridge	d																					12 46			
Wolverhampton [7]	a							11 41											12 40			12 56			
	d				11 22		11 32	11 42	11 45						12 17	12 22		12 32	12 41	12 45		12 59			
Coseley	d				11 27											12 27									
Tipton	d				11 29											12 29									
Dudley Port	d				11 31											12 31									
Sandwell & Dudley	d				11 35				11 57							12 35				12 55					
Smethwick Galton Bridge [7]	d				11 37											12 37									
Smethwick Rolfe Street	d				11 39											12 39									
Birmingham New Street [12]	a				11 46		11 55	11 59	12 06						12 32	12 46		12 54	12 58	13 06		13 15			
	d	11 34				11 50		12 04	12 10	12 14	12 30			12 34	12 37		12 50		13 04	13 10	13 14			13 30	
Adderley Park	d	11 38												12 38											
Stechford	d	11 42												12 42											
Lea Hall	d	11 44												12 44											
Marston Green	d	11 48								12 22				12 48							13 22				
Birmingham International ✈	a	11 51				11 59		12 13	12 19	12 25	12 39			12 51	12 56		12 59		13 13	13 19	13 25			13 39	
	d	11 51				12 00		12 14	12 20	12 25	12 40			12 51			13 00		13 14	13 20	13 25			13 40	
Hampton-in-Arden	d									12 28											13 28				
Berkswell	d									12 33											13 33				
Tile Hill	d									12 36				12 58							13 36				
Canley	d									12 40											13 40				
Coventry	a	12 01				12 10		12 24	12 30	12 44	12 50			13 04			13 10		13 24	13 30	13 44			13 50	
	d					12 11			12 31	12 44	12 51						13 10			13 31	13 44			13 51	
Rugby	d			12 20		12 25				12 55		13 20					13 25				13 55				14 20
Long Buckby	d			12 30						13 05		13 29									14 05				14 30
Northampton	a			12 42						13 17		13 41									14 17				14 42
London Euston [15] ⊖66	a			13 53		13 20			13 38	14 37	13 57	14 53					14 18			14 38	15 37			14 57	15 53

A To Bournemouth
B From Shrewsbury
C From Manchester Piccadilly to Bournemouth. ☕ from Birmingham New Street 🛒 to Birmingham New Street
D From Crewe
E From Chester
F From Preston
G From Manchester Piccadilly to Bournemouth
H From Aberystwyth
I From Liverpool Lime Street

Table 68R

Sundays

30 March to 11 May

Stafford - Wolverhampton - Birmingham - Coventry - Northampton

Network Diagram - refer to first Page of Table 67

		LM	AW	LM		VT	XC	VT	LM	LM	VT	LM	AW	XC		LM	AW	LM	VT	XC	VT	LM	LM	VT
		1	◇			◇1	◇1	◇1	1	1	◇1	1	◇	◇1		1	◇		◇1	◇1	◇1	1	1	◇1
			A				B	C		D		E	F	G			H			B	I		D	
			🛒			☕	☕🛒	☕			☕		🛒	🛒			🛒		☕	☕🛒	☕			☕
Stafford	d						13 25			13 40		14 18								14 25			14 40	
Penkridge	d									13 46													14 46	
Wolverhampton 7	a						13 40			13 56										14 40			14 56	
	d		13 08	13 22			13 41	13 45		13 59			14 08	14 15				14 22		14 41	14 45		14 59	
Coseley	d			13 27														14 27						
Tipton	d			13 29														14 29						
Dudley Port	d			13 31														14 31						
Sandwell & Dudley	d			13 35				13 56										14 35			14 56			
Smethwick Galton Bridge 7	d			13 37														14 37						
Smethwick Rolfe Street	d			13 39													←	14 39						
Birmingham New Street 12	a		13 23	13 46			13 58	14 06		14 15			14 23	14 31			14 23	14 46		14 58	15 06		15 15	
	d	13 34	13 36			13 50	14 04	14 10	14 14		14 30		14 36			14 34	14 36		14 50	15 04	15 10	15 14		15 30
Adderley Park	d	13 38											→			14 38								
Stechford	d	13 42														14 42								
Lea Hall	d	13 44														14 44								
Marston Green	d	13 48							14 22							14 48						15 22		
Birmingham International ✈	a	13 51	13 55			13 59	14 13	14 19	14 25		14 39					14 51	14 55		14 59	15 13	15 19	15 25		15 39
	d	13 51				14 01	14 14	14 20	14 25		14 40					14 51			15 01	15 14	15 20	15 25		15 40
Hampton-in-Arden	d								14 28													15 28		
Berkswell	d								14 33													15 33		
Tile Hill	d	13 58							14 36							14 58						15 36		
Canley	d								14 40													15 40		
Coventry	a	14 04				14 13	14 24	14 30	14 44		14 50					15 04			15 13	15 24	15 30	15 44		15 50
	d					14 14		14 31	14 44		14 51								15 14		15 31	15 44		15 51
Rugby	d					14 26			14 55			15 20							15 26			15 55		
Long Buckby	d								15 05			15 30										16 05		
Northampton	a								15 17			15 42										16 17		
London Euston 15 ⊖66	a					15 18		15 39	16 38		15 57	16 53							16 18		16 39	17 38		16 57

		LM	AW	XC	LM	AW	LM	VT	XC	VT		LM	LM	VT	LM	AW	XC	LM	AW	LM		VT	XC	VT	LM
		1	◇	◇1	1	◇		◇1	◇1	◇1		1	1	◇1	1	◇	◇1	1	◇			◇1	◇1	◇1	1
		E	J	K		A			B	L			D		E	F	K		H				B	I	
				🛒				☕	☕🛒	☕				☕		🛒	🛒		🛒			☕	☕🛒	☕	
Stafford	d	15 18							15 25				15 40		16 18								16 25		
Penkridge	d												15 46												
Wolverhampton 7	a								15 40				15 56										16 40		
	d		15 09	15 15			15 22		15 41	15 45			15 59			16 09	16 15			16 22			16 41	16 45	
Coseley	d						15 27													16 27					
Tipton	d						15 29													16 29					
Dudley Port	d						15 31													16 31					
Sandwell & Dudley	d						15 35			15 56										16 35				16 56	
Smethwick Galton Bridge 7	d						15 37													16 37					
Smethwick Rolfe Street	d					←	15 39												←	16 39					
Birmingham New Street 12	a		15 24	15 31		15 24	15 46		15 58	16 07			16 15			16 24	16 31		16 24	16 46			16 58	17 06	
	d		15 39		15 34	15 39		15 50	16 04	16 10		16 14		16 30		16 36		16 34	16 36			16 50	17 04	17 10	17 14
Adderley Park	d		→		15 38											→		16 38							
Stechford	d				15 42													16 42							
Lea Hall	d				15 44													16 44							
Marston Green	d				15 48							16 22						16 48							17 22
Birmingham International ✈	a				15 51	15 58		15 59	16 13	16 19		16 25		16 39				16 51	16 55			16 59	17 13	17 19	17 25
	d				15 51			16 01	16 14	16 21		16 25		16 40				16 51				17 00	17 14	17 20	17 25
Hampton-in-Arden	d											16 28													17 28
Berkswell	d											16 33													17 33
Tile Hill	d				15 58							16 36						16 58							17 36
Canley	d											16 40													17 40
Coventry	a				16 04			16 11	16 24	16 31		16 44		16 50				17 05				17 10	17 24	17 29	17 44
	d							16 11		16 31		16 44		16 51								17 11		17 29	17 44
Rugby	d	16 20						16 24				16 55			17 20							17 25			17 55
Long Buckby	d	16 29										17 05			17 30										18 05
Northampton	a	16 41										17 17			17 42										18 17
London Euston 15 ⊖66	a	17 53						17 17		17 38		18 37		17 57	18 53							18 18		18 38	19 37

A From Chester
B From Manchester Piccadilly to Bournemouth. ☕ from Birmingham New Street 🛒 to Birmingham New Street
C From Lancaster
D From Liverpool Lime Street
E From Crewe
F From Aberystwyth to Birmingham International
G From Manchester Piccadilly to Paignton
H From Aberystwyth
I From Edinburgh
J From Chester to Birmingham International
K From Manchester Piccadilly to Bristol Temple Meads
L From Glasgow Central

Table 68R

Sundays
30 March to 11 May

Stafford - Wolverhampton - Birmingham - Coventry - Northampton

Network Diagram - refer to first Page of Table 67

		LM	VT	XC	LM	LM	AW	LM	VT	XC	VT	LM	LM	VT	LM	AW	XC	LM	AW	LM	VT	XC
		1	◇1	◇1	1	1	◇		◇1	◇1	◇1	1	1	◇1	1	◇	◇1	1	◇		◇1	◇1
		A		B		C	D			E	F		A		C	G	H		I			E
			☕	🛒			🛒		☕	☕🛒	☕			☕		🛒	🛒		🛒		☕	☕🛒
Stafford	d	16 40				17 18				17 26			17 40		18 18							18 27
Penkridge	d	16 46											17 46									
Wolverhampton 7	a	16 56								17 40			17 56									18 40
	d	16 59		17 15			17 19	17 22		17 41	17 45		17 59			18 09	18 15			18 22		18 41
Coseley	d							17 27												18 27		
Tipton	d							17 29												18 29		
Dudley Port	d							17 31												18 31		
Sandwell & Dudley	d							17 35			17 56									18 35		
Smethwick Galton Bridge 7	d							17 37												18 37		
Smethwick Rolfe Street	d							17 39											←	18 39		
Birmingham New Street 12	a	17 15		17 31			17 35	17 46		17 58	18 07		18 15			18 27	18 31		18 27	18 46		18 58
	d		17 30		17 34		17 38		17 50	18 04	18 10	18 14		18 30		18 36		18 34	18 36		18 50	19 04
Adderley Park	d				17 38											↪		18 38				
Stechford	d				17 42													18 42				
Lea Hall	d				17 44													18 44				
Marston Green	d				17 48							18 22						18 48				
Birmingham International ✈	a		17 39		17 51		17 56		17 59	18 13	18 19	18 25		18 39				18 51	18 55		18 59	19 13
	d		17 40		17 51				18 00	18 14	18 21	18 25		18 40				18 51			19 01	19 14
Hampton-in-Arden	d											18 28										
Berkswell	d											18 33										
Tile Hill	d				17 58							18 36						18 58				
Canley	d											18 40										
Coventry	a		17 50		18 05				18 10	18 24	18 31	18 44		18 50				19 05			19 13	19 24
	d		17 51						18 11		18 31	18 44		18 51							19 14	
Rugby	d					18 20			18 26			18 55			19 20						19 26	
Long Buckby	d					18 30						19 05			19 30							
Northampton	a					18 42						19 17			19 42							
London Euston 15 ⊖66	a		18 57			19 53			19 18		19 38	20 38		19 57	20 53						20 18	

		VT	LM	LM	VT	LM	AW	XC	LM	AW	LM	XC	VT	LM	LM	VT	LM	AW	XC	LM	AW	LM	VT
		◇1	1	1	◇1	1	◇	◇1	1	◇		◇1	◇1	1	1	◇1	1	◇	◇1	1	◇		◇1
		J		A		C	K	B		D		L	F		A		C	M	B		N		J
		☕			☕			🛒				☕🛒	☕			☕		🛒	🛒		🛒		☕
Stafford	d			18 40		19 18						19 25			19 40		20 18						
Penkridge	d			18 46											19 46								
Wolverhampton 7	a			18 56								19 40			19 56								
	d	18 45		18 59			19 08	19 15			19 22	19 41	19 42		19 59			20 08	20 15			20 22	20 33
Coseley	d										19 27											20 27	
Tipton	d										19 29											20 29	
Dudley Port	d										19 31											20 31	
Sandwell & Dudley	d	18 56									19 35		19 56									20 35	
Smethwick Galton Bridge 7	d										19 37											20 37	
Smethwick Rolfe Street	d									←	19 39										←	20 39	
Birmingham New Street 12	a	19 06		19 15			19 25	19 31		19 25	19 46	19 58	20 06		20 15			20 23	20 31		20 23	20 46	20 51
	d	19 10	19 14		19 30		19 36		19 34	19 36		20 04	20 10	20 14		20 30		20 37		20 34	20 37		
Adderley Park	d						↪		19 38									↪		20 38			
Stechford	d								19 42											20 42			
Lea Hall	d								19 44											20 44			
Marston Green	d		19 22						19 48					20 22						20 48			
Birmingham International ✈	a	19 19	19 25		19 39				19 51	19 55		20 13	20 19	20 25		20 39				20 51	20 58		
	d	19 20	19 25		19 40				19 51			20 14	20 20	20 25		20 40				20 51			
Hampton-in-Arden	d		19 28											20 28									
Berkswell	d		19 33											20 33									
Tile Hill	d		19 36						19 58					20 36						20 58			
Canley	d		19 40											20 40									
Coventry	a	19 30	19 44		19 50				20 05			20 24	20 30	20 44		20 50				21 04			
	d	19 32	19 44		19 51								20 31	20 44		20 51							
Rugby	d		19 55			20 14								20 55		21 05	21 20						
Long Buckby	d		20 05			20 24								21 05			21 30						
Northampton	a		20 17			20 36								21 17			21 42						
London Euston 15 ⊖66	a	20 39	21 42		20 57	21 55							21 48	22 44		22 23	23 15						

A From Liverpool Lime Street
B From Manchester Piccadilly to Bristol Temple Meads
C From Crewe
D From Chester
E From Manchester Piccadilly to Bournemouth. ☕ from Birmingham New Street 🛒 to Birmingham New Street
F From Glasgow Central
G From Pwllheli to Birmingham International
H From Manchester Piccadilly to Plymouth
I From Pwllheli
J From Edinburgh
K From Chester to Birmingham International
L From Manchester Piccadilly to Southampton Central. ☕ from Birmingham New Street 🛒 to Birmingham New Street
M From Aberystwyth to Birmingham International
N From Aberystwyth

Table 68R

Sundays

30 March to 11 May

Stafford - Wolverhampton - Birmingham - Coventry - Northampton

Network Diagram - refer to first Page of Table 67

		XC	LM	LM	VT	LM	AW	XC	LM	AW		LM	LM	LM	VT	LM	AW	VT	XC	LM		VT	VT	LM	LM
		◇1	1	1	◇1	1		◇1		◇		1	1	1	◇1	1	◇	◇1	◇1			◇1	◇1	1	1
		A		B			C	D		E		F		B			G	H	I			J			B
Stafford	d	20 27		20 39				21 09		21 16		21 25		21 39				22 02	22 06						22 43
Penkridge	d			20 45										21 45											22 49
Wolverhampton 7	a	20 39		20 55				21 21		21 34				21 55				22 17	22 20						22 59
	d	20 41		21 00	21 05		21 12	21 22	21 25	21 35				22 00	22 05		22 09	22 18	22 22	22 25		22 34	22 37		23 00
Coseley	d								21 30											22 30					
Tipton	d								21 32											22 32					
Dudley Port	d								21 34											22 34					
Sandwell & Dudley	d				21 17				21 38						22 16					22 38			22 48		
Smethwick Galton Bridge 7	d								21 40											22 40					
Smethwick Rolfe Street	d								21 42											22 42					
Birmingham New Street 12	a	20 58		21 16	21 26		21 29	21 39	21 49	21 52				22 17	22 24		22 28	22 38	22 40	22 49		22 55	22 57		23 16
	d	21 04	21 14		21 30	21 34	21 37			21 55			22 14		22 30	22 34	22 37						23 01	23 14	
Adderley Park	d					21 38										22 38								23 19	
Stechford	d					21 42										22 42								23 22	
Lea Hall	d					21 44										22 45								23 25	
Marston Green	d		21 22			21 48							22 22			22 48								23 28	
Birmingham International	a	21 13	21 25		21 39	21 51	21 56			22 08			22 25		22 39	22 51	22 58						23 10	23 31	
	d	21 14	21 25		21 40	21 51							22 25		22 40	22 52							23 11	23 32	
Hampton-in-Arden	d		21 28										22 28											23 35	
Berkswell	d		21 33										22 33											23 40	
Tile Hill	d		21 36										22 36											23 43	
Canley	d		21 40										22 40											23 46	
Coventry	a	21 23	21 44		21 50	22 01							22 44		22 50	23 01							23 21	23 50	
	d		21 44		21 51								22 44		22 51								23 22		
Rugby	d		21 55		22 04							22 20	22 55		23 04								23 35		
Long Buckby	d		22 05									22 30	23 05												
Northampton	a		22 17									22 43	23 17										23s54		
London Euston 15 ⊖66	a		23 43		23 25										00 27								01 05		

		XC
		◇1
		I
Stafford	d	23 05
Penkridge	d	
Wolverhampton 7	a	23 18
	d	23 19
Coseley	d	
Tipton	d	
Dudley Port	d	
Sandwell & Dudley	d	
Smethwick Galton Bridge 7	d	
Smethwick Rolfe Street	d	
Birmingham New Street 12	a	23 36
	d	
Adderley Park	d	
Stechford	d	
Lea Hall	d	
Marston Green	d	
Birmingham International	a	
	d	
Hampton-in-Arden	d	
Berkswell	d	
Tile Hill	d	
Canley	d	
Coventry	a	
	d	
Rugby	d	
Long Buckby	d	
Northampton	a	
London Euston 15 ⊖66	a	

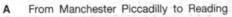

A From Manchester Piccadilly to Reading
B From Liverpool Lime Street
C From Chester
D From Manchester Piccadilly to Bristol Temple Meads
E From Holyhead
F From Crewe
G From Aberystwyth
H From Glasgow Central
I From Manchester Piccadilly
J From Edinburgh

Table 69

Mondays to Fridays

9 December to 16 May

Lichfield - Birmingham - Longbridge and Redditch

Network Diagram - refer to first Page of Table 67

Miles	Miles			LM	LM	LM	LM	LM	LM	LM	LM	LM		LM	LM	LM	XC ◇1	LM	LM	LM	LM	LM		LM	LM
0	—	**Lichfield Trent Valley**	d							06 08		06 20						06 50		07 10		07 20			07 38
1¼	—	**Lichfield City**	d							06 12		06 24				06 45		06 54		07 14		07 24			07 42
4¼	—	Shenstone	d							06 17						06 50				07 19					07 47
6¾	—	Blake Street	d					06 02		06 21		06 32				06 54		07 02		07 23		07 32			07 51
8½	—	Butlers Lane	d					06 04		06 23		06 34				06 56		07 04		07 25		07 34			07 53
9½	—	Four Oaks	d					06 07	06 17	06 26		06 37		06 47		06 59		07 07	07 17	07 28		07 37		07 47	07 56
11	—	Sutton Coldfield	d					06 10	06 21	06 29		06 40		06 51		07 02		07 10	07 21	07 31		07 40		07 51	08 00
12	—	Wylde Green	d					06 13	06 23	06 32		06 43		06 53		07 05		07 13	07 23	07 34		07 43		07 53	08 03
12¾	—	Chester Road	d					06 15	06 26	06 34		06 45		06 56		07 07		07 15	07 26	07 36		07 45		07 56	08 05
13¾	—	Erdington	d					06 17	06 27	06 36		06 47		06 57		07 09		07 17	07 27	07 38		07 47		07 57	08 07
14½	—	Gravelly Hill	d					06 20	06 30	06 39		06 49		07 00		07 11		07 19	07 30	07 40		07 50		08 00	08 10
15¾	—	Aston	d					06 23	06 34	06 42		06 53		07 04		07 14		07 23	07 34	07 44		07 53		08 04	08 13
17	—	Duddeston	d					06 26	06 36	06 45				07 06					07 36	07 46				08 06	08 16
18½	0	**Birmingham New Street 12**	a					06 31	06 41	06 49		06 59		07 11		07 21		07 30	07 41	07 51		08 02		08 11	08 20
—	—		d	05 53	06 03	06 13	06 23	06 33	06 43	06 53	06 59	07 03		07 13	07 19	07 23	07 30	07 33	07 43	07 53	07 59	08 03		08 13	08 22
19½	—	Five Ways	d	05 56	06 06	06 16	06 26	06 36	06 46	06 56		07 06		07 16		07 26		07 36	07 46	07 56		08 06		08 16	08 25
20	1½	University	d	06 00	06 10	06 20	06 30	06 40	06 50	07 00	07 05	07 10		07 20	07 25	07 30	07a36	07 40	07 50	08 00	08 05	08 10		08 20	08 29
20¾	—	Selly Oak	d	06 03	06 13	06 23	06 33	06 43	06 53	07 03		07 13		07 23		07 33		07 43	07 53	08 03		08 13		08 23	08 33
21¾	—	Bournville	d	06 05	06 15	06 25	06 35	06 45	06 55	07 05		07 15		07 25		07 35		07 45	07 55	08 05		08 15		08 25	08 35
22¾	—	Kings Norton	d	06 07	06 17	06 27	06 37	06 47	06 57	07 07		07 17		07 27		07 37		07 47	07 57	08 07		08 17		08 27	08 37
24¼	—	Northfield	d	06 10	06 20	06 30	06 40	06 50	07 00	07 10		07 20		07 30		07 40		07 50	08 00	08 10		08 20		08 30	08 40
25¼	—	Longbridge	d	06a14	06a24	06 34	06a44	06a54	07 05	07a14		07a24		07 34		07a44		07a54	08 04	08a14		08a24		08 34	08a44
28	9½	Barnt Green	d			06 39			07 09					07 39	07 41				08 09		08 18			08 39	
29¾	—	Alvechurch	d			06 43			07 14					07 43					08 13					08 43	
33	—	**Redditch**	a			06 52			07 22					07 52					08 22					08 52	
—	13	Bromsgrove	a								07 21				07 46						08 22				

		XC ◇1	LM	LM	LM	LM	LM	LM		LM	LM	XC ◇1	LM	LM	LM	LM	LM	LM		LM	XC ◇1	LM	LM	LM	LM
Lichfield Trent Valley	d		07 50				08 10				08 40		08 50				09 20					09 50			
Lichfield City	d		07 54		08 10		08 14	08 23			08 43		08 54			09 13	09 24			09 43		09 54			10 13
Shenstone	d						08 19	08 28			08 48					09 18				09 48					10 18
Blake Street	d		08 01				08 22	08 32			08 52		09 02			09 22	09 32			09 52		10 02			10 22
Butlers Lane	d		08 03				08 24	08 34			08 54		09 04			09 24	09 34			09 54		10 04			10 24
Four Oaks	d		08 06	08 15	08 20		08 27	08 37		08 47	08 57		09 07	09 17		09 27	09 37	09 47		09 57		10 07	10 17		10 27
Sutton Coldfield	d		08 10	08 18	08 23		08 31	08 40		08 51	09 01		09 11	09 21		09 31	09 41	09 51		10 01		10 11	10 21		10 31
Wylde Green	d		08 13	08 21	08 26		08 33	08 43		08 54	09 04		09 14	09 24		09 34	09 44	09 54		10 04		10 14	10 24		10 34
Chester Road	d		08 15	08 23	08 28		08 36	08 45		08 56	09 06		09 16	09 26		09 36	09 46	09 56		10 06		10 16	10 26		10 36
Erdington	d		08 17	08 25	08 29		08 37	08 47		08 58	09 08		09 18	09 28		09 38	09 48	09 58		10 08		10 18	10 28		10 38
Gravelly Hill	d		08 20		08 32		08 40	08 50		09 01	09 11		09 21	09 31		09 41	09 51	10 01		10 11		10 21	10 31		10 41
Aston	d		08 23		08 35		08 43	08 53		09 04	09 14		09 24	09 34		09 44	09 54	10 04		10 14		10 24	10 34		10 44
Duddeston	d				08 37		08 46	08 56		09 06				09 36				10 06					10 36		
Birmingham New Street 12	a		08 31	08 36	08 42		08 51	09 01		09 12	09 21		09 31	09 41		09 51	10 01	10 11		10 21		10 31	10 41		10 51
	d	08 30	08 33		08 43	08 49	08 53	09 03		09 14	09 23	09 30	09 33	09 43	09 49	09 53	10 03	10 13		10 23	10 30	10 33	10 43	10 49	10 53
Five Ways	d		08 36		08 46		08 56	09 06		09 17	09 26		09 36	09 46		09 56	10 06	10 16		10 26		10 36	10 46		10 56
University	d	08a36	08 40		08 50	08 55	09 00	09 10		09 21	09 30	09a36	09 40	09 50	09 55	10 00	10 10	10 20		10 30	10a36	10 40	10 50	10 55	11 00
Selly Oak	d		08 43		08 53		09 03	09 13		09 23	09 33		09 43	09 53		10 03	10 13	10 23		10 33		10 43	10 53		11 03
Bournville	d		08 45		08 55		09 05	09 15		09 25	09 35		09 45	09 55		10 05	10 15	10 25		10 35		10 45	10 55		11 05
Kings Norton	d		08 47		08 57		09 07	09 17		09 27	09 37		09 47	09 57		10 07	10 17	10 27		10 37		10 47	10 57		11 07
Northfield	d		08 50		09 00		09 10	09 20		09 30	09 40		09 50	10 00		10 10	10 20	10 30		10 40		10 50	11 00		11 10
Longbridge	d		08a54		09 06		09a14	09a24		09 36	09a44		09a54	10 06		10a14	10a24	10 36		10a44		10a54	11 06		11a14
Barnt Green	d				09 10					09 40				10 10				10 40					11 10		
Alvechurch	d				09 15					09 45				10 15				10 45					11 15		
Redditch	a				09 22					09 52				10 22				10 52					11 22		
Bromsgrove	a					09 09									10 09									11 09	

		LM	LM	LM		XC ◇1	LM	LM	LM	LM	LM	LM	LM	XC ◇1		LM	LM	LM	LM	LM	LM	LM	XC ◇1	LM	
Lichfield Trent Valley	d	10 20					10 50				11 20					11 50				12 20				12 50	
Lichfield City	d	10 24		10 43			10 54			11 13	11 24		11 43			11 54			12 13	12 24		12 43		12 54	
Shenstone	d			10 48						11 18			11 48						12 18			12 48			
Blake Street	d	10 32		10 52			11 02			11 22	11 32		11 52			12 02			12 22	12 32		12 52		13 02	
Butlers Lane	d	10 34		10 54			11 04			11 24	11 34		11 54			12 04			12 24	12 34		12 54		13 04	
Four Oaks	d	10 37	10 47	10 57			11 07	11 17		11 27	11 37	11 47	11 57			12 07	12 17		12 27	12 37	12 47	12 57		13 07	
Sutton Coldfield	d	10 41	10 51	11 01			11 11	11 21		11 31	11 41	11 51	12 01			12 11	12 21		12 31	12 41	12 51	13 01		13 11	
Wylde Green	d	10 44	10 54	11 04			11 14	11 24		11 34	11 44	11 54	12 04			12 14	12 24		12 34	12 44	12 54	13 04		13 14	
Chester Road	d	10 46	10 56	11 06			11 16	11 26		11 36	11 46	11 56	12 06			12 16	12 26		12 36	12 46	12 56	13 06		13 16	
Erdington	d	10 48	10 58	11 08			11 18	11 28		11 38	11 48	11 58	12 08			12 18	12 28		12 38	12 48	12 58	13 08		13 18	
Gravelly Hill	d	10 51	11 01	11 11			11 21	11 31		11 41	11 51	12 01	12 11			12 21	12 31		12 41	12 51	13 01	13 11		13 21	
Aston	d	10 54	11 04	11 14			11 24	11 34		11 44	11 54	12 04	12 14			12 24	12 34		12 44	12 54	13 04	13 14		13 24	
Duddeston	d		11 06					11 36				12 06					12 36				13 06				
Birmingham New Street 12	a	11 01	11 11	11 21			11 31	11 41		11 51	12 01	12 11	12 21			12 31	12 41		12 51	13 01	13 11	13 21		13 31	
	d	11 03	11 12	11 23		11 30	11 33	11 43	11 49	11 53	12 03	12 13	12 23	12 30		12 33	12 43	12 49	12 53	13 03	13 13	13 23	13 30	13 33	
Five Ways	d	11 06	11 15	11 26			11 36	11 46		11 56	12 06	12 16	12 26			12 36	12 46		12 56	13 06	13 17	13 26		13 36	
University	d	11 10	11 19	11 30		11a36	11 40	11 50	11 55	12 00	12 10	12 20	12 30	12a36		12 40	12 50	12 55	13 00	13 10	13 20	13 30	13a36	13 40	
Selly Oak	d	11 13	11 22	11 33			11 43	11 53		12 03	12 13	12 23	12 33			12 43	12 53		13 03	13 13	13 23	13 33		13 43	
Bournville	d	11 15	11 24	11 35			11 45	11 55		12 05	12 15	12 25	12 35			12 45	12 55		13 05	13 15	13 25	13 35		13 45	
Kings Norton	d	11 17	11 26	11 37			11 47	11 57		12 07	12 17	12 27	12 37			12 47	12 57		13 07	13 17	13 27	13 37		13 47	
Northfield	d	11 20	11 29	11 40			11 50	12 00		12 10	12 20	12 30	12 40			12 50	13 00		13 10	13 20	13 30	13 40		13 50	
Longbridge	d	11a24	11 35	11a44			11a54	12 06		12a14	12a22	12 36	12a44			12a53	13 06		13a14	13a24	13 36	13a45		13a54	
Barnt Green	d		11 39					12 10				12 40					13 10				13 40				
Alvechurch	d		11 44					12 15				12 45					13 15				13 45				
Redditch	a		11 51					12 22				12 52					13 22				13 52				
Bromsgrove	a								12 09									13 09							

Table 69

Mondays to Fridays

9 December to 16 May

Lichfield - Birmingham - Longbridge and Redditch

Network Diagram - refer to first Page of Table 67

		LM	LM	LM	LM	LM	LM	XC	LM	LM		LM	LM	LM	LM	LM	XC	LM	LM	LM		LM	LM	LM	LM
								◇1									◇1								
Lichfield Trent Valley	d				13 20				13 50					14 20				14 50					15 20		
Lichfield City	d			13 13	13 24		13 43		13 54				14 13	14 24		14 43		14 54				15 13	15 24		
Shenstone	d			13 18			13 48						14 18			14 48						15 18			
Blake Street	d			13 22	13 32		13 52		14 02				14 22	14 32		14 52		15 02				15 22	15 32		
Butlers Lane	d			13 24	13 34		13 54		14 04				14 24	14 34		14 54		15 04				15 24	15 34		
Four Oaks	d	13 17		13 27	13 37	13 47	13 57		14 07	14 17			14 27	14 37	14 47	14 57		15 07	15 17			15 27	15 37	15 47	
Sutton Coldfield	d	13 21		13 31	13 41	13 51	14 01		14 11	14 21			14 31	14 41	14 51	15 01		15 11	15 21			15 31	15 41	15 51	
Wylde Green	d	13 24		13 34	13 44	13 54	14 04		14 14	14 24			14 34	14 44	14 54	15 04		15 14	15 24			15 34	15 44	15 54	
Chester Road	d	13 26		13 36	13 46	13 56	14 06		14 16	14 26			14 36	14 46	14 56	15 06		15 16	15 26			15 36	15 46	15 56	
Erdington	d	13 28		13 38	13 48	13 58	14 08		14 18	14 28			14 38	14 48	14 58	15 08		15 18	15 28			15 38	15 48	15 58	
Gravelly Hill	d	13 31		13 41	13 51	14 01	14 11		14 21	14 31			14 41	14 51	15 01	15 11		15 21	15 31			15 41	15 51	16 01	
Aston	d	13 34		13 44	13 54	14 04	14 14		14 24	14 34			14 44	14 54	15 04	15 14		15 24	15 34			15 44	15 54	16 04	
Duddeston	d	13 36				14 06				14 36					15 06				15 36					16 06	
Birmingham New Street 12	a	13 41		13 51	14 01	14 11	14 21		14 31	14 41			14 51	15 01	15 11	15 21		15 31	15 41			15 51	16 01	16 11	
	d	13 43	13 49	13 53	14 03	14 13	14 23	14 30	14 33	14 43		14 49	14 53	15 03	15 13	15 23	15 30	15 33	15 43	15 49		15 53	16 03	16 13	16 19
Five Ways	d	13 46		13 56	14 06	14 16	14 26		14 36	14 46			14 56	15 06	15 16	15 26		15 36	15 46			15 56	16 06	16 16	
University	d	13 50	13 55	14 00	14 10	14 20	14 30	14a36	14 40	14 50		14 55	15 00	15 10	15 20	15 30	15a36	15 40	15 50	15 55		16 00	16 10	16 20	16 25
Selly Oak	d	13 53		14 03	14 13	14 23	14 33		14 43	14 53			15 03	15 13	15 23	15 33		15 43	15 53			16 03	16 13	16 23	
Bournville	d	13 55		14 05	14 15	14 25	14 35		14 45	14 55			15 05	15 15	15 25	15 35		15 45	15 55			16 05	16 15	16 25	
Kings Norton	d	13 57		14 07	14 17	14 27	14 37		14 47	14 57			15 07	15 17	15 27	15 37		15 47	15 57			16 08	16 17	16 27	
Northfield	d	14 00		14 10	14 20	14 30	14 40		14 50	15 00			15 10	15 20	15 30	15 40		15 50	16 00			16 11	16 20	16 30	
Longbridge	d	14 06		14a14	14a24	14 36	14a44		14a53	15 06			15a14	15a24	15 36	15a44		15a54	16 06			16a15	16a24	16 36	
Barnt Green	d	14 10				14 40				15 10					15 40				16 10					16 40	
Alvechurch	d	14 15				14 45				15 15					15 45				16 15					16 45	
Redditch	a	14 22				14 52				15 22					15 52				16 22					16 52	
Bromsgrove	a		14 09									15 09								16 09					16 40

		LM	XC	LM	LM	LM		LM	LM	LM	LM	LM	XC	LM	LM	LM		LM	LM	LM	LM	LM	LM	XC	LM
			◇1										◇1											◇1	
Lichfield Trent Valley	d			15 50					16 20					16 50						17 20			17 40		17 50
Lichfield City	d	15 43		15 54				16 13	16 24			16 43		16 54	17 05					17 24			17 43		17 54
Shenstone	d	15 48						16 18				16 48								17 29			17 48		
Blake Street	d	15 52		16 02				16 22	16 32			16 52		17 02	17 13					17 33			17 52		18 02
Butlers Lane	d	15 54		16 04				16 24	16 34			16 54		17 04	17 15					17 35			17 54		18 04
Four Oaks	d	15 57		16 07	16 17			16 27	16 37	16 47		16 57		17 07	17 18			17 27		17 38	17 47		17 57		18 07
Sutton Coldfield	d	16 01		16 11	16 21			16 31	16 41	16 51		17 01		17 11	17 21			17 31		17 41	17 51		18 01		18 11
Wylde Green	d	16 04		16 14	16 24			16 34	16 44	16 54		17 04		17 14	17 24			17 34		17 44	17 54		18 04		18 14
Chester Road	d	16 06		16 16	16 26			16 36	16 46	16 56		17 06		17 16	17 26			17 36		17 46	17 56		18 06		18 16
Erdington	d	16 08		16 18	16 28			16 38	16 48	16 58		17 08		17 18	17 28			17 38		17 48	17 58		18 08		18 18
Gravelly Hill	d	16 11		16 21	16 31			16 41	16 51	17 01		17 11		17 21	17 31			17 41		17 51	18 01		18 11		18 21
Aston	d	16 14		16 24	16 34			16 44	16 54	17 04		17 14		17 24	17 34			17 44		17 54	18 04		18 14		18 24
Duddeston	d				16 36					17 06					17 36						18 06				
Birmingham New Street 12	a	16 21		16 31	16 41			16 51	17 01	17 11		17 21		17 30	17 42			17 51		18 01	18 11		18 21		18 31
	d	16 23	16 30	16 33	16 43	16 49		16 53	17 03	17 13	17 19	17 23	17 30	17 33	17 43	17 49		17 53	17 59	18 03	18 13	18 19	18 23	18 30	18 33
Five Ways	d	16 26		16 36	16 46			16 56	17 06	17 16		17 26		17 36	17 46			17 56		18 06	18 16		18 26		18 36
University	d	16 30	16a36	16 40	16 50	16 55		17 00	17 10	17 20	17 25	17 30	17 36	17 40	17 50	17a55		18 00	18 05	18 10	18 20	18 25	18 30	18 36	18 40
Selly Oak	d	16 33		16 43	16 53			17 03	17 13	17 23		17 33		17 43	17 53			18 03		18 13	18 23		18 33		18 43
Bournville	d	16 35		16 45	16 55			17 05	17 15	17 25		17 35		17 45	17 55			18 05		18 15	18 25		18 35		18 45
Kings Norton	d	16 37		16 47	16 57			17 07	17 17	17 27		17 37		17 47	17 57			18 07		18 17	18 27		18 37		18 47
Northfield	d	16 40		16 50	17 00			17 10	17 20	17 30		17 40		17 50	18 00			18 10		18 20	18 30		18 40		18 50
Longbridge	d	16a44		16a53	17 06			17a14	17a24	17 36		17a44		17a54	18 06			18a14		18a24	18 34		18a44		18a54
Barnt Green	d				17 10					17 40					18 10						18 39				
Alvechurch	d				17 15					17 45					18 15						18 43				
Redditch	a				17 22					17 52					18 22						18 52				
Bromsgrove	a					17 09					17 40		17 51						18 21			18 44		18 49	

		LM		LM	LM	LM	LM	LM	XC	LM	LM	LM		LM	LM	LM	LM	XC	LM	LM	LM	LM		LM	LM
									◇1									◇1							
Lichfield Trent Valley	d			18 10	18 20					18 50					19 20				20 00			20 30			21 00
Lichfield City	d			18 13	18 24			18 43		18 54		19 13			19 24		19 43		20 04			20 34			21 04
Shenstone	d			18 18				18 48				19 18					19 48		20 09			20 39			21 09
Blake Street	d			18 22	18 32			18 52		19 02		19 22			19 32		19 52		20 13			20 43			21 13
Butlers Lane	d			18 24	18 34			18 54		19 04		19 24			19 34		19 54		20 15			20 45			21 15
Four Oaks	d	18 17		18 27	18 37	18 47		18 57		19 07	19 17	19 27			19 37	19 47	19 57		20 18			20 48			21 18
Sutton Coldfield	d	18 21		18 31	18 41	18 51		19 01		19 11	19 21	19 31			19 41	19 51	20 01		20 21			20 51			21 21
Wylde Green	d	18 24		18 34	18 44	18 54		19 04		19 14	19 24	19 34			19 44	19 54	20 04		20 24			20 54			21 24
Chester Road	d	18 26		18 36	18 46	18 56		19 06		19 16	19 26	19 36			19 46	19 56	20 06		20 26			20 56			21 26
Erdington	d	18 28		18 38	18 48	18 58		19 08		19 18	19 28	19 38			19 48	19 58	20 08		20 28			20 58			21 28
Gravelly Hill	d	18 31		18 41	18 51	19 01		19 11		19 21	19 31	19 41			19 51	20 01	20 11		20 30			21 00			21 30
Aston	d	18 34		18 44	18 54	19 04		19 14		19 24	19 34	19 44			19 54	20 04	20 14		20 33			21 03			21 33
Duddeston	d	18 36				19 06					19 36					20 06			20 36			21 06			21 36
Birmingham New Street 12	a	18 41		18 51	19 01	19 11		19 21		19 31	19 41	19 51			20 00	20 11	20 21		20 40			21 12			21 41
	d	18 43		18 53	19 03	19 13	19 19	19 23	19 30	19 33	19 43	19 53		19 59		20 13	20 23	20 30	20 44	20 53	20 59	21 13		21 23	21 43
Five Ways	d	18 46		18 56	19 06	19 16		19 26		19 36	19 46	19 56				20 16	20 26		20 47	20 56		21 16		21 26	21 46
University	d	18 50		19 00	19 10	19 20	19 25	19 30	19a36	19 40	19 50	20 00		20 05		20 20	20 30	20a36	20 51	21 00	21 05	21 20		21 30	21 50
Selly Oak	d	18 53		19 03	19 13	19 23		19 33		19 43	19 53	20 03				20 23	20 33		20 54	21 03		21 23		21 33	21 53
Bournville	d	18 55		19 05	19 15	19 25		19 35		19 45	19 55	20 05				20 25	20 35		20 56	21 05		21 25		21 35	21 55
Kings Norton	d	18 57		19 07	19 17	19 27		19 37		19 47	19 57	20 07				20 27	20 37		20 58	21 07		21 27		21 37	21 57
Northfield	d	19 00		19 10	19 20	19 30		19 40		19 50	20 00	20 10				20 30	20 40		21 01	21 10		21 30		21 40	22 00
Longbridge	d	19 06		19a14	19a24	19 36		19a44		19a54	20 04	20a14				20 34	20a44		21 05	21a14		21 34		21a44	22 04
Barnt Green	d	19 10				19 40					20 09					20 39			21 10			21 39			22 09
Alvechurch	d	19 15				19 45					20 13					20 43			21 14			21 43			22 13
Redditch	a	19 22				19 52					20 22					20 52			21 23			21 52			22 22
Bromsgrove	a						19 40							20 19							21 19				

Table 69

Mondays to Fridays

9 December to 16 May

Lichfield - Birmingham - Longbridge and Redditch

Network Diagram - refer to first Page of Table 67

		LM	LM	LM	LM	LM	LM	LM		LM	LM	LM
Lichfield Trent Valley	d			21 30		22 00				22 30	22 56	
Lichfield City	d			21 34		22 04				22 34	23 00	
Shenstone	d			21 39		22 09				22 39	23 05	
Blake Street	d			21 43		22 13				22 43	23 09	23 36
Butlers Lane	d			21 45		22 15				22 45	23 11	23 38
Four Oaks	d			21 48		22 18				22 48	23 14	23 41
Sutton Coldfield	d			21 51		22 21				22 51	23 17	23 44
Wylde Green	d			21 54		22 24				22 54	23 20	
Chester Road	d			21 56		22 26				22 56		
Erdington	d			21 58		22 28				22 58		
Gravelly Hill	d			22 00		22 30				23 00		
Aston	d			22 03		22 33				23 03		
Duddeston	d			22 06		22 36				23 06		
Birmingham New Street 12	a			22 12		22 41				23 11	23 31	23 59
	d	21 53	22 00	22 13	22 23	22 43	22 53	23 00		23 13	23 33	
Five Ways	d	21 56		22 16	22 26	22 46	22 56			23 16	23 36	
University	d	22 00	22 06	22 20	22 30	22 50	23 00	23 06		23 20	23 40	
Selly Oak	d	22 03		22 23	22 33	22 53	23 03			23 23	23 43	
Bournville	d	22 05		22 25	22 35	22 55	23 05			23 25	23 45	
Kings Norton	d	22 07		22 27	22 37	22 57	23 07			23 27	23 47	
Northfield	d	22 10		22 30	22 40	23 00	23 10			23 30	23 50	
Longbridge	d	22a14		22 34	22a44	23 04	23a14			23 34	23a54	
Barnt Green	d			22 39		23 09				23 39		
Alvechurch	d			22 43		23 13				23 43		
Redditch	a			22 52		23 22				23 52		
Bromsgrove	a		22 19					23 19				

Saturdays

14 December to 17 May

		XC	LM	LM	LM	LM	LM	LM	LM	LM		LM	LM	LM	XC	LM	LM	LM	LM	LM		LM	LM	XC	LM
		◇1													◇1 ⊥									◇1	
Lichfield Trent Valley	d											06 20				06 50				07 20					07 50
Lichfield City	d											06 24	06 38			06 54	07 08			07 24			07 43		07 54
Shenstone	d											06 29				06 59				07 29			07 48		
Blake Street	d						06 03					06 33				07 03				07 33			07 52		08 02
Butlers Lane	d						06 05					06 35				07 05				07 35			07 54		08 04
Four Oaks	d						06 08					06 38	06 48			07 08	07 18			07 38		07 47	07 57		08 07
Sutton Coldfield	d						06 11					06 41	06 51			07 11	07 21			07 41		07 51	08 01		08 11
Wylde Green	d						06 14					06 44	06 54			07 14	07 24			07 44		07 54	08 04		08 14
Chester Road	d						06 16					06 46	06 56			07 16	07 26			07 46		07 56	08 06		08 16
Erdington	d						06 17					06 48	06 58			07 18	07 28			07 47		07 58	08 08		08 18
Gravelly Hill	d						06 20					06 50	07 01			07 20	07 31			07 50		08 01	08 11		08 21
Aston	d						06 23					06 53	07 04			07 23	07 34			07 53		08 04	08 14		08 24
Duddeston	d						06 26					06 56	07 06			07 26	07 36					08 06			
Birmingham New Street 12	a						06 31					07 00	07 11			07 31	07 41			08 00		08 11	08 21		08 31
	d	05 42	05 53	06 03	06 13	06 23	06 33	06 43	06 49	06 53		07 03	07 13	07 23	07 30	07 33	07 43	07 49	07 53	08 03		08 13	08 23	08 30	08 33
Five Ways	d		05 56	06 06	06 16	06 26	06 36	06 46		06 56		07 06	07 16	07 26		07 36	07 46		07 56	08 06		08 16	08 26		08 36
University	d		06 00	06 10	06 20	06 30	06 40	06 50	06 55	07 00		07 10	07 20	07 30	07a36	07 40	07 50	07 55	08 00	08 10		08 20	08 30	08a36	08 40
Selly Oak	d		06 03	06 13	06 23	06 33	06 43	06 53		07 03		07 13	07 23	07 33		07 43	07 53		08 03	08 13		08 23	08 33		08 43
Bournville	d		06 05	06 15	06 25	06 35	06 45	06 55		07 05		07 15	07 25	07 35		07 45	07 55		08 05	08 15		08 25	08 35		08 45
Kings Norton	d		06 07	06 17	06 27	06 37	06 47	06 57		07 07		07 17	07 27	07 37		07 47	07 57		08 07	08 17		08 27	08 37		08 47
Northfield	d		06 10	06 20	06 30	06 40	06 50	07 00		07 10		07 20	07 30	07 40		07 50	08 00		08 10	08 20		08 30	08 40		08 50
Longbridge	d		06a14	06a24	06 36	06a44	06a54	07 06		07a14		07a24	07 36	07a44		07a54	08 06		08a14	08a24		08 36	08a44		08a54
Barnt Green	d				06 40			07 10					07 40				08 10					08 40			
Alvechurch	d				06 45			07 15					07 45				08 15					08 45			
Redditch	a				06 52			07 22					07 52				08 22					08 52			
Bromsgrove	a	06 03							07 09									08 09							

		LM	LM	LM	LM	LM		LM	XC	LM	LM	LM	LM	LM	LM	LM		XC	LM	LM	LM	LM	LM	LM	LM
									◇1 ⊥									◇1 ⊥							
Lichfield Trent Valley	d				08 20					08 50				09 20					09 50				10 20		
Lichfield City	d			08 13	08 24			08 43		08 54			09 13	09 24		09 43			09 54			10 13	10 24		10 43
Shenstone	d			08 18				08 48					09 18			09 48						10 18			10 48
Blake Street	d			08 22	08 32			08 52		09 02			09 22	09 32		09 52			10 02			10 22	10 32		10 52
Butlers Lane	d			08 24	08 34			08 54		09 04			09 24	09 34		09 54			10 04			10 24	10 34		10 54
Four Oaks	d	08 17		08 27	08 37	08 47		08 57		09 07	09 17		09 27	09 37	09 47	09 57			10 07	10 17		10 27	10 37	10 47	10 57
Sutton Coldfield	d	08 21		08 31	08 41	08 51		09 01		09 11	09 21		09 31	09 41	09 51	10 01			10 11	10 21		10 31	10 41	10 51	11 01
Wylde Green	d	08 24		08 34	08 44	08 54		09 04		09 14	09 24		09 34	09 44	09 54	10 04			10 14	10 24		10 34	10 44	10 54	11 04
Chester Road	d	08 26		08 36	08 46	08 56		09 06		09 16	09 26		09 36	09 46	09 56	10 06			10 16	10 26		10 36	10 46	10 56	11 06
Erdington	d	08 28		08 38	08 48	08 58		09 08		09 18	09 28		09 38	09 48	09 58	10 08			10 18	10 28		10 38	10 48	10 58	11 08
Gravelly Hill	d	08 31		08 41	08 51	09 01		09 11		09 21	09 31		09 41	09 51	10 01	10 11			10 21	10 31		10 41	10 51	11 01	11 11
Aston	d	08 34		08 44	08 54	09 04		09 14		09 24	09 34		09 44	09 54	10 04	10 14			10 24	10 34		10 44	10 54	11 04	11 14
Duddeston	d	08 36				09 06					09 36				10 06					10 36				11 06	
Birmingham New Street 12	a	08 41		08 51	09 01	09 11		09 21		09 31	09 41		09 51	10 01	10 11	10 21			10 31	10 41		10 51	11 01	11 11	11 21
	d	08 43	08 49	08 53	09 03	09 13		09 23	09 30	09 33	09 43	09 49	09 53	10 03	10 13	10 23		10 30	10 33	10 43	10 49	10 53	11 03	11 13	11 23
Five Ways	d	08 46		08 56	09 06	09 16		09 26		09 36	09 46		09 56	10 06	10 16	10 26			10 36	10 46		10 56	11 06	11 16	11 26
University	d	08 50	08 55	09 00	09 10	09 20		09 30	09a36	09 40	09 50	09 55	10 00	10 10	10 20	10 30		10a36	10 40	10 50	10 55	11 00	11 10	11 20	11 30
Selly Oak	d	08 53		09 03	09 13	09 23		09 33		09 43	09 53		10 03	10 13	10 23	10 33			10 43	10 53		11 03	11 13	11 23	11 33
Bournville	d	08 55		09 05	09 15	09 25		09 35		09 45	09 55		10 05	10 15	10 25	10 35			10 45	10 55		11 05	11 15	11 25	11 35
Kings Norton	d	08 57		09 07	09 17	09 27		09 37		09 47	09 57		10 07	10 17	10 27	10 37			10 47	10 57		11 07	11 17	11 27	11 37
Northfield	d	09 00		09 10	09 20	09 30		09 40		09 50	10 00		10 10	10 20	10 30	10 40			10 50	11 00		11 10	11 20	11 30	11 40
Longbridge	d	09 06		09a14	09a24	09 36		09a44		09a54	10 06		10a14	10a24	10 36	10a44			10a54	11 06		11a14	11a24	11 36	11a44
Barnt Green	d	09 10				09 40					10 10				10 40					11 10				11 40	
Alvechurch	d	09 15				09 45					10 15				10 45					11 15				11 45	
Redditch	a	09 22				09 52					10 22				10 52					11 22				11 52	
Bromsgrove	a		09 09									10 09									11 10				

Table 69

Saturdays

14 December to 17 May

Lichfield - Birmingham - Longbridge and Redditch

Network Diagram - refer to first Page of Table 67

		XC ◇1 🛒		LM	LM	LM	LM	LM	LM	LM	XC ◇1 🛒	LM		LM	LM	LM	LM	LM	LM	XC ◇1 🛒	LM	LM		LM	LM
Lichfield Trent Valley	d			10 50				11 20				11 50					12 20				12 50				
Lichfield City	d			10 54			11 13	11 24		11 43		11 54				12 13	12 24		12 43		12 54				13 13
Shenstone	d						11 18			11 48						12 18			12 48						13 18
Blake Street	d			11 02			11 22	11 32		11 52		12 02				12 22	12 32		12 52		13 02				13 22
Butlers Lane	d			11 04			11 24	11 34		11 54		12 04				12 24	12 34		12 54		13 04				13 24
Four Oaks	d			11 07	11 17		11 27	11 37	11 47	11 57		12 07		12 17		12 27	12 37	12 47	12 57		13 07	13 17			13 27
Sutton Coldfield	d			11 11	11 21		11 31	11 41	11 51	12 01		12 11		12 21		12 31	12 41	12 51	13 01		13 11	13 21			13 31
Wylde Green	d			11 14	11 24		11 34	11 44	11 54	12 04		12 14		12 24		12 34	12 44	12 54	13 04		13 14	13 24			13 34
Chester Road	d			11 16	11 26		11 36	11 46	11 56	12 06		12 16		12 26		12 36	12 46	12 56	13 06		13 16	13 26			13 36
Erdington	d			11 18	11 28		11 38	11 48	11 58	12 08		12 18		12 28		12 38	12 48	12 58	13 08		13 18	13 28			13 38
Gravelly Hill	d			11 21	11 31		11 41	11 51	12 01	12 11		12 21		12 31		12 41	12 51	13 01	13 11		13 21	13 31			13 41
Aston	d			11 24	11 34		11 44	11 54	12 04	12 14		12 24		12 34		12 44	12 54	13 04	13 14		13 24	13 34			13 44
Duddeston	d				11 36				12 06					12 36				13 06				13 36			
Birmingham New Street 12	a			11 31	11 41		11 51	12 01	12 11	12 21		12 31		12 41		12 51	13 01	13 11	13 21		13 31	13 41			13 51
	d	11 30		11 33	11 43	11 49	11 53	12 03	12 13	12 23	12 30	12 33		12 43	12 49	12 53	13 03	13 13	13 23	13 30	13 33	13 43		13 49	13 53
Five Ways	d			11 36	11 46		11 56	12 06	12 16	12 26		12 36		12 46		12 56	13 06	13 16	13 26		13 36	13 46			13 56
University	d	11a36		11 40	11 50	11 55	12 00	12 10	12 20	12 30	12a36	12 40		12 50	12 55	13 00	13 10	13 20	13 30	13a36	13 40	13 50		13 55	14 00
Selly Oak	d			11 43	11 53		12 03	12 13	12 23	12 33		12 43		12 53		13 03	13 13	13 23	13 33		13 43	13 53			14 03
Bournville	d			11 45	11 55		12 05	12 15	12 25	12 35		12 45		12 55		13 05	13 15	13 25	13 35		13 45	13 55			14 05
Kings Norton	d			11 47	11 57		12 07	12 17	12 27	12 37		12 47		12 57		13 07	13 17	13 27	13 37		13 47	13 57			14 07
Northfield	d			11 50	12 00		12 10	12 20	12 30	12 40		12 50		13 00		13 10	13 20	13 30	13 40		13 50	14 00			14 10
Longbridge	d			11a54	12 06		12a14	12a24	12 36	12a44		12a54		13 06		13a14	13a24	13 36	13a44		13a54	14 06			14a14
Barnt Green	d				12 10				12 40					13 10				13 40				14 10			
Alvechurch	d				12 15				12 45					13 15				13 45				14 15			
Redditch	a				12 22				12 52					13 22				13 52				14 22			
Bromsgrove	a					12 09									13 09									14 10	

		LM	LM	LM	XC ◇1 🛒	LM	LM	LM		LM	LM	LM	LM	XC ◇1 🛒	LM	LM	LM	LM		LM	LM	LM	LM	XC ◇1 🛒	LM
Lichfield Trent Valley	d	13 20				13 50					14 20				14 50					15 20					15 50
Lichfield City	d	13 24		13 43		13 54				14 13	14 24		14 43		14 54			15 13		15 24			15 43		15 54
Shenstone	d			13 48						14 18			14 48					15 18					15 48		
Blake Street	d	13 32		13 52		14 02				14 22	14 32		14 52		15 02			15 22		15 32			15 52		16 02
Butlers Lane	d	13 34		13 54		14 04				14 24	14 34		14 54		15 04			15 24		15 34			15 54		16 04
Four Oaks	d	13 37	13 47	13 57		14 07	14 17			14 27	14 37	14 47	14 57		15 07	15 17		15 27		15 37	15 47		15 57		16 07
Sutton Coldfield	d	13 41	13 51	14 01		14 11	14 21			14 31	14 41	14 51	15 01		15 11	15 21		15 31		15 41	15 51		16 01		16 11
Wylde Green	d	13 44	13 54	14 04		14 14	14 24			14 34	14 44	14 54	15 04		15 14	15 24		15 34		15 44	15 54		16 04		16 14
Chester Road	d	13 46	13 56	14 06		14 16	14 26			14 36	14 46	14 56	15 06		15 16	15 26		15 36		15 46	15 56		16 06		16 16
Erdington	d	13 48	13 58	14 08		14 18	14 28			14 38	14 48	14 58	15 08		15 18	15 28		15 38		15 48	15 58		16 08		16 18
Gravelly Hill	d	13 51	14 01	14 11		14 21	14 31			14 41	14 51	15 01	15 11		15 21	15 31		15 41		15 51	16 01		16 11		16 21
Aston	d	13 54	14 04	14 14		14 24	14 34			14 44	14 54	15 04	15 14		15 24	15 34		15 44		15 54	16 04		16 14		16 24
Duddeston	d		14 06				14 36					15 06				15 36					16 06				
Birmingham New Street 12	a	14 01	14 11	14 21		14 31	14 41			14 51	15 01	15 11	15 21		15 31	15 41		15 51		16 01	16 11		16 21		16 31
	d	14 03	14 13	14 23	14 30	14 33	14 43	14 49		14 53	15 03	15 13	15 23	15 30	15 33	15 43	15 49	15 53		16 03	16 13	16 19	16 23	16 30	16 33
Five Ways	d	14 06	14 16	14 26		14 36	14 46			14 56	15 06	15 16	15 26		15 36	15 46		15 56		16 06	16 16		16 26		16 36
University	d	14 10	14 20	14 30	14a36	14 40	14 50	14 55		15 00	15 10	15 20	15 30	15a36	15 40	15 50	15 55	16 00		16 10	16 20		16 30	16a36	16 40
Selly Oak	d	14 13	14 23	14 33		14 43	14 53			15 03	15 13	15 23	15 33		15 43	15 53		16 03		16 13	16 23		16 33		16 43
Bournville	d	14 15	14 25	14 35		14 45	14 55			15 05	15 15	15 25	15 35		15 45	15 55		16 05		16 15	16 25		16 35		16 45
Kings Norton	d	14 17	14 27	14 37		14 47	14 57			15 07	15 17	15 27	15 37		15 47	15 57		16 07		16 17	16 27		16 37		16 47
Northfield	d	14 20	14 30	14 40		14 50	15 00			15 10	15 20	15 30	15 40		15 50	16 00		16 10		16 20	16 30		16 40		16 50
Longbridge	d	14a24	14 36	14a44		14a54	15 06			15a14	15a24	15 36	15a44		15a54	16 06		16a14		16a24	16 36		16a44		16a54
Barnt Green	d		14 40				15 10					15 40				16 10					16 40				
Alvechurch	d		14 45				15 15					15 45				16 15					16 45				
Redditch	a		14 52				15 22					15 52				16 22					16 52				
Bromsgrove	a							15 09									16 09					16 43			

		LM	LM	LM		LM	LM	LM	LM	XC ◇1	LM	LM	LM	LM		LM	LM	LM	XC ◇1	LM	LM	LM	LM	LM	
Lichfield Trent Valley	d					16 20					16 50					17 20				17 50				18 20	
Lichfield City	d			16 13		16 24			16 43		16 54			17 13		17 24		17 43		17 54			18 13	18 24	
Shenstone	d			16 18					16 48					17 18				17 48					18 18		
Blake Street	d			16 22		16 32			16 52		17 02			17 22		17 32		17 52		18 02			18 22	18 32	
Butlers Lane	d			16 24		16 34			16 54		17 04			17 24		17 34		17 54		18 04			18 24	18 34	
Four Oaks	d	16 17		16 27		16 37	16 47		16 57		17 07	17 17		17 27		17 37	17 47	17 57		18 07	18 17		18 27	18 37	
Sutton Coldfield	d	16 21		16 31		16 41	16 51		17 01		17 11	17 21		17 31		17 41	17 51	18 01		18 11	18 21		18 31	18 41	
Wylde Green	d	16 24		16 34		16 44	16 54		17 04		17 14	17 24		17 34		17 44	17 54	18 04		18 14	18 24		18 34	18 44	
Chester Road	d	16 26		16 36		16 46	16 56		17 06		17 16	17 26		17 36		17 46	17 56	18 06		18 16	18 26		18 36	18 46	
Erdington	d	16 28		16 38		16 48	16 58		17 08		17 18	17 28		17 38		17 48	17 58	18 08		18 18	18 28		18 38	18 48	
Gravelly Hill	d	16 31		16 41		16 51	17 01		17 11		17 21	17 31		17 41		17 51	18 01	18 11		18 21	18 31		18 41	18 51	
Aston	d	16 34		16 44		16 54	17 04		17 14		17 24	17 34		17 44		17 54	18 04	18 14		18 24	18 34		18 44	18 54	
Duddeston	d	16 36					17 06					17 36					18 06				18 36				
Birmingham New Street 12	a	16 41		16 51		17 01	17 11		17 21		17 31	17 41		17 51		18 01	18 11	18 21		18 31	18 41		18 51	19 01	
	d	16 43	16 49	16 53		17 03	17 13	17 19	17 23	17 30	17 33	17 43	17 49	17 53		18 03	18 13	18 23	18 30	18 33	18 43	18 49	18 53	19 03	
Five Ways	d	16 46		16 56		17 06	17 16		17 26		17 36	17 46		17 56		18 06	18 16	18 26		18 36	18 46		18 56	19 06	
University	d	16 50	16 55	17 00		17 10	17 20		17 30	17 36	17 40	17 50	17 55	18 00		18 10	18 20	18 30	18a36	18 40	18 50	18 55	19 00	19 10	
Selly Oak	d	16 53		17 03		17 13	17 23		17 33		17 43	17 53		18 03		18 13	18 23	18 33		18 43	18 53		19 03	19 13	
Bournville	d	16 55		17 05		17 15	17 25		17 35		17 45	17 55		18 05		18 15	18 25	18 35		18 45	18 55		19 05	19 15	
Kings Norton	d	16 57		17 07		17 17	17 27		17 37		17 47	17 57		18 07		18 17	18 27	18 37		18 47	18 57		19 07	19 17	
Northfield	d	17 00		17 10		17 20	17 30		17 40		17 50	18 00		18 10		18 20	18 30	18 40		18 50	19 00		19 10	19 20	
Longbridge	d	17 06		17a14		17a24	17 36		17a44		17a54	18 06		18a14		18a24	18 36	18a44		18a54	19 06		19a14	19a24	
Barnt Green	d	17 10					17 40					18 10					18 40				19 10				
Alvechurch	d	17 15					17 45					18 15					18 45				19 15				
Redditch	a	17 22					17 52					18 22					18 52				19 22				
Bromsgrove	a		17 10					17 40		17 49			18 09									19 09			

Table 69

Saturdays

14 December to 17 May

Lichfield - Birmingham - Longbridge and Redditch

Network Diagram - refer to first Page of Table 67

		LM	LM	LM	XC	LM	LM	LM	LM	LM	LM	XC	LM	LM	LM	LM	LM	LM	LM	LM	LM	LM	LM
					◇1							◇1											
Lichfield Trent Valley	d					18 50			19 20				20 00			20 30		21 00		21 30		22 00	
Lichfield City	d			18 43		18 54		19 13	19 24		19 43		20 04			20 34		21 04		21 34		22 04	
Shenstone	d			18 48				19 18			19 48		20 09			20 39		21 09		21 39		22 09	
Blake Street	d			18 52		19 02		19 22	19 32		19 52		20 13			20 43		21 13		21 43		22 13	
Butlers Lane	d			18 54		19 04		19 24	19 34		19 54		20 15			20 45		21 15		21 45		22 15	
Four Oaks	d	18 47		18 57		19 07	19 17	19 27	19 37	19 47	19 57		20 18			20 48		21 18		21 48		22 18	
Sutton Coldfield	d	18 51		19 01		19 11	19 21	19 31	19 41	19 51	20 01		20 21			20 51		21 21		21 51		22 21	
Wylde Green	d	18 54		19 04		19 14	19 24	19 34	19 44	19 54	20 04		20 24			20 54		21 24		21 54		22 24	
Chester Road	d	18 56		19 06		19 16	19 26	19 36	19 46	19 56	20 06		20 26			20 56		21 26		21 56		22 26	
Erdington	d	18 58		19 08		19 18	19 28	19 38	19 48	19 58	20 08		20 28			20 58		21 28		21 58		22 28	
Gravelly Hill	d	19 01		19 11		19 21	19 31	19 41	19 51	20 01	20 11		20 30			21 00		21 30		22 00		22 30	
Aston	d	19 04		19 14		19 24	19 34	19 44	19 54	20 04	20 14		20 33			21 03		21 33		22 03		22 33	
Duddeston	d	19 06					19 36			20 06			20 36			21 06		21 36		22 06		22 36	
Birmingham New Street 12	a	19 11		19 21		19 31	19 41	19 51	20 01	20 11	20 20		20 41			21 12		21 41		22 11		22 41	
	d	19 13	19 19	19 23	19 30	19 33	19 43	19 53		20 13	20 23	20 30	20 43	20 53	20 59	21 13	21 23	21 43	21 53	22 13	22 23	22 43	22 53
Five Ways	d	19 16		19 26		19 36	19 46	19 56		20 16	20 26		20 46	20 56		21 16	21 26	21 46	21 56	22 16	22 26	22 46	22 56
University	d	19 20	19 25	19 30	19a36	19 40	19 50	20 00		20 20	20 30	20a36	20 50	21 00	21 05	21 20	21 30	21 50	22 00	22 20	22 30	22 50	23 00
Selly Oak	d	19 23		19 33		19 43	19 53	20 03		20 23	20 33		20 53	21 03		21 23	21 33	21 53	22 03	22 23	22 33	22 53	23 03
Bournville	d	19 25		19 35		19 45	19 55	20 05		20 25	20 35		20 55	21 05		21 25	21 35	21 55	22 05	22 25	22 35	22 55	23 05
Kings Norton	d	19 27		19 37		19 47	19 57	20 07		20 27	20 37		20 57	21 07		21 27	21 37	21 57	22 07	22 27	22 37	22 57	23 07
Northfield	d	19 30		19 40		19 50	20 00	20 10		20 30	20 40		21 00	21 10		21 30	21 40	22 00	22 10	22 30	22 40	23 00	23 10
Longbridge	d	19 36		19a44		19a54	20 04	20a14		20 34	20a44		21 04	21a14		21 34	21a44	22 04	22a14	22 34	22a44	23 04	23a14
Barnt Green	d	19 40					20 09			20 39			21 09			21 39		22 09		22 39		23 09	
Alvechurch	d	19 45					20 13			20 43			21 13			21 43		22 13		22 43		23 13	
Redditch	a	19 52					20 22			20 52			21 22			21 52		22 22		22 52		23 22	
Bromsgrove	a		19 39												21 19								

		LM	LM	LM
Lichfield Trent Valley	d	22 30	22 56	
Lichfield City	d	22 34	23 00	
Shenstone	d	22 39	23 05	
Blake Street	d	22 43	23 09	23 36
Butlers Lane	d	22 45	23 11	23 38
Four Oaks	d	22 48	23 14	23 41
Sutton Coldfield	d	22 51	23 17	23 44
Wylde Green	d	22 54	23 20	
Chester Road	d	22 56		
Erdington	d	22 58		
Gravelly Hill	d	23 00		
Aston	d	23 03		
Duddeston	d	23 06		
Birmingham New Street 12	a	23 11	23 31	23 59
	d	23 13	23 33	
Five Ways	d	23 16	23 36	
University	d	23 20	23 40	
Selly Oak	d	23 23	23 43	
Bournville	d	23 25	23 45	
Kings Norton	d	23 27	23 47	
Northfield	d	23 30	23 50	
Longbridge	d	23 34	23a54	
Barnt Green	d	23 39		
Alvechurch	d	23 43		
Redditch	a	23 53		
Bromsgrove	a			

Sundays

8 December to 11 May

		LM	LM	LM	LM	XC	LM	LM	XC	LM	LM	LM	LM	XC	XC	LM	LM	XC	LM	LM	LM	XC	XC
						◇1			◇1					◇1	◇1			◇1				◇1	◇1
														A	B							A	B
						🚲			🚲														
Lichfield Trent Valley	d						09 31	10 01		10 31	11 01		11 31			12 01	12 31		13 01		13 31		
Lichfield City	d						09 35	10 05		10 35	11 05		11 35			12 05	12 35		13 05		13 35		
Shenstone	d						09 40	10 10		10 40	11 10		11 40			12 10	12 40		13 10		13 40		
Blake Street	d						09 44	10 14		10 44	11 14		11 44			12 14	12 44		13 14		13 44		
Butlers Lane	d						09 46	10 16		10 46	11 16		11 46			12 16	12 46		13 16		13 46		
Four Oaks	d			09 19			09 49	10 19		10 49	11 19		11 49			12 19	12 49		13 19		13 49		
Sutton Coldfield	d			09 22			09 52	10 22		10 52	11 22		11 52			12 22	12 52		13 22		13 52		
Wylde Green	d			09 25			09 55	10 25		10 55	11 25		11 55			12 25	12 55		13 25		13 55		
Chester Road	d			09 27			09 57	10 27		10 57	11 27		11 57			12 27	12 57		13 27		13 57		
Erdington	d			09 29			09 59	10 29		10 59	11 29		11 59			12 29	12 59		13 29		13 59		
Gravelly Hill	d			09 31			10 01	10 31		11 01	11 31		12 01			12 31	13 01		13 31		14 01		
Aston	d			09 35			10 05	10 35		11 05	11 35		12 05			12 35	13 05		13 35		14 05		
Duddeston	d			09 37			10 07	10 37		11 07	11 37		12 07			12 37	13 07		13 37		14 07		
Birmingham New Street 12	a			09 42			10 12	10 42		11 12	11 42		12 12			12 42	13 12		13 42		14 12		
	d	08 55	09 15	09 45	10 00	10 12	10 15	10 45	11 12	11 15	11 45	12 00	12 15	12 30	12 33	12 45	13 15	13 30	13 45	13 58	14 15	14 30	14 33
Five Ways	d		09 19	09 49			10 19	10 49		11 19	11 49		12 19	≀	≀	12 49	13 19		13 49		14 19	≀	≀
University	d	09 01	09 23	09 53	10 06	10a18	10 23	10 53	11a18	11 23	11 53	12 06	12 23	12a36	12a39	12 53	13 23	13a36	13 53	14 04	14 23	14a36	14a39
Selly Oak	d		09 25	09 55			10 25	10 55		11 25	11 55		12 25			12 55	13 25		13 55		14 25		
Bournville	d		09 27	09 57			10 27	10 57		11 27	11 57		12 27			12 57	13 27		13 57		14 27		
Kings Norton	d		09 30	10 00			10 30	11 00		11 30	12 00		12 30			13 00	13 30		14 00		14 30		
Northfield	d		09 33	10 03			10 33	11 03		11 33	12 03		12 33			13 03	13 33		14 03		14 33		
Longbridge	d	09 09	09 36	10 06			10 36	11 06		11 36	12 06		12 36			13 06	13 36		14 06		14 36		
Barnt Green	d		09 40	10 10			10 40	11 10		11 40	12 10		12 40			13 10	13 40		14 10		14 40		
Alvechurch	d		09 45	10 15			10 45	11 15		11 45	12 15		12 45			13 15	13 45		14 15		14 45		
Redditch	a	09 24	09 53	10 23			10 53	11 23		11 53	12 23		12 53			13 23	13 53		14 23		14 53		
Bromsgrove	a				10 19							12 19								14 17			

A until 29 December, from 30 March

B from 5 January until 23 March

Table 69

Sundays

8 December to 11 May

Lichfield - Birmingham - Longbridge and Redditch

Network Diagram - refer to first Page of Table 67

		LM	LM	XC	LM	LM		LM	XC	LM	LM	XC	XC
				◇1					◇1			◇1	◇1
												A	B
				⚲					⚲				⚲
Lichfield Trent Valley	d	14 01	14 31		15 01			15 31		16 01	16 31		
Lichfield City	d	14 05	14 35		15 05			15 35		16 05	16 35		
Shenstone	d	14 10	14 40		15 10			15 40		16 10	16 40		
Blake Street	d	14 14	14 44		15 14			15 44		16 14	16 44		
Butlers Lane	d	14 16	14 46		15 16			15 46		16 16	16 46		
Four Oaks	d	14 19	14 49		15 19			15 49		16 19	16 49		
Sutton Coldfield	d	14 22	14 52		15 22			15 52		16 22	16 52		
Wylde Green	d	14 25	14 55		15 25			15 55		16 25	16 55		
Chester Road	d	14 27	14 57		15 27			15 57		16 27	16 57		
Erdington	d	14 29	14 59		15 29			15 59		16 29	16 59		
Gravelly Hill	d	14 31	15 01		15 31			16 01		16 31	17 01		
Aston	d	14 35	15 05		15 35			16 05		16 35	17 05		
Duddeston	d	14 37	15 07		15 37			16 07		16 37	17 07		
Birmingham New Street 12	a	14 42	15 12		15 42			16 12		16 42	17 12		
	d	14 45	15 15	15 30	15 45	15 58		16 15	16 30	16 45	17 15	17 30	17 30
Five Ways	d	14 49	15 19		15 49			16 19		16 49	17 19	⌇	⌇
University	d	14 53	15 23	15a36	15 53	16 04		16 23	16a36	16 53	17 23	17a36	17a36
Selly Oak	d	14 55	15 25		15 55			16 25		16 55	17 25		
Bournville	d	14 57	15 27		15 57			16 27		16 57	17 27		
Kings Norton	d	15 00	15 30		16 00			16 30		17 00	17 30		
Northfield	d	15 03	15 33		16 03			16 33		17 03	17 33		
Longbridge	d	15 06	15 36		16 06			16 36		17 06	17 36		
Barnt Green	d	15 10	15 40		16 10			16 40		17 10	17 40		
Alvechurch	d	15 15	15 45		16 15			16 45		17 15	17 45		
Redditch	a	15 23	15 53		16 23			16 53		17 23	17 53		
Bromsgrove	a					16 17							

		LM	LM	LM		XC	XC	LM	LM	LM	XC	XC	LM
						◇1	◇1				◇1	◇1	
						A	B				A	B	
							⚲					⚲	
Lichfield Trent Valley	d	17 01		17 31				18 01		18 31			19 01
Lichfield City	d	17 05		17 35				18 05		18 35			19 05
Shenstone	d	17 10		17 40				18 10		18 40			19 10
Blake Street	d	17 14		17 44				18 14		18 44			19 14
Butlers Lane	d	17 16		17 46				18 16		18 46			19 16
Four Oaks	d	17 19		17 49				18 19		18 49			19 19
Sutton Coldfield	d	17 22		17 52				18 22		18 52			19 22
Wylde Green	d	17 25		17 55				18 25		18 55			19 25
Chester Road	d	17 27		17 57				18 27		18 57			19 27
Erdington	d	17 29		17 59				18 29		18 59			19 29
Gravelly Hill	d	17 31		18 01				18 31		19 01			19 31
Aston	d	17 35		18 05				18 35		19 05			19 35
Duddeston	d	17 37		18 07				18 37		19 07			19 37
Birmingham New Street 12	a	17 42		18 12				18 42		19 12			19 42
	d	17 45	17 58	18 15		18 30	18 30	18 45	18 58	19 15	19 30	19 30	19 45
Five Ways	d	17 49		18 19		⌇	⌇	18 49		19 19	⌇	⌇	19 49
University	d	17 53	18 04	18 23		18a36	18a36	18 53	19 04	19 23	19a36	19a36	19 53
Selly Oak	d	17 55		18 25				18 55		19 25			19 55
Bournville	d	17 57		18 27				18 57		19 27			19 57
Kings Norton	d	18 00		18 30				19 00		19 30			20 00
Northfield	d	18 03		18 33				19 03		19 33			20 03
Longbridge	d	18 06		18 36				19 06		19 36			20 06
Barnt Green	d	18 10		18 40				19 10		19 40			20 10
Alvechurch	d	18 15		18 45				19 15		19 45			20 15
Redditch	a	18 23		18 53				19 23		19 53			20 23
Bromsgrove	a		18 17						19 17				

		LM		LM	LM	LM	LM	LM	LM	LM	LM	LM		LM
Lichfield Trent Valley	d			19 31	20 01		20 31	21 01		21 31	22 01	22 31		23 01
Lichfield City	d			19 35	20 05		20 35	21 05		21 35	22 05	22 35		23 05
Shenstone	d			19 40	20 10		20 40	21 10		21 40	22 10	22 40		23 10
Blake Street	d			19 44	20 14		20 44	21 14		21 44	22 14	22 44		23 14
Butlers Lane	d			19 46	20 16		20 46	21 16		21 46	22 16	22 46		23 16
Four Oaks	d			19 49	20 19		20 49	21 19		21 49	22 19	22 49		23 19
Sutton Coldfield	d			19 52	20 22		20 52	21 22		21 52	22 22	22 52		23 22
Wylde Green	d			19 55	20 25		20 55	21 25		21 55	22 25	22 55		23 25
Chester Road	d			19 57	20 27		20 57	21 27		21 57	22 27	22 57		
Erdington	d			19 59	20 29		20 59	21 29		21 59	22 29	22 59		
Gravelly Hill	d			20 01	20 31		21 01	21 31		22 01	22 31	23 01		
Aston	d			20 05	20 35		21 05	21 35		22 05	22 35	23 05		
Duddeston	d			20 07	20 37		21 07	21 37		22 07	22 37	23 07		
Birmingham New Street 12	a			20 12	20 42		21 12	21 42		22 12	22 42	23 12		23 39
	d	19 58		20 15	20 45	20 58	21 15	21 45	22 05	22 15	22 45	23 15		
Five Ways	d			20 19	20 49		21 19	21 49		22 19	22 49	23 19		
University	d	20 04		20 23	20 53	21 04	21 23	21 53	22 11	22 23	22 53	23 23		
Selly Oak	d			20 25	20 55		21 25	21 55		22 25	22 55	23 25		
Bournville	d			20 27	20 57		21 27	21 57		22 27	22 57	23 27		
Kings Norton	d			20 30	21 00		21 30	22 00		22 30	23 00	23 30		
Northfield	d			20 33	21 03		21 33	22 03		22 33	23 03	23 33		
Longbridge	d			20 36	21 06		21 36	22 06		22 36	23 06	23 36		
Barnt Green	d			20 40	21 10		21 40	22 10		22 40	23 10	23 40		
Alvechurch	d			20 45	21 15		21 45	22 15		22 45	23 15	23 45		
Redditch	a			20 53	21 23		21 53	22 23		22 53	23 23	23 53		
Bromsgrove	a	20 17				21 17			22 24					

A until 29 December, from 30 March

B from 5 January until 23 March

Table 69R

Mondays to Fridays

9 December to 16 May

Redditch and Longbridge - Birmingham - Lichfield

Network Diagram - refer to first Page of Table 67

Miles	Miles			LM	LM	LM	LM	LM	LM	LM	LM	LM	LM	LM	LM	LM	LM	LM	LM	LM	LM	XC	LM
																						◇1	
—	0	Bromsgrove	d					06 21			06 44						07 25					07 49	
0	—	**Redditch**	d							06 27				06 57					07 27				
3¼	—	Alvechurch	d							06 32				07 02					07 32				
5	3½	Barnt Green	d							06 38				07 08					07 38				
7¾	—	Longbridge	d			06 12	06 22		06 32	06 42		06 52	07 02	07 12	07 22			07 32	07 42		07 52		08 02
8¾	—	Northfield	d			06 14	06 24		06 34	06 44		06 54	07 04	07 14	07 24			07 34	07 44		07 54		08 04
10¼	—	Kings Norton	d			06 17	06 27		06 37	06 47		06 57	07 07	07 17	07 27			07 37	07 47		07 57		08 07
11¼	—	Bournville	d			06 19	06 29		06 39	06 49		06 59	07 09	07 19	07 29			07 39	07 49		07 59		08 09
12¼	—	Selly Oak	d			06 22	06 32		06 42	06 52		07 02	07 12	07 22	07 32			07 42	07 52		08 02		08 12
13	11½	University	d			06 25	06 35	06 39	06 45	06 55	06 59	07 05	07 15	07 25	07 35		07 40	07 45	07 55	07 59	08 05	08 08	08 15
13½	—	Five Ways	d			06 29	06 39		06 49	06 59		07 09	07 19	07 29	07 39			07 49	07 59		08 09		08 19
14½	13	**Birmingham New Street** [12]	a			06 33	06 43	06 47	06 52	07 02	07 06	07 13	07 22	07 34	07 42		07 47	07 53	08 03	08 09	08 13	08 15	08 23
—	—		d	06 03	06 25	06 35	06 45		06 55	07 04		07 15	07 25	07 35	07 45	07 47		07 55	08 04		08 15		08 25
16	—	Duddeston	d	06 07	06 29		06 49					07 19				07 52					08 19		
17¼	—	Aston	d	06 10	06 32	06 41	06 52		07 00	07 11		07 22	07 31	07 41		07 54		08 01	08 11		08 22		08 31
18½	—	Gravelly Hill	d	06 13	06 35	06 44	06 55		07 03	07 14		07 25	07 34	07 44		07 57		08 04	08 14		08 25		08 34
19¼	—	Erdington	d	06 16	06 38	06 47	06 58		07 06	07 15		07 28	07 36	07 47		08 00		08 06	08 15		08 28		08 37
20¼	—	Chester Road	d	06 18	06 40	06 48	07 00		07 08	07 18		07 30	07 38	07 48		08 02		08 08	08 18		08 30		08 38
21	—	Wylde Green	d	06 20	06 42	06 50	07 02		07 10	07 20		07 32	07 40	07 50		08 04		08 10	08 20		08 32		08 41
22	—	Sutton Coldfield	d	06 23	06 45	06 54	07 06		07 13	07 23		07 36	07 43	07 53	07 59	08 07		08 13	08 24		08 36		08 44
23½	—	Four Oaks	d	06 26	06 48	06 58	07a11		07 16	07 27		07a41	07 47		08 03	08a12		08 17	08 28		08a41		08 47
24½	—	Butlers Lane	d	06 28	06 50	07 00			07 18	07 29			07 49		08 05			08 19	08 30				08 49
26¼	—	Blake Street	d	06 31	06 53	07 02			07 21	07 31			07 51		08 07			08 21	08 32				08 52
28¾	—	Shenstone	d	06 35	06 57				07 25				07 55		08 11			08 25	08 36				08 56
31¾	—	**Lichfield City**	d	06a41	07 02	07 11			07 30	07 39			08 00	08a08	08a18			08 30	08 41				09a02
33	—	**Lichfield Trent Valley**	a		07 06	07 16			07 34	07 44			08 05					08 35	08 46				

		LM	LM	LM	XC	LM	LM	LM	LM	LM	LM	LM	LM	XC	LM	LM	LM	LM	LM	LM	LM	XC	LM
					◇1									◇1								◇1	
Bromsgrove	d				08 24			08 43				09 11						09 54					
Redditch	d	07 57					08 27				08 57					09 27				09 57			
Alvechurch	d	08 02					08 32				09 02					09 32				10 02			
Barnt Green	d	08 08					08 38				09 08					09 38				10 08			
Longbridge	d	08 12		08 22		08 32	08 42		08 52	09 02	09 12		09 22		09 32	09 42	09 52		10 02	10 12	10 22		10 32
Northfield	d	08 14		08 24		08 34	08 44		08 54	09 04	09 14		09 24		09 34	09 44	09 54		10 04	10 14	10 24		10 34
Kings Norton	d	08 17		08 27		08 37	08 47		08 57	09 07	09 17		09 27		09 37	09 47	09 57		10 07	10 17	10 27		10 37
Bournville	d	08 19		08 29		08 39	08 49		08 59	09 09	09 19		09 29		09 39	09 49	09 59		10 09	10 19	10 29		10 39
Selly Oak	d	08 22		08 32		08 42	08 52		09 02	09 12	09 22		09 32		09 42	09 52	10 02		10 12	10 22	10 32		10 42
University	d	08 25	08 29	08 35	08 39	08 45	08 55	08 59	09 05	09 15	09 25	09 29	09 35	09 39	09 45	09 55	10 05	10 09	10 15	10 25	10 35	10 39	10 45
Five Ways	d	08 29		08 39		08 49	08 59		09 09	09 19	09 29		09 39		09 49	09 59	10 09		10 19	10 29	10 39		10 49
Birmingham New Street [12]	a	08 33	08 38	08 43	08 45	08 53	09 03	09 07	09 13	09 23	09 33	09 42	09 43	09 45	09 53	10 03	10 13	10 22	10 23	10 33	10 43	10 45	10 53
	d	08 35		08 45		08 55	09 04		09 15	09 25	09 35		09 45		09 55	10 05	10 15		10 25	10 35	10 45		10 55
Duddeston	d			08 49					09 19				09 49				10 19				10 49		
Aston	d	08 41		08 52		09 01	09 11		09 22	09 31	09 41		09 52		10 01	10 11	10 22		10 31	10 39	10 52		11 01
Gravelly Hill	d	08 44		08 55		09 04	09 14		09 25	09 34	09 44		09 55		10 04	10 14	10 25		10 34	10 42	10 55		11 04
Erdington	d	08 47		08 58		09 07	09 17		09 28	09 37	09 47		09 58		10 07	10 17	10 28		10 37	10 45	10 58		11 07
Chester Road	d	08 48		09 00		09 08	09 18		09 30	09 38	09 48		10 00		10 08	10 18	10 30		10 38	10 46	11 00		11 08
Wylde Green	d	08 51		09 02		09 11	09 21		09 32	09 41	09 51		10 02		10 11	10 21	10 32		10 41	10 49	11 02		11 11
Sutton Coldfield	d	08 54		09 06		09 14	09 24		09 36	09 44	09 54		10 06		10 14	10 24	10 36		10 44	10 52	11 06		11 14
Four Oaks	d	08 57		09a11		09 17	09 27		09a41	09 47	09 57		10a11		10 17	10 27	10a41		10 47	10 55	11a11		11 17
Butlers Lane	d	08 59				09 19	09 29			09 49	09 59				10 19	10 29			10 49	10 57			11 19
Blake Street	d	09 02				09 22	09 32			09 52	10 02				10 22	10 32			10 52	11 00			11 22
Shenstone	d					09 26				09 56					10 26				10 56				11 26
Lichfield City	d	09 10				09a32	09 40			10a02	10 10				10a32	10 40			11a02	11 08			11a32
Lichfield Trent Valley	a	09 15					09 45				10 15					10 45				11 13			

		LM	LM	LM	LM	LM	LM	XC	LM	LM	LM	LM	LM	LM	LM	XC	LM	LM	LM	LM	LM	LM
								◇1								◇1						
Bromsgrove	d		10 43								11 43								12 43			
Redditch	d	10 27				10 57				11 27				11 57				12 27				12 57
Alvechurch	d	10 32				11 02				11 32				12 02				12 32				13 02
Barnt Green	d	10 38				11 08				11 38				12 08				12 38				13 08
Longbridge	d	10 42		10 52	11 02	11 12	11 22		11 32	11 42		11 52	12 02	12 12	12 22		12 32	12 42		12 52	13 02	13 12
Northfield	d	10 44		10 54	11 04	11 14	11 24		11 34	11 44		11 54	12 04	12 14	12 24		12 34	12 44		12 54	13 04	13 14
Kings Norton	d	10 47		10 57	11 07	11 17	11 27		11 37	11 47		11 57	12 07	12 17	12 27		12 37	12 47		12 57	13 07	13 17
Bournville	d	10 49		10 59	11 09	11 19	11 29		11 39	11 49		11 59	12 09	12 19	12 29		12 39	12 49		12 59	13 09	13 19
Selly Oak	d	10 52		11 02	11 12	11 22	11 32		11 42	11 52		12 02	12 12	12 22	12 32		12 42	12 52		13 02	13 12	13 22
University	d	10 55	10 59	11 05	11 15	11 25	11 35	11 39	11 45	11 55	11 59	12 05	12 15	12 25	12 35	12 39	12 45	12 55	12 59	13 05	13 15	13 25
Five Ways	d	10 59		11 09	11 19	11 29	11 39		11 49	11 59		12 09	12 19	12 29	12 39		12 49	12 59		13 09	13 19	13 29
Birmingham New Street [12]	a	11 02	11 13	11 13	11 23	11 33	11 43	11 45	11 53	12 03	12 11	12 13	12 23	12 33	12 43	12 45	12 52	13 03	13 13	13 13	13 23	13 33
	d	11 05		11 15	11 25	11 35	11 45		11 55	12 05		12 15	12 25	12 35	12 45		12 55	13 05		13 15	13 25	13 35
Duddeston	d			11 19			11 49					12 19			12 49					13 19		
Aston	d	11 11		11 22	11 31	11 41	11 52		12 01	12 11		12 22	12 31	12 41	12 52		13 01	13 11		13 22	13 31	13 41
Gravelly Hill	d	11 14		11 25	11 34	11 44	11 55		12 04	12 14		12 25	12 34	12 44	12 55		13 04	13 14		13 25	13 34	13 44
Erdington	d	11 17		11 28	11 37	11 47	11 58		12 07	12 17		12 28	12 37	12 47	12 58		13 07	13 17		13 28	13 37	13 47
Chester Road	d	11 18		11 30	11 38	11 48	12 00		12 08	12 18		12 30	12 38	12 48	13 00		13 08	13 18		13 30	13 38	13 48
Wylde Green	d	11 21		11 32	11 41	11 51	12 02		12 11	12 21		12 32	12 41	12 51	13 02		13 11	13 21		13 32	13 41	13 51
Sutton Coldfield	d	11 24		11 36	11 44	11 54	12 06		12 14	12 24		12 36	12 44	12 54	13 06		13 14	13 24		13 36	13 44	13 54
Four Oaks	d	11 27		11a41	11 47	11 57	12a11		12 17	12 27		12a41	12 47	12 57	13a11		13 17	13 27		13a41	13 47	13 57
Butlers Lane	d	11 29			11 49	11 59			12 19	12 29			12 49	12 59			13 19	13 29			13 49	13 59
Blake Street	d	11 32			11 52	12 02			12 22	12 32			12 52	13 02			13 22	13 32			13 52	14 02
Shenstone	d				11 56				12 26				12 56				13 26				13 56	
Lichfield City	d	11 40			12a02	12 10			12a32	12 40			13a02	13 10			13a32	13 40			14a02	14 10
Lichfield Trent Valley	a	11 45				12 15				12 45				13 15				13 45				14 15

Table 69R

Mondays to Fridays

9 December to 16 May

Redditch and Longbridge - Birmingham - Lichfield

Network Diagram - refer to first Page of Table 67

		LM	XC ◇1	LM	LM	LM	LM	LM	LM	LM	XC ◇1	LM	LM	LM	LM	LM	LM	LM	XC ◇1	LM	LM	LM	LM
Bromsgrove	d					13 43								14 43								15 43	
Redditch	d				13 27				13 57				14 27				14 57				15 27		
Alvechurch	d				13 32				14 02				14 32				15 02				15 32		
Barnt Green	d				13 38				14 08				14 38				15 08				15 38		
Longbridge	d	13 22		13 32	13 42		13 52	14 02	14 12	14 22		14 32	14 42		14 52	15 02	15 12	15 22		15 32	15 42		15 52
Northfield	d	13 24		13 34	13 44		13 54	14 04	14 14	14 24		14 34	14 44		14 54	15 04	15 14	15 24		15 34	15 44		15 54
Kings Norton	d	13 27		13 37	13 47		13 57	14 07	14 17	14 27		14 37	14 47		14 57	15 07	15 17	15 27		15 37	15 47		15 57
Bournville	d	13 29		13 39	13 49		13 59	14 09	14 19	14 29		14 39	14 49		14 59	15 09	15 19	15 29		15 39	15 49		15 59
Selly Oak	d	13 32		13 42	13 52		14 02	14 12	14 22	14 32		14 42	14 52		15 02	15 12	15 22	15 32		15 42	15 52		16 02
University	d	13 35	13 39	13 45	13 55	13 59	14 05	14 15	14 25	14 35	14 39	14 45	14 55	14 59	15 05	15 15	15 25	15 35	15 39	15 45	15 55	15 59	16 05
Five Ways	d	13 39		13 49	13 59		14 09	14 19	14 29	14 39		14 49	14 59		15 09	15 19	15 29	15 39		15 49	15 59		16 09
Birmingham New Street 12	a	13 43	13 45	13 53	14 03	14 12	14 13	14 23	14 33	14 43	14 45	14 53	15 03	15 11	15 13	15 23	15 33	15 43	15 45	15 53	16 03	16 13	16 13
	d	13 45		13 55	14 05		14 15	14 25	14 35	14 45		14 55	15 05		15 15	15 25	15 35	15 45		15 55	16 05		16 15
Duddeston	d	13 49					14 19			14 49					15 19			15 49					16 19
Aston	d	13 52		14 01	14 11		14 22	14 31	14 41	14 52		15 01	15 11		15 22	15 31	15 41	15 52		16 01	16 11		16 22
Gravelly Hill	d	13 55		14 04	14 14		14 25	14 34	14 44	14 55		15 04	15 14		15 25	15 34	15 44	15 55		16 04	16 14		16 25
Erdington	d	13 58		14 07	14 17		14 28	14 37	14 47	14 58		15 07	15 17		15 28	15 37	15 47	15 58		16 07	16 17		16 28
Chester Road	d	14 00		14 08	14 18		14 30	14 38	14 48	15 00		15 08	15 18		15 30	15 38	15 48	16 00		16 08	16 18		16 30
Wylde Green	d	14 02		14 11	14 21		14 32	14 41	14 51	15 02		15 11	15 21		15 32	15 41	15 51	16 02		16 11	16 21		16 32
Sutton Coldfield	d	14 06		14 14	14 24		14 36	14 44	14 54	15 06		15 14	15 24		15 36	15 44	15 54	16 06		16 14	16 24		16 36
Four Oaks	d	14a11		14 17	14 27		14a41	14 47	14 57	15a11		15 17	15 27		15a41	15 47	15 57	16a11		16 17	16 27		16a41
Butlers Lane	d			14 19	14 29			14 49	14 59			15 19	15 29			15 49	15 59			16 19	16 29		
Blake Street	d			14 22	14 32			14 52	15 02			15 22	15 32			15 52	16 02			16 22	16 32		
Shenstone	d			14 26				14 56				15 26				15 56				16 26			
Lichfield City	d			14a32	14 40			15a02	15 10			15a32	15 40			16a02	16 10			16a32	16 40		
Lichfield Trent Valley	a				14 45				15 15				15 45				16 15				16 45		

		LM	LM	LM	XC ◇1	LM	LM	LM	LM	LM	LM	LM	XC ◇1	LM	LM	LM	LM	LM	LM	LM	XC ◇1	LM
Bromsgrove	d							16 43								17 43						
Redditch	d		15 57				16 27				16 57				17 27				17 57			
Alvechurch	d		16 02				16 32				17 02				17 32				18 02			
Barnt Green	d		16 08				16 38	16 49			17 08				17 38				18 08			
Longbridge	d	16 02	16 12	16 22		16 32	16 42		16 52	17 02	17 12	17 22		17 32	17 42		17 52	18 02	18 12	18 22		18 32
Northfield	d	16 04	16 14	16 24		16 34	16 44		16 54	17 04	17 14	17 24		17 34	17 44		17 54	18 04	18 14	18 24		18 34
Kings Norton	d	16 07	16 17	16 27		16 37	16 47		16 57	17 07	17 17	17 27		17 37	17 47		17 57	18 07	18 17	18 27		18 37
Bournville	d	16 09	16 19	16 29		16 39	16 49		16 59	17 09	17 19	17 29		17 39	17 49		17 59	18 09	18 19	18 29		18 39
Selly Oak	d	16 12	16 22	16 32		16 42	16 52		17 02	17 12	17 22	17 32		17 42	17 52		18 02	18 12	18 22	18 32		18 42
University	d	16 15	16 25	16 35	16 39	16 45	16 55	16 59	17 05	17 15	17 25	17 35	17 39	17 45	17 55	17 59	18 05	18 15	18 25	18 35	18 39	18 45
Five Ways	d	16 19	16 29	16 39		16 49	16 59		17 09	17 19	17 29	17 39		17 49	17 59		18 09	18 19	18 29	18 39		18 49
Birmingham New Street 12	a	16 23	16 33	16 43	16 45	16 53	17 03	17 12	17 13	17 23	17 33	17 43	17 45	17 53	18 03	18 11	18 13	18 23	18 33	18 43	18 45	18 53
	d	16 25	16 35	16 45		16 55	17 05		17 15	17 25	17 35	17 45		17 55	18 05		18 15	18 25	18 35	18 45		18 55
Duddeston	d			16 49					17 19			17 49					18 19			18 49		
Aston	d	16 31	16 41	16 52		17 01	17 11		17 22	17 31	17 41	17 52		18 01	18 11		18 22	18 31	18 41	18 52		19 01
Gravelly Hill	d	16 34	16 44	16 55		17 04	17 14		17 25	17 34	17 44	17 55		18 04	18 14		18 25	18 34	18 44	18 55		19 04
Erdington	d	16 37	16 47	16 58		17 07	17 17		17 28	17 37	17 47	17 58		18 07	18 17		18 28	18 37	18 47	18 58		19 07
Chester Road	d	16 38	16 48	17 00		17 08	17 18		17 30	17 38	17 48	18 00		18 08	18 18		18 30	18 38	18 48	19 00		19 08
Wylde Green	d	16 41	16 51	17 02		17 11	17 21		17 32	17 41	17 51	18 02		18 11	18 21		18 32	18 41	18 51	19 02		19 11
Sutton Coldfield	d	16 44	16 54	17 06		17 14	17 24		17 36	17 44	17 54	18 06		18 14	18 24		18 36	18 44	18 54	19 06		19 14
Four Oaks	d	16 47	16 57	17a11		17 17	17 27		17a41	17 47	17 57	18a11		18 17	18 27		18a41	18 47	18 57	19a11		19 17
Butlers Lane	d	16 49	16 59			17 19	17 29			17 49	17 59			18 19	18 29			18 49	18 59			19 19
Blake Street	d	16 52	17 02			17 22	17 32			17 52	18 02			18 22	18 32			18 52	19 02			19 22
Shenstone	d	16 56				17 26	17 36			17 56	18 06			18 26				18 56				19 26
Lichfield City	d	17a02	17 10			17 31	17 41			18 01	18 11			18a32	18 40			19a02	19 10			19a32
Lichfield Trent Valley	a		17 15			17 36	17 46			18 06	18 16				18 45				19 15			

		LM	LM	LM	LM	LM	LM	XC ◇1	LM	LM	LM	LM	LM	LM	XC ◇1	LM	LM	LM	LM	LM	LM	XC ◇1	LM
Bromsgrove	d		18 43									19 47							20 55				
Redditch	d	18 27				18 57				19 27				19 57			20 27			20 57			21 27
Alvechurch	d	18 32				19 02				19 32				20 02			20 32			21 02			21 32
Barnt Green	d	18 38	18 49			19 08				19 38				20 08			20 38			21 08			21 38
Longbridge	d	18 42		18 52	19 02	19 12	19 22		19 32	19 42	19 52		20 02	20 12		20 30	20 42	20 57		21 12	21 27		21 42
Northfield	d	18 44		18 54	19 04	19 14	19 24		19 34	19 44	19 54		20 04	20 14		20 32	20 44	20 59		21 14	21 29		21 44
Kings Norton	d	18 47		18 57	19 07	19 17	19 27		19 37	19 47	19 57		20 07	20 17		20 35	20 47	21 02		21 17	21 32		21 47
Bournville	d	18 49		18 59	19 09	19 19	19 29		19 39	19 49	19 59		20 09	20 19		20 37	20 49	21 04		21 19	21 34		21 49
Selly Oak	d	18 52		19 02	19 12	19 22	19 32		19 42	19 52	20 02		20 12	20 22		20 40	20 52	21 07		21 22	21 37		21 52
University	d	18 55	18 59	19 05	19 15	19 25	19 35	19 39	19 45	19 55	20 05	20 09	20 15	20 25	20 35	20 42	20 55	21 10	21 14	21 25	21 40	21 45	21 55
Five Ways	d	18 59		19 09	19 19	19 29	19 39		19 49	19 59	20 09		20 19	20 29		20 46	20 59	21 14		21 29	21 44		21 59
Birmingham New Street 12	a	19 03	19 12	19 13	19 23	19 33	19 43	19 45	19 53	20 03	20 13	20 18	20 23	20 33	20 41	20 51	21 02	21 18	21 20	21 33	21 48	21 51	22 02
	d	19 05		19 15		19 35				20 05				20 35			21 05			21 35			22 05
Duddeston	d			19 19		19 39				20 09				20 39			21 09			21 39			22 09
Aston	d	19 11		19 22		19 42				20 12				20 42			21 12			21 42			22 12
Gravelly Hill	d	19 14		19 25		19 45				20 15				20 45			21 15			21 45			22 15
Erdington	d	19 17		19 28		19 48				20 18				20 48			21 18			21 48			22 18
Chester Road	d	19 18		19 30		19 50				20 20				20 50			21 20			21 50			22 20
Wylde Green	d	19 21		19 32		19 52				20 22				20 52			21 22			21 52			22 22
Sutton Coldfield	d	19 24		19 36		19 55				20 25				20 55			21 25			21 55			22 25
Four Oaks	d	19 27		19a41		19 58				20 28				20 58			21 28			21 58			22 28
Butlers Lane	d	19 29				20 00				20 30				21 00			21 30			22 00			22 30
Blake Street	d	19 32				20 03				20 33				21 03			21 33			22 03			22 33
Shenstone	d					20 07				20 37				21 07			21 37			22 07			22 37
Lichfield City	d	19 40				20 12				20 42				21 12			21 42			22 12			22 42
Lichfield Trent Valley	a	19 45				20 16				20 46				21 16			21 46			22 16			22 46

Table 69R

Mondays to Fridays

9 December to 16 May

Redditch and Longbridge - Birmingham - Lichfield

Network Diagram - refer to first Page of Table 67

		LM	LM	LM	LM	LM		LM	LM	LM
Bromsgrove	d				22 29					
Redditch	d		21 57			22 27			22 57	
Alvechurch	d		22 02			22 32			23 02	
Barnt Green	d		22 08			22 38			23 08	
Longbridge	d	21 57	22 12	22 27		22 42		22 52	23 12	23 30
Northfield	d	21 59	22 14	22 29		22 44		22 54	23 14	23 32
Kings Norton	d	22 02	22 17	22 32		22 47		22 57	23 17	23 35
Bournville	d	22 04	22 19	22 34		22 49		22 59	23 19	23 37
Selly Oak	d	22 07	22 22	22 37		22 52		23 02	23 22	23 40
University	d	22 10	22 25	22 40	22 44	22 55		23 05	23 25	23 43
Five Ways	d	22 14	22 29	22 44		22 59		23 09	23 29	23 47
Birmingham New Street 12	a	22 18	22 33	22 47	22 51	23 03		23 12	23 36	23 51
	d		22 35	22 55				23 15		
Duddeston	d		22 39	22 59				23 19		
Aston	d		22 42	23 02				23 22		
Gravelly Hill	d		22 45	23 05				23 25		
Erdington	d		22 48	23 08				23 28		
Chester Road	d		22 50	23 10				23 30		
Wylde Green	d		22 52	23 12				23 32		
Sutton Coldfield	d		22 55	23 15				23 35		
Four Oaks	d		22 58	23 18				23 38		
Butlers Lane	d		23 00	23 20				23 40		
Blake Street	d		23 03	23a24				23 43		
Shenstone	d		23 07					23 47		
Lichfield City	d		23 12					23a52		
Lichfield Trent Valley	a		23 16							

Saturdays

14 December to 17 May

		LM	LM	LM	LM	LM	LM	LM	LM	LM		LM	LM	LM	LM	XC ◇1	LM	LM	LM	LM		LM	XC ◇1	LM	LM
Bromsgrove	d								06 52							07 44		07 53							
Redditch	d						06 27					06 57			07 27					07 57					08 27
Alvechurch	d						06 32					07 02			07 32					08 02					08 32
Barnt Green	d						06 38					07 08			07 38					08 08					08 38
Longbridge	d			06 12	06 22	06 32	06 42	06 52		07 02		07 12	07 22	07 32	07 42		07 52		08 02	08 12		08 22		08 32	08 42
Northfield	d			06 14	06 24	06 34	06 44	06 54		07 04		07 14	07 24	07 34	07 44		07 54		08 04	08 14		08 24		08 34	08 44
Kings Norton	d			06 17	06 27	06 37	06 47	06 57		07 07		07 17	07 27	07 37	07 47		07 57		08 07	08 17		08 27		08 37	08 47
Bournville	d			06 19	06 29	06 39	06 49	06 59		07 09		07 19	07 29	07 39	07 49		07 59		08 09	08 19		08 29		08 39	08 49
Selly Oak	d			06 22	06 32	06 42	06 52	07 02		07 12		07 22	07 32	07 42	07 52		08 02		08 12	08 22		08 32		08 42	08 52
University	d			06 25	06 35	06 45	06 55	07 05	07 09	07 15		07 25	07 35	07 45	07 55	08 00	08 05	08 09	08 15	08 25		08 35	08 39	08 45	08 55
Five Ways	d			06 29	06 39	06 49	06 59	07 09		07 19		07 29	07 39	07 49	07 59		08 09		08 19	08 29		08 39		08 49	08 59
Birmingham New Street 12	a			06 33	06 43	06 53	07 02	07 13	07 16	07 23		07 33	07 43	07 53	08 03	08 08	08 13	08 16	08 23	08 33		08 43	08 45	08 53	09 03
	d	05 57	06 25	06 35		06 55	07 05	07 15		07 25		07 35	07 45	07 55	08 05		08 15		08 25	08 35		08 45		08 55	09 05
Duddeston	d	06 01	06 29			06 59		07 19					07 49				08 19					08 49			
Aston	d	06 04	06 32			07 02	07 11	07 22		07 31		07 41	07 52	08 01	08 11		08 22		08 31	08 41		08 52		09 01	09 11
Gravelly Hill	d	06 07	06 35			07 05	07 14	07 25		07 34		07 44	07 55	08 04	08 14		08 25		08 34	08 44		08 55		09 04	09 14
Erdington	d	06 10	06 38	06 44		07 08	07 17	07 28		07 37		07 47	07 58	08 07	08 17		08 28		08 37	08 47		08 58		09 07	09 17
Chester Road	d	06 12	06 40	06 46		07 10	07 18	07 30		07 38		07 48	08 00	08 08	08 18		08 30		08 38	08 48		09 00		09 08	09 18
Wylde Green	d	06 14	06 42	06 48		07 12	07 21	07 32		07 41		07 51	08 02	08 11	08 21		08 32		08 41	08 51		09 02		09 11	09 21
Sutton Coldfield	d	06 17	06 45	06 52		07 15	07 24	07 36		07 44		07 54	08 06	08 14	08 24		08 36		08 44	08 54		09 06		09 14	09 24
Four Oaks	d	06 20	06 48	06 55		07 18	07 27	07a41		07 47		07 57	08a11	08 17	08 27		08a41		08 47	08 57		09a11		09 17	09 27
Butlers Lane	d	06 22	06 50	06 57		07 20	07 29			07 49		07 59		08 19	08 29				08 49	08 59				09 19	09 29
Blake Street	d	06 24	06 53	07 00		07 23	07 32			07 52		08 02		08 22	08 32				08 52	09 02				09 22	09 32
Shenstone	d	06 28	06 57			07 27				07 56				08 26					08 56					09 26	
Lichfield City	d	06a34	07a02	07 08		07a32	07 40			08a02		08 10		08a32	08 40				09a02	09 10				09a32	09 40
Lichfield Trent Valley	a			07 12			07 45					08 14			08 45					09 15					09 45

		LM	LM	LM	LM	LM		XC ◇1	LM	LM	LM	LM	LM	LM	LM	LM		XC ◇1	LM	LM	LM	LM	LM	LM	LM
Bromsgrove	d	08 43									09 43				10 13						10 43				11 15
Redditch	d				08 57					09 27				09 57						10 27				10 57	
Alvechurch	d				09 02					09 32				10 02						10 32				11 02	
Barnt Green	d				09 08					09 38				10 08						10 38				11 08	
Longbridge	d		08 52	09 02	09 12	09 22			09 32	09 42		09 52	10 02	10 12		10 22			10 32	10 42		10 52	11 02	11 12	
Northfield	d		08 54	09 04	09 14	09 24			09 34	09 44		09 54	10 04	10 14		10 24			10 34	10 44		10 54	11 04	11 14	
Kings Norton	d		08 57	09 07	09 17	09 27			09 37	09 47		09 57	10 07	10 17		10 27			10 37	10 47		10 57	11 07	11 17	
Bournville	d		08 59	09 09	09 19	09 29			09 39	09 49		09 59	10 09	10 19		10 29			10 39	10 49		10 59	11 09	11 19	
Selly Oak	d		09 02	09 12	09 22	09 32			09 42	09 52		10 02	10 12	10 22		10 32			10 42	10 52		11 02	11 12	11 22	
University	d	08 59	09 05	09 15	09 25	09 35		09 39	09 45	09 55	09 59	10 05	10 15	10 25		10 35		10 39	10 45	10 55	10 59	11 05	11 15	11 25	
Five Ways	d		09 09	09 19	09 29	09 39			09 49	09 59		10 09	10 19	10 29		10 39			10 49	10 59		11 09	11 19	11 29	
Birmingham New Street 12	a	09 11	09 13	09 23	09 33	09 43		09 45	09 53	10 03	10 11	10 13	10 23	10 33	10 41	10 43		10 45	10 53	11 03	11 11	11 13	11 23	11 33	11 38
	d		09 15	09 25	09 35	09 45			09 55	10 05		10 15	10 25	10 35		10 45			10 55	11 05		11 15	11 25	11 35	
Duddeston	d		09 19			09 49						10 19				10 49						11 19			
Aston	d		09 22	09 31	09 41	09 52			10 01	10 11		10 22	10 31	10 41		10 52			11 01	11 11		11 22	11 31	11 41	
Gravelly Hill	d		09 25	09 34	09 44	09 55			10 04	10 14		10 25	10 34	10 44		10 55			11 04	11 14		11 25	11 34	11 44	
Erdington	d		09 28	09 37	09 47	09 58			10 07	10 17		10 28	10 37	10 47		10 58			11 07	11 17		11 28	11 37	11 47	
Chester Road	d		09 30	09 38	09 48	10 00			10 08	10 18		10 30	10 38	10 48		11 00			11 08	11 18		11 30	11 38	11 48	
Wylde Green	d		09 32	09 41	09 51	10 02			10 11	10 21		10 32	10 41	10 51		11 02			11 11	11 21		11 32	11 41	11 51	
Sutton Coldfield	d		09 36	09 44	09 54	10 06			10 14	10 24		10 36	10 44	10 54		11 06			11 14	11 24		11 36	11 44	11 54	
Four Oaks	d		09a41	09 47	09 57	10a11			10 17	10 27		10a41	10 47	10 57		11a11			11 17	11 27		11a41	11 47	11 57	
Butlers Lane	d			09 49	09 59				10 19	10 29			10 49	10 59					11 19	11 29			11 49	11 59	
Blake Street	d			09 52	10 02				10 22	10 32			10 52	11 02					11 22	11 32			11 52	12 02	
Shenstone	d			09 56					10 26				10 56						11 26				11 56		
Lichfield City	d			10a02	10 10				10a32	10 40			11a02	11 10					11a32	11 40			12a02	12 10	
Lichfield Trent Valley	a				10 15					10 45				11 15						11 45				12 15	

Table 69R

Saturdays

14 December to 17 May

Redditch and Longbridge - Birmingham - Lichfield

Network Diagram - refer to first Page of Table 67

		LM	XC	LM	LM	LM	LM	LM	LM		LM	XC	LM	LM	LM	LM	LM	LM	LM	LM	XC	LM	LM
			◇1 🛒									◇1 🛒									◇1 🛒		
Bromsgrove	d					11 43									15 43					16 12			
Redditch	d				11 27				11 57					15 27				15 57					16 27
Alvechurch	d				11 32				12 02					15 32				16 02					16 32
Barnt Green	d				11 38				12 08					15 38				16 08					16 38
Longbridge	d	11 22		11 32	11 42		11 52	12 02	12 12		15 22		15 32	15 42		15 52	16 02	16 12	16 22			16 32	16 42
Northfield	d	11 24		11 34	11 44		11 54	12 04	12 14		15 24		15 34	15 44		15 54	16 04	16 14	16 24			16 34	16 44
Kings Norton	d	11 27		11 37	11 47		11 57	12 07	12 17		15 27		15 37	15 47		15 57	16 07	16 17	16 27			16 37	16 47
Bournville	d	11 29		11 39	11 49		11 59	12 09	12 19	and at	15 29		15 39	15 49		15 59	16 09	16 19	16 29			16 39	16 49
Selly Oak	d	11 32		11 42	11 52		12 02	12 12	12 22	the same	15 32		15 42	15 52		16 02	16 12	16 22	16 32			16 42	16 52
University	d	11 35	11 39	11 45	11 55	11 59	12 05	12 15	12 25	minutes	15 35	15 39	15 45	15 55	15 59	16 05	16 15	16 25	16 35		16 39	16 45	16 55
Five Ways	d	11 39		11 49	11 59		12 09	12 19	12 29	past	15 39		15 49	15 59		16 09	16 19	16 29	16 39			16 49	16 59
Birmingham New Street 12	a	11 43	11 45	11 53	12 03	12 11	12 13	12 23	12 33	each	15 43	15 45	15 53	16 03	16 11	16 13	16 23	16 33	16 43	16 45	16 45	16 53	17 03
	d	11 45		11 55	12 05		12 15	12 25	12 35	hour until	15 45		15 55	16 05		16 15	16 25	16 35	16 45			16 55	17 05
Duddeston	d	11 49					12 19				15 49					16 19			16 49				
Aston	d	11 52		12 01	12 11		12 22	12 31	12 41		15 52		16 01	16 11		16 22	16 31	16 41	16 52			17 01	17 11
Gravelly Hill	d	11 55		12 04	12 14		12 25	12 34	12 44		15 55		16 04	16 14		16 25	16 34	16 44	16 55			17 04	17 14
Erdington	d	11 58		12 07	12 17		12 28	12 37	12 47		15 58		16 07	16 17		16 28	16 37	16 47	16 58			17 07	17 17
Chester Road	d	12 00		12 08	12 18		12 30	12 38	12 48		16 00		16 08	16 18		16 30	16 38	16 48	17 00			17 08	17 18
Wylde Green	d	12 02		12 11	12 21		12 32	12 41	12 51		16 02		16 11	16 21		16 32	16 41	16 51	17 02			17 11	17 21
Sutton Coldfield	d	12 06		12 14	12 24		12 36	12 44	12 54		16 06		16 14	16 24		16 36	16 44	16 54	17 06			17 14	17 24
Four Oaks	d	12a11		12 17	12 27		12a41	12 47	12 57		16a11		16 17	16 27		16a41	16 47	16 57	17a11			17 17	17 27
Butlers Lane	d			12 19	12 29			12 49	12 59				16 19	16 29			16 49	16 59				17 19	17 29
Blake Street	d			12 22	12 32			12 52	13 02				16 22	16 32			16 52	17 02				17 22	17 32
Shenstone	d			12 26				12 56					16 26				16 56					17 26	
Lichfield City	d			12a32	12 40			13a02	13 10				16a32	16 40			17a02	17 10				17a32	17 40
Lichfield Trent Valley	a				12 45				13 15					16 45				17 15					17 45

		LM	LM	LM	LM	LM	XC	LM	LM	LM	LM	LM	LM	LM	XC	LM	LM	LM	LM	LM	LM	LM	XC
							◇1 🛒								◇1 🛒								◇1 🛒
Bromsgrove	d	16 43								17 44								18 43					
Redditch	d				16 57				17 27				17 57				18 27				18 57		
Alvechurch	d				17 02				17 32				18 02				18 32				19 02		
Barnt Green	d				17 08				17 38				18 08				18 38				19 08		
Longbridge	d		16 52	17 02	17 12	17 22		17 32	17 42		17 52	18 02	18 12	18 22		18 32	18 42		18 52	19 02	19 12	19 22	
Northfield	d		16 54	17 04	17 14	17 24		17 34	17 44		17 54	18 04	18 14	18 24		18 34	18 44		18 54	19 04	19 14	19 24	
Kings Norton	d		16 57	17 07	17 17	17 27		17 37	17 47		17 57	18 07	18 17	18 27		18 37	18 47		18 57	19 07	19 17	19 27	
Bournville	d		16 59	17 09	17 19	17 29		17 39	17 49		17 59	18 09	18 19	18 29		18 39	18 49		18 59	19 09	19 19	19 29	
Selly Oak	d		17 02	17 12	17 22	17 32		17 42	17 52		18 02	18 12	18 22	18 32		18 42	18 52		19 02	19 12	19 22	19 32	
University	d	16 59	17 05	17 15	17 25	17 35	17 39	17 45	17 55	17 59	18 05	18 15	18 25	18 35	18 39	18 45	18 55	18 59	19 05	19 15	19 25	19 35	19 39
Five Ways	d		17 09	17 19	17 29	17 39		17 49	17 59		18 09	18 19	18 29	18 39		18 49	18 59		19 09	19 19	19 29	19 39	
Birmingham New Street 12	a	17 11	17 13	17 23	17 33	17 43	17 45	17 53	18 03	18 11	18 13	18 23	18 33	18 43	18 45	18 53	19 03	19 11	19 13	19 23	19 33	19 43	19 45
	d		17 15	17 25	17 35	17 45		17 55	18 05		18 15	18 25	18 35	18 45		18 55	19 05		19 15		19 35		
Duddeston	d		17 19			17 49					18 19			18 49					19 19		19 39		
Aston	d		17 22	17 31	17 41	17 52		18 01	18 11		18 22	18 31	18 41	18 52		19 01	19 11		19 22		19 42		
Gravelly Hill	d		17 25	17 34	17 44	17 55		18 04	18 14		18 25	18 34	18 44	18 55		19 04	19 14		19 25		19 45		
Erdington	d		17 28	17 37	17 47	17 58		18 07	18 17		18 28	18 37	18 47	18 58		19 07	19 17		19 28		19 48		
Chester Road	d		17 30	17 38	17 48	18 00		18 08	18 18		18 30	18 38	18 48	19 00		19 08	19 18		19 30		19 50		
Wylde Green	d		17 32	17 41	17 51	18 02		18 11	18 21		18 32	18 41	18 51	19 02		19 11	19 21		19 32		19 52		
Sutton Coldfield	d		17 36	17 44	17 54	18 06		18 14	18 24		18 36	18 44	18 54	19 06		19 14	19 24		19 36		19 55		
Four Oaks	d		17a41	17 47	17 57	18a11		18 17	18 27		18a41	18 47	18 57	19a11		19 17	19 27		19a41		19 58		
Butlers Lane	d			17 49	17 59			18 19	18 29			18 49	18 59			19 19	19 29				20 00		
Blake Street	d			17 52	18 02			18 22	18 32			18 52	19 02			19 22	19 32				20 03		
Shenstone	d			17 56				18 26				18 56				19 26					20 07		
Lichfield City	d			18a02	18 10			18a32	18 40			19a02	19 10			19a32	19 40				20 12		
Lichfield Trent Valley	a				18 15				18 45				19 15				19 45				20 16		

		LM	LM	LM	LM	LM	XC	LM	LM	LM	LM	LM	LM	LM	XC	LM	LM	XC	LM	LM	LM	LM
							◇1 🛒								◇1			◇1				
Bromsgrove	d										20 59				21 44							
Redditch	d		19 27			19 57			20 27			20 57		21 27			21 57			22 27		22 57
Alvechurch	d		19 32			20 02			20 32			21 02		21 32			22 02			22 32		23 02
Barnt Green	d		19 38			20 08			20 38			21 08		21 38			22 08			22 38		23 08
Longbridge	d	19 32	19 42	19 52	20 02	20 12		20 30	20 42	20 57		21 12	21 27	21 42		21 57	22 12		22 27	22 42	22 52	23 12
Northfield	d	19 34	19 44	19 54	20 04	20 14		20 32	20 44	20 59		21 14	21 29	21 44		21 59	22 14		22 29	22 44	22 54	23 14
Kings Norton	d	19 37	19 47	19 57	20 07	20 17		20 35	20 47	21 02		21 17	21 32	21 47		22 02	22 17		22 32	22 47	22 57	23 17
Bournville	d	19 39	19 49	19 59	20 09	20 19		20 37	20 49	21 04		21 19	21 34	21 49		22 04	22 19		22 34	22 49	22 59	23 19
Selly Oak	d	19 42	19 52	20 02	20 12	20 22		20 40	20 52	21 07		21 22	21 37	21 52		22 07	22 22		22 37	22 52	23 02	23 22
University	d	19 45	19 55	20 05	20 15	20 25	20 36	20 42	20 55	21 10	21 14	21 25	21 40	21 55	22 01	22 10	22 25	22 36	22 40	22 55	23 05	23 25
Five Ways	d	19 49	19 59	20 09	20 19	20 29		20 46	20 59	21 14		21 29	21 44	21 59		22 14	22 29		22 44	22 59	23 09	23 29
Birmingham New Street 12	a	19 53	20 03	20 13	20 23	20 33	20 42	20 51	21 03	21 18	21 20	21 33	21 48	22 03	22 07	22 18	22 33	22 42	22 48	23 04	23 13	23 33
	d		20 05			20 35			21 05			21 35		22 05			22 35		22 55		23 15	
Duddeston	d		20 09			20 39			21 09			21 39		22 09			22 39		22 59		23 19	
Aston	d		20 12			20 42			21 12			21 42		22 12			22 42		23 02		23 22	
Gravelly Hill	d		20 15			20 45			21 15			21 45		22 15			22 45		23 05		23 25	
Erdington	d		20 18			20 48			21 18			21 48		22 18			22 48		23 08		23 28	
Chester Road	d		20 20			20 50			21 20			21 50		22 20			22 50		23 10		23 30	
Wylde Green	d		20 22			20 52			21 22			21 52		22 22			22 52		23 12		23 32	
Sutton Coldfield	d		20 25			20 55			21 25			21 55		22 25			22 55		23 15		23 35	
Four Oaks	d		20 28			20 58			21 28			21 58		22 28			22 58		23 18		23 38	
Butlers Lane	d		20 30			21 00			21 30			22 00		22 30			23 00		23 20		23 40	
Blake Street	d		20 33			21 03			21 33			22 03		22 33			23 03		23a24		23 43	
Shenstone	d		20 37			21 07			21 37			22 07		22 37			23 07				23 47	
Lichfield City	d		20 42			21 12			21 42			22 12		22 42			23 12				23a52	
Lichfield Trent Valley	a		20 46			21 16			21 46			22 16		22 46			23 16					

Table 69R

Saturdays

14 December to 17 May

Redditch and Longbridge - Birmingham - Lichfield

Network Diagram - refer to first Page of Table 67

		LM
Bromsgrove	d	
Redditch	d	
Alvechurch	d	
Barnt Green	d	
Longbridge	d	23 30
Northfield	d	23 32
Kings Norton	d	23 35
Bournville	d	23 37
Selly Oak	d	23 40
University	d	23 43
Five Ways	d	23 47
Birmingham New Street 12	a	23 51
	d	
Duddeston	d	
Aston	d	
Gravelly Hill	d	
Erdington	d	
Chester Road	d	
Wylde Green	d	
Sutton Coldfield	d	
Four Oaks	d	
Butlers Lane	d	
Blake Street	d	
Shenstone	d	
Lichfield City	d	
Lichfield Trent Valley	a	

Sundays

8 December to 11 May

		LM	LM	LM	LM		LM	LM	LM	LM	XC	LM	LM	LM	XC	LM	LM	XC	LM	LM	LM	XC
											◇1 ⚲				◇1			◇1 ⚲				◇1
Bromsgrove	d			09 20				11 13						13 13							15 13	
Redditch	d				09 27		10 57		11 27	11 57		12 27	12 57			13 27	13 57		14 27	14 57		
Alvechurch	d				09 32		11 02		11 32	12 02		12 32	13 02			13 32	14 02		14 32	15 02		
Barnt Green	d				09 38		11 08		11 38	12 08		12 38	13 08			13 38	14 08		14 38	15 08		
Longbridge	d				09 43		11 13		11 43	12 13		12 43	13 13			13 43	14 13		14 43	15 13		
Northfield	d				09 45		11 15		11 45	12 15		12 45	13 15			13 45	14 15		14 45	15 15		
Kings Norton	d				09 48		11 18		11 48	12 18		12 48	13 18			13 48	14 18		14 48	15 18		
Bournville	d				09 51		11 21		11 51	12 21		12 51	13 21			13 51	14 21		14 51	15 21		
Selly Oak	d				09 53		11 23		11 53	12 23		12 53	13 23			13 53	14 23		14 53	15 23		
University	d			09 36	09 56	and every 30 minutes until	11 26	11 30	11 56	12 26	12 39	12 56	13 26	13 30	13 35	13 56	14 26	14 36	14 56	15 26	15 30	15 35
Five Ways	d				10 00		11 30		12 00	12 30		13 00	13 30			14 00	14 30		15 00	15 30		
Birmingham New Street 12	a			09 42	10 03		11 33	11 37	12 03	12 33	12 45	13 03	13 33	13 37	13 41	14 03	14 33	14 44	15 03	15 33	15 37	15 41
	d	09 06	09 36		10 06		11 36		12 06	12 36		13 06	13 36			14 06	14 36		15 06	15 36		
Duddeston	d	09 10	09 40		10 10		11 40		12 10	12 40		13 10	13 40			14 10	14 40		15 10	15 40		
Aston	d	09 13	09 43		10 13		11 43		12 13	12 43		13 13	13 43			14 13	14 43		15 13	15 43		
Gravelly Hill	d	09 16	09 46		10 16		11 46		12 16	12 46		13 16	13 46			14 16	14 46		15 16	15 46		
Erdington	d	09 19	09 49		10 19		11 49		12 19	12 49		13 19	13 49			14 19	14 49		15 19	15 49		
Chester Road	d	09 21	09 51		10 21		11 51		12 21	12 51		13 21	13 51			14 21	14 51		15 21	15 51		
Wylde Green	d	09 23	09 53		10 23		11 53		12 23	12 53		13 23	13 53			14 23	14 53		15 23	15 53		
Sutton Coldfield	d	09 26	09 56		10 26		11 56		12 26	12 56		13 26	13 56			14 26	14 56		15 26	15 56		
Four Oaks	d	09 29	09 59		10 29		11 59		12 29	12 59		13 29	13 59			14 29	14 59		15 29	15 59		
Butlers Lane	d	09 31	10 01		10 31		12 01		12 31	13 01		13 31	14 01			14 31	15 01		15 31	16 01		
Blake Street	d	09 34	10 04		10 34		12 04		12 34	13 04		13 34	14 04			14 34	15 04		15 34	16 04		
Shenstone	d	09 38	10 08		10 38		12 08		12 38	13 08		13 38	14 08			14 38	15 08		15 38	16 08		
Lichfield City	d	09 43	10 13		10 43		12 13		12 43	13 13		13 43	14 13			14 43	15 13		15 43	16 13		
Lichfield Trent Valley	a	09 47	10 17		10 47		12 17		12 47	13 17		13 47	14 17			14 47	15 17		15 47	16 17		

		LM	LM	XC	LM	LM	LM	XC	LM	LM	LM	XC	LM	LM	LM	XC	LM	LM	LM	XC	LM	LM	LM
				◇1 ⚲				◇1 ⚲				◇1 ⚲				◇1 ⚲				◇1 ⚲			
Bromsgrove	d						17 13				18 15				19 13				20 13				21 13
Redditch	d	15 27	15 57		16 27	16 57			17 27	17 57			18 27	18 57			19 27	19 57			20 27	20 57	
Alvechurch	d	15 32	16 02		16 32	17 02			17 32	18 02			18 32	19 02			19 32	20 02			20 32	21 02	
Barnt Green	d	15 38	16 08		16 38	17 08			17 38	18 08			18 38	19 08			19 38	20 08			20 38	21 08	
Longbridge	d	15 43	16 13		16 43	17 13			17 43	18 13			18 43	19 13			19 43	20 13			20 43	21 13	
Northfield	d	15 45	16 15		16 45	17 15			17 45	18 15			18 45	19 15			19 45	20 15			20 45	21 15	
Kings Norton	d	15 48	16 18		16 48	17 18			17 48	18 18			18 48	19 18			19 48	20 18			20 48	21 18	
Bournville	d	15 51	16 21		16 51	17 21			17 51	18 21			18 51	19 21			19 51	20 21			20 51	21 21	
Selly Oak	d	15 53	16 23		16 53	17 23			17 53	18 23			18 53	19 23			19 53	20 23			20 53	21 23	
University	d	15 56	16 26	16 35	16 56	17 26	17 30	17 35	17 56	18 26	18 30	18 35	18 56	19 26	19 30	19 35	19 56	20 26	20 30	20 38	20 56	21 26	21 30
Five Ways	d	16 00	16 30		17 00	17 30			18 00	18 30			19 00	19 30			20 00	20 30			21 00	21 30	
Birmingham New Street 12	a	16 03	16 33	16 41	17 03	17 33	17 37	17 41	18 03	18 33	18 37	18 41	19 03	19 33	19 37	19 41	20 03	20 33	20 37	20 44	21 03	21 33	21 37
	d	16 06	16 36		17 06	17 36			18 06	18 36			19 06	19 36			20 06	20 36			21 06	21 36	
Duddeston	d	16 10	16 40		17 10	17 40			18 10	18 40			19 10	19 40			20 10	20 40			21 10	21 40	
Aston	d	16 13	16 43		17 13	17 43			18 13	18 43			19 13	19 43			20 13	20 43			21 13	21 43	
Gravelly Hill	d	16 16	16 46		17 16	17 46			18 16	18 46			19 16	19 46			20 16	20 46			21 16	21 46	
Erdington	d	16 19	16 49		17 19	17 49			18 19	18 49			19 19	19 49			20 19	20 49			21 19	21 49	
Chester Road	d	16 21	16 51		17 21	17 51			18 21	18 51			19 21	19 51			20 21	20 51			21 21	21 51	
Wylde Green	d	16 23	16 53		17 23	17 53			18 23	18 53			19 23	19 53			20 23	20 53			21 23	21 53	
Sutton Coldfield	d	16 26	16 56		17 26	17 56			18 26	18 56			19 26	19 56			20 26	20 56			21 26	21 56	
Four Oaks	d	16 29	16 59		17 29	17 59			18 29	18 59			19 29	19 59			20 29	20 59			21 29	21 59	
Butlers Lane	d	16 31	17 01		17 31	18 01			18 31	19 01			19 31	20 01			20 31	21 01			21 31	22 01	
Blake Street	d	16 34	17 04		17 34	18 04			18 34	19 04			19 34	20 04			20 34	21 04			21 34	22 04	
Shenstone	d	16 38	17 08		17 38	18 08			18 38	19 08			19 38	20 08			20 38	21 08			21 38	22 08	
Lichfield City	d	16 43	17 13		17 43	18 13			18 43	19 13			19 43	20 13			20 43	21 13			21 43	22 13	
Lichfield Trent Valley	a	16 47	17 17		17 47	18 17			18 47	19 17			19 47	20 17			20 47	21 18			21 47	22 19	

Table 69R

Sundays

8 December to 11 May

Redditch and Longbridge - Birmingham - Lichfield

Network Diagram - refer to first Page of Table 67

		XC ◇1	LM	LM	XC ◇1	LM	LM
Bromsgrove	d						
Redditch	d		21 27	21 57		22 27	22 57
Alvechurch	d		21 32	22 02		22 32	23 02
Barnt Green	d		21 38	22 08		22 38	23 08
Longbridge	d		21 43	22 13		22 43	23 13
Northfield	d		21 45	22 15		22 45	23 15
Kings Norton	d		21 48	22 18		22 48	23 18
Bournville	d		21 51	22 21		22 51	23 21
Selly Oak	d		21 53	22 23		22 53	23 23
University	d	21 38	21 56	22 26	22 36	22 56	23 26
Five Ways	d		22 00	22 30		23 00	23 30
Birmingham New Street 12	a	21 44	22 03	22 33	22 42	23 03	23 33
	d		22 06	22 36		23 06	
Duddeston	d		22 10	22 40		23 10	
Aston	d		22 13	22 43		23 13	
Gravelly Hill	d		22 16	22 46		23 16	
Erdington	d		22 19	22 49		23 19	
Chester Road	d		22 21	22 51		23 21	
Wylde Green	d		22 23	22 53		23 23	
Sutton Coldfield	d		22 26	22 56		23 26	
Four Oaks	d		22 29	22 59		23 29	
Butlers Lane	d		22 31	23 01		23 31	
Blake Street	d		22 34	23 04		23 34	
Shenstone	d		22 38	23 08		23 38	
Lichfield City	d		22 43	23 13		23 43	
Lichfield Trent Valley	a		22 47	23 17		23 47	

Table 70

Birmingham - Walsall and Rugeley

Mondays to Fridays

9 December to 16 May

Network Diagram - refer to first Page of Table 67

Miles			LM MX A	LM	LM	LM 1	LM B	LM 1	LM	LM 1 C	LM		LM	LM	LM	LM	LM	LM	LM	LM	LM	LM		
—	Wolverhampton 7 68	d					06 14			06 59					07 49		08 20		08 49		09 19			
0	**Birmingham New Street 12**	d		05 33	05 56	06 21	06 41	06 57	07 07	07 27	07 39		07 57	08 07	08 27	08 42	08 57	09 12	09 27	09 42	09 57	10 12	and at the same minutes past each hour until	
1½	Duddeston	d			06 01	06 26		07 02		07 32			08 01		08 32		09 02		09 32		10 02			
2¾	Aston	d			06 04	06 29		07 05		07 35			08 05		08 35		09 05		09 35		10 05			
3½	Witton	d			06 06	06 31		07 07		07 37			08 07		08 37		09 07		09 37		10 07			
4¼	Perry Barr	d			06 09	06 33		07 09		07 39			08 09		08 39		09 09		09 39		10 09			
5¾	Hamstead	d		05 41	06 12	06 36		07 12		07 42			08 12		08 42		09 12		09 42		10 12			
8½	Tame Bridge Parkway	d		05 45	06 17	06 40	06 52	07 16	07 22	07 46	07 51		08 16	08 22	08 46	08 55	09 16	09 27	09 46	09 57	10 16	10 27		
9½	Bescot Stadium	d		05 48	06 19	06 42		07 18		07 48			08 18		08 48		09 18		09 48		10 18			
10¾	**Walsall**	a		05 55	06 25	06 48	06 59	07 24	07 29	07 54	07 59		08 24	08 29	08 54	09 03	09 24	09 34	09 54	10 05	10 24	10 34		
—		d			06 25		07 00		07 30		08 00			08 29		09 03		09 35				10 35		
14	Bloxwich	d			06 32		07 07		07 37		08 07					09 10		09 42				10 42		
14½	Bloxwich North	d			06 35		07 09		07 39		08 09					09 13		09 44				10 44		
16¾	Landywood	d	00 01		06 39		07 14		07 43		08 13					09 17		09 48				10 48		
18¾	Cannock	d	00 06		06 43		07 17		07 48		08 18			08 43		09 21		09 53				10 53		
20¾	Hednesford	d	00a12		06 48		07 22		07 53		08 23			08 48		09 26		09 58				10 58		
24¾	Rugeley Town	d			06 56		07 30		08 01		08 31			08 56		09 34		10 06				11 06		
26¼	**Rugeley Trent Valley**	a			07 00		07 36		08 05		08 36			09 00		09 38		10 10				11 13		

		LM	LM	LM	LM		LM	LM	LM	LM	LM	LM	LM	LM	LM		LM	LM	LM	LM	LM	LM	LM	LM	LM
Wolverhampton 7 68	d	12 49		13 19			13 49				14 49		15 19		15 49					16 49		17 19		17 49	
Birmingham New Street 12	d	13 27	13 42	13 57	14 12		14 27	14 42	14 57	15 12	15 27	15 42	15 57	16 12	16 27		16 42	16 57	17 12	17 27	17 42	17 57	18 12	18 27	18 42
Duddeston	d	13 32		14 02			14 32		15 02		15 32		16 02		16 32			17 02		17 32		18 02		18 32	
Aston	d	13 35		14 05			14 35		15 05		15 35		16 05		16 35			17 05		17 35		18 05		18 35	
Witton	d	13 37		14 07			14 37		15 07		15 37		16 07		16 37			17 07		17 37		18 07		18 37	
Perry Barr	d	13 39		14 09			14 39		15 09		15 39		16 09		16 39			17 09		17 39		18 09		18 39	
Hamstead	d	13 42		14 12			14 42		15 12		15 42		16 12		16 42			17 12		17 42		18 12		18 42	
Tame Bridge Parkway	d	13 46	13 57	14 16	14 27		14 46	14 57	15 16	15 27	15 46	15 54	16 16	16 24	16 46		16 57	17 16	17 27	17 46	17 57	18 16	18 27	18 46	18 54
Bescot Stadium	d	13 48		14 18			14 48		15 18		15 48		16 18		16 48			17 18		17 48		18 18		18 48	
Walsall	a	13 54	14 05	14 24	14 34		14 54	15 05	15 24	15 34	15 54	16 01	16 24	16 31	16 54		17 04	17 24	17 34	17 54	18 04	18 24	18 34	18 54	19 01
	d				14 35					15 35		16 02		16 32			17 05		17 35		18 05		18 35		19 02
Bloxwich	d				14 42					15 42		16 09		16 39			17 12		17 42		18 12		18 42		19 09
Bloxwich North	d				14 44					15 44		16 11		16 41			17 14		17 44		18 14		18 44		19 11
Landywood	d				14 48					15 48		16 15		16 45			17 18		17 48		18 18		18 48		19 15
Cannock	d				14 53					15 53		16 20		16 50			17 23		17 53		18 23		18 52		19 20
Hednesford	d				14 58					15 58		16 25		16 55			17 28		17 58		18 28		18 57		19 25
Rugeley Town	d				15 06					16 06		16 33		17 03			17 36		18 06		18 36		19 05		19 33
Rugeley Trent Valley	a				15 13					16 13		16 38		17 07			17 40		18 10		18 40		19 11		19 37

			LM	LM	LM	LM	LM	LM	LM	LM	LM		LM
Wolverhampton 7 68	d		18 19		19 19				21 19				
Birmingham New Street 12	d		18 57	19 22	19 57	20 22	20 57	21 17	21 47	22 17	22 47		23 18
Duddeston	d		19 02	19 27	20 02		21 02		21 52		22 52		23 23
Aston	d		19 05	19 30	20 05		21 05		21 55		22 55		23 26
Witton	d		19 07	19 32	20 07		21 07		21 57		22 57		23 28
Perry Barr	d		19 09	19 34	20 09		21 09		21 59		22 59		23 31
Hamstead	d		19 12	19 37	20 12		21 12		22 02		23 02		23 34
Tame Bridge Parkway	d		19 16	19 42	20 16	20 34	21 16	21 30	22 06	22 30	23 06		23 39
Bescot Stadium	d		19 18	19 45	20 18		21 18		22 08		23 08		23 41
Walsall	a		19 24	19 50	20 24	20 41	21 24	21 38	22 14	22 38	23 14		23 47
	d			19 51		20 42		21 39		22 39			23 47
Bloxwich	d			19 58		20 49		21 46		22 46			23 54
Bloxwich North	d			20 01		20 52		21 49		22 49			23 57
Landywood	d			20 05		20 56		21 53		22 53			00 01
Cannock	d			20 10		21 00		21 57		22 57			00 06
Hednesford	d			20 15		21 05		22 02		23 02			00a12
Rugeley Town	d			20 23		21 13		22 10		23 10			
Rugeley Trent Valley	a			20 28		21 18		22 15		23 15			

Saturdays

14 December to 17 May

		LM A	LM	LM	LM	LM	LM 1 C	LM	LM	LM		LM	LM	LM	LM	LM	LM	LM	LM	LM	LM	LM		
Wolverhampton 7 68	d			06 38			06 53		07 19			07 49		08 19		08 49				09 49		10 19		
Birmingham New Street 12	d		06 02		06 27	07 00	07 27	07 42	07 57	08 12		08 27	08 42	08 57	09 12	09 27	09 42	09 57	10 12	10 27	10 42	10 57	and at the same minutes past each hour until	
Duddeston	d		06 06		06 32		07 32		08 02			08 32		09 02		09 32		10 02		10 32		11 02		
Aston	d		06 09		06 35	07 06	07 35		08 05			08 35		09 05		09 35		10 05		10 35		11 05		
Witton	d		06 11		06 37		07 37		08 07			08 37		09 07		09 37		10 07		10 37		11 07		
Perry Barr	d		06 13		06 40	07 09	07 39		08 09			08 39		09 09		09 39		10 09		10 39		11 09		
Hamstead	d		06 16		06 43	07 12	07 42		08 12			08 42		09 12		09 42		10 12		10 42		11 12		
Tame Bridge Parkway	d		06 21		06 48	07 17	07 46	07 57	08 16	08 27		08 46	08 57	09 16	09 27	09 46	09 57	10 16	10 27	10 46	10 57	11 16		
Bescot Stadium	d		06 24		06 50		07 48		08 18			08 48		09 18		09 48		10 18		10 48		11 18		
Walsall	a		06 29	06 50	06 56	07 25	07 54	08 04	08 24	08 34		08 54	09 04	09 24	09 34	09 54	10 04	10 24	10 34	10 54	11 04	11 24		
	d		06 30		06 57	07 26		08 05		08 35			09 05		09 35		10 05		10 35		11 05			
Bloxwich	d		06 37		07 04	07 33		08 12					09 12				10 12				11 12			
Bloxwich North	d		06 39		07 06	07 35		08 14					09 14				10 14				11 14			
Landywood	d	00 01	06 43		07 10	07 39		08 18					09 18				10 18				11 18			
Cannock	d	00 06	06 48		07 15	07 44		08 23		08 49			09 23		09 49		10 23		10 49		11 23			
Hednesford	d	00a12	06a53		07 20	07 49		08 28		08 54			09 28		09 54		10 28		10 54		11 28			
Rugeley Town	d				07 28	07 57		08 36		09 02			09 36		10 02		10 36		11 02		11 36			
Rugeley Trent Valley	a				07 32	08 04		08 43		09 07			09 43		10 07		10 43		11 07		11 43			

A From Birmingham New Street **B** From Shrewsbury **C** From Crewe

For connections to Stafford please see Table 67

Table 70

Saturdays

14 December to 17 May

Birmingham - Walsall and Rugeley

Network Diagram - refer to first Page of Table 67

		LM	LM	LM	LM	LM	LM	LM	LM	LM	LM	LM	LM	LM	LM	LM	LM	LM
Wolverhampton 7 68 🚌	d		16 49		17 19		17 49		18 19		19 19		20 19		21 19		22 19	
Birmingham New Street 12	d	17 12	17 27	17 42	17 57	18 12	18 27	18 42	18 57	19 17	19 57	20 20	20 47	21 17	21 57	22 17	22 47	23 18
Duddeston	d		17 32		18 02		18 32		19 02	19 22	20 02		20 52		22 02		22 52	23 23
Aston	d		17 35		18 05		18 35		19 05	19 25	20 05		20 55		22 05		22 55	23 26
Witton	d		17 37		18 07		18 37		19 07	19 27	20 07		20 57		22 07		22 57	23 28
Perry Barr	d		17 39		18 09		18 39		19 09	19 29	20 09		20 59		22 09		22 59	23 31
Hamstead	d		17 42		18 12		18 42		19 12	19 32	20 12		21 02		22 12		23 02	23 34
Tame Bridge Parkway	d	17 27	17 46	17 57	18 16	18 27	18 46	18 57	19 16	19 37	20 16	20 32	21 06	21 31	22 16	22 31	23 06	23 39
Bescot Stadium	d		17 48		18 18		18 48		19 18	19 40	20 18		21 08		22 18		23 08	23 41
Walsall	a	17 34	17 54	18 04	18 24	18 34	18 54	19 04	19 24	19 45	20 24	20 40	21 14	21 38	22 24	22 38	23 14	23 47
	d	17 35		18 05		18 35		19 05		19 46		20 41		21 39		22 39		23 47
Bloxwich	d			18 12				19 12		19 53		20 48		21 46		22 46		23 54
Bloxwich North	d			18 14				19 14		19 56		20 50		21 49		22 49		23 57
Landywood	d			18 18				19 18		20 00		20 54		21 53		22 53		00 01
Cannock	d	17 49		18 23		18 49		19 23		20 05		20 59		21 57		22 57		00 06
Hednesford	d	17 54		18 28		18 54		19 28		20 10		21 04		22 02		23 02		00a12
Rugeley Town	d	18 02		18 36		19 02		19 36		20 18		21 12		22 10		23 10		
Rugeley Trent Valley	a	18 07		18 43		19 07		19 40		20 22		21 16		22 15		23 15		

Sundays

8 December to 11 May

		LM A	LM	LM		LM	LM	LM
Wolverhampton 7 68 🚌	d							
Birmingham New Street 12	d		09 17	09 40		22 17	22 40	23 17
Duddeston	d		09 21			22 21		23 21
Aston	d		09 24			22 24		23 24
Witton	d		09 26		and at	22 26		23 26
Perry Barr	d		09 29		the same	22 29		23 29
Hamstead	d		09 32		minutes	22 32		23 32
Tame Bridge Parkway	d		09 37	09 52	past	22 37	22 52	23 37
Bescot Stadium	d		09 39		each	22 39		23 39
Walsall	a		09 44	10 00	hour until	22 44	23 00	23 44
	d			10 01			23 01	
Bloxwich	d			10 08			23 08	
Bloxwich North	d			10 10			23 10	
Landywood	d	00§01		10 15			23 15	
Cannock	d	00§06		10 19			23 19	
Hednesford	d	00a12		10 24			23 24	
Rugeley Town	d			10 32			23 32	
Rugeley Trent Valley	a			10 37			23 37	

A not 8 December. From Birmingham New Street

For connections to Stafford please see Table 67

Table 70R

Rugeley and Walsall - Birmingham

Mondays to Fridays

9 December to 16 May

Network Diagram - refer to first Page of Table 67

Miles	Station		LM MX A	LM	LM	LM	LM	LM 1 B	LM	LM	LM	LM	LM	LM	LM	LM	LM	LM	LM	LM	LM	LM	LM
0	**Rugeley Trent Valley**	d			05 55		06 39		07 04		07 41		08 11		08 41		09 06		09 43				10 41
1½	Rugeley Town	d			05 59		06 43		07 08		07 45		08 15		08 45		09 10		09 47				10 45
5½	Hednesford	d			06 07		06 51		07 16		07 53		08 23		08 53		09 18		09 55				10 53
7½	Cannock	d			06 11		06 55		07 20		07 57		08 27		08 57		09 22		09 59				10 57
9½	Landywood	d			06 14		06 58		07 24		08 00		08 30		09 00		09 25		10 02				11 00
11¾	Bloxwich North	d			06 19		07 03		07 28		08 04		08 35		09 05		09 30		10 06				11 05
12¼	Bloxwich	d			06 21		07 05		07 30		08 06		08 37		09 07		09 32		10 08				11 07
15½	**Walsall**	a			06 28		07 12		07 38		08 14		08 44		09 13		09 39		10 16				11 14
—		d		06 01	06 29	07 01	07 13	07 30	07 38	08 01	08 14	08 30	08 45	09 01	09 15	09 31	09 46	10 01	10 16	10 31	10 45	11 01	11 15
16¾	Bescot Stadium	d		06 04	06 34	07 04		07 34		08 04		08 34		09 04		09 34		10 04		10 34		11 04	
17¾	Tame Bridge Parkway	d		06 07	06 37	07 07	07 19	07 37	07 44	08 07	08 20	08 37	08 51	09 07	09 21	09 37	09 52	10 07	10 22	10 37	10 51	11 07	11 21
20½	Hamstead	d		06 11	06 41	07 11		07 40		08 11		08 41		09 11		09 41		10 11		10 41		11 11	
22	Perry Barr	d		06 14	06 44	07 14		07 44		08 14		08 44		09 14		09 44		10 14		10 44		11 14	
22¾	Witton	d		06 16	06 46	07 16		07 46		08 16		08 47		09 16		09 46		10 16		10 46		11 16	
23½	Aston	d		06 19	06 49	07 19		07 49		08 18		08 50		09 19		09 49		10 19		10 49		11 19	
24¾	Duddeston	d	00 01	06 21	06 52	07 21		07 52		08 21		08 53		09 21		09 51		10 21		10 51		11 21	
26¼	**Birmingham New Street** 12	a	00 07	06 29	06 57	07 28	07 34	07 56	08 01	08 28	08 37	08 57	09 07	09 28	09 35	09 56	10 07	10 29	10 36	11 00	11 07	11 28	11 36
—	Wolverhampton 7 68	a		07 03				08 19		09 03				10 03		10 33		11 04		11 34		12 03	

Station		LM	LM	LM	LM	LM	LM	LM	LM	LM	LM	LM	LM	LM	LM	LM	LM	LM	LM	LM	LM	LM
Rugeley Trent Valley	d				11 41				12 41				13 41				14 41				15 41	
Rugeley Town	d				11 45				12 45				13 45				14 45				15 45	
Hednesford	d				11 53				12 53				13 53				14 53				15 53	
Cannock	d				11 57				12 57				13 57				14 57				15 57	
Landywood	d				12 00				13 00				14 00				15 00				16 00	
Bloxwich North	d				12 05				13 05				14 05				15 05				16 05	
Bloxwich	d				12 07				13 07				14 07				15 07				16 07	
Walsall	a				12 14				13 14				14 14				15 14				16 14	
	d	11 31	11 45	12 01	12 15	12 31	12 45	13 01	13 15	13 31	13 45	14 01	14 15	14 31	14 45	15 01	15 15	15 31	15 45	16 01	16 15	16 31
Bescot Stadium	d	11 34		12 04		12 34		13 04		13 34		14 04		14 34		15 04		15 34		16 04		16 34
Tame Bridge Parkway	d	11 37	11 51	12 07	12 21	12 37	12 51	13 07	13 21	13 37	13 51	14 07	14 21	14 37	14 51	15 07	15 21	15 37	15 51	16 07	16 21	16 37
Hamstead	d	11 41		12 11		12 41		13 11		13 41		14 11		14 41		15 11		15 41		16 11		16 41
Perry Barr	d	11 44		12 14		12 44		13 14		13 44		14 14		14 44		15 14		15 44		16 14		16 44
Witton	d	11 46		12 16		12 46		13 16		13 46		14 16		14 46		15 16		15 46		16 16		16 46
Aston	d	11 49		12 19		12 49		13 19		13 49		14 19		14 49		15 19		15 49		16 19		16 49
Duddeston	d	11 51		12 21		12 51		13 21		13 51		14 21		14 51		15 21		15 51		16 21		16 51
Birmingham New Street 12	a	12 04	12 06	12 28	12 36	13 00	13 07	13 29	13 36	14 00	14 07	14 28	14 36	15 00	15 07	15 29	15 36	16 00	16 07	16 30	16 36	17 00
Wolverhampton 7 68	a	12 33		13 03		13 34		14 04		14 33		15 03		15 33		16 04		16 33		17 04		17 33

Station		LM	LM	LM	LM	LM	LM	LM	LM	LM	LM	LM	LM	LM	LM	LM	LM	LM	LM	LM	LM	LM
Rugeley Trent Valley	d	16 16		16 41		17 12		17 46		18 16		18 46		19 14	19 42		20 40		21 40		22 35	
Rugeley Town	d	16 19		16 45		17 16		17 50		18 20		18 50		19 18	19 46		20 44		21 44		22 39	
Hednesford	d	16 27		16 53		17 24		17 58		18 28		18 58		19 26	19 54		20 52		21 52		22 48	
Cannock	d	16 31		16 57		17 28		18 02		18 32		19 02		19 30	19 58		20 56		21 56		22 52	
Landywood	d			17 00		17 31				18 35				19 33	20 01		20 59		21 59		22 56	
Bloxwich North	d			17 05		17 36				18 40				19 38	20 06		21 04		22 04		23 01	
Bloxwich	d			17 07		17 38				18 42				19 40	20 08		21 06		22 06		23 03	
Walsall	a	16 45		17 14		17 45		18 16		18 49		19 16		19 47	20 15		21 13		22 16		23 10	
	d	16 46	17 01	17 15	17 31	17 46	18 01	18 17	18 31	18 50	19 01	19 17	19 31	19 48	20 16	20 40	21 15	21 40	22 17	22 40	23 11	23 40
Bescot Stadium	d		17 04		17 34		18 04		18 34		19 04		19 34	19 52		20 43		21 43		22 44		23 43
Tame Bridge Parkway	d	16 52	17 07	17 21	17 37	17 52	18 07	18 23	18 37	18 56	19 07	19 23	19 37	19 55	20 22	20 46	21 21	21 46	22 23	22 47	23 17	23 46
Hamstead	d		17 11		17 41		18 11		18 41		19 11		19 41	20 00		20 50		21 50		22 51		23 50
Perry Barr	d		17 14		17 44		18 14		18 44		19 14		19 44	20 03		20 53		21 53		22 55		23 53
Witton	d		17 16		17 46		18 16		18 46		19 16		19 46	20 06		20 56		21 56		22 57		23 56
Aston	d		17 19		17 49		18 19		18 49		19 19		19 49	20 09		20 58		21 58		23 00		23 58
Duddeston	d		17 21		17 51		18 21		18 51		19 21		19 51	20 12		21 01		22 01		23 03		00 01
Birmingham New Street 12	a	17 07	17 29	17 35	18 00	18 06	18 28	18 39	19 00	19 11	19 28	19 39	19 56	20 18	20 37	21 07	21 35	22 07	22 40	23 09	23 33	00 07
Wolverhampton 7 68	a		18 03		18 33		19 03		19 33		20 04		20 33									

Saturdays

14 December to 17 May

Station		LM A	LM	LM	LM	LM	LM	LM	LM	LM	LM	LM	LM	LM	LM	LM	LM	LM	LM	LM	LM	LM	LM
Rugeley Trent Valley	d				06 26				07 39		08 12		08 45		09 12		09 45		10 12		10 45		11 12
Rugeley Town	d				06 30				07 43		08 16		08 48		09 16		09 48		10 16		10 48		11 16
Hednesford	d				06 38	06 58			07 51		08 24		08 56		09 24		09 56		10 24		10 56		11 24
Cannock	d				06 42	07 02			07 55		08 28		09 00		09 28		10 00		10 28		11 00		11 28
Landywood	d				06 45	07 05			07 58		08 31				09 31				10 31				11 31
Bloxwich North	d				06 50	07 10			08 03		08 36				09 36				10 36				11 36
Bloxwich	d				06 52	07 12			08 05		08 38				09 38				10 38				11 38
Walsall	a				06 59	07 19			08 12		08 45		09 14		09 45		10 14		10 45		11 14		11 45
	d		06 01	06 31	07 00	07 20	07 31	08 01	08 13	08 31	08 46	09 01	09 15	09 31	09 46	10 01	10 15	10 31	10 46	11 01	11 15	11 31	11 46
Bescot Stadium	d		06 04	06 34	07 04		07 34	08 04		08 34		09 04		09 34		10 04		10 34		11 04		11 34	
Tame Bridge Parkway	d		06 07	06 37	07 07	07 26	07 37	08 07	08 19	08 37	08 52	09 07	09 21	09 37	09 52	10 07	10 21	10 37	10 52	11 07	11 21	11 37	11 52
Hamstead	d		06 11	06 41	07 12		07 41	08 11		08 41		09 11		09 41		10 11		10 41		11 11		11 41	
Perry Barr	d		06 14	06 44	07 15		07 44	08 14		08 44		09 14		09 44		10 14		10 44		11 14		11 44	
Witton	d		06 16	06 46	07 17		07 46	08 16		08 46		09 16		09 46		10 16		10 46		11 16		11 46	
Aston	d		06 19	06 49	07 20		07 49	08 19		08 49		09 19		09 49		10 19		10 49		11 19		11 49	
Duddeston	d	00 01	06 21	06 51	07 23		07 51	08 21		08 51		09 21		09 51		10 21		10 51		11 21		11 51	
Birmingham New Street 12	a	00 07	06 28	06 58	07 28	07 44	07 58	08 28	08 37	08 56	09 06	09 29	09 36	09 56	10 06	10 29	10 36	10 56	11 06	11 28	11 36	11 56	12 06
Wolverhampton 7 68	a			07 33			08 33	09 03		09 33		10 03		10 33		11 03		11 33		12 03		12 33	

A From Walsall

B To Liverpool Lime Street

For connections from Stafford please see Table 67

Table 70R

Saturdays

14 December to 17 May

Rugeley and Walsall - Birmingham

Network Diagram - refer to first Page of Table 67

		LM	LM	LM	LM	LM	LM	LM	LM	LM	LM
Rugeley Trent Valley	d		11 45		12 12		12 45		13 11		13 45
Rugeley Town	d		11 48		12 16		12 48		13 15		13 48
Hednesford	d		11 56		12 24		12 56		13 23		13 56
Cannock	d		12 00		12 28		13 00		13 27		14 00
Landywood	d				12 31				13 30		
Bloxwich North	d				12 36				13 35		
Bloxwich	d				12 38				13 37		
Walsall	a		12 14		12 45		13 14		13 44		14 14
	d	12 01	12 15	12 31	12 46	13 01	13 15	13 31	13 45	14 01	14 15
Bescot Stadium	d	12 04		12 34		13 04		13 34		14 04	
Tame Bridge Parkway	d	12 07	12 21	12 37	12 52	13 07	13 21	13 37	13 51	14 07	14 21
Hamstead	d	12 11		12 41		13 11		13 41		14 11	
Perry Barr	d	12 14		12 44		13 14		13 44		14 14	
Witton	d	12 16		12 46		13 16		13 46		14 16	
Aston	d	12 19		12 49		13 19		13 49		14 19	
Duddeston	d	12 21		12 51		13 21		13 51		14 21	
Birmingham New Street 12	a	12 28	12 36	12 56	13 06	13 28	13 36	13 56	14 06	14 28	14 36
Wolverhampton 7 68	a	13 03		13 33		14 03		14 33		15 03	

		LM	LM	LM	LM	LM	LM	LM	LM	LM	LM	LM
Rugeley Trent Valley	d		14 11		14 45		15 11		15 45		16 11	
Rugeley Town	d		14 15		14 48		15 15		15 48		16 15	
Hednesford	d		14 23		14 56		15 23		15 56		16 23	
Cannock	d		14 27		15 00		15 27		16 00		16 27	
Landywood	d		14 30				15 30				16 30	
Bloxwich North	d		14 35				15 35				16 35	
Bloxwich	d		14 37				15 37				16 37	
Walsall	a		14 44		15 14		15 44		16 14		16 44	
	d	14 31	14 45	15 01	15 15	15 31	15 45	16 01	16 15	16 31	16 45	17 01
Bescot Stadium	d	14 34		15 04		15 34		16 04		16 34		17 04
Tame Bridge Parkway	d	14 37	14 51	15 07	15 21	15 37	15 51	16 07	16 21	16 37	16 51	17 07
Hamstead	d	14 41		15 11		15 41		16 11		16 41		17 11
Perry Barr	d	14 44		15 14		15 44		16 14		16 44		17 14
Witton	d	14 46		15 16		15 46		16 16		16 46		17 16
Aston	d	14 49		15 19		15 49		16 19		16 49		17 19
Duddeston	d	14 51		15 21		15 51		16 21		16 51		17 21
Birmingham New Street 12	a	14 56	15 06	15 28	15 36	15 56	16 06	16 28	16 36	16 56	17 06	17 28
Wolverhampton 7 68	a	15 33		16 03		16 33		17 04		17 33		18 03

		LM	LM	LM	LM	LM	LM	LM	LM
Rugeley Trent Valley	d	16 45		17 11		17 45		18 11	
Rugeley Town	d	16 48		17 15		17 48		18 15	
Hednesford	d	16 56		17 23		17 56		18 23	
Cannock	d	17 00		17 27		18 00		18 27	
Landywood	d			17 30				18 30	
Bloxwich North	d			17 35				18 35	
Bloxwich	d			17 37				18 37	
Walsall	a	17 14		17 44		18 14		18 44	
	d	17 15	17 31	17 45	18 01	18 15	18 31	18 45	19 01
Bescot Stadium	d		17 34		18 04		18 34		19 04
Tame Bridge Parkway	d	17 21	17 37	17 51	18 07	18 21	18 37	18 51	19 07
Hamstead	d		17 41		18 11		18 41		19 11
Perry Barr	d		17 44		18 14		18 44		19 14
Witton	d		17 46		18 16		18 46		19 16
Aston	d		17 49		18 19		18 49		19 19
Duddeston	d		17 51		18 21		18 51		19 21
Birmingham New Street 12	a	17 36	17 56	18 06	18 28	18 36	18 56	19 06	19 28
Wolverhampton 7 68	a		18 33		19 03		19 33		20 03

		LM	LM	LM	LM	LM	LM	LM	LM	LM	LM
Rugeley Trent Valley	d	18 45	19 12	19 50		20 39		21 35		22 35	
Rugeley Town	d	18 49	19 16	19 54		20 43		21 39		22 39	
Hednesford	d	18 57	19 24	20 02		20 51		21 47		22 47	
Cannock	d	19 01	19 28	20 06		20 55		21 51		22 51	
Landywood	d		19 31	20 09		20 58		21 54		22 54	
Bloxwich North	d		19 36	20 14		21 03		21 59		22 59	
Bloxwich	d		19 38	20 16		21 05		22 01		23 01	
Walsall	a	19 15	19 45	20 23		21 12		22 08		23 08	
	d	19 18	19 47	20 24	20 40	21 13	21 40	22 10	22 40	23 10	23 40
Bescot Stadium	d	19 23	19 51		20 43		21 43		22 43		23 43
Tame Bridge Parkway	d	19 26	19 54	20 30	20 46	21 19	21 46	22 16	22 46	23 16	23 46
Hamstead	d	19 30	19 59		20 50		21 50		22 49		23 49
Perry Barr	d	19 33	20 02		20 53		21 53		22 52		23 52
Witton	d	19 36	20 05		20 55		21 55		22 54		23 54
Aston	d	19 39	20 08		20 58		21 58		22 56		23 56
Duddeston	d	19 42	20 11		21 00		22 00		22 59		23 59
Birmingham New Street 12	a	19 46	20 16	20 44	21 06	21 37	22 07	22 33	23 04	23 34	00 03
Wolverhampton 7 68	a				21 33		22 33				

Sundays

8 December to 11 May

		LM	LM		LM	LM	LM A	LM B	LM	LM
Rugeley Trent Valley	d		09 48	and at the same minutes past each hour until		12 48			13 48	
Rugeley Town	d		09 52			12 52			13 52	
Hednesford	d		10 00			13 00			14 00	
Cannock	d		10 04			13 04			14 04	
Landywood	d		10 07			13 07			14 07	
Bloxwich North	d		10 12			13 12			14 12	
Bloxwich	d		10 14			13 14			14 14	
Walsall	a		10 21			13 21			14 21	
	d	10 00	10 23		13 00	13 23	14 00	14 03	14 23	15 00
Bescot Stadium	d	10 04			13 04		14 04	14 07		15 04
Tame Bridge Parkway	d	10 07	10 29		13 07	13 29	14 07	14 10	14 29	15 07
Hamstead	d	10 11			13 11		14 11	14 14		15 11
Perry Barr	d	10 14			13 14		14 14	14 17		15 14
Witton	d	10 17			13 17		14 17	14 20		15 17
Aston	d	10 20			13 20		14 20	14 23		15 20
Duddeston	d	10 23			13 23		14 23	14 26		15 23
Birmingham New Street 12	a	10 27	10 46		13 27	13 46	14 27	14 30	14 46	15 30
Wolverhampton 7 68	a									

		LM	LM	LM	LM	LM	LM	LM	LM	LM	LM	LM	LM
Rugeley Trent Valley	d	14 48		15 48		16 48		17 48		18 48		19 48	
Rugeley Town	d	14 52		15 52		16 52		17 52		18 52		19 52	
Hednesford	d	15 00		16 00		17 00		18 00		19 00		20 00	
Cannock	d	15 04		16 04		17 04		18 04		19 04		20 04	
Landywood	d	15 07		16 07		17 07		18 07		19 07		20 07	
Bloxwich North	d	15 12		16 12		17 12		18 12		19 12		20 12	
Bloxwich	d	15 14		16 14		17 14		18 14		19 14		20 14	
Walsall	a	15 21		16 21		17 21		18 21		19 21		20 21	
	d	15 23	16 00	16 23	17 00	17 23	18 00	18 23	19 00	19 23	20 00	20 23	21 00
Bescot Stadium	d		16 04		17 04		18 04		19 04		20 04		21 04
Tame Bridge Parkway	d	15 29	16 07	16 29	17 07	17 29	18 07	18 29	19 07	19 29	20 07	20 29	21 07
Hamstead	d		16 11		17 11		18 11		19 11		20 11		21 11
Perry Barr	d		16 14		17 14		18 14		19 14		20 14		21 14
Witton	d		16 17		17 17		18 17		19 17		20 17		21 17
Aston	d		16 20		17 20		18 20		19 20		20 20		21 20
Duddeston	d		16 23		17 23		18 23		19 23		20 23		21 23
Birmingham New Street 12	a	15 46	16 30	16 46	17 30	17 46	18 28	18 46	19 30	19 47	20 29	20 46	21 27
Wolverhampton 7 68	a												

		LM	LM	LM	LM	LM
Rugeley Trent Valley	d	20 48		21 48		22 48
Rugeley Town	d	20 52		21 52		22 52
Hednesford	d	21 00		22 00		23 00
Cannock	d	21 04		22 04		23 04
Landywood	d	21 07		22 07		23 07
Bloxwich North	d	21 12		22 12		23 12
Bloxwich	d	21 14		22 14		23 14
Walsall	a	21 21		22 21		23 21
	d	21 23	22 00	22 23	23 00	23 23
Bescot Stadium	d		22 04		23 04	
Tame Bridge Parkway	d	21 29	22 07	22 29	23 07	23 29
Hamstead	d		22 11		23 11	
Perry Barr	d		22 14		23 14	
Witton	d		22 17		23 17	
Aston	d		22 20		23 20	
Duddeston	d		22 23		23 23	
Birmingham New Street 12	a	21 46	22 27	22 47	23 27	23 46
Wolverhampton 7 68	a					

A until 29 December, from 16 February

B from 5 January until 9 February

For connections from Stafford please see Table 67

Network Diagram for Tables 71, 72

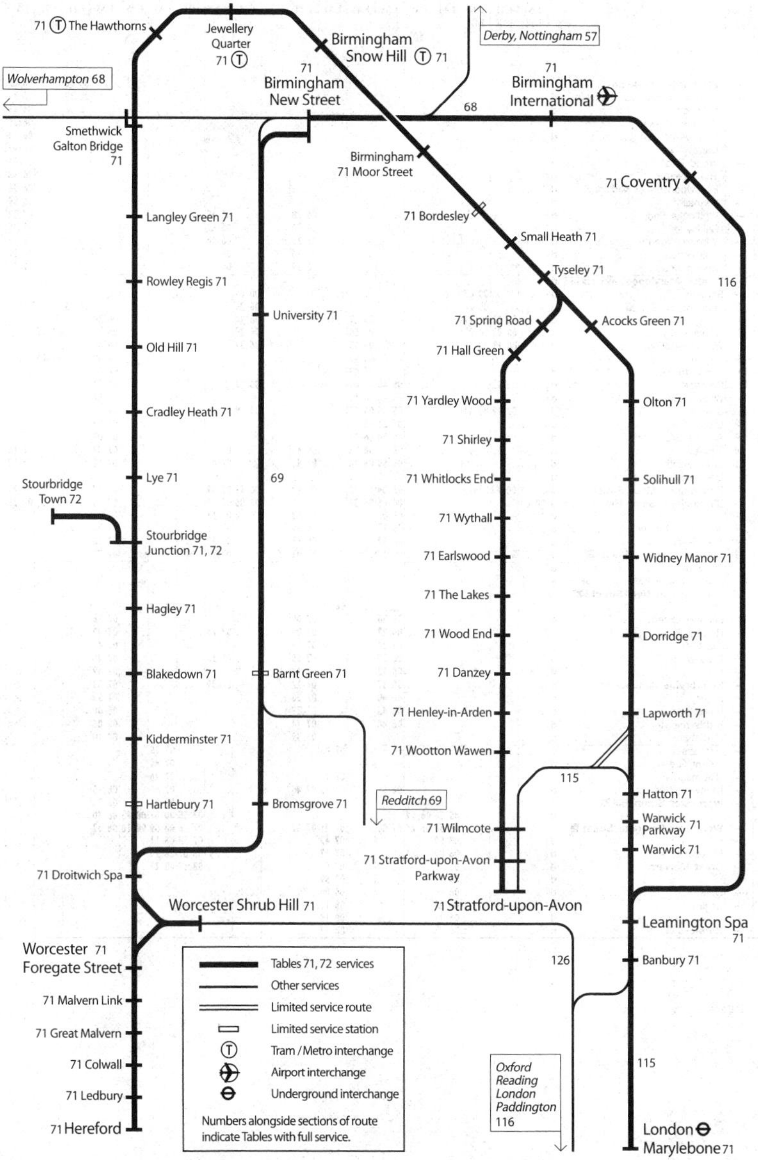

71 The Hawthorns
Jewellery Quarter 71
Birmingham Snow Hill 71
Derby, Nottingham 57
Wolverhampton 68
71 Birmingham New Street
71 Birmingham International
68
Smethwick Galton Bridge 71
Birmingham 71 Moor Street
71 Coventry
Langley Green 71
71 Bordesley
Small Heath 71
Tyseley 71
116
Rowley Regis 71
University 71
71 Spring Road
Acocks Green 71
Old Hill 71
71 Hall Green
Cradley Heath 71
71 Yardley Wood
Olton 71
71 Shirley
Lye 71
69
71 Whitlocks End
Solihull 71
Stourbridge Town 72
71 Wythall
Stourbridge Junction 71, 72
71 Earlswood
Widney Manor 71
71 The Lakes
Hagley 71
71 Wood End
Dorridge 71
Blakedown 71
Barnt Green 71
71 Danzey
71 Henley-in-Arden
Lapworth 71
Kidderminster 71
71 Wootton Wawen
115
Hatton 71
Hartlebury 71
Bromsgrove 71
Redditch 69
71 Wilmcote
Warwick Parkway 71
Warwick 71
71 Stratford-upon-Avon Parkway
71 Droitwich Spa
Worcester Shrub Hill 71
71 Stratford-upon-Avon
Leamington Spa 71
Worcester 71 Foregate Street
126
Banbury 71
71 Malvern Link
71 Great Malvern
71 Colwall
115
71 Ledbury
Oxford Reading London Paddington 116
71 Hereford
London Marylebone 71
Tables 71, 72 services
Other services
Limited service route
Limited service station
Tram / Metro interchange
Airport interchange
Underground interchange
Numbers alongside sections of route indicate Tables with full service.

TOCs operating on this network - Chiltern Railways (CH), London Midlands (LM), Cross Country (XC), First Great Western (GW)

Table 71

Mondays to Fridays

9 December to 16 May

Stratford-upon-Avon, Marylebone and Leamington Spa - Birmingham - Stourbridge, Worcester and Hereford

Network Diagram - see first Page of Table 71

Miles	Miles	Miles			LM	CH	CH	LM	GW	LM	LM	LM	LM		CH	LM	GW	LM	GW	LM	CH	CH	LM		LM
					MX	MX	MX																		
						◇	◇		[1]										◇[1] 🍴						
—	0	—	**Stratford-upon-Avon**	d																	06 08		06 28		
—	—	—	Stratford-upon-Avon Parkway	d																	06 12		06 32		
—	2¾	—	Wilmcote	d																	06 16		06 35		
—	6½	—	Wootton Wawen	d																			06x39		
—	8¼	—	Henley-in-Arden	d																			06 43		
—	11¼	—	Danzey	d																			06x47		
—	13	—	Wood End	d																			06x51		
—	14¼	—	The Lakes	d																			06x53		
—	15	—	Earlswood (West Midlands)	d																			06 56		
—	16	—	Wythall	d																			06 59		
—	17	—	Whitlocks End	d									06 28			06 45							07 02		
—	18	—	Shirley	d									06 30			06 52							07 05		
—	19¼	—	Yardley Wood	d									06 33			06 54							07 07		
—	20½	—	Hall Green	d									06 36			06 57							07 11		
—	21	—	Spring Road	d									06 39			06 59							07 13		
—	—	—	**London Marylebone** [10] ⊖115	d																					
—	—	—	Banbury	d			00 03								06 05										
—	—	0	**Leamington Spa** [8]	a			00 20								06 24						06 45				
—	—	—		d		00 05	00 21				05 47				06 24					06 30		06 52			
—	—	2	Warwick	d		00 09	00 25				05 50				06 29					06 33		06 57			
—	—	3¼	Warwick Parkway	d		00 13	00 29				05 53				06 32					06 36					
—	—	6	Hatton	d							05 57									06 40		07a04			
—	—	10¼	Lapworth	d							06 03									06 46					
—	—	12¾	Dorridge	d		00 23				05 40	06 07				06 43					06 53					07 09
—	—	14¾	Widney Manor	d						05 45	06 11									06 57					07 14
—	—	16¼	Solihull	d		00 29	00 41			05 48	06 15				06 49					07 01					07 17
—	—	18	Olton	d						05 51	06 18									07 04					07 20
—	—	19	Acocks Green	d						05 54	06 21									07 07					07 23
—	22	20	Tyseley	d						05 57	06 23		06 42			07 02				07 09			07 16		07 26
—	23	21	Small Heath	d						05 59	06 26		06 44			07 05				07 12			07 18		07 28
—	24	—	Bordesley	d																					
—	24¾	—	**Birmingham Moor Street**	d	00 06	00a43	00a55			06 04	06 30		06 49		06 59	07 09				07 17			07 23		07 33
—	25¼	—	**Birmingham Snow Hill** 🚊	a	00 08					06 06	06 34		06 51		07 06	07 12				07 19			07 25		07 35
—	—	—		d						06 08			06 53			07 13				07 24					07 37
—	26	—	Jewellery Quarter 🚊	d						06 10			06 55			07 15				07 26					07 39
—	28½	—	The Hawthorns 🚊	d						06 14			06 59			07 19				07 30					07 43
—	29¼	29	Smethwick Galton Bridge [7]	d						06 17			07 02			07 22				07 33					07 46
—	—	—	**Coventry**	a																					
—	—	—	**Birmingham Intl.** 68 ✈	a																					
0	—	24	**Birmingham New Street** [12] 68	a																					
—	—	—		d								06 59						07 19							
—	30½	30¼	Langley Green	d						06 20			07 05							07 36					
—	32¼	—	Rowley Regis	d						06 23			07 09			07 28				07 40					07 52
—	33½	—	Old Hill	d						06 27			07 12							07 43					
—	34¾	—	Cradley Heath	d						06 30			07 15			07 33				07 46					07 57
—	36¼	—	Lye	d						06 33			07 18							07 49					
—	37¼	—	**Stourbridge Junction** [2]	d						06 37			07 22			07a39				07 53					08a03
—	39¼	—	Hagley	d						06 40			07 26							07 57					
—	41	—	Blakedown	d						06 43			07 29							08 00					
—	44¼	—	**Kidderminster**	d						06 48			07 34							08 05					
—	47¾	—	Hartlebury	d									07 39							08 10					
2½	—	—	University	d								07 05						07 25							
10½	—	—	Barnt Green	d														07 41							
13	—	—	Bromsgrove	d								07 22						07 46							
19¼	53½	—	Droitwich Spa	d						06 59		07 32	07 46					07 56		08 18					
25	—	—	**Worcester Shrub Hill** [7]	a														08 03		08 26					
—	—	—		d				05 56	06 19								07 55	08 07	08 13	08 30					
25¾	58¾	—	**Worcester Foregate Street** [7]	a				05 58	06 25	07 09		07 41	07 57				07 58	08 09	08 16	08 32					
—	—	—		d				05 59				07 42					07 58	08 11							
32½	—	—	Malvern Link	d				06 08				07 52					08 07	08 20							
33¾	—	—	**Great Malvern**	a				06 11				07 54					08 12	08 22							
—	—	—		d				06 11				07 59													
36½	—	—	Colwall	d				06 16				08 04													
40¾	—	—	Ledbury	a				06 23				08 11													
—	—	—		d				06 25				08 12													
54½	—	—	**Hereford** [7]	a				06 49				08 32													

Table 71

Mondays to Fridays

9 December to 16 May

Stratford-upon-Avon, Marylebone and Leamington Spa - Birmingham - Stourbridge, Worcester and Hereford

Network Diagram - see first Page of Table 71

		LM	LM	LM	XC	CH	LM	XC	LM		LM	GW	LM	CH	LM	LM	LM		XC	LM	CH	CH	LM	LM	LM
					◇1	◇		◇1				1		◇					◇1		◇	◇			
					🚲			🚲				🚲							🚲						
Stratford-upon-Avon	d		06 52				07 19		07 26					07 33	07 43										08 26
Stratford-upon-Avon Parkway	d		06 56				07 23		07 30					07 37	07 47										08 30
Wilmcote	d		06 59											07 41	07 50										08 33
Wootton Wawen	d		07x03												07x54										08x37
Henley-in-Arden	d		07 07				07 35								07 58										08 41
Danzey	d		07x11												08x02										08x45
Wood End	d		07x15												08 05										08x49
The Lakes	d		07x17												08x08										08x51
Earlswood (West Midlands)	d		07 20				07 43								08 11										08 54
Wythall	d		07 23				07 46								08 14										08 57
Whitlocks End	d		07 26				07 49				08 07				08 16								08 34		09 00
Shirley	d		07 29				07 52				08 10				08 19								08 41		09 03
Yardley Wood	d		07 32				07 55				08 12				08 22								08 43		09 05
Hall Green	d		07 35				07 58				08 15				08 25								08 46		09 09
Spring Road	d		07 37				08 01				08 17				08 27								08 48		09 11
London Marylebone 10 ⊖115	d					06 05															06 45	07 15			
Banbury	d				06 54	07 03		07 26											07 56		08 00	08 07			
Leamington Spa 8	a				07 10	07 20		07 42							08 07				08 12		08 17	08 24			
	d			07 08	07 12	07 21		07 43					07 46				08 00		08 14		08 18	08 24			
Warwick	d			07 12		07 26							07 50				08 04				08 23	08 29			
Warwick Parkway	d			07 15		07 29							07 53				08 07					08 33			
Hatton	d			07 19		07 35							07 57				08 12				08a30				
Lapworth	d			07 24									08 03				08 17								
Dorridge	d			07 34		07 43			07 56				08 08			08 20	08 25							08 46	
Widney Manor	d			07 38		07 47			08 01				08 13			08 25	08 29							08 51	
Solihull	d			07 42		07 51			08 04				08 16			08 28	08 33					08 45		08 54	
Olton	d			07 45		07 55			08 08				08 19			08 32	08 36							08 57	
Acocks Green	d			07 48					08 11				08 22			08 35	08 39							09 00	
Tyseley	d		07 41	07 50					08 14		08 21		08 25		08 31	08 38	08 42						08 51	09 02	
Small Heath	d		07 43	07 53							08 23		08 27		08 33		08 45						08 54	09 05	
Bordesley	d																								
Birmingham Moor Street	d		07 48	07 58		08 03	08 08		08 19		08 28		08 32		08 38	08 42	08 49					08 54	08 58	09 09	09 18
Birmingham Snow Hill 🚋	a		07 50	08 00		08 10	08 10		08 21		08 30		08 35		08 40	08 47	08 52					08 59	09 01	09 12	09 20
	d		07 53	08 04			08 13		08 23		08 33		08 43				08 53						09 02	09 13	09 23
Jewellery Quarter 🚋	d		07 55	08 06			08 15		08 25		08 35		08 45				08 55						09 05	09 15	09 25
The Hawthorns 🚋	d		07 59	08 10			08 19		08 29		08 39		08 49				08 59						09 09	09 19	09 29
Smethwick Galton Bridge 7	d		08 02	08 13			08 22		08 32		08 42		08 52				09 02						09 11	09 22	09 32
Coventry	a				07 23														08 25						
Birmingham Intl. 68 ✈	a				07 37														08 37						
Birmingham New Street 12 68	a				07 48			08 14											08 48						
	d	07 59																		08 49					
Langley Green	d		08 05	08 16							08 45						09 05								09 35
Rowley Regis	d		08 08	08 20			08 28		08 38		08 49		08 58				09 08						09 17	09 28	09 38
Old Hill	d		08 12	08 23							08 52						09 12								09 42
Cradley Heath	d		08 15	08 26			08 33		08 43		08 55		09 03				09 15						09 22	09 33	09 45
Lye	d		08 18	08 29							08 58						09 18								09 48
Stourbridge Junction 2	d		08 22	08 33			08a40		08a48		09 02		09 09				09a22						09 28	09 39	09a52
Hagley	d		08 26	08 37									09 12										09 32		
Blakedown	d		08 29	08 40									09 15										09 35		
Kidderminster	d		08 34	08a45							09a10		09 20										09a39	09 47	
Hartlebury	d		08 39																					09 52	
University	d	08 05																		08 55					
Barnt Green	d	08 18																							
Bromsgrove	d	08 23																		09 10					
Droitwich Spa	d	08 32	08 47										09 31							09 20				10 00	
Worcester Shrub Hill 7	a												09 40												
	d											09 16													
Worcester Foregate Street 7	a	08 41	08 58									09 19								09 28				10 09	
	d	08 42										09 19								09 32					
Malvern Link	d	08 52										09 29								09 42					
Great Malvern	a	08 54										09 33								09 44					
	d	08 55																		09 45					
Colwall	d	09 00																		09 50					
Ledbury	a	09 07																		09 57					
	d	09 08																		09 59					
Hereford 7	a	09 28																		10 17					

Table 71

Mondays to Fridays

9 December to 16 May

Stratford-upon-Avon, Marylebone and Leamington Spa - Birmingham - Stourbridge, Worcester and Hereford

Network Diagram - see first Page of Table 71

		CH	LM	LM	XC	CH	XC	GW	LM	LM	LM	LM	CH	XC	CH	GW	LM	LM	LM	CH	XC	LM	LM
					◇1	◇	◇1						◇	◇1	◇	◇1				◇	◇1		
					🛒		🛒						🛒	🛒		☕				🛒 BZ	🛒		
Stratford-upon-Avon	d														09 14			09 26					
Stratford-upon-Avon Parkway	d														09 18			09 30					
Wilmcote	d														09 22			09 33					
Wootton Wawen	d																	09x37					
Henley-in-Arden	d																	09 41					
Danzey	d																	09x45					
Wood End	d																	09x49					
The Lakes	d																	09x51					
Earlswood (West Midlands)	d																	09 54					
Wythall	d																	09 57					
Whitlocks End	d									09 19		09 40						10 00					10 19
Shirley	d									09 22		09 42						10 03					10 22
Yardley Wood	d									09 24		09 45						10 05					10 24
Hall Green	d									09 27		09 48						10 09					10 27
Spring Road	d									09 29		09 51						10 11					10 29
London Marylebone 10 ⊖115	d					07 45							08 15							08 45			
Banbury	d				08 27	08 44	08 54						09 07	09 26						09 46	09 56		
Leamington Spa 8	a				08 43	09 03	09 10						09 24	09 42	09 52					10 03	10 11		
	d	08 30			08 44	09 04	09 12						09 25	09 43						10 04	10 13		
Warwick	d	08 35				09 09							09 30							10 10			
Warwick Parkway	d	08 38				09 14							09 34							10 14			
Hatton	d	08 44																					
Lapworth	d	08 50																					
Dorridge	d	08 55	09 10			09 25					09 28						09 46		10 09	10 25			
Widney Manor	d		09 14								09 33						09 51		10 14				
Solihull	d	09 01	09 18			09 31					09 36		09 46				09 54		10 17	10 32			
Olton	d		09 21								09 39						09 57		10 20				
Acocks Green	d		09 24								09 42						10 00		10 23				
Tyseley	d									09 32							10 02						10 32
Small Heath	d									09 35							10 05						10 35
Bordesley	d																						
Birmingham Moor Street	d	09a17	09 31			09a42				09 39	09 49	09 58	09 55				10 09	10 18	10 29	10a44			10 39
Birmingham Snow Hill 🚋	a		09 33							09 42	09 51	10 00	10 02				10 12	10 20	10 32				10 42
	d			09 33						09 43	09 53	10 03					10 13	10 23	10 33				10 43
Jewellery Quarter 🚋	d			09 35						09 45	09 55	10 05					10 15	10 25	10 35				10 45
The Hawthorns 🚋	d			09 39						09 49	09 59	10 09					10 19	10 29	10 39				10 49
Smethwick Galton Bridge 7	d			09 42						09 52	10 02	10 12					10 22	10 32	10 42				10 52
Coventry	a						09 23														10 24		
Birmingham Intl. 68 ✈	a						09 37														10 37		
Birmingham New Street 12 68	a				09 18		09 48							10 18							10 48		
	d								09 49													10 49	
Langley Green	d										10 05							10 35					
Rowley Regis	d			09 48						09 58	10 08	10 18					10 28	10 38	10 48				10 58
Old Hill	d										10 12							10 42					
Cradley Heath	d			09 53						10 03	10 15	10 23					10 33	10 45	10 53				11 03
Lye	d										10 18							10 48					
Stourbridge Junction 2	d			09 59						10 09	10a22	10 29					10 39	10a52	10 59				11 09
Hagley	d			10 03								10 33							11 03				
Blakedown	d			10 06								10 36							11 06				
Kidderminster	d			10a10						10 17		10a40					10 47		11a10				11 17
Hartlebury	d																10 52						
University	d								09 55													10 55	
Barnt Green	d																						
Bromsgrove	d								10 10													11 10	
Droitwich Spa	d								10 20	10 28							11 00					11 20	11 28
Worcester Shrub Hill 7	a																						11 36
	d							10 14								10 46							
Worcester Foregate Street 7	a							10 17	10 30	10 37						10 49	11 09					11 30	
	d							10 17	10 32	10 42						10 56						11 32	
Malvern Link	d							10 26	10 42	10 52						11 04						11 42	
Great Malvern	a							10 32	10 44	10 55						11 08						11 44	
	d								10 45							11 09						11 45	
Colwall	d								10 50							11 15						11 50	
Ledbury	a								10 57							11 22						11 57	
	d								10 59							11 24						11 59	
Hereford 7	a								11 19							11 43						12 19	

BZ Business Zone available offering greater comfort and an enhanced working environment. Supplement payable.

Table 71

Mondays to Fridays

9 December to 16 May

Stratford-upon-Avon, Marylebone and Leamington Spa - Birmingham - Stourbridge, Worcester and Hereford

Network Diagram - see first Page of Table 71

		GW	LM	CH	LM	LM	LM	CH	LM	CH		XC	CH	XC	GW	LM	LM	GW	LM	CH		XC	LM	LM
		◇1 ⊥		◇ ⊥						◇		◇1 ⊥	◇ ⊥	R 1 ⊥	◇			◇1 ⊓		◇ ⊥ BZ		◇1 ⊥		
Stratford-upon-Avon	d		10 03				10 26												11 03					
Stratford-upon-Avon Parkway	d		10 07				10 30												11 07					
Wilmcote	d						10 33																	
Wootton Wawen	d						10x37																	
Henley-in-Arden	d						10 41																	
Danzey	d						10x45																	
Wood End	d						10x49																	
The Lakes	d						10x51																	
Earlswood (West Midlands)	d						10 54																	
Wythall	d						10 57																	
Whitlocks End	d				10 40		11 00										11 19						11 40	
Shirley	d				10 42		11 03										11 22						11 42	
Yardley Wood	d				10 45		11 05										11 24						11 45	
Hall Green	d				10 48		11 09										11 27						11 48	
Spring Road	d				10 51		11 11										11 29						11 51	
London Marylebone 10 ⊖115	d			09 15						09 10			09 45							10 15				
Banbury	d			10 07						10 24		10 29	10 43	10 54						11 07		11 25		
Leamington Spa 8	a			10 24						10 41		10 46	11 00	11 10						11 24		11 41		
	d			10 25				10 32		10 42		10 47	11 01	11 12						11 25		11 43		
Warwick	d							10 38		10a46			11 06											
Warwick Parkway	d			10 32									11 09							11 32				
Hatton	d							10 44																
Lapworth	d							10 50																
Dorridge	d		10 29			10 46		10 55	11 09				11 19						11 29					11 46
Widney Manor	d		10 33			10 51			11 14										11 33					11 51
Solihull	d		10 37	10 45		10 54		11 01	11 17				11 24						11 37	11 45				11 54
Olton	d		10 40			10 57			11 20										11 40					11 57
Acocks Green	d		10 43			11 00			11 23										11 43					12 00
Tyseley	d					11 02											11 32							12 02
Small Heath	d					11 05											11 35							12 05
Bordesley	d																							
Birmingham Moor Street	d		10 49	10 54	10 59	11 09	11 18	11a17	11 29				11 33				11 39		11 49	11a59			11 58	12 09
Birmingham Snow Hill ⛴	a		10 52	11 01	11 02	11 12	11 20		11 32				11 42				11 42		11 52				12 00	12 12
	d		10 53		11 03	11 13	11 23		11 33								11 43		11 53				12 03	12 13
Jewellery Quarter ⛴	d		10 55		11 05	11 15	11 25		11 35								11 45		11 55				12 05	12 15
The Hawthorns ⛴	d		10 59		11 09	11 19	11 29		11 39								11 49		11 59				12 09	12 19
Smethwick Galton Bridge 7	d		11 02		11 12	11 22	11 32		11 42								11 52		12 02				12 12	12 22
Coventry	a													11 23										
Birmingham Intl. 68 ✈	a													11 37										
Birmingham New Street 12 68	a											11 18		11 48								12 18		
	d															11 49								
Langley Green	d		11 05				11 35												12 05					
Rowley Regis	d		11 08		11 18	11 28	11 38		11 48								11 58		12 08				12 18	12 28
Old Hill	d		11 12				11 42												12 12					
Cradley Heath	d		11 15		11 23	11 33	11 45		11 53								12 03		12 15				12 23	12 33
Lye	d		11 18				11 48												12 18					
Stourbridge Junction 2	d		11a22		11 29	11 39	11a52		11 59								12 09		12a22				12 29	12 39
Hagley	d				11 33				12 03														12 33	
Blakedown	d				11 36				12 06														12 36	
Kidderminster	d				11a40	11 47			12a10								12 17						12a40	12 47
Hartlebury	d					11 52																		12 52
University	d															11 55								
Barnt Green	d																							
Bromsgrove	d															12 10								
Droitwich Spa	d					12 00										12 20	12 28							13 00
Worcester Shrub Hill 7	a																12 36							
	d	11 36													12 14			12 46						
Worcester Foregate Street 7	a	11 41				12 09									12 16	12 30		12 49						13 09
	d														12 17	12 32		12 50						13 11
Malvern Link	d														12 26	12 42		12 59						13 21
Great Malvern	a														12 33	12 44		13 03						13 24
	d															12 45		13 10						
Colwall	d															12 50		13 16						
Ledbury	a															12 57		13 24						
	d															12 59		13 31						
Hereford 7	a															13 19		13 48						

BZ Business Zone available offering greater comfort and an enhanced working environment. Supplement payable.

Table 71

Mondays to Fridays

9 December to 16 May

Stratford-upon-Avon, Marylebone and Leamington Spa - Birmingham - Stourbridge, Worcester and Hereford

Network Diagram - see first Page of Table 71

		LM	LM	LM	GW	LM	CH		CH	XC	LM	CH	LM	LM	GW	LM	CH		LM	XC	LM	CH	XC	LM	LM
					◇1		◇		◇	◇1		◇			◇					◇1		◇	◇1		
					🚲		🚲			🚲										🚲			🚲		
Stratford-upon-Avon	d	11 26							11 35		12 03					12 26									13 03
Stratford-upon-Avon Parkway	d	11 30							11 39		12 07					12 30									13 07
Wilmcote	d	11 33							11 42							12 33									
Wootton Wawen	d	11x37														12x37									
Henley-in-Arden	d	11 41														12 41									
Danzey	d	11x45														12x45									
Wood End	d	11x49														12x49									
The Lakes	d	11x51														12x51									
Earlswood (West Midlands)	d	11 54														12 54									
Wythall	d	11 57														12 57									
Whitlocks End	d	12 00				12 19							12 40			13 00								13 19	
Shirley	d	12 03				12 22							12 42			13 03								13 22	
Yardley Wood	d	12 05				12 24							12 45			13 05								13 24	
Hall Green	d	12 09				12 27							12 48			13 09								13 27	
Spring Road	d	12 11				12 29							12 51			13 11								13 29	
London Marylebone 10 ⊖115	d						10 45					11 15										11 45			
Banbury	d						11 45			11 53		12 06								12 25		12 43	12 54		
Leamington Spa 8	a						12 03		12 06	12 10		12 23								12 42		13 00	13 10		
	d						12 04			12 11		12 23					12 32			12 43		13 01	13 12		
Warwick	d						12 09										12 38					13 06			
Warwick Parkway	d						12 13					12 29										13 09			
Hatton	d																12 44								
Lapworth	d																12 50								
Dorridge	d		12 09				12 24				12 29			12 46			12 55		13 09			13 19			13 29
Widney Manor	d		12 14								12 33			12 51					13 14						13 33
Solihull	d		12 17				12 31				12 37	12 43		12 54			13 01		13 17			13 24			13 37
Olton	d		12 20								12 40			12 57					13 20						13 40
Acocks Green	d		12 23								12 43			13 00					13 23						13 43
Tyseley	d					12 32								13 02										13 32	
Small Heath	d					12 35								13 05										13 35	
Bordesley	d																								
Birmingham Moor Street	d	12 18	12 29			12 39	12 42				12 49	12a59	12 58	13 09		13 18	13a17		13 29			13 33		13 39	13 49
Birmingham Snow Hill 🚊	a	12 20	12 32			12 42	12 48				12 52		13 00	13 12		13 20			13 32			13 42		13 42	13 52
	d	12 23	12 33			12 43					12 53		13 03	13 13		13 23			13 33					13 43	13 53
Jewellery Quarter 🚊	d	12 25	12 35			12 45					12 55		13 05	13 15		13 25			13 35					13 45	13 55
The Hawthorns 🚊	d	12 29	12 39			12 49					12 59		13 09	13 19		13 29			13 39					13 49	13 59
Smethwick Galton Bridge 7	d	12 32	12 42			12 52					13 02		13 12	13 22		13 32			13 42					13 52	14 02
Coventry	a									12 24													13 23		
Birmingham Intl. 68 ✈	a									12 37													13 37		
Birmingham New Street 12 68	a									12 48										13 18			13 49		
	d			12 49																	13 49				
Langley Green	d	12 35									13 05					13 35									14 05
Rowley Regis	d	12 38	12 48			12 58					13 08		13 18	13 28		13 38			13 48					13 58	14 08
Old Hill	d	12 42									13 12					13 42									14 12
Cradley Heath	d	12 45	12 53			13 03					13 15		13 23	13 33		13 45			13 53					14 03	14 15
Lye	d	12 48									13 18					13 48									14 18
Stourbridge Junction 2	d	12a52	12 59			13 09					13a22		13a31	13 39		13a52			13 59					14 09	14a22
Hagley	d		13 03																14 03						
Blakedown	d		13 06																14 06						
Kidderminster	d		13a10			13 17								13 47					14a10					14 17	
Hartlebury	d													13 52											
University	d			12 55																	13 55				
Barnt Green	d																								
Bromsgrove	d			13 10																	14 10				
Droitwich Spa	d			13 20		13 28								14 00							14 20			14 28	
Worcester Shrub Hill 7	a													14 08										14 36	
	d				13 33										14 14									14 42	
Worcester Foregate Street 7	a			13 30	13 36	13 37									14 17						14 30			14 44	
	d			13 32	13 42										14 17						14 32			14 44	
Malvern Link	d			13 42	13 51										14 26						14 42			14 53	
Great Malvern	a			13 44	13 56										14 35						14 44			14 55	
	d			13 45																	14 45				
Colwall	d			13 50																	14 50				
Ledbury	a			13 58																	14 57				
	d			14 00																	14 59				
Hereford 7	a			14 21																	15 19				

Table 71

Mondays to Fridays

9 December to 16 May

Stratford-upon-Avon, Marylebone and Leamington Spa - Birmingham - Stourbridge, Worcester and Hereford

Network Diagram - see first Page of Table 71

		CH	CH		XC	LM	GW	LM	LM	LM	CH	XC	LM		LM	LM	CH	LM	GW	LM	LM	CH	LM		XC
					R																				
		◇	◇		1		◇1				◇	◇1					◇		◇						◇1
		⚲			⚲		⚲				⚲	⚲					⚲ BZ								⚲
Stratford-upon-Avon	d								13 26							14 03					14 26				
Stratford-upon-Avon Parkway	d								13 30							14 07					14 30				
Wilmcote	d								13 33												14 33				
Wootton Wawen	d								13x37												14x37				
Henley-in-Arden	d								13 41												14 41				
Danzey	d								13x45												14x45				
Wood End	d								13x49												14x49				
The Lakes	d								13x51												14x51				
Earlswood (West Midlands)	d								13 54												14 54				
Wythall	d								13 57												14 57				
Whitlocks End	d					13 40			14 00						14 19			14 40			15 00				
Shirley	d					13 42			14 03						14 22			14 42			15 03				
Yardley Wood	d					13 45			14 05						14 25			14 45			15 05				
Hall Green	d					13 48			14 09						14 28			14 48			15 09				
Spring Road	d					13 51			14 11						14 30			14 51			15 11				
London Marylebone 10 ⊖115	d	12 15	12 18								12 45						13 15								
Banbury	d	13 07	13 21		13 26						13 43	13 54					14 06								14 26
Leamington Spa 8	a	13 24	13 38		13 43						14 00	14 10					14 23								14 41
	d	13 25	13 39		13 44						14 01	14 12					14 23					14 32			14 42
Warwick	d		13 43								14 06											14 38			
Warwick Parkway	d	13 32									14 10						14 29								
Hatton	d		13a51																			14 44			
Lapworth	d																					14 50			
Dorridge	d							13 46		14 09	14 20					14 29				14 46		14 55	15 09		
Widney Manor	d							13 51		14 14						14 33				14 51			15 14		
Solihull	d	13 45						13 54		14 17	14 26					14 37	14 43			14 54		15 01	15 17		
Olton	d							13 57		14 20						14 40				14 57			15 20		
Acocks Green	d							14 00		14 23						14 43				15 00			15 23		
Tyseley	d							14 02							14 33					15 02					
Small Heath	d							14 05							14 35					15 05					
Bordesley	d																								
Birmingham Moor Street	d	13a59				13 58		14 09	14 18	14 29	14 35				14 39	14 49	14a59	14 58		15 09	15 18	15a17	15 29		
Birmingham Snow Hill 🚋	a					14 00		14 12	14 20	14 32	14 42				14 42	14 52		15 00		15 12	15 20		15 32		
	d					14 03		14 13	14 23	14 33					14 43	14 53		15 03		15 13	15 23		15 33		
Jewellery Quarter 🚋	d					14 05		14 15	14 25	14 35					14 45	14 55		15 05		15 15	15 25		15 35		
The Hawthorns 🚋	d					14 09		14 19	14 29	14 39					14 49	14 59		15 09		15 19	15 29		15 39		
Smethwick Galton Bridge 7	d					14 12		14 22	14 32	14 42					14 52	15 02		15 12		15 22	15 32		15 42		
Coventry	a											14 23													
Birmingham Intl. 68 ✈	a											14 37													
Birmingham New Street 12 68	a				14 18							14 48													15 18
	d												14 49												
Langley Green	d								14 35							15 05					15 35				
Rowley Regis	d					14 18		14 28	14 38	14 48					14 58	15 08		15 18		15 28	15 38		15 48		
Old Hill	d								14 42							15 12					15 42				
Cradley Heath	d					14 23		14 33	14 45	14 53					15 03	15 15		15 23		15 33	15 45		15 53		
Lye	d								14 48							15 18					15 48				
Stourbridge Junction 2	d					14 29		14 39	14a52	14 59					15 09	15a22		15 29		15 39	15a52		15 59		
Hagley	d					14 33				15 03								15 33		15 42			16 03		
Blakedown	d					14 36				15 06								15 36		15 45			16 06		
Kidderminster	d					14a40		14 47		15a10					15 17			15a40		15 50			16a10		
Hartlebury	d							14 52												15 55					
University	d												14 55												
Barnt Green	d																								
Bromsgrove	d												15 10												
Droitwich Spa	d							15 00					15 20		15 28					16 04					
Worcester Shrub Hill 7	a							15 10												16 12					
	d						14 49												16 14	16 21					
Worcester Foregate Street 7	a						14 52						15 30		15 37				16 17	16 23					
	d						14 57						15 32						16 17						
Malvern Link	d						15 07						15 42						16 26						
Great Malvern	a						15 10						15 44						16 32						
	d												15 45												
Colwall	d												15 50												
Ledbury	a												15 57												
	d												15 59												
Hereford 7	a												16 19												

BZ Business Zone available offering greater comfort and an enhanced working environment. Supplement payable.

Table 71

Mondays to Fridays

9 December to 16 May

Stratford-upon-Avon, Marylebone and Leamington Spa - Birmingham - Stourbridge, Worcester and Hereford

Network Diagram - see first Page of Table 71

		CH	CH	XC	LM	LM	LM	CH	XC		LM	GW	LM	LM	LM	LM	CH	XC	LM		LM	LM	LM	CH	LM
		◇	◇	◇[1]				◇	◇[1]			◇[1]					◇	◇[1]						◇	
				⊤					⊤									⊤						⊤	
								BZ																	
Stratford-upon-Avon	d		14 35				15 03								15 26							16 03			
Stratford-upon-Avon Parkway	d		14 39				15 07								15 30							16 07			
Wilmcote	d		14 42												15 33										
Wootton Wawen	d														15x37										
Henley-in-Arden	d														15 41										
Danzey	d														15x45										
Wood End	d														15x49										
The Lakes	d														15x51										
Earlswood (West Midlands)	d														15 54										
Wythall	d														15 57										
Whitlocks End	d					15 19					15 40				16 00						16 18		16 40		
Shirley	d					15 22					15 42				16 03						16 21		16 42		
Yardley Wood	d					15 24					15 45				16 05						16 23		16 45		
Hall Green	d					15 27					15 48				16 09						16 26		16 48		
Spring Road	d					15 29					15 51				16 11						16 28		16 51		
London Marylebone [10] ⊖115	d	13 45						14 15									14 45							15 15	
Banbury	d	14 44		14 57				15 06	15 25								15 44	15 55						16 07	
Leamington Spa [8]	a	15 02	15 07	15 13				15 23	15 42								16 01	16 10						16 24	
	d	15 02		15 14				15 23	15 43								16 02	16 12						16 25	
Warwick	d	15 06															16 06								
Warwick Parkway	d	15 10						15 29									16 10							16 32	
Hatton	d																								
Lapworth	d																								
Dorridge	d	15 20					15 29							15 46		16 09	16 21					16 29			
Widney Manor	d						15 33							15 51		16 14						16 33			
Solihull	d	15 25					15 37	15 43						15 54		16 17	16 26					16 37		16 45	
Olton	d						15 40							15 57		16 20						16 40			
Acocks Green	d						15 43							16 00		16 23						16 43			
Tyseley	d					15 32								16 02							16 31				
Small Heath	d					15 35								16 05							16 34				
Bordesley	d																								
Birmingham Moor Street	d	15 34				15 39	15 49	15a59			15 58			16 09	16 18	16 29	16 35				16 39	16 49	16 58	16 54	
Birmingham Snow Hill 🚋	a	15 42				15 42	15 52				16 00			16 11	16 20	16 32	16 42				16 42	16 52	17 00	17 02	
	d					15 43	15 53				16 03			16 13	16 23	16 33					16 43	16 53	17 03		
Jewellery Quarter 🚋	d					15 45	15 55				16 05			16 15	16 25	16 35					16 46	16 55	17 05		
The Hawthorns 🚋	d					15 49	15 59				16 09			16 19	16 29	16 39					16 50	16 59	17 09		
Smethwick Galton Bridge [7]	d					15 52	16 02				16 12			16 22	16 32	16 42					16 53	17 02	17 12		
Coventry	a			15 25														16 23							
Birmingham Intl. 68 ✈	a			15 37														16 37							
Birmingham New Street [12] 68	a			15 48					16 18									16 48							
	d				15 49								16 19						16 49						17 19
Langley Green	d						16 05								16 35							17 05			
Rowley Regis	d					15 58	16 08				16 18			16 28	16 38	16 48					16 59	17 08	17 18		
Old Hill	d						16 12								16 42							17 12			
Cradley Heath	d					16 03	16 15				16 23			16 33	16 45	16 53					17 04	17 15	17 23		
Lye	d						16 18								16 48							17 18			
Stourbridge Junction [2]	d					16 08	16a22				16 29			16 39	16a52	16 59					17 10	17a22	17 29		
Hagley	d					16 12					16 33					17 03					17 14		17 33		
Blakedown	d					16 15					16 36					17 06					17 17		17 36		
Kidderminster	d					16 20					16a40			16 47		17a10					17 22		17a40		
Hartlebury	d													16 52							17 27				
University	d				15 55								16 25						16 55						17 25
Barnt Green	d																								
Bromsgrove	d				16 10								16 41						17 10						17 40
Droitwich Spa	d				16 20	16 31							16 51	17 00					17 20		17 37				17 52
Worcester Shrub Hill [7]	a												16 58						17 27						17 59
	d											16 41	17 06						17 32						18 04
Worcester Foregate Street [7]	a				16 30	16 40						16 44	17 08	17 09					17 34		17 46				18 06
	d				16 32								17 09						17 35						18 07
Malvern Link	d				16 42								17 18						17 44						18 16
Great Malvern	a				16 44								17 21						17 46						18 18
	d				16 45														17 47						18 19
Colwall	d				16 50														17 52						18 24
Ledbury	a				16 57														17 59						18 31
	d				16 59														18 00						18 31
Hereford [7]	a				17 19														18 22						18 51

BZ Business Zone available offering greater comfortand an enhanced working environment. Supplement payable.

Table 71

Mondays to Fridays

9 December to 16 May

Stratford-upon-Avon, Marylebone and Leamington Spa - Birmingham - Stourbridge, Worcester and Hereford

Network Diagram - see first Page of Table 71

		LM	GW	LM	CH		XC	LM	CH	LM	LM	CH	XC	LM	LM		CH	LM	LM	CH	LM	XC	CH	CH	GW
							◇■1 ⊤		◇			◇ ⊤	◇■1 ⊤				◇			◇		◇■1 ⊤	◇ ⊤ BZ	◇	■1
Stratford-upon-Avon	d			16 26															17 26					17 35	
Stratford-upon-Avon Parkway	d			16 30															17 30					17 39	
Wilmcote	d			16 33															17 33					17 42	
Wootton Wawen	d			16x37															17x37						
Henley-in-Arden	d			16 41															17 41						
Danzey	d			16x45															17x45						
Wood End	d			16x49															17x49						
The Lakes	d			16x51															17x51						
Earlswood (West Midlands)	d			16 54															17 54						
Wythall	d			16 57															17 57						
Whitlocks End	d			17 00							17 18							17 42	18 00						
Shirley	d			17 03							17 21							17 44	18 03						
Yardley Wood	d			17 05							17 23							17 47	18 05						
Hall Green	d			17 09							17 26							17 50	18 09						
Spring Road	d			17 11							17 28							17 52	18 11						
London Marylebone ■10 ⊖115	d								15 18			15 45					16 15			16 18			16 47		
Banbury	d						16 24		16 30			16 43	16 55							17 20		17 29	17 45		
Leamington Spa ■8	a						16 40		16 48			17 00	17 12				17 21			17 37		17 46	18 02	18 07	
	d				16 32		16 43		16 49			17 00	17 13				17 22			17 37		17 47	18 03		
Warwick	d				16 38				16 54			17 04								17 41					
Warwick Parkway	d											17 08					17 28			17 45			18 09		
Hatton	d				16 44				17a01																
Lapworth	d				16 50																				
Dorridge	d	16 46			16 55					17 09		17 18			17 28					17 55	18 03		18 20		
Widney Manor	d	16 51								17 14					17 33						18 07				
Solihull	d	16 54			17 01					17 17		17 24			17 36		17 41			18 01	18 11		18 25		
Olton	d	16 57								17 20					17 39						18 14				
Acocks Green	d	17 00								17 23					17 42						18 17				
Tyseley	d	17 02								17 25	17 31							17 56			18 20				
Small Heath	d	17 05								17 28	17 34							17 58			18 23				
Bordesley	d																								
Birmingham Moor Street	d	17 09		17 18	17a17					17 32	17 38	17 36			17 49		17 54	18 03	18 18	18 14	18 27		18a40		
Birmingham Snow Hill 🚊	a	17 12		17 20						17 35	17 41	17 44			17 51		18 02	18 05	18 20	18 21	18 29				
	d	17 13		17 23						17 36	17 43				17 53			18 08	18 23		18 31				
Jewellery Quarter 🚊	d	17 15		17 25						17 38	17 45				17 56			18 10	18 25		18 33				
The Hawthorns 🚊	d	17 19		17 29						17 42	17 49				18 00			18 14	18 29		18 38				
Smethwick Galton Bridge ■7	d	17 22		17 32						17 45	17 52				18 03			18 17	18 32		18 41				
Coventry	a												17 24												
Birmingham Intl. 68 ✈	a												17 37												
Birmingham New Street ■12 68	a						17 18						17 49									18 18			
	d							17 49						17 59											
Langley Green	d			17 35							17 55							18 20	18 35		18 44				
Rowley Regis	d	17 28		17 38						17 51	17 59				18 09			18 24	18 39		18 47				
Old Hill	d			17 42							18 02							18 27	18 42		18 50				
Cradley Heath	d	17 33		17 45						17 56	18 05				18 14			18 30	18 45		18 54				
Lye	d			17 48							18 08							18 33	18 48		18 57				
Stourbridge Junction ■2	d	17 38		17a52						18 01	18 12				18 20			18 37	18 52		19a02				
Hagley	d	17 42								18 05	18 16				18 24			18 41	18 56						
Blakedown	d	17 45								18 08	18 19				18 27			18 44	18 59						
Kidderminster	d	17 50								18 13	18a24				18 32			18a48	19a03						
Hartlebury	d									18 18					18 37										
University	d							17 55						18 05											
Barnt Green	d																								
Bromsgrove	d													18 21											
Droitwich Spa	d	18 01						18 17		18 26				18 34	18 46										
Worcester Shrub Hill ■7	a	18 13						18 25						18 42											
	d		18 19					18 32						18 53											19 08
Worcester Foregate Street ■7	a		18 21					18 34		18 36				18 55	18 55										19 11
	d		18 22					18 35						18 56											19 12
Malvern Link	d		18 31					18 44						19 05											19 21
Great Malvern	a		18 36					18 47						19 08											19 24
	d							18 49																	
Colwall	d							18 54																	
Ledbury	a							19 02																	
	d							19 04																	
Hereford ■7	a							19 24																	

BZ Business Zone available offering greater comfortand an enhanced working environment.
Supplement payable.

Table 71

Mondays to Fridays

9 December to 16 May

Stratford-upon-Avon, Marylebone and Leamington Spa - Birmingham - Stourbridge, Worcester and Hereford

Network Diagram - see first Page of Table 71

		LM	GW	XC	CH	LM	LM	CH	LM	CH	CH	XC	LM	LM	GW	LM	LM	CH	XC	CH	LM	GW	LM
			◇1	◇1				◇			◇	◇1						◇	◇1	◇		◇1	
																						A	
			☕	🛒				🛒				🛒							🛒			☕	
								BZ															
Stratford-upon-Avon	d					17 55								18 26			18 51			19 12			
Stratford-upon-Avon Parkway	d					17 59								18 30			18 55			19 16			
Wilmcote	d													18 33			18 58			19 20			
Wootton Wawen	d													18x37			19x03						
Henley-in-Arden	d					18 07								18 41			19 07						
Danzey	d													18x45									
Wood End	d													18x49									
The Lakes	d													18x51									
Earlswood (West Midlands)	d													18 54									
Wythall	d													18 57									
Whitlocks End	d					18 17			18 36					19 00			19 17						19 25
Shirley	d					18 20			18 38					19 03			19 19						19 27
Yardley Wood	d					18 23			18 41					19 05			19 22						19 30
Hall Green	d					18 26			18 44					19 09			19 25						19 33
Spring Road	d					18 28			18 46					19 11			19 28						19 35
London Marylebone 10 ⊖115	d							17 15			17 18							17 47					
Banbury	d			17 55						18 09	18 20	18 26						18 45	18 55				
Leamington Spa 8	a			18 11				18 22		18 26	18 37	18 45						19 02	19 11				
	d			18 12	18 17			18 22		18 27	18 37	18 46						19 03	19 12				
Warwick	d				18 22					18 32	18 41												
Warwick Parkway	d							18 28			18 45							19 09					
Hatton	d				18a29					18 38										19 36			
Lapworth	d									18 44													
Dorridge	d						18 23			18 50	18 55					18 59		19 20					
Widney Manor	d						18 28									19 04							
Solihull	d						18 31	18 41		18 55	19 01					19 07		19 26					
Olton	d						18 34									19 10							
Acocks Green	d						18 37									19 13							
Tyseley	d					18 32	18 39		18 49							19 16							19 38
Small Heath	d					18 34	18 42									19 18							19 39
Bordesley	d																						
Birmingham Moor Street	d					18 39	18 46	18 50	18 55	19 05	19a16			19 18		19 23	19 35	19 39					19 44
Birmingham Snow Hill ⛴	a					18 41	18 49	18 54	18 57	19 13				19 20		19 25	19 37	19 46					19 47
	d					18 43		18 56	18 59							19 27	19 40						
Jewellery Quarter ⛴	d					18 45			19 01							19 29	19 42						
The Hawthorns ⛴	d					18 49			19 05							19 33	19 46						
Smethwick Galton Bridge 7	d					18 52			19 08							19 36	19 49						
Coventry	a			18 24															19 23				
Birmingham Intl. 68 ✈	a			18 37															19 37				
Birmingham New Street 12 68	a			18 49								19 18							19 48				
	d	18 19											19 19								19 59		
Langley Green	d								19 11							19 39							
Rowley Regis	d					18 58		19 08	19 14							19 43	19 55						
Old Hill	d								19 18							19 46							
Cradley Heath	d					19 03			19 21							19 49	20 00						
Lye	d								19 24							19 52							
Stourbridge Junction 2	d					19 09		19 18	19a29							19 56	20a05						
Hagley	d					19 12										20 00							
Blakedown	d					19 15										20 03							
Kidderminster	d					19 20		19a31								20 08							
Hartlebury	d																						
University	d	18 25											19 25								20 05		
Barnt Green	d																						
Bromsgrove	d	18 45											19 41								20 19		
Droitwich Spa	d	18 57				19 31							19 52			20 19					20 29		
Worcester Shrub Hill 7	a	19 10											20 03								20 37		
	d		19 36										20 12		20 20							20 42	
Worcester Foregate Street 7	a		19 39			19 40							20 14		20 22	20 28						20 45	
	d		19 40										20 15		20 24							20 46	
Malvern Link	d		19 50										20 24		20 34							20 55	
Great Malvern	a		19 53										20 26		20 40							20 59	
	d		19 54										20 27									21 00	
Colwall	d		20 01										20 32									21 06	
Ledbury	a		20 08										20 39									21 14	
	d		20 10										20 40									21 16	
Hereford 7	a		20 29										21 03									21 34	

BZ Business Zone available offering greater comfortand an enhanced working environment. Supplement payable.

A The Cathedrals Express

Table 71

Mondays to Fridays

9 December to 16 May

Stratford-upon-Avon, Marylebone and Leamington Spa - Birmingham - Stourbridge, Worcester and Hereford

Network Diagram - see first Page of Table 71

		LM	CH	CH	LM	XC	CH	XC	LM	GW	LM	CH	LM	XC	CH	XC	CH	GW	LM	LM	CH	LM	XC
			◇	◇		◇[1]	◇	◇[1]		◇[1]		◇		◇[1]	◇	◇[1]	◇	◇[1]			◇		◇[1]
			⊼ BZ			⊼	⊼	⊼		⊏													
Stratford-upon-Avon	d	19 05			19 27								20 27				20 49					21 26	
Stratford-upon-Avon Parkway	d	19 08			19 30								20 30				20 53					21 30	
Wilmcote	d				19 33								20 33				20 56					21 33	
Wootton Wawen	d				19x38								20x38										
Henley-in-Arden	d				19 42								20 42									21 40	
Danzey	d				19x45								20x45										
Wood End	d				19x49								20x49									21x46	
The Lakes	d				19x51								20x51									21x48	
Earlswood (West Midlands)	d				19 54								20 54									21 51	
Wythall	d				19 57								20 57									21 54	
Whitlocks End	d				20 00								21 00									21 57	
Shirley	d				20 02								21 02									22 00	
Yardley Wood	d				20 05								21 05									22 02	
Hall Green	d				20 08								21 08									22 06	
Spring Road	d				20 11								21 11									22 08	
London Marylebone [10] ⊖115	d		18 15	18 18			18 47					19 15			19 45						20 15		
Banbury	d		19 09	19 25		19 31	19 45	19 56				20 09		20 28	20 43	20 54					21 12		21 33
Leamington Spa [8]	a		19 26	19 42		19 49	20 02	20 12				20 26		20 45	21 00	21 10	21 20				21 29		21 51
	d		19 27	19 42		19 50	20 03	20 13				20 27		20 46	21 01	21 12					21 30		21 52
Warwick	d			19 47			20 08								21 06								
Warwick Parkway	d		19 33	19 50			20 12					20 33			21 09						21 35		
Hatton	d			19a57											21 15								
Lapworth	d	19 25													21 21								
Dorridge	d	19 30	19 44				20 23				20 29	20 43			21 26					21 31	21 45		
Widney Manor	d	19 35									20 34									21 36			
Solihull	d	19 38	19 50				20 28				20 37	20 49			21 32					21 39	21 51		
Olton	d	19 41									20 40									21 42			
Acocks Green	d	19 44									20 42									21 45			
Tyseley	d	19 47									20 45									21 48		22 11	
Small Heath	d	19 49									20 47									21 50		22 13	
Bordesley	d																						
Birmingham Moor Street	d	19 54	19 59		20 18		20 38				20 52	21a03	21 18		21 41					21 55	22 00	22 18	
Birmingham Snow Hill 🚊	a	19 56	20 03		20 20		20 41				20 54		21 20		21 48					21 57	22 03	22 20	
	d	19 58	20 05		20 23		20 43				20 55		21 23							21 58	22 10	22 23	
Jewellery Quarter 🚊	d	20 00			20 25						20 58		21 25							22 01		22 25	
The Hawthorns 🚊	d	20 04	20 12		20 29		20 51				21 02		21 29							22 05	22 17	22 29	
Smethwick Galton Bridge [7]	d	20 07	20 16		20 32		20 55				21 05		21 32							22 07	22 20	22 32	
Coventry	a							20 24								21 23							
Birmingham Intl. 68 ✈	a							20 37								21 37							
Birmingham New Street [12] 68	a					20 18		20 48						21 22		21 49							22 17
	d								20 59										22 00				
Langley Green	d	20 10			20 35						21 08		21 35							22 10		22 35	
Rowley Regis	d	20 14	20 23		20 38		21 02				21 11		21 38							22 14	22 25	22 38	
Old Hill	d	20 17			20 42						21 14		21 42							22 17		22 42	
Cradley Heath	d	20 20			20 45						21 17		21 45							22 20	22 31	22 45	
Lye	d	20 23			20 48						21 20		21 48							22 23		22 48	
Stourbridge Junction [2]	d	20 27	20 34		20a52		21 13				21 24		21a52							22 27	22 37	22a52	
Hagley	d	20 31									21 28									22 30			
Blakedown	d	20 34									21 31									22 33			
Kidderminster	d	20 39	20a48				21a26				21 36									22 38	22a50		
Hartlebury	d																						
University	d								21 05										22 06				
Barnt Green	d																						
Bromsgrove	d								21 20										22 20				
Droitwich Spa	d	20 50							21 30		21 47								22 34	22 50			
Worcester Shrub Hill [7]	a	20 59									22 00								22 47	22 58			
	d									21 48	22 04							22 41		23 06			
Worcester Foregate Street [7]	a								21 38	21 51	22 06							22 44		23 08			
	d								21 41	21 54								22 45		23 08			
Malvern Link	d								21 51	22 04								22 54		23 17			
Great Malvern	a								21 53	22 07								22 59		23 19			
	d								21 54	22 20													
Colwall	d								21 59	22 27													
Ledbury	a								22 06	22 35													
	d								22 09	22 37													
Hereford [7]	a								22 29	22 55													

BZ Business Zone available offering greater comfortand an enhanced working environment. Supplement payable.

Table 71

Mondays to Fridays

9 December to 16 May

Stratford-upon-Avon, Marylebone and Leamington Spa - Birmingham - Stourbridge, Worcester and Hereford

Network Diagram - see first Page of Table 71

		CH	CH		XC	LM	LM	CH	LM	CH	XC	CH	CH	LM	CH	CH
		◇	◇		◇■1			◇		◇	◇■1	◇			◇	◇
Stratford-upon-Avon	d								22 33				23 15	23 30		
Stratford-upon-Avon Parkway	d								22 37					23 34		
Wilmcote	d								22 40							
Wootton Wawen	d															
Henley-in-Arden	d								22 46							
Danzey	d															
Wood End	d															
The Lakes	d															
Earlswood (West Midlands)	d															
Wythall	d								22 56							
Whitlocks End	d								22 58							
Shirley	d								23 01							
Yardley Wood	d								23 03							
Hall Green	d								23 06							
Spring Road	d								23 08							
London Marylebone ■10 ⊖115	d	20 18	20 45					21 15		21 45		22 15			22 45	23 07
Banbury	d	21 37	21 47		21 54			22 14		22 47	22 53	23 13			23 47	00 03
Leamington Spa ■8	a	21 55	22 04		22 10			22 31		23 04	23 09	23 30	23 38		00 04	00 20
	d	21 56	22 05		22 11			22 32		23 05	23 11	23 31			00 05	00 21
Warwick	d	22 01	22 10							23 09					00 09	00 25
Warwick Parkway	d		22 14					22 38		23 13		23 37			00 13	00 29
Hatton	d	22a08								23 19						
Lapworth	d									23 25						
Dorridge	d		22 24				22 33	22 48		23 30		23 47			00 23	
Widney Manor	d						22 38			23 34						
Solihull	d		22 29				22 41	22 54		23 38		23 53			00 29	00 41
Olton	d						22 44									
Acocks Green	d						22 47									
Tyseley	d						22 49		23 12							
Small Heath	d						22 52		23 14							
Bordesley	d															
Birmingham Moor Street	d		22 38				22 56	23 03	23 19	23 47		00a07		00 06	00a43	00a55
Birmingham Snow Hill ⛴	a		22 46				22 59	23 05	23 21	23 54				00 08		
	d						23 00	23 15								
Jewellery Quarter ⛴	d						23 03	23 18								
The Hawthorns ⛴	d						23 07	23 22								
Smethwick Galton Bridge ■7	d						23 10	23 25								
Coventry	a				22 22						23 24					
Birmingham Intl. 68 ✈	a				22 33						23 34					
Birmingham New Street ■12 68	a				22 45						00 02					
	d					23 00										
Langley Green	d						23 13	23 29								
Rowley Regis	d						23 16	23 33								
Old Hill	d						23 19	23 36								
Cradley Heath	d						23 23	23 40								
Lye	d						23 26	23 43								
Stourbridge Junction ■2	d						23 30	23a52								
Hagley	d						23 33									
Blakedown	d						23 36									
Kidderminster	d						23 41									
Hartlebury	d															
University	d					23 06										
Barnt Green	d															
Bromsgrove	d					23 19										
Droitwich Spa	d					23 29	23 52									
Worcester Shrub Hill ■7	a					23 37	00 01									
	d															
Worcester Foregate Street ■7	a															
	d															
Malvern Link	d															
Great Malvern	a															
	d															
Colwall	d															
Ledbury	a															
	d															
Hereford ■7	a															

Table 71

Saturdays

14 December to 17 May

Stratford-upon-Avon, Marylebone and Leamington Spa - Birmingham - Stourbridge, Worcester and Hereford

Network Diagram - see first Page of Table 71

		LM	CH	CH	CH	LM	LM	LM	GW	LM		LM	XC	LM	LM	GW	LM	LM	CH	LM		XC	LM	LM	GW
			◇	◇					◇1				◇1			◇1						◇1			◇1
													trolley			trolley						trolley			trolley
Stratford-upon-Avon	d																	07 00						07 43	
Stratford-upon-Avon Parkway	d																	07 04						07 47	
Wilmcote	d																	07 07						07 50	
Wootton Wawen	d																	07x11						07x54	
Henley-in-Arden	d																	07 15						07 58	
Danzey	d																	07x19						08x02	
Wood End	d																	07x23						08x05	
The Lakes	d																	07x25						08x08	
Earlswood (West Midlands)	d																	07 28						08 11	
Wythall	d																	07 31						08 14	
Whitlocks End	d														07 03			07 33						08 16	
Shirley	d														07 05			07 36						08 19	
Yardley Wood	d														07 08			07 39						08 22	
Hall Green	d														07 11			07 42						08 25	
Spring Road	d														07 14			07 44						08 27	
London Marylebone 10 ⊖115	d				00 20																				
Banbury	d			00 03	01 35								06 56						07 02			07 33			
Leamington Spa 8	a			00 20	01 58								07 13						07 20			07 50			
	d		00 05	00 21								06 29	07 14						07 21			07 51			
Warwick	d		00 09	00 25								06 32							07 25						
Warwick Parkway	d		00 13	00 29								06 35							07 29						
Hatton	d											06 39							07 34						
Lapworth	d											06 45													
Dorridge	d		00 23									06 49					07 26		07 42	08 07					
Widney Manor	d											06 53					07 31			08 12					
Solihull	d		00 29	00 41								06 57					07 34		07 48	08 15					
Olton	d											07 00					07 37			08 18					
Acocks Green	d		00a43									07 03					07 40			08 21					
Tyseley	d											07 06			07 17		07 42	07 48		08 24				08 31	
Small Heath	d											07 09			07 19		07 45	07 50						08 33	
Bordesley	d																								
Birmingham Moor Street	d	00 06	00a43	00a55				06 31		07 01		07 14			07 24		07 49	07 55	08a03	08 29				08 38	
Birmingham Snow Hill	a	00 08						06 33		07 03		07 16			07 26		07 52	07 57		08 31				08 40	
	d							06 35		07 05					07 28		07 53	08 03		08 33				08 43	
Jewellery Quarter	d							06 37		07 07					07 30		07 55	08 05		08 35				08 45	
The Hawthorns	d							06 41		07 11					07 34		07 59	08 09		08 39				08 49	
Smethwick Galton Bridge 7	d							06 44		07 14					07 37		08 02	08 12		08 42				08 52	
Coventry	a												07 25												
Birmingham Intl. 68 ✈	a												07 37												
Birmingham New Street 12 68	a												07 48									08 17			
	d						06 49							07 49									08 49		
Langley Green	d							06 47		07 17					07 40			08 15		08 45					
Rowley Regis	d							06 50		07 20					07 43		08 08	08 19		08 48				08 58	
Old Hill	d							06 54		07 24					07 47			08 22		08 52					
Cradley Heath	d							06 57		07 27					07 50		08 13	08 25		08 55				09 03	
Lye	d							07 00		07 30					07 53			08 28		08 58					
Stourbridge Junction 2	d							07 04		07 34					07a57		08 19	08a33		09a01				09a09	
Hagley	d							07 07		07 37							08 23								
Blakedown	d							07 10		07 40							08 26								
Kidderminster	d							07 15		07 45							08 31								
Hartlebury	d							07 20																	
University	d						06 55							07 55									08 55		
Barnt Green	d																								
Bromsgrove	d						07 10							08 10									09 10		
Droitwich Spa	d						07 20	07 28		07 56				08 20			08 42						09 20		
Worcester Shrub Hill 7	a							07 39		08 05															
	d					06 30			07 46	08 11						08 42									09 41
Worcester Foregate Street 7	a					06 32	07 30		07 49	08 13				08 30		08 44	08 51						09 30		09 44
	d					06 33	07 32		07 50	08 13				08 32		08 46							09 32		09 45
Malvern Link	d					06 42	07 42		07 59	08 22				08 42		08 54							09 42		09 54
Great Malvern	a					06 44	07 44		08 03	08 25				08 44		09 00							09 44		10 00
	d					06 45	07 45							08 45									09 45		
Colwall	d					06 50	07 50							08 50									09 50		
Ledbury	a					06 57	07 57							08 57									09 57		
	d					06 58	07 59							08 59									09 59		
Hereford 7	a					07 14	08 19							09 19									10 19		

Table 71

Saturdays

14 December to 17 May

Stratford-upon-Avon, Marylebone and Leamington Spa - Birmingham - Stourbridge, Worcester and Hereford

Network Diagram - see first Page of Table 71

		LM	XC	LM	CH	LM	CH	CH	CH	LM	XC	XC	LM	GW	LM	LM	GW	LM	LM	CH	LM	XC	CH
			◇1 🚲		◇		◇				◇1 🚲	◇1 🚲					◇1			◇		◇1 🚲	◇
Stratford-upon-Avon	d						07 56			08 26								09 03					09 14
Stratford-upon-Avon Parkway	d						08 00			08 30								09 07					09 18
Wilmcote	d						08 03			08 33													09 22
Wootton Wawen	d									08x37													
Henley-in-Arden	d									08 41													
Danzey	d									08x45													
Wood End	d									08x49													
The Lakes	d									08x51													
Earlswood (West Midlands)	d									08 54													
Wythall	d									08 57													
Whitlocks End	d			08 35						09 00						09 19			09 40				
Shirley	d			08 38						09 03						09 22			09 42				
Yardley Wood	d			08 40						09 05						09 24			09 45				
Hall Green	d			08 43						09 09						09 27			09 48				
Spring Road	d			08 45						09 11						09 29			09 51				
London Marylebone 10 ⊖115	d				07 00															08 00			
Banbury	d		07 54		08 05				08 14		08 33	08 54								09 08		09 24	
Leamington Spa 8	a		08 11		08 22		08 28		08 33		08 49	09 11								09 25		09 41	09 52
	d	07 56	08 12		08 23			08 30	08 34		08 50	09 12								09 26		09 42	
Warwick	d	08 00						08 34	08 38											09 30			
Warwick Parkway	d	08 03			08 29				08 42											09 34			
Hatton	d	08 07						08a42	08 47														
Lapworth	d	08 12							08 52														
Dorridge	d	08 21			08 39	08 46			08 57				09 09					09 29		09 44	09 46		
Widney Manor	d	08 25				08 51							09 14					09 33			09 51		
Solihull	d	08 29			08 45	08 54			09 03				09 17					09 37		09 50	09 54		
Olton	d	08 32				08 57							09 20					09 40			09 57		
Acocks Green	d	08 35				09 00							09 23					09 43			10 00		
Tyseley	d	08 37		08 48		09 02										09 32					10 02		
Small Heath	d	08 40		08 51		09 05										09 35					10 05		
Bordesley	d																						
Birmingham Moor Street	d	08 45		08 55	09 00	09 09			09a17	09 18			09 29			09 39		09 49	09 58	10 02	10 09		
Birmingham Snow Hill 🚋	a	08 48		08 58	09 07	09 12				09 20			09 32			09 42		09 52	10 00	10 09	10 12		
	d	08 53		09 03		09 13				09 23			09 33			09 43		09 53	10 03		10 13		
Jewellery Quarter 🚋	d	08 55		09 05		09 15				09 25			09 35			09 45		09 55	10 05		10 15		
The Hawthorns 🚋	d	08 59		09 09		09 19				09 29			09 39			09 49		09 59	10 09		10 19		
Smethwick Galton Bridge 7	d	09 02		09 12		09 22				09 32			09 42			09 52		10 02	10 12		10 22		
Coventry	a		08 23									09 23											
Birmingham Intl. 68 ✈	a		08 37									09 37											
Birmingham New Street 12 68	a		08 48								09 20	09 48										10 18	
	d														09 49								
Langley Green	d	09 05								09 35								10 05					
Rowley Regis	d	09 08		09 18		09 28				09 38			09 48			09 58		10 08	10 18		10 28		
Old Hill	d	09 12								09 42								10 12					
Cradley Heath	d	09 15		09 23		09 33				09 45			09 53			10 03		10 15	10 23		10 33		
Lye	d	09 18								09 48								10 18					
Stourbridge Junction 2	d	09 22		09 29		09 39				09a52			09 59			10 09		10a22	10 29		10 39		
Hagley	d	09 25		09 33									10 03						10 33				
Blakedown	d	09 28		09 36									10 06						10 36				
Kidderminster	d	09 33		09a40		09 47							10a10			10 17			10a40		10 47		
Hartlebury	d					09 52															10 52		
University	d														09 55								
Barnt Green	d																						
Bromsgrove	d														10 10								
Droitwich Spa	d	09 44				10 00									10 20	10 28					11 00		
Worcester Shrub Hill 7	a	09 52														10 36							
	d													10 15			10 46						
Worcester Foregate Street 7	a					10 09								10 17	10 30		10 49				11 09		
	d													10 18	10 32		10 50				11 10		
Malvern Link	d													10 27	10 42		10 59				11 19		
Great Malvern	a													10 32	10 44		11 02				11 21		
	d														10 45		11 07						
Colwall	d														10 50		11 13						
Ledbury	a														10 57		11 20						
	d														10 59		11 22						
Hereford 7	a														11 19		11 39						

Table 71

Saturdays

14 December to 17 May

Stratford-upon-Avon, Marylebone and Leamington Spa - Birmingham - Stourbridge, Worcester and Hereford

Network Diagram - see first Page of Table 71

		LM	LM	CH	XC	LM	LM	LM	CH	LM	LM	LM	CH	LM	XC	CH	CH	XC	GW	LM	LM	LM
				◇	◇ [1]				◇						◇ [1]	◇	◇	◇ [1]	◇			
Stratford-upon-Avon	d	09 26						10 03				10 26										11 03
Stratford-upon-Avon Parkway	d	09 30						10 07				10 30										11 07
Wilmcote	d	09 33										10 33										
Wootton Wawen	d	09x37										10x37										
Henley-in-Arden	d	09 41										10 41										
Danzey	d	09x45										10x45										
Wood End	d	09x49										10x49										
The Lakes	d	09x51										10x51										
Earlswood (West Midlands)	d	09 54										10 54										
Wythall	d	09 57										10 57										
Whitlocks End	d	10 00					10 19			10 40		11 00									11 19	
Shirley	d	10 03					10 22			10 42		11 03									11 22	
Yardley Wood	d	10 05					10 24			10 45		11 05									11 24	
Hall Green	d	10 09					10 27			10 48		11 09									11 27	
Spring Road	d	10 11					10 29			10 51		11 11									11 29	
London Marylebone [10] ⊖115	d			08 27					09 06							09 09	09 36					
Banbury	d			09 41	09 54				10 02						10 24	10 29	10 39	10 54				
Leamington Spa [8]	a			09 58	10 11				10 20						10 41	10 46	10 58	11 11				
	d			09 59	10 12				10 21				10 32		10 42	10 47	10 59	11 12				
Warwick	d			10 03									10 37			10a51	11 03					
Warwick Parkway	d			10 07					10 27								11 07					
Hatton	d												10 43									
Lapworth	d												10 48									
Dorridge	d		10 09	10 17				10 29			10 46		10 54	11 09			11 17					11 29
Widney Manor	d		10 14					10 33			10 51			11 14								11 33
Solihull	d		10 17	10 23				10 37	10 42		10 54		11 00	11 17			11 23					11 37
Olton	d		10 20					10 40			10 57			11 20								11 40
Acocks Green	d		10 23					10 43			11 00			11 23								11 43
Tyseley	d						10 32				11 02										11 32	
Small Heath	d						10 35				11 05										11 35	
Bordesley	d																					
Birmingham Moor Street	d	10 18	10 29	10 34			10 39	10 49	10a55	10 58	11 09	11 18	11a17	11 29			11 34				11 39	11 49
Birmingham Snow Hill	a	10 20	10 32	10 41			10 42	10 52		11 00	11 12	11 20		11 32			11 41				11 42	11 52
	d	10 23	10 33				10 43	10 53		11 03	11 13	11 23		11 33							11 43	11 53
Jewellery Quarter	d	10 25	10 35				10 45	10 55		11 05	11 15	11 25		11 35							11 45	11 55
The Hawthorns	d	10 29	10 39				10 49	10 59		11 09	11 19	11 29		11 39							11 49	11 59
Smethwick Galton Bridge [7]	d	10 32	10 42				10 52	11 02		11 12	11 22	11 32		11 42							11 52	12 02
Coventry	a				10 23													11 23				
Birmingham Intl. 68 ✈	a				10 37													11 37				
Birmingham New Street [12] 68	a				10 48										11 18			11 48				
	d					10 49														11 49		
Langley Green	d	10 35						11 05				11 35										12 05
Rowley Regis	d	10 38	10 48				10 58	11 08		11 18	11 28	11 38		11 48							11 58	12 08
Old Hill	d	10 42						11 12				11 42										12 12
Cradley Heath	d	10 45	10 53				11 03	11 15		11 23	11 33	11 45		11 53							12 03	12 15
Lye	d	10 48						11 18				11 48										12 18
Stourbridge Junction [2]	d	10a52	10 59				11 09	11a22		11 29	11 39	11a52		11 59							12 09	12a22
Hagley	d		11 03							11 33				12 03								
Blakedown	d		11 06							11 36				12 06								
Kidderminster	d		11a10				11 17			11a40	11 47			12a10							12 17	
Hartlebury	d										11 52											
University	d					10 55														11 55		
Barnt Green	d																					
Bromsgrove	d					11 10														12 10		
Droitwich Spa	d					11 20	11 28				12 00									12 20	12 28	
Worcester Shrub Hill [7]	a						11 36															
	d																		12 16			
Worcester Foregate Street [7]	a					11 30					12 09								12 18	12 30	12 37	
	d					11 32														12 32		
Malvern Link	d					11 42														12 42		
Great Malvern	a					11 44														12 44		
	d					11 45														12 45		
Colwall	d					11 50														12 50		
Ledbury	a					11 57														12 57		
	d					11 59														12 59		
Hereford [7]	a					12 19														13 19		

Table 71

Saturdays

14 December to 17 May

Stratford-upon-Avon, Marylebone and Leamington Spa - Birmingham - Stourbridge, Worcester and Hereford

Network Diagram - see first Page of Table 71

		CH	XC	LM	GW	LM	LM	LM	CH	CH	XC	LM	LM	GW	LM	CH	LM	LM	LM	CH	LM	XC	CH
		◇	◇1		◇1				◇	◇	◇1			◇1		◇						◇1	◇
																BZ							
Stratford-upon-Avon	d						11 26			11 37					12 03				12 26				
Stratford-upon-Avon Parkway	d						11 30			11 40					12 07				12 30				
Wilmcote	d						11 33			11 44									12 33				
Wootton Wawen	d						11x37												12x37				
Henley-in-Arden	d						11 41												12 41				
Danzey	d						11x45												12x45				
Wood End	d						11x49												12x49				
The Lakes	d						11x51												12x51				
Earlswood (West Midlands)	d						11 54												12 54				
Wythall	d						11 57												12 57				
Whitlocks End	d			11 40			12 00						12 19				12 40		13 00				
Shirley	d			11 42			12 03						12 22				12 42		13 03				
Yardley Wood	d			11 45			12 05						12 24				12 45		13 05				
Hall Green	d			11 48			12 09						12 27				12 48		13 09				
Spring Road	d			11 51			12 11						12 29				12 51		13 11				
London Marylebone 10 ⊖115	d	10 06							10 36							11 06							11 09
Banbury	d	11 02	11 24						11 41		11 54					12 04						12 24	12 32
Leamington Spa 8	a	11 20	11 41						11 58	12 08	12 11					12 23						12 41	12 50
	d	11 21	11 42						11 59		12 12					12 24				12 32		12 42	12 51
Warwick	d								12 03											12 37			12 56
Warwick Parkway	d	11 27							12 07							12 31							
Hatton	d																			12 43			13a03
Lapworth	d																			12 48			
Dorridge	d					11 46		12 09	12 17						12 29			12 46		12 54	13 09		
Widney Manor	d					11 51		12 14							12 33			12 51			13 14		
Solihull	d	11 42				11 54		12 17	12 23						12 37	12 45		12 54		13 00	13 17		
Olton	d					11 57		12 20							12 40			12 57			13 20		
Acocks Green	d					12 00		12 23							12 43			13 00			13 23		
Tyseley	d					12 02							12 32					13 02					
Small Heath	d					12 05							12 35					13 05					
Bordesley	d																						
Birmingham Moor Street	d	11a55		11 58		12 09	12 18	12 29	12 34				12 39		12 49	12a56	12 58	13 09	13 18	13a17	13 29		
Birmingham Snow Hill	a			12 00		12 12	12 20	12 32	12 41				12 42		12 52		13 00	13 12	13 20		13 32		
	d			12 03		12 13	12 23	12 33					12 43		12 53		13 03	13 13	13 23		13 33		
Jewellery Quarter	d			12 05		12 15	12 25	12 35					12 45		12 55		13 05	13 15	13 25		13 35		
The Hawthorns	d			12 09		12 19	12 29	12 39					12 49		12 59		13 09	13 19	13 29		13 39		
Smethwick Galton Bridge 7	d			12 12		12 22	12 32	12 42					12 52		13 02		13 12	13 22	13 32		13 42		
Coventry	a										12 23												
Birmingham Intl. 68 ✈	a										12 37												
Birmingham New Street 12 68	a		12 18								12 48											13 18	
	d											12 49											
Langley Green	d						12 35								13 05				13 35				
Rowley Regis	d			12 18		12 28	12 38	12 48					12 58		13 08		13 18	13 28	13 38		13 48		
Old Hill	d						12 42								13 12				13 42				
Cradley Heath	d			12 23		12 33	12 45	12 53					13 03		13 15		13 23	13 33	13 45		13 53		
Lye	d						12 48								13 18				13 48				
Stourbridge Junction 2	d			12 29		12 39	12a52	12 59					13 09		13a22		13 29	13 39	13a52		13 59		
Hagley	d			12 33				13 03									13 33				14 03		
Blakedown	d			12 36				13 06									13 36				14 06		
Kidderminster	d			12a40		12 47		13a10					13 17				13a40	13 47			14a10		
Hartlebury	d					12 52												13 52					
University	d											12 55											
Barnt Green	d																						
Bromsgrove	d											13 10											
Droitwich Spa	d					13 00						13 20	13 28					14 00					
Worcester Shrub Hill 7	a												13 36										
	d				12 46									13 41									
Worcester Foregate Street 7	a				12 49	13 09						13 30		13 44				14 09					
	d				12 50	13 10						13 32		13 45									
Malvern Link	d				12 59	13 19						13 42		13 54									
Great Malvern	a				13 03	13 21						13 44		14 00									
	d				13 06							13 45											
Colwall	d				13 13							13 50											
Ledbury	a				13 21							13 57											
	d				13 23							13 59											
Hereford 7	a				13 39							14 19											

BZ Business Zone available offering greater comfortand an enhanced working environment. Supplement payable.

Table 71

Saturdays

14 December to 17 May

Stratford-upon-Avon, Marylebone and Leamington Spa - Birmingham - Stourbridge, Worcester and Hereford

Network Diagram - see first Page of Table 71

		CH	XC	GW	LM	LM	LM	CH	XC	LM	LM	LM	LM	CH	CH	XC	LM	LM	GW	LM	CH	LM
		◇	◇[1]	◇				◇	◇[1]					◇	◇	◇[1]			◇[1]		◇	
			🛒					🛒	🛒							🛒			🛒			
Stratford-upon-Avon	d						12 52					13 26			13 37					14 03		
Stratford-upon-Avon Parkway	d						12 56					13 30			13 40					14 07		
Wilmcote	d											13 33			13 44							
Wootton Wawen	d											13x37										
Henley-in-Arden	d											13 41										
Danzey	d											13x45										
Wood End	d											13x49										
The Lakes	d											13x51										
Earlswood (West Midlands)	d											13 54										
Wythall	d											13 57										
Whitlocks End	d					13 18				13 40		14 00						14 19				14 40
Shirley	d					13 21				13 42		14 03						14 22				14 42
Yardley Wood	d					13 23				13 45		14 05						14 24				14 45
Hall Green	d					13 26				13 48		14 09						14 27				14 48
Spring Road	d					13 28				13 51		14 11						14 29				14 51
London Marylebone [10] ⊖115	d	11 36						12 06						12 36							13 06	
Banbury	d	12 41	12 54					13 02	13 24					13 41		13 54					14 02	
Leamington Spa [8]	a	12 58	13 11					13 20	13 41					13 58	14 08	14 11					14 20	
	d	12 59	13 12					13 21	13 42					13 59		14 12					14 21	
Warwick	d	13 03												14 03								
Warwick Parkway	d	13 07						13 27						14 07							14 27	
Hatton	d																					
Lapworth	d																					
Dorridge	d	13 17					13 28				13 46		14 09	14 17						14 29		
Widney Manor	d						13 33				13 51		14 14							14 33		
Solihull	d	13 23					13 37	13 42			13 54		14 17	14 23						14 37	14 42	
Olton	d						13 40				13 57		14 20							14 40		
Acocks Green	d						13 43				14 00		14 23							14 43		
Tyseley	d					13 31					14 02							14 32				
Small Heath	d					13 34					14 05							14 35				
Bordesley	d					13 36																
Birmingham Moor Street	d	13 34				13 39	13 49	13a55		13 58	14 09	14 18	14 29	14 34				14 39		14 49	14a55	14 58
Birmingham Snow Hill 🚋	a	13 41				13 42	13 52			14 00	14 12	14 20	14 32	14 41				14 42		14 52		15 00
	d					13 43	13 53			14 03	14 13	14 23	14 33					14 43		14 53		15 03
Jewellery Quarter 🚋	d					13 45	13 55			14 05	14 15	14 25	14 35					14 45		14 55		15 05
The Hawthorns 🚋	d					13 49	13 59			14 09	14 19	14 29	14 39					14 49		14 59		15 09
Smethwick Galton Bridge [7]	d					13 52	14 02			14 12	14 22	14 32	14 42					14 52		15 02		15 12
Coventry	a		13 23													14 23						
Birmingham Intl. 68 ✈	a		13 37													14 37						
Birmingham New Street [12] 68	a		13 48						14 18							14 48						
	d				13 49												14 49					
Langley Green	d						14 05					14 35								15 05		
Rowley Regis	d					13 58	14 08			14 18	14 28	14 38	14 48					14 58		15 08		15 18
Old Hill	d						14 12					14 42								15 12		
Cradley Heath	d					14 03	14 15			14 23	14 33	14 45	14 53					15 03		15 15		15 23
Lye	d						14 18					14 48								15 18		
Stourbridge Junction [2]	d					14 09	14a22			14 29	14 39	14a52	14 59					15 09		15a22		15 29
Hagley	d									14 33			15 03									15 33
Blakedown	d									14 36			15 06									15 36
Kidderminster	d					14 17				14a40	14 47		15a10					15 17				15a40
Hartlebury	d										14 52											
University	d				13 55												14 55					
Barnt Green	d																					
Bromsgrove	d				14 10												15 10					
Droitwich Spa	d				14 20	14 31					15 00						15 20	15 28				
Worcester Shrub Hill [7]	a					14 39												15 36				
	d			14 15		14 44													15 41			
Worcester Foregate Street [7]	a			14 17	14 30	14 46					15 09						15 30		15 44			
	d			14 18	14 32	14 46											15 32		15 45			
Malvern Link	d			14 27	14 42	14 55											15 42		15 54			
Great Malvern	a			14 32	14 44	14 57											15 44		16 00			
	d				14 45												15 45					
Colwall	d				14 50												15 50					
Ledbury	a				14 57												15 57					
	d				14 59												15 59					
Hereford [7]	a				15 19												16 17					

Table 71

Saturdays

14 December to 17 May

Stratford-upon-Avon, Marylebone and Leamington Spa - Birmingham - Stourbridge, Worcester and Hereford

Network Diagram - see first Page of Table 71

		LM	LM	CH	LM	XC	CH	CH	XC	GW	LM	LM	LM	CH	XC	LM	GW	LM	LM	LM	CH	CH	XC
						◇1 ⊥	◇	◇	◇1 ⊥	◇				◇	◇1 ⊥		◇1 ⊥				◇	◇	◇1 ⊥
Stratford-upon-Avon	d		14 26										14 52						15 26			15 37	
Stratford-upon-Avon Parkway	d		14 30										14 56						15 30			15 40	
Wilmcote	d		14 33																15 33			15 44	
Wootton Wawen	d		14x37																15x37				
Henley-in-Arden	d		14 41																15 41				
Danzey	d		14x45																15x45				
Wood End	d		14x49																15x49				
The Lakes	d		14x51																15x51				
Earlswood (West Midlands)	d		14 54																15 54				
Wythall	d		14 57																15 57				
Whitlocks End	d		15 00									15 19				15 40			16 00				
Shirley	d		15 03									15 22				15 42			16 03				
Yardley Wood	d		15 05									15 24				15 45			16 05				
Hall Green	d		15 09									15 27				15 48			16 09				
Spring Road	d		15 11									15 29				15 51			16 11				
London Marylebone 10 ⊖115	d						13 09	13 36						14 06							14 36		
Banbury	d					14 24	14 31	14 41	14 54					15 02	15 24						15 41		15 54
Leamington Spa 8	a					14 41	14 48	14 58	15 11					15 20	15 41						15 58	16 08	16 11
	d			14 32		14 42	14 49	14 59	15 12					15 21	15 42						15 59		16 12
Warwick	d			14 37			14 54	15 03													16 03		
Warwick Parkway	d							15 07						15 27							16 07		
Hatton	d			14 43			15a01																
Lapworth	d			14 48																			
Dorridge	d	14 46		14 54	15 09			15 17					15 28					15 46		16 09	16 17		
Widney Manor	d	14 51			15 14								15 33					15 51		16 14			
Solihull	d	14 54		15 00	15 17			15 23					15 37	15 42				15 54		16 17	16 23		
Olton	d	14 57			15 20								15 40					15 57		16 20			
Acocks Green	d	15 00			15 23								15 43					16 00		16 23			
Tyseley	d	15 02										15 32						16 02					
Small Heath	d	15 05										15 35						16 05					
Bordesley	d																						
Birmingham Moor Street	d	15 09	15 18	15a17	15 29			15 34				15 39	15 49	15a55		15 58		16 09	16 18	16 29	16 34		
Birmingham Snow Hill 🚊	a	15 12	15 20		15 32			15 41				15 42	15 52			16 00		16 12	16 20	16 32	16 41		
	d	15 13	15 23		15 33							15 43	15 53			16 03		16 13	16 23	16 33			
Jewellery Quarter 🚊	d	15 15	15 25		15 35							15 45	15 55			16 05		16 15	16 25	16 35			
The Hawthorns 🚊	d	15 19	15 29		15 39							15 49	15 59			16 09		16 19	16 29	16 39			
Smethwick Galton Bridge 7	d	15 22	15 32		15 42							15 52	16 02			16 12		16 22	16 32	16 42			
Coventry	a								15 23														16 23
Birmingham Intl. 68 ✈	a								15 37														16 37
Birmingham New Street 12 68	a					15 18			15 48						16 18								16 48
	d										15 49												
Langley Green	d		15 35										16 05						16 35				
Rowley Regis	d	15 28	15 38		15 48							15 58	16 08			16 18		16 28	16 38	16 48			
Old Hill	d		15 42										16 12						16 42				
Cradley Heath	d	15 33	15 45		15 53							16 03	16 15			16 23		16 33	16 45	16 53			
Lye	d		15 48										16 18						16 48				
Stourbridge Junction 2	d	15 39	15a52		15 59							16 09	16a22			16 29		16 39	16a52	16 59			
Hagley	d				16 03											16 33				17 03			
Blakedown	d				16 06											16 36				17 06			
Kidderminster	d	15 47			16a10							16 17				16a40		16 47		17a10			
Hartlebury	d	15 52																16 52					
University	d										15 55												
Barnt Green	d																						
Bromsgrove	d										16 10												
Droitwich Spa	d	16 00									16 20	16 28						17 00					
Worcester Shrub Hill 7	a																						
	d									16 14							16 41						
Worcester Foregate Street 7	a	16 09								16 17	16 30	16 37					16 44	17 09					
	d									16 17	16 32						16 47	17 10					
Malvern Link	d									16 26	16 42						16 55	17 19					
Great Malvern	a									16 32	16 44						17 00	17 21					
	d										16 45												
Colwall	d										16 50												
Ledbury	a										16 57												
	d										16 59												
Hereford 7	a										17 19												

Table 71

Saturdays

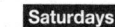

14 December to 17 May

Stratford-upon-Avon, Marylebone and Leamington Spa - Birmingham - Stourbridge, Worcester and Hereford

Network Diagram - see first Page of Table 71

		LM	LM	LM	CH	LM		GW	LM	LM	GW	LM	CH	LM	XC	CH		CH	XC	LM	LM	LM	CH	XC	LM
					◇			◇1							◇1	◇		◇	◇1				◇	◇1	
															⊥				⊥					⊥	
Stratford-upon-Avon	d			16 03								16 26										16 52			
Stratford-upon-Avon Parkway	d			16 07								16 30										16 56			
Wilmcote	d											16 33													
Wootton Wawen	d											16x37													
Henley-in-Arden	d											16 41													
Danzey	d											16x45													
Wood End	d											16x49													
The Lakes	d											16x51													
Earlswood (West Midlands)	d											16 54													
Wythall	d											16 57													
Whitlocks End	d		16 19			16 40						17 00									17 19				
Shirley	d		16 22			16 42						17 03									17 22				
Yardley Wood	d		16 24			16 45						17 05									17 24				
Hall Green	d		16 27			16 48						17 09									17 27				
Spring Road	d		16 29			16 51						17 11									17 29				
London Marylebone 10 ⊖115	d				15 06											15 09		15 36					16 06		
Banbury	d				16 02										16 24	16 32		16 41	16 54				17 02	17 24	
Leamington Spa 8	a				16 20										16 41	16 50		16 58	17 11				17 20	17 41	
	d				16 21								16 32		16 42	16 51		16 59	17 12				17 21	17 42	
Warwick	d												16 37			16 56		17 03							
Warwick Parkway	d				16 27													17 07					17 27		
Hatton	d												16 43			17a03									
Lapworth	d												16 48												
Dorridge	d			16 29						16 46			16 54	17 09				17 17				17 28			17 46
Widney Manor	d			16 33						16 51				17 14								17 33			17 51
Solihull	d			16 37	16 42					16 54			17 00	17 17				17 23				17 37	17 42		17 54
Olton	d			16 40						16 57				17 20								17 40			17 57
Acocks Green	d			16 43						17 00				17 23								17 43			18 00
Tyseley	d		16 32							17 02											17 32				18 02
Small Heath	d		16 35							17 05											17 35				18 05
Bordesley	d																								
Birmingham Moor Street	d		16 39	16 49	16a55	16 58				17 09		17 18	17a17	17 29				17 34			17 39	17 49	17 54		18 09
Birmingham Snow Hill ⛴	a		16 42	16 52		17 00				17 12		17 20		17 32				17 41			17 42	17 52	18 03		18 12
	d		16 43	16 53		17 03				17 13		17 23		17 33							17 43	17 53			18 13
Jewellery Quarter ⛴	d		16 45	16 55		17 05				17 15		17 25		17 35							17 45	17 55			18 15
The Hawthorns ⛴	d		16 49	16 59		17 09				17 19		17 29		17 39							17 49	17 59			18 19
Smethwick Galton Bridge 7	d		16 52	17 02		17 12				17 22		17 32		17 42							17 52	18 02			18 22
Coventry	a																		17 23						
Birmingham Intl. 68 ✈	a																		17 37						
Birmingham New Street 12 68	a														17 18				17 48					18 18	
	d	16 49							17 19											17 49					
Langley Green	d			17 05								17 35										18 05			18 25
Rowley Regis	d		16 58	17 08		17 18				17 28		17 38		17 48							17 58	18 08			18 28
Old Hill	d			17 12								17 42										18 12			18 32
Cradley Heath	d		17 03	17 15		17 23				17 33		17 45		17 53							18 03	18 15			18 35
Lye	d			17 18								17 48										18 18			18 38
Stourbridge Junction 2	d		17 09	17a22		17 29				17 39		17a52		17 59							18 09	18a22			18a42
Hagley	d					17 33								18 03							18 13				
Blakedown	d					17 36								18 06							18 16				
Kidderminster	d		17 17			17a40				17 47				18a10							18 21				
Hartlebury	d									17 56											18 27				
University	d	16 55																		17 55					
Barnt Green	d																								
Bromsgrove	d	17 10							17 40											18 10					
Droitwich Spa	d	17 20	17 28						17 50	18 03										18 20	18 36				
Worcester Shrub Hill 7	a								17 58	18 12										18 27					
	d							17 41			18 18									18 31					
Worcester Foregate Street 7	a	17 29	17 37					17 44			18 21									18 33	18 45				
	d	17 32						17 45			18 21									18 34					
Malvern Link	d	17 42						17 54			18 30									18 44					
Great Malvern	a	17 45						18 00			18 36									18 46					
	d	17 45																		18 47					
Colwall	d	17 50																		18 52					
Ledbury	a	17 57																		18 59					
	d	17 59																		19 00					
Hereford 7	a	18 16																		19 20					

Table 71

Saturdays

14 December to 17 May

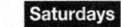

Stratford-upon-Avon, Marylebone and Leamington Spa - Birmingham - Stourbridge, Worcester and Hereford

Network Diagram - see first Page of Table 71

		GW	LM	LM	CH	CH	XC	LM	LM	GW	LM	CH	CH	LM	XC	LM	CH	GW	LM	GW	GW	CH
		◇1			◇	◇	◇1			◇1		◇			◇1		◇			◇1	◇1	◇
																				A	B	
		☕					🍴			☕		🍴 BZ			🍴					☕	☕	
Stratford-upon-Avon	d		17 26			17 35								18 08								
Stratford-upon-Avon Parkway	d		17 30			17 38								18 12								
Wilmcote	d		17 33			17 42								18 15								
Wootton Wawen	d		17x37											18x19								
Henley-in-Arden	d		17 41											18 23								
Danzey	d		17x45											18x27								
Wood End	d		17x49											18x31								
The Lakes	d		17x51											18x33								
Earlswood (West Midlands)	d		17 54											18 37								
Wythall	d		17 57											18 39								
Whitlocks End	d		18 00						18 19					18 42								
Shirley	d		18 03						18 22					18 45								
Yardley Wood	d		18 05						18 24					18 48								
Hall Green	d		18 09						18 27					18 51								
Spring Road	d		18 11						18 29					18 53								
London Marylebone 10 ⊖115	d				16 36							17 06					17 09					17 36
Banbury	d				17 41		17 54					18 03			18 24		18 32					18 41
Leamington Spa 8	a				17 58	18 07	18 11					18 22			18 41		18 50					18 58
	d				17 59		18 12					18 23	18 30		18 42		18 51					18 59
Warwick	d				18 03								18 35				18 56					19 03
Warwick Parkway	d				18 07							18 29										19 07
Hatton	d												18 41				19a03					
Lapworth	d												18 46									
Dorridge	d			18 09	18 17						18 28		18 51						19 00			19 17
Widney Manor	d			18 14							18 33								19 05			
Solihull	d			18 17	18 23						18 36	18 43	18 57						19 08			19 23
Olton	d			18 20							18 39								19 11			
Acocks Green	d			18 23							18 42								19 14			
Tyseley	d								18 32					18 57					19 17			
Small Heath	d								18 35					18 59					19 19			
Bordesley	d																					
Birmingham Moor Street	d		18 18	18 29	18a35				18 39		18 49	18 54	19a13	19 04					19 24			19a35
Birmingham Snow Hill 🚊	a		18 20	18 32					18 42		18 51	19 03		19 06					19 26			
	d		18 23	18 33							18 53								19 28			
Jewellery Quarter 🚊	d		18 25	18 35							18 55								19 30			
The Hawthorns 🚊	d		18 29	18 39							18 59								19 34			
Smethwick Galton Bridge 7	d		18 32	18 42							19 02								19 37			
Coventry	a						18 23															
Birmingham Intl. 68 ✈	a						18 37															
Birmingham New Street 12 68	a						18 48								19 18							
	d							18 49								19 19						
Langley Green	d			18 45							19 05								19 40			
Rowley Regis	d		18 38	18 48							19 09								19 43			
Old Hill	d			18 52							19 12								19 47			
Cradley Heath	d		18 43	18 55							19 15								19 50			
Lye	d			18 58							19 18								19 53			
Stourbridge Junction 2	d		18 48	19 02							19 22								19 57			
Hagley	d		18 52	19 06							19 26								20 01			
Blakedown	d		18 55	19 09							19 29								20 04			
Kidderminster	d		19 00	19a14							19 34								20 09			
Hartlebury	d		19 05																			
University	d							18 55								19 25						
Barnt Green	d																					
Bromsgrove	d							19 10								19 40						
Droitwich Spa	d		19 13					19 20			19 45					19 50			20 20			
Worcester Shrub Hill 7	a							19 27			19 53								20 30			
	d	18 53						19 35		19 42								20 20		20 45	20 46	
Worcester Foregate Street 7	a	18 55	19 22					19 37		19 45						20 00		20 22		20 49	20 49	
	d	18 57	19 23					19 38								20 00		20 25		20 50	20 50	
Malvern Link	d	19 05	19 32					19 48								20 10		20 34		20 59	20 59	
Great Malvern	a	19 09	19 35					19 50								20 13		20 40		21 02	21 02	
	d	19 09														20 25				21 03	21 03	
Colwall	d	19 15														20 30				21 09	21 09	
Ledbury	a	19 23														20 38				21 16	21 16	
	d	19 29														20 39				21 18	21 18	
Hereford 7	a	19 45														21 02				21 35	21 35	

A from 4 January until 8 February
B from 15 February

BZ Business Zone available offering greater comfortand an enhanced working environment. Supplement Payable.

Table 71

Saturdays

14 December to 17 May

Stratford-upon-Avon, Marylebone and Leamington Spa - Birmingham - Stourbridge, Worcester and Hereford

Network Diagram - see first Page of Table 71

		LM	XC	LM	CH	XC	LM	CH		XC	LM	CH	LM	GW	CH	LM	XC	CH		CH	XC	GW	LM	CH	XC
			◇1		◇	◇1		◇		◇1				◇1	◇		◇1	◇		◇	◇1	◇1		◇	◇1
														A								B			
			🛒		🛒	🛒				🛒															
					BZ																				
Stratford-upon-Avon	d	18 49					19 26					19 37				20 26									
Stratford-upon-Avon Parkway	d	18 53					19 30					19 40				20 30									
Wilmcote	d	18 56					19 33					19 44				20 33									
Wootton Wawen	d	19x00					19x37									20x37									
Henley-in-Arden	d	19 04					19 41									20 41									
Danzey	d	19x08					19x45									20x45									
Wood End	d	19x12					19x49									20x49									
The Lakes	d	19x14					19x51									20x51									
Earlswood (West Midlands)	d	19 17					19 54									20 54									
Wythall	d	19 20					19 57									20 57									
Whitlocks End	d	19 23					20 00									21 00									
Shirley	d	19 26					20 03									21 03									
Yardley Wood	d	19 28					20 05									21 05									
Hall Green	d	19 32					20 09									21 09									
Spring Road	d	19 34					20 11									21 11									
London Marylebone 10 ⊖115	d				18 06			18 36							19 06			19 09		19 36				20 00	
Banbury	d		18 54		19 03	19 24		19 41		19 54					20 02		20 29	20 34		20 43	20 54			21 05	21 25
Leamington Spa 8	a		19 11		19 22	19 41		19 58		20 10		20 17			20 20		20 45	20 53		21 00	21 11			21 22	21 43
	d		19 12		19 23	19 42		19 59		20 12					20 21		20 46	20 53		21 00	21 12			21 23	21 44
Warwick	d							20 03										20 58		21 05				21 27	
Warwick Parkway	d				19 29			20 07							20 27					21 08				21 32	
Hatton	d							20 12										21a05							
Lapworth	d							20 18																	
Dorridge	d			19 25				20 23					20 29							21 18			21 29	21 42	
Widney Manor	d			19 30									20 34										21 34		
Solihull	d			19 33	19 43			20 29					20 37		20 42					21 24			21 37	21 48	
Olton	d			19 36									20 40										21 40		
Acocks Green	d			19 39									20 43										21 43		
Tyseley	d	19 37		19 42									20 45										21 45		
Small Heath	d	19 39		19 44									20 48										21 48		
Bordesley	d																								
Birmingham Moor Street	d	19 44		19 52	19 56		20 18	20 40					20 52		20 58	21 18				21a35			21 52	21 58	
Birmingham Snow Hill 🚊	a	19 46		19 54	20 04		20 20	20 47					20 55		21 07	21 20							21 55	22 06	
	d			19 56			20 23						20 56			21 23							21 56		
Jewellery Quarter 🚊	d			19 58			20 25						20 58			21 25							21 58		
The Hawthorns 🚊	d			20 02			20 29						21 02			21 29							22 02		
Smethwick Galton Bridge 7	d			20 05			20 32						21 05			21 32							22 05		
Coventry	a		19 23							20 23											21 23				21 55
Birmingham Intl. 68 ✈	a		19 37							20 37											21 37				22 10
Birmingham New Street 12 68	a		19 48			20 18				20 48							21 15				21 48				22 21
	d										20 59														
Langley Green	d			20 08			20 35						21 08			21 35							22 08		
Rowley Regis	d			20 11			20 38						21 11			21 38							22 11		
Old Hill	d			20 15			20 42						21 15			21 42							22 15		
Cradley Heath	d			20 18			20 45						21 18			21 45							22 18		
Lye	d			20 21			20 48						21 21			21 48							22 21		
Stourbridge Junction 2	d			20 25			20a52						21 25			21a52							22 25		
Hagley	d			20 28									21 28										22 28		
Blakedown	d			20 31									21 31										22 31		
Kidderminster	d			20 36									21 36										22 36		
Hartlebury	d																								
University	d										21 05														
Barnt Green	d																								
Bromsgrove	d										21 20														
Droitwich Spa	d			20 48							21 30		21 48										22 48		
Worcester Shrub Hill 7	a			20 56							21 37		21 56										22 56		
	d			20 59							21 47			22 04								22 06	22 59		
Worcester Foregate Street 7	a			21 01							21 49			22 06								22 08	23 01		
	d			21 02							21 50			22 08								22 09	23 02		
Malvern Link	d			21 11							21 59			22 16								22 17	23 11		
Great Malvern	a			21 13							22 01			22 22								22 23	23 13		
	d										22 02														
Colwall	d										22 07														
Ledbury	a										22 14														
	d										22 15														
Hereford 7	a										22 35														

A from 15 February

B from 4 January until 8 February

BZ Business Zone available offering greater comfortand an enhanced working environment .Supplement Payable

Table 71

Saturdays

14 December to 17 May

Stratford-upon-Avon, Marylebone and Leamington Spa - Birmingham - Stourbridge, Worcester and Hereford

Network Diagram - see first Page of Table 71

Station		CH	LM	CH		XC	LM	CH	XC	LM	CH	LM
		◇				◇[1]		◇	◇[1]		◇	
Stratford-upon-Avon	d		21 26	21 35						22 33		23 30
Stratford-upon-Avon Parkway	d		21 30							22 37		23 34
Wilmcote	d		21 33							22 40		
Wootton Wawen	d											
Henley-in-Arden	d		21 40							22 47		
Danzey	d											
Wood End	d		21x46									
The Lakes	d		21x48									
Earlswood (West Midlands)	d		21 51									
Wythall	d		21 54							22 56		
Whitlocks End	d		21 57							22 59		
Shirley	d		22 00							23 02		
Yardley Wood	d		22 02							23 04		
Hall Green	d		22 06							23 07		
Spring Road	d		22 08							23 09		
London Marylebone [10] ⊖115	d	20 36						21 06			22 08	
Banbury	d	21 40				21 55		22 12	22 29		23 04	
Leamington Spa [8]	a	21 57		22 04		22 11		22 29	22 45		23 22	
	d	21 57				22 12		22 30	22 46		23 23	
Warwick	d	22 02						22 34			23 27	
Warwick Parkway	d	22 06						22 38			23 31	
Hatton	d							22 43				
Lapworth	d							22 49				
Dorridge	d	22 16					22 33	22 54			23 41	
Widney Manor	d						22 38				23 44	
Solihull	d	22 22					22 41	23 00			23 48	
Olton	d						22 44					
Acocks Green	d						22 47					
Tyseley	d		22 11				22 50			23 12		
Small Heath	d		22 13				22 52			23 15		
Bordesley	d											
Birmingham Moor Street	d	22a34	22 18				22 57	23 09		23 19	23a59	00 03
Birmingham Snow Hill	a		22 20				22 59	23 16		23 22		00 05
	d		22 23				23 01			23 23		
Jewellery Quarter	d		22 25				23 03			23 25		
The Hawthorns	d		22 29				23 07			23 29		
Smethwick Galton Bridge [7]	d		22 32				23 10			23 32		
Coventry	a					22 23						
Birmingham Intl. 68 ✈	a					22 36						
Birmingham New Street [12] 68	a					22 48			23 16			
	d											
Langley Green	d		22 35				23 13			23 35		
Rowley Regis	d		22 38				23 16			23 38		
Old Hill	d		22 42				23 20			23 42		
Cradley Heath	d		22 45				23 23			23 45		
Lye	d		22 48				23 26			23 48		
Stourbridge Junction [2]	d		22a52				23 30			23a52		
Hagley	d						23 33					
Blakedown	d						23 36					
Kidderminster	d						23 41					
Hartlebury	d											
University	d											
Barnt Green	d											
Bromsgrove	d											
Droitwich Spa	d						23 53					
Worcester Shrub Hill [7]	a						00 01					
	d											
Worcester Foregate Street [7]	a											
	d											
Malvern Link	d											
Great Malvern	a											
	d											
Colwall	d											
Ledbury	a											
	d											
Hereford [7]	a											

Table 71

Sundays

8 December to 9 February

Stratford-upon-Avon, Marylebone and Leamington Spa - Birmingham - Stourbridge, Worcester and Hereford

Network Diagram - see first Page of Table 71

		LM	LM	LM	GW	LM	LM	CH	LM	CH	XC	CH	CH	XC	GW	LM	LM	CH	LM	GW	LM	CH	LM
					◇1			◇		◇	◇1	◇	◇	◇1	◇1			◇		◇1		◇	
		A																					
Stratford-upon-Avon	d						09 29			09 38						10 29					11 29		
Stratford-upon-Avon Parkway	d						09 33			09 41						10 33					11 33		
Wilmcote	d						09 36			09 44						10 36					11 36		
Wootton Wawen	d																						
Henley-in-Arden	d						09 43									10 43					11 43		
Danzey	d																						
Wood End	d																						
The Lakes	d						09x49									10x49					11x49		
Earlswood (West Midlands)	d																						
Wythall	d						09 53									10 53					11 53		
Whitlocks End	d						09 56									10 56					11 56		
Shirley	d						09 59									10 59					11 59		
Yardley Wood	d						10 01									11 01					12 01		
Hall Green	d						10 05									11 05					12 05		
Spring Road	d						10 07									11 07					12 07		
London Marylebone 10 ⊖115	d							08 15				09 06	09 30					10 06				10 36	
Banbury	d							09 28			09 55	10 16	10 31	10 55				11 03				11 41	
Leamington Spa 8	a							09 46		10 05	10 11	10 33	10 49	11 11				11 20				11 58	
	d							09 46			10 12	10 34	10 50	11 12				11 21				11 59	
Warwick	d							09 51				10 38	10 54					11 25				12 03	
Warwick Parkway	d							09 54				10 42						11 29				12 07	
Hatton	d							10 00					11a01									12 12	
Lapworth	d							10 06														12 17	
Dorridge	d							10 11	10 27			10 52					11 27	11 39				12 23	12 27
Widney Manor	d								10 32								11 32						12 32
Solihull	d							10 16	10 35			10 58					11 35	11 45				12 29	12 35
Olton	d								10 38								11 38						12 38
Acocks Green	d								10 41								11 41						12 41
Tyseley	d						10 10									11 10					12 10		
Small Heath	d																						
Bordesley	d																						
Birmingham Moor Street	d	00 03		09 26			10 15	10 25	10 48			11 07				11 15	11 48	11 54			12 15	12 41	12 48
Birmingham Snow Hill ⛴	a	00 05		09 28			10 17	10 32	10 50			11 14				11 17	11 50	12 01			12 17	12 48	12 50
	d			09 30			10 22		10 52							11 22	11 52				12 22		12 52
Jewellery Quarter ⛴	d			09 32			10 24		10 54							11 24	11 54				12 24		12 54
The Hawthorns ⛴	d			09 36			10 28		10 58							11 28	11 58				12 28		12 58
Smethwick Galton Bridge 7	d			09 39			10 31		11 01							11 31	12 01				12 31		13 01
Coventry	a										10 24			11 24									
Birmingham Intl. 68 ✈	a										10 38			11 38									
Birmingham New Street 12 68	a										10 50			11 51									
	d					10 00													12 00				
Langley Green	d								11 04								12 04						13 04
Rowley Regis	d			09 45			10 37		11 07							11 37	12 07				12 37		13 07
Old Hill	d								11 10								12 10						13 10
Cradley Heath	d			09 50			10 42		11 14							11 42	12 14				12 42		13 14
Lye	d								11 17								12 17						13 17
Stourbridge Junction 2	d			09 55			10 47		11a20							11 47	12a20				12 47		13a20
Hagley	d			09 59			10 51									11 51					12 51		
Blakedown	d						10 54									11 54					12 54		
Kidderminster	d			10 05			10 59									11 59					12 59		
Hartlebury	d																						
University	d					10 06													12 06				
Barnt Green	d																						
Bromsgrove	d					10 20													12 21				
Droitwich Spa	d			10 17		10 30	11 11									12 11			12 32		13 11		
Worcester Shrub Hill 7	a			10 25		10 37	11 19									12 19			12 40				
	d		09 05	10 28	10 34	10 52	11 33								12 09				12 47	13 10			
Worcester Foregate Street 7	a		09 07	10 30	10 36	10 54	11 35								12 11				12 49	13 12	13 20		
	d		09 08	10 30	10 40	10 55	11 35								12 12				12 50	13 14			
Malvern Link	d		09 17	10 39	10 52	11 05	11 44								12 21				12 59	13 23			
Great Malvern	a		09 19	10 41	10 54	11 07	11 46								12 24				13 01	13 26			
	d		09 20			11 08									12 27				13 02	13 27			
Colwall	d		09 25			11 13									12 33				13 07	13 34			
Ledbury	a		09 31			11 20									12 40				13 14	13 41			
	d		09 32			11 21									12 42				13 15	13 52			
Hereford 7	a		09 48			11 39									12 59				13 32	14 08			

A not 8 December

Table 71

Sundays

8 December to 9 February

Stratford-upon-Avon, Marylebone and Leamington Spa - Birmingham - Stourbridge, Worcester and Hereford

Network Diagram - see first Page of Table 71

		CH	XC	CH	CH	LM	CH	LM	XC	LM	CH	XC	GW	LM	CH	LM	CH	XC	CH	XC	CH	LM	CH
		◇	◇1	◇	◇		◇		◇1		◇	◇1	◇1		◇		◇	◇1	◇	◇1	◇		◇
			🛒						🛒			🛒	🍽					🛒		🛒			🛒
Stratford-upon-Avon	d	11 38				12 29								13 29			13 38					14 29	
Stratford-upon-Avon Parkway	d	11 41				12 33								13 33			13 41					14 33	
Wilmcote	d	11 44				12 36								13 36			13 44					14 36	
Wootton Wawen	d																						
Henley-in-Arden	d					12 43								13 43								14 43	
Danzey	d																						
Wood End	d																						
The Lakes	d					12x49								13x49								14x49	
Earlswood (West Midlands)	d																						
Wythall	d					12 53								13 53								14 53	
Whitlocks End	d					12 56								13 56								14 56	
Shirley	d					12 59								13 58								14 59	
Yardley Wood	d					13 01								14 01								15 01	
Hall Green	d					13 05								14 04								15 05	
Spring Road	d					13 07								14 06								15 07	
London Marylebone 10 ⊖115	d			11 06	11 09		11 36				12 06				12 36				13 06		13 09		13 36
Banbury	d		11 55	12 03	12 31		12 41		12 55		13 03	13 35			13 41			13 55	14 03	14 24	14 31		14 41
Leamington Spa 8	a	12 05	12 11	12 20	12 49		12 58		13 11		13 20	13 50			13 58		14 05	14 11	14 20	14 40	14 49		14 58
	d		12 12	12 21	12 50		12 59		13 12		13 21	13 52			13 59			14 12	14 21	14 42	14 50		14 59
Warwick	d				12 54		13 03								14 03						14 54		15 03
Warwick Parkway	d			12 27			13 07				13 27				14 07				14 27				15 07
Hatton	d				13a01										14 12						15a01		
Lapworth	d														14 17								
Dorridge	d			12 37			13 17	13 27			13 37				14 23	14 27			14 37				15 17
Widney Manor	d							13 32								14 32							
Solihull	d			12 43			13 23	13 35			13 43				14 29	14 35			14 43				15 23
Olton	d							13 38								14 38							
Acocks Green	d							13 41								14 41							
Tyseley	d					13 10								14 09								15 10	
Small Heath	d																						
Bordesley	d																						
Birmingham Moor Street	d			12a57		13 15	13 32	13 48			13a57			14 14	14 38	14 48			14a57			15 15	15 32
Birmingham Snow Hill ⇌	a					13 17	13 39	13 50						14 17	14 47	14 50						15 17	15 39
	d					13 22		13 52						14 22		14 52						15 22	
Jewellery Quarter ⇌	d					13 24		13 54						14 24		14 54						15 24	
The Hawthorns ⇌	d					13 28		13 58						14 28		14 58						15 28	
Smethwick Galton Bridge 7	d					13 31		14 01						14 31		15 01						15 31	
Coventry	a		12 24						13 23									14 23					
Birmingham Intl. 68 ✈	a		12 38						13 37									14 37					
Birmingham New Street 12 68	a		12 50						13 48			14 19						14 48		15 09			
	d									13 58													
Langley Green	d							14 04								15 04							
Rowley Regis	d					13 37		14 07						14 37		15 07						15 37	
Old Hill	d							14 10								15 10							
Cradley Heath	d					13 42		14 14						14 42		15 14						15 42	
Lye	d							14 17								15 17							
Stourbridge Junction 2	d					13 47		14a20						14 47		15a20						15 47	
Hagley	d					13 51								14 51								15 51	
Blakedown	d													14 54									
Kidderminster	d					13 57								14 59								15 57	
Hartlebury	d																						
University	d									14 04													
Barnt Green	d																						
Bromsgrove	d									14 18													
Droitwich Spa	d					14 09				14 29				15 11								16 09	
Worcester Shrub Hill 7	a									14 36													
	d									14 50			15 08										
Worcester Foregate Street 7	a					14 18				14 52			15 11	15 20								16 18	
	d									14 53			15 12										
Malvern Link	d									15 02			15 21										
Great Malvern	a									15 04			15 24										
	d									15 06			15 25										
Colwall	d									15 11			15 31										
Ledbury	a									15 18			15 38										
	d									15 19			15 41										
Hereford 7	a									15 37			15 57										

Table 71

Sundays

8 December to 9 February

Stratford-upon-Avon, Marylebone and Leamington Spa - Birmingham - Stourbridge, Worcester and Hereford

Network Diagram - see first Page of Table 71

Station		LM		XC	LM	CH	XC	GW	LM	CH	LM	CH		XC	CH	LM	GW	XC	CH	LM	CH	LM		XC	LM
				◇1 🛒		◇	◇1 🛒	◇1		◇		◇		◇1 🛒	◇		◇1	◇1 🛒	◇		◇			◇1 🛒	
Stratford-upon-Avon	d								15 29			15 38								16 29					
Stratford-upon-Avon Parkway	d								15 33			15 41								16 33					
Wilmcote	d								15 36			15 44								16 36					
Wootton Wawen	d																								
Henley-in-Arden	d								15 43											16 43					
Danzey	d																								
Wood End	d																								
The Lakes	d								15x49											16x49					
Earlswood (West Midlands)	d																								
Wythall	d								15 53											16 53					
Whitlocks End	d								15 56											16 56					
Shirley	d								15 59											16 59					
Yardley Wood	d								16 01											17 01					
Hall Green	d								16 05											17 05					
Spring Road	d								16 07											17 07					
London Marylebone 10 ⊖115	d					14 06				14 36					15 06				15 09		15 36				
Banbury	d			14 55		15 03	15 25			15 41				15 55	16 03			16 25	16 32		16 41			16 55	
Leamington Spa 8	a			15 11		15 20	15 41			15 58		16 05		16 11	16 20			16 41	16 50		16 58			17 11	
	d			15 12		15 21	15 43			15 59				16 12	16 21			16 43	16 51		16 59			17 12	
Warwick	d									16 03									16 55		17 03				
Warwick Parkway	d					15 27				16 07					16 27						17 07				
Hatton	d									16 12									17a02						
Lapworth	d									16 17															
Dorridge	d	15 27				15 37				16 23	16 27				16 37						17 17	17 27			
Widney Manor	d	15 32									16 32											17 32			
Solihull	d	15 35				15 43				16 29	16 35				16 43						17 23	17 35			
Olton	d	15 38									16 38											17 38			
Acocks Green	d	15 41									16 41											17 41			
Tyseley	d								16 10											17 10					
Small Heath	d																								
Bordesley	d																								
Birmingham Moor Street	d	15 48				15a57			16 15	16 38	16 48				16a57	17 02				17 15	17 32	17 48			
Birmingham Snow Hill 🚋	a	15 50							16 17	16 45	16 50					17 04				17 17	17 39	17 50			
	d	15 52							16 22		16 52					17 05				17 22		17 52			
Jewellery Quarter 🚋	d	15 54							16 24		16 54									17 24		17 54			
The Hawthorns 🚋	d	15 58							16 28		16 58									17 28		17 58			
Smethwick Galton Bridge 7	d	16 01							16 31		17 01									17 31		18 01			
Coventry	a			15 23										16 23										17 23	
Birmingham Intl. 68 ✈	a			15 35										16 35										17 35	
Birmingham New Street 12 68	a			15 48			16 09							16 48				17 10						17 48	
	d				15 58																				17 58
Langley Green	d	16 04									17 04											18 04			
Rowley Regis	d	16 07							16 37		17 07									17 37		18 07			
Old Hill	d	16 10									17 10											18 10			
Cradley Heath	d	16 14							16 42		17 14									17 42		18 14			
Lye	d	16 17									17 17											18 17			
Stourbridge Junction 2	d	16a21							16 47		17a20					17 23				17 47		18a20			
Hagley	d								16 51							17 26				17 51					
Blakedown	d																								
Kidderminster	d								16 57							17 32				17 57					
Hartlebury	d																								
University	d				16 04																				18 04
Barnt Green	d																								
Bromsgrove	d				16 18																				18 18
Droitwich Spa	d				16 28				17 09							17 44				18 09					18 28
Worcester Shrub Hill 7	a				16 36											17 51									18 36
	d				16 39			17 11									18 05								18 39
Worcester Foregate Street 7	a				16 42			17 13	17 18								18 07			18 18					18 42
	d				16 42			17 14																	18 42
Malvern Link	d				16 51			17 23																	18 51
Great Malvern	a				16 54			17 25																	18 54
	d				17 03			17 26																	18 59
Colwall	d				17 09			17 31																	19 04
Ledbury	a				17 16			17 38																	19 11
	d				17 16			17 39																	19 12
Hereford 7	a				17 34			17 55																	19 30

Table 71

Sundays

8 December to 9 February

Stratford-upon-Avon, Marylebone and Leamington Spa - Birmingham - Stourbridge, Worcester and Hereford

Network Diagram - see first Page of Table 71

		CH	XC	GW	LM	CH	CH	XC		LM	CH	XC	GW	GW	LM	CH	CH	XC		LM	CH	XC	LM	CH	XC
		◇	◇1	◇1		◇	◇	◇1			◇	◇1	◇1	◇1		◇	◇	◇1			◇	◇1		◇	◇1
													A	B											
			🛒					🛒				🛒	🍽	🍽				🛒			BZ	🛒			🛒
Stratford-upon-Avon	d				17 29		17 38								18 29								19 29		
Stratford-upon-Avon Parkway	d				17 33		17 41								18 33								19 33		
Wilmcote	d				17 36		17 44								18 36								19 36		
Wootton Wawen	d																								
Henley-in-Arden	d				17 43										18 43								19 43		
Danzey	d																								
Wood End	d																								
The Lakes	d				17x49										18x49								19x49		
Earlswood (West Midlands)	d																								
Wythall	d				17 53										18 53								19 53		
Whitlocks End	d				17 56										18 56								19 56		
Shirley	d				17 59										18 59								19 59		
Yardley Wood	d				18 01										19 01								20 01		
Hall Green	d				18 05										19 05								20 05		
Spring Road	d				18 07										19 07								20 07		
London Marylebone 10 ⊖115	d	16 06				16 36					17 06					17 36	17 09				18 06			18 36	
Banbury	d	17 03	17 25			17 41		17 54			18 03	18 25				18 41	18 45	18 55			19 04	19 24		19 41	19 55
Leamington Spa 8	a	17 20	17 41			17 58	18 05	18 11			18 20	18 41				18 58	19 04	19 11			19 22	19 41		19 58	20 11
	d	17 21	17 43			17 59		18 12			18 21	18 43				18 59	19 05	19 12			19 23	19 42		19 59	20 12
Warwick	d					18 03										19 03	19 09							20 03	
Warwick Parkway	d	17 27				18 07					18 27					19 07					19 29			20 07	
Hatton	d					18 12											19a16								
Lapworth	d					18 17																			
Dorridge	d	17 37				18 22					18 37					19 17					19 40			20 17	
Widney Manor	d					18 26										19 20								20 20	
Solihull	d	17 43				18 29					18 43					19 24					19 46			20 24	
Olton	d																								
Acocks Green	d																								
Tyseley	d				18 10										19 10								20 10		
Small Heath	d																								
Bordesley	d																								
Birmingham Moor Street	d	17a57			18 15	18 39					18a57				19 15	19 34					20a00		20 15	20 34	
Birmingham Snow Hill 🚋	a				18 17	18 46									19 17	19 41							20 17	20 41	
	d				18 22										19 22								20 22		
Jewellery Quarter 🚋	d				18 24										19 24								20 24		
The Hawthorns 🚋	d				18 28										19 28								20 28		
Smethwick Galton Bridge 7	d				18 31										19 31								20 31		
Coventry	a							18 23										19 24				19 53			20 23
Birmingham Intl. 68 ✈	a							18 35										19 37				20 03			20 35
Birmingham New Street 12 68	a		18 09					18 48				19 11						19 48				20 15			20 48
	d									18 58										19 58					
Langley Green	d																								
Rowley Regis	d				18 37										19 37								20 37		
Old Hill	d																								
Cradley Heath	d				18 42										19 42								20 42		
Lye	d																								
Stourbridge Junction 2	d				18 47										19 47								20 47		
Hagley	d				18 51										19 51								20 51		
Blakedown	d				18 54																				
Kidderminster	d				18 59										19 57								20 57		
Hartlebury	d																								
University	d									19 04										20 04					
Barnt Green	d																								
Bromsgrove	d									19 18										20 18					
Droitwich Spa	d				19 11					19 28					20 09					20 31			21 09		
Worcester Shrub Hill 7	a				19 19					19 36					20 17					20 40			21 17		
	d			19 10						19 40			20 16	20 16						20 58			21 23		
Worcester Foregate Street 7	a			19 13						19 42			20 18	20 19						21 00			21 25		
	d			19 13									20 20	20 20									21 25		
Malvern Link	d			19 22									20 29	20 29									21 34		
Great Malvern	a			19 25									20 32	20 32									21 37		
	d												20 33	20 33											
Colwall	d												20 39	20 39											
Ledbury	a												20 46	20 46											
	d												20 48	20 48											
Hereford 7	a												21 04	21 04											

A from 5 January

B until 29 December

BZ Business Zone available offering greater comfortand an enhanced working environment.

Supplement payable.

Table 71

Sundays
8 December to 9 February

Stratford-upon-Avon, Marylebone and Leamington Spa - Birmingham - Stourbridge, Worcester and Hereford

Network Diagram - see first Page of Table 71

		LM	CH	CH	XC	GW	LM	CH	XC	LM	CH	XC	CH	XC	LM	CH	XC	CH
			◇	◇	◇1	◇1		◇	◇1		◇	◇1	◇	◇1		◇	◇1	◇
Stratford-upon-Avon	d			20 00														
Stratford-upon-Avon Parkway	d			20 03														
Wilmcote	d			20 06														
Wootton Wawen	d																	
Henley-in-Arden	d																	
Danzey	d																	
Wood End	d																	
The Lakes	d																	
Earlswood (West Midlands)	d																	
Wythall	d																	
Whitlocks End	d																	
Shirley	d																	
Yardley Wood	d																	
Hall Green	d																	
Spring Road	d																	
London Marylebone 10 ⊖115	d		19 06					19 30			20 06		20 30			21 00		22 08
Banbury	d		20 03		20 24			20 41	20 55		21 05	21 24	21 41	21 54		22 10	22 24	23 08
Leamington Spa 8	a		20 20	20 27	20 40			20 58	21 11		21 22	21 40	21 58	22 11		22 27	22 40	23 25
	d		20 21		20 42			20 59	21 12		21 23	21 41	21 59	22 12		22 28	22 42	23 26
Warwick	d							21 03			21 27		22 03			22 32		23 30
Warwick Parkway	d		20 27					21 07			21 31		22 07			22 36		23 34
Hatton	d							21 12								22 41		
Lapworth	d							21 17								22 46		
Dorridge	d		20 37					21 23			21 41		22 17			22 51		23 44
Widney Manor	d							21 26								22 55		
Solihull	d		20 43					21 30			21 47		22 23			22 58		23 50
Olton	d																	
Acocks Green	d																	
Tyseley	d																	
Small Heath	d																	
Bordesley	d																	
Birmingham Moor Street	d		20a57				21 41	21 39			22a03		22 32		22 52	23 08		23 59
Birmingham Snow Hill	a						21 43	21 46					22 39		22 54	23 15		00 06
	d						21 46								22 55			
Jewellery Quarter	d						21 48								22 57			
The Hawthorns	d						21 52								23 01			
Smethwick Galton Bridge 7	d						21 55								23 04			
Coventry	a				20 53				21 23			21 52		22 22			22 52	
Birmingham Intl. 68 ✈	a				21 03				21 35			22 02		22 32			23 02	
Birmingham New Street 12 68	a				21 15				21 48			22 14		22 43			23 13	
	d	20 58								22 05								
Langley Green	d																	
Rowley Regis	d						22 00								23 09			
Old Hill	d																	
Cradley Heath	d						22 05								23 14			
Lye	d																	
Stourbridge Junction 2	d						22 10								23 20			
Hagley	d						22 14								23 23			
Blakedown	d																	
Kidderminster	d						22 20								23 29			
Hartlebury	d																	
University	d	21 04								22 11								
Barnt Green	d																	
Bromsgrove	d	21 18								22 25								
Droitwich Spa	d	21 29					22 31			22 35					23 41			
Worcester Shrub Hill 7	a	21 36					22 39			22 44					23 49			
	d	21 40				22 12				22 48								
Worcester Foregate Street 7	a	21 42				22 14				22 50								
	d	21 43				22 16				22 51								
Malvern Link	d	21 52				22 25				23 00								
Great Malvern	a	21 54				22 28				23 02								
	d	21 56																
Colwall	d	22 01																
Ledbury	a	22 08																
	d	22 09																
Hereford 7	a	22 27																

Table 71

Sundays

16 February to 23 March

Stratford-upon-Avon, Marylebone and Leamington Spa - Birmingham - Stourbridge, Worcester and Hereford

Network Diagram - see first Page of Table 71

		LM	LM	LM	GW	LM	LM	CH	LM	CH		XC	CH	CH	XC	GW	LM	LM	CH	LM		GW	LM	CH	LM
					◇1			◇		◇		◇1	◇	◇	◇1	◇1			◇			◇1		◇	
												trolley			trolley	buffet						buffet			
Stratford-upon-Avon	d						09 29			09 38							10 29						11 29		
Stratford-upon-Avon Parkway	d						09 33			09 41							10 33						11 33		
Wilmcote	d						09 36			09 44							10 36						11 36		
Wootton Wawen	d																								
Henley-in-Arden	d						09 43										10 43						11 43		
Danzey	d																								
Wood End	d																								
The Lakes	d						09x49										10x49						11x49		
Earlswood (West Midlands)	d																								
Wythall	d						09 53										10 53						11 53		
Whitlocks End	d						09 56										10 56						11 56		
Shirley	d						09 59										10 59						11 59		
Yardley Wood	d						10 01										11 01						12 01		
Hall Green	d						10 05										11 05						12 05		
Spring Road	d						10 07										11 07						12 07		
London Marylebone 10 ⊖115	d							08 15					09 06	09 30					10 06					10 36	
Banbury	d							09 28				09 55	10 16	10 31	10 59				11 03					11 41	
Leamington Spa 8	a							09 46		10 05		10 11	10 33	10 49	11 15				11 20					11 58	
	d							09 46				10 12	10 34	10 50	11 16				11 21					11 59	
Warwick	d							09 51					10 38	10 54					11 25					12 03	
Warwick Parkway	d							09 54					10 42						11 29					12 07	
Hatton	d							10 00						11a01										12 12	
Lapworth	d							10 06																12 17	
Dorridge	d							10 11	10 27				10 52					11 27	11 39					12 23	12 27
Widney Manor	d								10 32									11 32							12 32
Solihull	d							10 16	10 35				10 58					11 35	11 45					12 29	12 35
Olton	d								10 38									11 38							12 38
Acocks Green	d								10 41									11 41							12 41
Tyseley	d						10 10										11 10						12 10		
Small Heath	d																								
Bordesley	d																								
Birmingham Moor Street	d	00 03		09 26			10 15	10 25	10 48				11 07				11 15	11 48	11 54				12 15	12 41	12 48
Birmingham Snow Hill ⛴	a	00 05		09 28			10 17	10 32	10 50				11 14				11 17	11 50	12 01				12 17	12 48	12 50
	d			09 30			10 22		10 52								11 22	11 52					12 22		12 52
Jewellery Quarter ⛴	d			09 32			10 24		10 54								11 24	11 54					12 24		12 54
The Hawthorns ⛴	d			09 36			10 28		10 58								11 28	11 58					12 28		12 58
Smethwick Galton Bridge 7	d			09 39			10 31		11 01								11 31	12 01					12 31		13 01
Coventry	a											10 24			11 27										
Birmingham Intl. 68 ✈	a											10 38			11 38										
Birmingham New Street 12 68	a											10 50			11 51										
	d					10 00														12 00					
Langley Green	d								11 04									12 04							13 04
Rowley Regis	d			09 45			10 37		11 07								11 37	12 07					12 37		13 07
Old Hill	d								11 10									12 10							13 10
Cradley Heath	d			09 50			10 42		11 14								11 42	12 14					12 42		13 14
Lye	d								11 17									12 17							13 17
Stourbridge Junction 2	d			09 55			10 47		11a20								11 47	12a20					12 47		13a20
Hagley	d			09 59			10 51										11 51						12 51		
Blakedown	d						10 54										11 54						12 54		
Kidderminster	d			10 05			10 59										11 59						12 59		
Hartlebury	d																								
University	d					10 06														12 06					
Barnt Green	d																								
Bromsgrove	d					10 20														12 21					
Droitwich Spa	d			10 17		10 30	11 11										12 11			12 32			13 11		
Worcester Shrub Hill 7	a			10 25		10 37	11 19										12 19			12 40					
	d		09 05	10 28	10 34	10 52	11 33									12 09				12 47		13 10			
Worcester Foregate Street 7	a		09 07	10 30	10 36	10 54	11 35									12 11				12 49		13 12	13 20		
	d		09 08	10 30	10 40	10 55	11 35									12 12				12 50		13 14			
Malvern Link	d		09 17	10 39	10 52	11 05	11 44									12 21				12 59		13 23			
Great Malvern	a		09 19	10 41	10 54	11 07	11 46									12 24				13 01		13 26			
	d		09 20			11 08										12 27				13 02		13 27			
Colwall	d		09 25			11 13										12 33				13 07		13 33			
Ledbury	a		09 31			11 20										12 40				13 14		13 41			
	d		09 32			11 21										12 42				13 15		13 52			
Hereford 7	a		09 48			11 39										12 59				13 32		14 08			

Table 71

Sundays

16 February to 23 March

Stratford-upon-Avon, Marylebone and Leamington Spa - Birmingham - Stourbridge, Worcester and Hereford

Network Diagram - see first Page of Table 71

		CH	XC	CH	CH	LM		CH	LM	XC	LM	CH	XC	GW	LM	CH		LM	CH	XC	CH	XC	CH	LM	CH
		◇	◇1	◇	◇			◇		◇1		◇	◇1	◇1		◇			◇	◇1	◇	◇1	◇		◇
			🛒							🛒			🛒	🍽						🛒		🛒			🛒
Stratford-upon-Avon	d	11 38				12 29									13 29				13 38					14 29	
Stratford-upon-Avon Parkway	d	11 41				12 33									13 33				13 41					14 33	
Wilmcote	d	11 44				12 36									13 36				13 44					14 36	
Wootton Wawen	d																								
Henley-in-Arden	d					12 43									13 43									14 43	
Danzey	d																								
Wood End	d																								
The Lakes	d					12x49									13x49									14x49	
Earlswood (West Midlands)	d																								
Wythall	d					12 53									13 53									14 53	
Whitlocks End	d					12 56									13 56									14 56	
Shirley	d					12 59									13 58									14 59	
Yardley Wood	d					13 01									14 01									15 01	
Hall Green	d					13 05									14 04									15 05	
Spring Road	d					13 07									14 06									15 07	
London Marylebone 10 ⊖115	d			11 06	11 09			11 36				12 06				12 36					13 06		13 09		13 36
Banbury	d		11 59	12 03	12 31			12 41		12 59		13 03	13 35			13 41				13 59	14 03	14 24	14 31		14 41
Leamington Spa 8	a	12 05	12 14	12 20	12 49			12 58		13 14		13 20	13 50			13 58			14 05	14 14	14 20	14 40	14 49		14 58
	d		12 15	12 21	12 50			12 59		13 15		13 21	13 52			13 59				14 15	14 21	14 42	14 50		14 59
Warwick	d				12 54			13 03								14 03							14 54		15 03
Warwick Parkway	d			12 27				13 07				13 27				14 07					14 27				15 07
Hatton	d				13a01											14 12							15a01		
Lapworth	d															14 17									
Dorridge	d			12 37				13 17	13 27			13 37				14 23		14 27			14 37				15 17
Widney Manor	d								13 32									14 32							
Solihull	d			12 43				13 23	13 35			13 43				14 29		14 35			14 43				15 23
Olton	d								13 38									14 38							
Acocks Green	d								13 41									14 41							
Tyseley	d					13 10									14 09									15 10	
Small Heath	d																								
Bordesley	d																								
Birmingham Moor Street	d			12a57		13 15		13 32	13 48			13a57			14 14	14 38		14 48			14a57			15 15	15 32
Birmingham Snow Hill 🚊	a					13 17		13 39	13 50						14 17	14 47		14 50						15 17	15 39
	d					13 22			13 52						14 22			14 52						15 22	
Jewellery Quarter 🚊	d					13 24			13 54						14 24			14 54						15 24	
The Hawthorns 🚊	d					13 28			13 58						14 28			14 58						15 28	
Smethwick Galton Bridge 7	d					13 31			14 01						14 31			15 01						15 31	
Coventry	a		12 26							13 26										14 26					
Birmingham Intl. 68 ✈	a		12 37							13 37										14 37					
Birmingham New Street 12 68	a		12 49							13 50			14 19							14 48		15 09			
	d										13 58														
Langley Green	d								14 04									15 04							
Rowley Regis	d					13 37			14 07						14 37			15 07						15 37	
Old Hill	d								14 10									15 10							
Cradley Heath	d					13 42			14 14						14 42			15 14						15 42	
Lye	d								14 17									15 17							
Stourbridge Junction 2	d					13 47			14a20						14 47			15a20						15 47	
Hagley	d					13 51									14 51									15 51	
Blakedown	d														14 54										
Kidderminster	d					13 57									14 59									15 57	
Hartlebury	d																								
University	d										14 04														
Barnt Green	d																								
Bromsgrove	d										14 18														
Droitwich Spa	d					14 09					14 29				15 11									16 09	
Worcester Shrub Hill 7	a										14 36														
	d										14 50			15 08											
Worcester Foregate Street 7	a					14 18					14 52			15 11	15 20									16 18	
	d										14 53			15 12											
Malvern Link	d										15 02			15 21											
Great Malvern	a										15 04			15 24											
	d										15 06			15 25											
Colwall	d										15 11			15 31											
Ledbury	a										15 18			15 38											
	d										15 19			15 41											
Hereford 7	a										15 37			15 57											

Table 71

Sundays

16 February to 23 March

Stratford-upon-Avon, Marylebone and Leamington Spa - Birmingham - Stourbridge, Worcester and Hereford

Network Diagram - see first Page of Table 71

		LM		XC	LM	CH	XC	GW	LM	CH	LM	CH		XC	CH	LM	GW	XC	CH	LM	CH	LM		XC	LM
				◇1		◇	◇1	◇1		◇		◇		◇1	◇		◇1	◇1	◇		◇			◇1	
				🛒			🛒							🛒				🛒						🛒	
Stratford-upon-Avon	d								15 29			15 38								16 29					
Stratford-upon-Avon Parkway	d								15 33			15 41								16 33					
Wilmcote	d								15 36			15 44								16 36					
Wootton Wawen	d																								
Henley-in-Arden	d								15 43											16 43					
Danzey	d																								
Wood End	d																								
The Lakes	d								15x49											16x49					
Earlswood (West Midlands)	d																								
Wythall	d								15 53											16 53					
Whitlocks End	d								15 56											16 56					
Shirley	d								15 59											16 59					
Yardley Wood	d								16 01											17 01					
Hall Green	d								16 05											17 05					
Spring Road	d								16 07											17 07					
London Marylebone 10 ⊖115	d					14 06				14 36					15 06				15 09		15 36				
Banbury	d			14 59		15 03	15 25			15 41				15 59	16 03			16 25	16 32		16 41			16 59	
Leamington Spa 8	a			15 14		15 20	15 41			15 58		16 05		16 14	16 20			16 41	16 50		16 58			17 14	
	d			15 15		15 21	15 43			15 59				16 15	16 21			16 43	16 51		16 59			17 15	
Warwick	d									16 03									16 55		17 03				
Warwick Parkway	d					15 27				16 07					16 27						17 07				
Hatton	d									16 12									17a02						
Lapworth	d									16 17															
Dorridge	d	15 27				15 37				16 23	16 27				16 37						17 17	17 27			
Widney Manor	d	15 32									16 32											17 32			
Solihull	d	15 35				15 43				16 29	16 35				16 43						17 23	17 35			
Olton	d	15 38									16 38											17 38			
Acocks Green	d	15 41									16 41											17 41			
Tyseley	d								16 10											17 10					
Small Heath	d																								
Bordesley	d																								
Birmingham Moor Street	d	15 48				15a57			16 15	16 38	16 48				16a57	17 02				17 15	17 32	17 48			
Birmingham Snow Hill 🚊	a	15 50							16 17	16 45	16 50					17 04				17 17	17 39	17 50			
	d	15 52							16 22		16 52					17 05				17 22		17 52			
Jewellery Quarter 🚊	d	15 54							16 24		16 54									17 24		17 54			
The Hawthorns 🚊	d	15 58							16 28		16 58									17 28		17 58			
Smethwick Galton Bridge 7	d	16 01							16 31		17 01									17 31		18 01			
Coventry	a			15 26										16 26										17 26	
Birmingham Intl. 68 ✈	a			15 37										16 37										17 37	
Birmingham New Street 12 68	a			15 50			16 09							16 50				17 10						17 50	
	d				15 58																				17 58
Langley Green	d	16 04									17 04											18 04			
Rowley Regis	d	16 07							16 37		17 07									17 37		18 07			
Old Hill	d	16 10									17 10											18 10			
Cradley Heath	d	16 14							16 42		17 14									17 42		18 14			
Lye	d	16 17									17 17											18 17			
Stourbridge Junction 2	d	16a21							16 47		17a20					17 23				17 47		18a20			
Hagley	d								16 51							17 26				17 51					
Blakedown	d																								
Kidderminster	d								16 57							17 32				17 57					
Hartlebury	d																								
University	d				16 04																				18 04
Barnt Green	d																								
Bromsgrove	d				16 18																				18 18
Droitwich Spa	d				16 28				17 09							17 44				18 09					18 28
Worcester Shrub Hill 7	a				16 36											17 51									18 36
	d				16 39			17 11									18 05								18 39
Worcester Foregate Street 7	a				16 42			17 13	17 18								18 07			18 18					18 42
	d				16 42			17 14																	18 42
Malvern Link	d				16 51			17 23																	18 51
Great Malvern	a				16 54			17 25																	18 54
	d				17 03			17 26																	18 59
Colwall	d				17 09			17 31																	19 04
Ledbury	a				17 16			17 38																	19 11
	d				17 16			17 39																	19 12
Hereford 7	a				17 34			17 55																	19 30

Table 71

Sundays

16 February to 23 March

Stratford-upon-Avon, Marylebone and Leamington Spa - Birmingham - Stourbridge, Worcester and Hereford

Network Diagram - see first Page of Table 71

	CH	XC	GW	LM	CH	CH	XC	LM	CH	XC	GW	LM	CH	CH	XC	LM	CH	XC	LM	CH	XC	LM
	◇	◇1	◇1		◇	◇	◇1		◇	◇1	◇1		◇	◇	◇1		◇	◇1		◇	◇1	
		🛒					🛒			🛒	☕				🛒		BZ	🛒			🛒	
Stratford-upon-Avon d				17 29		17 38						18 29							19 29			
Stratford-upon-Avon Parkway d				17 33		17 41						18 33							19 33			
Wilmcote d				17 36		17 44						18 36							19 36			
Wootton Wawen d																						
Henley-in-Arden d				17 43								18 43							19 43			
Danzey d																						
Wood End d																						
The Lakes d				17x49								18x49							19x49			
Earlswood (West Midlands) d																						
Wythall d				17 53								18 53							19 53			
Whitlocks End d				17 56								18 56							19 56			
Shirley d				17 59								18 59							19 59			
Yardley Wood d				18 01								19 01							20 01			
Hall Green d				18 05								19 05							20 05			
Spring Road d				18 07								19 07							20 07			
London Marylebone 10 ⊖115 d	16 06				16 36				17 06				17 36	17 09			18 06			18 36		
Banbury d	17 03	17 25			17 41		17 59		18 03	18 25			18 41	18 45	18 59		19 04	19 24		19 41	19 59	
Leamington Spa 8 a	17 20	17 41			17 58	18 05	18 14		18 20	18 41			18 58	19 04	19 14		19 22	19 41		19 58	20 14	
d	17 21	17 43			17 59		18 15		18 21	18 43			18 59	19 05	19 15		19 23	19 42		19 59	20 15	
Warwick d					18 03								19 03	19 09						20 03		
Warwick Parkway d	17 27				18 07				18 27				19 07				19 29			20 07		
Hatton d					18 12									19a16								
Lapworth d					18 17																	
Dorridge d	17 37				18 22				18 37				19 17				19 40			20 17		
Widney Manor d					18 26								19 20							20 20		
Solihull d	17 43				18 29				18 43				19 24				19 46			20 24		
Olton d																						
Acocks Green d																						
Tyseley d				18 10								19 10							20 10			
Small Heath d																						
Bordesley d																						
Birmingham Moor Street d	17a57			18 15	18 39				18a57			19 15	19 34				20a00		20 15	20 34		
Birmingham Snow Hill 🚊 a				18 17	18 46							19 17	19 41						20 17	20 41		
d				18 22								19 22							20 22			
Jewellery Quarter 🚊 d				18 24								19 24							20 24			
The Hawthorns 🚊 d				18 28								19 28							20 28			
Smethwick Galton Bridge 7 d				18 31								19 31							20 31			
Coventry a							18 26								19 27			19 53			20 27	
Birmingham Intl. 68 ✈ a							18 37								19 38			20 03			20 38	
Birmingham New Street 12 68 a		18 09					18 50			19 11					19 50			20 15			20 50	
d								18 58								19 58						20 58
Langley Green d																						
Rowley Regis d				18 37								19 37							20 37			
Old Hill d																						
Cradley Heath d				18 42								19 42							20 42			
Lye d																						
Stourbridge Junction 2 d				18 47								19 47							20 47			
Hagley d				18 51								19 51							20 51			
Blakedown d				18 54																		
Kidderminster d				18 59								19 57							20 57			
Hartlebury d																						
University d								19 04								20 04						21 04
Barnt Green d																						
Bromsgrove d								19 18								20 18						21 18
Droitwich Spa d				19 11				19 28				20 09				20 31			21 09			21 29
Worcester Shrub Hill 7 a				19 19				19 36				20 17				20 40			21 17			21 36
d			19 10					19 40			20 16					20 58			21 23			21 40
Worcester Foregate Street 7 a			19 13					19 42			20 18					21 00			21 25			21 42
d			19 13								20 20								21 25			21 43
Malvern Link d			19 22								20 29								21 34			21 52
Great Malvern a			19 25								20 32								21 37			21 54
d											20 33											21 56
Colwall d											20 39											22 01
Ledbury a											20 46											22 08
d											20 48											22 09
Hereford 7 a											21 04											22 27

BZ Business Zone available offering greater comfortand an enhanced working environment. Supplement payable.

Table 71

Sundays

16 February to 23 March

Stratford-upon-Avon, Marylebone and Leamington Spa - Birmingham - Stourbridge, Worcester and Hereford

Network Diagram - see first Page of Table 71

		CH	CH	XC		GW	LM	CH	XC	LM	CH	XC	CH	XC		LM	CH	XC	CH
		◇	◇	◇1		◇1		◇	◇1		◇	◇1	◇	◇1			◇	◇1	◇
Stratford-upon-Avon	d		20 00																
Stratford-upon-Avon Parkway	d		20 03																
Wilmcote	d		20 06																
Wootton Wawen	d																		
Henley-in-Arden	d																		
Danzey	d																		
Wood End	d																		
The Lakes	d																		
Earlswood (West Midlands)	d																		
Wythall	d																		
Whitlocks End	d																		
Shirley	d																		
Yardley Wood	d																		
Hall Green	d																		
Spring Road	d																		
London Marylebone 10 ⊖115	d	19 06						19 30			20 06		20 30				21 00		22 08
Banbury	d	20 03		20 26				20 41	21 00		21 05	21 24	21 41	21 59			22 10	22 24	23 08
Leamington Spa 8	a	20 20	20 27	20 42				20 58	21 16		21 22	21 40	21 58	22 15			22 27	22 40	23 25
	d	20 21		20 43				20 59	21 17		21 23	21 41	21 59	22 16			22 28	22 42	23 26
Warwick	d							21 03			21 27		22 03				22 32		23 30
Warwick Parkway	d	20 27						21 07			21 31		22 07				22 36		23 34
Hatton	d							21 12									22 41		
Lapworth	d							21 17									22 46		
Dorridge	d	20 37						21 23			21 41		22 17				22 51		23 44
Widney Manor	d							21 26									22 55		
Solihull	d	20 43						21 30			21 47		22 23				22 58		23 50
Olton	d																		
Acocks Green	d																		
Tyseley	d																		
Small Heath	d																		
Bordesley	d																		
Birmingham Moor Street	d	20a57					21 41	21 39			22a03		22 32			22 52	23 08		23 59
Birmingham Snow Hill	a						21 43	21 46					22 39			22 54	23 15		00 06
	d						21 46									22 55			
Jewellery Quarter	d						21 48									22 57			
The Hawthorns	d						21 52									23 01			
Smethwick Galton Bridge 7	d						21 55									23 04			
Coventry	a			20 54					21 27			21 52		22 26				22 52	
Birmingham Intl. 68 ✈	a			21 04					21 38			22 02		22 38				23 02	
Birmingham New Street 12 68	a			21 16					21 50			22 14		22 49				23 13	
	d									22 05									
Langley Green	d																		
Rowley Regis	d						22 00									23 09			
Old Hill	d																		
Cradley Heath	d						22 05									23 14			
Lye	d																		
Stourbridge Junction 2	d						22 10									23 20			
Hagley	d						22 14									23 23			
Blakedown	d																		
Kidderminster	d						22 20									23 29			
Hartlebury	d																		
University	d									22 11									
Barnt Green	d																		
Bromsgrove	d									22 25									
Droitwich Spa	d						22 31			22 35						23 41			
Worcester Shrub Hill 7	a						22 39			22 44						23 49			
	d					22 12				22 48									
Worcester Foregate Street 7	a					22 14				22 50									
	d					22 16				22 51									
Malvern Link	d					22 25				23 00									
Great Malvern	a					22 28				23 02									
	d																		
Colwall	d																		
Ledbury	a																		
	d																		
Hereford 7	a																		

Table 71

Sundays
30 March to 11 May

Stratford-upon-Avon, Marylebone and Leamington Spa - Birmingham - Stourbridge, Worcester and Hereford

Network Diagram - see first Page of Table 71

		LM	LM	LM	GW	LM	LM	CH	LM	CH		XC	CH	CH	XC	GW	LM	LM	CH	LM		GW	LM	CH	LM
					◇1			◇		◇		◇1	◇	◇	◇1	◇1			◇			◇1		◇	
												🛒			🛒	🍽						🍽			
Stratford-upon-Avon	d						09 29			09 38							10 29						11 29		
Stratford-upon-Avon Parkway	d						09 33			09 41							10 33						11 33		
Wilmcote	d						09 36			09 44							10 36						11 36		
Wootton Wawen	d																								
Henley-in-Arden	d						09 43										10 43						11 43		
Danzey	d																								
Wood End	d																								
The Lakes	d						09x49										10x49						11x49		
Earlswood (West Midlands)	d																								
Wythall	d						09 53										10 53						11 53		
Whitlocks End	d						09 56										10 56						11 56		
Shirley	d						09 59										10 59						11 59		
Yardley Wood	d						10 01										11 01						12 01		
Hall Green	d						10 05										11 05						12 05		
Spring Road	d						10 07										11 07						12 07		
London Marylebone 10 ⊖115	d							08 15					09 06	09 30					10 06					10 36	
Banbury	d							09 28				09 55	10 16	10 31	10 55				11 03					11 41	
Leamington Spa 8	a							09 46		10 05		10 11	10 33	10 49	11 11				11 20					11 58	
	d							09 46				10 12	10 34	10 50	11 12				11 21					11 59	
Warwick	d							09 51					10 38	10 54					11 25					12 03	
Warwick Parkway	d							09 54					10 42						11 29					12 07	
Hatton	d							10 00						11a01										12 12	
Lapworth	d							10 06																12 17	
Dorridge	d							10 11	10 27				10 52					11 27	11 39					12 23	12 27
Widney Manor	d								10 32									11 32							12 32
Solihull	d							10 16	10 35				10 58					11 35	11 45					12 29	12 35
Olton	d								10 38									11 38							12 38
Acocks Green	d								10 41									11 41							12 41
Tyseley	d						10 10										11 10						12 10		
Small Heath	d																								
Bordesley	d																								
Birmingham Moor Street	d	00 03		09 26			10 15	10 25	10 48				11 07				11 15	11 48	11 54				12 15	12 41	12 48
Birmingham Snow Hill 🚊	a	00 05		09 28			10 17	10 32	10 50				11 14				11 17	11 50	12 01				12 17	12 48	12 50
	d			09 30			10 22		10 52								11 22	11 52					12 22		12 52
Jewellery Quarter 🚊	d			09 32			10 24		10 54								11 24	11 54					12 24		12 54
The Hawthorns 🚊	d			09 36			10 28		10 58								11 28	11 58					12 28		12 58
Smethwick Galton Bridge 7	d			09 39			10 31		11 01								11 31	12 01					12 31		13 01
Coventry	a											10 24			11 24										
Birmingham Intl. 68 ✈	a											10 38			11 38										
Birmingham New Street 12 68	a											10 50			11 51										
	d					10 00														12 00					
Langley Green	d								11 04									12 04							13 04
Rowley Regis	d			09 45			10 37		11 07								11 37	12 07					12 37		13 07
Old Hill	d								11 10									12 10							13 10
Cradley Heath	d			09 50			10 42		11 14								11 42	12 14					12 42		13 14
Lye	d								11 17									12 17							13 17
Stourbridge Junction 2	d			09 55			10 47		11a20								11 47	12a20					12 47		13a20
Hagley	d			09 59			10 51										11 51						12 51		
Blakedown	d						10 54										11 54						12 54		
Kidderminster	d			10 05			10 59										11 59						12 59		
Hartlebury	d																								
University	d					10 06														12 06					
Barnt Green	d																								
Bromsgrove	d					10 20														12 21					
Droitwich Spa	d			10 17		10 30	11 11										12 11			12 32			13 11		
Worcester Shrub Hill 7	a			10 25		10 37	11 19										12 19			12 40					
	d		09 05	10 28	10 34	10 52	11 33									12 09				12 47		13 10			
Worcester Foregate Street 7	a		09 07	10 30	10 36	10 54	11 35									12 11				12 49		13 13	13 20		
	d		09 08	10 30	10 40	10 55	11 35									12 12				12 50		13 14			
Malvern Link	d		09 17	10 39	10 52	11 05	11 44									12 21				12 59		13 23			
Great Malvern	a		09 19	10 41	10 54	11 07	11 46									12 24				13 01		13 26			
	d		09 20			11 08										12 27				13 02		13 28			
Colwall	d		09 25			11 13										12 33				13 07		13 34			
Ledbury	a		09 31			11 20										12 40				13 14		13 41			
	d		09 32			11 21										12 42				13 15		13 52			
Hereford 7	a		09 48			11 39										12 59				13 32		14 08			

Table 71

Sundays

30 March to 11 May

Stratford-upon-Avon, Marylebone and Leamington Spa - Birmingham - Stourbridge, Worcester and Hereford

Network Diagram - see first Page of Table 71

		CH	XC	CH	CH	LM	CH	LM	XC	LM	CH	XC	GW	LM	CH	LM	CH	XC	CH	XC	CH	LM	CH
		◇	◇1 🛒	◇	◇		◇		◇1 🛒		◇	◇1 🛒	◇1 ⊡		◇		◇	◇1 🛒	◇	◇1 🛒	◇		◇ 🛒
Stratford-upon-Avon	d	11 38				12 29								13 29			13 38					14 29	
Stratford-upon-Avon Parkway	d	11 41				12 33								13 33			13 41					14 33	
Wilmcote	d	11 44				12 36								13 36			13 44					14 36	
Wootton Wawen	d																						
Henley-in-Arden	d					12 43								13 43								14 43	
Danzey	d																						
Wood End	d																						
The Lakes	d					12x49								13x49								14x49	
Earlswood (West Midlands)	d																						
Wythall	d					12 53								13 53								14 53	
Whitlocks End	d					12 56								13 56								14 56	
Shirley	d					12 59								13 58								14 59	
Yardley Wood	d					13 01								14 01								15 01	
Hall Green	d					13 05								14 04								15 05	
Spring Road	d					13 07								14 06								15 07	
London Marylebone 10 ⊖115	d			11 06	11 09		11 36				12 06				12 36				13 06		13 09		13 36
Banbury	d		11 55	12 03	12 31		12 41		12 55		13 03	13 37			13 41			13 55	14 03	14 24	14 31		14 41
Leamington Spa 8	a	12 05	12 11	12 20	12 49		12 58		13 11		13 20	13 52			13 58		14 05	14 11	14 20	14 40	14 49		14 58
	d		12 12	12 21	12 50		12 59		13 12		13 21	13 53			13 59			14 12	14 21	14 42	14 50		14 59
Warwick	d				12 54		13 03								14 03						14 54		15 03
Warwick Parkway	d			12 27			13 07				13 27				14 07				14 27				15 07
Hatton	d				13a01										14 12						15a01		
Lapworth	d														14 17								
Dorridge	d			12 37			13 17	13 27			13 37				14 23	14 27			14 37				15 17
Widney Manor	d							13 32								14 32							
Solihull	d			12 43			13 23	13 35			13 43				14 29	14 35			14 43				15 23
Olton	d							13 38								14 38							
Acocks Green	d							13 41								14 41							
Tyseley	d					13 10								14 09								15 10	
Small Heath	d																						
Bordesley	d																						
Birmingham Moor Street	d			12a57		13 15	13 32	13 48			13a57			14 14	14 38	14 48			14a57			15 15	15 32
Birmingham Snow Hill 🚊	a					13 17	13 39	13 50						14 17	14 47	14 50						15 17	15 39
	d					13 22		13 52						14 22		14 52						15 22	
Jewellery Quarter 🚊	d					13 24		13 54						14 24		14 54						15 24	
The Hawthorns 🚊	d					13 28		13 58						14 28		14 58						15 28	
Smethwick Galton Bridge 7	d					13 31		14 01						14 31		15 01						15 31	
Coventry	a		12 24						13 23									14 23					
Birmingham Intl. 68 ✈	a		12 38						13 37									14 37					
Birmingham New Street 12 68	a		12 50						13 48			14 19						14 48		15 09			
	d									13 58													
Langley Green	d							14 04								15 04							
Rowley Regis	d					13 37		14 07						14 37		15 07						15 37	
Old Hill	d							14 10								15 10							
Cradley Heath	d					13 42		14 14						14 42		15 14						15 42	
Lye	d							14 17								15 17							
Stourbridge Junction 2	d					13 47		14a20						14 47		15a20						15 47	
Hagley	d					13 51								14 51								15 51	
Blakedown	d													14 54									
Kidderminster	d					13 57								14 59								15 57	
Hartlebury	d																						
University	d									14 04													
Barnt Green	d																						
Bromsgrove	d									14 18													
Droitwich Spa	d					14 09				14 29				15 11								16 09	
Worcester Shrub Hill 7	a									14 36													
	d									14 50			15 08										
Worcester Foregate Street 7	a					14 18				14 52			15 11	15 20								16 18	
	d									14 53			15 12										
Malvern Link	d									15 02			15 21										
Great Malvern	a									15 04			15 24										
	d									15 06			15 25										
Colwall	d									15 11			15 31										
Ledbury	a									15 18			15 38										
	d									15 19			15 41										
Hereford 7	a									15 37			15 57										

Table 71

Sundays

30 March to 11 May

Stratford-upon-Avon, Marylebone and Leamington Spa - Birmingham - Stourbridge, Worcester and Hereford

Network Diagram - see first Page of Table 71

		LM		XC	LM	CH	XC	GW	LM	CH	LM	CH		XC	CH	LM	GW	XC	CH	LM	CH	LM		XC	LM
				◇1 🛒		◇	◇1 🛒	◇1		◇		◇		◇1 🛒	◇		◇1	◇1 🛒	◇		◇			◇1 🛒	
Stratford-upon-Avon	d								15 29			15 38								16 29					
Stratford-upon-Avon Parkway	d								15 33			15 41								16 33					
Wilmcote	d								15 36			15 44								16 36					
Wootton Wawen	d																								
Henley-in-Arden	d								15 43											16 43					
Danzey	d																								
Wood End	d																								
The Lakes	d								15x49											16x49					
Earlswood (West Midlands)	d																								
Wythall	d								15 53											16 53					
Whitlocks End	d								15 56											16 56					
Shirley	d								15 59											16 59					
Yardley Wood	d								16 01											17 01					
Hall Green	d								16 05											17 05					
Spring Road	d								16 07											17 07					
London Marylebone 10 ⊖115	d					14 06				14 36					15 06				15 09		15 36				
Banbury	d			14 55		15 03	15 25			15 41				15 55	16 03			16 25	16 32		16 41			16 55	
Leamington Spa 8	a			15 11		15 20	15 41			15 58		16 05		16 11	16 20			16 41	16 50		16 58			17 11	
	d			15 12		15 21	15 43			15 59				16 12	16 21			16 43	16 51		16 59			17 12	
Warwick	d									16 03									16 55		17 03				
Warwick Parkway	d					15 27				16 07					16 27						17 07				
Hatton	d									16 12									17a02						
Lapworth	d									16 17															
Dorridge	d	15 27				15 37				16 23	16 27				16 37						17 17	17 27			
Widney Manor	d	15 32									16 32											17 32			
Solihull	d	15 35				15 43				16 29	16 35				16 43						17 23	17 35			
Olton	d	15 38									16 38											17 38			
Acocks Green	d	15 41									16 41											17 41			
Tyseley	d								16 10											17 10					
Small Heath	d																								
Bordesley	d																								
Birmingham Moor Street	d	15 48				15a57			16 15	16 38	16 48				16a57	17 02				17 15	17 32	17 48			
Birmingham Snow Hill ⛴	a	15 50							16 17	16 45	16 50					17 04				17 17	17 39	17 50			
	d	15 52							16 22		16 52					17 05				17 22		17 52			
Jewellery Quarter ⛴	d	15 54							16 24		16 54									17 24		17 54			
The Hawthorns ⛴	d	15 58							16 28		16 58									17 28		17 58			
Smethwick Galton Bridge 7	d	16 01							16 31		17 01									17 31		18 01			
Coventry	a			15 23										16 23										17 23	
Birmingham Intl. 68 ✈	a			15 35										16 35										17 35	
Birmingham New Street 12 68	a			15 48			16 09							16 48				17 10						17 48	
	d				15 58																				17 58
Langley Green	d	16 04									17 04											18 04			
Rowley Regis	d	16 07							16 37		17 07									17 37		18 07			
Old Hill	d	16 10									17 10											18 10			
Cradley Heath	d	16 14							16 42		17 14									17 42		18 14			
Lye	d	16 17									17 17											18 17			
Stourbridge Junction 2	d	16a21							16 47		17a20					17 23				17 47		18a20			
Hagley	d								16 51							17 26				17 51					
Blakedown	d																								
Kidderminster	d								16 57							17 32				17 57					
Hartlebury	d																								
University	d				16 04																				18 04
Barnt Green	d																								
Bromsgrove	d				16 18																				18 18
Droitwich Spa	d				16 28				17 09							17 44				18 09					18 28
Worcester Shrub Hill 7	a				16 36											17 51									18 36
	d				16 39			17 09									18 05								18 39
Worcester Foregate Street 7	a				16 42			17 11	17 18								18 07			18 18					18 42
	d				16 42			17 12																	18 42
Malvern Link	d				16 51			17 21																	18 51
Great Malvern	a				16 54			17 23																	18 54
	d				17 03			17 24																	18 59
Colwall	d				17 09			17 29																	19 04
Ledbury	a				17 16			17 36																	19 11
	d				17 16			17 37																	19 12
Hereford 7	a				17 34			17 53																	19 30

Table 71

Sundays

30 March to 11 May

Stratford-upon-Avon, Marylebone and Leamington Spa - Birmingham - Stourbridge, Worcester and Hereford

Network Diagram - see first Page of Table 71

		CH	XC	GW	LM	CH	CH	XC		LM	CH	XC	GW	LM	CH	CH	XC	LM		CH	XC	LM	CH	XC	LM
		◇	◇■1	◇■1		◇	◇	◇■1			◇	◇■1	◇■1		◇	◇	◇■1			◇	◇■1		◇	◇■1	
			⊥					⊥				⊥	⊡				⊥				⊥			⊥	
																				BZ					
Stratford-upon-Avon	d				17 29		17 38							18 29								19 29			
Stratford-upon-Avon Parkway	d				17 33		17 41							18 33								19 33			
Wilmcote	d				17 36		17 44							18 36								19 36			
Wootton Wawen	d																								
Henley-in-Arden	d				17 43									18 43								19 43			
Danzey	d																								
Wood End	d																								
The Lakes	d				17x49									18x49								19x49			
Earlswood (West Midlands)	d																								
Wythall	d				17 53									18 53								19 53			
Whitlocks End	d				17 56									18 56								19 56			
Shirley	d				17 59									18 59								19 59			
Yardley Wood	d				18 01									19 01								20 01			
Hall Green	d				18 05									19 05								20 05			
Spring Road	d				18 07									19 07								20 07			
London Marylebone ■10 ⊖115	d	16 06				16 36					17 06				17 36	17 09				18 06			18 36		
Banbury	d	17 03	17 25			17 41		17 54			18 03	18 25			18 41	18 45	18 55			19 04	19 24		19 41	19 55	
Leamington Spa ■8	a	17 20	17 41			17 58	18 05	18 11			18 20	18 41			18 58	19 04	19 11			19 22	19 41		19 58	20 11	
	d	17 21	17 43			17 59		18 12			18 21	18 43			18 59	19 05	19 12			19 23	19 42		19 59	20 12	
Warwick	d					18 03									19 03	19 09							20 03		
Warwick Parkway	d	17 27				18 07					18 27				19 07					19 29			20 07		
Hatton	d					18 12										19a16									
Lapworth	d					18 17																			
Dorridge	d	17 37				18 22					18 37				19 17					19 40			20 17		
Widney Manor	d					18 26									19 20								20 20		
Solihull	d	17 43				18 29					18 43				19 24					19 46			20 24		
Olton	d																								
Acocks Green	d																								
Tyseley	d				18 10									19 10								20 10			
Small Heath	d																								
Bordesley	d																								
Birmingham Moor Street	d	17a57			18 15	18 39					18a57			19 15	19 34					20a00		20 15	20 34		
Birmingham Snow Hill 🚋	a				18 17	18 46								19 17	19 41							20 17	20 41		
	d				18 22									19 22								20 22			
Jewellery Quarter 🚋	d				18 24									19 24								20 24			
The Hawthorns 🚋	d				18 28									19 28								20 28			
Smethwick Galton Bridge ■7	d				18 31									19 31								20 31			
Coventry	a							18 23									19 24				19 53			20 23	
Birmingham Intl. 68 ✈	a							18 35									19 37				20 03			20 35	
Birmingham New Street ■12 68	a		18 09					18 48				19 11					19 48				20 15			20 48	
	d									18 58								19 58							20 58
Langley Green	d																								
Rowley Regis	d				18 37									19 37								20 37			
Old Hill	d																								
Cradley Heath	d				18 42									19 42								20 42			
Lye	d																								
Stourbridge Junction ■2	d				18 47									19 47								20 47			
Hagley	d				18 51									19 51								20 51			
Blakedown	d				18 54																				
Kidderminster	d				18 59									19 57								20 57			
Hartlebury	d																								
University	d									19 04								20 04							21 04
Barnt Green	d																								
Bromsgrove	d									19 18								20 18							21 18
Droitwich Spa	d				19 11					19 28				20 09				20 31				21 09			21 29
Worcester Shrub Hill ■7	a				19 19					19 36				20 17				20 40				21 17			21 36
	d			19 10						19 40			20 16					20 58				21 23			21 40
Worcester Foregate Street ■7	a			19 13						19 42			20 18					21 00				21 25			21 42
	d			19 13									20 20									21 25			21 43
Malvern Link	d			19 22									20 29									21 34			21 52
Great Malvern	a			19 25									20 32									21 37			21 54
	d												20 33												21 56
Colwall	d												20 39												22 01
Ledbury	a												20 46												22 08
	d												20 48												22 09
Hereford ■7	a												21 04												22 27

BZ Business Zone available offering greater comfort and an enhanced working environment
Supplement payable.

Table 71

Sundays
30 March to 11 May

Stratford-upon-Avon, Marylebone and Leamington Spa - Birmingham - Stourbridge, Worcester and Hereford

Network Diagram - see first Page of Table 71

		CH	CH	XC	GW	LM	CH	XC	LM	CH	XC	CH	XC	LM	CH	XC	CH
		◇	◇	◇1	◇1		◇	◇1		◇	◇1	◇	◇1		◇	◇1	◇
Stratford-upon-Avon	d		20 00														
Stratford-upon-Avon Parkway	d		20 03														
Wilmcote	d		20 06														
Wootton Wawen	d																
Henley-in-Arden	d																
Danzey	d																
Wood End	d																
The Lakes	d																
Earlswood (West Midlands)	d																
Wythall	d																
Whitlocks End	d																
Shirley	d																
Yardley Wood	d																
Hall Green	d																
Spring Road	d																
London Marylebone 10 ⊖115	d	19 06					19 30			20 06		20 30			21 00		22 08
Banbury	d	20 03		20 24			20 41	20 55		21 05	21 24	21 41	21 54		22 10	22 24	23 08
Leamington Spa 8	a	20 20	20 27	20 40			20 58	21 11		21 22	21 40	21 58	22 11		22 27	22 40	23 25
	d	20 21		20 42			20 59	21 12		21 23	21 41	21 59	22 12		22 28	22 42	23 26
Warwick	d						21 03			21 27		22 03			22 32		23 30
Warwick Parkway	d	20 27					21 07			21 31		22 07			22 36		23 34
Hatton	d						21 12								22 41		
Lapworth	d						21 17								22 46		
Dorridge	d	20 37					21 23			21 41		22 17			22 51		23 44
Widney Manor	d						21 26								22 55		
Solihull	d	20 43					21 30			21 47		22 23			22 58		23 50
Olton	d																
Acocks Green	d																
Tyseley	d																
Small Heath	d																
Bordesley	d																
Birmingham Moor Street	d	20a57				21 41	21 39			22a03		22 32		22 52	23 08		23 59
Birmingham Snow Hill 🚋	a					21 43	21 46					22 39		22 54	23 15		00 06
	d					21 46								22 55			
Jewellery Quarter 🚋	d					21 48								22 57			
The Hawthorns 🚋	d					21 52								23 01			
Smethwick Galton Bridge 7	d					21 55								23 04			
Coventry	a			20 53				21 23			21 52		22 22			22 52	
Birmingham Intl. 68 ✈	a			21 03				21 35			22 02		22 32			23 02	
Birmingham New Street 12 68	a			21 15				21 48			22 14		22 43			23 13	
	d								22 05								
Langley Green	d																
Rowley Regis	d					22 00								23 09			
Old Hill	d																
Cradley Heath	d					22 05								23 14			
Lye	d																
Stourbridge Junction 2	d					22 10								23 20			
Hagley	d					22 14								23 23			
Blakedown	d																
Kidderminster	d					22 20								23 29			
Hartlebury	d																
University	d								22 11								
Barnt Green	d																
Bromsgrove	d								22 25								
Droitwich Spa	d					22 31			22 35					23 41			
Worcester Shrub Hill 7	a					22 39			22 44					23 49			
	d				22 12				22 48								
Worcester Foregate Street 7	a				22 14				22 50								
	d				22 16				22 51								
Malvern Link	d				22 25				23 00								
Great Malvern	a				22 28				23 02								
	d																
Colwall	d																
Ledbury	a																
	d																
Hereford 7	a																

Table 71R

Mondays to Fridays

9 December to 16 May

Hereford, Worcester and Stourbridge - Birmingham - Leamington Spa, Marylebone and Stratford-upon-Avon

Network Diagram - see first Page of Table 71

Miles	Miles	Miles			CH	CH	CH	CH	LM	XC	CH	CH	CH	XC	CH	LM	LM	GW	LM	LM	CH	XC	LM
					MX																		
						◇		◇		◇1	◇			◇1	◇			◇1			◇	◇1	
								🛒		🛒								☕			🛒	🛒	
																					BZ		
0	—	—	**Hereford 7**	d														04 50					
13¾	—	—	Ledbury	a																			
—	—	—		d																			
18	—	—	Colwall	d																			
20¾	—	—	**Great Malvern**	a														05 14					
—	—	—		d														05 17	05 49				
22	—	—	Malvern Link	d														05 20	05 52				
28¾	0	—	**Worcester Foregate Street 7**	a														05 30	05 59				
—	—	—		d														05 31	06 02				
29½	—	—	**Worcester Shrub Hill 7**	a														05 35					
—	—	—		d													05 30						
34¼	5½	—	Droitwich Spa	d													05 38		06 11				
40½	—	—	Bromsgrove	d															06 21				
44	—	—	Barnt Green	d																			
52	—	—	University	d															06 39				
—	11	—	Hartlebury	d																			
—	14¾	—	**Kidderminster**	d													05 48				06 09		
—	17¾	—	Blakedown	d																			
—	19½	—	Hagley	d																			
—	21½	—	**Stourbridge Junction 2**	d													05 56				06 18		06 24
—	22¾	—	Lye	d													06 00						06 28
—	24	—	Cradley Heath	d													06 03						06 31
—	25½	—	Old Hill	d													06 07						06 34
—	26¾	—	Rowley Regis	d													06 10				06 30		06 38
—	28½	0	Langley Green	d													06 13						06 41
54½	—	6¼	**Birmingham New Street 12** 68	a															06 47				
—	—	—		d						06 04				06 33								07 04	
—	—	—	**Birmingham Intl.** 68 ✈	d						06 14												07 14	
—	—	—	**Coventry**	d						06 25												07 25	
—	29½	—	Smethwick Galton Bridge 7	d													06 17				06 38		06 44
—	30¼	—	The Hawthorns 🚋	d													06 19				06 42		06 46
—	32¾	—	Jewellery Quarter 🚋	d													06 23						06 50
—	33½	—	**Birmingham Snow Hill** 🚋	a													06 32				06 48		06 54
—	—	—		d					05 53							06 29	06 35			06 40	06 50		06 57
—	34	—	**Birmingham Moor Street**	d		05 15		05 46	05 56		06 10				06 28	06 32	06 38			06 43	06 55		07 00
—	34¾	—	Bordesley	d																			
—	35¾	9¼	Small Heath	d					05 59								06 41			06 46			07 03
—	36¾	10¼	Tyseley	d					06 02							06 37	06 45			06 49			07 07
—	—	11¼	Acocks Green	d					06 05								06 47						07 09
—	—	12¼	Olton	d					06 07								06 50						07 12
—	—	14	Solihull	d		05 24		05 55	06 11		06 19				06 38		06 54				07 04		07 16
—	—	15½	Widney Manor	d					06 14								06 57						07 19
—	—	17½	Dorridge	d				06 00	06 18		06 24				06 50		07a02						07 30
—	—	20	Lapworth	d					06 22														07 34
—	—	24¼	Hatton	d	00 05							06 32											07 39
—	—	27	Warwick Parkway	d	00 10	05 36	05 55	06 09			06 34				06 59						07 17		07 43
—	—	28¼	Warwick	d	00 13		05 58					06 40			07 02								07 46
—	—	30¼	**Leamington Spa 8**	a	00 17	05 41	06 02	06 14		06 36	06 40	06 45		06 58	07 06						07 22	07 37	07 51
—	—	—		d	00 18	05 41	06 03	06 15		06 37	06 40		06 52	07 00	07 06						07 23	07 38	
—	—	—	Banbury	d	00a41	05 59	06 21	06 33		06a53	06 58			07a18	07 24							07a55	
—	—	—	**London Marylebone 10** ⊖115	a		07 01	07 32	07 35			08 00				08 28						08 29		
—	37¾	—	Spring Road	d												06 39				06 52			
—	38¼	—	Hall Green	d												06 42				06 54			
—	39½	—	Yardley Wood	d												06 44				06 57			
—	40¾	—	Shirley	d												06 47				07 00			
—	41¾	—	Whitlocks End	d												06 50				07 03			
—	42¾	—	Wythall	d												06 53				07 05			
—	43¾	—	Earlswood (West Midlands)	d																07 08			
—	44½	—	The Lakes	d																07x10			
—	45¾	—	Wood End	d																07x12			
—	47½	—	Danzey	d																07x15			
—	50¼	—	Henley-in-Arden	d												07 03				07 20			
—	52¼	—	Wootton Wawen	d																07x23			
—	56	—	Wilmcote	d					06 39				07 20							07 29			
—	—	—	Stratford-upon-Avon Parkway	a					06 42				07 23			07 13				07 32			
—	58¾	—	**Stratford-upon-Avon**	a					06 45				07 27			07 16				07 35			

BZ Business Zone available offering greater comfort and an enhanced working environment Supplement payable..

Table 71R

Mondays to Fridays

9 December to 16 May

Hereford, Worcester and Stourbridge - Birmingham - Leamington Spa, Marylebone and Stratford-upon-Avon

Network Diagram - see first Page of Table 71

		CH	XC	CH	CH	CH	LM	GW	LM		LM	LM	GW	CH	LM	LM	XC	CH	LM		LM	XC	GW	CH	LM
		◇	◇1	◇	◇			◇1					1	◇			◇1	◇				◇1	◇1	◇	
																							A		
		🍴 BZ						Ø						🍴			🍴					🍴	Ø		
Hereford 7	d							05 28															06 42		
Ledbury	a							05 44															06 58		
	d							05 45															06 59		
Colwall	d							05 53															07 06		
Great Malvern	a							05 58															07 11		
	d							05 59								06 47					07 02		07 12		
Malvern Link	d							06 03								06 50					07 05		07 17		
Worcester Foregate Street 7	a							06 13								06 59					07 13		07 27		
	d							06 14					06 52			07 00			07 14		07 15		07 28		
Worcester Shrub Hill 7	a							06 17					06 54			07 02					07 17		07 31		
	d						06 12		06 26			06 35			06 56	07 07					07 23				
Droitwich Spa	d						06 20		06 34			06 43			07 04	07 15			07 23		07 34				
Bromsgrove	d								06 44							07 25									
Barnt Green	d																								
University	d								06 59							07 40					07 59				
Hartlebury	d						06 27					06 50			07 11				07 30						
Kidderminster	d						06 33					06 56		07 05	07 17			07 30	07 36						
Blakedown	d						06 37					07 00			07 21				07 40						
Hagley	d						06 41					07 04			07 25				07 44						
Stourbridge Junction 2	d	06 38					06 48					07 08		07 14	07 29			07 38	07 48						07 57
Lye	d						06 52					07 12			07 33										08 01
Cradley Heath	d						06 55					07 15		07 22	07 36			07 44	07 54						08 04
Old Hill	d						06 58					07 18			07 39										08 07
Rowley Regis	d	06 50					07 02					07 22		07 29	07 43			07 51	07 59						08 11
Langley Green	d						07 05					07 25			07 46										08 14
Birmingham New Street 12 68	a								07 06							07 47					08 09				
	d		07 33														08 04					08 33			
Birmingham Intl. 68 ✈	d																08 14								
Coventry	d																08 25								
Smethwick Galton Bridge 7	d	06 58					07 08					07 28		07 36	07 49			07 57	08 05						08 17
The Hawthorns 🚊	d						07 10					07 30		07 39	07 51			08 00	08 07						08 19
Jewellery Quarter 🚊	d						07 14					07 35		07 45	07 56				08 11						08 23
Birmingham Snow Hill 🚊	a	07 05					07 18					07 39		07 47	08 00			08 06	08 15						08 26
	d	07 06				07 19	07 23				07 35	07 40		07 50	08 03			08 07	08 17					08 22	08 28
Birmingham Moor Street	d	07 11				07 22	07 26				07 38	07 43		07 55	08 06			08 10	08 20					08 25	08 31
Bordesley	d																								
Small Heath	d						07 29				07 41				08 10										
Tyseley	d						07 32				07 45	07 48			08 13										
Acocks Green	d					07 29						07 51							08 26						
Olton	d					07 32						07 54							08 29						
Solihull	d	07 20				07 36						07 57		08 05				08 19	08 32					08 37	
Widney Manor	d					07 40						08 01							08 36						
Dorridge	d	07 27				07 52						08a06						08 24	08a41					08 52	
Lapworth	d					07 57																			
Hatton	d					08 03																			
Warwick Parkway	d	07 37		08 00										08 18				08 34						09 02	
Warwick	d			08 03		08 09												08 37						09 06	
Leamington Spa 8	a	07 43	07 58	08 07		08 19								08 23			08 37	08 41				08 58		09 10	
	d	07 44	07 59	08 08	08 18									08 24			08 38	08 42				09 00		09 11	
Banbury	d	08 03	08a15	08 25													08a54	09 00				09a18		09 30	
London Marylebone 10 ⊖115	a	09 03		09 32										09 36				09 59						10 36	
Spring Road	d						07 35				07 47				08 16										08 37
Hall Green	d						07 37				07 50				08 18										08 39
Yardley Wood	d						07 40				07 52				08 21										08 42
Shirley	d						07 43				07 56				08 24										08 45
Whitlocks End	d						07 46				07a58				08a27										08 48
Wythall	d						07 49																		08 51
Earlswood (West Midlands)	d						07 51																		08 53
The Lakes	d						07x54																		08x56
Wood End	d						07x56																		08x58
Danzey	d						07x59																		09x01
Henley-in-Arden	d						08 05																		09 06
Wootton Wawen	d						08x08																		09x09
Wilmcote	d				08 46		08 14																		09 15
Stratford-upon-Avon Parkway	a				08 48		08 17																		09 18
Stratford-upon-Avon	a				08 57		08 20																		09 21

BZ Business Zone available offering greater comfort and an enhanced working environment Supplement payable..

A The Cathedrals Express

Table 71R

Mondays to Fridays

9 December to 16 May

Hereford, Worcester and Stourbridge - Birmingham - Leamington Spa, Marylebone and Stratford-upon-Avon

Network Diagram - see first Page of Table 71

		LM	LM	LM	CH		LM	LM	XC	LM	GW	CH	LM	LM	CH		XC	CH	LM	LM	CH	LM	XC	GW	LM
					◇ 🛒				◇1 🛒		◇1 🛒	◇			◇		◇1 🛒				◇ 🛒		◇1 🛒		
Hereford 7	d			07 09						07 34															
Ledbury	a			07 24						07 49															
	d			07 25						07 50															
Colwall	d			07 31						07 56															
Great Malvern	a			07 36						08 00															
	d			07 37						08 05												08 38		08 50	
Malvern Link	d			07 40						08 08												08 41		08 53	
Worcester Foregate Street 7	a			07 48						08 16												08 49		09 03	
	d			07 49				08 02		08 24	08 26									08 38		08 51		09 03	
Worcester Shrub Hill 7	a			07 51							08 28									08 40				09 06	
	d	07 35		07 55																08 44					
Droitwich Spa	d	07 43		08 05				08 11		08 33										08 53		09 01			
Bromsgrove	d									08 43												09 11			
Barnt Green	d																								
University	d			08 29						08 59												09 29			
Hartlebury	d							08 18																	
Kidderminster	d	07 54			08 09			08 24											08 55	09 06					
Blakedown	d	07 59			08 14			08 28											08 59	09 10					
Hagley	d	08 03			08 19			08 31											09 03	09 14					
Stourbridge Junction 2	d	08 07	08 14		08 23			08 35					08 45	08 55					09 07	09 18					09 27
Lye	d		08 18					08 39						08 59											09 31
Cradley Heath	d	08 13	08 21		08 29			08 42					08 51	09 02					09 13	09 24					09 34
Old Hill	d		08 24					08 46						09 05											09 37
Rowley Regis	d	08 19	08 28		08 35			08 49					08 56	09 09					09 18	09 29					09 41
Langley Green	d		08 31					08 52						09 12											09 44
Birmingham New Street 12 68	a			08 38						09 07												09 42			
	d								09 04								09 33						10 04		
Birmingham Intl. 68 ✈	d								09 14														10 14		
Coventry	d								09 25														10 25		
Smethwick Galton Bridge 7	d	08 25	08 34		08 41			08 56					09 02	09 15					09 24	09 35					09 47
The Hawthorns 🚋	d	08 28	08 36		08 44			08 58					09 04	09 17					09 26	09 37					09 49
Jewellery Quarter 🚋	d	08 32	08 40		08 49			09 02					09 08	09 21					09 30	09 41					09 53
Birmingham Snow Hill 🚋	a	08 35	08 44		08 51			09 05					09 12	09 24					09 34	09 45					09 56
	d	08 37	08 47		08 52		08 57	09 07				09 12	09 17	09 28					09 37	09 47					09 58
Birmingham Moor Street	d	08 40	08 50		08 55		09 00	09 10				09 15	09 20	09 31				09 34	09 40	09 50	09 55				10 01
Bordesley	d																								
Small Heath	d	08 44						09 13											09 43						
Tyseley	d	08 47						09 17											09 47						
Acocks Green	d	08 50					09 06						09 26						09 49						10 07
Olton	d	08 53					09 09						09 28						09 52						10 10
Solihull	d	08 57			09 07		09 12					09 24	09 32					09 43	09 56		10 04				10 13
Widney Manor	d	09 00					09 16						09 35						09 59						10 17
Dorridge	d	09a05					09 20					09 29	09a41					09 52	10a04						10 21
Lapworth	d																	09 56							
Hatton	d														09 41			10 02							
Warwick Parkway	d				09 21							09 40									10 16				
Warwick	d											09 44			09 48			10 08							
Leamington Spa 8	a				09 26				09 37			09 48			09 52		09 59	10 17			10 21		10 37		
	d				09 27				09 38			09 49			09 53		10 00				10 22		10 38		
Banbury	d								09a54			10 07			10 13		10a17				10 40		10a54		
London Marylebone 10 ⊖115	a				10 39							11 11			11 29						11 34				
Spring Road	d		08 56					09 19						09 37						09 56					
Hall Green	d		08 59					09 22						09 39						09 59					
Yardley Wood	d		09 01					09 24						09 42						10 01					
Shirley	d		09 05					09 28						09 45						10 05					
Whitlocks End	d		09a07					09a30						09 48						10a07					
Wythall	d													09 51											
Earlswood (West Midlands)	d													09 53											
The Lakes	d													09x56											
Wood End	d													09x58											
Danzey	d													10x01											
Henley-in-Arden	d													10 06											
Wootton Wawen	d													10x09											
Wilmcote	d													10 15											
Stratford-upon-Avon Parkway	a						09 45							10 18											10 37
Stratford-upon-Avon	a						09 49							10 21											10 41

Table 71R

Mondays to Fridays

9 December to 16 May

Hereford, Worcester and Stourbridge - Birmingham - Leamington Spa, Marylebone and Stratford-upon-Avon

Network Diagram - see first Page of Table 71

		LM	LM	CH	CH	LM	LM	LM	LM	GW	XC	CH	LM	LM	XC	CH	LM	LM	LM	XC	CH	CH
				◇	◇					◇[1]	◇[1]	◇			◇[1]	◇				◇[1]	◇	
					ᴛ					ᴛ	ᴛ	ᴛ			ᴛ					ᴛ		
												BZ										
Hereford [7]	d		08 49																09 40			
Ledbury	a		09 05																09 56			
	d		09 08																09 58			
Colwall	d		09 14																10 04			
Great Malvern	a		09 18																10 08			
	d		09 19							09 54									10 10			
Malvern Link	d		09 22							09 56									10 13			
Worcester Foregate Street [7]	a		09 30							10 06									10 22			
	d	09 03	09 31							10 06							10 16		10 24			
Worcester Shrub Hill [7]	a		09 33							10 09												
	d		09 37						09 52													
Droitwich Spa	d	09 12	09 45						10 00								10 25		10 33			
Bromsgrove	d		09 54																10 43			
Barnt Green	d																					
University	d		10 09																10 59			
Hartlebury	d	09 19															10 32					
Kidderminster	d	09 25				09 36		09 55	10 10					10 25			10 40					
Blakedown	d	09 29				09 40		09 59						10 29								
Hagley	d	09 33				09 44		10 03						10 33								
Stourbridge Junction [2]	d	09 37				09 48	09 57	10 07	10 18				10 27	10 37			10 48	10 57				
Lye	d						10 01						10 31					11 01				
Cradley Heath	d	09 43				09 54	10 04	10 13	10 24				10 34	10 43			10 54	11 04				
Old Hill	d						10 07						10 37					11 07				
Rowley Regis	d	09 48				09 59	10 11	10 18	10 30				10 41	10 48			10 59	11 11				
Langley Green	d						10 14						10 44					11 14				
Birmingham New Street [12] 68	a		10 22																11 13			
	d										10 33				11 04					11 33		
Birmingham Intl. 68 ✈	d														11 14							
Coventry	d														11 25							
Smethwick Galton Bridge [7]	d	09 54				10 05	10 17	10 24	10 35				10 47	10 54			11 05	11 17				
The Hawthorns	d	09 56				10 07	10 19	10 26	10 37				10 49	10 56			11 07	11 19				
Jewellery Quarter	d	10 00				10 11	10 23	10 30	10 41				10 53	11 00			11 11	11 23				
Birmingham Snow Hill	a	10 03				10 15	10 26	10 34	10 45				10 56	11 03			11 15	11 26				
	d	10 07			10 12	10 17	10 28	10 37	10 47				10 58	11 07		11 12	11 17	11 28				
Birmingham Moor Street	d	10 10			10 15	10 20	10 31	10 40	10 50			10 55	11 01	11 10		11 15	11 20	11 31				11 34
Bordesley	d																					
Small Heath	d	10 13						10 43						11 13								
Tyseley	d	10 17						10 47						11 17								
Acocks Green	d					10 26		10 49					11 07				11 26					
Olton	d					10 29		10 52					11 10				11 29					
Solihull	d				10 24	10 32		10 56				11 04	11 13			11 24	11 32					11 43
Widney Manor	d					10 36		10 59					11 17				11 36					
Dorridge	d				10 29	10a42		11a04					11 21			11 29	11a42					11 52
Lapworth	d																					11 56
Hatton	d																				11 56	12 02
Warwick Parkway	d				10 38							11 16				11 38						
Warwick	d				10 42											11 42					12 02	12 08
Leamington Spa [8]	a				10 46						10 58	11 21			11 37	11 46				12 00	12 06	12 16
	d			10 42	10 46						11 00	11 22			11 38	11 46				12 01	12 07	
Banbury	d				11 04						11a17	11 40			11a56	12 04				12a17	12 25	
London Marylebone [10] ⊖115	a				12 08							12 34				13 08					13 33	
Spring Road	d	10 19					10 37		10 56					11 19				11 37				
Hall Green	d	10 22					10 39		10 59					11 22				11 39				
Yardley Wood	d	10 24					10 42		11 01					11 24				11 42				
Shirley	d	10 28					10 45		11 05					11 28				11 45				
Whitlocks End	d	10a30					10 48		11a07					11a30				11 48				
Wythall	d						10 51											11 51				
Earlswood (West Midlands)	d						10 53											11 53				
The Lakes	d						10x56											11x56				
Wood End	d						10x58											11x58				
Danzey	d						11x01											12x01				
Henley-in-Arden	d						11 06											12 06				
Wootton Wawen	d						11x09											12x09				
Wilmcote	d						11 15											12 15				
Stratford-upon-Avon Parkway	a			11 05			11 18						11 37					12 18				
Stratford-upon-Avon	a			11 16			11 21						11 41					12 21				

BZ Business Zone available offering greater comfort and an enhanced working environment.

Supplement Payable.

Table 71R

Mondays to Fridays

9 December to 16 May

Hereford, Worcester and Stourbridge - Birmingham - Leamington Spa, Marylebone and Stratford-upon-Avon

Network Diagram - see first Page of Table 71

		LM	LM	CH	GW	LM	LM	XC	CH	LM	LM	LM	XC	LM	LM	CH	GW	LM	LM	XC	CH	CH	LM
				◇	[R]			◇[1] ⏉	◇				◇[1] ⏉			◇ ⏉ BZ	◇[1] ⏉			◇[1] ⏉	◇	◇ ⏉	
Hereford [7]	d											10 40											
Ledbury	a											10 56											
	d											10 58											
Colwall	d											11 04											
Great Malvern	a											11 08											
	d				10 50							11 10			11 34								
Malvern Link	d				10 53							11 13			11 36								
Worcester Foregate Street [7]	a				11 03							11 22			11 46								
	d				11 03					11 16		11 24			11 51		12 06						12 16
Worcester Shrub Hill [7]	a				11 06												12 08						
	d		10 52																				
Droitwich Spa	d		11 00							11 25		11 33			12 00								12 25
Bromsgrove	d											11 43											
Barnt Green	d																						
University	d											11 59											
Hartlebury	d									11 32													12 32
Kidderminster	d	10 55	11 10				11 25			11 40				11 55	12 10				12 25				12 40
Blakedown	d	10 59					11 29							11 59					12 29				
Hagley	d	11 03					11 33							12 03					12 33				
Stourbridge Junction [2]	d	11 07	11 18			11 27	11 37			11 48	11 57			12 07	12 18			12 27	12 37				12 48
Lye	d					11 31					12 01							12 31					
Cradley Heath	d	11 13	11 24			11 34	11 43			11 54	12 04			12 13	12 24			12 34	12 43				12 54
Old Hill	d					11 37					12 07							12 37					
Rowley Regis	d	11 18	11 30			11 41	11 48			11 59	12 11			12 18	12 30			12 41	12 48				12 59
Langley Green	d					11 44					12 14							12 44					
Birmingham New Street [12] 68	a											12 11											
	d							12 04					12 33							13 04			
Birmingham Intl. 68 ✈	d							12 14												13 14			
Coventry	d							12 25												13 25			
Smethwick Galton Bridge [7]	d	11 24	11 35			11 47	11 54			12 05	12 17			12 24	12 35			12 47	12 54				13 05
The Hawthorns (tram)	d	11 26	11 37			11 49	11 56			12 07	12 19			12 26	12 37			12 49	12 56				13 07
Jewellery Quarter (tram)	d	11 30	11 41			11 53	12 00			12 11	12 23			12 30	12 41			12 53	13 00				13 11
Birmingham Snow Hill (tram)	a	11 34	11 45			11 56	12 03			12 15	12 26			12 34	12 45			12 56	13 03				13 15
	d	11 37	11 47			11 58	12 07		12 12	12 17	12 28			12 37	12 47			12 58	13 07			13 12	13 17
Birmingham Moor Street	d	11 40	11 50	11 55		12 01	12 10		12 15	12 20	12 31			12 40	12 50	12 55		13 01	13 10			13 15	13 20
Bordesley	d																						
Small Heath	d	11 43					12 13							12 43					13 13				
Tyseley	d	11 47					12 17							12 47					13 17				
Acocks Green	d	11 49				12 07				12 26				12 49				13 07					13 26
Olton	d	11 52				12 10				12 29				12 52				13 10					13 29
Solihull	d	11 56		12 03		12 13			12 24	12 32				12 56		13 04		13 13				13 24	13 32
Widney Manor	d	11 59				12 17				12 36				12 59				13 17					13 36
Dorridge	d	12a04				12 21			12 29	12a42				13a04				13 21				13 30	13a42
Lapworth	d																						
Hatton	d																						
Warwick Parkway	d			12 15					12 38							13 16						13 40	
Warwick	d								12 42													13 43	
Leamington Spa [8]	a			12 20				12 37	12 46				12 58			13 21				13 37		13 48	
	d			12 20				12 38	12 46				13 00			13 22				13 38	13 39	13 48	
Banbury	d			12 38				12a54	13 04				13a21			13 40				13a54		14 06	
London Marylebone [10] ⊖115	a			13 34					14 08							14 34						15 08	
Spring Road	d		11 56				12 19				12 37				12 56				13 19				
Hall Green	d		11 59				12 22				12 39				12 59				13 22				
Yardley Wood	d		12 01				12 24				12 42				13 01				13 24				
Shirley	d		12 05				12 28				12 45				13 05				13 28				
Whitlocks End	d		12a07				12a30				12 48				13a07				13a30				
Wythall	d										12 51												
Earlswood (West Midlands)	d										12 53												
The Lakes	d										12x56												
Wood End	d										12x58												
Danzey	d										13x01												
Henley-in-Arden	d										13 06												
Wootton Wawen	d										13x09												
Wilmcote	d										13 15										14 07		
Stratford-upon-Avon Parkway	a					12 37					13 18							13 37			14 10		
Stratford-upon-Avon	a					12 41					13 21							13 41			14 18		

BZ Business Zone available offering greater comfort and an enhanced working environment. Supplemant payable.

Table 71R

Mondays to Fridays

9 December to 16 May

Hereford, Worcester and Stourbridge - Birmingham - Leamington Spa, Marylebone and Stratford-upon-Avon

Network Diagram - see first Page of Table 71

		LM	LM	XC	CH	LM	LM	CH	GW	LM	LM	XC	CH	LM	LM	LM	XC	LM	LM	GW	CH	CH
				◇1				◇	◇			◇1	◇				◇1			◇1	◇	◇
Hereford 7	d		11 40													12 40				13 14		
Ledbury	a		11 56													12 56				13 30		
	d		11 58													12 58				13 31		
Colwall	d		12 04													13 04				13 39		
Great Malvern	a		12 09													13 08				13 44		
	d		12 10						12 50							13 10				13 45		
Malvern Link	d		12 13						12 53							13 13				13 50		
Worcester Foregate Street 7	a		12 22						13 03							13 21				14 00		
	d		12 24						13 03							13 24			13 51	14 01		
Worcester Shrub Hill 7	a								13 06											14 04		
	d						12 51							13 17								
Droitwich Spa	d		12 33				12 59							13 25		13 33			14 00			
Bromsgrove	d		12 43													13 43						
Barnt Green	d																					
University	d		12 59													13 59						
Hartlebury	d													13 32								
Kidderminster	d					12 55	13 10							13 40				13 55	14 10			
Blakedown	d					12 59												13 59				
Hagley	d					13 03												14 03				
Stourbridge Junction 2	d	12 57				13 07	13 18			13 27	13 37			13 48	13 57			14 07	14 18			
Lye	d	13 01								13 31					14 01							
Cradley Heath	d	13 04				13 13	13 24			13 34	13 43			13 54	14 04			14 13	14 24			
Old Hill	d	13 07								13 37					14 07							
Rowley Regis	d	13 11				13 18	13 30			13 41	13 48			13 59	14 11			14 18	14 30			
Langley Green	d	13 14								13 44					14 14							
Birmingham New Street 12 68	a		13 13													14 12						
	d			13 33								14 04					14 33					
Birmingham Intl. 68 ✈	d											14 14										
Coventry	d											14 24										
Smethwick Galton Bridge 7	d	13 17				13 24	13 35			13 47	13 54			14 05	14 17			14 24	14 35			
The Hawthorns	d	13 19				13 26	13 37			13 49	13 56			14 07	14 19			14 26	14 37			
Jewellery Quarter	d	13 23				13 30	13 41			13 53	14 00			14 11	14 23			14 30	14 41			
Birmingham Snow Hill	a	13 26				13 34	13 45			13 56	14 04			14 15	14 26			14 34	14 45			
	d	13 28				13 37	13 47			13 58	14 07		14 12	14 17	14 28			14 37	14 47			
Birmingham Moor Street	d	13 31			13 34	13 40	13 50	13 55		14 01	14 10		14 15	14 20	14 31			14 40	14 50			14 55
Bordesley	d																					
Small Heath	d					13 43					14 13							14 43				
Tyseley	d					13 47					14 17							14 47				
Acocks Green	d					13 49				14 07				14 26				14 49				
Olton	d					13 52				14 10				14 29				14 52				
Solihull	d				13 43	13 56		14 04		14 13			14 24	14 32				14 56				15 04
Widney Manor	d					13 59				14 17				14 36				14 59				
Dorridge	d				13 52	14a04				14 21			14 29	14a41				15a04				
Lapworth	d				13 56																	
Hatton	d				14 02																14 57	
Warwick Parkway	d							14 16					14 38									15 16
Warwick	d				14 08								14 42								15 03	
Leamington Spa 8	a			13 59	14 17			14 21				14 37	14 46				14 58				15 07	15 21
	d			14 00				14 22				14 38	14 46				15 00				15 08	15 22
Banbury	d			14a17				14 40				14a54	15 04				15a17				15 26	15 40
London Marylebone 10 ⊖115	a							15 34					16 08								16 34	16 36
Spring Road	d	13 37					13 56				14 19				14 37				14 56			
Hall Green	d	13 39					13 59				14 22				14 39				14 59			
Yardley Wood	d	13 42					14 02				14 24				14 42				15 01			
Shirley	d	13 45					14 05				14 28				14 45				15 05			
Whitlocks End	d	13 48					14a07				14a30				14 48				15a07			
Wythall	d	13 51													14 51							
Earlswood (West Midlands)	d	13 53													14 53							
The Lakes	d	13x56													14x56							
Wood End	d	13x58													14x58							
Danzey	d	14x01													15x01							
Henley-in-Arden	d	14 06													15 06							
Wootton Wawen	d	14x09													15x09							
Wilmcote	d	14 15													15 15							
Stratford-upon-Avon Parkway	a	14 18								14 37					15 18							
Stratford-upon-Avon	a	14 21								14 41					15 21							

Table 71R

Mondays to Fridays

9 December to 16 May

Hereford, Worcester and Stourbridge - Birmingham - Leamington Spa, Marylebone and Stratford-upon-Avon

Network Diagram - see first Page of Table 71

		LM	LM	XC	CH	LM	LM	LM	XC	GW	CH	LM	LM	CH	GW	LM	LM	XC	CH	LM	LM	LM	LM
				◇1 ⚲	◇ ⚲				◇1 ⚲	◇1 ⚲				◇ ⚲	◇			◇1 ⚲	◇ ⚲				
Hereford 7	d							13 43														14 40	
Ledbury	a							14 00														14 56	
	d							14 00														14 58	
Colwall	d							14 06														15 04	
Great Malvern	a							14 11														15 08	
	d					13 59		14 11		14 26					14 50							15 10	
Malvern Link	d					14 01		14 14		14 28					14 53							15 13	
Worcester Foregate Street 7	a					14 10		14 23		14 38					15 03							15 22	
	d					14 16		14 24		14 38					15 03							15 24	
Worcester Shrub Hill 7	a									14 41					15 06								
	d												14 52							15 15			
Droitwich Spa	d					14 25		14 33					15 00							15 23		15 33	
Bromsgrove	d							14 43														15 43	
Barnt Green	d																						
University	d							14 59														15 59	
Hartlebury	d					14 32														15 30			
Kidderminster	d		14 25			14 40						14 55	15 10				15 25			15 36			15 55
Blakedown	d		14 29									14 59					15 29			15 40			15 59
Hagley	d		14 33									15 03					15 33			15 44			16 03
Stourbridge Junction 2	d	14 27	14 37			14 48	14 57					15 07	15 18			15 27	15 37			15 48	15 57		16 07
Lye	d	14 31					15 01									15 31					16 01		
Cradley Heath	d	14 34	14 43			14 54	15 04					15 13	15 24			15 34	15 43			15 54	16 04		16 13
Old Hill	d	14 37					15 07									15 37					16 07		
Rowley Regis	d	14 41	14 48			14 59	15 11					15 18	15 30			15 41	15 48			15 59	16 11		16 18
Langley Green	d	14 44					15 14									15 44					16 14		
Birmingham New Street 12 68	a							15 11														16 13	
	d			15 04					15 33									16 04					
Birmingham Intl. 68 ✈	d			15 14														16 14					
Coventry	d			15 24														16 24					
Smethwick Galton Bridge 7	d	14 47	14 54			15 05	15 17					15 24	15 35			15 47	15 54			16 05	16 17		16 24
The Hawthorns 🚋	d	14 49	14 56			15 07	15 19					15 26	15 37			15 49	15 56			16 07	16 19		16 26
Jewellery Quarter 🚋	d	14 53	15 00			15 11	15 23					15 30	15 41			15 53	16 00			16 11	16 23		16 30
Birmingham Snow Hill 🚋	a	14 56	15 03			15 15	15 26					15 34	15 45			15 56	16 03			16 15	16 26		16 34
	d	14 58	15 07		15 12	15 17	15 28					15 37	15 47			15 58	16 07		16 12	16 17	16 28		16 37
Birmingham Moor Street	d	15 01	15 10		15 15	15 20	15 31				15 34	15 40	15 50	15 55		16 01	16 10		16 15	16 20	16 31		16 40
Bordesley	d																						
Small Heath	d		15 13									15 43					16 13						16 43
Tyseley	d		15 17									15 47					16 17				16 36		16 47
Acocks Green	d	15 07				15 26						15 49				16 07				16 26			16 49
Olton	d	15 10				15 29						15 52				16 10				16 29			16 52
Solihull	d	15 13			15 24	15 32					15 43	15 56		16 04		16 13			16 24	16 32			16 56
Widney Manor	d	15 17				15 36						15 59				16 17				16 36			16 59
Dorridge	d	15 21			15 30	15a42					15 52	16a04				16a22			16 29	16a42			17a04
Lapworth	d										15 56												
Hatton	d										16 02												
Warwick Parkway	d				15 39									16 17					16 39				
Warwick	d				15 43						16 08								16 43				
Leamington Spa 8	a			15 37	15 47				16 00		16 17			16 22				16 37	16 47				
	d			15 38	15 47				16 01					16 23				16 38	16 48				
Banbury	d			15a54	16 05				16a17					16 41				16a54	17 06				
London Marylebone 10 ⊖115	a				17 08									17 42					18 10				
Spring Road	d		15 19				15 37						15 56				16 19				16 38		
Hall Green	d		15 22				15 39						15 59				16 22				16 41		
Yardley Wood	d		15 24				15 42						16 01				16 24				16 43		
Shirley	d		15 28				15 45						16 05				16 28				16 46		
Whitlocks End	d		15a30				15 48						16a07				16a30				16 49		
Wythall	d						15 51														16 52		
Earlswood (West Midlands)	d						15 53														16 54		
The Lakes	d						15x56														16x56		
Wood End	d						15x58														16x58		
Danzey	d						16x01														17x01		
Henley-in-Arden	d						16 06														17 06		
Wootton Wawen	d						16x09														17x09		
Wilmcote	d						16 15														17 15		
Stratford-upon-Avon Parkway	a	15 37					16 18														17 18		
Stratford-upon-Avon	a	15 41					16 21														17 21		

Table 71R

Mondays to Fridays

9 December to 16 May

Hereford, Worcester and Stourbridge - Birmingham - Leamington Spa, Marylebone and Stratford-upon-Avon

Network Diagram - see first Page of Table 71

		LM	GW	GW	CH		XC	CH	LM	LM	XC	CH	LM	XC	CH		LM	LM	LM	CH	CH	LM	LM	LM	GW
			■1	◇■1	◇		◇■1	◇			◇■1	◇		◇■1						◇					
				☕			🛒				🛒			🛒											
Hereford ■7	d			15 14															15 40						
Ledbury	a			15 30															15 56						
	d			15 31															15 58						
Colwall	d			15 39															16 04						
Great Malvern	a			15 44															16 09						
	d	15 21	15 32	15 45															16 10						16 48
Malvern Link	d	15 23		15 49															16 13						16 51
Worcester Foregate Street ■7	a	15 32	15 41	15 59															16 21						17 01
	d	15 33	15 42	16 01													16 13		16 24				16 34	16 47	17 02
Worcester Shrub Hill ■7	a	15 35	15 44	16 04																			16 36		17 04
	d	15 47																					16 40		
Droitwich Spa	d	15 55															16 22		16 33				16 48	16 56	
Bromsgrove	d																		16 43						
Barnt Green	d																		16 49						
University	d																		16 59						
Hartlebury	d																16 29						16 55		
Kidderminster	d	16 06								16 23							16 35					16 53	17 01	17 06	
Blakedown	d	16 10								16 27							16 40					16 57		17 11	
Hagley	d	16 14								16 31							16 44					17 01		17 14	
Stourbridge Junction ■2	d	16 18							16 27	16 35							16 48	16 57				17 05	17 13	17 18	
Lye	d								16 31									17 01							
Cradley Heath	d	16 24							16 34	16 41							16 54	17 04				17 11	17 19	17 24	
Old Hill	d								16 37									17 07							
Rowley Regis	d	16 29							16 41	16 46							17 00	17 11				17 16	17 24	17 29	
Langley Green	d								16 44									17 14							
Birmingham New Street ■12 68	a																		17 12						
	d						16 33				17 04			17 33											
Birmingham Intl. 68 ✈	d										17 14														
Coventry	d										17 24														
Smethwick Galton Bridge ■7	d	16 35							16 47	16 52							17 05	17 17				17 22	17 29	17 35	
The Hawthorns 🚋	d	16 37							16 49	16 54							17 07	17 19				17 24	17 31	17 37	
Jewellery Quarter 🚋	d	16 41							16 53	16 58							17 15	17 23				17 28	17 35	17 41	
Birmingham Snow Hill 🚋	a	16 45							16 56	17 01							17 19	17 26				17 32	17 39	17 45	
	d	16 47						16 52	16 58	17 03		17 07	17 14				17 22	17 28				17 35	17 42	17 47	
Birmingham Moor Street	d	16 50						16 55	17 01	17 06		17 10	17 17		17 21		17 25	17 31				17 38	17 45	17 50	
Bordesley	d																								
Small Heath	d	16 53											17 20									17 41	17 48	17 53	
Tyseley	d	16 57							17 06				17 24					17 36				17 45	17 51	17 57	
Acocks Green	d								17 09								17 30					17 47	17 54		
Olton	d								17 11								17 33					17 50	17 56		
Solihull	d							17 03	17 15			17 18			17 30		17 36					17 54	18 00		
Widney Manor	d								17 18			17 22					17 40					17 57	18 03		
Dorridge	d								17a23			17 26			17 35		17a44					18 01	18a08		
Lapworth	d														17 39							18 05			
Hatton	d														17 45					17 56		18 10			
Warwick Parkway	d							17 15				17 35										18 14			
Warwick	d							17 18				17 39			17 51					18 02		18 17			
Leamington Spa ■8	a						16 58	17 22			17 37	17 43		17 59	18 01					18 07		18 21			
	d				16 49		17 00	17 23			17 38	17 43		18 00						18 08	18 17				
Banbury	d						17a17	17 41			17a54	18 02		18a18						18 27					
London Marylebone ■10 ⊖115	a							18 47				19 11								19 49					
Spring Road	d	16 59								17 12			17 26					17 38						17 59	
Hall Green	d	17 02								17 15			17 29					17 41						18 02	
Yardley Wood	d	17 04								17 17			17 31					17 43						18 04	
Shirley	d	17 08								17 21			17 35					17 46						18 08	
Whitlocks End	d	17a10								17 23			17a37					17 49						18 10	
Wythall	d									17 26								17 52						18 13	
Earlswood (West Midlands)	d																	17 54						18 15	
The Lakes	d																	17x56						18x18	
Wood End	d																	17x58						18x20	
Danzey	d																	18x01						18x23	
Henley-in-Arden	d									17 36								18 06						18 28	
Wootton Wawen	d																	18x09						18x31	
Wilmcote	d				17 22													18 15			18 45			18 37	
Stratford-upon-Avon Parkway	a				17 24					17 46								18 18			18 47			18 40	
Stratford-upon-Avon	a				17 35					17 49								18 21			18 52			18 43	

Table 71R

Mondays to Fridays

9 December to 16 May

Hereford, Worcester and Stourbridge - Birmingham - Leamington Spa, Marylebone and Stratford-upon-Avon

Network Diagram - see first Page of Table 71

		CH	LM	LM	XC	CH	LM	LM	LM	XC	GW	LM	CH	LM	LM	XC	LM	CH	CH	LM	LM	LM
		◇			◇1 🚲	◇				◇1 🚲	◇1 🚲		◇			◇1 🚲		◇	◇ 🚲			
Hereford 7	d								16 40								17 40					
Ledbury	a								16 56								17 56					
	d								16 58								18 01					
Colwall	d								17 04								18 07					
Great Malvern	a								17 08								18 11					
	d								17 10			17 41					18 12					
Malvern Link	d								17 13			17 44					18 15					
Worcester Foregate Street 7	a								17 21			17 52					18 23					
	d						17 16		17 24		17 28	17 53			17 56		18 24					
Worcester Shrub Hill 7	a										17 30	17 55										
	d																					18 37
Droitwich Spa	d						17 25		17 33						18 05		18 33					18 45
Bromsgrove	d								17 43								18 43					
Barnt Green	d																18 49					
University	d								17 59								18 59					
Hartlebury	d						17 32															
Kidderminster	d			17 25			17 38							18 00	18 16					18 38		18 55
Blakedown	d			17 29			17 42							18 05						18 42		19 00
Hagley	d			17 33			17 46							18 08						18 45		19 03
Stourbridge Junction 2	d		17 27	17 37			17 50	17 57						18 12	18 25					18 49		19 08
Lye	d		17 31					18 01							18 29					18 53		
Cradley Heath	d		17 34	17 43			17 56	18 04						18 18	18 32					18 56		19 14
Old Hill	d		17 37					18 07							18 36					19 00		
Rowley Regis	d		17 41	17 48			18 01	18 11						18 24	18 39					19 03		19 19
Langley Green	d		17 44					18 14							18 42					19 06		
Birmingham New Street 12 68	a								18 11								19 12					
	d				18 04					18 33						19 04						
Birmingham Intl. 68 ✈	d				18 14											19 14						
Coventry	d				18 24											19 24						
Smethwick Galton Bridge 7	d		17 47	17 54			18 07	18 17						18 29	18 46					19 10		19 25
The Hawthorns 🚊	d		17 49	17 56			18 09	18 19						18 31	18 48					19 12		19 27
Jewellery Quarter 🚊	d		17 53	18 00			18 13	18 23						18 36	18 52					19 16		19 31
Birmingham Snow Hill 🚊	a		17 56	18 03			18 17	18 26						18 41	18 55					19 20		19 35
	d	17 52	17 58	18 07		18 12	18 22	18 28					18 40	18 45	18 57				19 14	19 22	19 28	
Birmingham Moor Street	d	17 55	18 01	18 10		18 15	18 25	18 31					18 43	18 48	19 00				19 17	19 25	19 31	
Bordesley	d																					
Small Heath	d		18 04	18 13				18 34						18 51	19 03						19 34	
Tyseley	d		18 08	18 17				18 37						18 55	19 07						19 37	
Acocks Green	d		18 10				18 31							18 57						19 31		
Olton	d		18 13				18 33							19 00						19 34		
Solihull	d	18 05	18 17			18 24	18 37						18 52	19 04					19 26	19 37		
Widney Manor	d		18 20				18 40							19 07						19 41		
Dorridge	d	18 12	18 24			18 29	18a45						18 57	19 11					19 31	19a48		
Lapworth	d		18 28			18 34								19 15					19 35			
Hatton	d					18 40								19 20					19 41			
Warwick Parkway	d	18 22				18 45							19 06						19 46			
Warwick	d					18 49								19 26					19 49			
Leamington Spa 8	a	18 27			18 36	18 53				18 58			19 11	19 30		19 37			19 53			
	d	18 28			18 37	18 54				19 00			19 12			19 38		19 42	19 54			
Banbury	d	18 46			18a54	19 13				19a17			19 32			19a54			20 12			
London Marylebone 10 ⊖115	a	19 50				20 30							20 51						21 12			
Spring Road	d			18 19				18 40							19 09						19 40	
Hall Green	d			18 22				18 42							19 12						19 42	
Yardley Wood	d			18 24				18 45							19 14						19 45	
Shirley	d			18 28				18 48							19 18						19 48	
Whitlocks End	d			18a30				18 51							19a20						19 51	
Wythall	d							18 53													19 53	
Earlswood (West Midlands)	d							18 56													19 56	
The Lakes	d							18x58													19x58	
Wood End	d							19x00													20x00	
Danzey	d							19x03													20x02	
Henley-in-Arden	d							19 08													20 07	
Wootton Wawen	d							19x10													20x10	
Wilmcote	d							19 16										20 07			20 15	
Stratford-upon-Avon Parkway	a		18 56					19 19										20 10			20 18	
Stratford-upon-Avon	a		19 00					19 22										20 17			20 21	

Table 71R

Mondays to Fridays

9 December to 16 May

Hereford, Worcester and Stourbridge - Birmingham - Leamington Spa, Marylebone and Stratford-upon-Avon

Network Diagram - see first Page of Table 71

		LM	GW	GW	XC	XC	LM	CH	LM	LM	GW	XC	CH	XC	LM	CH	LM	LM	GW	GW	LM	CH	XC FO
			◇1		◇1	◇1		◇			◇1	◇1	◇	◇1		◇			◇1			◇	◇1
Hereford [7]	d						18 48								19 50						20 56		
Ledbury	a						19 03								20 06						21 12		
	d						19 04								20 09						21 14		
Colwall	d						19 10								20 15						21 20		
Great Malvern	a						19 14								20 19						21 25		
	d			18 50			19 15				19 44				20 20					21 15	21 25		
Malvern Link	d			18 53			19 18				19 46				20 22					21 18	21 28		
Worcester Foregate Street [7]	a			19 03			19 26				19 55				20 31					21 28	21 36		
	d	18 46	18 49	19 03			19 28			19 46	19 56				20 31			20 51	20 59	21 28	21 37		
Worcester Shrub Hill [7]	a		18 52	19 06							19 59				20 34				21 02	21 31	21 40		
	d														20 37								
Droitwich Spa	d	18 55					19 37			19 55					20 45			21 00					
Bromsgrove	d						19 47								20 55								
Barnt Green	d																						
University	d						20 09								21 14								
Hartlebury	d	19 02																					
Kidderminster	d	19 10								20 10								21 10					
Blakedown	d	19 15								20 15								21 15					
Hagley	d	19 18								20 18								21 18					
Stourbridge Junction [2]	d	19 24							19 57	20 24							20 57	21 24					
Lye	d	19 28							20 01	20 28							21 01	21 28					
Cradley Heath	d	19 31							20 04	20 31							21 04	21 31					
Old Hill	d	19 35							20 07	20 35							21 07	21 35					
Rowley Regis	d	19 38							20 11	20 38							21 11	21 38					
Langley Green	d	19 41							20 14	20 41							21 14	21 41					
Birmingham New Street [12] 68	a						20 18								21 20								
	d				19 33	20 04						20 33		21 04									22 04
Birmingham Intl. 68 ⇄	d					20 14								21 14									22 14
Coventry	d					20 24								21 24									22 25
Smethwick Galton Bridge [7]	d	19 45							20 17	20 45							21 17	21 45					
The Hawthorns	d	19 47							20 19	20 47							21 19	21 47					
Jewellery Quarter	d	19 51							20 23	20 51							21 23	21 51					
Birmingham Snow Hill	a	19 55							20 26	20 55							21 26	21 55					
	d	19 56						20 15	20 28	20 56						21 15	21 28	21 56					
Birmingham Moor Street	d	19 59						20 18	20 31	20 59						21 18	21 31	21 59					
Bordesley	d																						
Small Heath	d	20 03							20 34	21 03							21 34	22 03					
Tyseley	d	20 06							20 37	21 06							21 37	22 06					
Acocks Green	d	20 09								21 09								22 09					
Olton	d	20 12								21 12								22 12					
Solihull	d	20 15						20 27		21 15						21 27		22 15					
Widney Manor	d	20 19								21 19								22 19					
Dorridge	d	20a24						20 33		21a24						21 32		22a24					
Lapworth	d															21 37							
Hatton	d												21 09			21 43							
Warwick Parkway	d							20 43								21 48							
Warwick	d							20 47					21 16			21 51							
Leamington Spa [8]	a				20 03	20 37		20 51				20 58	21 20	21 37		21 55							22 36
	d				20 04	20 38		20 52				21 00	21 21	21 38		21 56						21 56	22 38
Banbury	d				20a21	20a54		21 13				21a17	21 46	21a54		22 14							22a54
London Marylebone [10] ⊖115	a							22 13					23 01			23 13							
Spring Road	d								20 40								21 40						
Hall Green	d								20 42								21 42						
Yardley Wood	d								20 45								21 45						
Shirley	d								20 48								21 48						
Whitlocks End	d								20 51								21 51						
Wythall	d								20 53								21 53						
Earlswood (West Midlands)	d								20 56								21 56						
The Lakes	d								20x58								21x58						
Wood End	d								21x00								22x00						
Danzey	d								21x02								22x02						
Henley-in-Arden	d								21 07								22 07						
Wootton Wawen	d								21x10								22x10						
Wilmcote	d								21 15								22 15					22 25	
Stratford-upon-Avon Parkway	a								21 18								22 18					22 27	
Stratford-upon-Avon	a								21 21								22 21					22 36	

Table 71R

Mondays to Fridays

9 December to 16 May

Hereford, Worcester and Stourbridge - Birmingham - Leamington Spa, Marylebone and Stratford-upon-Avon

Network Diagram - see first Page of Table 71

		XC FX	CH		LM	CH	LM	LM	CH	LM	GW	LM
		◇1									◇1	
Hereford 7	d							21 29			21 51	23 00
Ledbury	a							21 44			22 07	23 15
	d							21 45			22 09	23 16
Colwall	d							21 51			22 17	23 22
Great Malvern	a							21 55			22 22	23 26
	d							21 56			22 22	23 27
Malvern Link	d							21 59				23 30
Worcester Foregate Street 7	a							22 07			22 33	23 38
	d							22 10		22 17	22 34	23 39
Worcester Shrub Hill 7	a									22 19	22 38	23 44
	d						21 54			22 27		
Droitwich Spa	d						22 02	22 19		22 35		
Bromsgrove	d							22 29				
Barnt Green	d											
University	d							22 44				
Hartlebury	d											
Kidderminster	d						22 12			22 46		
Blakedown	d						22 17					
Hagley	d						22 20					
Stourbridge Junction 2	d				21 57		22 24			22 57		
Lye	d				22 01		22 28			23 01		
Cradley Heath	d				22 04		22 31			23 04		
Old Hill	d				22 07		22 35			23 07		
Rowley Regis	d				22 11		22 38			23 11		
Langley Green	d				22 14		22 41			23 14		
Birmingham New Street 12 68	a							22 51				
	d	22 04										
Birmingham Intl. 68 ✈	d	22 14										
Coventry	d	22 25										
Smethwick Galton Bridge 7	d				22 17		22 45			23 17		
The Hawthorns 🚋	d				22 19		22 47			23 19		
Jewellery Quarter 🚋	d				22 23		22 51			23 23		
Birmingham Snow Hill 🚋	a				22 26		22 55			23 26		
	d		22 12		22 28		22 57		23 30	23 33		
Birmingham Moor Street	d		22 15		22 31		23 00		23 33	23 36		
Bordesley	d											
Small Heath	d				22 34		23 03			23 39		
Tyseley	d		22 20		22 37		23 07		23 38	23 43		
Acocks Green	d		22 23				23 09		23 41			
Olton	d		22 26				23 12		23 44			
Solihull	d		22 30				23 16		23 48			
Widney Manor	d		22 33				23 19		23 51			
Dorridge	d		22 37				23 23		23 55			
Lapworth	d		22 41				23 27		23 59			
Hatton	d		22 47				23 32		00 05			
Warwick Parkway	d		22 52				23 36		00 10			
Warwick	d		22 55			23 34	23 39		00 13			
Leamington Spa 8	a	22 37	22 59			23 38	23 43		00 17			
	d	22 38	23 00			23 39			00 18			
Banbury	d	22a54	23a23			23a57			00a41			
London Marylebone 10 ⊖115	a											
Spring Road	d				22 40					23 45		
Hall Green	d				22 42					23 48		
Yardley Wood	d				22 45					23 50		
Shirley	d				22 48					23 54		
Whitlocks End	d				22 51					23a56		
Wythall	d				22 53							
Earlswood (West Midlands)	d				22 56							
The Lakes	d				22x58							
Wood End	d				23x00							
Danzey	d				23x02							
Henley-in-Arden	d				23 07							
Wootton Wawen	d				23x10							
Wilmcote	d				23 15							
Stratford-upon-Avon Parkway	a				23 18							
Stratford-upon-Avon	a				23 21							

Table 71R

Saturdays

14 December to 17 May

Hereford, Worcester and Stourbridge - Birmingham - Leamington Spa, Marylebone and Stratford-upon-Avon

Network Diagram - see first Page of Table 71

		CH	XC	CH	XC	CH	LM	LM	XC	GW	CH	LM	XC	CH	LM	LM	CH	LM	GW	CH	CH	XC	LM
			◇1	◇	◇1	◇			◇1	◇1	◇		◇1				◇		◇1	◇		◇1	
			🛒						🛒	🛒			🛒				🛒 BZ		🍽			🛒	
Hereford 7	d																		06 17				
Ledbury	a																		06 33				
	d																		06 34				
Colwall	d																		06 41				
Great Malvern	a																		06 46				
	d									05 56						06 21			06 49				
Malvern Link	d									05 59						06 24			06 53				
Worcester Foregate Street 7	a									06 08						06 31			07 02				
	d									06 09						06 33			07 04				
Worcester Shrub Hill 7	a									06 12									07 07				
	d						05 44	06 07							06 25			07 01					07 35
Droitwich Spa	d						05 52	06 15							06 33	06 42		07 09					07 43
Bromsgrove	d															06 52							07 53
Barnt Green	d																						
University	d															07 09							08 09
Hartlebury	d														06 40			07 16					
Kidderminster	d						06 02				06 37				06 46		07 12	07 22					
Blakedown	d						06 07								06 50			07 26					
Hagley	d						06 10								06 54			07 30					
Stourbridge Junction 2	d						06 14				06 45				07 01		07 22	07 34					
Lye	d						06 18								07 05			07 38					
Cradley Heath	d						06 21				06 51				07 08			07 41					
Old Hill	d						06 25								07 12			07 45					
Rowley Regis	d						06 28				06 57				07 15		07 33	07 48					
Langley Green	d						06 31								07 18			07 51					
Birmingham New Street 12 68	a							06 48								07 16							08 16
	d		06 04		06 33				07 04				07 33									08 04	
Birmingham Intl. 68 ✈	d		06 14						07 14													08 14	
Coventry	d		06 25						07 25													08 25	
Smethwick Galton Bridge 7	d						06 35				07 03				07 22		07 41	07 55					
The Hawthorns 🚋	d						06 37				07 05				07 24		07 44	07 57					
Jewellery Quarter 🚋	d						06 41								07 28			08 01					
Birmingham Snow Hill 🚋	a						06 45				07 11				07 32		07 49	08 05					
	d						06 50				07 12	07 20			07 36		07 51	08 07					
Birmingham Moor Street	d			06 15		06 42	06 53				07 15	07 23		07 33	07 39		07 55	08 10					
Bordesley	d																						
Small Heath	d						06 57					07 26						08 13					
Tyseley	d						07 00					07 29						08 17					
Acocks Green	d						07 03								07 47								
Olton	d						07 05								07 50								
Solihull	d			06 24		06 51	07 09				07 24			07 42	07 53		08 05						
Widney Manor	d						07 12								07 57								
Dorridge	d			06 29		06 56	07a18				07 30			07 50	08a03								
Lapworth	d			06 33										07 55									
Hatton	d	00 05		06 39										08 01						08 17			
Warwick Parkway	d	00 10		06 44		07 05					07 40						08 18						
Warwick	d	00 13		06 47							07 43			08 07						08 24			
Leamington Spa 8	a	00 17	06 37	06 51	06 58	07 10			07 37		07 47		07 58	08 17			08 23			08 28		08 37	
	d	00 18	06 38	06 52	07 00	07 11			07 38		07 48		08 00				08 24			08 29	08 30	08 38	
Banbury	d	00a41	06a54	07 10	07a17	07 29			07a54		08 07		08a17				08 44			08 50		08a54	
London Marylebone 10 ⊖115	a			08 23		08 30					09 11						09 47			10 17			
Spring Road	d											07 32						08 19					
Hall Green	d											07 34						08 22					
Yardley Wood	d											07 36						08 24					
Shirley	d											07 40						08 28					
Whitlocks End	d											07 42						08a30					
Wythall	d											07 45											
Earlswood (West Midlands)	d											07 47											
The Lakes	d											07x50											
Wood End	d											07x52											
Danzey	d											07x55											
Henley-in-Arden	d											08 01											
Wootton Wawen	d											08x04											
Wilmcote	d											08 10									08 58		
Stratford-upon-Avon Parkway	a											08 13									09 01		
Stratford-upon-Avon	a											08 16									09 09		

BZ Business Zone available offering greater comfort and an enhanced working environment. Supplement payable.

Table 71R

Saturdays

14 December to 17 May

Hereford, Worcester and Stourbridge - Birmingham - Leamington Spa, Marylebone and Stratford-upon-Avon

Network Diagram - see first Page of Table 71

		CH	LM	LM	LM	LM	GW	XC	CH	LM	LM	XC	CH	LM	LM	LM	CH	XC	CH	LM	LM	CH	LM
		◇					◇1 ⌀	◇1 ⚲	◇			◇1 ⚲	◇				◇	◇1 ⚲				◇ ⚲ BZ	
Hereford 7	d						07 10									07 40							
Ledbury	a						07 28									07 56							
	d						07 30									07 58							
Colwall	d						07 37									08 04							
Great Malvern	a						07 43									08 08							
	d					07 35	07 44									08 10							
Malvern Link	d					07 37	07 48									08 13							
Worcester Foregate Street 7	a					07 46	07 58									08 21							
	d					07 47	07 59									08 24							08 56
Worcester Shrub Hill 7	a						08 02																
	d													08 15									
Droitwich Spa	d					07 56								08 23		08 33							09 05
Bromsgrove	d															08 43							
Barnt Green	d																						
University	d															08 59							
Hartlebury	d													08 31									
Kidderminster	d			07 47		08 06			08 13					08 36								09 10	09 16
Blakedown	d			07 51		08 11								08 41									
Hagley	d			07 55		08 14								08 44									
Stourbridge Junction 2	d			07 59	08 05	08 19			08 26		08 35			08 48	08 57					09 07		09 20	09 27
Lye	d				08 09						08 39				09 01								09 31
Cradley Heath	d			08 04	08 12	08 25			08 32		08 42			08 54	09 04					09 13			09 34
Old Hill	d				08 15						08 46				09 07								09 37
Rowley Regis	d			08 10	08 19	08 30			08 37		08 49			08 59	09 11					09 18		09 31	09 41
Langley Green	d				08 22						08 52				09 14								09 44
Birmingham New Street 12 68	a															09 11							
	d							08 33				09 04						09 33					
Birmingham Intl. 68 ✈	d											09 14											
Coventry	d											09 25											
Smethwick Galton Bridge 7	d			08 16	08 25	08 36			08 43		08 56			09 05	09 17					09 24		09 39	09 47
The Hawthorns 🚋	d			08 18	08 27	08 38			08 45		08 58			09 07	09 19					09 26		09 42	09 49
Jewellery Quarter 🚋	d			08 22	08 31	08 42					09 02			09 11	09 23					09 30			09 53
Birmingham Snow Hill 🚋	a			08 26	08 35	08 45			08 51		09 05			09 15	09 26					09 34		09 47	09 56
	d		08 17	08 28	08 37	08 47			08 52	08 58	09 07		09 12	09 17	09 28					09 37	09 47	09 51	09 58
Birmingham Moor Street	d	08 15	08 20	08 31	08 40	08 50			08 55	09 01	09 10		09 15	09 20	09 31				09 34	09 40	09 50	09 55	10 01
Bordesley	d																						
Small Heath	d				08 43						09 13									09 43			
Tyseley	d				08 47						09 17									09 47			
Acocks Green	d		08 26		08 49					09 07				09 26						09 49			10 07
Olton	d		08 28		08 52					09 10				09 29						09 52			10 10
Solihull	d	08 24	08 32		08 56				09 05	09 13			09 24	09 32					09 43	09 56		10 05	10 13
Widney Manor	d		08 35		08 59					09 17				09 36						09 59			10 17
Dorridge	d	08 29	08a41		09a04					09 21			09 29	09a41					09 54	10a04			10 21
Lapworth	d																		09 58				
Hatton	d																09 41		10 03				
Warwick Parkway	d	08 39							09 19				09 39									10 19	
Warwick	d	08 43											09 42				09 48		10 09				
Leamington Spa 8	a	08 47						08 58	09 24			09 37	09 47				09 52	09 58	10 20			10 24	
	d	08 48						09 00	09 25			09 38	09 48				09 53	10 00				10 25	
Banbury	d	09 10						09a17	09 45			09a54	10 06				10 13	10a17				10 45	
London Marylebone 10 ⊖115	a	10 20							10 42				11 14				11 41					11 44	
Spring Road	d			08 37		08 56					09 19				09 37						09 56		
Hall Green	d			08 39		08 59					09 22				09 39						09 59		
Yardley Wood	d			08 42		09 01					09 24				09 42						10 01		
Shirley	d			08 45		09 05					09 28				09 45						10 05		
Whitlocks End	d			08 48		09a07					09a30				09 48						10a07		
Wythall	d			08 51											09 51								
Earlswood (West Midlands)	d			08 53											09 53								
The Lakes	d			08x56											09x56								
Wood End	d			08x58											09x58								
Danzey	d			09x01											10x01								
Henley-in-Arden	d			09 06											10 06								
Wootton Wawen	d			09x09											10x09								
Wilmcote	d			09 15											10 15								
Stratford-upon-Avon Parkway	a			09 18						09 45					10 18								10 37
Stratford-upon-Avon	a			09 21						09 49					10 21								10 41

BZ Business Zone available offering greater comfort and an enhanced working enviorment. Supplement payable.

Table 71R

Saturdays

14 December to 17 May

Hereford, Worcester and Stourbridge - Birmingham - Leamington Spa, Marylebone and Stratford-upon-Avon

Network Diagram - see first Page of Table 71

		LM		GW	XC	CH	CH	LM	LM	LM	XC	LM		LM	CH	LM	XC	GW	LM	LM	CH	LM		LM	LM
				◇1	◇1	◇	◇				◇1				◇		◇1	◇1			◇				
				restaurant	trolley						trolley						trolley	trolley							
								BZ																	
Hereford 7	d									08 40															09 40
Ledbury	a									08 56															09 56
	d									08 58															09 58
Colwall	d									09 04															10 04
Great Malvern	a									09 09															10 08
	d			08 43				09 00		09 10								09 51							10 10
Malvern Link	d			08 47				09 02		09 13								09 54							10 13
Worcester Foregate Street 7	a			08 56				09 11		09 22								10 03							10 21
	d			08 58				09 16		09 24								10 04				10 16			10 24
Worcester Shrub Hill 7	a			09 01														10 07							
	d													09 48		09 56									
Droitwich Spa	d							09 25		09 33				09 56		10 04						10 25			10 33
Bromsgrove	d									09 43						10 13									10 43
Barnt Green	d																								
University	d									09 59															10 59
Hartlebury	d							09 32														10 32			
Kidderminster	d	09 25						09 40				09 55		10 06						10 25		10 40			
Blakedown	d	09 29										09 59								10 29					
Hagley	d	09 33										10 03								10 33					
Stourbridge Junction 2	d	09 37						09 48	09 57			10 07		10 14					10 27	10 37		10 48		10 57	
Lye	d								10 01										10 31					11 01	
Cradley Heath	d	09 43						09 54	10 04			10 13		10 20					10 34	10 43		10 54		11 04	
Old Hill	d								10 07										10 37					11 07	
Rowley Regis	d	09 48						09 59	10 11			10 18		10 26					10 41	10 48		10 59		11 11	
Langley Green	d								10 14										10 44					11 14	
Birmingham New Street 12 68	a									10 11						10 41									11 11
	d				10 04						10 33						11 04								
Birmingham Intl. 68 ✈	d				10 14												11 14								
Coventry	d				10 25												11 25								
Smethwick Galton Bridge 7	d	09 54						10 05	10 17			10 24		10 31					10 47	10 54		11 05		11 17	
The Hawthorns (tram)	d	09 56						10 07	10 19			10 26		10 33					10 49	10 56		11 07		11 19	
Jewellery Quarter (tram)	d	10 00						10 11	10 23			10 30		10 37					10 53	11 00		11 11		11 23	
Birmingham Snow Hill (tram)	a	10 04						10 15	10 26			10 34		10 41					10 56	11 04		11 15		11 26	
	d	10 07					10 12	10 17	10 28			10 37		10 47					10 58	11 07	11 12	11 17		11 28	
Birmingham Moor Street	d	10 10					10 15	10 20	10 31			10 40		10 50	10 55				11 01	11 10	11 15	11 20		11 31	
Bordesley	d																								
Small Heath	d	10 13										10 43								11 13					
Tyseley	d	10 17										10 47								11 17					
Acocks Green	d							10 26				10 49							11 07			11 26			
Olton	d							10 29				10 52							11 10			11 29			
Solihull	d						10 24	10 32				10 56			11 04				11 13		11 24	11 32			
Widney Manor	d							10 36				10 59							11 17			11 36			
Dorridge	d						10 30	10a42				11a04							11 21		11 29	11a42			
Lapworth	d																								
Hatton	d																								
Warwick Parkway	d						10 40								11 15						11 39				
Warwick	d						10 44														11 42				
Leamington Spa 8	a				10 37		10 48				10 58				11 20		11 37				11 47				
	d				10 38	10 47	10 49				11 00				11 21		11 38				11 48				
Banbury	d				10a54		11 09				11a17				11 40		11a54				12 06				
London Marylebone 10 ⊖115	a						12 17								12 44						13 17				
Spring Road	d	10 19							10 37					10 56						11 19				11 37	
Hall Green	d	10 22							10 39					10 59						11 22				11 39	
Yardley Wood	d	10 24							10 42					11 01						11 24				11 42	
Shirley	d	10 28							10 45					11 05						11 28				11 45	
Whitlocks End	d	10a30							10 48					11a07						11a30				11 48	
Wythall	d								10 51															11 51	
Earlswood (West Midlands)	d								10 53															11 53	
The Lakes	d								10x56															11x56	
Wood End	d								10x58															11x58	
Danzey	d								11x01															12x01	
Henley-in-Arden	d								11 06															12 06	
Wootton Wawen	d								11x09															12x09	
Wilmcote	d								11 15															12 15	
Stratford-upon-Avon Parkway	a					11 08			11 18										11 37					12 18	
Stratford-upon-Avon	a					11 15			11 21										11 41					12 21	

BZ Business Zone available offering greater comfort and an enhanced working environment. Supplement payable.

Table 71R

Saturdays

14 December to 17 May

Hereford, Worcester and Stourbridge - Birmingham - Leamington Spa, Marylebone and Stratford-upon-Avon

Network Diagram - see first Page of Table 71

		XC	CH	CH	LM	LM	CH	GW		GW	LM	LM	XC	CH	LM	LM	LM	LM		LM	CH	XC	CH	LM	LM
		◇1 🚲	◇				◇	R		◇1 🚲			◇1 🚲	◇							◇	◇1 🚲	◇		
Hereford 7	d																10 40								
Ledbury	a																10 56								
	d																10 58								
Colwall	d																11 04								
Great Malvern	a																11 08								
	d							10 46		10 58							11 10			11 35					
Malvern Link	d							10 48		11 01							11 13			11 37					
Worcester Foregate Street 7	a							10 58		11 10							11 21			11 46					
	d							10 58		11 11							11 24			11 51					
Worcester Shrub Hill 7	a							11 01		11 14															
	d					10 52									11 17										
Droitwich Spa	d					11 00									11 25		11 33			12 00					
Bromsgrove	d																11 43								
Barnt Green	d																								
University	d																11 59								
Hartlebury	d														11 32										
Kidderminster	d				10 55	11 10						11 25			11 40			11 55		12 10					12 25
Blakedown	d				10 59							11 29						11 59							12 29
Hagley	d				11 03							11 33						12 03							12 33
Stourbridge Junction 2	d				11 07	11 18					11 27	11 37			11 48	11 57		12 07		12 18				12 27	12 37
Lye	d										11 31					12 01								12 31	
Cradley Heath	d				11 13	11 24					11 34	11 43			11 54	12 04		12 13		12 24				12 34	12 43
Old Hill	d										11 37					12 07								12 37	
Rowley Regis	d				11 18	11 30					11 41	11 48			11 59	12 11		12 18		12 30				12 41	12 48
Langley Green	d										11 44					12 14								12 44	
Birmingham New Street 12 68	a																12 11								
	d	11 33											12 04									12 33			
Birmingham Intl. 68 ✈	d												12 14												
Coventry	d												12 25												
Smethwick Galton Bridge 7	d				11 24	11 35					11 47	11 54			12 05	12 17		12 24		12 35				12 47	12 54
The Hawthorns 🚊	d				11 26	11 37					11 49	11 56			12 07	12 19		12 26		12 37				12 49	12 56
Jewellery Quarter 🚊	d				11 30	11 41					11 53	12 00			12 11	12 23		12 30		12 41				12 53	13 00
Birmingham Snow Hill 🚊	a				11 34	11 45					11 56	12 04			12 15	12 26		12 34		12 45				12 56	13 04
	d				11 37	11 47					11 58	12 07		12 12	12 17	12 28		12 37		12 47				12 58	13 07
Birmingham Moor Street	d			11 34	11 40	11 50	11 55				12 01	12 10		12 15	12 20	12 31		12 40		12 50			12 55	13 01	13 10
Bordesley	d																								
Small Heath	d				11 43							12 13						12 43							13 13
Tyseley	d				11 47							12 17						12 47							13 17
Acocks Green	d				11 49						12 07				12 26			12 49						13 07	
Olton	d				11 52						12 10				12 29			12 52						13 10	
Solihull	d			11 42	11 56		12 04				12 13			12 24	12 32			12 56					13 04	13 13	
Widney Manor	d				11 59						12 17				12 36			12 59						13 17	
Dorridge	d			11 53	12a04						12 21			12 29	12a42			13a04						13 21	
Lapworth	d			11 57																					
Hatton	d		11 58	12 02																					
Warwick Parkway	d						12 21							12 39									13 19		
Warwick	d		12 04	12 10										12 42											
Leamington Spa 8	a	11 58	12 08	12 20			12 26						12 37	12 47								12 59	13 24		
	d	12 00	12 09				12 27						12 38	12 48							12 51	13 02	13 25		
Banbury	d	12a17	12 27				12 46						12a54	13 08								13a19	13 44		
London Marylebone 10 ⊖115	a		13 47				13 50							14 18									14 47		
Spring Road	d					11 56						12 19				12 37				12 56					13 19
Hall Green	d					11 59						12 22				12 39				12 59					13 22
Yardley Wood	d					12 01						12 24				12 42				13 01					13 24
Shirley	d					12 05						12 28				12 45				13 05					13 28
Whitlocks End	d					12a07						12a30				12 48				13a07					13a30
Wythall	d															12 51									
Earlswood (West Midlands)	d															12 53									
The Lakes	d															12x56									
Wood End	d															12x58									
Danzey	d															13x01									
Henley-in-Arden	d															13 06									
Wootton Wawen	d															13x09									
Wilmcote	d															13 15					13 24				
Stratford-upon-Avon Parkway	a										12 37					13 18					13 26			13 37	
Stratford-upon-Avon	a										12 41					13 21					13 33			13 41	

Table 71R

Saturdays

14 December to 17 May

Hereford, Worcester and Stourbridge - Birmingham - Leamington Spa, Marylebone and Stratford-upon-Avon

Network Diagram - see first Page of Table 71

		XC	CH	LM	LM	LM	XC	GW	CH	CH	LM	LM	CH	GW	LM	LM	XC	CH	LM	LM	LM	LM
		◇1	◇				◇1	◇	◇				◇ BZ	◇1			◇1	◇				
Hereford 7	d					11 40								12 13							12 40	
Ledbury	a					11 56								12 30							12 56	
	d					11 58								12 31							12 58	
Colwall	d					12 04								12 38							13 04	
Great Malvern	a					12 08								12 43							13 08	
	d					12 10								12 44							13 10	
Malvern Link	d					12 13								12 48							13 13	
Worcester Foregate Street 7	a					12 21								12 58							13 21	
	d			12 16		12 24		12 41				12 51		12 59							13 24	
Worcester Shrub Hill 7	a							12 43						13 02								
	d																		13 17			
Droitwich Spa	d			12 25		12 33						13 00							13 25		13 33	
Bromsgrove	d					12 43															13 43	
Barnt Green	d																					
University	d					12 59															13 59	
Hartlebury	d			12 32															13 32			
Kidderminster	d			12 40							12 55	13 10				13 25			13 40			13 55
Blakedown	d										12 59					13 29						13 59
Hagley	d										13 03					13 33						14 03
Stourbridge Junction 2	d			12 48	12 57						13 07	13 18			13 27	13 37			13 48	13 57		14 07
Lye	d				13 01										13 31					14 01		
Cradley Heath	d			12 54	13 04						13 13	13 24			13 34	13 43			13 54	14 04		14 13
Old Hill	d				13 07										13 37					14 07		
Rowley Regis	d			12 59	13 11						13 18	13 30			13 41	13 48			13 59	14 11		14 18
Langley Green	d				13 14										13 44					14 14		
Birmingham New Street 12 68	a					13 11															14 11	
	d	13 04					13 33										14 04					
Birmingham Intl. 68 ✈	d	13 14															14 14					
Coventry	d	13 25															14 25					
Smethwick Galton Bridge 7	d			13 05	13 17						13 24	13 35			13 47	13 54			14 05	14 17		14 24
The Hawthorns	d			13 07	13 19						13 26	13 37			13 49	13 56			14 07	14 19		14 26
Jewellery Quarter	d			13 11	13 23						13 30	13 41			13 53	14 00			14 11	14 23		14 30
Birmingham Snow Hill	a			13 15	13 26						13 34	13 45			13 56	14 04			14 15	14 26		14 34
	d		13 12	13 17	13 28						13 37	13 47			13 58	14 07		14 12	14 17	14 28		14 37
Birmingham Moor Street	d		13 15	13 20	13 31					13 34	13 40	13 50	13 55		14 01	14 10		14 15	14 20	14 31		14 40
Bordesley	d																					
Small Heath	d										13 43					14 13						14 43
Tyseley	d										13 47					14 17						14 47
Acocks Green	d			13 26							13 49				14 07				14 26			14 49
Olton	d			13 29							13 52				14 10				14 29			14 52
Solihull	d		13 24	13 32						13 42	13 56		14 05		14 13			14 24	14 32			14 56
Widney Manor	d			13 36							13 59				14 17				14 36			14 59
Dorridge	d		13 29	13a42						13 54	14a04				14 21			14 29	14a42			15a04
Lapworth	d									13 58												
Hatton	d								13 58	14 03												
Warwick Parkway	d		13 39										14 18					14 39				
Warwick	d		13 42						14 04	14 09								14 42				
Leamington Spa 8	a	13 37	13 47				13 58		14 08	14 16			14 24				14 37	14 47				
	d	13 38	13 48				14 00		14 09				14 25				14 38	14 48				
Banbury	d	13a54	14 10				14a16		14 27				14 43				14a54	15 09				
London Marylebone 10 ⊖115	a		15 17						15 47				15 50					16 18				
Spring Road	d				13 37							13 56				14 19				14 37		
Hall Green	d				13 39							13 59				14 22				14 39		
Yardley Wood	d				13 42							14 01				14 24				14 42		
Shirley	d				13 45							14 05				14 28				14 45		
Whitlocks End	d				13 48							14a07				14a30				14 48		
Wythall	d				13 51															14 51		
Earlswood (West Midlands)	d				13 53															14 53		
The Lakes	d				13x56															14x56		
Wood End	d				13x58															14x58		
Danzey	d				14x01															15x01		
Henley-in-Arden	d				14 06															15 06		
Wootton Wawen	d				14x09															15x09		
Wilmcote	d				14 15															15 15		
Stratford-upon-Avon Parkway	a				14 18										14 37					15 18		
Stratford-upon-Avon	a				14 21										14 41					15 21		

BZ Business Zone available offering greater comfort and an enhanced working environment. Supplement payable.

Table 71R

Saturdays

14 December to 17 May

Hereford, Worcester and Stourbridge - Birmingham - Leamington Spa, Marylebone and Stratford-upon-Avon

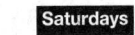

Network Diagram - see first Page of Table 71

		LM	CH	XC	CH	LM	LM	XC	CH	LM		LM	LM	XC	CH	CH	LM	LM	CH	GW		GW	LM	LM	XC
			◇	◇1 🍴	◇ 🍴			◇1 🍴	◇					◇1 🍴	◇				◇	◇1 🍴		◇			◇1 🍴
Hereford 7	d												13 40												
Ledbury	a												13 56												
	d												13 58												
Colwall	d												14 04												
Great Malvern	a												14 08												
	d	13 35											14 10							14 34		14 50			
Malvern Link	d	13 37											14 13							14 37		14 52			
Worcester Foregate Street 7	a	13 46											14 21							14 55		15 03			
	d	13 51								14 16			14 24							14 57		15 04			
Worcester Shrub Hill 7	a																			15 00		15 06			
	d																	14 52							
Droitwich Spa	d	14 00								14 25			14 33					15 00							
Bromsgrove	d												14 43												
Barnt Green	d																								
University	d												14 59												
Hartlebury	d									14 32															
Kidderminster	d	14 10					14 25			14 40							14 55	15 10						15 25	
Blakedown	d						14 29										14 59							15 29	
Hagley	d						14 33										15 03							15 33	
Stourbridge Junction 2	d	14 18				14 27	14 37			14 48		14 57					15 07	15 18					15 27	15 37	
Lye	d					14 31						15 01											15 31		
Cradley Heath	d	14 24				14 34	14 43			14 54		15 04					15 13	15 24					15 34	15 43	
Old Hill	d					14 37						15 07											15 37		
Rowley Regis	d	14 30				14 41	14 48			14 59		15 11					15 18	15 30					15 41	15 48	
Langley Green	d					14 44						15 14											15 44		
Birmingham New Street 12 68	a												15 11												
	d			14 33				15 04						15 33											16 04
Birmingham Intl. 68 ✈	d							15 14																	16 14
Coventry	d							15 25																	16 25
Smethwick Galton Bridge 7	d	14 35				14 47	14 54			15 05		15 17					15 24	15 35					15 47	15 54	
The Hawthorns 🚊	d	14 37				14 49	14 56			15 07		15 19					15 26	15 37					15 49	15 56	
Jewellery Quarter 🚊	d	14 41				14 53	15 00			15 11		15 23					15 30	15 41					15 53	16 00	
Birmingham Snow Hill 🚊	a	14 45				14 56	15 04			15 15		15 26					15 34	15 45					15 56	16 04	
	d	14 47				14 58	15 07		15 12	15 17		15 28					15 37	15 47					15 58	16 07	
Birmingham Moor Street	d	14 50			14 55	15 01	15 10		15 15	15 20		15 31				15 34	15 40	15 50	15 55				16 01	16 10	
Bordesley	d																								
Small Heath	d						15 13										15 43							16 13	
Tyseley	d						15 17										15 47							16 17	
Acocks Green	d					15 07				15 26							15 49						16 07		
Olton	d					15 10				15 29							15 52						16 10		
Solihull	d				15 04	15 13			15 24	15 32						15 42	15 56		16 04				16 13		
Widney Manor	d					15 17				15 36							15 59						16 17		
Dorridge	d					15 21			15 29	15a42						15 53	16a04						16 21		
Lapworth	d															15 57									
Hatton	d														15 58	16 03									
Warwick Parkway	d				15 16				15 39										16 16						
Warwick	d								15 42						16 04	16 08									
Leamington Spa 8	a			14 58	15 22			15 37	15 47					16 00	16 08	16 16			16 22						16 37
	d		14 49	15 00	15 23			15 38	15 48					16 02	16 09				16 23						16 38
Banbury	d			15a19	15 42			15a54	16 07					16a19	16 27				16 44						16a54
London Marylebone 10 ⊖115	a				16 47				17 22						17 44				17 47						
Spring Road	d	14 56					15 19					15 37						15 56						16 19	
Hall Green	d	14 59					15 22					15 39						15 59						16 22	
Yardley Wood	d	15 01					15 24					15 42						16 01						16 24	
Shirley	d	15 05					15 28					15 45						16 05						16 28	
Whitlocks End	d	15a07					15a30					15 48						16a07						16a30	
Wythall	d											15 51													
Earlswood (West Midlands)	d											15 53													
The Lakes	d											15x56													
Wood End	d											15x58													
Danzey	d											16x01													
Henley-in-Arden	d											16 06													
Wootton Wawen	d											16x09													
Wilmcote	d		15 22									16 15													
Stratford-upon-Avon Parkway	a		15 24			15 37						16 18											16 37		
Stratford-upon-Avon	a		15 33			15 41						16 21											16 41		

Table 71R

Saturdays

14 December to 17 May

Hereford, Worcester and Stourbridge - Birmingham - Leamington Spa, Marylebone and Stratford-upon-Avon

Network Diagram - see first Page of Table 71

		CH	LM	LM	LM	LM	LM	CH	XC	LM	GW	CH	LM	LM	XC	CH	LM	LM	LM	XC	CH	CH	LM
		◇						◇	◇1		◇1	◇			◇1	◇				◇1	◇		
Hereford 7	d				14 40						15 13								15 40				
Ledbury	a				14 56						15 30								15 56				
	d				14 58						15 31								15 58				
Colwall	d				15 04						15 38								16 04				
Great Malvern	a				15 08						15 43								16 08				
	d				15 10		15 30				15 44								16 10				
Malvern Link	d				15 13		15 32				15 48								16 13				
Worcester Foregate Street 7	a				15 21		15 41				15 58								16 21				
	d		15 16		15 24		15 46				15 59						16 14		16 24				
Worcester Shrub Hill 7	a										16 02												
	d									15 54													
Droitwich Spa	d		15 25		15 33		15 55			16 02							16 23		16 33				
Bromsgrove	d				15 43					16 12									16 43				
Barnt Green	d																						
University	d				15 59														16 59				
Hartlebury	d		15 32														16 31						
Kidderminster	d		15 40			15 55	16 10							16 25			16 36						16 55
Blakedown	d					15 59								16 29			16 41						16 59
Hagley	d					16 03								16 32			16 44						17 03
Stourbridge Junction 2	d		15 48	15 57		16 07	16 18						16 27	16 36			16 48	16 57					17 07
Lye	d			16 01									16 31					17 01					
Cradley Heath	d		15 54	16 04		16 13	16 24						16 34	16 42			16 54	17 04					17 13
Old Hill	d			16 07									16 37					17 07					
Rowley Regis	d		15 59	16 11		16 18	16 30						16 41	16 48			17 00	17 11					17 18
Langley Green	d			16 14									16 44					17 14					
Birmingham New Street 12 68	a				16 11					16 45									17 11				
	d								16 33						17 04					17 33			
Birmingham Intl. 68 ✈	d														17 14								
Coventry	d														17 25								
Smethwick Galton Bridge 7	d		16 05	16 17		16 24	16 35						16 47	16 53			17 05	17 17					17 24
The Hawthorns 🚋	d		16 07	16 19		16 26	16 37						16 49	16 55			17 07	17 19					17 26
Jewellery Quarter 🚋	d		16 11	16 23		16 30	16 41						16 53	17 00			17 11	17 23					17 30
Birmingham Snow Hill 🚋	a		16 15	16 26		16 34	16 45						16 56	17 03			17 15	17 26					17 34
	d	16 12	16 17	16 28		16 37	16 47						16 58	17 06		17 12	17 17	17 28					17 37
Birmingham Moor Street	d	16 15	16 20	16 31		16 40	16 50					16 55	17 01	17 09		17 15	17 20	17 31				17 34	17 40
Bordesley	d																						
Small Heath	d					16 43	16 53							17 13									17 43
Tyseley	d			16 36		16 47	16 57							17 16				17 36					17 47
Acocks Green	d		16 26			16 49							17 07				17 26						17 49
Olton	d		16 29			16 52							17 10				17 29						17 52
Solihull	d	16 24	16 32			16 56						17 04	17 13			17 24	17 32					17 42	17 56
Widney Manor	d		16 36			16 59							17 17				17 36						17 59
Dorridge	d	16 29	16a42			17a04							17 21			17 29	17a42					17 54	18a04
Lapworth	d																					17 58	
Hatton	d																					18 03	
Warwick Parkway	d	16 39										17 16				17 39							
Warwick	d	16 42														17 42					18 03	18 09	
Leamington Spa 8	a	16 47							16 59			17 22			17 37	17 47				18 00	18 07	18 19	
	d	16 48						16 51	17 00			17 23			17 38	17 48				18 02	18 08		
Banbury	d	17 08							17a17			17 45			17a54	18 08				18a18	18 26		
London Marylebone 10 ⊖115	a	18 20										18 47				19 16					19 24		
Spring Road	d			16 38			16 59							17 19				17 38					
Hall Green	d			16 41			17 02							17 21				17 41					
Yardley Wood	d			16 43			17 04							17 24				17 43					
Shirley	d			16 46			17 08							17 27				17 47					
Whitlocks End	d			16 49			17a10							17 30				17a49					
Wythall	d			16 52										17 32									
Earlswood (West Midlands)	d			16 54										17 35									
The Lakes	d			16x56										17x37									
Wood End	d			16x58										17x40									
Danzey	d			17x01										17x43									
Henley-in-Arden	d			17 06										17 48									
Wootton Wawen	d			17x09										17x51									
Wilmcote	d			17 15				17 24						17 56									
Stratford-upon-Avon Parkway	a			17 18				17 26					17 37	17 59									
Stratford-upon-Avon	a			17 21				17 32					17 43	18 03									

Table 71R

Saturdays

14 December to 17 May

Hereford, Worcester and Stourbridge - Birmingham - Leamington Spa, Marylebone and Stratford-upon-Avon

Network Diagram - see first Page of Table 71

		LM	GW	GW	CH	LM	LM	LM	LM	XC	LM	CH	XC	CH	LM	LM	GW	LM	LM	XC	LM	XC
			◇1 ⌶		◇					◇1 ⌶		◇	◇1 ⌶	◇			◇1 ⌶			◇1 ⌶		◇1 ⌶
Hereford 7	d										16 40										17 40	
Ledbury	a										16 56										17 56	
	d										16 58										17 58	
Colwall	d										17 04										18 04	
Great Malvern	a										17 08										18 08	
	d		16 34	16 50							17 10						17 49	18 00			18 10	
Malvern Link	d		16 37	16 52							17 13						17 52	18 02			18 13	
Worcester Foregate Street 7	a		16 54	17 04							17 21						18 01	18 11			18 21	
	d	16 47	16 55	17 04							17 24				17 47		18 02	18 12			18 24	
Worcester Shrub Hill 7	a		16 58	17 06													18 05	18 14				
	d							17 15										18 18				
Droitwich Spa	d	16 56						17 23			17 34				17 56			18 26			18 33	
Bromsgrove	d										17 44										18 43	
Barnt Green	d																					
University	d										17 59										18 59	
Hartlebury	d							17 31														
Kidderminster	d	17 06					17 25	17 36							18 06			18 36				
Blakedown	d	17 11					17 29	17 41							18 11			18 41				
Hagley	d	17 14					17 33	17 44							18 14			18 44				
Stourbridge Junction 2	d	17 18				17 27	17 37	17 48	17 57						18 18	18 27		18 48	18 57			
Lye	d					17 31			18 01							18 31			19 01			
Cradley Heath	d	17 24				17 34	17 43	17 54	18 04						18 24	18 34		18 54	19 04			
Old Hill	d					17 37			18 07							18 37			19 07			
Rowley Regis	d	17 29				17 41	17 48	18 00	18 11						18 30	18 41		19 00	19 11			
Langley Green	d					17 44			18 14							18 44			19 14			
Birmingham New Street 12 68	a										18 11										19 11	
	d									18 04			18 33							19 04		19 33
Birmingham Intl. 68 ✈	d									18 14										19 14		
Coventry	d									18 25										19 25		
Smethwick Galton Bridge 7	d	17 35				17 47	17 54	18 05	18 17						18 35	18 47		19 05	19 17			
The Hawthorns	d	17 37				17 49	17 56	18 07	18 19						18 37	18 49		19 07	19 19			
Jewellery Quarter	d	17 41				17 53	18 00	18 11	18 23						18 41	18 53		19 11	19 23			
Birmingham Snow Hill	a	17 45				17 56	18 04	18 15	18 26						18 45	18 56		19 15	19 26			
	d	17 47			17 52	17 58	18 07	18 17	18 28					18 42	18 50	18 58		19 17	19 28			
Birmingham Moor Street	d	17 50			17 55	18 01	18 10	18 20	18 31					18 45	18 53	19 01		19 20	19 31			
Bordesley	d																					
Small Heath	d	17 53					18 13	18 23							18 56	19 04		19 23	19 34			
Tyseley	d	17 57					18 17	18 26							19 00	19 08		19 27	19 37			
Acocks Green	d					18 07		18 29							19 02			19 29				
Olton	d					18 10		18 31							19 05			19 32				
Solihull	d				18 04	18 13		18 35						18 54	19 09			19 36				
Widney Manor	d					18 17		18 38							19 12			19 39				
Dorridge	d					18a22		18a43						18 59	19a17			19a44				
Lapworth	d																					
Hatton	d																					
Warwick Parkway	d				18 16									19 08								
Warwick	d				18 19									19 11								
Leamington Spa 8	a				18 24					18 37			18 58	19 16						19 37		20 01
	d				18 25					18 38		18 51	19 00	19 17						19 38		20 03
Banbury	d				18 45					18a54			19a17	19 35						19a54		20a18
London Marylebone 10 ⊖115	a				19 50									20 40								
Spring Road	d	17 59					18 19		18 37							19 10			19 40			
Hall Green	d	18 02					18 22		18 39							19 13			19 42			
Yardley Wood	d	18 04					18 24		18 42							19 15			19 45			
Shirley	d	18 08					18 28		18 45							19 19			19 48			
Whitlocks End	d	18 10					18a30		18 48							19a21			19 51			
Wythall	d	18 13							18 51										19 53			
Earlswood (West Midlands)	d	18 15							18 53										19 56			
The Lakes	d	18x18							18x56										19x58			
Wood End	d	18x20							18x58										20x00			
Danzey	d	18x23							19x01										20x02			
Henley-in-Arden	d	18 28							19 06										20 07			
Wootton Wawen	d	18x31							19x09										20x10			
Wilmcote	d	18 37							19 15			19 22							20 15			
Stratford-upon-Avon Parkway	a	18 40							19 18			19 24							20 18			
Stratford-upon-Avon	a	18 43							19 21			19 32							20 21			

Table 71R

Saturdays

14 December to 17 May

Hereford, Worcester and Stourbridge - Birmingham - Leamington Spa, Marylebone and Stratford-upon-Avon

Network Diagram - see first Page of Table 71

		GW	CH	CH	LM	GW	LM	XC		CH	XC	CH	LM	GW	XC	LM	CH	CH		LM	LM	GW	GW	CH	LM
		◇1		◇				◇1 ✠		◇	◇1 ✠	◇		◇1	◇1			◇				◇1			
Hereford 7	d												19 11			20 00						20 20			
Ledbury	a												19 27			20 15						20 36			
	d												19 27			20 16						20 40			
Colwall	d												19 33			20 22						20 47			
Great Malvern	a												19 38			20 26						20 52			
	d	18 35				18 50							19 38			20 27						20 53	21 15		
Malvern Link	d	18 38				18 52							19 41			20 30						20 57	21 17		
Worcester Foregate Street 7	a	18 47				19 03							19 50			20 38						21 09	21 27		
	d	18 49			18 51	19 04							19 53	20 02		20 40						21 11	21 27		
Worcester Shrub Hill 7	a	18 51				19 06								20 05								21 14	21 30		
	d																				20 52				
Droitwich Spa	d				19 00								20 02			20 49					21 00				
Bromsgrove	d															20 59									
Barnt Green	d																								
University	d															21 14									
Hartlebury	d				19 07																				
Kidderminster	d				19 13		19 43						20 12								21 10				
Blakedown	d				19 17		19 47						20 17								21 15				
Hagley	d				19 21		19 50						20 20								21 18				
Stourbridge Junction 2	d				19 25		19 56						20 24							20 57	21 22				21 57
Lye	d				19 29		20 00						20 28							21 01	21 26				22 01
Cradley Heath	d				19 32		20 03						20 31							21 04	21 29				22 04
Old Hill	d				19 35		20 07						20 35							21 07	21 33				22 07
Rowley Regis	d				19 39		20 10						20 38							21 11	21 36				22 11
Langley Green	d				19 42		20 13						20 41							21 14	21 39				22 14
Birmingham New Street 12 68	a															21 20									
	d							20 04			20 33				21 04										
Birmingham Intl. 68 ✈	d							20 14							21 14										
Coventry	d							20 25							21 25										
Smethwick Galton Bridge 7	d				19 45		20 17						20 45							21 17	21 43				22 17
The Hawthorns 🚋	d				19 47		20 19						20 47							21 19	21 45				22 19
Jewellery Quarter 🚋	d				19 51		20 23						20 51							21 23	21 49				22 23
Birmingham Snow Hill 🚋	a				19 55		20 26						20 55							21 26	21 53				22 26
	d			19 42	19 57		20 28						20 57					21 22		21 28	21 54			22 15	22 28
Birmingham Moor Street	d			19 45	20 00		20 31					20 45	21 00					21 25		21 31	21 57			22 18	22 31
Bordesley	d																								
Small Heath	d				20 03		20 34						21 03							21 34	22 01				22 34
Tyseley	d				20 07		20 37						21 07							21 37	22 04			22 23	22 37
Acocks Green	d				20 09								21 09								22 07			22 26	
Olton	d				20 12								21 12								22 10			22 29	
Solihull	d			19 54	20 16							20 54	21 16					21 34			22 13			22 33	
Widney Manor	d				20 19								21 19					21 38			22 17			22 36	
Dorridge	d			19 59	20a24							20 59	21a24					21 42			22a22			22 40	
Lapworth	d			20 03								21 03						21 47						22 44	
Hatton	d		20 00	20 09								21 09						21 52						22 49	
Warwick Parkway	d		20 06	20 14								21 14						21 57						22 54	
Warwick	d		20 09	20 17								21 17					21 55	22 01						22 58	
Leamington Spa 8	a		20 17	20 22				20 37			20 59	21 21			21 37		22 04	22 05						23 03	
	d			20 23				20 38		20 53	21 00	21 21			21 38			22 05						23 03	
Banbury	d			20 46				20a54			21a19	21 41			21a54			22 23						23a24	
London Marylebone 10 ⊖115	a			21 58								23 00						23 35							
Spring Road	d						20 40													21 40					22 40
Hall Green	d						20 42													21 42					22 42
Yardley Wood	d						20 45													21 45					22 45
Shirley	d						20 48													21 48					22 48
Whitlocks End	d						20 51													21 51					22 51
Wythall	d						20 53													21 53					22 53
Earlswood (West Midlands)	d						20 56													21 56					22 56
The Lakes	d						20x58													21x58					22x58
Wood End	d						21x00													22x00					23x00
Danzey	d						21x02													22x02					23x02
Henley-in-Arden	d						21 07													22 07					23 07
Wootton Wawen	d						21x10													22x10					23x10
Wilmcote	d						21 15			21 22										22 15					23 15
Stratford-upon-Avon Parkway	a						21 18			21 24										22 18					23 18
Stratford-upon-Avon	a						21 21			21 32										22 21					23 21

Table 71R

Saturdays

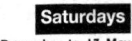

14 December to 17 May

Hereford, Worcester and Stourbridge - Birmingham - Leamington Spa, Marylebone and Stratford-upon-Avon

Network Diagram - see first Page of Table 71

Station		LM	LM	LM		LM	GW ■	LM
Hereford ■	d		21 35					22 50
Ledbury	a		21 50					23 05
	d		21 51					23 06
Colwall	d		21 57					23 12
Great Malvern	a		22 02					23 16
	d	21 30	22 03				22 41	23 17
Malvern Link	d	21 32	22 06				22 44	23 20
Worcester Foregate Street ■	a	21 42	22 14				22 52	23 27
	d	21 42	22 15				22 53	23 28
Worcester Shrub Hill ■	a	21 45	22 18				22 56	23 34
	d	21 54				22 47		
Droitwich Spa	d	22 02				22 55		
Bromsgrove	d							
Barnt Green	d							
University	d							
Hartlebury	d							
Kidderminster	d	22 12				23 05		
Blakedown	d	22 17				23 10		
Hagley	d	22 20				23 14		
Stourbridge Junction ■	d	22 24		22 57		23 18		
Lye	d	22 28		23 01				
Cradley Heath	d	22 31		23 04				
Old Hill	d	22 35		23 07				
Rowley Regis	d	22 38		23 11				
Langley Green	d	22 41		23 14				
Birmingham New Street ■ 68	a							
	d							
Birmingham Intl. 68 ✈	d							
Coventry	d							
Smethwick Galton Bridge ■	d	22 45		23 17				
The Hawthorns 🚋	d	22 47		23 19				
Jewellery Quarter 🚋	d	22 51		23 23				
Birmingham Snow Hill 🚋	a	22 55		23 26		23 36		
	d	22 56		23 28		23 37		
Birmingham Moor Street	d	22 59		23 31		23 40		
Bordesley	d							
Small Heath	d	23 03		23 34		23 43		
Tyseley	d	23 06		23 38		23 47		
Acocks Green	d	23 09				23 49		
Olton	d	23 12				23 52		
Solihull	d	23 15				23 56		
Widney Manor	d	23 19				23 59		
Dorridge	d	23a24				00 03		
Lapworth	d					00 06		
Hatton	d					00 12		
Warwick Parkway	d					00 15		
Warwick	d					00 18		
Leamington Spa ■	a					00 24		
	d							
Banbury	d							
London Marylebone ■ ⊖115	a							
Spring Road	d			23 40				
Hall Green	d			23 43				
Yardley Wood	d			23 45				
Shirley	d			23 49				
Whitlocks End	d			23a51				
Wythall	d							
Earlswood (West Midlands)	d							
The Lakes	d							
Wood End	d							
Danzey	d							
Henley-in-Arden	d							
Wootton Wawen	d							
Wilmcote	d							
Stratford-upon-Avon Parkway	a							
Stratford-upon-Avon	a							

Table 71R

Sundays

8 December to 9 February

Hereford, Worcester and Stourbridge - Birmingham - Leamington Spa, Marylebone and Stratford-upon-Avon

Network Diagram - see first Page of Table 71

		LM	CH	CH	XC	LM	CH	LM	CH	CH		XC	CH	CH	LM	GW	CH	LM	XC	CH		LM	LM	CH	CH
			◇	◇	◇**1**		◇		◇	◇		◇**1**	◇	◇		◇**1**	◇		◇**1**	◇				◇	◇
		A																							
					🛒							☕					🛒		☕						
																	BZ								
Hereford ■7	d																						10 06		
Ledbury	a																						10 22		
	d																						10 22		
Colwall	d																						10 29		
Great Malvern	a																						10 33		
	d														09 07	09 20						10 07	10 34		
Malvern Link	d														09 09	09 23						10 09	10 37		
Worcester Foregate Street ■7	a														09 19	09 31						10 18	10 45		
	d														09 20	09 32						10 19	10 46		
Worcester Shrub Hill ■7	a														09 22	09 34						10 21	10 48		
	d					09 02									09 26							10 25	10 55		
Droitwich Spa	d					09 10									09 34							10 33	11 03		
Bromsgrove	d					09 20																	11 13		
Barnt Green	d																								
University	d					09 36																	11 30		
Hartlebury	d																								
Kidderminster	d														09 44			10 14				10 45			
Blakedown	d														09 49			10 18							
Hagley	d														09 52			10 22				10 51			
Stourbridge Junction ■2	d														09 56			10 26				10 55			
Lye	d																	10 30							
Cradley Heath	d														10 02			10 33				11 01			
Old Hill	d																	10 36							
Rowley Regis	d														10 07			10 40				11 06			
Langley Green	d																	10 43							
Birmingham New Street ■12 68	a					09 42																	11 37		
	d				09 04							10 04							11 04						
Birmingham Intl. 68 ✈	d				09 14							10 14							11 14						
Coventry	d				09 25							10 25							11 25						
Smethwick Galton Bridge ■7	d														10 13			10 46				11 12			
The Hawthorns 🚊	d														10 15			10 48				11 14			
Jewellery Quarter 🚊	d														10 19			10 52				11 18			
Birmingham Snow Hill 🚊	a														10 22			10 55				11 21			
	d						09 12	09 27						10 12	10 26			10 57		11 12		11 25			
Birmingham Moor Street	d		08 25	08 55			09 15	09 30		09 55				10 15	10 29		10 55	11 00		11 15		11 28			11 55
Bordesley	d																								
Small Heath	d																								
Tyseley	d							09 35							10 34							11 33			
Acocks Green	d																	11 06							
Olton	d																	11 09							
Solihull	d		08 34	09 04			09 24			10 04				10 24			11 04	11 12		11 24					12 04
Widney Manor	d																	11 16							
Dorridge	d	00 03	08 39	09 09			09 29			10 09				10 29			11 10	11a21		11 29					12 09
Lapworth	d	00 06												10 33											
Hatton	d	00 12							09 55					10 38										11 55	
Warwick Parkway	d	00 15	08 49	09 19			09 39			10 19				10 44			11 20			11 39					12 19
Warwick	d	00 18	08 52				09 42		10 01					10 47						11 42				12 01	
Leamington Spa ■8	a	00 24	08 57	09 24	09 37		09 47		10 05	10 24		10 37		10 51			11 25		11 37	11 47				12 05	12 24
	d		08 58	09 25	09 38		09 48		10 06	10 25		10 38	10 50	10 52			11 26		11 38	11 48				12 06	12 25
Banbury	d		09 16	09 43	09a54		10 06		10 24	10 43		10a54		11 10			11 44		11a54	12 06				12 24	12 43
London Marylebone ■10 ⊖115	a		10 21	10 44			11 17		11 41	11 44				12 17			12 44			13 17				13 41	13 44
Spring Road	d							09 37							10 37							11 36			
Hall Green	d							09 40							10 39							11 38			
Yardley Wood	d							09 42							10 42							11 41			
Shirley	d							09 45							10 45							11 44			
Whitlocks End	d							09 48							10 48							11 47			
Wythall	d							09 51							10 50							11 49			
Earlswood (West Midlands)	d																								
The Lakes	d							09x53							10x53							11x52			
Wood End	d																								
Danzey	d																								
Henley-in-Arden	d							10 01							11 00							11 59			
Wootton Wawen	d																								
Wilmcote	d							10 09					11 16		11 08							12 07			
Stratford-upon-Avon Parkway	a							10 12					11 18		11 11							12 10			
Stratford-upon-Avon	a							10 15					11 29		11 15							12 14			

BZ Business Zone available offering greater comfort and an enhanced working environment. Supplement payable.

A not 8 December

Table 71R

Sundays

8 December to 9 February

Hereford, Worcester and Stourbridge - Birmingham - Leamington Spa, Marylebone and Stratford-upon-Avon

Network Diagram - see first Page of Table 71

		LM	XC	CH	CH	LM	GW	XC	CH	LM	XC	CH	LM	XC	XC	LM	CH	CH	LM	XC	CH	CH	LM
			◇[1]	◇	◇		◇[1]	◇[1]	◇		◇[1]	◇		◇[1]	◇[1]		◇	◇		◇[1]	◇	◇	
														A	B								
			🛒					🛒			☕			🛒	🛒					☕			
Hereford [7]	d															12 00							
Ledbury	a															12 16							
	d															12 16							
Colwall	d															12 23							
Great Malvern	a															12 27							
	d					10 57	11 15						12 07			12 30							
Malvern Link	d					10 59	11 18						12 09			12 33							
Worcester Foregate Street [7]	a					11 08	11 27						12 19			12 41							
	d					11 09	11 28						12 20			12 42							13 26
Worcester Shrub Hill [7]	a					11 11	11 30						12 22			12 44							
	d					11 27							12 26			12 55							
Droitwich Spa	d					11 35							12 35			13 03							13 35
Bromsgrove	d															13 13							
Barnt Green	d																						
University	d															13 30							
Hartlebury	d																						
Kidderminster	d					11 45							12 45										13 45
Blakedown	d												12 49										
Hagley	d					11 51							12 53										13 52
Stourbridge Junction [2]	d	11 26				11 55				12 26			12 57						13 26				13 56
Lye	d	11 30								12 30									13 30				
Cradley Heath	d	11 33				12 01				12 33			13 03						13 33				14 02
Old Hill	d	11 36								12 36									13 36				
Rowley Regis	d	11 40				12 06				12 40			13 08						13 40				14 07
Langley Green	d	11 43								12 43									13 43				
Birmingham New Street [12] 68	a															13 37							
	d		12 04					12 33			13 04			13 33	13 33					14 04			
Birmingham Intl. 68 ✈	d		12 14								13 14									14 14			
Coventry	d		12 25								13 25									14 25			
Smethwick Galton Bridge [7]	d	11 46				12 12				12 46			13 13						13 46				14 12
The Hawthorns 🚋	d	11 48				12 14				12 48			13 15						13 48				14 14
Jewellery Quarter 🚋	d	11 52				12 18				12 52			13 19						13 52				14 18
Birmingham Snow Hill 🚋	a	11 55				12 21				12 55			13 22						13 55				14 21
	d	11 57			12 12	12 26				12 57		13 12	13 27						13 57			14 12	14 27
Birmingham Moor Street	d	12 00			12 15	12 30			12 55	13 00		13 15	13 30					13 55	14 00			14 15	14 30
Bordesley	d																						
Small Heath	d																						
Tyseley	d					12 35							13 35										14 35
Acocks Green	d	12 06								13 06									14 06				
Olton	d	12 09								13 09									14 09				
Solihull	d	12 12			12 24				13 04	13 12		13 24						14 04	14 12			14 24	
Widney Manor	d	12 16								13 16									14 16				
Dorridge	d	12a21			12 29				13 09	13a21		13 29						14 09	14a21			14 29	
Lapworth	d				12 33																	14 33	
Hatton	d				12 38												13 55					14 38	
Warwick Parkway	d				12 44				13 19			13 39						14 19				14 44	
Warwick	d				12 47							13 42					14 01					14 47	
Leamington Spa [8]	a		12 37		12 51			12 59	13 24		13 37	13 47		13 58	13 59		14 05	14 24		14 37		14 51	
	d		12 38	12 50	12 52			13 00	13 25		13 38	13 48		13 59	14 00		14 06	14 25		14 38	14 50	14 52	
Banbury	d		12a54		13 10			13a17	13 43		13a54	14 06		14a17	14a17		14 24	14 43		14a54		15 10	
London Marylebone [10] ⊖115	a				14 17				14 44			15 17					15 41	15 44				16 17	
Spring Road	d					12 37							13 37										14 37
Hall Green	d					12 40							13 40										14 40
Yardley Wood	d					12 42							13 42										14 42
Shirley	d					12 45							13 45										14 45
Whitlocks End	d					12 48							13 48										14 48
Wythall	d					12 51							13 51										14 51
Earlswood (West Midlands)	d																						
The Lakes	d					12x53							13x53										14x53
Wood End	d																						
Danzey	d																						
Henley-in-Arden	d					13 01							14 01										15 01
Wootton Wawen	d																						
Wilmcote	d			13 16		13 09							14 09								15 16		15 09
Stratford-upon-Avon Parkway	a			13 18		13 12							14 12								15 18		15 12
Stratford-upon-Avon	a			13 29		13 15							14 15								15 29		15 15

A until 29 December

B from 5 January

Table 71R

Sundays

8 December to 9 February

Hereford, Worcester and Stourbridge - Birmingham - Leamington Spa, Marylebone and Stratford-upon-Avon

Network Diagram - see first Page of Table 71

		GW		XC	CH	LM	XC	CH	LM	GW	XC	XC		LM	GW	CH	CH	LM	XC	CH	CH	LM		LM	XC
		◇1		◇1	◇		◇1	◇		◇1	◇1	◇1			◇1	◇	◇		◇1	◇	◇				◇1
											A	B													
				🛒			☕	🛒		☕	🛒	🛒			☕				☕						🛒
Hereford 7	d									13 33				14 05	14 35										
Ledbury	a									13 51				14 21	14 53										
	d									13 52				14 21	14 55										
Colwall	d									13 59				14 28	15 02										
Great Malvern	a									14 04				14 32	15 06										
	d	13 15								14 11				14 33	15 07										
Malvern Link	d	13 18								14 15				14 36	15 11										
Worcester Foregate Street 7	a	13 26								14 24				14 44	15 20										
	d	13 27							14 24	14 26				14 45	15 22							15 28			
Worcester Shrub Hill 7	a	13 29								14 29				14 47	15 24										
	d													14 55										15 46	
Droitwich Spa	d								14 33					15 03								15 37		15 54	
Bromsgrove	d													15 13											
Barnt Green	d																								
University	d													15 30											
Hartlebury	d																								
Kidderminster	d								14 43													15 47		16 04	
Blakedown	d								14 48															16 09	
Hagley	d								14 52													15 54		16 13	
Stourbridge Junction 2	d					14 26			14 56									15 26				15 58		16 17	
Lye	d					14 30												15 30							
Cradley Heath	d					14 33			15 02									15 33				16 04			
Old Hill	d					14 36												15 36							
Rowley Regis	d					14 40			15 07									15 40				16 09			
Langley Green	d					14 43												15 43							
Birmingham New Street 12 68	a													15 37											
	d			14 33			15 04				15 33	15 33							16 04						16 33
Birmingham Intl. 68 ✈	d						15 14												16 14						
Coventry	d						15 25												16 25						
Smethwick Galton Bridge 7	d					14 46			15 12									15 46				16 14		16 30	
The Hawthorns 🚊	d					14 48			15 14									15 48				16 16			
Jewellery Quarter 🚊	d					14 52			15 18									15 52				16 20			
Birmingham Snow Hill 🚊	a					14 55			15 21									15 55				16 23		16 36	
	d					14 57		15 12	15 27									15 57			16 12	16 27		16 43	
Birmingham Moor Street	d				14 55	15 00		15 15	15 30								15 55	16 00			16 15	16 30		16a45	
Bordesley	d																								
Small Heath	d																								
Tyseley	d								15 35													16 36			
Acocks Green	d					15 06												16 06							
Olton	d					15 09												16 09							
Solihull	d				15 04	15 12		15 24									16 04	16 12			16 24				
Widney Manor	d					15 16												16 16							
Dorridge	d				15 09	15a21		15 29									16 09	16a21			16 29				
Lapworth	d																				16 33				
Hatton	d															15 55					16 38				
Warwick Parkway	d				15 19			15 39									16 19				16 44				
Warwick	d							15 42								16 01					16 47				
Leamington Spa 8	a			14 59	15 24		15 37	15 47			15 58	15 59				16 05	16 24		16 37		16 51				16 59
	d			15 00	15 25		15 38	15 48			15 59	16 00				16 06	16 25		16 38	16 51	16 52				17 00
Banbury	d			15a18	15 43		15a54	16 06			16a17	16a17				16 24	16 43		16a54		17 10				17a17
London Marylebone 10 ⊖115	a				16 44			17 17								17 40	17 43				18 17				
Spring Road	d								15 37													16 38			
Hall Green	d								15 40													16 41			
Yardley Wood	d								15 42													16 43			
Shirley	d								15 45													16 46			
Whitlocks End	d								15 48													16 49			
Wythall	d								15 51													16 52			
Earlswood (West Midlands)	d																								
The Lakes	d								15x53													16x54			
Wood End	d																								
Danzey	d																								
Henley-in-Arden	d								16 01													17 02			
Wootton Wawen	d																								
Wilmcote	d								16 09											17 17		17 10			
Stratford-upon-Avon Parkway	a								16 12											17 19		17 13			
Stratford-upon-Avon	a								16 15											17 30		17 16			

A from 5 January

B until 29 December

Table 71R

Sundays

8 December to 9 February

Hereford, Worcester and Stourbridge - Birmingham - Leamington Spa, Marylebone and Stratford-upon-Avon

Network Diagram - see first Page of Table 71

		CH	LM	XC	CH	LM	XC	XC	LM	GW	CH	CH	LM	XC	CH	LM	XC	LM	GW	CH	CH	XC	CH
		◇		◇1	◇		◇1	◇1		◇1	◇	◇		◇1	◇		◇1		◇1	◇	◇	◇1	◇
							A	B															
				☕			🛒	🛒		☕				☕			🛒					☕	
Hereford 7	d								16 09	16 34													
Ledbury	a								16 25	16 51													
	d								16 25	16 52													
Colwall	d								16 32	17 00													
Great Malvern	a								16 36	17 04													
	d								16 37	17 05													
Malvern Link	d								16 40	17 09													
Worcester Foregate Street 7	a								16 48	17 20													
	d					16 26			16 49	17 22						17 27			18 26				
Worcester Shrub Hill 7	a								16 51	17 25									18 29				
	d								16 55									17 57					
Droitwich Spa	d					16 35			17 03							17 36		18 05					
Bromsgrove	d								17 13									18 15					
Barnt Green	d																						
University	d								17 30									18 30					
Hartlebury	d																						
Kidderminster	d					16 45										17 46							
Blakedown	d															17 51							
Hagley	d					16 52										17 55							
Stourbridge Junction 2	d		16 26			16 56							17 26			17 59							
Lye	d		16 30										17 30										
Cradley Heath	d		16 33			17 02							17 33			18 05							
Old Hill	d		16 36										17 36										
Rowley Regis	d		16 40			17 07							17 40			18 10							
Langley Green	d		16 43										17 43										
Birmingham New Street 12 68	a								17 37									18 37					
	d			17 04			17 33	17 33						18 04			18 33					19 04	
Birmingham Intl. 68 ✈	d			17 14										18 14								19 14	
Coventry	d			17 25										18 25								19 25	
Smethwick Galton Bridge 7	d		16 46			17 12							17 46			18 15							
The Hawthorns 🚊	d		16 48			17 14							17 48			18 17							
Jewellery Quarter 🚊	d		16 52			17 18							17 52			18 21							
Birmingham Snow Hill 🚊	a		16 55			17 21							17 55			18 24							
	d		16 57		17 12	17 27							17 57		18 12	18 27							19 15
Birmingham Moor Street	d	16 55	17 00		17 15	17 30						17 55	18 00		18 15	18 30					18 55		19 18
Bordesley	d																						
Small Heath	d																						
Tyseley	d					17 35										18 37							
Acocks Green	d		17 06										18 06										
Olton	d		17 09										18 09										
Solihull	d	17 04	17 12		17 24							18 04	18 12		18 24						19 04		19 26
Widney Manor	d		17 16										18 16										19 30
Dorridge	d	17 09	17a21		17 29							18 09	18a21		18 29						19 09		19 34
Lapworth	d																						19 38
Hatton	d										17 55												19 43
Warwick Parkway	d	17 19			17 39							18 19			18 39						19 19		19 48
Warwick	d				17 42						18 01				18 42								19 51
Leamington Spa 8	a	17 24		17 37	17 47		17 59	18 00			18 05	18 24		18 37	18 47		18 59				19 24	19 37	19 56
	d	17 25		17 38	17 48		18 00	18 01			18 06	18 25		18 38	18 48		19 00			19 05	19 25	19 38	19 57
Banbury	d	17 43		17a54	18 06		18a18	18a19			18 24	18 43		18a54	19 06		19a17				19 43	19a54	20 15
London Marylebone 10 ⊖115	a	18 44			19 17						19 41	19 44			20 17						20 43		21 50
Spring Road	d					17 37										18 39							
Hall Green	d					17 40										18 42							
Yardley Wood	d					17 42										18 44							
Shirley	d					17 45										18 47							
Whitlocks End	d					17 48										18 50							
Wythall	d					17 51										18 53							
Earlswood (West Midlands)	d																						
The Lakes	d					17x53										18x55							
Wood End	d																						
Danzey	d																						
Henley-in-Arden	d					18 01										19 03							
Wootton Wawen	d																						
Wilmcote	d					18 09										19 11				19 26			
Stratford-upon-Avon Parkway	a					18 12										19 14				19 28			
Stratford-upon-Avon	a					18 15										19 17				19 39			

A from 5 January

B until 29 December

Table 71R

Sundays
8 December to 9 February

Hereford, Worcester and Stourbridge - Birmingham - Leamington Spa, Marylebone and Stratford-upon-Avon

Network Diagram - see first Page of Table 71

		LM	XC	LM		GW	CH	XC	CH	LM	XC	LM	XC	GW		CH	LM	LM	LM	LM	LM
			◇1			◇1	◇	◇1	◇		◇1		◇1	◇1		◇					
Hereford 7	d			18 09		18 30												20 06			22 40
Ledbury	a			18 25		18 47												20 22			22 56
	d			18 25		18 48												20 22			22 57
Colwall	d			18 32		18 55												20 29			23 04
Great Malvern	a			18 36		19 00												20 33			23 08
	d			18 37		19 11								20 15				20 37		22 10	23 09
Malvern Link	d			18 40		19 14								20 18				20 40		22 12	23 11
Worcester Foregate Street 7	a			18 48		19 24								20 27				20 48		22 22	23 21
	d	18 26		18 49		19 29						19 49		20 28				20 49	21 18	22 23	23 22
Worcester Shrub Hill 7	a			18 51		19 31						19 51		20 30				20 51	21 20	22 25	23 25
	d			18 55						19 38		19 55					20 36	20 55	21 25	22 29	
Droitwich Spa	d	18 35		19 03						19 46		20 03					20 44	21 03	21 33	22 37	
Bromsgrove	d			19 13								20 13						21 13			
Barnt Green	d																				
University	d			19 30								20 30						21 30			
Hartlebury	d																				
Kidderminster	d	18 45								19 56							20 54		21 43	22 47	
Blakedown	d																				
Hagley	d	18 51								20 03							21 00		21 49	22 53	
Stourbridge Junction 2	d	18 55								20 07							21 04		21 53	22 57	
Lye	d																				
Cradley Heath	d	19 01								20 13							21 10		21 59	23 03	
Old Hill	d																				
Rowley Regis	d	19 06								20 18							21 15		22 04	23 08	
Langley Green	d																				
Birmingham New Street 12 68	a			19 37								20 37						21 37			
	d		19 33					20 04			20 33		21 04								
Birmingham Intl. 68 ✈	d							20 14					21 14								
Coventry	d							20 25					21 24								
Smethwick Galton Bridge 7	d	19 12								20 23							21 20		22 09	23 14	
The Hawthorns 🚊	d	19 14								20 25							21 22		22 11	23 16	
Jewellery Quarter 🚊	d	19 18								20 29							21 26		22 15	23 20	
Birmingham Snow Hill 🚊	a	19 21								20 33							21 30		22 19	23 25	
	d	19 23							20 15	20 34						21 15	21 31		22 21		
Birmingham Moor Street	d	19a25							20 18	20a37						21 18	21a34		22a23		
Bordesley	d																				
Small Heath	d																				
Tyseley	d																				
Acocks Green	d																				
Olton	d																				
Solihull	d								20 27							21 27					
Widney Manor	d								20 30							21 30					
Dorridge	d								20 33							21 34					
Lapworth	d																				
Hatton	d						20 17														
Warwick Parkway	d								20 43							21 44					
Warwick	d						20 23		20 46							21 47					
Leamington Spa 8	a		19 59				20 27	20 37	20 50		20 58		21 34			21 51					
	d		20 00				20 28	20 38	20 51		21 00					21 52					
Banbury	d		20a18				20 48	20a54	21 09		21a17					22 15					
London Marylebone 10 ⊖115	a						22 08		22 41							23 47					
Spring Road	d																				
Hall Green	d																				
Yardley Wood	d																				
Shirley	d																				
Whitlocks End	d																				
Wythall	d																				
Earlswood (West Midlands)	d																				
The Lakes	d																				
Wood End	d																				
Danzey	d																				
Henley-in-Arden	d																				
Wootton Wawen	d																				
Wilmcote	d																				
Stratford-upon-Avon Parkway	a																				
Stratford-upon-Avon	a																				

Table 71R

Sundays

16 February to 23 March

Hereford, Worcester and Stourbridge - Birmingham - Leamington Spa, Marylebone and Stratford-upon-Avon

Network Diagram - see first Page of Table 71

		LM	CH	CH	XC	LM	CH	LM	CH	CH		XC	CH	CH	LM	GW	CH	LM	XC	CH		LM	LM	CH	CH
			◇	◇	◇1		◇		◇	◇		◇1	◇	◇		◇1	◇		◇1	◇				◇	◇
					🍴							☕					🍴 BZ		☕						
Hereford 7	d																						10 06		
Ledbury	a																						10 22		
	d																						10 22		
Colwall	d																						10 29		
Great Malvern	a																						10 33		
	d														09 07	09 20						10 07	10 34		
Malvern Link	d														09 09	09 23						10 09	10 37		
Worcester Foregate Street 7	a														09 19	09 31						10 18	10 45		
	d														09 20	09 32						10 19	10 46		
Worcester Shrub Hill 7	a														09 22	09 34						10 21	10 48		
	d					09 02									09 26							10 25	10 55		
Droitwich Spa	d					09 10									09 34							10 33	11 03		
Bromsgrove	d					09 20																	11 13		
Barnt Green	d																								
University	d					09 36																	11 30		
Hartlebury	d																								
Kidderminster	d														09 44			10 14				10 45			
Blakedown	d														09 49			10 18							
Hagley	d														09 52			10 22				10 51			
Stourbridge Junction 2	d														09 56			10 26				10 55			
Lye	d																	10 30							
Cradley Heath	d														10 02			10 33				11 01			
Old Hill	d																	10 36							
Rowley Regis	d														10 07			10 40				11 06			
Langley Green	d																	10 43							
Birmingham New Street 12 68	a					09 42																	11 37		
	d				09 04							10 04							11 04						
Birmingham Intl. 68 ✈	d				09 14							10 14							11 14						
Coventry	d				09 25							10 25							11 25						
Smethwick Galton Bridge 7	d														10 13			10 46				11 12			
The Hawthorns 🚊	d														10 15			10 48				11 14			
Jewellery Quarter 🚊	d														10 19			10 52				11 18			
Birmingham Snow Hill 🚊	a														10 22			10 55				11 21			
	d						09 12	09 27						10 12	10 26			10 57		11 12		11 25			
Birmingham Moor Street	d		08 25	08 55			09 15	09 30		09 55				10 15	10 29		10 55	11 00		11 15		11 28			11 55
Bordesley	d																								
Small Heath	d																								
Tyseley	d							09 35							10 34							11 33			
Acocks Green	d																	11 06							
Olton	d																	11 09							
Solihull	d		08 34	09 04			09 24			10 04				10 24			11 04	11 12		11 24					12 04
Widney Manor	d																	11 16							
Dorridge	d	00 03	08 39	09 09			09 29			10 09				10 29			11 10	11a21		11 29					12 09
Lapworth	d	00 06												10 33											
Hatton	d	00 12							09 55					10 38										11 55	
Warwick Parkway	d	00 15	08 49	09 19			09 39			10 19				10 44			11 20			11 39					12 19
Warwick	d	00 18	08 52				09 42		10 01					10 47						11 42				12 01	
Leamington Spa 8	a	00 24	08 57	09 24	09 37		09 47		10 05	10 24		10 37		10 51			11 25		11 37	11 47				12 05	12 24
	d		08 58	09 25	09 38		09 48		10 06	10 25		10 38	10 50	10 52			11 26		11 38	11 48				12 06	12 25
Banbury	d		09 16	09 43	09a54		10 06		10 24	10 43		10a54		11 10			11 44		11a54	12 06				12 24	12 43
London Marylebone 10 ⊖115	a		10 21	10 44			11 17		11 41	11 44				12 17			12 44			13 17				13 41	13 44
Spring Road	d							09 37							10 37							11 36			
Hall Green	d							09 40							10 39							11 38			
Yardley Wood	d							09 42							10 42							11 41			
Shirley	d							09 45							10 45							11 44			
Whitlocks End	d							09 48							10 48							11 47			
Wythall	d							09 51							10 50							11 49			
Earlswood (West Midlands)	d																								
The Lakes	d							09x53							10x53							11x52			
Wood End	d																								
Danzey	d																								
Henley-in-Arden	d							10 01							11 00							11 59			
Wootton Wawen	d																								
Wilmcote	d							10 09					11 16		11 08							12 07			
Stratford-upon-Avon Parkway	a							10 12					11 18		11 11							12 10			
Stratford-upon-Avon	a							10 15					11 29		11 15							12 14			

BZ Business Zone available offering greater comfort and an enhanced working environment. Supplement payable.

Table 71R

Sundays

16 February to 23 March

Hereford, Worcester and Stourbridge - Birmingham - Leamington Spa, Marylebone and Stratford-upon-Avon

Network Diagram - see first Page of Table 71

		LM	XC	CH	CH	LM		GW	XC	CH	LM	XC	CH	LM	XC	LM		CH	CH	LM	XC	CH	CH	LM	GW
			◇1	◇	◇			◇1	◇1	◇		◇1	◇		◇1			◇	◇		◇1	◇	◇		◇1
			[trolley]						[trolley]			[restaurant]			[trolley]						[restaurant]				
Hereford 7	d															12 00									
Ledbury	a															12 16									
	d															12 16									
Colwall	d															12 23									
Great Malvern	a															12 27									
	d					10 57		11 15						12 07		12 30									13 15
Malvern Link	d					10 59		11 18						12 09		12 33									13 18
Worcester Foregate Street 7	a					11 08		11 27						12 19		12 41									13 26
	d					11 09		11 28						12 20		12 42								13 26	13 27
Worcester Shrub Hill 7	a					11 11		11 30						12 22		12 44									13 29
	d					11 27								12 26		12 55									
Droitwich Spa	d					11 35								12 35		13 03								13 35	
Bromsgrove	d															13 13									
Barnt Green	d																								
University	d															13 30									
Hartlebury	d																								
Kidderminster	d					11 45								12 45										13 45	
Blakedown	d													12 49											
Hagley	d					11 51								12 53										13 52	
Stourbridge Junction 2	d	11 26				11 55					12 26			12 57						13 26				13 56	
Lye	d	11 30									12 30									13 30					
Cradley Heath	d	11 33				12 01					12 33			13 03						13 33				14 02	
Old Hill	d	11 36									12 36									13 36					
Rowley Regis	d	11 40				12 06					12 40			13 08						13 40				14 07	
Langley Green	d	11 43									12 43									13 43					
Birmingham New Street 12 68	a															13 37									
	d		12 04						12 33			13 04			13 33						14 04				
Birmingham Intl. 68 ✈	d		12 14									13 14									14 14				
Coventry	d		12 25									13 25									14 25				
Smethwick Galton Bridge 7	d	11 46				12 12					12 46			13 13						13 46				14 12	
The Hawthorns 🚊	d	11 48				12 14					12 48			13 15						13 48				14 14	
Jewellery Quarter 🚊	d	11 52				12 18					12 52			13 19						13 52				14 18	
Birmingham Snow Hill 🚊	a	11 55				12 21					12 55			13 22						13 55				14 21	
	d	11 57			12 12	12 26					12 57		13 12	13 27						13 57			14 12	14 27	
Birmingham Moor Street	d	12 00			12 15	12 30				12 55	13 00		13 15	13 30					13 55	14 00			14 15	14 30	
Bordesley	d																								
Small Heath	d																								
Tyseley	d					12 35								13 35										14 35	
Acocks Green	d	12 06									13 06									14 06					
Olton	d	12 09									13 09									14 09					
Solihull	d	12 12			12 24					13 04	13 12		13 24						14 04	14 12			14 24		
Widney Manor	d	12 16									13 16									14 16					
Dorridge	d	12a21			12 29					13 09	13a21		13 29						14 09	14a21			14 29		
Lapworth	d				12 33																		14 33		
Hatton	d				12 38													13 55					14 38		
Warwick Parkway	d				12 44					13 19			13 39						14 19				14 44		
Warwick	d				12 47								13 42					14 01					14 47		
Leamington Spa 8	a		12 37		12 51				12 59	13 24		13 37	13 47		13 59			14 05	14 24		14 37		14 51		
	d		12 38	12 50	12 52				13 00	13 25		13 38	13 48		14 00			14 06	14 25		14 38	14 50	14 52		
Banbury	d		12a54		13 10				13a17	13 43		13a54	14 06		14a17			14 24	14 43		14a54		15 10		
London Marylebone 10 ⊖115	a				14 17					14 44			15 17					15 41	15 44				16 17		
Spring Road	d					12 37								13 37										14 37	
Hall Green	d					12 40								13 40										14 40	
Yardley Wood	d					12 42								13 42										14 42	
Shirley	d					12 45								13 45										14 45	
Whitlocks End	d					12 48								13 48										14 48	
Wythall	d					12 51								13 51										14 51	
Earlswood (West Midlands)	d																								
The Lakes	d					12x53								13x53										14x53	
Wood End	d																								
Danzey	d																								
Henley-in-Arden	d					13 01								14 01										15 01	
Wootton Wawen	d																								
Wilmcote	d			13 16		13 09								14 09								15 16		15 09	
Stratford-upon-Avon Parkway	a			13 18		13 12								14 12								15 18		15 12	
Stratford-upon-Avon	a			13 29		13 15								14 15								15 29		15 15	

Table 71R

Sundays

16 February to 23 March

Hereford, Worcester and Stourbridge - Birmingham - Leamington Spa, Marylebone and Stratford-upon-Avon

Network Diagram - see first Page of Table 71

		XC		CH	LM	XC	CH	LM	GW	XC	LM	GW		CH	CH	LM	XC	CH	CH	LM	LM	XC		CH	LM
		◇1		◇		◇1	◇		◇1	◇1		◇1		◇	◇		◇1	◇	◇			◇1		◇	
		🛒				☕	🛒		☕	🛒		☕					☕					🛒			
Hereford 7	d								13 33		14 05	14 35													
Ledbury	a								13 51		14 21	14 53													
	d								13 52		14 21	14 55													
Colwall	d								13 59		14 28	15 02													
Great Malvern	a								14 04		14 32	15 06													
	d								14 11		14 33	15 07													
Malvern Link	d								14 15		14 36	15 11													
Worcester Foregate Street 7	a								14 24		14 44	15 20													
	d							14 24	14 26		14 45	15 22								15 28					
Worcester Shrub Hill 7	a								14 29		14 47	15 24													
	d										14 55										15 46				
Droitwich Spa	d							14 33			15 03									15 37	15 54				
Bromsgrove	d										15 13														
Barnt Green	d																								
University	d										15 30														
Hartlebury	d																								
Kidderminster	d							14 43												15 47	16 04				
Blakedown	d							14 48													16 09				
Hagley	d							14 52												15 54	16 13				
Stourbridge Junction 2	d				14 26			14 56								15 26				15 58	16 17				16 26
Lye	d				14 30											15 30									16 30
Cradley Heath	d				14 33			15 02								15 33				16 04					16 33
Old Hill	d				14 36											15 36									16 36
Rowley Regis	d				14 40			15 07								15 40				16 09					16 40
Langley Green	d				14 43											15 43									16 43
Birmingham New Street 12 68	a										15 37														
	d	14 33				15 04				15 33							16 04					16 33			
Birmingham Intl. 68 ✈	d					15 14											16 14								
Coventry	d					15 25											16 25								
Smethwick Galton Bridge 7	d				14 46			15 12								15 46				16 14	16 30				16 46
The Hawthorns	d				14 48			15 14								15 48				16 16					16 48
Jewellery Quarter	d				14 52			15 18								15 52				16 20					16 52
Birmingham Snow Hill	a				14 55			15 21								15 55				16 23	16 36				16 55
	d				14 57		15 12	15 27								15 57			16 12	16 27	16 43				16 57
Birmingham Moor Street	d			14 55	15 00		15 15	15 30							15 55	16 00			16 15	16 30	16a45			16 55	17 00
Bordesley	d																								
Small Heath	d																								
Tyseley	d							15 35												16 36					
Acocks Green	d				15 06											16 06									17 06
Olton	d				15 09											16 09									17 09
Solihull	d			15 04	15 12		15 24								16 04	16 12			16 24					17 04	17 12
Widney Manor	d				15 16											16 16									17 16
Dorridge	d			15 09	15a21		15 29								16 09	16a21			16 29					17 09	17a21
Lapworth	d																		16 33						
Hatton	d													15 55					16 38						
Warwick Parkway	d			15 19			15 39								16 19				16 44					17 19	
Warwick	d						15 42							16 01					16 47						
Leamington Spa 8	a	14 59		15 24		15 37	15 47			15 58				16 05	16 24		16 37		16 51			16 59		17 24	
	d	15 00		15 25		15 38	15 48			15 59				16 06	16 25		16 38	16 51	16 52			17 00		17 25	
Banbury	d	15a18		15 43		15a54	16 06			16a17				16 24	16 43		16a54		17 10			17a17		17 43	
London Marylebone 10 ⊖115	a			16 44			17 17							17 40	17 43				18 17					18 44	
Spring Road	d							15 37												16 38					
Hall Green	d							15 40												16 41					
Yardley Wood	d							15 42												16 43					
Shirley	d							15 45												16 46					
Whitlocks End	d							15 48												16 49					
Wythall	d							15 51												16 52					
Earlswood (West Midlands)	d																								
The Lakes	d							15x53												16x54					
Wood End	d																								
Danzey	d																								
Henley-in-Arden	d							16 01												17 02					
Wootton Wawen	d																								
Wilmcote	d							16 09										17 17		17 10					
Stratford-upon-Avon Parkway	a							16 12										17 19		17 13					
Stratford-upon-Avon	a							16 15										17 30		17 16					

Table 71R

Sundays

16 February to 23 March

Hereford, Worcester and Stourbridge - Birmingham - Leamington Spa, Marylebone and Stratford-upon-Avon

Network Diagram - see first Page of Table 71

		XC	CH	LM	XC	LM	GW	CH	CH	LM	XC	CH	LM	XC	LM	GW	CH	CH	XC	CH	LM	XC	LM
		◇1	◇		◇1		◇1	◇	◇		◇1	◇		◇1		◇1	◇	◇	◇1	◇		◇1	
		☕			🛒		☕				☕			🛒					☕			🛒	
Hereford 7	d					16 09	16 34																18 09
Ledbury	a					16 25	16 51																18 25
	d					16 25	16 52																18 25
Colwall	d					16 32	17 00																18 32
Great Malvern	a					16 36	17 04																18 36
	d					16 37	17 05																18 37
Malvern Link	d					16 40	17 09																18 40
Worcester Foregate Street 7	a					16 48	17 20																18 48
	d			16 26		16 49	17 22						17 27			18 26					18 26		18 49
Worcester Shrub Hill 7	a					16 51	17 25									18 29							18 51
	d					16 55									17 57								18 55
Droitwich Spa	d			16 35		17 03							17 36		18 05						18 35		19 03
Bromsgrove	d					17 13									18 15								19 13
Barnt Green	d																						
University	d					17 30									18 30								19 30
Hartlebury	d																						
Kidderminster	d			16 45									17 46								18 45		
Blakedown	d												17 51										
Hagley	d			16 52									17 55								18 51		
Stourbridge Junction 2	d			16 56						17 26			17 59								18 55		
Lye	d									17 30													
Cradley Heath	d			17 02						17 33			18 05								19 01		
Old Hill	d									17 36													
Rowley Regis	d			17 07						17 40			18 10								19 06		
Langley Green	d									17 43													
Birmingham New Street 12 68	a					17 37									18 37								19 37
	d	17 04			17 33						18 04			18 33					19 04			19 33	
Birmingham Intl. 68 ✈	d	17 14									18 14								19 14				
Coventry	d	17 25									18 25								19 25				
Smethwick Galton Bridge 7	d			17 12						17 46			18 15								19 12		
The Hawthorns 🚊	d			17 14						17 48			18 17								19 14		
Jewellery Quarter 🚊	d			17 18						17 52			18 21								19 18		
Birmingham Snow Hill 🚊	a			17 21						17 55			18 24								19 21		
	d		17 12	17 27						17 57		18 12	18 27							19 15	19 23		
Birmingham Moor Street	d		17 15	17 30					17 55	18 00		18 15	18 30					18 55		19 18	19a25		
Bordesley	d																						
Small Heath	d																						
Tyseley	d			17 35									18 37										
Acocks Green	d									18 06													
Olton	d									18 09													
Solihull	d		17 24						18 04	18 12		18 24						19 04		19 26			
Widney Manor	d									18 16										19 30			
Dorridge	d		17 29						18 09	18a21		18 29						19 09		19 34			
Lapworth	d																			19 38			
Hatton	d							17 55												19 43			
Warwick Parkway	d		17 39						18 19			18 39						19 19		19 48			
Warwick	d		17 42					18 01				18 42								19 51			
Leamington Spa 8	a	17 37	17 47		17 59			18 05	18 24		18 37	18 47		18 59				19 24	19 37	19 56		19 59	
	d	17 38	17 48		18 00			18 06	18 25		18 38	18 48		19 00			19 05	19 25	19 38	19 57		20 00	
Banbury	d	17a54	18 06		18a18			18 24	18 43		18a54	19 06		19a17				19 43	19a54	20 15		20a18	
London Marylebone 10 ⊖115	a		19 17					19 41	19 44			20 17						20 43		21 50			
Spring Road	d			17 37									18 39										
Hall Green	d			17 40									18 42										
Yardley Wood	d			17 42									18 44										
Shirley	d			17 45									18 47										
Whitlocks End	d			17 48									18 50										
Wythall	d			17 51									18 53										
Earlswood (West Midlands)	d																						
The Lakes	d			17x53									18x55										
Wood End	d																						
Danzey	d																						
Henley-in-Arden	d			18 01									19 03										
Wootton Wawen	d																						
Wilmcote	d			18 09									19 11				19 26						
Stratford-upon-Avon Parkway	a			18 12									19 14				19 28						
Stratford-upon-Avon	a			18 15									19 17				19 39						

Table 71R

Sundays

16 February to 23 March

Hereford, Worcester and Stourbridge - Birmingham - Leamington Spa, Marylebone and Stratford-upon-Avon

Network Diagram - see first Page of Table 71

		GW	CH	XC	CH	LM	XC	LM	XC	GW	CH	LM	LM	LM	LM	LM
		◇1	◇	◇1	◇		◇1		◇1	◇1	◇					
Hereford 7	d	18 30											20 06			22 40
Ledbury	a	18 47											20 22			22 56
	d	18 48											20 22			22 57
Colwall	d	18 55											20 29			23 04
Great Malvern	a	19 00											20 33			23 08
	d	19 11								20 15			20 37		22 10	23 09
Malvern Link	d	19 14								20 18			20 40		22 12	23 11
Worcester Foregate Street 7	a	19 24								20 27			20 48		22 22	23 21
	d	19 29						19 49		20 28			20 49	21 18	22 23	23 22
Worcester Shrub Hill 7	a	19 31						19 51		20 30			20 51	21 20	22 25	23 25
	d					19 38		19 55				20 36	20 55	21 25	22 29	
Droitwich Spa	d					19 46		20 03				20 44	21 03	21 33	22 37	
Bromsgrove	d							20 13					21 13			
Barnt Green	d															
University	d							20 30					21 30			
Hartlebury	d															
Kidderminster	d					19 56						20 54		21 43	22 47	
Blakedown	d															
Hagley	d					20 03						21 00		21 49	22 53	
Stourbridge Junction 2	d					20 07						21 04		21 53	22 57	
Lye	d															
Cradley Heath	d					20 13						21 10		21 59	23 03	
Old Hill	d															
Rowley Regis	d					20 18						21 15		22 04	23 08	
Langley Green	d															
Birmingham New Street 12 68	a							20 37					21 37			
	d			20 04			20 33		21 04							
Birmingham Intl. 68 ✈	d			20 14					21 14							
Coventry	d			20 25					21 24							
Smethwick Galton Bridge 7	d					20 23						21 20		22 09	23 14	
The Hawthorns	d					20 25						21 22		22 11	23 16	
Jewellery Quarter	d					20 29						21 26		22 15	23 20	
Birmingham Snow Hill	a					20 33						21 30		22 19	23 25	
	d				20 15	20 34					21 15	21 31		22 21		
Birmingham Moor Street	d				20 18	20a37					21 18	21a34		22a23		
Bordesley	d															
Small Heath	d															
Tyseley	d															
Acocks Green	d															
Olton	d															
Solihull	d				20 27						21 27					
Widney Manor	d				20 30						21 30					
Dorridge	d				20 33						21 34					
Lapworth	d															
Hatton	d		20 17													
Warwick Parkway	d				20 43						21 44					
Warwick	d		20 23		20 46						21 47					
Leamington Spa 8	a		20 27	20 37	20 50		20 58		21 34		21 51					
	d		20 28	20 38	20 51		21 00				21 52					
Banbury	d		20 48	20a54	21 09		21a17				22 15					
London Marylebone 10 ⊖115	a		22 08		22 41						23 47					
Spring Road	d															
Hall Green	d															
Yardley Wood	d															
Shirley	d															
Whitlocks End	d															
Wythall	d															
Earlswood (West Midlands)	d															
The Lakes	d															
Wood End	d															
Danzey	d															
Henley-in-Arden	d															
Wootton Wawen	d															
Wilmcote	d															
Stratford-upon-Avon Parkway	a															
Stratford-upon-Avon	a															

Table 71R

Sundays

30 March to 11 May

Hereford, Worcester and Stourbridge - Birmingham - Leamington Spa, Marylebone and Stratford-upon-Avon

Network Diagram - see first Page of Table 71

Station		LM	CH	CH	XC	LM	CH	LM	CH	CH		XC	CH	CH	LM	GW	CH	LM	XC	CH		LM	LM	CH	CH
			◇	◇	◇1		◇		◇	◇		◇1	◇	◇		◇1	◇		◇1	◇				◇	◇
Hereford 7	d																						10 06		
Ledbury	a																						10 22		
	d																						10 22		
Colwall	d																						10 29		
Great Malvern	a																						10 33		
	d														09 07	09 20						10 07	10 34		
Malvern Link	d														09 09	09 23						10 09	10 37		
Worcester Foregate Street 7	a														09 19	09 31						10 18	10 45		
	d														09 20	09 32						10 19	10 46		
Worcester Shrub Hill 7	a														09 22	09 34						10 21	10 48		
	d					09 02									09 26							10 25	10 55		
Droitwich Spa	d					09 10									09 34							10 33	11 03		
Bromsgrove	d					09 20																	11 13		
Barnt Green	d																								
University	d					09 36																	11 30		
Hartlebury	d																								
Kidderminster	d														09 44			10 14				10 45			
Blakedown	d														09 49			10 18							
Hagley	d														09 52			10 22				10 51			
Stourbridge Junction 2	d														09 56			10 26				10 55			
Lye	d																	10 30							
Cradley Heath	d														10 02			10 33				11 01			
Old Hill	d																	10 36							
Rowley Regis	d														10 07			10 40				11 06			
Langley Green	d																	10 43							
Birmingham New Street 12 68	a					09 42																	11 37		
	d				09 04							10 04							11 04						
Birmingham Intl. 68 ✈	d				09 14							10 14							11 14						
Coventry	d				09 25							10 25							11 25						
Smethwick Galton Bridge 7	d														10 13			10 46				11 12			
The Hawthorns 🚊	d														10 15			10 48				11 14			
Jewellery Quarter 🚊	d														10 19			10 52				11 18			
Birmingham Snow Hill 🚊	a														10 22			10 55				11 21			
	d						09 12	09 27						10 12	10 26			10 57		11 12		11 25			
Birmingham Moor Street	d		08 25	08 55			09 15	09 30		09 55				10 15	10 29		10 55	11 00		11 15		11 28			11 55
Bordesley	d																								
Small Heath	d																								
Tyseley	d							09 35							10 34							11 33			
Acocks Green	d																	11 06							
Olton	d																	11 09							
Solihull	d		08 34	09 04			09 24			10 04				10 24			11 04	11 12		11 24					12 04
Widney Manor	d																	11 16							
Dorridge	d	00 03	08 39	09 09			09 29			10 09				10 29			11 10	11a21		11 29					12 09
Lapworth	d	00 06												10 33											
Hatton	d	00 12							09 55					10 38										11 55	
Warwick Parkway	d	00 15	08 49	09 19			09 39			10 19				10 44			11 20			11 39					12 19
Warwick	d	00 18	08 52				09 42		10 01					10 47						11 42				12 01	
Leamington Spa 8	a	00 24	08 57	09 24	09 37		09 47		10 05	10 24		10 37		10 51			11 25		11 37	11 47				12 05	12 24
	d		08 58	09 25	09 38		09 48		10 06	10 25		10 38	10 50	10 52			11 26		11 38	11 48				12 06	12 25
Banbury	d		09 16	09 43	09a54		10 06		10 24	10 43		10a54		11 10			11 44		11a54	12 06				12 24	12 43
London Marylebone 10 ⊖115	a		10 21	10 44			11 17		11 41	11 44				12 17			12 44			13 17				13 41	13 44
Spring Road	d							09 37							10 37							11 36			
Hall Green	d							09 40							10 39							11 38			
Yardley Wood	d							09 42							10 42							11 41			
Shirley	d							09 45							10 45							11 44			
Whitlocks End	d							09 48							10 48							11 47			
Wythall	d							09 51							10 50							11 49			
Earlswood (West Midlands)	d																								
The Lakes	d							09x53							10x53							11x52			
Wood End	d																								
Danzey	d																								
Henley-in-Arden	d							10 01							11 00							11 59			
Wootton Wawen	d																								
Wilmcote	d							10 09					11 16		11 08							12 07			
Stratford-upon-Avon Parkway	a							10 12					11 18		11 11							12 10			
Stratford-upon-Avon	a							10 15					11 29		11 15							12 14			

BZ Business Zone available offering greater comfort and an enhanced working environment. Supplement payable.

Table 71R

Sundays

30 March to 11 May

Hereford, Worcester and Stourbridge - Birmingham - Leamington Spa, Marylebone and Stratford-upon-Avon

Network Diagram - see first Page of Table 71

		LM	XC	CH	CH	LM	GW	XC	CH	LM	XC	CH	LM	XC	LM	CH	CH	LM	XC	CH	CH	LM	GW
			◇1	◇	◇		◇1	◇1	◇		◇1	◇		◇1		◇	◇		◇1	◇	◇		◇1
			🛒					🛒			☕			🛒					☕				
Hereford 7	d														12 00								
Ledbury	a														12 16								
	d														12 16								
Colwall	d														12 23								
Great Malvern	a														12 27								
	d					10 57	11 15						12 07		12 30								13 15
Malvern Link	d					10 59	11 18						12 09		12 33								13 18
Worcester Foregate Street 7	a					11 08	11 27						12 19		12 41								13 26
	d					11 09	11 28						12 20		12 42							13 26	13 27
Worcester Shrub Hill 7	a					11 11	11 30						12 22		12 44								13 29
	d					11 27							12 26		12 55								
Droitwich Spa	d					11 35							12 35		13 03							13 35	
Bromsgrove	d														13 13								
Barnt Green	d																						
University	d														13 30								
Hartlebury	d																						
Kidderminster	d					11 45							12 45									13 45	
Blakedown	d												12 49										
Hagley	d					11 51							12 53									13 52	
Stourbridge Junction 2	d	11 26				11 55				12 26			12 57					13 26				13 56	
Lye	d	11 30								12 30								13 30					
Cradley Heath	d	11 33				12 01				12 33			13 03					13 33				14 02	
Old Hill	d	11 36								12 36								13 36					
Rowley Regis	d	11 40				12 06				12 40			13 08					13 40				14 07	
Langley Green	d	11 43								12 43								13 43					
Birmingham New Street 12 68	a														13 37								
	d		12 04					12 33			13 04			13 33					14 04				
Birmingham Intl. 68 ✈	d		12 14								13 14								14 14				
Coventry	d		12 25								13 25								14 25				
Smethwick Galton Bridge 7	d	11 46				12 12				12 46			13 13					13 46				14 12	
The Hawthorns 🚋	d	11 48				12 14				12 48			13 15					13 48				14 14	
Jewellery Quarter 🚋	d	11 52				12 18				12 52			13 19					13 52				14 18	
Birmingham Snow Hill 🚋	a	11 55				12 21				12 55			13 22					13 55				14 21	
	d	11 57			12 12	12 26				12 57		13 12	13 27					13 57			14 12	14 27	
Birmingham Moor Street	d	12 00			12 15	12 30			12 55	13 00		13 15	13 30				13 55	14 00			14 15	14 30	
Bordesley	d																						
Small Heath	d																						
Tyseley	d					12 35							13 35									14 35	
Acocks Green	d	12 06								13 06								14 06					
Olton	d	12 09								13 09								14 09					
Solihull	d	12 12			12 24				13 04	13 12		13 24					14 04	14 12			14 24		
Widney Manor	d	12 16								13 16								14 16					
Dorridge	d	12a21			12 29				13 09	13a21		13 29					14 09	14a21			14 29		
Lapworth	d				12 33																14 33		
Hatton	d				12 38											13 55					14 38		
Warwick Parkway	d				12 44				13 19			13 39					14 19				14 44		
Warwick	d				12 47							13 42				14 01					14 47		
Leamington Spa 8	a		12 37		12 51			12 59	13 24		13 37	13 47		13 58		14 05	14 24		14 37		14 51		
	d		12 38	12 50	12 52			13 00	13 25		13 38	13 48		13 59		14 06	14 25		14 38	14 50	14 52		
Banbury	d		12a54		13 10			13a17	13 43		13a54	14 06		14a17		14 24	14 43		14a54		15 10		
London Marylebone 10 ⊖115	a				14 17				14 44			15 17				15 41	15 44				16 17		
Spring Road	d					12 37							13 37									14 37	
Hall Green	d					12 40							13 40									14 40	
Yardley Wood	d					12 42							13 42									14 42	
Shirley	d					12 45							13 45									14 45	
Whitlocks End	d					12 48							13 48									14 48	
Wythall	d					12 51							13 51									14 51	
Earlswood (West Midlands)	d																						
The Lakes	d					12x53							13x53									14x53	
Wood End	d																						
Danzey	d																						
Henley-in-Arden	d					13 01							14 01									15 01	
Wootton Wawen	d																						
Wilmcote	d			13 16		13 09							14 09							15 16		15 09	
Stratford-upon-Avon Parkway	a			13 18		13 12							14 12							15 18		15 12	
Stratford-upon-Avon	a			13 29		13 15							14 15							15 29		15 15	

Table 71R

Sundays

30 March to 11 May

Hereford, Worcester and Stourbridge - Birmingham - Leamington Spa, Marylebone and Stratford-upon-Avon

Network Diagram - see first Page of Table 71

		XC		CH	LM	XC	CH	LM	GW	XC	LM	GW		CH	CH	LM	XC	CH	CH	LM	LM	XC		CH	LM
		◇1		◇		◇1	◇		◇1	◇1		◇1		◇	◇		◇1	◇	◇			◇1		◇	
		🛒				☕	🛒		☕	🛒		☕					☕					🛒			
Hereford 7	d								13 33		14 05	14 35													
Ledbury	a								13 51		14 21	14 53													
	d								13 52		14 21	14 55													
Colwall	d								13 59		14 28	15 02													
Great Malvern	a								14 04		14 32	15 06													
	d								14 11		14 33	15 07													
Malvern Link	d								14 15		14 36	15 11													
Worcester Foregate Street 7	a								14 24		14 44	15 20													
	d							14 24	14 26		14 45	15 22								15 28					
Worcester Shrub Hill 7	a								14 29		14 47	15 24													
	d										14 55										15 46				
Droitwich Spa	d							14 33			15 03									15 37	15 54				
Bromsgrove	d										15 13														
Barnt Green	d																								
University	d										15 30														
Hartlebury	d																								
Kidderminster	d							14 43												15 47	16 04				
Blakedown	d							14 48													16 09				
Hagley	d							14 52												15 54	16 13				
Stourbridge Junction 2	d				14 26			14 56								15 26				15 58	16 17				16 26
Lye	d				14 30											15 30									16 30
Cradley Heath	d				14 33			15 02								15 33				16 04					16 33
Old Hill	d				14 36											15 36									16 36
Rowley Regis	d				14 40			15 07								15 40				16 09					16 40
Langley Green	d				14 43											15 43									16 43
Birmingham New Street 12 68	a										15 37														
	d	14 33				15 04				15 33							16 04					16 33			
Birmingham Intl. 68 ✈	d					15 14											16 14								
Coventry	d					15 25											16 25								
Smethwick Galton Bridge 7	d				14 46			15 12								15 46				16 14	16 30				16 46
The Hawthorns 🚋	d				14 48			15 14								15 48				16 16					16 48
Jewellery Quarter 🚋	d				14 52			15 18								15 52				16 20					16 52
Birmingham Snow Hill 🚋	a				14 55			15 21								15 55				16 23	16 36				16 55
	d				14 57		15 12	15 27								15 57			16 12	16 27	16 43				16 57
Birmingham Moor Street	d			14 55	15 00		15 15	15 30							15 55	16 00			16 15	16 30	16a45			16 55	17 00
Bordesley	d																								
Small Heath	d																								
Tyseley	d							15 35												16 36					
Acocks Green	d				15 06											16 06									17 06
Olton	d				15 09											16 09									17 09
Solihull	d			15 04	15 12		15 24								16 04	16 12			16 24					17 04	17 12
Widney Manor	d				15 16											16 16									17 16
Dorridge	d			15 09	15a21		15 29								16 09	16a21			16 29					17 09	17a21
Lapworth	d																		16 33						
Hatton	d													15 55					16 38						
Warwick Parkway	d			15 19			15 39								16 19				16 44					17 19	
Warwick	d						15 42							16 01					16 47						
Leamington Spa 8	a	14 59		15 24		15 37	15 47			15 58				16 05	16 24		16 37		16 51			16 59		17 24	
	d	15 00		15 25		15 38	15 48			15 59				16 06	16 25		16 38	16 51	16 52			17 00		17 25	
Banbury	d	15a18		15 43		15a54	16 06			16a17				16 24	16 43		16a54		17 10			17a17		17 43	
London Marylebone 10 ⊖115	a			16 44			17 17							17 40	17 43				18 17					18 44	
Spring Road	d							15 37												16 38					
Hall Green	d							15 40												16 41					
Yardley Wood	d							15 42												16 43					
Shirley	d							15 45												16 46					
Whitlocks End	d							15 48												16 49					
Wythall	d							15 51												16 52					
Earlswood (West Midlands)	d																								
The Lakes	d							15x53												16x54					
Wood End	d																								
Danzey	d																								
Henley-in-Arden	d							16 01												17 02					
Wootton Wawen	d																								
Wilmcote	d							16 09										17 17		17 10					
Stratford-upon-Avon Parkway	a							16 12										17 19		17 13					
Stratford-upon-Avon	a							16 15										17 30		17 16					

Table 71R

Sundays

30 March to 11 May

Hereford, Worcester and Stourbridge - Birmingham - Leamington Spa, Marylebone and Stratford-upon-Avon

Network Diagram - see first Page of Table 71

		XC	CH	LM	XC	LM	GW	CH		CH	LM	XC	CH	LM	XC	LM	GW	CH		CH	XC	CH	LM	XC	LM
		◇1	◇		◇1		◇1	◇		◇		◇1	◇		◇1		◇1	◇		◇	◇1	◇		◇1	
		☕			🛒		☕					☕			🛒						☕			🛒	
Hereford 7	d					16 09	16 34																		18 09
Ledbury	a					16 25	16 51																		18 25
	d					16 25	16 52																		18 25
Colwall	d					16 32	17 00																		18 32
Great Malvern	a					16 36	17 04																		18 36
	d					16 37	17 05																		18 37
Malvern Link	d					16 40	17 09																		18 40
Worcester Foregate Street 7	a					16 48	17 19																		18 48
	d			16 26		16 49	17 22							17 27			18 26						18 26		18 49
Worcester Shrub Hill 7	a					16 51	17 25										18 29								18 51
	d					16 55										17 57									18 55
Droitwich Spa	d			16 35		17 03								17 36		18 05							18 35		19 03
Bromsgrove	d					17 13										18 15									19 13
Barnt Green	d																								
University	d					17 30										18 30									19 30
Hartlebury	d																								
Kidderminster	d			16 45										17 46									18 45		
Blakedown	d													17 51											
Hagley	d			16 52										17 55									18 51		
Stourbridge Junction 2	d			16 56							17 26			17 59									18 55		
Lye	d										17 30														
Cradley Heath	d			17 02							17 33			18 05									19 01		
Old Hill	d										17 36														
Rowley Regis	d			17 07							17 40			18 10									19 06		
Langley Green	d										17 43														
Birmingham New Street 12 68	a					17 37										18 37									19 37
	d	17 04			17 33							18 04			18 33						19 04			19 33	
Birmingham Intl. 68 ✈	d	17 14										18 14									19 14				
Coventry	d	17 25										18 25									19 25				
Smethwick Galton Bridge 7	d			17 12							17 46			18 15									19 12		
The Hawthorns 🚊	d			17 14							17 48			18 17									19 14		
Jewellery Quarter 🚊	d			17 18							17 52			18 21									19 18		
Birmingham Snow Hill 🚊	a			17 21							17 55			18 24									19 21		
	d		17 12	17 27							17 57		18 12	18 27								19 15	19 23		
Birmingham Moor Street	d		17 15	17 30						17 55	18 00		18 15	18 30						18 55		19 18	19a25		
Bordesley	d																								
Small Heath	d																								
Tyseley	d			17 35										18 37											
Acocks Green	d										18 06														
Olton	d										18 09														
Solihull	d		17 24							18 04	18 12		18 24							19 04		19 26			
Widney Manor	d										18 16											19 30			
Dorridge	d		17 29							18 09	18a21		18 29							19 09		19 34			
Lapworth	d																					19 38			
Hatton	d							17 55														19 43			
Warwick Parkway	d		17 39							18 19			18 39							19 19		19 48			
Warwick	d		17 42					18 01					18 42									19 51			
Leamington Spa 8	a	17 37	17 47		17 59			18 05		18 24		18 37	18 47		18 59					19 24	19 37	19 56		19 59	
	d	17 38	17 48		18 00			18 06		18 25		18 38	18 48		19 00			19 05		19 25	19 38	19 57		20 00	
Banbury	d	17a54	18 06		18a19			18 24		18 43		18a54	19 06		19a17					19 43	19a54	20 15		20a18	
London Marylebone 10 ⊖115	a		19 17					19 41		19 44			20 17							20 43		21 50			
Spring Road	d			17 37										18 39											
Hall Green	d			17 40										18 42											
Yardley Wood	d			17 42										18 44											
Shirley	d			17 45										18 47											
Whitlocks End	d			17 48										18 50											
Wythall	d			17 51										18 53											
Earlswood (West Midlands)	d																								
The Lakes	d			17x53										18x55											
Wood End	d																								
Danzey	d																								
Henley-in-Arden	d			18 01										19 03											
Wootton Wawen	d																								
Wilmcote	d			18 09										19 11				19 26							
Stratford-upon-Avon Parkway	a			18 12										19 14				19 28							
Stratford-upon-Avon	a			18 15										19 17				19 39							

Table 71R

Sundays
30 March to 11 May

Hereford, Worcester and Stourbridge - Birmingham - Leamington Spa, Marylebone and Stratford-upon-Avon

Network Diagram - see first Page of Table 71

		GW	CH	XC		CH	LM	XC	LM	XC	GW	CH	LM	LM		LM	LM	LM
		◇■1	◇	◇■1		◇		◇■1		◇■1	◇■1	◇						
				🍴				🛒		🛒								
Hereford ■7	d	18 30												20 06				22 40
Ledbury	a	18 47												20 22				22 56
	d	18 48												20 22				22 57
Colwall	d	18 55												20 29				23 04
Great Malvern	a	19 00												20 33				23 08
	d	19 11									20 15			20 37			22 10	23 09
Malvern Link	d	19 14									20 18			20 40			22 12	23 11
Worcester Foregate Street ■7	a	19 24									20 27			20 48			22 22	23 21
	d	19 29							19 49		20 28			20 49		21 18	22 23	23 22
Worcester Shrub Hill ■7	a	19 31							19 51		20 30			20 51		21 20	22 25	23 25
	d						19 38		19 55				20 36	20 55		21 25	22 29	
Droitwich Spa	d						19 46		20 03				20 44	21 03		21 33	22 37	
Bromsgrove	d								20 13					21 13				
Barnt Green	d																	
University	d								20 30					21 30				
Hartlebury	d																	
Kidderminster	d						19 56						20 54			21 43	22 47	
Blakedown	d																	
Hagley	d						20 03						21 00			21 49	22 53	
Stourbridge Junction ■2	d						20 07						21 04			21 53	22 57	
Lye	d																	
Cradley Heath	d						20 13						21 10			21 59	23 03	
Old Hill	d																	
Rowley Regis	d						20 18						21 15			22 04	23 08	
Langley Green	d																	
Birmingham New Street ■12 68	a								20 37					21 37				
	d			20 04				20 33		21 04								
Birmingham Intl. 68 ✈	d			20 14						21 14								
Coventry	d			20 25						21 24								
Smethwick Galton Bridge ■7	d						20 23						21 20			22 09	23 14	
The Hawthorns 🚋	d						20 25						21 22			22 11	23 16	
Jewellery Quarter 🚋	d						20 29						21 26			22 15	23 20	
Birmingham Snow Hill 🚋	a						20 33						21 30			22 19	23 25	
	d					20 15	20 34					21 15	21 31			22 21		
Birmingham Moor Street	d					20 18	20a37					21 18	21a34			22a23		
Bordesley	d																	
Small Heath	d																	
Tyseley	d																	
Acocks Green	d																	
Olton	d																	
Solihull	d					20 27						21 27						
Widney Manor	d					20 30						21 30						
Dorridge	d					20 33						21 34						
Lapworth	d																	
Hatton	d		20 17															
Warwick Parkway	d					20 43						21 44						
Warwick	d		20 23			20 46						21 47						
Leamington Spa ■8	a		20 27	20 37		20 50		20 58		21 34		21 51						
	d		20 28	20 38		20 51		21 00				21 52						
Banbury	d		20 48	20a54		21 09		21a17				22 15						
London Marylebone ■10 ⊖115	a		22 08			22 41						23 47						
Spring Road	d																	
Hall Green	d																	
Yardley Wood	d																	
Shirley	d																	
Whitlocks End	d																	
Wythall	d																	
Earlswood (West Midlands)	d																	
The Lakes	d																	
Wood End	d																	
Danzey	d																	
Henley-in-Arden	d																	
Wootton Wawen	d																	
Wilmcote	d																	
Stratford-upon-Avon Parkway	a																	
Stratford-upon-Avon	a																	

Table 72

Mondays to Saturdays

9 December to 17 May

Stourbridge Junction - Stourbridge Town

Network Diagram - see first Page of Table 71

Miles			LM SX	LM	LM SX	LM	LM SX	LM SX		LM	LM SX	LM	LM	LM	LM	LM	LM	and at the same minutes past each hour until	LM	LM	LM	LM	LM	LM
0	Stourbridge Junction ■	d	05 47	05 58	06 08	06 19	06 29	06 39		06 49	06 59	07 09	07 19	07 29	07 39	07 49	07 59		21 09	21 19	21 29	21 39	21 49	21 59
0¾	Stourbridge Town	a	05 50	06 01	06 11	06 22	06 32	06 42		06 52	07 02	07 12	07 22	07 32	07 42	07 52	08 02		21 12	21 22	21 32	21 42	21 52	22 02

		LM	LM	LM	LM	LM	LM		LM	LM	LM
Stourbridge Junction ■	d	22 09	22 19	22 29	22 39	22 52	23 02		23 19	23 31	23 54
Stourbridge Town	a	22 12	22 22	22 32	22 42	22 55	23 05		23 22	23 34	23 57

Sundays

8 December to 11 May

		LM	LM	LM	LM	LM	LM	and at the same minutes past each hour until	LM	LM	LM	LM		LM	LM	LM
Stourbridge Junction ■	d	09 43	10 00	10 11	10 21	10 41	10 54		18 11	18 21	18 41	18 54		19 11	19 21	19 47
Stourbridge Town	a	09 46	10 03	10 14	10 24	10 44	10 57		18 14	18 24	18 44	18 57		19 14	19 24	19 50

Table 72R

Mondays to Saturdays

9 December to 17 May

Stourbridge Town - Stourbridge Junction

Network Diagram - see first Page of Table 71

Miles			LM SX	LM SX	LM SO	LM SX	LM SX	LM SX		LM SO	LM SX	LM	LM SX	LM	LM	LM	LM	LM	LM	and at the same minutes past each hour until
0	Stourbridge Town	d	05 52	06 03	06 10	06 13	06 24	06 34		06 40	06 44	06 54	07 04	07 14	07 24	07 34	07 44	07 54	08 04	
0¾	Stourbridge Junction ■	a	05 55	06 06	06 13	06 16	06 27	06 37		06 43	06 47	06 57	07 07	07 17	07 27	07 37	07 47	07 57	08 07	

		LM	LM	LM	LM	LM	LM		LM	LM	LM	LM	LM	LM		LM	LM	LM
Stourbridge Town	d	21 14	21 24	21 34	21 44	21 54	22 04		22 14	22 24	22 34	22 44	22 57	23 07		23 24	23 36	23 59
Stourbridge Junction ■	a	21 17	21 27	21 37	21 47	21 57	22 07		22 17	22 27	22 37	22 47	23 00	23 10		23 27	23 39	00 02

Sundays

8 December to 11 May

		LM	LM	LM	LM	LM	LM	and at the same minutes past each hour until	LM	LM	LM	LM		LM	LM	LM
Stourbridge Town	d	09 49	10 05	10 16	10 36	10 46	11 00		18 16	18 36	18 46	19 00		19 16	19 36	19 55
Stourbridge Junction ■	a	09 52	10 08	10 19	10 39	10 49	11 03		18 19	18 39	18 49	19 03		19 19	19 39	19 58

Network Diagram for Tables 74, 75, 76

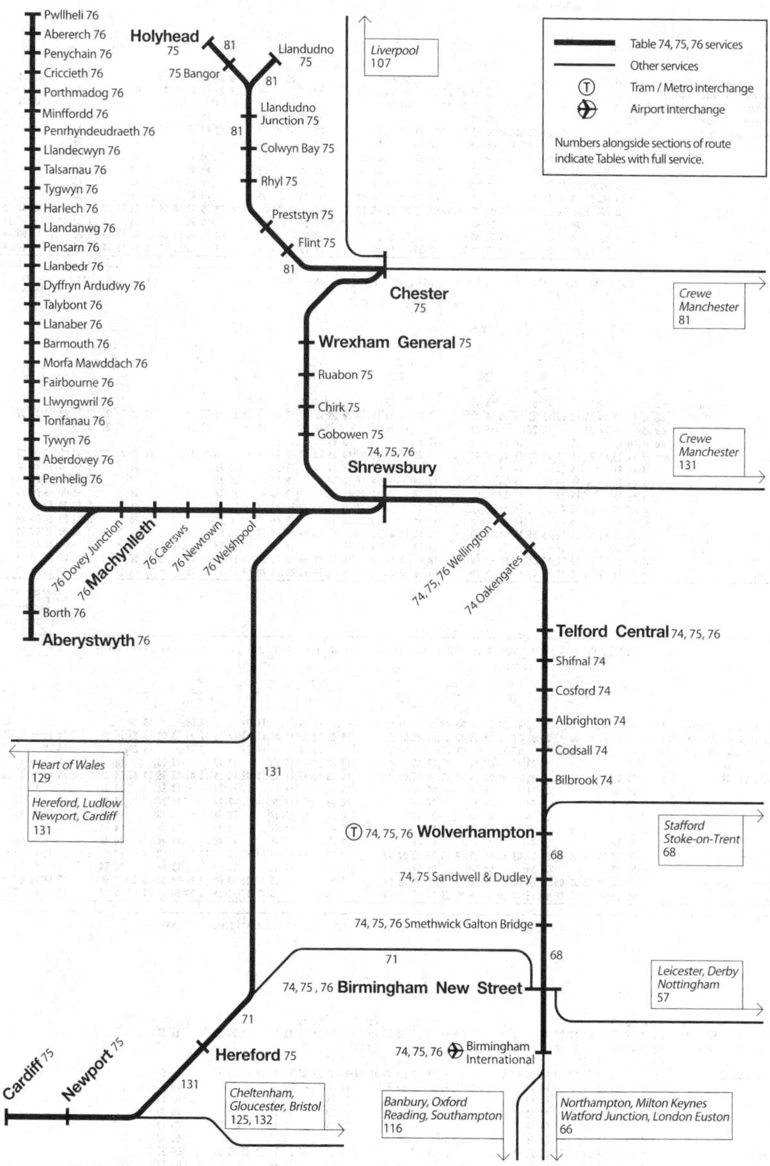

Pwllheli 76
Abererch 76
Penychain 76
Criccieth 76
Porthmadog 76
Minffordd 76
Penrhyndeudraeth 76
Llandecwyn 76
Talsarnau 76
Tygwyn 76
Harlech 76
Llandanwg 76
Pensarn 76
Llanbedr 76
Dyffryn Ardudwy 76
Talybont 76
Llanaber 76
Barmouth 76
Morfa Mawddach 76
Fairbourne 76
Llwyngwril 76
Tonfanau 76
Tywyn 76
Aberdovey 76
Penhelig 76
Holyhead
75
81
75 Bangor
Llandudno
75
81
Llandudno Junction 75
81
Colwyn Bay 75
Rhyl 75
Prestatyn 75
Flint 75
81
Liverpool
107
Table 74, 75, 76 services
Other services
Tram / Metro interchange
Airport interchange
Numbers alongside sections of route indicate Tables with full service.
Chester
75
Crewe
Manchester
81
Wrexham General 75
Ruabon 75
Chirk 75
Gobowen 75
74, 75, 76
Shrewsbury
Crewe
Manchester
131
76 Dovey Junction
76 Machynlleth
76 Caersws
76 Newtown
76 Welshpool
74, 75, 76 Wellington
74 Oakengates
Borth 76
Aberystwyth 76
Telford Central 74, 75, 76
Shifnal 74
Cosford 74
Albrighton 74
Codsall 74
Bilbrook 74
Heart of Wales
129
Hereford, Ludlow
Newport, Cardiff
131
131
74, 75, 76 Wolverhampton
68
Stafford
Stoke-on-Trent
68
74, 75 Sandwell & Dudley
74, 75, 76 Smethwick Galton Bridge
71
68
Leicester, Derby
Nottingham
57
74, 75, 76 Birmingham New Street
71
Hereford 75
74, 75, 76 Birmingham International
Cardiff 75
Newport 75
131
Cheltenham,
Gloucester, Bristol
125, 132
Banbury, Oxford
Reading, Southampton
116
Northampton, Milton Keynes
Watford Junction, London Euston
66

TOCs operating on this network - Arriva Trains Wales (AW), London Midland (LM), Cross Country (XC)

Table 74

Mondays to Fridays

9 December to 16 May

Birmingham - Wolverhampton - Telford - Shrewsbury

Network Diagram - see first Page of Table 74

Miles		AW MO A	AW WFO B	AW TThO B	AW MX	LM	AW ◇ C 🛒	LM	AW ◇ D 🛒	LM		LM	AW ◇ C 🛒	LM	AW ◇ E 🛒	LM	AW ◇ C 🛒	LM	AW ◇ E 🛒	LM		AW ◇ C 🛒	LM	AW ◇ E 🛒
—	Birmingham International 68 d								07 08				08 08		09 09		10 08		11 08			12 08		13 08
0	**Birmingham New Street** 68 d					05 51	06 25		07 23	07 26		08 05	08 23	09 05	09 23	10 05	10 23	11 05	11 23	12 05		12 23	13 05	13 23
4	Smethwick Galton Bridge 68 d						06 30		07 29				08 29		09 29		10 29		11 29			12 29		13 29
5¼	Sandwell & Dudley 68 d					05 59						08 13		09 13		10 13		11 14		12 13			13 13	
13	**Wolverhampton 7** d		00 02	00 02	00 20	06 13	06 43	06 48	07 42	07 45		08 25	08 42	09 25	09 42	10 25	10 43	11 25	11 42	12 25		12 42	13 25	13 42
17	Bilbrook d		00 08	00 08		06 19		06 54		07 51		08 31		09 31		10 31		11 31		12 31			13 31	
17½	Codsall d		00 11	00 11		06 22		06 57		07 54		08 34		09 34		10 34		11 34		12 34			13 34	
20¾	Albrighton d		00 15	00 15		06 26		07 01		07 58		08 38		09 38		10 38		11 38		12 38			13 38	
22¼	Cosford d	00 02	00 19	00 19		06 30		07 05		08 02		08 41		09 41		10 41		11 41		12 41			13 41	
25½	Shifnal d	00 07	00 24	00 24		06 35		07 10		08 07		08 46		09 46		10 46		11 46		12 46			13 46	
28½	Telford Central d	00 13	00 30	00 30	00 36	06 40	06 59	07 15	07 59	08 12		08 52	08 59	09 52	09 58	10 52	10 59	11 52	11 58	12 52		12 58	13 52	13 59
29½	Oakengates d	00 15	00 32	00 32		06 43		07 18		08 15		08 54		09 54		10 54		11 54		12 54			13 54	
32½	Wellington (Shropshire) d	00 20	00 37	00 37	00 43	06 48	07 06	07 23	08 05	08 20		09 00	09 06	10 00	10 05	11 00	11 06	12 00	12 05	13 00		13 06	14 00	14 06
43	**Shrewsbury** a	00 35	00 53	00 53	01 02	07 01	07 18	07 36	08 19	08 33		09 15	09 19	10 15	10 19	11 15	11 19	12 15	12 18	13 15		13 19	14 15	14 19

	LM	AW ◇ C 🛒	LM	AW ◇ E 🛒	LM	AW R C 🛒		LM	AW ◇ D 🛒	LM	LM	AW ◇ C 🛒	LM	AW ◇ F 🛒	LM	AW ◇ C		LM	AW ◇ G	LM	AW TThO	AW MWFO		
Birmingham International 68 d		14 08		15 08		16 09			17 08			18 09		19 04		20 04			21 04					
Birmingham New Street 68 d	14 05	14 23	15 05	15 23	16 05	16 23		17 05	17 23	17 46	18 05	18 23	19 05	19 23	20 05	20 23		21 05	21 23	22 12	23 32	23 32		
Smethwick Galton Bridge 68 d		14 29		15 27		16 29			17 29			18 29		19 29		20 29			21 29	22 20				
Sandwell & Dudley 68 d	14 13		15 13		16 13			17 13			18 13		19 13		20 13			21 13		22 23				
Wolverhampton 7 d	14 25	14 42	15 25	15 42	16 25	16 43		17 25	17 42	18 07	18 25	18 42	19 25	19 42	20 25	20 42		21 25	21 42	22 43	00 02	00 02		
Bilbrook d	14 31		15 31		16 31			17 31		18 13	18 31		19 31		20 31			21 31		22 49	00 08	00 08		
Codsall d	14 34		15 34		16 34			17 34		18 16	18 34		19 34		20 34			21 34		22 52	00 11	00 11		
Albrighton d	14 38		15 38		16 38			17 38		18 20	18 38		19 38		20 38			21 38		22 56	00 15	00 15		
Cosford d	14 41		15 41		16 41			17 41		18 24	18 41		19 41		20 41			21 41		22 59	00 19	00 19		
Shifnal d	14 46		15 46		16 46			17 46		18 28	18 46		19 46		20 46			21 46		23 04	00 24	00 24		
Telford Central d	14 52	14 59	15 52	15 58	16 52	16 59		17 52	18 01	18 34	18 52	18 59	19 52	19 59	20 52	20 58		21 52	21 58	23 10	00 30	00 30		
Oakengates d	14 54		15 54		16 54			17 54		18 36	18 54		19 54		20 54			21 54		23 12	00 32	00 32		
Wellington (Shropshire) d	15 00	15 06	16 00	16 05	17 00	17 06		18 00	18 06	18 42	19 00	19 06	20 00	20 06	21 00	21 05		22 00	22 06	23 18	00 37	00 37		
Shrewsbury a	15 15	15 19	16 15	16 19	17 15	17 19		18 15	18 20	18 56	19 15	19 19	20 15	20 19	21 15	21 18		22 14	22 18	23 30	00 52	00 53		

Saturdays

14 December to 17 May

	AW B	AW	AW ◇ C 🛒	LM	AW ◇ E 🛒	LM	AW ◇ C 🛒	LM	AW ◇ E 🛒		LM	AW ◇ C 🛒	LM	AW ◇ E 🛒	LM	AW ◇ C 🛒	LM	AW ◇ E 🛒	LM		AW ◇ C 🛒	LM	AW ◇ E 🛒	LM
Birmingham International 68 d					07 09		08 09		09 09			10 09		11 09		12 09		13 09			14 09		15 09	
Birmingham New Street 68 d			06 23	07 05	07 22	08 05	08 23	09 05	09 23		10 05	10 23	11 05	11 23	12 05	12 23	13 05	13 23	14 05		14 23	15 05	15 23	16 05
Smethwick Galton Bridge 68 d			06 29		07 28		08 29		09 29			10 30		11 29		12 29		13 29			14 29		15 29	
Sandwell & Dudley 68 d				07 13		08 13		09 13			10 13		11 13		12 13		13 13		14 13			15 13		16 13
Wolverhampton 7 d	00 02	00 20	06 42	07 25	07 41	08 25	08 42	09 25	09 42		10 25	10 43	11 25	11 42	12 25	12 42	13 25	13 42	14 25		14 42	15 25	15 42	16 25
Bilbrook d	00 08			07 31		08 31		09 31			10 31		11 31		12 31		13 31		14 31			15 31		16 31
Codsall d	00 11			07 34		08 34		09 34			10 34		11 34		12 34		13 34		14 34			15 34		16 34
Albrighton d	00 15			07 38		08 38		09 38			10 38		11 38		12 38		13 38		14 38			15 38		16 38
Cosford d	00 19			07 41		08 41		09 41			10 41		11 41		12 41		13 41		14 41			15 41		16 41
Shifnal d	00 24			07 46		08 46		09 46			10 46		11 46		12 46		13 46		14 46			15 46		16 46
Telford Central d	00 30	00 36	06 59	07 52	07 57	08 52	08 59	09 52	09 58		10 52	10 59	11 52	11 58	12 52	12 59	13 52	13 59	14 52		14 58	15 52	15 59	16 52
Oakengates d	00 32			07 54		08 54		09 54			10 54		11 54		12 54		13 54		14 54			15 54		16 54
Wellington (Shropshire) d	00 37	00 43	07 05	08 00	08 05	09 00	09 05	10 00	10 05		11 00	11 06	12 00	12 06	13 00	13 07	14 00	14 05	15 00		15 06	16 00	16 06	17 00
Shrewsbury a	00 53	01 00	07 18	08 15	08 20	09 15	09 20	10 15	10 19		11 15	11 20	12 15	12 19	13 15	13 23	14 15	14 18	15 15		15 19	16 15	16 19	17 15

	AW R C 🛒	LM	AW ◇ E 🛒	LM	AW ◇ C 🛒		LM	AW ◇ F 🛒	LM	AW ◇ C	LM	AW ◇ F	LM	AW H	LM		AW
Birmingham International 68 d	16 09		17 09		18 09			19 09		20 09		21 09					
Birmingham New Street 68 d	16 23	17 05	17 23	18 05	18 23		19 05	19 23	20 05	20 23	21 05	21 23	22 05	22 55	23 08		23 35
Smethwick Galton Bridge 68 d	16 29		17 30		18 29			19 29		20 29		21 29			23 16		
Sandwell & Dudley 68 d		17 13		18 13			19 13		20 13		21 13		22 13		23 19		
Wolverhampton 7 d	16 42	17 25	17 42	18 25	18 42		19 25	19 42	20 25	20 42	21 25	21 41	22 25	23 13	23 35		23 54
Bilbrook d		17 31		18 31			19 31		20 31		21 31		22 31				00 01
Codsall d		17 34		18 34			19 34		20 34		21 34		22 34				00 04
Albrighton d		17 38		18 38			19 38		20 38		21 38		22 38				00 08
Cosford d		17 41		18 41			19 41		20 41		21 41		22 41				00 12
Shifnal d		17 46		18 46			19 46		20 46		21 46		22 46				00 17
Telford Central d	16 58	17 52	17 58	18 52	18 58		19 52	19 59	20 52	20 58	21 52	21 58	22 52	23 29	23 52		00 22
Oakengates d		17 54		18 54			19 54		20 54		21 54		22 54				00 25
Wellington (Shropshire) d	17 05	18 00	18 06	19 00	19 05		20 00	20 05	21 00	21 05	22 00	22 04	23 00	23 36	23 58		00 30
Shrewsbury a	17 19	18 15	18 19	19 15	19 19		20 15	20 19	21 15	21 19	22 14	22 21	23 15	23 49	00 11		00 43

A From Birmingham International
B From Birmingham New Street
C To Aberystwyth
D To Llandudno
E To Holyhead
F To Chester
G To Manchester Piccadilly
H To Crewe

Table 74

Sundays

8 December to 11 May

Birmingham - Wolverhampton - Telford - Shrewsbury

Network Diagram - see first Page of Table 74

		AW	AW	AW	AW	AW	AW	AW	AW	AW	AW	AW	AW	AW	AW	AW	AW	AW	AW	AW	AW	AW
						◇	◇		◇	◇		◇	◇		◇	◇		◇	◇	◇		
						A	B		A	B		A	B		C	B		A	B	A		
							🛒		🛒	🛒		🛒	🛒		🛒	🛒		🛒				
Birmingham International 68	d			09 51		10 48	12 08		13 07	14 07		15 07	16 07		17 07	18 07		19 07	20 07	21 08	22 11	23 08
Birmingham New Street 68	d			10 04		11 05	12 24		13 24	14 24		15 24	16 24		17 24	18 24		19 24	20 24	21 24	22 24	23 24
Smethwick Galton Bridge 68	d																					
Sandwell & Dudley 68	d																					
Wolverhampton 7 🚌	d		00 18	10 22	11 06	11 27	12 42	13 06	13 42	14 43	15 06	15 43	16 43	17 06	17 43	18 43	19 06	19 43	20 43	21 43	22 42	23 46
Bilbrook	d	00 01		10 28	11 12	11 33		13 12			15 12			17 12			19 12			21 49	22 48	23 52
Codsall	d	00 04		10 31	11 15	11 35		13 15			15 15			17 15			19 15			21 51	22 50	23 54
Albrighton	d	00 08		10 35	11 19	11 40		13 19			15 19			17 19			19 19			21 56	22 55	23 59
Cosford	d	00 12		10 39	11 23	11 43		13 23			15 23			17 23			19 23			21 59	22 58	00 02
Shifnal	d	00 17		10 44	11 28	11 48		13 28			15 28			17 28			19 28			22 04	23 03	00 07
Telford Central	d	00 22	00 36	10 49	11 34	11 54	12 59	13 34	13 58	14 59	15 34	15 59	16 59	17 34	17 59	18 59	19 34	19 59	20 59	22 10	23 09	00 13
Oakengates	d	00 25		10 51	11 37	11 56		13 37			15 37			17 37			19 37			22 12	23 11	00 15
Wellington (Shropshire)	d	00 30	00 43	10 57	11 43	12 01	13 05	13 43	14 04	15 06	15 43	16 06	17 06	17 43	18 05	19 06	19 43	20 06	21 06	22 17	23 16	00 20
Shrewsbury	a	00 43	00 59	11 12	11 58	12 15	13 18	13 58	14 18	15 19	15 58	16 22	17 19	17 59	18 19	19 19	19 58	20 19	21 19	22 30	23 32	00 35

A To Chester
B To Aberystwyth
C To Holyhead

Table 74R

Mondays to Fridays

9 December to 16 May

Shrewsbury - Telford - Wolverhampton - Birmingham

Network Diagram - see first Page of Table 74

Miles				AW	AW	LM	LM	AW	LM		LM	AW	LM	AW	AW	LM	AW	LM	AW		LM	AW	LM	AW	LM	AW
				MX											BHX											
				◇				◇				◇			◇		◇		◇			◇		◇		◇
				A		B		A				C			E		F		G			H		G		H
												🛒			🛒		🛒		🛒			🛒		🛒		🛒
0	**Shrewsbury**		d		05 18	05 24	05 58	06 33	06 55		07 15	07 33	07 47		08 32	08 47	09 33	09 47	10 32		10 47	11 33	11 47	12 33	12 47	13 33
10½	Wellington (Shropshire)		d		05 31	05 37	06 11	06 46	07 09		07 28	07 46	08 00		08 45	09 00	09 46	10 00	10 46		11 00	11 46	12 00	12 46	13 00	13 46
13½	Oakengates		d			05 42	06 16				07 33		08 05			09 05		10 05			11 05		12 05		13 05	
14½	Telford Central		d		05 38	05 45	06 19	06 53	07 15		07 37	07 53	08 08		08 52	09 08	09 53	10 08	10 52		11 08	11 53	12 08	12 53	13 08	13 53
17½	Shifnal		d			05 50	06 24				07 42		08 13			09 13		10 13			11 13		12 13		13 13	
20¾	Cosford		d			05 55	06 29				07 47		08 18			09 18		10 18			11 18		12 18		13 18	
22¼	Albrighton		d	00 01		05 58	06 32				07 50		08 21			09 21		10 21			11 21		12 21		13 21	
25½	Codsall		d	00 06		06 04	06 38				07 56		08 27			09 27		10 27			11 27		12 27		13 27	
26	Bilbrook		d	00 08		06 06	06 40				07 58		08 29			09 29		10 29			11 29		12 29		13 29	
30	**Wolverhampton** 7	🚌	a	00 17	05 58	06 13	06 47	07 11	07 33		08 05	08 11	08 36		09 10	09 36	10 10	10 36	11 09		11 36	12 11	12 36	13 10	13 36	14 09
37¾	Sandwell & Dudley	68	a			06 27	07 04		07 42				08 46			09 46		10 46			11 46		12 46		13 46	
39	Smethwick Galton Bridge	68	a		06 10	06 31	07 08	07 23				08 22			09 22		10 21		11 20			12 22		13 22		14 22
43	**Birmingham New Street** 12	68	a		06 15	06 39	07 17	07 30	07 52		08 23	08 29	08 55		09 29	09 55	10 30	10 55	11 30		11 55	12 30	12 55	13 29	13 56	14 30
—	Birmingham International	68	a		06 50			07 50				08 50			09 49		10 49		11 49			12 49		13 49		14 49

			LM	AW	LM		AW	LM	AW	LM	AW	LM	AW	LM	AW		LM	LM	AW	LM	AW	AW	AW
																					MWFO	TThO	
				◇			◇		◇		◇		◇		◇				◇		◇	◇	◇
				G			H		G		H		G		C				C		G	G	A
				🛒			🛒		🛒		🛒		🛒		🛒								
Shrewsbury		d	13 47	14 33	14 47		15 33	15 47	16 32	16 47	17 33	17 47	18 33	18 47	19 33		19 47	20 47	21 33	21 47	22 18	22 18	23 26
Wellington (Shropshire)		d	14 00	14 46	15 00		15 46	16 00	16 45	17 00	17 46	18 00	18 46	19 00	19 46		20 00	21 00	21 46	22 00	22 32	22 32	23 40
Oakengates		d	14 05		15 05			16 05		17 05		18 05		19 05			20 05	21 05		22 05			23 44
Telford Central		d	14 08	14 53	15 08		15 53	16 08	16 52	17 08	17 53	18 08	18 53	19 08	19 53		20 08	21 08	21 53	22 08	22 38	22 38	23 47
Shifnal		d	14 13		15 13			16 13		17 13		18 13		19 13			20 13	21 13		22 13			23 52
Cosford		d	14 18		15 18			16 18		17 18		18 18		19 18			20 18	21 18		22 18			23 57
Albrighton		d	14 21		15 21			16 21		17 21		18 21		19 21			20 21	21 21		22 21			00 01
Codsall		d	14 27		15 27			16 27		17 27		18 27		19 27			20 27	21 27		22 27			00 06
Bilbrook		d	14 29		15 29			16 29		17 29		18 29		19 29			20 29	21 29		22 29			00 08
Wolverhampton 7	🚌	a	14 36	15 11	15 36		16 11	16 36	17 09	17 36	18 11	18 36	19 11	19 36	20 11		20 36	21 36	22 09	22 36	22 55	22 55	00 17
Sandwell & Dudley	68	a	14 46		15 46			16 46		17 46		18 46		19 46			20 47	21 46		22 47			
Smethwick Galton Bridge	68	a		15 22			16 22		17 22		18 22		19 22		20 22				22 20				
Birmingham New Street 12	68	a	14 55	15 30	15 55		16 30	16 55	17 30	17 55	18 30	18 55	19 30	19 55	20 29		20 56	21 55	22 33	22 55	23 27	23 28	
Birmingham International	68	a		15 49			16 49		17 49		18 49		19 50		20 49								

Saturdays

14 December to 17 May

			AW	AW	LM	AW	LM	AW	LM	AW	LM		AW	LM	AW	LM	AW	LM	AW	LM	AW		LM	AW	LM	AW
			◇					◇		◇			◇		◇		◇		◇		◇			◇		◇
			A					C		G			F		G		H		G		H			G		H
								🛒		🛒			🛒		🛒		🛒		🛒		🛒			🛒		🛒
Shrewsbury		d		05 22	05 29	06 33	06 47	07 31	07 47	08 33	08 47		09 33	09 47	10 33	10 47	11 33	11 47	12 33	12 47	13 33		13 47	14 33	14 47	15 33
Wellington (Shropshire)		d		05 35	05 42	06 46	07 00	07 44	08 00	08 46	09 00		09 46	10 00	10 46	11 00	11 46	12 00	12 46	13 00	13 46		14 00	14 46	15 00	15 46
Oakengates		d			05 47		07 05		08 05		09 05			10 05		11 05		12 05		13 05			14 05		15 05	
Telford Central		d		05 42	05 50	06 53	07 08	07 51	08 08	08 53	09 08		09 53	10 08	10 53	11 08	11 53	12 08	12 53	13 08	13 53		14 08	14 53	15 08	15 53
Shifnal		d			05 55		07 13		08 13		09 13			10 13		11 13		12 13		13 13			14 13		15 13	
Cosford		d			06 00		07 18		08 18		09 18			10 18		11 18		12 18		13 18			14 18		15 18	
Albrighton		d	00 01		06 03		07 21		08 21		09 21			10 21		11 21		12 21		13 21			14 21		15 21	
Codsall		d	00 06		06 09		07 27		08 27		09 27			10 27		11 27		12 27		13 27			14 27		15 27	
Bilbrook		d	00 08		06 11		07 29		08 29		09 29			10 29		11 29		12 29		13 29			14 29		15 29	
Wolverhampton 7	🚌	a	00 17	06 01	06 18	07 11	07 36	08 08	08 36	09 11	09 36		10 11	10 36	11 11	11 36	12 11	12 36	13 10	13 36	14 11		14 36	15 11	15 36	16 11
Sandwell & Dudley	68	a			06 31		07 46		08 46		09 46			10 46		11 47		12 46		13 46			14 46		15 46	
Smethwick Galton Bridge	68	a		06 13	06 35	07 23		08 20		09 23			10 22		11 22		12 22		13 22		14 22			15 22		16 22
Birmingham New Street 12	68	a		06 20	06 45	07 28	07 55	08 26	08 55	09 27	09 55		10 28	10 55	11 28	11 56	12 28	12 55	13 28	13 55	14 28		14 55	15 28	15 55	16 28
Birmingham International	68	a		06 49		07 50		08 50		09 49			10 50		11 50		12 50		13 50		14 50			15 49		16 50

			LM	AW	LM	AW	LM		AW	LM	AW	LM	LM	AW	LM	AW	AW
				◇		◇			◇		◇			◇		◇	◇
				G		H			G		C			C		G	A
				🛒		🛒			🛒		🛒						
Shrewsbury		d	15 47	16 32	16 47	17 33	17 47		18 33	18 47	19 33	19 47	20 47	21 33	21 47	22 31	23 26
Wellington (Shropshire)		d	16 00	16 45	17 00	17 46	18 00		18 46	19 00	19 46	20 00	21 00	21 46	22 00	22 45	23 40
Oakengates		d	16 05		17 05		18 05			19 05		20 05	21 05		22 05		23 44
Telford Central		d	16 08	16 52	17 08	17 53	18 08		18 53	19 08	19 53	20 08	21 08	21 53	22 08	22 51	23 47
Shifnal		d	16 13		17 13		18 13			19 13		20 13	21 13		22 13		23 52
Cosford		d	16 18		17 18		18 18			19 18		20 18	21 18		22 18		23 57
Albrighton		d	16 21		17 21		18 21			19 21		20 21	21 21		22 21		00 02
Codsall		d	16 27		17 27		18 27			19 27		20 27	21 27		22 27		00 07
Bilbrook		d	16 29		17 29		18 29			19 29		20 29	21 29		22 29		00 09
Wolverhampton 7	🚌	a	16 36	17 07	17 36	18 11	18 36		19 11	19 36	20 10	20 36	21 36	22 08	22 36	23 07	00 16
Sandwell & Dudley	68	a	16 46		17 46		18 46			19 46		20 46	21 47		22 45		
Smethwick Galton Bridge	68	a		17 20		18 22			19 22		20 21			22 19			
Birmingham New Street 12	68	a	16 55	17 26	17 55	18 28	18 55		19 28	19 55	20 26	20 55	21 55	22 32	22 55	23 29	
Birmingham International	68	a		17 49		18 50			19 50		20 50						

A From Chester
B To Rugeley Trent Valley
C From Aberystwyth
D
E not 21 April, 5 May. From Holyhead
F From Barmouth and Aberystwyth
G From Holyhead
H From Pwllheli and Aberystwyth

Table 74R

Sundays

8 December to 11 May

Shrewsbury - Telford - Wolverhampton - Birmingham

Network Diagram - see first Page of Table 74

		AW	AW	AW	AW	AW	AW		AW	AW	AW	AW	AW	AW	AW	AW	AW		AW	AW	AW	AW	AW	AW
		◇				◇	◇			◇	◇		◇	◇		◇	◇			◇	◇		◇	◇
						A	B			A	B		A	B		A	C			A	B	A	B	A
							🛒			🛒	🛒			🛒		🛒	🛒				🛒			
Shrewsbury	d		08 10	09 09	09 55	10 20	11 40		12 10	12 31	13 31	14 10	14 31	15 33	16 10	16 40	17 33		18 10	18 31	19 31	20 23	21 31	22 23
Wellington (Shropshire)	d		08 24	09 23	10 09	10 34	11 54		12 24	12 45	13 45	14 23	14 45	15 47	16 23	16 54	17 47		18 23	18 45	19 45	20 37	21 45	22 37
Oakengates	d		08 28	09 27	10 14				12 29			14 29			16 29				18 29			20 41		22 43
Telford Central	d		08 31	09 30	10 17	10 40	12 00		12 32	12 51	13 51	14 32	14 51	15 53	16 32	17 00	17 53		18 32	18 51	19 51	20 44	21 51	22 45
Shifnal	d		08 36	09 35	10 22				12 37			14 37			16 37				18 37			20 49		22 51
Cosford	d		08 41	09 40	10 28				12 43			14 43			16 43				18 43			20 54		22 56
Albrighton	d		08 44	09 43	10 31				12 46			14 46			16 46				18 46			20 57		22 59
Codsall	d		08 50	09 48	10 37				12 52			14 52			16 52				18 52			21 02		23 05
Bilbrook	d		08 52	09 50	10 39				12 55			14 54			16 54				18 54			21 04		23 07
Wolverhampton [7] 🚋	a		08 59	09 57	10 50	10 56	12 16		13 03	13 07	14 07	15 03	15 07	16 09	17 03	17 15	18 09		19 03	19 07	20 07	21 11	22 07	23 14
Sandwell & Dudley 68	a																							
Smethwick Galton Bridge 68	a																							
Birmingham New Street [12] 68	a		09 15	10 14		11 13	12 32			13 23	14 23		15 24	16 24		17 35	18 27			19 25	20 23	21 29	22 28	
Birmingham International 68	a		09 31	10 32		11 31	12 56			13 55	14 55		15 58	16 55		17 56	18 55			19 55	20 58	21 56	22 58	

A From Chester

B From Aberystwyth

C From Pwllheli

Table 75

Mondays to Fridays

9 December to 16 May

Birmingham - Shrewsbury - Chester - Holyhead

Network Diagram - see first Page of Table 74

Miles	Miles	Station			AW	AW	AW	VT	AW	AW	AW	AW	AW
					MX		BHX	D	BHX				
								◇1		◇	◇	◇	◇
					A					[T]	[T]	[T]	[T]
0	—	Birmingham International	68 ✈	d							07 08		09 09
8¼	—	**Birmingham New Street** 12	68	d							07 23		09 23
12¼	—	Smethwick Galton Bridge 4	68	d							07 29		09 29
21	—	**Wolverhampton** 7	74 ⛴	d							07 42		09 42
45¼	—	Telford Central	74	d							07 59		09 58
49½	—	Wellington (Shropshire)	74	d							08 05		10 05
—	0	**Cardiff Central** 7	131	d						05 10		07 21	
—	11¾	Newport (South Wales)	131	d						05 28		07 36	
—	55¼	Hereford	131	d						06 25		08 27	
59¾	106	**Shrewsbury**		a						07 20	08 19	09 19	10 19
—	—			d		05 20	06 10		07 00	07 24	08 21	09 24	10 23
77½	124	Gobowen		d		05 39	06 30		07 19	07 43	08 40	09 43	10 42
80½	127	Chirk		d	00 03	05 45	06 35		07 25	07 48	08 46	09 48	10 48
84¾	131¼	Ruabon		d	00 09	05 51	06 42		07 31	07 54	08 52	09 54	10 54
89¾	136¼	Wrexham General		a	00 14	05 57	06 49		07 39	08 01	08 59	10 01	11 00
—	—			d	00 15	06 04		07 00		08 02	09 00	10 02	11 01
101¾	148¼	Chester		a	00 35	06 24		07 16		08 20	09 17	10 19	11 19
114¼	160¾	Flint	81	a						08 37	09 37	10 38	11 37
128¼	174¾	Prestatyn	81	a						08 51	09 51	10 52	11 51
131¾	178¼	Rhyl	81	a						08 57	09 57	10 58	11 57
142¼	188½	Colwyn Bay	81	a						09 11	10 11	11 08	12 07
146¼	192½	Llandudno Junction	81	a						09 16	10 16	11 14	12 13
149¼	195½	Llandudno	81	a						09 26	10 30		
167½	214	Bangor (Gwynedd)	81	a								11 38	12 30
192½	238¾	Holyhead	81	a								12 23	13 13

Station		AW	AW	AW	AW	AW	AW	AW	AW	AW	AW	AW
								R		R	R	
										1		
		◇	◇	◇	◇	◇	◇		◇	B		◇
		[T]	[T]	[T]	[T]	[T]	[T]	[T]	[T]	⊠[T]	[T]	[T]
Birmingham International	d		11 08		13 08		15 08		17 08			19 04
Birmingham New Street	d		11 23		13 23		15 23		17 23			19 23
Smethwick Galton Bridge	d		11 29		13 29		15 27		17 29			19 29
Wolverhampton	d		11 42		13 42		15 42		17 42			19 42
Telford Central	d		11 58		13 59		15 58		18 01			19 59
Wellington (Shropshire)	d		12 05		14 06		16 05		18 06			20 06
Cardiff Central	d	09 21		11 21		13 21		15 21		17 16		
Newport (South Wales)	d	09 36		11 36		13 36		15 36		17 31		
Hereford	d	10 27		12 27		14 27		16 27		18 25		
Shrewsbury	a	11 19	12 18	13 19	14 19	15 19	16 19	17 19	18 20	19 08		20 19
	d	11 24	12 22	13 24	14 22	15 24	16 24	17 24	18 24	19 09	19 24	20 24
Gobowen	d	11 43	12 42	13 43	14 42	15 43	16 43	17 43	18 43		19 43	20 43
Chirk	d	11 48	12 47	13 48	14 47	15 48	16 49	17 48	18 49		19 49	20 49
Ruabon	d	11 54	12 54	13 54	14 54	15 54	16 55	17 54	18 55		19 55	20 55
Wrexham General	a	12 01	13 00	14 01	15 00	16 01	17 01	18 01	19 03	19 41	20 01	21 01
	d	12 02	13 00	14 02	15 00	16 02	17 02	18 02	19 05	19 43	20 02	21 02
Chester	a	12 19	13 19	14 19	15 20	16 20	17 21	18 20	19 21	20 01	20 21	21 19
Flint	a	12 35	13 36	14 35	15 36	16 37	17 39	18 36	19 46	20 18	20 48	
Prestatyn	a	12 49	13 50	14 49	15 50	16 51	17 53	18 50	20 00		21 02	
Rhyl	a	12 55	13 56	14 55	15 56	16 57	17 59	18 56	20 06	20 34	21 08	
Colwyn Bay	a	13 05	14 06	15 05	16 06	17 07	18 13	19 06	20 20	20 46	21 22	
Llandudno Junction	a	13 11	14 12	15 11	16 13	17 13	18 19	19 12	20 25	20 53	21 27	
Llandudno	a								20 43			
Bangor (Gwynedd)	a	13 29	14 35	15 29	16 42	17 35	18 44	19 32		21 09	21 51	
Holyhead	a	14 13	15 08	16 15	17 15	18 19	19 16	20 18		21 45	22 35	

Station			AW	AW	AW
			◇	◇	
				C	
Birmingham International	68 ✈	d		21 04	
Birmingham New Street 12	68	d		21 23	
Smethwick Galton Bridge 4	68	d		21 29	
Wolverhampton 7	74 ⛴	d		21 42	
Telford Central	74	d		21 58	
Wellington (Shropshire)	74	d		22 06	
Cardiff Central 7	131	d	19 34		
Newport (South Wales)	131	d	19 48		
Hereford	131	d	20 39		
Shrewsbury		a	21 37	22 18	
		d	21 39	22 24	23 37
Gobowen		d	21 58	22 43	23 57
Chirk		d	22 03	22 49	00 03
Ruabon		d	22 09	22 55	00 09
Wrexham General		a	22 13	23 01	00 14
		d	22 14	23 01	00 15
Chester		a	22 34	23 19	00 35
Flint	81	a	23 10		
Prestatyn	81	a	23 24		
Rhyl	81	a	23 30		
Colwyn Bay	81	a	23 44		
Llandudno Junction	81	a	23 49		
Llandudno	81	a			
Bangor (Gwynedd)	81	a	00 13		
Holyhead	81	a	00 48		

A From Shrewsbury
D To London Euston

B 1 ⊠ to Shrewsbury [T] from Shrewsbury

C To Manchester Piccadilly

For connections from London Euston please see Table 66

For connections from Manchester Piccadilly and Crewe please see Table 131

For full services between Birmingham New Street, Wolverhampton and Shrewsbury see table 74

For full details of all trains between Chester and Holyhead see Table 81

Table 75

Saturdays

14 December to 17 May

Birmingham - Shrewsbury - Chester - Holyhead

Network Diagram - see first Page of Table 74

		AW	AW	AW	AW	AW	AW	AW	AW	AW	AW	AW	AW	AW	AW	AW	AW	AW	AW	AW	AW	AW
															■			■				
					◇	◇	◇	◇	◇	◇	◇	◇	◇	◇		◇			◇	◇	◇	
		A		B																		
				🛒	🛒	🛒	🛒	🛒	🛒	🛒	🛒	🛒	🛒	🛒	🛒	🛒			🛒			
Birmingham International 68 ✈	d					07 09		09 09		11 09		13 09		15 09		17 09			19 09		21 09	
Birmingham New Street 12 68	d					07 22		09 23		11 23		13 23		15 23		17 23			19 23		21 23	
Smethwick Galton Bridge 4 68	d					07 28		09 29		11 29		13 29		15 29		17 30			19 29		21 29	
Wolverhampton 7 74	d					07 41		09 42		11 42		13 42		15 42		17 42			19 42		21 41	
Telford Central 74	d					07 57		09 58		11 58		13 59		15 59		17 58			19 59		21 58	
Wellington (Shropshire) 74	d					08 05		10 05		12 06		14 05		16 06		18 06			20 05		22 04	
Cardiff Central 7 131	d				05 20		07 21		09 21		11 21		13 21		15 21			17 21		19 34		
Newport (South Wales) 131	d				05 35		07 36		09 36		11 36		13 36		15 36			17 35		19 48		
Hereford 131	d				06 26		08 27		10 28		12 28		14 26		16 27			18 27		20 39		
Shrewsbury	a				07 22	08 20	09 19	10 19	11 20	12 19	13 20	14 18	15 18	16 19	17 19	18 19		19 19	20 19	21 35	22 21	
	d		05 20	06 10	07 24	08 21	09 24	10 23	11 24	12 22	13 24	14 22	15 24	16 22	17 24	18 22		19 24	20 24	21 37	22 23	23 33
Gobowen	d		05 39	06 30	07 43	08 40	09 43	10 42	11 43	12 42	13 43	14 41	15 43	16 42	17 43	18 42		19 43	20 43	21 56	22 42	23 52
Chirk	d	00 03	05 45	06 35	07 48	08 46	09 48	10 48	11 48	12 47	13 48	14 47	15 48	16 47	17 48	18 47		19 48	20 49	22 01	22 48	23 58
Ruabon	d	00 09	05 51	06 42	07 54	08 52	09 54	10 54	11 54	12 54	13 54	14 53	15 54	16 54	17 54	18 54		19 54	20 55	22 07	22 54	00 04
Wrexham General	a	00 14	05 57	06 48	08 00	08 59	10 01	11 00	12 01	13 00	14 01	14 59	16 01	17 00	18 01	19 01		20 01	21 01	22 13	23 00	00 10
	d	00 15	05 58	06 50	08 01	09 00	10 02	11 01	12 02	13 00	14 02	15 00	16 02	17 03	18 03	19 02	19 46	20 02	21 02	22 13	23 01	00 14
Chester	a	00 35	06 16	07 08	08 18	09 17	10 19	11 21	12 19	13 18	14 19	15 20	16 22	17 19	18 21	19 20	20 05	20 21	21 21	22 31	23 20	00 33
Flint 81	a				08 35	09 36	10 35	11 38	12 35	13 35	14 35	15 36	16 38	17 38	18 38	19 46		20 46		22 51		
Prestatyn 81	a				08 49	09 50	10 49	11 52	12 49	13 49	14 49	15 50	16 52	17 52	18 52	20 00		21 00		23 04		
Rhyl 81	a				08 55	09 56	10 55	11 58	12 55	13 55	14 55	15 56	16 58	17 58	18 58	20 06		21 06		23 10		
Colwyn Bay 81	a				09 05	10 06	11 05	12 08	13 05	14 05	15 05	16 06	17 08	18 12	19 08	20 20		21 19		23 24		
Llandudno Junction 81	a				09 11	10 12	11 11	12 14	13 11	14 11	15 11	16 12	17 14	18 17	19 14	20 25		21 24		23 38		
Llandudno 81	a																					
Bangor (Gwynedd) 81	a				09 34	10 30	11 34	12 32	13 29	14 34	15 29	16 36	17 36	18 41	19 32	20 47		21 42				
Holyhead 81	a				10 14	11 05	12 09	13 12	14 13	15 08	16 13	17 11	18 20	19 13	20 18	21 31		22 25				

Sundays

8 December to 11 May

		AW	AW	AW	AW	AW	AW	AW	AW	AW	AW
						■		■			
				◇	◇		◇		◇	◇	
			🛒		🛒		🛒	🛒	🛒	🛒	
Birmingham International 68 ✈	d			10 48	13 07		15 07		17 07	19 07	
Birmingham New Street 12 68	d			11 05	13 24		15 24		17 24	19 24	
Smethwick Galton Bridge 4 68	d										
Wolverhampton 7 74	d			11 27	13 42		15 43		17 43	19 43	
Telford Central 74	d			11 54	13 58		15 59		17 59	19 59	
Wellington (Shropshire) 74	d			12 01	14 04		16 06		18 05	20 06	
Cardiff Central 7 131	d					13 22		15 22			
Newport (South Wales) 131	d					13 36		15 36			
Hereford 131	d					14 26		16 28			
Shrewsbury	a			12 15	14 18	15 21	16 22	17 23	18 19	20 19	
	d		10 16	12 17	14 20	15 22	16 24	17 30	18 20	20 22	
Gobowen	d		10 35	12 37	14 39	15 42	16 43	17 49	18 40	20 42	
Chirk	d		10 41	12 42	14 45	15 47	16 49	17 55	18 45	20 47	
Ruabon	d		10 47	12 49	14 51	15 54	16 55	18 01	18 51	20 54	
Wrexham General	a		10 53	12 55	14 57	16 00	17 01	18 07	18 57	21 00	
	d		10 54	12 56	14 58	16 00	17 06	18 08	18 58	21 01	22 35
Chester	a		11 13	13 20	15 18	16 18	17 26	18 25	19 17	21 20	22 53
Flint 81	a					16 50		18 43	19 52		
Prestatyn 81	a					17 04		18 57	20 06		
Rhyl 81	a					17 10		19 03	20 12		
Colwyn Bay 81	a					17 24		19 17	20 26		
Llandudno Junction 81	a					17 29		19 22	20 31		
Llandudno 81	a										
Bangor (Gwynedd) 81	a					17 52		19 47	20 53		
Holyhead 81	a					18 37		20 18	21 30		

A From Shrewsbury

B To Manchester Piccadilly

C From Shrewsbury

For connections from London Euston please see Table 66

For connections from Manchester Piccadilly and Crewe please see Table 131

For full services between Birmingham New Street, Wolverhampton and Shrewsbury see table 74

For full details of all trains between Chester and Holyhead see Table 81

Table 75R

Mondays to Fridays

9 December to 16 May

Holyhead - Chester - Shrewsbury - Birmingham

Network Diagram - see first Page of Table 74

Miles	Miles				AW	AW	AW	AW	AW	AW	AW		AW	AW	AW	AW	AW	AW	AW	AW	AW		AW	AW	AW	AW
								BHX	BHX	BHX																
								[R]						[R]			[R]									
					◇	◇	◇	■1	◇	◇	◇		◇		◇	◇		◇	◇	◇	◇		◇	◇	◇	
						A	B	C	D	E							F		G							B
						⚲	⚲	☒	⚲	⚲	⚲		⚲	⚲	⚲	⚲	⚲	⚲	⚲	⚲	⚲		⚲	⚲	⚲	
0	0	**Holyhead**	81	d		04 25	05 14	05 33	05 14		06 28		07 15		08 05	09 23	10 40	11 27	12 32	13 28	14 34		15 44	16 50	17 30	
24¾	24¾	Bangor (Gwynedd)	81	d		04 57	05 43	06 01	05 43		07 06		08 02		09 02	10 02	11 07	12 00	13 07	14 07	15 04		16 23	17 18	18 09	
43¼	43¼	Llandudno	81	d										08 30												
46¼	46¼	Llandudno Junction	81	d		05 15	06 07	06 19	06 07		07 24		08 25	08 39	09 25	10 25	11 25	12 23	13 25	14 25	15 27		16 46	17 37	18 33	
50¼	50¼	Colwyn Bay	81	d		05 21	06 13	06 27	06 13		07 30		08 31	08 45	09 31	10 31	11 31	12 29	13 31	14 31	15 33			17 43		
60½	60½	Rhyl	81	d		05 31	06 23	06 38	06 23		07 40		08 41	08 56	09 41	10 41	11 41	12 40	13 41	14 41	15 44			17 53		
64	64	Prestatyn	81	d		05 37	06 29		06 29		07 46		08 47		09 47	10 47	11 47	12 45	13 47	14 47	15 49			17 59		
78	78	Flint	81	d		05 50	06 42	06 55	06 42		07 59		09 00		10 00	11 00	12 00	12 59	14 00	15 00	16 03			18 12		
90½	90½	Chester		d	05 13	06 18	07 15	07 15	07 02		08 19		09 19	09 26	10 20	11 30	12 19	13 30	14 19	15 30	16 19		17 30	18 28	19 17	20 22
102½	102½	Wrexham General		a	05 29	06 35	07 31	07 31			08 34			09 42	10 35	11 45	12 34	13 46	14 34	15 46	16 35		17 46	18 44	19 33	20 38
—	—			d	05 29	06 37	07 47	07 32		07 47	08 34			09 42	10 36	11 45	12 34	13 46	14 34	15 46	16 35		17 48	18 45	19 33	20 39
107½	107½	Ruabon		a	05 36	06 43	07 54			07 54	08 41			09 49	10 42	11 53	12 41	13 53	14 41	15 53	16 42		17 54	18 51	19 40	20 47
111¾	111¾	**Chirk**		a	05 42	06 50	08 01			08 01	08 47			09 55	10 48	11 59	12 47	13 59	14 47	15 59	16 48		18 01	18 57	19 46	20 52
114¾	114¾	Gobowen ■7		a	05 48	06 55	08 06			08 06	08 52			10 01	10 53	12 05	12 53	14 05	14 52	16 05	16 53		18 06	19 03	19 52	20 58
132¾	132¾	**Shrewsbury**		a	06 09	07 16	08 28	08 07	08 25	08 28	09 13		10 26	10 22	11 14	12 27	13 14	14 27	15 13	16 27	17 14		18 27	19 24	20 14	21 18
—	—																									
—	183½	Hereford	131	a		08 10		08 54			10 09				12 06		14 09		16 09		18 12			20 15		
—	227	Newport (South Wales)	131	a		09 00		09 41			11 01			11 53	12 56		14 53		16 59		19 00			21 15		
—	238¾	**Cardiff Central**	131	a		09 21		09 58			11 15			12 09	13 22		15 11		17 15		19 21			21 42		
143	—	Wellington (Shropshire)	74	a	06 46		08 44		08 45				10 46			12 45		14 45		16 45			18 46			
147	—	Telford Central	74	a	06 53		08 51		08 52				10 51			12 53		14 53		16 52			18 53			
171½	—	**Wolverhampton**	74	a	07 11		09 09		09 10				11 09			13 10		15 11		17 09			19 11			
180¼	—	Smethwick Galton Bridge	68 ⇜	a	07 23		09 22		09 22				11 20			13 22		15 22		17 22			19 22			
184	—	**Birmingham New Street**	68	a	07 30		09 29		09 29				11 30			13 29		15 30		17 30			19 30			
192½	—	Birmingham International	68	a	07 50		09 49		09 49				11 49			13 49		15 49		17 49			19 50			

			AW	AW	AW	AW
				MW FO	TThO	
			BHX			
				◇	◇	◇
Holyhead	81	d		19 21	19 21	
Bangor (Gwynedd)	81	d		20 00	20 00	
Llandudno	81	d				
Llandudno Junction	81	d		20 23	20 23	
Colwyn Bay	81	d		20 29	20 29	
Rhyl	81	d		20 39	20 39	
Prestatyn	81	d		20 45	20 45	
Flint	81	d		20 58	20 58	
Chester		d		21 21	21 21	22 28
Wrexham General		a		21 37	21 37	22 44
		d	20 49	21 37	21 37	22 44
Ruabon		a	20 57	21 44	21 44	22 51
Chirk		a	21 02	21 50	21 50	22 57
Gobowen ■7		a	21 08	21 55	21 55	23 02
Shrewsbury		a	21 28	22 16	22 16	23 23
Hereford	131	a				
Newport (South Wales)	131	a				
Cardiff Central	131	a				
Wellington (Shropshire)	74	a		22 31	22 31	23 39
Telford Central	74	a		22 37	22 37	23 47
Wolverhampton	74	a		22 55	22 55	00 17
Smethwick Galton Bridge	68 ⇜	a				
Birmingham New Street	68	a		23 27	23 28	
Birmingham International	68	a				

A ⚲ from Chester
B 21 April, 5 May
C ■1 to Chester
D not 21 April, 5 May
E not 21 April, 5 May. ⚲ from Shrewsbury
F To Llanelli
G To Maesteg

For connections to Crewe and Manchester Piccadilly please see Table 131

For connections to London Euston please see Table 66

For full services between Birmingham New Street, Wolverhampton and Shrewsbury see table 74

For full details of all trains between Chester and Holyhead see Table 81

Table 75R

Saturdays

14 December to 17 May

Holyhead - Chester - Shrewsbury - Birmingham

Network Diagram - see first Page of Table 74

			AW	AW	AW	AW	AW	AW	AW	AW	AW	AW	AW	AW	AW	AW	AW	AW	AW
									R										
			◇	◇	◇	◇	◇	◇		◇	◇	◇	◇	◇	◇	◇		◇	◇
											A								
			trolley	trolley	trolley	trolley	trolley	trolley	trolley	trolley	trolley	trolley	trolley	trolley	trolley	trolley			
Holyhead	81	d	04 25	05 22	06 35	07 15	08 20	09 23	10 33	11 23	12 38	13 28	14 23	15 23	16 50	17 30		19 21	
Bangor (Gwynedd)	81	d	04 57	06 01	07 07	08 02	09 02	10 02	11 05	12 02	13 07	14 07	14 53	16 02	17 18	18 09		20 00	
Llandudno	81	d																	
Llandudno Junction	81	d	05 15	06 24	07 25	08 25	09 25	10 25	11 25	12 25	13 25	14 25	15 16	16 25	17 36	18 32		20 23	
Colwyn Bay	81	d	05 21	06 30	07 31	08 31	09 31	10 31	11 31	12 31	13 31	14 31	15 22	16 31	17 42	18 38		20 29	
Rhyl	81	d	05 31	06 40	07 41	08 41	09 41	10 41	11 41	12 41	13 41	14 41	15 33	16 41	17 52	18 48		20 39	
Prestatyn	81	d	05 37	06 46	07 47	08 47	09 47	10 47	11 47	12 47	13 47	14 47	15 38	16 47	17 58	18 54		20 45	
Flint	81	d	05 50	06 59	08 00	09 00	10 00	11 00	12 00	13 00	14 00	15 00	15 52	17 00	18 11	19 07		20 58	
Chester		d	06 12	07 21	08 19	09 20	10 19	11 30	12 19	13 30	14 19	15 30	16 19	17 28	18 29	19 28	20 27	21 20	22 28
Wrexham General		a	06 35	07 37	08 34	09 36	10 34	11 46	12 34	13 46	14 34	15 46	16 35	17 44	18 45	19 44	20 43	21 36	22 44
		d	06 38	07 37	08 34	09 36	10 35	11 46	12 34	13 46	14 34	15 46	16 35	17 44	18 45	19 44	20 43	21 37	22 44
Ruabon		a	06 44	07 44	08 41	09 43	10 42	11 53	12 41	13 53	14 41	15 53	16 42	17 51	18 52	19 51	20 50	21 43	22 51
Chirk		a	06 51	07 50	08 47	09 49	10 48	11 59	12 47	13 59	14 47	15 59	16 48	17 57	18 58	19 57	20 56	21 50	22 57
Gobowen 7		a	06 56	07 56	08 52	09 55	10 53	12 05	12 52	14 05	14 52	16 05	16 53	18 03	19 03	20 02	21 02	21 56	23 02
Shrewsbury		a	07 17	08 20	09 13	10 29	11 14	12 27	13 13	14 28	15 13	16 27	17 14	18 24	19 24	20 26	21 22	22 17	23 23
Hereford	131	a	08 11		10 05		12 04		14 09		16 03		18 05		20 15				
Newport (South Wales)	131	a	09 01		10 55		12 54		15 04		16 54		18 55		21 14				
Cardiff Central	131	a	09 22		11 14		13 15		15 24		17 08		19 15		21 43				
Wellington (Shropshire)	74	a		08 46		10 46		12 45		14 45		16 45		18 46				22 44	23 39
Telford Central	74	a		08 53		10 53		12 53		14 53		16 51		18 53				22 50	23 47
Wolverhampton	74	a		09 11		11 11		13 10		15 11		17 07		19 11				23 07	00 16
Smethwick Galton Bridge	68 ⇌	a		09 23		11 22		13 22		15 22		17 20		19 22					
Birmingham New Street	68	a		09 27		11 28		13 28		15 28		17 26		19 28				23 29	
Birmingham International	68	a		09 49		11 50		13 50		15 49		17 49		19 50					

Sundays

8 December to 11 May

			AW	AW	AW	AW	AW	AW	AW	AW	AW	AW	AW	AW
										R				
				◇	◇	◇	◇	◇	◇			◇		
					trolley	trolley		trolley		trolley				
Holyhead	81	d				10 20				16 25				
Bangor (Gwynedd)	81	d				10 59				17 04				
Llandudno	81	d												
Llandudno Junction	81	d				11 22				17 25				
Colwyn Bay	81	d				11 28				17 31				
Rhyl	81	d				11 41				17 44				
Prestatyn	81	d				11 46				17 49				
Flint	81	d				12 00				18 03				
Chester		d	08 08	09 22	11 31	12 21	13 31	15 31	17 31	18 24	19 26	21 26	22 04	23 00
Wrexham General		a	08 26	09 38	11 47	12 38	13 47	15 47	17 47	18 40	19 42	21 42	22 22	
		d		09 38	11 48	12 38	13 48	15 48	17 48	18 41	19 42	21 44		
Ruabon		a		09 45	11 54	12 45	13 54	15 54	17 54	18 47	19 49	21 50		
Chirk		a		09 51	12 01	12 51	14 01	16 01	18 01	18 53	19 55	21 57		
Gobowen 7		a		09 57	12 06	12 57	14 06	16 06	18 06	18 59	20 00	22 02		
Shrewsbury		a		10 18	12 27	13 18	14 27	16 27	18 27	19 20	20 21	22 22		00 14
Hereford	131	a				14 17				20 18				
Newport (South Wales)	131	a				15 07				21 14				
Cardiff Central	131	a				15 31				21 36				
Wellington (Shropshire)	74	a		10 34	12 45		14 45	16 53	18 45		20 36	22 37		
Telford Central	74	a		10 40	12 51		14 51	16 59	18 51		20 44	22 45		
Wolverhampton	74	a		10 56	13 07		15 07	17 15	19 07		21 11	23 14		
Smethwick Galton Bridge	68 ⇌	a												
Birmingham New Street	68	a		11 13	13 23		15 24	17 35	19 25		21 29			
Birmingham International	68	a		11 31	13 55		15 58	17 56	19 55		21 56			

A To Maesteg

For connections to Crewe and Manchester Piccadilly please see Table 131

For connections to London Euston please see Table 66

For full services between Birmingham New Street, Wolverhampton and Shrewsbury see table 74

For full details of all trains between Chester and Holyhead see Table 81

Table 76

Mondays to Fridays

9 December to 16 May

Birmingham - Shrewsbury - Aberystwyth, Barmouth and Pwllheli

Network Diagram - see first Page of Table 74

Miles	Miles			AW	AW	AW	AW	AW	AW	AW	AW			AW		AW		AW		AW FX	AW FO		AW		AW
								BHX			A			A		A		A		■	■		A		
					◇		◇		◇	◇	◇			◇		◇		◇					◇		◇
									🚲		🚲			🚲		🚲		🚲		🚲	🚲		🚲		
—	—	Birmingham International 68 ✈	d								08 08			10 08		12 08		14 08		16 09	16 09		18 09		20 04
0	—	**Birmingham New Street** [12] 68	d						06 25		08 23			10 23		12 23		14 23		16 23	16 23		18 23		20 23
4	—	Smethwick Galton Bridge [4] 68	d						06 30		08 29			10 29		12 29		14 29		16 29	16 29		18 29		20 29
12¾	—	**Wolverhampton** [7] 74	d						06 43		08 42			10 43		12 42		14 42		16 43	16 43		18 42		20 42
28¼	—	Telford Central 74	d						06 59		08 59			10 59		12 58		14 59		16 59	16 59		18 59		20 58
32¼	—	Wellington (Shropshire) 74	d						07 06		09 06			11 06		13 06		15 06		17 06	17 06		19 06		21 05
42¾	—	**Shrewsbury**	a						07 18		09 19			11 19		13 19		15 19		17 19	17 19		19 19		21 18
—	—		d						07 27		09 27			11 27		13 27		15 27		17 27	17 27		19 30		21 42
62½	—	Welshpool	d						07 49		09 49			11 49		13 49		15 49		17 49	17 49		19 52		22 04
76½	—	Newtown (Powys)	d						08 04		10 04			12 04		14 04		16 04		18 04	18 04		20 07		22 20
82	—	Caersws	d						08 13		10 13			12 13		14 13		16 13		18 13	18 13		20 16		22 29
103¾	0	**Machynlleth** [4]	a						08 46		10 46			12 46		14 46		16 46		18 46	18 46		20 47		23 00
—	—																								23 07
—	—		d	04 35	05 07	06 35	06 47	08 07	08 48	08 57	10 51	10 55		12 51	12 55	14 51	14 56	16 51	17 05	18 48	18 51	18 59	20 49	21 20	23 14
107¾	4	Dovey Junction [4]	d	04 42	05 14	06 42	06 54	08 14	08 55	09 04	10 58	11 02		12 58	13 02	14 58	15 03	16 58	17 12	18 55	18 58	19 06	20 56	21 27	23 25
116	—	Borth	d	04 53		06 53		08 25	09 06		11 09			13 09		15 09		17 09		19 06	19 09		21 07		23 44
124¼	—	**Aberystwyth**	a	05 12		07 10		08 44	09 25		11 25			13 25		15 25		17 25		19 25	19 25		21 25		20 04
—	9	Penhelig	d		05x22		07x02			09x12		11x10			13x10		15x11		17x20			19x14		21x35	
—	10	Aberdovey	d		05 27		07 06			09 16		11 15			13 14		15 15		17 24			19 19		21 39	
—	13½	Tywyn	a		05 33		07 16			09 26		11 24			13 24		15 25		17 34			19 28		21 49	
—	—		d		05 34		07 16			09 29		11 32			13 24		15 25		17 35			19 30		21 49	
—	16	Tonfanau	d		05x37		07x20			09x33		11x35			13x28		15x29		17x38			19x33		21x53	
—	20	Llwyngwril	d		05x44		07x26			09x39		11x42			13x34		15x35		17x45			19x40		21x59	
—	22¾	Fairbourne	d		05 52		07 34			09 47		11 50			13 42		15 43		17 53			19 48		22 07	
—	23¾	Morfa Mawddach	d		05x53		07x36			09x49		11x52			13x44		15x45		17x54			19x49		22x09	
—	25½	**Barmouth**	a		06 03		07 45			09 58		12 01			13 53		15 54		18 04			20 03		22 18	
—	—		d		06 09		07 47			10 01		12 02			13 56		15 57		18 05					22 21	
—	26¾	Llanaber	d		06x12		07x49			10x03		12x05			13x58		16x00		18x09					22x23	
—	29¼	Talybont	d				07x53			10x07		12x09			14x02		16x03		18x12					22x27	
—	30¼	Dyffryn Ardudwy	d				07x56			10x10		12x12			14x05		16x06		18x15					22x30	
—	32½	Llanbedr	d				08x00			10x14		12x16			14x09		16x10		18x19					22x34	
—	33¼	Pensarn	d				08x02			10x16		12x18			14x11		16x12		18x21					22x36	
—	34	Llandanwg	d				08x04			10x18		12x20			14x13		16x14		18x23					22x38	
—	35¾	Harlech	a		06 27		08 10			10 25		12 26			14 20		16 21		18 29					22 45	
—	—		d		06 27		08 25			10 25		12 27			14 31		16 29		18 33					22 45	
—	38½	Tygwyn	d				08x29			10x29		12x30			14x35		16x32		18x36					22x49	
—	39¼	Talsarnau	d				08x31			10x31		12x33			14x37		16x35		18x39					22x51	
—	40½	Llandecwyn	d				08x34			10x34		12x36			14x40		16x38		18x42					22x54	
—	41¼	Penrhyndeudraeth	d				08 38			10 38		12 40			14 44		16 42		18 46					22 58	
—	42½	Minffordd	d		06 44		08 42			10 42		12 43			14 48		16 45		18 49					23 02	
—	44½	Porthmadog	a		06 48		08 49			10 49		12 51			14 55		16 52		18 56					23 09	
—	—		d		06 52		08 50			10 50		12 51			14 56		16 53		18 57					23 10	
—	49½	Criccieth	d		06 59		08 57			10 57		12 59			15 03		17 00		19 04					23 17	
—	54	Penychain	d		07x05		09x02			11x02		13x04			15x08		17x05		19x09					23x22	
—	55½	Abererch	d				09x05			11x05		13x07			15x11		17x08		19x12					23x25	
—	57½	**Pwllheli**	a		07 14		09 12			11 12		13 13			15 20		17 17		19 21					23 32	

A 🚲 to Aberystwyth

For connections from London Euston please see Table 66

For connections from Manchester Piccadilly and Crewe please see Table 131

For full services between Birmingham New Street, Wolverhampton and Shrewsbury see table 74

Table 76

Saturdays

14 December to 17 May

Birmingham - Shrewsbury - Aberystwyth, Barmouth and Pwllheli

Network Diagram - see first Page of Table 74

		AW	AW ◇	AW	AW ◇	AW ◇ 🛒	AW ◇	AW A ◇ 🛒		AW ◇ 🛒		AW A ◇ 🛒		AW A ◇ 🛒		AW ■ 🛒	AW A ◇ 🛒		AW ◇
Birmingham International 68 ✈	d							08 09		10 09		12 09		14 09		16 09	18 09		20 09
Birmingham New Street 12 68	d					06 23		08 23		10 23		12 23		14 23		16 23	18 23		20 23
Smethwick Galton Bridge 4 68	d					06 29		08 29		10 30		12 29		14 29		16 29	18 29		20 29
Wolverhampton 7 74 ⛴	d					06 42		08 42		10 43		12 42		14 42		16 42	18 42		20 42
Telford Central 74	d					06 59		08 59		10 59		12 59		14 58		16 58	18 58		20 58
Wellington (Shropshire) 74	d					07 05		09 05		11 06		13 07		15 06		17 05	19 05		21 05
Shrewsbury	a					07 18		09 20		11 20		13 23		15 19		17 19	19 19		21 19
	d					07 27		09 27		11 27		13 27		15 27		17 27	19 30		21 42
Welshpool	d					07 49		09 49		11 49		13 49		15 49		17 49	19 52		22 04
Newtown (Powys)	d					08 04		10 04		12 04		14 04		16 04		18 04	20 07		22 20
Caersws	d					08 13		10 13		12 13		14 13		16 13		18 13	20 16		22 29
Machynlleth 4	a					08 47		10 46		12 46		14 49		16 46		18 46	20 47		22 59
	d	04 35	05 07	06 35	06 47	08 48	08 57	10 51	10 55	12 51	12 55	14 54	14 56	16 51	16 58	18 48	20 49	21 18	23 04
Dovey Junction 4	d	04 42	05 14	06 42	06 54	08 55	09 04	10 58	11 02	12 58	13 02	15 01	15 03	16 58	17 05	18 55	20 56	21 25	23 11
Borth	d	04 53		06 53		09 06		11 09		13 09		15 12		17 09		19 06	21 07		23 22
Aberystwyth	a	05 12		07 10		09 25		11 25		13 25		15 28		17 25		19 25	21 25		23 41
Penhelig	d		05x22		07x02		09x12		11x10		13x10		15x11		17x13			21x33	
Aberdovey	d		05 27		07 06		09 16		11 15		13 14		15 15		17 17			21 37	
Tywyn	a		05 33		07 16		09 26		11 24		13 24		15 24		17 27			21 47	
	d		05 34		07 16		09 29		11 24		13 24		15 25		17 30			21 50	
Tonfanau	d		05x37		07x20		09x33		11x28		13x28		15x28		17x33			21x54	
Llwyngwril	d		05x44		07x26		09x39		11x34		13x34		15x35		17x40			22x00	
Fairbourne	d		05 52		07 34		09 47		11 43		13 42		15 43		17 48			22 08	
Morfa Mawddach	d		05x53		07x36		09x49		11x44		13x44		15x44		17x49			22x10	
Barmouth	a		06 04		07 45		09 58		11 53		13 53		15 54		17 59			22 19	
	d		06 09		07 47		10 01		11 56		13 56		15 57		18 01			22 22	
Llanaber	d		06x12		07x49		10x03		11x58		13x58		16x00		18x05			22x24	
Talybont	d				07x53		10x07		12x02		14x02		16x03		18x08			22x28	
Dyffryn Ardudwy	d				07x56		10x10		12x05		14x05		16x06		18x11			22x31	
Llanbedr	d				08x00		10x14		12x09		14x09		16x10		18x15			22x35	
Pensarn	d				08x02		10x16		12x11		14x11		16x12		18x17			22x37	
Llandanwg	d				08x04		10x18		12x13		14x13		16x14		18x19			22x39	
Harlech	a		06 27		08 10		10 25		12 20		14 20		16 21		18 25			22 46	
	d		06 27		08 25		10 25		12 22		14 31		16 27		18 33			22 46	
Tygwyn	d				08x29		10x29		12x25		14x35		16x30		18x36			22x50	
Talsarnau	d				08x31		10x31		12x28		14x37		16x33		18x39			22x52	
Llandecwyn	d				08x34		10x34		12x31		14x40		16x36		18x42			22x55	
Penrhyndeudraeth	d				08 38		10 38		12 35		14 44		16 40		18 46			22 59	
Minffordd	d		06 44		08 42		10 42		12 38		14 48		16 43		18 49			23 03	
Porthmadog	a		06 48		08 49		10 49		12 46		14 55		16 50		18 56			23 10	
	d		06 52		08 50		10 50		12 46		14 56		16 51		18 57			23 11	
Criccieth	d		06 59		08 57		10 57		12 54		15 03		16 58		19 04			23 18	
Penychain	d		07x05		09x02		11x02		12x59		15x08		17x03		19x09			23x23	
Abererch	d				09x05		11x05		13x02		15x11		17x06		19x12			23x26	
Pwllheli	a		07 14		09 12		11 12		13 11		15 20		17 15		19 21			23 33	

A 🛒 to Aberystwyth

For connections from London Euston please see Table 66

For connections from Manchester Piccadilly and Crewe please see Table 131

For full services between Birmingham New Street, Wolverhampton and Shrewsbury see table 74

Table 76

Sundays

8 December to 11 May

Birmingham - Shrewsbury - Aberystwyth, Barmouth and Pwllheli

Network Diagram - see first Page of Table 74

		AW	AW	AW	AW	AW	AW		AW	AW
				◇	◇	◇	◇		◇	◇
					🍴	🍴	🍴		🍴	
							A			
Birmingham International 68 ✈	d				12 08	14 07	16 07		18 07	20 07
Birmingham New Street 12 68	d				12 24	14 24	16 24		18 24	20 24
Smethwick Galton Bridge 4 68	d									
Wolverhampton 7 74	d				12 42	14 43	16 43		18 43	20 43
Telford Central 74	d				12 59	14 59	16 59		18 59	20 59
Wellington (Shropshire) 74	d				13 05	15 06	17 06		19 06	21 06
Shrewsbury	a				13 18	15 19	17 19		19 19	21 19
	d			11 26	13 27	15 27	17 27		19 27	21 30
Welshpool	d			11 49	13 49	15 49	17 49		19 49	21 52
Newtown (Powys)	d			12 05	14 04	16 04	18 04		20 04	22 07
Caersws	d			12 14	14 13	16 13	18 13		20 13	22 16
Machynlleth 4	a			12 46	14 46	16 46	18 46		20 46	22 47
	d	08 50	10 50	12 48	14 48	16 48	18 51	18 55	20 48	22 49
Dovey Junction 4	d	08 57	10 57	12 55	14 55	16 55	18 58	19 02	20 55	22 56
Borth	d	09 08	11 08	13 06	15 06	17 06	19 09		21 06	23 07
Aberystwyth	a	09 25	11 25	13 25	15 25	17 25	19 25		21 25	23 26
Penhelig	d							19x10		
Aberdovey	d							19 14		
Tywyn	a							19 20		
	d							19 21		
Tonfanau	d							19x24		
Llwyngwril	d							19x31		
Fairbourne	d							19 39		
Morfa Mawddach	d							19x41		
Barmouth	a							19 48		
	d							19 49		
Llanaber	d							19x53		
Talybont	d							19x56		
Dyffryn Ardudwy	d							20x00		
Llanbedr	d							20x04		
Pensarn	d							20x07		
Llandanwg	d							20x09		
Harlech	a							20 15		
	d							20 18		
Tygwyn	d							20x21		
Talsarnau	d							20x24		
Llandecwyn	d							20x27		
Penrhyndeudraeth	d							20 31		
Minffordd	d							20 35		
Porthmadog	a							20 40		
	d							20 41		
Criccieth	d							20 48		
Penychain	d							20x53		
Abererch	d							20x57		
Pwllheli	a							21 07		

A 🍴 to Aberystwyth

For connections from London Euston please see Table 66

For connections from Manchester Piccadilly and Crewe please see Table 131

For full services between Birmingham New Street, Wolverhampton and Shrewsbury see table 74

Table 76R

Mondays to Fridays

9 December to 16 May

Pwllheli - Barmouth, Aberystwyth - Shrewsbury - Birmingham

Network Diagram - see first Page of Table 74

Miles	Miles	Miles			AW MX	AW	AW	AW	AW	AW	AW	AW	AW	AW	AW	AW	AW	AW	AW	AW	AW	AW	AW	AW FO	AW
						◇	◇	◇	◇	◇	◇	◇	◇	◇	◇	◇	◇	◇	◇	◇	◇		◇		
					A		B			B		B		B		B									
						🍴	🍴	🍴		🍴	🍴	🍴	🍴	🍴	🍴	🍴	🍴		🍴						
—	0	—	**Pwllheli**	d					06 29	07 24		09 34		11 37		13 38		15 37		17 45			20 05		
—	1¾	—	Abererch	d					06x32	07x27		09x37		11x40		13x41		15x40		17x48			20x08		
—	3¼	—	Penychain	d					06x35	07x30		09x40		11x43		13x44		15x43		17x51			20x11		
—	7¾	—	Criccieth	d					06 43	07 38		09 48		11 51		13 52		15 51		17 59			20 19		
—	12¾	—	Porthmadog	a					06 51	07 45		09 56		11 59		14 00		15 59		18 07			20 27		
—	—	—		d					06 53	07 47		09 58		12 01		14 02		16 01		18 09			20 29		
—	15	—	Minffordd	d					06 57	07 51		10 02		12 05		14 06		16 05		18 13			20 33		
—	16¼	—	Penrhyndeudraeth	d					07 01	07 55		10 06		12 09		14 10		16 09		18 17			20 37		
—	17	—	Llandecwyn	d					07x03	07x57		10x08		12x11		14x12		16x11		18x19			20x39		
—	18¼	—	Talsarnau	d					07x05	08x00		10x10		12x13		14x14		16x13		18x21			20x41		
—	19	—	Tygwyn	d					07x08	08x02		10x13		12x16		14x17		16x16		18x24			20x44		
—	21½	—	Harlech	a					07 15	08 08		10 21		12 23		14 24		16 23		18 30			20 51		
—	—	—		d					07 17	08 21		10 25		12 27		14 28		16 29		18 33			20 53		
—	23½	—	Llandanwg	d					07x21	08x25		10x29		12x31		14x32		16x34		18x38			20x57		
—	24¼	—	Pensarn	d					07x23	08x26		10x31		12x33		14x34		16x35		18x40			20x59		
—	30½	—	Llanbedr	d					07x25	08x29		10x33		12x35		14x36		16x37		18x41			21x01		
—	27	—	Dyffryn Ardudwy	d					07x29	08x33		10x37		12x39		14x40		16x41		18x45			21x05		
—	28¼	—	Talybont	d					07x32	08x36		10x40		12x42		14x43		16x44		18x48			21x08		
—	25	—	Llanaber	d					07x37	08x40		10x45		12x47		14x48		16x49		18x53			21x13		
—	32	—	**Barmouth**	a					07 41	08 45		10 49		12 51		14 52		16 53		18 57			21 18		
—	—	—		d			06 46		07 47	08 52		11 03		12 54		14 55		16 56		19 00			21 20		
—	33¾	—	Morfa Mawddach	d			06x50		07x51	08x56		11x07		12x58		14x59		17x00		19x04			21x24	22 22	
—	34¾	—	Fairbourne	d			06 54		07 55	09 00		11 11		13 02		15 03		17 04		19 08			21 28	22x27	
—	37¼	—	Llwyngwril	d			07x00		08x01	09x06		11x17		13x08		15x09		17x10		19x14			21x34	22 30	
—	41½	—	Tonfanau	d			07x07		08x09	09x13		11x24		13x15		15x16		17x17		19x21			21x41	22x37	
—	44¼	—	Tywyn	a			07 13		08 12	09 19		11 30		13 21		15 23		17 23		19 27			21 48	22x44	
—	—	—		d			07 17		08 16	09 27		11 32		13 25		15 26		17 35		19 29			21 50	22 47	
—	47½	—	Aberdovey	d			07 23		08 22	09 33		11 38		13 31		15 32		17 41		19 35			21 56	22 49	
—	48½	—	Penhelig	d			07x25		08x24	09x35		11x40		13x33		15x35		17x43		19x37			21x59	22 55	
0	—	—	**Aberystwyth**	d		05 14		07 30			09 30		11 30		13 30		15 30		17 30		19 30	21 36			23 53
8¼	—	—	Borth	d	00 06	05 27		07 43			09 43		11 43		13 43		15 43		17 43		19 43	21 49			00 06
16½	53½	—	Dovey Junction 4	d	00 17	05 38	07 38	07 54	08 37	09 47	09 54	11 53	11 56	13 46	13 54	15 46	15 54	17 56	17 59	19 50	19 54	22 00	22 11	23 14	00 17
20½	57½	—	**Machynlleth 4**	a	00 24	05 45	07 46	08 02	08 47	09 55	10 02	12 00	12 02	13 53	14 02	15 54	16 02	18 03	18 06	20 00	20 03	22 07	22 22	23 21	00 24
—	—	—																							
—	—	—		d		05 47	08 07			10 07		12 07		14 07		16 07			18 08		20 07				
42¼	—	—	Caersws	d		06 13	08 33			10 33		12 33		14 33		16 33			18 33		20 36				
47¾	—	—	Newtown (Powys)	d		06 25	08 46			10 46		12 46		14 46		16 46			18 46		20 48				
61¾	—	—	Welshpool	d		06 41	09 01			11 01		13 01		15 01		17 01			19 01		21 04				
81½	—	—	**Shrewsbury**	a		07 11	09 26			11 26		13 26		15 26		17 27			19 26		21 28				
—	—	—		d		07 33	09 33			11 33		13 33		15 33		17 33			19 33		21 33				
92	—	10¼	Wellington (Shropshire) 74	d		07 46	09 46			11 46		13 46		15 46		17 46			19 46		21 46				
96	—	14½	Telford Central 74	d		07 53	09 53			11 53		13 53		15 53		17 53			19 53		21 53				
112	—	30	**Wolverhampton 7** 74 ⛴	a		08 11	10 10			12 11		14 09		16 11		18 11			20 11		22 09				
120¾	—	38¾	Smethwick Galton Bridge 68	a		08 22	10 21			12 22		14 22		16 22		18 22			20 22		22 20				
124¾	—	42½	**Birmingham New Street 12** 68	a		08 29	10 30			12 30		14 30		16 30		18 30			20 29		22 33				
—	—	—	Birmingham International 68 ✈	a		08 50	10 49			12 49		14 49		16 49		18 49			20 49						

A 🍴 From Aberystwyth

B 🍴 from Machynlleth

For connections to Crewe and Manchester Piccadilly please see Table 131

For connections to London Euston please see Table 66

For full services between Birmingham New Street, Wolverhampton and Shrewsbury see table 74

Table 76R

Saturdays

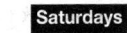

14 December to 17 May

Pwllheli - Barmouth, Aberystwyth - Shrewsbury - Birmingham

Network Diagram - see first Page of Table 74

		AW	AW	AW	AW	AW	AW	AW		AW	AW	AW	AW	AW	AW	AW	AW	AW		AW	AW	AW	AW
			◇	◇	◇	◇	◇	◇		◇	◇	◇	◇	◇	◇	◇	◇	◇		◇		◇	
		A		B			B			B		B		B									
			🚲	🚲	🚲		🚲	🚲		🚲	🚲	🚲	🚲	🚲	🚲		🚲						
Pwllheli	d					06 29	07 24			09 34		11 30		13 38		15 37		17 45				20 05	
Abererch	d					06x32	07x27			09x37		11x33		13x41		15x40		17x48				20x08	
Penychain	d					06x35	07x30			09x40		11x36		13x44		15x43		17x51				20x11	
Criccieth	d					06 43	07 38			09 48		11 44		13 52		15 51		17 59				20 19	
Porthmadog	a					06 51	07 45			09 56		11 52		14 00		15 59		18 07				20 27	
	d					06 53	07 47			09 58		11 54		14 02		16 01		18 08				20 29	
Minffordd	d					06 57	07 51			10 02		11 58		14 06		16 05		18 13				20 33	
Penrhyndeudraeth	d					07 01	07 55			10 06		12 02		14 10		16 09		18 16				20 37	
Llandecwyn	d					07x03	07x57			10x08		12x04		14x12		16x11		18x18				20x39	
Talsarnau	d					07x05	08x00			10x10		12x06		14x14		16x13		18x21				20x41	
Tygwyn	d					07x08	08x02			10x13		12x09		14x17		16x16		18x23				20x44	
Harlech	a					07 16	08 10			10 21		12 15		14 24		16 23		18 29				20 51	
	d					07 17	08 21			10 25		12 22		14 28		16 29		18 35				20 53	
Llandanwg	d					07x21	08x25			10x29		12x26		14x32		16x34		18x40				20x58	
Pensarn	d					07x23	08x26			10x31		12x28		14x34		16x35		18x41				21x00	
Llanbedr	d					07x25	08x29			10x33		12x30		14x36		16x37		18x43				21x01	
Dyffryn Ardudwy	d					07x29	08x33			10x37		12x34		14x40		16x41		18x47				21x05	
Talybont	d					07x32	08x36			10x40		12x37		14x43		16x44		18x50				21x08	
Llanaber	d					07x37	08x40			10x45		12x42		14x48		16x49		18x54				21x13	
Barmouth	a					07 41	08 45			10 49		12 46		14 52		16 53		18 59				21 18	
	d			06 46		07 47	08 52			10 52		12 50		14 55		16 56		19 01				21 20	
Morfa Mawddach	d			06x50		07x51	08x56			10x56		12x54		14x59		17x00		19x05				21x24	
Fairbourne	d			06 54		07 55	09 00			11 00		12 58		15 03		17 04		19 09				21 28	
Llwyngwril	d			07x00		08x01	09x06			11x06		13x04		15x09		17x10		19x15				21x34	
Tonfanau	d			07x07		08x08	09x13			11x13		13x11		15x16		17x17		19x22				21x41	
Tywyn	a			07 13		08 12	09 19			11 19		13 17		15 23		17 23		19 29				21 48	
	d			07 17		08 16	09 27			11 24		13 25		15 26		17 28		19 30				21 50	
Aberdovey	d			07 23		08 22	09 33			11 30		13 31		15 32		17 34		19 36				21 56	
Penhelig	d			07x25		08x24	09x35			11x32		13x33		15x34		17x36		19x39				21x59	
Aberystwyth	d		05 14		07 30			09 30			11 30		13 30		15 30		17 30			19 30	21 36		23 46
Borth	d	00 06	05 27		07 43			09 43			11 43		13 43		15 43		17 43			19 43	21 49		23 59
Dovey Junction 4	d	00 17	05 38	07 38	07 54	08 37	09 47	09 54		11 45	11 54	13 46	13 54	15 46	15 54	17 49	17 54	19 51		19 54	22 00	22 11	00 10
Machynlleth 4	a	00 24	05 45	07 46	08 02	08 47	09 55	10 02		11 55	12 02	13 55	14 02	15 54	16 02	17 59	18 03	20 02		20 03	22 07	22 22	00 17
	d		05 47	08 07			10 07			12 07		14 07		16 07			18 07			20 07			
Caersws	d		06 13	08 34			10 34			12 34		14 34		16 34			18 34			20 36			
Newtown (Powys)	d		06 25	08 46			10 46			12 46		14 46		16 46			18 46			20 48			
Welshpool	d		06 41	09 02			11 02			13 02		15 02		17 02			19 02			21 04			
Shrewsbury	a		07 11	09 26			11 26			13 26		15 26		17 26			19 26			21 28			
	d		07 31	09 33			11 33			13 33		15 33		17 33			19 33			21 33			
Wellington (Shropshire) 74	d		07 44	09 46			11 46			13 46		15 46		17 46			19 46			21 46			
Telford Central 74	d		07 51	09 53			11 53			13 53		15 53		17 53			19 53			21 53			
Wolverhampton 7 74 🚌	a		08 08	10 11			12 11			14 11		16 11		18 11			20 10			22 08			
Smethwick Galton Bridge 68	a		08 20	10 22			12 22			14 22		16 22		18 22			20 21			22 19			
Birmingham New Street 12 68	a		08 26	10 28			12 28			14 28		16 28		18 28			20 26			22 32			
Birmingham International 68 ✈	a		08 50	10 50			12 50			14 50		16 50		18 50			20 50						

A From Aberystwyth

B 🚲 from Machynlleth

For connections to Crewe and Manchester Piccadilly please see Table 131

For connections to London Euston please see Table 66

For full services between Birmingham New Street, Wolverhampton and Shrewsbury see table 74

Table 76R

Sundays

8 December to 11 May

Pwllheli - Barmouth, Aberystwyth - Shrewsbury - Birmingham

Network Diagram - see first Page of Table 74

		AW	AW	AW	AW	AW	AW	AW	AW	AW	AW
			◇	◇	◇	◇	◇	◇	◇		
						A					
			(trolley)	(trolley)	(trolley)	(trolley)	(trolley)	(trolley)			
Pwllheli	d					13 48					
Abererch	d					13x51					
Penychain	d					13x54					
Criccieth	d					14 02					
Porthmadog	a					14 10					
	d					14 12					
Minffordd	d					14 16					
Penrhyndeudraeth	d					14 20					
Llandecwyn	d					14x22					
Talsarnau	d					14x24					
Tygwyn	d					14x27					
Harlech	a					14 32					
	d					14 34					
Llandanwg	d					14x38					
Pensarn	d					14x40					
Llanbedr	d					14x42					
Dyffryn Ardudwy	d					14x46					
Talybont	d					14x49					
Llanaber	d					14x54					
Barmouth	a					14 59					
	d					15 01					
Morfa Mawddach	d					15x05					
Fairbourne	d					15 09					
Llwyngwril	d					15x15					
Tonfanau	d					15x22					
Tywyn	a					15 27					
	d					15 28					
Aberdovey	d					15 35					
Penhelig	d					15x37					
Aberystwyth	d		09 30	11 30	13 30		15 30	17 30	19 30	21 30	23 30
Borth	d		09 43	11 43	13 43		15 43	17 43	19 43	21 43	23 43
Dovey Junction 4	d	00 10	09 54	11 54	13 54	15 49	15 54	17 54	19 54	21 54	23 54
Machynlleth 4	a	00 17	10 03	12 03	14 03	15 59	16 02	18 03	20 03	22 01	00 01
	d		10 07	12 07	14 07	16 07		18 07	20 07		
Caersws	d		10 33	12 33	14 33	16 33		18 33	20 33		
Newtown (Powys)	d		10 45	12 45	14 45	16 45		18 45	20 46		
Welshpool	d		11 01	13 01	15 01	17 01		19 01	21 01		
Shrewsbury	a		11 25	13 25	15 26	17 27		19 25	21 25		
	d		11 40	13 31	15 33	17 33		19 31	21 31		
Wellington (Shropshire) 74	d		11 54	13 45	15 47	17 47		19 45	21 45		
Telford Central 74	d		12 00	13 51	15 53	17 53		19 51	21 51		
Wolverhampton 7 74	a		12 16	14 07	16 09	18 09		20 07	22 07		
Smethwick Galton Bridge 68	a										
Birmingham New Street 12 68	a		12 32	14 23	16 24	18 27		20 23	22 28		
Birmingham International 68	a		12 56	14 55	16 55	18 55		20 58	22 58		

A (trolley) from Machynlleth

For connections to Crewe and Manchester Piccadilly please see Table 131

For connections to London Euston please see Table 66

For full services between Birmingham New Street, Wolverhampton and Shrewsbury see table 74

Network Diagram for Tables 78, 79, 84, 85, 86

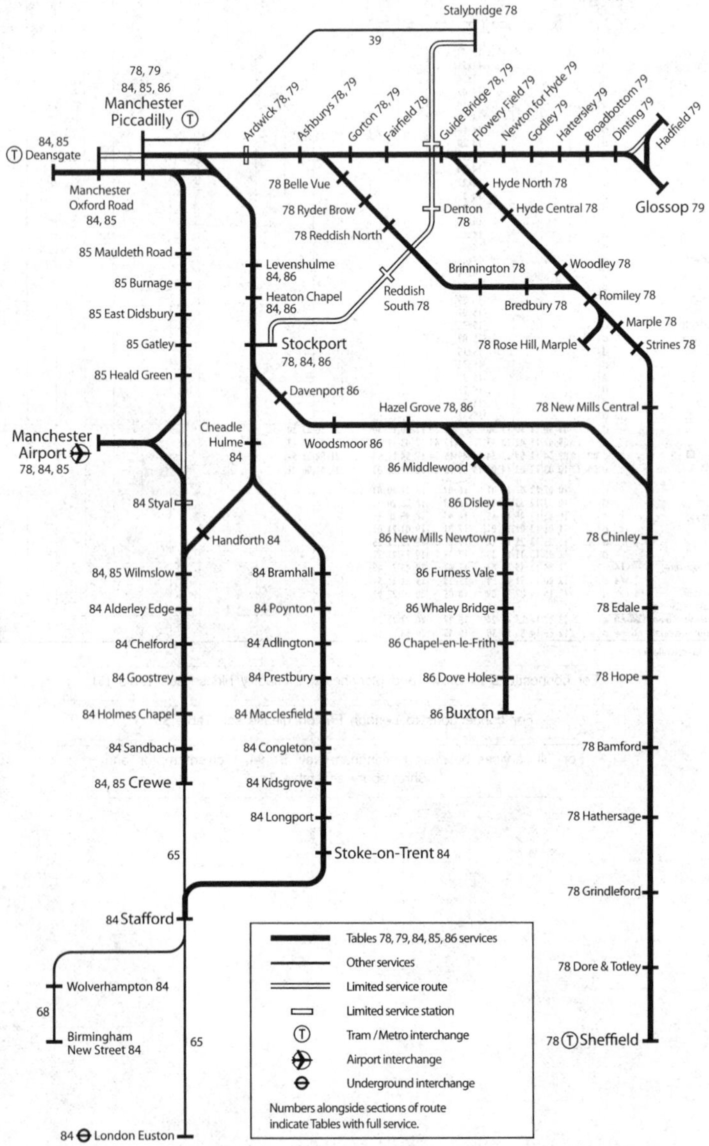

TOCs operating on this network - Northern (NT), First TransPennine Express (TP), Cross Country (XC), East Midlands Trains (EM) Virgin Trains (VT), Arriva Trains Wales (AW)

Table 78

Mondays to Fridays

9 December to 16 May

Sheffield, Chinley, Marple and Romiley Manchester and Manchester Airport

Network Diagram - see first Page of Table 78

Miles	Miles	Miles			TP	TP	TP	TP	TP	NT	NT	TP	NT		NT	NT	EM	NT	NT	NT	NT	NT	TP		NT
					MO	MX	MX		FO																
					◇1	◇1	◇1	◇1	◇1			◇1					◇						◇1		
						A	B	C	D	E		F				E	G		E			H	I		
0	—	—	**Sheffield 7**	d	03 25	03 25	03 25	05 11	05 11			06 11					06 20						07 09		
4¾	—	—	Dore & Totley	d													06 27						07 15		
9¾	—	—	Grindleford	d													06 35								
11¼	—	—	Hathersage	d													06 39								
13	—	—	Bamford	d													06 43								
14¾	—	—	Hope (Derbyshire)	d													06 47								
20	—	—	Edale	d													06 55								
25½	—	0	**Chinley**	d													07 03								
—	—	8½	Hazel Grove 86	a																					
—	—	—	Stockport 86	a								06 53					07 22						07 53		
29¼	—	—	New Mills Central	d							06 13				06 33			07 00			07 17				
30¾	—	—	Strines	d							06 16							07 03							
33	—	—	**Marple**	d							06 19				06 38			07 06			07 22				
—	0	—	**Rose Hill Marple**	d									06 31							07 14					07 41
34¼	2	—	**Romiley**	d							06 23		06 36		06 41			07 12		07 19	07 25				07 46
—	3¼	—	Woodley	d									06 39							07 22					07 50
—	4¾	—	Hyde Central	d									06 42							07 25					07 53
—	6	—	Hyde North	d									06 45							07 28					07 56
—	7¾	—	Guide Bridge	d						06 27			06 49			06 57			07 27	07 32		07 48			08 00
—	9	—	Fairfield	d									06 52							07 35					08 03
—	10	—	Gorton	d						06 30			06 54						07 30			07 51			
35½	—	—	Bredbury	d							06 26				06 44			07 15			07 28				
36½	—	—	Brinnington	d							06 28				06 47			07 18			07 31				
38¼	—	—	Reddish North	d							06 31				06 50			07 21			07 34				
39¼	—	—	Ryder Brow	d							06 34							07 24			07 37				
39½	—	—	Belle Vue	d							06 36							07 26							
40½	11	—	Ashburys	d						06 33	06 39				06 56	07 04		07 29	07 33		07 41				08 06
41½	12	—	Ardwick	d															07 35						
42	12½	8¾	**Manchester Piccadilly 10**	a	04 20	04 52	04 53	06 02	06 02	06 40	06 47	07 02	07 05		07 02	07 12	07 34	07 36	07 41	07 45	07 47	08 00	08 02		08 13
—	—	—	**Manchester Airport** 85	a	04 40	05 12		06 28	06 33			07 29											08 26		

		NT	NT	NT	NT	EM	NT	NT	NT		NT	TP	NT	NT	NT	NT	NT	EM	NT		NT	TP	NT	NT	NT
						◇						◇1						◇				◇1			
			H			G	H					I	H	H				G	H			I	E		
Sheffield 7	d				07 12	07 32						08 05						08 41				09 11			
Dore & Totley	d				07 19	07 39						08 11													
Grindleford	d				07 29																				
Hathersage	d				07 32																				
Bamford	d				07 36																				
Hope (Derbyshire)	d				07 39																				
Edale	d				07 47																				
Chinley	d				07 55	08 03						08 32													
Hazel Grove 86	a					08 16																			
Stockport 86	a					08 24						08 53						09 25				09 53			
New Mills Central	d	07 39			08 02				08 24								09 04								
Strines	d	07 42							08 27								09 07								
Marple	d	07 45		07 59	08 09				08 30						08 53		09 10							09 48	
Rose Hill Marple	d							08 13			08 35					08 54					09 24				09 54
Romiley	d	07 49		08 03	08 13			08 18	08 34		08 40				08 56	08 59	09 14				09 29			09 51	09 59
Woodley	d							08 21								09 02					09 32				10 02
Hyde Central	d							08 24								09 05					09 35				10 05
Hyde North	d							08 27								09 08									10 08
Guide Bridge	d		08 10				08 26	08 31					08 49	09 02		09 12			09 27		09 42		09 57		10 12
Fairfield	d							08 34													09 45				
Gorton	d		08 14				08 30						08 52			09 16			09 31		09 47				10 16
Bredbury	d	07 52		08 06					08 37		08 43				08 59		09 17							09 54	
Brinnington	d	07 54		08 09					08 39		08 45				09 02		09 19							09 57	
Reddish North	d	07 57		08 12					08 42		08 48				09 05		09 22							10 00	
Ryder Brow	d			08 14					08 45															10 02	
Belle Vue	d			08 16					08 46															10 04	
Ashburys	d		08 17	08 21			08 33		08 49				08 56	09 07	09 11				09 33				10 02	10 07	
Ardwick	d			08 23																					
Manchester Piccadilly 10	a	08 09	08 25	08 30	08 33	08 36	08 41	08 45	08 56		08 59	09 02	09 02	09 15	09 19	09 27	09 34	09 36	09 40		09 57	10 02	10 10	10 13	10 27
Manchester Airport 85	a											09 33										10 26			

A until 27 December, from 25 March
B from 31 December until 21 March
C until 2 January, FX from 6 January until 6 February, from 10 February
D from 3 January until 7 February
E From Hadfield
F From Doncaster
G From Nottingham to Liverpool Lime Street
H From Manchester Piccadilly
I From Cleethorpes

Table 78

Mondays to Fridays

9 December to 16 May

Sheffield, Chinley, Marple and Romiley Manchester and Manchester Airport

Network Diagram - see first Page of Table 78

		NT	EM	NT	NT	TP	TP	NT	NT	NT	NT	EM	NT	NT	TP	NT	NT	NT	NT	EM	NT	NT
						FO																
			◇			◇1	◇1					◇			◇1					◇		
			A	B		C	D		B			A	B		E		B			A	B	
						🚲	🚲								🚲							
Sheffield 7 🚢	d	09 14	09 41			10 11	10 11				10 14	10 41			11 11					11 41		
Dore & Totley	d	09 21									10 21											
Grindleford	d	09 29									10 29											
Hathersage	d	09 32									10 32											
Bamford	d	09 36									10 36											
Hope (Derbyshire)	d	09 39									10 39											
Edale	d	09 47									10 47											
Chinley	d	09 55									10 55											
Hazel Grove 86	a																					
Stockport 86	a		10 25			10 53	10 53					11 25			11 53					12 24		
New Mills Central	d	10 01						10 30			11 02					11 30			12 01			
Strines	d							10 33														
Marple	d	10 07						10 36			11 07					11 36			12 07			
Rose Hill Marple	d				10 24					10 54				11 24				11 54				12 24
Romiley	d	10 11			10 29			10 39		10 59	11 11			11 29		11 39		11 59	12 11			12 29
Woodley	d				10 32					11 02				11 32				12 02				12 32
Hyde Central	d				10 35					11 05				11 35				12 05				12 35
Hyde North	d									11 08								12 08				
Guide Bridge	d			10 27	10 42				10 57	11 12			11 27	11 42			11 57	12 12			12 27	12 42
Fairfield	d				10 45									11 45								12 45
Gorton	d				10 47					11 16				11 47				12 16				12 47
Bredbury	d	10 14						10 42			11 14					11 42			12 14			
Brinnington	d	10 16						10 45			11 16					11 45			12 16			
Reddish North	d	10 19						10 48			11 19					11 48			12 19			
Ryder Brow	d							10 50								11 50						
Belle Vue	d															11 52						
Ashburys	d			10 32				10 55	11 02				11 32			11 55	12 02				12 32	
Ardwick	d																					
Manchester Piccadilly 10 🚢	a	10 32	10 36	10 40	10 57	11 02	11 02	11 02	11 10	11 27	11 32	11 36	11 40	11 57	12 02	12 02	12 10	12 27	12 32	12 36	12 40	12 57
Manchester Airport 85 ✈	a					11 26	11 34								12 26							

		TP	NT	NT	NT	NT	EM	NT	NT	TP	NT	NT	NT	NT	EM	NT	NT	TP	NT	NT	NT	NT	EM
		◇1					◇			◇1					◇			◇1					◇
		E		B			A	B		E		B			A	B		E		B			A
		🚲								🚲								🚲					
Sheffield 7 🚢	d	12 11				12 14	12 40			13 11					13 43			14 11				14 14	14 40
Dore & Totley	d					12 21																14 21	
Grindleford	d					12 29																14 29	
Hathersage	d					12 32																14 32	
Bamford	d					12 36																14 36	
Hope (Derbyshire)	d					12 39																14 39	
Edale	d					12 47																14 47	
Chinley	d					12 55																14 55	
Hazel Grove 86	a																						
Stockport 86	a	12 53					13 25			13 53					14 25			14 53					15 25
New Mills Central	d		12 30			13 01					13 30			14 02					14 30			15 02	
Strines	d		12 33																14 33				
Marple	d		12 36			13 07					13 36			14 07					14 36			15 07	
Rose Hill Marple	d				12 54				13 24				13 54				14 24				14 54		
Romiley	d		12 39		12 59	13 11			13 29		13 39		13 59	14 11			14 29		14 40		14 59	15 11	
Woodley	d				13 02				13 32				14 02				14 32				15 02		
Hyde Central	d				13 05				13 35				14 05				14 35				15 05		
Hyde North	d				13 08								14 08								15 08		
Guide Bridge	d			12 57	13 12			13 27	13 42			13 57	14 12			14 27	14 42			14 57	15 12		
Fairfield	d								13 45								14 45						
Gorton	d				13 16				13 48				14 16				14 47				15 16		
Bredbury	d		12 42			13 14					13 42			14 14					14 43			15 14	
Brinnington	d		12 45			13 16					13 45			14 16					14 45			15 16	
Reddish North	d		12 48			13 19					13 48			14 19					14 48			15 19	
Ryder Brow	d		12 50								13 50								14 50				
Belle Vue	d										13 52												
Ashburys	d		12 55	13 02				13 32			13 55	14 02				14 32			14 55	15 02			
Ardwick	d																						
Manchester Piccadilly 10 🚢	a	13 02	13 02	13 10	13 27	13 32	13 36	13 40	13 57	14 02	14 02	14 11	14 27	14 32	14 36	14 41	14 57	15 02	15 02	15 11	15 27	15 32	15 36
Manchester Airport 85 ✈	a	13 26								14 26								15 26					

A From Norwich to Liverpool Lime Street
B From Hadfield
C until 7 February. From Cleethorpes
D FX until 6 February, from 10 February. From Cleethorpes
E From Cleethorpes

Table 78

Mondays to Fridays

9 December to 16 May

Sheffield, Chinley, Marple and Romiley Manchester and Manchester Airport

Network Diagram - see first Page of Table 78

		NT	NT	TP	TP	NT	NT	NT	NT		EM	NT	NT	TP	NT	NT	NT	NT	NT		NT	EM	NT	NT	NT
				◇1	◇1						◇			◇1								◇			
		A		B	C		A				D	A		E	F						F	D	F		
Sheffield 7	d			15 11	15 11						15 41			16 11					16 14			16 41			
Dore & Totley	d																		16 21						
Grindleford	d																		16 29						
Hathersage	d																		16 32						
Bamford	d																		16 36						
Hope (Derbyshire)	d																		16 39						
Edale	d																		16 47						
Chinley	d																		16 55						
Hazel Grove 86	a																								
Stockport 86	a			15 53	15 53						16 25			16 53								17 25			
New Mills Central	d					15 30			16 02							16 37			17 01						
Strines	d															16 40									
Marple	d					15 36			16 07							16 43	16 52		17 06						17 35
Rose Hill Marple	d		15 24					15 54					16 24					16 54						17 24	
Romiley	d		15 29			15 39		15 59	16 11				16 29			16 47	16 55	16 59	17 10					17 29	17 38
Woodley	d		15 32					16 02					16 32					17 02						17 32	
Hyde Central	d		15 35					16 05					16 35					17 05						17 35	
Hyde North	d							16 08										17 08							
Guide Bridge	d	15 27	15 42				15 57	16 12				16 27	16 42		16 48			17 12			17 17		17 35	17 42	
Fairfield	d		15 45										16 45											17 45	
Gorton	d		15 47					16 16					16 47					17 16						17 47	
Bredbury	d					15 42			16 14							16 50			17 13						17 41
Brinnington	d					15 45			16 16							16 52									17 44
Reddish North	d					15 48			16 19							16 55									17 47
Ryder Brow	d					15 50										16 58									17 49
Belle Vue	d					15 52																			17 51
Ashburys	d	15 32				15 55	16 02					16 33			16 55	17 03					17 27		17 40		17 54
Ardwick	d																								
Manchester Piccadilly 10	a	15 41	15 57	16 02	16 02	16 02	16 11	16 27	16 32		16 36	16 41	16 57	17 02	17 04	17 09	17 15	17 27	17 29		17 34	17 37	17 48	17 57	18 00
Manchester Airport 85	a			16 26	16 34									17 33											

		TP	NT	NT	NT		NT	NT	EM	TP	NT	NT	NT	NT	NT		EM	NT	NT	TP	NT	NT	NT	EM	NT
		◇1							◇	◇1							◇			◇1				◇	
		E		F				F	D	E	F		F				D	A		E		A		D	A
Sheffield 7	d	17 11					17 14		17 41	18 11					18 14		18 42			19 11			19 14	19 40	
Dore & Totley	d						17 21								18 21								19 20		
Grindleford	d						17 29								18 29								19 29		
Hathersage	d						17 32								18 32								19 32		
Bamford	d						17 36																19 36		
Hope (Derbyshire)	d						17 40								18 38								19 39		
Edale	d						17 47								18 45								19 47		
Chinley	d						17 55								18 53								19 55		
Hazel Grove 86	a																								
Stockport 86	a	17 53							18 25	18 53							19 25			19 53				20 25	
New Mills Central	d		17 47				18 02								19 02						19 30		20 02		
Strines	d						18 05								19 05										
Marple	d		17 52				18 08					18 37			19 08						19 36		20 07		
Rose Hill Marple	d				17 54									18 54					19 24						
Romiley	d		17 56		17 59		18 11					18 40		18 59	19 12				19 29		19 39		20 11		
Woodley	d				18 03									19 02					19 32						
Hyde Central	d				18 06									19 05					19 35						
Hyde North	d				18 08									19 08											
Guide Bridge	d			17 58	18 12			18 18			18 46		19 02	19 12				19 27	19 43			19 57			20 27
Fairfield	d				18 15														19 46						
Gorton	d				18 18						18 49			19 17					19 49						20 30
Bredbury	d						18 14					18 43			19 15						19 42		20 14		
Brinnington	d											18 46			19 17						19 45		20 16		
Reddish North	d											18 49			19 20						19 48		20 19		
Ryder Brow	d											18 51									19 50				
Belle Vue	d											18 53									19 52				
Ashburys	d			18 07				18 27			18 55	18 59	19 07	19 21				19 32			19 55	20 02			20 33
Ardwick	d																								
Manchester Piccadilly 10	a	18 02	18 10	18 14	18 27		18 31	18 34	18 36	19 02	19 02	19 05	19 16	19 28	19 32		19 36	19 41	19 58	20 01	20 02	20 11	20 32	20 36	20 41
Manchester Airport 85	a	18 26								19 28										20 39					

A From Hadfield
B until 7 February, from 24 March. From Cleethorpes
C from 10 February until 21 March. From Cleethorpes
D From Norwich to Liverpool Lime Street
E From Cleethorpes
F From Manchester Piccadilly

Table 78

Mondays to Fridays

9 December to 16 May

Sheffield, Chinley, Marple and Romiley Manchester and Manchester Airport

Network Diagram - see first Page of Table 78

		TP FX ◇1 A	TP ◇1 B	NT	NT C	EM ◇ D	NT	NT	NT C	TP FX ◇1 A	TP FX ◇1 E	TP ◇1 F	NT	NT C	NT	NT
Sheffield 7	d	20 11	20 11			20 31		20 36		22 11	22 11	22 11			22 47	
Dore & Totley	d							20 43							22 54	
Grindleford	d							20 50							23 01	
Hathersage	d							20 54							23 05	
Bamford	d							20 57							23 08	
Hope (Derbyshire)	d							21 01							23 12	
Edale	d							21 08							23 19	
Chinley	d							21 16							23 27	
Hazel Grove 86	a															
Stockport 86	a	20 53	20 53			21 20				22 53	22 53	22 53			23 47	
New Mills Central	d			20 30				21 30					22 30			23 30
Strines	d			20 33									22 33			23 33
Marple	d			20 36				21 36					22 36			23 36
Rose Hill Marple	d						21 11									
Romiley	d			20 40			21 16	21 39					22 40			23 40
Woodley	d						21 19									
Hyde Central	d						21 22									
Hyde North	d						21 25									
Guide Bridge	d				21 01		21 29		21 57					22 57		
Fairfield	d						21 32									
Gorton	d						21 34		22 00					23 00		
Bredbury	d			20 43				21 42					22 43			23 43
Brinnington	d			20 45				21 45					22 45			23 45
Reddish North	d			20 48				21 48					22 48			23 48
Ryder Brow	d			20 50				21 50					22 50			23 51
Belle Vue	d							21 52								23 52
Ashburys	d			20 55	21 05			21 55	22 03				22 55	23 03		23 55
Ardwick	d															
Manchester Piccadilly 10	a	21 02	21 02	21 02	21 14	21 32	21 42	22 05	22 11	23 02	23 02	23 02	23 02	23 11	00 02	00 03
Manchester Airport 85	a		21 36								23 25	23 26				

Saturdays

14 December to 17 May

		TP ◇1	TP ◇1	TP ◇1 G	NT C	EM ◇ H	NT	NT C	NT	TP ◇1 I	NT	NT C	NT	EM ◇ H	NT C	NT	TP ◇1 I	NT	NT C	NT	NT	EM ◇ H	NT C
Sheffield 7	d	03 25	05 11	06 11		06 20				07 09			07 12	07 32			08 05				08 14	08 41	
Dore & Totley	d					06 27				07 15			07 19	07 40			08 11				08 21		
Grindleford	d					06 35							07 29								08 29		
Hathersage	d					06 39							07 32								08 32		
Bamford	d					06 43							07 36								08 36		
Hope (Derbyshire)	d					06 47							07 39								08 39		
Edale	d					06 55							07 47								08 47		
Chinley	d					07 03							07 55	08 03			08 32				08 55		
Hazel Grove 86	a													08 16									
Stockport 86	a			06 53		07 22				07 53				08 24			08 53					09 25	
New Mills Central	d						07 00						08 01								09 01		
Strines	d						07 03						08 04								09 04		
Marple	d						07 06				07 36		08 07					08 36			09 07		
Rose Hill Marple	d								07 25							08 25				08 54			
Romiley	d						07 12		07 30		07 39		08 11			08 30		08 39		08 59	09 11		
Woodley	d								07 33							08 33				09 02			
Hyde Central	d								07 36							08 36				09 05			
Hyde North	d								07 39											09 08			
Guide Bridge	d				06 57			07 27	07 44			07 57			08 27	08 44			08 57	09 12			09 27
Fairfield	d								07 47							08 47							
Gorton	d				07 00				07 50						08 30					09 16			
Bredbury	d						07 15				07 42		08 14					08 42			09 14		
Brinnington	d						07 18				07 45		08 16					08 45			09 16		
Reddish North	d						07 21				07 48		08 19					08 48			09 19		
Ryder Brow	d						07 24				07 50							08 50					
Belle Vue	d						07 26				07 52												
Ashburys	d				07 03		07 29	07 32			07 55	08 02			08 33			08 55	09 02				09 32
Ardwick	d																						
Manchester Piccadilly 10	a	04 52	06 04	07 02	07 10	07 34	07 36	07 40	07 58	08 02	08 02	08 10	08 32	08 36	08 40	08 57	09 02	09 02	09 10	09 27	09 32	09 36	09 40
Manchester Airport 85	a	05 12	06 28	07 29						08 26							09 26						

A from 30 December until 20 March. From Cleethorpes
B until 27 December, FO from 3 January until 14 March, from 21 March. From Cleethorpes
C From Hadfield
D From Norwich
E until 26 December. From Cleethorpes
F FO until 14 March, from 21 March. From Cleethorpes
G From Doncaster
H From Nottingham to Liverpool Lime Street
I From Cleethorpes

Table 78

Saturdays

14 December to 17 May

Sheffield, Chinley, Marple and Romiley Manchester and Manchester Airport

Network Diagram - see first Page of Table 78

		NT		TP ◇1 A	NT	NT B	NT	NT	EM ◇ C	NT B	NT	TP ◇1 A		NT	NT B	NT	NT	EM ◇ C	NT B	NT	TP ◇1 A	NT		NT B	NT
Sheffield 7	d			09 11				09 14	09 41			10 11					10 14	10 41			11 11				
Dore & Totley	d							09 21									10 21								
Grindleford	d							09 29									10 29								
Hathersage	d							09 32									10 32								
Bamford	d							09 36									10 36								
Hope (Derbyshire)	d							09 39									10 39								
Edale	d							09 47									10 47								
Chinley	d							09 55									10 55								
Hazel Grove 86	a																								
Stockport 86	a			09 53					10 25			10 53						11 25			11 53				
New Mills Central	d							10 01									11 01								
Strines	d							10 04																	
Marple	d				09 36			10 07						10 36			11 07					11 36			
Rose Hill Marple	d	09 24					09 54				10 24					10 54				11 24					11 54
Romiley	d	09 29			09 39		09 59	10 11			10 29			10 39		10 59	11 11			11 29		11 39			11 59
Woodley	d	09 32					10 02				10 32					11 02				11 32					12 02
Hyde Central	d	09 35					10 05				10 35					11 05				11 35					12 05
Hyde North	d						10 08									11 08									12 08
Guide Bridge	d	09 42				09 57	10 12			10 27	10 42				10 57	11 12			11 27	11 42				11 57	12 12
Fairfield	d	09 45									10 45									11 45					
Gorton	d	09 47					10 16				10 47					11 16				11 47					12 16
Bredbury	d				09 42			10 14						10 42			11 14					11 42			
Brinnington	d				09 45			10 16						10 45			11 16					11 45			
Reddish North	d				09 48			10 19						10 48			11 19					11 48			
Ryder Brow	d				09 50									10 50								11 50			
Belle Vue	d				09 52																	11 52			
Ashburys	d				09 55	10 02				10 32				10 55	11 02				11 32			11 55		12 02	
Ardwick	d																								
Manchester Piccadilly 10	a	09 57		10 02	10 02	10 10	10 27	10 32	10 36	10 40	10 57	11 02		11 02	11 10	11 27	11 32	11 36	11 40	11 57	12 02	12 02		12 10	12 27
Manchester Airport 85	a			10 32								11 32									12 26				

		NT	EM ◇ C	NT B	NT	TP ◇1 A	NT	NT B		NT	NT	EM ◇ C	NT B	NT	TP ◇1 A	NT	NT B	NT		NT	EM ◇ C	NT B	NT	TP ◇1 A	NT
Sheffield 7	d	11 14	11 41			12 11					12 14	12 41			13 11					13 14	13 41			14 11	
Dore & Totley	d	11 21									12 21									13 21					
Grindleford	d	11 29									12 29									13 29					
Hathersage	d	11 32									12 32									13 32					
Bamford	d	11 36									12 36									13 36					
Hope (Derbyshire)	d	11 39									12 39									13 39					
Edale	d	11 47									12 47									13 47					
Chinley	d	11 55									12 55									13 55					
Hazel Grove 86	a																								
Stockport 86	a		12 24			12 53						13 25			13 53						14 25			14 53	
New Mills Central	d	12 01									13 01									14 01					
Strines	d	12 04																		14 04					
Marple	d	12 07					12 36				13 07					13 36				14 07					14 37
Rose Hill Marple	d				12 24					12 54				13 24				13 54					14 24		
Romiley	d	12 11			12 29		12 39			12 59	13 11			13 29		13 39		13 59		14 11			14 29		14 40
Woodley	d				12 32					13 02				13 32				14 02					14 32		
Hyde Central	d				12 35					13 05				13 35				14 05					14 35		
Hyde North	d									13 08								14 08							
Guide Bridge	d			12 27	12 42			12 57		13 12			13 27	13 42			13 57	14 12				14 27	14 42		
Fairfield	d				12 45									13 45									14 45		
Gorton	d				12 47					13 16				13 47				14 16					14 47		
Bredbury	d	12 14					12 42				13 14					13 42				14 14					14 43
Brinnington	d	12 16					12 45				13 16					13 45				14 16					14 46
Reddish North	d	12 19					12 48				13 19					13 48				14 19					14 49
Ryder Brow	d						12 50									13 50									14 51
Belle Vue	d															13 52									
Ashburys	d			12 32			12 55	13 02					13 32			13 55	14 04					14 33			14 56
Ardwick	d																								
Manchester Piccadilly 10	a	12 32	12 36	12 40	12 57	13 02	13 02	13 10		13 27	13 32	13 36	13 40	13 57	14 02	14 02	14 11	14 28		14 32	14 36	14 40	14 57	15 02	15 03
Manchester Airport 85	a					13 33									14 26									15 26	

A From Cleethorpes

B From Hadfield

C From Norwich to Liverpool Lime Street

Table 78

Saturdays

14 December to 17 May

Sheffield, Chinley, Marple and Romiley Manchester and Manchester Airport

Network Diagram - see first Page of Table 78

Station		NT A	NT	NT	EM ◇ B	NT A	NT	TP ◇1 C	NT	NT A		NT	NT	EM ◇ B	NT A	NT	TP ◇1 C	NT	NT A	NT		NT	EM ◇ B	NT A	NT
Sheffield 7	d			14 14	14 41			15 11					15 14	15 41			16 11					16 14	16 41		
Dore & Totley	d			14 21									15 21									16 21			
Grindleford	d			14 29									15 29									16 29			
Hathersage	d			14 32									15 32									16 32			
Bamford	d			14 36									15 36									16 36			
Hope (Derbyshire)	d			14 39									15 39									16 39			
Edale	d			14 47									15 47									16 47			
Chinley	d			14 55									15 55									16 55			
Hazel Grove 86	a																								
Stockport 86	a				15 25			15 53						16 25			16 53						17 25		
New Mills Central	d			15 01									16 01									17 01			
Strines	d												16 04												
Marple	d			15 07					15 37				16 07					16 37				17 07			
Rose Hill Marple	d		14 54				15 24					15 54				16 24				16 54					17 24
Romiley	d		14 59	15 11			15 29		15 40			15 59	16 11			16 29		16 40		16 59		17 11			17 29
Woodley	d		15 02				15 32					16 02				16 32				17 02					17 32
Hyde Central	d		15 05				15 35					16 05				16 35				17 05					17 35
Hyde North	d		15 08									16 08								17 08					
Guide Bridge	d	14 57	15 12			15 27	15 42			15 57		16 12			16 27	16 42			16 57	17 12				17 27	17 42
Fairfield	d						15 45									16 45									17 45
Gorton	d		15 16				15 47					16 16				16 47				17 16					17 47
Bredbury	d			15 14					15 43				16 14					16 43				17 14			
Brinnington	d			15 16					15 46				16 16					16 46				17 16			
Reddish North	d			15 19					15 49				16 19					16 49				17 19			
Ryder Brow	d								15 51									16 51							
Belle Vue	d								15 53																
Ashburys	d	15 04				15 33			15 56	16 04					16 33			16 56	17 04					17 33	
Ardwick	d																								
Manchester Piccadilly 10	a	15 11	15 27	15 32	15 36	15 40	15 57	16 02	16 03	16 11		16 27	16 33	16 36	16 40	16 57	17 02	17 03	17 11	17 27		17 32	17 37	17 40	17 57
Manchester Airport 85	a							16 34									17 33								

Station		TP ◇1 D	TP ◇1 E	NT	NT A	NT		NT	EM ◇ B	NT A	NT	TP ◇1 C	NT	NT A	NT	NT		EM ◇ B	NT A	NT	TP ◇1 C	NT A	NT	NT	EM ◇ B
Sheffield 7	d	17 11	17 11					17 14	17 38			18 11				18 14		18 38			19 11			19 14	19 40
Dore & Totley	d							17 21								18 21								19 21	
Grindleford	d							17 29								18 28								19 29	
Hathersage	d							17 32								18 32								19 32	
Bamford	d							17 36								18 35								19 36	
Hope (Derbyshire)	d							17 39								18 39								19 39	
Edale	d							17 47								18 46								19 47	
Chinley	d							17 55								18 54								19 55	
Hazel Grove 86	a																								
Stockport 86	a	17 53	17 53						18 26			18 53						19 24			19 53				20 25
New Mills Central	d							18 01								19 01								20 01	
Strines	d							18 04								19 04									
Marple	d			17 37				18 07					18 37			19 07								20 07	
Rose Hill Marple	d					17 54					18 24				18 54					19 24			19 54		
Romiley	d			17 40		17 59		18 11			18 29		18 40		18 59	19 11				19 29			19 59	20 11	
Woodley	d					18 02					18 32				19 02					19 32			20 02		
Hyde Central	d					18 05					18 35				19 05					19 35			20 05		
Hyde North	d					18 08									19 08								20 08		
Guide Bridge	d				17 57	18 12				18 27	18 42			18 57	19 13				19 27	19 43		19 57	20 12		
Fairfield	d										18 45									19 46					
Gorton	d					18 16					18 47				19 17					19 49			20 16		
Bredbury	d			17 43				18 14					18 43			19 14								20 14	
Brinnington	d			17 46				18 16					18 46			19 16								20 16	
Reddish North	d			17 49				18 19					18 49			19 19								20 19	
Ryder Brow	d			17 51									18 51												
Belle Vue	d			17 53									18 53												
Ashburys	d			17 57	18 04					18 33			18 56	19 04					19 33			20 04			
Ardwick	d																								
Manchester Piccadilly 10	a	18 02	18 02	18 03	18 11	18 27		18 32	18 37	18 40	18 57	19 02	19 03	19 11	19 27	19 32		19 35	19 40	20 00	20 01	20 11	20 27	20 32	20 36
Manchester Airport 85	a	18 26	18 34									19 28									20 39				

A From Hadfield
B From Norwich to Liverpool Lime Street
C From Cleethorpes
D 14 December, 21 December, 28 December. From Cleethorpes
E from 4 January. From Cleethorpes

Table 78

Saturdays

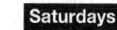

14 December to 17 May

Sheffield, Chinley, Marple and Romiley Manchester and Manchester Airport

Network Diagram - see first Page of Table 78

		TP	NT	NT	EM	NT	NT	NT		NT	NT	NT	NT	NT
		◇1			◇									
		A		B	C			B			B	D	E	
Sheffield 7	d	20 11			20 32		20 35					22 24	22 24	
Dore & Totley	d						20 42					22 31	22 31	
Grindleford	d						20 50					22 38	22 38	
Hathersage	d						20 53					22 41	22 41	
Bamford	d						20 57					22 45	22 45	
Hope (Derbyshire)	d						21 00					22 48	22 48	
Edale	d						21 08					22 56	22 56	
Chinley	d						21 16					23 04	23 04	
Hazel Grove 86	a													
Stockport 86	a	20 53			21 20								23 21	
New Mills Central	d		20 30				21 30			22 30				23 30
Strines	d		20 33							22 33				23 33
Marple	d		20 36				21 36			22 36				23 36
Rose Hill Marple	d					21 12								
Romiley	d		20 40			21 17	21 39			22 40				23 40
Woodley	d					21 20								
Hyde Central	d					21 23								
Hyde North	d					21 26								
Guide Bridge	d			20 57		21 30		21 57			22 57			
Fairfield	d					21 33								
Gorton	d			21 00				22 00			23 00			
Bredbury	d		20 43				21 42			22 43				23 43
Brinnington	d		20 45				21 45			22 45				23 45
Reddish North	d		20 48				21 48			22 48				23 48
Ryder Brow	d		20 51				21 50			22 51				23 51
Belle Vue	d		20 52				21 52			22 52				23 52
Ashburys	d		20 55	21 04			21 55	22 04		22 55	23 04			23 55
Ardwick	d													
Manchester Piccadilly 10	a	21 02	21 03	21 11	21 32	21 42	22 05	22 11		23 03	23 11	23 34	23 38	00 02
Manchester Airport 85	a	21 36												

Sundays

8 December to 11 May

		TP	TP	TP	TP	NT	NT	TP	NT	EM		NT	TP	NT	NT	EM	NT	TP	NT	EM		NT	TP	NT	NT
		◇1	◇1	◇1	◇1			◇1		◇			◇1			◇		◇1		◇			◇1		
		F	G	H	I		B		B	J		B	A	B		J	B	A	B	J		B	A	B	
Sheffield 7	d	07 50	07 50	09 10	09 10	09 20		10 10		10 41			11 10		11 14	11 39		12 10		12 37			13 10		13 13
Dore & Totley	d					09 27				10 48					11 21										13 20
Grindleford	d					09 34									11 29										13 28
Hathersage	d					09 38									11 32										13 31
Bamford	d					09 41									11 36										13 35
Hope (Derbyshire)	d					09 45									11 39										13 38
Edale	d					09 52									11 47										13 46
Chinley	d					10 00									11 55										13 54
Hazel Grove 86	a																								
Stockport 86	a	08 31	08 31	09 54	09 54					11 25			11 53			12 25		12 52		13 25			13 53		
New Mills Central	d					10 07									12 01										14 00
Strines	d					10 10									12 04										14 03
Marple	d					10 13									12 07										14 07
Rose Hill Marple	d																								
Romiley	d					10 17									12 11										14 10
Woodley	d																								
Hyde Central	d																								
Hyde North	d																								
Guide Bridge	d						10 28		10 58			11 28		11 58			12 28		12 58			13 28		13 58	
Fairfield	d																								
Gorton	d						10 31		11 01			11 31		12 01			12 31		13 01			13 31		14 01	
Bredbury	d					10 20									12 14										14 13
Brinnington	d					10 22									12 16										14 16
Reddish North	d					10 25									12 19										14 19
Ryder Brow	d																								
Belle Vue	d																								
Ashburys	d						10 34		11 04			11 34		12 04			12 34		13 04			13 34		14 04	
Ardwick	d																								
Manchester Piccadilly 10	a	08 40	08 40	10 01	10 01	10 37	10 42	11 04	11 12	11 37		11 42	12 06	12 12	12 31	12 37	12 42	13 07	13 12	13 37		13 42	14 06	14 12	14 31
Manchester Airport 85	a	09 07	09 10	10 26	10 31								12 27					13 28					14 27		

A From Cleethorpes
B From Hadfield
C From Norwich
D from 15 February until 22 March
E until 8 February, from 29 March
F until 29 December, from 16 February
G from 5 January until 9 February
H until 9 February, from 30 March
I from 16 February until 23 March
J From Nottingham to Liverpool Lime Street

Table 78

Sundays

8 December to 11 May

Sheffield, Chinley, Marple and Romiley Manchester and Manchester Airport

Network Diagram - see first Page of Table 78

	EM		NT	TP	NT	EM	NT	TP	TP	NT	NT		EM	NT	TP	NT	NT	EM	NT	TP	NT		NT	EM
	◇			◇1		◇		◇1	◇1				◇		◇1			◇		◇1				◇
	A		B	C	B	D	B	E	F	B			A	B	G	B	H	I	B	G	B			D
Sheffield 7 d	13 39			14 11		14 37		15 11	15 11		15 14		15 43		16 11		16 15	16 39		17 11			17 14	17 44
Dore & Totley d											15 21						16 23						17 21	
Grindleford d											15 29						16 30						17 29	
Hathersage d											15 32						16 33						17 32	
Bamford d											15 36						16 37						17 36	
Hope (Derbyshire) d											15 39						16 40						17 39	
Edale d											15 47						16 48						17 47	
Chinley d											15 55						16 56						17 55	
Hazel Grove 86 a																								
Stockport 86 a	14 25			14 53		15 25		15 53	15 53				16 25		16 53			17 28		17 53				18 25
New Mills Central d											16 01						17 02						18 01	
Strines d											16 04						17 05						18 04	
Marple d											16 07						17 08						18 07	
Rose Hill Marple d																								
Romiley d											16 11						17 12						18 11	
Woodley d																								
Hyde Central d																								
Hyde North d																								
Guide Bridge d			14 28		14 58		15 28			15 58				16 28		16 58			17 28		17 58			
Fairfield d																								
Gorton d			14 31		15 01		15 31			16 01				16 31		17 01			17 31		18 01			
Bredbury d											16 14						17 15						18 14	
Brinnington d											16 16						17 17						18 16	
Reddish North d											16 19						17 20						18 19	
Ryder Brow d																								
Belle Vue d																								
Ashburys d			14 34		15 04		15 34			16 04				16 34		17 04			17 34		18 04			
Ardwick d																								
Manchester Piccadilly 10 a	14 37		14 42	15 06	15 12	15 37	15 42	16 06	16 06	16 12	16 31		16 37	16 42	17 06	17 12	17 32	17 37	17 42	18 06	18 12		18 31	18 37
Manchester Airport 85 a				15 28				16 27	16 34						17 27					18 27				

	NT	TP	NT	EM	NT	TP	TP		TP	NT	NT	EM	NT	TP	NT	EM	TP		NT	NT	NT			
		◇1		◇		◇1	◇1		◇1			◇		◇1		◇	◇1							
	B	G	B	D	B	J	K		F	B		L	B	G	B	L	G		B					
Sheffield 7 d		18 11		18 37		19 11	19 11		19 11		19 14	19 35		20 11		20 35	21 11			22 17				
Dore & Totley d											19 21									22 24				
Grindleford d											19 29									22 32				
Hathersage d											19 32									22 35				
Bamford d											19 36									22 39				
Hope (Derbyshire) d											19 39									22 42				
Edale d											19 47									22 50				
Chinley d											19 55									22 58				
Hazel Grove 86 a																								
Stockport 86 a		18 53		19 25		19 53	19 53		19 53			20 25		20 53		21 24	21 53			23 16				
New Mills Central d											20 01										23 01			
Strines d											20 04										23 04			
Marple d											20 07										23 07			
Rose Hill Marple d																								
Romiley d											20 11										23 11			
Woodley d																								
Hyde Central d																								
Hyde North d																								
Guide Bridge d	18 28		18 58		19 28					19 58			20 28		20 58				21 58					
Fairfield d																								
Gorton d	18 31		19 01		19 31					20 01			20 31		21 01				22 01					
Bredbury d											20 14										23 14			
Brinnington d											20 16										23 16			
Reddish North d											20 19										23 19			
Ryder Brow d																								
Belle Vue d																								
Ashburys d	18 34		19 04		19 34					20 04			20 34		21 04				22 04					
Ardwick d																								
Manchester Piccadilly 10 a	18 42	19 06	19 12	19 37	19 42	20 08	20 09		20 09	20 12	20 32	20 38	20 42	21 06	21 12	21 36	22 06		22 12	23 29	23 31			
Manchester Airport 85 a		19 27				20 28	20 29		20 30					21 27			22 28							

A From Nottingham to Liverpool Lime Street
B From Hadfield
C From Doncaster
D From Norwich to Liverpool Lime Street
E until 23 March. From Cleethorpes
F from 30 March. From Cleethorpes
G From Cleethorpes
H from 30 March
I From Peterborough to Liverpool Lime Street
J from 5 January until 23 March
K until 29 December. From Cleethorpes
L From Norwich

Table 78R

Mondays to Fridays

9 December to 16 May

Manchester Airport and Manchester Romiley, Marple, Chinley and Sheffield

Network Diagram - see first Page of Table 78

Miles	Miles	Miles			TP ◇1 A	TP MX ◇1 B	NT	NT	NT C	NT	NT	NT D	NT	NT D	NT E	NT D	TP ◇1 F	NT G	NT	NT	EM ◇ H	NT D	NT
—	—	—	**Manchester Airport** 85	d	05 20												06 55						
0	0	—	**Manchester Piccadilly** 10	a	05 33												07 13						
—	—	—		d	05 44	05 44	05 50	06 14	06 18	06 35	06 41	06 48	06 57	07 02	07 08	07 18	07 19		07 24	07 39	07 42	07 48	07 54
0½	0½	—	Ardwick	d																			
1½	1½	—	Ashburys	d				06 18	06 22		06 45	06 52		07 06	07 12	07 22			07 28			07 52	
2½	—	—	Belle Vue	d							06 47								07 30				
2¾	—	—	Ryder Brow	d				06 21			06 49								07 32				
3¾	—	—	Reddish North	d				06 24			06 52				07 17				07 35				
5½	—	—	Brinnington	d				06 27			06 55				07 20				07 38				
6½	—	—	Bredbury	d				06 30			06 58				07 23				07 41				
—	2½	—	Gorton	d						06 41						07 24				07 45		07 54	
—	3½	—	Fairfield	d						06 43										07 47			
—	4¾	—	Guide Bridge	a					06 27	06 46		06 57		07 11		07 28				07 50		07 58	
—	—	—		d						06 46										07 50			
—	6½	—	Hyde North	d						06 50										07 54			
—	7¾	—	Hyde Central	d						06 53										07 57			
—	9¼	—	Woodley	d						06 56										08 00			
7½	10½	—	**Romiley**	d				06 33		06 59	07 02		07 10		07 26				07 44	08 03			08 06
—	12½	—	Rose Hill Marple	a						07 05										08 09			
9	—	—	**Marple**	d				06 37			07 06		07 14		07 30				07a49				08 10
11¼	—	—	Strines	d																			
12¾	—	—	New Mills Central	a				06 45			07 12		07 20		07 35								08 16
—	—	—		d											07 40								
—	—	—	Stockport 86	d	05 52	05 52	06 00										07 27				07 54		
—	—	0	Hazel Grove 86	d			06 07																
16½	—	8½	**Chinley**	d			06 18								07 49								
22	—	—	Edale	d			06 26								07 57								
27¼	—	—	Hope (Derbyshire)	d			06 32								08 03								
29	—	—	Bamford	d			06 35								08 06								
30¾	—	—	Hathersage	d			06 39								08 10								
32¼	—	—	Grindleford	d			06 42								08 13			←					
37¾	—	—	Dore & Totley	d			06 51								08 22		08 02	08 22			08 27		
42	—	—	**Sheffield** 7	a	06 40	06 40	07 01								↪		08 11	08 32			08 34		

		NT D	NT	NT	NT	TP ◇1 F	NT D	NT	EM ◇ H	NT	NT C	NT	NT	NT	NT C	TP ◇1 F	NT	EM ◇ H	NT	NT C	NT	NT	NT C
Manchester Airport 85	d					07 53										08 55							
Manchester Piccadilly 10	a					08 12										09 13							
	d	08 04	08 07	08 14	08 17	08 20	08 29	08 35	08 43	08 45	08 48	08 51	09 05	09 14	09 18	09 20	09 35	09 43	09 45	09 48	10 05	10 14	10 18
Ardwick	d																						
Ashburys	d	08 08		08 18			08 33				08 52			09 18	09 22					09 52		10 18	10 22
Belle Vue	d			08 20																		10 20	
Ryder Brow	d			08 21										09 21								10 21	
Reddish North	d			08 24						08 52				09 24					09 52			10 24	
Brinnington	d			08 27						08 56				09 27					09 56			10 27	
Bredbury	d			08 30						08 59				09 30					09 59			10 30	
Gorton	d				08 23							08 57	09 11				09 41				10 11		
Fairfield	d				08 25							08 59					09 43						
Guide Bridge	a	08 13	08 16		08 28		08 38				08 57	09 02	09 15		09 27		09 46			09 57	10 15		10 27
	d		08 16		08 28							09 02	09 15				09 46				10 15		
Hyde North	d				08 32								09 19								10 19		
Hyde Central	d		08 21		08 35							09 07	09 22				09 51				10 22		
Woodley	d				08 38							09 10	09 25				09 54				10 25		
Romiley	d		08 26	08 33	08 41			08 48		09 02		09 14	09 28	09 33			09 58		10 02		10 28	10 33	
Rose Hill Marple	a		08 32		08 47							09 20	09 34				10 04				10 34		
Marple	d			08a39				08 52		09 06				09a38					10 06			10 37	
Strines	d							08 56											10 10				
New Mills Central	a							08 59		09 11									10 14			10 45	
	d									09 11													
Stockport 86	d					08 28			08 54							09 28		09 54					
Hazel Grove 86	d																						
Chinley	d									09 20													
Edale	d									09 30													
Hope (Derbyshire)	d									09 36													
Bamford	d									09 39													
Hathersage	d									09 42													
Grindleford	d									09 46													
Dore & Totley	d									09 56													
Sheffield 7	a					09 08			09 34	10 06						10 08		10 34					

A until 30 December, MO from 6 January until 17 March, from 24 March. To Cleethorpes
B from 31 December until 21 March. To Cleethorpes
C To Hadfield
D To Manchester Piccadilly
E To Sheffield
F To Cleethorpes
G From Manchester Piccadilly
H From Liverpool Lime Street to Norwich

Table 78R

Mondays to Fridays

9 December to 16 May

Manchester Airport and Manchester Romiley, Marple, Chinley and Sheffield

Network Diagram - see first Page of Table 78

		TP	NT	EM		NT	NT	NT	NT	NT	TP	NT	EM	NT		NT	NT	NT	NT	TP	NT	EM	NT	NT	
		◇1		◇							◇1		◇							◇1		◇			
		A		B			C			C	A		B			C			C	A		B		C	
Manchester Airport 85 ✈	d	09 55									10 55									11 55					
Manchester Piccadilly 10	a	10 13									11 13									12 13					
	d	10 20	10 35	10 43		10 45	10 48	11 05	11 14	11 18	11 20	11 35	11 43	11 45		11 48	12 05	12 14	12 18	12 20	12 35	12 43	12 45	12 48	
Ardwick	d																								
Ashburys	d						10 52		11 18	11 22						11 52		12 18	12 22					12 52	
Belle Vue	d																	12 20							
Ryder Brow	d								11 21									12 21							
Reddish North	d					10 52			11 24					11 52				12 24					12 52		
Brinnington	d					10 56			11 27					11 56				12 27					12 56		
Bredbury	d					10 59			11 30					11 59				12 30					12 59		
Gorton	d		10 41					11 11				11 41					12 11				12 41				
Fairfield	d		10 43									11 43									12 43				
Guide Bridge	a		10 46				10 57	11 15		11 27		11 46				11 57	12 15		12 27		12 46			12 57	
	d		10 46					11 15				11 46					12 15				12 46				
Hyde North	d							11 19									12 19								
Hyde Central	d		10 51					11 22				11 51					12 22				12 51				
Woodley	d		10 54					11 25				11 54					12 25				12 54				
Romiley	d		10 58			11 02		11 28	11 33			11 58		12 02			12 28	12 33			12 58		13 02		
Rose Hill Marple	a		11 04					11 34				12 04					12 34				13 04				
Marple	d					11 06			11 37					12 06				12 37					13 06		
Strines	d								11 41																
New Mills Central	a					11 11			11 45					12 13				12 45					13 11		
	d					11 11																	13 11		
Stockport 86	d	10 28		10 54							11 28		11 54							12 28		12 54			
Hazel Grove 86	d																								
Chinley	d					11 19																	13 19		
Edale	d					11 28																	13 28		
Hope (Derbyshire)	d					11 34																	13 34		
Bamford	d					11 37																	13 37		
Hathersage	d					11 40																	13 40		
Grindleford	d					11 44																	13 44		
Dore & Totley	d					11 56																	13 56		
Sheffield 7	a	11 08		11 33		12 05					12 08		12 34							13 08		13 35	14 06		

		NT	NT	NT	TP	NT	EM	NT	NT	NT		NT	NT	TP	NT	EM	NT	NT	NT	NT		NT	TP	NT	EM
					◇1		◇							◇1		◇							◇1		◇
				C	A		B		C				C	A		B		C				C	A		B
Manchester Airport 85 ✈	d				12 55									13 55									14 55		
Manchester Piccadilly 10	a				13 13									14 13									15 13		
	d	13 05	13 14	13 18	13 20	13 35	13 43	13 45	13 48	14 05		14 14	14 18	14 20	14 35	14 43	14 45	14 48	15 05	15 14		15 18	15 20	15 35	15 43
Ardwick	d																								
Ashburys	d		13 18	13 22					13 52			14 18	14 22					14 52		15 18		15 22			
Belle Vue	d											14 20													
Ryder Brow	d		13 21									14 21								15 21					
Reddish North	d		13 24					13 52				14 24					14 52			15 24					
Brinnington	d		13 27					13 56				14 27					14 56			15 27					
Bredbury	d		13 30					13 59				14 30					14 59			15 30					
Gorton	d	13 11				13 41				14 11					14 41				15 11					15 41	
Fairfield	d					13 43									14 43									15 43	
Guide Bridge	a	13 15		13 27		13 46			13 57	14 15			14 27		14 46			14 57	15 15			15 27		15 46	
	d	13 15				13 46				14 15					14 46				15 15					15 46	
Hyde North	d	13 19								14 19									15 19						
Hyde Central	d	13 22				13 51				14 22					14 51				15 22					15 51	
Woodley	d	13 25				13 54				14 25					14 54				15 25					15 54	
Romiley	d	13 28	13 33			13 58		14 02		14 28		14 33			14 58		15 02		15 28	15 33				15 58	
Rose Hill Marple	a	13 34				14 04				14 34					15 04				15 34					16 04	
Marple	d		13 37					14 06				14 37					15 06			15 37					
Strines	d		13 41																	15 41					
New Mills Central	a		13 45					14 13				14 45					15 11			15 45					
	d																15 11								
Stockport 86	d				13 28		13 54							14 28		14 54							15 28		15 54
Hazel Grove 86	d																								
Chinley	d																15 19								
Edale	d																15 28								
Hope (Derbyshire)	d																15 34								
Bamford	d																15 37								
Hathersage	d																15 40								
Grindleford	d																15 44								
Dore & Totley	d																15 56								
Sheffield 7	a				14 08		14 34							15 08		15 34	16 06						16 08		16 34

A To Cleethorpes
B From Liverpool Lime Street to Norwich
C To Hadfield

Table 78R

Mondays to Fridays

9 December to 16 May

Manchester Airport and Manchester Romiley, Marple, Chinley and Sheffield

Network Diagram - see first Page of Table 78

Station		NT	NT A	NT	NT	NT A		TP ◇1 B	NT	NT A	EM ◇ C	NT	NT	NT A	NT	NT A		NT	TP ◇1 B	NT	NT	NT A	EM ◇ D	NT	NT A
Manchester Airport 85	d							15 55											16 55						
Manchester Piccadilly 10	a							16 13											17 13						
	d	15 45	15 48	16 02	16 05	16 15		16 20	16 23	16 35	16 43	16 45	16 48	16 59	17 03	17 15		17 18	17 20	17 21	17 33	17 37	17 43	17 48	17 59
Ardwick	d														17 06										
Ashburys	d		15 52	16 06		16 19				16 39		16 49		17 03	17 08	17 19					17 37	17 41			18 03
Belle Vue	d			16 08											17 11						17 39				
Ryder Brow	d			16 10											17 13						17 41				
Reddish North	d	15 52		16 13					16 30			16 54			17 15			17 25			17 44			17 55	
Brinnington	d	15 56		16 16					16 34			16 57			17 19						17 47			17 59	
Bredbury	d	15 59		16 19					16 37			17 00			17 22			17 31			17 50			18 02	
Gorton	d				16 11					16 41			16 54			17 21						17 43			18 05
Fairfield	d				16 13								16 57												
Guide Bridge	a		15 57		16 16	16 24				16 45			17 00	17 08		17 25				17 29		17 47			18 09
	d				16 16								17 00							17 29					
Hyde North	d				16 20								17 04							17 33					
Hyde Central	d				16 23								17 06							17 36					
Woodley	d				16 26								17 09							17 39					
Romiley	d	16 02		16 22	16 29				16 40			17 03	17 13		17 25			17 34		17 42	17 53			18 05	
Rose Hill Marple	a				16 35								17 19							17 48					
Marple	d	16 06		16 26					16a44			17 07			17a29			17 37			17 57			18 08	
Strines	d	16 10										17 11									18 01				
New Mills Central	a	16 13		16 32								17 15						17 44			18 05			18 14	
	d	16 13										17 15												18 14	
Stockport 86	d							16 28			16 54								17 28				17 54		
Hazel Grove 86	d																								
Chinley	d	16 21									17 09	17 21											18 09	18 21	
Edale	d	16 30										17 30												18 30	
Hope (Derbyshire)	d	16 36										17 36												18 36	
Bamford	d	16 39										17 39												18 39	
Hathersage	d	16 42										17 42												18 42	
Grindleford	d	16 46										17 46												18 46	
Dore & Totley	d	16 56									17 31	17 56							18 03				18 40	18 56	
Sheffield 7	a	17 06						17 08			17 39	18 06							18 10				18 47	19 05	

Station		NT		NT	NT	NT E	TP ◇1 B	NT	EM ◇ C	NT	NT E	NT		TP ◇1 B	NT E	EM ◇ D	NT	NT E	TP ◇1 B	NT	EM ◇ D	NT		NT E	TP FX ◇1 B
Manchester Airport 85	d						17 55							18 55					19 55						20 47
Manchester Piccadilly 10	a						18 13							19 13					20 13						21 13
	d	18 03		18 05	18 14	18 18	18 20	18 35	18 43	18 45	18 48	19 14		19 18	19 18	19 43	19 45	19 48	20 20	20 35	20 43	20 45		20 48	21 20
Ardwick	d			18 08																					
Ashburys	d	18 07		18 10	18 18						18 52	19 18			19 22		19 49	19 52						20 52	
Belle Vue	d	18 09			18 20												19 51								
Ryder Brow	d	18 11			18 21							19 21					19 53								
Reddish North	d	18 14			18 24					18 52		19 24					19 56					20 52			
Brinnington	d	18 17			18 27					18 56		19 27					19 59					20 56			
Bredbury	d	18 20			18 30					18 59		19 30					20 02					20 59			
Gorton	d					18 24		18 41							19 24			19 54		20 41					
Fairfield	d			18 14				18 43												20 43					
Guide Bridge	a			18 17		18 27		18 46			18 57				19 28			19 58		20 46				20 57	
	d			18 17				18 46												20 46					
Hyde North	d			18 21				18 50												20 50					
Hyde Central	d			18 24				18 53												20 53					
Woodley	d			18 27				18 56												20 56					
Romiley	d	18 23		18 30	18 33			18 59		19 02		19 33					20 05			20 59		21 02			
Rose Hill Marple	a			18 36				19 05												21 05					
Marple	d	18a28			18 37					19 06		19 37					20 09					21 06			
Strines	d				18 41												20 13								
New Mills Central	a				18 46					19 11		19 44					20 18					21 11			
	d									19 11												21 11			
Stockport 86	d						18 28		18 54					19 26		19 54			20 28		20 54				21 28
Hazel Grove 86	d																								
Chinley	d									19 19												21 19			
Edale	d									19 28												21 28			
Hope (Derbyshire)	d									19 34												21 34			
Bamford	d									19 37												21 37			
Hathersage	d									19 40												21 40			
Grindleford	d									19 44												21 44			
Dore & Totley	d						19 03			19 56				20 01					21 03			21 52			
Sheffield 7	a						19 09		19 33	20 06				20 08		20 35			21 10		21 34	22 03			22 09

A To Manchester Piccadilly
B To Cleethorpes
C From Liverpool Lime Street to Norwich
D From Liverpool Lime Street to Nottingham
E To Hadfield

Table 78R

Mondays to Fridays

9 December to 16 May

Manchester Airport and Manchester Romiley, Marple, Chinley and Sheffield

Network Diagram - see first Page of Table 78

		TP FO ◇[1] A	NT	NT B	TP ◇[1] C	TP FX ◇[1] D	EM ◇ E	NT	NT B	NT	NT F	TP ◇[1] C	TP FX ◇[1] D
Manchester Airport 85 ⇐	d	20 47			21 47							23 30	
Manchester Piccadilly [10] car	a	21 13			22 13							23 48	
	d	21 20	21 45	21 48	22 20	22 20	22 28	22 45	22 48	23 24	23 27	23 52	23 52
Ardwick	d												
Ashburys	d		21 49	21 52				22 49	22 52	23 28	23 31		
Belle Vue	d		21 51							23 30			
Ryder Brow	d		21 53					22 52		23 32			
Reddish North	d		21 56					22 55		23 35			
Brinnington	d		21 59					22 58		23 38			
Bredbury	d		22 02					23 01		23 41			
Gorton	d			21 54					22 54		23 33		
Fairfield	d												
Guide Bridge	a			21 58					22 58		23 37		
	d												
Hyde North	d												
Hyde Central	d												
Woodley	d												
Romiley	d		22 05					23 04		23 44			
Rose Hill Marple	a												
Marple	d		22 09					23 08		23 48			
Strines	d		22 13							23 52			
New Mills Central	a		22 18					23 15		23 57			
	d												
Stockport 86	d	21 28					22 38						
Hazel Grove 86	d												
Chinley	d						22 53						
Edale	d						23 01						
Hope (Derbyshire)	d						23 07						
Bamford	d						23 11						
Hathersage	d						23 15						
Grindleford	d						23 19						
Dore & Totley	d						23 28						
Sheffield [7] car	a	22 10			23 16	23 16	23 35					01 19	01 19

Saturdays

14 December to 17 May

		TP ◇[1] A	NT	NT B	NT	NT B	NT	NT B	TP ◇[1] A	NT G	EM ◇ H	NT	NT I	NT B	NT	NT	NT B	TP ◇[1] A	NT	EM ◇ H	NT	NT B	NT
Manchester Airport 85 ⇐	d	05 20							06 55									07 53					
Manchester Piccadilly [10] car	a	05 33							07 13									08 12					
	d	05 44	05 50	06 16	06 35	06 48	07 03	07 18	07 19	07 39	07 42	07 44		07 48	08 03	08 14	08 18	08 20	08 35	08 43	08 45	08 48	09 03
Ardwick	d																						
Ashburys	d			06 20	06 39	06 52	07 07	07 22						07 52		08 18	08 22					08 52	
Belle Vue	d				06 41		07 09									08 20							
Ryder Brow	d				06 43		07 11									08 21							
Reddish North	d				06 46		07 14					07 52				08 24					08 52		
Brinnington	d				06 49		07 17					07 56				08 27					08 56		
Bredbury	d				06 52		07 20					07 59				08 30					08 59		
Gorton	d					06 54				07 45					08 09				08 41				09 09
Fairfield	d									07 47									08 43				
Guide Bridge	a			06 25		06 58		07 27		07 50				07 57	08 13		08 27		08 46			08 57	09 13
	d									07 50					08 13				08 46				09 13
Hyde North	d									07 54					08 17								09 17
Hyde Central	d									07 57					08 20				08 51				09 20
Woodley	d									08 00			←		08 23				08 54				09 23
Romiley	d				06 55		07 23			08 03		08 02	08 03		08 26	08 33			08 58		09 02		09 26
Rose Hill Marple	a									↳			08 10			08 39			09 04				
Marple	d				06 59		07a28					08 06			08a31						09 06		09a31
Strines	d																				09 10		
New Mills Central	a				07 04							08 11									09 13		
	d				07 04							08 11									09 13		
Stockport 86	d	05 52	06 00						07 27		07 54							08 28		08 54			
Hazel Grove 86	d		06 07																				
Chinley	d		06 18		07 12							08 19									09 21		
Edale	d		06 26		07 21							08 28									09 30		
Hope (Derbyshire)	d		06 32		07 27							08 34									09 36		
Bamford	d		06 35		07 30							08 37									09 39		
Hathersage	d		06 39		07 33							08 40									09 42		
Grindleford	d		06 42		07 37							08 44									09 46		
Dore & Totley	d		06 51		07 47				08 02		08 27	08 56									09 56		
Sheffield [7] car	a	06 40	07 01		07 57				08 11		08 34	09 06						09 08		09 34	10 06		

A To Cleethorpes
B To Hadfield
C until 27 December, FO from 3 January until 14 March, from 21 March
D from 30 December until 20 March
E From Liverpool Lime Street to Nottingham
F To Glossop
G To Rose Hill Marple
H From Liverpool Lime Street to Norwich
I From Manchester Piccadilly

Table 78R

Saturdays

14 December to 17 May

Manchester Airport and Manchester Romiley, Marple, Chinley and Sheffield

Network Diagram - see first Page of Table 78

		NT	NT A	TP ◇1 B	NT	EM ◇ C		NT	NT A	NT	NT	NT A	TP ◇1 B	NT	EM ◇ C	NT		NT A	NT	NT	NT A	TP ◇1 B	NT	EM ◇ C	NT
Manchester Airport 85	d			08 55									09 55									10 55			
Manchester Piccadilly 10	a			09 13									10 13									11 13			
	d	09 14	09 18	09 20	09 35	09 43		09 45	09 48	10 03	10 14	10 18	10 20	10 35	10 43	10 45		10 48	11 03	11 14	11 18	11 20	11 35	11 43	11 45
Ardwick	d																								
Ashburys	d	09 18	09 22						09 52		10 18	10 22						10 52		11 18	11 22				
Belle Vue	d										10 20														
Ryder Brow	d	09 21									10 21									11 21					
Reddish North	d	09 24						09 52			10 24					10 52				11 24					11 52
Brinnington	d	09 27						09 56			10 28					10 56				11 27					11 56
Bredbury	d	09 30						09 59			10 30					10 59				11 30					11 59
Gorton	d				09 41					10 09				10 41					11 09				11 41		
Fairfield	d				09 43									10 43									11 43		
Guide Bridge	a		09 27		09 46				09 57	10 13		10 27		10 46				10 57	11 13		11 27		11 46		
	d				09 46					10 13				10 46					11 13				11 46		
Hyde North	d									10 17									11 17						
Hyde Central	d				09 51					10 20				10 51					11 20				11 51		
Woodley	d				09 54					10 23				10 54					11 23				11 54		
Romiley	d	09 33			09 58			10 02		10 26	10 33			10 58		11 02			11 26	11 33			11 58		12 02
Rose Hill Marple	a	09 39			10 04						10 39			11 04						11 39			12 04		
Marple	d							10 06		10a31						11 06			11a31						12 06
Strines	d							10 10																	12 10
New Mills Central	a							10 13								11 11									12 13
	d							10 13								11 11									12 13
Stockport 86	d			09 28		09 54							10 28		10 54							11 28		11 54	
Hazel Grove 86	d																								
Chinley	d							10 21								11 19									12 21
Edale	d							10 30								11 28									12 30
Hope (Derbyshire)	d							10 36								11 34									12 36
Bamford	d							10 39								11 37									12 39
Hathersage	d							10 42								11 40									12 42
Grindleford	d							10 46								11 44									12 46
Dore & Totley	d							10 56								11 56									12 56
Sheffield 7	a			10 08		10 34		11 06					11 08		11 34	12 06						12 08		12 34	13 06

		NT A		NT	NT	NT A	TP ◇1 B	NT	EM ◇ C	NT	NT A	NT		NT	NT A	TP ◇1 B	NT	EM ◇ C	NT	NT A	NT	NT		NT A	TP ◇1 B
Manchester Airport 85	d						11 55									12 55									13 55
Manchester Piccadilly 10	a						12 13									13 13									14 13
	d	11 48		12 03	12 14	12 18	12 20	12 35	12 43	12 45	12 48	13 03		13 14	13 18	13 20	13 35	13 43	13 45	13 48	14 03	14 14		14 18	14 20
Ardwick	d																								
Ashburys	d	11 52			12 18	12 22					12 52			13 18	13 22					13 52		14 18		14 22	
Belle Vue	d				12 20																	14 20			
Ryder Brow	d				12 21									13 21								14 21			
Reddish North	d				12 24					12 52				13 24					13 52			14 24			
Brinnington	d				12 27					12 56				13 27					13 56			14 27			
Bredbury	d				12 30					12 59				13 30					13 59			14 30			
Gorton	d			12 09				12 41				13 09					13 41				14 09				
Fairfield	d							12 43									13 43								
Guide Bridge	a	11 57		12 13		12 27		12 46			12 57	13 13			13 27		13 46			13 57	14 13			14 27	
	d			12 13				12 46				13 13					13 46				14 13				
Hyde North	d			12 17								13 17									14 17				
Hyde Central	d			12 20				12 51				13 20					13 51				14 20				
Woodley	d			12 23				12 54				13 23					13 54				14 23				
Romiley	d			12 26	12 33			12 58		13 02		13 26		13 33			13 58		14 02		14 26	14 33			
Rose Hill Marple	a				12 39			13 04						13 39			14 04					14 39			
Marple	d			12a31						13 06		13a31							14 06		14a31				
Strines	d																		14 10						
New Mills Central	a									13 11									14 13						
	d									13 11									14 13						
Stockport 86	d						12 28		12 54							13 28		13 54							14 28
Hazel Grove 86	d																								
Chinley	d									13 19									14 21						
Edale	d									13 28									14 30						
Hope (Derbyshire)	d									13 34									14 36						
Bamford	d									13 37									14 39						
Hathersage	d									13 40									14 42						
Grindleford	d									13 44									14 46						
Dore & Totley	d									13 56									14 56						
Sheffield 7	a						13 08		13 34	14 06						14 08		14 34	15 06						15 08

A To Hadfield

B To Cleethorpes

C From Liverpool Lime Street to Norwich

Table 78R

Saturdays

14 December to 17 May

Manchester Airport and Manchester Romiley, Marple, Chinley and Sheffield

Network Diagram - see first Page of Table 78

Station		NT	EM ◇ A	NT	NT B	NT	NT	NT B		TP ◇1 C	NT	EM ◇ A	NT	NT B	NT	NT	NT B	TP ◇1 C		NT	EM ◇ A	NT	NT B	NT	NT
Manchester Airport 85 ✈	d									14 55								15 55							
Manchester Piccadilly 10	a									15 13								16 13							
	d	14 35	14 43	14 45	14 48	15 03	15 14	15 18		15 20	15 35	15 43	15 45	15 48	16 03	16 14	16 18	16 20		16 35	16 43	16 45	16 48	17 03	17 14
Ardwick	d																								
Ashburys	d				14 52		15 18	15 22						15 52		16 18	16 22						16 52		17 18
Belle Vue	d															16 20									
Ryder Brow	d						15 21									16 21									17 21
Reddish North	d			14 52			15 24						15 52			16 24						16 52			17 24
Brinnington	d			14 56			15 27						15 56			16 27						16 56			17 27
Bredbury	d			14 59			15 30						15 59			16 30						16 59			17 30
Gorton	d	14 41				15 09					15 41				16 09					16 41				17 09	
Fairfield	d	14 43									15 43									16 43					
Guide Bridge	a	14 46			14 57	15 13		15 27			15 46			15 57	16 13		16 27			16 46			16 57	17 13	
	d	14 46				15 13					15 46				16 13					16 46				17 13	
Hyde North	d					15 17									16 17									17 17	
Hyde Central	d	14 51				15 20					15 51				16 20					16 51				17 20	
Woodley	d	14 54				15 23					15 54				16 23					16 54				17 23	
Romiley	d	14 58		15 02		15 26	15 33				15 58		16 02		16 26	16 33				16 58		17 02		17 26	17 33
Rose Hill Marple	a	15 04					15 39				16 04					16 39				17 04					17 39
Marple	d			15 06		15a31							16 06		16a31							17 06		17a31	
Strines	d												16 10												
New Mills Central	a			15 11									16 13									17 11			
	d			15 11									16 13									17 11			
Stockport 86	d		14 54							15 28		15 54						16 28			16 54				
Hazel Grove 86	d																								
Chinley	d			15 19									16 21								17 09	17 19			
Edale	d			15 28									16 30									17 28			
Hope (Derbyshire)	d			15 34									16 36									17 34			
Bamford	d			15 37									16 39									17 37			
Hathersage	d			15 40									16 42									17 40			
Grindleford	d			15 44									16 46									17 44			
Dore & Totley	d			15 56									16 56								17 31	17 56			
Sheffield 7	a		15 34	16 06						16 08		16 34	17 06					17 08			17 37	18 06			

Station		NT B	TP ◇1 C	NT		EM ◇ D	NT	NT B	NT	NT	NT B	TP ◇1 C	NT	EM ◇ A		NT	NT B	NT	TP ◇1 C	EM ◇ D	NT	NT B	TP ◇1 C	NT	
Manchester Airport 85 ✈	d		16 55									17 55							18 55				19 55		
Manchester Piccadilly 10	a		17 13									18 13							19 13				20 13		
	d	17 18	17 20	17 35		17 43	17 45	17 48	18 03	18 14	18 18	18 20	18 35	18 43		18 45	18 48	19 14	19 18	19 43	19 45	19 48	20 20	20 35	
Ardwick	d																								
Ashburys	d	17 22						17 52		18 18	18 22						18 52	19 18			19 49	19 52			
Belle Vue	d									18 20											19 51				
Ryder Brow	d									18 21								19 21			19 53				
Reddish North	d						17 52			18 24						18 52		19 24			19 56				
Brinnington	d						17 56			18 27						18 56		19 27			19 59				
Bredbury	d						17 59			18 30						18 59		19 30			20 02				
Gorton	d			17 41					18 09				18 41									19 54		20 41	
Fairfield	d			17 43									18 43											20 43	
Guide Bridge	a	17 27		17 46				17 57	18 13		18 27		18 46				18 57					19 58		20 46	
	d			17 46					18 13				18 46											20 46	
Hyde North	d								18 17				18 50											20 50	
Hyde Central	d			17 51					18 20				18 53											20 53	
Woodley	d			17 54					18 23				18 56											20 56	
Romiley	d			17 58			18 02		18 26	18 33			18 59			19 02		19 33			20 05			20 59	
Rose Hill Marple	a			18 04						18 39			19 05					19 39						21 05	
Marple	d						18 06		18a31							19 06					20 09				
Strines	d						18 10														20 13				
New Mills Central	a						18 13									19 11					20 18				
	d						18 13									19 11									
Stockport 86	d		17 28			17 54						18 28		18 54					19 26	19 54			20 28		
Hazel Grove 86	d																								
Chinley	d					18 08	18 21									19 19									
Edale	d						18 30									19 28									
Hope (Derbyshire)	d						18 36									19 34									
Bamford	d						18 39									19 37									
Hathersage	d						18 42									19 40									
Grindleford	d						18 46									19 44									
Dore & Totley	d		18 03				18 56					19 03				19 56			20 01				21 03		
Sheffield 7	a		18 10			18 36	19 06					19 09		19 33		20 06			20 08	20 36			21 14		

A From Liverpool Lime Street to Norwich
B To Hadfield
C To Cleethorpes
D From Liverpool Lime Street to Nottingham

Table 78R

Saturdays

14 December to 17 May

Manchester Airport and Manchester Romiley, Marple, Chinley and Sheffield

Network Diagram - see first Page of Table 78

		EM	NT	NT	TP	EM	NT	NT	TP	EM	NT	NT	NT	NT	NT	NT
		◇			◇ 1	◇			◇ 1	◇						
		A		B		A		B		A		C	D		E	F
Manchester Airport 85 ✈	d				20 47				21 47							
Manchester Piccadilly 10	a				21 13				22 13							
	d	20 43	20 45	20 48	21 20	21 43	21 45	21 48	22 20	22 28	22 45	22 48	22 48	23 24	23 27	23 27
Ardwick	d															
Ashburys	d			20 52			21 49	21 52			22 49	22 52	22 52	23 28	23 31	23 31
Belle Vue	d						21 51				22 51			23 30		
Ryder Brow	d						21 53				22 53			23 32		
Reddish North	d		20 52				21 56				22 56			23 35		
Brinnington	d		20 56				21 59				22 59			23 38		
Bredbury	d		20 59				22 02				23 02			23 41		
Gorton	d							21 54				22 54	22 55		23 33	23 34
Fairfield	d															
Guide Bridge	a			20 57				21 58				22 58	22 59		23 37	23 38
	d															
Hyde North	d															
Hyde Central	d															
Woodley	d															
Romiley	d		21 02				22 05				23 05			23 44		
Rose Hill Marple	a															
Marple	d		21 06				22 09				23 09			23 48		
Strines	d						22 13				23 13			23 52		
New Mills Central	a		21 11				22 18				23 18			23 57		
	d		21 11													
Stockport 86	d	20 54			21 28	21 52				22 38						
Hazel Grove 86	d															
Chinley	d		21 19							22 53						
Edale	d		21 28							23 01						
Hope (Derbyshire)	d		21 34							23 07						
Bamford	d		21 37							23 11						
Hathersage	d		21 40							23 15						
Grindleford	d		21 44							23 19						
Dore & Totley	d		21 52							23 28						
Sheffield 7	a	21 34	22 03		22 10	22 31			23 16	23 35						

Sundays

8 December to 11 May

		NT	TP	TP	TP	NT	NT	NT	NT	NT	TP	NT	NT	NT	TP	NT	EM	NT	NT	TP	EM	NT	NT
			◇ 1	◇ 1	◇ 1						◇ 1				◇ 1		◇			◇ 1	◇		
			G	H	I	B		B	B	B		B		B		B	J	B	B		K		B
Manchester Airport 85 ✈	d		08 40	08 41							10 44				11 55					12 55			
Manchester Piccadilly 10	a		08 54	08 55							10 58				12 09					13 07			
	d	07 45	08 58	08 58	08 58	09 18	09 22	09 48	10 18	10 48	11 18	11 18	11 45	11 48	12 18	12 18	12 44	12 48	13 18	13 20	13 44	13 45	13 48
Ardwick	d																						
Ashburys	d					09 22		09 52	10 22	10 52		11 22		11 52		12 22		12 52	13 22				13 52
Belle Vue	d																						
Ryder Brow	d																						
Reddish North	d	07 52					09 29						11 52									13 52	
Brinnington	d	07 56					09 33						11 56									13 56	
Bredbury	d	07 59					09 36						11 59									13 59	
Gorton	d					09 24		09 56	10 24	10 54		11 24		11 54		12 24		12 54	13 24				13 54
Fairfield	d																						
Guide Bridge	a					09 28		10 00	10 28	10 58		11 28		11 58		12 28		12 58	13 28				13 58
	d																						
Hyde North	d																						
Hyde Central	d																						
Woodley	d																						
Romiley	d	08 02					09 39						12 02									14 02	
Rose Hill Marple	a																						
Marple	d	08 06					09 43						12 06									14 06	
Strines	d	08 10					09 47						12 10									14 10	
New Mills Central	a	08 14					09 51						12 14									14 14	
	d	08 14					09 51						12 14									14 14	
Stockport 86	d		09 07	09 07	09 08						11 27				12 28		12 55			13 28	13 54		
Hazel Grove 86	d																						
Chinley	d	08 23					09 59						12 23									14 23	
Edale	d	08 32					10 08						12 32									14 32	
Hope (Derbyshire)	d	08 38					10 14						12 38									14 38	
Bamford	d	08 41					10 17						12 41									14 41	
Hathersage	d	08 45					10 20						12 45									14 45	
Grindleford	d	08 48					10 24						12 48									14 48	
Dore & Totley	d	08 57					10 35						12 57									14 57	
Sheffield 7	a	09 06	09 45	09 45	09 45		10 44				12 07		13 05		13 08		13 38			14 08	14 37	15 05	

A From Liverpool Lime Street to Nottingham
B To Hadfield
C until 8 February, from 29 March. To Hadfield
D from 15 February until 22 March. To Hadfield
E until 8 February, from 29 March. To Glossop
F from 15 February until 22 March. To Glossop
G until 9 February
H from 30 March
I from 16 February until 23 March
J To Norwich
K From Liverpool Lime Street to Norwich

Table 78R

Sundays

8 December to 11 May

Manchester Airport and Manchester Romiley, Marple, Chinley and Sheffield

Network Diagram - see first Page of Table 78

		NT	TP	EM	NT	NT		NT	TP	EM	EM	NT	NT	NT	TP	TP		EM	NT	NT	TP	EM	EM	NT	NT
			◇1	◇					◇1	◇	◇				◇1	◇1		◇			◇1	◇	◇		
		A		B	C	A		A		D	E		A	A	F	G		B	A	A		H	I		A
Manchester Airport 85 ✈	d		13 55						14 55						15 55	15 55					16 55				
Manchester Piccadilly 10	a		14 09						15 09						16 09	16 09					17 09				
	d	14 18	14 20	14 44	14 45	14 48		15 18	15 20	15 44	15 44	15 45	15 48	16 18	16 20	16 20		16 44	16 48	17 18	17 20	17 44	17 44	17 45	17 48
Ardwick	d																								
Ashburys	d	14 22				14 52		15 22					15 52	16 22					16 52	17 22					17 52
Belle Vue	d																								
Ryder Brow	d																								
Reddish North	d				14 52							15 52												17 52	
Brinnington	d				14 56							15 56												17 56	
Bredbury	d				14 59							15 59												17 59	
Gorton	d	14 24				14 54		15 24					15 54	16 24					16 54	17 24					17 54
Fairfield	d																								
Guide Bridge	a	14 28				14 58		15 28					15 58	16 28					16 58	17 28					17 58
	d																								
Hyde North	d																								
Hyde Central	d																								
Woodley	d																								
Romiley	d				15 02							16 02												18 02	
Rose Hill Marple	a																								
Marple	d				15 06							16 06												18 06	
Strines	d				15 10							16 10												18 10	
New Mills Central	a				15 14							16 14												18 14	
	d				15 14							16 14												18 14	
Stockport 86	d		14 28	14 54					15 28	15 54	15 54				16 28	16 28		16 54			17 28	17 54	17 54		
Hazel Grove 86	d																								
Chinley	d				15 23							16 23												18 23	
Edale	d				15 32							16 32												18 32	
Hope (Derbyshire)	d				15 38							16 38												18 38	
Bamford	d				15 41							16 41												18 41	
Hathersage	d				15 45							16 45												18 45	
Grindleford	d				15 48							16 48												18 48	
Dore & Totley	d				15 57							16 57												18 57	
Sheffield 7	a		15 08	15 35	16 05				16 09	16 37	16 39	17 06			17 08	17 11		17 34			18 08	18 36	18 41	19 06	

		NT		TP	EM	NT	NT	TP	EM	NT	NT	TP		EM	NT	TP	EM	TP	NT	TP
				◇1	◇			◇1	◇			◇1		◇		◇1	◇	◇1		◇1
		A			B	A	A		J		A			J	A		J			
Manchester Airport 85 ✈	d			17 55				18 55				19 55				20 55		21 55		22 55
Manchester Piccadilly 10	a			18 09				19 09				20 09				21 09		22 09		23 09
	d	18 18		18 20	18 44	18 48	19 18	19 20	19 44	19 45	19 48	20 18		20 44	20 48	21 20	22 11	22 15	22 20	23 20
Ardwick	d																			
Ashburys	d	18 22				18 52	19 22				19 52				20 52					
Belle Vue	d																			
Ryder Brow	d																			
Reddish North	d									19 52									22 27	
Brinnington	d									19 56									22 31	
Bredbury	d									19 59									22 34	
Gorton	d	18 24				18 54	19 24				19 54				20 54					
Fairfield	d																			
Guide Bridge	a	18 28				18 58	19 28				19 58				20 58					
	d																			
Hyde North	d																			
Hyde Central	d																			
Woodley	d																			
Romiley	d									20 02									22 37	
Rose Hill Marple	a																			
Marple	d									20 06									22 40	
Strines	d									20 10									22 44	
New Mills Central	a									20 14									22 49	
	d									20 14										
Stockport 86	d			18 28	18 54			19 28	19 54			20 27		20 54		21 28	22 28	22 23		23 28
Hazel Grove 86	d																			
Chinley	d									20 23							22 43			
Edale	d									20 32							22 51			
Hope (Derbyshire)	d									20 38							22 57			
Bamford	d									20 41							23 00			
Hathersage	d									20 45							23 03			
Grindleford	d									20 48							23 07			
Dore & Totley	d									20 57							23 17			
Sheffield 7	a			19 08	19 35			20 08	20 35	21 06		21 08		21 34		22 12	23 24	23 04		00 15

A To Hadfield
B From Liverpool Lime Street to Norwich
C from 30 March
D until 9 February, from 30 March. From Liverpool Lime Street to Norwich
E from 16 February until 23 March. From Liverpool Lime Street to Norwich
F until 29 December, from 30 March. To Cleethorpes
G from 5 January until 23 March
H until 9 February, from 30 March. From Liverpool Lime Street to Nottingham
I from 16 February until 23 March. From Liverpool Lime Street to Nottingham
J From Liverpool Lime Street to Nottingham

Table 79

Mondays to Fridays

9 December to 16 May

Manchester - Glossop and Hadfield

Network Diagram - see first Page of Table 78

Miles	Miles			NT	NT	NT	NT	NT	NT	NT	NT	NT		NT	NT	NT	NT	NT	NT	NT	NT	NT	NT
0	—	**Manchester Picc.** [10] 78 ⛴	d	06 18	06 48	07 02	07 18	07 48	08 04	08 29	08 48	09 18		15 48	16 15	16 35	16 59	17 15	17 37	17 59	18 18	18 48	19 18
0½	—	Ardwick 78	d																				
1½	—	Ashburys 78	d	06 22	06 52	07 06	07 22	07 52	08 08	08 33	08 52	09 22		15 52	16 19	16 39	17 03	17 19	17 41	18 03		18 52	19 22
2½	—	Gorton 78	d				07 24	07 54								16 41		17 21	17 43	18 05	18 24		19 24
4¾	—	Guide Bridge 78	d	06 27	06 57	07 11	07 28	07 58	08 13	08 38	08 57	09 27	and	15 57	16 24	16 45	17 09	17 25	17 47	18 09	18 27	18 57	19 28
6¾	—	Flowery Field	d	06 30	07 00	07 14	07 31	08 01	08 16	08 41	09 00	09 30	every 30	16 00	16 27	16 48	17 12	17 28	17 50	18 12	18 30	19 00	19 31
7½	—	Newton for Hyde	d	06 32	07 02	07 16	07 33	08 03	08 18	08 43	09 02	09 32	minutes	16 02	16 29	16 50	17 14	17 30	17 52	18 14	18 32	19 02	19 33
8½	—	Godley	d	06 34	07 04	07 18	07 35	08 05	08 20	08 45	09 04	09 34	until	16 04	16 31	16 52	17 16	17 32	17 54	18 16	18 34	19 04	19 35
9	—	Hattersley	d	06 36	07 06	07 20	07 37	08 07	08 22	08 47	09 06	09 36		16 06	16 33	16 54	17 19	17 34	17 56	18 18	18 36	19 06	19 37
10	—	Broadbottom	d	06 38	07 08	07 22	07 39	08 09	08 24	08 49	09 08	09 38		16 08	16 35	16 56	17 22	17 36	17 59	18 21	18 39	19 08	19 39
12¼	0	Dinting [3]	d	06 45	07 15	07 28	07 48	08 15	08 30	08 55	09 15	09 45		16 15	16 41	17 02	17 27	17 42	18 05	18 27	18 44	19 15	19 45
13¼	—	**Glossop**	a	06 48							09 19	09 48		16 18	16 44	17 05	17 31	17 45	18 08	18 30	18 48	19 18	19 48
—	—		d	06 51							09 21	09 51		16 21	16 47	17 08	17 33	17 48	18 13	18 33	18 50	19 21	19 51
15	0¾	**Hadfield**	a	06 58	07 17	07 30	07 50	08 17	08 32	08 57	09 28	09 58		16 28	16 53	17 14	17 39	17 54	18 19	18 39	18 57	19 28	19 58

		NT	NT	NT	NT	NT
Manchester Picc. [10] 78 ⛴	d	19 48	20 48	21 48	22 48	23 27
Ardwick 78	d					
Ashburys 78	d	19 52	20 52	21 52	22 52	23 31
Gorton 78	d	19 54		21 54	22 54	23 33
Guide Bridge 78	d	19 58	20 57	21 58	22 58	23 37
Flowery Field	d	20 01	21 00	22 01	23 01	23 40
Newton for Hyde	d	20 03	21 02	22 03	23 03	23 42
Godley	d	20 05	21 04	22 05	23 05	23 44
Hattersley	d	20 07	21 06	22 07	23 07	23 46
Broadbottom	d	20 09	21 08	22 09	23 09	23 48
Dinting [3]	d	20 15	21 15	22 15	23 15	23 54
Glossop	a	20 18	21 18	22 18	23 18	
	d	20 21	21 21	22 21	23 21	
Hadfield	a	20 28	21 28	22 28	23 28	23 56

Saturdays

14 December to 17 May

		NT	NT	NT		NT	NT	NT	NT	NT A	NT B	NT A	NT B
Manchester Picc. [10] 78 ⛴	d	06 16	06 48	07 18		18 48	19 48	20 48	21 48	22 48	22 48	23 27	23 27
Ardwick 78	d												
Ashburys 78	d	06 20	06 52	07 22		18 52	19 52	20 52	21 52	22 52	22 52	23 31	23 31
Gorton 78	d		06 54		and		19 54		21 54	22 54	22 55	23 33	23 34
Guide Bridge 78	d	06 25	06 58	07 27	every 30	18 57	19 58	20 57	21 58	22 58	22 59	23 37	23 38
Flowery Field	d	06 28	07 01	07 30	minutes	19 00	20 01	21 00	22 01	23 01	23 03	23 40	23 42
Newton for Hyde	d	06 30	07 03	07 32	until	19 02	20 03	21 02	22 03	23 03	23 06	23 42	23 45
Godley	d	06 32	07 05	07 34		19 04	20 05	21 04	22 05	23 05	23 08	23 44	23 47
Hattersley	d	06 34	07 07	07 36		19 06	20 07	21 06	22 07	23 07	23 10	23 46	23 49
Broadbottom	d	06 36	07 09	07 38		19 08	20 09	21 08	22 09	23 09	23 13	23 48	23 52
Dinting [3]	d	06 44	07 15	07 45		19 15	20 15	21 15	22 15	23 15	23 19	23 54	23 58
Glossop	a	06 47	07 18	07 48		19 18	20 18	21 18	22 18	23 18	23 23		
	d	06 50	07 21	07 51		19 21	20 21	21 21	22 21	23 21	23 25		
Hadfield	a	06 58	07 28	07 58		19 28	20 28	21 28	22 28	23 28	23 33	23 56	00 01

Sundays

8 December to 11 May

		NT	NT	NT		NT	NT
Manchester Picc. [10] 78 ⛴	d	09 18	09 48	10 18		19 48	20 48
Ardwick 78	d						
Ashburys 78	d	09 22	09 52	10 22		19 52	20 52
Gorton 78	d	09 24	09 56	10 24		19 54	20 54
Guide Bridge 78	d	09 28	10 00	10 28	and	19 58	20 58
Flowery Field	d	09 31	10 03	10 31	every 30	20 01	21 01
Newton for Hyde	d	09 33	10 05	10 33	minutes	20 03	21 03
Godley	d	09 35	10 07	10 35	until	20 05	21 05
Hattersley	d	09 37	10 09	10 37		20 07	21 07
Broadbottom	d	09 39	10 11	10 39		20 09	21 09
Dinting [3]	d	09 46	10 17	10 46		20 16	21 16
Glossop	a	09 49	10 20	10 49		20 19	21 19
	d	09 52	10 23	10 52		20 22	21 22
Hadfield	a	09 58	10 29	10 58		20 28	21 28

A until 8 February, from 29 March

B from 15 February until 22 March

Table 79R

Hadfield and Glossop - Manchester

Mondays to Fridays

9 December to 16 May

Network Diagram - see first Page of Table 78

Miles	Miles			NT	NT	NT	NT	NT	NT	NT	NT	NT	NT		NT	NT		NT	NT	NT
0	0	**Hadfield**	d	06 00	06 30	07 00	07 21	07 40	07 57	08 21	08 35	09 00	09 30	and every 30 minutes until	13 00	13 30	and every 30 minutes until	15 30	16 00	16 30
1¾	—	**Glossop**	a	06 05	06 35	07 05	07 26	07 45	08 02	08 26	08 40	09 05	09 35		13 05	13 35		15 35	16 05	
—	—		d	06 08	06 38	07 08	07 29	07 48	08 05	08 29	08 43	09 08	09 38		13 08	13 38		15 38	16 08	
2¾	0¾	Dinting 3	d	06 11	06 41	07 11	07 32	07 51	08 08	08 33	08 46	09 11	09 41		13 11	13 41		15 41	16 11	16 32
5	—	Broadbottom	d	06 15	06 45	07 15	07 36	07 56	08 12	08 37	08 50	09 15	09 45		13 15	13 45		15 45	16 15	16 36
6	—	Hattersley	d	06 18	06 48	07 18	07 39	07 59	08 15	08 40	08 53	09 18	09 48		13 18	13 48		15 48	16 18	16 39
6½	—	Godley	d	06 20	06 50	07 20	07 41	08 01	08 17	08 42	08 55	09 20	09 50		13 20	13 50		15 50	16 20	16 41
7½	—	Newton for Hyde	d	06 22	06 52	07 22	07 43	08 04	08 20	08 44	08 57	09 22	09 52		13 22	13 52		15 52	16 22	16 43
8¼	—	Flowery Field	d	06 24	06 54	07 24	07 45	08 06	08 22	08 46	08 59	09 24	09 54		13 24	13 54		15 54	16 24	16 45
10¼	—	Guide Bridge 78	a	06 27	06 57	07 27	07 48	08 10	08 25	08 49	09 02	09 27	09 57		13 27	13 57		15 57	16 27	16 48
12½	—	Gorton 78	a	06 30		07 30	07 51	08 13	08 29	08 52		09 31								
13½	—	Ashburys 78	a	06 33	07 04	07 33		08 17	08 33	08 56	09 07	09 33	10 02		13 32	14 02		16 02	16 33	16 55
14½	—	Ardwick 78	a			07 35														
15	—	**Manchester Picc. 10** 78 ⛴	a	06 40	07 12	07 41	08 00	08 25	08 41	09 02	09 15	09 40	10 10		13 40	14 11		16 11	16 41	17 04

		NT	NT	NT	NT	NT	NT	NT	NT	NT	NT	NT	NT	NT
Hadfield	d	16 56	17 17	17 44	17 59	18 28	18 44	19 00	19 30	20 00	20 30	21 30	22 30	23 59
Glossop	a							19 05	19 35	20 05	20 35	21 35	22 35	00 05
	d							19 08	19 38	20 08	20 38	21 38	22 38	
Dinting 3	d	16 58	17 19	17 46	18 01	18 30	18 47	19 11	19 41	20 11	20 41	21 41	22 41	
Broadbottom	d	17 02	17 23	17 50	18 05	18 34	18 51	19 15	19 45	20 15	20 45	21 45	22 45	
Hattersley	d	17 05	17 26		18 08	18 37	18 53	19 18	19 48	20 18	20 48	21 48	22 48	
Godley	d	17 07	17 28		18 10	18 39	18 55	19 20	19 50	20 20	20 50	21 50	22 50	
Newton for Hyde	d	17 09	17 30	17 54	18 13	18 41	18 57	19 22	19 52	20 22	20 52	21 52	22 52	
Flowery Field	d	17 11	17 32		18 15	18 43	18 59	19 24	19 54	20 24	20 55	21 54	22 54	
Guide Bridge 78	a	17 17	17 35	17 58	18 18	18 46	19 02	19 27	19 57	20 27	21 01	21 57	22 57	
Gorton 78	a					18 49				20 30		22 00	23 00	
Ashburys 78	a	17 27	17 40	18 07	18 27	18 55	19 07	19 32	20 02	20 33	21 05	22 03	23 03	
Ardwick 78	a													
Manchester Picc. 10 78 ⛴	a	17 34	17 48	18 14	18 34	19 02	19 16	19 41	20 11	20 41	21 14	22 11	23 11	

Saturdays

14 December to 17 May

		NT	NT	NT	NT	NT		NT	NT	NT		NT	NT	NT	NT	NT	NT	NT A
Hadfield	d	06 30	07 00	07 30	08 00	08 30	and every 30 minutes until	13 00	13 30	14 00	and at the same minutes past each hour until	18 30	19 00	19 30	20 30	21 30	22 30	23{59
Glossop	a	06 35	07 05	07 35	08 05	08 35		13 05	13 35	14 05		18 35	19 05	19 35	20 35	21 35	22 35	00}05
	d	06 38	07 08	07 38	08 08	08 38		13 08	13 38	14 08		18 38	19 08	19 38	20 38	21 38	22 38	
Dinting 3	d	06 41	07 11	07 41	08 11	08 41		13 11	13 41	14 11		18 41	19 11	19 41	20 41	21 41	22 41	
Broadbottom	d	06 45	07 15	07 45	08 15	08 45		13 15	13 45	14 15		18 45	19 15	19 45	20 45	21 45	22 45	
Hattersley	d	06 48	07 18	07 48	08 18	08 48		13 18	13 48	14 18		18 48	19 18	19 48	20 48	21 48	22 48	
Godley	d	06 50	07 20	07 50	08 20	08 50		13 20	13 50	14 20		18 50	19 20	19 50	20 50	21 50	22 50	
Newton for Hyde	d	06 52	07 22	07 52	08 22	08 52		13 22	13 52	14 22		18 52	19 22	19 52	20 52	21 52	22 52	
Flowery Field	d	06 54	07 24	07 54	08 24	08 54		13 24	13 54	14 24		18 54	19 24	19 54	20 54	21 54	22 54	
Guide Bridge 78	a	06 57	07 27	07 57	08 27	08 57		13 27	13 57	14 27		18 57	19 27	19 57	20 57	21 57	22 57	
Gorton 78	a	07 00			08 30										21 00	22 00	23 00	
Ashburys 78	a	07 03	07 32	08 02	08 33	09 02		13 32	14 04	14 33		19 04	19 33	20 04	21 04	22 04	23 04	
Ardwick 78	a																	
Manchester Picc. 10 78 ⛴	a	07 10	07 40	08 10	08 40	09 10		13 40	14 11	14 40		19 11	19 40	20 11	21 11	22 11	23 11	

Sundays

8 December to 11 May

		NT B	NT		NT	NT
Hadfield	d	00{04	10 01	and every 30 minutes until	20 31	21 31
Glossop	a	00}11	10 06		20 36	21 36
	d		10 09		20 39	21 39
Dinting 3	d		10 12		20 42	21 42
Broadbottom	d		10 16		20 46	21 46
Hattersley	d		10 19		20 49	21 49
Godley	d		10 21		20 51	21 51
Newton for Hyde	d		10 23		20 53	21 53
Flowery Field	d		10 25		20 55	21 55
Guide Bridge 78	a		10 28		20 58	21 58
Gorton 78	a		10 31		21 01	22 01
Ashburys 78	a		10 34		21 04	22 04
Ardwick 78	a					
Manchester Picc. 10 78 ⛴	a		10 42		21 12	22 12

A until 8 February, from 29 March

B from 16 February until 23 March

Network Diagram for Tables 81, 102

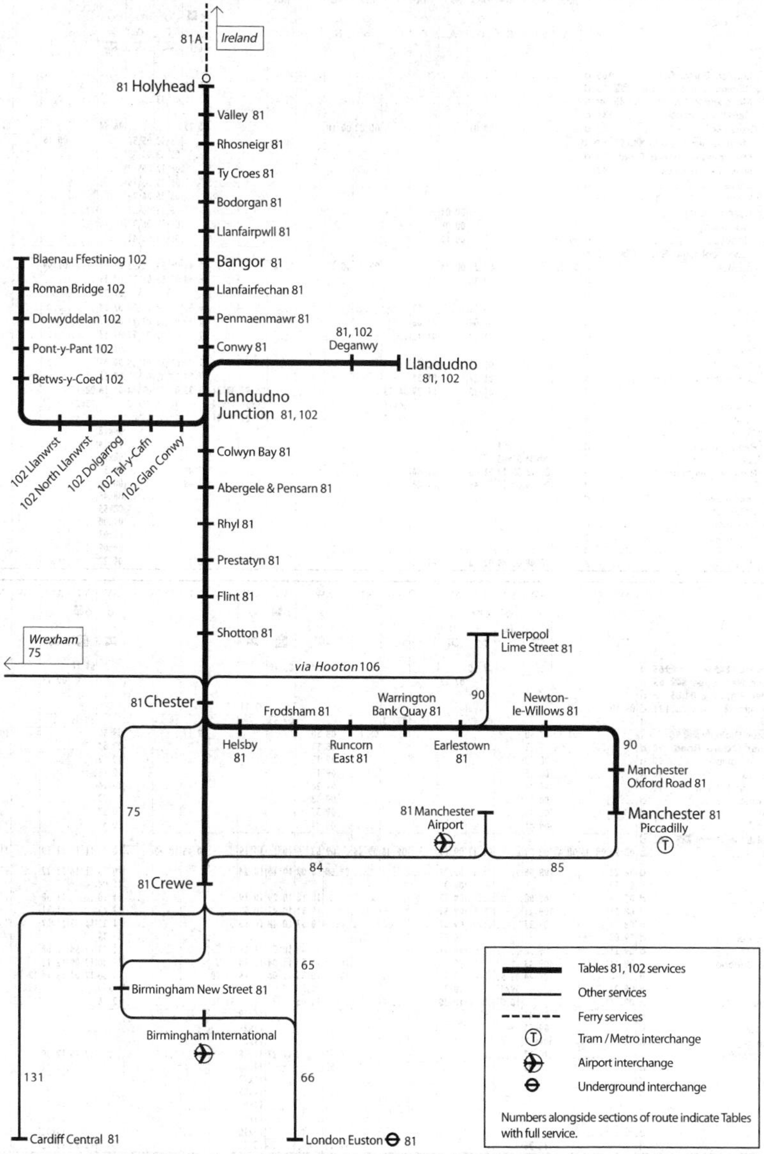

TOCs operating on this network - Northern (NT), Arriva Trains Wales (AW), Virgin Trains (VT)

Table 81

Mondays to Fridays

9 December to 16 May

Crewe and Manchester - Chester and North Wales

Network Diagram - see first Page of Table 81

Miles	Miles		AW	AW	AW	AW	AW	AW	AW	AW	AW		AW	AW	AW	VT	AW	AW	AW	AW	NT		AW	AW
			MX	MX	MO	MO	MO	MX		MX	MO		MX											
				◇	◇	◇		◇		◇	◇					◇1	◇	◇	◇					◇
			A	B	C	D	A	E		B	B						F	G						
																⊠	╤	╤	╤					╤
—	—	London Euston 15 ⊖65 d																						
—	—	Birmingham New Street 12 65 d														05 30								
—	—	Manchester Airport 84,85 ✈ d															05 33							
—	—	Cardiff Central 7 131 d																						
0	—	**Crewe** 10 d				00 01				00 02	00 10					06 23			06 54				07 23	
—	0	**Manchester Pic'dilly** 10 90 ⛴ d											00 25				05 50	05 50			06 18			06 50
—	0½	**Manchester Oxford Road** 90 d															05 53	05 53						06 53
—	16¼	Newton-le-Willows 90 d															06 12	06 12						07 11
—	18	Earlestown 8 90 d															06 15	06 15						07 15
—	22	Warrington Bank Quay 90 d															06 26	06 26						07 22
—	27	Runcorn East d					00 04										06 33	06 33						07 29
—	30¼	Frodsham d					00 08										06 37	06 37						07 34
—	32¾	Helsby d	00 03				00 12										06 41	06 41						07 38
—	—	Liverpool Lime Street 10 106 d																						
21	40¼	**Chester** a	00 15			00 22	00 24			00 27	00 33		01 29			06 43	06 53	06 53	07 11		07 45		07 46	07 50
—	—	d				00 38		00 40								06 44	06 55	06 55	07 19					07 55
29	—	Shotton d																	07 28					08 04
33½	—	Flint d				00 51		00 53								06 57	07 08	07 08	07 34					08 10
47½	—	Prestatyn d				01 04		01 06								07 10	07 21	07 21	07 47					08 23
51	—	Rhyl d				01 10		01 12								07 16	07 27	07 27	07 53					08 29
55¼	—	Abergele & Pensarn d																	07 59					08 35
61½	—	Colwyn Bay d				01 21		01 23								07 26	07 38	07 38	08 07					08 43
65½	0	**Llandudno Junction** a				01 27		01 28								07 32	07 43	07 43	08 12					08 51
—	—	d				01 28		01 29	06 13					06 51	07 31	07 33	07 44	07 44	08 16	08 17				
—	1¼	Deganwy d							06x16					06x54	07x34		07x48	07x48		08x20				
—	3	**Llandudno** a							06 23					07 01	07 41		08 01	08 01		08 25				
66½	—	Conwy d																	08x18					
70¾	—	Penmaenmawr d			00x01														08x24					
73¼	—	Llanfairfechan d		00x04	00x05														08x28					
80¾	—	**Bangor (Gwynedd)** a		00 13	00 14	01 45		01 46								07 49			08 37					
—	—	d		00 14	00 15	01 45		01 46								07 49			08 38					
84½	—	Llanfairpwll d																	08x45					
93½	—	Bodorgan d																	08x55					
96¼	—	Ty Croes d																	09x00					
98	—	Rhosneigr d																	09x03					
102	—	Valley d																	09x09					
105½	—	**Holyhead** a		00 48	00 49	02 20		02 15								08 23			09 22					

	AW	AW	NT	AW	AW	VT	AW		AW	NT	AW		VT	AW	AW	NT	AW		AW	VT	AW	AW	NT	AW
	◇			◇	◇	◇1	◇				◇		◇1	◇					◇	◇1	◇			
					H		D														D			
	╤			╤		⊠	╤				╤		⊠	╤					╤	⊠	╤			
London Euston 15 ⊖65 d						07 10							08 10							09 10				
Birmingham New Street 12 65 d							07 23														09 23			
Manchester Airport 84,85 ✈ d																								
Cardiff Central 7 131 d	05 10													07 21										
Crewe 10 d		08 23				08 49			09 23				09 53				10 23			10 49				11 23
Manchester Pic'dilly 10 90 ⛴ d			07 17	07 50						08 17	08 50					09 17			09 50				10 17	
Manchester Oxford Road 90 d				07 53							08 53								09 53					
Newton-le-Willows 90 d				08 12							09 12								10 12					
Earlestown 8 90 d				08 15							09 15								10 15					
Warrington Bank Quay 90 d				08 24							09 26								10 26					
Runcorn East d				08 31							09 33								10 33					
Frodsham d				08 36							09 37								10 37					
Helsby d				08 41							09 41								10 41					
Liverpool Lime Street 10 106 d																								
Chester a	08 20	08 46	08 47	08 53		09 13	09 17		09 46	09 48	09 53		10 13	10 19		10 45	10 46		10 53	11 13	11 19		11 45	11 46
d	08 22			08 55			09 23				09 58	10 02	10 16	10 24					10 55	11 16	11 22			
Shotton d	08 32						09 32												11 04					
Flint d	08 38			09 08			09 38					10 18	10 29	10 39					11 10		11 38			
Prestatyn d	08 51			09 21			09 51					10 31	10 42	10 52					11 23		11 51			
Rhyl d	08 57			09 27			09 57					10 37	10 48	10 58					11 29	11 43	11 57			
Abergele & Pensarn d	09 03						10 03												11 35					
Colwyn Bay d	09 11			09 38			10 11					10 48	10 59	11 09					11 43	11 54	12 08			
Llandudno Junction a	09 16			09 43			10 16				10 34	10 53	11 04	11 14					11 48	12 00	12 13			
d	09 18			09 44	09 53		10 18				10 36	10 55	11 06	11 15	11 28				11 50	12 01	12 14	12 28		
Deganwy d	09x21				09x56		10x21					10x58			11x31				11x54			12x31		
Llandudno a	09 26				10 01		10 30					11 06			11 38				12 06			12 38		
Conwy d				09x46										11x18										
Penmaenmawr d				09x53										11x24										
Llanfairfechan d				09x57										11x28										
Bangor (Gwynedd) a				10 07							10 51		11 27	11 38						12 16	12 30			
d				10 08							10 53			11 40						12 17	12 32			
Llanfairpwll d														11x47							12x38			
Bodorgan d														11x57							12x48			
Ty Croes d														12x01							12x53			
Rhosneigr d														12x04							12x56			
Valley d														12x10							13x02			
Holyhead a				10 36							11 22			12 23						12 50	13 13			

A From Manchester Piccadilly
B From Cardiff Central
C From Crewe
D From Birmingham International
E From Birmingham New Street
F until 27 December, from 24 March
G from 30 December until 21 March
H From Blaenau Ffestiniog

Table 81

Mondays to Fridays

9 December to 16 May

Crewe and Manchester - Chester and North Wales

Network Diagram - see first Page of Table 81

		AW	AW	VT		AW	NT	AW	AW	VT	AW	AW	NT	AW		AW	VT	AW	NT	AW	AW	VT	AW	AW
		◇	◇	◇[1]		◇			◇	◇[1]	◇					◇	◇[1]	◇			◇	◇[1]	◇	◇
			A								B												A	B
		🛒		⊠		🛒			🛒	🍴	🛒					🛒	🍴	🛒			🛒	🍴		🛒
London Euston [15] ⊖65	d			10 10						11 10							12 10					13 10		
Birmingham New Street [12] 65	d										11 23													13 23
Manchester Airport 84,85 ✈	d																							
Cardiff Central [7] 131	d					09 21												11 21						
Crewe [10]	d			11 49				12 23		12 49				13 23			13 49			14 23		14 49		
Manchester Pic'dilly [10] 90	d	10 50					11 17		11 50				12 17			12 50			13 17		13 50			
Manchester Oxford Road 90	d	10 53							11 53							12 53					13 53			
Newton-le-Willows 90	d	11 12							12 12							13 12					14 12			
Earlestown [8] 90	d	11 15							12 15							13 15					14 15			
Warrington Bank Quay 90	d	11 26							12 26							13 26					14 26			
Runcorn East	d	11 33							12 33							13 33					14 33			
Frodsham	d	11 37							12 37							13 37					14 37			
Helsby	d	11 41							12 41							13 41					14 41			
Liverpool Lime Street [10] 106	d																							
Chester	a	11 53		12 13		12 19	12 45	12 46	12 53	13 13	13 19		13 45	13 46		13 53	14 13	14 19	14 45	14 46	14 53	15 13		15 20
	d	11 55				12 23			12 55		13 24					13 55		14 23			14 55			15 22
Shotton	d	12 04							13 04							14 04					15 04			
Flint	d	12 10				12 36			13 10		13 37					14 10		14 36			15 10			15 37
Prestatyn	d	12 23				12 49			13 23		13 50					14 23		14 49			15 23			15 50
Rhyl	d	12 29				12 55			13 29		13 56					14 29		14 55			15 29			15 56
Abergele & Pensarn	d	12 35							13 35							14 35					15 35			
Colwyn Bay	d	12 43				13 06			13 43		14 07					14 43		15 06			15 43			16 07
Llandudno Junction	a	12 48				13 11			13 48		14 12					14 48		15 11			15 48			16 13
	d	12 50	12 53			13 12			13 50		14 13	14 28				14 50		15 12			15 50		16 05	16 19
Deganwy	d		12x56						13x54			14x31				14x54					15x54		16x08	
Llandudno	a		13 03						14 06			14 38				15 06					16 06		16 17	
Conwy	d	12x52									14x16													16x23
Penmaenmawr	d	12x58									14x22													16x29
Llanfairfechan	d	13x02									14x26													16x32
Bangor (Gwynedd)	a	13 15				13 29					14 35							15 29						16 42
	d					13 30					14 37							15 31						16 43
Llanfairpwll	d					13x36												15x38						
Bodorgan	d					13x46												15x48						
Ty Croes	d					13x51												15x52						
Rhosneigr	d					13x54												15x55						
Valley	d					14x00												16x01						
Holyhead	a					14 13					15 08							16 15						17 15

		NT	AW	AW	VT	AW	NT	AW	AW	VT		AW	AW	NT	AW	AW	AW	VT	AW	AW		AW	NT	AW	AW
																			[R]						
				◇	◇[1]	◇			◇	◇[1]		◇				◇	◇	◇[1]							◇
												B				A									
				🛒	🍴	🛒			🛒	🍴		🛒					🛒	🍴	🛒			🛒			🛒
London Euston [15] ⊖65	d				14 10					15 10								16 10							
Birmingham New Street [12] 65	d											15 23													
Manchester Airport 84,85 ✈	d																								
Cardiff Central [7] 131	d					13 21													15 21						
Crewe [10]	d		15 23		15 49			16 23		16 49					17 23			17 49						18 23	
Manchester Pic'dilly [10] 90	d	14 17		14 50			15 17		15 50					16 17			16 50					17 19	17 09		17 50
Manchester Oxford Road 90	d			14 53					15 53								16 53					17 22			17 53
Newton-le-Willows 90	d			15 12					16 12								17 12					17 40			18 11
Earlestown [8] 90	d			15 15					16 15								17 15					17 44			18 14
Warrington Bank Quay 90	d			15 26					16 26								17 26					17 53			18 24
Runcorn East	d			15 33					16 33								17 33					18 00			18 31
Frodsham	d			15 37					16 37								17 37					18 05			18 36
Helsby	d			15 41					16 41								17 41					18 09			18 40
Liverpool Lime Street [10] 106	d																								
Chester	a	15 45	15 46	15 53	16 13	16 20	16 45	16 46	16 54	17 13		17 21		17 45	17 46		17 53	18 08	18 20			18 23	18 35	18 46	18 53
	d			15 55		16 25			16 55			17 25					17 55	18 10	18 24						18 55
Shotton	d			16 04					17 04			17 34					18 04								19 04
Flint	d			16 10		16 38			17 10			17 40					18 10	18 23	18 37						19 10
Prestatyn	d			16 23		16 51			17 23			17 53					18 23	18 36	18 50						19 23
Rhyl	d			16 29		16 57			17 29			17 59					18 29	18 42	18 56						19 29
Abergele & Pensarn	d			16 35					17 35			18 05					18 35								19 35
Colwyn Bay	d			16 43		17 08			17 43			18 13					18 43	18 53	19 07						19 43
Llandudno Junction	a			16 48		17 13			17 49			18 19					18 49	18 58	19 12						19 48
	d			16 50		17 13			17 50			18 23	18 26			18 41	18 51	19 00	19 16	19 28					19 50
Deganwy	d			16x54					17x54				18x29			18x44	18x55			19x31					
Llandudno	a			17 05					18 06				18 36			18 54	19 06			19 38					
Conwy	d					17x16						18x25													19x52
Penmaenmawr	d					17x22						18x31													19x58
Llanfairfechan	d					17x26						18x35													20x02
Bangor (Gwynedd)	a					17 35						18 44						19 21	19 32						20 12
	d					17 37						18 45							19 33						20 13
Llanfairpwll	d					17x44													19x40						
Bodorgan	d					17x54													19x50						
Ty Croes	d					17x58													19x54						
Rhosneigr	d					18x01													19x57						
Valley	d					18x07													20x03						
Holyhead	a					18 19						19 16							20 18						20 45

A From Blaenau Ffestiniog

B From Birmingham International

Table 81

Mondays to Fridays

9 December to 16 May

Crewe and Manchester - Chester and North Wales

Network Diagram - see first Page of Table 81

	AW	VT	VT	AW	NT		AW	AW	AW	VT	VT	AW	AW	NT	AW		AW	AW BHX	VT	VT	AW	AW	AW	NT
	■	◇1	◇1	◇					■	◇1	◇1	■	◇					■	■ 1	■ 1	◇	◇		
	A	⊠	⊠	B 🛒					C 🛒	D ⊠	⊠	E 🛒	F					G ⊠	☕	☕		B 🛒		
London Euston 15 ⊖65 d		17 10	17 10							18 10	18 10								19 10	19 10				
Birmingham New Street 12 65 d				17 23																		19 23		
Manchester Airport 84,85 ✈ d																								
Cardiff Central 7 131 d	16 21								17 16									18 21						
Crewe 10 d	18 45	18 57	18 57				19 23			19 56	19 56				20 23			20 42	20 49	20 50			21 00	
Manchester Pic'dilly 10 90 ⇌ d					18 17			18 50						19 17			19 50							20 17
Manchester Oxford Road 90 d								18 53									19 53							
Newton-le-Willows 90 d								19 12									20 12							
Earlestown 8 90 d								19 16									20 15							
Warrington Bank Quay 90 d								19 26									20 26							
Runcorn East d								19 33									20 33							
Frodsham d								19 37									20 37							
Helsby d								19 41									20 41							
Liverpool Lime Street 10 106 d																								
Chester a	19 05	19 16	19 16	19 21	19 45		19 46	19 53	20 01	20 15	20 15			20 45	20 46		20 53	21 01	21 13	21 13		21 19	21 23	21 45
d			19 23	19 32					20 06		20 26	20 34							21 17		22 04			
Shotton d				19 41								20 43									22 13			
Flint d			19 36	19 47					20 18			20 49							21 30		22 19			
Prestatyn d			19 49	20 00								21 02							21 43		22 32			
Rhyl d			19 55	20 06					20 35		20 53	21 08							21 50		22 38			
Abergele & Pensarn d				20 12								21 14									22 44			
Colwyn Bay d			20 06	20 20					20 47		21 04	21 22							22 01		22 52			
Llandudno Junction a			20 11	20 25					20 53		21 09	21 27							22 06		22 57			
d			20 13	20 30					20 54		21 10	21 29	21 32						22 07		22 59			
Deganwy d				20x33									21x35											
Llandudno a				20 43									21 46											
Conwy d												21x31									23x01			
Penmaenmawr d												21x37									23x07			
Llanfairfechan d												21x41									23x12			
Bangor (Gwynedd) a			20 28						21 09		21 25	21 51							22 22		23 21			
d			20 29						21 11		21 27	21 52							22 24		23 22			
Llanfairpwll d												21x58									23x29			
Bodorgan d												22x08									23x39			
Ty Croes d												22x13									23x44			
Rhosneigr d												22x16									23x47			
Valley d												22x21									23x53			
Holyhead a			20 59						21 45		21 59	22 35							22 56		00 05			

	AW		AW	VT	AW	NT	AW	AW	AW	AW	AW		NT	AW	AW	AW	NT							
				◇1	◇				◇						◇	◇								
				☕					H															
London Euston 15 ⊖65 d				20 10																				
Birmingham New Street 12 65 d									21 23						22 55									
Manchester Airport 84,85 ✈ d	20 32							21 32																
Cardiff Central 7 131 d					19 34											20 55								
Crewe 10 d			21 36	21 49			22 23				23 23				23 57	00 02								
Manchester Pic'dilly 10 90 ⇌ d	20 50					21 17		21 50		22 12			22 17	23 14			23 17							
Manchester Oxford Road 90 d	20 53							21 53		22 29				23 17										
Newton-le-Willows 90 d	21 12							22 12		22 47				23 36										
Earlestown 8 90 d	21 15							22 15		22 50				23 39										
Warrington Bank Quay 90 d	21 24							22 24		22 59				23 48										
Runcorn East d	21 33							22 31		23 06				23 55										
Frodsham d	21 37							22 35		23 10				23 59										
Helsby d	21 41							22 39		23 14				00 03										
Liverpool Lime Street 10 106 d																								
Chester a	21 55		21 59	22 13	22 34	22 45	22 45	22 51	23 19	23 26	23 44		23 45	00 15	00 18	00 27	00 43							
d					22 56										00 40									
Shotton d					23 05																			
Flint d					23 11										00 53									
Prestatyn d					23 24										01 06									
Rhyl d					23 30										01 12									
Abergele & Pensarn d					23 36																			
Colwyn Bay d					23 44										01 23									
Llandudno Junction a					23 49										01 28									
d					23 52										01 29									
Deganwy d																								
Llandudno a																								
Conwy d					23x54																			
Penmaenmawr d					23x59																			
Llanfairfechan d					00x04																			
Bangor (Gwynedd) a					00 13										01 46									
d					00 14										01 46									
Llanfairpwll d																								
Bodorgan d																								
Ty Croes d																								
Rhosneigr d																								
Valley d																								
Holyhead a					00 48										02 15									

A From Swansea
B From Birmingham International
C 🛒 from Chester
D To Wrexham General
E From Shrewsbury
F From Blaenau Ffestiniog
G From Llanelli. ⊠ from Crewe
H From Birmingham International to Manchester Piccadilly

Table 81

Saturdays

14 December to 17 May

Crewe and Manchester - Chester and North Wales

Network Diagram - see first Page of Table 81

	AW	AW	AW	AW	AW	AW	AW	AW	VT		AW	AW	AW	NT	AW	AW	AW	AW	NT		AW	AW	AW	AW
		◇	◇		◇				◇■1		◇	◇				◇	◇					◇	◇	◇
	A	B	B		C																		D	E
									🍽		🛒	🛒				🛒	🛒					🛒		🛒
London Euston ■15 ⊖65 d																								
Birmingham New Street ■12 65 d									05 30															07 22
Manchester Airport 84,85 ✈ d											05 33													
Cardiff Central ■7 131 d																	05 20							
Crewe ■10 d		00 02							06 23			07 03			07 23						08 23			
Manchester Pic'dilly ■10 90 ⛴ d				00 25							05 50			06 18		06 50			07 17			07 50		
Manchester Oxford Road 90 d											05 53					06 53						07 53		
Newton-le-Willows 90 d											06 12					07 11						08 12		
Earlestown ■8 90 d											06 15					07 15						08 15		
Warrington Bank Quay 90 d											06 26					07 22						08 24		
Runcorn East d											06 33					07 29						08 31		
Frodsham d											06 37					07 34						08 36		
Helsby d	00 03										06 41					07 38						08 41		
Liverpool Lime Street ■10 106 d																								
Chester a	00 15	00 27		01 29					06 43		06 53	07 23		07 45	07 46	07 50	08 18		08 45		08 46	08 53		09 17
d					00 40				06 44		06 55	07 25				07 55	08 22					08 55		09 24
Shotton d											07 04					08 04						09 04		
Flint d					00 53				06 57		07 10	07 39				08 10	08 36					09 10		09 37
Prestatyn d					01 06				07 10		07 23	07 52				08 23	08 49					09 23		09 50
Rhyl d					01 12				07 16		07 29	07 58				08 29	08 55					09 29		09 56
Abergele & Pensarn d											07 35					08 35						09 35		
Colwyn Bay d					01 23				07 27		07 43	08 09				08 43	09 06					09 43		10 07
Llandudno Junction a					01 28				07 33		07 48	08 14				08 48	09 11					09 48		10 12
d					01 29	06 13	06 51	07 31	07 33		07 50	08 15	08 28			08 50	09 12	09 28				09 50	10 03	10 13
Deganwy d						06x16	06x54	07x34			07x54		08x31			08x54		09x31				09x54	10x06	
Llandudno a						06 23	07 01	07 41			08 06		08 38			09 06		09 38				10 06	10 13	
Conwy d												08x17					09x15							
Penmaenmawr d												08x23					09x21							
Llanfairfechan d			00x04									08x27					09x25							
Bangor (Gwynedd) a			00 13		01 46				07 49			08 36					09 34							10 30
d			00 14		01 46				07 50			08 38					09 36							10 31
Llanfairpwll d												08x44												10x38
Bodorgan d												08x54					09x51							
Ty Croes d												08x59					09x55							
Rhosneigr d												09x02					09x58							
Valley d												09x08												10x56
Holyhead a			00 48		02 15				08 23			09 21					10 14							11 05

	AW	NT	AW	AW	VT		AW	AW	NT	AW	AW	VT	AW	AW	NT		AW	AW	AW	VT	AW	NT	AW	AW
				◇	◇■1		◇				◇	◇■1	◇					◇	◇	◇■1	◇			◇
													E						D					
				🛒	🍽		🛒				🛒	🍽	🛒					🛒		🍽	🛒			🛒
London Euston ■15 ⊖65 d					08 10							09 10								10 10				
Birmingham New Street ■12 65 d													09 23											
Manchester Airport 84,85 ✈ d																								
Cardiff Central ■7 131 d							07 21														09 21			
Crewe ■10 d			09 23		09 49					10 23		10 49					11 23			11 49			12 23	
Manchester Pic'dilly ■10 90 ⛴ d		08 17		08 50					09 17		09 50				10 17			10 50				11 17		11 50
Manchester Oxford Road 90 d				08 53							09 53							10 53						11 53
Newton-le-Willows 90 d				09 12							10 12							11 12						12 12
Earlestown ■8 90 d				09 15							10 15							11 15						12 15
Warrington Bank Quay 90 d				09 26							10 26							11 26						12 26
Runcorn East d				09 33							10 33							11 33						12 33
Frodsham d				09 37							10 37							11 37						12 37
Helsby d				09 41							10 41							11 41						12 41
Liverpool Lime Street ■10 106 d																								
Chester a		09 46	09 46	09 53	10 13		10 19		10 45	10 46	10 53	11 13	11 21		11 45		11 46	11 53		12 13	12 19	12 45	12 46	12 53
d				09 55			10 23				10 55	11 16	11 24					11 55			12 23			12 55
Shotton d				10 04							11 04							12 04						13 04
Flint d				10 10			10 36				11 10		11 39					12 10			12 36			13 10
Prestatyn d				10 23			10 49				11 23		11 52					12 23			12 49			13 23
Rhyl d				10 29			10 55				11 29	11 43	11 58					12 29			12 55			13 29
Abergele & Pensarn d				10 35							11 35							12 35						13 35
Colwyn Bay d				10 43			11 06				11 43	11 54	12 09					12 43			13 06			13 43
Llandudno Junction a				10 48			11 11				11 48	12 00	12 14					12 48			13 11			13 48
d	10 28			10 50			11 12	11 26			11 50	12 01	12 15	12 28				12 50	12 53		13 12			13 50
Deganwy d	10x31			10x54				11x29			11x54			12x31					12x56					13x54
Llandudno a	10 38			11 06				11 36			12 06			12 38					13 03					14 06
Conwy d							11x15											12x52						
Penmaenmawr d							11x21											12x58						
Llanfairfechan d							11x25											13x02						
Bangor (Gwynedd) a							11 34					12 16	12 32					13 15			13 29			
d							11 36					12 17	12 33								13 30			
Llanfairpwll d													12x40								13x36			
Bodorgan d													12x50								13x46			
Ty Croes d													12x55								13x51			
Rhosneigr d													12x58								13x54			
Valley d													13x04								14x00			
Holyhead a							12 09					12 50	13 12								14 13			

A From Manchester Piccadilly
B From Cardiff Central
C From Birmingham New Street
D From Blaenau Ffestiniog
E From Birmingham International

Table 81

Saturdays

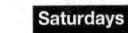

14 December to 17 May

Crewe and Manchester - Chester and North Wales

Network Diagram - see first Page of Table 81

	VT		AW	AW	NT	AW	AW	VT	AW	AW	NT		AW	AW	VT	AW	AW	AW	NT	AW	AW		VT	AW
	◇1		◇				◇	◇1	◇					◇	◇1	◇	◇				◇		◇1	◇
			A													B	A							
	R		T				T	R	T					T	R		T				T		R	T
London Euston [15] ⊖65 d	11 10							12 10							13 10								14 10	
Birmingham New Street [12] 65 d			11 23														13 23							
Manchester Airport .. 84,85 ✈ d																								
Cardiff Central [7] 131 d									11 21															13 21
Crewe [10] d	12 49					13 23		13 49					14 23		14 49					15 23			15 49	
Manchester Pic'dilly [10] 90 ⇌ d					12 17		12 50				13 17			13 50					14 17		14 50			
Manchester Oxford Road 90 d							12 53							13 53							14 53			
Newton-le-Willows 90 d							13 12							14 12							15 12			
Earlestown [8] 90 d							13 15							14 15							15 15			
Warrington Bank Quay 90 d							13 26							14 26							15 26			
Runcorn East d							13 33							14 33							15 33			
Frodsham d							13 37							14 37							15 37			
Helsby d							13 41							14 41							15 41			
Liverpool Lime Street [10] 106 d																								
Chester a	13 13		13 18		13 45	13 46	13 53	14 13	14 19		14 45		14 46	14 53	15 13		15 20		15 45	15 46	15 53		16 10	16 22
d			13 22				13 55		14 23					14 55			15 22				15 55		16 12	16 24
Shotton d							14 04							15 04							16 04			
Flint d			13 36				14 10		14 36					15 10			15 37				16 10		16 25	16 39
Prestatyn d			13 49				14 23		14 49					15 23			15 50				16 23		16 38	16 52
Rhyl d			13 55				14 29		14 55					15 29			15 56				16 29		16 45	16 58
Abergele & Pensarn d							14 35							15 35							16 35			
Colwyn Bay d			14 06				14 43		15 06					15 43			16 07				16 43		16 56	17 09
Llandudno Junction a			14 11				14 48		15 11					15 48			16 12				16 48		17 01	17 14
d			14 12	14 28			14 50		15 12	15 30				15 50		16 03	16 14	16 26			16 50		17 02	17 14
Deganwy d				14x31			14x54			15x33				15x54		16x06		16x29			16x54			
Llandudno a				14 38			15 06			15 40				16 06		16 13		16 36			17 06			
Conwy d			14x15														16x16							17x17
Penmaenmawr d			14x21														16x22							17x23
Llanfairfechan d			14x25														16x27							17x27
Bangor (Gwynedd) a			14 34						15 29								16 36						17 17	17 36
d			14 36						15 29								16 37						17 19	17 38
Llanfairpwll d									15x36															17x45
Bodorgan d									15x46															17x55
Ty Croes d									15x51															17x59
Rhosneigr d									15x54															18x02
Valley d									16x00															18x08
Holyhead a			15 08						16 13								17 11						17 51	18 20

	AW	NT	AW	AW	VT	AW	AW		NT	AW	AW	AW	VT	AW	AW	NT	AW		AW	VT	VT	AW	AW	NT
														■										
				◇	◇1	◇					◇	◇	◇1						◇	◇1	◇1	◇		
						A					B											A		
				T	R	T						T	R	T					T	☒	R	T		
London Euston [15] ⊖65 d					15 10								16 10							17 10	17 10			
Birmingham New Street [12] 65 d						15 23																17 23		
Manchester Airport .. 84,85 ✈ d																								
Cardiff Central [7] 131 d														15 21										
Crewe [10] d			16 23		16 49					17 23			17 49				18 23			18 52	18 52			
Manchester Pic'dilly [10] 90 ⇌ d		15 17		15 50					16 17			16 50				17 17			17 50					18 17
Manchester Oxford Road 90 d				15 53								16 53							17 53					
Newton-le-Willows 90 d				16 12								17 12							18 11					
Earlestown [8] 90 d				16 15								17 15							18 14					
Warrington Bank Quay 90 d				16 26								17 26							18 25					
Runcorn East d				16 33								17 33							18 32					
Frodsham d				16 37								17 37							18 36					
Helsby d				16 41								17 41							18 40					
Liverpool Lime Street [10] 106 d																								
Chester a		16 45	16 46	16 53	17 13	17 19			17 45	17 46		17 53	18 09	18 21		18 45	18 46		18 52	19 11	19 12	19 20		19 45
d				16 55		17 24						17 55	18 16	18 24					18 55		19 18	19 32		
Shotton d				17 04		17 33						18 04							19 04			19 41		
Flint d				17 10		17 39						18 10	18 29	18 39					19 10		19 31	19 47		
Prestatyn d				17 23		17 52						18 23	18 42	18 52					19 23		19 45	20 00		
Rhyl d				17 29		17 58						18 29	18 49	18 58					19 29		19 51	20 06		
Abergele & Pensarn d				17 35		18 04						18 35							19 35			20 12		
Colwyn Bay d				17 43		18 12						18 43	19 00	19 09					19 43		20 02	20 20		
Llandudno Junction a				17 48		18 17						18 49	19 05	19 14					19 48		20 07	20 25		
d	17 28			17 50		18 19	18 26				18 41	18 50	19 06	19 15	19 28				19 50		20 09	20 27	20 30	
Deganwy d	17x31			17x54			18x29				18x44	18x55			19x31				19x54				20x33	
Llandudno a	17 38			18 06			18 36				18 54	19 06			19 38				20 06				20 40	
Conwy d						18x21																20x29		
Penmaenmawr d						18x27																20x35		
Llanfairfechan d						18x32																20x39		
Bangor (Gwynedd) a						18 41							19 21	19 32							20 24	20 47		
d						18 43							19 23	19 33							20 25	20 48		
Llanfairpwll d														19x40								20x55		
Bodorgan d														19x50								21x05		
Ty Croes d														19x55								21x10		
Rhosneigr d														19x58								21x13		
Valley d														20x04								21x19		
Holyhead a						19 13							19 55	20 18							20 58	21 31		

A From Birmingham International

B From Blaenau Ffestiniog

Table 81

Saturdays

14 December to 17 May

Crewe and Manchester - Chester and North Wales

Network Diagram - see first Page of Table 81

		AW	AW	VT	AW	AW	NT	AW	AW	AW	AW	NT	AW	AW	AW	AW	NT	AW	AW	AW	AW	AW
				◇ 1	R	◇ A				◇ B	◇				◇	Bus				◇ B		
London Euston 15 ⊖65	d			18 10																		
Birmingham New Street 12 65	d									19 23										21 23		
Manchester Airport 84,85 ✈	d												20 32									
Cardiff Central 7 131	d				17 21										19 34							
Crewe 10	d	19 23		19 49				20 23			21 00			21 36				22 23				23 21
Manchester Pic'dilly 10 90	d		18 50				19 17		19 50			20 17	20 50				21 17		21 50		22 26	
Manchester Oxford Road 90	d		18 53						19 53				20 53						21 53		22 29	
Newton-le-Willows 90	d		19 12						20 12				21 12						22 12		22 47	
Earlestown 8 90	d		19 16						20 15				21 15						22 15		22 50	
Warrington Bank Quay 90	d		19 27						20 30				21 27						22 24		22 59	
Runcorn East	d		19 34						20 37				21 34						22 31		23 06	
Frodsham	d		19 38						20 41				21 38						22 35		23 10	
Helsby	d		19 42						20 45				21 42						22 39		23 14	
Liverpool Lime Street 10 106	d																					
Chester	a	19 46	19 54	20 13	20 21		20 45	20 46	20 57	21 21	21 21	21 45	21 57	22 01	22 31		22 45	22 45	22 54	23 20	23 26	23 42
	d				20 32						21 26				22 36							
Shotton	d				20 41						21 35				22 45							
Flint	d				20 47						21 41				22 51							
Prestatyn	d				21 00						21 54				23 05							
Rhyl	d				21 06						22 00				23 11							
Abergele & Pensarn	d										22 06				23 17							
Colwyn Bay	d				21 19						22 14				23 25							
Llandudno Junction	a				21 24						22 19				23 38							
	d				21 26	21 32					22 21					23 48						
Deganwy	d					21x35																
Llandudno	a					21 46																
Conwy	d										22x23											
Penmaenmawr	d										22x30											
Llanfairfechan	d										22x34											
Bangor (Gwynedd)	a				21 42						22 43					00 13						
	d				21 43						22 45					00 13						
Llanfairpwll	d				21x50																	
Bodorgan	d				22x00																	
Ty Croes	d				22x04																	
Rhosneigr	d				22x07																	
Valley	d				22x13																	
Holyhead	a				22 25						23 18					00 48						

		NT	AW	AW	NT
				◇	
London Euston 15 ⊖65	d				
Birmingham New Street 12 65	d				
Manchester Airport 84,85 ✈	d				
Cardiff Central 7 131	d			20 55	
Crewe 10	d			23 58	
Manchester Pic'dilly 10 90	d	22 17	23 14		23 17
Manchester Oxford Road 90	d		23 17		
Newton-le-Willows 90	d		23 36		
Earlestown 8 90	d		23 39		
Warrington Bank Quay 90	d		23 48		
Runcorn East	d		23 55		
Frodsham	d		23 59		
Helsby	d		00 03		
Liverpool Lime Street 10 106	d				
Chester	a	23 45	00 17	00 24	00 43
	d				
Shotton	d				
Flint	d				
Prestatyn	d				
Rhyl	d				
Abergele & Pensarn	d				
Colwyn Bay	d				
Llandudno Junction	a				
	d				
Deganwy	d				
Llandudno	a				
Conwy	d				
Penmaenmawr	d				
Llanfairfechan	d				
Bangor (Gwynedd)	a				
	d				
Llanfairpwll	d				
Bodorgan	d				
Ty Croes	d				
Rhosneigr	d				
Valley	d				
Holyhead	a				

A From Blaenau Ffestiniog

B From Birmingham International

Table 81

Sundays

8 December to 11 May

Crewe and Manchester - Chester and North Wales

Network Diagram - see first Page of Table 81

		AW	AW	AW	AW	AW	NT	AW	VT	AW	AW	AW	AW	NT	AW	AW	AW	AW	AW	AW	AW	NT	AW
					◇				◇1		◇				◇			◇	◇				◇
		A	B				C							D				E				D	
			🚌	🚌					☕						🛒	🛒			🛒	🛒			🛒
London Euston 15 ⊖65	d																						
Birmingham New Street 12 65	d																	11 05					
Manchester Airport 84,85 ✈	d																						
Cardiff Central 7 131	d																						
Crewe 10	d				09 24	10 07			10 42	11 05	11 27		11 57		12 27		12 54		13 27		13 57		14 27
Manchester Pic'dilly 10 90 ⇌	d			07 28			09 22	09 56				10 55		11 22		11 56				12 56		13 22	
Manchester Oxford Road 90	d			07 33				09 59				10 56				11 59				12 59			
Newton-le-Willows 90	d			08 03				10 18				11 18				12 18				13 18			
Earlestown 8 90	d			08 13				10 21				11 21				12 21				13 21			
Warrington Bank Quay 90	d			08 38				10 28				11 30				12 28				13 29			
Runcorn East	d			08 58				10 35				11 37				12 35				13 36			
Frodsham	d			09 13				10 40				11 41				12 39				13 40			
Helsby	d	00 03		09 18				10 44				11 45				12 43				13 44			
Liverpool Lime Street 10 106	d																						
Chester	a	00 17		09 38	09 46	10 30	10 47	10 59	11 02	11 30	11 50	11 57	12 20	12 46	12 52	12 55	13 19	13 20	13 51	13 56	14 20	14 46	14 51
	d				09 48				11 07		12 03				13 02				14 02				15 02
Shotton	d				09 57						12 12				13 11				14 11				15 11
Flint	d				10 03						12 18				13 17				14 17				15 17
Prestatyn	d				10 16				11 30		12 31				13 30				14 30				15 30
Rhyl	d				10 22				11 37		12 37				13 36				14 36				15 36
Abergele & Pensarn	d				10 28										13 42				14 42				15 42
Colwyn Bay	d				10 36				11 48		12 48				13 50				14 50				15 50
Llandudno Junction	a				10 41				11 53		12 53				13 55				14 55				15 55
	d				10 43				11 54		12 54				13 57				14 57				15 57
Deganwy	d																						
Llandudno	a																						
Conwy	d				10x45										13x59								15x59
Penmaenmawr	d				10x51										14x05								16x05
Llanfairfechan	d				10x55										14x10								16x10
Bangor (Gwynedd)	a				11 03				12 09		13 11				14 19				15 12				16 19
	d		00 13		11 04				12 11		13 12				14 21				15 14				16 20
Llanfairpwll	d				11x11														15x21				
Bodorgan	d				11x21														15x31				
Ty Croes	d				11x26														15x35				
Rhosneigr	d				11x29														15x38				
Valley	d				11x35														15x44				
Holyhead	a		00 48		11 49				12 43		13 42				14 53				15 55				16 53

		AW	AW	AW	AW	AW	AW	NT	AW	AW	VT	AW	AW	AW	VT	AW	NT	AW	AW	VT	VT	AW	AW
							■									■							
			◇		◇				◇		◇1	◇	◇		◇1			◇		◇1	◇1	◇	
			E					D				E					D					E	
		🛒	🛒			🛒	🛒			🛒	☕	🛒			☕	🛒			🛒	☕	☕	🛒	
London Euston 15 ⊖65	d										15 08				16 08					17 08	17 08		
Birmingham New Street 12 65	d		13 24									15 24										17 24	
Manchester Airport 84,85 ✈	d																						
Cardiff Central 7 131	d						13 22									15 22							
Crewe 10	d			14 57	15 27				16 27		16 52		17 27		17 52			18 27		18 56	18 56		19 24
Manchester Pic'dilly 10 90 ⇌	d	13 56				14 56		15 22		15 56				16 56			17 22		17 56				
Manchester Oxford Road 90	d	13 59				14 59				15 59				16 59					17 59				
Newton-le-Willows 90	d	14 18				15 18				16 18				17 18					18 18				
Earlestown 8 90	d	14 21				15 21				16 21				17 21					18 21				
Warrington Bank Quay 90	d	14 28				15 29				16 28				17 28					18 28				
Runcorn East	d	14 35				15 36				16 35				17 35					18 35				
Frodsham	d	14 39				15 40				16 39				17 39					18 39				
Helsby	d	14 43				15 44				16 43				17 43					18 43				
Liverpool Lime Street 10 106	d																						
Chester	a	14 55	15 18	15 20	15 49	15 56	16 18	16 48	16 49	16 55	17 14	17 26	17 49	17 55	18 15	18 25	18 46	18 49	18 55	19 14	19 14	19 17	19 45
	d				16 02		16 36		17 02				18 02			18 29		18 52			19 22	19 38	
Shotton	d				16 11		16 45		17 11				18 11			18 38		19 01				19 47	
Flint	d				16 17		16 51		17 17				18 17			18 44		19 07			19 35	19 53	
Prestatyn	d				16 30		17 04		17 30				18 30			18 57		19 21			19 48	20 06	
Rhyl	d				16 36		17 10		17 36				18 36			19 03		19 27			19 55	20 12	
Abergele & Pensarn	d				16 42		17 16		17 42				18 42			19 09		19 33				20 18	
Colwyn Bay	d				16 50		17 24		17 50				18 50			19 17		19 41			20 06	20 26	
Llandudno Junction	a				16 55		17 29		17 55				18 55			19 22		19 46			20 11	20 31	
	d				16 57		17 31		17 57				18 57			19 24		19 47			20 12	20 33	
Deganwy	d																						
Llandudno	a																						
Conwy	d						17x33		17x59							19x26		19x49				20x35	
Penmaenmawr	d						17x39		18x05							19x32		19x55				20x41	
Llanfairfechan	d						17x43		18x10							19x37		19x59				20x45	
Bangor (Gwynedd)	a				17 13		17 52		18 19				19 12			19 47		20 08			20 27	20 53	
	d				17 15		17 54		18 20				19 14			19 48		20 10			20 29	20 55	
Llanfairpwll	d				17x21		18x00						19x21										
Bodorgan	d				17x31		18x10						19x31										
Ty Croes	d				17x36		18x15						19x35										
Rhosneigr	d				17x39		18x19						19x39										
Valley	d				17x45		18x25						19x45										
Holyhead	a				17 57		18 37		18 54				19 54			20 18		20 44			20 59	21 30	

A not 8 December. From Manchester Piccadilly
B not 8 December. From Llandudno Junction
C From Wigan Wallgate
D From Southport
E From Birmingham International

Table 81

Sundays

8 December to 11 May

Crewe and Manchester - Chester and North Wales

Network Diagram - see first Page of Table 81

	AW		VT	VT	NT	AW	AW	VT	AW	AW	AW		AW	NT	AW	AW	AW	AW	AW	AW	AW		AW	
			◇1	◇1				◇1	◇	◇					◇		◇			◇			◇	
					A				B					A			B			B				
London Euston 15 ⊖65 d			18 08	18 08				19 08																
Birmingham New Street 12 65 d									19 24								21 24			22 55				
Manchester Airport 84,85 ✈ d																								
Cardiff Central 7 131 d																							21 04	
Crewe 10 d			19 52	19 52		20 27		20 55		21 27			22 03		22 29		23 06		23 38	00 01			00 10	
Manchester Pic'dilly 10 90 d	18 56				19 22		19 56				20 56			21 22		21 56		22 56			23 25			
Manchester Oxford Road 90 d	18 59						19 59				20 59					21 59		22 59			23 28			
Newton-le-Willows 90 d	19 18						20 18				21 18					22 18		23 18			23 47			
Earlestown 8 90 d	19 21						20 21				21 21					22 21		23 21			23 50			
Warrington Bank Quay 90 d	19 29						20 30				21 28					22 28		23 28			23 57			
Runcorn East d	19 36						20 37				21 35					22 35		23 35			00 04			
Frodsham d	19 40						20 41				21 39					22 39		23 39			00 08			
Helsby d	19 44						20 45				21 43					22 43		23 43			00 12			
Liverpool Lime Street 10 106 d																								
Chester a	19 56		20 11	20 11	20 46	20 50	20 57	21 14	21 20	21 50	21 55		22 26	22 46	22 52	22 55	23 31	23 55	00 01	00 22	00 24		00 33	
d				20 18				21 17		22 00					23 00					00 38				
Shotton d										22 09					23 09									
Flint d				20 31				21 30		22 15					23 15					00 51				
Prestatyn d				20 44				21 43		22 28					23 28					01 04				
Rhyl d				20 51				21 50		22 34					23 34					01 10				
Abergele & Pensarn d										22 40														
Colwyn Bay d				21 02				22 01		22 48					23 45					01 21				
Llandudno Junction a				21 07				22 06		22 53					23 50					01 27				
d				21 08				22 07		22 55					23 51					01 28				
Deganwy d																								
Llandudno a																								
Conwy d															23x54									
Penmaenmawr d															00x01									
Llanfairfechan d															00x05									
Bangor (Gwynedd) a				21 23				22 22		23 10					00 14					01 45				
d				21 25				22 24		23 12					00 15					01 45				
Llanfairpwll d										23x18														
Bodorgan d										23x28														
Ty Croes d										23x33														
Rhosneigr d										23x36														
Valley d										23x42														
Holyhead a				21 54				22 56		23 55					00 49					02 20				

A From Southport

B From Birmingham International

Table 81R

Mondays to Fridays

9 December to 16 May

North Wales and Chester - Manchester and Crewe

Network Diagram - see first Page of Table 81

Miles	Miles			AW A	AW B	AW	AW	AW ◇ C	AW	AW		AW	NT	AW ◇ D 🚲	VT ◇[1] ⊠	AW ◇	AW	NT	AW BHX ◇ E 🚲	AW 🚲		AW ◇ F 🚲	AW BHX ■ [1] G ⊠	VT ◇[1] H ⊠	VT ◇[1] ⊠
0	—	**Holyhead**	d											04 25	04 48				05 14			05 14	05 33		05 51
3½	—	Valley	d											04x31											
7½	—	Rhosneigr	d																						
9¼	—	Ty Croes	d																						
12	—	Bodorgan	d																						
21	—	Llanfairpwll	d											04x48											
24¾	—	**Bangor (Gwynedd)**	a											04 55	05 14				05 41			05 41	06 00		06 17
—	—		d											04 57	05 14				05 43			05 43	06 01		06 18
32¼	—	Llanfairfechan	d																05x50			05x50			
34¾	—	Penmaenmawr	d																05x54			05x54			
39	—	Conwy	d																06x01			06x01			
—	0	**Llandudno**	d																						
—	1¾	Deganwy	d																						
40	3	**Llandudno Junction**	a											05 13	05 32				06 05			06 05	06 18		06 35
—	—		d						04 38					05 15	05 32	05 46			06 07			06 07	06 19		06 36
44	—	Colwyn Bay	d						04 44					05 21	05 38	05 52			06 13			06 13	06 27		06 42
50¼	—	Abergele & Pensarn	d						04 51																
54½	—	Rhyl	d						04 57					05 31	05 49	06 02			06 23			06 23	06 38		06 53
58	—	Prestatyn	d						05 02					05 37		06 08			06 29			06 29			06 58
72	—	Flint	d						05 16					05 50		06 21			06 42			06 42	06 55		07 12
76¼	—	Shotton	d						05 22							06 27			06 48			06 48			
84¼	0	**Chester**	a						05 33					06 05	06 17	06 38			06 59			07 00	07 10		07 26
—	—		d	03 34	03 34	04 22	04 55	05 13	05 37	05 38		05 51	06 02	06 18	06 26	06 40	06 43	06 58	07 02	07 12		07 15	07 15	07 35	07 35
—	—	Liverpool Lime Street [10] 106	a																						
—	7½	Helsby	d							05 47						06 49				07 21					
—	10	Frodsham	d							05 51						06 53				07 25					
—	13¼	Runcorn East	d							05 56						06 59				07 31					
—	18¼	Warrington Bank Quay 90	a							06 05						07 06				07 38					
—	22¼	Earlestown [8] 90	a							06 12						07 14				07 46					
—	24	Newton-le-Willows 90	a							06 15						07 17				07 49					
—	39¾	**Manchester Oxford Road** 90	a							06 35						07 41				08 09					
—	40¼	**Manchester Pic'dilly** [10] 90 ⇌	a	04 41	04 41					06 44			07 30			07 50		08 29		08 18					
105½	—	**Crewe** [10]	a			04 44	05 20		05 58			06 15			06 47		07 04		07 27					07 54	07 54
—	—	Cardiff Central [7] 131	a											09 21									09 58		
—	—	Manchester Airport 84,85 ✈	a		05 04																				
—	—	Birmingham New Street [12] 65	a			05 59		07 30											09 29			09 29			
—	—	London Euston [15] ⊖65	a												08 34									09 41	09 41

		AW ◇ 🚲	AW	AW	NT	AW ◇ 🚲		VT ◇[1] ⊠	AW ◇ 🚲	AW	AW	NT	AW ◇ C 🚲	AW ■ 🚲	VT ◇[1] ⊠	AW ◇ 🚲		AW	NT	AW ◇ 🚲	VT ◇[1] ⊠	AW ◇ 🚲	AW ◇ I	AW	NT
Holyhead	d					06 28		06 55					07 15							08 05	08 55				
Valley	d					06x34							07x21							08x11					
Rhosneigr	d					06x40							07x26							08x17					
Ty Croes	d					06x43							07x30							08x20					
Bodorgan	d					06x48							07x34							08x25					
Llanfairpwll	d					06x57							07x44							08x34					
Bangor (Gwynedd)	a					07 05		07 21					07 52							08 42	09 21				
	d					07 06		07 22					08 02							09 02	09 22				
Llanfairfechan	d												08x09							09x09					
Penmaenmawr	d												08x13							09x13					
Conwy	d												08x19							09x19					
Llandudno	d	06 34	07 08						07 45	08 02				08 30								09 45	10 08		
Deganwy	d	06x38	07x12						07x49	08x06				08x34								09x49	10x12		
Llandudno Junction	a	06 42	07 18			07 22		07 39	07 53	08 12			08 23	08 38						09 23	09 39	09 53	10 18		
	d	06 44				07 24		07 40	07 54				08 25	08 39		08 54				09 25	09 40	09 54			
Colwyn Bay	d	06 50				07 30		07 47	08 00				08 31	08 45		09 00				09 31	09 47	10 00			
Abergele & Pensarn	d	06 57							08 07							09 07						10 07			
Rhyl	d	07 03				07 40		07 58	08 13				08 41	08 56		09 13				09 41	09 58	10 13			
Prestatyn	d	07 08				07 46		08 04	08 19				08 47			09 19				09 47	10 04	10 19			
Flint	d	07 21				07 59		08 17	08 32				09 00			09 32				10 00	10 17	10 32			
Shotton	d	07 27							08 38							09 38						10 38			
Chester	a	07 38				08 14		08 31	08 50				09 14	09 23		09 50				10 15	10 31	10 50			
	d	07 40		07 55	08 04	08 19		08 35	08 52		08 55	09 04	09 19	09 26	09 35	09 52		09 55	10 04	10 20	10 35	10 52		10 55	11 04
Liverpool Lime Street [10] 106	a																								
Helsby	d	07 49							09 01							10 01						11 01			
Frodsham	d	07 53							09 05							10 05						11 05			
Runcorn East	d	07 59							09 11							10 11						11 11			
Warrington Bank Quay 90	a	08 06							09 18							10 18						11 18			
Earlestown [8] 90	a	08 15							09 26							10 26						11 26			
Newton-le-Willows 90	a	08 18							09 29							10 29						11 29			
Manchester Oxford Road 90	a	08 41							09 48							10 48						11 48			
Manchester Pic'dilly [10] 90 ⇌	a	08 50			09 35				09 57			10 35				10 57			11 35			11 57			12 35
Crewe [10]	a			08 18				08 54			09 18		09 40		09 54			10 18			10 54			11 18	
Cardiff Central [7] 131	a					11 15								12 09						13 22					
Manchester Airport 84,85 ✈	a																								
Birmingham New Street [12] 65	a												11 30												
London Euston [15] ⊖65	a							10 39							11 39						12 39				

A from 30 December until 21 March
B until 27 December, from 24 March
C To Birmingham International
D 🚲 from Chester
E not 21 April, 5 May. To Birmingham International
F 21 April, 5 May. To Birmingham International
G [1] to Chester
H From Wrexham General
I To Blaenau Ffestiniog

Table 81R

Mondays to Fridays

9 December to 16 May

North Wales and Chester - Manchester and Crewe

Network Diagram - see first Page of Table 81

		AW		VT	AW	AW	AW	NT	AW	VT	AW	AW		AW	NT	AW	VT	AW	AW	AW	NT	AW		VT	AW
									■																
		◇		◇1	◇					◇1	◇					◇	◇1	◇	◇			◇		◇1	◇
		A							B							A			C			D			
		⊥		☕	⊥				⊥	☕	⊥					⊥	☕	⊥				⊥		☕	⊥
Holyhead	d	09 23							10 40							11 27						12 32			
Valley	d	09x29														11x33									
Rhosneigr	d	09x34																				12x42			
Ty Croes	d	09x38																				12x46			
Bodorgan	d	09x42																				12x50			
Llanfairpwll	d	09x52														11x51									
Bangor (Gwynedd)	a	10 00							11 06							11 59						13 05			
	d	10 02							11 07							12 00	12 24					13 07			13 31
Llanfairfechan	d	10x09														12x07									13x38
Penmaenmawr	d	10x13														12x11									13x42
Conwy	d	10x19														12x17									13x48
Llandudno	d				10 44	11 12					11 44	12 08						12 44	13 08						
Deganwy	d				10x48	11x16					11x48	12x12						12x48	13x12						
Llandudno Junction	a	10 23			10 52	11 20			11 23		11 52	12 18				12 22	12 40	12 52	13 18			13 23			13 53
	d	10 25			10 53				11 25		11 53					12 23	12 42	12 53				13 25			13 55
Colwyn Bay	d	10 31			10 59				11 31		11 59					12 29	12 48	12 59				13 31			14 01
Abergele & Pensarn	d				11 06						12 06							13 06							14 08
Rhyl	d	10 41			11 12				11 41		12 12					12 40	12 59	13 12				13 41			14 14
Prestatyn	d	10 47			11 18				11 47		12 18					12 45	13 05	13 18				13 47			14 19
Flint	d	11 00			11 31				12 00		12 31					12 59	13 18	13 31				14 00			14 33
Shotton	d				11 37						12 37							13 37							14 39
Chester	a	11 15			11 49				12 16		12 49					13 13	13 32	13 49				14 15			14 50
	d	11 30		11 35	11 50		11 55	12 04	12 19	12 35	12 50			12 55	13 04	13 30	13 35	13 50		13 55	14 04	14 19		14 35	14 52
Liverpool Lime Street 10 106	a																								
Helsby	d				12 00						13 00							14 00							15 01
Frodsham	d				12 04						13 04							14 04							15 05
Runcorn East	d				12 09						13 09							14 09							15 11
Warrington Bank Quay 90	a				12 18						13 18							14 18							15 18
Earlestown 8 90	a				12 26						13 26							14 26							15 26
Newton-le-Willows 90	a				12 29						13 29							14 29							15 29
Manchester Oxford Road 90	a				12 48						13 48							14 48							15 48
Manchester Pic'dilly 10 90 ⛴	a				12 57			13 35			13 57				14 35			14 57			15 35				15 57
Crewe 10	a			11 54			12 18			12 54				13 18			13 54			14 18				14 54	
Cardiff Central 7 131	a								15 11													17 15			
Manchester Airport 84,85 ✈	a																								
Birmingham New Street 12 65	a	13 29														15 30									
London Euston 15 ⊖65	a			13 39						14 39							15 39							16 39	

		AW	AW	NT	AW	VT	AW	AW		NT	AW	AW	VT	AW	NT	AW	AW	AW		VT	AW	NT	AW	AW	AW
					◇	◇1	◇				◇	◇	◇1			◇	◇	◇		◇1			◇	◇	
					A												C	A							
					⊥	☕	⊥				⊥	⊥	☕			⊥		⊥		⊠			⊥	⊥	
Holyhead	d				13 28	13 58						14 34						15 44						16 50	
Valley	d				13x34													15x50							
Rhosneigr	d				13x39													15x55							
Ty Croes	d				13x43													15x59							
Bodorgan	d				13x47													16x03							
Llanfairpwll	d				13x57													16x13							
Bangor (Gwynedd)	a				14 05	14 24						15 01						16 21						17 16	
	d				14 07	14 25						15 04						16 23						17 18	
Llanfairfechan	d											15x11						16x30							
Penmaenmawr	d											15x15						16x34							
Conwy	d											15x21						16x40							
Llandudno	d	14 08					14 40				15 08					16 06	16 20						17 05		
Deganwy	d	14x12					14x44				15x12					16x10	16x24						17x09		
Llandudno Junction	a	14 18			14 23	14 42	14 48				15 16	15 26				16 14	16 28	16 44					17 13	17 35	
	d				14 25	14 43	14 49				15 17	15 27				16 15		16 46					17 15	17 37	
Colwyn Bay	d				14 31	14 50	14 55				15 23	15 33				16 21							17 21	17 43	
Abergele & Pensarn	d						15 02				15 30					16 28							17 27		
Rhyl	d				14 41	15 00	15 08				15 36	15 44				16 34							17 33	17 53	
Prestatyn	d				14 47		15 14				15 42	15 49				16 39							17 39	17 59	
Flint	d				15 00		15 27				15 55	16 03				16 53							17 52	18 12	
Shotton	d						15 33				16 01					16 59							17 58		
Chester	a				15 15	15 27	15 44				16 13	16 17				17 10		17 26					18 11	18 26	
	d		14 55	15 04	15 30	15 35	15 46	15 55		16 04	16 22	16 19	16 35	16 55	17 04	17 19		17 30		17 35	17 55	18 04	18 16	18 28	18 49
Liverpool Lime Street 10 106	a																								
Helsby	d						15 55				16 31					17 28							18 25		18 59
Frodsham	d						15 59				16 35					17 33							18 30		19 03
Runcorn East	d						16 04				16 41					17 38							18 35		19 08
Warrington Bank Quay 90	a						16 12				16 51					17 49							18 45		19 18
Earlestown 8 90	a						16 26				16 59					17 57							18 57		19 26
Newton-le-Willows 90	a						16 29				17 01					17 59							18 59		19 29
Manchester Oxford Road 90	a						16 48				17 21					18 19							19 21		19 48
Manchester Pic'dilly 10 90 ⛴	a			16 35			16 57			17 35	17 30				18 35	18 28						19 35	19 29		19 52
Crewe 10	a		15 18			15 54		16 18					16 54	17 18						17 54	18 18				
Cardiff Central 7 131	a											19 21												21 42	
Manchester Airport 84,85 ✈	a																								20 18
Birmingham New Street 12 65	a				17 30													19 30							
London Euston 15 ⊖65	a					17 39							18 39							19 39					

A To Birmingham International
B To Llanelli
C To Blaenau Ffestiniog
D To Maesteg

Table 81R

Mondays to Fridays

9 December to 16 May

North Wales and Chester - Manchester and Crewe

Network Diagram - see first Page of Table 81

		AW	AW	AW		NT	VT	AW	AW	AW	AW	NT	AW	AW		AW	AW	AW	NT	VT	AW	AW	NT	AW
																	MW FO	TThO						
			◇				◇ 1	◇	◇				◇	◇			◇	◇		◇ 1	◇	◇		
			A						B															
Holyhead	d		17 30										18 23				19 21	19 21				20 37		
Valley	d		17x36										18x29				19x27	19x27						
Rhosneigr	d		17x41										18x34				19x32	19x32						
Ty Croes	d		17x45										18x38				19x36	19x36						
Bodorgan	d		17x49										18x42				19x40	19x40						
Llanfairpwll	d		17x59										18x52				19x50	19x50						
Bangor (Gwynedd)	a		18 07										19 00				19 58	19 58				21 04		
	d		18 09										19 02				20 00	20 00		20 20		21 06		
Llanfairfechan	d		18x16										19x09				20x07	20x07				21x13		
Penmaenmawr	d		18x20										19x13				20x11	20x11				21x17		
Conwy	d		18x26										19x19				20x17	20x17				21x23		
Llandudno	d	18 08						18 44	19 03	19 13				19 42							20 43			21 45
Deganwy	d	18x12						18x48	19x07	19x17				19x46							20x47			21x49
Llandudno Junction	a	18 18	18 30					18 52	19 11	19 21			19 24	19 50			20 21	20 21		20 36	20 51	21 27		21 53
	d		18 33					18 53					19 26	19 51			20 23	20 23		20 38	20 52	21 29		21 55
Colwyn Bay	d							18 59					19 32	19 57			20 29	20 29		20 44	20 58	21 35		22 01
Abergele & Pensarn	d							19 06						20 04							21 05	21 42		22 09
Rhyl	d							19 12					19 42	20 10			20 39	20 39		20 55	21 11	21 48		22 16
Prestatyn	d							19 18					19 48	20 16			20 45	20 45		21 01	21 17	21 53		22 22
Flint	d							19 31					20 01	20 29			20 58	20 58		21 14	21 30	22 07		22 37
Shotton	d							19 37						20 35							21 36	22 13		22 44
Chester	a		19 14					19 49					20 16	20 47			21 15	21 15		21 28	21 47	22 23		22 55
	d			18 55		19 04	19 35	19 50			19 55	20 04	20 18	20 50		20 55	21 21	21 21	21 30	21 35	21 52	22 26	22 48	23 01
Liverpool Lime Street 10 106	a																							
Helsby	d							20 00						20 59							22 01			
Frodsham	d							20 04						21 03							22 05			
Runcorn East	d							20 09						21 09							22 11			
Warrington Bank Quay 90	a							20 18						21 18							22 18			
Earlestown 8 90	a							20 26						21 26							22 26			
Newton-le-Willows 90	a							20 29						21 29							22 29			
Manchester Oxford Road 90	a							20 48						21 48							22 50			
Manchester Pic'dilly 10 90	a					20 34		20 52				21 34		21 57					22 59		22 58		00 18	
Crewe 10	a			19 18			19 54				20 18		20 41			21 18				21 54		22 50		23 26
Cardiff Central 7 131	a																							
Manchester Airport 84,85	a							21 18																
Birmingham New Street 12 65	a																23 27	23 28		22 50				
London Euston 15 ⊖65	a						21 43																	

		AW
		◇
		C
Holyhead	d	
Valley	d	
Rhosneigr	d	
Ty Croes	d	
Bodorgan	d	
Llanfairpwll	d	
Bangor (Gwynedd)	a	
	d	
Llanfairfechan	d	
Penmaenmawr	d	
Conwy	d	
Llandudno	d	
Deganwy	d	
Llandudno Junction	a	
	d	
Colwyn Bay	d	
Abergele & Pensarn	d	
Rhyl	d	
Prestatyn	d	
Flint	d	
Shotton	d	
Chester	a	
	d	23 22
Liverpool Lime Street 10 106	a	
Helsby	d	23 31
Frodsham	d	23 35
Runcorn East	d	23 41
Warrington Bank Quay 90	a	23 49
Earlestown 8 90	a	23 56
Newton-le-Willows 90	a	23 59
Manchester Oxford Road 90	a	
Manchester Pic'dilly 10 90	a	00 28
Crewe 10	a	
Cardiff Central 7 131	a	
Manchester Airport 84,85	a	
Birmingham New Street 12 65	a	
London Euston 15 ⊖65	a	

A To Shrewsbury **B** To Blaenau Ffestiniog **C** From Birmingham International

Table 81R

Saturdays

14 December to 17 May

North Wales and Chester - Manchester and Crewe

Network Diagram - see first Page of Table 81

		AW	AW	AW	AW	AW	AW	NT	AW	AW		AW	NT	AW	VT	AW	AW	AW	AW	NT		AW	VT	AW	AW
									◇	◇					◇[1]	◇	◇					◇	◇[1]	◇	
														A		B									
									🚲					🚲	🍽	🚲	🚲					🚲	🍽	🚲	
Holyhead	d								04 25							05 22						06 35	06 52		
Valley	d								04x32							05x28						06x41			
Rhosneigr	d															05x33									
Ty Croes	d															05x37									
Bodorgan	d															05x41									
Llanfairpwll	d								04x49							05x51						06x58			
Bangor (Gwynedd)	a								04 56							05 59						07 05	07 18		
	d								04 57							06 01						07 07	07 20		
Llanfairfechan	d															06x08									
Penmaenmawr	d															06x12									
Conwy	d															06x18									
Llandudno	d																06 34	07 08						07 45	08 08
Deganwy	d																06x38	07x12						07x49	08x12
Llandudno Junction	a								05 13							06 22	06 42	07 18				07 23	07 36	07 53	08 18
	d				04 38				05 15			05 37				06 24	06 44					07 25	07 38	07 54	
Colwyn Bay	d				04 44				05 21			05 43				06 30	06 50					07 31	07 44	08 00	
Abergele & Pensarn	d				04 51							05 50					06 57							08 07	
Rhyl	d				04 57				05 31			05 56				06 40	07 03					07 41	07 55	08 13	
Prestatyn	d				05 02				05 37			06 01				06 46	07 08					07 47	08 01	08 19	
Flint	d				05 16				05 50			06 15				06 59	07 21					08 00	08 15	08 32	
Shotton	d				05 22							06 21					07 27							08 38	
Chester	a				05 33				06 04			06 33				07 15	07 38					08 16	08 28	08 50	
	d	03 36	04 22	04 55	05 37	05 38	05 51	06 02	06 12	06 13		06 35	06 58	07 12	07 17	07 21	07 40		07 55	08 04		08 19	08 35	08 52	
Liverpool Lime Street [10] 106	a																								
Helsby	d					05 47				06 22				07 21			07 49							09 01	
Frodsham	d					05 51				06 26				07 25			07 53							09 05	
Runcorn East	d					05 56				06 32				07 31			07 59							09 11	
Warrington Bank Quay 90	a					06 05				06 39				07 38			08 06							09 18	
Earlestown [8] 90	a					06 12				06 47				07 46			08 15							09 26	
Newton-le-Willows 90	a					06 15				06 50				07 49			08 18							09 29	
Manchester Oxford Road 90	a					06 35				07 09				08 09			08 41							09 48	
Manchester Pic'dilly [10] 90 ⛴	a	04 41				06 44		07 30		07 18			08 29	08 18			08 45			09 35				09 52	
Crewe [10]	a		04 44	05 20	05 58		06 15					06 59			07 36				08 18				08 54		
Cardiff Central [7] 131	a								09 22													11 14			
Manchester Airport 84,85 ✈	a	05 04																							
Birmingham New Street [12] 65	a		05 58													09 27									
London Euston [15] ⊖65	a														09 30								10 39		

		AW	NT	AW	VT	AW		AW	AW	NT	AW	VT	AW	AW	AW	NT		AW	VT	AW	AW	AW	AW	NT	AW
																									■
				◇	◇[1]	◇					◇	◇[1]	◇					◇	◇[1]	◇	◇				
				B														B		C					
				🚲	🍽	🚲					🚲	🍽	🚲					🚲	🍽		🚲				🚲
Holyhead	d			07 15	07 55						08 20	08 55						09 23							10 33
Valley	d			07x21							08x26							09x29							10x39
Rhosneigr	d			07x26							08x32							09x34							
Ty Croes	d			07x30							08x35							09x38							
Bodorgan	d			07x34							08x40							09x42							
Llanfairpwll	d			07x44							08x49							09x52							10x56
Bangor (Gwynedd)	a			07 52	08 21						08 57	09 21						10 00							11 03
	d			08 02	08 22						09 02	09 22						10 02							11 05
Llanfairfechan	d			08x09							09x09							10x09							
Penmaenmawr	d			08x13							09x13							10x13							
Conwy	d			08x19							09x19							10x19							
Llandudno	d					08 45		09 08					09 45	10 08						10 22	10 44	11 08			
Deganwy	d					08x49		09x12					09x49	10x12						10x26	10x48	11x12			
Llandudno Junction	a			08 23	08 39	08 53		09 18			09 23	09 39	09 53	10 18				10 23		10 32	10 52	11 18			11 21
	d			08 25	08 40	08 54					09 25	09 40	09 54					10 25			10 53				11 25
Colwyn Bay	d			08 31	08 47	09 00					09 31	09 47	10 00					10 31			10 59				11 31
Abergele & Pensarn	d					09 07							10 07								11 06				
Rhyl	d			08 41	08 58	09 13					09 41	09 58	10 13					10 41			11 12				11 41
Prestatyn	d			08 47	09 04	09 19					09 47	10 03	10 19					10 47			11 18				11 47
Flint	d			09 00	09 17	09 32					10 00		10 32					11 00			11 31				12 00
Shotton	d					09 38							10 38								11 37				
Chester	a			09 15	09 31	09 50					10 16	10 28	10 50					11 16			11 49				12 16
	d	08 55	09 04	09 20	09 35	09 52			09 55	10 04	10 19	10 35	10 52		10 55	11 04		11 30	11 35		11 50		11 55	12 04	12 19
Liverpool Lime Street [10] 106	a																								
Helsby	d					10 01							11 01								12 00				
Frodsham	d					10 05							11 05								12 04				
Runcorn East	d					10 11							11 11								12 09				
Warrington Bank Quay 90	a					10 18							11 18								12 18				
Earlestown [8] 90	a					10 26							11 26								12 26				
Newton-le-Willows 90	a					10 29							11 29								12 29				
Manchester Oxford Road 90	a					10 48							11 48								12 48				
Manchester Pic'dilly [10] 90 ⛴	a		10 35			10 52				11 35			11 52			12 35					12 52			13 35	
Crewe [10]	a	09 18			09 54				10 18			10 54			11 18				11 54				12 18		
Cardiff Central [7] 131	a										13 15														15 24
Manchester Airport 84,85 ✈	a																								
Birmingham New Street [12] 65	a			11 28														13 28							
London Euston [15] ⊖65	a				11 39							12 39							13 39						

A From Shrewsbury

B To Birmingham International

C To Blaenau Ffestiniog

Table 81R

Saturdays

14 December to 17 May

North Wales and Chester - Manchester and Crewe

Network Diagram - see first Page of Table 81

		VT ◇1		AW ◇	AW	AW	NT	AW ◇ A	VT ◇1	AW ◇	AW ◇ B	AW		NT	AW ◇ C	VT ◇1	AW ◇	AW	AW	NT	AW ◇ A	VT ◇1		AW ◇	AW
Holyhead	d							11 23							12 38						13 28	13 58			
Valley	d							11x29													13x34				
Rhosneigr	d							11x34													13x39				
Ty Croes	d							11x38													13x43				
Bodorgan	d							11x42													13x47				
Llanfairpwll	d							11x52													13x57				
Bangor (Gwynedd)	a							12 00							13 05						14 05	14 24			
	d							12 02							13 07		13 31				14 07	14 25			
Llanfairfechan	d							12x09									13x38								
Penmaenmawr	d							12x13									13x42								
Conwy	d							12x19									13x48								
Llandudno	d			11 44	12 08					12 44	13 08							14 08						14 42	
Deganwy	d			11x48	12x12					12x48	13x12							14x12						14x46	
Llandudno Junction	a			11 52	12 18			12 23		12 52	13 18				13 23		13 53	14 18			14 23	14 42		14 50	
	d			11 53				12 25		12 53					13 25		13 55				14 25	14 43		14 51	
Colwyn Bay	d			11 59				12 31		12 59					13 31		14 01				14 31	14 50		14 57	
Abergele & Pensarn	d			12 06						13 06							14 08							15 04	
Rhyl	d			12 12				12 41		13 12					13 41		14 14				14 41	15 00		15 10	
Prestatyn	d			12 18				12 47		13 18					13 47		14 19				14 47			15 16	
Flint	d			12 31				13 00		13 31					14 00		14 33				15 00			15 29	
Shotton	d			12 37						13 37							14 39							15 35	
Chester	a			12 49				13 15		13 49					14 14		14 50				15 17	15 27		15 46	
	d	12 35		12 50		12 55	13 04	13 30	13 35	13 50		13 55		14 04	14 19	14 35	14 52		14 55	15 04	15 30	15 35		15 48	15 55
Liverpool Lime Street 10 106	a																								
Helsby	d			13 00						14 00							15 01							15 57	
Frodsham	d			13 04						14 04							15 05							16 02	
Runcorn East	d			13 09						14 09							15 11							16 07	
Warrington Bank Quay 90	a			13 18						14 18							15 18							16 16	
Earlestown 8 90	a			13 26						14 26							15 26							16 26	
Newton-le-Willows 90	a			13 29						14 29							15 29							16 29	
Manchester Oxford Road 90	a			13 48						14 48							15 48							16 48	
Manchester Pic'dilly 10 90	a			13 52			14 35			14 57				15 35			15 52			16 35				16 57	
Crewe 10	a	12 54				13 18			13 54			14 18				14 54			15 18			15 54			16 18
Cardiff Central 7 131	a														17 08										
Manchester Airport 84,85	a																								
Birmingham New Street 12 65	a							15 28													17 26				
London Euston 15 ⊖65	a	14 39							15 39							16 39						17 39			

		NT	AW ◇	VT ◇1	AW	AW ◇	AW	AW		NT	AW ◇ A	VT ◇1	AW ◇ B	AW ◇	AW	AW	NT	AW ◇		AW ◇	AW	AW ◇ D	AW	NT	AW ◇
Holyhead	d		14 23								15 23							16 50				17 30			
Valley	d										15x29											17x36			
Rhosneigr	d										15x34											17x41			
Ty Croes	d										15x38											17x45			
Bodorgan	d										15x42											17x49			
Llanfairpwll	d										15x52											17x59			
Bangor (Gwynedd)	a		14 52								16 00							17 16				18 07			
	d		14 53								16 02							17 18				18 09			
Llanfairfechan	d		15x00								16x09											18x16			
Penmaenmawr	d		15x04								16x13											18x20			
Conwy	d		15x10								16x19											18x26			
Llandudno	d				15 08	15 44	16 08						16 20	16 44	17 08					17 44	18 08				18 44
Deganwy	d				15x12	15x48	16x12						16x24	16x48	17x12					17x48	18x12				18x48
Llandudno Junction	a		15 15		15 18	15 52	16 18				16 23		16 30	16 52	17 18			17 34		17 52	18 18	18 30			18 52
	d		15 16			15 53					16 25			16 53				17 36		17 53		18 32			18 53
Colwyn Bay	d		15 22			15 59					16 31			16 59				17 42		17 59		18 38			18 59
Abergele & Pensarn	d					16 06								17 06						18 06					19 06
Rhyl	d		15 33			16 12					16 41			17 12				17 52		18 12		18 48			19 12
Prestatyn	d		15 38			16 18					16 47			17 18				17 58		18 18		18 54			19 18
Flint	d		15 52			16 31					17 00			17 31				18 11		18 31		19 07			19 31
Shotton	d					16 37								17 37						18 37					19 37
Chester	a		16 05			16 49					17 15			17 49				18 25		18 49		19 24			19 49
	d	16 04	16 19	16 35		16 50		16 55		17 04	17 28	17 35		17 50		17 55	18 04	18 29		18 50			18 55	19 04	19 50
Liverpool Lime Street 10 106	a																								
Helsby	d					17 00								18 00						19 00					20 00
Frodsham	d					17 04								18 04						19 04					20 04
Runcorn East	d					17 09								18 09						19 09					20 09
Warrington Bank Quay 90	a					17 18								18 18						19 18					20 18
Earlestown 8 90	a					17 26								18 26						19 26					20 26
Newton-le-Willows 90	a					17 29								18 29						19 29					20 29
Manchester Oxford Road 90	a					17 48								18 48						19 48					20 48
Manchester Pic'dilly 10 90	a	17 35				17 57				18 35				18 57			19 35			19 52				20 34	20 57
Crewe 10	a			16 54				17 18				17 54				18 18							19 18		
Cardiff Central 7 131	a		19 15															21 43							
Manchester Airport 84,85	a																			20 13					
Birmingham New Street 12 65	a										19 28														
London Euston 15 ⊖65	a			18 39																					

A To Birmingham International
B To Blaenau Ffestiniog
C To Maesteg
D To Shrewsbury

Table 81R

North Wales and Chester - Manchester and Crewe

Saturdays

14 December to 17 May

Network Diagram - see first Page of Table 81

		AW	AW	AW		NT	AW	VT	AW	AW	AW	AW	NT	AW		AW	AW	NT	AW	AW	AW
		◇ A					◇	◇	◇			◇					◇	B		B	C
Holyhead	d						18 23					19 21					20 37				
Valley	d						18x29					19x27									
Rhosneigr	d						18x34					19x32									
Ty Croes	d						18x38					19x36									
Bodorgan	d						18x42					19x40									
Llanfairpwll	d						18x52					19x50									
Bangor (Gwynedd)	a						19 00					19 58					21 05				
	d						19 02					20 00					21 06				
Llanfairfechan	d						19x09					20x07					21x13				
Penmaenmawr	d						19x13					20x11					21x17				
Conwy	d						19x19					20x17					21x23				
Llandudno	d	19 03	19 13						19 42	20 08				20 43					21 45		
Deganwy	d	19x07	19x17						19x46	20x12				20x47					21x49		
Llandudno Junction	a	19 11	19 21				19 23		19 50	20 18		20 21		20 51			21 28		21 53		
	d						19 25		19 51			20 23		20 52			21 29		21 55		
Colwyn Bay	d						19 31		19 57			20 29		20 58			21 35		22 01		
Abergele & Pensarn	d								20 04					21 05			21 42		22 09		
Rhyl	d						19 41		20 10			20 39		21 11			21 48		22 16		
Prestatyn	d						19 47		20 16			20 45		21 17			21 54		22 22		
Flint	d						20 00		20 29			20 58		21 30			22 07		22 37		
Shotton	d								20 35					21 36			22 13		22 44		
Chester	a						20 15		20 47			21 15		21 47			22 23		22 55		
	d			19 55		20 04	20 17	20 35	20 50		20 55	21 20	21 30			21 52	22 26	22 48	23 01	23 22	23 22
Liverpool Lime Street 10 106	a																				
Helsby	d								20 59							22 01				23 31	23 42
Frodsham	d								21 03							22 05				23 35	23 47
Runcorn East	d								21 09							22 11				23 41	00 02
Warrington Bank Quay 90	a								21 16							22 19				23 50	00 22
Earlestown 8 90	a								21 26							22 26				23 58	00 47
Newton-le-Willows 90	a								21 29							22 30				00 01	00 57
Manchester Oxford Road 90	a								21 48							22 50					
Manchester Pic'dilly 10 90	a					21 34			21 57				22 59			22 58		00 16		00 26	01 32
Crewe 10	a			20 18			20 41	20 54			21 18						22 50		23 26		
Cardiff Central 7 131	a																				
Manchester Airport 84,85	a																				
Birmingham New Street 12 65	a											23 29									
London Euston 15 ⊖65	a																				

Sundays

8 December to 11 May

		AW	AW	AW	NT	AW	AW	AW	AW	AW		NT	VT	AW	AW	AW	AW	VT	AW	NT		AW	VT	VT	AW
		D			E	◇ F		◇		◇		E	◇1	◇ F		◇		◇1		E			◇1	◇1	◇ F
Holyhead	d									08 45						10 20		10 55					11 50		
Valley	d															10x26									
Rhosneigr	d															10x31									
Ty Croes	d															10x35									
Bodorgan	d															10x39									
Llanfairpwll	d															10x49									
Bangor (Gwynedd)	a									09 12						10 57		11 21					12 16		
	d									09 13						10 59		11 22					12 17		
Llanfairfechan	d															11x06									
Penmaenmawr	d															11x10									
Conwy	d															11x16									
Llandudno	d																								
Deganwy	d																								
Llandudno Junction	a									09 29						11 20		11 38					12 34		
	d									09 35						11 22		11 40					12 35		
Colwyn Bay	d									09 41						11 28		11 46					12 42		
Abergele & Pensarn	d									09 48						11 35									
Rhyl	d									09 54						11 41		11 57					12 53		
Prestatyn	d									09 59						11 46		12 03					12 59		
Flint	d									10 13						12 00		12 16							
Shotton	d									10 19						12 06									
Chester	a									10 30						12 18		12 30					13 24		
	d		08 40	08 41	09 01	09 22	09 39	09 42	10 36	10 39		11 04	11 28	11 31	11 36	12 21	12 24	12 32	12 36	13 04		13 20	13 30	13 30	13 31
Liverpool Lime Street 10 106	a																								
Helsby	d			08 50				09 51	10 45						11 45				12 45						
Frodsham	d			08 54				09 55	10 49						11 49				12 49						
Runcorn East	d	00 02		08 59				10 00	10 54						11 54				12 54						
Warrington Bank Quay 90	a	00 22		09 10				10 09	11 03						12 03				13 03						
Earlestown 8 90	a	00 47		09 16				10 19	11 10						12 10				13 10						
Newton-le-Willows 90	a	00 57		09 19				10 22	11 13						12 13				13 13						
Manchester Oxford Road 90	a			09 39				10 41	11 33						12 32				13 32						
Manchester Pic'dilly 10 90	a	01 32		09 48	10 22			10 50	11 41			12 32			12 41				13 41	14 33					
Crewe 10	a		09 04				10 02			11 03			11 47				12 47	12 53				13 43	13 50	13 50	
Cardiff Central 7 131	a															15 31									
Manchester Airport 84,85	a																								
Birmingham New Street 12 65	a					11 13								13 23											15 24
London Euston 15 ⊖65	a												13 46					14 44					15 45	15 45	

A To Blaenau Ffestiniog
B until 8 February, from 29 March
C from 15 February until 22 March
D from 16 February until 23 March. From Chester
E To Southport
F To Birmingham International

Table 81R

Sundays

8 December to 11 May

North Wales and Chester - Manchester and Crewe

Network Diagram - see first Page of Table 81

		AW	AW	VT	VT	AW		NT	AW	VT	AW	AW	AW	NT	AW	AW		VT	AW	AW	VT	AW	AW	NT	AW
				◇■1	◇■1				◇	◇■1			◇		◇	◇		◇■1	◇	■	◇■1				◇
								A	B					A		B								A	
		🛒		☕	☕	🛒			🛒	☕			🛒					☕		🛒	☕				
Holyhead	d				12 50					13 55			14 30		15 30					16 25					17 30
Valley	d												14x36							16x31					
Rhosneigr	d												14x42							16x36					
Ty Croes	d												14x45							16x40					
Bodorgan	d												14x50							16x44					
Llanfairpwll	d												14x59							16x54					
Bangor (Gwynedd)	a				13 16					14 21			15 07		15 56					17 02					17 57
	d				13 18					14 22			15 08		15 58					17 04					17 59
Llanfairfechan	d														16x05										18x06
Penmaenmawr	d														16x09										18x10
Conwy	d														16x15										18x16
Llandudno	d																								
Deganwy	d																								
Llandudno Junction	a				13 34					14 39			15 25		16 19					17 20					18 20
	d				13 36					14 40			15 26		16 25					17 25					18 24
Colwyn Bay	d				13 42					14 46			15 32		16 31					17 31					18 30
Abergele & Pensarn	d												15 39		16 38					17 38					18 37
Rhyl	d				13 53					14 57			15 45		16 44					17 44					18 43
Prestatyn	d				13 59					15 03			15 51		16 49					17 49					18 48
Flint	d				14 13								16 04		17 03					18 03					19 02
Shotton	d												16 10		17 09					18 11					19 10
Chester	a				14 26					15 31			16 21		17 20					18 21					19 21
	d	13 36	14 23	14 33	14 33	14 36		15 04	15 31	15 33	15 36	16 27	16 36	17 04	17 22	17 31		17 35	17 36	18 24	18 35	18 36	18 57	19 04	19 22
Liverpool Lime Street ■10 106	a																								
Helsby	d	13 45				14 45					15 45		16 45						17 45			18 45			
Frodsham	d	13 49				14 49					15 49		16 49						17 49			18 49			
Runcorn East	d	13 54				14 54					15 54		16 54						17 54			18 54			
Warrington Bank Quay 90	a	14 03				15 03					16 03		17 03						18 03			19 03			
Earlestown ■8 90	a	14 10				15 10					16 10		17 10						18 10			19 10			
Newton-le-Willows 90	a	14 13				15 13					16 13		17 13						18 13			19 13			
Manchester Oxford Road 90	a	14 32				15 32					16 32		17 32						18 32			19 32			
Manchester Pic'dilly ■10 90 ⛴	a	14 41				15 41		16 33			16 41		17 41	18 33					18 41			19 41		20 33	
Crewe ■10	a		14 46	14 52	14 53					15 52		16 51			17 44			17 53			18 53		19 19		19 47
Cardiff Central ■7 131	a																			21 36					
Manchester Airport 84,85 ✈	a																								
Birmingham New Street ■12 65	a								17 35							19 25									
London Euston ■15 ⊖65	a			16 41	16 44					17 44								19 45			20 46				

		AW		VT	AW	AW	AW	AW	VT	AW	NT	AW		AW	AW	AW	AW	AW	AW						
				◇			◇		◇			◇					◇	◇							
		B					B				C								D						
				☕			🛒		☕																
Holyhead	d						18 25					19 40					20 35	21 40							
Valley	d						18x31										20x41								
Rhosneigr	d						18x36										20x46								
Ty Croes	d						18x40										20x50								
Bodorgan	d						18x44										20x54								
Llanfairpwll	d						18x54										21x04								
Bangor (Gwynedd)	a						19 02					20 07					21 12	22 07							
	d						19 04					20 09					21 14	22 09							
Llanfairfechan	d											20x16					21x21								
Penmaenmawr	d											20x20					21x25								
Conwy	d											20x26					21x31								
Llandudno	d																								
Deganwy	d																								
Llandudno Junction	a						19 20					20 30					21 35	22 25							
	d						19 24					20 37					21 37	22 27							
Colwyn Bay	d						19 30					20 43					21 43	22 33							
Abergele & Pensarn	d						19 37					20 50					21 50								
Rhyl	d						19 43					20 56					21 56	22 43							
Prestatyn	d						19 48					21 01					22 01	22 49							
Flint	d						20 02					21 15					22 15	23 02							
Shotton	d						20 10					21 21					22 21								
Chester	a						20 19					21 33					22 32	23 16							
	d	19 26		19 35	19 36	19 50	20 27	20 36	20 37	20 50	21 04	21 35		21 36	21 50	22 09	22 35		23 00						
Liverpool Lime Street ■10 106	a																								
Helsby	d				19 45			20 45						21 45		22 18									
Frodsham	d				19 49			20 49						21 49		22 22									
Runcorn East	d				19 54			20 54						21 54		22 27									
Warrington Bank Quay 90	a				20 03			21 03						22 03		22 36									
Earlestown ■8 90	a				20 10			21 10						22 12		22 47									
Newton-le-Willows 90	a				20 13			21 13						22 14		22 50									
Manchester Oxford Road 90	a				20 32			21 32						22 34		23 09									
Manchester Pic'dilly ■10 90 ⛴	a				20 41			21 41			22 33			22 38		23 18									
Crewe ■10	a			19 56		20 13	20 48		20 56	21 13		21 59			22 13		22 59		23 21						
Cardiff Central ■7 131	a																								
Manchester Airport 84,85 ✈	a																								
Birmingham New Street ■12 65	a	21 29					21 52																		
London Euston ■15 ⊖65	a																								

A To Southport
B To Birmingham International
C To Wigan Wallgate
D To Shrewsbury

Table 81A

Holyhead - Dun Laoghaire - Dublin

9 December to 11 May
Network Diagram - see first Page of Table 81

		AW	AW	AW	AW	AW
		R	R	R	R	R
			A			
Holyhead	d	02 40	10 30	11 50	14 10	17 15
Dun Laoghaire	a		12 39			
Dublin Ferryport §	a	05 55		13 39	17 25	19 15

§ Bus connections to/from city centre and railway stations

A from 24 March

Table 81A-R

Dublin - Dun Laoghaire - Holyhead

9 December to 11 May
Network Diagram - see first Page of Table 81

		AW	AW	AW	AW		AW
		R	R	R	R		R
				A			
Dublin Ferryport §	d	08 45	08 05		14 30		20 55
Dun Laoghaire	d			13 30			
Holyhead	a	10 34	11 30	15 29	16 30		00 20

§ Bus connections to/from city centre and railway stations

A from 24 March

Network Diagram for Tables 82, 83, 94

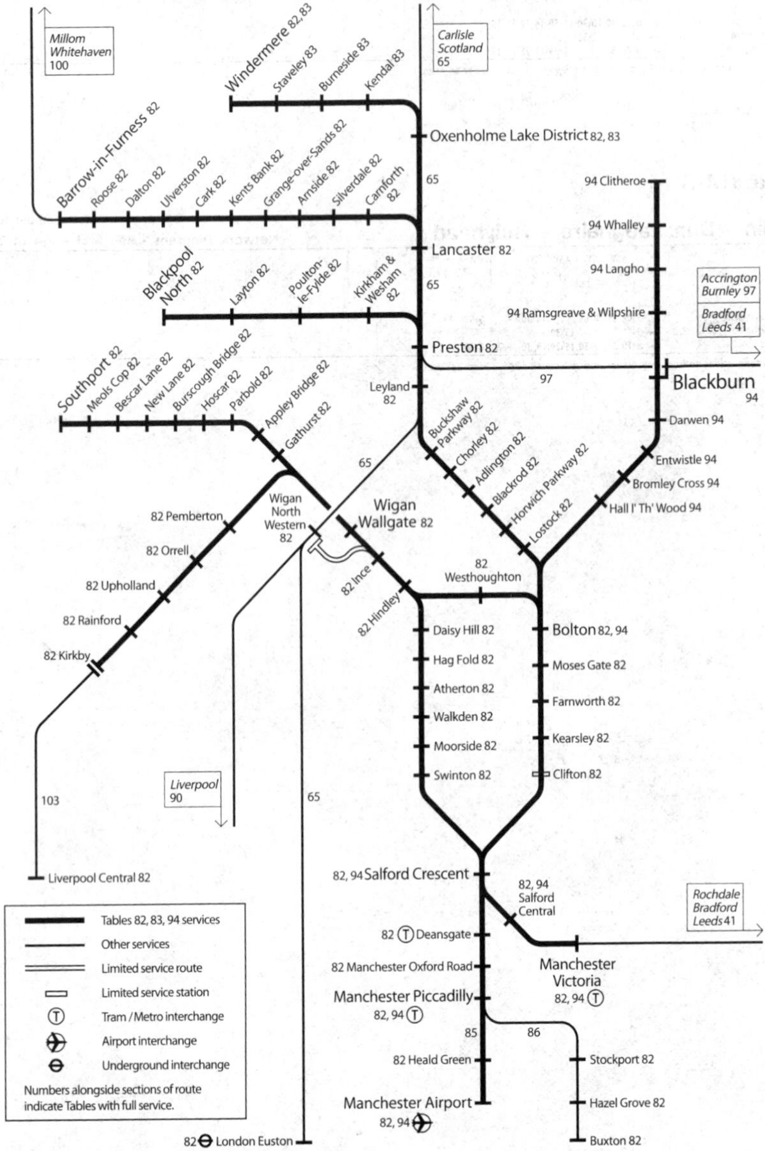

TOCs operating on this network - First TransPennine Express (TP), Northern (NT)

Table 82

Mondays to Fridays

9 December to 7 February

Manchester - Bolton - Wigan, Kirkby, Southport, Preston, Blackpool North and Barrow-in-Furness

Network Diagram - see first Page of Table 82

Miles	Miles	Miles	Miles	Miles	Station		NT	TP	TP	TP	NT	TP	TP	TP	NT	NT	NT	NT	TP	NT	TP	NT	NT	NT
							MX	MX	MX					MX										
								◇1	◇1	◇1		1	◇1	◇1					◇1		◇1			
							A	B	C	D	E		D	C	F			G	H 🚲					F
0	0	0	—	—	**Manchester Airport** 85 ✈	d				00 01			05 29						05 58		06 18			
1½	1½	1½	—	—	Heald Green 85	d													06 02					
—	—	—	—	—	Buxton 86	d																		05 59
—	—	—	—	—	Hazel Grove 86	d																		06 33
—	—	—	—	—	Stockport 84	d																		06 41
9¾	9¾	9¾	—	—	**Manchester Piccadilly** 10 🚇	d			00 16	00 16			05 44	05 44					06 13		06 33			06 53
10¼	10¼	10¼	—	—	**Manchester Oxford Road**	d							05 47	05 47					06 17		06 36			06 57
10½	10½	10½	—	—	Deansgate 🚇	d																		06 59
—	—	—	—	—	Rochdale 41	d																		
—	—	—	0	—	**Manchester Victoria** 🚇	d									05 55	06 00				06 17		06 38	06 45	
—	—	—	0¾	—	Salford Central	d																06 40	06 48	
12	12	12	1¾	—	**Salford Crescent**	a							05 52	05 52	05 59	06 04				06 23	06 41	06 44	06 51	07 02
—	—	—	—	—		d							05 52	05 52	06 00	06 05				06 24	06 41	06 45	06 52	07 03
—	—	—	5¾	—	Swinton	d																	06 58	
—	—	—	6½	—	Moorside	d																		
—	—	—	8¼	—	Walkden	d																	07 03	
—	—	—	11¾	—	Atherton	d																	07 08	
—	—	—	13	—	Hag Fold	d																		
—	—	—	13¼	—	Daisy Hill	d																	07 12	
15	15	15	—	—	Clifton	d																		
18	18	18	—	—	Kearsley	d																06 52		
18¾	18	18¾	—	—	Farnworth	d																06 54		
19¾	19¾	19¾	—	—	Moses Gate	d																06 57		
21	21	21	—	—	**Bolton**	a			00s30	00s30			06 02	06 02	06 11	06 15				06 34	06 51	07 00		07 16
—	—	—	—	—		d							06 03	06 03		06 15				06 34	06 52	07 01		
—	—	25½	—	—	Westhoughton	d										06 23								
—	—	28	15¾	—	Hindley	d										06 27							07 16	
—	—	29½	17¼	0	Ince	d																		
—	—	—	—	0¾	Wigan North Western	a													06 42			07 19		
—	—	30½	18¼	—	**Wigan Wallgate**	a										06 32							07 21	
—	—	—	—	—		d										06 34	06 37						07 23	
—	—	—	20	—	Pemberton	d										06 38								
—	—	—	22	—	Orrell	d										06 42								
—	—	—	23¼	—	Upholland	d										06 45								
—	—	—	25¼	—	Rainford	d										06 49								
—	—	—	30½	—	**Kirkby**	a										07 01								
—	—	33¼	—	—	Gathurst	d											06 41						07 27	
—	—	35	—	—	Appley Bridge	d											06 45						07 31	
—	—	37¼	—	—	Parbold	d											06 49						07 35	
—	—	38¾	—	—	Hoscar	d											06 52							
—	—	40¼	—	—	Burscough Bridge	d											06 55						07 39	
—	—	41½	—	—	New Lane	d											06 57							
—	—	43½	—	—	Bescar Lane	d											07 01							
—	—	46¾	—	—	Meols Cop	d											07 06						07 47	
—	—	48	—	—	**Southport**	a											07 15						07 56	
24	24	—	—	—	Lostock	d														06 39				
26	26	—	—	—	Horwich Parkway	d							06 10	06 10						06 43	06 58			
27½	27½	—	—	—	Blackrod	d														06 46				
29½	29½	—	—	—	Adlington (Lancashire)	d														06 50				
33½	33½	—	—	—	Chorley	d	00 03						06 17	06 17						06 55	07 06			
36	36	—	—	—	Buckshaw Parkway	d	00 07						06 21	06 21						06 59	07 09			
37	37	—	—	—	Leyland	d	00 14						06 27	06 27						07 06				
41	41	—	—	—	**Preston** 8 65,97	a	00 19		01s01	01s04			06 32	06 32					06 56	07 11	07 18			
—	—	—	—	—		d	00 21				05 19		06 35	06 35					06 57	07 13	07 20			
48¾	—	—	—	—	Kirkham & Wesham 97	a	00 30						06 44	06 44						07 22				
55¼	—	—	—	—	Poulton-le-Fylde 97	a	00 38						06 54	06 54						07 30				
57¼	—	—	—	—	Layton 97	a	00 43						06 58	06 58						07 34				
58½	—	—	—	—	**Blackpool North** 97	a	00 50		01 27	01 29			07 05	07 05						07 41				
—	62	—	—	—	**Lancaster** 6 65	a					05 39								07 13		07 35			
—	—	—	—	—		d					05 41	05 45						07 08	07 13		07 36			
—	81	—	—	—	Oxenholme Lake District 65	a						06 20							07 27					
—	91	—	—	—	Windermere 83	a						06 40												
—	68	—	—	—	Carnforth	d					05 51							07a17			07 44			
—	71¾	—	—	—	Silverdale	d					05 57										07 50			
—	74	—	—	—	Arnside	d					06 01										07 54			
—	77¼	—	—	—	Grange-over-Sands	d					06 07										08 00			
—	79½	—	—	—	Kents Bank	d					06 11										08 03			
—	81½	—	—	—	Cark	d					06 15										08 08			
—	87½	—	—	—	Ulverston	d		00 07			06 24										08 16			
—	90¾	—	—	—	Dalton	d		00 15			06 32										08 24			
—	95	—	—	—	Roose	d		00 21			06 38										08 30			
—	96¾	—	—	—	**Barrow-in-Furness**	a		00 30			06 48										08 39			

A From Manchester Victoria
B From Manchester Airport
C from 31 December
D until 30 December, MO from 6 January
E To Carlisle
F To Clitheroe
G To Leeds
H To Edinburgh

The Sunday service between Manchester Victoria and Wigan Wallgate via Atherton is funded by TfGM and will operate whilst funding exists

Table 82

Mondays to Fridays

9 December to 7 February

Manchester - Bolton - Wigan, Kirkby, Southport, Preston, Blackpool North and Barrow-in-Furness

Network Diagram - see first Page of Table 82

Station			TP	NT	NT	NT	NT	NT	NT	NT	TP	NT	NT	NT	NT	NT	NT	NT	TP	NT	NT	NT	TP
			◇1								◇1								◇1				◇1
			A	B		C		D			E	F		G	H	B		C				D	I
			🛒								🛒								🛒				🛒
Manchester Airport	85 ✈	d	07 00								07 25								07 56		08 01		
Heald Green	85	d									07 29										08 05		
Buxton	86	d								06 23			06 53										
Hazel Grove	86	d								07 00			07 27										
Stockport	84	d								07 10			07 37										
Manchester Piccadilly 10	🚊	d	07 15							07 27	07 45		07 54						08 15		08 22		
Manchester Oxford Road		d	07 18							07 30			07 57						08 19		08 26		08 31
Deansgate	🚊	d								07 32			07 59								08 28		
Rochdale	41	d																					
Manchester Victoria	🚊	d		07 01	07 06		07 17	07 23	07 27			07 47		08 00		08 03	08 11			08 22		08 29	
Salford Central		d		07 04	07 09		07 19	07 26	07 30			07 50		08 03		08 08	08 13			08 25		08 32	
Salford Crescent		a		07 07	07 12		07 24	07 29	07 32	07 37		07 53	08 04	08 07		08 12	08 17			08 29	08 33	08 37	
		d		07 08	07 13		07 25	07 30	07 32	07 37		07 53	08 04	08 08		08 13	08 17			08 30	08 34	08 37	
Swinton		d		07 14								08 00				08 19							
Moorside		d		07 17								08 02				08 22							
Walkden		d		07 20					07 42			08 06				08 25							
Atherton		d		07 26					07 48			08 11				08 31							
Hag Fold		d		07 28								08 14				08 33							
Daisy Hill		d		07 31					07 51			08 17				08 36							
Clifton		d																					
Kearsley		d								07 45													
Farnworth		d								07 47													
Moses Gate		d								07 49													
Bolton		a			07 23		07 35	07 41		07 53	07 59		08 14	08 19			08 27		08 32	08 40	08 44	08 49	08 52
		d			07 23		07 35			07 53	07 59		08 15				08 28		08 33	08 40	08 45		08 52
Westhoughton		d			07 31	←				08 01							08 35	←			08 53		
Hindley		d		07 39	07 35	07 39						08 21				08 43	08 39	08 43					
Ince		d		→		07 42										→	08 42	08 46					
Wigan North Western		a	07 43							08 16													
Wigan Wallgate		a			07 40	07 45			08 03			08 26					08 45	08 49			09 00		
		d			07 41	07 46						08 28					08 47	08 51			09 05		
Pemberton		d				07 50												08 55					
Orrell		d				07 54												08 59					
Upholland		d				07 58												09 02					
Rainford		d				08 01												09 06					
Kirkby		a				08 13												09 18					
Gathurst		d			07 46							08 32					08 51						
Appley Bridge		d			07 49							08 36					08 55				09 11		
Parbold		d			07 53												08 59				09 15		
Hoscar		d			07 56																		
Burscough Bridge		d			07 59							08 42					09 03				09 20		
New Lane		d			08 02																		
Bescar Lane		d			08 05																		
Meols Cop		d			08 10												09 11						
Southport		a			08 20							08 59					09 20				09 36		
Lostock		d					07 42						08 20							08 45			08 57
Horwich Parkway		d					07 46						08 24						08 39	08 49			09 01
Blackrod		d					07 49													08 52			
Adlington (Lancashire)		d					07 53						08 29							08 56			
Chorley		d					07 58				08 11		08 34						08 47	09 01			09 08
Buckshaw Parkway		d					08 01						08 37							09 05			09 12
Leyland		d					08 08						08 43							09 12			
Preston 8	65,97	a	07 57				08 14				08 22		08 49						08 58	09 17			09 22
		d	07 58				08 15				08 24		08 51						08 59	09 19			09 25
Kirkham & Wesham	97	a					08 25													09 28			
Poulton-le-Fylde	97	a					08 33												09 16	09 36			
Layton	97	a					08 37													09 43			
Blackpool North	97	a					08 44						09 16						09 25	09 50			
Lancaster 6	65	a	08 14								08 39												09 40
		d									08 40				08 48								09 41
Oxenholme Lake District	65	a									08 54												
Windermere	83	a																					
Carnforth		d													08 57								09 49
Silverdale		d													09 03								09 55
Arnside		d													09 08								09 59
Grange-over-Sands		d													09 14								10 05
Kents Bank		d													09 18								10 08
Cark		d													09 22								10 13
Ulverston		d													09 31								10 21
Dalton		d													09 39								10 29
Roose		d													09 45								10 35
Barrow-in-Furness		a													09 55								10 44

A To Glasgow Central
B To Kirkby
C From Manchester Victoria
D To Blackburn
E To Edinburgh
F From Huddersfield
G To Clitheroe
H From Morecambe to Carlisle
I 🛒 to Preston

The Sunday service between Manchester Victoria and Wigan Wallgate via Atherton is funded by TfGM and will operate whilst funding exists

Table 82

Mondays to Fridays

9 December to 7 February

Manchester - Bolton - Wigan, Kirkby, Southport, Preston, Blackpool North and Barrow-in-Furness

Network Diagram - see first Page of Table 82

	NT	NT	TP	NT	NT	TP	NT	NT	NT	NT	NT	NT	NT	NT	TP		NT	NT	TP	NT	NT	NT
			◇1			◇1									◇1				◇1			
	A				B	C	D							E				B	F			G
			🚲			🚲									🚲				🚲			
Manchester Airport 85 ✈ d			08 25			09 00					09 03				09 29				10 00			
Heald Green 85 d			08 29												09 33							
Buxton 86 d																						
Hazel Grove 86 d				08 32													09 33					
Stockport 84 d				08 41													09 41					
Manchester Piccadilly 10 d			08 46	08 54		09 16					09 22				09 46		09 54		10 16			
Manchester Oxford Road d			08 49	08 58		09 19					09 26				09 49		09 58		10 19			
Deansgate d			08 51	09 00							09 28				09 51		10 00					
Rochdale 41 d	08 00											09 04										
Manchester Victoria d	08 33	08 46			09 00			09 07	09 10	09 22		09 33	09 46					10 00			10 07	10 10
Salford Central d	08 37	08 49			09 03			09 10	09 13	09 25		09 36	09 49					10 03			10 10	10 13
Salford Crescent a	08 40	08 52	08 56	09 04	09 07			09 13	09 16	09 29	09 33	09 39	09 52		09 56		10 04	10 07			10 13	10 16
d	08 41	08 53	08 56	09 04	09 08			09 13	09 17	09 30	09 34	09 41	09 53		09 56		10 04	10 08			10 13	10 17
Swinton d		08 59							09 23				09 59									10 23
Moorside d									09 26													10 26
Walkden d		09 04							09 29				10 04									10 29
Atherton d		09 09							09 35				10 09									10 35
Hag Fold d									09 37													10 37
Daisy Hill d		09 13							09 40				10 13									10 40
Clifton d																						
Kearsley d	08 48											09 48										
Farnworth d	08 50											09 50										
Moses Gate d	08 53											09 53										
Bolton a	08 56		09 06	09 14	09 19			09 23		09 40	09 45	09 56			10 06		10 14	10 19			10 23	
d	08 57		09 07	09 15				09 24		09 40	09 45	09 57			10 07		10 15				10 24	
Westhoughton d								09 31			09 53										10 31	
Hindley d		09 17						09 35	09 45		09 57		10 17								10 35	10 45
Ince d									09 48													10 48
Wigan North Western a						09 43																
Wigan Wallgate a	09 15	09 22						09 44	09 51		10 02	10 14	10 22								10 44	10 51
d		09 24							09 52		10 03		10 24									10 52
Pemberton d									09 56													10 56
Orrell d									10 00													11 00
Upholland d									10 04													11 04
Rainford d									10 07													11 07
Kirkby a									10 19													11 19
Gathurst d		09 28											10 28									
Appley Bridge d		09 32									10 10		10 32									
Parbold d		09 36									10 14		10 36									
Hoscar d		09 39																				
Burscough Bridge d		09 42									10 18		10 40									
New Lane d		09 44																				
Bescar Lane d		09 48																				
Meols Cop d		09 53											10 48									
Southport a		10 02									10 35		10 57									
Lostock d				09 20						09 45							10 20					
Horwich Parkway d			09 13	09 24						09 49					10 13		10 24					
Blackrod d										09 52												
Adlington (Lancashire) d										09 56												
Chorley d			09 21	09 32						10 01					10 21		10 32					
Buckshaw Parkway d			09 24	09 35						10 05					10 24		10 35					
Leyland d				09 42						10 12							10 42					
Preston 8 65,97 a			09 33	09 50		09 57				10 17					10 33		10 50		10 56			
d			09 38			09 59				10 19					10 38	10 45			10 57			
Kirkham & Wesham 97 a										10 28												
Poulton-le-Fylde 97 a			09 56							10 36					10 56							
Layton 97 a										10 40												
Blackpool North 97 a			10 05							10 50					11 05							
Lancaster 6 65 a						10 15										11 00			11 13			
d							10 25							10 49		11 01				11 23		
Oxenholme Lake District 65 a																11 17						
Windermere 83 a																11 39						
Carnforth d							10 35							10a58						11 33		
Silverdale d							10 41													11 39		
Arnside d							10 46													11 43		
Grange-over-Sands d							10 52													11 49		
Kents Bank d							10 55													11 53		
Cark d							10 59													11 57		
Ulverston d							11 07													12 06		
Dalton d							11 16													12 14		
Roose d							11 22													12 20		
Barrow-in-Furness a							11 30													12 28		

A From Todmorden
B To Clitheroe
C To Glasgow Central
D From Morecambe
E From Morecambe to Leeds
F To Edinburgh
G From Stalybridge

The Sunday service between Manchester Victoria and Wigan Wallgate via Atherton is funded by TfGM and will operate whilst funding exists

Table 82

Mondays to Fridays

9 December to 7 February

Manchester - Bolton - Wigan, Kirkby, Southport, Preston, Blackpool North and Barrow-in-Furness

Network Diagram - see first Page of Table 82

	NT	NT	NT	NT	TP	NT	NT	TP	NT	NT	NT	NT	NT	NT	TP	NT	TP	NT	TP	NT	NT
		◇			◇1			◇1				◇			◇1		◇1		◇1		
							A	B		C								A	D		C
					[trolley]			[trolley]							[trolley]				[trolley]		
Manchester Airport 85 ✈ d		10 03			10 29			11 00				11 03			11 29				12 00		
Heald Green 85 d					10 33										11 33						
Buxton 86 d																					
Hazel Grove 86 d						10 33										11 33					
Stockport 84 d						10 41										11 41					
Manchester Piccadilly 10 d		10 22			10 46	10 54		11 16				11 22			11 46	11 54			12 16		
Manchester Oxford Road d		10 26			10 49	10 58		11 19				11 26			11 49	11 58			12 19		
Deansgate d		10 28			10 51	11 00						11 28			11 51	12 00					
Rochdale 41 d			10 05										11 04								
Manchester Victoria d	10 22		10 33	10 46			11 00		11 07	11 10	11 22		11 33	11 46				12 00		12 07	12 10
Salford Central d	10 25		10 36	10 49			11 03		11 10	11 13	11 25		11 36	11 49				12 03		12 10	12 13
Salford Crescent a	10 29	10 33	10 39	10 52	10 56	11 04	11 07		11 13	11 16	11 29	11 33	11 39	11 52	11 56	12 04		12 07		12 13	12 16
d	10 30	10 34	10 40	10 53	10 56	11 04	11 08		11 13	11 17	11 30	11 34	11 40	11 53	11 56	12 04		12 08		12 13	12 17
Swinton d				10 59						11 23				11 59							12 23
Moorside d										11 26											12 26
Walkden d				11 04						11 29				12 04							12 29
Atherton d				11 09						11 35				12 09							12 35
Hag Fold d										11 37											12 37
Daisy Hill d				11 13						11 40				12 13							12 40
Clifton d																					
Kearsley d			10 47										11 47								
Farnworth d			10 49										11 49								
Moses Gate d			10 52										11 52								
Bolton a	10 40	10 45	10 55		11 06	11 14	11 19		11 23		11 40	11 45	11 55		12 06	12 14		12 19		12 23	
d	10 40	10 45	10 56		11 07	11 15			11 24		11 40	11 45	11 56		12 07	12 15				12 24	
Westhoughton d		10 53							11 31			11 53								12 31	
Hindley d		10 57		11 17					11 35	11 45		11 57		12 17						12 35	12 45
Ince d										11 48											12 48
Wigan North Western a								11 43											12 43		
Wigan Wallgate a		11 02	11 13	11 22					11 44	11 51		12 02	12 13	12 22						12 44	12 51
d		11 03		11 24						11 52		12 03		12 24							12 52
Pemberton d										11 56											12 56
Orrell d										12 00											13 00
Upholland d										12 04											13 04
Rainford d										12 07											13 07
Kirkby a										12 19											13 19
Gathurst d				11 28										12 28							
Appley Bridge d		11 10		11 32								12 10		12 32							
Parbold d		11 14		11 36								12 14		12 36							
Hoscar d				11 39																	
Burscough Bridge d		11 18		11 42								12 18		12 41							
New Lane d				11 44																	
Bescar Lane d				11 48																	
Meols Cop d				11 53										12 49							
Southport a		11 35		12 02								12 35		12 59							
Lostock d	10 45					11 20					11 45					12 20					
Horwich Parkway d	10 49				11 13	11 24					11 49				12 13	12 24					
Blackrod d	10 52										11 52										
Adlington (Lancashire) d	10 56										11 56										
Chorley d	11 01				11 21	11 32					12 01				12 21	12 32					
Buckshaw Parkway d	11 05				11 24	11 35					12 05				12 24	12 35					
Leyland d	11 12					11 42					12 12					12 42					
Preston 8 65,97 a	11 17				11 33	11 50		11 57			12 17				12 33	12 50			12 57		
d	11 19				11 38			11 58			12 19				12 38		12 45		12 59		
Kirkham & Wesham 97 a	11 28										12 28										
Poulton-le-Fylde 97 a	11 36				11 56						12 36				12 56						
Layton 97 a	11 43										12 43										
Blackpool North 97 a	11 50				12 05						12 50				13 05						
Lancaster 6 65 a								12 14									13 00		13 14		
d								12 15									13 01		13 15		
Oxenholme Lake District 65 a																	13 17		13 29		
Windermere 83 a																	13 39				
Carnforth d								12 22													
Silverdale d																					
Arnside d								12 30													
Grange-over-Sands d								12 36													
Kents Bank d																					
Cark d																					
Ulverston d								12 48													
Dalton d																					
Roose d																					
Barrow-in-Furness a								13 09													

A To Clitheroe
B [trolley] to Preston
C From Stalybridge
D To Edinburgh

The Sunday service between Manchester Victoria and Wigan Wallgate via Atherton is funded by TfGM and will operate whilst funding exists

Table 82

Mondays to Fridays

9 December to 7 February

Manchester - Bolton - Wigan, Kirkby, Southport, Preston, Blackpool North and Barrow-in-Furness

Network Diagram - see first Page of Table 82

Station			NT	NT	NT	NT	TP	NT	NT	TP	TP	NT	NT	NT	NT	NT	NT	TP	NT	NT	NT	NT	NT	NT
				◇			◇1			◇1	◇1				◇			◇1						
									A	B	C		D							E	A		D	F
Manchester Airport	85	✈ d		12 03			12 29			13 00					13 03			13 29						
Heald Green	85	d					12 33											13 33						
Buxton	86	d																						
Hazel Grove	86	d						12 33											13 33					
Stockport	84	d						12 41											13 41					
Manchester Piccadilly 10		d		12 22			12 46	12 54		13 16					13 22			13 46	13 54					
Manchester Oxford Road		d		12 26			12 49	12 58		13 19					13 26			13 49	13 58					
Deansgate		d		12 28			12 51	13 00							13 28			13 51	14 00					
Rochdale	41	d			12 04											13 04								
Manchester Victoria		d	12 22		12 33	12 46			13 00			13 07	13 10	13 22		13 33	13 46				14 00	14 07	14 10	
Salford Central		d	12 25		12 36	12 49			13 03			13 10	13 13	13 25		13 36	13 49				14 03	14 10	14 13	
Salford Crescent		a	12 29	12 33	12 39	12 52	12 56	13 04	13 07			13 13	13 16	13 29	13 33	13 39	13 52	13 56	14 04		14 07	14 13	14 16	
		d	12 30	12 34	12 40	12 53	12 56	13 04	13 08			13 13	13 17	13 30	13 34	13 40	13 53	13 56	14 04		14 08	14 13	14 17	
Swinton		d				12 59							13 23				13 59						14 23	
Moorside		d											13 26										14 26	
Walkden		d				13 04							13 29				14 04						14 29	
Atherton		d				13 09							13 35				14 09						14 35	
Hag Fold		d											13 37										14 37	
Daisy Hill		d				13 13							13 40				14 13						14 40	
Clifton		d																						
Kearsley		d			12 47											13 47								
Farnworth		d			12 49											13 49								
Moses Gate		d			12 52											13 52								
Bolton		a	12 40	12 45	12 55		13 06	13 14	13 19			13 23		13 40	13 45	13 55		14 06	14 14		14 19	14 23		
		d	12 40	12 45	12 56		13 07	13 15				13 24		13 40	13 45	13 56		14 07	14 15			14 24		
Westhoughton		d		12 53								13 31			13 53							14 31		
Hindley		d		12 57		13 17						13 35	13 45		13 57		14 17					14 35	14 45	
Ince		d											13 48										14 48	
Wigan North Western		a								13 43														
Wigan Wallgate		a		13 02	13 13	13 22						13 44	13 51		14 02	14 13	14 22					14 44	14 51	
		d		13 03		13 24							13 52		14 03		14 24						14 52	
Pemberton		d											13 56										14 56	
Orrell		d											14 00										15 00	
Upholland		d											14 04										15 04	
Rainford		d											14 07										15 07	
Kirkby		a											14 19										15 19	
Gathurst		d				13 28											14 28							
Appley Bridge		d		13 10		13 32									14 10		14 32							
Parbold		d		13 14		13 36									14 14		14 36							
Hoscar		d				13 39																		
Burscough Bridge		d		13 18		13 42									14 18		14 41							
New Lane		d				13 44																		
Bescar Lane		d				13 48																		
Meols Cop		d				13 53											14 49							
Southport		a		13 35		14 02									14 35		14 59							
Lostock		d	12 45					13 20						13 45					14 20					
Horwich Parkway		d	12 49				13 13	13 24						13 49				14 13	14 24					
Blackrod		d	12 52											13 52										
Adlington (Lancashire)		d	12 56											13 56										
Chorley		d	13 01				13 21	13 32						14 01				14 21	14 32					
Buckshaw Parkway		d	13 05				13 24	13 35						14 05				14 24	14 35					
Leyland		d	13 12					13 42						14 12					14 42					
Preston 8	65,97	a	13 17				13 33	13 50		13 57				14 17				14 33	14 50					
		d	13 19				13 38			13 58				14 19				14 38						
Kirkham & Wesham	97	a	13 28											14 28										
Poulton-le-Fylde	97	a	13 36				13 56							14 36				14 56						
Layton	97	a	13 43											14 42										
Blackpool North	97	a	13 50				14 05							14 50				15 05						
Lancaster 6	65	a								14 14														
		d									13 34									13 48				14 21
Oxenholme Lake District	65	a																						
Windermere	83	a																						
Carnforth		d									13 42									13a57				14 31
Silverdale		d																						14 37
Arnside		d									13 51													14 41
Grange-over-Sands		d									13 56													14 47
Kents Bank		d																						14 51
Cark		d																						14 55
Ulverston		d									14 09													15 04
Dalton		d																						15 12
Roose		d																						15 20
Barrow-in-Furness		a									14 29													15 26

A To Clitheroe
B To Glasgow Central
C From Windermere
D From Stalybridge
E From Heysham Harbour to Leeds
F From Morecambe

The Sunday service between Manchester Victoria and Wigan Wallgate via Atherton is funded by TfGM and will operate whilst funding exists

Table 82

Mondays to Fridays

9 December to 7 February

Manchester - Bolton - Wigan, Kirkby, Southport, Preston, Blackpool North and Barrow-in-Furness

Network Diagram - see first Page of Table 82

Station		TP	NT	NT	NT	NT	TP	NT	NT	NT	NT	NT	NT	NT	TP	NT	NT	NT	NT	TP	NT	NT	NT
		◇1		◇			◇1								◇1	◇				◇1			
		A							B		C		D	E	F			B					C
		🛒					🛒								🛒					🛒			
Manchester Airport 85 ✈	d	14 00		14 03			14 29								15 00	15 03				15 29			
Heald Green 85	d						14 33													15 33			
Buxton 86	d																						
Hazel Grove 86	d							14 33													15 33		
Stockport 84	d							14 41													15 41		
Manchester Piccadilly 10 🚊	d	14 16		14 22			14 46	14 54							15 16	15 22				15 46	15 54		
Manchester Oxford Road	d	14 19		14 26			14 49	14 58							15 19	15 26				15 49	15 58		
Deansgate 🚊	d			14 28			14 51	15 00								15 28				15 51	16 00		
Rochdale 41	d				14 04												15 04						
Manchester Victoria 🚊	d		14 22		14 33	14 46			15 00	15 07	15 10	15 22					15 33	15 40	15 46			16 07	16 10
Salford Central	d		14 25		14 36	14 49			15 03	15 10	15 13	15 25					15 36	15 43	15 49			16 10	16 13
Salford Crescent	a		14 29	14 33	14 39	14 52	14 56	15 04	15 07	15 13	15 16	15 29				15 33	15 39	15 46	15 52	15 56	16 04	16 13	16 16
	d		14 30	14 34	14 40	14 53	14 56	15 04	15 08	15 13	15 17	15 30				15 34	15 40	15 47	15 53	15 56	16 04	16 13	16 17
Swinton	d					14 59					15 23								15 59				16 23
Moorside	d										15 26												16 26
Walkden	d					15 04					15 29								16 04				16 29
Atherton	d					15 09					15 35								16 09				16 35
Hag Fold	d										15 37												16 37
Daisy Hill	d					15 13					15 40								16 13				16 40
Clifton	d																						
Kearsley	d				14 47												15 47						
Farnworth	d				14 49												15 49						
Moses Gate	d				14 52												15 52					16 21	
Bolton	a		14 40	14 45	14 55		15 06	15 14	15 19	15 23		15 40				15 45	15 55	15 59		16 06	16 19	16 25	
	d		14 40	14 45	14 56		15 07	15 15		15 24		15 40				15 45	15 56			16 07		16 25	
Westhoughton	d			14 53						15 31						15 53						16 33	
Hindley	d			14 57		15 17				15 35	15 45					15 57			16 17			16 37	16 45
Ince	d										15 48												16 48
Wigan North Western	a	14 43													15 43								
Wigan Wallgate	a			15 02	15 13	15 22				15 44	15 51					16 02	16 13		16 22			16 46	16 51
	d			15 03		15 24					15 58					16 03			16 24				16 52
Pemberton	d										16 02												16 56
Orrell	d										16 06												17 00
Upholland	d										16 09												17 04
Rainford	d										16 13												17 07
Kirkby	a										16 25												17 19
Gathurst	d					15 28										16 08			16 28				
Appley Bridge	d			15 10		15 32										16 11			16 32				
Parbold	d			15 14		15 36										16 15			16 36				
Hoscar	d															16 18							
Burscough Bridge	d			15 18		15 40										16 21			16 40				
New Lane	d															16 24							
Bescar Lane	d															16 27							
Meols Cop	d					15 48										16 32			16 48				
Southport	a			15 35		15 57										16 42			16 57				
Lostock	d		14 45					15 20				15 45								16 11			
Horwich Parkway	d		14 49				15 13	15 24				15 49								16 15			
Blackrod	d		14 52									15 52											
Adlington (Lancashire)	d		14 56									15 56											
Chorley	d		15 01				15 21	15 32				16 01								16 23			
Buckshaw Parkway	d		15 05				15 24	15 35				16 05								16 26			
Leyland	d		15 12					15 42				16 12											
Preston 8 65,97	a	14 57	15 17				15 33	15 50				16 19			15 57					16 35			
	d	14 58	15 19				15 38								15 58					16 38			
Kirkham & Wesham 97	a		15 28																	16 47			
Poulton-le-Fylde 97	a		15 36				15 56													16 57			
Layton 97	a		15 43																	17 00			
Blackpool North 97	a		15 50				16 05													17 07			
Lancaster 6 65	a	15 14													16 14								
	d	15 15											15 35	16 04	16 15								
Oxenholme Lake District 65	a	15 29																					
Windermere 83	a																						
Carnforth	d												15 45	16a32	16 23								
Silverdale	d												15 51		16 29								
Arnside	d												15 56		16 33								
Grange-over-Sands	d												16 02		16 39								
Kents Bank	d												16 05		16 42								
Cark	d												16 09		16 47								
Ulverston	d												16 17		16 55								
Dalton	d												16 26		17 03								
Roose	d												16 32		17 09								
Barrow-in-Furness	a												16 39		17 18								

A To Edinburgh
B To Clitheroe
C From Stalybridge
D To Carlisle
E To Leeds
F 🛒 to Preston

The Sunday service between Manchester Victoria and Wigan Wallgate via Atherton is funded by TfGM and will operate whilst funding exists

Table 82

Mondays to Fridays

9 December to 7 February

Manchester - Bolton - Wigan, Kirkby, Southport, Preston, Blackpool North and Barrow-in-Furness

Network Diagram - see first Page of Table 82

		NT A		TP FO ◇1 B	NT	TP FX ◇1 B		NT	NT C	NT ◇	NT	NT		TP ◇1	NT	NT	NT C	TP ◇1 D	NT E	NT	TP FX ◇1	TP FO ◇1		NT	NT F
Manchester Airport 85	d			16 00		16 00				16 03				16 29				17 00							
Heald Green 85	d													16 33											
Buxton 86	d										15 29														
Hazel Grove 86	d										16 04					16 30									
Stockport 84	d										16 12					16 41									
Manchester Piccadilly 10	d			16 16		16 16				16 22	16 27			16 46		16 54		17 15							
Manchester Oxford Road	d			16 19		16 19				16 26	16 30			16 49		16 58		17 18							
Deansgate	d									16 28	16 33					17 00									
Rochdale 41	d											16 04													17 03
Manchester Victoria	d							16 20	16 23			16 36			16 46		17 00		17 07	17 10				17 20	17 23
Salford Central	d							16 23	16 26			16 39			16 49		17 03		17 10	17 12				17 23	17 27
Salford Crescent	a							16 26	16 30	16 34	16 38	16 42			16 52	17 04	17 07		17 13	17 16				17 26	17 29
	d							16 27	16 31	16 34	16 38	16 43			16 53	17 04	17 08		17 13	17 17				17 27	17 30
Swinton	d														16 59					17 23					
Moorside	d														17 02					17 26					
Walkden	d														17 05					17 31					
Atherton	d														17 11				17 26	17 37					
Hag Fold	d														17 14					17 39					
Daisy Hill	d														17 17				17 30	17 43					
Clifton	d																								
Kearsley	d											16 50													
Farnworth	d											16 52													
Moses Gate	d											16 55													
Bolton	a			16 32		16 32		16 37	16 42	16 45	16 48	16 58		17 05		17 14	17 19	17 31						17 37	17 42
	d			16 33		16 33		16 37		16 45	16 49	16 59		17 06		17 15		17 32						17 37	
Westhoughton	d									16 53		17 06													
Hindley	d									16 57		17 10			17 21					17 48					
Ince	d														17 24					17 51					
Wigan North Western	a																								
Wigan Wallgate	a									17 02		17 19			17 31				17 39	17 54					
	d									17 03									17 40	17 55					
Pemberton	d																			17 59					
Orrell	d																			18 03					
Upholland	d																			18 07					
Rainford	d																			18 10					
Kirkby	a																			18 22					
Gathurst	d									17 08									17 45						
Appley Bridge	d									17 11									17 48						
Parbold	d									17 15									17 53						
Hoscar	d																								
Burscough Bridge	d									17 20									17 58						
New Lane	d																								
Bescar Lane	d																								
Meols Cop	d									17 27									18 05						
Southport	a									17 37									18 15						
Lostock	d							16 43			16 54					17 20								17 43	
Horwich Parkway	d							16 47			16 58					17 24								17 47	
Blackrod	d							16 51			17 01													17 51	
Adlington (Lancashire)	d							16 55			17 05													17 55	
Chorley	d			16 45		16 45		17 00			17 10			17 19		17 32		17 44						18 00	
Buckshaw Parkway	d							17 04			17 13					17 35								18 03	
Leyland	d							17 11			17 21					17 42								18 11	
Preston 8 65,97	a			16 58		16 56		17 19			17 26			17 30		17 51		17 57						18 16	
	d			16 58		16 58	17 05	17 21			17 28			17 32				17 58			18 05			18 18	
Kirkham & Wesham 97	a							17 30						17 41										18 27	
Poulton-le-Fylde 97	a							17 38						17 51										18 35	
Layton 97	a							17 43						17 54										18 39	
Blackpool North 97	a							17 50						18 02										18 46	
Lancaster 6 65	a			17 14		17 14	17 23				17 48							18 14			18 20				
	d	16 46		17 15	17 20	17 15	17 24				17 48							18 15			18 22	18 22			
Oxenholme Lake District 65	a			17 28		17 29	17 41											18 29							
Windermere 83	a						18 01																		
Carnforth	d	16 56			17 29						17 58										18 30	18 30			
Silverdale	d	17 03			17 35						18 03										18 36	18 36			
Arnside	d	17 07			17 40						18 08										18 40	18 40			
Grange-over-Sands	d	17 13			17 46						18 14										18 46	18 46			
Kents Bank	d	17 17			17 49						18 18										18 49	18 49			
Cark	d	17 21			17 54						18 22										18 54	18 54			
Ulverston	d	17 30			18 02						18 31										19 02	19 02			
Dalton	d	17 39			18 10						18 39										19 10	19 10			
Roose	d	17 45			18 17						18 45										19 16	19 16			
Barrow-in-Furness	a	17 55			18 25						18 56										19 25	19 25			

A To Millom
B To Edinburgh
C To Clitheroe
D To Glasgow Central
E From Stalybridge
F To Blackburn

The Sunday service between Manchester Victoria and Wigan Wallgate via Atherton is funded by TfGM and will operate whilst funding exists

Table 82

Mondays to Fridays

9 December to 7 February

Manchester - Bolton - Wigan, Kirkby, Southport, Preston, Blackpool North and Barrow-in-Furness

Network Diagram - see first Page of Table 82

		NT	NT	NT	NT	NT	TP	TP		NT	NT	TP	TP		NT	NT	NT	NT	NT	NT	TP	NT	NT
							FX					FX	FO										
		◇					1	◇1				◇1	◇1					◇			◇1		
											A	B	B				C						A
								⚲				⚲	⚲								⚲		
Manchester Airport 85 ✈	d	17 03						17 29				18 00	18 00					18 03			18 29		
Heald Green 85	d							17 33													18 33		
Buxton 86	d		16 29							16 59												17 59	
Hazel Grove 86	d		17 04							17 33												18 33	
Stockport 84	d		17 12							17 41												18 41	
Manchester Piccadilly 10	d	17 22	17 27					17 46		17 54		18 16	18 16					18 22			18 46	18 54	
Manchester Oxford Road	d	17 26	17 30					17 49		17 58		18 19	18 19					18 27			18 49	18 58	
Deansgate	d		17 33					17 51		18 00								18 29			18 51	19 00	
Rochdale 41	d																18 02						
Manchester Victoria	d			17 36	17 40	17 45					18 00				18 10	18 20	18 23		18 33	18 45			19 00
Salford Central	d			17 39	17 43	17 48					18 03				18 13	18 23	18 26		18 36	18 48			19 03
Salford Crescent	a	17 34	17 38	17 42	17 46	17 51		17 55		18 04	18 07				18 16	18 26	18 30	18 35	18 39	18 51	18 56	19 04	19 07
	d	17 34	17 38	17 43	17 47	17 52		17 55		18 04	18 08				18 17	18 27	18 31	18 35	18 40	18 52	18 56	19 04	19 08
Swinton	d					17 58									18 23					18 58			
Moorside	d					18 01									18 26					19 01			
Walkden	d					18 05									18 29					19 04			
Atherton	d				18 00	18 11									18 35					19 10			
Hag Fold	d					18 13									18 37					19 12			
Daisy Hill	d				18 04	18 17									18 40					19 15			
Clifton	d			17 48																			
Kearsley	d			17 53															18 47				
Farnworth	d			17 55															18 49				
Moses Gate	d			17 57															18 52				
Bolton	a	17 45	17 48	18 01				18 05		18 14	18 19					18 37	18 42	18 45	18 55		19 06	19 19	19 20
	d	17 45	17 49	18 01				18 06		18 15						18 37		18 45	18 56		19 07		
Westhoughton	d	17 53		18 09														18 53	19 03				
Hindley	d			18 13		18 22									18 45			18 57	19 09	19 20			
Ince	d					18 25									18 48					19 23			
Wigan North Western	a											18 43	18 42		18 56								
Wigan Wallgate	a	18 01		18 22	18 12	18 28												19 02	19 18	19 30			
	d	18 02			18 15	18 29												19 03					
Pemberton	d					18 33																	
Orrell	d					18 37																	
Upholland	d					18 41																	
Rainford	d					18 44																	
Kirkby	a					18 55																	
Gathurst	d				18 20													19 08					
Appley Bridge	d	18 09			18 24													19 11					
Parbold	d	18 13			18 28													19 15					
Hoscar	d				18 31																		
Burscough Bridge	d	18 17			18 35													19 19					
New Lane	d				18 37																		
Bescar Lane	d				18 41																		
Meols Cop	d	18 26			18 46													19 27					
Southport	a	18 35			18 55													19 37					
Lostock	d		17 54					18 11		18 20						18 42					19 11		
Horwich Parkway	d		17 59					18 15		18 24						18 46					19 15		
Blackrod	d		18 02							18 27						18 49							
Adlington (Lancashire)	d		18 06													18 53							
Chorley	d		18 11					18 23		18 34						18 58					19 23		
Buckshaw Parkway	d		18 14					18 26		18 37						19 02					19 26		
Leyland	d									18 44						19 10							
Preston 8 65,97	a		18 25					18 35		18 49		18 57	18 57			19 18					19 35		
	d		18 26					18 40	18 43	18 51		18 58	18 59	19 05		19 19					19 38		
Kirkham & Wesham 97	a							18 49								19 28							
Poulton-le-Fylde 97	a		18 43					18 59								19 36					19 56		
Layton 97	a							19 02								19 43							
Blackpool North 97	a		18 55					19 09		19 15						19 50					20 05		
Lancaster 6 65	a								18 58			19 14		19 21									
	d						18 27		18 59			19 15		19 22									
Oxenholme Lake District 65	a						18 42					19 29	19 28	19 38									
Windermere 83	a						19 04							19 59									
Carnforth	d								19 07														
Silverdale	d								19 13														
Arnside	d								19 17														
Grange-over-Sands	d								19 23														
Kents Bank	d								19 26														
Cark	d								19 31														
Ulverston	d								19 39														
Dalton	d								19 47														
Roose	d								19 53														
Barrow-in-Furness	a								20 02														

A To Clitheroe **B** To Edinburgh **C** To Blackburn

The Sunday service between Manchester Victoria and Wigan Wallgate via Atherton is funded by TfGM and will operate whilst funding exists

Table 82

Mondays to Fridays

9 December to 7 February

Manchester - Bolton - Wigan, Kirkby, Southport, Preston, Blackpool North and Barrow-in-Furness

Network Diagram - see first Page of Table 82

		NT	TP	NT	NT	NT	TP	NT	TP	NT	NT	NT	TP	NT	NT	TP	NT	NT	NT	TP	NT FO	NT FX	TP
			◇1	◇			◇1		◇1		◇		◇1			◇1		◇		◇1			◇1
		A						B	C					B				D			B	B	E
Manchester Airport	85 ✈ d		19 00	19 03			19 29		20 00		20 03		20 29					21 03		21 29			22 00
Heald Green	85 d						19 33						20 33							21 33			
Buxton	86 d																						
Hazel Grove	86 d																						
Stockport	84 d																						
Manchester Piccadilly 10	⇌ d		19 16	19 20			19 46		20 16		20 20		20 46					21 20		21 46			22 16
Manchester Oxford Road	d		19 19	19 24			19 49		20 19		20 24		20 49					21 24		21 49			22 19
Deansgate	⇌ d			19 26			19 51				20 26		20 51					21 26		21 51			
Rochdale	41 d																						
Manchester Victoria	⇌ d				19 28	19 35		20 00		20 22		20 35		21 00			21 22		21 35		22 00	22 00	
Salford Central	d				19 31	19 38		20 03		20 25		20 38		21 03			21 25		21 38		22 04		
Salford Crescent	a			19 29	19 34	19 41	19 56	20 07		20 29	20 33	20 41	20 56	21 07			21 30	21 33	21 41	21 56	22 07	22 07	22 24
	d			19 30	19 35	19 42	19 56	20 08		20 30	20 34	20 42	20 56	21 08			21 30	21 34	21 42	21 56	22 08	22 08	22 24
Swinton	d					19 48						20 48							21 48				
Moorside	d					19 51						20 51							21 51				
Walkden	d					19 54						20 54							21 54				
Atherton	d					20 00						21 00							22 00				
Hag Fold	d					20 02						21 02							22 02				
Daisy Hill	d					20 05						21 05							22 05				
Clifton	d																						
Kearsley	d																						
Farnworth	d																						
Moses Gate	d																						
Bolton	a		19 32	19 40	19 45		20 06	20 19		20 40	20 45		21 06	21 19			21 40	21 45		22 06	22 19	22 19	22 34
	d		19 33	19 40	19 45		20 07			20 40	20 45		21 07				21 40	21 45		22 07			22 35
Westhoughton	d			19 48							20 53							21 53					
Hindley	d			19 52		20 10					20 57	21 10						21 57	22 10				
Ince	d					20 13						21 13							22 13				
Wigan North Western	a								20 43														22 48
Wigan Wallgate	a			19 57		20 20					21 02	21 20						22 02	22 20				
	d			19 59							21 03							22 03					
Pemberton	d																						
Orrell	d																						
Upholland	d																						
Rainford	d																						
Kirkby	a																						
Gathurst	d			20 03							21 08							22 08					
Appley Bridge	d			20 07							21 11							22 11					
Parbold	d			20 11							21 15							22 15					
Hoscar	d										21 18												
Burscough Bridge	d			20 15							21 21							22 20					
New Lane	d										21 24												
Bescar Lane	d										21 27												
Meols Cop	d			20 23							21 32							22 27					
Southport	a			20 32							21 42							22 37					
Lostock	d				19 50					20 45							21 45						
Horwich Parkway	d				19 54		20 13			20 49			21 13				21 49			22 13			
Blackrod	d				19 57					20 52							21 52						
Adlington (Lancashire)	d				20 01					20 56							21 56						
Chorley	d		19 44		20 06		20 21			21 01			21 21				22 01			22 21			
Buckshaw Parkway	d				20 10		20 24			21 05			21 24				22 04			22 24			
Leyland	d				20 18					21 12							22 12						
Preston 8	65,97 a		19 57		20 23		20 33		20 57	21 17			21 33				22 17			22 35			23 08
	d		19 59		20 25		20 38		20 58	21 19			21 38			21 47	22 19			22 38			23 11
Kirkham & Wesham	97 a				20 34					21 28							22 28						
Poulton-le-Fylde	97 a				20 42		20 56			21 36			21 56				22 36			22 55			
Layton	97 a				20 46					21 40							22 42						
Blackpool North	97 a				20 54		21 05			21 48			22 05				22 50			23 04			
Lancaster 6	65 a		20 14						21 14							22 02							23 26
	d	19 24	20 15						21 15						21 20	22 03							23 27
Oxenholme Lake District	65 a								21 29														
Windermere	83 a																						
Carnforth	d	19a34	20 23												21 30	22 11							23 35
Silverdale	d		20 29												21 37	22 17							23 41
Arnside	d		20 33												21 41	22 21							23 45
Grange-over-Sands	d		20 39												21 47	22 27							23 51
Kents Bank	d		20 42												21 51	22 30							23 54
Cark	d		20 47												21 55	22 35							23 59
Ulverston	d		20 55												22 03	22 43							00 07
Dalton	d		21 03												22 12	22 51							00 15
Roose	d		21 09												22 18	22 57							00 21
Barrow-in-Furness	a		21 18												22 27	23 06							00 30

A From Morecambe to Leeds
B To Clitheroe
C To Edinburgh
D until 27 December
E until 27 December, FO from 3 January

The Sunday service between Manchester Victoria and Wigan Wallgate via Atherton is funded by TfGM and will operate whilst funding exists

Table 82

Mondays to Fridays

9 December to 7 February

Manchester - Bolton - Wigan, Kirkby, Southport, Preston, Blackpool North and Barrow-in-Furness

Network Diagram - see first Page of Table 82

Station		TP FX ◇1 A	NT FO	NT FX	NT ◇ B	NT FX ◇ A	NT FO	NT FX	TP ◇1 B	TP FX ◇1 A	NT	NT FO C	NT FX C	NT FO	NT FX	NT FO	NT FX
Manchester Airport 85 ✈	d				22 19				22 29								
Heald Green 85	d								22 33								
Buxton 86	d																
Hazel Grove 86	d																
Stockport 84	d										22 34						
Manchester Piccadilly 10	d	22 16			22 35				22 46	22 46	22 50						
Manchester Oxford Road	d	22 19			22 39	22 39			22 49	22 49	22 53						
Deansgate	d				22 41	22 41			22 51	22 51	22 55						
Rochdale 41	d																
Manchester Victoria	d		22 22	22 22			22 45	22 45				23 00	23 00	23 20	23 20	23 23	23 23
Salford Central	d		22 25				22 48					23 03		23 23		23 26	
Salford Crescent	a	22 24	22 29	22 29	22 46	22 46	22 51	22 51	22 56	22 56	22 59	23 07	23 07	23 26	23 26	23 31	23 31
	d	22 24	22 30	22 30	22 46	22 46	22 52	22 52	22 56	22 56	22 59	23 08	23 08	23 26	23 26	23 32	23 32
Swinton	d						22 58	22 58						23 33	23 33		
Moorside	d						23 01	23 01						23 35	23 35		
Walkden	d						23 04	23 04						23 39	23 39		
Atherton	d						23 10	23 10						23 44	23 44		
Hag Fold	d						23 12	23 12						23 47	23 47		
Daisy Hill	d						23 15	23 15						23 50	23 50		
Clifton	d																
Kearsley	d										23 07						
Farnworth	d										23 09						
Moses Gate	d										23 11						
Bolton	a	22 34	22 40	22 40	22 56	22 56			23 06	23 06	23 15	23 19	23 19			23 42	23 42
	d	22 35	22 40	22 40	22 57	22 57			23 07	23 07	23 15					23 42	23 42
Westhoughton	d				23 04	23 04					23 23						
Hindley	d				23 08	23 08	23 20	23 20			23 27			23 54	23 54		
Ince	d						23 23	23 23						23 57	23 57		
Wigan North Western	a	22 48															
Wigan Wallgate	a				23 13	23 13	23 30	23 30			23 38			00 04	00 04		
	d				23 15	23 15											
Pemberton	d																
Orrell	d																
Upholland	d																
Rainford	d																
Kirkby	a																
Gathurst	d				23 19	23 19											
Appley Bridge	d				23 23	23 23											
Parbold	d				23 27	23 27											
Hoscar	d																
Burscough Bridge	d				23 31	23 31											
New Lane	d																
Bescar Lane	d																
Meols Cop	d				23 39	23 39											
Southport	a				23 48	23 48											
Lostock	d		22 45	22 45												23 47	23 47
Horwich Parkway	d		22 49	22 49					23 13	23 13						23 51	23 51
Blackrod	d		22 52	22 52												23 54	23 54
Adlington (Lancashire)	d		22 56	22 56												23 58	23 58
Chorley	d		23 01	23 01					23 21	23 21						00 03	00 03
Buckshaw Parkway	d		23 05	23 05					23 24	23 24						00 07	00 07
Leyland	d		23 12	23 12												00 14	00 14
Preston 8 65,97	a	23 08	23 17	23 17					23 33	23 33						00 19	00 19
	d	23 11	23 19	23 19					23 35	23 35						00 21	00 21
Kirkham & Wesham 97	a		23 28	23 28												00 30	00 30
Poulton-le-Fylde 97	a		23 36	23 36					23 52	23 52						00 38	00 38
Layton 97	a		23 40	23 40												00 43	00 43
Blackpool North 97	a		23 48	23 48					00 01	00 01						00 50	00 50
Lancaster 6 65	a	23 26															
	d	23 27															
Oxenholme Lake District 65	a																
Windermere 83	a																
Carnforth	d	23 35															
Silverdale	d	23 41															
Arnside	d	23 45															
Grange-over-Sands	d	23 51															
Kents Bank	d	23 54															
Cark	d	23 59															
Ulverston	d	00 07															
Dalton	d	00 15															
Roose	d	00 21															
Barrow-in-Furness	a	00 30															

A from 30 December **B** until 27 December, FO from 3 January **C** To Blackburn

The Sunday service between Manchester Victoria and Wigan Wallgate via Atherton is funded by TfGM and will operate whilst funding exists

Table 82

Mondays to Fridays

10 February to 16 May

Manchester - Bolton - Wigan, Kirkby, Southport, Preston, Blackpool North and Barrow-in-Furness

Network Diagram - see first Page of Table 82

Station			TP MO ◇1 A	NT MX B	TP MX ◇1 C	TP MX ◇1 D	TP ◇1 E	NT F	TP 1	TP ◇1 G	TP ◇1 H		TP MX ◇1 D	NT I	NT	NT	NT J	TP ◇1 K 🍴	NT	TP ◇1	NT		NT	NT I	TP ◇1 L 🍴	NT M
Manchester Airport	85 ✈	d	00 01				00 01			05 29	05 29							05 58		06 18					07 00	
Heald Green	85	d																06 02								
Buxton	86	d																						05 59		
Hazel Grove	86	d																						06 33		
Stockport	84	d																						06 41		
Manchester Piccadilly 10	🚊	d	00 16			00 16	00 16			05 44	05 44		05 44					06 13		06 33				06 53	07 15	
Manchester Oxford Road		d								05 47	05 47		05 47					06 17		06 36				06 57	07 18	
Deansgate	🚊	d																						06 59		
Rochdale	41	d																								
Manchester Victoria	🚊	d												05 55	06 00				06 17		06 38		06 45			07 01
Salford Central		d																			06 40		06 48			07 04
Salford Crescent		a								05 52	05 52		05 52	05 59	06 04				06 23	06 41	06 44		06 51	07 02		07 07
		d								05 52	05 52		05 52	06 00	06 05				06 24	06 41	06 45		06 52	07 03		07 08
Swinton		d																					06 58			07 14
Moorside		d																								07 17
Walkden		d																					07 03			07 20
Atherton		d																					07 08			07 26
Hag Fold		d																								07 28
Daisy Hill		d																					07 12			07 31
Clifton		d																								
Kearsley		d																			06 52					
Farnworth		d																			06 54					
Moses Gate		d																			06 57					
Bolton		a	00s30			00s30	00s30			06 02	06 02		06 02	06 11	06 15				06 34	06 51	07 00			07 16		
		d								06 03	06 03		06 03		06 15				06 34	06 52	07 01					
Westhoughton		d													06 23											
Hindley		d													06 27								07 16			07 39
Ince		d																								↳
Wigan North Western		a																06 42			07 19				07 43	
Wigan Wallgate		a													06 32								07 21			
		d													06 34	06 37							07 23			
Pemberton		d													06 38											
Orrell		d													06 42											
Upholland		d													06 45											
Rainford		d													06 49											
Kirkby		a													07 01											
Gathurst		d														06 41							07 27			
Appley Bridge		d														06 45							07 31			
Parbold		d														06 49							07 35			
Hoscar		d														06 52										
Burscough Bridge		d														06 55							07 39			
New Lane		d														06 57										
Bescar Lane		d														07 01										
Meols Cop		d														07 06							07 47			
Southport		a														07 15							07 56			
Lostock		d																	06 39							
Horwich Parkway		d								06 10	06 10		06 10						06 43	06 58						
Blackrod		d																	06 46							
Adlington (Lancashire)		d																	06 50							
Chorley		d		00 03						06 17	06 17		06 17						06 55	07 06						
Buckshaw Parkway		d		00 07						06 21	06 21		06 21						06 59	07 09						
Leyland		d		00 14							06 27		06 27						07 06							
Preston 8	65,97	a	01 01	00 19		01s01	01s04			06 31	06 32		06 32					06 56	07 11	07 18					07 57	
		d		00 21				05 19		06 33	06 35		06 35					06 57	07 13	07 20					07 58	
Kirkham & Wesham	97	a		00 30						06 42	06 44		06 44						07 22							
Poulton-le-Fylde	97	a		00 38						06 53	06 54		06 54						07 30							
Layton	97	a		00 43						06 56	06 58		06 58						07 34							
Blackpool North	97	a		00 50		01 27	01 29			07 03	07 05		07 05						07 41							
Lancaster 6	65	a						05 39										07 13		07 35					08 14	
		d						05 41	05 45								07 08	07 13		07 36						
Oxenholme Lake District	65	a							06 20									07 27								
Windermere	83	a							06 40																	
Carnforth		d						05 51									07a17			07 44						
Silverdale		d						05 57												07 50						
Arnside		d						06 01												07 54						
Grange-over-Sands		d						06 07												08 00						
Kents Bank		d						06 11												08 03						
Cark		d						06 15												08 08						
Ulverston		d			00 07			06 24												08 16						
Dalton		d			00 15			06 32												08 24						
Roose		d			00 21			06 38												08 30						
Barrow-in-Furness		a			00 30			06 48												08 39						

A until 17 March
B From Manchester Victoria
C From Manchester Airport
D until 21 March
E from 24 March
F To Carlisle
G MO until 31 March, also from 25 March until 28 March, from 28 April
H from 1 April until 25 April
I To Clitheroe
J To Leeds
K To Edinburgh
L To Glasgow Central
M To Kirkby

The Sunday service between Manchester Victoria and Wigan Wallgate via Atherton is funded by TfGM and will operate whilst funding exists

Table 82

Mondays to Fridays

10 February to 16 May

Manchester - Bolton - Wigan, Kirkby, Southport, Preston, Blackpool North and Barrow-in-Furness

Network Diagram - see first Page of Table 82

		NT	NT	NT	NT	NT	NT	TP	NT	NT	NT	NT	NT	NT	NT	TP	NT	NT	NT	TP	NT	NT	TP
								◇1								◇1				◇1			◇1
			A		B			C	D		E	F	G		A				B	H	I		
								🛒								🛒				🛒			🛒
Manchester Airport 85 ✈	d							07 25								07 56		08 01					08 25
Heald Green 85	d							07 29										08 05					08 29
Buxton 86	d						06 23			06 53													
Hazel Grove 86	d						07 00			07 27													
Stockport 84	d						07 10			07 37													
Manchester Piccadilly 10 🚇	d						07 27	07 45		07 54						08 15		08 22					08 46
Manchester Oxford Road	d						07 30			07 57						08 19		08 26		08 31			08 49
Deansgate 🚇	d						07 32			07 59								08 28					08 51
Rochdale 41	d																				08 00		
Manchester Victoria 🚇	d	07 06		07 17	07 23	07 27			07 47		08 00		08 03	08 11			08 22		08 29		08 33	08 46	
Salford Central	d	07 09		07 19	07 26	07 30			07 50		08 03		08 08	08 13			08 25		08 32		08 37	08 49	
Salford Crescent	a	07 12		07 24	07 29	07 32	07 37		07 53	08 04	08 07		08 12	08 17			08 29	08 33	08 37		08 40	08 52	08 56
	d	07 13		07 25	07 30	07 32	07 37		07 53	08 04	08 08		08 13	08 17			08 30	08 34	08 37		08 41	08 53	08 56
Swinton	d								08 00				08 19									08 59	
Moorside	d								08 02				08 22										
Walkden	d					07 42			08 06				08 25									09 04	
Atherton	d					07 48			08 11				08 31									09 09	
Hag Fold	d								08 14				08 33										
Daisy Hill	d					07 51			08 17				08 36									09 13	
Clifton	d																						
Kearsley	d						07 45														08 48		
Farnworth	d						07 47														08 50		
Moses Gate	d						07 49														08 53		
Bolton	a	07 23		07 35	07 41		07 53	07 59		08 14	08 19			08 27		08 32	08 40	08 44	08 49	08 52	08 56		09 06
	d	07 23		07 35			07 53	07 59		08 15				08 28		08 33	08 40	08 45		08 52	08 57		09 07
Westhoughton	d	07 31	←				08 01							08 35	←			08 53					
Hindley	d	07 35	07 39						08 21				08 43	08 39	08 43							09 17	
Ince	d		07 42										→	08 42	08 46								
Wigan North Western	a						08 16																
Wigan Wallgate	a	07 40	07 45			08 03			08 26					08 45	08 49			09 00			09 15	09 22	
	d	07 41	07 46						08 28					08 47	08 51			09 05				09 24	
Pemberton	d		07 50												08 55								
Orrell	d		07 54												08 59								
Upholland	d		07 58												09 02								
Rainford	d		08 01												09 06								
Kirkby	a		08 13												09 18								
Gathurst	d	07 46							08 32					08 51								09 28	
Appley Bridge	d	07 49							08 36					08 55				09 11				09 32	
Parbold	d	07 53												08 59				09 15				09 36	
Hoscar	d	07 56																				09 39	
Burscough Bridge	d	07 59							08 42					09 03				09 20				09 42	
New Lane	d	08 02																				09 44	
Bescar Lane	d	08 05																				09 48	
Meols Cop	d	08 10												09 11								09 53	
Southport	a	08 20							08 59					09 20				09 36				10 02	
Lostock	d			07 42						08 20							08 45			08 57			
Horwich Parkway	d			07 46						08 24						08 39	08 49			09 01			09 13
Blackrod	d			07 49													08 52						
Adlington (Lancashire)	d			07 53						08 29							08 56						
Chorley	d			07 58				08 11		08 34						08 47	09 01			09 08			09 21
Buckshaw Parkway	d			08 01						08 37							09 05			09 12			09 24
Leyland	d			08 08						08 43							09 12						
Preston 8 65,97	a			08 14				08 22		08 49						08 58	09 17			09 22			09 33
	d			08 15				08 24		08 51						08 59	09 19			09 25			09 38
Kirkham & Wesham 97	a			08 25													09 28						
Poulton-le-Fylde 97	a			08 33												09 16	09 36						09 56
Layton 97	a			08 37													09 43						
Blackpool North 97	a			08 44						09 16						09 25	09 50						10 05
Lancaster 6 65	a							08 39												09 40			
	d							08 40				08 48								09 41			
Oxenholme Lake District 65	a							08 54															
Windermere 83	a																						
Carnforth	d											08 57								09 49			
Silverdale	d											09 03								09 55			
Arnside	d											09 08								09 59			
Grange-over-Sands	d											09 14								10 05			
Kents Bank	d											09 18								10 08			
Cark	d											09 22								10 13			
Ulverston	d											09 31								10 21			
Dalton	d											09 39								10 29			
Roose	d											09 45								10 35			
Barrow-in-Furness	a											09 55								10 44			

A From Manchester Victoria
B To Blackburn
C To Edinburgh
D From Huddersfield
E To Clitheroe
F From Morecambe to Carlisle
G To Kirkby
H 🛒 to Preston
I From Todmorden

The Sunday service between Manchester Victoria and Wigan Wallgate via Atherton is funded by TfGM and will operate whilst funding exists

Table 82

Mondays to Fridays

10 February to 16 May

Manchester - Bolton - Wigan, Kirkby, Southport, Preston, Blackpool North and Barrow-in-Furness

Network Diagram - see first Page of Table 82

		NT		NT	TP	NT	NT	NT	NT	NT	NT	NT		NT	TP	NT	NT	TP	NT	NT	NT		NT	NT
					◇1										◇1			◇1						◇
				A	B	C								D			A	E			F			
Manchester Airport 85 ✈	d				09 00					09 03					09 29			10 00						10 03
Heald Green 85	d														09 33									
Buxton 86	d																							
Hazel Grove 86	d	08 32														09 33								
Stockport 84	d	08 41														09 41								
Manchester Piccadilly 10	d	08 54			09 16					09 22					09 46	09 54		10 16						10 22
Manchester Oxford Road	d	08 58			09 19					09 26					09 49	09 58		10 19						10 26
Deansgate	d	09 00								09 28					09 51	10 00								10 28
Rochdale 41	d										09 04													
Manchester Victoria	d			09 00			09 07	09 10	09 22		09 33	09 46					10 00			10 07	10 10		10 22	
Salford Central	d			09 03			09 10	09 13	09 25		09 36	09 49					10 03			10 10	10 13		10 25	
Salford Crescent	a	09 04		09 07			09 13	09 16	09 29	09 33	09 39	09 52			09 56	10 04	10 07			10 13	10 16		10 29	10 33
	d	09 04		09 08			09 13	09 17	09 30	09 34	09 41	09 53			09 56	10 04	10 08			10 13	10 17		10 30	10 34
Swinton	d							09 23				09 59									10 23			
Moorside	d							09 26													10 26			
Walkden	d							09 29				10 04									10 29			
Atherton	d							09 35				10 09									10 35			
Hag Fold	d							09 37													10 37			
Daisy Hill	d							09 40				10 13									10 40			
Clifton	d																							
Kearsley	d										09 48													
Farnworth	d										09 50													
Moses Gate	d										09 53													
Bolton	a	09 14		09 19			09 23		09 40	09 45	09 56				10 06	10 14	10 19			10 23			10 40	10 45
	d	09 15					09 24		09 40	09 45	09 57				10 07	10 15				10 24			10 40	10 45
Westhoughton	d						09 31			09 53										10 31				10 53
Hindley	d						09 35	09 45		09 57		10 17								10 35	10 45			10 57
Ince	d							09 48													10 48			
Wigan North Western	a				09 43																			
Wigan Wallgate	a						09 44	09 51		10 02	10 14	10 22								10 44	10 51			11 02
	d							09 52		10 03		10 24									10 52			11 03
Pemberton	d							09 56													10 56			
Orrell	d							10 00													11 00			
Upholland	d							10 04													11 04			
Rainford	d							10 07													11 07			
Kirkby	a							10 19													11 19			
Gathurst	d											10 28												
Appley Bridge	d									10 10		10 32												11 10
Parbold	d									10 14		10 36												11 14
Hoscar	d																							
Burscough Bridge	d									10 18		10 40												11 18
New Lane	d																							
Bescar Lane	d																							
Meols Cop	d											10 48												
Southport	a									10 35		10 57												11 35
Lostock	d	09 20							09 45							10 20							10 45	
Horwich Parkway	d	09 24							09 49						10 13	10 24							10 49	
Blackrod	d								09 52														10 52	
Adlington (Lancashire)	d								09 56														10 56	
Chorley	d	09 32							10 01						10 21	10 32							11 01	
Buckshaw Parkway	d	09 35							10 05						10 24	10 35							11 05	
Leyland	d	09 42							10 12							10 42							11 12	
Preston 8 65,97	a	09 50			09 57				10 17						10 33	10 50		10 56					11 17	
	d				09 59				10 19						10 38 10 45			10 57					11 19	
Kirkham & Wesham 97	a								10 28														11 28	
Poulton-le-Fylde 97	a								10 36						10 56								11 36	
Layton 97	a								10 40														11 43	
Blackpool North 97	a								10 50						11 05								11 50	
Lancaster 6 65	a				10 15										11 00			11 13						
	d					10 25								10 49	11 01				11 23					
Oxenholme Lake District 65	a														11 17									
Windermere 83	a														11 39									
Carnforth	d					10 35								10a58					11 33					
Silverdale	d					10 41													11 39					
Arnside	d					10 46													11 43					
Grange-over-Sands	d					10 52													11 49					
Kents Bank	d					10 55													11 53					
Cark	d					10 59													11 57					
Ulverston	d					11 07													12 06					
Dalton	d					11 16													12 14					
Roose	d					11 22													12 20					
Barrow-in-Furness	a					11 30													12 28					

A To Clitheroe
B To Glasgow Central
C From Morecambe
D From Morecambe to Leeds
E To Edinburgh
F From Stalybridge

The Sunday service between Manchester Victoria and Wigan Wallgate via Atherton is funded by TfGM and will operate whilst funding exists

Table 82

Mondays to Fridays

10 February to 16 May

Manchester - Bolton - Wigan, Kirkby, Southport, Preston, Blackpool North and Barrow-in-Furness

Network Diagram - see first Page of Table 82

			NT	NT	TP	NT	NT	TP	NT	NT	NT	NT	NT	NT	TP	NT	TP	NT	TP	NT	NT	NT	NT	NT
					◇1			◇1				◇			◇1		◇1		◇1				◇	
							A	B		C								A	D		C			
					🚲			🚲							🚲				🚲					
Manchester Airport	85 ✈	d			10 29			11 00				11 03			11 29				12 00				12 03	
Heald Green	85	d			10 33										11 33									
Buxton	86	d																						
Hazel Grove	86	d				10 33										11 33								
Stockport	84	d				10 41										11 41								
Manchester Piccadilly 10	🚊	d			10 46	10 54		11 16				11 22			11 46	11 54			12 16				12 22	
Manchester Oxford Road		d			10 49	10 58		11 19				11 26			11 49	11 58			12 19				12 26	
Deansgate	🚊	d			10 51	11 00						11 28			11 51	12 00							12 28	
Rochdale	41	d	10 05										11 04											12 04
Manchester Victoria	🚊	d	10 33	10 46			11 00		11 07	11 10	11 22		11 33	11 46				12 00		12 07	12 10	12 22		12 33
Salford Central		d	10 36	10 49			11 03		11 10	11 13	11 25		11 36	11 49				12 03		12 10	12 13	12 25		12 36
Salford Crescent		a	10 39	10 52	10 56	11 04	11 07		11 13	11 16	11 29	11 33	11 39	11 52	11 56	12 04		12 07		12 13	12 16	12 29	12 33	12 39
		d	10 40	10 53	10 56	11 04	11 08		11 13	11 17	11 30	11 34	11 40	11 53	11 56	12 04		12 08		12 13	12 17	12 30	12 34	12 40
Swinton		d		10 59						11 23				11 59							12 23			
Moorside		d								11 26											12 26			
Walkden		d		11 04						11 29				12 04							12 29			
Atherton		d		11 09						11 35				12 09							12 35			
Hag Fold		d								11 37											12 37			
Daisy Hill		d		11 13						11 40				12 13							12 40			
Clifton		d																						
Kearsley		d	10 47										11 47											12 47
Farnworth		d	10 49										11 49											12 49
Moses Gate		d	10 52										11 52											12 52
Bolton		a	10 55		11 06	11 14	11 19		11 23		11 40	11 45	11 55		12 06	12 14		12 19		12 23		12 40	12 45	12 55
		d	10 56		11 07	11 15			11 24		11 40	11 45	11 56		12 07	12 15				12 24		12 40	12 45	12 56
Westhoughton		d							11 31			11 53								12 31			12 53	
Hindley		d		11 17					11 35	11 45		11 57		12 17						12 35	12 45		12 57	
Ince		d								11 48											12 48			
Wigan North Western		a						11 43											12 43					
Wigan Wallgate		a	11 13	11 22					11 44	11 51		12 02	12 13	12 22						12 44	12 51		13 02	13 13
		d		11 24						11 52		12 03		12 24							12 52		13 03	
Pemberton		d								11 56											12 56			
Orrell		d								12 00											13 00			
Upholland		d								12 04											13 04			
Rainford		d								12 07											13 07			
Kirkby		a								12 19											13 19			
Gathurst		d		11 28										12 28										
Appley Bridge		d		11 32								12 10		12 32									13 10	
Parbold		d		11 36								12 14		12 36									13 14	
Hoscar		d		11 39																				
Burscough Bridge		d		11 42								12 18		12 41									13 18	
New Lane		d		11 44																				
Bescar Lane		d		11 48																				
Meols Cop		d		11 53										12 49										
Southport		a		12 02								12 35		12 59									13 35	
Lostock		d				11 20					11 45					12 20						12 45		
Horwich Parkway		d			11 13	11 24					11 49				12 13	12 24						12 49		
Blackrod		d									11 52											12 52		
Adlington (Lancashire)		d									11 56											12 56		
Chorley		d			11 21	11 32					12 01				12 21	12 32						13 01		
Buckshaw Parkway		d			11 24	11 35					12 05				12 24	12 35						13 05		
Leyland		d				11 42					12 12					12 42						13 12		
Preston 8	65,97	a			11 33	11 50		11 57			12 17				12 33	12 50			12 57			13 17		
		d			11 38			11 58			12 19				12 38		12 45		12 59			13 19		
Kirkham & Wesham	97	a									12 28											13 28		
Poulton-le-Fylde	97	a			11 56						12 36				12 56							13 36		
Layton	97	a									12 43											13 43		
Blackpool North	97	a			12 05						12 50				13 05							13 50		
Lancaster 6	65	a						12 14									13 00		13 14					
		d						12 15									13 01		13 15					
Oxenholme Lake District	65	a															13 17		13 29					
Windermere	83	a															13 39							
Carnforth		d						12 22																
Silverdale		d																						
Arnside		d						12 30																
Grange-over-Sands		d						12 36																
Kents Bank		d																						
Cark		d																						
Ulverston		d						12 48																
Dalton		d																						
Roose		d																						
Barrow-in-Furness		a						13 09																

A To Clitheroe
B 🚲 to Preston
C From Stalybridge
D To Edinburgh

The Sunday service between Manchester Victoria and Wigan Wallgate via Atherton is funded by TfGM and will operate whilst funding exists

Table 82

Mondays to Fridays

10 February to 16 May

Manchester - Bolton - Wigan, Kirkby, Southport, Preston, Blackpool North and Barrow-in-Furness

Network Diagram - see first Page of Table 82

Station	Table		NT	TP ◇1	NT	NT A	TP ◇1 B	TP ◇1 C	NT	NT D	NT	NT ◇	NT	NT	TP ◇1	NT	NT E	NT A	NT	NT D	NT F	TP ◇1 G	NT
Manchester Airport	85 ✈	d		12 29			13 00					13 03			13 29							14 00	
Heald Green	85	d		12 33											13 33								
Buxton	86	d																					
Hazel Grove	86	d			12 33											13 33							
Stockport	84	d			12 41											13 41							
Manchester Piccadilly 10		d		12 46	12 54		13 16					13 22			13 46	13 54						14 16	
Manchester Oxford Road		d		12 49	12 58		13 19					13 26			13 49	13 58						14 19	
Deansgate		d		12 51	13 00							13 28			13 51	14 00							
Rochdale	41	d											13 04										
Manchester Victoria		d	12 46			13 00			13 07	13 10	13 22		13 33	13 46				14 00	14 07	14 10			14 22
Salford Central		d	12 49			13 03			13 10	13 13	13 25		13 36	13 49				14 03	14 10	14 13			14 25
Salford Crescent		a	12 52	12 56	13 04	13 07			13 13	13 16	13 29	13 33	13 39	13 52	13 56	14 04		14 07	14 13	14 16			14 29
		d	12 53	12 56	13 04	13 08			13 13	13 17	13 30	13 34	13 40	13 53	13 56	14 04		14 08	14 13	14 17			14 30
Swinton		d	12 59							13 23				13 59						14 23			
Moorside		d								13 26										14 26			
Walkden		d	13 04							13 29				14 04						14 29			
Atherton		d	13 09							13 35				14 09						14 35			
Hag Fold		d								13 37										14 37			
Daisy Hill		d	13 13							13 40				14 13						14 40			
Clifton		d																					
Kearsley		d											13 47										
Farnworth		d											13 49										
Moses Gate		d											13 52										
Bolton		a		13 06	13 14	13 19			13 23		13 40	13 45	13 55		14 06	14 14		14 19	14 23				14 40
		d		13 07	13 15				13 24		13 40	13 45	13 56		14 07	14 15			14 24				14 40
Westhoughton		d							13 31			13 53							14 31				
Hindley		d	13 17						13 35	13 45		13 57		14 17					14 35	14 45			
Ince		d								13 48										14 48			
Wigan North Western		a					13 43															14 43	
Wigan Wallgate		a	13 22						13 44	13 51		14 02	14 13	14 22					14 44	14 51			
		d	13 24							13 52		14 03		14 24						14 52			
Pemberton		d								13 56										14 56			
Orrell		d								14 00										15 00			
Upholland		d								14 04										15 04			
Rainford		d								14 07										15 07			
Kirkby		a								14 19										15 19			
Gathurst		d	13 28											14 28									
Appley Bridge		d	13 32									14 10		14 32									
Parbold		d	13 36									14 14		14 36									
Hoscar		d	13 39																				
Burscough Bridge		d	13 42									14 18		14 41									
New Lane		d	13 44																				
Bescar Lane		d	13 48																				
Meols Cop		d	13 53											14 49									
Southport		a	14 02									14 35		14 59									
Lostock		d			13 20						13 45					14 20							14 45
Horwich Parkway		d		13 13	13 24						13 49				14 13	14 24							14 49
Blackrod		d									13 52												14 52
Adlington (Lancashire)		d									13 56												14 56
Chorley		d		13 21	13 32						14 01				14 21	14 32							15 01
Buckshaw Parkway		d		13 24	13 35						14 05				14 24	14 35							15 05
Leyland		d			13 42						14 12					14 42							15 12
Preston 8	65,97	a		13 33	13 50		13 57				14 17				14 33	14 50						14 57	15 17
		d		13 38			13 58				14 19				14 38							14 58	15 19
Kirkham & Wesham	97	a									14 28												15 28
Poulton-le-Fylde	97	a		13 56							14 36				14 56								15 36
Layton	97	a									14 42												15 43
Blackpool North	97	a		14 05							14 50				15 05								15 50
Lancaster 6	65	a					14 14															15 14	
		d						13 34									13 48				14 21	15 15	
Oxenholme Lake District	65	a																				15 29	
Windermere	83	a																					
Carnforth		d						13 42									13a57				14 31		
Silverdale		d																			14 37		
Arnside		d						13 51													14 41		
Grange-over-Sands		d						13 56													14 47		
Kents Bank		d																			14 51		
Cark		d																			14 55		
Ulverston		d						14 09													15 04		
Dalton		d																			15 12		
Roose		d																			15 20		
Barrow-in-Furness		a						14 29													15 26		

A To Clitheroe
B To Glasgow Central
C From Windermere
D From Stalybridge
E From Heysham Harbour to Leeds
F From Morecambe
G To Edinburgh

The Sunday service between Manchester Victoria and Wigan Wallgate via Atherton is funded by TfGM and will operate whilst funding exists

Table 82

Mondays to Fridays

10 February to 16 May

Manchester - Bolton - Wigan, Kirkby, Southport, Preston, Blackpool North and Barrow-in-Furness

Network Diagram - see first Page of Table 82

Station		NT	NT	NT	NT	TP	NT	NT	TP	NT	NT	NT	NT	NT	NT	NT	NT	TP	NT	NT	NT	NT
		◇				◇1			◇1					◇				◇1				
					A			B	C	D		E				B					E	F
						⚯			⚯									⚯				
Manchester Airport 85 ✈	d	14 03				14 29			15 00					15 03				15 29				
Heald Green 85	d					14 33												15 33				
Buxton 86	d																					
Hazel Grove 86	d						14 33												15 33			
Stockport 84	d						14 41												15 41			
Manchester Piccadilly 10 ⇌	d	14 22				14 46	14 54		15 16					15 22				15 46	15 54			
Manchester Oxford Road	d	14 26				14 49	14 58		15 19					15 26				15 49	15 58			
Deansgate ⇌	d	14 28				14 51	15 00							15 28				15 51	16 00			
Rochdale 41	d		14 04												15 04							
Manchester Victoria ⇌	d		14 33	14 46				15 00			15 07	15 10	15 22		15 33	15 40	15 46			16 07	16 10	
Salford Central	d		14 36	14 49				15 03			15 10	15 13	15 25		15 36	15 43	15 49			16 10	16 13	
Salford Crescent	a	14 33	14 39	14 52		14 56	15 04	15 07			15 13	15 16	15 29	15 33	15 39	15 46	15 52	15 56	16 04	16 13	16 16	
	d	14 34	14 40	14 53		14 56	15 04	15 08			15 13	15 17	15 30	15 34	15 40	15 47	15 53	15 56	16 04	16 13	16 17	
Swinton	d			14 59								15 23					15 59				16 23	
Moorside	d											15 26									16 26	
Walkden	d			15 04								15 29					16 04				16 29	
Atherton	d			15 09								15 35					16 09				16 35	
Hag Fold	d											15 37									16 37	
Daisy Hill	d			15 13								15 40					16 13				16 40	
Clifton	d																					
Kearsley	d		14 47												15 47							
Farnworth	d		14 49												15 49							
Moses Gate	d		14 52												15 52					16 21		
Bolton	a	14 45	14 55			15 06	15 14	15 19			15 23		15 40	15 45	15 55	15 59		16 06	16 19	16 25		
	d	14 45	14 56			15 07	15 15				15 24		15 40	15 45	15 56			16 07		16 25		
Westhoughton	d	14 53									15 31			15 53						16 33		
Hindley	d	14 57		15 17							15 35	15 45		15 57			16 17			16 37	16 45	
Ince	d											15 48									16 48	
Wigan North Western	a								15 43													
Wigan Wallgate	a	15 02	15 13	15 22							15 44	15 51		16 02	16 13		16 22			16 46	16 51	
	d	15 03		15 24								15 58		16 03			16 24				16 52	
Pemberton	d											16 02									16 56	
Orrell	d											16 06									17 00	
Upholland	d											16 09									17 04	
Rainford	d											16 13									17 07	
Kirkby	a											16 25									17 19	
Gathurst	d			15 28										16 08			16 28					
Appley Bridge	d	15 10		15 32										16 11			16 32					
Parbold	d	15 14		15 36										16 15			16 36					
Hoscar	d													16 18								
Burscough Bridge	d	15 18		15 40										16 21			16 40					
New Lane	d													16 24								
Bescar Lane	d													16 27								
Meols Cop	d			15 48										16 32			16 48					
Southport	a	15 35		15 57										16 42			16 57					
Lostock	d						15 20						15 45					16 11				
Horwich Parkway	d					15 13	15 24						15 49					16 15				
Blackrod	d												15 52									
Adlington (Lancashire)	d												15 56									
Chorley	d					15 21	15 32						16 01					16 23				
Buckshaw Parkway	d					15 24	15 35						16 05					16 26				
Leyland	d						15 42						16 12									
Preston 8 65,97	a					15 33	15 50		15 57				16 19					16 35				
	d					15 38 15 46			15 58									16 38				
Kirkham & Wesham 97	a																	16 47				
Poulton-le-Fylde 97	a					15 56												16 57				
Layton 97	a																	17 00				
Blackpool North 97	a					16 05												17 07				
Lancaster 6 65	a					16 01			16 15													
	d				15 35	16 02				16 04												16 46
Oxenholme Lake District 65	a																					
Windermere 83	a																					
Carnforth	d				15 45	16 10				16a32												16 56
Silverdale	d				15 51	16 16																17 03
Arnside	d				15 56	16 20																17 07
Grange-over-Sands	d				16 02	16 25																17 13
Kents Bank	d				16 05	16 29																17 17
Cark	d				16 09	16 33																17 21
Ulverston	d				16 17	16 41																17 30
Dalton	d				16 26	16 49																17 39
Roose	d				16 32	16 55																17 45
Barrow-in-Furness	a				16 39	17 04																17 55

A To Carlisle
B To Clitheroe
C ⚯ to Preston
D To Leeds
E From Stalybridge
F To Millom

The Sunday service between Manchester Victoria and Wigan Wallgate via Atherton is funded by TfGM and will operate whilst funding exists

Table 82

Mondays to Fridays

10 February to 16 May

Manchester - Bolton - Wigan, Kirkby, Southport, Preston, Blackpool North and Barrow-in-Furness

Network Diagram - see first Page of Table 82

			TP	TP	NT	NT	NT		NT	NT	NT	TP	NT	NT	TP	NT	NT		NT	TP	NT	NT	NT	NT	NT	NT
			FO	FX																						
			◇1	◇1			◇					◇1			◇1					◇1			◇			
			A	A		B									C	B	D			E		F				
			🛒	🛒								🛒			🛒					🛒						
Manchester Airport	85 ✈	d	16 00	16 00			16 03					16 29			17 00								17 03			
Heald Green	85	d										16 33														
Buxton	86	d								15 29														16 29		
Hazel Grove	86	d								16 04				16 30										17 04		
Stockport	84	d								16 12				16 41										17 12		
Manchester Piccadilly 10	🚊	d	16 16	16 16			16 22			16 27		16 46		16 54	17 15								17 22	17 27		
Manchester Oxford Road		d	16 19	16 19			16 26			16 30		16 49		16 58	17 18					17 13			17 26	17 30		
Deansgate	🚊	d					16 28			16 33				17 00										17 33		
Rochdale	41	d									16 04											17 03				
Manchester Victoria	🚊	d			16 20	16 23					16 36		16 46			17 00	17 07		17 10		17 20	17 23			17 36	17 40
Salford Central		d			16 23	16 26					16 39		16 49			17 03	17 10		17 12		17 23	17 27			17 39	17 43
Salford Crescent		a			16 26	16 30	16 34			16 38	16 42		16 52	17 04		17 07	17 13		17 16		17 26	17 29	17 34	17 38	17 42	17 46
		d			16 27	16 31	16 34			16 38	16 43		16 53	17 04		17 08	17 13		17 17		17 27	17 30	17 34	17 38	17 43	17 47
Swinton		d											16 59						17 23							
Moorside		d											17 02						17 26							
Walkden		d											17 05						17 31							
Atherton		d											17 11				17 26		17 37							18 00
Hag Fold		d											17 14						17 39							
Daisy Hill		d											17 17				17 30		17 43							18 04
Clifton		d																							17 48	
Kearsley		d									16 50														17 53	
Farnworth		d									16 52														17 55	
Moses Gate		d									16 55														17 57	
Bolton		a	16 32		16 37	16 42	16 45			16 48	16 58	17 05		17 14		17 19				17 30	17 37	17 42	17 45	17 48	18 01	
		d	16 33	16u33	16 37		16 45			16 49	16 59	17 06		17 15						17 32	17 37		17 45	17 49	18 01	
Westhoughton		d					16 53				17 06												17 53		18 09	
Hindley		d					16 57				17 10		17 21						17 48						18 13	
Ince		d											17 24						17 51							
Wigan North Western		a																								
Wigan Wallgate		a					17 02				17 19		17 31				17 39		17 54				18 01		18 22	18 12
		d					17 03										17 40		17 55				18 02			18 15
Pemberton		d																	17 59							
Orrell		d																	18 03							
Upholland		d																	18 07							
Rainford		d																	18 10							
Kirkby		a																	18 22							
Gathurst		d					17 08										17 45									18 20
Appley Bridge		d					17 11										17 48						18 09			18 24
Parbold		d					17 15										17 53						18 13			18 28
Hoscar		d																								18 31
Burscough Bridge		d					17 20										17 58						18 17			18 35
New Lane		d																								18 37
Bescar Lane		d																								18 41
Meols Cop		d					17 27										18 05						18 26			18 46
Southport		a					17 37										18 15						18 35			18 55
Lostock		d			16 43					16 54				17 20							17 43			17 54		
Horwich Parkway		d			16 47					16 58				17 24							17 47			17 59		
Blackrod		d			16 51					17 01											17 51			18 02		
Adlington (Lancashire)		d			16 55					17 05											17 55			18 06		
Chorley		d	16 45	16 45	17 00					17 10		17 19		17 32						17 44	18 00			18 11		
Buckshaw Parkway		d			17 04					17 13				17 35						17 48	18 03			18 14		
Leyland		d			17 11					17 21				17 42							18 11					
Preston 8	65,97	a	16 58	16 58	17 19					17 26		17 30		17 51	17 55					18 01	18 16			18 25		
		d	16 58	16 58	17 21					17 28		17 32			17 58					18 05	18 18			18 26		
Kirkham & Wesham	97	a			17 30							17 41									18 27					
Poulton-le-Fylde	97	a			17 38							17 51									18 35			18 43		
Layton	97	a			17 43							17 54									18 39					
Blackpool North	97	a			17 50							18 02									18 46			18 55		
Lancaster 6	65	a	17 14	17 14						17 48					18 15					18 21						
		d	17 15	17 15					17 20	17 48					18 15					18 21						
Oxenholme Lake District	65	a	17 29	17 29											18 29					18 37						
Windermere	83	a																		19 00						
Carnforth		d							17 29	17 58																
Silverdale		d							17 35	18 03																
Arnside		d							17 40	18 08																
Grange-over-Sands		d							17 46	18 14																
Kents Bank		d							17 49	18 18																
Cark		d							17 54	18 22																
Ulverston		d							18 02	18 31																
Dalton		d							18 10	18 39																
Roose		d							18 17	18 45																
Barrow-in-Furness		a							18 25	18 56																

A To Edinburgh
B To Clitheroe
C To Glasgow Central
D From Stalybridge
E 🛒 to Preston
F To Blackburn

The Sunday service between Manchester Victoria and Wigan Wallgate via Atherton is funded by TfGM and will operate whilst funding exists

Table 82

Mondays to Fridays

10 February to 16 May

Manchester - Bolton - Wigan, Kirkby, Southport, Preston, Blackpool North and Barrow-in-Furness

Network Diagram - see first Page of Table 82

	NT	TP	TP		NT	NT	TP	TP	TP	NT	NT	NT	NT	NT	NT	TP	NT	NT	NT	TP	NT
							FX	FO	FO												
		◇1	◇1				◇1	◇1	◇1				◇			◇1				◇1	◇
						A	B	C	D			E						A	F		
			⊥				⊥	⊥	⊥							⊥					
Manchester Airport 85 ✈ d			17 29				18 00	18 00	18 00				18 03			18 29				19 00	19 03
Heald Green 85 d			17 33													18 33					
Buxton 86 d					16 59												17 59				
Hazel Grove 86 d					17 33												18 33				
Stockport 84 d					17 41												18 41				
Manchester Piccadilly 10 d			17 46		17 54		18 16	18 16	18 16				18 22			18 46	18 54			19 16	19 20
Manchester Oxford Road d			17 49		17 58		18 19	18 19	18 19				18 27			18 49	18 58			19 19	19 24
Deansgate d			17 51		18 00								18 29			18 51	19 00				19 26
Rochdale 41 d												18 02									
Manchester Victoria d	17 45					18 00				18 10	18 20	18 23		18 33	18 45			19 00			
Salford Central d	17 48					18 03				18 13	18 23	18 26		18 36	18 48			19 03			
Salford Crescent a	17 51		17 55		18 04	18 07				18 16	18 26	18 30	18 35	18 39	18 51	18 56	19 04	19 07			19 29
d	17 52		17 55		18 04	18 08				18 17	18 27	18 31	18 35	18 40	18 52	18 56	19 04	19 08			19 30
Swinton d	17 58									18 23					18 58						
Moorside d	18 01									18 26					19 01						
Walkden d	18 05									18 29					19 04						
Atherton d	18 11									18 35					19 10						
Hag Fold d	18 13									18 37					19 12						
Daisy Hill d	18 17									18 40					19 15						
Clifton d																					
Kearsley d														18 47							
Farnworth d														18 49							
Moses Gate d														18 52							
Bolton a			18 05		18 14	18 19					18 37	18 42	18 45	18 55		19 06	19 19	19 20		19 32	19 40
d			18 06		18 15						18 37		18 45	18 56		19 07				19 33	19 40
Westhoughton d													18 53	19 03							19 48
Hindley d	18 22									18 45			18 57	19 09	19 20						19 52
Ince d	18 25									18 48					19 23						
Wigan North Western a							18 43	18 42	18 42	18 56											
Wigan Wallgate a	18 28												19 02	19 18	19 30						19 57
d	18 29												19 03								19 59
Pemberton d	18 33																				
Orrell d	18 37																				
Upholland d	18 41																				
Rainford d	18 44																				
Kirkby a	18 55																				
Gathurst d													19 08								20 03
Appley Bridge d													19 11								20 07
Parbold d													19 15								20 11
Hoscar d																					
Burscough Bridge d													19 19								20 15
New Lane d																					
Bescar Lane d																					
Meols Cop d													19 27								20 23
Southport a													19 37								20 32
Lostock d			18 11		18 20						18 42					19 11					
Horwich Parkway d			18 15		18 24						18 46					19 15					
Blackrod d					18 27						18 49										
Adlington (Lancashire) d											18 53										
Chorley d			18 23		18 34						18 58					19 23				19 44	
Buckshaw Parkway d			18 26		18 37						19 02					19 26					
Leyland d					18 44						19 10										
Preston 8 65,97 a			18 35		18 49		18 57	18 56	18 56		19 18					19 35				19 57	
d			18 40	18 43	18 51		18 58	18 58	18 59		19 19					19 38				19 59	
Kirkham & Wesham 97 a			18 49								19 28										
Poulton-le-Fylde 97 a			18 59								19 36					19 56					
Layton 97 a			19 02								19 43										
Blackpool North 97 a			19 09		19 15						19 50					20 05					
Lancaster 8 65 a				18 58			19 14	19 16	19 16											20 14	
d		18 26		18 59			19 15	19 16	19 17										19 24	20 15	
Oxenholme Lake District 65 a							19 29	19 30	19 31												
Windermere 83 a																					
Carnforth d		18 34		19 07															19a34	20 23	
Silverdale d		18 40		19 13																20 29	
Arnside d		18 44		19 17																20 33	
Grange-over-Sands d		18 50		19 23																20 39	
Kents Bank d		18 53		19 26																20 42	
Cark d		18 58		19 31																20 47	
Ulverston d		19 06		19 39																20 55	
Dalton d		19 14		19 47																21 03	
Roose d		19 20		19 53																21 09	
Barrow-in-Furness a		19 29		20 02																21 18	

A To Clitheroe
B To Edinburgh
C until 21 March. To Edinburgh
D from 28 March. To Edinburgh
E To Blackburn
F From Morecambe to Leeds

The Sunday service between Manchester Victoria and Wigan Wallgate via Atherton is funded by TfGM and will operate whilst funding exists

Table 82

Mondays to Fridays

10 February to 16 May

Manchester - Bolton - Wigan, Kirkby, Southport, Preston, Blackpool North and Barrow-in-Furness

Network Diagram - see first Page of Table 82

		NT	NT	TP	NT	TP	NT	NT	NT	TP	NT	NT	TP	NT	NT	NT	TP	NT	NT	TP	TP	NT	NT
																		FO	FX		FX	FO	FX
				◇1		◇1		◇		◇1			◇1		◇		◇1			◇1	◇1		
					A	B					A							A	A	C	D		
Manchester Airport 85 ✈	d			19 29		20 00		20 03		20 29					21 03		21 29			22 00			
Heald Green 85	d			19 33						20 33							21 33						
Buxton 86	d																						
Hazel Grove 86	d																						
Stockport 84	d																						
Manchester Piccadilly 10	d			19 46		20 16		20 20		20 46					21 20		21 46			22 16	22 16		
Manchester Oxford Road	d			19 49		20 19		20 24		20 49					21 24		21 49			22 19	22 19		
Deansgate	d			19 51				20 26		20 51					21 26		21 51						
Rochdale 41	d																						
Manchester Victoria	d	19 28	19 35		20 00		20 22		20 35		21 00			21 22		21 35		22 00	22 00			22 22	22 22
Salford Central	d	19 31	19 38		20 03		20 25		20 38		21 03			21 25		21 38		22 04				22 25	
Salford Crescent	a	19 34	19 41	19 56	20 07		20 29	20 33	20 41	20 56	21 07			21 30	21 33	21 41	21 56	22 07	22 07	22 24	22 24	22 29	22 29
	d	19 35	19 42	19 56	20 08		20 30	20 34	20 42	20 56	21 08			21 30	21 34	21 42	21 56	22 08	22 08	22 24	22 24	22 30	22 30
Swinton	d		19 48						20 48							21 48							
Moorside	d		19 51						20 51							21 51							
Walkden	d		19 54						20 54							21 54							
Atherton	d		20 00						21 00							22 00							
Hag Fold	d		20 02						21 02							22 02							
Daisy Hill	d		20 05						21 05							22 05							
Clifton	d																						
Kearsley	d																						
Farnworth	d																						
Moses Gate	d																						
Bolton	a	19 45		20 06	20 19		20 40	20 45		21 06	21 19			21 40	21 45		22 06	22 19	22 19	22 34	22 34	22 40	22 40
	d	19 45		20 07			20 40	20 45		21 07				21 40	21 45		22 07			22 35	22 35	22 40	22 40
Westhoughton	d							20 53							21 53								
Hindley	d		20 10					20 57	21 10						21 57	22 10							
Ince	d		20 13						21 13							22 13							
Wigan North Western	a					20 43														22 48	22 48		
Wigan Wallgate	a		20 20					21 02	21 20						22 02	22 20							
	d							21 03							22 03								
Pemberton	d																						
Orrell	d																						
Upholland	d																						
Rainford	d																						
Kirkby	a																						
Gathurst	d							21 08							22 08								
Appley Bridge	d							21 11							22 11								
Parbold	d							21 15							22 15								
Hoscar	d							21 18															
Burscough Bridge	d							21 21							22 20								
New Lane	d							21 24															
Bescar Lane	d							21 27															
Meols Cop	d							21 32							22 27								
Southport	a							21 42							22 37								
Lostock	d	19 50					20 45							21 45								22 45	22 45
Horwich Parkway	d	19 54		20 13			20 49			21 13				21 49			22 13					22 49	22 49
Blackrod	d	19 57					20 52							21 52								22 52	22 52
Adlington (Lancashire)	d	20 01					20 56							21 56								22 56	22 56
Chorley	d	20 06		20 21			21 01			21 21				22 01			22 21					23 01	23 01
Buckshaw Parkway	d	20 10		20 24			21 05			21 24				22 04			22 24					23 05	23 05
Leyland	d	20 18					21 12							22 12								23 12	23 12
Preston 8 65,97	a	20 23		20 33		20 57	21 17			21 33				22 17			22 35			23 08	23 08	23 17	23 17
	d	20 25		20 38		20 58	21 19			21 38			21 47	22 19			22 38			23 11	23 11	23 19	23 19
Kirkham & Wesham 97	a	20 34					21 28							22 28								23 28	23 28
Poulton-le-Fylde 97	a	20 42		20 56			21 36			21 56				22 36			22 55					23 36	23 36
Layton 97	a	20 46					21 40							22 42								23 40	23 40
Blackpool North 97	a	20 54		21 05			21 48			22 05				22 50			23 04					23 48	23 48
Lancaster 6 65	a					21 14							22 02							23 26	23 26		
	d					21 15						21 20	22 03							23 27	23 27		
Oxenholme Lake District 65	a					21 29																	
Windermere 83	a																						
Carnforth	d											21 30	22 11							23 35	23 35		
Silverdale	d											21 37	22 17							23 41	23 41		
Arnside	d											21 41	22 21							23 45	23 45		
Grange-over-Sands	d											21 47	22 27							23 51	23 51		
Kents Bank	d											21 51	22 30							23 54	23 54		
Cark	d											21 55	22 35							23 59	23 59		
Ulverston	d											22 03	22 43							00 07	00 07		
Dalton	d											22 12	22 51							00 15	00 15		
Roose	d											22 18	22 57							00 21	00 21		
Barrow-in-Furness	a											22 27	23 06							00 30	00 30		

A To Clitheroe
B To Edinburgh
C FO until 14 March, from 21 March
D until 20 March

The Sunday service between Manchester Victoria and Wigan Wallgate via Atherton is funded by TfGM and will operate whilst funding exists

Table 82

Mondays to Fridays

10 February to 16 May

Manchester - Bolton - Wigan, Kirkby, Southport, Preston, Blackpool North and Barrow-in-Furness

Network Diagram - see first Page of Table 82

		NT	NT	NT		NT	TP	TP	NT	NT	NT	NT	NT	NT		NT
			FX	FO		FX		FX		FO	FX	FO	FX	FO		FX
		◇	◇				◇■1	◇■1								
		A	B				A	B		C	C					
Manchester Airport 85 ✈	d	22 19					22 29									
Heald Green 85	d						22 33									
Buxton 86	d															
Hazel Grove 86	d															
Stockport 84	d								22 34							
Manchester Piccadilly ■10	d	22 35					22 46	22 46	22 50							
Manchester Oxford Road	d	22 39	22 39				22 49	22 49	22 53							
Deansgate	d	22 41	22 41				22 51	22 51	22 55							
Rochdale 41	d															
Manchester Victoria	d			22 45		22 45				23 00	23 00	23 20	23 20	23 23		23 23
Salford Central	d			22 48						23 03		23 23		23 26		
Salford Crescent	a	22 46	22 46	22 51		22 51	22 56	22 56	22 59	23 07	23 07	23 26	23 26	23 31		23 31
	d	22 46	22 46	22 52		22 52	22 56	22 56	22 59	23 08	23 08	23 26	23 26	23 32		23 32
Swinton	d			22 58		22 58						23 33	23 33			
Moorside	d			23 01		23 01						23 35	23 35			
Walkden	d			23 04		23 04						23 39	23 39			
Atherton	d			23 10		23 10						23 44	23 44			
Hag Fold	d			23 12		23 12						23 47	23 47			
Daisy Hill	d			23 15		23 15						23 50	23 50			
Clifton	d															
Kearsley	d								23 07							
Farnworth	d								23 09							
Moses Gate	d								23 11							
Bolton	a	22 56	22 56				23 06	23 06	23 15	23 19	23 19			23 42		23 42
	d	22 57	22 57				23 07	23 07	23 15					23 42		23 42
Westhoughton	d	23 04	23 04						23 23							
Hindley	d	23 08	23 08	23 20		23 20			23 27			23 54	23 54			
Ince	d			23 23		23 23						23 57	23 57			
Wigan North Western	a															
Wigan Wallgate	a	23 13	23 13	23 30		23 30			23 38			00 04	00 04			
	d	23 15	23 15													
Pemberton	d															
Orrell	d															
Upholland	d															
Rainford	d															
Kirkby	a															
Gathurst	d	23 19	23 19													
Appley Bridge	d	23 23	23 23													
Parbold	d	23 27	23 27													
Hoscar	d															
Burscough Bridge	d	23 31	23 31													
New Lane	d															
Bescar Lane	d															
Meols Cop	d	23 39	23 39													
Southport	a	23 48	23 48													
Lostock	d													23 47		23 47
Horwich Parkway	d						23 13	23 13						23 51		23 51
Blackrod	d													23 54		23 54
Adlington (Lancashire)	d													23 58		23 58
Chorley	d						23 21	23 21						00 03		00 03
Buckshaw Parkway	d						23 24	23 24						00 07		00 07
Leyland	d													00 14		00 14
Preston ■8 65,97	a						23 33	23 33						00 19		00 19
	d						23 35	23 35						00 21		00 21
Kirkham & Wesham 97	a													00 30		00 30
Poulton-le-Fylde 97	a						23 52	23 52						00 38		00 38
Layton 97	a													00 43		00 43
Blackpool North 97	a						00 01	00 01						00 50		00 50
Lancaster ■6 65	a															
	d															
Oxenholme Lake District 65	a															
Windermere 83	a															
Carnforth	d															
Silverdale	d															
Arnside	d															
Grange-over-Sands	d															
Kents Bank	d															
Cark	d															
Ulverston	d															
Dalton	d															
Roose	d															
Barrow-in-Furness	a															

A FO until 14 March, from 21 March **B** until 20 March **C** To Blackburn

The Sunday service between Manchester Victoria and Wigan Wallgate via Atherton is funded by TfGM and will operate whilst funding exists

Table 82

Saturdays

14 December to 28 December

Manchester - Bolton - Wigan, Kirkby, Southport, Preston, Blackpool North and Barrow-in-Furness

Network Diagram - see first Page of Table 82

		NT	TP	TP	TP	TP	NT	TP	NT	NT		TP	NT	NT	NT	NT	TP	NT	NT	NT		NT	NT	NT	NT
			◇1	◇1	◇1	1		◇1				◇1					◇1								
		A		B			C	D								C	E	F	G	H			A		I
Manchester Airport	85 ✈ d		00 01		05 29			05 58				06 18					07 00								
Heald Green	85 d							06 02																	
Buxton	86 d															05 59									
Hazel Grove	86 d															06 33									
Stockport	84 d															06 41									
Manchester Piccadilly 10	d		00 16		05 44			06 13				06 33				06 53	07 15								
Manchester Oxford Road	d				05 47			06 17				06 36				06 57	07 18								
Deansgate	d															06 59									
Rochdale	41 d																								
Manchester Victoria	d						05 55		06 00	06 17				06 38	06 45					07 01		07 06		07 17	07 23
Salford Central	d													06 40	06 48					07 04		07 09		07 19	07 26
Salford Crescent	a				05 52		05 59		06 04	06 23		06 41		06 44	06 51	07 02				07 07		07 12		07 24	07 29
	d				05 52		06 00		06 05	06 24		06 41		06 45	06 52	07 03				07 08		07 13		07 25	07 30
Swinton	d														06 58					07 14					
Moorside	d																			07 17					
Walkden	d														07 03					07 20					
Atherton	d														07 08					07 26					
Hag Fold	d																			07 28					
Daisy Hill	d														07 12					07 31					
Clifton	d																								
Kearsley	d													06 52											
Farnworth	d													06 54											
Moses Gate	d													06 57											
Bolton	a		00s30		06 02		06 11		06 15	06 34		06 51		07 00		07 16						07 23		07 35	07 41
	d				06 03				06 15	06 34		06 52		07 01								07 23		07 35	
Westhoughton	d								06 23													07 31	↤		
Hindley	d								06 27						07 16					07 39		07 35	07 39		
Ince	d																			↪			07 42		
Wigan North Western	a							06 42						07 19			07 43								
Wigan Wallgate	a								06 32						07 21							07 40	07 45		
	d								06 34				06 37		07 23							07 41	07 46		
Pemberton	d								06 38														07 50		
Orrell	d								06 42														07 54		
Upholland	d								06 45														07 58		
Rainford	d								06 49														08 01		
Kirkby	a								07 01														08 13		
Gathurst	d												06 41		07 27							07 46			
Appley Bridge	d												06 45		07 31							07 49			
Parbold	d												06 49		07 35							07 53			
Hoscar	d												06 52									07 56			
Burscough Bridge	d												06 55		07 39							07 59			
New Lane	d												06 57									08 02			
Bescar Lane	d												07 01									08 05			
Meols Cop	d												07 06		07 47							08 10			
Southport	a												07 15		07 56							08 20			
Lostock	d									06 39														07 42	
Horwich Parkway	d				06 10					06 43		06 58												07 46	
Blackrod	d									06 46														07 49	
Adlington (Lancashire)	d									06 50														07 53	
Chorley	d	00 03			06 17					06 55		07 06												07 58	
Buckshaw Parkway	d	00 07			06 21					06 59		07 09												08 01	
Leyland	d	00 14			06 27					07 06														08 08	
Preston 8	65,97 a	00 19	01s04		06 32			06 56		07 11		07 18					07 57							08 14	
	d	00 21			06 35			06 57		07 13		07 20					07 58							08 15	
Kirkham & Wesham	97 a	00 30			06 44					07 22														08 25	
Poulton-le-Fylde	97 a	00 38			06 54					07 30														08 33	
Layton	97 a	00 43			06 58					07 34														08 37	
Blackpool North	97 a	00 50	01 29		07 05					07 41														08 44	
Lancaster 6	65 a							07 13				07 35					08 14								
	d					05 45		07 13				07 36						08 23	09 02						
Oxenholme Lake District	65 a					06 20		07 27																	
Windermere	83 a					06 40																			
Carnforth	d											07 44						08a32	09 11						
Silverdale	d											07 50							09 17						
Arnside	d											07 54							09 21						
Grange-over-Sands	d											08 00							09 27						
Kents Bank	d											08 03							09 31						
Cark	d											08 08							09 35						
Ulverston	d			00 07								08 16							09 44						
Dalton	d			00 15								08 24							09 52						
Roose	d			00 21								08 30							09 58						
Barrow-in-Furness	a			00 30								08 39							10 06						

A From Manchester Victoria
B From Manchester Airport
C To Clitheroe
D To Edinburgh
E To Glasgow Central
F To Leeds
G From Morecambe to Carlisle
H To Kirkby
I To Blackburn

The Sunday service between Manchester Victoria and Wigan Wallgate via Atherton is funded by TfGM and will operate whilst funding exists

Table 82

Saturdays

14 December to 28 December

Manchester - Bolton - Wigan, Kirkby, Southport, Preston, Blackpool North and Barrow-in-Furness

Network Diagram - see first Page of Table 82

Station			TP ◇1 A	NT	NT	NT B	NT C	NT	NT D	TP ◇1	NT	NT	NT E	NT F	NT	TP ◇1	NT	TP ◇1 G	NT B	NT	NT	NT H	TP ◇1 I	
Manchester Airport	85 ✈	d	07 25							07 56		08 01				08 25							09 00	
Heald Green	85	d	07 29									08 05				08 29								
Buxton	86	d															07 59							
Hazel Grove	86	d			07 32												08 33							
Stockport	84	d			07 40												08 41							
Manchester Piccadilly 10		d	07 45		07 54					08 15		08 22				08 46	08 54						09 16	
Manchester Oxford Road		d			07 57					08 19		08 26				08 49	08 58						09 19	
Deansgate		d			07 59							08 28				08 51	09 00							
Rochdale	41	d												08 00										
Manchester Victoria		d		07 27		08 00	08 03	08 11			08 22		08 29	08 33	08 46				09 00	09 07	09 10			
Salford Central		d		07 30		08 03	08 08	08 14			08 25		08 32	08 36	08 49				09 03	09 10	09 13			
Salford Crescent		a		07 32	08 04	08 07	08 12	08 17			08 29	08 33	08 37	08 40	08 52	08 56	09 04		09 07	09 13	09 16		09 24	
		d		07 32	08 04	08 08	08 13	08 17			08 30	08 34	08 37	08 41	08 53	08 56	09 04		09 08	09 13	09 17		09 24	
Swinton		d					08 19								08 59						09 23			
Moorside		d					08 22														09 26			
Walkden		d		07 42			08 25								09 04						09 29			
Atherton		d		07 48			08 31								09 09						09 35			
Hag Fold		d					08 33														09 37			
Daisy Hill		d		07 51			08 36								09 13						09 40			
Clifton		d																						
Kearsley		d												08 47										
Farnworth		d												08 49										
Moses Gate		d												08 52										
Bolton		a	07 59		08 14	08 19		08 27		08 32	08 40	08 44	08 49	08 55		09 06	09 14		09 19	09 23			09 34	
		d	07 59		08 15			08 28		08 33	08 40	08 45		08 56		09 07	09 15			09 24			09 35	
Westhoughton		d						08 35	←			08 53								09 31				
Hindley		d					08 41	08 39	08 41						09 17					09 35	09 45			
Ince		d					↪		08 44												09 48			
Wigan North Western		a																						
Wigan Wallgate		a		08 03				08 48	08 50			09 00		09 14	09 22					09 44	09 51			
		d							08 51			09 05			09 24						09 52			
Pemberton		d							08 55												09 56			
Orrell		d							08 59												10 00			
Upholland		d							09 03												10 04			
Rainford		d							09 06												10 07			
Kirkby		a							09 18												10 19			
Gathurst		d													09 28									
Appley Bridge		d										09 11			09 32									
Parbold		d										09 15			09 36									
Hoscar		d													09 39									
Burscough Bridge		d										09 20			09 42									
New Lane		d													09 44									
Bescar Lane		d													09 48									
Meols Cop		d													09 53									
Southport		a										09 36			10 02									
Lostock		d			08 20						08 45						09 20							
Horwich Parkway		d			08 24					08 39	08 49						09 24							
Blackrod		d									08 52													
Adlington (Lancashire)		d			08 29						08 56													
Chorley		d	08 11		08 34					08 47	09 01					09 19	09 32							
Buckshaw Parkway		d			08 37						09 05						09 35							
Leyland		d			08 43						09 12						09 42							
Preston 8	65,97	a	08 22		08 50					08 58	09 17					09 30	09 50						09 55	
		d	08 24							08 59	09 19					09 32		09 45					09 59	10 09
Kirkham & Wesham	97	a									09 28													
Poulton-le-Fylde	97	a								09 16	09 36													10 26
Layton	97	a									09 43													
Blackpool North	97	a								09 25	09 50													10 35
Lancaster 6	65	a	08 39													09 47		10 00					10 14	
		d														09 48		10 01				10 49		
Oxenholme Lake District	65	a														10 03								
Windermere	83	a														10 27								
Carnforth		d																10 09				10a58		
Silverdale		d																10 15						
Arnside		d																10 19						
Grange-over-Sands		d																10 25						
Kents Bank		d																10 28						
Cark		d																10 33						
Ulverston		d																10 41						
Dalton		d																10 49						
Roose		d																10 55						
Barrow-in-Furness		a																11 04						

A To Edinburgh
B To Clitheroe
C To Kirkby
D From Manchester Victoria
E To Blackburn
F From Hebden Bridge
G From Blackpool North
H From Morecambe to Leeds
I To Glasgow Central

The Sunday service between Manchester Victoria and Wigan Wallgate via Atherton is funded by TfGM and will operate whilst funding exists

Table 82

Saturdays

14 December to 28 December

Manchester - Bolton - Wigan, Kirkby, Southport, Preston, Blackpool North and Barrow-in-Furness

Network Diagram - see first Page of Table 82

	NT		NT	NT	NT	NT	TP		NT	NT	TP		NT	NT	NT	NT	NT	NT	NT	NT	TP		NT	NT
							◇1				◇1										◇1			
				A						B	C		D					A						B
Manchester Airport 85 d			09 03				09 29				10 00						10 03				10 29			
Heald Green 85 d							09 33														10 33			
Buxton 86 d																								
Hazel Grove 86 d									09 33														10 33	
Stockport 84 d									09 41														10 41	
Manchester Piccadilly 10 d			09 22				09 46		09 54		10 16						10 22				10 46		10 54	
Manchester Oxford Road d			09 26				09 49		09 58		10 19						10 26				10 49		10 58	
Deansgate d			09 28				09 51		10 00								10 28				10 51		11 00	
Rochdale 41 d					09 04														10 05					
Manchester Victoria d	09 22			09 29	09 33	09 46				10 00				10 07	10 10	10 22		10 29	10 33	10 46				11 00
Salford Central d	09 25			09 32	09 36	09 49				10 03				10 10	10 13	10 25		10 32	10 36	10 49				11 03
Salford Crescent a	09 29		09 33	09 37	09 39	09 52	09 56		10 04	10 07				10 13	10 16	10 29	10 33	10 37	10 39	10 52	10 56		11 04	11 07
d	09 30		09 34	09 37	09 41	09 53	09 56		10 04	10 08				10 13	10 17	10 30	10 34	10 37	10 40	10 53	10 56		11 04	11 08
Swinton d						09 59									10 23					10 59				
Moorside d															10 26									
Walkden d						10 04									10 29					11 04				
Atherton d						10 09									10 35					11 09				
Hag Fold d															10 37									
Daisy Hill d						10 13									10 40					11 13				
Clifton d																								
Kearsley d					09 48														10 47					
Farnworth d					09 50														10 49					
Moses Gate d					09 53														10 52					
Bolton a	09 40		09 44	09 49	09 56		10 06		10 14	10 19				10 23		10 40	10 45	10 49	10 55		11 06		11 14	11 19
d	09 40		09 45		09 57		10 07		10 15					10 24		10 40	10 45		10 56		11 07		11 15	
Westhoughton d			09 53											10 31			10 53							
Hindley d			09 57			10 17								10 35	10 45		10 57			11 17				
Ince d															10 48									
Wigan North Western a																								
Wigan Wallgate a			10 02		10 14	10 22								10 44	10 51		11 02		11 13	11 22				
d			10 03			10 24									10 52		11 03			11 24				
Pemberton d															10 56									
Orrell d															11 00									
Upholland d															11 04									
Rainford d															11 07									
Kirkby a															11 19									
Gathurst d						10 28														11 28				
Appley Bridge d			10 10			10 32											11 10			11 32				
Parbold d			10 14			10 36											11 14			11 36				
Hoscar d																				11 39				
Burscough Bridge d			10 18			10 40											11 18			11 42				
New Lane d																				11 44				
Bescar Lane d																				11 48				
Meols Cop d						10 48														11 53				
Southport a			10 35			10 57											11 35			12 02				
Lostock d	09 45								10 20							10 45							11 20	
Horwich Parkway d	09 49						10 13		10 24							10 49					11 13		11 24	
Blackrod d	09 52															10 52								
Adlington (Lancashire) d	09 56															10 56								
Chorley d	10 01						10 21		10 32							11 01					11 21		11 32	
Buckshaw Parkway d	10 05						10 24		10 35							11 05					11 24		11 35	
Leyland d	10 12								10 42							11 12							11 42	
Preston 8 65,97 a	10 17						10 33		10 50		10 56					11 17					11 33		11 50	
d	10 19						10 38	10 45			10 57					11 19					11 38			
Kirkham & Wesham 97 a	10 28															11 28								
Poulton-le-Fylde 97 a	10 36						10 56									11 36					11 56			
Layton 97 a	10 40															11 43								
Blackpool North 97 a	10 50						11 05									11 50					12 05			
Lancaster 6 65 a								11 00			11 13													
d								11 01					11 28											
Oxenholme Lake District 65 a								11 17																
Windermere 83 a								11 39																
Carnforth d													11 37											
Silverdale d													11 43											
Arnside d													11 48											
Grange-over-Sands d													11 54											
Kents Bank d													11 57											
Cark d													12 02											
Ulverston d													12 10											
Dalton d													12 18											
Roose d													12 24											
Barrow-in-Furness a													12 32											

A To Blackburn
B To Clitheroe
C To Edinburgh
D To Carlisle

The Sunday service between Manchester Victoria and Wigan Wallgate via Atherton is funded by TfGM and will operate whilst funding exists

Table 82

Saturdays

14 December to 28 December

Manchester - Bolton - Wigan, Kirkby, Southport, Preston, Blackpool North and Barrow-in-Furness

Network Diagram - see first Page of Table 82

Station			TP	NT	NT	NT	NT	NT	NT	TP	NT	TP	NT	TP	NT	NT	NT	NT	NT	NT	TP	NT	NT	TP
			◇1							◇1		◇1	A	◇1 B 🚲							◇1		A	◇1 C 🚲
Manchester Airport	85 ✈	d	11 00				11 03			11 29				12 00				12 03			12 29			13 00
Heald Green	85	d								11 33											12 33			
Buxton	86	d																						
Hazel Grove	86	d									11 33											12 33		
Stockport	84	d									11 41											12 41		
Manchester Piccadilly 10	🚋	d	11 16				11 22			11 46	11 54			12 16				12 22			12 46	12 54		13 16
Manchester Oxford Road		d	11 19				11 26			11 49	11 58			12 19				12 26			12 49	12 58		13 19
Deansgate	🚋	d					11 28			11 51	12 00							12 28			12 51	13 00		
Rochdale	41	d						11 04											12 04					
Manchester Victoria	🚋	d		11 07	11 10	11 22		11 33	11 46				12 00		12 07	12 10	12 22		12 33	12 46			13 00	
Salford Central		d		11 10	11 13	11 25		11 36	11 49				12 03		12 10	12 13	12 25		12 36	12 49			13 03	
Salford Crescent		a		11 13	11 16	11 29	11 33	11 39	11 52	11 56	12 04		12 07		12 13	12 16	12 29	12 33	12 39	12 52	12 56	13 04	13 07	
		d		11 13	11 17	11 30	11 34	11 40	11 53	11 56	12 04		12 08		12 13	12 17	12 30	12 34	12 40	12 53	12 56	13 04	13 08	
Swinton		d			11 23				11 59							12 23				12 59				
Moorside		d			11 26											12 26								
Walkden		d			11 29				12 04							12 29				13 04				
Atherton		d			11 35				12 09							12 35				13 09				
Hag Fold		d			11 37											12 37								
Daisy Hill		d			11 40				12 13							12 40				13 13				
Clifton		d																						
Kearsley		d						11 47											12 47					
Farnworth		d						11 49											12 49					
Moses Gate		d						11 52											12 52					
Bolton		a		11 23		11 40	11 45	11 55		12 06	12 14		12 19		12 23		12 40	12 45	12 55		13 06	13 14	13 19	
		d		11 24		11 40	11 45	11 56		12 07	12 15				12 24		12 40	12 45	12 56		13 07	13 15		
Westhoughton		d		11 31			11 53								12 31			12 53						
Hindley		d		11 35	11 45		11 57		12 17						12 35	12 45		12 57		13 17				
Ince		d			11 48											12 48								
Wigan North Western		a	11 43											12 43										13 43
Wigan Wallgate		a		11 44	11 51		12 02	12 13	12 22						12 44	12 51		13 02	13 13	13 22				
		d			11 52		12 03		12 24							12 52		13 03		13 24				
Pemberton		d			11 56											12 56								
Orrell		d			12 00											13 00								
Upholland		d			12 04											13 04								
Rainford		d			12 07											13 07								
Kirkby		a			12 19											13 19								
Gathurst		d							12 28											13 28				
Appley Bridge		d					12 10		12 32									13 10		13 32				
Parbold		d					12 14		12 36									13 14		13 36				
Hoscar		d																		13 39				
Burscough Bridge		d					12 18		12 41									13 18		13 42				
New Lane		d																		13 44				
Bescar Lane		d																		13 48				
Meols Cop		d							12 49											13 53				
Southport		a					12 35		12 59									13 35		14 02				
Lostock		d				11 45					12 20						12 45					13 20		
Horwich Parkway		d				11 49				12 13	12 24						12 49				13 13	13 24		
Blackrod		d				11 52											12 52							
Adlington (Lancashire)		d				11 56											12 56							
Chorley		d				12 01				12 21	12 32						13 01				13 21	13 32		
Buckshaw Parkway		d				12 05				12 24	12 35						13 05				13 24	13 35		
Leyland		d				12 12					12 42						13 12					13 42		
Preston 8	65,97	a	11 57			12 17				12 33	12 50			12 57			13 17				13 33	13 50		13 57
		d	11 58			12 19				12 38		12 45		12 58			13 19				13 38			13 58
Kirkham & Wesham	97	a				12 28											13 28							
Poulton-le-Fylde	97	a				12 36				12 56							13 36				13 56			
Layton	97	a				12 43											13 43							
Blackpool North	97	a				12 50				13 05							13 50				14 05			
Lancaster 6	65	a	12 14									13 00		13 14										14 14
		d	12 15									13 01		13 15										
Oxenholme Lake District	65	a										13 17		13 29										
Windermere	83	a										13 39												
Carnforth		d	12 22																					
Silverdale		d																						
Arnside		d	12 30																					
Grange-over-Sands		d	12 36																					
Kents Bank		d																						
Cark		d																						
Ulverston		d	12 48																					
Dalton		d																						
Roose		d																						
Barrow-in-Furness		a	13 09																					

A To Clitheroe **B** To Edinburgh **C** To Glasgow Central

The Sunday service between Manchester Victoria and Wigan Wallgate via Atherton is funded by TfGM and will operate whilst funding exists

Table 82

Saturdays

14 December to 28 December

Manchester - Bolton - Wigan, Kirkby, Southport, Preston, Blackpool North and Barrow-in-Furness

Network Diagram - see first Page of Table 82

Station		NT	NT	NT	NT	TP	NT	NT	NT	NT	TP		NT	NT	TP	NT	NT	NT	NT	NT	NT	TP
											◇1				◇1							◇1
		A			B									C	D							
															🚲							
Manchester Airport 85 ✈	d							13 03			13 29				14 00				14 03			14 29
Heald Green 85	d										13 33											14 33
Buxton 86	d																					
Hazel Grove 86	d												13 33									
Stockport 84	d												13 41									
Manchester Piccadilly 10 ⇌	d							13 22			13 46		13 54		14 16				14 22			14 46
Manchester Oxford Road	d							13 26			13 49		13 58		14 19				14 26			14 49
Deansgate ⇌	d							13 28			13 51		14 00						14 28			14 51
Rochdale 41	d								13 04											14 04		
Manchester Victoria ⇌	d		13 07	13 10			13 22		13 33	13 46				14 00		14 07	14 10	14 22		14 33	14 46	
Salford Central	d		13 10	13 13			13 25		13 36	13 49				14 03		14 10	14 13	14 25		14 36	14 49	
Salford Crescent	a		13 13	13 16			13 29	13 33	13 39	13 52	13 56		14 04	14 07		14 13	14 16	14 29	14 33	14 39	14 52	14 56
	d		13 13	13 17			13 30	13 34	13 40	13 53	13 56		14 04	14 08		14 13	14 17	14 30	14 34	14 40	14 53	14 56
Swinton	d			13 23						13 59							14 23				14 59	
Moorside	d			13 26													14 26					
Walkden	d			13 29						14 04							14 29				15 04	
Atherton	d			13 35						14 09							14 35				15 09	
Hag Fold	d			13 37													14 37					
Daisy Hill	d			13 40						14 13							14 40				15 13	
Clifton	d																					
Kearsley	d								13 47											14 47		
Farnworth	d								13 49											14 49		
Moses Gate	d								13 52											14 52		
Bolton	a		13 23				13 40	13 45	13 55		14 06		14 14	14 19		14 23		14 40	14 45	14 55		15 06
	d		13 24				13 40	13 45	13 56		14 07		14 15			14 24		14 40	14 45	14 56		15 07
Westhoughton	d		13 31					13 53								14 31			14 53			
Hindley	d		13 35	13 45				13 57		14 17						14 35	14 45		14 57		15 17	
Ince	d			13 48													14 48					
Wigan North Western	a														14 43							
Wigan Wallgate	a		13 44	13 51				14 02	14 13	14 22						14 44	14 51		15 02	15 13	15 22	
	d			13 52				14 03		14 24							14 52		15 03		15 24	
Pemberton	d			13 56													14 56					
Orrell	d			14 00													15 00					
Upholland	d			14 04													15 04					
Rainford	d			14 07													15 07					
Kirkby	a			14 19													15 19					
Gathurst	d									14 28											15 28	
Appley Bridge	d							14 10		14 32									15 10		15 32	
Parbold	d							14 14		14 36									15 14		15 36	
Hoscar	d																					
Burscough Bridge	d							14 18		14 41									15 18		15 40	
New Lane	d																					
Bescar Lane	d																					
Meols Cop	d									14 49											15 48	
Southport	a							14 35		14 59									15 35		15 57	
Lostock	d						13 45						14 20					14 45				
Horwich Parkway	d						13 49				14 13		14 24					14 49				15 13
Blackrod	d						13 52											14 52				
Adlington (Lancashire)	d						13 56											14 56				
Chorley	d						14 01				14 21		14 32					15 01				15 21
Buckshaw Parkway	d						14 05				14 24		14 35					15 05				15 24
Leyland	d						14 12						14 42					15 12				
Preston 8 65,97	a						14 17				14 33		14 50		14 57			15 17				15 33
	d					14 06	14 19				14 38	14 45			14 58			15 19				15 38
Kirkham & Wesham 97	a						14 28											15 28				
Poulton-le-Fylde 97	a						14 36				14 56							15 36				15 56
Layton 97	a						14 42											15 43				
Blackpool North 97	a						14 50				15 05							15 50				16 05
Lancaster 6 65	a					14 21						15 00			15 14							
	d	13 32			13 48	14 22						15 01			15 15							
Oxenholme Lake District 65	a											15 17			15 29							
Windermere 83	a											15 39										
Carnforth	d	13 41			13a58	14 30																
Silverdale	d	13 47																				
Arnside	d	13 52				14 39																
Grange-over-Sands	d	13 58				14 44																
Kents Bank	d	14 01																				
Cark	d	14 06																				
Ulverston	d	14 14				14 57																
Dalton	d	14 22																				
Roose	d	14 28																				
Barrow-in-Furness	a	14 36				15 17																

A To Carlisle
B From Heysham Harbour to Leeds
C To Clitheroe
D To Edinburgh

The Sunday service between Manchester Victoria and Wigan Wallgate via Atherton is funded by TfGM and will operate whilst funding exists

Table 82

Saturdays

14 December to 28 December

Manchester - Bolton - Wigan, Kirkby, Southport, Preston, Blackpool North and Barrow-in-Furness

Network Diagram - see first Page of Table 82

		NT	NT	NT	NT	NT	TP	NT	NT	NT	NT	NT	TP	NT	NT	NT	NT	NT	TP		NT	NT	NT
							◇1						◇1						◇1				
			A								A						B	C	D			A	
																			🍴				
Manchester Airport 85 ✈	d						15 00		15 03				15 29						16 00				16 03
Heald Green 85	d												15 33										
Buxton 86	d																						
Hazel Grove 86	d	14 33												15 33									
Stockport 84	d	14 41												15 41									
Manchester Piccadilly 10 ⛴	d	14 54					15 16		15 22				15 46	15 54					16 16				16 22
Manchester Oxford Road	d	14 58					15 19		15 26				15 49	15 58					16 19				16 26
Deansgate ⛴	d	15 00							15 28				15 51	16 00									16 28
Rochdale 41	d									15 04													
Manchester Victoria ⛴	d		15 00	15 07	15 10			15 22		15 33	15 40	15 46			16 07	16 10					16 20	16 23	
Salford Central	d		15 03	15 10	15 13			15 25		15 36	15 43	15 49			16 10	16 13					16 23	16 26	
Salford Crescent	a	15 04	15 08	15 13	15 16			15 29	15 33	15 39	15 46	15 52	15 56	16 04	16 13	16 16					16 26	16 30	16 34
	d	15 04	15 08	15 13	15 17			15 30	15 34	15 40	15 47	15 53	15 56	16 04	16 13	16 17					16 27	16 31	16 34
Swinton	d				15 23							15 59				16 23							
Moorside	d				15 26											16 26							
Walkden	d				15 29							16 04				16 29							
Atherton	d				15 35							16 09				16 35							
Hag Fold	d				15 37											16 37							
Daisy Hill	d				15 40							16 13				16 40							
Clifton	d																						
Kearsley	d									15 47													
Farnworth	d									15 49													
Moses Gate	d									15 52													
Bolton	a	15 14	15 19	15 23				15 40	15 45	15 55	15 59		16 06	16 14	16 23				16 32		16 37	16 42	16 45
	d	15 15		15 24				15 40	15 45	15 56			16 07	16 15	16 24				16 33		16 37		16 46
Westhoughton	d			15 31					15 53						16 31								16 53
Hindley	d			15 35	15 45				15 57			16 17			16 35	16 45							16 57
Ince	d				15 48											16 48							
Wigan North Western	a						15 43																
Wigan Wallgate	a			15 44	15 51				16 02	16 13		16 22			16 44	16 51							17 02
	d				15 52				16 03			16 24				16 52							17 03
Pemberton	d				15 56											16 56							
Orrell	d				16 00											17 00							
Upholland	d				16 04											17 04							
Rainford	d				16 07											17 07							
Kirkby	a				16 19											17 19							
Gathurst	d								16 08			16 28											17 08
Appley Bridge	d								16 11			16 32											17 11
Parbold	d								16 15			16 36											17 15
Hoscar	d								16 18														
Burscough Bridge	d								16 21			16 40											17 20
New Lane	d								16 24														
Bescar Lane	d								16 27														
Meols Cop	d								16 32			16 48											17 27
Southport	a								16 42			16 57											17 37
Lostock	d	15 20						15 45					16 11	16 20							16 43		
Horwich Parkway	d	15 24						15 49					16 15	16 24							16 47		
Blackrod	d							15 52													16 51		
Adlington (Lancashire)	d							15 56													16 55		
Chorley	d	15 32						16 01					16 23	16 32					16 45		17 00		
Buckshaw Parkway	d	15 35						16 05					16 26	16 35							17 04		
Leyland	d	15 42						16 12						16 42							17 11		
Preston 8 65,97	a	15 50					15 57	16 19					16 35	16 50					16 56		17 19		
	d						15 58						16 38						16 58	17 05	17 20		
Kirkham & Wesham 97	a												16 47								17 30		
Poulton-le-Fylde 97	a												16 57								17 38		
Layton 97	a												17 00								17 43		
Blackpool North 97	a												17 07								17 50		
Lancaster 6 65	a						16 14												17 14	17 20			
	d					15 20	16 15										16 40	17 00	17 15	17 21			
Oxenholme Lake District 65	a																		17 29	17 37			
Windermere 83	a																			17 58			
Carnforth	d					15 30	16 23										16a49	17 10					
Silverdale	d					15 36	16 29											17 17					
Arnside	d					15 40	16 33											17 21					
Grange-over-Sands	d					15 46	16 39											17 27					
Kents Bank	d					15 50	16 42											17 31					
Cark	d					15 54	16 47											17 35					
Ulverston	d					16 03	16 55											17 44					
Dalton	d					16 11	17 03											17 53					
Roose	d					16 19	17 09											17 59					
Barrow-in-Furness	a					16 25	17 18											18 07					

A To Clitheroe
B From Morecambe to Leeds
C To Millom
D To Edinburgh

The Sunday service between Manchester Victoria and Wigan Wallgate via Atherton is funded by TfGM and will operate whilst funding exists

Table 82

Saturdays

14 December to 28 December

Manchester - Bolton - Wigan, Kirkby, Southport, Preston, Blackpool North and Barrow-in-Furness

Network Diagram - see first Page of Table 82

		NT	NT	NT	TP	NT	NT	NT	TP	NT	NT	NT	NT	NT	NT	TP	NT	NT	NT	TP	NT
					◇1				◇1							◇1				◇1	
							A		B 🛒			C							A	D 🛒	
Manchester Airport 85 ⇌	d				16 29				17 00				17 03			17 29				18 00	
Heald Green 85	d				16 33											17 33					
Buxton 86	d																				
Hazel Grove 86	d					16 30												17 33			
Stockport 84	d					16 41												17 41			
Manchester Piccadilly 10 ⇌	d				16 46	16 54			17 15				17 23			17 46		17 54		18 16	
Manchester Oxford Road	d				16 49	16 58			17 18				17 26			17 49		17 58		18 19	
Deansgate ⇌	d				16 51	17 00										17 51		18 00			
Rochdale 41	d	16 04										17 03									
Manchester Victoria ⇌	d	16 36	16 46				17 00	17 07		17 10	17 20	17 23		17 36	17 40		17 50		18 00		18 10
Salford Central	d	16 39	16 49				17 03	17 10		17 13	17 23	17 26		17 39	17 43		17 53		18 03		18 13
Salford Crescent	a	16 42	16 52		16 56	17 04	17 07	17 13		17 17	17 26	17 30	17 33	17 42	17 46	17 55	17 58	18 04	18 07		18 16
	d	16 43	16 53		16 56	17 04	17 08	17 13		17 17	17 27	17 31	17 34	17 43	17 47	17 55	17 59	18 04	18 08		18 17
Swinton	d		16 59							17 23							18 05				18 23
Moorside	d		17 02							17 26							18 08				18 26
Walkden	d		17 05							17 29							18 11				18 29
Atherton	d		17 11							17 35					18 00		18 17				18 35
Hag Fold	d		17 14							17 37							18 19				18 37
Daisy Hill	d		17 17							17 41					18 04		18 22				18 40
Clifton	d													17 48							
Kearsley	d	16 50												17 53							
Farnworth	d	16 52												17 55							
Moses Gate	d	16 55												17 57							
Bolton	a	16 58			17 06	17 14	17 19	17 23	17 32		17 37	17 42	17 44	18 01		18 05		18 14	18 19		
	d	16 59			17 07	17 15		17 24	17 32		17 37		17 46	18 01		18 06		18 15			
Westhoughton	d	17 06						17 31					17 53	18 09							
Hindley	d	17 10	17 21					17 35		17 45				18 13			18 27				18 45
Ince	d		17 24							17 48											18 48
Wigan North Western	a																			18 43	18 56
Wigan Wallgate	a	17 19	17 27					17 44		17 51			18 01	18 22	18 12		18 32				
	d		17 29							17 52			18 02		18 15		18 33				
Pemberton	d									17 56							18 37				
Orrell	d									18 00							18 41				
Upholland	d									18 04							18 45				
Rainford	d									18 07							18 48				
Kirkby	a									18 19							19 00				
Gathurst	d		17 33												18 20						
Appley Bridge	d		17 37										18 09		18 24						
Parbold	d		17 41										18 13		18 28						
Hoscar	d														18 31						
Burscough Bridge	d		17 45										18 18		18 35						
New Lane	d														18 37						
Bescar Lane	d														18 41						
Meols Cop	d		17 53										18 26		18 46						
Southport	a		18 02										18 36		18 55						
Lostock	d					17 20					17 43					18 11		18 20			
Horwich Parkway	d				17 13	17 24					17 47					18 15		18 24			
Blackrod	d										17 51										
Adlington (Lancashire)	d										17 55										
Chorley	d				17 21	17 32			17 46		18 00					18 23		18 32			
Buckshaw Parkway	d				17 24	17 35					18 03					18 26		18 35			
Leyland	d					17 42					18 11							18 42			
Preston 8 65,97	a				17 33	17 50			17 56		18 16					18 35		18 48		18 57	
	d				17 38 / 17 45				18 00		18 18					18 40 / 18 45		18 49		18 58	
Kirkham & Wesham 97	a				17 47						18 27					18 49					
Poulton-le-Fylde 97	a				17 57						18 35					18 59					
Layton 97	a				18 00						18 39					19 02					
Blackpool North 97	a				18 08						18 46					19 09		19 16			
Lancaster 6 65	a				18 00				18 16							19 00				19 14	
	d			17 36	18 01				18 16							19 01				19 15	
Oxenholme Lake District 65	a								18 31											19 29	
Windermere 83	a																				
Carnforth	d			17 45	18 09											19 09					
Silverdale	d			17 51	18 15											19 15					
Arnside	d			17 56	18 19											19 19					
Grange-over-Sands	d			18 02	18 25											19 25					
Kents Bank	d			18 05	18 28											19 28					
Cark	d			18 10	18 33											19 33					
Ulverston	d			18 18	18 41											19 41					
Dalton	d			18 26	18 49											19 49					
Roose	d			18 33	18 55											19 55					
Barrow-in-Furness	a			18 43	19 04											20 04					

A To Clitheroe
B To Glasgow Central
C To Blackburn
D To Edinburgh

The Sunday service between Manchester Victoria and Wigan Wallgate via Atherton is funded by TfGM and will operate whilst funding exists

Table 82

Saturdays

14 December to 28 December

Manchester - Bolton - Wigan, Kirkby, Southport, Preston, Blackpool North and Barrow-in-Furness

Network Diagram - see first Page of Table 82

Station		NT	NT	NT	NT	NT	TP	NT	NT	NT	TP	NT	NT	NT	TP	TP	NT	NT	NT	NT	NT	TP
							◇1				◇1				◇1	◇1						◇1
			A						B	C								B				
Manchester Airport	85 ✈ d			18 03			18 29				19 00	19 03			19 29	20 00				20 03		20 29
Heald Green	85 d						18 33								19 33							20 33
Buxton	86 d																					
Hazel Grove	86 d							18 33														
Stockport	84 d							18 41														
Manchester Piccadilly 10	⇌ d			18 22			18 46	18 54			19 16	19 20			19 46	20 16				20 20		20 46
Manchester Oxford Road	d			18 27			18 49	18 58			19 19	19 24			19 49	20 19				20 24		20 49
Deansgate	⇌ d			18 29			18 51	19 00				19 26			19 51					20 26		20 51
Rochdale	41 d		18 02																			
Manchester Victoria	⇌ d	18 20	18 23		18 33	18 45			19 00				19 28	19 35				20 00	20 22		20 35	
Salford Central	d	18 23	18 26		18 36	18 48			19 03				19 31	19 38				20 04	20 25		20 38	
Salford Crescent	a	18 26	18 30	18 34	18 39	18 51	18 56	19 04	19 08			19 29	19 34	19 41	19 56			20 07	20 29	20 33	20 41	20 56
	d	18 27	18 31	18 34	18 40	18 52	18 56	19 04	19 08			19 30	19 35	19 42	19 56			20 08	20 30	20 35	20 42	20 56
Swinton	d					18 58								19 48							20 48	
Moorside	d					19 01								19 51							20 51	
Walkden	d					19 04								19 54							20 54	
Atherton	d					19 10								20 00							21 00	
Hag Fold	d					19 12								20 02							21 02	
Daisy Hill	d					19 15								20 05							21 05	
Clifton	d																					
Kearsley	d				18 47																	
Farnworth	d				18 49																	
Moses Gate	d				18 52																	
Bolton	a	18 37	18 42	18 45	18 55		19 06	19 19	19 20		19 32	19 40	19 45		20 06			20 19	20 40	20 45		21 06
	d	18 37		18 46	18 56		19 07				19 33	19 40	19 45		20 07				20 40	20 45		21 07
Westhoughton	d			18 53	19 03							19 48								20 53		
Hindley	d			18 57	19 09	19 20						19 52		20 10						20 57	21 10	
Ince	d					19 23								20 13							21 13	
Wigan North Western	a															20 43						
Wigan Wallgate	a			19 02	19 18	19 30						19 57		20 20						21 02	21 20	
	d			19 03								19 59								21 03		
Pemberton	d																					
Orrell	d																					
Upholland	d																					
Rainford	d																					
Kirkby	a																					
Gathurst	d			19 08								20 03								21 08		
Appley Bridge	d			19 11								20 07								21 11		
Parbold	d			19 15								20 11								21 15		
Hoscar	d																			21 18		
Burscough Bridge	d			19 19								20 15								21 21		
New Lane	d																			21 24		
Bescar Lane	d																			21 27		
Meols Cop	d			19 27								20 23								21 32		
Southport	a			19 37								20 32								21 42		
Lostock	d	18 42					19 11						19 50						20 45			
Horwich Parkway	d	18 46					19 15						19 54		20 13				20 49			21 13
Blackrod	d	18 49											19 57						20 52			
Adlington (Lancashire)	d	18 53											20 01						20 56			
Chorley	d	18 58					19 23				19 44		20 06		20 21				21 01			21 21
Buckshaw Parkway	d	19 02					19 26						20 10		20 24				21 05			21 24
Leyland	d	19 10											20 18						21 12			
Preston 8	65,97 a	19 18					19 35				19 57		20 23		20 33	20 57			21 17			21 33
	d	19 19					19 38				19 59		20 25		20 38		20 45		21 19			21 38
Kirkham & Wesham	97 a	19 28											20 34						21 28			
Poulton-le-Fylde	97 a	19 36					19 56						20 42		20 56				21 36			21 56
Layton	97 a	19 43											20 47						21 40			
Blackpool North	97 a	19 50					20 05						20 54		21 05				21 48			22 05
Lancaster 6	65 a										20 14						21 08					
	d									19 24	20 15						21 11					
Oxenholme Lake District	65 a																					
Windermere	83 a																					
Carnforth	d									19a33	20 23						21 21					
Silverdale	d										20 29						21 27					
Arnside	d										20 33						21 32					
Grange-over-Sands	d										20 39						21 38					
Kents Bank	d										20 42						21 41					
Cark	d										20 47						21 45					
Ulverston	d										20 55						21 53					
Dalton	d										21 03						22 02					
Roose	d										21 09						22 08					
Barrow-in-Furness	a										21 18						22 17					

A To Blackburn B To Clitheroe C From Morecambe to Leeds

The Sunday service between Manchester Victoria and Wigan Wallgate via Atherton is funded by TfGM and will operate whilst funding exists

Table 82

Saturdays

14 December to 28 December

Manchester - Bolton - Wigan, Kirkby, Southport, Preston, Blackpool North and Barrow-in-Furness

Network Diagram - see first Page of Table 82

			NT	TP	NT	NT	NT	TP	NT	TP	NT	NT	NT	TP	NT	NT	NT	NT
				◇1				◇1		◇1				◇1				
			A						A							B		
Manchester Airport	85 ✈	d				21 03		21 29		22 00		22 19		22 29				
Heald Green	85	d						21 33						22 33				
Buxton	86	d																
Hazel Grove	86	d																
Stockport	84	d													22 40			
Manchester Piccadilly 10	⇌	d				21 20		21 46		22 16		22 35		22 46	22 54			
Manchester Oxford Road		d				21 24		21 49		22 19		22 39		22 49	22 58			
Deansgate	⇌	d				21 26		21 51				22 41		22 51	23 00			
Rochdale	41	d																
Manchester Victoria	⇌	d	21 00		21 22		21 35		22 00		22 22		22 45			23 05	23 16	23 20
Salford Central		d	21 03		21 25		21 38		22 03		22 25		22 48			23 08	23 19	23 23
Salford Crescent		a	21 07		21 30	21 34	21 41	21 56	22 07		22 29	22 46	22 51	22 56	23 03	23 11	23 22	23 26
		d	21 08		21 30	21 35	21 42	21 56	22 08		22 30	22 46	22 52	22 56	23 05	23 12	23 22	23 26
Swinton		d					21 48						22 58					23 33
Moorside		d					21 51						23 01					23 35
Walkden		d					21 54						23 04					23 39
Atherton		d					22 00						23 10					23 44
Hag Fold		d					22 02						23 12					23 47
Daisy Hill		d					22 05						23 15					23 50
Clifton		d																
Kearsley		d													23 12			
Farnworth		d													23 14			
Moses Gate		d													23 17			
Bolton		a	21 19		21 40	21 45		22 06	22 19	22 32	22 40	22 56		23 06	23 20	23 23	23 32	
		d			21 40	21 45		22 07		22 32	22 40	22 57		23 07	23 21		23 33	
Westhoughton		d				21 53						23 04			23 28			
Hindley		d				21 57	22 10					23 08	23 20		23 32			23 54
Ince		d					22 13						23 23					23 57
Wigan North Western		a																
Wigan Wallgate		a				22 02	22 20					23 13	23 30		23 41			00 04
		d				22 03						23 15						
Pemberton		d																
Orrell		d																
Upholland		d																
Rainford		d																
Kirkby		a																
Gathurst		d				22 08						23 19						
Appley Bridge		d				22 11						23 23						
Parbold		d				22 15						23 27						
Hoscar		d																
Burscough Bridge		d				22 20						23 31						
New Lane		d																
Bescar Lane		d																
Meols Cop		d				22 27						23 39						
Southport		a				22 37						23 48						
Lostock		d			21 45						22 45						23 38	
Horwich Parkway		d			21 49			22 13			22 49			23 13			23 42	
Blackrod		d			21 52						22 52						23 45	
Adlington (Lancashire)		d			21 56						22 56						23 49	
Chorley		d			22 01			22 21			23 01			23 21			23 54	
Buckshaw Parkway		d			22 04			22 24			23 05			23 24			23 57	
Leyland		d			22 12						23 12						00 04	
Preston 8	65,97	a			22 17			22 35		22 53	23 17			23 33			00 10	
		d		21 47	22 19			22 38		22 55	23 19			23 35			00 11	
Kirkham & Wesham	97	a			22 28						23 28						00 21	
Poulton-le-Fylde	97	a			22 36			22 55			23 36			23 52			00 29	
Layton	97	a			22 42						23 40						00 34	
Blackpool North	97	a			22 50			23 04			23 48			00 01			00 40	
Lancaster 6	65	a		22 02						23 10								
		d		22 03						23 11								
Oxenholme Lake District	65	a																
Windermere	83	a																
Carnforth		d		22 11						23 19								
Silverdale		d		22 17						23 25								
Arnside		d		22 21						23 29								
Grange-over-Sands		d		22 27						23 35								
Kents Bank		d		22 30						23 38								
Cark		d		22 35						23 43								
Ulverston		d		22 43						23 51								
Dalton		d		22 51						23 59								
Roose		d		22 57						00 05								
Barrow-in-Furness		a		23 06						00 14								

A To Clitheroe

B To Blackburn

The Sunday service between Manchester Victoria and Wigan Wallgate via Atherton is funded by TfGM and will operate whilst funding exists

Table 82

Saturdays

4 January to 8 February

Manchester - Bolton - Wigan, Kirkby, Southport, Preston, Blackpool North and Barrow-in-Furness

Network Diagram - see first Page of Table 82

	NT	TP	TP	TP	TP	NT	TP	NT	NT		TP	NT	NT	NT	NT	TP	NT	NT	NT		NT	NT	NT	NT
		◇1	◇1	◇1	1		◇1				◇1					◇1								
	A		B			C	D 🛒								C	E 🛒	F	G	H			A		I
Manchester Airport 85 ✈ d		00 01		05 29			05 58				06 18					07 00								
Heald Green 85 d							06 02																	
Buxton 86 d															05 59									
Hazel Grove 86 d															06 33									
Stockport 84 d															06 41									
Manchester Piccadilly 10 ⇌ d		00 16		05 44			06 13				06 33				06 53	07 15								
Manchester Oxford Road d				05 47			06 17				06 36				06 57	07 18								
Deansgate ⇌ d															06 59									
Rochdale 41 d																								
Manchester Victoria ⇌ d						05 55		06 00	06 17				06 38	06 45					07 01		07 06		07 17	07 23
Salford Central d													06 40	06 48					07 04		07 09		07 19	07 26
Salford Crescent a				05 52		05 59		06 04	06 23		06 41		06 44	06 51	07 02				07 07		07 12		07 24	07 29
d				05 52		06 00		06 05	06 24		06 41		06 45	06 52	07 03				07 08		07 13		07 25	07 30
Swinton d														06 58					07 14					
Moorside d																			07 17					
Walkden d														07 03					07 20					
Atherton d														07 08					07 26					
Hag Fold d																			07 28					
Daisy Hill d														07 12					07 31					
Clifton d																								
Kearsley d													06 52											
Farnworth d													06 54											
Moses Gate d													06 57											
Bolton a		00s30		06 02		06 11		06 15	06 34		06 51		07 00		07 16						07 23		07 35	07 41
d				06 03				06 15	06 34		06 52		07 01								07 23		07 35	
Westhoughton d								06 23													07 31	←		
Hindley d								06 27						07 16					07 39		07 35	07 39		
Ince d																			↪			07 42		
Wigan North Western a							06 42						07 19			07 43								
Wigan Wallgate a								06 32						07 21							07 40	07 45		
d								06 34				06 37		07 23							07 41	07 46		
Pemberton d								06 38														07 50		
Orrell d								06 42														07 54		
Upholland d								06 45														07 58		
Rainford d								06 49														08 01		
Kirkby a								07 01														08 13		
Gathurst d												06 41		07 27							07 46			
Appley Bridge d												06 45		07 31							07 49			
Parbold d												06 49		07 35							07 53			
Hoscar d												06 52									07 56			
Burscough Bridge d												06 55		07 39							07 59			
New Lane d												06 57									08 02			
Bescar Lane d												07 01									08 05			
Meols Cop d												07 06		07 47							08 10			
Southport a												07 15		07 56							08 20			
Lostock d									06 39														07 42	
Horwich Parkway d				06 10					06 43		06 58												07 46	
Blackrod d									06 46														07 49	
Adlington (Lancashire) d									06 50														07 53	
Chorley d	00 03			06 17					06 55		07 06												07 58	
Buckshaw Parkway d	00 07			06 21					06 59		07 09												08 01	
Leyland d	00 14			06 27					07 06														08 08	
Preston 8 65,97 a	00 19	01s04		06 32			06 56		07 11		07 18					07 57							08 14	
d	00 21			06 35			06 57		07 13		07 20					07 58							08 15	
Kirkham & Wesham 97 a	00 30			06 44					07 22														08 25	
Poulton-le-Fylde 97 a	00 38			06 54					07 30														08 33	
Layton 97 a	00 43			06 58					07 34														08 37	
Blackpool North 97 a	00 50	01 29		07 05					07 41														08 44	
Lancaster 6 65 a							07 13				07 35					08 14								
d					05 45		07 13				07 36						08 23	09 02						
Oxenholme Lake District 65 a					06 20		07 27																	
Windermere 83 a					06 40																			
Carnforth d											07 44						08a32	09 11						
Silverdale d											07 50							09 17						
Arnside d											07 54							09 21						
Grange-over-Sands d											08 00							09 27						
Kents Bank d											08 03							09 31						
Cark d											08 08							09 35						
Ulverston d			00 07								08 16							09 44						
Dalton d			00 15								08 24							09 52						
Roose d			00 21								08 30							09 58						
Barrow-in-Furness a			00 30								08 39							10 06						

A From Manchester Victoria
B From Manchester Airport
C To Clitheroe
D To Edinburgh
E To Glasgow Central
F To Leeds
G From Morecambe to Carlisle
H To Kirkby
I To Blackburn

The Sunday service between Manchester Victoria and Wigan Wallgate via Atherton is funded by TfGM and will operate whilst funding exists

Table 82

Saturdays

4 January to 8 February

Manchester - Bolton - Wigan, Kirkby, Southport, Preston, Blackpool North and Barrow-in-Furness

Network Diagram - see first Page of Table 82

			TP	NT	NT	NT	NT	NT	NT	TP	NT	NT	NT	NT	NT	TP	NT	TP	NT	NT	NT	NT	TP	TP
			◇1							◇1						◇1		◇1					◇1	
			A			B	C		D				E	F				G	B			H	I	
			🚲																				🚲	
Manchester Airport	85 ✈	d	07 25							07 56		08 01				08 25							09 00	
Heald Green	85	d	07 29									08 05				08 29								
Buxton	86	d															07 59							
Hazel Grove	86	d			07 32												08 33							
Stockport	84	d			07 40												08 41							
Manchester Piccadilly 10	⛴	d	07 45		07 54					08 15		08 22				08 46	08 54						09 16	
Manchester Oxford Road		d			07 57					08 19		08 26				08 49	08 58						09 19	
Deansgate	⛴	d			07 59							08 28				08 51	09 00							
Rochdale	41	d												08 00										
Manchester Victoria	⛴	d		07 27		08 00	08 03	08 11			08 22		08 29	08 33	08 46				09 00	09 07	09 10			
Salford Central		d		07 30		08 03	08 08	08 14			08 25		08 32	08 36	08 49				09 03	09 10	09 13			
Salford Crescent		a		07 32	08 04	08 07	08 12	08 17			08 29	08 33	08 37	08 40	08 52	08 56	09 04		09 07	09 13	09 16		09 24	
		d		07 32	08 04	08 08	08 13	08 17			08 30	08 34	08 37	08 41	08 53	08 56	09 04		09 08	09 13	09 17		09 24	
Swinton		d					08 19								08 59						09 23			
Moorside		d					08 22														09 26			
Walkden		d		07 42			08 25								09 04						09 29			
Atherton		d		07 48			08 31								09 09						09 35			
Hag Fold		d					08 33														09 37			
Daisy Hill		d		07 51			08 36								09 13						09 40			
Clifton		d																						
Kearsley		d												08 47										
Farnworth		d												08 49										
Moses Gate		d												08 52										
Bolton		a	07 59		08 14	08 19		08 27		08 32	08 40	08 44	08 49	08 55		09 06	09 14		09 19	09 23			09 34	
		d	07 59		08 15			08 28		08 33	08 40	08 45		08 56		09 07	09 15			09 24			09 35	
Westhoughton		d						08 35	←			08 53								09 31				
Hindley		d					08 41	08 39	08 41						09 17					09 35	09 45			
Ince		d					→		08 44												09 48			
Wigan North Western		a																						
Wigan Wallgate		a		08 03				08 48	08 50			09 00		09 14	09 22					09 44	09 51			
		d							08 51			09 05			09 24						09 52			
Pemberton		d							08 55												09 56			
Orrell		d							08 59												10 00			
Upholland		d							09 03												10 04			
Rainford		d							09 06												10 07			
Kirkby		a							09 18												10 19			
Gathurst		d													09 28									
Appley Bridge		d										09 11			09 32									
Parbold		d										09 15			09 36									
Hoscar		d													09 39									
Burscough Bridge		d										09 20			09 42									
New Lane		d													09 44									
Bescar Lane		d													09 48									
Meols Cop		d													09 53									
Southport		a										09 36			10 02									
Lostock		d			08 20						08 45						09 20							
Horwich Parkway		d			08 24					08 39	08 49						09 24							
Blackrod		d									08 52													
Adlington (Lancashire)		d			08 29						08 56													
Chorley		d	08 11		08 34					08 47	09 01					09 19	09 32							
Buckshaw Parkway		d			08 37						09 05						09 35							
Leyland		d			08 43						09 12						09 42							
Preston 8	65,97	a	08 22		08 50					08 58	09 17					09 30	09 50						09 55	
		d	08 24							08 59	09 19					09 32		09 45					09 59	10 09
Kirkham & Wesham	97	a									09 28													
Poulton-le-Fylde	97	a								09 16	09 36													10 26
Layton	97	a									09 43													
Blackpool North	97	a								09 25	09 50													10 35
Lancaster 6	65	a	08 39													09 47		10 00					10 14	
		d														09 48		10 01				10 49		
Oxenholme Lake District	65	a														10 03								
Windermere	83	a														10 27								
Carnforth		d																10 09				10a58		
Silverdale		d																10 15						
Arnside		d																10 19						
Grange-over-Sands		d																10 25						
Kents Bank		d																10 28						
Cark		d																10 33						
Ulverston		d																10 41						
Dalton		d																10 49						
Roose		d																10 55						
Barrow-in-Furness		a																11 04						

A To Edinburgh
B To Clitheroe
C To Kirkby
D From Manchester Victoria
E To Blackburn
F From Hebden Bridge
G From Blackpool North
H From Morecambe to Leeds
I To Glasgow Central

The Sunday service between Manchester Victoria and Wigan Wallgate via Atherton is funded by TfGM and will operate whilst funding exists

Table 82

Saturdays

4 January to 8 February

Manchester - Bolton - Wigan, Kirkby, Southport, Preston, Blackpool North and Barrow-in-Furness

Network Diagram - see first Page of Table 82

		NT	NT	NT	NT	NT	TP		NT	NT	TP	NT	NT	NT	NT	NT	NT	NT	NT	TP	NT	NT
							◇1				◇1									◇1		
				A						B	C	D					A					B
											🚲											
Manchester Airport 85 ✈	d		09 03				09 29				10 00					10 03				10 29		
Heald Green 85	d						09 33													10 33		
Buxton 86	d																					
Hazel Grove 86	d								09 33												10 33	
Stockport 84	d								09 41												10 41	
Manchester Piccadilly 10	d		09 22				09 46		09 54		10 16					10 22				10 46	10 54	
Manchester Oxford Road	d		09 26				09 49		09 58		10 19					10 26				10 49	10 58	
Deansgate	d		09 28				09 51		10 00							10 28				10 51	11 00	
Rochdale 41	d				09 04													10 05				
Manchester Victoria	d	09 22		09 29	09 33	09 46				10 00			10 07	10 10	10 22		10 29	10 33	10 46			11 00
Salford Central	d	09 25		09 32	09 36	09 49				10 03			10 10	10 13	10 25		10 32	10 36	10 49			11 03
Salford Crescent	a	09 29	09 33	09 37	09 39	09 52	09 56		10 04	10 07			10 13	10 16	10 29	10 33	10 37	10 39	10 52	10 56	11 04	11 07
	d	09 30	09 34	09 37	09 41	09 53	09 56		10 04	10 08			10 13	10 17	10 30	10 34	10 37	10 40	10 53	10 56	11 04	11 08
Swinton	d					09 59								10 23					10 59			
Moorside	d													10 26								
Walkden	d					10 04								10 29					11 04			
Atherton	d					10 09								10 35					11 09			
Hag Fold	d													10 37								
Daisy Hill	d					10 13								10 40					11 13			
Clifton	d																					
Kearsley	d				09 48													10 47				
Farnworth	d				09 50													10 49				
Moses Gate	d				09 53													10 52				
Bolton	a	09 40	09 44	09 49	09 56		10 06		10 14	10 19			10 23		10 40	10 45	10 49	10 55		11 06	11 14	11 19
	d	09 40	09 45		09 57		10 07		10 15				10 24		10 40	10 45		10 56		11 07	11 15	
Westhoughton	d		09 53										10 31			10 53						
Hindley	d		09 57			10 17							10 35	10 45		10 57			11 17			
Ince	d													10 48								
Wigan North Western	a																					
Wigan Wallgate	a		10 02		10 14	10 22							10 44	10 51		11 02		11 13	11 22			
	d		10 03			10 24								10 52		11 03			11 24			
Pemberton	d													10 56								
Orrell	d													11 00								
Upholland	d													11 04								
Rainford	d													11 07								
Kirkby	a													11 19								
Gathurst	d					10 28													11 28			
Appley Bridge	d		10 10			10 32										11 10			11 32			
Parbold	d		10 14			10 36										11 14			11 36			
Hoscar	d																		11 39			
Burscough Bridge	d		10 18			10 40										11 18			11 42			
New Lane	d																		11 44			
Bescar Lane	d																		11 48			
Meols Cop	d					10 48													11 53			
Southport	a		10 35			10 57										11 35			12 02			
Lostock	d	09 45							10 20						10 45						11 20	
Horwich Parkway	d	09 49					10 13		10 24						10 49					11 13	11 24	
Blackrod	d	09 52													10 52							
Adlington (Lancashire)	d	09 56													10 56							
Chorley	d	10 01					10 21		10 32						11 01					11 21	11 32	
Buckshaw Parkway	d	10 05					10 24		10 35						11 05					11 24	11 35	
Leyland	d	10 12							10 42						11 12						11 42	
Preston 8 65,97	a	10 17					10 33		10 50		10 56				11 17					11 33	11 50	
	d	10 19					10 38	10 45			10 57				11 19					11 38		
Kirkham & Wesham 97	a	10 28													11 28							
Poulton-le-Fylde 97	a	10 36					10 56								11 36					11 56		
Layton 97	a	10 40													11 43							
Blackpool North 97	a	10 50					11 05								11 50					12 05		
Lancaster 6 65	a							11 00			11 13											
	d							11 01				11 28										
Oxenholme Lake District 65	a							11 17														
Windermere 83	a							11 39														
Carnforth	d											11 37										
Silverdale	d											11 43										
Arnside	d											11 48										
Grange-over-Sands	d											11 54										
Kents Bank	d											11 57										
Cark	d											12 02										
Ulverston	d											12 10										
Dalton	d											12 18										
Roose	d											12 24										
Barrow-in-Furness	a											12 32										

A To Blackburn
B To Clitheroe
C To Edinburgh
D To Carlisle

The Sunday service between Manchester Victoria and Wigan Wallgate via Atherton is funded by TfGM and will operate whilst funding exists

Table 82

Saturdays
4 January to 8 February

Manchester - Bolton - Wigan, Kirkby, Southport, Preston, Blackpool North and Barrow-in-Furness

Network Diagram - see first Page of Table 82

		TP	VT	NT	NT	NT	NT	NT		NT	TP	NT	NT	TP	TP	NT	NT	NT		NT	NT	NT	TP	NT	TP
		◇1									◇1			◇1									◇1		◇1
			A										B												
			🚌											🛒	🚌										🛒
Manchester Airport 85 ✈	d	11 00					11 03				11 29			12 00						12 03			12 29		13 00
Heald Green 85	d										11 33												12 33		
Buxton 86	d																								
Hazel Grove 86	d											11 33												12 33	
Stockport 84	d											11 41												12 41	
Manchester Piccadilly 10 🚊	d	11 16					11 22				11 46	11 54		12 16						12 22			12 46	12 54	13 16
Manchester Oxford Road	d	11 19					11 26				11 49	11 58		12 19						12 26			12 49	12 58	13 19
Deansgate 🚊	d						11 28				11 51	12 00								12 28			12 51	13 00	
Rochdale 41	d							11 04													12 04				
Manchester Victoria 🚊	d			11 07	11 10	11 22		11 33		11 46			12 00			12 07	12 10	12 22			12 33	12 46			
Salford Central	d			11 10	11 13	11 25		11 36		11 49			12 03			12 10	12 13	12 25			12 36	12 49			
Salford Crescent	a			11 13	11 16	11 29	11 33	11 39		11 52	11 56	12 04	12 07			12 13	12 16	12 29		12 33	12 39	12 52	12 56	13 04	
	d			11 13	11 17	11 30	11 34	11 40		11 53	11 56	12 04	12 08			12 13	12 17	12 30		12 34	12 40	12 53	12 56	13 04	
Swinton	d				11 23					11 59							12 23					12 59			
Moorside	d				11 26												12 26								
Walkden	d				11 29					12 04							12 29					13 04			
Atherton	d				11 35					12 09							12 35					13 09			
Hag Fold	d				11 37												12 37								
Daisy Hill	d				11 40					12 13							12 40					13 13			
Clifton	d																								
Kearsley	d							11 47													12 47				
Farnworth	d							11 49													12 49				
Moses Gate	d							11 52													12 52				
Bolton	a			11 23		11 40	11 45	11 55			12 06	12 14	12 19			12 23		12 40		12 45	12 55		13 06	13 14	
	d			11 24		11 40	11 45	11 56			12 07	12 15				12 24		12 40		12 45	12 56		13 07	13 15	
Westhoughton	d			11 31			11 53									12 31				12 53					
Hindley	d			11 35	11 45		11 57			12 17						12 35	12 45			12 57		13 17			
Ince	d				11 48												12 48								
Wigan North Western	a	11 43												12 43											13 43
Wigan Wallgate	a			11 44	11 51		12 02	12 13		12 22						12 44	12 51			13 02	13 13	13 22			
	d				11 52		12 03			12 24							12 52			13 03		13 24			
Pemberton	d				11 56												12 56								
Orrell	d				12 00												13 00								
Upholland	d				12 04												13 04								
Rainford	d				12 07												13 07								
Kirkby	a				12 19												13 19								
Gathurst	d									12 28												13 28			
Appley Bridge	d						12 10			12 32										13 10		13 32			
Parbold	d						12 14			12 36										13 14		13 36			
Hoscar	d																					13 39			
Burscough Bridge	d						12 18			12 41										13 18		13 42			
New Lane	d																					13 44			
Bescar Lane	d																					13 48			
Meols Cop	d									12 49												13 53			
Southport	a						12 35			12 59										13 35		14 02			
Lostock	d					11 45						12 20						12 45						13 20	
Horwich Parkway	d					11 49					12 13	12 24						12 49					13 13	13 24	
Blackrod	d					11 52												12 52							
Adlington (Lancashire)	d					11 56												12 56							
Chorley	d					12 01					12 21	12 32						13 01					13 21	13 32	
Buckshaw Parkway	d					12 05					12 24	12 35						13 05					13 24	13 35	
Leyland	d					12 12						12 42						13 12						13 42	
Preston 8 65,97	a	11 57				12 17					12 33	12 50		12 57				13 17					13 33	13 50	13 57
	d	11 58				12 19					12 38			12 58				13 19					13 38		13 58
Kirkham & Wesham 97	a					12 28												13 28							
Poulton-le-Fylde 97	a					12 36					12 56							13 36					13 56		
Layton 97	a					12 43												13 43							
Blackpool North 97	a					12 50					13 05							13 50					14 05		
Lancaster 6 65	a	12 14												13 15											14 15
	d	12 15	12 20												12 25										
Oxenholme Lake District 65	a		13 05																						
Windermere 83	a														13 12										
Carnforth	d	12 22																							
Silverdale	d																								
Arnside	d	12 30																							
Grange-over-Sands	d	12 36																							
Kents Bank	d																								
Cark	d																								
Ulverston	d	12 48																							
Dalton	d																								
Roose	d																								
Barrow-in-Furness	a	13 09																							

A To Carlisle

B To Clitheroe

The Sunday service between Manchester Victoria and Wigan Wallgate via Atherton is funded by TfGM and will operate whilst funding exists

Table 82

Saturdays

4 January to 8 February

Manchester - Bolton - Wigan, Kirkby, Southport, Preston, Blackpool North and Barrow-in-Furness

Network Diagram - see first Page of Table 82

Station		VT	NT	NT	NT	TP	NT	NT	VT	TP	TP	NT	NT	NT	NT	TP	NT	NT	TP	VT	NT	NT
																◇1			◇1			
		A	B				A	C	A									B		A		
Manchester Airport 85 ✈	d												13 03			13 29			14 00			
Heald Green 85	d															13 33						
Buxton 86	d																					
Hazel Grove 86	d																13 33					
Stockport 84	d																13 41					
Manchester Piccadilly 10	d												13 22			13 46	13 54		14 16			
Manchester Oxford Road	d												13 26			13 49	13 58		14 19			
Deansgate	d												13 28			13 51	14 00					
Rochdale 41	d													13 04								
Manchester Victoria	d		13 00	13 07	13 10							13 22		13 33	13 46			14 00			14 07	14 10
Salford Central	d		13 03	13 10	13 13							13 25		13 36	13 49			14 03			14 10	14 13
Salford Crescent	a		13 07	13 13	13 16							13 29	13 33	13 39	13 52	13 56	14 04	14 07			14 13	14 16
	d		13 08	13 13	13 17							13 30	13 34	13 40	13 53	13 56	14 04	14 08			14 13	14 17
Swinton	d				13 23										13 59							14 23
Moorside	d				13 26																	14 26
Walkden	d				13 29										14 04							14 29
Atherton	d				13 35										14 09							14 35
Hag Fold	d				13 37																	14 37
Daisy Hill	d				13 40										14 13							14 40
Clifton	d																					
Kearsley	d													13 47								
Farnworth	d													13 49								
Moses Gate	d													13 52								
Bolton	a		13 19	13 23								13 40	13 45	13 55		14 06	14 14	14 19			14 23	
	d			13 24								13 40	13 45	13 56		14 07	14 15				14 24	
Westhoughton	d			13 31									13 53								14 31	
Hindley	d			13 35	13 45								13 57		14 17						14 35	14 45
Ince	d				13 48																	14 48
Wigan North Western	a																		14 43			
Wigan Wallgate	a			13 44	13 51								14 02	14 13	14 22						14 44	14 51
	d				13 52								14 03		14 24							14 52
Pemberton	d				13 56																	14 56
Orrell	d				14 00																	15 00
Upholland	d				14 04																	15 04
Rainford	d				14 07																	15 07
Kirkby	a				14 19																	15 19
Gathurst	d														14 28							
Appley Bridge	d												14 10		14 32							
Parbold	d												14 14		14 36							
Hoscar	d																					
Burscough Bridge	d												14 18		14 41							
New Lane	d																					
Bescar Lane	d																					
Meols Cop	d														14 49							
Southport	a												14 35		14 59							
Lostock	d											13 45					14 20					
Horwich Parkway	d											13 49				14 13	14 24					
Blackrod	d											13 52										
Adlington (Lancashire)	d											13 56										
Chorley	d											14 01				14 21	14 32					
Buckshaw Parkway	d											14 05				14 24	14 35					
Leyland	d											14 12					14 42					
Preston 8 65,97	a											14 17				14 33	14 50		14 57			
	d									14 06		14 19				14 38			14 58			
Kirkham & Wesham 97	a											14 28										
Poulton-le-Fylde 97	a											14 36				14 56						
Layton 97	a											14 42										
Blackpool North 97	a											14 50				15 05						
Lancaster 6 65	a									14 21									15 15			
	d	13 05				13 25	13 32	13 48	14 05	14 22	14 25									15 05		
Oxenholme Lake District 65	a	13 50							14 50											15 50		
Windermere 83	a					14 12					15 12											
Carnforth	d						13 41	13a58		14 30												
Silverdale	d						13 47															
Arnside	d						13 52			14 39												
Grange-over-Sands	d						13 58			14 44												
Kents Bank	d						14 01															
Cark	d						14 06															
Ulverston	d						14 14			14 57												
Dalton	d						14 22															
Roose	d						14 28															
Barrow-in-Furness	a						14 36			15 17												

A To Carlisle **B** To Clitheroe **C** From Heysham Harbour to Leeds

The Sunday service between Manchester Victoria and Wigan Wallgate via Atherton is funded by TfGM and will operate whilst funding exists

Table 82

Saturdays

4 January to 8 February

Manchester - Bolton - Wigan, Kirkby, Southport, Preston, Blackpool North and Barrow-in-Furness

Network Diagram - see first Page of Table 82

	NT	NT	NT	NT	TP	NT	NT	NT	NT	NT	NT	TP	VT	TP	TP	NT	NT	NT	NT	TP	NT	NT
					◇1		A					bus	B bus	◇1	bus			A		◇1		
Manchester Airport 85 ✈ d		14 03			14 29									15 00		15 03				15 29		
Heald Green 85 d					14 33															15 33		
Buxton 86 d																						
Hazel Grove 86 d						14 33															15 33	
Stockport 84 d						14 41															15 41	
Manchester Piccadilly 10 d		14 22			14 46	14 54								15 16		15 22				15 46	15 54	
Manchester Oxford Road d		14 26			14 49	14 58								15 19		15 26				15 49	15 58	
Deansgate d		14 28			14 51	15 00										15 28				15 51	16 00	
Rochdale 41 d			14 04														15 04					
Manchester Victoria d	14 22		14 33	14 46			15 00	15 07	15 10		15 22						15 33	15 40	15 46			16 07
Salford Central d	14 25		14 36	14 49			15 03	15 10	15 13		15 25						15 36	15 43	15 49			16 10
Salford Crescent a	14 29	14 33	14 39	14 52	14 56	15 04	15 08	15 13	15 16		15 29					15 33	15 39	15 46	15 52	15 56	16 04	16 13
d	14 30	14 34	14 40	14 53	14 56	15 04	15 08	15 13	15 17		15 30					15 34	15 40	15 47	15 53	15 56	16 04	16 13
Swinton d				14 59					15 23										15 59			
Moorside d									15 26													
Walkden d				15 04					15 29										16 04			
Atherton d				15 09					15 35										16 09			
Hag Fold d									15 37													
Daisy Hill d				15 13					15 40										16 13			
Clifton d																						
Kearsley d			14 47														15 47					
Farnworth d			14 49														15 49					
Moses Gate d			14 52														15 52					
Bolton a	14 40	14 45	14 55		15 06	15 14	15 19	15 23			15 40					15 45	15 55	15 59		16 06	16 14	16 23
d	14 40	14 45	14 56		15 07	15 15		15 24			15 40					15 45	15 56			16 07	16 15	16 24
Westhoughton d		14 53						15 31								15 53						16 31
Hindley d		14 57		15 17				15 35	15 45							15 57			16 17			16 35
Ince d									15 48													
Wigan North Western a														15 43								
Wigan Wallgate a		15 02	15 13	15 22				15 44	15 51							16 02	16 13		16 22			16 44
d		15 03		15 24					15 52							16 03			16 24			
Pemberton d									15 56													
Orrell d									16 00													
Upholland d									16 04													
Rainford d									16 07													
Kirkby a									16 19													
Gathurst d				15 28												16 08			16 28			
Appley Bridge d		15 10		15 32												16 11			16 32			
Parbold d		15 14		15 36												16 15			16 36			
Hoscar d																16 18						
Burscough Bridge d		15 18		15 40												16 21			16 40			
New Lane d																16 24						
Bescar Lane d																16 27						
Meols Cop d				15 48												16 32			16 48			
Southport a		15 35		15 57												16 42			16 57			
Lostock d	14 45					15 20					15 45									16 11	16 20	
Horwich Parkway d	14 49				15 13	15 24					15 49									16 15	16 24	
Blackrod d	14 52										15 52											
Adlington (Lancashire) d	14 56										15 56											
Chorley d	15 01				15 21	15 32					16 01									16 23	16 32	
Buckshaw Parkway d	15 05				15 24	15 35					16 05									16 26	16 35	
Leyland d	15 12					15 42					16 12										16 42	
Preston 8 65,97 a	15 17				15 33	15 50					16 19			15 57						16 35	16 50	
d	15 19				15 38									15 58						16 38		
Kirkham & Wesham 97 a	15 28																			16 47		
Poulton-le-Fylde 97 a	15 36				15 56															16 57		
Layton 97 a	15 43																			17 00		
Blackpool North 97 a	15 50				16 05															17 07		
Lancaster 6 65 a														16 14								
d										15 20		15 25	16 05	16 15	16 25							
Oxenholme Lake District 65 a													16 50									
Windermere 83 a												16 12			17 12							
Carnforth d										15 30				16 23								
Silverdale d										15 36				16 29								
Arnside d										15 40				16 33								
Grange-over-Sands d										15 46				16 39								
Kents Bank d										15 50				16 42								
Cark d										15 54				16 47								
Ulverston d										16 03				16 55								
Dalton d										16 11				17 03								
Roose d										16 19				17 09								
Barrow-in-Furness a										16 25				17 18								

A To Clitheroe

B To Carlisle

The Sunday service between Manchester Victoria and Wigan Wallgate via Atherton is funded by TfGM and will operate whilst funding exists

Table 82

Saturdays

4 January to 8 February

Manchester - Bolton - Wigan, Kirkby, Southport, Preston, Blackpool North and Barrow-in-Furness

Network Diagram - see first Page of Table 82

		TP	NT	NT	NT	NT	NT	NT	NT	NT	VT	TP	NT	TP		VT	NT	TP	TP	NT	NT	NT	NT
		◇1	A			B				C	D			◇1		D		◇1		B			
Manchester Airport 85 ✈	d	16 00					16 03							16 29				17 00					
Heald Green 85	d													16 33									
Buxton 86	d																						
Hazel Grove 86	d																16 30						
Stockport 84	d																16 41						
Manchester Piccadilly 10	d	16 16					16 22							16 46			16 54	17 15					
Manchester Oxford Road	d	16 19					16 26							16 49			16 58	17 18					
Deansgate	d						16 28							16 51			17 00						
Rochdale 41	d							16 04															
Manchester Victoria	d			16 10	16 20	16 23		16 36	16 46											17 00	17 07	17 10	17 20
Salford Central	d			16 13	16 23	16 26		16 39	16 49											17 03	17 10	17 13	17 23
Salford Crescent	a			16 16	16 26	16 30	16 34	16 42	16 52					16 56			17 04			17 07	17 13	17 17	17 26
	d			16 17	16 27	16 31	16 34	16 43	16 53					16 56			17 04			17 08	17 13	17 17	17 27
Swinton	d			16 23					16 59													17 23	
Moorside	d			16 26					17 02													17 26	
Walkden	d			16 29					17 05													17 29	
Atherton	d			16 35					17 11													17 35	
Hag Fold	d			16 37					17 14													17 37	
Daisy Hill	d			16 40					17 17													17 41	
Clifton	d																						
Kearsley	d							16 50															
Farnworth	d							16 52															
Moses Gate	d							16 55															
Bolton	a	16 32			16 37	16 42	16 45	16 58						17 06			17 14			17 19	17 23		17 37
	d	16 33			16 37		16 46	16 59						17 07			17 15				17 24		17 37
Westhoughton	d						16 53	17 06													17 31		
Hindley	d			16 45			16 57	17 10	17 21												17 35	17 45	
Ince	d			16 48					17 24													17 48	
Wigan North Western	a																						
Wigan Wallgate	a			16 51			17 02	17 19	17 27												17 44	17 51	
	d			16 52			17 03		17 29													17 52	
Pemberton	d			16 56																		17 56	
Orrell	d			17 00																		18 00	
Upholland	d			17 04																		18 04	
Rainford	d			17 07																		18 07	
Kirkby	a			17 19																		18 19	
Gathurst	d						17 08		17 33														
Appley Bridge	d						17 11		17 37														
Parbold	d						17 15		17 41														
Hoscar	d																						
Burscough Bridge	d						17 20		17 45														
New Lane	d																						
Bescar Lane	d																						
Meols Cop	d						17 27		17 53														
Southport	a						17 37		18 02														
Lostock	d				16 43												17 20						17 43
Horwich Parkway	d				16 47									17 13			17 24						17 47
Blackrod	d				16 51																		17 51
Adlington (Lancashire)	d				16 55																		17 55
Chorley	d	16 45			17 00									17 21			17 32						18 00
Buckshaw Parkway	d				17 04									17 24			17 35						18 03
Leyland	d				17 11												17 42						18 11
Preston 8 65,97	a	16 56			17 19									17 33			17 50	17 56					18 16
	d	16 58			17 20									17 38	17 45			17 57					18 18
Kirkham & Wesham 97	a				17 30									17 47									18 27
Poulton-le-Fylde 97	a				17 38									17 57									18 35
Layton 97	a				17 43									18 00									18 39
Blackpool North 97	a				17 50									18 08									18 46
Lancaster 6 65	a	17 15													18 00			18 14					
	d		16 40							17 00	17 05	17 25	17 36		18 01	18 05			18 25				
Oxenholme Lake District 65	a										17 50					18 50							
Windermere 83	a											18 12							19 12				
Carnforth	d		16a49							17 10			17 45		18 09								
Silverdale	d									17 17			17 51		18 15								
Arnside	d									17 21			17 56		18 19								
Grange-over-Sands	d									17 27			18 02		18 25								
Kents Bank	d									17 31			18 05		18 28								
Cark	d									17 35			18 10		18 33								
Ulverston	d									17 44			18 18		18 41								
Dalton	d									17 53			18 26		18 49								
Roose	d									17 59			18 33		18 55								
Barrow-in-Furness	a									18 07			18 43		19 04								

A From Morecambe to Leeds
B To Clitheroe
C To Millom
D To Carlisle

The Sunday service between Manchester Victoria and Wigan Wallgate via Atherton is funded by TfGM and will operate whilst funding exists

Table 82

Saturdays

4 January to 8 February

Manchester - Bolton - Wigan, Kirkby, Southport, Preston, Blackpool North and Barrow-in-Furness

Network Diagram - see first Page of Table 82

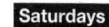

		NT		NT	NT	NT	TP		VT	NT	NT	NT		TP	NT	NT	TP	VT	NT	NT	NT	NT		NT	TP
							◇1							◇1											◇1
		A							B			C			D			B		A					
Manchester Airport 85	d			17 03			17 29							18 00							18 03				18 27
Heald Green 85	d						17 33																		18 31
Buxton 86	d																								
Hazel Grove 86	d										17 33														
Stockport 84	d										17 41														
Manchester Piccadilly 10	d			17 23			17 46				17 54			18 16							18 22				18 46
Manchester Oxford Road	d			17 26			17 49				17 58			18 19							18 27				18 49
Deansgate	d						17 51				18 00										18 29				18 51
Rochdale 41	d	17 03																		18 02					
Manchester Victoria	d	17 23			17 36	17 40				17 50		18 00				18 10			18 20	18 23		18 33		18 45	
Salford Central	d	17 26			17 39	17 43				17 53		18 03				18 13			18 23	18 26		18 36		18 48	
Salford Crescent	a	17 30		17 33	17 42	17 46	17 55			17 58	18 04	18 07				18 16			18 26	18 30	18 34	18 39		18 51	18 56
	d	17 31		17 34	17 43	17 47	17 55			17 59	18 04	18 08				18 17			18 27	18 31	18 34	18 40		18 52	18 56
Swinton	d									18 05						18 23								18 58	
Moorside	d									18 08						18 26								19 01	
Walkden	d									18 11						18 29								19 04	
Atherton	d					18 00				18 17						18 35								19 10	
Hag Fold	d									18 19						18 37								19 12	
Daisy Hill	d					18 04				18 22						18 40								19 15	
Clifton	d				17 48																				
Kearsley	d				17 53																	18 47			
Farnworth	d				17 55																	18 49			
Moses Gate	d				17 57																	18 52			
Bolton	a	17 42		17 44	18 01		18 05				18 14	18 19							18 37	18 42	18 45	18 55			19 06
	d			17 46	18 01		18 06				18 15								18 37		18 46	18 56			19 07
Westhoughton	d			17 53	18 09																18 53	19 03			
Hindley	d				18 13					18 27						18 45					18 57	19 09		19 20	
Ince	d															18 48								19 23	
Wigan North Western	a													18 43		18 56									
Wigan Wallgate	a			18 01	18 22	18 12				18 32											19 02	19 18		19 30	
	d			18 02		18 15				18 33											19 03				
Pemberton	d									18 37															
Orrell	d									18 41															
Upholland	d									18 45															
Rainford	d									18 48															
Kirkby	a									19 00															
Gathurst	d					18 20															19 08				
Appley Bridge	d			18 09		18 24															19 11				
Parbold	d			18 13		18 28															19 15				
Hoscar	d					18 31																			
Burscough Bridge	d			18 18		18 35															19 19				
New Lane	d					18 37																			
Bescar Lane	d					18 41																			
Meols Cop	d			18 26		18 46															19 27				
Southport	a			18 36		18 55															19 37				
Lostock	d						18 11				18 20								18 42						19 11
Horwich Parkway	d						18 15				18 24								18 46						19 15
Blackrod	d																		18 49						
Adlington (Lancashire)	d																		18 53						
Chorley	d						18 23				18 32								18 58						19 23
Buckshaw Parkway	d						18 26				18 35								19 02						19 26
Leyland	d										18 42								19 10						
Preston 8 65,97	a						18 35				18 48			18 57					19 18						19 35
	d						18 40	18 45			18 49			18 58				19 05	19 19						19 38
Kirkham & Wesham 97	a						18 49												19 28						
Poulton-le-Fylde 97	a						18 59												19 36						19 56
Layton 97	a						19 02												19 43						
Blackpool North 97	a						19 09				19 16								19 50						20 05
Lancaster 6 65	a							19 00						19 15				19 55							
	d							19 01	19 05						19 24		19 25	20 00							
Oxenholme Lake District 65	a								19 50									20 45							
Windermere 83	a																20 12								
Carnforth	d							19 09							19a33										
Silverdale	d							19 15																	
Arnside	d							19 19																	
Grange-over-Sands	d							19 25																	
Kents Bank	d							19 28																	
Cark	d							19 33																	
Ulverston	d							19 41																	
Dalton	d							19 49																	
Roose	d							19 55																	
Barrow-in-Furness	a							20 04																	

A To Blackburn
B To Carlisle
C To Clitheroe
D From Morecambe to Leeds

The Sunday service between Manchester Victoria and Wigan Wallgate via Atherton is funded by TfGM and will operate whilst funding exists

Table 82

Saturdays

4 January to 8 February

Manchester - Bolton - Wigan, Kirkby, Southport, Preston, Blackpool North and Barrow-in-Furness

Network Diagram - see first Page of Table 82

		NT	NT	TP	TP	NT	NT	NT		VT	NT	TP	NT	NT	NT	NT	NT	NT		TP	NT	NT	NT	TP	NT
				◇1								◇1								◇1				◇1	
			A							B			A								A				
					bus			bus		bus					bus								bus		
Manchester Airport 85 ✈	d			19 00		19 03						19 29					20 03			20 29					21 03
Heald Green 85	d											19 33								20 33					
Buxton 86	d																								
Hazel Grove 86	d	18 33																							
Stockport 84	d	18 41																							
Manchester Piccadilly 10 ⛴	d	18 54		19 16		19 20						19 46					20 20			20 46					21 20
Manchester Oxford Road	d	18 58		19 19		19 24						19 49					20 24			20 49					21 24
Deansgate ⛴	d	19 00				19 26						19 51					20 26			20 51					21 26
Rochdale 41	d																								
Manchester Victoria ⛴	d		19 00				19 28				19 35		20 00	20 22				20 35			21 00	21 22			
Salford Central	d		19 03				19 31				19 38		20 04	20 25				20 38			21 03	21 25			
Salford Crescent	a	19 04	19 08			19 29	19 34				19 41	19 56	20 07	20 29			20 33	20 41		20 56	21 07	21 30			21 34
	d	19 04	19 08			19 30	19 35				19 42	19 56	20 08	20 30			20 35	20 42		20 56	21 08	21 30			21 35
Swinton	d										19 48							20 48							
Moorside	d										19 51							20 51							
Walkden	d										19 54							20 54							
Atherton	d										20 00							21 00							
Hag Fold	d										20 02							21 02							
Daisy Hill	d										20 05							21 05							
Clifton	d																								
Kearsley	d																								
Farnworth	d																								
Moses Gate	d																								
Bolton	a	19 19	19 20	19 32		19 40	19 45					20 06	20 19	20 40			20 45			21 06	21 19	21 40			21 45
	d			19 33		19 40	19 45					20 07		20 40			20 45			21 07		21 40			21 45
Westhoughton	d					19 48											20 53								21 53
Hindley	d					19 52					20 10						20 57	21 10							21 57
Ince	d										20 13							21 13							
Wigan North Western	a																								
Wigan Wallgate	a					19 57					20 20						21 02	21 20							22 02
	d					19 59											21 03								22 03
Pemberton	d																								
Orrell	d																								
Upholland	d																								
Rainford	d																								
Kirkby	a																								
Gathurst	d					20 03											21 08								22 08
Appley Bridge	d					20 07											21 11								22 11
Parbold	d					20 11											21 15								22 15
Hoscar	d																21 18								
Burscough Bridge	d					20 15											21 21								22 20
New Lane	d																21 24								
Bescar Lane	d																21 27								
Meols Cop	d					20 23											21 32								22 27
Southport	a					20 32											21 42								22 37
Lostock	d						19 50							20 45								21 45			
Horwich Parkway	d						19 54							20 49								21 49			
Blackrod	d						19 57							20 52								21 52			
Adlington (Lancashire)	d						20 01							20 56								21 56			
Chorley	d			19 44			20a09	20 15						21a04	21 15							22a04	22 15		
Buckshaw Parkway	d							20 25							21 25								22 25		
Leyland	d							20 37							21 37								22 37		
Preston 8 65,97	a			19 57				20 57				20 37			21 57					21 36			22 57		
	d			19 59						20 05		20 38				20 45				21 38				21 47	
Kirkham & Wesham 97	a																								
Poulton-le-Fylde 97	a											20 56								21 56					
Layton 97	a																								
Blackpool North 97	a											21 05								22 03					
Lancaster 6 65	a			20 14						20 55						21 08								22 02	
	d			20 15	20 25					21 00						21 11								22 03	
Oxenholme Lake District 65	a									21 45															
Windermere 83	a				21 12																				
Carnforth	d			20 23												21 21								22 11	
Silverdale	d			20 29												21 27								22 17	
Arnside	d			20 33												21 32								22 21	
Grange-over-Sands	d			20 39												21 38								22 27	
Kents Bank	d			20 42												21 41								22 30	
Cark	d			20 47												21 45								22 35	
Ulverston	d			20 55												21 53								22 43	
Dalton	d			21 03												22 02								22 51	
Roose	d			21 09												22 08								22 57	
Barrow-in-Furness	a			21 18												22 17								23 06	

A To Clitheroe   **B** To Carlisle

The Sunday service between Manchester Victoria and Wigan Wallgate via Atherton is funded by TfGM and will operate whilst funding exists

Table 82

Saturdays

4 January to 8 February

Manchester - Bolton - Wigan, Kirkby, Southport, Preston, Blackpool North and Barrow-in-Furness

Network Diagram - see first Page of Table 82

			NT	TP	NT	NT	NT	TP	NT	NT	TP	NT	NT	NT	NT
				◇1				◇1			◇1				
					A								B		
							🚌								
Manchester Airport	85 ✈	d		21 29					22 19		22 29				
Heald Green	85	d		21 33							22 33				
Buxton	86	d													
Hazel Grove	86	d													
Stockport	84	d										22 40			
Manchester Piccadilly 10	🚊	d		21 46					22 35		22 46	22 54			
Manchester Oxford Road		d		21 49					22 39		22 49	22 58			
Deansgate	🚊	d		21 51					22 41		22 51	23 00			
Rochdale	41	d													
Manchester Victoria	🚊	d	21 35		22 00	22 22				22 45			23 05	23 16	23 20
Salford Central		d	21 38		22 03	22 25				22 48			23 08	23 19	23 23
Salford Crescent		a	21 41	21 56	22 07	22 29			22 46	22 51	22 56	23 03	23 11	23 22	23 26
		d	21 42	21 56	22 08	22 30			22 46	22 52	22 56	23 05	23 12	23 22	23 26
Swinton		d	21 48							22 58					23 33
Moorside		d	21 51							23 01					23 35
Walkden		d	21 54							23 04					23 39
Atherton		d	22 00							23 10					23 44
Hag Fold		d	22 02							23 12					23 47
Daisy Hill		d	22 05							23 15					23 50
Clifton		d													
Kearsley		d										23 12			
Farnworth		d										23 14			
Moses Gate		d										23 17			
Bolton		a		22 07	22 19	22 40			22 56		23 06	23 20	23 23	23 32	
		d				22 40			22 57		23 07	23 21		23 33	
Westhoughton		d							23 04			23 28			
Hindley		d	22 10						23 08	23 20		23 32			23 54
Ince		d	22 13							23 23					23 57
Wigan North Western		a													
Wigan Wallgate		a	22 20						23 13	23 30		23 41			00 04
		d							23 15						
Pemberton		d													
Orrell		d													
Upholland		d													
Rainford		d													
Kirkby		a													
Gathurst		d							23 19						
Appley Bridge		d							23 23						
Parbold		d							23 27						
Hoscar		d													
Burscough Bridge		d							23 31						
New Lane		d													
Bescar Lane		d													
Meols Cop		d							23 39						
Southport		a							23 48						
Lostock		d				22 45								23 38	
Horwich Parkway		d				22 49								23 42	
Blackrod		d				22 52								23 45	
Adlington (Lancashire)		d				22 56								23 49	
Chorley		d				23a04	23 15							23a56	
Buckshaw Parkway		d					23 25								
Leyland		d					23 37								
Preston 8	65,97	a					23 57				23 36				
		d						22 55			23 38				
Kirkham & Wesham	97	a													
Poulton-le-Fylde	97	a									23 55				
Layton	97	a													
Blackpool North	97	a									00 02				
Lancaster 6	65	a						23 10							
		d						23 11							
Oxenholme Lake District	65	a													
Windermere	83	a													
Carnforth		d						23 19							
Silverdale		d						23 25							
Arnside		d						23 29							
Grange-over-Sands		d						23 35							
Kents Bank		d						23 38							
Cark		d						23 43							
Ulverston		d						23 51							
Dalton		d						23 59							
Roose		d						00 05							
Barrow-in-Furness		a						00 14							

A To Clitheroe   **B** To Blackburn

The Sunday service between Manchester Victoria and Wigan Wallgate via Atherton is funded by TfGM and will operate whilst funding exists

Table 82

Saturdays
15 February to 17 May

Manchester - Bolton - Wigan, Kirkby, Southport, Preston, Blackpool North and Barrow-in-Furness

Network Diagram - see first Page of Table 82

Station		NT	TP	TP	TP	TP	TP	NT	TP	NT		NT	TP	NT	NT	NT	NT	TP	NT	NT		NT	NT	NT	NT
			◇1	◇1	◇1	◇1	1		◇1				◇1					◇1							
		A		B	C	D		E	F								E	G	H	I		J		A	
									🚲									🚲							
Manchester Airport	85 ✈ d		00 01		05 29	05 29			05 58				06 18					07 00							
Heald Green	85 d								06 02																
Buxton	86 d																05 59								
Hazel Grove	86 d																06 33								
Stockport	84 d																06 41								
Manchester Piccadilly 10	⇌ d		00 16		05 44	05 44			06 13				06 33				06 53	07 15							
Manchester Oxford Road	d				05 47	05 47			06 17				06 36				06 57	07 18							
Deansgate	⇌ d																06 59								
Rochdale	41 d																								
Manchester Victoria	⇌ d							05 55		06 00		06 17			06 38	06 45						07 01	07 06		07 17
Salford Central	d														06 40	06 48						07 04	07 09		07 19
Salford Crescent	a				05 52	05 52		05 59		06 04		06 23	06 41		06 44	06 51	07 02					07 07	07 12		07 24
	d				05 52	05 52		06 00		06 05		06 24	06 41		06 45	06 52	07 03					07 08	07 13		07 25
Swinton	d															06 58						07 14			
Moorside	d																					07 17			
Walkden	d															07 03						07 20			
Atherton	d															07 08						07 26			
Hag Fold	d																					07 28			
Daisy Hill	d															07 12						07 31			
Clifton	d																								
Kearsley	d														06 52										
Farnworth	d														06 54										
Moses Gate	d														06 57										
Bolton	a		00s30		06 02	06 02		06 11		06 15		06 34	06 51		07 00		07 16						07 23		07 35
	d				06 03	06 03				06 15		06 34	06 52		07 01								07 23		07 35
Westhoughton	d									06 23													07 31	←	
Hindley	d									06 27						07 16						07 39	07 35	07 39	
Ince	d																					→		07 42	
Wigan North Western	a								06 42						07 19			07 43							
Wigan Wallgate	a									06 32						07 21							07 40	07 45	
	d									06 34				06 37		07 23							07 41	07 46	
Pemberton	d									06 38														07 50	
Orrell	d									06 42														07 54	
Upholland	d									06 45														07 58	
Rainford	d									06 49														08 01	
Kirkby	a									07 01														08 13	
Gathurst	d													06 41		07 27							07 46		
Appley Bridge	d													06 45		07 31							07 49		
Parbold	d													06 49		07 35							07 53		
Hoscar	d													06 52									07 56		
Burscough Bridge	d													06 55		07 39							07 59		
New Lane	d													06 57									08 02		
Bescar Lane	d													07 01									08 05		
Meols Cop	d													07 06		07 47							08 10		
Southport	a													07 15		07 56							08 20		
Lostock	d											06 39													07 42
Horwich Parkway	d				06 10	06 10						06 43	06 58												07 46
Blackrod	d											06 46													07 49
Adlington (Lancashire)	d											06 50													07 53
Chorley	d	00 03			06 17	06 17						06 55	07 06												07 58
Buckshaw Parkway	d	00 07			06 21	06 21						06 59	07 09												08 01
Leyland	d	00 14				06 27						07 06													08 08
Preston 8	65,97 a	00 19	01s04		06 31	06 32			06 56			07 11	07 18					07 57							08 14
	d	00 21			06 33	06 35			06 57			07 13	07 20					07 58							08 15
Kirkham & Wesham	97 a	00 30			06 42	06 44						07 22													08 25
Poulton-le-Fylde	97 a	00 38			06 53	06 54						07 30													08 33
Layton	97 a	00 43			06 56	06 58						07 34													08 37
Blackpool North	97 a	00 50	01 29		07 03	07 05						07 41													08 44
Lancaster 6	65 a								07 13				07 35					08 14							
	d						05 45		07 13				07 36						08 23	09 02					
Oxenholme Lake District	65 a						06 20		07 27																
Windermere	83 a						06 40																		
Carnforth	d												07 44						08a32	09 11					
Silverdale	d												07 50							09 17					
Arnside	d												07 54							09 21					
Grange-over-Sands	d												08 00							09 27					
Kents Bank	d												08 03							09 31					
Cark	d												08 08							09 35					
Ulverston	d			00 07									08 16							09 44					
Dalton	d			00 15									08 24							09 52					
Roose	d			00 21									08 30							09 58					
Barrow-in-Furness	a			00 30									08 39							10 06					

A From Manchester Victoria
B From Manchester Airport
C 29 March, 3 May, 10 May, 17 May
D until 26 April, not 29 March
E To Clitheroe
F To Edinburgh
G To Glasgow Central
H To Leeds
I From Morecambe to Carlisle
J To Kirkby

The Sunday service between Manchester Victoria and Wigan Wallgate via Atherton is funded by TfGM and will operate whilst funding exists

Table 82

Saturdays

15 February to 17 May

Manchester - Bolton - Wigan, Kirkby, Southport, Preston, Blackpool North and Barrow-in-Furness

Network Diagram - see first Page of Table 82

		NT	TP	NT	NT	NT		NT	NT	NT	TP	NT	NT	NT	NT	NT		TP	NT	TP	NT	NT	TP		NT
			◇1								◇1							◇1		◇1			◇1		
		A	B			C		D		E				A	F					G	C	H	I		
			🚲																				🚲		
Manchester Airport 85 ✈	d		07 25								07 56		08 01					08 25					09 00		
Heald Green 85	d		07 29										08 05					08 29							
Buxton 86	d																		07 59						
Hazel Grove 86	d				07 32														08 33						
Stockport 84	d				07 40														08 41						
Manchester Piccadilly 10	d		07 45		07 54						08 15		08 22					08 46	08 54				09 16		
Manchester Oxford Road	d				07 57						08 19		08 26					08 49	08 58				09 19		
Deansgate	d				07 59								08 28					08 51	09 00						
Rochdale 41	d														08 00										
Manchester Victoria	d	07 23		07 27		08 00		08 03	08 11			08 22		08 29	08 33	08 46					09 00				09 07
Salford Central	d	07 26		07 30		08 03		08 08	08 14			08 25		08 32	08 36	08 49					09 03				09 10
Salford Crescent	a	07 29		07 32	08 04	08 07		08 12	08 17			08 29	08 33	08 37	08 40	08 52		08 56	09 04		09 07				09 13
	d	07 30		07 32	08 04	08 08		08 13	08 17			08 30	08 34	08 37	08 41	08 53		08 56	09 04		09 08				09 13
Swinton	d							08 19								08 59									
Moorside	d							08 22																	
Walkden	d			07 42				08 25								09 04									
Atherton	d			07 48				08 31								09 09									
Hag Fold	d							08 33																	
Daisy Hill	d			07 51				08 36								09 13									
Clifton	d																								
Kearsley	d														08 47										
Farnworth	d														08 49										
Moses Gate	d														08 52										
Bolton	a	07 41	07 59		08 14	08 19			08 27		08 32	08 40	08 44	08 49	08 55			09 06	09 14		09 19				09 23
	d		07 59		08 15				08 28		08 33	08 40	08 45		08 56			09 07	09 15						09 24
Westhoughton	d								08 35	⟵			08 53												09 31
Hindley	d							08 41	08 39	08 41						09 17									09 35
Ince	d							↪		08 44															
Wigan North Western	a																						09 43		
Wigan Wallgate	a			08 03					08 48	08 50			09 00		09 14	09 22									09 44
	d									08 51			09 05			09 24									
Pemberton	d									08 55															
Orrell	d									08 59															
Upholland	d									09 03															
Rainford	d									09 06															
Kirkby	a									09 18															
Gathurst	d															09 28									
Appley Bridge	d												09 11			09 32									
Parbold	d												09 15			09 36									
Hoscar	d															09 39									
Burscough Bridge	d												09 20			09 42									
New Lane	d															09 44									
Bescar Lane	d															09 48									
Meols Cop	d															09 53									
Southport	a												09 36			10 02									
Lostock	d				08 20							08 45							09 20						
Horwich Parkway	d				08 24						08 39	08 49							09 24						
Blackrod	d											08 52													
Adlington (Lancashire)	d				08 29							08 56													
Chorley	d		08 11		08 34						08 47	09 01						09 19	09 32						
Buckshaw Parkway	d				08 37							09 05							09 35						
Leyland	d				08 43							09 12							09 42						
Preston 8 65,97	a		08 22		08 50						08 58	09 17						09 30	09 50				09 57		
	d		08 24								08 59	09 19						09 32		09 45			09 59	10 09	
Kirkham & Wesham 97	a											09 28													
Poulton-le-Fylde 97	a										09 16	09 36												10 26	
Layton 97	a											09 43													
Blackpool North 97	a										09 25	09 50												10 33	
Lancaster 6 65	a		08 39															09 47		10 00			10 15		
	d																	09 48		10 01		10 49			
Oxenholme Lake District 65	a																	10 03							
Windermere 83	a																	10 27							
Carnforth	d																			10 09		10a58			
Silverdale	d																			10 15					
Arnside	d																			10 19					
Grange-over-Sands	d																			10 25					
Kents Bank	d																			10 28					
Cark	d																			10 33					
Ulverston	d																			10 41					
Dalton	d																			10 49					
Roose	d																			10 55					
Barrow-in-Furness	a																			11 04					

A To Blackburn
B To Edinburgh
C To Clitheroe
D To Kirkby
E From Manchester Victoria
F From Hebden Bridge
G From Blackpool North
H From Morecambe to Leeds
I To Glasgow Central

The Sunday service between Manchester Victoria and Wigan Wallgate via Atherton is funded by TfGM and will operate whilst funding exists

Table 82

Saturdays
15 February to 17 May

Manchester - Bolton - Wigan, Kirkby, Southport, Preston, Blackpool North and Barrow-in-Furness

Network Diagram - see first Page of Table 82

	NT		NT	NT	NT	NT	NT	TP		NT	NT		TP	NT	NT	NT	NT	NT	NT	NT	NT		TP	NT
								◇1					◇1										◇1	
					A						B		C	D					A					
Manchester Airport 85 ✈ d				09 03				09 29					10 00					10 03					10 29	
Heald Green 85 d								09 33															10 33	
Buxton 86 d																								
Hazel Grove 86 d										09 33														10 33
Stockport 84 d										09 41														10 41
Manchester Piccadilly 10 d				09 22				09 46		09 54			10 16					10 22					10 46	10 54
Manchester Oxford Road d				09 26				09 49		09 58			10 19					10 26					10 49	10 58
Deansgate d				09 28				09 51		10 00								10 28					10 51	11 00
Rochdale 41 d						09 04														10 05				
Manchester Victoria d	09 10		09 22		09 29	09 33	09 46				10 00				10 07	10 10	10 22		10 29	10 33	10 46			
Salford Central d	09 13		09 25		09 32	09 36	09 49				10 03				10 10	10 13	10 25		10 32	10 36	10 49			
Salford Crescent a	09 16		09 29	09 33	09 37	09 39	09 52	09 56		10 04	10 07				10 13	10 16	10 29	10 33	10 37	10 39	10 52		10 56	11 04
d	09 17		09 30	09 34	09 37	09 41	09 53	09 56		10 04	10 08				10 13	10 17	10 30	10 34	10 37	10 40	10 53		10 56	11 04
Swinton d	09 23						09 59									10 23					10 59			
Moorside d	09 26															10 26								
Walkden d	09 29						10 04									10 29					11 04			
Atherton d	09 35						10 09									10 35					11 09			
Hag Fold d	09 37															10 37								
Daisy Hill d	09 40						10 13									10 40					11 13			
Clifton d																								
Kearsley d						09 48														10 47				
Farnworth d						09 50														10 49				
Moses Gate d						09 53														10 52				
Bolton a			09 40	09 44	09 49	09 56		10 06		10 14	10 19				10 23		10 40	10 45	10 49	10 55			11 06	11 14
d			09 40	09 45		09 57		10 07		10 15					10 24		10 40	10 45		10 56			11 07	11 15
Westhoughton d				09 53											10 31			10 53						
Hindley d	09 45			09 57			10 17								10 35	10 45		10 57			11 17			
Ince d	09 48															10 48								
Wigan North Western a																								
Wigan Wallgate a	09 51			10 02		10 14	10 22								10 44	10 51		11 02		11 13	11 22			
d	09 52			10 03			10 24									10 52		11 03			11 24			
Pemberton d	09 56															10 56								
Orrell d	10 00															11 00								
Upholland d	10 04															11 04								
Rainford d	10 07															11 07								
Kirkby a	10 19															11 19								
Gathurst d							10 28														11 28			
Appley Bridge d				10 10			10 32											11 10			11 32			
Parbold d				10 14			10 36											11 14			11 36			
Hoscar d																					11 39			
Burscough Bridge d				10 18			10 40											11 18			11 42			
New Lane d																					11 44			
Bescar Lane d																					11 48			
Meols Cop d							10 48														11 53			
Southport a				10 35			10 57											11 35			12 02			
Lostock d			09 45							10 20							10 45							11 20
Horwich Parkway d			09 49					10 13		10 24							10 49						11 13	11 24
Blackrod d			09 52														10 52							
Adlington (Lancashire) d			09 56														10 56							
Chorley d			10 01					10 21		10 32							11 01						11 21	11 32
Buckshaw Parkway d			10 05					10 24		10 35							11 05						11 24	11 35
Leyland d			10 12							10 42							11 12							11 42
Preston 8 65,97 a			10 17					10 33		10 50			10 56				11 17						11 33	11 50
d			10 19					10 38	10 45				10 57				11 19						11 38	
Kirkham & Wesham 97 a			10 28														11 28							
Poulton-le-Fylde 97 a			10 36					10 56									11 36						11 56	
Layton 97 a			10 40														11 43							
Blackpool North 97 a			10 50					11 05									11 50						12 05	
Lancaster 6 65 a									11 00				11 13											
d									11 01					11 28										
Oxenholme Lake District 65 a									11 17															
Windermere 83 a									11 39															
Carnforth d														11 37										
Silverdale d														11 43										
Arnside d														11 48										
Grange-over-Sands d														11 54										
Kents Bank d														11 57										
Cark d														12 02										
Ulverston d														12 10										
Dalton d														12 18										
Roose d														12 24										
Barrow-in-Furness a														12 32										

A To Blackburn
B To Clitheroe
C To Edinburgh
D To Carlisle

The Sunday service between Manchester Victoria and Wigan Wallgate via Atherton is funded by TfGM and will operate whilst funding exists

Table 82

Saturdays

15 February to 17 May

Manchester - Bolton - Wigan, Kirkby, Southport, Preston, Blackpool North and Barrow-in-Furness

Network Diagram - see first Page of Table 82

Station		NT	TP	NT	NT	NT	NT	NT		NT	TP	NT	TP	NT	TP	NT	NT	NT		NT	NT	NT	TP	NT	NT
		A	◇1								◇1		◇1	A	◇1 B 🚃								◇1		A
Manchester Airport 85 ✈	d		11 00				11 03				11 29				12 00					12 03			12 29		
Heald Green 85	d										11 33												12 33		
Buxton 86	d																								
Hazel Grove 86	d											11 33												12 33	
Stockport 84	d											11 41												12 41	
Manchester Piccadilly 10 🚇	d		11 16				11 22				11 46	11 54			12 16					12 22			12 46	12 54	
Manchester Oxford Road	d		11 19				11 26				11 49	11 58			12 19					12 26			12 49	12 58	
Deansgate 🚇	d						11 28				11 51	12 00								12 28			12 51	13 00	
Rochdale 41	d							11 04													12 04				
Manchester Victoria 🚇	d	11 00		11 07	11 10	11 22		11 33		11 46				12 00		12 07	12 10	12 22			12 33	12 46			13 00
Salford Central	d	11 03		11 10	11 13	11 25		11 36		11 49				12 03		12 10	12 13	12 25			12 36	12 49			13 03
Salford Crescent	a	11 07		11 13	11 16	11 29	11 33	11 39		11 52	11 56	12 04		12 07		12 13	12 16	12 29		12 33	12 39	12 52	12 56	13 04	13 07
	d	11 08		11 13	11 17	11 30	11 34	11 40		11 53	11 56	12 04		12 08		12 13	12 17	12 30		12 34	12 40	12 53	12 56	13 04	13 08
Swinton	d				11 23					11 59							12 23					12 59			
Moorside	d				11 26												12 26								
Walkden	d				11 29					12 04							12 29					13 04			
Atherton	d				11 35					12 09							12 35					13 09			
Hag Fold	d				11 37												12 37								
Daisy Hill	d				11 40					12 13							12 40					13 13			
Clifton	d																								
Kearsley	d							11 47													12 47				
Farnworth	d							11 49													12 49				
Moses Gate	d							11 52													12 52				
Bolton	a	11 19		11 23		11 40	11 45	11 55			12 06	12 14		12 19		12 23		12 40		12 45	12 55		13 06	13 14	13 19
	d			11 24		11 40	11 45	11 56			12 07	12 15				12 24		12 40		12 45	12 56		13 07	13 15	
Westhoughton	d			11 31			11 53									12 31				12 53					
Hindley	d			11 35	11 45		11 57			12 17						12 35	12 45			12 57		13 17			
Ince	d				11 48												12 48								
Wigan North Western	a		11 43												12 43										
Wigan Wallgate	a			11 44	11 51		12 02	12 13		12 22						12 44	12 51			13 02	13 13	13 22			
	d				11 52		12 03			12 24							12 52			13 03		13 24			
Pemberton	d				11 56												12 56								
Orrell	d				12 00												13 00								
Upholland	d				12 04												13 04								
Rainford	d				12 07												13 07								
Kirkby	a				12 19												13 19								
Gathurst	d									12 28												13 28			
Appley Bridge	d						12 10			12 32										13 10		13 32			
Parbold	d						12 14			12 36										13 14		13 36			
Hoscar	d																					13 39			
Burscough Bridge	d						12 18			12 41										13 18		13 42			
New Lane	d																					13 44			
Bescar Lane	d																					13 48			
Meols Cop	d									12 49												13 53			
Southport	a						12 35			12 59										13 35		14 02			
Lostock	d					11 45						12 20						12 45						13 20	
Horwich Parkway	d					11 49					12 13	12 24						12 49					13 13	13 24	
Blackrod	d					11 52												12 52							
Adlington (Lancashire)	d					11 56												12 56							
Chorley	d					12 01					12 21	12 32						13 01					13 21	13 32	
Buckshaw Parkway	d					12 05					12 24	12 35						13 05					13 24	13 35	
Leyland	d					12 12						12 42						13 12						13 42	
Preston 8 65,97	a		11 57			12 17					12 33	12 50			12 57			13 17					13 33	13 50	
	d		11 58			12 19					12 38		12 45		12 58			13 19					13 38		
Kirkham & Wesham 97	a					12 28												13 28							
Poulton-le-Fylde 97	a					12 36					12 56							13 36					13 56		
Layton 97	a					12 43												13 43							
Blackpool North 97	a					12 50					13 05							13 50					14 05		
Lancaster 6 65	a		12 14										13 00		13 14										
	d		12 15										13 01		13 15										
Oxenholme Lake District 65	a												13 17		13 29										
Windermere 83	a												13 39												
Carnforth	d		12 22																						
Silverdale	d																								
Arnside	d		12 30																						
Grange-over-Sands	d		12 36																						
Kents Bank	d																								
Cark	d																								
Ulverston	d		12 48																						
Dalton	d																								
Roose	d																								
Barrow-in-Furness	a		13 09																						

A To Clitheroe **B** To Edinburgh

The Sunday service between Manchester Victoria and Wigan Wallgate via Atherton is funded by TfGM and will operate whilst funding exists

Table 82

Saturdays

15 February to 17 May

Manchester - Bolton - Wigan, Kirkby, Southport, Preston, Blackpool North and Barrow-in-Furness

Network Diagram - see first Page of Table 82

	TP	NT	NT	NT	NT	TP	NT	NT	NT	NT	TP	NT	TP	NT	TP	NT	NT	NT	NT	NT	NT
	◇1										◇1		◇1		◇1						
	A	B			C									D	E						
	⚮														⚮						
Manchester Airport 85 ✈ d	13 00							13 03			13 29				14 00				14 03		
Heald Green 85 d											13 33										
Buxton 86 d																					
Hazel Grove 86 d												13 33									
Stockport 84 d												13 41									
Manchester Piccadilly 10 ⇌ d	13 16							13 22			13 46	13 54			14 16				14 22		
Manchester Oxford Road d	13 19							13 26			13 49	13 58			14 19				14 26		
Deansgate ⇌ d								13 28			13 51	14 00							14 28		
Rochdale 41 d									13 04											14 04	
Manchester Victoria ⇌ d			13 07	13 10			13 22		13 33	13 46				14 00		14 07	14 10	14 22		14 33	14 46
Salford Central d			13 10	13 13			13 25		13 36	13 49				14 03		14 10	14 13	14 25		14 36	14 49
Salford Crescent a			13 13	13 16			13 29	13 33	13 39	13 52	13 56	14 04		14 07		14 13	14 16	14 29	14 33	14 39	14 52
d			13 13	13 17			13 30	13 34	13 40	13 53	13 56	14 04		14 08		14 13	14 17	14 30	14 34	14 40	14 53
Swinton d				13 23						13 59							14 23				14 59
Moorside d				13 26													14 26				
Walkden d				13 29						14 04							14 29				15 04
Atherton d				13 35						14 09							14 35				15 09
Hag Fold d				13 37													14 37				
Daisy Hill d				13 40						14 13							14 40				15 13
Clifton d																					
Kearsley d									13 47											14 47	
Farnworth d									13 49											14 49	
Moses Gate d									13 52											14 52	
Bolton a			13 23				13 40	13 45	13 55		14 06	14 14		14 19		14 23		14 40	14 45	14 55	
d			13 24				13 40	13 45	13 56		14 07	14 15				14 24		14 40	14 45	14 56	
Westhoughton d			13 31					13 53								14 31			14 53		
Hindley d			13 35	13 45				13 57		14 17						14 35	14 45		14 57		15 17
Ince d				13 48													14 48				
Wigan North Western a	13 43														14 43						
Wigan Wallgate a			13 44	13 51				14 02	14 13	14 22						14 44	14 51		15 02	15 13	15 22
d				13 52				14 03		14 24							14 52		15 03		15 24
Pemberton d				13 56													14 56				
Orrell d				14 00													15 00				
Upholland d				14 04													15 04				
Rainford d				14 07													15 07				
Kirkby a				14 19													15 19				
Gathurst d										14 28											15 28
Appley Bridge d								14 10		14 32									15 10		15 32
Parbold d								14 14		14 36									15 14		15 36
Hoscar d																					
Burscough Bridge d								14 18		14 41									15 18		15 40
New Lane d																					
Bescar Lane d																					
Meols Cop d										14 49											15 48
Southport a								14 35		14 59									15 35		15 57
Lostock d							13 45					14 20						14 45			
Horwich Parkway d							13 49				14 13	14 24						14 49			
Blackrod d							13 52											14 52			
Adlington (Lancashire) d							13 56											14 56			
Chorley d							14 01				14 21	14 32						15 01			
Buckshaw Parkway d							14 05				14 24	14 35						15 05			
Leyland d							14 12					14 42						15 12			
Preston 8 65,97 a	13 57						14 17				14 33	14 50			14 57			15 17			
d	13 58					14 06	14 19				14 38		14 45		14 58			15 19			
Kirkham & Wesham 97 a							14 28											15 28			
Poulton-le-Fylde 97 a							14 36				14 56							15 36			
Layton 97 a							14 42											15 43			
Blackpool North 97 a							14 50				15 05							15 50			
Lancaster 6 65 a	14 14					14 21							15 00		15 14						
d		13 32			13 48	14 22							15 01		15 15						
Oxenholme Lake District 65 a													15 17		15 29						
Windermere 83 a													15 39								
Carnforth d		13 41			13a58	14 30															
Silverdale d		13 47																			
Arnside d		13 52				14 39															
Grange-over-Sands d		13 58				14 44															
Kents Bank d		14 01																			
Cark d		14 06																			
Ulverston d		14 14				14 57															
Dalton d		14 22																			
Roose d		14 28																			
Barrow-in-Furness a		14 36				15 17															

A To Glasgow Central
B To Carlisle
C From Heysham Harbour to Leeds
D To Clitheroe
E To Edinburgh

The Sunday service between Manchester Victoria and Wigan Wallgate via Atherton is funded by TfGM and will operate whilst funding exists

Table 82

Saturdays
15 February to 17 May

Manchester - Bolton - Wigan, Kirkby, Southport, Preston, Blackpool North and Barrow-in-Furness

Network Diagram - see first Page of Table 82

	NT	TP ◇1		NT	NT A	TP ◇1 B 🚲	NT C	NT	NT	NT	NT	NT	NT A	NT	TP ◇1	NT	NT	NT	NT D	TP ◇1 E 🚲		NT
Manchester Airport 85 ✈ d		14 29				15 00					15 03				15 29					16 00		
Heald Green 85 d		14 33													15 33							
Buxton 86 d																						
Hazel Grove 86 d				14 33												15 33						
Stockport 84 d				14 41												15 41						
Manchester Piccadilly 10 d		14 46		14 54		15 16					15 22				15 46	15 54				16 16		
Manchester Oxford Road d		14 49		14 58		15 19					15 26				15 49	15 58				16 19		
Deansgate d		14 51		15 00							15 28				15 51	16 00						
Rochdale 41 d												15 04										
Manchester Victoria d					15 00			15 07	15 10	15 22		15 33	15 40	15 46			16 07	16 10				16 20
Salford Central d					15 03			15 10	15 13	15 25		15 36	15 43	15 49			16 10	16 13				16 23
Salford Crescent a		14 56		15 04	15 08			15 13	15 16	15 29	15 33	15 39	15 46	15 52	15 56	16 04	16 13	16 16				16 26
d		14 56		15 04	15 08			15 13	15 17	15 30	15 34	15 40	15 47	15 53	15 56	16 04	16 13	16 17				16 27
Swinton d									15 23					15 59				16 23				
Moorside d									15 26									16 26				
Walkden d									15 29					16 04				16 29				
Atherton d									15 35					16 09				16 35				
Hag Fold d									15 37									16 37				
Daisy Hill d									15 40					16 13				16 40				
Clifton d																						
Kearsley d												15 47										
Farnworth d												15 49										
Moses Gate d												15 52										
Bolton a		15 06		15 14	15 19			15 23		15 40	15 45	15 55	15 59		16 06	16 14	16 23			16 32		16 37
d		15 07		15 15				15 24		15 40	15 45	15 56			16 07	16 15	16 24			16 33		16 37
Westhoughton d								15 31			15 53						16 31					
Hindley d								15 35	15 45		15 57			16 17			16 35	16 45				
Ince d									15 48									16 48				
Wigan North Western a						15 43																
Wigan Wallgate a								15 44	15 51		16 02	16 13		16 22			16 44	16 51				
d									15 52		16 03			16 24				16 52				
Pemberton d									15 56									16 56				
Orrell d									16 00									17 00				
Upholland d									16 04									17 04				
Rainford d									16 07									17 07				
Kirkby a									16 19									17 19				
Gathurst d											16 08			16 28								
Appley Bridge d											16 11			16 32								
Parbold d											16 15			16 36								
Hoscar d											16 18											
Burscough Bridge d											16 21			16 40								
New Lane d											16 24											
Bescar Lane d											16 27											
Meols Cop d											16 32			16 48								
Southport a											16 42			16 57								
Lostock d				15 20						15 45					16 11	16 20						16 43
Horwich Parkway d		15 13		15 24						15 49					16 15	16 24						16 47
Blackrod d										15 52												16 51
Adlington (Lancashire) d										15 56												16 55
Chorley d		15 21		15 32						16 01					16 23	16 32				16 45		17 00
Buckshaw Parkway d		15 24		15 35						16 05					16 26	16 35						17 04
Leyland d				15 42						16 12						16 42						17 11
Preston 8 65,97 a		15 33		15 50		15 57				16 19					16 35	16 50				16 58		17 19
d		15 38	15 46			15 58									16 38					16 58	17 05	17 20
Kirkham & Wesham 97 a															16 47							17 30
Poulton-le-Fylde 97 a		15 56													16 57							17 38
Layton 97 a															17 00							17 43
Blackpool North 97 a		16 05													17 07							17 50
Lancaster 6 65 a			16 01			16 15														17 14	17 20	
d	15 20		16 02				16 40												17 00	17 15	17 21	
Oxenholme Lake District 65 a																				17 29	17 37	
Windermere 83 a																					17 58	
Carnforth d	15 30		16 10				16a49												17 10			
Silverdale d	15 36		16 16																17 17			
Arnside d	15 40		16 20																17 21			
Grange-over-Sands d	15 46		16 25																17 27			
Kents Bank d	15 50		16 29																17 31			
Cark d	15 54		16 33																17 35			
Ulverston d	16 03		16 41																17 44			
Dalton d	16 11		16 49																17 53			
Roose d	16 19		16 55																17 59			
Barrow-in-Furness a	16 25		17 04																18 07			

A To Clitheroe
B 🚲 to Preston
C From Morecambe to Leeds
D To Millom
E To Edinburgh

The Sunday service between Manchester Victoria and Wigan Wallgate via Atherton is funded by TfGM and will operate whilst funding exists

Table 82

Saturdays

15 February to 17 May

Manchester - Bolton - Wigan, Kirkby, Southport, Preston, Blackpool North and Barrow-in-Furness

Network Diagram - see first Page of Table 82

		NT	NT	NT	NT	NT		TP		NT	NT	NT	TP	NT	NT	NT		NT	NT	NT	TP		NT	NT	NT
								◇1					◇1								◇1				
		A									A		B 🍴			C									A
Manchester Airport 85 ✈	d		16 03					16 29					17 00					17 03			17 29				
Heald Green 85	d							16 33													17 33				
Buxton 86	d																								
Hazel Grove 86	d									16 30														17 33	
Stockport 84	d									16 41														17 41	
Manchester Piccadilly 10	d		16 22					16 46		16 54			17 15					17 23			17 46			17 54	
Manchester Oxford Road	d		16 26					16 49		16 58			17 18					17 26			17 49			17 58	
Deansgate	d		16 28					16 51		17 00											17 51			18 00	
Rochdale 41	d			16 04												17 03									
Manchester Victoria	d	16 23		16 36	16 46						17 00	17 07		17 10	17 20	17 23			17 36	17 40			17 50		18 00
Salford Central	d	16 26		16 39	16 49						17 03	17 10		17 13	17 23	17 26			17 39	17 43			17 53		18 03
Salford Crescent	a	16 30	16 34	16 42	16 52			16 56		17 04	17 07	17 13		17 17	17 26	17 30		17 33	17 42	17 46	17 55		17 58	18 04	18 07
	d	16 31	16 34	16 43	16 53			16 56		17 04	17 08	17 13		17 17	17 27	17 31		17 34	17 43	17 47	17 55		17 59	18 04	18 08
Swinton	d				16 59									17 23									18 05		
Moorside	d				17 02									17 26									18 08		
Walkden	d				17 05									17 29									18 11		
Atherton	d				17 11									17 35						18 00			18 17		
Hag Fold	d				17 14									17 37									18 19		
Daisy Hill	d				17 17									17 41						18 04			18 22		
Clifton	d																		17 48						
Kearsley	d			16 50															17 53						
Farnworth	d			16 52															17 55						
Moses Gate	d			16 55															17 57						
Bolton	a	16 42	16 45	16 58				17 06		17 14	17 19	17 23	17 32		17 37	17 42		17 44	18 01		18 05			18 14	18 19
	d		16 46	16 59				17 07		17 15		17 24	17 32		17 37			17 46	18 01		18 06			18 15	
Westhoughton	d		16 53	17 06								17 31						17 53	18 09						
Hindley	d		16 57	17 10	17 21							17 35		17 45					18 13				18 27		
Ince	d				17 24									17 48											
Wigan North Western	a																								
Wigan Wallgate	a		17 02	17 19	17 27							17 44		17 51				18 01	18 22	18 12			18 32		
	d		17 03		17 29									17 52				18 02		18 15			18 33		
Pemberton	d													17 56									18 37		
Orrell	d													18 00									18 41		
Upholland	d													18 04									18 45		
Rainford	d													18 07									18 48		
Kirkby	a													18 19									19 00		
Gathurst	d		17 08		17 33															18 20					
Appley Bridge	d		17 11		17 37													18 09		18 24					
Parbold	d		17 15		17 41													18 13		18 28					
Hoscar	d																			18 31					
Burscough Bridge	d		17 20		17 45													18 18		18 35					
New Lane	d																			18 37					
Bescar Lane	d																			18 41					
Meols Cop	d		17 27		17 53													18 26		18 46					
Southport	a		17 37		18 02													18 36		18 55					
Lostock	d									17 20					17 43						18 11			18 20	
Horwich Parkway	d							17 13		17 24					17 47						18 15			18 24	
Blackrod	d														17 51										
Adlington (Lancashire)	d														17 55										
Chorley	d							17 21		17 32			17 46		18 00						18 23			18 32	
Buckshaw Parkway	d							17 24		17 35					18 03						18 26			18 35	
Leyland	d									17 42					18 11									18 42	
Preston 8 65,97	a							17 33		17 50			17 56		18 16						18 35			18 48	
	d							17 38	17 45				18 00		18 18						18 40	18 45		18 49	
Kirkham & Wesham 97	a							17 47							18 27						18 49				
Poulton-le-Fylde 97	a							17 57							18 35						18 59				
Layton 97	a							18 00							18 39						19 02				
Blackpool North 97	a							18 08							18 46						19 09			19 16	
Lancaster 6 65	a								18 00				18 16									19 00			
	d					17 36			18 01				18 16									19 01			
Oxenholme Lake District 65	a												18 31												
Windermere 83	a																								
Carnforth	d					17 45			18 09													19 09			
Silverdale	d					17 51			18 15													19 15			
Arnside	d					17 56			18 19													19 19			
Grange-over-Sands	d					18 02			18 25													19 25			
Kents Bank	d					18 05			18 28													19 28			
Cark	d					18 10			18 33													19 33			
Ulverston	d					18 18			18 41													19 41			
Dalton	d					18 26			18 49													19 49			
Roose	d					18 33			18 55													19 55			
Barrow-in-Furness	a					18 43			19 04													20 04			

A To Clitheroe **B** To Glasgow Central **C** To Blackburn

The Sunday service between Manchester Victoria and Wigan Wallgate via Atherton is funded by TfGM and will operate whilst funding exists

Table 82

Saturdays

15 February to 17 May

Manchester - Bolton - Wigan, Kirkby, Southport, Preston, Blackpool North and Barrow-in-Furness

Network Diagram - see first Page of Table 82

		TP	NT	NT	NT	NT	NT	NT	TP	NT	NT	NT	TP	NT	NT	NT	TP	TP	NT	NT	NT	NT
		◇1							◇1				◇1				◇1	◇1				
		A			B						C	D								C		
Manchester Airport	85 ✈ d	18 00				18 03			18 29				19 00	19 03			19 29	20 00				20 03
Heald Green	85 d								18 33								19 33					
Buxton	86 d																					
Hazel Grove	86 d									18 33												
Stockport	84 d									18 41												
Manchester Piccadilly 10	d	18 16				18 22			18 46	18 54			19 16	19 20			19 46	20 16				20 20
Manchester Oxford Road	d	18 19				18 27			18 49	18 58			19 19	19 24			19 49	20 19				20 24
Deansgate	d					18 29			18 51	19 00				19 26			19 51					20 26
Rochdale	41 d				18 02																	
Manchester Victoria	d		18 10	18 20	18 23		18 33	18 45			19 00				19 28	19 35				20 00	20 22	
Salford Central	d		18 13	18 23	18 26		18 36	18 48			19 03				19 31	19 38				20 04	20 25	
Salford Crescent	a		18 16	18 26	18 30	18 34	18 39	18 51	18 56	19 04	19 08			19 29	19 34	19 41	19 56			20 07	20 29	20 33
	d		18 17	18 27	18 31	18 34	18 40	18 52	18 56	19 04	19 08			19 30	19 35	19 42	19 56			20 08	20 30	20 35
Swinton	d		18 23					18 58								19 48						
Moorside	d		18 26					19 01								19 51						
Walkden	d		18 29					19 04								19 54						
Atherton	d		18 35					19 10								20 00						
Hag Fold	d		18 37					19 12								20 02						
Daisy Hill	d		18 40					19 15								20 05						
Clifton	d																					
Kearsley	d						18 47															
Farnworth	d						18 49															
Moses Gate	d						18 52															
Bolton	a			18 37	18 42	18 45	18 55		19 06	19 19	19 20		19 32	19 40	19 45		20 06			20 19	20 40	20 45
	d			18 37		18 46	18 56		19 07				19 33	19 40	19 45		20 07				20 40	20 45
Westhoughton	d					18 53	19 03							19 48								20 53
Hindley	d		18 45			18 57	19 09	19 20						19 52		20 10						20 57
Ince	d		18 48					19 23								20 13						
Wigan North Western	a	18 43	18 56															20 43				
Wigan Wallgate	a					19 02	19 18	19 30						19 57		20 20						21 02
	d					19 03								19 59								21 03
Pemberton	d																					
Orrell	d																					
Upholland	d																					
Rainford	d																					
Kirkby	a																					
Gathurst	d					19 08								20 03								21 08
Appley Bridge	d					19 11								20 07								21 11
Parbold	d					19 15								20 11								21 15
Hoscar	d																					21 18
Burscough Bridge	d					19 19								20 15								21 21
New Lane	d																					21 24
Bescar Lane	d																					21 27
Meols Cop	d					19 27								20 23								21 32
Southport	a					19 37								20 32								21 42
Lostock	d			18 42					19 11						19 50						20 45	
Horwich Parkway	d			18 46					19 15						19 54		20 13				20 49	
Blackrod	d			18 49											19 57						20 52	
Adlington (Lancashire)	d			18 53											20 01						20 56	
Chorley	d			18 58					19 23				19 44		20 06		20 21				21 01	
Buckshaw Parkway	d			19 02					19 26						20 10		20 24				21 05	
Leyland	d			19 10											20 18						21 12	
Preston 8	65,97 a	18 57		19 18					19 35				19 57		20 23		20 33	20 57			21 17	
	d	18 58		19 19					19 38				19 59		20 25		20 38		20 45		21 19	
Kirkham & Wesham	97 a			19 28											20 34						21 28	
Poulton-le-Fylde	97 a			19 36					19 56						20 42		20 56				21 36	
Layton	97 a			19 43											20 47						21 40	
Blackpool North	97 a			19 50					20 05						20 54		21 05				21 48	
Lancaster 6	65 a	19 14											20 14						21 08			
	d	19 15										19 24	20 15						21 11			
Oxenholme Lake District	65 a	19 29																				
Windermere	83 a																					
Carnforth	d											19a33	20 23						21 21			
Silverdale	d												20 29						21 27			
Arnside	d												20 33						21 32			
Grange-over-Sands	d												20 39						21 38			
Kents Bank	d												20 42						21 41			
Cark	d												20 47						21 45			
Ulverston	d												20 55						21 53			
Dalton	d												21 03						22 02			
Roose	d												21 09						22 08			
Barrow-in-Furness	a												21 18						22 17			

A To Edinburgh
B To Blackburn
C To Clitheroe
D From Morecambe to Leeds

The Sunday service between Manchester Victoria and Wigan Wallgate via Atherton is funded by TfGM and will operate whilst funding exists

Table 82

Saturdays

15 February to 17 May

Manchester - Bolton - Wigan, Kirkby, Southport, Preston, Blackpool North and Barrow-in-Furness

Network Diagram - see first Page of Table 82

Station		NT	TP	NT	NT	NT	TP	TP	NT	TP	NT	TP	TP	NT	NT	TP	NT	TP	NT	NT	NT	TP	NT
			◇1					1		◇1		◇1	◇1			◇1		◇1				1	
				A			B 🚌	B			A	B	C			C				D		B	C
Manchester Airport 85 ✈	d		20 29			21 03				21 29		22 00	22 00		22 19			22 29					
Heald Green 85	d		20 33							21 33								22 33					
Buxton 86	d																						
Hazel Grove 86	d																						
Stockport 84	d																		22 40				
Manchester Piccadilly 10	d		20 46			21 20				21 46		22 16	22 16		22 35			22 46	22 54				
Manchester Oxford Road	d		20 49			21 24				21 49		22 19	22 19		22 39			22 49	22 58				
Deansgate	d		20 51			21 26				21 51					22 41			22 51	23 00				
Rochdale 41	d																						
Manchester Victoria	d	20 35		21 00	21 22				21 35		22 00			22 22			22 45			23 05	23 16		
Salford Central	d	20 38		21 03	21 25				21 38		22 03			22 25			22 48			23 08	23 19		
Salford Crescent	a	20 41	20 56	21 07	21 30	21 34			21 41	21 56	22 07			22 29	22 46		22 51	22 56	23 03	23 11	23 22		
	d	20 42	20 56	21 08	21 30	21 35			21 42	21 56	22 08			22 30	22 46		22 52	22 56	23 05	23 12	23 22		
Swinton	d	20 48							21 48								22 58						
Moorside	d	20 51							21 51								23 01						
Walkden	d	20 54							21 54								23 04						
Atherton	d	21 00							22 00								23 10						
Hag Fold	d	21 02							22 02								23 12						
Daisy Hill	d	21 05							22 05								23 15						
Clifton	d																						
Kearsley	d																		23 12				
Farnworth	d																		23 14				
Moses Gate	d																		23 17				
Bolton	a		21 06	21 19	21 40	21 45				22 06	22 19	22 32	22 32	22 40	22 56			23 06	23 20	23 23	23 32		
	d		21 07		21 40	21 45				22 07		22 32	22 32	22 40	22 57			23 07	23 21		23 33		
Westhoughton	d					21 53									23 04				23 28				
Hindley	d	21 10				21 57			22 10						23 08		23 20		23 32				
Ince	d	21 13							22 13								23 23						
Wigan North Western	a																						
Wigan Wallgate	a	21 20				22 02			22 20						23 13		23 30		23 41				
	d					22 03									23 15								
Pemberton	d																						
Orrell	d																						
Upholland	d																						
Rainford	d																						
Kirkby	a																						
Gathurst	d					22 08									23 19								
Appley Bridge	d					22 11									23 23								
Parbold	d					22 15									23 27								
Hoscar	d																						
Burscough Bridge	d					22 20									23 31								
New Lane	d																						
Bescar Lane	d																						
Meols Cop	d					22 27									23 39								
Southport	a					22 37									23 48								
Lostock	d				21 45									22 45							23 38		
Horwich Parkway	d		21 13		21 49					22 13				22 49				23 13			23 42		
Blackrod	d				21 52									22 52							23 45		
Adlington (Lancashire)	d				21 56									22 56							23 49		
Chorley	d		21 21		22 01					22 21				23 01				23 21			23 54		
Buckshaw Parkway	d		21 24		22 04					22 24				23 05				23 24			23 57		
Leyland	d				22 12									23 12							00 04		
Preston 8 65,97	a		21 33		22 17					22 35		22 53	22 55	23 17				23 33			00 10		
	d		21 38		22 19					22 38				23 19				23 35			00 11		
Kirkham & Wesham 97	a				22 28									23 28							00 21		
Poulton-le-Fylde 97	a		21 56		22 36					22 55				23 36				23 52			00 29		
Layton 97	a				22 42									23 40							00 34		
Blackpool North 97	a		22 05		22 50					23 04				23 48				00 01			00 40		
Lancaster 6 65	a																						
	d						21 35									22 25							23 11
Oxenholme Lake District 65	a																						
Windermere 83	a																						
Carnforth	d						22a00	22 11								22 33						23 19	23 21
Silverdale	d							22 17								22 39						23 25	23 27
Arnside	d							22 21								22 43						23 29	23 32
Grange-over-Sands	d							22 27								22 49						23 35	23 38
Kents Bank	d							22 30								22 52						23 38	23 41
Cark	d							22 35								22 57						23 43	23 45
Ulverston	d							22 43								23 05						23 51	23 53
Dalton	d							22 51								23 13						23 59	00 02
Roose	d							22 57								23 19						00 05	00 08
Barrow-in-Furness	a							23 06								23 28						00 14	00 17

A To Clitheroe
B from 29 March
C until 22 March
D To Blackburn

The Sunday service between Manchester Victoria and Wigan Wallgate via Atherton is funded by TfGM and will operate whilst funding exists

Table 82

Saturdays

15 February to 17 May

Manchester - Bolton - Wigan, Kirkby, Southport, Preston, Blackpool North and Barrow-in-Furness

Network Diagram - see first Page of Table 82

Station	Table		NT
Manchester Airport	85 ✈	d	
Heald Green	85	d	
Buxton	86	d	
Hazel Grove	86	d	
Stockport	84	d	
Manchester Piccadilly 10		d	
Manchester Oxford Road		d	
Deansgate		d	
Rochdale	41	d	
Manchester Victoria		d	23 20
Salford Central		d	23 23
Salford Crescent		a	23 26
		d	23 26
Swinton		d	23 33
Moorside		d	23 35
Walkden		d	23 39
Atherton		d	23 44
Hag Fold		d	23 47
Daisy Hill		d	23 50
Clifton		d	
Kearsley		d	
Farnworth		d	
Moses Gate		d	
Bolton		a	
		d	
Westhoughton		d	
Hindley		d	23 54
Ince		d	23 57
Wigan North Western		a	
Wigan Wallgate		a	00 04
		d	
Pemberton		d	
Orrell		d	
Upholland		d	
Rainford		d	
Kirkby		a	
Gathurst		d	
Appley Bridge		d	
Parbold		d	
Hoscar		d	
Burscough Bridge		d	
New Lane		d	
Bescar Lane		d	
Meols Cop		d	
Southport		a	
Lostock		d	
Horwich Parkway		d	
Blackrod		d	
Adlington (Lancashire)		d	
Chorley		d	
Buckshaw Parkway		d	
Leyland		d	
Preston 8	65,97	a	
		d	
Kirkham & Wesham	97	a	
Poulton-le-Fylde	97	a	
Layton	97	a	
Blackpool North	97	a	
Lancaster 6	65	a	
		d	
Oxenholme Lake District	65	a	
Windermere	83	a	
Carnforth		d	
Silverdale		d	
Arnside		d	
Grange-over-Sands		d	
Kents Bank		d	
Cark		d	
Ulverston		d	
Dalton		d	
Roose		d	
Barrow-in-Furness		a	

The Sunday service between Manchester Victoria and Wigan Wallgate via Atherton is funded by TfGM and will operate whilst funding exists

Table 82

Sundays

8 December to 29 December

Manchester - Bolton - Wigan, Kirkby, Southport, Preston, Blackpool North and Barrow-in-Furness

Network Diagram - see first Page of Table 82

		NT	TP	TP	TP	NT	TP	NT	NT	NT	TP	TP	NT	NT	TP	NT	NT	TP	TP	TP	NT	NT	TP
		A	(bus)	◇1 B	(bus)	C	◇1			C	◇1	◇1 D (trolley)			◇1	C		◇1	◇1 E (trolley)	◇1		F	◇1
Manchester Airport 85 ✈	d		00 05		05 30		07 48				08 49	09 00			09 29				10 00				10 30
Heald Green 85	d																						
Buxton 86	d																						
Hazel Grove 86	d													09 12									
Stockport 84	d								08 22					09 22								10 12	
Manchester Piccadilly 10	d		00 30		05 55		08 03		08 35		09 03	09 16		09 35	09 46				10 15			10 24	10 46
Manchester Oxford Road	d						08 06		08 38		09 07	09 19		09 38	09 49				10 18			10 38	10 49
Deansgate	d						08 08		08 40		09 08			09 40	09 51							10 40	10 51
Rochdale 41	d																						
Manchester Victoria	d					08 01		08 25		09 00			09 25			10 00	10 09				10 25		
Salford Central	d																						
Salford Crescent	a					08 07	08 11	08 29	08 44	09 05	09 12		09 29	09 44	09 54	10 06	10 16				10 29	10 44	10 54
	d					08 08	08 12	08 30	08 44	09 07	09 12		09 30	09 44	09 55	10 08	10 17				10 30	10 44	10 55
Swinton	d																10 23						
Moorside	d																10 26						
Walkden	d																10 29						
Atherton	d																10 35						
Hag Fold	d																10 37						
Daisy Hill	d																10 40						
Clifton	d																						
Kearsley	d																						
Farnworth	d																						
Moses Gate	d																						
Bolton	a		00s55		06s20	08 19	08 22	08 40	08 54	09 18	09 22		09 40	09 54	10 05	10 19			10 31		10 40	10 54	11 05
	d						08 22	08 40	08 55		09 23		09 40	09 55	10 05				10 32		10 40	10 55	11 05
Westhoughton	d								09 02					10 02								11 02	
Hindley	d								09 06					10 06			10 45					11 06	
Ince	d																10 48						
Wigan North Western	a											09 42											
Wigan Wallgate	a								09 11					10 11			10 55					11 11	
	d								09 13					10 13								11 13	
Pemberton	d																						
Orrell	d																						
Upholland	d																						
Rainford	d																						
Kirkby	a																						
Gathurst	d								09 17					10 17								11 17	
Appley Bridge	d								09 21					10 21								11 21	
Parbold	d								09 25					10 25								11 25	
Hoscar	d																						
Burscough Bridge	d								09 29					10 29								11 29	
New Lane	d																						
Bescar Lane	d																						
Meols Cop	d								09 37					10 37								11 37	
Southport	a								09 46					10 46								11 46	
Lostock	d							08 45					09 45								10 45		
Horwich Parkway	d						08 29	08 49			09 29		09 49		10 12						10 49		11 12
Blackrod	d							08 52					09 52								10 52		
Adlington (Lancashire)	d							08 56					09 56								10 56		
Chorley	d						08 36	09 01			09 37		10 01		10 19				10 43		11 01		11 19
Buckshaw Parkway	d						08 40	09 05			09 40		10 05		10 23						11 05		11 23
Leyland	d	00 04						09 12					10 12								11 12		
Preston 8 65,97	a	00 10	01s30		06s55		08 50	09 18			09 51	09 57	10 18		10 33				10 54		11 20		11 33
	d	00 11					08 54	09 20			09 52	09 58	10 20		10 35				10 57	11 14	11 21		11 35
Kirkham & Wesham 97	a	00 21						09 29					10 29								11 31		
Poulton-le-Fylde 97	a	00 29					09 11	09 37			10 09		10 37		10 52						11 39		11 52
Layton 97	a	00 34						09 42					10 42								11 44		
Blackpool North 97	a	00 40	02 10		07 35		09 19	09 49			10 17		10 49		11 01						11 49		12 01
Lancaster 6 65	a											10 14							11 14	11 31			
	d											10 15						10 22	11 14	11 32			
Oxenholme Lake District 65	a											10 29						10 37	11 28				
Windermere 83	a																	10 58					
Carnforth	d																			11 39			
Silverdale	d																			11 45			
Arnside	d																			11 49			
Grange-over-Sands	d																			11 54			
Kents Bank	d																						
Cark	d																			12 00			
Ulverston	d																			12 08			
Dalton	d																			12 17			
Roose	d			00 05																			
Barrow-in-Furness	a			00 14																12 30			

A not 8 December. From Manchester Victoria
B not 8 December. From Manchester Airport
C To Clitheroe
D To Edinburgh
E To Glasgow Central
F From Chester

The Sunday service between Manchester Victoria and Wigan Wallgate via Atherton is funded by TfGM and will operate whilst funding exists

Table 82

Sundays

8 December to 29 December

Manchester - Bolton - Wigan, Kirkby, Southport, Preston, Blackpool North and Barrow-in-Furness

Network Diagram - see first Page of Table 82

	NT	NT	NT	NT	TP	NT	NT	NT	TP	TP	NT	NT	TP	NT	TP	NT	NT	NT	TP	NT	NT	NT
					◇1				◇1	◇1			◇1		◇1				◇1			
	A					A		B		C		D		A	E					A		F
Manchester Airport 85 d					11 30					12 00			12 30		13 00				13 30			
Heald Green 85 d																						
Buxton 86 d																						
Hazel Grove 86 d																		13 12				
Stockport 84 d				11 11								12 21						13 22				
Manchester Piccadilly 10 d				11 26	11 46					12 14		12 35	12 46		13 16			13 35	13 46			
Manchester Oxford Road d				11 38	11 49					12 17		12 38	12 49		13 19			13 38	13 49			
Deansgate d				11 40	11 51							12 40	12 51					13 40	13 51			
Rochdale 41 d																						
Manchester Victoria d	11 00	11 12	11 25			12 00	12 09				12 25			13 00		13 12	13 25			14 00	14 12	
Salford Central d																						
Salford Crescent a	11 06	11 16	11 29	11 44	11 54	12 06	12 13				12 29	12 44	12 54	13 06		13 16	13 29	13 44	13 54	14 06	14 16	
d	11 08	11 17	11 30	11 44	11 55	12 08	12 17				12 30	12 44	12 55	13 08		13 17	13 30	13 44	13 55	14 08	14 17	
Swinton d		11 23					12 23									13 23					14 23	
Moorside d		11 26					12 26									13 26					14 26	
Walkden d		11 29					12 29									13 29					14 29	
Atherton d		11 35					12 35									13 35					14 35	
Hag Fold d		11 37					12 37									13 37					14 37	
Daisy Hill d		11 40					12 40									13 40					14 40	
Clifton d																						
Kearsley d																						
Farnworth d																						
Moses Gate d																						
Bolton a	11 19		11 40	11 54	12 05	12 19					12 40	12 54	13 05	13 19			13 40	13 54	14 05	14 19		
d			11 40	11 55	12 05						12 40	12 55	13 05				13 40	13 55	14 05			
Westhoughton d				12 02								13 02						14 02				
Hindley d		11 45		12 06			12 45					13 06				13 45		14 06			14 45	
Ince d		11 48					12 48									13 48					14 48	
Wigan North Western a										12 42					13 43							
Wigan Wallgate a		11 55		12 11			12 55					13 11				13 55		14 11			14 55	
d				12 13								13 13						14 13				
Pemberton d																						
Orrell d																						
Upholland d																						
Rainford d																						
Kirkby a																						
Gathurst d				12 17								13 17						14 17				
Appley Bridge d				12 21								13 21						14 21				
Parbold d				12 25								13 25						14 25				
Hoscar d																						
Burscough Bridge d				12 29								13 29						14 29				
New Lane d																						
Bescar Lane d																						
Meols Cop d				12 37								13 37						14 37				
Southport a				12 46								13 46						14 46				
Lostock d			11 45								12 45						13 45					
Horwich Parkway d			11 49		12 12						12 49		13 12				13 49		14 12			
Blackrod d			11 52								12 52						13 52					
Adlington (Lancashire) d			11 56								12 56						13 56					
Chorley d			12 01		12 19						13 01		13 19				14 01		14 19			
Buckshaw Parkway d			12 05		12 23						13 05		13 23				14 05		14 23			
Leyland d			12 12								13 12						14 12					
Preston 8 65,97 a			12 18		12 33					12 57	13 18		13 33		13 57		14 18		14 33			
d			12 20		12 35				12 48	12 57	13 20		13 35		13 58		14 20		14 35			
Kirkham & Wesham 97 a			12 29								13 29						14 29					
Poulton-le-Fylde 97 a			12 37		12 52						13 37		13 52				14 37		14 52			
Layton 97 a			12 42								13 42						14 42					
Blackpool North 97 a			12 49		13 01						13 49		14 01				14 49		15 01			
Lancaster 6 65 a									13 03	13 14					14 14							
d								12 48	13 04	13 14					14 15							14 27
Oxenholme Lake District 65 a										13 28					14 29							
Windermere 83 a																						
Carnforth d								12a57	13 12													14a59
Silverdale d									13 18													
Arnside d									13 22													
Grange-over-Sands d									13 28													
Kents Bank d									13 31													
Cark d									13 36													
Ulverston d									13 44													
Dalton d									13 52													
Roose d									13 58													
Barrow-in-Furness a									14 07													

A To Clitheroe
B From Morecambe to Leeds
C To Edinburgh
D From Chester
E To Glasgow Central
F To Leeds

The Sunday service between Manchester Victoria and Wigan Wallgate via Atherton is funded by TfGM and will operate whilst funding exists

Table 82

Sundays

8 December to 29 December

Manchester - Bolton - Wigan, Kirkby, Southport, Preston, Blackpool North and Barrow-in-Furness

Network Diagram - see first Page of Table 82

		TP	NT	NT	TP	NT	TP	NT	NT	NT	TP	NT	TP	NT	NT	NT	TP	NT	NT	NT	NT	TP
		◇1			◇1		◇1				◇1		◇1				◇1					◇1
		A		B		C						C	A			B		C			D	E
		trolley											trolley									trolley
Manchester Airport 85 ✈	d	14 00			14 30		15 00				15 30		16 00				16 30					17 00
Heald Green 85	d																					
Buxton 86	d																					
Hazel Grove 86	d									15 07												
Stockport 84	d			14 21						15 22						16 21						
Manchester Piccadilly 10	d	14 14		14 35	14 46		15 14			15 35	15 46		16 14			16 35	16 46					17 14
Manchester Oxford Road	d	14 18		14 38	14 49		15 18			15 38	15 49		16 18			16 38	16 49					17 18
Deansgate	d			14 40	14 51					15 40	15 51					16 40	16 51					
Rochdale 41	d																					
Manchester Victoria	d		14 25			15 00		15 12	15 25			16 00		16 12	16 25			17 00	17 12			
Salford Central	d																					
Salford Crescent	a		14 29	14 44	14 54	15 06		15 16	15 29	15 44	15 54	16 06		16 16	16 29	16 44	16 54	17 06	17 16			
	d		14 30	14 44	14 55	15 08		15 17	15 30	15 44	15 55	16 08		16 17	16 30	16 44	16 55	17 08	17 17			
Swinton	d							15 23						16 23					17 23			
Moorside	d							15 26						16 26					17 26			
Walkden	d							15 29						16 29					17 29			
Atherton	d							15 35						16 35					17 35			
Hag Fold	d							15 37						16 37					17 37			
Daisy Hill	d							15 40						16 40					17 40			
Clifton	d																					
Kearsley	d																					
Farnworth	d																					
Moses Gate	d																					
Bolton	a		14 40	14 54	15 05	15 19			15 40	15 54	16 05	16 19			16 40	16 54	17 05	17 19				
	d		14 40	14 55	15 05				15 40	15 55	16 05				16 40	16 55	17 05					
Westhoughton	d			15 02						16 02						17 02						
Hindley	d			15 06				15 45		16 06				16 45		17 06			17 45			
Ince	d							15 48						16 48					17 48			
Wigan North Western	a	14 42					15 42						16 42									17 42
Wigan Wallgate	a			15 11				15 55		16 11				16 55		17 11			17 55			
	d			15 13						16 13						17 13						
Pemberton	d																					
Orrell	d																					
Upholland	d																					
Rainford	d																					
Kirkby	a																					
Gathurst	d			15 17						16 17						17 17						
Appley Bridge	d			15 21						16 21						17 21						
Parbold	d			15 25						16 25						17 25						
Hoscar	d																					
Burscough Bridge	d			15 29						16 29						17 29						
New Lane	d																					
Bescar Lane	d																					
Meols Cop	d			15 37						16 37						17 37						
Southport	a			15 46						16 46						17 46						
Lostock	d		14 45						15 45						16 45							
Horwich Parkway	d		14 49		15 12				15 49		16 12				16 49		17 12					
Blackrod	d		14 52						15 52						16 52							
Adlington (Lancashire)	d		14 56						15 56						16 56							
Chorley	d		15 01		15 19				16 01		16 19				17 01		17 19					
Buckshaw Parkway	d		15 05		15 23				16 05		16 23				17 05		17 23					
Leyland	d		15 13						16 12						17 12							
Preston 8 65,97	a	14 57	15 18		15 33		15 57		16 18		16 33		16 57		17 18		17 33					17 57
	d	14 57	15 20		15 35		15 57		16 20		16 35		16 57		17 20		17 35					17 57
Kirkham & Wesham 97	a		15 29						16 29						17 29							
Poulton-le-Fylde 97	a		15 37		15 52				16 37		16 52				17 37		17 52					
Layton 97	a		15 43						16 42						17 42							
Blackpool North 97	a		15 49		16 01				16 49		17 01				17 49		18 01					
Lancaster 6 65	a	15 14					16 14						17 14									18 14
	d	15 14					16 14						17 14							17 30	18 04	18 14
Oxenholme Lake District 65	a	15 28											17 28									18 28
Windermere 83	a																					
Carnforth	d						16 23													17 40	18a13	
Silverdale	d						16 29													17 46		
Arnside	d						16 33													17 51		
Grange-over-Sands	d						16 38													17 57		
Kents Bank	d						16 42													18 00		
Cark	d						16 46													18 04		
Ulverston	d						16 54													18 12		
Dalton	d						17 03													18 21		
Roose	d						17 08													18 27		
Barrow-in-Furness	a						17 18													18 34		

A To Edinburgh
B From Chester
C To Clitheroe
D From Morecambe to Leeds
E To Glasgow Central

The Sunday service between Manchester Victoria and Wigan Wallgate via Atherton is funded by TfGM and will operate whilst funding exists

Table 82

Sundays

8 December to 29 December

Manchester - Bolton - Wigan, Kirkby, Southport, Preston, Blackpool North and Barrow-in-Furness

Network Diagram - see first Page of Table 82

	NT	NT	TP	NT	TP	NT	NT	NT	TP	NT	NT	TP	NT	NT	TP	NT	NT	NT	TP	NT
			◇1		◇1				◇1			◇1			◇1				◇1	
				A	B			C		A	D					A		C		A
					🚲															
Manchester Airport 85 ✈ d			17 30		18 00				18 30			19 00			19 30				20 30	
Heald Green 85 d																				
Buxton 86 d																				
Hazel Grove 86 d		17 12												19 07						
Stockport 84 d		17 22						18 21						19 22				20 21		
Manchester Piccadilly [10] ⇌ d		17 35	17 46		18 14			18 35	18 46			19 14		19 35	19 46			20 35	20 46	
Manchester Oxford Road d		17 38	17 49		18 18			18 38	18 49			19 18		19 38	19 49			20 38	20 49	
Deansgate ⇌ d		17 40	17 51					18 40	18 51					19 40	19 51			20 40	20 51	
Rochdale 41 d																				
Manchester Victoria ⇌ d	17 25			18 00		18 12	18 25			19 00			19 25			20 00	20 25			21 00
Salford Central d																				
Salford Crescent a	17 29	17 44	17 54	18 06		18 16	18 29	18 44	18 54	19 06		19 22	19 29	19 44	19 54	20 06	20 29	20 44	20 54	21 06
d	17 30	17 44	17 55	18 08		18 17	18 30	18 44	18 55	19 08		19 23	19 30	19 44	19 55	20 08	20 30	20 44	20 55	21 08
Swinton d						18 23														
Moorside d						18 26														
Walkden d						18 29														
Atherton d						18 35														
Hag Fold d						18 37														
Daisy Hill d						18 40														
Clifton d																				
Kearsley d																				
Farnworth d																				
Moses Gate d																				
Bolton a	17 40	17 54	18 05	18 19	18 31		18 40	18 54	19 05	19 19		19 33	19 40	19 54	20 05	20 19	20 40	20 54	21 05	21 19
d	17 40	17 55	18 05		18 31		18 40	18 55	19 05			19 33	19 40	19 55	20 05		20 40	20 55	21 05	
Westhoughton d		18 02						19 02						20 02				21 02		
Hindley d		18 06				18 45		19 06						20 06				21 06		
Ince d						18 48														
Wigan North Western a																				
Wigan Wallgate a		18 11				18 55		19 11						20 11				21 11		
d		18 13						19 13						20 13				21 13		
Pemberton d																				
Orrell d																				
Upholland d																				
Rainford d																				
Kirkby a																				
Gathurst d		18 17						19 17						20 17				21 17		
Appley Bridge d		18 21						19 21						20 21				21 21		
Parbold d		18 25						19 25						20 25				21 25		
Hoscar d																				
Burscough Bridge d		18 29						19 29						20 29				21 29		
New Lane d																				
Bescar Lane d																				
Meols Cop d		18 37						19 37						20 37				21 37		
Southport a		18 46						19 46						20 46				21 46		
Lostock d	17 45						18 45						19 45				20 45			
Horwich Parkway d	17 49		18 12				18 49		19 12				19 49		20 12		20 49		21 12	
Blackrod d	17 52						18 52						19 52				20 52			
Adlington (Lancashire) d	17 56						18 56						19 56				20 56			
Chorley d	18 01		18 19		18 43		19 01		19 19			19 45	20 01		20 19		21 01		21 19	
Buckshaw Parkway d	18 05		18 23				19 05		19 23				20 05		20 23		21 05		21 23	
Leyland d	18 12						19 14						20 14				21 12			
Preston [8] 65,97 a	18 18		18 33		18 54		19 19		19 33			19 57	20 19		20 33		21 18		21 33	
d	18 20		18 35 / 19 06		18 57 / 19 06		19 21		19 35			20 06	20 21		20 35		21 20		21 35	
Kirkham & Wesham 97 a	18 29						19 30						20 30				21 29			
Poulton-le-Fylde 97 a	18 37		18 52				19 38		19 52				20 38		20 52		21 37		21 52	
Layton 97 a	18 42						19 42						20 43				21 42			
Blackpool North 97 a	18 49		19 01				19 49		20 01				20 49		21 01		21 49		22 01	
Lancaster [6] 65 a			19 22		19 14 / 19 22							20 23								
d			19 22		19 14 / 19 22						20 20	20 24								
Oxenholme Lake District 65 a					19 28															
Windermere 83 a																				
Carnforth d			19 31		19 31						20a29	20 32								
Silverdale d			19 36		19 36							20 38								
Arnside d			19 41		19 41							20 42								
Grange-over-Sands d			19 46		19 46							20 48								
Kents Bank d			19 50		19 50							20 51								
Cark d			19 54		19 54							20 56								
Ulverston d			20 02		20 02							21 04								
Dalton d			20 11		20 11							21 12								
Roose d			20 16		20 16							21 18								
Barrow-in-Furness a			20 26		20 26							21 27								

A To Clitheroe
B To Edinburgh
C From Chester
D From Morecambe to Leeds

The Sunday service between Manchester Victoria and Wigan Wallgate via Atherton is funded by TfGM and will operate whilst funding exists

Table 82

Sundays

8 December to 29 December

Manchester - Bolton - Wigan, Kirkby, Southport, Preston, Blackpool North and Barrow-in-Furness

Network Diagram - see first Page of Table 82

			TP	NT	NT		TP	NT	NT	NT	TP
			◇1				◇1				◇1
			A					B		C	
Manchester Airport	85 ✈	d					21 30				22 30
Heald Green	85	d									
Buxton	86	d									
Hazel Grove	86	d			21 07						
Stockport	84	d			21 22					22 21	
Manchester Piccadilly 10		d			21 35		21 46			22 35	22 46
Manchester Oxford Road		d			21 38		21 49			22 38	22 49
Deansgate		d			21 40		21 51			22 40	22 51
Rochdale	41	d									
Manchester Victoria		d		21 25				22 00			
Salford Central		d									
Salford Crescent		a		21 29	21 44		21 54	22 06		22 44	22 54
		d		21 30	21 44		21 55	22 08		22 44	22 55
Swinton		d									
Moorside		d									
Walkden		d									
Atherton		d									
Hag Fold		d									
Daisy Hill		d									
Clifton		d									
Kearsley		d									
Farnworth		d									
Moses Gate		d									
Bolton		a		21 40	21 54		22 05	22 19		22 54	23 05
		d		21 40	21 55		22 05			22 55	23 05
Westhoughton		d			22 02					23 02	
Hindley		d			22 06					23 06	
Ince		d									
Wigan North Western		a									
Wigan Wallgate		a			22 15					23 15	
		d									
Pemberton		d									
Orrell		d									
Upholland		d									
Rainford		d									
Kirkby		a									
Gathurst		d									
Appley Bridge		d									
Parbold		d									
Hoscar		d									
Burscough Bridge		d									
New Lane		d									
Bescar Lane		d									
Meols Cop		d									
Southport		a									
Lostock		d		21 45							23 10
Horwich Parkway		d		21 49							23 14
Blackrod		d		21 52							23 17
Adlington (Lancashire)		d		21 56							23 20
Chorley		d		22 01			22 17				23 25
Buckshaw Parkway		d		22 05							23 28
Leyland		d		22 12							23 34
Preston 8	65,97	a		22 18			22 27				23 42
		d		22 20			22 29				23 47
Kirkham & Wesham	97	a		22 29							23 56
Poulton-le-Fylde	97	a		22 37			22 46				00 05
Layton	97	a		22 42							
Blackpool North	97	a		22 49			22 55				00 14
Lancaster 6	65	a									
		d	21 22						22 05		
Oxenholme Lake District	65	a									
Windermere	83	a									
Carnforth		d	21 30						22 15		
Silverdale		d	21 36						22 21		
Arnside		d	21 40						22 26		
Grange-over-Sands		d	21 46						22 32		
Kents Bank		d	21 49						22 35		
Cark		d	21 54						22 39		
Ulverston		d	22 02						22 47		
Dalton		d	22 10						22 56		
Roose		d	22 16						23 02		
Barrow-in-Furness		a	22 25						23 09		

A From Windermere **B** To Blackburn **C** From Chester

The Sunday service between Manchester Victoria and Wigan Wallgate via Atherton is funded by TfGM and will operate whilst funding exists

Table 82

Sundays

5 January to 9 February

Manchester - Bolton - Wigan, Kirkby, Southport, Preston, Blackpool North and Barrow-in-Furness

Network Diagram - see first Page of Table 82

		NT	TP	TP	TP	TP	NT	NT	NT	TP	NT	NT	NT	TP	NT	NT	NT	VT	TP	NT	NT	NT	VT
				◇1		◇1				◇1				◇1					◇1				
				A				B				B				B	C	D			B		D
		🚌	🚌		🚌		🚌	🚌		🍴	🚌	🚌			🚌	🚌		🚌		🚌	🚌		🚌
Manchester Airport 85 ✈	d		00 05		05 30	07 48				08 49				09 29					10 30				
Heald Green 85	d																						
Buxton 86	d																						
Hazel Grove 86	d												09 12										
Stockport 84	d								08 22				09 22				10 12					11 11	
Manchester Piccadilly 10 🚊	d		00 30		05 55	08 03			08 35	09 03			09 35	09 46			10 24		10 46			11 26	
Manchester Oxford Road	d					08 06			08 38	09 07			09 38	09 49			10 38		10 49			11 38	
Deansgate 🚊	d					08 08			08 40	09 08			09 40	09 51			10 40		10 51			11 40	
Rochdale 41	d																						
Manchester Victoria 🚊	d							08 05				09 05				10 05					11 05		
Salford Central	d																						
Salford Crescent	a					08 11		08 15	08 44	09 12		09 15	09 44	09 54		10 15	10 44		10 54		11 15	11 44	
	d					08 12			08 44	09 12			09 44	09 55			10 44		10 55			11 44	
Swinton	d																						
Moorside	d																						
Walkden	d																						
Atherton	d																						
Hag Fold	d																						
Daisy Hill	d																						
Clifton	d																						
Kearsley	d																						
Farnworth	d																						
Moses Gate	d																						
Bolton	a		00s55		06s20	08 22			08 54	09 22			09 54	10 05			10 54		11 05			11 54	
	d					08 22			08 55	09 23			09 55	10 05			10 55		11 05			11 55	
Westhoughton	d								09 02				10 02				11 02					12 02	
Hindley	d								09 06				10 06				11 06					12 06	
Ince	d																						
Wigan North Western	a																						
Wigan Wallgate	a								09 11				10 11				11 11					12 11	
	d								09 13				10 13				11 13					12 13	
Pemberton	d																						
Orrell	d																						
Upholland	d																						
Rainford	d																						
Kirkby	a																						
Gathurst	d								09 17				10 17				11 17					12 17	
Appley Bridge	d								09 21				10 21				11 21					12 21	
Parbold	d								09 25				10 25				11 25					12 25	
Hoscar	d																						
Burscough Bridge	d								09 29				10 29				11 29					12 29	
New Lane	d																						
Bescar Lane	d																						
Meols Cop	d								09 37				10 37				11 37					12 37	
Southport	a								09 46				10 46				11 46					12 46	
Lostock	d																						
Horwich Parkway	d					08 29				09 29				10 12					11 12				
Blackrod	d																						
Adlington (Lancashire)	d																						
Chorley	d	00 05				08a36	09 15			09a37	10 15			10a19	11 15				11a19	12 15			
Buckshaw Parkway	d	00 15					09 25				10 25				11 25					12 25			
Leyland	d	00 27					09 37				10 37				11 37					12 37			
Preston 8 65,97	a	00s47	01s30		06s55		09 57				10 57				11 57					12 57			
	d																						
Kirkham & Wesham 97	a	01s12																					
Poulton-le-Fylde 97	a	01s32																					
Layton 97	a	01s42																					
Blackpool North 97	a	01 52	02 10		07 35																		
Lancaster 6 65	a																						
	d																	10 15					11 15
Oxenholme Lake District 65	a																	11 00					12 00
Windermere 83	a																						
Carnforth	d																						
Silverdale	d																						
Arnside	d																						
Grange-over-Sands	d																						
Kents Bank	d																						
Cark	d																						
Ulverston	d																						
Dalton	d																						
Roose	d			00 05																			
Barrow-in-Furness	a			00 14																			

A From Preston
B From Salford Crescent
C From Chester
D To Carlisle

The Sunday service between Manchester Victoria and Wigan Wallgate via Atherton is funded by TfGM and will operate whilst funding exists

Table 82

Sundays

5 January to 9 February

Manchester - Bolton - Wigan, Kirkby, Southport, Preston, Blackpool North and Barrow-in-Furness

Network Diagram - see first Page of Table 82

		TP	TP	TP	NT	VT		NT	NT	TP	TP	NT	NT	VT	TP	VT		NT	NT	TP	NT	VT	TP	TP	NT
		◇1		◇1							◇1				◇1								◇1	◇1	
						A		B	C				D	E		A		B			F	G		H	B
			🚌		🚌	🚌		🚌		🚌		🚌		🚌		🚌		🚌		🚌		🚌			🚌
Manchester Airport 85 ✈	d			11 30							12 30												13 30	14 00	
Heald Green 85	d																								
Buxton 86	d																								
Hazel Grove 86	d																		13 12						
Stockport 84	d								12 21										13 22						
Manchester Piccadilly 10	d			11 46					12 35		12 46								13 35				13 46	14 14	
Manchester Oxford Road	d			11 49					12 38		12 49								13 38				13 49	14 18	
Deansgate	d			11 51					12 40		12 51								13 40				13 51		
Rochdale 41	d																								
Manchester Victoria	d							12 05										13 05							14 05
Salford Central	d																								
Salford Crescent	a			11 54				12 15	12 44		12 54							13 15	13 44				13 54		14 15
	d			11 55					12 44		12 55								13 44				13 55		
Swinton	d																								
Moorside	d																								
Walkden	d																								
Atherton	d																								
Hag Fold	d																								
Daisy Hill	d																								
Clifton	d																								
Kearsley	d																								
Farnworth	d																								
Moses Gate	d																								
Bolton	a			12 05					12 54		13 05								13 54				14 05		
	d			12 05					12 55		13 05								13 55				14 05		
Westhoughton	d								13 02										14 02						
Hindley	d								13 06										14 06						
Ince	d																								
Wigan North Western	a																							14 42	
Wigan Wallgate	a								13 11										14 11						
	d								13 13										14 13						
Pemberton	d																								
Orrell	d																								
Upholland	d																								
Rainford	d																								
Kirkby	a																								
Gathurst	d								13 17										14 17						
Appley Bridge	d								13 21										14 21						
Parbold	d								13 25										14 25						
Hoscar	d																								
Burscough Bridge	d								13 29										14 29						
New Lane	d																								
Bescar Lane	d																								
Meols Cop	d								13 37										14 37						
Southport	a								13 46										14 46						
Lostock	d																								
Horwich Parkway	d			12 12							13 12												14 12		
Blackrod	d																								
Adlington (Lancashire)	d																								
Chorley	d			12a19	13 15						13a19	14 15											14 19		
Buckshaw Parkway	d				13 25							14 25											14 23		
Leyland	d				13 37							14 37													
Preston 8 65,97	a				13 57							14 57											14 34	14 57	
	d	11 14												12 40	12 48							13 40	14 36	14 57	
Kirkham & Wesham 97	a																								
Poulton-le-Fylde 97	a																						14 55		
Layton 97	a																								
Blackpool North 97	a																						15 04		
Lancaster 6 65	a	11 30												13 30	13 03							14 30		15 14	
	d	11 31	11 40			11 45				12 30			12 48	13 35	13 04	13 10				13 15	14 27	14 35		15 14	
Oxenholme Lake District 65	a					12 30								14 20		13 55						15 20		15 28	
Windermere 83	a		12 27							13 17										14 02					
Carnforth	d	11 39											12a57		13 12						14a59				
Silverdale	d	11 45													13 18										
Arnside	d	11 49													13 22										
Grange-over-Sands	d	11 54													13 28										
Kents Bank	d														13 31										
Cark	d	12 00													13 36										
Ulverston	d	12 08													13 44										
Dalton	d	12 17													13 52										
Roose	d														13 58										
Barrow-in-Furness	a	12 30													14 07										

A To Carlisle
B From Salford Crescent
C From Chester
D From Morecambe to Leeds
E From Wigan North Western to Carlisle
F To Leeds
G From Wigan North Western
H To Edinburgh

The Sunday service between Manchester Victoria and Wigan Wallgate via Atherton is funded by TfGM and will operate whilst funding exists

Table 82

Sundays
5 January to 9 February

Manchester - Bolton - Wigan, Kirkby, Southport, Preston, Blackpool North and Barrow-in-Furness

Network Diagram - see first Page of Table 82

	NT		NT	TP	TP	NT	NT	NT	TP	TP	NT		NT	NT	TP	NT	NT	NT	TP	NT	NT		TP	
				◇1	◇1				◇1	◇1					◇1				◇1				◇1	
			A			B				C	B			A		B		D	E					
Manchester Airport 85 d				14 30	15 00				15 30	16 00					16 30				17 00				17 30	
Heald Green 85 d																								
Buxton 86 d																								
Hazel Grove 86 d								15 07													17 12			
Stockport 84 d			14 21					15 22						16 21							17 22			
Manchester Piccadilly 10 d			14 35	14 46	15 14			15 35	15 46	16 14				16 35	16 46				17 14		17 35		17 46	
Manchester Oxford Road d	14 24		14 38	14 49	15 18		15 24	15 38	15 49	16 18			16 24	16 38	16 49				17 18	17 24	17 38		17 49	
Deansgate d			14 40	14 51				15 40	15 51					16 40	16 51						17 40		17 51	
Rochdale 41 d																								
Manchester Victoria d						15 05					16 05					17 05								
Salford Central d																								
Salford Crescent a	14 28		14 44	14 54		15 15	15 28	15 44	15 54		16 15		16 28	16 44	16 54	17 15				17 28	17 44		17 54	
d	14 29		14 44	14 55			15 29	15 44	15 55				16 29	16 44	16 55					17 29	17 44		17 55	
Swinton d																								
Moorside d																								
Walkden d																								
Atherton d																								
Hag Fold d																								
Daisy Hill d																								
Clifton d																								
Kearsley d																								
Farnworth d																								
Moses Gate d																								
Bolton a	14 39		14 54	15 05			15 39	15 54	16 05				16 39	16 54	17 05					17 39	17 54		18 05	
d	14 39		14 55	15 05			15 39	15 55	16 05				16 39	16 55	17 05					17 39	17 55		18 05	
Westhoughton d			15 02					16 02						17 02							18 02			
Hindley d			15 06					16 06						17 06							18 06			
Ince d																								
Wigan North Western a					15 42					16 42									17 42					
Wigan Wallgate a			15 11					16 11						17 11							18 11			
d			15 13					16 13						17 13							18 13			
Pemberton d																								
Orrell d																								
Upholland d																								
Rainford d																								
Kirkby a																								
Gathurst d			15 17					16 17						17 17							18 17			
Appley Bridge d			15 21					16 21						17 21							18 21			
Parbold d			15 25					16 25						17 25							18 25			
Hoscar d																								
Burscough Bridge d			15 29					16 29						17 29							18 29			
New Lane d																								
Bescar Lane d																								
Meols Cop d			15 37					16 37						17 37							18 37			
Southport a			15 46					16 46						17 46							18 46			
Lostock d	14 44						15 44						16 44							17 44				
Horwich Parkway d	14 48			15 12			15 48		16 12				16 48		17 12					17 48			18 12	
Blackrod d	14 51						15 51						16 51							17 51				
Adlington (Lancashire) d	14 55						15 55						16 55							17 55				
Chorley d	15 00			15 19			16 00		16 19				17 00		17 19					18 00			18 19	
Buckshaw Parkway d	15 04			15 23			16 04		16 23				17 04		17 23					18 04			18 23	
Leyland d	15 13						16 12						17 12							18 12				
Preston 8 65,97 a	15 18			15 33	15 57		16 18		16 33	16 57			17 18		17 33				17 57	18 18			18 33	
d	15 20			15 35	15 57		16 20		16 35	16 57			17 20		17 35				17 57	18 20			18 35	19 06
Kirkham & Wesham 97 a	15 29						16 29						17 29							18 29				
Poulton-le-Fylde 97 a	15 37			15 52			16 37		16 52				17 37		17 52					18 37			18 52	
Layton 97 a	15 43						16 42						17 42							18 42				
Blackpool North 97 a	15 49			16 01			16 49		17 01				17 49		18 01					18 49			19 01	
Lancaster 6 65 a					16 14					17 14									18 14					19 22
d					16 14					17 14							17 30	18 04	18 14					19 22
Oxenholme Lake District 65 a										17 28									18 28					
Windermere 83 a																								
Carnforth d					16 23												17 40	18a13						19 31
Silverdale d					16 29												17 46							19 36
Arnside d					16 33												17 51							19 41
Grange-over-Sands d					16 38												17 57							19 46
Kents Bank d					16 42												18 00							19 50
Cark d					16 46												18 04							19 54
Ulverston d					16 54												18 12							20 02
Dalton d					17 03												18 21							20 11
Roose d					17 08												18 27							20 16
Barrow-in-Furness a					17 18												18 34							20 26

A From Chester
B From Salford Crescent
C To Edinburgh
D From Morecambe to Leeds
E To Glasgow Central

The Sunday service between Manchester Victoria and Wigan Wallgate via Atherton is funded by TfGM and will operate whilst funding exists

Table 82

Sundays

5 January to 9 February

Manchester - Bolton - Wigan, Kirkby, Southport, Preston, Blackpool North and Barrow-in-Furness

Network Diagram - see first Page of Table 82

	TP ◇1 A 🍴		NT B 🚌	NT	NT C	TP ◇1	NT B 🚌	NT D	TP ◇1	NT	NT	TP ◇1	NT B 🚌	NT	NT C	TP ◇1	NT B 🚌	NT	TP ◇1 E	TP ◇1	NT B 🚌	NT
Manchester Airport 85 ✈ d	18 00					18 30			19 00			19 30				20 30				21 30		
Heald Green 85 d																						
Buxton 86 d																						
Hazel Grove 86 d											19 07							21 07				
Stockport 84 d					18 21						19 22				20 21			21 22				
Manchester Piccadilly 10 🚇 d	18 14				18 35	18 46			19 14		19 35	19 46			20 35	20 46		21 35		21 46		
Manchester Oxford Road d	18 18			18 24	18 38	18 49			19 18	19 24	19 38	19 49		20 24	20 38	20 49		21 38		21 49		
Deansgate 🚇 d					18 40	18 51					19 40	19 51			20 40	20 51		21 40		21 51		
Rochdale 41 d																						
Manchester Victoria 🚇 d			18 05				19 05						20 05				21 05				22 05	
Salford Central d																						
Salford Crescent a			18 15	18 28	18 44	18 54	19 15		19 22	19 28	19 44	19 54	20 15	20 28	20 44	20 54	21 15	21 44		21 54	22 15	
d				18 29	18 44	18 55			19 23	19 29	19 44	19 55		20 29	20 44	20 55		21 44		21 55		
Swinton d																						
Moorside d																						
Walkden d																						
Atherton d																						
Hag Fold d																						
Daisy Hill d																						
Clifton d																						
Kearsley d																						
Farnworth d																						
Moses Gate d																						
Bolton a	18 31			18 39	18 54	19 05			19 33	19 39	19 54	20 05		20 39	20 54	21 05		21 54		22 05		
d	18 31			18 39	18 55	19 05			19 33	19 39	19 55	20 05		20 39	20 55	21 05		21 55		22 05		
Westhoughton d					19 02						20 02				21 02			22 02				
Hindley d					19 06						20 06				21 06			22 06				
Ince d																						
Wigan North Western a																				22 18		
Wigan Wallgate a					19 11						20 11				21 11			22 15				
d					19 13						20 13				21 13							
Pemberton d																						
Orrell d																						
Upholland d																						
Rainford d																						
Kirkby a																						
Gathurst d					19 17						20 17				21 17							
Appley Bridge d					19 21						20 21				21 21							
Parbold d					19 25						20 25				21 25							
Hoscar d																						
Burscough Bridge d					19 29						20 29				21 29							
New Lane d																						
Bescar Lane d																						
Meols Cop d					19 37						20 37				21 37							
Southport a					19 46						20 46				21 46							
Lostock d				18 44						19 44				20 44								
Horwich Parkway d				18 48		19 12				19 48		20 12		20 48		21 12						
Blackrod d				18 51						19 51				20 51								
Adlington (Lancashire) d				18 55						19 55				20 55								
Chorley d	18 43			19 00		19 19			19 45	20 00		20 19		21 00		21 19						
Buckshaw Parkway d				19 04		19 23				20 04		20 23		21 04		21 23						
Leyland d				19 14						20 14				21 12								
Preston 8 65,97 a	18 54			19 19		19 33			19 57	20 19		20 33		21 18		21 33				22 44		
d	18 57	19 06		19 21		19 35			20 06	20 21		20 35		21 20		21 35				22 45		
Kirkham & Wesham 97 a				19 30						20 30				21 29								
Poulton-le-Fylde 97 a				19 38		19 52				20 38		20 52		21 37		21 52				23 02		
Layton 97 a				19 42						20 43				21 42								
Blackpool North 97 a				19 49		20 01				20 49		21 01		21 49		22 01				23 11		
Lancaster 6 65 a	19 14	19 22							20 23													
d	19 14	19 22						20 20	20 24										21 22			22 05
Oxenholme Lake District 65 a	19 28																					
Windermere 83 a																						
Carnforth d		19 31						20a29	20 32										21 30			22 15
Silverdale d		19 36							20 38										21 36			22 21
Arnside d		19 41							20 42										21 40			22 26
Grange-over-Sands d		19 46							20 48										21 46			22 32
Kents Bank d		19 50							20 51										21 49			22 35
Cark d		19 54							20 56										21 54			22 39
Ulverston d		20 02							21 04										22 02			22 47
Dalton d		20 11							21 12										22 10			22 56
Roose d		20 16							21 18										22 16			23 02
Barrow-in-Furness a		20 26							21 27										22 25			23 09

A To Edinburgh
B From Salford Crescent
C From Chester
D From Morecambe to Leeds
E From Windermere

The Sunday service between Manchester Victoria and Wigan Wallgate via Atherton is funded by TfGM and will operate whilst funding exists

Table 82

Sundays
5 January to 9 February

Manchester - Bolton - Wigan, Kirkby, Southport, Preston, Blackpool North and Barrow-in-Furness

Network Diagram - see first Page of Table 82

Station	Table		NT	NT	TP	NT
					◇1	
				A		B
			🚌			🚌
Manchester Airport	85 ✈	d			22 30	
Heald Green	85	d				
Buxton	86	d				
Hazel Grove	86	d				
Stockport	84	d		22 21		
Manchester Piccadilly 10	⇌	d		22 35	22 46	
Manchester Oxford Road		d		22 38	22 49	
Deansgate	⇌	d		22 40	22 51	
Rochdale	41	d				
Manchester Victoria	⇌	d				23 05
Salford Central		d				
Salford Crescent		a		22 44	22 54	23 15
		d		22 44	22 55	
Swinton		d				
Moorside		d				
Walkden		d				
Atherton		d				
Hag Fold		d				
Daisy Hill		d				
Clifton		d				
Kearsley		d				
Farnworth		d				
Moses Gate		d				
Bolton		a		22 54	23 05	
		d		22 55	23 05	
Westhoughton		d		23 02		
Hindley		d		23 06		
Ince		d				
Wigan North Western		a			23 18	
Wigan Wallgate		a		23 15		
		d				
Pemberton		d				
Orrell		d				
Upholland		d				
Rainford		d				
Kirkby		a				
Gathurst		d				
Appley Bridge		d				
Parbold		d				
Hoscar		d				
Burscough Bridge		d				
New Lane		d				
Bescar Lane		d				
Meols Cop		d				
Southport		a				
Lostock		d				
Horwich Parkway		d				
Blackrod		d				
Adlington (Lancashire)		d				
Chorley		d	22 15			
Buckshaw Parkway		d	22 25			
Leyland		d	22 37		23 40	
Preston 8	65,97	a	22s57		23 45	
		d			23 47	
Kirkham & Wesham	97	a	23s22		23 56	
Poulton-le-Fylde	97	a	23s42		00 06	
Layton	97	a	23s52			
Blackpool North	97	a	00 02		00 15	
Lancaster 6	65	a				
		d				
Oxenholme Lake District	65	a				
Windermere	83	a				
Carnforth		d				
Silverdale		d				
Arnside		d				
Grange-over-Sands		d				
Kents Bank		d				
Cark		d				
Ulverston		d				
Dalton		d				
Roose		d				
Barrow-in-Furness		a				

A From Chester

B From Salford Crescent

The Sunday service between Manchester Victoria and Wigan Wallgate via Atherton is funded by TfGM and will operate whilst funding exists

Table 82

Sundays

16 February to 23 March

Manchester - Bolton - Wigan, Kirkby, Southport, Preston, Blackpool North and Barrow-in-Furness

Network Diagram - see first Page of Table 82

		NT	NT	TP	TP	NT	TP	NT	TP	NT	NT	NT	TP	NT	NT	TP	TP	NT	TP	TP	TP	NT	NT
							◇1		◇1				◇1			◇1	◇1		◇1	◇1	◇1		
		A	B			C				C				C			D	E			F	C	
				🚌	🚌	🚌				🚌		🚌		🚌	🚌							🚌	🚌
																	✕				✕		
Manchester Airport 85 ✈	d			00 05	05 30				08 48				09 29				10 00			10 30	11 00		
Heald Green 85	d																						
Buxton 86	d																						
Hazel Grove 86	d										09 12												
Stockport 84	d							08 22			09 22							10 12					
Manchester Piccadilly 10 ⇌	d			00 30	05 55		08 16	08 35	09 03		09 35		09 46				10 14	10 24		10 46	11 14		
Manchester Oxford Road	d						08 19	08 38	09 07		09 38		09 49				10 17	10 38		10 49	11 18		
Deansgate ⇌	d						08 21	08 40	09 08		09 40		09 51					10 40		10 51			
Rochdale 41	d																						
Manchester Victoria ⇌	d					08 05				09 05				10 05								11 05	
Salford Central	d																						
Salford Crescent	a					08 15	08 24	08 44	09 12	09 15	09 44		09 54	10 15				10 44		10 54		11 15	
	d						08 25	08 44	09 12		09 44		09 55					10 44		10 55			
Swinton	d																						
Moorside	d																						
Walkden	d																						
Atherton	d																						
Hag Fold	d																						
Daisy Hill	d																						
Clifton	d																						
Kearsley	d																						
Farnworth	d																						
Moses Gate	d																						
Bolton	a			00s55	06s20		08 35	08 54	09 22		09 54		10 05					10 54		11 05			
	d						08 35	08 55	09 23		09 55		10 05					10 55		11 05			
Westhoughton	d							09 02			10 02							11 02					
Hindley	d							09 06			10 06							11 06					
Ince	d																						
Wigan North Western	a																10 41						
Wigan Wallgate	a							09 11			10 11							11 11					
	d							09 13			10 13							11 13					
Pemberton	d																						
Orrell	d																						
Upholland	d																						
Rainford	d																						
Kirkby	a																						
Gathurst	d							09 17			10 17							11 17					
Appley Bridge	d							09 21			10 21							11 21					
Parbold	d							09 25			10 25							11 25					
Hoscar	d																						
Burscough Bridge	d							09 29			10 29							11 29					
New Lane	d																						
Bescar Lane	d																						
Meols Cop	d							09 37			10 37							11 37					
Southport	a							09 46			10 46							11 46					
Lostock	d																						
Horwich Parkway	d																						
Blackrod	d																						
Adlington (Lancashire)	d																						
Chorley	d											09 15			10 15								11 15
Buckshaw Parkway	d											09 25			10 25								11 25
Leyland	d		00 04									09 37			10 37								11 37
Preston 8 65,97	a		00 10	01s30	06s55		09 05		09 52			09 57	10 38		10 57		11 00			11 37	11 59		11 57
	d		00 11				09 06		09 54				10 43				11 09		11 14	11 37	11 59		
Kirkham & Wesham 97	a		00 21																				
Poulton-le-Fylde 97	a		00 29				09 23		10 11				11 03							11 55			
Layton 97	a		00 34																				
Blackpool North 97	a		00 40	02 10	07 35		09 32		10 20				11 10							12 04			
Lancaster 6 65	a																11 25		11 30		12 16		
	d															10 22	11 25		11 31		12 16		
Oxenholme Lake District 65	a															10 37	11 42				12 30		
Windermere 83	a															10 58							
Carnforth	d																		11 39				
Silverdale	d																		11 45				
Arnside	d																		11 49				
Grange-over-Sands	d																		11 54				
Kents Bank	d																						
Cark	d																		12 00				
Ulverston	d																		12 08				
Dalton	d	00 02																	12 17				
Roose	d	00 08																					
Barrow-in-Furness	a	00 17																	12 30				

A From Lancaster
B From Manchester Victoria
C From Salford Crescent
D To Edinburgh
E From Chester
F To Glasgow Central

The Sunday service between Manchester Victoria and Wigan Wallgate via Atherton is funded by TfGM and will operate whilst funding exists

Table 82

Sundays

16 February to 23 March

Manchester - Bolton - Wigan, Kirkby, Southport, Preston, Blackpool North and Barrow-in-Furness

Network Diagram - see first Page of Table 82

Station		NT	NT	TP	NT	NT		TP	TP	NT	NT	TP	TP	NT	NT	NT		TP	NT	NT	TP	NT	NT	TP	TP
				◇1				◇1	◇1			◇1	◇1					◇1			◇1			◇1	◇1
					A	B			C		D		E	A					A	F	C		D		
					(bus)				(trolley)				(trolley)	(bus)					(bus)		(trolley)				
Manchester Airport 85 ✈	d			11 30					12 00			12 30	13 00					13 30			14 00			14 30	15 00
Heald Green 85	d																								
Buxton 86	d																								
Hazel Grove 86	d															13 12									
Stockport 84	d		11 11								12 21					13 22							14 21		
Manchester Piccadilly 10	d		11 26	11 46					12 14		12 35	12 46	13 14			13 35		13 46			14 14		14 35	14 46	15 14
Manchester Oxford Road	d	11 24	11 38	11 49					12 18	12 24	12 38	12 49	13 18		13 24	13 38		13 49			14 18	14 24	14 38	14 49	15 18
Deansgate	d		11 40	11 51							12 40	12 51				13 40		13 51					14 40	14 51	
Rochdale 41	d																								
Manchester Victoria	d				12 05									13 05					14 05						
Salford Central	d																								
Salford Crescent	a	11 28	11 44	11 54	12 15					12 28	12 44	12 54		13 15	13 28	13 44		13 54	14 15			14 28	14 44	14 54	
	d	11 29	11 44	11 55						12 29	12 44	12 55			13 29	13 44		13 55				14 29	14 44	14 55	
Swinton	d																								
Moorside	d																								
Walkden	d																								
Atherton	d																								
Hag Fold	d																								
Daisy Hill	d																								
Clifton	d																								
Kearsley	d																								
Farnworth	d																								
Moses Gate	d																								
Bolton	a	11 39	11 54	12 05						12 39	12 54	13 05			13 39	13 54		14 05				14 39	14 54	15 05	
	d	11 39	11 55	12 05						12 39	12 55	13 05			13 39	13 55		14 05				14 39	14 55	15 05	
Westhoughton	d		12 02								13 02					14 02							15 02		
Hindley	d		12 06								13 06					14 06							15 06		
Ince	d																								
Wigan North Western	a								12 42				13 42								14 42				15 42
Wigan Wallgate	a		12 11								13 11					14 11							15 11		
	d		12 13								13 13					14 13							15 13		
Pemberton	d																								
Orrell	d																								
Upholland	d																								
Rainford	d																								
Kirkby	a																								
Gathurst	d		12 17								13 17					14 17							15 17		
Appley Bridge	d		12 21								13 21					14 21							15 21		
Parbold	d		12 25								13 25					14 25							15 25		
Hoscar	d																								
Burscough Bridge	d		12 29								13 29					14 29							15 29		
New Lane	d																								
Bescar Lane	d																								
Meols Cop	d		12 37								13 37					14 37							15 37		
Southport	a		12 46								13 46					14 46							15 46		
Lostock	d	11 44								12 44					13 44							14 44			
Horwich Parkway	d	11 48		12 12						12 48		13 12			13 48			14 12				14 48		15 12	
Blackrod	d	11 51								12 51					13 51							14 51			
Adlington (Lancashire)	d	11 55								12 55					13 55							14 55			
Chorley	d	12 01		12 19						13 00		13 19			14 00			14 19				15 00		15 19	
Buckshaw Parkway	d	12 05		12 23						13 04		13 23			14 04			14 23				15 04		15 23	
Leyland	d	12 12								13 12					14 12							15 13			
Preston 8 65,97	a	12 18		12 33					12 57	13 18		13 33	13 57		14 18			14 33			14 57	15 18		15 33	15 57
	d	12 20		12 35				12 48	12 57	13 20		13 35	13 57		14 20			14 35			14 57	15 20		15 35	15 57
Kirkham & Wesham 97	a	12 29								13 29					14 29							15 29			
Poulton-le-Fylde 97	a	12 37		12 52						13 37		13 52			14 37			14 52				15 37		15 52	
Layton 97	a	12 42								13 42					14 42							15 43			
Blackpool North 97	a	12 50		12 58						13 49		13 58			14 49			14 58				15 49		15 58	
Lancaster 6 65	a							13 03	13 14				14 14								15 14				16 14
	d					12 48		13 04	13 14				14 14							14 27	15 14				16 14
Oxenholme Lake District 65	a								13 28				14 28								15 28				
Windermere 83	a																								
Carnforth	d					12a57		13 12												14a59					16 23
Silverdale	d							13 18																	16 29
Arnside	d							13 22																	16 33
Grange-over-Sands	d							13 28																	16 38
Kents Bank	d							13 31																	16 42
Cark	d							13 36																	16 46
Ulverston	d							13 44																	16 54
Dalton	d							13 52																	17 03
Roose	d							13 58																	17 08
Barrow-in-Furness	a							14 07																	17 18

A From Salford Crescent
B From Morecambe to Leeds
C To Edinburgh
D From Chester
E To Glasgow Central
F To Leeds

The Sunday service between Manchester Victoria and Wigan Wallgate via Atherton is funded by TfGM and will operate whilst funding exists

Table 82

Sundays

16 February to 23 March

Manchester - Bolton - Wigan, Kirkby, Southport, Preston, Blackpool North and Barrow-in-Furness

Network Diagram - see first Page of Table 82

	NT	NT	NT	TP	TP	NT	NT	NT	TP	NT	NT	NT	TP	NT	NT	TP		TP		NT	NT
				◇1	◇1				◇1				◇1			◇1		◇1			
	A				B	A		C		A		D	E					B		A	
	[bus]				[trolley]	[bus]				[bus]			[trolley]					[trolley]		[bus]	
Manchester Airport 85 ✈ d				15 30	16 00				16 30				17 00			17 30		18 00			
Heald Green 85 d																					
Buxton 86 d																					
Hazel Grove 86 d			15 07												17 12						
Stockport 84 d			15 22					16 21							17 22						
Manchester Piccadilly 10 ⇌ d			15 35	15 46	16 14			16 35	16 46				17 14		17 35	17 46		18 14			
Manchester Oxford Road d		15 24	15 38	15 49	16 18		16 24	16 38	16 49				17 18	17 24	17 38	17 49		18 18			18 24
Deansgate ⇌ d			15 40	15 51				16 40	16 51						17 40	17 51					
Rochdale 41 d																					
Manchester Victoria ⇌ d	15 05					16 05				17 05										18 05	
Salford Central d																					
Salford Crescent a	15 15	15 28	15 44	15 54		16 15	16 28	16 44	16 54	17 15				17 28	17 44	17 54				18 15	18 28
d		15 29	15 44	15 55			16 29	16 44	16 55					17 29	17 44	17 55					18 29
Swinton d																					
Moorside d																					
Walkden d																					
Atherton d																					
Hag Fold d																					
Daisy Hill d																					
Clifton d																					
Kearsley d																					
Farnworth d																					
Moses Gate d																					
Bolton a		15 39	15 54	16 05			16 39	16 54	17 05					17 39	17 54	18 05		18 31			18 39
d		15 39	15 55	16 05			16 39	16 55	17 05					17 39	17 55	18 05		18 31			18 39
Westhoughton d			16 02					17 02							18 02						
Hindley d			16 06					17 06							18 06						
Ince d																					
Wigan North Western a					16 42								17 42								
Wigan Wallgate a			16 11					17 11							18 11						
d			16 13					17 13							18 13						
Pemberton d																					
Orrell d																					
Upholland d																					
Rainford d																					
Kirkby a																					
Gathurst d			16 17					17 17							18 17						
Appley Bridge d			16 21					17 21							18 21						
Parbold d			16 25					17 25							18 25						
Hoscar d																					
Burscough Bridge d			16 29					17 29							18 29						
New Lane d																					
Bescar Lane d																					
Meols Cop d			16 37					17 37							18 37						
Southport a			16 46					17 46							18 46						
Lostock d		15 44					16 44							17 44							18 44
Horwich Parkway d		15 48		16 12			16 48		17 12					17 48		18 12					18 48
Blackrod d		15 51					16 51							17 51							18 51
Adlington (Lancashire) d		15 55					16 55							17 55							18 55
Chorley d		16 00		16 19			17 00		17 19					18 00		18 19		18 43			19 00
Buckshaw Parkway d		16 04		16 23			17 04		17 23					18 04		18 23					19 04
Leyland d		16 12					17 12							18 12							19 14
Preston 8 65,97 a		16 18		16 33	16 57		17 18		17 33				17 57	18 18		18 33		18 54			19 19
d		16 20		16 35	16 57		17 20		17 35				17 57	18 20		18 35	19 06	18 57	19 06		19 21
Kirkham & Wesham 97 a		16 29					17 29							18 29							19 30
Poulton-le-Fylde 97 a		16 37		16 52			17 37		17 52					18 37		18 52					19 38
Layton 97 a		16 42					17 42							18 42							19 42
Blackpool North 97 a		16 49		16 58			17 49		17 58					18 49		18 58					19 49
Lancaster 6 65 a					17 14								18 14				19 22	19 14	19 22		
d					17 14						17 30	18 04	18 14				19 22	19 14	19 22		
Oxenholme Lake District 65 a					17 28								18 28					19 28			
Windermere 83 a																					
Carnforth d											17 40	18a13					19 31		19 31		
Silverdale d											17 46						19 36		19 36		
Arnside d											17 51						19 41		19 41		
Grange-over-Sands d											17 57						19 46		19 46		
Kents Bank d											18 00						19 50		19 50		
Cark d											18 04						19 54		19 54		
Ulverston d											18 12						20 02		20 02		
Dalton d											18 21						20 11		20 11		
Roose d											18 27						20 16		20 16		
Barrow-in-Furness a											18 34						20 26		20 26		

A From Salford Crescent
B To Edinburgh
C From Chester
D From Morecambe to Leeds
E To Glasgow Central

The Sunday service between Manchester Victoria and Wigan Wallgate via Atherton is funded by TfGM and will operate whilst funding exists

Table 82

Sundays

16 February to 23 March

Manchester - Bolton - Wigan, Kirkby, Southport, Preston, Blackpool North and Barrow-in-Furness

Network Diagram - see first Page of Table 82

		NT	TP	NT	NT	TP	NT	NT	TP	NT	NT	NT	TP	NT	TP	NT	NT	TP	NT	NT	NT	TP	NT
			◇1			◇1			◇1				◇1		◇1			◇1				◇1	
		A		B	C					B		A		B	D				B		A		B
				🚌						🚌				🚌					🚌				🚌
Manchester Airport 85 ✈	d		18 30			19 00			19 30				20 30					21 30				22 30	
Heald Green 85	d																						
Buxton 86	d																						
Hazel Grove 86	d							19 07									21 07						
Stockport 84	d	18 21						19 22				20 21					21 22				22 21		
Manchester Piccadilly 10 🚇	d	18 35	18 46			19 14		19 35	19 46			20 35	20 46				21 35	21 46			22 35	22 46	
Manchester Oxford Road	d	18 38	18 49			19 18	19 24	19 38	19 49		20 24	20 38	20 49			21 24	21 38	21 49			22 38	22 49	
Deansgate 🚇	d	18 40	18 51					19 40	19 51			20 40	20 51				21 40	21 51			22 40	22 51	
Rochdale 41	d																						
Manchester Victoria 🚇	d			19 05						20 05				21 05					22 05				23 05
Salford Central	d																						
Salford Crescent	a	18 44	18 54	19 15		19 22	19 28	19 44	19 54	20 15	20 28	20 44	20 54	21 15		21 28	21 44	21 54	22 15		22 44	22 54	23 15
	d	18 44	18 55			19 23	19 29	19 44	19 55		20 29	20 44	20 55			21 29	21 44	21 55			22 44	22 55	
Swinton	d																						
Moorside	d																						
Walkden	d																						
Atherton	d																						
Hag Fold	d																						
Daisy Hill	d																						
Clifton	d																						
Kearsley	d																						
Farnworth	d																						
Moses Gate	d																						
Bolton	a	18 54	19 05			19 33	19 39	19 54	20 05		20 39	20 54	21 05			21 39	21 54	22 05			22 54	23 05	
	d	18 55	19 05			19 33	19 39	19 55	20 05		20 39	20 55	21 05			21 39	21 55	22 05			22 55	23 05	
Westhoughton	d	19 02						20 02				21 02					22 02				23 02		
Hindley	d	19 06						20 06				21 06					22 06				23 06		
Ince	d																						
Wigan North Western	a																						
Wigan Wallgate	a	19 11						20 11				21 11					22 15				23 15		
	d	19 13						20 13				21 13											
Pemberton	d																						
Orrell	d																						
Upholland	d																						
Rainford	d																						
Kirkby	a																						
Gathurst	d	19 17						20 17				21 17											
Appley Bridge	d	19 21						20 21				21 21											
Parbold	d	19 25						20 25				21 25											
Hoscar	d																						
Burscough Bridge	d	19 29						20 29				21 29											
New Lane	d																						
Bescar Lane	d																						
Meols Cop	d	19 37						20 37				21 37											
Southport	a	19 46						20 46				21 46											
Lostock	d						19 44				20 44					21 44						23 10	
Horwich Parkway	d		19 12				19 48		20 12		20 48		21 12			21 48						23 14	
Blackrod	d						19 51				20 51					21 51						23 17	
Adlington (Lancashire)	d						19 55				20 55					21 55						23 20	
Chorley	d		19 19			19 45	20 00		20 19		21 00		21 19			22 00		22 17				23 25	
Buckshaw Parkway	d		19 23				20 04		20 23		21 04		21 23			22 04						23 28	
Leyland	d						20 14				21 12					22 12						23 34	
Preston 8 65,97	a		19 33			19 57	20 19		20 33		21 18		21 31			22 18		22 27				23 42	
	d		19 35			20 06	20 21		20 35		21 20		21 33			22 20		22 29				23 44	
Kirkham & Wesham 97	a						20 30				21 29					22 29						23 53	
Poulton-le-Fylde 97	a		19 52				20 38		20 52		21 37		21 50			22 37		22 46				00 02	
Layton 97	a						20 43				21 42					22 42							
Blackpool North 97	a		19 58				20 49		20 58		21 49		21 59			22 49		22 53				00 10	
Lancaster 6 65	a					20 23																	
	d				20 20	20 24									21 22					22 05			
Oxenholme Lake District 65	a																						
Windermere 83	a																						
Carnforth	d				20a29	20 32									21 30					22 15			
Silverdale	d					20 38									21 36					22 21			
Arnside	d					20 42									21 40					22 26			
Grange-over-Sands	d					20 48									21 46					22 32			
Kents Bank	d					20 51									21 49					22 35			
Cark	d					20 56									21 54					22 39			
Ulverston	d					21 04									22 02					22 47			
Dalton	d					21 12									22 10					22 56			
Roose	d					21 18									22 16					23 02			
Barrow-in-Furness	a					21 27									22 25					23 09			

A From Chester
B From Salford Crescent
C From Morecambe to Leeds
D From Windermere

The Sunday service between Manchester Victoria and Wigan Wallgate via Atherton is funded by TfGM and will operate whilst funding exists

Table 82

Sundays

30 March to 11 May

Manchester - Bolton - Wigan, Kirkby, Southport, Preston, Blackpool North and Barrow-in-Furness

Network Diagram - see first Page of Table 82

Station		NT	TP	TP	TP	TP	NT	NT	NT	TP		NT	NT	NT	TP	TP	NT	TP	NT	NT		TP	TP	NT	NT
				1		◇1				◇1					◇1	◇1		◇1				◇1	◇1		
		A		B			C					C				D	C			E			F	C	
			(bus)		(bus)		(bus)					(bus)				(trolley)	(bus)						(trolley)	(bus)	
Manchester Airport 85 ✈	d		00 05		05 30	07 48				08 48					09 29	10 00						10 30	11 00		
Heald Green 85	d																								
Buxton 86	d																								
Hazel Grove 86	d													09 12											
Stockport 84	d								08 22					09 22						10 12					
Manchester Piccadilly 10	d		00 30		05 55	08 03			08 35	09 03				09 35	09 46	10 15				10 24		10 46	11 14		
Manchester Oxford Road	d					08 06		08 25	08 38	09 06			09 24	09 38	09 49	10 18			10 24	10 38		10 49	11 18		11 24
Deansgate	d					08 08			08 40	09 08				09 40	09 51					10 40		10 51			
Rochdale 41	d																								
Manchester Victoria	d						08 05					09 05					10 05							11 05	
Salford Central	d																								
Salford Crescent	a					08 11	08 15	08 29	08 44	09 11		09 15	09 28	09 44	09 54		10 15		10 28	10 44		10 54		11 15	11 28
	d					08 12		08 30	08 44	09 12			09 29	09 44	09 55				10 29	10 44		10 55			11 29
Swinton	d																								
Moorside	d																								
Walkden	d																								
Atherton	d																								
Hag Fold	d																								
Daisy Hill	d																								
Clifton	d																								
Kearsley	d																								
Farnworth	d																								
Moses Gate	d																								
Bolton	a		00s55		06s20	08 22		08 40	08 54	09 22			09 39	09 54	10 05				10 39	10 54		11 05			11 39
	d					08 22		08 40	08 55	09 22			09 39	09 55	10 05				10 39	10 55		11 05			11 39
Westhoughton	d								09 02					10 02						11 02					
Hindley	d								09 06					10 06						11 06					
Ince	d																								
Wigan North Western	a															10 42							11 42		
Wigan Wallgate	a								09 11					10 11						11 11					
	d								09 13					10 13						11 13					
Pemberton	d																								
Orrell	d																								
Upholland	d																								
Rainford	d																								
Kirkby	a																								
Gathurst	d								09 17					10 17						11 17					
Appley Bridge	d								09 21					10 21						11 21					
Parbold	d								09 25					10 25						11 25					
Hoscar	d																								
Burscough Bridge	d								09 29					10 29						11 29					
New Lane	d																								
Bescar Lane	d																								
Meols Cop	d								09 37					10 37						11 37					
Southport	a								09 46					10 46						11 46					
Lostock	d							08 45					09 44						10 44						11 44
Horwich Parkway	d					08 29		08 49		09 29			09 48		10 12				10 48			11 12			11 48
Blackrod	d							08 52					09 51						10 51						11 51
Adlington (Lancashire)	d							08 56					09 55						10 55						11 55
Chorley	d					08 36		09 01		09 36			10 00		10 19				11 00			11 19			12 00
Buckshaw Parkway	d					08 40		09 05		09 40			10 04		10 23				11 04			11 23			12 04
Leyland	d	00 04						09 12					10 12						11 12						12 12
Preston 8 65,97	a	00 10	01s30		06s55	08 50		09 18		09 50			10 18		10 33	10 57			11 20			11 33	11 57		12 18
	d	00 11				08 54		09 20		09 52			10 20		10 35	11 10		11 14	11 21			11 35	11 57		12 20
Kirkham & Wesham 97	a	00 21						09 29					10 29						11 31						12 29
Poulton-le-Fylde 97	a	00 29				09 11		09 37		10 09			10 37		10 52				11 39			11 52			12 37
Layton 97	a	00 34						09 42					10 42						11 44						12 42
Blackpool North 97	a	00 40	02 10		07 35	09 19		09 49		10 18			10 49		11 01				11 49			12 01			12 49
Lancaster 6 65	a															11 25		11 30					12 14		
	d															11 26		11 31					12 14		
Oxenholme Lake District 65	a															11 41							12 28		
Windermere 83	a																								
Carnforth	d																	11 39							
Silverdale	d																	11 45							
Arnside	d																	11 49							
Grange-over-Sands	d																	11 54							
Kents Bank	d																								
Cark	d																	12 00							
Ulverston	d																	12 08							
Dalton	d																	12 17							
Roose	d			00 05																					
Barrow-in-Furness	a			00 14														12 30							

A From Manchester Victoria
B From Carnforth
C From Salford Crescent
D To Edinburgh
E From Chester
F To Glasgow Central

The Sunday service between Manchester Victoria and Wigan Wallgate via Atherton is funded by TfGM and will operate whilst funding exists

Table 82

Sundays

30 March to 11 May

Manchester - Bolton - Wigan, Kirkby, Southport, Preston, Blackpool North and Barrow-in-Furness

Network Diagram - see first Page of Table 82

		NT	TP	NT	NT	TP	TP	NT	NT	TP	TP	NT	NT	NT	TP	NT	NT	TP	NT	NT	TP	TP	NT
			◇1			◇1	◇1			◇1	◇1				◇1			◇1			◇1	◇1	
				A 🚌	B		C		D		E	A 🚌				A 🚌	F	C		D			A 🚌
Manchester Airport 85 ✈	d		11 30				12 00			12 30	13 00				13 30			14 00			14 30	15 00	
Heald Green 85	d																						
Buxton 86	d																						
Hazel Grove 86	d													13 12									
Stockport 84	d	11 11							12 21					13 22						14 21			
Manchester Piccadilly 10	d	11 26	11 46				12 14		12 35	12 46	13 14			13 35	13 46			14 14		14 35	14 46	15 14	
Manchester Oxford Road	d	11 38	11 49				12 18	12 24	12 38	12 49	13 18		13 24	13 38	13 49			14 18	14 24	14 38	14 49	15 18	
Deansgate	d	11 40	11 51						12 40	12 51				13 40	13 51					14 40	14 51		
Rochdale 41	d																						
Manchester Victoria	d			12 05								13 05				14 05							15 05
Salford Central	d																						
Salford Crescent	a	11 44	11 54	12 15				12 28	12 44	12 54		13 15	13 28	13 44	13 54	14 15			14 28	14 44	14 54		15 15
	d	11 44	11 55					12 29	12 44	12 55			13 29	13 44	13 55				14 29	14 44	14 55		
Swinton	d																						
Moorside	d																						
Walkden	d																						
Atherton	d																						
Hag Fold	d																						
Daisy Hill	d																						
Clifton	d																						
Kearsley	d																						
Farnworth	d																						
Moses Gate	d																						
Bolton	a	11 54	12 05					12 39	12 54	13 05			13 39	13 54	14 05				14 39	14 54	15 05		
	d	11 55	12 05					12 39	12 55	13 05			13 39	13 55	14 05				14 39	14 55	15 05		
Westhoughton	d	12 02							13 02					14 02						15 02			
Hindley	d	12 06							13 06					14 06						15 06			
Ince	d																						
Wigan North Western	a						12 42				13 42							14 42				15 42	
Wigan Wallgate	a	12 11							13 11					14 11						15 11			
	d	12 13							13 13					14 13						15 13			
Pemberton	d																						
Orrell	d																						
Upholland	d																						
Rainford	d																						
Kirkby	a																						
Gathurst	d	12 17							13 17					14 17						15 17			
Appley Bridge	d	12 21							13 21					14 21						15 21			
Parbold	d	12 25							13 25					14 25						15 25			
Hoscar	d																						
Burscough Bridge	d	12 29							13 29					14 29						15 29			
New Lane	d																						
Bescar Lane	d																						
Meols Cop	d	12 37							13 37					14 37						15 37			
Southport	a	12 46							13 46					14 46						15 46			
Lostock	d							12 44					13 44						14 44				
Horwich Parkway	d		12 12					12 48		13 12			13 48		14 12				14 48		15 12		
Blackrod	d							12 51					13 51						14 51				
Adlington (Lancashire)	d							12 55					13 55						14 55				
Chorley	d		12 19					13 00		13 19			14 00		14 19				15 00		15 19		
Buckshaw Parkway	d		12 23					13 04		13 23			14 04		14 23				15 04		15 23		
Leyland	d							13 12					14 12						15 13				
Preston 8 65,97	a		12 33				12 57	13 18		13 33	13 57		14 18		14 33			14 57	15 18		15 33	15 57	
	d		12 35			12 48	12 57	13 20		13 35	13 57		14 20		14 35			14 57	15 20		15 35	15 57	
Kirkham & Wesham 97	a							13 29					14 29						15 29				
Poulton-le-Fylde 97	a		12 52					13 37		13 52			14 37		14 52				15 37		15 52		
Layton 97	a							13 42					14 42						15 43				
Blackpool North 97	a		13 01					13 49		14 01			14 49		15 01				15 49		16 01		
Lancaster 6 65	a					13 03	13 14				14 14							15 14				16 14	
	d				12 48	13 04	13 14				14 14						14 27	15 14				16 14	
Oxenholme Lake District 65	a						13 28				14 28							15 28					
Windermere 83	a																						
Carnforth	d				12a57	13 12											14a59					16 23	
Silverdale	d					13 18																16 29	
Arnside	d					13 22																16 33	
Grange-over-Sands	d					13 28																16 38	
Kents Bank	d					13 31																16 42	
Cark	d					13 36																16 46	
Ulverston	d					13 44																16 54	
Dalton	d					13 52																17 03	
Roose	d					13 58																17 08	
Barrow-in-Furness	a					14 07																17 18	

A From Salford Crescent
B From Morecambe to Leeds
C To Edinburgh
D From Chester
E To Glasgow Central
F To Leeds

The Sunday service between Manchester Victoria and Wigan Wallgate via Atherton is funded by TfGM and will operate whilst funding exists

Table 82

Sundays

30 March to 11 May

Manchester - Bolton - Wigan, Kirkby, Southport, Preston, Blackpool North and Barrow-in-Furness

Network Diagram - see first Page of Table 82

Station		NT	NT	TP ◇[1]	TP ◇[1] A	NT B	NT	NT C	TP ◇[1]	NT B	NT	NT D	TP ◇[1] E	NT	NT	TP ◇[1]	TP ◇[1] A	NT B	TP ◇[1]	NT	NT C	TP ◇[1]
Manchester Airport 85	d			15 30	16 00				16 30				17 00			17 30	18 00					18 30
Heald Green 85	d																					
Buxton 86	d																					
Hazel Grove 86	d		15 07												17 12							
Stockport 84	d		15 22					16 21							17 22						18 21	
Manchester Piccadilly [10]	d		15 35	15 46	16 14			16 35	16 46				17 14		17 35	17 46	18 14				18 35	18 46
Manchester Oxford Road	d	15 24	15 38	15 49	16 18		16 24	16 38	16 49				17 18	17 24	17 38	17 49	18 17			18 24	18 38	18 49
Deansgate	d		15 40	15 51				16 40	16 51						17 40	17 51					18 40	18 51
Rochdale 41	d																					
Manchester Victoria	d					16 05				17 05								18 05				
Salford Central	d																					
Salford Crescent	a	15 28	15 44	15 54		16 15	16 28	16 44	16 54	17 15				17 28	17 44	17 54		18 15		18 28	18 44	18 54
	d	15 29	15 44	15 55			16 29	16 44	16 55					17 29	17 44	17 55				18 29	18 44	18 55
Swinton	d																					
Moorside	d																					
Walkden	d																					
Atherton	d																					
Hag Fold	d																					
Daisy Hill	d																					
Clifton	d																					
Kearsley	d																					
Farnworth	d																					
Moses Gate	d																					
Bolton	a	15 39	15 54	16 05			16 39	16 54	17 05					17 39	17 54	18 05				18 39	18 54	19 05
	d	15 39	15 55	16 05			16 39	16 55	17 05					17 39	17 55	18 05				18 39	18 55	19 05
Westhoughton	d		16 02					17 02							18 02						19 02	
Hindley	d		16 06					17 06							18 06						19 06	
Ince	d																					
Wigan North Western	a				16 42								17 42				18 42					
Wigan Wallgate	a		16 11					17 11							18 11						19 11	
	d		16 13					17 13							18 13						19 13	
Pemberton	d																					
Orrell	d																					
Upholland	d																					
Rainford	d																					
Kirkby	a																					
Gathurst	d		16 17					17 17							18 17						19 17	
Appley Bridge	d		16 21					17 21							18 21						19 21	
Parbold	d		16 25					17 25							18 25						19 25	
Hoscar	d																					
Burscough Bridge	d		16 29					17 29							18 29						19 29	
New Lane	d																					
Bescar Lane	d																					
Meols Cop	d		16 37					17 37							18 37						19 37	
Southport	a		16 46					17 46							18 46						19 46	
Lostock	d	15 44					16 44							17 44						18 44		
Horwich Parkway	d	15 48		16 12			16 48		17 12					17 48		18 12				18 48		19 12
Blackrod	d	15 51					16 51							17 51						18 51		
Adlington (Lancashire)	d	15 55					16 55							17 55						18 55		
Chorley	d	16 00		16 19			17 00		17 19					18 00		18 19				19 00		19 19
Buckshaw Parkway	d	16 04		16 23			17 04		17 23					18 04		18 23				19 04		19 23
Leyland	d	16 12					17 12							18 12						19 14		
Preston [8] 65,97	a	16 18		16 33	16 57		17 18		17 33				17 57	18 18		18 33	18 57			19 19		19 33
	d	16 20		16 35	16 57		17 20		17 35				17 57	18 20		18 35	18 57		19 06	19 21		19 35
Kirkham & Wesham 97	a	16 29					17 29							18 29						19 30		
Poulton-le-Fylde 97	a	16 37		16 52			17 37		17 52					18 37		18 52				19 38		19 52
Layton 97	a	16 42					17 42							18 42						19 42		
Blackpool North 97	a	16 49		17 01			17 49		18 01					18 49		19 01				19 49		20 01
Lancaster [6] 65	a				17 14								18 14				19 14		19 22			
	d				17 14						17 30	18 04	18 14				19 14		19 22			
Oxenholme Lake District 65	a				17 28								18 28				19 28					
Windermere 83	a																					
Carnforth	d										17 40	18a13							19 31			
Silverdale	d										17 46								19 36			
Arnside	d										17 51								19 41			
Grange-over-Sands	d										17 57								19 46			
Kents Bank	d										18 00								19 50			
Cark	d										18 04								19 54			
Ulverston	d										18 12								20 02			
Dalton	d										18 21								20 11			
Roose	d										18 27								20 16			
Barrow-in-Furness	a										18 34								20 26			

A To Edinburgh
B From Salford Crescent
C From Chester
D From Morecambe to Leeds
E To Glasgow Central

The Sunday service between Manchester Victoria and Wigan Wallgate via Atherton is funded by TfGM and will operate whilst funding exists

Table 82

Sundays

30 March to 11 May

Manchester - Bolton - Wigan, Kirkby, Southport, Preston, Blackpool North and Barrow-in-Furness

Network Diagram - see first Page of Table 82

	NT	NT	TP	NT	NT	TP	NT		NT	NT	TP	NT	TP	NT	NT	TP	NT		NT	NT	TP	NT	
			◇1			◇1					◇1		◇1			◇1					◇1		
	A	B					A			C		A	D				A			C		A	
	🚌						🚌					🚌					🚌					🚌	
Manchester Airport 85 ✈ d			19 00			19 30					20 30					21 30					22 30		
Heald Green 85 d																							
Buxton 86 d																							
Hazel Grove 86 d					19 07										21 07								
Stockport 84 d					19 22					20 21					21 22					22 21			
Manchester Piccadilly 10 🚇 d			19 14		19 35	19 46				20 35	20 46				21 35	21 46				22 35	22 46		
Manchester Oxford Road d			19 18	19 24	19 38	19 49			20 24	20 38	20 49			21 24	21 38	21 49				22 38	22 49		
Deansgate 🚇 d					19 40	19 51				20 40	20 51				21 40	21 51				22 40	22 51		
Rochdale 41 d																							
Manchester Victoria 🚇 d	19 05						20 05					21 05					22 05					23 05	
Salford Central d																							
Salford Crescent a	19 15		19 22	19 28	19 44	19 54	20 15		20 28	20 44	20 54	21 15		21 28	21 44	21 54	22 15			22 44	22 54	23 15	
d			19 23	19 29	19 44	19 55			20 29	20 44	20 55			21 29	21 44	21 55				22 44	22 55		
Swinton d																							
Moorside d																							
Walkden d																							
Atherton d																							
Hag Fold d																							
Daisy Hill d																							
Clifton d																							
Kearsley d																							
Farnworth d																							
Moses Gate d																							
Bolton a			19 33	19 39	19 54	20 05			20 39	20 54	21 05			21 39	21 54	22 05				22 54	23 05		
d			19 33	19 39	19 55	20 05			20 39	20 55	21 05			21 39	21 55	22 05				22 55	23 05		
Westhoughton d					20 02					21 02					22 02					23 02			
Hindley d					20 06					21 06					22 06					23 06			
Ince d																							
Wigan North Western a																							
Wigan Wallgate a					20 11					21 11					22 15					23 15			
d					20 13					21 13													
Pemberton d																							
Orrell d																							
Upholland d																							
Rainford d																							
Kirkby a																							
Gathurst d					20 17					21 17													
Appley Bridge d					20 21					21 21													
Parbold d					20 25					21 25													
Hoscar d																							
Burscough Bridge d					20 29					21 29													
New Lane d																							
Bescar Lane d																							
Meols Cop d					20 37					21 37													
Southport a					20 46					21 46													
Lostock d				19 44					20 44					21 44							23 10		
Horwich Parkway d				19 48		20 12			20 48		21 12			21 48							23 14		
Blackrod d				19 51					20 51					21 51							23 17		
Adlington (Lancashire) d				19 55					20 55					21 55							23 20		
Chorley d			19 45	20 00		20 19			21 00		21 19			22 00		22 17					23 25		
Buckshaw Parkway d				20 04		20 23			21 04		21 23			22 04							23 28		
Leyland d				20 14					21 12					22 12							23 34		
Preston 8 65,97 a			19 57	20 19		20 33			21 18		21 33			22 18		22 27					23 42		
d			20 06	20 21		20 35			21 20		21 35			22 20		22 29					23 47		
Kirkham & Wesham 97 a				20 30					21 29					22 29							23 56		
Poulton-le-Fylde 97 a				20 38		20 52			21 37		21 52			22 37		22 46					00 05		
Layton 97 a				20 43					21 42					22 42									
Blackpool North 97 a				20 49		21 01			21 49		22 01			22 49		22 55					00 14		
Lancaster 6 65 a			20 23																				
d		20 20	20 24										21 22						22 05				
Oxenholme Lake District 65 a																							
Windermere 83 a																							
Carnforth d		20a29	20 32										21 30						22 15				
Silverdale d			20 38										21 36						22 21				
Arnside d			20 42										21 40						22 26				
Grange-over-Sands d			20 48										21 46						22 32				
Kents Bank d			20 51										21 49						22 35				
Cark d			20 56										21 54						22 39				
Ulverston d			21 04										22 02						22 47				
Dalton d			21 12										22 10						22 56				
Roose d			21 18										22 16						23 02				
Barrow-in-Furness a			21 27										22 25						23 09				

A From Salford Crescent
B From Morecambe to Leeds
C From Chester
D From Windermere

The Sunday service between Manchester Victoria and Wigan Wallgate via Atherton is funded by TfGM and will operate whilst funding exists

Table 82R

Mondays to Fridays

9 December to 7 February

Barrow-in-Furness, Blackpool North, Preston, Southport, Kirkby and Wigan - Bolton - Manchester

Network Diagram - see first Page of Table 82

Miles	Miles	Miles	Miles	Miles			TP	TP	NT	TP	TP	TP	TP	TP	TP		NT	TP	NT	NT	NT	TP	NT	NT	NT
							MO	MO	MX	MX		TW ThO			MO										
							◇1	◇1		◇1	◇1	◇1	◇1	◇1	◇1			◇1				◇1			
							A	B	C	D	E	D	F		G						H				I
—	0	—	—	—	**Barrow-in-Furness**	d								04 35								05 32			
—	1¾	—	—	—	Roose	d																			
—	6	—	—	—	Dalton	d																			
—	9¼	—	—	—	Ulverston	d								04 51								05 48			
—	15¼	—	—	—	Cark	d																			
—	17¼	—	—	—	Kents Bank	d																			
—	19½	—	—	—	Grange-over-Sands	d								05 03								06 00			
—	22¾	—	—	—	Arnside	d								05 09								06 06			
—	25	—	—	—	Silverdale	d																			
—	28¾	—	—	—	Carnforth	d								05 19								06 16			06 43
—	—	—	—	—	Windermere 83	d																			
—	—	—	—	—	Oxenholme Lake District 65	d																			
—	34¾	—	—	—	**Lancaster** 6 65	a								05 27								06 24			06 52
—	—	—	—	—		d																06 24			
0	—	—	—	—	**Blackpool North** 97	d				03 37	03 37							05 39						06 19	
1¼	—	—	—	—	Layton 97	d																		06 22	
3¼	—	—	—	—	Poulton-le-Fylde 97	d												05 45						06 26	
9¾	—	—	—	—	Kirkham & Wesham 97	d																		06 36	
—	55¾	—	—	—	**Preston** 8 65,97	a												06 03				06 43		06 46	
—	—	—	—	—		d				04u02	04u02	05 12	05 12		05 12			06 05				06 44		06 48	
21½	59¾	—	—	—	Leyland	d												06 10						06 53	
23¾	62	—	—	—	Buckshaw Parkway	d																		06 58	
26	64¼	—	—	—	Chorley	d						05 22	05 22		05 22			06 17				06 54		07 02	
29	67¼	—	—	—	Adlington (Lancashire)	d			00 02															07 07	
31	69¼	—	—	—	Blackrod	d			00 06									06 23						07 11	
32½	70¾	—	—	—	Horwich Parkway	d			00 09			05 29	05 29		05 29			06 26				07 01		07 15	
34½	72¾	—	—	—	Lostock	d			00 13									06 30						07 20	
—	—	0	—	—	**Southport**	d																	06 23		
—	—	1¼	—	—	Meols Cop	d																	06 28		
—	—	4½	—	—	Bescar Lane	d																			
—	—	6½	—	—	New Lane	d																			
—	—	7¾	—	—	Burscough Bridge	d																	06 36		
—	—	9¼	—	—	Hoscar	d																			
—	—	10¾	—	—	Parbold	d																	06 41		
—	—	13	—	—	Appley Bridge	d																	06 45		
—	—	14¾	—	—	Gathurst	d																	06 49		
—	—	—	0	—	**Kirkby**	d																			
—	—	—	5¼	—	Rainford	d																			
—	—	—	7¼	—	Upholland	d																			
—	—	—	8½	—	Orrell	d																			
—	—	—	10½	—	Pemberton	d																			
—	—	17½	12¼	—	**Wigan Wallgate**	a																	06 54		
—	—	—	—	—		d											06 03		06 31	06 36			06 55		
—	—	—	—	0	Wigan North Western	d																			
—	—	18½	13¼	0¾	Ince	d											06 06			06 39					
—	—	20	14¾	—	Hindley	d											06 09		06 36	06 42					
—	—	22½	—	—	Westhoughton	d													06 41				07 03		
37½	75¾	27	—	—	**Bolton**	a			00 17			05 40	05 40		05 40			06 34	06 52			07 07	07 11	07 25	
—	—	—	—	—		d	00 02	00 02	00 17	04u31	04u31	05 40	05 40		05 40			06 35	06 53		06 56	07 08	07 12	07 25	
38¼	76½	27¾	—	—	Moses Gate	d															06 59				
39¾	78	29¼	—	—	Farnworth	d															07 01				
40½	78¾	30	—	—	Kearsley	d															07 03				
43½	81¾	33	—	—	Clifton	d															07 07				
—	—	—	17¼	—	Daisy Hill	d											06 13			06 46					
—	—	—	17½	—	Hag Fold	d											06 16			06 49					
—	—	—	18¾	—	Atherton	d											06 19			06 52					
—	—	—	22¼	—	Walkden	d											06 24			06 58					
—	—	—	24	—	Moorside	d											06 28			07 01					
—	—	—	24¾	—	Swinton	d											06 30			07 04					
46½	84¾	36	28¾	—	**Salford Crescent**	a						05 52	05 52		05 52		06 38	06 47	07 05	07 11	07 15		07 24	07 38	
—	—	—	—	—		d						05 53	05 53		05 53		06 38	06 47	07 08	07 11	07 16		07 25	07 38	
—	—	—	29¾	—	Salford Central	d											06 41			07 14	07 19			07 41	
—	—	—	30½	—	**Manchester Victoria** ⛴	a			00 36								06 46			07 20	07 22			07 47	
—	—	—	—	—	Rochdale 41	a																			
48	86¼	37½	—	—	Deansgate ⛴	a												06 51	07 11				07 28		
48¼	86½	37¾	—	—	**Manchester Oxford Road**	a						05 57	05 57		05 57			06 52	07 13			07 23	07 30		
48¾	87	38¼	—	—	**Manchester Piccadilly** 10 ⛴	a	00 17	00 18		04 46	04 46	06 00	06 00		06 00			06 56	07 17			07 27	07 34		
—	—	—	—	—	Stockport 84	a													07 34						
—	—	—	—	—	Hazel Grove 86	a													07 45						
—	—	—	—	—	Buxton 86	a																			
57	95¼	46½	—	—	Heald Green 85	a												07 10							
58½	96¾	48	—	—	**Manchester Airport** 85 ✈	a	00 34	00 35			05 05	06 16	06 17		06 21			07 15				07 46	07 53		

A from 6 January. From Blackpool North
B until 30 December. From Blackpool North
C From Blackpool North
D from 31 December
E until 30 December, MO from 6 January
F until 27 December, FO from 3 January
G from 30 December
H From Blackburn
I From Skipton

The Sunday service between Wigan Wallgate and Manchester Victoria via Atherton is funded by TfGM and will operate whilst funding exists

Table 82R

Mondays to Fridays

9 December to 7 February

Barrow-in-Furness, Blackpool North, Preston, Southport, Kirkby and Wigan - Bolton - Manchester

Network Diagram - see first Page of Table 82

		NT	TP	NT	NT	NT	NT	TP	NT	NT	TP	NT	NT	NT	NT	NT	TP	TP	NT	NT	NT	NT
			◇1					◇1			◇1						◇1	◇1				
		A		B				C		A					A		C	C			B	
			⚯					⚯			⚯						⚯	⚯				
Barrow-in-Furness	d							06 15								07 14	06 48					
Roose	d							06 19									06 52					
Dalton	d							06 26								07 23	06 59					
Ulverston	d							06 34								07 32	07 07					
Cark	d							06 42								07 40	07 15					
Kents Bank	d							06 46									07 19					
Grange-over-Sands	d							06 50								07 47	07 23					
Arnside	d							06 56								07 53	07 29					
Silverdale	d							07 00								07 58	07 33					
Carnforth	d							07 07								08 06	07 40					
Windermere 83	d																					
Oxenholme Lake District 65	d																					
Lancaster 6 65	a							07 15								08 16	07 48					
	d							07 23									07 48					
Blackpool North 97	d		06 40				06 53				07 11			07 18				07 36				
Layton 97	d		06 43								07 14			07 21				07 39				
Poulton-le-Fylde 97	d		06 47								07 18			07 26				07 43				
Kirkham & Wesham 97	d		06 57								07 27			07 35				07 53				
Preston 8 65,97	a		07 07				07 15	07 41			07 38			07 46			08 07	08 03				
	d		07 09				07 17	07 43			07 47			07 47			08 12					08 21
Leyland	d						07 22							07 53								08 27
Buckshaw Parkway	d						07 28							07 58								08 31
Chorley	d		07 18				07 32				07 56			08 02			08 22					08 35
Adlington (Lancashire)	d						07 37							08 07								08 40
Blackrod	d						07 41							08 11								08 43
Horwich Parkway	d		07 26				07 45							08 15								08 47
Lostock	d		07 30				07 49							08 20								08 50
Southport	d				06 52							07 21									07 59	
Meols Cop	d				06 57							07 26									08 04	
Bescar Lane	d				07 02																	
New Lane	d				07 06																	
Burscough Bridge	d				07 08							07 34									08 12	
Hoscar	d				07 12																	
Parbold	d				07 15							07 39									08 17	
Appley Bridge	d				07 19							07 43									08 21	
Gathurst	d				07 22							07 47									08 24	
Kirkby	d								07 11													
Rainford	d								07 19													
Upholland	d								07 23													
Orrell	d								07 27													
Pemberton	d								07 30													
Wigan Wallgate	a				07 28				07 35			07 51									08 29	
	d			07 15	07 29				07 37			07 53	08 00						08 13		08 30	
Wigan North Western	d					07 22		07 56												08 20		
Ince	d			07 18		07 25			07 40										08 16			
Hindley	d			07 21		07 29			07 43			07 58							08 19	08 25	08 35	
Westhoughton	d					07 33						08 03								08 29		
Bolton	a		07 34			07 42	07 54				08 08	08 11		08 25			08 34			08 38		08 55
	d	07 30	07 35			07 43	07 55			07 59	08 08	08 12		08 25	08 31		08 35			08 39		08 56
Moses Gate	d					07 46				08 02										08 42		
Farnworth	d					07 48				08 04										08 44		
Kearsley	d					07 50				08 06										08 46		
Clifton	d																					
Daisy Hill	d			07 26	07 39				07 47				08 07						08 23		08 39	
Hag Fold	d			07 29					07 50										08 26			
Atherton	d			07 32	07 43				07 53				08 12						08 29		08 44	
Walkden	d			07 38					07 59				08 18						08 35		08 50	
Moorside	d			07 41					08 03										08 39			
Swinton	d			07 44					08 06										08 42		08 55	
Salford Crescent	a	07 43	07 47	07 51	07 59	08 02	08 07		08 13	08 17		08 24	08 29	08 38	08 43		08 46		08 50	08 56	09 02	09 08
	d	07 43	07 47	07 51	08 00	08 02	08 08		08 13	08 17		08 25	08 30	08 38	08 44		08 47		08 51	08 56	09 02	09 09
Salford Central	d	07 46		07 55	08 03	08 05			08 16	08 20			08 32	08 41	08 46				08 54	08 59	09 04	
Manchester Victoria 🚊	a	07 53		08 00	08 08	08 12			08 20	08 25			08 38	08 47	08 52				08 59	09 06	09 09	
Rochdale 41	a								08 51													
Deansgate 🚊	a		07 51				08 11					08 28										09 12
Manchester Oxford Road	a		07 53				08 14	08 22			08 25	08 31					08 52					09 14
Manchester Piccadilly 10 🚊	a		07 57				08 18	08 26				08 35					08 56					09 18
Stockport 84	a						08 34															09 34
Hazel Grove 86	a						08 45															09 45
Buxton 86	a																					
Heald Green 85	a		08 10									08 47					09 09					
Manchester Airport 85 ✈	a		08 17					08 47				08 53					09 17					

A From Clitheroe B To Stalybridge C ⚯ from Preston

The Sunday service between Wigan Wallgate and Manchester Victoria via Atherton is funded by TfGM and will operate whilst funding exists

Table 82R

Mondays to Fridays

9 December to 7 February

Barrow-in-Furness, Blackpool North, Preston, Southport, Kirkby and Wigan - Bolton - Manchester

Network Diagram - see first Page of Table 82

			TP	TP	NT	NT	NT	NT	NT	NT	TP	NT	NT	NT	TP	TP	NT	NT	NT	NT	NT	NT	TP	TP
			FX	FO																			FX	
			◇1	◇1							◇1				◇1	◇1							◇1	◇1
			A	A	B	C				D			E		F		C					D	G	
			🛒	🛒							🛒				🛒								🛒	🛒
Barrow-in-Furness		d			08 00											08 50							08 50	
Roose		d			08 04																			
Dalton		d			08 10											08 59							08 59	
Ulverston		d			08 19											09 07							09 07	
Cark		d			08 27											09 15							09 15	
Kents Bank		d			08 32																			
Grange-over-Sands		d			08 36											09 22							09 22	
Arnside		d			08 42											09 28							09 28	
Silverdale		d			08 47											09 32							09 32	
Carnforth		d			08 54											09 39							09 39	
Windermere	83	d																						
Oxenholme Lake District	65	d	08 10	08 10											09 11									
Lancaster 6	65	a	08 25	08 25	09 05										09 26	09 46							09 46	
		d	08 26	08 26	09 07										09 26	09 47							09 47	
Blackpool North	97	d							08 20		08 44										09 20			09 40
Layton	97	d							08 23												09 23			
Poulton-le-Fylde	97	d							08 27		08 50										09 27			09 46
Kirkham & Wesham	97	d							08 37												09 37			
Preston 8	65,97	a	08 44	08 44	09 30				08 47		09 08				09 45	10 07					09 47		10 07	10 04
		d	08 45	08 45					08 49		09 10			09 23	09 45						09 49		10 12	10 12
Leyland		d							08 54					09 29							09 54			
Buckshaw Parkway		d							08 59		09 17			09 33							09 59			
Chorley		d							09 03		09 21			09 38							10 03		10 22	10 22
Adlington (Lancashire)		d							09 08												10 08			
Blackrod		d							09 12												10 12			
Horwich Parkway		d							09 16		09 28			09 46							10 16			
Lostock		d							09 20					09 50							10 20			
Southport		d					08 25						09 02						09 24					
Meols Cop		d					08 30						09 07											
Bescar Lane		d																						
New Lane		d																						
Burscough Bridge		d					08 38						09 15						09 36					
Hoscar		d																						
Parbold		d					08 43						09 20						09 41					
Appley Bridge		d					08 47						09 24						09 45					
Gathurst		d					08 50						09 27											
Kirkby		d						08 21												09 32				
Rainford		d						08 29												09 40				
Upholland		d						08 33												09 44				
Orrell		d						08 36												09 47				
Pemberton		d						08 39												09 50				
Wigan Wallgate		a					08 55	08 45					09 32						09 51	09 56				
		d					08 56	08 50				09 20	09 32					09 46	09 53	09 58				
Wigan North Western		d	08 58	08 58											09 58									
Ince		d						08 53												10 01				
Hindley		d						08 57				09 25	09 37						09 58	10 04				
Westhoughton		d					09 04					09 29						09 54	10 02					
Bolton		a					09 12		09 25		09 34	09 38		09 55				10 02	10 12		10 25		10 34	10 34
		d				09 03	09 13		09 25	09 31	09 35	09 39		09 56			10 00	10 03	10 13		10 25	10 31	10 34	10 34
Moses Gate		d										09 42												
Farnworth		d										09 44												
Kearsley		d										09 46												
Clifton		d																						
Daisy Hill		d						09 01					09 41							10 09				
Hag Fold		d						09 04												10 12				
Atherton		d						09 06					09 45							10 15				
Walkden		d						09 12					09 50							10 20				
Moorside		d						09 15												10 24				
Swinton		d						09 18					09 55							10 26				
Salford Crescent		a				09 14	09 25	09 27	09 38	09 43	09 47	09 56	10 03	10 08			10 13	10 15	10 25	10 34	10 38	10 43	10 46	10 46
		d				09 15	09 26	09 27	09 38	09 44	09 47	09 56	10 03	10 09			10 13	10 15	10 26	10 35	10 38	10 44	10 47	10 47
Salford Central		d				09 18		09 31	09 41	09 46		09 59	10 05				10 16	10 17		10 37	10 41	10 46		
Manchester Victoria	🚌	a				09 22		09 38	09 47	09 52		10 06	10 10				10 21	10 25		10 43	10 47	10 52		
Rochdale	41	a																10 51						
Deansgate	🚌	a					09 29				09 51			10 12					10 29				10 50	10 50
Manchester Oxford Road		a	09 23	09 23			09 31				09 52			10 14	10 23				10 31				10 52	10 52
Manchester Piccadilly 10	🚌	a	09 27	09 27			09 35				09 56			10 18	10 27				10 35				10 56	10 56
Stockport	84	a												10 34										
Hazel Grove	86	a												10 45										
Buxton	86	a																						
Heald Green	85	a									10 10												11 09	11 09
Manchester Airport	85 ✈	a	09 47	09 51			09 53				10 17				10 47				10 53				11 15	11 15

A From Edinburgh
B From Maryport
C From Blackburn
D From Clitheroe
E To Stalybridge
F From Glasgow Central
G 🛒 from Preston

The Sunday service between Wigan Wallgate and Manchester Victoria via Atherton is funded by TfGM and will operate whilst funding exists

Table 82R

Mondays to Fridays

9 December to 7 February

Barrow-in-Furness, Blackpool North, Preston, Southport, Kirkby and Wigan - Bolton - Manchester

Network Diagram - see first Page of Table 82

		NT	NT	NT	NT	TP	NT	NT	NT	NT	NT	NT	TP	NT	NT	NT	TP	NT	NT	NT	NT	NT
						◇1			◇				◇1				◇1		◇			
		A		B		C	D					E			B		F					G
						✠							✠				✠					
Barrow-in-Furness	d						10 09															
Roose	d						10 13															
Dalton	d						10 19															
Ulverston	d						10 28															
Cark	d						10 35															
Kents Bank	d						10 40															
Grange-over-Sands	d						10 44															
Arnside	d						10 50															
Silverdale	d						10 55															
Carnforth	d	09 56					11 07															12 02
Windermere 83	d																10 51					
Oxenholme Lake District 65	d					10 10											11 08					
Lancaster 6 65	a	10 08				10 24	11 18										11 25					12 11
	d					10 25											11 25					
Blackpool North 97	d										10 20		10 44								11 20	
Layton 97	d										10 23										11 23	
Poulton-le-Fylde 97	d										10 27		10 50								11 27	
Kirkham & Wesham 97	d										10 37										11 37	
Preston 8 65,97	a					10 44					10 47		11 08				11 44				11 47	
	d				10 23	10 45					10 49		11 10			11 23	11 45				11 49	
Leyland	d				10 29						10 54					11 29					11 54	
Buckshaw Parkway	d				10 33						10 59		11 17			11 33					11 59	
Chorley	d				10 38						11 03		11 21			11 38					12 03	
Adlington (Lancashire)	d										11 08										12 08	
Blackrod	d										11 12										12 12	
Horwich Parkway	d				10 46						11 16		11 28			11 46					12 16	
Lostock	d				10 50						11 20					11 50					12 20	
Southport	d			09 55					10 24						10 55				11 24			
Meols Cop	d			10 00											11 00							
Bescar Lane	d			10 05											11 05							
New Lane	d			10 09											11 09							
Burscough Bridge	d			10 11					10 36						11 11				11 36			
Hoscar	d			10 15											11 15							
Parbold	d			10 18					10 41						11 18				11 41			
Appley Bridge	d			10 22					10 45						11 22				11 45			
Gathurst	d			10 25											11 25							
Kirkby	d									10 32										11 32		
Rainford	d									10 40										11 40		
Upholland	d									10 44										11 44		
Orrell	d									10 47										11 47		
Pemberton	d									10 50										11 50		
Wigan Wallgate	a			10 30					10 51	10 56					11 30				11 51	11 56		
	d		10 20	10 32				10 48	10 53	10 58				11 20	11 32			11 48	11 53	11 58		
Wigan North Western	d					10 58											11 57					
Ince	d									11 01										12 01		
Hindley	d		10 25	10 37					10 58	11 04				11 25	11 37				11 58	12 04		
Westhoughton	d		10 29						11 02					11 29					12 02			
Bolton	a		10 38		10 55			11 02	11 12		11 25		11 34	11 38		11 55		12 02	12 12		12 25	
	d		10 39		10 56			11 03	11 13		11 25	11 31	11 35	11 39		11 56		12 03	12 13		12 25	
Moses Gate	d		10 42											11 42								
Farnworth	d		10 44											11 44								
Kearsley	d		10 46											11 46								
Clifton	d																					
Daisy Hill	d			10 41						11 09					11 41					12 09		
Hag Fold	d									11 12										12 12		
Atherton	d			10 45						11 15					11 45					12 15		
Walkden	d			10 50						11 20					11 50					12 20		
Moorside	d									11 24										12 24		
Swinton	d			10 55						11 26					11 55					12 26		
Salford Crescent	a		10 56	11 02	11 08			11 16	11 25	11 34	11 38	11 43	11 47	11 56	12 02	12 08		12 16	12 25	12 34	12 38	
	d		10 56	11 03	11 09			11 16	11 26	11 34	11 38	11 44	11 47	11 56	12 03	12 09		12 16	12 26	12 34	12 38	
Salford Central	d		10 59	11 05				11 18		11 36	11 41	11 46		11 59	12 05			12 18		12 36	12 41	
Manchester Victoria ⇌	a		11 06	11 09				11 25		11 43	11 47	11 52		12 06	12 09			12 25		12 43	12 47	
Rochdale 41	a							11 51										12 51				
Deansgate ⇌	a				11 12				11 29				11 51			12 12			12 29			
Manchester Oxford Road	a				11 14	11 23			11 31				11 52			12 14	12 22		12 31			
Manchester Piccadilly 10 ⇌	a				11 18	11 27			11 35				11 56			12 18	12 26		12 35			
Stockport 84	a				11 34											12 34						
Hazel Grove 86	a				11 45											12 45						
Buxton 86	a																					
Heald Green 85	a												12 10									
Manchester Airport 85 ✈	a					11 47			11 53				12 17				12 47		12 53			

A From Leeds to Morecambe
B To Stalybridge
C From Edinburgh
D From Sellafield
E From Clitheroe
F ✠ from Preston
G From Leeds to Heysham Harbour

The Sunday service between Wigan Wallgate and Manchester Victoria via Atherton is funded by TfGM and will operate whilst funding exists

Table 82R

Mondays to Fridays

9 December to 7 February

Barrow-in-Furness, Blackpool North, Preston, Southport, Kirkby and Wigan - Bolton - Manchester

Network Diagram - see first Page of Table 82

		TP	NT	TP	NT	NT	NT	TP	NT		NT	NT	NT	NT	NT	TP	NT	NT	NT		TP	TP	TP	NT	NT
																							FX		
		◇1		◇1				◇1				◇				◇1					◇1	◇1	◇1		◇
			A			B		C	D						A			B			E	F			
Barrow-in-Furness	d	11 20							12 10														13 20		
Roose	d								12 14																
Dalton	d	11 29							12 20														13 29		
Ulverston	d	11 37							12 28														13 37		
Cark	d	11 45							12 36														13 45		
Kents Bank	d								12 40																
Grange-over-Sands	d	11 52							12 44														13 52		
Arnside	d	11 58							12 50														13 58		
Silverdale	d	12 02							12 54														14 02		
Carnforth	d	12 09							13 02														14 09		
Windermere 83	d																					12 52			
Oxenholme Lake District 65	d							12 10													13 10	13 12			
Lancaster 6 65	a	12 17						12 25	13 14												13 25	13 30	14 17		
	d	12 17						12 26													13 25		14 17		
Blackpool North 97	d			11 44										12 20		12 41									
Layton 97	d													12 23											
Poulton-le-Fylde 97	d			11 50										12 27		12 47									
Kirkham & Wesham 97	d													12 37											
Preston 8 65,97	a	12 37		12 08				12 44						12 47		13 05					13 44		14 37		
	d			12 10			12 23	12 45						12 49		13 10			13 23		13 44				
Leyland	d						12 29							12 54					13 29						
Buckshaw Parkway	d			12 17			12 33							12 59		13 17			13 33						
Chorley	d			12 21			12 38							13 03		13 21			13 38						
Adlington (Lancashire)	d													13 08											
Blackrod	d													13 12											
Horwich Parkway	d			12 28			12 46							13 16		13 28			13 46						
Lostock	d						12 50							13 20					13 50						
Southport	d					12 00						12 24						12 54							13 24
Meols Cop	d					12 05												12 59							
Bescar Lane	d																	13 04							
New Lane	d																	13 08							
Burscough Bridge	d					12 13						12 36						13 11							13 36
Hoscar	d																	13 15							
Parbold	d					12 18						12 41						13 18							13 41
Appley Bridge	d					12 22						12 45						13 22							13 45
Gathurst	d					12 25												13 25							
Kirkby	d												12 32												
Rainford	d												12 40												
Upholland	d												12 44												
Orrell	d												12 47												
Pemberton	d												12 50												
Wigan Wallgate	a					12 30						12 51	12 56					13 30							13 51
	d				12 20	12 32					12 48	12 53	12 58				13 20	13 32						13 48	13 53
Wigan North Western	d							12 58													13 58				
Ince	d												13 01												
Hindley	d				12 25	12 37						12 58	13 04				13 25	13 37							13 58
Westhoughton	d				12 29							13 02					13 29								14 02
Bolton	a			12 34	12 38		12 55				13 02	13 12		13 25		13 34	13 38		13 55					14 02	14 12
	d		12 31	12 35	12 39		12 56				13 03	13 13		13 25	13 31	13 35	13 39		13 56					14 03	14 13
Moses Gate	d				12 42												13 42								
Farnworth	d				12 44												13 44								
Kearsley	d				12 46												13 46								
Clifton	d																								
Daisy Hill	d					12 41							13 09					13 41							
Hag Fold	d												13 12												
Atherton	d					12 45							13 15					13 45							
Walkden	d					12 50							13 20					13 50							
Moorside	d												13 24												
Swinton	d					12 55							13 26					13 55							
Salford Crescent	a		12 43	12 47	12 56	13 02	13 08				13 15	13 25	13 34	13 38	13 43	13 47	13 56	14 02	14 08					14 15	14 25
	d		12 44	12 47	12 56	13 03	13 09				13 15	13 26	13 34	13 38	13 44	13 47	13 56	14 03	14 09					14 15	14 26
Salford Central	d		12 46		12 59	13 05					13 17		13 36	13 41	13 46		13 59	14 05						14 17	
Manchester Victoria 🚊	a		12 52		13 06	13 09					13 25		13 43	13 47	13 52		14 06	14 09						14 25	
Rochdale 41	a										13 51													14 51	
Deansgate 🚊	a			12 51			13 12					13 29				13 51			14 12						14 29
Manchester Oxford Road	a			12 52			13 14	13 23				13 31				13 52			14 14		14 22				14 31
Manchester Piccadilly 10 🚊	a			12 56			13 18	13 27				13 35				13 56			14 18		14 26				14 35
Stockport 84	a						13 34												14 34						
Hazel Grove 86	a						13 45												14 45						
Buxton 86	a																								
Heald Green 85	a			13 10												14 10									
Manchester Airport 85 ✈	a			13 17				13 46				13 53				14 17					14 46				14 53

A From Clitheroe
B To Stalybridge
C From Edinburgh
D From Carlisle
E From Glasgow Central
F To Barrow-in-Furness

The Sunday service between Wigan Wallgate and Manchester Victoria via Atherton is funded by TfGM and will operate whilst funding exists

Table 82R

Mondays to Fridays

9 December to 7 February

Barrow-in-Furness, Blackpool North, Preston, Southport, Kirkby and Wigan - Bolton - Manchester

Network Diagram - see first Page of Table 82

		NT	NT	NT	TP	NT	NT	NT	NT	TP	TP	TP	NT	NT	NT	NT	NT	TP	NT	NT	NT	TP	TP
										FO	FO	FX										FX	FO
					◇1					◇1	◇1	◇1	◇					◇1				◇1	◇1
				A			B			C	D	D				E	A					F	F
					(trolley)					(trolley)	(trolley)	(trolley)						(trolley)				(trolley)	(trolley)
Barrow-in-Furness	d									13 20													
Roose	d																						
Dalton	d									13 29													
Ulverston	d									13 37													
Cark	d									13 45													
Kents Bank	d																						
Grange-over-Sands	d									13 52													
Arnside	d									13 58													
Silverdale	d									14 02													
Carnforth	d									14 09							15 02						
Windermere 83	d																						
Oxenholme Lake District 65	d											14 10											15 09
Lancaster 6 65	a									14 17		14 24					15 15						15 23
	d									14 17	14 24	14 25										15 22	15 24
Blackpool North 97	d		13 20		13 44										14 20			14 40					
Layton 97	d		13 23												14 23								
Poulton-le-Fylde 97	d		13 27		13 50										14 27			14 46					
Kirkham & Wesham 97	d		13 37												14 37								
Preston 8 65,97	a		13 47		14 08					14 37	14 42	14 45			14 47			15 04				15 40	15 42
	d		13 49		14 10			14 23		14 47		14 45			14 49			15 10			15 23	15 45	15 45
Leyland	d		13 54					14 29							14 54						15 29		
Buckshaw Parkway	d		13 59		14 17			14 33							14 59			15 17			15 33		
Chorley	d		14 03		14 21			14 38		14 57		14 55			15 03			15 21			15 38		
Adlington (Lancashire)	d		14 08												15 08								
Blackrod	d		14 12												15 12								
Horwich Parkway	d		14 16		14 28			14 46							15 16			15 28			15 46		
Lostock	d		14 20					14 50							15 20						15 50		
Southport	d						14 00						14 24							14 54			
Meols Cop	d						14 05													14 59			
Bescar Lane	d																			15 04			
New Lane	d																			15 08			
Burscough Bridge	d						14 13						14 36							15 11			
Hoscar	d																			15 15			
Parbold	d						14 18						14 41							15 18			
Appley Bridge	d						14 22						14 45							15 22			
Gathurst	d						14 25													15 25			
Kirkby	d	13 32												14 32									
Rainford	d	13 40												14 40									
Upholland	d	13 44												14 44									
Orrell	d	13 47												14 47									
Pemberton	d	13 50												14 50									
Wigan Wallgate	a	13 56					14 30						14 51	14 56						15 30			
	d	13 58				14 20	14 32		14 48				14 53	14 58					15 20	15 32			
Wigan North Western	d																					15 58	15 58
Ince	d	14 01												15 01									
Hindley	d	14 04				14 25	14 37						14 58	15 04					15 25	15 37			
Westhoughton	d					14 29							15 02						15 29				
Bolton	a		14 25		14 34	14 38		14 55	15 02	15 08		15 07	15 12		15 25			15 34	15 38		15 55		
	d		14 25	14 31	14 35	14 39		14 56	15 03	15 09		15 07	15 13		15 25		15 31	15 35	15 39		15 56		
Moses Gate	d					14 42													15 42				
Farnworth	d					14 44													15 44				
Kearsley	d					14 46													15 46				
Clifton	d																						
Daisy Hill	d	14 09					14 41							15 09						15 41			
Hag Fold	d	14 12												15 12									
Atherton	d	14 15					14 45							15 15						15 45			
Walkden	d	14 20					14 50							15 20						15 50			
Moorside	d	14 24												15 24									
Swinton	d	14 26					14 55							15 26						15 55			
Salford Crescent	a	14 34	14 38	14 43	14 47	14 56	15 02	15 08	15 15	15 20		15 19	15 25	15 33	15 38		15 43	15 47	15 56	16 02	16 08		
	d	14 34	14 38	14 44	14 47	14 56	15 03	15 09	15 15	15 21		15 19	15 26	15 34	15 38		15 44	15 47	15 56	16 03	16 09		
Salford Central	d	14 36	14 41	14 46		14 59	15 05		15 17					15 36	15 41		15 46		15 59	16 05			
Manchester Victoria (tram)	a	14 43	14 47	14 52		15 06	15 10		15 25					15 43	15 47		15 54		16 06	16 11			
Rochdale 41	a								15 51														
Deansgate (tram)	a				14 51			15 12					15 29					15 51			16 12		
Manchester Oxford Road	a				14 52			15 14		15 25		15 24	15 31					15 52			16 14	16 23	16 23
Manchester Piccadilly 10 (tram)	a				14 56			15 18		15 29		15 28	15 35					15 56			16 18	16 27	16 27
Stockport 84	a							15 34													16 34		
Hazel Grove 86	a							15 45													16 43		
Buxton 86	a																				17 24		
Heald Green 85	a				15 10													16 10				16 40	16 40
Manchester Airport 85 ✈	a				15 17					15 47		15 47	15 53					16 17				16 47	16 47

A From Clitheroe
B To Stalybridge
C (trolley) from Preston
D From Edinburgh
E From Leeds to Morecambe
F From Glasgow Central

The Sunday service between Wigan Wallgate and Manchester Victoria via Atherton is funded by TfGM and will operate whilst funding exists

Table 82R

Mondays to Fridays

9 December to 7 February

Barrow-in-Furness, Blackpool North, Preston, Southport, Kirkby and Wigan - Bolton - Manchester

Network Diagram - see first Page of Table 82

		NT	NT	NT	NT	NT	NT	TP	TP	NT		NT	NT	TP	NT	NT	NT	NT	NT	NT		TP	NT	NT
			◇					◇1	◇1					◇1			◇					◇1		
				A			B	C				D		E						A				
								🛒	🛒					🛒								🛒		
Barrow-in-Furness	d						15 18	14 40							16 10									
Roose	d						15 22								16 14									
Dalton	d						15 28								16 20									
Ulverston	d						15 37	14 56							16 28									
Cark	d						15 44								16 36									
Kents Bank	d						15 49								16 40									
Grange-over-Sands	d						15 53	15 08							16 44									
Arnside	d						15 59	15 14							16 50									
Silverdale	d						16 03								16 54									
Carnforth	d						16 11	15 24							17 02									
Windermere	83 d																							
Oxenholme Lake District	65 d													16 14										
Lancaster 6	65 a						16 22	15 32						16 29	17 14									
	d							15 32						16 29										
Blackpool North	97 d					15 20			15 40										16 20			16 40		
Layton	97 d					15 23													16 23			16 43		
Poulton-le-Fylde	97 d					15 27			15 46										16 27			16 47		
Kirkham & Wesham	97 d					15 37													16 37			16 57		
Preston 8	65,97 a					15 47		15 51	16 04					16 48					16 47			17 08		
	d					15 49		16 10					16 22	16 49					16 49			17 10		
Leyland	d					15 54							16 28						16 54					
Buckshaw Parkway	d					15 59		16 17					16 32						16 59			17 17		
Chorley	d					16 03		16 21					16 37						17 03			17 21		
Adlington (Lancashire)	d					16 08													17 08					
Blackrod	d					16 12													17 12					
Horwich Parkway	d					16 16		16 28					16 45						17 16			17 28		
Lostock	d					16 20							16 49						17 20					
Southport	d		15 24									15 58					16 24							16 54
Meols Cop	d											16 03												16 59
Bescar Lane	d																							17 04
New Lane	d																							17 08
Burscough Bridge	d		15 36									16 11					16 36							17 11
Hoscar	d																							17 15
Parbold	d		15 41									16 16					16 41							17 18
Appley Bridge	d		15 45									16 20					16 45							17 22
Gathurst	d											16 24												17 25
Kirkby	d				15 32													16 32						
Rainford	d				15 40													16 40						
Upholland	d				15 44													16 44						
Orrell	d				15 47													16 47						
Pemberton	d				15 50													16 50						
Wigan Wallgate	a		15 51		15 56							16 29					16 51	16 56						17 30
	d	15 48	15 53		15 58					16 20		16 30				16 48	16 53	16 58					17 20	17 32
Wigan North Western	d																							
Ince	d				16 01							16 33						17 01						
Hindley	d		15 58		16 04					16 25		16 37					16 58	17 04					17 25	17 37
Westhoughton	d		16 02							16 29							17 02						17 29	
Bolton	a	16 02	16 12			16 25		16 34		16 38			16 54			17 02	17 12		17 25			17 34	17 38	
	d	16 03	16 13	16 18		16 25		16 35		16 39			16 55			17 03	17 13		17 25	17 31		17 35	17 39	
Moses Gate	d									16 42													17 42	
Farnworth	d									16 44													17 44	
Kearsley	d									16 46													17 46	
Clifton	d																							
Daisy Hill	d				16 09							16 41						17 08						17 41
Hag Fold	d				16 12													17 11						
Atherton	d				16 15							16 45						17 14						17 45
Walkden	d				16 20							16 50						17 19						17 50
Moorside	d				16 24													17 23						
Swinton	d				16 26							16 55						17 25						17 55
Salford Crescent	a	16 15	16 25	16 31	16 34	16 38		16 47		16 56		17 02	17 07			17 15	17 25	17 33	17 38	17 43		17 47	17 56	18 02
	d	16 15	16 26	16 31	16 34	16 38		16 47		16 56		17 03	17 08			17 15	17 26	17 33	17 38	17 44		17 47	17 56	18 03
Salford Central	d	16 17		16 34	16 37	16 41				16 59		17 05				17 17		17 36	17 41	17 46			17 59	18 05
Manchester Victoria	🚊 a	16 23		16 41	16 43	16 47				17 06		17 13				17 23		17 43	17 47	17 53			18 06	18 11
Rochdale	41 a	16 51														17 51								
Deansgate	🚊 a							16 51					17 12									17 51		
Manchester Oxford Road	a		16 31					16 52					17 14	17 26			17 30					17 52		
Manchester Piccadilly 10	🚊 a		16 35					16 56					17 19	17 30			17 35					17 56		
Stockport	84 a												17 32											
Hazel Grove	86 a												17 39											
Buxton	86 a												18 14											
Heald Green	85 a							17 10									17 47					18 10		
Manchester Airport	85 ✈ a		16 53					17 17						17 47			17 53					18 17		

A From Clitheroe
B From Carlisle
C 🛒 from Preston
D To Huddersfield
E From Edinburgh

The Sunday service between Wigan Wallgate and Manchester Victoria via Atherton is funded by TfGM and will operate whilst funding exists

Table 82R

Mondays to Fridays

9 December to 7 February

Barrow-in-Furness, Blackpool North, Preston, Southport, Kirkby and Wigan - Bolton - Manchester

Network Diagram - see first Page of Table 82

		NT	NT	TP	NT	NT	NT	TP	TP	TP	TP	NT	NT	NT	NT	NT	NT	NT	TP	NT	NT	TP	NT
								FX	FO										FX				
				◇1	◇			◇1	◇1	◇1	◇1				◇				◇1			◇1	
			A					B			C			A				A		D	E		
				🚲				🚲	🚲		🚲												
Barrow-in-Furness	d									17 21											18 03		
Roose	d																				18 07		
Dalton	d									17 30											18 13		
Ulverston	d									17 39											18 21		
Cark	d									17 46											18 29		
Kents Bank	d																				18 33		
Grange-over-Sands	d									17 53											18 37		
Arnside	d									17 59											18 43		
Silverdale	d																				18 47		
Carnforth	d									18 08										18 26	18 55		
Windermere	83 d							17 06											18 05				
Oxenholme Lake District	65 d							17 30											18 22				
Lancaster 6	65 a							17 47		18 17									18 39	18 40	19 05		
	d							17 48			18 25								18 40		19 06		
Blackpool North	97 d			17 20													18 20					18 40	
Layton	97 d			17 23													18 23						
Poulton-le-Fylde	97 d			17 27													18 27					18 46	
Kirkham & Wesham	97 d																18 37						
Preston 8	65,97 a			17 45				18 06			18 45						18 47		18 58		19 31	19 04	
	d			17 47			17 56	18 08	18 08		18 45						18 49		19 10			19 10	
Leyland	d						18 01										18 54						
Buckshaw Parkway	d						18 05	18 15	18 15								18 59		19 17			19 17	
Chorley	d			17 56			18 09	18 19	18 19								19 03		19 21			19 21	
Adlington (Lancashire)	d						18 15										19 08						
Blackrod	d						18 19										19 12						
Horwich Parkway	d						18 21	18 26	18 26								19 16		19 28			19 28	
Lostock	d							18 30	18 30								19 20						
Southport	d				17 24										18 17								19 00
Meols Cop	d				17 29										18 22								19 05
Bescar Lane	d														18 27								
New Lane	d														18 31								
Burscough Bridge	d				17 37										18 33								19 13
Hoscar	d														18 37								
Parbold	d				17 42										18 40								19 18
Appley Bridge	d				17 46										18 44								19 22
Gathurst	d														18 47								19 25
Kirkby	d					17 32										18 32							
Rainford	d					17 40										18 40							
Upholland	d					17 44										18 44							
Orrell	d					17 47										18 47							
Pemberton	d					17 50										18 50							
Wigan Wallgate	a				17 52	17 57									18 52	18 56							19 30
	d	17 39			17 54	17 59						18 20	18 32		18 53	18 58							19 32
Wigan North Western	d										18 59												
Ince	d					18 02										19 01							
Hindley	d					18 05						18 25	18 37		18 58	19 04							19 37
Westhoughton	d	17 47			18 02							18 29			19 02								
Bolton	a	17 55		18 08	18 12		18 30	18 34	18 34			18 38			19 12		19 25		19 35			19 35	
	d	17 56	18 02	18 08	18 12		18 30	18 35	18 35			18 39		19 02	19 13		19 25	19 31	19 35			19 35	
Moses Gate	d											18 42											
Farnworth	d											18 44											
Kearsley	d											18 46											
Clifton	d																						
Daisy Hill	d					18 09							18 41			19 08							19 41
Hag Fold	d					18 12										19 11							
Atherton	d					18 15							18 45			19 14							19 45
Walkden	d					18 20							18 50			19 19							19 50
Moorside	d					18 24										19 23							
Swinton	d					18 26							18 55			19 25							19 55
Salford Crescent	a	18 08	18 15		18 25	18 32	18 42	18 47	18 47			18 56	19 02	19 14	19 25	19 33	19 38	19 44	19 48			19 48	20 02
	d	18 09	18 15		18 25	18 33	18 42	18 47	18 47			18 56	19 03	19 15	19 26	19 33	19 38	19 44	19 48			19 48	20 03
Salford Central	d		18 17			18 35	18 45					18 59	19 05	19 17		19 36	19 41	19 46					20 05
Manchester Victoria 🚊	a		18 24			18 43	18 50					19 06	19 11	19 23		19 43	19 47	19 53					20 11
Rochdale	41 a		18 47																				
Deansgate 🚊	a	18 12						18 51	18 51						19 29				19 52			19 52	
Manchester Oxford Road	a	18 14		18 23	18 31			18 52	18 52		19 24				19 31				19 53			19 53	
Manchester Piccadilly 10 🚊	a	18 18		18 27	18 35			18 56	18 56		19 29				19 35				19 57			19 57	
Stockport	84 a	18 34																					
Hazel Grove	86 a	18 43																					
Buxton	86 a	19 24																					
Heald Green	85 a			18 40				19 10	19 10										20 11			20 11	
Manchester Airport	85 ✈ a			18 47	18 53			19 17	19 17		19 47				19 53				20 17			20 17	

A From Clitheroe
B 🚲 from Preston
C From Edinburgh
D From Leeds to Morecambe
E From Carlisle

The Sunday service between Wigan Wallgate and Manchester Victoria via Atherton is funded by TfGM and will operate whilst funding exists

Table 82R

Mondays to Fridays

9 December to 7 February

Barrow-in-Furness, Blackpool North, Preston, Southport, Kirkby and Wigan - Bolton - Manchester

Network Diagram - see first Page of Table 82

	TP	TP		NT	NT	NT	NT	TP	TP	TP	NT	NT		NT	NT		TP	TP	NT		TP			NT
		FO							FO	FX				FX										FO
	◇1	◇1			◇			◇1	◇1	◇1		◇		◇			◇1	◇1			◇1			
	A			B			C	D				E		F					C					
	🚲																🚲							
Barrow-in-Furness d																		20 10						
Roose d																		20 14						
Dalton d																		20 21						
Ulverston d																		20 29						
Cark d																		20 37						
Kents Bank d																		20 41						
Grange-over-Sands d																		20 45						
Arnside d																		20 51						
Silverdale d																		20 55						
Carnforth d																		21 02						
Windermere 83 d		18 56						18 56																
Oxenholme Lake District 65 d	19 09	19 16						19 16									20 16							
Lancaster 6 65 a	19 24	19 32						19 32									20 31	21 10						
d	19 24	19 32						19 32									20 31	21 11						
Blackpool North 97 d						19 20			19 40	19 44					20 20						20 44			
Layton 97 d						19 23									20 23									
Poulton-le-Fylde 97 d						19 28			19 46	19 50					20 27						20 50			
Kirkham & Wesham 97 d						19 37									20 37									
Preston 8 65,97 a	19 44	19 51				19 47		19 51	20 04	20 08					20 47		20 50	21 30			21 08			
d	19 45					19 49		20 10	20 10	20 10					20 49		20 51				21 10			
Leyland d						19 54									20 54									
Buckshaw Parkway d						19 59		20 17	20 17	20 17					20 59						21 17			
Chorley d						20 03		20 21	20 21	20 21					21 03						21 21			
Adlington (Lancashire) d						20 08									21 08									
Blackrod d						20 12									21 12									
Horwich Parkway d						20 16		20 28	20 28	20 28					21 16						21 28			
Lostock d						20 20									21 20									
Southport d					19 23							20 23		20 23										
Meols Cop d					19 28							20 28		20 28										
Bescar Lane d																								
New Lane d																								
Burscough Bridge d					19 36							20 36		20 36										
Hoscar d																								
Parbold d					19 41							20 41		20 41										
Appley Bridge d					19 45							20 45		20 45										
Gathurst d					19 48							20 48		20 48										
Kirkby d																								
Rainford d																								
Upholland d																								
Orrell d																								
Pemberton d																								
Wigan Wallgate a					19 53							20 53		20 53										
d					19 55						20 29	20 55		20 55										21 29
Wigan North Western d	19 59																							
Ince d											20 32													21 32
Hindley d					20 00						20 35	21 00		21 00										21 35
Westhoughton d					20 04							21 04		21 04										
Bolton a					20 12	20 25		20 34	20 34	20 34		21 12		21 12	21 25						21 34			
d				20 02	20 13	20 25	20 31	20 35	20 35	20 35		21 13		21 13	21 25				21 31		21 35			
Moses Gate d																								
Farnworth d																								
Kearsley d																								
Clifton d																								
Daisy Hill d											20 39													21 39
Hag Fold d											20 42													21 42
Atherton d											20 45													21 45
Walkden d											20 51													21 51
Moorside d											20 54													21 54
Swinton d											20 57													21 57
Salford Crescent a				20 15	20 25	20 38	20 43	20 47	20 47	20 47	21 04	21 25		21 25	21 38				21 43		21 47			22 04
d				20 15	20 26	20 38	20 44	20 47	20 47	20 47	21 05	21 26		21 26	21 38				21 44		21 47			22 05
Salford Central d				20 17		20 41	20 46				21 07				21 41				21 46					22 07
Manchester Victoria 🚊 a				20 24		20 47	20 52				21 13				21 47				21 52					22 13
Rochdale 41 a																								
Deansgate 🚊 a					20 29			20 51	20 51	20 51		21 29		21 29							21 51			
Manchester Oxford Road a	20 23				20 31			20 52	20 52	20 52		21 31		21 34			21 26				21 52			
Manchester Piccadilly 10 🚊 a	20 27				20 35			20 56	20 56	20 56		21 35					21 30				21 56			
Stockport 84 a																								
Hazel Grove 86 a																								
Buxton 86 a																								
Heald Green 85 a								21 10	21 10	21 10											22 10			
Manchester Airport 85 ✈ a	20 46				20 52			21 17	21 17	21 17		21 53					21 47				22 17			

A From Glasgow Central
B From Blackburn
C From Clitheroe
D 13 December, 20 December, 27 December
E until 27 December, FO from 3 January
F from 30 December

The Sunday service between Wigan Wallgate and Manchester Victoria via Atherton is funded by TfGM and will operate whilst funding exists

Table 82R

Mondays to Fridays

9 December to 7 February

Barrow-in-Furness, Blackpool North, Preston, Southport, Kirkby and Wigan - Bolton - Manchester

Network Diagram - see first Page of Table 82

Station	Table		NT	NT	NT	NT	NT	NT	NT	TP	TP	TP	TP	NT	NT	NT	NT	NT	NT	TP	NT	NT	TP	TP	NT
			FX	FO	FX	FX	FO	FX	FO	FX			FX		FO	FX								FX	
										◇1	◇1	◇1	◇1				◇			◇1			◇1	◇1	
								A	A	B	C	D	E						F	G		A	C	B	
Barrow-in-Furness		d												21 43											
Roose		d												21 47											
Dalton		d												21 53											
Ulverston		d												22 01											
Cark		d												22 09											
Kents Bank		d												22 13											
Grange-over-Sands		d												22 17											
Arnside		d												22 23											
Silverdale		d												22 27											
Carnforth		d												22 35											
Windermere	83	d																		22 45					
Oxenholme Lake District	65	d										22 10	22 10							23 05					
Lancaster [6]	65	a										22 24	22 24	22 45						23 22					
		d										22 25	22 25	22 46					23 02	23 22					
Blackpool North	97	d				21 20	21 20			21 44	21 44							22 20					22 45	22 45	23 13
Layton	97	d				21 23	21 23											22 23							23 16
Poulton-le-Fylde	97	d				21 27	21 27			21 50	21 50							22 27					22 51	22 51	23 20
Kirkham & Wesham	97	d				21 37	21 37											22 37							23 30
Preston [8]	65,97	a				21 47	21 47			22 08	22 08	22 44	22 44	23 11				22 47	23 23	23 42			23 09	23 09	23 40
		d				21 49	21 49			22 10	22 10	22 45	22 45					22 49					23 10	23 10	23 42
Leyland		d				21 54	21 54											22 55							23 48
Buckshaw Parkway		d				21 59	21 59			22 17	22 17							23 00					23 17	23 17	23 52
Chorley		d				22 03	22 03			22 21	22 21							23 04					23 21	23 21	23 58
Adlington (Lancashire)		d				22 08	22 08											23 09							00 02
Blackrod		d				22 12	22 12											23 13							00 06
Horwich Parkway		d				22 16	22 16			22 28	22 28							23 17					23 28	23 28	00 09
Lostock		d				22 20	22 20											23 20							00 13
Southport		d		21 23	21 23												22 18				23 10				
Meols Cop		d		21 28	21 28												22 23				23 15				
Bescar Lane		d															22 28								
New Lane		d															22 32								
Burscough Bridge		d		21 36	21 36												22 34				23 23				
Hoscar		d															22 38								
Parbold		d		21 41	21 41												22 41				23 28				
Appley Bridge		d		21 45	21 45												22 45				23 32				
Gathurst		d		21 48	21 48												22 48				23 35				
Kirkby		d																							
Rainford		d																							
Upholland		d																							
Orrell		d																							
Pemberton		d																							
Wigan Wallgate		a		21 53	21 53												22 53				23 44				
		d	21 29	21 55	21 55										22 29	22 29	22 55								
Wigan North Western		d										22 58	22 58												
Ince		d	21 32												22 32	22 32									
Hindley		d	21 35	22 00	22 00										22 35	22 35	23 00								
Westhoughton		d		22 04	22 04												23 04								
Bolton		a		22 12	22 12	22 25	22 25			22 34	22 34						23 12	23 25					23 34	23 34	00 17
		d		22 13	22 13	22 25	22 25	22 31	22 31	22 35	22 35						23 13	23 26				23 31	23 35	23 35	00 17
Moses Gate		d																							
Farnworth		d																							
Kearsley		d																							
Clifton		d																							
Daisy Hill		d	21 39												22 39	22 39									
Hag Fold		d	21 42												22 42	22 42									
Atherton		d	21 45												22 45	22 45									
Walkden		d	21 51												22 51	22 51									
Moorside		d	21 54												22 54	22 54									
Swinton		d	21 57												22 57	22 57									
Salford Crescent		a	22 04	22 25	22 25	22 38	22 38	22 43	22 43	22 47	22 47				23 04	23 04	23 25	23 38				23 43	23 47	23 47	
		d	22 05	22 26	22 26	22 38	22 38	22 44	22 44	22 47	22 47				23 05	23 05	23 26	23 39				23 44	23 47	23 47	
Salford Central		d		22 28			22 41		22 46						23 07										
Manchester Victoria		a	22 13	22 34	22 34	22 46	22 47	22 52	22 54						23 13	23 13		23 44				23 50			00 36
Rochdale	41	a																							
Deansgate		a								22 51	22 51						23 29								
Manchester Oxford Road		a								22 52	22 52	23 23	23 23				23 31								
Manchester Piccadilly [10]		a								22 57	22 57	23 27	23 28				23 39						23 55	23 55	
Stockport	84	a																							
Hazel Grove	86	a																							
Buxton	86	a																							
Heald Green	85	a									23 10												00 16		
Manchester Airport	85	a									23 17	23 46											00 23		

- **A** From Clitheroe
- **B** from 30 December
- **C** until 27 December, FO from 3 January
- **D** until 27 December, FO from 3 January. From Edinburgh
- **E** from 30 December. From Edinburgh
- **F** From Morecambe
- **G** To Blackpool North

The Sunday service between Wigan Wallgate and Manchester Victoria via Atherton is funded by TfGM and will operate whilst funding exists

Table 82R

Mondays to Fridays

10 February to 16 May

Barrow-in-Furness, Blackpool North, Preston, Southport, Kirkby and Wigan - Bolton - Manchester

Network Diagram - see first Page of Table 82

		TP	TP	NT	TP	TP	TP	TP	TP	TP	NT	TP	NT	NT	NT	TP	NT	NT	NT	TP	NT	TP	NT
			MO	MX	MX		MO																
		◇1	◇1		◇1	◇1	◇1	◇1	◇1	◇1		◇1				◇1				◇1		◇1	
		A	B	C	D	E	F		E	D					G				H	I	J		K
																						🚲	
Barrow-in-Furness	d							04 35								05 32				06 15			
Roose	d																			06 19			
Dalton	d																			06 26			
Ulverston	d							04 51								05 48				06 34			
Cark	d																			06 42			
Kents Bank	d																			06 46			
Grange-over-Sands	d							05 03								06 00				06 50			
Arnside	d							05 09								06 06				06 56			
Silverdale	d																			07 00			
Carnforth	d							05 19								06 16			06 43	07 07			
Windermere 83	d																						
Oxenholme Lake District 65	d																						
Lancaster 6 65	a							05 27								06 24			06 52	07 15			
	d															06 24				07 15			
Blackpool North 97	d				03 37	03 37						05 39						06 19				06 40	
Layton 97	d																	06 22				06 43	
Poulton-le-Fylde 97	d											05 45						06 26				06 47	
Kirkham & Wesham 97	d																	06 36				06 57	
Preston 8 65,97	a											06 03				06 43		06 46		07 34		07 07	
	d				04u02	04u02	04 02		05 12	05 12		06 05				06 44		06 48				07 09	
Leyland	d											06 10						06 53					
Buckshaw Parkway	d																	06 58					
Chorley	d								05 22	05 22		06 17				06 54		07 02				07 18	
Adlington (Lancashire)	d			00 02														07 07					
Blackrod	d			00 06								06 23						07 11					
Horwich Parkway	d			00 09					05 29	05 29		06 26				07 01		07 15				07 26	
Lostock	d			00 13								06 30						07 20				07 30	
Southport	d																06 23						
Meols Cop	d																06 28						
Bescar Lane	d																						
New Lane	d																						
Burscough Bridge	d																06 36						
Hoscar	d																						
Parbold	d																06 41						
Appley Bridge	d																06 45						
Gathurst	d																06 49						
Kirkby	d																						
Rainford	d																						
Upholland	d																						
Orrell	d																						
Pemberton	d																						
Wigan Wallgate	a																06 54						
	d										06 03		06 31	06 36			06 55						07 15
Wigan North Western	d																						
Ince	d										06 06			06 39									07 18
Hindley	d										06 09		06 36	06 42									07 21
Westhoughton	d												06 41				07 03						
Bolton	a			00 17					05 40	05 40		06 34	06 52			07 07	07 11	07 25				07 34	
	d	00 02	00 02	00 17	04u31	04u31	04u31		05 40	05 40		06 35	06 53		06 56	07 08	07 12	07 25			07 30	07 35	
Moses Gate	d														06 59								
Farnworth	d														07 01								
Kearsley	d														07 03								
Clifton	d														07 07								
Daisy Hill	d										06 13			06 46									07 26
Hag Fold	d										06 16			06 49									07 29
Atherton	d										06 19			06 52									07 32
Walkden	d										06 24			06 58									07 38
Moorside	d										06 28			07 01									07 41
Swinton	d										06 30			07 04									07 44
Salford Crescent	a								05 52	05 52	06 38	06 47	07 05	07 11	07 15		07 24	07 38			07 43	07 47	07 51
	d								05 53	05 53	06 38	06 47	07 08	07 11	07 16		07 25	07 38			07 43	07 47	07 51
Salford Central	d										06 41			07 14	07 19			07 41			07 46		07 55
Manchester Victoria 🚊	a			00 36							06 46			07 20	07 22			07 47			07 53		08 00
Rochdale 41	a																						
Deansgate 🚊	a											06 51	07 11				07 28					07 51	
Manchester Oxford Road	a								05 57	05 57		06 52	07 13			07 23	07 30					07 53	
Manchester Piccadilly 10 🚊	a	00 17	00 18		04 46	04 46	04 46		06 00	06 00		06 56	07 17			07 27	07 34					07 57	
Stockport 84	a												07 34										
Hazel Grove 86	a												07 45										
Buxton 86	a																						
Heald Green 85	a											07 10										08 10	
Manchester Airport 85 ✈	a	00 34	00 35			05 05	05 05		06 17	06 22		07 15				07 46	07 53					08 17	

A 10 February. From Blackpool North
B from 17 February. From Blackpool North
C From Blackpool North
D until 21 March
E from 24 March
F until 17 March
G From Blackburn
H From Skipton
I To Blackpool North
J From Clitheroe
K To Stalybridge

The Sunday service between Wigan Wallgate and Manchester Victoria via Atherton is funded by TfGM and will operate whilst funding exists

Table 82R

Mondays to Fridays

10 February to 16 May

Barrow-in-Furness, Blackpool North, Preston, Southport, Kirkby and Wigan - Bolton - Manchester

Network Diagram - see first Page of Table 82

			NT	NT	NT	NT	TP		NT	TP	NT	NT	NT	NT	NT	TP	TP		NT	NT	NT	NT	TP	NT	NT	NT
							◇1			◇1						◇1	◇1						◇1			
							A		B					B		A	A				C		D	E	F	
							🚲			🚲						🚲	🚲						🚲			
Barrow-in-Furness		d													07 14	06 48								08 00		
Roose		d														06 52								08 04		
Dalton		d													07 23	06 59								08 10		
Ulverston		d													07 32	07 07								08 19		
Cark		d													07 40	07 15								08 27		
Kents Bank		d														07 19								08 32		
Grange-over-Sands		d													07 47	07 23								08 36		
Arnside		d													07 53	07 29								08 42		
Silverdale		d													07 58	07 33								08 47		
Carnforth		d													08 06	07 40								08 54		
Windermere	83	d																								
Oxenholme Lake District	65	d																					08 10			
Lancaster 6	65	a													08 16	07 48							08 25	09 05		
		d					07 23									07 48							08 26	09 07		
Blackpool North	97	d			06 53					07 11			07 18				07 36									
Layton	97	d								07 14			07 21				07 39									
Poulton-le-Fylde	97	d								07 18			07 26				07 43									
Kirkham & Wesham	97	d								07 27			07 35				07 53									
Preston 8	65,97	a			07 15		07 41			07 38			07 46			08 07	08 03						08 44	09 30		
		d			07 17		07 43			07 47			07 47			08 12						08 21	08 45			
Leyland		d			07 22								07 53									08 27				
Buckshaw Parkway		d			07 28								07 58									08 31				
Chorley		d			07 32					07 56			08 02			08 22						08 35				
Adlington (Lancashire)		d			07 37								08 07									08 40				
Blackrod		d			07 41								08 11									08 43				
Horwich Parkway		d			07 45								08 15									08 47				
Lostock		d			07 49								08 20									08 50				
Southport		d	06 52								07 21										07 59					08 25
Meols Cop		d	06 57								07 26										08 04					08 30
Bescar Lane		d	07 02																							
New Lane		d	07 06																							
Burscough Bridge		d	07 08								07 34										08 12					08 38
Hoscar		d	07 12																							
Parbold		d	07 15								07 39										08 17					08 43
Appley Bridge		d	07 19								07 43										08 21					08 47
Gathurst		d	07 22								07 47										08 24					08 50
Kirkby		d				07 11																				
Rainford		d				07 19																				
Upholland		d				07 23																				
Orrell		d				07 27																				
Pemberton		d				07 30																				
Wigan Wallgate		a	07 28			07 35					07 51										08 29					08 55
		d	07 29			07 37					07 53	08 00							08 13		08 30					08 56
Wigan North Western		d		07 22			07 56													08 20			08 58			
Ince		d		07 25		07 40													08 16							
Hindley		d		07 29		07 43					07 58								08 19	08 25	08 35					
Westhoughton		d		07 33							08 03									08 29						09 04
Bolton		a		07 42	07 54					08 08	08 11		08 25			08 34				08 38		08 55				09 12
		d		07 43	07 55				07 59	08 08	08 12		08 25	08 31		08 35				08 39		08 56			09 03	09 13
Moses Gate		d		07 46					08 02											08 42						
Farnworth		d		07 48					08 04											08 44						
Kearsley		d		07 50					08 06											08 46						
Clifton		d																								
Daisy Hill		d	07 39			07 47						08 07							08 23		08 39					
Hag Fold		d				07 50													08 26							
Atherton		d	07 43			07 53						08 12							08 29		08 44					
Walkden		d				07 59						08 18							08 35		08 50					
Moorside		d				08 03													08 39							
Swinton		d				08 06													08 42		08 55					
Salford Crescent		a	07 59	08 02	08 07	08 13			08 17		08 24	08 29	08 38	08 43		08 46			08 50	08 56	09 02	09 08			09 14	09 25
		d	08 00	08 02	08 08	08 13			08 17		08 25	08 30	08 38	08 44		08 47			08 51	08 56	09 02	09 09			09 15	09 26
Salford Central		d	08 03	08 05		08 16			08 20			08 32	08 41	08 46					08 54	08 59	09 04				09 18	
Manchester Victoria 🚊		a	08 08	08 12		08 20			08 25			08 38	08 47	08 52					08 59	09 06	09 09				09 22	
Rochdale	41	a				08 51																				
Deansgate 🚊		a			08 11						08 28											09 12				09 29
Manchester Oxford Road		a			08 14		08 22			08 25	08 31					08 52						09 14	09 23			09 31
Manchester Piccadilly 10 🚊		a			08 18		08 26				08 35					08 56						09 18	09 27			09 35
Stockport	84	a			08 34																	09 34				
Hazel Grove	86	a			08 45																	09 45				
Buxton	86	a																								
Heald Green	85	a									08 47					09 09										
Manchester Airport ✈	85	a					08 47				08 53					09 17							09 47			09 53

A 🚲 from Preston
B From Clitheroe
C To Stalybridge
D From Edinburgh
E From Maryport
F From Blackburn

The Sunday service between Wigan Wallgate and Manchester Victoria via Atherton is funded by TfGM and will operate whilst funding exists

Table 82R

Mondays to Fridays

10 February to 16 May

Barrow-in-Furness, Blackpool North, Preston, Southport, Kirkby and Wigan - Bolton - Manchester

Network Diagram - see first Page of Table 82

			NT		NT	NT	TP	NT	NT	NT	TP	TP	NT		NT	NT	NT	NT	NT	NT	TP	NT	NT		NT	TP
							◇1				◇1	◇1									◇1					◇1
						A			B		C		D		E					A			B			F
							🚲				🚲										🚲					🚲
Barrow-in-Furness		d										08 50														
Roose		d																								
Dalton		d										08 59														
Ulverston		d										09 07														
Cark		d										09 15														
Kents Bank		d																								
Grange-over-Sands		d										09 22														
Arnside		d										09 28														
Silverdale		d										09 32														
Carnforth		d										09 39	09 56													
Windermere	83	d																								
Oxenholme Lake District	65	d									09 11															10 10
Lancaster 6	65	a									09 26	09 46	10 08													10 24
		d									09 26	09 47														10 25
Blackpool North	97	d			08 20		08 44												09 20		09 40					
Layton	97	d			08 23														09 23							
Poulton-le-Fylde	97	d			08 27		08 50												09 27		09 46					
Kirkham & Wesham	97	d			08 37														09 37							
Preston 8	65,97	a			08 47		09 08				09 45	10 07							09 47		10 04					10 44
		d			08 49		09 10			09 23	09 45								09 49		10 12				10 23	10 45
Leyland		d			08 54					09 29									09 54						10 29	
Buckshaw Parkway		d			08 59		09 17			09 33									09 59						10 33	
Chorley		d			09 03		09 21			09 38									10 03		10 22				10 38	
Adlington (Lancashire)		d			09 08														10 08							
Blackrod		d			09 12														10 12							
Horwich Parkway		d			09 16		09 28			09 46									10 16						10 46	
Lostock		d			09 20					09 50									10 20						10 50	
Southport		d							09 02								09 24						09 55			
Meols Cop		d							09 07														10 00			
Bescar Lane		d																					10 05			
New Lane		d																					10 09			
Burscough Bridge		d							09 15								09 36						10 11			
Hoscar		d																					10 15			
Parbold		d							09 20								09 41						10 18			
Appley Bridge		d							09 24								09 45						10 22			
Gathurst		d							09 27														10 25			
Kirkby		d	08 21															09 32								
Rainford		d	08 29															09 40								
Upholland		d	08 33															09 44								
Orrell		d	08 36															09 47								
Pemberton		d	08 39															09 50								
Wigan Wallgate		a	08 45						09 32								09 51	09 56					10 30			
		d	08 50					09 20	09 32							09 46	09 53	09 58				10 20	10 32			
Wigan North Western		d									09 58															10 58
Ince		d	08 53															10 01								
Hindley		d	08 57					09 25	09 37								09 58	10 04				10 25	10 37			
Westhoughton		d						09 29								09 54	10 02					10 29				
Bolton		a			09 25		09 34	09 38		09 55						10 02	10 12		10 25		10 34	10 38			10 55	
		d			09 25	09 31	09 35	09 39		09 56					10 00	10 03	10 13		10 25	10 31	10 34	10 39			10 56	
Moses Gate		d						09 42														10 42				
Farnworth		d						09 44														10 44				
Kearsley		d						09 46														10 46				
Clifton		d																								
Daisy Hill		d	09 01						09 41									10 09					10 41			
Hag Fold		d	09 04															10 12								
Atherton		d	09 06						09 45									10 15					10 45			
Walkden		d	09 12						09 50									10 20					10 50			
Moorside		d	09 15															10 24								
Swinton		d	09 18						09 55									10 26					10 55			
Salford Crescent		a	09 27		09 38	09 43	09 47	09 56	10 03	10 08					10 13	10 15	10 25	10 34	10 38	10 43	10 46	10 56	11 02		11 08	
		d	09 27		09 38	09 44	09 47	09 56	10 03	10 09					10 13	10 15	10 26	10 35	10 38	10 44	10 47	10 56	11 03		11 09	
Salford Central		d	09 31		09 41	09 46		09 59	10 05						10 16	10 17		10 37	10 41	10 46		10 59	11 05			
Manchester Victoria ⇌		a	09 38		09 47	09 52		10 06	10 10						10 21	10 25		10 43	10 47	10 52		11 06	11 09			
Rochdale	41	a														10 51										
Deansgate ⇌		a					09 51			10 12							10 29				10 50				11 12	
Manchester Oxford Road		a					09 52			10 14	10 23						10 31				10 52				11 14	11 23
Manchester Piccadilly 10 ⇌		a					09 56			10 18	10 27						10 35				10 56				11 18	11 27
Stockport	84	a								10 34															11 34	
Hazel Grove	86	a								10 45															11 45	
Buxton	86	a																								
Heald Green	85	a					10 10														11 09					
Manchester Airport	85 ✈	a					10 17				10 47						10 53				11 15					11 47

A From Clitheroe
B To Stalybridge
C From Glasgow Central
D From Leeds to Morecambe
E From Blackburn
F From Edinburgh

The Sunday service between Wigan Wallgate and Manchester Victoria via Atherton is funded by TfGM and will operate whilst funding exists

Table 82R

Mondays to Fridays

10 February to 16 May

Barrow-in-Furness, Blackpool North, Preston, Southport, Kirkby and Wigan - Bolton - Manchester

Network Diagram - see first Page of Table 82

Station		NT	NT	NT	NT	NT	NT	TP	NT	NT	NT	TP	NT	NT	NT	NT	NT	TP	NT	TP	NT	NT	NT
				◇				◇1				◇1		◇				◇1		◇1			
		A					B			C		D					E		B			C	
								🛒				🛒								🛒			
Barrow-in-Furness	d	10 09																11 20					
Roose	d	10 13																					
Dalton	d	10 19																11 29					
Ulverston	d	10 28																11 37					
Cark	d	10 35																11 45					
Kents Bank	d	10 40																					
Grange-over-Sands	d	10 44																11 52					
Arnside	d	10 50																11 58					
Silverdale	d	10 55																12 02					
Carnforth	d	11 07															12 02	12 09					
Windermere 83	d											10 51											
Oxenholme Lake District 65	d											11 08											
Lancaster 6 65	a	11 18										11 25					12 11	12 17					
	d											11 25						12 17					
Blackpool North 97	d					10 20		10 44								11 20				11 44			
Layton 97	d					10 23										11 23							
Poulton-le-Fylde 97	d					10 27		10 50								11 27				11 50			
Kirkham & Wesham 97	d					10 37										11 37							
Preston 8 65,97	a					10 47		11 08				11 44				11 47		12 37		12 08			
	d					10 49		11 10			11 23	11 45				11 49				12 10			12 23
Leyland	d					10 54					11 29					11 54							12 29
Buckshaw Parkway	d					10 59		11 17			11 33					11 59				12 17			12 33
Chorley	d					11 03		11 21			11 38					12 03				12 21			12 38
Adlington (Lancashire)	d					11 08										12 08							
Blackrod	d					11 12										12 12							
Horwich Parkway	d					11 16		11 28			11 46					12 16				12 28			12 46
Lostock	d					11 20					11 50					12 20							12 50
Southport	d			10 24						10 55				11 24								12 00	
Meols Cop	d									11 00												12 05	
Bescar Lane	d									11 05													
New Lane	d									11 09													
Burscough Bridge	d			10 36						11 11				11 36								12 13	
Hoscar	d									11 15													
Parbold	d			10 41						11 18				11 41								12 18	
Appley Bridge	d			10 45						11 22				11 45								12 22	
Gathurst	d									11 25												12 25	
Kirkby	d				10 32										11 32								
Rainford	d				10 40										11 40								
Upholland	d				10 44										11 44								
Orrell	d				10 47										11 47								
Pemberton	d				10 50										11 50								
Wigan Wallgate	a			10 51	10 56					11 30				11 51	11 56							12 30	
	d		10 48	10 53	10 58				11 20	11 32			11 48	11 53	11 58						12 20	12 32	
Wigan North Western	d											11 57											
Ince	d				11 01										12 01								
Hindley	d			10 58	11 04				11 25	11 37				11 58	12 04						12 25	12 37	
Westhoughton	d			11 02					11 29					12 02							12 29		
Bolton	a		11 02	11 12		11 25		11 34	11 38		11 55		12 02	12 12		12 25				12 34	12 38		12 55
	d		11 03	11 13		11 25	11 31	11 35	11 39		11 56		12 03	12 13		12 25			12 31	12 35	12 39		12 56
Moses Gate	d								11 42												12 42		
Farnworth	d								11 44												12 44		
Kearsley	d								11 46												12 46		
Clifton	d																						
Daisy Hill	d				11 09					11 41					12 09							12 41	
Hag Fold	d				11 12										12 12								
Atherton	d				11 15					11 45					12 15							12 45	
Walkden	d				11 20					11 50					12 20							12 50	
Moorside	d				11 24										12 24								
Swinton	d				11 26					11 55					12 26							12 55	
Salford Crescent	a		11 16	11 25	11 34	11 38	11 43	11 47	11 56	12 02	12 08		12 16	12 25	12 34	12 38			12 43	12 47	12 56	13 02	13 08
	d		11 16	11 26	11 34	11 38	11 44	11 47	11 56	12 03	12 09		12 16	12 26	12 34	12 38			12 44	12 47	12 56	13 03	13 09
Salford Central	d		11 18		11 36	11 41	11 46		11 59	12 05			12 18		12 36	12 41			12 46		12 59	13 05	
Manchester Victoria ⇌	a		11 25		11 43	11 47	11 52		12 06	12 09			12 25		12 43	12 47			12 52		13 06	13 09	
Rochdale 41	a		11 51										12 51										
Deansgate ⇌	a			11 29				11 51			12 12			12 29						12 51			13 12
Manchester Oxford Road	a			11 31				11 52			12 14	12 22		12 31						12 52			13 14
Manchester Piccadilly 10 ⇌	a			11 35				11 56			12 18	12 26		12 35						12 56			13 18
Stockport 84	a										12 34												13 34
Hazel Grove 86	a										12 45												13 45
Buxton 86	a																						
Heald Green 85	a							12 10												13 10			
Manchester Airport 85 ✈	a			11 53				12 17				12 47		12 53						13 17			

A From Sellafield
B From Clitheroe
C To Stalybridge
D 🛒 from Preston
E From Leeds to Heysham Harbour

The Sunday service between Wigan Wallgate and Manchester Victoria via Atherton is funded by TfGM and will operate whilst funding exists

Table 82R

Mondays to Fridays

10 February to 16 May

Barrow-in-Furness, Blackpool North, Preston, Southport, Kirkby and Wigan - Bolton - Manchester

Network Diagram - see first Page of Table 82

		TP	NT	NT	NT	NT	NT	NT	TP	NT	NT	NT	TP	TP	TP	NT	NT	NT	NT	NT	TP	NT
															FX							
		◇1			◇				◇1				◇1	◇1	◇1		◇				◇1	
		A	B					C			D		E	F						C		
		⊥							⊥				⊥								⊥	
Barrow-in-Furness	d		12 10												13 20							
Roose	d		12 14																			
Dalton	d		12 20												13 29							
Ulverston	d		12 28												13 37							
Cark	d		12 36												13 45							
Kents Bank	d		12 40																			
Grange-over-Sands	d		12 44												13 52							
Arnside	d		12 50												13 58							
Silverdale	d		12 54												14 02							
Carnforth	d		13 02												14 09							
Windermere	83 d													12 52								
Oxenholme Lake District	65 d	12 10											13 10	13 12								
Lancaster 6	65 a	12 25	13 14										13 25	13 30	14 17							
	d	12 26											13 25		14 17							
Blackpool North	97 d						12 20		12 41										13 20		13 44	
Layton	97 d						12 23												13 23			
Poulton-le-Fylde	97 d						12 27		12 47										13 27		13 50	
Kirkham & Wesham	97 d						12 37												13 37			
Preston 8	65,97 a	12 44					12 47		13 05				13 44		14 37				13 47		14 08	
	d	12 45					12 49		13 10			13 23	13 44						13 49		14 10	
Leyland	d						12 54					13 29							13 54			
Buckshaw Parkway	d						12 59		13 17			13 33							13 59		14 17	
Chorley	d						13 03		13 21			13 38							14 03		14 21	
Adlington (Lancashire)	d						13 08												14 08			
Blackrod	d						13 12												14 12			
Horwich Parkway	d						13 16		13 28			13 46							14 16		14 28	
Lostock	d						13 20					13 50							14 20			
Southport	d				12 24						12 54						13 24					
Meols Cop	d										12 59											
Bescar Lane	d										13 04											
New Lane	d										13 08											
Burscough Bridge	d				12 36						13 11						13 36					
Hoscar	d										13 15											
Parbold	d				12 41						13 18						13 41					
Appley Bridge	d				12 45						13 22						13 45					
Gathurst	d										13 25											
Kirkby	d					12 32												13 32				
Rainford	d					12 40												13 40				
Upholland	d					12 44												13 44				
Orrell	d					12 47												13 47				
Pemberton	d					12 50												13 50				
Wigan Wallgate	a				12 51	12 56					13 30						13 51	13 56				
	d			12 48	12 53	12 58				13 20	13 32					13 48	13 53	13 58				14 20
Wigan North Western	d	12 58											13 58									
Ince	d					13 01												14 01				
Hindley	d				12 58	13 04				13 25	13 37						13 58	14 04				14 25
Westhoughton	d				13 02					13 29							14 02					14 29
Bolton	a			13 02	13 12		13 25		13 34	13 38		13 55				14 02	14 12		14 25		14 34	14 38
	d			13 03	13 13		13 25	13 31	13 35	13 39		13 56				14 03	14 13		14 25	14 31	14 35	14 39
Moses Gate	d									13 42												14 42
Farnworth	d									13 44												14 44
Kearsley	d									13 46												14 46
Clifton	d																					
Daisy Hill	d					13 09					13 41							14 09				
Hag Fold	d					13 12												14 12				
Atherton	d					13 15					13 45							14 15				
Walkden	d					13 20					13 50							14 20				
Moorside	d					13 24												14 24				
Swinton	d					13 26					13 55							14 26				
Salford Crescent	a			13 15	13 25	13 34	13 38	13 43	13 47	13 56	14 02	14 08				14 15	14 25	14 34	14 38	14 43	14 47	14 56
	d			13 15	13 26	13 34	13 38	13 44	13 47	13 56	14 03	14 09				14 15	14 26	14 34	14 38	14 44	14 47	14 56
Salford Central	d			13 17		13 36	13 41	13 46		13 59	14 05					14 17		14 36	14 41	14 46		14 59
Manchester Victoria ⇌	a			13 25		13 43	13 47	13 52		14 06	14 09					14 25		14 43	14 47	14 52		15 06
Rochdale	41 a			13 51												14 51						
Deansgate ⇌	a				13 29				13 51			14 12					14 29				14 51	
Manchester Oxford Road	a	13 23			13 31				13 52			14 14	14 22				14 31				14 52	
Manchester Piccadilly 10 ⇌	a	13 27			13 35				13 56			14 18	14 26				14 35				14 56	
Stockport	84 a											14 34										
Hazel Grove	86 a											14 45										
Buxton	86 a																					
Heald Green	85 a								14 10												15 10	
Manchester Airport	85 ✈ a	13 46			13 53				14 17				14 46				14 53				15 17	

A From Edinburgh
B From Carlisle
C From Clitheroe
D To Stalybridge
E From Glasgow Central
F To Barrow-in-Furness

The Sunday service between Wigan Wallgate and Manchester Victoria via Atherton is funded by TfGM and will operate whilst funding exists

Table 82R

Mondays to Fridays

10 February to 16 May

Barrow-in-Furness, Blackpool North, Preston, Southport, Kirkby and Wigan - Bolton - Manchester

Network Diagram - see first Page of Table 82

		NT	NT	NT	TP	TP	TP	NT	NT	NT	NT	NT	TP	NT	NT	NT	TP	NT	NT	NT	NT	NT	NT
					FO	FO	FX																
					◇1	◇1	◇1	◇					◇1				◇1		◇				
		A			B	C	C				D	E					F			E			G
					(trolley)	(trolley)	(trolley)						(trolley)				(trolley)						
Barrow-in-Furness	d				13 20																		15 18
Roose	d																						15 22
Dalton	d				13 29																		15 28
Ulverston	d				13 37																		15 37
Cark	d				13 45																		15 44
Kents Bank	d																						15 49
Grange-over-Sands	d				13 52																		15 53
Arnside	d				13 58																		15 59
Silverdale	d				14 02																		16 03
Carnforth	d				14 09						15 02												16 11
Windermere 83	d																						
Oxenholme Lake District 65	d						14 10										15 09						
Lancaster [6] 65	a				14 17		14 24				15 15						15 23						16 22
	d				14 17	14 24	14 25										15 24						
Blackpool North 97	d									14 20			14 40									15 20	
Layton 97	d									14 23												15 23	
Poulton-le-Fylde 97	d									14 27			14 46									15 27	
Kirkham & Wesham 97	d									14 37												15 37	
Preston [8] 65,97	a				14 37	14 42	14 45			14 47			15 04				15 43					15 47	
	d		14 23		14 47		14 45			14 49			15 10			15 23	15 45					15 49	
Leyland	d		14 29							14 54						15 29						15 54	
Buckshaw Parkway	d		14 33							14 59			15 17			15 33						15 59	
Chorley	d		14 38		14 57		14 55			15 03			15 21			15 38						16 03	
Adlington (Lancashire)	d									15 08												16 08	
Blackrod	d									15 12												16 12	
Horwich Parkway	d		14 46							15 16			15 28			15 46						16 16	
Lostock	d		14 50							15 20						15 50						16 20	
Southport	d	14 00						14 24							14 54				15 24				
Meols Cop	d	14 05													14 59								
Bescar Lane	d														15 04								
New Lane	d														15 08								
Burscough Bridge	d	14 13						14 36							15 11				15 36				
Hoscar	d														15 15								
Parbold	d	14 18						14 41							15 18				15 41				
Appley Bridge	d	14 22						14 45							15 22				15 45				
Gathurst	d	14 25													15 25								
Kirkby	d								14 32												15 32		
Rainford	d								14 40												15 40		
Upholland	d								14 44												15 44		
Orrell	d								14 47												15 47		
Pemberton	d								14 50												15 50		
Wigan Wallgate	a	14 30						14 51	14 56						15 30				15 51		15 56		
	d	14 32		14 48				14 53	14 58					15 20	15 32			15 48	15 53		15 58		
Wigan North Western	d																15 58						
Ince	d								15 01												16 01		
Hindley	d	14 37						14 58	15 04					15 25	15 37				15 58		16 04		
Westhoughton	d							15 02						15 29					16 02				
Bolton	a		14 55	15 02	15 08		15 07	15 12		15 25			15 34	15 38		15 55		16 02	16 12			16 25	
	d		14 56	15 03	15 09		15 07	15 13		15 25		15 31	15 35	15 39		15 56		16 03	16 13	16 18		16 25	
Moses Gate	d													15 42									
Farnworth	d													15 44									
Kearsley	d													15 46									
Clifton	d																						
Daisy Hill	d	14 41							15 09						15 41						16 09		
Hag Fold	d								15 12												16 12		
Atherton	d	14 45							15 15						15 45						16 15		
Walkden	d	14 50							15 20						15 50						16 20		
Moorside	d								15 24												16 24		
Swinton	d	14 55							15 26						15 55						16 26		
Salford Crescent	a	15 02	15 08	15 15	15 20		15 19	15 25	15 33	15 38		15 43	15 47	15 56	16 02	16 08		16 15	16 25	16 31	16 34	16 38	
	d	15 03	15 09	15 15	15 21		15 19	15 26	15 34	15 38		15 44	15 47	15 56	16 03	16 09		16 15	16 26	16 31	16 34	16 38	
Salford Central	d	15 05		15 17					15 36	15 41		15 46		15 59	16 05			16 17		16 34	16 37	16 41	
Manchester Victoria 🚊	a	15 10		15 25					15 43	15 47		15 54		16 06	16 11			16 23		16 41	16 43	16 47	
Rochdale 41	a			15 51														16 51					
Deansgate 🚊	a		15 12					15 29					15 51			16 12							
Manchester Oxford Road	a		15 14		15 25		15 24	15 31					15 52			16 14	16 23		16 31				
Manchester Piccadilly [10] 🚊	a		15 18		15 29		15 28	15 35					15 56			16 18	16 27		16 35				
Stockport 84	a		15 34													16 34							
Hazel Grove 86	a		15 45													16 43							
Buxton 86	a															17 24							
Heald Green 85	a												16 10				16 40						
Manchester Airport 85 ✈	a				15 47		15 47	15 53					16 17				16 47		16 53				

A To Stalybridge
B (trolley) from Preston
C From Edinburgh
D From Leeds to Morecambe
E From Clitheroe
F From Glasgow Central
G From Carlisle

The Sunday service between Wigan Wallgate and Manchester Victoria via Atherton is funded by TfGM and will operate whilst funding exists

Table 82R

Mondays to Fridays

10 February to 16 May

Barrow-in-Furness, Blackpool North, Preston, Southport, Kirkby and Wigan - Bolton - Manchester

Network Diagram - see first Page of Table 82

		TP	TP	NT	NT	NT		TP	NT	NT	NT	NT	NT	NT	TP	NT		NT	NT	NT	TP	NT	NT	NT	TP
		◇1	◇1					◇1			◇				◇1						◇1	◇			◇1
		A			B			C						D						D					A
		🛒	🛒					🛒							🛒						🛒				🛒
Barrow-in-Furness	d	14 40							16 10																
Roose	d								16 14																
Dalton	d								16 20																
Ulverston	d	14 56							16 28																
Cark	d								16 36																
Kents Bank	d								16 40																
Grange-over-Sands	d	15 08							16 44																
Arnside	d	15 14							16 50																
Silverdale	d								16 54																
Carnforth	d	15 24							17 02																
Windermere 83	d																								
Oxenholme Lake District 65	d							16 14																	
Lancaster 6 65	a	15 32						16 29	17 14																
	d	15 32						16 29																	17 45
Blackpool North 97	d		15 40										16 20		16 40						17 20				
Layton 97	d												16 23		16 43						17 23				
Poulton-le-Fylde 97	d		15 46										16 27		16 47						17 27				
Kirkham & Wesham 97	d												16 37		16 57										
Preston 8 65,97	a	15 51	16 04					16 48					16 47		17 08						17 45				18 03
	d	16 10				16 22		16 49					16 49		17 10						17 47			17 56	18 05
Leyland	d					16 28							16 54											18 01	
Buckshaw Parkway	d	16 17				16 32							16 59		17 17									18 05	
Chorley	d	16 21				16 37							17 03		17 21						17 56			18 09	
Adlington (Lancashire)	d												17 08											18 15	
Blackrod	d												17 12											18 19	
Horwich Parkway	d	16 28				16 45							17 16		17 28									18 21	
Lostock	d					16 49							17 20											18 26	
Southport	d				15 58						16 24							16 54				17 24			
Meols Cop	d				16 03													16 59				17 29			
Bescar Lane	d																	17 04							
New Lane	d																	17 08							
Burscough Bridge	d				16 11						16 36							17 11				17 37			
Hoscar	d																	17 15							
Parbold	d				16 16						16 41							17 18				17 42			
Appley Bridge	d				16 20						16 45							17 22				17 46			
Gathurst	d				16 24													17 25							
Kirkby	d											16 32											17 32		
Rainford	d											16 40											17 40		
Upholland	d											16 44											17 44		
Orrell	d											16 47											17 47		
Pemberton	d											16 50											17 50		
Wigan Wallgate	a				16 29						16 51	16 56						17 30				17 52	17 57		
	d			16 20	16 30					16 48	16 53	16 58				17 20		17 32	17 39			17 54	17 59		
Wigan North Western	d																								18 17
Ince	d				16 33							17 01											18 02		
Hindley	d			16 25	16 37						16 58	17 04				17 25		17 37					18 05		
Westhoughton	d			16 29							17 02					17 29			17 47			18 02			
Bolton	a	16 34		16 38		16 54				17 02	17 12		17 25		17 34	17 38			17 55		18 08	18 12		18 31	
	d	16 35		16 39		16 55				17 03	17 13		17 25	17 31	17 35	17 39			17 56	18 02	18 08	18 12		18 31	
Moses Gate	d			16 42												17 42									
Farnworth	d			16 44												17 44									
Kearsley	d			16 46												17 46									
Clifton	d																								
Daisy Hill	d				16 41							17 08						17 41					18 09		
Hag Fold	d											17 11											18 12		
Atherton	d				16 45							17 14						17 45					18 15		
Walkden	d				16 50							17 19						17 50					18 20		
Moorside	d											17 23											18 24		
Swinton	d				16 55							17 25						17 55					18 26		
Salford Crescent	a	16 47		16 56	17 02	17 07				17 15	17 25	17 33	17 38	17 43	17 47	17 56		18 02	18 08	18 15		18 25	18 32	18 43	
	d	16 47		16 56	17 03	17 08				17 15	17 26	17 33	17 38	17 44	17 47	17 56		18 03	18 09	18 15		18 25	18 33	18 43	
Salford Central	d			16 59	17 05					17 17		17 36	17 41	17 46		17 59		18 05		18 17			18 35	18 46	
Manchester Victoria 🚊	a			17 06	17 13					17 23		17 43	17 47	17 53		18 06		18 11		18 24			18 43	18 51	
Rochdale 41	a									17 51										18 47					
Deansgate 🚊	a	16 51				17 12									17 51				18 12						18 47
Manchester Oxford Road	a	16 52				17 14		17 26			17 30				17 52				18 14		18 23	18 31			18 48
Manchester Piccadilly 10 🚊	a	16 56				17 19		17 30			17 35				17 56				18 18		18 27	18 35			18 52
Stockport 84	a					17 32													18 34						
Hazel Grove 86	a					17 39													18 43						
Buxton 86	a					18 14													19 24						
Heald Green 85	a	17 10									17 47				18 10						18 40				19 05
Manchester Airport 85 ✈	a	17 17						17 47			17 53				18 17						18 47	18 53			19 13

A 🛒 from Preston
B To Huddersfield
C From Edinburgh
D From Clitheroe

The Sunday service between Wigan Wallgate and Manchester Victoria via Atherton is funded by TfGM and will operate whilst funding exists

Table 82R

Mondays to Fridays

10 February to 16 May

Barrow-in-Furness, Blackpool North, Preston, Southport, Kirkby and Wigan - Bolton - Manchester

Network Diagram - see first Page of Table 82

		TP	TP	TP	NT	NT	NT	NT	NT	NT	NT	TP	NT	NT	TP	NT	TP	NT	NT	NT	NT	TP
		◇1	◇1	◇1				◇				◇1			◇1		◇1		◇			◇1
			A				B				B	C	D	E			F	G			B	
Barrow-in-Furness	d	17 21												18 03								
Roose	d													18 07								
Dalton	d	17 30												18 13								
Ulverston	d	17 39												18 21								
Cark	d	17 46												18 29								
Kents Bank	d													18 33								
Grange-over-Sands	d	17 53												18 37								
Arnside	d	17 59												18 43								
Silverdale	d													18 47								
Carnforth	d	18 08											18 26	18 55								
Windermere 83	d			18 02								18 02										
Oxenholme Lake District 65	d			18 22								18 22					19 09					
Lancaster 6 65	a	18 17		18 39								18 39	18 40	19 05			19 24					
	d		18 25	18 40								18 40		19 06			19 24					
Blackpool North 97	d									18 20					18 40					19 20		19 44
Layton 97	d									18 23										19 23		
Poulton-le-Fylde 97	d									18 27					18 46					19 28		19 50
Kirkham & Wesham 97	d									18 37										19 37		
Preston 8 65,97	a		18 45	18 58						18 47		18 58		19 31	19 04		19 44			19 47		20 08
	d		18 45							18 49		19 10			19 10		19 45			19 49		20 10
Leyland	d									18 54										19 54		
Buckshaw Parkway	d									18 59		19 17			19 17					19 59		20 17
Chorley	d									19 03		19 21			19 21					20 03		20 21
Adlington (Lancashire)	d									19 08										20 08		
Blackrod	d									19 12										20 12		
Horwich Parkway	d									19 16		19 28			19 28					20 16		20 28
Lostock	d									19 20										20 20		
Southport	d							18 17								19 00			19 23			
Meols Cop	d							18 22								19 05			19 28			
Bescar Lane	d							18 27														
New Lane	d							18 31														
Burscough Bridge	d							18 33								19 13			19 36			
Hoscar	d							18 37														
Parbold	d							18 40								19 18			19 41			
Appley Bridge	d							18 44								19 22			19 45			
Gathurst	d							18 47								19 25			19 48			
Kirkby	d								18 32													
Rainford	d								18 40													
Upholland	d								18 44													
Orrell	d								18 47													
Pemberton	d								18 50													
Wigan Wallgate	a							18 52	18 56							19 30			19 53			
	d				18 20	18 32		18 53	18 58							19 32			19 55			
Wigan North Western	d		18 59														19 59					
Ince	d								19 01													
Hindley	d				18 25	18 37		18 58	19 04							19 37			20 00			
Westhoughton	d				18 29			19 02											20 04			
Bolton	a				18 38			19 12		19 25		19 35			19 35				20 12	20 25		20 34
	d				18 39		19 02	19 13		19 25	19 31	19 35			19 35			20 02	20 13	20 25	20 31	20 35
Moses Gate	d				18 42																	
Farnworth	d				18 44																	
Kearsley	d				18 46																	
Clifton	d																					
Daisy Hill	d					18 41			19 08							19 41						
Hag Fold	d								19 11													
Atherton	d					18 45			19 14							19 45						
Walkden	d					18 50			19 19							19 50						
Moorside	d								19 23													
Swinton	d					18 55			19 25							19 55						
Salford Crescent	a				18 56	19 02	19 14	19 25	19 33	19 38	19 44	19 48			19 48	20 02		20 15	20 25	20 38	20 43	20 47
	d				18 56	19 03	19 15	19 26	19 33	19 38	19 44	19 48			19 48	20 03		20 15	20 26	20 38	20 44	20 47
Salford Central	d				18 59	19 05	19 17		19 36	19 41	19 46					20 05		20 17		20 41	20 46	
Manchester Victoria	a				19 06	19 11	19 23		19 43	19 47	19 53					20 11		20 24		20 47	20 52	
Rochdale 41	a																					
Deansgate	a							19 29				19 52			19 52				20 29			20 51
Manchester Oxford Road	a		19 24					19 31				19 53			19 53		20 23		20 31			20 52
Manchester Piccadilly 10	a		19 29					19 35				19 57			19 57		20 27		20 35			20 56
Stockport 84	a																					
Hazel Grove 86	a																					
Buxton 86	a																					
Heald Green 85	a											20 11			20 11							21 10
Manchester Airport 85	a		19 47					19 53				20 17			20 17		20 46		20 52			21 17

A From Edinburgh
B From Clitheroe
C until 21 March
D From Leeds to Morecambe
E From Carlisle
F From Glasgow Central
G From Blackburn

The Sunday service between Wigan Wallgate and Manchester Victoria via Atherton is funded by TfGM and will operate whilst funding exists

Table 82R

Mondays to Fridays

10 February to 16 May

Barrow-in-Furness, Blackpool North, Preston, Southport, Kirkby and Wigan - Bolton - Manchester

Network Diagram - see first Page of Table 82

	NT	NT	NT	NT	TP	TP	TP	TP	NT	TP	TP	NT	NT	NT	NT	NT	NT	NT	NT	TP	TP	TP
			FX		FX	FO				FX		FO	FX	FO	FX	FX	FO	FX	FO	FX		
		◇	◇		◇1	◇1	◇1	◇1		◇1	◇1									◇1	◇1	◇1
		A	B		C	D	E		F	B	A							F	F	B	A	G
					🍴	🍴	🍴															🍴
Barrow-in-Furness d								20 10														
Roose d								20 14														
Dalton d								20 21														
Ulverston d								20 29														
Cark d								20 37														
Kents Bank d								20 41														
Grange-over-Sands d								20 45														
Arnside d								20 51														
Silverdale d								20 55														
Carnforth d								21 02														
Windermere 83 d																						
Oxenholme Lake District 65 d					20 16	20 16	20 16															22 10
Lancaster 6 65 a					20 31	20 31	20 31	21 10														22 24
d					20 31	20 31	20 31	21 11														22 25
Blackpool North 97 d				20 20						20 44	20 44					21 20	21 20			21 44	21 44	
Layton 97 d				20 23												21 23	21 23					
Poulton-le-Fylde 97 d				20 27						20 50	20 50					21 27	21 27			21 50	21 50	
Kirkham & Wesham 97 d				20 37												21 37	21 37					
Preston 8 65,97 a				20 47	20 50	20 50	20 50	21 30		21 08	21 08					21 47	21 47			22 08	22 08	22 44
d				20 49	20 51	20 51	20 51			21 10	21 10					21 49	21 49			22 10	22 10	22 45
Leyland d				20 54												21 54	21 54					
Buckshaw Parkway d				20 59						21 17	21 17					21 59	21 59			22 17	22 17	
Chorley d				21 03						21 21	21 21					22 03	22 03			22 21	22 21	
Adlington (Lancashire) d				21 08												22 08	22 08					
Blackrod d				21 12												22 12	22 12					
Horwich Parkway d				21 16						21 28	21 28					22 16	22 16			22 28	22 28	
Lostock d				21 20												22 20	22 20					
Southport d		20 23	20 23											21 23	21 23							
Meols Cop d		20 28	20 28											21 28	21 28							
Bescar Lane d																						
New Lane d																						
Burscough Bridge d		20 36	20 36											21 36	21 36							
Hoscar d																						
Parbold d		20 41	20 41											21 41	21 41							
Appley Bridge d		20 45	20 45											21 45	21 45							
Gathurst d		20 48	20 48											21 48	21 48							
Kirkby d																						
Rainford d																						
Upholland d																						
Orrell d																						
Pemberton d																						
Wigan Wallgate a		20 53	20 53											21 53	21 53							
d	20 29	20 55	20 55									21 29	21 29	21 55	21 55							
Wigan North Western d																						22 58
Ince d	20 32											21 32	21 32									
Hindley d	20 35	21 00	21 00									21 35	21 35	22 00	22 00							
Westhoughton d		21 04	21 04											22 04	22 04							
Bolton a		21 12	21 12	21 25						21 34	21 34			22 12	22 12	22 25	22 25			22 34	22 34	
d		21 13	21 13	21 25					21 31	21 35	21 35			22 13	22 13	22 25	22 25	22 31	22 31	22 35	22 35	
Moses Gate d																						
Farnworth d																						
Kearsley d																						
Clifton d																						
Daisy Hill d	20 39											21 39	21 39									
Hag Fold d	20 42											21 42	21 42									
Atherton d	20 45											21 45	21 45									
Walkden d	20 51											21 51	21 51									
Moorside d	20 54											21 54	21 54									
Swinton d	20 57											21 57	21 57									
Salford Crescent a	21 04	21 25	21 25	21 38					21 43	21 47	21 47	22 04	22 04	22 25	22 25	22 38	22 38	22 43	22 43	22 47	22 47	
d	21 05	21 26	21 26	21 38					21 44	21 47	21 47	22 05	22 05	22 26	22 26	22 38	22 38	22 44	22 44	22 47	22 47	
Salford Central d	21 07			21 41					21 46			22 07		22 28			22 41		22 46			
Manchester Victoria ⇌ a	21 13			21 47					21 52			22 13	22 13	22 34	22 34	22 46	22 47	22 52	22 54			
Rochdale 41 a																						
Deansgate ⇌ a		21 29	21 29							21 51	21 51									22 51	22 51	
Manchester Oxford Road a		21 31	21 34		21 26	21 26	21 26			21 52	21 52									22 52	22 52	23 23
Manchester Piccadilly 10 ⇌ a		21 35			21 30	21 30	21 30			21 56	21 56									22 57	22 57	23 27
Stockport 84 a																						
Hazel Grove 86 a																						
Buxton 86 a																						
Heald Green 85 a											22 10										23 10	
Manchester Airport 85 ✈ a		21 53				21 47	21 49				22 20										23 17	23 46

A FO until 14 March, from 21 March
B until 20 March
C until 20 March. From Edinburgh
D until 21 March. From Edinburgh
E from 24 March. From Edinburgh
F From Clitheroe
G FO until 14 March, from 21 March. From Edinburgh

The Sunday service between Wigan Wallgate and Manchester Victoria via Atherton is funded by TfGM and will operate whilst funding exists

Table 82R

Mondays to Fridays

10 February to 16 May

Barrow-in-Furness, Blackpool North, Preston, Southport, Kirkby and Wigan - Bolton - Manchester

Network Diagram - see first Page of Table 82

Station		TP FX ◇1 A 🍴	NT	NT FO	NT FX	NT ◇	NT	NT B	TP ◇1 C	NT	NT D	TP ◇1 E	TP FX ◇1 F	NT
Barrow-in-Furness	d		21 43											
Roose	d		21 47											
Dalton	d		21 53											
Ulverston	d		22 01											
Cark	d		22 09											
Kents Bank	d		22 13											
Grange-over-Sands	d		22 17											
Arnside	d		22 23											
Silverdale	d		22 27											
Carnforth	d		22 35											
Windermere 83	d								22 45					
Oxenholme Lake District 65	d	22 10							23 05					
Lancaster [6] 65	a	22 24	22 45						23 22					
	d	22 25	22 46					23 02	23 22					
Blackpool North 97	d						22 20					22 45	22 45	23 13
Layton 97	d						22 23							23 16
Poulton-le-Fylde 97	d						22 27					22 51	22 51	23 20
Kirkham & Wesham 97	d						22 37							23 30
Preston [8] 65,97	a	22 44	23 11				22 47	23 23	23 42			23 09	23 09	23 40
	d	22 45					22 49					23 10	23 10	23 42
Leyland	d						22 55							23 48
Buckshaw Parkway	d						23 00					23 17	23 17	23 52
Chorley	d						23 04					23 21	23 21	23 58
Adlington (Lancashire)	d						23 09							00 02
Blackrod	d						23 13							00 06
Horwich Parkway	d						23 17					23 28	23 28	00 09
Lostock	d						23 20							00 13
Southport	d					22 18				23 10				
Meols Cop	d					22 23				23 15				
Bescar Lane	d					22 28								
New Lane	d					22 32								
Burscough Bridge	d					22 34				23 23				
Hoscar	d					22 38								
Parbold	d					22 41				23 28				
Appley Bridge	d					22 45				23 32				
Gathurst	d					22 48				23 35				
Kirkby	d													
Rainford	d													
Upholland	d													
Orrell	d													
Pemberton	d													
Wigan Wallgate	a					22 53				23 44				
	d			22 29	22 29	22 55								
Wigan North Western	d	22 58												
Ince	d			22 32	22 32									
Hindley	d			22 35	22 35	23 00								
Westhoughton	d					23 04								
Bolton	a					23 12	23 25					23 34	23 34	00 17
	d					23 13	23 26				23 31	23 35	23 35	00 17
Moses Gate	d													
Farnworth	d													
Kearsley	d													
Clifton	d													
Daisy Hill	d			22 39	22 39									
Hag Fold	d			22 42	22 42									
Atherton	d			22 45	22 45									
Walkden	d			22 51	22 51									
Moorside	d			22 54	22 54									
Swinton	d			22 57	22 57									
Salford Crescent	a			23 04	23 04	23 25	23 38				23 43	23 47	23 47	
	d			23 05	23 05	23 26	23 39				23 44	23 47	23 47	
Salford Central	d			23 07										
Manchester Victoria 🚋	a			23 13	23 13		23 44				23 50			00 36
Rochdale 41	a													
Deansgate 🚋	a					23 29								
Manchester Oxford Road	a	23 23				23 31								
Manchester Piccadilly [10] 🚋	a	23 28				23 39						23 55	23 55	
Stockport 84	a													
Hazel Grove 86	a													
Buxton 86	a													
Heald Green 85	a											00 16		
Manchester Airport 85 ✈	a											00 23		

A until 20 March. From Edinburgh
B From Morecambe
C To Blackpool North
D From Clitheroe
E FO until 14 March, from 21 March
F until 20 March

The Sunday service between Wigan Wallgate and Manchester Victoria via Atherton is funded by TfGM and will operate whilst funding exists

Table 82R

Saturdays

14 December to 28 December

Barrow-in-Furness, Blackpool North, Preston, Southport, Kirkby and Wigan - Bolton - Manchester

Network Diagram - see first Page of Table 82

		NT	TP	TP	TP	TP	NT	NT	NT	TP		NT	NT	TP	NT	NT	NT	TP	NT	NT		NT	NT	NT	NT
			◇1	◇1	◇1	◇1				◇1				◇1				◇1							
		A							B											C		D			D
Barrow-in-Furness	d				04 35					05 32								06 15							
Roose	d																	06 19							
Dalton	d																	06 26							
Ulverston	d				04 51					05 48								06 34							
Cark	d																	06 42							
Kents Bank	d																	06 46							
Grange-over-Sands	d				05 03					06 00								06 50							
Arnside	d				05 09					06 06								06 56							
Silverdale	d																	07 00							
Carnforth	d				05 19					06 16								07 07		07 42					
Windermere 83	d																								
Oxenholme Lake District 65	d																								
Lancaster 6 65	a				05 27					06 24								07 15		07 50					
	d									06 24								07 23							
Blackpool North 97	d		03 37			05 39							06 19	06 40			06 53							07 18	
Layton 97	d												06 22	06 43										07 21	
Poulton-le-Fylde 97	d					05 45							06 26	06 47										07 25	
Kirkham & Wesham 97	d												06 36	06 57										07 35	
Preston 8 65,97	a					06 03				06 43			06 46	07 07			07 15	07 41						07 46	
	d		04u02	05 12		06 05				06 44			06 48	07 09			07 17	07 43						07 47	
Leyland	d					06 10							06 53				07 22							07 53	
Buckshaw Parkway	d												06 58				07 28							07 58	
Chorley	d			05 22		06 17				06 54			07 02	07 18			07 32							08 02	
Adlington (Lancashire)	d	00 02											07 07				07 37							08 07	
Blackrod	d	00 06				06 23							07 11				07 41							08 11	
Horwich Parkway	d	00 09		05 29		06 26				07 01			07 15	07 26			07 45							08 15	
Lostock	d	00 13				06 30							07 20	07 30			07 49							08 20	
Southport	d											06 23											07 21		
Meols Cop	d											06 28											07 26		
Bescar Lane	d																								
New Lane	d																								
Burscough Bridge	d											06 36											07 34		
Hoscar	d																								
Parbold	d											06 41											07 39		
Appley Bridge	d											06 45											07 43		
Gathurst	d											06 49											07 47		
Kirkby	d																		07 11						
Rainford	d																		07 19						
Upholland	d																		07 23						
Orrell	d																		07 27						
Pemberton	d																		07 30						
Wigan Wallgate	a											06 54							07 35				07 51		
	d						06 31	06 36				06 55			07 15				07 37				07 53		
Wigan North Western	d															07 22		07 56							
Ince	d							06 39							07 18	07 25			07 40						
Hindley	d						06 36	06 42							07 21	07 29			07 43				07 58		
Westhoughton	d						06 41					07 03				07 33							08 03		
Bolton	a	00 17		05 40		06 34	06 52			07 07		07 11	07 25	07 34		07 42	07 54						08 11	08 25	
	d	00 17	04u31	05 40		06 35	06 53		06 57	07 08		07 12	07 25	07 35		07 43	07 55					07 59	08 12	08 25	08 31
Moses Gate	d								07 00							07 46						08 02			
Farnworth	d								07 02							07 48						08 04			
Kearsley	d								07 04							07 50						08 06			
Clifton	d								07 08																
Daisy Hill	d							06 46							07 26				07 47						
Hag Fold	d							06 49							07 29				07 50						
Atherton	d							06 52							07 32				07 53						
Walkden	d							06 58							07 38				07 59						
Moorside	d							07 01							07 41				08 03						
Swinton	d							07 04							07 44				08 06						
Salford Crescent	a			05 52		06 47	07 05	07 11	07 16			07 24	07 38	07 47	07 53	08 02	08 07		08 13			08 17	08 24	08 38	08 43
	d			05 53		06 47	07 08	07 12	07 17			07 25	07 38	07 47	07 53	08 02	08 08		08 13			08 17	08 25	08 38	08 44
Salford Central	d							07 15	07 20				07 41		07 56	08 05			08 16			08 20		08 41	08 46
Manchester Victoria ⇌	a	00 36						07 18	07 25				07 47		07 59	08 12			08 20			08 25		08 47	08 52
Rochdale 41	a																		08 51						
Deansgate ⇌	a					06 51	07 11					07 28		07 51			08 11						08 28		
Manchester Oxford Road	a			05 57		06 52	07 13			07 23		07 30		07 53			08 14	08 22					08 31		
Manchester Piccadilly 10 ⇌	a		04 46	06 00		06 56	07 17			07 27		07 34		07 57			08 18	08 26					08 35		
Stockport 84	a						07 34										08 34								
Hazel Grove 86	a						07 45										08 45								
Buxton 86	a																								
Heald Green 85	a					07 10								08 10									08 47		
Manchester Airport 85 ✈	a		05 05	06 17		07 15				07 47		07 53		08 17				08 47					08 53		

A From Blackpool North
B From Blackburn
C From Leeds
D From Clitheroe

The Sunday service between Wigan Wallgate and Manchester Victoria via Atherton is funded by TfGM and will operate whilst funding exists

Table 82R

Saturdays

14 December to 28 December

Barrow-in-Furness, Blackpool North, Preston, Southport, Kirkby and Wigan - Bolton - Manchester

Network Diagram - see first Page of Table 82

	TP ◇1	NT	NT	NT	NT	TP ◇1	NT	NT	NT	NT	NT	NT	TP ◇1	TP ◇1	NT	NT	NT	TP ◇1	TP ◇1	TP ◇1	NT	NT
						A	B				C	D						E			B	
Barrow-in-Furness d												08 20	07 33						08 50			
Roose d												08 24	07 37									
Dalton d												08 30	07 44						08 59			
Ulverston d												08 38	07 52						09 07			
Cark d												08 46	08 00						09 15			
Kents Bank d												08 50	08 04									
Grange-over-Sands d												08 54	08 08						09 22			
Arnside d												09 00	08 14						09 28			
Silverdale d												09 04	08 18						09 32			
Carnforth d												09 11	08 25						09 39			
Windermere 83 d																				09 37		
Oxenholme Lake District 65 d						08 10												09 10		09 57		
Lancaster 6 65 a						08 25						09 24	08 33					09 25	09 46	10 13		
d						08 26							08 33					09 25	09 47	10 14		
Blackpool North 97 d	07 44									08 20				08 40								
Layton 97 d	07 47									08 23												
Poulton-le-Fylde 97 d	07 51									08 27				08 46								
Kirkham & Wesham 97 d	08 01									08 37												
Preston 8 65,97 a	08 11					08 44				08 47			08 52	09 04				09 44	10 07	10 33		
d	08 12				08 21	08 45				08 49			09 10				09 23	09 44				
Leyland d					08 27					08 54							09 29					
Buckshaw Parkway d					08 31					08 59			09 17				09 33					
Chorley d	08 22				08 35					09 03			09 21				09 38					
Adlington (Lancashire) d					08 40					09 08												
Blackrod d					08 43					09 12												
Horwich Parkway d					08 47					09 16			09 28				09 46					
Lostock d					08 50					09 20							09 50					
Southport d				07 54				08 25								09 00						
Meols Cop d				07 59				08 30								09 05						
Bescar Lane d				08 04																		
New Lane d				08 08																		
Burscough Bridge d				08 10				08 38								09 13						
Hoscar d				08 14																		
Parbold d				08 17				08 43								09 18						
Appley Bridge d				08 21				08 47								09 22						
Gathurst d				08 24				08 50								09 25						
Kirkby d									08 21													
Rainford d									08 29													
Upholland d									08 33													
Orrell d									08 36													
Pemberton d									08 39													
Wigan Wallgate a				08 29				08 55	08 45							09 30						
d		08 13		08 29				08 56	08 50						09 20	09 31						09 46
Wigan North Western d			08 20			08 58												09 58				
Ince d		08 16							08 53													
Hindley d		08 19	08 25	08 34					08 57						09 25	09 36						
Westhoughton d			08 29					09 04							09 29							09 54
Bolton a	08 34		08 38		08 55			09 12		09 25			09 34		09 38		09 55					10 02
d	08 35		08 39		08 56		09 02	09 13		09 25	09 31		09 35		09 39		09 56				10 00	10 03
Moses Gate d			08 42												09 42							
Farnworth d			08 44												09 44							
Kearsley d			08 46												09 46							
Clifton d																						
Daisy Hill d		08 23		08 39					09 01							09 40						
Hag Fold d		08 26							09 04													
Atherton d		08 29		08 43					09 06							09 44						
Walkden d		08 35		08 49					09 12							09 48						
Moorside d		08 39							09 15													
Swinton d		08 42		08 54					09 18							09 54						
Salford Crescent a	08 46	08 50	08 56	09 01	09 08		09 14	09 25	09 27	09 38	09 43		09 47		09 56	10 01	10 08				10 13	10 15
d	08 47	08 51	08 56	09 02	09 09		09 15	09 26	09 27	09 38	09 44		09 47		09 56	10 02	10 09				10 13	10 15
Salford Central d		08 54	08 59	09 04			09 18		09 31	09 41	09 46				09 59	10 03					10 16	10 17
Manchester Victoria a		08 57	09 06	09 10			09 22		09 38	09 47	09 52				10 06	10 11					10 21	10 25
Rochdale 41 a							09 54															10 51
Deansgate a					09 12			09 29					09 51				10 12					
Manchester Oxford Road a	08 52				09 14	09 23		09 31					09 52				10 14	10 22				
Manchester Piccadilly 10 a	08 56				09 18	09 27		09 35					09 56				10 18	10 26				
Stockport 84 a					09 34												10 34					
Hazel Grove 86 a					09 45												10 45					
Buxton 86 a																						
Heald Green 85 a	09 09												10 10									
Manchester Airport 85 a	09 17					09 47		09 53					10 17					10 46				

A From Edinburgh
B From Blackburn
C From Clitheroe
D From Maryport
E From Glasgow Central

The Sunday service between Wigan Wallgate and Manchester Victoria via Atherton is funded by TfGM and will operate whilst funding exists

Table 82R

Saturdays

14 December to 28 December

Barrow-in-Furness, Blackpool North, Preston, Southport, Kirkby and Wigan - Bolton - Manchester

Network Diagram - see first Page of Table 82

		NT		NT	NT	NT	NT	TP	NT	NT	NT	TP		NT	NT	NT	NT	NT	NT	NT	TP	NT		NT	NT
						A	B	◇1				◇1 C		D	E					B	◇1				
Barrow-in-Furness	d													10 09											
Roose	d													10 13											
Dalton	d													10 19											
Ulverston	d													10 28											
Cark	d													10 36											
Kents Bank	d													10 40											
Grange-over-Sands	d													10 44											
Arnside	d													10 50											
Silverdale	d													10 55											
Carnforth	d					10 01								11 03											
Windermere 83	d																								
Oxenholme Lake District 65	d											10 10													
Lancaster 6 65	a					10 13						10 24		11 12											
	d											10 25													
Blackpool North 97	d				09 20			09 40											10 20		10 44				
Layton 97	d				09 23														10 23						
Poulton-le-Fylde 97	d				09 27			09 46											10 27		10 50				
Kirkham & Wesham 97	d				09 37														10 37						
Preston 8 65,97	a				09 47			10 04				10 43							10 47		11 08				
	d				09 49			10 12			10 23	10 45							10 49		11 10				11 23
Leyland	d				09 54						10 29								10 54						11 29
Buckshaw Parkway	d				09 59						10 33								10 59		11 17				11 33
Chorley	d				10 03			10 22			10 38								11 03		11 21				11 38
Adlington (Lancashire)	d				10 08														11 08						
Blackrod	d				10 12														11 12						
Horwich Parkway	d				10 16						10 46								11 16		11 28				11 46
Lostock	d				10 20						10 50								11 20						11 50
Southport	d	09 24								09 55							10 24							10 55	
Meols Cop	d									10 00														11 00	
Bescar Lane	d									10 05														11 05	
New Lane	d									10 09														11 09	
Burscough Bridge	d	09 36								10 11							10 36							11 11	
Hoscar	d									10 15														11 15	
Parbold	d	09 41								10 18							10 41							11 18	
Appley Bridge	d	09 45								10 22							10 45							11 22	
Gathurst	d									10 25														11 25	
Kirkby	d			09 32														10 32							
Rainford	d			09 40														10 40							
Upholland	d			09 44														10 44							
Orrell	d			09 47														10 47							
Pemberton	d			09 50														10 50							
Wigan Wallgate	a	09 51		09 56						10 30							10 51	10 56						11 30	
	d	09 53		09 58					10 20	10 32						10 48	10 53	10 58				11 20		11 32	
Wigan North Western	d											10 58													
Ince	d			10 01														11 01							
Hindley	d	09 58		10 04					10 25	10 37							10 58	11 04				11 25		11 37	
Westhoughton	d	10 02							10 29								11 02					11 29			
Bolton	a	10 12			10 25			10 34	10 38		10 55					11 02	11 12		11 25		11 34	11 38			11 55
	d	10 13			10 25		10 31	10 34	10 39		10 56				10 59	11 03	11 13		11 25	11 31	11 35	11 39			11 56
Moses Gate	d								10 42													11 42			
Farnworth	d								10 44													11 44			
Kearsley	d								10 46													11 46			
Clifton	d																								
Daisy Hill	d			10 09						10 41								11 09						11 41	
Hag Fold	d			10 12														11 12							
Atherton	d			10 15						10 45								11 15						11 45	
Walkden	d			10 20						10 50								11 20						11 50	
Moorside	d			10 24														11 24							
Swinton	d			10 26						10 55								11 26						11 55	
Salford Crescent	a	10 25		10 34	10 38		10 43	10 46	10 56	11 02	11 08				11 11	11 16	11 25	11 34	11 38	11 43	11 47	11 56		12 02	12 08
	d	10 26		10 35	10 38		10 44	10 47	10 56	11 03	11 09				11 12	11 16	11 26	11 34	11 38	11 44	11 47	11 56		12 03	12 09
Salford Central	d			10 37	10 41		10 46		10 59	11 05					11 15	11 18		11 36	11 41	11 46		11 59		12 05	
Manchester Victoria ⇌	a			10 43	10 47		10 52		11 06	11 11					11 20	11 25		11 43	11 47	11 52		12 06		12 11	
Rochdale 41	a															11 51									
Deansgate ⇌	a	10 29						10 50			11 12						11 29				11 51				12 12
Manchester Oxford Road	a	10 31						10 52			11 14	11 23					11 31				11 52				12 14
Manchester Piccadilly 10 ⇌	a	10 35						10 56			11 18	11 27					11 35				11 56				12 18
Stockport 84	a										11 34														12 34
Hazel Grove 86	a										11 45														12 45
Buxton 86	a																								
Heald Green 85	a							11 09													12 10				
Manchester Airport 85 ✈	a	10 53						11 15				11 47					11 53				12 17				

A From Leeds to Morecambe
B From Clitheroe
C From Edinburgh
D From Sellafield to Morecambe
E From Blackburn

The Sunday service between Wigan Wallgate and Manchester Victoria via Atherton is funded by TfGM and will operate whilst funding exists

Table 82R

Saturdays

14 December to 28 December

Barrow-in-Furness, Blackpool North, Preston, Southport, Kirkby and Wigan - Bolton - Manchester

Network Diagram - see first Page of Table 82

	TP ◇1	NT A	NT	NT	NT	NT	NT B	TP ◇1	NT C	TP ◇1	NT	NT	NT	TP ◇1 D	NT E	NT	NT	NT	NT	NT C	TP ◇1	NT
Barrow-in-Furness d								11 20							12 10							
Roose d															12 14							
Dalton d								11 29							12 20							
Ulverston d								11 37							12 28							
Cark d								11 45							12 36							
Kents Bank d															12 40							
Grange-over-Sands d								11 52							12 44							
Arnside d								11 58							12 50							
Silverdale d								12 02							12 54							
Carnforth d							12 02	12 09							13 02							
Windermere 83 d	10 48																					
Oxenholme Lake District 65 d	11 08													12 10								
Lancaster 6 65 a	11 26						12 11	12 17						12 25	13 14							
d	11 26							12 17						12 26								
Blackpool North 97 d						11 20				11 41									12 20		12 40	
Layton 97 d						11 23													12 23			
Poulton-le-Fylde 97 d						11 27				11 47									12 27		12 46	
Kirkham & Wesham 97 d						11 37													12 37			
Preston 8 65,97 a	11 45					11 47		12 37		12 05				12 44					12 47		13 04	
d	11 46					11 49				12 10			12 23	12 45					12 49		13 10	
Leyland d						11 54							12 29						12 54			
Buckshaw Parkway d						11 59				12 17			12 33						12 59		13 17	
Chorley d						12 03				12 21			12 38						13 03		13 21	
Adlington (Lancashire) d						12 08													13 08			
Blackrod d						12 12													13 12			
Horwich Parkway d						12 16				12 28			12 46						13 16		13 28	
Lostock d						12 20							12 50						13 20			
Southport d				11 24								12 00					12 24					
Meols Cop d												12 05										
Bescar Lane d																						
New Lane d																						
Burscough Bridge d				11 36								12 13					12 36					
Hoscar d																						
Parbold d				11 41								12 18					12 41					
Appley Bridge d				11 45								12 22					12 45					
Gathurst d												12 25										
Kirkby d					11 32													12 32				
Rainford d					11 40													12 40				
Upholland d					11 44													12 44				
Orrell d					11 47													12 47				
Pemberton d					11 50													12 50				
Wigan Wallgate a				11 51	11 56							12 30					12 51	12 56				
d			11 48	11 53	11 58						12 20	12 32				12 48	12 53	12 58				13 20
Wigan North Western d	11 58													12 58								
Ince d					12 01													13 01				
Hindley d				11 58	12 04						12 25	12 37					12 58	13 04				13 25
Westhoughton d				12 02							12 29						13 02					13 29
Bolton a			12 02	12 12		12 25				12 34	12 38		12 55			13 02	13 12		13 25		13 34	13 38
d		12 00	12 03	12 13		12 25			12 31	12 35	12 39		12 56			13 03	13 13		13 25	13 31	13 35	13 39
Moses Gate d											12 42											13 42
Farnworth d											12 44											13 44
Kearsley d											12 46											13 46
Clifton d																						
Daisy Hill d					12 09							12 41						13 09				
Hag Fold d					12 12													13 12				
Atherton d					12 15							12 45						13 15				
Walkden d					12 20							12 50						13 20				
Moorside d					12 24													13 24				
Swinton d					12 26							12 55						13 26				
Salford Crescent a		12 13	12 16	12 25	12 34	12 38			12 43	12 47	12 56	13 02	13 08			13 15	13 25	13 34	13 38	13 43	13 47	13 56
d		12 13	12 16	12 26	12 34	12 38			12 44	12 47	12 56	13 03	13 09			13 15	13 26	13 34	13 38	13 44	13 47	13 56
Salford Central d		12 16	12 18		12 36	12 41			12 46		12 59	13 05				13 17		13 36	13 41	13 46		13 59
Manchester Victoria ⇌ a		12 22	12 25		12 43	12 47			12 52		13 06	13 11				13 25		13 43	13 47	13 52		14 06
Rochdale 41 a			12 51													13 51						
Deansgate ⇌ a				12 29						12 51			13 12				13 29				13 51	
Manchester Oxford Road a	12 23			12 31						12 52			13 14	13 23			13 31				13 52	
Manchester Piccadilly 10 ⇌ a	12 27			12 35						12 56			13 18	13 27			13 35				13 56	
Stockport 84 a													13 34									
Hazel Grove 86 a													13 45									
Buxton 86 a																						
Heald Green 85 a										13 10											14 10	
Manchester Airport 85 ✈ a	12 47			12 53						13 17				13 47			13 53				14 17	

A From Blackburn
B From Leeds to Heysham Harbour
C From Clitheroe
D From Edinburgh
E From Carlisle

The Sunday service between Wigan Wallgate and Manchester Victoria via Atherton is funded by TfGM and will operate whilst funding exists

Table 82R

Saturdays

14 December to 28 December

Barrow-in-Furness, Blackpool North, Preston, Southport, Kirkby and Wigan - Bolton - Manchester

Network Diagram - see first Page of Table 82

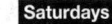

		NT	NT	TP	TP	TP	NT	NT	NT	NT	NT	TP	NT	NT	NT	NT	TP	NT	NT	NT	NT	NT
				◇1	◇1	◇1						◇1					◇1					
				A							B						C	D				B
				🚲													🚲					
Barrow-in-Furness	d					13 20												14 16				
Roose	d																	14 20				
Dalton	d					13 29												14 26				
Ulverston	d					13 37												14 35				
Cark	d					13 45												14 42				
Kents Bank	d																	14 47				
Grange-over-Sands	d					13 52												14 51				
Arnside	d					13 58												14 57				
Silverdale	d					14 02												15 01				
Carnforth	d					14 09												15 08				
Windermere 83	d				12 52																	
Oxenholme Lake District 65	d			13 10	13 13												14 10					
Lancaster 6 65	a			13 25	13 29	14 17											14 24	15 19				
	d			13 25	13 29	14 17											14 25					
Blackpool North 97	d									13 20		13 44									14 20	
Layton 97	d									13 23											14 23	
Poulton-le-Fylde 97	d									13 27		13 50									14 27	
Kirkham & Wesham 97	d									13 37											14 37	
Preston 8 65,97	a			13 44	13 49	14 37				13 47		14 08					14 45				14 47	
	d		13 23	13 44						13 49		14 10			14 23		14 45				14 49	
Leyland	d		13 29							13 54					14 29						14 54	
Buckshaw Parkway	d		13 33							13 59		14 17			14 33						14 59	
Chorley	d		13 38							14 03		14 21			14 38		14 55				15 03	
Adlington (Lancashire)	d									14 08											15 08	
Blackrod	d									14 12											15 12	
Horwich Parkway	d		13 46							14 16		14 28			14 46						15 16	
Lostock	d		13 50							14 20					14 50						15 20	
Southport	d	12 54						13 24						14 00					14 24			
Meols Cop	d	12 59												14 05								
Bescar Lane	d	13 04																				
New Lane	d	13 08																				
Burscough Bridge	d	13 11						13 36						14 13					14 36			
Hoscar	d	13 15																				
Parbold	d	13 18						13 41						14 18					14 41			
Appley Bridge	d	13 22						13 45						14 22					14 45			
Gathurst	d	13 25												14 25								
Kirkby	d								13 32											14 32		
Rainford	d								13 40											14 40		
Upholland	d								13 44											14 44		
Orrell	d								13 47											14 47		
Pemberton	d								13 50											14 50		
Wigan Wallgate	a	13 30						13 51	13 56					14 30					14 51	14 56		
	d	13 32					13 48	13 53	13 58				14 20	14 32		14 48			14 53	14 58		
Wigan North Western	d			13 58																		
Ince	d								14 01											15 01		
Hindley	d	13 37						13 58	14 04				14 25	14 37					14 58	15 04		
Westhoughton	d							14 02					14 29						15 02			
Bolton	a		13 55				14 02	14 12		14 25		14 34	14 38		14 55	15 02	15 07		15 12		15 25	
	d		13 56				14 03	14 13		14 25	14 31	14 35	14 39		14 56	15 03	15 07		15 13		15 25	15 31
Moses Gate	d												14 42									
Farnworth	d												14 44									
Kearsley	d												14 46									
Clifton	d																					
Daisy Hill	d	13 41							14 09					14 41						15 09		
Hag Fold	d								14 12											15 12		
Atherton	d	13 45							14 15					14 45						15 15		
Walkden	d	13 50							14 20					14 50						15 20		
Moorside	d								14 24											15 24		
Swinton	d	13 55							14 26					14 55						15 26		
Salford Crescent	a	14 02	14 08				14 15	14 25	14 34	14 38	14 43	14 47	14 56	15 02	15 08	15 15	15 19		15 25	15 34	15 38	15 43
	d	14 03	14 09				14 15	14 26	14 34	14 38	14 44	14 47	14 56	15 03	15 09	15 15	15 19		15 26	15 34	15 38	15 44
Salford Central	d	14 05					14 17		14 36	14 41	14 46		14 59	15 05		15 17				15 36	15 41	15 48
Manchester Victoria ⇌	a	14 10					14 25		14 43	14 47	14 52		15 06	15 11		15 25				15 43	15 47	15 54
Rochdale 41	a						14 51									15 51						
Deansgate ⇌	a		14 12					14 29				14 51			15 12				15 29			
Manchester Oxford Road	a		14 14	14 22				14 31				14 52			15 14		15 24		15 31			
Manchester Piccadilly 10 ⇌	a		14 18	14 26				14 35				14 56			15 18		15 28		15 35			
Stockport 84	a		14 34												15 34							
Hazel Grove 86	a		14 45												15 45							
Buxton 86	a																					
Heald Green 85	a											15 10										
Manchester Airport 85 ✈	a			14 45				14 53				15 17					15 47		15 53			

A From Glasgow Central
B From Clitheroe
C From Edinburgh
D From Whitehaven

The Sunday service between Wigan Wallgate and Manchester Victoria via Atherton is funded by TfGM and will operate whilst funding exists

Table 82R

Saturdays

14 December to 28 December

Barrow-in-Furness, Blackpool North, Preston, Southport, Kirkby and Wigan - Bolton - Manchester

Network Diagram - see first Page of Table 82

		TP	NT	NT	NT	TP	NT	NT	NT	NT	NT	NT	TP	TP	TP	NT	NT	NT	TP	NT	NT	NT	NT
		◇1				◇1							◇1	◇1	◇1				◇1				
						A			B			C							D				
						🚲													🚲				
Barrow-in-Furness	d												15 25							16 29			
Roose	d																			16 33			
Dalton	d																			16 39			
Ulverston	d												15 41							16 47			
Cark	d																			16 55			
Kents Bank	d																			16 59			
Grange-over-Sands	d												15 53							17 03			
Arnside	d												15 59							17 09			
Silverdale	d																			17 13			
Carnforth	d											15 36	16 09							17 21			
Windermere 83	d													14 52									
Oxenholme Lake District 65	d					15 09								15 12					16 14				
Lancaster 6 65	a					15 23						15 45	16 17	15 28					16 29	17 33			
	d					15 24							16 17	15 28					16 29				
Blackpool North 97	d	14 40									15 20				15 40								
Layton 97	d										15 23												
Poulton-le-Fylde 97	d	14 46									15 27				15 46								
Kirkham & Wesham 97	d										15 37												
Preston 8 65,97	a	15 04				15 42					15 47		16 37	15 48	16 04				16 48				
	d	15 10			15 23	15 45					15 49			16 10				16 22	16 49				
Leyland	d				15 29						15 54							16 28					
Buckshaw Parkway	d	15 17			15 33						15 59			16 17				16 32					
Chorley	d	15 21			15 38						16 03			16 21				16 37					
Adlington (Lancashire)	d										16 08												
Blackrod	d										16 12												
Horwich Parkway	d	15 28			15 46						16 16			16 28				16 45					
Lostock	d				15 50						16 20							16 49					
Southport	d			14 54				15 24									16 00					16 24	
Meols Cop	d			14 59													16 05						
Bescar Lane	d			15 04																			
New Lane	d			15 08																			
Burscough Bridge	d			15 11				15 36									16 13					16 36	
Hoscar	d			15 15																			
Parbold	d			15 18				15 41									16 18					16 41	
Appley Bridge	d			15 22				15 45									16 22					16 45	
Gathurst	d			15 25													16 25						
Kirkby	d									15 32													16 32
Rainford	d									15 40													16 40
Upholland	d									15 44													16 44
Orrell	d									15 47													16 47
Pemberton	d									15 50													16 50
Wigan Wallgate	a			15 30				15 51		15 56							16 30					16 51	16 56
	d		15 20	15 32			15 48	15 53		15 58						16 20	16 32				16 48	16 53	16 58
Wigan North Western	d					15 58																	
Ince	d									16 01													17 01
Hindley	d		15 25	15 37				15 58		16 04						16 25	16 37					16 58	17 04
Westhoughton	d		15 29					16 02								16 29						17 02	
Bolton	a	15 34	15 38		15 55		16 02	16 12			16 25			16 34		16 38		16 54			17 02	17 12	
	d	15 35	15 39		15 56		16 03	16 13	16 17		16 25			16 35		16 39		16 55			17 03	17 13	
Moses Gate	d		15 42													16 42							
Farnworth	d		15 44													16 44							
Kearsley	d		15 46													16 46							
Clifton	d																						
Daisy Hill	d			15 41						16 09							16 41						17 08
Hag Fold	d									16 12													17 11
Atherton	d			15 45						16 15							16 45						17 14
Walkden	d			15 50						16 20							16 50						17 19
Moorside	d									16 24													17 23
Swinton	d			15 55						16 26							16 55						17 25
Salford Crescent	a	15 47	15 56	16 02	16 08		16 15	16 25	16 30	16 33	16 38			16 47		16 56	17 02	17 07			17 15	17 25	17 33
	d	15 47	15 56	16 03	16 09		16 15	16 26	16 30	16 34	16 38			16 47		16 56	17 03	17 08			17 15	17 26	17 33
Salford Central	d		15 59	16 05			16 17		16 33	16 37	16 41					16 59	17 05				17 17		17 36
Manchester Victoria 🚊	a		16 06	16 11			16 23		16 41	16 43	16 47					17 06	17 11				17 23		17 43
Rochdale 41	a						16 51														17 51		
Deansgate 🚊	a	15 51			16 12									16 51				17 10				17 29	
Manchester Oxford Road	a	15 52			16 14	16 23		16 31						16 52				17 12	17 26			17 31	
Manchester Piccadilly 10 🚊	a	15 56			16 18	16 27		16 35						16 56				17 17	17 30			17 35	
Stockport 84	a				16 34													17 34					
Hazel Grove 86	a				16 45													17 43					
Buxton 86	a																	18 24					
Heald Green 85	a	16 10				16 40								17 10								17 47	
Manchester Airport 85 ✈	a	16 17				16 47		16 53						17 17					17 47			17 53	

A From Glasgow Central
B From Clitheroe
C From Leeds to Morecambe
D From Edinburgh

The Sunday service between Wigan Wallgate and Manchester Victoria via Atherton is funded by TfGM and will operate whilst funding exists

Table 82R

Saturdays

14 December to 28 December

Barrow-in-Furness, Blackpool North, Preston, Southport, Kirkby and Wigan - Bolton - Manchester

Network Diagram - see first Page of Table 82

		NT	NT	TP	NT	NT	NT	NT	TP	NT	NT	NT	TP	TP	NT	NT	TP	NT	NT	NT	NT	NT	NT
				◇1					◇1				◇1	◇1			◇1						
			A					A									B	C	D	A			
																	🚲						
Barrow-in-Furness	d													17 21					18 03				
Roose	d																		18 07				
Dalton	d													17 30					18 13				
Ulverston	d													17 39					18 21				
Cark	d													17 46					18 29				
Kents Bank	d																		18 33				
Grange-over-Sands	d													17 53					18 37				
Arnside	d													17 59					18 43				
Silverdale	d																		18 47				
Carnforth	d													18 08				18 26	18 55				
Windermere 83	d												17 06										
Oxenholme Lake District 65	d												17 30										
Lancaster 6 65	a												17 47	18 17				18 38	19 05				
	d												17 48	18 17			18 25		19 06				
Blackpool North 97	d	16 20		16 40					17 20														18 20
Layton 97	d	16 23		16 43					17 23														18 23
Poulton-le-Fylde 97	d	16 27		16 47					17 27														18 27
Kirkham & Wesham 97	d	16 37		16 57																			18 37
Preston 8 65,97	a	16 47		17 08					17 45				18 06	18 37			18 45		19 31				18 47
	d	16 49		17 10			17 23		17 47			17 56	18 08				18 45						18 49
Leyland	d	16 54					17 29					18 01											18 54
Buckshaw Parkway	d	16 59		17 17			17 33					18 05	18 15										18 59
Chorley	d	17 03		17 21			17 38		17 56			18 09	18 19										19 03
Adlington (Lancashire)	d	17 08										18 15											19 08
Blackrod	d	17 12										18 19											19 12
Horwich Parkway	d	17 16		17 28			17 46					18 21	18 26										19 16
Lostock	d	17 20					17 50						18 30										19 20
Southport	d					16 54				17 24						17 54					18 17		
Meols Cop	d					16 59				17 29						17 59					18 22		
Bescar Lane	d					17 04										18 04					18 27		
New Lane	d					17 08										18 08					18 31		
Burscough Bridge	d					17 11				17 37						18 11					18 33		
Hoscar	d					17 15										18 15					18 37		
Parbold	d					17 18				17 42						18 18					18 40		
Appley Bridge	d					17 22				17 46						18 22					18 44		
Gathurst	d					17 25										18 25					18 47		
Kirkby	d										17 32											18 32	
Rainford	d										17 40											18 40	
Upholland	d										17 44											18 44	
Orrell	d										17 47											18 47	
Pemberton	d										17 50											18 50	
Wigan Wallgate	a					17 30				17 52	17 57					18 30					18 52	18 56	
	d				17 20	17 32				17 54	17 59				18 20	18 32					18 53	18 58	
Wigan North Western	d																18 59						
Ince	d										18 02											19 01	
Hindley	d				17 25	17 37					18 05				18 25	18 37					18 58	19 04	
Westhoughton	d				17 29					18 02					18 29						19 02		
Bolton	a	17 25		17 34	17 38		17 55		18 08	18 12		18 30	18 34		18 38						19 12		19 25
	d	17 25	17 31	17 35	17 39		17 56	18 02	18 08	18 12		18 30	18 35		18 39					19 02	19 13		19 25
Moses Gate	d				17 42										18 42								
Farnworth	d				17 44										18 44								
Kearsley	d				17 46										18 46								
Clifton	d																						
Daisy Hill	d					17 41					18 09					18 41						19 08	
Hag Fold	d										18 12											19 11	
Atherton	d					17 45					18 15					18 45						19 14	
Walkden	d					17 50					18 20					18 50						19 19	
Moorside	d										18 24											19 23	
Swinton	d					17 55					18 26					18 55						19 25	
Salford Crescent	a	17 38	17 43	17 47	17 56	18 02	18 08	18 14		18 25	18 33	18 42	18 47		18 56	19 02				19 14	19 25	19 33	19 38
	d	17 38	17 44	17 47	17 56	18 03	18 09	18 15		18 25	18 33	18 42	18 47		18 56	19 03				19 15	19 26	19 33	19 38
Salford Central	d	17 41	17 47		17 59	18 05		18 17			18 36	18 45			18 59	19 05				19 17		19 36	19 41
Manchester Victoria ⇌	a	17 47	17 53		18 06	18 11		18 24			18 43	18 50			19 06	19 11				19 23		19 43	19 47
Rochdale 41	a							18 47															
Deansgate ⇌	a			17 51			18 12						18 51								19 29		
Manchester Oxford Road	a			17 52			18 14		18 23	18 31			18 52				19 24				19 31		
Manchester Piccadilly 10 ⇌	a			17 56			18 18		18 27	18 35			18 56				19 29				19 35		
Stockport 84	a						18 34																
Hazel Grove 86	a						18 45																
Buxton 86	a																						
Heald Green 85	a			18 10					18 40				19 10										
Manchester Airport 85 ✈	a			18 17					18 47	18 53			19 17				19 46				19 53		

A From Clitheroe
B From Edinburgh
C From Leeds to Morecambe
D From Carlisle

The Sunday service between Wigan Wallgate and Manchester Victoria via Atherton is funded by TfGM and will operate whilst funding exists

Table 82R

Saturdays

14 December to 28 December

Barrow-in-Furness, Blackpool North, Preston, Southport, Kirkby and Wigan - Bolton - Manchester

Network Diagram - see first Page of Table 82

		NT	TP	NT	NT	TP	TP	NT	NT	NT	TP	TP	NT	NT	NT	NT	TP	NT	NT	NT	TP	NT
			◇1			◇1	◇1				◇1	◇1					◇1				◇1	
		A			B	C				A		D				A						
						⚮						⚮										
Barrow-in-Furness	d						19 17															21 43
Roose	d						19 21															21 47
Dalton	d						19 28															21 53
Ulverston	d						19 36															22 01
Cark	d						19 44															22 09
Kents Bank	d						19 48															22 13
Grange-over-Sands	d						19 52															22 17
Arnside	d						19 58															22 23
Silverdale	d						20 02															22 27
Carnforth	d						20 09															22 35
Windermere 83	d																				21 40	
Oxenholme Lake District 65	d					19 09						20 13									22 00	
Lancaster 6 65	a					19 24	20 17					20 27									22 17	22 45
	d					19 24	20 18					20 28									22 17	22 46
Blackpool North 97	d		18 40						19 20		19 44				20 20		20 44			21 20		
Layton 97	d								19 23						20 23					21 23		
Poulton-le-Fylde 97	d		18 46						19 28		19 50				20 27		20 50			21 27		
Kirkham & Wesham 97	d								19 37						20 37					21 37		
Preston 8 65,97	a		19 04			19 44	20 37		19 47		20 08	20 46			20 47		21 08			21 47	22 38	23 11
	d		19 10			19 45			19 49		20 10	20 48			20 49		21 10			21 49		
Leyland	d								19 54						20 54					21 54		
Buckshaw Parkway	d		19 17						19 59		20 17				20 59		21 17			21 59		
Chorley	d		19 21			19 55			20 03		20 21				21 03		21 21			22 03		
Adlington (Lancashire)	d								20 08						21 08					22 08		
Blackrod	d								20 12						21 12					22 12		
Horwich Parkway	d		19 28						20 16		20 28				21 16		21 28			22 16		
Lostock	d								20 20						21 20					22 20		
Southport	d			19 00				19 23						20 23					21 23			
Meols Cop	d			19 05				19 28						20 28					21 28			
Bescar Lane	d																					
New Lane	d																					
Burscough Bridge	d			19 13				19 36						20 36					21 36			
Hoscar	d																					
Parbold	d			19 18				19 41						20 41					21 41			
Appley Bridge	d			19 22				19 45						20 45					21 45			
Gathurst	d			19 25				19 48						20 48					21 48			
Kirkby	d																					
Rainford	d																					
Upholland	d																					
Orrell	d																					
Pemberton	d																					
Wigan Wallgate	a			19 30				19 53						20 53					21 53			
	d			19 32				19 55					20 29	20 55				21 29	21 55			
Wigan North Western	d																					
Ince	d												20 32					21 32				
Hindley	d			19 37				20 00					20 35	21 00				21 35	22 00			
Westhoughton	d							20 04						21 04					22 04			
Bolton	a		19 35			20 08		20 12	20 25		20 34			21 12	21 25		21 34		22 12	22 25		
	d	19 32	19 35		20 02	20 09		20 13	20 25	20 31	20 35			21 13	21 25	21 31	21 35		22 13	22 25		
Moses Gate	d																					
Farnworth	d																					
Kearsley	d																					
Clifton	d																					
Daisy Hill	d			19 41									20 39					21 39				
Hag Fold	d												20 42					21 42				
Atherton	d			19 45									20 45					21 45				
Walkden	d			19 50									20 51					21 51				
Moorside	d												20 54					21 54				
Swinton	d			19 55									20 57					21 57				
Salford Crescent	a	19 44	19 48	20 02	20 15			20 25	20 38	20 43	20 47		21 04	21 25	21 38	21 43	21 47	22 04	22 25	22 38		
	d	19 45	19 48	20 03	20 15			20 26	20 38	20 44	20 47		21 05	21 26	21 38	21 44	21 47	22 05	22 26	22 38		
Salford Central	d	19 47		20 05	20 17				20 41	20 46			21 07		21 41	21 46		22 07	22 28	22 41		
Manchester Victoria 🚊	a	19 53		20 11	20 24				20 47	20 52			21 13		21 47	21 52		22 13	22 34	22 47		
Rochdale 41	a																					
Deansgate 🚊	a		19 52					20 29			20 51			21 29			21 51					
Manchester Oxford Road	a		19 53			20 23		20 31			20 52	21 23		21 31			21 52					
Manchester Piccadilly 10 🚊	a		19 57			20 27		20 35			20 56	21 27		21 35			21 56					
Stockport 84	a																					
Hazel Grove 86	a																					
Buxton 86	a																					
Heald Green 85	a		20 11								21 10						22 10					
Manchester Airport 85 ✈	a		20 17			20 46		20 52			21 17	21 46		21 53			22 20					

A From Clitheroe
B From Blackburn
C From Glasgow Central
D From Edinburgh

The Sunday service between Wigan Wallgate and Manchester Victoria via Atherton is funded by TfGM and will operate whilst funding exists

Table 82R

Saturdays

14 December to 28 December

Barrow-in-Furness, Blackpool North, Preston, Southport, Kirkby and Wigan - Bolton - Manchester

Network Diagram - see first Page of Table 82

		NT	TP	NT	NT	NT	TP	NT		NT	NT
			◇1				◇1				
		A								A	
Barrow-in-Furness	d										
Roose	d										
Dalton	d										
Ulverston	d										
Cark	d										
Kents Bank	d										
Grange-over-Sands	d										
Arnside	d										
Silverdale	d										
Carnforth	d										
Windermere 83	d										
Oxenholme Lake District 65	d										
Lancaster 6 65	a										
	d										
Blackpool North 97	d		21 44			22 20	22 45				23 02
Layton 97	d					22 23					23 05
Poulton-le-Fylde 97	d		21 50			22 27	22 51				23 09
Kirkham & Wesham 97	d					22 37					23 19
Preston 8 65,97	a		22 08			22 47	23 09				23 29
	d		22 10			22 49	23 10				23 31
Leyland	d					22 54					23 36
Buckshaw Parkway	d		22 17			22 59	23 17				23 41
Chorley	d		22 21			23 03	23 20				23 45
Adlington (Lancashire)	d					23 08					23 50
Blackrod	d					23 12					23 54
Horwich Parkway	d		22 28			23 16	23 28				23 58
Lostock	d					23 20					00 02
Southport	d				22 18			23 10			
Meols Cop	d				22 23			23 15			
Bescar Lane	d				22 28						
New Lane	d				22 32						
Burscough Bridge	d				22 34			23 23			
Hoscar	d				22 38						
Parbold	d				22 41			23 28			
Appley Bridge	d				22 45			23 32			
Gathurst	d				22 48			23 35			
Kirkby	d										
Rainford	d										
Upholland	d										
Orrell	d										
Pemberton	d										
Wigan Wallgate	a				22 53			23 44			
	d			22 29	22 55						
Wigan North Western	d										
Ince	d			22 32							
Hindley	d			22 35	23 00						
Westhoughton	d				23 04						
Bolton	a		22 34		23 12	23 25	23 34				00 07
	d	22 31	22 35		23 13	23 25	23 35			23 38	00 07
Moses Gate	d										
Farnworth	d										
Kearsley	d										
Clifton	d										
Daisy Hill	d			22 39							
Hag Fold	d			22 42							
Atherton	d			22 45							
Walkden	d			22 51							
Moorside	d			22 54							
Swinton	d			22 57							
Salford Crescent	a	22 43	22 47	23 04	23 25	23 38	23 47			23 50	
	d	22 44	22 47	23 05	23 26	23 38	23 47			23 53	
Salford Central	d	22 46		23 07							
Manchester Victoria 🚋	a	22 52		23 13		23 47				00 01	00 26
Rochdale 41	a										
Deansgate 🚋	a		22 51		23 29						
Manchester Oxford Road	a		22 52		23 31						
Manchester Piccadilly 10 🚋	a		22 57		23 39		23 55				
Stockport 84	a										
Hazel Grove 86	a										
Buxton 86	a										
Heald Green 85	a		23 10				00 16				
Manchester Airport 85 ✈	a		23 17				00 23				

A From Clitheroe

The Sunday service between Wigan Wallgate and Manchester Victoria via Atherton is funded by TfGM and will operate whilst funding exists

Table 82R

Saturdays

4 January to 8 February

Barrow-in-Furness, Blackpool North, Preston, Southport, Kirkby and Wigan - Bolton - Manchester

Network Diagram - see first Page of Table 82

		NT	TP	TP	TP	TP	NT	NT	NT	TP		NT	NT	TP	NT	NT	NT	TP	NT	NT		NT	NT	NT	NT
			◇1	◇1	◇1	◇1				◇1				◇1				◇1							
		A							B											C		D			D
Barrow-in-Furness	d				04 35					05 32								06 15							
Roose	d																	06 19							
Dalton	d																	06 26							
Ulverston	d				04 51					05 48								06 34							
Cark	d																	06 42							
Kents Bank	d																	06 46							
Grange-over-Sands	d				05 03					06 00								06 50							
Arnside	d				05 09					06 06								06 56							
Silverdale	d																	07 00							
Carnforth	d				05 19					06 16								07 07		07 42					
Windermere 83	d																								
Oxenholme Lake District 65	d																								
Lancaster 6 65	a				05 27					06 24								07 15		07 50					
	d									06 24								07 23							
Blackpool North 97	d		03 37			05 39							06 19	06 40			06 53							07 18	
Layton 97	d												06 22	06 43										07 21	
Poulton-le-Fylde 97	d					05 45							06 26	06 47										07 25	
Kirkham & Wesham 97	d												06 36	06 57										07 35	
Preston 8 65,97	a					06 03				06 43			06 46	07 07			07 15	07 41						07 46	
	d		04u02	05 12		06 05				06 44			06 48	07 09			07 17	07 43						07 47	
Leyland	d					06 10							06 53				07 22							07 53	
Buckshaw Parkway	d												06 58				07 28							07 58	
Chorley	d			05 22		06 17				06 54			07 02	07 18			07 32							08 02	
Adlington (Lancashire)	d	00 02											07 07				07 37							08 07	
Blackrod	d	00 06				06 23							07 11				07 41							08 11	
Horwich Parkway	d	00 09		05 29		06 26				07 01			07 15	07 26			07 45							08 15	
Lostock	d	00 13				06 30							07 20	07 30			07 49							08 20	
Southport	d											06 23											07 21		
Meols Cop	d											06 28											07 26		
Bescar Lane	d																								
New Lane	d																								
Burscough Bridge	d											06 36											07 34		
Hoscar	d																								
Parbold	d											06 41											07 39		
Appley Bridge	d											06 45											07 43		
Gathurst	d											06 49											07 47		
Kirkby	d																		07 11						
Rainford	d																		07 19						
Upholland	d																		07 23						
Orrell	d																		07 27						
Pemberton	d																		07 30						
Wigan Wallgate	a											06 54							07 35				07 51		
	d						06 31	06 36				06 55			07 15				07 37				07 53		
Wigan North Western	d															07 22		07 56							
Ince	d							06 39							07 18	07 25			07 40						
Hindley	d						06 36	06 42							07 21	07 29			07 43				07 58		
Westhoughton	d						06 41					07 03				07 33							08 03		
Bolton	a	00 17		05 40		06 34	06 52			07 07		07 11	07 25	07 34		07 42	07 54						08 11	08 25	
	d	00 17	04u31	05 40		06 35	06 53		06 57	07 08		07 12	07 25	07 35		07 43	07 55					07 59	08 12	08 25	08 31
Moses Gate	d								07 00							07 46						08 02			
Farnworth	d								07 02							07 48						08 04			
Kearsley	d								07 04							07 50						08 06			
Clifton	d								07 08																
Daisy Hill	d							06 46							07 26				07 47						
Hag Fold	d							06 49							07 29				07 50						
Atherton	d							06 52							07 32				07 53						
Walkden	d							06 58							07 38				07 59						
Moorside	d							07 01							07 41				08 03						
Swinton	d							07 04							07 44				08 06						
Salford Crescent	a			05 52		06 47	07 05	07 11	07 16			07 24	07 38	07 47	07 53	08 02	08 07		08 13			08 17	08 24	08 38	08 43
	d			05 53		06 47	07 08	07 12	07 17			07 25	07 38	07 47	07 53	08 02	08 08		08 13			08 17	08 25	08 38	08 44
Salford Central	d							07 15	07 20				07 41		07 56	08 05			08 16			08 20		08 41	08 46
Manchester Victoria 🚋	a	00 36						07 18	07 25				07 47		07 59	08 12			08 20			08 25		08 47	08 52
Rochdale 41	a																		08 51						
Deansgate 🚋	a					06 51	07 11					07 28		07 51			08 11						08 28		
Manchester Oxford Road	a			05 57		06 52	07 13			07 23		07 30		07 53			08 14	08 22					08 31		
Manchester Piccadilly 10 🚋	a		04 46	06 00		06 56	07 17			07 27		07 34		07 57			08 18	08 26					08 35		
Stockport 84	a						07 34										08 34								
Hazel Grove 86	a						07 45										08 45								
Buxton 86	a																								
Heald Green 85	a					07 10								08 10									08 47		
Manchester Airport 85 ✈	a		05 05	06 17		07 15				07 47		07 53		08 17				08 47					08 53		

A From Blackpool North
B From Blackburn
C From Leeds
D From Clitheroe

The Sunday service between Wigan Wallgate and Manchester Victoria via Atherton is funded by TfGM and will operate whilst funding exists

Table 82R

Saturdays

4 January to 8 February

Barrow-in-Furness, Blackpool North, Preston, Southport, Kirkby and Wigan - Bolton - Manchester

Network Diagram - see first Page of Table 82

		TP	NT	NT	NT	NT	TP	NT	NT	NT	NT	NT	NT	TP	TP	NT	NT	NT	TP	TP	TP	NT	NT
		◇1					◇1							◇1	◇1				◇1	◇1	◇1		
							A	B				C	D						E			B	
Barrow-in-Furness	d												08 20	07 33						08 50			
Roose	d												08 24	07 37									
Dalton	d												08 30	07 44						08 59			
Ulverston	d												08 38	07 52						09 07			
Cark	d												08 46	08 00						09 15			
Kents Bank	d												08 50	08 04									
Grange-over-Sands	d												08 54	08 08						09 22			
Arnside	d												09 00	08 14						09 28			
Silverdale	d												09 04	08 18						09 32			
Carnforth	d												09 11	08 25						09 39			
Windermere 83	d																				09 37		
Oxenholme Lake District 65	d						08 10												09 10		09 57		
Lancaster 6 65	a						08 25						09 24	08 33					09 25	09 46	10 13		
	d						08 26							08 33					09 25	09 47	10 14		
Blackpool North 97	d	07 44									08 20				08 40								
Layton 97	d	07 47									08 23												
Poulton-le-Fylde 97	d	07 51									08 27				08 46								
Kirkham & Wesham 97	d	08 01									08 37												
Preston 8 65,97	a	08 11					08 44				08 47			08 52	09 04				09 44	10 07	10 33		
	d	08 12				08 21	08 45				08 49				09 10			09 23	09 44				
Leyland	d					08 27					08 54							09 29					
Buckshaw Parkway	d					08 31					08 59				09 17			09 33					
Chorley	d	08 22				08 35					09 03				09 21			09 38					
Adlington (Lancashire)	d					08 40					09 08												
Blackrod	d					08 43					09 12												
Horwich Parkway	d					08 47					09 16				09 28			09 46					
Lostock	d					08 50					09 20							09 50					
Southport	d				07 54				08 25								09 00						
Meols Cop	d				07 59				08 30								09 05						
Bescar Lane	d				08 04																		
New Lane	d				08 08																		
Burscough Bridge	d				08 10				08 38								09 13						
Hoscar	d				08 14																		
Parbold	d				08 17				08 43								09 18						
Appley Bridge	d				08 21				08 47								09 22						
Gathurst	d				08 24				08 50								09 25						
Kirkby	d									08 21													
Rainford	d									08 29													
Upholland	d									08 33													
Orrell	d									08 36													
Pemberton	d									08 39													
Wigan Wallgate	a				08 29				08 55	08 45							09 30						
	d		08 13		08 29				08 56	08 50						09 20	09 31						09 46
Wigan North Western	d			08 20			08 58												09 58				
Ince	d		08 16							08 53													
Hindley	d		08 19	08 25	08 34					08 57						09 25	09 36						
Westhoughton	d			08 29					09 04							09 29							09 54
Bolton	a	08 34		08 38		08 55			09 12		09 25				09 34	09 38		09 55					10 02
	d	08 35		08 39		08 56		09 02	09 13		09 25	09 31			09 35	09 39		09 56				10 00	10 03
Moses Gate	d			08 42												09 42							
Farnworth	d			08 44												09 44							
Kearsley	d			08 46												09 46							
Clifton	d																						
Daisy Hill	d		08 23		08 39					09 01							09 40						
Hag Fold	d		08 26							09 04													
Atherton	d		08 29		08 43					09 06							09 44						
Walkden	d		08 35		08 49					09 12							09 48						
Moorside	d		08 39							09 15													
Swinton	d		08 42		08 54					09 18							09 54						
Salford Crescent	a	08 46	08 50	08 56	09 01	09 08		09 14	09 25	09 27	09 38	09 43			09 47	09 56	10 01	10 08				10 13	10 15
	d	08 47	08 51	08 56	09 02	09 09		09 15	09 26	09 27	09 38	09 44			09 47	09 56	10 02	10 09				10 13	10 15
Salford Central	d		08 54	08 59	09 04			09 18		09 31	09 41	09 46				09 59	10 03					10 16	10 17
Manchester Victoria ⇌	a		08 57	09 06	09 10			09 22		09 38	09 47	09 52				10 06	10 11					10 21	10 25
Rochdale 41	a							09 54															10 51
Deansgate ⇌	a					09 12			09 29						09 51			10 12					
Manchester Oxford Road	a	08 52				09 14	09 23		09 31						09 52			10 14	10 22				
Manchester Piccadilly 10 ⇌	a	08 56				09 18	09 27		09 35						09 56			10 18	10 26				
Stockport 84	a					09 34												10 34					
Hazel Grove 86	a					09 45												10 45					
Buxton 86	a																						
Heald Green 85	a	09 09													10 10								
Manchester Airport 85 ✈	a	09 17					09 47		09 53						10 17				10 46				

A From Edinburgh
B From Blackburn
C From Clitheroe
D From Maryport
E From Glasgow Central

The Sunday service between Wigan Wallgate and Manchester Victoria via Atherton is funded by TfGM and will operate whilst funding exists

Table 82R

Saturdays
4 January to 8 February

Barrow-in-Furness, Blackpool North, Preston, Southport, Kirkby and Wigan - Bolton - Manchester

Network Diagram - see first Page of Table 82

Station		NT		NT	NT	NT	NT	TP	NT	NT	NT	TP		NT	NT	NT	NT	NT	NT	NT	TP	NT		NT	NT
								◇1				◇1									◇1				
						A	B					C		D	E					B					
												⚲													
Barrow-in-Furness	d													10 09											
Roose	d													10 13											
Dalton	d													10 19											
Ulverston	d													10 28											
Cark	d													10 36											
Kents Bank	d													10 40											
Grange-over-Sands	d													10 44											
Arnside	d													10 50											
Silverdale	d													10 55											
Carnforth	d					10 01								11 03											
Windermere 83	d																								
Oxenholme Lake District 65	d											10 10													
Lancaster 6 65	a					10 13						10 24		11 12											
	d											10 25													
Blackpool North 97	d				09 20			09 40											10 20		10 44				
Layton 97	d				09 23														10 23						
Poulton-le-Fylde 97	d				09 27			09 46											10 27		10 50				
Kirkham & Wesham 97	d				09 37														10 37						
Preston 8 65,97	a				09 47			10 04				10 43							10 47		11 08				
	d				09 49			10 12			10 23	10 45							10 49		11 10				11 23
Leyland	d				09 54						10 29								10 54						11 29
Buckshaw Parkway	d				09 59						10 33								10 59		11 17				11 33
Chorley	d				10 03			10 22			10 38								11 03		11 21				11 38
Adlington (Lancashire)	d				10 08														11 08						
Blackrod	d				10 12														11 12						
Horwich Parkway	d				10 16						10 46								11 16		11 28				11 46
Lostock	d				10 20						10 50								11 20						11 50
Southport	d	09 24								09 55							10 24							10 55	
Meols Cop	d									10 00														11 00	
Bescar Lane	d									10 05														11 05	
New Lane	d									10 09														11 09	
Burscough Bridge	d	09 36								10 11							10 36							11 11	
Hoscar	d									10 15														11 15	
Parbold	d	09 41								10 18							10 41							11 18	
Appley Bridge	d	09 45								10 22							10 45							11 22	
Gathurst	d									10 25														11 25	
Kirkby	d			09 32														10 32							
Rainford	d			09 40														10 40							
Upholland	d			09 44														10 44							
Orrell	d			09 47														10 47							
Pemberton	d			09 50														10 50							
Wigan Wallgate	a	09 51		09 56						10 30							10 51	10 56						11 30	
	d	09 53		09 58					10 20	10 32						10 48	10 53	10 58				11 20		11 32	
Wigan North Western	d											10 58													
Ince	d			10 01														11 01							
Hindley	d	09 58		10 04					10 25	10 37							10 58	11 04				11 25		11 37	
Westhoughton	d	10 02							10 29								11 02					11 29			
Bolton	a	10 12			10 25			10 34	10 38		10 55					11 02	11 12		11 25		11 34	11 38			11 55
	d	10 13			10 25		10 31	10 34	10 39		10 56				10 59	11 03	11 13		11 25	11 31	11 35	11 39			11 56
Moses Gate	d								10 42													11 42			
Farnworth	d								10 44													11 44			
Kearsley	d								10 46													11 46			
Clifton	d																								
Daisy Hill	d			10 09						10 41								11 09						11 41	
Hag Fold	d			10 12														11 12							
Atherton	d			10 15						10 45								11 15						11 45	
Walkden	d			10 20						10 50								11 20						11 50	
Moorside	d			10 24														11 24							
Swinton	d			10 26						10 55								11 26						11 55	
Salford Crescent	a	10 25		10 34	10 38		10 43	10 46	10 56	11 02	11 08				11 11	11 16	11 25	11 34	11 38	11 43	11 47	11 56		12 02	12 08
	d	10 26		10 35	10 38		10 44	10 47	10 56	11 03	11 09				11 12	11 16	11 26	11 34	11 38	11 44	11 47	11 56		12 03	12 09
Salford Central	d			10 37	10 41		10 46		10 59	11 05					11 15	11 18		11 36	11 41	11 46		11 59		12 05	
Manchester Victoria ⇌	a			10 43	10 47		10 52		11 06	11 11					11 20	11 25		11 43	11 47	11 52		12 06		12 11	
Rochdale 41	a															11 51									
Deansgate ⇌	a	10 29						10 50			11 12						11 29				11 51				12 12
Manchester Oxford Road	a	10 31						10 52			11 14	11 23					11 31				11 52				12 14
Manchester Piccadilly 10 ⇌	a	10 35						10 56			11 18	11 27					11 35				11 56				12 18
Stockport 84	a										11 34														12 34
Hazel Grove 86	a										11 45														12 45
Buxton 86	a																								
Heald Green 85	a							11 09													12 10				
Manchester Airport 85 ✈	a	10 53						11 15				11 47					11 53				12 17				

A From Leeds to Morecambe
B From Clitheroe
C From Edinburgh
D From Sellafield to Morecambe
E From Blackburn

The Sunday service between Wigan Wallgate and Manchester Victoria via Atherton is funded by TfGM and will operate whilst funding exists

Table 82R

Saturdays

4 January to 8 February

Barrow-in-Furness, Blackpool North, Preston, Southport, Kirkby and Wigan - Bolton - Manchester

Network Diagram - see first Page of Table 82

Station		TP	NT	NT	NT	NT	NT	NT	TP	NT	TP	NT	NT	NT	TP	NT	TP	NT	NT	NT	NT	NT	TP
		◇1							◇1		◇1				◇1								◇1
			A					B		C					D	E						C	
															🚲		🚌						
Barrow-in-Furness	d								11 20							12 10							
Roose	d															12 14							
Dalton	d								11 29							12 20							
Ulverston	d								11 37							12 28							
Cark	d								11 45							12 36							
Kents Bank	d															12 40							
Grange-over-Sands	d								11 52							12 44							
Arnside	d								11 58							12 50							
Silverdale	d								12 02							12 54							
Carnforth	d							12 02	12 09							13 02							
Windermere	83 d	10 48															12 45						
Oxenholme Lake District	65 d	11 08													12 10								
Lancaster 6	65 a	11 26						12 11	12 17						12 25	13 14	13 24						
	d	11 26							12 17						12 26								
Blackpool North	97 d						11 20				11 41										12 20		12 40
Layton	97 d						11 23														12 23		
Poulton-le-Fylde	97 d						11 27				11 47										12 27		12 46
Kirkham & Wesham	97 d						11 37														12 37		
Preston 8	65,97 a	11 45					11 47		12 37		12 05				12 44						12 47		13 04
	d	11 46					11 49				12 10			12 23	12 45						12 49		13 10
Leyland	d						11 54							12 29							12 54		
Buckshaw Parkway	d						11 59				12 17			12 33							12 59		13 17
Chorley	d						12 03				12 21			12 38							13 03		13 21
Adlington (Lancashire)	d						12 08														13 08		
Blackrod	d						12 12														13 12		
Horwich Parkway	d						12 16				12 28			12 46							13 16		13 28
Lostock	d						12 20							12 50							13 20		
Southport	d				11 24								12 00						12 24				
Meols Cop	d												12 05										
Bescar Lane	d																						
New Lane	d																						
Burscough Bridge	d				11 36								12 13						12 36				
Hoscar	d																						
Parbold	d				11 41								12 18						12 41				
Appley Bridge	d				11 45								12 22						12 45				
Gathurst	d												12 25										
Kirkby	d					11 32														12 32			
Rainford	d					11 40														12 40			
Upholland	d					11 44														12 44			
Orrell	d					11 47														12 47			
Pemberton	d					11 50														12 50			
Wigan Wallgate	a				11 51	11 56							12 30						12 51	12 56			
	d			11 48	11 53	11 58						12 20	12 32					12 48	12 53	12 58			
Wigan North Western	d	11 58													12 58								
Ince	d					12 01														13 01			
Hindley	d				11 58	12 04						12 25	12 37						12 58	13 04			
Westhoughton	d				12 02							12 29							13 02				
Bolton	a			12 02	12 12		12 25				12 34	12 38		12 55				13 02	13 12		13 25		13 34
	d		12 00	12 03	12 13		12 25			12 31	12 35	12 39		12 56				13 03	13 13		13 25	13 31	13 35
Moses Gate	d											12 42											
Farnworth	d											12 44											
Kearsley	d											12 46											
Clifton	d																						
Daisy Hill	d					12 09							12 41							13 09			
Hag Fold	d					12 12														13 12			
Atherton	d					12 15							12 45							13 15			
Walkden	d					12 20							12 50							13 20			
Moorside	d					12 24														13 24			
Swinton	d					12 26							12 55							13 26			
Salford Crescent	a		12 13	12 16	12 25	12 34	12 38			12 43	12 47	12 56	13 02	13 08				13 15	13 25	13 34	13 38	13 43	13 47
	d		12 13	12 16	12 26	12 34	12 38			12 44	12 47	12 56	13 03	13 09				13 15	13 26	13 34	13 38	13 44	13 47
Salford Central	d		12 16	12 18		12 36	12 41			12 46		12 59	13 05					13 17		13 36	13 41	13 46	
Manchester Victoria 🚊	a		12 22	12 25		12 43	12 47			12 52		13 06	13 11					13 25		13 43	13 47	13 52	
Rochdale	41 a			12 51														13 51					
Deansgate 🚊	a				12 29						12 51			13 12					13 29				13 51
Manchester Oxford Road	a	12 23			12 31						12 52			13 14	13 23				13 31				13 52
Manchester Piccadilly 10 🚊	a	12 27			12 35						12 56			13 18	13 27				13 35				13 56
Stockport	84 a													13 34									
Hazel Grove	86 a													13 45									
Buxton	86 a																						
Heald Green	85 a										13 10												14 10
Manchester Airport	85 ✈ a	12 47			12 53						13 17				13 47				13 53				14 17

A From Blackburn
B From Leeds to Heysham Harbour
C From Clitheroe
D From Edinburgh
E From Carlisle

The Sunday service between Wigan Wallgate and Manchester Victoria via Atherton is funded by TfGM and will operate whilst funding exists

Table 82R

Saturdays
4 January to 8 February

Barrow-in-Furness, Blackpool North, Preston, Southport, Kirkby and Wigan - Bolton - Manchester

Network Diagram - see first Page of Table 82

		NT	NT	NT		TP	TP	TP	VT	NT	NT	NT	NT	NT		TP	NT	NT	NT	NT	TP	VT	NT	NT
						◇1	◇1									◇1					◇1			
									A					B								A	C	
								bus	bus													bus		
						trolley															trolley			
Barrow-in-Furness	d						13 20																14 16	
Roose	d																						14 20	
Dalton	d						13 29																14 26	
Ulverston	d						13 37																14 35	
Cark	d						13 45																14 42	
Kents Bank	d																						14 47	
Grange-over-Sands	d						13 52																14 51	
Arnside	d						13 58																14 57	
Silverdale	d						14 02																15 01	
Carnforth	d						14 09																15 08	
Windermere 83	d							13 45																
Oxenholme Lake District 65	d								13 40													14 00		
Lancaster 6 65	a						14 17	14 24	14 25													14 45	15 19	
	d					13 25	14 17														14 25			
Blackpool North 97	d												13 20			13 44								
Layton 97	d												13 23											
Poulton-le-Fylde 97	d												13 27			13 50								
Kirkham & Wesham 97	d												13 37											
Preston 8 65,97	a					13 43	14 37						13 47			14 08					14 44			
	d			13 23		13 44							13 49			14 10			14 23		14 45			
Leyland	d			13 29									13 54						14 29					
Buckshaw Parkway	d			13 33									13 59			14 17			14 33					
Chorley	d			13 38									14 03			14 21			14 38		14 55			
Adlington (Lancashire)	d												14 08											
Blackrod	d												14 12											
Horwich Parkway	d			13 46									14 16			14 28			14 46					
Lostock	d			13 50									14 20						14 50					
Southport	d		12 54								13 24							14 00						14 24
Meols Cop	d		12 59															14 05						
Bescar Lane	d		13 04																					
New Lane	d		13 08																					
Burscough Bridge	d		13 11								13 36							14 13						14 36
Hoscar	d		13 15																					
Parbold	d		13 18								13 41							14 18						14 41
Appley Bridge	d		13 22								13 45							14 22						14 45
Gathurst	d		13 25															14 25						
Kirkby	d											13 32												
Rainford	d											13 40												
Upholland	d											13 44												
Orrell	d											13 47												
Pemberton	d											13 50												
Wigan Wallgate	a		13 30								13 51	13 56						14 30						14 51
	d	13 20	13 32							13 48	13 53	13 58					14 20	14 32		14 48				14 53
Wigan North Western	d					13 57																		
Ince	d											14 01												
Hindley	d	13 25	13 37								13 58	14 04					14 25	14 37						14 58
Westhoughton	d	13 29									14 02						14 29							15 02
Bolton	a	13 38		13 55						14 02	14 12		14 25			14 34	14 38		14 55	15 02	15 06			15 12
	d	13 39		13 56						14 03	14 13		14 25	14 31		14 35	14 39		14 56	15 03	15 07			15 13
Moses Gate	d	13 42															14 42							
Farnworth	d	13 44															14 44							
Kearsley	d	13 46															14 46							
Clifton	d																							
Daisy Hill	d		13 41									14 09						14 41						
Hag Fold	d											14 12												
Atherton	d		13 45									14 15						14 45						
Walkden	d		13 50									14 20						14 50						
Moorside	d											14 24												
Swinton	d		13 55									14 26						14 55						
Salford Crescent	a	13 56	14 02	14 08						14 15	14 25	14 34	14 38	14 43		14 47	14 56	15 02	15 08	15 15	15 18			15 25
	d	13 56	14 03	14 09						14 15	14 26	14 34	14 38	14 44		14 47	14 56	15 03	15 09	15 15	15 19			15 26
Salford Central	d	13 59	14 05							14 17		14 36	14 41	14 46			14 59	15 05		15 17				
Manchester Victoria (tram)	a	14 06	14 10							14 25		14 43	14 47	14 52			15 06	15 11		15 25				
Rochdale 41	a									14 51										15 51				
Deansgate (tram)	a			14 12							14 29					14 51			15 12					15 29
Manchester Oxford Road	a			14 14		14 22					14 31					14 52			15 14		15 23			15 31
Manchester Piccadilly 10 (tram)	a			14 18		14 26					14 35					14 56			15 18		15 27			15 35
Stockport 84	a			14 34															15 34					
Hazel Grove 86	a			14 45															15 45					
Buxton 86	a																							
Heald Green 85	a															15 10								
Manchester Airport 85 (plane)	a					14 47					14 53					15 17					15 47			15 53

A From Carlisle
B From Clitheroe
C From Whitehaven

The Sunday service between Wigan Wallgate and Manchester Victoria via Atherton is funded by TfGM and will operate whilst funding exists

Table 82R

Saturdays

4 January to 8 February

Barrow-in-Furness, Blackpool North, Preston, Southport, Kirkby and Wigan - Bolton - Manchester

Network Diagram - see first Page of Table 82

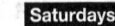

		NT	NT	TP	NT	TP	NT	NT	NT	TP		VT	NT
						◇1				◇1			
					A							B	C
Barrow-in-Furness	d												
Roose	d												
Dalton	d												
Ulverston	d												
Cark	d												
Kents Bank	d												
Grange-over-Sands	d												
Arnside	d												
Silverdale	d												
Carnforth	d												15 36
Windermere 83	d			14 45									
Oxenholme Lake District 65	d											14 40	
Lancaster 6 65	a			15 24								15 25	15 45
	d									15 24			
Blackpool North 97	d		14 20			14 40							
Layton 97	d		14 23										
Poulton-le-Fylde 97	d		14 27			14 46							
Kirkham & Wesham 97	d		14 37										
Preston 8 65,97	a		14 47			15 04				15 42			
	d		14 49			15 10			15 23	15 44			
Leyland	d		14 54						15 29				
Buckshaw Parkway	d		14 59			15 17			15 33				
Chorley	d		15 03			15 21			15 38				
Adlington (Lancashire)	d		15 08										
Blackrod	d		15 12										
Horwich Parkway	d		15 16			15 28			15 46				
Lostock	d		15 20						15 50				
Southport	d							14 54					
Meols Cop	d							14 59					
Bescar Lane	d							15 04					
New Lane	d							15 08					
Burscough Bridge	d							15 11					
Hoscar	d							15 15					
Parbold	d							15 18					
Appley Bridge	d							15 22					
Gathurst	d							15 25					
Kirkby	d	14 32											
Rainford	d	14 40											
Upholland	d	14 44											
Orrell	d	14 47											
Pemberton	d	14 50											
Wigan Wallgate	a	14 56						15 30					
	d	14 58					15 20	15 32					
Wigan North Western	d									15 58			
Ince	d	15 01											
Hindley	d	15 04					15 25	15 37					
Westhoughton	d						15 29						
Bolton	a		15 25			15 34	15 38		15 55				
	d		15 25		15 31	15 35	15 39		15 56				
Moses Gate	d						15 42						
Farnworth	d						15 44						
Kearsley	d						15 46						
Clifton	d												
Daisy Hill	d	15 09						15 41					
Hag Fold	d	15 12											
Atherton	d	15 15						15 45					
Walkden	d	15 20						15 50					
Moorside	d	15 24											
Swinton	d	15 26						15 55					
Salford Crescent	a	15 34	15 38		15 43	15 47	15 56	16 02	16 08				
	d	15 34	15 38		15 44	15 47	15 56	16 03	16 09				
Salford Central	d	15 36	15 41		15 48		15 59	16 05					
Manchester Victoria	a	15 43	15 47		15 54		16 06	16 11					
Rochdale 41	a												
Deansgate	a					15 51			16 12				
Manchester Oxford Road	a					15 52			16 14	16 22			
Manchester Piccadilly 10	a					15 56			16 18	16 26			
Stockport 84	a								16 34				
Hazel Grove 86	a								16 45				
Buxton 86	a												
Heald Green 85	a					16 10				16 39			
Manchester Airport 85	a					16 17				16 47			

		NT	NT	NT	NT	NT	TP	NT		NT	NT	TP	TP
							◇1					1	
				A									
Barrow-in-Furness	d											15 25	
Roose	d												
Dalton	d												
Ulverston	d											15 41	
Cark	d												
Kents Bank	d												
Grange-over-Sands	d											15 53	
Arnside	d											15 59	
Silverdale	d												
Carnforth	d											16 09	
Windermere 83	d												15 45
Oxenholme Lake District 65	d												
Lancaster 6 65	a											16 17	16 24
	d											16 29	
Blackpool North 97	d					15 20	15 40						
Layton 97	d					15 23							
Poulton-le-Fylde 97	d					15 27	15 46						
Kirkham & Wesham 97	d					15 37							
Preston 8 65,97	a					15 47	16 04					16 47	
	d					15 49	16 10				16 22	16 49	
Leyland	d					15 54					16 28		
Buckshaw Parkway	d					15 59	16 17				16 32		
Chorley	d					16 03	16 21				16 37		
Adlington (Lancashire)	d					16 08							
Blackrod	d					16 12							
Horwich Parkway	d					16 16	16 28				16 45		
Lostock	d					16 20					16 49		
Southport	d		15 24							16 00			
Meols Cop	d									16 05			
Bescar Lane	d												
New Lane	d												
Burscough Bridge	d		15 36							16 13			
Hoscar	d												
Parbold	d		15 41							16 18			
Appley Bridge	d		15 45							16 22			
Gathurst	d									16 25			
Kirkby	d				15 32								
Rainford	d				15 40								
Upholland	d				15 44								
Orrell	d				15 47								
Pemberton	d				15 50								
Wigan Wallgate	a		15 51		15 56					16 30			
	d	15 48	15 53		15 58			16 20		16 32			
Wigan North Western	d												
Ince	d				16 01								
Hindley	d		15 58		16 04			16 25		16 37			
Westhoughton	d		16 02					16 29					
Bolton	a	16 02	16 12			16 25	16 34	16 38			16 54		
	d	16 03	16 13	16 17		16 25	16 35	16 39			16 55		
Moses Gate	d							16 42					
Farnworth	d							16 44					
Kearsley	d							16 46					
Clifton	d												
Daisy Hill	d				16 09					16 41			
Hag Fold	d				16 12								
Atherton	d				16 15					16 45			
Walkden	d				16 20					16 50			
Moorside	d				16 24								
Swinton	d				16 26					16 55			
Salford Crescent	a	16 15	16 25	16 30	16 33	16 38	16 47	16 56		17 02	17 07		
	d	16 15	16 26	16 30	16 34	16 38	16 47	16 56		17 03	17 08		
Salford Central	d	16 17		16 33	16 37	16 41		16 59		17 05			
Manchester Victoria	a	16 23		16 41	16 43	16 47		17 06		17 11			
Rochdale 41	a	16 51											
Deansgate	a						16 51				17 10		
Manchester Oxford Road	a		16 31				16 52				17 12	17 25	
Manchester Piccadilly 10	a		16 35				16 56				17 17	17 28	
Stockport 84	a										17 34		
Hazel Grove 86	a										17 43		
Buxton 86	a										18 24		
Heald Green 85	a						17 10						
Manchester Airport 85	a		16 53				17 17					17 47	

A From Clitheroe

B From Carlisle

C From Leeds to Morecambe

The Sunday service between Wigan Wallgate and Manchester Victoria via Atherton is funded by TfGM and will operate whilst funding exists

Table 82R

Saturdays

4 January to 8 February

Barrow-in-Furness, Blackpool North, Preston, Southport, Kirkby and Wigan - Bolton - Manchester

Network Diagram - see first Page of Table 82

Station		VT	VT	TP	VT	NT		NT	NT	NT	NT	NT	TP	NT	NT	NT		NT	TP	NT	NT	NT	TP	TP	TP
													◇1						◇1				◇1	◇1	
		A	A		A							B						B							
		🚌	🚌	🚌	🚌																				🚌
Barrow-in-Furness	d					16 29																		17 21	
Roose	d					16 33																			
Dalton	d					16 39																		17 30	
Ulverston	d					16 47																		17 39	
Cark	d					16 55																		17 46	
Kents Bank	d					16 59																			
Grange-over-Sands	d					17 03																		17 53	
Arnside	d					17 09																		17 59	
Silverdale	d					17 13																			
Carnforth	d					17 21																		18 09	
Windermere 83	d			16 45																					17 45
Oxenholme Lake District 65	d	15 40	16 00		16 40																				
Lancaster 6 65	a	16 25	16 45	17 24	17 25	17 33																			18 24
	d																						17 48		
Blackpool North 97	d										16 20		16 40						17 20						
Layton 97	d										16 23		16 43						17 23						
Poulton-le-Fylde 97	d										16 27		16 47						17 27						
Kirkham & Wesham 97	d										16 37		16 57												
Preston 8 65,97	a										16 47		17 08						17 45				18 06	18 44	
	d										16 49		17 10			17 23			17 47			17 56	18 08	18 45	
Leyland	d										16 54					17 29						18 01			
Buckshaw Parkway	d										16 59		17 17			17 33						18 05	18 15		
Chorley	d										17 03		17 21			17 38			17 56			18 09	18 19		
Adlington (Lancashire)	d										17 08											18 15			
Blackrod	d										17 12											18 19			
Horwich Parkway	d										17 16		17 28			17 46						18 21	18 26		
Lostock	d										17 20					17 50							18 30		
Southport	d								16 24						16 54					17 24					
Meols Cop	d														16 59					17 29					
Bescar Lane	d														17 04										
New Lane	d														17 08										
Burscough Bridge	d								16 36						17 11					17 37					
Hoscar	d														17 15										
Parbold	d								16 41						17 18					17 42					
Appley Bridge	d								16 45						17 22					17 46					
Gathurst	d														17 25										
Kirkby	d									16 32											17 32				
Rainford	d									16 40											17 40				
Upholland	d									16 44											17 44				
Orrell	d									16 47											17 47				
Pemberton	d									16 50											17 50				
Wigan Wallgate	a								16 51	16 56					17 30					17 52	17 57				
	d							16 48	16 53	16 58				17 20	17 32					17 54	17 59				
Wigan North Western	d																							18 58	
Ince	d									17 01											18 02				
Hindley	d								16 58	17 04				17 25	17 37						18 05				
Westhoughton	d								17 02					17 29						18 02					
Bolton	a							17 02	17 12		17 25		17 34	17 38		17 55			18 08	18 12		18 30	18 34		
	d							17 03	17 13		17 25	17 31	17 35	17 39		17 56		18 02	18 08	18 12		18 30	18 35		
Moses Gate	d													17 42											
Farnworth	d													17 44											
Kearsley	d													17 46											
Clifton	d																								
Daisy Hill	d									17 08					17 41						18 09				
Hag Fold	d									17 11											18 12				
Atherton	d									17 14					17 45						18 15				
Walkden	d									17 19					17 50						18 20				
Moorside	d									17 23											18 24				
Swinton	d									17 25					17 55						18 26				
Salford Crescent	a							17 15	17 25	17 33	17 38	17 43	17 47	17 56	18 02	18 08		18 14		18 25	18 33	18 42	18 47		
	d							17 15	17 26	17 33	17 38	17 44	17 47	17 56	18 03	18 09		18 15		18 25	18 33	18 42	18 47		
Salford Central	d							17 17		17 36	17 41	17 47		17 59	18 05			18 17			18 36	18 45			
Manchester Victoria 🚊	a							17 23		17 43	17 47	17 53		18 06	18 11			18 24			18 43	18 50			
Rochdale 41	a							17 51										18 47							
Deansgate 🚊	a								17 29				17 51			18 12							18 51		
Manchester Oxford Road	a								17 31				17 52			18 14			18 23	18 31			18 52	19 23	
Manchester Piccadilly 10 🚊	a								17 35				17 56			18 18			18 27	18 35			18 56	19 27	
Stockport 84	a															18 34									
Hazel Grove 86	a															18 45									
Buxton 86	a																								
Heald Green 85	a								17 47				18 10						18 40				19 10		
Manchester Airport 85 ✈	a								17 53				18 17						18 47	18 53			19 17	19 46	

A From Carlisle

B From Clitheroe

The Sunday service between Wigan Wallgate and Manchester Victoria via Atherton is funded by TfGM and will operate whilst funding exists

Table 82R

Saturdays

4 January to 8 February

Barrow-in-Furness, Blackpool North, Preston, Southport, Kirkby and Wigan - Bolton - Manchester

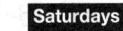

Network Diagram - see first Page of Table 82

	VT		NT	NT	NT	NT	NT	NT	NT	NT	VT		NT	TP	NT	NT	TP	NT	NT	NT	TP		VT	TP
														◇1			◇1							
	A				B	A	C				A		C			D			C				A	
	🚌										🚌										🚌		🚌	🚌
																	🍴							
Barrow-in-Furness d						18 03																		
Roose d						18 07																		
Dalton d						18 13																		
Ulverston d						18 21																		
Cark d						18 29																		
Kents Bank d						18 33																		
Grange-over-Sands d						18 37																		
Arnside d						18 43																		
Silverdale d						18 47																		
Carnforth d					18 26	18 55																		
Windermere 83 d																								18 55
Oxenholme Lake District 65 d	17 40																						18 40	
Lancaster 6 65 a	18 25				18 38	19 05																	19 25	19 34
d						19 06											19 22						19 30	
Blackpool North 97 d										18 20				18 40										
Layton 97 d										18 23														
Poulton-le-Fylde 97 d										18 27				18 46										
Kirkham & Wesham 97 d										18 37														
Preston 8 65,97 a						19 31				18 47				19 04			19 41						20 20	
d										18 49	19 05			19 10			19 45				20 20		20 25	
Leyland d										18 54														
Buckshaw Parkway d										18 59				19 17										
Chorley d										19 03				19 21			19 55			20 19				
Adlington (Lancashire) d										19 08										20 23				
Blackrod d										19 12										20 28				
Horwich Parkway d										19 16				19 28			20 02			20 32				
Lostock d										19 20										20 35				
Southport d				17 54				18 17							19 00			19 23						
Meols Cop d				17 59				18 22							19 05			19 28						
Bescar Lane d				18 04				18 27																
New Lane d				18 08				18 31																
Burscough Bridge d				18 11				18 33							19 13			19 36						
Hoscar d				18 15				18 37																
Parbold d				18 18				18 40							19 18			19 41						
Appley Bridge d				18 22				18 44							19 22			19 45						
Gathurst d				18 25				18 47							19 25			19 48						
Kirkby d									18 32															
Rainford d									18 40															
Upholland d									18 44															
Orrell d									18 47															
Pemberton d									18 50															
Wigan Wallgate a				18 30				18 52	18 56						19 30			19 53						
d			18 20	18 32				18 53	18 58						19 32			19 55						
Wigan North Western d											19a50												21a10	
Ince d									19 01															
Hindley d			18 25	18 37				18 58	19 04						19 37			20 00						
Westhoughton d			18 29					19 02										20 04						
Bolton a			18 38					19 12		19 25				19 35			20 08	20 12		20 40	20 46			
d			18 39				19 02	19 13		19 25			19 32	19 35		20 02	20 08	20 13	20 31	20 41				
Moses Gate d			18 42																					
Farnworth d			18 44																					
Kearsley d			18 46																					
Clifton d																								
Daisy Hill d				18 41					19 08						19 41									
Hag Fold d									19 11															
Atherton d				18 45					19 14						19 45									
Walkden d				18 50					19 19						19 50									
Moorside d									19 23															
Swinton d				18 55					19 25						19 55									
Salford Crescent a			18 56	19 02			19 14	19 25	19 33	19 38			19 44	19 48	20 02	20 15		20 25	20 43	20 53				
d			18 56	19 03			19 15	19 26	19 33	19 38			19 45	19 48	20 03	20 15		20 26	20 44	20 54				
Salford Central d			18 59	19 05			19 17		19 36	19 41			19 47		20 05	20 17			20 46	20 57				
Manchester Victoria 🚊 a			19 06	19 11			19 23		19 43	19 47			19 53		20 11	20 24			20 52	21 02				
Rochdale 41 a																								
Deansgate 🚊 a								19 29						19 52				20 29						
Manchester Oxford Road a								19 31						19 53			20 23	20 31						
Manchester Piccadilly 10 🚊 a								19 35						19 57			20 27	20 35						
Stockport 84 a																								
Hazel Grove 86 a																								
Buxton 86 a																								
Heald Green 85 a														20 11										
Manchester Airport 85 ✈ a								19 53						20 17			20 46	20 52						

A From Carlisle
B From Leeds to Morecambe
C From Clitheroe
D From Blackburn

The Sunday service between Wigan Wallgate and Manchester Victoria via Atherton is funded by TfGM and will operate whilst funding exists

Table 82R

Saturdays
4 January to 8 February

Barrow-in-Furness, Blackpool North, Preston, Southport, Kirkby and Wigan - Bolton - Manchester

Network Diagram - see first Page of Table 82

		TP	VT	NT	NT	NT	NT	TP		VT	NT	NT	NT	TP	NT	TP	VT	NT		TP	TP	NT	VT	NT	NT
		◇1																			◇1				
			A			B				A			B				A						A		
			🚌					🚌		🚌						🚌	🚌	🚌		🚌			🚌		
Barrow-in-Furness	d	19 17																				21 43			
Roose	d	19 21																				21 47			
Dalton	d	19 28																				21 53			
Ulverston	d	19 36																				22 01			
Cark	d	19 44																				22 09			
Kents Bank	d	19 48																				22 13			
Grange-over-Sands	d	19 52																				22 17			
Arnside	d	19 58																				22 23			
Silverdale	d	20 02																				22 27			
Carnforth	d	20 09																				22 35			
Windermere	83 d																			20 55					
Oxenholme Lake District	65 d									20 05							20 40						22 05		
Lancaster 6	65 a	20 17								20 50							21 25			21 34		22 45	22 50		
	d	20 18								20 55							21 30				22 17	22 46	22 55		
Blackpool North	97 d																								
Layton	97 d																								
Poulton-le-Fylde	97 d																								
Kirkham & Wesham	97 d																								
Preston 8	65,97 a	20 37								21 45							22 20				22 38	23 11	23 45		
	d		20 30					21 20		21 50						22 20	22 25	22 28							
Leyland	d																	22 48							
Buckshaw Parkway	d																	23 00							
Chorley	d						21 19								22 20			23a10							
Adlington (Lancashire)	d						21 24								22 25										
Blackrod	d						21 27								22 28										
Horwich Parkway	d						21 31								22 32										
Lostock	d						21 35								22 36										
Southport	d				20 23							21 23													22 18
Meols Cop	d				20 28							21 28													22 23
Bescar Lane	d																								22 28
New Lane	d																								22 32
Burscough Bridge	d				20 36							21 36													22 34
Hoscar	d																								22 38
Parbold	d				20 41							21 41													22 41
Appley Bridge	d				20 45							21 45													22 45
Gathurst	d				20 48							21 48													22 48
Kirkby	d																								
Rainford	d																								
Upholland	d																								
Orrell	d																								
Pemberton	d																								
Wigan Wallgate	a				20 53							21 53													22 53
	d			20 29	20 55						21 29	21 55												22 29	22 55
Wigan North Western	d		21a15							22a35							23a10								
Ince	d			20 32							21 32													22 32	
Hindley	d			20 35	21 00						21 35	22 00												22 35	23 00
Westhoughton	d				21 04							22 04													23 04
Bolton	a				21 12		21 40	21 46				22 12			22 41	22s45									23 12
	d				21 13	21 31	21 41					22 13	22 31	22 38	22 42										23 13
Moses Gate	d																								
Farnworth	d																								
Kearsley	d																								
Clifton	d																								
Daisy Hill	d			20 39							21 39													22 39	
Hag Fold	d			20 42							21 42													22 42	
Atherton	d			20 45							21 45													22 45	
Walkden	d			20 51							21 51													22 51	
Moorside	d			20 54							21 54													22 54	
Swinton	d			20 57							21 57													22 57	
Salford Crescent	a			21 04	21 25	21 43	21 53				22 04	22 25	22 43	22 50	22 54									23 04	23 25
	d			21 05	21 26	21 44	21 54				22 05	22 26	22 44	22 51	22 55									23 05	23 26
Salford Central	d			21 07		21 46	21 56				22 07	22 28	22 46		22 58									23 07	
Manchester Victoria 🚊	a			21 13		21 52	22 03				22 13	22 34	22 52		23 03									23 13	
Rochdale	41 a																								
Deansgate 🚊	a				21 29									22 54											23 29
Manchester Oxford Road	a				21 31									22 56											23 31
Manchester Piccadilly 10 🚊	a				21 35									23 00		23 11									23 39
Stockport	84 a																								
Hazel Grove	86 a																								
Buxton	86 a																								
Heald Green	85 a													23 11											
Manchester Airport	85 ✈ a				21 53									23 16											

A From Carlisle **B** From Clitheroe

The Sunday service between Wigan Wallgate and Manchester Victoria via Atherton is funded by TfGM and will operate whilst funding exists

Table 82R

Saturdays

4 January to 8 February

Barrow-in-Furness, Blackpool North, Preston, Southport, Kirkby and Wigan - Bolton - Manchester

Network Diagram - see first Page of Table 82

			NT	NT A	NT		TP	NT
Barrow-in-Furness		d						
Roose		d						
Dalton		d						
Ulverston		d						
Cark		d						
Kents Bank		d						
Grange-over-Sands		d						
Arnside		d						
Silverdale		d						
Carnforth		d						
Windermere	83	d						
Oxenholme Lake District	65	d						
Lancaster 6	65	a						
		d						
Blackpool North	97	d						
Layton	97	d						
Poulton-le-Fylde	97	d						
Kirkham & Wesham	97	d						
Preston 8	65,97	a						
		d					23 20	23 40
Leyland		d						00 01
Buckshaw Parkway		d						00 12
Chorley		d			23 20			00s22
Adlington (Lancashire)		d			23 25			00s28
Blackrod		d			23 28			00s33
Horwich Parkway		d			23 32			00s37
Lostock		d			23 36			00s43
Southport		d	23 10					
Meols Cop		d	23 15					
Bescar Lane		d						
New Lane		d						
Burscough Bridge		d	23 23					
Hoscar		d						
Parbold		d	23 28					
Appley Bridge		d	23 32					
Gathurst		d	23 35					
Kirkby		d						
Rainford		d						
Upholland		d						
Orrell		d						
Pemberton		d						
Wigan Wallgate		a	23 44					
		d						
Wigan North Western		d						
Ince		d						
Hindley		d						
Westhoughton		d						
Bolton		a			23 41		23s45	00s58
		d		23 38	23 42			
Moses Gate		d						
Farnworth		d						
Kearsley		d						
Clifton		d						
Daisy Hill		d						
Hag Fold		d						
Atherton		d						
Walkden		d						
Moorside		d						
Swinton		d						
Salford Crescent		a		23 50	23 54			01s23
		d		23 53	23 55			
Salford Central		d						
Manchester Victoria		a		00 01	00 03			01 33
Rochdale	41	a						
Deansgate		a						
Manchester Oxford Road		a						
Manchester Piccadilly 10		a					00s10	
Stockport	84	a						
Hazel Grove	86	a						
Buxton	86	a						
Heald Green	85	a						
Manchester Airport	85 ✈	a					00 36	

A From Clitheroe

The Sunday service between Wigan Wallgate and Manchester Victoria via Atherton is funded by TfGM and will operate whilst funding exists

Table 82R

Saturdays
15 February to 17 May

Barrow-in-Furness, Blackpool North, Preston, Southport, Kirkby and Wigan - Bolton - Manchester

Network Diagram - see first Page of Table 82

		NT	TP	TP	TP	TP	NT	NT	NT	TP		TP	NT	NT	TP	NT	NT	NT	NT	TP		NT	NT	NT	NT
			◇1	◇1	◇1	◇1				◇1		◇1			◇1					◇1					
		A							B			C										D	E		
Barrow-in-Furness	d				04 35					05 32		06 15													
Roose	d											06 19													
Dalton	d											06 26													
Ulverston	d				04 51					05 48		06 34													
Cark	d											06 42													
Kents Bank	d											06 46													
Grange-over-Sands	d				05 03					06 00		06 50													
Arnside	d				05 09					06 06		06 56													
Silverdale	d											07 00													
Carnforth	d				05 19					06 16		07 07										07 42			
Windermere 83	d																								
Oxenholme Lake District 65	d																								
Lancaster 6 65	a				05 27					06 24		07 15										07 50			
	d									06 24		07 15								07 23					
Blackpool North 97	d		03 37			05 39								06 19	06 40			06 53							07 18
Layton 97	d													06 22	06 43										07 21
Poulton-le-Fylde 97	d					05 45								06 26	06 47										07 25
Kirkham & Wesham 97	d													06 36	06 57										07 35
Preston 8 65,97	a					06 03				06 43		07 34		06 46	07 07			07 15		07 41					07 46
	d		04u02	05 12		06 05				06 44				06 48	07 09			07 17		07 43					07 47
Leyland	d					06 10								06 53				07 22							07 53
Buckshaw Parkway	d													06 58				07 28							07 58
Chorley	d			05 22		06 17				06 54				07 02	07 18			07 32							08 02
Adlington (Lancashire)	d	00 02												07 07				07 37							08 07
Blackrod	d	00 06				06 23								07 11				07 41							08 11
Horwich Parkway	d	00 09		05 29		06 26				07 01				07 15	07 26			07 45							08 15
Lostock	d	00 13				06 30								07 20	07 30			07 49							08 20
Southport	d												06 23											07 21	
Meols Cop	d												06 28											07 26	
Bescar Lane	d																								
New Lane	d																								
Burscough Bridge	d												06 36											07 34	
Hoscar	d																								
Parbold	d												06 41											07 39	
Appley Bridge	d												06 45											07 43	
Gathurst	d												06 49											07 47	
Kirkby	d																		07 11						
Rainford	d																		07 19						
Upholland	d																		07 23						
Orrell	d																		07 27						
Pemberton	d																		07 30						
Wigan Wallgate	a												06 54						07 35					07 51	
	d						06 31	06 36					06 55			07 15			07 37					07 53	
Wigan North Western	d																07 22			07 56					
Ince	d							06 39								07 18	07 25		07 40						
Hindley	d						06 36	06 42								07 21	07 29		07 43					07 58	
Westhoughton	d						06 41						07 03				07 33							08 03	
Bolton	a	00 17		05 40		06 34	06 52			07 07			07 11	07 25	07 34		07 42	07 54						08 11	08 25
	d	00 17	04u31	05 40		06 35	06 53		06 57	07 08			07 12	07 25	07 35		07 43	07 55					07 59	08 12	08 25
Moses Gate	d								07 00								07 46						08 02		
Farnworth	d								07 02								07 48						08 04		
Kearsley	d								07 04								07 50						08 06		
Clifton	d								07 08																
Daisy Hill	d							06 46								07 26			07 47						
Hag Fold	d							06 49								07 29			07 50						
Atherton	d							06 52								07 32			07 53						
Walkden	d							06 58								07 38			07 59						
Moorside	d							07 01								07 41			08 03						
Swinton	d							07 04								07 44			08 06						
Salford Crescent	a			05 52		06 47	07 05	07 11	07 16				07 24	07 38	07 47	07 53	08 02	08 07	08 13				08 17	08 24	08 38
	d			05 53		06 47	07 08	07 12	07 17				07 25	07 38	07 47	07 53	08 02	08 08	08 13				08 17	08 25	08 38
Salford Central	d							07 15	07 20					07 41		07 56	08 05		08 16				08 20		08 41
Manchester Victoria ⇌	a	00 36						07 18	07 25					07 47		07 59	08 12		08 20				08 25		08 47
Rochdale 41	a																		08 51						
Deansgate ⇌	a					06 51	07 11						07 28		07 51			08 11						08 28	
Manchester Oxford Road	a			05 57		06 52	07 13			07 23			07 30		07 53			08 14		08 22				08 31	
Manchester Piccadilly 10 ⇌	a		04 46	06 00		06 56	07 17			07 27			07 34		07 57			08 18		08 26				08 35	
Stockport 84	a						07 34											08 34							
Hazel Grove 86	a						07 45											08 45							
Buxton 86	a																								
Heald Green 85	a					07 10									08 10									08 47	
Manchester Airport 85 ✈	a		05 05	06 17		07 15				07 45			07 53		08 17					08 47				08 53	

A From Blackpool North
B From Blackburn
C To Blackpool North
D From Leeds
E From Clitheroe

The Sunday service between Wigan Wallgate and Manchester Victoria via Atherton is funded by TfGM and will operate whilst funding exists

Table 82R

Saturdays

15 February to 17 May

Barrow-in-Furness, Blackpool North, Preston, Southport, Kirkby and Wigan - Bolton - Manchester

Network Diagram - see first Page of Table 82

		NT	TP	NT	NT	NT	NT	TP	NT	NT	NT	NT	NT	NT	TP	TP	NT	NT	NT	TP	TP	TP	NT
			◇1					◇1							◇1	◇1				◇1	◇1	◇1	
		A						B	C				A	D						E			C
Barrow-in-Furness	d													08 20	07 33						08 50		
Roose	d													08 24	07 37								
Dalton	d													08 30	07 44						08 59		
Ulverston	d													08 38	07 52						09 07		
Cark	d													08 46	08 00						09 15		
Kents Bank	d													08 50	08 04								
Grange-over-Sands	d													08 54	08 08						09 22		
Arnside	d													09 00	08 14						09 28		
Silverdale	d													09 04	08 18						09 32		
Carnforth	d													09 11	08 25						09 39		
Windermere	83 d																					09 37	
Oxenholme Lake District	65 d							08 10												09 10		09 57	
Lancaster 6	65 a							08 25						09 24	08 33					09 25	09 46	10 13	
	d							08 26							08 33					09 25	09 47	10 14	
Blackpool North	97 d		07 44									08 20				08 40							
Layton	97 d		07 47									08 23											
Poulton-le-Fylde	97 d		07 51									08 27				08 46							
Kirkham & Wesham	97 d		08 01									08 37											
Preston 8	65,97 a		08 11					08 44				08 47			08 52	09 04				09 44	10 07	10 33	
	d		08 12				08 21	08 45				08 49			09 10				09 23	09 44			
Leyland	d						08 27					08 54							09 29				
Buckshaw Parkway	d						08 31					08 59			09 17				09 33				
Chorley	d		08 22				08 35					09 03			09 21				09 38				
Adlington (Lancashire)	d						08 40					09 08											
Blackrod	d						08 43					09 12											
Horwich Parkway	d						08 47					09 16			09 28				09 46				
Lostock	d						08 50					09 20							09 50				
Southport	d					07 54				08 25								09 00					
Meols Cop	d					07 59				08 30								09 05					
Bescar Lane	d					08 04																	
New Lane	d					08 08																	
Burscough Bridge	d					08 10				08 38								09 13					
Hoscar	d					08 14																	
Parbold	d					08 17				08 43								09 18					
Appley Bridge	d					08 21				08 47								09 22					
Gathurst	d					08 24				08 50								09 25					
Kirkby	d										08 21												
Rainford	d										08 29												
Upholland	d										08 33												
Orrell	d										08 36												
Pemberton	d										08 39												
Wigan Wallgate	a					08 29				08 55	08 45							09 30					
	d			08 13		08 29				08 56	08 50						09 20	09 31					
Wigan North Western	d				08 20			08 58												09 58			
Ince	d			08 16							08 53												
Hindley	d			08 19	08 25	08 34					08 57						09 25	09 36					
Westhoughton	d				08 29					09 04							09 29						
Bolton	a		08 34		08 38		08 55			09 12		09 25			09 34		09 38		09 55				
	d	08 31	08 35		08 39		08 56		09 02	09 13		09 25	09 31		09 35		09 39		09 56				10 00
Moses Gate	d				08 42												09 42						
Farnworth	d				08 44												09 44						
Kearsley	d				08 46												09 46						
Clifton	d																						
Daisy Hill	d			08 23		08 39					09 01							09 40					
Hag Fold	d			08 26							09 04												
Atherton	d			08 29		08 43					09 06							09 44					
Walkden	d			08 35		08 49					09 12							09 48					
Moorside	d			08 39							09 15												
Swinton	d			08 42		08 54					09 18							09 54					
Salford Crescent	a	08 43	08 46	08 50	08 56	09 01	09 08		09 14	09 25	09 27	09 38	09 43		09 47		09 56	10 01	10 08				10 13
	d	08 44	08 47	08 51	08 56	09 02	09 09		09 15	09 26	09 27	09 38	09 44		09 47		09 56	10 02	10 09				10 13
Salford Central	d	08 46		08 54	08 59	09 04			09 18		09 31	09 41	09 46				09 59	10 03					10 16
Manchester Victoria	a	08 52		08 57	09 06	09 10			09 22		09 38	09 47	09 52				10 06	10 11					10 21
Rochdale	41 a								09 54														
Deansgate	a						09 12			09 29					09 51				10 12				
Manchester Oxford Road	a		08 52				09 14	09 23		09 31					09 52				10 14	10 22			
Manchester Piccadilly 10	a		08 56				09 18	09 27		09 35					09 56				10 18	10 26			
Stockport	84 a						09 34												10 34				
Hazel Grove	86 a						09 45												10 45				
Buxton	86 a																						
Heald Green	85 a		09 09												10 10								
Manchester Airport	85 a		09 17					09 47		09 53					10 17					10 46			

A From Clitheroe
B From Edinburgh
C From Blackburn
D From Maryport
E From Glasgow Central

The Sunday service between Wigan Wallgate and Manchester Victoria via Atherton is funded by TfGM and will operate whilst funding exists

Table 82R

Saturdays

15 February to 17 May

Barrow-in-Furness, Blackpool North, Preston, Southport, Kirkby and Wigan - Bolton - Manchester

Network Diagram - see first Page of Table 82

		NT	NT	NT	NT	NT	NT	TP	NT	NT	NT	TP	NT	NT	NT	NT	NT	NT	NT	TP	NT	NT
								◇1				◇1								◇1		
						A	B					C	D	E					B			
												🍴										
Barrow-in-Furness	d												10 09									
Roose	d												10 13									
Dalton	d												10 19									
Ulverston	d												10 28									
Cark	d												10 36									
Kents Bank	d												10 40									
Grange-over-Sands	d												10 44									
Arnside	d												10 50									
Silverdale	d												10 55									
Carnforth	d					10 01							11 03									
Windermere	83 d																					
Oxenholme Lake District	65 d											10 10										
Lancaster 6	65 a					10 13						10 24	11 12									
	d											10 25										
Blackpool North	97 d				09 20			09 40										10 20		10 44		
Layton	97 d				09 23													10 23				
Poulton-le-Fylde	97 d				09 27			09 46										10 27		10 50		
Kirkham & Wesham	97 d				09 37													10 37				
Preston 8	65,97 a				09 47			10 04				10 43						10 47		11 08		
	d				09 49			10 12			10 23	10 45						10 49		11 10		
Leyland	d				09 54						10 29							10 54				
Buckshaw Parkway	d				09 59						10 33							10 59		11 17		
Chorley	d				10 03			10 22			10 38							11 03		11 21		
Adlington (Lancashire)	d				10 08													11 08				
Blackrod	d				10 12													11 12				
Horwich Parkway	d				10 16						10 46							11 16		11 28		
Lostock	d				10 20						10 50							11 20				
Southport	d		09 24							09 55						10 24						10 55
Meols Cop	d									10 00												11 00
Bescar Lane	d									10 05												11 05
New Lane	d									10 09												11 09
Burscough Bridge	d		09 36							10 11						10 36						11 11
Hoscar	d									10 15												11 15
Parbold	d		09 41							10 18						10 41						11 18
Appley Bridge	d		09 45							10 22						10 45						11 22
Gathurst	d									10 25												11 25
Kirkby	d			09 32													10 32					
Rainford	d			09 40													10 40					
Upholland	d			09 44													10 44					
Orrell	d			09 47													10 47					
Pemberton	d			09 50													10 50					
Wigan Wallgate	a		09 51	09 56						10 30						10 51	10 56					11 30
	d	09 46	09 53	09 58					10 20	10 32					10 48	10 53	10 58				11 20	11 32
Wigan North Western	d											10 58										
Ince	d			10 01													11 01					
Hindley	d		09 58	10 04					10 25	10 37						10 58	11 04				11 25	11 37
Westhoughton	d	09 54	10 02						10 29							11 02					11 29	
Bolton	a	10 02	10 12		10 25			10 34	10 38		10 55				11 02	11 12		11 25		11 34	11 38	
	d	10 03	10 13		10 25		10 31	10 34	10 39		10 56			10 59	11 03	11 13		11 25	11 31	11 35	11 39	
Moses Gate	d								10 42												11 42	
Farnworth	d								10 44												11 44	
Kearsley	d								10 46												11 46	
Clifton	d																					
Daisy Hill	d			10 09						10 41							11 09					11 41
Hag Fold	d			10 12													11 12					
Atherton	d			10 15						10 45							11 15					11 45
Walkden	d			10 20						10 50							11 20					11 50
Moorside	d			10 24													11 24					
Swinton	d			10 26						10 55							11 26					11 55
Salford Crescent	a	10 15	10 25	10 34	10 38		10 43	10 46	10 56	11 02	11 08			11 11	11 16	11 25	11 34	11 38	11 43	11 47	11 56	12 02
	d	10 15	10 26	10 35	10 38		10 44	10 47	10 56	11 03	11 09			11 12	11 16	11 26	11 34	11 38	11 44	11 47	11 56	12 03
Salford Central	d	10 17		10 37	10 41		10 46		10 59	11 05				11 15	11 18		11 36	11 41	11 46		11 59	12 05
Manchester Victoria ⇌	a	10 25		10 43	10 47		10 52		11 06	11 11				11 20	11 25		11 43	11 47	11 52		12 06	12 11
Rochdale	41 a	10 51													11 51							
Deansgate ⇌	a		10 29					10 50			11 12					11 29				11 51		
Manchester Oxford Road	a		10 31					10 52			11 14	11 23				11 31				11 52		
Manchester Piccadilly 10 ⇌	a		10 35					10 56			11 18	11 27				11 35				11 56		
Stockport	84 a										11 34											
Hazel Grove	86 a										11 45											
Buxton	86 a																					
Heald Green	85 a							11 09												12 10		
Manchester Airport	85 ✈ a		10 53					11 15				11 47				11 53				12 17		

A From Leeds to Morecambe
B From Clitheroe
C From Edinburgh
D From Sellafield to Morecambe
E From Blackburn

The Sunday service between Wigan Wallgate and Manchester Victoria via Atherton is funded by TfGM and will operate whilst funding exists

Table 82R

Saturdays

15 February to 17 May

Barrow-in-Furness, Blackpool North, Preston, Southport, Kirkby and Wigan - Bolton - Manchester

Network Diagram - see first Page of Table 82

		NT	TP	NT	NT	NT	NT	NT	NT	TP	NT	TP	NT	NT	NT	TP	NT	NT	NT	NT	NT	NT	TP
			◇1							◇1		◇1				◇1							◇1
				A					B		C					D 🚲	E					C	
Barrow-in-Furness	d									11 20							12 10						
Roose	d																12 14						
Dalton	d									11 29							12 20						
Ulverston	d									11 37							12 28						
Cark	d									11 45							12 36						
Kents Bank	d																12 40						
Grange-over-Sands	d									11 52							12 44						
Arnside	d									11 58							12 50						
Silverdale	d									12 02							12 54						
Carnforth	d								12 02	12 09							13 02						
Windermere	83 d		10 48																				
Oxenholme Lake District	65 d		11 08													12 10							
Lancaster 6	65 a		11 26						12 11	12 17						12 25	13 14						
	d		11 26							12 17						12 26							
Blackpool North	97 d							11 20				11 41									12 20		12 40
Layton	97 d							11 23													12 23		
Poulton-le-Fylde	97 d							11 27				11 47									12 27		12 46
Kirkham & Wesham	97 d							11 37													12 37		
Preston 8	65,97 a		11 45					11 47		12 37		12 05				12 44					12 47		13 04
	d	11 23	11 46					11 49				12 10			12 23	12 45					12 49		13 10
Leyland	d	11 29						11 54							12 29						12 54		
Buckshaw Parkway	d	11 33						11 59				12 17			12 33						12 59		13 17
Chorley	d	11 38						12 03				12 21			12 38						13 03		13 21
Adlington (Lancashire)	d							12 08													13 08		
Blackrod	d							12 12													13 12		
Horwich Parkway	d	11 46						12 16				12 28			12 46						13 16		13 28
Lostock	d	11 50						12 20							12 50						13 20		
Southport	d					11 24								12 00					12 24				
Meols Cop	d													12 05									
Bescar Lane	d																						
New Lane	d																						
Burscough Bridge	d					11 36								12 13					12 36				
Hoscar	d																						
Parbold	d					11 41								12 18					12 41				
Appley Bridge	d					11 45								12 22					12 45				
Gathurst	d													12 25									
Kirkby	d						11 32													12 32			
Rainford	d						11 40													12 40			
Upholland	d						11 44													12 44			
Orrell	d						11 47													12 47			
Pemberton	d						11 50													12 50			
Wigan Wallgate	a					11 51	11 56							12 30					12 51	12 56			
	d				11 48	11 53	11 58						12 20	12 32				12 48	12 53	12 58			
Wigan North Western	d		11 58													12 58							
Ince	d						12 01													13 01			
Hindley	d					11 58	12 04						12 25	12 37					12 58	13 04			
Westhoughton	d					12 02							12 29						13 02				
Bolton	a	11 55			12 02	12 12		12 25				12 34	12 38		12 55			13 02	13 12		13 25		13 34
	d	11 56		12 00	12 03	12 13		12 25			12 31	12 35	12 39		12 56			13 03	13 13		13 25	13 31	13 35
Moses Gate	d												12 42										
Farnworth	d												12 44										
Kearsley	d												12 46										
Clifton	d																						
Daisy Hill	d						12 09							12 41						13 09			
Hag Fold	d						12 12													13 12			
Atherton	d						12 15							12 45						13 15			
Walkden	d						12 20							12 50						13 20			
Moorside	d						12 24													13 24			
Swinton	d						12 26							12 55						13 26			
Salford Crescent	a	12 08		12 13	12 16	12 25	12 34	12 38			12 43	12 47	12 56	13 02	13 08			13 15	13 25	13 34	13 38	13 43	13 47
	d	12 09		12 13	12 16	12 26	12 34	12 38			12 44	12 47	12 56	13 03	13 09			13 15	13 26	13 34	13 38	13 44	13 47
Salford Central	d			12 16	12 18		12 36	12 41			12 46		12 59	13 05				13 17		13 36	13 41	13 46	
Manchester Victoria	🚊 a			12 22	12 25		12 43	12 47			12 52		13 06	13 11				13 25		13 43	13 47	13 52	
Rochdale	41 a				12 51													13 51					
Deansgate	🚊 a	12 12				12 29						12 51			13 12				13 29				13 51
Manchester Oxford Road	a	12 14	12 23			12 31						12 52			13 14	13 23			13 31				13 52
Manchester Piccadilly 10	🚊 a	12 18	12 27			12 35						12 56			13 18	13 27			13 35				13 56
Stockport	84 a	12 34													13 34								
Hazel Grove	86 a	12 45													13 45								
Buxton	86 a																						
Heald Green	85 a											13 10											14 10
Manchester Airport	85 ✈ a		12 47			12 53						13 17				13 47			13 53				14 17

A From Blackburn
B From Leeds to Heysham Harbour
C From Clitheroe
D From Edinburgh
E From Carlisle

The Sunday service between Wigan Wallgate and Manchester Victoria via Atherton is funded by TfGM and will operate whilst funding exists

Table 82R

Saturdays

15 February to 17 May

Barrow-in-Furness, Blackpool North, Preston, Southport, Kirkby and Wigan - Bolton - Manchester

Network Diagram - see first Page of Table 82

Station		NT	NT	NT	TP		TP	TP	NT	NT	NT	NT	NT	TP	NT		NT	NT	NT	TP	NT	NT	NT	NT	NT
					◇1 A 🚲		◇1	◇1					B	◇1						◇1 C 🚲	D				B
Barrow-in-Furness	d							13 20													14 16				
Roose	d																				14 20				
Dalton	d							13 29													14 26				
Ulverston	d							13 37													14 35				
Cark	d							13 45													14 42				
Kents Bank	d																				14 47				
Grange-over-Sands	d							13 52													14 51				
Arnside	d							13 58													14 57				
Silverdale	d							14 02													15 01				
Carnforth	d							14 09													15 08				
Windermere 83	d						12 52																		
Oxenholme Lake District 65	d				13 10		13 13													14 10					
Lancaster 6 65	a				13 25		13 29	14 17												14 24	15 19				
	d				13 25		13 29	14 17												14 25					
Blackpool North 97	d											13 20		13 44										14 20	
Layton 97	d											13 23												14 23	
Poulton-le-Fylde 97	d											13 27		13 50										14 27	
Kirkham & Wesham 97	d											13 37												14 37	
Preston 8 65,97	a				13 44		13 49	14 37				13 47		14 08						14 45				14 47	
	d			13 23	13 44							13 49		14 10				14 23		14 45				14 49	
Leyland	d			13 29								13 54						14 29						14 54	
Buckshaw Parkway	d			13 33								13 59		14 17				14 33						14 59	
Chorley	d			13 38								14 03		14 21				14 38		14 55				15 03	
Adlington (Lancashire)	d											14 08												15 08	
Blackrod	d											14 12												15 12	
Horwich Parkway	d			13 46								14 16		14 28				14 46						15 16	
Lostock	d			13 50								14 20						14 50						15 20	
Southport	d		12 54							13 24							14 00					14 24			
Meols Cop	d		12 59														14 05								
Bescar Lane	d		13 04																						
New Lane	d		13 08																						
Burscough Bridge	d		13 11							13 36							14 13					14 36			
Hoscar	d		13 15																						
Parbold	d		13 18							13 41							14 18					14 41			
Appley Bridge	d		13 22							13 45							14 22					14 45			
Gathurst	d		13 25														14 25								
Kirkby	d										13 32												14 32		
Rainford	d										13 40												14 40		
Upholland	d										13 44												14 44		
Orrell	d										13 47												14 47		
Pemberton	d										13 50												14 50		
Wigan Wallgate	a		13 30							13 51	13 56						14 30					14 51	14 56		
	d	13 20	13 32						13 48	13 53	13 58				14 20		14 32		14 48			14 53	14 58		
Wigan North Western	d				13 58																				
Ince	d										14 01												15 01		
Hindley	d	13 25	13 37							13 58	14 04				14 25		14 37					14 58	15 04		
Westhoughton	d	13 29								14 02					14 29							15 02			
Bolton	a	13 38		13 55					14 02	14 12		14 25		14 34	14 38			14 55	15 02	15 07		15 12		15 25	
	d	13 39		13 56					14 03	14 13		14 25	14 31	14 35	14 39			14 56	15 03	15 07		15 13		15 25	15 31
Moses Gate	d	13 42													14 42										
Farnworth	d	13 44													14 44										
Kearsley	d	13 46													14 46										
Clifton	d																								
Daisy Hill	d		13 41								14 09						14 41						15 09		
Hag Fold	d										14 12												15 12		
Atherton	d		13 45								14 15						14 45						15 15		
Walkden	d		13 50								14 20						14 50						15 20		
Moorside	d										14 24												15 24		
Swinton	d		13 55								14 26						14 55						15 26		
Salford Crescent	a	13 56	14 02	14 08					14 15	14 25	14 34	14 38	14 43	14 47	14 56		15 02	15 08	15 15	15 19		15 25	15 34	15 38	15 43
	d	13 56	14 03	14 09					14 15	14 26	14 34	14 38	14 44	14 47	14 56		15 03	15 09	15 15	15 19		15 26	15 34	15 38	15 44
Salford Central	d	13 59	14 05						14 17		14 36	14 41	14 46		14 59		15 05		15 17				15 36	15 41	15 48
Manchester Victoria 🚊	a	14 06	14 10						14 25		14 43	14 47	14 52		15 06		15 11		15 25				15 43	15 47	15 54
Rochdale 41	a								14 51										15 51						
Deansgate 🚊	a			14 12						14 29				14 51				15 12				15 29			
Manchester Oxford Road	a			14 14	14 22					14 31				14 52				15 14		15 24		15 31			
Manchester Piccadilly 10 🚊	a			14 18	14 26					14 35				14 56				15 18		15 28		15 35			
Stockport 84	a			14 34														15 34							
Hazel Grove 86	a			14 45														15 45							
Buxton 86	a																								
Heald Green 85	a													15 10											
Manchester Airport 85 ✈	a				14 45					14 53				15 17						15 47		15 53			

A From Glasgow Central
B From Clitheroe
C From Edinburgh
D From Whitehaven

The Sunday service between Wigan Wallgate and Manchester Victoria via Atherton is funded by TfGM and will operate whilst funding exists

Table 82R

Saturdays

15 February to 17 May

Barrow-in-Furness, Blackpool North, Preston, Southport, Kirkby and Wigan - Bolton - Manchester

Network Diagram - see first Page of Table 82

Station			TP ◇1	NT	NT	NT	TP ◇1 A	NT	NT	NT B	NT	NT	NT C	TP ◇1	TP ◇1	TP ◇1	NT	NT	NT	TP ◇1 D	TP ◇1 E	NT	NT
Barrow-in-Furness		d												15 25								16 29	
Roose		d																				16 33	
Dalton		d																				16 39	
Ulverston		d												15 41								16 47	
Cark		d																				16 55	
Kents Bank		d																				16 59	
Grange-over-Sands		d												15 53								17 03	
Arnside		d												15 59								17 09	
Silverdale		d																				17 13	
Carnforth		d											15 36	16 09								17 21	
Windermere	83	d													14 52								
Oxenholme Lake District	65	d					15 09								15 12					16 14	16 14		
Lancaster 6	65	a					15 23						15 45	16 17	15 28					16 29	16 29	17 33	
		d					15 24							16 17	15 28					16 29	16 29		
Blackpool North	97	d	14 40									15 20				15 40							
Layton	97	d										15 23											
Poulton-le-Fylde	97	d	14 46									15 27				15 46							
Kirkham & Wesham	97	d										15 37											
Preston 8	65,97	a	15 04				15 42					15 47		16 37	15 48	16 04				16 48	16 48		
		d	15 10			15 23	15 45					15 49			16 10				16 22	16 49	16 49		
Leyland		d				15 29						15 54							16 28				
Buckshaw Parkway		d	15 17			15 33						15 59			16 17				16 32				
Chorley		d	15 21			15 38						16 03			16 21				16 37				
Adlington (Lancashire)		d										16 08											
Blackrod		d										16 12											
Horwich Parkway		d	15 28			15 46						16 16			16 28				16 45				
Lostock		d				15 50						16 20							16 49				
Southport		d			14 54				15 24									16 00					
Meols Cop		d			14 59													16 05					
Bescar Lane		d			15 04																		
New Lane		d			15 08																		
Burscough Bridge		d			15 11				15 36									16 13					
Hoscar		d			15 15																		
Parbold		d			15 18				15 41									16 18					
Appley Bridge		d			15 22				15 45									16 22					
Gathurst		d			15 25													16 25					
Kirkby		d									15 32												
Rainford		d									15 40												
Upholland		d									15 44												
Orrell		d									15 47												
Pemberton		d									15 50												
Wigan Wallgate		a			15 30				15 51		15 56							16 30					
		d		15 20	15 32			15 48	15 53		15 58						16 20	16 32					16 48
Wigan North Western		d					15 58																
Ince		d									16 01												
Hindley		d		15 25	15 37				15 58		16 04						16 25	16 37					
Westhoughton		d		15 29					16 02								16 29						
Bolton		a	15 34	15 38		15 55		16 02	16 12			16 25			16 34		16 38		16 54				17 02
		d	15 35	15 39		15 56		16 03	16 13	16 17		16 25			16 35		16 39		16 55				17 03
Moses Gate		d		15 42													16 42						
Farnworth		d		15 44													16 44						
Kearsley		d		15 46													16 46						
Clifton		d																					
Daisy Hill		d			15 41						16 09							16 41					
Hag Fold		d									16 12												
Atherton		d			15 45						16 15							16 45					
Walkden		d			15 50						16 20							16 50					
Moorside		d									16 24												
Swinton		d			15 55						16 26							16 55					
Salford Crescent		a	15 47	15 56	16 02	16 08		16 15	16 25	16 30	16 33	16 38			16 47		16 56	17 02	17 07				17 15
		d	15 47	15 56	16 03	16 09		16 15	16 26	16 30	16 34	16 38			16 47		16 56	17 03	17 08				17 15
Salford Central		d		15 59	16 05			16 17		16 33	16 37	16 41					16 59	17 05					17 17
Manchester Victoria	⛴	a		16 06	16 11			16 23		16 41	16 43	16 47					17 06	17 11					17 23
Rochdale	41	a						16 51															17 51
Deansgate	⛴	a	15 51			16 12									16 51				17 10				
Manchester Oxford Road		a	15 52			16 14	16 23		16 31						16 52				17 12	17 26	17 26		
Manchester Piccadilly 10	⛴	a	15 56			16 18	16 27		16 35						16 56				17 17	17 30	17 30		
Stockport	84	a				16 34													17 34				
Hazel Grove	86	a				16 45													17 43				
Buxton	86	a																	18 24				
Heald Green	85	a	16 10				16 40								17 10						17 42		
Manchester Airport	85 ✈	a	16 17				16 47		16 53						17 17					17 46	17 50		

A From Glasgow Central
B From Clitheroe
C From Leeds to Morecambe
D from 29 March. From Edinburgh
E until 22 March. From Edinburgh

The Sunday service between Wigan Wallgate and Manchester Victoria via Atherton is funded by TfGM and will operate whilst funding exists

Table 82R

Saturdays

15 February to 17 May

Barrow-in-Furness, Blackpool North, Preston, Southport, Kirkby and Wigan - Bolton - Manchester

Network Diagram - see first Page of Table 82

		NT	NT	NT	NT	TP	NT	NT	NT	NT	TP	NT	NT	NT	TP	TP	NT	NT	TP	NT	NT	NT	NT
						◇1					◇1				◇1	◇1			◇1				
					A					A									B 🍴	C	D	A	
Barrow-in-Furness	d															17 21					18 03		
Roose	d																				18 07		
Dalton	d															17 30					18 13		
Ulverston	d															17 39					18 21		
Cark	d															17 46					18 29		
Kents Bank	d																				18 33		
Grange-over-Sands	d															17 53					18 37		
Arnside	d															17 59					18 43		
Silverdale	d																				18 47		
Carnforth	d															18 08				18 26	18 55		
Windermere 83	d														17 06								
Oxenholme Lake District 65	d														17 30								
Lancaster 6 65	a														17 47	18 17				18 38	19 05		
	d														17 48	18 17			18 25		19 06		
Blackpool North 97	d			16 20		16 40					17 20												
Layton 97	d			16 23		16 43					17 23												
Poulton-le-Fylde 97	d			16 27		16 47					17 27												
Kirkham & Wesham 97	d			16 37		16 57																	
Preston 8 65,97	a			16 47		17 08					17 45				18 06	18 37			18 45		19 31		
	d			16 49		17 10			17 23		17 47			17 56	18 08				18 45				
Leyland	d			16 54					17 29					18 01									
Buckshaw Parkway	d			16 59		17 17			17 33					18 05	18 15								
Chorley	d			17 03		17 21			17 38		17 56			18 09	18 19								
Adlington (Lancashire)	d			17 08										18 15									
Blackrod	d			17 12										18 19									
Horwich Parkway	d			17 16		17 28			17 46					18 21	18 26								
Lostock	d			17 20					17 50						18 30								
Southport	d	16 24						16 54				17 24						17 54					18 17
Meols Cop	d							16 59				17 29						17 59					18 22
Bescar Lane	d							17 04										18 04					18 27
New Lane	d							17 08										18 08					18 31
Burscough Bridge	d	16 36						17 11				17 37						18 11					18 33
Hoscar	d							17 15										18 15					18 37
Parbold	d	16 41						17 18				17 42						18 18					18 40
Appley Bridge	d	16 45						17 22				17 46						18 22					18 44
Gathurst	d							17 25										18 25					18 47
Kirkby	d		16 32										17 32										
Rainford	d		16 40										17 40										
Upholland	d		16 44										17 44										
Orrell	d		16 47										17 47										
Pemberton	d		16 50										17 50										
Wigan Wallgate	a	16 51	16 56					17 30				17 52	17 57					18 30					18 52
	d	16 53	16 58				17 20	17 32				17 54	17 59				18 20	18 32					18 53
Wigan North Western	d																		18 59				
Ince	d		17 01										18 02										
Hindley	d	16 58	17 04				17 25	17 37					18 05				18 25	18 37					18 58
Westhoughton	d	17 02					17 29					18 02					18 29						19 02
Bolton	a	17 12		17 25		17 34	17 38		17 55		18 08	18 12		18 30	18 34		18 38						19 12
	d	17 13		17 25	17 31	17 35	17 39		17 56	18 02	18 08	18 12		18 30	18 35		18 39					19 02	19 13
Moses Gate	d						17 42										18 42						
Farnworth	d						17 44										18 44						
Kearsley	d						17 46										18 46						
Clifton	d																						
Daisy Hill	d		17 08					17 41					18 09					18 41					
Hag Fold	d		17 11										18 12										
Atherton	d		17 14					17 45					18 15					18 45					
Walkden	d		17 19					17 50					18 20					18 50					
Moorside	d		17 23										18 24										
Swinton	d		17 25					17 55					18 26					18 55					
Salford Crescent	a	17 25	17 33	17 38	17 43	17 47	17 56	18 02	18 08	18 14		18 25	18 33	18 42	18 47		18 56	19 02				19 14	19 25
	d	17 26	17 33	17 38	17 44	17 47	17 56	18 03	18 09	18 15		18 25	18 33	18 42	18 47		18 56	19 03				19 15	19 26
Salford Central	d		17 36	17 41	17 47		17 59	18 05		18 17			18 36	18 45			18 59	19 05				19 17	
Manchester Victoria 🚇	a		17 43	17 47	17 53		18 06	18 11		18 24			18 43	18 50			19 06	19 11				19 23	
Rochdale 41	a									18 47													
Deansgate 🚇	a	17 29				17 51			18 12						18 51								19 29
Manchester Oxford Road	a	17 31				17 52			18 14		18 23	18 31			18 52				19 24				19 31
Manchester Piccadilly 10 🚇	a	17 35				17 56			18 18		18 27	18 35			18 56				19 29				19 35
Stockport 84	a								18 34														
Hazel Grove 86	a								18 45														
Buxton 86	a																						
Heald Green 85	a	17 47				18 10					18 40				19 10								
Manchester Airport 85 ✈	a	17 53				18 17					18 47	18 53			19 17				19 47				19 53

A From Clitheroe
B From Edinburgh
C From Leeds to Morecambe
D From Carlisle

The Sunday service between Wigan Wallgate and Manchester Victoria via Atherton is funded by TfGM and will operate whilst funding exists

Table 82R

Saturdays

15 February to 17 May

Barrow-in-Furness, Blackpool North, Preston, Southport, Kirkby and Wigan - Bolton - Manchester

Network Diagram - see first Page of Table 82

			NT	NT	NT	TP	NT	TP	TP	NT	NT	NT	NT	TP	TP	NT	NT	NT	NT	TP	NT	NT	NT
						◇1		◇1	◇1					◇1	◇1					◇1			
					A			B		C			A		D				A				
Barrow-in-Furness		d							19 17														
Roose		d							19 21														
Dalton		d							19 28														
Ulverston		d							19 36														
Cark		d							19 44														
Kents Bank		d							19 48														
Grange-over-Sands		d							19 52														
Arnside		d							19 58														
Silverdale		d							20 02														
Carnforth		d							20 09														
Windermere	83	d																					
Oxenholme Lake District	65	d						19 09							20 13								
Lancaster 6	65	a						19 24	20 17						20 27								
		d						19 24	20 18						20 28								
Blackpool North	97	d		18 20		18 40						19 20		19 44				20 20		20 44			21 20
Layton	97	d		18 23								19 23						20 23					21 23
Poulton-le-Fylde	97	d		18 27		18 46						19 28		19 50				20 27		20 50			21 27
Kirkham & Wesham	97	d		18 37								19 37						20 37					21 37
Preston 8	65,97	a		18 47		19 04		19 44	20 37			19 47		20 08	20 46			20 47		21 08			21 47
		d		18 49		19 10		19 45				19 49		20 10	20 48			20 49		21 10			21 49
Leyland		d		18 54								19 54						20 54					21 54
Buckshaw Parkway		d		18 59		19 17						19 59		20 17				20 59		21 17			21 59
Chorley		d		19 03		19 21						20 03		20 21				21 03		21 21			22 03
Adlington (Lancashire)		d		19 08								20 08						21 08					22 08
Blackrod		d		19 12								20 12						21 12					22 12
Horwich Parkway		d		19 16		19 28						20 16		20 28				21 16		21 28			22 16
Lostock		d		19 20								20 20						21 20					22 20
Southport		d					19 00				19 23						20 23					21 23	
Meols Cop		d					19 05				19 28						20 28					21 28	
Bescar Lane		d																					
New Lane		d																					
Burscough Bridge		d					19 13				19 36						20 36					21 36	
Hoscar		d																					
Parbold		d					19 18				19 41						20 41					21 41	
Appley Bridge		d					19 22				19 45						20 45					21 45	
Gathurst		d					19 25				19 48						20 48					21 48	
Kirkby		d	18 32																				
Rainford		d	18 40																				
Upholland		d	18 44																				
Orrell		d	18 47																				
Pemberton		d	18 50																				
Wigan Wallgate		a	18 56				19 30				19 53						20 53					21 53	
		d	18 58				19 32				19 55					20 29	20 55				21 29	21 55	
Wigan North Western		d						19 59															
Ince		d	19 01													20 32					21 32		
Hindley		d	19 04				19 37				20 00					20 35	21 00				21 35	22 00	
Westhoughton		d									20 04						21 04					22 04	
Bolton		a		19 25		19 35					20 12	20 25		20 34			21 12	21 25		21 34		22 12	22 25
		d		19 25	19 32	19 35				20 02	20 13	20 25	20 31	20 35			21 13	21 25	21 31	21 35		22 13	22 25
Moses Gate		d																					
Farnworth		d																					
Kearsley		d																					
Clifton		d																					
Daisy Hill		d	19 08				19 41									20 39					21 39		
Hag Fold		d	19 11													20 42					21 42		
Atherton		d	19 14				19 45									20 45					21 45		
Walkden		d	19 19				19 50									20 51					21 51		
Moorside		d	19 23													20 54					21 54		
Swinton		d	19 25				19 55									20 57					21 57		
Salford Crescent		a	19 33	19 38	19 44	19 48	20 02			20 15	20 25	20 38	20 43	20 47		21 04	21 25	21 38	21 43	21 47	22 04	22 25	22 38
		d	19 33	19 38	19 45	19 48	20 03			20 15	20 26	20 38	20 44	20 47		21 05	21 26	21 38	21 44	21 47	22 05	22 26	22 38
Salford Central		d	19 36	19 41	19 47		20 05			20 17		20 41	20 46			21 07		21 41	21 46		22 07	22 28	22 41
Manchester Victoria	⇌	a	19 43	19 47	19 53		20 11			20 24		20 47	20 52			21 13		21 47	21 52		22 13	22 34	22 47
Rochdale	41	a																					
Deansgate	⇌	a				19 52					20 29			20 51			21 29			21 51			
Manchester Oxford Road		a				19 53		20 23			20 31			20 52	21 23		21 31			21 52			
Manchester Piccadilly 10	⇌	a				19 57		20 27			20 35			20 56	21 27		21 35			21 56			
Stockport	84	a																					
Hazel Grove	86	a																					
Buxton	86	a																					
Heald Green	85	a				20 11								21 10						22 10			
Manchester Airport	85 ✈	a				20 17		20 47			20 52			21 17	21 46		21 53			22 20			

A From Clitheroe
B From Glasgow Central
C From Blackburn
D From Edinburgh

The Sunday service between Wigan Wallgate and Manchester Victoria via Atherton is funded by TfGM and will operate whilst funding exists

Table 82R

Saturdays

15 February to 17 May

Barrow-in-Furness, Blackpool North, Preston, Southport, Kirkby and Wigan - Bolton - Manchester

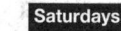

Network Diagram - see first Page of Table 82

		TP	TP	TP	NT	NT	NT	TP	NT		NT	NT	TP	NT	NT	NT
			◇1	1				◇1					◇1			
		A	B	A	B		C								C	
		🚌				🚌										
Barrow-in-Furness	d			21 43	21 43											
Roose	d			21 47	21 47											
Dalton	d			21 53	21 53											
Ulverston	d			22 01	22 01											
Cark	d			22 09	22 09											
Kents Bank	d			22 13	22 13											
Grange-over-Sands	d			22 17	22 17											
Arnside	d			22 23	22 23											
Silverdale	d			22 27	22 27											
Carnforth	d			22a35	22 35											
Windermere 83	d	21 40	21 40													
Oxenholme Lake District 65	d		22 00													
Lancaster 6 65	a	22s18	22 19		22 46											
	d					23 00										
Blackpool North 97	d							21 44				22 20	22 45			23 02
Layton 97	d											22 23				23 05
Poulton-le-Fylde 97	d							21 50				22 27	22 51			23 09
Kirkham & Wesham 97	d											22 37				23 19
Preston 8 65,97	a	23 00				23 40		22 08				22 47	23 09			23 29
	d							22 10				22 49	23 10			23 31
Leyland	d											22 54				23 36
Buckshaw Parkway	d							22 17				22 59	23 17			23 41
Chorley	d							22 21				23 03	23 21			23 45
Adlington (Lancashire)	d											23 08				23 50
Blackrod	d											23 12				23 54
Horwich Parkway	d							22 28				23 16	23 28			23 58
Lostock	d											23 20				00 02
Southport	d										22 18			23 10		
Meols Cop	d										22 23			23 15		
Bescar Lane	d										22 28					
New Lane	d										22 32					
Burscough Bridge	d										22 34			23 23		
Hoscar	d										22 38					
Parbold	d										22 41			23 28		
Appley Bridge	d										22 45			23 32		
Gathurst	d										22 48			23 35		
Kirkby	d															
Rainford	d															
Upholland	d															
Orrell	d															
Pemberton	d															
Wigan Wallgate	a										22 53			23 44		
	d								22 29		22 55					
Wigan North Western	d															
Ince	d								22 32							
Hindley	d								22 35		23 00					
Westhoughton	d										23 04					
Bolton	a							22 34			23 12	23 25	23 34			00 07
	d						22 31	22 35			23 13	23 25	23 35		23 38	00 07
Moses Gate	d															
Farnworth	d															
Kearsley	d															
Clifton	d															
Daisy Hill	d								22 39							
Hag Fold	d								22 42							
Atherton	d								22 45							
Walkden	d								22 51							
Moorside	d								22 54							
Swinton	d								22 57							
Salford Crescent	a						22 43	22 47	23 04		23 25	23 38	23 47		23 50	
	d						22 44	22 47	23 05		23 26	23 38	23 47		23 53	
Salford Central	d						22 46		23 07							
Manchester Victoria ⇌	a						22 52		23 13			23 47			00 01	00 26
Rochdale 41	a															
Deansgate ⇌	a							22 51			23 29					
Manchester Oxford Road	a							22 52			23 31					
Manchester Piccadilly 10 ⇌	a							22 57			23 39		23 55			
Stockport 84	a															
Hazel Grove 86	a															
Buxton 86	a															
Heald Green 85	a							23 10					00 16			
Manchester Airport 85 ✈	a							23 17					00 23			

A from 29 March **B** until 22 March **C** From Clitheroe

The Sunday service between Wigan Wallgate and Manchester Victoria via Atherton is funded by TfGM and will operate whilst funding exists

Table 82R

Sundays
8 December to 29 December

Barrow-in-Furness, Blackpool North, Preston, Southport, Kirkby and Wigan - Bolton - Manchester

Network Diagram - see first Page of Table 82

Station		NT	TP	TP	TP	NT	NT	NT	TP	NT	NT	NT	NT	TP	NT	NT	TP	NT	NT	NT	TP	NT	NT
					◇1				◇1					◇1			◇1				◇1		
		A				B		C					D			B			E	D			
Barrow-in-Furness	d																09 17						
Roose	d																09 21						
Dalton	d																09 28						
Ulverston	d																09 36						
Cark	d																09 44						
Kents Bank	d																09 48						
Grange-over-Sands	d																09 52						
Arnside	d																09 58						
Silverdale	d																10 02						
Carnforth	d																10 09		10 31				
Windermere 83	d																						
Oxenholme Lake District 65	d																						
Lancaster 6 65	a																10 17		10 40				
	d																10 24						
Blackpool North 97	d		03 20	05 20	07 48		08 20		08 44			09 20		09 44				10 20			10 44		
Layton 97	d						08 23					09 23						10 23					
Poulton-le-Fylde 97	d				07 54		08 27		08 50			09 27		09 50				10 27			10 50		
Kirkham & Wesham 97	d						08 37					09 37						10 37					
Preston 8 65,97	a				08 12		08 47		09 08			09 47		10 08			10 42	10 47			11 08		
	d		04u00	06u00	08 13		08 49		09 10			09 49		10 10			10 47	10 49			11 11		
Leyland	d						08 54					09 54						10 54					
Buckshaw Parkway	d						08 59		09 17			09 59		10 17				10 59			11 18		
Chorley	d				08 23		09 03		09 21			10 03		10 21			10 57	11 03			11 22		
Adlington (Lancashire)	d						09 08					10 08						11 08					
Blackrod	d						09 12					10 12						11 12					
Horwich Parkway	d				08 30		09 16		09 28			10 16		10 28				11 16			11 29		
Lostock	d	00 02					09 20					10 20						11 20					
Southport	d										09 10					10 05							11 05
Meols Cop	d										09 15					10 10							11 10
Bescar Lane	d																						
New Lane	d																						
Burscough Bridge	d										09 23					10 18							11 18
Hoscar	d																						
Parbold	d										09 28					10 23							11 23
Appley Bridge	d										09 32					10 27							11 27
Gathurst	d										09 35					10 30							11 30
Kirkby	d																						
Rainford	d																						
Upholland	d																						
Orrell	d																						
Pemberton	d																						
Wigan Wallgate	a										09 40					10 35							11 35
	d					08 40				09 15	09 41				10 15	10 36						11 15	11 36
Wigan North Western	d																						
Ince	d									09 18					10 18							11 18	
Hindley	d					08 45				09 22	09 46				10 22	10 41						11 22	11 41
Westhoughton	d					08 49					09 51					10 46							11 46
Bolton	a	00 07			08 37	08 57	09 25		09 34		09 59	10 25		10 34		10 54	11 08	11 25			11 35		11 54
	d	00 07	04u35	06u35	08 37	08 58	09 25	09 31	09 35		09 59	10 25	10 31	10 36		10 54	11 09	11 25		11 31	11 36		11 54
Moses Gate	d																						
Farnworth	d																						
Kearsley	d																						
Clifton	d																						
Daisy Hill	d									09 26					10 26							11 26	
Hag Fold	d									09 29					10 29							11 29	
Atherton	d									09 31					10 31							11 31	
Walkden	d									09 37					10 37							11 37	
Moorside	d									09 41					10 40							11 40	
Swinton	d									09 43					10 43							11 43	
Salford Crescent	a				08 49		09 38	09 43	09 47	09 51	10 12	10 38	10 43	10 48	10 50	11 07		11 38		11 43	11 48	11 50	12 07
	d				08 50		09 38	09 44	09 47	09 51	10 12	10 38	10 44	10 48	10 51	11 07		11 38		11 44	11 48	11 51	12 07
Salford Central	d																						
Manchester Victoria ⇌	a	00 26					09 45	09 52		09 57		10 45	10 52		10 57			11 45		11 52		11 57	
Rochdale 41	a																						
Deansgate ⇌	a				08 53	09 14			09 51		10 16			10 52		11 11					11 52		12 11
Manchester Oxford Road	a				08 55	09 17			09 52		10 18			10 53		11 13	11 23				11 53		12 13
Manchester Piccadilly 10 ⇌	a		05b00	07b00	08 59	09 21			09 56		10 22			10 57		11 19	11 27				11 57		12 19
Stockport 84	a					09 31					10 33					11 30							12 33
Hazel Grove 86	a																						12 42
Buxton 86	a																						
Heald Green 85	a																						
Manchester Airport 85 ✈	a		05 25	07 25	09 14				10 15					11 12			11 47				12 14		

A not 8 December. From Blackpool North
B To Chester
C From Blackburn
D From Clitheroe
E From Leeds to Morecambe
b Stops to pick up only

The Sunday service between Wigan Wallgate and Manchester Victoria via Atherton is funded by TfGM and will operate whilst funding exists

Table 82R

Sundays

8 December to 29 December

Barrow-in-Furness, Blackpool North, Preston, Southport, Kirkby and Wigan - Bolton - Manchester

Network Diagram - see first Page of Table 82

		TP	NT	NT	TP	NT	NT	TP	NT	NT	NT	TP	NT	NT	TP	NT	NT	NT	TP	NT	NT	TP	NT
		◇1			◇1			◇1				◇1			◇1				◇1			◇1	
				A			B	C		D	A							A			B	C	
								🚲														🚲	
Barrow-in-Furness	d	10 25													12 33	13 10							
Roose	d	10 29														13 14							
Dalton	d	10 36														13 20							
Ulverston	d	10 44													12 49	13 29							
Cark	d	10 52														13 36							
Kents Bank	d	10 56														13 41							
Grange-over-Sands	d	11 00													13 01	13 45							
Arnside	d	11 06													13 07	13 51							
Silverdale	d	11 10														13 55							
Carnforth	d	11 17								12 35					13 17	14 03							
Windermere 83	d																						
Oxenholme Lake District 65	d							12 10														14 10	
Lancaster 6 65	a	11 25						12 24		12 44					13 25	14 15						14 24	
	d	11 25						12 25							13 25							14 25	
Blackpool North 97	d		11 20		11 44				12 20			12 44					13 20		13 44				14 20
Layton 97	d		11 23						12 23								13 23						14 23
Poulton-le-Fylde 97	d		11 27		11 50				12 27			12 50					13 27		13 50				14 27
Kirkham & Wesham 97	d		11 37						12 37								13 37						14 37
Preston 8 65,97	a	11 44	11 47		12 08			12 43	12 47			13 08			13 44		13 47		14 08			14 43	14 47
	d	11 49	11 49		12 10			12 45	12 50			13 11			13 45		13 50		14 11			14 45	14 50
Leyland	d		11 54						12 55								13 55						14 55
Buckshaw Parkway	d		11 59		12 17				13 00			13 18					14 00		14 18				15 00
Chorley	d	11 58	12 03		12 21				13 04			13 22					14 04		14 22				15 04
Adlington (Lancashire)	d		12 08						13 09								14 09						15 09
Blackrod	d		12 12						13 12								14 12						15 12
Horwich Parkway	d		12 16		12 28				13 16			13 29					14 16		14 29				15 16
Lostock	d		12 20						13 20								14 20						15 20
Southport	d						12 05							13 05							14 05		
Meols Cop	d						12 10							13 10							14 10		
Bescar Lane	d																						
New Lane	d																						
Burscough Bridge	d						12 18							13 18							14 18		
Hoscar	d																						
Parbold	d						12 23							13 23							14 23		
Appley Bridge	d						12 27							13 27							14 27		
Gathurst	d						12 30							13 30							14 30		
Kirkby	d																						
Rainford	d																						
Upholland	d																						
Orrell	d																						
Pemberton	d																						
Wigan Wallgate	a						12 35							13 35							14 35		
	d					12 15	12 36						13 15	13 36						14 15	14 36		
Wigan North Western	d							12 58							13 58							14 58	
Ince	d					12 18							13 18							14 18			
Hindley	d					12 22	12 41						13 22	13 41						14 22	14 41		
Westhoughton	d						12 46							13 46							14 46		
Bolton	a	12 09	12 25		12 34		12 54		13 25			13 35		13 54			14 25		14 35		14 54		15 25
	d	12 10	12 25	12 31	12 35		12 54		13 25		13 31	13 36		13 54			14 25	14 31	14 36		14 54		15 26
Moses Gate	d																						
Farnworth	d																						
Kearsley	d																						
Clifton	d																						
Daisy Hill	d					12 26							13 26							14 26			
Hag Fold	d					12 29							13 29							14 29			
Atherton	d					12 31							13 31							14 31			
Walkden	d					12 37							13 37							14 37			
Moorside	d					12 40							13 40							14 40			
Swinton	d					12 43							13 43							14 43			
Salford Crescent	a		12 38	12 43	12 47	12 50	13 07		13 38		13 43	13 48	13 50	14 07			14 38	14 43	14 48	14 50	15 07		15 38
	d		12 38	12 44	12 47	12 51	13 07		13 38		13 44	13 48	13 51	14 07			14 38	14 44	14 48	14 51	15 07		15 38
Salford Central	d																						
Manchester Victoria 🚊	a		12 45	12 52		12 57			13 45		13 52		13 57				14 45	14 52		14 57			15 45
Rochdale 41	a																						
Deansgate 🚊	a				12 51		13 11					13 52		14 11					14 52		15 11		
Manchester Oxford Road	a	12 24			12 52		13 13	13 23				13 53		14 13	14 23				14 53		15 13	15 23	
Manchester Piccadilly 10 🚊	a	12 28			12 56		13 19	13 27				13 57		14 19	14 27				14 57		15 19	15 27	
Stockport 84	a						13 30							14 33							15 31		
Hazel Grove 86	a													14 42									
Buxton 86	a																						
Heald Green 85	a																						
Manchester Airport 85 ✈	a	12 46			13 14			13 47				14 14			14 47				15 13			15 47	

A From Clitheroe
B To Chester
C From Edinburgh
D From Leeds to Morecambe

The Sunday service between Wigan Wallgate and Manchester Victoria via Atherton is funded by TfGM and will operate whilst funding exists

Table 82R

Sundays

8 December to 29 December

Barrow-in-Furness, Blackpool North, Preston, Southport, Kirkby and Wigan - Bolton - Manchester

Network Diagram - see first Page of Table 82

Station			NT	TP	NT	NT	TP	NT	NT	TP	NT	NT	TP	NT	NT	NT	TP	NT	NT	TP	NT	NT	TP
				◇1			◇1			◇1			◇1				◇1			◇1			◇1
			A						A			B	C		D	A				E		A	
Barrow-in-Furness		d					14 25																
Roose		d					14 29																
Dalton		d					14 36																
Ulverston		d					14 44																
Cark		d					14 52																
Kents Bank		d					14 56																
Grange-over-Sands		d					15 00																
Arnside		d					15 06																
Silverdale		d					15 10																
Carnforth		d					15 17								16 37								
Windermere	83	d																					
Oxenholme Lake District	65	d											16 10							17 09			
Lancaster 6	65	a					15 25						16 24		16 46					17 23			
		d					15 25						16 25							17 24			
Blackpool North	97	d		14 44				15 20		15 44				16 20			16 44				17 20		17 44
Layton	97	d						15 23						16 23							17 23		
Poulton-le-Fylde	97	d		14 50				15 27		15 50				16 27			16 50				17 27		17 50
Kirkham & Wesham	97	d						15 37						16 37							17 37		
Preston 8	65,97	a		15 08			15 44	15 47		16 08			16 43	16 47			17 08			17 42	17 47		18 08
		d		15 10			15 45	15 49		16 11			16 45	16 49			17 10			17 45	17 49		18 10
Leyland		d						15 54						16 54							17 54		
Buckshaw Parkway		d		15 17				15 59		16 18				16 59			17 17				17 59		18 17
Chorley		d		15 21				16 03		16 22				17 03			17 21				18 03		18 21
Adlington (Lancashire)		d						16 08						17 08							18 08		
Blackrod		d						16 11						17 12							18 12		
Horwich Parkway		d		15 28				16 15		16 29				17 16			17 28				18 16		18 28
Lostock		d						16 20						17 20							18 20		
Southport		d				15 05						16 05							17 05				
Meols Cop		d				15 10						16 10							17 10				
Bescar Lane		d																					
New Lane		d																					
Burscough Bridge		d				15 18						16 18							17 18				
Hoscar		d																					
Parbold		d				15 23						16 23							17 23				
Appley Bridge		d				15 27						16 27							17 27				
Gathurst		d				15 30						16 30							17 30				
Kirkby		d																					
Rainford		d																					
Upholland		d																					
Orrell		d																					
Pemberton		d																					
Wigan Wallgate		a				15 35						16 35							17 35				
		d			15 15	15 36					16 15	16 36						17 15	17 36				
Wigan North Western		d					15 58						16 58							17 58			
Ince		d			15 18						16 18							17 18					
Hindley		d			15 22	15 41					16 22	16 41						17 22	17 41				
Westhoughton		d				15 46						16 46							17 46				
Bolton		a		15 34		15 54		16 25		16 35		16 54		17 25			17 34		17 54		18 25		18 34
		d	15 31	15 35		15 54		16 25	16 31	16 36		16 54		17 25		17 31	17 35		17 54		18 25	18 31	18 35
Moses Gate		d																					
Farnworth		d																					
Kearsley		d																					
Clifton		d																					
Daisy Hill		d			15 26						16 26							17 26					
Hag Fold		d			15 29						16 29							17 29					
Atherton		d			15 31						16 31							17 31					
Walkden		d			15 37						16 37							17 37					
Moorside		d			15 40						16 40							17 40					
Swinton		d			15 43						16 43							17 43					
Salford Crescent		a	15 43	15 47	15 50	16 07		16 38	16 43	16 48	16 50	17 07		17 38		17 43	17 47	17 50	18 07		18 38	18 43	18 47
		d	15 44	15 47	15 51	16 07		16 38	16 44	16 48	16 51	17 07		17 38		17 44	17 47	17 51	18 07		18 38	18 44	18 47
Salford Central		d																					
Manchester Victoria	⇌	a	15 52		15 57			16 45	16 52		16 57			17 45		17 52		17 57			18 45	18 52	
Rochdale	41	a																					
Deansgate	⇌	a		15 51		16 11				16 52		17 11					17 51		18 11				18 51
Manchester Oxford Road		a		15 52		16 13	16 23			16 53		17 13	17 23				17 52		18 13	18 23			18 52
Manchester Piccadilly 10	⇌	a		15 56		16 19	16 27			16 57		17 19	17 27				17 56		18 19	18 27			18 56
Stockport	84	a				16 32						17 30							18 31				
Hazel Grove	86	a				16 42													18 42				
Buxton	86	a																					
Heald Green	85	a																					
Manchester Airport	85 ✈	a		16 12			16 47			17 13			17 47				18 12			18 47			19 12

A From Clitheroe
B To Chester
C From Edinburgh
D From Leeds to Morecambe
E From Glasgow Central

The Sunday service between Wigan Wallgate and Manchester Victoria via Atherton is funded by TfGM and will operate whilst funding exists

Table 82R

Sundays

8 December to 29 December

Barrow-in-Furness, Blackpool North, Preston, Southport, Kirkby and Wigan - Bolton - Manchester

Network Diagram - see first Page of Table 82

		NT	TP	NT	NT	TP	NT	TP		NT	TP	NT	NT	TP	NT	TP	NT	NT		TP	NT	TP	NT	NT	NT
			◇**1**			◇**1**		◇**1**			◇**1**			◇**1**		◇**1**				◇**1**		◇**1**			
		A	B		C		D				E		D		A	B				F	D				D
			🛒								🛒					🛒									
Barrow-in-Furness	d					18 17											19 48								
Roose	d					18 21											19 52								
Dalton	d					18 28											19 58								
Ulverston	d					18 36											20 07								
Cark	d					18 44											20 14								
Kents Bank	d					18 48											20 19								
Grange-over-Sands	d					18 52											20 23								
Arnside	d					18 58											20 29								
Silverdale	d					19 02											20 33								
Carnforth	d				19 04	19 09											20 41								
Windermere 83	d																			20 40					
Oxenholme Lake District 65	d		18 10								19 09					20 10				21 00					
Lancaster 6 65	a		18 24		19 13	19 17					19 24					20 24	20 52			21 18					
	d		18 25			19 17					19 24					20 25									
Blackpool North 97	d			18 20				18 44				19 20		19 44				20 20				20 44		21 20	
Layton 97	d			18 23								19 23						20 23						21 23	
Poulton-le-Fylde 97	d			18 27				18 50				19 27		19 50				20 27				20 50		21 27	
Kirkham & Wesham 97	d			18 37								19 37						20 37						21 37	
Preston 8 65,97	a		18 43	18 47		19 37		19 08			19 44	19 47		20 08		20 43		20 47				21 08		21 47	
	d		18 45	18 49				19 10			19 45	19 49		20 10		20 46		20 49				21 10		21 49	
Leyland	d			18 54								19 54						20 54						21 54	
Buckshaw Parkway	d			18 59				19 17				19 59		20 17				20 59				21 17		21 59	
Chorley	d			19 03				19 21				20 03		20 21				21 03				21 21		22 03	
Adlington (Lancashire)	d			19 08								20 08						21 08						22 08	
Blackrod	d			19 12								20 12						21 12						22 12	
Horwich Parkway	d			19 16				19 28				20 16		20 28				21 16				21 28		22 16	
Lostock	d			19 20								20 20						21 20						22 20	
Southport	d	18 05								19 05					20 05								21 05		
Meols Cop	d	18 10								19 10					20 10								21 10		
Bescar Lane	d																								
New Lane	d																								
Burscough Bridge	d	18 18								19 18					20 18								21 18		
Hoscar	d																								
Parbold	d	18 23								19 23					20 23								21 23		
Appley Bridge	d	18 27								19 27					20 27								21 27		
Gathurst	d	18 30								19 30					20 30								21 30		
Kirkby	d																								
Rainford	d																								
Upholland	d																								
Orrell	d																								
Pemberton	d																								
Wigan Wallgate	a	18 35								19 35					20 35								21 35		
	d	18 36								19 36					20 36								21 36		
Wigan North Western	d		18 58								19 59														
Ince	d																								
Hindley	d	18 41								19 41					20 41								21 41		
Westhoughton	d	18 46								19 46					20 46								21 46		
Bolton	a	18 54		19 25				19 34		19 54		20 25		20 34	20 54			21 25				21 34	21 54	22 25	
	d	18 54		19 25			19 31	19 35		19 54		20 25	20 31	20 35	20 54			21 25			21 31	21 35	21 54	22 25	22 31
Moses Gate	d																								
Farnworth	d																								
Kearsley	d																								
Clifton	d																								
Daisy Hill	d																								
Hag Fold	d																								
Atherton	d																								
Walkden	d																								
Moorside	d																								
Swinton	d																								
Salford Crescent	a	19 08		19 38			19 43	19 47		20 07		20 38	20 43	20 47	21 07			21 38			21 43	21 47	22 07	22 38	22 43
	d	19 09		19 38			19 44	19 47		20 07		20 38	20 44	20 47	21 07			21 38			21 44	21 47	22 07	22 38	22 44
Salford Central	d																								
Manchester Victoria 🚊	a			19 45			19 51					20 45	20 52					21 45			21 52			22 45	22 52
Rochdale 41	a																								
Deansgate 🚊	a	19 12						19 51		20 11				20 51	21 11							21 51	22 11		
Manchester Oxford Road	a	19 15	19 23					19 52		20 13	20 23			20 52	21 13	21 21						21 52	22 13		
Manchester Piccadilly 10 🚊	a	19 19	19 27					19 56		20 19	20 27			20 56	21 19	21 25						21 56	22 19		
Stockport 84	a	19 30								20 32					21 30								22 32		
Hazel Grove 86	a									20 42													22 42		
Buxton 86	a																								
Heald Green 85	a																								
Manchester Airport 85 ✈	a		19 47					20 12			20 45			21 12		21 45						22 12			

A To Chester
B From Edinburgh
C From Leeds to Morecambe
D From Clitheroe
E From Glasgow Central
F To Barrow-in-Furness

The Sunday service between Wigan Wallgate and Manchester Victoria via Atherton is funded by TfGM and will operate whilst funding exists

Table 82R

Sundays

8 December to 29 December

Barrow-in-Furness, Blackpool North, Preston, Southport, Kirkby and Wigan - Bolton - Manchester

Network Diagram - see first Page of Table 82

		TP	TP	NT	NT	TP
		◇1	◇1			◇1
			A		B	
			✠			
Barrow-in-Furness	d					
Roose	d					
Dalton	d					
Ulverston	d					
Cark	d					
Kents Bank	d					
Grange-over-Sands	d					
Arnside	d					
Silverdale	d					
Carnforth	d					
Windermere	83 d					
Oxenholme Lake District	65 d		21 51			
Lancaster 6	65 a		22 06			
	d		22 06			
Blackpool North	97 d	21 44				23 02
Layton	97 d					
Poulton-le-Fylde	97 d	21 50				23 08
Kirkham & Wesham	97 d					23 17
Preston 8	65,97 a	22 08	22 25			23 28
	d	22 10	22 26			23 29
Leyland	d					23 34
Buckshaw Parkway	d	22 17				23 38
Chorley	d	22 21				23 42
Adlington (Lancashire)	d					23 46
Blackrod	d					23 50
Horwich Parkway	d	22 28				23 53
Lostock	d					23 57
Southport	d			22 05		
Meols Cop	d			22 10		
Bescar Lane	d					
New Lane	d					
Burscough Bridge	d			22 18		
Hoscar	d					
Parbold	d			22 23		
Appley Bridge	d			22 27		
Gathurst	d			22 30		
Kirkby	d					
Rainford	d					
Upholland	d					
Orrell	d					
Pemberton	d					
Wigan Wallgate	a			22 35		
	d			22 36		
Wigan North Western	d		22 39			
Ince	d					
Hindley	d			22 41		
Westhoughton	d			22 46		
Bolton	a	22 34		22 54		00 02
	d	22 35		22 54	23 31	00 02
Moses Gate	d					
Farnworth	d					
Kearsley	d					
Clifton	d					
Daisy Hill	d					
Hag Fold	d					
Atherton	d					
Walkden	d					
Moorside	d					
Swinton	d					
Salford Crescent	a	22 47		23 07	23 43	
	d	22 47		23 07	23 44	
Salford Central	d					
Manchester Victoria	⇌ a				23 52	
Rochdale	41 a					
Deansgate	⇌ a	22 51		23 11		
Manchester Oxford Road	a	22 52	23 04	23 15		
Manchester Piccadilly 10	⇌ a	22 56	23 08	23 19		00 18
Stockport	84 a			23 34		
Hazel Grove	86 a					
Buxton	86 a					
Heald Green	85 a					
Manchester Airport	85 ✈ a	23 15	23 24			00 35

A From Edinburgh

B From Clitheroe

The Sunday service between Wigan Wallgate and Manchester Victoria via Atherton is funded by TfGM and will operate whilst funding exists

Table 82R

Sundays
5 January to 9 February

Barrow-in-Furness, Blackpool North, Preston, Southport, Kirkby and Wigan - Bolton - Manchester

Network Diagram - see first Page of Table 82

		NT	TP	TP	TP	NT	TP	NT	TP	NT		TP	TP	NT	NT	NT	NT	NT	TP	TP		VT	NT	TP	TP
							◇1					◇1	◇1							◇1				◇1	◇1
		A				B		B		C				D	B								E		
		🚌	🚌	🚌	🚌	🚌		🚌	🚌						🚌				🚌			🚌			
Barrow-in-Furness	d												09 17												10 25
Roose	d												09 21												10 29
Dalton	d												09 28												10 36
Ulverston	d												09 36												10 44
Cark	d												09 44												10 52
Kents Bank	d												09 48												10 56
Grange-over-Sands	d												09 52												11 00
Arnside	d												09 58												11 06
Silverdale	d												10 02												11 10
Carnforth	d												10 09										10 31		11 17
Windermere 83	d																								
Oxenholme Lake District 65	d																								
Lancaster 6 65	a												10 17										10 40		11 25
	d												10 24											10 53	11 25
Blackpool North 97	d		03 20	05 20																					
Layton 97	d																								
Poulton-le-Fylde 97	d																								
Kirkham & Wesham 97	d																								
Preston 8 65,97	a												10 42											11 11	11 44
	d		04u00	06u00	07 50				08 20										09 20			09 30			
Leyland	d	00 01																							
Buckshaw Parkway	d	00 12																							
Chorley	d	00s22			08a15		08 23		08a45			08 52					09 24		09a45	09 52					
Adlington (Lancashire)	d	00s28															09 28								
Blackrod	d	00s33															09 32								
Horwich Parkway	d	00s37					08 30					08 59					09 36			09 59					
Lostock	d	00s43															09 40								
Southport	d																	09 10							
Meols Cop	d																	09 15							
Bescar Lane	d																								
New Lane	d																								
Burscough Bridge	d																	09 23							
Hoscar	d																								
Parbold	d																	09 28							
Appley Bridge	d																	09 32							
Gathurst	d																	09 35							
Kirkby	d																								
Rainford	d																								
Upholland	d																								
Orrell	d																								
Pemberton	d																								
Wigan Wallgate	a																	09 40							
	d									08 40						09 15		09 41							
Wigan North Western	d																					10a15			
Ince	d															09 18									
Hindley	d									08 45						09 22		09 46							
Westhoughton	d									08 49								09 51							
Bolton	a	00s58					08 37			08 57		09 05					09 45	09 59		10 05					
	d		04u35	06u35			08 37			08 58		09 06		09 31			09 45	09 59		10 06					
Moses Gate	d																								
Farnworth	d																								
Kearsley	d																								
Clifton	d																								
Daisy Hill	d															09 26									
Hag Fold	d															09 29									
Atherton	d															09 31									
Walkden	d															09 37									
Moorside	d															09 41									
Swinton	d															09 43									
Salford Crescent	a	01s23					08 49					09 18		09 43		09 51	09 58	10 12		10 18					
	d					07 50	08 50	08 50				09 18		09 44	09 50	09 53	09 58	10 12		10 18					
Salford Central	d																								
Manchester Victoria ⛴	a	01 33				08 00		09 00							10 00										
Rochdale 41	a																								
Deansgate ⛴	a						08 53			09 14		09 22						10 16		10 22					
Manchester Oxford Road	a						08 55			09 17		09 23		09 49		10 00	10 04	10 18		10 23					
Manchester Piccadilly 10 ⛴	a		05b00	07b00			08 59			09 21		09 27						10 22		10 30					
Stockport 84	a									09 31								10 33							
Hazel Grove 86	a																								
Buxton 86	a																								
Heald Green 85	a																								
Manchester Airport 85 ✈	a		05 25	07 25			09 14					09 47								10 46					

A From Preston
B To Salford Crescent
C To Chester
D From Blackburn
E From Leeds to Morecambe
b Stops to pick up only

The Sunday service between Wigan Wallgate and Manchester Victoria via Atherton is funded by TfGM and will operate whilst funding exists

Table 82R

Sundays

5 January to 9 February

Barrow-in-Furness, Blackpool North, Preston, Southport, Kirkby and Wigan - Bolton - Manchester

Network Diagram - see first Page of Table 82

Station			NT	NT	NT	NT	NT	TP	TP	VT	NT	NT	NT	NT	NT	TP	TP	VT	NT	NT	NT	NT	NT	TP
									◇1								◇1							
			A	B			C				A	B							A	B			C	
Barrow-in-Furness		d																						
Roose		d																						
Dalton		d																						
Ulverston		d																						
Cark		d																						
Kents Bank		d																						
Grange-over-Sands		d																						
Arnside		d																						
Silverdale		d																						
Carnforth		d																						
Windermere	83	d																						
Oxenholme Lake District	65	d																						
Lancaster 6	65	a																						
		d																						
Blackpool North	97	d																						
Layton	97	d																						
Poulton-le-Fylde	97	d																						
Kirkham & Wesham	97	d																						
Preston 8	65,97	a																						
		d						10 20		10 30						11 20		11 30						12 20
Leyland		d																						
Buckshaw Parkway		d																						
Chorley		d				10 24		10a45	10 52					11 24		11a45	11 52					12 24		12a45
Adlington (Lancashire)		d				10 28								11 28								12 28		
Blackrod		d				10 32								11 32								12 32		
Horwich Parkway		d				10 36			10 59					11 36			11 59					12 36		
Lostock		d				10 40								11 40								12 40		
Southport		d					10 05								11 05								12 05	
Meols Cop		d					10 10								11 10								12 10	
Bescar Lane		d																						
New Lane		d																						
Burscough Bridge		d					10 18								11 18								12 18	
Hoscar		d																						
Parbold		d					10 23								11 23								12 23	
Appley Bridge		d					10 27								11 27								12 27	
Gathurst		d					10 30								11 30								12 30	
Kirkby		d																						
Rainford		d																						
Upholland		d																						
Orrell		d																						
Pemberton		d																						
Wigan Wallgate		a					10 35								11 35								12 35	
		d			10 15		10 36						11 15		11 36						12 18		12 36	
Wigan North Western		d								11a15								12a15						
Ince		d			10 18								11 18								12 21			
Hindley		d			10 22		10 41						11 22		11 41						12 25		12 41	
Westhoughton		d					10 46								11 46								12 46	
Bolton		a				10 45	10 54		11 05					11 45	11 54		12 05					12 45	12 54	
		d	10 32			10 45	10 54		11 06		11 32			11 45	11 54		12 06		12 32			12 45	12 54	
Moses Gate		d																						
Farnworth		d																						
Kearsley		d																						
Clifton		d																						
Daisy Hill		d			10 26								11 26								12 29			
Hag Fold		d			10 29								11 29								12 32			
Atherton		d			10 31								11 31								12 34			
Walkden		d			10 37								11 37								12 40			
Moorside		d			10 41								11 41								12 44			
Swinton		d			10 43								11 43								12 46			
Salford Crescent		a	10 44		10 51	10 58	11 07		11 18		11 44		11 51	11 58	12 07		12 18		12 44		12 54	12 58	13 07	
		d	10 45	10 50	10 53	10 58	11 07		11 18		11 45	11 50	11 53	11 58	12 07		12 18		12 45	12 50	12 54	12 58	13 07	
Salford Central		d																						
Manchester Victoria	⇌	a		11 00								12 00								13 00				
Rochdale	41	a																						
Deansgate	⇌	a					11 11		11 22						12 11		12 22						13 11	
Manchester Oxford Road		a	10 50		11 00	11 04	11 13		11 23		11 50		12 00	12 04	12 13		12 23		12 50		13 00	13 04	13 13	
Manchester Piccadilly 10	⇌	a					11 19		11 27						12 19		12 27						13 19	
Stockport	84	a					11 30								12 33								13 30	
Hazel Grove	86	a													12 42									
Buxton	86	a																						
Heald Green	85	a																						
Manchester Airport	85 ✈	a							11 47								12 47							

A From Clitheroe B To Salford Crescent C To Chester

The Sunday service between Wigan Wallgate and Manchester Victoria via Atherton is funded by TfGM and will operate whilst funding exists

Table 82R

Sundays

5 January to 9 February

Barrow-in-Furness, Blackpool North, Preston, Southport, Kirkby and Wigan - Bolton - Manchester

Network Diagram - see first Page of Table 82

		TP	VT	TP	TP	NT	NT	NT	NT	NT	TP	TP	VT	TP	NT	TP	TP	NT	VT	NT	NT	NT
		◇1			◇1							◇1				◇1						
						A	B						C		D				E	A	B	
			🚌	🚌			🚌				🚌		🚌	🚌			🚌		🚌		🚌	
Barrow-in-Furness	d															12 33		13 10				
Roose	d																	13 14				
Dalton	d																	13 20				
Ulverston	d															12 49		13 29				
Cark	d																	13 36				
Kents Bank	d																	13 41				
Grange-over-Sands	d															13 01		13 45				
Arnside	d															13 07		13 51				
Silverdale	d																	13 55				
Carnforth	d														12 35	13 17		14 03				
Windermere 83	d			10 50										11 40			12 40					
Oxenholme Lake District 65	d																		13 33			
Lancaster 6 65	a			11 54										12 44	12 44	13 25	13 44	14 15	14 18			
	d		11 35		12 26								12 35			13 25						
Blackpool North 97	d																					
Layton 97	d																					
Poulton-le-Fylde 97	d																					
Kirkham & Wesham 97	d																					
Preston 8 65,97	a		12 25		12 42								13 25			13 44						
	d		12 30								13 20		13 30									
Leyland	d																					
Buckshaw Parkway	d																					
Chorley	d	12 52							13 24		13a45	13 52										
Adlington (Lancashire)	d								13 29													
Blackrod	d								13 32													
Horwich Parkway	d	12 59							13 36			13 59										
Lostock	d								13 40													
Southport	d									13 05												
Meols Cop	d									13 10												
Bescar Lane	d																					
New Lane	d																					
Burscough Bridge	d									13 18												
Hoscar	d																					
Parbold	d									13 23												
Appley Bridge	d									13 27												
Gathurst	d									13 30												
Kirkby	d																					
Rainford	d																					
Upholland	d																					
Orrell	d																					
Pemberton	d																					
Wigan Wallgate	a									13 35												
	d							13 18		13 36												14 18
Wigan North Western	d		13a15										14a15									
Ince	d							13 21														14 21
Hindley	d							13 25		13 41												14 25
Westhoughton	d									13 46												
Bolton	a	13 05							13 45	13 54		14 05										
	d	13 06				13 32			13 45	13 54		14 06								14 32		
Moses Gate	d																					
Farnworth	d																					
Kearsley	d																					
Clifton	d																					
Daisy Hill	d							13 29														14 29
Hag Fold	d							13 32														14 32
Atherton	d							13 34														14 34
Walkden	d							13 40														14 40
Moorside	d							13 44														14 44
Swinton	d							13 46														14 46
Salford Crescent	a	13 18				13 44		13 54	13 58	14 07		14 18								14 44		14 54
	d	13 18				13 45	13 50	13 54	13 58	14 07		14 18								14 45	14 50	14 54
Salford Central	d																					
Manchester Victoria 🚊	a						14 00														15 00	
Rochdale 41	a																					
Deansgate 🚊	a	13 22								14 11		14 22										
Manchester Oxford Road	a	13 23				13 50		14 00	14 04	14 13		14 23								14 50		15 00
Manchester Piccadilly 10 🚊	a	13 27								14 19		14 27										
Stockport 84	a									14 33												
Hazel Grove 86	a									14 42												
Buxton 86	a																					
Heald Green 85	a																					
Manchester Airport 85 ✈	a	13 47										14 47										

A From Clitheroe
B To Salford Crescent
C From Penrith North Lakes
D From Leeds to Morecambe
E From Carlisle

The Sunday service between Wigan Wallgate and Manchester Victoria via Atherton is funded by TfGM and will operate whilst funding exists

Table 82R

Sundays

5 January to 9 February

Barrow-in-Furness, Blackpool North, Preston, Southport, Kirkby and Wigan - Bolton - Manchester

Network Diagram - see first Page of Table 82

		NT	NT	TP	TP	TP	NT	VT	VT	NT	TP	NT	NT	NT	TP	NT	NT	TP	NT	NT	NT	TP	NT
					◇1						◇1				◇1			◇1				◇1	
			A					B	C	D		E					D		E		A	F	
				bus	cycle	bus		bus	bus			bus							bus			cycle	
Barrow-in-Furness	d														14 25								
Roose	d														14 29								
Dalton	d														14 36								
Ulverston	d														14 44								
Cark	d														14 52								
Kents Bank	d														14 56								
Grange-over-Sands	d														15 00								
Arnside	d														15 06								
Silverdale	d														15 10								
Carnforth	d														15 17								
Windermere 83	d					13 40																	
Oxenholme Lake District 65	d							14 30	14 40													16 10	
Lancaster 6 65	a					14 44		15 15	15 25						15 25							16 24	
	d				14 24										15 25							16 25	
Blackpool North 97	d						14 20				14 44					15 20		15 44					16 20
Layton 97	d						14 23									15 23							16 23
Poulton-le-Fylde 97	d						14 27				14 50					15 27		15 50					16 27
Kirkham & Wesham 97	d						14 37									15 37							16 37
Preston 8 65,97	a				14 43		14 47				15 08				15 44	15 47		16 08				16 43	16 47
	d			14 20	14 46		14 50				15 10				15 45	15 49		16 10				16 45	16 49
Leyland	d						14 55									15 54							16 54
Buckshaw Parkway	d						15 00				15 17					15 59		16 17					16 59
Chorley	d	14 24		14a45			15 04				15 21					16 03		16 21					17 03
Adlington (Lancashire)	d	14 29					15 09									16 08							17 08
Blackrod	d	14 32					15 12									16 11							17 12
Horwich Parkway	d	14 36					15 16				15 28					16 15		16 28					17 16
Lostock	d	14 40					15 20									16 20							17 20
Southport	d		14 05											15 05							16 05		
Meols Cop	d		14 10											15 10							16 10		
Bescar Lane	d																						
New Lane	d																						
Burscough Bridge	d		14 18											15 18							16 18		
Hoscar	d																						
Parbold	d		14 23											15 23							16 23		
Appley Bridge	d		14 27											15 27							16 27		
Gathurst	d		14 30											15 30							16 30		
Kirkby	d																						
Rainford	d																						
Upholland	d																						
Orrell	d																						
Pemberton	d																						
Wigan Wallgate	a		14 35											15 35							16 35		
	d		14 36										15 18	15 36						16 18	16 36		
Wigan North Western	d				15 00										15 58							16 58	
Ince	d												15 21							16 21			
Hindley	d		14 41										15 25	15 41						16 25	16 41		
Westhoughton	d		14 46											15 46							16 46		
Bolton	a	14 45	14 54				15 25				15 34			15 54		16 25		16 34			16 54		17 25
	d	14 45	14 54				15 26			15 32	15 35			15 54		16 25	16 32	16 35			16 54		17 25
Moses Gate	d																						
Farnworth	d																						
Kearsley	d																						
Clifton	d																						
Daisy Hill	d												15 29							16 29			
Hag Fold	d												15 32							16 32			
Atherton	d												15 34							16 34			
Walkden	d												15 40							16 40			
Moorside	d												15 44							16 44			
Swinton	d												15 46							16 46			
Salford Crescent	a	14 58	15 07				15 38			15 44	15 47		15 54	16 07		16 38	16 44	16 47		16 54	17 07		17 38
	d	14 58	15 07				15 38			15 45	15 47	15 50	15 54	16 07		16 38	16 45	16 47	16 50	16 54	17 07		17 38
Salford Central	d																						
Manchester Victoria ⇌	a											16 00							17 00				
Rochdale 41	a																						
Deansgate ⇌	a		15 11								15 51			16 11				16 51			17 11		
Manchester Oxford Road	a	15 04	15 13		15 24		15 44			15 50	15 52		16 00	16 13	16 23	16 44	16 50	16 52		17 00	17 13	17 23	17 44
Manchester Piccadilly 10 ⇌	a		15 19		15 28						15 56			16 19	16 27			16 56			17 19	17 27	
Stockport 84	a		15 31											16 32							17 30		
Hazel Grove 86	a													16 42									
Buxton 86	a																						
Heald Green 85	a																						
Manchester Airport 85 ✈	a				15 47						16 12				16 47			17 13				17 47	

A To Chester
B From Penrith North Lakes
C From Carlisle
D From Clitheroe
E To Salford Crescent
F From Edinburgh

The Sunday service between Wigan Wallgate and Manchester Victoria via Atherton is funded by TfGM and will operate whilst funding exists

Table 82R

Sundays

5 January to 9 February

Barrow-in-Furness, Blackpool North, Preston, Southport, Kirkby and Wigan - Bolton - Manchester

Network Diagram - see first Page of Table 82

Station		NT A	NT B	TP ◇1	NT C (bus)	NT	NT	TP ◇1 D (trolley)	NT	NT B	TP ◇1	NT C (bus)	NT E	TP ◇1 F (trolley)	NT	NT A	TP ◇1	NT B	TP ◇1	NT C (bus)	NT	TP ◇1 D (trolley)
Barrow-in-Furness	d																18 17					
Roose	d																18 21					
Dalton	d																18 28					
Ulverston	d																18 36					
Cark	d																18 44					
Kents Bank	d																18 48					
Grange-over-Sands	d																18 52					
Arnside	d																18 58					
Silverdale	d																19 02					
Carnforth	d	16 37														19 04	19 09					
Windermere 83	d																					
Oxenholme Lake District 65	d							17 09						18 10								19 09
Lancaster 6 65	a	16 46						17 23						18 24		19 13	19 17					19 24
	d							17 24						18 25			19 17					19 24
Blackpool North 97	d			16 44					17 20		17 44				18 20				18 44			
Layton 97	d								17 23						18 23							
Poulton-le-Fylde 97	d			16 50					17 27		17 50				18 27				18 50			
Kirkham & Wesham 97	d								17 37						18 37							
Preston 8 65,97	a			17 08				17 42	17 47		18 08			18 43	18 47		19 37		19 08			19 44
	d			17 10				17 45	17 49		18 10			18 45	18 49				19 10			19 45
Leyland	d								17 54						18 54							
Buckshaw Parkway	d			17 17					17 59		18 17				18 59				19 17			
Chorley	d			17 21					18 03		18 21				19 03				19 21			
Adlington (Lancashire)	d								18 08						19 08							
Blackrod	d								18 12						19 12							
Horwich Parkway	d			17 28					18 16		18 28				19 16				19 28			
Lostock	d								18 20						19 20							
Southport	d						17 05						18 05								19 05	
Meols Cop	d						17 10						18 10								19 10	
Bescar Lane	d																					
New Lane	d																					
Burscough Bridge	d						17 18						18 18								19 18	
Hoscar	d																					
Parbold	d						17 23						18 23								19 23	
Appley Bridge	d						17 27						18 27								19 27	
Gathurst	d						17 30						18 30								19 30	
Kirkby	d																					
Rainford	d																					
Upholland	d																					
Orrell	d																					
Pemberton	d																					
Wigan Wallgate	a						17 35						18 35								19 35	
	d					17 18	17 36						18 36								19 36	
Wigan North Western	d							17 58						18 58								19 59
Ince	d					17 21																
Hindley	d					17 25	17 41						18 41								19 41	
Westhoughton	d						17 46						18 46								19 46	
Bolton	a			17 34			17 54		18 25		18 34		18 54		19 25				19 34		19 54	
	d		17 32	17 35			17 54		18 25	18 32	18 35		18 54		19 25			19 32	19 35		19 54	
Moses Gate	d																					
Farnworth	d																					
Kearsley	d																					
Clifton	d																					
Daisy Hill	d					17 29																
Hag Fold	d					17 32																
Atherton	d					17 34																
Walkden	d					17 40																
Moorside	d					17 44																
Swinton	d					17 46																
Salford Crescent	a		17 44	17 47		17 54	18 07		18 38	18 44	18 47		19 08		19 38			19 44	19 47		20 07	
	d		17 45	17 47	17 50	17 54	18 07		18 38	18 45	18 47	18 50	19 09		19 38			19 45	19 47	19 50	20 07	
Salford Central	d																					
Manchester Victoria ⇌	a				18 00							19 00								20 00		
Rochdale 41	a																					
Deansgate ⇌	a			17 51			18 11				18 51		19 12						19 51		20 11	
Manchester Oxford Road	a		17 50	17 52		18 00	18 13	18 23	18 44	18 50	18 52		19 15	19 23	19 44			19 50	19 52		20 13	20 23
Manchester Piccadilly 10 ⇌	a			17 56			18 19	18 27			18 56		19 19	19 27					19 56		20 19	20 27
Stockport 84	a						18 31						19 30								20 32	
Hazel Grove 86	a						18 42														20 42	
Buxton 86	a																					
Heald Green 85	a																					
Manchester Airport 85 ✈	a			18 13				18 47			19 13			19 47					20 13			20 45

A From Leeds to Morecambe
B From Clitheroe
C To Salford Crescent
D From Glasgow Central
E To Chester
F From Edinburgh

The Sunday service between Wigan Wallgate and Manchester Victoria via Atherton is funded by TfGM and will operate whilst funding exists

Table 82R

Sundays

5 January to 9 February

Barrow-in-Furness, Blackpool North, Preston, Southport, Kirkby and Wigan - Bolton - Manchester

Network Diagram - see first Page of Table 82

		NT	NT	TP	NT	NT	TP	NT	NT	TP		NT	TP	NT	NT	NT	TP	NT	TP	NT		NT	TP	NT	NT
				◇1			◇1			◇1			◇1				◇1						◇1		
			A		B	C	D			E		A		B		A		B					D	A	
					🚌		🚲							🚌				🚌	🚌				🚲		🚌
Barrow-in-Furness	d							19 48																	
Roose	d							19 52																	
Dalton	d							19 58																	
Ulverston	d							20 07																	
Cark	d							20 14																	
Kents Bank	d							20 19																	
Grange-over-Sands	d							20 23																	
Arnside	d							20 29																	
Silverdale	d							20 33																	
Carnforth	d							20 41																	
Windermere 83	d									20 40													21 51		
Oxenholme Lake District 65	d						20 10			21 00													22 06		
Lancaster 8 65	a						20 24	20 52		21 18													22 06		
	d						20 25																		
Blackpool North 97	d	19 20		19 44					20 20				20 44				21 35								
Layton 97	d	19 23							20 23																
Poulton-le-Fylde 97	d	19 27		19 50					20 27				20 50				21 41								
Kirkham & Wesham 97	d	19 37							20 37																
Preston 8 65,97	a	19 47		20 08			20 43		20 47				21 08				21 59						22 25		
	d	19 49		20 10			20 46		20 49				21 10				22 00		22 10				22 33		
Leyland	d	19 54							20 54																
Buckshaw Parkway	d	19 59		20 17					20 59				21 17												
Chorley	d	20 03		20 21					21 03				21 21							22 21					
Adlington (Lancashire)	d	20 08							21 08											22 26					
Blackrod	d	20 12							21 12											22 29					
Horwich Parkway	d	20 16		20 28					21 16				21 28							22 33					
Lostock	d	20 20							21 20											22 37					
Southport	d					20 05									21 05							22 05			
Meols Cop	d					20 10									21 10							22 10			
Bescar Lane	d																								
New Lane	d																								
Burscough Bridge	d					20 18									21 18							22 18			
Hoscar	d																								
Parbold	d					20 23									21 23							22 23			
Appley Bridge	d					20 27									21 27							22 27			
Gathurst	d					20 30									21 30							22 30			
Kirkby	d																								
Rainford	d																								
Upholland	d																								
Orrell	d																								
Pemberton	d																								
Wigan Wallgate	a					20 35									21 35							22 35			
	d					20 36									21 36							22 36			
Wigan North Western	d																22 14						22 46		
Ince	d																								
Hindley	d					20 41									21 41							22 41			
Westhoughton	d					20 46									21 46							22 46			
Bolton	a	20 25		20 34		20 54			21 25				21 34		21 54		22 27		22 36	22 42		22 54			
	d	20 25	20 32	20 35		20 54			21 25			21 32	21 35		21 54	22 32	22 36			22 42		22 54		23 31	
Moses Gate	d																								
Farnworth	d																								
Kearsley	d																								
Clifton	d																								
Daisy Hill	d																								
Hag Fold	d																								
Atherton	d																								
Walkden	d																								
Moorside	d																								
Swinton	d																								
Salford Crescent	a	20 38	20 44	20 47		21 07			21 38			21 44	21 47		22 07	22 44	22 48			22 55		23 07		23 43	
	d	20 38	20 45	20 47	20 50	21 07			21 38			21 45	21 47	21 50	22 07	22 45	22 48	22 50		22 55		23 07		23 44	23 50
Salford Central	d																								
Manchester Victoria ⇌	a				21 00									22 00				23 00							00 01
Rochdale 41	a																								
Deansgate ⇌	a			20 51		21 11							21 51		22 11		22 52					23 11			
Manchester Oxford Road	a	20 44	20 50	20 52		21 13	21 21		21 44			21 50	21 52		22 13	22 50	22 53			23 01		23 15	23 19	23 50	
Manchester Piccadilly 10 ⇌	a			20 56		21 19	21 25						21 56		22 19		22 57					23 19	23 24		
Stockport 84	a					21 30									22 32							23 34			
Hazel Grove 86	a														22 42										
Buxton 86	a																								
Heald Green 85	a																								
Manchester Airport 85 ✈	a			21 13			21 45						22 12				23 16						23 40		

A From Clitheroe
B To Salford Crescent
C To Chester
D From Edinburgh
E To Barrow-in-Furness

The Sunday service between Wigan Wallgate and Manchester Victoria via Atherton is funded by TfGM and will operate whilst funding exists

Table 82R

Sundays
5 January to 9 February

Barrow-in-Furness, Blackpool North, Preston, Southport, Kirkby and Wigan - Bolton - Manchester

Network Diagram - see first Page of Table 82

Station			TP ◇1	TP 🚌
Barrow-in-Furness		d		
Roose		d		
Dalton		d		
Ulverston		d		
Cark		d		
Kents Bank		d		
Grange-over-Sands		d		
Arnside		d		
Silverdale		d		
Carnforth		d		
Windermere	83	d		
Oxenholme Lake District	65	d		
Lancaster 8	65	a		
		d		
Blackpool North	97	d	23 02	
Layton	97	d		
Poulton-le-Fylde	97	d	23 08	
Kirkham & Wesham	97	d	23 17	
Preston 8	65,97	a	23 28	
		d	23 32	23 40
Leyland		d	23 37	
Buckshaw Parkway		d		
Chorley		d		
Adlington (Lancashire)		d		
Blackrod		d		
Horwich Parkway		d		
Lostock		d		
Southport		d		
Meols Cop		d		
Bescar Lane		d		
New Lane		d		
Burscough Bridge		d		
Hoscar		d		
Parbold		d		
Appley Bridge		d		
Gathurst		d		
Kirkby		d		
Rainford		d		
Upholland		d		
Orrell		d		
Pemberton		d		
Wigan Wallgate		a		
		d		
Wigan North Western		d	23 48	
Ince		d		
Hindley		d		
Westhoughton		d		
Bolton		a	00 01	00 06
		d	00 02	
Moses Gate		d		
Farnworth		d		
Kearsley		d		
Clifton		d		
Daisy Hill		d		
Hag Fold		d		
Atherton		d		
Walkden		d		
Moorside		d		
Swinton		d		
Salford Crescent		a		
		d		
Salford Central		d		
Manchester Victoria	🚊	a		
Rochdale	41	a		
Deansgate	🚊	a		
Manchester Oxford Road		a		
Manchester Piccadilly 10	🚊	a	00 17	
Stockport	84	a		
Hazel Grove	86	a		
Buxton	86	a		
Heald Green	85	a		
Manchester Airport	85 ✈	a	00 34	

The Sunday service between Wigan Wallgate and Manchester Victoria via Atherton is funded by TfGM and will operate whilst funding exists

Table 82R

Sundays

16 February to 23 March

Barrow-in-Furness, Blackpool North, Preston, Southport, Kirkby and Wigan - Bolton - Manchester

Network Diagram - see first Page of Table 82

		NT	TP	TP	TP	NT	TP	NT	NT	NT	TP	NT	NT	NT	NT	NT	TP	NT	NT	NT	NT	TP	NT
		A	🚌	🚌	🚌	B 🚌	◇1	B 🚌	C	D	◇1	B 🚌				E	◇1	B 🚌			C	◇1	F
Barrow-in-Furness	d																					09 17	
Roose	d																					09 21	
Dalton	d																					09 28	
Ulverston	d																					09 36	
Cark	d																					09 44	
Kents Bank	d																					09 48	
Grange-over-Sands	d																					09 52	
Arnside	d																					09 58	
Silverdale	d																					10 02	
Carnforth	d																					10 09	10 31
Windermere 83	d																						
Oxenholme Lake District 65	d																					10 17	10 40
Lancaster 6 65	a																					10 22	
	d																						
Blackpool North 97	d		03 20	05 20							08 38						09 36						
Layton 97	d																						
Poulton-le-Fylde 97	d										08 44						09 42						
Kirkham & Wesham 97	d																						
Preston 8 65,97	a										09 01						10 00					10 40	
	d		04u00	06u00	07 50						09 04						10 04					10 42	
Leyland	d																						
Buckshaw Parkway	d																						
Chorley	d				08a15		08 23							09 24						10 24			
Adlington (Lancashire)	d													09 28						10 28			
Blackrod	d													09 32						10 32			
Horwich Parkway	d						08 30							09 36						10 36			
Lostock	d	00 02												09 40						10 40			
Southport	d														09 10						10 05		
Meols Cop	d														09 15						10 10		
Bescar Lane	d																						
New Lane	d																						
Burscough Bridge	d														09 23						10 18		
Hoscar	d																						
Parbold	d														09 28						10 23		
Appley Bridge	d														09 32						10 27		
Gathurst	d														09 35						10 30		
Kirkby	d																						
Rainford	d																						
Upholland	d																						
Orrell	d																						
Pemberton	d																						
Wigan Wallgate	a														09 40						10 35		
	d								08 40				09 15		09 41				10 15		10 36		
Wigan North Western	d																						
Ince	d												09 18						10 18				
Hindley	d								08 45				09 22		09 46				10 22		10 41		
Westhoughton	d								08 49						09 51						10 46		
Bolton	a	00 07					08 37		08 57		09 34			09 45	09 59		10 34			10 45	10 54		
	d	00 07	04u35	06u35			08 37		08 58	09 31	09 35			09 45	09 59	10 32	10 36			10 45	10 54		
Moses Gate	d																						
Farnworth	d																						
Kearsley	d																						
Clifton	d																						
Daisy Hill	d												09 26						10 26				
Hag Fold	d												09 29						10 29				
Atherton	d												09 31						10 31				
Walkden	d												09 37						10 37				
Moorside	d												09 41						10 41				
Swinton	d												09 43						10 43				
Salford Crescent	a						08 49			09 43	09 47		09 51	09 58	10 12	10 44	10 48		10 51	10 58	11 07		
	d					07 50	08 50	08 50		09 44	09 47	09 50	09 53	09 58	10 12	10 45	10 48	10 50	10 53	10 58	11 07		
Salford Central	d																						
Manchester Victoria ⇌	a	00 26				08 00		09 00				10 00						11 00					
Rochdale 41	a																						
Deansgate ⇌	a						08 53		09 14		09 51				10 16		10 52				11 11		
Manchester Oxford Road	a						08 55		09 17	09 49	09 52		10 00	10 04	10 18	10 50	10 53		11 00	11 04	11 13	11 21	
Manchester Piccadilly 10 ⇌	a		05b00	07b00			08 59		09 21		09 56				10 22		10 57				11 19	11 25	
Stockport 84	a								09 31						10 33						11 30		
Hazel Grove 86	a																						
Buxton 86	a																						
Heald Green 85	a																						
Manchester Airport 85 ✈	a		05 25	07 25			09 14				10 15						11 14					11 45	

A From Blackpool North
B To Salford Crescent
C To Chester
D From Blackburn
E From Clitheroe
F From Leeds to Morecambe
b Stops to pick up only

The Sunday service between Wigan Wallgate and Manchester Victoria via Atherton is funded by TfGM and will operate whilst funding exists

Table 82R

Sundays

16 February to 23 March

Barrow-in-Furness, Blackpool North, Preston, Southport, Kirkby and Wigan - Bolton - Manchester

Network Diagram - see first Page of Table 82

Station			NT	TP	NT	NT	NT	NT	TP	TP	NT	NT	TP	NT	NT	NT	TP	NT	NT	NT	TP	NT	NT	NT
				◇1						◇1			◇1				◇1				◇1			
			A		B							A		B		C	D		E	A		B		
					🚌				🚌					🚌			🛒					🚌		
Barrow-in-Furness		d								10 25														
Roose		d								10 29														
Dalton		d								10 36														
Ulverston		d								10 44														
Cark		d								10 52														
Kents Bank		d								10 56														
Grange-over-Sands		d								11 00														
Arnside		d								11 06														
Silverdale		d								11 10														
Carnforth		d								11 17										12 35				
Windermere	83	d																						
Oxenholme Lake District	65	d															12 10							
Lancaster 6	65	a								11 25							12 24		12 44					
		d								11 25							12 25							
Blackpool North	97	d		10 38							11 20		11 45					12 20			12 41			
Layton	97	d									11 23							12 23						
Poulton-le-Fylde	97	d		10 44							11 27		11 51					12 27			12 47			
Kirkham & Wesham	97	d									11 37							12 37						
Preston 8	65,97	a		11 02						11 44	11 47		12 09				12 43	12 47			13 05			
		d		11 04					11 10	11 45	11 52		12 11				12 45	12 50			13 09			
Leyland		d									11 57							12 55						
Buckshaw Parkway		d									12 03		12 18					13 00			13 16			
Chorley		d					11 24		11a35		12 07		12 22					13 04			13 20			
Adlington (Lancashire)		d					11 28				12 11							13 09						
Blackrod		d					11 32				12 15							13 12						
Horwich Parkway		d					11 36				12 19		12 29					13 16			13 27			
Lostock		d					11 40				12 22							13 20						
Southport		d						11 05								12 05								13 05
Meols Cop		d						11 10								12 10								13 10
Bescar Lane		d																						
New Lane		d																						
Burscough Bridge		d						11 18								12 18								13 18
Hoscar		d																						
Parbold		d						11 23								12 23								13 23
Appley Bridge		d						11 27								12 27								13 27
Gathurst		d						11 30								12 30								13 30
Kirkby		d																						
Rainford		d																						
Upholland		d																						
Orrell		d																						
Pemberton		d																						
Wigan Wallgate		a						11 35								12 35								13 35
		d				11 15		11 36							12 18	12 36							13 18	13 36
Wigan North Western		d								12 00							12 58							
Ince		d				11 18									12 21								13 21	
Hindley		d				11 22		11 41							12 25	12 41							13 25	13 41
Westhoughton		d						11 46								12 46								13 46
Bolton		a		11 35			11 45	11 54			12 27		12 35			12 54		13 25			13 34			13 54
		d	11 32	11 35			11 45	11 54			12 28	12 32	12 36			12 54		13 25		13 32	13 35			13 54
Moses Gate		d																						
Farnworth		d																						
Kearsley		d																						
Clifton		d																						
Daisy Hill		d				11 26									12 29								13 29	
Hag Fold		d				11 29									12 32								13 32	
Atherton		d				11 31									12 34								13 34	
Walkden		d				11 37									12 40								13 40	
Moorside		d				11 41									12 44								13 44	
Swinton		d				11 43									12 46								13 46	
Salford Crescent		a	11 44	11 47		11 51	11 58	12 07			12 39	12 44	12 48		12 54	13 07		13 38		13 44	13 47		13 54	14 07
		d	11 45	11 48	11 50	11 53	11 58	12 07			12 40	12 45	12 48	12 50	12 54	13 07		13 38		13 45	13 48	13 50	13 54	14 07
Salford Central		d																						
Manchester Victoria 🚊		a			12 00									13 00								14 00		
Rochdale	41	a																						
Deansgate 🚊		a		11 51				12 11					12 52			13 11					13 51			14 11
Manchester Oxford Road		a	11 50	11 53		12 00	12 04	12 13		12 25	12 45	12 50	12 53		13 00	13 13	13 23	13 44		13 50	13 53		14 00	14 13
Manchester Piccadilly 10 🚊		a		11 56				12 19		12 29			12 57			13 19	13 27				13 56			14 19
Stockport	84	a						12 33								13 30								14 33
Hazel Grove	86	a						12 42																14 42
Buxton	86	a																						
Heald Green	85	a																						
Manchester Airport	85 ✈	a		12 13						12 46			13 15				13 47				14 14			

A From Clitheroe
B To Salford Crescent
C To Chester
D From Edinburgh
E From Leeds to Morecambe

The Sunday service between Wigan Wallgate and Manchester Victoria via Atherton is funded by TfGM and will operate whilst funding exists

Table 82R

Sundays

16 February to 23 March

Barrow-in-Furness, Blackpool North, Preston, Southport, Kirkby and Wigan - Bolton - Manchester

Network Diagram - see first Page of Table 82

		TP		NT	NT	NT	TP	NT	NT	NT	TP	NT		NT	TP	NT	NT	NT	TP	NT	NT	TP		NT	NT
		◇1					◇1				◇1				◇1				◇1			◇1			
						A		B		C	D			A		B					A			B	
								🚌			🍴					🚌								🚌	
Barrow-in-Furness	d	12 33		13 10															14 25						
Roose	d			13 14															14 29						
Dalton	d			13 20															14 36						
Ulverston	d	12 49		13 29															14 44						
Cark	d			13 36															14 52						
Kents Bank	d			13 41															14 56						
Grange-over-Sands	d	13 01		13 45															15 00						
Arnside	d	13 07		13 51															15 06						
Silverdale	d			13 55															15 10						
Carnforth	d	13 17		14 03															15 17						
Windermere 83	d																								
Oxenholme Lake District 65	d										14 10														
Lancaster 6 65	a	13 25		14 15							14 24								15 25						
	d	13 25									14 25								15 25						
Blackpool North 97	d				13 20		13 44					14 20			14 45					15 20		15 45			
Layton 97	d				13 23							14 23								15 23					
Poulton-le-Fylde 97	d				13 27		13 50					14 27			14 51					15 27		15 51			
Kirkham & Wesham 97	d				13 37							14 37								15 37					
Preston 8 65,97	a	13 44			13 47		14 08				14 43	14 47			15 09				15 44	15 47		16 09			
	d	13 45			13 50		14 11				14 45	14 50			15 11				15 45	15 49		16 11			
Leyland	d				13 55							14 55								15 54					
Buckshaw Parkway	d				14 00		14 18					15 00			15 18					15 59		16 18			
Chorley	d				14 04		14 22					15 04			15 22					16 03		16 22			
Adlington (Lancashire)	d				14 09							15 09								16 08					
Blackrod	d				14 12							15 12								16 11					
Horwich Parkway	d				14 16		14 29					15 16			15 29					16 15		16 29			
Lostock	d				14 20							15 20								16 20					
Southport	d									14 05								15 05							
Meols Cop	d									14 10								15 10							
Bescar Lane	d																								
New Lane	d																								
Burscough Bridge	d									14 18								15 18							
Hoscar	d																								
Parbold	d									14 23								15 23							
Appley Bridge	d									14 27								15 27							
Gathurst	d									14 30								15 30							
Kirkby	d																								
Rainford	d																								
Upholland	d																								
Orrell	d																								
Pemberton	d																								
Wigan Wallgate	a									14 35								15 35							
	d								14 18	14 36							15 18	15 36							16 18
Wigan North Western	d	13 58									14 58								15 58						
Ince	d								14 21								15 21								16 21
Hindley	d								14 25	14 41							15 25	15 41							16 25
Westhoughton	d									14 46								15 46							
Bolton	a				14 25		14 35			14 54		15 25			15 35			15 54		16 25		16 35			
	d				14 25	14 32	14 36			14 54		15 26		15 32	15 36			15 54		16 25	16 32	16 36			
Moses Gate	d																								
Farnworth	d																								
Kearsley	d																								
Clifton	d																								
Daisy Hill	d								14 29								15 29								16 29
Hag Fold	d								14 32								15 32								16 32
Atherton	d								14 34								15 34								16 34
Walkden	d								14 40								15 40								16 40
Moorside	d								14 44								15 44								16 44
Swinton	d								14 46								15 46								16 46
Salford Crescent	a				14 38	14 44	14 48		14 54	15 07		15 38		15 44	15 48		15 54	16 07		16 38	16 44	16 48			16 54
	d				14 38	14 45	14 48	14 50	14 54	15 07		15 38		15 45	15 48	15 50	15 54	16 07		16 38	16 45	16 48		16 50	16 54
Salford Central	d																								
Manchester Victoria 🚋	a							15 00								16 00								17 00	
Rochdale 41	a																								
Deansgate 🚋	a						14 52			15 11					15 52			16 11				16 52			
Manchester Oxford Road	a	14 23			14 44	14 50	14 53		15 00	15 13	15 23	15 44		15 50	15 53		16 00	16 13	16 23	16 44	16 50	16 53			17 00
Manchester Piccadilly 10 🚋	a	14 27					14 57			15 19	15 27				15 57			16 19	16 27			16 57			
Stockport 84	a									15 31								16 32							
Hazel Grove 86	a																	16 42							
Buxton 86	a																								
Heald Green 85	a																								
Manchester Airport 85 ✈	a	14 47					15 13				15 47				16 13				16 47			17 13			

A From Clitheroe
B To Salford Crescent
C To Chester
D From Edinburgh

The Sunday service between Wigan Wallgate and Manchester Victoria via Atherton is funded by TfGM and will operate whilst funding exists

Table 82R

Sundays

16 February to 23 March

Barrow-in-Furness, Blackpool North, Preston, Southport, Kirkby and Wigan - Bolton - Manchester

Network Diagram - see first Page of Table 82

			NT	TP	NT	NT	NT	TP	NT	NT	NT	TP	NT	NT	TP	NT	NT	TP	NT	NT	TP	NT	TP	NT
				◇1				◇1				◇1			◇1			◇1			◇1		◇1	
			A	B		C	D		E			F		D		E	A	B		C		D		E
				🚲					🚌			🚲				🚌		🚲						🚌
Barrow-in-Furness		d																			18 17			
Roose		d																			18 21			
Dalton		d																			18 28			
Ulverston		d																			18 36			
Cark		d																			18 44			
Kents Bank		d																			18 48			
Grange-over-Sands		d																			18 52			
Arnside		d																			18 58			
Silverdale		d																			19 02			
Carnforth		d				16 37														19 04	19 09			
Windermere	83	d																						
Oxenholme Lake District	65	d		16 10								17 09						18 10						
Lancaster 6	65	a		16 24		16 46						17 23						18 24		19 13	19 17			
		d		16 25								17 24						18 25			19 17			
Blackpool North	97	d			16 20			16 45					17 20		17 45				18 20				18 45	
Layton	97	d			16 23								17 23						18 23					
Poulton-le-Fylde	97	d			16 27			16 51					17 27		17 51				18 27				18 51	
Kirkham & Wesham	97	d			16 37								17 37						18 37					
Preston 8	65,97	a		16 43	16 47			17 09				17 42	17 47		18 09			18 43	18 47		19 37		19 09	
		d		16 45	16 49			17 11				17 45	17 49		18 11			18 45	18 49				19 11	
Leyland		d			16 54								17 54						18 54					
Buckshaw Parkway		d			16 59			17 18					17 59		18 18				18 59				19 18	
Chorley		d			17 03			17 22					18 03		18 22				19 03				19 22	
Adlington (Lancashire)		d			17 08								18 08						19 08					
Blackrod		d			17 12								18 12						19 12					
Horwich Parkway		d			17 16			17 29					18 16		18 29				19 16				19 29	
Lostock		d			17 20								18 20						19 20					
Southport		d	16 05								17 05						18 05							
Meols Cop		d	16 10								17 10						18 10							
Bescar Lane		d																						
New Lane		d																						
Burscough Bridge		d	16 18								17 18						18 18							
Hoscar		d																						
Parbold		d	16 23								17 23						18 23							
Appley Bridge		d	16 27								17 27						18 27							
Gathurst		d	16 30								17 30						18 30							
Kirkby		d																						
Rainford		d																						
Upholland		d																						
Orrell		d																						
Pemberton		d																						
Wigan Wallgate		a	16 35								17 35						18 35							
		d	16 36							17 18	17 36						18 36							
Wigan North Western		d		16 58								17 58						18 58						
Ince		d								17 21														
Hindley		d	16 41							17 25	17 41						18 41							
Westhoughton		d	16 46								17 46						18 46							
Bolton		a	16 54		17 25			17 35			17 54		18 25		18 35		18 54		19 25				19 35	
		d	16 54		17 25		17 32	17 36			17 54		18 25	18 32	18 36		18 54		19 25			19 32	19 36	
Moses Gate		d																						
Farnworth		d																						
Kearsley		d																						
Clifton		d																						
Daisy Hill		d								17 29														
Hag Fold		d								17 32														
Atherton		d								17 34														
Walkden		d								17 40														
Moorside		d								17 44														
Swinton		d								17 46														
Salford Crescent		a	17 07		17 38		17 44	17 48		17 54	18 07		18 38	18 44	18 48		19 08		19 38			19 44	19 48	
		d	17 07		17 38		17 45	17 48	17 50	17 54	18 07		18 38	18 45	18 48	18 50	19 09		19 38			19 45	19 48	19 50
Salford Central		d																						
Manchester Victoria	🚊	a							18 00							19 00								20 00
Rochdale	41	a																						
Deansgate	🚊	a	17 11					17 52			18 11				18 52		19 12						19 52	
Manchester Oxford Road		a	17 13	17 23	17 44		17 50	17 53		18 00	18 13	18 23	18 44	18 50	18 53		19 15	19 23	19 44			19 50	19 53	
Manchester Piccadilly 10	🚊	a	17 19	17 27				17 57			18 19	18 27			18 57		19 19	19 27					19 57	
Stockport	84	a	17 30								18 31						19 30							
Hazel Grove	86	a									18 42													
Buxton	86	a																						
Heald Green	85	a																						
Manchester Airport	85 ✈	a		17 47				18 13				18 47			19 13			19 47					20 13	

A To Chester
B From Edinburgh
C From Leeds to Morecambe
D From Clitheroe
E To Salford Crescent
F From Glasgow Central

The Sunday service between Wigan Wallgate and Manchester Victoria via Atherton is funded by TfGM and will operate whilst funding exists

Table 82R

Sundays

16 February to 23 March

Barrow-in-Furness, Blackpool North, Preston, Southport, Kirkby and Wigan - Bolton - Manchester

Network Diagram - see first Page of Table 82

		NT	TP	NT		NT	TP	NT	NT	TP	NT	NT	TP	NT		TP	NT	NT	NT	NT	TP	NT	TP	NT
			◇1				◇1			◇1			◇1			◇1					◇1		◇1	
			A			B		C	D	E			F	B			C			B		C	E	
Barrow-in-Furness	d										19 48													
Roose	d										19 52													
Dalton	d										19 58													
Ulverston	d										20 07													
Cark	d										20 14													
Kents Bank	d										20 19													
Grange-over-Sands	d										20 23													
Arnside	d										20 29													
Silverdale	d										20 33													
Carnforth	d										20 41													
Windermere 83	d												20 40											
Oxenholme Lake District 65	d		19 09							20 10			21 00										21 51	
Lancaster 6 65	a		19 24							20 24	20 52		21 18										22 06	
	d		19 24							20 25													22 06	
Blackpool North 97	d			19 20			19 45					20 20				20 45			21 20		21 45			
Layton 97	d			19 23								20 23							21 23					
Poulton-le-Fylde 97	d			19 27			19 51					20 27				20 51			21 27		21 51			
Kirkham & Wesham 97	d			19 37								20 37							21 37					
Preston 8 65,97	a		19 44	19 47			20 09			20 43		20 47				21 09			21 47		22 09		22 25	
	d		19 45	19 49			20 11			20 46		20 49				21 11			21 49		22 11		22 26	
Leyland	d			19 54								20 54							21 54					
Buckshaw Parkway	d			19 59			20 18					20 59				21 18			21 59		22 18			
Chorley	d			20 03			20 22					21 03				21 22			22 03		22 22			
Adlington (Lancashire)	d			20 08								21 08							22 08					
Blackrod	d			20 12								21 12							22 12					
Horwich Parkway	d			20 16			20 29					21 16				21 29			22 16		22 29			
Lostock	d			20 20								21 20							22 20					
Southport	d	19 05							20 05									21 05						22 05
Meols Cop	d	19 10							20 10									21 10						22 10
Bescar Lane	d																							
New Lane	d																							
Burscough Bridge	d	19 18							20 18									21 18						22 18
Hoscar	d																							
Parbold	d	19 23							20 23									21 23						22 23
Appley Bridge	d	19 27							20 27									21 27						22 27
Gathurst	d	19 30							20 30									21 30						22 30
Kirkby	d																							
Rainford	d																							
Upholland	d																							
Orrell	d																							
Pemberton	d																							
Wigan Wallgate	a	19 35							20 35									21 35						22 35
	d	19 36							20 36									21 36						22 36
Wigan North Western	d		19 59																				22 39	
Ince	d																							
Hindley	d	19 41							20 41									21 41						22 41
Westhoughton	d	19 46							20 46									21 46						22 46
Bolton	a	19 54		20 25			20 35		20 54			21 25				21 35		21 54	22 25		22 35			22 54
	d	19 54		20 25		20 32	20 36		20 54			21 25		21 32		21 36		21 54	22 25	22 32	22 36			22 54
Moses Gate	d																							
Farnworth	d																							
Kearsley	d																							
Clifton	d																							
Daisy Hill	d																							
Hag Fold	d																							
Atherton	d																							
Walkden	d																							
Moorside	d																							
Swinton	d																							
Salford Crescent	a	20 07		20 38		20 44	20 48		21 07			21 38		21 44		21 48		22 07	22 38	22 44	22 48			23 07
	d	20 07		20 38		20 45	20 48	20 50	21 07			21 38		21 45		21 48	21 50	22 07	22 38	22 45	22 48	22 50		23 07
Salford Central	d																							
Manchester Victoria	a							21 00									22 00					23 00		
Rochdale 41	a																							
Deansgate	a	20 11					20 52		21 11							21 52		22 11			22 52			23 11
Manchester Oxford Road	a	20 13	20 23	20 44		20 50	20 53		21 13	21 21		21 44		21 50		21 53		22 13	22 44	22 50	22 53		23 04	23 15
Manchester Piccadilly 10	a	20 19	20 27				20 57		21 19	21 25						21 57		22 19			22 57		23 08	23 19
Stockport 84	a	20 32							21 30									22 32						23 34
Hazel Grove 86	a	20 42																22 42						
Buxton 86	a																							
Heald Green 85	a																							
Manchester Airport 85	a		20 45				21 13			21 45						22 13					23 16		23 24	

A From Glasgow Central
B From Clitheroe
C To Salford Crescent
D To Chester
E From Edinburgh
F To Barrow-in-Furness

The Sunday service between Wigan Wallgate and Manchester Victoria via Atherton is funded by TfGM and will operate whilst funding exists

Table 82R

Sundays

16 February to 23 March

Barrow-in-Furness, Blackpool North, Preston, Southport, Kirkby and Wigan - Bolton - Manchester

Network Diagram - see first Page of Table 82

Station			NT A	NT 🚌	TP ◇1
Barrow-in-Furness		d			
Roose		d			
Dalton		d			
Ulverston		d			
Cark		d			
Kents Bank		d			
Grange-over-Sands		d			
Arnside		d			
Silverdale		d			
Carnforth		d			
Windermere	83	d			
Oxenholme Lake District	65	d			
Lancaster 6	65	a			
		d			
Blackpool North	97	d			23 01
Layton	97	d			
Poulton-le-Fylde	97	d			23 07
Kirkham & Wesham	97	d			23 17
Preston 8	65,97	a			23 27
		d			23 29
Leyland		d			23 34
Buckshaw Parkway		d			23 38
Chorley		d			23 42
Adlington (Lancashire)		d			23 46
Blackrod		d			23 50
Horwich Parkway		d			23 53
Lostock		d			23 57
Southport		d			
Meols Cop		d			
Bescar Lane		d			
New Lane		d			
Burscough Bridge		d			
Hoscar		d			
Parbold		d			
Appley Bridge		d			
Gathurst		d			
Kirkby		d			
Rainford		d			
Upholland		d			
Orrell		d			
Pemberton		d			
Wigan Wallgate		a			
		d			
Wigan North Western		d			
Ince		d			
Hindley		d			
Westhoughton		d			
Bolton		a			00 02
		d	23 31		00 02
Moses Gate		d			
Farnworth		d			
Kearsley		d			
Clifton		d			
Daisy Hill		d			
Hag Fold		d			
Atherton		d			
Walkden		d			
Moorside		d			
Swinton		d			
Salford Crescent		a	23 43		
		d	23 44	23 50	
Salford Central		d			
Manchester Victoria	🚊	a		00 01	
Rochdale	41	a			
Deansgate	🚊	a			
Manchester Oxford Road		a	23 50		
Manchester Piccadilly 10	🚊	a			00 18
Stockport	84	a			
Hazel Grove	86	a			
Buxton	86	a			
Heald Green	85	a			
Manchester Airport	85 ✈	a			00 35

A From Clitheroe

The Sunday service between Wigan Wallgate and Manchester Victoria via Atherton is funded by TfGM and will operate whilst funding exists

Table 82R

Sundays

30 March to 11 May

Barrow-in-Furness, Blackpool North, Preston, Southport, Kirkby and Wigan - Bolton - Manchester

Network Diagram - see first Page of Table 82

Station		NT	TP	TP	NT	TP	NT	NT	NT	TP	TP	NT	TP	NT	NT	NT	NT	NT	TP	NT	NT	NT	NT
						◇1				◇1			◇1						◇1				
		A			B		B	C				D		B				E		B		C	F
			bus	bus	bus		bus				bus			bus						bus			bus
Barrow-in-Furness	d									09 17													
Roose	d									09 21													
Dalton	d									09 28													
Ulverston	d									09 36													
Cark	d									09 44													
Kents Bank	d									09 48													
Grange-over-Sands	d									09 52													
Arnside	d									09 58													
Silverdale	d									10 02													
Carnforth	d									10a09	10 20												10 40
Windermere 83	d																						
Oxenholme Lake District 65	d																						
Lancaster 6 65	a										10 45												11 05
	d																						
Blackpool North 97	d		03 20	05 20		07 48			08 20				08 44				09 20		09 44				
Layton 97	d								08 23								09 23						
Poulton-le-Fylde 97	d					07 54			08 27				08 50				09 27		09 50				
Kirkham & Wesham 97	d								08 37								09 37						
Preston 8 65,97	a					08 12			08 47				09 08				09 47		10 08				
	d		04u00	06u00		08 13			08 49				09 10				09 49		10 10				
Leyland	d								08 54								09 54						
Buckshaw Parkway	d								08 59				09 17				09 59		10 17				
Chorley	d					08 23			09 03				09 21				10 03		10 21				
Adlington (Lancashire)	d								09 08								10 08						
Blackrod	d								09 12								10 12						
Horwich Parkway	d					08 30			09 16				09 28				10 16		10 28				
Lostock	d	00 02							09 20								10 20						
Southport	d															09 10						10 05	
Meols Cop	d															09 15						10 10	
Bescar Lane	d																						
New Lane	d																						
Burscough Bridge	d															09 23						10 18	
Hoscar	d																						
Parbold	d															09 28						10 23	
Appley Bridge	d															09 32						10 27	
Gathurst	d															09 35						10 30	
Kirkby	d																						
Rainford	d																						
Upholland	d																						
Orrell	d																						
Pemberton	d																						
Wigan Wallgate	a															09 40						10 35	
	d							08 40							09 15	09 41					10 15	10 36	
Wigan North Western	d																						
Ince	d														09 18						10 18		
Hindley	d							08 45							09 22	09 46					10 22	10 41	
Westhoughton	d							08 49								09 51						10 46	
Bolton	a	00 07				08 37		08 57	09 25				09 34			09 59	10 25		10 34			10 54	
	d	00 07	04u35	06u35		08 37		08 58	09 25			09 31	09 35			09 59	10 25	10 32	10 36			10 54	
Moses Gate	d																						
Farnworth	d																						
Kearsley	d																						
Clifton	d																						
Daisy Hill	d														09 26						10 26		
Hag Fold	d														09 29						10 29		
Atherton	d														09 31						10 31		
Walkden	d														09 37						10 37		
Moorside	d														09 41						10 41		
Swinton	d														09 43						10 43		
Salford Crescent	a					08 49			09 38			09 43	09 47		09 51	10 12	10 38	10 44	10 48		10 51	11 07	
	d				07 50	08 50	08 50		09 38			09 44	09 47	09 50	09 53	10 12	10 40	10 45	10 48	10 50	10 53	11 07	
Salford Central	d																						
Manchester Victoria ⇌	a	00 26			08 00		09 00							10 00						11 00			
Rochdale 41	a																						
Deansgate ⇌	a					08 53		09 14					09 51			10 16			10 52			11 11	
Manchester Oxford Road	a					08 55		09 17	09 44			09 49	09 52		10 00	10 18	10 45	10 50	10 53		11 00	11 13	
Manchester Piccadilly 10 ⇌	a		05b00	07b00		08 59		09 21					09 56			10 22			10 57			11 19	
Stockport 84	a							09 31								10 33						11 30	
Hazel Grove 86	a																						
Buxton 86	a																						
Heald Green 85	a																						
Manchester Airport 85 ✈	a		05 25	07 25		09 14							10 15						11 14				

A From Blackpool North
B To Salford Crescent
C To Chester
D From Blackburn
E From Clitheroe
F To Morecambe
b Stops to pick up only

The Sunday service between Wigan Wallgate and Manchester Victoria via Atherton is funded by TfGM and will operate whilst funding exists

Table 82R

Sundays

30 March to 11 May

Barrow-in-Furness, Blackpool North, Preston, Southport, Kirkby and Wigan - Bolton - Manchester

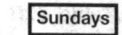

Network Diagram - see first Page of Table 82

		TP	NT	NT	TP	NT	NT	NT	TP	NT	NT	TP	NT	NT	NT	TP	NT	NT	NT	TP	NT	NT	NT
		◇1			◇1				◇1			◇1				◇1				◇1			
				A		B					A		B		C	D		E	A		B		
Barrow-in-Furness	d								10 25														
Roose	d								10 29														
Dalton	d								10 36														
Ulverston	d								10 44														
Cark	d								10 52														
Kents Bank	d								10 56														
Grange-over-Sands	d								11 00														
Arnside	d								11 06														
Silverdale	d								11 10														
Carnforth	d								11 17									12 35					
Windermere 83	d																						
Oxenholme Lake District 65	d															12 10							
Lancaster 6 65	a								11 25							12 24		12 44					
	d								11 25							12 25							
Blackpool North 97	d		10 20		10 44					11 20		11 44					12 20			12 40			
Layton 97	d		10 23							11 23							12 23						
Poulton-le-Fylde 97	d		10 27		10 50					11 27		11 50					12 27			12 46			
Kirkham & Wesham 97	d		10 37							11 37							12 37						
Preston 8 65,97	a		10 47		11 08				11 44	11 47		12 08				12 43	12 47			13 04			
	d	10 47	10 49		11 11				11 47	11 49		12 10				12 45	12 50			13 08			
Leyland	d		10 54							11 54							12 55						
Buckshaw Parkway	d		10 59		11 18					11 59		12 17					13 00			13 15			
Chorley	d	10 57	11 03		11 22				11 57	12 03		12 21					13 04			13 19			
Adlington (Lancashire)	d		11 08							12 08							13 09						
Blackrod	d		11 12							12 12							13 12						
Horwich Parkway	d		11 16		11 29					12 16		12 28					13 16			13 26			
Lostock	d		11 20							12 20							13 20						
Southport	d							11 05							12 05								13 05
Meols Cop	d							11 10							12 10								13 10
Bescar Lane	d																						
New Lane	d																						
Burscough Bridge	d							11 18							12 18								13 18
Hoscar	d																						
Parbold	d							11 23							12 23								13 23
Appley Bridge	d							11 27							12 27								13 27
Gathurst	d							11 30							12 30								13 30
Kirkby	d																						
Rainford	d																						
Upholland	d																						
Orrell	d																						
Pemberton	d																						
Wigan Wallgate	a							11 35							12 35								13 35
	d						11 15	11 36						12 18	12 36							13 18	13 36
Wigan North Western	d															12 58							
Ince	d						11 18							12 21								13 21	
Hindley	d						11 22	11 41						12 25	12 41							13 25	13 41
Westhoughton	d							11 46							12 46								13 46
Bolton	a	11 08	11 25		11 35			11 54	12 08	12 25		12 34			12 54		13 25			13 33			13 54
	d	11 09	11 25	11 32	11 36			11 54	12 09	12 25	12 32	12 35			12 54		13 25		13 32	13 35			13 54
Moses Gate	d																						
Farnworth	d																						
Kearsley	d																						
Clifton	d																						
Daisy Hill	d						11 26							12 29								13 29	
Hag Fold	d						11 29							12 32								13 32	
Atherton	d						11 31							12 34								13 34	
Walkden	d						11 37							12 40								13 40	
Moorside	d						11 41							12 44								13 44	
Swinton	d						11 43							12 46								13 46	
Salford Crescent	a		11 38	11 44	11 48		11 51	12 07		12 38	12 44	12 47		12 54	13 07		13 38		13 44	13 47		13 54	14 07
	d		11 38	11 45	11 48	11 50	11 53	12 07		12 38	12 45	12 47	12 50	12 54	13 07		13 38		13 45	13 48	13 50	13 54	14 07
Salford Central	d																						
Manchester Victoria ⇌	a					12 00							13 00								14 00		
Rochdale 41	a																						
Deansgate ⇌	a				11 52			12 11				12 51			13 11					13 51			14 11
Manchester Oxford Road	a	11 23	11 44	11 50	11 53		12 00	12 13	12 23	12 44	12 50	12 52		13 00	13 13	13 23	13 44		13 50	13 53		14 00	14 13
Manchester Piccadilly 10 ⇌	a	11 27			11 57			12 19	12 27			12 56			13 19	13 27				13 56			14 19
Stockport 84	a							12 33							13 30								14 33
Hazel Grove 86	a							12 42															14 42
Buxton 86	a																						
Heald Green 85	a																						
Manchester Airport 85 ✈	a	11 47			12 14				12 42			13 14				13 47				14 13			

A From Clitheroe
B To Salford Crescent
C To Chester
D From Edinburgh
E From Leeds to Morecambe

The Sunday service between Wigan Wallgate and Manchester Victoria via Atherton is funded by TfGM and will operate whilst funding exists

Table 82R

Sundays

30 March to 11 May

Barrow-in-Furness, Blackpool North, Preston, Southport, Kirkby and Wigan - Bolton - Manchester

Network Diagram - see first Page of Table 82

		TP		NT	NT	NT	TP	NT	NT	NT	TP	NT		NT	TP	NT	NT	NT	TP	NT	NT	TP		NT	NT
		◇1					◇1				◇1				◇1				◇1			◇1			
						A		B		C	D			A		B					A			B	
								🚌			🚲					🚌								🚌	
Barrow-in-Furness	d	12 33		13 10															14 25						
Roose	d			13 14															14 29						
Dalton	d			13 20															14 36						
Ulverston	d	12 49		13 29															14 44						
Cark	d			13 36															14 52						
Kents Bank	d			13 41															14 56						
Grange-over-Sands	d	13 01		13 45															15 00						
Arnside	d	13 07		13 51															15 06						
Silverdale	d			13 55															15 10						
Carnforth	d	13 17		14 03															15 17						
Windermere	83 d																								
Oxenholme Lake District	65 d										14 10														
Lancaster 6	65 a	13 25		14 15							14 24								15 25						
	d	13 25									14 25								15 25						
Blackpool North	97 d				13 20		13 44					14 20			14 44					15 20		15 44			
Layton	97 d				13 23							14 23								15 23					
Poulton-le-Fylde	97 d				13 27		13 50					14 27			14 50					15 27		15 50			
Kirkham & Wesham	97 d				13 37							14 37								15 37					
Preston 8	65,97 a	13 44			13 47		14 08				14 43	14 47			15 08				15 44	15 47		16 08			
	d	13 45			13 50		14 11				14 45	14 50			15 10				15 45	15 49		16 11			
Leyland	d				13 55							14 55								15 54					
Buckshaw Parkway	d				14 00		14 18					15 00			15 17					15 59		16 18			
Chorley	d				14 04		14 22					15 04			15 21					16 03		16 22			
Adlington (Lancashire)	d				14 09							15 09								16 08					
Blackrod	d				14 12							15 12								16 11					
Horwich Parkway	d				14 16		14 29					15 16			15 28					16 15		16 29			
Lostock	d				14 20							15 20								16 20					
Southport	d									14 05								15 05							
Meols Cop	d									14 10								15 10							
Bescar Lane	d																								
New Lane	d																								
Burscough Bridge	d									14 18								15 18							
Hoscar	d																								
Parbold	d									14 23								15 23							
Appley Bridge	d									14 27								15 27							
Gathurst	d									14 30								15 30							
Kirkby	d																								
Rainford	d																								
Upholland	d																								
Orrell	d																								
Pemberton	d																								
Wigan Wallgate	a									14 35								15 35							
	d								14 18	14 36							15 18	15 36							16 18
Wigan North Western	d	13 58									14 58								15 58						
Ince	d								14 21								15 21								16 21
Hindley	d								14 25	14 41							15 25	15 41							16 25
Westhoughton	d									14 46								15 46							
Bolton	a				14 25		14 35			14 54		15 25			15 34			15 54		16 25		16 35			
	d				14 25	14 32	14 36			14 54		15 26		15 32	15 35			15 54		16 25	16 32	16 36			
Moses Gate	d																								
Farnworth	d																								
Kearsley	d																								
Clifton	d																								
Daisy Hill	d								14 29								15 29								16 29
Hag Fold	d								14 32								15 32								16 32
Atherton	d								14 34								15 34								16 34
Walkden	d								14 40								15 40								16 40
Moorside	d								14 44								15 44								16 44
Swinton	d								14 46								15 46								16 46
Salford Crescent	a				14 38	14 44	14 48		14 54	15 07		15 38		15 44	15 47		15 54	16 07		16 38	16 44	16 48			16 54
	d				14 38	14 45	14 48	14 50	14 54	15 07		15 38		15 45	15 47	15 50	15 54	16 07		16 38	16 45	16 48		16 50	16 54
Salford Central	d																								
Manchester Victoria	⇌ a							15 00								16 00								17 00	
Rochdale	41 a																								
Deansgate	⇌ a						14 52			15 11					15 51			16 11				16 52			
Manchester Oxford Road	a	14 23			14 44	14 50	14 53		15 00	15 13	15 23	15 44		15 50	15 52		16 00	16 13	16 23	16 44	16 50	16 53			17 00
Manchester Piccadilly 10	⇌ a	14 27					14 57			15 19	15 27				15 56			16 19	16 27			16 57			
Stockport	84 a									15 31								16 32							
Hazel Grove	86 a																	16 42							
Buxton	86 a																								
Heald Green	85 a																								
Manchester Airport	85 ✈ a	14 47					15 13				15 47				16 12				16 47			17 13			

A From Clitheroe
B To Salford Crescent
C To Chester
D From Edinburgh

The Sunday service between Wigan Wallgate and Manchester Victoria via Atherton is funded by TfGM and will operate whilst funding exists

Table 82R

Sundays
30 March to 11 May

Barrow-in-Furness, Blackpool North, Preston, Southport, Kirkby and Wigan - Bolton - Manchester

Network Diagram - see first Page of Table 82

	NT	TP	NT	NT	NT	TP	NT		NT	NT	TP	NT	NT	TP	NT	NT	TP		NT	NT	TP	NT	TP	NT
		◇1				◇1					◇1			◇1			◇1				◇1		◇1	
	A	B		C	D		E				F		D		E	A	B			C		D		E
		✠					🚌				✠				🚌		✠							🚌
Barrow-in-Furness d																					18 17			
Roose d																					18 21			
Dalton d																					18 28			
Ulverston d																					18 36			
Cark d																					18 44			
Kents Bank d																					18 48			
Grange-over-Sands d																					18 52			
Arnside d																					18 58			
Silverdale d																					19 02			
Carnforth d				16 37																19 04	19 09			
Windermere 83 d																								
Oxenholme Lake District 65 d		16 10									17 09						18 10							
Lancaster 6 65 a		16 24		16 46							17 23						18 24			19 13	19 17			
d		16 25									17 24						18 25				19 17			
Blackpool North 97 d			16 20			16 44						17 20		17 44					18 20				18 44	
Layton 97 d			16 23									17 23							18 23					
Poulton-le-Fylde 97 d			16 27			16 50						17 27		17 50					18 27				18 50	
Kirkham & Wesham 97 d			16 37									17 37							18 37					
Preston 8 65,97 a		16 43	16 47			17 08					17 42	17 47		18 08			18 43		18 47		19 37		19 08	
d		16 45	16 49			17 10					17 45	17 49		18 10			18 45		18 49				19 10	
Leyland d			16 54									17 54							18 54					
Buckshaw Parkway d			16 59			17 17						17 59		18 17					18 59				19 17	
Chorley d			17 03			17 21						18 03		18 21					19 03				19 21	
Adlington (Lancashire) d			17 08									18 08							19 08					
Blackrod d			17 12									18 12							19 12					
Horwich Parkway d			17 16			17 28						18 16		18 28					19 16				19 28	
Lostock d			17 20									18 20							19 20					
Southport d	16 05									17 05						18 05								
Meols Cop d	16 10									17 10						18 10								
Bescar Lane d																								
New Lane d																								
Burscough Bridge d	16 18									17 18						18 18								
Hoscar d																								
Parbold d	16 23									17 23						18 23								
Appley Bridge d	16 27									17 27						18 27								
Gathurst d	16 30									17 30						18 30								
Kirkby d																								
Rainford d																								
Upholland d																								
Orrell d																								
Pemberton d																								
Wigan Wallgate a	16 35									17 35						18 35								
d	16 36								17 18	17 36						18 36								
Wigan North Western d		16 58									17 58						18 58							
Ince d									17 21															
Hindley d	16 41								17 25	17 41						18 41								
Westhoughton d	16 46									17 46						18 46								
Bolton a	16 54		17 25			17 34				17 54		18 25		18 34		18 54			19 25				19 34	
d	16 54		17 25		17 32	17 35				17 54		18 25	18 32	18 35		18 54			19 25			19 32	19 35	
Moses Gate d																								
Farnworth d																								
Kearsley d																								
Clifton d																								
Daisy Hill d									17 29															
Hag Fold d									17 32															
Atherton d									17 34															
Walkden d									17 40															
Moorside d									17 44															
Swinton d									17 46															
Salford Crescent a	17 07		17 38		17 44	17 47			17 54	18 07		18 38	18 44	18 47		19 08			19 38			19 44	19 47	
d	17 07		17 38		17 45	17 47	17 50		17 54	18 07		18 38	18 45	18 47	18 50	19 09			19 38			19 45	19 47	19 50
Salford Central d																								
Manchester Victoria ⇌ a							18 00								19 00									
Rochdale 41 a																								20 00
Deansgate ⇌ a	17 11					17 51				18 11				18 51		19 12							19 51	
Manchester Oxford Road a	17 13	17 23	17 44		17 50	17 52			18 00	18 13	18 23	18 44	18 50	18 52		19 15	19 23		19 44			19 50	19 52	
Manchester Piccadilly 10 ⇌ a	17 19	17 27				17 56				18 19	18 27			18 56		19 19	19 27						19 56	
Stockport 84 a	17 30									18 31						19 30								
Hazel Grove 86 a										18 42														
Buxton 86 a																								
Heald Green 85 a																								
Manchester Airport 85 ✈ a		17 47				18 13					18 47			19 13			19 47						20 13	

A To Chester
B From Edinburgh
C From Leeds to Morecambe
D From Clitheroe
E To Salford Crescent
F From Glasgow Central

The Sunday service between Wigan Wallgate and Manchester Victoria via Atherton is funded by TfGM and will operate whilst funding exists

Table 82R

Sundays

30 March to 11 May

Barrow-in-Furness, Blackpool North, Preston, Southport, Kirkby and Wigan - Bolton - Manchester

Network Diagram - see first Page of Table 82

		NT	TP	NT		NT	TP	NT	NT	TP	NT	NT	TP	NT		TP	NT	NT	NT	NT	TP	NT	TP	NT
			◇1				◇1			◇1			◇1			◇1					◇1		◇1	
			A			B		C	D	E			F	B			C			B		C	E	
								🚌									🚌					🚌		
			🚲							🚲													🚲	
Barrow-in-Furness	d										19 48													
Roose	d										19 52													
Dalton	d										19 58													
Ulverston	d										20 07													
Cark	d										20 14													
Kents Bank	d										20 19													
Grange-over-Sands	d										20 23													
Arnside	d										20 29													
Silverdale	d										20 33													
Carnforth	d										20 41													
Windermere 83	d												20 40											
Oxenholme Lake District 65	d		19 09							20 10			21 00										21 51	
Lancaster 6 65	a		19 24							20 24	20 52		21 18										22 06	
	d		19 24							20 25													22 06	
Blackpool North 97	d			19 20			19 44					20 20				20 44			21 20		21 44			
Layton 97	d			19 23								20 23							21 23					
Poulton-le-Fylde 97	d			19 27			19 50					20 27				20 50			21 27		21 50			
Kirkham & Wesham 97	d			19 37								20 37							21 37					
Preston 8 65,97	a		19 44	19 47			20 08			20 43		20 47				21 08			21 47		22 08		22 25	
	d		19 45	19 49			20 10			20 46		20 49				21 10			21 49		22 10		22 26	
Leyland	d			19 54								20 54							21 54					
Buckshaw Parkway	d			19 59			20 17					20 59				21 17			21 59		22 17			
Chorley	d			20 03			20 21					21 03				21 21			22 03		22 21			
Adlington (Lancashire)	d			20 08								21 08							22 08					
Blackrod	d			20 12								21 12							22 12					
Horwich Parkway	d			20 16			20 28					21 16				21 28			22 16		22 28			
Lostock	d			20 20								21 20							22 20					
Southport	d	19 05							20 05									21 05						22 05
Meols Cop	d	19 10							20 10									21 10						22 10
Bescar Lane	d																							
New Lane	d																							
Burscough Bridge	d	19 18							20 18									21 18						22 18
Hoscar	d																							
Parbold	d	19 23							20 23									21 23						22 23
Appley Bridge	d	19 27							20 27									21 27						22 27
Gathurst	d	19 30							20 30									21 30						22 30
Kirkby	d																							
Rainford	d																							
Upholland	d																							
Orrell	d																							
Pemberton	d																							
Wigan Wallgate	a	19 35							20 35									21 35						22 35
	d	19 36							20 36									21 36						22 36
Wigan North Western	d		19 59																				22 39	
Ince	d																							
Hindley	d	19 41							20 41									21 41						22 41
Westhoughton	d	19 46							20 46									21 46						22 46
Bolton	a	19 54		20 25			20 34		20 54			21 25				21 34		21 54	22 25		22 34			22 54
	d	19 54		20 25		20 32	20 35		20 54			21 25		21 32		21 35		21 54	22 25	22 32	22 35			22 54
Moses Gate	d																							
Farnworth	d																							
Kearsley	d																							
Clifton	d																							
Daisy Hill	d																							
Hag Fold	d																							
Atherton	d																							
Walkden	d																							
Moorside	d																							
Swinton	d																							
Salford Crescent	a	20 07		20 38		20 44	20 47		21 07			21 38		21 44		21 47		22 07	22 38	22 44	22 47			23 07
	d	20 07		20 38		20 45	20 47	20 50	21 07			21 38		21 45		21 47	21 50	22 07	22 38	22 45	22 47	22 50		23 07
Salford Central	d																							
Manchester Victoria 🚊	a							21 00									22 00					23 00		
Rochdale 41	a																							
Deansgate 🚊	a	20 11					20 51		21 11							21 51		22 11			22 51			23 11
Manchester Oxford Road	a	20 13	20 23	20 44		20 50	20 52		21 13	21 21		21 44		21 50		21 52		22 13	22 44	22 50	22 52		23 04	23 15
Manchester Piccadilly 10 🚊	a	20 19	20 27				20 56		21 19	21 25						21 56		22 19			22 56		23 08	23 19
Stockport 84	a	20 32							21 30									22 32						23 34
Hazel Grove 86	a	20 42																22 42						
Buxton 86	a																							
Heald Green 85	a																							
Manchester Airport 85 ✈	a		20 45				21 13			21 45						22 12					23 15		23 24	

A From Glasgow Central
B From Clitheroe
C To Salford Crescent
D To Chester
E From Edinburgh
F To Barrow-in-Furness

The Sunday service between Wigan Wallgate and Manchester Victoria via Atherton is funded by TfGM and will operate whilst funding exists

Table 82R

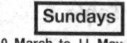

Sundays
30 March to 11 May

Barrow-in-Furness, Blackpool North, Preston, Southport, Kirkby and Wigan - Bolton - Manchester

Network Diagram - see first Page of Table 82

Station			NT	NT	TP
					◇1
			A		
				🚌	
Barrow-in-Furness		d			
Roose		d			
Dalton		d			
Ulverston		d			
Cark		d			
Kents Bank		d			
Grange-over-Sands		d			
Arnside		d			
Silverdale		d			
Carnforth		d			
Windermere	83	d			
Oxenholme Lake District	65	d			
Lancaster 6	65	a			
		d			
Blackpool North	97	d			23 02
Layton	97	d			
Poulton-le-Fylde	97	d			23 08
Kirkham & Wesham	97	d			23 17
Preston 8	65,97	a			23 28
		d			23 29
Leyland		d			23 34
Buckshaw Parkway		d			23 38
Chorley		d			23 42
Adlington (Lancashire)		d			23 46
Blackrod		d			23 50
Horwich Parkway		d			23 53
Lostock		d			23 57
Southport		d			
Meols Cop		d			
Bescar Lane		d			
New Lane		d			
Burscough Bridge		d			
Hoscar		d			
Parbold		d			
Appley Bridge		d			
Gathurst		d			
Kirkby		d			
Rainford		d			
Upholland		d			
Orrell		d			
Pemberton		d			
Wigan Wallgate		a			
		d			
Wigan North Western		d			
Ince		d			
Hindley		d			
Westhoughton		d			
Bolton		a			00 02
		d	23 31		00 02
Moses Gate		d			
Farnworth		d			
Kearsley		d			
Clifton		d			
Daisy Hill		d			
Hag Fold		d			
Atherton		d			
Walkden		d			
Moorside		d			
Swinton		d			
Salford Crescent		a	23 43		
		d	23 44	23 50	
Salford Central		d			
Manchester Victoria	🚊	a		00 01	
Rochdale	41	a			
Deansgate	🚊	a			
Manchester Oxford Road		a	23 50		
Manchester Piccadilly 10	🚊	a			00 18
Stockport	84	a			
Hazel Grove	86	a			
Buxton	86	a			
Heald Green	85	a			
Manchester Airport	85 ✈	a			00 35

A From Clitheroe

The Sunday service between Wigan Wallgate and Manchester Victoria via Atherton is funded by TfGM and will operate whilst funding exists

Table 83

Oxenholme - Lake District - Windermere

Mondays to Fridays

9 December to 16 May

Network Diagram - see first Page of Table 82

Miles			TP	TP	TP	TP	TP	TP	TP	TP	TP	TP	TP	TP	TP	TP	TP	TP	TP	TP	TP	TP	TP
															FX	FO		FX		FO			
			1	1	1	1	1	◇1	1	◇1	1	1	1	1	◇1	1	◇1	1	1	◇1	1	1	1
			A					B		C				D	E	F	G	H	I	J			
0	Oxenholme Lake District	d	06 20	07 33	08 27	09 14	10 27	11 18	12 28	13 18	14 17	15 36	16 28	17 35	17 42	18 35	18 37	18 43	19 35	19 39	20 22	21 15	22 20
2¼	Kendal	d	06 25	07 37	08 31	09 18	10 31	11 22	12 32	13 22	14 21	15 40	16 32	17 39	17 46	18 39	18 42	18 47	19 39	19 43	20 26	21 19	22 24
4	Burneside	d		07 41	08 35	09 22	10 35	11 26	12 36	13 26	14 25	15 44	16 36	17 43	17 50		18 45	18 51	19 43	19 47	20 30		22 27
6½	Staveley	d		07 46	08 40	09 27	10 40	11 31	12 41	13 31	14 30	15 50	16 41	17 48	17 55		18 50	18 56	19 48	19 52	20 35		22 32
10	Windermere	a	06 40	07 52	08 46	09 33	10 46	11 39	12 47	13 39	14 36	15 56	16 47	17 54	18 01	18 52	19 00	19 04	19 54	19 59	20 42	21 32	22 39

Saturdays

14 December to 8 February

		TP	TP	TP	TP	TP	TP	TP	TP	TP	TP	TP	TP	TP	TP	TP	TP	TP
		1	1	1	1	◇1	◇1		1	◇1	1	◇1	1	◇1	1	1	1	1
		A				B	B	K (bus)	L	M	L	N	L	N	L	L	L	L
Oxenholme Lake District	d	06 20	07 22	08 27	09 14	10 04	11 18	12 20	12 28	13 18	14 17	15 18	16 28	17 38	18 35	19 35	20 22	21 15
Kendal	d	06 25	07 26	08 31	09 18	10 08	11 22		12 32	13 22	14 21	15 22	16 32	17 42	18 39	19 39	20 26	21 19
Burneside	d		07 30	08 35	09 22	10 12	11 26		12 36	13 26	14 25	15 26	16 36	17 46	18 43	19 43	20 30	21 23
Staveley	d		07 35	08 40	09 27	10 17	11 31		12 41	13 31	14 30	15 31	16 41	17 51	18 48	19 48	20 35	21 28
Windermere	a	06 40	07 41	08 46	09 33	10 27	11 39	12 42	12 47	13 39	14 36	15 39	16 47	17 58	18 54	19 54	20 42	21 34

Saturdays

15 February to 17 May

		TP	TP	TP	TP	TP	TP	TP	TP	TP	TP	TP	TP	TP	TP	TP	TP	TP
		1	1	1	1	◇1	◇1	1	◇1	1	◇1	1	◇1	1	1	1	1	
		A				B	B		C		C		B				O	P (bus)
Oxenholme Lake District	d	06 20	07 22	08 27	09 14	10 04	11 18	12 28	13 18	14 17	15 18	16 28	17 38	18 35	19 35	20 22	21 15	21 20
Kendal	d	06 25	07 26	08 31	09 18	10 08	11 22	12 32	13 22	14 21	15 22	16 32	17 42	18 39	19 39	20 26	21 19	
Burneside	d		07 30	08 35	09 22	10 12	11 26	12 36	13 26	14 25	15 26	16 36	17 46	18 43	19 43	20 30	21 23	
Staveley	d		07 35	08 40	09 27	10 17	11 31	12 41	13 31	14 30	15 31	16 41	17 51	18 48	19 48	20 35	21 28	
Windermere	a	06 40	07 41	08 46	09 33	10 27	11 39	12 47	13 39	14 36	15 39	16 47	17 58	18 54	19 54	20 42	21 34	21 42

Sundays

8 December to 29 December

		TP	TP	TP	TP	TP	TP	TP	TP	TP	TP	TP
		◇1	1	1	1	1	1	1	1	1	1	1
		A										
Oxenholme Lake District	d	10 38	11 37	12 33	13 35	14 35	15 35	16 21	17 35	18 35	19 28	20 16
Kendal	d	10 42	11 41	12 37	13 39	14 39	15 39	16 25	17 39	18 39	19 32	20 20
Burneside	d		11 45	12 41	13 43	14 43	15 43	16 29	17 43	18 43		20 23
Staveley	d		11 50	12 46	13 48	14 49	15 48	16 34	17 48	18 48		20 28
Windermere	a	10 58	11 56	12 52	13 54	14 55	15 54	16 40	17 54	18 54	19 44	20 35

Sundays

5 January to 9 February

		TP	TP	TP	TP	TP	TP
		1	1	1	1	1	1
Oxenholme Lake District	d	15 35	16 21	17 35	18 35	19 28	20 16
Kendal	d	15 39	16 25	17 39	18 39	19 32	20 20
Burneside	d	15 43	16 29	17 43	18 43		20 23
Staveley	d	15 48	16 34	17 48	18 48		20 28
Windermere	a	15 54	16 40	17 54	18 54	19 44	20 35

Sundays

16 February to 23 March

		TP	TP	TP	TP	TP	TP	TP	TP	TP	TP	TP
		◇1	1	1	1	1	1	1	1	1	1	1
		A										
Oxenholme Lake District	d	10 38	11 37	12 33	13 35	14 35	15 35	16 21	17 35	18 35	19 28	20 16
Kendal	d	10 42	11 41	12 37	13 39	14 39	15 39	16 25	17 39	18 39	19 32	20 20
Burneside	d		11 45	12 41	13 43	14 43	15 43	16 29	17 43	18 43		20 23
Staveley	d		11 50	12 46	13 48	14 49	15 48	16 34	17 48	18 48		20 28
Windermere	a	10 58	11 56	12 52	13 54	14 55	15 54	16 40	17 54	18 54	19 44	20 35

A From Lancaster
B From Manchester Airport
C From Preston
D FO until 31 January, from 7 February
E until 6 February. From Manchester Airport
F until 7 February
G from 10 February. From Manchester Oxford Road
H until 6 February. From Lancaster
I FX until 6 February, from 10 February
J until 7 February. From Manchester Airport
K from 4 January
L 14 December, 21 December, 28 December
M 14 December, 21 December, 28 December. From Preston
N 14 December, 21 December, 28 December. From Manchester Airport
O until 22 March
P from 29 March

Refer to table 65 for buses from Lancaster to Windermere

Table 83

Sundays

30 March to 11 May

Oxenholme - Lake District - Windermere

Network Diagram - see first Page of Table 82

		TP	TP	TP	TP	TP	TP	TP		TP	TP	TP	TP
			1	1	1	1	1	1		1	1	1	1
		🚌											
Oxenholme Lake District	d	10 40	11 40	12 33	13 35	14 35	15 35	16 21		17 35	18 35	19 28	20 16
Kendal	d		11 44	12 37	13 39	14 39	15 39	16 25		17 39	18 39	19 32	20 20
Burneside	d			12 41	13 43	14 43	15 43	16 29		17 43	18 43		20 23
Staveley	d			12 46	13 48	14 49	15 48	16 34		17 48	18 48		20 28
Windermere	a	11 02	11 56	12 52	13 54	14 55	15 54	16 40		17 54	18 54	19 44	20 35

Refer to table 65 for buses from Lancaster to Windermere

Table 83R

Windermere - Oxenholme - Lake District

Mondays to Fridays

9 December to 16 May

Network Diagram - see first Page of Table 82

Miles			TP	TP	TP	TP	TP	TP	TP	TP	TP	TP	TP	TP	TP	TP	TP	TP	TP	TP	TP	TP	TP
														FX	FO		FX	FO			FO		
			1	1	1	1	◇1	1	◇1	1	1	1	1	◇1	1	◇1	◇1	◇1	1	1	1	1	1
							A		B				C	D	E	F	D	G	H	H	E		
0	**Windermere**	d	06 58	07 56	08 50	09 45	10 51	11 45	12 52	13 44	14 58	16 00	17 06	17 06	18 02	18 02	18 05	18 56	19 08	19 59	20 03	20 50	21 40
3½	Staveley	d	07 03	08 02	.	09 50	.	11 50	12 57	13 49	15 03	.	17 11	17 11	18 07	18 07		19 01	19 13	20 04		20 55	21 45
6	Burneside	d	07 08	08 07	.	09 55	.	11 55	13 02	13 54	15 08	.	17 16	17 16	18 12	18 12		19 06	19 18	20 09		21 00	21 50
7¾	Kendal	d	07 12	08 11	09 01	09 59	11 03	11 59	13 06	13 58	15 12	16 12	17 20	17 20	18 16	18 16	18 17	19 10	19 22	20 13	20 14	21 04	21 54
10	**Oxenholme Lake District**	a	07 17	08 16	09 06	10 04	11 08	12 04	13 11	14 03	15 18	16 17	17 25	17 25	18 21	18 21	18 22	19 15	19 27	20 18	20 19	21 09	21 59

		TP
		◇1
		I
Windermere	d	22 45
Staveley	d	22 50
Burneside	d	22 55
Kendal	d	22 59
Oxenholme Lake District	a	23 04

Saturdays

14 December to 8 February

		TP	TP	TP	TP	TP	TP	TP	TP	TP	TP	TP	TP	TP	TP	TP	TP	TP
		1	1	1	◇1	◇1	1	◇1	1	◇1	1	◇1	1	1		1	1	◇1
					J	A		K	L	M	L	M	L	L	N	L	L	K
															🚌			
Windermere	d	06 58	07 46	08 50	09 37	10 48	11 45	12 52	13 44	14 52	15 50	17 06	18 02	19 04	19 45	19 59	20 45	21 40
Staveley	d	07 03	07 51	.	09 42	10 53	11 50	12 57	13 49	14 57	15 55	17 11	18 07	19 09		20 04		21 45
Burneside	d	07 08	07 56	.	09 47	10 58	11 55	13 02	13 54	15 02	16 00	17 16	18 12	19 14		20 09		21 50
Kendal	d	07 12	08 00	09 01	09 51	11 03	11 59	13 06	13 58	15 06	16 04	17 20	18 16	19 18		20 13	20 56	21 54
Oxenholme Lake District	a	07 17	08 05	09 06	09 56	11 08	12 04	13 12	14 03	15 11	16 09	17 25	18 21	19 23	19 59	20 18	21 01	21 59

Saturdays

15 February to 17 May

		TP	TP	TP	TP	TP	TP	TP	TP	TP	TP	TP	TP	TP	TP	TP	TP
		1	1	1	◇1	◇1	1	◇1	1	◇1	1	◇1	1	1	1	1	◇1
					J	A		J		A		A					O
Windermere	d	06 58	07 46	08 50	09 37	10 48	11 45	12 52	13 44	14 52	15 50	17 06	18 02	19 04	19 59	20 45	21 40
Staveley	d	07 03	07 51	.	09 42	10 53	11 50	12 57	13 49	14 57	15 55	17 11	18 07	19 09	20 04	.	21 45
Burneside	d	07 08	07 56	.	09 47	10 58	11 55	13 02	13 54	15 02	16 00	17 16	18 12	19 14	20 09	.	21 50
Kendal	d	07 12	08 00	09 01	09 51	11 03	11 59	13 06	13 58	15 06	16 04	17 20	18 16	19 18	20 13	20 56	21 54
Oxenholme Lake District	a	07 17	08 05	09 06	09 56	11 08	12 04	13 12	14 03	15 11	16 09	17 25	18 21	19 23	20 18	21 01	21 59

Sundays

8 December to 29 December

		TP	TP	TP	TP	TP	TP	TP	TP	TP	TP	TP
		1	1	1	1	1	1	1	1	1	1	◇1
												B
Windermere	d	11 00	11 58	12 58	13 58	15 00	15 58	16 45	18 04	19 00	19 48	20 40
Staveley	d	.	12 03	13 03	14 03	.	16 03	16 50	18 09	19 05	.	20 45
Burneside	d	.	12 08	13 08	14 08	.	16 08	16 55	18 14	19 10	.	20 50
Kendal	d	11 12	12 12	13 12	14 12	15 12	16 12	16 59	18 18	19 14	19 59	20 54
Oxenholme Lake District	a	11 17	12 17	13 17	14 18	15 17	16 17	17 04	18 23	19 19	20 04	20 59

Sundays

5 January to 9 February

		TP	TP	TP	TP	TP	TP	TP
			1	1	1	1	1	◇1
								B
		🚌						
Windermere	d	14 50	15 58	16 45	18 04	19 00	19 48	20 40
Staveley	d	.	16 03	16 50	18 09	19 05	.	20 45
Burneside	d	.	16 08	16 55	18 14	19 10	.	20 50
Kendal	d	.	16 12	16 59	18 18	19 14	19 59	20 54
Oxenholme Lake District	a	15 04	16 17	17 04	18 23	19 19	20 04	20 59

A To Manchester Airport
B To Barrow-in-Furness
C FO until 31 January, from 7 February
D until 6 February. To Manchester Airport
E until 7 February
F from 10 February. To Preston
G until 7 February. To Preston
H FX until 6 February, from 10 February
I To Blackpool North
J To Preston
K 14 December, 21 December, 28 December. To Preston
L 14 December, 21 December, 28 December
M 14 December, 21 December, 28 December. To Manchester Airport
N from 4 January
O until 22 March. To Lancaster

Refer to table 65 for buses from Windermere to Lancaster

Table 83R

Sundays

16 February to 23 March

Windermere - Oxenholme - Lake District

Network Diagram - see first Page of Table 82

		TP	TP	TP	TP	TP	TP	TP		TP	TP	TP	TP
		1	1	1	1	1	1	1		1	1	1	◇1
													A
Windermere	d	11 00	11 58	12 58	13 58	15 00	15 58	16 45		18 04	19 00	19 48	20 40
Staveley	d		12 03	13 03	14 03		16 03	16 50		18 09	19 05		20 45
Burneside	d		12 08	13 08	14 08		16 08	16 55		18 14	19 10		20 50
Kendal	d	11 12	12 12	13 12	14 12	15 12	16 12	16 59		18 18	19 14	19 59	20 54
Oxenholme Lake District	a	11 17	12 17	13 17	14 18	15 17	16 17	17 04		18 23	19 19	20 04	20 59

Sundays

30 March to 11 May

		TP	TP	TP	TP	TP	TP	TP	TP	TP		TP	TP
			1	1	1	1	1	1	1	1		1	◇1
		🚌											A
Windermere	d	10 53	12 00	12 58	13 58	15 00	15 58	16 45	18 04	19 00		19 48	20 40
Staveley	d			13 03	14 03		16 03	16 50	18 09	19 05			20 45
Burneside	d			13 08	14 08		16 08	16 55	18 14	19 10			20 50
Kendal	d		12 12	13 12	14 12	15 12	16 12	16 59	18 18	19 14		19 59	20 54
Oxenholme Lake District	a	11 07	12 17	13 17	14 18	15 17	16 17	17 04	18 23	19 19		20 04	20 59

A To Barrow-in-Furness

Refer to table 65 for buses from Windermere to Lancaster

Table 84

Mondays to Fridays

9 December to 16 May

Stoke-on-Trent and Crewe - Manchester Airport, Stockport and Manchester

Network Diagram - see first Page of Table 78

Miles	Miles	Miles			VT	NT	NT	NT	NT	NT	NT	VT	NT		NT	TP	AW	NT	NT	NT	NT	NT	EM		XC
					MO	MX	MX	MX																	
					◇1							◇1				◇1							◇		◇1
					A	B	C	D		E			F			G		H		I		B	J		
					☕																				
—	—	—	London Euston 15 ⊖65	d																					
—	—	—	Birmingham New Street 12 68	d																					05 57
—	—	—	Wolverhampton 7 68	d																					06 16
—	—	—	Stafford 65,67	d																					06 30
0	—	—	**Stoke-on-Trent** 50	d																	06 30				06 51
3	—	—	Longport 50	d																	06 34				
6¼	—	—	Kidsgrove 50	d																	06 38				
—	0	—	**Crewe** 10	d			00 44	00 44			05 48	06 11					06 27								
—	4¾	—	Sandbach	d							05 55														
—	8½	—	Holmes Chapel	d							06 00														
—	10½	—	Goostrey	d							06 03														
—	14¼	—	Chelford	d							06 07														
—	17¼	—	Alderley Edge	d							06 11								06 49						
—	19	0	**Wilmslow**	d						05 46	06 15	06 27					06 45		06 52						
—	—	2	Styal	d																					
—	—	4¼	**Manchester Airport** ✈	a				01 08		05 53															
—	20½	—	Handforth	d							06 18								06 55						
11¾	—	—	Congleton	d																	06 45				07 03
19¾	—	—	**Macclesfield**	a																	06 52				07 11
—	—	—		d											06 22						06 53				07 12
22½	—	—	Prestbury	d											06 26						06 57				
24½	—	—	Adlington (Cheshire)	d											06 29						07 00				
26½	—	—	Poynton	d											06 33						07 04				
28	—	—	Bramhall	d											06 35						07 07				
29½	22¾	—	Cheadle Hulme	d							06 22				06 38				06 59		07 11				
31¾	25	—	**Stockport**	a							06 27	06 36			06 43		06 55		07 04		07 15				07 25
—	—	—		d	00 01	00 04			06 05		06 27	06 37	06 41		06 43	06 53	06 55	06 58	07 04	07 10	07 16	07 19	07 22		07 26
31¾	26½	—	Heaton Chapel	d							06 31				06 46				07 08	07 15					
34¾	28	—	Levenshulme	d							06 34				06 49				07 11	07 18					
37¾	31	—	**Manchester Picc.** 10 85,89	a	00 12	00 18	01 20	01 36	06 14	06 25	06 42	06 48	06 52		06 58	07 02	07 07	07 10	07 20	07 26	07 27	07 30	07 34		07 34
—	—	—		d									06 53							07 27			07 34		
38¼	31½	—	**Manchester Oxford Rd** 85,89	a									06 56							07 29			07 37		
38¾	32	—	Deansgate 85,89	a									06 59							07 32					

		NT	NT	NT	NT	NT	XC	TP	NT		AW	NT	NT	NT	VT	NT	XC	EM	NT		NT	NT	VT	NT	NT
							◇1	◇1			◇				◇1		◇1	◇					◇1		
				H				K	H		L		M	N		B		J						O	
							🛒	🛒							⊠		🛒						⊠		
London Euston 15 ⊖65	d														06 16								06 36		
Birmingham New Street 12 68	d						06 22										06 57								
Wolverhampton 7 68	d						06 41										07 15								
Stafford 65,67	d						06 55										07 30								
Stoke-on-Trent 50	d						07 14					07 17			07 45										07 57
Longport 50	d											07 21													
Kidsgrove 50	d											07 26													08 04
Crewe 10	d	06 33	06 49								07 27			07 22			07 52					07 56	08 11		
Sandbach	d	06 40	06 56											07 35								08 03			
Holmes Chapel	d	06 43	07 00											07 41								08 07			
Goostrey	d		07 03											07 45											
Chelford	d		07 08											07 51											
Alderley Edge	d	06 53	07 12			07 30								07 56					07 53			08 16			
Wilmslow	d	06 57	07 16			07 33					07 45			08 00			08 09		07 56			08 19	08 27		
Styal	d																		07 59						
Manchester Airport ✈	a	07 04																	08 04						
Handforth	d		07 19			07 37								08 03								08 22			
Congleton	d											07 33													08 11
Macclesfield	a						07 30					07 40			08 01										08 18
	d				07 15		07 31					07 40			08 02						08 06				08 19
Prestbury	d				07 20							07 45									08 10				08 23
Adlington (Cheshire)	d				07 24							07 48													08 26
Poynton	d				07 27							07 52									08 15				08 30
Bramhall	d				07 30							07 55									08 17				08 33
Cheadle Hulme	d		07 24		07 34	07 42						07 59		08 09							08 20	08 27			08 37
Stockport	a		07 29		07 41	07 47	07 45				07 54	08 04		08 14	08 16		08 20				08 27	08 31	08 36		08 41
	d		07 29	07 31	07 41	07 48	07 50	07 53	07 57		07 54	08 04	08 10	08 14	08 17	08 19	08 21	08 24			08 28	08 31	08 37	08 41	08 42
Heaton Chapel	d		07 33									08 08		08 18								08 36			08 45
Levenshulme	d		07 36									08 11		08 21							08 32				08 48
Manchester Picc. 10 85,89	a	07 42	07 44	07 45	07 56	07 58	07 59	08 02	08 09		08 10	08 21	08 25	08 27	08 28	08 29	08 34	08 36	08 42		08 42	08 45	08 49	08 52	08 56
	d													08 29				08 37						08 54	
Manchester Oxford Rd 85,89	a													08 31				08 40						08 56	
Deansgate 85,89	a													08 38										09 00	

A From London Euston
B From Chester
C from 31 December until 21 March
D until 27 December, from 25 March
E until 27 December
F From Buxton to Clitheroe
G From Doncaster to Manchester Airport
H From Hazel Grove
I From Buxton to Wigan North Western
J From Nottingham to Liverpool Lime Street
K From Cleethorpes to Manchester Airport
L From Cardiff Central
M From Buxton
N To Salford Crescent
O From Hazel Grove to Preston

Table 84

Mondays to Fridays

9 December to 16 May

Stoke-on-Trent and Crewe - Manchester Airport, Stockport and Manchester

Network Diagram - see first Page of Table 78

			XC	TP	VT	AW		NT	NT	VT	NT	EM	XC	NT	NT	VT		NT	NT	XC	TP	VT	AW	NT	NT	VT
			◇1	◇1	◇1	◇				◇1		◇	◇1			◇1				◇1	◇1	◇1	◇			◇1
				A		B			C		D	E	F					G		H	A		I		C	
			⊥	⊥	⊠	⊥				⊠			⊥			⊠				⊥	⊥	⊠	⊥			⊠
London Euston 15	⊖65	d			06 55					07 20						07 35						08 00				08 20
Birmingham New Street 12	68	d	07 31										07 57							08 31						
Wolverhampton 7	68 ⛴	d	07 49										08 15							08 49						
Stafford	65,67	d	08 01										08 30							09 01						
Stoke-on-Trent	50	d	08 20		08 25					08 48			08 55						08 58	09 20		09 25				09 48
Longport	50	d																								
Kidsgrove	50	d																	09 05							
Crewe 10		d				08 28								08 31	08 50	09 11							09 30			
Sandbach		d												08 38	08 57											
Holmes Chapel		d												08 42	09 02											
Goostrey		d												08 45	09 05											
Chelford		d												08 50	09 09											
Alderley Edge		d						08 49						08 54	09 13									09 49		
Wilmslow		d				08 45		08 52						08 57	09 17	09 27							09 47	09 51		
Styal		d																								
Manchester Airport	✈	a												09 04												
Handforth		d						08 55							09 20									09 54		
Congleton		d																	09 12							
Macclesfield		a	08 36		08 41								09 11						09 19			09 41				
		d	08 37		08 41								09 12						09 20			09 41				
Prestbury		d																	09 24							
Adlington (Cheshire)		d																	09 27							
Poynton		d																	09 30							
Bramhall		d																	09 33							
Cheadle Hulme		d						08 59							09 24				09 37					09 59		
Stockport		a	08 50		08 55	08 59		09 04		09 16			09 27		09 29	09 36			09 41	09 49		09 55	09 57	10 04		10 16
		d	08 50	08 53	08 56	08 59		09 04	09 12	09 17	09 21	09 25	09 28		09 29	09 37		09 41	09 42	09 50	09 53	09 56	09 58	10 04	10 12	10 17
Heaton Chapel		d						09 08			09 25				09 33				09 45					10 08		
Levenshulme		d						09 11			09 28				09 36				09 48					10 11		
Manchester Picc. 10	85,89 ⛴	a	08 59	09 02	09 07	09 14		09 20	09 26	09 28	09 35	09 36	09 38	09 42	09 44	09 49		09 52	09 56	09 59	10 02	10 07	10 14	10 20	10 27	10 28
		d										09 37						09 54								
Manchester Oxford Rd	85,89	a										09 40						09 56								
Deansgate	85,89 ⛴	a																10 00								

				NT	EM	XC	NT	NT	VT	NT	NT	XC		TP	VT	AW	NT	NT	VT	NT	EM	XC		NT	NT	VT
					◇	◇1			◇1			◇1		◇1	◇1	◇			◇1		◇	◇1				◇1
				D	J	F				G		B		A		I		C		D	J	K				
						⊥			⊠			⊥		⊥	⊠	⊥			⊠			⊥				⊠
London Euston 15	⊖65	d							08 40						09 00				09 20							09 40
Birmingham New Street 12	68	d				08 57						09 31										09 57				
Wolverhampton 7	68 ⛴	d				09 15						09 49										10 15				
Stafford	65,67	d				09 30						10 01										10 30				
Stoke-on-Trent	50	d				09 55					09 58	10 20			10 25				10 48			10 55				
Longport	50	d																								
Kidsgrove	50	d									10 05															
Crewe 10		d					09 33	09 50	10 11							10 31								10 34	10 50	11 11
Sandbach		d					09 40	09 57																10 41	10 57	
Holmes Chapel		d					09 44	10 02																10 45	11 02	
Goostrey		d						10 05																	11 05	
Chelford		d						10 09																	11 09	
Alderley Edge		d					09 53	10 13									10 49							10 54	11 13	
Wilmslow		d					09 57	10 17	10 27							10 49	10 52							10 57	11 17	11 27
Styal		d																								
Manchester Airport	✈	a					10 04																	11 04		
Handforth		d						10 20									10 55								11 20	
Congleton		d									10 12															
Macclesfield		a				10 11					10 19				10 41							11 11				
		d				10 12					10 20				10 41							11 12				
Prestbury		d									10 24															
Adlington (Cheshire)		d									10 27															
Poynton		d									10 30															
Bramhall		d									10 33															
Cheadle Hulme		d						10 24			10 37						10 59								11 24	
Stockport		a				10 27		10 29	10 36		10 41	10 49			10 55	10 58	11 04		11 16			11 27			11 29	11 36
		d		10 21	10 26	10 28		10 29	10 37	10 41	10 42	10 50		10 53	10 56	10 58	11 04	11 12	11 17	11 21	11 26	11 28			11 29	11 37
Heaton Chapel		d		10 25				10 33			10 45						11 08			11 25					11 33	
Levenshulme		d		10 28				10 36			10 48						11 11			11 28					11 36	
Manchester Picc. 10	85,89 ⛴	a		10 35	10 36	10 38	10 42	10 43	10 49	10 52	10 56	10 59		11 02	11 07	11 15	11 20	11 27	11 28	11 35	11 36	11 38		11 42	11 44	11 49
		d			10 37					10 54											11 37					
Manchester Oxford Rd	85,89	a			10 40					10 56											11 40					
Deansgate	85,89 ⛴	a								11 00																

A From Cleethorpes to Manchester Airport
B From Cardiff Central
C From Buxton
D From Chester
E From Nottingham to Liverpool Lime Street
F From Southampton Central
G From Hazel Grove to Preston
H From Bristol Temple Meads
I From Carmarthen
J From Norwich to Liverpool Lime Street
K From Bournemouth

Table 84

Mondays to Fridays

9 December to 16 May

Stoke-on-Trent and Crewe - Manchester Airport, Stockport and Manchester

Network Diagram - see first Page of Table 78

	NT	NT	XC	TP	VT	AW		NT	NT	VT	NT	EM	XC	NT	NT	VT		NT	NT	XC	TP	VT	AW	NT
			◇1	◇1	◇1	◇				◇1		◇	◇1			◇1				◇1	◇1	◇1	◇	
	A		B	C		D			E		F	G	H					A		I	C		D	
			⌶	⌶	⊠	⌶				⊠			⌶			⊠				⌶	⌶	⊏	⌶	
London Euston 15 ⊖65 d					10 00					10 20						10 40						11 00		
Birmingham New Street 12 68 d			10 31										10 57							11 31				
Wolverhampton 7 68 d			10 49										11 15							11 49				
Stafford 65,67 d			11 01										11 30							12 01				
Stoke-on-Trent 50 d		10 58	11 20		11 25					11 48			11 55						11 58	12 20		12 25		
Longport 50 d																								
Kidsgrove 50 d		11 05																	12 05					
Crewe 10 d						11 31								11 34	11 50	12 11							12 31	
Sandbach d														11 41	11 57									
Holmes Chapel d														11 45	12 02									
Goostrey d															12 05									
Chelford d															12 09									
Alderley Edge d								11 48						11 54	12 13									12 49
Wilmslow d						11 48		11 51						11 57	12 17	12 27							12 49	12 52
Styal d																								
Manchester Airport ✈ a														12 04										
Handforth d								11 54							12 20									12 55
Congleton d		11 12																	12 12					
Macclesfield a		11 19			11 41								12 11						12 19			12 41		
d		11 20			11 41								12 12						12 20			12 41		
Prestbury d		11 24																	12 24					
Adlington (Cheshire) d		11 27																	12 27					
Poynton d		11 30																	12 30					
Bramhall d		11 33																	12 33					
Cheadle Hulme d		11 37						11 59							12 24				12 37					12 59
Stockport a		11 41	11 49		11 55	11 58		12 04		12 16			12 26		12 29	12 36			12 41	12 49		12 55	12 58	13 04
d	11 41	11 42	11 50	11 53	11 56	11 58		12 04	12 12	12 17	12 21	12 25	12 27		12 29	12 37		12 41	12 42	12 50	12 53	12 56	12 58	13 04
Heaton Chapel d		11 45						12 08			12 25				12 33				12 45					13 08
Levenshulme d		11 48						12 11			12 28				12 36				12 48					13 11
Manchester Picc. 10 85,89 a	11 52	11 56	11 59	12 02	12 07	12 15		12 20	12 27	12 28	12 35	12 36	12 38	12 42	12 44	12 49		12 52	12 56	12 59	13 02	13 07	13 15	13 20
d	11 54											12 37						12 54						
Manchester Oxford Rd 85,89 a	11 56											12 40						12 56						
Deansgate 85,89 a	12 00																	13 00						

	NT	VT		NT	EM	XC	NT	NT	VT	NT	NT	XC		TP	VT	AW	NT	NT	VT	NT	EM	XC		NT
		◇1			◇	◇1			◇1			◇1		◇1	◇1	◇			◇1		◇	◇1		
	E			F	G	H				A		I		C		J		E		F	G	H		
		⊏				⌶			⊏			⌶		⌶	⊏	⌶			⊏			⌶		
London Euston 15 ⊖65 d		11 20							11 40						12 00				12 20					
Birmingham New Street 12 68 d						11 57						12 31										12 57		
Wolverhampton 7 68 d						12 15						12 49										13 15		
Stafford 65,67 d						12 30						13 01										13 30		
Stoke-on-Trent 50 d		12 48				12 55					12 58	13 20			13 25				13 48			13 55		
Longport 50 d																								
Kidsgrove 50 d											13 05													
Crewe 10 d							12 34	12 50	13 11							13 31								13 34
Sandbach d							12 41	12 57																13 41
Holmes Chapel d							12 45	13 02																13 45
Goostrey d								13 05																
Chelford d								13 09																
Alderley Edge d							12 54	13 13									13 48							13 54
Wilmslow d							12 57	13 17	13 27							13 48	13 51							13 57
Styal d																								
Manchester Airport ✈ a							13 04																	14 04
Handforth d								13 20									13 54							
Congleton d											13 12													
Macclesfield a						13 11					13 19				13 41							14 11		
d						13 12					13 20				13 41							14 12		
Prestbury d											13 24													
Adlington (Cheshire) d											13 27													
Poynton d											13 30													
Bramhall d											13 33													
Cheadle Hulme d								13 24			13 37						13 59							
Stockport a		13 16				13 27		13 29	13 36		13 41	13 49			13 55	13 58	14 04		14 16			14 27		
d	13 12	13 17		13 21	13 26	13 28		13 29	13 37	13 41	13 42	13 50		13 53	13 56	13 58	14 04	14 12	14 17	14 21	14 26	14 28		
Heaton Chapel d				13 25				13 33			13 45						14 08			14 25				
Levenshulme d				13 28				13 36			13 48						14 11			14 28				
Manchester Picc. 10 85,89 a	13 27	13 28		13 35	13 36	13 38	13 42	13 44	13 49	13 52	13 56	13 59		14 02	14 07	14 15	14 20	14 27	14 28	14 35	14 36	14 38		14 42
d					13 37					13 54											14 37			
Manchester Oxford Rd 85,89 a					13 40					13 56											14 40			
Deansgate 85,89 a										14 00														

A From Hazel Grove to Preston
B From Paignton
C From Cleethorpes to Manchester Airport
D From Milford Haven
E From Buxton
F From Chester
G From Norwich to Liverpool Lime Street
H From Bournemouth
I From Bristol Temple Meads
J From Fishguard Harbour

Table 84

Mondays to Fridays

9 December to 16 May

Stoke-on-Trent and Crewe - Manchester Airport, Stockport and Manchester

Network Diagram - see first Page of Table 78

	NT	VT	NT	NT	XC	TP	VT	AW		NT	NT	VT	NT	EM	XC	NT	NT	VT		NT	NT	XC	TP	VT
		◇1			◇1	◇1	◇1	◇				◇1		◇	◇1			◇1				◇1	◇1	◇1
			A		B	C		D			E		F	G	H					I		J	C	
		⊡			⊥	⊥	⊡	⊥				⊡			⊥			⊡				⊥	⊥	⊡
London Euston [15] ⊖65 d		12 40					13 00					13 20						13 40						14 00
Birmingham New Street [12] 68 d					13 31										13 57							14 31		
Wolverhampton [7] 68 d					13 49										14 15							14 49		
Stafford 65,67 d					14 01										14 30							15 01		
Stoke-on-Trent 50 d				13 58	14 20		14 25					14 48			14 55						14 58	15 20		15 25
Longport 50 d																								
Kidsgrove 50 d				14 05																	15 05			
Crewe [10] d	13 50	14 11						14 31								14 34	14 50	15 11						
Sandbach d	13 57															14 41	14 57							
Holmes Chapel d	14 02															14 45	15 02							
Goostrey d	14 05																15 05							
Chelford d	14 09																15 09							
Alderley Edge d	14 13									14 49						14 54	15 13							
Wilmslow d	14 17	14 27						14 49		14 52						14 57	15 17	15 27						
Styal d																								
Manchester Airport ✈ a																15 04								
Handforth d	14 20									14 55							15 20							
Congleton d				14 12																	15 12			
Macclesfield a				14 19			14 41								15 11						15 19			15 41
d				14 20			14 41								15 12						15 20			15 41
Prestbury d				14 24																	15 24			
Adlington (Cheshire) d				14 27																	15 27			
Poynton d				14 30																	15 30			
Bramhall d				14 33																	15 33			
Cheadle Hulme d	14 24			14 37						14 59							15 24				15 37			
Stockport a	14 29	14 36		14 41	14 49		14 55	14 58		15 04		15 16			15 27		15 29	15 36			15 41	15 49		15 55
d	14 29	14 37	14 41	14 42	14 50	14 53	14 56	14 58		15 04	15 12	15 17	15 21	15 26	15 28		15 29	15 37		15 41	15 42	15 50	15 53	15 56
Heaton Chapel d	14 33			14 45						15 08			15 25				15 33				15 45			
Levenshulme d	14 36			14 48						15 11			15 28				15 36				15 48			
Manchester Picc. [10] 85,89 a	14 44	14 49	14 52	14 56	14 59	15 02	15 07	15 15		15 20	15 27	15 28	15 35	15 36	15 38	15 40	15 44	15 49		15 52	15 56	15 59	16 02	16 07
d			14 54											15 37		15 42				15 54				
Manchester Oxford Rd 85,89 a			14 56											15 40		15 46				15 56				
Deansgate 85,89 a			15 00																	16 00				

	AW	NT	NT	VT		NT	EM	XC	NT	NT	VT	NT	NT	XC		TP	VT	AW	NT	VT	NT	EM	XC	NT
	◇			◇1			◇	◇1			◇1			◇1		◇1	◇1	◇		◇1		◇	◇1	
	K		L			F	G	H				A		M		C		D			F	G	H	
	⊥			⊡				⊥			⊡			⊥		⊥	⊡	⊥		⊡			⊥	
London Euston [15] ⊖65 d				14 20							14 40						15 00			15 20				
Birmingham New Street [12] 68 d								14 57						15 31									15 57	
Wolverhampton [7] 68 d								15 15						15 50									16 15	
Stafford 65,67 d								15 30						16 02									16 31	
Stoke-on-Trent 50 d				15 48				15 55					15 58	16 21			16 25			16 48			16 55	
Longport 50 d																								
Kidsgrove 50 d													16 05											
Crewe [10] d	15 29								15 33	15 50	16 11							16 31						16 34
Sandbach d									15 40	15 57														16 41
Holmes Chapel d									15 44	16 02														16 45
Goostrey d										16 05														
Chelford d										16 09														
Alderley Edge d		15 48							15 53	16 13									16 49					16 54
Wilmslow d	15 47	15 51							15 56	16 17	16 27							16 48	16 52					16 57
Styal d									15 59															
Manchester Airport ✈ a									16 04															17 04
Handforth d		15 54								16 20									16 55					
Congleton d													16 12											
Macclesfield a								16 11					16 19				16 41						17 11	
d								16 12					16 20				16 41						17 12	
Prestbury d													16 24											
Adlington (Cheshire) d													16 27											
Poynton d													16 30											
Bramhall d													16 33											
Cheadle Hulme d		15 59								16 24			16 37						16 59					
Stockport a	15 58	16 04		16 16				16 27		16 29	16 36		16 41	16 49			16 55	16 58	17 04	17 16			17 27	
d	15 58	16 04	16 12	16 17		16 21	16 26	16 28		16 29	16 37	16 41	16 42	16 50		16 53	16 56	16 58	17 04	17 17	17 21	17 26	17 28	
Heaton Chapel d		16 08				16 25				16 33			16 45						17 08		17 25			
Levenshulme d		16 11				16 28				16 36			16 48						17 11		17 28			
Manchester Picc. [10] 85,89 a	16 15	16 20	16 25	16 28		16 35	16 36	16 38	16 42	16 44	16 49	16 52	16 56	16 59		17 02	17 07	17 14	17 20	17 28	17 35	17 37	17 38	17 42
d			16 27				16 37					16 54										17 37		
Manchester Oxford Rd 85,89 a			16 29				16 40					16 56										17 40		
Deansgate 85,89 a			16 32									17 00												

A From Hazel Grove to Preston
B From Paignton
C From Cleethorpes to Manchester Airport
D From Milford Haven
E From Buxton
F From Chester
G From Norwich to Liverpool Lime Street
H From Bournemouth
I From Hazel Grove to Bolton
J From Bristol Temple Meads
K From Carmarthen
L From Buxton to Barrow-in-Furness
M From Penzance

Table 84

Mondays to Fridays

9 December to 16 May

Stoke-on-Trent and Crewe - Manchester Airport, Stockport and Manchester

Network Diagram - see first Page of Table 78

		NT	VT	NT	XC	TP	VT	AW	NT	NT		VT	NT	EM	XC	NT	NT	VT	NT	NT		XC	TP	VT
			◇■1		◇■1	◇■1	◇■1	◇				◇■1		◇	◇■1			◇■1				◇■1	◇■1	◇■1
					A	B		C		D			E	F	G				H			I	B	
			☕		🛒	🛒	☕	🛒				☕			🛒			☕				🛒	🛒	☒
London Euston ■15 ⊖65 d			15 40				16 00					16 20						16 40						17 00
Birmingham New Street ■12 68 d					16 31										16 57							17 31		
Wolverhampton ■7 68 🚌 d					16 49										17 15							17 50		
Stafford 65,67 d					17 01										17 30							18 02		
Stoke-on-Trent 50 d				16 58	17 19		17 25					17 48			17 55					17 58		18 21		18 25
Longport 50 d																								
Kidsgrove 50 d				17 05																18 05				
Crewe ■10 d		16 50	17 11					17 30								17 33	17 50	18 11						
Sandbach d		16 57														17 40	17 57							
Holmes Chapel d		17 02														17 44	18 02							
Goostrey d		17 05															18 05							
Chelford d		17 09															18 09							
Alderley Edge d		17 13							17 48							17 53	18 13							
Wilmslow d		17 17	17 27					17 47	17 51							17 56	18 17	18 27						
Styal d																17 59								
Manchester Airport ✈ a																18 04								
Handforth d		17 20							17 54								18 20							
Congleton d				17 12																18 12				
Macclesfield a				17 19			17 41								18 11					18 19				18 41
d				17 20			17 41								18 12					18 20				18 41
Prestbury d				17 24																18 24				
Adlington (Cheshire) d				17 27																18 27				
Poynton d				17 30																18 30				
Bramhall d				17 33																18 33				
Cheadle Hulme d		17 24		17 36					17 59								18 24			18 37				
Stockport a		17 29	17 36	17 41	17 49		17 55	17 57	18 04			18 16			18 27		18 29	18 36		18 41		18 49		18 55
d		17 29	17 37	17 42	17 50	17 53	17 56	17 58	18 04	18 12		18 17	18 21	18 26	18 28		18 29	18 37	18 41	18 42		18 50	18 53	18 56
Heaton Chapel d		17 33		17 45					18 08				18 25				18 33			18 45				
Levenshulme d		17 36		17 48					18 11				18 28				18 36			18 48				
Manchester Picc. ■10 85,89 🚌 a		17 44	17 49	17 56	17 58	18 02	18 07	18 13	18 20	18 27		18 28	18 35	18 36	18 38	18 42	18 44	18 49	18 52	18 56		18 59	19 02	19 07
d														18 37					18 54					
Manchester Oxford Rd 85,89 a														18 40					18 56					
Deansgate 85,89 🚌 a																			19 00					

	AW	NT	VT	NT	NT	EM		XC	NT	VT	NT	XC	TP	VT	AW	NT		VT	NT	NT	EM	XC	NT	VT
	R														R									
			◇■1			◇		◇■1		◇■1		◇■1	◇■1	◇■1				◇■1			◇	◇■1		◇■1
	J	D			E	F		G				A	B		C	D				E	F	G		
	🛒		☒					🛒		☒		🛒	🛒	☒	🛒			☒				🛒		☒
London Euston ■15 ⊖65 d			17 20							17 40				18 00				18 20						18 40
Birmingham New Street ■12 68 d								17 57				18 31										18 57		
Wolverhampton ■7 68 🚌 d								18 15				18 49										19 15		
Stafford 65,67 d								18 30				19 01										19 29		
Stoke-on-Trent 50 d			18 49					18 55			18 58	19 20		19 25				19 48				19 55		
Longport 50 d																								
Kidsgrove 50 d											19 05													
Crewe ■10 d	18 31			18 34					18 50	19 11					19 31								19 50	20 11
Sandbach d				18 41					18 57														19 57	
Holmes Chapel d				18 45					19 02														20 02	
Goostrey d									19 05														20 05	
Chelford d									19 09														20 09	
Alderley Edge d				18 54					19 13														20 13	
Wilmslow d	18 48			18 57					19 17	19 27					19 48				19 56				20 17	20 27
Styal d																								
Manchester Airport ✈ a				19 05															20 04					
Handforth d									19 20														20 20	
Congleton d											19 12													
Macclesfield a								19 11			19 19			19 41								20 11		
d								19 12			19 20			19 41								20 12		
Prestbury d											19 24													
Adlington (Cheshire) d											19 27													
Poynton d											19 30													
Bramhall d											19 33													
Cheadle Hulme d									19 24		19 37												20 24	
Stockport a	18 58		19 16					19 27	19 29	19 36	19 41	19 48		19 55	19 58			20 16				20 27	20 29	20 36
d	18 58	19 12	19 17		19 21	19 26		19 28	19 29	19 37	19 42	19 50	19 53	19 56	19 58	20 12		20 17		20 21	20 26	20 28	20 29	20 37
Heaton Chapel d		19 15									19 45					20 15								
Levenshulme d		19 18									19 48					20 18								
Manchester Picc. ■10 85,89 🚌 a	19 15	19 28	19 28	19 29	19 35	19 36		19 38	19 43	19 49	19 56	19 59	20 01	20 07	20 15	20 26		20 28	20 31	20 34	20 36	20 37	20 43	20 49
d				19 31		19 37													20 31		20 37			
Manchester Oxford Rd 85,89 a				19 35		19 40													20 35		20 40			
Deansgate 85,89 🚌 a																								

A From Bristol Temple Meads
B From Cleethorpes to Manchester Airport
C From Carmarthen
D From Buxton
E From Chester
F From Norwich to Liverpool Lime Street
G From Bournemouth
H From Buxton to Bolton
I From Paignton
J From Milford Haven

Table 84

Mondays to Fridays

9 December to 16 May

Stoke-on-Trent and Crewe - Manchester Airport, Stockport and Manchester

Network Diagram - see first Page of Table 78

	NT	XC	TP	AW	VT	VT	VT	NT	VT	NT	NT	EM	NT	XC	NT	VT	NT	XC	VT	AW	NT
					FX	ThFO	FO				FX										
				R	R		R		R												
		◇1	◇1		1	◇	1		1			◇		◇1		◇1		◇1	◇1	◇	
		A	B	C				D		E	F	G	H	I				J		K	D
London Euston 15 ⊖65 d					19 00	18 57	19 00		19 20							19 40			20 00		
Birmingham New Street 12 68 d		19 31												19 57				20 31			
Wolverhampton 7 68 d		19 49												20 16				20 49			
Stafford 65,67 d		20 01												20 30		21 04					
Stoke-on-Trent 50 d	19 58	20 20			20 25		20 25		20 48					20 55			20 58	21 19	21 25		
Longport 50 d																					
Kidsgrove 50 d	20 05																21 05				
Crewe 10 d				20 23		20s33									20 50	21 23				21 31	
Sandbach d															20 57						
Holmes Chapel d															21 02						
Goostrey d															21 05						
Chelford d															21 09						
Alderley Edge d															21 13						
Wilmslow d				20 40						20 56	20 56				21 17	21 38				21 48	
Styal d																					
Manchester Airport a										21 04	21 04										
Handforth d															21 20						
Congleton d	20 12																21 12				
Macclesfield a	20 19				20 41		20 41							21 11			21 19		21 40		
d	20 20				20 41		20 41							21 12			21 20		21 41		
Prestbury d	20 24																21 24				
Adlington (Cheshire) d	20 27																21 27				
Poynton d	20 30																21 30				
Bramhall d	20 33																21 33				
Cheadle Hulme d	20 37														21 24		21 37				
Stockport a	20 41	20 48		20 51	20 55		20 55		21 16					21 25	21 29		21 41	21 47	21 54	21 58	
d	20 42	20 50	20 53	20 52	20 56		20 56	21 12	21 17			21 20	21 21	21 26	21 29		21 42	21 49	21 55	21 59	22 12
Heaton Chapel d	20 45							21 15									21 45				22 15
Levenshulme d	20 48							21 18									21 48				22 18
Manchester Picc. 10 85,89 a	20 56	20 58	21 02	21 06	21 07	21 09	21 10	21 28	21 28	21 31	21 32	21 32	21 34	21 39	21 42	21 57	21 57	21 59	22 07	22 13	22 28
d										21 31											
Manchester Oxford Rd 85,89 a										21 35											
Deansgate 85,89 a																					

	NT	XC	NT	NT	VT	NT	NT	TP	VT	NT	NT	XC	VT	AW	NT	NT	NT	NT	XC	AW	VT
						FX										FX					
		◇1			◇1			◇1	◇1			◇1	◇1	◇					◇1	◇	◇1
	L	I		M		F	H	B			E	I		N	D	F	O			P	Q
London Euston 15 ⊖65 d					20 40				21 00				21 40								22 50
Birmingham New Street 12 68 d		20 57										21 57							22 30	21 23	
Wolverhampton 7 68 d		21 16										22 16							22 48	21 42	
Stafford 65,67 d		21 32										22 30							23 01		
Stoke-on-Trent 50 d		21 55							22 28	22 18		22 55	23 07						23 21		01s20
Longport 50 d																					
Kidsgrove 50 d										22 25											
Crewe 10 d			21 45		22 13									23 04				23 12			
Sandbach d			21 52															23 19			
Holmes Chapel d			21 58															23 24			
Goostrey d			22 01															23 27			
Chelford d			22 07															23 31			
Alderley Edge d			22 12															23 35			
Wilmslow d	21 55		22 15		22 29	21 56					22 56			23 22		22 56		23 39			
Styal d																					
Manchester Airport a	22 02					22 16					23 04					23 16					
Handforth d			22 19															23 42			
Congleton d										22 32											
Macclesfield a		22 11							22 44	22 40		23 11	23 23								01s37
d		22 12							22 44	22 48		23 12	23 23								
Prestbury d										22 53											
Adlington (Cheshire) d										22 56											
Poynton d										22 59											
Bramhall d										23 02											
Cheadle Hulme d			22 24							23 05								23 46			
Stockport a		22 25	22 29		22 38				22 58	23 10		23 25	23 37	23 30				23 51			01s58
d		22 26	22 29	22 34	22 39		22 48	22 53	22 59	23 10		23 26	23 38	23 31	23 41		23 48	23 51			
Heaton Chapel d				22 38						23 14								23 55			
Levenshulme d				22 41						23 17								23 58			
Manchester Picc. 10 85,89 a	22 30	22 34	22 43	22 48	22 48	22 58	22 59	23 02	23 11	23 25	23 33	23 34	23 46	23 48	23 53	23 58	00 02	00 07	00 12	00 28	02 09
d	22 31			22 50																	
Manchester Oxford Rd 85,89 a	22 35			22 52																	
Deansgate 85,89 a				22 55																	

- **A** From Exeter St Davids
- **B** From Cleethorpes
- **C** From Milford Haven
- **D** From Buxton
- **E** until 27 December, FO from 3 January until 14 March, from 21 March
- **F** from 30 December until 20 March
- **G** From Norwich
- **H** From Chester
- **I** From Bournemouth
- **J** From Bristol Temple Meads
- **K** From Carmarthen
- **L** until 27 December, FX from 24 March
- **M** To Wigan Wallgate
- **N** From Cardiff Central
- **O** From Sheffield
- **P** From Birmingham International
- **Q** not 25 December, 26 December, 1 January

Table 84

Saturdays

14 December to 17 May

Stoke-on-Trent and Crewe - Manchester Airport, Stockport and Manchester

Network Diagram - see first Page of Table 78

	NT	NT	NT	NT	TP	AW	NT	NT	NT		EM	XC	NT	NT	NT	NT	XC	TP	NT		AW	NT	NT	NT
					◇1						◇	◇1					◇1	◇1			◇			
	A			B	C			D	A		E				F			G	H		I		D	A
																	🛒							
London Euston [15] ⊖65 d																								
Birmingham New Street [12] 68 d												05 57					06 31							
Wolverhampton [7] 68 ⛴ d												06 16					06 49							
Stafford 65,67 d												06 30					07 01							
Stoke-on-Trent 50 d												06 51				06 57	07 19							
Longport 50 d																								
Kidsgrove 50 d																07 04								
Crewe [10] d		00 44				06 27							06 33	06 49							07 27			
Sandbach d													06 40	06 56										
Holmes Chapel d													06 44	07 00										
Goostrey d														07 03										
Chelford d														07 08										
Alderley Edge d							06 49						06 53	07 12								07 49		
Wilmslow d			05 46			06 45	06 52						06 57	07 16							07 44	07 52		
Styal d																								
Manchester Airport ✈ a		01 08	05 53										07 04											
Handforth d							06 55							07 19								07 55		
Congleton d												07 03				07 11								
Macclesfield a												07 11				07 18	07 36							
d												07 12				07 19	07 37							
Prestbury d																07 23								
Adlington (Cheshire) d																07 26								
Poynton d																07 29								
Bramhall d																07 32								
Cheadle Hulme d							06 59							07 24		07 36						07 59		
Stockport a						06 55	07 04					07 25		07 29		07 40	07 49				07 54	08 04		
d	00 04			06 41	06 53	06 55	07 04	07 12	07 19		07 22	07 26		07 29	07 40	07 41	07 50	07 53	07 57		07 54	08 04	08 10	08 19
Heaton Chapel d							07 08	07 16						07 33		07 45						08 08	08 15	
Levenshulme d							07 11	07 19						07 36		07 48						08 11	08 18	
Manchester Picc. [10] 85,89 ⛴ a	00 18	01 36	06 25	06 52	07 02	07 07	07 20	07 28	07 30		07 34	07 34	07 42	07 44	07 52	07 56	07 59	08 02	08 09		08 10	08 20	08 26	08 29
d				06 53							07 34				07 54									
Manchester Oxford Rd 85,89 a				06 56							07 37				07 56									
Deansgate 85,89 ⛴ a				06 59											07 59									

	XC	EM	NT	NT	VT		NT	NT	XC	TP	VT	AW	NT	NT	VT		NT	EM	XC	NT	NT	VT	NT	NT
	◇1	◇			◇1				◇1	◇1	◇1	◇			◇1			◇	◇1			◇1		
		E					J			G		I		D			A	E	K				F	
	🛒				🍽				🛒		🍽	🛒			🍽				🛒			🍽		
London Euston [15] ⊖65 d					06 36						06 55				07 20							07 35		
Birmingham New Street [12] 68 d	06 57								07 31										07 57					
Wolverhampton [7] 68 ⛴ d	07 15								07 49										08 15					
Stafford 65,67 d	07 30								08 01										08 30					
Stoke-on-Trent 50 d								07 57	08 20		08 25				08 48				08 55					08 58
Longport 50 d																								
Kidsgrove 50 d								08 04																09 05
Crewe [10] d	07 52		07 30	07 55	08 11							08 28								08 31	08 50	09 11		
Sandbach d			07 37	08 02																08 38	08 57			
Holmes Chapel d			07 41	08 06																08 42	09 02			
Goostrey d			07 44																	08 45	09 05			
Chelford d			07 49																	08 50	09 09			
Alderley Edge d			07 53	08 15									08 49							08 54	09 13			
Wilmslow d	08 09		07 56	08 19	08 27							08 45	08 52							08 57	09 17	09 27		
Styal d			07 59																					
Manchester Airport ✈ a			08 04																	09 04				
Handforth d				08 22									08 55								09 20			
Congleton d								08 11																09 12
Macclesfield a								08 18	08 36		08 41								09 11					09 19
d								08 19	08 37		08 41								09 12					09 20
Prestbury d								08 23																09 24
Adlington (Cheshire) d								08 26																09 27
Poynton d								08 30																09 30
Bramhall d								08 33																09 33
Cheadle Hulme d				08 26				08 37					08 59								09 24			09 37
Stockport a	08 20			08 31	08 36			08 41	08 49		08 55	08 58	09 04		09 16				09 27		09 29	09 36		09 41
d	08 20	08 24		08 31	08 37		08 41	08 42	08 50	08 53	08 56	08 59	09 04	09 12	09 17		09 21	09 25	09 28		09 29	09 37	09 41	09 42
Heaton Chapel d				08 36				08 45					09 08				09 25				09 33			09 45
Levenshulme d								08 48					09 11				09 28				09 36			09 48
Manchester Picc. [10] 85,89 ⛴ a	08 34	08 36	08 42	08 45	08 49		08 52	08 56	08 59	09 02	09 07	09 15	09 20	09 27	09 28		09 35	09 36	09 38	09 42	09 44	09 49	09 52	09 56
d		08 37					08 54											09 37					09 54	
Manchester Oxford Rd 85,89 a		08 40					08 56											09 40					09 56	
Deansgate 85,89 ⛴ a							09 00																10 00	

A From Chester
B From Buxton to Clitheroe
C From Doncaster to Manchester Airport
D From Buxton
E From Nottingham to Liverpool Lime Street
F From Hazel Grove to Preston
G From Cleethorpes to Manchester Airport
H From Hazel Grove
I From Cardiff Central
J From Buxton to Preston
K From Southampton Central

Table 84

Saturdays

14 December to 17 May

Stoke-on-Trent and Crewe - Manchester Airport, Stockport and Manchester

Network Diagram - see first Page of Table 78

Station			XC		TP	VT	AW	NT	NT	VT	NT	EM	XC		NT	NT	VT	NT	NT	XC	TP	VT	AW		NT	NT
			◇1		◇1	◇1	◇			◇1		◇	◇1				◇1			◇1	◇1	◇1	◇			
			A		B		C		D		E	F	G					H		I	B		C			D
London Euston 15	⊖65	d				08 00				08 20							08 40					09 00				
Birmingham New Street 12	68	d	08 31										08 57							09 31						
Wolverhampton 7	68	d	08 49										09 15							09 49						
Stafford	65,67	d	09 01										09 30							10 01						
Stoke-on-Trent	50	d	09 20			09 25				09 48			09 55						09 58	10 20		10 25				
Longport	50	d																								
Kidsgrove	50	d																	10 05							
Crewe 10		d					09 30								09 34	09 50	10 11						10 31			
Sandbach		d													09 41	09 57										
Holmes Chapel		d													09 45	10 02										
Goostrey		d														10 05										
Chelford		d														10 09										
Alderley Edge		d						09 49							09 54	10 13									10 49	
Wilmslow		d					09 47	09 52							09 57	10 17	10 27						10 49		10 52	
Styal		d																								
Manchester Airport	✈	a													10 04											
Handforth		d						09 55								10 20									10 55	
Congleton		d																	10 12							
Macclesfield		a				09 41							10 11						10 19			10 41				
		d				09 41							10 12						10 20			10 41				
Prestbury		d																	10 24							
Adlington (Cheshire)		d																	10 27							
Poynton		d																	10 30							
Bramhall		d																	10 33							
Cheadle Hulme		d						10 00								10 24			10 37						10 59	
Stockport		a	09 49			09 55	09 57	10 05		10 16			10 27			10 29	10 36		10 41	10 49		10 55	10 58		11 04	
		d	09 50		09 53	09 56	09 58	10 06	10 12	10 17	10 21	10 26	10 28			10 29	10 37	10 41	10 42	10 50	10 53	10 56	10 58		11 04	11 12
Heaton Chapel		d						10 09			10 25					10 33			10 45						11 08	
Levenshulme		d						10 12			10 28					10 36			10 48						11 11	
Manchester Picc. 10	85,89	a	09 59		10 02	10 07	10 14	10 20	10 27	10 28	10 35	10 36	10 38		10 42	10 43	10 49	10 52	10 56	10 59	11 02	11 07	11 15		11 20	11 27
		d										10 37						10 54								
Manchester Oxford Rd	85,89	a										10 40						10 56								
Deansgate	85,89	a																11 00								

Station			VT	NT	EM	XC	NT	NT	VT		NT	NT	XC	TP	VT	AW	NT	NT	VT		NT	EM	XC	NT	NT	VT
			◇1		◇	◇1			◇1				◇1	◇1	◇1	◇			◇1			◇	◇1			◇1
				E	F	J					H		K	B		L		D			E	F	J			
London Euston 15	⊖65	d	09 20						09 40						10 00				10 20							10 40
Birmingham New Street 12	68	d				09 57							10 31										10 57			
Wolverhampton 7	68	d				10 15							10 49										11 15			
Stafford	65,67	d				10 30							11 01										11 30			
Stoke-on-Trent	50	d	10 48			10 55						10 58	11 20		11 25				11 48				11 55			
Longport	50	d																								
Kidsgrove	50	d										11 05														
Crewe 10		d					10 34	10 50	11 11							11 31								11 34	11 50	12 11
Sandbach		d					10 41	10 57																11 41	11 57	
Holmes Chapel		d					10 45	11 02																11 45	12 02	
Goostrey		d						11 05																	12 05	
Chelford		d						11 09																	12 09	
Alderley Edge		d					10 54	11 13									11 49							11 54	12 13	
Wilmslow		d					10 57	11 17	11 27							11 48	11 52							11 57	12 17	12 27
Styal		d																								
Manchester Airport	✈	a					11 04																	12 04		
Handforth		d						11 20									11 55								12 20	
Congleton		d										11 12														
Macclesfield		a				11 11						11 19			11 41								12 11			
		d				11 12						11 20			11 41								12 12			
Prestbury		d										11 24														
Adlington (Cheshire)		d										11 27														
Poynton		d										11 30														
Bramhall		d										11 33														
Cheadle Hulme		d						11 24				11 37					11 59								12 24	
Stockport		a	11 16			11 27		11 29	11 36			11 41	11 49		11 55	11 58	12 04		12 16				12 26		12 29	12 36
		d	11 17	11 21	11 26	11 28		11 29	11 37		11 41	11 42	11 50	11 53	11 56	11 58	12 04	12 12	12 17		12 21	12 25	12 27		12 29	12 37
Heaton Chapel		d		11 25				11 33				11 45					12 08				12 25				12 33	
Levenshulme		d		11 28				11 36				11 48					12 11				12 28				12 36	
Manchester Picc. 10	85,89	a	11 28	11 35	11 36	11 38	11 42	11 44	11 49		11 52	11 56	11 59	12 02	12 07	12 15	12 20	12 27	12 28		12 35	12 36	12 38	12 42	12 44	12 49
		d			11 37						11 54											12 37				
Manchester Oxford Rd	85,89	a			11 40						11 56											12 40				
Deansgate	85,89	a									12 00															

A From Bristol Temple Meads
B From Cleethorpes to Manchester Airport
C From Carmarthen
D From Buxton
E From Chester
F From Norwich to Liverpool Lime Street
G From Southampton Central
H From Hazel Grove to Preston
I From Cardiff Central
J From Bournemouth
K From Paignton
L From Milford Haven

Table 84

Saturdays

14 December to 17 May

Stoke-on-Trent and Crewe - Manchester Airport, Stockport and Manchester

Network Diagram - see first Page of Table 78

		NT	NT	XC	TP	VT	AW	NT	NT	VT	NT	EM	XC	NT	NT	VT	NT	NT	XC	TP	VT	AW
				◇[1]	◇[1]	◇[1]	◇			◇[1]		◇	◇[1]			◇[1]			◇[1]	◇[1]	◇[1]	◇
		A		B	C		D		E		F	G	H				A		B	C		I
				🛒		🍴	🛒			🍴			🛒			🍴			🛒		🍴	🛒
London Euston [15] ⊖65	d					11 00				11 20						11 40					12 00	
Birmingham New Street [12] 68	d			11 31									11 57						12 31			
Wolverhampton [7] 68 ⇌	d			11 49									12 15						12 49			
Stafford 65,67	d			12 01									12 30						13 01			
Stoke-on-Trent 50	d		11 58	12 20		12 25				12 48			12 55					12 58	13 20		13 25	
Longport 50	d																					
Kidsgrove 50	d		12 05															13 05				
Crewe [10]	d						12 31							12 34	12 50	13 11						13 31
Sandbach	d													12 41	12 57							
Holmes Chapel	d													12 45	13 02							
Goostrey	d														13 05							
Chelford	d														13 09							
Alderley Edge	d							12 49						12 54	13 13							
Wilmslow	d						12 49	12 52						12 57	13 17	13 27						13 48
Styal	d																					
Manchester Airport ✈	a													13 04								
Handforth	d							12 55							13 20							
Congleton	d		12 12															13 12				
Macclesfield	a		12 19			12 41							13 11					13 19			13 41	
	d		12 20			12 41							13 12					13 20			13 41	
Prestbury	d		12 24															13 24				
Adlington (Cheshire)	d		12 27															13 27				
Poynton	d		12 30															13 30				
Bramhall	d		12 33															13 33				
Cheadle Hulme	d		12 37					12 59							13 24			13 37				
Stockport	a		12 41	12 49		12 55	12 58	13 04		13 16			13 27		13 29	13 36		13 41	13 49		13 55	13 58
	d	12 41	12 42	12 50	12 53	12 56	12 58	13 04	13 12	13 17	13 21	13 26	13 28		13 29	13 37	13 41	13 42	13 50	13 53	13 56	13 58
Heaton Chapel	d		12 45					13 08			13 25				13 33			13 45				
Levenshulme	d		12 48					13 11			13 28				13 36			13 48				
Manchester Picc. [10] 85,89 ⇌	a	12 52	12 56	12 59	13 02	13 07	13 15	13 20	13 25	13 28	13 35	13 36	13 38	13 42	13 44	13 49	13 52	13 56	13 59	14 02	14 07	14 15
	d	12 54										13 37					13 54					
Manchester Oxford Rd 85,89	a	12 56										13 40					13 56					
Deansgate 85,89 ⇌	a	13 00															14 00					

		NT	NT	VT	NT	EM	XC	NT	NT	VT	NT	NT	XC	TP	VT	AW	NT	NT	VT	NT	EM	XC	NT
				◇[1]		◇	◇[1]			◇[1]			◇[1]	◇[1]	◇[1]	◇			◇[1]		◇	◇[1]	
			E		F	G	H				A		J	C		D		E		F	G	H	
				🍴			🛒			🍴			🛒		🍴	🛒			🍴			🛒	
London Euston [15] ⊖65	d			12 20						12 40					13 00				13 20				
Birmingham New Street [12] 68	d						12 57						13 31									13 57	
Wolverhampton [7] 68 ⇌	d						13 15						13 49									14 15	
Stafford 65,67	d						13 30						14 01									14 30	
Stoke-on-Trent 50	d			13 48			13 55					13 58	14 20		14 25				14 48			14 55	
Longport 50	d																						
Kidsgrove 50	d											14 05											
Crewe [10]	d							13 34	13 50	14 11						14 31							14 34
Sandbach	d							13 41	13 57														14 41
Holmes Chapel	d							13 45	14 02														14 45
Goostrey	d								14 05														
Chelford	d								14 09														
Alderley Edge	d	13 49						13 54	14 13								14 49						14 54
Wilmslow	d	13 52						13 57	14 17	14 27						14 49	14 52						14 57
Styal	d																						
Manchester Airport ✈	a							14 04															15 04
Handforth	d	13 55							14 20								14 55						
Congleton	d											14 12											
Macclesfield	a						14 11					14 19			14 41							15 11	
	d						14 12					14 20			14 41							15 12	
Prestbury	d											14 24											
Adlington (Cheshire)	d											14 27											
Poynton	d											14 30											
Bramhall	d											14 33											
Cheadle Hulme	d	13 59							14 24			14 37					14 59						
Stockport	a	14 04		14 16			14 27		14 29	14 36		14 41	14 49		14 55	14 58	15 04		15 16			15 27	
	d	14 04	14 12	14 17	14 21	14 26	14 28		14 29	14 37	14 41	14 42	14 50	14 53	14 56	14 58	15 04	15 12	15 17	15 21	15 26	15 28	
Heaton Chapel	d	14 08			14 25				14 33			14 45					15 08			15 25			
Levenshulme	d	14 11			14 28				14 36			14 48					15 11			15 28			
Manchester Picc. [10] 85,89 ⇌	a	14 20	14 27	14 28	14 35	14 36	14 38	14 42	14 44	14 49	14 52	14 56	14 59	15 02	15 07	15 15	15 20	15 27	15 28	15 35	15 36	15 38	15 42
	d					14 37					14 54										15 37		
Manchester Oxford Rd 85,89	a					14 40					14 56										15 40		
Deansgate 85,89 ⇌	a										15 00												

A From Hazel Grove to Preston
B From Bristol Temple Meads
C From Cleethorpes to Manchester Airport
D From Milford Haven
E From Buxton
F From Chester
G From Norwich to Liverpool Lime Street
H From Bournemouth
I From Fishguard Harbour
J From Paignton

Table 84

Saturdays

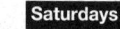

14 December to 17 May

Stoke-on-Trent and Crewe - Manchester Airport, Stockport and Manchester

Network Diagram - see first Page of Table 78

	NT	VT	NT	NT	XC		TP	VT	AW	NT	NT	VT	NT	EM	XC		NT	NT	VT	NT	NT	XC	TP	VT
		◇1			◇1		◇1	◇1	◇			◇1		◇	◇1				◇1			◇1	◇1	◇1
			A		B		C		D		E		F	G	H					A		I	C	
London Euston 15 ⊖65 d		13 40						14 00				14 20							14 40					15 00
Birmingham New Street 12 68 d					14 31										14 57							15 31		
Wolverhampton 7 68 d					14 49										15 15							15 49		
Stafford 65,67 d					15 01										15 30							16 01		
Stoke-on-Trent 50 d				14 58	15 20			15 25				15 48			15 55						15 58	16 20		16 25
Longport 50 d																								
Kidsgrove 50 d				15 05																	16 05			
Crewe 10 d	14 50	15 11							15 28								15 33	15 50	16 11					
Sandbach d	14 57																15 40	15 57						
Holmes Chapel d	15 02																15 44	16 02						
Goostrey d	15 05																	16 05						
Chelford d	15 09																	16 09						
Alderley Edge d	15 13									15 49							15 53	16 13						
Wilmslow d	15 17	15 27							15 45	15 52							15 56	16 17	16 27					
Styal d																	15 59							
Manchester Airport ✈ a																	16 04							
Handforth d	15 20									15 55								16 20						
Congleton d				15 12																	16 12			
Macclesfield a				15 19				15 41							16 11						16 19			16 41
d				15 20				15 41							16 12						16 20			16 41
Prestbury d				15 24																	16 24			
Adlington (Cheshire) d				15 27																	16 27			
Poynton d				15 30																	16 30			
Bramhall d				15 33																	16 33			
Cheadle Hulme d	15 24			15 37						15 59								16 24			16 37			
Stockport a	15 29	15 36		15 41	15 49			15 55	15 58	16 04		16 16			16 27			16 29	16 36		16 41	16 49		16 55
d	15 29	15 37	15 41	15 42	15 50		15 53	15 56	15 58	16 04	16 12	16 17	16 21	16 26	16 28			16 29	16 37	16 41	16 42	16 50	16 53	16 56
Heaton Chapel d	15 33			15 45						16 08			16 25					16 33			16 45			
Levenshulme d	15 36			15 48						16 11			16 28					16 36			16 48			
Manchester Picc. 10 85,89 a	15 44	15 49	15 52	15 56	15 59		16 02	16 07	16 15	16 20	16 27	16 28	16 35	16 36	16 38		16 42	16 44	16 49	16 52	16 56	16 59	17 02	17 07
d			15 54											16 37						16 54				
Manchester Oxford Rd 85,89 a			15 56											16 40						16 56				
Deansgate 85,89 a			16 00																	17 00				

	AW		NT	NT	VT	NT	EM	XC	NT	NT	VT		NT	XC	TP	VT	AW	NT	NT	VT	NT		EM	XC
	◇				◇1		◇	◇1			◇1			◇1	◇1	◇1	◇			◇1			◇	◇1
	J			E		F	G	H						B	C		D		E		F		G	H
London Euston 15 ⊖65 d					15 20						15 40					16 00				16 20				
Birmingham New Street 12 68 d								15 57						16 31										16 57
Wolverhampton 7 68 d								16 15						16 49										17 15
Stafford 65,67 d								16 30						17 01										17 30
Stoke-on-Trent 50 d					16 48			16 55					16 58	17 20		17 25				17 48				17 55
Longport 50 d																								
Kidsgrove 50 d													17 05											
Crewe 10 d	16 31								16 34	16 50	17 11						17 28							
Sandbach d									16 41	16 57														
Holmes Chapel d									16 45	17 02														
Goostrey d										17 05														
Chelford d										17 09														
Alderley Edge d			16 49						16 54	17 13								17 49						
Wilmslow d	16 48		16 52						16 57	17 17	17 27						17 45	17 52						
Styal d																								
Manchester Airport ✈ a									17 04															
Handforth d			16 55							17 20								17 55						
Congleton d													17 12											
Macclesfield a								17 11					17 19			17 41								18 11
d								17 12					17 20			17 41								18 12
Prestbury d													17 24											
Adlington (Cheshire) d													17 27											
Poynton d													17 30											
Bramhall d													17 33											
Cheadle Hulme d			16 59							17 24			17 37					17 59						
Stockport a	16 58		17 04		17 16			17 27		17 29	17 36		17 41	17 49		17 55	17 58	18 04		18 16				18 27
d	16 58		17 04	17 12	17 17	17 21	17 26	17 28		17 29	17 37		17 42	17 50	17 53	17 56	17 58	18 04	18 12	18 17	18 21		18 27	18 28
Heaton Chapel d			17 08			17 25				17 33			17 45					18 08			18 25			
Levenshulme d			17 11			17 28				17 36			17 48					18 11			18 28			
Manchester Picc. 10 85,89 a	17 14		17 20	17 27	17 28	17 35	17 37	17 38	17 42	17 44	17 49		17 56	17 59	18 02	18 07	18 15	18 20	18 27	18 28	18 35		18 37	18 38
d							17 37																18 37	
Manchester Oxford Rd 85,89 a							17 40																18 40	
Deansgate 85,89 a																								

A From Hazel Grove to Preston
B From Bristol Temple Meads
C From Cleethorpes to Manchester Airport
D From Carmarthen
E From Buxton
F From Chester
G From Norwich to Liverpool Lime Street
H From Bournemouth
I From Penzance
J From Milford Haven

Table 84

Saturdays

14 December to 17 May

Stoke-on-Trent and Crewe - Manchester Airport, Stockport and Manchester

Network Diagram - see first Page of Table 78

	NT	NT	VT ◇1 ☕	NT A	NT	XC ◇1 B 🛒	TP ◇1 C		VT ◇1 ☕	AW R D 🛒	NT E	VT ◇1 ☕	NT	NT F	EM ◇ G	XC ◇1 H 🛒	NT		VT ◇1 ☕	NT	XC ◇1 I 🛒	TP ◇1 C	VT ◇1 ☕	AW R J 🛒
London Euston 15 ⊖65 d			16 40						17 00			17 20							17 40				18 00	
Birmingham New Street 12 68 d						17 31										17 57					18 31			
Wolverhampton 7 68 🚋 d						17 49										18 15					18 49			
Stafford 65,67 d						18 01										18 30					19 01			
Stoke-on-Trent 50 d					17 58	18 20			18 25			18 48				18 55				18 58	19 20		19 25	
Longport 50 d																								
Kidsgrove 50 d					18 05															19 05				
Crewe 10 d	17 33	17 50	18 11							18 31			18 34				18 50		19 11					19 31
Sandbach d	17 40	17 57											18 41				18 57							
Holmes Chapel d	17 44	18 02											18 45				19 02							
Goostrey d		18 05															19 05							
Chelford d		18 09															19 09							
Alderley Edge d	17 53	18 13											18 54				19 13							
Wilmslow d	17 56	18 17	18 27							18 48			18 57				19 17		19 27					19 48
Styal d	17 59																							
Manchester Airport ✈ a	18 04												19 05											
Handforth d		18 20															19 20							
Congleton d					18 12															19 12				
Macclesfield a					18 19				18 41							19 11				19 19			19 41	
d					18 20				18 41							19 12				19 20			19 41	
Prestbury d					18 24															19 24				
Adlington (Cheshire) d					18 27															19 27				
Poynton d					18 30															19 30				
Bramhall d					18 33															19 33				
Cheadle Hulme d		18 24			18 37												19 24			19 37				
Stockport a		18 29	18 36		18 41	18 49			18 55	18 58		19 16				19 27	19 29		19 36	19 41	19 49		19 55	19 58
d		18 29	18 37	18 41	18 42	18 50	18 53		18 56	18 58	19 12	19 17		19 21	19 25	19 28	19 29		19 37	19 42	19 50	19 53	19 56	19 58
Heaton Chapel d		18 33			18 45						19 15									19 45				
Levenshulme d		18 36			18 48						19 18									19 48				
Manchester Picc. 10 85,89 🚋 a	18 42	18 44	18 49	18 52	18 56	18 59	19 02		19 07	19 15	19 28	19 28	19 31	19 35	19 35	19 38	19 42		19 49	19 56	19 59	20 01	20 07	20 15
d				18 54									19 32		19 36									
Manchester Oxford Rd 85,89 a				18 56									19 36		19 39									
Deansgate 85,89 🚋 a				19 00																				

	NT E	VT ◇1 ☕	NT		NT F	EM ◇ G	XC ◇1 H 🛒	NT	VT ◇1 ☕	NT	XC ◇1 K 🛒	TP ◇1 C	VT ◇1 ☕		AW R D 🛒	NT E	VT ◇1 ☕	NT	EM ◇ L	NT F	XC ◇1 H	NT	VT ◇1 ☕	
London Euston 15 ⊖65 d		18 20							18 40				19 00				19 20						19 40	
Birmingham New Street 12 68 d							18 57				19 31										19 57			
Wolverhampton 7 68 🚋 d							19 15				19 49										20 15			
Stafford 65,67 d							19 30				20 01										20 30			
Stoke-on-Trent 50 d		19 48					19 55			19 58	20 20		20 25				20 48				20 55			
Longport 50 d																								
Kidsgrove 50 d										20 05														
Crewe 10 d								19 50	20 11						20 29							20 50	21 19	
Sandbach d								19 57														20 57		
Holmes Chapel d								20 02														21 02		
Goostrey d								20 05														21 05		
Chelford d								20 09														21 09		
Alderley Edge d								20 13														21 13		
Wilmslow d			19 56					20 17	20 27						20 46			20 56				21 17	21 34	
Styal d																								
Manchester Airport ✈ a			20 04															21 04						
Handforth d								20 20														21 20		
Congleton d										20 12														
Macclesfield a							20 11			20 19	20 36		20 41								21 11			
d							20 12			20 20	20 37		20 41								21 12			
Prestbury d										20 24														
Adlington (Cheshire) d										20 27														
Poynton d										20 30														
Bramhall d										20 33														
Cheadle Hulme d								20 24		20 37												21 24		
Stockport a		20 16					20 27	20 29	20 36	20 41	20 49		20 55		20 59		21 16				21 25	21 29	21 44	
d	20 12	20 17			20 21	20 26	20 28	20 29	20 37	20 42	20 50	20 53	20 56		21 00	21 12	21 17		21 20	21 21	21 26	21 29	21 45	
Heaton Chapel d	20 15									20 45						21 15								
Levenshulme d	20 18									20 48						21 18								
Manchester Picc. 10 85,89 🚋 a	20 28	20 28	20 31		20 34	20 36	20 37	20 43	20 49	20 56	20 59	21 02	21 07		21 16	21 28	21 28	21 31	21 32	21 34	21 39	21 43	21 53	
d			20 32			20 37												21 32						
Manchester Oxford Rd 85,89 a			20 36			20 40												21 36						
Deansgate 85,89 🚋 a																								

A From Hazel Grove to Bolton
B From Paignton
C From Cleethorpes to Manchester Airport
D From Milford Haven
E From Buxton
F From Chester
G From Norwich to Liverpool Lime Street
H From Bournemouth
I From Bristol Temple Meads
J From Carmarthen
K From Exeter St Davids
L From Norwich

Table 84

Saturdays

14 December to 17 May

Stoke-on-Trent and Crewe - Manchester Airport, Stockport and Manchester

Network Diagram - see first Page of Table 78

		NT	XC	AW	NT	NT	XC	NT	VT	NT		NT	VT	NT	XC	NT	VT	AW	NT	NT		NT	XC		
			◇1	◇			◇1		◇1				◇1		◇1		◇1	◇					◇1		
			A	B	C		D			E		F	G		D	H		I	J	K		J			
				🛒					☕				☕				☕								
London Euston 15 ⊖65	d								20 20				20 31				21 00								
Birmingham New Street 12 68	d		20 31				20 57								21 57								22 31		
Wolverhampton 7 68	d		20 49				21 15								22 15								22 49		
Stafford 65,67	d		21 01				21 30								22 30		22 34						23 02		
Stoke-on-Trent 50	d	20 58	21 21				21 53		22 05					22 18	22 51								23 21		
Longport 50	d																								
Kidsgrove 50	d	21 05												22 25											
Crewe 10	d			21 31				21 50					22 36				22 59	23 06				23 13			
Sandbach	d							21 57														23 20			
Holmes Chapel	d							22 02														23 24			
Goostrey	d							22 05														23 27			
Chelford	d							22 09														23 32			
Alderley Edge	d							22 13														23 36			
Wilmslow	d			21 48		21 55		22 17									23 15	23 24	23 15			23 39			
Styal	d																								
Manchester Airport ✈	a					22 04													23 23						
Handforth	d							22 20														23 42			
Congleton	d	21 12												22 32											
Macclesfield	a	21 19	21 38				22 11		22 21					22 39	23 07								23 38		
	d	21 20	21 39				22 12		22 21					22 40	23 08								23 39		
Prestbury	d	21 24												22 44											
Adlington (Cheshire)	d	21 27												22 47											
Poynton	d	21 30												22 50											
Bramhall	d	21 33												22 53											
Cheadle Hulme	d	21 37						22 24						22 56								23 47			
Stockport	a	21 41	21 53	21 58			22 25	22 29	22 35					23 01	23 20		23 24	23 32				23 51	23 53		
	d	21 42	21 54	21 58	22 12		22 26	22 29	22 36	22 40		22 48		23 01	23 21	23 23	23 25	23 33		23 41		23 52	23 54		
Heaton Chapel	d	21 45			22 16					22 44				23 05								23 55			
Levenshulme	d	21 48			22 19					22 47				23 08								23 58			
Manchester Picc. 10 85,89	a	21 57	22 04	22 13	22 28	22 30	22 34	22 43	22 51	22 53		22 59	23 05	23 16	23 30	23 38	23 38	23 49	23 51	23 53		00 07	00 10		
	d					22 31				22 54															
Manchester Oxford Rd 85,89	a					22 35				22 56															
Deansgate 85,89	a									23 00															

Sundays

8 December to 11 May

		NT	NT	TP	AW	NT	NT	NT	TP	AW		NT	NT	XC	VT	NT	VT	AW	NT	NT		NT	NT	XC	EM
				◇1					◇1					◇1	◇1		◇1	◇						◇1	◇
		L	M	N		C	O		N			C	P					Q		C		M			R
														🛒	☕		☕							🛒	
London Euston 15 ⊖65	d														08 10		08 20								
Birmingham New Street 12 68	d													09 01										10 01	
Wolverhampton 7 68	d													09 19										10 19	
Stafford 65,67	d													09 33										10 33	
Stoke-on-Trent 50	d																10 21							10 52	
Longport 50	d																								
Kidsgrove 50	d																								
Crewe 10	d				08 28					09 28				09 56	10 19			10 28							
Sandbach	d																								
Holmes Chapel	d																								
Goostrey	d																								
Chelford	d																								
Alderley Edge	d							09 19								10 19							10 46		
Wilmslow	d				08 48			09 23		09 47				10 13	10 34	10 23		10 47					10 49		
Styal	d																						10 53		
Manchester Airport ✈	a																						11 00		
Handforth	d							09 26								10 26									
Congleton	d																								
Macclesfield	a																10 36							11 08	
	d																10 38		10 44					11 09	
Prestbury	d																		10 48						
Adlington (Cheshire)	d																		10 51						
Poynton	d																		10 54						
Bramhall	d																		10 57						
Cheadle Hulme	d							09 30								10 30			11 00						
Stockport	a							09 38						10 21	10 43	10 35	10 50	10 58	11 05					11 22	
	d	00 04	08 22	08 31		09 08	09 22	09 40	09 54			10 04	10 12	10 22	10 44	10 39	10 52	10 58	11 05	11 12		11 11		11 23	11 26
Heaton Chapel	d					09 12		09 44				10 08				10 43						11 15			
Levenshulme	d					09 15		09 47				10 13				10 46						11 18			
Manchester Picc. 10 85,89	a	00 16	08 33	08 40	09 11	09 23	09 33	09 54	10 01	10 11		10 20	10 22	10 37	10 55	10 56	11 03	11 14	11 19	11 23		11 24	11 26	11 31	11 37
	d		08 35				09 35						10 24									11 26			11 38
Manchester Oxford Rd 85,89	a		08 37				09 37						10 26									11 28			11 41
Deansgate 85,89	a		08 40				09 40						10 40									11 40			

A From Bristol Temple Meads
B From Carmarthen
C From Buxton
D From Bournemouth
E To Wigan Wallgate
F From Chester
G from 4 January until 8 February
H until 8 February, from 29 March. From Sheffield
I until 8 February, from 29 March. From Maesteg
J until 8 February, from 29 March
K until 8 February, from 29 March. From Buxton
L from 15 December until 9 February, from 30 March. From Chester
M To Southport
N From Sheffield to Manchester Airport
O From Hazel Grove to Southport
P From Chester to Southport
Q From Shrewsbury
R From Nottingham to Liverpool Lime Street

Table 84

Sundays

8 December to 11 May

Stoke-on-Trent and Crewe - Manchester Airport, Stockport and Manchester

Network Diagram - see first Page of Table 78

	NT	AW	VT	TP	NT	NT	EM	XC	NT	TP	VT	AW	NT	NT	NT	EM	XC	VT	NT	TP	AW	NT
		◇	◇1	◇1			◇	◇1		◇1	◇1	◇				◇	◇1	◇1		◇1	◇	
		A		B	C	D	E	F		B		A	C		G	E	H			B	A	
		⊼	☕					⊼			☕	⊼					⊼	☕			⊼	
London Euston 15 ⊖65 d			09 20								10 20							11 20				
Birmingham New Street 12 68 d								11 01									12 01					
Wolverhampton 7 68 ⛴ d								11 19									12 19					
Stafford 65,67 d								11 33									12 33					
Stoke-on-Trent 50 d			11 22					11 52			12 25						12 53	13 11				13 25
Longport 50 d																						
Kidsgrove 50 d																						13 32
Crewe 10 d	10 56	11 23										12 28							12 56		13 29	
Sandbach d	11 03																		13 03			
Holmes Chapel d	11 08																		13 08			
Goostrey d	11 11																		13 11			
Chelford d	11 15																		13 15			
Alderley Edge d	11 19								12 17					12 51					13 19			
Wilmslow d	11 23	11 42							12 21			12 48		12 54					13 23		13 49	
Styal d														12 58								
Manchester Airport ✈ a														13 05								
Handforth d	11 26								12 24										13 26			
Congleton d																						13 39
Macclesfield a			11 37					12 09			12 40						13 10	13 26				13 46
d			11 38					12 10			12 42						13 11	13 28				13 47
Prestbury d																						13 51
Adlington (Cheshire) d																						13 54
Poynton d																						13 57
Bramhall d																						14 00
Cheadle Hulme d	11 30								12 28										13 30			14 03
Stockport a	11 37		11 51					12 22	12 33		12 55	12 58					13 28	13 41	13 37		14 00	14 08
d	11 37		11 53	11 53	12 11	12 21	12 26	12 27	12 33	12 53	12 56	12 58	13 12		13 22	13 26	13 29	13 42	13 37	13 53	14 00	14 08
Heaton Chapel d	11 41				12 15				12 37				13 16						13 41			
Levenshulme d	11 44				12 19				12 40				13 19						13 44			
Manchester Picc. 10 85,89 ⛴ a	11 53	12 02	12 04	12 06	12 26	12 32	12 37	12 40	12 46	13 07	13 08	13 15	13 27	13 31	13 33	13 37	13 40	13 53	13 55	14 06	14 19	14 21
d						12 35	12 38								13 35	13 38						
Manchester Oxford Rd 85,89 a						12 37	12 41								13 37	13 41						
Deansgate 85,89 ⛴ a						12 40									13 40							

	NT	VT	NT	EM	XC	XC	VT	NT	XC	TP	VT	AW	NT	VT	NT	NT	EM	XC	VT	NT	XC
		◇1		◇	◇1	◇1	◇1		◇1	◇1	◇1	◇		◇1			◇	◇1	◇1		◇1
	C		D	E	I	J				K		A	C			G	L	M			N
		☕			⊼	⊼	☕		⊼		☕	⊼		☕				⊼	☕		⊼
London Euston 15 ⊖65 d		12 17					12 37				12 57			13 17					13 37		
Birmingham New Street 12 68 d					13 00	13 01			13 31									14 01			14 31
Wolverhampton 7 68 ⛴ d					13 18	13 19			13 49									14 19			14 49
Stafford 65,67 d					13 33	13 34												14 34			
Stoke-on-Trent 50 d		13 50			13 56	13 57			14 21		14 26			14 50				14 57			15 21
Longport 50 d																					
Kidsgrove 50 d																					
Crewe 10 d							14 13					14 28							15 13	14 56	
Sandbach d																				15 03	
Holmes Chapel d																				15 08	
Goostrey d																				15 11	
Chelford d																				15 15	
Alderley Edge d								14 19							14 51					15 19	
Wilmslow d							14 29	14 23				14 48			14 54				15 29	15 23	
Styal d															14 58						
Manchester Airport ✈ a															15 05						
Handforth d								14 26												15 26	
Congleton d																					
Macclesfield a					14 13	14 14					14 42							15 14			
d					14 14	14 15					14 42							15 15			
Prestbury d																					
Adlington (Cheshire) d																					
Poynton d																					
Bramhall d																					
Cheadle Hulme d								14 30												15 30	
Stockport a		14 18			14 27	14 28	14 38	14 37			14 56	15 00		15 18				15 28	15 38	15 37	
d	14 12	14 19	14 21	14 26	14 28	14 29	14 39	14 37		14 53	14 57	15 00	15 12	15 19		15 22	15 26	15 29	15 39	15 37	
Heaton Chapel d	14 16							14 41					15 16							15 41	
Levenshulme d	14 19							14 44					15 19							15 44	
Manchester Picc. 10 85,89 ⛴ a	14 27	14 29	14 33	14 37	14 39	14 40	14 50	14 53	14 57	15 06	15 09	15 15	15 27	15 29	15 32	15 33	15 37	15 40	15 50	15 53	15 59
d			14 35	14 38												15 35	15 38				
Manchester Oxford Rd 85,89 a			14 37	14 41												15 37	15 41				
Deansgate 85,89 ⛴ a			14 40													15 40					

A From Cardiff Central
B From Cleethorpes to Manchester Airport
C From Buxton
D From Chester to Southport
E From Nottingham to Liverpool Lime Street
F From Reading
G From Hazel Grove to Southport
H From Southampton Central
I from 16 February until 23 March. From Bournemouth
J until 9 February, from 30 March. From Bournemouth
K From Doncaster to Manchester Airport
L From Norwich to Liverpool Lime Street
M From Bournemouth
N From Paignton

Table 84

Sundays

8 December to 11 May

Stoke-on-Trent and Crewe - Manchester Airport, Stockport and Manchester

Network Diagram - see first Page of Table 78

		TP	VT	AW	NT	VT	NT	EM	XC	XC	VT	NT	NT	XC	TP	VT	AW	NT	VT	NT	NT	EM	XC
		◇1 A	◇1	◇ B	C	◇1	D	◇ E	◇1 F	◇1 G	◇1			◇1 H	◇1 A	◇1	R I	C	◇1		J	◇ K	◇1 L
London Euston 15 ⊖65	d		13 57			14 17					14 37					14 57			15 17				
Birmingham New Street 12 68	d								15 00	15 01				15 31									16 01
Wolverhampton 7 68	d								15 18	15 19				15 49									16 19
Stafford 65,67	d								15 33	15 34													16 34
Stoke-on-Trent 50	d		15 26			15 50			15 56	15 57			16 01	16 21		16 25			16 50				16 57
Longport 50	d																						
Kidsgrove 50	d												16 08										
Crewe 10	d			15 28							16 13						16 28						
Sandbach	d																						
Holmes Chapel	d																						
Goostrey	d																						
Chelford	d																						
Alderley Edge	d											16 19								16 51			
Wilmslow	d			15 47							16 29	16 23					16 47			16 54			
Styal	d																			16 58			
Manchester Airport	a																			17 05			
Handforth	d											16 26											
Congleton	d												16 15										
Macclesfield	a		15 42						16 13	16 14			16 22			16 42							17 14
	d		15 42						16 14	16 15			16 23			16 42							17 15
Prestbury	d												16 27										
Adlington (Cheshire)	d												16 30										
Poynton	d												16 33										
Bramhall	d												16 36										
Cheadle Hulme	d											16 30	16 39										
Stockport	a		15 56	15 58		16 18			16 27	16 28	16 38	16 37	16 44			16 56	16 58		17 18				17 28
	d	15 53	15 57	15 58	16 12	16 19	16 21	16 26	16 28	16 29	16 39	16 37	16 44		16 53	16 57	16 58	17 12	17 19		17 22	17 29	17 29
Heaton Chapel	d				16 16							16 41						17 16					
Levenshulme	d				16 19							16 44						17 19					
Manchester Picc. 10 85,89	a	16 06	16 09	16 15	16 27	16 29	16 33	16 37	16 39	16 40	16 50	16 53	16 58	16 59	17 06	17 09	17 15	17 27	17 29	17 31	17 33	17 37	17 40
	d						16 35	16 38													17 35	17 38	
Manchester Oxford Rd 85,89	a						16 37	16 41													17 37	17 41	
Deansgate 85,89	a						16 40														17 40		

		VT	NT	XC	TP	VT	AW	NT	VT	NT	EM	XC	VT	NT	XC	TP	VT	AW	NT	VT	NT	NT
		◇1		◇1 H	◇1 A	◇1	R M	C	◇1	D	◇ N	◇1 L	◇1		◇1 O	◇1 A	◇1	R I	C	◇1		J
London Euston 15 ⊖65	d	15 37				15 57			16 17				16 37				16 57			17 17		
Birmingham New Street 12 68	d			16 31								17 01			17 31							
Wolverhampton 7 68	d			16 49								17 19			17 49							
Stafford 65,67	d											17 36										
Stoke-on-Trent 50	d			17 21		17 26			17 50			17 57			18 21		18 26			18 50		
Longport 50	d																					
Kidsgrove 50	d																					
Crewe 10	d	17 13	16 56				17 28						18 13					18 28				
Sandbach	d		17 03																			
Holmes Chapel	d		17 08																			
Goostrey	d		17 11																			
Chelford	d		17 15																			
Alderley Edge	d		17 19											18 19							18 51	
Wilmslow	d	17 29	17 23				17 45						18 29	18 23				18 47			18 54	
Styal	d																				18 58	
Manchester Airport	a																				19 05	
Handforth	d		17 26											18 26								
Congleton	d																					
Macclesfield	a					17 42						18 14					18 42					
	d					17 42						18 15					18 42					
Prestbury	d																					
Adlington (Cheshire)	d																					
Poynton	d																					
Bramhall	d																					
Cheadle Hulme	d		17 30											18 30								
Stockport	a	17 38	17 37			17 56	17 58		18 18			18 28	18 38	18 37			18 56	18 58		19 18		
	d	17 39	17 37		17 53	17 57	17 58	18 12	18 19	18 21	18 26	18 29	18 39	18 37		18 53	18 57	18 58	19 12	19 19		19 22
Heaton Chapel	d		17 41					18 16						18 41					19 16			
Levenshulme	d		17 44					18 19						18 44					19 19			
Manchester Picc. 10 85,89	a	17 50	17 53	17 56	18 06	18 09	18 17	18 27	18 29	18 33	18 37	18 40	18 50	18 53	18 56	19 06	19 09	19 15	19 27	19 29	19 31	19 33
	d									18 35	18 38											19 35
Manchester Oxford Rd 85,89	a									18 37	18 41											19 37
Deansgate 85,89	a									18 40												19 40

A From Cleethorpes to Manchester Airport
B From Carmarthen
C From Buxton
D From Chester to Southport
E From Nottingham to Liverpool Lime Street
F from 16 February until 23 March. From Bournemouth
G until 9 February, from 30 March. From Bournemouth
H From Plymouth
I From Cardiff Central
J From Hazel Grove to Southport
K From Peterborough to Liverpool Lime Street
L From Bournemouth
M From Milford Haven
N From Norwich to Liverpool Lime Street
O From Bristol Temple Meads

Table 84

Sundays

8 December to 11 May

Stoke-on-Trent and Crewe - Manchester Airport, Stockport and Manchester

Network Diagram - see first Page of Table 78

Station		EM	XC	VT	NT	XC	TP	TP	VT	AW		NT	VT	NT	EM	XC	VT	NT	NT	XC		TP	VT	AW	NT
										R														R	
		◇	◇1	◇1		◇1	◇1	◇1	◇1				◇1		◇	◇1	◇1			◇1		◇1	◇1		
		A	B			C	D	E		F		G		H	I	B				J		K		L	G
			🚲	🍴		🚲			🍴	🚲			🍴			🚲	🍴			🚲			🍴		
London Euston 15 ⊖65	d			17 37					17 57				18 17				18 37						18 57		
Birmingham New Street 12 68	d		18 01			18 31										19 01				19 31					
Wolverhampton 7 68	d		18 19			18 49										19 19				19 49					
Stafford 65,67	d		18 36													19 38									
Stoke-on-Trent 50	d		18 57			19 21			19 26				19 50			19 57			20 01	20 21			20 26		
Longport 50	d																								
Kidsgrove 50	d																		20 08						
Crewe 10	d			19 13	18 56					19 28							20 13							20 28	
Sandbach	d				19 03																				
Holmes Chapel	d				19 08																				
Goostrey	d				19 11																				
Chelford	d				19 15																				
Alderley Edge	d				19 19													20 19							
Wilmslow	d			19 29	19 23					19 47							20 29	20 23						20 46	
Styal	d																								
Manchester Airport ✈	a																								
Handforth	d				19 26													20 26							
Congleton	d																		20 15						
Macclesfield	a		19 15						19 42							20 14			20 22				20 42		
	d		19 15						19 42							20 15			20 23				20 42		
Prestbury	d																		20 27						
Adlington (Cheshire)	d																		20 30						
Poynton	d																		20 33						
Bramhall	d																		20 36						
Cheadle Hulme	d				19 30													20 30	20 39						
Stockport	a		19 28	19 38	19 37				19 56	19 58			20 18			20 28	20 38	20 37	20 44				20 56	20 57	
	d	19 26	19 29	19 39	19 37		19 53	19 53	19 57	19 58		20 12	20 19	20 21	20 26	20 29	20 39	20 37	20 44			20 53	20 57	20 57	21 12
Heaton Chapel	d				19 41							20 16						20 41							21 16
Levenshulme	d				19 44							20 19						20 44							21 19
Manchester Picc. 10 85,89	a	19 37	19 40	19 50	19 53	19 58	20 08	20 09	20 09	20 17		20 27	20 29	20 33	20 38	20 40	20 50	20 53	20 58	21 00		21 06	21 09	21 14	21 27
	d	19 38												20 35											
Manchester Oxford Rd 85,89	a	19 41												20 37											
Deansgate 85,89	a													20 40											

Station		VT	NT	NT	EM	XC		VT	NT	XC	TP	VT	AW	NT	VT	NT		XC	NT	VT	NT	NT	NT	NT	XC
													R												
		◇1			◇	◇1		◇1		◇1	◇1	◇1			◇1			◇1		◇1					◇1
				M	I	B				J	K		F	G		N		B			G	O	P		B
		🍴				🚲		🍴				🍴	🚲		🍴					🍴					
London Euston 15 ⊖65	d	19 17						19 37				19 57			20 15					20 35					
Birmingham New Street 12 68	d					20 01				20 31								21 01							22 01
Wolverhampton 7 68	d					20 19				20 53								21 19							22 20
Stafford 65,67	d					20 37												21 37		22 00					22 37
Stoke-on-Trent 50	d	20 50				20 57				21 22		21 26			21 50			21 57						22 39	22 57
Longport 50	d																								
Kidsgrove 50	d																							22 46	
Crewe 10	d							21 14	20 56				21 28							22 21					
Sandbach	d								21 03																
Holmes Chapel	d								21 08																
Goostrey	d								21 11																
Chelford	d								21 16																
Alderley Edge	d		20 51						21 21										22 19				22 51		
Wilmslow	d		20 54					21 30	21 24				21 45						22 23	22 36			22 54		
Styal	d		20 58																				22 58		
Manchester Airport ✈	a		21 05																				23 05		
Handforth	d								21 27										22 26						
Congleton	d																							22 53	
Macclesfield	a					21 15						21 42						22 14						23 00	23 12
	d					21 15						21 42						22 15						23 01	23 13
Prestbury	d																							23 05	
Adlington (Cheshire)	d																							23 08	
Poynton	d																							23 11	
Bramhall	d																							23 14	
Cheadle Hulme	d								21 32										22 30					23 17	
Stockport	a	21 18				21 28		21 39	21 37			21 56	21 58		22 18			22 27	22 37	22 45				23 22	23 27
	d	21 19		21 22	21 24	21 29		21 40	21 38		21 53	21 57	21 58	22 12	22 19	22 21		22 28	22 37	22 46	23 12	23 16		23 23	23 28
Heaton Chapel	d								21 41					22 16					22 41		23 16				
Levenshulme	d								21 44					22 19					22 44		23 19				
Manchester Picc. 10 85,89	a	21 29	21 31	21 33	21 36	21 40		21 50	21 53	21 57	22 06	22 09	22 19	22 27	22 29	22 33		22 39	22 53	22 57	23 27	23 29	23 32	23 37	23 41
	d			21 35												22 35									
Manchester Oxford Rd 85,89	a			21 37												22 37									
Deansgate 85,89	a			21 40												22 40									

A From Norwich to Liverpool Lime Street
B From Bournemouth
C From Penzance
D from 5 January until 23 March. From Sheffield to Manchester Airport
E until 29 December, from 30 March. From Cleethorpes to Manchester Airport
F From Milford Haven
G From Buxton
H From Chester to Southport
I From Norwich
J From Bristol Temple Meads
K From Cleethorpes to Manchester Airport
L From Cardiff Central
M From Hazel Grove to Wigan Wallgate
N From Chester to Wigan Wallgate
O From Sheffield
P until 29 December, from 16 February until 23 March

Table 84

Sundays

8 December to 11 May

Stoke-on-Trent and Crewe - Manchester Airport, Stockport and Manchester

Network Diagram - see first Page of Table 78

		NT		VT	VT
				◇1	◇1
				⊡	⊡
London Euston 15 ⊖65	d			21 25	21 51
Birmingham New Street 12 68	d				
Wolverhampton 7 68 ⇌	d				
Stafford 65,67	d				23s55
Stoke-on-Trent 50	d			23 29	
Longport 50	d				
Kidsgrove 50	d				
Crewe 10	d	22 56			00s21
Sandbach	d	23 03			
Holmes Chapel	d	23 08			
Goostrey	d	23 11			
Chelford	d	23 15			
Alderley Edge	d	23 19			
Wilmslow	d	23 23			
Styal	d				
Manchester Airport ✈	a				
Handforth	d	23 26			
Congleton	d				
Macclesfield	a			23 45	
	d			23 46	
Prestbury	d				
Adlington (Cheshire)	d				
Poynton	d				
Bramhall	d				
Cheadle Hulme	d	23 30			
Stockport	a	23 35		23 59	00s50
	d	23 37		00 01	
Heaton Chapel	d	23 41			
Levenshulme	d	23 44			
Manchester Picc. 10 85,89 ⇌	a	23 53		00 12	01 00
	d				
Manchester Oxford Rd 85,89	a				
Deansgate 85,89 ⇌	a				

Table 84R

Mondays to Fridays

9 December to 16 May

Manchester, Stockport and Manchester Airport - Crewe and Stoke-on-Trent

Network Diagram - see first Page of Table 78

Miles	Miles	Miles			NT MX	TP MX	TP MX	TP MX	TP MX	VT	XC	TP MX	TP MX	NT	NT	TP	NT	VT	XC	NT	NT	VT	NT
										◇1	◇1		◇1			◇1		◇1	◇1			◇1	
					A	B	B	B	B		C	B	B	D	E	F	G		H				I
						🚌	🚌	🚌	🚌	⊠	⚒	🚌	⚒					⊠	⚒			⊠	
0	0	—	Deansgate 85,89 ⛴	d																			
0½	0½	—	**Manchester Oxford Rd** 85,89	d																			
1	1	—	**Manchester Picc.** 10 85,89 ⛴	a																			
—	—	—		d		00 05	00 15	03 55	05 05	05 05	05 11	05 20	05 35	05 35	05 38	05 44	05 50	05 55	06 00		06 06	06 10	06 18
4	4	—	Levenshulme	d																	06 11		
5½	5½	—	Heaton Chapel	d																	06 14		
7	7	—	**Stockport**	a						05 12						05 52	05 59	06 02	06 07		06 18	06 17	06 27
—	—	—		d						05 13								06 03	06 08		06 19	06 18	
9¼	9¼	—	Cheadle Hulme	d																	06 26		
9¾	—	—	Bramhall	d																			
12¼	—	—	Poynton	d																			
14¼	—	—	Adlington (Cheshire)	d																			
16¼	—	—	Prestbury	d																			
19	—	—	**Macclesfield**	a																		06 30	
—	—	—		d																06 03		06 31	
27	—	—	Congleton	d																06 10			
—	11½	—	Handforth	d																	06 30		
—	—	0	**Manchester Airport** ✈	d		00a20	00a40	04a20	05a30			05a45	05a51	06 05	06 05								
—	—	2¼	Styal	d																			
—	13	4	**Wilmslow**	d	00 01									06 17	06 17			06 11	06 16		06 34		
—	14¾	—	Alderley Edge	d	00 04									06 20	06 20						06 37		
—	17¾	—	Chelford	d	00 08									06 24	06 24								
—	21½	—	Goostrey	d	00 13									06 29	06 29								
—	23½	—	Holmes Chapel	d	00 16									06 32	06 32						06 47		
—	27¼	—	Sandbach	d	00 20									06 36	06 36						06 53		
—	32	—	**Crewe** 10	a	00 30					05 34	05 44			06 46	06 46			06 27	06 33		07 04		
32½	—	—	Kidsgrove 50	a																06 16			
35¾	—	—	Longport 50	a																			
38¾	—	—	**Stoke-on-Trent** 50	a							06 06									06 26		06 46	
—	—	—	Stafford 65,67	a						05 54	06 24								06 57				
—	—	—	Wolverhampton 7 68 ⛴	a							06 39								07 13				
—	—	—	Birmingham New Street 12 68	a							06 57								07 33				
—	—	—	London Euston 15 ⊖65	a						07 29								08 08				08 23	

		NT	VT	AW	NT	VT	VT	NT	NT	VT	NT	XC	VT	NT	TP	NT	XC	AW	VT	NT	NT	NT	NT
			◇1	◇		◇1	◇1			◇1		◇1	◇1		◇1		1	◇	◇1				
		J		K					L			H		I	F	M	C	N					L
			⊠	⚒		⊠	⊠			⊠		⚒	⊠		⚒		⚒	⚒	⊠				
Deansgate 85,89 ⛴	d															07 11							
Manchester Oxford Rd 85,89	d															07 15							
Manchester Picc. 10 85,89 ⛴	a															07 17							
	d	06 21	06 27	06 30	06 32	06 35	06 43	06 46	06 49	07 00	07 03	07 07	07 15	07 17	07 19	07 21	07 27	07 30	07 35	07 38	07 46	07 49	07 52
Levenshulme	d	06 28			06 37				06 55		07 09					07 28				07 43			
Heaton Chapel	d	06 31			06 40				06 58		07 12					07 31				07 46			
Stockport	a	06 34	06 34	06 38	06 44	06 42	06 50		07 01		07 16	07 14	07 22	07 26	07 27	07 34	07 34	07 38	07 42	07 50		07 57	08 01
	d		06 35	06 39	06 45	06 43	06 51			07u07	07 18	07 16	07 23				07 35	07 39	07 43	07 51		07 58	
Cheadle Hulme	d				06 51						07 24									07 55		08 02	
Bramhall	d				06 54																	08 05	
Poynton	d				06 57																	08 08	
Adlington (Cheshire)	d				07 01																	08 11	
Prestbury	d				07 04																	08 14	
Macclesfield	a		06 47		07 07	06 55											07 47		07 55			08 18	
	d		06 48		07 08	06 56											07 49		07 56			08 18	
Congleton	d				07 15																	08 26	
Handforth	d										07 28									07 59			
Manchester Airport ✈	d							07 11													08 10		
Styal	d																				08 17		
Wilmslow	d			06 46			06 59	07 21			07 31							07 46		08 02	08 21		
Alderley Edge	d							07 24			07 34									08a08	08 24		
Chelford	d										07 38												
Goostrey	d										07 43												
Holmes Chapel	d							07 32			07 46										08 32		
Sandbach	d							07 36			07 51										08 36		
Crewe 10	a			07 05			07 15	07 46			08 01							08 05			08 46		
Kidsgrove 50	a																					08 32	
Longport 50	a																						
Stoke-on-Trent 50	a		07 04		07 30	07 11						07 43	07 48				08 06		08 11			08 42	
Stafford 65,67	a		07 27				07 35					08 01					08 24						
Wolverhampton 7 68 ⛴	a		07 43									08 15					08 39						
Birmingham New Street 12 68	a		08 05									08 34					08 58						
London Euston 15 ⊖65	a		09 34			08 46	08 53			09 00			09 24						09 52				

A From Manchester Picc.
B from 31 December until 21 March
C To Bournemouth
D until 27 December, from 24 March
E from 30 December until 21 March
F From Manchester Airport to Cleethorpes
G To Sheffield
H To Bristol Temple Meads
I To Chester
J To Hazel Grove
K To Milford Haven
L To Buxton
M From Wigan Wallgate to Hazel Grove
N To Carmarthen

Table 84R

Mondays to Fridays

9 December to 16 May

Manchester, Stockport and Manchester Airport - Crewe and Stoke-on-Trent

Network Diagram - see first Page of Table 78

	VT ◇1 ⊠	NT	XC ◇1 A 🛒	VT ◇1 ⊠	NT B	TP ◇1 C 🛒	XC ◇1 D 🛒	AW ◇ E 🛒	VT ◇1 ⊠	NT	NT	NT	NT F	VT ◇1 ⊠	NT	XC ◇1 G 🛒	VT ◇1 ⊠	NT B	TP ◇1 C 🛒	XC ◇1 D 🛒	AW ◇ H 🛒
Deansgate 85,89 d																					
Manchester Oxford Rd 85,89 d																					
Manchester Picc. 10 85,89 a																					
d	07 55	08 04	08 07	08 15	08 17	08 20	08 27	08 30	08 35	08 38	08 46	08 48	08 52	08 55	09 04	09 07	09 15	09 17	09 20	09 27	09 30
Levenshulme d		08 09								08 43			08 58		09 09						
Heaton Chapel d		08 12								08 46			09 01		09 12						
Stockport a	08 03	08 16	08 15	08 22	08 27	08 28	08 34	08 38	08 42	08 50		08 57	09 04	09 03	09 16	09 15	09 22	09 27	09 28	09 34	09 38
d	08 04	08 17	08 16	08 23			08 35	08 39	08 43	08 51		08 58		09 04	09 17	09 16	09 23			09 35	09 39
Cheadle Hulme d		08 24								08 55		09 02			09 24						
Bramhall d												09 05									
Poynton d												09 08									
Adlington (Cheshire) d												09 11									
Prestbury d												09 14									
Macclesfield a							08 47		08 55			09 18								09 47	
d							08 49		08 56			09 18								09 49	
Congleton d												09 26									
Handforth d		08 28								08 59					09 28						
Manchester Airport ✈ d											09 11										
Styal d																					
Wilmslow d	08 11	08 31						08 46		09 02	09 18			09 11	09 31						09 46
Alderley Edge d		08 34								09 05	09 21				09 34						
Chelford d		08 38													09 38						
Goostrey d		08 43													09 43						
Holmes Chapel d		08 46									09 29				09 46						
Sandbach d		08 52									09 34				09 51						
Crewe 10 a	08 27	09 04						09 07		09 23	09 44			09 29	10 01						10 05
Kidsgrove 50 a												09 32									
Longport 50 a																					
Stoke-on-Trent 50 a			08 43	08 48			09 06		09 11			09 42				09 43	09 48			10 06	
Stafford 65,67 a			09 02				09 24									10 02				10 24	
Wolverhampton 7 68 a			09 15				09 39									10 15				10 39	
Birmingham New Street 12 68 a			09 32				09 58									10 33				10 58	
London Euston 15 ⊖65 a	10 06			10 24					10 43					11 08			11 24				

	VT ◇1 ⊠	NT	NT	NT	NT F	VT ◇1 ⊠	NT	XC ◇1 G 🛒	VT ◇1 ⊠	NT B	TP ◇1 C 🛒	XC ◇1 D 🛒	AW ◇ E 🛒	VT ◇1 ⊠	NT	NT	NT	NT F	VT ◇1 ⊠	NT	XC ◇1 G 🛒	VT ◇1 ☕
Deansgate 85,89 d																						
Manchester Oxford Rd 85,89 d																						
Manchester Picc. 10 85,89 a																						
d	09 35	09 38	09 46	09 48	09 52	09 55	10 04	10 07	10 15	10 17	10 20	10 27	10 30	10 35	10 38	10 46	10 48	10 52	10 55	11 04	11 07	11 15
Levenshulme d		09 43			09 58		10 09								10 43			10 58		11 09		
Heaton Chapel d		09 46			10 01		10 12								10 46			11 01		11 12		
Stockport a	09 42	09 50		09 57	10 04	10 03	10 16	10 15	10 22	10 27	10 28	10 34	10 38	10 42	10 50		10 57	11 04	11 03	11 16	11 15	11 22
d	09 43	09 51		09 58		10 04	10 17	10 16	10 23			10 35	10 39	10 43	10 51		10 58		11 04	11 17	11 16	11 23
Cheadle Hulme d		09 55		10 02			10 24								10 55		11 02			11 24		
Bramhall d				10 05													11 05					
Poynton d				10 08													11 08					
Adlington (Cheshire) d				10 11													11 11					
Prestbury d				10 14													11 14					
Macclesfield a	09 55			10 18								10 47		10 55			11 18					
d	09 56			10 18								10 49		10 56			11 18					
Congleton d				10 26													11 26					
Handforth d		09 59					10 28								10 59					11 28		
Manchester Airport ✈ d			10 11													11 11						
Styal d																11 17						
Wilmslow d		10 02	10 21			10 11	10 31						10 46		11 02	11 21			11 11	11 31		
Alderley Edge d		10a06	10 24				10 34								11a08	11 24				11 34		
Chelford d							10 38													11 38		
Goostrey d							10 43													11 43		
Holmes Chapel d			10 32				10 46									11 32				11 46		
Sandbach d			10 36				10 51									11 36				11 51		
Crewe 10 a			10 46			10 27	11 01						11 05			11 46			11 27	12 01		
Kidsgrove 50 a				10 32													11 32					
Longport 50 a																						
Stoke-on-Trent 50 a	10 11			10 42				10 43	10 48			11 06		11 11			11 42				11 43	11 48
Stafford 65,67 a								11 01				11 24									12 02	
Wolverhampton 7 68 a								11 15				11 39									12 15	
Birmingham New Street 12 68 a								11 33				11 58									12 33	
London Euston 15 ⊖65 a	11 43					12 05			12 24					12 43					13 05			13 24

A To Paignton
B To Chester
C From Manchester Airport to Cleethorpes
D To Bournemouth
E To Milford Haven
F To Buxton
G To Bristol Temple Meads
H To Carmarthen

Table 84R

Mondays to Fridays

9 December to 16 May

Manchester, Stockport and Manchester Airport - Crewe and Stoke-on-Trent

Network Diagram - see first Page of Table 78

	NT	TP	XC	AW	VT		NT	NT	NT	NT	VT	NT	XC	VT	NT		TP	XC	AW	VT	NT	NT	NT	NT
																			R					
		◇1	◇1	◇	◇1						◇1		◇1	◇1			◇1	◇1		◇1				
	A	B	C	D						E			F		A		B	C	G					E
Deansgate 85,89 d																								
Manchester Oxford Rd 85,89 d																								
Manchester Picc. 10 85,89 a																								
d	11 17	11 20	11 27	11 30	11 35		11 38	11 46	11 48	11 52	11 55	12 04	12 07	12 15	12 17		12 20	12 27	12 30	12 35	12 38	12 46	12 48	12 52
Levenshulme d							11 43			11 58		12 09									12 43			12 58
Heaton Chapel d							11 46			12 01		12 12									12 46			13 01
11 27	11 28	11 34	11 38	11 42		11 50		11 57	12 04	12 03	12 16	12 15	12 22	12 27		12 28	12 34	12 38	12 42	12 50		12 57	13 04
d			11 35	11 39	11 43		11 51		11 58		12 04	12 17	12 16	12 23				12 35	12 39	12 43	12 51		12 58	
Cheadle Hulme d							11 55		12 02			12 24									12 55		13 02	
Bramhall d									12 05														13 05	
Poynton d									12 08														13 08	
Adlington (Cheshire) d									12 11														13 11	
Prestbury d									12 14														13 14	
Macclesfield a			11 47		11 55				12 18									12 47		12 55			13 18	
d			11 49		11 56				12 18									12 49		12 56			13 18	
Congleton d									12 26														13 26	
Handforth d							11 59					12 28									12 59			
Manchester Airport ✈ d								12 11														13 11		
Styal d																						13 17		
Wilmslow d				11 46			12 02	12 20			12 11	12 31							12 46		13 02	13 21		
Alderley Edge d							12a06	12 23				12 34									13a08	13 24		
Chelford d												12 38												
Goostrey d												12 43												
Holmes Chapel d								12 31				12 46										13 32		
Sandbach d								12 35				12 51										13 36		
Crewe 10 a				12 05				12 45			12 27	13 01							13 05			13 46		
Kidsgrove 50 a									12 32														13 32	
Longport 50 a																								
Stoke-on-Trent 50 a			12 06		12 11				12 42				12 43	12 47				13 06		13 11			13 42	
Stafford 65,67 a			12 24										13 01					13 24						
Wolverhampton 7 68 a			12 39										13 16					13 39						
Birmingham New Street 12 68 a			12 58										13 33					13 58						
London Euston 15 ⊖65 a					13 43						14 05			14 24						14 43				

	VT		NT	XC	VT	NT	TP	XC	AW	VT	NT		NT	NT	NT	VT	NT	XC	VT	NT	TP		XC	AW
									R															R
	◇1			◇1	◇1		◇1	◇1		◇1						◇1		◇1	◇1		◇1		◇1	
				H		A	B	C	I						E			J		A	B		C	G
Deansgate 85,89 d																								
Manchester Oxford Rd 85,89 d																								
Manchester Picc. 10 85,89 a																								
d	12 55		13 04	13 07	13 15	13 17	13 20	13 27	13 30	13 35	13 38		13 46	13 48	13 52	13 55	14 04	14 07	14 15	14 17	14 20		14 27	14 30
Levenshulme d			13 09								13 43				13 58		14 09							
Heaton Chapel d			13 12								13 46				14 01		14 12							
Stockport a	13 03		13 16	13 15	13 22	13 27	13 28	13 34	13 38	13 42	13 50			13 57	14 04	14 03	14 16	14 15	14 22	14 27	14 28		14 34	14 38
d	13 04		13 17	13 16	13 23			13 35	13 39	13 43	13 51			13 58		14 04	14 17	14 16	14 23				14 35	14 39
Cheadle Hulme d			13 24								13 55			14 02			14 24							
Bramhall d														14 05										
Poynton d														14 08										
Adlington (Cheshire) d														14 11										
Prestbury d														14 14										
Macclesfield a								13 47		13 55				14 18									14 47	
d								13 49		13 56				14 18									14 49	
Congleton d														14 26										
Handforth d			13 28								13 59						14 28							
Manchester Airport ✈ d													14 10											
Styal d																								
Wilmslow d	13 11		13 31						13 46		14 02		14 20			14 11	14 31							14 46
Alderley Edge d			13 34								14a06		14 23				14 34							
Chelford d			13 38														14 38							
Goostrey d			13 43														14 43							
Holmes Chapel d			13 46										14 31				14 46							
Sandbach d			13 51										14 35				14 51							
Crewe 10 a	13 29		14 01						14 05				14 45			14 27	15 01							15 05
Kidsgrove 50 a														14 32										
Longport 50 a																								
Stoke-on-Trent 50 a				13 43	13 48			14 06		14 11				14 42				14 43	14 48				15 06	
Stafford 65,67 a				14 01				14 24										15 02					15 24	
Wolverhampton 7 68 a				14 15				14 39										15 15					15 39	
Birmingham New Street 12 68 a				14 33				14 58										15 33					15 58	
London Euston 15 ⊖65 a	15 09				15 24					15 43						16 05			16 24					

A To Chester
B From Manchester Airport to Cleethorpes
C To Bournemouth
D To Carmarthen
E To Buxton
F To Exeter St Davids
G To Milford Haven
H To Bristol Temple Meads
I To Tenby
J To Paignton

Table 84R

Mondays to Fridays

9 December to 16 May

Manchester, Stockport and Manchester Airport - Crewe and Stoke-on-Trent

Network Diagram - see first Page of Table 78

Station		VT	NT	NT	NT	NT	VT	NT	XC	VT	NT	TP	XC	AW	VT	NT	NT	NT	NT	VT	NT	XC	VT
														R									
		◇1					◇1		◇1	◇1		◇1	◇1		◇1					◇1		◇1	◇1
						A			B		C	D	E	F					A			B	
Deansgate 85,89	d																						
Manchester Oxford Rd 85,89	d																						
Manchester Picc. 10 85,89	a																						
	d	14 35	14 38	14 46	14 48	14 52	14 55	15 04	15 07	15 15	15 17	15 20	15 27	15 30	15 35	15 38	15 46	15 48	15 52	15 55	16 04	16 07	16 15
Levenshulme	d		14 43			14 58		15 09								15 43			15 58		16 09		
Heaton Chapel	d		14 46			15 01		15 12								15 46			16 01		16 12		
Stockport	a	14 42	14 50		14 57	15 04	15 03	15 16	15 15	15 22	15 27	15 28	15 34	15 38	15 42	15 50		15 57	16 04	16 03	16 16	16 15	16 22
	d	14 43	14 51		14 58		15 04	15 17	15 16	15 23			15 35	15 39	15 43	15 51		15 58		16 04	16 17	16 16	16 23
Cheadle Hulme	d		14 55		15 02			15 24								15 55		16 02			16 24		
Bramhall	d				15 05													16 05					
Poynton	d				15 08													16 08					
Adlington (Cheshire)	d				15 11													16 11					
Prestbury	d				15 14													16 14					
Macclesfield	a	14 55			15 18								15 47		15 55			16 18					
	d	14 56			15 18								15 49		15 56			16 18					
Congleton	d				15 26													16 26					
Handforth	d		14 59					15 28								15 59					16 28		
Manchester Airport	d			15 10													16 11						
Styal	d																						
Wilmslow	d		15 02	15 20			15 11	15 31						15 46		16 02	16 19			16 11	16 31		
Alderley Edge	d		15a08	15 23				15 34								16a06	16 22				16 34		
Chelford	d							15 38													16 38		
Goostrey	d							15 43													16 43		
Holmes Chapel	d			15 31				15 46									16 30				16 46		
Sandbach	d			15 35				15 51									16 34				16 51		
Crewe 10	a			15 45			15 27	16 01						16 05			16 44			16 27	17 01		
Kidsgrove 50	a				15 32													16 32					
Longport 50	a																						
Stoke-on-Trent 50	a	15 11			15 42				15 43	15 48			16 06		16 11			16 42				16 43	16 49
Stafford 65,67	a								16 02				16 24									17 02	
Wolverhampton 7 68	a								16 15				16 39									17 15	
Birmingham New Street 12 68	a								16 33				16 58									17 33	
London Euston 15 ⊖65	a	16 43					17 05			17 24					17 43					18 05			18 24

Station		NT	TP	XC	AW	VT	NT	NT	NT	NT	VT	NT	NT	XC	NT	VT	NT	TP	NT	XC	AW	VT
					R																R	
			◇1	◇1		◇1					◇1			◇1		◇1		◇1		◇1		◇1
		C	D	E	G					A		H		I	C			D	J	E	I	
Deansgate 85,89	d																17 10					
Manchester Oxford Rd 85,89	d																17 13					
Manchester Picc. 10 85,89	a																17 15					
	d	16 17	16 20	16 27	16 30	16 35	16 38	16 46	16 48	16 51	16 55	16 58	17 03	17 05	17 09	17 15	17 17	17 20	17 23	17 27	17 30	17 35
Levenshulme	d						16 43					17 03	17 08						17 28			
Heaton Chapel	d						16 46					17 06	17 11						17 31			
Stockport	a	16 27	16 28	16 34	16 38	16 42	16 50		16 57	17 02	17 03	17 10	17 15	17 12	17 17	17 22	17 27	17 28	17 35	17 35	17 39	17 42
	d			16 35	16 39	16 43	16 51		16 58		17 04		17 16	17 13		17 23	17 28			17 35	17 39	17 43
Cheadle Hulme	d						16 55		17 02				17 24				17 32					
Bramhall	d								17 05								17 35					
Poynton	d								17 08								17 38					
Adlington (Cheshire)	d								17 11								17 41					
Prestbury	d								17 14								17 44					
Macclesfield	a			16 47		16 55			17 18					17 25			17 48					17 55
	d			16 49		16 56			17 18					17 27			17 48					17 56
Congleton	d								17 25								17 56					
Handforth	d						16 59						17 28									
Manchester Airport	d							17 11														
Styal	d							17 17														
Wilmslow	d				16 46		17 03	17 21			17 11		17 31							17 44	17 46	
Alderley Edge	d						17a08	17 24					17 34									
Chelford	d												17 38									
Goostrey	d												17 43									
Holmes Chapel	d							17 32					17 46									
Sandbach	d							17 36					17 51									
Crewe 10	a				17 05			17 46			17 27		18 01							18 04	18 07	
Kidsgrove 50	a								17 31													
Longport 50	a																					
Stoke-on-Trent 50	a			17 06		17 11			17 41					17 43		17 49	18 10					18 11
Stafford 65,67	a			17 24										18 03						18 27		
Wolverhampton 7 68	a			17 39										18 14						18 39		
Birmingham New Street 12 68	a			17 58										18 32						18 58		
London Euston 15 ⊖65	a					18 43					19 09					19 26						19 43

A To Buxton
B To Bristol Temple Meads
C To Chester
D From Manchester Airport to Cleethorpes
E To Bournemouth
F To Carmarthen
G To Milford Haven
H To Hazel Grove
I To Cardiff Central
J To Chinley

Table 84R

Mondays to Fridays

9 December to 16 May

Manchester, Stockport and Manchester Airport - Crewe and Stoke-on-Trent

Network Diagram - see first Page of Table 78

		NT	NT	NT	NT	VT	XC	NT	VT	NT	TP	NT	XC	AW	VT	NT	NT	NT	NT	VT	NT	XC	VT
						◇1	◇1		◇1		◇1		◇1	◇	◇1		1			◇1		◇1	◇1
					A		B			C	D	E	F	G			H		A			I	
						⊠	⚲		⊠		⚲		⚲		⊠					⊠		⚲	☕
Deansgate 85,89	d											18 12											
Manchester Oxford Rd 85,89	d											18 16											
Manchester Picc. 10 85,89	a											18 18											
	d	17 38	17 46	17 48	17 52	17 55	18 05	18 08	18 15	18 17	18 20	18 21	18 27	18 30	18 35	18 38	18 46	18 48	18 52	18 55	19 04	19 07	19 15
Levenshulme	d	17 43			17 58			18 13				18 28				18 43			18 58		19 09		
Heaton Chapel	d	17 46			18 01			18 16				18 31				18 46			19 01		19 12		
Stockport	a	17 50		17 57	18 04	18 03	18 12	18 20	18 22	18 27	18 28	18 34	18 34	18 38	18 42	18 50		18 57	19 04	19 03	19 16	19 15	19 22
	d	17 51		17 58		18 04	18 13	18 21	18 23				18 35	18 39	18 43	18 51		18 58		19 04	19 17	19 16	19 23
Cheadle Hulme	d	17 55		18 02				18 25								18 55		19 02			19 24		
Bramhall	d			18 05														19 05					
Poynton	d			18 08														19 08					
Adlington (Cheshire)	d			18 11														19 11					
Prestbury	d			18 14														19 14					
Macclesfield	a			18 17			18 25								18 55			19 18					19 35
	d			18 18			18 26								18 56			19 18					19 36
Congleton	d			18 26									18 54					19 26					
Handforth	d	17 59						18 29								18 59					19 28		
Manchester Airport ✈	d		18 11														19 14						
Styal	d		18 17																				
Wilmslow	d	18 02	18 21			18 11		18 31						18 46		19 02	19 26			19 11	19 31		
Alderley Edge	d	18 05	18 24					18 34								19a08	19a31				19 34		
Chelford	d							18 38													19 38		
Goostrey	d							18 43													19 43		
Holmes Chapel	d		18 32					18 46													19 46		
Sandbach	d	18 16	18 36					18 50													19 51		
Crewe 10	a	18 26	18 46			18 28		19 00						19 05						19 27	20 01		
Kidsgrove 50	a			18 32														19 32					
Longport 50	a																						
Stoke-on-Trent 50	a			18 42			18 43		18 48				19 06		19 11			19 42				19 43	19 51
Stafford 65,67	a						19 01						19 24									20 03	
Wolverhampton 7 68	a						19 15						19 39									20 16	
Birmingham New Street 12 68	a						19 33						19 58									20 33	
London Euston 15 ⊖65	a					20 08			20 24						20 42					21 06			21 26

		NT	TP	NT	XC	AW	NT	NT	NT	VT	NT	XC	VT	NT	TP	XC	AW	NT	NT	NT	NT	TP FX	VT
			◇1		◇1	◇				◇1		◇1	◇1		◇1	◇1	◇						◇1
		C	D	J	K	G	L		A					C	M		N	O		A		P	
					⚲					☕			☕									🚌	☕
Deansgate 85,89	d																						
Manchester Oxford Rd 85,89	d						19 43											20 43					
Manchester Picc. 10 85,89	a						19 45											20 45					
	d	19 17	19 18	19 22	19 27	19 30	19 46	19 48	19 51	19 55	20 04	20 07	20 15	20 17	20 20	20 27	20 30	20 46	20 48	20 52	21 04	21 15	21 15
Levenshulme	d			19 28					19 58		20 09									20 58	21 09		
Heaton Chapel	d			19 31					20 01		20 12									21 01	21 12		
Stockport	a	19 27	19 26	19 34	19 34	19 38		19 56	20 04	20 03	20 15	20 15	20 22	20 27	20 28	20 34	20 38		20 57	21 04	21 16		21 22
	d				19 35	19 39		19 58		20 04	20 17	20 16	20 23			20 35	20 39		20 58		21 17		21 23
Cheadle Hulme	d							20 02			20 23								21 02		21 24		
Bramhall	d							20 05											21 05				
Poynton	d							20 08											21 08				
Adlington (Cheshire)	d							20 11											21 11				
Prestbury	d							20 14											21 14				
Macclesfield	a				19 47			20 18					20 35			20 47			21 18				21 35
	d				19 49			20 18					20 36			20 49			21 18				21 36
Congleton	d							20 26											21 26				
Handforth	d										20 27										21 28		
Manchester Airport ✈	d						20 14											21 15				21a30	
Styal	d																						
Wilmslow	d					19 46	20a24			20 11	20 30						20 46	21a25			21 31		
Alderley Edge	d										20 33										21 34		
Chelford	d										20 37										21 38		
Goostrey	d										20 42										21 43		
Holmes Chapel	d										20 45										21 46		
Sandbach	d										20 51										21 51		
Crewe 10	a					20 05				20 27	21 03						21 06				22 01		
Kidsgrove 50	a							20 32											21 32				
Longport 50	a																						
Stoke-on-Trent 50	a				20 06			20 42				20 43	20 51			21 06			21 42				21 51
Stafford 65,67	a				20 26					20 47		21 02				21 24							
Wolverhampton 7 68	a				20 42							21 15				21 39							
Birmingham New Street 12 68	a				21 00							21 33				22 00							
London Euston 15 ⊖65	a									22 13			22 33										23 48

A To Buxton
B To Plymouth
C To Chester
D From Manchester Airport to Cleethorpes
E From Wigan Wallgate to Buxton
F To Bournemouth
G To Carmarthen
H 1 from Wilmslow
I To Bristol Temple Meads
J To Hazel Grove
K To Southampton Central
L until 27 December
M From Manchester Airport to Sheffield
N To Cardiff Central
O until 2 January, FX from 6 January until 6 February, from 10 February
P from 30 December until 20 March

Table 84R

Mondays to Fridays

9 December to 16 May

Manchester, Stockport and Manchester Airport - Crewe and Stoke-on-Trent

Network Diagram - see first Page of Table 78

		NT	TP	XC	AW	TP FX	NT	NT FX	NT	NT	NT	XC	TP FX	NT	AW	TP FO	NT	NT FX	NT	TP FX	NT	NT
			◇■1	◇■1	◇							◇■1			◇	◇■1						
		A	B		C	D 🚌	E	D 🚌		F			D 🚌	A	C	G	E	D 🚌		D 🚌		F
Deansgate 85,89 ⛴	d																					
Manchester Oxford Rd 85,89	d						21 43										22 43					
Manchester Picc. 10 85,89 ⛴	a						21 45										22 45					
	d	21 17	21 20	21 27	21 35	21 45	21 47	21 47	21 48	21 52	22 04	22 07	22 15	22 17	22 36	22 40	22 46	22 47	22 48	22 50	23 04	23 10
Levenshulme	d									21 58	22 09										23 09	
Heaton Chapel	d									22 01	22 12										23 12	
Stockport	a	21 27	21 28	21 34	21 43				21 57	22 04	22 16	22 15		22 27	22 43				22 57		23 16	23 19
	d			21 35	21 44				21 58		22 17	22 16			22 44				22 58		23 16	
Cheadle Hulme	d								22 02		22 24								23 02		23 23	
Bramhall	d								22 05										23 05			
Poynton	d								22 08										23 08			
Adlington (Cheshire)	d								22 11										23 11			
Prestbury	d								22 14										23 14			
Macclesfield	a			21 47					22 18			22 28							23 20			
	d			21 49					22 18			22 29										
Congleton	d								22 26													
Handforth	d										22 28										23 27	
Manchester Airport ✈	d					22a10	22 14	22 27					22a30			22a57	23 14	23 27		23a15		
Styal	d																					
Wilmslow	d				21 51		22a22	22a47			22 31				22 52		23a22	23a47			23 31	
Alderley Edge	d										22 34										23a36	
Chelford	d										22 38											
Goostrey	d										22 43											
Holmes Chapel	d										22 46											
Sandbach	d										22 51											
Crewe 10	a				22 11						23 01				23 10							
Kidsgrove 50	a								22 32													
Longport 50	a																					
Stoke-on-Trent 50	a			22 07					22 42			22 46										
Stafford 65,67	a			22 25								23 06										
Wolverhampton 7 68 ⛴	a			22 39								23 19										
Birmingham New Street 12 68	a			22 58								23 39										
London Euston 15 ⊖65	a																					

		NT	TP FX	NT	NT	TP FX
			D 🚌	A		D 🚌
Deansgate 85,89 ⛴	d					
Manchester Oxford Rd 85,89	d					
Manchester Picc. 10 85,89 ⛴	a					
	d	23 14	23 15	23 17	23 38	23 45
Levenshulme	d				23 44	
Heaton Chapel	d				23 47	
Stockport	a	23 23		23 26	23 50	
	d	23 23			23 51	
Cheadle Hulme	d	23 27			23 55	
Bramhall	d	23 30				
Poynton	d	23 33				
Adlington (Cheshire)	d	23 37				
Prestbury	d	23 40				
Macclesfield	a	23 46				
	d					
Congleton	d					
Handforth	d				23 59	
Manchester Airport ✈	d		23a30			00a10
Styal	d					
Wilmslow	d				00 01	
Alderley Edge	d				00 04	
Chelford	d				00 08	
Goostrey	d				00 13	
Holmes Chapel	d				00 16	
Sandbach	d				00 20	
Crewe 10	a				00 30	
Kidsgrove 50	a					
Longport 50	a					
Stoke-on-Trent 50	a					
Stafford 65,67	a					
Wolverhampton 7 68 ⛴	a					
Birmingham New Street 12 68	a					
London Euston 15 ⊖65	a					

A To Chester
B From Manchester Airport to Cleethorpes
C To Shrewsbury
D from 30 December until 20 March
E until 27 December, FO from 3 January until 14 March, from 21 March
F To Buxton
G From Hull

Table 84R

Saturdays

14 December to 17 May

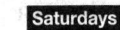

Manchester, Stockport and Manchester Airport - Crewe and Stoke-on-Trent

Network Diagram - see first Page of Table 78

		NT	XC	VT	NT	TP	NT	VT	NT	XC		NT	VT	NT	AW	VT	NT	NT	NT	VT		NT	XC	VT	NT
			◇1	◇1		◇1		◇1		◇1			◇1		◇	◇1				◇1			◇1	◇1	
		A	B			C	D			E				F	G				H				E		F
			🛒	🍴				🍴		🛒			🍴		🛒	🍴				🍴			🛒	🍴	
Deansgate 85,89 ⛴	d																								
Manchester Oxford Rd 85,89	d																								
Manchester Picc. 10 85,89 ⛴	a																								
	d		05 11	05 25	05 35	05 44	05 50	05 55		06 00		06 06	06 10	06 18	06 30	06 35	06 45	06 46	06 49	06 55		07 03	07 07	07 15	07 17
Levenshulme	d											06 11							06 55			07 09			
Heaton Chapel	d											06 14							06 58			07 12			
Stockport	a			05 33		05 52	05 59	06 02		06 07		06 18	06 17	06 27	06 38	06 42	06 53		07 01	07 03		07 16	07 14	07 22	07 27
	d			05 34				06 03		06 08		06 19	06 18		06 39	06 43	06 54			07 04		07 18	07 16	07 23	
Cheadle Hulme	d											06 26					06 58					07 24			
Bramhall	d																07 01								
Poynton	d																07 04								
Adlington (Cheshire)	d																07 07								
Prestbury	d																07 10								
Macclesfield	a									06 20			06 30			06 55	07 14								
	d								06 03	06 21			06 31			06 56	07 14								
Congleton	d								06 10								07 22								
Handforth	d											06 30										07 28			
Manchester Airport ✈	d				06 05													07 11							
Styal	d																								
Wilmslow	d	00 01		05 41	06 14			06 11				06 33			06 46			07 21		07 11		07 31			
Alderley Edge	d	00 04			06 17							06 36						07 24				07 34			
Chelford	d	00 08			06 21																	07 38			
Goostrey	d	00 13			06 25																	07 43			
Holmes Chapel	d	00 16			06 28							06 44						07 32				07 46			
Sandbach	d	00 20			06 33							06 49						07 36				07 51			
Crewe 10	a	00 30	05 41	05 57	06 43			06 27				06 59			07 05			07 46		07 27		08 01			
Kidsgrove 50	a								06 16								07 28								
Longport 50	a																								
Stoke-on-Trent 50	a		06 07						06 26	06 38			06 46			07 11	07 40						07 43	07 48	
Stafford 65,67	a		06 25	06 18						06 57													08 02		
Wolverhampton 7 68 ⛴	a		06 39							07 12													08 15		
Birmingham New Street 12 68	a		06 57							07 33													08 34		
London Euston 15 ⊖65	a			07 53				08 10					08 28			08 46				09 05				09 24	

		TP	NT	XC	AW	VT		NT	NT	NT	NT	VT	NT	XC	VT	NT		TP	XC	AW	VT	NT	NT	NT	NT
		◇1		◇1	◇	◇1						◇1		◇1	◇1			◇1	◇1	◇	◇1				
		C	I	B	J						H			K		F		C	B	G					H
				🛒	🛒	🍴						🍴		🛒	🍴				🛒	🛒	🍴				
Deansgate 85,89 ⛴	d		07 11																						
Manchester Oxford Rd 85,89	d		07 15																						
Manchester Picc. 10 85,89 ⛴	a		07 17																						
	d	07 19	07 21	07 27	07 30	07 35		07 38	07 46	07 49	07 52	07 55	08 04	08 07	08 15	08 17		08 20	08 27	08 30	08 35	08 38	08 46	08 48	08 52
Levenshulme	d		07 28					07 43			07 58		08 09									08 43			08 58
Heaton Chapel	d		07 31					07 46					08 12									08 46			09 01
Stockport	a	07 27	07 34	07 34	07 38	07 42		07 50		07 57	08 02	08 03	08 16	08 15	08 22	08 27		08 28	08 34	08 38	08 42	08 50		08 57	09 04
	d			07 35	07 39	07 43		07 51		07 58		08 04	08 17	08 16	08 23				08 35	08 39	08 43	08 51		08 58	
Cheadle Hulme	d							07 55		08 02			08 24									08 55		09 02	
Bramhall	d									08 05														09 05	
Poynton	d									08 08														09 08	
Adlington (Cheshire)	d									08 11														09 11	
Prestbury	d									08 14														09 14	
Macclesfield	a			07 47		07 55				08 18									08 47		08 55			09 18	
	d			07 49		07 56				08 18									08 49		08 56			09 18	
Congleton	d									08 26														09 26	
Handforth	d							07 59					08 28									08 59			
Manchester Airport ✈	d								08 10														09 11		
Styal	d								08 17																
Wilmslow	d				07 46			08 02	08 21			08 11	08 31							08 46		09 02	09 18		
Alderley Edge	d							08a08	08 24				08 34									09a06	09 21		
Chelford	d												08 38												
Goostrey	d												08 43												
Holmes Chapel	d								08 32				08 46										09 29		
Sandbach	d								08 36				08 51										09 34		
Crewe 10	a				08 05				08 46			08 27	09 01							09 05			09 44		
Kidsgrove 50	a									08 32														09 32	
Longport 50	a																								
Stoke-on-Trent 50	a			08 06		08 11				08 42				08 43	08 48				09 06		09 11			09 42	
Stafford 65,67	a			08 25										09 02					09 25						
Wolverhampton 7 68 ⛴	a			08 39										09 15					09 39						
Birmingham New Street 12 68	a			08 58										09 33					09 58						
London Euston 15 ⊖65	a					09 43						10 11			10 24						10 43				

A From Manchester Picc.
B To Bournemouth
C From Manchester Airport to Cleethorpes
D To Sheffield
E To Bristol Temple Meads
F To Chester
G To Milford Haven
H To Buxton
I From Wigan Wallgate to Hazel Grove
J To Carmarthen
K To Paignton

Table 84R

Saturdays

14 December to 17 May

Manchester, Stockport and Manchester Airport - Crewe and Stoke-on-Trent

Network Diagram - see first Page of Table 78

		VT	NT	XC	VT	NT	TP	XC	AW	VT	NT	NT	NT	NT	VT	NT	XC	VT	NT	TP	XC	AW
		◇1		◇1	◇1		◇1	◇1	◇	◇1					◇1		◇1	◇1		◇1	◇1	◇
				A		B	C	D	E					F			A		B	C	D	G
		☕		🛒	☕			🛒	🛒	☕					☕		🛒	☕			🛒	🛒
Deansgate 85,89 ⛴	d																					
Manchester Oxford Rd 85,89	d																					
Manchester Picc. 10 85,89 ⛴	a																					
	d	08 55	09 04	09 07	09 15	09 17	09 20	09 27	09 30	09 35	09 38	09 46	09 48	09 52	09 55	10 04	10 07	10 15	10 17	10 20	10 27	10 30
Levenshulme	d		09 09								09 43			09 58		10 09						
Heaton Chapel	d		09 12								09 46			10 01		10 12						
Stockport	a	09 03	09 16	09 15	09 22	09 27	09 28	09 34	09 38	09 42	09 50		09 57	10 04	10 03	10 16	10 15	10 22	10 27	10 28	10 34	10 38
	d	09 04	09 17	09 16	09 23			09 35	09 39	09 43	09 51		09 58		10 04	10 17	10 16	10 23			10 35	10 39
Cheadle Hulme	d		09 24								09 55		10 02			10 24						
Bramhall	d												10 05									
Poynton	d												10 08									
Adlington (Cheshire)	d												10 11									
Prestbury	d												10 14									
Macclesfield	a							09 47		09 55			10 18								10 47	
	d							09 49		09 56			10 18								10 49	
Congleton	d												10 26									
Handforth	d		09 28								09 59					10 28						
Manchester Airport ✈	d											10 11										
Styal	d																					
Wilmslow	d	09 11	09 31						09 46		10 02	10 21			10 11	10 31						10 46
Alderley Edge	d		09 34								10a06	10 24				10 34						
Chelford	d		09 38													10 38						
Goostrey	d		09 43													10 43						
Holmes Chapel	d		09 46									10 32				10 46						
Sandbach	d		09 51									10 36				10 51						
Crewe 10	a	09 29	10 01						10 05			10 46			10 27	11 01						11 05
Kidsgrove 50	a												10 32									
Longport 50	a																					
Stoke-on-Trent 50	a			09 43	09 48			10 06		10 11			10 42				10 43	10 48			11 06	
Stafford 65,67	a			10 02				10 25									11 02				11 25	
Wolverhampton 7 68 ⛴	a			10 15				10 39									11 15				11 39	
Birmingham New Street 12 68	a			10 33				10 58									11 33				11 59	
London Euston 15 ⊖65	a	11 08			11 24					11 43					12 05			12 24				

		VT	NT	NT	NT	NT	VT	NT	XC	VT	NT	TP	XC	AW	VT	NT	NT	NT	NT	VT	NT	XC	VT
		◇1					◇1		◇1	◇1		◇1	◇1	◇	◇1					◇1		◇1	◇1
						F			A		B	C	D	E					F			H	
		☕					☕		🛒	☕			🛒	🛒	☕					☕		🛒	☕
Deansgate 85,89 ⛴	d																						
Manchester Oxford Rd 85,89	d																						
Manchester Picc. 10 85,89 ⛴	a																						
	d	10 35	10 38	10 46	10 48	10 52	10 55	11 04	11 07	11 15	11 17	11 20	11 27	11 30	11 35	11 38	11 46	11 48	11 52	11 55	12 04	12 07	12 15
Levenshulme	d		10 43			10 58		11 09								11 43			11 58		12 09		
Heaton Chapel	d		10 46			11 01		11 12								11 46			12 01		12 12		
Stockport	a	10 42	10 50		10 57	11 04	11 03	11 16	11 15	11 22	11 27	11 28	11 34	11 38	11 42	11 50		11 57	12 04	12 03	12 16	12 15	12 22
	d	10 43	10 51		10 58		11 04	11 17	11 16	11 23			11 35	11 39	11 43	11 51		11 58		12 04	12 17	12 16	12 23
Cheadle Hulme	d		10 55		11 02			11 24								11 55		12 02			12 24		
Bramhall	d				11 05													12 05					
Poynton	d				11 08													12 08					
Adlington (Cheshire)	d				11 11													12 11					
Prestbury	d				11 14													12 14					
Macclesfield	a	10 55			11 18								11 47		11 55			12 18					
	d	10 56			11 18								11 49		11 56			12 18					
Congleton	d				11 26													12 26					
Handforth	d		10 59					11 28								11 59					12 28		
Manchester Airport ✈	d			11 11													12 11						
Styal	d			11 17																			
Wilmslow	d		11 02	11 21			11 11	11 31						11 46		12 02	12 20			12 11	12 31		
Alderley Edge	d		11a06	11 24				11 34								12a06	12 23				12 34		
Chelford	d							11 38													12 38		
Goostrey	d							11 43													12 43		
Holmes Chapel	d			11 32				11 46									12 31				12 46		
Sandbach	d			11 36				11 51									12 35				12 51		
Crewe 10	a			11 46			11 27	12 01						12 05			12 45			12 27	13 01		
Kidsgrove 50	a				11 32													12 32					
Longport 50	a																						
Stoke-on-Trent 50	a	11 11			11 42				11 43	11 48			12 06		12 11			12 42				12 43	12 48
Stafford 65,67	a								12 02				12 24									13 02	
Wolverhampton 7 68 ⛴	a								12 15				12 39									13 14	
Birmingham New Street 12 68	a								12 33				12 58									13 32	
London Euston 15 ⊖65	a	12 43					13 05			13 24					13 43					14 05			14 24

A To Bristol Temple Meads
B To Chester
C From Manchester Airport to Cleethorpes
D To Bournemouth
E To Carmarthen
F To Buxton
G To Milford Haven
H To Exeter St Davids

Table 84R

Saturdays

14 December to 17 May

Manchester, Stockport and Manchester Airport - Crewe and Stoke-on-Trent

Network Diagram - see first Page of Table 78

		NT	TP	XC	AW	VT	NT	NT	NT	NT	VT	NT	XC	VT	NT	TP	XC	AW	VT	NT	NT	NT
					R													R				
			◇1	◇1		◇1					◇1		◇1	◇1		◇1	◇1		◇1			
		A	B	C	D					E			F		A	B	C	G				
				[trolley]	[trolley]	[restaurant]					[restaurant]		[trolley]	[restaurant]			[trolley]	[trolley]	[restaurant]			
Deansgate 85,89 ⛴	d																					
Manchester Oxford Rd 85,89	d																					
Manchester Picc. 10 85,89 ⛴	a																					
	d	12 17	12 20	12 27	12 30	12 35	12 38	12 46	12 48	12 52	12 55	13 04	13 07	13 15	13 17	13 20	13 27	13 30	13 35	13 38	13 46	13 48
Levenshulme	d						12 43			12 58		13 09								13 43		
Heaton Chapel	d						12 46			13 01		13 12								13 46		
Stockport	a	12 27	12 28	12 34	12 38	12 42	12 50		12 57	13 04	13 03	13 16	13 15	13 22	13 27	13 28	13 34	13 38	13 42	13 50		13 57
	d			12 35	12 39	12 43	12 51		12 58		13 04	13 17	13 16	13 23			13 35	13 39	13 43	13 51		13 58
Cheadle Hulme	d						12 55		13 02			13 24								13 55		14 02
Bramhall	d								13 05													14 05
Poynton	d								13 08													14 08
Adlington (Cheshire)	d								13 11													14 11
Prestbury	d								13 14													14 14
Macclesfield	a			12 47		12 55			13 18								13 47		13 55			14 18
	d			12 49		12 56			13 18								13 49		13 56			14 18
Congleton	d								13 26													14 26
Handforth	d						12 59					13 28								13 59		
Manchester Airport ✈	d							13 11													14 11	
Styal	d							13 17														
Wilmslow	d				12 46		13 02	13 21			13 11	13 31						13 46		14 02	14 20	
Alderley Edge	d						13a06	13 24				13 34								14a06	14 23	
Chelford	d											13 38										
Goostrey	d											13 43										
Holmes Chapel	d							13 32				13 46									14 31	
Sandbach	d							13 36				13 51									14 35	
Crewe 10	a				13 05			13 46			13 29	14 01						14 05			14 45	
Kidsgrove 50	a								13 32													14 32
Longport 50	a																					
Stoke-on-Trent 50	a			13 06		13 11			13 42				13 43	13 48			14 06		14 11			14 42
Stafford 65,67	a			13 25									14 02				14 25					
Wolverhampton 7 68 ⛴	a			13 39									14 15				14 39					
Birmingham New Street 12 68	a			13 58									14 33				14 58					
London Euston 15 ⊖65	a					14 43					15 09			15 24					15 43			

		NT	VT	NT	XC	VT	NT	TP	XC	AW	VT	NT	NT	NT	NT	VT	NT	XC	VT	NT	TP	XC	AW
										R													R
			◇1		◇1	◇1		◇1	◇1		◇1					◇1		◇1	◇1		◇1	◇1	
		E			H		A	B	C	D					E			F		A	B	C	G
			[restaurant]		[trolley]	[restaurant]			[trolley]	[trolley]	[restaurant]					[restaurant]		[trolley]	[restaurant]			[trolley]	[trolley]
Deansgate 85,89 ⛴	d																						
Manchester Oxford Rd 85,89	d																						
Manchester Picc. 10 85,89 ⛴	a																						
	d	13 52	13 55	14 04	14 07	14 15	14 17	14 20	14 27	14 30	14 35	14 38	14 46	14 48	14 52	14 55	15 04	15 07	15 15	15 17	15 20	15 27	15 30
Levenshulme	d	13 58		14 09								14 43			14 58		15 09						
Heaton Chapel	d	14 01		14 12								14 46			15 01		15 12						
Stockport	a	14 04	14 03	14 16	14 15	14 22	14 27	14 28	14 34	14 38	14 42	14 50		14 57	15 04	15 03	15 16	15 15	15 22	15 27	15 28	15 34	15 38
	d		14 04	14 17	14 16	14 23			14 35	14 39	14 43	14 51		14 58		15 04	15 17	15 16	15 23			15 35	15 39
Cheadle Hulme	d			14 24								14 55		15 02			15 24						
Bramhall	d													15 05									
Poynton	d													15 08									
Adlington (Cheshire)	d													15 11									
Prestbury	d													15 14									
Macclesfield	a								14 47		14 55			15 18								15 47	
	d								14 49		14 56			15 18								15 49	
Congleton	d													15 26									
Handforth	d			14 28								14 59					15 28						
Manchester Airport ✈	d												15 11										
Styal	d																						
Wilmslow	d		14 11	14 31						14 46		15 02	15 20			15 11	15 31						15 46
Alderley Edge	d			14 34								15a06	15 23				15 34						
Chelford	d			14 38													15 38						
Goostrey	d			14 43													15 43						
Holmes Chapel	d			14 46									15 31				15 46						
Sandbach	d			14 51									15 35				15 51						
Crewe 10	a		14 27	15 01						15 05			15 45			15 27	16 01						16 05
Kidsgrove 50	a													15 32									
Longport 50	a																						
Stoke-on-Trent 50	a				14 43	14 48			15 06		15 11			15 42				15 43	15 48			16 06	
Stafford 65,67	a				15 02				15 25									16 02				16 24	
Wolverhampton 7 68 ⛴	a				15 16				15 39									16 16				16 39	
Birmingham New Street 12 68	a				15 33				15 58									16 33				16 58	
London Euston 15 ⊖65	a		16 05			16 24					16 43					17 05			17 24				

A To Chester
B From Manchester Airport to Cleethorpes
C To Bournemouth
D To Milford Haven
E To Buxton
F To Bristol Temple Meads
G To Pembroke Dock
H To Paignton

Table 84R

Saturdays

14 December to 17 May

Manchester, Stockport and Manchester Airport - Crewe and Stoke-on-Trent

Network Diagram - see first Page of Table 78

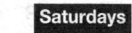

		VT	NT	NT	NT	NT	VT	NT	XC	VT	NT	TP	XC	AW	VT	NT	NT	NT	NT	VT	NT	XC	NT
														R									
		◇1					◇1		◇1	◇1		◇1	◇1		◇1					◇1		◇1	
						A			B		C	D	E	F					A			G	H
Deansgate 85,89	d																						
Manchester Oxford Rd 85,89	d																						
Manchester Picc. 10 85,89	a																						
	d	15 35	15 38	15 46	15 48	15 52	15 55	16 04	16 07	16 15	16 17	16 20	16 27	16 30	16 35	16 38	16 46	16 48	16 51	16 55	17 03	17 06	17 09
Levenshulme	d		15 43			15 58		16 09								16 43			16 58		17 08		17 14
Heaton Chapel	d		15 46			16 01		16 12								16 46			17 01		17 11		17 17
Stockport	a	15 42	15 50		15 57	16 04	16 03	16 16	16 15	16 22	16 27	16 28	16 34	16 38	16 42	16 50		16 57	17 04	17 03	17 15	17 14	17 21
	d	15 43	15 51		15 58		16 04	16 17	16 16	16 23			16 35	16 39	16 43	16 51		16 58		17 04	17 16	17 15	
Cheadle Hulme	d		15 55		16 02			16 24								16 55		17 02			17 22		
Bramhall	d				16 05													17 05					
Poynton	d				16 08													17 08					
Adlington (Cheshire)	d				16 11													17 11					
Prestbury	d				16 14													17 14					
Macclesfield	a	15 55			16 18								16 47		16 55			17 18				17 26	
	d	15 56			16 18								16 49		16 56			17 18				17 27	
Congleton	d				16 26													17 25					
Handforth	d		15 59					16 28								16 59					17 26		
Manchester Airport ✈	d			16 11													17 11						
Styal	d																17 17						
Wilmslow	d		16 02	16 19			16 11	16 31						16 46		17 02	17 21			17 11	17 29		
Alderley Edge	d		16a06	16 22				16 34								17a06	17 24				17 32		
Chelford	d							16 38													17 36		
Goostrey	d							16 43													17 41		
Holmes Chapel	d			16 30				16 46									17 32				17 44		
Sandbach	d			16 34				16 51									17 36				17 49		
Crewe 10	a			16 44			16 27	17 01						17 05			17 46			17 27	18 01		
Kidsgrove 50	a				16 32													17 31					
Longport 50	a																						
Stoke-on-Trent 50	a	16 11			16 42				16 43	16 48			17 06		17 11			17 41				17 44	
Stafford 65,67	a								17 02				17 25									18 03	
Wolverhampton 7 68	a								17 16				17 39									18 15	
Birmingham New Street 12 68	a								17 33				17 58									18 33	
London Euston 15 ⊖65	a	17 43					18 05			18 24					18 43					19 09			

		VT	NT	TP	XC	AW	VT	NT	NT	NT	NT	VT	XC	NT	VT	NT	TP	XC	AW	VT	NT	NT
						R																
		◇1		◇1	◇1		◇1					◇1	◇1		◇1		◇1	◇1	◇	◇1		1
			C	D	E	G					A		B			C	D	E	I			J
Deansgate 85,89	d																					
Manchester Oxford Rd 85,89	d																					
Manchester Picc. 10 85,89	a																					
	d	17 15	17 17	17 20	17 27	17 30	17 35	17 38	17 46	17 48	17 52	17 55	18 05	18 08	18 15	18 17	18 20	18 27	18 30	18 35	18 38	18 46
Levenshulme	d							17 43			17 58			18 13							18 43	
Heaton Chapel	d							17 46			18 01			18 16							18 46	
Stockport	a	17 22	17 27	17 28	17 35	17 38	17 42	17 50		17 57	18 04	18 03	18 12	18 20	18 22	18 27	18 28	18 34	18 38	18 42	18 50	
	d	17 23			17 36	17 39	17 43	17 51		17 58		18 04	18 13	18 22	18 23			18 35	18 39	18 43	18 51	
Cheadle Hulme	d							17 55		18 02				18 30							18 55	
Bramhall	d									18 05												
Poynton	d									18 08												
Adlington (Cheshire)	d									18 11												
Prestbury	d									18 14												
Macclesfield	a						17 55			18 18			18 25							18 55		
	d						17 56			18 18			18 26							18 56		
Congleton	d				17 54					18 26								18 54				
Handforth	d							17 59						18 34							18 59	
Manchester Airport ✈	d								18 11													19 14
Styal	d								18 17													
Wilmslow	d					17 46		18 02	18 21			18 11		18 37					18 46		19 02	19 26
Alderley Edge	d							18a06	18 24					18 40							19a06	19a31
Chelford	d													18 44								
Goostrey	d													18 48								
Holmes Chapel	d								18 32					18 51								
Sandbach	d								18 36					18 56								
Crewe 10	a					18 05			18 46			18 27		19 06					19 08			
Kidsgrove 50	a									18 32												
Longport 50	a																					
Stoke-on-Trent 50	a	17 49			18 06		18 11			18 42			18 43		18 48			19 06		19 11		
Stafford 65,67	a				18 25								19 02					19 25				
Wolverhampton 7 68	a				18 40								19 15					19 39				
Birmingham New Street 12 68	a				18 58								19 33					19 59				
London Euston 15 ⊖65	a	19 24					19 43					20 05			20 26					20 59		

A To Buxton
B To Bristol Temple Meads
C To Chester
D From Manchester Airport to Cleethorpes
E To Bournemouth
F To Milford Haven
G To Cardiff Central
H To Hazel Grove
I To Carmarthen
J 1 from Wilmslow

Table 84R

Saturdays

14 December to 17 May

Manchester, Stockport and Manchester Airport - Crewe and Stoke-on-Trent

Network Diagram - see first Page of Table 78

	NT	NT	VT	NT	XC	NT	TP		NT	XC	AW	VT	NT	NT	NT	NT	XC		NT	TP	XC	AW	VT	NT
			◇1		◇1		◇1			◇1	◇	◇1					◇1			◇1	◇1	◇	◇1	
		A			B	C	D		E	F	G				A				C	H		G		
Deansgate 85,89 d																								
Manchester Oxford Rd 85,89 d													19 43											20 43
Manchester Picc. 10 85,89 a													19 45											20 45
d	18 48	18 52	18 55	19 04	19 07	19 17	19 18		19 22	19 27	19 30	19 35	19 46	19 48	19 51	20 04	20 07		20 17	20 20	20 27	20 30	20 35	20 46
Levenshulme d		18 58		19 09					19 28						19 58	20 09								
Heaton Chapel d		19 01		19 12					19 31						20 01	20 12								
Stockport a	18 57	19 04	19 03	19 16	19 15	19 27	19 26		19 34	19 34	19 38	19 42		19 57	20 04	20 16	20 15		20 27	20 28	20 34	20 38	20 42	
d	18 58		19 04	19 17	19 16					19 35	19 39	19 43		19 58		20 17	20 16				20 35	20 39	20 43	
Cheadle Hulme d	19 02			19 24										20 02		20 24								
Bramhall d	19 05													20 05										
Poynton d	19 08													20 08										
Adlington (Cheshire) d	19 11													20 11										
Prestbury d	19 14													20 14										
Macclesfield a	19 18									19 47		19 55		20 18							20 47		20 55	
d	19 18									19 49		19 56		20 18							20 49		20 56	
Congleton d	19 26													20 26										
Handforth d				19 28												20 28								
Manchester Airport d													20 14											21 15
Styal d																								
Wilmslow d			19 11	19 31							19 46		20a24			20 31						20 46		21a25
Alderley Edge d				19 34												20 34								
Chelford d				19 38												20 38								
Goostrey d				19 43												20 43								
Holmes Chapel d				19 46												20 46								
Sandbach d				19 51												20 51								
Crewe 10 a			19 27	20 01							20 05					21 01						21 05		
Kidsgrove 50 a	19 32													20 32										
Longport 50 a																								
Stoke-on-Trent 50 a	19 42				19 43					20 06		20 11		20 42			20 43				21 06		21 11	
Stafford 65,67 a					20 02					20 25							21 02				21 26			
Wolverhampton 7 68 a					20 15					20 39							21 15				21 39			
Birmingham New Street 12 68 a					20 33					20 58							21 32				21 58			
London Euston 15 ⊖65 a			21 20									22 00											23 02	

	NT	NT	NT		XC	NT	TP	XC	AW	NT	NT	NT	NT		NT	AW	NT	NT	TP	NT	NT	NT	NT	
					◇1		◇1	◇1	◇															
		A				C	H		I			A			C	I			J		A		C	
Deansgate 85,89 d																			22 54					
Manchester Oxford Rd 85,89 d										21 43							22 43		22 57					
Manchester Picc. 10 85,89 a										21 45							22 45		23 00					
d	20 48	20 52	21 04		21 07	21 17	21 20	21 27	21 35	21 46	21 48	21 52	22 05		22 17	22 35	22 46	22 46	23 01	23 04	23 10	23 14	23 17	
Levenshulme d		20 58	21 09									21 58	22 09							23 09				
Heaton Chapel d		21 01	21 12									22 01	22 12							23 12				
Stockport a	20 57	21 04	21 16			21 27	21 28	21 34	21 43		21 57	22 04	22 16		22 27	22 43		22 57		23 16	23 19	23 24	23 26	
d	20 58		21 17					21 35	21 44		21 58		22 17			22 44		22 58		23 16		23 25		
Cheadle Hulme d	21 02		21 24								22 02		22 24					23 02		23 21		23 29		
Bramhall d	21 05										22 05							23 05				23 32		
Poynton d	21 08										22 08							23 08				23 35		
Adlington (Cheshire) d	21 11										22 11							23 11				23 38		
Prestbury d	21 14										22 14							23 14				23 41		
Macclesfield a	21 18							21 47			22 18							23 20				23 48		
d	21 18							21 49			22 18													
Congleton d	21 26										22 26													
Handforth d			21 28										22 28							23 25				
Manchester Airport d										22 14							23 14		23a16					
Styal d																								
Wilmslow d			21 31						21 51	22a22			22 31			22 52	23a22			23 28				
Alderley Edge d			21 34										22 34							23 31				
Chelford d			21 38										22 38							23 35				
Goostrey d			21 43										22 43							23 40				
Holmes Chapel d			21 46										22 46							23 43				
Sandbach d			21 51										22 51							23 48				
Crewe 10 a			22 01						22 11				23 01			23 10				23 58				
Kidsgrove 50 a	21 32										22 32													
Longport 50 a																								
Stoke-on-Trent 50 a	21 42				21 43			22 06			22 42													
Stafford 65,67 a					22 02			22 28																
Wolverhampton 7 68 a					22 14			22 43																
Birmingham New Street 12 68 a					22 32			23 01																
London Euston 15 ⊖65 a																								

A To Buxton
B To Bristol Temple Meads
C To Chester
D From Manchester Airport to Cleethorpes
E To Hazel Grove
F To Southampton Central
G To Cardiff Central
H From Manchester Airport to Sheffield
I To Shrewsbury
J from 4 January until 8 February. From Bolton

Table 84R

Saturdays

14 December to 17 May

Manchester, Stockport and Manchester Airport - Crewe and Stoke-on-Trent

Network Diagram - see first Page of Table 78

		NT A	NT B
Deansgate 85,89	d		
Manchester Oxford Rd 85,89	d		
Manchester Picc. 10 85,89	a		
	d	23 25	23 37
Levenshulme	d	23 30	23 42
Heaton Chapel	d	23 33	23 45
Stockport	a	23 37	23 49
	d	23 38	23 50
Cheadle Hulme	d	23 42	23 54
Bramhall	d		
Poynton	d		
Adlington (Cheshire)	d		
Prestbury	d		
Macclesfield	a		
	d		
Congleton	d		
Handforth	d	23 46	23 58
Manchester Airport	d		
Styal	d		
Wilmslow	d	23 49	00 01
Alderley Edge	d	23a53	00a05
Chelford	d		
Goostrey	d		
Holmes Chapel	d		
Sandbach	d		
Crewe 10	a		
Kidsgrove 50	a		
Longport 50	a		
Stoke-on-Trent 50	a		
Stafford 65,67	a		
Wolverhampton 7 68	a		
Birmingham New Street 12 68	a		
London Euston 15 ⊖65	a		

Sundays

8 December to 29 December

		NT	TP	TP	VT	VT	XC	TP	NT	NT	NT	TP	NT	VT	NT	XC	AW	NT	NT	VT	XC	AW	VT
			◇1	1	◇1	◇1	◇1	◇1				◇1		◇1		◇1	◇			◇1	◇1	R	◇1
		C					D				E	F			G	D	H	E			D	I	
Deansgate 85,89	d														09 15								
Manchester Oxford Rd 85,89	d														09 18								
Manchester Picc. 10 85,89	a														09 21								
	d		07 29	07 48	08 05	08 20	08 27	08 29	08 41	08 50	08 55	08 58	09 04	09 20	09 22	09 27	09 30	09 51	10 05	10 20	10 27	10 30	10 35
Levenshulme	d										09 00		09 08					09 58	10 10				
Heaton Chapel	d										09 03		09 11					10 01	10 13				
Stockport	a				08 13	08 28	08 34			08 59	09 07	09 06	09 16	09 27	09 31	09 35	09 39	10 04	10 17	10 28	10 34	10 39	10 43
	d				08 14	08 28	08 36			09 01			09 18	09 27		09 36	09 39		10 19	10 29	10 36	10 39	10 43
Cheadle Hulme	d									09 06			09 22						10 23				
Bramhall	d									09 09													
Poynton	d									09 12													
Adlington (Cheshire)	d									09 15													
Prestbury	d									09 18													
Macclesfield	a					08 41				09 22				09 40		09 48					10 48		10 55
	d					08 42								09 40		09 49					10 49		10 55
Congleton	d																						
Handforth	d												09 26						10 27				
Manchester Airport	d		07a44	08a06				08a43	09 06														
Styal	d								09 10														
Wilmslow	d	00 01			08 22		08 43		09 15				09 29				09 47		10 30	10 36		10 48	
Alderley Edge	d	00a05							09a22				09 32						10a36				
Chelford	d												09 36										
Goostrey	d												09 41										
Holmes Chapel	d												09 44										
Sandbach	d												09 49										
Crewe 10	a				08 39		09 01						09 59				10 06			10 53		11 07	
Kidsgrove 50	a																						
Longport 50	a																						
Stoke-on-Trent 50	a					08 59								09 57		10 05					11 06		11 12
Stafford 65,67	a				09 01		09 25									10 26					11 27		
Wolverhampton 7 68	a						09 40									10 42					11 41		
Birmingham New Street 12 68	a						09 58									10 59					11 59		
London Euston 15 ⊖65	a				10 58	11 02								12 09						12 57			13 00

A from 15 February until 22 March
B until 8 February, from 29 March
C not 8 December. From Manchester Picc.
D To Bournemouth
E To Buxton
F From Manchester Airport to Sheffield
G From Wigan Wallgate to Chester
H To Cardiff Central
I To Milford Haven

Table 84R

Sundays

8 December to 29 December

Manchester, Stockport and Manchester Airport - Crewe and Stoke-on-Trent

Network Diagram - see first Page of Table 78

	NT	NT	NT	VT	TP		AW	XC	VT	NT	NT	VT	NT	VT	TP		XC	AW	VT	EM	NT	NT	VT	NT
				◇1	◇1		R	◇1	◇1			◇1		◇1	◇1		◇1	R	◇1	◇			◇1	
		A			B		C	D			A				E		D	F		G		A		
Deansgate 85,89 d																								
Manchester Oxford Rd 85,89 d																					12 43			
Manchester Picc. 10 85,89 a																					12 45			
d	10 41	10 52	11 05	11 15	11 18		11 24	11 27	11 35	11 41	11 52	11 55	12 04	12 15	12 18		12 26	12 30	12 35	12 44	12 47	12 52	12 55	13 04
Levenshulme d		10 58	11 11								11 58		12 09									12 58		13 09
Heaton Chapel d		11 01	11 14								12 01		12 12									13 01		13 12
Stockport a		11 04	11 17	11 23	11 27		11 34	11 34	11 43	11 50	12 04	12 04	12 16	12 23	12 28		12 35	12 39	12 44	12 53		13 04	13 04	13 16
d			11 18	11 23			11 40	11 36	11 43	11 51		12 05	12 16	12 23			12 35	12 40	12 44				13 05	13 17
Cheadle Hulme d			11 22							11 56			12 22											13 21
Bramhall d										11 59														
Poynton d										12 02														
Adlington (Cheshire) d										12 04														
Prestbury d										12 07														
Macclesfield a								11 49	11 56	12 11							12 48		12 57					
d								11 49	11 56	12 11							12 49		12 57					
Congleton d										12 19														
Handforth d			11 26										12 26											13 25
Manchester Airport ✈ d	11 10																				13 12			
Styal d	11 14																				13 16			
Wilmslow d	11 17		11 29				11 47					12 12	12 29					12 48			13 23		13 12	13 28
Alderley Edge d	11a22		11 32										12a35								13a29			13 31
Chelford d			11 36																					13 35
Goostrey d			11 41																					13 40
Holmes Chapel d			11 44																					13 43
Sandbach d			11 49																					13 48
Crewe 10 a			11 59				12 07					12 28						13 07					13 28	13 58
Kidsgrove 50 a										12 25														
Longport 50 a																								
Stoke-on-Trent 50 a				11 50				12 06	12 13	12 35				12 50			13 06		13 14					
Stafford 65,67 a								12 24									13 24							
Wolverhampton 7 68 a								12 40									13 40							
Birmingham New Street 12 68 a								12 58									13 58							
London Euston 15 ⊖65 a				13 28					13 48			14 10		14 27					14 48				15 08	

	XC		VT	TP	XC	AW	VT	NT	VT	NT	XC		VT	TP	XC	AW	VT	NT	NT	VT	NT		XC	VT
	◇1		◇1	◇1	◇1	R	◇1		◇1		◇1		◇1	◇1	◇1	R	◇1			◇1			◇1	◇1
	H			B	D	C		A			I			B	D	F			A				I	
Deansgate 85,89 d																								
Manchester Oxford Rd 85,89 d																								
Manchester Picc. 10 85,89 a																								
d	13 07		13 15	13 20	13 27	13 30	13 35	13 52	13 55	14 04	14 07		14 15	14 20	14 27	14 30	14 35	14 41	14 52	14 55	15 04		15 07	15 15
Levenshulme d								13 58		14 09									14 58		15 09			
Heaton Chapel d								14 01		14 12									15 01		15 12			
Stockport a			13 22	13 28	13 35	13 39	13 42	14 04	14 03	14 16			14 22	14 28	14 34	14 38	14 42	14 49	15 04	15 03	15 16			15 22
d			13 22		13 36	13 40	13 42		14 04	14 17			14 22		14 36	14 39	14 42	14 51		15 04	15 17			15 22
Cheadle Hulme d										14 22								14 56			15 22			
Bramhall d																		14 59						
Poynton d																		15 02						
Adlington (Cheshire) d																		15 04						
Prestbury d																		15 07						
Macclesfield a					13 48		13 55								14 48		14 55	15 11						
d					13 49		13 55								14 49		14 55	15 11						
Congleton d																		15 19						
Handforth d										14 26											15 26			
Manchester Airport ✈ d																								
Styal d																								
Wilmslow d						13 47			14 11	14 29						14 47				15 11	15 29			
Alderley Edge d										14a35											15 32			
Chelford d																					15 36			
Goostrey d																					15 40			
Holmes Chapel d																					15 43			
Sandbach d																					15 48			
Crewe 10 a						14 07			14 27							15 07				15 27	15 58			
Kidsgrove 50 a																		15 25						
Longport 50 a																								
Stoke-on-Trent 50 a	13 42		13 49		14 06		14 12				14 42		14 49		15 06		15 12	15 37					15 42	15 49
Stafford 65,67 a					14 24										15 24									
Wolverhampton 7 68 a	14 13				14 40						15 13				15 40								16 13	
Birmingham New Street 12 68 a	14 31				14 58						15 31				15 58								16 31	
London Euston 15 ⊖65 a			15 26				15 48		16 07				16 26				16 48			17 09				17 27

A To Buxton
B From Manchester Airport to Cleethorpes
C To Cardiff Central
D To Bournemouth
E From Manchester Airport to Doncaster
F To Milford Haven
G To Norwich
H To Paignton
I To Bristol Temple Meads

Table 84R

Sundays

8 December to 29 December

Manchester, Stockport and Manchester Airport - Crewe and Stoke-on-Trent

Network Diagram - see first Page of Table 78

	TP	XC	AW	VT	NT	VT	NT		XC	VT	TP	XC	AW	VT	NT	NT	VT		NT	XC	VT	TP	XC	AW
	◇1 A	◇1 B 🛒	R C 🛒	◇1 🍴	D	◇1 🍴			◇1 E 🛒	◇1 🍴	◇1 A	◇1 B 🛒	R C 🛒	◇1 🍴		D	◇1 🍴			◇1 F 🛒	◇1 🍴	◇1 A	◇1 B 🛒	R C 🛒
Deansgate 85,89 d																								
Manchester Oxford Rd 85,89 d																								
Manchester Picc. 10 85,89 a																								
d	15 20	15 27	15 30	15 35	15 52	15 55	16 04		16 07	16 15	16 20	16 27	16 30	16 35	16 41	16 52	16 55		17 04	17 07	17 15	17 20	17 27	17 30
Levenshulme d					15 58		16 09									16 58			17 09					
Heaton Chapel d					16 01		16 12									17 01			17 12					
Stockport a	15 28	15 35	15 39	15 42	16 04	16 03	16 16			16 22	16 28	16 34	16 39	16 42		17 04	17 03		17 16		17 22	17 28	17 34	17 39
d		15 36	15 39	15 42		16 04	16 17			16 23		16 36	16 39	16 42			17 04		17 17		17 22		17 36	17 39
Cheadle Hulme d							16 22												17 22					
Bramhall d																								
Poynton d																								
Adlington (Cheshire) d																								
Prestbury d																								
Macclesfield a		15 48		15 55								16 48		16 55									17 48	
d		15 49		15 55								16 49		16 55									17 49	
Congleton d																								
Handforth d							16 26												17 26					
Manchester Airport ✈ d															17 06									
Styal d															17 10									
Wilmslow d			15 47			16 11	16 29						16 47		17 15		17 11		17 29					17 47
Alderley Edge d							16a35								17a21				17 32					
Chelford d																			17 36					
Goostrey d																			17 40					
Holmes Chapel d																			17 43					
Sandbach d																			17 48					
Crewe 10 a			16 06			16 27							17 06				17 27		17 58					18 07
Kidsgrove 50 a																								
Longport 50 a																								
Stoke-on-Trent 50 a		16 06		16 12					16 42	16 48		17 06		17 12						17 42	17 49		18 06	
Stafford 65,67 a		16 24										17 25											18 26	
Wolverhampton 7 68 a		16 40							17 13			17 40								18 13			18 40	
Birmingham New Street 12 68 a		16 58							17 31			17 58								18 31			18 58	
London Euston 15 ⊖65 a				17 46		18 09				18 27				18 48			19 07				19 27			

	VT	NT	VT		NT	XC	VT	TP	XC	AW	VT	NT	NT		NT	VT	NT	XC	VT	TP	XC	AW	VT
	◇1 🍴	D	◇1 🍴			◇1 E 🛒	◇1 🍴	◇1 A	◇1 G 🛒	R C 🛒	◇1 🍴				D	◇1 🍴		◇1 E 🛒	◇1 🍴	◇1 A	◇1 H 🛒	◇ C	◇1 🍴
Deansgate 85,89 d																							
Manchester Oxford Rd 85,89 d																							
Manchester Picc. 10 85,89 a																							
d	17 35	17 52	17 55		18 04	18 07	18 15	18 20	18 27	18 30	18 35	18 41	18 42		18 52	18 55	19 04	19 07	19 15	19 20	19 27	19 30	19 35
Levenshulme d		17 58			18 09										18 58		19 09						
Heaton Chapel d		18 01			18 12										19 01		19 12						
Stockport a	17 42	18 04	18 03		18 16		18 22	18 28	18 34	18 39	18 42		18 50		19 04	19 03	19 16		19 22	19 28	19 34	19 39	19 41
d	17 42		18 04		18 17		18 22		18 36	18 39	18 42		18 52			19 04	19 17		19 22		19 36	19 39	19 41
Cheadle Hulme d					18 22								18 57				19 22						
Bramhall d													19 00										
Poynton d													19 03										
Adlington (Cheshire) d													19 06										
Prestbury d													19 09										
Macclesfield a	17 55								18 48		18 55		19 13								19 48		19 54
d	17 55								18 49		18 55		19 13								19 49		19 54
Congleton d													19 21										
Handforth d					18 26												19 26						
Manchester Airport ✈ d												19 06											
Styal d												19 10											
Wilmslow d			18 11		18 29					18 47		19 15				19 11	19 29					19 47	
Alderley Edge d					18a35							19a21					19 32						
Chelford d																	19 36						
Goostrey d																	19 40						
Holmes Chapel d																	19 43						
Sandbach d																	19 48						
Crewe 10 a			18 27							19 06						19 27	19 58					20 07	
Kidsgrove 50 a													19 28										
Longport 50 a																							
Stoke-on-Trent 50 a	18 12					18 42	18 49		19 06		19 12		19 40					19 42	19 49		20 06		20 11
Stafford 65,67 a									19 24												20 26		
Wolverhampton 7 68 a						19 13			19 40									20 13			20 39		
Birmingham New Street 12 68 a						19 31			19 58									20 31			20 58		
London Euston 15 ⊖65 a	19 48		20 08				20 27				20 48					21 10			21 31				21 58

A From Manchester Airport to Cleethorpes
B To Bournemouth
C To Cardiff Central
D To Buxton
E To Bristol Temple Meads
F To Plymouth
G To Southampton Central
H To Reading

Table 84R

Sundays

8 December to 29 December

Manchester, Stockport and Manchester Airport - Crewe and Stoke-on-Trent

Network Diagram - see first Page of Table 78

		NT	NT	XC	TP	VT	AW	NT	NT	VT	NT	XC	TP	AW	NT	NT	NT	XC	TP	AW	NT	NT	TP
				◇1	◇1	◇1	◇			◇1		◇1	◇1					◇1	◇1				◇1
		A		B	C		D		A				E			A			E		A		E
						🍴				🍴													
Deansgate 85,89	d																						
Manchester Oxford Rd 85,89	d																						
Manchester Picc. 10 85,89	a																						
	d	19 52	20 04	20 07	20 18	20 21	20 30	20 41	20 52	20 55	21 04	21 07	21 20	21 34	21 41	21 52	22 04	22 07	22 15	22 35	22 52	23 04	23 20
Levenshulme	d	19 58	20 09						20 58		21 09					21 58	22 09				22 58	23 09	
Heaton Chapel	d	20 01	20 12						21 01		21 12					22 01	22 12				23 01	23 12	
Stockport	a	20 04	20 16	20 15	20 26	20 27	20 38		21 04	21 03	21 16	21 15	21 28		21 49	22 04	22 16	22 15	22 23		23 04	23 16	23 28
	d		20 17	20 16		20 27	20 39			21 03	21 17	21 16			21 52		22 17	22 16				23 17	
Cheadle Hulme	d		20 22								21 22				21 56		22 22					23 21	
Bramhall	d														21 59								
Poynton	d														22 02								
Adlington (Cheshire)	d														22 05								
Prestbury	d														22 08								
Macclesfield	a			20 28		20 40				21 15		21 28			22 12			22 28					
	d			20 29		20 40				21 15		21 29			22 13			22 29					
Congleton	d														22 20								
Handforth	d		20 26								21 26						22 26					23 25	
Manchester Airport ✈	d							21 06															
Styal	d							21 10															
Wilmslow	d		20 29				20 47	21 15			21 29			21 50			22 29			22 50		23 28	
Alderley Edge	d		20a37					21a21			21 32						22a35					23a35	
Chelford	d										21 36												
Goostrey	d										21 40												
Holmes Chapel	d										21 43												
Sandbach	d										21 48												
Crewe 10	a						21 07				21 58			22 13						23 13			
Kidsgrove 50	a														22 26								
Longport 50	a																						
Stoke-on-Trent 50	a			20 46		20 57				21 32		21 46			22 36			22 46					
Stafford 65,67	a			21 08								22 06						23 04					
Wolverhampton 7 68 🚌	a			21 21								22 20						23 18					
Birmingham New Street 12 68	a			21 39								22 40						23 36					
London Euston 15 ⊖65	a					22 57				23 49													

Sundays

5 January to 9 February

		NT	TP	TP	VT	VT	XC	NT	NT	NT	TP	TP	NT	VT	NT	XC	TP	AW	NT	NT	VT	XC	AW
																							1
			◇1	1	◇1	◇1	◇1				◇1	◇1		◇1		◇1	◇1	◇			◇1	◇1	
		F					G			A	E	H			I	G	H	D	A			G	J
					🍴	🍴	🚲							🍴		🚲		🚲			🍴	🚲	🚲
Deansgate 85,89 🚌	d											08 53			09 15		09 22						
Manchester Oxford Rd 85,89	d											08 56			09 18		09 24						
Manchester Picc. 10 85,89 🚌	a											08 59			09 21		09 27						
	d		07 29	07 48	08 05	08 20	08 27	08 41	08 50	08 55	08 58	09 01	09 04	09 20	09 22	09 27	09 29	09 30	09 51	10 05	10 20	10 27	10 30
Levenshulme	d									09 00			09 08						09 58	10 10			
Heaton Chapel	d									09 03			09 11						10 01	10 13			
Stockport	a				08 13	08 28	08 34		08 59	09 07	09 06		09 16	09 27	09 31	09 35		09 39	10 04	10 17	10 28	10 34	10 39
	d				08 14	08 28	08 36		09 01				09 18	09 27		09 36		09 39		10 19	10 29	10 36	10 39
Cheadle Hulme	d								09 06				09 22							10 23			
Bramhall	d								09 09														
Poynton	d								09 12														
Adlington (Cheshire)	d								09 15														
Prestbury	d								09 18														
Macclesfield	a					08 41			09 22					09 40		09 48						10 48	
	d					08 42								09 40		09 49						10 49	
Congleton	d																						
Handforth	d												09 26							10 27			
Manchester Airport ✈	d		07a44	08a06				09 06				09a14					09a47						
Styal	d							09 10															
Wilmslow	d	00 01			08 22		08 43	09 15					09 29					09 47		10 30	10 36		10 48
Alderley Edge	d	00a05						09a22					09 32							10a36			
Chelford	d												09 36										
Goostrey	d												09 41										
Holmes Chapel	d												09 44										
Sandbach	d												09 49										
Crewe 10	a				08 39		09 01						09 59					10 06			10 53		11 07
Kidsgrove 50	a																						
Longport 50	a																						
Stoke-on-Trent 50	a					08 59								09 57		10 05						11 06	
Stafford 65,67	a				09 01		09 25									10 26						11 27	
Wolverhampton 7 68 🚌	a						09 40									10 42						11 41	
Birmingham New Street 12 68	a						09 58									10 59						11 59	
London Euston 15 ⊖65	a				10 58	11 02								12 09							12 57		

A To Buxton
B To Bristol Temple Meads
C From Manchester Airport to Cleethorpes
D To Cardiff Central
E From Manchester Airport to Sheffield
F From Manchester Picc.
G To Bournemouth
H From Chorley
I From Wigan Wallgate to Chester
J To Milford Haven

Table 84R

Sundays

5 January to 9 February

Manchester, Stockport and Manchester Airport - Crewe and Stoke-on-Trent

Network Diagram - see first Page of Table 78

	TP	VT	NT	NT	NT		VT	TP	AW	XC	TP	VT	NT	NT	VT		NT	VT	TP	XC	TP	AW	VT	EM
	◇1 A	◇1 ☕		B			◇1 ☕	◇1 C	R D 🛒	◇1 E 🛒	◇1 A	◇1 ☕		B	◇1 ☕			◇1 ☕	◇1 C	◇1 E 🛒	◇1 A	R F 🛒	◇1 ☕	◇ G
Deansgate 85,89 d	10 22										11 22										12 22			
Manchester Oxford Rd 85,89 d	10 27										11 24										12 24			
Manchester Picc. 10 85,89 a	10 30										11 27										12 27			
d	10 32	10 35	10 41	10 52	11 05		11 15	11 18	11 24	11 27	11 29	11 35	11 41	11 52	11 55		12 04	12 15	12 18	12 26	12 29	12 30	12 35	12 44
Levenshulme d				10 58	11 11									11 58			12 09							
Heaton Chapel d				11 01	11 14									12 01			12 12							
Stockport a		10 43		11 04	11 17		11 23	11 27	11 34	11 34		11 43	11 50	12 04	12 04		12 16	12 23	12 28	12 35		12 39	12 44	12 53
d		10 43			11 18		11 23		11 40	11 36		11 43	11 51		12 05		12 16	12 23		12 35		12 40	12 44	
Cheadle Hulme d					11 22								11 56				12 22							
Bramhall d													11 59											
Poynton d													12 02											
Adlington (Cheshire) d													12 04											
Prestbury d													12 07											
Macclesfield a		10 55								11 49		11 56	12 11							12 48			12 57	
d		10 55								11 49		11 56	12 11							12 49			12 57	
Congleton d													12 19											
Handforth d					11 26												12 26							
Manchester Airport ✈ d	10a46		11 10								11a47										12a47			
Styal d			11 14																					
Wilmslow d			11 17		11 29				11 47						12 12		12 29					12 48		
Alderley Edge d			11a22		11 32												12a35							
Chelford d					11 36																			
Goostrey d					11 41																			
Holmes Chapel d					11 44																			
Sandbach d					11 49																			
Crewe 10 a					11 59				12 07						12 28							13 07		
Kidsgrove 50 a													12 25											
Longport 50 a																								
Stoke-on-Trent 50 a		11 12					11 50			12 06		12 13	12 35					12 50		13 06			13 14	
Stafford 65,67 a										12 24										13 24				
Wolverhampton 7 68 a										12 40										13 40				
Birmingham New Street 12 68 a										12 58										13 58				
London Euston 15 ⊖65 a		13 00					13 28					13 48			14 10			14 27					14 48	

	NT		NT	VT	NT	XC	VT	TP	XC	TP	AW		VT	NT	VT	NT	XC	VT	TP	XC	TP		AW	VT
			B	◇1 ☕		◇1 H 🛒	◇1 ☕	◇1 C	◇1 E 🛒	◇1 A	R D 🛒		◇1 ☕	B	◇1 ☕		◇1 I 🛒	◇1 ☕	◇1 C	◇1 E 🛒	◇1 A		R F 🛒	◇1 ☕
Deansgate 85,89 d										13 22											14 22			
Manchester Oxford Rd 85,89 d	12 43									13 24											14 24			
Manchester Picc. 10 85,89 a	12 45									13 27											14 27			
d	12 47		12 52	12 55	13 04	13 07	13 15	13 20	13 27	13 29	13 30		13 35	13 52	13 55	14 04	14 07	14 15	14 20	14 27	14 29		14 30	14 35
Levenshulme d			12 58		13 09									13 58		14 09								
Heaton Chapel d			13 01		13 12									14 01		14 12								
Stockport a			13 04	13 04	13 16		13 22	13 28	13 35		13 39		13 42	14 04	14 03	14 16		14 22	14 28	14 34			14 38	14 42
d				13 05	13 17		13 22		13 36		13 40		13 42		14 04	14 17		14 22		14 36			14 39	14 42
Cheadle Hulme d					13 21											14 22								
Bramhall d																								
Poynton d																								
Adlington (Cheshire) d																								
Prestbury d																								
Macclesfield a									13 48				13 55							14 48				14 55
d									13 49				13 55							14 49				14 55
Congleton d																								
Handforth d					13 25											14 26								
Manchester Airport ✈ d	13 12									13a47											14a47			
Styal d	13 16																							
Wilmslow d	13 23			13 12	13 28						13 47				14 11	14 29							14 47	
Alderley Edge d	13a29				13 31											14a35								
Chelford d					13 35																			
Goostrey d					13 40																			
Holmes Chapel d					13 43																			
Sandbach d					13 48																			
Crewe 10 a				13 28	13 58						14 07				14 27								15 07	
Kidsgrove 50 a																								
Longport 50 a																								
Stoke-on-Trent 50 a						13 42	13 49		14 06				14 12				14 42	14 49		15 06				15 12
Stafford 65,67 a									14 24											15 24				
Wolverhampton 7 68 a						14 13			14 40								15 13			15 40				
Birmingham New Street 12 68 a						14 31			14 58								15 31			15 58				
London Euston 15 ⊖65 a				15 08			15 26						15 48		16 07			16 26						16 48

A From Chorley
B To Buxton
C From Manchester Airport to Sheffield
D To Cardiff Central
E To Bournemouth
F To Milford Haven
G To Norwich
H To Paignton
I To Bristol Temple Meads

Table 84R

Sundays

5 January to 9 February

Manchester, Stockport and Manchester Airport - Crewe and Stoke-on-Trent

Network Diagram - see first Page of Table 78

	NT	NT	VT	NT	XC	VT	TP		XC	AW	VT	NT	VT	NT	XC	VT	TP		XC	AW	VT	NT	NT	VT
										R										R				
			◇1		◇1	◇1	◇1		◇1		◇1		◇1		◇1	◇1	◇1		◇1		◇1			◇1
		A			B		C		D	E		A			B		C		D	E			A	
Deansgate 85,89 d																								
Manchester Oxford Rd 85,89 d																								
Manchester Picc. 10 85,89 a																								
d	14 41	14 52	14 55	15 04	15 07	15 15	15 20		15 27	15 30	15 35	15 52	15 55	16 04	16 07	16 15	16 20		16 27	16 30	16 35	16 41	16 52	16 55
Levenshulme d		14 58		15 09								15 58		16 09									16 58	
Heaton Chapel d		15 01		15 12								16 01		16 12									17 01	
Stockport a	14 49	15 04	15 03	15 16		15 22	15 28		15 35	15 39	15 42	16 04	16 03	16 16		16 22	16 28		16 34	16 39	16 42		17 04	17 03
d	14 51		15 04	15 17		15 22			15 36	15 39	15 42		16 04	16 17		16 23			16 36	16 39	16 42			17 04
Cheadle Hulme d	14 56			15 22										16 22										
Bramhall d	14 59																							
Poynton d	15 02																							
Adlington (Cheshire) d	15 04																							
Prestbury d	15 07																							
Macclesfield a	15 11								15 48		15 55								16 48		16 55			
d	15 11								15 49		15 55								16 49		16 55			
Congleton d	15 19																							
Handforth d				15 26										16 26										
Manchester Airport d																						17 06		
Styal d																						17 10		
Wilmslow d			15 11	15 29						15 47			16 11	16 29						16 47		17 15		17 11
Alderley Edge d				15 32										16a35								17a21		
Chelford d				15 36																				
Goostrey d				15 40																				
Holmes Chapel d				15 43																				
Sandbach d				15 48																				
Crewe 10 a			15 27	15 58						16 06			16 27							17 06				17 27
Kidsgrove 50 a	15 25																							
Longport 50 a																								
Stoke-on-Trent 50 a	15 37				15 42	15 49			16 06		16 12				16 42	16 48			17 06		17 12			
Stafford 65,67 a									16 24										17 25					
Wolverhampton 7 68 a					16 13				16 40						17 13				17 40					
Birmingham New Street 12 68 a					16 31				16 58						17 31				17 58					
London Euston 15 ⊖65 a			17 09			17 27					17 46		18 09			18 27					18 48			19 07

	NT	XC	VT		TP	XC	AW	VT	NT	VT	NT	XC	VT		TP	XC	AW	VT	NT	NT	NT	VT	NT	
							R										R							
		◇1	◇1		◇1	◇1		◇1		◇1		◇1	◇1		◇1	◇1		◇1				◇1		
		F			C	D	E		A			B			C	G	E				A			
Deansgate 85,89 d																								
Manchester Oxford Rd 85,89 d																								
Manchester Picc. 10 85,89 a																								
d	17 04	17 07	17 15		17 20	17 27	17 30	17 35	17 52	17 55	18 04	18 07	18 15		18 20	18 27	18 30	18 35	18 41	18 42	18 52	18 55	19 04	
Levenshulme d	17 09								17 58		18 09										18 58		19 09	
Heaton Chapel d	17 12								18 01		18 12										19 01		19 12	
Stockport a	17 16		17 22		17 28	17 34	17 39	17 42	18 04	18 03	18 16		18 22		18 28	18 34	18 39	18 42		18 50	19 04	19 03	19 16	
d	17 17		17 22			17 36	17 39	17 42		18 04	18 17		18 22			18 36	18 39	18 42		18 52		19 04	19 17	
Cheadle Hulme d	17 22										18 22									18 57			19 22	
Bramhall d																				19 00				
Poynton d																				19 03				
Adlington (Cheshire) d																				19 06				
Prestbury d																				19 09				
Macclesfield a						17 48		17 55								18 48		18 55		19 13				
d						17 49		17 55								18 49		18 55		19 13				
Congleton d																				19 21				
Handforth d	17 26										18 26												19 26	
Manchester Airport d																			19 06					
Styal d																			19 10					
Wilmslow d	17 29						17 47			18 11	18 29						18 47		19 15			19 11	19 29	
Alderley Edge d	17 32										18a35								19a21				19 32	
Chelford d	17 36																						19 36	
Goostrey d	17 40																						19 40	
Holmes Chapel d	17 43																						19 43	
Sandbach d	17 48																						19 48	
Crewe 10 a	17 58						18 07			18 27							19 06					19 27	19 58	
Kidsgrove 50 a																				19 28				
Longport 50 a																								
Stoke-on-Trent 50 a		17 42	17 49			18 06		18 12				18 42	18 49			19 06		19 12		19 40				
Stafford 65,67 a						18 26										19 24								
Wolverhampton 7 68 a		18 13				18 40						19 13				19 40								
Birmingham New Street 12 68 a		18 31				18 58						19 31				19 58								
London Euston 15 ⊖65 a			19 27					19 48		20 08			20 27					20 48				21 10		

A To Buxton
B To Bristol Temple Meads
C From Manchester Airport to Sheffield
D To Bournemouth
E To Cardiff Central
F To Plymouth
G To Southampton Central

Table 84R

Sundays

5 January to 9 February

Manchester, Stockport and Manchester Airport - Crewe and Stoke-on-Trent

Network Diagram - see first Page of Table 78

		XC	VT	TP	XC	AW	VT	NT	NT	XC		TP	VT	AW	NT	NT	VT	NT	XC	TP		AW	NT	NT	NT
		◇1	◇1	◇1	◇1	◇	◇1			◇1		◇1	◇1	◇			◇1		◇1	◇1					
		A		B	C	D		E		A		B		D		E				B				E	
		🛒	☕		🛒		☕						☕				☕								
Deansgate 85,89 ⛴	d																								
Manchester Oxford Rd 85,89	d																								
Manchester Picc. 10 85,89 ⛴	a																								
	d	19 07	19 15	19 20	19 27	19 30	19 35	19 52	20 04	20 07		20 18	20 21	20 30	20 41	20 52	20 55	21 04	21 07	21 20		21 34	21 41	21 52	22 04
Levenshulme	d							19 58	20 09							20 58		21 09						21 58	22 09
Heaton Chapel	d							20 01	20 12							21 01		21 12						22 01	22 12
Stockport	a		19 22	19 28	19 34	19 39	19 41	20 04	20 16	20 15		20 26	20 27	20 38		21 04	21 03	21 16	21 15	21 28			21 49	22 04	22 16
	d		19 22		19 36	19 39	19 41		20 17	20 16			20 27	20 39			21 03	21 17	21 16				21 52		22 17
Cheadle Hulme	d								20 22									21 22					21 56		22 22
Bramhall	d																						21 59		
Poynton	d																						22 02		
Adlington (Cheshire)	d																						22 05		
Prestbury	d																						22 08		
Macclesfield	a				19 48		19 54			20 28			20 40				21 15		21 28				22 12		
	d				19 49		19 54			20 29			20 40				21 15		21 29				22 13		
Congleton	d																						22 20		
Handforth	d								20 26									21 26							22 26
Manchester Airport ✈	d														21 06										
Styal	d														21 10										
Wilmslow	d					19 47			20 29					20 47	21 15			21 29				21 50			22 29
Alderley Edge	d								20a37						21a21			21 32							22a35
Chelford	d																	21 36							
Goostrey	d																	21 40							
Holmes Chapel	d																	21 43							
Sandbach	d																	21 48							
Crewe 10	a					20 07								21 07				21 58				22 13			
Kidsgrove 50	a																						22 26		
Longport 50	a																								
Stoke-on-Trent 50	a	19 42	19 49		20 06		20 11			20 46			20 57				21 32		21 46				22 36		
Stafford 65,67	a				20 26					21 08									22 06						
Wolverhampton 7 68 ⛴	a	20 13			20 39					21 21									22 20						
Birmingham New Street 12 68	a	20 31			20 58					21 39									22 40						
London Euston 15 ⊖65	a		21 31				21 58						22 57				23 49								

		XC	TP	AW	NT	NT		TP
		◇1	◇1					◇1
			B		E			B
Deansgate 85,89 ⛴	d							
Manchester Oxford Rd 85,89	d							
Manchester Picc. 10 85,89 ⛴	a							
	d	22 07	22 15	22 35	22 52	23 04		23 20
Levenshulme	d				22 58	23 09		
Heaton Chapel	d				23 01	23 12		
Stockport	a	22 15	22 23		23 04	23 16		23 28
	d	22 16				23 17		
Cheadle Hulme	d					23 21		
Bramhall	d							
Poynton	d							
Adlington (Cheshire)	d							
Prestbury	d							
Macclesfield	a	22 28						
	d	22 29						
Congleton	d							
Handforth	d					23 25		
Manchester Airport ✈	d							
Styal	d							
Wilmslow	d			22 50		23 28		
Alderley Edge	d					23a35		
Chelford	d							
Goostrey	d							
Holmes Chapel	d							
Sandbach	d							
Crewe 10	a			23 13				
Kidsgrove 50	a							
Longport 50	a							
Stoke-on-Trent 50	a	22 46						
Stafford 65,67	a	23 04						
Wolverhampton 7 68 ⛴	a	23 18						
Birmingham New Street 12 68	a	23 36						
London Euston 15 ⊖65	a							

A To Bristol Temple Meads
B From Manchester Airport to Sheffield
C To Reading
D To Cardiff Central
E To Buxton

Table 84R

Sundays

16 February to 23 March

Manchester, Stockport and Manchester Airport - Crewe and Stoke-on-Trent

Network Diagram - see first Page of Table 78

		VT	VT	XC	TP	TP	NT	NT	NT	TP		TP	NT	VT	NT	XC	AW	TP	NT	NT		VT	XC	AW	VT
																								R	
		◇1	◇1	◇1	◇1	◇1				◇1		◇1		◇1		◇1	◇	◇1				◇1	◇1		◇1
				A					B	C		D			E	A	F	G	B				A	H	
		☕	☕	🛒										☕		🛒	🛒					☕	🛒	🛒	☕
Deansgate 85,89	d											08 53			09 15										
Manchester Oxford Rd 85,89	d											08 56			09 18										
Manchester Picc. 10 85,89	a											08 59			09 21										
	d	08 05	08 20	08 27	08 30	08 39	08 41	08 50	08 55	08 58		09 01	09 04	09 20	09 22	09 27	09 30	09 38	09 51	10 05		10 20	10 27	10 30	10 35
Levenshulme	d								09 00				09 08						09 58	10 10					
Heaton Chapel	d								09 03				09 11						10 01	10 13					
Stockport	a	08 13	08 28	08 34				08 59	09 07	09 07			09 16	09 27	09 31	09 35	09 39		10 04	10 17		10 28	10 34	10 39	10 43
	d	08 14	08 28	08 36				09 01					09 18	09 27		09 36	09 39			10 19		10 29	10 36	10 39	10 43
Cheadle Hulme	d							09 06					09 22							10 23					
Bramhall	d							09 09																	
Poynton	d							09 12																	
Adlington (Cheshire)	d							09 15																	
Prestbury	d							09 18																	
Macclesfield	a		08 41					09 22						09 40		09 48							10 48		10 55
	d		08 42											09 40		09 49							10 49		10 55
Congleton	d																								
Handforth	d												09 26							10 27					
Manchester Airport ✈	d				08a47	08a54	09 06					09a14						09a55							
Styal	d						09 10																		
Wilmslow	d	08 22		08 43			09 15						09 29				09 47			10 30		10 36		10 48	
Alderley Edge	d						09a22						09 32							10a36					
Chelford	d												09 36												
Goostrey	d												09 41												
Holmes Chapel	d												09 44												
Sandbach	d												09 49												
Crewe 10	a	08 39		09 01									09 59				10 06					10 53		11 07	
Kidsgrove 50	a																								
Longport 50	a																								
Stoke-on-Trent 50	a		08 59											09 57		10 05							11 06		11 12
Stafford 65,67	a	09 01		09 25												10 26							11 27		
Wolverhampton 7 68	a			09 40												10 42							11 41		
Birmingham New Street 12 68	a			09 58												10 59							11 59		
London Euston 15 ⊖65	a	10 58	11 02											12 09								12 57			13 00

		NT	NT	NT	VT	TP		AW	XC	VT	NT	NT	VT	NT	VT	TP		XC	AW	VT	EM	NT	NT	VT	NT
								R											R						
					◇1	◇1			◇1	◇1			◇1		◇1	◇1		◇1		◇1	◇			◇1	
			B			I		F	A			B				I		A	H		J		B		
					☕			🛒	🛒	☕			☕		☕			🛒	🛒	☕				☕	
Deansgate 85,89	d																								
Manchester Oxford Rd 85,89	d																					12 43			
Manchester Picc. 10 85,89	a																					12 45			
	d	10 41	10 52	11 05	11 15	11 18		11 24	11 27	11 35	11 41	11 52	11 55	12 04	12 15	12 18		12 26	12 30	12 35	12 44	12 47	12 52	12 55	13 04
Levenshulme	d		10 58	11 11								11 58		12 09									12 58		13 09
Heaton Chapel	d		11 01	11 14								12 01		12 12									13 01		13 12
Stockport	a		11 04	11 17	11 23	11 27		11 34	11 34	11 43	11 50	12 04	12 04	12 16	12 23	12 28		12 35	12 39	12 44	12 53		13 04	13 04	13 16
	d			11 18	11 23			11 40	11 36	11 43	11 51		12 05	12 16	12 23			12 35	12 40	12 44				13 05	13 17
Cheadle Hulme	d			11 22							11 56			12 22											13 21
Bramhall	d										11 59														
Poynton	d										12 02														
Adlington (Cheshire)	d										12 04														
Prestbury	d										12 07														
Macclesfield	a								11 49	11 56	12 11							12 48		12 57					
	d								11 49	11 56	12 11							12 49		12 57					
Congleton	d										12 19														
Handforth	d			11 26										12 26											13 25
Manchester Airport ✈	d	11 10																				13 12			
Styal	d	11 14																				13 16			
Wilmslow	d	11 17		11 29				11 47					12 12	12 29					12 48			13 23		13 12	13 28
Alderley Edge	d	11a22		11 32										12a35								13a29			13 31
Chelford	d			11 36																					13 35
Goostrey	d			11 41																					13 40
Holmes Chapel	d			11 44																					13 43
Sandbach	d			11 49																					13 48
Crewe 10	a			11 59				12 07					12 28						13 07					13 28	13 58
Kidsgrove 50	a										12 25														
Longport 50	a																								
Stoke-on-Trent 50	a				11 50				12 06	12 13	12 35				12 50			13 06		13 14					
Stafford 65,67	a								12 24									13 24							
Wolverhampton 7 68	a								12 40									13 40							
Birmingham New Street 12 68	a								12 58									13 58							
London Euston 15 ⊖65	a				13 28					13 48			14 10		14 28					14 48				15 08	

A To Bournemouth
B To Buxton
C To Sheffield
D From Chorley
E From Wigan Wallgate to Chester
F To Cardiff Central
G From Stalybridge
H To Milford Haven
I From Manchester Airport to Sheffield
J To Norwich

Table 84R

Sundays

16 February to 23 March

Manchester, Stockport and Manchester Airport - Crewe and Stoke-on-Trent

Network Diagram - see first Page of Table 78

	XC		VT	TP	XC	AW	VT	NT	VT	NT	XC		VT	TP	XC	AW	VT	NT	NT	NT	VT		NT	XC
						R										R								
	◇1		◇1	◇1	◇1		◇1		◇1		◇1		◇1	◇1	◇1		◇1				◇1			◇1
	A			B	C	D		E			A			B	C	F				E				A
Deansgate 85,89 d																								
Manchester Oxford Rd 85,89 d																								
Manchester Picc. 10 85,89 a																								
d	13 07		13 15	13 20	13 27	13 30	13 35	13 52	13 55	14 04	14 07		14 15	14 20	14 27	14 30	14 35	14 41	14 41	14 52	14 55		15 04	15 07
Levenshulme d								13 58		14 09										14 58			15 09	
Heaton Chapel d								14 01		14 12										15 01			15 12	
Stockport a			13 22	13 28	13 35	13 39	13 42	14 04	14 03	14 16			14 22	14 28	14 34	14 38	14 42		14 49	15 04	15 03		15 16	
d			13 22		13 36	13 40	13 42		14 04	14 17			14 22		14 36	14 39	14 42		14 51		15 04		15 17	
Cheadle Hulme d										14 22									14 56				15 22	
Bramhall d																			14 59					
Poynton d																			15 02					
Adlington (Cheshire) d																			15 04					
Prestbury d																			15 07					
Macclesfield a					13 48		13 55								14 48		14 55		15 11					
d					13 49		13 55								14 49		14 55		15 11					
Congleton d																			15 19					
Handforth d										14 26													15 26	
Manchester Airport ✈ d																		15 06						
Styal d																		15 11						
Wilmslow d						13 47			14 11	14 29						14 47		15 15			15 11		15 29	
Alderley Edge d										14a35								15a21					15 32	
Chelford d																							15 36	
Goostrey d																							15 40	
Holmes Chapel d																							15 43	
Sandbach d																							15 48	
Crewe 10 a						14 07			14 27							15 07					15 27		15 58	
Kidsgrove 50 a																			15 25					
Longport 50 a																								
Stoke-on-Trent 50 a	13 42		13 49		14 06		14 12				14 42		14 49		15 06		15 12		15 37					15 42
Stafford 65,67 a					14 24										15 24									
Wolverhampton 7 68 a	14 13				14 40						15 13				15 40									16 13
Birmingham New Street 12 68 a	14 31				14 58						15 31				15 58									16 31
London Euston 15 ⊖65 a			15 26				15 48		16 07				16 26				16 48				17 09			

	VT	TP	XC	AW	VT	NT	VT		NT	XC	VT	TP	XC	AW	VT	NT	NT		VT	NT	XC	VT	TP	XC
				R										R										
	◇1	◇1	◇1		◇1		◇1			◇1	◇1	◇1	◇1		◇1				◇1		◇1	◇1	◇1	◇1
		B	C	D		E				A		B	C	D			E				A		B	C
Deansgate 85,89 d																								
Manchester Oxford Rd 85,89 d																								
Manchester Picc. 10 85,89 a																								
d	15 15	15 20	15 27	15 30	15 35	15 52	15 55		16 04	16 07	16 15	16 20	16 27	16 30	16 35	16 41	16 52		16 55	17 04	17 07	17 15	17 20	17 27
Levenshulme d						15 58			16 09								16 58			17 09				
Heaton Chapel d						16 01			16 12								17 01			17 12				
Stockport a	15 22	15 28	15 35	15 39	15 42	16 04	16 03		16 16		16 22	16 28	16 34	16 39	16 42		17 04		17 03	17 16		17 22	17 28	17 34
d	15 22		15 36	15 39	15 42		16 04		16 17		16 23		16 36	16 39	16 42				17 04	17 17		17 22		17 36
Cheadle Hulme d									16 22											17 22				
Bramhall d																								
Poynton d																								
Adlington (Cheshire) d																								
Prestbury d																								
Macclesfield a			15 48		15 55								16 48		16 55									17 48
d			15 49		15 55								16 49		16 55									17 49
Congleton d																								
Handforth d									16 26											17 26				
Manchester Airport ✈ d																17 06								
Styal d																17 10								
Wilmslow d				15 47			16 11		16 29					16 47		17 15			17 11	17 29				
Alderley Edge d									16a35							17a21				17 32				
Chelford d																				17 36				
Goostrey d																				17 40				
Holmes Chapel d																				17 43				
Sandbach d																				17 48				
Crewe 10 a				16 06			16 27							17 06					17 27	17 58				
Kidsgrove 50 a																								
Longport 50 a																								
Stoke-on-Trent 50 a	15 49		16 06		16 12					16 42	16 48		17 06		17 12						17 42	17 49		18 06
Stafford 65,67 a			16 24										17 25											18 26
Wolverhampton 7 68 a			16 40							17 13			17 40								18 13			18 40
Birmingham New Street 12 68 a			16 58							17 31			17 58								18 31			18 58
London Euston 15 ⊖65 a	17 27				17 46		18 09				18 27				18 48				19 07			19 27		

A To Bristol Temple Meads
B From Manchester Airport to Sheffield
C To Bournemouth
D To Cardiff Central
E To Buxton
F To Milford Haven

Table 84R

Sundays

16 February to 23 March

Manchester, Stockport and Manchester Airport - Crewe and Stoke-on-Trent

Network Diagram - see first Page of Table 78

	AW	VT	NT		VT	NT	XC	VT	TP	XC	AW	VT	NT		NT	NT	VT	NT	XC	VT	TP	XC	AW
	R										R												
		◇1			◇1		◇1	◇1	◇1	◇1		◇1					◇1		◇1	◇1	◇1	◇1	◇
	A		B				C		D	E	A					B			C		D	F	A
	⊥	☕			☕		⊥	☕		⊥	⊥	☕					☕		⊥	☕		⊥	
Deansgate 85,89 d																							
Manchester Oxford Rd 85,89 d																							
Manchester Picc. 10 85,89 a																							
d	17 30	17 35	17 52		17 55	18 04	18 07	18 15	18 20	18 27	18 30	18 35	18 41		18 42	18 52	18 55	19 04	19 07	19 15	19 20	19 27	19 30
Levenshulme d			17 58			18 09										18 58		19 09					
Heaton Chapel d			18 01			18 12										19 01		19 12					
Stockport a	17 39	17 42	18 04		18 03	18 16		18 22	18 28	18 34	18 39	18 42			18 50	19 04	19 03	19 16		19 22	19 28	19 34	19 39
d	17 39	17 42			18 04	18 17		18 22		18 36	18 39	18 42			18 52		19 04	19 17		19 22		19 36	19 39
Cheadle Hulme d						18 22									18 57			19 22					
Bramhall d															19 00								
Poynton d															19 03								
Adlington (Cheshire) d															19 06								
Prestbury d															19 09								
Macclesfield a		17 55								18 48		18 55			19 13							19 48	
d		17 55								18 49		18 55			19 13							19 49	
Congleton d															19 21								
Handforth d						18 26												19 26					
Manchester Airport ✈ d													19 06										
Styal d													19 10										
Wilmslow d	17 47				18 11	18 29					18 47		19 15				19 11	19 29					19 47
Alderley Edge d						18a35							19a21					19 32					
Chelford d																		19 36					
Goostrey d																		19 40					
Holmes Chapel d																		19 43					
Sandbach d																		19 48					
Crewe 10 a	18 07				18 27						19 06						19 27	19 58					20 07
Kidsgrove 50 a															19 28								
Longport 50 a																							
Stoke-on-Trent 50 a		18 12					18 42	18 49		19 06		19 12			19 40				19 42	19 49		20 06	
Stafford 65,67 a										19 24												20 26	
Wolverhampton 7 68 a							19 13			19 40									20 13			20 39	
Birmingham New Street 12 68 a							19 31			19 58									20 31			20 58	
London Euston 15 ⊖65 a		19 48			20 08			20 27				20 48					21 10			21 31			

	VT	NT	NT	XC	TP	VT	AW	NT	NT		VT	NT	XC	TP	AW	NT	NT	NT	XC		TP	AW	NT	NT
	◇1			◇1	◇1	◇1	◇				◇1		◇1	◇1					◇1		◇1			
		B		C	D		A		B					D			B				D		B	
	☕					☕					☕													
Deansgate 85,89 d																								
Manchester Oxford Rd 85,89 d																								
Manchester Picc. 10 85,89 a																								
d	19 35	19 52	20 04	20 07	20 18	20 21	20 30	20 41	20 52		20 55	21 04	21 07	21 20	21 34	21 41	21 52	22 04	22 07		22 15	22 35	22 52	23 04
Levenshulme d		19 58	20 09						20 58			21 09					21 58	22 09					22 58	23 09
Heaton Chapel d		20 01	20 12						21 01			21 12					22 01	22 12					23 01	23 12
Stockport a	19 41	20 04	20 16	20 15	20 26	20 27	20 38		21 04		21 03	21 16	21 15	21 28		21 49	22 04	22 16	22 15		22 23		23 04	23 16
d	19 41		20 17	20 16		20 27	20 39				21 03	21 17	21 16			21 52		22 17	22 16					23 17
Cheadle Hulme d			20 22									21 22				21 56		22 22						23 21
Bramhall d																21 59								
Poynton d																22 02								
Adlington (Cheshire) d																22 05								
Prestbury d																22 08								
Macclesfield a	19 54			20 28		20 40					21 15		21 28			22 12			22 28					
d	19 54			20 29		20 40					21 15		21 29			22 13			22 29					
Congleton d																22 20								
Handforth d			20 26									21 26						22 26						23 25
Manchester Airport ✈ d								21 06																
Styal d								21 10																
Wilmslow d			20 29				20 47	21 15				21 29			21 50			22 29				22 50		23 28
Alderley Edge d			20a37					21a21				21 32						22a35						23a35
Chelford d												21 36												
Goostrey d												21 40												
Holmes Chapel d												21 43												
Sandbach d												21 48												
Crewe 10 a							21 07					21 58			22 13							23 13		
Kidsgrove 50 a																22 26								
Longport 50 a																								
Stoke-on-Trent 50 a	20 11			20 46		20 57					21 32		21 46			22 36			22 46					
Stafford 65,67 a				21 08									22 06						23 04					
Wolverhampton 7 68 a				21 21									22 20						23 18					
Birmingham New Street 12 68 a				21 39									22 40						23 36					
London Euston 15 ⊖65 a	21 58					22 57					23 49													

A To Cardiff Central
B To Buxton
C To Bristol Temple Meads
D From Manchester Airport to Sheffield
E To Southampton Central
F To Reading

Table 84R

Sundays

16 February to 23 March

Manchester, Stockport and Manchester Airport - Crewe and Stoke-on-Trent

Network Diagram - see first Page of Table 78

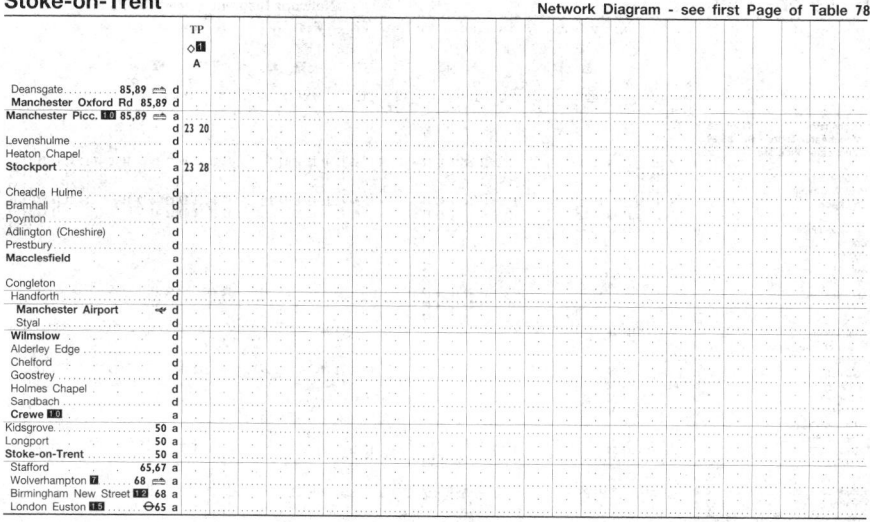

		TP
		◇1
		A
Deansgate 85,89 ⛴	d	
Manchester Oxford Rd 85,89	d	
Manchester Picc. 10 85,89 ⛴	a	
	d	23 20
Levenshulme	d	
Heaton Chapel	d	
Stockport	a	23 28
	d	
Cheadle Hulme	d	
Bramhall	d	
Poynton	d	
Adlington (Cheshire)	d	
Prestbury	d	
Macclesfield	a	
	d	
Congleton	d	
Handforth	d	
Manchester Airport ✈	d	
Styal	d	
Wilmslow	d	
Alderley Edge	d	
Chelford	d	
Goostrey	d	
Holmes Chapel	d	
Sandbach	d	
Crewe 10	a	
Kidsgrove 50	a	
Longport 50	a	
Stoke-on-Trent 50	a	
Stafford 65,67	a	
Wolverhampton 7 68 ⛴	a	
Birmingham New Street 12 68	a	
London Euston 15 ⊖65	a	

Sundays

30 March to 11 May

		NT	TP	TP	VT	VT	XC	TP	NT	NT		NT	TP	NT	VT	NT	XC	AW	NT	NT		VT	XC	AW	VT
																								R	
			◇1	1	◇1	◇1	◇1	◇1					◇1		◇1		◇1	◇				◇1	◇1		◇1
		B					C					D	A			E	C	F	D				C	G	
					☕	☕	🛒								☕		🛒	🛒				☕	🛒	🛒	☕
Deansgate 85,89 ⛴	d															09 15									
Manchester Oxford Rd 85,89	d															09 18									
Manchester Picc. 10 85,89 ⛴	a															09 21									
	d		07 29	07 50	08 05	08 20	08 27	08 29	08 41	08 50		08 55	08 58	09 04	09 20	09 22	09 27	09 30	09 51	10 05		10 20	10 27	10 30	10 35
Levenshulme	d											09 00		09 08					09 58	10 11					
Heaton Chapel	d											09 03		09 11					10 01	10 14					
Stockport	a				08 13	08 28	08 34			08 59		09 07	09 07	09 16	09 27	09 31	09 35	09 39	10 04	10 17		10 28	10 35	10 39	10 43
	d				08 14	08 28	08 36			09 01				09 18	09 27		09 36	09 39		10 19		10 29	10 37	10 39	10 43
Cheadle Hulme	d									09 06				09 22						10 23					
Bramhall	d									09 09															
Poynton	d									09 12															
Adlington (Cheshire)	d									09 15															
Prestbury	d									09 18															
Macclesfield	a					08 41				09 22					09 40		09 48						10 49		10 56
	d					08 42									09 40		09 49						10 50		10 56
Congleton	d																								
Handforth	d													09 26						10 27					
Manchester Airport ✈	d		07a43	08a04				08a43	09 06																
Styal	d								09 10																
Wilmslow	d	00 01			08 22		08 43		09 15					09 29				09 47		10 30		10 37		10 48	
Alderley Edge	d	00a05							09a22					09 32						10a36					
Chelford	d													09 36											
Goostrey	d													09 41											
Holmes Chapel	d													09 44											
Sandbach	d													09 49											
Crewe 10	a				08 39		09 01							09 59				10 06				10 53		11 07	
Kidsgrove 50	a																								
Longport 50	a																								
Stoke-on-Trent 50	a					08 59									09 57		10 05						11 07		11 13
Stafford 65,67	a				09 01		09 25										10 26						11 27		
Wolverhampton 7 68 ⛴	a						09 40										10 42						11 41		
Birmingham New Street 12 68	a						09 58										10 59						11 59		
London Euston 15 ⊖65	a				10 58	11 02									12 09							12 57			13 00

A From Manchester Airport to Sheffield
B From Manchester Picc.
C To Bournemouth
D To Buxton
E From Wigan Wallgate to Chester
F To Cardiff Central
G To Milford Haven

Table 84R

Sundays
30 March to 11 May

Manchester, Stockport and Manchester Airport - Crewe and Stoke-on-Trent

Network Diagram - see first Page of Table 78

	NT	NT	NT	VT	TP		AW	XC	VT	NT	NT	VT	NT	VT	TP		XC	AW	VT	EM	NT	NT	VT	NT
		A		◇1	◇1 B		R C	◇1 D	◇1		A	◇1		◇1	◇1 E		◇1 D	R F	◇1	◇ G		A	◇1	
Deansgate 85,89 d																								
Manchester Oxford Rd 85,89 d																					12 43			
Manchester Picc. 10 85,89 a																					12 45			
d	10 41	10 52	11 05	11 15	11 18		11 24	11 27	11 35	11 41	11 52	11 55	12 04	12 15	12 18		12 26	12 30	12 35	12 44	12 47	12 52	12 55	13 04
Levenshulme d		10 58	11 11								11 58		12 09									12 58		13 09
Heaton Chapel d		11 01	11 14								12 01		12 12									13 01		13 12
Stockport a		11 04	11 17	11 23	11 27		11 34	11 34	11 43	11 50	12 04	12 04	12 16	12 23	12 28		12 34	12 39	12 44	12 53		13 04	13 04	13 16
d			11 18	11 23			11 40	11 36	11 43	11 51		12 05	12 16	12 23			12 35	12 40	12 44				13 05	13 17
Cheadle Hulme d			11 22							11 56			12 22											13 21
Bramhall d										11 59														
Poynton d										12 02														
Adlington (Cheshire) d										12 04														
Prestbury d										12 07														
Macclesfield a								11 49	11 56	12 11							12 48		12 57					
d								11 49	11 56	12 11							12 49		12 57					
Congleton d										12 19														
Handforth d			11 26										12 26											13 25
Manchester Airport ✈ d	11 10																				13 12			
Styal d	11 14																				13 16			
Wilmslow d	11 17		11 29				11 47					12 12	12 29					12 48			13 23		13 12	13 28
Alderley Edge d	11a22		11 32										12a35								13a29			13 31
Chelford d			11 36																					13 35
Goostrey d			11 41																					13 40
Holmes Chapel d			11 44																					13 43
Sandbach d			11 49																					13 48
Crewe 10 a			11 59				12 07					12 28						13 07					13 28	13 58
Kidsgrove 50 a										12 25														
Longport 50 a																								
Stoke-on-Trent 50 a				11 50				12 06	12 13	12 35				12 50			13 06		13 14					
Stafford 65,67 a								12 24									13 24							
Wolverhampton 7 68 a								12 40									13 40							
Birmingham New Street 12 68 a								12 58									13 58							
London Euston 15 ⊖65 a				13 28					13 48			14 10		14 28					14 48				15 08	

	XC		VT	TP	XC	AW	VT	NT	VT	NT	XC		VT	TP	XC	AW	VT	NT	NT	VT	NT		XC	VT
	◇1 H		◇1	◇1 B	◇1 D	R C	◇1	A	◇1		◇1 I		◇1	◇1 B	◇1 D	R F	◇1		A	◇1			◇1 I	◇1
Deansgate 85,89 d																								
Manchester Oxford Rd 85,89 d																								
Manchester Picc. 10 85,89 a																								
d	13 07		13 15	13 20	13 27	13 30	13 35	13 52	13 55	14 04	14 07		14 15	14 20	14 27	14 30	14 35	14 41	14 52	14 55	15 04		15 07	15 15
Levenshulme d								13 58		14 09									14 58		15 09			
Heaton Chapel d								14 01		14 12									15 01		15 12			
Stockport a			13 22	13 28	13 35	13 39	13 42	14 04	14 03	14 16			14 22	14 28	14 34	14 38	14 42	14 49	15 04	15 03	15 16			15 22
d			13 22		13 36	13 40	13 42		14 04	14 17			14 22		14 36	14 39	14 42	14 51		15 04	15 17			15 22
Cheadle Hulme d										14 22								14 56			15 22			
Bramhall d																		14 59						
Poynton d																		15 02						
Adlington (Cheshire) d																		15 04						
Prestbury d																		15 07						
Macclesfield a					13 48		13 55								14 48		14 55	15 11						
d					13 49		13 55								14 49		14 55	15 11						
Congleton d																		15 19						
Handforth d										14 26											15 26			
Manchester Airport ✈ d																								
Styal d																								
Wilmslow d						13 47			14 11	14 29						14 47				15 11	15 29			
Alderley Edge d										14a35											15 32			
Chelford d																					15 36			
Goostrey d																					15 40			
Holmes Chapel d																					15 43			
Sandbach d																					15 48			
Crewe 10 a						14 07			14 27							15 07				15 27	15 58			
Kidsgrove 50 a																		15 25						
Longport 50 a																								
Stoke-on-Trent 50 a	13 42		13 49		14 06		14 12				14 42		14 49		15 06		15 12	15 37					15 42	15 49
Stafford 65,67 a					14 24										15 24									
Wolverhampton 7 68 a	14 13				14 40						15 13				15 40								16 13	
Birmingham New Street 12 68 a	14 31				14 58						15 31				15 58								16 31	
London Euston 15 ⊖65 a			15 26				15 48		16 07				16 26				16 48			17 09				17 27

A To Buxton
B From Manchester Airport to Cleethorpes
C To Cardiff Central
D To Bournemouth
E From Manchester Airport to Doncaster
F To Milford Haven
G To Norwich
H To Paignton
I To Bristol Temple Meads

Table 84R

Sundays

30 March to 11 May

Manchester, Stockport and Manchester Airport - Crewe and Stoke-on-Trent

Network Diagram - see first Page of Table 78

Station		TP	XC	AW	VT	NT	VT	NT		XC	VT	TP	XC	AW	VT	NT	NT	VT		NT	XC	VT	TP	XC	AW
		◇1 A	◇1 B	R C	◇1	D	◇1			◇1 E	◇1	◇1 A	◇1 B	R C	◇1		D	◇1			◇1 F	◇1	◇1 A	◇1 B	R C
Deansgate 85,89	d																								
Manchester Oxford Rd 85,89	d																								
Manchester Picc. 10 85,89	a																								
	d	15 20	15 27	15 30	15 35	15 52	15 55	16 04		16 07	16 15	16 20	16 27	16 30	16 35	16 41	16 52	16 55		17 04	17 07	17 15	17 20	17 27	17 30
Levenshulme	d					15 58		16 09									16 58			17 09					
Heaton Chapel	d					16 01		16 12									17 01			17 12					
Stockport	a	15 28	15 35	15 39	15 42	16 04	16 03	16 16			16 22	16 28	16 34	16 39	16 42		17 04	17 03		17 16		17 22	17 28	17 34	17 39
	d		15 36	15 39	15 42		16 04	16 17			16 23		16 36	16 39	16 42			17 04		17 17		17 22		17 36	17 39
Cheadle Hulme	d							16 22												17 22					
Bramhall	d																								
Poynton	d																								
Adlington (Cheshire)	d																								
Prestbury	d																								
Macclesfield	a		15 48		15 55								16 48		16 55									17 48	
	d		15 49		15 55								16 49		16 55									17 49	
Congleton	d																								
Handforth	d							16 26												17 26					
Manchester Airport ✈	d															17 06									
Styal	d															17 10									
Wilmslow	d			15 47			16 11	16 29						16 47		17 15		17 11		17 29					17 47
Alderley Edge	d							16a35								17a21				17 32					
Chelford	d																			17 36					
Goostrey	d																			17 40					
Holmes Chapel	d																			17 43					
Sandbach	d																			17 48					
Crewe 10	a			16 06			16 27							17 06				17 27		17 58					18 07
Kidsgrove 50	a																								
Longport 50	a																								
Stoke-on-Trent 50	a		16 06		16 12					16 42	16 48		17 06		17 12						17 42	17 49		18 06	
Stafford 65,67	a		16 24										17 25											18 26	
Wolverhampton 7 68	a		16 40							17 13			17 40								18 13			18 40	
Birmingham New Street 12 68	a		16 58							17 31			17 58								18 31			18 58	
London Euston 15 ⊖65	a				17 46		18 09				18 27				18 48			19 07				19 27			

Station		VT	NT	VT		NT	XC	VT	TP	XC	AW	VT	NT	NT		NT	VT	NT	XC	VT	TP	XC	AW	VT	
		◇1	D	◇1			◇1 E	◇1	◇1 A	◇1 G	R C	◇1				D	◇1		◇1 E	◇1	◇1 A	◇1 H	◇ C	◇1	
Deansgate 85,89	d																								
Manchester Oxford Rd 85,89	d																								
Manchester Picc. 10 85,89	a																								
	d	17 35	17 52	17 55		18 04	18 07	18 15	18 20	18 27	18 30	18 35	18 41	18 42		18 52	18 55	19 04	19 07	19 15	19 20	19 27	19 30	19 35	
Levenshulme	d		17 58			18 09										18 58		19 09							
Heaton Chapel	d		18 01			18 12										19 01		19 12							
Stockport	a	17 42	18 04	18 03		18 16		18 22	18 28	18 34	18 39	18 42		18 50		19 04	19 03	19 16		19 22	19 28	19 34	19 39	19 41	
	d	17 42		18 04		18 17		18 22		18 36	18 39	18 42		18 52			19 04	19 17		19 22		19 36	19 39	19 41	
Cheadle Hulme	d					18 22								18 57				19 22							
Bramhall	d													19 00											
Poynton	d													19 03											
Adlington (Cheshire)	d													19 06											
Prestbury	d													19 09											
Macclesfield	a	17 55								18 48		18 55		19 13								19 48		19 54	
	d	17 55								18 49		18 55		19 13								19 49		19 54	
Congleton	d													19 21											
Handforth	d					18 26												19 26							
Manchester Airport ✈	d												19 06												
Styal	d												19 10												
Wilmslow	d			18 11		18 29					18 47		19 15				19 11	19 29					19 47		
Alderley Edge	d					18a35							19a21					19 32							
Chelford	d																	19 36							
Goostrey	d																	19 40							
Holmes Chapel	d																	19 43							
Sandbach	d																	19 48							
Crewe 10	a			18 27							19 06						19 27	19 58					20 07		
Kidsgrove 50	a													19 28											
Longport 50	a																								
Stoke-on-Trent 50	a	18 12					18 42	18 49		19 06		19 12		19 40					19 42	19 49		20 06		20 11	
Stafford 65,67	a									19 24												20 26			
Wolverhampton 7 68	a						19 13			19 40									20 13			20 39			
Birmingham New Street 12 68	a						19 31			19 58									20 31			20 58			
London Euston 15 ⊖65	a	19 48		20 08				20 27				20 48					21 10			21 31				21 58	

A From Manchester Airport to Cleethorpes
B To Bournemouth
C To Cardiff Central
D To Buxton
E To Bristol Temple Meads
F To Plymouth
G To Southampton Central
H To Reading

Table 84R

Sundays
30 March to 11 May

Manchester, Stockport and Manchester Airport - Crewe and Stoke-on-Trent

Network Diagram - see first Page of Table 78

		NT	NT	XC	TP	VT	AW	NT	NT	VT	NT	XC	TP	AW	NT	NT	NT	XC	TP	AW	NT	NT	TP
				◇1	◇1	◇1	◇			◇1		◇1	◇1					◇1	◇1				◇1
		A		B	C		D		A				E			A			E		A		E
Deansgate 85,89	d																						
Manchester Oxford Rd 85,89	d																						
Manchester Picc. 10 85,89	a																						
	d	19 52	20 04	20 07	20 18	20 21	20 30	20 41	20 52	20 55	21 04	21 07	21 20	21 34	21 41	21 52	22 04	22 07	22 15	22 35	22 52	23 04	23 20
Levenshulme	d	19 58	20 09						20 58		21 09					21 58	22 09				22 58	23 09	
Heaton Chapel	d	20 01	20 12						21 01		21 12					22 01	22 12				23 01	23 12	
Stockport	a	20 04	20 16	20 15	20 26	20 27	20 38		21 04	21 03	21 16	21 15	21 28		21 49	22 04	22 16	22 15	22 23		23 04	23 16	23 28
	d		20 17	20 16		20 27	20 39			21 03	21 17	21 16			21 52		22 17	22 16				23 17	
Cheadle Hulme	d		20 22								21 22				21 56		22 22					23 21	
Bramhall	d														21 59								
Poynton	d														22 02								
Adlington (Cheshire)	d														22 05								
Prestbury	d														22 08								
Macclesfield	a			20 28		20 40				21 15		21 28			22 12			22 28					
	d			20 29		20 40				21 15		21 29			22 13			22 29					
Congleton	d														22 20								
Handforth	d		20 26								21 26						22 26					23 25	
Manchester Airport	d							21 06															
Styal	d							21 10															
Wilmslow	d		20 29				20 47	21 15			21 29			21 50			22 29			22 50		23 28	
Alderley Edge	d		20a37					21a21			21 32						22a35					23a35	
Chelford	d										21 36												
Goostrey	d										21 40												
Holmes Chapel	d										21 43												
Sandbach	d										21 48												
Crewe 10	a						21 07				21 58			22 13						23 13			
Kidsgrove 50	a														22 26								
Longport 50	a																						
Stoke-on-Trent 50	a			20 46		20 57				21 32		21 46			22 36			22 46					
Stafford 65,67	a			21 08								22 06						23 04					
Wolverhampton 7 68	a			21 21								22 20						23 18					
Birmingham New Street 12 68	a			21 39								22 40						23 36					
London Euston 15 ⊖65	a					22 57				23 49													

A To Buxton
B To Bristol Temple Meads
C From Manchester Airport to Cleethorpes
D To Cardiff Central
E From Manchester Airport to Sheffield

Table 85

Manchester Airport - Manchester

Mondays to Fridays

9 December to 16 May

Network Diagram - see first Page of Table 78

Miles	Station		TP ◇1 A	TP MX ◇1 B	TP MO ◇1	TP MX C bus	NT FX D bus	NT MX B	TP MX C bus	TP ◇1 A	NT MX C bus		NT A	TP MX C bus	TP MX C bus	TP ◇1 A	TP ◇1 A	AW ◇ E trolley	TP ◇1 A	TP ◇1 trolley	NT F		TP ◇1	TP ◇1 trolley	NT
—	Crewe 10	84 d						00 44																	
—	Wilmslow	84 d																			05 46				
0	**Manchester Airport**	✈ d	00 01	00 38	00 48	00 55	01 00	01 20	03 55	04 13	04 15		04 38	05 03	05 10	05 20	05 29	05 33	05 37	05 58	06 01		06 18	06 30	06 41
1½	Heald Green	d																		06 02	06 04				
3	Gatley	d																			06 07				
4¼	East Didsbury	d																			06 10				
5¼	Burnage	d																			06 12				
6¼	Mauldeth Road	d																			06 14				
9¼	**Manchester Piccadilly 10**	a	00 14	00 51	01 01	01 20	01 25	01 36	04 20	04 27	04 40		04 51	05 28	05 35	05 33	05 42	05 48	05 51	06 12	06 25		06 31	06 44	06 56
—		d															05 44	05 50		06 13			06 33		06 58
—	**Manchester Oxford Rd.**	a															05 46	05 52		06 15			06 35		07 00
—	Deansgate	a																							

Station		NT	TP ◇1 trolley	TP ◇1 trolley	TP ◇1 trolley	NT	TP ◇1 trolley		TP ◇1 trolley	NT	NT	TP ◇1 trolley	TP ◇1 trolley	NT	TP ◇1 trolley	NT	TP ◇1 trolley		TP ◇1 trolley	NT	NT	TP ◇1 trolley	TP ◇1 trolley	NT	TP ◇1 trolley
Crewe 10	84 d					06 33																			
Wilmslow	84 d					06 57										07 56									
Manchester Airport	✈ d	06 46	06 55	07 00	07 06	07 17	07 25		07 35	07 38	07 46	07 53	07 56	08 01	08 06	08 17	08 25		08 35	08 41	08 46	08 55	09 00	09 03	09 06
Heald Green	d	06 49				07 20	07 29			07 42	07 49			08 05		08 20	08 29				08 49				
Gatley	d	06 52				07 23				07 45	07 52		08 02			08 23	08 33				08 52				
East Didsbury	d	06 55				07 26				07 48	07 55		08 05			08 26	08 36				08 55				
Burnage	d	06 57				07 28					07 57					08 28					08 57				
Mauldeth Road	d	06 59				07 30					07 59					08 30					08 59				
Manchester Piccadilly 10	a	07 11	07 13	07 13	07 22	07 42	07 43		07 49	07 57	08 11	08 12	08 13	08 21	08 22	08 42	08 44		08 49	08 58	09 11	09 13	09 14	09 18	09 22
	d			07 15						07 59			08 15	08 22			08 46			09 01			09 16	09 22	
Manchester Oxford Rd.	a			07 17						08 01			08 17	08 24			08 48			09 03			09 18	09 24	
Deansgate	a													08 28			08 51							09 28	

Station		NT	TP ◇1 trolley		TP ◇1 trolley	NT	NT	TP ◇1 trolley	TP ◇1 trolley	NT ◇	TP ◇1 trolley	NT	TP ◇1 trolley	TP ◇1 trolley	NT	NT	TP ◇1 trolley	TP ◇1 trolley	NT ◇	TP ◇1 trolley	NT			
Crewe 10	84 d	08 31										09 33									10 34	and at the same minutes past each hour until		
Wilmslow	84 d	08 57										09 57									10 57			
Manchester Airport	✈ d	09 17	09 29		09 35	09 41	09 46	09 55	10 00	10 03	10 06	10 17	10 29	10 35	10 41	10 46	10 55	11 00	11 03	11 06	11 17			
Heald Green	d	09 20	09 33				09 49					10 20	10 33			10 49					11 20			
Gatley	d	09 23					09 52					10 23				10 52					11 23			
East Didsbury	d	09 26					09 55					10 26				10 55					11 26			
Burnage	d	09 28					09 57					10 28				10 57					11 28			
Mauldeth Road	d	09 30					09 59					10 30				10 59					11 30			
Manchester Piccadilly 10	a	09 42	09 44		09 52	09 59	10 11	10 13	10 14	10 18	10 22	10 42	10 44	10 52	10 59	11 11	11 13	11 14	11 18	11 22	11 42			
	d		09 46			10 01			10 16	10 22			10 46		11 01			11 16	11 22					
Manchester Oxford Rd.	a		09 48			10 03			10 18	10 24			10 48		11 03			11 18	11 24					
Deansgate	a		09 51							10 28			10 51						11 28					

Station		TP ◇1 trolley	TP ◇1 trolley	NT	NT	TP ◇1 trolley	TP ◇1 trolley	NT ◇	TP ◇1 trolley	NT		TP ◇1 trolley	TP ◇1 trolley	NT	NT	TP ◇1 trolley	TP ◇1 trolley	NT ◇	TP ◇1 trolley	NT		TP ◇1 trolley	NT	NT	TP ◇1 trolley
Crewe 10	84 d									13 34										14 34					
Wilmslow	84 d									13 57										14 57					
Manchester Airport	✈ d	13 29	13 35	13 41	13 46	13 55	14 00	14 03	14 06	14 17		14 29	14 35	14 41	14 46	14 55	15 00	15 03	15 06	15 17		15 35	15 41	15 46	15 55
Heald Green	d	13 33			13 49					14 20		14 33			14 49					15 20				15 49	
Gatley	d				13 52					14 23					14 52					15 23				15 52	
East Didsbury	d				13 55					14 26					14 55					15 26				15 55	
Burnage	d				13 57					14 28					14 57					15 28				15 57	
Mauldeth Road	d				13 59					14 30					14 59					15 30				15 59	
Manchester Piccadilly 10	a	13 44	13 52	13 59	14 11	14 13	14 14	14 18	14 22	14 42		14 44	14 52	14 59	15 11	15 13	15 14	15 18	15 22	15 40		15 52	15 59	16 11	16 13
	d	13 46		14 01			14 16	14 22				14 46		15 01			15 16	15 22		15 42			16 01		
Manchester Oxford Rd.	a	13 48		14 03			14 18	14 24				14 48		15 03			15 18	15 24		15 46			16 03		
Deansgate	a	13 51						14 28				14 51						15 28							

Station		TP ◇1 trolley	NT ◇	TP ◇1 trolley	NT	TP ◇1 trolley		TP FO ◇1 trolley	TP FX ◇1 trolley	NT	NT	TP ◇1 trolley	TP ◇1 G trolley	TP ◇1 H trolley	NT ◇	TP FX ◇1 trolley		NT	TP ◇1 trolley	NT	NT	TP ◇1 trolley	TP ◇1 trolley	NT ◇	NT
Crewe 10	84 d				15 33													16 34							17 33
Wilmslow	84 d				15 56													16 57							17 56
Manchester Airport	✈ d	16 00	16 03	16 06	16 17	16 29		16 34	16 35	16 41	16 46	16 55	17 00	17 00	17 03	17 06		17 17	17 35	17 41	17 46	17 55	18 00	18 03	18 17
Heald Green	d				16 20	16 33					16 49							17 20			17 49				18 20
Gatley	d				16 23						16 52							17 23			17 52				18 23
East Didsbury	d				16 26						16 55							17 26			17 55				18 26
Burnage	d				16 28						16 57							17 28			17 57				18 28
Mauldeth Road	d				16 30						16 59							17 30			17 59				18 30
Manchester Piccadilly 10	a	16 14	16 18	16 22	16 42	16 44		16 52	16 52	16 59	17 11	17 13	17 13	17 14	17 21	17 22		17 42	17 52	17 59	18 11	18 13	18 14	18 18	18 42
	d	16 16	16 22			16 46				17 01			17 15	17 15	17 22					18 01			18 16	18 22	
Manchester Oxford Rd.	a	16 18	16 24			16 48				17 03			17 17	17 17	17 25					18 02			18 18	18 24	
Deansgate	a		16 28																					18 29	

A until 30 December, MO from 6 January until 17 March, from 24 March
B until 27 December, from 25 March
C from 31 December until 21 March
D from 30 December until 20 March
E until 27 December, from 24 March
F until 27 December
G from 10 February
H until 7 February

Table 85

Manchester Airport - Manchester

Mondays to Fridays

9 December to 16 May

Network Diagram - see first Page of Table 78

	TP	NT	NT	TP	TP	NT	NT		TP	TP	NT	NT	TP	TP	NT	NT	TP		TP	AW	TP	NT	NT	NT FX
	◇1			◇1	◇1	◇			◇1	◇1			◇1	◇1	◇		◇1		◇1		◇1	◇		
																						A	B	C
														trolley										
Crewe 10 84 d							18 34																	
Wilmslow 84 d							18 57									19 56							20 56	20 56
Manchester Airport ✈ d	18 35	18 41	18 46	18 55	19 00	19 03	19 09		19 20	19 29	19 41	19 46	19 55	20 00	20 03	20 09	20 20		20 29	20 32	20 47	21 03	21 09	21 09
Heald Green d			18 49				19 12			19 33		19 49				20 12			20 33		20 51		21 12	21 12
Gatley d			18 52				19 15					19 52				20 15					20 54		21 15	21 15
East Didsbury d			18 55				19 18					19 55				20 18					20 57		21 18	21 18
Burnage d			18 57				19 20					19 57				20 20					20 59		21 20	21 20
Mauldeth Road d			18 59				19 22					19 59				20 22					21 02		21 22	21 22
Manchester Piccadilly 10 🚊 a	18 52	18 59	19 11	19 13	19 14	19 18	19 29		19 36	19 44	19 59	20 11	20 13	20 14	20 18	20 31	20 36		20 44	20 48	21 13	21 18	21 31	21 32
d		19 01			19 16	19 20	19 31			19 46	20 01			20 16	20 20	20 31			20 46	20 50		21 20	21 31	
Manchester Oxford Rd. a		19 03			19 18	19 22	19 35			19 48	20 03			20 18	20 22	20 35			20 48	20 52		21 22	21 35	
Deansgate 🚊 a						19 26				19 51					20 26				20 51			21 26		

	TP	NT FX	TP		AW	TP FX	NT FO	TP	TP	TP FX	NT	NT FX	TP FO		NT	TP FX	TP	TP FX	NT	NT FX	TP FX	TP FX	TP FO	
	◇1		◇1					◇1	◇1				◇1		◇	◇1	◇1					◇1	◇1	
						C		B	B	C	D	C			B	E	B	C	B	C	C	E		
						bus				bus		bus						bus		bus	bus			
Crewe 10 84 d																								
Wilmslow 84 d											21 55	21 56							22 56	22 56				
Manchester Airport ✈ d	21 20	21 25	21 29		21 32	21 40	21 41	21 47	22 00	22 05	22 07	22 16	22 18		22 19	22 22	22 29	23 05	23 09	23 16	23 17	23 24	23 24	
Heald Green d			21 33					21 51			22 11	22 21					22 33		23 12	23 21				
Gatley d								21 54			22 14	22 29							23 15	23 29				
East Didsbury d								21 57			22 16	22 37							23 18	23 37				
Burnage d								21 59			22 18	22 42							23 20	23 42				
Mauldeth Road d								22 02			22 20	22 47							23 22	23 47				
Manchester Piccadilly 10 🚊 a	21 36	21 38	21 44		21 48	22 05	21 59	22 13	22 14	22 30	22 30	22 58	22 31		22 33	22 35	22 44	23 30	23 33	23 58	23 42	23 37	23 38	
d			21 46		21 50		22 01		22 16		22 31				22 35		22 46							
Manchester Oxford Rd. a			21 48		21 52		22 03		22 18		22 35				22 37		22 48							
Deansgate 🚊 a			21 51												22 41		22 51							

	TP	TP FX
	◇1	
	B	C
		bus
Crewe 10 84 d		
Wilmslow 84 d		
Manchester Airport ✈ d	23 30	23 40
Heald Green d		
Gatley d		
East Didsbury d		
Burnage d		
Mauldeth Road d		
Manchester Piccadilly 10 🚊 a	23 48	00 05
d		
Manchester Oxford Rd. a		
Deansgate 🚊 a		

Saturdays

14 December to 17 May

	TP	TP	NT	TP	NT	TP	TP	AW	TP		TP	NT	TP	TP	NT	NT	TP	TP	TP		NT	TP	TP	NT
	◇1	◇1		◇1		◇1	◇1	◇	◇1		◇1		◇1	◇1			◇1	◇1	◇1			◇1	◇1	
								trolley			trolley							trolley				trolley		
Crewe 10 84 d			00 44																		06 33			
Wilmslow 84 d												05 46									06 57			
Manchester Airport ✈ d	00 01	00 38	01 20	04 13	04 34	05 20	05 29	05 33	05 37		05 58	06 01	06 18	06 30	06 41	06 46	06 55	07 00	07 06		07 17	07 25	07 35	07 38
Heald Green d											06 02	06 04				06 49					07 20	07 29		07 42
Gatley d												06 07				06 52					07 23			07 45
East Didsbury d												06 10				06 55					07 26			07 48
Burnage d												06 12				06 57					07 28			
Mauldeth Road d												06 14				06 59					07 30			
Manchester Piccadilly 10 🚊 a	00 14	00 51	01 36	04 27	04 47	05 33	05 42	05 48	05 51		06 12	06 25	06 31	06 44	06 56	07 11	07 13	07 13	07 22		07 42	07 43	07 49	07 57
d							05 44	05 50			06 13		06 33		06 58			07 15						07 59
Manchester Oxford Rd. a							05 46	05 52			06 15		06 35		07 00			07 17						08 01
Deansgate 🚊 a																								

A until 27 December, from 10 February
B until 27 December, FO from 3 January until 14 March, from 21 March
C from 30 December until 20 March
D until 27 December, FX from 24 March
E until 26 December, from 24 March

Table 85

Saturdays

14 December to 17 May

Manchester Airport - Manchester

Network Diagram - see first Page of Table 78

		NT		TP	TP	NT	TP	NT	TP	TP	NT	NT		TP	TP	NT	TP	NT	TP	TP	NT	NT		TP	TP
				◇1	◇1		◇1		◇1	◇1				◇1	◇1		◇1		◇1	◇1				◇1	◇1
															🚲										🚲
Crewe 10	84 d							07 30										08 31							
Wilmslow	84 d							07 56										08 57							
Manchester Airport ✈	d	07 46		07 53	07 56	08 01	08 06	08 17	08 25	08 35	08 41	08 46		08 55	09 00	09 03	09 06	09 17	09 29	09 35	09 41	09 46		09 55	10 00
Heald Green	d	07 49				08 05		08 20	08 29			08 49						09 20	09 33			09 49			
Gatley	d	07 52			08 02			08 23	08 33			08 52						09 23				09 52			
East Didsbury	d	07 55			08 05			08 26	08 36			08 55						09 26				09 55			
Burnage	d	07 57						08 28				08 57						09 28				09 57			
Mauldeth Road	d	07 59						08 30				08 59						09 30				09 59			
Manchester Piccadilly 10 🚊	a	08 11		08 12	08 13	08 21	08 22	08 42	08 44	08 49	08 58	09 11		09 13	09 14	09 18	09 22	09 42	09 44	09 52	09 59	10 11		10 13	10 14
	d				08 15	08 22			08 46		09 01				09 16	09 22			09 46		10 01				10 16
Manchester Oxford Rd.	a				08 17	08 24			08 48		09 03				09 18	09 24			09 48		10 03				10 18
Deansgate 🚊	a					08 28			08 51							09 28			09 51						

		NT	TP	NT	TP	TP	NT	NT		TP	TP	NT	TP	NT	TP	TP	NT	NT		TP	TP	NT	TP	NT	TP
			◇1		◇1	◇1				◇1	◇1		◇1		◇1	◇1				◇1	◇1		◇1		◇1
																					🚲				
Crewe 10	84 d			09 34										10 34										11 34	
Wilmslow	84 d			09 57										10 57										11 57	
Manchester Airport ✈	d	10 03	10 06	10 17	10 29	10 35	10 41	10 46		10 55	11 00	11 03	11 06	11 17	11 29	11 35	11 41	11 46		11 55	12 00	12 03	12 06	12 17	12 29
Heald Green	d			10 20	10 33			10 49						11 20	11 33			11 49						12 20	12 33
Gatley	d			10 23				10 52						11 23				11 52						12 23	
East Didsbury	d			10 26				10 55						11 26				11 55						12 26	
Burnage	d			10 28				10 57						11 28				11 57						12 28	
Mauldeth Road	d			10 30				10 59						11 30				11 59						12 30	
Manchester Piccadilly 10 🚊	a	10 18	10 22	10 42	10 44	10 52	10 59	11 11		11 13	11 14	11 18	11 22	11 42	11 44	11 52	11 59	12 11		12 13	12 14	12 18	12 22	12 42	12 44
	d	10 22			10 46		11 01				11 16	11 22			11 46		12 01				12 16	12 22			12 46
Manchester Oxford Rd.	a	10 24			10 48		11 03				11 18	11 24			11 48		12 03				12 18	12 24			12 48
Deansgate 🚊	a	10 28			10 51							11 28			11 51							12 28			12 51

		TP	NT	NT		TP	TP	NT	TP	TP	NT	TP	TP	NT		NT	TP	TP	NT	TP	NT	TP	TP	NT	
		◇1				◇1	◇1		◇1	◇1		◇1	◇1				◇1	◇1		◇1		◇1	◇1		
									A	B															
							🚲											🚲							
Crewe 10	84 d										12 34										13 34				
Wilmslow	84 d										12 57										13 57				
Manchester Airport ✈	d	12 35	12 41	12 46		12 55	13 00	13 03	13 05	13 06	13 17	13 29	13 35	13 41		13 46	13 55	14 00	14 03	14 06	14 17	14 29	14 35	14 41	
Heald Green	d			12 49							13 20	13 33				13 49					14 20	14 33			
Gatley	d			12 52							13 23					13 52					14 23				
East Didsbury	d			12 55							13 26					13 55					14 26				
Burnage	d			12 57							13 28					13 57					14 28				
Mauldeth Road	d			12 59							13 30					13 59					14 30				
Manchester Piccadilly 10 🚊	a	12 52	12 59	13 11		13 13	13 14	13 18	13 22	13 22	13 42	13 44	13 52	13 59		14 11	14 13	14 14	14 18	14 22	14 42	14 44	14 52	14 59	
	d		13 01				13 16	13 22				13 46		14 01				14 16	14 22			14 46		15 01	
Manchester Oxford Rd.	a		13 03				13 18	13 24				13 48		14 03				14 18	14 24			14 48		15 03	
Deansgate 🚊	a							13 28				13 51							14 28			14 51			

		NT	TP	TP	TP	NT	TP	NT	TP	NT		NT	TP	TP	NT	TP	NT	TP	TP	NT		NT	TP	TP	NT
			◇1	◇1	◇1		◇1		◇1				◇1	◇1		◇1		◇1	◇1				◇1	◇1	
				B	C																				
				🚲										🚲										🚲	
Crewe 10	84 d							14 34									15 33								
Wilmslow	84 d							14 57									15 56								
Manchester Airport ✈	d	14 46	14 55	15 00	15 00	15 03	15 06	15 17	15 35	15 41		15 46	15 55	16 00	16 03	16 06	16 17	16 29	16 35	16 41		16 46	16 55	17 00	17 03
Heald Green	d	14 49						15 20				15 49					16 20	16 33				16 49			
Gatley	d	14 52						15 23				15 52					16 23					16 52			
East Didsbury	d	14 55						15 26				15 55					16 26					16 55			
Burnage	d	14 57						15 28				15 57					16 28					16 57			
Mauldeth Road	d	14 59						15 30				15 59					16 30					16 59			
Manchester Piccadilly 10 🚊	a	15 11	15 13	15 14	15 14	15 18	15 22	15 42	15 52	15 59		16 11	16 13	16 14	16 18	16 22	16 42	16 44	16 52	16 59		17 11	17 13	17 13	17 21
	d			15 16	15 16	15 22				16 01				16 16	16 22			16 46		17 01				17 15	17 23
Manchester Oxford Rd.	a			15 18	15 18	15 24				16 03				16 18	16 24			16 48		17 03				17 17	17 25
Deansgate 🚊	a					15 28									16 28			16 51							

		TP	NT	TP	NT	NT		TP	TP	NT	NT	TP	NT	NT	TP	TP		NT	NT	TP	TP	NT	NT	TP	TP
		◇1		◇1				◇1	◇1			◇1			◇1	◇1				◇1	◇1			◇1	◇1
																									B
									🚲																
Crewe 10	84 d		16 34								17 33								18 34						
Wilmslow	84 d		16 57								17 56								18 57						
Manchester Airport ✈	d	17 06	17 17	17 35	17 41	17 46		17 55	18 00	18 03	18 17	18 35	18 41	18 46	18 55	19 00		19 03	19 09	19 20	19 29	19 41	19 46	19 55	20 00
Heald Green	d		17 20			17 49					18 20			18 49					19 12		19 33		19 49		
Gatley	d		17 23			17 52					18 23			18 52					19 15				19 52		
East Didsbury	d		17 26			17 55					18 26			18 55					19 18				19 55		
Burnage	d		17 28			17 57					18 28			18 57					19 20				19 57		
Mauldeth Road	d		17 30			17 59					18 30			18 59					19 22				19 59		
Manchester Piccadilly 10 🚊	a	17 22	17 42	17 52	17 59	18 11		18 13	18 14	18 18	18 42	18 52	18 59	19 11	19 13	19 14		19 18	19 31	19 36	19 44	19 59	20 11	20 13	20 14
	d				18 01				18 16	18 22			19 01			19 16		19 20	19 32		19 46	20 01			20 16
Manchester Oxford Rd.	a				18 04				18 18	18 24			19 03			19 18		19 22	19 36		19 48	20 03			20 18
Deansgate 🚊	a									18 29								19 26			19 51				

A from 4 January until 8 February

B from 15 February

C until 8 February

Table 85

Saturdays

14 December to 17 May

Manchester Airport - Manchester

Network Diagram - see first Page of Table 78

		NT	NT	TP	TP	AW	TP	NT	NT	TP	TP	NT	TP	TP	NT	NT	TP	TP	TP	NT	NT
				◇1	◇1		◇1			◇1	◇1		◇1	◇1 A			◇1	◇1	◇1	B	C (bus)
Crewe 10	84 d																				
Wilmslow	84 d		19 56						20 56						21 55					23 15	
Manchester Airport	d	20 03	20 09	20 20	20 29	20 32	20 47	21 03	21 09	21 20	21 29	21 42	21 47	22 00	22 08	22 19	22 22	22 29	23 24	23 27	23 35
Heald Green	d		20 12		20 33		20 51		21 12		21 33		21 51		22 12			22 33		23 30	23 40
Gatley	d		20 15				20 54		21 15				21 54		22 15					23 33	23 48
East Didsbury	d		20 18				20 57		21 18				21 57		22 17					23 36	23 56
Burnage	d		20 20				20 59		21 20				21 59		22 19					23 38	00 01
Mauldeth Road	d		20 22				21 02		21 22				22 02		22 21					23 40	00 06
Manchester Piccadilly 10	a	20 18	20 31	20 36	20 44	20 48	21 13	21 17	21 31	21 36	21 44	22 00	22 13	22 14	22 30	22 33	22 37	22 44	23 38	23 51	00 17
	d	20 20	20 32		20 46	20 50		21 20	21 32		21 46	22 01		22 16	22 31	22 35		22 46			
Manchester Oxford Rd.	a	20 22	20 36		20 48	20 52		21 22	21 36		21 48	22 03		22 18	22 35	22 37		22 48			
Deansgate	a	20 26			20 51			21 26			21 51					22 41		22 51			

Sundays

8 December to 29 December

		TP	TP	TP	TP	NT	TP	TP	NT	TP	TP	NT	NT	TP	TP	TP	TP	NT	TP	NT	TP	NT	TP
		(bus)	◇1	◇1	(bus)		◇1	◇1		◇1	◇1			◇1	◇1	◇1 (trolley)	◇1		◇1		◇1 (trolley)		◇1
Crewe 10	84 d																						
Wilmslow	84 d																						
Manchester Airport	d	00 05	01 22	04 43	05 30	06 14	06 24	07 24	07 30	07 48	08 20	08 24	08 35	08 40	08 49	09 00	09 03	09 06	09 29	09 35	10 00	10 06	10 20
Heald Green	d					06 17			07 33			08 27						09 09				10 09	
Gatley	d					06 20			07 36			08 30						09 12				10 12	
East Didsbury	d					06 23			07 39			08 33						09 15				10 15	
Burnage	d					06 25			07 41			08 35						09 17				10 17	
Mauldeth Road	d					06 27			07 43			08 37						09 19				10 19	
Manchester Piccadilly 10	a	00 30	01 36	04 57	05 55	06 36	06 38	07 37	07 54	08 01	08 37	08 44	08 48	08 54	09 02	09 13	09 17	09 26	09 43	09 48	10 14	10 26	10 37
	d									08 03			08 50		09 03	09 16			09 46	09 50	10 15		
Manchester Oxford Rd.	a									08 05			08 52		09 05	09 18			09 48	09 52	10 17		
Deansgate	a									08 08			08 55		09 08				09 51				

		TP	NT	TP	NT	TP	TP	NT	TP	TP	NT	TP	TP	NT	TP	TP	NT	TP	TP	NT	TP	TP	NT
		◇1		◇1		◇1	◇1		◇1	◇1 (trolley)		◇1	◇1		◇1	◇1 (trolley)		◇1	◇1		◇1	◇1 (trolley)	
Crewe 10	84 d																						
Wilmslow	84 d				10 49												12 54						
Manchester Airport	d	10 30	10 35	10 44	11 06	11 20	11 30	11 33	11 55	12 00	12 08	12 20	12 30	12 35	12 55	13 00	13 09	13 20	13 30	13 35	13 55	14 00	14 09
Heald Green	d				11 09						12 11						13 12						14 13
Gatley	d				11 12						12 14						13 15						14 16
East Didsbury	d				11 15						12 17						13 18						14 18
Burnage	d				11 17						12 19						13 20						14 20
Mauldeth Road	d				11 19						12 21						13 22						14 22
Manchester Piccadilly 10	a	10 44	10 48	10 58	11 26	11 34	11 44	11 48	12 09	12 13	12 29	12 34	12 44	12 48	13 07	13 14	13 31	13 37	13 44	13 48	14 09	14 14	14 31
	d	10 46	10 50				11 46	11 50		12 14	12 30		12 46	12 50		13 16			13 46	13 50		14 14	
Manchester Oxford Rd.	a	10 48	10 52				11 48	11 52		12 16	12 34		12 48	12 52		13 18			13 48	13 52		14 16	
Deansgate	a	10 51					11 51						12 51						13 51				

		TP	TP	NT	TP	TP	NT	TP	TP	NT	TP	TP	NT	TP	TP	NT	TP	TP	NT	TP	TP	NT
		◇1	◇1		◇1	◇1		◇1	◇1		◇1	◇1 (trolley)		◇1	◇1		◇1	◇1 (trolley)		◇1	◇1	
Crewe 10	84 d																					
Wilmslow	84 d						14 54												16 54			
Manchester Airport	d	14 20	14 30	14 35	14 55	15 00	15 09	15 20	15 30	15 35	15 55	16 00	16 09	16 20	16 30	16 35	16 55	17 00	17 09	17 20	17 30	17 35
Heald Green	d						15 12						16 12						17 12			
Gatley	d						15 15						16 15						17 15			
East Didsbury	d						15 18						16 18						17 18			
Burnage	d						15 20						16 20						17 20			
Mauldeth Road	d						15 22						16 22						17 22			
Manchester Piccadilly 10	a	14 37	14 44	14 48	15 09	15 13	15 32	15 37	15 44	15 48	16 09	16 14	16 31	16 37	16 44	16 48	17 09	17 14	17 31	17 37	17 44	17 48
	d		14 46	14 50		15 14			15 46	15 50		16 14			16 46	16 50		17 14			17 46	17 50
Manchester Oxford Rd.	a		14 48	14 52		15 16			15 48	15 52		16 16			16 48	16 52		17 16			17 48	17 52
Deansgate	a		14 51						15 51						16 51						17 51	

		TP	TP	NT	TP	TP	NT	TP	TP	NT	TP	TP	NT	TP	NT	TP	TP	NT	TP	NT	TP	TP	NT
		◇1	◇1 (trolley)		◇1	◇1		◇1	◇1		◇1	◇1		◇1		◇1	◇1		◇1		◇1	◇1	
Crewe 10	84 d																						
Wilmslow	84 d									18 54										20 54			
Manchester Airport	d	17 55	18 00	18 09	18 20	18 30	18 35	18 55	19 00	19 09	19 20	19 30	19 35	19 55	20 09	20 20	20 30	20 35	20 55	21 09	21 20	21 30	21 35
Heald Green	d			18 12						19 12					20 12					21 12			
Gatley	d			18 15						19 15					20 15					21 15			
East Didsbury	d			18 18						19 18					20 18					21 18			
Burnage	d			18 20						19 20					20 20					21 20			
Mauldeth Road	d			18 22						19 22					20 22					21 22			
Manchester Piccadilly 10	a	18 09	18 14	18 31	18 37	18 44	18 48	19 09	19 13	19 31	19 37	19 44	19 48	20 09	20 31	20 37	20 44	20 48	21 09	21 31	21 37	21 43	21 48
	d		18 14			18 46	18 50		19 14			19 46	19 50				20 46	20 50				21 46	21 50
Manchester Oxford Rd.	a		18 16			18 48	18 52		19 16			19 48	19 52				20 48	20 52				21 48	21 52
Deansgate	a					18 51						19 51					20 51					21 51	

A from 15 February

B until 8 February, from 29 March

C from 15 February until 22 March

Table 85

Manchester Airport - Manchester

Sundays

8 December to 29 December

Network Diagram - see first Page of Table 78

		TP ◇1	NT	TP ◇1	NT	TP ◇1
Crewe 10	84 d					
Wilmslow	84 d				22 54	
Manchester Airport ✈	d	21 55	22 09	22 55	23 09	23 20
Heald Green	d		22 12		23 12	
Gatley	d		22 15		23 15	
East Didsbury	d		22 18		23 18	
Burnage	d		22 20		23 20	
Mauldeth Road	d		22 22		23 22	
Manchester Piccadilly 10 ⛴	a	22 09	22 31	23 09	23 32	23 37
	d					
Manchester Oxford Rd.	a					
Deansgate ⛴	a					

Sundays

5 January to 9 February

		TP 🚌	TP ◇1	TP ◇1	TP 🚌	NT	TP ◇1	TP ◇1	NT	TP ◇1		TP ◇1	NT	TP ◇1	TP ◇1 🍴	NT	TP ◇1	TP ◇1	NT	NT		TP ◇1	TP ◇1	TP ◇1	NT
Crewe 10	84 d																								
Wilmslow	84 d																								
Manchester Airport ✈	d	00 05	01 22	04 43	05 30	06 14	06 24	07 24	07 30	07 48		08 20	08 24	08 40	08 49	09 03	09 22	09 29	10 03	10 06		10 20	10 30	10 44	11 03
Heald Green	d					06 17			07 33				08 27							10 09					
Gatley	d					06 20			07 36				08 30							10 12					
East Didsbury	d					06 23			07 39				08 33							10 15					
Burnage	d					06 25			07 41				08 35							10 17					
Mauldeth Road	d					06 27			07 43				08 37							10 19					
Manchester Piccadilly 10 ⛴	a	00 30	01 36	04 57	05 55	06 36	06 38	07 37	07 54	08 01		08 37	08 44	08 54	09 02	09 16	09 36	09 43	10 17	10 26		10 37	10 44	10 58	11 17
	d									08 03					09 03	09 18		09 46	10 19				10 46		11 18
Manchester Oxford Rd.	a									08 05					09 05	09 20		09 48	10 21				10 48		11 20
Deansgate ⛴	a									08 08					09 08			09 51					10 51		

		NT	TP ◇1	TP ◇1	TP ◇1	NT		NT	TP ◇1	TP ◇1	TP ◇1	NT	NT	TP ◇1	TP ◇1	TP ◇1		TP ◇1 🍴	NT	NT	TP ◇1	TP ◇1	TP ◇1	TP ◇1	NT
Crewe 10	84 d																								
Wilmslow	84 d	10 49											12 54												
Manchester Airport ✈	d	11 06	11 20	11 30	11 55	12 03		12 08	12 20	12 30	12 55	13 03	13 09	13 20	13 30	13 55		14 00	14 03	14 09	14 20	14 30	14 55	15 00	15 03
Heald Green	d	11 09						12 11					13 12							14 13					
Gatley	d	11 12						12 14					13 15							14 16					
East Didsbury	d	11 15						12 17					13 18							14 18					
Burnage	d	11 17						12 19					13 20							14 20					
Mauldeth Road	d	11 19						12 21					13 22							14 22					
Manchester Piccadilly 10 ⛴	a	11 26	11 34	11 44	12 09	12 17		12 29	12 34	12 44	13 07	13 17	13 31	13 37	13 44	14 09		14 14	14 17	14 31	14 37	14 44	15 09	15 13	15 17
	d			11 46		12 18		12 30		12 46		13 18			13 46			14 14	14 18			14 46		15 14	15 18
Manchester Oxford Rd.	a			11 48		12 20		12 34		12 48		13 20			13 48			14 16	14 20			14 48		15 16	15 20
Deansgate ⛴	a			11 51						12 51					13 51							14 51			

		NT		TP ◇1	TP ◇1	TP ◇1	TP ◇1 🍴	NT	NT	TP ◇1	TP ◇1	TP ◇1		TP ◇1 🍴	NT	NT	TP ◇1	TP ◇1	TP ◇1	TP ◇1 🍴	NT	NT		TP ◇1	TP ◇1
Crewe 10	84 d																								
Wilmslow	84 d	14 54														16 54									
Manchester Airport ✈	d	15 09		15 20	15 30	15 55	16 00	16 03	16 09	16 20	16 30	16 55		17 00	17 03	17 09	17 20	17 30	17 55	18 00	18 03	18 09		18 20	18 30
Heald Green	d	15 12							16 12							17 12						18 12			
Gatley	d	15 15							16 15							17 15						18 15			
East Didsbury	d	15 18							16 18							17 18						18 18			
Burnage	d	15 20							16 20							17 20						18 20			
Mauldeth Road	d	15 22							16 22							17 22						18 22			
Manchester Piccadilly 10 ⛴	a	15 32		15 37	15 44	16 09	16 14	16 17	16 31	16 37	16 44	17 09		17 14	17 17	17 31	17 37	17 44	18 09	18 14	18 17	18 31		18 37	18 44
	d				15 46		16 14	16 18			16 46			17 14	17 18			17 46		18 14	18 18				18 46
Manchester Oxford Rd.	a				15 48		16 16	16 20			16 48			17 16	17 20			17 48		18 16	18 20				18 48
Deansgate ⛴	a				15 51						16 51							17 51							18 51

		TP ◇1	TP ◇1	NT	NT	TP ◇1	TP ◇1	TP ◇1		NT	NT	TP ◇1	TP ◇1	TP ◇1	NT	NT	TP ◇1	TP ◇1		TP ◇1	NT	TP ◇1	TP ◇1	TP ◇1	
Crewe 10	84 d																								
Wilmslow	84 d				18 54											20 54									
Manchester Airport ✈	d	18 55	19 00	19 03	19 09	19 20	19 30	19 55		20 03	20 09	20 20	20 30	20 55	21 03	21 09	21 20	21 30		21 55	22 09	22 30	22 55	23 20	
Heald Green	d				19 12						20 12					21 12					22 12				
Gatley	d				19 15						20 15					21 15					22 15				
East Didsbury	d				19 18						20 18					21 18					22 18				
Burnage	d				19 20						20 20					21 20					22 20				
Mauldeth Road	d				19 22						20 22					21 22					22 22				
Manchester Piccadilly 10 ⛴	a	19 09	19 13	19 17	19 31	19 37	19 44	20 09		20 15	20 31	20 37	20 44	21 09	21 15	21 31	21 37	21 43		22 09	22 31	22 43	23 09	23 37	
	d		19 14	19 18			19 46			20 17			20 46		21 17			21 46				22 46			
Manchester Oxford Rd.	a		19 16	19 20			19 48			20 19			20 48		21 19			21 48				22 48			
Deansgate ⛴	a						19 51						20 51					21 51				22 51			

Table 85

Sundays

16 February to 23 March

Manchester Airport - Manchester

Network Diagram - see first Page of Table 78

		NT	TP	TP	NT	NT		TP	NT	TP	TP	NT	NT	TP	TP	NT		NT	TP	TP	TP	TP	NT	NT	TP
		🚌	🚌	🚌	🚌	🚌		🚌	🚌	◇1	◇1			◇1	◇1 trolley				◇1	◇1	◇1	◇1 trolley			◇1
Crewe 10	84 d																								
Wilmslow	84 d																							10 49	
Manchester Airport ✈	d		00 05	05 30	06 10	07 10		07 40	08 10	08 48	09 00	09 03	09 06	09 29	10 00	10 03		10 06	10 20	10 30	10 44	11 00	11 03	11 06	11 20
Heald Green	d				06 15	07 15			08 15				09 09					10 09						11 09	
Gatley	d				06 23	07 23			08 23				09 12					10 12						11 12	
East Didsbury	d				06 31	07 31			08 31				09 15					10 15						11 15	
Burnage	d	00 01			06 36	07 36			08 36				09 17					10 17						11 17	
Mauldeth Road	d	00 06			06 41	07 41			08 41				09 19					10 19						11 19	
Manchester Piccadilly 10	a	00 17	00 30	05 55	06 52	07 52		08 05	08 52	09 02	09 13	09 16	09 26	09 43	10 12	10 17		10 26	10 37	10 44	10 58	11 14	11 17	11 26	11 36
	d									09 03		09 18		09 46	10 14	10 19				10 46		11 14	11 18		
Manchester Oxford Rd.	a									09 05		09 20		09 48	10 16	10 21				10 48		11 16	11 20		
Deansgate	a									09 08				09 51						10 51					

		TP		TP	TP	NT	NT	TP	TP	TP	TP	NT		NT	TP	TP	TP	TP	NT	NT	TP	TP		TP	TP
		◇1		◇1	◇1 trolley			◇1	◇1	◇1	◇1 trolley				◇1	◇1	◇1	◇1 trolley			◇1	◇1		◇1	◇1
Crewe 10	84 d																								
Wilmslow	84 d													12 54											
Manchester Airport ✈	d	11 30		11 55	12 00	12 03	12 08	12 20	12 30	12 55	13 00	13 03		13 09	13 20	13 30	13 55	14 00	14 03	14 09	14 20	14 30		14 55	15 00
Heald Green	d						12 11							13 12						14 13					
Gatley	d						12 14							13 15						14 16					
East Didsbury	d						12 17							13 18						14 18					
Burnage	d						12 19							13 20						14 20					
Mauldeth Road	d						12 21							13 22						14 22					
Manchester Piccadilly 10	a	11 44		12 09	12 14	12 17	12 29	12 37	12 44	13 07	13 14	13 17		13 31	13 37	13 44	14 09	14 14	14 17	14 31	14 37	14 44		15 09	15 13
	d	11 46			12 14	12 18	12 30		12 46		13 14	13 18				13 46		14 14	14 18			14 46			15 14
Manchester Oxford Rd.	a	11 48			12 16	12 20	12 34		12 48		13 16	13 20				13 48		14 16	14 20			14 48			15 16
Deansgate	a	11 51							12 51							13 51						14 51			

		NT	NT	TP	TP	TP	TP	NT		NT	TP	TP	TP	TP	NT	NT	TP	TP		TP	TP	NT	NT	TP	TP
				◇1	◇1	◇1	◇1 trolley				◇1	◇1	◇1	◇1 trolley			◇1	◇1		◇1	◇1 trolley			◇1	◇1
Crewe 10	84 d																								
Wilmslow	84 d		14 54													16 54									
Manchester Airport ✈	d	15 03	15 09	15 20	15 30	15 55	16 00	16 03		16 09	16 20	16 30	16 55	17 00	17 03	17 09	17 20	17 30		17 55	18 00	18 03	18 09	18 20	18 30
Heald Green	d		15 12							16 12						17 12							18 12		
Gatley	d		15 15							16 15						17 15							18 15		
East Didsbury	d		15 18							16 18						17 18							18 18		
Burnage	d		15 20							16 20						17 20							18 20		
Mauldeth Road	d		15 22							16 22						17 22							18 22		
Manchester Piccadilly 10	a	15 17	15 32	15 37	15 44	16 09	16 14	16 17		16 31	16 37	16 44	17 09	17 14	17 17	17 31	17 37	17 44		18 09	18 14	18 17	18 31	18 37	18 44
	d	15 18			15 46		16 14	16 18				16 46		17 14	17 18			17 46			18 14	18 18			18 46
Manchester Oxford Rd.	a	15 20			15 48		16 16	16 20				16 48		17 16	17 20			17 48			18 16	18 20			18 48
Deansgate	a				15 51							16 51						17 51							18 51

		TP	TP	NT		NT	TP	TP	TP	NT	NT	TP	TP	TP		NT	NT	TP	TP	TP	NT	TP	NT	TP	
		◇1	◇1				◇1	◇1	◇1			◇1	◇1	◇1				◇1	◇1	◇1		◇1		◇1	
Crewe 10	84 d																								
Wilmslow	84 d					18 54											20 54						22 54		
Manchester Airport ✈	d	18 55	19 00	19 03		19 09	19 20	19 30	19 55	20 03	20 09	20 20	20 30	20 55		21 03	21 09	21 20	21 30	21 55	22 09	22 55	23 09	23 24	
Heald Green	d					19 12					20 12						21 12				22 12		23 12		
Gatley	d					19 15					20 15						21 15				22 15		23 15		
East Didsbury	d					19 18					20 18						21 18				22 18		23 18		
Burnage	d					19 20					20 20						21 20				22 20		23 20		
Mauldeth Road	d					19 22					20 22						21 22				22 22		23 22		
Manchester Piccadilly 10	a	19 09	19 13	19 17		19 31	19 37	19 44	20 09	20 15	20 31	20 37	20 44	21 09		21 15	21 31	21 37	21 43	22 09	22 31	23 09	23 32	23 38	
	d		19 14	19 18				19 46		20 17			20 46			21 17			21 46						
Manchester Oxford Rd.	a		19 16	19 20				19 48		20 19			20 48			21 19			21 48						
Deansgate	a							19 51					20 51						21 51						

Sundays

30 March to 11 May

		TP	TP	TP	TP	NT	TP	TP	NT	TP		TP	NT	TP	TP	NT	NT	TP	TP	TP		NT	NT	TP	TP
		🚌	◇1	◇1	🚌		◇1	◇1		◇1		◇1		◇1	◇1			◇1	◇1	◇1 trolley				◇1	◇1
Crewe 10	84 d																								
Wilmslow	84 d																								
Manchester Airport ✈	d	00 05	01 22	04 43	05 30	06 14	06 24	07 24	07 30	07 48		08 10	08 24	08 41	08 48	09 03	09 06	09 22	09 29	10 00		10 03	10 06	10 20	10 30
Heald Green	d					06 17			07 33				08 27				09 09						10 09		
Gatley	d					06 20			07 36				08 30				09 12						10 12		
East Didsbury	d					06 23			07 39				08 33				09 15						10 15		
Burnage	d					06 25			07 41				08 35				09 17						10 17		
Mauldeth Road	d					06 27			07 43				08 37				09 19						10 19		
Manchester Piccadilly 10	a	00 30	01 36	04 57	05 55	06 36	06 38	07 37	07 54	08 01		08 24	08 44	08 55	09 02	09 16	09 26	09 36	09 43	10 13		10 17	10 26	10 37	10 44
	d									08 03					09 03	09 18			09 46	10 15		10 19			10 46
Manchester Oxford Rd.	a									08 05					09 05	09 20			09 48	10 17		10 21			10 48
Deansgate	a									08 08					09 08				09 51						10 51

Table 85

Manchester Airport - Manchester

Sundays

30 March to 11 May

Network Diagram - see first Page of Table 78

	TP ◇1		TP ◇1 🛒	NT	NT	TP ◇1	TP ◇1	TP ◇1	TP ◇1 🛒	NT	NT		TP ◇1	TP ◇1	TP ◇1	TP ◇1 🛒	NT	NT	TP ◇1	TP ◇1	TP ◇1		TP ◇1 🛒	NT
Crewe 10 ... 84 d																								
Wilmslow ... 84 d					10 49													12 54						
Manchester Airport ✈ d	10 44		11 00	11 03	11 06	11 20	11 30	11 55	12 00	12 03	12 08		12 20	12 30	12 55	13 00	13 03	13 09	13 20	13 30	13 55		14 00	14 03
Heald Green d					11 09						12 11							13 12						
Gatley d					11 12						12 14							13 15						
East Didsbury d					11 15						12 17							13 18						
Burnage d					11 17						12 19							13 20						
Mauldeth Road d					11 19						12 21							13 22						
Manchester Piccadilly 10 🚊 a	10 58		11 14	11 17	11 26	11 34	11 44	12 09	12 14	12 17	12 29		12 34	12 44	13 07	13 14	13 17	13 31	13 37	13 44	14 09		14 14	14 17
d			11 14	11 18			11 46		12 14	12 18	12 30			12 46		13 14	13 18			13 46			14 14	14 18
Manchester Oxford Rd. a			11 16	11 20			11 48		12 16	12 20	12 34			12 48		13 16	13 20			13 48			14 16	14 20
Deansgate 🚊 a							11 51							12 51						13 51				

	NT	TP ◇1	TP ◇1	TP ◇1	TP ◇1	NT	NT		TP ◇1	TP ◇1	TP ◇1	TP ◇1 🛒	NT	NT	TP ◇1	TP ◇1	TP ◇1		TP ◇1 🛒	NT	NT	TP ◇1	TP ◇1	TP ◇1
Crewe 10 ... 84 d																								
Wilmslow ... 84 d							14 54														16 54			
Manchester Airport ✈ d	14 09	14 20	14 30	14 55	15 00	15 03	15 09		15 20	15 30	15 55	16 00	16 03	16 09	16 20	16 30	16 55		17 00	17 03	17 09	17 20	17 30	17 55
Heald Green d	14 13						15 12							16 12							17 12			
Gatley d	14 16						15 15							16 15							17 15			
East Didsbury d	14 18						15 18							16 18							17 18			
Burnage d	14 20						15 20							16 20							17 20			
Mauldeth Road d	14 22						15 22							16 22							17 22			
Manchester Piccadilly 10 🚊 a	14 31	14 37	14 44	15 09	15 13	15 17	15 32		15 37	15 44	16 09	16 14	16 17	16 31	16 37	16 44	17 09		17 14	17 17	17 31	17 37	17 44	18 09
d			14 46		15 14	15 18				15 46		16 14	16 18			16 46			17 14	17 18			17 46	
Manchester Oxford Rd. a			14 48		15 16	15 20				15 48		16 16	16 20			16 48			17 16	17 20			17 48	
Deansgate 🚊 a			14 51							15 51						16 51							17 51	

	TP ◇1 🛒	NT	NT		TP ◇1	TP ◇1	TP ◇1	TP ◇1	NT	NT	TP ◇1	TP ◇1	TP ◇1		NT	NT	TP ◇1	TP ◇1	TP ◇1	NT	NT	TP ◇1	TP ◇1	
Crewe 10 ... 84 d																								
Wilmslow ... 84 d										18 54											20 54			
Manchester Airport ✈ d	18 00	18 03	18 09		18 20	18 30	18 55	19 00	19 03	19 09	19 20	19 30	19 55		20 03	20 09	20 20	20 30	20 55	21 03	21 09	21 20	21 30	
Heald Green d			18 12							19 12						20 12					21 12			
Gatley d			18 15							19 15						20 15					21 15			
East Didsbury d			18 18							19 18						20 18					21 18			
Burnage d			18 20							19 20						20 20					21 20			
Mauldeth Road d			18 22							19 22						20 22					21 22			
Manchester Piccadilly 10 🚊 a	18 13	18 17	18 31		18 37	18 44	19 09	19 13	19 17	19 31	19 37	19 44	20 09		20 15	20 31	20 37	20 44	21 09	21 15	21 31	21 37	21 43	
d	18 14	18 18				18 46		19 14	19 18			19 46			20 17			20 46		21 17			21 46	
Manchester Oxford Rd. a	18 16	18 20				18 48		19 16	19 20			19 48			20 19			20 48		21 19			21 48	
Deansgate 🚊 a						18 51						19 51						20 51					21 51	

	TP ◇1	NT	TP ◇1	TP ◇1
Crewe 10 ... 84 d				
Wilmslow ... 84 d				
Manchester Airport ✈ d	21 55	22 09	22 55	23 20
Heald Green d		22 12		
Gatley d		22 15		
East Didsbury d		22 18		
Burnage d		22 20		
Mauldeth Road d		22 22		
Manchester Piccadilly 10 🚊 a	22 09	22 31	23 09	23 37
d				
Manchester Oxford Rd. a				
Deansgate 🚊 a				

Table 85R

Mondays to Fridays

9 December to 16 May

Manchester - Manchester Airport

Network Diagram - see first Page of Table 78

Miles		TP	TP	TP	TP	TP	TP	TP	TP	NT	TP	TP	NT	NT	TP	AW	TP	TP	TP	TP	TP	TP
		MX	MX	MX	MO	MO	MX	MO	MO	FX		MX	MO	MX	MO			MX		MX	MX	MX
			◇1		◇1	◇1	◇1	◇1	◇1		◇1				◇1		◇1	◇1	◇1			◇1
		A	B	A	C	D	B	E	F	G	H	A		B		I	H	B	H	A	A	A
		🚌		🚌						🚌		🚌								🚌	🚌	🛒
—	Deansgate 84,89 🚊 d																					
—	**Manchester Oxford Rd.** 84,89 d																					
0	**Manchester Piccadilly** [10] 84,89 🚊 a																					
—	d	00ʃ05		00ʃ15	00ʃ18	00ʃ34	00ʃ42	00ʃ44	00ʃ47	01ʃ30	03ʃ44	03ʃ55	04 21	04ʃ21	04 24	04ʃ46	04ʃ49	04ʃ56	05ʃ00	05ʃ05	05ʃ20	05ʃ35
3½	Mauldeth Road d		00ʃ04																			
4½	Burnage d		00ʃ07																			
5½	East Didsbury d		00ʃ10																			
6¾	Gatley d		00ʃ13																			
8¼	Heald Green d		00ʃ17																			
9¾	**Manchester Airport** ✈ a	00ʃ20	00ʃ23	00ʃ40	00ʃ34	00ʃ48	00ʃ57	00ʃ57	01ʃ01	01ʃ55	04ʃ00	04ʃ20	04 33	04ʃ35	04 40	05ʃ04	05ʃ05	05ʃ12	05ʃ19	05ʃ30	05ʃ45	05ʃ51
—	Wilmslow 84 a																					
—	Crewe [10] 84 a																					

	NT	NT	NT	TP	TP	TP	TP	TP	TP	TP	TP	NT	NT	TP	NT	TP	NT	TP	TP	NT	NT
				TW ThO		MO			MO		FO										
				◇1	◇1	◇1	◇1	◇1	◇1	◇1	◇1			◇1		◇1		◇1	◇1		
	I	J		K	L	M	N	O	P	Q	R										
Deansgate 84,89 🚊 d																				07 28	
Manchester Oxford Rd. 84,89 d				05ʃ58	05ʃ58	05ʃ58	05ʃ58								06 58				07 24	07 32	
Manchester Piccadilly [10] 84,89 🚊 a				06ʃ00	06ʃ00	06ʃ00	06ʃ00								07 00				07 27	07 34	
d	05ʃ35	05ʃ38	05 58	06ʃ01	06ʃ01	06ʃ01	06ʃ01	06ʃ08	06ʃ08	06ʃ12	06ʃ12	06 15	06 46	06 54	07 02	07 06	07 14	07 22	07 28	07 36	07 46
Mauldeth Road d	05ʃ42	05ʃ42										06 22	06 53				07 21				07 53
Burnage d	05ʃ44	05ʃ44										06 24	06 55				07 23				07 55
East Didsbury d	05ʃ46	05ʃ46										06 26	06 57				07 25				07 57
Gatley d	05ʃ49	05ʃ49										06 29	06 59				07 27				07 59
Heald Green d	05ʃ52	05ʃ52										06 32	07 02				07 30				08 02
Manchester Airport ✈ a	05ʃ57	06ʃ00	06 14	06ʃ16	06ʃ17	06ʃ21	06ʃ22	06ʃ24	06ʃ26	06ʃ28	06ʃ33	06 39	07 07	07 12	07 22	07 29	07 38	07 41	07 46	07 53	08 06
Wilmslow 84 a	06ʃ11	06ʃ11											07 20								08 20
Crewe [10] 84 a	06ʃ46	06ʃ46											07 46								08 46

	TP	NT	TP	NT	TP	TP	NT	NT	TP	TP	NT	TP	NT	TP	TP	TP	NT	NT	TP	TP	NT	TP
																FO						
	◇1		◇1		◇1	◇1			◇1	◇1		◇1		◇1	◇1	◇1			◇1	◇1		◇1
															S	T						
	🛒		🛒		🛒	🛒			🛒	🛒		🛒		🛒	🛒	🛒			🛒	🛒		🛒
Deansgate 84,89 🚊 d							08 29										09 29			09 51		
Manchester Oxford Rd. 84,89 d		07 58				08 24	08 33			08 54	08 58				09ʃ24	09ʃ24	09 33			09 54	09 58	
Manchester Piccadilly [10] 84,89 🚊 a		08 01				08 26	08 35			08 56	09 00				09ʃ27	09ʃ27	09 35			09 56	10 00	
d	07 54	08 02	08 06	08 14	08 24	08 28	08 37	08 46	08 54	08 58	09 02	09 06	09 14	09 24	09ʃ29	09ʃ29	09 37	09 46	09 54	09 58	10 02	10 06
Mauldeth Road d				08 21				08 53					09 21					09 53				
Burnage d				08 23				08 55					09 23					09 55				
East Didsbury d				08 25				08 57				09 16	09 25					09 57				
Gatley d				08 27				08 59					09 27					09 59				
Heald Green d				08 30			08 47	09 02		09 10			09 30					10 02		10 10		
Manchester Airport ✈ a	08 12	08 22	08 26	08 38	08 42	08 47	08 53	09 07	09 12	09 17	09 22	09 33	09 38	09 42	09ʃ47	09ʃ51	09 53	10 07	10 12	10 17	10 22	10 26
Wilmslow 84 a								09 18										10 20				
Crewe [10] 84 a								09 44										10 46				

	NT	TP	TP	NT	NT	TP	TP	NT	TP	TP	NT	TP	TP	NT	NT	TP	TP	NT	TP	NT	TP	TP
									FO													
		◇1	◇1			◇1	◇1		◇1	◇1		◇1	◇1	◇		◇1	◇1		◇1		◇1	◇1
									T	S												
		🛒	🛒			🛒	🛒		🛒	🛒		🛒	🛒			🛒	🛒		🛒		🛒	🛒
Deansgate 84,89 🚊 d				10 29			10 50							11 29			11 51					
Manchester Oxford Rd. 84,89 d			10 24	10 33			10 53	10 58				11 24		11 33			11 54	11 58				12 24
Manchester Piccadilly [10] 84,89 🚊 a			10 27	10 35			10 56	11 00				11 27		11 35			11 56	12 00				12 26
d	10 14	10 24	10 29	10 37	10 46	10 54	10 57	11 02	11ʃ06	11ʃ06	11 14	11 29	11 32	11 37	11 46	11 54	11 58	12 02	12 06	12 14	12 24	12 28
Mauldeth Road d	10 21				10 53						11 21				11 53					12 21		
Burnage d	10 23				10 55						11 23				11 55					12 23		
East Didsbury d	10 25				10 57						11 25				11 57					12 25		
Gatley d	10 27				10 59						11 27				11 59					12 27		
Heald Green d	10 30				11 02		11 09				11 30				12 02		12 10			12 30		
Manchester Airport ✈ a	10 38	10 42	10 47	10 53	11 07	11 12	11 15	11 22	11ʃ26	11ʃ34	11 40	11 47	11 50	11 53	12 06	12 12	12 17	12 22	12 26	12 38	12 42	12 47
Wilmslow 84 a					11 20										12 19							
Crewe [10] 84 a					11 46										12 45							

A from 31 December until 21 March
B until 27 December, from 25 March
C from 6 January until 10 February
D from 6 January until 10 February, from 31 March
E until 30 December
F from 17 February until 24 March
G from 30 December until 20 March
H until 30 December, MO from 6 January until 17 March, from 24 March
I until 27 December, from 24 March
J from 30 December until 21 March
K from 31 December until 6 February
L until 27 December, FO from 3 January until 7 February, from 24 March
M from 30 December until 3 February
N from 10 February until 21 March
O until 7 February, MX from 11 February until 14 March, from 18 March
P from 10 February until 17 March
Q until 2 January, FX from 6 January until 6 February, from 10 February
R from 3 January until 7 February
S FX until 6 February, from 10 February
T until 7 February

Table 85R

Mondays to Fridays

9 December to 16 May

Manchester - Manchester Airport

Network Diagram - see first Page of Table 78

	NT	NT	TP	TP	NT FX	TP	NT		TP	TP	NT	NT	TP	TP	NT	TP	NT		TP	TP	NT	NT	TP	TP
	◇		◇1	◇1		◇1			◇1	◇1	◇		◇1	◇1		◇1			◇1	◇1	◇		◇1	◇1
			🚲	🚲		🚲			🚲	🚲			🚲	🚲		🚲			🚲	🚲			🚲	🚲
Deansgate 84,89 🚊 d	12 29			12 51							13 29			13 51							14 29			14 51
Manchester Oxford Rd. 84,89 d	12 33			12 54	12 58					13 24	13 33			13 54	13 58					14 24	14 33			14 54
Manchester Piccadilly 10 84,89 🚊 a	12 35			12 56	13 00					13 27	13 35			13 56	14 00					14 26	14 35			14 56
d	12 37	12 46	12 54	12 58	13 02	13 06	13 14		13 24	13 29	13 37	13 46	13 54	13 58	14 02	14 06	14 14		14 24	14 28	14 37	14 46	14 54	14 58
Mauldeth Road d		12 53					13 21					13 53					14 21					14 53		
Burnage d		12 55					13 23					13 55					14 23					14 55		
East Didsbury d		12 57					13 25					13 57					14 25					14 57		
Gatley d		12 59					13 27					13 59					14 27					14 59		
Heald Green d		13 02		13 10			13 30					14 02		14 10			14 30					15 02		15 10
Manchester Airport ✈ a	12 53	13 07	13 12	13 17	13 22	13 26	13 38		13 42	13 46	13 53	14 06	14 12	14 17	14 22	14 26	14 38		14 42	14 46	14 53	15 06	15 12	15 17
Wilmslow 84 a		13 20										14 19										15 19		
Crewe 10 84 a		13 46										14 45										15 45		

	NT	TP	NT		TP	TP FX	TP FO	NT	NT	TP	TP	NT	TP		TP	NT	TP FO	TP FX	TP FO	TP	NT	NT	TP	
		◇1			◇1	◇1	◇1	◇		◇1	◇1		◇1		◇1		◇1	◇1	◇1	◇1	◇		◇1	
													A		B		C		D					
		🚲			🚲	🚲	🚲			🚲	🚲		🚲		🚲		🚲	🚲	🚲	🚲			🚲	
Deansgate 84,89 🚊 d								15 29			15 51													
Manchester Oxford Rd. 84,89 d	14 58					15 25	15 27	15 33			15 54	15 58								16 24	16 33			
Manchester Piccadilly 10 84,89 🚊 a	15 00					15 28	15 29	15 35			15 56	16 00								16 27	16 35			
d	15 02	15 06	15 14		15 24	15 29	15 31	15 37	15 46	15 54	15 58	16 02	16 06		16 06	16 14	16 24	16 24	16 24	16 29	16 37	16 46	16 54	
Mauldeth Road d			15 21						15 53							16 21						16 53		
Burnage d			15 23						15 55							16 23						16 55		
East Didsbury d			15 25						15 57							16 25						16 57		
Gatley d			15 27						15 59							16 27						16 59		
Heald Green d			15 30						16 02		16 10					16 30				16 40		17 02		
Manchester Airport ✈ a	15 22	15 26	15 38		15 42	15 47	15 47	15 53	16 07	16 12	16 17	16 22	16 26		16 34	16 38	16 41	16 42	16 46	16 47	16 53	17 07	17 12	
Wilmslow 84 a									16 19													17 20		
Crewe 10 84 a									16 44													17 46		

	TP	NT	TP	NT	TP	NT	NT	TP	TP		NT	TP	NT	TP FX	TP	NT	NT	TP	TP		TP FX	NT	TP	NT
	◇1		◇1		◇1	◇		◇1	◇1			◇1		◇1	◇1	◇		◇1	◇1		◇1		◇1	
																		E	F		E			
	🚲		🚲		🚲			🚲	🚲			🚲		🚲	🚲			🚲	🚲		🚲		🚲	
Deansgate 84,89 🚊 d	16 51								17 51									18 47						
Manchester Oxford Rd. 84,89 d	16 54	16 58			17 28	17 33			17 54		17 58				18 24	18 33		18 50				18 58		
Manchester Piccadilly 10 84,89 🚊 a	16 56	17 00			17 30	17 35			17 56		18 00				18 27	18 35		18 52				19 00		
d	16 58	17 02	17 06	17 14	17 32	17 37	17 46	17 54	17 58		18 02	18 06	18 14	18 24	18 29	18 37	18 46	18 54	18 54		18 56	19 02	19 06	19 14
Mauldeth Road d				17 21			17 53						18 21				18 53							19 21
Burnage d				17 23			17 55						18 23				18 55							19 23
East Didsbury d			17 17	17 25			17 57						18 25				18 57							19 25
Gatley d			17 20	17 27			17 59						18 27				18 59							19 27
Heald Green d	17 10		17 23	17 30		17 47	18 02		18 10				18 30		18 40		19 02	19 05						19 30
Manchester Airport ✈ a	17 17	17 22	17 33	17 39	17 47	17 53	18 07	18 12	18 17		18 22	18 26	18 38	18 42	18 47	18 53	19 08	19 13	19 13		19 15	19 23	19 28	19 38
Wilmslow 84 a							18 20										19 23							
Crewe 10 84 a							18 46																	

	TP	NT	TP	NT	AW		TP	TP	TP	NT	TP	NT	AW	TP	NT		TP	TP FX	TP	TP	NT	TP	TP FX	NT
	◇1	◇	◇1				◇1	◇1	◇1	◇	◇1		◇	◇1			◇1		◇1	◇1	◇	◇1		
				G								H					I	J	K	L	I	I	J	I
																		🚌					🚌	
	🚲		🚲					🚲	🚲										🚲	🚲				
Deansgate 84,89 🚊 d		19 29					19 52			20 29				20 51							21 29			
Manchester Oxford Rd. 84,89 d	19 26	19 33		19 43	19 49		19 55		20 25	20 33		20 43	20 49	20 54	20 58				21 28	21 28	21 33			21 43
Manchester Piccadilly 10 84,89 🚊 a	19 29	19 35		19 45	19 52		19 57		20 27	20 35		20 45	20 52	20 56	21 00				21 30	21 30	21 35			21 45
d	19 31	19 37	19 40	19 46	19 54		19 59	20 13	20 29	20 37	20 40	20 46	20 54	20 58	21 02		21 08	21 15	21 32	21 32	21 37	21 40	21 45	21 47
Mauldeth Road d				19 53				20 21				20 53					21 14							21 53
Burnage d				19 55				20 23				20 55					21 16							21 55
East Didsbury d				19 57				20 26				20 57					21 19							21 57
Gatley d				19 59				20 29				20 59					21 22							21 59
Heald Green d				20 02			20 12	20 32				21 02		21 10			21 25							22 02
Manchester Airport ✈ a	19 47	19 53	19 59	20 07	20 18		20 17	20 39	20 46	20 52	20 57	21 07	21 18	21 17	21 23		21 36	21 30	21 47	21 49	21 53	21 57	22 10	22 10
Wilmslow 84 a				20 24								21 25												22 22
Crewe 10 84 a																								

A until 7 February, from 24 March
B from 10 February until 21 March
C from 14 February
D until 7 February
E from 10 February
F until 7 February, FO from 14 February
G until 27 December
H until 2 January, FX from 6 January until 6 February, from 10 February
I until 27 December, FO from 3 January until 14 March, from 21 March
J from 30 December until 20 March
K until 27 December, FO from 3 January until 21 March
L from 24 March

Table 85R

Manchester - Manchester Airport

Mondays to Fridays

9 December to 16 May

Network Diagram - see first Page of Table 78

	NT FX A 🚌	TP FO ◇1 B	TP ◇1 C	TP FX A 🚌		TP ◇1 D	NT D	NT FX A 🚌	TP FX A 🚌	TP ◇1 D	TP FX ◇1 E	TP ◇1 F	TP FX A 🚌	TP ◇1 D 🛒		TP FX A 🚌	TP ◇1 D
Deansgate 84,89 🚊 d		21 51	21 51							22 51							
Manchester Oxford Rd. 84,89 d		21 54	21 54				22 43			22 55				23 24			
Manchester Piccadilly 10 84,89 🚊 a		21 56	21 56				22 45			22 57				23 27			
d	21 47	21 58	21 58	22 15		22 40	22 46	22 47	22 50	22 59	23 06	23 06	23 15	23 29		23 45	23 55
Mauldeth Road d	21 58						22 53	22 58									00 04
Burnage d	22 03						22 55	23 03									00 07
East Didsbury d	22 09						22 57	23 09									00 10
Gatley d	22 14						22 59	23 14									00 13
Heald Green d	22 22	22 10	22 10				23 02	23 22		23 10							00 17
Manchester Airport ✈ a	22 27	22 17	22 20	22 30		22 57	23 08	23 27	23 15	23 17	23 25	23 26	23 30	23 46		00 10	00 23
Wilmslow 84 a	22 47						23 22	23 47									
Crewe 10 84 a																	

Saturdays

14 December to 17 May

	TP ◇1	TP ◇1	TP ◇1	NT	AW	TP ◇1	TP ◇1	TP ◇1	NT		NT	TP ◇1	TP ◇1	TP ◇1	NT	NT	TP ◇1	NT	TP ◇1		NT	TP ◇1	TP ◇1 G	TP ◇1 H
Deansgate 84,89 🚊 d																								
Manchester Oxford Rd. 84,89 d												05 58						06 58					07 24	07 24
Manchester Piccadilly 10 84,89 🚊 a												06 00						07 00					07 27	07 27
d		00 42	03 44	04 15	04 46	04 49	04 53	04 56	05 35		05 58	06 01	06 08	06 12	06 15	06 46	06 54	07 02	07 06		07 14	07 23	07 28	07 28
Mauldeth Road d	00 04								05 42						06 22	06 53					07 21			
Burnage d	00 07								05 44						06 24	06 55					07 23			
East Didsbury d	00 10								05 46						06 26	06 57					07 25			
Gatley d	00 13								05 49						06 29	06 59					07 27			
Heald Green d	00 17								05 52						06 32	07 02					07 30			
Manchester Airport ✈ a	00 23	00 57	04 00	04 30	05 04	05 05	05 08	05 12	05 57		06 14	06 17	06 24	06 28	06 39	07 07	07 12	07 22	07 29		07 38	07 42	07 45	07 47
Wilmslow 84 a									06 11							07 20								
Crewe 10 84 a									06 43							07 46								

	NT	NT	TP ◇1	NT I	NT J		TP ◇1	NT	TP ◇1	TP ◇1	NT	NT	TP ◇1	TP ◇1	NT		TP ◇1	NT	TP ◇1	TP ◇1 🛒	NT	NT	TP ◇1	TP ◇1
Deansgate 84,89 🚊 d	07 28										08 29										09 29			09 51
Manchester Oxford Rd. 84,89 d	07 32			07 57	07 58					08 24	08 33			08 54	08 58					09 24	09 33			09 54
Manchester Piccadilly 10 84,89 🚊 a	07 34			08 01	08 01					08 26	08 35			08 56	09 00					09 27	09 35			09 56
d	07 36	07 46	07 54	08 02	08 02		08 06	08 14	08 24	08 28	08 37	08 46	08 54	08 58	09 02		09 06	09 14	09 24	09 29	09 37	09 46	09 54	09 58
Mauldeth Road d		07 53						08 21				08 53						09 21				09 53		
Burnage d		07 55						08 23				08 55						09 23				09 55		
East Didsbury d		07 57						08 25				08 57					09 16	09 25				09 57		
Gatley d		07 59						08 27				08 59						09 27				09 59		
Heald Green d		08 02						08 30			08 47	09 02		09 10				09 30				10 02		10 10
Manchester Airport ✈ a	07 53	08 06	08 12	08 22	08 22		08 26	08 38	08 42	08 47	08 53	09 07	09 12	09 17	09 22		09 26	09 38	09 42	09 47	09 53	10 07	10 12	10 17
Wilmslow 84 a		08 20										09 18										10 20		
Crewe 10 84 a		08 46										09 44										10 46		

	NT		TP ◇1	NT	TP ◇1	TP ◇1 🛒	NT	NT	TP ◇1	TP ◇1	NT		TP ◇1	NT	TP ◇1	TP ◇1 🛒	NT	NT	TP ◇1	TP ◇1	NT		TP ◇1	NT
Deansgate 84,89 🚊 d							10 29			10 50							11 29			11 51				
Manchester Oxford Rd. 84,89 d	09 58					10 24	10 33			10 53	10 58					11 24	11 33			11 54	11 58			
Manchester Piccadilly 10 84,89 🚊 a	10 00					10 26	10 35			10 56	11 00					11 27	11 35			11 56	12 00			
d	10 02		10 06	10 14	10 24	10 28	10 37	10 46	10 54	10 57	11 02		11 06	11 14	11 24	11 29	11 37	11 46	11 54	11 58	12 02		12 06	12 14
Mauldeth Road d				10 21				10 53						11 21				11 53						12 21
Burnage d				10 23				10 55						11 23				11 55						12 23
East Didsbury d				10 25				10 57						11 25				11 57						12 25
Gatley d				10 27				10 59						11 27				11 59						12 27
Heald Green d				10 30				11 02		11 09				11 30				12 02		12 10				12 30
Manchester Airport ✈ a	10 22		10 32	10 38	10 42	10 46	10 53	11 07	11 12	11 15	11 22		11 32	11 38	11 42	11 47	11 53	12 07	12 12	12 17	12 22		12 26	12 38
Wilmslow 84 a								11 20										12 19						
Crewe 10 84 a								11 46										12 45						

A from 30 December until 20 March
B from 3 January until 7 February
C until 27 December, FO from 14 February until 14 March, from 21 March
D until 27 December, FO from 3 January until 14 March, from 21 March
E until 26 December
F FO until 14 March, from 21 March
G from 15 February
H until 8 February
I from 15 February until 22 March
J until 8 February, from 29 March

Table 85R

Saturdays

14 December to 17 May

Manchester - Manchester Airport

Network Diagram - see first Page of Table 78

	TP	TP	NT	NT	TP	TP	NT	TP	NT	TP	TP	NT	NT	TP	TP	NT	TP	NT	TP	TP	TP
	◇1	◇1			◇1	◇1		◇1		◇1	◇1			◇1	◇1		◇1		◇1	◇1	◇1
											🚲									A 🚲	B 🚲
Deansgate 84,89 d			12 29			12 51						13 29			13 51						
Manchester Oxford Rd. 84,89 d		12 25	12 33			12 54	12 58				13 24	13 33			13 54	13 58				14 23	14 24
Manchester Piccadilly 10 84,89 a		12 27	12 35			12 56	13 00				13 27	13 35			13 56	14 00				14 26	14 26
d	12 24	12 29	12 37	12 46	12 54	12 58	13 02	13 06	13 14	13 24	13 29	13 37	13 46	13 54	13 58	14 02	14 06	14 14	14 24	14 28	14 28
Mauldeth Road d				12 53					13 21				13 53					14 21			
Burnage d				12 55					13 23				13 55					14 23			
East Didsbury d				12 57					13 25				13 57					14 25			
Gatley d				12 59					13 27				13 59					14 27			
Heald Green d				13 02		13 10			13 30				14 02		14 10			14 30			
Manchester Airport a	12 42	12 47	12 53	13 07	13 12	13 17	13 22	13 33	13 38	13 42	13 47	13 53	14 07	14 12	14 17	14 22	14 26	14 38	14 42	14 47	14 45
Wilmslow 84 a				13 20									14 19								
Crewe 10 84 a				13 46									14 45								

	NT	NT	TP	TP	NT	TP	NT	TP	TP	TP	NT	NT	TP	TP	NT	TP	NT	TP	TP	TP	NT	NT
			◇1	◇1		◇1		◇1	◇1	◇1			◇1	◇1		◇1		◇1	◇1	◇1		
									B 🚲	A 🚲									A 🚲	B 🚲		
Deansgate 84,89 d	14 29			14 51							15 29			15 51								
Manchester Oxford Rd. 84,89 d	14 33			14 54	14 58				15 25	15 25	15 33			15 54	15 58				16 24	16 24	16 33	
Manchester Piccadilly 10 84,89 a	14 35			14 56	15 00				15 28	15 27	15 35			15 56	16 00				16 26	16 27	16 35	
d	14 37	14 46	14 54	14 58	15 02	15 06	15 14	15 24	15 29	15 29	15 37	15 46	15 54	15 58	16 02	16 06	16 14	16 24	16 28	16 29	16 37	16 46
Mauldeth Road d		14 53					15 21					15 53					16 21					16 53
Burnage d		14 55					15 23					15 55					16 23					16 55
East Didsbury d		14 57					15 25					15 57					16 25					16 57
Gatley d		14 59					15 27					15 59					16 27					16 59
Heald Green d		15 02		15 10			15 30					16 02		16 10			16 30		16 39	16 40		17 02
Manchester Airport a	14 53	15 07	15 12	15 17	15 22	15 26	15 38	15 42	15 47	15 47	15 53	16 07	16 12	16 17	16 22	16 34	16 37	16 42	16 47	16 47	16 53	17 07
Wilmslow 84 a		15 19										16 19										17 20
Crewe 10 84 a		15 45										16 44										17 46

	TP	TP	NT	TP	NT	TP	TP	TP	TP	NT	NT	TP	TP	NT	TP	TP	NT	TP	TP	NT	NT	TP
	◇1	◇1		◇1		1	◇1	◇1	◇1			◇1	◇1		◇1	◇1		◇1	◇1			◇1
						A	C 🚲	D 🚲	E 🚲						D	F						
Deansgate 84,89 d		16 51								17 29			17 51									
Manchester Oxford Rd. 84,89 d		16 54	16 58			17 26	17 28	17 28	17 28	17 33			17 54	17 58					18 24	18 33		
Manchester Piccadilly 10 84,89 a		16 56	17 00			17 28	17 30	17 30	17 30	17 35			17 56	18 00					18 27	18 35		
d	16 54	16 58	17 02	17 06	17 14	17 30	17 32	17 32	17 32	17 37	17 46	17 54	17 58	18 02	18 06	18 06	18 14	18 24	18 29	18 37	18 46	18 54
Mauldeth Road d					17 21						17 53						18 21				18 53	
Burnage d					17 23						17 55						18 23				18 55	
East Didsbury d				17 17	17 25						17 57						18 25				18 57	
Gatley d				17 20	17 27						17 59						18 27				18 59	
Heald Green d		17 10		17 23	17 30				17 43	17 47	18 02		18 10				18 30		18 40		19 02	
Manchester Airport a	17 12	17 17	17 22	17 33	17 38	17 47	17 46	17 47	17 50	17 53	18 07	18 12	18 17	18 22	18 26	18 34	18 38	18 42	18 47	18 53	19 08	19 13
Wilmslow 84 a											18 20										19 23	
Crewe 10 84 a											18 46											

	NT	TP	NT	TP	TP	TP	NT	TP	NT	AW	TP	TP	TP	TP	TP	NT	TP	NT	TP	NT	TP
		◇1		◇1	◇1	◇1		◇1		◇	◇1	◇1	◇1	◇1	◇1		◇1		◇1		◇1
				A	D 🚲	B 🚲				🚲			A 🚲	D 🚲	B 🚲				B		
Deansgate 84,89 d							19 29				19 52					20 29			20 51		
Manchester Oxford Rd. 84,89 d	18 58			19 25	19 26	19 26	19 33		19 43	19 49	19 55		20 24	20 25	20 25	20 33		20 43	20 54	20 58	
Manchester Piccadilly 10 84,89 a	19 00			19 27	19 29	19 29	19 35		19 45	19 52	19 57		20 27	20 27	20 27	20 35		20 45	20 56	21 00	
d	19 02	19 06	19 14	19 28	19 31	19 31	19 37	19 40	19 46	19 54	19 59	20 13	20 29	20 29	20 29	20 37	20 40	20 46	20 58	21 02	21 08
Mauldeth Road d			19 21						19 53			20 21						20 53			21 14
Burnage d			19 23						19 55			20 23						20 55			21 16
East Didsbury d			19 25						19 57			20 26						20 57			21 19
Gatley d			19 27						19 59			20 29						20 59			21 22
Heald Green d			19 30						20 02		20 12	20 32						21 02	21 10		21 25
Manchester Airport a	19 23	19 28	19 38	19 46	19 46	19 47	19 53	19 59	20 07	20 13	20 17	20 39	20 46	20 46	20 47	20 52	20 57	21 07	21 17	21 19	21 36
Wilmslow 84 a									20 24									21 25			
Crewe 10 84 a																					

A from 4 January until 8 February
B from 15 February
C from 29 March
D 14 December, 21 December, 28 December
E from 15 February until 22 March
F from 4 January

Table 85R

Saturdays

14 December to 17 May

Manchester - Manchester Airport

Network Diagram - see first Page of Table 78

	TP	NT	TP	NT	TP	TP		NT	TP	TP	TP
	◇1		◇1		◇1	◇1			◇1		◇1
	A				A				A	B	A
	🚲										
Deansgate 84,89 🚌 d		21 29			21§51				22§51	22§54	
Manchester Oxford Rd. 84,89 d	21§24	21 33		21 43	21§54			22 43	22§55	22§57	
Manchester Piccadilly 10 84,89 🚌 a	21§27	21 35		21 45	21§56			22 45	22§57	23§00	
d	21§29	21 37	21 40	21 46	21§58	22 40		22 46	22§59	23§01	23§55
Mauldeth Road d				21 53				22 53			00§04
Burnage d				21 55				22 55			00§07
East Didsbury d				21 57				22 57			00§10
Gatley d				21 59				22 59			00§13
Heald Green d				22 02	22§10			23 02	23§10	23§11	00§17
Manchester Airport ✈ a	21§46	21 53	21 57	22 08	22§20	22 57		23 08	23§17	23§16	00§23
Wilmslow 84 a				22 22				23 22			
Crewe 10 84 a											

Sundays

8 December to 29 December

	TP	TP	TP	TP	TP	NT	TP	NT	TP		TP	TP	NT	TP	TP	TP	NT	TP	TP		NT	TP	NT	TP
	◇1	◇1	◇1		◇1		◇1				◇1	◇1		1	◇1	◇1		◇1	◇1			◇1		◇1
	C	C																						
				🚌					🚌															
Deansgate 84,89 🚌 d																			08 53					09 51
Manchester Oxford Rd. 84,89 d																			08 56		09 03			09 54
Manchester Piccadilly 10 84,89 🚌 a																			08 59		09 06			09 56
d		00§31	04 06	05u00	05 21	05 41	06 38	06 41	07u00		07 29	07 38	07 41	07 48	08 29	08 38	08 41	08 47	09 01		09 07	09 38	09 41	09 58
Mauldeth Road d	00§04					05 48		06 50					07 48				08 48						09 48	
Burnage d	00§07					05 50		06 52					07 50				08 50						09 50	
East Didsbury d	00§10					05 52		06 54					07 52				08 52						09 52	
Gatley d	00§13					05 54		06 56					07 54				08 54						09 54	
Heald Green d	00§17					05 57		06 59					07 57				08 57						09 57	
Manchester Airport ✈ a	00§23	00§46	04 23	05 25	05 38	06 03	06 55	07 05	07 25		07 44	07 55	08 02	08 06	08 43	08 53	09 04	09 07	09 14		09 22	09 55	10 03	10 15
Wilmslow 84 a																	09 15							
Crewe 10 84 a																								

	NT	TP	TP	NT	TP		NT	TP	TP	NT	TP	NT	TP	TP	TP		NT	TP	NT	TP	TP	TP	NT	TP
		◇1	◇1		◇1			◇1	◇1		◇1		◇1	◇1	◇1			◇1		◇1	◇1	◇1		◇1
																					🚲			
Deansgate 84,89 🚌 d					10 52						11 52							12 51						13 52
Manchester Oxford Rd. 84,89 d	10 00				10 54		11 00	11 25			11 54	12 00		12 26			12 43	12 53	13 00		13 24			13 54
Manchester Piccadilly 10 84,89 🚌 a	10 03				10 57		11 03	11 27			11 57	12 02		12 28			12 45	12 56	13 02		13 27			13 57
d	10 07	10 12	10 38	10 41	10 58		11 07	11 29	11 38	11 43	11 58	12 06	12 13	12 33	12 38		12 47	12 57	13 04	13 14	13 30	13 38	13 41	13 58
Mauldeth Road d				10 48						11 49							12 54						13 48	
Burnage d				10 50						11 51							12 56						13 50	
East Didsbury d				10 52						11 53							12 58						13 52	
Gatley d				10 54						11 56							13 00						13 54	
Heald Green d				10 57						11 59							13 03						13 57	
Manchester Airport ✈ a	10 24	10 26	10 54	11 01	11 12		11 24	11 47	11 54	12 06	12 14	12 20	12 27	12 46	12 52		13 08	13 14	13 18	13 28	13 47	13 52	14 03	14 14
Wilmslow 84 a				11 17													13 19							
Crewe 10 84 a																								

	NT		TP	TP	TP	TP	NT	TP	TP	TP	NT		TP	NT	TP	TP	TP	NT	TP	NT	TP		TP	TP
			◇1	◇1	◇1	◇1		◇1	◇1	◇1			◇1		◇1	◇1	◇1		◇1		◇1		◇1	◇1
									🚲														🚲	
Deansgate 84,89 🚌 d						14 52							15 51						16 52					
Manchester Oxford Rd. 84,89 d	13 59			14 24		14 54	15 00		15 24				15 53	16 00		16 24			16 54	17 00			17 23	
Manchester Piccadilly 10 84,89 🚌 a	14 01			14 27		14 57	15 02		15 27				15 56	16 02		16 27			16 57	17 02			17 27	
d	14 04		14 13	14 29	14 38	14 58	15 04	15 13	15 29	15 38	15 41		15 57	16 04	16 13	16 29	16 38	16 41	16 58	17 04	17 13		17 29	17 38
Mauldeth Road d											15 48							16 48						
Burnage d											15 50							16 50						
East Didsbury d											15 52							16 52						
Gatley d											15 54							16 54						
Heald Green d											15 57							16 57						
Manchester Airport ✈ a	14 21		14 27	14 47	14 52	15 13	15 20	15 28	15 47	15 52	16 03		16 12	16 21	16 27	16 47	16 52	17 02	17 13	17 21	17 27		17 47	17 52
Wilmslow 84 a																		17 13						
Crewe 10 84 a																								

A from 15 February

B from 4 January until 8 February

C not 8 December

Table 85R

Sundays

8 December to 29 December

Manchester - Manchester Airport

Network Diagram - see first Page of Table 78

	NT	TP	NT		TP	TP	TP	NT	TP	NT	TP	TP	TP		NT	TP	NT	TP	TP	TP	NT	TP	NT
		◇1			◇1	◇1 🚲	◇1		◇1		◇1	◇1 🚲	◇1			◇1		◇1	◇1 🚲	◇1		◇1	
Deansgate 84,89 🚊 d		17 51							18 51							19 51						20 51	
Manchester Oxford Rd. 84,89 d		17 53	18 00			18 24			18 53	19 00		19 24				19 53	20 00		20 25			20 53	21 00
Manchester Piccadilly 10 84,89 🚊 a		17 56	18 02			18 27			18 56	19 02		19 27				19 56	20 02		20 27			20 56	21 02
d	17 41	17 57	18 04		18 13	18 29	18 38	18 41	18 57	19 04	19 13	19 29	19 38		19 41	19 57	20 04	20 13	20 29	20 38	20 41	20 57	21 04
Mauldeth Road d	17 48							18 48							19 48						20 48		
Burnage d	17 50							18 50							19 50						20 50		
East Didsbury d	17 52							18 52							19 52						20 52		
Gatley d	17 54							18 54							19 54						20 54		
Heald Green d	17 57							18 57							19 57						20 57		
Manchester Airport ✈ a	18 03	18 12	18 21		18 27	18 47	18 52	19 02	19 12	19 21	19 27	19 47	19 52		20 03	20 12	20 23	20 29	20 45	20 52	21 01	21 12	21 20
Wilmslow 84 a								19 13													21 12		
Crewe 10 84 a																							

	TP	TP	AW	NT	TP	NT	TP	AW	TP		NT	TP	NT	TP	NT
	◇1	◇1 🚲			◇1		◇1		◇1			◇1		◇1 🚲	
Deansgate 84,89 🚊 d					21 51							22 51			
Manchester Oxford Rd. 84,89 d		21 22			21 53	22 00						22 53	22 58	23 05	23 47
Manchester Piccadilly 10 84,89 🚊 a		21 25			21 56	22 02						22 56	23 01	23 08	23 50
d	21 13	21 28	21 34	21 41	21 57	22 04	22 13	22 35	22 38		22 46	22 57	23 01	23 09	23 52
Mauldeth Road d				21 48							22 53				
Burnage d				21 50							22 55				
East Didsbury d				21 52							22 57				
Gatley d				21 54							22 59				
Heald Green d				21 57							23 02				
Manchester Airport ✈ a	21 27	21 45		22 03	22 12	22 21	22 28		22 52		23 08	23 15	23 17	23 24	00 07
Wilmslow 84 a			21 50					22 50							
Crewe 10 84 a			22 13					23 13							

Sundays

5 January to 9 February

	TP	TP	TP	TP	NT	TP	NT	TP	TP		TP	NT	TP	TP	NT	TP	TP	NT	TP		TP	NT	NT	TP
	◇1	◇1	🚌	◇1		◇1		🚌	◇1		◇1		1	◇1		◇1	◇1		◇1		◇1			◇1
Deansgate 84,89 🚊 d																	08 53		09 22					
Manchester Oxford Rd. 84,89 d																	08 56	09 03	09 24				09 57	
Manchester Piccadilly 10 84,89 🚊 a																	08 59	09 05	09 27				10 00	
d	00 31	04 06	05u00	05 21	05 41	06 38	06 41	07u00	07 29		07 38	07 41	07 48	08 38	08 41	08 47	09 01	09 07	09 29		09 38	09 41	10 01	10 12
Mauldeth Road d					05 48		06 50					07 48			08 48							09 48		
Burnage d					05 50		06 52					07 50			08 50							09 50		
East Didsbury d					05 52		06 54					07 52			08 52							09 52		
Gatley d					05 54		06 56					07 54			08 54							09 54		
Heald Green d					05 57		06 59					07 57			08 57							09 57		
Manchester Airport ✈ a	00 46	04 23	05 25	05 38	06 03	06 55	07 05	07 25	07 44		07 55	08 02	08 06	08 53	09 04	09 10	09 14	09 21	09 47		09 55	10 03	10 15	10 26
Wilmslow 84 a															09 15									
Crewe 10 84 a																								

	TP	TP	NT	TP	TP		NT	NT	TP	TP	TP	NT	NT	TP	TP		TP	NT	TP	TP	TP	NT	TP	TP
	◇1	◇1		◇1	◇1				◇1	◇1	◇1			◇1	◇1		◇1		◇1	◇1	◇1		◇1	◇1 🚲
Deansgate 84,89 🚊 d	10 22			11 22						12 22					13 22					14 22				
Manchester Oxford Rd. 84,89 d	10 27			11 24				11 58		12 24		12 43	12 58		13 24			13 58		14 24		14 58		15 26
Manchester Piccadilly 10 84,89 🚊 a	10 30			11 27				12 01		12 27		12 45	13 01		13 27			14 01		14 27		15 01		15 28
d	10 32	10 38	10 41	11 29	11 38		11 43	12 02	12 13	12 29	12 38	12 47	13 02	13 14	13 29		13 38	14 02	14 13	14 29	14 38	15 02	15 13	15 30
Mauldeth Road d			10 48				11 49					12 54												
Burnage d			10 50				11 51					12 56												
East Didsbury d			10 52				11 53					12 58												
Gatley d			10 54				11 56					13 00												
Heald Green d			10 57				11 59					13 03												
Manchester Airport ✈ a	10 46	10 54	11 01	11 47	11 54		12 06	12 15	12 27	12 47	12 52	13 08	13 18	13 28	13 47		13 52	14 15	14 27	14 47	14 52	15 15	15 28	15 47
Wilmslow 84 a			11 17									13 19												
Crewe 10 84 a																								

	TP		NT	TP	NT	TP	TP	TP	NT	TP	NT		TP	TP	TP	NT	TP	NT	TP	TP	TP		NT	TP
	◇1			◇1		◇1	◇1	◇1		◇1			◇1	◇1 🚲	◇1		◇1		◇1	◇1 🚲	◇1			◇1
Deansgate 84,89 🚊 d				15 51						16 51							17 51							18 51
Manchester Oxford Rd. 84,89 d				15 53	15 58		16 24			16 53	16 58			17 23			17 53	17 58		18 24				18 53
Manchester Piccadilly 10 84,89 🚊 a				15 56	16 01		16 27			16 56	17 01			17 27			17 56	18 01		18 27				18 56
d	15 38		15 41	15 57	16 02	16 13	16 29	16 38	16 41	16 57	17 02		17 13	17 29	17 38	17 41	17 57	18 02	18 13	18 29	18 38		18 41	18 57
Mauldeth Road d			15 48						16 48							17 48							18 48	
Burnage d			15 50						16 50							17 50							18 50	
East Didsbury d			15 52						16 52							17 52							18 52	
Gatley d			15 54						16 54							17 54							18 54	
Heald Green d			15 57						16 57							17 57							18 57	
Manchester Airport ✈ a	15 52		16 03	16 12	16 15	16 27	16 47	16 52	17 02	17 13	17 15		17 27	17 47	17 52	18 03	18 13	18 15	18 27	18 47	18 52		19 02	19 13
Wilmslow 84 a									17 13														19 13	
Crewe 10 84 a																								

Table 85R

Sundays

5 January to 9 February

Manchester - Manchester Airport

Network Diagram - see first Page of Table 78

	NT	TP ◇1	TP ◇1 🛒		TP ◇1	NT	TP ◇1	NT	TP ◇1	TP ◇1 🛒	TP ◇1	NT	TP ◇1		NT	TP ◇1	TP ◇1 🛒	AW	NT	TP ◇1	NT	TP ◇1	AW	
Deansgate 84,89 🚊 d							19 51						20 51							21 51				
Manchester Oxford Rd. 84,89 d	18 58		19 24				19 53	19 58		20 25			20 53		20 58		21 22			21 53	21 58			
Manchester Piccadilly 10 84,89 🚊 a	19 01		19 27				19 56	20 01		20 27			20 56		21 01		21 25			21 56	22 01			
d	19 02	19 13	19 29		19 38	19 41	19 57	20 02	20 13	20 29	20 38	20 41	20 57		21 02	21 13	21 28	21 34	21 41	21 57	22 02	22 13	22 35	
Mauldeth Road d						19 48						20 48							21 48					
Burnage d						19 50						20 50							21 50					
East Didsbury d						19 52						20 52							21 52					
Gatley d						19 54						20 54							21 54					
Heald Green d						19 57						20 57							21 57					
Manchester Airport ✈ a	19 16	19 27	19 47		19 52	20 03	20 13	20 23	20 28	20 45	20 52	21 01	21 13		21 15	21 27	21 45		22 03	22 12	22 15	22 28		
Wilmslow 84 a												21 12						21 50					22 50	
Crewe 10 84 a																		22 13					23 13	

	TP ◇1	NT	TP ◇1	NT	TP ◇1 🛒	NT
Deansgate 84,89 🚊 d			22 52			
Manchester Oxford Rd. 84,89 d			22 54	22 58	23 22	23 47
Manchester Piccadilly 10 84,89 🚊 a			22 57	23 01	23 24	23 50
d	22 38	22 46	22 58	23 01	23 26	23 52
Mauldeth Road d		22 53				
Burnage d		22 55				
East Didsbury d		22 57				
Gatley d		22 59				
Heald Green d		23 02				
Manchester Airport ✈ a	22 52	23 08	23 16	23 17	23 40	00 07
Wilmslow 84 a						
Crewe 10 84 a						

Sundays

16 February to 23 March

	TP ◇1	TP 🚌	NT 🚌	NT 🚌	TP 🚌	NT 🚌	TP ◇1	TP ◇1	NT		TP ◇1	TP ◇1	NT	TP ◇1	NT	TP ◇1	NT	TP ◇1	TP ◇1		NT	TP ◇1	NT	TP ◇1
Deansgate 84,89 🚊 d												08 53				09 51						10 52		
Manchester Oxford Rd. 84,89 d												08 56	09 03			09 53	09 57					10 54	10 58	11 22
Manchester Piccadilly 10 84,89 🚊 a												08 59	09 05			09 56	10 00					10 57	11 01	11 25
d		05u00	05 25	06 25	07u00	07 25	08 30	08 39	08 41		08 47	09 01	09 07	09 38	09 41	09 57	10 01	10 12	10 38		10 41	10 58	11 02	11 27
Mauldeth Road d	00 04		05 36	06 36		07 36			08 48						09 48						10 48			
Burnage d	00 07		05 41	06 41		07 41			08 50						09 50						10 50			
East Didsbury d	00 10		05 47	06 47		07 47			08 52						09 52						10 52			
Gatley d	00 13		05 52	06 52		07 52			08 54						09 54						10 54			
Heald Green d	00 17		06 00	07 00		08 00			08 57						09 57						10 57			
Manchester Airport ✈ a	00 23	05 25	06 05	07 05	07 25	08 05	08 47	08 54	09 04		09 07	09 14	09 21	09 55	10 03	10 15	10 15	10 31	10 54		11 01	11 14	11 17	11 45
Wilmslow 84 a									09 15												11 17			
Crewe 10 84 a																								

	TP ◇1	NT	TP ◇1	NT	TP ◇1		TP ◇1	TP ◇1	NT	TP ◇1	NT	TP ◇1	TP ◇1 🛒	TP ◇1	TP ◇1		NT	TP ◇1	TP ◇1	TP ◇1	NT	TP ◇1	NT	TP ◇1
Deansgate 84,89 🚊 d			11 51							12 52					13 51							14 52		
Manchester Oxford Rd. 84,89 d			11 54	11 58			12 26		12 43	12 54	12 58		13 24		13 54		13 58		14 24			14 54	14 58	
Manchester Piccadilly 10 84,89 🚊 a			11 56	12 01			12 29		12 45	12 57	13 01		13 27		13 56		14 01		14 27			14 57	15 01	
d	11 38	11 43	11 58	12 02	12 13		12 31	12 38	12 47	12 58	13 02	13 14	13 30	13 38	13 58		14 02	14 13	14 29	14 38	14 41	14 58	15 02	15 13
Mauldeth Road d		11 49							12 54												14 48			
Burnage d		11 51							12 56												14 50			
East Didsbury d		11 53							12 58												14 52			
Gatley d		11 56							13 00												14 54			
Heald Green d		11 59							13 03												14 57			
Manchester Airport ✈ a	11 54	12 06	12 13	12 15	12 27		12 46	12 52	13 08	13 15	13 18	13 28	13 47	13 52	14 14		14 15	14 27	14 47	14 52	15 02	15 13	15 15	15 28
Wilmslow 84 a									13 19												15 14			
Crewe 10 84 a																								

	TP ◇1 🛒		TP ◇1	NT	TP ◇1	NT	TP ◇1	TP ◇1	TP ◇1	NT	TP ◇1		NT	TP ◇1	TP ◇1 🛒	TP ◇1	NT	TP ◇1	NT	TP ◇1	TP ◇1 🛒		TP ◇1	NT
Deansgate 84,89 🚊 d					15 52						16 52							17 52						
Manchester Oxford Rd. 84,89 d	15 24				15 54	15 58		16 24			16 54		16 58		17 23			17 54	17 58		18 24			
Manchester Piccadilly 10 84,89 🚊 a	15 27				15 57	16 01		16 27			16 57		17 01		17 27			17 57	18 01		18 27			
d	15 29		15 38	15 41	15 58	16 02	16 13	16 29	16 38	16 41	16 58		17 02	17 13	17 29	17 38	17 41	17 58	18 02	18 13	18 29		18 38	18 41
Mauldeth Road d				15 48						16 48							17 48							18 48
Burnage d				15 50						16 50							17 50							18 50
East Didsbury d				15 52						16 52							17 52							18 52
Gatley d				15 54						16 54							17 54							18 54
Heald Green d				15 57						16 57							17 57							18 57
Manchester Airport ✈ a	15 47		15 52	16 03	16 13	16 15	16 27	16 47	16 52	17 02	17 13		17 15	17 27	17 47	17 52	18 03	18 13	18 15	18 27	18 47		18 52	19 02
Wilmslow 84 a										17 13														19 13
Crewe 10 84 a																								

Table 85R

Sundays

16 February to 23 March

Manchester - Manchester Airport

Network Diagram - see first Page of Table 78

	TP	NT	TP		TP	TP	NT	TP	NT	TP	TP	TP	NT		TP	NT	TP	TP	AW	NT	TP	NT	TP
	◇1		◇1		◇1 🚲	◇1		◇1		◇1	◇1 🚲	◇1			◇1		◇1	◇1 🚲			◇1		◇1
Deansgate 84,89 d	18 52							19 52							20 52						21 52		
Manchester Oxford Rd. 84,89 d	18 54	18 58			19 24			19 54	19 58		20 25				20 54	20 58		21 22			21 54	21 58	
Manchester Piccadilly 10 84,89 a	18 57	19 01			19 27			19 57	20 01		20 27				20 57	21 01		21 25			21 57	22 01	
d	18 58	19 02	19 13		19 29	19 38	19 41	19 58	20 02	20 13	20 29	20 38	20 41		20 58	21 02	21 13	21 28	21 34	21 41	21 58	22 02	22 13
Mauldeth Road d							19 48						20 48							21 48			
Burnage d							19 50						20 50							21 50			
East Didsbury d							19 52						20 52							21 52			
Gatley d							19 54						20 54							21 54			
Heald Green d							19 57						20 57							21 57			
Manchester Airport ✈ a	19 13	19 16	19 27		19 47	19 52	20 03	20 13	20 15	20 28	20 45	20 52	21 01		21 13	21 15	21 27	21 45		22 03	22 13	22 15	22 28
Wilmslow 84 a													21 12						21 50				
Crewe 10 84 a																			22 13				

	AW	TP	NT	TP	NT	TP	NT
		◇1		◇1		◇1 🚲	
Deansgate 84,89 d				22 52			
Manchester Oxford Rd. 84,89 d				22 54	22 58	23 05	23 47
Manchester Piccadilly 10 84,89 a				22 57	23 01	23 08	23 50
d	22 35	22 38	22 46	22 58	23 01	23 09	23 52
Mauldeth Road d			22 53				
Burnage d			22 55				
East Didsbury d			22 57				
Gatley d			22 59				
Heald Green d			23 02				
Manchester Airport ✈ a		22 52	23 08	23 16	23 17	23 24	00 07
Wilmslow 84 a	22 50						
Crewe 10 84 a	23 13						

Sundays

30 March to 11 May

	TP	TP	TP	TP	TP	NT	TP	NT	TP		TP	TP	NT	TP	TP	TP	NT	TP	TP		NT	TP	NT	TP
	◇1	◇1	◇1	🚌	◇1		◇1		🚌		◇1	◇1		1	◇1	◇1		◇1	◇1			◇1		◇1
Deansgate 84,89 d																			08 53					09 51
Manchester Oxford Rd. 84,89 d																			08 56		09 03			09 54
Manchester Piccadilly 10 84,89 a																			08 59		09 05			09 56
d		00 31	04 06	05u00	05 21	05 41	06 38	06 41	07u00		07 29	07 38	07 41	07 50	08 29	08 38	08 41	08 47	09 01		09 07	09 38	09 41	09 58
Mauldeth Road d	00 04					05 48		06 50					07 48				08 48						09 48	
Burnage d	00 07					05 50		06 52					07 50				08 50						09 50	
East Didsbury d	00 10					05 52		06 54					07 52				08 52						09 52	
Gatley d	00 13					05 54		06 56					07 54				08 54						09 54	
Heald Green d	00 17					05 57		06 59					07 57				08 57						09 57	
Manchester Airport ✈ a	00 23	00 46	04 23	05 25	05 38	06 03	06 55	07 05	07 25		07 43	07 55	08 02	08 04	08 43	08 53	09 04	09 07	09 14		09 21	09 55	10 03	10 15
Wilmslow 84 a																	09 15							
Crewe 10 84 a																								

	NT	TP	TP	NT	TP		TP	TP	NT	TP	NT	TP	TP	TP	NT		TP	NT	TP	TP	TP	TP	NT	TP
		◇1	◇1		◇1		◇1	◇1		◇1		◇1	◇1	◇1			◇1		◇1	◇1 🚲	◇1	◇1		◇1
Deansgate 84,89 d					10 52					11 52							12 51					13 51		
Manchester Oxford Rd. 84,89 d	09 58				10 54		11 25			11 54	11 58		12 25		12 43		12 53	12 58		13 24		13 54	13 58	
Manchester Piccadilly 10 84,89 a	10 00				10 57		11 27			11 57	12 01		12 27		12 45		12 56	13 01		13 27		13 56	14 01	
d	10 02	10 12	10 38	10 41	10 58		11 29	11 38	11 43	11 58	12 02	12 13	12 28	12 38	12 47		12 57	13 02	13 14	13 30	13 38	13 58	14 02	14 13
Mauldeth Road d				10 48					11 49						12 54									
Burnage d				10 50					11 51						12 56									
East Didsbury d				10 52					11 53						12 58									
Gatley d				10 54					11 56						13 00									
Heald Green d				10 57					11 59						13 03									
Manchester Airport ✈ a	10 15	10 26	10 54	11 01	11 14		11 47	11 54	12 06	12 14	12 15	12 27	12 42	12 52	13 08		13 14	13 18	13 28	13 47	13 52	14 13	14 15	14 27
Wilmslow 84 a				11 17											13 19									
Crewe 10 84 a																								

	TP		TP	TP	NT	TP	TP	TP	NT	TP	NT		TP	TP	TP	NT	TP	NT	TP	TP	TP		NT	TP
	◇1		◇1	◇1		◇1	◇1 🚲	◇1		◇1			◇1	◇1	◇1		◇1		◇1	◇1 🚲	◇1			◇1
Deansgate 84,89 d				14 52						15 51							16 52							17 51
Manchester Oxford Rd. 84,89 d	14 24			14 54	14 58		15 24			15 53	15 58			16 24			16 54	16 58		17 23				17 53
Manchester Piccadilly 10 84,89 a	14 27			14 57	15 01		15 27			15 56	16 01			16 27			16 57	17 01		17 27				17 56
d	14 29		14 38	14 58	15 02	15 13	15 29	15 38	15 41	15 57	16 02		16 13	16 29	16 38	16 41	16 58	17 02	17 13	17 29	17 38		17 41	17 57
Mauldeth Road d									15 48							16 48							17 48	
Burnage d									15 50							16 50							17 50	
East Didsbury d									15 52							16 52							17 52	
Gatley d									15 54							16 54							17 54	
Heald Green d									15 57							16 57							17 57	
Manchester Airport ✈ a	14 47		14 52	15 13	15 15	15 28	15 47	15 52	16 03	16 12	16 15		16 34	16 47	16 52	17 02	17 13	17 15	17 27	17 47	17 52		18 03	18 13
Wilmslow 84 a																17 13								
Crewe 10 84 a																								

Table 85R

Sundays

30 March to 11 May

Manchester - Manchester Airport

Network Diagram - see first Page of Table 78

		NT	TP	TP	TP	NT	TP	NT	TP	TP	TP	NT	TP	NT	TP	TP	TP	NT	TP	NT	TP	TP
			◇1	◇1 (trolley)	◇1		◇1		◇1	◇1 (trolley)	◇1		◇1		◇1	◇1 (trolley)	◇1		◇1		◇1	◇1 (trolley)
Deansgate 84,89 (ferry)	d						18 51						19 51						20 51			
Manchester Oxford Rd. 84,89	d	17 58		18 24			18 53	18 58		19 24			19 53	19 58		20 25			20 53	20 58		21 22
Manchester Piccadilly 10 84,89 (ferry)	a	18 01		18 27			18 56	19 01		19 27			19 56	20 01		20 27			20 56	21 01		21 25
	d	18 02	18 13	18 29	18 38	18 41	18 57	19 02	19 13	19 29	19 38	19 41	19 57	20 02	20 13	20 29	20 38	20 41	20 57	21 02	21 13	21 28
Mauldeth Road	d					18 48						19 48						20 48				
Burnage	d					18 50						19 50						20 50				
East Didsbury	d					18 52						19 52						20 52				
Gatley	d					18 54						19 54						20 54				
Heald Green	d					18 57						19 57						20 57				
Manchester Airport (plane)	a	18 15	18 27	18 47	18 52	19 02	19 13	19 16	19 27	19 47	19 52	20 03	20 13	20 15	20 30	20 45	20 52	21 01	21 13	21 15	21 27	21 45
Wilmslow 84	a					19 13												21 12				
Crewe 10 84	a																					

		AW	NT	TP	NT	TP	AW	TP	NT	TP	NT	TP	NT
				◇1		◇1		◇1		◇1		◇1 (trolley)	
Deansgate 84,89 (ferry)	d			21 51						22 51			
Manchester Oxford Rd. 84,89	d			21 53	21 58					22 53	22 58	23 05	23 47
Manchester Piccadilly 10 84,89 (ferry)	a			21 56	22 01					22 56	23 01	23 08	23 50
	d	21 34	21 41	21 57	22 02	22 13	22 35	22 38	22 46	22 57	23 01	23 09	23 52
Mauldeth Road	d		21 48						22 53				
Burnage	d		21 50						22 55				
East Didsbury	d		21 52						22 57				
Gatley	d		21 54						22 59				
Heald Green	d		21 57						23 02				
Manchester Airport (plane)	a		22 03	22 12	22 15	22 28		22 52	23 08	23 15	23 17	23 24	00 07
Wilmslow 84	a	21 50					22 50						
Crewe 10 84	a	22 13					23 13						

Table 86

Buxton and Hazel Grove - Manchester

Mondays to Fridays

9 December to 16 May

Network Diagram - see first Page of Table 78

Miles			NT	NT	NT	NT	NT	NT	NT	EM	NT	NT	NT	NT	NT	NT	NT	NT	NT	NT	NT	NT	NT
										◇													
			A		B		C			D		E		E		E		E		E		E	
0	**Buxton**	d	05 59		06 23		06 53		07 24		07 49		08 27		09 27		10 29		11 29		12 29		13 26
3	Dove Holes	d			06 29				07 30				08 33		09 33		10 35				12 35		
5¼	Chapel-en-le-Frith	d	06 08		06 34		07 02		07 35		07 58		08 38		09 38		10 40		11 38		12 40		13 35
9½	Whaley Bridge	d	06 14		06 40		07 08		07 41		08 04		08 44		09 44		10 46		11 44		12 46		13 41
10½	Furness Vale	d	06 17		06 43		07 11		07 44				08 47		09 47		10 49		11 47		12 49		13 44
11½	New Mills Newtown	d	06 20		06 46		07 15		07 47		08 09		08 50		09 50		10 52		11 50		12 52		13 48
13¼	Disley	d	06 24		06 49		07 19		07 51		08 13		08 54		09 54		10 55		11 54		12 55		13 51
14¾	Middlewood	d			06 53				07 55				08 58		09 58				11 58				13 55
17	**Hazel Grove**	a	06 32		06 59		07 27		08 00		08 21		09 03		10 03		11 03		12 03		13 03		14 01
—		d	06 33	06 50	07 00	07 22	07 27	07 48	08 01	08 17	08 22	08 32	09 04	09 33	10 04	10 33	11 04	11 33	12 04	12 33	13 04	13 33	14 01
18	Woodsmoor	d	06 35	06 52	07 02	07 24	07 30	07 50	08 03			08 34	09 06	09 35	10 06	10 35	11 06	11 35	12 06	12 35	13 06	13 35	14 03
18¾	Davenport	d	06 37	06 54	07 04	07 27	07 32	07 53	08 06			08 37	09 08	09 37	10 08	10 37	11 08	11 37	12 08	12 37	13 08	13 37	14 05
19¾	**Stockport**	84 a	06 41	06 58	07 08	07 31	07 37	07 57	08 10	08 24		08 41	09 12	09 41	10 12	10 41	11 12	11 41	12 12	12 41	13 12	13 41	14 09
21¼	Heaton Chapel	84 a			07 15		07 41																
22¾	Levenshulme	84 a			07 18		07 44																
25¾	**Manchester Picc.** 10	84 a	06 52	07 10	07 26	07 45	07 52	08 09	08 25	08 36	08 37	08 52	09 26	09 52	10 27	10 52	11 27	11 52	12 27	12 52	13 27	13 52	14 27
—	Manchester Oxford Road	a	06 56		07 29		07 56			08 40		08 56		09 56		10 56		11 56		12 56		13 56	
—	Deansgate	a	06 59		07 32		07 59					09 00		10 00		11 00		12 00		13 00		14 00	

		NT	NT	NT	NT	NT	NT	NT	NT	NT	NT	NT	NT	NT	NT
		E		F	G	E	C	C		F					
Buxton	d		14 29		15 29		16 29	16 59	17 29	17 59	18 29	19 29	20 29	21 29	22 56
Dove Holes	d		14 35				16 35				18 35		20 35		23 02
Chapel-en-le-Frith	d		14 40		15 38		16 40	17 08	17 38	18 08	18 40	19 38	20 40	21 38	23 07
Whaley Bridge	d		14 46		15 44		16 46	17 14	17 44	18 14	18 46	19 44	20 46	21 44	23 13
Furness Vale	d		14 49		15 47		16 49	17 17	17 47	18 17	18 49	19 47	20 49	21 47	23 16
New Mills Newtown	d		14 52		15 50		16 52	17 20	17 50	18 20	18 52	19 50	20 52	21 50	23 19
Disley	d		14 55		15 54		16 55	17 24	17 54	18 24	18 55	19 54	20 55	21 54	23 22
Middlewood	d				15 58				17 58			19 58		21 58	23 26
Hazel Grove	a		15 03		16 03		17 03	17 32	18 03	18 32	19 03	20 03	21 03	22 03	23 31
	d	14 33	15 04	15 33	16 04	16 30	17 04	17 33	18 04	18 33	19 04	20 04	21 04	22 04	23 32
Woodsmoor	d	14 35	15 06	15 35	16 06	16 32	17 06	17 35	18 06	18 35	19 06	20 06	21 06	22 06	23 34
Davenport	d	14 37	15 08	15 37	16 08	16 34	17 08	17 37	18 08	18 37	19 08	20 08	21 08	22 08	23 36
Stockport	84 a	14 41	15 12	15 41	16 12	16 40	17 12	17 41	18 12	18 41	19 11	20 11	21 12	22 12	23 40
Heaton Chapel	84 a										19 15	20 15	21 15	22 15	
Levenshulme	84 a										19 18	20 18	21 18	22 18	
Manchester Picc. 10	84 a	14 52	15 27	15 52	16 25	16 52	17 25	17 52	18 27	18 52	19 28	20 26	21 28	22 28	23 53
Manchester Oxford Road	a	14 56		15 56	16 29	16 56	17 29	17 56		18 56					
Deansgate	a	15 00		16 00	16 32	17 00	17 32	18 00		19 00					

Saturdays

14 December to 17 May

		NT	NT	NT	NT	NT	EM	NT	NT	NT	NT	NT	NT	NT	NT	NT	NT	NT	NT	NT	NT	NT	NT
							◇																
		A		E			D	E		E		E		E		E		E		E		E	
Buxton	d	05 59	06 27			07 24		07 59	08 27		09 27		10 29		11 29		12 29		13 29		14 29		15 29
Dove Holes	d		06 33			07 30			08 33		09 33		10 35				12 35				14 35		
Chapel-en-le-Frith	d	06 08	06 38			07 35		08 08	08 38		09 38		10 40		11 38		12 40		13 38		14 40		15 38
Whaley Bridge	d	06 14	06 44			07 41		08 14	08 44		09 44		10 46		11 44		12 46		13 44		14 46		15 44
Furness Vale	d	06 17	06 47			07 44		08 17	08 47		09 47		10 49		11 47		12 49		13 47		14 49		15 47
New Mills Newtown	d	06 20	06 50			07 47		08 20	08 50		09 50		10 52		11 50		12 52		13 50		14 52		15 50
Disley	d	06 24	06 53			07 51		08 24	08 54		09 54		10 55		11 54		12 55		13 54		14 55		15 54
Middlewood	d		06 57			07 55			08 58		09 58				11 58				13 58				15 58
Hazel Grove	a	06 32	07 03			08 00		08 32	09 03		10 03		11 03		12 03		13 03		14 03		15 03		16 03
	d	06 33	07 03	07 32	07 48	08 01	08 17	08 33	09 04	09 33	10 04	10 33	11 04	11 33	12 04	12 33	13 04	13 33	14 04	14 33	15 04	15 33	16 04
Woodsmoor	d	06 35	07 05	07 34	07 50	08 03		08 35	09 06	09 35	10 06	10 35	11 06	11 35	12 06	12 35	13 06	13 35	14 06	14 35	15 06	15 35	16 06
Davenport	d	06 37	07 07	07 36	07 53	08 06		08 37	09 08	09 37	10 08	10 37	11 08	11 37	12 08	12 37	13 08	13 37	14 08	14 37	15 08	15 37	16 08
Stockport	84 a	06 41	07 12	07 40	07 57	08 10	08 24	08 41	09 12	09 41	10 12	10 41	11 12	11 41	12 12	12 41	13 12	13 41	14 12	14 41	15 12	15 41	16 12
Heaton Chapel	84 a		07 16			08 15																	
Levenshulme	84 a		07 19			08 18																	
Manchester Picc. 10	84 a	06 52	07 28	07 52	08 09	08 26	08 36	08 52	09 27	09 52	10 27	10 52	11 27	11 52	12 27	12 52	13 25	13 52	14 27	14 52	15 27	15 52	16 27
Manchester Oxford Road	a	06 56		07 56			08 40	08 56		09 56		10 56		11 56		12 56		13 56		14 56		15 56	
Deansgate	a	06 59		07 59				09 00		10 00		11 00		12 00		13 00		14 00		15 00		16 00	

		NT	NT	NT	NT	NT	NT	NT	NT	NT	NT	NT
		E		C		F					H	I
Buxton	d		16 29		17 29		18 29	19 29	20 29	21 29	22 56	22 56
Dove Holes	d		16 35				18 35		20 35		23 02	23 02
Chapel-en-le-Frith	d		16 40		17 38		18 40	19 38	20 40	21 38	23 07	23 07
Whaley Bridge	d		16 46		17 44		18 46	19 44	20 46	21 44	23 13	23 13
Furness Vale	d		16 49		17 47		18 49	19 47	20 49	21 47	23 16	23 16
New Mills Newtown	d		16 52		17 50		18 52	19 50	20 52	21 50	23 19	23 19
Disley	d		16 55		17 54		18 55	19 54	20 55	21 54	23 22	23 22
Middlewood	d				17 58			19 58		21 58	23 26	23 26
Hazel Grove	a		17 03		18 03		19 03	20 03	21 03	22 03	23 30	23 30
	d	16 30	17 04	17 33	18 04	18 33	19 04	20 04	21 04	22 04	23 32	23 32
Woodsmoor	d	16 32	17 06	17 35	18 06	18 35	19 06	20 06	21 06	22 06	23 33	23 34
Davenport	d	16 34	17 08	17 37	18 08	18 37	19 08	20 08	21 08	22 08	23 35	23 36
Stockport	84 a	16 40	17 12	17 41	18 12	18 41	19 12	20 12	21 12	22 12	23 40	23 40
Heaton Chapel	84 a						19 15	20 15	21 15	22 16		
Levenshulme	84 a						19 18	20 18	21 18	22 19		
Manchester Picc. 10	84 a	16 52	17 27	17 52	18 27	18 52	19 28	20 28	21 28	22 28		23 53
Manchester Oxford Road	a	16 56		17 56		18 56						
Deansgate	a	17 00		18 00		19 00						

A To Clitheroe
B To Wigan North Western
C To Blackpool North
D From Nottingham to Liverpool Lime Street
E To Preston
F To Bolton
G To Barrow-in-Furness
H from 15 February until 22 March
I until 8 February, from 29 March

Table 86

Sundays

8 December to 11 May

Buxton and Hazel Grove - Manchester

Network Diagram - see first Page of Table 78

			NT	NT A	NT	NT	NT	NT	NT A	NT	NT	NT A	NT	NT	NT A	NT	NT	NT A	NT	NT	NT B	NT	NT
Buxton		d	08 23		09 21	10 29	11 28	12 29		13 29	14 29		15 29	16 29		17 29	18 29		19 29	20 29		21 29	22 27
Dove Holes		d	08 29			10 35		12 35			14 35			16 35			18 35			20 35			22 33
Chapel-en-le-Frith		d	08 34		09 30	10 40	11 37	12 40		13 38	14 40		15 38	16 40		17 38	18 40		19 38	20 40		21 38	22 38
Whaley Bridge		d	08 40		09 36	10 46	11 43	12 46		13 44	14 46		15 44	16 46		17 44	18 46		19 44	20 46		21 44	22 44
Furness Vale		d	08 43		09 39	10 49	11 46	12 49		13 47	14 49		15 47	16 49		17 47	18 49		19 47	20 49		21 47	22 47
New Mills Newtown		d	08 46		09 42	10 52	11 49	12 52		13 50	14 52		15 50	16 52		17 50	18 52		19 50	20 52		21 50	22 50
Disley		d	08 49		09 46	10 55	11 53	12 55		13 54	14 55		15 54	16 55		17 54	18 55		19 54	20 55		21 54	22 53
Middlewood		d	08 53		09 49		11 56			13 58			15 58			17 58			19 58			21 58	22 57
Hazel Grove		a	08 59		09 55	11 03	12 02	13 03		14 03	15 03		16 03	17 03		18 03	19 03		20 03	21 03		22 03	23 03
		d	09 00	09 12	09 55	11 04	12 02	13 04	13 12	14 04	15 04	15 07	16 04	17 04	17 12	18 04	19 04	19 07	20 04	21 04	21 07	22 04	23 04
Woodsmoor		d	09 02	09 14	09 57	11 06	12 04	13 06	13 14	14 06	15 06	15 09	16 06	17 06	17 15	18 06	19 06	19 09	20 06	21 06	21 09	22 06	23 06
Davenport		d	09 04	09 16	09 59	11 08	12 06	13 08	13 16	14 08	15 08	15 11	16 08	17 08	17 17	18 08	19 08	19 11	20 08	21 08	21 11	22 08	23 08
Stockport	84	a	09 08	09 20	10 04	11 12	12 11	13 12	13 20	14 12	15 12	15 15	16 12	17 12	17 21	18 12	19 12	19 15	20 12	21 12	21 15	22 12	23 12
Heaton Chapel	84	a	09 12		10 08		12 15	13 16		14 16	15 16		16 16	17 16		18 16	19 16		20 16	21 16		22 16	23 16
Levenshulme	84	a	09 15		10 11		12 18	13 19		14 19	15 19		16 19	17 19		18 19	19 19		20 19	21 19		22 19	23 19
Manchester Picc. 10	84	a	09 23	09 33	10 20	11 23	12 26	13 27	13 33	14 27	15 27	15 33	16 27	17 27	17 33	18 27	19 27	19 33	20 27	21 27	21 33	22 27	23 27
Manchester Oxford Road		a		09 37					13 37			15 37			17 37			19 37			21 37		
Deansgate		a		09 40					13 40			15 40			17 40			19 40			21 40		

A To Southport

B To Wigan Wallgate

Table 86R

Manchester - Hazel Grove and Buxton

Mondays to Fridays

9 December to 16 May

Network Diagram - see first Page of Table 78

Miles		NT A	NT	NT	NT B	NT	NT C		NT	NT D	NT	NT D	NT	NT D	NT	NT D	NT		NT D	NT	NT D	NT	NT D	NT
—	Deansgate 84,85,89 d				07 11		08 12			09 12		10 12		11 12		12 12			13 12		14 12		15 12	
—	Manchester Oxford Road 84,85,89 d				07 15		08 15			09 16		10 16		11 16		12 16			13 16		14 16		15 16	
0	**Manchester Picc.** 10 84 d	05 50	06 21	06 49	07 21	07 52	08 20		08 52	09 21	09 52	10 21	10 52	11 21	11 52	12 21	12 52		13 21	13 52	14 21	14 52	15 21	15 52
3	Levenshulme 84 d		06 28	06 55	07 28		08 28		08 58	09 28	09 58	10 28	10 58	11 28	11 58	12 28	12 58		13 28	13 58	14 28	14 58	15 28	15 58
4½	Heaton Chapel 84 d		06 31	06 58	07 31		08 31		09 01	09 31	10 01	10 31	11 01	11 31	12 01	12 31	13 01		13 31	14 01	14 31	15 01	15 31	16 01
6	**Stockport** 84 d	06 00	06 35	07 02	07 35	08 01	08 35		09 05	09 35	10 05	10 35	11 05	11 35	12 05	12 35	13 05		13 35	14 05	14 35	15 05	15 35	16 05
7	Davenport d		06 39	07 06	07 39	08 05	08 39		09 09	09 39	10 09	10 39	11 09	11 39	12 09	12 39	13 09		13 39	14 09	14 39	15 09	15 39	16 09
7¾	Woodsmoor d		06 41	07 08	07 41	08 07	08 41		09 11	09 41	10 11	10 41	11 11	11 41	12 11	12 41	13 11		13 41	14 11	14 41	15 11	15 41	16 11
8¾	**Hazel Grove** a	06 06	06 45	07 10	07 45	08 09	08 45		09 13	09 45	10 13	10 45	11 13	11 45	12 13	12 45	13 13		13 45	14 13	14 45	15 13	15 45	16 13
—	d			07 10		08 10			09 13		10 13		11 13		12 13		13 13			14 13		15 13		16 13
11	Middlewood d			07 15					09 18		10 18				12 18					14 18				16 18
12½	Disley d			07 19		08 17			09 22		10 22		11 20		12 22		13 20			14 22		15 20		16 22
14¼	New Mills Newtown d			07 22		08 20			09 25		10 25		11 24		12 25		13 24			14 25		15 24		16 25
15¼	Furness Vale d			07 25		08 23			09 28		10 28		11 26		12 28		13 26			14 28		15 26		16 28
16¼	Whaley Bridge d			07 28		08 26			09 31		10 31		11 29		12 31		13 29			14 31		15 29		16 31
20½	Chapel-en-le-Frith d			07 35		08 33			09 38		10 38		11 36		12 38		13 36			14 38		15 36		16 38
22¾	Dove Holes d			07 40					09 43				11 41				13 41					15 41		
25¾	**Buxton** a			07 50		08 44			09 53		10 51		11 51		12 51		13 51			14 51		15 51		16 51

	NT D	NT	NT		NT D	NT E	NT	NT B	NT	NT	NT	NT	NT		NT
Deansgate 84,85,89 d	16 12				17 12			18 12							
Manchester Oxford Road 84,85,89 d	16 16				17 17			18 16							
Manchester Picc. 10 84 d	16 21	16 51	16 58		17 22	17 23	17 52	18 21	18 52	19 22	19 51	20 52	21 52		23 10
Levenshulme 84 d	16 28		17 03			17 28	17 58	18 28	18 58	19 28	19 58	20 58	21 58		
Heaton Chapel 84 d	16 31		17 06			17 31	18 01	18 31	19 01	19 31	20 01	21 01	22 01		
Stockport 84 d	16 35	17 03	17 10		17 32	17 35	18 05	18 35	19 05	19 35	20 05	21 05	22 05		23 20
Davenport d	16 39	17 06	17 14			17 39	18 09	18 39	19 09	19 39	20 09	21 09	22 09		23 23
Woodsmoor d	16 41	17 08	17 16			17 41	18 11	18 41	19 11	19 41	20 11	21 11	22 11		23 25
Hazel Grove a	16 43	17 10	17 20		17 39	17 43	18 13	18 43	19 13	19 45	20 13	21 13	22 13		23 27
d	16 46	17 11			17 39		18 13	18 46	19 13		20 13	21 13	22 13		23 28
Middlewood d		17 15					18 18		19 18			21 18			23 32
Disley d	16 53	17 19			17 46		18 22	18 53	19 22		20 20	21 22	22 20		23 36
New Mills Newtown d	16 56	17 23			17 50		18 25	18 56	19 25		20 24	21 25	22 24		23 40
Furness Vale d	16 59	17 26					18 28	18 59	19 28		20 26	21 28	22 26		23 42
Whaley Bridge d	17 02	17 29			17 54		18 31	19 02	19 31		20 29	21 31	22 29		23 45
Chapel-en-le-Frith d	17 09	17 36			18 02		18 39	19 09	19 38		20 36	21 38	22 36		23 52
Dove Holes d	17 14						18 44	19 14			20 41		22 41		23 57
Buxton a	17 24	17 50			18 14		18 54	19 24	19 51		20 51	21 51	22 51		00 07

Saturdays

14 December to 17 May

	NT A	NT	NT B	NT	NT C	NT	NT D	NT	NT D		NT	NT D	NT	NT D	NT	NT D	NT	NT D	NT		NT D	NT	NT D	NT
Deansgate 84,85,89 d			07 11		08 12		09 12		10 12			11 12		12 12		13 12		14 12			15 12		16 12	
Manchester Oxford Road 84,85,89 d			07 15		08 15		09 16		10 16			11 16		12 16		13 16		14 16			15 16		16 16	
Manchester Picc. 10 84 d	05 50	06 49	07 21	07 52	08 20	08 52	09 21	09 52	10 21		10 52	11 21	11 52	12 21	12 52	13 21	13 52	14 21	14 52		15 21	15 52	16 21	16 51
Levenshulme 84 d		06 55	07 28	07 58	08 28	08 58	09 28	09 58	10 28		10 58	11 28	11 58	12 28	12 58	13 28	13 58	14 28	14 58		15 28	15 58	16 28	16 58
Heaton Chapel 84 d		06 58	07 31		08 31	09 01	09 31	10 01	10 31		11 01	11 31	12 01	12 31	13 01	13 31	14 01	14 31	15 01		15 31	16 01	16 31	17 01
Stockport 84 d	06 00	07 02	07 35	08 02	08 35	09 05	09 35	10 05	10 35		11 05	11 35	12 05	12 35	13 05	13 35	14 05	14 35	15 05		15 35	16 05	16 35	17 05
Davenport d		07 06	07 39	08 07	08 39	09 09	09 39	10 09	10 39		11 09	11 39	12 09	12 39	13 09	13 39	14 09	14 39	15 09		15 39	16 09	16 39	17 09
Woodsmoor d		07 08	07 41	08 09	08 41	09 11	09 41	10 11	10 41		11 11	11 41	12 11	12 41	13 11	13 41	14 11	14 41	15 11		15 41	16 11	16 41	17 11
Hazel Grove a	06 06	07 10	07 45	08 11	08 45	09 13	09 45	10 13	10 45		11 13	11 45	12 13	12 45	13 13	13 45	14 13	14 45	15 13		15 45	16 13	16 45	17 13
d		07 10		08 11		09 13		10 13			11 13		12 13		13 13		14 13		15 13			16 13		17 13
Middlewood d		07 15				09 18		10 18					12 18				14 18					16 18		
Disley d		07 19		08 18		09 22		10 22			11 20		12 22		13 20		14 22		15 20			16 22		17 20
New Mills Newtown d		07 22		08 22		09 25		10 25			11 24		12 25		13 24		14 25		15 24			16 25		17 24
Furness Vale d		07 25		08 24		09 28		10 28			11 26		12 28		13 26		14 28		15 26			16 28		17 26
Whaley Bridge d		07 28		08 27		09 31		10 31			11 29		12 31		13 29		14 31		15 29			16 31		17 29
Chapel-en-le-Frith d		07 35		08 34		09 38		10 38			11 36		12 38		13 36		14 38		15 36			16 38		17 36
Dove Holes d		07 40				09 43					11 41				13 41				15 41					17 41
Buxton a		07 50		08 48		09 53		10 51			11 51		12 51		13 51		14 51		15 51			16 51		17 51

	NT	NT D	NT	NT D	NT		NT	NT	NT	NT	NT
Deansgate 84,85,89 d		17 10		18 12							
Manchester Oxford Road 84,85,89 d		17 15		18 16							
Manchester Picc. 10 84 d	17 09	17 21	17 52	18 21	18 52		19 22	19 51	20 52	21 52	23 10
Levenshulme 84 d	17 14	17 28	17 58	18 28	18 58		19 28	19 58	20 58	21 58	
Heaton Chapel 84 d	17 17	17 31	18 01	18 31	19 01		19 31	20 01	21 01	22 01	
Stockport 84 d	17 32	17 35	18 05	18 35	19 05		19 35	20 05	21 05	22 05	23 20
Davenport d		17 39	18 09	18 39	19 09		19 39	20 09	21 09	22 09	23 23
Woodsmoor d		17 41	18 11	18 41	19 11		19 41	20 11	21 11	22 11	23 25
Hazel Grove a	17 39	17 43	18 13	18 45	19 13		19 45	20 13	21 13	22 13	23 27
d		17 46	18 13		19 13			20 13	21 13	22 13	23 28
Middlewood d		17 50			19 18				21 18		23 32
Disley d		17 54	18 20		19 22			20 20	21 22	22 20	23 36
New Mills Newtown d		17 58	18 24		19 25			20 24	21 25	22 24	23 40
Furness Vale d		18 00	18 26		19 28			20 26	21 28	22 26	23 42
Whaley Bridge d		18 03	18 29		19 31			20 29	21 31	22 29	23 45
Chapel-en-le-Frith d		18 10	18 36		19 38			20 36	21 38	22 36	23 52
Dove Holes d			18 41					20 41		22 41	23 57
Buxton a		18 24	18 51		19 51			20 51	21 51	22 51	00 07

A To Sheffield
B From Wigan Wallgate
C From Blackpool North
D From Preston
E To Chinley

Table 86R

Sundays

8 December to 11 May

Manchester - Hazel Grove and Buxton

Network Diagram - see first Page of Table 78

	NT	NT	NT	NT	NT A	NT	NT	NT A	NT	NT	NT A
Deansgate 84,85,89 d					12 11			14 11			16 11
Manchester Oxford Road 84,85,89 d					12 17			14 17			16 17
Manchester Picc. 10 84 d	08 55	09 51	10 52	11 52	12 22	12 52	13 52	14 22	14 52	15 52	16 22
Levenshulme 84 d	09 00	09 58	10 58	11 58		12 58	13 58		14 58	15 58	
Heaton Chapel 84 d	09 03	10 01	11 01	12 01		13 01	14 01		15 01	16 01	
Stockport 84 d	09 10	10 05	11 05	12 05	12 33	13 05	14 05	14 33	15 05	16 05	16 33
Davenport d	09 13	10 09	11 09	12 09	12 37	13 09	14 09	14 37	15 09	16 09	16 37
Woodsmoor d	09 15	10 11	11 11	12 11	12 39	13 11	14 11	14 39	15 11	16 11	16 39
Hazel Grove a	09 17	10 13	11 13	12 13	12 42	13 13	14 13	14 42	15 13	16 13	16 42
d	09 18	10 13	11 13	12 13		13 13	14 13		15 13	16 13	
Middlewood d	09 22	10 18		12 18			14 18			16 18	
Disley d	09 26	10 22	11 20	12 22		13 20	14 22		15 20	16 22	
New Mills Newtown d	09 30	10 25	11 24	12 25		13 24	14 25		15 24	16 25	
Furness Vale d	09 32	10 28	11 26	12 28		13 26	14 28		15 26	16 28	
Whaley Bridge d	09 35	10 31	11 29	12 31		13 29	14 31		15 29	16 31	
Chapel-en-le-Frith d	09 42	10 38	11 36	12 38		13 36	14 38		15 36	16 38	
Dove Holes d	09 47		11 41			13 41			15 41		
Buxton a	09 57	10 51	11 51	12 51		13 51	14 51		15 51	16 51	

	NT	NT	NT A	NT	NT	NT A	NT	NT	NT A	NT
Deansgate 84,85,89 d			18 11			20 11			22 11	
Manchester Oxford Road 84,85,89 d			18 17			20 17			22 17	
Manchester Picc. 10 84 d	16 52	17 52	18 22	18 52	19 52	20 22	20 52	21 52	22 22	22 52
Levenshulme 84 d	16 58	17 58		18 58	19 58		20 58	21 58		22 58
Heaton Chapel 84 d	17 01	18 01		19 01	20 01		21 01	22 01		23 01
Stockport 84 d	17 05	18 05	18 32	19 05	20 05	20 33	21 05	22 05	22 33	23 05
Davenport d	17 09	18 09	18 36	19 09	20 09	20 36	21 09	22 09	22 37	23 09
Woodsmoor d	17 11	18 11	18 38	19 11	20 11	20 38	21 11	22 11	22 39	23 11
Hazel Grove a	17 13	18 13	18 42	19 13	20 13	20 42	21 13	22 13	22 42	23 13
d	17 13	18 13		19 13	20 13		21 13	22 13		23 13
Middlewood d		18 18			20 18			22 18		23 18
Disley d	17 20	18 22		19 20	20 22		21 20	22 22		23 22
New Mills Newtown d	17 24	18 25		19 24	20 25		21 24	22 25		23 25
Furness Vale d	17 26	18 28		19 26	20 28		21 26	22 28		23 28
Whaley Bridge d	17 29	18 31		19 29	20 31		21 29	22 31		23 31
Chapel-en-le-Frith d	17 36	18 38		19 36	20 38		21 36	22 38		23 38
Dove Holes d	17 41			19 41			21 41			23 43
Buxton a	17 51	18 51		19 51	20 51		21 51	22 51		23 53

A From Southport

Network Diagram for Tables 88, 89, 90, 91

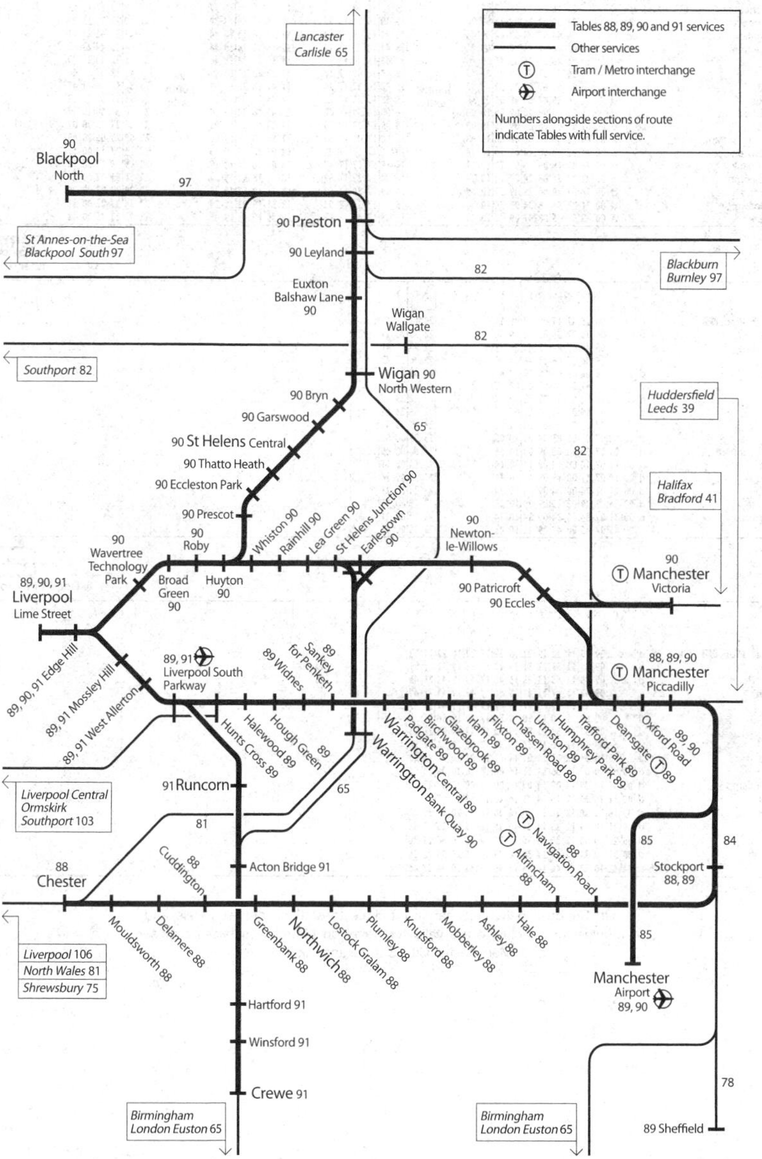

TOCs operating on this network - Virgin Trains (VT), First TransPennine Express (TP), Northern (NT), London Midland (LM) Arriva Trains Wales (ATW), East Midlands Trains (EM)

Table 88

Mondays to Fridays

9 December to 16 May

Manchester - Northwich and Chester

Network Diagram - see first Page of Table 88

Miles			NT MX	NT	NT	NT	NT		NT	NT	NT	NT	NT	NT		NT	NT	NT
0	**Manchester Picc. 10**	84 d		06 18	07 17	08 17	09 17		15 17	16 17		17 09		18 17		21 17	22 17	23 17
6½	**Stockport**	84 d		06 30	07 30	08 30	09 30		15 30	16 30	16 58	17 19	17 58	18 30		21 30	22 28	23 27
14¾	Navigation Road	d		06 44	07 44	08 44	09 44		15 44	16 44	17 12	17 33	18 12	18 44		21 44	22 42	23 41
15¼	**Altrincham**	a		06 46	07 46	08 46	09 46		15 46	16 46	17 14	17 35	18 14	18 46		21 46	22 44	23 43
—		d		06 46	07 46	08 46	09 46		15 46	16 46	17 14	17 35	18 14	18 46		21 46	22 44	23 43
16	Hale	d		06 49	07 49	08 49	09 49	and hourly until	15 49	16 49	17 17	17 38	18 17	18 49	and hourly until	21 49	22 47	23 46
17¾	Ashley	d		06 52	07 52	08 52	09 52		15 52	16 52	17 20	17 41	18 20	18 52		21 52	22 50	23 49
18½	Mobberley	d		06 55	07 55	08 55	09 55		15 55	16 55	17 23	17 44	18 23	18 55		21 55	22 53	23 52
22¼	Knutsford	d		07 00	08 00	09 00	10 00		16 00	16 59	17 28	17 49	18 28	19 00		22 00	22 58	23 57
24¾	Plumley	d	00 02	07 05	08 05	09 05	10 05		16 05	17 03	17 33	17 53	18 33	19 05		22 05	23 03	00 02
26¾	Lostock Gralam	d	00 05	07 08	08 08	09 08	10 08		16 08	17 07	17 36	17 56	18 36	19 08		22 08	23 06	00 05
28¼	**Northwich**	d	00 11	07 14	08 14	09 14	10 14		16 14	17 12	17 42	18 02	18 42	19 14		22 14	23 12	00 11
30	Greenbank	d	00 16	07 19	08 19	09 19	10 19		16 19	17 17	17 47	18 06	18 47	19 19		22 19	23 17	00 16
32¾	Cuddington	d	00 21	07 24	08 24	09 24	10 24		16 24	17 22	17 52	18 11	18 52	19 24		22 24	23 22	00 21
35¾	Delamere	d	00 26	07 29	08 29	09 29	10 29		16 29	17 26	17 57	18 16	18 57	19 29		22 29	23 27	00 26
38¾	Mouldsworth	d	00 31	07 34	08 34	09 34	10 34		16 34	17 31	18 02	18 21	19 02	19 34		22 34	23 32	00 31
45¼	**Chester**	81 a	00 43	07 45	08 47	09 48	10 45		16 45	17 45	18 13	18 35	19 14	19 45		22 45	23 45	00 43

Saturdays

14 December to 17 May

		NT	NT	NT	NT	NT		NT	NT
Manchester Picc. 10	84 d		06 18	07 17	08 17	09 17		22 17	23 17
Stockport	84 d		06 30	07 30	08 30	09 30		22 30	23 27
Navigation Road	d		06 44	07 44	08 44	09 44		22 44	23 41
Altrincham	a		06 46	07 46	08 46	09 46		22 46	23 43
	d		06 46	07 46	08 46	09 46		22 46	23 43
Hale	d		06 49	07 49	08 49	09 49		22 49	23 46
Ashley	d		06 52	07 52	08 52	09 52	and hourly until	22 52	23 49
Mobberley	d		06 55	07 55	08 55	09 55		22 55	23 52
Knutsford	d		07 00	08 00	09 00	10 00		23 00	23 57
Plumley	d	00 02	07 05	08 05	09 05	10 05		23 05	00 02
Lostock Gralam	d	00 05	07 08	08 08	09 08	10 08		23 08	00 05
Northwich	d	00 11	07 14	08 14	09 14	10 14		23 14	00 11
Greenbank	d	00 16	07 19	08 19	09 19	10 19		23 19	00 16
Cuddington	d	00 21	07 24	08 24	09 24	10 24		23 24	00 21
Delamere	d	00 26	07 29	08 29	09 29	10 29		23 29	00 26
Mouldsworth	d	00 31	07 34	08 34	09 34	10 34		23 34	00 31
Chester	81 a	00 43	07 45	08 45	09 46	10 45		23 45	00 43

Sundays

8 December to 11 May

		NT A	NT	NT	NT	NT	NT	NT	NT
Manchester Picc. 10	84 d		09 22	11 22	13 22	15 22	17 22	19 22	21 22
Stockport	84 d		09 31	11 31	13 31	15 32	17 31	19 31	21 31
Navigation Road	d		09 45	11 45	13 45	15 45	17 45	19 45	21 45
Altrincham	a		09 47	11 47	13 47	15 46	17 47	19 47	21 47
	d		09 47	11 47	13 47	15 47	17 47	19 47	21 47
Hale	d		09 50	11 50	13 50	15 50	17 50	19 50	21 50
Ashley	d		09 53	11 53	13 53	15 53	17 53	19 53	21 53
Mobberley	d		09 56	11 56	13 56	15 56	17 56	19 56	21 56
Knutsford	d		10 01	12 01	14 01	16 01	18 01	20 01	22 01
Plumley	d	00 02	10 07	12 06	14 06	16 06	18 06	20 06	22 06
Lostock Gralam	d	00 05	10 09	12 09	14 09	16 09	18 09	20 09	22 09
Northwich	d	00 11	10 15	12 15	14 15	16 15	18 15	20 15	22 15
Greenbank	d	00 16	10 20	12 20	14 20	16 20	18 20	20 20	22 20
Cuddington	d	00 21	10 25	12 25	14 25	16 25	18 25	20 25	22 25
Delamere	d	00 26	10 30	12 30	14 30	16 30	18 30	20 30	22 30
Mouldsworth	d	00 31	10 35	12 35	14 35	16 35	18 35	20 35	22 35
Chester	81 a	00 43	10 47	12 46	14 46	16 48	18 46	20 46	22 46

A not 8 December

On Sundays only, National Rail Tickets to stations between Hale and Mouldsworth inclusive are valid for travel on Metrolink services between Manchester City Centre and Altrincham

Table 88R

Chester and Northwich - Manchester

Mondays to Fridays
9 December to 16 May

Network Diagram - see first Page of Table 88

Miles	Station			NT	NT	NT	NT	NT		NT	NT	NT	NT	NT
0	**Chester**	81	d	06 02	06 33	06 58	07 33	08 04		18 04	19 04	20 04	21 30	22 48
6½	Mouldsworth		d	06 13	06 44	07 10	07 44	08 15		18 15	19 15	20 15	21 42	22 59
9½	Delamere		d	06 18	06 49	07 15	07 49	08 20		18 20	19 20	20 20	21 47	23 04
12½	Cuddington		d	06 23	06 54	07 19	07 54	08 25		18 25	19 25	20 25	21 51	23 09
15¼	Greenbank		d	06 28	06 59	07 24	07 59	08 30		18 30	19 30	20 30	21 56	23 14
17	**Northwich**		d	06 33	07 04	07 29	08 04	08 35		18 35	19 35	20 35	22 01	23 19
18½	Lostock Gralam		d	06 36	07 07	07 32	08 07	08 38	and	18 38	19 38	20 38	22 04	23 22
20½	Plumley		d	06 40	07 11	07 36	08 11	08 42	hourly	18 42	19 42	20 42	22 08	23 26
23	Knutsford		d	06 45	07 16	07 42	08 16	08 47	until	18 47	19 47	20 47	22 14	23 31
26¾	Mobberley		d	06 49	07 21	07 46	08 21	08 52		18 52	19 52	20 52	22 18	23 36
27½	Ashley		d	06 53	07 24	07 50	08 24	08 55		18 55	19 55	20 55	22 22	23 39
29¼	Hale		d	06 56	07 28	07 54	08 28	08 59		18 59	19 59	20 59	22 25	23 42
30	**Altrincham**	🚋	a	07 01	07 32	07 58	08 32	09 03		19 03	20 03	21 03	22 30	23 47
—			d	07 01	07 33	07 59	08 33	09 04		19 04	20 04	21 04	22 30	23 47
30½	Navigation Road	🚋	d	07 04	07 35	08 01	08 35	09 06		19 06	20 06	21 06	22 33	23 49
38¾	**Stockport**	84	a	07 18	07 56	08 19	08 56	09 21		19 21	20 21	21 21	22 47	00 03
44¾	**Manchester Picc.** 10	81 🚋	a	07 30		08 29		09 35		19 35	20 34	21 34	22 59	00 18

Saturdays
14 December to 17 May

Station			NT	NT	NT		NT	NT	NT	NT	NT A	NT B
Chester	81	d	06 02	06 58	08 04		18 04	19 04	20 04	21 30	22 48	22 48
Mouldsworth		d	06 13	07 10	08 15		18 15	19 15	20 15	21 42	22 59	22 59
Delamere		d	06 18	07 15	08 20		18 20	19 20	20 20	21 47	23 04	23 04
Cuddington		d	06 23	07 19	08 25		18 25	19 25	20 25	21 51	23 09	23 09
Greenbank		d	06 28	07 24	08 30		18 30	19 30	20 30	21 56	23 14	23 14
Northwich		d	06 33	07 29	08 35		18 35	19 35	20 35	22 01	23 19	23 19
Lostock Gralam		d	06 36	07 32	08 38	and	18 38	19 38	20 38	22 04	23 22	23 22
Plumley		d	06 40	07 36	08 42	hourly	18 42	19 42	20 42	22 08	23 26	23 26
Knutsford		d	06 45	07 42	08 47	until	18 47	19 47	20 47	22 14	23 31	23 31
Mobberley		d	06 49	07 46	08 52		18 52	19 52	20 52	22 18	23 36	23 36
Ashley		d	06 53	07 50	08 55		18 55	19 55	20 55	22 22	23 39	23 39
Hale		d	06 56	07 54	08 59		18 59	19 59	20 59	22 25	23 42	23 42
Altrincham	🚋	a	07 01	07 58	09 03		19 03	20 03	21 03	22 30	23 47	23 47
		d	07 01	07 59	09 04		19 04	20 04	21 04	22 30	23 47	23 47
Navigation Road	🚋	d	07 04	08 01	09 06		19 06	20 06	21 06	22 33	23 49	23 49
Stockport	84	a	07 18	08 19	09 21		19 21	20 21	21 21	22 47	00 03	00 04
Manchester Picc. 10	81 🚋	a	07 30	08 29	09 35		19 35	20 34	21 34	22 59	00 16	

Sundays
8 December to 11 May

Station			NT	NT	NT	NT	NT	NT	NT
Chester	81	d	09 01	11 04	13 04	15 04	17 04	19 04	21 04
Mouldsworth		d	09 12	11 15	13 15	15 15	17 15	19 15	21 15
Delamere		d	09 17	11 20	13 20	15 20	17 20	19 20	21 20
Cuddington		d	09 21	11 25	13 25	15 25	17 25	19 25	21 25
Greenbank		d	09 26	11 30	13 30	15 30	17 30	19 30	21 30
Northwich		d	09 31	11 35	13 35	15 35	17 35	19 35	21 35
Lostock Gralam		d		11 38	13 38	15 38	17 38	19 38	21 38
Plumley		d	09 36	11 42	13 42	15 42	17 42	19 42	21 42
Knutsford		d	09 41	11 47	13 47	15 47	17 47	19 47	21 47
Mobberley		d	09 45	11 52	13 52	15 52	17 52	19 52	21 52
Ashley		d		11 55	13 55	15 55	17 55	19 55	21 55
Hale		d	09 50	11 59	13 59	15 59	17 59	19 59	21 59
Altrincham	🚋	a	09 55	12 03	14 03	16 03	18 03	20 03	22 03
		d	09 55	12 04	14 04	16 04	18 04	20 04	22 04
Navigation Road	🚋	d	09 57	12 06	14 06	16 06	18 06	20 06	22 06
Stockport	84	a	10 12	12 21	14 21	16 21	18 21	20 21	22 21
Manchester Picc. 10	81 🚋	a	10 22	12 32	14 33	16 33	18 33	20 33	22 33

A until 8 February, from 29 March
B from 15 February until 22 March

On Sundays only, National Rail Tickets from stations between Mouldsworth and Hale inclusive are valid for travel on Metrolink services between Altrincham and Manchester City Centre

Table 89

Mondays to Fridays

9 December to 16 May

Manchester Airport and Manchester - Warrington Central - Liverpool

Network Diagram - see first Page of Table 88

Miles	Station		NT MX A	NT B	NT MX C	NT	NT	NT	NT	NT	TP ◇[1]		NT	EM ◇ D	NT	NT	TP ◇[1] E [trolley]	NT	EM ◇ D	NT	NT		TP ◇[1] F [trolley]	NT	EM ◇ D
0	**Manchester Airport** 85 ✈	d		04 38						06 41						07 38					08 41				
—	Sheffield [7] 78	d												06 20					07 32						08 41
—	Stockport 84	d												07 22					08 24						09 25
9¾	**ManchesterPicc** [10] 78,84,85	d		04 53	04 53				06 47	06 58	07 07			07 34		07 59	08 07		08 37		09 01		09 07		09 37
10¼	**Manchester Oxford Road** 84,85	d						06 22	06 50	07 01	07 10			07 37	07 39	08 03	08 12	08 15	08 41	08 44	09 04		09 12	09 16	09 41
10¾	Deansgate 84,85	d						06 24							07 41			08 17		08 46				09 18	
13¾	Trafford Park	d						06 29							07 46									09 23	
14½	Humphrey Park	d						06 31																09 25	
15¾	Urmston	d						06 33	06 57						07 49			08 24		08 52				09 27	
16¼	Chassen Road	d						06 35										08 26							
16¾	Flixton	d						06 38							07 52			08 28						09 30	
19	Irlam	d						06 42	07 02						07 56			08 32		08 57				09 34	
20¼	Glazebrook	d						06 45							07 59			08 35							
23	Birchwood	d						06 49	07 08		07 23				08 04		08 25	08 40		09 03			09 25	09 40	
24½	Padgate	d						06 52							08 07					09 06					
26¼	**Warrington Central**	a						06 56	07 16		07 27			07 53	08 10		08 30	08 45	08 57	09 09			09 30	09 45	09 57
—		d	00 02			06 03	06 37	06 56			07 28		07 35	07 53	08 11		08 30	08 45	08 57	09 10			09 30	09 45	09 57
28¾	Sankey for Penketh	d	00 05			06 07	06 41	07 00					07 39		08 15					09 14					
32½	Widnes	d	00 11			06 12	06 46	07 06					07 44	08 01	08 20			08 53	09 05	09 19				09 53	10 05
34¼	Hough Green	d	00 13			06 15	06 49	07 09					07 47	08 05	08 24			08 56		09 23				09 56	
36½	Halewood	d	00 18			06 20	06 54	07 13					07 52		08 28					09 27					
37½	Hunts Cross 103	d	00 21			06 23	06 57	07 17					07 55	08s10	08 32					09 30					
39¼	L'pool Sth Parkway [7] 91,103 ✈	d	00 27			06 27	07 01	07 22					07 59	08 18	08 37		08 47	09 06	09 15	09 36			09 47	10 06	10 15
40¼	West Allerton 91	a				06 31	07 05	07 25					08 03		08 40			09 09		09 39				10 09	
41	Mossley Hill 91	a				06 33	07 07	07 28					08 06		08 43			09 12		09 41				10 12	
43	Edge Hill 90,91	a				06 39	07 13	07 34					08 11		08 48					09 47					
44¾	**Liverpool Lime Street** [10] 90,91	a	00 41	05 38	05 38	06 45	07 18	07 40		07 49	07 53		08 18	08 31	08 55	08 59	08 58	09 24	09 31	09 53	09 48		09 58	10 24	10 31

Station		NT	NT	TP ◇[1] G [trolley]	NT	EM ◇ H	NT		NT	TP ◇[1] G [trolley]	NT	EM ◇ H	NT	NT	TP ◇[1] G [trolley]	NT	EM ◇ H		NT	NT	TP ◇[1] G [trolley]	NT	EM ◇ H	NT	NT
Manchester Airport 85 ✈	d		09 41						10 41					11 41						12 41					13 41
Sheffield [7] 78	d					09 41						10 41					11 41						12 40		
Stockport 84	d					10 26						11 26					12 25						13 26		
ManchesterPicc [10] 78,84,85	d		10 01	10 07		10 37			11 01	11 07		11 37		12 01	12 07		12 37			13 01	13 07		13 37		14 01
Manchester Oxford Road 84,85	d	09 44	10 04	10 12	10 16	10 41	10 44		11 04	11 12	11 16	11 41	11 44	12 04	12 12	12 16	12 41		12 44	13 04	13 12	13 16	13 41	13 44	14 04
Deansgate 84,85	d	09 46			10 18		10 46				11 18		11 46			12 18			12 46			13 18		13 46	
Trafford Park	d										11 23											13 23			
Humphrey Park	d										11 25											13 25			
Urmston	d	09 52			10 24		10 52				11 27		11 52			12 24			12 52			13 27		13 52	
Chassen Road	d				10 26											12 26									
Flixton	d				10 29						11 30					12 29						13 30			
Irlam	d	09 57			10 33		10 57				11 34		11 57			12 33			12 57			13 34		13 57	
Glazebrook	d				10 36											12 36									
Birchwood	d	10 03		10 25	10 40		11 03			11 25	11 40		12 03		12 25	12 40			13 03		13 25	13 40		14 03	
Padgate	d	10 06					11 06						12 06						13 06					14 06	
Warrington Central	a	10 09		10 30	10 45	10 57	11 09			11 30	11 45	11 57	12 09		12 30	12 45	12 57		13 09		13 30	13 45	13 57	14 09	
	d	10 10		10 30	10 46	10 57	11 10			11 30	11 45	11 57	12 10		12 30	12 46	12 57		13 10		13 30	13 45	13 57	14 10	
Sankey for Penketh	d	10 14					11 14						12 14						13 14					14 14	
Widnes	d	10 19			10 54	11 05	11 19				11 53	12 05	12 19			12 54	13 05		13 19			13 53	14 05	14 19	
Hough Green	d	10 23			10 57		11 23				11 56		12 23			12 57			13 23			13 56		14 23	
Halewood	d	10 27					11 27						12 27						13 27					14 27	
Hunts Cross 103	d	10 30					11 30						12 30						13 30					14 30	
L'pool Sth Parkway [7] 91,103 ✈	d	10 36		10 47	11 06	11 15	11 36			11 47	12 06	12 15	12 36		12 47	13 06	13 15		13 36		13 47	14 06	14 15	14 36	
West Allerton 91	a	10 39			11 09		11 39				12 09		12 39			13 09			13 39			14 09		14 39	
Mossley Hill 91	a	10 41			11 12		11 41				12 12		12 41			13 12			13 41			14 12		14 41	
Edge Hill 90,91	a	10 47					11 47						12 47						13 47					14 47	
Liverpool Lime Street [10] 90,91	a	10 53	10 48	10 58	11 24	11 31	11 53		11 48	11 58	12 24	12 31	12 52	12 48	12 58	13 24	13 31		13 53	13 48	13 58	14 24	14 31	14 53	14 48

A From Manchester Oxford Road
B until 30 December, MO from 6 January until 17 March, from 24 March
C from 31 December until 21 March
D From Nottingham
E From Hull
F From Newcastle
G From Scarborough
H From Norwich

Table 89

Mondays to Fridays

9 December to 16 May

Manchester Airport and Manchester - Warrington Central - Liverpool

Network Diagram - see first Page of Table 88

		TP	NT	EM	NT	NT	TP	NT	EM		NT	NT	TP	NT	EM	NT	NT	TP	NT		EM	NT	NT	TP	NT
		◇1		◇			◇1		◇				◇1		◇			◇1			◇			◇1	
		A		B			A		B				A		B			A			B			A	
		🛒					🛒						🛒					🛒						🛒	
Manchester Airport 85 ✈	d					14 41						15 41					16 41						17 41		
Sheffield 7 78 🚋	d			13 43					14 40						15 41						16 41				
Stockport 84	d			14 26					15 26						16 26						17 26				
ManchesterPicc 10 78,84,85 🚋	d	14 07		14 37		15 01	15 07		15 37			16 01	16 07		16 37		17 01	17 07			17 37		18 01	18 07	
Manchester Oxford Road 84,85	d	14 12	14 16	14 41	14 44	15 04	15 12	15 16	15 41		15 44	16 04	16 12	16 16	16 41	16 44	17 04	17 11	17 15		17 42	17 44	18 04	18 12	18 16
Deansgate 84,85 🚋	d		14 18		14 46			15 18			15 46			16 18		16 46			17 17			17 46			18 18
Trafford Park	d							15 23								16 51			17 22			17 51			18 23
Humphrey Park	d							15 25											17 24			17 53			18 25
Urmston	d		14 24		14 52			15 27			15 52			16 24		16 54			17 27			17 55			18 27
Chassen Road	d		14 26											16 26					17 29			17 57			18 29
Flixton	d		14 29					15 30						16 29		16 57			17 31			18 00			18 32
Irlam	d		14 33		14 57			15 34			15 57			16 33		17 01			17 35		17 52	18 04			18 36
Glazebrook	d		14 36											16 36					17 38			18 07			
Birchwood	d	14 25	14 40		15 03		15 25	15 40			16 03		16 25	16 40		17 07		17 25	17 43		17 58	18 11		18 25	18 41
Padgate	d				15 06						16 06			16 43		17 10			17 46			18 14			
Warrington Central	a	14 30	14 45	14 57	15 09		15 30	15 45	15 57		16 09		16 30	16 47	16 57	17 13		17 30	17 50		18 03	18 18		18 30	18 46
	d	14 30	14 46	14 57	15 10		15 30	15 45	15 57		16 10		16 30	16 47	16 57	17 14		17 30	17 50		18 03	18 18		18 30	18 47
Sankey for Penketh	d				15 14						16 14					17 18			17 54						18 51
Widnes	d		14 54	15 05	15 19			15 53	16 05		16 19			16 55	17 05	17 23			18 00		18 11				18 56
Hough Green	d		14 57		15 23			15 56			16 23			16 58		17 27			18 03			18 28			18 59
Halewood	d				15 27			16 01			16 27					17 31			18 07						19 04
Hunts Cross 103	d				15 30						16 30					17 34			18 10			18 33			19 07
L'pool Sth Parkway 7 91,103 ✈	d	14 47	15 06	15 15	15 36		15 47	16 07	16 15		16 38		16 47	17 07	17 15	17 38		17 47	18 15		18 22	18 38		18 47	19 13
West Allerton 91	a		15 09		15 39			16 10			16 41			17 10		17 41			18 19			18 41			19 16
Mossley Hill 91	a		15 12		15 41			16 13			16 43			17 13		17 44			18 21			18 44			19 18
Edge Hill 90,91	a				15 47						16 49					17 49			18 30			18 50			19 26
Liverpool Lime Street 10 90,91	a	14 58	15 24	15 31	15 53	15 48	15 58	16 25	16 31		16 55	16 48	16 58	17 25	17 31	17 58	17 48	18 01	18 38		18 35	18 57	18 59	19 01	19 35

		EM	NT	NT	TP		NT	EM	NT	NT	TP	NT	EM	NT	TP		NT	NT	NT	NT	TP	NT	NT		
																		FX	FO	FO					
		◇			◇1			◇			◇1		◇		◇1						◇1				
		B			A			B			A		B		A						A				
					🛒																				
Manchester Airport 85 ✈	d			18 41						19 41										21 41					
Sheffield 7 78 🚋	d	17 41						18 42					19 40												
Stockport 84	d	18 26						19 26					20 26												
ManchesterPicc 10 78,84,85 🚋	d	18 37		19 01	19 07			19 37		20 01	20 07		20 37		21 07			21 38	21 40	22 01	22 07				
Manchester Oxford Road 84,85	d	18 41	18 44	19 04	19 12			19 41	19 44	20 04	20 12		20 41	20 44	21 12			21 44	21 44	22 04	22 12		23 27		
Deansgate 84,85 🚋	d		18 46						19 46					20 46				21 46	21 46				23 29		
Trafford Park	d		18 51						19 51					20 51				21 51	21 51				23 34		
Humphrey Park	d		18 53						19 53					20 53				21 53	21 53				23 36		
Urmston	d		18 55						19 55					20 55				21 55	21 55				23 38		
Chassen Road	d		18 57						19 57					20 57				21 57	21 57				23 40		
Flixton	d		19 00						20 00					21 00				22 00	22 00				23 43		
Irlam	d		19 04						20 04					21 04				22 04	22 04				23 47		
Glazebrook	d		19 07						20 07					21 07				22 07	22 07				23 50		
Birchwood	d		19 11		19 25				20 11		20 25			21 11	21 25			22 11	22 11		22 25		23 54		
Padgate	d		19 14						20 14					21 14				22 14	22 14				23 57		
Warrington Central	a	18 57	19 20		19 30			19 57	20 18		20 30		20 57	21 20	21 30			22 22	22 22		22 30		00 01		
	d	18 57			19 30		19 49	19 57	20 18		20 30	20 49	20 57		21 30		21 49				22 30	22 58	00 02		
Sankey for Penketh	d						19 53					20 53					21 53					23 02	00 05		
Widnes	d	19 05					19 58	20 05				20 58	21 05				21 58					23 07	00 11		
Hough Green	d						20 02		20 28			21 01					22 01					23 10	00 13		
Halewood	d						20 06					21 06					22 06					23 15	00 18		
Hunts Cross 103	d	19 12					20 09		20 33			21 09					22 09					23 18	00 21		
L'pool Sth Parkway 7 91,103 ✈	d	19 18			19 47		20 13	20 16	20 38		20 47	21 12	21 20		21 47		22 12				22 47	23 22	00 27		
West Allerton 91	a						20 15		20 41			21 15					22 15					23 25			
Mossley Hill 91	a						20 18		20 44			21 18					22 18					23 27			
Edge Hill 90,91	a						20 23					21 23					22 23					23 32			
Liverpool Lime Street 10 90,91	a	19 34		19 48	20 01		20 30	20 35	20 56	20 48	21 01	21 30	21 35		22 00		22 30			22 48	23 01	23 39	00 41		

A From Scarborough

B From Norwich

Table 89

Saturdays

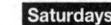

14 December to 17 May

Manchester Airport and Manchester - Warrington Central - Liverpool

Network Diagram - see first Page of Table 88

	NT A	NT	NT	NT	NT	NT	TP ◇1	NT	EM ◇ B	NT	NT	TP ◇1 C	NT	EM ◇ B	NT	NT	TP ◇1 D	NT	EM ◇ B	NT	NT	TP ◇1 E
Manchester Airport 85 d		04 34				06 41					07 38					08 41					09 41	
Sheffield 7 78 d									06 20					07 32					08 41			
Stockport 84 d									07 22					08 24					09 25			
ManchesterPicc 10 78,84,85 d		04 49				06 58	07 07		07 34		07 59	08 07		08 37		09 01	09 07		09 37		10 01	10 07
Manchester Oxford Road 84,85 d					06 22	07 01	07 10		07 37	07 39	08 03	08 12	08 15	08 41	08 44	09 04	09 12	09 16	09 41	09 44	10 04	10 12
Deansgate 84,85 d					06 24					07 41			08 17		08 46			09 18		09 46		
Trafford Park d					06 29					07 46								09 23				
Humphrey Park d					06 31													09 25				
Urmston d					06 33					07 49			08 24		08 52			09 27		09 52		
Chassen Road d					06 35								08 26									
Flixton d					06 38					07 52			08 28					09 30				
Irlam d					06 42					07 56			08 32		08 57			09 34		09 57		
Glazebrook d					06 45					07 59			08 35									
Birchwood d					06 49		07 23			08 04		08 25	08 40		09 03		09 25	09 40		10 03		10 25
Padgate d					06 52					08 07					09 06					10 06		
Warrington Central a					06 56		07 27		07 53	08 10		08 30	08 45	08 57	09 09		09 30	09 45	09 57	10 09		10 30
d	00 02		06 03	06 37	06 56		07 28	07 40	07 53	08 11		08 30	08 45	08 57	09 10		09 30	09 45	09 57	10 10		10 30
Sankey for Penketh d	00 05		06 07	06 41	07 00			07 44		08 15					09 14					10 14		
Widnes d	00 11		06 12	06 46	07 06			07 49	08 01	08 20			08 53	09 05	09 19			09 53	10 05	10 19		
Hough Green d	00 13		06 15	06 49	07 09			07 52	08 05	08 24			08 56		09 23			09 56		10 23		
Halewood d	00 18		06 20	06 54	07 13			07 57		08 28					09 27					10 27		
Hunts Cross 103 d	00 21		06 23	06 57	07 17			08 00	08s10	08 32					09 30					10 30		
L'pool Sth Parkway 7 91,103 d	00 27		06 27	07 01	07 22			08 03	08 18	08 37		08 47	09 06	09 15	09 36		09 47	10 06	10 15	10 36		10 47
West Allerton 91 a			06 31	07 05	07 25			08 06		08 40			09 09		09 39			10 09		10 39		
Mossley Hill 91 a			06 33	07 07	07 28			08 09		08 43			09 12		09 41			10 12		10 41		
Edge Hill 90,91 a			06 39	07 13	07 34			08 14		08 48					09 47					10 47		
Liverpool Lime Street 10 90,91 a	00 41	05 32	06 45	07 18	07 40	07 49	07 53	08 21	08 31	08 55	08 59	08 58	09 24	09 31	09 53	09 48	09 58	10 24	10 31	10 53	10 48	10 58

	NT	EM ◇ F	NT	NT	TP ◇1 E	NT	EM ◇ F	NT	NT	TP ◇1 E	NT	EM ◇ F	NT	NT	TP ◇1 E	NT	EM ◇ F	NT	NT	TP ◇1 E	NT
Manchester Airport 85 d				10 41					11 41					12 41					13 41		
Sheffield 7 78 d		09 41					10 41					11 41					12 41				
Stockport 84 d		10 26					11 26					12 25					13 26				
ManchesterPicc 10 78,84,85 d		10 37		11 01	11 07		11 37		12 01	12 07		12 37		13 01	13 07		13 37		14 01	14 07	
Manchester Oxford Road 84,85 d	10 16	10 41	10 44	11 04	11 12	11 16	11 41	11 44	12 04	12 12	12 16	12 41	12 44	13 04	13 12	13 16	13 41	13 44	14 04	14 12	14 16
Deansgate 84,85 d	10 18		10 46			11 18		11 46			12 18		12 46			13 18		13 46			14 18
Trafford Park d						11 23										13 23					
Humphrey Park d						11 25										13 25					
Urmston d	10 24		10 52			11 27		11 52			12 24		12 52			13 27		13 52			14 24
Chassen Road d	10 26										12 26										14 26
Flixton d	10 29					11 30					12 29					13 30					14 29
Irlam d	10 33		10 57			11 34		11 57			12 33		12 57			13 34		13 57			14 33
Glazebrook d	10 36										12 36										14 36
Birchwood d	10 40		11 03		11 25	11 40		12 03		12 25	12 40		13 03		13 25	13 40		14 03		14 25	14 40
Padgate d			11 06					12 06					13 06					14 06			
Warrington Central a	10 45	10 57	11 09		11 30	11 45	11 57	12 09		12 30	12 45	12 57	13 09		13 30	13 45	13 57	14 09		14 30	14 45
d	10 46	10 57	11 10		11 30	11 45	11 57	12 10		12 30	12 46	12 57	13 10		13 30	13 45	13 57	14 10		14 30	14 46
Sankey for Penketh d			11 14					12 14					13 14					14 14			
Widnes d	10 54	11 05	11 19			11 53	12 05	12 19			12 54	13 05	13 19			13 53	14 05	14 19			14 54
Hough Green d	10 57		11 23			11 56		12 23			12 57		13 23			13 56		14 23			14 57
Halewood d			11 27					12 27					13 27					14 27			
Hunts Cross 103 d			11 30					12 30					13 30					14 30			
L'pool Sth Parkway 7 91,103 d	11 06	11 15	11 36		11 47	12 06	12 15	12 37		12 47	13 06	13 15	13 36		13 47	14 06	14 15	14 36		14 47	15 06
West Allerton 91 a	11 09		11 39			12 09		12 39			13 09		13 39			14 09		14 39			15 09
Mossley Hill 91 a	11 12		11 41			12 12		12 41			13 12		13 41			14 12		14 41			15 12
Edge Hill 90,91 a			11 47					12 47					13 47					14 47			
Liverpool Lime Street 10 90,91 a	11 24	11 31	11 53	11 48	11 58	12 24	12 31	12 55	12 48	12 58	13 24	13 31	13 53	13 48	13 58	14 24	14 31	14 53	14 48	14 58	15 24

	EM ◇ F	NT	NT	TP ◇1 E	NT	EM ◇ F	NT	NT	TP ◇1 E	NT	EM ◇ F	NT	NT	TP ◇1 E	NT	EM ◇ F	NT	NT	TP ◇1 E	NT	EM ◇ F	NT
Manchester Airport 85 d			14 41					15 41					16 41					17 41				
Sheffield 7 78 d	13 41					14 41					15 41					16 41					17 38	
Stockport 84 d	14 26					15 26					16 26					17 26					18 27	
ManchesterPicc 10 78,84,85 d	14 37		15 01	15 07		15 37		16 01	16 07		16 37		17 01	17 07		17 37		18 01	18 07		18 37	
Manchester Oxford Road 84,85 d	14 41	14 44	15 04	15 12	15 16	15 41	15 44	16 04	16 12	16 16	16 41	16 44	17 04	17 11	17 15	17 42	17 44	18 04	18 12	18 16	18 41	18 44
Deansgate 84,85 d		14 46			15 18		15 46			16 18		16 46			17 17		17 46			18 18		18 46
Trafford Park d					15 23							16 51			17 22		17 51			18 23		18 51
Humphrey Park d					15 25										17 24		17 53			18 25		18 53
Urmston d		14 52			15 27		15 52			16 24		16 54			17 27		17 55			18 27		18 55
Chassen Road d										16 26					17 29		17 57			18 29		18 57
Flixton d					15 30					16 29		16 57			17 31		18 00			18 32		19 00
Irlam d		14 57			15 34		15 57			16 33		17 01			17 35	17 52	18 04			18 36		19 04
Glazebrook d										16 36					17 38		18 07					19 07
Birchwood d		15 03		15 25	15 40		16 03		16 25	16 40		17 07		17 25	17 43	17 58	18 11		18 25	18 41		19 11
Padgate d		15 06					16 06			16 43		17 10			17 46		18 14					19 14
Warrington Central a	14 57	15 09		15 30	15 45	15 57	16 09		16 30	16 47	16 57	17 13		17 30	17 50	18 03	18 18		18 30	18 46	18 57	19 20
d	14 57	15 10		15 30	15 45	15 57	16 10		16 30	16 47	16 57	17 14		17 30	17 50	18 03	18 18		18 30	18 47	18 58	
Sankey for Penketh d		15 14					16 14					17 18			17 54					18 51		
Widnes d	15 05	15 19			15 53	16 05	16 19			16 55	17 05	17 23			18 00	18 11				18 56	19 06	
Hough Green d		15 23			15 56		16 23			16 58		17 27			18 02		18 28			18 59		
Halewood d		15 27			16 01		16 27					17 31			18 07					19 04		
Hunts Cross 103 d		15 30					16 30					17 34			18 10		18 33			19 07	19 13	
L'pool Sth Parkway 7 91,103 d	15 15	15 36		15 47	16 07	16 15	16 36		16 47	17 07	17 15	17 39		17 47	18 15	18 22	18 38		18 47	19 11	19 19	
West Allerton 91 a		15 39			16 10		16 39			17 10		17 41			18 19		18 41			19 14		
Mossley Hill 91 a		15 41			16 13		16 41			17 13		17 44			18 21		18 44			19 17		
Edge Hill 90,91 a		15 47					16 47					17 49			18 30		18 50			19 26		
Liverpool Lime Street 10 90,91 a	15 31	15 53	15 48	15 58	16 25	16 31	16 54	16 48	16 58	17 25	17 31	17 58	17 48	18 01	18 38	18 35	18 57	18 59	19 01	19 35	19 35	

A From Manchester Oxford Road
B From Nottingham
C From Hull
D From Newcastle
E From Scarborough
F From Norwich

Table 89

Saturdays

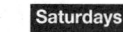

14 December to 17 May

Manchester Airport and Manchester - Warrington Central - Liverpool

Network Diagram - see first Page of Table 88

	NT	TP ◇1 A	NT		EM ◇ B	NT	NT	TP ◇1 A	EM ◇ B	NT	NT	TP ◇1 A	NT		NT	NT	TP ◇1 A	NT	NT
Manchester Airport 85 ✈ d	18 41						19 41									21 42			
Sheffield 7 78 🚌 d					18 38				19 40										
Stockport 84 d					19 25				20 26										
ManchesterPicc 10 78,84,85 🚌 d	19 01	19 07			19 36		20 01	20 07	20 37			21 07			21 40	22 01	22 07		
Manchester Oxford Road 84,85 d	19 04	19 12			19 41	19 44	20 04	20 12	20 41		20 44	21 12			21 44	22 04	22 12		23 20
Deansgate 84,85 🚌 d						19 46					20 46				21 46				23 22
Trafford Park d						19 51					20 51				21 51				23 27
Humphrey Park d						19 53					20 53				21 53				23 29
Urmston d						19 55					20 55				21 55				23 31
Chassen Road d						19 57					20 57				21 57				23 33
Flixton d						20 00					21 00				22 00				23 36
Irlam d						20 04					21 04				22 04				23 40
Glazebrook d						20 07					21 07				22 07				23 43
Birchwood d		19 25				20 11		20 25			21 11	21 25			22 11		22 25		23 47
Padgate d						20 14					21 14				22 14				23 50
Warrington Central a		19 30			19 57	20 18		20 30	20 57		21 20	21 30			22 22		22 30		23 54
d		19 30	19 34		19 57	20 18		20 30	20 57	20 49		21 30	21 49				22 30	22 49	23 54
Sankey for Penketh d			19 38							20 53			21 53					22 53	23 58
Widnes d			19 43		20 05				21 05	20 58			21 58					22 58	00 04
Hough Green d			19 46			20 28				21 01			22 01					23 01	00 06
Halewood d			19 51							21 06			22 06					23 06	00 11
Hunts Cross 103 d			19 54			20 33				21 09			22 09					23 09	00 14
L'pool Sth Parkway 7 91,103 ✈ d		19 47	19 59		20 15	20 38		20 47	21 20	21 15		21 47	22 12				22 47	23 12	00 20
West Allerton 91 a			20 03			20 41				21 19			22 15					23 15	
Mossley Hill 91 a			20 05			20 44				21 21			22 18					23 18	
Edge Hill 90,91 a			20 11							21 27			22 23					23 23	
Liverpool Lime Street 10 90,91 a	19 48	20 00	20 17		20 30	20 55	20 48	21 00	21 32	21 34		22 00	22 30			22 48	23 00	23 30	00 34

Sundays

8 December to 29 December

	NT C	NT	NT	NT	TP ◇1	NT	NT	TP ◇1 D	NT		NT	TP ◇1	EM ◇ E	NT	NT	TP ◇1 F	EM ◇ E	NT	NT		TP ◇1 A	EM ◇ E	NT	NT
Manchester Airport 85 ✈ d				08 35			09 35				10 35				11 33				12 35					13 35
Sheffield 7 78 🚌 d													10 41				11 39					12 37		
Stockport 84 d													11 26				12 26					13 26		
ManchesterPicc 10 78,84,85 🚌 d				08 50	09 12		09 50	10 10			10 50	11 10	11 38		11 50	12 07	12 38		12 50		13 07	13 38		13 50
Manchester Oxford Road 84,85 d		08 08	08 45	08 53	09 15	09 45	09 53	10 14	10 45		10 53	11 13	11 42	11 45	11 53	12 12	12 42	12 45	12 52		13 12	13 42	13 45	13 53
Deansgate 84,85 🚌 d		08 10	08 47	08 55		09 47			10 47					11 47				12 47					13 47	
Trafford Park d																								
Humphrey Park d																								
Urmston d		08 16	08 53			09 53			10 53					11 53				12 53					13 53	
Chassen Road d																								
Flixton d																								
Irlam d		08 21	08 58			09 58			10 58					11 58				12 58					13 58	
Glazebrook d																								
Birchwood d		08 27	09 04		09 29	10 04		10 27	11 04			11 27		12 04		12 25		13 04			13 25		14 04	
Padgate d																								
Warrington Central a		08 31	09 09		09 33	10 09		10 32	11 09			11 31	11 58	12 09		12 30	12 58	13 09			13 30	13 58	14 09	
d		08 31	09 09		09 34	10 09		10 32	11 09			11 32	11 59	12 09		12 30	12 58	13 09			13 30	13 58	14 09	
Sankey for Penketh d																								
Widnes d	00 04	08 39	09 17			10 17			11 17				12 06	12 17			13 06	13 17				14 06	14 17	
Hough Green d	00 06	08 44	09 21			10 21			11 21					12 21				13 21					14 21	
Halewood d	00 11	08 48	09 25			10 25			11 25					12 25				13 25					14 25	
Hunts Cross 103 d	00 14	08 51	09 28			10 28			11 28					12 28				13 28					14 28	
L'pool Sth Parkway 7 91,103 ✈ d	00 20	08 55	09 33		09 47	10 33		10 49	11 33			11 46	12 17	12 33		12 47	13 17	13 33			13 47	14 16	14 33	
West Allerton 91 a		08 58	09 36			10 36			11 36					12 36				13 36					14 36	
Mossley Hill 91 a		09 02	09 39			10 39			11 39					12 39				13 39					14 39	
Edge Hill 90,91 a																								
Liverpool Lime Street 10 90,91 a	00 34	09 12	09 51	09 53	10 00	10 50	10 54	10 59	11 50		11 54	11 58	12 30	12 50	12 54	12 58	13 30	13 50	13 54		13 58	14 30	14 50	14 54

A From Scarborough
B From Norwich
C not 8 December. From Manchester Oxford Road
D From York
E From Nottingham
F From Newcastle

Table 89

Sundays

8 December to 29 December

Manchester Airport and Manchester - Warrington Central - Liverpool

Network Diagram - see first Page of Table 88

		TP		EM	NT	NT	TP	EM	NT	NT	TP	EM		NT	NT	TP	EM	NT	NT	TP	EM	NT		NT	TP
		◇1		◇			◇1	◇			◇1	◇				◇1	◇			◇1	◇				◇1
		A		B			C	D			A	B				C	E			A	D				C
Manchester Airport 85 ✈	d					14 35				15 35					16 35				17 35					18 35	
Sheffield 7 78 🚌	d			13 39				14 37				15 43					16 39				17 44				
Stockport 84	d			14 26				15 26				16 26					17 29				18 26				
ManchesterPicc 10 78,84,85 🚌	d	14 06		14 38		14 50	15 07	15 38		15 50	16 07	16 38			16 50	17 07	17 38		17 50	18 07	18 38			18 50	19 07
Manchester Oxford Road 84,85	d	14 11		14 42	14 45	14 53	15 12	15 42	15 45	15 53	16 12	16 42		16 45	16 53	17 12	17 42	17 45	17 53	18 12	18 42	18 45		18 53	19 12
Deansgate 84,85 🚌	d				14 47				15 47					16 47				17 47				18 47			
Trafford Park	d																								
Humphrey Park	d																								
Urmston	d				14 53				15 53					16 53				17 53				18 53			
Chassen Road	d																								
Flixton	d																								
Irlam	d				14 58				15 58					16 58				17 58				18 58			
Glazebrook	d																								
Birchwood	d	14 25			15 04		15 26		16 04		16 25			17 04		17 26		18 04		18 25		19 04			19 26
Padgate	d																								
Warrington Central	a	14 29		14 58	15 09		15 30	15 58	16 09		16 30	16 58		17 09		17 30	17 58	18 09		18 30	18 58	19 09			19 30
	d	14 30		14 58	15 09		15 31	15 58	16 09		16 30	16 58		17 09		17 31	17 58	18 09		18 30	18 58	19 09			19 31
Sankey for Penketh	d																								
Widnes	d			15 06	15 17			16 06	16 17			17 06		17 17			18 06	18 17			19 06	19 17			
Hough Green	d				15 21				16 21					17 21				18 21				19 21			
Halewood	d				15 25				16 25					17 25				18 25				19 25			
Hunts Cross 103	d				15 28				16 28					17 28				18 28				19 28			
L'pool Sth Parkway 7 91,103 ✈	d	14 47		15 16	15 33		15 47	16 16	16 33		16 47	17 16		17 33		17 47	18 16	18 33		18 48	19 17	19 33			19 47
West Allerton 91	a				15 36				16 36					17 36				18 36				19 36			
Mossley Hill 91	a				15 39				16 39					17 39				18 39				19 39			
Edge Hill 90,91	a																								
Liverpool Lime Street 10 90,91	a	14 57		15 30	15 50	15 54	15 58	16 30	16 50	16 54	16 58	17 30		17 50	17 54	17 58	18 30	18 50	18 54	18 58	19 30	19 50		19 54	19 58

		EM	NT	NT	TP	NT	NT	TP		NT	NT	TP	NT	NT
		◇			◇1			◇1				◇1		
		D			A			C				A		🚌
Manchester Airport 85 ✈	d			19 35			20 35				21 35		22 27	
Sheffield 7 78 🚌	d	18 37												
Stockport 84	d	19 26												
ManchesterPicc 10 78,84,85 🚌	d	19 38		19 50	20 07		20 50	21 07			21 50	22 07	22 41	
Manchester Oxford Road 84,85	d	19 42	19 45	19 53	20 12	20 45	20 53	21 12		21 45	21 53	22 12	22 45	23 00
Deansgate 84,85 🚌	d		19 47			20 47				21 47			22 47	
Trafford Park	d													
Humphrey Park	d													
Urmston	d		19 53			20 53				21 53			22 53	
Chassen Road	d													
Flixton	d													
Irlam	d		19 58			20 58				21 58			22 58	
Glazebrook	d													
Birchwood	d		20 04		20 25	21 04		21 26		22 04		22 25	23 04	
Padgate	d													
Warrington Central	a	19 58	20 09		20 30	21 09		21 30		22 09		22 30	23 09	
	d	19 58	20 09		20 30	21 09		21 31		22 09		22 30	23 09	
Sankey for Penketh	d													
Widnes	d	20 06	20 17			21 17				22 17			23 17	
Hough Green	d		20 21			21 21				22 21			23 21	
Halewood	d		20 25			21 25				22 25			23 25	
Hunts Cross 103	d		20 28			21 28				22 28			23 28	
L'pool Sth Parkway 7 91,103 ✈	d	20 16	20 33		20 47	21 33		21 47		22 33		22 47	23 33	
West Allerton 91	a		20 36			21 36				22 36			23 36	
Mossley Hill 91	a		20 39			21 39				22 39			23 39	
Edge Hill 90,91	a													
Liverpool Lime Street 10 90,91	a	20 30	20 50	20 54	20 58	21 50	21 54	21 58		22 50	22 54	22 58	23 50	01 11

A From Scarborough
B From Nottingham
C From Middlesbrough
D From Norwich
E From Peterborough

Table 89

Sundays

5 January to 11 May

Manchester Airport and Manchester - Warrington Central - Liverpool

Network Diagram - see first Page of Table 88

Station		NT	NT	NT	NT	NT		TP	NT	NT	NT	TP	NT	NT	NT	TP		NT	EM	NT	NT	TP	NT	EM	NT
		A	(bus)			(bus)		◇1			(bus)	◇1 B			(bus)	◇1			◇ C		(bus)	◇1 D		◇ C	
Manchester Airport 85 ✈	d								09 03				10 03					11 03					12 03		
Sheffield 7 78	d																		10 41					11 39	
Stockport 84	d																		11 26					12 26	
ManchesterPicc 10 78,84,85	d							09 12	09 18			10 10	10 19			11 10		11 18	11 38			12 07	12 18	12 38	
Manchester Oxford Road 84,85	d		07 55	08 08	08 45	08 55		09 15	09 21	09 45	09 55	10 14	10 22	10 45	10 55	11 13		11 22	11 42	11 45	11 55	12 12	12 22	12 42	12 45
Deansgate 84,85	d			08 10	08 47					09 47				10 47						11 47					12 47
Trafford Park	d																								
Humphrey Park	d																								
Urmston	d			08 16	08 53					09 53				10 53						11 53					12 53
Chassen Road	d																								
Flixton	d																								
Irlam	d			08 21	08 58					09 58				10 58						11 58					12 58
Glazebrook	d																								
Birchwood	d			08 27	09 04			09 29		10 04		10 27		11 04		11 27				12 04		12 25			13 04
Padgate	d																								
Warrington Central	a			08 31	09 09			09 33		10 09		10 32		11 09		11 31			11 58	12 09		12 30		12 58	13 09
	d			08 31	09 09			09 34		10 09		10 32		11 09		11 32			11 59	12 09		12 30		12 58	13 09
Sankey for Penketh	d																								
Widnes	d	00 04		08 39	09 17					10 17				11 17					12 06	12 17				13 06	13 17
Hough Green	d	00 06		08 44	09 21					10 21				11 21						12 21					13 21
Halewood	d	00 11		08 48	09 25					10 25				11 25						12 25					13 25
Hunts Cross 103	d	00 14		08 51	09 28					10 28				11 28						12 28					13 28
L'pool Sth Parkway 7 91,103 ✈	d	00 20		08 55	09 33			09 47		10 33		10 49		11 33		11 46			12 17	12 33		12 47		13 17	13 33
West Allerton 91	a			08 58	09 36					10 36				11 36						12 36					13 36
Mossley Hill 91	a			09 02	09 39					10 39				11 39						12 39					13 39
Edge Hill 90,91	a																								
Liverpool Lime Street 10 90,91	a	00 34	10 06	09 12	09 51	11 06		10 00	10 03	10 50	12 06	10 59	11 03	11 50	13 06	11 58		12 02	12 30	12 50	14 06	12 58	13 03	13 30	13 50

Station		NT		TP	NT	EM	NT	NT	TP	NT	EM	NT		NT	TP	NT	EM	NT	NT	TP	NT	EM		NT	NT
		(bus)		◇1 E		◇ C		(bus)	◇1 F		◇ C			(bus)	◇1 F		◇ G		(bus)	◇1 F		◇ C			(bus)
Manchester Airport 85 ✈	d				13 03					14 03						15 03					16 03				
Sheffield 7 78	d					12 37					13 39						14 37					15 43			
Stockport 84	d					13 26					14 26						15 26					16 26			
ManchesterPicc 10 78,84,85	d			13 07	13 18	13 38			14 06	14 18	14 38				15 07	15 18	15 38			16 07	16 18	16 38			
Manchester Oxford Road 84,85	d	12 55		13 12	13 22	13 42	13 45	13 55	14 11	14 22	14 42	14 45		14 55	15 12	15 22	15 42	15 45	15 55	16 12	16 22	16 42		16 45	16 55
Deansgate 84,85	d						13 47					14 47						15 47						16 47	
Trafford Park	d																								
Humphrey Park	d																								
Urmston	d						13 53					14 53						15 53						16 53	
Chassen Road	d																								
Flixton	d																								
Irlam	d						13 58					14 58						15 58						16 58	
Glazebrook	d																								
Birchwood	d			13 25			14 04		14 25			15 04			15 26			16 04		16 25				17 04	
Padgate	d																								
Warrington Central	a			13 30		13 58	14 09		14 29		14 58	15 09			15 30		15 58	16 09		16 30		16 58		17 09	
	d			13 30		13 58	14 09		14 30		14 58	15 09			15 31		15 58	16 09		16 30		16 58		17 09	
Sankey for Penketh	d																								
Widnes	d					14 06	14 17				15 06	15 17					16 06	16 17				17 06		17 17	
Hough Green	d						14 21					15 21						16 21						17 21	
Halewood	d						14 25					15 25						16 25						17 25	
Hunts Cross 103	d						14 28					15 28						16 28						17 28	
L'pool Sth Parkway 7 91,103 ✈	d			13 47		14 16	14 33		14 47		15 16	15 33			15 47		16 16	16 33		16 47		17 16		17 33	
West Allerton 91	a						14 36					15 36						16 36						17 36	
Mossley Hill 91	a						14 39					15 39						16 39						17 39	
Edge Hill 90,91	a																								
Liverpool Lime Street 10 90,91	a	15 06		13 58	14 03	14 30	14 50	16 06	14 57	15 03	15 30	15 50		17 06	15 58	16 03	16 30	16 50	18 06	16 58	17 03	17 30		17 50	19 06

A From Manchester Oxford Road
B From York
C From Nottingham
D From Scarborough
E From Middlesbrough
F From Newcastle
G From Norwich

Table 89

Sundays

5 January to 11 May

Manchester Airport and Manchester - Warrington Central - Liverpool

Network Diagram - see first Page of Table 88

		TP	NT	EM	NT	NT	TP	NT	EM	NT	NT	TP	NT	EM	NT	NT	TP	NT	NT	NT	TP	NT
		◇1		◇			◇1		◇			◇1		◇			◇1				◇1	
		A		B			A		C			A		C			A				A	
						bus					bus					bus				bus		
Manchester Airport 85 ✈	d		17 03					18 03					19 03					20 03				21 03
Sheffield 7 78	d			16 39					17 44					18 37								
Stockport 84	d			17 29					18 26					19 26								
ManchesterPicc 10 78,84,85	d	17 07	17 18	17 38			18 07	18 18	18 38			19 07	19 18	19 38			20 07	20 17			21 07	21 17
Manchester Oxford Road 84,85	d	17 12	17 22	17 42	17 45	17 55	18 12	18 22	18 42	18 45	18 55	19 12	19 22	19 42	19 45	19 55	20 12	20 21	20 45	20 55	21 12	21 21
Deansgate 84,85	d				17 47					18 47					19 47				20 47			
Trafford Park	d																					
Humphrey Park	d																					
Urmston	d				17 53					18 53					19 53				20 53			
Chassen Road	d																					
Flixton	d																					
Irlam	d				17 58					18 58					19 58				20 58			
Glazebrook	d																					
Birchwood	d	17 26			18 04		18 25			19 04		19 26			20 04		20 25		21 04		21 26	
Padgate	d																					
Warrington Central	a	17 30		17 58	18 09		18 30		18 58	19 09		19 30		19 58	20 09		20 30		21 09		21 30	
	d	17 31		17 58	18 09		18 30		18 58	19 09		19 31		19 58	20 09		20 30		21 09		21 31	
Sankey for Penketh	d																					
Widnes	d			18 06	18 17				19 06	19 17				20 06	20 17				21 17			
Hough Green	d				18 21					19 21					20 21				21 21			
Halewood	d				18 25					19 25					20 25				21 25			
Hunts Cross 103	d				18 28					19 28					20 28				21 28			
L'pool Sth Parkway 7 91,103 ✈	d	17 47		18 16	18 33		18 48		19 17	19 33		19 47		20 16	20 33		20 47		21 33		21 47	
West Allerton 91	a				18 36					19 36					20 36				21 36			
Mossley Hill 91	a				18 39					19 39					20 39				21 39			
Edge Hill 90,91	a																					
Liverpool Lime Street 10 90,91	a	17 58	18 03	18 30	18 50	20 06	18 58	19 02	19 30	19 50	21 06	19 58	20 02	20 30	20 50	22 06	20 58	21 03	21 50	23 06	21 58	22 03

		NT	NT	TP	NT	NT
				◇1		
				A		
			bus			bus
Manchester Airport 85 ✈	d				22 27	
Sheffield 7 78	d					
Stockport 84	d					
ManchesterPicc 10 78,84,85	d			22 07	22 41	
Manchester Oxford Road 84,85	d	21 45	21 55	22 12	22 45	23 00
Deansgate 84,85	d	21 47			22 47	
Trafford Park	d					
Humphrey Park	d					
Urmston	d	21 53			22 53	
Chassen Road	d					
Flixton	d					
Irlam	d	21 58			22 58	
Glazebrook	d					
Birchwood	d	22 04		22 25	23 04	
Padgate	d					
Warrington Central	a	22 09		22 30	23 09	
	d	22 09		22 30	23 09	
Sankey for Penketh	d					
Widnes	d	22 17			23 17	
Hough Green	d	22 21			23 21	
Halewood	d	22 25			23 25	
Hunts Cross 103	d	22 28			23 28	
L'pool Sth Parkway 7 91,103 ✈	d	22 33		22 47	23 33	
West Allerton 91	a	22 36			23 36	
Mossley Hill 91	a	22 39			23 39	
Edge Hill 90,91	a					
Liverpool Lime Street 10 90,91	a	22 50	00 06	22 58	23 50	01 11

A From Newcastle **B** From Peterborough **C** From Norwich

Table 89R

Mondays to Fridays

9 December to 16 May

Liverpool - Warrington Central - Manchester and Manchester Airport

Network Diagram - see first Page of Table 88

Miles			NT MX	NT MO	NT MX	NT MX	NT	NT	NT	NT	TP	NT	EM	NT	NT	NT	TP	NT	EM	NT	NT	TP	NT
			A		B	C					◇1 D		◇ E				◇1 D		◇ E			◇1 D	
0	**Liverpool Lime Street** 10 90,91	d		03 38	03 38	03 58	05 13	05 50		06 13	06 15	06 21	06 47	06 50	07 13		07 15	07 26	07 42	07 45	08 13	08 22	08 26
1¾	Edge Hill 90,91	d						05 54						06 54				07 30					08 30
3¾	Mossley Hill 91	d						05 59				06 29		06 59				07 35		07 53			08 35
4½	West Allerton 91	d						06 01				06 31		07 01				07 37		07 56			08 37
5½	L'pool Sth Parkway 7 91,103 ✈	d						06 04			06 25	06 34	06 57	07 04			07 25	07 40	07 53	07 59		08 32	08 40
7¼	Hunts Cross 103	d						06 08						07 08					07 59	08 04			
8¼	Halewood	d						06 10						07 10						08 07			
10½	Hough Green	d	00 03					06 14				06 41		07 14				07 47		08 11			08 47
12¼	Widnes	d	00 06					06 18				06 45	07 07	07 18			07 33		08 05	08 15			08 50
16	Sankey for Penketh	d	00 11					06 23						07 23						08 20			
18½	**Warrington Central**	a	00 16					06 29			06 37	06 53	07 15	07 29			07 39	07 56	08 13	08 25		08 44	08 58
—		d	00 17						06 02		06 38	06 53	07 15			07 22	07 40	07 57	08 13	08 25		08 45	08 59
20¼	Padgate	d							06 05			06 56				07 25		08 00					09 02
21¾	Birchwood	d							06 08		06 43	07 00	07 20			07 28	07 45	08 03	08 18	08 30		08 50	09 05
24½	Glazebrook	d							06 13			07 05				07 33		08 08					
25¾	Irlam	d							06 16			07 08				07 36	07 50	08 11		08 37			09 11
28	Flixton	d							06 20			07 13				07 40		08 15		08 41			09 15
28½	Chassen Road	d							06 22			07 15				07 42		08 17		08 43			
29	Urmston	d							06 24			07 17				07 44		08 19		08 46			09 18
30¼	Humphrey Park	d							06 26			07 20				07 46		08 21		08 49			09 20
31	Trafford Park	d							06 29			07 22				07 49		08 24		08 52			09 23
34	Deansgate 84,85	a							06 36			07 31				07 58		08 32		09 00			09 30
34½	**Manchester Oxford Road** 84,85	a							06 39	06 56	06 59	07 35	07 38		07 56	08 03	08 04	08 36	08 38	09 04	08 56	09 05	09 35
35	**ManchesterPicc** 10 78,84,85	a	00 40	04 20	04 20	04 40	05 56		06 44	07 00	07 08		07 41		08 01		08 08		08 41		09 00	09 09	
—	Stockport 84	a											07 53						08 53				
—	Sheffield 7 78	a											08 34						09 34				
44¾	**Manchester Airport** 85,84 ✈	a		04 33	04 35		06 14			07 22					08 22						09 22		

		EM	NT	NT	TP	NT	EM	NT	NT	TP	NT	EM	NT	NT	TP	NT	EM	NT	NT FX	TP	NT	EM
		◇ E			◇1 D		◇ E			◇1 D		◇ E			◇1 D		◇ E			◇1 D		◇ E
Liverpool Lime Street 10 90,91	d	08 52	08 55	09 13	09 22	09 27	09 52	09 55	10 13	10 22	10 27	10 52	10 55	11 13	11 22	11 27	11 52	11 55	12 13	12 22	12 27	12 52
Edge Hill 90,91	d		08 59					09 59					10 59					11 59				
Mossley Hill 91	d		09 04			09 35		10 04			10 35		11 04			11 35		12 04			12 35	
West Allerton 91	d		09 06			09 37		10 06			10 37		11 06			11 37		12 06			12 37	
L'pool Sth Parkway 7 91,103 ✈	d	09 03	09 09		09 32	09 40	10 03	10 09		10 32	10 40	11 03	11 09		11 32	11 40	12 03	12 09		12 32	12 40	13 03
Hunts Cross 103	d		09 13					10 13					11 13					12 13				
Halewood	d		09 16					10 16					11 16					12 16				
Hough Green	d		09 20			09 47		10 20			10 47		11 20			11 47		12 20			12 47	
Widnes	d	09 11	09 23			09 50	10 11	10 23			10 50	11 11	11 23			11 50	12 11	12 23			12 50	13 11
Sankey for Penketh	d		09 28					10 28					11 28					12 28				
Warrington Central	a	09 18	09 33		09 44	09 58	10 18	10 33		10 44	10 58	11 18	11 33		11 44	11 58	12 18	12 33		12 44	12 58	13 18
	d	09 19	09 34		09 45	09 59	10 19	10 34		10 45	10 59	11 19	11 34		11 45	11 59	12 19	12 34		12 45	12 59	13 19
Padgate	d					10 02					11 02					12 02					13 02	
Birchwood	d		09 38		09 50	10 05		10 38		10 50	11 05		11 38		11 50	12 05		12 38		12 50	13 05	
Glazebrook	d					10 10										12 10						
Irlam	d		09 44			10 13		10 44			11 11		11 44			12 13		12 44			13 11	
Flixton	d					10 17					11 15					12 17					13 15	
Chassen Road	d					10 19										12 19						
Urmston	d		09 49			10 21		10 49			11 18		11 49			12 21		12 49			13 18	
Humphrey Park	d										11 20										13 20	
Trafford Park	d										11 23										13 23	
Deansgate 84,85	a		09 59			10 30		10 59			11 30		11 59			12 30		12 59			13 30	
Manchester Oxford Road 84,85	a	09 39	10 04	09 56	10 05	10 35	10 39	11 04	10 56	11 05	11 35	11 39	12 04	11 56	12 05	12 35	12 39	13 04	12 56	13 05	13 35	13 39
ManchesterPicc 10 78,84,85	a	09 41		10 00	10 09		10 41		11 00	11 09		11 41		12 00	12 09		12 41		13 00	13 09		13 41
Stockport 84	a	09 53					10 53					11 53					12 53					13 53
Sheffield 7 78	a	10 34					11 33					12 34					13 35					14 34
Manchester Airport 85,84 ✈	a			10 22					11 22					12 22					13 22			

A From Liverpool Lime Street
B until 27 December, from 25 March
C from 31 December until 21 March
D To Scarborough
E To Norwich

Table 89R

Mondays to Fridays

9 December to 16 May

Liverpool - Warrington Central - Manchester and Manchester Airport

Network Diagram - see first Page of Table 88

		NT	NT	TP	NT	EM		NT	NT	TP	NT	EM	NT	NT	TP	NT		EM	NT	NT	TP	NT	EM	NT	NT
				◇[1]		◇				◇[1]		◇			◇[1]			◇			◇[1]		◇		
				A		B				A		B			C			B			A		D		
				🛒						🛒					🛒						🛒				
Liverpool Lime Street [10] 90,91	d	12 55	13 13	13 22	13 27	13 52		13 55	14 13	14 22	14 27	14 52	14 55	15 13	15 22	15 27		15 52	15 55	16 13	16 22	16 27	16 52	16 55	17 06
Edge Hill 90,91	d	12 59						13 59					14 59						15 59					16 59	
Mossley Hill 91	d	13 04			13 35			14 04			14 35		15 04			15 35			16 04			16 35		17 04	
West Allerton 91	d	13 06			13 37			14 06			14 37		15 06			15 37			16 06			16 37		17 06	
L'pool Sth Parkway [7] 91,103 ✈	d	13 09		13 32	13 40	14 03		14 09		14 32	14 40	15 03	15 09		15 32	15 40		16 03	16 09		16 32	16 40	17 03	17 09	
Hunts Cross 103	d	13 13						14 13					15 13						16 13					17 13	
Halewood	d	13 16						14 16					15 16						16 16					17 16	
Hough Green	d	13 20			13 47			14 20			14 47		15 20			15 47			16 20			16 47		17 20	
Widnes	d	13 23			13 50	14 11		14 23			14 50	15 11	15 23			15 50		16 11	16 23			16 50	17 11	17 23	
Sankey for Penketh	d	13 28						14 28					15 28						16 28					17 28	
Warrington Central	a	13 33		13 44	13 58	14 18		14 33		14 44	14 58	15 18	15 33		15 44	15 58		16 18	16 33		16 44	16 58	17 18	17 33	
	d	13 34		13 45	13 59	14 19		14 34		14 45	14 59	15 19	15 34		15 45	15 59		16 19	16 34		16 45	16 59	17 19	17 34	
Padgate	d				14 02						15 02					16 02						17 02			
Birchwood	d	13 38		13 50	14 05			14 38		14 50	15 05		15 38		15 50	16 05			16 38		16 50	17 05		17 38	
Glazebrook	d				14 10											16 10									
Irlam	d	13 44			14 13			14 44			15 11		15 44			16 13			16 44			17 11		17 44	
Flixton	d				14 17						15 15					16 17						17 15			
Chassen Road	d				14 19											16 19									
Urmston	d	13 49			14 21			14 49			15 18		15 49			16 21			16 49			17 18		17 49	
Humphrey Park	d										15 20											17 20			
Trafford Park	d										15 23											17 23			
Deansgate 84,85 ⛴	a	13 59			14 30			14 59			15 30		15 59			16 30			16 59			17 30		17 59	
Manchester Oxford Road 84,85	a	14 04	13 56	14 05	14 35	14 39		15 04	14 56	15 05	15 35	15 39	16 04	15 56	16 05	16 35		16 38	17 04	16 56	17 05	17 35	17 38	18 04	17 56
ManchesterPicc [10] 78,84,85 ⛴	a		14 00	14 09		14 41			15 00	15 09		15 41		16 00	16 09			16 41		17 00	17 09		17 41		18 00
Stockport 84	a					14 53						15 53						16 53					17 53		
Sheffield [7] 78 ⛴	a					15 34						16 34						17 39					18 47		
Manchester Airport 85,84 ✈	a		14 22						15 22					16 22						17 22					18 22

		TP		NT	EM	NT	NT	TP	NT	EM	NT	TP		NT	EM	NT	NT	TP	NT	EM	NT	TP		NT	
		◇[1]			◇			◇[1]		◇		◇[1]			◇			◇[1]		◇		◇[1]			
		A			B			A		D		E			D			F		D		F			
		🛒																							
Liverpool Lime Street [10] 90,91	d	17 22		17 25	17 52	17 55	18 13	18 22	18 25	18 52	18 55	19 22			19 52	19 55	20 09	20 22	20 55	21 37	21 55	22 30		23 38	
Edge Hill 90,91	d			17 29		17 59			18 29		18 59					19 59			20 59		21 59			23 42	
Mossley Hill 91	d			17 34		18 04			18 34		19 04					20 04			21 04		22 04			23 47	
West Allerton 91	d			17 36		18 06			18 36		19 06					20 06			21 06		22 06			23 50	
L'pool Sth Parkway [7] 91,103 ✈	d	17 32		17 39	18 03	18 09		18 32	18 39	19 03	19 09	19 32			20 03	20 09		20 32	21 09	21 47	22 09	22 40		23 53	
Hunts Cross 103	d			17 43		18 13			18 43		19 13					20 13			21 13		22 13			23 56	
Halewood	d			17 46		18 16			18 46		19 16					20 16			21 16		22 16			23 59	
Hough Green	d			17 50		18 20			18 50		19 20					20 20			21 20		22 20			00 03	
Widnes	d			17 53	18 11	18 23			18 53	19 11	19 23				20 11	20 23			21 23	21 55	22 23			00 06	
Sankey for Penketh	d			17 58		18 28			18 58		19 28					20 28			21 28		22 28			00 11	
Warrington Central	a	17 44		18 03	18 18	18 33		18 44	19 03	19 18	19 34	19 44			20 18	20 34		20 44	21 33	22 03	22 33	22 52		00 16	
	d	17 45		18 04	18 19	18 34		18 45	19 04	19 19		19 45		19 56	20 19			20 45	21 34	22 03	22 34	22 53		00 17	
Padgate	d			18 07					19 07					19 59					21 37		22 37				
Birchwood	d	17 50		18 10		18 38		18 50	19 10			19 50		20 02				20 50	21 40		22 40	22 58			
Glazebrook	d								19 15					20 07					21 45		22 45				
Irlam	d			18 16		18 44			19 18					20 10					21 48		22 48				
Flixton	d			18 20										20 14					21 52		22 52				
Chassen Road	d													20 16					21 54		22 54				
Urmston	d			18 23		18 49			19 23					20 18					21 56		22 56				
Humphrey Park	d													20 20					21 58		22 58				
Trafford Park	d													20 23					22 01		23 01				
Deansgate 84,85 ⛴	a			18 31		18 59			19 31					20 30					22 08		23 08				
Manchester Oxford Road 84,85	a	18 05		18 36	18 39	19 04	18 56	19 05	19 36	19 39		20 05		20 35	20 39		20 56	21 06	22 13	22 23	23 13	23 14			
ManchesterPicc [10] 78,84,85 ⛴	a	18 09			18 41		19 00	19 09		19 41		20 09			20 41		21 00	21 09		22 26		23 19		00 40	
Stockport 84	a				18 53					19 53					20 53					22 37					
Sheffield [7] 78 ⛴	a				19 33					20 35					21 34					23 35					
Manchester Airport 85,84 ✈	a						19 23										21 23								

A To Scarborough
B To Norwich
C To Middlesbrough
D To Nottingham
E To Hull
F To York

Table 89R

Saturdays

14 December to 17 May

Liverpool - Warrington Central - Manchester and Manchester Airport

Network Diagram - see first Page of Table 88

	NT	NT	NT	NT	NT		TP	NT	EM	NT	NT	TP	NT	EM	NT		NT	TP	NT	EM	NT	NT	TP	NT
							◇1		◇			◇1		◇				◇1		◇			◇1	
	A						B		C			B		C				B		C			B	
Liverpool Lime Street 10 90,91 d		03 38	05 13	05 50	06 13		06 15	06 21	06 49	06 55	07 13	07 15	07 26	07 42	07 45		08 13	08 22	08 26	08 52	08 55	09 13	09 22	09 27
Edge Hill 90,91 d				05 54						06 59			07 30						08 30		08 59			
Mossley Hill 91 d				05 59				06 29		07 04			07 35		07 53				08 35		09 04			09 35
West Allerton 91 d				06 01				06 31		07 06			07 37		07 56				08 37		09 06			09 37
L'pool Sth Parkway 7 91,103 ✈ d				06 04			06 25	06 34	06 59	07 09		07 25	07 40	07 52	07 59			08 32	08 40	09 03	09 09		09 32	09 40
Hunts Cross 103 d				06 08						07 13				07 59	08 04						09 13			
Halewood d				06 10						07 16					08 07						09 16			
Hough Green d	00 03			06 14				06 41		07 20			07 47		08 11				08 47		09 20			09 47
Widnes d	00 06			06 18				06 45	07 07	07 23		07 33		08 05	08 15				08 50	09 11	09 23			09 50
Sankey for Penketh d	00 11			06 23						07 28					08 20						09 28			
Warrington Central a	00 16			06 28			06 37	06 53	07 15	07 34		07 39	07 56	08 13	08 25			08 44	08 58	09 18	09 33		09 44	09 58
d	00 17						06 38	06 53	07 15			07 40	07 57	08 13	08 25			08 45	08 59	09 19	09 34		09 45	09 59
Padgate d								06 56					08 00						09 02					10 02
Birchwood d							06 43	07 00	07 20			07 45	08 03	08 18	08 30			08 50	09 05		09 38		09 50	10 05
Glazebrook d								07 05					08 08											10 10
Irlam d								07 08				07 50	08 11		08 37				09 11		09 44			10 13
Flixton d								07 13					08 15		08 41				09 15					10 17
Chassen Road d								07 15					08 17		08 43									10 19
Urmston d								07 17					08 19		08 46				09 18		09 49			10 21
Humphrey Park d								07 20					08 21		08 49				09 20					
Trafford Park d								07 22					08 24		08 52				09 23					
Deansgate 84,85 🚊 a								07 31					08 32		09 00				09 30		09 59			10 30
Manchester Oxford Road 84,85 a					06 56		06 59	07 35	07 38		07 56	08 04	08 36	08 38	09 04		08 56	09 05	09 35	09 39	10 04	09 56	10 05	10 35
ManchesterPicc 10 78,84,85 🚊 a	00 40	04 14	05 56		07 00		07 08		07 41		08 01	08 08		08 41			09 00	09 09		09 41		10 00	10 09	
Stockport 84 a									07 53					08 53						09 53				
Sheffield 7 78 🚊 a									08 34					09 34						10 34				
Manchester Airport 85,84 ✈ a		04 30	06 14		07 22						08 22						09 22					10 22		

	EM		NT	NT	TP	NT	EM	NT	NT	TP	NT		EM	NT	NT	TP	NT	EM	NT	NT	TP		NT	EM
	◇				◇1		◇			◇1			◇			◇1		◇			◇1			◇
	C				B		C			B			C			B		C			B			C
Liverpool Lime Street 10 90,91 d	09 52		09 55	10 13	10 22	10 27	10 52	10 55	11 13	11 22	11 27		11 52	11 55	12 13	12 22	12 27	12 52	12 55	13 13	13 22		13 27	13 52
Edge Hill 90,91 d			09 59					10 59						11 59					12 59					
Mossley Hill 91 d			10 04			10 35		11 04			11 35			12 04			12 35		13 04				13 35	
West Allerton 91 d			10 06			10 37		11 06			11 37			12 06			12 37		13 06				13 37	
L'pool Sth Parkway 7 91,103 ✈ d	10 03		10 09		10 32	10 40	11 03	11 09		11 32	11 40		12 03	12 09		12 32	12 40	13 03	13 09		13 32		13 40	14 03
Hunts Cross 103 d			10 13					11 13						12 13					13 13					
Halewood d			10 16					11 16						12 16					13 16					
Hough Green d			10 20			10 47		11 20			11 47			12 20			12 47		13 20				13 47	
Widnes d	10 11		10 23			10 50	11 11	11 23			11 50		12 11	12 23			12 50	13 11	13 23				13 50	14 11
Sankey for Penketh d			10 28					11 28						12 28					13 28					
Warrington Central a	10 18		10 33		10 44	10 58	11 18	11 33		11 44	11 58		12 18	12 33		12 44	12 58	13 18	13 33		13 44		13 58	14 18
d	10 19		10 34		10 45	10 59	11 19	11 34		11 45	11 59		12 19	12 34		12 45	12 59	13 19	13 34		13 45		13 59	14 19
Padgate d						11 02					12 02						13 02						14 02	
Birchwood d			10 38		10 50	11 05		11 38		11 50	12 05			12 38		12 50	13 05		13 38		13 50		14 05	
Glazebrook d											12 10												14 10	
Irlam d			10 44			11 11		11 44			12 13			12 44			13 11		13 44				14 13	
Flixton d						11 15					12 17						13 15						14 17	
Chassen Road d											12 19												14 19	
Urmston d			10 49			11 18		11 49			12 21			12 49			13 18		13 49				14 21	
Humphrey Park d						11 20											13 20							
Trafford Park d						11 23											13 23							
Deansgate 84,85 🚊 a			10 59			11 30		11 59			12 30			12 59			13 30		13 59				14 30	
Manchester Oxford Road 84,85 a	10 39		11 04	10 56	11 05	11 35	11 39	12 04	11 56	12 05	12 35		12 39	13 04	12 56	13 05	13 35	13 39	14 04	13 56	14 05		14 35	14 39
ManchesterPicc 10 78,84,85 🚊 a	10 41			11 00	11 09		11 41		12 00	12 09			12 41		13 00	13 09		13 41		14 00	14 09			14 41
Stockport 84 a	10 53						11 53						12 53					13 53						14 53
Sheffield 7 78 🚊 a	11 34						12 34						13 34					14 34						15 34
Manchester Airport 85,84 ✈ a				11 22					12 22						13 22					14 22				

	NT	NT	TP	NT	EM	NT	NT		TP	NT	EM	NT	NT	TP	NT	EM	NT		NT	TP	NT	EM	NT	NT
			◇1		◇				◇1		◇			◇1		◇				◇1		◇		
			B		C				B		C			B		D				B		C		
Liverpool Lime Street 10 90,91 d	13 55	14 13	14 22	14 27	14 52	14 55	15 13		15 22	15 27	15 52	15 55	16 13	16 22	16 27	16 52	16 55		17 06	17 22	17 25	17 52	17 55	18 13
Edge Hill 90,91 d	13 59					14 59						15 59					16 59				17 29		17 59	
Mossley Hill 91 d	14 04			14 35		15 04				15 35		16 04			16 35		17 04				17 34		18 04	
West Allerton 91 d	14 06			14 37		15 06				15 37		16 06			16 37		17 06				17 36		18 06	
L'pool Sth Parkway 7 91,103 ✈ d	14 09		14 32	14 40	15 03	15 09			15 32	15 40	16 03	16 09		16 32	16 40	17 03	17 09			17 32	17 39	18 03	18 09	
Hunts Cross 103 d	14 13					15 13						16 13					17 13				17 43		18 13	
Halewood d	14 16					15 16						16 16					17 16				17 46		18 16	
Hough Green d	14 20			14 47		15 20				15 47		16 20			16 47		17 20				17 50		18 20	
Widnes d	14 23			14 50	15 11	15 23				15 50	16 11	16 23			16 50	17 11	17 23				17 54	18 11	18 23	
Sankey for Penketh d	14 28					15 28						16 28					17 28				17 58		18 28	
Warrington Central a	14 33		14 44	14 58	15 18	15 33			15 44	15 58	16 18	16 33		16 44	16 58	17 18	17 33			17 44	18 03	18 18	18 33	
d	14 34		14 45	14 59	15 19	15 34			15 45	15 59	16 19	16 34		16 45	16 59	17 19	17 34			17 45	18 04	18 19	18 34	
Padgate d				15 02						16 02					17 02						18 07			
Birchwood d	14 38		14 50	15 05		15 38			15 50	16 05		16 38		16 50	17 05		17 38			17 50	18 10		18 38	
Glazebrook d										16 10														
Irlam d	14 44			15 11		15 44				16 13		16 44			17 11		17 44				18 16		18 44	
Flixton d				15 15						16 17					17 15						18 20			
Chassen Road d										16 19														
Urmston d	14 49			15 18		15 49				16 21		16 49			17 18		17 49				18 23		18 49	
Humphrey Park d				15 20											17 20									
Trafford Park d				15 23											17 23									
Deansgate 84,85 🚊 a	14 59			15 30		15 59				16 30		16 59			17 30		17 59				18 31		18 59	
Manchester Oxford Road 84,85 a	15 04	14 56	15 05	15 35	15 39	16 04	15 56		16 05	16 35	16 38	17 04	16 56	17 05	17 35	17 38	18 04		17 56	18 05	18 36	18 39	19 04	18 56
ManchesterPicc 10 78,84,85 🚊 a		15 00	15 09		15 41		16 00		16 09		16 41		17 00	17 09		17 41			18 00	18 09		18 41		19 00
Stockport 84 a					15 53						16 53					17 53						18 53		
Sheffield 7 78 🚊 a					16 34						17 37					18 36						19 33		
Manchester Airport 85,84 ✈ a		15 22					16 22						17 22						18 22					19 23

A From Liverpool Lime Street
B To Scarborough
C To Norwich
D To Nottingham

Table 89R

Saturdays

14 December to 17 May

Liverpool - Warrington Central - Manchester and Manchester Airport

Network Diagram - see first Page of Table 88

		TP	NT	EM		NT	TP	NT	EM	NT	NT	TP	EM	NT		EM	NT	TP	NT
		◇1		◇			◇1		◇			◇1	◇			◇		◇1	
		A		B			C		B			C	B			B		C	
Liverpool Lime Street 10 90,91	d	18 22	18 25	18 52		18 55	19 22		19 52	19 55	20 09	20 22	20 52	20 55		21 37	21 55	22 30	23 38
Edge Hill 90,91	d		18 29			18 59				19 59				20 59			21 59		23 42
Mossley Hill 91	d		18 34			19 04				20 04				21 04			22 04		23 47
West Allerton 91	d		18 36			19 06				20 06				21 06			22 06		23 50
L'pool Sth Parkway 7 91,103 ✈	d	18 32	18 39	19 03		19 09	19 32		20 03	20 09		20 32	21 03	21 09		21 47	22 09	22 40	23 53
Hunts Cross 103	d		18 43			19 13				20 13				21 13			22 13		23 56
Halewood	d		18 46			19 16				20 16				21 16			22 16		23 59
Hough Green	d		18 50			19 20				20 20				21 20			22 20		00 03
Widnes	d		18 53	19 11		19 23			20 11	20 23			21 11	21 23		21 55	22 23		00 06
Sankey for Penketh	d		18 58			19 28				20 28				21 28			22 28		00 11
Warrington Central	a	18 44	19 03	19 18		19 34	19 44		20 18	20 34		20 44	21 18	21 33		22 03	22 33	22 52	00 16
	d	18 45	19 04	19 19			19 45	19 56	20 19			20 45	21 19	21 34		22 03	22 34	22 53	00 17
Padgate	d		19 07					19 59						21 37			22 37		
Birchwood	d	18 50	19 10				19 50	20 02				20 50		21 40			22 40	22 58	
Glazebrook	d		19 15					20 07						21 45			22 45		
Irlam	d		19 18					20 10						21 48			22 48		
Flixton	d							20 14						21 52			22 52		
Chassen Road	d							20 16						21 54			22 54		
Urmston	d		19 23					20 18						21 56			22 56		
Humphrey Park	d							20 20						21 58			22 58		
Trafford Park	d							20 23						22 01			23 01		
Deansgate 84,85 🚊	a		19 31					20 30						22 08			23 08		
Manchester Oxford Road 84,85	a	19 05	19 36	19 39			20 05	20 35	20 39		20 56	21 06	21 38	22 13		22 23	23 13	23 14	
ManchesterPicc 10 78,84,85 🚊	a	19 09		19 41			20 09		20 41		21 00	21 09	21 41			22 26		23 19	00 39
Stockport 84	a			19 53					20 53				21 51			22 37			
Sheffield 7 78 🚊	a			20 36					21 34				22 31			23 35			
Manchester Airport 85,84 ✈	a										21 19								

Sundays

8 December to 29 December

		NT	NT	TP	NT	NT	TP	NT	NT	TP		NT	NT	TP	NT	NT	TP	NT	EM	NT		TP	NT	EM	NT
				◇1			◇1			◇1				◇1			◇1		◇			◇1		◇	
		D		E			A			F				A			F		G			A		G	
Liverpool Lime Street 10 90,91	d		08 05	08 22	08 28	09 01	09 22	09 27	10 01	10 22		10 28	11 01	11 22	11 26	12 01	12 22	12 26	12 52	13 01		13 22	13 26	13 52	14 01
Edge Hill 90,91	d																								
Mossley Hill 91	d				08 36			09 35				10 36			11 34			12 34					13 34		
West Allerton 91	d				08 38			09 37				10 38			11 36			12 36					13 36		
L'pool Sth Parkway 7 91,103 ✈	d			08 32	08 41		09 32	09 40		10 32		10 41		11 32	11 39		12 32	12 39	13 03			13 32	13 39	14 03	
Hunts Cross 103	d				08 45			09 44				10 45			11 43			12 43					13 43		
Halewood	d				08 47			09 47				10 47			11 46			12 46					13 46		
Hough Green	d	00 03			08 51			09 51				10 51			11 50			12 50					13 50		
Widnes	d	00 06			08 55			09 54				10 55			11 53			12 53	13 11				13 53	14 11	
Sankey for Penketh	d	00 11																							
Warrington Central	a	00 16		08 44	09 03		09 44	10 02		10 44		11 03		11 44	12 01		12 44	13 01	13 18			13 44	14 01	14 18	
	d	00 17		08 45	09 03		09 45	10 03		10 45		11 03		11 45	12 02		12 45	13 02	13 19			13 45	14 02	14 19	
Padgate	d																								
Birchwood	d			08 50	09 08		09 50	10 07		10 50		11 08		11 50	12 06		12 50	13 06				13 50	14 06		
Glazebrook	d																								
Irlam	d				09 14			10 13				11 14			12 12			13 12					14 12		
Flixton	d																								
Chassen Road	d																								
Urmston	d				09 19			10 18				11 19			12 17			13 17					14 17		
Humphrey Park	d																								
Trafford Park	d																								
Deansgate 84,85 🚊	a				09 29			10 28				11 29			12 28			13 28					14 28		
Manchester Oxford Road 84,85	a		09 02	09 05	09 33	09 59	10 05	10 32	10 59	11 05		11 33	11 59	12 05	12 31	12 59	13 05	13 32	13 39	13 57		14 05	14 32	14 38	14 59
ManchesterPicc 10 78,84,85 🚊	a	00 39	09 06	09 10		10 03	10 09		11 03	11 09			12 02	12 09		13 02	13 09		13 41	14 01		14 09		14 41	15 02
Stockport 84	a																		13 53					14 53	
Sheffield 7 78 🚊	a																		14 37					15 35	
Manchester Airport 85,84 ✈	a		09 22			10 24			11 24				12 20			13 18				14 21					15 20

A To Scarborough
B To Nottingham
C To York
D not 8 December. From Liverpool Lime Street
E To Hull
F To Middlesbrough
G To Norwich

Table 89R

Sundays

8 December to 29 December

Liverpool - Warrington Central - Manchester and Manchester Airport

Network Diagram - see first Page of Table 88

		TP ◇1 A		NT	EM ◇ B	NT	TP ◇1 C	NT	EM ◇ B	NT	TP ◇1 A	NT		EM ◇ D	NT	TP ◇1 C	NT	EM ◇ B	NT	TP ◇1 C	NT	EM ◇ D		NT	TP ◇1 E
Liverpool Lime Street 10 90,91	d	14 22		14 26	14 52	15 01	15 22	15 26	15 52	16 01	16 22	16 26		16 52	17 01	17 22	17 26	17 52	18 01	18 22	18 26	18 52		19 01	19 22
Edge Hill 90,91	d																								
Mossley Hill 91	d			14 34				15 33				16 34					17 34				18 34				
West Allerton 91	d			14 36				15 36				16 36					17 36				18 36				
L'pool Sth Parkway 7 91,103 ✈	d	14 32		14 39	15 03		15 32	15 39	16 03		16 32	16 39		17 03		17 32	17 39	18 03		18 32	18 39	19 03			19 32
Hunts Cross 103	d			14 43				15 43				16 43					17 43				18 43				
Halewood	d			14 46				15 45				16 46					17 46				18 46				
Hough Green	d			14 50				15 49				16 50					17 50				18 50				
Widnes	d			14 53	15 11			15 53	16 11			16 53		17 11			17 53	18 11			18 53	19 11			
Sankey for Penketh	d																								
Warrington Central	a	14 44		15 01	15 18		15 44	16 01	16 18		16 44	17 01		17 18		17 44	18 01	18 18		18 44	19 01	19 18			19 44
	d	14 45		15 02	15 19		15 45	16 01	16 19		16 45	17 02		17 19		17 45	18 02	18 19		18 45	19 02	19 19			19 45
Padgate	d																								
Birchwood	d	14 50		15 06			15 50	16 06			16 50	17 06				17 50	18 06			18 50	19 06				19 50
Glazebrook	d																								
Irlam	d			15 12				16 12				17 12					18 12				19 12				
Flixton	d																								
Chassen Road	d																								
Urmston	d			15 17				16 17				17 17					18 17				19 17				
Humphrey Park	d																								
Trafford Park	d																								
Deansgate 84,85 🚊	a			15 28				16 28				17 28					18 28				19 28				
Manchester Oxford Road 84,85	a	15 05		15 32	15 38	15 59	16 05	16 31	16 38	16 59	17 05	17 32		17 38	17 59	18 05	18 32	18 39	18 59	19 05	19 32	19 39		19 59	20 05
ManchesterPicc 10 78,84,85 🚊	a	15 09			15 41	16 02	16 09		16 41	17 02	17 09			17 41	18 02	18 09		18 41	19 02	19 09		19 41		20 02	20 09
Stockport 84	a				15 53				16 53					17 53				18 53				19 53			
Sheffield 7 78 🚊	a				16 37				17 34					18 36				19 35				20 35			
Manchester Airport 85,84 ✈	a					16 21				17 21					18 21				19 21					20 23	

		NT	EM ◇ D	NT	TP ◇1 F	NT	NT	EM ◇ D		NT	TP ◇1 E	NT 🚌	NT	NT	NT	NT 🚌
Liverpool Lime Street 10 90,91	d	19 26	19 52	20 01	20 22	20 26	21 01	21 21		21 26	21 52	22 01	22 13	22 26	23 01	23 01
Edge Hill 90,91	d															
Mossley Hill 91	d	19 34				20 34				21 34				22 34		
West Allerton 91	d	19 36				20 36				21 36				22 36		
L'pool Sth Parkway 7 91,103 ✈	d	19 39	20 03		20 32	20 39		21 31		21 39	22 02			22 39		
Hunts Cross 103	d	19 43				20 43				21 43				22 43		
Halewood	d	19 46				20 46				21 46				22 46		
Hough Green	d	19 50				20 50				21 50				22 50		
Widnes	d	19 53	20 11			20 53		21 39		21 53				22 53		
Sankey for Penketh	d															
Warrington Central	a	20 01	20 18		20 44	21 01		21 47		22 01	22 14			23 01		
	d	20 02	20 19		20 45	21 02		21 47		22 02	22 15			23 02		
Padgate	d															
Birchwood	d	20 06			20 50	21 06				22 06	22 20			23 06		
Glazebrook	d															
Irlam	d	20 12				21 12				22 12				23 12		
Flixton	d															
Chassen Road	d															
Urmston	d	20 17				21 17				22 17				23 17		
Humphrey Park	d															
Trafford Park	d															
Deansgate 84,85 🚊	a	20 28				21 28				22 27				23 27		
Manchester Oxford Road 84,85	a	20 32	20 39	20 59	21 05	21 32	21 59	22 06		22 31	22 35	00 12	22 58	23 31	23 47	01 12
ManchesterPicc 10 78,84,85 🚊	a		20 41	21 02	21 09		22 02	22 09			22 39		23 01		23 50	
Stockport 84	a		20 53					22 20								
Sheffield 7 78 🚊	a		21 34					23 24								
Manchester Airport 85,84 ✈	a			21 20			22 21						23 17		00 07	

A To Middlesbrough
B To Norwich
C To Scarborough
D To Nottingham
E To York
F To Newcastle

Table 89R

Sundays

5 January to 11 May

Liverpool - Warrington Central - Manchester and Manchester Airport

Network Diagram - see first Page of Table 88

		NT	NT	NT	NT	TP		TP	NT	NT	NT	TP	NT	NT	NT	TP		NT	NT	NT	TP	NT	NT	NT	TP
						◇1		◇1				◇1				◇1					◇1				◇1
		A				B		C				D			E	F					D				F
			🚌	🚌						🚌				🚌					🚌				🚌		
Liverpool Lime Street ■10 90,91	d		06 48	07 48	08 12	08 22		08 22	08 28	08 48	09 13	09 22	09 27	09 48	10 13	10 22		10 28	10 48	11 13	11 22	11 26	11 48	12 13	12 22
Edge Hill 90,91	d																								
Mossley Hill 91	d								08 36				09 35					10 36				11 34			
West Allerton 91	d								08 38				09 37					10 38				11 36			
L'pool Sth Parkway ■7 91,103 ✈	d					08 32		08 32	08 41			09 32	09 40			10 32		10 41			11 32	11 39			12 32
Hunts Cross 103	d								08 45				09 44					10 45				11 43			
Halewood	d								08 47				09 47					10 47				11 46			
Hough Green	d	00 03							08 51				09 51					10 51				11 50			
Widnes	d	00 06							08 55				09 54					10 55				11 53			
Sankey for Penketh	d	00 11																							
Warrington Central	a	00 16				08 44		08 44	09 03			09 44	10 02			10 44		11 03			11 44	12 01			12 44
	d	00 17				08 45		08 45	09 03			09 45	10 03			10 45		11 03			11 45	12 02			12 45
Padgate	d																								
Birchwood	d					08 50		08 50	09 08			09 50	10 07			10 50		11 08			11 50	12 06			12 50
Glazebrook	d																								
Irlam	d								09 14				10 13					11 14				12 12			
Flixton	d																								
Chassen Road	d																								
Urmston	d								09 19				10 18					11 19				12 17			
Humphrey Park	d																								
Trafford Park	d																								
Deansgate 84,85 🚊	a								09 29				10 28					11 29				12 28			
Manchester Oxford Road 84,85	a		08 59	09 59	08 57	09 05		09 06	09 33	10 59	09 56	10 05	10 32	11 59	10 57	11 05		11 33	12 59	11 57	12 05	12 31	13 59	12 57	13 05
ManchesterPicc ■10 78,84,85 🚊	a	00 39			09 05	09 10		09 10			10 00	10 09			11 01	11 09				12 01	12 09			13 01	13 09
Stockport 84	a																								
Sheffield ■7 78 🚊	a																								
Manchester Airport 85,84 ✈	a				09 21						10 15				11 17					12 15				13 18	

		NT		NT	EM	NT	TP	NT	NT	EM	NT	TP		NT	NT	EM	EM	EM	NT	TP	NT	NT		EM	NT
					◇		◇1			◇		◇1				◇	◇	◇		◇1				◇	
					G		D			G		F				H	I	J		D				G	
				🚌					🚌						🚌							🚌			
Liverpool Lime Street ■10 90,91	d	12 26		12 48	12 52	13 13	13 22	13 26	13 48	13 52	14 13	14 22		14 26	14 48	14 52	14 52	14 52	15 13	15 22	15 26	15 48		15 52	16 13
Edge Hill 90,91	d																								
Mossley Hill 91	d	12 34						13 34						14 34							15 33				
West Allerton 91	d	12 36						13 36						14 36							15 36				
L'pool Sth Parkway ■7 91,103 ✈	d	12 39			13 03		13 32	13 39		14 03		14 32		14 39		15 03	15 03	15 03		15 32	15 39			16 03	
Hunts Cross 103	d	12 43						13 43						14 43							15 43				
Halewood	d	12 46						13 46						14 46							15 45				
Hough Green	d	12 50						13 50						14 50							15 49				
Widnes	d	12 53			13 11			13 53		14 11				14 53		15 11	15 11	15 11			15 53			16 11	
Sankey for Penketh	d																								
Warrington Central	a	13 01			13 18		13 44	14 01		14 18		14 44		15 01		15 18	15 18	15 18		15 44	16 01			16 18	
	d	13 02			13 19		13 45	14 02		14 19		14 45		15 02		15 19	15 19	15 19		15 45	16 01			16 19	
Padgate	d																								
Birchwood	d	13 06					13 50	14 06				14 50		15 06						15 50	16 06				
Glazebrook	d																								
Irlam	d	13 12						14 12						15 12							16 12				
Flixton	d																								
Chassen Road	d																								
Urmston	d	13 17						14 17						15 17							16 17				
Humphrey Park	d																								
Trafford Park	d																								
Deansgate 84,85 🚊	a	13 28						14 28						15 28							16 28				
Manchester Oxford Road 84,85	a	13 32		14 59	13 39	13 57	14 05	14 32	15 59	14 38	14 57	15 05		15 32	16 59	15 38	15 38	15 39	15 57	16 05	16 31	17 59		16 38	16 57
ManchesterPicc ■10 78,84,85 🚊	a				13 41	14 01	14 09			14 41	15 01	15 09				15 41	15 41	15 41	16 01	16 09				16 41	17 01
Stockport 84	a				13 53					14 53						15 53	15 53	15 53						16 53	
Sheffield ■7 78 🚊	a				14 37					15 35						16 37	16 39	16 37						17 34	
Manchester Airport 85,84 ✈	a					14 15					15 15								16 15						17 15

- **A** From Liverpool Lime Street
- **B** until 9 February, from 30 March. To Hull
- **C** from 16 February until 23 March. To Hull
- **D** To Scarborough
- **E** from 16 February until 23 March
- **F** To Middlesbrough
- **G** To Norwich
- **H** until 9 February. To Norwich
- **I** from 16 February until 23 March. To Norwich
- **J** from 30 March. To Norwich

Table 89R

Sundays

5 January to 11 May

Liverpool - Warrington Central - Manchester and Manchester Airport

Network Diagram - see first Page of Table 88

		TP	NT	NT	EM	EM	NT	TP	NT	NT	EM	NT	TP	NT	NT	EM	NT	NT	TP	NT	NT	EM
		◇1			◇	◇		◇1			◇		◇1			◇			◇1			◇
		A			B	C		D			E		D			F	G	H	I			F
				bus						bus					bus						bus	
Liverpool Lime Street [10] 90,91	d	16 22	16 26	16 48	16 52	16 52	17 13	17 22	17 26	17 48	17 52	18 13	18 22	18 26	18 48	18 52	19 13	19 13	19 22	19 26	19 48	19 52
Edge Hill 90,91	d																					
Mossley Hill 91	d		16 34						17 34					18 34						19 34		
West Allerton 91	d		16 36						17 36					18 36						19 36		
L'pool Sth Parkway [7] 91,103 ✈	d	16 32	16 39		17 03	17 03		17 32	17 39		18 03		18 32	18 39		19 03			19 32	19 39		20 03
Hunts Cross 103	d		16 43						17 43					18 43						19 43		
Halewood	d		16 46						17 46					18 46						19 46		
Hough Green	d		16 50						17 50					18 50						19 50		
Widnes	d		16 53		17 11	17 11			17 53		18 11			18 53		19 11				19 53		20 11
Sankey for Penketh	d																					
Warrington Central	a	16 44	17 01		17 18	17 18		17 44	18 01		18 18		18 44	19 01		19 18			19 44	20 01		20 18
	d	16 45	17 02		17 19	17 19		17 45	18 02		18 19		18 45	19 02		19 19			19 45	20 02		20 19
Padgate	d																					
Birchwood	d	16 50	17 06					17 50	18 06				18 50	19 06					19 50	20 06		
Glazebrook	d																					
Irlam	d		17 12						18 12					19 12						20 12		
Flixton	d																					
Chassen Road	d																					
Urmston	d		17 17						18 17					19 17						20 17		
Humphrey Park	d																					
Trafford Park	d																					
Deansgate 84,85 ⛴	a		17 28						18 28					19 28						20 28		
Manchester Oxford Road 84,85	a	17 05	17 32	18 59	17 38	17 38	17 57	18 05	18 32	19 59	18 39	18 57	19 05	19 32	20 59	19 39	19 57	19 57	20 05	20 32	21 59	20 39
ManchesterPicc [10] 78,84,85 ⛴	a	17 09			17 41	17 41	18 01	18 09			18 41	19 01	19 09			19 41	20 01	20 01	20 09			20 41
Stockport 84	a				17 53	17 53					18 53					19 53						20 53
Sheffield [7] 78 ⛴	a				18 36	18 41					19 35					20 35						21 34
Manchester Airport 85,84 ✈	a						18 15					19 16					20 15	20 23				

		NT	TP	NT	NT	NT	EM	NT	TP	NT	NT	NT	NT	NT
			◇1				◇		◇1					
			J				F		I					
					bus					bus				bus
Liverpool Lime Street [10] 90,91	d	20 13	20 22	20 26	20 48	21 13	21 21	21 26	21 52	22 01	22 13	22 26	23 01	23 01
Edge Hill 90,91	d													
Mossley Hill 91	d			20 34				21 34				22 34		
West Allerton 91	d			20 36				21 36				22 36		
L'pool Sth Parkway [7] 91,103 ✈	d		20 32	20 39			21 31	21 39	22 02			22 39		
Hunts Cross 103	d			20 43				21 43				22 43		
Halewood	d			20 46				21 46				22 46		
Hough Green	d			20 50				21 50				22 50		
Widnes	d			20 53			21 39	21 53				22 53		
Sankey for Penketh	d													
Warrington Central	a		20 44	21 01			21 47	22 01	22 14			23 01		
	d		20 45	21 02			21 47	22 02	22 15			23 02		
Padgate	d													
Birchwood	d		20 50	21 06				22 06	22 20			23 06		
Glazebrook	d													
Irlam	d			21 12				22 12				23 12		
Flixton	d													
Chassen Road	d													
Urmston	d			21 17				22 17				23 17		
Humphrey Park	d													
Trafford Park	d													
Deansgate 84,85 ⛴	a			21 28				22 27				23 27		
Manchester Oxford Road 84,85	a	20 57	21 05	21 32	22 59	21 57	22 06	22 31	22 35	00 12	22 58	23 31	23 47	01 12
ManchesterPicc [10] 78,84,85 ⛴	a	21 01	21 09			22 01	22 09		22 39		23 01		23 50	
Stockport 84	a						22 20							
Sheffield [7] 78 ⛴	a						23 24							
Manchester Airport 85,84 ✈	a	21 15				22 15					23 17		00 07	

A To Middlesbrough
B until 9 February, from 30 March. To Nottingham
C from 16 February until 23 March. To Nottingham
D To Scarborough
E To Norwich
F To Nottingham
G from 16 February
H until 9 February
I To York
J To Newcastle

Table 90

Mondays to Fridays

9 December to 16 May

Manchester, Preston, Wigan and Newton-le-Willows - St Helens and Liverpool

Network Diagram - see first Page of Table 88

Miles	Miles	Miles	Miles		TP	NT	NT	NT	NT	NT	NT	NT	NT		NT	AW	AW	AW	NT	NT	NT	NT	NT	
					MO	MX	MO	MX	MO	MX	MO	MX												
																	◇	◇						
					A	B	B	B	C	D	B	D				E	F	G			H			
—	—	—	0	**Manchester Airport** 85 d	00 01												05 33							
—	—	—	9¾	**Manchester Piccadilly** d													05 50	05 50						
—	—	—	10¼	**Manchester Oxford Road** d													05 53	05 53						
0	—	—	—	**Manchester Victoria** d											05 39					06 09				
4	—	—	14½	Eccles d											05 46					06 16				
5	—	—	15½	Patricroft d											05 49					06 19				
—	—	—	—	Blackpool North 97 d	01a46																			
—	0	0	—	**Preston** 65,82 d																				
—	4	4	—	Leyland 82 d																				
—	6¾	6¾	—	Euxton Balshaw Lane d																				
—	15	15	—	**Wigan North Western** 65 a																				
—	—	—	—	d															06 08			06 38	06 47	
15½	—	22	26	**Newton-le-Willows** d								00 08			06 01		06 12	06 12		06 31			07 00	
—	—	—	—	Warrington Bank Quay d												06 06								
17	—	23½	27½	Earlestown d								00 16			06 04	06a12	06 15	06 15		06 34	06 50		07 03	
—	—	—	—	Warrington Bank Quay a													06 25	06 25			07 01			
19¾	—	26¼	30¼	**St Helens Junction** d					00 01			00 28			06 09					06 39			07 09	
21	—	27½	31½	Lea Green d					00 07	00 05		00 35			06 12					06 42			07 12	
22¾	—	29¼	33¼	Rainhill d					00 15	00 13		00 43			06 16					06 46			07 16	
24¼	—	30¼	34¼	Whiston d					00 25	00 23		00 53			06 19					06 49			07 19	
—	18¾	—	—	Bryn d															06 15			06 45		
—	20	—	—	Garswood d							00 07								06 19			06 49		
—	23¾	—	—	**St Helens Central** a							00 27								06 25			06 55		
—	—	—	—	d							00 27		05 56						06 26			06 56		
—	25¼	—	—	Thatto Heath d				00 05			00 37		05 59						06 29			06 59		
—	26¼	—	—	Eccleston Park d				00 15					06 02						06 32			07 02		
—	27¼	—	—	Prescot d				00 21			00 47		06 04						06 34			07 04		
26¼	29½	32¾	36¾	Huyton d				00 31	00 35	00 33	00 57	01 03	06 08		06 23				06 38	06 53		07 08	07 23	
26¾	30	33¼	37¼	Roby d			00 01	00 35	00 39	00 37	01 01	01 07	06 10		06 25				06 40	06 55		07 10	07 25	
28¼	31½	34¾	38¾	Broad Green d			00 08	00 42	00 46	00 44	01 08	01 14	06 13		06 28				06 43	06 58		07 13	07 28	
29¼	32½	35¾	39¾	Wavertree Technology Park d		00 02	00 18	00 52	00 56	00 54	01 18	01 24	06 16		06 31				06 46	07 01		07 16	07 31	
30	33¼	36½	40½	Edge Hill 91 d		00 12		01 02		01 04		01 34	06 19		06 34				06 49	07 04		07 19	07 35	
31¾	35	38¼	42¼	**Liverpool Lime Street** 91 a		00 20	00 33	01 10	01 11	01 12	01 33	01 42	06 28		06 43				06 58	07 13		07 28	07 41	

	AW	AW	NT	NT	NT	NT	NT	AW	NT		AW	NT	AW	NT	NT	NT	NT	NT	AW		NT	NT	NT	AW
	◇	◇									◇		◇						◇					◇
	I	J						E			K		L		H			M	N				O	L
Manchester Airport 85 d			06 41																		08 41			
Manchester Piccadilly d		06 50	06 58								07 50								08 50		09 01			
Manchester Oxford Road d		06 53	07 01								07 53								08 53		09 04			
Manchester Victoria d					07 09				07 39					08 09				08 39						
Eccles d					07 16				07 46					08 16				08 46						
Patricroft d					07 19				07 49					08 19				08 49						
Blackpool North 97 d							07 02																	
Preston 65,82 d							07 30																09 04	
Leyland 82 d							07 35																09 09	
Euxton Balshaw Lane d							07 40																09 14	
Wigan North Western 65 a							07 50																09 24	
d				07 08		07 38	07 50					07 58				08 28						09 08	09 24	
Newton-le-Willows d		07 11	07 19		07 31				08 01		08 12			08 31				09 01	09 12		09 22			
Warrington Bank Quay d	07 07							07 39					08 08											09 19
Earlestown d	07a14	07 15			07 34			07a46	08 04		08 15		08a15	08 34	08 50			09 04	09 15					09a26
Warrington Bank Quay a		07 22									08 23				09 01				09 25					
St Helens Junction d			07 24		07 39				08 09					08 39				09 09			09 27			
Lea Green d					07 42				08 12					08 42				09 12						
Rainhill d			07 29		07 46				08 16					08 46				09 16						
Whiston d					07 49				08 19					08 49				09 19						
Bryn d				07 15		07 45						08 05				08 35						09 15		
Garswood d				07 19		07 49	07 59					08 09				08 39						09 19		
St Helens Central a				07 25		07 55	08 06					08 15				08 45						09 25	09 39	
d				07 26		07 56	08 06					08 16				08 46	08 56					09 26	09 39	
Thatto Heath d				07 29		07 59						08 19				08 49	08 59					09 29		
Eccleston Park d				07 32		08 02						08 22				08 52	09 02					09 32		
Prescot d				07 34		08 04	08 12					08 24				08 54	09 04					09 34		
Huyton d			07 34	07 38	07 53	08 08	08 16		08 23			08 28		08 53		08 58	09 08	09 23				09 38	09 48	
Roby d				07 40	07 55	08 10			08 25			08 30		08 55		09 00	09 10	09 25				09 40		
Broad Green d				07 43	07 58	08 13	08 20		08 28			08 33		08 58		09 03	09 13	09 28				09 43		
Wavertree Technology Park d			07 39	07 46	08 01	08 16	08 24		08 31			08 36		09 01		09 06	09 16	09 31			09 38	09 46		
Edge Hill 91 d				07 49	08 04	08 19			08 34			08 39		09 04		09 09	09 19	09 34				09 49		
Liverpool Lime Street 91 a			07 49	07 58	08 13	08 28	08 35		08 43			08 50		09 13		09 18	09 28	09 43			09 48	09 58	10 01	

A from 6 January until 10 February
B From Wigan North Western
C From Manchester Oxford Road
D From Manchester Victoria
E From Chester to Manchester Piccadilly
F until 27 December, from 24 March. To Llandudno
G from 30 December until 21 March. To Llandudno
H From Liverpool Lime Street
I From Llandudno Junction to Manchester Piccadilly
J To Llandudno Junction
K To Holyhead
L From Llandudno to Manchester Piccadilly
M To Llandundo & Holyhead
N To Llandudno
O To Liverpool South Pw Hl

Table 90

Mondays to Fridays

9 December to 16 May

Manchester, Preston, Wigan and Newton-le-Willows - St Helens and Liverpool

Network Diagram - see first Page of Table 88

		NT	NT A	NT	NT B	AW ◇ C	NT	NT	NT D	AW ◇ E	NT	NT A	NT	NT B	AW ◇ F	NT	NT	NT D	AW ◇ G	NT	NT A	NT	NT B
Manchester Airport 85	d						09 41									10 41							
Manchester Piccadilly 10	d					09 50	10 01								10 50	11 01							
Manchester Oxford Road	d					09 53	10 04								10 53	11 04							
Manchester Victoria	d				09 39									10 39									11 39
Eccles	d				09 46									10 46									11 46
Patricroft	d				09 49									10 49									11 49
Blackpool North 97	d								09 35									10 35					
Preston 8 65,82	d								10 04									11 04					
Leyland 82	d								10 09									11 09					
Euxton Balshaw Lane	d								10 14									11 14					
Wigan North Western 65	a								10 24									11 24					
	d			09 38				10 08	10 24				10 38				11 08	11 24				11 38	
Newton-le-Willows	d				10 01	10 12	10 22							11 01	11 12	11 22							12 01
Warrington Bank Quay	d	09 22								10 19	10 22								11 19	11 22			
Earlestown 8	d	09 34	09 50		10 04	10 15				10a26	10 34	10 50		11 04	11 15				11a26	11 34	11 50		12 04
Warrington Bank Quay	a		10 01			10 25						10 59			11 25						12 01		
St Helens Junction	d	09 39			10 09		10 27				10 39			11 09		11 27				11 39			12 09
Lea Green	d	09 42			10 12						10 42			11 12						11 42			12 12
Rainhill	d	09 46			10 16						10 46			11 16						11 46			12 16
Whiston	d	09 49			10 19						10 49			11 19						11 49			12 19
Bryn	d			09 45				10 15					10 45				11 15					11 45	
Garswood	d			09 49				10 19					10 49				11 19					11 49	
St Helens Central	a			09 55				10 25	10 39				10 55				11 25	11 39				11 55	
	d			09 56				10 26	10 39				10 56				11 26	11 39				11 56	
Thatto Heath	d			09 59				10 29					10 59				11 29					11 59	
Eccleston Park	d			10 02				10 32					11 02				11 32					12 02	
Prescot	d			10 04				10 34					11 04				11 34					12 04	
Huyton	d	09 53		10 08	10 23			10 38	10 48		10 53		11 08	11 23			11 38	11 48		11 53		12 08	12 23
Roby	d	09 55		10 10	10 25			10 40			10 55		11 10	11 25			11 40			11 55		12 10	12 25
Broad Green	d	09 58		10 13	10 28			10 43			10 58		11 13	11 28			11 43			11 58		12 13	12 28
Wavertree Technology Park	d	10 01		10 16	10 31		10 38	10 46			11 01		11 16	11 31		11 38	11 46			12 01		12 16	12 31
Edge Hill 91	d	10 04		10 19	10 34			10 49			11 04		11 19	11 34			11 49			12 04		12 19	12 34
Liverpool Lime Street 10 91	a	10 13		10 28	10 43		10 48	10 58	11 01		11 13		11 28	11 43		11 48	11 58	12 01		12 13		12 28	12 43

		AW ◇ C	NT	NT	NT D	AW ◇ G	NT	NT A	NT	NT B	AW ◇ C	NT	NT	NT D	AW ◇ G	NT	NT A	NT	NT B	AW ◇ C	NT	NT
Manchester Airport 85	d		11 41									12 41									13 41	
Manchester Piccadilly 10	d	11 50	12 01								12 50	13 01								13 50	14 01	
Manchester Oxford Road	d	11 53	12 04								12 53	13 04								13 53	14 04	
Manchester Victoria	d									12 39									13 39			
Eccles	d									12 46									13 46			
Patricroft	d									12 49									13 49			
Blackpool North 97	d				11 35									12 35								
Preston 8 65,82	d				12 04									13 04								
Leyland 82	d				12 09									13 09								
Euxton Balshaw Lane	d				12 14									13 14								
Wigan North Western 65	a				12 24									13 23								
	d			12 08	12 24				12 38				13 08	13 24				13 38				14 08
Newton-le-Willows	d	12 12	12 22							13 01	13 12	13 22							14 01	14 12	14 22	
Warrington Bank Quay	d					12 19	12 22								13 19	13 22						
Earlestown 8	d	12 15				12a26	12 34	12 50		13 04	13 15				13a26	13 34	13 50		14 04	14 15		
Warrington Bank Quay	a	12 25						13 01			13 25						14 01			14 25		
St Helens Junction	d		12 27				12 39			13 09		13 27				13 39			14 09		14 27	
Lea Green	d						12 42			13 12						13 42			14 12			
Rainhill	d						12 46			13 16						13 46			14 16			
Whiston	d						12 49			13 19						13 49			14 19			
Bryn	d			12 15					12 45				13 15					13 45				14 15
Garswood	d			12 19					12 49				13 19					13 49				14 19
St Helens Central	a			12 25	12 39				12 55				13 25	13 39				13 55				14 25
	d			12 26	12 39				12 56				13 26	13 39				13 56				14 26
Thatto Heath	d			12 29					12 59				13 29					13 59				14 29
Eccleston Park	d			12 32					13 02				13 32					14 02				14 32
Prescot	d			12 34					13 04				13 34					14 04				14 34
Huyton	d			12 38	12 48		12 53		13 08	13 23			13 38	13 48		13 53		14 08	14 23			14 38
Roby	d			12 40			12 55		13 10	13 25			13 40			13 55		14 10	14 25			14 40
Broad Green	d			12 43			12 58		13 13	13 28			13 43			13 58		14 13	14 28			14 43
Wavertree Technology Park	d		12 38	12 46			13 01		13 16	13 31		13 38	13 46			14 01		14 16	14 31		14 38	14 46
Edge Hill 91	d			12 49			13 04		13 19	13 34			13 50			14 04		14 19	14 34			14 49
Liverpool Lime Street 10 91	a		12 48	12 58	13 01		13 13		13 28	13 43		13 48	13 58	14 01		14 13		14 28	14 43		14 48	14 58

A From Liverpool Lime Street
B From Stalybridge
C To Llandudno
D To Liverpool South Pw Hl
E From Llandudno Junction to Manchester Piccadilly
F To Bangor (Gwynedd)
G From Llandudno to Manchester Piccadilly

Table 90

Mondays to Fridays

9 December to 16 May

Manchester, Preston, Wigan and Newton-le-Willows - St Helens and Liverpool

Network Diagram - see first Page of Table 88

		NT	AW	NT	NT	NT	NT	AW		NT	NT	NT	AW	NT	NT	NT	TP	NT		AW	NT	NT	NT	AW	NT
			◇					◇					◇				◇1			◇				◇	
		A	B		C		D	E				A	F		C		G	D		E				B	
Manchester Airport 85	d									14 41							15 00				15 41				
Manchester Piccadilly 10	d							14 50		15 01							15 16			15 50	16 01				
Manchester Oxford Road	d							14 53		15 04							15 19			15 53	16 04				
Manchester Victoria	d						14 39											15 39							
Eccles	d						14 46											15 46							
Patricroft	d						14 49											15 49							
Blackpool North 97	d	13 35										14 35											15 35		
Preston 8 65,82	d	14 04										15 04											16 04		
Leyland 82	d	14 09										15 09											16 09		
Euxton Balshaw Lane	d	14 14										15 14											16 14		
Wigan North Western 65	a	14 24										15 24					15 43						16 24		
	d	14 24				14 38					15 08	15 24				15 38						16 08	16 24		
Newton-le-Willows	d						15 01	15 12		15 22								16 01		16 12	16 22				
Warrington Bank Quay	d		14 19	14 22									15 19	15 22										16 19	16 22
Earlestown 8	d		14a26	14 34	14 50		15 04	15 15					15a26	15 34	15 50			16 04		16 15				16a26	16 34
Warrington Bank Quay	a				15 01			15 25							16 01					16 26					
St Helens Junction	d			14 39			15 09			15 27				15 39				16 09			16 27				16 39
Lea Green	d			14 42			15 12							15 42				16 12							16 42
Rainhill	d			14 46			15 16							15 46				16 16							16 46
Whiston	d			14 49			15 19							15 49				16 19							16 49
Bryn	d					14 45					15 15					15 45						16 15			
Garswood	d					14 49					15 19					15 49						16 19			
St Helens Central	a	14 39				14 55					15 25	15 39				15 55						16 25	16 39		
	d	14 39				14 56					15 26	15 39				15 56						16 26	16 39		
Thatto Heath	d					14 59					15 29					15 59						16 29			
Eccleston Park	d					15 02					15 32					16 02						16 32			
Prescot	d					15 04					15 34					16 04						16 34			
Huyton	d	14 48		14 53		15 08	15 23				15 38	15 48		15 53		16 08		16 23				16 38	16 48		16 53
Roby	d			14 55		15 10	15 25				15 40			15 55		16 10		16 25				16 40			16 55
Broad Green	d			14 58		15 13	15 28				15 43			15 58		16 13		16 28				16 43			16 58
Wavertree Technology Park	d			15 01		15 16	15 31			15 38	15 46			16 01		16 16		16 31			16 38	16 46			17 01
Edge Hill 91	d			15 04		15 19	15 34				15 49			16 04		16 19		16 34				16 49			17 04
Liverpool Lime Street 10 91	a	15 01		15 13		15 28	15 43			15 48	15 58	16 01		16 13		16 28		16 43			16 48	16 58	17 05		17 13

		NT	AW	NT		AW	NT	NT	NT	NT	AW	NT	AW	NT		AW	NT	NT	NT	NT	NT	NT	TP	AW	
																							FO		
			◇			◇							◇			◇							◇1	◇	
			B	D		E					H		B			I				C			J	B	
Manchester Airport 85	d						16 41											17 41					18 00		
Manchester Piccadilly 10	d					16 50	17 01				17 19					17 50		18 01					18 16		
Manchester Oxford Road	d					16 53	17 04				17 22					17 53		18 04					18 19		
Manchester Victoria	d			16 39						17 09				17 37											
Eccles	d			16 46						17 16				17 46				18 11							
Patricroft	d			16 49						17 19				17 49											
Blackpool North 97	d								16 35												17 35				
Preston 8 65,82	d								17 04												18 04				
Leyland 82	d								17 09												18 09				
Euxton Balshaw Lane	d								17 14												18 14				
Wigan North Western 65	a								17 24												18 24		18 42		
	d	16 38						17 08	17 24			17 38					18 08		18 21		18 24	18 35			
Newton-le-Willows	d			17 01		17 12	17 22			17 31	17 40			18 01		18 11		18 24	18 33						
Warrington Bank Quay	d		16 51										17 49											18 46	
Earlestown 8	d		16a59	17 04		17 15				17 34	17 44		17a57	18 04		18 14			18 35	18 50				18a57	
Warrington Bank Quay	a					17 25					17 52					18 23				19 01					
St Helens Junction	d			17 09			17 27			17 39				18 09				18 29	18 41						
Lea Green	d			17 12						17 42				18 12				18 32	18 44						
Rainhill	d			17 16						17 46				18 16				18 36	18 48						
Whiston	d			17 19						17 49				18 19					18 51						
Bryn	d	16 45						17 15				17 45					18 15					18 45			
Garswood	d	16 49						17 19				17 49					18 19					18 49			
St Helens Central	a	16 55						17 25	17 39			17 55					18 25				18 39	18 55			
	d	16 56						17 26	17 39			17 56					18 26				18 39	18 56			
Thatto Heath	d	16 59						17 29				17 59					18 29					18 59			
Eccleston Park	d	17 02						17 32				18 02					18 32					19 02			
Prescot	d	17 04						17 34				18 04					18 34					19 04			
Huyton	d	17 08		17 23				17 38	17 48	17 53		18 08		18 23			18 38	18 41	18 54		18 48	19 08			
Roby	d	17 10		17 25				17 40		17 55		18 10		18 25				18 43	18 56			19 10			
Broad Green	d	17 13		17 28				17 43		17 58		18 13		18 28				18 46	19 00			19 13			
Wavertree Technology Park	d	17 16		17 31			17 38	17 46		18 01		18 16		18 31			18 43	18 49	19 03			19 16			
Edge Hill 91	d	17 19		17 34				17 49		18 04		18 19		18 34			18 46		19 06			19 19			
Liverpool Lime Street 10 91	a	17 28		17 43			17 48	17 58	18 01	18 13		18 28		18 43			18 54	18 59	19 15		19 02	19 28			

A To Liverpool South Pw Hl
B From Llandudno to Manchester Piccadilly
C From Liverpool Lime Street
D From Stalybridge
E To Llandudno
F From Bangor (Gwynedd) to Manchester Piccadilly
G from 10 February. To Lancaster
H To Chester
I To Holyhead
J until 7 February. To Windermere

Table 90

Mondays to Fridays

9 December to 16 May

Manchester, Preston, Wigan and Newton-le-Willows - St Helens and Liverpool

Network Diagram - see first Page of Table 88

		NT	AW	NT	NT	NT	AW	NT	NT	AW	NT	NT	NT	NT	AW	NT	AW	NT	AW	NT	AW	NT	AW
																						FO	
															◇				◇				◇
			A		B		C			A					D		A		E		A		E
Manchester Airport 85 ✈	d			18 41							19 41						20 32				21 32	21 41	
Manchester Piccadilly 10	d		18 50	19 01						19 50	20 01						20 50				21 50	22 01	
Manchester Oxford Road	d		18 53	19 04						19 53	20 04						20 53				21 53	22 04	
Manchester Victoria	d	18 39							19 39							20 39				21 39			
Eccles	d	18 46							19 46							20 46				21 46			
Patricroft	d	18 49							19 49							20 49				21 49			
Blackpool North 97	d					18 35							19 35					20 35					
Preston 8 65,82	d					19 04							20 04					21 04					
Leyland 82	d					19 09							20 09					21 09					
Euxton Balshaw Lane	d					19 14							20 14					21 14					
Wigan North Western 65	a					19 24							20 24					21 23					
	d				19 08	19 24						20 08	20 24	20 38				21 23					
Newton-le-Willows	d	19 01	19 12	19 22					20 01	20 12	20 22					21 01	21 12			22 01	22 12	22 22	
Warrington Bank Quay	d						19 19	19 25							20 19				21 19				22 19
Earlestown 8	d	19 04	19 16				19a26	19 34	20 04	20 15					20a26	21 04	21 15		21a26	22 04	22 15		22a26
Warrington Bank Quay	a		19 24							20 25							21 24				22 23		
St Helens Junction	d	19 09		19 27				19 39	20 09		20 27					21 09				22 09		22 27	
Lea Green	d	19 12						19 42	20 12							21 12				22 12			
Rainhill	d	19 16						19 46	20 16							21 16				22 16			
Whiston	d	19 19						19 49	20 19							21 19				22 19			
Bryn	d				19 15							20 15		20 45				21 30					
Garswood	d				19 19							20 19		20 49				21 34					
St Helens Central	a				19 25	19 39						20 25	20 39	20 55				21 40					
	d				19 26	19 39						20 26	20 39	20 56				21 41					
Thatto Heath	d				19 29							20 29		20 59				21 44					
Eccleston Park	d				19 32							20 32		21 02				21 47					
Prescot	d				19 34							20 34		21 04				21 49					
Huyton	d	19 23			19 38	19 48		19 53	20 23			20 38	20 48	21 08		21 23		21 53		22 23			
Roby	d	19 25			19 40			19 55	20 25			20 40		21 10		21 25		21 55		22 25			
Broad Green	d	19 28			19 43			19 58	20 28			20 43		21 13		21 28		21 58		22 28			
Wavertree Technology Park	d	19 31		19 38	19 46			20 01	20 31		20 38	20 46		21 16		21 31		22 03		22 31		22 38	
Edge Hill 91	d	19 34			19 49			20 04	20 34			20 49		21 19		21 34		22 06		22 34			
Liverpool Lime Street 10 91	a	19 43		19 48	19 58	20 02		20 13	20 43		20 48	20 58	21 02	21 28		21 43		22 16		22 43		22 48	

		AW	NT	NT	NT	NT	NT	NT	AW	NT	NT	NT
			FO	FO	FX	FO	FX	FO		FX	FX	FX
		A							A			
					🚌					🚌	🚌	🚌
Manchester Airport 85 ✈	d											
Manchester Piccadilly 10	d	22 12							23 14			
Manchester Oxford Road	d	22 29							23 17			
Manchester Victoria	d			22 39				23 09			22 39	23 09
Eccles	d			22 46				23 16			22 58	23 28
Patricroft	d			22 49				23 19			23 08	23 38
Blackpool North 97	d					22 14	22 14					
Preston 8 65,82	d					22 43	22 43					
Leyland 82	d					22 48	22 48					
Euxton Balshaw Lane	d					22 53	22 53					
Wigan North Western 65	a					23 02	23 05					
	d		22 25		22 25	23 03				23 15		
Newton-le-Willows	d	22 47		23 01				23 31	23 36		23 38	00 08
Warrington Bank Quay	d											
Earlestown 8	d	22 50		23 04				23 34	23 39		23 46	00 16
Warrington Bank Quay	a	22 58							23 47			
St Helens Junction	d			23 09				23 39			23 58	00 28
Lea Green	d			23 12				23 42			00 05	00 35
Rainhill	d			23 16				23 46			00 13	00 43
Whiston	d			23 19				23 49			00 23	00 53
Bryn	d		22 32		22 38	23 10				23 28		
Garswood	d		22 36		22 45	23 14				23 35		
St Helens Central	a		22 42		23 05	23 20				23 55		
	d		22 43		23 05	23 21				23 55		
Thatto Heath	d		22 46		23 15	23 24				00 05		
Eccleston Park	d		22 49		23 25	23 27				00 15		
Prescot	d		22 51		23 31	23 29				00 21		
Huyton	d		22 55	23 23	23 41	23 33		23 53		00 31	00 33	01 03
Roby	d		22 57	23 25	23 45	23 35		23 55		00 35	00 37	01 07
Broad Green	d		23 00	23 28	23 52	23 38		23 58		00 42	00 44	01 14
Wavertree Technology Park	d		23 03	23 31	00 02	23 41		00 01		00 52	00 54	01 24
Edge Hill 91	d		23 06	23 34	00 12	23 46		00 04		01 02	01 04	01 34
Liverpool Lime Street 10 91	a		23 15	23 43	00 20	23 56		00 13		01 10	01 12	01 42

A To Chester
B until 21 March
C From Chester to Manchester Airport
D From Llandudno to Manchester Airport
E From Llandudno to Manchester Piccadilly

Table 90

Saturdays

14 December to 28 December

Manchester, Preston, Wigan and Newton-le-Willows - St Helens and Liverpool

Network Diagram - see first Page of Table 88

		NT	NT	NT	AW	AW	NT	NT	NT	AW		NT	NT	AW	NT	NT	NT	NT	NT	AW		NT	AW	NT	AW
		A			B	◇ C				◇ B		D		◇ C						E			◇ C		◇ F
Manchester Airport 85 ✈	d					05 33									06 41										
Manchester Piccadilly 10	d					05 50								06 50	06 58								07 50		
Manchester Oxford Road	d					05 53								06 53	07 01								07 53		
Manchester Victoria	d			05 39				06 09									07 09					07 39			
Eccles	d			05 46				06 16									07 16					07 46			
Patricroft	d			05 49				06 19									07 19					07 49			
Blackpool North 97	d																		07 02						
Preston 8 65,82	d																		07 30						
Leyland 82	d																		07 35						
Euxton Balshaw Lane	d																		07 40						
Wigan North Western 65	a																		07 50						
	d						06 08		06 38				06 47			07 08		07 38	07 50					07 58	
Newton-le-Willows	d			06 01		06 12		06 31					07 00	07 11	07 19		07 31					08 01	08 12		
Warrington Bank Quay	d				06 06					06 40										07 39					08 08
Earlestown 8	d			06 04	06a12	06 15		06 34		06a47		06 50	07 03	07 15			07 34			07a46		08 04	08 15		08a15
Warrington Bank Quay	a					06 25						07 01		07 22									08 23		
St Helens Junction	d			06 09				06 39					07 09		07 24		07 39					08 09			
Lea Green	d			06 12				06 42					07 12				07 42					08 12			
Rainhill	d			06 16				06 46					07 16		07 29		07 46					08 16			
Whiston	d			06 19				06 49					07 19				07 49					08 19			
Bryn	d						06 15		06 45							07 15		07 45						08 05	
Garswood	d						06 19		06 49							07 19		07 49	07 59					08 09	
St Helens Central	a						06 25		06 55							07 25		07 55	08 06					08 15	
	d		05 56				06 26		06 56							07 26		07 56	08 06					08 16	
Thatto Heath	d		05 59				06 29		06 59							07 29		07 59						08 19	
Eccleston Park	d		06 02				06 32		07 02							07 32		08 02						08 22	
Prescot	d		06 04				06 34		07 04							07 34		08 04	08 12					08 24	
Huyton	d		06 08	06 23			06 38	06 53	07 08				07 23		07 34	07 38	07 53	08 08	08 16			08 23		08 28	
Roby	d		06 10	06 25			06 40	06 55	07 10				07 25			07 40	07 55	08 10				08 25		08 30	
Broad Green	d		06 13	06 28			06 43	06 58	07 13				07 28			07 43	07 58	08 13	08 20			08 28		08 33	
Wavertree Technology Park	d	00 01	06 16	06 31			06 46	07 01	07 16				07 31		07 39	07 46	08 01	08 16	08 24			08 31		08 36	
Edge Hill 91	d	00 04	06 19	06 34			06 49	07 04	07 19				07 35			07 49	08 04	08 19				08 34		08 39	
Liverpool Lime Street 10 91	a	00 13	06 28	06 43			06 58	07 13	07 28				07 43		07 49	07 58	08 13	08 28	08 35			08 43		08 50	

		NT	NT	NT	NT	NT		AW	NT	NT	NT	AW	NT	NT	NT	NT		AW	NT	NT	NT	AW	NT	NT	NT
			D			G		◇ C			H	◇ F		D		G		◇ C			H	◇ F		D	
Manchester Airport 85 ✈	d								08 41										09 41						
Manchester Piccadilly 10	d							08 50	09 01									09 50	10 01						
Manchester Oxford Road	d							08 53	09 04									09 53	10 04						
Manchester Victoria	d	08 09				08 39										09 39									
Eccles	d	08 16				08 46										09 46									
Patricroft	d	08 19				08 49										09 49									
Blackpool North 97	d										08 35										09 35				
Preston 8 65,82	d										09 04										10 04				
Leyland 82	d										09 09										10 09				
Euxton Balshaw Lane	d										09 14										10 14				
Wigan North Western 65	a										09 24										10 24				
	d			08 28						09 08	09 24				09 38					10 08	10 24				10 38
Newton-le-Willows	d	08 31				09 01		09 12	09 22							10 01		10 12	10 22						
Warrington Bank Quay	d											09 19	09 22									10 19	10 22		
Earlestown 8	d	08 34	08 50			09 04		09 15				09a26	09 34	09 50		10 04		10 15				10a26	10 34	10 50	
Warrington Bank Quay	a		09 01					09 25						10 01				10 25						11 01	
St Helens Junction	d	08 39				09 09			09 27				09 39			10 09			10 27				10 39		
Lea Green	d	08 42				09 12							09 42			10 12							10 42		
Rainhill	d	08 46				09 16							09 46			10 16							10 46		
Whiston	d	08 49				09 19							09 49			10 19							10 49		
Bryn	d			08 35						09 15					09 45					10 15					10 45
Garswood	d			08 39						09 19					09 49					10 19					10 49
St Helens Central	a			08 45						09 25	09 39				09 55					10 25	10 39				10 55
	d			08 46	08 56					09 26	09 39				09 56					10 26	10 39				10 56
Thatto Heath	d			08 49	08 59					09 29					09 59					10 29					10 59
Eccleston Park	d			08 52	09 02					09 32					10 02					10 32					11 02
Prescot	d			08 54	09 04					09 34					10 04					10 34					11 04
Huyton	d	08 53		08 58	09 08	09 23				09 38	09 48		09 53		10 08	10 23				10 38	10 48		10 53		11 08
Roby	d	08 55		09 00	09 10	09 25				09 40			09 55		10 10	10 25				10 40			10 55		11 10
Broad Green	d	08 58		09 03	09 13	09 28				09 43			09 58		10 13	10 28				10 43			10 58		11 13
Wavertree Technology Park	d	09 01		09 06	09 16	09 31			09 38	09 46			10 01		10 16	10 31			10 38	10 46			11 01		11 16
Edge Hill 91	d	09 04		09 09	09 19	09 34				09 49			10 04		10 17	10 34				10 49			11 04		11 19
Liverpool Lime Street 10 91	a	09 13		09 18	09 28	09 43			09 48	09 58	10 01		10 13		10 26	10 43			10 48	10 58	11 02		11 13		11 28

A From Manchester Victoria
B From Chester to Manchester Piccadilly
C To Llandudno
D From Liverpool Lime Street
E From Shrewsbury to Manchester Piccadilly
F From Llandudno to Manchester Piccadilly
G From Stalybridge
H To Liverpool South Pw Hl

Table 90

Saturdays

14 December to 28 December

Manchester, Preston, Wigan and Newton-le-Willows - St Helens and Liverpool

Network Diagram - see first Page of Table 88

		NT A		AW ◇ B	NT	NT	NT C	AW ◇ D	NT	NT E	NT	NT A		AW ◇ F	NT	NT	NT C	AW ◇ D	NT	NT E	NT	NT A		AW ◇ F	NT
Manchester Airport 85	d				10 41										11 41										12 41
Manchester Piccadilly 10	d			10 50	11 01									11 50	12 01									12 50	13 01
Manchester Oxford Road	d			10 53	11 04									11 53	12 04									12 53	13 04
Manchester Victoria	d	10 39										11 39										12 39			
Eccles	d	10 46										11 46										12 46			
Patricroft	d	10 49										11 49										12 49			
Blackpool North 97	d						10 35										11 35								
Preston 8 65,82	d						11 04										12 04								
Leyland 82	d						11 09										12 09								
Euxton Balshaw Lane	d						11 14										12 14								
Wigan North Western 65	a						11 24										12 24								
	d					11 08	11 24				11 38					12 08	12 24				12 38				
Newton-le-Willows	d	11 01		11 12	11 22							12 01		12 12	12 22							13 01		13 12	13 22
Warrington Bank Quay	d							11 19	11 22									12 19	12 22						
Earlestown 8	d	11 04		11 15				11a26	11 34	11 50		12 04		12 15				12a26	12 34	12 50		13 04		13 15	
Warrington Bank Quay	a			11 25						12 01				12 25						13 01				13 25	
St Helens Junction	d	11 09			11 27				11 39			12 09			12 27				12 39			13 09			13 27
Lea Green	d	11 12							11 42			12 12							12 42			13 12			
Rainhill	d	11 16							11 46			12 16							12 46			13 16			
Whiston	d	11 19							11 49			12 19							12 49			13 19			
Bryn	d					11 15					11 45					12 15					12 45				
Garswood	d					11 19					11 49					12 19					12 49				
St Helens Central	a					11 25	11 39				11 55					12 25	12 39				12 55				
	d					11 26	11 39				11 56					12 26	12 39				12 56				
Thatto Heath	d					11 29					11 59					12 29					12 59				
Eccleston Park	d					11 32					12 02					12 32					13 02				
Prescot	d					11 34					12 04					12 34					13 04				
Huyton	d	11 23				11 38	11 48		11 53		12 08	12 23				12 38	12 48		12 53		13 08	13 23			
Roby	d	11 25				11 40			11 55		12 10	12 25				12 40			12 55		13 10	13 25			
Broad Green	d	11 28				11 43			11 58		12 13	12 28				12 43			12 58		13 13	13 28			
Wavertree Technology Park	d	11 31			11 38	11 46			12 01		12 16	12 31			12 38	12 46			13 01		13 16	13 31			13 38
Edge Hill 91	d	11 34				11 49			12 04		12 19	12 34				12 49			13 04		13 19	13 34			
Liverpool Lime Street 10 91	a	11 43			11 48	11 58	12 01		12 13		12 28	12 43			12 48	12 58	13 01		13 13		13 28	13 43			13 48

		NT	NT C	AW ◇ D	NT	NT E	NT	NT A		AW ◇ F	NT	NT	NT C	AW ◇ D	NT	NT E	NT	NT A		AW ◇ F	NT	NT	NT C	AW ◇ G	NT
Manchester Airport 85	d										13 41										14 41				
Manchester Piccadilly 10	d									13 50	14 01									14 50	15 01				
Manchester Oxford Road	d									13 53	14 04									14 53	15 04				
Manchester Victoria	d							13 39										14 39							
Eccles	d							13 46										14 46							
Patricroft	d							13 49										14 49							
Blackpool North 97	d		12 35										13 35										14 35		
Preston 8 65,82	d		13 04										14 04										15 04		
Leyland 82	d		13 09										14 09										15 09		
Euxton Balshaw Lane	d		13 14										14 14										15 14		
Wigan North Western 65	a		13 23										14 24										15 23		
	d	13 08	13 24				13 38					14 08	14 24				14 38					15 08	15 24		
Newton-le-Willows	d							14 01		14 12	14 22							15 01		15 12	15 22				
Warrington Bank Quay	d			13 19	13 22									14 19	14 22									15 19	15 22
Earlestown 8	d			13a26	13 34	13 50		14 04		14 15				14a26	14 34	14 50		15 04		15 15				15a26	15 34
Warrington Bank Quay	a					14 01				14 25						15 01				15 25					
St Helens Junction	d				13 39			14 09			14 27				14 39			15 09			15 27				15 39
Lea Green	d				13 42			14 12							14 42			15 12							15 42
Rainhill	d				13 46			14 16							14 46			15 16							15 46
Whiston	d				13 49			14 19							14 49			15 19							15 49
Bryn	d	13 15					13 45					14 15					14 45					15 15			
Garswood	d	13 19					13 49					14 19					14 49					15 19			
St Helens Central	a	13 25	13 39				13 55					14 25	14 39				14 55					15 25	15 39		
	d	13 26	13 39				13 56					14 26	14 39				14 56					15 26	15 39		
Thatto Heath	d	13 29					13 59					14 29					14 59					15 29			
Eccleston Park	d	13 32					14 02					14 32					15 02					15 32			
Prescot	d	13 34					14 04					14 34					15 04					15 34			
Huyton	d	13 38	13 48		13 53		14 08	14 23				14 38	14 48		14 53		15 08	15 23				15 38	15 48		15 53
Roby	d	13 40			13 55		14 10	14 25				14 40			14 55		15 10	15 25				15 40			15 55
Broad Green	d	13 43			13 58		14 13	14 28				14 44			14 58		15 13	15 28				15 43			15 58
Wavertree Technology Park	d	13 46			14 01		14 16	14 31			14 38	14 47			15 01		15 16	15 31			15 38	15 46			16 01
Edge Hill 91	d	13 50			14 04		14 19	14 34				14 50			15 04		15 19	15 34				15 49			16 04
Liverpool Lime Street 10 91	a	13 58	14 01		14 13		14 28	14 43			14 48	14 58	15 01		15 13		15 28	15 43			15 48	15 58	16 02		16 13

A From Stalybridge
B To Bangor (Gwynedd)
C To Liverpool South Pw Hl
D From Llandudno to Manchester Piccadilly
E From Liverpool Lime Street
F To Llandudno
G From Bangor (Gwynedd) to Manchester Piccadilly

Table 90

Saturdays

14 December to 28 December

Manchester, Preston, Wigan and Newton-le-Willows - St Helens and Liverpool

Network Diagram - see first Page of Table 88

		NT	NT	NT		AW	NT	NT	NT	AW	NT	NT	NT	AW		NT	NT	NT	AW	NT	NT	NT	AW	NT	
		A		B		◇ C 🛒				◇ D 🛒			B	◇ C 🛒					◇ D 🛒			B	◇ C 🛒		
Manchester Airport 85 ✈	d						15 41									16 41									
Manchester Piccadilly 10 🚇	d					15 50	16 01							16 50		17 01							17 50		
Manchester Oxford Road	d					15 53	16 04							16 53		17 04							17 53		
Manchester Victoria 🚇	d			15 39									16 39							17 09		17 39			
Eccles	d			15 46									16 46							17 16		17 46			
Patricroft	d			15 49									16 49							17 19		17 49			
Blackpool North 97	d								15 35									16 35							
Preston 8 65,82	d								16 04									17 04							
Leyland 82	d								16 09									17 09							
Euxton Balshaw Lane	d								16 14									17 14							
Wigan North Western 65	a								16 23									17 24							
	d		15 38					16 08	16 24			16 38					17 08	17 24			17 38			18 08	
Newton-le-Willows	d			16 01		16 12	16 22						17 01	17 12		17 22				17 31		18 01	18 11		
Warrington Bank Quay	d									16 19	16 22								17 19						
Earlestown 8	d	15 50		16 04		16 15				16a26	16 34		17 04	17 15					17a26	17 34		18 04	18 14		
Warrington Bank Quay	a	16 01				16 25								17 25									18 24		
St Helens Junction	d			16 09			16 27				16 39		17 09			17 27				17 39		18 09			
Lea Green	d			16 12							16 42		17 12							17 42		18 12			
Rainhill	d			16 16							16 46		17 16							17 46		18 16			
Whiston	d			16 19							16 49		17 19							17 49		18 19			
Bryn	d		15 45					16 15				16 45					17 15				17 45			18 15	
Garswood	d		15 49					16 19				16 49					17 19				17 49			18 19	
St Helens Central	a		15 55					16 25	16 39			16 55					17 25	17 39			17 55			18 25	
	d		15 56					16 26	16 39			16 56					17 26	17 39			17 56			18 26	
Thatto Heath	d		15 59					16 29				16 59					17 29				17 59			18 29	
Eccleston Park	d		16 02					16 32				17 02					17 32				18 02			18 32	
Prescot	d		16 04					16 34				17 04					17 34				18 04			18 34	
Huyton	d		16 08	16 23				16 38	16 48		16 53	17 08	17 23				17 38	17 48		17 53	18 08	18 23		18 38	
Roby	d		16 10	16 25				16 40			16 55	17 10	17 25				17 40			17 55	18 10	18 25			
Broad Green	d		16 13	16 28				16 44			16 58	17 13	17 28				17 43			17 58	18 13	18 28			
Wavertree Technology Park	d		16 16	16 31			16 38	16 47			17 01	17 16	17 31			17 38	17 46			18 01	18 16	18 31		18 43	
Edge Hill 91	d		16 19	16 34				16 50			17 04	17 19	17 34				17 49			18 04	18 19	18 34		18 46	
Liverpool Lime Street 10 91	a		16 28	16 43			16 48	16 58	17 05		17 13	17 28	17 43			17 48	17 58	18 01		18 13	18 28	18 43		18 54	

		NT	AW	NT	NT	NT	NT	NT	AW	NT		NT	NT	AW	NT	NT	AW	NT	NT	NT		NT	TP	AW	NT
			◇ D 🛒		A			B	E					◇ F 🛒			E						◇1 G	◇ D	
Manchester Airport 85 ✈	d	17 41								18 41								19 41					20 00		
Manchester Piccadilly 10 🚇	d	18 01							18 50	19 01							19 50	20 01					20 16		
Manchester Oxford Road	d	18 04							18 53	19 04							19 53	20 04					20 19		
Manchester Victoria 🚇	d							18 39								19 39									20 39
Eccles	d	18 11						18 46								19 46									20 46
Patricroft	d							18 49								19 49									20 49
Blackpool North 97	d					17 35							18 35							19 35					
Preston 8 65,82	d					18 04							19 04							20 04					
Leyland 82	d					18 09							19 09							20 09					
Euxton Balshaw Lane	d					18 14							19 14							20 14					
Wigan North Western 65	a					18 24							19 23							20 24			20 43		
	d			18 21		18 24	18 35					19 08	19 24						20 08	20 24		20 38			
Newton-le-Willows	d	18 24		18 33				19 01	19 12	19 22						20 01	20 12	20 22							21 01
Warrington Bank Quay	d		18 19											19 19	19 22									20 19	
Earlestown 8	d		18a26	18 35	18 50			19 04	19 16					19a26	19 34	20 04	20 15							20a26	21 04
Warrington Bank Quay	a				19 01				19 26								20 29								
St Helens Junction	d	18 29		18 41				19 09		19 27					19 39	20 09		20 27							21 09
Lea Green	d	18 32		18 44				19 12							19 42	20 12									21 12
Rainhill	d	18 36		18 48				19 16							19 46	20 16									21 16
Whiston	d			18 51				19 19							19 49	20 19									21 19
Bryn	d						18 45					19 15							20 15			20 45			
Garswood	d						18 49					19 19							20 19			20 49			
St Helens Central	a					18 39	18 55					19 25	19 39						20 25	20 39		20 55			
	d					18 39	18 56					19 26	19 39						20 26	20 39		20 56			
Thatto Heath	d						18 59					19 29							20 29			20 59			
Eccleston Park	d						19 02					19 32							20 32			21 02			
Prescot	d						19 04					19 34							20 34			21 04			
Huyton	d	18 41		18 54		18 48	19 08	19 23				19 38	19 48		19 53	20 23			20 38	20 48		21 08			21 23
Roby	d	18 43		18 56			19 10	19 25				19 40			19 55	20 25			20 40			21 10			21 25
Broad Green	d	18 46		19 00			19 13	19 28				19 44			19 58	20 28			20 43			21 13			21 28
Wavertree Technology Park	d	18 49		19 03			19 16	19 31		19 38		19 47			20 01	20 31		20 38	20 46			21 16			21 31
Edge Hill 91	d			19 06			19 19	19 34				19 50			20 04	20 34			20 49			21 19			21 34
Liverpool Lime Street 10 91	a	18 59		19 15		19 02	19 28	19 43		19 48		19 58	20 02		20 13	20 43		20 48	20 58	21 02		21 28			21 43

A From Liverpool Lime Street
B From Stalybridge
C To Llandudno
D From Llandudno to Manchester Piccadilly
E To Chester
F From Llandudno to Manchester Airport
G To Preston

Table 90

Saturdays

14 December to 28 December

Manchester, Preston, Wigan and Newton-le-Willows - St Helens and Liverpool

Network Diagram - see first Page of Table 88

		AW	NT	AW	NT	AW		NT	AW	NT	AW	NT	NT	NT	AW	AW
				◇												
		A		B		A			C		A				A	C
Manchester Airport 85 ✈	d	20 32						21 42								
Manchester Piccadilly 10	d	20 50				21 50		22 01			22 26				23 14	
Manchester Oxford Road	d	20 53				21 53		22 04			22 29				23 17	
Manchester Victoria	d				21 39							22 39		23 09		
Eccles	d				21 46							22 46		23 16		
Patricroft	d				21 49							22 49		23 19		
Blackpool North 97	d		20 35										22 14			
Preston 8 65,82	d		21 04										22 43			
Leyland 82	d		21 09										22 48			
Euxton Balshaw Lane	d		21 14										22 53			
Wigan North Western 65	a		21 23										23 02			
	d		21 23							22 25			23 03			
Newton-le-Willows	d	21 12			22 01	22 12		22 22			22 47	23 01		23 31	23 36	
Warrington Bank Quay	d			21 19					22 19							23 50
Earlestown 8	d	21 15		21a26	22 04	22 15			22a26		22 50	23 04		23 34	23 39	23a58
Warrington Bank Quay	a	21 26				22 23					22 58				23 47	
St Helens Junction	d				22 09			22 27				23 09		23 39		
Lea Green	d				22 12							23 12		23 42		
Rainhill	d				22 16							23 16		23 46		
Whiston	d				22 19							23 19		23 49		
Bryn	d		21 30							22 32			23 10			
Garswood	d		21 34							22 36			23 14			
St Helens Central	a		21 40							22 42			23 20			
	d		21 41							22 43			23 21			
Thatto Heath	d		21 44							22 46			23 24			
Eccleston Park	d		21 47							22 49			23 27			
Prescot	d		21 49							22 51			23 29			
Huyton	d		21 53		22 23					22 55		23 23	23 33	23 53		
Roby	d		21 55		22 25					22 57		23 25	23 35	23 55		
Broad Green	d		21 58		22 28					23 00		23 28	23 38	23 58		
Wavertree Technology Park	d		22 03		22 31			22 38		23 03		23 31	23 41	00 01		
Edge Hill 91	d		22 06		22 34					23 06		23 34	23 46	00 04		
Liverpool Lime Street 10 91	a		22 16		22 43			22 48		23 15		23 43	23 56	00 13		

Saturdays

4 January to 8 February

		NT	NT	NT	AW	AW	NT	NT	NT	AW		NT	NT	AW	NT	NT	NT	NT	NT	AW		NT	AW	NT	AW
						◇				◇				◇									◇		◇
		D			C	E 🛒				C		F		E 🛒						G 🛒			E 🛒		B 🛒
Manchester Airport 85 ✈	d					05 33									06 41										
Manchester Piccadilly 10	d					05 50								06 50	06 58								07 50		
Manchester Oxford Road	d					05 53								06 53	07 01								07 53		
Manchester Victoria	d			05 39				06 09									07 09					07 39			
Eccles	d			05 46				06 16									07 16					07 46			
Patricroft	d			05 49				06 19									07 19					07 49			
Blackpool North 97	d																		07 02						
Preston 8 65,82	d																		07 30						
Leyland 82	d																		07 35						
Euxton Balshaw Lane	d																		07 40						
Wigan North Western 65	a																		07 50						
	d						06 08		06 38				06 47			07 08		07 38	07 50					07 58	
Newton-le-Willows	d			06 01		06 12		06 31					07 00	07 11	07 19		07 31					08 01	08 12		
Warrington Bank Quay	d				06 06					06 40										07 39					08 08
Earlestown 8	d			06 04	06a12	06 15		06 34		06a47		06 50	07 03	07 15			07 34			07a46		08 04	08 15		08a15
Warrington Bank Quay	a					06 25						07 01		07 22									08 23		
St Helens Junction	d			06 09				06 39					07 09		07 24		07 39					08 09			
Lea Green	d			06 12				06 42					07 12				07 42					08 12			
Rainhill	d			06 16				06 46					07 16		07 29		07 46					08 16			
Whiston	d			06 19				06 49					07 19				07 49					08 19			
Bryn	d						06 15		06 45							07 15		07 45						08 05	
Garswood	d						06 19		06 49							07 19		07 49	07 59					08 09	
St Helens Central	a						06 25		06 55							07 25		07 55	08 06					08 15	
	d		05 56				06 26		06 56							07 26		07 56	08 06					08 16	
Thatto Heath	d		05 59				06 29		06 59							07 29		07 59						08 19	
Eccleston Park	d		06 02				06 32		07 02							07 32		08 02						08 22	
Prescot	d		06 04				06 34		07 04							07 34		08 04	08 12					08 24	
Huyton	d		06 08	06 23			06 38	06 53	07 08				07 23		07 34	07 38	07 53	08 08	08 16			08 23		08 28	
Roby	d		06 10	06 25			06 40	06 55	07 10				07 25			07 40	07 55	08 10				08 25		08 30	
Broad Green	d		06 13	06 28			06 43	06 58	07 13				07 28			07 43	07 58	08 13	08 20			08 28		08 33	
Wavertree Technology Park	d	00 01	06 16	06 31			06 46	07 01	07 16				07 31		07 39	07 46	08 01	08 16	08 24			08 31		08 36	
Edge Hill 91	d	00 04	06 19	06 34			06 49	07 04	07 19				07 35			07 49	08 04	08 19				08 34		08 39	
Liverpool Lime Street 10 91	a	00 13	06 28	06 43			06 58	07 13	07 28				07 43		07 49	07 58	08 13	08 28	08 35			08 43		08 50	

A To Chester
B From Llandudno to Manchester Piccadilly
C From Chester to Manchester Piccadilly
D From Manchester Victoria
E To Llandudno
F From Liverpool Lime Street
G From Shrewsbury to Manchester Piccadilly

Table 90

Saturdays

4 January to 8 February

Manchester, Preston, Wigan and Newton-le-Willows - St Helens and Liverpool

Network Diagram - see first Page of Table 88

		NT	NT A	NT	NT	NT B		AW ◇ C	NT	NT	NT D	AW ◇ E	NT	NT A	NT	NT B		AW ◇ C	NT	NT	NT D	AW ◇ E	NT	NT A	NT
Manchester Airport 85	d								08 41										09 41						
Manchester Piccadilly 10	d							08 50	09 01									09 50	10 01						
Manchester Oxford Road	d							08 53	09 04									09 53	10 04						
Manchester Victoria	d	08 09				08 39										09 39									
Eccles	d	08 16				08 46										09 46									
Patricroft	d	08 19				08 49										09 49									
Blackpool North 97	d										08 35										09 35				
Preston 8 65,82	d										09 04										10 04				
Leyland 82	d										09 09										10 09				
Euxton Balshaw Lane	d										09 14										10 14				
Wigan North Western 65	a										09 24										10 24				
	d			08 28						09 08	09 24				09 38					10 08	10 24				10 38
Newton-le-Willows	d	08 31				09 01		09 12	09 22							10 01		10 12	10 22						
Warrington Bank Quay	d											09 19	09 22									10 19	10 22		
Earlestown 8	d	08 34	08 50			09 04		09 15				09a26	09 34	09 50		10 04		10 15				10a26	10 34	10 50	
Warrington Bank Quay	a		09 01					09 25						10 01				10 25						11 01	
St Helens Junction	d	08 39				09 09			09 27				09 39			10 09			10 27				10 39		
Lea Green	d	08 42				09 12							09 42			10 12							10 42		
Rainhill	d	08 46				09 16							09 46			10 16							10 46		
Whiston	d	08 49				09 19							09 49			10 19							10 49		
Bryn	d			08 35						09 15					09 45					10 15					10 45
Garswood	d			08 39						09 19					09 49					10 19					10 49
St Helens Central	a			08 45						09 25	09 39				09 55					10 25	10 39				10 55
	d			08 46	08 56					09 26	09 39				09 56					10 26	10 39				10 56
Thatto Heath	d			08 49	08 59					09 29					09 59					10 29					10 59
Eccleston Park	d			08 52	09 02					09 32					10 02					10 32					11 02
Prescot	d			08 54	09 04					09 34					10 04					10 34					11 04
Huyton	d	08 53		08 58	09 08	09 23				09 38	09 48		09 53		10 08	10 23				10 38	10 48		10 53		11 08
Roby	d	08 55		09 00	09 10	09 25				09 40			09 55		10 10	10 25				10 40			10 55		11 10
Broad Green	d	08 58		09 03	09 13	09 28				09 43			09 58		10 13	10 28				10 43			10 58		11 13
Wavertree Technology Park	d	09 01		09 06	09 16	09 31			09 38	09 46			10 01		10 16	10 31			10 38	10 46			11 01		11 16
Edge Hill 91	d	09 04		09 09	09 19	09 34				09 49			10 04		10 17	10 34				10 49			11 04		11 19
Liverpool Lime Street 10 91	a	09 13		09 18	09 28	09 43			09 48	09 58	10 01		10 13		10 26	10 43			10 48	10 58	11 02		11 13		11 28

		NT B		AW ◇ F	NT	NT	NT D	AW ◇ E	NT	NT A	NT	NT B		AW ◇ C	NT	NT	NT D	AW ◇ E	NT	NT A	NT	TP ◇1 G		NT B	AW ◇ C
Manchester Airport 85	d				10 41										11 41							12 00			
Manchester Piccadilly 10	d			10 50	11 01									11 50	12 01							12 16			12 50
Manchester Oxford Road	d			10 53	11 04									11 53	12 04							12 19			12 53
Manchester Victoria	d	10 39										11 39												12 39	
Eccles	d	10 46										11 46												12 46	
Patricroft	d	10 49										11 49												12 49	
Blackpool North 97	d						10 35										11 35								
Preston 8 65,82	d						11 04										12 04								
Leyland 82	d						11 09										12 09								
Euxton Balshaw Lane	d						11 14										12 14								
Wigan North Western 65	a						11 24										12 24					12 43			
	d					11 08	11 24				11 38					12 08	12 24				12 38				
Newton-le-Willows	d	11 01		11 12	11 22							12 01		12 12	12 22									13 01	13 12
Warrington Bank Quay	d							11 19	11 22									12 19	12 22						
Earlestown 8	d	11 04		11 15				11a26	11 34	11 50		12 04		12 15				12a26	12 34	12 50				13 04	13 15
Warrington Bank Quay	a			11 25						12 01				12 25						13 01					13 25
St Helens Junction	d	11 09			11 27				11 39			12 09			12 27				12 39					13 09	
Lea Green	d	11 12							11 42			12 12							12 42					13 12	
Rainhill	d	11 16							11 46			12 16							12 46					13 16	
Whiston	d	11 19							11 49			12 19							12 49					13 19	
Bryn	d					11 15					11 45					12 15					12 45				
Garswood	d					11 19					11 49					12 19					12 49				
St Helens Central	a					11 25	11 39				11 55					12 25	12 39				12 55				
	d					11 26	11 39				11 56					12 26	12 39				12 56				
Thatto Heath	d					11 29					11 59					12 29					12 59				
Eccleston Park	d					11 32					12 02					12 32					13 02				
Prescot	d					11 34					12 04					12 34					13 04				
Huyton	d	11 23				11 38	11 48		11 53		12 08	12 23				12 38	12 48		12 53		13 08			13 23	
Roby	d	11 25				11 40			11 55		12 10	12 25				12 40			12 55		13 10			13 25	
Broad Green	d	11 28				11 43			11 58		12 13	12 28				12 43			12 58		13 13			13 28	
Wavertree Technology Park	d	11 31			11 38	11 46			12 01		12 16	12 31			12 38	12 46			13 01		13 16			13 31	
Edge Hill 91	d	11 34				11 49			12 04		12 19	12 34				12 49			13 04		13 19			13 34	
Liverpool Lime Street 10 91	a	11 43			11 48	11 58	12 01		12 13		12 28	12 43			12 48	12 58	13 01		13 13		13 28			13 43	

A From Liverpool Lime Street
B From Stalybridge
C To Llandudno
D To Liverpool South Pw Hl
E From Llandudno to Manchester Piccadilly
F To Bangor (Gwynedd)
G To Lancaster

Table 90

Saturdays
4 January to 8 February

Manchester, Preston, Wigan and Newton-le-Willows - St Helens and Liverpool

Network Diagram - see first Page of Table 88

		NT	NT	NT	AW	NT	NT	NT	TP	NT	AW	NT	NT	NT	AW	NT	NT	NT	TP	NT	AW	NT	NT
					◇				◇1		◇				◇				◇1		◇		
				A	B		C		D	E	F			A	B		C		D	E	F		
					🚲				🚲		🚲				🚲				🚲		🚲		
Manchester Airport 85 ✈	d	12 41							13 00			13 41							14 00			14 41	
Manchester Piccadilly 10	d	13 01							13 16		13 50	14 01							14 16		14 50	15 01	
Manchester Oxford Road	d	13 04							13 19		13 53	14 04							14 19		14 53	15 04	
Manchester Victoria	d									13 39										14 39			
Eccles	d									13 46										14 46			
Patricroft	d									13 49										14 49			
Blackpool North 97	d			12 35										13 35									
Preston 8 65,82	d			13 04										14 04									
Leyland 82	d			13 09										14 09									
Euxton Balshaw Lane	d			13 14										14 14									
Wigan North Western 65	a			13 23					13 43					14 24					14 43				
	d		13 08	13 24				13 38					14 08	14 24				14 38					15 08
Newton-le-Willows	d	13 22								14 01	14 12	14 22								15 01	15 12	15 22	
Warrington Bank Quay	d				13 19	13 22									14 19	14 22							
Earlestown 8	d				13a26	13 34	13 50			14 04	14 15				14a26	14 34	14 50			15 04	15 15		
Warrington Bank Quay	a						14 01				14 25						15 01				15 25		
St Helens Junction	d	13 27				13 39				14 09		14 27				14 39				15 09		15 27	
Lea Green	d					13 42				14 12						14 42				15 12			
Rainhill	d					13 46				14 16						14 46				15 16			
Whiston	d					13 49				14 19						14 49				15 19			
Bryn	d		13 15					13 45					14 15					14 45					15 15
Garswood	d		13 19					13 49					14 19					14 49					15 19
St Helens Central	a		13 25	13 39				13 55					14 25	14 39				14 55					15 25
	d		13 26	13 39				13 56					14 26	14 39				14 56					15 26
Thatto Heath	d		13 29					13 59					14 29					14 59					15 29
Eccleston Park	d		13 32					14 02					14 32					15 02					15 32
Prescot	d		13 34					14 04					14 34					15 04					15 34
Huyton	d		13 38	13 48		13 53		14 08		14 23			14 38	14 48		14 53		15 08		15 23			15 38
Roby	d		13 40			13 55		14 10		14 25			14 40			14 55		15 10		15 25			15 40
Broad Green	d		13 43			13 58		14 13		14 28			14 44			14 58		15 13		15 28			15 43
Wavertree Technology Park	d	13 38	13 46			14 01		14 16		14 31		14 38	14 47			15 01		15 16		15 31		15 38	15 46
Edge Hill 91	d		13 50			14 04		14 19		14 34			14 50			15 04		15 19		15 34			15 49
Liverpool Lime Street 10 91	a	13 48	13 58	14 01		14 13		14 28		14 43		14 48	14 58	15 01		15 13		15 28		15 43		15 48	15 58

		NT	AW	NT	NT	NT	NT	AW	NT	NT	NT	AW	NT	NT	NT	AW	NT	NT	NT	AW	NT	NT
			◇					◇				◇				◇				◇		
		A	G		C		E	F				B			E	F				B		
			🚲					🚲				🚲				🚲				🚲		
Manchester Airport 85 ✈	d								15 41								16 41					
Manchester Piccadilly 10	d							15 50	16 01							16 50	17 01					
Manchester Oxford Road	d							15 53	16 04							16 53	17 04					
Manchester Victoria	d						15 39								16 39						17 09	
Eccles	d						15 46								16 46						17 16	
Patricroft	d						15 49								16 49						17 19	
Blackpool North 97	d	14 35									15 35								16 35			
Preston 8 65,82	d	15 04									16 04								17 04			
Leyland 82	d	15 09									16 09								17 09			
Euxton Balshaw Lane	d	15 14									16 14								17 14			
Wigan North Western 65	a	15 23									16 23								17 24			
	d	15 24				15 38				16 08	16 24			16 38				17 08	17 24			17 38
Newton-le-Willows	d						16 01	16 12	16 22						17 01	17 12	17 22				17 31	
Warrington Bank Quay	d		15 19	15 22								16 19	16 22							17 19		
Earlestown 8	d		15a26	15 34	15 50		16 04	16 15				16a26	16 34		17 04	17 15				17a26	17 34	
Warrington Bank Quay	a				16 01			16 25								17 25						
St Helens Junction	d			15 39			16 09		16 27				16 39		17 09		17 27				17 39	
Lea Green	d			15 42			16 12						16 42		17 12						17 42	
Rainhill	d			15 46			16 16						16 46		17 16						17 46	
Whiston	d			15 49			16 19						16 49		17 19						17 49	
Bryn	d					15 45				16 15				16 45				17 15				17 45
Garswood	d					15 49				16 19				16 49				17 19				17 49
St Helens Central	a	15 39				15 55				16 25	16 39			16 55				17 25	17 39			17 55
	d	15 39				15 56				16 26	16 39			16 56				17 26	17 39			17 56
Thatto Heath	d					15 59				16 29				16 59				17 29				17 59
Eccleston Park	d					16 02				16 32				17 02				17 32				18 02
Prescot	d					16 04				16 34				17 04				17 34				18 04
Huyton	d	15 48		15 53		16 08	16 23			16 38	16 48		16 53	17 08	17 23			17 38	17 48		17 53	18 08
Roby	d			15 55		16 10	16 25			16 40			16 55	17 10	17 25			17 40			17 55	18 10
Broad Green	d			15 58		16 13	16 28			16 44			16 58	17 13	17 28			17 43			17 58	18 13
Wavertree Technology Park	d			16 01		16 16	16 31		16 38	16 47			17 01	17 16	17 31		17 38	17 46			18 01	18 16
Edge Hill 91	d			16 04		16 19	16 34			16 50			17 04	17 19	17 34			17 49			18 04	18 19
Liverpool Lime Street 10 91	a	16 02		16 13		16 28	16 43		16 48	16 58	17 05		17 13	17 28	17 43		17 48	17 58	18 01		18 13	18 28

A To Liverpool South Pw Hl
B From Llandudno to Manchester Piccadilly
C From Liverpool Lime Street
D To Lancaster
E From Stalybridge
F To Llandudno
G From Bangor (Gwynedd) to Manchester Piccadilly

Table 90

Saturdays

4 January to 8 February

Manchester, Preston, Wigan and Newton-le-Willows - St Helens and Liverpool

Network Diagram - see first Page of Table 88

		NT	AW	NT	NT	AW	NT	NT	NT	NT	TP	NT	TP	AW	NT	NT	NT	AW	NT	NT	AW	NT	NT
			◇			◇					◇[1]		◇[1]					◇					
		A	B			C		D			E	A	F	G				H			G		
			🛒			🛒					🛒							🛒					
Manchester Airport 85 ✈	d				17 41						18 00				18 41							19 41	
Manchester Piccadilly [10]	d		17 50		18 01						18 16			18 50	19 01						19 50	20 01	
Manchester Oxford Road	d		17 53		18 04						18 19			18 53	19 04						19 53	20 04	
Manchester Victoria	d	17 39										18 39								19 39			
Eccles	d	17 46			18 11							18 46								19 46			
Patricroft	d	17 49										18 49								19 49			
Blackpool North 97	d								17 35								18 35						19 19
Preston [8] 65,82	d								18 04				18 45				19 04						19 46
Leyland 82	d								18 09								19 09						19 52
Euxton Balshaw Lane	d								18 14								19 14						19 56
Wigan North Western 65	a								18 24		18 43		18 58				19 23						20 06
	d			18 08			18 21		18 24	18 35						19 08	19 24						20 08
Newton-le-Willows	d	18 01	18 11		18 24		18 33					19 01		19 12	19 22					20 01	20 12	20 22	
Warrington Bank Quay	d					18 19												19 19	19 22				
Earlestown [8]	d	18 04	18 14			18a26	18 35	18 50				19 04		19 16				19a26	19 34	20 04	20 15		
Warrington Bank Quay	a		18 24					19 01						19 26							20 29		
St Helens Junction	d	18 09			18 29		18 41					19 09			19 27				19 39	20 09		20 27	
Lea Green	d	18 12			18 32		18 44					19 12							19 42	20 12			
Rainhill	d	18 16			18 36		18 48					19 16							19 46	20 16			
Whiston	d	18 19					18 51					19 19							19 49	20 19			
Bryn	d			18 15						18 45						19 15							20 16
Garswood	d			18 19						18 49						19 19							20 19
St Helens Central	a			18 25					18 39	18 55						19 25	19 39						20 26
	d			18 26					18 39	18 56						19 26	19 39						20 26
Thatto Heath	d			18 29						18 59						19 29							20 30
Eccleston Park	d			18 32						19 02						19 32							20 32
Prescot	d			18 34						19 04						19 34							20 34
Huyton	d	18 23		18 38	18 41		18 54		18 48	19 08		19 23				19 38	19 48		19 53	20 23			20 38
Roby	d	18 25			18 43		18 56			19 10		19 25				19 40			19 55	20 25			20 40
Broad Green	d	18 28			18 46		19 00			19 13		19 28				19 44			19 58	20 28			20 44
Wavertree Technology Park	d	18 31		18 43	18 49		19 03			19 16		19 31			19 38	19 47			20 01	20 31		20 38	20 47
Edge Hill 91	d	18 34		18 46			19 06			19 19		19 34				19 50			20 04	20 34			20 50
Liverpool Lime Street [10] 91	a	18 43		18 54	18 59		19 15		19 02	19 28		19 43			19 48	19 58	20 02		20 13	20 43		20 48	20 58

		AW	NT	NT	NT	NT	AW	AW	NT	NT	AW	NT	AW	NT	NT	AW	NT	NT	NT	NT	AW	AW
		◇						◇														
		C					G	C			G		I			G					G	I
					🚌										🚌					🚌		
Manchester Airport 85 ✈	d						20 32					21 42										
Manchester Piccadilly [10]	d						20 50				21 50	22 01				22 26					23 14	
Manchester Oxford Road	d						20 53				21 53	22 04				22 29					23 17	
Manchester Victoria	d					20 39				21 39							22 39		23 09			
Eccles	d					20 46				21 46							22 46		23 16			
Patricroft	d					20 49				21 49							22 49		23 19			
Blackpool North 97	d																					
Preston [8] 65,82	d				20 17										21 59					23 00		
Leyland 82	d				20 37										22 19					23 20		
Euxton Balshaw Lane	d				20 49										22 31					23 32		
Wigan North Western 65	a				21 14										22 56					23s57		
	d		20 24	20 38					21 23					22 25				23 03				
Newton-le-Willows	d					21 01	21 12			22 01	22 12	22 22				22 47	23 01		23 31		23 36	
Warrington Bank Quay	d	20 19						21 19					22 19									23 50
Earlestown [8]	d	20a26				21 04	21 15	21a26		22 04	22 15		22a26			22 50	23 04		23 34		23 39	23a58
Warrington Bank Quay	a						21 26				22 23					22 58					23 47	
St Helens Junction	d					21 09				22 09		22 27					23 09		23 39			
Lea Green	d					21 12				22 12							23 12		23 42			
Rainhill	d					21 16				22 16							23 16		23 46			
Whiston	d					21 19				22 19							23 19		23 49			
Bryn	d			20 45					21 30					22 32				23 10				
Garswood	d			20 49					21 34					22 36				23 14				
St Helens Central	a		20 39	20 55					21 40					22 42				23 20		00s32		
	d		20 39	20 56					21 41					22 43				23 21				
Thatto Heath	d			20 59					21 44					22 46				23 24				
Eccleston Park	d			21 02					21 47					22 49				23 27				
Prescot	d			21 04					21 49					22 51				23 29				
Huyton	d		20 48	21 08		21 23			21 53	22 23				22 55			23 23	23 33	23 53			
Roby	d			21 10		21 25			21 55	22 25				22 57			23 25	23 35	23 55			
Broad Green	d			21 13		21 28			21 58	22 28				23 00			23 28	23 38	23 58			
Wavertree Technology Park	d			21 16		21 31			22 03	22 31		22 38		23 03			23 31	23 41	00 01			
Edge Hill 91	d			21 19		21 34			22 06	22 34				23 06			23 34	23 46	00 04			
Liverpool Lime Street [10] 91	a		21 02	21 28		21 43			22 16	22 43		22 48		23 15			23 43	23 56	00 13	01 07		

A From Stalybridge
B To Llandudno
C From Llandudno to Manchester Piccadilly
D From Liverpool Lime Street
E To Lancaster
F From Barrow-in-Furness to Manchester Airport
G To Chester
H From Llandudno to Manchester Airport
I From Chester to Manchester Piccadilly

Table 90

Saturdays

15 February to 22 March

Manchester, Preston, Wigan and Newton-le-Willows - St Helens and Liverpool

Network Diagram - see first Page of Table 88

	NT A	NT	NT	AW B	AW ◇ C	NT	NT	NT	AW ◇ B		NT D	NT	AW ◇ C	NT	NT	NT	NT	NT	AW E		NT	AW ◇ C	NT	AW ◇ F
Manchester Airport 85 ✈ d					05 33									06 41										
Manchester Piccadilly 10 d					05 50								06 50	06 58								07 50		
Manchester Oxford Road d					05 53								06 53	07 01								07 53		
Manchester Victoria d			05 39				06 09									07 09					07 39			
Eccles d			05 46				06 16									07 16					07 46			
Patricroft d			05 49				06 19									07 19					07 49			
Blackpool North 97 d																		07 02						
Preston 8 65,82 d																		07 30						
Leyland 82 d																		07 35						
Euxton Balshaw Lane d																		07 40						
Wigan North Western 65 a																		07 50						
d						06 08		06 38				06 47			07 08		07 38	07 50					07 58	
Newton-le-Willows d			06 01		06 12		06 31					07 00	07 11	07 19		07 31					08 01	08 12		
Warrington Bank Quay d				06 06					06 40										07 39					08 08
Earlestown 8 d			06 04	06a12	06 15		06 34		06a47		06 50	07 03	07 15			07 34			07a46		08 04	08 15		08a15
Warrington Bank Quay a					06 25						07 01		07 22									08 23		
St Helens Junction d			06 09				06 39					07 09		07 24		07 39					08 09			
Lea Green d			06 12				06 42					07 12				07 42					08 12			
Rainhill d			06 16				06 46					07 16		07 29		07 46					08 16			
Whiston d			06 19				06 49					07 19				07 49					08 19			
Bryn d						06 15		06 45							07 15		07 45						08 05	
Garswood d						06 19		06 49							07 19		07 49	07 59					08 09	
St Helens Central a						06 25		06 55							07 25		07 55	08 06					08 15	
d		05 56				06 26		06 56							07 26		07 56	08 06					08 16	
Thatto Heath d		05 59				06 29		06 59							07 29		07 59						08 19	
Eccleston Park d		06 02				06 32		07 02							07 32		08 02						08 22	
Prescot d		06 04				06 34		07 04							07 34		08 04	08 12					08 24	
Huyton d		06 08	06 23			06 38	06 53	07 08				07 23		07 34	07 38	07 53	08 08	08 16			08 23		08 28	
Roby d		06 10	06 25			06 40	06 55	07 10				07 25			07 40	07 55	08 10				08 25		08 30	
Broad Green d		06 13	06 28			06 43	06 58	07 13				07 28			07 43	07 58	08 13	08 20			08 28		08 33	
Wavertree Technology Park d	00 01	06 16	06 31			06 46	07 01	07 16				07 31		07 39	07 46	08 01	08 16	08 24			08 31		08 36	
Edge Hill 91 d	00 04	06 19	06 34			06 49	07 04	07 19				07 35			07 49	08 04	08 19				08 34		08 39	
Liverpool Lime Street 10 91 a	00 13	06 28	06 43			06 58	07 13	07 28				07 43		07 49	07 58	08 13	08 28	08 35			08 43		08 50	

	NT	NT D	NT	NT	NT G		AW ◇ C	NT	NT	NT H	AW ◇ F	NT	NT D	NT	TP ◇1 I		NT G	AW ◇ C	NT	NT	NT H	AW ◇ F	NT	NT D
Manchester Airport 85 ✈ d								08 41							09 00				09 41					
Manchester Piccadilly 10 d							08 50	09 01							09 16			09 50	10 01					
Manchester Oxford Road d							08 53	09 04							09 19			09 53	10 04					
Manchester Victoria d	08 09				08 39												09 39							
Eccles d	08 16				08 46												09 46							
Patricroft d	08 19				08 49												09 49							
Blackpool North 97 d										08 35											09 35			
Preston 8 65,82 d										09 04											10 04			
Leyland 82 d										09 09											10 09			
Euxton Balshaw Lane d										09 14											10 14			
Wigan North Western 65 a										09 24					09 43						10 24			
d			08 28						09 08	09 24				09 38						10 08	10 24			
Newton-le-Willows d	08 31				09 01		09 12	09 22									10 01	10 12	10 22					
Warrington Bank Quay d											09 19	09 22										10 19	10 22	
Earlestown 8 d	08 34	08 50			09 04		09 15				09a26	09 34	09 50				10 04	10 15				10a26	10 34	10 50
Warrington Bank Quay a		09 01					09 25						10 01					10 25						11 01
St Helens Junction d	08 39				09 09			09 27				09 39					10 09		10 27				10 39	
Lea Green d	08 42				09 12							09 42					10 12						10 42	
Rainhill d	08 46				09 16							09 46					10 16						10 46	
Whiston d	08 49				09 19							09 49					10 19						10 49	
Bryn d			08 35						09 15					09 45						10 15				
Garswood d			08 39						09 19					09 49						10 19				
St Helens Central a			08 45						09 25	09 39				09 55						10 25	10 39			
d			08 46	08 56					09 26	09 39				09 56						10 26	10 39			
Thatto Heath d			08 49	08 59					09 29					09 59						10 29				
Eccleston Park d			08 52	09 02					09 32					10 02						10 32				
Prescot d			08 54	09 04					09 34					10 04						10 34				
Huyton d	08 53		08 58	09 08	09 23				09 38	09 48		09 53		10 08			10 23			10 38	10 48		10 53	
Roby d	08 55		09 00	09 10	09 25				09 40			09 55		10 10			10 25			10 40			10 55	
Broad Green d	08 58		09 03	09 13	09 28				09 43			09 58		10 13			10 28			10 43			10 58	
Wavertree Technology Park d	09 01		09 06	09 16	09 31			09 38	09 46			10 01		10 16			10 31		10 38	10 46			11 01	
Edge Hill 91 d	09 04		09 09	09 18	09 34				09 49			10 04		10 17			10 34			10 49			11 04	
Liverpool Lime Street 10 91 a	09 13		09 18	09 28	09 43			09 48	09 58	10 01		10 13		10 26			10 43		10 48	10 58	11 02		11 13	

A From Manchester Victoria
B From Chester to Manchester Piccadilly
C To Llandudno
D From Liverpool Lime Street
E From Shrewsbury to Manchester Piccadilly
F From Llandudno to Manchester Piccadilly
G From Stalybridge
H To Liverpool South Pw Hl
I To Blackpool North

Table 90

Saturdays

15 February to 22 March

Manchester, Preston, Wigan and Newton-le-Willows - St Helens and Liverpool

Network Diagram - see first Page of Table 88

	NT		NT	AW	NT	NT	NT	AW	NT	NT	NT		NT	AW	NT	NT	NT	AW	NT	NT	NT		NT	AW
				◇				◇						◇				◇						◇
			A	B			C	D		E			A	F			C	D		E			A	F
Manchester Airport 85 d					10 41										11 41									
Manchester Piccadilly 10 d				10 50	11 01									11 50	12 01									12 50
Manchester Oxford Road d				10 53	11 04									11 53	12 04									12 53
Manchester Victoria d			10 39										11 39										12 39	
Eccles d			10 46										11 46										12 46	
Patricroft d			10 49										11 49										12 49	
Blackpool North 97 d							10 35										11 35							
Preston 8 65,82 d							11 04										12 04							
Leyland 82 d							11 09										12 09							
Euxton Balshaw Lane d							11 14										12 14							
Wigan North Western 65 a							11 24										12 24							
d	10 38					11 08	11 24				11 38					12 08	12 24				12 38			
Newton-le-Willows d			11 01	11 12	11 22								12 01	12 12	12 22								13 01	13 12
Warrington Bank Quay d								11 19	11 22									12 19	12 22					
Earlestown 8 d			11 04	11 15				11a26	11 34	11 50			12 04	12 15				12a26	12 34	12 50			13 04	13 15
Warrington Bank Quay a				11 25						12 01				12 25						13 01				13 25
St Helens Junction d			11 09		11 27				11 39				12 09		12 27				12 39				13 09	
Lea Green d			11 12						11 42				12 12						12 42				13 12	
Rainhill d			11 16						11 46				12 16						12 46				13 16	
Whiston d			11 19						11 49				12 19						12 49				13 19	
Bryn d	10 45					11 15					11 45					12 15					12 45			
Garswood d	10 49					11 19					11 49					12 19					12 49			
St Helens Central a	10 55					11 25	11 39				11 55					12 25	12 39				12 55			
d	10 56					11 26	11 39				11 56					12 26	12 39				12 56			
Thatto Heath d	10 59					11 29					11 59					12 29					12 59			
Eccleston Park d	11 02					11 32					12 02					12 32					13 02			
Prescot d	11 04					11 34					12 04					12 34					13 04			
Huyton d	11 08		11 23			11 38	11 48		11 53		12 08		12 23			12 38	12 48		12 53		13 08		13 23	
Roby d	11 10		11 25			11 40			11 55		12 10		12 25			12 40			12 55		13 10		13 25	
Broad Green d	11 13		11 28			11 43			11 58		12 13		12 28			12 43			12 58		13 13		13 28	
Wavertree Technology Park d	11 16		11 31		11 38	11 46			12 01		12 16		12 31		12 38	12 46			13 01		13 16		13 31	
Edge Hill 91 d	11 19		11 34			11 49			12 04		12 19		12 34			12 49			13 04		13 19		13 34	
Liverpool Lime Street 10 91 a	11 28		11 43		11 48	11 58	12 01		12 13		12 28		12 43		12 48	12 58	13 01		13 13		13 28		13 43	

	NT	NT	NT	AW	NT	NT	NT		NT	AW	NT	NT	NT	AW	NT	NT	NT		NT	AW	NT	NT	NT	AW
				◇						◇				◇						◇				◇
			C	D		E			A	F			C	D		E			A	F			C	G
Manchester Airport 85 d	12 41										13 41										14 41			
Manchester Piccadilly 10 d	13 01									13 50	14 01									14 50	15 01			
Manchester Oxford Road d	13 04									13 53	14 04									14 53	15 04			
Manchester Victoria d									13 39										14 39					
Eccles d									13 46										14 46					
Patricroft d									13 49										14 49					
Blackpool North 97 d			12 35										13 35										14 35	
Preston 8 65,82 d			13 04										14 04										15 04	
Leyland 82 d			13 09										14 09										15 09	
Euxton Balshaw Lane d			13 14										14 14										15 14	
Wigan North Western 65 a			13 23										14 24										15 23	
d		13 08	13 24				13 38					14 08	14 24				14 38					15 08	15 24	
Newton-le-Willows d	13 22								14 01	14 12	14 22								15 01	15 12	15 22			
Warrington Bank Quay d				13 19	13 22									14 19	14 22									15 19
Earlestown 8 d				13a26	13 34	13 50			14 04	14 15				14a26	14 34	14 50			15 04	15 15				15a26
Warrington Bank Quay a						14 01				14 25						15 01				15 25				
St Helens Junction d	13 27				13 39				14 09		14 27				14 39				15 09		15 27			
Lea Green d					13 42				14 12						14 42				15 12					
Rainhill d					13 46				14 16						14 46				15 16					
Whiston d					13 49				14 19						14 49				15 19					
Bryn d		13 15					13 45					14 15					14 45					15 15		
Garswood d		13 19					13 49					14 19					14 49					15 19		
St Helens Central a		13 25	13 39				13 55					14 25	14 39				14 55					15 25	15 39	
d		13 26	13 39				13 56					14 26	14 39				14 56					15 26	15 39	
Thatto Heath d		13 29					13 59					14 29					14 59					15 29		
Eccleston Park d		13 32					14 02					14 32					15 02					15 32		
Prescot d		13 34					14 04					14 34					15 04					15 34		
Huyton d		13 38	13 50		13 53		14 08		14 23			14 38	14 48		14 53		15 08		15 23			15 38	15 48	
Roby d		13 40			13 55		14 10		14 25			14 40			14 55		15 10		15 25			15 40		
Broad Green d		13 43			13 58		14 13		14 28			14 44			14 58		15 13		15 28			15 43		
Wavertree Technology Park d	13 38	13 46			14 01		14 16		14 31		14 38	14 47			15 01		15 16		15 31		15 38	15 46		
Edge Hill 91 d		13 50			14 04		14 19		14 34			14 50			15 04		15 19		15 34			15 49		
Liverpool Lime Street 10 91 a	13 48	13 58	14 02		14 13		14 28		14 43		14 48	14 58	15 01		15 13		15 28		15 43		15 48	15 58	16 02	

A From Stalybridge
B To Bangor (Gwynedd)
C To Liverpool South Pw Hl
D From Llandudno to Manchester Piccadilly
E From Liverpool Lime Street
F To Llandudno
G From Bangor (Gwynedd) to Manchester Piccadilly

Table 90

Saturdays

15 February to 22 March

Manchester, Preston, Wigan and Newton-le-Willows - St Helens and Liverpool

Network Diagram - see first Page of Table 88

	NT	NT A	NT	TP ◇1 B	NT C	AW ◇ D	NT	NT	NT	AW ◇ E	NT	NT	NT C	AW ◇ D	NT	NT	NT	AW ◇ E	NT	NT	NT C
Manchester Airport 85 ✈ d				15 00			15 41								16 41						
Manchester Piccadilly 10 d				15 16		15 50	16 01							16 50	17 01						
Manchester Oxford Road d				15 19		15 53	16 04							16 53	17 04						
Manchester Victoria d					15 39								16 39						17 09		17 39
Eccles d					15 46								16 46						17 16		17 46
Patricroft d					15 49								16 49						17 19		17 49
Blackpool North 97 d									15 35								16 35				
Preston 8 65,82 d									16 04								17 04				
Leyland 82 d									16 09								17 09				
Euxton Balshaw Lane d									16 14								17 14				
Wigan North Western 65 a				15 43					16 23								17 24				
d			15 38					16 08	16 24			16 38				17 08	17 24			17 38	
Newton-le-Willows d					16 01	16 12	16 22						17 01	17 12	17 22				17 31		18 01
Warrington Bank Quay d	15 22									16 19	16 22							17 19			
Earlestown 8 d	15 34	15 50			16 04	16 15				16a26	16 34		17 04	17 15				17a26	17 34		18 04
Warrington Bank Quay a		16 01				16 25								17 25							
St Helens Junction d	15 39				16 09		16 27				16 39		17 09		17 27				17 39		18 09
Lea Green d	15 42				16 12						16 42		17 12						17 42		18 12
Rainhill d	15 46				16 16						16 46		17 16						17 46		18 16
Whiston d	15 49				16 19						16 49		17 19						17 49		18 19
Bryn d			15 45					16 15				16 45				17 15				17 45	
Garswood d			15 49					16 19				16 49				17 19				17 49	
St Helens Central a			15 55					16 25	16 39			16 55				17 25	17 39			17 55	
d			15 56					16 26	16 39			16 56				17 26	17 39			17 56	
Thatto Heath d			15 59					16 29				16 59				17 29				17 59	
Eccleston Park d			16 02					16 32				17 02				17 32				18 02	
Prescot d			16 04					16 34				17 04				17 34				18 04	
Huyton d	15 53		16 08		16 23			16 38	16 48		16 53	17 08	17 23			17 38	17 48		17 53	18 08	18 23
Roby d	15 55		16 10		16 25			16 40			16 55	17 10	17 25			17 40			17 55	18 10	18 25
Broad Green d	15 58		16 13		16 28			16 44			16 58	17 13	17 28			17 43			17 58	18 13	18 28
Wavertree Technology Park d	16 01		16 16		16 31		16 38	16 47			17 01	17 16	17 31		17 38	17 46			18 01	18 16	18 31
Edge Hill 91 d	16 04		16 19		16 34			16 50			17 04	17 19	17 34			17 49			18 04	18 19	18 34
Liverpool Lime Street 10 91 a	16 13		16 28		16 43		16 48	16 58	17 05		17 13	17 28	17 43		17 48	17 58	18 01		18 13	18 28	18 43

	AW ◇ D	NT	NT	AW ◇ E	NT	NT A	NT	NT	NT C	AW F	NT	NT	NT	AW ◇ G	NT	NT	AW F	NT	NT	NT	NT	TP ◇1 H
Manchester Airport 85 ✈ d			17 41								18 41							19 41				20 00
Manchester Piccadilly 10 d	17 50		18 01							18 50	19 01						19 50	20 01				20 16
Manchester Oxford Road d	17 53		18 04							18 53	19 04						19 53	20 04				20 19
Manchester Victoria d									18 39							19 39						
Eccles d			18 11						18 46							19 46						
Patricroft d									18 49							19 49						
Blackpool North 97 d							17 35						18 35							19 35		
Preston 8 65,82 d							18 04						19 04							20 04		
Leyland 82 d							18 09						19 09							20 09		
Euxton Balshaw Lane d							18 14						19 14							20 14		
Wigan North Western 65 a							18 24						19 23							20 24		20 43
d		18 08			18 21		18 24	18 35				19 08	19 24						20 08	20 24	20 38	
Newton-le-Willows d	18 11		18 24		18 33				19 01	19 12	19 22					20 01	20 12	20 22				
Warrington Bank Quay d				18 19										19 19	19 22							
Earlestown 8 d	18 14			18a26	18 35	18 50			19 04	19 16				19a26	19 34	20 04	20 15					
Warrington Bank Quay a	18 24					19 01				19 26							20 29					
St Helens Junction d			18 29		18 41				19 09		19 27				19 39	20 09		20 27				
Lea Green d			18 32		18 44				19 12						19 42	20 12						
Rainhill d			18 36		18 48				19 16						19 46	20 16						
Whiston d					18 51				19 19						19 49	20 19						
Bryn d		18 15						18 45				19 15							20 15		20 45	
Garswood d		18 19						18 49				19 19							20 19		20 49	
St Helens Central a		18 25					18 39	18 55				19 25	19 39						20 25	20 39	20 55	
d		18 26					18 39	18 56				19 26	19 39						20 26	20 39	20 56	
Thatto Heath d		18 29						18 59				19 29							20 29		20 59	
Eccleston Park d		18 32						19 02				19 32							20 32		21 02	
Prescot d		18 34						19 04				19 34							20 34		21 04	
Huyton d		18 38	18 41		18 54		18 48	19 08	19 23			19 38	19 48		19 53	20 23			20 38	20 48	21 08	
Roby d			18 43		18 56			19 10	19 25			19 40			19 55	20 25			20 40		21 10	
Broad Green d			18 46		19 00			19 13	19 28			19 44			19 58	20 28			20 43		21 13	
Wavertree Technology Park d		18 43	18 49		19 03			19 16	19 31		19 38	19 47			20 01	20 31		20 38	20 46		21 16	
Edge Hill 91 d		18 46			19 06			19 19	19 34			19 50			20 04	20 34			20 49		21 19	
Liverpool Lime Street 10 91 a		18 54	18 59		19 15		19 02	19 28	19 43		19 48	19 58	20 02		20 13	20 43		20 48	20 58	21 02	21 28	

A From Liverpool Lime Street
B To Lancaster
C From Stalybridge
D To Llandudno
E From Llandudno to Manchester Piccadilly
F To Chester
G From Llandudno to Manchester Airport
H To Preston

Table 90

Saturdays
15 February to 22 March

Manchester, Preston, Wigan and Newton-le-Willows - St Helens and Liverpool

Network Diagram - see first Page of Table 88

		AW	NT	AW	NT	AW	NT	AW	NT	AW	NT	AW	NT	NT	NT	AW
		◇ A		B		◇ A		B		C		B				B
Manchester Airport 85 ✈	d			20 32					21 42							
Manchester Piccadilly (10) ⛴	d			20 50				21 50	22 01			22 26				23 14
Manchester Oxford Road	d			20 53				21 53	22 04			22 29				23 17
Manchester Victoria ⛴	d		20 39				21 39						22 39		23 09	
Eccles	d		20 46				21 46						22 46		23 16	
Patricroft	d		20 49				21 49						22 49		23 19	
Blackpool North 97	d				20 35									22 14		
Preston (8) 65,82	d				21 04									22 43		
Leyland 82	d				21 09									22 48		
Euxton Balshaw Lane	d				21 14									22 53		
Wigan North Western 65	a				21 23									23 02		
	d				21 23						22 25			23 03		
Newton-le-Willows	d		21 01	21 12			22 01	22 12	22 22			22 47	23 01		23 31	23 36
Warrington Bank Quay	d	20 19				21 19				22 19						
Earlestown (8)	d	20a26	21 04	21 15		21a26	22 04	22 15		22a26		22 50	23 04		23 34	23 39
Warrington Bank Quay	a			21 26				22 23				22 58				23 47
St Helens Junction	d		21 09				22 09		22 27				23 09		23 39	
Lea Green	d		21 12				22 12						23 12		23 42	
Rainhill	d		21 16				22 16						23 16		23 46	
Whiston	d		21 19				22 19						23 19		23 49	
Bryn	d				21 30						22 32			23 10		
Garswood	d				21 34						22 36			23 14		
St Helens Central	a				21 40						22 42			23 20		
	d				21 41						22 43			23 21		
Thatto Heath	d				21 44						22 46			23 24		
Eccleston Park	d				21 47						22 49			23 27		
Prescot	d				21 49						22 51			23 29		
Huyton	d		21 23		21 53		22 23				22 55		23 23	23 33	23 53	
Roby	d		21 25		21 55		22 25				22 57		23 25	23 35	23 55	
Broad Green	d		21 28		21 58		22 28				23 00		23 28	23 38	23 58	
Wavertree Technology Park	d		21 31		22 03		22 31		22 38		23 03		23 31	23 41	00 01	
Edge Hill 91	d		21 34		22 06		22 34				23 06		23 34	23 46	00 04	
Liverpool Lime Street (10) 91	a		21 43		22 16		22 43		22 48		23 15		23 43	23 56	00 13	

Saturdays
29 March to 17 May

		NT	NT	NT	AW	AW	NT	NT	NT	AW	NT	NT	AW	NT	NT	NT	NT	NT	AW	NT	AW	NT	AW
		D			C	◇ E 🚲				◇ C	F		◇ E 🚲						G 🚲		◇ E 🚲		◇ A 🚲
Manchester Airport 85 ✈	d					05 33								06 41									
Manchester Piccadilly (10) ⛴	d					05 50							06 50	06 58							07 50		
Manchester Oxford Road	d					05 53							06 53	07 01							07 53		
Manchester Victoria ⛴	d			05 39				06 09								07 09				07 39			
Eccles	d			05 46				06 16								07 16				07 46			
Patricroft	d			05 49				06 19								07 19				07 49			
Blackpool North 97	d																	07 02					
Preston (8) 65,82	d																	07 30					
Leyland 82	d																	07 35					
Euxton Balshaw Lane	d																	07 40					
Wigan North Western 65	a																	07 50					
	d						06 08		06 38			06 47			07 08		07 38	07 50				07 58	
Newton-le-Willows	d			06 01		06 12		06 31				07 00	07 11	07 19		07 31				08 01	08 12		
Warrington Bank Quay	d				06 06					06 40									07 39				08 08
Earlestown (8)	d			06 04	06a12	06 15		06 34		06a47	06 50	07 03	07 15			07 34			07a46	08 04	08 15		08a15
Warrington Bank Quay	a					06 25					07 01		07 22								08 23		
St Helens Junction	d			06 09				06 39				07 09		07 24		07 39				08 09			
Lea Green	d			06 12				06 42				07 12				07 42				08 12			
Rainhill	d			06 16				06 46				07 16		07 29		07 46				08 16			
Whiston	d			06 19				06 49				07 19				07 49				08 19			
Bryn	d						06 15		06 45						07 15		07 45					08 05	
Garswood	d						06 19		06 49						07 19		07 49	07 59				08 09	
St Helens Central	a						06 25		06 55						07 25		07 55	08 06				08 15	
	d		05 56				06 26		06 56						07 26		07 56	08 06				08 16	
Thatto Heath	d		05 59				06 29		06 59						07 29		07 59					08 19	
Eccleston Park	d		06 02				06 32		07 02						07 32		08 02					08 22	
Prescot	d		06 04				06 34		07 04						07 34		08 04	08 12				08 24	
Huyton	d		06 08	06 23			06 38	06 53	07 08			07 23		07 34	07 38	07 53	08 08	08 16		08 23		08 28	
Roby	d		06 10	06 25			06 40	06 55	07 10			07 25			07 40	07 55	08 10			08 25		08 30	
Broad Green	d		06 13	06 28			06 43	06 58	07 13			07 28			07 43	07 58	08 13	08 20		08 28		08 33	
Wavertree Technology Park	d	00 01	06 16	06 31			06 46	07 01	07 16			07 31		07 39	07 46	08 01	08 16	08 24		08 31		08 36	
Edge Hill 91	d	00 04	06 19	06 34			06 49	07 04	07 19			07 35			07 49	08 04	08 19			08 34		08 39	
Liverpool Lime Street (10) 91	a	00 13	06 28	06 43			06 58	07 13	07 28			07 43		07 49	07 58	08 13	08 28	08 35		08 43		08 50	

A From Llandudno to Manchester Piccadilly
B To Chester
C From Chester to Manchester Piccadilly
D From Manchester Victoria
E To Llandudno
F From Liverpool Lime Street
G From Shrewsbury to Manchester Piccadilly

Table 90

Saturdays

29 March to 17 May

Manchester, Preston, Wigan and Newton-le-Willows - St Helens and Liverpool

Network Diagram - see first Page of Table 88

Station		NT	NT A	NT	NT	NT B		AW ◇ C	NT	NT	NT D	AW ◇ E	NT	NT A	NT	TP ◇1 F		NT B	AW ◇ C	NT	NT	NT D	AW ◇ E	NT	NT A
Manchester Airport 85 ✈	d								08 41							09 00				09 41					
Manchester Piccadilly 10	d							08 50	09 01							09 16			09 50	10 01					
Manchester Oxford Road	d							08 53	09 04							09 19			09 53	10 04					
Manchester Victoria	d	08 09				08 39												09 39							
Eccles	d	08 16				08 46												09 46							
Patricroft	d	08 19				08 49												09 49							
Blackpool North 97	d										08 35											09 35			
Preston 8 65,82	d										09 04											10 04			
Leyland 82	d										09 09											10 09			
Euxton Balshaw Lane	d										09 14											10 14			
Wigan North Western 65	a										09 24					09 43						10 24			
	d			08 28						09 08	09 24				09 38						10 08	10 24			
Newton-le-Willows	d	08 31				09 01		09 12	09 22									10 01	10 12	10 22					
Warrington Bank Quay	d											09 19	09 22										10 19	10 22	
Earlestown 8	d	08 34	08 50			09 04		09 15				09a26	09 34	09 50				10 04	10 15				10a26	10 34	10 50
Warrington Bank Quay	a		09 01					09 25						10 01					10 25						11 01
St Helens Junction	d	08 39				09 09			09 27				09 39					10 09		10 27				10 39	
Lea Green	d	08 42				09 12							09 42					10 12						10 42	
Rainhill	d	08 46				09 16							09 46					10 16						10 46	
Whiston	d	08 49				09 19							09 49					10 19						10 49	
Bryn	d			08 35						09 15					09 45						10 15				
Garswood	d			08 39						09 19					09 49						10 19				
St Helens Central	a			08 45						09 25	09 39				09 55						10 25	10 39			
	d			08 46	08 56					09 26	09 39				09 56						10 26	10 39			
Thatto Heath	d			08 49	08 59					09 29					09 59						10 29				
Eccleston Park	d			08 52	09 02					09 32					10 02						10 32				
Prescot	d			08 54	09 04					09 34					10 04						10 34				
Huyton	d	08 53		08 58	09 08	09 23				09 38	09 48		09 53		10 08			10 23			10 38	10 48		10 53	
Roby	d	08 55		09 00	09 10	09 25				09 40			09 55		10 10			10 25			10 40			10 55	
Broad Green	d	08 58		09 03	09 13	09 28				09 43			09 58		10 13			10 28			10 43			10 58	
Wavertree Technology Park	d	09 01		09 06	09 16	09 31			09 38	09 46			10 01		10 16			10 31		10 38	10 46			11 01	
Edge Hill 91	d	09 04		09 09	09 19	09 34				09 49			10 04		10 17			10 34			10 49			11 04	
Liverpool Lime Street 10 91	a	09 13		09 18	09 28	09 43			09 48	09 58	10 01		10 13		10 26			10 43		10 48	10 58	11 02		11 13	

Station		NT		NT B	AW ◇ G	NT	NT	NT D	AW ◇ E	NT	NT A	NT		NT B	AW ◇ C	NT	NT	NT D	AW ◇ E	NT	NT A	NT		NT B	AW ◇ C
Manchester Airport 85 ✈	d					10 41										11 41									
Manchester Piccadilly 10	d				10 50	11 01									11 50	12 01									12 50
Manchester Oxford Road	d				10 53	11 04									11 53	12 04									12 53
Manchester Victoria	d			10 39										11 39										12 39	
Eccles	d			10 46										11 46										12 46	
Patricroft	d			10 49										11 49										12 49	
Blackpool North 97	d							10 35										11 35							
Preston 8 65,82	d							11 04										12 04							
Leyland 82	d							11 09										12 09							
Euxton Balshaw Lane	d							11 14										12 14							
Wigan North Western 65	a							11 24										12 24							
	d	10 38					11 08	11 24				11 38					12 08	12 24				12 38			
Newton-le-Willows	d			11 01	11 12	11 22								12 01	12 12	12 22								13 01	13 12
Warrington Bank Quay	d								11 19	11 22									12 19	12 22					
Earlestown 8	d			11 04	11 15				11a26	11 34	11 50			12 04	12 15				12a26	12 34	12 50			13 04	13 15
Warrington Bank Quay	a				11 25						12 01				12 25						13 01				13 25
St Helens Junction	d			11 09		11 27				11 39				12 09		12 27				12 39				13 09	
Lea Green	d			11 12						11 42				12 12						12 42				13 12	
Rainhill	d			11 16						11 46				12 16						12 46				13 16	
Whiston	d			11 19						11 49				12 19						12 49				13 19	
Bryn	d	10 45					11 15					11 45					12 15					12 45			
Garswood	d	10 49					11 19					11 49					12 19					12 49			
St Helens Central	a	10 55					11 25	11 39				11 55					12 25	12 39				12 55			
	d	10 56					11 26	11 39				11 56					12 26	12 39				12 56			
Thatto Heath	d	10 59					11 29					11 59					12 29					12 59			
Eccleston Park	d	11 02					11 32					12 02					12 32					13 02			
Prescot	d	11 04					11 34					12 04					12 34					13 04			
Huyton	d	11 08		11 23			11 38	11 48		11 53		12 08		12 23			12 38	12 48		12 53		13 08		13 23	
Roby	d	11 10		11 25			11 40			11 55		12 10		12 25			12 40			12 55		13 10		13 25	
Broad Green	d	11 13		11 28			11 43			11 58		12 13		12 28			12 43			12 58		13 13		13 28	
Wavertree Technology Park	d	11 16		11 31		11 38	11 46			12 01		12 16		12 31		12 38	12 46			13 01		13 16		13 31	
Edge Hill 91	d	11 19		11 34			11 49			12 04		12 19		12 34			12 49			13 04		13 19		13 34	
Liverpool Lime Street 10 91	a	11 28		11 43		11 48	11 58	12 01		12 13		12 28		12 43		12 48	12 58	13 01		13 13		13 28		13 43	

A From Liverpool Lime Street
B From Stalybridge
C To Llandudno
D To Liverpool South Pw Hl
E From Llandudno to Manchester Piccadilly
F To Blackpool North
G To Bangor (Gwynedd)

Table 90

Saturdays

29 March to 17 May

Manchester, Preston, Wigan and Newton-le-Willows - St Helens and Liverpool

Network Diagram - see first Page of Table 88

	NT	NT	NT A	AW ◇ B	NT	NT C	NT		NT D	AW ◇ E	NT	NT	NT A	AW ◇ B	NT	NT C	NT		NT D	AW ◇ E	NT	NT	NT A	AW ◇ F
Manchester Airport 85 ✈ d	12 41										13 41										14 41			
Manchester Piccadilly 10 d	13 01									13 50	14 01									14 50	15 01			
Manchester Oxford Road d	13 04									13 53	14 04									14 53	15 04			
Manchester Victoria d									13 39										14 39					
Eccles d									13 46										14 46					
Patricroft d									13 49										14 49					
Blackpool North 97 d			12 35										13 35										14 35	
Preston 8 65,82 d			13 04										14 04										15 04	
Leyland 82 d			13 09										14 09										15 09	
Euxton Balshaw Lane d			13 14										14 14										15 14	
Wigan North Western 65 a			13 23										14 24										15 23	
d		13 08	13 24				13 38					14 08	14 24				14 38					15 08	15 24	
Newton-le-Willows d	13 22								14 01	14 12	14 22								15 01	15 12	15 22			
Warrington Bank Quay d				13 19	13 22									14 19	14 22									15 19
Earlestown 8 d				13a26	13 34	13 50			14 04	14 15				14a26	14 34	14 50			15 04	15 15				15a26
Warrington Bank Quay a						14 01				14 25						15 01				15 25				
St Helens Junction d	13 27				13 39				14 09		14 27				14 39				15 09		15 27			
Lea Green d					13 42				14 12						14 42				15 12					
Rainhill d					13 46				14 16						14 46				15 16					
Whiston d					13 49				14 19						14 49				15 19					
Bryn d		13 15					13 45					14 15					14 45					15 15		
Garswood d		13 19					13 49					14 19					14 49					15 19		
St Helens Central a		13 25	13 39				13 55					14 25	14 39				14 55					15 25	15 39	
d		13 26	13 39				13 56					14 26	14 39				14 56					15 26	15 39	
Thatto Heath d		13 29					13 59					14 29					14 59					15 29		
Eccleston Park d		13 32					14 02					14 32					15 02					15 32		
Prescot d		13 34					14 04					14 34					15 04					15 34		
Huyton d		13 38	13 48		13 53		14 08		14 23			14 38	14 48		14 53		15 08		15 23			15 38	15 48	
Roby d		13 40			13 55		14 10		14 25			14 40			14 55		15 10		15 25			15 40		
Broad Green d		13 43			13 58		14 13		14 28			14 44			14 58		15 13		15 28			15 43		
Wavertree Technology Park d	13 38	13 46			14 01		14 16		14 31		14 38	14 47			15 01		15 16		15 31		15 38	15 46		
Edge Hill 91 d		13 50			14 04		14 19		14 34			14 50			15 04		15 19		15 34			15 49		
Liverpool Lime Street 10 91 a	13 48	13 58	14 01		14 13		14 28		14 43		14 48	14 58	15 01		15 13		15 28		15 43		15 48	15 58	16 02	

	NT	NT C	NT		TP ◇1 G	NT D	AW ◇ E	NT	NT	NT	AW ◇ B	NT	NT		NT D	AW ◇ E	NT	NT	NT	AW ◇ B	NT	NT	NT D	
Manchester Airport 85 ✈ d					15 00			15 41									16 41							
Manchester Piccadilly 10 d					15 16		15 50	16 01								16 50	17 01							
Manchester Oxford Road d					15 19		15 53	16 04								16 53	17 04							
Manchester Victoria d						15 39									16 39						17 09		17 39	
Eccles d						15 46									16 46						17 16		17 46	
Patricroft d						15 49									16 49						17 19		17 49	
Blackpool North 97 d										15 35									16 35					
Preston 8 65,82 d										16 04									17 04					
Leyland 82 d										16 09									17 09					
Euxton Balshaw Lane d										16 14									17 14					
Wigan North Western 65 a					15 43					16 23									17 24					
d			15 38						16 08	16 24			16 38					17 08	17 24			17 38		
Newton-le-Willows d						16 01	16 12	16 22							17 01	17 12	17 22				17 31		18 01	
Warrington Bank Quay d	15 22										16 19	16 22								17 19				
Earlestown 8 d	15 34	15 50				16 04	16 15				16a26	16 34			17 04	17 15				17a26	17 34		18 04	
Warrington Bank Quay a		16 01					16 25									17 25								
St Helens Junction d	15 39					16 09		16 27				16 39			17 09		17 27				17 39		18 09	
Lea Green d	15 42					16 12						16 42			17 12						17 42		18 12	
Rainhill d	15 46					16 16						16 46			17 16						17 46		18 16	
Whiston d	15 49					16 19						16 49			17 19						17 49		18 19	
Bryn d			15 45						16 15				16 45					17 15				17 45		
Garswood d			15 49						16 19				16 49					17 19				17 49		
St Helens Central a			15 55						16 25	16 39			16 55					17 25	17 39			17 55		
d			15 56						16 26	16 39			16 56					17 26	17 39			17 56		
Thatto Heath d			15 59						16 29				16 59					17 29				17 59		
Eccleston Park d			16 02						16 32				17 02					17 32				18 02		
Prescot d			16 04						16 34				17 04					17 34				18 04		
Huyton d	15 53		16 08			16 23			16 38	16 48		16 53	17 08		17 23			17 38	17 48		17 53	18 08	18 23	
Roby d	15 55		16 10			16 25			16 40			16 55	17 10		17 25			17 40			17 55	18 10	18 25	
Broad Green d	15 58		16 13			16 28			16 44			16 58	17 13		17 28			17 43			17 58	18 13	18 28	
Wavertree Technology Park d	16 01		16 16			16 31		16 38	16 47			17 01	17 16		17 31		17 38	17 46			18 01	18 16	18 31	
Edge Hill 91 d	16 04		16 19			16 34			16 50			17 04	17 19		17 34			17 49			18 04	18 19	18 34	
Liverpool Lime Street 10 91 a	16 13		16 28			16 43		16 48	16 58	17 05		17 13	17 28		17 43		17 48	17 58	18 01		18 13	18 28	18 43	

A To Liverpool South Pw Hl
B From Llandudno to Manchester Piccadilly
C From Liverpool Lime Street
D From Stalybridge
E To Llandudno
F From Bangor (Gwynedd) to Manchester Piccadilly
G To Lancaster

Table 90

Saturdays

29 March to 17 May

Manchester, Preston, Wigan and Newton-le-Willows - St Helens and Liverpool

Network Diagram - see first Page of Table 88

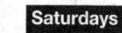

	AW	NT	NT	AW	NT	NT	NT	NT	NT		AW	NT	NT	NT	AW	NT	NT	AW	NT		NT	NT	NT	TP
	◇ A 🛒			◇ B 🛒		C			D		E				◇ F 🛒			E						◇1 G
Manchester Airport 85 ✈ d			17 41									18 41							19 41					20 00
Manchester Piccadilly 10 ⛴ d	17 50		18 01								18 50	19 01						19 50	20 01					20 16
Manchester Oxford Road d	17 53		18 04								18 53	19 04						19 53	20 04					20 19
Manchester Victoria ⛴ d									18 39								19 39							
Eccles d			18 11						18 46								19 46							
Patricroft d									18 49								19 49							
Blackpool North 97 d							17 35							18 35								19 35		
Preston 8 65,82 d							18 04							19 04								20 04		
Leyland 82 d							18 09							19 09								20 09		
Euxton Balshaw Lane d							18 14							19 14								20 14		
Wigan North Western 65 a							18 24							19 23								20 24		20 43
d		18 08			18 21		18 24	18 35					19 08	19 24							20 08	20 24	20 38	
Newton-le-Willows d	18 11		18 24		18 33				19 01		19 12	19 22					20 01	20 12	20 22					
Warrington Bank Quay d				18 19											19 19	19 22								
Earlestown 8 d	18 14			18a26	18 35	18 50			19 04		19 16				19a26	19 34	20 04	20 15						
Warrington Bank Quay a	18 24					19 01					19 26							20 29						
St Helens Junction d			18 29		18 41				19 09			19 27				19 39	20 09		20 27					
Lea Green d			18 32		18 44				19 12							19 42	20 12							
Rainhill d			18 36		18 48				19 16							19 46	20 16							
Whiston d					18 51				19 19							19 49	20 19							
Bryn d		18 15						18 45					19 15								20 15		20 45	
Garswood d		18 19						18 49					19 19								20 19		20 49	
St Helens Central a		18 25					18 39	18 55					19 25	19 39							20 25	20 39	20 55	
d		18 26					18 39	18 56					19 26	19 39							20 26	20 39	20 56	
Thatto Heath d		18 29						18 59					19 29								20 29		20 59	
Eccleston Park d		18 32						19 02					19 32								20 32		21 02	
Prescot d		18 34						19 04					19 34								20 34		21 04	
Huyton d		18 38	18 41		18 54		18 48	19 08	19 23				19 38	19 48		19 53	20 23				20 38	20 48	21 08	
Roby d			18 43		18 56			19 10	19 25				19 40			19 55	20 25				20 40		21 10	
Broad Green d			18 46		19 00			19 13	19 28				19 44			19 58	20 28				20 43		21 13	
Wavertree Technology Park d		18 43	18 49		19 03			19 16	19 31			19 38	19 47			20 01	20 31		20 38		20 46		21 16	
Edge Hill 91 d		18 46			19 06			19 19	19 34				19 50			20 04	20 34				20 49		21 19	
Liverpool Lime Street 10 91 a		18 54	18 59		19 15		19 02	19 28	19 43			19 48	19 58	20 02		20 13	20 43		20 48		20 58	21 02	21 28	

	AW	NT	AW	NT	AW		NT	AW	NT	AW	NT	AW	NT	NT	NT		AW	AW
	◇ B		E		◇ B			E		H		E					E	H
Manchester Airport 85 ✈ d			20 32						21 42									
Manchester Piccadilly 10 ⛴ d			20 50					21 50	22 01			22 26					23 14	
Manchester Oxford Road d			20 53					21 53	22 04			22 29					23 17	
Manchester Victoria ⛴ d		20 39					21 39						22 39		23 09			
Eccles d		20 46					21 46						22 46		23 16			
Patricroft d		20 49					21 49						22 49		23 19			
Blackpool North 97 d				20 35										22 14				
Preston 8 65,82 d				21 04										22 43				
Leyland 82 d				21 09										22 48				
Euxton Balshaw Lane d				21 14										22 53				
Wigan North Western 65 a				21 23										23 02				
d				21 23							22 25			23 03				
Newton-le-Willows d		21 01	21 12				22 01	22 12	22 22			22 47	23 01		23 31		23 36	
Warrington Bank Quay d	20 19				21 19					22 19								23 50
Earlestown 8 d	20a26	21 04	21 15		21a26		22 04	22 15		22a26		22 50	23 04		23 34		23 39	23a58
Warrington Bank Quay a			21 26					22 23				22 58					23 47	
St Helens Junction d		21 09					22 09		22 27				23 09		23 39			
Lea Green d		21 12					22 12						23 12		23 42			
Rainhill d		21 16					22 16						23 16		23 46			
Whiston d		21 19					22 19						23 19		23 49			
Bryn d				21 30							22 32			23 10				
Garswood d				21 34							22 36			23 14				
St Helens Central a				21 40							22 42			23 20				
d				21 41							22 43			23 21				
Thatto Heath d				21 44							22 46			23 24				
Eccleston Park d				21 47							22 49			23 27				
Prescot d				21 49							22 51			23 29				
Huyton d		21 23		21 53			22 23				22 55		23 23	23 33	23 53			
Roby d		21 25		21 55			22 25				22 57		23 25	23 35	23 55			
Broad Green d		21 28		21 58			22 28				23 00		23 28	23 38	23 58			
Wavertree Technology Park d		21 31		22 03			22 31		22 38		23 03		23 31	23 41	00 01			
Edge Hill 91 d		21 34		22 06			22 34				23 06		23 34	23 46	00 04			
Liverpool Lime Street 10 91 a		21 43		22 16			22 43		22 48		23 15		23 43	23 56	00 13			

A To Llandudno
B From Llandudno to Manchester Piccadilly
C From Liverpool Lime Street
D From Stalybridge
E To Chester
F From Llandudno to Manchester Airport
G To Preston
H From Chester to Manchester Piccadilly

Table 90

Sundays

8 December to 29 December

Manchester, Preston, Wigan and Newton-le-Willows - St Helens and Liverpool

Network Diagram - see first Page of Table 88

		NT	AW	NT	NT	NT	AW	NT	NT	AW	AW	AW	NT	NT	AW	AW	NT	NT	AW	AW	NT	NT	AW
		A	B				C			◇ C	B	C			B	C			B	C			B
			🚌									🚲				🚲			🚲	🚲			🚲
Manchester Airport 85 ✈	d				08 35			09 35					10 35				11 33				12 35		
Manchester Piccadilly 10	d		07 28		08 50			09 50			09 56		10 50		10 55		11 50		11 56		12 50		12 56
Manchester Oxford Road	d		07 33		08 53			09 53			09 59		10 53		10 56		11 53		11 59		12 52		12 59
Manchester Victoria	d																						
Eccles	d				09 01			10 00					11 00				12 00				13 00		
Patricroft	d																						
Blackpool North 97	d					08 50			09 50					10 50				11 50				12 50	
Preston 8 65,82	d					09 15			10 15					11 15				12 15				13 15	
Leyland 82	d					09 21			10 21					11 21				12 21				13 21	
Euxton Balshaw Lane	d					09 25			10 25					11 25				12 25				13 25	
Wigan North Western 65	a					09 35			10 35					11 35				12 35				13 35	
	d			08 36		09 36			10 36					11 36				12 36				13 36	
Newton-le-Willows	d		08 03		09 14			10 13			10 18		11 13		11 18		12 13		12 18		13 12		13 18
Warrington Bank Quay	d						09 10			10 12		11 03				12 03				13 03			
Earlestown 8	d		08 13		09 16		09a16	10 15		10a19	10 21	11a10	11 15		11 21	12a10	12 15		12 21	13a10	13 15		13 21
Warrington Bank Quay	a		08 38								10 27				11 29				12 27				13 28
St Helens Junction	d				09 21			10 20					11 20				12 20				13 20		
Lea Green	d				09 24			10 23					11 23				12 23				13 23		
Rainhill	d				09 28			10 27					11 27				12 27				13 27		
Whiston	d				09 31			10 30					11 30				12 30				13 30		
Bryn	d																						
Garswood	d			08 46		09 46			10 46					11 46				12 46				13 46	
St Helens Central	a			08 52		09 52			10 52					11 52				12 52				13 52	
	d			08 53		09 53			10 53					11 53				12 53				13 53	
Thatto Heath	d			08 56		09 56			10 56					11 56				12 56				13 56	
Eccleston Park	d																						
Prescot	d			09 00		10 00			11 00					12 00				13 00				14 00	
Huyton	d			09 05	09 36	10 05		10 35	11 05				11 35	12 05			12 35	13 05			13 35	14 05	
Roby	d			09 07	09 38	10 07		10 37	11 07				11 37	12 07			12 37	13 07			13 37	14 07	
Broad Green	d			09 10	09 41	10 10		10 40	11 10				11 40	12 10			12 40	13 10			13 39	14 10	
Wavertree Technology Park	d	00 01		09 13	09 44	10 13		10 43	11 13				11 43	12 13			12 43	13 13			13 42	14 13	
Edge Hill 91	d	00 04																					
Liverpool Lime Street 10 91	a	00 13		09 22	09 53	10 24		10 54	11 24				11 54	12 24			12 54	13 24			13 54	14 24	

		AW	NT	NT	AW	AW	NT	NT	AW	AW	NT	NT	AW	AW	NT	NT	AW	AW	NT	NT	AW	AW	NT
		C			B	C			B	C			B	◇ D			B	◇ C			B	C	
		🚲			🚲	🚲			🚲				🚲	🚲							🚲		
Manchester Airport 85 ✈	d		13 35				14 35				15 35				16 35				17 35				18 35
Manchester Piccadilly 10	d		13 50		13 56		14 50		14 56		15 50		15 56		16 50		16 56		17 50		17 56		18 50
Manchester Oxford Road	d		13 53		13 59		14 53		14 59		15 53		15 59		16 53		16 59		17 53		17 59		18 53
Manchester Victoria	d																						
Eccles	d		14 00				15 00				16 00				17 00				18 00				19 00
Patricroft	d																						
Blackpool North 97	d			13 50				14 50				15 50				16 50				17 50			
Preston 8 65,82	d			14 15				15 15				16 15				17 15				18 15			
Leyland 82	d			14 21				15 21				16 21				17 21				18 21			
Euxton Balshaw Lane	d			14 25				15 25				16 25				17 25				18 25			
Wigan North Western 65	a			14 35				15 35				16 35				17 35				18 35			
	d			14 36				15 36				16 36				17 36				18 36			
Newton-le-Willows	d		14 13		14 18		15 13		15 18		16 13		16 18		17 13		17 18		18 13		18 18		19 13
Warrington Bank Quay	d	14 03				15 03				16 03				17 03				18 03				19 03	
Earlestown 8	d	14a10	14 15		14 21	15a10	15 15		15 21	16a10	16 15		16 21	17a10	17 15		17 21	18a10	18 15		18 21	19a10	19 15
Warrington Bank Quay	a				14 27				15 28				16 27				17 27				18 27		
St Helens Junction	d		14 20				15 20				16 20				17 20				18 20				19 20
Lea Green	d		14 23				15 23				16 23				17 23				18 23				19 23
Rainhill	d		14 27				15 27				16 27				17 27				18 27				19 27
Whiston	d		14 30				15 30				16 30				17 30				18 30				19 30
Bryn	d																						
Garswood	d			14 46				15 46				16 46				17 46				18 46			
St Helens Central	a			14 52				15 52				16 52				17 52				18 52			
	d			14 53				15 53				16 53				17 53				18 53			
Thatto Heath	d			14 56				15 56				16 56				17 56				18 56			
Eccleston Park	d																						
Prescot	d			15 00				16 00				17 00				18 00				19 00			
Huyton	d		14 35	15 05			15 35	16 05			16 35	17 05			17 35	18 05			18 35	19 05			19 35
Roby	d		14 37	15 07			15 37	16 07			16 37	17 07			17 37	18 07			18 37	19 07			19 37
Broad Green	d		14 40	15 10			15 40	16 10			16 40	17 10			17 40	18 10			18 40	19 10			19 40
Wavertree Technology Park	d		14 43	15 13			15 43	16 13			16 43	17 13			17 43	18 13			18 43	19 13			19 43
Edge Hill 91	d																						
Liverpool Lime Street 10 91	a		14 54	15 24			15 54	16 24			16 54	17 24			17 54	18 24			18 54	19 24			19 54

A not 8 December. From Manchester Victoria
B To Chester
C From Chester to Manchester Piccadilly
D From Holyhead to Manchester Piccadilly

Table 90

Sundays

8 December to 29 December

Manchester, Preston, Wigan and Newton-le-Willows - St Helens and Liverpool

Network Diagram - see first Page of Table 88

		NT	AW	AW	NT	NT	AW	AW	NT	NT	AW	NT	AW	NT	AW	AW	NT	NT	AW	NT	AW	NT
			A	B			A	B			A		B		A	B			A		A	
																	🚌			🚌		🚌
Manchester Airport 85 ✈	d				19 35				20 35					21 35								
Manchester Piccadilly [10] ⛴	d		18 56		19 50		19 56		20 50		20 56			21 50	21 56				22 56		23 25	
Manchester Oxford Road	d		18 59		19 53		19 59		20 53		20 59			21 53	21 59				22 59	23 00	23 28	
Manchester Victoria ⛴	d																					
Eccles	d				20 00				21 00					22 00						23 15		
Patricroft	d																					
Blackpool North 97	d	18 50				19 50				20 50		21 50						22 44				
Preston [8] 65,82	d	19 15				20 15				21 15		22 15						23 09				
Leyland 82	d	19 21				20 21				21 21		22 21						23 15				
Euxton Balshaw Lane	d	19 25				20 25				21 25		22 25						23 19				
Wigan North Western 65	a	19 35				20 35				21 35		22 36						23 30				
	d	19 36				20 36				21 36							22 47					23 47
Newton-le-Willows	d		19 18		20 13		20 18		21 13		21 18			22 13	22 18				23 18	23 40	23 47	
Warrington Bank Quay	d			20 03				21 03					22 04			22 36						
Earlestown [8]	d		19 21	20a10	20 15		20 21	21a10	21 15		21 21		22a12	22 15	22 21	22a47			23 21	23 48	23 50	
Warrington Bank Quay	a		19 28				20 29				21 27				22 27				23 27		23 56	
St Helens Junction	d				20 20				21 20					22 20						00 01		
Lea Green	d				20 23				21 23					22 23						00 07		
Rainhill	d				20 27				21 27					22 27						00 15		
Whiston	d				20 30				21 30					22 30						00 25		
Bryn	d																					
Garswood	d	19 46				20 46				21 46							23 07					00 07
St Helens Central	a	19 52				20 52				21 52							23 27					00 27
	d	19 53				20 53				21 53							23 27					00 27
Thatto Heath	d	19 56				20 56				21 56							23 37					00 37
Eccleston Park	d																					
Prescot	d	20 00				21 00				22 00							23 47					00 47
Huyton	d	20 05			20 35	21 05			21 35	22 05				22 35			23 57			00 35		00 57
Roby	d	20 07			20 37	21 07			21 37	22 07				22 37			00 01			00 39		01 01
Broad Green	d	20 10			20 40	21 10			21 40	22 10				22 40			00 08			00 46		01 08
Wavertree Technology Park	d	20 13			20 43	21 13			21 43	22 13				22 43			00 18			00 56		01 18
Edge Hill 91	d																					
Liverpool Lime Street [10] 91	a	20 24			20 54	21 24			21 54	22 24				22 54			00 33			01 11		01 33

Sundays

5 January to 9 February

		NT	AW	NT	NT	NT	NT	NT	NT	AW	NT	NT	NT	NT	AW	AW	NT	NT	NT	NT	AW	AW	NT
															◇								
		C	A							B					B	A					B	A	
			🚌	🚌	🚌		🚌	🚌	🚌			🚌	🚌	🚌				🚌	🚌	🚌	🚲		
Manchester Airport 85 ✈	d					09 03					10 03						11 03						12 03
Manchester Piccadilly [10] ⛴	d		07 28			09 18					10 19					09 56	11 18					10 55	12 18
Manchester Oxford Road	d		07 33			09 21	07 55				10 22	08 55				09 59	11 22	09 55				10 56	12 22
Manchester Victoria ⛴	d																						
Eccles	d						08 10					09 10						10 10					
Patricroft	d																						
Blackpool North 97	d																						
Preston [8] 65,82	d				07 44				08 44					09 44						10 44			
Leyland 82	d				08 04				09 04					10 04						11 04			
Euxton Balshaw Lane	d				08 16				09 16					10 16						11 16			
Wigan North Western 65	a				08 41				09 41					10 41						11 41			
	d			07 47	08 41			08 47	09 41				09 47	10 41					10 47	11 41			
Newton-le-Willows	d		08 03				08 35					09 35				10 18		10 35				11 18	
Warrington Bank Quay	d									09 10					10 12						11 03		
Earlestown [8]	d		08 13				08 43			09a16		09 43			10a19	10 21		10 43			11a10	11 21	
Warrington Bank Quay	a		08 38													10 27						11 29	
St Helens Junction	d						08 55					09 55						10 55					
Lea Green	d						09 02					10 02						11 02					
Rainhill	d						09 10					10 10						11 10					
Whiston	d						09 20					10 20						11 20					
Bryn	d																						
Garswood	d			08 07				09 07					10 07						11 07				
St Helens Central	a			08 27				09 27					10 27						11 27				
	d			08 27				09 27					10 27						11 27				
Thatto Heath	d			08 37				09 37					10 37						11 37				
Eccleston Park	d																						
Prescot	d			08 47				09 47					10 47						11 47				
Huyton	d			08 57			09 30	09 57				10 30	10 57					11 30	11 57				
Roby	d			09 01			09 34	10 01				10 34	11 01					11 34	12 01				
Broad Green	d			09 08			09 41	10 08				10 41	11 08					11 41	12 08				
Wavertree Technology Park	d	00 01		09 18			09 51	10 18				10 51	11 18					11 51	12 18				
Edge Hill 91	d	00 04																					
Liverpool Lime Street [10] 91	a	00 13		09 33	09 41	10 03	10 06	10 33	10 41		11 03	11 06	11 33	11 41			12 02	12 06	12 33	12 41			13 03

A To Chester **B** From Chester to Manchester Piccadilly **C** From Manchester Victoria

Table 90

Sundays

5 January to 9 February

Manchester, Preston, Wigan and Newton-le-Willows - St Helens and Liverpool

Network Diagram - see first Page of Table 88

	NT	NT	NT	AW A	AW B		NT	NT	NT	NT	AW A	AW B	NT	NT	NT		NT	AW A	AW B	NT	NT	NT	NT	AW A
	bus	bus	bus	trolley	trolley			bus	bus	bus	trolley	trolley		bus	bus		bus	trolley	trolley		bus	bus		trolley
Manchester Airport 85 ✈ d							13 03						14 03							15 03				
Manchester Piccadilly 10 d					11 56		13 18					12 56	14 18						13 56	15 18				
Manchester Oxford Road d	10 55				11 59		13 22	11 55				12 59	14 22	12 55					13 59	15 22	13 55			
Manchester Victoria d																								
Eccles d	11 10							12 10						13 10							14 10			
Patricroft d																								
Blackpool North 97 d																							14 50	
Preston 8 65,82 d			11 44							12 44							13 44						15 15	
Leyland 82 d			12 04							13 04							14 04						15 21	
Euxton Balshaw Lane d			12 16							13 16							14 16						15 25	
Wigan North Western 65 a			12 41							13 41							14 41						15 37	
d		11 47	12 41						12 47	13 41					13 47		14 41					14 47		
Newton-le-Willows d	11 35				12 18			12 35				13 18		13 35					14 18		14 35			
Warrington Bank Quay d				12 03							13 03							14 03						15 03
Earlestown 8 d	11 43			12a10	12 21			12 43			13a10	13 21		13 43				14a10	14 21		14 43			15a10
Warrington Bank Quay a					12 27							13 28							14 27					
St Helens Junction d	11 55							12 55						13 55							14 55			
Lea Green d	12 02							13 02						14 02							15 02			
Rainhill d	12 10							13 10						14 10							15 10			
Whiston d	12 20							13 20						14 20							15 20			
Bryn d																								
Garswood d		12 07							13 07						14 07							15 07		
St Helens Central a		12 27							13 27						14 27							15 27		
d		12 27							13 27						14 27							15 27		
Thatto Heath d		12 37							13 37						14 37							15 37		
Eccleston Park d																								
Prescot d		12 47							13 47						14 47							15 47		
Huyton d	12 30	12 57						13 30	13 57					14 30	14 57						15 30	15 57		
Roby d	12 34	13 01						13 34	14 01					14 34	15 01						15 34	16 01		
Broad Green d	12 41	13 08						13 41	14 08					14 41	15 08						15 41	16 08		
Wavertree Technology Park d	12 51	13 18						13 51	14 18					14 51	15 18						15 51	16 18		
Edge Hill 91 d																								
Liverpool Lime Street 10 91 a	13 06	13 33	13 41				14 03	14 06	14 33	14 41			15 03	15 06	15 33		15 41			16 03	16 06	16 33		

	AW B		NT	NT	NT	NT	AW A	AW B	NT	NT	NT		NT	AW ◇ C	AW B	NT	NT	NT	NT	AW ◇ A	AW B		NT	NT
	trolley			bus	bus			trolley		bus	bus			trolley			bus	bus			trolley			bus
Manchester Airport 85 ✈ d			16 03						17 03							18 03							19 03	
Manchester Piccadilly 10 d	14 56		16 18					15 56	17 18						16 56	18 18					17 56		19 18	
Manchester Oxford Road d	14 59		16 22	14 55				15 59	17 22	15 55					16 59	18 22	16 55				17 59		19 22	17 55
Manchester Victoria d																								
Eccles d				15 10						16 10							17 10							18 10
Patricroft d																								
Blackpool North 97 d						15 50							16 50						17 50					
Preston 8 65,82 d						16 15							17 15						18 15					
Leyland 82 d						16 21							17 21						18 21					
Euxton Balshaw Lane d						16 25							17 25						18 25					
Wigan North Western 65 a						16 37							17 37						18 37					
d					15 47						16 47							17 47						
Newton-le-Willows d	15 18			15 35				16 18		16 35					17 18		17 35				18 18			18 35
Warrington Bank Quay d							16 03							17 03						18 03				
Earlestown 8 d	15 21			15 43			16a10	16 21		16 43				17a10	17 21		17 43			18a10	18 21			18 43
Warrington Bank Quay a	15 28							16 27							17 27						18 27			
St Helens Junction d				15 55						16 55							17 55							18 55
Lea Green d				16 02						17 02							18 02							19 02
Rainhill d				16 10						17 10							18 10							19 10
Whiston d				16 20						17 20							18 20							19 20
Bryn d																								
Garswood d					16 07						17 07							18 07						
St Helens Central a					16 27						17 27							18 27						
d					16 27						17 27							18 27						
Thatto Heath d					16 37						17 37							18 37						
Eccleston Park d																								
Prescot d					16 47						17 47							18 47						
Huyton d				16 30	16 57					17 30	17 57						18 30	18 57						19 30
Roby d				16 34	17 01					17 34	18 01						18 34	19 01						19 34
Broad Green d				16 41	17 08					17 41	18 08						18 41	19 08						19 41
Wavertree Technology Park d				16 51	17 18					17 51	18 18						18 51	19 18						19 51
Edge Hill 91 d																								
Liverpool Lime Street 10 91 a			17 03	17 06	17 33				18 03	18 06	18 33					19 02	19 06	19 33					20 02	20 06

A From Chester to Manchester Piccadilly **B** To Chester **C** From Holyhead to Manchester Piccadilly

Table 90

Sundays

5 January to 9 February

Manchester, Preston, Wigan and Newton-le-Willows - St Helens and Liverpool

Network Diagram - see first Page of Table 88

	NT	NT	AW	AW	NT	NT	NT	NT	AW	AW	NT	NT	NT	NT	AW	AW	NT	NT	TP	NT	AW	AW
																			◇1			
			A	B					A	B					A	B			C		A	B
	(bus)					(bus)	(bus)					(bus)	(bus)				(bus)	(bus)				
Manchester Airport 85 ✈ d					20 03						21 03											
Manchester Piccadilly 10 d				18 56	20 17					19 56	21 17					20 56						21 56
Manchester Oxford Road d				18 59	20 21	18 55				19 59	21 21	19 55				20 59	20 55					21 59
Manchester Victoria d																						
Eccles d						19 10						20 10					21 10					
Patricroft d																						
Blackpool North 97 d		18 50						19 50						20 50					21 35	21 50		
Preston 8 65,82 d		19 15						20 15						21 15					22 00	22 15		
Leyland 82 d		19 21						20 21						21 21						22 21		
Euxton Balshaw Lane d		19 25						20 25						21 25						22 25		
Wigan North Western 65 a		19 37						20 37						21 37					22 14	22 36		
d	18 47						19 47						20 47					21 47				
Newton-le-Willows d				19 18		19 35				20 18		20 35				21 18	21 35					22 18
Warrington Bank Quay d			19 03						20 03						21 03						22 04	
Earlestown 8 d			19a10	19 21		19 43			20a10	20 21		20 43			21a10	21 21	21 43				22a12	22 21
Warrington Bank Quay a				19 28						20 29						21 27						22 27
St Helens Junction d						19 55						20 55					21 55					
Lea Green d						20 02						21 02					22 02					
Rainhill d						20 10						21 10					22 10					
Whiston d						20 20						21 20					22 20					
Bryn d																						
Garswood d	19 07						20 07						21 07					22 07				
St Helens Central a	19 27						20 27						21 27					22 27				
d	19 27						20 27						21 27					22 27				
Thatto Heath d	19 37						20 37						21 37					22 37				
Eccleston Park d																						
Prescot d	19 47						20 47						21 47					22 47				
Huyton d	19 57					20 30	20 57					21 30	21 57				22 30	22 57				
Roby d	20 01					20 34	21 01					21 34	22 01				22 34	23 01				
Broad Green d	20 08					20 41	21 08					21 41	22 08				22 41	23 08				
Wavertree Technology Park d	20 18					20 51	21 18					21 51	22 18				22 51	23 18				
Edge Hill 91 d																						
Liverpool Lime Street 10 91 a	20 33				21 03	21 06	21 33				22 03	22 06	22 33				23 06	23 33				

	NT	AW	NT	NT	AW	NT	TP	NT	AW
							◇1		
		A			B		C		B
	(bus)		(bus)			(bus)		(bus)	
Manchester Airport 85 ✈ d									
Manchester Piccadilly 10 d					22 56				23 25
Manchester Oxford Road d	21 55				22 59	23 00			23 28
Manchester Victoria d									
Eccles d	22 10					23 15			
Patricroft d									
Blackpool North 97 d				22 44			23 02		
Preston 8 65,82 d				23 09			23 32		
Leyland 82 d				23 15			23 37		
Euxton Balshaw Lane d				23 19					
Wigan North Western 65 a				23 30			23 47		
d			22 47					23 47	
Newton-le-Willows d	22 35				23 18	23 40			23 47
Warrington Bank Quay d		22 36							
Earlestown 8 d	22 43	22a47			23 21	23 48			23 50
Warrington Bank Quay a					23 27				23 56
St Helens Junction d	22 55					00 01			
Lea Green d	23 02					00 07			
Rainhill d	23 10					00 15			
Whiston d	23 20					00 25			
Bryn d									
Garswood d			23 07					00 07	
St Helens Central a			23 27					00 27	
d			23 27					00 27	
Thatto Heath d			23 37					00 37	
Eccleston Park d									
Prescot d			23 47					00 47	
Huyton d	23 30		23 57			00 35		00 57	
Roby d	23 34		00 01			00 39		01 01	
Broad Green d	23 41		00 08			00 46		01 08	
Wavertree Technology Park d	23 51		00 18			00 56		01 18	
Edge Hill 91 d									
Liverpool Lime Street 10 91 a	00 06		00 33			01 11		01 33	

A From Chester to Manchester Piccadilly

B To Chester

C To Manchester Airport

Table 90

Sundays

16 February to 11 May

Manchester, Preston, Wigan and Newton-le-Willows - St Helens and Liverpool

Network Diagram - see first Page of Table 88

	NT	AW	AW	NT	NT	NT	NT	NT	NT		AW	NT	NT	NT	NT	AW	AW	NT	NT		NT	NT	AW	AW
																◇								
	A	B	C								D					D	C						D	C
		🚌	🚌	🚌	🚌		🚌	🚌					🚌	🚌					🚌		🚌		🛒	
Manchester Airport 85 ✈ d						09 03						10 03						11 03						
Manchester Piccadilly 10 d			07 28			09 18						10 19					09 56	11 18						10 55
Manchester Oxford Road d			07 33			09 21	07 55					10 22	08 55				09 59	11 22	09 55					10 56
Manchester Victoria d																								
Eccles d							08 10						09 10						10 10					
Patricroft d																								
Blackpool North 97 d									08 50						09 50							10 50		
Preston 8 65,82 d					07 44				09 15						10 18							11 18		
Leyland 82 d					08 04				09 21						10 24							11 24		
Euxton Balshaw Lane d					08 16				09 25						10 28							11 28		
Wigan North Western 65 a					08 41				09 37						10 41							11 41		
d				07 47	08 41			08 47						09 47							10 47			
Newton-le-Willows d			08 03				08 35						09 35				10 18		10 35					11 18
Warrington Bank Quay d		00 22									09 10					10 12							11 03	
Earlestown 8 d		00a47	08 13				08 43				09a16		09 43			10a19	10 21		10 43				11a10	11 21
Warrington Bank Quay a			08 38														10 27							11 29
St Helens Junction d							08 55						09 55						10 55					
Lea Green d							09 02						10 02						11 02					
Rainhill d							09 10						10 10						11 10					
Whiston d							09 20						10 20						11 20					
Bryn d																								
Garswood d				08 07				09 07						10 07							11 07			
St Helens Central a				08 27				09 27						10 27							11 27			
d				08 27				09 27						10 27							11 27			
Thatto Heath d				08 37				09 37						10 37							11 37			
Eccleston Park d																								
Prescot d				08 47				09 47						10 47							11 47			
Huyton d				08 57			09 30	09 57					10 30	10 57					11 30		11 57			
Roby d				09 01			09 34	10 01					10 34	11 01					11 34		12 01			
Broad Green d				09 08			09 41	10 08					10 41	11 08					11 41		12 08			
Wavertree Technology Park d	00 01			09 18			09 51	10 18					10 51	11 18					11 51		12 18			
Edge Hill 91 d	00 04																							
Liverpool Lime Street 10 91 a	00 13			09 33	09 41	10 03	10 06	10 33				11 03	11 06	11 33				12 02	12 06		12 33			

	NT	NT	NT	NT	AW		AW	NT	NT	NT	NT	AW	AW	NT	NT		NT	NT	AW	AW	NT	NT	NT	NT
					D		C					D	C						D	C				
		🚌	🚌		🛒		🛒		🚌	🚌		🛒	🛒		🚌		🚌		🛒	🛒		🚌	🚌	
Manchester Airport 85 ✈ d	12 03							13 03						14 03							15 03			
Manchester Piccadilly 10 d	12 18						11 56	13 18					12 56	14 18						13 56	15 18			
Manchester Oxford Road d	12 22	10 55					11 59	13 22	11 55				12 59	14 22	12 55					13 59	15 22	13 55		
Manchester Victoria d																								
Eccles d		11 10							12 10						13 10							14 10		
Patricroft d																								
Blackpool North 97 d				11 50							12 50							13 50						14 50
Preston 8 65,82 d				12 15							13 15							14 15						15 15
Leyland 82 d				12 21							13 21							14 21						15 21
Euxton Balshaw Lane d				12 25							13 25							14 25						15 25
Wigan North Western 65 a				12 37							13 37							14 37						15 37
d			11 47							12 47							13 47						14 47	
Newton-le-Willows d		11 35					12 18		12 35				13 18		13 35					14 18		14 35		
Warrington Bank Quay d					12 03							13 03							14 03					
Earlestown 8 d		11 43			12a10		12 21		12 43			13a10	13 21		13 43				14a10	14 21		14 43		
Warrington Bank Quay a							12 27						13 28							14 27				
St Helens Junction d		11 55							12 55						13 55							14 55		
Lea Green d		12 02							13 02						14 02							15 02		
Rainhill d		12 10							13 10						14 10							15 10		
Whiston d		12 20							13 20						14 20							15 20		
Bryn d																								
Garswood d			12 07							13 07							14 07						15 07	
St Helens Central a			12 27							13 27							14 27						15 27	
d			12 27							13 27							14 27						15 27	
Thatto Heath d			12 37							13 37							14 37						15 37	
Eccleston Park d																								
Prescot d			12 47							13 47							14 47						15 47	
Huyton d		12 30	12 57						13 30	13 57					14 30		14 57					15 30	15 57	
Roby d		12 34	13 01						13 34	14 01					14 34		15 01					15 34	16 01	
Broad Green d		12 41	13 08						13 41	14 08					14 41		15 08					15 41	16 08	
Wavertree Technology Park d		12 51	13 18						13 51	14 18					14 51		15 18					15 51	16 18	
Edge Hill 91 d																								
Liverpool Lime Street 10 91 a	13 03	13 06	13 33					14 03	14 06	14 33				15 03	15 06		15 33				16 03	16 06	16 33	

A From Manchester Victoria
B until 23 March. From Chester to Manchester Piccadilly
C To Chester
D From Chester to Manchester Piccadilly

Table 90

Sundays

16 February to 11 May

Manchester, Preston, Wigan and Newton-le-Willows - St Helens and Liverpool

Network Diagram - see first Page of Table 88

		AW		AW	NT	NT	NT	NT	AW	AW	NT	NT		NT	NT	AW	AW	NT	NT	NT	NT	AW		AW	NT
																◇						◇			
		A		B					A	B						C	B					A		B	
						bus	bus					bus		bus					bus	bus					
		trolley		trolley						trolley						trolley								trolley	
Manchester Airport 85 ✈	d				16 03						17 03							18 03							19 03
Manchester Piccadilly 10	d			14 56	16 18					15 56	17 18						16 56	18 18						17 56	19 18
Manchester Oxford Road	d			14 59	16 22	14 55				15 59	17 22	15 55					16 59	18 22	16 55					17 59	19 22
Manchester Victoria	d																								
Eccles	d					15 10						16 10							17 10						
Patricroft	d																								
Blackpool North 97	d							15 50							16 50						17 50				
Preston 8 65,82	d							16 15							17 15						18 15				
Leyland 82	d							16 21							17 21						18 21				
Euxton Balshaw Lane	d							16 25							17 25						18 25				
Wigan North Western 65	a							16 37							17 37						18 37				
	d						15 47							16 47						17 47					
Newton-le-Willows	d			15 18		15 35				16 18		16 35					17 18		17 35					18 18	
Warrington Bank Quay	d	15 03							16 03							17 03						18 03			
Earlestown 8	d	15a10		15 21		15 43			16a10	16 21		16 43				17a10	17 21		17 43			18a10		18 21	
Warrington Bank Quay	a			15 28						16 27							17 27							18 27	
St Helens Junction	d					15 55						16 55							17 55						
Lea Green	d					16 02						17 02							18 02						
Rainhill	d					16 10						17 10							18 10						
Whiston	d					16 20						17 20							18 20						
Bryn	d																								
Garswood	d						16 07							17 07						18 07					
St Helens Central	a						16 27							17 27						18 27					
	d						16 27							17 27						18 27					
Thatto Heath	d						16 37							17 37						18 37					
Eccleston Park	d																								
Prescot	d						16 47							17 47						18 47					
Huyton	d					16 30	16 57					17 30		17 57					18 30	18 57					
Roby	d					16 34	17 01					17 34		18 01					18 34	19 01					
Broad Green	d					16 41	17 08					17 41		18 08					18 41	19 08					
Wavertree Technology Park	d					16 51	17 18					17 51		18 18					18 51	19 18					
Edge Hill 91	d																								
Liverpool Lime Street 10 91	a				17 03	17 06	17 33				18 03	18 06		18 33				19 02	19 06	19 33					20 02

		NT	NT	NT	AW	AW	NT	NT		NT	NT	AW	AW	NT	NT	NT	NT	AW		AW	NT	NT	NT	AW	AW
					A	B						A	B					A		B				A	B
		bus	bus					bus		bus					bus	bus					bus	bus			
Manchester Airport 85 ✈	d						20 03							21 03											
Manchester Piccadilly 10	d					18 56	20 17						19 56	21 17						20 56					21 56
Manchester Oxford Road	d	17 55				18 59	20 21	18 55					19 59	21 21	19 55					20 59	20 55				21 59
Manchester Victoria	d																								
Eccles	d	18 10						19 10							20 10						21 10				
Patricroft	d																								
Blackpool North 97	d			18 50							19 50						20 50						21 50		
Preston 8 65,82	d			19 15							20 15						21 15						22 15		
Leyland 82	d			19 21							20 21						21 21						22 21		
Euxton Balshaw Lane	d			19 25							20 25						21 25						22 25		
Wigan North Western 65	a			19 37							20 37						21 37						22 36		
	d		18 47							19 47						20 47						21 47			
Newton-le-Willows	d	18 35				19 18		19 35					20 18		20 35					21 18	21 35				22 18
Warrington Bank Quay	d				19 03							20 03						21 03						22 04	
Earlestown 8	d	18 43			19a10	19 21		19 43				20a10	20 21		20 43			21a10		21 21	21 43			22a12	22 21
Warrington Bank Quay	a					19 28							20 29							21 27					22 27
St Helens Junction	d	18 55						19 55							20 55						21 55				
Lea Green	d	19 02						20 02							21 02						22 02				
Rainhill	d	19 10						20 10							21 10						22 10				
Whiston	d	19 20						20 20							21 20						22 20				
Bryn	d																								
Garswood	d		19 07							20 07						21 07						22 07			
St Helens Central	a		19 27							20 27						21 27						22 27			
	d		19 27							20 27						21 27						22 27			
Thatto Heath	d		19 37							20 37						21 37						22 37			
Eccleston Park	d																								
Prescot	d		19 47							20 47						21 47						22 47			
Huyton	d	19 30	19 57					20 30		20 57					21 30	21 57					22 30	22 57			
Roby	d	19 34	20 01					20 34		21 01					21 34	22 01					22 34	23 01			
Broad Green	d	19 41	20 08					20 41		21 08					21 41	22 08					22 41	23 08			
Wavertree Technology Park	d	19 51	20 18					20 51		21 18					21 51	22 18					22 51	23 18			
Edge Hill 91	d																								
Liverpool Lime Street 10 91	a	20 06	20 33				21 03	21 06		21 33				22 03	22 06	22 33					23 06	23 33			

A From Chester to Manchester Piccadilly
B To Chester
C From Holyhead to Manchester Piccadilly

Table 90

Sundays

16 February to 11 May

Manchester, Preston, Wigan and Newton-le-Willows - St Helens and Liverpool

Network Diagram - see first Page of Table 88

			NT	AW A	NT		NT	AW B	NT	AW B	NT
Manchester Airport	85	d									
Manchester Piccadilly 10		d						22 56		23 25	
Manchester Oxford Road		d	21 55					22 59	23 00	23 28	
Manchester Victoria		d									
Eccles		d	22 10						23 15		
Patricroft		d									
Blackpool North	97	d					22 44				
Preston 8	65,82	d					23 09				
Leyland	82	d					23 15				
Euxton Balshaw Lane		d					23 19				
Wigan North Western	65	a					23 30				
		d			22 47						23 47
Newton-le-Willows		d	22 35					23 18	23 40	23 47	
Warrington Bank Quay		d		22 36							
Earlestown 8		d	22 43	22a47				23 21	23 48	23 50	
Warrington Bank Quay		a						23 27		23 56	
St Helens Junction		d	22 55						00 01		
Lea Green		d	23 02						00 07		
Rainhill		d	23 10						00 15		
Whiston		d	23 20						00 25		
Bryn		d									
Garswood		d			23 07						00 07
St Helens Central		a			23 27						00 27
		d			23 27						00 27
Thatto Heath		d			23 37						00 37
Eccleston Park		d									
Prescot		d			23 47						00 47
Huyton		d	23 30		23 57				00 35		00 57
Roby		d	23 34		00 01				00 39		01 01
Broad Green		d	23 41		00 08				00 46		01 08
Wavertree Technology Park		d	23 51		00 18				00 56		01 18
Edge Hill	91	d									
Liverpool Lime Street 10	91	a	00 06		00 33				01 11		01 33

A From Chester to Manchester Piccadilly

B To Chester

Table 90R

Mondays to Fridays

9 December to 16 May

Liverpool and St Helens - Newton-le-Willows, Wigan, Preston and Manchester

Network Diagram - see first Page of Table 88

Miles	Miles	Miles	Miles			NT MO A	NT MX A	NT MX A	NT MX B	NT	NT	AW C	NT	NT	NT	NT	NT	AW ◇ D	NT	NT	NT	NT	NT
0	0	0	—	**Liverpool Lime Street 10** 91	d				03 58	05 13	05 31		05 46	06 01	06 13	06 16	06 31		06 46		06 57	07 01	07 13
1¾	1¾	1¾	—	Edge Hill 91	d						05 35		05 50	06 05		06 20	06 35		06 50			07 05	
2½	2½	2½	—	Wavertree Technology Park	d					05 19	05 37		05 52	06 07	06 19	06 22	06 37		06 52			07 07	07 19
3½	3½	3½	—	Broad Green	d						05 40		05 55	06 10		06 25	06 40		06 55			07 10	
5	5	5	—	Roby	d						05 44		05 59	06 14		06 29	06 44		06 59			07 14	
5½	5½	5½	—	Huyton	d						05 46		06 01	06 16		06 31	06 46		07 01		07 06	07 16	
—	7¼	—	—	Prescot	d						05 51			06 21			06 51					07 21	
—	8¾	—	—	Eccleston Park	d						05 53			06 23			06 53					07 23	
—	9¾	—	—	Thatto Heath	d			00 06			05 56			06 26			06 56					07 26	
—	11¼	—	—	**St Helens Central**	a			00 16			05 59			06 29			06 59				07 15	07 29	
—	—	—	—		d			00 16			06 00			06 30			07 00				07 15	07 30	
—	15	—	—	Garswood	d			00 36			06 07			06 37			07 07					07 37	
—	16¼	—	—	Bryn	d			00 43			06 10			06 40			07 10					07 40	
7½	—	7½	—	Whiston	d		00 04						06 05			06 35			07 05				
9	—	9	—	Rainhill	d		00 14						06 08			06 38			07 08				
10¾	—	10¾	—	Lea Green	d	00 05	00 22						06 11			06 41			07 11				07 28
12	—	12	—	**St Helens Junction**	d	00 12	00 29			05 29			06 14		06 29	06 44			07 14				07 31
—	—	—	—	Warrington Bank Quay	d							06 06						07 07					
14¾	—	14¾	—	Earlestown 8	d	00 24	00 41					06 12	06 19			06 50		07 14	07 19				
—	—	—	—	Warrington Bank Quay	a											07 01							
16¼	—	16¼	0	**Newton-le-Willows**	d	00 32	00 49			05 35		06 15	06 22		06 35			07 17	07 22				07 37
—	20	23¼	—	**Wigan North Western** 65	a			00s56			06 21			06 51			07 21				07 30	07 51	
—	—	—	—		d															07 22	07 31		
—	28¼	31½	—	Euxton Balshaw Lane	d			01s21													07 41		
—	31	34¼	—	Leyland 82	a			01s33													07 46		
—	35	38¼	—	**Preston 8** 65,82	a			01s53													07 56		
—	52½	—	—	Blackpool North 97	a																		
26¾	—	—	10½	Patricroft	d		01 19						06 33						07 33				
27¾	—	—	11½	Eccles	d	00 57	01 29						06 36						07 36				
31¾	—	—	—	**Manchester Victoria**	a		01 48						06 49						07 49	08 12			
—	—	—	15¾	**Manchester Oxford Road**	a	01 12						06 35			06 56			07 41					07 56
—	—	—	16¼	**Manchester Piccadilly 10**	a				04 40	05 56		06 44			07 00			07 50					08 01
—	—	—	26	**Manchester Airport** 85	a					06 14					07 22								08 22

		AW C	NT E	TP ◇1 F	AW ◇ G	NT	NT	NT	NT	NT	NT	NT	TP ◇1 H	TP FO ◇1 I	NT	NT J	NT	NT	AW ◇ G	NT	NT K	NT	TP ◇1 L
Liverpool Lime Street 10 91	d		07 16				07 31	07 46	07 57	08 01	08 13	08 16			08 31	08 44	08 57	09 01		09 13		09 16	
Edge Hill 91	d		07 20				07 35	07 50		08 05		08 20			08 35	08 50		09 05				09 20	
Wavertree Technology Park	d		07 22				07 37	07 52		08 07	08 19	08 22			08 37	08 52		09 07		09 19		09 22	
Broad Green	d		07 25				07 40	07 55		08 10		08 25			08 40	08 55		09 10				09 25	
Roby	d		07 29				07 44	07 59		08 14		08 29			08 44	08 59		09 14				09 29	
Huyton	d		07 31				07 46	08 01	08 06	08 16		08 31			08 46	09 01	09 06	09 16				09 31	
Prescot	d						07 51			08 21					08 51			09 21					
Eccleston Park	d						07 53			08 23					08 53			09 23					
Thatto Heath	d						07 56			08 26					08 56			09 26					
St Helens Central	a						07 59		08 15	08 29					08 59		09 15	09 29					
	d						08 00		08 15	08 30					09 00		09 15	09 30					
Garswood	d						08 07			08 37					09 07			09 37					
Bryn	d						08 10			08 40					09 10			09 40					
Whiston	d		07 35					08 05				08 35				09 05						09 35	
Rainhill	d		07 38					08 08				08 38				09 08						09 38	
Lea Green	d		07 41					08 11				08 41				09 11						09 41	
St Helens Junction	d		07 44					08 14			08 29	08 44				09 14				09 29		09 44	
Warrington Bank Quay	d	07 39			08 08														09 19		09 22		
Earlestown 8	d	07 46	07 49		08 16			08 19				08 50				09 19			09 26		09a33	09 50	
Warrington Bank Quay	a											09 01										10 01	
Newton-le-Willows	d	07 49	07 52		08 19			08 22			08 35					09 22			09 29	09 35			
Wigan North Western 65	a						08 21		08 30	08 51					09 21		09 30	09 51					
	d			07 56		08 20			08 31				08 58	08 58			09 31						09 58
Euxton Balshaw Lane	d								08 41								09 41						
Leyland 82	a								08 46								09 46						
Preston 8 65,82	a								08 56								09 54						
Blackpool North 97	a																10 21						
Patricroft	d		08 03					08 33								09 33							
Eccles	d		08 06					08 36								09 36							
Manchester Victoria	a		08 19			09 06		08 50								09 47							
Manchester Oxford Road	a	08 09		08 22	08 41						08 56		09 23	09 23					09 48	09 56			10 23
Manchester Piccadilly 10	a	08 18		08 26	08 50						09 00		09 27	09 27					09 57	10 00			10 27
Manchester Airport 85	a			08 47							09 22		09 47	09 51						10 22			10 47

A From Liverpool Lime Street
B from 31 December until 21 March
C From Chester
D From Llandudno Junction
E To Huddersfield
F From Barrow-in-Furness
G From Llandudno
H FX until 6 February, from 10 February. From Edinburgh
I until 7 February. From Edinburgh
J To Stalybridge
K To Liverpool Lime Street
L From Glasgow Central

Table 90R

Mondays to Fridays

9 December to 16 May

Liverpool and St Helens - Newton-le-Willows, Wigan, Preston and Manchester

Network Diagram - see first Page of Table 88

		NT	NT A	NT	NT	AW ◇ B	NT	NT C	NT	TP ◇1 D	NT	NT A	NT E	AW ◇ F	NT C	TP ◇1 G	NT	NT	NT	TP ◇1 H	NT	NT A	NT E
Liverpool Lime Street 10 91	d	09 31	09 46	09 57	10 01		10 13		10 16		10 31	10 46	10 57				11 01	11 13	11 16		11 31	11 46	11 57
Edge Hill 91	d	09 35	09 50		10 05				10 20		10 35	10 50					11 05		11 20		11 35	11 50	
Wavertree Technology Park	d	09 37	09 52		10 07		10 19		10 22		10 37	10 52					11 07	11 19	11 22		11 37	11 52	
Broad Green	d	09 40	09 55		10 10				10 25		10 40	10 55					11 10		11 25		11 40	11 55	
Roby	d	09 44	09 59		10 14				10 29		10 44	10 59					11 14		11 29		11 44	11 59	
Huyton	d	09 46	10 01	10 06	10 16				10 31		10 46	11 01	11 06				11 16		11 31		11 46	12 01	12 06
Prescot	d	09 51			10 21						10 51						11 21				11 51		
Eccleston Park	d	09 53			10 23						10 53						11 23				11 53		
Thatto Heath	d	09 56			10 26						10 56						11 26				11 56		
St Helens Central	a	09 59		10 15	10 29						10 59		11 15				11 29				11 59		12 15
	d	10 00		10 15	10 30						11 00		11 15				11 30				12 00		12 15
Garswood	d	10 07			10 37						11 07						11 37				12 07		
Bryn	d	10 10			10 40						11 10						11 40				12 10		
Whiston	d		10 05						10 35			11 05							11 35			12 05	
Rainhill	d		10 08						10 38			11 08							11 38			12 08	
Lea Green	d		10 11						10 41			11 11							11 41			12 11	
St Helens Junction	d		10 14				10 29		10 44			11 14						11 29	11 44			12 14	
Warrington Bank Quay	d					10 19		10 22						11 19	11 22								
Earlestown 8	d		10 19			10 26		10a33	10 50			11 19		11 26	11a33				11 50			12 19	
Warrington Bank Quay	a								10 59										12 01				
Newton-le-Willows	d		10 22			10 29	10 35					11 22		11 29				11 35				12 22	
Wigan North Western 65	a	10 21		10 30	10 51						11 21		11 30				11 51				12 21		12 30
	d			10 31						10 58			11 31			11 43				11 57			12 31
Euxton Balshaw Lane	d			10 41									11 41										12 41
Leyland 82	a			10 46									11 46										12 46
Preston 8 65,82	a			10 54									11 54			11 57							12 54
Blackpool North 97	a			11 21									12 21										13 21
Patricroft	d		10 33									11 33										12 33	
Eccles	d		10 36									11 36										12 36	
Manchester Victoria	a		10 49									11 49										12 50	
Manchester Oxford Road	a					10 48	10 56			11 23				11 48				11 56		12 22			
Manchester Piccadilly 10	a					10 57	11 00			11 27				11 57				12 00		12 26			
Manchester Airport 85 ✈	a						11 22			11 47								12 22		12 47			

		NT	AW ◇ F	NT FX	NT C	NT	TP ◇1 D	NT	NT A	NT E	NT	AW ◇ F	NT	NT C	NT	TP ◇1 I	NT	NT A	NT E	NT	AW ◇ F	NT
Liverpool Lime Street 10 91	d	12 01		12 13		12 16		12 31	12 46	12 57	13 01		13 13		13 16		13 31	13 46	13 57	14 01		14 13
Edge Hill 91	d	12 05				12 20		12 35	12 50		13 05				13 20		13 35	13 50		14 05		
Wavertree Technology Park	d	12 07		12 19		12 22		12 37	12 52		13 07		13 19		13 22		13 37	13 52		14 07		14 19
Broad Green	d	12 10				12 25		12 40	12 55		13 10				13 25		13 40	13 55		14 10		
Roby	d	12 14				12 29		12 44	12 59		13 14				13 29		13 44	13 59		14 14		
Huyton	d	12 16				12 31		12 46	13 01	13 06	13 16				13 31		13 46	14 01	14 06	14 16		
Prescot	d	12 21						12 51			13 21						13 51			14 21		
Eccleston Park	d	12 23						12 53			13 23						13 53			14 23		
Thatto Heath	d	12 26						12 56			13 26						13 56			14 26		
St Helens Central	a	12 29						12 59		13 15	13 29						13 59		14 15	14 29		
	d	12 30						13 00		13 15	13 30						14 00		14 15	14 30		
Garswood	d	12 37						13 07			13 37						14 07			14 37		
Bryn	d	12 40						13 10			13 40						14 10			14 40		
Whiston	d					12 35			13 05						13 35			14 05				
Rainhill	d					12 38			13 08						13 38			14 08				
Lea Green	d					12 41			13 11						13 41			14 11				
St Helens Junction	d			12 29		12 44			13 14				13 29		13 44			14 14				14 29
Warrington Bank Quay	d		12 19		12 22							13 19		13 22							14 19	
Earlestown 8	d		12 26		12a33	12 50			13 19			13 26		13a33	13 50			14 19			14 26	
Warrington Bank Quay	a					13 01									14 01							
Newton-le-Willows	d		12 29	12 35					13 22			13 29	13 35					14 22			14 29	14 35
Wigan North Western 65	a	12 51						13 21		13 30	13 51						14 21		14 30	14 51		
	d						12 58			13 31						13 58			14 31			
Euxton Balshaw Lane	d									13 41									14 41			
Leyland 82	a									13 46									14 46			
Preston 8 65,82	a									13 54									14 54			
Blackpool North 97	a									14 21									15 21			
Patricroft	d								13 33									14 33				
Eccles	d								13 36									14 36				
Manchester Victoria	a								13 47									14 50				
Manchester Oxford Road	a		12 48	12 56			13 23					13 48	13 56			14 22					14 48	14 56
Manchester Piccadilly 10	a		12 57	13 00			13 27					13 57	14 00			14 26					14 57	15 00
Manchester Airport 85 ✈	a			13 22			13 46						14 22			14 46						15 22

A To Stalybridge
B From Llandudno Junction
C To Liverpool Lime Street
D From Edinburgh
E From Liverpool South Pw Hl
F From Llandudno
G From Manchester Airport to Barrow-in-Furness
H From Windermere
I From Glasgow Central

Table 90R

Mondays to Fridays

9 December to 16 May

Liverpool and St Helens - Newton-le-Willows, Wigan, Preston and Manchester

Network Diagram - see first Page of Table 88

Station		NT A	NT	NT	NT B	NT C	AW ◇ D	NT A	TP ◇[1] E	NT	NT	NT	TP ◇[1] F	NT	NT G	NT C	NT	AW ◇ H	NT	NT A	NT	NT	AW ◇ H
Liverpool Lime Street [10] 91	d		14 16	14 31	14 46	14 57				15 01	15 13	15 16		15 31	15 46	15 57	16 01		16 13		16 16	16 31	
Edge Hill 91	d		14 20	14 35	14 50					15 05		15 20		15 35	15 50		16 05				16 20	16 35	
Wavertree Technology Park	d		14 22	14 37	14 52					15 07	15 19	15 22		15 37	15 52		16 07		16 19		16 22	16 37	
Broad Green	d		14 25	14 40	14 55					15 10		15 25		15 40	15 55		16 10				16 25	16 40	
Roby	d		14 29	14 44	14 59					15 14		15 29		15 44	15 59		16 14				16 29	16 44	
Huyton	d		14 31	14 46	15 01	15 06				15 16		15 31		15 46	16 01	16 06	16 16				16 31	16 46	
Prescot	d			14 51						15 21				15 51			16 21					16 51	
Eccleston Park	d			14 53						15 23				15 53			16 23					16 53	
Thatto Heath	d			14 56						15 26				15 56			16 26					16 56	
St Helens Central	a			14 59		15 15				15 29				15 59		16 15	16 29					16 59	
	d			15 00		15 15				15 30				16 00		16 15	16 30					17 00	
Garswood	d			15 07						15 37				16 07			16 37					17 07	
Bryn	d			15 10						15 40				16 10			16 40					17 10	
Whiston	d		14 35		15 05							15 35			16 05						16 35		
Rainhill	d		14 38		15 08							15 38			16 08						16 38		
Lea Green	d		14 41		15 11							15 41			16 11						16 41		
St Helens Junction	d		14 44		15 14						15 29	15 44			16 14				16 29		16 44		
Warrington Bank Quay	d	14 22					15 19	15 22										16 19		16 22			16 51
Earlestown [8]	d	14a33	14 50		15 19		15 26	15a33				15 50			16 19			16 26		16a33	16 49		16 59
Warrington Bank Quay	a		15 01									16 01											
Newton-le-Willows	d				15 22		15 29				15 35				16 22			16 29	16 35		16 52		17 02
Wigan North Western 65	a			15 21		15 30				15 51				16 21		16 30	16 51					17 21	
	d					15 31			15 43				15 58			16 31							
Euxton Balshaw Lane	d					15 41										16 41							
Leyland 82	a					15 46										16 46							
Preston [8] 65,82	a					15 54			15 57							16 54							
Blackpool North 97	a					16 21										17 21							
Patricroft	d				15 33										16 33						17 03		
Eccles	d				15 36										16 36						17 06		
Manchester Victoria	a				15 49										16 49						17 19		
Manchester Oxford Road	a						15 48				15 56		16 23					16 48	16 56				17 21
Manchester Piccadilly [10]	a						15 57				16 00		16 27					16 57	17 00				17 30
Manchester Airport 85 ✈	a										16 22		16 47						17 22				

Station		NT G	NT C	NT	NT	NT	NT I	NT	AW ◇ H	NT	TP ◇[1] J	NT	NT	TP FO ◇[1] K	NT	NT	NT	AW ◇ H	TP ◇[1] L	NT	NT	NT
Liverpool Lime Street [10] 91	d	16 46	16 57	17 01	17 06	17 10	17 19	17 27		17 35		17 42	17 46		18 01	18 13	18 16			18 31	18 46	19 01
Edge Hill 91	d	16 50		17 05		17 14		17 31		17 39			17 50		18 05		18 20			18 35	18 50	19 05
Wavertree Technology Park	d	16 52		17 07	17 12	17 16		17 33		17 41		17 47	17 52		18 07	18 19	18 22			18 37	18 52	19 07
Broad Green	d	16 55		17 10		17 19		17 36		17 44		17 50	17 55		18 10		18 25			18 40	18 55	19 10
Roby	d	16 59		17 14		17 23		17 40		17 48			17 59		18 14		18 29			18 44	18 59	19 14
Huyton	d	17 01	17 06	17 16	17 20	17 25	17 29	17 42		17 50		17 55	18 01		18 16		18 31			18 46	19 01	19 16
Prescot	d			17 21			17 34					18 00			18 21					18 51		19 21
Eccleston Park	d			17 23			17 36					18 03			18 23					18 53		19 23
Thatto Heath	d			17 26			17 39					18 05			18 26					18 56		19 26
St Helens Central	a		17 15	17 29			17 42	17 51				18 09			18 29					18 59		19 29
	d		17 15	17 30			17 43	17 51				18 09			18 30					19 00		19 30
Garswood	d			17 37			17 50					18 17			18 37					19 07		19 37
Bryn	d			17 40			17 53					18 20			18 40					19 10		19 40
Whiston	d	17 05				17 29				17 54			18 05				18 35				19 05	
Rainhill	d	17 08				17 32				17 57			18 08				18 38				19 08	
Lea Green	d	17 11			17 26	17 35				18 00			18 11				18 41				19 11	
St Helens Junction	d	17 14			17 29	17 39				18 03			18 14			18 29	18 44				19 14	
Warrington Bank Quay	d								17 49									18 46				
Earlestown [8]	d	17 19				17 44			17 57	18 08			18 19				18 50	18 57			19 19	
Warrington Bank Quay	a																19 01					
Newton-le-Willows	d	17 22			17 35	17 47			18 00	18 11			18 22			18 35		19 00			19 22	
Wigan North Western 65	a		17 30	17 51			18 05	18 04				18 27			18 49					19 21		19 51
	d		17 31					18 05			18 17	18 30		18 43	18 49				18 59			
Euxton Balshaw Lane	d		17 41					18 16				18 40			19 01							
Leyland 82	a		17 46					18 21				18 47			19 06							
Preston [8] 65,82	a		17 54					18 31				18 53		18 57	19 15							
Blackpool North 97	a		18 24									19 22										
Patricroft	d	17 33				17 58				18 22											19 33	
Eccles	d	17 36				18 01				18 25			18 34								19 36	
Manchester Victoria	a	17 47				18 14				18 37			18 47								19 49	
Manchester Oxford Road	a				17 56				18 19		18 48					18 56		19 21	19 24			
Manchester Piccadilly [10]	a				18 00				18 28		18 52					19 00		19 29	19 29			
Manchester Airport 85 ✈	a				18 22						19 13					19 23			19 47			

A To Liverpool Lime Street
B To Stalybridge
C From Liverpool South Pw Hl
D From Bangor (Gwynedd)
E From Manchester Airport to Lancaster
F From Glasgow Central
G To Huddersfield
H From Llandudno
I until 21 March
J from 10 February. From Lancaster
K until 7 February. From Manchester Airport to Windermere
L From Edinburgh

Table 90R

Mondays to Fridays

9 December to 16 May

Liverpool and St Helens - Newton-le-Willows, Wigan, Preston and Manchester

Network Diagram - see first Page of Table 88

		AW	NT	NT	NT	TP	NT	AW	NT	NT		NT	NT	AW	NT	NT	AW	NT	TP	TP		TP FX	NT FO	NT FX	NT FX
						◇1		◇						◇			◇		◇1	◇1		◇1			
		A	B			C		D						D			D		E	F		G	H		
						🚲														🚲		🚲			🚌
Liverpool Lime Street 10 91	d			19 12	19 23		19 42		20 09	20 12		20 25	20 42		21 12	21 42		22 12					23 02		23 02
Edge Hill 91	d			19 16			19 46			20 16			20 46		21 16	21 46		22 16					23 06		23 09
Wavertree Technology Park	d			19 18			19 48		20 15	20 18			20 48		21 18	21 48		22 18					23 08		23 19
Broad Green	d			19 21			19 51			20 21			20 51		21 21	21 51		22 21					23 11		23 29
Roby	d			19 25			19 55			20 25			20 55		21 25	21 55		22 25					23 15		23 36
Huyton	d			19 27	19 32		19 57			20 27		20 34	20 57		21 27	21 57		22 27					23 17		23 40
Prescot	d						20 02						21 02			22 02							23 22		23 50
Eccleston Park	d						20 04						21 04			22 04							23 24		23 56
Thatto Heath	d						20 07						21 07			22 07							23 27		00 06
St Helens Central	a				19 40		20 10					20 42	21 10			22 10							23 30		00 16
	d				19 41		20 11					20 43	21 11			22 11							23 31		00 16
Garswood	d						20 18						21 18			22 18							23 38		00 36
Bryn	d						20 21						21 21			22 21							23 41		00 43
Whiston	d			19 31						20 31					21 31			22 31							
Rainhill	d			19 34						20 34					21 34			22 34							
Lea Green	d			19 37						20 37					21 37			22 37							
St Helens Junction	d			19 40					20 25	20 40					21 40			22 40							
Warrington Bank Quay	d	19 19	19 25					20 19						21 19			22 19								
Earlestown 8	d	19 26	19a33	19 45				20 26		20 45				21 26	21 45		22 26	22 45							
Warrington Bank Quay	a																								
Newton-le-Willows	d	19 29		19 48				20 29	20 35	20 48				21 29	21 48		22 29	22 48							
Wigan North Western 65	a				19 54		20 32					20 57	21 32			22 28							23 48		00s56
	d				19 55	19 59						20 57				22 28			22 50	22 58		22 58	23 48	23 48	
Euxton Balshaw Lane	d				20 05							21 08				22 39							23 59	23 59	01s21
Leyland 82	a				20 10							21 16				22 44							00 04	00 04	01s33
Preston 8 65,82	a				20 18							21 22				22 55			23 08				00 13	00 13	01s53
Blackpool North 97	a				20 44							21 53				23 22									
Patricroft	d			19 59						20 59					21 59			22 59							
Eccles	d			20 02						21 02					22 02			23 02							
Manchester Victoria	a			20 16						21 15					22 15			23 15							
Manchester Oxford Road	a	19 48				20 23		20 48	20 56					21 48			22 50			23 23		23 23			
Manchester Piccadilly 10	a	19 52				20 27		20 52	21 00					21 57			22 58			23 27		23 28			
Manchester Airport 85 ✈	a	20 18				20 46		21 18	21 23											23 46					

		NT FO	NT FX
			🚌
Liverpool Lime Street 10 91	d	23 16	23 16
Edge Hill 91	d	23 20	23 23
Wavertree Technology Park	d	23 22	23 33
Broad Green	d	23 26	23 43
Roby	d	23 30	23 50
Huyton	d	23 32	23 54
Prescot	d		
Eccleston Park	d		
Thatto Heath	d		
St Helens Central	a		
	d		
Garswood	d		
Bryn	d		
Whiston	d	23 36	00 04
Rainhill	d	23 39	00 14
Lea Green	d	23 42	00 22
St Helens Junction	d	23 45	00 29
Warrington Bank Quay	d		
Earlestown 8	d	23 50	00 41
Warrington Bank Quay	a		
Newton-le-Willows	d	23 53	00 49
Wigan North Western 65	a		
	d		
Euxton Balshaw Lane	d		
Leyland 82	a		
Preston 8 65,82	a		
Blackpool North 97	a		
Patricroft	d	00 04	01 19
Eccles	d	00 07	01 29
Manchester Victoria	a	00 21	01 48
Manchester Oxford Road	a		
Manchester Piccadilly 10	a		
Manchester Airport 85 ✈	a		

A From Chester
B To Liverpool Lime Street
C From Glasgow Central
D From Llandudno
E From Manchester Airport to Barrow-in-Furness
F until 27 December, FO from 3 January until 14 March, from 21 March. From Edinburgh
G from 30 December until 20 March. From Edinburgh
H until 21 March

Table 90R

Saturdays

14 December to 28 December

Liverpool and St Helens - Newton-le-Willows, Wigan, Preston and Manchester

Network Diagram - see first Page of Table 88

		NT	NT	NT	AW	NT	NT	NT	AW	NT	NT	NT	NT	NT	NT	NT	AW	NT	TP	AW	NT	NT	NT
									◇										◇[1]	◇			
		A			B				B			C					D 🚲	E	F	G 🚲			
Liverpool Lime Street [10] 91	d		05 13	05 31		05 46	06 01	06 13		06 16	06 31	06 46		06 57	07 01	07 13		07 16				07 31	07 46
Edge Hill 91	d			05 35		05 50	06 05			06 20	06 35	06 50			07 05			07 20				07 35	07 50
Wavertree Technology Park	d		05 19	05 37		05 52	06 07	06 19		06 22	06 37	06 52			07 07	07 19		07 22				07 37	07 52
Broad Green	d			05 40		05 55	06 10			06 25	06 40	06 55			07 10			07 25				07 40	07 55
Roby	d			05 44		05 59	06 14			06 29	06 44	06 59			07 14			07 29				07 44	07 59
Huyton	d			05 46		06 01	06 16			06 31	06 46	07 01		07 06	07 16			07 31				07 46	08 01
Prescot	d			05 51			06 21				06 51				07 21							07 51	
Eccleston Park	d			05 53			06 23				06 53				07 23							07 53	
Thatto Heath	d			05 56			06 26				06 56				07 26							07 56	
St Helens Central	a			05 59			06 29				06 59			07 15	07 29							07 59	
	d			06 00			06 30				07 00			07 15	07 30							08 00	
Garswood	d			06 07			06 37				07 07				07 37							08 07	
Bryn	d			06 10			06 40				07 10				07 40							08 10	
Whiston	d					06 05				06 35		07 05						07 35					08 05
Rainhill	d					06 08				06 38		07 08						07 38					08 08
Lea Green	d					06 11				06 41		07 11				07 28		07 41					08 11
St Helens Junction	d		05 29			06 14		06 29		06 44		07 14				07 31		07 44					08 14
Warrington Bank Quay	d				06 06				06 40								07 39			08 08			
Earlestown [8]	d				06 12	06 19			06 47	06 50		07 19					07 46	07 49		08 16			08 19
Warrington Bank Quay	a									07 01													
Newton-le-Willows	d		05 35		06 15	06 22		06 35	06 50			07 22				07 37	07 49	07 52		08 19			08 22
Wigan North Western 65	a			06 21			06 51				07 21			07 30	07 51							08 21	
	d												07 22	07 31					07 56		08 20		
Euxton Balshaw Lane	d													07 41									
Leyland 82	a													07 46									
Preston [8] 65,82	a													07 54									
Blackpool North 97	a													08 21									
Patricroft	d	00 04				06 33						07 33						08 03					08 33
Eccles	d	00 07				06 36						07 36						08 06					08 36
Manchester Victoria 🚊	a	00 21				06 49						07 49	08 12					08 19			09 06		08 50
Manchester Oxford Road	a				06 35			06 56	07 09							07 56	08 09		08 22	08 41			
Manchester Piccadilly [10] 🚊	a		05 56		06 44			07 00	07 18							08 01	08 18		08 26	08 45			
Manchester Airport 85 ✈	a		06 14					07 22								08 22			08 47				

		NT	NT	NT	NT	TP	NT	NT	NT	NT	AW	NT	NT	NT	TP	NT	NT	NT	NT	AW	NT	NT	NT
						◇[1]					◇				◇[1]					◇			
						H 🚲		C			G 🚲		I		J 🚲		C			G 🚲		I	
Liverpool Lime Street [10] 91	d	07 57	08 01	08 13	08 16		08 31	08 44	08 57	09 01		09 13		09 16		09 31	09 46	09 57	10 01		10 13		10 16
Edge Hill 91	d		08 05		08 20		08 35	08 50		09 05				09 20		09 35	09 50		10 05				10 20
Wavertree Technology Park	d		08 07	08 19	08 22		08 37	08 52		09 07		09 19		09 22		09 37	09 52		10 07		10 19		10 22
Broad Green	d		08 10		08 25		08 40	08 55		09 10				09 25		09 40	09 55		10 10				10 25
Roby	d		08 14		08 29		08 44	08 59		09 14				09 29		09 44	09 59		10 14				10 29
Huyton	d	08 06	08 16		08 31		08 46	09 01	09 06	09 16				09 31		09 46	10 01	10 06	10 16				10 31
Prescot	d		08 21				08 51			09 21						09 51			10 21				
Eccleston Park	d		08 23				08 53			09 23						09 53			10 23				
Thatto Heath	d		08 26				08 56			09 26						09 56			10 26				
St Helens Central	a	08 15	08 29				08 59		09 15	09 29						09 59		10 15	10 29				
	d	08 15	08 30				09 00		09 15	09 30						10 00		10 15	10 30				
Garswood	d		08 37				09 07			09 37						10 07			10 37				
Bryn	d		08 40				09 10			09 40						10 10			10 40				
Whiston	d				08 35			09 05						09 35			10 05						10 35
Rainhill	d				08 38			09 08						09 38			10 08						10 38
Lea Green	d				08 41			09 11						09 41			10 11						10 41
St Helens Junction	d			08 29	08 44			09 14				09 29		09 44			10 14				10 29		10 44
Warrington Bank Quay	d										09 19		09 22							10 19		10 22	
Earlestown [8]	d				08 50			09 19			09 26		09a33	09 50			10 19			10 26		10a33	10 50
Warrington Bank Quay	a				09 01									10 01									11 01
Newton-le-Willows	d			08 35				09 22			09 29	09 35					10 22			10 29	10 35		
Wigan North Western 65	a	08 30	08 51				09 21		09 30	09 51						10 21		10 30	10 51				
	d	08 31				08 58			09 31						09 58			10 31					
Euxton Balshaw Lane	d	08 41							09 41									10 41					
Leyland 82	a	08 46							09 46									10 46					
Preston [8] 65,82	a	08 54							09 54									10 54					
Blackpool North 97	a	09 21							10 21									11 21					
Patricroft	d							09 33									10 33						
Eccles	d							09 36									10 36						
Manchester Victoria 🚊	a							09 47									10 49						
Manchester Oxford Road	a			08 56		09 23					09 48	09 56			10 22					10 48	10 56		
Manchester Piccadilly [10] 🚊	a			09 00		09 27					09 52	10 00			10 26					10 52	11 00		
Manchester Airport 85 ✈	a			09 22		09 47						10 22			10 46						11 22		

A From Liverpool Lime Street
B From Chester
C To Stalybridge
D From Shrewsbury
E To Huddersfield
F From Barrow-in-Furness
G From Llandudno
H From Edinburgh
I To Liverpool Lime Street
J From Glasgow Central

Table 90R

Saturdays

14 December to 28 December

Liverpool and St Helens - Newton-le-Willows, Wigan, Preston and Manchester

Network Diagram - see first Page of Table 88

		TP ◇1 A		NT	NT B	NT C	AW ◇ D	NT E	TP ◇1 F	NT	NT	NT		TP ◇1 G	NT	NT B	NT C	NT	AW ◇ D	NT	NT E	NT		TP ◇1 A	NT
Liverpool Lime Street 10 91	d			10 31	10 46	10 57				11 01	11 13	11 16			11 31	11 46	11 57	12 01		12 13		12 16			12 31
Edge Hill 91	d			10 35	10 50					11 05		11 20			11 35	11 50		12 05				12 20			12 35
Wavertree Technology Park	d			10 37	10 52					11 07	11 19	11 22			11 37	11 52		12 07		12 19		12 22			12 37
Broad Green	d			10 40	10 55					11 10		11 25			11 40	11 55		12 10				12 25			12 40
Roby	d			10 44	10 59					11 14		11 29			11 44	11 59		12 14				12 29			12 44
Huyton	d			10 46	11 01	11 06				11 16		11 31			11 46	12 01	12 06	12 16				12 31			12 46
Prescot	d			10 51						11 21					11 51			12 21							12 51
Eccleston Park	d			10 53						11 23					11 53			12 23							12 53
Thatto Heath	d			10 56						11 26					11 56			12 26							12 56
St Helens Central	a			10 59		11 15				11 29					11 59		12 15	12 29							12 59
	d			11 00		11 15				11 30					12 00		12 15	12 30							13 00
Garswood	d			11 07						11 37					12 07			12 37							13 07
Bryn	d			11 10						11 40					12 10			12 40							13 10
Whiston	d				11 05							11 35				12 05						12 35			
Rainhill	d				11 08							11 38				12 08						12 38			
Lea Green	d				11 11							11 41				12 11						12 41			
St Helens Junction	d				11 14						11 29	11 44				12 14				12 29		12 44			
Warrington Bank Quay	d						11 19	11 22											12 19		12 22				
Earlestown 8	d				11 19		11 26	11a33				11 50				12 19			12 26		12a33	12 50			
Warrington Bank Quay	a											12 01										13 01			
Newton-le-Willows	d				11 22		11 29				11 35					12 22			12 29	12 35					
Wigan North Western 65	a			11 21		11 30				11 51					12 21		12 30	12 51							13 21
	d	10 58				11 31			11 43					11 58			12 31							12 58	
Euxton Balshaw Lane	d					11 41											12 41								
Leyland 82	a					11 46											12 46								
Preston 8 65,82	a					11 54			11 57								12 54								
Blackpool North 97	a					12 21											13 21								
Patricroft	d				11 33											12 33									
Eccles	d				11 36											12 36									
Manchester Victoria	a				11 49											12 49									
Manchester Oxford Road	a	11 23					11 48				11 56			12 23					12 48	12 56				13 23	
Manchester Piccadilly 10	a	11 27					11 52				12 00			12 27					12 52	13 00				13 27	
Manchester Airport 85	a	11 47									12 22			12 47						13 22				13 47	

		NT B	NT C	NT	AW ◇ D	NT	NT E	NT		TP ◇1 H	NT	NT B	NT C	NT	AW ◇ D	NT	NT E	NT		NT	NT B	NT C	AW ◇ I	NT E	TP ◇1 F
Liverpool Lime Street 10 91	d	12 46	12 57	13 01		13 13		13 16			13 31	13 46	13 57	14 01		14 13		14 16		14 31	14 46	14 57			
Edge Hill 91	d	12 50		13 05				13 20			13 35	13 50		14 05				14 20		14 35	14 50				
Wavertree Technology Park	d	12 52		13 07		13 19		13 22			13 37	13 52		14 07		14 19		14 22		14 37	14 52				
Broad Green	d	12 55		13 10				13 25			13 40	13 55		14 10				14 25		14 40	14 55				
Roby	d	12 59		13 14				13 29			13 44	13 59		14 14				14 29		14 44	14 59				
Huyton	d	13 01	13 06	13 16				13 31			13 46	14 01	14 06	14 16				14 31		14 46	15 01	15 06			
Prescot	d			13 21							13 51			14 21						14 51					
Eccleston Park	d			13 23							13 53			14 23						14 53					
Thatto Heath	d			13 26							13 56			14 26						14 56					
St Helens Central	a		13 15	13 29							13 59		14 15	14 29						14 59		15 15			
	d		13 15	13 30							14 00		14 15	14 30						15 00		15 15			
Garswood	d			13 37							14 07			14 37						15 07					
Bryn	d			13 40							14 10			14 40						15 10					
Whiston	d	13 05						13 35				14 05						14 35			15 05				
Rainhill	d	13 08						13 38				14 08						14 38			15 08				
Lea Green	d	13 11						13 41				14 11						14 41			15 11				
St Helens Junction	d	13 14				13 29		13 44				14 14				14 29		14 44			15 14				
Warrington Bank Quay	d				13 19		13 22								14 19		14 22						15 19	15 22	
Earlestown 8	d	13 19			13 26		13a33	13 50				14 19			14 26		14a33	14 50			15 19		15 26	15a33	
Warrington Bank Quay	a							14 01										15 01							
Newton-le-Willows	d	13 22			13 29	13 35						14 22			14 29	14 35					15 22		15 29		
Wigan North Western 65	a		13 30	13 51							14 21		14 30	14 51						15 21		15 30			
	d		13 31							13 58			14 31									15 31			15 43
Euxton Balshaw Lane	d		13 41										14 41									15 41			
Leyland 82	a		13 46										14 46									15 46			
Preston 8 65,82	a		13 54										14 54									15 54			15 57
Blackpool North 97	a		14 21										15 21									16 21			
Patricroft	d	13 33										14 33									15 33				
Eccles	d	13 36										14 36									15 36				
Manchester Victoria	a	13 49										14 50									15 49				
Manchester Oxford Road	a				13 48	13 56				14 22					14 48	14 56							15 48		
Manchester Piccadilly 10	a				13 52	14 00				14 26					14 57	15 00							15 52		
Manchester Airport 85	a					14 22				14 45						15 22									

A From Edinburgh
B To Stalybridge
C From Liverpool South Pw Hl
D From Llandudno
E To Liverpool Lime Street
F From Manchester Airport to Barrow-in-Furness
G From Windermere
H From Glasgow Central
I From Bangor (Gwynedd)

Table 90R

Saturdays

14 December to 28 December

Liverpool and St Helens - Newton-le-Willows, Wigan, Preston and Manchester

Network Diagram - see first Page of Table 88

		NT	NT	NT		TP	NT	NT	NT	NT	AW	NT	NT	NT		NT	NT	NT	NT	AW	NT	NT	NT	NT	
						◇[1]					◇									◇					
						A		B	C		D		E				B	C		D					
						🛒					🛒									🛒					
Liverpool Lime Street [10] 91	d	15 01	15 13	15 16			15 31	15 46	15 57	16 01		16 13		16 16		16 31	16 46	16 57	17 01		17 06	17 10	17 19	17 27	
Edge Hill 91	d	15 05		15 20			15 35	15 50		16 05				16 20		16 35	16 50		17 05			17 14		17 31	
Wavertree Technology Park	d	15 07	15 19	15 22			15 37	15 52		16 07		16 19		16 22		16 37	16 52		17 07		17 12	17 16		17 33	
Broad Green	d	15 10		15 25			15 40	15 55		16 10				16 25		16 40	16 55		17 10			17 19		17 36	
Roby	d	15 14		15 29			15 44	15 59		16 14				16 29		16 44	16 59		17 14			17 23		17 40	
Huyton	d	15 16		15 31			15 46	16 01	16 06	16 16				16 31		16 46	17 01	17 06	17 16		17 20	17 25	17 29	17 42	
Prescot	d	15 21					15 51			16 21						16 51			17 21				17 34		
Eccleston Park	d	15 23					15 53			16 23						16 53			17 23				17 36		
Thatto Heath	d	15 26					15 56			16 26						16 56			17 26				17 39		
St Helens Central	a	15 29					15 59		16 15	16 29						16 59		17 15	17 29				17 42	17 51	
	d	15 30					16 00		16 15	16 30						17 00		17 15	17 30				17 43	17 51	
Garswood	d	15 37					16 07			16 37						17 07			17 37				17 50		
Bryn	d	15 40					16 10			16 40						17 10			17 40				17 53		
Whiston	d			15 35				16 05						16 35			17 05					17 29			
Rainhill	d			15 38				16 08						16 38			17 08					17 32			
Lea Green	d			15 41				16 11						16 41			17 11				17 25	17 35			
St Helens Junction	d		15 29	15 44				16 14				16 29		16 44			17 14				17 28	17 39			
Warrington Bank Quay	d										16 19		16 22							17 19					
Earlestown [8]	d			15 50				16 19			16 26		16a33	16 49			17 19			17 26		17 44			
Warrington Bank Quay	a			16 01																					
Newton-le-Willows	d		15 35					16 22			16 29	16 35		16 52			17 22			17 29	17 34	17 47			
Wigan North Western 65	a	15 51					16 21		16 30	16 51						17 21		17 30	17 51				18 05	18 04	
	d					15 58			16 31									17 31						18 05	
Euxton Balshaw Lane	d								16 41									17 41						18 16	
Leyland 82	a								16 46									17 46						18 21	
Preston [8] 65,82	a								16 54									17 54						18 31	
Blackpool North 97	a								17 21									18 24							
Patricroft	d							16 33						17 03			17 33					17 58			
Eccles	d							16 36						17 06			17 36					18 01			
Manchester Victoria ⛴	a							16 49						17 19			17 47					18 14			
Manchester Oxford Road	a		15 56			16 23					16 48	16 56								17 48	17 56				
Manchester Piccadilly [10] ⛴	a		16 00			16 27					16 57	17 00								17 57	18 00				
Manchester Airport 85 ✈	a		16 22			16 47						17 22									18 22				

		NT	NT	NT	NT	AW	NT	NT	TP	NT		NT	NT	AW	NT	NT	NT	NT	TP	AW		NT	NT	NT	NT
						◇			◇[1]					◇					◇[1]	◇					
						D			F					D	E				G	D					
						🛒			🛒					🛒											
Liverpool Lime Street [10] 91	d	17 35	17 42	17 46	18 01		18 13	18 16		18 31		18 46	19 01			19 12	19 23	19 42				20 09	20 12	20 25	20 42
Edge Hill 91	d	17 39		17 50	18 05			18 20		18 35		18 50	19 05			19 16		19 46					20 16		20 46
Wavertree Technology Park	d	17 41	17 47	17 52	18 07		18 19	18 22		18 37		18 52	19 07			19 18		19 48				20 15	20 18		20 48
Broad Green	d	17 44	17 50	17 55	18 10			18 25		18 40		18 55	19 10			19 21		19 51					20 21		20 51
Roby	d	17 48		17 59	18 14			18 29		18 44		18 59	19 14			19 25		19 55					20 25		20 55
Huyton	d	17 50	17 55	18 01	18 16			18 31		18 46		19 01	19 16			19 27	19 32	19 57					20 27	20 34	20 57
Prescot	d		18 00		18 21					18 51			19 21					20 02							21 02
Eccleston Park	d		18 03		18 23					18 53			19 23					20 04							21 04
Thatto Heath	d		18 05		18 26					18 56			19 26					20 07							21 07
St Helens Central	a		18 09		18 29					18 59			19 29				19 40	20 10						20 42	21 10
	d		18 09		18 30					19 00			19 30				19 41	20 11						20 43	21 11
Garswood	d		18 17		18 37					19 07			19 37					20 18							21 18
Bryn	d		18 20		18 40					19 10			19 40					20 21							21 21
Whiston	d	17 54		18 05				18 35				19 05				19 31							20 31		
Rainhill	d	17 57		18 08				18 38				19 08				19 34							20 34		
Lea Green	d	18 00		18 11				18 41				19 11				19 37							20 37		
St Helens Junction	d	18 03		18 14			18 29	18 44				19 14				19 40						20 25	20 40		
Warrington Bank Quay	d					18 19								19 19	19 22					20 19					
Earlestown [8]	d	18 08		18 19		18 26		18 50				19 19		19 26	19a33	19 45				20 26			20 45		
Warrington Bank Quay	a							19 01																	
Newton-le-Willows	d	18 11		18 22		18 29	18 35					19 22		19 29		19 48				20 29		20 35	20 48		
Wigan North Western 65	a		18 27		18 49					19 21			19 51				19 54	20 32						20 57	21 32
	d		18 30		18 49				18 59								19 55		20 43					20 57	
Euxton Balshaw Lane	d		18 40		19 01												20 05							21 08	
Leyland 82	a		18 45		19 06												20 10							21 16	
Preston [8] 65,82	a		18 53		19 15												20 18		20 57					21 22	
Blackpool North 97	a		19 22														20 44							21 53	
Patricroft	d	18 22										19 33				19 59							20 59		
Eccles	d	18 25		18 34								19 36				20 02							21 02		
Manchester Victoria ⛴	a	18 37		18 47								19 49				20 15							21 15		
Manchester Oxford Road	a					18 48	18 56		19 24					19 48						20 48		20 56			
Manchester Piccadilly [10] ⛴	a					18 57	19 00		19 29					19 52						20 57		21 00			
Manchester Airport 85 ✈	a						19 23		19 46					20 13								21 19			

A From Glasgow Central
B To Stalybridge
C From Liverpool South Pw Hl
D From Llandudno
E To Liverpool Lime Street
F From Edinburgh
G From Manchester Airport

Table 90R

Saturdays

14 December to 28 December

Liverpool and St Helens - Newton-le-Willows, Wigan, Preston and Manchester

Network Diagram - see first Page of Table 88

			AW	NT	NT	AW	NT		NT	NT	AW
			◇								
			A			B					B
Liverpool Lime Street 10	91	d		21 12	21 42		22 12		23 02	23 16	
Edge Hill	91	d		21 16	21 46		22 16		23 06	23 20	
Wavertree Technology Park		d		21 18	21 48		22 18		23 08	23 22	
Broad Green		d		21 21	21 51		22 21		23 11	23 26	
Roby		d		21 25	21 55		22 25		23 15	23 30	
Huyton		d		21 27	21 57		22 27		23 17	23 32	
Prescot		d			22 02				23 22		
Eccleston Park		d			22 04				23 24		
Thatto Heath		d			22 07				23 27		
St Helens Central		a			22 10				23 30		
		d			22 11				23 31		
Garswood		d			22 18				23 38		
Bryn		d			22 21				23 41		
Whiston		d		21 31			22 31			23 36	
Rainhill		d		21 34			22 34			23 39	
Lea Green		d		21 37			22 37			23 42	
St Helens Junction		d		21 40			22 40			23 45	
Warrington Bank Quay		d	21 19			22 19					23 50
Earlestown 8		d	21 26	21 45		22 27	22 45			23 50	23 58
Warrington Bank Quay		a									
Newton-le-Willows		d	21 29	21 48		22 30	22 48			23 53	00 02
Wigan North Western	65	a			22 28				23 48		
		d			22 28				23 48		
Euxton Balshaw Lane		d			22 39				23 59		
Leyland	82	a			22 44				00 04		
Preston 8	65,82	a			22 55				00 13		
Blackpool North	97	a			23 22						
Patricroft		d		21 59			22 59			00 04	
Eccles		d		22 02			23 02			00 07	
Manchester Victoria	⛴	a		22 15			23 15			00 21	
Manchester Oxford Road		a	21 48			22 50					
Manchester Piccadilly 10	⛴	a	21 57			22 58					00 26
Manchester Airport	85 ✈	a									

Saturdays

4 January to 8 February

			NT	NT	NT	AW	NT	NT	NT	AW	NT		NT	NT	NT	NT	NT	NT	AW	NT	TP		AW	NT	NT	NT
										◇											◇1		◇			
			C			B				B				D					E 🍴	F	G		A 🍴			
Liverpool Lime Street 10	91	d		05 13	05 31		05 46	06 01	06 13		06 16		06 31	06 46		06 57	07 01	07 13		07 16					07 31	07 46
Edge Hill	91	d			05 35		05 50	06 05			06 20		06 35	06 50			07 05			07 20					07 35	07 50
Wavertree Technology Park		d		05 19	05 37		05 52	06 07	06 19		06 22		06 37	06 52			07 07	07 19		07 22					07 37	07 52
Broad Green		d			05 40		05 55	06 10			06 25		06 40	06 55			07 10			07 25					07 40	07 55
Roby		d			05 44		05 59	06 14			06 29		06 44	06 59			07 14			07 29					07 44	07 59
Huyton		d			05 46		06 01	06 16			06 31		06 46	07 01		07 06	07 16			07 31					07 46	08 01
Prescot		d			05 51			06 21					06 51				07 21								07 51	
Eccleston Park		d			05 53			06 23					06 53				07 23								07 53	
Thatto Heath		d			05 56			06 26					06 56				07 26								07 56	
St Helens Central		a			05 59			06 29					06 59			07 15	07 29								07 59	
		d			06 00			06 30					07 00			07 15	07 30								08 00	
Garswood		d			06 07			06 37					07 07				07 37								08 07	
Bryn		d			06 10			06 40					07 10				07 40								08 10	
Whiston		d					06 05				06 35			07 05						07 35						08 05
Rainhill		d					06 08				06 38			07 08						07 38						08 08
Lea Green		d					06 11				06 41			07 11				07 28		07 41						08 11
St Helens Junction		d		05 29			06 14		06 29		06 44			07 14				07 31		07 44						08 14
Warrington Bank Quay		d				06 06				06 40									07 39				08 08			
Earlestown 8		d				06 12	06 19			06 47	06 50			07 19					07 46	07 49			08 16			08 19
Warrington Bank Quay		a									07 01															
Newton-le-Willows		d		05 35		06 15	06 22		06 35	06 50				07 22				07 37	07 49	07 52			08 19			08 22
Wigan North Western	65	a			06 21			06 51					07 21			07 30	07 51								08 21	
		d													07 22	07 31					07 56			08 20		
Euxton Balshaw Lane		d														07 41										
Leyland	82	a														07 46										
Preston 8	65,82	a														07 54										
Blackpool North	97	a														08 21										
Patricroft		d	00 04				06 33							07 33						08 03						08 33
Eccles		d	00 07				06 36							07 36						08 06						08 36
Manchester Victoria	⛴	a	00 21				06 49							07 49	08 12					08 19				09 06		08 50
Manchester Oxford Road		a				06 35			06 56	07 09								07 56	08 09		08 22		08 41			
Manchester Piccadilly 10	⛴	a		05 56		06 44			07 00	07 18								08 01	08 18		08 26		08 45			
Manchester Airport	85 ✈	a		06 14					07 22									08 22			08 47					

A From Llandudno
B From Chester
C From Liverpool Lime Street
D To Stalybridge
E From Shrewsbury
F To Huddersfield
G From Barrow-in-Furness

Table 90R

Saturdays

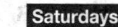

4 January to 8 February

Liverpool and St Helens - Newton-le-Willows, Wigan, Preston and Manchester

Network Diagram - see first Page of Table 88

			NT	NT	NT	NT	TP		NT	NT	NT	NT	AW	NT	NT	NT	TP		NT	NT	NT	NT	AW	NT	NT	NT
							◇1 A			B			◇ C		D		◇1 E			B			◇ C		D	
Liverpool Lime Street 10	91	d	07 57	08 01	08 13	08 16			08 31	08 44	08 57	09 01		09 13		09 16			09 31	09 46	09 57	10 01		10 13		10 16
Edge Hill	91	d		08 05		08 20			08 35	08 50		09 05				09 20			09 35	09 50		10 05				10 20
Wavertree Technology Park		d		08 07	08 19	08 22			08 37	08 52		09 07		09 19		09 22			09 37	09 52		10 07		10 19		10 22
Broad Green		d		08 10		08 25			08 40	08 55		09 10				09 25			09 40	09 55		10 10				10 25
Roby		d		08 14		08 29			08 44	08 59		09 14				09 29			09 44	09 59		10 14				10 29
Huyton		d	08 06	08 16		08 31			08 46	09 01	09 06	09 16				09 31			09 46	10 01	10 06	10 16				10 31
Prescot		d		08 21					08 51			09 21							09 51			10 21				
Eccleston Park		d		08 23					08 53			09 23							09 53			10 23				
Thatto Heath		d		08 26					08 56			09 26							09 56			10 26				
St Helens Central		a	08 15	08 29					08 59		09 15	09 29							09 59		10 15	10 29				
		d	08 15	08 30					09 00		09 15	09 30							10 00		10 15	10 30				
Garswood		d		08 37					09 07			09 37							10 07			10 37				
Bryn		d		08 40					09 10			09 40							10 10			10 40				
Whiston		d				08 35				09 05						09 35				10 05						10 35
Rainhill		d				08 38				09 08						09 38				10 08						10 38
Lea Green		d				08 41				09 11						09 41				10 11						10 41
St Helens Junction		d			08 29	08 44				09 14				09 29		09 44				10 14				10 29		10 44
Warrington Bank Quay		d											09 19		09 22								10 19		10 22	
Earlestown 8		d				08 50				09 19			09 26		09a33	09 50				10 19			10 26		10a33	10 50
Warrington Bank Quay		a				09 01										10 01										11 01
Newton-le-Willows		d			08 35					09 22			09 29	09 35						10 22			10 29	10 35		
Wigan North Western	65	a	08 30	08 51					09 21		09 30	09 51							10 21		10 30	10 51				
		d	08 31				08 58				09 31						09 58				10 31					
Euxton Balshaw Lane		d	08 41								09 41										10 41					
Leyland	82	a	08 46								09 46										10 46					
Preston 8	65,82	a	08 54								09 54										10 54					
Blackpool North	97	a	09 21								10 21										11 21					
Patricroft		d								09 33										10 33						
Eccles		d								09 36										10 36						
Manchester Victoria		a								09 47										10 49						
Manchester Oxford Road		a			08 56		09 23						09 48	09 56			10 22						10 48	10 56		
Manchester Piccadilly 10		a			09 00		09 27						09 52	10 00			10 26						10 52	11 00		
Manchester Airport	85	a			09 22		09 47							10 22			10 46							11 22		

			TP		NT	NT	NT	AW	NT	TP	NT	NT	NT		TP	NT	NT	NT	AW	NT	TP	NT	NT		NT	TP
			◇1 A			B	F	◇ C	D	◇1 G					◇1 H		B	F	◇ C	D	◇1 I					◇1 A
Liverpool Lime Street 10	91	d			10 31	10 46	10 57				11 01	11 13	11 16			11 31	11 46	11 57				12 01	12 13		12 16	
Edge Hill	91	d			10 35	10 50					11 05		11 20			11 35	11 50					12 05			12 20	
Wavertree Technology Park		d			10 37	10 52					11 07	11 19	11 22			11 37	11 52					12 07	12 19		12 22	
Broad Green		d			10 40	10 55					11 10		11 25			11 40	11 55					12 10			12 25	
Roby		d			10 44	10 59					11 14		11 29			11 44	11 59					12 14			12 29	
Huyton		d			10 46	11 01	11 06				11 16		11 31			11 46	12 01	12 06				12 16			12 31	
Prescot		d			10 51						11 21					11 51						12 21				
Eccleston Park		d			10 53						11 23					11 53						12 23				
Thatto Heath		d			10 56						11 26					11 56						12 26				
St Helens Central		a			10 59		11 15				11 29					11 59		12 15				12 29				
		d			11 00		11 15				11 30					12 00		12 15				12 30				
Garswood		d			11 07						11 37					12 07						12 37				
Bryn		d			11 10						11 40					12 10						12 40				
Whiston		d				11 05							11 35				12 05								12 35	
Rainhill		d				11 08							11 38				12 08								12 38	
Lea Green		d				11 11							11 41				12 11								12 41	
St Helens Junction		d				11 14						11 29	11 44				12 14						12 29		12 44	
Warrington Bank Quay		d						11 19	11 22										12 19	12 22						
Earlestown 8		d				11 19		11 26	11a33				11 50				12 19		12 26	12a33					12 50	
Warrington Bank Quay		a											12 01												13 01	
Newton-le-Willows		d				11 22		11 29				11 35					12 22		12 29				12 35			
Wigan North Western	65	a			11 21		11 30				11 51					12 21		12 30				12 51				
		d	10 58				11 31			11 43					11 58			12 31			12 43					12 58
Euxton Balshaw Lane		d					11 41											12 41								
Leyland	82	a					11 46											12 46								
Preston 8	65,82	a					11 54			11 57								12 54			12 57					
Blackpool North	97	a					12 21											13 21								
Patricroft		d				11 33											12 33									
Eccles		d				11 36											12 36									
Manchester Victoria		a				11 49											12 49									
Manchester Oxford Road		a	11 23					11 48				11 56			12 23				12 48				12 56			13 23
Manchester Piccadilly 10		a	11 27					11 52				12 00			12 27				12 52				13 00			13 27
Manchester Airport	85	a	11 47									12 22			12 47								13 22			13 47

A From Edinburgh
B To Stalybridge
C From Llandudno
D To Liverpool Lime Street
E From Glasgow Central
F From Liverpool South Pw Hl
G From Manchester Airport to Barrow-in-Furness
H From Windermere
I From Manchester Airport to Lancaster

Table 90R

Saturdays

4 January to 8 February

Liverpool and St Helens - Newton-le-Willows, Wigan, Preston and Manchester

Network Diagram - see first Page of Table 88

			NT	NT	NT	AW	NT	TP	NT		NT	NT	TP	NT	NT	NT	AW	NT	TP		NT	NT	NT	NT	NT	NT
						◇		◇**1**					◇**1**				◇		◇**1**							
				A	B	C	D	E					F		A	B	C	D	E						A	B
						[trolley]		[trolley]					[trolley]				[trolley]		[trolley]							
Liverpool Lime Street **10**	91	d	12 31	12 46	12 57				13 01		13 13	13 16		13 31	13 46	13 57					14 01	14 13	14 16	14 31	14 46	14 57
Edge Hill	91	d	12 35	12 50					13 05			13 20		13 35	13 50						14 05		14 20	14 35	14 50	
Wavertree Technology Park		d	12 37	12 52					13 07		13 19	13 22		13 37	13 52						14 07	14 19	14 22	14 37	14 52	
Broad Green		d	12 40	12 55					13 10			13 25		13 40	13 55						14 10		14 25	14 40	14 55	
Roby		d	12 44	12 59					13 14			13 29		13 44	13 59						14 14		14 29	14 44	14 59	
Huyton		d	12 46	13 01	13 06				13 16			13 31		13 46	14 01	14 06					14 16		14 31	14 46	15 01	15 06
Prescot		d	12 51						13 21					13 51							14 21			14 51		
Eccleston Park		d	12 53						13 23					13 53							14 23			14 53		
Thatto Heath		d	12 56						13 26					13 56							14 26			14 56		
St Helens Central		a	12 59		13 15				13 29					13 59		14 15					14 29			14 59		15 15
		d	13 00		13 15				13 30					14 00		14 15					14 30			15 00		15 15
Garswood		d	13 07						13 37					14 07							14 37			15 07		
Bryn		d	13 10						13 40					14 10							14 40			15 10		
Whiston		d		13 05								13 35			14 05								14 35		15 05	
Rainhill		d		13 08								13 38			14 08								14 38		15 08	
Lea Green		d		13 11								13 41			14 11								14 41		15 11	
St Helens Junction		d		13 14							13 29	13 44			14 14							14 29	14 44		15 14	
Warrington Bank Quay		d				13 19	13 22										14 19	14 22								
Earlestown **8**		d		13 19		13 26	13a33					13 50			14 19		14 26	14a33					14 50		15 19	
Warrington Bank Quay		a										14 01											15 01			
Newton-le-Willows		d		13 22		13 29					13 35				14 22		14 29					14 35			15 22	
Wigan North Western	65	a	13 21		13 30				13 51					14 21		14 30					14 51			15 21		15 30
		d			13 31			13 43					13 57			14 31			14 43							15 31
Euxton Balshaw Lane		d			13 41											14 41										15 41
Leyland	82	a			13 46											14 46										15 46
Preston **8**	65,82	a			13 54			13 57								14 54			14 57							15 54
Blackpool North	97	a			14 21											15 21										16 21
Patricroft		d		13 33											14 33										15 33	
Eccles		d		13 36											14 36										15 36	
Manchester Victoria	[tram]	a		13 49											14 50										15 49	
Manchester Oxford Road		a				13 48					13 56		14 22				14 48					14 56				
Manchester Piccadilly **10**	[tram]	a				13 52					14 00		14 26				14 57					15 00				
Manchester Airport	85 [air]	a									14 22		14 47									15 22				

			AW	NT	TP		NT	NT	NT	TP	NT	NT	NT	NT	AW		NT	NT	NT	NT	NT	NT	NT	AW	NT	
			◇		◇**1**					◇**1**					◇									◇		
			G	D	H					F		A	B		C			D			A	B		C		
			[trolley]							[trolley]					[trolley]									[trolley]		
Liverpool Lime Street **10**	91	d					15 01	15 13	15 16		15 31	15 46	15 57	16 01			16 13		16 16	16 31	16 46	16 57	17 01		17 06	
Edge Hill	91	d					15 05		15 20		15 35	15 50		16 05					16 20	16 35	16 50		17 05			
Wavertree Technology Park		d					15 07	15 19	15 22		15 37	15 52		16 07			16 19		16 22	16 37	16 52		17 07		17 12	
Broad Green		d					15 10		15 25		15 40	15 55		16 10					16 25	16 40	16 55		17 10			
Roby		d					15 14		15 29		15 44	15 59		16 14					16 29	16 44	16 59		17 14			
Huyton		d					15 16		15 31		15 46	16 01	16 06	16 16					16 31	16 46	17 01	17 06	17 16		17 20	
Prescot		d					15 21				15 51			16 21						16 51			17 21			
Eccleston Park		d					15 23				15 53			16 23						16 53			17 23			
Thatto Heath		d					15 26				15 56			16 26						16 56			17 26			
St Helens Central		a					15 29				15 59		16 15	16 29						16 59		17 15	17 29			
		d					15 30				16 00		16 15	16 30						17 00		17 15	17 30			
Garswood		d					15 37				16 07			16 37						17 07			17 37			
Bryn		d					15 40				16 10			16 40						17 10			17 40			
Whiston		d							15 35			16 05							16 35		17 05					
Rainhill		d							15 38			16 08							16 38		17 08					
Lea Green		d							15 41			16 11							16 41		17 11				17 25	
St Helens Junction		d						15 29	15 44			16 14					16 29		16 44		17 14				17 28	
Warrington Bank Quay		d	15 19	15 22											16 19			16 22						17 19		
Earlestown **8**		d	15 26	15a33					15 50			16 19			16 26			16a33	16 49		17 19			17 26		
Warrington Bank Quay		a							16 01																	
Newton-le-Willows		d	15 29					15 35				16 22			16 29		16 35		16 52		17 22			17 29	17 34	
Wigan North Western	65	a					15 51				16 21		16 30	16 51						17 21		17 30	17 51			
		d			15 43					15 58			16 31									17 31				
Euxton Balshaw Lane		d											16 41									17 41				
Leyland	82	a											16 46									17 46				
Preston **8**	65,82	a			15 57								16 54									17 54				
Blackpool North	97	a											17 21									18 24				
Patricroft		d										16 33							17 03		17 33					
Eccles		d										16 36							17 06		17 36					
Manchester Victoria	[tram]	a										16 49							17 19		17 47					
Manchester Oxford Road		a	15 48					15 56		16 22					16 48		16 56							17 48	17 56	
Manchester Piccadilly **10**	[tram]	a	15 52					16 00		16 26					16 57		17 00							17 57	18 00	
Manchester Airport	85 [air]	a						16 22		16 47							17 22								18 22	

A To Stalybridge
B From Liverpool South Pw Hl
C From Llandudno
D To Liverpool Lime Street
E From Manchester Airport to Lancaster
F From Lancaster
G From Bangor (Gwynedd)
H From Manchester Airport to Barrow-in-Furness

Table 90R

Saturdays

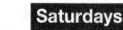

4 January to 8 February

Liverpool and St Helens - Newton-le-Willows, Wigan, Preston and Manchester

Network Diagram - see first Page of Table 88

		NT	NT	NT	NT	NT	NT	AW	TP	NT	NT	NT	TP	NT	NT	NT	AW	NT	NT	NT	NT	AW	NT
								◇ A 🍴	◇[1] B 🍴				◇[1] C				◇ A 🍴	D				◇ A	
Liverpool Lime Street [10] 91	d	17 10	17 19	17 27	17 35	17 42	17 46			18 01	18 13	18 16		18 31	18 46	19 01			19 12	19 23	19 42		20 09
Edge Hill 91	d	17 14		17 31	17 39		17 50			18 05		18 20		18 35	18 50	19 05			19 16		19 46		
Wavertree Technology Park	d	17 16		17 33	17 41	17 47	17 52			18 07	18 19	18 22		18 37	18 52	19 07			19 18		19 48		20 15
Broad Green	d	17 19		17 36	17 44	17 50	17 55			18 10		18 25		18 40	18 55	19 10			19 21		19 51		
Roby	d	17 23		17 40	17 48		17 59			18 14		18 29		18 44	18 59	19 14			19 25		19 55		
Huyton	d	17 25	17 29	17 42	17 50	17 55	18 01			18 16		18 31		18 46	19 01	19 16			19 27	19 32	19 57		
Prescot	d		17 34			18 00				18 21				18 51		19 21					20 02		
Eccleston Park	d		17 36			18 03				18 23				18 53		19 23					20 04		
Thatto Heath	d		17 39			18 05				18 26				18 56		19 26					20 07		
St Helens Central	a		17 42	17 51		18 09				18 29				18 59		19 29				19 40	20 10		
	d		17 43	17 51		18 09				18 30				19 00		19 30				19 41	20 11		
Garswood	d		17 50			18 17				18 37				19 07		19 37					20 18		
Bryn	d		17 53			18 20				18 40				19 10		19 40					20 21		
Whiston	d	17 29			17 54		18 05					18 35			19 05				19 31				
Rainhill	d	17 32			17 57		18 08					18 38			19 08				19 34				
Lea Green	d	17 35			18 00		18 11					18 41			19 11				19 37				
St Helens Junction	d	17 39			18 03		18 14				18 29	18 44			19 14				19 40				20 25
Warrington Bank Quay	d							18 19									19 19	19 22				20 19	
Earlestown [8]	d	17 44			18 08		18 19	18 26				18 50			19 19		19 26	19a33	19 45			20 26	
Warrington Bank Quay	a											19 01											
Newton-le-Willows	d	17 47			18 11		18 22	18 29			18 35				19 22		19 29		19 48			20 29	20 35
Wigan North Western 65	a		18 05	18 04		18 27				18 49				19 21		19 51				19 54	20 32		
	d			18 05		18 30			18 43	18 49			18 58							19 55			
Euxton Balshaw Lane	d			18 16		18 40				19 01										20 05			
Leyland 82	a			18 21		18 45				19 06										20 10			
Preston [8] 65,82	a			18 31		18 53			18 57	19 15										20 18			
Blackpool North 97	a					19 22														20 44			
Patricroft	d	17 58			18 22										19 33				19 59				
Eccles	d	18 01			18 25		18 34								19 36				20 02				
Manchester Victoria	a	18 14			18 37		18 47								19 49				20 15				
Manchester Oxford Road	a							18 48			18 56		19 23				19 48					20 48	20 56
Manchester Piccadilly [10]	a							18 57			19 00		19 27				19 52					20 57	21 00
Manchester Airport 85 ✈	a										19 23		19 46				20 13						21 19

		NT	NT	NT	AW	NT	NT	AW	NT	NT	NT	NT	AW
					◇ A			E			🚌		E
Liverpool Lime Street [10] 91	d	20 12	20 25	20 42		21 12	21 42		22 12	23 02		23 16	
Edge Hill 91	d	20 16		20 46		21 16	21 46		22 16	23 06		23 20	
Wavertree Technology Park	d	20 18		20 48		21 18	21 48		22 18	23 08		23 22	
Broad Green	d	20 21		20 51		21 21	21 51		22 21	23 11		23 26	
Roby	d	20 25		20 55		21 25	21 55		22 25	23 15		23 30	
Huyton	d	20 27	20 34	20 57		21 27	21 57		22 27	23 17		23 32	
Prescot	d			21 02			22 02			23 22			
Eccleston Park	d			21 04			22 04			23 24			
Thatto Heath	d			21 07			22 07			23 27			
St Helens Central	a		20 42	21 10			22 10			23 30			
	d		20 43	21 11			22 11			23 31			
Garswood	d			21 18			22 18			23 38			
Bryn	d			21 21			22 21			23 41			
Whiston	d	20 31				21 31			22 31			23 36	
Rainhill	d	20 34				21 34			22 34			23 39	
Lea Green	d	20 37				21 37			22 37			23 42	
St Helens Junction	d	20 40				21 40			22 40			23 45	
Warrington Bank Quay	d				21 19			22 19					23 50
Earlestown [8]	d	20 45			21 26	21 45		22 27	22 45			23 50	23 58
Warrington Bank Quay	a												
Newton-le-Willows	d	20 48			21 29	21 48		22 30	22 48			23 53	00 02
Wigan North Western 65	a		20 57	21 32			22 28			23 48			
	d		20 57				22 28				23 58		
Euxton Balshaw Lane	d		21 08				22 39				00 23		
Leyland 82	a		21 16				22 44				00 35		
Preston [8] 65,82	a		21 22				22 55				00 55		
Blackpool North 97	a		21 53				23 22						
Patricroft	d	20 59				21 59			22 59			00 04	
Eccles	d	21 02				22 02			23 02			00 07	
Manchester Victoria	a	21 15				22 15			23 15			00 21	
Manchester Oxford Road	a				21 48			22 50					
Manchester Piccadilly [10]	a				21 57			22 58					00 26
Manchester Airport 85 ✈	a												

A From Llandudno
B From Manchester Airport to Lancaster
C From Barrow-in-Furness
D To Liverpool Lime Street
E From Chester

Table 90R

Saturdays

15 February to 22 March

Liverpool and St Helens - Newton-le-Willows, Wigan, Preston and Manchester

Network Diagram - see first Page of Table 88

Station			NT	NT	NT	AW	NT	NT	NT	AW	NT		NT	NT	NT	NT	NT	NT	AW	NT	TP		AW	NT	NT	NT
			A			B				◇ B				C					D ⚲	E	◇1 F		◇ G ⚲			
Liverpool Lime Street 10	91	d		05 13	05 31		05 46	06 01	06 13		06 16		06 31	06 46		06 57	07 01	07 13		07 16					07 31	07 46
Edge Hill	91	d			05 35		05 50	06 05			06 20		06 35	06 50			07 05			07 20					07 35	07 50
Wavertree Technology Park		d		05 19	05 37		05 52	06 07	06 19		06 22		06 37	06 52			07 07	07 19		07 22					07 37	07 52
Broad Green		d			05 40		05 55	06 10			06 25		06 40	06 55			07 10			07 25					07 40	07 55
Roby		d			05 44		05 59	06 14			06 29		06 44	06 59			07 14			07 29					07 44	07 59
Huyton		d			05 46		06 01	06 16			06 31		06 46	07 01		07 06	07 16			07 31					07 46	08 01
Prescot		d			05 51			06 21					06 51				07 21								07 51	
Eccleston Park		d			05 53			06 23					06 53				07 23								07 53	
Thatto Heath		d			05 56			06 26					06 56				07 26								07 56	
St Helens Central		a			05 59			06 29					06 59			07 15	07 29								07 59	
		d			06 00			06 30					07 00			07 15	07 30								08 00	
Garswood		d			06 07			06 37					07 07				07 37								08 07	
Bryn		d			06 10			06 40					07 10				07 40								08 10	
Whiston		d					06 05				06 35			07 05						07 35						08 05
Rainhill		d					06 08				06 38			07 08						07 38						08 08
Lea Green		d					06 11				06 41			07 11				07 28		07 41						08 11
St Helens Junction		d		05 29			06 14		06 29		06 44			07 14				07 31		07 44						08 14
Warrington Bank Quay		d				06 06				06 40									07 39				08 08			
Earlestown 8		d				06 12	06 19			06 47	06 50			07 19					07 46	07 49			08 16			08 19
Warrington Bank Quay		a									07 01															
Newton-le-Willows		d		05 35		06 15	06 22		06 35	06 50				07 22				07 37	07 49	07 52			08 19			08 22
Wigan North Western	65	a			06 21			06 51					07 21			07 30	07 51								08 21	
		d													07 22	07 31					07 56			08 20		
Euxton Balshaw Lane		d														07 41										
Leyland	82	a														07 46										
Preston 8	65,82	a														07 54										
Blackpool North	97	a														08 21										
Patricroft		d	00 04				06 33							07 33						08 03						08 33
Eccles		d	00 07				06 36							07 36						08 06						08 36
Manchester Victoria ⛴		a	00 21				06 49							07 49	08 12					08 19				09 06		08 50
Manchester Oxford Road		a				06 35			06 56	07 09								07 56	08 09		08 22		08 41			
Manchester Piccadilly 10 ⛴		a		05 56		06 44			07 00	07 18								08 01	08 18		08 26		08 45			
Manchester Airport ✈	85	a		06 14					07 22									08 22			08 47					

Station			NT	NT	NT	NT	TP		NT	NT	NT	AW	NT	TP	NT	NT	NT		TP	NT	NT	NT	NT	AW	NT	NT
							◇1 H ⚲			C		◇ G ⚲	I	◇1 J ⚲					◇1 K ⚲		C			◇ G ⚲		I
Liverpool Lime Street 10	91	d	07 57	08 01	08 13	08 16			08 31	08 44	08 57				09 01	09 13	09 18			09 31	09 46	09 57	10 01		10 13	
Edge Hill	91	d		08 05		08 20			08 35	08 50					09 05		09 20			09 35	09 50		10 05			
Wavertree Technology Park		d		08 07	08 19	08 22			08 37	08 52					09 07	09 19	09 22			09 37	09 52		10 07		10 19	
Broad Green		d		08 10		08 25			08 40	08 55					09 10		09 25			09 40	09 55		10 10			
Roby		d		08 14		08 29			08 44	08 59					09 14		09 29			09 44	09 59		10 14			
Huyton		d	08 06	08 16		08 31			08 46	09 01	09 06				09 16		09 31			09 46	10 01	10 06	10 16			
Prescot		d		08 21					08 51						09 21					09 51			10 21			
Eccleston Park		d		08 23					08 53						09 23					09 53			10 23			
Thatto Heath		d		08 26					08 56						09 26					09 56			10 26			
St Helens Central		a	08 15	08 29					08 59		09 15				09 29					09 59		10 15	10 29			
		d	08 15	08 30					09 00		09 15				09 30					10 00		10 15	10 30			
Garswood		d		08 37					09 07						09 37					10 07			10 37			
Bryn		d		08 40					09 10						09 40					10 10			10 40			
Whiston		d				08 35				09 05							09 35				10 05					
Rainhill		d				08 38				09 08							09 38				10 08					
Lea Green		d				08 41				09 11							09 41				10 11					
St Helens Junction		d			08 29	08 44				09 14						09 29	09 44				10 14				10 29	
Warrington Bank Quay		d										09 19	09 22											10 19		10 22
Earlestown 8		d				08 50				09 19		09 26	09a33				09 50				10 19			10 26		10a33
Warrington Bank Quay		a				09 01											10 01									
Newton-le-Willows		d			08 35					09 22		09 29				09 35					10 22			10 29	10 35	
Wigan North Western	65	a	08 30	08 51					09 21		09 30				09 51					10 21		10 30	10 51			
		d	08 31				08 58				09 31			09 43					09 58			10 31				
Euxton Balshaw Lane		d	08 41								09 41											10 41				
Leyland	82	a	08 46								09 46											10 46				
Preston 8	65,82	a	08 54								09 54			09 57								10 54				
Blackpool North	97	a	09 21								10 21			10 33								11 21				
Patricroft		d								09 33											10 33					
Eccles		d								09 36											10 36					
Manchester Victoria ⛴		a								09 47											10 49					
Manchester Oxford Road		a			08 56		09 23					09 48				09 56			10 22					10 48	10 56	
Manchester Piccadilly 10 ⛴		a			09 00		09 27					09 52				10 00			10 26					10 52	11 00	
Manchester Airport ✈	85	a			09 22		09 47									10 22			10 46						11 22	

A From Liverpool Lime Street
B From Chester
C To Stalybridge
D From Shrewsbury
E To Huddersfield
F From Lancaster
G From Llandudno
H From Edinburgh
I To Liverpool Lime Street
J From Manchester Airport. ⚲ to Preston
K From Glasgow Central

Table 90R

Saturdays

15 February to 22 March

Liverpool and St Helens - Newton-le-Willows, Wigan, Preston and Manchester

Network Diagram - see first Page of Table 88

		NT		TP	NT	NT	NT	AW	NT	TP	NT	NT		NT	TP	NT	NT	NT	NT	AW	NT	NT		NT	TP
				◇[1]				◇		◇[1]					◇[1]					◇					◇[1]
				A		B	C	D	E	F					G		B	C		D		E			A
				🛒				🛒												🛒					🛒
Liverpool Lime Street [10]	91 d	10 16			10 31	10 46	10 57				11 01	11 13		11 16		11 31	11 46	11 57	12 01		12 13			12 16	
Edge Hill	91 d	10 20			10 35	10 50					11 05			11 20		11 35	11 50		12 05					12 20	
Wavertree Technology Park	d	10 22			10 37	10 52					11 07	11 19		11 22		11 37	11 52		12 07		12 19			12 22	
Broad Green	d	10 25			10 40	10 55					11 10			11 25		11 40	11 55		12 10					12 25	
Roby	d	10 29			10 44	10 59					11 14			11 29		11 44	11 59		12 14					12 29	
Huyton	d	10 31			10 46	11 01	11 06				11 16			11 31		11 46	12 01	12 06	12 16					12 31	
Prescot	d				10 51						11 21					11 51			12 21						
Eccleston Park	d				10 53						11 23					11 53			12 23						
Thatto Heath	d				10 56						11 26					11 56			12 26						
St Helens Central	a				10 59		11 15				11 29					11 59		12 15	12 29						
	d				11 00		11 15				11 30					12 00		12 15	12 30						
Garswood	d				11 07						11 37					12 07			12 37						
Bryn	d				11 10						11 40					12 10			12 40						
Whiston	d	10 35				11 05								11 35			12 05							12 35	
Rainhill	d	10 38				11 08								11 38			12 08							12 38	
Lea Green	d	10 41				11 11								11 41			12 11							12 41	
St Helens Junction	d	10 44				11 14						11 29		11 44			12 14				12 29			12 44	
Warrington Bank Quay	d							11 19	11 22											12 19		12 22			
Earlestown [8]	d	10 50				11 19		11 26	11a33					11 50			12 19			12 26		12a33		12 50	
Warrington Bank Quay	a	11 01												12 01										13 01	
Newton-le-Willows	d					11 22		11 29				11 35					12 22			12 29	12 35				
Wigan North Western	65 a				11 21		11 30				11 51					12 21		12 30	12 51						
	d			10 58			11 31			11 43					11 58			12 31							12 58
Euxton Balshaw Lane	d						11 41											12 41							
Leyland	82 a						11 46											12 46							
Preston [8]	65,82 a						11 54			11 57								12 54							
Blackpool North	97 a						12 21											13 21							
Patricroft	d					11 33											12 33								
Eccles	d					11 36											12 36								
Manchester Victoria	⛴ a					11 49											12 49								
Manchester Oxford Road	a			11 23				11 48				11 56			12 23					12 48	12 56				13 23
Manchester Piccadilly [10]	⛴ a			11 27				11 52				12 00			12 27					12 52	13 00				13 27
Manchester Airport	85 ✈ a			11 47								12 22			12 47						13 22				13 47

		NT	NT	NT	NT	AW	NT	NT		NT	TP	NT	NT	NT	NT	AW	NT	NT		NT	NT	NT	NT	AW	NT
						◇					◇[1]					◇								◇	
			B	C		D		E			H		B	C		D		E				B	C	I	E
						🛒					🛒					🛒								🛒	
Liverpool Lime Street [10]	91 d	12 31	12 46	12 57	13 01		13 13			13 16		13 31	13 46	13 57	14 01		14 13			14 16	14 31	14 46	14 57		
Edge Hill	91 d	12 35	12 50		13 05					13 20		13 35	13 50		14 05					14 20	14 35	14 50			
Wavertree Technology Park	d	12 37	12 52		13 07		13 19			13 22		13 37	13 52		14 07		14 19			14 22	14 37	14 52			
Broad Green	d	12 40	12 55		13 10					13 25		13 40	13 55		14 10					14 25	14 40	14 55			
Roby	d	12 44	12 59		13 14					13 29		13 44	13 59		14 14					14 29	14 44	14 59			
Huyton	d	12 46	13 01	13 06	13 16					13 31		13 46	14 01	14 06	14 16					14 31	14 46	15 01	15 06		
Prescot	d	12 51			13 21							13 51			14 21						14 51				
Eccleston Park	d	12 53			13 23							13 53			14 23						14 53				
Thatto Heath	d	12 56			13 26							13 56			14 26						14 56				
St Helens Central	a	12 59		13 15	13 29							13 59		14 15	14 29						14 59		15 15		
	d	13 00		13 15	13 30							14 00		14 15	14 30						15 00		15 15		
Garswood	d	13 07			13 37							14 07			14 37						15 07				
Bryn	d	13 10			13 40							14 10			14 40						15 10				
Whiston	d		13 05							13 35			14 05							14 35		15 05			
Rainhill	d		13 08							13 38			14 08							14 38		15 08			
Lea Green	d		13 11							13 41			14 11							14 41		15 11			
St Helens Junction	d		13 14				13 29			13 44			14 14				14 29			14 44		15 14			
Warrington Bank Quay	d					13 19		13 22								14 19		14 22						15 19	15 22
Earlestown [8]	d		13 19			13 26		13a33		13 50			14 19			14 26		14a33		14 50		15 19		15 26	15a33
Warrington Bank Quay	a									14 01										15 01					
Newton-le-Willows	d		13 22			13 29	13 35						14 22			14 29	14 35					15 22		15 29	
Wigan North Western	65 a	13 21		13 30	13 51							14 21		14 30	14 51						15 21		15 30		
	d			13 31							13 58			14 31									15 31		
Euxton Balshaw Lane	d			13 41										14 41									15 41		
Leyland	82 a			13 46										14 46									15 46		
Preston [8]	65,82 a			13 54										14 54									15 54		
Blackpool North	97 a			14 21										15 21									16 21		
Patricroft	d		13 33										14 33									15 33			
Eccles	d		13 36										14 36									15 36			
Manchester Victoria	⛴ a		13 49										14 50									15 49			
Manchester Oxford Road	a					13 48	13 56				14 22					14 48	14 56							15 48	
Manchester Piccadilly [10]	⛴ a					13 52	14 00				14 26					14 57	15 00							15 52	
Manchester Airport	85 ✈ a						14 22				14 45						15 22								

A From Edinburgh
B To Stalybridge
C From Liverpool South Pw Hl
D From Llandudno
E To Liverpool Lime Street
F From Manchester Airport to Barrow-in-Furness
G From Windermere
H From Glasgow Central
I From Bangor (Gwynedd)

Table 90R

Saturdays

15 February to 22 March

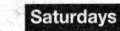

Liverpool and St Helens - Newton-le-Willows, Wigan, Preston and Manchester

Network Diagram - see first Page of Table 88

			TP	NT	NT	NT	TP	NT	NT	NT	NT	AW	NT	NT	NT	NT	NT	NT	NT	AW	NT	NT	NT
			◇1				◇1					◇								◇			
			A				B		C	D		E		F			C	D		E			
			🚲				🚲					🚲								🚲			
Liverpool Lime Street 10	91	d		15 01	15 13	15 16		15 31	15 46	15 57	16 01		16 13		16 16	16 31	16 46	16 57	17 01		17 06	17 10	17 19
Edge Hill	91	d		15 05		15 20		15 35	15 50		16 05				16 20	16 35	16 50		17 05			17 14	
Wavertree Technology Park		d		15 07	15 19	15 22		15 37	15 52		16 07		16 19		16 22	16 37	16 52		17 07		17 12	17 16	
Broad Green		d		15 10		15 25		15 40	15 55		16 10				16 25	16 40	16 55		17 10			17 19	
Roby		d		15 14		15 29		15 44	15 59		16 14				16 29	16 44	16 59		17 14			17 23	
Huyton		d		15 16		15 31		15 46	16 01	16 06	16 16				16 31	16 46	17 01	17 06	17 16		17 20	17 25	17 29
Prescot		d		15 21				15 51			16 21					16 51			17 21				17 34
Eccleston Park		d		15 23				15 53			16 23					16 53			17 23				17 36
Thatto Heath		d		15 26				15 56			16 26					16 56			17 26				17 39
St Helens Central		a		15 29				15 59		16 15	16 29					16 59		17 15	17 29				17 42
		d		15 30				16 00		16 15	16 30					17 00		17 15	17 30				17 43
Garswood		d		15 37				16 07			16 37					17 07			17 37				17 50
Bryn		d		15 40				16 10			16 40					17 10			17 40				17 53
Whiston		d				15 35			16 05						16 35		17 05					17 29	
Rainhill		d				15 38			16 08						16 38		17 08					17 32	
Lea Green		d				15 41			16 11						16 41		17 11				17 25	17 35	
St Helens Junction		d			15 29	15 44			16 14				16 29		16 44		17 14				17 28	17 39	
Warrington Bank Quay		d										16 19		16 22						17 19			
Earlestown 8		d				15 50			16 19			16 26		16a33	16 49		17 19			17 26		17 44	
Warrington Bank Quay		a				16 01																	
Newton-le-Willows		d			15 35				16 22			16 29	16 35		16 52		17 22			17 29	17 34	17 47	
Wigan North Western	65	a		15 51				16 21		16 30	16 51					17 21		17 30	17 51				18 05
		d	15 43				15 58			16 31								17 31					
Euxton Balshaw Lane		d								16 41								17 41					
Leyland	82	a								16 46								17 46					
Preston 8	65,82	a	15 57							16 54								17 54					
Blackpool North	97	a								17 21								18 24					
Patricroft		d							16 33						17 03		17 33					17 58	
Eccles		d							16 36						17 06		17 36					18 01	
Manchester Victoria	⛴	a							16 49						17 19		17 47					18 14	
Manchester Oxford Road		a			15 56		16 23					16 48	16 56							17 48	17 56		
Manchester Piccadilly 10	⛴	a			16 00		16 27					16 57	17 00							17 57	18 00		
Manchester Airport	85 ✈	a			16 22		16 47						17 22								18 22		

			NT	NT	NT	NT	NT	AW	NT	NT	TP	NT	NT	NT	AW	NT	NT	NT	TP	NT	TP	AW	NT	NT
								◇			◇1				◇				◇1		◇1	◇		
								E			G				E	F			B		H	E		
								🚲			🚲				🚲				🚲					
Liverpool Lime Street 10	91	d	17 27	17 35	17 42	17 46	18 01		18 13	18 16		18 31	18 46	19 01			19 12	19 23		19 42			20 09	20 12
Edge Hill	91	d	17 31	17 39		17 50	18 05			18 20		18 35	18 50	19 05			19 16			19 46				20 16
Wavertree Technology Park		d	17 33	17 41	17 47	17 52	18 07		18 19	18 22		18 37	18 52	19 07			19 18			19 48			20 15	20 18
Broad Green		d	17 36	17 44	17 50	17 55	18 10			18 25		18 40	18 55	19 10			19 21			19 51				20 21
Roby		d	17 40	17 48		17 59	18 14			18 29		18 44	18 59	19 14			19 25			19 55				20 25
Huyton		d	17 42	17 50	17 55	18 01	18 16			18 31		18 46	19 01	19 16			19 27	19 32		19 57				20 27
Prescot		d			18 00		18 21					18 51		19 21						20 02				
Eccleston Park		d			18 03		18 23					18 53		19 23						20 04				
Thatto Heath		d			18 05		18 26					18 56		19 26						20 07				
St Helens Central		a	17 51		18 09		18 29					18 59		19 29				19 40		20 10				
		d	17 51		18 09		18 30					19 00		19 30				19 41		20 11				
Garswood		d			18 17		18 37					19 07		19 37						20 18				
Bryn		d			18 20		18 40					19 10		19 40						20 21				
Whiston		d		17 54		18 05				18 35			19 05				19 31							20 31
Rainhill		d		17 57		18 08				18 38			19 08				19 34							20 34
Lea Green		d		18 00		18 11				18 41			19 11				19 37							20 37
St Helens Junction		d		18 03		18 14			18 29	18 44			19 14				19 40						20 25	20 40
Warrington Bank Quay		d						18 19							19 19	19 22						20 19		
Earlestown 8		d		18 08		18 19		18 26		18 50			19 19		19 26	19a33	19 45					20 26		20 45
Warrington Bank Quay		a								19 01														
Newton-le-Willows		d		18 11		18 22		18 29	18 35				19 22		19 29		19 48					20 29	20 35	20 48
Wigan North Western	65	a	18 04		18 27		18 49					19 21		19 51				19 54		20 32				
		d	18 05		18 30		18 49				18 59							19 55	19 59		20 43			
Euxton Balshaw Lane		d	18 16		18 40		19 01											20 05						
Leyland	82	a	18 21		18 45		19 06											20 10						
Preston 8	65,82	a	18 31		18 53		19 15											20 18			20 57			
Blackpool North	97	a			19 22													20 44						
Patricroft		d		18 22									19 33				19 59							20 59
Eccles		d		18 25		18 34							19 36				20 02							21 02
Manchester Victoria	⛴	a		18 37		18 47							19 49				20 15							21 15
Manchester Oxford Road		a						18 48	18 56		19 24				19 48				20 23			20 48	20 56	
Manchester Piccadilly 10	⛴	a						18 57	19 00		19 29				19 52				20 27			20 57	21 00	
Manchester Airport	85 ✈	a							19 23		19 47				20 13				20 47				21 19	

A From Manchester Airport to Lancaster
B From Glasgow Central
C To Stalybridge
D From Liverpool South Pw Hl
E From Llandudno
F To Liverpool Lime Street
G From Edinburgh
H From Manchester Airport

Table 90R

Saturdays

15 February to 22 March

Liverpool and St Helens - Newton-le-Willows, Wigan, Preston and Manchester

Network Diagram - see first Page of Table 88

Station			NT	NT	AW	NT	NT	AW	NT	NT	NT
					◇ A			B			
Liverpool Lime Street 10	91	d	20 25	20 42		21 12	21 42		22 12	23 02	23 16
Edge Hill	91	d		20 46		21 16	21 46		22 16	23 06	23 20
Wavertree Technology Park		d		20 48		21 18	21 48		22 18	23 08	23 22
Broad Green		d		20 51		21 21	21 51		22 21	23 11	23 26
Roby		d		20 55		21 25	21 55		22 25	23 15	23 30
Huyton		d	20 34	20 57		21 27	21 57		22 27	23 17	23 32
Prescot		d		21 02			22 02			23 22	
Eccleston Park		d		21 04			22 04			23 24	
Thatto Heath		d		21 07			22 07			23 27	
St Helens Central		a	20 42	21 10			22 10			23 30	
		d	20 43	21 11			22 11			23 31	
Garswood		d		21 18			22 18			23 38	
Bryn		d		21 21			22 21			23 41	
Whiston		d				21 31			22 31		23 36
Rainhill		d				21 34			22 34		23 39
Lea Green		d				21 37			22 37		23 42
St Helens Junction		d				21 40			22 40		23 45
Warrington Bank Quay		d			21 19			22 19			
Earlestown 8		d			21 26	21 45		22 27	22 45		23 50
Warrington Bank Quay		a									
Newton-le-Willows		d			21 29	21 48		22 30	22 48		23 53
Wigan North Western	65	a	20 57	21 32			22 28			23 48	
		d	20 57				22 28			23 48	
Euxton Balshaw Lane		d	21 08				22 39			23 59	
Leyland	82	a	21 16				22 44			00 04	
Preston 8	65,82	a	21 22				22 55			00 13	
Blackpool North	97	a	21 53				23 22				
Patricroft		d				21 59			22 59		00 04
Eccles		d				22 02			23 02		00 07
Manchester Victoria	⇌	a				22 15			23 15		00 21
Manchester Oxford Road		a			21 48			22 50			
Manchester Piccadilly 10	⇌	a			21 57			22 58			
Manchester Airport	85 ✈	a									

Saturdays

29 March to 17 May

Station			NT	NT	NT	AW	NT	NT	NT	AW	NT	NT	NT
			C			B				◇ B			D
Liverpool Lime Street 10	91	d		05 13	05 31		05 46	06 01	06 13		06 16	06 31	06 46
Edge Hill	91	d			05 35		05 50	06 05			06 20	06 35	06 50
Wavertree Technology Park		d		05 19	05 37		05 52	06 07	06 19		06 22	06 37	06 52
Broad Green		d			05 40		05 55	06 10			06 25	06 40	06 55
Roby		d			05 44		05 59	06 14			06 29	06 44	06 59
Huyton		d			05 46		06 01	06 16			06 31	06 46	07 01
Prescot		d			05 51			06 21				06 51	
Eccleston Park		d			05 53			06 23				06 53	
Thatto Heath		d			05 56			06 26				06 56	
St Helens Central		a			05 59			06 29				06 59	
		d			06 00			06 30				07 00	
Garswood		d			06 07			06 37				07 07	
Bryn		d			06 10			06 40				07 10	
Whiston		d					06 05				06 35		07 05
Rainhill		d					06 08				06 38		07 08
Lea Green		d					06 11				06 41		07 11
St Helens Junction		d		05 29			06 14		06 29		06 44		07 14
Warrington Bank Quay		d				06 06				06 40			
Earlestown 8		d				06 12	06 19			06 47	06 50		07 19
Warrington Bank Quay		a									07 01		
Newton-le-Willows		d		05 35		06 15	06 22		06 35	06 50			07 22
Wigan North Western	65	a			06 21			06 51				07 21	
		d											
Euxton Balshaw Lane		d											
Leyland	82	a											
Preston 8	65,82	a											
Blackpool North	97	a											
Patricroft		d	00 04				06 33						07 33
Eccles		d	00 07				06 36						07 36
Manchester Victoria	⇌	a	00 21				06 49						07 49
Manchester Oxford Road		a				06 35			06 56	07 09			
Manchester Piccadilly 10	⇌	a		05 56		06 44			07 00	07 18			
Manchester Airport	85 ✈	a		06 14					07 22				

Station			NT	NT	NT	NT	AW	NT	TP	AW	NT	NT	NT
							E 🍴	F	◇1 G	◇ A 🍴			
Liverpool Lime Street 10	91	d		06 57	07 01	07 13		07 16				07 31	07 46
Edge Hill	91	d			07 05			07 20				07 35	07 50
Wavertree Technology Park		d			07 07	07 19		07 22				07 37	07 52
Broad Green		d			07 10			07 25				07 40	07 55
Roby		d			07 14			07 29				07 44	07 59
Huyton		d		07 06	07 16			07 31				07 46	08 01
Prescot		d			07 21							07 51	
Eccleston Park		d			07 23							07 53	
Thatto Heath		d			07 26							07 56	
St Helens Central		a		07 15	07 29							07 59	
		d		07 15	07 30							08 00	
Garswood		d			07 37							08 07	
Bryn		d			07 40							08 10	
Whiston		d						07 35					08 05
Rainhill		d						07 38					08 08
Lea Green		d				07 28		07 41					08 11
St Helens Junction		d				07 31		07 44					08 14
Warrington Bank Quay		d					07 39			08 08			
Earlestown 8		d					07 46	07 49		08 16			08 19
Warrington Bank Quay		a											
Newton-le-Willows		d				07 37	07 49	07 52		08 19			08 22
Wigan North Western	65	a		07 30	07 51							08 21	
		d	07 22	07 31					07 56		08 20		
Euxton Balshaw Lane		d		07 41									
Leyland	82	a		07 46									
Preston 8	65,82	a		07 54									
Blackpool North	97	a		08 21									
Patricroft		d						08 03					08 33
Eccles		d						08 06					08 36
Manchester Victoria	⇌	a	08 12					08 19			09 06		08 50
Manchester Oxford Road		a				07 56	08 09		08 22	08 41			
Manchester Piccadilly 10	⇌	a				08 01	08 18		08 26	08 45			
Manchester Airport	85 ✈	a				08 22			08 47				

A From Llandudno
B From Chester
C From Liverpool Lime Street
D To Stalybridge
E From Shrewsbury
F To Huddersfield
G From Lancaster

Table 90R

Saturdays

29 March to 17 May

Liverpool and St Helens - Newton-le-Willows, Wigan, Preston and Manchester

Network Diagram - see first Page of Table 88

			NT	NT	NT	NT	TP ◇1 A		NT	NT B	NT	AW ◇ C	NT D	TP ◇1 E	NT	NT	NT		TP ◇1 F	NT	NT B	NT	NT	AW ◇ C	NT	NT D
Liverpool Lime Street 10	91	d	07 57	08 01	08 13	08 16			08 31	08 44	08 57				09 01	09 13	09 16			09 31	09 46	09 57	10 01		10 13	
Edge Hill	91	d		08 05		08 20			08 35	08 50					09 05		09 20			09 35	09 50		10 05			
Wavertree Technology Park		d		08 07	08 19	08 22			08 37	08 52					09 07	09 19	09 22			09 37	09 52		10 07		10 19	
Broad Green		d		08 10		08 25			08 40	08 55					09 10		09 25			09 40	09 55		10 10			
Roby		d		08 14		08 29			08 44	08 59					09 14		09 29			09 44	09 59		10 14			
Huyton		d	08 06	08 16		08 31			08 46	09 01	09 06				09 16		09 31			09 46	10 01	10 06	10 16			
Prescot		d		08 21					08 51						09 21					09 51			10 21			
Eccleston Park		d		08 23					08 53						09 23					09 53			10 23			
Thatto Heath		d		08 26					08 56						09 26					09 56			10 26			
St Helens Central		a	08 15	08 29					08 59		09 15				09 29					09 59		10 15	10 29			
		d	08 15	08 30					09 00		09 15				09 30					10 00		10 15	10 30			
Garswood		d		08 37					09 07						09 37					10 07			10 37			
Bryn		d		08 40					09 10						09 40					10 10			10 40			
Whiston		d				08 35				09 05							09 35				10 05					
Rainhill		d				08 38				09 08							09 38				10 08					
Lea Green		d				08 41				09 11							09 41				10 11					
St Helens Junction		d			08 29	08 44				09 14						09 29	09 44				10 14				10 29	
Warrington Bank Quay		d										09 19	09 22											10 19		10 22
Earlestown 8		d				08 50				09 19		09 26	09a33				09 50				10 19			10 26		10a33
Warrington Bank Quay		a				09 01											10 01									
Newton-le-Willows		d			08 35					09 22		09 29				09 35					10 22			10 29	10 35	
Wigan North Western	65	a	08 30	08 51					09 21		09 30				09 51					10 21		10 30	10 51			
		d	08 31				08 58				09 31			09 43					09 58			10 31				
Euxton Balshaw Lane		d	08 41								09 41											10 41				
Leyland	82	a	08 46								09 46											10 46				
Preston 8	65,82	a	08 54								09 54			09 57								10 54				
Blackpool North	97	a	09 21								10 21			10 33								11 21				
Patricroft		d								09 33											10 33					
Eccles		d								09 36											10 36					
Manchester Victoria		a								09 47											10 49					
Manchester Oxford Road		a			08 56		09 23					09 48				09 56			10 22					10 48	10 56	
Manchester Piccadilly 10		a			09 00		09 27					09 52				10 00			10 26					10 52	11 00	
Manchester Airport	85	a			09 22		09 47									10 22			10 46						11 22	

			NT		TP ◇1 A	NT	NT B	NT G	AW ◇ C	NT D	TP ◇1 H	NT	NT		NT	TP ◇1 I	NT	NT B	NT G	NT	AW ◇ C	NT	NT D		NT	TP ◇1 A
Liverpool Lime Street 10	91	d	10 16			10 31	10 46	10 57				11 01	11 13		11 16		11 31	11 46	11 57	12 01		12 13			12 16	
Edge Hill	91	d	10 20			10 35	10 50					11 05			11 20		11 35	11 50		12 05					12 20	
Wavertree Technology Park		d	10 22			10 37	10 52					11 07	11 19		11 22		11 37	11 52		12 07		12 19			12 22	
Broad Green		d	10 25			10 40	10 55					11 10			11 25		11 40	11 55		12 10					12 25	
Roby		d	10 29			10 44	10 59					11 14			11 29		11 44	11 59		12 14					12 29	
Huyton		d	10 31			10 46	11 01	11 06				11 16			11 31		11 46	12 01	12 06	12 16					12 31	
Prescot		d				10 51						11 21					11 51			12 21						
Eccleston Park		d				10 53						11 23					11 53			12 23						
Thatto Heath		d				10 56						11 26					11 56			12 26						
St Helens Central		a				10 59		11 15				11 29					11 59		12 15	12 29						
		d				11 00		11 15				11 30					12 00		12 15	12 30						
Garswood		d				11 07						11 37					12 07			12 37						
Bryn		d				11 10						11 40					12 10			12 40						
Whiston		d	10 35				11 05								11 35			12 05							12 35	
Rainhill		d	10 38				11 08								11 38			12 08							12 38	
Lea Green		d	10 41				11 11								11 41			12 11							12 41	
St Helens Junction		d	10 44				11 14						11 29		11 44			12 14				12 29			12 44	
Warrington Bank Quay		d							11 19	11 22											12 19		12 22			
Earlestown 8		d	10 50				11 19		11 26	11a33					11 50			12 19			12 26		12a33		12 50	
Warrington Bank Quay		a	11 01												12 01										13 01	
Newton-le-Willows		d					11 22		11 29				11 35					12 22			12 29	12 35				
Wigan North Western	65	a				11 21		11 30				11 51					12 21		12 30	12 51						
		d			10 58			11 31			11 43					11 58			12 31							12 58
Euxton Balshaw Lane		d						11 41											12 41							
Leyland	82	a						11 46											12 46							
Preston 8	65,82	a						11 54			11 57								12 54							
Blackpool North	97	a						12 21											13 21							
Patricroft		d					11 33											12 33								
Eccles		d					11 36											12 36								
Manchester Victoria		a					11 49											12 49								
Manchester Oxford Road		a			11 23				11 48				11 56			12 23					12 48	12 56				13 23
Manchester Piccadilly 10		a			11 27				11 52				12 00			12 27					12 52	13 00				13 27
Manchester Airport	85	a			11 47								12 22			12 47						13 22				13 47

A From Edinburgh
B To Stalybridge
C From Llandudno
D To Liverpool Lime Street
E From Manchester Airport. Trolley to Preston
F From Glasgow Central
G From Liverpool South Pw Hl
H From Manchester Airport to Barrow-in-Furness
I From Windermere

Table 90R

Saturdays

29 March to 17 May

Liverpool and St Helens - Newton-le-Willows, Wigan, Preston and Manchester

Network Diagram - see first Page of Table 88

Station			NT	NT	NT	AW	NT	NT	NT		TP	NT	NT	NT	NT	AW	NT	NT	NT		NT	NT	NT	AW	NT	TP
				A	B	◇ C		D			◇1 E		A	B		◇ C		D				A	B	◇ F	D	◇1 G
Liverpool Lime Street 10	91	d	12 31	12 46	12 57		13 13		13 16			13 31	13 46	13 57	14 01		14 13		14 16		14 31	14 46	14 57			
Edge Hill	91	d	12 35	12 50					13 20			13 35	13 50		14 05				14 20		14 35	14 50				
Wavertree Technology Park		d	12 37	12 52			13 19		13 22			13 37	13 52		14 07		14 19		14 22		14 37	14 52				
Broad Green		d	12 40	12 55					13 25			13 40	13 55		14 10				14 25		14 40	14 55				
Roby		d	12 44	12 59					13 29			13 44	13 59		14 14				14 29		14 44	14 59				
Huyton		d	12 46	13 01	13 06				13 31			13 46	14 01	14 06	14 16				14 31		14 46	15 01	15 06			
Prescot		d	12 51									13 51			14 21						14 51					
Eccleston Park		d	12 53									13 53			14 23						14 53					
Thatto Heath		d	12 56									13 56			14 26						14 56					
St Helens Central		a	12 59		13 15							13 59		14 15	14 29						14 59		15 15			
		d	13 00		13 15							14 00		14 15	14 30						15 00		15 15			
Garswood		d	13 07									14 07			14 37						15 07					
Bryn		d	13 10									14 10			14 40						15 10					
Whiston		d		13 05					13 35				14 05						14 35			15 05				
Rainhill		d		13 08					13 38				14 08						14 38			15 08				
Lea Green		d		13 11					13 41				14 11						14 41			15 11				
St Helens Junction		d		13 14			13 29		13 44				14 14				14 29		14 44			15 14				
Warrington Bank Quay		d				13 19		13 22								14 19		14 22						15 19	15 22	
Earlestown 8		d		13 19		13 26		13a33	13 50				14 19			14 26		14a33	14 50			15 19		15 26	15a33	
Warrington Bank Quay		a							14 01										15 01							
Newton-le-Willows		d		13 22		13 29	13 35						14 22			14 29	14 35					15 22		15 29		
Wigan North Western	65	a	13 21		13 30							14 21		14 30	14 51						15 21		15 30			
		d			13 31						13 58			14 31									15 31			15 43
Euxton Balshaw Lane		d			13 41									14 41									15 41			
Leyland	82	a			13 46									14 46									15 46			
Preston 8	65,82	a			13 54									14 54									15 54			15 57
Blackpool North	97	a			14 21									15 21									16 21			
Patricroft		d		13 33									14 33									15 33				
Eccles		d		13 36									14 36									15 36				
Manchester Victoria		a		13 49									14 50									15 49				
Manchester Oxford Road		a				13 48	13 56				14 22					14 48	14 56							15 48		
Manchester Piccadilly 10		a				13 52	14 00				14 26					14 57	15 00							15 52		
Manchester Airport	85	a					14 22				14 45						15 22									

Station			NT	NT	NT		TP	NT	NT	NT	NT	AW	NT	NT	NT		NT	NT	NT	NT	AW	NT	NT	NT	NT	
							◇1 E		A	B		◇ C		D				A	B		◇ C					
Liverpool Lime Street 10	91	d	15 01	15 13	15 16			15 31	15 46	15 57	16 01		16 13		16 16		16 31	16 46	16 57	17 01		17 06	17 10	17 19	17 27	
Edge Hill	91	d	15 05		15 20			15 35	15 50		16 05				16 20		16 35	16 50		17 05			17 14		17 31	
Wavertree Technology Park		d	15 07	15 19	15 22			15 37	15 52		16 07		16 19		16 22		16 37	16 52		17 07		17 12	17 16		17 33	
Broad Green		d	15 10		15 25			15 40	15 55		16 10				16 25		16 40	16 55		17 10			17 19		17 36	
Roby		d	15 14		15 29			15 44	15 59		16 14				16 29		16 44	16 59		17 14			17 23		17 40	
Huyton		d	15 16		15 31			15 46	16 01	16 06	16 16				16 31		16 46	17 01	17 06	17 16		17 20	17 25	17 29	17 42	
Prescot		d	15 21					15 51			16 21						16 51			17 21				17 34		
Eccleston Park		d	15 23					15 53			16 23						16 53			17 23				17 36		
Thatto Heath		d	15 26					15 56			16 26						16 56			17 26				17 39		
St Helens Central		a	15 29					15 59		16 15	16 29						16 59		17 15	17 29				17 42	17 51	
		d	15 30					16 00		16 15	16 30						17 00		17 15	17 30				17 43	17 51	
Garswood		d	15 37					16 07			16 37						17 07			17 37				17 50		
Bryn		d	15 40					16 10			16 40						17 10			17 40				17 53		
Whiston		d			15 35				16 05						16 35			17 05					17 29			
Rainhill		d			15 38				16 08						16 38			17 08					17 32			
Lea Green		d			15 41				16 11						16 41			17 11				17 26	17 35			
St Helens Junction		d		15 29	15 44				16 14				16 29		16 44			17 14				17 29	17 39			
Warrington Bank Quay		d										16 19		16 22							17 19					
Earlestown 8		d			15 50				16 19			16 26		16a33	16 49			17 19			17 26		17 44			
Warrington Bank Quay		a			16 01																					
Newton-le-Willows		d		15 35					16 22			16 29	16 35		16 52			17 22			17 29	17 35	17 47			
Wigan North Western	65	a	15 51					16 21		16 30	16 51						17 21		17 30	17 51				18 05	18 04	
		d					15 58			16 31									17 31						18 05	
Euxton Balshaw Lane		d								16 41									17 41						18 16	
Leyland	82	a								16 46									17 46						18 21	
Preston 8	65,82	a								16 54									17 54						18 31	
Blackpool North	97	a								17 21									18 24							
Patricroft		d							16 33						17 03			17 33					17 58			
Eccles		d							16 36						17 06			17 36					18 01			
Manchester Victoria		a							16 49						17 19			17 47					18 14			
Manchester Oxford Road		a		15 56			16 23					16 48	16 56								17 48	17 56				
Manchester Piccadilly 10		a		16 00			16 27					16 57	17 00								17 57	18 00				
Manchester Airport	85	a		16 22			16 47						17 22									18 22				

A To Stalybridge
B From Liverpool South Pw Hl
C From Llandudno
D To Liverpool Lime Street
E From Glasgow Central
F From Bangor (Gwynedd)
G From Manchester Airport to Lancaster

Table 90R

Saturdays

29 March to 17 May

Liverpool and St Helens - Newton-le-Willows, Wigan, Preston and Manchester

Network Diagram - see first Page of Table 88

Station		NT	NT	NT	NT	AW ◇ A 🚲	NT	NT	TP ◇1 B 🚲	NT		NT	NT
Liverpool Lime Street 10 91	d	17 35	17 42	17 46	18 01		18 13	18 16		18 31		18 46	19 01
Edge Hill 91	d	17 39		17 50	18 05			18 20		18 35		18 50	19 05
Wavertree Technology Park	d	17 41	17 47	17 52	18 07		18 19	18 22		18 37		18 52	19 07
Broad Green	d	17 44	17 50	17 55	18 10			18 25		18 40		18 55	19 10
Roby	d	17 48		17 59	18 14			18 29		18 44		18 59	19 14
Huyton	d	17 50	17 55	18 01	18 16			18 31		18 46		19 01	19 16
Prescot	d		18 00		18 21					18 51			19 21
Eccleston Park	d		18 03		18 23					18 53			19 23
Thatto Heath	d		18 05		18 26					18 56			19 26
St Helens Central	a		18 09		18 29					18 59			19 29
	d		18 09		18 30					19 00			19 30
Garswood	d		18 17		18 37					19 07			19 37
Bryn	d		18 20		18 40					19 10			19 40
Whiston	d	17 54		18 05				18 35				19 05	
Rainhill	d	17 57		18 08				18 38				19 08	
Lea Green	d	18 00		18 11				18 41				19 11	
St Helens Junction	d	18 03		18 14			18 29	18 44				19 14	
Warrington Bank Quay	d					18 19							
Earlestown 8	d	18 08		18 19		18 26		18 50				19 19	
Warrington Bank Quay	a							19 01					
Newton-le-Willows	d	18 11		18 22		18 29	18 35					19 22	
Wigan North Western 65	a		18 27		18 49					19 21			19 51
	d		18 30		18 49				18 59				
Euxton Balshaw Lane	d		18 40		19 01								
Leyland 82	a		18 45		19 06								
Preston 8 65,82	a		18 53		19 15								
Blackpool North 97	a		19 22										
Patricroft	d	18 22										19 33	
Eccles	d	18 25		18 34								19 36	
Manchester Victoria 🚆	a	18 37		18 47								19 49	
Manchester Oxford Road	a					18 48	18 56		19 24				
Manchester Piccadilly 10 🚆	a					18 57	19 00		19 29				
Manchester Airport 85 ✈	a						19 23		19 47				

Station		AW ◇ A 🚲	NT C	NT	NT	TP ◇1 D 🚲	NT	TP ◇1 E		AW ◇ A	NT	NT	NT
Liverpool Lime Street 10 91	d			19 12	19 23		19 42				20 09	20 12	20 25
Edge Hill 91	d			19 16			19 46					20 16	
Wavertree Technology Park	d			19 18			19 48				20 15	20 18	
Broad Green	d			19 21			19 51					20 21	
Roby	d			19 25			19 55					20 25	
Huyton	d			19 27	19 32		19 57					20 27	20 34
Prescot	d						20 02						
Eccleston Park	d						20 04						
Thatto Heath	d						20 07						
St Helens Central	a				19 40		20 10						20 42
	d				19 41		20 11						20 43
Garswood	d						20 18						
Bryn	d						20 21						
Whiston	d			19 31								20 31	
Rainhill	d			19 34								20 34	
Lea Green	d			19 37								20 37	
St Helens Junction	d			19 40							20 25	20 40	
Warrington Bank Quay	d	19 19	19 22							20 19			
Earlestown 8	d	19 26	19a33	19 45						20 26		20 45	
Warrington Bank Quay	a												
Newton-le-Willows	d	19 29		19 48						20 29	20 35	20 48	
Wigan North Western 65	a				19 54		20 32						20 57
	d				19 55	19 59		20 43					20 57
Euxton Balshaw Lane	d				20 05								21 08
Leyland 82	a				20 10								21 16
Preston 8 65,82	a				20 18			20 57					21 22
Blackpool North 97	a				20 44								21 53
Patricroft	d			19 59								20 59	
Eccles	d			20 02								21 02	
Manchester Victoria 🚆	a			20 15								21 15	
Manchester Oxford Road	a	19 48				20 23				20 48	20 56		
Manchester Piccadilly 10 🚆	a	19 52				20 27				20 57	21 00		
Manchester Airport 85 ✈	a	20 13				20 47					21 19		

Station		NT	AW ◇ A	NT	NT	AW F		NT	NT	NT	AW F
Liverpool Lime Street 10 91	d	20 42		21 12	21 42			22 12	23 02	23 16	
Edge Hill 91	d	20 46		21 16	21 46			22 16	23 06	23 20	
Wavertree Technology Park	d	20 48		21 18	21 48			22 18	23 08	23 22	
Broad Green	d	20 51		21 21	21 51			22 21	23 11	23 26	
Roby	d	20 55		21 25	21 55			22 25	23 15	23 30	
Huyton	d	20 57		21 27	21 57			22 27	23 17	23 32	
Prescot	d	21 02			22 02				23 22		
Eccleston Park	d	21 04			22 04				23 24		
Thatto Heath	d	21 07			22 07				23 27		
St Helens Central	a	21 10			22 10				23 30		
	d	21 11			22 11				23 31		
Garswood	d	21 18			22 18				23 38		
Bryn	d	21 21			22 21				23 41		
Whiston	d			21 31				22 31		23 36	
Rainhill	d			21 34				22 34		23 39	
Lea Green	d			21 37				22 37		23 42	
St Helens Junction	d			21 40				22 40		23 45	
Warrington Bank Quay	d		21 19			22 19					23 50
Earlestown 8	d		21 26	21 45		22 27		22 45		23 50	23 58
Warrington Bank Quay	a										
Newton-le-Willows	d		21 29	21 48		22 30		22 48		23 53	00 02
Wigan North Western 65	a	21 32			22 28				23 48		
	d				22 28				23 48		
Euxton Balshaw Lane	d				22 39				23 59		
Leyland 82	a				22 44				00 04		
Preston 8 65,82	a				22 55				00 13		
Blackpool North 97	a				23 22						
Patricroft	d			21 59				22 59		00 04	
Eccles	d			22 02				23 02		00 07	
Manchester Victoria 🚆	a			22 15				23 15		00 21	
Manchester Oxford Road	a		21 48			22 50					
Manchester Piccadilly 10 🚆	a		21 57			22 58					00 26
Manchester Airport 85 ✈	a										

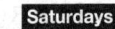

A From Llandudno
B From Edinburgh
C To Liverpool Lime Street
D From Glasgow Central
E From Manchester Airport
F From Chester

Table 90R

Sundays

8 December to 29 December

Liverpool and St Helens - Newton-le-Willows, Wigan, Preston and Manchester

Network Diagram - see first Page of Table 88

Station			AW	NT	NT	NT	AW	NT	NT	AW	NT		NT	AW	NT	NT	AW	NT	TP	NT	AW		NT	TP	NT	AW
			A	B			C			◇ C				C 🚲			C 🚲		◇[1] D 🚲		C 🚲			◇[1] E		C 🚲
Liverpool Lime Street [10]	91	d			08 05	08 31		09 01	09 31		10 01		10 31		11 01	11 31		12 01		12 31			13 01		13 31	
Edge Hill	91	d																								
Wavertree Technology Park		d			08 11	08 37		09 07	09 37		10 07		10 37		11 07	11 37		12 07		12 37			13 07		13 37	
Broad Green		d			08 14	08 40		09 10	09 40		10 10		10 40		11 10	11 40		12 10		12 40			13 10		13 40	
Roby		d			08 17	08 43		09 13	09 43		10 13		10 43		11 13	11 43		12 13		12 43			13 13		13 43	
Huyton		d			08 20	08 46		09 16	09 46		10 16		10 46		11 16	11 46		12 16		12 46			13 16		13 46	
Prescot		d				08 50			09 50				10 50			11 50				12 50					13 50	
Eccleston Park		d																								
Thatto Heath		d				08 54			09 54				10 54			11 54				12 54					13 54	
St Helens Central		a				08 57			09 57				10 57			11 57				12 57					13 57	
		d				08 58			09 58				10 58			11 58				12 58					13 58	
Garswood		d				09 05			10 05				11 05			12 05				13 05					14 05	
Bryn		d																								
Whiston		d			08 23			09 19			10 19				11 19			12 19					13 19			
Rainhill		d			08 26			09 22			10 22				11 22			12 22					13 22			
Lea Green		d			08 30			09 26			10 26				11 26			12 26					13 26			
St Helens Junction		d			08 33			09 29			10 29				11 29			12 29					13 29			
Warrington Bank Quay		d					09 10			10 12				11 03			12 03				13 03					14 03
Earlestown [8]		d			08 37		09 16	09 33		10 19	10 33			11 10	11 33		12 10	12 33			13 10		13 33			14 10
Warrington Bank Quay		a																								
Newton-le-Willows		d	00 02		08 40		09 19	09 36		10 22	10 36			11 13	11 36		12 13	12 36			13 13		13 36			14 13
Wigan North Western	65	a				09 13			10 13				11 13			12 13				13 13					14 13	
		d				09 14			10 14				11 14			12 14			12 58	13 14				13 58	14 14	
Euxton Balshaw Lane		d				09 24			10 26				11 24			12 24				13 24					14 24	
Leyland	82	a				09 29			10 31				11 29			12 29				13 29					14 29	
Preston [8]	65,82	a				09 37			10 39				11 37			12 37				13 37					14 37	
Blackpool North	97	a				10 07			11 09				12 07			13 07				14 07					15 05	
Patricroft		d		00 04																						
Eccles		d		00 07	08 52			09 48			10 48				11 48			12 48					13 48			
Manchester Victoria		a		00 21																						
Manchester Oxford Road		a			09 02		09 39	09 59		10 41	10 59			11 33	11 59		12 32	12 59	13 23		13 32		13 57	14 23		14 32
Manchester Piccadilly [10]		a	00 26		09 06		09 48	10 03		10 50	11 03			11 41	12 02		12 41	13 02	13 27		13 41		14 01	14 27		14 41
Manchester Airport	85	a			09 22			10 24			11 24				12 20			13 18	13 47				14 21	14 47		

Station			NT	TP	NT	AW	NT		TP	TP	NT	AW	NT	TP	NT	AW	NT		TP	NT	AW	NT	TP	NT	AW	NT
				◇[1] D 🚲		C 🚲			◇[1] F	◇[1] E		C		◇[1] D 🚲		◇ G 🚲			◇[1] H 🚲		◇ C		◇[1] D 🚲		C	
Liverpool Lime Street [10]	91	d	14 01		14 31		15 01				15 31		16 01		16 31		17 01			17 31		18 01		18 31		19 01
Edge Hill	91	d																								
Wavertree Technology Park		d	14 07		14 37		15 07				15 37		16 07		16 37		17 07			17 37		18 07		18 37		19 07
Broad Green		d	14 10		14 40		15 10				15 40		16 10		16 40		17 10			17 40		18 10		18 40		19 10
Roby		d	14 13		14 43		15 13				15 43		16 13		16 43		17 13			17 43		18 13		18 43		19 13
Huyton		d	14 16		14 46		15 16				15 46		16 16		16 46		17 16			17 46		18 16		18 46		19 16
Prescot		d			14 50						15 50				16 50					17 50				18 50		
Eccleston Park		d																								
Thatto Heath		d			14 54						15 54				16 54					17 54				18 54		
St Helens Central		a			14 57						15 57				16 57					17 57				18 57		
		d			14 58						15 58				16 58					17 58				18 58		
Garswood		d			15 05						16 05				17 05					18 05				19 05		
Bryn		d																								
Whiston		d	14 19				15 19						16 19				17 19					18 19				19 19
Rainhill		d	14 22				15 22						16 22				17 22					18 22				19 22
Lea Green		d	14 26				15 26						16 26				17 26					18 26				19 26
St Helens Junction		d	14 29				15 29						16 29				17 29					18 29				19 29
Warrington Bank Quay		d				15 03						16 03				17 03					18 03				19 03	
Earlestown [8]		d	14 33			15 10	15 33					16 10	16 33			17 10	17 33				18 10	18 33			19 10	19 33
Warrington Bank Quay		a																								
Newton-le-Willows		d	14 36			15 13	15 36					16 13	16 36			17 13	17 36				18 13	18 36			19 13	19 36
Wigan North Western	65	a			15 13						16 13				17 13					18 13				19 13		
		d		14 58	15 14				15 43	15 58	16 14			16 58	17 14				17 58	18 14			18 58	19 14		
Euxton Balshaw Lane		d			15 24						16 24				17 24					18 24				19 24		
Leyland	82	a			15 29						16 29				17 29					18 29				19 29		
Preston [8]	65,82	a			15 37				15 57		16 37				17 37					18 37				19 37		
Blackpool North	97	a			16 07						17 07				18 07					19 07				20 07		
Patricroft		d																								
Eccles		d	14 48				15 48						16 48				17 48					18 48				19 48
Manchester Victoria		a																								
Manchester Oxford Road		a	14 59	15 23		15 32	15 59			16 23		16 32	16 59	17 23		17 32	17 59		18 23		18 32	18 59	19 23		19 32	19 59
Manchester Piccadilly [10]		a	15 02	15 27		15 41	16 02			16 27		16 41	17 02	17 27		17 41	18 02		18 27		18 41	19 02	19 27		19 41	20 02
Manchester Airport	85	a	15 20	15 47			16 21			16 47			17 21	17 47			18 21		18 47			19 21	19 47			20 23

A not 8 December. From Chester
B not 8 December. From Liverpool Lime Street
C From Chester
D From Edinburgh
E From Barrow-in-Furness
F From Manchester Airport to Barrow-in-Furness
G From Holyhead
H From Glasgow Central

Table 90R

Sundays

8 December to 29 December

Liverpool and St Helens - Newton-le-Willows, Wigan, Preston and Manchester

Network Diagram - see first Page of Table 88

	TP		NT	AW	NT	NT	AW	NT	NT	AW	NT		TP	AW	NT	NT	NT
	◇1												◇1				
	A			B			B			B			C	B			
	🚲												🚲			🚌	
Liverpool Lime Street 10 . 91 d			19 31		20 01	20 31		21 01	21 31		22 13					22 31	23 01
Edge Hill 91 d																	
Wavertree Technology Park d			19 37		20 07	20 37		21 07	21 37							22 46	
Broad Green d			19 40		20 10	20 40		21 10	21 40							22 56	
Roby d			19 43		20 13	20 43		21 13	21 43							23 03	
Huyton d			19 46		20 16	20 46		21 16	21 46							23 07	
Prescot d			19 50			20 50			21 50							23 17	
Eccleston Park d																	
Thatto Heath d			19 54			20 54			21 54							23 27	
St Helens Central a			19 57			20 57			21 57							23 37	
d			19 58			20 58			21 58							23 37	
Garswood d			20 05			21 05			22 05							23 57	
Bryn d																	
Whiston d					20 19			21 19									
Rainhill d					20 22			21 22									
Lea Green d					20 26			21 26									
St Helens Junction d					20 29			21 29									
Warrington Bank Quay d				20 03			21 03			22 04				22 36			
Earlestown 8 d				20 10	20 33		21 10	21 33		22 12				22 47			
Warrington Bank Quay a																	
Newton-le-Willows d				20 13	20 36		21 13	21 36		22 15				22 50			
Wigan North Western 65 a			20 13			21 13			22 13							00s17	
d	19 59		20 14			21 14			22 14				22 39		23 14		
Euxton Balshaw Lane d			20 24			21 24			22 24								
Leyland 82 a			20 29			21 29			22 29						23 28	00s46	
Preston 8 65,82 a			20 37			21 37			22 37						23 36	01s06	
Blackpool North 97 a			21 07			22 07			23 07						00 05	02 01	
Patricroft d																	
Eccles d					20 48			21 48									
Manchester Victoria 🚊 a																	
Manchester Oxford Road a	20 23			20 32	20 59		21 32	21 59		22 34	22 58		23 04	23 09			23 47
Manchester Piccadilly 10 🚊 a	20 27			20 41	21 02		21 41	22 02		22 38	23 01		23 08	23 18			23 50
Manchester Airport 85 ✈ a	20 45				21 20			22 21			23 17		23 24				00 07

Sundays

5 January to 9 February

	AW	NT	NT	NT	NT	AW	NT	NT	AW		NT	AW	NT	NT	AW	NT	NT	AW	NT		NT	AW	NT	TP
									◇															◇1
	B	D	E			B			B			B			B			B				B		F
			🚌		🚌			🚌			🚌	🚲		🚌	🚲		🚌	🚲			🚌	🚲		🚲
Liverpool Lime Street 10 . 91 d				08 12	08 14		09 13	09 14			10 14		11 13	11 14		12 13	12 14		13 13		13 14		14 13	
Edge Hill 91 d																								
Wavertree Technology Park d																								
Broad Green d																								
Roby d																								
Huyton d																								
Prescot d																								
Eccleston Park d																								
Thatto Heath d																								
St Helens Central a																								
d																								
Garswood d																								
Bryn d																								
Whiston d																								
Rainhill d																								
Lea Green d																								
St Helens Junction d																								
Warrington Bank Quay d						09 10			10 12			11 03			12 03			13 03				14 03		
Earlestown 8 d						09 16			10 19			11 10			12 10			13 10				14 10		
Warrington Bank Quay a																								
Newton-le-Willows d	00 02					09 19			10 22			11 13			12 13			13 13				14 13		
Wigan North Western 65 a					09 14			10 14			11 14			12 14			13 14				14 14			
d					09 14			10 14			11 14			12 14			13 14				14 14			15 00
Euxton Balshaw Lane d			00 23		09 39			10 39			11 39			12 39			13 39				14 39			
Leyland 82 a			00 35		09 51			10 51			11 51			12 51			13 51				14 51			
Preston 8 65,82 a			00 55		10 11			11 11			12 11			13 11			14 11				15 11			
Blackpool North 97 a																								
Patricroft d		00 04																						
Eccles d		00 07																						
Manchester Victoria 🚊 a		00 21																						
Manchester Oxford Road a				08 57		09 39	09 56		10 41			11 33	11 57		12 32	12 57		13 32	13 57			14 32	14 57	15 24
Manchester Piccadilly 10 🚊 a	00 26			09 05		09 48	10 00		10 50			11 41	12 01		12 41	13 01		13 41	14 01			14 41	15 01	15 28
Manchester Airport 85 ✈ a				09 21			10 15						12 15			13 18			14 15				15 15	15 47

A From Glasgow Central
B From Chester
C From Edinburgh
D From Liverpool Lime Street
E From Wigan North Western
F From Lancaster

Table 90R

Sundays

5 January to 9 February

Liverpool and St Helens - Newton-le-Willows, Wigan, Preston and Manchester

Network Diagram - see first Page of Table 88

Station		AW	NT	NT	TP	TP	AW	NT	NT	TP	AW	NT	NT	TP	AW	NT	NT	TP	AW	NT	NT	TP	AW
					◇1	◇1				◇1	◇			◇1	◇			◇1				◇1	
		A			B	C	A			D	E			F	A			D	A			F	A
		⊥								⊥	⊥			⊥				⊥				⊥	
Liverpool Lime Street [10] 91	d		15 13					16 13				17 13				18 13				19 13			
Edge Hill 91	d																						
Wavertree Technology Park	d																						
Broad Green	d																						
Roby	d																						
Huyton	d																						
Prescot	d																						
Eccleston Park	d																						
Thatto Heath	d																						
St Helens Central	a																						
	d																						
Garswood	d																						
Bryn	d																						
Whiston	d																						
Rainhill	d																						
Lea Green	d																						
St Helens Junction	d																						
Warrington Bank Quay	d	15 03					16 03				17 03				18 03				19 03				20 03
Earlestown [8]	d	15 10					16 10				17 10				18 10				19 10				20 10
Warrington Bank Quay	a																						
Newton-le-Willows	d	15 13					16 13				17 13				18 13				19 13				20 13
Wigan North Western 65	a																						
	d			15 14	15 43	15 58			16 14	16 58			17 14	17 58			18 14	18 58			19 14	19 59	
Euxton Balshaw Lane	d			15 24					16 24				17 24				18 24				19 24		
Leyland 82	a			15 29					16 29				17 29				18 29				19 29		
Preston [8] 65,82	a			15 37	15 57				16 37				17 37				18 37				19 37		
Blackpool North 97	a			16 07					17 07				18 07				19 07				20 07		
Patricroft	d																						
Eccles	d																						
Manchester Victoria 🚊	a																						
Manchester Oxford Road	a	15 32	15 57			16 23	16 32	16 57		17 23	17 32	17 57		18 23	18 32	18 57		19 23	19 32	19 57		20 23	20 32
Manchester Piccadilly [10] 🚊	a	15 41	16 01			16 27	16 41	17 01		17 27	17 41	18 01		18 27	18 41	19 01		19 27	19 41	20 01		20 27	20 41
Manchester Airport 85 ✈	a		16 15			16 47		17 15		17 47		18 15		18 47		19 16		19 47		20 23		20 45	

Station		NT	NT	AW	NT	NT	AW	TP	NT	TP	TP	NT	NT	NT	AW	TP	TP	NT	NT
								◇1		◇1	◇1					◇1	◇1		
				A			A	G		H	D				A	H	G		
											⊥	🚌						🚌	
Liverpool Lime Street [10] 91	d	20 13			21 13							21 18		22 13				22 31	23 01
Edge Hill 91	d																		
Wavertree Technology Park	d											21 33						22 46	
Broad Green	d											21 43						22 56	
Roby	d											21 50						23 03	
Huyton	d											21 54						23 07	
Prescot	d											22 04						23 17	
Eccleston Park	d																		
Thatto Heath	d											22 14						23 27	
St Helens Central	a											22 24						23 37	
	d											22 24						23 37	
Garswood	d											22 44						23 57	
Bryn	d																		
Whiston	d																		
Rainhill	d																		
Lea Green	d																		
St Helens Junction	d																		
Warrington Bank Quay	d			21 03			22 04								22 36				
Earlestown [8]	d			21 10			22 12								22 47				
Warrington Bank Quay	a																		
Newton-le-Willows	d			21 13			22 15								22 50				
Wigan North Western 65	a											23 04						00s17	
	d		20 14			21 14		22 14	22 14	22 27	22 46		23 14			23 27	23 48		
Euxton Balshaw Lane	d		20 24			21 24			22 24										
Leyland 82	a		20 29			21 29			22 29				23 28			23 40		00s46	
Preston [8] 65,82	a		20 37			21 37			22 37	22 44			23 36			23 45		01s06	
Blackpool North 97	a		21 07			22 07			23 07	23 11			00 05			00 15		02 01	
Patricroft	d																		
Eccles	d																		
Manchester Victoria 🚊	a																		
Manchester Oxford Road	a	20 57		21 32	21 57		22 34	22 53			23 19			22 58	23 09				23 47
Manchester Piccadilly [10] 🚊	a	21 01		21 41	22 01		22 38	22 57			23 24			23 01	23 18		00 17		23 50
Manchester Airport 85 ✈	a	21 15			22 15			23 16			23 40			23 17			00 34		00 07

A From Chester
B From Manchester Airport to Barrow-in-Furness
C From Barrow-in-Furness
D From Edinburgh
E From Holyhead
F From Glasgow Central
G From Blackpool North
H From Manchester Airport

Table 90R

Sundays

16 February to 11 May

Liverpool and St Helens - Newton-le-Willows, Wigan, Preston and Manchester

Network Diagram - see first Page of Table 88

Station		AW A	NT B	AW C	NT	AW D	NT	NT	NT	AW ◇ D		NT E	AW D	NT E	NT F	NT	TP ◇1 G	AW D	NT	NT		TP ◇1 H	AW D	NT	NT
Liverpool Lime Street 10 91	d				08 12			09 13				10 13				11 13			12 13					13 13	
Edge Hill 91	d																								
Wavertree Technology Park	d																								
Broad Green	d																								
Roby	d																								
Huyton	d																								
Prescot	d																								
Eccleston Park	d																								
Thatto Heath	d																								
St Helens Central	a																								
	d																								
Garswood	d																								
Bryn	d																								
Whiston	d																								
Rainhill	d																								
Lea Green	d																								
St Helens Junction	d																								
Warrington Bank Quay	d			00 22		09 10				10 12			11 03					12 03					13 03		
Earlestown 8	d			00 47		09 16				10 19			11 10					12 10					13 10		
Warrington Bank Quay	a																								
Newton-le-Willows	d	00 02		00 57		09 19				10 22			11 13					12 13					13 13		
Wigan North Western 65	a																								
	d						09 11		10 11					11 11	11 11		12 00			12 14		12 58			13 14
Euxton Balshaw Lane	d						09 21		10 21					11 21	11 21					12 24					13 24
Leyland 82	a						09 26		10 26					11 26	11 26					12 29					13 29
Preston 8 65,82	a						09 36		10 32					11 33	11 33					12 37					13 37
Blackpool North 97	a						10 07		11 07					12 00	12 07					13 07					14 07
Patricroft	d		00 04																						
Eccles	d		00 07																						
Manchester Victoria	a		00 21																						
Manchester Oxford Road	a				08 57	09 39		09 56		10 41		10 57	11 33			11 57	12 25	12 32	12 57			13 23	13 32	13 57	
Manchester Piccadilly 10	a	00 26		01 32	09 05	09 48		10 00		10 50		11 01	11 41			12 01	12 29	12 41	13 01			13 27	13 41	14 01	
Manchester Airport 85	a				09 21			10 15				11 17				12 15	12 46		13 18			13 47		14 15	

Station		TP ◇1 I	AW D	NT	NT	TP ◇1 H		AW D	NT	NT	TP ◇1 J	TP ◇1 I	AW D	NT	NT	TP ◇1 H		AW ◇ K	NT	NT	TP ◇1 L	AW ◇ D	NT	NT	TP ◇1 H
Liverpool Lime Street 10 91	d			14 13					15 13					16 13					17 13				18 13		
Edge Hill 91	d																								
Wavertree Technology Park	d																								
Broad Green	d																								
Roby	d																								
Huyton	d																								
Prescot	d																								
Eccleston Park	d																								
Thatto Heath	d																								
St Helens Central	a																								
	d																								
Garswood	d																								
Bryn	d																								
Whiston	d																								
Rainhill	d																								
Lea Green	d																								
St Helens Junction	d																								
Warrington Bank Quay	d		14 03					15 03					16 03					17 03				18 03			
Earlestown 8	d		14 10					15 10					16 10					17 10				18 10			
Warrington Bank Quay	a																								
Newton-le-Willows	d		14 13					15 13					16 13					17 13				18 13			
Wigan North Western 65	a																								
	d	13 58			14 14	14 58				15 14	15 43	15 58			16 14	16 58				17 14	17 58			18 14	18 58
Euxton Balshaw Lane	d				14 24					15 24					16 24					17 24				18 24	
Leyland 82	a				14 29					15 29					16 29					17 29				18 29	
Preston 8 65,82	a				14 37					15 37	15 57				16 37					17 37				18 37	
Blackpool North 97	a				15 07					16 07					17 07					18 07				19 07	
Patricroft	d																								
Eccles	d																								
Manchester Victoria	a																								
Manchester Oxford Road	a	14 23	14 32	14 57		15 23		15 32	15 57			16 23	16 32	16 57		17 23		17 32	17 57		18 23	18 32	18 57		19 23
Manchester Piccadilly 10	a	14 27	14 41	15 01		15 27		15 41	16 01			16 27	16 41	17 01		17 27		17 41	18 01		18 27	18 41	19 01		19 27
Manchester Airport 85	a	14 47		15 15		15 47			16 15			16 47		17 15		17 47			18 15		18 47		19 16		19 47

A from 30 March. From Chester
B From Liverpool Lime Street
C until 23 March. From Chester
D From Chester
E until 23 March
F from 30 March
G until 23 March. From Barrow-in-Furness
H From Edinburgh
I From Barrow-in-Furness
J From Manchester Airport to Barrow-in-Furness
K From Holyhead
L From Glasgow Central

Table 90R

Sundays

16 February to 11 May

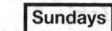

Liverpool and St Helens - Newton-le-Willows, Wigan, Preston and Manchester

Network Diagram - see first Page of Table 88

		AW		NT	NT	TP	AW	NT	NT	AW	NT	NT		AW	NT	TP	NT	NT	NT	NT	AW	NT		
						◇1										◇1								
		A				B	A			A				A		C					A			
																	bus			bus				
						bicycle										bicycle								
Liverpool Lime Street 10 91	d			19 13				20 13			21 13						21 18		22 13	22 31		23 01		
Edge Hill 91	d																							
Wavertree Technology Park	d																21 33			22 46				
Broad Green	d																21 43			22 56				
Roby	d																21 50			23 03				
Huyton	d																21 54			23 07				
Prescot	d																22 04			23 17				
Eccleston Park	d																							
Thatto Heath	d																22 14			23 27				
St Helens Central	a																22 24			23 37				
	d																22 24			23 37				
Garswood	d																22 44			23 57				
Bryn	d																							
Whiston	d																							
Rainhill	d																							
Lea Green	d																							
St Helens Junction	d																							
Warrington Bank Quay	d	19 03					20 03			21 03				22 04							22 36			
Earlestown 8	d	19 10					20 10			21 10				22 12							22 47			
Warrington Bank Quay	a																							
Newton-le-Willows	d	19 13					20 13			21 13				22 15							22 50			
Wigan North Western 65	a																23 04			00s17				
	d				19 14	19 59			20 14			21 14			22 14	22 39		23 14						
Euxton Balshaw Lane	d				19 24				20 24			21 24			22 24									
Leyland 82	a				19 29				20 29			21 29			22 29			23 28		00s46				
Preston 8 65,82	a				19 37				20 37			21 37			22 37			23 36		01s06				
Blackpool North 97	a				20 07				21 07			22 07			23 07			00 05		02 01				
Patricroft	d																							
Eccles	d																							
Manchester Victoria	a																							
Manchester Oxford Road	a	19 32		19 57		20 23	20 32	20 57		21 32	21 57			22 34		23 04			22 58		23 09	23 47		
Manchester Piccadilly 10	a	19 41		20 01		20 27	20 41	21 01		21 41	22 01			22 38		23 08			23 01		23 18	23 50		
Manchester Airport 85 ✈	a			20 15		20 45		21 15			22 15					23 24			23 17			00 07		

A From Chester

B From Glasgow Central

C From Edinburgh

Table 91

Mondays to Fridays

9 December to 16 May

Crewe and Runcorn - Liverpool

Network Diagram - see first Page of Table 88

Miles	Station	VT MO ◇1 A ☕	NT MX B	LM 1	NT C	LM 1	NT C	LM 1	NT B	LM 1	VT ◇1 ⊠	NT C	LM 1 D	EM ◇ E	LM 1	NT B	TP ◇1 F 🛒	LM 1 D	VT ◇1 ⊠	NT B	EM ◇ E	LM 1 G
—	London Euston ⊖65 d										05 27								07 07			
—	Birmingham New Street 12 65 d									06 01			06 36		07 01			07 36				08 01
0	**Crewe 10** 65 d			05 40		06 02		06 32		06 58	07 25		07 34		07 58			08 32	08 43			08 58
7½	Winsford d					06 10		06 41		07 06			07 43		08 05							09 07
11¾	Hartford d					06 15		06 46		07 11			07 48		08 10							09 12
14½	Acton Bridge d					06 19		06 51		07 15			07 52		08 14							
22½	**Runcorn** a			05 58		06 27		06 59		07 23	07 42		08 00		08 22			08 50	09 02			09 21
—	d	00 07		06 02		06 28		06 59		07 24	07 42		08 01		08 23			08 50	09 02			09 22
30	**Liverpool South Parkway 7** ✈ a			06 10		06 36		07 08		07 32			08 09		08 31			08 59				09 30
—	d		00 27	06 10	06 27	06 37	07 01	07 08	07 22	07 33		07 59	08 10	08 18	08 31	08 37	08 47	08 59		09 06	09 15	09 31
31	West Allerton d				06 31		07 05		07 25			08 03				08 40				09 09		
31¾	Mossley Hill d				06 33		07 07		07 28			08 06				08 43				09 12		
33¾	Edge Hill 90 d				06 39		07 13		07 34			08 11				08 48						
35½	**Liverpool Lime Street 10** 90 a	00 30	00 41	06 22	06 45	06 49	07 18	07 22	07 40	07 44	08 01	08 18	08 21	08 31	08 44	08 55	08 58	09 10	09 23	09 24	09 31	09 42

Station	NT B	TP ◇1 H 🛒	LM 1	VT ◇1 ⊠	NT B	EM ◇ E	LM 1	NT I	NT B	TP ◇1 J 🛒	LM 1	VT ◇1 ⊠	NT B	EM ◇ K	LM 1	NT I	NT B	TP ◇1 J 🛒	LM 1	VT ◇1 ⊠	NT B	EM ◇ K
London Euston ⊖65 d				08 07								09 07								10 07		
Birmingham New Street 12 65 d			08 36				09 01				09 36				10 01				10 36			
Crewe 10 65 d			09 32				09 58				10 32	10 43			10 57				11 32	11 43		
Winsford d							10 06								11 07							
Hartford d							10 11								11 12							
Acton Bridge d							10 16															
Runcorn a			09 50	10 00			10 24				10 50	11 00			11 21				11 50	12 00		
d			09 50	10 00			10 24				10 50	11 00			11 22				11 50	12 00		
Liverpool South Parkway 7 ✈ a			09 59				10 33				10 59				11 30				11 59			
d	09 36	09 47	09 59		10 06	10 15	10 33	10 36	10 36	10 47	10 59		11 06	11 15	11 31	11 36	11 36	11 47	11 59		12 06	12 15
West Allerton d	09 39				10 09				10 39				11 10				11 39				12 10	
Mossley Hill d	09 41				10 12				10 41				11 12				11 41				12 12	
Edge Hill 90 d	09 47								10 47								11 47					
Liverpool Lime Street 10 90 a	09 53	09 58	10 10	10 21	10 24	10 31	10 44	10 49	10 53	10 58	11 10	11 21	11 24	11 31	11 42	11 49	11 53	11 58	12 10	12 21	12 24	12 31

Station	LM 1	NT I	NT B	TP ◇1 J 🛒	LM 1	VT ◇1 ☕	NT B	EM ◇ K	LM 1	NT I	NT B	TP ◇1 J 🛒	LM 1	VT ◇1 ☕	NT B	EM ◇ K	LM 1	NT I	NT B	TP ◇1 J 🛒	LM 1
London Euston ⊖65 d						11 07								12 07							
Birmingham New Street 12 65 d	11 01				11 36				12 01				12 36				13 01				13 36
Crewe 10 65 d	11 57				12 32	12 43			12 58				13 32	13 43			13 57				14 32
Winsford d	12 07								13 07								14 07				
Hartford d	12 12								13 12								14 12				
Acton Bridge d	12 16																				
Runcorn a	12 24				12 50	13 00			13 21				13 50	14 00			14 21				14 50
d	12 25				12 50	13 00			13 22				13 50	14 00			14 22				14 50
Liverpool South Parkway 7 ✈ a	12 33				12 59				13 30				13 59				14 30				14 59
d	12 33	12 36	12 36	12 47	12 59		13 06	13 15	13 31	13 36	13 36	13 47	13 59		14 06	14 15	14 31	14 36	14 36	14 47	14 59
West Allerton d			12 39				13 10				13 39				14 10				14 39		
Mossley Hill d			12 41				13 12				13 41				14 12				14 41		
Edge Hill 90 d			12 47								13 47								14 47		
Liverpool Lime Street 10 90 a	12 44	12 49	12 52	12 58	13 10	13 21	13 24	13 31	13 42	13 49	13 53	13 58	14 10	14 21	14 24	14 31	14 42	14 49	14 53	14 58	15 10

Station	VT ◇1 ☕	NT B	EM ◇ K	LM 1	NT I	NT B	TP ◇1 J 🛒	LM 1	VT ◇1 ☕	NT B	EM ◇ K	LM 1	NT I	NT B	TP ◇1 J 🛒	LM 1	VT ◇1 ☕	NT B	EM ◇ K	LM 1	NT B	TP ◇1 J 🛒
London Euston ⊖65 d	13 07								14 07								15 07					
Birmingham New Street 12 65 d				14 01				14 36				15 01				15 36				16 01		
Crewe 10 65 d	14 43			14 57				15 32	15 43			15 57				16 32	16 43			16 58		
Winsford d				15 07								16 09								17 07		
Hartford d				15 12								16 13								17 12		
Acton Bridge d												16 18								17 16		
Runcorn a	15 00			15 21				15 50	16 00			16 26				16 50	17 00			17 24		
d	15 00			15 22				15 50	16 00			16 26				16 50	17 00			17 25		
Liverpool South Parkway 7 ✈ a				15 30				15 59				16 35				16 59				17 33		
d		15 06	15 15	15 31	15 36	15 36	15 47	15 59		16 07	16 15	16 35	16 36	16 38	16 47	16 59		17 07	17 15	17 34	17 38	17 47
West Allerton d		15 10				15 39				16 11				16 41				17 11			17 41	
Mossley Hill d		15 12				15 41				16 13				16 43				17 13			17 45	
Edge Hill 90 d						15 47								16 49							17 49	
Liverpool Lime Street 10 90 a	15 21	15 24	15 31	15 42	15 49	15 53	15 58	16 10	16 21	16 25	16 31	16 45	16 49	16 55	16 58	17 10	17 21	17 25	17 31	17 45	17 58	18 01

A From London Euston
B From Manchester Oxford Road
C From Warrington Central
D From Birmingham International
E From Nottingham
F From Hull
G From Walsall
H From Newcastle
I To Blackpool North
J From Scarborough
K From Norwich

Table 91

Crewe and Runcorn - Liverpool

Mondays to Fridays

9 December to 16 May

Network Diagram - see first Page of Table 88

		LM	VT	NT	EM	LM	NT	TP	LM	VT		NT	EM	LM	VT	TP	LM	VT	NT	EM		VT	NT	TP
		1	◇1		◇	1		◇1	1	◇1			◇	1	◇1	◇1	1	◇1		◇		◇1		◇1
				A	B		A	C				A	B			C			D	B			A	C
			☕					🛒		⊠					⊠	🛒		⊠				⊠		
London Euston ⊖65 d			16 07							17 07					17 33			18 07				18 33		
Birmingham New Street 12 65 d		16 36				17 01			17 36					18 01			18 36							
Crewe 10 65 d		17 32	17 43			17 57			18 32	18 43				19 04	19 16		19 32	19 43				20 17		
Winsford d						18 07								19 12			19 41							
Hartford d						18 12			18 44								19 46							
Acton Bridge d						18 16			18 48															
Runcorn a		17 50	18 00			18 24			18 56	19 00				19 25	19 33		19 56	20 00				20 34		
d		17 50	18 00			18 25			18 57	19 00				19 25	19 33		19 56	20 00				20 34		
Liverpool South Parkway 7 ✈ a		17 59				18 33			19 05					19 34			20 05							
d		17 59		18 15	18 22	18 34	18 38	18 47	19 06			19 13	19 18	19 34		19 47	20 05		20 13	20 16			20 38	20 47
West Allerton d				18 19			18 41					19 16							20 16				20 41	
Mossley Hill d				18 21			18 44					19 18							20 18				20 44	
Edge Hill 90 d				18 30			18 50					19 26							20 24					
Liverpool Lime Street 10 90 a		18 10	18 21	18 38	18 35	18 45	18 57	19 01	19 16	19 21		19 35	19 34	19 45	19 51	20 01	20 16	20 21	20 30	20 35		20 53	20 56	21 01

	LM	VT	NT	EM	TP	LM		VT	NT	TP	LM	VT	NT
		R											
	1	1		◇	◇1	1		◇1		◇1	1	◇1	
			D	B	C				D	C			D
		☕						☕				☕	
London Euston ⊖65 d		19 07						20 07				21 07	
Birmingham New Street 12 65 d	19 35					20 36					21 36		
Crewe 10 65 d	20 32					21 32		21 48			22 32	22 48	
Winsford d	20 41					21 39					22 39		
Hartford d	20 46					21 44					22 44		
Acton Bridge d											22 48		
Runcorn a	20 56	21 00				21 54		22 05			22 56	23 05	
d	20 56	21 00				21 54		22 05			22 57	23 05	
Liverpool South Parkway 7 ✈ a	21 05					22 03					23 07		
d	21 05		21 12	21 20	21 47	22 03			22 12	22 47	23 07		23 22
West Allerton d			21 15						22 15				23 25
Mossley Hill d			21 18						22 18				23 27
Edge Hill 90 d			21 23						22 23				23 32
Liverpool Lime Street 10 90 a	21 16	21 21	21 30	21 35	22 00	22 15		22 25	22 30	23 01	23 21	23 24	23 39

Saturdays

14 December to 17 May

	NT	LM	NT	LM	NT	LM	NT	LM	NT		LM	EM	LM	NT	TP	LM	VT	NT	EM		LM	NT	TP	LM
		1		1		1		1			1	◇	1		◇1	1	◇1		◇		1		◇1	1
	A		D		D		A		D			E		A	F			A	E			A	G	
																	☕							
London Euston ⊖65 d																	07 07							
Birmingham New Street 12 65 d								06 01			06 36		07 01			07 36					08 01			08 36
Crewe 10 65 d		05 48		06 12		06 32		06 58			07 34		08 00			08 32	08 43				08 58			09 32
Winsford d						06 41		07 06			07 43		08 07								09 07			
Hartford d						06 46		07 11			07 48		08 12								09 12			
Acton Bridge d						06 51		07 15			07 52		08 16											
Runcorn a		06 07		06 31		06 59		07 23			08 00		08 24			08 50	09 00				09 21			09 50
d		06 08		06 31		06 59		07 24			08 01		08 25			08 50	09 00				09 22			09 50
Liverpool South Parkway 7 ✈ a		06 15		06 40		07 08		07 32			08 09		08 33			08 59					09 30			09 59
d	00 27	06 15	06 27	06 40	07 01	07 08	07 22	07 33	08 03		08 10	08 18	08 34	08 37	08 47	08 59		09 06	09 15		09 31	09 36	09 47	09 59
West Allerton d			06 31		07 05		07 25		08 06					08 40				09 09				09 39		
Mossley Hill d			06 33		07 07		07 28		08 09					08 43				09 12				09 41		
Edge Hill 90 d			06 39		07 13		07 34		08 14					08 48								09 47		
Liverpool Lime Street 10 90 a	00 41	06 26	06 45	06 52	07 18	07 20	07 40	07 44	08 21		08 21	08 31	08 46	08 55	08 58	09 10	09 21	09 24	09 31		09 42	09 53	09 58	10 10

	VT	NT	EM	LM	NT		NT	TP	LM	VT	NT	EM	LM	NT	NT		TP	LM	VT	NT	EM	LM	NT	NT
	◇1		◇	1				◇1	1	◇1		◇	1				◇1	1	◇1		◇	1		
		A	E		H		A	C			A	B		H	A		C			A	B		H	A
	☕									☕									☕					
London Euston ⊖65 d	08 07									09 07									10 07					
Birmingham New Street 12 65 d				09 01					09 36				10 01					10 36				11 01		
Crewe 10 65 d	09 43			09 57					10 32	10 43			10 57					11 32	11 43			11 57		
Winsford d				10 06									11 07									12 07		
Hartford d				10 11									11 12									12 12		
Acton Bridge d				10 15																		12 16		
Runcorn a	10 00			10 23					10 50	11 00			11 21					11 51	12 00			12 24		
d	10 00			10 24					10 50	11 00			11 22					11 51	12 00			12 25		
Liverpool South Parkway 7 ✈ a				10 32					10 59				11 30					12 00				12 33		
d		10 06	10 15	10 33	10 36		10 36	10 47	10 59		11 06	11 15	11 31	11 36	11 36		11 47	12 00		12 06	12 15	12 34	12 36	12 37
West Allerton d		10 09					10 39				11 10				11 39					12 10				12 40
Mossley Hill d		10 12					10 41				11 12				11 41					12 12				12 42
Edge Hill 90 d							10 47								11 47									12 48
Liverpool Lime Street 10 90 a	10 21	10 24	10 31	10 44	10 49		10 53	10 58	11 10	11 21	11 24	11 31	11 42	11 49	11 53		11 58	12 11	12 21	12 24	12 31	12 44	12 49	12 55

A From Manchester Oxford Road
B From Norwich
C From Scarborough
D From Warrington Central
E From Nottingham
F From Hull
G From Newcastle
H To Blackpool North

Table 91

Saturdays

14 December to 17 May

Crewe and Runcorn - Liverpool

Network Diagram - see first Page of Table 88

	TP ◇1 A	LM 1	VT ◇1	NT B	EM ◇ C	LM 1	NT D		NT B	TP ◇1 A	LM 1	VT ◇1	NT B	EM ◇ C	LM 1	NT D	NT B		TP ◇1 A	LM 1	VT ◇1	NT B	EM ◇ C	LM 1
London Euston ⊖65 d			11 07									12 07									13 07			
Birmingham New Street 12 65 d		11 36				12 01					12 36				13 01					13 36				14 01
Crewe 10 65 d		12 32	12 43			12 57					13 32	13 43			13 57					14 32	14 43			14 57
Winsford d						13 07									14 07									15 07
Hartford d						13 12									14 12									15 12
Acton Bridge d																								
Runcorn a		12 50	13 00			13 21					13 50	14 00			14 21					14 50	15 00			15 21
d		12 50	13 00			13 22					13 50	14 00			14 22					14 50	15 00			15 22
Liverpool South Parkway 7 ✈ a		12 59				13 30					13 59				14 30					14 59				15 30
d	12 47	12 59		13 06	13 15	13 31	13 36		13 36	13 47	13 59		14 06	14 15	14 31	14 36	14 36		14 47	14 59		15 06	15 15	15 31
West Allerton d				13 10					13 39				14 10				14 39					15 10		
Mossley Hill d				13 12					13 41				14 12				14 41					15 12		
Edge Hill 90 d									13 47								14 47							
Liverpool Lime Street 10 90 a	12 58	13 10	13 21	13 24	13 31	13 42	13 49		13 53	13 58	14 10	14 21	14 24	14 31	14 42	14 49	14 53		14 58	15 10	15 21	15 24	15 31	15 42

	NT D	NT B	TP ◇1 A		LM 1	VT ◇1	NT B	EM ◇ C	LM 1	NT D	NT B	TP ◇1 A	LM 1		VT ◇1	NT B	EM ◇ C	LM 1	NT B	TP ◇1 A	LM 1	VT ◇1	NT B	
London Euston ⊖65 d						14 07									15 07							16 07		
Birmingham New Street 12 65 d					14 36				15 01				15 36					16 01			16 36			
Crewe 10 65 d					15 32	15 43			15 57				16 32		16 43			16 57			17 32	17 43		
Winsford d									16 07									17 07						
Hartford d									16 12									17 12						
Acton Bridge d									16 16									17 16						
Runcorn a					15 50	16 00			16 24				16 50		17 00			17 24			17 50	18 00		
d					15 50	16 00			16 25				16 50		17 00			17 25			17 50	18 00		
Liverpool South Parkway 7 ✈ a					15 59				16 33				16 59					17 33			17 59			
d	15 36	15 36	15 47		15 59		16 07	16 15	16 34	16 36	16 36	16 47	16 59			17 07	17 15	17 34	17 39	17 47	17 59		18 15	
West Allerton d		15 39					16 11				16 39					17 11			17 42				18 19	
Mossley Hill d		15 41					16 13				16 41					17 13			17 45				18 21	
Edge Hill 90 d		15 47									16 47								17 50				18 30	
Liverpool Lime Street 10 90 a	15 49	15 53	15 58		16 10	16 21	16 25	16 31	16 45	16 49	16 54	16 58	17 10		17 21	17 25	17 31	17 45	17 58	18 01	18 10	18 21	18 38	

	EM ◇ C	LM 1	VT ◇1	NT B	TP ◇1 A	LM 1	VT ◇1	NT B	EM ◇ C		LM 1	TP ◇1 A	NT E	VT ◇1	EM ◇ C	LM 1	VT ◇1	NT B	TP ◇1 A		VT ◇1	NT E	EM ◇ C	LM 1
London Euston ⊖65 d			16 33				17 07							18 07			18 33				19 07			
Birmingham New Street 12 65 d		17 01				17 36					18 01					19 01								20 01
Crewe 10 65 d		17 57				18 33	18 47				18 59			19 43		19 58					20 47			21 06
Winsford d		18 07									19 08					20 07								21 15
Hartford d		18 12				18 44					19 13					20 12								21 20
Acton Bridge d		18 16														20 16								
Runcorn a		18 24	18 31			18 52	19 04				19 22			20 00		20 24	20 31				21 05			21 29
d		18 25	18 31			18 53	19 04				19 23			20 00		20 25	20 32				21 05			21 30
Liverpool South Parkway 7 ✈ a		18 33				19 02					19 31					20 33								21 38
d	18 22	18 34		18 38	18 47	19 02		19 11	19 19		19 32	19 47	19 59		20 15	20 34		20 38	20 47			21 15	21 20	21 39
West Allerton d				18 41				19 15					20 03					20 41				21 19		
Mossley Hill d				18 44				19 18					20 05					20 44				21 21		
Edge Hill 90 d				18 50				19 26					20 11									21 27		
Liverpool Lime Street 10 90 a	18 35	18 45	18 52	18 57	19 01	19 14	19 23	19 35	19 35		19 44	20 00	20 17	20 21	20 30	20 46	20 52	20 55	21 00		21 25	21 34	21 32	21 50

	TP ◇1 A	NT E	VT ◇1	TP ◇1 A	NT E
London Euston ⊖65 d			20 11		
Birmingham New Street 12 65 d					
Crewe 10 65 d			22 06		
Winsford d					
Hartford d					
Acton Bridge d					
Runcorn a			22 24		
d			22 24		
Liverpool South Parkway 7 ✈ a					
d	21 47	22 12		22 47	23 12
West Allerton d		22 15			23 15
Mossley Hill d		22 18			23 18
Edge Hill 90 d		22 23			23 23
Liverpool Lime Street 10 90 a	22 00	22 30	22 46	23 00	23 30

A From Scarborough
B From Manchester Oxford Road
C From Norwich
D To Blackpool North
E From Warrington Central

Table 91

Sundays

8 December to 11 May

Crewe and Runcorn - Liverpool

Network Diagram - see first Page of Table 88

	NT	NT	NT	TP	NT		TP	VT	LM	NT	TP	VT	LM	EM	NT		TP	VT	LM	EM	NT	VT	TP	LM
				◇1			◇1	◇1	1		◇1	◇1	1	◇			◇1	◇1	1	◇		◇1	◇1	1
	A	B	B	C	B		D			B	C			E	B		F			E	B		G	
								☕				☕						☕				☕		
London Euston ⊖65 d								08 15				09 15						10 15				11 15		
Birmingham New Street 12 65 d									09 42				10 42						11 42					12 35
Crewe 10 65 d								10 30	10 38			11 32	11 38					12 34	12 38			13 15		13 31
Winsford d									10 45				11 45						12 45					13 38
Hartford d									10 50				11 50						12 50					13 43
Acton Bridge d																								
Runcorn a								10 47	11 00			11 49	12 01					12 51	13 01			13 32		13 54
d								10 47	11 01			11 49	12 01					12 51	13 01			13 32		13 54
Liverpool South Parkway 7 ✈ a									11 09				12 10						13 10					14 03
d	00 20	08 55	09 33	09 47	10 33		10 49		11 10	11 33	11 46		12 10	12 17	12 33		12 47		13 10	13 17	13 33		13 47	14 03
West Allerton d		08 58	09 36		10 36					11 36					12 36						13 36			
Mossley Hill d		09 02	09 39		10 39					11 39					12 39						13 39			
Edge Hill 90 d																								
Liverpool Lime Street 10 90 a	00 34	09 12	09 51	10 00	10 50		10 59	11 09	11 21	11 50	11 58	12 10	12 21	12 30	12 50		12 58	13 12	13 21	13 30	13 50	13 54	13 58	14 14

	VT		EM	NT	TP	LM	VT	EM	NT	TP	LM		VT	EM	NT	TP	LM	VT	EM	NT	TP		LM	VT
	◇1		◇		◇1	1	◇1	◇		◇1	1		◇1	◇		◇1	1	◇1	◇		◇1		1	◇1
			E	B	H			E	B	H				I	B	H			E	B	H			
	☕						☕						☕					☕						☕
London Euston ⊖65 d	12 05						13 05						14 05					15 05						16 05
Birmingham New Street 12 65 d						13 35					14 35						15 35						16 35	
Crewe 10 65 d	13 45					14 31	14 45				15 31		15 45				16 31	16 45					17 31	17 45
Winsford d						14 38					15 38						16 38						17 38	
Hartford d						14 43					15 43						16 43						17 43	
Acton Bridge d																								
Runcorn a	14 02					14 53	15 02				15 53		16 02				16 54	17 02					17 54	18 02
d	14 02					14 54	15 02				15 54		16 02				16 54	17 02					17 54	18 02
Liverpool South Parkway 7 ✈ a						15 02					16 02						17 03						18 03	
d			14 16	14 33	14 47	15 03		15 16	15 33	15 47	16 03			16 16	16 33	16 47	17 03		17 16	17 33	17 47		18 03	
West Allerton d				14 36					15 36						16 36					17 36				
Mossley Hill d				14 39					15 39						16 39					17 39				
Edge Hill 90 d																								
Liverpool Lime Street 10 90 a	14 24		14 30	14 50	14 57	15 14	15 24	15 30	15 50	15 58	16 14		16 24	16 30	16 50	16 58	17 14	17 22	17 30	17 50	17 58		18 14	18 22

	EM	NT	TP	LM	VT	EM	NT		TP	LM	VT	EM	NT	TP	LM	VT	NT		TP	VT	VT	NT	TP	NT
	◇		◇1	1	◇1	◇			◇1	1	◇1	◇		◇1	1	◇1			◇1	◇1	◇1		◇1	
	J	B	H			I	B		H			I	B	H			B		H			B	H	K
					☕						☕					☕				☕	☕			
London Euston ⊖65 d					17 05						18 05					19 05				20 05	20 08			
Birmingham New Street 12 65 d				17 35						18 35					19 35									
Crewe 10 65 d				18 31	18 46					19 31	19 45				20 31	20 49				21 46	21 55			
Winsford d				18 38						19 38					20 38									
Hartford d				18 43						19 43					20 43									
Acton Bridge d																								
Runcorn a				18 54	19 02					19 53	20 02				20 54	21 06				22 03	22 12			
d				18 54	19 02					19 54	20 02				20 54	21 06				22 03	22 12			
Liverpool South Parkway 7 ✈ a				19 03						20 02					21 03									
d	18 16	18 33	18 48	19 03		19 17	19 33		19 47	20 03		20 16	20 33	20 47	21 03		21 33		21 47			22 33	22 47	23 33
West Allerton d		18 36					19 36						20 36				21 36					22 36		23 36
Mossley Hill d		18 39					19 39						20 39				21 39					22 39		23 39
Edge Hill 90 d																								
Liverpool Lime Street 10 90 a	18 30	18 50	18 58	19 14	19 25	19 30	19 50		19 58	20 14	20 21	20 30	20 50	20 58	21 14	21 27	21 50		21 58	22 23	22 33	22 50	22 58	23 50

	VT
	◇1
	☕
London Euston ⊖65 d	21 21
Birmingham New Street 12 65 d	
Crewe 10 65 d	23 45
Winsford d	
Hartford d	
Acton Bridge d	
Runcorn a	00 07
d	00 07
Liverpool South Parkway 7 ✈ a	
d	
West Allerton d	
Mossley Hill d	
Edge Hill 90 d	
Liverpool Lime Street 10 90 a	00 30

A not 8 December. From Manchester Oxford Road
B From Manchester Oxford Road
C From Manchester Piccadilly
D From York
E From Nottingham
F From Scarborough
G From Middlesbrough
H From Newcastle
I From Norwich
J From Peterborough
K From Manchester Airport

Table 91R

Mondays to Fridays

9 December to 16 May

Liverpool - Runcorn and Crewe

Network Diagram - see first Page of Table 88

Miles	Station		LM	VT	NT	VT	TP	NT	LM	EM	NT	VT	LM	TP	NT	LM	EM	NT	VT	LM	TP	NT	LM
			MX 1	◇1		◇1	◇1		1	◇		◇1	1	◇1		1	◇		◇1	1	◇1		1
			A		B		C	D		E	B			C	D		E	D			C	D	
				⊠		⊠	T					⊠		T					⊠		T		
0	**Liverpool Lime Street 10** 90	d		05 27	05 50	06 05	06 15	06 21	06 30	06 47	06 50	07 00	07 04	07 15	07 26	07 34	07 42	07 45	07 47	08 04	08 22	08 26	08 34
1¾	Edge Hill 90	d			05 54						06 54				07 30							08 30	
3¾	Mossley Hill	d			05 59			06 29			06 59				07 35			07 53				08 35	
4½	West Allerton	d			06 01			06 31			07 01				07 37			07 56				08 37	
5½	**Liverpool South Parkway 7** ✈	a			06 04		06 25	06 34	06 39	06 57	07 04		07 13	07 25	07 40	07 44	07 52	07 59		08 14	08 32	08 40	08 43
—		d							06 40				07 14			07 45				08 15			08 44
13	**Runcorn**	a		05 42		06 20			06 47				07 21			07 53			08 02	08 24			08 51
—		d		05 43		06 21			06 48			07u15	07 22			07 53			08 03	08 24			08 52
21	Acton Bridge	d	00 02						06 57				07 32							08 34			09 02
23¾	Hartford	d	00 07						07 02				07 37			08 04							09 06
28	Winsford	d	00 11						07 06							08 08							09 11
35½	**Crewe 10** 65	a	00 22	06 00					07 14				07 48			08 16			08 21	08 47			09 19
—	Birmingham New Street 12 65	a							08 17				08 47			09 18				09 47			10 17
—	London Euston ⊖65	a		07 51		08 23						09 04							10 01				

Station		VT	EM	NT	LM	TP	NT	LM	VT	EM	NT	LM	NT	TP	NT	LM	VT	EM	NT	LM	NT	TP
		◇1	◇		1	◇1		1	◇1	◇		1		◇1		1	◇1	◇		1		◇1
			E	D		C	D			E	D		F	C	D			E	D		G	C
		⊠				T			⊠					T			⊠					T
Liverpool Lime Street 10 90	d	08 47	08 52	08 55	09 04	09 22	09 27	09 34	09 47	09 52	09 55	10 04	10 16	10 22	10 27	10 34	10 47	10 52	10 55	11 04	11 16	11 22
Edge Hill 90	d			08 59							09 59								10 59			
Mossley Hill	d			09 04			09 35				10 04				10 35				11 04			
West Allerton	d			09 06			09 37				10 06				10 37				11 06			
Liverpool South Parkway 7 ✈	a		09 02	09 09	09 15	09 32	09 40	09 43		10 02	10 09	10 15	10 27	10 32	10 40	10 43		11 02	11 09	11 15	11 27	11 32
	d				09 15			09 44				10 15				10 44				11 15		
Runcorn	a	09 02			09 24			09 51	10 02			10 24				10 51	11 02			11 24		
	d	09 03			09 25			09 52	10 03			10 25				10 52	11 03			11 25		
Acton Bridge	d																					
Hartford	d							10 04								11 04						
Winsford	d							10 08								11 08						
Crewe 10 65	a	09 23			09 45			10 16	10 21			10 45				11 16	11 21			11 45		
Birmingham New Street 12 65	a				10 47			11 17				11 47				12 17				12 47		
London Euston ⊖65	a	11 05							11 59								12 59					

Station		NT	LM	VT	EM	NT	LM	NT	TP	NT	LM	VT	EM	NT	LM	NT	TP	NT	LM	VT	EM	NT	LM
			1	◇1	◇		1		◇1		1	◇1	◇		1		◇1		1	◇1	◇		1
		D			E	D		G	C	D			E	D		G	C	D			E	D	
				⊐					T			⊐					T			⊐			
Liverpool Lime Street 10 90	d	11 27	11 34	11 47	11 52	11 55	12 04	12 16	12 22	12 27	12 34	12 47	12 52	12 55	13 04	13 16	13 22	13 27	13 34	13 47	13 52	13 55	14 04
Edge Hill 90	d					11 59								12 59								13 59	
Mossley Hill	d	11 35				12 04				12 35				13 04				13 35				14 04	
West Allerton	d	11 37				12 06				12 37				13 06				13 37				14 06	
Liverpool South Parkway 7 ✈	a	11 40	11 43		12 02	12 09	12 15	12 27	12 32	12 40	12 43		13 02	13 09	13 15	13 27	13 32	13 40	13 43		14 02	14 09	14 15
	d		11 44				12 15				12 44				13 15				13 44				14 15
Runcorn	a		11 51	12 02			12 24				12 51	13 02			13 24				13 51	14 02			14 24
	d		11 52	12 03			12 25				12 52	13 03			13 25				13 52	14 03			14 25
Acton Bridge	d										13 02												
Hartford	d		12 04								13 06								14 04				
Winsford	d		12 08								13 11								14 08				
Crewe 10 65	a		12 16	12 21			12 45				13 19	13 23			13 45				14 16	14 21			14 45
Birmingham New Street 12 65	a		13 17				13 47				14 18				14 51				15 18				15 47
London Euston ⊖65	a			14 00								15 05								15 59			

Station		NT	TP	NT	LM	VT	EM	NT	LM	NT	TP	NT	LM	VT	EM	NT	LM	NT	TP	NT	LM	VT	EM
			◇1		1	◇1	◇		1		◇1		1	◇1	◇		1		◇1		1	◇1	◇
		G	C	D			E	D		G	H	D			E	D		G	C	D			I
			T			⊐					T			⊐					T			⊐	
Liverpool Lime Street 10 90	d	14 15	14 22	14 27	14 34	14 47	14 52	14 55	15 04	15 16	15 22	15 27	15 34	15 47	15 52	15 55	16 04	16 16	16 22	16 27	16 34	16 47	16 52
Edge Hill 90	d							14 59								15 59							
Mossley Hill	d			14 35				15 04				15 35				16 04				16 35			
West Allerton	d			14 37				15 06				15 37				16 06				16 37			
Liverpool South Parkway 7 ✈	a	14 26	14 32	14 40	14 43		15 02	15 09	15 15	15 27	15 32	15 40	15 43		16 02	16 09	16 15	16 27	16 32	16 40	16 43		17 02
	d				14 44				15 15				15 44				16 15				16 44		
Runcorn	a				14 51	15 02			15 24				15 51	16 02			16 24				16 52	17 02	
	d				14 52	15 03			15 25				15 52	16 03			16 25				16 52	17 03	
Acton Bridge	d																				17 01		
Hartford	d				15 04								16 04								17 06		
Winsford	d				15 08								16 08										
Crewe 10 65	a				15 16	15 21			15 45				16 16	16 21			16 45				17 20		
Birmingham New Street 12 65	a				16 17				16 48				17 17				17 47				18 16		
London Euston ⊖65	a					17 00								17 59								19 02	

A From Liverpool Lime Street
B To Warrington Central
C To Scarborough
D To Manchester Oxford Road
E To Norwich
F From Preston
G From Blackpool North
H To Middlesbrough
I To Nottingham

Table 91R

Mondays to Fridays

9 December to 16 May

Liverpool - Runcorn and Crewe

Network Diagram - see first Page of Table 88

	NT	LM	TP	NT	LM	VT	EM		NT	LM	TP	NT	LM	VT	EM	NT	LM		TP	LM	VT	EM	NT	LM
		[1]	◇[1]		[1]	◇[1]	◇			[1]	◇[1]		[1]	◇[1]	◇		[1]		◇[1]	[1]	◇[1]	◇		[1]
	A		B	A			C		A		B	A			D	E			F			D	E	
			ꝏ			⊠								⊠							☕			
Liverpool Lime Street [10] 90 d	16 55	17 04	17 22	17 25	17 34	17 47	17 52		17 55	18 04	18 22	18 25	18 34	18 47	18 52	18 55	19 11		19 22	19 34	19 48	19 52	19 55	20 04
Edge Hill 90 d	16 59			17 29					17 59			18 29				18 59							19 59	
Mossley Hill d	17 04			17 34					18 04			18 34				19 04							20 04	
West Allerton d	17 06			17 36					18 06			18 36				19 06							20 06	
Liverpool South Parkway [7] ✈ a	17 09	17 15	17 32	17 39	17 43		18 02		18 09	18 14	18 32	18 39	18 43		19 02	19 09	19 20		19 32	19 43		20 02	20 09	20 15
d		17 15			17 44					18 15			18 44				19 21			19 44				20 15
Runcorn a		17 24			17 51	18 02				18 24			18 51	19 02			19 28			19 51	20 03			20 24
d		17 25			17 52	18 03				18 24			18 52	19 03			19 29			19 52	20 04			20 24
Acton Bridge d					18 01												19 40							
Hartford d					18 06								19 04							20 04				
Winsford d		17 39								18 38			19 08							20 08				
Crewe [10] 65 a		17 47			18 18	18 22				18 47			19 16	19 21			19 53			20 16	20 21			20 45
Birmingham New Street [12] 65 a		18 48			19 17					19 48			20 19				20 47			21 17				21 47
London Euston ⊖65 a						20 07								21 04							22 09			

	TP	LM	VT		NT	LM	EM	NT	TP	LM	LM	NT
	◇[1]	[1]	◇[1]			[1]	◇		◇[1]	[1]	[1]	
	G				A		D	A	G			H
			☕									
Liverpool Lime Street [10] 90 d	20 22	20 34	20 48		20 55	21 34	21 37	21 55	22 30	22 34	23 34	23 38
Edge Hill 90 d					20 59			21 59				23 42
Mossley Hill d					21 04			22 04				23 47
West Allerton d					21 06			22 06				23 50
Liverpool South Parkway [7] ✈ a	20 32	20 43			21 09	21 43	21 47	22 09	22 40	22 44	23 44	23 53
d		20 44				21 44				22 45	23 45	
Runcorn a		20 51	21 03			21 51				22 54	23 53	
d		20 52	21 04			21 52				22 54	23 53	
Acton Bridge d										23 03	00 02	
Hartford d		21 04				22 04				23 08	00 07	
Winsford d		21 08				22 08				23 12	00 11	
Crewe [10] 65 a		21 16	21 21			22 18				23 21	00 22	
Birmingham New Street [12] 65 a		22 17				23 27						
London Euston ⊖65 a			23 57									

Saturdays

14 December to 17 May

	LM	VT	NT	TP	NT	LM	VT	EM	NT		LM	TP	VT	NT	LM	EM	NT	VT	LM		TP	NT	LM	VT
	[1]	◇[1]		◇[1]		[1]	◇[1]	◇			[1]	◇[1]	◇[1]		[1]	◇		◇[1]	[1]		◇[1]		[1]	◇[1]
	I		E	B	A			C	E			B		A		C	A				B	A		
		☕					☕						☕					☕						☕
Liverpool Lime Street [10] 90 d		05 47	05 50	06 15	06 21	06 32	06 45	06 49	06 55		07 04	07 15	07 19	07 26	07 34	07 42	07 45	07 47	08 04		08 22	08 26	08 34	08 47
Edge Hill 90 d			05 54						06 59					07 30								08 30		
Mossley Hill d			05 59		06 29				07 04					07 35			07 53					08 35		
West Allerton d			06 01		06 31				07 06					07 37			07 56					08 37		
Liverpool South Parkway [7] ✈ a			06 04	06 25	06 34	06 41		06 59	07 09		07 13	07 25		07 40	07 43	07 52	07 59		08 14		08 32	08 40	08 43	
d						06 42					07 14				07 44				08 15				08 44	
Runcorn a		06 02				06 49	07 00				07 21		07 35		07 51			08 02	08 24				08 51	09 02
d		06 03				06 50	07 01				07 22		07 36		07 52			08 03	08 24				08 52	09 03
Acton Bridge d	00 02										07 32								08 34				09 02	
Hartford d	00 07					07 02					07 36				08 04								09 06	
Winsford d	00 11					07 06									08 08								09 11	
Crewe [10] 65 a	00 22					07 14	07 18				07 47		07 52		08 16			08 21	08 47				09 19	09 23
Birmingham New Street [12] 65 a						08 17					08 48				09 17				09 47				10 17	
London Euston ⊖65 a		08 05					09 00						09 47					10 06						11 05

	EM	NT	LM	TP	NT		LM	VT	EM	NT	LM	NT	TP	NT	LM		VT	EM	NT	LM	NT	TP	NT	LM
	◇		[1]	◇[1]			[1]	◇[1]	◇		[1]		◇[1]		[1]		◇[1]	◇		[1]		◇[1]		[1]
	C	A		B	A				C	A		J	B	A				C	A		J	B	A	
								☕									☕							
Liverpool Lime Street [10] 90 d	08 52	08 55	09 04	09 22	09 27		09 34	09 47	09 52	09 55	10 04	10 16	10 22	10 27	10 34		10 47	10 52	10 55	11 04	11 16	11 22	11 27	11 34
Edge Hill 90 d		08 59								09 59									10 59					
Mossley Hill d		09 04			09 35					10 04				10 35					11 04				11 35	
West Allerton d		09 06			09 37					10 06				10 37					11 06				11 37	
Liverpool South Parkway [7] ✈ a	09 02	09 09	09 15	09 32	09 40		09 43		10 02	10 09	10 15	10 27	10 32	10 40	10 43			11 02	11 09	11 15	11 27	11 32	11 40	11 43
d			09 15				09 44				10 15				10 44					11 15				11 44
Runcorn a			09 24				09 51	10 02			10 24				10 51		11 02			11 24				11 51
d			09 25				09 52	10 03			10 25				10 52		11 03			11 25				11 52
Acton Bridge d																								
Hartford d							10 04								11 04									12 04
Winsford d							10 08								11 08									12 08
Crewe [10] 65 a			09 45				10 16	10 21			10 45				11 16		11 21			11 45				12 16
Birmingham New Street [12] 65 a			10 47				11 17				11 47				12 17					12 47				13 17
London Euston ⊖65 a								11 59									12 59							

A To Manchester Oxford Road
B To Scarborough
C To Norwich
D To Nottingham
E To Warrington Central
F To Hull
G To York
H To Manchester Piccadilly
I From Liverpool Lime Street
J From Blackpool North

Table 91R

Saturdays

14 December to 17 May

Liverpool - Runcorn and Crewe

Network Diagram - see first Page of Table 88

	VT	EM	NT	LM	NT	TP	NT		LM	VT	EM	NT	LM	NT	TP	NT	LM		VT	EM	NT	LM	NT	TP
	◇1	◇		1		◇1			1	◇1	◇		1		◇1		1		◇1	◇		1		◇1
		A	B		C	D	B				A	B		C	D	B				A	B		C	D
	☕									☕									☕					
Liverpool Lime Street 10 90 d	11 47	11 52	11 55	12 04	12 16	12 22	12 27		12 34	12 47	12 52	12 55	13 04	13 16	13 22	13 27	13 34		13 47	13 52	13 55	14 04	14 15	14 22
Edge Hill 90 d			11 59									12 59									13 59			
Mossley Hill d			12 04				12 35					13 04				13 35					14 04			
West Allerton d			12 06				12 37					13 06				13 37					14 06			
Liverpool South Parkway 7 ⇌ a		12 02	12 09	12 15	12 27	12 32	12 40		12 43		13 02	13 09	13 15	13 27	13 32	13 40	13 43			14 02	14 09	14 15	14 26	14 32
d				12 15					12 44				13 15				13 44					14 15		
Runcorn a	12 02			12 24					12 51	13 02			13 24				13 51		14 02			14 24		
d	12 03			12 25					12 52	13 03			13 25				13 52		14 03			14 25		
Acton Bridge d									13 02															
Hartford d									13 06								14 04							
Winsford d									13 11								14 08							
Crewe 10 65 a	12 21			12 45					13 19	13 23			13 45				14 16		14 21			14 45		
Birmingham New Street 12 65 a				13 47					14 17				14 47				15 17					15 47		
London Euston ⊖65 a	14 00									15 05									15 59					

	NT	LM	VT		EM	NT	LM	NT	TP	NT	LM	VT	EM		NT	LM	NT	TP	NT	LM	VT	EM	NT	
		1	◇1		◇		1		◇1		1	◇1	◇			1		◇1		1	◇1	◇		
	B				A	B		C	D	B			A		B		C	D	B			E	B	
			☕									☕									☕			
Liverpool Lime Street 10 90 d	14 27	14 34	14 47		14 52	14 55	15 04	15 16	15 22	15 27	15 34	15 47	15 52		15 55	16 04	16 16	16 22	16 27	16 34	16 47	16 52	16 55	
Edge Hill 90 d						14 59									15 59								16 59	
Mossley Hill d	14 35					15 04				15 35					16 04				16 35				17 04	
West Allerton d	14 37					15 06				15 37					16 06				16 37				17 06	
Liverpool South Parkway 7 ⇌ a	14 40	14 43			15 02	15 09	15 15	15 27	15 32	15 40	15 43		16 02		16 09	16 15	16 28	16 32	16 40	16 43		17 02	17 09	
d		14 44					15 15				15 44					16 15				16 44				
Runcorn a		14 51	15 02				15 24				15 51	16 02				16 24				16 51	17 02			
d		14 52	15 03				15 25				15 52	16 03				16 25				16 52	17 03			
Acton Bridge d																				17 02				
Hartford d		15 04									16 04									17 06				
Winsford d		15 08									16 08													
Crewe 10 65 a		15 16	15 21				15 45				16 16	16 21				16 45				17 17	17 22			
Birmingham New Street 12 65 a		16 17					16 47				17 17					17 47				18 17				
London Euston ⊖65 a			16 59									17 59									19 01			

	LM	TP	NT	LM	VT	EM	NT	LM	TP		NT	LM	VT	EM	NT	LM	TP	LM	VT		EM	NT	TP	LM
	1	◇1		1	◇1	◇		1	◇1			1	◇1	◇		1	◇1	1	◇1		◇		◇1	1
		D	B			A	B		D		B			E	F		G				E	F	G	
					☕								☕						☕					
Liverpool Lime Street 10 90 d	17 04	17 22	17 25	17 34	17 47	17 52	17 55	18 04	18 22		18 25	18 34	18 47	18 52	18 55	19 04	19 22	19 34	19 48		19 52	19 55	20 22	20 34
Edge Hill 90 d			17 29				17 59				18 29				18 59							19 59		
Mossley Hill d			17 34				18 04				18 34				19 04							20 04		
West Allerton d			17 36				18 06				18 36				19 06							20 06		
Liverpool South Parkway 7 ⇌ a	17 15	17 32	17 39	17 43		18 02	18 09	18 14	18 32		18 39	18 43		19 02	19 09	19 14	19 32	19 43			20 02	20 09	20 32	20 43
d	17 15			17 44				18 15				18 44				19 14		19 44						20 44
Runcorn a	17 24			17 51	18 02			18 24				18 51	19 02			19 23		19 51	20 03					20 51
d	17 25			17 52	18 03			18 24				18 52	19 03			19 23		19 52	20 04					20 52
Acton Bridge d				18 02												19 36								
Hartford d				18 06								19 04						20 04						21 03
Winsford d	17 39							18 38				19 08						20 08						21 08
Crewe 10 65 a	17 47			18 20				18 46				19 19				19 49		20 16	20 21					21 16
Birmingham New Street 12 65 a	18 47			19 17				19 47				20 19				20 48		21 17						22 20
London Euston ⊖65 a					19 59								21 15						22 15					

	EM	NT	LM	EM	NT		LM	TP	NT
	◇		1	◇			1	◇1	
	E	B		E	B			G	H
Liverpool Lime Street 10 90 d	20 52	20 55	21 34	21 37	21 55		22 04	22 30	23 38
Edge Hill 90 d		20 59			21 59				23 42
Mossley Hill d		21 04			22 04				23 47
West Allerton d		21 06			22 06				23 50
Liverpool South Parkway 7 ⇌ a	21 02	21 09	21 43	21 47	22 09		22 14	22 40	23 53
d			21 44				22 14		
Runcorn a			21 51				22 22		
d			21 52				22 23		
Acton Bridge d									
Hartford d			22 04				22 34		
Winsford d			22 08				22 39		
Crewe 10 65 a			22 16				22 48		
Birmingham New Street 12 65 a			23 20						
London Euston ⊖65 a									

A To Norwich
B To Manchester Oxford Road
C From Blackpool North
D To Scarborough
E To Nottingham
F To Warrington Central
G To York
H To Manchester Piccadilly

Table 91R

Sundays

8 December to 11 May

Liverpool - Runcorn and Crewe

Network Diagram - see first Page of Table 88

			VT	TP	NT	VT	TP		NT	VT	TP	NT	VT	TP	NT	LM	VT		TP	NT	LM	VT	EM	TP	NT	LM
			◇1	◇1		◇1	◇1			◇1	◇1		◇1	◇1		1	◇1		◇1		1	◇1	◇	◇1		1
				A	B		C		B		D	B		C	B				D	B			E	C	B	
			☕			☕				☕			☕				☕					☕				
Liverpool Lime Street 10	90	d	08 15	08 22	08 28	08 38	09 22		09 27	09 38	10 22	10 28	10 38	11 22	11 26	11 34	11 47		12 22	12 26	12 34	12 47	12 52	13 22	13 26	13 34
Edge Hill	90	d																								
Mossley Hill		d			08 36				09 35			10 36			11 34					12 34					13 34	
West Allerton		d			08 38				09 37			10 38			11 36					12 36					13 36	
Liverpool South Parkway 7 ✈		a		08 32	08 41		09 32		09 40		10 32	10 41		11 32	11 39	11 43			12 32	12 39	12 43		13 02	13 32	13 39	13 43
		d														11 44					12 44					13 44
Runcorn		a	08 34			08 53				09 53			10 53			11 51	12 02				12 51	13 02				13 51
		d	08 35			08 54				09 54			10 54			11 52	12 03				12 52	13 03				13 52
Acton Bridge		d																								
Hartford		d														12 03					13 03					14 03
Winsford		d														12 08					13 08					14 08
Crewe 10	65	a	08 52			09 11				10 12			11 12			12 18	12 21				13 17	13 21				14 17
Birmingham New Street 12	65	a														13 15					14 15					15 15
London Euston ⊖	65	a	11 06			11 37				12 32			13 13				14 04					15 04				

			VT		EM	TP	NT	LM	VT	EM	TP	NT	LM		VT	EM	VT	TP	NT	LM	VT	EM	TP		NT	LM
			◇1		◇	◇1		1	◇1	◇	◇1		1		◇1	◇	◇1	◇1		1	◇1	◇	◇1			1
					E	D	B			E	C	B				E		D	B			F	C		B	
			☕						☕						☕		☕				☕					
Liverpool Lime Street 10	90	d	13 47		13 52	14 22	14 26	14 34	14 47	14 52	15 22	15 26	15 34		15 47	15 52	16 18	16 22	16 26	16 34	16 47	16 52	17 22		17 26	17 34
Edge Hill	90	d																								
Mossley Hill		d					14 34					15 33							16 34						17 34	
West Allerton		d					14 36					15 36							16 36						17 36	
Liverpool South Parkway 7 ✈		a			14 02	14 32	14 39	14 43		15 02	15 32	15 39	15 43			16 02		16 32	16 39	16 43		17 02	17 32		17 39	17 43
		d						14 44					15 44							16 44						17 44
Runcorn		a	14 02					14 51	15 02				15 51		16 02		16 33			16 51	17 02					17 51
		d	14 03					14 52	15 03				15 52		16 03		16 34			16 52	17 03					17 52
Acton Bridge		d																								
Hartford		d						15 03					16 03							17 03						18 03
Winsford		d						15 08					16 08							17 08						18 08
Crewe 10	65	a	14 21					15 17	15 21				16 17		16 21		16 51			17 17	17 21					18 17
Birmingham New Street 12	65	a						16 15					17 15							18 15						19 15
London Euston ⊖	65	a	16 04						17 04						18 03		18 44				19 04					

			VT	EM	TP	NT	LM	VT	EM		TP	NT	LM	VT	EM	TP	NT	LM	VT		EM	NT	LM	TP	NT	
			◇1	◇	◇1		1	◇1	◇		◇1		1	◇1	◇	◇1		1	◇1		◇		1	◇1		
				E	C	B			F		G	B			F	H	B				F	B		G	B	
			☕					☕						☕					☕							
Liverpool Lime Street 10	90	d	17 47	17 52	18 22	18 26	18 34	18 47	18 52		19 22	19 26	19 34	19 47	19 52	20 22	20 26	20 34	20 47		21 21	21 26	21 34	21 52	22 26	
Edge Hill	90	d																								
Mossley Hill		d				18 34						19 34					20 34					21 34			22 34	
West Allerton		d				18 36						19 36					20 36					21 36			22 36	
Liverpool South Parkway 7 ✈		a		18 02	18 32	18 39	18 43		19 02		19 32	19 39	19 43		20 02	20 32	20 39	20 43			21 31	21 39	21 43	22 02	22 39	
		d					18 44						19 44					20 44					21 44			
Runcorn		a	18 02				18 51	19 02					19 51	20 02				20 51	21 02				21 51			
		d	18 03				18 52	19 03					19 52	20 03				20 52	21 03				21 52			
Acton Bridge		d																								
Hartford		d					19 03						20 03					21 03					22 03			
Winsford		d					19 08						20 08					21 08					22 08			
Crewe 10	65	a	18 21				19 17	19 21					20 16	20 22				21 16	21 21				22 18			
Birmingham New Street 12	65	a					20 15						21 16					22 17					23 16			
London Euston ⊖	65	a	20 05					21 04						22 28					23 54							

A To Hull
B To Manchester Oxford Road
C To Scarborough
D To Middlesbrough
E To Norwich
F To Nottingham
G To York
H To Newcastle

Table 94

Mondays to Fridays

9 December to 16 May

Manchester and Bolton - Blackburn - Clitheroe

Network Diagram - see first Page of Table 82

Miles	Station		NT	NT	NT	NT	NT	NT	NT		NT	NT	NT	NT	NT	NT	NT	NT	NT	NT	NT FO	NT FX
0	**Manchester Victoria**	82 d		05 55		07 23	08 00	08 29	09 00		15 00	15 40	16 23	17 00	17 23	18 00	18 23	19 00	20 00	21 00	22 00	22 00
0¾	Salford Central	82 d				07 26	08 03	08 32	09 03		15 03	15 43	16 26	17 03	17 27	18 03	18 26	19 03	20 03	21 03	22 04	
—	Manchester Piccadilly 10	82 d			06 53																	
1¾	Salford Crescent	82 d		06 00	07 03	07 30	08 08	08 37	09 08		15 08	15 47	16 31	17 08	17 30	18 08	18 31	19 08	20 08	21 08	22 08	22 08
10¾	**Bolton**	82 d		06 12	07 19	07 42	08 20	08 49	09 20		15 20	16 00	16 43	17 20	17 43	18 20	18 44	19 20	20 20	21 20	22 20	22 20
12½	Hall I' Th' Wood	d		06 17	07 24	07 47	08 25	08 54	09 25		15 25	16 05	16 48	17 25	17 48	18 25	18 49	19 25	20 25	21 25	22 25	22 25
13½	Bromley Cross	d		06 20	07 27	07 53	08 28	08 57	09 28	and	15 28	16 11	16 51	17 28	17 55	18 28	18 54	19 28	20 28	21 28	22 28	22 28
16½	Entwistle	d				07x59	08x34		09x34	hourly	15x34	16x17	16x57	17x34		18x34		19x34	20x34	21x34	22x34	22x34
20¼	Darwen	a		06 31	07 39	08 06	08 41	09 09	09 41	until	15 41	16 24	17 04	17 41	18 07	18 41	19 06	19 41	20 41	21 41	22 41	22 41
—		d		06 42	07 39	08 11	08 41	09 11	09 41		15 41	16 24	17 11	17 41	18 07	18 41	19 11	19 41	20 41	21 41	22 41	22 41
—	Blackpool North	97 d																				
—	Preston 8	97 d																				
24½	**Blackburn**	a		06 49	07 46	08 20	08 50	09 20	09 50		15 50	16 31	17 20	17 52	18 16	18 48	19 21	19 51	20 50	21 50	22 50	22 50
—		d	06 25	06 52	07 47		08 52		09 52		15 52	16 32	17 20	17 55		18 49		19 52	20 52	21 52	22 51	22 51
27¼	Ramsgreave & Wilpshire	d	06 31	06 58	07 53		08 58		09 58		15 58	16 38	17 26	18 00		18 55		19 58	20 58	21 58	22 57	22 57
29¾	Langho	d	06 35	07 02	07 57		09 02		10 02		16 02	16 42	17 31	18 04		18 59		20 02	21 02	22 02	23 01	23 01
31¾	Whalley	d	06 39	07 06	08 01		09 06		10 06		16 06	16 46	17 35	18 08		19 03		20 06	21 06	22 06	23 05	23 05
34¼	**Clitheroe**	a	06 50	07 17	08 12		09 17		10 17		16 17	16 57	17 45	18 19		19 14		20 17	21 17	22 17	23 16	23 16

Station		NT FO	NT FX
Manchester Victoria	82 d	23 00	23 00
Salford Central	82 d	23 03	
Manchester Piccadilly 10	82 d		
Salford Crescent	82 d	23 08	23 08
Bolton	82 d	23 20	23 20
Hall I' Th' Wood	d	23 25	23 25
Bromley Cross	d	23 28	23 28
Entwistle	d	23x34	23x34
Darwen	a	23 41	23 41
	d	23 41	23 41
Blackpool North	97 d		
Preston 8	97 d		
Blackburn	a	23 51	23 51
	d		
Ramsgreave & Wilpshire	d		
Langho	d		
Whalley	d		
Clitheroe	a		

Saturdays

14 December to 17 May

Station		NT	NT	NT	NT	NT	NT	NT	NT	NT	NT	NT		NT	NT	NT	NT	NT	NT	NT	NT	NT
Manchester Victoria	82 d		05 55		07 23	08 00	08 29	09 00	09 29	10 00	10 29	11 00		14 00	15 00	15 40	16 23	17 00	17 23	18 00	18 23	19 00
Salford Central	82 d				07 26	08 03	08 32	09 03	09 32	10 03	10 32	11 03		14 03	15 03	15 43	16 26	17 03	17 26	18 03	18 26	19 03
Manchester Piccadilly 10	82 d			06 53																		
Salford Crescent	82 d		06 00	07 03	07 30	08 08	08 37	09 08	09 37	10 08	10 37	11 08		14 08	15 08	15 47	16 31	17 08	17 31	18 08	18 31	19 08
Bolton	82 d		06 12	07 19	07 42	08 20	08 49	09 20	09 49	10 20	10 49	11 20		14 20	15 20	16 00	16 43	17 20	17 43	18 20	18 43	19 20
Hall I' Th' Wood	d		06 17	07 24	07 47	08 25	08 54	09 25	09 54	10 25	10 54	11 25		14 25	15 25	16 05	16 48	17 25	17 48	18 25	18 48	19 25
Bromley Cross	d		06 20	07 27	07 53	08 28	08 57	09 28	09 57	10 28	10 57	11 28	and	14 28	15 28	16 10	16 51	17 28	17 55	18 28	18 54	19 28
Entwistle	d				07x59	08x34		09x34		10x34		11x34	hourly	14x34	15x34	16x16	16x57	17x34		18x34		19x34
Darwen	a		06 31	07 39	08 06	08 41	09 09	09 41	10 09	10 41	11 09	11 41	until	14 41	15 41	16 23	17 04	17 41	18 07	18 41	19 06	19 41
	d		06 42	07 39	08 11	08 41	09 11	09 41	10 11	10 41	11 11	11 41		14 41	15 41	16 23	17 11	17 41	18 07	18 41	19 11	19 41
Blackpool North	97 d																					
Preston 8	97 d																					
Blackburn	a		06 49	07 46	08 20	08 50	09 20	09 50	10 20	10 50	11 20	11 50		14 50	15 49	16 30	17 19	17 51	18 21	18 48	19 21	19 51
	d	06 25	06 52	07 47		08 52		09 52		10 52		11 52		14 52	15 52	16 31	17 19	17 53		18 49		19 52
Ramsgreave & Wilpshire	d	06 31	06 58	07 53		08 58		09 58		10 58		11 58		14 58	15 58	16 37	17 25	17 59		18 55		19 58
Langho	d	06 35	07 02	07 57		09 02		10 02		11 02		12 02		15 02	16 02	16 41	17 30	18 03		18 59		20 02
Whalley	d	06 39	07 06	08 01		09 06		10 06		11 06		12 06		15 06	16 06	16 45	17 34	18 07		19 03		20 06
Clitheroe	a	06 50	07 17	08 12		09 17		10 17		11 17		12 17		15 17	16 17	16 56	17 44	18 18		19 14		20 17

Station		NT	NT	NT	NT
Manchester Victoria	82 d	20 00	21 00	22 00	23 05
Salford Central	82 d	20 04	21 03	22 03	23 08
Manchester Piccadilly 10	82 d				
Salford Crescent	82 d	20 08	21 08	22 08	23 12
Bolton	82 d	20 20	21 20	22 20	23 24
Hall I' Th' Wood	d	20 25	21 25	22 25	23 29
Bromley Cross	d	20 28	21 28	22 28	23 32
Entwistle	d	20x34	21x34	22x34	23x38
Darwen	a	20 41	21 41	22 41	23 45
	d	20 41	21 41	22 41	23 45
Blackpool North	97 d				
Preston 8	97 d				
Blackburn	a	20 50	21 50	22 50	23 54
	d	20 52	21 52	22 51	
Ramsgreave & Wilpshire	d	20 58	21 58	22 57	
Langho	d	21 02	22 02	23 01	
Whalley	d	21 06	22 06	23 05	
Clitheroe	a	21 17	22 17	23 16	

Table 94

Sundays

8 December to 29 December

Manchester and Bolton - Blackburn - Clitheroe

Network Diagram - see first Page of Table 82

		NT	NT	NT	NT	NT	NT	NT	NT		NT		NT
Manchester Victoria 82 ⛴	d	08 01		09 00	10 00	11 00	12 00		13 00		21 00		22 00
Salford Central 82	d												
Manchester Piccadilly 10 82 ⛴	d												
Salford Crescent 82	d	08 08		09 07	10 08	11 08	12 08		13 08		21 08		22 08
Bolton 82	d	08 20		09 19	10 20	11 20	12 20		13 20		21 20		22 20
Hall I' Th' Wood	d	08 25		09 24	10 25	11 25	12 25		13 25		21 25		22 25
Bromley Cross	d	08 28		09 27	10 28	11 28	12 28		13 28	and	21 28		22 28
Entwistle	d	08x34		09x33	10x34	11x34	12x34		13x34	hourly	21x34		22x34
Darwen	a	08 41		09 40	10 41	11 41	12 41		13 41	until	21 41		22 41
	d	08 41		09 40	10 41	11 41	12 41		13 41		21 41		22 41
Blackpool North 97	d		08 10										
Preston 8 97	d		08 39					13 18					
Blackburn	a	08 48	08 59	09 48	10 48	11 48	12 48	13 37	13 48		21 48		22 50
	d	08 54	09 04	09 50	10 50	11 50	12 50	13 39	13 50		21 50		
Ramsgreave & Wilpshire	d	09 00	09 11	09 56	10 56	11 56	12 56	13 45	13 56		21 56		
Langho	d	09 04	09 16	10 00	11 00	12 00	13 00	13 50	14 00		22 00		
Whalley	d	09 08	09 20	10 04	11 04	12 04	13 04	13 55	14 04		22 04		
Clitheroe	a	09 19	09 27	10 15	11 15	12 15	13 15	14 01	14 15		22 15		

Sundays

5 January to 11 May

		NT	NT	NT	NT	NT	NT	NT	NT		NT		NT
Manchester Victoria 82 ⛴	d												
Salford Central 82	d												
Manchester Piccadilly 10 82 ⛴	d												
Salford Crescent 82	d	08 08		09 07	10 10	11 10	12 10		13 10		21 10		22 10
Bolton 82	d	08 20		09 19	10 22	11 22	12 22		13 22		21 22		22 22
Hall I' Th' Wood	d	08 25		09 24	10 27	11 27	12 27		13 27		21 27		22 27
Bromley Cross	d	08 28		09 27	10 30	11 30	12 30		13 30	and	21 30		22 30
Entwistle	d	08x34		09x33	10x36	11x36	12x36		13x36	hourly	21x36		22x36
Darwen	a	08 41		09 40	10 43	11 43	12 43		13 43	until	21 43		22 43
	d	08 41		09 40	10 43	11 43	12 43		13 43		21 43		22 43
Blackpool North 97	d		08 10										
Preston 8 97	d		08 39					13 18					
Blackburn	a	08 48	08 59	09 48	10 50	11 50	12 50	13 37	13 50		21 50		22 52
	d	08 54	09 04	09 50	10 51	11 51	12 51	13 39	13 51		21 51		
Ramsgreave & Wilpshire	d	09 00	09 11	09 56	10 57	11 57	12 57	13 45	13 57		21 57		
Langho	d	09 04	09 16	10 00	11 01	12 01	13 01	13 50	14 01		22 01		
Whalley	d	09 08	09 20	10 04	11 05	12 05	13 05	13 55	14 05		22 05		
Clitheroe	a	09 19	09 27	10 15	11 16	12 16	13 16	14 01	14 16		22 16		

Table 94R

Mondays to Fridays

9 December to 16 May

Clitheroe - Blackburn - Bolton and Manchester

Network Diagram - see first Page of Table 82

Miles			NT	NT	NT	NT	NT	NT	NT	NT		NT	NT	NT	NT	NT	NT	NT	NT	NT	NT	NT FX
0	**Clitheroe**	d		06 40	07 07	07 40		08 26		09 40	and hourly until	13 40	14 40	15 26	16 40	17 09	18 09	18 40		19 40	20 40	21 40
2½	Whalley	d		06 46	07 13	07 45		08 32		09 46		13 46	14 46	15 32	16 46	17 15	18 15	18 46		19 46	20 46	21 46
4½	Langho	d		06 50	07 17	07 49		08 36		09 50		13 50	14 50	15 36	16 49	17 19	18 19	18 50		19 50	20 50	21 50
7	Ramsgreave & Wilpshire	d		06 55	07 22	07 54		08 41		09 55		13 55	14 55	15 41	16 55	17 24	18 24	18 55		19 55	20 55	21 55
9¾	**Blackburn**	a		07 01	07 28	08 01		08 47		10 01		14 01	15 01	15 48	17 01	17 30	18 30	19 01		20 01	21 01	22 01
—		d	06 28	07 02	07 29	08 03	08 31	09 03	09 31	10 03		14 03	15 03	15 52	17 03	17 31	18 31	19 03	19 31	20 03	21 03	22 03
—	Preston 8 97	a																				
—	Blackpool North 97	a																				
14	Darwen	a	06 35	07 09	07 37	08 10	08 38	09 11	09 38	10 10		14 10	15 10	15 59	17 10	17 38	18 38	19 10	19 38	20 10	21 10	22 10
—		d	06 35	07 09	07 40	08 10	08 42	09 11	09 41	10 10		14 10	15 10	15 59	17 10	17 41	18 41	19 10	19 42	20 10	21 10	22 10
17¾	Entwistle	d	06x42	07x16		08x17				10x17		14x17	15x17		17x17	17x48	18x48	19x17	19x49	20x17	21x17	22x17
20¾	Bromley Cross	d	06 48	07 22	07 51	08 23	08 52	09 22	09 52	10 23		14 23	15 23	16 10	17 23	17 54	18 54	19 23	19 54	20 23	21 23	22 23
21¾	Hall I' Th' Wood	d	06 50	07 24	07 53	08 25	08 57	09 25	09 55	10 25		14 25	15 25	16 13	17 25	17 56	18 56	19 25	19 57	20 25	21 25	22 25
23½	**Bolton** 82	a	06 55	07 30	07 58	08 30	09 02	09 30	10 00	10 30		14 30	15 30	16 18	17 30	18 01	19 01	19 31	20 02	20 30	21 30	22 30
32½	Salford Crescent 82	a	07 15	07 43	08 17	08 43	09 14	09 43	10 13	10 43		14 43	15 43	16 31	17 43	18 15	19 14	19 44	20 15	20 43	21 43	22 43
—	Manchester Piccadilly 10 82 ⛴	a																				
33½	Salford Central 82	a	07 18	07 46	08 20	08 46	09 18	09 46	10 16	10 46		14 46	15 46	16 34	17 46	18 17	19 17	19 46	20 17	20 46	21 46	
34¼	**Manchester Victoria** 82 ⛴	a	07 22	07 53	08 25	08 52	09 22	09 52	10 21	10 52		14 52	15 54	16 41	17 53	18 24	19 23	19 53	20 24	20 52	21 52	22 52

		NT FO	NT	NT
Clitheroe	d	21 40	22 40	23 24
Whalley	d	21 46	22 46	23 30
Langho	d	21 50	22 50	23 34
Ramsgreave & Wilpshire	d	21 55	22 55	23 39
Blackburn	a	22 01	23 01	23 45
	d	22 03	23 03	
Preston 8 97	a			
Blackpool North 97	a			
Darwen	a	22 10	23 10	
	d	22 10	23 10	
Entwistle	d	22x17	23x17	
Bromley Cross	d	22 23	23 23	
Hall I' Th' Wood	d	22 25	23 25	
Bolton 82	a	22 30	23 30	
Salford Crescent 82	a	22 43	23 43	
Manchester Piccadilly 10 82 ⛴	a			
Salford Central 82	a	22 46		
Manchester Victoria 82 ⛴	a	22 54	23 50	

Saturdays

14 December to 17 May

		NT	NT	NT	NT	NT	NT	NT	NT	NT	NT	NT	NT	NT	NT	NT	NT	NT	NT	NT	NT	NT	NT	NT
Clitheroe	d		07 07	07 40		08 26		09 40		10 40		11 40	12 40	13 40	14 40	15 26	16 40	17 09	18 09	18 40		19 40	20 40
Whalley	d		07 13	07 45		08 32		09 46		10 46		11 46	12 46	13 46	14 46	15 32	16 46	17 15	18 15	18 46		19 46	20 46
Langho	d		07 17	07 49		08 36		09 50		10 50		11 50	12 50	13 50	14 50	15 36	16 50	17 19	18 19	18 50		19 50	20 50
Ramsgreave & Wilpshire	d		07 22	07 54		08 41		09 55		10 55		11 55	12 55	13 55	14 55	15 41	16 55	17 24	18 24	18 55		19 55	20 55
Blackburn	a		07 28	08 01		08 47		10 01		11 01		12 01	13 01	14 01	15 01	15 47	17 01	17 30	18 30	19 01		20 01	21 01
	d	06 29	07 29	08 03	08 31	09 03	09 31	10 03	10 31	11 03	11 31	12 03	13 03	14 03	15 03	15 51	17 03	17 31	18 31	19 03	19 31	20 03	21 03
Preston 8 97	a																						
Blackpool North 97	a																						
Darwen	a	06 36	07 37	08 10	08 38	09 11	09 38	10 10	10 38	11 10	11 38	12 10	13 10	14 10	15 10	15 58	17 10	17 38	18 38	19 10	19 38	20 10	21 10
	d	06 36	07 40	08 10	08 41	09 11	09 41	10 10	10 41	11 10	11 41	12 10	13 10	14 10	15 10	15 58	17 10	17 41	18 41	19 10	19 42	20 10	21 10
Entwistle	d	06x43		08x17				10x17		11x17		12x17	13x17	14x17	15x17		17x17	17x48	18x48	19x17	19x49	20x17	21x17
Bromley Cross	d	06 49	07 51	08 23	08 51	09 22	09 52	10 23	10 52	11 23	11 52	12 23	13 23	14 23	15 23	16 09	17 23	17 54	18 54	19 23	19 54	20 23	21 23
Hall I' Th' Wood	d	06 51	07 53	08 25	08 56	09 25	09 55	10 25	10 54	11 25	11 55	12 25	13 25	14 25	15 25	16 12	17 25	17 56	18 56	19 26	19 57	20 25	21 25
Bolton 82	a	06 56	07 58	08 30	09 01	09 30	10 00	10 30	10 59	11 30	12 00	12 30	13 30	14 30	15 30	16 17	17 30	18 01	19 01	19 31	20 02	20 30	21 30
Salford Crescent 82	a	07 16	08 17	08 43	09 14	09 43	10 13	10 43	11 11	11 43	12 13	12 43	13 43	14 43	15 43	16 30	17 43	18 14	19 14	19 44	20 15	20 43	21 43
Manchester Piccadilly 10 82 ⛴	a																						
Salford Central 82	a	07 19	08 20	08 46	09 18	09 46	10 16	10 46	11 15	11 46	12 16	12 46	13 46	14 46	15 46	16 33	17 46	18 17	19 17	19 47	20 17	20 46	21 46
Manchester Victoria 82 ⛴	a	07 25	08 25	08 52	09 22	09 52	10 21	10 52	11 20	11 52	12 22	12 52	13 52	14 52	15 54	16 41	17 53	18 24	19 23	19 53	20 24	20 52	21 52

		NT	NT	NT
Clitheroe	d	21 40	22 46	23 24
Whalley	d	21 46	22 52	23 30
Langho	d	21 50	22 56	23 34
Ramsgreave & Wilpshire	d	21 55	23 01	23 39
Blackburn	a	22 01	23 07	23 45
	d	22 03	23 09	
Preston 8 97	a			
Blackpool North 97	a			
Darwen	a	22 10	23 16	
	d	22 10	23 16	
Entwistle	d	22x17	23x23	
Bromley Cross	d	22 23	23 29	
Hall I' Th' Wood	d	22 25	23 31	
Bolton 82	a	22 30	23 36	
Salford Crescent 82	a	22 43	23 50	
Manchester Piccadilly 10 82 ⛴	a			
Salford Central 82	a	22 46		
Manchester Victoria 82 ⛴	a	22 52	00 01	

Table 94R

Sundays

8 December to 29 December

Clitheroe - Blackburn - Bolton and Manchester

Network Diagram - see first Page of Table 82

		NT	NT	NT	NT	NT		NT	NT	NT	NT	NT	NT	NT		NT
Clitheroe	d		09 40	10 40	10 55	11 40	and hourly until	14 40	15 18	15 40	16 40	17 40	18 40	19 40	and hourly until	22 40
Whalley	d		09 46	10 46	11 01	11 46		14 46	15 24	15 46	16 46	17 46	18 46	19 46		22 46
Langho	d		09 50	10 50	11 06	11 50		14 50	15 29	15 50	16 50	17 50	18 50	19 50		22 50
Ramsgreave & Wilpshire	d		09 55	10 55	11 11	11 55		14 55	15 34	15 55	16 55	17 55	18 55	19 55		22 55
Blackburn	a		10 01	11 01	11 20	12 01		15 01	15 43	16 01	17 01	18 01	19 01	20 01		23 01
	d	09 03	10 03	11 03	11 22	12 03		15 03	15 44	16 04	17 03	18 03	19 03	20 03		23 03
Preston 8	97 a				11 46				16 04							
Blackpool North	97 a								16 33							
Darwen	a	09 10	10 09	11 10		12 10		15 10		16 12	17 10	18 10	19 10	20 10		23 10
	d	09 10	10 09	11 10		12 10		15 10		16 12	17 10	18 10	19 10	20 10		23 10
Entwistle	d	09x17	10x16	11x17		12x17		15x17			17x17	18x17	19x17	20x17		23x17
Bromley Cross	d	09 23	10 23	11 23		12 23		15 23		16 23	17 23	18 23	19 23	20 23		23 23
Hall I' Th' Wood	d	09 25	10 24	11 25		12 25		15 25		16 25	17 25	18 25	19 25	20 25		23 25
Bolton	82 a	09 30	10 30	11 30		12 30		15 30		16 30	17 30	18 30	19 30	20 30		23 30
Salford Crescent	82 a	09 43	10 43	11 43		12 43		15 43		16 43	17 43	18 43	19 43	20 43		23 43
Manchester Piccadilly 10 82	a															
Salford Central	82 a															
Manchester Victoria	82 a	09 52	10 52	11 52		12 52		15 52		16 52	17 52	18 52	19 51	20 52		23 52

Sundays

5 January to 11 May

		NT	NT	NT	NT	NT		NT	NT	NT	NT		NT	NT
Clitheroe	d		09 40	10 40	10 55	11 40	and hourly until	14 40	15 18	15 40	16 40	and hourly until	21 40	22 40
Whalley	d		09 46	10 46	11 01	11 46		14 46	15 24	15 46	16 46		21 46	22 46
Langho	d		09 50	10 50	11 06	11 50		14 50	15 29	15 50	16 50		21 50	22 50
Ramsgreave & Wilpshire	d		09 55	10 55	11 11	11 55		14 55	15 34	15 55	16 55		21 55	22 55
Blackburn	a		10 01	11 01	11 20	12 01		15 01	15 43	16 01	17 01		22 01	23 01
	d	09 03	10 03	11 03	11 22	12 03		15 03	15 44	16 04	17 03		22 03	23 03
Preston 8	97 a				11 46				16 04					
Blackpool North	97 a								16 33					
Darwen	a	09 10	10 09	11 10		12 10		15 10		16 12	17 10		22 10	23 10
	d	09 10	10 09	11 10		12 10		15 10		16 12	17 10		22 10	23 10
Entwistle	d	09x17	10x16	11x17		12x17		15x17			17x17		22x17	23x17
Bromley Cross	d	09 23	10 23	11 23		12 23		15 23		16 23	17 23		22 23	23 23
Hall I' Th' Wood	d	09 25	10 25	11 26		12 26		15 26		16 26	17 26		22 26	23 25
Bolton	82 a	09 30	10 31	11 31		12 31		15 31		16 31	17 31		22 31	23 30
Salford Crescent	82 a	09 43	10 44	11 44		12 44		15 44		16 44	17 44		22 44	23 43
Manchester Piccadilly 10 82	a													
Salford Central	82 a													
Manchester Victoria	82 a													

Network Diagram for Tables 97, 98, 99, 100

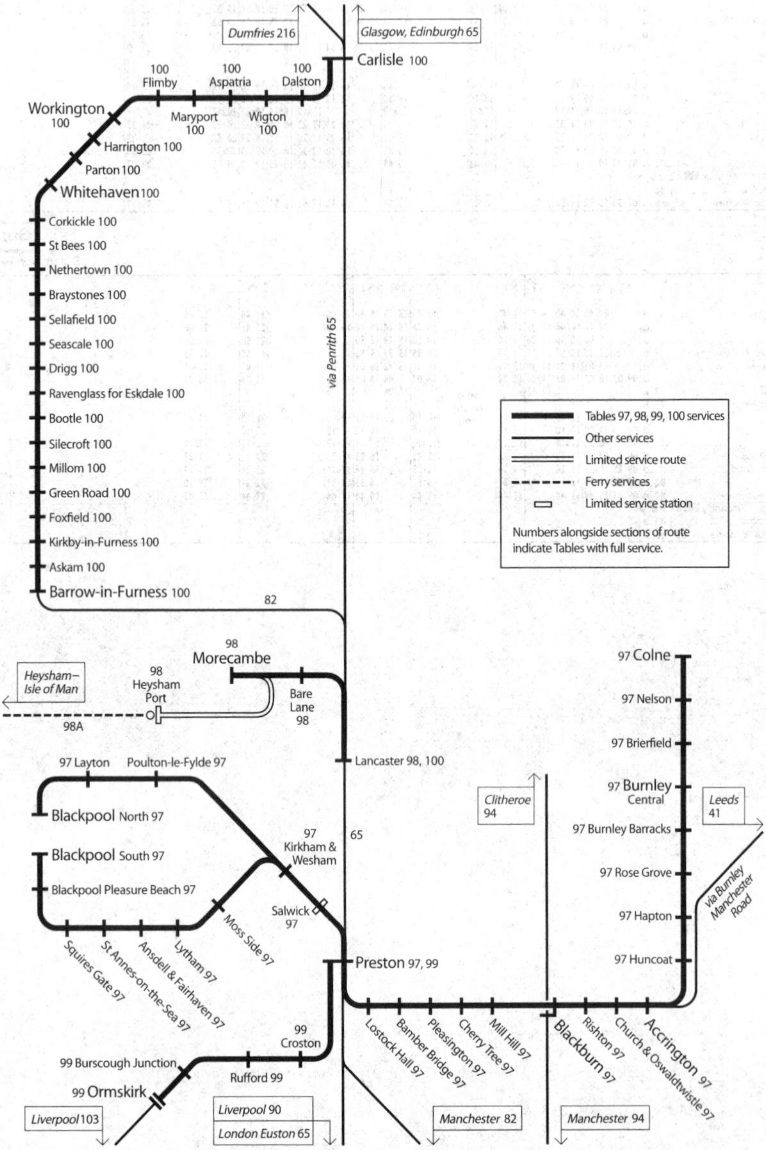

Dumfries 216
Glasgow, Edinburgh 65
Carlisle 100
100 Flimby
100 Aspatria
100 Dalston
Workington 100
Maryport 100
Wigton 100
Harrington 100
Parton 100
Whitehaven 100
Corkickle 100
St Bees 100
Nethertown 100
Braystones 100
Sellafield 100
Seascale 100
Drigg 100
Ravenglass for Eskdale 100
Bootle 100
Silecroft 100
Millom 100
Green Road 100
Foxfield 100
Kirkby-in-Furness 100
Askam 100
Barrow-in-Furness 100
82
via Penrith 65
Tables 97, 98, 99, 100 services
Other services
Limited service route
Ferry services
Limited service station
Numbers alongside sections of route indicate Tables with full service.
98 Morecambe
Heysham–Isle of Man
98 Heysham Port
98A
Bare Lane 98
Lancaster 98, 100
97 Layton
Poulton-le-Fylde 97
Blackpool North 97
97 Kirkham & Wesham
65
Blackpool South 97
Blackpool Pleasure Beach 97
Salwick 97
Moss Side 97
Squires Gate 97
St Annes-on-the-Sea 97
Ansdell & Fairhaven 97
Lytham 97
Preston 97, 99
99 Croston
99 Burscough Junction
99 Ormskirk
Rufford 99
Liverpool 103
Liverpool 90
London Euston 65
Manchester 82
Manchester 94
Clitheroe 94
97 Colne
97 Nelson
97 Brierfield
97 Burnley Central
Leeds 41
97 Burnley Barracks
97 Rose Grove
97 Hapton
97 Huncoat
via Burnley Manchester Road
Lostock Hall 97
Bamber Bridge 97
Pleasington 97
Cherry Tree 97
Mill Hill 97
Blackburn 97
Rishton 97
Church & Oswaldtwistle 97
Accrington 97

TOCs operating on this network - Northern (NT), First TransPennine Express (TP)

Table 97

Mondays to Fridays

9 December to 21 March

Colne, Burnley, Accrington and Blackburn - Preston - Blackpool

Network Diagram - see first Page of Table 97

Miles	Miles			TP MO ◇1 A	TP MO ◇1 B	TP MO ◇1 C	TP MX ◇1 D	NT MX E	TP MO ◇1 F	TP ◇1 G	NT	NT E		NT	TP ◇1 H	NT	NT E	NT	NT	NT I	TP ◇1 J	NT E		NT	TP ◇1 J
0	—	**Colne**	d								05 41					06 47			07 48						
2	—	Nelson	d								05 45					06 51			07 52						
3¼	—	Brierfield	d								05 48					06 54			07 55						
5½	—	**Burnley Central**	d								05 53					06 59			08 00						
—	—	Burnley Barracks	d								05x55					07x01			08x02						
—	—	Leeds 10	41 d																						
—	—	Burnley Manchester Road	41 d											06 52				07 53						08 52	
7	—	Rose Grove	d								05 58					07 05			08 05						
8½	—	Hapton	d								06x01								08x08						
10	—	Huncoat	d								06 04					07 09			08 11						
11¾	—	Accrington	d								06 09			07 06		07 14		08 06	08 16					09 06	
12½	—	Church & Oswaldtwistle	d								06 11			07 09				08 09							
14¼	—	Rishton	d								06 14					07 18			08 20						
18	—	**Blackburn**	a								06 23			07 16		07 24		08 16	08 26					09 14	
—	—	Clitheroe	94 d																						
—	—	**Blackburn**	d								06 25			07 16		07 35		08 16	08 35					09 15	
19¼	—	Mill Hill (Lancashire)	d								06 28					07 38		08 20	08 38						
20	—	Cherry Tree	d								06 30					07 40			08 40						
21	—	Pleasington	d								06x32					07x42			08x42						
26	—	Bamber Bridge	d								06 39			07 26		07 49		08 28	08 49						
27¼	—	Lostock Hall	d								06 42			07 28		07 52		08 31	08 52						
30	—	**Preston 8**	a								06 50			07 36		08 00		08 39	09 00					09 32	
—	—		d					00 21	06 33	06 35	07 00	07 13		07 38	07 42	08 02	08 15	08 41	09 02	08 51	08 59	09 19		09 34	09 38
35¼	5¼	Salwick	d								07 07					08 09									
37¾	7¾	Kirkham & Wesham	d					00 30	06 43	06 44	07 11	07 22			07 51	08 13	08 25		09 11			09 28			
41	—	Moss Side	d								07 17					08 19			09 17						
43½	—	Lytham	d								07 21					08 23			09 21						
44¾	—	Ansdell & Fairhaven	d								07 24					08 26			09 24						
46¾	—	St Annes-on-the-Sea	d								07 28					08 30			09 28						
48¼	—	Squires Gate	d								07 32					08 34			09 32						
49½	—	Blackpool Pleasure Beach	d								07 34					08 36			09 34						
50	—	**Blackpool South**	a								07 38					08 41			09 39						
—	14¼	Poulton-le-Fylde	d	00 02	00 05	00 06	00 08	00 38	06 53	06 54		07 30		07 54	08 01		08 33	08 57			09 16	09 36		09 51	09 56
—	16¼	Layton	d					00 43	06 56	06 58		07 34			08 04		08 37					09 43			
—	17½	**Blackpool North**	a	00 10	00 14	00 15	00 16	00 50	07 03	07 05		07 41		08 05	08 11		08 44	09 06		09 16	09 25	09 50		10 01	10 05

		NT K	NT	NT E	NT	TP ◇1 J	NT K	NT		NT E	NT	TP ◇1 J	NT L	NT	NT E	NT	TP ◇1 J	NT L		NT	NT E	NT	TP ◇1 J	NT L	NT
Colne	d		08 41					09 51						10 51						11 51					12 51
Nelson	d		08 45					09 55						10 55						11 55					12 55
Brierfield	d		08 48					09 58						10 58						11 58					12 58
Burnley Central	d		09 03					10 03						11 03						12 03					13 03
Burnley Barracks	d		09x05					10x05						11x05						12x05					13x05
Leeds 10	41 d																								
Burnley Manchester Road	41 d				09 52						10 52					11 52						12 52			
Rose Grove	d		09 08					10 08						11 08						12 08					13 08
Hapton	d		09x11					10x11						11x11						12x11					13x11
Huncoat	d		09 14					10 14						11 14						12 14					13 14
Accrington	d		09 19		10 06			10 19			11 06			11 19		12 06				12 19		13 06			13 19
Church & Oswaldtwistle	d		09 21					10 21						11 21						12 21					13 21
Rishton	d		09 24					10 24						11 24						12 24					13 24
Blackburn	a		09 33		10 14			10 34			11 14			11 33		12 14				12 33		13 14			13 33
Clitheroe	94 d																								
Blackburn	d		09 34		10 15			10 35			11 15			11 35		12 15				12 35		13 15			13 35
Mill Hill (Lancashire)	d		09 37					10 38						11 38						12 38					13 38
Cherry Tree	d		09 39					10 40						11 40						12 40					13 40
Pleasington	d		09x42					10x42						11x42						12x42					13x42
Bamber Bridge	d		09 49					10 49						11 49						12 49					13 49
Lostock Hall	d		09 51					10 52						11 52						12 52					13 52
Preston 8	a		10 00		10 32			11 00			11 32			12 00		12 32				13 00		13 32			14 00
	d	09 55	10 01	10 19	10 34	10 38	10 55	11 02		11 19	11 34	11 38	11 55	12 02	12 19	12 34	12 38	12 55		13 02	13 19	13 34	13 38	13 55	14 02
Salwick	d													12 09											
Kirkham & Wesham	d	10 05	10 11	10 28			11 05	11 11		11 28			12 05	12 13	12 28			13 05		13 11	13 28			14 05	14 11
Moss Side	d		10 17					11 17						12 19						13 17					14 17
Lytham	d		10 21					11 21						12 23						13 21					14 21
Ansdell & Fairhaven	d		10 24					11 24						12 26						13 24					14 24
St Annes-on-the-Sea	d		10 28					11 28						12 30						13 28					14 28
Squires Gate	d		10 31					11 32						12 34						13 32					14 32
Blackpool Pleasure Beach	d		10 34					11 34						12 36						13 34					14 34
Blackpool South	a		10 39					11 39						12 41						13 39					14 39
Poulton-le-Fylde	d			10 36	10 51	10 56				11 36	11 50	11 56			12 36	12 50	12 56				13 36	13 50	13 56		
Layton	d			10 41						11 43					12 43						13 43				
Blackpool North	a	10 21		10 50	11 01	11 05	11 21			11 50	12 00	12 05	12 21		12 50	13 00	13 05	13 21			13 50	14 00	14 05	14 21	

A from 17 February. From Manchester Airport
B until 30 December. From Manchester Airport
C from 6 January until 10 February. From Manchester Airport
D From Windermere
E From Manchester Victoria
F from 10 February. From Manchester Airport
G until 7 February, MX from 11 February. From Manchester Airport
H From Barrow-in-Furness
I From Buxton
J From Manchester Airport
K From Liverpool Lime Street
L From Liverpool South Pw Hl

Table 97

Mondays to Fridays

9 December to 21 March

Colne, Burnley, Accrington and Blackburn - Preston - Blackpool

Network Diagram - see first Page of Table 97

	NT A	NT	TP ◇1 B	NT C	NT	NT A	NT	TP ◇1 B	NT C	NT	NT	TP ◇1 B	NT C	NT	NT A	TP ◇1 B	NT	NT C	NT	NT A	NT D
Colne d					13 51					14 51				15 51					16 51		
Nelson d					13 55					14 55				15 55					16 55		
Brierfield d					13 58					14 58				15 58					16 58		
Burnley Central d					14 03					15 03				16 03					17 03		
Burnley Barracks d					14x05					15x05				16x05					17x05		
Leeds 10 41 d																					
Burnley Manchester Road 41 d		13 52					14 52				15 52						16 52				
Rose Grove d					14 08					15 08				16 08					17 08		
Hapton d					14x11					15x11				16x11					17x11		
Huncoat d					14 14					15 14				16 14					17 14		
Accrington d		14 06			14 19		15 06			15 19	16 06			16 19			17 06		17 19		
Church & Oswaldtwistle d					14 21					15 21				16 21					17 21		
Rishton d					14 24					15 24				16 24					17 24		
Blackburn a		14 14			14 33		15 14			15 33	16 14			16 33			17 14		17 33		
Clitheroe 94 d																					
Blackburn d		14 15			14 35		15 15			15 35	16 15			16 35			17 15		17 35		
Mill Hill (Lancashire) d					14 38					15 38				16 38					17 38		
Cherry Tree d					14 40					15 40				16 40					17 40		
Pleasington d					14x42					15x42				16x42					17x42		
Bamber Bridge d					14 49					15 49				16 49					17 49		
Lostock Hall d					14 52					15 52				16 52					17 52		
Preston 8 a		14 32			15 00		15 32			16 00	16 32			17 00			17 32		18 00		
d	14 19	14 34	14 38	14 55	15 02	15 19	15 34	15 38	15 55	16 02	16 34	16 38	16 55	17 02	17 21	17 32	17 35	17 55	18 02	18 18	18 26
Salwick d										16 09											
Kirkham & Wesham d	14 28			15 05	15 11	15 28			16 05	16 13		16 47	17 05	17 11	17 30	17 42		18 05	18 11	18 27	
Moss Side d					15 17					16 19				17 17					18 17		
Lytham d					15 21					16 23				17 21					18 21		
Ansdell & Fairhaven d					15 24					16 26				17 24					18 24		
St Annes-on-the-Sea d					15 28					16 30				17 28					18 28		
Squires Gate d					15 32					16 34				17 32					18 32		
Blackpool Pleasure Beach d					15 34					16 36				17 34					18 34		
Blackpool South a					15 39					16 41				17 39					18 39		
Poulton-le-Fylde d	14 36	14 50	14 56			15 36	15 50	15 56			16 50	16 57	17 12		17 38	17 51	17 56	18 13		18 35	18 43
Layton d	14 42					15 43						17 00			17 43	17 54				18 39	
Blackpool North a	14 50	15 00	15 05	15 21		15 50	16 00	16 05	16 21		17 00	17 07	17 21		17 50	18 02	18 06	18 24		18 46	18 55

	NT	TP ◇1 B	NT D	NT E	NT	NT	NT A	NT	NT	TP ◇1 B	NT E	NT A	NT	NT	TP ◇1 B	NT F	NT A	NT	NT E	TP ◇1 B	NT A	NT
Colne d					17 51				18 55					19 51				20 51				21 46
Nelson d					17 55				18 59					19 55				20 55				21 50
Brierfield d					17 58				19 02					19 58				20 58				21 53
Burnley Central d					18 03				19 07					20 03				21 03				21 58
Burnley Barracks d					18x05				19x09					20x05				21x05				22x00
Leeds 10 41 d																						
Burnley Manchester Road 41 d	17 52							18 52					19 52			20 40						
Rose Grove d					18 08				19 12					20 08				21 08				22 03
Hapton d					18x11				19x15					20x11				21 11				22x06
Huncoat d					18 14				19 18					20 14				21x14				22 09
Accrington d	18 06				18 19			19 06	19 23				20 06	20 19				21 19				22 14
Church & Oswaldtwistle d					18 21				19 25					20 21				21 21				22 16
Rishton d					18 24				19 28					20 24				21 24				22 19
Blackburn a	18 14				18 33			19 14	19 33				20 14	20 33				21 33				22 24
Clitheroe 94 d																						
Blackburn d	18 15				18 35	18 44		19 15	19 35				20 15	20 35				21 35				22 25
Mill Hill (Lancashire) d					18 38				19 38					20 38				21 38				22 28
Cherry Tree d					18 40				19 40					20 40				21 40				22 30
Pleasington d					18x42				19x42					20x42				21x42				22x32
Bamber Bridge d					18 49				19 49					20 49				21 49				22 39
Lostock Hall d					18 52				19 52					20 52				21 52				22 42
Preston 8 a	18 33				19 00	19 05		19 32	20 00				20 32	21 00		21 48		22 02				22 50
d	18 34	18 40	18 51	18 54	19 02	19 08	19 19	19 34	20 02	19 38	20 19	20 25	20 34	21 02	20 38		21 19		21 24	21 38	22 19	22 51
Salwick d																						
Kirkham & Wesham d		18 49		19 04	19 11		19 28		20 11			20 34		21 11			21 28				22 28	23 01
Moss Side d					19 17				20 17					21 17								23 07
Lytham d					19 21				20 21					21 21								23 11
Ansdell & Fairhaven d					19 24				20 24					21 24								23 14
St Annes-on-the-Sea d					19 28				20 28					21 28								23 18
Squires Gate d					19 32				20 32					21 32								23 21
Blackpool Pleasure Beach d					19 34				20 34					21 34								23 24
Blackpool South a					19 39				20 39					21 39								23 28
Poulton-le-Fylde d	18 50	18 59					19 36	19 50		19 56		20 42	20 50		20 56		21 36			21 56	22 36	
Layton d		19 02					19 43					20 47					21 40				22 42	
Blackpool North a	19 00	19 09	19 15	19 22		19 33	19 50	20 00		20 05	20 44	20 54	21 00		21 05		21 48		21 53	22 05	22 50	

A From Manchester Victoria
B From Manchester Airport
C From Liverpool South Pw Hl
D From Buxton
E From Liverpool Lime Street
F not 25 December, 26 December. From Hebden Bridge

Table 97

Mondays to Fridays

9 December to 21 March

Colne, Burnley, Accrington and Blackburn - Preston - Blackpool

Network Diagram - see first Page of Table 97

		TP	NT	NT	NT	NT	TP	TP
		◇1					◇1	◇1
		A	B		C		A	D
Colne	d					22 56		
Nelson	d					23 00		
Brierfield	d					23 03		
Burnley Central	d					23 08		
Burnley Barracks	d					23x10		
Leeds 10 41	d							
Burnley Manchester Road 41	d			22 23				
Rose Grove	d					23 13		
Hapton	d							
Huncoat	d							
Accrington	d			22 38		23 20		
Church & Oswaldtwistle	d							
Rishton	d							
Blackburn	a			22 46		23 28		
Clitheroe 94	d							
Blackburn	d			22 46		23 30		
Mill Hill (Lancashire)	d					23 33		
Cherry Tree	d							
Pleasington	d							
Bamber Bridge	d					23 41		
Lostock Hall	d					23 43		
Preston 8	a			23 03		23 54		
	d	22 38	22 57	23 05	23 19		23 35	23 51
Salwick	d							
Kirkham & Wesham	d				23 28			
Moss Side	d							
Lytham	d							
Ansdell & Fairhaven	d							
St Annes-on-the-Sea	d							
Squires Gate	d							
Blackpool Pleasure Beach	d							
Blackpool South	a							
Poulton-le-Fylde	d	22 55		23 22	23 36		23 52	00 08
Layton	d				23 40			
Blackpool North	a	23 04	23 22	23 32	23 48		00 01	00 16

Mondays to Fridays

24 March to 16 May

		TP	TP MO	TP MX	NT MX	TP	TP	NT	NT	NT	TP	NT	NT	NT	NT	NT	TP	NT	NT	TP	NT	NT	NT
		◇1	◇1	◇1		◇1	◇1				◇1						◇1			◇1			
		E	F	D	C	G	H		C		I		C	J		K	A ✠	C	J	A ✠	B		C
Colne	d							05 41				06 47			07 48							08 41	
Nelson	d							05 45				06 51			07 52							08 45	
Brierfield	d							05 48				06 54			07 55							08 48	
Burnley Central	d							05 53				06 59			08 00							09 03	
Burnley Barracks	d							05x55				07x01			08x02							09x05	
Leeds 10 41	d									05 51				06 51					07 51				
Burnley Manchester Road 41	d									06 57				07 57					08 57				
Rose Grove	d							05 58				07 05			08 05							09 08	
Hapton	d							06x01							08x08							09x11	
Huncoat	d							06 04				07 09			08 11							09 14	
Accrington	d							06 09		07 06		07 14		08 06	08 16				09 06			09 19	
Church & Oswaldtwistle	d							06 11		07 09				08 09								09 21	
Rishton	d							06 14				07 18			08 20							09 24	
Blackburn	a							06 23		07 16		07 24		08 16	08 26				09 14			09 33	
Clitheroe 94	d																						
Blackburn	d							06 25		07 16		07 35		08 16	08 35				09 15			09 34	
Mill Hill (Lancashire)	d							06 28				07 38		08 20	08 38							09 37	
Cherry Tree	d							06 30				07 40			08 40							09 39	
Pleasington	d							06x32				07x42			08x42							09x42	
Bamber Bridge	d							06 39		07 26		07 49		08 28	08 49							09 49	
Lostock Hall	d							06 42		07 28		07 52		08 31	08 52							09 51	
Preston 8	a							06 50		07 36		08 00		08 39	09 00				09 32			10 00	
	d				00 21	06 33	06 35	07 00	07 13	07 38	07 42	08 02	08 15	08 41	09 02	08 51	08 59	09 19	09 34	09 38	09 55	10 01	10 19
Salwick	d							07 07				08 09											
Kirkham & Wesham	d				00 30	06 43	06 44	07 11	07 22		07 51	08 13	08 25		09 11			09 28			10 05	10 11	10 28
Moss Side	d							07 17				08 19			09 17							10 17	
Lytham	d							07 21				08 23			09 21							10 21	
Ansdell & Fairhaven	d							07 24				08 26			09 24							10 24	
St Annes-on-the-Sea	d							07 28				08 30			09 28							10 28	
Squires Gate	d							07 32				08 34			09 32							10 31	
Blackpool Pleasure Beach	d							07 34				08 36			09 34							10 34	
Blackpool South	a							07 38				08 41			09 39							10 39	
Poulton-le-Fylde	d	00 02	00 05	00 08	00 38	06 53	06 54		07 30	07 54	08 01		08 33	08 57			09 16	09 36	09 51	09 56			10 36
Layton	d				00 43	06 56	06 58		07 34		08 04		08 37					09 43					10 41
Blackpool North	a	00 10	00 14	00 16	00 50	07 03	07 05		07 41	08 05	08 11		08 44	09 05		09 16	09 25	09 50	10 01	10 05	10 21		10 50

- **A** From Manchester Airport
- **B** From Liverpool Lime Street
- **C** From Manchester Victoria
- **D** From Windermere
- **E** 24 March. From Manchester Airport
- **F** from 31 March. From Manchester Airport
- **G** until 31 March, from 28 April. From Manchester Airport
- **H** from 1 April until 25 April. From Manchester Airport
- **I** From Barrow-in-Furness
- **J** From York
- **K** From Buxton

Table 97

Mondays to Fridays

24 March to 16 May

Colne, Burnley, Accrington and Blackburn - Preston - Blackpool

Network Diagram - see first Page of Table 97

		NT	TP	NT	NT	NT		NT	TP	NT	NT	NT	NT	TP	NT	NT		NT	NT	TP	NT	NT	NT	NT	TP
			◇1						◇1					◇1						◇1					◇1
		A	B 🛒	C		D		A	B 🛒	E		D	A	B 🛒	E			D	A	B 🛒	E		D	A	B 🛒
Colne	d				09 51						10 51					11 51						12 51			
Nelson	d				09 55						10 55					11 55						12 55			
Brierfield	d				09 58						10 58					11 58						12 58			
Burnley Central	d				10 03						11 03					12 03						13 03			
Burnley Barracks	d				10x05						11x05					12x05						13x05			
Leeds 10 41	d	08 51						09 53					10 53						11 53					12 53	
Burnley Manchester Road 41	d	09 57						10 57					11 57						12 57					13 57	
Rose Grove	d				10 08						11 08					12 08						13 08			
Hapton	d				10x11						11x11					12x11						13x11			
Huncoat	d				10 14						11 14					12 14						13 14			
Accrington	d	10 06			10 19			11 06			11 19		12 06			12 19			13 06			13 19		14 06	
Church & Oswaldtwistle	d				10 21						11 21					12 21						13 21			
Rishton	d				10 24						11 24					12 24						13 24			
Blackburn	a	10 14			10 34			11 14			11 33		12 14			12 33			13 14			13 33		14 14	
Clitheroe 94	d																								
Blackburn	d	10 15			10 35			11 15			11 35		12 15			12 35			13 15			13 35		14 15	
Mill Hill (Lancashire)	d				10 38						11 38					12 38						13 38			
Cherry Tree	d				10 40						11 40					12 40						13 40			
Pleasington	d				10x42						11x42					12x42						13x42			
Bamber Bridge	d				10 49						11 49					12 49						13 49			
Lostock Hall	d				10 52						11 52					12 52						13 52			
Preston 8	a	10 32			11 00			11 32			12 00		12 32			13 00			13 32			14 00		14 32	
	d	10 34	10 38	10 55	11 02	11 19		11 34	11 38	11 55	12 02	12 19	12 34	12 38	12 55	13 02		13 19	13 34	13 38	13 55	14 02	14 19	14 34	14 38
Salwick	d										12 09														
Kirkham & Wesham	d			11 05	11 11	11 28				12 05	12 13	12 28			13 05	13 11		13 28			14 05	14 11	14 28		
Moss Side	d				11 17						12 19					13 17						14 17			
Lytham	d				11 21						12 23					13 21						14 21			
Ansdell & Fairhaven	d				11 24						12 26					13 24						14 24			
St Annes-on-the-Sea	d				11 28						12 30					13 28						14 28			
Squires Gate	d				11 32						12 34					13 32						14 32			
Blackpool Pleasure Beach	d				11 34						12 36					13 34						14 34			
Blackpool South	a				11 39						12 41					13 39						14 39			
Poulton-le-Fylde	d	10 51	10 56			11 36		11 50	11 56			12 36	12 50	12 56				13 36	13 50	13 56			14 36	14 50	14 56
Layton	d					11 43						12 43						13 43					14 42		
Blackpool North	a	11 01	11 05	11 21		11 50		12 00	12 05	12 21		12 50	13 00	13 05	13 21			13 50	14 00	14 05	14 21		14 50	15 00	15 05

		NT		NT	NT	NT	TP	NT	NT	NT	TP	NT		NT	NT	TP	NT	NT	NT	NT	NT	NT		TP	NT
							◇1				◇1					◇1								◇1	
		E			D	A	B 🛒	E		A	B 🛒	E			D	B 🛒	A	E		D	F	A		B 🛒	F
Colne	d			13 51					14 51					15 51					16 51						
Nelson	d			13 55					14 55					15 55					16 55						
Brierfield	d			13 58					14 58					15 58					16 58						
Burnley Central	d			14 03					15 03					16 03					17 03						
Burnley Barracks	d			14x05					15x05					16x05					17x05						
Leeds 10 41	d					13 53				14 53							15 52					16 51			
Burnley Manchester Road 41	d					14 57				15 57							16 58					17 57			
Rose Grove	d			14 08					15 08					16 08					17 08						
Hapton	d			14x11					15x11					16x11					17x11						
Huncoat	d			14 14					15 14					16 14					17 14						
Accrington	d			14 19		15 06			15 19	16 06				16 19			17 06		17 19			18 06			
Church & Oswaldtwistle	d			14 21					15 21					16 21					17 21						
Rishton	d			14 24					15 24					16 24					17 24						
Blackburn	a			14 33		15 14			15 33	16 14				16 33			17 14		17 33			18 14			
Clitheroe 94	d																								
Blackburn	d			14 35		15 15			15 35	16 15				16 35			17 15		17 35			18 15			
Mill Hill (Lancashire)	d			14 38					15 38					16 38					17 38						
Cherry Tree	d			14 40					15 40					16 40					17 40						
Pleasington	d			14x42					15x42					16x42					17x42						
Bamber Bridge	d			14 49					15 49					16 49					17 49						
Lostock Hall	d			14 52					15 52					16 52					17 52						
Preston 8	a			15 00		15 32			16 00	16 32				17 00			17 32		18 00			18 33			
	d	14 55		15 02	15 19	15 34	15 38	15 55	16 02	16 34	16 38	16 55		17 02	17 21	17 32	17 35	17 55	18 02	18 18	18 26	18 34		18 40	18 51
Salwick	d								16 09																
Kirkham & Wesham	d	15 05		15 11	15 28			16 05	16 13		16 47	17 05		17 11	17 30	17 42		18 05	18 11	18 27				18 49	
Moss Side	d			15 17					16 19					17 17					18 17						
Lytham	d			15 21					16 23					17 21					18 21						
Ansdell & Fairhaven	d			15 24					16 26					17 24					18 24						
St Annes-on-the-Sea	d			15 28					16 30					17 28					18 28						
Squires Gate	d			15 32					16 34					17 32					18 32						
Blackpool Pleasure Beach	d			15 34					16 36					17 34					18 34						
Blackpool South	a			15 39					16 41					17 39					18 39						
Poulton-le-Fylde	d				15 36	15 50	15 56			16 50	16 57	17 12			17 38	17 51	17 56	18 13		18 35	18 43	18 50		18 59	
Layton	d				15 43						17 00				17 43	17 54				18 39				19 02	
Blackpool North	a	15 21			15 50	16 00	16 05	16 21		17 00	17 07	17 21			17 50	18 02	18 06	18 24		18 46	18 55	19 00		19 09	19 15

A From York
B From Manchester Airport
C From Liverpool Lime Street
D From Manchester Victoria
E From Liverpool South Pw Hl
F From Buxton

Table 97

Mondays to Fridays

24 March to 16 May

Colne, Burnley, Accrington and Blackburn - Preston - Blackpool

Network Diagram - see first Page of Table 97

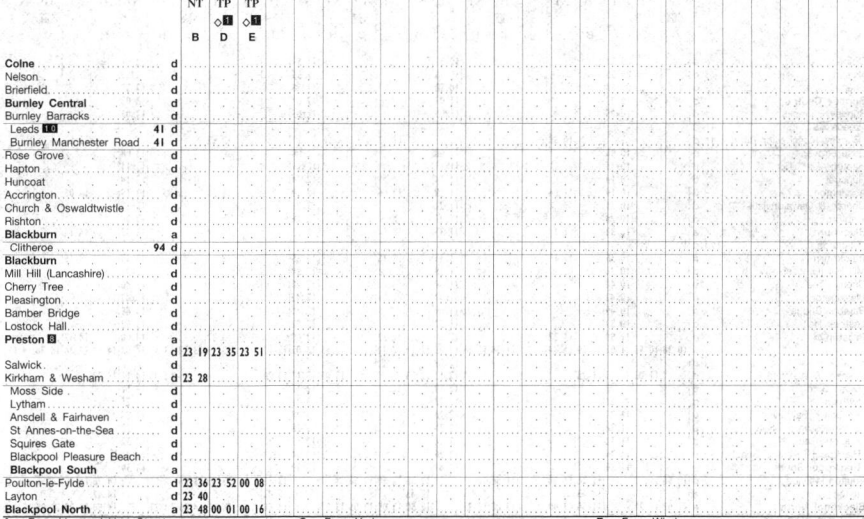

		NT A	NT	NT	NT B	NT C	NT	TP ◇1 D	NT A	NT B	NT C	NT	TP ◇1 D	NT	NT B	NT A	TP ◇1 D	NT B	NT C	NT	TP ◇1 D	NT	NT A
Colne	d		17 51				18 55					19 51		20 51						21 46		22 56	
Nelson	d		17 55				18 59					19 55		20 55						21 50		23 00	
Brierfield	d		17 58				19 02					19 58		20 58						21 53		23 03	
Burnley Central	d		18 03				19 07					20 03		21 03						21 58		23 08	
Burnley Barracks	d		18x05				19x09					20x05		21x05						22x00		23x10	
Leeds 10 41	d					17 51					18 51								20 51				
Burnley Manchester Road 41	d					18 57					19 57								21 56				
Rose Grove	d		18 08				19 12					20 08		21 08						22 03		23 13	
Hapton	d		18x11				19x15					20x11		21 11						22x06			
Huncoat	d		18 14				19 18					20 14		21x14						22 09			
Accrington	d		18 19			19 06	19 23				20 06	20 19		21 19					22 05	22 14		23 20	
Church & Oswaldtwistle	d		18 21				19 25					20 21		21 21						22 16			
Rishton	d		18 24				19 28					20 24		21 24						22 19			
Blackburn	a		18 33			19 14	19 33				20 14	20 33		21 33					22 13	22 24		23 28	
Clitheroe 94	d																						
Blackburn	d		18 35	18 44		19 15	19 35				20 15	20 35		21 35					22 14	22 25		23 30	
Mill Hill (Lancashire)	d		18 38				19 38					20 38		21 38						22 28		23 33	
Cherry Tree	d		18 40				19 40					20 40		21 40						22 30			
Pleasington	d		18x42				19x42					20x42		21x42						22x32			
Bamber Bridge	d		18 49				19 49					20 49		21 49						22 39		23 41	
Lostock Hall	d		18 52				19 52					20 52		21 52						22 42		23 43	
Preston 8	a		19 00	19 05		19 32	20 00				20 32	21 00		22 02					22 31	22 50		23 54	
	d	18 54	19 02	19 08	19 19	19 34	20 02	19 38	20 19	20 25	20 34	21 02	20 38		21 19	21 24	21 38	22 19	22 32	22 51	22 38		22 57
Salwick	d																						
Kirkham & Wesham	d	19 04	19 11		19 28		20 11			20 34		21 11			21 28			22 28		23 01			
Moss Side	d		19 17				20 17					21 17								23 07			
Lytham	d		19 21				20 21					21 21								23 11			
Ansdell & Fairhaven	d		19 24				20 24					21 24								23 14			
St Annes-on-the-Sea	d		19 28				20 28					21 28								23 18			
Squires Gate	d		19 32				20 32					21 32								23 21			
Blackpool Pleasure Beach	d		19 34				20 34					21 34								23 24			
Blackpool South	a		19 39				20 39					21 39								23 28			
Poulton-le-Fylde	d				19 36	19 50		19 56		20 42	20 50		20 56		21 36		21 56	22 36	22 49		22 55		
Layton	d				19 43					20 47					21 40			22 42					
Blackpool North	a	19 22		19 33	19 50	20 00		20 05	20 44	20 54	21 00		21 05		21 48	21 53	22 05	22 50	22 59		23 04		23 22

		NT B	TP ◇1 D	TP ◇1 E
Colne	d			
Nelson	d			
Brierfield	d			
Burnley Central	d			
Burnley Barracks	d			
Leeds 10 41	d			
Burnley Manchester Road 41	d			
Rose Grove	d			
Hapton	d			
Huncoat	d			
Accrington	d			
Church & Oswaldtwistle	d			
Rishton	d			
Blackburn	a			
Clitheroe 94	d			
Blackburn	d			
Mill Hill (Lancashire)	d			
Cherry Tree	d			
Pleasington	d			
Bamber Bridge	d			
Lostock Hall	d			
Preston 8	a			
	d	23 19	23 35	23 51
Salwick	d			
Kirkham & Wesham	d	23 28		
Moss Side	d			
Lytham	d			
Ansdell & Fairhaven	d			
St Annes-on-the-Sea	d			
Squires Gate	d			
Blackpool Pleasure Beach	d			
Blackpool South	a			
Poulton-le-Fylde	d	23 36	23 52	00 08
Layton	d	23 40		
Blackpool North	a	23 48	00 01	00 16

A From Liverpool Lime Street
B From Manchester Victoria
C From York
D From Manchester Airport
E From Windermere

Table 97

Saturdays

14 December to 22 March

Colne, Burnley, Accrington and Blackburn - Preston - Blackpool

Network Diagram - see first Page of Table 97

		TP	NT	TP	NT	NT	NT	TP	NT	NT		NT	NT	NT	NT	TP	NT	NT	NT	NT		TP	TP	NT	NT
		◇1		◇1				◇1								◇1						◇1	◇1		
		A	B	C		B		D		E		B		E		C	B		E			F	G	B	
Colne	d				05 41				06 51						07 51					08 51					
Nelson	d				05 45				06 55						07 55					08 55					
Brierfield	d				05 48				06 58						07 58					08 58					
Burnley Central	d				05 53				07 03						08 03					09 03					
Burnley Barracks	d				05x55				07x05						08x05					09x05					
Leeds 10 41	d																								
Burnley Manchester Road 41	d						06 53						07 53					08 52							09 52
Rose Grove	d				05 58				07 08						08 08					09 08					
Hapton	d				06x01				07x11						08x11					09x11					
Huncoat	d				06 04				07 14						08 14					09 14					
Accrington	d				06 09		07 06		07 19				08 06		08 19			09 06		09 19					10 06
Church & Oswaldtwistle	d				06 11				07 21						08 21					09 21					
Rishton	d				06 14				07 24						08 24					09 24					
Blackburn	a				06 23		07 14		07 33				08 14		08 33			09 14		09 33					10 14
Clitheroe 94	d																								
Blackburn	d				06 25		07 16		07 35				08 15		08 35			09 15		09 35					10 15
Mill Hill (Lancashire)	d				06 28				07 38				08 18		08 38					09 38					
Cherry Tree	d				06 30				07 40						08 40					09 40					
Pleasington	d				06x32				07x42						08x42					09x42					
Bamber Bridge	d				06 39		07 26		07 49				08 27		08 49					09 49					
Lostock Hall	d				06 42		07 28		07 52				08 30		08 52					09 52					
Preston 8	a				06 50		07 36		08 00				08 38		09 00			09 32		10 00					10 32
	d		00 21	06 35	07 00	07 13	07 38	07 42	08 02	07 55		08 15	08 40	08 55	09 02	08 59	09 19	09 34	09 55	10 02		10 09	10 09	10 19	10 34
Salwick	d				07 07				08 09																
Kirkham & Wesham	d		00 30	06 44	07 11	07 22		07 51	08 13			08 25		09 05	09 11		09 28		10 05	10 11				10 28	
Moss Side	d				07 17				08 19						09 17					10 17					
Lytham	d				07 21				08 23						09 21					10 21					
Ansdell & Fairhaven	d				07 24				08 26						09 24					10 24					
St Annes-on-the-Sea	d				07 28				08 30						09 28					10 28					
Squires Gate	d				07 32				08 34						09 32					10 32					
Blackpool Pleasure Beach	d				07 34				08 36						09 34					10 34					
Blackpool South	a				07 38				08 41						09 39					10 39					
Poulton-le-Fylde	d	00 08	00 38	06 54		07 30	07 54	08 01				08 33	08 56			09 16	09 36	09 51				10 26	10 26	10 36	10 51
Layton	d		00 43	06 58		07 34		08 04				08 37					09 43							10 41	
Blackpool North	a	00 16	00 50	07 05		07 41	08 05	08 11		08 21		08 44	09 05	09 21		09 25	09 50	10 01	10 21			10 33	10 35	10 50	11 01

		TP	NT	NT	NT	NT		TP	NT	NT	NT	NT	TP	NT	NT	NT		NT	TP	NT	NT	NT	NT	TP	NT
		◇1						◇1					◇1						◇1					◇1	
		C	E		B			C	H		B		C	H		B			C	H		B		C	H
Colne	d			09 51						10 51					11 51						12 51				
Nelson	d			09 55						10 55					11 55						12 55				
Brierfield	d			09 58						10 58					11 58						12 58				
Burnley Central	d			10 03						11 03					12 03						13 03				
Burnley Barracks	d			10x05						11x05					12x05						13x05				
Leeds 10 41	d																								
Burnley Manchester Road 41	d					10 52						11 52						12 52					13 52		
Rose Grove	d			10 08						11 08					12 08						13 08				
Hapton	d			10x11						11x11					12x11						13x11				
Huncoat	d			10 14						11 14					12 14						13 14				
Accrington	d			10 19		11 06				11 19		12 06			12 19			13 06			13 19		14 06		
Church & Oswaldtwistle	d			10 21						11 21					12 21						13 21				
Rishton	d			10 24						11 24					12 24						13 24				
Blackburn	a			10 33		11 14				11 33		12 14			12 33			13 14			13 33		14 14		
Clitheroe 94	d																								
Blackburn	d			10 35		11 15				11 35		12 15			12 35			13 15			13 35		14 15		
Mill Hill (Lancashire)	d			10 38						11 38					12 38						13 38				
Cherry Tree	d			10 40						11 40					12 40						13 40				
Pleasington	d			10x42						11x42					12x42						13x42				
Bamber Bridge	d			10 49						11 49					12 49						13 49				
Lostock Hall	d			10 52						11 52					12 52						13 52				
Preston 8	a			11 00		11 32				12 00		12 32			13 00			13 32			14 00		14 32		
	d	10 38	10 55	11 02	11 19	11 34		11 38	11 55	12 02	12 19	12 34	12 38	12 55	13 02	13 19		13 34	13 38	13 55	14 02	14 19	14 34	14 38	14 55
Salwick	d									12 09															
Kirkham & Wesham	d		11 05	11 11	11 28				12 05	12 13	12 28			13 05	13 11	13 28				14 05	14 11	14 28			15 05
Moss Side	d			11 17						12 19					13 17						14 17				
Lytham	d			11 21						12 23					13 21						14 21				
Ansdell & Fairhaven	d			11 24						12 26					13 24						14 24				
St Annes-on-the-Sea	d			11 28						12 30					13 28						14 28				
Squires Gate	d			11 32						12 34					13 32						14 32				
Blackpool Pleasure Beach	d			11 34						12 36					13 34						14 34				
Blackpool South	a			11 39						12 41					13 39						14 39				
Poulton-le-Fylde	d	10 56			11 36	11 50		11 56			12 36	12 50	12 56			13 36		13 50	13 56			14 36	14 50	14 56	
Layton	d				11 43						12 43					13 43						14 42			
Blackpool North	a	11 05	11 21		11 50	12 00		12 05	12 21		12 50	13 00	13 05	13 21		13 50		14 00	14 05	14 21		14 50	15 00	15 05	15 21

A From Windermere
B From Manchester Victoria
C From Manchester Airport
D From Barrow-in-Furness
E From Liverpool Lime Street
F from 15 February. From Manchester Airport
G until 8 February. From Manchester Airport
H From Liverpool South Pw Hl

Table 97

Saturdays

14 December to 22 March

Colne, Burnley, Accrington and Blackburn - Preston - Blackpool

Network Diagram - see first Page of Table 97

		NT		NT	NT	TP	NT	NT	NT	TP	NT	NT		NT	NT	TP	NT	NT	NT	NT	TP	NT		NT	NT
						◇1				◇1						◇1					◇1				
				A		B	C			B	C			A		B	C		A		B	D		E	
Colne	d	13 51						14 51				15 51						16 51							17 51
Nelson	d	13 55						14 55				15 55						16 55							17 55
Brierfield	d	13 58						14 58				15 58						16 58							17 58
Burnley Central	d	14 03						15 03				16 03						17 03							18 03
Burnley Barracks	d	14x05						15x05				16x05						17x05							18x05
Leeds 10 41	d																								
Burnley Manchester Road 41	d				14 52				15 52						16 52					17 52					
Rose Grove	d	14 08						15 08				16 08						17 08							18 08
Hapton	d	14x11						15x11				16x11						17x11							18x11
Huncoat	d	14 14						15 14				16 14						17 14							18 14
Accrington	d	14 19			15 06			15 19	16 06			16 19			17 06			17 19		18 06					18 19
Church & Oswaldtwistle	d	14 21						15 21				16 21						17 21							18 21
Rishton	d	14 24						15 24				16 24						17 24							18 24
Blackburn	a	14 33			15 14			15 33	16 14			16 33			17 14			17 34		18 14					18 34
Clitheroe 94	d																								
Blackburn	d	14 35			15 15			15 35	16 15			16 35			17 15			17 35		18 15					18 35
Mill Hill (Lancashire)	d	14 38						15 38				16 38						17 38							18 38
Cherry Tree	d	14 40						15 40				16 40						17 40							18 40
Pleasington	d	14x42						15x42				16x42						17x42							18x42
Bamber Bridge	d	14 49						15 49				16 49						17 49							18 49
Lostock Hall	d	14 52						15 52				16 52						17 52							18 52
Preston 8	a	15 00			15 32			16 00	16 32			17 00			17 32			18 00		18 33					19 00
	d	15 02		15 19	15 34	15 38	15 55	16 02	16 34	16 38	16 55	17 02		17 20	17 34	17 38	17 55	18 02	18 18	18 34	18 40	18 49		18 54	19 02
Salwick	d							16 09																	
Kirkham & Wesham	d	15 11		15 28			16 05	16 13		16 47	17 05	17 11		17 30		17 47	18 05	18 11	18 27		18 49			19 04	19 11
Moss Side	d	15 17						16 19				17 17						18 17							19 17
Lytham	d	15 21						16 23				17 21						18 21							19 21
Ansdell & Fairhaven	d	15 24						16 26				17 24						18 24							19 24
St Annes-on-the-Sea	d	15 28						16 30				17 28						18 28							19 28
Squires Gate	d	15 32						16 34				17 32						18 32							19 32
Blackpool Pleasure Beach	d	15 34						16 36				17 34						18 34							19 34
Blackpool South	a	15 39						16 41				17 39						18 39							19 39
Poulton-le-Fylde	d			15 36	15 50	15 56			16 50	16 57	17 12			17 38	17 50	17 57	18 13		18 35	18 50	18 59				
Layton	d			15 43						17 00				17 43		18 00			18 39		19 02				
Blackpool North	a			15 50	16 00	16 05	16 21		17 00	17 07	17 21			17 50	17 58	18 08	18 24		18 46	19 00	19 09	19 16		19 22	

		NT	NT	NT	TP	NT	NT	NT		NT	NT	TP	NT	NT	NT	NT	NT	TP		TP	NT	NT	TP	TP	NT
					◇1							◇1						◇1		◇1			◇1		
		A			B	F	E	G				B	H	F		G	E	I		J	F	G	J	F	
Colne	d			18 51							19 51				20 51										21 46
Nelson	d			18 55							19 55				20 55										21 50
Brierfield	d			18 58							19 58				20 58										21 53
Burnley Central	d			19 03							20 03				21 03										21 58
Burnley Barracks	d			19x05							20x05				21x05										22x00
Leeds 10 41	d																								
Burnley Manchester Road 41	d		18 52							19 52			20 40												
Rose Grove	d			19 08							20 08				21 08										22 03
Hapton	d			19x11							20x11				21x11										22x06
Huncoat	d			19 14							20 14				21 14										22 09
Accrington	d		19 06	19 19						20 06	20 19				21 19										22 14
Church & Oswaldtwistle	d			19 21							20 21				21 21										22 16
Rishton	d			19 24							20 24				21 24										22 19
Blackburn	a		19 14	19 33						20 14	20 33				21 33										22 24
Clitheroe 94	d																								
Blackburn	d		19 15	19 35						20 15	20 35				21 35										22 25
Mill Hill (Lancashire)	d			19 38							20 38				21 38										22 28
Cherry Tree	d			19 40							20 40				21 40										22 30
Pleasington	d			19x42							20x42				21x42										22x32
Bamber Bridge	d			19 49							20 49				21 49										22 39
Lostock Hall	d			19 52							20 52				21 52										22 42
Preston 8	a		19 32	20 00						20 32	21 00		21 48		22 02										22 50
	d	19 19	19 34	20 02	19 38	20 10	20 19	20 25		20 34	21 02	20 38		21 10		21 19	21 24	21 38		21 38	22 10	22 19	22 38	22 40	22 51
Salwick	d																								
Kirkham & Wesham	d	19 28		20 11		20 20		20 34			21 11			21 20		21 28					22 20	22 28		22 49	23 01
Moss Side	d			20 17							21 17														23 07
Lytham	d			20 21							21 21														23 11
Ansdell & Fairhaven	d			20 24							21 24														23 14
St Annes-on-the-Sea	d			20 28							21 28														23 18
Squires Gate	d			20 32							21 32														23 21
Blackpool Pleasure Beach	d			20 34							21 34														23 24
Blackpool South	a			20 39							21 39														23 28
Poulton-le-Fylde	d	19 36	19 50		19 56	20 28		20 42		20 50		20 56		21 28		21 36		21 56		21 56	22 28	22 36	22 55	22 58	
Layton	d	19 43				20 33		20 47						21 33		21 40					22 33	22 42			
Blackpool North	a	19 50	20 00		20 05	20 39	20 44	20 54		21 00		21 05		21 39		21 48	21 53	22 03		22 05	22 39	22 50	23 04	23 05	

A From Manchester Victoria
B From Manchester Airport
C From Liverpool South Pw Hl
D From Hazel Grove
E From Liverpool Lime Street
F from 4 January until 8 February
G from 15 February. From Manchester Victoria
H From Hebden Bridge
I from 4 January until 8 February. From Manchester Airport
J from 15 February. From Manchester Airport

Table 97

Saturdays

14 December to 22 March

Colne, Burnley, Accrington and Blackburn - Preston - Blackpool

Network Diagram - see first Page of Table 97

		NT	NT	NT	NT	NT	TP	TP
							◇1	◇1
		A		B		C	D	E
Colne	d				22 56			
Nelson	d				23 00			
Brierfield	d				23 03			
Burnley Central	d				23 08			
Burnley Barracks	d				23x10			
Leeds 10 41	d							
Burnley Manchester Road 41	d		22 23					
Rose Grove	d				23 13			
Hapton	d							
Huncoat	d							
Accrington	d		22 38		23 20			
Church & Oswaldtwistle	d							
Rishton	d							
Blackburn	a		22 46		23 28			
Clitheroe 94	d							
Blackburn	d		22 46		23 30			
Mill Hill (Lancashire)	d				23 33			
Cherry Tree	d							
Pleasington	d							
Bamber Bridge	d				23 41			
Lostock Hall	d				23 43			
Preston 8	a		23 03		23 54			
	d	22 57	23 05	23 10		23 19	23 35	23 38
Salwick	d							
Kirkham & Wesham	d			23 20		23 28		
Moss Side	d							
Lytham	d							
Ansdell & Fairhaven	d							
St Annes-on-the-Sea	d							
Squires Gate	d							
Blackpool Pleasure Beach	d							
Blackpool South	a							
Poulton-le-Fylde	d		23 22	23 28		23 36	23 52	23 55
Layton	d			23 33		23 40		
Blackpool North	a	23 22	23 32	23 39		23 48	00 01	00 02

Saturdays

29 March to 17 May

		TP	NT	TP	TP	NT	NT	NT	TP	NT	NT	NT	NT	NT	NT	TP	NT	NT	NT	NT	TP	NT	NT
		◇1		◇1	◇1				◇1							◇1					◇1		
		F	G	H	I		G		J		A	G	K	A		L	G	K	A		L	G	K
Colne	d					05 41				06 51					07 51					08 51			
Nelson	d					05 45				06 55					07 55					08 55			
Brierfield	d					05 48				06 58					07 58					08 58			
Burnley Central	d					05 53				07 03					08 03					09 03			
Burnley Barracks	d					05x55				07x05					08x05					09x05			
Leeds 10 41	d							05 51					06 51					07 51					08 51
Burnley Manchester Road 41	d							06 57					07 57					08 57					09 57
Rose Grove	d					05 58				07 08					08 08					09 08			
Hapton	d					06x01				07x11					08x11					09x11			
Huncoat	d					06 04				07 14					08 14					09 14			
Accrington	d					06 09		07 06		07 19			08 06		08 19			09 06		09 19			10 06
Church & Oswaldtwistle	d					06 11				07 21					08 21					09 21			
Rishton	d					06 14				07 24					08 24					09 24			
Blackburn	a					06 23		07 16		07 33			08 14		08 33			09 14		09 33			10 14
Clitheroe 94	d																						
Blackburn	d					06 25		07 16		07 35			08 15		08 35			09 15		09 35			10 15
Mill Hill (Lancashire)	d					06 28				07 38			08 18		08 38					09 38			
Cherry Tree	d					06 30				07 40					08 40					09 40			
Pleasington	d					06x32				07x42					08x42					09x42			
Bamber Bridge	d					06 39		07 26		07 49			08 27		08 49					09 49			
Lostock Hall	d					06 42		07 28		07 52			08 30		08 52					09 52			
Preston 8	a					06 50		07 36		08 00			08 38		09 00			09 32		10 00			10 32
	d		00 21	06 33	06 35	07 00	07 13	07 38	07 42	08 02	07 55	08 15	08 40	08 55	09 02	08 59	09 19	09 34	09 55	10 02	10 09	10 19	10 34
Salwick	d					07 07				08 09													
Kirkham & Wesham	d		00 30	06 43	06 44	07 11	07 22		07 51	08 13		08 25		09 05	09 11		09 28		10 05	10 11		10 28	
Moss Side	d					07 17				08 19					09 17					10 17			
Lytham	d					07 21				08 23					09 21					10 21			
Ansdell & Fairhaven	d					07 24				08 26					09 24					10 24			
St Annes-on-the-Sea	d					07 28				08 30					09 28					10 28			
Squires Gate	d					07 32				08 34					09 32					10 32			
Blackpool Pleasure Beach	d					07 34				08 36					09 34					10 34			
Blackpool South	a					07 38				08 41					09 39					10 39			
Poulton-le-Fylde	d	00 08	00 38	06 53	06 54		07 30	07 54	08 01			08 33	08 56			09 16	09 36	09 51			10 26	10 36	10 51
Layton	d		00 43	06 56	06 58		07 34		08 04			08 37					09 43					10 41	
Blackpool North	a	00 16	00 50	07 03	07 05		07 41	08 05	08 11		08 21	08 44	09 05	09 21		09 25	09 50	10 01	10 21		10 33	10 50	11 01

A From Liverpool Lime Street
B from 4 January until 8 February
C from 15 February. From Manchester Victoria
D from 15 February. From Manchester Airport
E from 4 January until 8 February. From Manchester Airport
F From Windermere
G From Manchester Victoria
H 29 March, 3 May, 10 May, 17 May. From Manchester Airport
I from 5 April until 26 April. From Manchester Airport
J From Barrow-in-Furness
K From York
L From Manchester Airport

Table 97

Saturdays
29 March to 17 May

Colne, Burnley, Accrington and Blackburn - Preston - Blackpool

Network Diagram - see first Page of Table 97

		TP ◇1 A	NT B	NT	NT C	NT D		TP ◇1 A	NT E	NT	NT C	NT D	TP ◇1 A	NT E	NT	NT C		NT D	TP ◇1 A	NT E	NT	NT C	NT D	TP ◇1 A	NT E
Colne	d			09 51						10 51					11 51						12 51				
Nelson	d			09 55						10 55					11 55						12 55				
Brierfield	d			09 58						10 58					11 58						12 58				
Burnley Central	d			10 03						11 03					12 03						13 03				
Burnley Barracks	d			10x05						11x05					12x05						13x05				
Leeds 10 41	d					09 53						10 53						11 53					12 53		
Burnley Manchester Road 41	d					10 57						11 57						12 57					13 57		
Rose Grove	d			10 08						11 08					12 08						13 08				
Hapton	d			10x11						11x11					12x11						13x11				
Huncoat	d			10 14						11 14					12 14						13 14				
Accrington	d			10 19		11 06				11 19		12 06			12 19			13 06			13 19		14 06		
Church & Oswaldtwistle	d			10 21						11 21					12 21						13 21				
Rishton	d			10 24						11 24					12 24						13 24				
Blackburn	a			10 33		11 14				11 33		12 14			12 33			13 14			13 33		14 14		
Clitheroe 94	d																								
Blackburn	d			10 35		11 15				11 35		12 15			12 35			13 15			13 35		14 15		
Mill Hill (Lancashire)	d			10 38						11 38					12 38						13 38				
Cherry Tree	d			10 40						11 40					12 40						13 40				
Pleasington	d			10x42						11x42					12x42						13x42				
Bamber Bridge	d			10 49						11 49					12 49						13 49				
Lostock Hall	d			10 52						11 52					12 52						13 52				
Preston 8	a			11 00		11 32				12 00		12 32			13 00			13 32			14 00		14 32		
	d	10 38	10 55	11 02	11 19	11 34		11 38	11 55	12 02	12 19	12 34	12 38	12 55	13 02	13 19		13 34	13 38	13 55	14 02	14 19	14 34	14 38	14 55
Salwick	d									12 09															
Kirkham & Wesham	d		11 05	11 11	11 28				12 05	12 13	12 28			13 05	13 11	13 28				14 05	14 11	14 28			15 05
Moss Side	d			11 17						12 19					13 17						14 17				
Lytham	d			11 21						12 23					13 21						14 21				
Ansdell & Fairhaven	d			11 24						12 26					13 24						14 24				
St Annes-on-the-Sea	d			11 28						12 30					13 28						14 28				
Squires Gate	d			11 32						12 34					13 32						14 32				
Blackpool Pleasure Beach	d			11 34						12 36					13 34						14 34				
Blackpool South	a			11 39						12 41					13 39						14 39				
Poulton-le-Fylde	d	10 56			11 36	11 50		11 56			12 36	12 50	12 56			13 36		13 50	13 56			14 36	14 50	14 56	
Layton	d				11 43						12 43					13 43						14 42			
Blackpool North	a	11 05	11 21		11 50	12 00		12 05	12 21		12 50	13 00	13 05	13 21		13 50		14 00	14 05	14 21		14 50	15 00	15 05	15 21

		NT		NT C	NT D	TP ◇1 A	NT E	NT	NT D	TP ◇1 A	NT E	NT		NT C	NT D	TP ◇1 A	NT E	NT	NT C	NT D	TP ◇1 A	NT F		NT B	NT
Colne	d	13 51						14 51				15 51						16 51							17 51
Nelson	d	13 55						14 55				15 55						16 55							17 55
Brierfield	d	13 58						14 58				15 58						16 58							17 58
Burnley Central	d	14 03						15 03				16 03						17 03							18 03
Burnley Barracks	d	14x05						15x05				16x05						17x05							18x05
Leeds 10 41	d				13 53				14 53						15 52					16 51					
Burnley Manchester Road 41	d				14 57				15 57						16 58					17 57					
Rose Grove	d	14 08						15 08				16 08						17 08							18 08
Hapton	d	14x11						15x11				16x11						17x11							18x11
Huncoat	d	14 14						15 14				16 14						17 14							18 14
Accrington	d	14 19			15 06			15 19	16 06			16 19			17 06			17 19		18 06					18 19
Church & Oswaldtwistle	d	14 21						15 21				16 21						17 21							18 21
Rishton	d	14 24						15 24				16 24						17 24							18 24
Blackburn	a	14 33			15 14			15 33	16 14			16 33			17 14			17 34		18 14					18 34
Clitheroe 94	d																								
Blackburn	d	14 35			15 15			15 35	16 15			16 35			17 15			17 35		18 15					18 35
Mill Hill (Lancashire)	d	14 38						15 38				16 38						17 38							18 38
Cherry Tree	d	14 40						15 40				16 40						17 40							18 40
Pleasington	d	14x42						15x42				16x42						17x42							18x42
Bamber Bridge	d	14 49						15 49				16 49						17 49							18 49
Lostock Hall	d	14 52						15 52				16 52						17 52							18 52
Preston 8	a	15 00			15 32			16 00	16 32			17 00			17 32			18 00		18 33					19 00
	d	15 02		15 19	15 34	15 38	15 55	16 02	16 34	16 38	16 55	17 02		17 20	17 34	17 38	17 55	18 02	18 18	18 34	18 40	18 49		18 54	19 02
Salwick	d							16 09																	
Kirkham & Wesham	d	15 11		15 28			16 05	16 13		16 47	17 05	17 11		17 30		17 47	18 05	18 11	18 27		18 49			19 04	19 11
Moss Side	d	15 17						16 19				17 17						18 17							19 17
Lytham	d	15 21						16 23				17 21						18 21							19 21
Ansdell & Fairhaven	d	15 24						16 26				17 24						18 24							19 24
St Annes-on-the-Sea	d	15 28						16 30				17 28						18 28							19 28
Squires Gate	d	15 32						16 34				17 32						18 32							19 32
Blackpool Pleasure Beach	d	15 34						16 36				17 34						18 34							19 34
Blackpool South	a	15 39						16 41				17 39						18 39							19 39
Poulton-le-Fylde	d			15 36	15 50	15 56			16 50	16 57	17 12			17 38	17 50	17 57	18 13		18 35	18 50	18 59				
Layton	d			15 43						17 00				17 43		18 00			18 39		19 02				
Blackpool North	a			15 50	16 00	16 05	16 21		17 00	17 07	17 21			17 50	17 58	18 08	18 24		18 46	19 00	19 09	19 16		19 22	

A From Manchester Airport
B From Liverpool Lime Street
C From Manchester Victoria
D From York
E From Liverpool South Pw Hl
F From Hazel Grove

Table 97

Saturdays
29 March to 17 May

Colne, Burnley, Accrington and Blackburn - Preston - Blackpool

Network Diagram - see first Page of Table 97

		NT	NT	NT	TP	NT	NT	NT	NT	TP	NT	NT	NT	TP	NT	NT	NT	TP	NT	NT	NT	TP
					◇1					◇1				◇1				◇1				◇1
		A	B		C	D	A	B		C		A	D	C	A	B		C		D	A	C
Colne	d			18 51					19 51		20 51						21 46		22 56			
Nelson	d			18 55					19 55		20 55						21 50		23 00			
Brierfield	d			18 58					19 58		20 58						21 53		23 03			
Burnley Central	d			19 03					20 03		21 03						21 58		23 08			
Burnley Barracks	d			19x05					20x05		21x05						22x00		23x10			
Leeds 10 41	d		17 51					18 51								20 51						
Burnley Manchester Road 41	d		18 57					19 57								21 56						
Rose Grove	d			19 08					20 08		21 08						22 03		23 13			
Hapton	d			19x11					20x11		21x11						22x06					
Huncoat	d			19 14					20 14		21 14						22 09					
Accrington	d		19 06	19 19				20 06	20 19		21 19					22 05	22 14		23 20			
Church & Oswaldtwistle	d			19 21					20 21		21 21						22 16					
Rishton	d			19 24					20 24		21 24						22 19					
Blackburn	a		19 14	19 33				20 14	20 33		21 33					22 13	22 24		23 28			
Clitheroe 94	d																					
Blackburn	d		19 15	19 35				20 15	20 35		21 35					22 14	22 25		23 30			
Mill Hill (Lancashire)	d			19 38					20 38		21 38						22 28		23 33			
Cherry Tree	d			19 40					20 40		21 40						22 30					
Pleasington	d			19x42					20x42		21x42						22x32					
Bamber Bridge	d			19 49					20 49		21 49						22 39		23 41			
Lostock Hall	d			19 52					20 52		21 52						22 42		23 43			
Preston 8	a		19 32	20 00				20 32	21 00		22 02					22 31	22 50		23 54			
	d	19 19	19 34	20 02	19 38	20 19	20 25	20 34	21 02	20 38		21 19	21 24	21 38	22 19	22 32	22 51	22 38		22 57	23 19	23 35
Salwick	d																					
Kirkham & Wesham	d	19 28		20 11			20 34		21 11			21 28			22 28		23 01				23 28	
Moss Side	d			20 17					21 17								23 07					
Lytham	d			20 21					21 21								23 11					
Ansdell & Fairhaven	d			20 24					21 24								23 14					
St Annes-on-the-Sea	d			20 28					21 28								23 18					
Squires Gate	d			20 32					21 32								23 21					
Blackpool Pleasure Beach	d			20 34					21 34								23 24					
Blackpool South	a			20 39					21 39								23 28					
Poulton-le-Fylde	d	19 36	19 50		19 56		20 42	20 50		20 56		21 36		21 56	22 36	22 49		22 55			23 36	23 52
Layton	d	19 43					20 47					21 40			22 42						23 40	
Blackpool North	a	19 50	20 00		20 05	20 44	20 54	21 00		21 05		21 48	21 53	22 05	22 50	22 59		23 04		23 22	23 48	00 01

Sundays
8 December to 29 December

		NT	TP	NT	NT	NT	TP	NT	NT	TP	NT	NT	NT	TP	NT	NT	NT	NT	TP	NT	NT	NT	TP
			◇1				◇1			◇1				◇1					◇1				◇1
		E	C		A	D	C	A		C	D		A	C	D		A		C	D		A	C
Colne	d			09 17														11 36					
Nelson	d			09 21														11 40					
Brierfield	d			09 24														11 43					
Burnley Central	d			09 29														11 48					
Burnley Barracks	d			09x31														11x50					
Leeds 10 41	d																						
Burnley Manchester Road 41	d								09 46			10 34				11 34					12 34		
Rose Grove	d			09 34														11 53					
Hapton	d			09x37														11x56					
Huncoat	d			09 40														11 59					
Accrington	d			09 45					09 59			10 48				11 47		12 04			12 47		
Church & Oswaldtwistle	d			09 47														12 06					
Rishton	d			09 50														12 09					
Blackburn	a			09 55					10 07			10 56				11 55		12 14			12 55		
Clitheroe 94	d																						
Blackburn	d			09 57					10 07			10 56				11 56		12 16			12 56		
Mill Hill (Lancashire)	d			10 00														12 19					
Cherry Tree	d			10 02														12 21					
Pleasington	d			10x04														12x23					
Bamber Bridge	d			10 11														12 30					
Lostock Hall	d			10 14														12 33					
Preston 8	a			10 22					10 27			11 13				12 13		12 42			13 13		
	d	00 11	08 54		09 20	09 39	09 52	10 20	10 29	10 35	10 40	11 15	11 21	11 35	11 39	12 14	12 20		12 35	12 39	13 14	13 20	13 35
Salwick	d																						
Kirkham & Wesham	d	00 21			09 29			10 29					11 31				12 29					13 29	
Moss Side	d																						
Lytham	d																						
Ansdell & Fairhaven	d																						
St Annes-on-the-Sea	d																						
Squires Gate	d																						
Blackpool Pleasure Beach	d																						
Blackpool South	a																						
Poulton-le-Fylde	d	00 29	09 11		09 37	09 57	10 09	10 37	10 46	10 52	10 57	11 32	11 39	11 52	11 57	12 31	12 37		12 52	12 57	13 31	13 37	13 52
Layton	d	00 34			09 42			10 42					11 44				12 42					13 42	
Blackpool North	a	00 40	09 19		09 49	10 07	10 17	10 49	10 53	11 01	11 09	11 39	11 49	12 01	12 07	12 38	12 49		13 01	13 07	13 38	13 49	14 01

A From Manchester Victoria
B From York
C From Manchester Airport
D From Liverpool Lime Street
E not 8 December. From Manchester Victoria

Table 97

Sundays

8 December to 29 December

Colne, Burnley, Accrington and Blackburn - Preston - Blackpool

Network Diagram - see first Page of Table 97

		NT	NT	NT	NT	TP		NT	NT	NT	TP	NT	NT	NT	NT	NT		TP	NT	NT	NT	TP	NT	NT	NT
						◇1					◇1							◇1				◇1			
		A		B		C		A		B	C	A	D		B			C	A		B	C	A		B
Colne	d				13 36											15 36									
Nelson	d				13 40											15 40									
Brierfield	d				13 43											15 43									
Burnley Central	d				13 48											15 48									
Burnley Barracks	d				13x50											15x50									
Leeds 10 41	d																								
Burnley Manchester Road 41	d		13 34						14 34					15 34						16 34				17 34	
Rose Grove	d				13 53											15 53									
Hapton	d				13x56											15x56									
Huncoat	d				13 59											15 59									
Accrington	d		13 47		14 04				14 47					15 47		16 04				16 47				17 47	
Church & Oswaldtwistle	d				14 06											16 06									
Rishton	d				14 09											16 09									
Blackburn	a		13 55		14 14				14 55					15 55		16 14				16 55				17 55	
Clitheroe 94	d												15 18												
Blackburn	d		13 56		14 16				14 56				15 44	15 56		16 16				16 56				17 56	
Mill Hill (Lancashire)	d				14 19											16 19									
Cherry Tree	d				14 21											16 21									
Pleasington	d				14x23											16x23									
Bamber Bridge	d				14 30								15 54			16 30									
Lostock Hall	d				14 33								15 56			16 33									
Preston 8	a		14 13		14 41				15 13				16 04	16 13		16 42				17 13				18 13	
	d	13 39	14 14	14 20		14 35		14 38	15 14	15 20	15 35	15 39	16 06	16 14	16 20			16 35	16 39	17 14	17 20	17 35	17 39	18 14	18 20
Salwick	d																								
Kirkham & Wesham	d			14 29						15 29			16 16		16 29						17 29				18 29
Moss Side	d																								
Lytham	d																								
Ansdell & Fairhaven	d																								
St Annes-on-the-Sea	d																								
Squires Gate	d																								
Blackpool Pleasure Beach	d																								
Blackpool South	a																								
Poulton-le-Fylde	d	13 57	14 30	14 37		14 52		14 55	15 32	15 37	15 52	15 57	16 24	16 31	16 37			16 52	16 57	17 31	17 37	17 52	17 57	18 31	18 37
Layton	d			14 42						15 43					16 42						17 42				18 42
Blackpool North	a	14 07	14 38	14 49		15 01		15 05	15 39	15 49	16 01	16 07	16 33	16 38	16 49			17 01	17 07	17 38	17 49	18 01	18 07	18 38	18 49

		NT		TP	NT	NT	NT	TP	NT	NT	NT	NT		TP	NT	NT	NT	TP	NT	NT	NT	NT		TP	NT
				◇1				◇1						◇1				◇1						◇1	
				C	A		B	C	A		B			C	A		B	C	A		B			C	A
Colne	d	17 36										19 36										21 36			
Nelson	d	17 40										19 40										21 40			
Brierfield	d	17 43										19 43										21 43			
Burnley Central	d	17 48										19 48										21 48			
Burnley Barracks	d	17x50										19x50										21x50			
Leeds 10 41	d																								
Burnley Manchester Road 41	d					18 34				19 34						20 34				21 34					
Rose Grove	d	17 53										19 53										21 53			
Hapton	d	17x56										19x56										21x56			
Huncoat	d	17 59										19 59										21 59			
Accrington	d	18 04				18 47				19 47		20 04				20 47				21 47		22 04			
Church & Oswaldtwistle	d	18 06										20 06										22 06			
Rishton	d	18 09										20 09										22 09			
Blackburn	a	18 14				18 55				19 56		20 14				20 55				21 55		22 14			
Clitheroe 94	d																								
Blackburn	d	18 16				18 56				19 57		20 16				20 56				21 56		22 16			
Mill Hill (Lancashire)	d	18 19										20 19										22 19			
Cherry Tree	d	18 21										20 21										22 21			
Pleasington	d	18x23										20x23										22x23			
Bamber Bridge	d	18 30										20 30										22 30			
Lostock Hall	d	18 33										20 33										22 33			
Preston 8	a	18 42				19 13				20 14		20 42				21 13				22 13		22 44			
	d			18 35	18 39	19 14	19 21	19 35	19 39	20 15	20 21			20 35	20 39	21 14	21 20	21 35	21 39	22 14	22 20			22 29	22 39
Salwick	d																								
Kirkham & Wesham	d						19 30				20 30						21 29				22 29				
Moss Side	d																								
Lytham	d																								
Ansdell & Fairhaven	d																								
St Annes-on-the-Sea	d																								
Squires Gate	d																								
Blackpool Pleasure Beach	d																								
Blackpool South	a																								
Poulton-le-Fylde	d			18 52	18 57	19 31	19 38	19 52	19 57	20 32	20 38			20 52	20 57	21 31	21 37	21 52	21 57	22 31	22 37			22 46	22 57
Layton	d						19 42				20 43						21 42				22 42				
Blackpool North	a			19 01	19 07	19 38	19 49	20 01	20 07	20 39	20 49			21 01	21 07	21 38	21 49	22 01	22 07	22 38	22 49			22 55	23 07

A From Liverpool Lime Street
B From Manchester Victoria
C From Manchester Airport
D From Hellifield

Table 97

Sundays

8 December to 29 December

Colne, Burnley, Accrington and Blackburn - Preston - Blackpool

Network Diagram - see first Page of Table 97

		NT	NT	NT	TP
					◇1
		A		B	C
		🚌			
Colne	d				
Nelson	d				
Brierfield	d				
Burnley Central	d				
Burnley Barracks	d				
Leeds 10	41 d				
Burnley Manchester Road	41 d	22 10	22 18		
Rose Grove	d				
Hapton	d				
Huncoat	d				
Accrington	d	22 30	22 31		
Church & Oswaldtwistle	d				
Rishton	d				
Blackburn	a	22 48	22 39		
Clitheroe	94 d				
Blackburn	d	22 48	22 39		
Mill Hill (Lancashire)	d				
Cherry Tree	d				
Pleasington	d				
Bamber Bridge	d				
Lostock Hall	d				
Preston 8	a	23 18	22 54		
	d	23 18	22 56	23 39	23 47
Salwick	d				
Kirkham & Wesham	d				23 56
Moss Side	d				
Lytham	d				
Ansdell & Fairhaven	d				
St Annes-on-the-Sea	d				
Squires Gate	d				
Blackpool Pleasure Beach	d				
Blackpool South	a				
Poulton-le-Fylde	d	23 58	23 13	23 56	00 05
Layton	d				
Blackpool North	a	00 13	23 19	00 05	00 14

Sundays

5 January to 9 February

		NT	TP	NT	TP	NT	NT	TP	NT	NT		TP	NT	NT	NT	TP	NT	NT	TP	NT		NT	NT	TP	NT
			◇1		◇1			◇1				◇1				◇1			◇1					◇1	
																								C	
Colne	d			09 17											11 36								13 36		
Nelson	d			09 21											11 40								13 40		
Brierfield	d			09 24											11 43								13 43		
Burnley Central	d			09 29											11 48								13 48		
Burnley Barracks	d			09x31											11x50								13x50		
Leeds 10	41 d																								
Burnley Manchester Road	41 d						09 46			10 34				11 34				12 34				13 34			
Rose Grove	d			09 34											11 53								13 53		
Hapton	d			09x37											11x56								13x56		
Huncoat	d			09 40											11 59								13 59		
Accrington	d			09 45			09 59			10 48				11 47	12 04			12 47				13 47	14 04		
Church & Oswaldtwistle	d			09 47											12 06								14 06		
Rishton	d			09 50											12 09								14 09		
Blackburn	a			09 55			10 07			10 56				11 55	12 14			12 55				13 55	14 14		
Clitheroe	94 d																								
Blackburn	d			09 57			10 07			10 56				11 56	12 16			12 56				13 56	14 16		
Mill Hill (Lancashire)	d			10 00											12 19								14 19		
Cherry Tree	d			10 02											12 21								14 21		
Pleasington	d			10x04											12x23								14x23		
Bamber Bridge	d			10 11											12 30								14 30		
Lostock Hall	d			10 14											12 33								14 33		
Preston 8	a			10 22			10 27			11 13				12 13	12 42			13 13				14 13	14 41		
	d	00 10	08 54		09 53	10 00	10 29	10 35	10 55	11 15		11 35	11 55	12 14		12 35	12 55	13 14	13 35	13 55		14 14		14 36	14 55
Salwick	d																								
Kirkham & Wesham	d	00 20				10 10			11 05				12 05				13 05			14 05					15 05
Moss Side	d																								
Lytham	d																								
Ansdell & Fairhaven	d																								
St Annes-on-the-Sea	d																								
Squires Gate	d																								
Blackpool Pleasure Beach	d																								
Blackpool South	a																								
Poulton-le-Fylde	d	00 28	09 11		10 10	10 18	10 46	10 52	11 13	11 32		11 52	12 13	12 31		12 52	13 13	13 31	13 52	14 13		14 30		14 55	15 13
Layton	d	00 33				10 22			11 17				12 17				13 17			14 17					15 17
Blackpool North	a	00 39	09 20		10 18	10 29	10 53	11 01	11 24	11 39		12 01	12 24	12 38		13 01	13 24	13 38	14 01	14 24		14 38		15 04	15 24

A From Hebden Bridge
B From Wigan North Western
C From Manchester Airport

Table 97

Sundays

5 January to 9 February

Colne, Burnley, Accrington and Blackburn - Preston - Blackpool

Network Diagram - see first Page of Table 97

		NT	NT	TP	NT	NT		NT	NT	NT	TP	NT	NT	NT	TP	NT		NT	NT	NT	TP	NT	NT	NT	TP
				◇1							◇1				◇1						◇1				◇1
			A	B	C	D			A		B	C		A	B	C			A		B	C		A	B
Colne	d									15 36										17 36					
Nelson	d									15 40										17 40					
Brierfield	d									15 43										17 43					
Burnley Central	d									15 48										17 48					
Burnley Barracks	d									15x50										17x50					
Leeds 10 41	d																								
Burnley Manchester Road 41	d	14 34						15 34					16 34					17 34					18 34		
Rose Grove	d									15 53										17 53					
Hapton	d									15x56										17x56					
Huncoat	d									15 59										17 59					
Accrington	d	14 47						15 47		16 04			16 47					17 47		18 04			18 47		
Church & Oswaldtwistle	d									16 06										18 06					
Rishton	d									16 09										18 09					
Blackburn	a	14 55						15 55		16 14			16 55					17 55		18 14			18 55		
Clitheroe 94	d					15 18																			
Blackburn	d	14 56				15 44		15 56		16 16			16 56					17 56		18 16			18 56		
Mill Hill (Lancashire)	d									16 19										18 19					
Cherry Tree	d									16 21										18 21					
Pleasington	d									16x23										18x23					
Bamber Bridge	d					15 54				16 30										18 30					
Lostock Hall	d					15 56				16 33										18 33					
Preston 8	a	15 13				16 04		16 13		16 42			17 13					18 13		18 42			19 13		
	d	15 14	15 20	15 35	15 39	16 06		16 14	16 20		16 35	16 39	17 14	17 20	17 35	17 39		18 14	18 20		18 35	18 39	19 14	19 21	19 35
Salwick	d																								
Kirkham & Wesham	d		15 29			16 16			16 29					17 29					18 29					19 30	
Moss Side	d																								
Lytham	d																								
Ansdell & Fairhaven	d																								
St Annes-on-the-Sea	d																								
Squires Gate	d																								
Blackpool Pleasure Beach	d																								
Blackpool South	a																								
Poulton-le-Fylde	d	15 32	15 37	15 52	15 57	16 24		16 31	16 37		16 52	16 57	17 31	17 37	17 52	17 57		18 31	18 37		18 52	18 57	19 31	19 38	19 52
Layton	d		15 43						16 42					17 42					18 42					19 42	
Blackpool North	a	15 39	15 49	16 01	16 07	16 33		16 38	16 49		17 01	17 07	17 38	17 49	18 01	18 07		18 38	18 49		19 01	19 07	19 38	19 49	20 01

		NT		NT	NT	NT	TP	NT	NT	NT	TP	NT		NT	NT	NT	NT	TP	NT	NT	NT	TP			
							◇1				◇1							◇1				◇1			
		C			A		B	C		A	B	C					C	B	E (bus)		C	B			
Colne	d					19 36										21 36									
Nelson	d					19 40										21 40									
Brierfield	d					19 43										21 43									
Burnley Central	d					19 48										21 48									
Burnley Barracks	d					19x50										21x50									
Leeds 10 41	d																								
Burnley Manchester Road 41	d			19 34					20 34					21 34					22 10	22 18					
Rose Grove	d					19 53										21 53									
Hapton	d					19x56										21x56									
Huncoat	d					19 59										21 59									
Accrington	d			19 47		20 04			20 47					21 47		22 04			22 30	22 31					
Church & Oswaldtwistle	d					20 06										22 06									
Rishton	d					20 09										22 09									
Blackburn	a			19 56		20 14			20 55					21 55		22 14			22 48	22 39					
Clitheroe 94	d																								
Blackburn	d			19 57		20 16			20 56					21 56		22 16			22 48	22 39					
Mill Hill (Lancashire)	d					20 19										22 19									
Cherry Tree	d					20 21										22 21									
Pleasington	d					20x23										22x23									
Bamber Bridge	d					20 30										22 30									
Lostock Hall	d					20 33										22 33									
Preston 8	a			20 14		20 42			21 13					22 13		22 44			23 18	22 54					
	d	19 39		20 15	20 21		20 35	20 39	21 14	21 20	21 35	21 39		22 14	22 20		22 39	22 45	23 18	22 56	23 39	23 47			
Salwick	d																								
Kirkham & Wesham	d				20 30					21 29					22 29							23 57			
Moss Side	d																								
Lytham	d																								
Ansdell & Fairhaven	d																								
St Annes-on-the-Sea	d																								
Squires Gate	d																								
Blackpool Pleasure Beach	d																								
Blackpool South	a																								
Poulton-le-Fylde	d	19 57		20 32	20 38		20 52	20 57	21 31	21 37	21 52	21 57		22 31	22 37		22 57	23 02	23 58	23 13	23 56	00 06			
Layton	d				20 43					21 42					22 42										
Blackpool North	a	20 07		20 39	20 49		21 01	21 07	21 38	21 49	22 01	22 07		22 38	22 49		23 07	23 11	00 13	23 19	00 05	00 15			

A From Manchester Oxford Road
B From Manchester Airport
C From Wigan North Western
D From Hellifield
E From Hebden Bridge

Table 97

Sundays

16 February to 23 March

Colne, Burnley, Accrington and Blackburn - Preston - Blackpool

Network Diagram - see first Page of Table 97

			NT	NT	TP	NT	NT	TP	NT	NT	NT	NT	TP	NT	NT	NT	TP	NT	NT	NT	NT	TP	NT	NT
					◇1			◇1					◇1				◇1					◇1		
			A		B		C	D				C	D			C	D			E		D	C	
Colne		d								09 17											11 36			
Nelson		d								09 21											11 40			
Brierfield		d								09 24											11 43			
Burnley Central		d								09 29											11 48			
Burnley Barracks		d								09x31											11x50			
Leeds 10	41	d																						
Burnley Manchester Road	41	d									09 46			10 34				11 34						12 34
Rose Grove		d								09 34											11 53			
Hapton		d								09x37											11x56			
Huncoat		d								09 40											11 59			
Accrington		d								09 45	09 59			10 48				11 47			12 04			12 47
Church & Oswaldtwistle		d								09 47											12 06			
Rishton		d								09 50											12 09			
Blackburn		a								09 55	10 07			10 56				11 55			12 14			12 55
Clitheroe	94	d																						
Blackburn		d								09 57	10 07			10 56				11 56			12 16			12 56
Mill Hill (Lancashire)		d								10 00											12 19			
Cherry Tree		d								10 02											12 21			
Pleasington		d								10x04											12x23			
Bamber Bridge		d								10 11											12 30			
Lostock Hall		d								10 14											12 33			
Preston 8		a								10 25	10 27			11 13				12 13			12 41			13 13
		d	00 11	08 49	09 06	09 21	09 39	09 54	10 21	10 26	10 29	10 39	10 43	11 15	11 21	11 34	11 37	12 14	11 44	12 20	12 42	12 35	12 39	13 14
Salwick		d																						
Kirkham & Wesham		d	00 21	08 58		09 31			10 31	10 36					11 31				11 53	12 29	12 52			
Moss Side		d		09 06						10 42									12 01		12 58			
Lytham		d		09 10						10 46									12 05		13 02			
Ansdell & Fairhaven		d		09 13						10 49									12 08		13 05			
St Annes-on-the-Sea		d		09 17						10 53									12 12		13 09			
Squires Gate		d		09 20						10 57									12 15		13 13			
Blackpool Pleasure Beach		d		09 23						10 59									12 18		13 15			
Blackpool South		a		09 25						11 04									12 21		13 20			
Poulton-le-Fylde		d	00 29		09 23	09 39	09 57	10 11	10 39		10 46	10 57	11 03	11 32	11 39	11 51	11 55	12 31		12 37		12 52	12 57	13 31
Layton		d	00 34			09 43			10 43						11 43					12 42				
Blackpool North		a	00 40		09 32	09 48	10 07	10 20	10 48		10 53	11 07	11 10	11 39	11 48	12 00	12 04	12 38		12 50		12 58	13 07	13 38

			NT	TP	NT	NT	NT	NT	NT	TP	NT	NT	NT	TP	NT	NT	NT	NT	NT	NT	TP	NT	NT	NT
				◇1						◇1				◇1							◇1			
			E	D	C			E		D	C		E	D	C		F		E		D	C		E
Colne		d							13 36											15 36				
Nelson		d							13 40											15 40				
Brierfield		d							13 43											15 43				
Burnley Central		d							13 48											15 48				
Burnley Barracks		d							13x50											15x50				
Leeds 10	41	d																						
Burnley Manchester Road	41	d				13 34						14 34						15 34					16 34	
Rose Grove		d							13 53											15 53				
Hapton		d							13x56											15x56				
Huncoat		d							13 59											15 59				
Accrington		d				13 47			14 04			14 47						15 47		16 04			16 47	
Church & Oswaldtwistle		d							14 06											16 06				
Rishton		d							14 09											16 09				
Blackburn		a				13 55			14 14			14 55						15 55		16 14			16 55	
Clitheroe	94	d															15 18							
Blackburn		d				13 56			14 16			14 56					15 44	15 56		16 16			16 56	
Mill Hill (Lancashire)		d							14 19											16 19				
Cherry Tree		d							14 21											16 21				
Pleasington		d							14x23											16x23				
Bamber Bridge		d							14 30								15 54			16 30				
Lostock Hall		d							14 33								15 56			16 33				
Preston 8		a				14 13			14 41			15 13					16 04	16 13		16 41			17 13	
		d	13 20	13 35	13 39	14 14	13 44	14 20	14 42	14 35	14 39	15 14	15 20	15 35	15 39	15 44	16 06	16 14	16 20	16 41	16 35	16 39	17 14	17 20
Salwick		d																						
Kirkham & Wesham		d	13 29				13 53	14 29	14 52				15 29			15 53	16 16		16 29	16 52				17 29
Moss Side		d					14 01		14 59							16 01				16 58				
Lytham		d					14 05		15 03							16 05				17 02				
Ansdell & Fairhaven		d					14 08		15 06							16 08				17 05				
St Annes-on-the-Sea		d					14 12		15 10							16 12				17 09				
Squires Gate		d					14 15		15 13							16 15				17 13				
Blackpool Pleasure Beach		d					14 18		15 16							16 18				17 15				
Blackpool South		a					14 20		15 21							16 21				17 20				
Poulton-le-Fylde		d	13 37	13 52	13 57	14 30		14 37		14 52	14 57	15 32	15 37	15 52	15 57		16 24	16 31	16 37		16 52	16 57	17 31	17 37
Layton		d	13 42					14 42					15 43						16 42					17 42
Blackpool North		a	13 49	13 58	14 07	14 38		14 49		14 58	15 07	15 39	15 49	15 58	16 07		16 33	16 38	16 49		16 58	17 07	17 38	17 49

A From Manchester Victoria
B From Manchester Piccadilly
C From Wigan North Western
D From Manchester Airport
E From Manchester Oxford Road
F From Hellifield

Table 97

Sundays

16 February to 23 March

Colne, Burnley, Accrington and Blackburn - Preston - Blackpool

Network Diagram - see first Page of Table 97

		TP	NT	NT	NT	NT	NT	TP	NT	NT	NT	TP	NT	NT	NT	NT	NT	TP	NT	NT	NT	TP
		◇1						◇1				◇1						◇1				◇1
		A	B			C		A	B		C	A	B			C		A	B		C	A
Colne	d						17 36										19 36					
Nelson	d						17 40										19 40					
Brierfield	d						17 43										19 43					
Burnley Central	d						17 48										19 48					
Burnley Barracks	d						17x50										19x50					
Leeds 10 41	d																					
Burnley Manchester Road 41	d			17 34						18 34				19 34						20 34		
Rose Grove	d						17 53										19 53					
Hapton	d						17x56										19x56					
Huncoat	d						17 59										19 59					
Accrington	d			17 47			18 04			18 47				19 47			20 04			20 47		
Church & Oswaldtwistle	d						18 06										20 06					
Rishton	d						18 09										20 09					
Blackburn	a			17 55			18 14			18 55				19 56			20 14			20 55		
Clitheroe 94	d																					
Blackburn	d			17 56			18 16			18 56				19 57			20 16			20 56		
Mill Hill (Lancashire)	d						18 19										20 19					
Cherry Tree	d						18 21										20 21					
Pleasington	d						18x23										20x23					
Bamber Bridge	d						18 30										20 30					
Lostock Hall	d						18 33										20 33					
Preston 8	a			18 13			18 41			19 13				20 14			20 41			21 13		
	d	17 35	17 39	18 14	17 44	18 20	18 41	18 35	18 39	19 14	19 21	19 35	19 39	20 15	19 44	20 21	20 41	20 35	20 39	21 14	21 20	21 33
Salwick	d																					
Kirkham & Wesham	d				17 53	18 29	18 52				19 30				19 53	20 30	20 52				21 29	
Moss Side	d				18 01		18 59								20 01		20 58					
Lytham	d				18 05		19 03								20 05		21 02					
Ansdell & Fairhaven	d				18 08		19 06								20 08		21 05					
St Annes-on-the-Sea	d				18 12		19 10								20 12		21 09					
Squires Gate	d				18 15		19 13								20 15		21 13					
Blackpool Pleasure Beach	d				18 18		19 16								20 18		21 15					
Blackpool South	a				18 21		19 20								20 21		21 20					
Poulton-le-Fylde	d	17 52	17 57	18 31		18 37		18 52	18 57	19 31	19 38	19 52	19 57	20 32		20 38		20 52	20 57	21 31	21 37	21 50
Layton	d					18 42					19 42					20 43					21 42	
Blackpool North	a	17 58	18 07	18 38		18 49		18 58	19 07	19 38	19 49	19 58	20 07	20 39		20 49		20 58	21 07	21 38	21 49	21 59

		NT	NT	NT	NT	TP	NT	NT	NT	NT	TP
						◇1					◇1
		B		C		A	B	D 🚌		B	A
Colne	d				21 36						
Nelson	d				21 40						
Brierfield	d				21 43						
Burnley Central	d				21 48						
Burnley Barracks	d				21x50						
Leeds 10 41	d										
Burnley Manchester Road 41	d		21 34					22 10	22 18		
Rose Grove	d				21 53						
Hapton	d				21x56						
Huncoat	d				21 59						
Accrington	d		21 47		22 04			22 30	22 31		
Church & Oswaldtwistle	d				22 06						
Rishton	d				22 09						
Blackburn	a		21 55		22 14			22 48	22 39		
Clitheroe 94	d										
Blackburn	d		21 56		22 16			22 48	22 39		
Mill Hill (Lancashire)	d				22 19						
Cherry Tree	d				22 21						
Pleasington	d				22x23						
Bamber Bridge	d				22 30						
Lostock Hall	d				22 33						
Preston 8	a		22 13		22 44			23 18	22 54		
	d	21 39	22 14	22 20		22 29	22 39	23 18	22 56	23 39	23 44
Salwick	d										
Kirkham & Wesham	d			22 29							23 53
Moss Side	d										
Lytham	d										
Ansdell & Fairhaven	d										
St Annes-on-the-Sea	d										
Squires Gate	d										
Blackpool Pleasure Beach	d										
Blackpool South	a										
Poulton-le-Fylde	d	21 57	22 31	22 37		22 46	22 57	23 58	23 13	23 56	00 02
Layton	d			22 42							
Blackpool North	a	22 07	22 38	22 49		22 53	23 07	00 13	23 19	00 05	00 10

A From Manchester Airport
B From Wigan North Western
C From Manchester Oxford Road
D From Hebden Bridge

Table 97

Sundays

30 March to 11 May

Colne, Burnley, Accrington and Blackburn - Preston - Blackpool

Network Diagram - see first Page of Table 97

		NT	NT	TP	NT	NT	TP	NT	NT	NT	TP	NT	NT	NT	TP	NT	NT	NT	NT	NT	TP	NT	NT
				◇1			◇1				◇1				◇1						◇1		
		A		B	C	D	B	C			B	D	E	C	B	D	E		C		B	D	E
Colne	d								09 17											11 36			
Nelson	d								09 21											11 40			
Brierfield	d								09 24											11 43			
Burnley Central	d								09 29											11 48			
Burnley Barracks	d								09x31											11x50			
Leeds 10 41	d									08 45			09 35				10 35						11 35
Burnley Manchester Road 41	d									09 50			10 39				11 39						12 39
Rose Grove	d								09 34											11 53			
Hapton	d								09x37											11x56			
Huncoat	d								09 40											11 59			
Accrington	d								09 45	09 59			10 48				11 47			12 04			12 47
Church & Oswaldtwistle	d								09 47											12 06			
Rishton	d								09 50											12 09			
Blackburn	a								09 55	10 07			10 56				11 55			12 14			12 55
Clitheroe 94	d																						
Blackburn	d								09 57	10 07			10 56				11 56			12 16			12 56
Mill Hill (Lancashire)	d								10 00											12 19			
Cherry Tree	d								10 02											12 21			
Pleasington	d								10x04											12x23			
Bamber Bridge	d								10 11											12 30			
Lostock Hall	d								10 14											12 33			
Preston 8	a								10 22	10 27			11 13				12 13			12 41			13 13
	d	00 11	08 49	08 54	09 20	09 39	09 52	10 20	10 23	10 29	10 35	10 39	11 15	11 21	11 35	11 39	12 14	11 44	12 20	12 42	12 35	12 39	13 14
Salwick	d																						
Kirkham & Wesham	d	00 21	08 58		09 29			10 29	10 33					11 31				11 53	12 29	12 52			
Moss Side	d		09 06						10 39									12 01		12 58			
Lytham	d		09 10						10 43									12 05		13 02			
Ansdell & Fairhaven	d		09 13						10 46									12 08		13 05			
St Annes-on-the-Sea	d		09 17						10 50									12 12		13 09			
Squires Gate	d		09 20						10 54									12 15		13 13			
Blackpool Pleasure Beach	d		09 23						10 56									12 18		13 15			
Blackpool South	a		09 25						11 01									12 21		13 20			
Poulton-le-Fylde	d	00 29		09 11	09 37	09 57	10 09	10 37		10 46	10 52	10 57	11 32	11 39	11 52	11 57	12 31		12 37		12 52	12 57	13 31
Layton	d	00 34			09 42			10 42						11 44					12 42				
Blackpool North	a	00 40		09 19	09 49	10 07	10 18	10 49		10 53	11 01	11 07	11 39	11 49	12 01	12 07	12 38		12 49		13 01	13 07	13 38

		NT	TP	NT	NT	NT	NT	NT	TP	NT	NT	NT	TP	NT	NT	NT	NT	NT	NT	TP	NT	NT	NT
			◇1						◇1				◇1							◇1			
		C	B	D	E		C		B	D	E	C	B	D		F	E	C		B	D	E	C
Colne	d							13 36											15 36				
Nelson	d							13 40											15 40				
Brierfield	d							13 43											15 43				
Burnley Central	d							13 48											15 48				
Burnley Barracks	d							13x50											15x50				
Leeds 10 41	d				12 35						13 35						14 35					15 35	
Burnley Manchester Road 41	d				13 39						14 39						15 39					16 39	
Rose Grove	d							13 53											15 53				
Hapton	d							13x56											15x56				
Huncoat	d							13 59											15 59				
Accrington	d				13 47			14 04			14 47						15 47		16 04			16 47	
Church & Oswaldtwistle	d							14 06											16 06				
Rishton	d							14 09											16 09				
Blackburn	a				13 55			14 14			14 55						15 55		16 14			16 55	
Clitheroe 94	d															15 18							
Blackburn	d				13 56			14 16			14 56					15 44	15 56		16 16			16 56	
Mill Hill (Lancashire)	d							14 19											16 19				
Cherry Tree	d							14 21											16 21				
Pleasington	d							14x23											16x23				
Bamber Bridge	d							14 30								15 54			16 30				
Lostock Hall	d							14 33								15 56			16 33				
Preston 8	a				14 13			14 41			15 13					16 04	16 13		16 41			17 13	
	d	13 20	13 35	13 39	14 14	13 44	14 20	14 42	14 35	14 39	15 14	15 20	15 35	15 39	15 44	16 06	16 14	16 20	16 41	16 35	16 39	17 14	17 20
Salwick	d																						
Kirkham & Wesham	d	13 29				13 53	14 29	14 52				15 29			15 53	16 16		16 29	16 52				17 29
Moss Side	d					14 01		14 59							16 01				16 58				
Lytham	d					14 05		15 03							16 05				17 02				
Ansdell & Fairhaven	d					14 08		15 06							16 08				17 05				
St Annes-on-the-Sea	d					14 12		15 10							16 12				17 09				
Squires Gate	d					14 15		15 13							16 15				17 13				
Blackpool Pleasure Beach	d					14 18		15 16							16 18				17 15				
Blackpool South	a					14 20		15 21							16 21				17 20				
Poulton-le-Fylde	d	13 37	13 52	13 57	14 30		14 37		14 52	14 57	15 32	15 37	15 52	15 57		16 24	16 31	16 37		16 52	16 57	17 31	17 37
Layton	d	13 42					14 42					15 43						16 42					17 42
Blackpool North	a	13 49	14 01	14 07	14 38		14 49		15 01	15 07	15 39	15 49	16 01	16 07		16 33	16 38	16 49		17 01	17 07	17 38	17 49

A From Manchester Victoria
B From Manchester Airport
C From Manchester Oxford Road
D From Wigan North Western
E From York
F From Hellifield

Table 97

Sundays
30 March to 11 May

Colne, Burnley, Accrington and Blackburn - Preston - Blackpool

Network Diagram - see first Page of Table 97

		TP ◇1 A	NT B	NT C	NT	NT D	NT	TP ◇1 A	NT B	NT C	NT D	TP ◇1 A	NT B	NT C	NT	NT D	NT	TP ◇1 A	NT B	NT C	NT D	TP ◇1 A
Colne	d						17 36										19 36					
Nelson	d						17 40										19 40					
Brierfield	d						17 43										19 43					
Burnley Central	d						17 48										19 48					
Burnley Barracks	d						17x50										19x50					
Leeds 10 41	d			16 35						17 35				18 35						19 35		
Burnley Manchester Road 41	d			17 39						18 39				19 39						20 39		
Rose Grove	d						17 53										19 53					
Hapton	d						17x56										19x56					
Huncoat	d						17 59										19 59					
Accrington	d			17 47			18 04			18 47				19 47			20 04			20 47		
Church & Oswaldtwistle	d						18 06										20 06					
Rishton	d						18 09										20 09					
Blackburn	a			17 55			18 14			18 55				19 56			20 14			20 55		
Clitheroe 94	d																					
Blackburn	d			17 56			18 16			18 56				19 57			20 16			20 56		
Mill Hill (Lancashire)	d						18 19										20 19					
Cherry Tree	d						18 21										20 21					
Pleasington	d						18x23										20x23					
Bamber Bridge	d						18 30										20 30					
Lostock Hall	d						18 33										20 33					
Preston 8	a			18 13			18 41			19 13				20 14			20 41			21 13		
	d	17 35	17 39	18 14	17 44	18 20	18 41	18 35	18 39	19 14	19 21	19 35	19 39	20 15	19 44	20 21	20 41	20 35	20 39	21 14	21 20	21 35
Salwick	d																					
Kirkham & Wesham	d				17 53	18 29	18 52				19 30				19 53	20 30	20 52				21 29	
Moss Side	d				18 01		18 59								20 01		20 58					
Lytham	d				18 05		19 03								20 05		21 02					
Ansdell & Fairhaven	d				18 08		19 06								20 08		21 05					
St Annes-on-the-Sea	d				18 12		19 10								20 12		21 09					
Squires Gate	d				18 15		19 13								20 15		21 13					
Blackpool Pleasure Beach	d				18 18		19 16								20 18		21 15					
Blackpool South	a				18 21		19 20								20 21		21 20					
Poulton-le-Fylde	d	17 52	17 57	18 31		18 37		18 52	18 57	19 31	19 38	19 52	19 57	20 32		20 38		20 52	20 57	21 31	21 37	21 52
Layton	d					18 42					19 42					20 43					21 42	
Blackpool North	a	18 01	18 07	18 38		18 49		19 01	19 07	19 38	19 49	20 01	20 07	20 39		20 49		21 01	21 07	21 38	21 49	22 01

		NT B	NT C	NT D	NT	TP ◇1 A	NT B	NT B	TP ◇1 A
Colne	d				21 36				
Nelson	d				21 40				
Brierfield	d				21 43				
Burnley Central	d				21 48				
Burnley Barracks	d				21x50				
Leeds 10 41	d		20 35						
Burnley Manchester Road 41	d		21 39						
Rose Grove	d				21 53				
Hapton	d				21x56				
Huncoat	d				21 59				
Accrington	d		21 47		22 04				
Church & Oswaldtwistle	d				22 06				
Rishton	d				22 09				
Blackburn	a		21 55		22 14				
Clitheroe 94	d								
Blackburn	d		21 56		22 16				
Mill Hill (Lancashire)	d				22 19				
Cherry Tree	d				22 21				
Pleasington	d				22x23				
Bamber Bridge	d				22 30				
Lostock Hall	d				22 33				
Preston 8	a		22 13		22 44				
	d	21 39	22 14	22 20		22 29	22 39	23 39	23 47
Salwick	d								
Kirkham & Wesham	d			22 29					23 56
Moss Side	d								
Lytham	d								
Ansdell & Fairhaven	d								
St Annes-on-the-Sea	d								
Squires Gate	d								
Blackpool Pleasure Beach	d								
Blackpool South	a								
Poulton-le-Fylde	d	21 57	22 31	22 37		22 46	22 57	23 56	00 05
Layton	d			22 42					
Blackpool North	a	22 07	22 38	22 49		22 55	23 07	00 05	00 14

A From Manchester Airport
B From Wigan North Western
C From York
D From Manchester Oxford Road

Table 97R

Mondays to Fridays

9 December to 21 March

Blackpool - Preston - Blackburn, Accrington, Burnley and Colne

Network Diagram - see first Page of Table 97

Miles	Miles			NT	NT	NT	NT	TP	NT	NT	NT	TP		NT	NT	NT	TP	NT	NT	TP	NT	NT		NT	TP
								◇1				◇1					◇1			◇1					◇1
					A			B		C		B		D		E	F	C				C			B
					🚌							🛒					🛒								🛒
—	0	**Blackpool North**	d			04 56	05 29	05 39		06 19	06 28	06 40		06 53		07 02	07 11	07 18	07 29	07 36		08 20		08 29	08 44
—	1¼	Layton	d							06 22		06 43					07 14	07 21		07 39		08 23			
—	3¼	Poulton-le-Fylde	d			05 02	05 35	05 45		06 26	06 34	06 47				07 08	07 18	07 26	07 35	07 43		08 27		08 35	08 50
0	—	**Blackpool South**	d						05 42						06 42						07 42				
0½	—	Blackpool Pleasure Beach	d						05 44						06 44						07 44				
1¾	—	Squires Gate	d						05 46						06 46						07 46				
3¼	—	St Annes-on-the-Sea	d						05 50						06 50						07 50				
5¼	—	Ansdell & Fairhaven	d						05 53						06 53						07 53				
6½	—	Lytham	d						05 56						06 56						07 56				
9	—	Moss Side	d						06 01						07 01						08 01				
12¼	9¾	Kirkham & Wesham	d						06 08	06 36		06 57			07 09		07 27	07 35		07 53	08 09	08 37			
14¾	12¼	Salwick	d												07 13						08 13				
20	17½	**Preston** 8	a			05 20	05 52	06 03	06 19	06 46	06 52	07 07		07 15	07 20	07 28	07 38	07 46	07 52	08 03	08 20	08 47		08 52	09 08
—	—		d	04 47	04 57	05 22	05 54		06 21		06 54				07 22				07 54		08 22			08 54	
22¾	—	Lostock Hall	d						06 26						07 27						08 27				
24	—	Bamber Bridge	d						06 29						07 30						08 30				
29	—	Pleasington	d						06x37						07x38						08x38				
30	—	Cherry Tree	d						06 40						07 41						08 41				
30¾	—	Mill Hill (Lancashire)	d						06 42						07 43						08 43				
32	—	**Blackburn**	a	05 03	05 27	05 39	06 09		06 46		07 09				07 50				08 09		08 47			09 09	
—	—	Clitheroe 94	a																						
—	—	**Blackburn**	d	05 04	05 27	05 39	06 10		06 48		07 10				07 51				08 10		08 48			09 10	
35¾	—	Rishton	d			05 44			06 53						07 56						08 53				
37½	—	Church & Oswaldtwistle	d			05 47			06 56						07 59						08 56				
38¼	—	**Accrington**	d	05 11	05 45	05 50	06 19		06 59		07 19				08 02				08 19		08 59			09 19	
40	—	Huncoat	d			05 55			07 04						08 06						09 03				
41½	—	Hapton	d			05x58			07x07						08x09						09x06				
43	—	Rose Grove	d			06 01			07 10						08 12						09 09				
—	—	Burnley Manchester Road 41	a		06 05		06 30				07 31								08 30					09 32	
—	—	Leeds 10 41	a																						
44	—	Burnley Barracks	d						07x13						08x15						09x12				
44½	—	**Burnley Central**	d	05 21		06 05			07 15						08 18						09 15				
46¾	—	Brierfield	d			06 10			07 20						08 22						09 19				
48	—	Nelson	d			06 13			07 23						08 25						09 22				
50	—	**Colne**	a	05 34		06 21			07 31						08 34						09 31				

		NT	NT	NT	NT	TP	NT	NT		NT	NT	TP	NT	NT	NT	NT	TP	NT		NT	NT	NT	TP	NT	NT
						◇1						◇1					◇1						◇1		
			C		G	B		C			G	B		C		G	B			C		G	B		C
						🛒						🛒					🛒						🛒		
Blackpool North	d		09 20	09 29	09 35	09 40		10 20		10 29	10 35	10 44		11 20	11 29	11 35	11 44			12 20	12 29	12 35	12 41		13 20
Layton	d		09 23					10 23						11 23						12 23					13 23
Poulton-le-Fylde	d		09 27	09 35		09 46		10 27		10 35		10 50		11 27	11 35		11 50			12 27	12 35		12 47		13 27
Blackpool South	d	08 44					09 44						10 44					11 44						12 44	
Blackpool Pleasure Beach	d	08 46					09 46						10 46					11 46						12 46	
Squires Gate	d	08 48					09 48						10 48					11 48						12 48	
St Annes-on-the-Sea	d	08 52					09 52						10 52					11 52						12 52	
Ansdell & Fairhaven	d	08 55					09 55						10 55					11 55						12 55	
Lytham	d	08 58					09 58						10 58					11 58						12 58	
Moss Side	d	09 03					10 03						11 03					12 03						13 03	
Kirkham & Wesham	d	09 10	09 37		09 52		10 10	10 37			10 52		11 10	11 37		11 52		12 10		12 37		12 50		13 10	13 37
Salwick	d																								
Preston 8	a	09 20	09 47	09 52	10 02	10 04	10 20	10 47		10 52	11 02	11 08	11 20	11 47	11 52	12 02	12 08	12 20		12 47	12 52	13 00	13 05	13 20	13 47
	d	09 22		09 54			10 22			10 54			11 22		11 54			12 22			12 54			13 22	
Lostock Hall	d	09 27					10 27						11 27					12 27						13 27	
Bamber Bridge	d	09 30					10 30						11 30					12 30						13 30	
Pleasington	d	09x38					10x38						11x38					12x38						13x38	
Cherry Tree	d	09 41					10 41						11 41					12 41						13 41	
Mill Hill (Lancashire)	d	09 43					10 43						11 43					12 43						13 43	
Blackburn	a	09 47		10 09			10 46			11 09			11 46		12 09			12 46			13 09			13 46	
Clitheroe 94	a																								
Blackburn	d	09 48		10 10			10 48			11 10			11 48		12 10			12 48			13 10			13 48	
Rishton	d	09 53					10 53						11 53					12 53						13 53	
Church & Oswaldtwistle	d	09 56					10 56						11 56					12 56						13 56	
Accrington	d	09 59		10 19			10 59			11 19			11 59		12 19			12 59			13 19			13 59	
Huncoat	d	10 04					11 03						12 03					13 03						14 03	
Hapton	d	10x07					11x06						12x06					13x06						14x06	
Rose Grove	d	10 10					11 09						12 09					13 09						14 09	
Burnley Manchester Road 41	a			10 32						11 30					12 30						13 30				
Leeds 10 41	a																								
Burnley Barracks	d	10x13					11x12						12x12					13x12						14x12	
Burnley Central	d	10 15					11 15						12 15					13 15						14 15	
Brierfield	d	10 20					11 19						12 19					13 19						14 19	
Nelson	d	10 23					11 22						12 22					13 22						14 22	
Colne	a	10 31					11 31						12 31					13 31						14 31	

A To Hebden Bridge
B To Manchester Airport
C To Manchester Victoria
D To Hazel Grove
E To Liverpool Lime Street
F To Manchester Oxford Road
G To Liverpool South Pw Hl

Table 97R

Mondays to Fridays

9 December to 21 March

Blackpool - Preston - Blackburn, Accrington, Burnley and Colne

Network Diagram - see first Page of Table 97

		NT	NT A	TP ◇1 B	NT	NT C	NT	NT A	TP ◇1 B	NT	NT C	NT	NT D	TP ◇1 B	NT	NT C	NT	NT D	TP ◇1 B	NT	NT	TP ◇1 B
Blackpool North	d	13 29	13 35	13 44		14 20	14 29	14 35	14 40		15 20	15 29	15 35	15 40		16 20	16 29	16 35	16 40		17 14	17 20
Layton	d					14 23					15 23					16 23			16 43			17 23
Poulton-le-Fylde	d	13 35		13 50		14 27	14 35		14 46		15 27	15 35		15 46		16 27	16 35		16 47		17 20	17 27
Blackpool South	d				13 44					14 44					15 44					16 46		
Blackpool Pleasure Beach	d				13 46					14 46					15 46					16 47		
Squires Gate	d				13 48					14 48					15 48					16 48		
St Annes-on-the-Sea	d				13 52					14 52					15 52					16 52		
Ansdell & Fairhaven	d				13 55					14 55					15 55					16 55		
Lytham	d				13 58					14 58					15 58					16 58		
Moss Side	d				14 03					15 03					16 02					17 03		
Kirkham & Wesham	d		13 52		14 10	14 37		14 50		15 10	15 37		15 50		16 10	16 37		16 50	16 57	17 10	17 29	
Salwick	d														16 15							
Preston 8	a	13 52	14 02	14 08	14 20	14 47	14 52	15 00	15 04	15 20	15 47	15 52	16 00	16 04	16 22	16 47	16 52	17 01	17 08	17 20	17 44	17 45
	d	13 54			14 22		14 54			15 22		15 54			16 22		16 54			17 22	17 44	
Lostock Hall	d				14 27					15 27					16 27					17 27	17 51	
Bamber Bridge	d				14 30					15 30					16 30					17 30	17 54	
Pleasington	d				14x38					15x38					16x38					17x38	18x01	
Cherry Tree	d				14 41					15 41					16 41					17 41	18 05	
Mill Hill (Lancashire)	d				14 43					15 43					16 43					17 43	18 08	
Blackburn	a	14 09			14 46		15 09			15 47		16 09			16 48		17 09			17 48	18 11	
Clitheroe 94	a																					
Blackburn	d	14 10			14 48		15 10			15 48		16 10			16 50		17 10			17 58	18 11	
Rishton	d				14 53					15 53					16 55					18 03		
Church & Oswaldtwistle	d				14 56					15 56					16 58					18 06		
Accrington	d	14 19			14 59		15 19			15 59		16 19			17 01		17 19			18 09	18 19	
Huncoat	d				15 03					16 03					17 05					18 13		
Hapton	d				15x06					16x06					17x08					18x16		
Rose Grove	d				15 09					16 09					17 11					18 19		
Burnley Manchester Road 41	a	14 31					15 31					16 31					17 31				18 31	
Leeds 10 41	a																					
Burnley Barracks	d				15x12					16x12					17x14					18x22		
Burnley Central	d				15 15					16 15					17 18					18 25		
Brierfield	d				15 19					16 19					17 21					18 29		
Nelson	d				15 22					16 22					17 24					18 32		
Colne	a				15 31					16 31					17 33					18 41		

		NT D	NT	NT C	NT	NT D	TP ◇1 B	NT	NT C	NT D	TP FO ◇1 E	TP ◇1 F	NT	NT C	NT	NT D	TP ◇1 G	NT	NT C	TP ◇1 G	NT	NT H	NT C
Blackpool North	d	17 35		18 20	18 29	18 35	18 40		19 20	19 35	19 40	19 44		20 20	20 29	20 35	20 44		21 20	21 44		22 14	22 20
Layton	d			18 23					19 23					20 23					21 23				22 23
Poulton-le-Fylde	d			18 27	18 35		18 46		19 28		19 46	19 50		20 27	20 35		20 50		21 27	21 50			22 27
Blackpool South	d		17 44					18 44					19 44					20 44			22 00		
Blackpool Pleasure Beach	d		17 46					18 46					19 46					20 46			22 02		
Squires Gate	d		17 48					18 48					19 48					20 48			22 04		
St Annes-on-the-Sea	d		17 52					18 52					19 52					20 52			22 08		
Ansdell & Fairhaven	d		17 55					18 55					19 55					20 55			22 11		
Lytham	d		17 58					18 58					19 58					20 58			22 14		
Moss Side	d		18 03					19 03					20 03					21 03			22 19		
Kirkham & Wesham	d	17 52	18 10	18 37		18 50		19 10	19 37	19 50			20 10	20 37		20 52		21 10	21 37		22 26		22 37
Salwick	d																						
Preston 8	a	18 02	18 20	18 47	18 52	19 00	19 04	19 20	19 47	20 00	20 04	20 08	20 20	20 47	20 53	21 02	21 08	21 20	21 47	22 08	22 36	22 41	22 47
	d		18 24		18 54			19 22					20 22		20 54			21 22			22 38		
Lostock Hall	d		18 30					19 27					20 27					21 27			22 43		
Bamber Bridge	d		18 33					19 30					20 30					21 30			22 46		
Pleasington	d		18x41					19x38					20x38					21x38			22x54		
Cherry Tree	d		18 44					19 41					20 41					21 41			22 57		
Mill Hill (Lancashire)	d		18 46					19 43					20 43					21 43			22 59		
Blackburn	a		18 52		19 09			19 46					20 46		21 10			21 46			23 06		
Clitheroe 94	a																						
Blackburn	d		18 53		19 10			19 48					20 48		21 10			21 48			23 07		
Rishton	d		18 58					19 53					20 53					21 53			23 12		
Church & Oswaldtwistle	d		19 01					19 56					20 56					21 56			23 15		
Accrington	d		19 04		19 19			19 59					20 59		21 19			21 59			23 18		
Huncoat	d		19 08					20 03					21 03					22 03			23 22		
Hapton	d		19x11					20x06					21x06					22x06			23x25		
Rose Grove	d		19 14					20 09					21 09					22 09			23 28		
Burnley Manchester Road 41	a				19 32										21 32								
Leeds 10 41	a																						
Burnley Barracks	d		19x17					20x12					21x12					22x12			23x31		
Burnley Central	d		19 20					20 15					21 15					22 15			23 34		
Brierfield	d		19 24					20 19					21 19					22 19			23 38		
Nelson	d		19 27					20 22					21 22					22 22			23 41		
Colne	a		19 36					20 31					21 31					22 31			23 50		

A To Liverpool South Pw Hl
B To Manchester Airport
C To Manchester Victoria
D To Liverpool Lime Street
E until 7 February. To Manchester Airport
F FX until 6 February, from 10 February. To Manchester Airport
G To Manchester Piccadilly
H To Wigan North Western

Table 97R

Mondays to Fridays

9 December to 21 March

Blackpool - Preston - Blackburn, Accrington, Burnley and Colne

Network Diagram - see first Page of Table 97

		TP	NT	NT
		◇1		
		A	B	
Blackpool North	d	22 45	23 13	
Layton	d		23 16	
Poulton-le-Fylde	d	22 51	23 20	
Blackpool South	d			23 30
Blackpool Pleasure Beach	d			23 32
Squires Gate	d			23 34
St Annes-on-the-Sea	d			23 38
Ansdell & Fairhaven	d			23 41
Lytham	d			23 44
Moss Side	d			23 49
Kirkham & Wesham	d		23 30	23 56
Salwick	d			
Preston 8	a	23 09	23 40	00 08
	d			
Lostock Hall	d			
Bamber Bridge	d			
Pleasington	d			
Cherry Tree	d			
Mill Hill (Lancashire)	d			
Blackburn	a			
Clitheroe 94	a			
Blackburn	d			
Rishton	d			
Church & Oswaldtwistle	d			
Accrington	d			
Huncoat	d			
Hapton	d			
Rose Grove	d			
Burnley Manchester Road 41	a			
Leeds 10 41	a			
Burnley Barracks	d			
Burnley Central	d			
Brierfield	d			
Nelson	d			
Colne	a			

Mondays to Fridays

24 March to 16 May

		NT	NT	NT	TP	NT	NT	NT	TP	NT	NT	NT	TP	NT	NT	TP	NT	NT	NT	TP	NT	NT	NT
					◇1				◇1				◇1			◇1				◇1			
				C	A		B	C	A	D		E	F	B	C			B	C	A		B	C
									🚲				🚲							🚲			
Blackpool North	d		04 56	05 29	05 39		06 19	06 28	06 40	06 53		07 02	07 11	07 18	07 29	07 36		08 20	08 29	08 44		09 20	09 29
Layton	d						06 22		06 43				07 14	07 21		07 39		08 23				09 23	
Poulton-le-Fylde	d		05 02	05 35	05 45		06 26	06 34	06 47			07 08	07 18	07 26	07 35	07 43		08 27	08 35	08 50		09 27	09 35
Blackpool South	d					05 42					06 42						07 42				08 44		
Blackpool Pleasure Beach	d					05 44					06 44						07 44				08 46		
Squires Gate	d					05 46					06 46						07 46				08 48		
St Annes-on-the-Sea	d					05 50					06 50						07 50				08 52		
Ansdell & Fairhaven	d					05 53					06 53						07 53				08 55		
Lytham	d					05 56					06 56						07 56				08 58		
Moss Side	d					06 01					07 01						08 01				09 03		
Kirkham & Wesham	d					06 08	06 36		06 57		07 09		07 27	07 35		07 53	08 09	08 37			09 10	09 37	
Salwick	d										07 13						08 13						
Preston 8	a		05 20	05 52	06 03	06 19	06 46	06 52	07 07	07 15	07 20	07 28	07 38	07 46	07 52	08 03	08 20	08 47	08 52	09 08	09 20	09 47	09 52
	d	04 47	05 22	05 54		06 21		06 54			07 22				07 54		08 22		08 54		09 22		09 54
Lostock Hall	d					06 26					07 27						08 27				09 27		
Bamber Bridge	d					06 29					07 30						08 30				09 30		
Pleasington	d					06x37					07x38						08x38				09x38		
Cherry Tree	d					06 40					07 41						08 41				09 41		
Mill Hill (Lancashire)	d					06 42					07 43						08 43				09 43		
Blackburn	a	05 03	05 39	06 09		06 46		07 09			07 50				08 10		08 47		09 09		09 47		10 09
Clitheroe 94	a																						
Blackburn	d	05 04	05 39	06 10		06 48		07 10			07 51				08 10		08 48		09 10		09 48		10 10
Rishton	d		05 44			06 53					07 56						08 53				09 53		
Church & Oswaldtwistle	d		05 47			06 56					07 59						08 56				09 56		
Accrington	d	05 11	05 50	06 17		06 59		07 17			08 02				08 18		08 59		09 17		09 59		10 17
Huncoat	d		05 55			07 04					08 06						09 03				10 04		
Hapton	d		05x58			07x07					08x09						09x06				10x07		
Rose Grove	d		06 01			07 10					08 12						09 09				10 10		
Burnley Manchester Road 41	a			06 26				07 26							08 26				09 26				10 26
Leeds 10 41	a			07 39				08 39							09 39				10 38				11 39
Burnley Barracks	d					07x13					08x15						09x12				10x13		
Burnley Central	d	05 21	06 05			07 15					08 18						09 15				10 15		
Brierfield	d		06 10			07 20					08 22						09 19				10 20		
Nelson	d		06 13			07 23					08 25						09 22				10 23		
Colne	a	05 34	06 21			07 31					08 34						09 31				10 31		

A To Manchester Airport
B To Manchester Victoria
C To York
D To Hazel Grove
E To Liverpool Lime Street
F To Manchester Oxford Road

Table 97R

Mondays to Fridays

24 March to 16 May

Blackpool - Preston - Blackburn, Accrington, Burnley and Colne

Network Diagram - see first Page of Table 97

		NT A	TP ◇1 B	NT	NT C	NT D		NT A	TP ◇1 B	NT	NT C	NT D	NT A	TP ◇1 B	NT	NT C		NT D	NT A	TP ◇1 B	NT	NT C	NT D	NT A	TP ◇1 B
Blackpool North	d	09 35	09 40		10 20	10 29		10 35	10 44		11 20	11 29	11 35	11 44		12 20		12 29	12 35	12 41		13 20	13 29	13 35	13 44
Layton	d				10 23						11 23					12 23						13 23			
Poulton-le-Fylde	d		09 46		10 27	10 35			10 50		11 27	11 35		11 50		12 27		12 35		12 47		13 27	13 35		13 50
Blackpool South	d			09 44						10 44					11 44						12 44				
Blackpool Pleasure Beach	d			09 46						10 46					11 46						12 46				
Squires Gate	d			09 48						10 48					11 48						12 48				
St Annes-on-the-Sea	d			09 52						10 52					11 52						12 52				
Ansdell & Fairhaven	d			09 55						10 55					11 55						12 55				
Lytham	d			09 58						10 58					11 58						12 58				
Moss Side	d			10 03						11 03					12 03						13 03				
Kirkham & Wesham	d	09 52		10 10	10 37			10 52		11 10	11 37		11 52		12 10	12 37			12 50		13 10	13 37		13 52	
Salwick	d																								
Preston 8	a	10 02	10 04	10 20	10 47	10 52		11 02	11 08	11 20	11 47	11 52	12 02	12 08	12 20	12 47		12 52	13 00	13 05	13 20	13 47	13 52	14 02	14 08
	d			10 22		10 54				11 22		11 54			12 22			12 54			13 22		13 54		
Lostock Hall	d			10 27						11 27					12 27						13 27				
Bamber Bridge	d			10 30						11 30					12 30						13 30				
Pleasington	d			10x38						11x38					12x38						13x38				
Cherry Tree	d			10 41						11 41					12 41						13 41				
Mill Hill (Lancashire)	d			10 43						11 43					12 43						13 43				
Blackburn	a			10 46		11 09				11 46		12 09			12 46			13 09			13 46		14 10		
Clitheroe 94	a																								
Blackburn	d			10 48		11 10				11 48		12 10			12 48			13 10			13 48		14 10		
Rishton	d			10 53						11 53					12 53						13 53				
Church & Oswaldtwistle	d			10 56						11 56					12 56						13 56				
Accrington	d			10 59		11 17				11 59		12 17			12 59			13 17			13 59		14 17		
Huncoat	d			11 03						12 03					13 03						14 03				
Hapton	d			11x06						12x06					13x06						14x06				
Rose Grove	d			11 09						12 09					13 09						14 09				
Burnley Manchester Road 41	a					11 27						12 26						13 26					14 26		
Leeds 10 41	a					12 37						13 40						14 39					15 39		
Burnley Barracks	d			11x12						12x12					13x12						14x12				
Burnley Central	d			11 15						12 15					13 15						14 15				
Brierfield	d			11 19						12 19					13 19						14 19				
Nelson	d			11 22						12 22					13 22						14 22				
Colne	a			11 31						12 31					13 31						14 31				

		NT		NT C	NT D	NT A	TP ◇1 B	NT	NT C	NT D	NT E	TP ◇1 B		NT	NT C	NT D	NT E	TP ◇1 B	NT	NT D	TP ◇1 B	NT E		NT	NT C
Blackpool North	d			14 20	14 29	14 35	14 40		15 20	15 29	15 35	15 40			16 20	16 29	16 35	16 40		17 14	17 20	17 35			18 20
Layton	d			14 23					15 23						16 23			16 43			17 23				18 23
Poulton-le-Fylde	d			14 27	14 35		14 46		15 27	15 35		15 46			16 27	16 35		16 47		17 20	17 27				18 27
Blackpool South	d	13 44						14 44						15 44					16 46					17 44	
Blackpool Pleasure Beach	d	13 46						14 46						15 46					16 47					17 46	
Squires Gate	d	13 48						14 48						15 48					16 48					17 48	
St Annes-on-the-Sea	d	13 52						14 52						15 52					16 52					17 52	
Ansdell & Fairhaven	d	13 55						14 55						15 55					16 55					17 55	
Lytham	d	13 58						14 58						15 58					16 58					17 58	
Moss Side	d	14 03						15 03						16 02					17 03					18 03	
Kirkham & Wesham	d	14 10		14 37		14 50		15 10	15 37		15 50			16 10	16 37		16 50	16 57	17 10	17 29		17 52		18 10	18 37
Salwick	d													16 15											
Preston 8	a	14 20		14 47	14 52	15 00	15 04	15 20	15 47	15 52	16 00	16 04		16 22	16 47	16 52	17 01	17 08	17 20	17 44	17 45	18 02		18 20	18 47
	d	14 22			14 54			15 22		15 54				16 22		16 54			17 22	17 44				18 24	
Lostock Hall	d	14 27						15 27						16 27					17 27	17 51				18 30	
Bamber Bridge	d	14 30						15 30						16 30					17 30	17 54				18 33	
Pleasington	d	14x38						15x38						16x38					17x38	18 01				18x41	
Cherry Tree	d	14 41						15 41						16 41					17 41	18 05				18 44	
Mill Hill (Lancashire)	d	14 43						15 43						16 43					17 43	18 08				18 46	
Blackburn	a	14 46			15 09			15 47		16 09				16 48		17 09			17 48	18 11				18 52	
Clitheroe 94	a																								
Blackburn	d	14 48			15 10			15 48		16 10				16 50		17 10			17 58	18 11				18 53	
Rishton	d	14 53						15 53						16 55					18 03					18 58	
Church & Oswaldtwistle	d	14 56						15 56						16 58					18 06					19 01	
Accrington	d	14 59			15 17			15 59		16 17				17 01		17 17			18 09	18 19				19 04	
Huncoat	d	15 03						16 03						17 05					18 13					19 08	
Hapton	d	15x06						16x06						17x08					18x16					19x11	
Rose Grove	d	15 09						16 09						17 11					18 19					19 14	
Burnley Manchester Road 41	a				15 26					16 26						17 26				18 27					
Leeds 10 41	a				16 39					17 39						18 39				19 39					
Burnley Barracks	d	15x12						16x12						17x14					18x22					19x17	
Burnley Central	d	15 15						16 15						17 18					18 25					19 20	
Brierfield	d	15 19						16 19						17 21					18 29					19 24	
Nelson	d	15 22						16 22						17 24					18 32					19 27	
Colne	a	15 31						16 31						17 33					18 41					19 36	

A To Liverpool South Pw Hl
B To Manchester Airport
C To Manchester Victoria
D To York
E To Liverpool Lime Street

Table 97R

Mondays to Fridays

24 March to 16 May

Blackpool - Preston - Blackburn, Accrington, Burnley and Colne

Network Diagram - see first Page of Table 97

		NT	NT	TP	NT	NT	NT	TP	NT	NT	NT	NT	TP	NT	NT	TP	NT	NT	NT	TP	NT	NT
				◇1				◇1					◇1			◇1				◇1		
		A	B	C		D	B	C		D	A	B	C		D	C		E	D	C	D	
Blackpool North	d	18 29	18 35	18 40		19 20	19 35	19 44		20 20	20 29	20 35	20 44		21 20	21 44		22 14	22 20	22 45	23 13	
Layton	d					19 23				20 23					21 23				22 23		23 16	
Poulton-le-Fylde	d	18 35		18 46		19 28		19 50		20 27	20 35		20 50		21 27	21 50			22 27	22 51	23 20	
Blackpool South	d				18 44				19 44					20 44			22 00					23 30
Blackpool Pleasure Beach	d				18 46				19 46					20 46			22 02					23 32
Squires Gate	d				18 48				19 48					20 48			22 04					23 34
St Annes-on-the-Sea	d				18 52				19 52					20 52			22 08					23 38
Ansdell & Fairhaven	d				18 55				19 55					20 55			22 11					23 41
Lytham	d				18 58				19 58					20 58			22 14					23 44
Moss Side	d				19 03				20 03					21 03			22 19					23 49
Kirkham & Wesham	d		18 50		19 10	19 37	19 50		20 10	20 37		20 52		21 10	21 37		22 26		22 37		23 30	23 56
Salwick	d																					
Preston 8	a	18 52	19 00	19 04	19 20	19 47	20 00	20 08	20 20	20 47	20 53	21 02	21 08	21 20	21 47	22 08	22 36	22 41	22 47	23 09	23 40	00 08
	d	18 54			19 22				20 22		20 54			21 22			22 38					
Lostock Hall	d				19 27				20 27					21 27			22 43					
Bamber Bridge	d				19 30				20 30					21 30			22 46					
Pleasington	d				19x38				20x38					21x38			22x54					
Cherry Tree	d				19 41				20 41					21 41			22 57					
Mill Hill (Lancashire)	d				19 43				20 43					21 43			22 59					
Blackburn	a	19 09			19 46				20 46		21 10			21 46			23 06					
Clitheroe 94	a																					
Blackburn	d	19 10			19 48				20 48		21 10			21 48			23 07					
Rishton	d				19 53				20 53					21 53			23 12					
Church & Oswaldtwistle	d				19 56				20 56					21 56			23 15					
Accrington	d	19 17			19 59				20 59		21 18			21 59			23 18					
Huncoat	d				20 03				21 03					22 03			23 22					
Hapton	d				20x06				21x06					22x06			23x25					
Rose Grove	d				20 09				21 09					22 09			23 28					
Burnley Manchester Road 41	a	19 26									21 27											
Leeds 10 41	a	20 38									22 36											
Burnley Barracks	d				20x12				21x12					22x12			23x31					
Burnley Central	d				20 15				21 15					22 15			23 34					
Brierfield	d				20 19				21 19					22 19			23 38					
Nelson	d				20 22				21 22					22 22			23 41					
Colne	a				20 31				21 31					22 31			23 50					

Saturdays

14 December to 22 March

		NT	NT	NT	NT	TP	NT	NT	NT	TP	NT	NT	NT	NT	NT	TP	NT	NT	NT	NT	TP	NT	TP
						◇1				◇1						◇1					◇1		◇1
			F			C		D		C	G		B	D		C		D		H	C		I
Blackpool North	d			04 56	05 29	05 39		06 19	06 28	06 40	06 53		07 02	07 18	07 29	07 44		08 20	08 29	08 35	08 40		09 14
Layton	d							06 22		06 43				07 21		07 47		08 23					
Poulton-le-Fylde	d			05 02	05 35	05 45		06 26	06 34	06 47			07 08	07 25	07 35	07 51		08 27	08 35		08 46		09 20
Blackpool South	d						05 42					06 42					07 42					08 44	
Blackpool Pleasure Beach	d						05 44					06 44					07 44					08 46	
Squires Gate	d						05 46					06 46					07 46					08 48	
St Annes-on-the-Sea	d						05 50					06 50					07 50					08 52	
Ansdell & Fairhaven	d						05 53					06 53					07 53					08 55	
Lytham	d						05 56					06 56					07 56					08 58	
Moss Side	d						06 01					07 01					08 01					09 03	
Kirkham & Wesham	d						06 08	06 36		06 57		07 09		07 35		08 01	08 09	08 37				09 10	
Salwick	d											07 13					08 14						
Preston 8	a			05 20	05 52	06 03	06 19	06 46	06 52	07 07	07 15	07 20	07 28	07 46	07 52	08 11	08 21	08 47	08 52	09 02	09 04	09 20	09 41
	d	04 47	04 57	05 22	05 54		06 21		06 54			07 22			07 54		08 22		08 54			09 22	
Lostock Hall	d						06 26					07 27					08 27					09 27	
Bamber Bridge	d						06 29					07 30					08 30					09 30	
Pleasington	d						06x37					07x38					08x38					09x38	
Cherry Tree	d						06 40					07 41					08 41					09 41	
Mill Hill (Lancashire)	d						06 42					07 43					08 43					09 43	
Blackburn	a	05 03	05 27	05 38	06 09		06 45		07 09			07 50			08 09		08 46		09 09			09 46	
Clitheroe 94	a																						
Blackburn	d	05 04	05 27	05 39	06 10		06 48		07 10			07 51			08 10		08 48		09 10			09 48	
Rishton	d			05 44			06 53					07 56					08 53					09 53	
Church & Oswaldtwistle	d			05 47			06 56					07 59					08 56					09 56	
Accrington	d	05 11	05 45	05 50	06 19		06 59		07 19			08 02			08 19		08 59		09 19			09 59	
Huncoat	d			05 54			07 03					08 06					09 03					10 03	
Hapton	d			05x57			07x06					08x09					09x06					10x06	
Rose Grove	d			06 00			07 09					08 12					09 09					10 09	
Burnley Manchester Road 41	a		06 05		06 30				07 31						08 30				09 32				
Leeds 10 41	a																						
Burnley Barracks	d						07x12					08x15					09x12					10x12	
Burnley Central	d	05 21		06 05			07 15					08 18					09 15					10 15	
Brierfield	d			06 09			07 19					08 22					09 19					10 19	
Nelson	d			06 12			07 22					08 25					09 22					10 22	
Colne	a	05 34		06 21			07 31					08 34					09 31					10 31	

A To York
B To Liverpool Lime Street
C To Manchester Airport
D To Manchester Victoria
E To Wigan North Western
F To Hebden Bridge
G To Hazel Grove
H To Liverpool South Pw Hl
I To Barrow-in-Furness

Table 97R

Saturdays

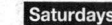

14 December to 22 March

Blackpool - Preston - Blackburn, Accrington, Burnley and Colne

Network Diagram - see first Page of Table 97

		NT A	NT	NT B	TP ◇1 C	NT		NT A	NT	NT B	TP ◇1 C	NT	NT A	NT	NT B	TP ◇1 C		NT	NT A	NT	NT B	TP ◇1 C	NT	NT A	NT
Blackpool North	d	09 20	09 29	09 35	09 40			10 20	10 29	10 35	10 44		11 20	11 29	11 35	11 41			12 20	12 29	12 35	12 40		13 20	13 29
Layton	d	09 23						10 23					11 23						12 23					13 23	
Poulton-le-Fylde	d	09 27	09 35		09 46			10 27	10 35		10 50		11 27	11 35		11 47			12 27	12 35		12 46		13 27	13 35
Blackpool South	d					09 44						10 44						11 44					12 44		
Blackpool Pleasure Beach	d					09 46						10 46						11 46					12 46		
Squires Gate	d					09 48						10 48						11 48					12 48		
St Annes-on-the-Sea	d					09 52						10 52						11 52					12 52		
Ansdell & Fairhaven	d					09 55						10 55						11 55					12 55		
Lytham	d					09 58						10 58						11 58					12 58		
Moss Side	d					10 03						11 03						12 03					13 03		
Kirkham & Wesham	d	09 37		09 52		10 10		10 37		10 52		11 10	11 37		11 52			12 10	12 37		12 50		13 10	13 37	
Salwick	d																								
Preston 8	a	09 47	09 52	10 02	10 04	10 20		10 47	10 52	11 02	11 08	11 20	11 47	11 52	12 02	12 05		12 20	12 47	12 52	13 00	13 04	13 20	13 47	13 52
	d		09 54			10 22			10 54			11 22		11 54				12 22		12 54			13 22		13 54
Lostock Hall	d					10 27						11 27						12 27					13 27		
Bamber Bridge	d					10 30						11 30						12 30					13 30		
Pleasington	d					10x38						11x38						12x38					13x38		
Cherry Tree	d					10 41						11 41						12 41					13 41		
Mill Hill (Lancashire)	d					10 43						11 43						12 43					13 43		
Blackburn	a		10 09			10 46			11 09			11 46		12 09				12 46		13 09			13 46		14 09
Clitheroe 94	a																								
Blackburn	d		10 10			10 48			11 10			11 48		12 10				12 48		13 10			13 48		14 10
Rishton	d					10 53						11 53						12 53					13 53		
Church & Oswaldtwistle	d					10 56						11 56						12 56					13 56		
Accrington	d		10 19			10 59			11 19			11 59		12 19				12 59		13 19			13 59		14 19
Huncoat	d					11 03						12 03						13 03					14 03		
Hapton	d					11x06						12x06						13x06					14x06		
Rose Grove	d					11 09						12 09						13 09					14 09		
Burnley Manchester Road 41	a		10 32						11 30					12 30						13 30					14 31
Leeds 10 41	a																								
Burnley Barracks	d					11x12						12x12						13x12					14x12		
Burnley Central	d					11 15						12 15						13 15					14 15		
Brierfield	d					11 19						12 19						13 19					14 19		
Nelson	d					11 22						12 22						13 22					14 22		
Colne	a					11 31						12 31						13 31					14 31		

		NT B		TP ◇1 C	NT	NT A	NT	NT B	TP ◇1 C	NT	NT A	NT		NT D	TP ◇1 C	NT	NT A	NT	NT D	TP ◇1 C	NT	NT		TP ◇1 C	NT D
Blackpool North	d	13 35		13 44		14 20	14 29	14 35	14 40		15 20	15 29		15 35	15 40		16 20	16 29	16 35	16 40		17 14		17 20	17 35
Layton	d					14 23					15 23						16 23			16 43				17 23	
Poulton-le-Fylde	d			13 50		14 27	14 35		14 46		15 27	15 35			15 46		16 27	16 35		16 47		17 20		17 27	
Blackpool South	d				13 44					14 44						15 44					16 44				
Blackpool Pleasure Beach	d				13 46					14 46						15 46					16 46				
Squires Gate	d				13 48					14 48						15 48					16 48				
St Annes-on-the-Sea	d				13 52					14 52						15 52					16 52				
Ansdell & Fairhaven	d				13 55					14 55						15 55					16 55				
Lytham	d				13 58					14 58						15 58					16 58				
Moss Side	d				14 03					15 03						16 03					17 03				
Kirkham & Wesham	d	13 52			14 10	14 37		14 50		15 10	15 37			15 50		16 10	16 37		16 52	16 57	17 10	17 29			17 52
Salwick	d															16 15									
Preston 8	a	14 02		14 08	14 20	14 47	14 52	15 00	15 04	15 20	15 47	15 52		16 00	16 04	16 22	16 47	16 52	17 02	17 08	17 20	17 42		17 45	18 02
	d				14 22		14 54			15 22		15 54				16 22		16 54			17 22	17 44			
Lostock Hall	d				14 27					15 27						16 27					17 27	17 51			
Bamber Bridge	d				14 30					15 30						16 30					17 30	17 54			
Pleasington	d				14x38					15x38						16x38					17x38	18x01			
Cherry Tree	d				14 41					15 41						16 41					17 41	18 05			
Mill Hill (Lancashire)	d				14 43					15 43						16 43					17 43	18 08			
Blackburn	a				14 46		15 09			15 46		16 09				16 48		17 09			17 47	18 11			
Clitheroe 94	a																								
Blackburn	d				14 48		15 10			15 48		16 10				16 50		17 10			17 48	18 11			
Rishton	d				14 53					15 53						16 55					17 53				
Church & Oswaldtwistle	d				14 56					15 56						16 58					17 56				
Accrington	d				14 59		15 19			15 59		16 19				17 01		17 19			17 59	18 19			
Huncoat	d				15 03					16 03						17 05					18 03				
Hapton	d				15x06					16x06						17x08					18x06				
Rose Grove	d				15 09					16 09						17 11					18 09				
Burnley Manchester Road 41	a						15 31					16 31						17 31				18 31			
Leeds 10 41	a																								
Burnley Barracks	d				15x12					16x12						17x14					18x12				
Burnley Central	d				15 15					16 15						17 16					18 15				
Brierfield	d				15 19					16 19						17 21					18 19				
Nelson	d				15 22					16 22						17 24					18 22				
Colne	a				15 31					16 31						17 33					18 31				

A To Manchester Victoria
B To Liverpool South Pw Hl
C To Manchester Airport
D To Liverpool Lime Street

Table 97R

Saturdays

14 December to 22 March

Blackpool - Preston - Blackburn, Accrington, Burnley and Colne

Network Diagram - see first Page of Table 97

		NT	NT	NT	NT	TP	NT	TP		NT	NT	NT	NT	TP	NT	NT	NT	NT		NT	TP	TP	NT	NT	NT
						◇1		◇1						◇1							◇1				
			A		B	C		D		E	F	D	G	H		F	D			G	H	D		F	D
Blackpool North	d		18 20	18 29	18 35	18 40		19 14		19 19	19 20	19 35	19 35	19 44		20 20	20 20	20 29		20 35	20 44	20 44		21 20	21 20
Layton	d		18 23								19 23	19 38				20 23	20 23					20 47		21 23	21 23
Poulton-le-Fylde	d		18 27	18 35		18 46		19 20			19 28	19 43		19 50		20 27	20 28	20 35			20 50	20 51		21 27	21 28
Blackpool South	d	17 44					18 44								19 44								20 44		
Blackpool Pleasure Beach	d	17 46					18 46								19 46								20 46		
Squires Gate	d	17 48					18 48								19 48								20 48		
St Annes-on-the-Sea	d	17 52					18 52								19 52								20 52		
Ansdell & Fairhaven	d	17 55					18 55								19 55								20 55		
Lytham	d	17 58					18 58								19 58								20 58		
Moss Side	d	18 03					19 03								20 03								21 03		
Kirkham & Wesham	d	18 10	18 37		18 50		19 10			19 34	19 37	19 51	19 52		20 10	20 37	20 36			20 52		21 00	21 10	21 37	21 36
Salwick	d																								
Preston 8	a	18 22	18 47	18 52	19 00	19 04	19 20	19 38		19 44	19 47	20 02	20 02	20 08	20 20	20 47	20 47	20 53		21 02	21 08	21 10	21 20	21 47	21 47
	d	18 24		18 54			19 22								20 22			20 54					21 22		
Lostock Hall	d	18 30					19 27								20 27								21 27		
Bamber Bridge	d	18 33					19 30								20 30								21 30		
Pleasington	d	18x41					19x38								20x38								21x38		
Cherry Tree	d	18 44					19 41								20 41								21 41		
Mill Hill (Lancashire)	d	18 46					19 43								20 43								21 43		
Blackburn	a	18 52		19 09			19 46								20 46			21 10					21 46		
Clitheroe 94	a																								
Blackburn	d	18 53		19 10			19 48								20 48			21 10					21 48		
Rishton	d	18 58					19 53								20 53								21 53		
Church & Oswaldtwistle	d	19 01					19 56								20 56								21 56		
Accrington	d	19 04		19 19			19 59								20 59			21 19					21 59		
Huncoat	d	19 08					20 03								21 03								22 03		
Hapton	d	19x11					20x06								21x06								22x06		
Rose Grove	d	19 14					20 09								21 09								22 09		
Burnley Manchester Road 41	a			19 32														21 32							
Leeds 10 41	a																								
Burnley Barracks	d	19x17					20x12								21x12								22x12		
Burnley Central	d	19 20					20 15								21 15								22 15		
Brierfield	d	19 24					20 19								21 19								22 19		
Nelson	d	19 27					20 22								21 22								22 22		
Colne	a	19 36					20 31								21 31								22 31		

		TP	TP	NT		NT	NT	NT	TP	TP	NT	NT	NT	NT
		◇1							◇1					
		H	D			G	F	D	H	D	F	D		
													🚌	
Blackpool North	d	21 44	21 44			22 14	22 20	22 20	22 45	22 45	23 02	23 02		
Layton	d		21 47				22 23	22 23			23 05	23 05		
Poulton-le-Fylde	d	21 50	21 51				22 27	22 28	22 51	22 51	23 09	23 10		
Blackpool South	d			22 00										23 30
Blackpool Pleasure Beach	d			22 02										23 32
Squires Gate	d			22 04										23 34
St Annes-on-the-Sea	d			22 08										23 38
Ansdell & Fairhaven	d			22 11										23 41
Lytham	d			22 14										23 44
Moss Side	d			22 19										23 49
Kirkham & Wesham	d		22 00	22 26			22 37	22 36			23 19	23 18		23 56
Salwick	d													
Preston 8	a	22 08	22 10	22 36		22 41	22 47	22 47	23 09	23 09	23 29	23 29		00 08
	d			22 38										
Lostock Hall	d			22 43										
Bamber Bridge	d			22 46										
Pleasington	d			22 54										
Cherry Tree	d			22 57										
Mill Hill (Lancashire)	d			22 59										
Blackburn	a			23 06										
Clitheroe 94	a													
Blackburn	d												23 14	
Rishton	d												23 24	
Church & Oswaldtwistle	d												23 36	
Accrington	d												23 40	
Huncoat	d												23 46	
Hapton	d												23 52	
Rose Grove	d												23 58	
Burnley Manchester Road 41	a													
Leeds 10 41	a													
Burnley Barracks	d												00 02	
Burnley Central	d												00 07	
Brierfield	d												00 15	
Nelson	d												00 20	
Colne	a												00 28	

A To Manchester Victoria
B To Liverpool Lime Street
C To Manchester Airport
D from 4 January until 8 February
E from 4 January until 8 February. To Liverpool Lime Street
F from 15 February. To Manchester Victoria
G from 15 February. To Liverpool Lime Street
H from 15 February. To Manchester Airport

Table 97R

Saturdays

29 March to 17 May

Blackpool - Preston - Blackburn, Accrington, Burnley and Colne

Network Diagram - see first Page of Table 97

Station		NT	NT	NT A	TP ◇1 B	NT	NT C	NT A	TP ◇1 B	NT D	NT	NT E	NT C	NT A	TP ◇1 B	NT	NT C	NT A	NT F	TP ◇1 B	NT	TP ◇1 G	NT C
Blackpool North	d		04 56	05 29	05 39		06 19	06 28	06 40	06 53		07 02	07 18	07 29	07 44		08 20	08 29	08 35	08 40		09 14	09 20
Layton	d						06 22		06 43				07 21		07 47		08 23						09 23
Poulton-le-Fylde	d		05 02	05 35	05 45		06 26	06 34	06 47			07 08	07 25	07 35	07 51		08 27	08 35		08 46		09 20	09 27
Blackpool South	d					05 42					06 42					07 42					08 44		
Blackpool Pleasure Beach	d					05 44					06 44					07 44					08 46		
Squires Gate	d					05 46					06 46					07 46					08 48		
St Annes-on-the-Sea	d					05 50					06 50					07 50					08 52		
Ansdell & Fairhaven	d					05 53					06 53					07 53					08 55		
Lytham	d					05 56					06 56					07 56					08 58		
Moss Side	d					06 01					07 01					08 01					09 03		
Kirkham & Wesham	d					06 08	06 36		06 57		07 09		07 35		08 01	08 09	08 37				09 10		09 37
Salwick	d										07 13					08 14							
Preston 8	a		05 20	05 52	06 03	06 19	06 46	06 52	07 07	07 15	07 20	07 28	07 46	07 52	08 11	08 21	08 47	08 52	09 02	09 04	09 20	09 41	09 47
	d	04 47	05 22	05 54		06 21		06 54			07 22			07 54		08 22		08 54			09 22		
Lostock Hall	d					06 26					07 27					08 27					09 27		
Bamber Bridge	d					06 29					07 30					08 30					09 30		
Pleasington	d					06x37					07x38					08x38					09x38		
Cherry Tree	d					06 40					07 41					08 41					09 41		
Mill Hill (Lancashire)	d					06 42					07 43					08 43					09 43		
Blackburn	a	05 03	05 38	06 09		06 45		07 09			07 50			08 09		08 46		09 09			09 46		
Clitheroe 94	a																						
Blackburn	d	05 04	05 39	06 10		06 48		07 10			07 51			08 10		08 48		09 10			09 48		
Rishton	d		05 44			06 53					07 56					08 53					09 53		
Church & Oswaldtwistle	d		05 47			06 56					07 59					08 56					09 56		
Accrington	d	05 11	05 50	06 17		06 59		07 17			08 02			08 17		08 59		09 17			09 59		
Huncoat	d		05 54			07 03					08 06					09 03					10 03		
Hapton	d		05x57			07x06					08x09					09x06					10x06		
Rose Grove	d		06 00			07 09					08 12					09 09					10 09		
Burnley Manchester Road 41	a			06 26				07 26						08 26				09 26					
Leeds 10 41	a			07 39				08 39						09 39				10 38					
Burnley Barracks	d					07x12					08x15					09x12					10x12		
Burnley Central	d	05 21	06 05			07 15					08 18					09 15					10 15		
Brierfield	d		06 09			07 19					08 22					09 19					10 19		
Nelson	d		06 12			07 22					08 25					09 22					10 22		
Colne	a	05 34	06 21			07 31					08 34					09 31					10 31		

Station		NT A	NT F	TP ◇1 B	NT	NT C	NT A	NT F	TP ◇1 B	NT	NT C	NT A	NT F	TP ◇1 B	NT	NT C	NT A	NT F	TP ◇1 B	NT	NT C	NT A	NT F
Blackpool North	d	09 29	09 35	09 40		10 20	10 29	10 35	10 44		11 20	11 29	11 35	11 41		12 20	12 29	12 35	12 40		13 20	13 29	13 35
Layton	d					10 23					11 23					12 23					13 23		
Poulton-le-Fylde	d	09 35		09 46		10 27	10 35		10 50		11 27	11 35		11 47		12 27	12 35		12 46		13 27	13 35	
Blackpool South	d				09 44					10 44					11 44					12 44			
Blackpool Pleasure Beach	d				09 46					10 46					11 46					12 46			
Squires Gate	d				09 48					10 48					11 48					12 48			
St Annes-on-the-Sea	d				09 52					10 52					11 52					12 52			
Ansdell & Fairhaven	d				09 55					10 55					11 55					12 55			
Lytham	d				09 58					10 58					11 58					12 58			
Moss Side	d				10 03					11 03					12 03					13 03			
Kirkham & Wesham	d		09 52		10 10	10 37		10 52		11 10	11 37		11 52		12 10	12 37		12 50		13 10	13 37		13 52
Salwick	d																						
Preston 8	a	09 52	10 02	10 04	10 20	10 47	10 52	11 02	11 08	11 20	11 47	11 52	12 02	12 05	12 20	12 47	12 51	13 00	13 04	13 20	13 47	13 52	14 02
	d	09 54			10 22		10 54			11 22		11 54			12 22		12 53			13 22		13 54	
Lostock Hall	d				10 27					11 27					12 27					13 27			
Bamber Bridge	d				10 30					11 30					12 30					13 30			
Pleasington	d				10x38					11x38					12x38					13x38			
Cherry Tree	d				10 41					11 41					12 41					13 41			
Mill Hill (Lancashire)	d				10 43					11 43					12 43					13 43			
Blackburn	a	10 09			10 46		11 09			11 46		12 09			12 46		13 08			13 46		14 09	
Clitheroe 94	a																						
Blackburn	d	10 10			10 48		11 10			11 48		12 10			12 48		13 09			13 48		14 10	
Rishton	d				10 53					11 53					12 53					13 53			
Church & Oswaldtwistle	d				10 56					11 56					12 56					13 56			
Accrington	d	10 18			10 59		11 17			11 59		12 17			12 59		13 16			13 59		14 17	
Huncoat	d				11 03					12 03					13 03					14 03			
Hapton	d				11x06					12x06					13x06					14x06			
Rose Grove	d				11 09					12 09					13 09					14 09			
Burnley Manchester Road 41	a	10 26					11 27					12 26					13 25					14 26	
Leeds 10 41	a	11 39					12 39					13 39					14 39					15 39	
Burnley Barracks	d				11x12					12x12					13x12					14x12			
Burnley Central	d				11 15					12 15					13 15					14 15			
Brierfield	d				11 19					12 19					13 19					14 19			
Nelson	d				11 22					12 22					13 22					14 22			
Colne	a				11 31					12 31					13 31					14 31			

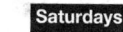

A To York
B To Manchester Airport
C To Manchester Victoria
D To Hazel Grove
E To Liverpool Lime Street
F To Liverpool South Pw Hl
G To Barrow-in-Furness

Table 97R

Saturdays

29 March to 17 May

Blackpool - Preston - Blackburn, Accrington, Burnley and Colne

Network Diagram - see first Page of Table 97

		TP ◇1 A	NT	NT B	NT C	NT D	TP ◇1 A	NT	NT B	NT C	NT E	TP ◇1 A	NT	NT B	NT C	NT E	TP ◇1 A	NT	NT C	TP ◇1 A	NT E	NT
Blackpool North	d	13 44		14 20	14 29	14 35	14 40		15 20	15 29	15 35	15 40		16 20	16 29	16 35	16 40		17 14	17 20	17 35	
Layton	d			14 23					15 23					16 23			16 43			17 23		
Poulton-le-Fylde	d	13 50		14 27	14 35		14 46		15 27	15 35		15 46		16 27	16 35		16 47		17 20	17 27		
Blackpool South	d		13 44					14 44					15 44					16 44				17 44
Blackpool Pleasure Beach	d		13 46					14 46					15 46					16 46				17 46
Squires Gate	d		13 48					14 48					15 48					16 48				17 48
St Annes-on-the-Sea	d		13 52					14 52					15 52					16 52				17 52
Ansdell & Fairhaven	d		13 55					14 55					15 55					16 55				17 55
Lytham	d		13 58					14 58					15 58					16 58				17 58
Moss Side	d		14 03					15 03					16 03					17 03				18 03
Kirkham & Wesham	d		14 10	14 37		14 50		15 10	15 37		15 50		16 10	16 37		16 52	16 57	17 10	17 29		17 52	18 10
Salwick	d												16 15									
Preston 8	a	14 08	14 20	14 47	14 52	15 00	15 04	15 20	15 47	15 52	16 00	16 04	16 22	16 47	16 52	17 02	17 08	17 20	17 42	17 45	18 02	18 22
	d		14 22		14 54			15 22		15 54			16 22		16 54			17 22	17 44			18 24
Lostock Hall	d		14 27					15 27					16 27					17 27	17 51			18 30
Bamber Bridge	d		14 30					15 30					16 30					17 30	17 54			18 33
Pleasington	d		14x38					15x38					16x38					17x38	18 01			18x41
Cherry Tree	d		14 41					15 41					16 41					17 41	18 05			18 44
Mill Hill (Lancashire)	d		14 43					15 43					16 43					17 43	18 08			18 46
Blackburn	a		14 46		15 09			15 46		16 09			16 48		17 09			17 47	18 11			18 52
Clitheroe 94	a																					
Blackburn	d		14 48		15 10			15 48		16 10			16 50		17 10			17 48	18 11			18 53
Rishton	d		14 53					15 53					16 55					17 53				18 58
Church & Oswaldtwistle	d		14 56					15 56					16 58					17 56				19 01
Accrington	d		14 59		15 17			15 59		16 17			17 01		17 17			17 59	18 19			19 04
Huncoat	d		15 03					16 03					17 05					18 03				19 08
Hapton	d		15x06					16x06					17x08					18x06				19x11
Rose Grove	d		15 09					16 09					17 11					18 09				19 14
Burnley Manchester Road 41	a				15 26					16 26					17 26				18 27			
Leeds 10 41	a				16 39					17 39					18 39				19 38			
Burnley Barracks	d		15x12					16x12					17x14					18x12				19x17
Burnley Central	d		15 15					16 15					17 16					18 15				19 20
Brierfield	d		15 19					16 19					17 21					18 19				19 24
Nelson	d		15 22					16 22					17 24					18 22				19 27
Colne	a		15 31					16 31					17 33					18 31				19 36

		NT B	NT C	NT E	TP ◇1 A	NT	NT B	NT E	TP ◇1 A	NT	NT B	NT C	NT E	TP ◇1 A	NT	NT B	TP ◇1 A	NT	NT E	NT B	TP ◇1 A	NT B	NT (bus)
Blackpool North	d	18 20	18 29	18 35	18 40		19 20	19 35	19 44		20 20	20 29	20 35	20 44		21 20	21 44		22 14	22 20	22 45	23 02	
Layton	d	18 23					19 23				20 23					21 23				22 23		23 05	
Poulton-le-Fylde	d	18 27	18 35		18 46		19 28		19 50		20 27	20 35		20 50		21 27	21 50			22 27	22 51	23 09	
Blackpool South	d					18 44				19 44					20 44			22 00					
Blackpool Pleasure Beach	d					18 46				19 46					20 46			22 02					
Squires Gate	d					18 48				19 48					20 48			22 04					
St Annes-on-the-Sea	d					18 52				19 52					20 52			22 08					
Ansdell & Fairhaven	d					18 55				19 55					20 55			22 11					
Lytham	d					18 58				19 58					20 58			22 14					
Moss Side	d					19 03				20 03					21 03			22 19					
Kirkham & Wesham	d	18 37		18 50		19 10	19 37	19 52		20 10	20 37		20 52		21 10	21 37		22 26		22 37		23 19	
Salwick	d																						
Preston 8	a	18 47	18 52	19 00	19 04	19 20	19 47	20 02	20 08	20 20	20 47	20 53	21 02	21 08	21 20	21 47	22 08	22 36	22 41	22 47	23 09	23 29	
	d		18 54			19 22				20 22		20 54			21 22			22 38					
Lostock Hall	d					19 27				20 27					21 27			22 43					
Bamber Bridge	d					19 30				20 30					21 30			22 46					
Pleasington	d					19x38				20x38					21x38			22 54					
Cherry Tree	d					19 41				20 41					21 41			22 57					
Mill Hill (Lancashire)	d					19 43				20 43					21 43			22 59					
Blackburn	a		19 09			19 46				20 46		21 10			21 46			23 06					
Clitheroe 94	a																						
Blackburn	d		19 10			19 48				20 48		21 10			21 48								23 14
Rishton	d					19 53				20 53					21 53								23 24
Church & Oswaldtwistle	d					19 56				20 56					21 56								23 36
Accrington	d		19 17			19 59				20 59		21 18			21 59								23 40
Huncoat	d					20 03				21 03					22 03								23 46
Hapton	d					20x06				21x06					22x06								23 52
Rose Grove	d					20 09				21 09					22 09								23 58
Burnley Manchester Road 41	a		19 26									21 27											
Leeds 10 41	a		20 38									22 35											
Burnley Barracks	d					20x12				21x12					22x12								00 02
Burnley Central	d					20 15				21 15					22 15								00 07
Brierfield	d					20 19				21 19					22 19								00 15
Nelson	d					20 22				21 22					22 22								00 20
Colne	a					20 31				21 31					22 31								00 28

A To Manchester Airport
B To Manchester Victoria
C To York
D To Liverpool South Pw Hl
E To Liverpool Lime Street

Table 97R

Saturdays

29 March to 17 May

Blackpool - Preston - Blackburn, Accrington, Burnley and Colne

Network Diagram - see first Page of Table 97

		NT
Blackpool North	d	
Layton	d	
Poulton-le-Fylde	d	
Blackpool South	d	23 30
Blackpool Pleasure Beach	d	23 32
Squires Gate	d	23 34
St Annes-on-the-Sea	d	23 38
Ansdell & Fairhaven	d	23 41
Lytham	d	23 44
Moss Side	d	23 49
Kirkham & Wesham	d	23 56
Salwick	d	
Preston 8	a	00 08
	d	
Lostock Hall	d	
Bamber Bridge	d	
Pleasington	d	
Cherry Tree	d	
Mill Hill (Lancashire)	d	
Blackburn	a	
Clitheroe 94	a	
Blackburn	d	
Rishton	d	
Church & Oswaldtwistle	d	
Accrington	d	
Huncoat	d	
Hapton	d	
Rose Grove	d	
Burnley Manchester Road 41	a	
Leeds 10 41	a	
Burnley Barracks	d	
Burnley Central	d	
Brierfield	d	
Nelson	d	
Colne	a	

Sundays

8 December to 29 December

		NT	TP	NT	NT	NT	TP	NT	NT	NT	NT	TP	NT	NT	NT	TP	NT	NT	NT	NT	TP	NT	NT
			◇1				◇1					◇1				◇1					◇1		
		A (bus)	B		C	D	B	E		D		B	E		D	B	E		D		B	E	
Blackpool North	d		07 48		08 10	08 20	08 44	08 50	09 01	09 20		09 44	09 50	10 11	10 20	10 44	10 50	11 13	11 20		11 44	11 50	12 11
Layton	d					08 23				09 23					10 23				11 23				
Poulton-le-Fylde	d		07 54		08 16	08 27	08 50	08 56	09 07	09 27		09 50	09 56	10 17	10 27	10 50	10 56	11 19	11 27		11 50	11 56	12 17
Blackpool South	d																						
Blackpool Pleasure Beach	d																						
Squires Gate	d																						
St Annes-on-the-Sea	d																						
Ansdell & Fairhaven	d																						
Lytham	d																						
Moss Side	d																						
Kirkham & Wesham	d				08 26	08 37				09 37					10 37				11 37				
Salwick	d																						
Preston 8	a		08 12		08 36	08 47	09 08	09 14	09 24	09 47		10 08	10 14	10 34	10 47	11 08	11 14	11 36	11 47		12 08	12 14	12 34
	d			08 16	08 39				09 27		10 05			10 39				11 38		12 05			12 39
Lostock Hall	d			08 21	08 45						10 11									12 11			
Bamber Bridge	d			08 24	08 48						10 14									12 14			
Pleasington	d										10x21									12x21			
Cherry Tree	d										10 24									12 24			
Mill Hill (Lancashire)	d										10 27									12 27			
Blackburn	a			08 35	08 59				09 42		10 30			10 54				11 54		12 30			12 54
Clitheroe 94	a				09 27																		
Blackburn	d			08 37					09 44		10 31			10 55				11 55		12 31			12 55
Rishton	d										10 36									12 36			
Church & Oswaldtwistle	d										10 39									12 39			
Accrington	d			08 44					09 51		10 42			11 02				12 02		12 42			13 02
Huncoat	d										10 47									12 47			
Hapton	d										10x50									12x50			
Rose Grove	d			08 51							10 53									12 53			
Burnley Manchester Road 41	a								10 04					11 15				12 15					13 15
Leeds 10 41	a																						
Burnley Barracks	d	00 02									10x56									12x56			
Burnley Central	d	00 07		08 56							10 58									12 58			
Brierfield	d	00 15		09 00							11 03									13 03			
Nelson	d	00 20		09 03							11 06									13 06			
Colne	a	00 28		09 12							11 14									13 14			

A not 8 December. From Blackburn
B To Manchester Airport
C To Hellifield
D To Manchester Victoria
E To Liverpool Lime Street

Table 97R

Sundays

8 December to 29 December

Blackpool - Preston - Blackburn, Accrington, Burnley and Colne

Network Diagram - see first Page of Table 97

		NT	TP	NT	NT	NT	NT	NT	TP	NT	NT	NT	TP	NT	NT	NT	NT	TP	NT	NT	NT	TP	NT
			◇1						◇1				◇1					◇1				◇1	
		A	B	C	D		A		B	C		A	B	C		A		B	C		A	B	C
Blackpool North	d	12 20	12 44	12 50		13 13	13 20		13 44	13 50	14 11	14 20	14 44	14 50	15 13	15 20		15 44	15 50	16 11	16 20	16 44	16 50
Layton	d	12 23					13 23					14 23				15 23					16 23		
Poulton-le-Fylde	d	12 27	12 50	12 56		13 19	13 27		13 50	13 56	14 17	14 27	14 50	14 56	15 19	15 27		15 50	15 56	16 17	16 27	16 50	16 56
Blackpool South	d																						
Blackpool Pleasure Beach	d																						
Squires Gate	d																						
St Annes-on-the-Sea	d																						
Ansdell & Fairhaven	d																						
Lytham	d																						
Moss Side	d																						
Kirkham & Wesham	d	12 37					13 37					14 37				15 37					16 37		
Salwick	d																						
Preston 8	a	12 47	13 08	13 14		13 36	13 47		14 08	14 14	14 34	14 47	15 08	15 14	15 36	15 47		16 08	16 14	16 34	16 47	17 08	17 14
	d				13 18	13 38		14 05			14 39				15 38		16 05			16 39			
Lostock Hall	d				13 23			14 11									16 11						
Bamber Bridge	d				13 26			14 14									16 14						
Pleasington	d							14x21									16x21						
Cherry Tree	d							14 24									16 24						
Mill Hill (Lancashire)	d							14 27									16 27						
Blackburn	a				13 37	13 54		14 30			14 54				15 54		16 30			16 54			
Clitheroe 94	a				14 01																		
Blackburn	d					13 55		14 31			14 55				15 55		16 31			16 55			
Rishton	d							14 36									16 36						
Church & Oswaldtwistle	d							14 39									16 39						
Accrington	d					14 02		14 42			15 02				16 02		16 42			17 02			
Huncoat	d							14 47									16 47						
Hapton	d							14x50									16x50						
Rose Grove	d							14 53									16 53						
Burnley Manchester Road 41	a					14 15					15 15				16 15					17 15			
Leeds 10 41	a																						
Burnley Barracks	d							14x56									16x56						
Burnley Central	d							14 58									16 58						
Brierfield	d							15 03									17 03						
Nelson	d							15 06									17 06						
Colne	a							15 14									17 14						

		NT	NT	NT	TP	NT	NT	NT	TP	NT	NT	NT	NT	TP	NT	NT	NT	TP	NT	NT	NT	NT
					◇1				◇1					◇1				◇1				
			A		B	C		A	B	C		A		B	C		A	B	C		A	
Blackpool North	d	17 11	17 20		17 44	17 50	18 11	18 20	18 44	18 50	19 13	19 20		19 44	19 50	20 11	20 20	20 44	20 50	21 13	21 20	
Layton	d		17 23					18 23				19 23					20 23				21 23	
Poulton-le-Fylde	d	17 17	17 27		17 50	17 56	18 17	18 27	18 50	18 56	19 19	19 27		19 50	19 56	20 17	20 27	20 50	20 56	21 19	21 27	
Blackpool South	d																					
Blackpool Pleasure Beach	d																					
Squires Gate	d																					
St Annes-on-the-Sea	d																					
Ansdell & Fairhaven	d																					
Lytham	d																					
Moss Side	d																					
Kirkham & Wesham	d		17 37					18 37				19 37					20 37				21 37	
Salwick	d																					
Preston 8	a	17 34	17 47		18 08	18 14	18 36	18 47	19 08	19 14	19 36	19 47		20 08	20 14	20 34	20 47	21 08	21 14	21 36	21 47	
	d	17 39		18 05			18 39				19 38		20 05			20 39				21 39		22 05
Lostock Hall	d			18 10									20 11									22 10
Bamber Bridge	d			18 13									20 14									22 13
Pleasington	d			18x20									20x21									22x20
Cherry Tree	d			18 23									20 24									22 23
Mill Hill (Lancashire)	d			18 26									20 27									22 26
Blackburn	a	17 54		18 29			18 54				19 54		20 30			20 54				21 54		22 29
Clitheroe 94	a																					
Blackburn	d	17 55		18 30			18 55				19 55		20 31			20 55				21 55		22 30
Rishton	d			18 35									20 36									22 35
Church & Oswaldtwistle	d			18 38									20 39									22 38
Accrington	d	18 02		18 41			19 02				20 02		20 42			21 02				22 02		22 41
Huncoat	d			18 46									20 47									22 46
Hapton	d			18x49									20x50									22x49
Rose Grove	d			18 52									20 53									22 52
Burnley Manchester Road 41	a	18 15					19 15				20 15					21 15				22 15		
Leeds 10 41	a																					
Burnley Barracks	d			18x55									20x56									22x55
Burnley Central	d			18 57									20 58									22 57
Brierfield	d			19 02									21 03									23 02
Nelson	d			19 05									21 06									23 05
Colne	a			19 13									21 14									23 13

A To Manchester Victoria
B To Manchester Airport
C To Liverpool Lime Street
D To Hellifield

Table 97R

Sundays

8 December to 29 December

Blackpool - Preston - Blackburn, Accrington, Burnley and Colne

Network Diagram - see first Page of Table 97

		TP	NT	NT	TP
		◇1			◇1
		A	B	B	A
Blackpool North	d	21 44	21 50	22 44	23 02
Layton	d				
Poulton-le-Fylde	d	21 50	21 56	22 50	23 08
Blackpool South	d				
Blackpool Pleasure Beach	d				
Squires Gate	d				
St Annes-on-the-Sea	d				
Ansdell & Fairhaven	d				
Lytham	d				
Moss Side	d				
Kirkham & Wesham	d				23 17
Salwick	d				
Preston 8	a	22 08	22 14	23 08	23 28
	d				
Lostock Hall	d				
Bamber Bridge	d				
Pleasington	d				
Cherry Tree	d				
Mill Hill (Lancashire)	d				
Blackburn	a				
Clitheroe 94	a				
Blackburn	d				
Rishton	d				
Church & Oswaldtwistle	d				
Accrington	d				
Huncoat	d				
Hapton	d				
Rose Grove	d				
Burnley Manchester Road 41	a				
Leeds 10 41	a				
Burnley Barracks	d				
Burnley Central	d				
Brierfield	d				
Nelson	d				
Colne	a				

Sundays

5 January to 9 February

		NT	TP	NT	NT	TP	NT	NT	NT	TP		NT	NT	TP	NT	NT	NT	TP	NT	NT		TP	NT	NT	NT
			◇1			◇1				◇1				◇1				◇1				◇1			
		C 🚌			D																		D		
Blackpool North	d		07 48		08 10	08 44	08 53	09 01		09 44		09 53	10 11	10 44	10 53	11 13		11 44	11 53	12 11		12 44		12 53	13 13
Layton	d						08 56					09 56			10 56				11 56					12 56	
Poulton-le-Fylde	d		07 54		08 16	08 50	09 01	09 07		09 50		10 01	10 17	10 50	11 01	11 19		11 50	12 01	12 17		12 50		13 01	13 19
Blackpool South	d																								
Blackpool Pleasure Beach	d																								
Squires Gate	d																								
St Annes-on-the-Sea	d																								
Ansdell & Fairhaven	d																								
Lytham	d																								
Moss Side	d																								
Kirkham & Wesham	d				08 26		09 09					10 09			11 09				12 09					13 09	
Salwick	d																								
Preston 8	a		08 12		08 36	09 08	09 20	09 24		10 08		10 20	10 34	11 08	11 20	11 36		12 08	12 20	12 34		13 08		13 20	13 36
	d			08 16	08 39			09 27	10 05				10 39			11 38	12 05			12 39			13 18		13 38
Lostock Hall	d			08 21	08 45				10 11								12 11						13 23		
Bamber Bridge	d			08 24	08 48				10 14								12 14						13 26		
Pleasington	d								10x21								12x21								
Cherry Tree	d								10 24								12 24								
Mill Hill (Lancashire)	d								10 27								12 27								
Blackburn	a			08 35	08 59			09 42	10 30				10 54			11 54	12 30			12 54			13 37		13 54
Clitheroe 94	a				09 27																		14 01		
Blackburn	d			08 37				09 44	10 31				10 55			11 55	12 31			12 55					13 55
Rishton	d								10 36								12 36								
Church & Oswaldtwistle	d								10 39								12 39								
Accrington	d			08 44				09 51	10 42				11 02			12 02	12 42			13 02					14 02
Huncoat	d								10 47								12 47								
Hapton	d								10x50								12x50								
Rose Grove	d			08 51					10 53								12 53								
Burnley Manchester Road 41	a							10 04					11 15			12 15				13 15					14 15
Leeds 10 41	a																								
Burnley Barracks	d	00 02							10x56								12x56								
Burnley Central	d	00 07		08 56					10 58								12 58								
Brierfield	d	00 15		09 00					11 03								13 03								
Nelson	d	00 20		09 03					11 06								13 06								
Colne	a	00 28		09 12					11 14								13 14								

A To Manchester Airport
B To Wigan North Western
C From Blackburn
D To Hellifield

Table 97R

Sundays

5 January to 9 February

Blackpool - Preston - Blackburn, Accrington, Burnley and Colne

Network Diagram - see first Page of Table 97

		NT	TP ◇1	NT	NT	NT A		TP ◇1 B	NT C	NT	NT A	NT	TP ◇1 B	NT C	NT	NT A		TP ◇1 B	NT C	NT	NT A	NT	TP ◇1 B	NT C	NT
Blackpool North	d		13 44	13 53	14 11	14 20		14 44	14 50	15 13	15 20		15 44	15 50	16 11	16 20		16 44	16 50	17 11	17 20		17 44	17 50	18 11
Layton	d			13 56		14 23					15 23					16 23					17 23				
Poulton-le-Fylde	d		13 50	14 01	14 17	14 27		14 50	14 56	15 19	15 27		15 50	15 56	16 17	16 27		16 50	16 56	17 17	17 27		17 50	17 56	18 17
Blackpool South	d																								
Blackpool Pleasure Beach	d																								
Squires Gate	d																								
St Annes-on-the-Sea	d																								
Ansdell & Fairhaven	d																								
Lytham	d																								
Moss Side	d																								
Kirkham & Wesham	d			14 09		14 37					15 37					16 37					17 37				
Salwick	d																								
Preston 8	a		14 08	14 20	14 34	14 47		15 08	15 14	15 36	15 47		16 08	16 14	16 34	16 47		17 08	17 14	17 34	17 47		13 08	18 14	18 36
	d	14 05			14 39					15 38		16 05			16 39					17 39		18 05			18 39
Lostock Hall	d	14 11										16 11										18 10			
Bamber Bridge	d	14 14										16 14										18 13			
Pleasington	d	14x21										16x21										18x20			
Cherry Tree	d	14 24										16 24										18 23			
Mill Hill (Lancashire)	d	14 27										16 27										18 26			
Blackburn	a	14 30			14 54					15 54		16 30			16 54					17 54		18 29			18 54
Clitheroe 94	a																								
Blackburn	d	14 31			14 55					15 55		16 31			16 55					17 55		18 30			18 55
Rishton	d	14 36										16 36										18 35			
Church & Oswaldtwistle	d	14 39										16 39										18 38			
Accrington	d	14 42			15 02					16 02		16 42			17 02					18 02		18 41			19 02
Huncoat	d	14 47										16 47										18 46			
Hapton	d	14x50										16x50										18x49			
Rose Grove	d	14 53										16 53										18 52			
Burnley Manchester Road 41	a				15 15					16 15					17 15					18 15					19 15
Leeds 10 41	a																								
Burnley Barracks	d	14x56										16x56										18x55			
Burnley Central	d	14 58										16 58										18 57			
Brierfield	d	15 03										17 03										19 02			
Nelson	d	15 06										17 06										19 05			
Colne	a	15 14										17 14										19 13			

		NT A		TP ◇1 B	NT C	NT	NT A	NT	TP ◇1 B	NT C	NT	NT A		TP ◇1 B	NT C	NT	NT	TP ◇1 B	NT	NT C	NT C	TP ◇1 B			
Blackpool North	d	18 20		18 44	18 50	19 13	19 20		19 44	19 50	20 11	20 20		20 44	20 50	21 13	21 20	21 35		21 50	22 44	23 02			
Layton	d	18 23					19 23					20 23					21 23								
Poulton-le-Fylde	d	18 27		18 50	18 56	19 19	19 27		19 50	19 56	20 17	20 27		20 50	20 56	21 19	21 27	21 41		21 56	22 50	23 08			
Blackpool South	d																								
Blackpool Pleasure Beach	d																								
Squires Gate	d																								
St Annes-on-the-Sea	d																								
Ansdell & Fairhaven	d																								
Lytham	d																								
Moss Side	d																								
Kirkham & Wesham	d	18 37					19 37					20 37					21 37					23 17			
Salwick	d																								
Preston 8	a	18 47		19 08	19 14	19 36	19 47		20 08	20 14	20 34	20 47		21 08	21 14	21 36	21 47	21 59		22 14	23 08	23 28			
	d					19 38		20 05			20 39					21 39			22 05						
Lostock Hall	d							20 11											22 10						
Bamber Bridge	d							20 14											22 13						
Pleasington	d							20x21											22x20						
Cherry Tree	d							20 24											22 23						
Mill Hill (Lancashire)	d							20 27											22 26						
Blackburn	a					19 54		20 30			20 54					21 54			22 29						
Clitheroe 94	a																								
Blackburn	d					19 55		20 31			20 55					21 55			22 30						
Rishton	d							20 36											22 35						
Church & Oswaldtwistle	d							20 39											22 38						
Accrington	d					20 02		20 42			21 02					22 02			22 41						
Huncoat	d							20 47											22 46						
Hapton	d							20x50											22x49						
Rose Grove	d							20 53											22 52						
Burnley Manchester Road 41	a					20 15					21 15					22 15									
Leeds 10 41	a																								
Burnley Barracks	d							20x56											22x55						
Burnley Central	d							20 58											22 57						
Brierfield	d							21 03											23 02						
Nelson	d							21 06											23 05						
Colne	a							21 14											23 13						

A To Manchester Oxford Road **B** To Manchester Airport **C** To Wigan North Western

Table 97R

Sundays

16 February to 23 March

Blackpool - Preston - Blackburn, Accrington, Burnley and Colne

Network Diagram - see first Page of Table 97

		NT	NT	NT	NT	TP	NT	NT	NT	TP	NT	NT	NT	NT	TP	NT	NT	NT	NT	TP	NT	NT	NT
						◇1				◇1					◇1					◇1			
		A		B		C	D			C		D			C	D		E		C	D		E
		🚌																					
Blackpool North	d			08 10	08 20	08 38	08 50	09 01	09 20	09 36		09 50	10 11	10 20	10 38	10 50	11 13	11 20		11 45	11 50	12 11	12 20
Layton	d				08 23				09 23					10 23				11 23					12 23
Poulton-le-Fylde	d			08 16	08 28	08 44	08 56	09 07	09 28	09 42		09 56	10 17	10 28	10 44	10 56	11 19	11 27		11 51	11 56	12 17	12 27
Blackpool South	d										09 28								11 27				
Blackpool Pleasure Beach	d										09 30								11 29				
Squires Gate	d										09 32								11 31				
St Annes-on-the-Sea	d										09 36								11 35				
Ansdell & Fairhaven	d										09 39								11 38				
Lytham	d										09 42								11 41				
Moss Side	d										09 47								11 46				
Kirkham & Wesham	d			08 26	08 36				09 36		09 54			10 36				11 37	11 53				12 37
Salwick	d																						
Preston 8	a			08 36	08 47	09 01	09 14	09 24	09 47	10 00	10 04	10 14	10 34	10 47	11 02	11 14	11 36	11 47	12 03	12 09	12 14	12 34	12 47
	d		08 16	08 39				09 27			10 06		10 39				11 38		12 05			12 39	
Lostock Hall	d		08 21	08 45							10 12								12 11				
Bamber Bridge	d		08 24	08 48							10 15								12 14				
Pleasington	d										10x22								12x21				
Cherry Tree	d										10 25								12 24				
Mill Hill (Lancashire)	d										10 28								12 27				
Blackburn	a		08 35	08 59				09 42			10 31		10 54				11 54		12 30			12 54	
Clitheroe 94	a			09 27																			
Blackburn	d		08 37					09 44			10 32		10 55				11 55		12 31			12 55	
Rishton	d										10 37								12 36				
Church & Oswaldtwistle	d										10 40								12 39				
Accrington	d		08 44					09 51			10 43		11 02				12 02		12 42			13 02	
Huncoat	d										10 48								12 47				
Hapton	d										10x51								12x50				
Rose Grove	d		08 51								10 54								12 53				
Burnley Manchester Road 41	a							10 04					11 15				12 15					13 15	
Leeds 10 41	a																						
Burnley Barracks	d	00 02									10x57								12x56				
Burnley Central	d	00 07	08 56								10 59								12 58				
Brierfield	d	00 15	09 00								11 04								13 03				
Nelson	d	00 20	09 03								11 07								13 06				
Colne	a	00 28	09 12								11 15								13 14				

		NT	TP	NT	NT	NT	NT	NT	TP	NT	NT	NT	NT	TP	NT	NT	NT	NT	TP	NT	NT	NT	NT
			◇1						◇1					◇1					◇1				
			C	D	B		E		C	D		E		C	D		E		C	D		E	
Blackpool North	d		12 41	12 50		13 13	13 20		13 44	13 50	14 11	14 20		14 45	14 50	15 13	15 20		15 45	15 50	16 11	16 20	
Layton	d						13 23					14 23					15 23					16 23	
Poulton-le-Fylde	d		12 47	12 56		13 19	13 27		13 50	13 56	14 17	14 27		14 51	14 56	15 19	15 27		15 51	15 56	16 17	16 27	
Blackpool South	d	12 24						13 27					14 27					15 27					16 27
Blackpool Pleasure Beach	d	12 26						13 29					14 29					15 29					16 29
Squires Gate	d	12 28						13 31					14 31					15 31					16 31
St Annes-on-the-Sea	d	12 32						13 35					14 35					15 35					16 35
Ansdell & Fairhaven	d	12 35						13 38					14 38					15 38					16 38
Lytham	d	12 38						13 41					14 41					15 41					16 41
Moss Side	d	12 43						13 46					14 46					15 46					16 46
Kirkham & Wesham	d	12 50					13 37	13 53				14 37	14 53				15 37	15 53				16 37	16 53
Salwick	d																						
Preston 8	a	13 01	13 05	13 14		13 36	13 47	14 03	14 08	14 14	14 34	14 47	15 03	15 09	15 14	15 36	15 47	16 03	16 09	16 14	16 34	16 47	17 03
	d				13 18	13 38		14 05			14 39					15 38		16 05			16 39		
Lostock Hall	d				13 23			14 11										16 11					
Bamber Bridge	d				13 26			14 14										16 14					
Pleasington	d							14x21										16x21					
Cherry Tree	d							14 24										16 24					
Mill Hill (Lancashire)	d							14 27										16 27					
Blackburn	a				13 37	13 54		14 30			14 54					15 54		16 30			16 54		
Clitheroe 94	a				14 01																		
Blackburn	d					13 55		14 31			14 55					15 55		16 31			16 55		
Rishton	d							14 36										16 36					
Church & Oswaldtwistle	d							14 39										16 39					
Accrington	d					14 02		14 42			15 02					16 02		16 42			17 02		
Huncoat	d							14 47										16 47					
Hapton	d							14x50										16x50					
Rose Grove	d							14 53										16 53					
Burnley Manchester Road 41	a					14 15					15 15					16 15					17 15		
Leeds 10 41	a																						
Burnley Barracks	d							14x56										16x56					
Burnley Central	d							14 58										16 58					
Brierfield	d							15 03										17 03					
Nelson	d							15 06										17 06					
Colne	a							15 14										17 14					

A From Blackburn
B To Hellifield
C To Manchester Airport
D To Wigan North Western
E To Manchester Oxford Road

Table 97R

Sundays

16 February to 23 March

Blackpool - Preston - Blackburn, Accrington, Burnley and Colne

Network Diagram - see first Page of Table 97

		TP ◇1 A		NT B	NT	NT C	NT	TP ◇1 A	NT B	NT	NT C	NT		TP ◇1 A	NT B	NT	NT C	NT	TP ◇1 A	NT B	NT	NT C		NT	TP ◇1 A
Blackpool North	d	16 45		16 50	17 11	17 20		17 45	17 50	18 11	18 20			18 45	18 50	19 13	19 20		19 45	19 50	20 11	20 20			20 45
Layton	d					17 23					18 23						19 23					20 23			
Poulton-le-Fylde	d	16 51		16 56	17 17	17 27		17 51	17 56	18 17	18 27			18 51	18 56	19 19	19 27		19 51	19 56	20 17	20 27			20 51
Blackpool South	d						17 24					18 27						19 27						20 27	
Blackpool Pleasure Beach	d						17 26					18 29						19 29						20 29	
Squires Gate	d						17 28					18 31						19 31						20 31	
St Annes-on-the-Sea	d						17 32					18 35						19 35						20 35	
Ansdell & Fairhaven	d						17 35					18 38						19 38						20 38	
Lytham	d						17 38					18 41						19 41						20 41	
Moss Side	d						17 43					18 46						19 46						20 46	
Kirkham & Wesham	d					17 37	17 50				18 37	18 53					19 37	19 53				20 37		20 53	
Salwick	d																								
Preston 8	a	17 09		17 14	17 34	17 47	18 00	18 09	18 14	18 36	18 47	19 03		19 09	19 14	19 36	19 47	20 03	20 09	20 14	20 34	20 47		21 03	21 09
	d				17 39		18 05			18 39						19 38		20 05			20 39			21 05	
Lostock Hall	d						18 11											20 11						21 10	
Bamber Bridge	d						18 14											20 14						21 13	
Pleasington	d						18x21											20x21						21x20	
Cherry Tree	d						18 24											20 24						21 23	
Mill Hill (Lancashire)	d						18 27											20 27						21 26	
Blackburn	a				17 54		18 30			18 54						19 54		20 30			20 54			21 29	
Clitheroe 94	a																								
Blackburn	d				17 55		18 31			18 55						19 55		20 31			20 55			21 29	
Rishton	d						18 36											20 36						21 34	
Church & Oswaldtwistle	d						18 39											20 39						21 37	
Accrington	d				18 02		18 42			19 02						20 02		20 42			21 02			21 40	
Huncoat	d						18 47											20 47						21 45	
Hapton	d						18x50											20x50						21x48	
Rose Grove	d						18 53											20 53						21 51	
Burnley Manchester Road 41	a				18 15					19 15						20 15					21 15				
Leeds 10 41	a																								
Burnley Barracks	d						18x56											20x56						21x55	
Burnley Central	d						18 58											20 58						22a01	
Brierfield	d						19 03											21 03							
Nelson	d						19 06											21 06							
Colne	a						19 14											21 14							

		NT B	NT	NT C	NT	TP ◇1 A	NT B	NT B		TP ◇1 A
Blackpool North	d	20 50	21 13	21 20		21 45	21 50	22 44		23 01
Layton	d			21 23						
Poulton-le-Fylde	d	20 56	21 19	21 27		21 51	21 56	22 50		23 07
Blackpool South	d				21 27					
Blackpool Pleasure Beach	d				21 29					
Squires Gate	d				21 31					
St Annes-on-the-Sea	d				21 35					
Ansdell & Fairhaven	d				21 38					
Lytham	d				21 41					
Moss Side	d				21 46					
Kirkham & Wesham	d			21 37	21 53					23 17
Salwick	d									
Preston 8	a	21 14	21 36	21 47	22 03	22 09	22 14	23 08		23 27
	d		21 39		22 05					
Lostock Hall	d				22 11					
Bamber Bridge	d				22 14					
Pleasington	d				22x21					
Cherry Tree	d				22 24					
Mill Hill (Lancashire)	d				22 27					
Blackburn	a		21 54		22 30					
Clitheroe 94	a									
Blackburn	d		21 55		22 31					
Rishton	d				22 36					
Church & Oswaldtwistle	d				22 39					
Accrington	d		22 02		22 42					
Huncoat	d				22 47					
Hapton	d				22x50					
Rose Grove	d				22 53					
Burnley Manchester Road 41	a		22 15							
Leeds 10 41	a									
Burnley Barracks	d				22x56					
Burnley Central	d				22 58					
Brierfield	d				23 03					
Nelson	d				23 06					
Colne	a				23 14					

A To Manchester Airport **B** To Wigan North Western **C** To Manchester Oxford Road

Table 97R

Sundays

30 March to 11 May

Blackpool - Preston - Blackburn, Accrington, Burnley and Colne

Network Diagram - see first Page of Table 97

		NT	TP	NT	NT	NT	TP	NT	NT	NT	NT	TP	NT	NT	NT	TP	NT	NT	NT	NT	TP	NT	NT
			◇1				◇1					◇1				◇1					◇1		
		A 🚌	B		C	D	B	E	F	D		B	E	F	D	B	E	F	D		B	E	F
Blackpool North	d		07 48		08 10	08 20	08 44	08 50	09 01	09 20		09 44	09 50	10 11	10 20	10 44	10 50	11 13	11 20		11 44	11 50	12 11
Layton	d					08 23				09 23					10 23				11 23				
Poulton-le-Fylde	d		07 54		08 16	08 27	08 50	08 56	09 07	09 27		09 50	09 56	10 17	10 27	10 50	10 56	11 19	11 27		11 50	11 56	12 17
Blackpool South	d										09 28									11 27			
Blackpool Pleasure Beach	d										09 30									11 29			
Squires Gate	d										09 32									11 31			
St Annes-on-the-Sea	d										09 36									11 35			
Ansdell & Fairhaven	d										09 39									11 38			
Lytham	d										09 42									11 41			
Moss Side	d										09 47									11 46			
Kirkham & Wesham	d				08 26	08 37				09 37	09 54				10 37				11 37	11 53			
Salwick	d																						
Preston 8	a		08 12		08 36	08 47	09 08	09 14	09 24	09 47	10 04	10 08	10 14	10 34	10 47	11 08	11 14	11 36	11 47	12 03	12 08	12 14	12 34
	d			08 16	08 39				09 27		10 06			10 37				11 37		12 05			12 37
Lostock Hall	d			08 21	08 45						10 12									12 11			
Bamber Bridge	d			08 24	08 48						10 15									12 14			
Pleasington	d										10x22									12x21			
Cherry Tree	d										10 25									12 24			
Mill Hill (Lancashire)	d										10 28									12 27			
Blackburn	a			08 35	08 59				09 42		10 31			10 53				11 53		12 30			12 52
Clitheroe 94	a				09 27																		
Blackburn	d			08 37					09 44		10 32			10 54				11 54		12 31			12 54
Rishton	d										10 37									12 36			
Church & Oswaldtwistle	d										10 40									12 39			
Accrington	d			08 44					09 51		10 43			11 01				12 01		12 42			13 01
Huncoat	d										10 48									12 47			
Hapton	d										10x51									12x50			
Rose Grove	d			08 51							10 54									12 53			
Burnley Manchester Road 41	a								10 00					11 10				12 10					13 10
Leeds 10 41	a								11 21					12 22				13 22					14 22
Burnley Barracks	d	00 02									10x57									12x56			
Burnley Central	d	00 07		08 56							10 59									12 58			
Brierfield	d	00 15		09 00							11 04									13 03			
Nelson	d	00 20		09 03							11 07									13 06			
Colne	a	00 28		09 12							11 15									13 14			

		NT	NT	TP	NT	NT	NT	NT	NT	TP	NT	NT	NT	NT	TP	NT	NT	NT	NT	TP	NT	NT	NT
				◇1						◇1					◇1					◇1			
		D		B	E	C	F	D		B	E	F	D		B	E	F	D		B	E	F	D
Blackpool North	d	12 20		12 40	12 50		13 13	13 20		13 44	13 50	14 11	14 20		14 44	14 50	15 13	15 20		15 44	15 50	16 11	16 20
Layton	d	12 23						13 23					14 23					15 23					16 23
Poulton-le-Fylde	d	12 27		12 46	12 56		13 19	13 27		13 50	13 56	14 17	14 27		14 50	14 56	15 19	15 27		15 50	15 56	16 17	16 27
Blackpool South	d		12 24						13 27					14 27					15 27				
Blackpool Pleasure Beach	d		12 26						13 29					14 29					15 29				
Squires Gate	d		12 28						13 31					14 31					15 31				
St Annes-on-the-Sea	d		12 32						13 35					14 35					15 35				
Ansdell & Fairhaven	d		12 35						13 38					14 38					15 38				
Lytham	d		12 38						13 41					14 41					15 41				
Moss Side	d		12 43						13 46					14 46					15 46				
Kirkham & Wesham	d	12 37	12 50					13 37	13 53				14 37	14 53				15 37	15 53				16 37
Salwick	d																						
Preston 8	a	12 47	13 01	13 04	13 14		13 36	13 47	14 03	14 08	14 14	14 34	14 47	15 03	15 08	15 14	15 36	15 47	16 03	16 08	16 14	16 34	16 47
	d					13 18	13 37		14 05			14 37					15 37		16 05			16 37	
Lostock Hall	d					13 23			14 11										16 11				
Bamber Bridge	d					13 26			14 14										16 14				
Pleasington	d								14x21										16x21				
Cherry Tree	d								14 24										16 24				
Mill Hill (Lancashire)	d								14 27										16 27				
Blackburn	a					13 37	13 53		14 30			14 52					15 53		16 30			16 52	
Clitheroe 94	a					14 01																	
Blackburn	d						13 54		14 31			14 54					15 54		16 31			16 54	
Rishton	d								14 36										16 36				
Church & Oswaldtwistle	d								14 39										16 39				
Accrington	d						14 01		14 42			15 01					16 01		16 42			17 01	
Huncoat	d								14 47										16 47				
Hapton	d								14x50										16x50				
Rose Grove	d								14 53										16 53				
Burnley Manchester Road 41	a						14 10					15 10					16 10					17 10	
Leeds 10 41	a						15 22					16 22					17 22					18 22	
Burnley Barracks	d								14x56										16x56				
Burnley Central	d								14 58										16 58				
Brierfield	d								15 03										17 03				
Nelson	d								15 06										17 06				
Colne	a								15 14										17 14				

A From Blackburn
B To Manchester Airport
C To Hellifield
D To Manchester Oxford Road
E To Wigan North Western
F To York

Table 97R

Sundays

30 March to 11 May

Blackpool - Preston - Blackburn, Accrington, Burnley and Colne

Network Diagram - see first Page of Table 97

Station		NT		TP	NT	NT	NT	NT	TP	NT	NT	NT		NT	TP	NT	NT	NT	NT	TP	NT	NT		NT	NT
				◇1					◇1						◇1					◇1					
				A	B	C	D		A	B	C	D			A	B	C	D		A	B			D	
Blackpool North	d			16 44	16 50	17 11	17 20		17 44	17 50	18 11	18 20			18 44	18 50	19 13	19 20		19 44	19 50	20 11		20 20	
Layton	d						17 23					18 23						19 23						20 23	
Poulton-le-Fylde	d			16 50	16 56	17 17	17 27		17 50	17 56	18 17	18 27			18 50	18 56	19 19	19 27		19 50	19 56	20 17		20 27	
Blackpool South	d	16 27						17 24						18 27					19 27						20 27
Blackpool Pleasure Beach	d	16 29						17 26						18 29					19 29						20 29
Squires Gate	d	16 31						17 28						18 31					19 31						20 31
St Annes-on-the-Sea	d	16 35						17 32						18 35					19 35						20 35
Ansdell & Fairhaven	d	16 38						17 35						18 38					19 38						20 38
Lytham	d	16 41						17 38						18 41					19 41						20 41
Moss Side	d	16 46						17 43						18 46					19 46						20 46
Kirkham & Wesham	d	16 53					17 37	17 50				18 37		18 53				19 37	19 53					20 37	20 53
Salwick	d																								
Preston 8	a	17 03		17 08	17 14	17 34	17 47	18 00	18 08	18 14	18 34	18 47		19 03	19 08	19 14	19 36	19 47	20 03	20 08	20 14	20 34		20 47	21 03
	d					17 37		18 05			18 37						19 37		20 05			20 37			21 05
Lostock Hall	d							18 11											20 11						21 10
Bamber Bridge	d							18 14											20 14						21 13
Pleasington	d							18x21											20x21						21x20
Cherry Tree	d							18 24											20 24						21 23
Mill Hill (Lancashire)	d							18 27											20 27						21 26
Blackburn	a					17 52		18 30			18 52						19 53		20 30			20 52			21 29
Clitheroe 94	a																								
Blackburn	d					17 54		18 31			18 54						19 54		20 31			20 54			21 29
Rishton	d							18 36											20 36						21 34
Church & Oswaldtwistle	d							18 39											20 39						21 37
Accrington	d					18 01		18 42			19 01						20 01		20 42			21 01			21 40
Huncoat	d							18 47											20 47						21 45
Hapton	d							18x50											20x50						21x48
Rose Grove	d							18 53											20 53						21 51
Burnley Manchester Road 41	a					18 10					19 10						20 10					21 10			
Leeds 10 41	a					19 22					20 22						21 22					22 21			
Burnley Barracks	d							18x56											20x56						21x55
Burnley Central	d							18 58											20 58						22a01
Brierfield	d							19 03											21 03						
Nelson	d							19 06											21 06						
Colne	a							19 14											21 14						

Station		TP	NT	NT	NT	NT	TP	NT		NT	TP
		◇1					◇1				◇1
		A	B		D		A	B		B	A
Blackpool North	d	20 44	20 50	21 13	21 20		21 44	21 50		22 44	23 02
Layton	d				21 23						
Poulton-le-Fylde	d	20 50	20 56	21 19	21 27		21 50	21 56		22 50	23 08
Blackpool South	d					21 27					
Blackpool Pleasure Beach	d					21 29					
Squires Gate	d					21 31					
St Annes-on-the-Sea	d					21 35					
Ansdell & Fairhaven	d					21 38					
Lytham	d					21 41					
Moss Side	d					21 46					
Kirkham & Wesham	d				21 37	21 53					23 17
Salwick	d										
Preston 8	a	21 08	21 14	21 36	21 47	22 03	22 08	22 14		23 08	23 28
	d			21 39		22 05					
Lostock Hall	d					22 11					
Bamber Bridge	d					22 14					
Pleasington	d					22x21					
Cherry Tree	d					22 24					
Mill Hill (Lancashire)	d					22 27					
Blackburn	a			21 54		22 30					
Clitheroe 94	a										
Blackburn	d			21 55		22 31					
Rishton	d					22 36					
Church & Oswaldtwistle	d					22 39					
Accrington	d			22 02		22 42					
Huncoat	d					22 47					
Hapton	d					22x50					
Rose Grove	d					22 53					
Burnley Manchester Road 41	a			22 12							
Leeds 10 41	a			23 23							
Burnley Barracks	d					22x56					
Burnley Central	d					22 58					
Brierfield	d					23 03					
Nelson	d					23 06					
Colne	a					23 14					

A To Manchester Airport
B To Wigan North Western
C To York
D To Manchester Oxford Road

Table 98

Lancaster - Morecambe and Heysham

Mondays to Fridays

9 December to 16 May

Network Diagram - see first Page of Table 97

Miles				TP 1	NT	NT	NT	NT	NT	NT	NT	NT	NT	NT	NT	NT	NT	NT	NT	NT	NT	NT	NT
0	**Lancaster 6**	82	d	05 45	06 38	07 21	08 04	08 35	09 15	09 48	10 20	11 26	12 02	12 20	13 39	14 25	15 24	16 04	16 20	16 49	17 27	18 02	18 49	19 42
2½	Bare Lane		d	05 51	06 44	07 27	08 10	08 41	09 21	09 54	10 26	11 32	12 08	12 26	13 45	14 31	15 30	16 10	16 26	16 55	17 33	18 08	18 55	19 48
4¼	**Morecambe**		a	05 55	06 49	07 32	08 15	08 46	09 26	09 59	10 31	11 37	12 13	12 30	13 50	14 36	15 35	16 14	16 30	17 00	17 38	18 13	19 01	19 53
—			d											12 34										
8½	**Heysham Harbour**		a											12 48										

			NT	NT	NT	NT
Lancaster 6	82	d	20 36	21 34	22 07	22 36
Bare Lane		d	20 42	21 40	22 13	22 42
Morecambe		a	20 47	21 45	22 17	22 47
		d				
Heysham Harbour		a				

Saturdays

14 December to 17 May

			TP 1	NT	NT	NT	NT	NT	NT	NT	NT	NT	NT	NT	NT	NT	NT	NT	NT	NT	NT	NT	NT	NT
Lancaster 6	82	d	05 45	06 36	07 21	07 53	08 27	09 27	10 05	10 18	11 20	12 02	12 25	13 24	14 43	15 24	15 49	16 05	16 51	17 26	18 20	18 47	19 30	20 10
Bare Lane		d	05 51	06 42	07 27	07 59	08 33	09 33	10 11	10 25	11 26	12 08	12 32	13 30	14 49	15 30	15 56	16 11	16 57	17 32	18 26	18 53	19 36	20 16
Morecambe		a	05 55	06 47	07 32	08 04	08 38	09 39	10 16	10 31	11 31	12 13	12 36	13 35	14 54	15 35	16 02	16 16	17 02	17 37	18 31	18 59	19 40	20 20
		d											12 40											
Heysham Harbour		a											12 54											

			NT A (bus)	NT B	NT A (bus)	NT B	NT B	NT A (bus)
Lancaster 6	82	d	20 55	21 07	21 55	22 07	22 35	22 55
Bare Lane		d	21 10	21 13	22 10	22 13	22 41	23 10
Morecambe		a	21 20	21 17	22 20	22 17	22 46	23 20
		d						
Heysham Harbour		a						

Sundays

8 December to 11 May

			NT C	NT D (bus)	NT	NT	NT	NT	NT	NT	NT
Lancaster 6	82	d	10 45	11 05	12 05	13 00	14 27	15 05	16 51	19 25	21 18
Bare Lane		d	10 51	11 20	12 11	13 06	14 34	15 11	16 56	19 31	21 24
Morecambe		a	10 57	11 30	12 16	13 12	14 38	15 16	17 03	19 37	21 29
		d									
Heysham Harbour		a									

A from 29 March
B until 22 March
C until 23 March
D from 30 March

Table 98R

Mondays to Fridays

9 December to 16 May

Heysham and Morecambe - Lancaster

Network Diagram - see first Page of Table 97

Miles				NT	NT	NT	NT	NT	NT	NT	NT	NT	NT	NT
0	Heysham Harbour		d											13 15
4¼	Morecambe		a											13 28
—			d	06 10	06 57	07 42	08 22	08 51	09 32	10 03	10 34	11 45	12 38	13 31
6	Bare Lane		d	06 14	07 01	07 46	08 26	08 55	09 36	10 07	10 38	11 49	12 42	13 36
8½	Lancaster 6	82	a	06 20	07 07	07 52	08 32	09 01	09 44	10 14	10 45	11 56	12 49	13 42

Miles				NT	NT	NT	NT	NT	NT	NT	NT	NT	NT
0	Heysham Harbour		d										
4¼	Morecambe		a										
—			d	13 54	14 40	15 45	16 19	16 35	17 08	17 42	18 19	19 08	20 14
6	Bare Lane		d	13 58	14 44	15 49	16a23	16 39	17 12	17 46	18 23	19 12	20 18
8½	Lancaster 6	82	a	14 04	14 51	15 56		16 46	17 19	17 53	18 29	19 19	20 24

			NT	NT	NT	NT
Heysham Harbour		d				
Morecambe		a				
		d	20 54	21 48	22 21	22 51
Bare Lane		d	20 58	21 52	22 25	22 55
Lancaster 6	82	a	21 05	21 59	22 32	23 01

Saturdays

14 December to 17 May

			NT	NT	NT	NT	NT	NT	NT	NT	NT	NT	NT
Heysham Harbour		d											13 15
Morecambe		a											13 28
		d	06 10	06 57	07 36	08 10	08 42	09 41	10 34	10 55	11 38	12 32	13 31
Bare Lane		d	06 14	07 01	07 40	08 14	08 46	09 45	10 38	10 59	11 42	12 36	13 36
Lancaster 6	82	a	06 21	07 08	07 47	08 21	08 52	09 52	10 45	11 06	11 49	12 43	13 42

			NT	NT	NT	NT	NT	NT	NT	NT	NT	NT
Heysham Harbour		d										
Morecambe		a										
		d	13 57	15 02	15 44	16 21	16 34	17 07	17 55	18 41	19 09	19 55	20 34
Bare Lane		d	14 01	15 06	15 48	16 25	16 38	17 11	17 59	18 45	19 13	19 59	20 38
Lancaster 6	82	a	14 08	15 13	15 55	16 32	16 44	17 18	18 07	18 53	19 20	20 06	20 45

			NT A	NT B 🚌	NT A	NT B 🚌
Heysham Harbour		d				
Morecambe		a				
		d	21 25	21 25	22 20	22 25
Bare Lane		d	21 29	21 35	22 24	22 35
Lancaster 6	82	a	21 36	21 50	22 31	22 50

Sundays

8 December to 11 May

			NT	NT	NT	NT	NT	NT	NT	NT
Heysham Harbour		d								
Morecambe		a								
		d	11 45	12 20	13 23	14 46	15 21	17 45	20 00	21 41
Bare Lane		d	11 49	12 24	13 27	14a50	15 25	17 49	20 04	21 45
Lancaster 6	82	a	11 55	12 31	13 34		15 32	17 55	20 11	21 51

A until 22 March

B from 29 March

Table 98A

To and from The Isle of Man via Heysham and Liverpool

Mondays to Fridays
9 December to 16 May
One Class only on ship
Network Diagram - see first Page of Table 97

		VT	VT	VT	VT	VT
			MFO			
		A	B	C	D	E
Liverpool Landing Stage	d		11 15			19 15
Heysham Harbour	d	02 15		12 00	14 15	
Douglas (Isle of Man)	a	05 45	14 00	15 30	17 45	22 00

Saturdays
14 December to 17 May

		VT	VT	VT	VT
		F	G	H	I
Liverpool Landing Stage	d	11 15			19 15
Heysham Harbour	d		12 00	14 15	
Douglas (Isle of Man)	a	14 00	15 30	17 45	22 00

Sundays
8 December to 11 May

		VT	VT	VT
		J	K	L
Liverpool Landing Stage	d			19 15
Heysham Harbour	d	12 00	14 15	
Douglas (Isle of Man)	a	15 30	17 45	22 00

Mondays to Fridays
9 December to 16 May

		VT	VT	VT	VT
		MFO			
		B	M	E	N
Douglas (Isle of Man)	d	07 30	08 45	15 00	19 45
Heysham Harbour	a		12 15		23 15
Liverpool Landing Stage	a	10 15		17 45	

Saturdays
14 December to 17 May

		VT	VT	VT
		F	H	H
Douglas (Isle of Man)	d	07 30	08 45	15 00
Heysham Harbour	a		12 15	
Liverpool Landing Stage	a	10 15		17 45

Sundays
8 December to 11 May

		VT	VT	VT
		L	O	P
Douglas (Isle of Man)	d	08 45	15 00	19 45
Heysham Harbour	a	12 15		23 15
Liverpool Landing Stage	a		17 45	

A not 25 December, 26 December, 1 January
B from 28 March until 28 April, also from 17 April until 24 April
C from 29 April
D until 28 April, not 25 December
E from 28 March, not 18 April
F from 29 March until 26 April
G 3 May, 10 May, 17 May
H from 29 March
I from 29 March, not 19 April
J 4 May, 11 May
K from 30 March until 27 April
L from 30 March
M not 25 December
N until 28 April, not 24 December, 25 December, 31 December
O from 30 March until 4 May
P until 10 May, not 4 May

Table 99

Mondays to Saturdays

9 December to 17 May

Ormskirk - Preston

Network Diagram - see first Page of Table 97

Miles			NT	NT	NT	NT	NT	NT	NT	NT	NT		NT	NT	NT
0	**Ormskirk**	d	06 58	08 06	09 17	10 36	12 17	13 36	15 17	16 36	17 52		19 06	20 47	22 47
2½	Burscough Junction	d	07 02	08 10	09 21	10 40	12 21	13 40	15 21	16 40	17 56		19 10	20 51	22 51
5½	Rufford	d	07 07	08 15	09 25	10 45	12 25	13 45	15 25	16 45	18 01		19 15	20 55	22 55
8	Croston	d	07 11	08 19	09 30	10 49	12 30	13 49	15 30	16 49	18 06		19 19	21 00	23 00
15	**Preston** 8	a	07 29	08 36	09 47	11 08	12 47	14 08	15 47	17 08	18 23		19 38	21 17	23 17

For connections from Liverpool Central please see Table 103

No Sunday Service

Table 99R

Mondays to Saturdays

9 December to 17 May

Preston - Ormskirk

Network Diagram - see first Page of Table 97

Miles			NT	NT	NT	NT	NT	NT		NT	NT	NT	NT	NT	NT
0	**Preston** 8	d	06 25	07 33	08 41	09 59	11 29	12 59		14 29	15 59	17 10	18 34	20 08	22 08
7	Croston	d	06 36	07 45	08 52	10 11	11 41	13 11		14 41	16 11	17 22	18 47	20 19	22 20
9½	Rufford	d	06 41	07 50	08 57	10 16	11 46	13 16		14 46	16 16	17 27	18 51	20 24	22 24
12½	Burscough Junction	d	06 46	07 55	09 02	10 21	11 51	13 21		14 51	16 21	17 32	18 56	20 29	22 29
15	**Ormskirk**	a	06 55	08 04	09 11	10 30	12 00	13 30		15 00	16 30	17 41	19 05	20 38	22 38

For connections to Liverpool Central please see Table 103

No Sunday Service

Table 100

Barrow-in-Furness - Whitehaven and Carlisle

Mondays to Fridays

9 December to 16 May

Network Diagram - see first Page of Table 97

Miles			NT	NT	NT	NT	NT	NT	NT	NT	NT
—	Lancaster 6	82 d			05 41				08 48		
0	**Barrow-in-Furness**	d		05 58	06 50	07 58		09 10	10 10	11 22	12 33
6	Askam	d		06 08	07 00	08 08		09 20	10 20	11 32	12 43
9¼	Kirkby-in-Furness	d		06 12	07x04	08x12		09x24	10x24	11x36	12x47
11¼	Foxfield	d		06x16	07x08	08x15		09x27	10x27	11x39	12x50
13½	Green Road	d		06x20	07x12	08x19		09x31	10x31	11x43	12x54
16	Millom	a		06 27	07 19	08 25		09 37	10 37	11 49	13 00
—		d		06 27	07 19	08 26		09 38	10 38	11 49	13 01
19	Silecroft	d		06x32	07 24			09x42	10x42	11x54	13x05
24½	Bootle	d		06x39	07x31			09x49	10x49	12x00	13x12
29¼	Ravenglass for Eskdale	d		06 45	07 37	08 41		09 55	10 55	12 06	13 18
31	Drigg	d		06x49	07x41			09x58	10x58	12x09	13x21
33¼	Seascale	d		06 52	07 44	08 47		10 01	11 01	12 13	13 24
35	Sellafield	d		06 59	07 51	08a55		10 07	11 08	12 18	13 30
37	Braystones	d		07x02	07x54						
38¼	Nethertown	d		07x05	07x57						
41¼	St Bees	d		07 09	08 01			10 16	11 17	12 27	13 40
44¾	Corkickle	d		07x14	08x06			10x21	11x22	12x32	13x45
45¾	**Whitehaven**	a		07 18	08 10			10 24	11 25	12 35	13 48
—		d	06 30	07 25	08 11		09 02	10 24	11 27	12 36	13 50
47	Parton	d	06x33	07x28	08x15		09x05	10x28	11x30	12x40	13x53
50½	Harrington	d	06x41	07x36	08x23		09x13	10x36	11x38	12x48	14x01
52¼	**Workington**	d	06 48	07 43	08 29		09 20	10 42	11 45	12 54	14 08
56	Flimby	d	06x52	07x48	08x34		09x24	10x47	11x49	12x59	14x12
58	Maryport	d	06 56	07 51	08 37		09 28	10 50	11 53	13 02	14 16
65½	Aspatria	d	07x05	08x01	08x47		09x37	11x00	12x02	13x12	14x25
71¾	Wigton	d	07 17	08 13	08 59		09 49	11 12	12 14	13 24	14 37
81¼	Dalston	d	07x26	08x21	09x07		09x58	11x20	12x23	13x32	14x46
85¼	**Carlisle 8**	a	07 38	08 35	09 21		10 13	11 35	12 38	13 46	15 00

Miles			NT	NT	NT	NT	NT	NT	NT	NT	NT	NT
—	Lancaster 6	82 d			15 35		16 46					
0	**Barrow-in-Furness**	d	13 35	14 54	16 41	17 28	18 05		19 35		21 30	
6	Askam	d	13 45	15 04	16 51	17 40	18 15		19 45		21 40	
9¼	Kirkby-in-Furness	d	13x49	15x08	16x55	17x44	18x19		19x49		21x44	
11¼	Foxfield	d	13x52	15x11	16x58	17x48	18x22		19x52		21x47	
13½	Green Road	d	13x56	15x15	17x02	17x51	18x26		19x56		21x51	
16	Millom	a	14 02	15 21	17 08	17 58	18 35		20 05		22 00	
—		d	14 02	15 22	17 09	17 58						
19	Silecroft	d	14x07	15x26	17x13	18x03						
24½	Bootle	d	14x13	15x33	17x20	18x09						
29¼	Ravenglass for Eskdale	d	14 19	15 39	17 26	18 15						
31	Drigg	d	14x22	15x42	17x29	18x18						
33¼	Seascale	d	14 26	15 45	17 32	18 22						
35	Sellafield	d	14 31	15 51	17 39	18 27						
37	Braystones	d	14x35			18x31						
38¼	Nethertown	d	14x37			18x33						
41¼	St Bees	d	14 42	16 00	17 49	18 45						
44¾	Corkickle	d	14x47	16x05	17x54	18x50						
45¾	**Whitehaven**	a	14 50	16 09	17 57	18 53						
—		d	14 52	16 11	17 58	18 55		19 34		20 30		21 51
47	Parton	d	14x55	16x15	18x02	18x58		19x37		20x33		21x54
50½	Harrington	d	15x03	16x23	18x10	19x06		19x45		20x41		22x02
52¼	**Workington**	d	15 10	16 29	18 16	19 12		19 52		20 48		22a11
56	Flimby	d	15x14	16x34	18x21	19x17		19x56		20x52		
58	Maryport	d	15 18	16 37	18 26	19 20		20 00		20 56		
65½	Aspatria	d	15x27	16x47	18x36	19x30		20x09		21x05		
71¾	Wigton	d	15 39	16 59	18 48	19 42		20 21		21 17		
81¼	Dalston	d	15x48	17x07	18x56	19x50		20x30		21x26		
85¼	**Carlisle 8**	a	16 02	17 21	19 08	20 04		20 44		21 39		

Saturdays

14 December to 17 May

		NT	NT	NT	NT	NT	NT	NT	NT	NT
Lancaster 6	82 d							09 02		
Barrow-in-Furness	d		05 58	07 05	07 58		09 10	10 10	11 22	
Askam	d		06 08	07 15	08 08		09 20	10 20	11 32	
Kirkby-in-Furness	d		06x12	07x19	08x12		09x24	10x24	11x36	
Foxfield	d		06x15	07x23	08x15		09x27	10x27	11x39	
Green Road	d		06x19	07x27	08x19		09x31	10x31	11x43	
Millom	a		06 23	07 34	08 25		09 37	10 37	11 49	
	d		06 24	07 34	08 26		09 38	10 38	11 49	
Silecroft	d		06x28	07x39			09x42	10x42	11x54	
Bootle	d		06x35	07x46			09x49	10x49	12x00	
Ravenglass for Eskdale	d		06 40	07 52	08 41		09 55	10 55	12 06	
Drigg	d		06x43	07x56			09x58	10x58	12x09	
Seascale	d		06 49	07 59	08 47		10 01	11 01	12 13	
Sellafield	d		06 54	08 06	08a55		10 07	11 08	12 18	
Braystones	d		06x57	08x09						
Nethertown	d		07x00	08x12						
St Bees	d		07 04	08 16			10 16	11 17	12 27	
Corkickle	d		07x09	08x21			10x21	11x22	12x32	
Whitehaven	a		07 13	08 25			10 24	11 25	12 40	
	d	06 30	07 19	08 26		09 15	10 24	11 27		12 54
Parton	d	06x33	07x22	08x30		09x18	10x28	11x30		12x57
Harrington	d	06x41	07x30	08x38		09x26	10x36	11x38		13x05
Workington	d	06 48	07 37	08 44		09 33	10 42	11 45		13 12
Flimby	d	06x52	07x41	08x49		09x37	10x47	11x49		13x16
Maryport	d	06 56	07 45	08 52		09 41	10 50	11 53		13 20
Aspatria	d	07x05	07x54	09x02		09x50	11x00	12x02		13x29
Wigton	d	07 17	08 06	09 14		10 02	11 12	12 14		13 41
Dalston	d	07x26	08x15	09x22		10x11	11x20	12x23		13x50
Carlisle 8	a	07 38	08 27	09 36		10 24	11 35	12 38		14 04

		NT	NT	NT	NT	NT	NT	NT	NT	NT	NT
Lancaster 6	82 d	11 28		13 32			17 00				
Barrow-in-Furness	d	12 33	13 50	14 54	15 33	17 25	18 10		19 35		21 30
Askam	d	12 43	14 00	15 04	15 43	17 35	18 20		19 45		21 40
Kirkby-in-Furness	d	12x47	14x04	15x08	15x47	17x39	18x24		19x49		21x44
Foxfield	d	12x50	14x07	15x11	15x50	17x42	18x27		19x52		21x47
Green Road	d	12x54	14x11	15x15	15x54	17x46	18x31		19x56		21x51
Millom	a	13 01	14 17	15 21	16 00	17 52	18 40		20 05		22 00
	d	13 01	14 18	15 22	16 01	17 53					
Silecroft	d	13x05	14x22	15x26	16x05	17x57					
Bootle	d	13x12	14x29	15x33	16x12	18x04					
Ravenglass for Eskdale	d	13 18	14 35	15 39	16 18	18 10					
Drigg	d	13x21	14x38	15x42	16x21	18x13					
Seascale	d	13 24	14 41	15 45	16 24	18 16					
Sellafield	d	13 30	14 47	15 51	16 30	18 22					
Braystones	d				16x34	18x26					
Nethertown	d				16x36	18x28					
St Bees	d	13 40	14 56	16 00	16 46	18 33					
Corkickle	d	13x45	15x01	16x05	16x51	18x38					
Whitehaven	a	13 48	15 04	16 09	16 54	18 41					
	d	13 50	15 05	16 11	16 56	18 43		19 34		20 30	
Parton	d	13x53	15x09	16x15	17x00	18x46		19x37		20x33	
Harrington	d	14x01	15x17	16x23	17x08	18x54		19x45		20x41	
Workington	d	14 08	15 23	16 29	17 14	19 01		19 52		20 48	
Flimby	d	14x12	15x28	16x34	17x19	19x05		19x56		20x52	
Maryport	d	14 16	15 31	16 37	17 22	19 09		20 00		20 56	
Aspatria	d	14x25	15x41	16x47	17x32	19x18		20x09		21x05	
Wigton	d	14 37	15 53	16 59	17 44	19 30		20 21		21 17	
Dalston	d	14x46	16x01	17x07	17x52	19x39		20x30		21x26	
Carlisle 8	a	15 00	16 15	17 21	18 06	19 53		20 44		21 39	

Sundays

8 December to 11 May

		NT	NT	NT	NT
Lancaster 6	82 d				
Barrow-in-Furness	d				
Askam	d				
Kirkby-in-Furness	d				
Foxfield	d				
Green Road	d				
Millom	a				
	d				
Silecroft	d				
Bootle	d				
Ravenglass for Eskdale	d				
Drigg	d				
Seascale	d				
Sellafield	d				
Braystones	d				
Nethertown	d				
St Bees	d				
Corkickle	d				
Whitehaven	a				
	d	12 33	14 30	16 30	19 30
Parton	d	12x36	14x33	16x33	19x33
Harrington	d	12x44	14x41	16x41	19x41
Workington	d	12 51	14 48	16 48	19 48
Flimby	d	12x55	14x52	16x52	19x52
Maryport	d	12 59	14 56	16 56	19 56
Aspatria	d	13x08	15x05	17x05	20x05
Wigton	d	13 18	15 15	17 15	20 15
Dalston	d	13x27	15x24	17x24	20x24
Carlisle 8	a	13 42	15 40	17 40	20 40

No Sunday Service Barrow-in-Furness to Whitehaven

Table 100R

Mondays to Fridays

9 December to 16 May

Carlisle and Whitehaven - Barrow-in-Furness

Network Diagram - see first Page of Table 97

Miles			NT	NT	NT	NT	NT	NT	NT	NT	NT	NT	NT	NT	NT	NT	NT	NT	NT	NT	NT	NT
0	**Carlisle** 8	d				07 44		08 38	09 38	10 43	11 50	12 47	14 20	15 12	16 31	17 27	18 14	19 15		20 37	21 50	
4	Dalston	d				07x52		08x46	09x46	10x51	11x58	12x55	14x28	15x20	16x39	17x35	18x22	19x23		20x45	21x58	
11½	Wigton	d				08 02		08 56	09 56	11 01	12 08	13 05	14 38	15 30	16 49	17 44	18 32	19 33		20 55	22 08	
19¾	Aspatria	d				08x12		09x06	10x06	11x11	12x18	13x15	14x48	15x40	16x59	17x54	18x42	19x43		21x05	22x18	
27¼	Maryport	d		06 00		08 23		09 17	10 17	11 22	12 29	13 26	14 59	15 51	17 10	18 05	18 53	19 54		21 16	22 29	
29¼	Flimby	d		06x03		08x26		09x20	10x20	11x25	12x32	13x29	15x02	15x54	17x13	18x08	18x56	19x57		21x19	22x32	
33	**Workington**	d		06 09		08 34		09 28	10 28	11 33	12 40	13 37	15 10	16 02	17 21	18 16	19 04	20 05		21 27	22 40	
34¾	Harrington	d		06 13		08x38		09x32	10x32	11x37	12x44	13x41	15x14	16x06	17x25	18x20	19x08	20x09		21x31	22x44	
38¼	Parton	d		06X21		08x46		09x40	10x40	11x45	12x52	13x49	15x22	16x14	17x33	18x28	19x16	20x17		21x39	22x52	
39½	**Whitehaven**	a		06 26		08 54		09 46	10 46	11 51	12 58	13 55	15 28	16 20	17 39	18 34	19 25	20 25		21 47	23 00	
—		d		06 28	07 25			09 48	10 48	11 53	13 00	13 57	15 30	16 22	17 41	18 36						
40½	Corkickle	d		06 30	07x27			09x50	10x50	11x55	13x02	13x59	15x32	16x24	17x43	18x38						
44	St Bees	d		06 35	07 32			09 55	10 55	12 00	13 07	14 04	15 37	16 30	17 48	18 44						
47	Nethertown	d		06x39					10x59	12x04			15x41		17x52							
48¼	Braystones	d		06 42					11x02	12x07			15x44		17x55							
50¼	Sellafield	d		06 48	07 45		09 05	10 06	11 08	12 13	13 18	14 15	15 55	16 43	18 04	18 55						
52	Seascale	d		06 51	07 48		09 08	10 10	11 11	12 16	13 21	14 18	15 58	16 47	18 07	18 59						
54¼	Drigg	d		06 54	07x51		09X11	10x13	11x14	12x19	13x24	14x21	16x02	16x50	18x11	19x02						
56	Ravenglass for Eskdale	d		06 58	07 55		09 15	10 16	11 18	12 23	13 28	14 25	16 05	16 54	18 14	19 05						
60¾	Bootle	d		07x03	08x00		09X20	10x22	11x23	12x28	13x33	14x30	16x11	17x00	18x20	19x11						
66¼	Silecroft	d		07x10	08x07		09X27	10x28	11x30	12x35	13x40	14x37	16x18	17x07	18x27	19x17						
69¼	Millom	a		07 16	08 12		09 33	10 35	11 36	12 41	13 46	14 43	16 25	17 14	18 34	19 24						
—		d	06 10	07 17	08 12		09 34	10 35	11 36	12 42	13 47	14 44	16 26	17 14	18 35	19 24			20 12			22 08
71¾	Green Road	d	06x14	07x21	08x16		09X38	10x39	11x40	12x46	13x51	14x48	16x30	17x19	18x39	19x28			20x16			22x12
73¾	Foxfield	d	06x17	07x24	08x20		09X41	10x43	11x44	12x49	13x54	14x51	16x34	17x23	18x43	19x32			20x19			22x15
76	Kirkby-in-Furness	d	06x21	07x28	08x24		09X45	10x47	11x48	12x53	13x58	14x55	16x39	17x27	18x48	19x36			20x23			22x19
79¼	Askam	d	06x26	07 33	08 29		09 50	10 52	11 53	12 58	14 03	15 00	16 44	17 32	18 53	19 41			20x28			22x24
85¼	**Barrow-in-Furness**	a	06x42	07 49	08 45		10 05	11 09	12 08	13 14	14 20	15 16	17 01	17 48	19 10	19 58			20x45			22 41
—	Lancaster 6 82	a	08 04	09 07			11 18		13 14			16 22		19 05								

Saturdays

14 December to 17 May

		NT	NT	NT	NT	NT	NT	NT	NT	NT	NT	NT	NT	NT	NT	NT	NT	NT	NT	NT	NT
Carlisle 8	d			07 44		08 38	09 38	10 43	11 39		12 47	14 20	15 25	16 31	17 40	18 14	19 00	20 05		21 45	
Dalston	d			07x52		08x46	09x46	10x51	11x47		12x55	14x28	15x33	16x39	17x48	18x22	19x08	20x13		21x53	
Wigton	d			08 02		08 56	09 56	11 01	11 57		13 05	14 38	15 43	16 49	17 58	18 32	19 18	20 22		22 03	
Aspatria	d			08x12		09x06	10x06	11x11	12x07		13x15	14x48	15x53	16x59	18x08	18x42	19x28	20x32		22x13	
Maryport	d		06 23	08 23		09 17	10 17	11 22	12 18		13 26	14 59	16 04	17 10	18 19	18 53	19 39	20 42		22 24	
Flimby	d		06x26	08x26		09x20	10x20	11x25	12x21		13x29	15x02	16x07	17x13	18x22	18x56	19x42	20x45		22x27	
Workington	d		06 34	08 34		09 28	10 28	11 33	12 29		13 37	15 10	16 16	17 21	18 30	19 04	19 50	20 54		22 35	
Harrington	d		06 38	08x38		09x32	10x32	11x37	12x33		13x41	15x14	16x19	17x25	18x34	19x08	19x54	20x57		22x39	
Parton	d		06X46	08x46		09x40	10x40	11x45	12x41		13x49	15x22	16x28	17x33	18x42	19x16	20x02	21x06		22x47	
Whitehaven	a		06 52	08 54		09 46	10 46	11 51	12 49		13 55	15 28	16 34	17 39	18 48	19 25	20 10	21 15		22 55	
	d		06 54			09 48	10 48	11 53		12 54	13 57	15 30	16 36	17 41	18 50						
Corkickle	d		06x56			09x50	10x50	11x55		12x56	13x59	15x32	16x38	17x43	18x52						
St Bees	d		07 04			09 55	10 55	12 00		13 01	14 04	15 37	16 43	17 48	18 57						
Nethertown	d		07x08				10x59	12 05				15x41		17x52							
Braystones	d		07x11				11x02	12 08				15x44		17x55							
Sellafield	d		07 16		09 05	10 06	11 08	12 14		13 11	14 15	15 50	16 54	18 01	19 08						
Seascale	d		07 20		09 08	10 10	11 11	12 17		13 15	14 18	15 53	16 57	18 04	19 11						
Drigg	d		07x23		09X11	10x13	11x14	12x20		13x18	14x21	15x56	17x00	18x07	19x14						
Ravenglass for Eskdale	d		07 27		09 15	10 16	11 18	12 24		13 22	14 25	16 00	17 04	18 11	19 18						
Bootle	d		07x32		09X20	10x22	11x23	12x29		13x27	14x30	16x05	17x09	18x16	19x23						
Silecroft	d		07x39		09X27	10x28	11x30	12x36		13x34	14x37	16x12	17x16	18x23	19x30						
Millom	a		07 45		09 33	10 35	11 36	12 42		13 40	14 43	16 18	17 22	18 29	19 36						
	d	06 10	07 46		09 34	10 35	11 36	12 43		13 41	14 44	16 19	17 23	18 30	19 37				20 12		22 08
Green Road	d	06x14	07x50		09X38	10x39	11x40	12x47		13 45	14x48	16x23	17x27	18x34	19x41				20x16		22x12
Foxfield	d	06x17	07x53		09X41	10x43	11x44	12x50		13x48	14x51	16x26	17x30	18x37	19x45				20x19		22x15
Kirkby-in-Furness	d	06x21	07x57		09X45	10x47	11x48	12x54		13x52	14x55	16x30	17x34	18x41	19x49				20x23		22x19
Askam	d	06x26	08 02		09 50	10 52	11 53	12 59		13 57	15 00	16 35	17 39	18 46	19 54				20x28		22 24
Barrow-in-Furness	a	06x42	08 20		10 05	11 09	12 08	13 15		14 16	15 16	16 53	17 55	19 04	20 11				20 45		22 41
Lancaster 6 82	a	08 04	09 24		11 20		13 14			15 19			19 05								

Sundays

8 December to 11 May

		NT	NT	NT	NT
Carlisle 8	d	14 10	17 10	19 10	21 10
Dalston	d	14x18	17x18	19x18	21x18
Wigton	d	14 27	17 27	19 27	21 27
Aspatria	d	14x37	17x37	19x37	21x37
Maryport	d	14 47	17 47	19 47	21 47
Flimby	d	14x50	17x50	19x50	21x50
Workington	d	14 59	17 59	19 59	21 59
Harrington	d	15x02	18x02	20x02	22x02
Parton	d	15x11	18x11	20x11	22x11
Whitehaven	a	15 20	18 20	20 20	22 20
	d				
Corkickle	d				
St Bees	d				
Nethertown	d				
Braystones	d				
Sellafield	d				
Seascale	d				
Drigg	d				
Ravenglass for Eskdale	d				
Bootle	d				
Silecroft	d				
Millom	a				
	d				
Green Road	d				
Foxfield	d				
Kirkby-in-Furness	d				
Askam	d				
Barrow-in-Furness	a				
Lancaster 6 82	a				

No Sunday Service Whitehaven to Barrow-in-Furness

Network Diagram for Tables 101, 103, 104, 105, 106, 107, 109

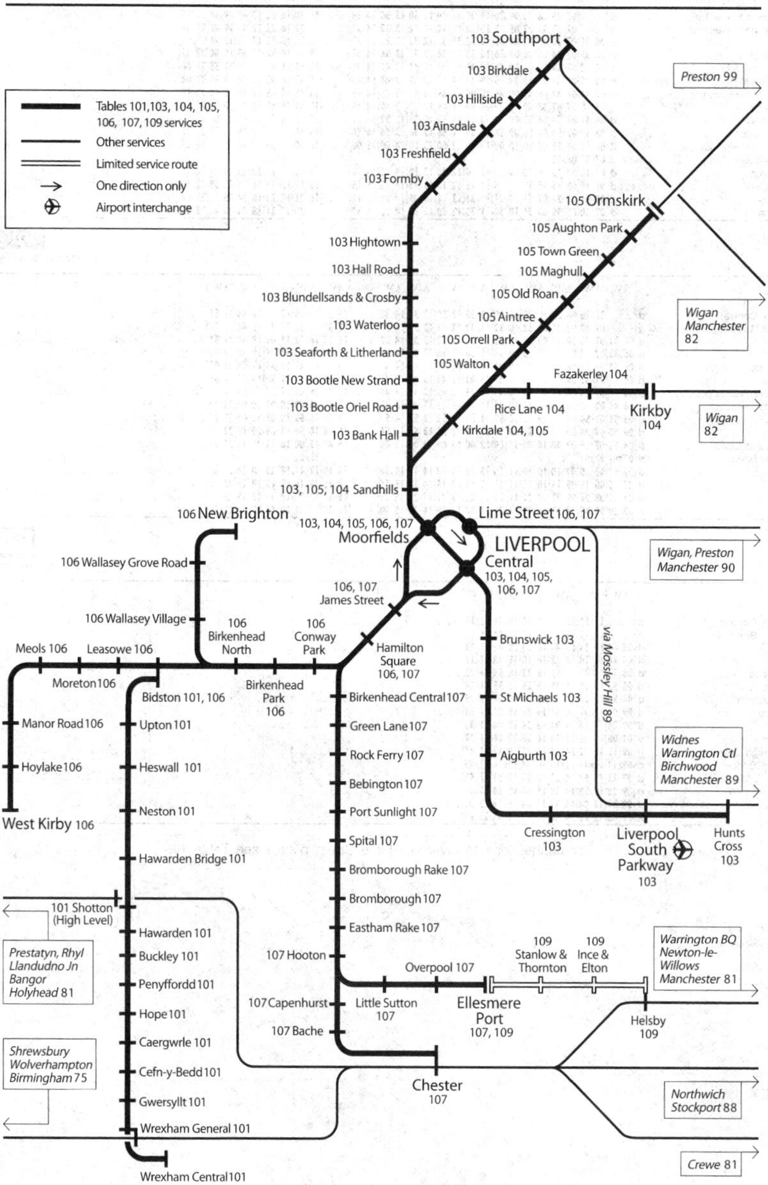

Tables 101,103, 104, 105, 106, 107, 109 services
Other services
Limited service route
One direction only
Airport interchange
103 Southport
103 Birkdale
103 Hillside
103 Ainsdale
103 Freshfield
103 Formby
103 Hightown
103 Hall Road
103 Blundellsands & Crosby
103 Waterloo
103 Seaforth & Litherland
103 Bootle New Strand
103 Bootle Oriel Road
103 Bank Hall
103, 105, 104 Sandhills
Preston 99
105 Ormskirk
105 Aughton Park
105 Town Green
105 Maghull
105 Old Roan
105 Aintree
105 Orrell Park
105 Walton
Wigan Manchester 82
Fazakerley 104
Rice Lane 104
Kirkdale 104, 105
Kirkby 104
Wigan 82
106 New Brighton
103, 104, 105, 106, 107 Moorfields
Lime Street 106, 107
LIVERPOOL
Central 103, 104, 105, 106, 107
Wigan, Preston Manchester 90
106 Wallasey Grove Road
106 Wallasey Village
106, 107 James Street
106 Birkenhead North
106 Conway Park
Hamilton Square 106, 107
Meols 106
Leasowe 106
Moreton 106
Bidston 101, 106
Birkenhead Park 106
Brunswick 103
via Mossley Hill 89
Birkenhead Central 107
St Michaels 103
Manor Road 106
Upton 101
Green Lane 107
Hoylake 106
Heswall 101
Rock Ferry 107
Aigburth 103
Widnes Warrington Ctl Birchwood Manchester 89
Bebington 107
Neston 101
Port Sunlight 107
West Kirby 106
Spital 107
Cressington 103
Liverpool South Parkway 103
Hunts Cross 103
Hawarden Bridge 101
Bromborough Rake 107
101 Shotton (High Level)
Bromborough 107
Eastham Rake 107
Prestatyn, Rhyl Llandudno Jn Bangor Holyhead 81
Hawarden 101
Buckley 101
107 Hooton
Overpool 107
109 Stanlow & Thornton
109 Ince & Elton
Warrington BQ Newton-le-Willows Manchester 81
Penyffordd 101
Hope 101
107 Capenhurst
Little Sutton 107
Ellesmere Port 107, 109
Helsby 109
107 Bache
Caergwrle 101
Shrewsbury Wolverhampton Birmingham 75
Cefn-y-Bedd 101
Chester 107
Northwich Stockport 88
Gwersyllt 101
Wrexham General 101
Crewe 81
Wrexham Central 101

TOCs operating on this network - Arriva Trains Wales (AW), Merseyrail (ME), Northern (NT)

Table 101

Mondays to Fridays

9 December to 16 May

Wrexham - Bidston

Network Diagram - see first Page of Table 101

Miles			AW	AW BHX	AW	AW BHX	AW	AW BHX	AW	AW BHX	AW		AW BHX	AW	AW BHX	AW	AW
0	**Wrexham Central**	d		07 28	08 30	09 30	10 30	11 30	12 30	13 30	14 30		15 30	16 30	17 43	19 44	21 55
0½	**Wrexham General**	a		07 30	08 32	09 32	10 32	11 32	12 32	13 32	14 32		15 32	16 32	17 45	19 46	21 57
—		d	06 31	07 30	08 32	09 32	10 32	11 32	12 32	13 32	14 32		15 32	16 32	17 45	19 46	21 57
2¼	Gwersyllt	d	06 35	07 34	08 36	09 36	10 36	11 36	12 36	13 36	14 36		15 36	16 36	17 49	19 50	22 01
4	Cefn-y-Bedd	d	06 40	07 39	08 41	09 41	10 41	11 41	12 41	13 41	14 41		15 41	16 41	17 54	19 55	22 06
4¾	Caergwrle	d	06 42	07 41	08 43	09 43	10 43	11 43	12 43	13 43	14 43		15 43	16 43	17 56	19 57	22 08
5¼	Hope (Flintshire)	d	06 44	07 43	08 45	09 45	10 45	11 45	12 45	13 45	14 45		15 45	16 45	17 58	19 59	22 10
7¼	Penyffordd	d	06 48	07 47	08 49	09 49	10 49	11 49	12 49	13 49	14 49		15 49	16 49	18 02	20 03	22 14
8½	Buckley	d	06 51	07 50	08 52	09 52	10 52	11 52	12 52	13 52	14 52		15 52	16 52	18 05	20 06	22 17
10½	Hawarden	d	06 55	07 54	08 56	09 56	10 56	11 56	12 56	13 56	14 56		15 56	16 56	18 09	20 10	22 21
12¾	Shotton High Level	d	06 59	07 59	09 00	10 00	11 00	12 00	13 00	14 00	15 00		16 00	17 00	18 13	20 14	22 25
13¼	Hawarden Bridge	d	07x01	08x01										17x02			
18¾	Neston	d	07 10	08 10	09 10	10 10	11 10	12 10	13 10	14 10	15 10		16 10	17 11	18 23	20 24	22 35
21¼	Heswall	d	07 15	08 15	09 15	10 15	11 15	12 15	13 15	14 15	15 15		16 15	17 16	18 28	20 29	22 40
25½	Upton	d	07 21	08 21	09 21	10 21	11 21	12 21	13 21	14 21	15 21		16 21	17 22	18 34	20 35	22 46
27½	**Bidston**	a	07 30	08 30	09 31	10 30	11 30	12 30	13 30	14 30	15 30		16 30	17 31	18 45	20 44	22 55

Saturdays

14 December to 17 May

		AW	AW	AW	AW	AW	AW	AW	AW	AW		AW	AW	AW	AW	AW
Wrexham Central	d		07 28	08 30	09 30	10 30	11 30	12 30	13 30	14 30		15 30	16 30	17 43	19 44	21 55
Wrexham General	a		07 30	08 32	09 32	10 32	11 32	12 32	13 32	14 32		15 32	16 32	17 45	19 46	21 57
	d	06 31	07 30	08 32	09 32	10 32	11 32	12 32	13 32	14 32		15 32	16 32	17 45	19 46	21 57
Gwersyllt	d	06 35	07 34	08 36	09 36	10 36	11 36	12 36	13 36	14 36		15 36	16 36	17 49	19 50	22 01
Cefn-y-Bedd	d	06 40	07 39	08 41	09 41	10 41	11 41	12 41	13 41	14 41		15 41	16 41	17 54	19 55	22 06
Caergwrle	d	06 42	07 41	08 43	09 43	10 43	11 43	12 43	13 43	14 43		15 43	16 43	17 56	19 57	22 08
Hope (Flintshire)	d	06 44	07 43	08 45	09 45	10 45	11 45	12 45	13 45	14 45		15 45	16 45	17 58	19 59	22 10
Penyffordd	d	06 48	07 47	08 49	09 49	10 49	11 49	12 49	13 49	14 49		15 49	16 49	18 02	20 03	22 14
Buckley	d	06 51	07 50	08 52	09 52	10 52	11 52	12 52	13 52	14 52		15 52	16 52	18 05	20 06	22 17
Hawarden	d	06 55	07 54	08 56	09 56	10 56	11 56	12 56	13 56	14 56		15 56	16 56	18 09	20 10	22 21
Shotton High Level	d	06 59	07 59	09 00	10 00	11 00	12 00	13 00	14 00	15 00		16 00	17 00	18 13	20 14	22 25
Hawarden Bridge	d	07x01	08x01										17x02			
Neston	d	07 10	08 10	09 10	10 10	11 10	12 10	13 10	14 10	15 10		16 10	17 11	18 23	20 24	22 35
Heswall	d	07 15	08 15	09 15	10 15	11 15	12 15	13 15	14 15	15 15		16 15	17 16	18 28	20 29	22 40
Upton	d	07 21	08 21	09 21	10 21	11 21	12 21	13 21	14 21	15 21		16 21	17 22	18 34	20 35	22 46
Bidston	a	07 30	08 30	09 31	10 30	11 30	12 30	13 30	14 30	15 30		16 30	17 31	18 45	20 44	22 55

Sundays

8 December to 11 May

		AW	AW	AW	AW	AW	AW
Wrexham Central	d		11 11	13 41	16 11	18 41	21 10
Wrexham General	a		11 13	13 43	16 13	18 43	21 12
	d	08 44	11 14	13 44	16 14	18 44	21 13
Gwersyllt	d	08 48	11 18	13 48	16 18	18 48	21 17
Cefn-y-Bedd	d	08 53	11 23	13 53	16 23	18 53	21 22
Caergwrle	d	08 55	11 25	13 55	16 25	18 55	21 24
Hope (Flintshire)	d	08 57	11 27	13 57	16 27	18 57	21 26
Penyffordd	d	09 01	11 31	14 01	16 31	19 01	21 30
Buckley	d	09 04	11 34	14 04	16 34	19 04	21 33
Hawarden	d	09 08	11 38	14 08	16 38	19 08	21 37
Shotton High Level	d	09 12	11 42	14 12	16 42	19 12	21 41
Hawarden Bridge	d	09x14	11x44	14x14	16x44	19x14	21x43
Neston	d	09 23	11 53	14 23	16 53	19 23	21 52
Heswall	d	09 28	11 58	14 28	16 58	19 28	21 57
Upton	d	09 34	12 04	14 34	17 04	19 34	22 03
Bidston	a	09 42	12 12	14 42	17 13	19 43	22 12

For connections to Liverpool Lime Street please see Table 106

Table 101R

Bidston - Wrexham

Mondays to Fridays

9 December to 16 May

Network Diagram - see first Page of Table 101

Miles			AW BHX	AW	AW BHX		AW	AW BHX	AW	AW BHX	AW	AW BHX	AW	AW BHX	AW		AW BHX	AW	AW
0	**Bidston**	d		07 31	08 31		09 32	10 32	11 32	12 32	13 32	14 32	15 32	16 35	17 45		18 46	20 56	22 56
2	Upton	d		07 32	08 32		09 33	10 33	11 33	12 33	13 33	14 33	15 33	16 36	17 46		18 47	20 57	22 57
6¼	Heswall	d		07 39	08 39		09 40	10 40	11 40	12 40	13 40	14 40	15 40	16 43	17 53		18 54	21 04	23 04
8¾	Neston	d		07 44	08 44		09 45	10 45	11 45	12 45	13 45	14 45	15 45	16 48	17 58		18 59	21 09	23 09
14¼	Hawarden Bridge	d		07x53	08x53									16x57	18x07				
14¾	Shotton High Level	d		07 55	08 55		09 55	10 55	11 55	12 55	13 55	14 55	15 55	16 59	18 09		19 09	21 19	23 20
17½	Hawarden	d		08 00	09 00		10 00	11 00	12 00	13 00	14 00	15 00	16 00	17 04	18 14		19 14	21 24	23 25
19	Buckley	d		08 05	09 05		10 05	11 05	12 05	13 05	14 05	15 05	16 05	17 09	18 19		19 19	21 29	23 30
20¼	Penyffordd	d		08 08	09 08		10 08	11 08	12 08	13 08	14 08	15 08	16 08	17 12	18 22		19 22	21 32	23 33
22¼	Hope (Flintshire)	d		08 12	09 12		10 12	11 12	12 12	13 12	14 12	15 12	16 12	17 16	18 26		19 26	21 36	23 37
22¾	Caergwrle	d		08 14	09 14		10 14	11 14	12 14	13 14	14 14	15 14	16 14	17 18	18 28		19 28	21 38	23 39
23½	Cefn-y-Bedd	d		08 16	09 16		10 16	11 16	12 16	13 16	14 16	15 16	16 16	17 20	18 30		19 30	21 40	23 41
25¼	Gwersyllt	d		08 20	09 20		10 20	11 20	12 20	13 20	14 20	15 20	16 20	17 24	18 34		19 34	21 44	23 47
27	**Wrexham General**	a		08 27	09 27		10 27	11 27	12 27	13 27	14 27	15 27	16 27	17 31	18 41		19 41	21 51	23 54
—		d	07 10	08 27	09 27		10 27	11 27	12 27	13 27	14 27	15 27	16 27	17 31	18 41		19 41	21 51	
27½	**Wrexham Central**	a	07 13	08 32	09 32		10 32	11 32	12 32	13 32	14 32	15 32	16 32	17 36	18 46		19 46	21 56	

Saturdays

14 December to 17 May

		AW	AW	AW	AW	AW	AW	AW	AW	AW		AW	AW	AW	AW	AW	AW
Bidston	d		07 31	08 31	09 32	10 32	11 32	12 32	13 32	14 32		15 32	16 35	17 45	18 46	20 56	22 56
Upton	d		07 32	08 32	09 33	10 33	11 33	12 33	13 33	14 33		15 33	16 36	17 46	18 47	20 57	22 57
Heswall	d		07 39	08 39	09 40	10 40	11 40	12 40	13 40	14 40		15 40	16 43	17 53	18 54	21 04	23 04
Neston	d		07 44	08 44	09 45	10 45	11 45	12 45	13 45	14 45		15 45	16 48	17 58	18 59	21 09	23 09
Hawarden Bridge	d		07x53	08x53									16x57	18x07			
Shotton High Level	d		07 55	08 55	09 55	10 55	11 55	12 55	13 55	14 55		15 55	16 59	18 09	19 09	21 19	23 20
Hawarden	d		08 00	09 00	10 00	11 00	12 00	13 00	14 00	15 00		16 00	17 04	18 14	19 14	21 24	23 25
Buckley	d		08 05	09 05	10 05	11 05	12 05	13 05	14 05	15 05		16 05	17 09	18 19	19 19	21 29	23 30
Penyffordd	d		08 08	09 08	10 08	11 08	12 08	13 08	14 08	15 08		16 08	17 12	18 22	19 22	21 32	23 33
Hope (Flintshire)	d		08 12	09 12	10 12	11 12	12 12	13 12	14 12	15 12		16 12	17 16	18 26	19 26	21 36	23 37
Caergwrle	d		08 14	09 14	10 14	11 14	12 14	13 14	14 14	15 14		16 14	17 18	18 28	19 28	21 38	23 39
Cefn-y-Bedd	d		08 16	09 16	10 16	11 16	12 16	13 16	14 16	15 16		16 16	17 20	18 30	19 30	21 40	23 41
Gwersyllt	d		08 20	09 20	10 20	11 20	12 20	13 20	14 20	15 20		16 20	17 24	18 34	19 34	21 44	23 47
Wrexham General	a		08 27	09 27	10 27	11 27	12 27	13 27	14 27	15 27		16 27	17 31	18 41	19 41	21 51	23 54
	d	07 10	08 27	09 27	10 27	11 27	12 27	13 27	14 27	15 27		16 27	17 31	18 41	19 41	21 51	
Wrexham Central	a	07 13	08 32	09 32	10 32	11 32	12 32	13 32	14 32	15 32		16 32	17 36	18 46	19 46	21 56	

Sundays

8 December to 11 May

		AW	AW	AW	AW	AW	AW
Bidston	d	09 57	12 27	14 57	17 27	19 57	22 27
Upton	d	09 58	12 28	14 58	17 28	19 58	22 28
Heswall	d	10 05	12 35	15 05	17 35	20 05	22 35
Neston	d	10 10	12 40	15 10	17 40	20 10	22 40
Hawarden Bridge	d	10x19	12x49	15x19	17x49	20x19	22x49
Shotton High Level	d	10 21	12 51	15 21	17 51	20 21	22 51
Hawarden	d	10 26	12 56	15 26	17 56	20 26	22 56
Buckley	d	10 31	13 01	15 31	18 01	20 31	23 01
Penyffordd	d	10 34	13 04	15 34	18 04	20 34	23 04
Hope (Flintshire)	d	10 38	13 08	15 38	18 08	20 38	23 08
Caergwrle	d	10 40	13 10	15 40	18 10	20 40	23 10
Cefn-y-Bedd	d	10 42	13 12	15 42	18 12	20 42	23 12
Gwersyllt	d	10 46	13 16	15 46	18 16	20 46	23 16
Wrexham General	a	10 51	13 23	15 53	18 23	20 53	23 26
	d	10 52	13 24	15 54	18 24	20 54	
Wrexham Central	a	10 59	13 29	15 59	18 29	20 59	

For connections from Liverpool Lime Street please see Table 106

Table 102

Mondays to Fridays

9 December to 16 May

Llandudno - Blaenau Ffestiniog

Network Diagram - see first Page of Table 81

Miles				AW ◇	AW ◇	AW ◇	AW ◇	AW ◇	AW ◇
0	**Llandudno**	81	d			10 08	13 08	16 20	19 03
1¾	Deganwy	81	d			10x12	13x12	16x24	19x07
3	**Llandudno Junction**	81	d	05 35	07 39	10 28	13 30	16 33	19 20
5	Glan Conwy		d		07x42	10x31	13x33	16x36	19x23
8½	Tal-y-Cafn		d		07 48	10 37	13 39	16 42	19 29
11½	Dolgarrog		d		07x53	10x42	13x44	16x47	19x34
14½	North Llanrwst		d		08x00	10x48	13x50	16x53	19x40
15	Llanrwst		d	05 53	08 02	10 50	13 52	16 55	19 42
18½	Betws-y-Coed		d	05 59	08 08	10 56	13 58	17 01	19 48
22¾	Pont-y-Pant		d		08x16	11x04	14x06	17x09	19x56
24¼	Dolwyddelan		d		08x19	11x07	14x09	17x12	19x59
26	Roman Bridge		d		08x23	11x11	14x13	17x16	20x03
31	**Blaenau Ffestiniog**		a	06 29	08 42	11 30	14 32	17 35	20 20

Saturdays

14 December to 17 May

			AW ◇	AW ◇	AW ◇	AW ◇	AW ◇	AW ◇
Llandudno	81	d			10 22	13 08	16 20	19 03
Deganwy	81	d			10x26	13x12	16x24	19x07
Llandudno Junction	81	d	05 35	07 39	10 34	13 30	16 33	19 18
Glan Conwy		d		07x42	10x37	13x33	16x36	19x23
Tal-y-Cafn		d		07 48	10 43	13 39	16 42	19 29
Dolgarrog		d		07x53	10x48	13x44	16x47	19x34
North Llanrwst		d		08x00	10x54	13x50	16x53	19x40
Llanrwst		d	05 53	08 02	10 56	13 52	16 55	19 42
Betws-y-Coed		d	05 59	08 08	11 02	13 58	17 01	19 48
Pont-y-Pant		d		08x16	11x10	14x06	17x09	19x56
Dolwyddelan		d		08x19	11x13	14x09	17x12	19x59
Roman Bridge		d		08x23	11x17	14x13	17x16	20x03
Blaenau Ffestiniog		a	06 29	08 42	11 36	14 32	17 35	20 20

For connections from Crewe, Chester, Rhyl and Bangor (Gwynedd) please see Table 81

On Sundays a bus service is available at Llandudno Junction

Table 102R

Mondays to Fridays

9 December to 16 May

Blaenau Ffestiniog - Llandudno

Network Diagram - see first Page of Table 81

Miles				AW ◇	AW ◇	AW ◇	AW ◇	AW ◇	AW ◇
—	**Blaenau Ffestiniog**		d	06 30	08 46	11 46	14 57	17 37	20 23
—	Roman Bridge		d	06x40	08x56	11x56	15x07	17x47	20x33
6¾	Dolwyddelan		d	06x43	09x00	12x00	15x11	17x51	20x37
8¼	Pont-y-Pant		d	06x46	09x03	12x03	15x14	17x54	20x40
12½	Betws-y-Coed		d	06 56	09 13	12 13	15 24	18 04	20 50
16	Llanrwst		d	07 02	09 19	12 19	15 30	18 10	20 56
16½	North Llanrwst		d	07x03	09x20	12x20	15x31	18x11	20x57
19½	Dolgarrog		d	07x09	09x27	12x27	15x38	18x18	21x04
22½	Tal-y-Cafn		d	07x15	09x33	12x33	15x44	18x24	21x10
26	Glan Conwy		d	07x21	09x39	12x39	15x50	18x30	21x16
28	**Llandudno Junction**	81	a	07 26	09 48	12 44	15 57	18 35	21 21
29¼	Deganwy	81	a		09x56	12x56	16x08	18x44	21x35
31	**Llandudno**	81	a		10 01	13 03	16 17	18 54	21 46

Saturdays

14 December to 17 May

			AW ◇	AW ◇	AW ◇	AW ◇	AW ◇	AW ◇
Blaenau Ffestiniog		d	06 30	08 46	11 46	14 57	17 37	20 23
Roman Bridge		d	06x40	08x56	11x56	15x07	17x47	20x33
Dolwyddelan		d	06x43	09x00	12x00	15x11	17x51	20x37
Pont-y-Pant		d	06x46	09x03	12x03	15x14	17x54	20x40
Betws-y-Coed		d	06 56	09 13	12 13	15 24	18 04	20 50
Llanrwst		d	07 02	09 19	12 19	15 30	18 10	20 56
North Llanrwst		d	07x03	09x20	12x20	15x31	18x11	20x57
Dolgarrog		d	07x09	09x27	12x27	15x38	18x18	21x04
Tal-y-Cafn		d	07x15	09x33	12x33	15x44	18x24	21x10
Glan Conwy		d	07x21	09x39	12x39	15x50	18x30	21x16
Llandudno Junction	81	a	07 31	09 44	12 44	15 59	18 35	21 21
Deganwy	81	a		10x06	12x56	16x06	18x44	21x35
Llandudno	81	a		10 13	13 03	16 13	18 54	21 46

For connections to Bangor (Gwynedd), Rhyl, Chester and Crewe please see Table 81

On Sundays a bus service is available at Llandudno Junction

Table 103

Hunts Cross - Southport

Mondays to Saturdays

9 December to 17 May

Network Diagram - see first Page of Table 101

Miles			ME	ME	ME SX	ME SO	ME SX	ME SO	ME SX	ME SO	ME SX		ME SO	ME	ME SX	ME SO	ME SX	ME SO	ME SX	ME SO	ME SX		ME SO	ME SX	ME SO
0	**Hunts Cross**	89 d							06 06	06 06	06 21		06 21	06 36	06 51	06 51	07 06	07 06	07 21	07 21	07 36		07 36	07 51	07 51
1½	**Liverpool Sth Parkway 7**	89 ✈ d							06 09	06 09	06 24		06 24	06 39	06 54	06 54	07 09	07 09	07 24	07 24	07 39		07 39	07 54	07 54
2½	Cressington	d							06 12	06 12	06 27		06 27	06 42	06 57	06 57	07 12	07 12	07 27	07 27	07 42		07 42	07 57	07 57
3¼	Aigburth	d							06 14	06 14	06 29		06 29	06 44	06 59	06 59	07 14	07 14	07 29	07 29	07 44		07 44	07 59	07 59
4½	St Michaels	d							06 16	06 16	06 31		06 31	06 46	07 01	07 01	07 16	07 16	07 31	07 31	07 46		07 46	08 01	08 01
5¾	Brunswick	d							06 19	06 19	06 34		06 34	06 49	07 04	07 04	07 19	07 19	07 34	07 34	07 49		07 49	08 04	08 04
7¼	**Liverpool Central 10**	a							06 23	06 23	06 38		06 38	06 53	07 08	07 08	07 23	07 23	07 38	07 38	07 53		07 53	08 08	08 08
—		d					06 08	06 08	06 23	06 23	06 38		06 38	06 53	07 08	07 08	07 23	07 23	07 38	07 38	07 53		07 53	08 08	08 08
7¾	**Moorfields 10**	d					06 11	06 11	06 26	06 26	06 41		06 41	06 56	07 11	07 11	07 26	07 26	07 41	07 41	07 56		07 56	08 11	08 11
9¼	Sandhills	d			05 59	05 59	06 15	06 15	06 30	06 30	06 45		06 45	07 00	07 15	07 15	07 30	07 30	07 45	07 45	08 00		08 00	08 15	08 15
10	Bank Hall	d			06 01	06 01	06 17	06 17	06 32	06 32	06 47		06 47	07 02	07 17	07 17	07 32	07 32	07 47	07 47	08 02		08 02	08 17	08 17
10¾	Bootle Oriel Road	d			06 03	06 03	06 19	06 19	06 34	06 34	06 49		06 49	07 04	07 19	07 19	07 34	07 34	07 49	07 49	08 04		08 04	08 19	08 19
11	Bootle New Strand	d			06 05	06 05	06 21	06 21	06 36	06 36	06 51		06 51	07 06	07 21	07 21	07 36	07 36	07 51	07 51	08 06		08 06	08 21	08 21
12	Seaforth & Litherland	d			06 07	06 07	06 23	06 23	06 38	06 38	06 53		06 53	07 08	07 23	07 23	07 38	07 38	07 53	07 53	08 08		08 08	08 23	08 23
13¼	Waterloo (Merseyside)	d			06 09	06 09	06 25	06 25	06 40	06 40	06 55		06 55	07 10	07 25	07 25	07 40	07 40	07 55	07 55	08 10		08 10	08 25	08 25
14¼	Blundellsands & Crosby	d			06 12	06 12	06 28	06 28	06 43	06 43	06 58		06 58	07 13	07 28	07 28	07 43	07 43	07 58	07 58	08 13		08 13	08 28	08 28
15	Hall Road	d			06 14	06 14	06 30	06 30	06 45	06 45	07 00		07 00	07 15	07 30	07 30	07 45	07 45	08 00	08 00	08 15		08 15	08 30	08 30
17	Hightown	d		00 02	06 17	06 17	06 33	06 33	06 48	06 48	07 03		07 03	07 18	07 33	07 33	07 48	07 48	08 03	08 03	08 18		08 18	08 33	08 33
19	Formby	d		00 06	06 21	06 21	06 37	06 37	06 52	06 52	07 07		07 07	07 22	07 37	07 37	07 52	07 52	08 07	08 07	08 22		08 22	08 37	08 37
20	Freshfield	d		00 08	06 23	06 23	06 39	06 39	06 54	06 54	07 09		07 09	07 24	07 39	07 39	07 54	07 54	08 09	08 09	08 24		08 24	08 39	08 39
22¾	Ainsdale	d		00 12	06 27	06 27	06 43	06 43	06 58	06 58	07 13		07 13	07 28	07 43	07 43	07 58	07 58	08 13	08 13	08 28		08 28	08 43	08 43
24½	Hillside	d		00 15	06 30	06 30	06 46	06 46	07 01	07 01	07 16		07 16	07 31	07 46	07 46	08 01	08 01	08 16	08 16	08 31		08 31	08 46	08 46
25¼	Birkdale	d	00 02	00 17	06 32	06 32	06 48	06 48	07 03	07 03	07 18		07 18	07 33	07 48	07 48	08 03	08 03	08 18	08 18	08 33		08 33	08 48	08 48
26¼	**Southport**	a	00 09	00 24	06 37	06 39	06 53	06 55	07 08	07 10	07 23		07 25	07 40	07 53	07 55	08 08	08 10	08 23	08 25	08 38		08 40	08 53	08 55

		ME SX	ME SO	ME SX	ME SO	ME SX	ME SO		ME	ME	ME SX	ME SO	ME		ME	ME SX	ME SO		ME SX	ME SO	ME	ME	ME SX	ME SO
Hunts Cross	89 d	08 06	08 06	08 21	08 21	08 36	08 36		08 51	09 06	09 21	09 21	09 36		13 51	14 06	14 06		14 21	14 21	14 36	14 51	15 06	15 06
Liverpool Sth Parkway 7	89 ✈ d	08 09	08 09	08 24	08 24	08 39	08 39		08 54	09 09	09 24	09 24	09 39		13 54	14 09	14 09		14 24	14 24	14 39	14 54	15 09	15 09
Cressington	d	08 12	08 12	08 27	08 27	08 42	08 42		08 57	09 12	09 27	09 27	09 42		13 57	14 12	14 12		14 27	14 27	14 42	14 57	15 12	15 12
Aigburth	d	08 14	08 14	08 29	08 29	08 44	08 44		08 59	09 14	09 29	09 29	09 44		13 59	14 14	14 14		14 29	14 29	14 44	14 59	15 14	15 14
St Michaels	d	08 16	08 16	08 31	08 31	08 46	08 46		09 01	09 16	09 31	09 31	09 46		14 01	14 16	14 16		14 31	14 31	14 46	15 01	15 16	15 16
Brunswick	d	08 19	08 19	08 34	08 34	08 49	08 49		09 04	09 19	09 34	09 34	09 49		14 04	14 19	14 19		14 34	14 34	14 49	15 04	15 19	15 19
Liverpool Central 10	a	08 23	08 23	08 38	08 38	08 53	08 53		09 08	09 23	09 38	09 38	09 53		14 08	14 23	14 23		14 38	14 38	14 53	15 08	15 23	15 23
	d	08 23	08 23	08 38	08 38	08 53	08 53		09 08	09 23	09 38	09 38	09 53		14 08	14 23	14 23		14 38	14 38	14 53	15 08	15 23	15 23
Moorfields 10	d	08 26	08 26	08 40	08 41	08 55	08 56		09 11	09 26	09 40	09 41	09 56	and every 15 minutes until	14 11	14 26	14 26		14 41	14 41	14 56	15 11	15 26	15 26
Sandhills	d	08 30	08 30	08 44	08 45	08 59	09 00		09 15	09 30	09 44	09 45	10 00		14 15	14 30	14 30		14 45	14 45	15 00	15 15	15 30	15 30
Bank Hall	d	08 32	08 32	08 46	08 47	09 01	09 02		09 17	09 32	09 46	09 47	10 02		14 17	14 32	14 32		14 47	14 47	15 02	15 17	15 32	15 32
Bootle Oriel Road	d	08 34	08 34	08 48	08 49	09 03	09 04		09 19	09 34	09 48	09 49	10 04		14 19	14 34	14 34		14 49	14 49	15 04	15 19	15 34	15 34
Bootle New Strand	d	08 36	08 36	08 50	08 51	09 05	09 06		09 21	09 36	09 50	09 51	10 06		14 21	14 36	14 36		14 51	14 51	15 06	15 21	15 36	15 36
Seaforth & Litherland	d	08 38	08 38	08 52	08 53	09 07	09 08		09 23	09 38	09 52	09 53	10 08		14 23	14 38	14 38		14 53	14 53	15 08	15 23	15 38	15 38
Waterloo (Merseyside)	d	08 40	08 40	08 54	08 55	09 09	09 10		09 25	09 40	09 54	09 55	10 10		14 25	14 40	14 40		14 55	14 55	15 10	15 25	15 40	15 40
Blundellsands & Crosby	d	08 43	08 43	08 57	08 58	09 12	09 13		09 28	09 43	09 57	09 58	10 13		14 28	14 43	14 43		14 58	14 58	15 13	15 28	15 43	15 43
Hall Road	d	08 45	08 45	08 59	09 00	09 14	09 15		09 30	09 45	09 59	10 00	10 15		14 30	14 45	14 45		15 00	15 00	15 15	15 30	15 45	15 45
Hightown	d	08 48	08 48	09 02	09 03	09 17	09 18		09 33	09 48	10 02	10 03	10 18		14 33	14 48	14 48		15 03	15 03	15 18	15 33	15 48	15 48
Formby	d	08 52	08 52	09 06	09 07	09 21	09 22		09 37	09 52	10 06	10 07	10 22		14 37	14 52	14 52		15 07	15 07	15 22	15 37	15 52	15 52
Freshfield	d	08 54	08 54	09 08	09 09	09 23	09 24		09 39	09 54	10 08	10 09	10 24		14 39	14 54	14 54		15 09	15 09	15 24	15 39	15 54	15 54
Ainsdale	d	08 58	08 58	09 12	09 13	09 27	09 28		09 43	09 58	10 12	10 13	10 28		14 43	14 58	14 58		15 13	15 13	15 28	15 43	15 58	15 58
Hillside	d	09 01	09 01	09 15	09 16	09 30	09 31		09 46	10 01	10 15	10 16	10 31		14 46	15 01	15 01		15 16	15 16	15 31	15 46	16 01	16 01
Birkdale	d	09 03	09 03	09 17	09 18	09 32	09 33		09 48	10 03	10 17	10 18	10 33		14 48	15 03	15 03		15 18	15 18	15 33	15 48	16 03	16 03
Southport	a	09 08	09 10	09 23	09 25	09 38	09 40		09 55	10 10	10 24	10 25	10 40		14 55	15 08	15 10		15 23	15 25	15 40	15 55	16 08	16 10

		ME SX	ME SO	ME SX		ME SO	ME SX	ME SO	ME SX	ME SO	ME SX	ME SO	ME SX	ME SO		ME SX	ME SO	ME SX	ME SX	ME SO	ME		ME	
Hunts Cross	89 d	15 21	15 21	15 36		15 36	15 51	15 51	16 06	16 06	16 21	16 21	16 36	16 36		16 51	16 51		17 06	17 06	17 21		18 51	
Liverpool Sth Parkway 7	89 ✈ d	15 24	15 24	15 39		15 39	15 54	15 54	16 09	16 09	16 24	16 24	16 39	16 39		16 54	16 54		17 09	17 09	17 24		18 54	
Cressington	d	15 27	15 27	15 42		15 42	15 57	15 57	16 12	16 12	16 27	16 27	16 42	16 42		16 57	16 57		17 12	17 12	17 27		18 57	
Aigburth	d	15 29	15 29	15 44		15 44	15 59	15 59	16 14	16 14	16 29	16 29	16 44	16 44		16 59	16 59		17 14	17 14	17 29		18 59	
St Michaels	d	15 31	15 31	15 46		15 46	16 01	16 01	16 16	16 16	16 31	16 31	16 46	16 46		17 01	17 01		17 16	17 16	17 31		19 01	
Brunswick	d	15 34	15 34	15 49		15 49	16 04	16 04	16 19	16 19	16 34	16 34	16 49	16 49		17 04	17 04		17 19	17 19	17 34		19 04	
Liverpool Central 10	a	15 38	15 38	15 53		15 53	16 08	16 08	16 23	16 23	16 38	16 38	16 53	16 53		17 08	17 08		17 23	17 23	17 38		19 08	
	d	15 38	15 38	15 53		15 53	16 08	16 08	16 23	16 23	16 38	16 38	16 53	16 53		17 08	17 08	17 13	17 23	17 23	17 38		19 08	
Moorfields 10	d	15 41	15 41	15 56		15 56	16 11	16 11	16 26	16 26	16 41	16 41	16 56	16 56		17 11	17 11	17 16	17 26	17 26	17 41	and every 15 minutes until	19 11	
Sandhills	d	15 45	15 45	16 00		16 00	16 15	16 15	16 30	16 30	16 45	16 45	17 00	17 00		17 15	17 15	17 20	17 30	17 30	17 45		19 15	
Bank Hall	d	15 47	15 47	16 02		16 02	16 17	16 17	16 32	16 32	16 47	16 47	17 02	17 02		17 17	17 17	17 22	17 32	17 32	17 47		19 17	
Bootle Oriel Road	d	15 49	15 49	16 04		16 04	16 19	16 19	16 34	16 34	16 49	16 49	17 04	17 04		17 19	17 19	17 24	17 34	17 34	17 49		19 19	
Bootle New Strand	d	15 51	15 51	16 06		16 06	16 21	16 21	16 36	16 36	16 51	16 51	17 06	17 06		17 21	17 21	17 26	17 36	17 36	17 51		19 21	
Seaforth & Litherland	d	15 53	15 53	16 08		16 08	16 23	16 23	16 38	16 38	16 53	16 53	17 08	17 08		17 23	17 23	17 28	17 38	17 38	17 53		19 23	
Waterloo (Merseyside)	d	15 55	15 55	16 10		16 10	16 25	16 25	16 40	16 40	16 55	16 55	17 10	17 10		17 25	17 25	17 30	17 40	17 40	17 55		19 25	
Blundellsands & Crosby	d	15 58	15 58	16 13		16 13	16 28	16 28	16 43	16 43	16 58	16 58	17 13	17 13		17 28	17 28	17 33	17 43	17 43	17 58		19 28	
Hall Road	d	16 00	16 00	16 15		16 15	16 30	16 30	16 45	16 45	17 00	17 00	17 15	17 15		17 30	17 30	17 35	17 45	17 45	18 00		19 30	
Hightown	d	16 03	16 03	16 18		16 18	16 33	16 33	16 48	16 48	17 03	17 03	17 18	17 18		17 33	17 33	17 38	17 48	17 48	18 03		19 33	
Formby	d	16 07	16 07	16 22		16 22	16 37	16 37	16 52	16 52	17 07	17 07	17 22	17 22		17 37	17 37	17 42	17 52	17 52	18 07		19 37	
Freshfield	d	16 09	16 09	16 24		16 24	16 39	16 39	16 54	16 54	17 09	17 09	17 24	17 24		17 39	17 39	17 44	17 54	17 54	18 09		19 39	
Ainsdale	d	16 13	16 13	16 28		16 28	16 43	16 43	16 58	16 58	17 13	17 13	17 28	17 28		17 43	17 43	17 48	17 58	17 58	18 13		19 43	
Hillside	d	16 16	16 16	16 31		16 31	16 46	16 46	17 01	17 01	17 16	17 16	17 31	17 31		17 46	17 46	17 51	18 01	18 01	18 16		19 46	
Birkdale	d	16 18	16 18	16 33		16 33	16 48	16 48	17 03	17 03	17 18	17 18	17 33	17 33		17 48	17 48	17 53	18 03	18 03	18 18		19 48	
Southport	a	16 23	16 25	16 38		16 40	16 53	16 55	17 08	17 10	17 23	17 25	17 38	17 40		17 53	17 55	18 00	18 09	18 10	18 25		19 55	

For alternative trains between Liverpool and Sandhills see tables 104 and 105

Table 103

Hunts Cross - Southport

Mondays to Saturdays

9 December to 17 May

Network Diagram - see first Page of Table 101

Station		ME		ME	ME	ME
Hunts Cross 89	d	19 06		22 51	23 06	23 21
Liverpool Sth Parkway 7 89 ✈	d	19 09		22 54	23 09	23 24
Cressington	d	19 12		22 57	23 12	23 27
Aigburth	d	19 14		22 59	23 14	23 29
St Michaels	d	19 16		23 01	23 16	23 31
Brunswick	d	19 19		23 04	23 19	23 34
Liverpool Central 10	a	19 23		23 08	23 23	23 38
	d	19 23		23 08	23 23	23 38
Moorfields 10	d	19 25		23 10	23 25	23 40
Sandhills	d	19 29	and	23 14	23 29	23 44
Bank Hall	d	19 31	every 15	23 16	23 31	23 46
Bootle Oriel Road	d	19 33	minutes	23 18	23 33	23 48
Bootle New Strand	d	19 35	until	23 20	23 35	23 50
Seaforth & Litherland	d	19 37		23 22	23 37	23 52
Waterloo (Merseyside)	d	19 39		23 24	23 39	23 54
Blundellsands & Crosby	d	19 42		23 27	23 42	23 57
Hall Road	d	19 44		23 29	23 44	23 59
Hightown	d	19 47		23 32	23 47	00 02
Formby	d	19 51		23 36	23 51	00 06
Freshfield	d	19 53		23 38	23 53	00 08
Ainsdale	d	19 57		23 42	23 57	00 12
Hillside	d	20 00		23 45	23 59	00 15
Birkdale	d	20 02		23 47	00 02	00 17
Southport	a	20 09		23 54	00 09	00 24

Sundays

8 December to 11 May

Station		ME	ME	ME	ME		ME	ME	ME
Hunts Cross 89	d				08 06		22 36	23 06	
Liverpool Sth Parkway 7 89 ✈	d				08 09		22 39	23 09	
Cressington	d				08 12		22 42	23 12	
Aigburth	d				08 14		22 44	23 14	
St Michaels	d				08 16		22 46	23 16	
Brunswick	d				08 19		22 49	23 19	
Liverpool Central 10	a				08 23		22 53	23 23	
	d			08 08	08 23		22 53	23 23	23 38
Moorfields 10	d			08 10	08 25	and	22 55	23 25	23 40
Sandhills	d			08 14	08 29	every 30	22 59	23 29	23 44
Bank Hall	d			08 16	08 31	minutes	23 01	23 31	23 46
Bootle Oriel Road	d			08 18	08 33	until	23 03	23 33	23 48
Bootle New Strand	d			08 20	08 35		23 05	23 35	23 50
Seaforth & Litherland	d			08 22	08 37		23 07	23 37	23 52
Waterloo (Merseyside)	d			08 24	08 39		23 09	23 39	23 54
Blundellsands & Crosby	d			08 27	08 42		23 12	23 42	23 57
Hall Road	d			08 29	08 44		23 14	23 44	23 59
Hightown	d		00 02	08 32	08 47		23 17	23 47	00 02
Formby	d		00 06	08 36	08 51		23 21	23 51	00 06
Freshfield	d		00 08	08 38	08 53		23 23	23 53	00 08
Ainsdale	d		00 12	08 42	08 57		23 27	23 57	00 12
Hillside	d		00 15	08 45	09 00		23 30	23 59	00 15
Birkdale	d	00 02	00 17	08 47	09 02		23 32	00 02	00 17
Southport	a	00 09	00 24	08 52	09 09		23 39	00 09	00 24

r

For alternative trains between Liverpool and Sandhills see tables 104 and 105

Table 103R

Southport - Hunts Cross

Mondays to Saturdays

9 December to 17 May

Network Diagram - see first Page of Table 101

Miles			ME	ME	ME	ME	ME	ME	ME SX	ME SO	ME	ME	ME SX	ME SO	ME SX	ME	ME SX	ME		ME	ME	ME
0	**Southport**	d		05 38	05 53	06 08	06 23	06 43	06 58	06 58	07 13	07 28	07 38	07 43	07 48	07 58	08 03	08 13		17 58	18 13	18 28
1	Birkdale	d		05 42	05 57	06 12	06 27	06 47	07 02	07 02	07 17	07 32	07 42	07 47	07 52	08 02	08 07	08 17		18 02	18 17	18 32
2	Hillside	d		05 44	05 59	06 14	06 29	06 49	07 04	07 04	07 19	07 34	07 44	07 49	07 54	08 04	08 09	08 19		18 04	18 19	18 34
3½	Ainsdale	d		05 47	06 02	06 17	06 32	06 52	07 07	07 07	07 22	07 37	07 47	07 52	07 57	08 07	08 12	08 22		18 07	18 22	18 37
6¼	Freshfield	d		05 51	06 06	06 21	06 36	06 56	07 11	07 11	07 26	07 41	07 51	07 56	08 01	08 11	08 16	08 26		18 11	18 26	18 41
7¼	Formby	d		05 53	06 08	06 23	06 38	06 58	07 13	07 13	07 28	07 43	07 53	07 58	08 03	08 13	08 18	08 28		18 13	18 28	18 43
9¼	Hightown	d		05 57	06 12	06 27	06 42	07 02	07 17	07 17	07 32	07 47	07 57	08 02	08 07	08 17	08 22	08 32		18 17	18 32	18 47
11¼	Hall Road	d		06 00	06 15	06 30	06 45	07 05	07 20	07 20	07 35	07 50	08 00	08 05	08 10	08 20	08 25	08 35		18 20	18 35	18 50
12	Blundellsands & Crosby	d		06 02	06 17	06 32	06 47	07 07	07 22	07 22	07 37	07 52	08 02	08 07	08 12	08 22	08 27	08 37	and every 15 minutes until	18 22	18 37	18 52
13	Waterloo (Merseyside)	d		06 05	06 20	06 35	06 50	07 10	07 25	07 25	07 40	07 55	08 05	08 10	08 15	08 25	08 30	08 40		18 25	18 40	18 55
14¼	Seaforth & Litherland	d		06 07	06 22	06 37	06 52	07 12	07 27	07 27	07 42	07 57	08 07	08 12	08 17	08 27	08 32	08 42		18 27	18 42	18 57
15¼	Bootle New Strand	d		06 10	06 25	06 40	06 55	07 15	07 30	07 30	07 45	08 00	08 10	08 15	08 20	08 30	08 35	08 45		18 30	18 45	19 00
15½	Bootle Oriel Road	d		06 11	06 26	06 41	06 56	07 16	07 31	07 31	07 46	08 01	08 11	08 16	08 21	08 31	08 36	08 46		18 31	18 46	19 01
16¼	Bank Hall	d		06 18	06 33	06 48	07 03	07 18	07 33	07 33	07 48	08 03	08 18	08 18	08 23	08 33	08 38	08 48		18 33	18 48	19 03
17	Sandhills	d	06 06	06 21	06 36	06 51	07 06	07 21	07 36	07 36	07 51	08 06	08 21	08 21	08 27	08 36	08 42	08 51		18 36	18 51	19 06
18½	**Moorfields** 10	d	06 10	06 25	06 40	06 55	07 10	07 25	07 40	07 40	07 55	08 10	08 25	08 25	08 31	08 40	08 46	08 55		18 40	18 55	19 10
19	**Liverpool Central** 10	a	06 13	06 28	06 43	06 58	07 13	07 28	07 43	07 43	07 58	08 13	08 28	08 28	08 33	08 43	08 48	08 58		18 43	18 58	19 13
—		d	06 14	06 29	06 43	06 59	07 14	07 29	07 44	07 44	07 59	08 14	08 29	08 29		08 44		08 59		18 44	18 59	19 14
20½	Brunswick	d	06 17	06 32	06 47	07 02	07 17	07 32	07 47	07 47	08 02	08 17	08 32	08 32		08 47		09 02		18 47	19 02	19 17
21¾	St Michaels	d	06 20	06 35	06 49	07 05	07 20	07 35	07 50	07 50	08 05	08 20	08 35	08 35		08 50		09 05		18 50	19 05	19 20
23	Aigburth	d	06 22	06 37	06 52	07 07	07 22	07 37	07 52	07 52	08 07	08 22	08 37	08 37		08 52		09 07		18 52	19 07	19 22
23¾	Cressington	d	06 24	06 39	06 54	07 09	07 24	07 39	07 54	07 54	08 09	08 24	08 39	08 39		08 54		09 09		18 54	19 09	19 24
24¾	**Liverpool Sth Parkway** 7 89 ✈	d	06 27	06 42	06 56	07 12	07 27	07 42	07 57	07 57	08 12	08 27	08 42	08 42		08 57		09 12		18 57	19 12	19 27
26¼	**Hunts Cross** 89	a	06 32	06 47	07 02	07 17	07 32	07 47	08 01	08 02	08 17	08 32	08 47	08 47		09 02		09 17		19 02	19 16	19 32

		ME	ME	ME	ME		ME	ME	ME		ME	ME	ME	ME	ME	ME
Southport	d	18 43	18 58	19 13	19 28		20 43	20 58	21 13		21 58	22 13	22 28	22 43	22 58	23 16
Birkdale	d	18 47	19 02	19 17	19 32		20 47	21 02	21 17		22 02	22 17	22 32	22 47	23 02	23 20
Hillside	d	18 49	19 04	19 19	19 34		20 49	21 04	21 19		22 04	22 19	22 34	22 49	23 04	23 22
Ainsdale	d	18 52	19 07	19 22	19 37		20 52	21 07	21 22		22 07	22 22	22 37	22 52	23 07	23 25
Freshfield	d	18 56	19 11	19 26	19 41		20 56	21 11	21 26		22 11	22 26	22 41	22 56	23 11	23 29
Formby	d	18 58	19 13	19 28	19 43		20 58	21 13	21 28		22 13	22 28	22 43	22 58	23 13	23 31
Hightown	d	19 02	19 17	19 32	19 47		21 02	21 17	21 32		22 17	22 32	22 47	23 02	23 17	23 35
Hall Road	d	19 05	19 20	19 35	19 50		21 05	21 20	21 35		22 20	22 35	22 50	23 05	23 20	23 38
Blundellsands & Crosby	d	19 07	19 22	19 37	19 52		21 07	21 22	21 37		22 22	22 37	22 52	23 07	23 22	23 40
Waterloo (Merseyside)	d	19 10	19 25	19 40	19 55	and every 15 minutes until	21 10	21 25	21 40	and every 15 minutes until	22 25	22 40	22 55	23 10	23 25	23 43
Seaforth & Litherland	d	19 12	19 27	19 42	19 57		21 12	21 27	21 42		22 27	22 42	22 57	23 12	23 27	23 45
Bootle New Strand	d	19 15	19 30	19 45	20 00		21 15	21 30	21 45		22 30	22 45	23 00	23 15	23 30	23 48
Bootle Oriel Road	d	19 16	19 31	19 46	20 01		21 16	21 31	21 46		22 31	22 46	23 01	23 16	23 31	23 49
Bank Hall	d	19 18	19 33	19 48	20 03		21 18	21 33	21 48		22 33	22 48	23 03	23 18	23 33	23 51
Sandhills	d	19 21	19 36	19 51	20 06		21 21	21 36	21 51		22 36	22 51	23 06	23 21	23 36	23 55
Moorfields 10	d	19 25	19 40	19 55	20 10		21 25	21 40	21 55		22 40	22 55	23 10	23 25	23 40	23 58
Liverpool Central 10	a	19 28	19 43	19 58	20 13		21 28	21 43	21 58		22 43	22 58	23 13	23 28	23 43	00 01
	d	19 29	19 44	19 59	20 14		21 29	21 44	21 59		22 44	22 59	23 14	23 29	23 44	
Brunswick	d	19 32	19 47	20 02	20 17		21 32	21 47	22 02		22 47	23 02	23 17	23 32	23 47	
St Michaels	d	19 35	19 50	20 05	20 20		21 35	21 50	22 05		22 50	23 05	23 20	23 35	23 50	
Aigburth	d	19 37	19 52	20 07	20 22		21 37	21 52	22 07		22 52	23 07	23 22	23 37	23 52	
Cressington	d	19 39	19 54	20 09	20 24		21 39	21 54	22 09		22 54	23 09	23 24	23 39	23 54	
Liverpool Sth Parkway 7 89 ✈	d	19 42	19 57	20 12	20 27		21 42	21 57	22 12		22 57	23 12	23 27	23 42	23 57	
Hunts Cross 89	a	19 47	20 02	20 16	20 32		21 47	22 01	22 17		23 02	23 18	23 32	23 47	00 02	

Sundays

8 December to 11 May

		ME	ME		ME	ME
Southport	d		07 58		22 58	23 16
Birkdale	d		08 02		23 02	23 20
Hillside	d		08 04		23 04	23 22
Ainsdale	d		08 07		23 07	23 25
Freshfield	d		08 11		23 11	23 29
Formby	d		08 13		23 13	23 31
Hightown	d		08 17		23 17	23 35
Hall Road	d		08 20		23 20	23 38
Blundellsands & Crosby	d		08 22		23 22	23 40
Waterloo (Merseyside)	d		08 25	and every 30 minutes until	23 25	23 43
Seaforth & Litherland	d		08 27		23 27	23 45
Bootle New Strand	d		08 30		23 30	23 48
Bootle Oriel Road	d		08 31		23 31	23 49
Bank Hall	d		08 33		23 33	23 51
Sandhills	d		08 36		23 36	23 55
Moorfields 10	d		08 40		23 40	23 58
Liverpool Central 10	a		08 43		23 43	00 01
	d	08 14	08 44		23 44	
Brunswick	d	08 17	08 47		23 47	
St Michaels	d	08 20	08 50		23 50	
Aigburth	d	08 22	08 52		23 52	
Cressington	d	08 24	08 54		23 54	
Liverpool Sth Parkway 7 89 ✈	d	08 27	08 57		23 57	
Hunts Cross 89	a	08 32	09 02		00 02	

For alternative trains between Liverpool and Sandhills see tables 104 and 105

Table 104

Mondays to Saturdays

9 December to 17 May

Liverpool Central - Kirkby

Network Diagram - see first Page of Table 101

Miles			ME	ME	ME	ME	ME		ME	ME	ME		ME	ME SO	ME SX	ME SO	ME SX	ME		ME
0	**Liverpool Central** 10	d		05 55	06 25	06 50	07 20	and every 15 minutes until	08 35	08 50	09 05	and every 15 minutes until	19 05	19 25	19 25	19 55	19 55	20 25	and every 30 minutes until	23 55
0½	**Moorfields** 10	d		05 57	06 27	06 52	07 22		08 37	08 52	09 07		19 07	19 27	19 27	19 57	19 57	20 27		23 57
2	Sandhills	d	00 01	06 01	06 31	06 56	07 26		08 41	08 56	09 11		19 11	19 31	19 31	20 01	20 01	20 31		00 01
3	Kirkdale	d	00 04	06 04	06 34	06 59	07 29		08 44	08 59	09 14		19 14	19 34	19 34	20 04	20 04	20 34		00 04
4¼	Rice Lane	d	00 07	06 07	06 37	07 02	07 32		08 47	09 02	09 17		19 17	19 37	19 37	20 07	20 07	20 37		00 07
5¾	Fazakerley	d	00 10	06 10	06 40	07 03	07 34		08 49	09 05	09 19		19 19	19 40	19 40	20 10	20 10	20 40		00 10
7½	**Kirkby**	a	00 13	06 13	06 43	07 08	07 38		08 53	09 08	09 23		19 23	19 43	19 45	20 13	20 15	20 43		00 13

Sundays

8 December to 11 May

		ME	ME		ME
Liverpool Central 10	d		08 25	and every 30 minutes until	23 55
Moorfields 10	d		08 27		23 57
Sandhills	d	00 01	08 31		00 01
Kirkdale	d	00 04	08 34		00 04
Rice Lane	d	00 07	08 37		00 07
Fazakerley	d	00 10	08 40		00 10
Kirkby	a	00 13	08 43		00 13

For additional trains Liverpool-Kirkdale see table 105

For additional trains Liverpool-Sandhills see tables 103 & 105

Table 104R

Mondays to Saturdays

9 December to 17 May

Kirby - Liverpool Central

Network Diagram - see first Page of Table 101

Miles			ME	ME	ME	ME		ME	ME		ME
0	**Kirkby**	d	05 48	06 18	06 48	07 13	and every 15 minutes until	19 28	19 48	and every 30 minutes until	23 18
1¾	Fazakerley	d	05 51	06 21	06 51	07 16		19 31	19 51		23 21
3¼	Rice Lane	d	05 54	06 24	06 54	07 19		19 34	19 54		23 24
4½	Kirkdale	d	05 57	06 27	06 57	07 22		19 37	19 57		23 27
5½	Sandhills	d	06 00	06 30	07 00	07 25		19 40	20 00		23 30
7	**Moorfields** 10	d	06 03	06 33	07 03	07 28		19 43	20 03		23 33
7½	**Liverpool Central** 10	a	06 06	06 36	07 06	07 31		19 46	20 06		23 36

Sundays

8 December to 11 May

		ME		ME
Kirkby	d	08 18	and every 30 minutes until	23 18
Fazakerley	d	08 21		23 21
Rice Lane	d	08 24		23 24
Kirkdale	d	08 27		23 27
Sandhills	d	08 30		23 30
Moorfields 10	d	08 33		23 33
Liverpool Central 10	a	08 36		23 36

For additional trains Liverpool-Kirkdale see table 105

For additional trains Liverpool-Sandhills see tables 103 & 105

Table 105

Liverpool Central - Ormskirk

Mondays to Saturdays

9 December to 17 May

Network Diagram - see first Page of Table 101

Miles			ME	ME	ME		ME	ME	ME		ME	ME	ME
0	**Liverpool Central** 10	d		06 10	06 40	and every 15 minutes until	19 10	19 40	20 10	and every 30 minutes until	22 40	23 10	23 40
0½	**Moorfields** 10	d		06 14	06 44		19 14	19 44	20 12		22 42	23 12	23 42
2	Sandhills	d		06 18	06 48		19 18	19 48	20 16		22 46	23 16	23 46
3	Kirkdale	d		06 21	06 51		19 21	19 51	20 19		22 49	23 19	23 49
4¼	Walton (Merseyside)	d		06 23	06 53		19 23	19 53	20 22		22 52	23 22	23 52
4½	Orrell Park	d		06 25	06 55		19 25	19 55	20 23		22 53	23 23	23 53
5½	Aintree	d		06 27	06 57		19 27	19 57	20 26		22 56	23 26	23 56
6¼	Old Roan	d		06 29	06 59		19 29	19 59	20 28		22 58	23 28	23 58
8	Maghull	d	00 01	06 32	07 02		19 32	20 02	20 31		23 01	23 31	00 01
10½	Town Green	d	00 05	06 36	07 06		19 36	20 06	20 35		23 05	23 35	00 05
11½	Aughton Park	d	00 07	06 39	07 09		19 39	20 09	20 37		23 07	23 37	00 07
12¾	**Ormskirk**	a	00 12	06 44	07 14		19 44	20 13	20 43		23 13	23 42	00 12

Sundays

8 December to 11 May

		ME	ME		ME	ME	ME
Liverpool Central 10	d		08 10	and every 30 minutes until	22 40	23 10	23 40
Moorfields 10	d		08 12		22 42	23 12	23 42
Sandhills	d		08 16		22 46	23 16	23 46
Kirkdale	d		08 19		22 49	23 19	23 49
Walton (Merseyside)	d		08 22		22 52	23 22	23 52
Orrell Park	d		08 23		22 53	23 23	23 53
Aintree	d		08 26		22 56	23 26	23 56
Old Roan	d		08 28		22 58	23 28	23 58
Maghull	d	00 01	08 31		23 01	23 31	00 01
Town Green	d	00 05	08 35		23 05	23 35	00 05
Aughton Park	d	00 07	08 37		23 07	23 37	00 07
Ormskirk	a	00 12	08 43		23 13	23 42	00 12

For Additional trains between Liverpool and Kirkdale see table 104

For Additional trains between Liverpool and Sandhills see tables 103 & 104

Table 105R

Ormskirk - Liverpool Central

Mondays to Saturdays

9 December to 17 May

Network Diagram - see first Page of Table 101

Miles			ME	ME	ME		ME	ME		ME
0	**Ormskirk**	d	05 50	06 20	06 50	and every 15 minutes until	19 20	19 50	and every 30 minutes until	23 20
1¼	Aughton Park	d	05 53	06 23	06 53		19 23	19 53		23 23
2¼	Town Green	d	05 55	06 25	06 55		19 25	19 55		23 25
4¾	Maghull	d	06 00	06 30	07 00		19 30	20 00		23 30
6½	Old Roan	d	06 03	06 33	07 03		19 33	20 03		23 33
7¼	Aintree	d	06 05	06 35	07 05		19 35	20 05		23 35
8¼	Orrell Park	d	06 07	06 37	07 07		19 37	20 07		23 37
8½	Walton (Merseyside)	d	06 09	06 39	07 09		19 39	20 09		23 39
9¾	Kirkdale	d	06 12	06 42	07 12		19 42	20 12		23 42
10¾	Sandhills	d	06 14	06 44	07 14		19 44	20 14		23 44
12¼	**Moorfields** 10	d	06 18	06 48	07 18		19 48	20 18		23 48
12¾	**Liverpool Central** 10	a	06 20	06 50	07 20		19 50	20 20		23 50

Sundays

8 December to 11 May

		ME		ME
Ormskirk	d	08 20	and every 30 minutes until	23 20
Aughton Park	d	08 23		23 23
Town Green	d	08 25		23 25
Maghull	d	08 30		23 30
Old Roan	d	08 33		23 33
Aintree	d	08 35		23 35
Orrell Park	d	08 37		23 37
Walton (Merseyside)	d	08 39		23 39
Kirkdale	d	08 42		23 42
Sandhills	d	08 44		23 44
Moorfields 10	d	08 48		23 48
Liverpool Central 10	a	08 50		23 50

For Additional trains between Liverpool and Kirkdale see table 104

For Additional trains between Liverpool and Sandhills see tables 103 & 104

Table 106

Liverpool & Birkenhead - New Brighton & West Kirby

Mondays to Saturdays

9 December to 17 May

Network Diagram - see first Page of Table 101

Miles	Miles			ME	ME	ME	ME	ME	ME	ME	ME	ME	ME	ME	ME	ME	ME		ME	ME	ME	ME	ME	ME
0	0	Moorfields 10	d			06 16	06 21	06 46	06 51	07 16	07 21	07 31	07 36	07 46	07 51	08 01	08 06		18 16	18 21	18 31	18 36	18 46	18 51
0½	0½	Liverpool Lime Street 10	d			06 18	06 23	06 48	06 53	07 18	07 23	07 33	07 38	07 48	07 53	08 03	08 08		18 18	18 23	18 33	18 38	18 48	18 53
1	1	Liverpool Central 10	d			06 20	06 25	06 50	06 55	07 20	07 25	07 35	07 40	07 50	07 55	08 05	08 10		18 20	18 25	18 35	18 40	18 50	18 55
1½	1½	James Street	d			06 22	06 27	06 52	06 57	07 22	07 27	07 37	07 42	07 52	07 57	08 07	08 12		18 22	18 27	18 37	18 42	18 52	18 57
2¾	2¾	Hamilton Square	d			06 25	06 30	06 55	07 00	07 25	07 30	07 40	07 45	07 55	08 00	08 10	08 15		18 25	18 30	18 40	18 45	18 55	19 00
3¼	3¼	Conway Park	d			06 27	06 32	06 57	07 02	07 27	07 32	07 42	07 47	07 57	08 02	08 12	08 17	and at	18 27	18 32	18 42	18 47	18 57	19 02
4	4	Birkenhead Park	d			06 29	06 34	06 59	07 04	07 29	07 34	07 44	07 49	07 59	08 04	08 14	08 19	the same	18 29	18 34	18 44	18 49	18 59	19 04
4¾	4¾	Birkenhead North	d		00 02	06 32	06 37	07 02	07 07	07 32	07 37	07 47	07 52	08 02	08 07	08 17	08 22	minutes	18 32	18 37	18 47	18 52	19 02	19 07
—	6¼	Wallasey Village	d		00 07	06 37		07 07		07 37		07 52		08 07		08 22		past	18 37		18 52		19 07	
—	6½	Wallasey Grove Road	d		00 08	06 38		07 08		07 38		07 53		08 08		08 23		each	18 38		18 53		19 08	
—	7¾	**New Brighton**	a		00 13	06 43		07 13		07 43		07 58		08 13		08 28		hour until	18 43		18 58		19 13	
5¼	—	Bidston	d				06 40		07 10		07 40		07 55		08 10		08 25			18 40		18 55		19 10
6½	—	Leasowe	d				06 42		07 12		07 42		07 57		08 12		08 27			18 42		18 57		19 12
7	—	Moreton (Merseyside)	d				06 44		07 14		07 44		07 59		08 14		08 29			18 44		18 59		19 14
8¼	—	Meols	d				06 48		07 18		07 48		08 03		08 18		08 33			18 48		19 03		19 18
9½	—	Manor Road	d				06 50		07 20		07 50		08 05		08 20		08 35			18 50		19 05		19 20
10	—	Hoylake	d	00 02			06 52		07 22		07 52		08 07		08 22		08 37			18 52		19 07		19 22
11¼	—	**West Kirby**	a	00 07			06 57		07 27		07 57		08 12		08 27		08 42			18 57		19 12		19 27

		ME	ME			ME	ME	ME	ME		ME	ME	ME	ME		ME	ME	ME
Moorfields 10	d	19 01	19 06			19 16	19 31	19 46	20 01		22 16	22 31	22 46	23 01		23 16	23 31	23 46
Liverpool Lime Street 10	d	19 03	19 08			19 18	19 33	19 48	20 03		22 18	22 33	22 48	23 03		23 18	23 33	23 48
Liverpool Central 10	d	19 05	19 10			19 20	19 35	19 50	20 05		22 20	22 35	22 50	23 05		23 20	23 35	23 50
James Street	d	19 07	19 12			19 22	19 37	19 52	20 07		22 22	22 37	22 52	23 07		23 22	23 37	23 52
Hamilton Square	d	19 10	19 15			19 25	19 40	19 55	20 10		22 25	22 40	22 55	23 10		23 25	23 40	23 55
Conway Park	d	19 12	19 17			19 27	19 42	19 57	20 12	and at	22 27	22 42	22 57	23 12		23 27	23 42	23 57
Birkenhead Park	d	19 14	19 19			19 29	19 44	19 59	20 14	the same	22 29	22 44	22 59	23 14		23 29	23 44	23 59
Birkenhead North	d	19 17	19 22			19 32	19 47	20 02	20 17	minutes	22 32	22 47	23 02	23 17		23 32	23 47	00 02
Wallasey Village	d	19 22				19 37		20 07		past	22 37		23 07			23 37		00 07
Wallasey Grove Road	d	19 23				19 38		20 08		each	22 38		23 08			23 38		00 08
New Brighton	a	19 28				19 43		20 13		hour until	22 43		23 13			23 43		00 13
Bidston	d		19 25				19 50		20 20			22 50		23 20			23 50	
Leasowe	d		19 27				19 52		20 22			22 52		23 22			23 52	
Moreton (Merseyside)	d		19 29				19 54		20 24			22 54		23 24			23 54	
Meols	d		19 33				19 58		20 28			22 58		23 28			23 58	
Manor Road	d		19 35				20 00		20 30			23 00		23 30			23 59	
Hoylake	d		19 37				20 02		20 32			23 02		23 32			00 02	
West Kirby	a		19 42				20 07		20 37			23 07		23 37			00 07	

Sundays

8 December to 11 May

		ME	ME	ME	ME	ME	ME		ME	ME	ME	ME		ME	ME	ME	ME
Moorfields 10	d			08 01	08 16	08 31	08 46		22 01	22 16	22 31	22 46		23 01	23 16	23 31	23 46
Liverpool Lime Street 10	d			08 03	08 18	08 33	08 48		22 03	22 18	22 33	22 48		23 03	23 18	23 33	23 48
Liverpool Central 10	d			08 05	08 20	08 35	08 50		22 05	22 20	22 35	22 50		23 05	23 20	23 35	23 50
James Street	d			08 07	08 22	08 37	08 52		22 07	22 22	22 37	22 52		23 07	23 22	23 37	23 52
Hamilton Square	d			08 10	08 25	08 40	08 55		22 10	22 25	22 40	22 55		23 10	23 25	23 40	23 55
Conway Park	d			08 12	08 27	08 42	08 57	and at	22 12	22 27	22 42	22 57		23 12	23 27	23 42	23 57
Birkenhead Park	d			08 14	08 29	08 44	08 59	the same	22 14	22 29	22 44	22 59		23 14	23 29	23 44	23 59
Birkenhead North	d		00 02	08 17	08 32	08 47	09 02	minutes	22 17	22 32	22 47	23 02		23 17	23 32	23 47	00 02
Wallasey Village	d		00 07		08 37		09 07	past		22 37		23 07			23 37		00 07
Wallasey Grove Road	d		00 08		08 38		09 08	each		22 38		23 08			23 38		00 08
New Brighton	a		00 13		08 43		09 13	hour until		22 43		23 13			23 43		00 13
Bidston	d			08 20		08 50			22 20		22 50			23 20		23 50	
Leasowe	d			08 22		08 52			22 22		22 52			23 22		23 52	
Moreton (Merseyside)	d			08 24		08 54			22 24		22 54			23 24		23 54	
Meols	d			08 28		08 58			22 28		22 58			23 28		23 58	
Manor Road	d			08 30		09 00			22 30		23 00			23 30		23 59	
Hoylake	d	00 02		08 32		09 02			22 32		23 02			23 32		00 02	
West Kirby	a	00 07		08 37		09 07			22 37		23 07			23 37		00 07	

For alternative trains between Liverpool and Hamilton Square refer to table 107

Table 106R

Mondays to Saturdays

9 December to 17 May

West Kirby & New Brighton - Birkenhead & Liverpool

Network Diagram - see first Page of Table 101

Miles	Miles			ME	ME	ME	ME	ME	ME	ME	ME	ME	ME	ME	ME		ME	ME	ME	ME	ME	ME	ME
0	—	**West Kirby**	d		05 51		06 21		06 51		07 06		07 21		07 36	and at the same minutes past each hour until		17 51		18 06		18 21	
1	—	Hoylake	d		05 54		06 24		06 54		07 09		07 24		07 39			17 54		18 09		18 24	
1¾	—	Manor Road	d		05 56		06 26		06 56		07 11		07 26		07 41			17 56		18 11		18 26	
3	—	Meols	d		05 58		06 28		06 58		07 13		07 28		07 43			17 58		18 13		18 28	
4¼	—	Moreton (Merseyside)	d		06 01		06 31		07 01		07 16		07 31		07 46			18 01		18 16		18 31	
4¾	—	Leasowe	d		06 03		06 33		07 03		07 18		07 33		07 48			18 03		18 18		18 33	
5¾	—	Bidston	d		06 06		06 36		07 06		07 21		07 36		07 51			18 06		18 21		18 36	
—	0	**New Brighton**	d	05 53		06 23		06 53		07 08		07 23		07 38			17 53		18 08		18 23		18 38
—	1¼	Wallasey Grove Road	d	05 57		06 27		06 57		07 12		07 27		07 42			17 57		18 12		18 27		18 42
—	1½	Wallasey Village	d	05 59		06 29		06 59		07 14		07 29		07 44			17 59		18 14		18 29		18 44
6½	3	Birkenhead North	d	06 04	06 09	06 34	06 39	07 04	07 09	07 19	07 24	07 34	07 39	07 49	07 54		18 04	18 09	18 19	18 24	18 34	18 39	18 49
7½	3¾	Birkenhead Park	d	06 06	06 11	06 36	06 41	07 06	07 11	07 21	07 26	07 36	07 41	07 51	07 56		18 06	18 11	18 21	18 26	18 36	18 41	18 51
8¼	4½	Conway Park	d	06 09	06 14	06 39	06 44	07 09	07 14	07 24	07 29	07 39	07 44	07 54	07 59		18 09	18 14	18 24	18 29	18 39	18 44	18 54
8¾	5	Hamilton Square	d	06 11	06 16	06 41	06 46	07 11	07 16	07 26	07 31	07 41	07 46	07 56	08 01		18 11	18 16	18 26	18 31	18 41	18 46	18 56
8¾	6¼	James Street	d	06 14	06 19	06 44	06 49	07 14	07 19	07 29	07 34	07 44	07 49	07 59	08 04		18 14	18 19	18 29	18 34	18 44	18 49	18 59
10¼	7¾	Moorfields [10]	a	06 16	06 21	06 46	06 51	07 16	07 21	07 31	07 36	07 46	07 51	08 01	08 06		18 16	18 21	18 31	18 36	18 46	18 51	19 01
9¾	7¼	Liverpool Lime Street [10]	a	06 18	06 23	06 48	06 53	07 18	07 23	07 33	07 38	07 48	07 53	08 03	08 08		18 18	18 23	18 33	18 38	18 48	18 53	19 03
9¼	6¾	**Liverpool Central** [10]	a	06 20	06 25	06 50	06 55	07 20	07 25	07 35	07 40	07 50	07 55	08 05	08 10		18 20	18 25	18 35	18 40	18 50	18 55	19 05

		ME	ME	ME	ME	ME		ME	ME	ME	ME	ME	ME	ME
West Kirby	d	18 36		19 01		19 31	and at the same minutes past each hour until		22 01		22 31		23 01	
Hoylake	d	18 39		19 04		19 34			22 04		22 34		23 04	
Manor Road	d	18 41		19 06		19 36			22 06		22 36		23 06	
Meols	d	18 43		19 08		19 38			22 08		22 38		23 08	
Moreton (Merseyside)	d	18 46		19 11		19 41			22 11		22 41		23 11	
Leasowe	d	18 48		19 13		19 43			22 13		22 43		23 13	
Bidston	d	18 51		19 16		19 46			22 16		22 46		23 16	
New Brighton	d		18 53		19 23			21 53		22 23		22 53		23 23
Wallasey Grove Road	d		18 57		19 27			21 57		22 27		22 57		23 27
Wallasey Village	d		18 59		19 29			21 59		22 29		22 59		23 29
Birkenhead North	d	18 54	19 04	19 19	19 34	19 49		22 04	22 19	22 34	22 49	23 04	23 19	23 34
Birkenhead Park	d	18 56	19 06	19 21	19 36	19 51		22 06	22 21	22 36	22 51	23 06	23 21	23 36
Conway Park	d	18 59	19 09	19 24	19 39	19 54		22 09	22 24	22 39	22 54	23 09	23 24	23 39
Hamilton Square	d	19 01	19 11	19 26	19 41	19 56		22 11	22 26	22 41	22 56	23 11	23 26	23 41
James Street	d	19 04	19 14	19 29	19 44	19 59		22 14	22 29	22 44	22 59	23 14	23 29	23 44
Moorfields [10]	a	19 06	19 16	19 31	19 46	20 01		22 16	22 31	22 46	23 01	23 16	23 31	23 46
Liverpool Lime Street [10]	a	19 08	19 18	19 33	19 48	20 03		22 18	22 33	22 48	23 03	23 18	23 33	23 48
Liverpool Central [10]	a	19 10	19 20	19 35	19 50	20 05		22 20	22 35	22 50	23 05	23 20	23 35	23 50

Sundays

8 December to 11 May

		ME	ME	ME	ME		ME	ME	ME	ME	ME	ME	ME
West Kirby	d		08 01		08 31	and at the same minutes past each hour until		22 01		22 31		23 01	
Hoylake	d		08 04		08 34			22 04		22 34		23 04	
Manor Road	d		08 06		08 36			22 06		22 36		23 06	
Meols	d		08 08		08 38			22 08		22 38		23 08	
Moreton (Merseyside)	d		08 11		08 41			22 11		22 41		23 11	
Leasowe	d		08 13		08 43			22 13		22 43		23 13	
Bidston	d		08 16		08 46			22 16		22 46		23 16	
New Brighton	d	07 53		08 23			21 53		22 23		22 53		23 23
Wallasey Grove Road	d	07 57		08 27			21 57		22 27		22 57		23 27
Wallasey Village	d	07 59		08 29			21 59		22 29		22 59		23 29
Birkenhead North	d	08 04	08 19	08 34	08 49		22 04	22 19	22 34	22 49	23 04	23 19	23 34
Birkenhead Park	d	08 06	08 21	08 36	08 51		22 06	22 21	22 36	22 51	23 06	23 21	23 36
Conway Park	d	08 09	08 24	08 39	08 54		22 09	22 24	22 39	22 54	23 09	23 24	23 39
Hamilton Square	d	08 11	08 26	08 41	08 56		22 11	22 26	22 41	22 56	23 11	23 26	23 41
James Street	d	08 14	08 29	08 44	08 59		22 14	22 29	22 44	22 59	23 14	23 29	23 44
Moorfields [10]	a	08 16	08 31	08 46	09 01		22 16	22 31	22 46	23 01	23 16	23 31	23 46
Liverpool Lime Street [10]	a	08 18	08 33	08 48	09 03		22 18	22 33	22 48	23 03	23 18	23 33	23 48
Liverpool Central [10]	a	08 20	08 35	08 50	09 05		22 20	22 35	22 50	23 05	23 20	23 35	23 50

For alternative trains between Hamilton Square and Liverpool see table 107

Table 107

Mondays to Saturdays

9 December to 17 May

Liverpool - Chester & Ellesmere Port

Network Diagram - see first Page of Table 101

Miles	Miles			ME	ME	ME	ME	ME	ME	ME	ME	ME	ME	ME	ME SX	ME SO	ME SX	ME	ME SX	ME	ME SO	ME SX	ME SO
0	—	Moorfields 10	d			05 36	05 56	06 06	06 26	06 41	06 56	07 11	07 26	07 41	07 53	07 56		08 11	08 18	08 26	08 41	08 41	08 48
0½	—	Liverpool Lime Street 10	d			05 38	05 58	06 08	06 28	06 43	06 58	07 13	07 28	07 43	07 55	07 58		08 13	08 20	08 28	08 43	08 43	08 50
1	—	Liverpool Central 10	d			05 40	06 00	06 10	06 30	06 45	07 00	07 15	07 30	07 45	07 57	08 00		08 15	08 22	08 30	08 45	08 45	08 52
1½	—	James Street	d			05 42	06 02	06 12	06 32	06 47	07 02	07 17	07 32	07 47	07 59	08 02		08 17	08 24	08 32	08 47	08 47	08 54
2¾	—	Hamilton Square	d			05 45	06 05	06 15	06 35	06 50	07 05	07 20	07 35	07 50	08 02	08 05		08 20	08 27	08 35	08 50	08 50	08 57
3	—	Birkenhead Central	d			05 47	06 07	06 17	06 37	06 52	07 07	07 22	07 37	07 52	08 05	08 07		08 22	08 30	08 37	08 52	08 53	09 00
3¾	—	Green Lane	d			05 49	06 09	06 19	06 39	06 54	07 09	07 24	07 39	07 54	08 07	08 09		08 24	08 32	08 39	08 54	08 55	09 02
4½	—	Rock Ferry	d			05 52	06 12	06 22	06 42	06 57	07 12	07 27	07 42	07 57	08 09	08 12		08 27	08 34	08 42	08 57	08 57	09 04
5½	—	Bebington	d			05 54	06 14	06 24	06 44	06 59	07 14	07 29	07 44	07 59	08 12	08 14		08 29	08 37	08 44	08 59	09 00	09 07
6½	—	Port Sunlight	d		00 01	05 56	06 16	06 26	06 46	07 01	07 16	07 31	07 46	08 01	08 14	08 16		08 31	08 39	08 46	09 01	09 02	09 09
7	—	Spital	d		00 03	05 58	06 18	06 28	06 48	07 03	07 18	07 33	07 48	08 03	08 16	08 18		08 33	08 41	08 48	09 03	09 04	09 11
7¾	—	Bromborough Rake	d		00 05	06 00	06 20	06 30	06 50	07 05	07 20	07 35	07 50	08 05	08 18	08 20		08 35	08 43	08 50	09 05	09 06	09 13
8½	—	Bromborough	d		00 07	06 02	06 22	06 32	06 52	07 07	07 22	07 37	07 52	08 07	08 20	08 22		08 37	08 45	08 52	09 07	09 08	09 15
9	—	Eastham Rake	d		00 10	06 05	06 25	06 35	06 55	07 10	07 25	07 40	07 55	08 10	08 22	08 25		08 40	08 47	08 55	09 10	09 10	09 17
10	0	Hooton	d		00 12	06 07	06 27	06 37	06 57	07 12	07 27	07 42	07 57	08 12	08 24	08 27	08 29	08 42	08 49	08 57	09 12	09 12	09 19
—	1½	Little Sutton	d	00 01			06 31		07 01		07 31		08 01			08 31	08 34			09 01			09 24
—	2½	Overpool	d	00 03			06 33		07 03		07 33		08 03			08 33	08 36			09 03			09 26
—	4	**Ellesmere Port**	a	00 07			06 38		07 08		07 38		08 08			08 38	08 39			09 08			09 32
13	—	Capenhurst	d		00 17	06 12		06 42		07 17		07 47		08 17	08 29			08 47	08 54		09 17	09 17	
16¾	—	Bache	d		00 22	06 17		06 47		07 22		07 52		08 22	08 35			08 52	09 00		09 22	09 23	
18¼	—	**Chester**	a		00 26	06 26		06 56		07 26		07 56		08 27	08 38			08 57	09 06		09 27	09 27	

		ME SO	ME SX	ME	ME SO	ME SX	ME	ME	ME	ME	ME	ME	ME	ME	ME	ME	ME	ME	ME	ME	ME
Moorfields 10	d	08 56	08 56	09 11	09 18	09 19	09 26	09 41	09 48	09 56	10 11	10 18	10 26	10 41	10 48	10 56	11 11	11 18	11 26	11 41	11 48
Liverpool Lime Street 10	d	08 58	08 58	09 13	09 20	09 21	09 28	09 43	09 50	09 58	10 13	10 20	10 28	10 43	10 50	10 58	11 13	11 20	11 28	11 43	11 50
Liverpool Central 10	d	09 00	09 00	09 15	09 22	09 23	09 30	09 45	09 52	10 00	10 15	10 22	10 30	10 45	10 52	11 00	11 15	11 22	11 30	11 45	11 52
James Street	d	09 02	09 02	09 17	09 24	09 25	09 32	09 47	09 54	10 02	10 17	10 24	10 32	10 47	10 54	11 02	11 17	11 24	11 32	11 47	11 54
Hamilton Square	d	09 05	09 05	09 20	09 27	09 28	09 35	09 50	09 57	10 05	10 20	10 27	10 35	10 50	10 57	11 05	11 20	11 27	11 35	11 50	11 57
Birkenhead Central	d	09 07	09 07	09 22	09 30	09 30	09 37	09 52	10 00	10 07	10 22	10 30	10 37	10 52	11 00	11 07	11 22	11 30	11 37	11 52	12 00
Green Lane	d	09 09	09 09	09 24	09 32	09 32	09 39	09 54	10 02	10 09	10 24	10 32	10 39	10 54	11 02	11 09	11 24	11 32	11 39	11 54	12 02
Rock Ferry	d	09 12	09 12	09 27	09 34	09 35	09 42	09 57	10 04	10 12	10 27	10 34	10 42	10 57	11 04	11 12	11 27	11 34	11 42	11 57	12 04
Bebington	d	09 14	09 14	09 29	09 37	09 37	09 44	09 59	10 07	10 14	10 29	10 37	10 44	10 59	11 07	11 14	11 29	11 37	11 44	11 59	12 07
Port Sunlight	d	09 16	09 16	09 31	09 39	09 39	09 46	10 01	10 09	10 16	10 31	10 39	10 46	11 01	11 09	11 16	11 31	11 39	11 46	12 01	12 09
Spital	d	09 18	09 18	09 33	09 41	09 41	09 48	10 03	10 11	10 18	10 33	10 41	10 48	11 03	11 11	11 18	11 33	11 41	11 48	12 03	12 11
Bromborough Rake	d	09 20	09 20	09 35	09 43	09 43	09 50	10 05	10 13	10 20	10 35	10 43	10 50	11 05	11 13	11 20	11 35	11 43	11 50	12 05	12 13
Bromborough	d	09 22	09 22	09 37	09 45	09 45	09 52	10 07	10 15	10 22	10 37	10 45	10 52	11 07	11 15	11 22	11 37	11 45	11 52	12 07	12 15
Eastham Rake	d	09 25	09 25	09 40	09 47	09 48	09 55	10 10	10 17	10 25	10 40	10 47	10 55	11 10	11 17	11 25	11 40	11 47	11 55	12 10	12 17
Hooton	d	09 27	09 27	09 42	09 49	09 50	09 57	10 12	10 19	10 27	10 42	10 49	10 57	11 12	11 19	11 27	11 42	11 49	11 57	12 12	12 19
Little Sutton	d		09 31		09 54	09 54			10 24			10 54			11 24			11 54			12 24
Overpool	d		09 33		09 56	09 56			10 26			10 56			11 26			11 56			12 26
Ellesmere Port	a		09 38		10 00	10 00			10 30			11 00			11 30			12 00			12 31
Capenhurst	d			09 47				10 17			10 47			11 17			11 47			12 17	
Bache	d	09 36		09 52			10 06	10 22		10 36	10 52		11 06	11 22		11 36	11 52		12 06	12 22	
Chester	a	09 41		09 57			10 11	10 27		10 41	10 57		11 11	11 27		11 41	11 57		12 11	12 27	

		ME	ME	ME	ME	ME	ME		ME	ME	ME	ME	ME	ME	ME	ME	ME	ME	ME SX	ME	ME	ME SO	ME SX
Moorfields 10	d	11 56	12 11	12 18	12 26	12 41	12 48		14 56	15 11	15 18	15 26	15 41	15 48	15 56	16 11	16 18	16 26	16 33	16 41	16 48	16 56	16 56
Liverpool Lime Street 10	d	11 58	12 13	12 20	12 28	12 43	12 50		14 58	15 13	15 20	15 28	15 43	15 50	15 58	16 13	16 20	16 28	16 35	16 43	16 50	16 58	16 58
Liverpool Central 10	d	12 00	12 15	12 22	12 30	12 45	12 52		15 00	15 15	15 22	15 30	15 45	15 52	16 00	16 15	16 22	16 30	16 37	16 45	16 52	17 00	17 00
James Street	d	12 02	12 17	12 24	12 32	12 47	12 54		15 02	15 17	15 24	15 32	15 47	15 54	16 02	16 17	16 24	16 32	16 39	16 47	16 54	17 02	17 02
Hamilton Square	d	12 05	12 20	12 27	12 35	12 50	12 57		15 05	15 20	15 27	15 35	15 50	15 57	16 05	16 20	16 27	16 35	16 42	16 50	16 57	17 05	17 05
Birkenhead Central	d	12 07	12 22	12 30	12 37	12 52	13 00		15 07	15 22	15 30	15 37	15 52	16 00	16 07	16 22	16 30	16 37	16 45	16 52	17 00	17 07	17 07
Green Lane	d	12 09	12 24	12 32	12 39	12 54	13 02	and at the same minutes past each hour until	15 09	15 24	15 32	15 39	15 54	16 02	16 09	16 24	16 32	16 39	16 47	16 54	17 02	17 09	17 09
Rock Ferry	d	12 12	12 27	12 34	12 42	12 57	13 04		15 12	15 27	15 34	15 42	15 57	16 04	16 12	16 27	16 34	16 42	16 49	16 57	17 04	17 12	17 12
Bebington	d	12 14	12 29	12 37	12 44	12 59	13 07		15 14	15 29	15 37	15 44	15 59	16 07	16 14	16 29	16 37	16 44	16 52	16 59	17 07	17 14	17 14
Port Sunlight	d	12 16	12 31	12 39	12 46	13 01	13 09		15 16	15 31	15 39	15 46	16 01	16 09	16 16	16 31	16 39	16 46	16 54	17 01	17 09	17 16	17 16
Spital	d	12 18	12 33	12 41	12 48	13 03	13 11		15 18	15 33	15 41	15 48	16 03	16 11	16 18	16 33	16 41	16 48	16 56	17 03	17 11	17 18	17 18
Bromborough Rake	d	12 20	12 35	12 43	12 50	13 05	13 13		15 20	15 35	15 43	15 50	16 05	16 13	16 20	16 35	16 43	16 50	16 58	17 05	17 13	17 20	17 20
Bromborough	d	12 22	12 37	12 45	12 52	13 07	13 15		15 22	15 37	15 45	15 52	16 07	16 15	16 22	16 37	16 45	16 52	17 00	17 07	17 15	17 22	17 22
Eastham Rake	d	12 25	12 40	12 47	12 55	13 10	13 17		15 25	15 40	15 47	15 55	16 10	16 17	16 25	16 40	16 47	16 55	17 02	17 10	17 17	17 25	17 25
Hooton	d	12 27	12 42	12 49	12 57	13 12	13 19		15 27	15 42	15 49	15 57	16 12	16 19	16 27	16 42	16 49	16 57	17 04	17 12	17 19	17 27	17 27
Little Sutton	d			12 54			13 24				15 54			16 24			16 54		17 09		17 24		
Overpool	d			12 56			13 26				15 56			16 26			16 56		17 11		17 26		
Ellesmere Port	a			13 00			13 30				16 00			16 30			17 00		17 16		17 30		
Capenhurst	d		12 47			13 17				15 47			16 17			16 47				17 17			17 32
Bache	d	12 36	12 52		13 06	13 22			15 36	15 52		16 06	16 22		16 36	16 52		17 06		17 22		17 36	17 37
Chester	a	12 41	12 57		13 11	13 27			15 41	15 57		16 11	16 27		16 41	16 57		17 11		17 27		17 41	17 41

For alternative trains between Hamilton Square and Liverpool see table 106

Table 107

Mondays to Saturdays

9 December to 17 May

Liverpool - Chester & Ellesmere Port

Network Diagram - see first Page of Table 101

		ME SX	ME	ME	ME SO	ME SX	ME SX	ME	ME	ME	ME	ME	ME	ME	ME	ME	ME	ME	ME	ME	ME	ME	ME
Moorfields 10	d	17 03	17 11	17 18	17 26	17 26	17 33	17 41	17 48	17 56	18 11	18 18	18 26	18 41	18 48	18 56	19 11	19 26	19 41	19 56	20 11	20 27	20 41
Liverpool Lime Street 10	d	17 05	17 13	17 20	17 28	17 28	17 35	17 43	17 50	17 58	18 13	18 20	18 28	18 43	18 50	18 58	19 13	19 28	19 43	19 58	20 13	20 29	20 43
Liverpool Central 10	d	17 07	17 15	17 22	17 30	17 30	17 37	17 45	17 52	18 00	18 15	18 22	18 30	18 45	18 52	19 00	19 15	19 30	19 45	20 00	20 15	20 31	20 45
James Street	d	17 09	17 17	17 24	17 32	17 32	17 39	17 47	17 54	18 02	18 17	18 24	18 32	18 47	18 54	19 02	19 17	19 32	19 47	20 02	20 17	20 33	20 47
Hamilton Square	d	17 12	17 20	17 27	17 35	17 35	17 42	17 50	17 57	18 05	18 20	18 27	18 35	18 50	18 57	19 05	19 20	19 35	19 50	20 05	20 20	20 36	20 50
Birkenhead Central	d	17 15	17 22	17 30	17 37	17 37	17 45	17 52	18 00	18 07	18 22	18 30	18 37	18 52	19 00	19 07	19 22	19 37	19 52	20 07	20 22	20 38	20 52
Green Lane	d	17 17	17 24	17 32	17 39	17 39	17 47	17 54	18 02	18 09	18 24	18 32	18 39	18 54	19 02	19 09	19 24	19 39	19 54	20 09	20 24	20 40	20 54
Rock Ferry	d	17 19	17 27	17 34	17 42	17 42	17 49	17 57	18 04	18 12	18 27	18 34	18 42	18 57	19 04	19 12	19 27	19 42	19 57	20 12	20 27	20 43	20 57
Bebington	d	17 22	17 29	17 37	17 44	17 44	17 52	17 59	18 07	18 14	18 29	18 37	18 44	18 59	19 07	19 14	19 29	19 44	19 59	20 14	20 29	20 45	20 59
Port Sunlight	d	17 24	17 31	17 39	17 46	17 46	17 54	18 01	18 09	18 16	18 31	18 39	18 46	19 01	19 09	19 16	19 31	19 46	20 01	20 16	20 31	20 47	21 01
Spital	d	17 26	17 33	17 41	17 48	17 48	17 56	18 03	18 11	18 18	18 33	18 41	18 48	19 03	19 11	19 18	19 33	19 48	20 03	20 18	20 33	20 49	21 03
Bromborough Rake	d	17 28	17 35	17 43	17 50	17 50	17 58	18 05	18 13	18 20	18 35	18 43	18 50	19 05	19 13	19 20	19 35	19 50	20 05	20 20	20 35	20 51	21 05
Bromborough	d	17 30	17 37	17 45	17 52	17 52	18 00	18 07	18 15	18 22	18 37	18 45	18 52	19 07	19 15	19 22	19 37	19 52	20 07	20 22	20 37	20 53	21 07
Eastham Rake	d	17 32	17 40	17 47	17 55	17 55	18 02	18 10	18 17	18 25	18 40	18 47	18 55	19 10	19 17	19 25	19 40	19 55	20 10	20 25	20 40	20 56	21 10
Hooton	d	17 34	17 42	17 49	17 57	17 57	18 04	18 12	18 19	18 27	18 42	18 49	18 57	19 12	19 19	19 27	19 42	19 57	20 12	20 27	20 42	20 58	21 12
Little Sutton	d	17 39		17 54			18 09		18 24			18 54			19 24			20 01		20 31		21 02	
Overpool	d	17 41		17 56			18 11		18 26			18 56			19 26			20 03		20 33		21 04	
Ellesmere Port	a	17 46		18 00			18 16		18 30			19 00			19 30			20 08		20 38		21 09	
Capenhurst	d		17 47			18 02		18 17			18 47			19 17			19 47		20 17		20 47		21 17
Bache	d		17 52		18 06	18 07		18 22		18 36	18 52		19 06	19 22		19 36	19 52		20 22		20 52		21 22
Chester	a		17 57		18 11	18 11		18 26		18 39	18 56		19 10	19 26		19 41	19 56		20 26		20 56		21 26

		ME	ME	ME	ME	ME	ME	ME	ME	ME	ME	ME	ME
Moorfields 10	d	20 56	21 11	21 26	21 41	21 56	22 11	22 26	22 41	22 56	23 11	23 26	23 41
Liverpool Lime Street 10	d	20 58	21 13	21 28	21 43	21 58	22 13	22 28	22 43	22 58	23 13	23 28	23 43
Liverpool Central 10	d	21 00	21 15	21 30	21 45	22 00	22 15	22 30	22 45	23 00	23 15	23 30	23 45
James Street	d	21 02	21 17	21 32	21 47	22 02	22 17	22 32	22 47	23 02	23 17	23 32	23 47
Hamilton Square	d	21 05	21 20	21 35	21 50	22 05	22 20	22 35	22 50	23 05	23 20	23 35	23 50
Birkenhead Central	d	21 07	21 22	21 37	21 52	22 07	22 22	22 37	22 52	23 07	23 22	23 37	23 52
Green Lane	d	21 09	21 24	21 39	21 54	22 09	22 24	22 39	22 54	23 09	23 24	23 39	23 54
Rock Ferry	d	21 12	21 27	21 42	21 57	22 12	22 27	22 42	22 57	23 12	23 27	23 42	23 57
Bebington	d	21 14	21 29	21 44	21 59	22 14	22 29	22 44	22 59	23 14	23 29	23 44	23 59
Port Sunlight	d	21 16	21 31	21 46	22 01	22 16	22 31	22 46	23 01	23 16	23 31	23 46	00 01
Spital	d	21 18	21 33	21 48	22 03	22 18	22 33	22 48	23 03	23 18	23 33	23 48	00 03
Bromborough Rake	d	21 20	21 35	21 50	22 05	22 20	22 35	22 50	23 05	23 20	23 35	23 50	00 05
Bromborough	d	21 22	21 37	21 52	22 07	22 22	22 37	22 52	23 07	23 22	23 37	23 52	00 07
Eastham Rake	d	21 25	21 40	21 55	22 10	22 25	22 40	22 55	23 10	23 25	23 40	23 55	00 10
Hooton	d	21 27	21 42	21 57	22 12	22 27	22 42	22 57	23 12	23 27	23 42	23 57	00 12
Little Sutton	d	21 31		22 01		22 31		23 01		23 31		00 01	
Overpool	d	21 33		22 03		22 33		23 03		23 33		00 03	
Ellesmere Port	a	21 38		22 08		22 38		23 08		23 37		00 07	
Capenhurst	d		21 47		22 17		22 47		23 17		23 47		00 17
Bache	d		21 52		22 22		22 52		23 22		23 52		00 22
Chester	a		21 56		22 26		22 56		23 26		23 56		00 26

Sundays

8 December to 11 May

		ME	ME A	ME	ME	ME	ME		ME	ME	ME	ME	ME	ME	ME	ME
Moorfields 10	d			07 56	08 11	08 26	08 41		21 56	22 11	22 26	22 41	22 56	23 11	23 26	23 41
Liverpool Lime Street 10	d			07 58	08 13	08 28	08 43		21 58	22 13	22 28	22 43	22 58	23 13	23 28	23 43
Liverpool Central 10	d			08 00	08 15	08 30	08 45		22 00	22 15	22 30	22 45	23 00	23 15	23 30	23 45
James Street	d			08 02	08 17	08 32	08 47		22 02	22 17	22 32	22 47	23 02	23 17	23 32	23 47
Hamilton Square	d			08 05	08 20	08 35	08 50		22 05	22 20	22 35	22 50	23 05	23 20	23 35	23 50
Birkenhead Central	d			08 07	08 22	08 37	08 52		22 07	22 22	22 37	22 52	23 07	23 22	23 37	23 52
Green Lane	d			08 09	08 24	08 39	08 54	and at	22 09	22 24	22 39	22 54	23 09	23 24	23 39	23 54
Rock Ferry	d			08 12	08 27	08 42	08 57	the same	22 12	22 27	22 42	22 57	23 12	23 27	23 42	23 57
Bebington	d			08 14	08 29	08 44	08 59	minutes	22 14	22 29	22 44	22 59	23 14	23 29	23 44	23 59
Port Sunlight	d		00 01	08 16	08 31	08 46	09 01	past	22 16	22 31	22 46	23 01	23 16	23 31	23 46	00 01
Spital	d		00 03	08 18	08 33	08 48	09 03	each	22 18	22 33	22 48	23 03	23 18	23 33	23 48	00 03
Bromborough Rake	d		00 05	08 20	08 35	08 50	09 05	hour until	22 20	22 35	22 50	23 05	23 20	23 35	23 50	00 05
Bromborough	d		00 07	08 22	08 37	08 52	09 07		22 22	22 37	22 52	23 07	23 22	23 37	23 52	00 07
Eastham Rake	d		00 10	08 25	08 40	08 55	09 10		22 25	22 40	22 55	23 10	23 25	23 40	23 55	00 10
Hooton	d		00 12	08 27	08 42	08 57	09 12		22 27	22 42	22 57	23 12	23 27	23 42	23 57	00 12
Little Sutton	d	00 01		08 31		09 01			22 31		23 01		23 31		00 01	
Overpool	d	00 03		08 33		09 03			22 33		23 03		23 33		00 03	
Ellesmere Port	a	00 07		08 38		09 08			22 38		23 08		23 37		00 07	
Capenhurst	d		00 17		08 47		09 17			22 47		23 17		23 47		00 17
Bache	d		00 22		08 52		09 22			22 52		23 22		23 52		00 22
Chester	a		00 26		08 56		09 26			22 56		23 26		23 56		00 26

A not 8 December

For alternative trains between Hamilton Square and Liverpool see table 106

Table 107R

Mondays to Saturdays

9 December to 17 May

Chester, Ellesmere Port - Liverpool

Network Diagram - see first Page of Table 101

Miles	Miles			ME	ME	ME	ME	ME	ME	ME	ME SX	ME SO	ME SX	ME SO	ME SX	ME SX	ME	ME SX	ME SO	ME SX	ME SX	ME SO	ME SO
0	—	**Chester**	d			05 55		06 30		07 00			07 22	07 30		07 37		07 52	08 00		08 07		08 15
1½	—	Bache	d			05 58		06 33		07 03			07 26	07 33		07 41		07 56	08 03		08 11		08 18
5¼	—	Capenhurst	d			06 04		06 39		07 09			07 32	07 39		07 47		08 02	08 09		08 17		08 24
—	0	**Ellesmere Port**	d				06 17		06 47		07 17	07 19			07 31		07 49			08 01		08 12	
—	1½	Overpool	d				06 20		06 50		07 20	07 22			07 34		07 52			08 04		08 15	
—	2½	Little Sutton	d				06 22		06 52		07 22	07 24			07 36		07 54			08 06		08 17	
8¼	4	Hooton	d	05 39	05 59	06 09	06 26	06 44	06 56	07 14	07 26	07 29	07 36	07 44	07 44	07 51	07 59	08 06	08 14	08 14	08 21	08 21	08 29
9¼	—	Eastham Rake	d	05 41	06 01	06 11	06 28	06 46	06 58	07 16	07 28	07 31	07 38	07 46	07 46	07 53	08 01	08 08	08 16	08 16	08 23	08 23	08 31
9¾	—	Bromborough	d	05 43	06 03	06 13	06 31	06 48	07 01	07 18	07 31	07 33	07 41	07 48	07 48	07 56	08 03	08 11	08 18	08 18	08 26	08 26	08 33
10½	—	Bromborough Rake	d	05 45	06 05	06 15	06 33	06 50	07 03	07 20	07 33	07 35	07 43	07 50	07 50	07 58	08 05	08 13	08 20	08 20	08 28	08 28	08 35
11¼	—	Spital	d	05 47	06 07	06 17	06 35	06 52	07 05	07 22	07 35	07 37	07 45	07 52	07 52	08 00	08 07	08 15	08 22	08 22	08 30	08 30	08 37
11¾	—	Port Sunlight	d	05 49	06 09	06 19	06 37	06 54	07 07	07 24	07 37	07 39	07 47	07 54	07 54	08 02	08 09	08 17	08 24	08 24	08 32	08 32	08 39
12¾	—	Bebington	d	05 51	06 11	06 21	06 39	06 56	07 09	07 26	07 39	07 41	07 49	07 56	07 56	08 04	08 11	08 19	08 26	08 26	08 34	08 34	08 41
13¾	—	Rock Ferry	d	05 54	06 14	06 24	06 42	06 59	07 12	07 29	07 42	07 44	07 52	07 59	07 59	08 07	08 14	08 22	08 29	08 29	08 37	08 37	08 44
14½	—	Green Lane	d	05 57	06 17	06 27	06 44	07 02	07 14	07 32	07 44	07 47	07 54	08 02	08 02	08 09	08 17	08 24	08 32	08 32	08 39	08 39	08 47
15	—	Birkenhead Central	d	05 59	06 19	06 34	06 49	07 04	07 19	07 34	07 47	07 49	07 57	08 04	08 04	08 12	08 19	08 27	08 34	08 34	08 42	08 42	08 49
15½	—	Hamilton Square	d	06 01	06 21	06 36	06 51	07 06	07 21	07 36	07 49	07 51	07 59	08 06	08 06	08 14	08 21	08 29	08 36	08 36	08 44	08 44	08 51
16¾	—	James Street	d	06 04	06 24	06 39	06 54	07 09	07 24	07 39	07 52	07 54	08 02	08 09	08 09	08 17	08 24	08 32	08 39	08 39	08 47	08 47	08 54
17	—	Moorfields 10	a	06 06	06 26	06 41	06 56	07 11	07 26	07 41	07 53	07 56	08 03	08 11	08 11	08 18	08 26	08 33	08 41	08 41	08 48	08 48	08 56
17½	—	Liverpool Lime Street 10	a	06 08	06 28	06 43	06 58	07 13	07 28	07 43	07 55	07 58	08 05	08 13	08 13	08 20	08 28	08 35	08 43	08 43	08 50	08 50	08 58
18	—	**Liverpool Central 10**	a	06 10	06 30	06 45	07 00	07 15	07 30	07 45	07 57	08 00	08 07	08 15	08 15	08 22	08 30	08 37	08 45	08 45	08 52	08 52	09 00

		ME SX	ME	ME SO	ME SX	ME	ME	ME	ME	ME	ME		ME	ME	ME	ME	ME	ME	ME	ME	ME	ME	ME
Chester	d		08 31			08 45	09 01		09 15	09 31			16 45	17 01		17 15	17 31		17 45	18 01		18 15	18 30
Bache	d		08 35			08 48	09 05		09 18	09 35			16 48	17 05		17 18	17 35		17 48	18 05		18 18	18 33
Capenhurst	d					08 54			09 24				16 54			17 24			17 54			18 24	18 39
Ellesmere Port	d	08 17		08 42	08 42			09 12			09 42				17 12			17 42			18 12		
Overpool	d	08 20		08 45	08 45			09 15			09 45				17 15			17 45			18 15		
Little Sutton	d	08 22		08 47	08 47			09 17			09 47				17 17			17 47			18 17		
Hooton	d	08 29	08 44	08 51	08 52	08 59	09 14	09 21	09 29	09 44	09 51	and at the same minutes past each hour until	16 59	17 14	17 21	17 29	17 44	17 51	17 59	18 14	18 21	18 29	18 44
Eastham Rake	d	08 31	08 46	08 53	08 54	09 01	09 16	09 23	09 31	09 46	09 53		17 01	17 16	17 23	17 31	17 46	17 53	18 01	18 16	18 23	18 31	18 46
Bromborough	d	08 33	08 48	08 56	08 56	09 03	09 18	09 26	09 33	09 48	09 56		17 03	17 18	17 26	17 33	17 48	17 56	18 03	18 18	18 26	18 33	18 48
Bromborough Rake	d	08 35	08 50	08 58	08 58	09 05	09 20	09 28	09 35	09 50	09 58		17 05	17 20	17 28	17 35	17 50	17 58	18 05	18 20	18 28	18 35	18 50
Spital	d	08 37	08 52	09 00	09 00	09 07	09 22	09 30	09 37	09 52	10 00		17 07	17 22	17 30	17 37	17 52	18 00	18 07	18 22	18 30	18 37	18 52
Port Sunlight	d	08 39	08 54	09 02	09 02	09 09	09 24	09 32	09 39	09 54	10 02		17 09	17 24	17 32	17 39	17 54	18 02	18 09	18 24	18 32	18 39	18 54
Bebington	d	08 41	08 56	09 04	09 04	09 11	09 26	09 34	09 41	09 56	10 04		17 11	17 26	17 34	17 41	17 56	18 04	18 11	18 26	18 34	18 41	18 56
Rock Ferry	d	08 44	08 59	09 07	09 07	09 14	09 29	09 37	09 44	09 59	10 07		17 14	17 29	17 37	17 44	17 59	18 07	18 14	18 29	18 37	18 44	18 59
Green Lane	d	08 47	09 02	09 09	09 10	09 17	09 32	09 39	09 47	10 02	10 09		17 17	17 32	17 39	17 47	18 02	18 09	18 17	18 32	18 39	18 47	19 02
Birkenhead Central	d	08 49	09 04	09 12	09 12	09 19	09 34	09 42	09 49	10 04	10 12		17 19	17 34	17 42	17 49	18 04	18 12	18 19	18 34	18 42	18 49	19 04
Hamilton Square	d	08 51	09 06	09 14	09 14	09 21	09 36	09 44	09 51	10 06	10 14		17 21	17 36	17 44	17 51	18 06	18 14	18 21	18 36	18 44	18 51	19 06
James Street	d	08 54	09 09	09 17	09 17	09 24	09 39	09 47	09 54	10 09	10 17		17 24	17 39	17 47	17 54	18 09	18 17	18 24	18 39	18 47	18 54	19 09
Moorfields 10	a	08 56	09 11	09 18	09 19	09 26	09 41	09 48	09 56	10 11	10 18		17 26	17 41	17 48	17 56	18 11	18 18	18 26	18 41	18 48	18 56	19 11
Liverpool Lime Street 10	a	08 58	09 13	09 20	09 21	09 28	09 43	09 50	09 58	10 13	10 20		17 28	17 43	17 50	17 58	18 13	18 20	18 28	18 43	18 50	18 58	19 13
Liverpool Central 10	a	09 00	09 15	09 22	09 23	09 30	09 45	09 52	10 00	10 15	10 22		17 30	17 45	17 52	18 00	18 15	18 22	18 30	18 45	18 52	19 00	19 15

		ME	ME	ME	ME	ME	ME	ME	ME	ME	ME	ME	ME	ME	ME	ME	ME	ME	ME	ME	ME
Chester	d		19 00		19 30		20 00		20 30		21 00		21 30		22 00		22 30		23 00		23 30
Bache	d		19 03		19 33		20 03		20 33		21 03		21 33		22 03		22 33		23 03		23 33
Capenhurst	d		19 09		19 39		20 09		20 39		21 09		21 39		22 09		22 39		23 09		23 39
Ellesmere Port	d	18 46		19 16		19 49		20 19		20 49		21 19		21 49		22 19		22 49		23 19	
Overpool	d	18 49		19 19		19 52		20 22		20 52		21 22		21 52		22 22		22 52		23 22	
Little Sutton	d	18 51		19 21		19 54		20 24		20 54		21 24		21 54		22 24		22 54		23 24	
Hooton	d	18 59	19 14	19 29	19 44	20 00	20 14	20 29	20 44	20 59	21 14	21 29	21 44	21 59	22 14	22 29	22 44	22 59	23 14	23 29	23 45
Eastham Rake	d	19 01	19 16	19 31	19 46	20 02	20 16	20 31	20 46	21 01	21 16	21 31	21 46	22 01	22 16	22 31	22 46	23 01	23 16	23 31	
Bromborough	d	19 03	19 18	19 33	19 48	20 04	20 18	20 33	20 48	21 03	21 18	21 33	21 48	22 03	22 18	22 33	22 48	23 03	23 18	23 33	
Bromborough Rake	d	19 05	19 20	19 35	19 50	20 06	20 20	20 35	20 50	21 05	21 20	21 35	21 50	22 05	22 20	22 35	22 50	23 05	23 20	23 35	
Spital	d	19 07	19 22	19 37	19 52	20 08	20 22	20 37	20 52	21 07	21 22	21 37	21 52	22 07	22 22	22 37	22 52	23 07	23 22	23 37	
Port Sunlight	d	19 09	19 24	19 39	19 54	20 10	20 24	20 39	20 54	21 09	21 24	21 39	21 54	22 09	22 24	22 39	22 54	23 09	23 24	23 39	
Bebington	d	19 11	19 26	19 41	19 56	20 12	20 26	20 41	20 56	21 11	21 26	21 41	21 56	22 11	22 26	22 41	22 56	23 11	23 26	23 41	
Rock Ferry	d	19 14	19 29	19 44	19 59	20 15	20 29	20 44	20 59	21 14	21 29	21 44	21 59	22 14	22 29	22 44	22 59	23 14	23 29	23 44	
Green Lane	d	19 17	19 32	19 47	20 02	20 18	20 32	20 47	21 02	21 17	21 32	21 47	22 02	22 17	22 32	22 47	23 02	23 17	23 32	23 47	
Birkenhead Central	d	19 19	19 34	19 49	20 04	20 20	20 34	20 49	21 04	21 19	21 34	21 49	22 04	22 19	22 34	22 49	23 04	23 19	23 34	23 49	
Hamilton Square	d	19 21	19 36	19 51	20 06	20 22	20 36	20 51	21 06	21 21	21 36	21 51	22 06	22 21	22 36	22 51	23 06	23 21	23 36	23 51	
James Street	d	19 24	19 39	19 54	20 09	20 25	20 39	20 54	21 09	21 24	21 39	21 54	22 09	22 24	22 39	22 54	23 09	23 24	23 39	23 54	
Moorfields 10	a	19 26	19 41	19 56	20 11	20 27	20 41	20 56	21 11	21 26	21 41	21 56	22 11	22 26	22 41	22 56	23 11	23 26	23 41	23 56	
Liverpool Lime Street 10	a	19 28	19 43	19 58	20 13	20 29	20 43	20 58	21 13	21 28	21 43	21 58	22 13	22 28	22 43	22 58	23 13	23 28	23 43	23 58	
Liverpool Central 10	a	19 30	19 45	20 00	20 15	20 31	20 45	21 00	21 15	21 30	21 45	22 00	22 15	22 30	22 45	23 00	23 15	23 30	23 45	23 59	

For alternative trains between Hamilton Square and Liverpool see table 106

Table 107R

Sundays

8 December to 11 May

Chester, Ellesmere Port - Liverpool

Network Diagram - see first Page of Table 101

		ME	ME	ME	ME	ME		ME	ME	ME	ME	ME	ME	ME	ME
Chester	d			08 00		08 30			22 00		22 30		23 00		23 30
Bache	d			08 03		08 33			22 03		22 33		23 03		23 33
Capenhurst	d			08 09		08 39			22 09		22 39		23 09		23 39
Ellesmere Port	d		07 49		08 19			21 49		22 19		22 49		23 19	
Overpool	d		07 52		08 22			21 52		22 22		22 52		23 22	
Little Sutton	d		07 54		08 24			21 54		22 24		22 54		23 24	
Hooton	d	07 44	07 59	08 14	08 29	08 44	and at	21 59	22 14	22 29	22 44	22 59	23 14	23 29	23 45
Eastham Rake	d	07 46	08 01	08 16	08 31	08 46	the same	22 01	22 16	22 31	22 46	23 01	23 16	23 31	
Bromborough	d	07 48	08 03	08 18	08 33	08 48	minutes	22 03	22 18	22 33	22 48	23 03	23 18	23 33	
Bromborough Rake	d	07 50	08 05	08 20	08 35	08 50	past	22 05	22 20	22 35	22 50	23 05	23 20	23 35	
Spital	d	07 52	08 07	08 22	08 37	08 52	each	22 07	22 22	22 37	22 52	23 07	23 22	23 37	
Port Sunlight	d	07 54	08 09	08 24	08 39	08 54	hour until	22 09	22 24	22 39	22 54	23 09	23 24	23 39	
Bebington	d	07 56	08 11	08 26	08 41	08 56		22 11	22 26	22 41	22 56	23 11	23 26	23 41	
Rock Ferry	d	07 59	08 14	08 29	08 44	08 59		22 14	22 29	22 44	22 59	23 14	23 29	23 44	
Green Lane	d	08 02	08 17	08 32	08 47	09 02		22 17	22 32	22 47	23 02	23 17	23 32	23 47	
Birkenhead Central	d	08 04	08 19	08 34	08 49	09 04		22 19	22 34	22 49	23 04	23 19	23 34	23 49	
Hamilton Square	d	08 06	08 21	08 36	08 51	09 06		22 21	22 36	22 51	23 06	23 21	23 36	23 51	
James Street	d	08 09	08 24	08 39	08 54	09 09		22 24	22 39	22 54	23 09	23 24	23 39	23 54	
Moorfields 10	a	08 11	08 26	08 41	08 56	09 11		22 26	22 41	22 56	23 11	23 26	23 41	23 56	
Liverpool Lime Street 10	a	08 13	08 28	08 43	08 58	09 13		22 28	22 43	22 58	23 13	23 28	23 43	23 58	
Liverpool Central 10	a	08 15	08 30	08 45	09 00	09 15		22 30	22 45	23 00	23 15	23 30	23 45	23 59	

For alternative trains between Hamilton Square and Liverpool see table 106

Table 109

Mondays to Fridays

9 December to 16 May

Ellesmere Port - Helsby

Network Diagram - see first Page of Table 101

Miles			NT	NT	NT	NT
0	**Ellesmere Port**	d	06 19	06 53	15 34	16 04
2½	Stanlow & Thornton	d	06 23	06 57	15 38	16 08
3¼	Ince & Elton	d	06 26	07 00	15 41	16 11
5¼	**Helsby**	a	06 30	07 03	15 45	16 14
—	Warrington Bank Quay 81	a		07 23		16 34

Saturdays

14 December to 17 May

		NT	NT	NT	NT
Ellesmere Port	d	06 19	06 56	15 34	16 04
Stanlow & Thornton	d	06 23	07 00	15 38	16 08
Ince & Elton	d	06 26	07 03	15 41	16 11
Helsby	a	06 30	07 07	15 45	16 14
Warrington Bank Quay 81	a				16 34

No Sunday Service

Table 109R

Mondays to Fridays

9 December to 16 May

Helsby - Ellesmere Port

Network Diagram - see first Page of Table 101

Miles			NT	NT	NT	NT
—	Warrington Bank Quay 81	d	05 49			
0	**Helsby**	d	06 03	06 33	15 17	15 48
2	Ince & Elton	d	06 06	06 36	15 20	15 51
2¾	Stanlow & Thornton	d	06 08	06 38	15 22	15 53
5¼	**Ellesmere Port**	a	06 15	06 45	15 28	15 59

Saturdays

14 December to 17 May

		NT	NT	NT	NT
Warrington Bank Quay 81	d	05 49			
Helsby	d	06 03	06 33	15 17	15 48
Ince & Elton	d	06 06	06 36	15 20	15 51
Stanlow & Thornton	d	06 08	06 38	15 22	15 53
Ellesmere Port	a	06 15	06 45	15 28	15 59

No Sunday Service

Network Diagram for Tables 114, 115

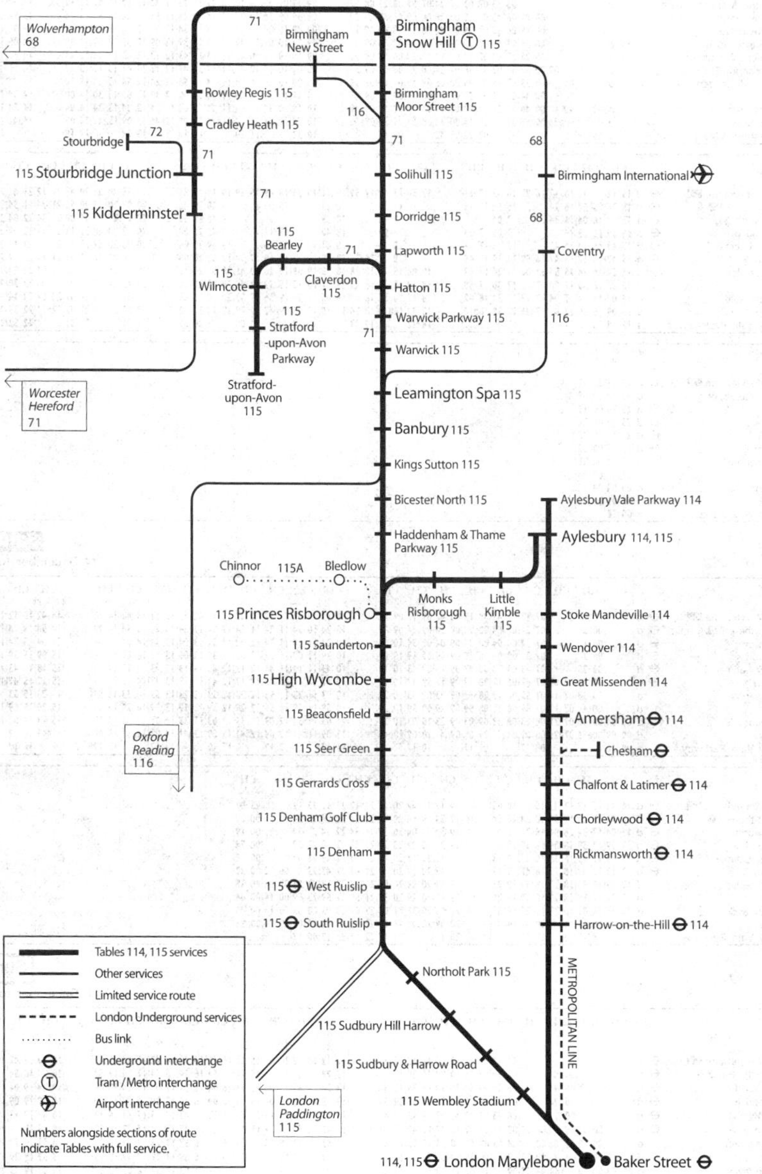
Wolverhampton 68
71
Birmingham New Street
Birmingham Snow Hill Ⓣ 115
Rowley Regis 115
Birmingham Moor Street 115
116
Cradley Heath 115
Stourbridge
72
71
71
68
115 Stourbridge Junction
Solihull 115
Birmingham International
115 Kidderminster
71
Dorridge 115
68
115 Bearley
71
Lapworth 115
Coventry
115 Wilmcote
Claverdon 115
Hatton 115
115 Stratford -upon-Avon Parkway
Warwick Parkway 115
116
71
Warwick 115
Stratford-upon-Avon 115
Worcester Hereford 71
Leamington Spa 115
Banbury 115
Kings Sutton 115
Bicester North 115
Aylesbury Vale Parkway 114
Haddenham & Thame Parkway 115
Aylesbury 114, 115
Chinnor
115A
Bledlow
Monks Risborough 115
Little Kimble 115
115 Princes Risborough
Stoke Mandeville 114
115 Saunderton
Wendover 114
115 High Wycombe
Great Missenden 114
115 Beaconsfield
Amersham 114
Oxford Reading 116
115 Seer Green
Chesham
115 Gerrards Cross
Chalfont & Latimer 114
115 Denham Golf Club
Chorleywood 114
115 Denham
Rickmansworth 114
115 West Ruislip
115 South Ruislip
Harrow-on-the-Hill 114
Northolt Park 115
METROPOLITAN LINE
115 Sudbury Hill Harrow
115 Sudbury & Harrow Road
115 Wembley Stadium
London Paddington 115
114, 115 London Marylebone
Baker Street
Tables 114, 115 services
Other services
Limited service route
London Underground services
Bus link
Underground interchange
Tram / Metro interchange
Airport interchange
Numbers alongside sections of route indicate Tables with full service.

TOCs operating on this network - Chiltern Railways (CH)

Table 114

Mondays to Fridays

9 December to 16 May

London - Amersham and Aylesbury

Network Diagram - see first Page of Table 114

Miles				CH MX	CH MO	CH MX	CH	CH	CH	CH	CH	CH		CH	CH	CH	CH	CH	CH	CH	CH	CH		CH	CH	CH
0	London Marylebone 10	⊖	d				06 33	07 03	07 24	07 57	08 27	08 57		09 27	09 42	10 12	10 42	11 12	11 42	12 12	12 42	13 12		13 42	14 12	14 42
9	Harrow-on-the-Hill 3 §	⊖	d			00 09	06 45	07 15	07 36	08 09	08 39	09 09		09 39	09 54	10 24	10 54	11 24	11 54	12 24	12 54	13 24		13 54	14 24	14 54
17	Rickmansworth §	⊖	d			00 19	06 55	07 25	07 46	08 19	08 49	09 19		09 49	10 04	10 34	11 04	11 34	12 04	12 34	13 04	13 34		14 04	14 34	15 04
19¼	Chorleywood §	⊖	d			00 24	07 00	07 30	07 51	08 24	08 54	09 24		09 54	10 09	10 39	11 09	11 39	12 09	12 39	13 09	13 39		14 09	14 39	15 09
21½	Chalfont & Latimer §	⊖	d			00 28	07 04	07 34	07 55	08 28	08 58	09 28		09 58	10 13	10 43	11 13	11 43	12 13	12 43	13 13	13 43		14 13	14 43	15 13
23½	Amersham §	⊖	d		00 02	00 32	07 08	07 38	07 59	08 32	09 02	09 32		10 02	10 17	10 47	11 17	11 47	12 17	12 47	13 17	13 47		14 17	14 47	15 17
28¾	Great Missenden		d		00 08	00 38	07 15	07 45	08 06	08 39	09 09	09 39		10 09	10 24	10 54	11 24	11 54	12 24	12 54	13 24	13 54		14 24	14 54	15 24
33¼	Wendover		d		00 14	00 44	07 21	07 52	08 12	08 45	09 15	09 45		10 15	10 30	11 00	11 30	12 00	12 30	13 00	13 30	14 00		14 30	15 00	15 30
35¼	Stoke Mandeville		d	00 04	00 18	00 48	07 25	07 57	08 17	08 49	09 19	09 49		10 19	10 34	11 04	11 34	12 04	12 34	13 04	13 34	14 04		14 34	15 04	15 34
37¾	Aylesbury		d	00 09	00a26	00a56	07 30	08 14	08 34	08a56	09 36	09a56		10 24	10a41	11 12	11a41	12 09	12a41	13 09	13a41	14 09		14a41	15 09	15a41
40½	Aylesbury Vale Parkway		a	00 18			07 39	08 22	08 42		09 44			10 33		11 20		12 18		13 18		14 18			15 18	

			CH	CH	CH	CH	CH	CH		CH	CH	CH	CH	CH	CH	CH	CH	CH		CH	CH	CH	CH	CH	CH	CH
London Marylebone 10	⊖	d	15 12	15 42	16 12	16 27	16 42	17 11		17 30	17 42	17 59	18 11	18 32	18 43	18 59	19 18	19 33		19 55	20 21	20 42	21 12	21 42	22 12	22 42
Harrow-on-the-Hill 3 §	⊖	d	15 24	15 54	16 24		16 54	17 23			17 54		18 23		18 55		19 30	19 45		20 07	20 33	20 55	21 24	21 54	22 24	22 54
Rickmansworth §	⊖	d	15 34	16 04	16 34		17 04				18 04		18 35				19 40	19 55		20 17	20 43	21 08	21 34	22 04	22 34	23 04
Chorleywood §	⊖	d	15 39	16 09	16 39		17 09	17 37			18 09		18 40		19 11		19 45	20 00		20 22	20 48	21 13	21 39	22 09	22 39	23 09
Chalfont & Latimer §	⊖	d	15 43	16 13	16 43		17 13	17 41			18 13		18 44		19 15		19 49	20 04		20 26	20 52	21 17	21 43	22 13	22 43	23 13
Amersham §	⊖	d	15 47	16 17	16 47	16 59	17 17	17 45			18 17	18 31	18 48		19 19	19 34	19 53	20 08		20 30	20 56	21 21	21 47	22 17	22 47	23 17
Great Missenden		d	15 54	16 24	16 54	17 06	17 24	17 52		18 06	18 24	18 38	18 55	19 09	19 26	19 41	20 00	20 15		20 37	21 03	21 27	21 54	22 24	22 54	23 24
Wendover		d	16 00	16 30	17 00	17 12	17 30	17 58		18 12	18 30	18 44	19 01	19 15	19 32	19 48	20 06	20 21		20 43	21 09	21 33	22 00	22 30	23 00	23 30
Stoke Mandeville		d	16 04	16 34	17 04	17 17	17 34	18 02		18 17	18 34	18 49	19 05	19 20	19 36	19 53	20 10	20 25		20 47	21 13	21 37	22 04	22 34	23 04	23 34
Aylesbury		d	16 09	16 39	17 09	17a25	17 39	18a10		18 24	18a41	18 54	19a10	19 25	19a42	19 59	20a17	20 30		20 53	21a20	21 42	22a11	22 39	23 09	23a41
Aylesbury Vale Parkway		a	16 18	16 48	17 18		17 48			18 32		19 03		19 34		20 08		20 39		21 01		21 53		22 52	23 18	

			CH	CH
London Marylebone 10	⊖	d	23 12	23 57
Harrow-on-the-Hill 3 §	⊖	d	23 24	00 09
Rickmansworth §	⊖	d	23 34	00 19
Chorleywood §	⊖	d	23 39	00 24
Chalfont & Latimer §	⊖	d	23 43	00 28
Amersham §	⊖	d	23 47	00 32
Great Missenden		d	23 54	00 38
Wendover		d	23 59	00 44
Stoke Mandeville		d	00 04	00 48
Aylesbury		d	00 09	00a56
Aylesbury Vale Parkway		a	00 18	

Saturdays

14 December to 17 May

			CH	CH	CH	CH	CH	CH	CH	CH	CH		CH	CH	CH	CH	CH	CH	CH	CH	CH		CH	CH	CH	CH
London Marylebone 10	⊖	d				07 12	07 42	08 12	08 42	09 12	09 42		10 12	10 42	11 12	11 42	12 12	12 42	13 12	13 42	14 12		14 42	15 12	15 42	16 12
Harrow-on-the-Hill 3 §	⊖	d		00 09		07 24	07 54	08 24	08 54	09 24	09 54		10 24	10 54	11 24	11 54	12 24	12 54	13 24	13 54	14 24		14 54	15 24	15 54	16 24
Rickmansworth §	⊖	d		00 19		07 34	08 04	08 34	09 04	09 34	10 04		10 34	11 04	11 34	12 04	12 34	13 04	13 34	14 04	14 34		15 04	15 34	16 04	16 34
Chorleywood §	⊖	d		00 24		07 39	08 09	08 39	09 09	09 39	10 09		10 39	11 09	11 39	12 09	12 39	13 09	13 39	14 09	14 39		15 09	15 39	16 09	16 39
Chalfont & Latimer §	⊖	d		00 28		07 43	08 13	08 43	09 13	09 43	10 13		10 43	11 13	11 43	12 13	12 43	13 13	13 43	14 13	14 43		15 13	15 43	16 13	16 43
Amersham §	⊖	d		00 32	07 05	07 47	08 17	08 47	09 17	09 47	10 17		10 47	11 17	11 47	12 17	12 47	13 17	13 47	14 17	14 47		15 17	15 47	16 17	16 47
Great Missenden		d		00 38	07 11	07 53	08 23	08 53	09 23	09 53	10 23		10 53	11 23	11 53	12 23	12 53	13 23	13 53	14 23	14 53		15 23	15 53	16 23	16 53
Wendover		d		00 44	07 17	07 59	08 29	08 59	09 29	09 59	10 29		10 59	11 29	11 59	12 29	12 59	13 29	13 59	14 29	14 59		15 29	15 59	16 29	16 59
Stoke Mandeville		d	00 04	00 48	07 21	08 03	08 33	09 03	09 33	10 03	10 33		11 03	11 33	12 03	12 33	13 03	13 33	14 03	14 33	15 03		15 33	16 03	16 33	17 03
Aylesbury		d	00 09	00a56	07a29	08 09	08a41	09 09	09a41	10 09	10a41		11 09	11a41	12 09	12a41	13 09	13a41	14 09	14a41	15 09		15a41	16 09	16a41	17 09
Aylesbury Vale Parkway		a	00 18			08 17		09 17		10 17			11 17		12 17		13 17		14 17		15 17			16 17		17 17

			CH	CH	CH	CH	CH		CH	CH	CH	CH	CH	CH		CH
London Marylebone 10	⊖	d	16 42	17 12	17 42	18 12	18 42		19 12	19 42	20 12	21 12	22 12	23 12		23 57
Harrow-on-the-Hill 3 §	⊖	d	16 54	17 24	17 54	18 24	18 54		19 24	19 54	20 24	21 24	22 24	23 24		00 09
Rickmansworth §	⊖	d	17 04	17 34	18 04	18 34	19 04		19 34	20 04	20 34	21 34	22 34	23 34		00 19
Chorleywood §	⊖	d	17 09	17 39	18 09	18 39	19 09		19 39	20 09	20 39	21 39	22 39	23 39		00 24
Chalfont & Latimer §	⊖	d	17 13	17 43	18 13	18 43	19 13		19 43	20 13	20 43	21 43	22 43	23 43		00 28
Amersham §	⊖	d	17 17	17 47	18 17	18 47	19 17		19 47	20 17	20 47	21 47	22 47	23 47	00 02	00 32
Great Missenden		d	17 23	17 53	18 23	18 53	19 23		19 53	20 23	20 53	21 53	22 53	23 53	00 08	00 38
Wendover		d	17 29	17 59	18 29	18 59	19 29		19 59	20 29	20 59	21 59	22 59	23 59	00 14	00 44
Stoke Mandeville		d	17 33	18 03	18 33	19 03	19 33		20 03	20 33	21 03	22 03	23 03	00 03	00 18	00 48
Aylesbury		d	17a41	18 09	18a41	19 09	19a41		20 09	20a41	21 09	22 09	23 09	00 09	00a26	00a56
Aylesbury Vale Parkway		a		18 17		19 17			20 17		21 17	22 17	23 17	00 17		

Sundays

8 December to 11 May

			CH	CH	CH	CH	CH	CH	CH	CH	CH		CH	CH	CH	CH	CH	CH	CH	CH	CH		CH	CH	CH	CH
London Marylebone 10	⊖	d					08 12	09 12	10 12	11 12	12 12		13 12	14 12	14 42	15 12	15 42	16 12	16 42	17 12	17 42		18 12	18 42	19 12	19 42
Harrow-on-the-Hill 3 §	⊖	d			00 09		08 24	09 24	10 24	11 24	12 24		13 24	14 24	14 54	15 24	15 54	16 24	16 54	17 24	17 54		18 24	18 54	19 24	19 54
Rickmansworth §	⊖	d			00 19		08 34	09 34	10 34	11 34	12 34		13 34	14 34	15 04	15 34	16 04	16 34	17 04	17 34	18 04		18 34	19 04	19 34	20 04
Chorleywood §	⊖	d			00 24		08 39	09 39	10 39	11 39	12 39		13 39	14 39	15 09	15 39	16 09	16 39	17 09	17 39	18 09		18 39	19 09	19 39	20 09
Chalfont & Latimer §	⊖	d			00 28		08 43	09 43	10 43	11 43	12 43		13 43	14 43	15 13	15 43	16 13	16 43	17 13	17 43	18 13		18 43	19 13	19 43	20 13
Amersham §	⊖	d		00 02	00 32	08 17	08 47	09 47	10 47	11 47	12 47		13 47	14 47	15 17	15 47	16 17	16 47	17 17	17 47	18 17		18 47	19 17	19 47	20 17
Great Missenden		d		00 08	00 38	08 23	08 53	09 53	10 53	11 53	12 53		13 53	14 53	15 23	15 53	16 23	16 53	17 23	17 53	18 23		18 53	19 23	19 53	20 23
Wendover		d		00 14	00 44	08 29	08 59	09 59	10 59	11 59	12 59		13 59	14 59	15 29	15 59	16 29	16 59	17 29	17 59	18 29		18 59	19 29	19 59	20 29
Stoke Mandeville		d	00 03	00 18	00 48	08 33	09 03	10 03	11 03	12 03	13 03		14 03	15 03	15 33	16 03	16 33	17 03	17 33	18 03	18 33		19 03	19 33	20 03	20 33
Aylesbury		d	00 09	00a26	00a56	08a41	09 09	10 09	11 09	12 09	13 09		14 09	15 09	15a41	16 09	16a41	17 09	17a41	18 09	18a41		19 09	19a41	20 09	20a41
Aylesbury Vale Parkway		a	00 17				09 17	10 17	11 17	12 17	13 17		14 17	15 17		16 17		17 17		18 17			19 17		20 17	

§ London Underground Limited (Metropolitan Line) services operate between Harrow-on-the-Hill, Rickmansworth, Chorleywood, Chalfont & Latimer and Amersham

Table 114

Sundays

8 December to 11 May

London - Amersham and Aylesbury

Network Diagram - see first Page of Table 114

			CH	CH	CH	CH	CH	CH
London Marylebone 10	⊖	d	20 12	20 42	21 12	21 42	22 27	23 27
Harrow-on-the-Hill 3 §	⊖	d	20 24	20 54	21 24	21 54	22 39	23 39
Rickmansworth §	⊖	d	20 34	21 04	21 34	22 04	22 49	23 49
Chorleywood §	⊖	d	20 39	21 09	21 39	22 09	22 54	23 54
Chalfont & Latimer §	⊖	d	20 43	21 13	21 43	22 13	22 58	23 58
Amersham §	⊖	d	20 47	21 17	21 47	22 17	23 02	00 02
Great Missenden		d	20 53	21 23	21 53	22 23	23 08	00 08
Wendover		d	20 59	21 29	21 59	22 29	23 14	00 14
Stoke Mandeville		d	21 03	21 33	22 03	22 33	23 18	00 18
Aylesbury		d	21 09	21a41	22 09	22a41	23 24	00a26
Aylesbury Vale Parkway		a	21 17		22 17		23 32	

§ London Underground Limited (Metropolitan Line) services operate between Harrow-on-the-Hill, Rickmansworth, Chorleywood, Chalfont & Latimer and Amersham

Table 114R

Aylesbury and Amersham - London

Mondays to Fridays

9 December to 16 May

Network Diagram - see first Page of Table 114

Miles			CH	CH	CH	CH	CH	CH		CH	CH	CH	CH	CH	CH	CH	CH	CH		CH	CH	CH	CH	CH	CH
0	**Aylesbury Vale Parkway**	d	05 15	05 44		06 19		06 51			07 23		07 49	08 08	08 28	09 00	09 30	10 00			11 00		12 00		13 00
2¾	**Aylesbury**	d	05 20	05 49	06 07	06 24	06 38	06 56		07 10	07 28	07 42	08 00	08 13	08 33	09 05	09 35	10 05		10 35	11 05	11 35	12 05	12 35	13 05
5¼	Stoke Mandeville	d	05 25	05 54	06 11	06 29	06 43	07 01		07 15	07 33	07 47	08 05	08 18	08 37	09 09	09 39	10 09		10 39	11 09	11 39	12 09	12 39	13 09
7¼	Wendover	d	05 29	05 58	06 15	06 33	06 47	07 05		07 19	07 37	07 51	08 09	08 22	08 41	09 13	09 43	10 13		10 43	11 13	11 43	12 13	12 43	13 13
11¾	Great Missenden	d	05 36	06 04	06 21	06 40	06 53	07 12		07 25	07 44	07 57	08 16	08 28	08 47	09 19	09 49	10 19		10 49	11 19	11 49	12 19	12 49	13 19
17	**Amersham** § ⊖	d	05 43	06 11	06 28	06 47	07 00	07 19		07 32	07 51	08 04	08 23	08 35	08 54	09 26	09 56	10 26		10 56	11 26	11 56	12 26	12 56	13 26
19	Chalfont & Latimer § ⊖	d		06 15	06 32		07 04			07 36		08 08		08 39	08 58	09 30	10 00	10 30		11 00	11 30	12 00	12 30	13 00	13 30
21¼	Chorleywood § ⊖	d		06 18	06 35		07 07			07 39		08 11		08 42	09 01	09 33	10 03	10 33		11 03	11 33	12 03	12 33	13 03	13 33
23½	Rickmansworth § ⊖	d		06 23	06 40		07 12					08 16			09 06	09 38	10 08	10 38		11 08	11 38	12 08	12 38	13 08	13 38
31½	Harrow-on-the-Hill 3 § ⊖	d	06 01	06 34	06 51		07 23			07 54		08 27		08 57	09 17	09 49	10 19	10 49		11 19	11 49	12 19	12 49	13 19	13 49
40½	**London Marylebone** 10 ⊖	a	06 16	06 49	07 07	07 19	07 38	07 53		08 09	08 22	08 42	08 59	09 12	09 33	10 05	10 35	11 05		11 35	12 05	12 35	13 05	13 35	14 05

		CH	CH	CH		CH	CH	CH	CH	CH	CH	CH	CH	CH		CH	CH	CH	CH	CH	CH
Aylesbury Vale Parkway	d	13 30		14 30		15 00		16 00	16 30	17 00	17 27		18 18			19 18		20 24		21 30	22 30
Aylesbury	d	13 35	14 05	14 35		15 05	15 35	16 05	16 35	17 05	17 32	18 03	18 30	19 03		19 35	20 05	20 35	21 05	21 35	22 35
Stoke Mandeville	d	13 39	14 09	14 39		15 09	15 39	16 09	16 39	17 09	17 36	18 08	18 34	19 07		19 39	20 09	20 39	21 09	21 39	22 39
Wendover	d	13 43	14 13	14 43		15 13	15 43	16 13	16 43	17 13	17 40	18 12	18 38	19 11		19 43	20 13	20 43	21 13	21 43	22 43
Great Missenden	d	13 49	14 19	14 49		15 19	15 49	16 19	16 49	17 19	17 46	18 18	18 44	19 17		19 49	20 19	20 49	21 19	21 49	22 49
Amersham § ⊖	d	13 56	14 26	14 56		15 26	15 56	16 26	16 56	17 26	17 53	18 24	18 51	19 24		19 56	20 26	20 56	21 26	21 56	22 56
Chalfont & Latimer § ⊖	d	14 00	14 30	15 00		15 30	16 00	16 30	17 00	17 30	17 57	18 28	18 55	19 28		20 00	20 30	21 00	21 30	22 00	23 00
Chorleywood § ⊖	d	14 03	14 33	15 03		15 33	16 03	16 33	17 03	17 33	18 00	18 32	18 58	19 31		20 03	20 33	21 03	21 33	22 03	23 03
Rickmansworth § ⊖	d	14 08	14 38	15 08		15 38	16 08	16 38	17 08	17 38	18 05	18 36	19 03	19 36		20 08	20 38	21 08	21 38	22 08	23 08
Harrow-on-the-Hill 3 § ⊖	d	14 19	14 49	15 19		15 49	16 19	16 49	17 19	17 49	18 16	18 47	19 14	19 47		20 19	20 49	21 19	21 49	22 19	23 19
London Marylebone 10 ⊖	a	14 35	15 05	15 35		16 05	16 35	17 05	17 35	18 05	18 32	19 03	19 30	20 03		20 35	21 05	21 35	22 05	22 35	23 35

Saturdays

14 December to 17 May

		CH	CH	CH	CH	CH	CH	CH	CH	CH		CH	CH	CH	CH	CH	CH	CH	CH	CH		CH	CH	CH	CH
Aylesbury Vale Parkway	d			07 00	07 30		08 30		09 30			10 30		11 30		12 30		13 30		14 30			15 30		16 30
Aylesbury	d	06 05	06 35	07 05	07 35	08 05	08 35	09 05	09 35	10 05		10 35	11 05	11 35	12 05	12 35	13 05	13 35	14 05	14 35		15 05	15 35	16 05	16 35
Stoke Mandeville	d	06 09	06 39	07 09	07 39	08 09	08 39	09 09	09 39	10 09		10 39	11 09	11 39	12 09	12 39	13 09	13 39	14 09	14 39		15 09	15 39	16 09	16 39
Wendover	d	06 13	06 43	07 13	07 43	08 13	08 43	09 13	09 43	10 13		10 43	11 13	11 43	12 13	12 43	13 13	13 43	14 13	14 43		15 13	15 43	16 13	16 43
Great Missenden	d	06 19	06 49	07 19	07 49	08 19	08 49	09 19	09 49	10 19		10 49	11 19	11 49	12 19	12 49	13 19	13 49	14 19	14 49		15 19	15 49	16 19	16 49
Amersham § ⊖	d	06 26	06a58	07 26	07 56	08 26	08 56	09 26	09 56	10 26		10 56	11 26	11 56	12 26	12 56	13 26	13 56	14 26	14 56		15 26	15 56	16 26	16 56
Chalfont & Latimer § ⊖	d	06 30		07 30	08 00	08 30	09 00	09 30	10 00	10 30		11 00	11 30	12 00	12 30	13 00	13 30	14 00	14 30	15 00		15 30	16 00	16 30	17 00
Chorleywood § ⊖	d	06 33		07 33	08 03	08 33	09 03	09 33	10 03	10 33		11 03	11 33	12 03	12 33	13 03	13 33	14 03	14 33	15 03		15 33	16 03	16 33	17 03
Rickmansworth § ⊖	d	06 38		07 38	08 08	08 38	09 08	09 38	10 08	10 38		11 08	11 38	12 08	12 38	13 08	13 38	14 08	14 38	15 08		15 38	16 08	16 38	17 08
Harrow-on-the-Hill 3 § ⊖	d	06 49		07 49	08 19	08 49	09 19	09 49	10 19	10 49		11 19	11 49	12 19	12 49	13 19	13 49	14 19	14 49	15 19		15 49	16 19	16 49	17 19
London Marylebone 10 ⊖	a	07 05		08 05	08 35	09 05	09 35	10 05	10 35	11 05		11 35	12 05	12 35	13 05	13 35	14 05	14 35	15 05	15 35		16 05	16 35	17 05	17 35

		CH	CH	CH	CH	CH		CH	CH	CH	CH
Aylesbury Vale Parkway	d		17 30		18 30			19 46	20 46	21 46	
Aylesbury	d	17 05	17 35	18 05	18 35	19 05		20 05	21 05	22 05	23 20
Stoke Mandeville	d	17 09	17 39	18 09	18 39	19 09		20 09	21 09	22 09	23 24
Wendover	d	17 13	17 43	18 13	18 43	19 13		20 13	21 13	22 13	23 28
Great Missenden	d	17 19	17 49	18 19	18 49	19 19		20 19	21 19	22 19	23 34
Amersham § ⊖	d	17 26	17 56	18 26	18 56	19 26		20 26	21 26	22 26	23a43
Chalfont & Latimer § ⊖	d	17 30	18 00	18 30	19 00	19 30		20 30	21 30	22 30	
Chorleywood § ⊖	d	17 33	18 03	18 33	19 03	19 33		20 33	21 33	22 33	
Rickmansworth § ⊖	d	17 38	18 08	18 38	19 08	19 38		20 38	21 38	22 38	
Harrow-on-the-Hill 3 § ⊖	d	17 49	18 19	18 49	19 19	19 49		20 49	21 49	22 49	
London Marylebone 10 ⊖	a	18 05	18 35	19 05	19 35	20 05		21 05	22 05	23 05	

Sundays

8 December to 11 May

		CH	CH	CH	CH	CH	CH	CH	CH	CH		CH	CH	CH	CH	CH	CH	CH	CH	CH		CH	CH	CH	CH
Aylesbury Vale Parkway	d	07 30	08 30	09 00	09 30	10 00	10 30	11 30	12 30	13 30		14 30		15 30		16 30		17 30		18 30			19 30		20 30
Aylesbury	d	07 35	08 35	09 05	09 35	10 05	10 35	11 35	12 35	13 35		14 35	15 05	15 35	16 05	16 35	17 05	17 35	18 05	18 35		19 05	19 35	20 05	20 35
Stoke Mandeville	d	07 39	08 39	09 09	09 39	10 09	10 39	11 39	12 39	13 39		14 39	15 09	15 39	16 09	16 39	17 09	17 39	18 09	18 39		19 09	19 39	20 09	20 39
Wendover	d	07 43	08 43	09 13	09 43	10 13	10 43	11 43	12 43	13 43		14 43	15 13	15 43	16 13	16 43	17 13	17 43	18 13	18 43		19 13	19 43	20 13	20 43
Great Missenden	d	07 49	08 49	09 19	09 49	10 19	10 49	11 49	12 49	13 49		14 49	15 19	15 49	16 19	16 49	17 19	17 49	18 19	18 49		19 19	19 49	20 19	20 49
Amersham § ⊖	d	07 56	08 56	09 26	09 56	10 26	10 56	11 56	12 56	13 56		14 56	15 26	15 56	16 26	16 56	17 26	17 56	18 26	18 56		19 26	19 56	20 26	20 56
Chalfont & Latimer § ⊖	d	08 00	09 00	09 30	10 00	10 30	11 00	12 00	13 00	14 00		15 00	15 30	16 00	16 30	17 00	17 30	18 00	18 30	19 00		19 30	20 00	20 30	21 00
Chorleywood § ⊖	d	08 03	09 03	09 33	10 03	10 33	11 03	12 03	13 03	14 03		15 03	15 33	16 03	16 33	17 03	17 33	18 03	18 33	19 03		19 33	20 03	20 33	21 03
Rickmansworth § ⊖	d	08 08	09 08	09 38	10 08	10 38	11 08	12 08	13 08	14 08		15 08	15 38	16 08	16 38	17 08	17 38	18 08	18 38	19 08		19 38	20 08	20 38	21 08
Harrow-on-the-Hill 3 § ⊖	d	08 19	09 19	09 49	10 19	10 49	11 19	12 19	13 19	14 19		15 19	15 49	16 19	16 49	17 19	17 49	18 19	18 49	19 19		19 49	20 19	20 49	21 19
London Marylebone 10 ⊖	a	08 35	09 35	10 05	10 35	11 05	11 35	12 35	13 35	14 35		15 35	16 05	16 35	17 05	17 35	18 05	18 35	19 05	19 35		20 05	20 35	21 05	21 35

		CH	CH	CH	CH
Aylesbury Vale Parkway	d		21 30		22 30
Aylesbury	d	21 05	21 35	22 05	22 35
Stoke Mandeville	d	21 09	21 39	22 09	22 39
Wendover	d	21 13	21 43	22 13	22 43
Great Missenden	d	21 19	21 49	22 19	22 49
Amersham § ⊖	d	21 26	21 56	22a28	22 56
Chalfont & Latimer § ⊖	d	21 30	22 00		23 00
Chorleywood § ⊖	d	21 33	22 03		23 03
Rickmansworth § ⊖	d	21 38	22 08		23 08
Harrow-on-the-Hill 3 § ⊖	d	21 49	22 19		23 19
London Marylebone 10 ⊖	a	22 05	22 35		23 35

§ London Underground Limited (Metropolitan Line) services operate between Harrow-on-the-Hill, Rickmansworth, Chorleywood, Chalfont & Latimer and Amersham

Table 115

Mondays to Fridays

9 December to 16 May

London - High Wycombe, Aylesbury, Banbury, Stratford-upon-Avon, Birmingham Snow Hill and Kidderminster

Network Diagram - see first Page of Table 114

Miles	Miles	Miles			CH MX ◇	CH MX ◇	CH MO	CH MX	CH MX	CH MO	CH MX	CH MO	CH MX	CH	CH	LM	CH	CH ◇	CH	CH	CH	CH ◇
—	—	—	**London Marylebone** [10] ⊖	d							00 05		00 10		05 58			06 05	06 20		06 28	06 45
—	—	0	**London Paddington** [15] ⊖	d																		
6½	—	—	Wembley Stadium	d									00 19		06 07				06 30		06 37	
8	—	—	Sudbury & Harrow Road	d																		
8¾	—	—	Sudbury Hill Harrow	d																		
9¾	—	—	Northolt Park	d									00 24		06 12						06 42	
11½	—	—	South Ruislip § ⊖	d						00 02			00 28		06 18							
13¼	—	—	West Ruislip [3] § ⊖	d						00 06			00 32						06 38		06a52	
16	—	—	Denham	d						00 10			00 37		06 24				06 43			
17	—	—	Denham Golf Club	d						00 13					06 27							
18¾	—	—	Gerrards Cross [1]	d					00 02	00 17	00 24		00 42		06 30				06 47			07 04
21¼	—	—	Seer Green	d					00 06	00 21			00 46		06 35				06 52			
23	—	—	Beaconsfield	d					00 10	00 25	00 30		00 50		06 39				06 55			07 10
27¾	—	—	**High Wycombe** [1]	d					00 16	00 31	00 36		00 56	06 04	06a48				07 01			07 16
32¾	—	—	Saunderton	d				00 01		00 37			01 02	06 11					07 07			
36	—	—	**Princes Risborough** [2]	d				00 07	00 26	00 42	00 45	00 48	01 09	06 17					07 13	07 18		07 25
—	1½	—	Monks Risborough	d					00 30			00 51	01 12							07 22		
—	3	—	Little Kimble	d					00 34			00 55	01 16							07 26		
—	7½	—	**Aylesbury**	a					00 44			01 06	01 27							07 36		
4¾	—	—	Haddenham & Thame Parkway	d			00 02	00 14		00 49	00 52			06 24					07 20			07 32
54¾	—	—	**Bicester North** [3]	d			00 16	00 27		01 02	01 05			06a39				06 47	07 33			07 45
65¼	—	—	Kings Sutton	d				00 38		01 13								06 57	07 44			
68¾	—	—	**Banbury**	d		00 03	00a35	00a46		01a20	01a22							07 03	07a51			08 00
88¾	—	—	**Leamington Spa** [8]	d	00 05	00 21											06 52	07 21				08 18
90¾	—	—	Warwick	d	00 09	00 25											06 57	07 26				08 23
92	—	—	Warwick Parkway	d	00 13	00 29												07 29				
94¾	—	—	Hatton	d													07 05	07 35				08 30
—	—	7¾	Claverdon	d												06x31	07 11					08 36
—	—	10	Bearley	d												06x35	07 16					08 42
—	—	11½	Wilmcote	d												06 39	07 20					08 46
—	—	—	Stratford-upon-Avon Parkway	a												06 42	07 23					08 48
—	—	15¼	**Stratford-upon-Avon**	a												06 45	07 27					08 57
99	—	—	Lapworth	a																		
101½	—	—	Dorridge	a	00 22													07 42				
104¾	—	—	Solihull	a	00 28	00 40												07 50				
111¼	—	—	**Birmingham Moor Street**	a	00 43	00 55												08 02				
112	—	—	**Birmingham Snow Hill**	a														08 10				
—	—	—	Rowley Regis	a																		
—	—	—	Cradley Heath	a																		
—	—	—	**Stourbridge Junction** [2]	a																		
—	—	—	**Kidderminster**	a																		

Miles	Miles	Miles			CH	CH	CH ◇	CH	CH	CH	CH	CH ◇	CH	CH	CH	CH	CH ◇	CH	CH	CH
—	—	—	**London Marylebone** [10] ⊖	d	06 48	07 10	07 15	07 21		07 28	07 31	07 45	07 48	07 35	07 51	08 07	08 15	08 20	08 23	08 31
—	—	0	**London Paddington** [15] ⊖	d																
6½	—	—	Wembley Stadium	d	06 57			07 30						07 45	08 00	08 17			08 33	
8	—	—	Sudbury & Harrow Road	d																
8¾	—	—	Sudbury Hill Harrow	d	07 01										08 05					
9¾	—	—	Northolt Park	d	07 03									07 51	08 08					
11½	—	—	South Ruislip § ⊖	d	07 10	07 31								08 02		08 28				
13¼	—	—	West Ruislip [3] § ⊖	d							07 46				08 13					08 46
16	—	—	Denham	d	07 15						07 51				08 18					08 51
17	—	—	Denham Golf Club	d	07 18										08 21					
18¾	—	—	Gerrards Cross [1]	d	07a24			07 43		07 47	07a59			08 10	08a27			08 41	08 47	08a58
21¼	—	—	Seer Green	d						07 52				08 14					08 52	
23	—	—	Beaconsfield	d				07 49		07 55			08 11	08 17				08 47	08 55	
27¾	—	—	**High Wycombe** [1]	d		07 47		07 55		08a04		08 09	08 17	08a24		08 45		08 53	09a04	
32¾	—	—	Saunderton	d				08 01										09 00		
36	—	—	**Princes Risborough** [2]	d		07 57		08 06	08 12				08a30			08 54		09 06		
—	1½	—	Monks Risborough	d					08 16									09 10		
—	3	—	Little Kimble	d					08 20									09 14		
—	7½	—	**Aylesbury**	a					08 30									09 24		
4¾	—	—	Haddenham & Thame Parkway	d		08 04		08 13								09 01				
54¾	—	—	**Bicester North** [3]	d		08 17		08a28				08 31				09 14				
65¼	—	—	Kings Sutton	d		08 28										09 25				
68¾	—	—	**Banbury**	d		08a37	08 07					08 44				09a34	09 07			
88¾	—	—	**Leamington Spa** [8]	d			08 24					09 04					09 25			
90¾	—	—	Warwick	d			08 29					09 09					09 30			
92	—	—	Warwick Parkway	d			08 33					09 14					09 34			
94¾	—	—	Hatton	d																
—	—	7¾	Claverdon	d																
—	—	10	Bearley	d																
—	—	11½	Wilmcote	d																
—	—	—	Stratford-upon-Avon Parkway	a																
—	—	15¼	**Stratford-upon-Avon**	a																
99	—	—	Lapworth	a																
101½	—	—	Dorridge	a								09 24								
104¾	—	—	Solihull	a			08 44					09 30					09 45			
111¼	—	—	**Birmingham Moor Street**	a			08 53					09 42					09 54			
112	—	—	**Birmingham Snow Hill**	a			08 59										10 02			
—	—	—	Rowley Regis	a																
—	—	—	Cradley Heath	a																
—	—	—	**Stourbridge Junction** [2]	a																
—	—	—	**Kidderminster**	a																

§ London Underground Limited (Central Line) also operate services between South Ruislip and West Ruislip at frequent intervals

For complete service between Banbury and Leamington (Birmingham), please refer to table 71

Table 115

Mondays to Fridays

9 December to 16 May

London - High Wycombe, Aylesbury, Banbury, Stratford-upon-Avon, Birmingham Snow Hill and Kidderminster

Network Diagram - see first Page of Table 114

		CH ◇ ⚲ BZ	CH	CH	CH	CH ◇ ⚲	CH ◇	CH	CH	CH	CH ◇ ⚲	CH	CH	CH ◇ ⚲ BZ	CH	CH	CH	CH	CH ◇ ⚲	CH	CH
London Marylebone 10 ⊖	d	08 45	08 48	08 35	08 51	09 15	09 10		09 20	09 23	09 45	09 48	09 52	10 15	10 18	10 21		10 25	10 45	10 48	10 52
London Paddington 15 ⊖	d																				
Wembley Stadium	d			08 45	09 00					09 34			10 01					10 34			11 01
Sudbury & Harrow Road	d																				
Sudbury Hill Harrow	d				09 05								10 05								11 05
Northolt Park	d			08 51	09 08								10 08								11 08
South Ruislip § ⊖	d			09 02			09 28			09 42								10 42			
West Ruislip 3 § ⊖	d				09 13								10 13								11 13
Denham	d				09 18								10 18								11 18
Denham Golf Club	d				09 21								10 21								
Gerrards Cross 1	d			09 10	09a27				09 41	09 51		10 05	10a29			10 41		10 51		11 05	11a25
Seer Green	d			09 14					09 45							10 45					
Beaconsfield	d		09 11	09 17					09 49	09 58		10 10				10 49		10 58		11 10	
High Wycombe 1	d	09 10	09 17	09a24			09 44		09 55	10a07	10 09	10 16			10 47	10 55		11a07	11 09	11 16	
Saunderton	d								10 02							11 02					
Princes Risborough 2	d		09 26				09 53	10 00	10a11			10 25			10 56	11a11	11 23			11 25	
Monks Risborough	d							10 04									11 27				
Little Kimble	d																11 31				
Aylesbury	a							10 18									11 43				
Haddenham & Thame Parkway	d		09 32				09 59					10 32			11 03					11 32	
Bicester North 3	d	09 32	09a48				10 11				10 30	10a46			11a18				11 30	11a46	
Kings Sutton	d																				
Banbury	d	09 46				10 07	10 24				10 43			11 07					11 45		
Leamington Spa 3	d	10 04				10 25	10 42				11 01			11 25					12 04		
Warwick	d	10 10					10 47				11 06								12 09		
Warwick Parkway	d	10 14				10 32					11 09			11 32					12 13		
Hatton	d																				
Claverdon	d																				
Bearley	d																				
Wilmcote	d																				
Stratford-upon-Avon Parkway	a						11 05														
Stratford-upon-Avon	a						11 16														
Lapworth	a																				
Dorridge	a	10 24									11 18								12 23		
Solihull	a	10 31				10 44					11 24			11 44					12 30		
Birmingham Moor Street	a	10 44				10 53					11 32			11 59					12 41		
Birmingham Snow Hill	a					11 01					11 42								12 48		
Rowley Regis	a																				
Cradley Heath	a																				
Stourbridge Junction 2	a																				
Kidderminster	a																				

		CH ◇	CH	CH	CH	CH	CH ◇	CH	CH	CH	CH ◇ ⚲	CH ◇	CH	CH	CH ◇ ⚲	CH	CH	CH ◇ ⚲ BZ
London Marylebone 10 ⊖	d	11 15	11 18	11 21		11 30	11 45	11 48		11 52	12 15	12 18	12 21	12 25	12 45	12 48	12 52	13 15
London Paddington 15 ⊖	d								11 36									
Wembley Stadium	d					11 40				12 01				12 34			13 01	
Sudbury & Harrow Road	d																	
Sudbury Hill Harrow	d									12 05							13 05	
Northolt Park	d									12 08							13 08	
South Ruislip § ⊖	d								12 01					12 42				
West Ruislip 3 § ⊖	d								12 08	12 13							13 13	
Denham	d									12 18							13 18	
Denham Golf Club	d									12 21							13 21	
Gerrards Cross 1	d			11 41		11 53		12 05		12a27			12 41	12 51		13 05	13a27	
Seer Green	d			11 45									12 45					
Beaconsfield	d			11 49		11 59		12 10					12 49	12 58		13 10		
High Wycombe 1	d		11 46	11 55		12a08	12 09	12 16				12 41	12 55	13a07	13 09	13 16		
Saunderton	d			12 02									13 02					
Princes Risborough 2	d		11 55	12a11	12 23			12 25				12 50	13 09			13 25		
Monks Risborough	d				12 27								13 12					
Little Kimble	d												13 16					
Aylesbury	a				12 41								13 27					
Haddenham & Thame Parkway	d		12 02					12 32				12 56				13 32		
Bicester North 3	d		12 15				12 30	12a46				13 08			13 30	13a46		
Kings Sutton	d		12 26															
Banbury	d	12 06	12a35				12 43				13 07	13 21			13 43			14 06
Leamington Spa 3	d	12 23					13 01				13 25	13 39			14 01			14 23
Warwick	d						13 06					13 43			14 06			
Warwick Parkway	d	12 29					13 09				13 32				14 10			14 29
Hatton	d											13 51						
Claverdon	d											13 57						
Bearley	d											14 02						
Wilmcote	d											14 07						
Stratford-upon-Avon Parkway	a											14 10						
Stratford-upon-Avon	a											14 18						
Lapworth	a																	
Dorridge	a						13 18								14 19			
Solihull	a	12 42					13 24				13 44				14 25			14 42
Birmingham Moor Street	a	12 59					13 32				13 59				14 34			14 59
Birmingham Snow Hill	a						13 42								14 42			
Rowley Regis	a																	
Cradley Heath	a																	
Stourbridge Junction 2	a																	
Kidderminster	a																	

§ London Underground Limited (Central Line) also operate services between South Ruislip and West Ruislip at frequent intervals

BZ Business Zone available offering greater comfort and an enhanced working environment. Supplement payable.

For complete service between Banbury and Leamington (Birmingham), please refer to table 71

Table 115

Mondays to Fridays

9 December to 16 May

London - High Wycombe, Aylesbury, Banbury, Stratford-upon-Avon, Birmingham Snow Hill and Kidderminster

Network Diagram - see first Page of Table 114

Station		CH	CH	CH	CH	CH	CH	CH	CH	CH	CH	CH
					◇			◇				
London Marylebone 10 ⊖	d	13 18	13 21	13 25	13 45	13 48	13 52	14 15	14 18	14 21		14 25
London Paddington 15 ⊖	d											
Wembley Stadium	d			13 34			14 01					14 34
Sudbury & Harrow Road	d											
Sudbury Hill Harrow	d						14 05					
Northolt Park	d						14 08					
South Ruislip § ⊖	d			13 42								14 42
West Ruislip 3 § ⊖	d						14 13					
Denham	d						14 18					
Denham Golf Club	d						14 21					
Gerrards Cross 1	d		13 40	13 51		14 05	14a27			14 41		14 51
Seer Green	d		13 44							14 45		
Beaconsfield	d		13 48	13 58		14 10				14 49		14 58
High Wycombe 1	d	13 46	13 54	14a07	14 09	14 16			14 47	14 55		15a07
Saunderton	d		14 00							15 02		
Princes Risborough 2	d	13 55	14 07			14 25			14 56	15a11	15 23	
Monks Risborough	d		14 10								15 27	
Little Kimble	d										15 31	
Aylesbury	a		14 24								15 44	
Haddenham & Thame Parkway	d	14 02				14 32			15 03			
Bicester North 3	d	14a17			14 30	14a46			15 16			
Kings Sutton	d								15 27			
Banbury	d				14 44			15 06	15a36			
Leamington Spa 8	d				15 02			15 23				
Warwick	d				15 06							
Warwick Parkway	d				15 10			15 29				
Hatton	d											
Claverdon	d											
Bearley	d											
Wilmcote	d											
Stratford-upon-Avon Parkway	a											
Stratford-upon-Avon	a											
Lapworth	a											
Dorridge	a				15 19							
Solihull	a				15 25			15 42				
Birmingham Moor Street	a				15 33			15 59				
Birmingham Snow Hill	a				15 42							
Rowley Regis	a											
Cradley Heath	a											
Stourbridge Junction 2	a											
Kidderminster	a											

Station		CH	CH	CH	CH	CH	CH	CH	CH	CH
		◇			◇ trolley	◇			◇ trolley	
London Marylebone 10 ⊖	d	14 45	14 48	14 52	15 15	15 18	15 21	15 25	15 45	15 48
London Paddington 15 ⊖	d									
Wembley Stadium	d			15 01				15 34		
Sudbury & Harrow Road	d									
Sudbury Hill Harrow	d			15 05						
Northolt Park	d			15 08						
South Ruislip § ⊖	d			15 12						
West Ruislip 3 § ⊖	d							15 43		
Denham	d			15 18				15 48		
Denham Golf Club	d			15 21						
Gerrards Cross 1	d		15 05	15a27			15 40	15 53		16 05
Seer Green	d						15 44			
Beaconsfield	d		15 10				15 48	15 59		16 10
High Wycombe 1	d	15 09	15 16			15 46	15 54	16a08	16 09	16 16
Saunderton	d						16 00			
Princes Risborough 2	d		15 25			15 55	16 09			16 25
Monks Risborough	d						16 12			
Little Kimble	d						16 16			
Aylesbury	a						16 28			
Haddenham & Thame Parkway	d		15 32			16 02				16 32
Bicester North 3	d	15 31	15a46			16 15			16 30	16a46
Kings Sutton	d									
Banbury	d	15 44			16 07	16 30			16 43	
Leamington Spa 8	d	16 02			16 25	16 49			17 00	
Warwick	d	16 06				16 54			17 04	
Warwick Parkway	d	16 10			16 32				17 08	
Hatton	d					17 05				
Claverdon	d					17 12				
Bearley	d									
Wilmcote	d					17 22				
Stratford-upon-Avon Parkway	a					17 24				
Stratford-upon-Avon	a					17 35				
Lapworth	a									
Dorridge	a	16 20							17 17	
Solihull	a	16 26			16 44				17 23	
Birmingham Moor Street	a	16 34			16 53				17 35	
Birmingham Snow Hill	a	16 42			17 02				17 44	
Rowley Regis	a									
Cradley Heath	a									
Stourbridge Junction 2	a									
Kidderminster	a									

Station		CH	CH	CH	CH	CH	CH	CH	CH	CH
				◇	◇					
London Marylebone 10 ⊖	d	16 00	15 52	16 15	16 18	16 21	16 24	16 27	16 30	16 36
London Paddington 15 ⊖	d									
Wembley Stadium	d	16 09	16 01				16 33			
Sudbury & Harrow Road	d								16 40	
Sudbury Hill Harrow	d		16 05							
Northolt Park	d		16 08						16 43	
South Ruislip § ⊖	d		16 16						16 51	
West Ruislip 3 § ⊖	d								16a58	
Denham	d		16 22				16 43			
Denham Golf Club	d		16 24							
Gerrards Cross 1	d	16 22	16a30				16 48			16 56
Seer Green	d						16 53			
Beaconsfield	d	16 28				16 42				17 03
High Wycombe 1	d	16a37				16 48	17 01			17a12
Saunderton	d					16 54				
Princes Risborough 2	d					17 00	17 12			
Monks Risborough	d						17 15			
Little Kimble	d						17 19			
Aylesbury	a						17 30	17 25		
Haddenham & Thame Parkway	d				16 55	17 06				
Bicester North 3	d				17 07	17 18				
Kings Sutton	d					17 28				
Banbury	d				17 20	17a40				
Leamington Spa 8	d			17 22	17 37					
Warwick	d				17 41					
Warwick Parkway	d			17 28	17 45					
Hatton	d									
Claverdon	d									
Bearley	d									
Wilmcote	d									
Stratford-upon-Avon Parkway	a									
Stratford-upon-Avon	a									
Lapworth	a									
Dorridge	a				17 55					
Solihull	a			17 40	18 01					
Birmingham Moor Street	a			17 50	18 10					
Birmingham Snow Hill	a			18 02	18 21					
Rowley Regis	a									
Cradley Heath	a									
Stourbridge Junction 2	a									
Kidderminster	a									

Station		CH	CH	CH	CH	CH	CH	CH
		◇ trolley BZ						◇ trolley BZ
London Marylebone 10 ⊖	d	16 47		16 50	16 54	17 02	16 57	17 15
London Paddington 15 ⊖	d							
Wembley Stadium	d					17 11		
Sudbury & Harrow Road	d							
Sudbury Hill Harrow	d						17 08	
Northolt Park	d						17 11	
South Ruislip § ⊖	d						17 18	
West Ruislip 3 § ⊖	d				17 08			
Denham	d				17 13			
Denham Golf Club	d						17 25	
Gerrards Cross 1	d				17 18	17 24	17a30	
Seer Green	d				17 22			
Beaconsfield	d				17 26	17 30		
High Wycombe 1	d			17 16	17 32	17a39		
Saunderton	d							
Princes Risborough 2	d			17 25	17 47			
Monks Risborough	d				17 51			
Little Kimble	d				17 55			
Aylesbury	a				18 08			
Haddenham & Thame Parkway	d			17 31				
Bicester North 3	d	17 31		17a46				
Kings Sutton	d							
Banbury	d	17 45						
Leamington Spa 8	d	18 03	18 17					18 22
Warwick	d		18 22					
Warwick Parkway	d	18 09						18 28
Hatton	d		18 30					
Claverdon	d		18 36					
Bearley	d		18 41					
Wilmcote	d		18 45					
Stratford-upon-Avon Parkway	a		18 47					
Stratford-upon-Avon	a		18 52					
Lapworth	a							
Dorridge	a	18 19						
Solihull	a	18 25						18 41
Birmingham Moor Street	a	18 40						18 49
Birmingham Snow Hill	a							18 54
Rowley Regis	a							19 07
Cradley Heath	a							
Stourbridge Junction 2	a							19 17
Kidderminster	a							19 31

§ London Underground Limited (Central Line) also operate services between South Ruislip and West Ruislip at frequent intervals

BZ Business Zone available offering greater comfort and an enhanced working environment. Supplement payable.

For complete service between Banbury and Leamington (Birmingham), please refer to table 71

Table 115

Mondays to Fridays

9 December to 16 May

London - High Wycombe, Aylesbury, Banbury, Stratford-upon-Avon, Birmingham Snow Hill and Kidderminster

Network Diagram - see first Page of Table 114

		CH ◇	CH	CH	CH	CH	CH	CH	CH ◇	CH	CH	CH	CH	CH	CH ◇ BZ	CH ◇	CH	CH	CH
London Marylebone 10 ⊖	d	17 18		17 21	17 24	17 27	17 30	17 36	17 47	17 50	17 53	18 02	17 56	17 59	18 15	18 18	18 21	18 24	18 29
London Paddington 15 ⊖	d																		
Wembley Stadium	d				17 33							18 11						18 33	
Sudbury & Harrow Road	d					17 39													18 39
Sudbury Hill Harrow	d												18 08						
Northolt Park	d					17 42							18 11						18 42
South Ruislip § ⊖	d					17 51							18 18						18 51
West Ruislip 3 § ⊖	d					17a58					18 08								18a58
Denham	d				17 43						18 13							18 42	
Denham Golf Club	d												18 25						
Gerrards Cross 1	d				17 48			17 56			18 18	18 24	18a31					18 47	
Seer Green	d				17 53						18 22							18 52	
Beaconsfield	d			17 44				18 03			18 26	18 31					18 44		
High Wycombe 1	d			17 50	18 01			18a12		18 17	18 32	18a40					18 50	19 00	
Saunderton	d			17 56													18 56		
Princes Risborough 2	d		18 00	18 02	18 10					18 28	18 43						19 02	19a11	
Monks Risborough	d										18 47								
Little Kimble	d										18 51								
Aylesbury	a		18 18				18 23				19 02			18 53					
Haddenham & Thame Parkway	d	17 55		18 09						18 36						18 57	19 09		
Bicester North 3	d	18 07		18 22	18a28				18 31	18 49						19 08	19a25		
Kings Sutton	d			18 33												19 18			
Banbury	d	18 20		18a42					18 45	19a07					19 09	19 25			
Leamington Spa 8	d	18 37							19 03						19 27	19 42			
Warwick	d	18 41														19 47			
Warwick Parkway	d	18 45							19 09						19 33	19 50			
Hatton	d															19 57			
Claverdon	d																		
Bearley	d																		
Wilmcote	d															20 07			
Stratford-upon-Avon Parkway	a															20 10			
Stratford-upon-Avon	a															20 17			
Lapworth	a																		
Dorridge	a	18 55							19 19						19 43				
Solihull	a	19 00							19 25						19 49				
Birmingham Moor Street	a	19 16							19 38						19 58				
Birmingham Snow Hill ⇌	a								19 46						20 03				
Rowley Regis	a														20 22				
Cradley Heath	a																		
Stourbridge Junction 2	a														20 33				
Kidderminster	a														20 48				

		CH	CH	CH ◇	CH	CH	CH	CH	CH	CH	CH ◇	CH	CH	CH	CH ◇	CH	CH	CH	CH ◇
London Marylebone 10 ⊖	d	18 32	18 36	18 47	18 50		18 53	19 02	18 56	18 59	19 15	19 21	19 24	19 27	19 45	19 48		19 52	20 15
London Paddington 15 ⊖	d																		
Wembley Stadium	d							19 11						19 36				20 01	
Sudbury & Harrow Road	d																	20 04	
Sudbury Hill Harrow	d								19 08									20 07	
Northolt Park	d								19 11				19 35					20 10	
South Ruislip § ⊖	d								19 18					19 43					
West Ruislip 3 § ⊖	d						19 08											20 15	
Denham	d						19 13							19 48				20 19	
Denham Golf Club	d								19 25									20 22	
Gerrards Cross 1	d		18 56				19 18	19 24	19a31				19 45	19 53		20 07		20a30	
Seer Green	d						19 22						19 49			20 11			
Beaconsfield	d		19 02				19 26	19 31					19 53	19 59		20 15			
High Wycombe 1	d		19a11		19 17		19 32	19a40				19 44	19 59	20a08	20 09	20 21			
Saunderton	d												20 05						
Princes Risborough 2	d				19 28	19 36	19a45					19 53	20a13			20 32	20 42		
Monks Risborough	d					19 40											20 46		
Little Kimble	d					19 44											20 50		
Aylesbury	a	19 24				19 55				19 58							21 01		
Haddenham & Thame Parkway	d				19 36							19 59				20 40			
Bicester North 3	d			19 30	19a52							20 10			20 30	20a56			20 59
Kings Sutton	d																		
Banbury	d			19 45							20 09	20a26			20 43				21 12
Leamington Spa 8	d			20 03							20 27				21 01				21 30
Warwick	d			20 08											21 06				
Warwick Parkway	d			20 12							20 33				21 09				21 35
Hatton	d														21 15				
Claverdon	d																		
Bearley	d																		
Wilmcote	d																		
Stratford-upon-Avon Parkway	a																		
Stratford-upon-Avon	a																		
Lapworth	a														21 20				
Dorridge	a			20 22							20 42				21 25				21 45
Solihull	a			20 28							20 48				21 31				21 50
Birmingham Moor Street	a			20 36							21 03				21 40				21 59
Birmingham Snow Hill ⇌	a			20 41											21 48				22 03
Rowley Regis	a			21 00															22 25
Cradley Heath	a																		22 30
Stourbridge Junction 2	a			21 11															22 36
Kidderminster	a			21 26															22 50

§ London Underground Limited (Central Line) also operate services between South Ruislip and West Ruislip at frequent intervals

BZ Business Zone available offering greater comfort and an enhanced working environment. Supplement payable.

For complete service between Banbury and Leamington (Birmingham), please refer to table 71

Table 115

Mondays to Fridays

9 December to 16 May

London - High Wycombe, Aylesbury, Banbury, Stratford-upon-Avon, Birmingham Snow Hill and Kidderminster

Network Diagram - see first Page of Table 114

		CH	CH	CH	CH	CH	CH	CH	CH	CH	CH	CH	CH	CH	CH	CH	CH	CH	CH	CH	CH	CH	CH	CH	CH	CH	CH	CH	CH	CH
																								FX	FO	FX	FX	FO	FO
		◇			◇			◇				◇				◇			◇				◇							
London Marylebone 10 ⊖	d	20 18	20 24	20 27	20 45	20 48	20 52	21 15	21 18		21 24	21 45	21 48		21 52	22 15	22 18	22 24	22 45	22 48		23 00	23 07	23 20	23 30	23 45	00 05	00 10	00 20	00 25
London Paddington 15 ⊖	d																													
Wembley Stadium	d			20 36			21 01				21 33		21 57		22 01			22 33		22 57		23 09		23 29	23 39	23 54		00 19		00 34
Sudbury & Harrow Road	d																													
Sudbury Hill Harrow	d						21 05																							
Northolt Park	d						21 08								22 06							23 14			23 44	23 59		00 24		00 39
South Ruislip § ⊖	d			20 43							21 40							22 40				23 20			23 47	00 02		00 28		00 43
West Ruislip 3 § ⊖	d						21 13								22 11							23 24			23 51	00 06		00 32		00 47
Denham	d			20 48			21 18				21 46				22 16			22 46				23 29			23 55	00 10		00 37		00 52
Denham Golf Club	d						21 21								22 19							23 31			23 58	00 13				
Gerrards Cross 1	d		20 44	20 53		21 07	21a29		21 37		21 51		22 09		22 23		22 37	22 51		23 08		23 35		23 42	00 02	00 17	00 24	00 42	00 39	00 57
Seer Green	d		20 48								21 56							22 56				23 40			00 06	00 21		00 46		01 01
Beaconsfield	d		20 52	20 59		21 14			21 44		21 59		22 15		22 29		22 44	22 59		23 14		23 44		23 49	00 10	00 25	00 30	00 50	00 45	01 05
High Wycombe 1	d	20 45	20 58	21a08	21 09	21 20			21 50		22a08	22 09	22 21		22a38		22 50	23a08	23 09	23 20		23 50		23 55	00 16	00 31	00 36	00 56	00 51	01 11
Saunderton	d		21 05						21 56								22 56							00 01				01 02		01 17
Princes Risborough 2	d	20 56	21 12			21 29			22 02	22 11			22 31	22 34			23 02			23 28	23 34	00a03		00 07	00 26	00 41	00 45	01 09	01 00	01 24
Monks Risborough	d		21 16							22 15				22 37							23 37				00 30	00 45		01 12		01 27
Little Kimble	d		21 20							22 19				22 41							23 41				00 34	00 49		01 16		01 31
Aylesbury	a		21 30							22 29				22 52							23 52				00 44	01 01		01 27		01 42
Haddenham & Thame Parkway	d	21 04			21 22	21 36			22 09			22 22	22 38				23 09		23 22	23 34				00 14			00 52		01 07	
Bicester North 3	d	21 18			21 34	21a51		22 00	22 22			22 34	22a54			22 59	23a25		23 34	23a47			23 50	00 27			01 05		01 20	
Kings Sutton	d	21 29																						00 38						
Banbury	d	21 37			21 47			22 14	22a40			22 47				23 13			23 47				00 03	00a46			01a22		01 35	
Leamington Spa 8	d	21 56			22 05			22 32				23 05				23 31			00 05				00 21						01a58	
Warwick	d	22 01			22 10							23 09							00 09				00 25							
Warwick Parkway	d				22 14			22 38				23 13				23 37			00 13				00 29							
Hatton	d	22 09										23 19																		
Claverdon	d	22 15																												
Bearley	d	22 20																												
Wilmcote	d	22 25																												
Stratford-upon-Avon Parkway	a	22 27																												
Stratford-upon-Avon	a	22 36																												
Lapworth	a											23 24																		
Dorridge	a				22 23			22 47				23 29				23 46			00 22											
Solihull	a				22 29			22 53				23 37				23 52			00 28				00 40							
Birmingham Moor Street	a				22 37			23 02				23 46				00 07			00 43				00 55							
Birmingham Snow Hill ⇌	a				22 46			23 05				23 54																		
Rowley Regis	a							23 32																						
Cradley Heath	a							23 39																						
Stourbridge Junction 2	a							23 52																						
Kidderminster	a																													

§ London Underground Limited (Central Line) also operate services between South Ruislip and West Ruislip at frequent intervals

For complete service between Banbury and Leamington (Birmingham), please refer to table 71

Table 115

Saturdays

14 December to 17 May

London - High Wycombe, Aylesbury, Banbury, Stratford-upon-Avon, Birmingham Snow Hill and Kidderminster

Network Diagram - see first Page of Table 114

Station		CH ◇	CH ◇	CH	CH	CH FO	CH FO	CH	CH	CH ◇
London Marylebone 10 ⊖	d					00 20	00 25		06 30	07 00
London Paddington 15 ⊖	d									
Wembley Stadium	d						00 34		06 39	
Sudbury & Harrow Road	d									
Sudbury Hill Harrow	d									
Northolt Park	d						00 39		06 44	
South Ruislip § ⊖	d				00 02		00 43		06 47	
West Ruislip 3 § ⊖	d				00 06		00 47		06 51	
Denham	d				00 10		00 52		06 55	
Denham Golf Club	d				00 13				06 58	
Gerrards Cross 1	d				00 17	00 39	00 57		07 01	
Seer Green	d				00 21		01 01		07 06	
Beaconsfield	d				00 25	00 45	01 05		07 09	
High Wycombe 1	d				00 31	00 51	01 11	06 12	07 15	07 24
Saunderton	d			00 01			01 17	06 18	07 21	
Princes Risborough 2	d			00 07	00 41	01 00	01 24	06 24	07 28	07 34
Monks Risborough	d				00 45		01 27		07 31	
Little Kimble	d				00 49		01 31		07 35	
Aylesbury	a				01 01		01 42		07 46	
Haddenham & Thame Parkway	d			00 14		01 07		06 31		07 40
Bicester North 3	d			00 27		01 20		06 45		07 52
Kings Sutton	d			00 38				06 55		
Banbury	d		00 03	00a46		01 35		07 02		08 05
Leamington Spa 8	d	00 05	00 21			01a58		07 21		08 23
Warwick	d	00 09	00 25					07 25		
Warwick Parkway	d	00 13	00 29					07 29		08 29
Hatton	d							07 34		
Claverdon	d									
Bearley	d									
Wilmcote	d									
Stratford-upon-Avon Parkway	a									
Stratford-upon-Avon	a									
Lapworth	a									
Dorridge	a	00 22						07 41		08 38
Solihull	a	00 28	00 40					07 47		08 45
Birmingham Moor Street	a	00 43	00 55					08 03		08 59
Birmingham Snow Hill ⛴	a									09 07
Rowley Regis	a									
Cradley Heath	a									
Stourbridge Junction 2	a									
Kidderminster	a									

Station		CH	CH	CH ◇	CH ◇	CH	CH	CH ◇	CH ◇	CH
London Marylebone 10 ⊖	d		07 30	08 00	08 27		08 39	09 06	09 09	09 15
London Paddington 15 ⊖	d									
Wembley Stadium	d		07 39				08 48			09 24
Sudbury & Harrow Road	d									
Sudbury Hill Harrow	d									
Northolt Park	d		07 44				08 53			
South Ruislip § ⊖	d		07 47				08 56			09 31
West Ruislip 3 § ⊖	d		07 51				09 00			
Denham	d		07 55				09 04			09 37
Denham Golf Club	d		07 58				09 07			
Gerrards Cross 1	d		08 01		08 44		09 10		09 29	09a47
Seer Green	d		08 06				09 15			
Beaconsfield	d		08 09		08 50		09 18		09 35	
High Wycombe 1	d		08 15	08 24	08 56		09a27		09 41	
Saunderton	d		08 21		09 02				09 47	
Princes Risborough 2	d		08 28	08 34	09 08	09 15			09 54	
Monks Risborough	d		08 31			09 19				
Little Kimble	d		08 35			09 23				
Aylesbury	a		08 46			09 34				
Haddenham & Thame Parkway	d			08 40	09 15				10 01	
Bicester North 3	d			08 52	09 27			09 49	10 14	
Kings Sutton	d			09 02						
Banbury	d			09 08	09 41			10 02	10 29	
Leamington Spa 8	d	08 30		09 26	09 59			10 21	10 47	
Warwick	d	08 34		09 30	10 03				10 51	
Warwick Parkway	d			09 34	10 07			10 27		
Hatton	d	08 42								
Claverdon	d	08 48								
Bearley	d	08 53								
Wilmcote	d	08 58								
Stratford-upon-Avon Parkway	a	09 01							11 08	
Stratford-upon-Avon	a	09 09							11 15	
Lapworth	a									
Dorridge	a			09 43	10 16					
Solihull	a			09 49	10 22			10 41		
Birmingham Moor Street	a			10 01	10 33			10 55		
Birmingham Snow Hill ⛴	a			10 09	10 41					
Rowley Regis	a									
Cradley Heath	a									
Stourbridge Junction 2	a									
Kidderminster	a									

Station		CH ◇	CH	CH	CH ◇	CH	CH	CH ◇	CH	CH ◇ 🛒 BZ
London Marylebone 10 ⊖	d	09 36		09 39	10 06	10 09	10 16	10 36	10 39	11 06
London Paddington 15 ⊖	d									
Wembley Stadium	d			09 48			10 25		10 48	
Sudbury & Harrow Road	d									
Sudbury Hill Harrow	d									
Northolt Park	d			09 53					10 53	
South Ruislip § ⊖	d						10 32			
West Ruislip 3 § ⊖	d			09 58					10 58	
Denham	d			10 02			10 38		11 02	
Denham Golf Club	d			10 05					11 05	
Gerrards Cross 1	d			10 08		10 29	10 43		11 08	
Seer Green	d			10 13					11 13	
Beaconsfield	d			10 16		10 35			11 16	
High Wycombe 1	d	09 59		10a25		10 41	10 53	11 01	11a25	
Saunderton	d					10 47				
Princes Risborough 2	d	10 08	10 15			10 54	11 04	11 10		
Monks Risborough	d		10 19				11 08			
Little Kimble	d		10 23				11 12			
Aylesbury	a		10 34				11 23			
Haddenham & Thame Parkway	d	10 14				11 01		11 16		
Bicester North 3	d	10 25			10 49	11a17		11 28		11 49
Kings Sutton	d									
Banbury	d	10 39			11 02			11 41		12 04
Leamington Spa 8	d	10 59			11 21			11 59		12 24
Warwick	d	11 03						12 03		
Warwick Parkway	d	11 07			11 27			12 07		12 31
Hatton	d									
Claverdon	d									
Bearley	d									
Wilmcote	d									
Stratford-upon-Avon Parkway	a									
Stratford-upon-Avon	a									
Lapworth	a									
Dorridge	a	11 16						12 16		
Solihull	a	11 22			11 41			12 22		12 45
Birmingham Moor Street	a	11 33			11 55			12 33		12 56
Birmingham Snow Hill ⛴	a	11 41						12 41		
Rowley Regis	a									
Cradley Heath	a									
Stourbridge Junction 2	a									
Kidderminster	a									

Station		CH ◇	CH	CH ◇	CH	CH ◇ 🛒	CH	CH	CH ◇	CH
London Marylebone 10 ⊖	d	11 09	11 16	11 36	11 39	12 06	12 09		12 36	12 39
London Paddington 15 ⊖	d									
Wembley Stadium	d		11 25		11 48		12 18			12 48
Sudbury & Harrow Road	d									
Sudbury Hill Harrow	d									
Northolt Park	d				11 53					12 53
South Ruislip § ⊖	d		11 32		11 56					12 56
West Ruislip 3 § ⊖	d				12 00					13 00
Denham	d		11 38		12 04					13 04
Denham Golf Club	d				12 07					13 07
Gerrards Cross 1	d	11 29	11 43		12 10		12 31			13 10
Seer Green	d				12 15					13 15
Beaconsfield	d	11 35			12 18		12 37			13 18
High Wycombe 1	d	11 41	11 53	11 59	12a27		12 43		13 01	13a27
Saunderton	d	11 47					12 49			
Princes Risborough 2	d	11 54	12 04	12 08			12 55	13 00	13 10	
Monks Risborough	d		12 08					13 04		
Little Kimble	d		12 12					13 08		
Aylesbury	a		12 23					13 19		
Haddenham & Thame Parkway	d	12 01		12 14			13 03		13 16	
Bicester North 3	d	12 14		12 25		12 49	13a19		13 28	
Kings Sutton	d	12 26								
Banbury	d	12 32		12 41		13 02			13 41	
Leamington Spa 8	d	12 51		12 59		13 21			13 59	
Warwick	d	12 56		13 03					14 03	
Warwick Parkway	d			13 07		13 27			14 07	
Hatton	d	13 08								
Claverdon	d	13 14								
Bearley	d	13 19								
Wilmcote	d	13 24								
Stratford-upon-Avon Parkway	a	13 26								
Stratford-upon-Avon	a	13 33								
Lapworth	a									
Dorridge	a			13 16					14 16	
Solihull	a			13 22		13 41			14 22	
Birmingham Moor Street	a			13 33		13 55			14 33	
Birmingham Snow Hill ⛴	a			13 41					14 41	
Rowley Regis	a									
Cradley Heath	a									
Stourbridge Junction 2	a									
Kidderminster	a									

§ London Underground Limited (Central Line) also operate services between South Ruislip and West Ruislip at frequent intervals

BZ Business Zone available offering greater comfort and an enhanced working environment. Supplement payable.

For complete service between Banbury and Leamington (Birmingham), please refer to table 71

Table 115

Saturdays

14 December to 17 May

London - High Wycombe, Aylesbury, Banbury, Stratford-upon-Avon, Birmingham Snow Hill and Kidderminster

Network Diagram - see first Page of Table 114

		CH	CH	CH	CH	CH	CH	CH	CH	CH	CH	CH	CH	CH	CH	CH	CH	CH	CH
		◇	◇		◇		◇			◇		◇	◇			◇		◇	
London Marylebone 10 ⊖	d	13 06	13 09		13 36	13 39	14 06	14 09		14 36	14 39	15 06	15 09		15 15	15 36	15 39	16 06	16 09
London Paddington 15 ⊖	d																		
Wembley Stadium	d		13 18			13 48		14 18			14 48				15 24		15 48		
Sudbury & Harrow Road	d																		
Sudbury Hill Harrow	d																		
Northolt Park	d					13 53					14 53						15 53		
South Ruislip § ⊖	d					13 56					14 56				15 31				
West Ruislip 3 § ⊖	d					14 00					15 00						15 58		
Denham	d					14 04					15 04				15 36		16 02		
Denham Golf Club	d					14 07					15 07						16 05		
Gerrards Cross 1	d		13 29			14 10		14 31			15 10		15 29		15 41		16 08		16 29
Seer Green	d					14 15					15 15						16 13		
Beaconsfield	d		13 35			14 18		14 37			15 18		15 35		15 47		16 16		16 35
High Wycombe 1	d		13 41		13 59	14a27		14 43		15 01	15a27		15 41		15a58	15 59	16a27		16 41
Saunderton	d		13 47					14 49					15 47						16 47
Princes Risborough 2	d		13 54	14 00	14 08			14 55	15 00	15 10			15 54	16 00		16 08			16 54
Monks Risborough	d			14 04					15 04					16 04					
Little Kimble	d			14 08										16 08					
Aylesbury	a			14 19					15 18					16 19					
Haddenham & Thame Parkway	d		14 01		14 14			15 03		15 16			16 01			16 14			17 01
Bicester North 3	d	13 49	14 14		14 25		14 49	15a19		15 28		15 49	16 14			16 25		16 49	17a17
Kings Sutton	d		14 25										16 26						
Banbury	d	14 02	14 31		14 41		15 02			15 41		16 02	16 32			16 41		17 02	
Leamington Spa 8	d	14 21	14 49		14 59		15 21			15 59		16 21	16 51			16 59		17 21	
Warwick	d		14 54		15 03					16 03			16 56			17 03			
Warwick Parkway	d	14 27			15 07		15 27			16 07		16 27				17 07		17 27	
Hatton	d		15 08										17 08						
Claverdon	d		15 14										17 14						
Bearley	d												17 19						
Wilmcote	d		15 22										17 24						
Stratford-upon-Avon Parkway	a		15 24										17 26						
Stratford-upon-Avon	a		15 33										17 32						
Lapworth	a																		
Dorridge	a				15 16					16 16						17 16			
Solihull	a	14 41			15 22		15 41			16 22		16 41				17 22		17 41	
Birmingham Moor Street	a	14 55			15 33		15 55			16 33		16 55				17 33		17 53	
Birmingham Snow Hill	a				15 41					16 41						17 41		18 03	
Rowley Regis	a																		
Cradley Heath	a																		
Stourbridge Junction 2	a																		
Kidderminster	a																		

		CH	CH	CH	CH	CH	CH	CH	CH	CH	CH	CH	CH	CH	CH	CH	CH	CH	CH
				◇		◇ BZ	◇			◇		◇ BZ				◇		◇	◇
London Marylebone 10 ⊖	d		16 15	16 36	16 39	17 06	17 09		17 15	17 36	17 39	18 06	18 09		18 15	18 36	18 39	19 06	19 09
London Paddington 15 ⊖	d																		
Wembley Stadium	d		16 24		16 48				17 24		17 48				18 24		18 48		
Sudbury & Harrow Road	d																		
Sudbury Hill Harrow	d																		
Northolt Park	d				16 53						17 53						18 53		
South Ruislip § ⊖	d		16 31						17 31						18 31				
West Ruislip 3 § ⊖	d				16 58						17 58						18 58		
Denham	d		16 36		17 02				17 36		18 02				18 36		19 02		
Denham Golf Club	d				17 05						18 05						19 05		
Gerrards Cross 1	d		16a44		17 08		17 29		17a44		18 08		18 29		18a44		19 08		19 29
Seer Green	d				17 13						18 13						19 13		
Beaconsfield	d				17 16		17 35				18 16		18 35				19 16		19 35
High Wycombe 1	d			17 01	17a25		17 41			17 59	18a25		18 41			19 00	19a25		19 41
Saunderton	d						17 47						18 47						19 47
Princes Risborough 2	d	17 00		17 10			17 54	18 00		18 08			18 54	19 00		19 10			19 54
Monks Risborough	d	17 04						18 04						19 04					
Little Kimble	d	17 08						18 08						19 08					
Aylesbury	a	17 19						18 19						19 19					
Haddenham & Thame Parkway	d			17 16			18 01			18 14			19 01			19 16			20 01
Bicester North 3	d			17 28		17 49	18 14			18 25		18 49	19 14			19 28		19 49	20 14
Kings Sutton	d						18 26												20 26
Banbury	d			17 41		18 03	18 32			18 41		19 03	19a32			19 41		20 02	20 34
Leamington Spa 8	d			17 59		18 23	18 51			18 59		19 23				19 59		20 21	20 53
Warwick	d			18 03			18 56			19 03						20 03			20 58
Warwick Parkway	d			18 07		18 29				19 07		19 29				20 07		20 27	
Hatton	d						19 04									20 12			21 06
Claverdon	d						19 10												21 12
Bearley	d						19 16												21 18
Wilmcote	d						19 22												21 22
Stratford-upon-Avon Parkway	a						19 24												21 24
Stratford-upon-Avon	a						19 32												21 32
Lapworth	a															20 17			
Dorridge	a			18 16						19 16						20 22			
Solihull	a			18 22		18 41				19 22		19 41				20 28		20 41	
Birmingham Moor Street	a			18 35		18 53				19 35		19 55				20 39		20 55	
Birmingham Snow Hill	a					19 03						20 04				20 47		21 07	
Rowley Regis	a																		
Cradley Heath	a																		
Stourbridge Junction 2	a																		
Kidderminster	a																		

§ London Underground Limited (Central Line) also operate services between South Ruislip and West Ruislip at frequent intervals

BZ Business Zone available offering greater comfort and an enhanced working environment. Supplement payable.

For complete service between Banbury and Leamington (Birmingham), please refer to table 71

Table 115

Saturdays

14 December to 17 May

London - High Wycombe, Aylesbury, Banbury, Stratford-upon-Avon, Birmingham Snow Hill and Kidderminster

Network Diagram - see first Page of Table 114

		CH	CH	CH	CH	CH	CH	CH	CH	CH	CH	CH	CH	CH	CH	CH	CH	CH
			◇		◇		◇		◇			◇						
London Marylebone 10 ⊖	d	19 16	19 36	19 39	20 00	20 04	20 36	20 40	21 06	21 09	21 35	22 08	22 18	22 40	23 15	23 18	23 45	00 10
London Paddington 15 ⊖	d																	
Wembley Stadium	d	19 25		19 48		20 13				21 18			22 27	22 50	23 25	23 29	23 55	00 19
Sudbury & Harrow Road	d																	
Sudbury Hill Harrow	d																	
Northolt Park	d			19 53		20 18				21 23			22 32			23 34		00 24
South Ruislip § ⊖	d	19 32				20 21				21 26			22 35			23 37		00 27
West Ruislip 3 § ⊖	d			19 58		20 25				21 30			22 39			23 41		00 31
Denham	d	19 37		20 02		20 29				21 34			22 43			23 45		00 35
Denham Golf Club	d			20 05		20 32				21 37			22 46			23 48		00 38
Gerrards Cross 1	d	19 43		20 08		20 36		21 00		21 41	21 55		22 50	23 03	23 38	23 52	00 08	00 42
Seer Green	d	19 47				20 40				21 45			22 54			23 56		00 46
Beaconsfield	d	19 51		20 14		20 44		21 06		21 49	22 02		22 58	23 10	23 45	23 59	00 15	00 50
High Wycombe 1	d	19 57	20 01	20a23	20 25	20 50	21 00	21 12	21 29	21 55	22 08		23 04	23 16	23 51	00 06	00 21	00 56
Saunderton	d					20 56				22 01			23 10			00 12		01 02
Princes Risborough 2	d	20 08	20 11		20 34	21 03	21 09	21 23	21 39	22 08	22 19		23 17	23 26	00 02	00 19	00 31	01 09
Monks Risborough	d	20 12				21 06				22 11			23 20			00 22		01 12
Little Kimble	d	20 16				21 10				22 15			23 24			00 26		01 16
Aylesbury	a	20 27				21 20				22 25			23 35			00 37		01 27
Haddenham & Thame Parkway	d		20 17		20 40		21 15	21 30	21 46		22 26			23 33	00 10		00 38	
Bicester North 3	d		20 30		20 52		21 27	21 43	21 58		22a45	22 51		23 46	00 24		00 51	
Kings Sutton	d							21 54						23 58			01 02	
Banbury	d		20 43		21 05		21 40	22a07	22 12			23 04		00a07	00a42		01a11	
Leamington Spa 8	d		21 00		21 23		21 57		22 30			23 23						
Warwick	d		21 05		21 27		22 02		22 34			23 27						
Warwick Parkway	d		21 08		21 32		22 06		22 38			23 31						
Hatton	d								22 43									
Claverdon	d																	
Bearley	d																	
Wilmcote	d																	
Stratford-upon-Avon Parkway	a																	
Stratford-upon-Avon	a																	
Lapworth	a								22 48									
Dorridge	a		21 18		21 41		22 15		22 53			23 40						
Solihull	a		21 23		21 47		22 21		22 59			23 47						
Birmingham Moor Street	a		21 35		21 57		22 34		23 08			23 59						
Birmingham Snow Hill ⛴	a				22 06				23 16									
Rowley Regis	a																	
Cradley Heath	a																	
Stourbridge Junction 2	a																	
Kidderminster	a																	

§ London Underground Limited (Central Line) also operate services between South Ruislip and West Ruislip at frequent intervals

For complete service between Banbury and Leamington (Birmingham), please refer to table 71

Table 115

Sundays

8 December to 11 May

London - High Wycombe, Aylesbury, Banbury, Stratford-upon-Avon, Birmingham Snow Hill and Kidderminster

Network Diagram - see first Page of Table 114

		CH	CH	CH	CH	CH	CH	CH	CH	CH	CH	CH	CH	CH	CH	CH	CH	CH	CH
								◇		◇	◇		◇		◇		◇	◇	◇
London Marylebone 10 ⊖	d				00 10	07 35	07 50	08 15	08 30	09 06	09 30	09 33	10 06	10 09	10 36	10 28	11 06	11 09	11 36
London Paddington 15 ⊖	d																		
Wembley Stadium	d				00 19	07 44	07 59		08 40			09 42		10 18		10 37		11 18	
Sudbury & Harrow Road	d																		
Sudbury Hill Harrow	d																		
Northolt Park	d				00 24		08 04		08 45			09 47				10 42			
South Ruislip § ⊖	d				00 27	07 51	08 07		08 50			09 50				10 50			
West Ruislip 3 § ⊖	d				00 31		08 11		08 54							10 53			
Denham	d				00 35	07 56	08 15		08 58			09 56				10 58			
Denham Golf Club	d				00 38		08 18					09 58							
Gerrards Cross 1	d			00 08	00 42	08 01	08 22	08 32	09 03	09 23		10 03		10 31		11 03		11 31	
Seer Green	d				00 46		08 26		09 08			10 07				11 07			
Beaconsfield	d			00 15	00 50	08 08	08 30	08 38	09 11	09 28		10 10		10 37		11 10		11 37	
High Wycombe 1	d		00 06	00 21	00 56	08 14	08 36	08 44	09 17	09 34		10 16		10 43	11 01	11 16		11 43	12 01
Saunderton	d		00 12		01 02		08 42		09 23			10 23				11 23			
Princes Risborough 2	d	00 02	00 19	00 31	01 09	08 23	08a52	08 54	09 30	09 44		10 30		10 53	11 10	11 30		11 53	12 10
Monks Risborough	d		00 22		01 12				09 33			10 33				11 33			
Little Kimble	d		00 26		01 16				09 37			10 37				11 37			
Aylesbury	a		00 37		01 27				09 48			10 48				11 48			
Haddenham & Thame Parkway	d	00 10		00 38		08 30		09 00		09 51				11 00	11 16			12 00	12 16
Bicester North 3	d	00 24		00 51		08 45		09 12		10 03	10 13		10 49	11a16	11 28		11 49	12 13	12 28
Kings Sutton	d			01 02				09 22			10 25							12 25	
Banbury	d	00a42		01a11		09a02		09 28		10 16	10 31		11 03		11 41		12 03	12 31	12 41
Leamington Spa 8	d							09 46		10 34	10 50		11 21		11 59		12 21	12 50	12 59
Warwick	d							09 51		10 38	10 54		11 25		12 03			12 54	13 03
Warwick Parkway	d							09 54		10 42			11 29		12 07		12 27		13 07
Hatton	d							10 00			11 02				12 12			13 02	
Claverdon	d																		
Bearley	d																		
Wilmcote	d										11 16							13 16	
Stratford-upon-Avon Parkway	a										11 18							13 18	
Stratford-upon-Avon	a										11 29							13 29	
Lapworth	a							10 06							12 17				
Dorridge	a							10 10		10 51			11 38		12 22		12 36		13 16
Solihull	a							10 16		10 57			11 44		12 28		12 42		13 22
Birmingham Moor Street	a							10 24		11 06			11 53		12 40		12 57		13 31
Birmingham Snow Hill	a							10 32		11 14			12 01		12 48				13 39
Rowley Regis	a																		
Cradley Heath	a																		
Stourbridge Junction 2	a																		
Kidderminster	a																		

		CH	CH	CH	CH	CH	CH	CH	CH	CH	CH	CH	CH	CH	CH	CH	CH	CH	CH
			◇			◇		◇	◇		◇ 🚲		◇			◇		◇	◇
London Marylebone 10 ⊖	d	11 28	12 06	12 09	12 25	12 36	12 28	13 06	13 09	13 25	13 36	13 28	14 06	14 09	14 25	14 36	14 28	15 06	15 09
London Paddington 15 ⊖	d																		
Wembley Stadium	d	11 37		12 18			12 37		13 18			13 37		14 18			14 37		15 18
Sudbury & Harrow Road	d																		
Sudbury Hill Harrow	d																		
Northolt Park	d	11 42					12 42					13 42					14 42		
South Ruislip § ⊖	d	11 50					12 50					13 50					14 50		
West Ruislip 3 § ⊖	d						12 53										14 53		
Denham	d	11 55					12 58					13 55					14 58		
Denham Golf Club	d	11 58										13 58							
Gerrards Cross 1	d	12 03		12 31	12 44		13 03		13 31	13 44		14 03		14 31	14 44		15 03		15 31
Seer Green	d	12 07					13 07					14 07					15 07		
Beaconsfield	d	12 10		12 37	12 50		13 10		13 37	13 50		14 10		14 37	14 50		15 10		15 37
High Wycombe 1	d	12 16		12 43	12a59	13 01	13 16		13 43	13a59	14 01	14 16		14 43	14a59	15 01	15 16		15 43
Saunderton	d	12 23					13 23					14 23					15 23		
Princes Risborough 2	d	12 30		12 53		13 10	13 30		13 53		14 10	14 30		14 53		15 10	15 30		15 53
Monks Risborough	d	12 33					13 33					14 33					15 33		
Little Kimble	d	12 37					13 37					14 37					15 37		
Aylesbury	a	12 48					13 48					14 48					15 48		
Haddenham & Thame Parkway	d			13 00		13 16			14 00		14 16			15 00		15 16			16 00
Bicester North 3	d		12 49	13a16		13 28		13 49	14 13		14 28		14 49	15a16		15 28		15 49	16 13
Kings Sutton	d								14 25										16 26
Banbury	d		13 03			13 41		14 03	14 31		14 41		15 03			15 41		16 03	16 32
Leamington Spa 8	d		13 21			13 59		14 21	14 50		14 59		15 21			15 59		16 21	16 51
Warwick	d					14 03			14 54		15 03					16 03			16 55
Warwick Parkway	d		13 27			14 07		14 27			15 07		15 27			16 07		16 27	
Hatton	d					14 12			15 02							16 12			17 03
Claverdon	d																		
Bearley	d																		
Wilmcote	d								15 16										17 17
Stratford-upon-Avon Parkway	a								15 18										17 19
Stratford-upon-Avon	a								15 29										17 30
Lapworth	a					14 17										16 17			
Dorridge	a		13 36			14 22		14 36			15 16		15 36			16 22		16 36	
Solihull	a		13 42			14 28		14 42			15 22		15 42			16 28		16 42	
Birmingham Moor Street	a		13 57			14 37		14 57			15 31		15 57			16 37		16 57	
Birmingham Snow Hill	a					14 47					15 39					16 45			
Rowley Regis	a																		
Cradley Heath	a																		
Stourbridge Junction 2	a																		
Kidderminster	a																		

§ London Underground Limited (Central Line) also operate services between South Ruislip and West Ruislip at frequent intervals

For complete service between Banbury and Leamington (Birmingham), please refer to table 71

Table 115

Sundays

8 December to 11 May

London - High Wycombe, Aylesbury, Banbury, Stratford-upon-Avon, Birmingham Snow Hill and Kidderminster

Network Diagram - see first Page of Table 114

		CH	CH ◇	CH	CH ◇	CH	CH	CH ◇	CH	CH ◇
London Marylebone 10 ⊖	d	15 25	15 36	15 28	16 06	16 09	16 25	16 36	16 28	17 06
London Paddington 15 ⊖	d									
Wembley Stadium	d			15 37		16 18			16 37	
Sudbury & Harrow Road	d									
Sudbury Hill Harrow	d									
Northolt Park	d			15 42					16 42	
South Ruislip § ⊖	d			15 50					16 50	
West Ruislip 3 § ⊖	d								16 53	
Denham	d			15 55					16 58	
Denham Golf Club	d			15 58						
Gerrards Cross 1	d	15 44		16 03		16 31	16 44		17 03	
Seer Green	d			16 07					17 07	
Beaconsfield	d	15 50		16 10		16 37	16 50		17 10	
High Wycombe 1	d	15a59	16 01	16 16		16 43	16a59	17 01	17 16	
Saunderton	d			16 23					17 23	
Princes Risborough 2	d		16 10	16 30		16 53		17 10	17 30	
Monks Risborough	d			16 33					17 33	
Little Kimble	d			16 37					17 37	
Aylesbury	a			16 48					17 48	
Haddenham & Thame Parkway	d		16 16			17 00		17 16		
Bicester North 3	d		16 28		16 49	17a16		17 28		17 49
Kings Sutton	d									
Banbury	d		16 41		17 03			17 41		18 03
Leamington Spa 8	d		16 59		17 21			17 59		18 21
Warwick	d		17 03					18 03		
Warwick Parkway	d		17 07		17 27			18 07		18 27
Hatton	d							18 12		
Claverdon	d									
Bearley	d									
Wilmcote	d									
Stratford-upon-Avon Parkway	a									
Stratford-upon-Avon	a									
Lapworth	a							18 17		
Dorridge	a		17 16		17 36			18 22		18 36
Solihull	a		17 22		17 42			18 29		18 42
Birmingham Moor Street	a		17 31		17 57			18 38		18 57
Birmingham Snow Hill	a		17 39					18 46		
Rowley Regis	a									
Cradley Heath	a									
Stourbridge Junction 2	a									
Kidderminster	a									

		CH ◇	CH	CH ◇	CH	CH ◇ BZ	CH	CH	CH ◇	CH
London Marylebone 10 ⊖	d	17 09	17 25	17 36	17 28	18 06	18 09	18 25	18 36	18 28
London Paddington 15 ⊖	d									
Wembley Stadium	d	17 18			17 37		18 18			18 37
Sudbury & Harrow Road	d									
Sudbury Hill Harrow	d									
Northolt Park	d				17 42					18 42
South Ruislip § ⊖	d				17 50					18 50
West Ruislip 3 § ⊖	d									18 53
Denham	d				17 55					18 58
Denham Golf Club	d				17 58					
Gerrards Cross 1	d	17 31	17 44		18 03		18 31	18 44		19 03
Seer Green	d				18 07					19 07
Beaconsfield	d	17 37	17 50		18 10		18 37	18 50		19 10
High Wycombe 1	d	17 43	17a59	18 01	18 16		18 43	18a59	19 01	19 16
Saunderton	d				18 23					19 23
Princes Risborough 2	d	17 53		18 10	18 30		18 53		19 10	19 30
Monks Risborough	d				18 33					19 33
Little Kimble	d				18 37					19 37
Aylesbury	a				18 48					19 48
Haddenham & Thame Parkway	d	18 00		18 16			19 00		19 16	
Bicester North 3	d	18 13		18 28		18 49	19a16		19 28	
Kings Sutton	d	18 26								
Banbury	d	18 45		18 41		19 04			19 41	
Leamington Spa 8	d	19 05		18 59		19 23			19 59	
Warwick	d	19 09		19 03					20 03	
Warwick Parkway	d			19 07		19 29			20 07	
Hatton	d	19 16								
Claverdon	d									
Bearley	d									
Wilmcote	d	19 26								
Stratford-upon-Avon Parkway	a	19 28								
Stratford-upon-Avon	a	19 39								
Lapworth	a									
Dorridge	a			19 16		19 39			20 16	
Solihull	a			19 23		19 45			20 23	
Birmingham Moor Street	a			19 33		20 00			20 33	
Birmingham Snow Hill	a			19 41					20 41	
Rowley Regis	a									
Cradley Heath	a									
Stourbridge Junction 2	a									
Kidderminster	a									

		CH ◇	CH	CH ◇	CH	CH ◇	CH	CH ◇	CH	CH ◇
London Marylebone 10 ⊖	d	19 06	19 09	19 30	19 35	20 06	20 09	20 30	20 35	21 00
London Paddington 15 ⊖	d									
Wembley Stadium	d		19 18		19 44		20 18		20 44	
Sudbury & Harrow Road	d									
Sudbury Hill Harrow	d									
Northolt Park	d				19 49				20 49	
South Ruislip § ⊖	d				19 52				20 52	
West Ruislip 3 § ⊖	d				19 56				20 56	
Denham	d				20 00				21 00	
Denham Golf Club	d				20 03					
Gerrards Cross 1	d		19 31	19 48	20 07		20 31	20 48	21 05	21 18
Seer Green	d				20 11				21 10	
Beaconsfield	d		19 37	19 54	20 14		20 37	20 54	21 13	21 24
High Wycombe 1	d		19 43	20 01	20 20	20 31	20 43	21 01	21 19	21 30
Saunderton	d				20 27				21 25	
Princes Risborough 2	d		19 53	20 10	20 34		20 53	21 10	21 32	21 39
Monks Risborough	d				20 37				21 35	
Little Kimble	d				20 41				21 39	
Aylesbury	a				20 52				21 50	
Haddenham & Thame Parkway	d		20 00	20 16			21 00	21 16		21 45
Bicester North 3	d	19 49	20 13	20 28		20 52	21 13	21 28		21 57
Kings Sutton	d		20 27							
Banbury	d	20 03	20a35	20 41		21 05	21a32	21 41		22 10
Leamington Spa 8	d	20 21		20 59		21 23		21 59		22 28
Warwick	d			21 03		21 27		22 03		22 32
Warwick Parkway	d	20 27		21 07		21 31		22 07		22 36
Hatton	d			21 12						22 41
Claverdon	d									
Bearley	d									
Wilmcote	d									
Stratford-upon-Avon Parkway	a									
Stratford-upon-Avon	a									
Lapworth	a			21 17						22 46
Dorridge	a	20 36		21 22		21 40		22 16		22 51
Solihull	a	20 42		21 29		21 46		22 22		22 58
Birmingham Moor Street	a	20 57		21 38		22 03		22 31		23 07
Birmingham Snow Hill	a			21 46				22 39		23 15
Rowley Regis	a									
Cradley Heath	a									
Stourbridge Junction 2	a									
Kidderminster	a									

		CH	CH	CH ◇	CH	CH	CH	CH
London Marylebone 10 ⊖	d	21 35	21 38	22 08	22 38	23 10	23 45	
London Paddington 15 ⊖	d							
Wembley Stadium	d		21 47		22 47	23 19	23 54	
Sudbury & Harrow Road	d							
Sudbury Hill Harrow	d							
Northolt Park	d		21 52		22 52		23 59	
South Ruislip § ⊖	d		21 55		22 55		00 02	
West Ruislip 3 § ⊖	d		21 59		22 59		00 06	
Denham	d		22 03		23 03		00 10	
Denham Golf Club	d		22 06		23 06		00 13	
Gerrards Cross 1	d	21 54	22 09		23 10	23 32	00 17	
Seer Green	d		22 14		23 14		00 21	
Beaconsfield	d	22 01	22 17		23 18	23 38	00 25	
High Wycombe 1	d	22 07	22 23		23 24	23 44	00 31	
Saunderton	d		22 29		23 30		00 37	
Princes Risborough 2	d	22 16	22 40		23 37	23 55	00 42	00 48
Monks Risborough	d		22 43		23 40			00 51
Little Kimble	d		22 47		23 44			00 55
Aylesbury	a		22 58		23 55			01 06
Haddenham & Thame Parkway	d	22 23		22 43		00 02	00 49	
Bicester North 3	d	22a39		22 55		00 16	01 02	
Kings Sutton	d						01 13	
Banbury	d			23 08		00a35	01a20	
Leamington Spa 8	d			23 26				
Warwick	d			23 30				
Warwick Parkway	d			23 34				
Hatton	d							
Claverdon	d							
Bearley	d							
Wilmcote	d							
Stratford-upon-Avon Parkway	a							
Stratford-upon-Avon	a							
Lapworth	a							
Dorridge	a			23 43				
Solihull	a			23 49				
Birmingham Moor Street	a			23 58				
Birmingham Snow Hill	a			00 06				
Rowley Regis	a							
Cradley Heath	a							
Stourbridge Junction 2	a							
Kidderminster	a							

§ London Underground Limited (Central Line) also operate services between South Ruislip and West Ruislip at frequent intervals

Supplement payable.

For complete service between Banbury and Leamington (Birmingham), please refer to table 71

Table 115R

Mondays to Fridays

9 December to 16 May

Kidderminster, Birmingham Snow Hill, Stratford-upon-Avon, Banbury, Aylesbury and High Wycombe - London

Network Diagram - see first Page of Table 114

Miles	Miles	Miles			CH MX	CH	CH	CH	CH	CH	CH	CH ◇	CH	CH	CH	CH	CH	CH	CH ◇ ⚲	CH	CH	CH
—	—	—	**Kidderminster**	d																		
—	—	—	**Stourbridge Junction** 2	d																		
—	—	—	Cradley Heath	d																		
—	—	—	Rowley Regis	d																		
0	—	—	**Birmingham Snow Hill**	d																		
0¾	—	—	**Birmingham Moor Street**	d								05 15							05 46			
7¼	—	—	Solihull	d								05 24							05 55			
10½	—	—	Dorridge	d															06 00			
13	—	—	Lapworth	d																		
—	—	0	**Stratford-upon-Avon**	d																		
—	—	—	Stratford-upon-Avon Parkway	d																		
—	—	2¾	Wilmcote	d																		
—	—	4¼	Bearley	d																		
—	—	7¼	Claverdon	d																		
17¼	—	9¼	Hatton	d																		
20	—	12	Warwick Parkway	d								05 36						05 55	06 09			
21¼	—	13¼	Warwick	d														05 58				
23¼	—	15¼	**Leamington Spa** 8	d								05 41						06 03	06 15			
43¼	—	—	**Banbury**	d				05 20			05 37	05 59						06 21	06 33			
46¾	—	—	Kings Sutton	d												06 09						
57¼	—	—	**Bicester North** 3	d				05 33			05 52	06 12				06 20		06 33	06 45			
70¼	—	—	Haddenham & Thame Parkway	d				05 44			06 05	06 23				06 33		06 45				
—	0	—	**Aylesbury**	d		05 05	05 15		05 35					06 24	06 14							06 56
—	4½	—	Little Kimble	d		05 13			05 43													
—	6	—	Monks Risborough	d		05 17			05 47													
76	7½	—	**Princes Risborough** 2	d		05 21	05 29		05 52		06 12				06 31		06 44	06 53				
79¼	—	—	Saunderton	d		05 26			05 57													
84¼	—	—	**High Wycombe** 1	d		05 32	05 39	05 58	06 04	06 10	06 22				06 41	06 47	06 54				07 08	
89	—	—	Beaconsfield	d		05 38	05 45		06 10	06 17	06 28				06 48		07 01				07 15	
90¾	—	—	Seer Green	d		05 41			06 13							06 54						
93¼	—	—	Gerrards Cross 1	d		05 46	05 51		06 18	06 23	06 34		06 45		06 54	06 59					07 21	
95	—	—	Denham Golf Club	d		05 49							06 48									
96	—	—	Denham	d		05 52	05 56			06 27						07 03						
98¾	—	—	West Ruislip 3 § ⊖	d		06 01		06 11			06 40									07 18		
100½	—	—	South Ruislip § ⊖	d		06 05				06 33					07 02						07 29	
102¼	—	—	Northolt Park	d		06 09				06 37			06 57							07 24		
103¼	—	—	Sudbury Hill Harrow	d						06 40										07 28		
104	—	—	Sudbury & Harrow Road	d									07 01									
105½	—	—	Wembley Stadium	d	00 04	06 14	06 06	06 19		06 44					07 09							
—	—	12	**London Paddington** 15 ⊖	a																		
112	—	—	**London Marylebone** 10 ⊖	a	00 17	06 26	06 19	06 31	06 42	06 56	07 00	07 01	07 15	07 19	07 22	07 25	07 29	07 32	07 35	07 43	07 46	07 53

Miles	Miles	Miles			CH	CH	CH ◇	CH	LM	CH	CH	CH	CH	CH	CH ◇	CH BZ ◇ ⚲	CH	CH	CH	CH
—	—	—	**Kidderminster**	d												06 09				
—	—	—	**Stourbridge Junction** 2	d												06 18				
—	—	—	Cradley Heath	d																
—	—	—	Rowley Regis	d												06 30				
0	—	—	**Birmingham Snow Hill**	d												06 50				
0¾	—	—	**Birmingham Moor Street**	d			06 10								06 28	06 55				
7¼	—	—	Solihull	d			06 19								06 38	07 04				
10½	—	—	Dorridge	d			06 24								06 50					
13	—	—	Lapworth	d																
—	—	0	**Stratford-upon-Avon**	d				06 08	07 26											
—	—	—	Stratford-upon-Avon Parkway	d				06 12	07a29											
—	—	2¾	Wilmcote	d				06 16												
—	—	4¼	Bearley	d																
—	—	7¼	Claverdon	d				06 23												
17¼	—	9¼	Hatton	d				06 32												
20	—	12	Warwick Parkway	d			06 34								06 59	07 17				
21¼	—	13¼	Warwick	d				06 40							07 02					
23¼	—	15¼	**Leamington Spa** 8	d			06 40	06a45							07 06	07 23				
43¼	—	—	**Banbury**	d			06 58								07 24					
46¾	—	—	Kings Sutton	d																
57¼	—	—	**Bicester North** 3	d		06 53	07 10					07 15			07 38					
70¼	—	—	Haddenham & Thame Parkway	d		07 06						07 28			07 49					
—	0	—	**Aylesbury**	d	06 44								07 28				07 44			
—	4½	—	Little Kimble	d	06 53												07 53			
—	6	—	Monks Risborough	d	06 57												07 57			
76	7½	—	**Princes Risborough** 2	d	07 01	07 14								07 44			08a03			08 05
79¼	—	—	Saunderton	d	07 06															08 10
84¼	—	—	**High Wycombe** 1	d	07 13	07 25					07 32	07 42		07 55					08 10	08 16
89	—	—	Beaconsfield	d	07 20						07 39	07 49		08 03					08 17	08 23
90¾	—	—	Seer Green	d	07 23							07 52								08 26
93¼	—	—	Gerrards Cross 1	d	07 28					07 40	07 45	07 57						08 17	08 23	08 31
95	—	—	Denham Golf Club	d						07 43										
96	—	—	Denham	d	07 32						07 50								08 27	
98¾	—	—	West Ruislip 3 § ⊖	d							07 55							08 24		
100½	—	—	South Ruislip § ⊖	d						07 50									08 33	
102¼	—	—	Northolt Park	d						07 54								08 30		
103¼	—	—	Sudbury Hill Harrow	d														08 33		
104	—	—	Sudbury & Harrow Road	d						07 58										
105½	—	—	Wembley Stadium	d	07 43						08 04								08 40	
—	—	12	**London Paddington** 15 ⊖	a																
112	—	—	**London Marylebone** 10 ⊖	a	07 56	07 59	08 00			08 12	08 16	08 19	08 22	08 25	08 28	08 29		08 46	08 53	08 56

§ London Underground Limited (Central Line) also operate services between South Ruislip and West Ruislip at frequent intervals

For complete service between Banbury and Leamington (Birmingham), please refer to table 71

Table 115R

Mondays to Fridays

9 December to 16 May

Kidderminster, Birmingham Snow Hill, Stratford-upon-Avon, Banbury, Aylesbury and High Wycombe - London

Network Diagram - see first Page of Table 114

		CH	CH	CH	CH	CH	CH	CH	CH	CH	CH	CH	CH	CH	CH	CH	CH	CH	CH	CH	CH	CH	CH	CH	CH	CH	CH	CH	CH	LM	LM	CH	CH	CH	CH	CH	CH
				◇ 🍴 BZ					◇	◇ 🍴					◇					◇	◇ 🍴			◇				◇	◇ 🍴					◇ 🍴			
Kidderminster	d									07 05					07 30						08 09																
Stourbridge Junction 2	d			06 38						07 14					07 38						08 23																
Cradley Heath	d									07 22					07 44						08 29																
Rowley Regis	d			06 50						07 29					07 51						08 35																
Birmingham Snow Hill	d			07 06						07 50					08 07					08 22	08 52			09 12										10 12			
Birmingham Moor Street	d			07 11						07 55					08 10					08 25	08 55			09 15					09 55					10 15			
Solihull	d			07 20						08 05					08 19					08 37	09 07			09 24					10 04					10 24			
Dorridge	d			07 27											08 24					08 52				09 29										10 29			
Lapworth	d																																				
Stratford-upon-Avon	d								07 33																			09 14		10 03	11 03						
Stratford-upon-Avon Parkway	d								07 37																			09 18		10a06	11a06						
Wilmcote	d								07 41																			09 22									
Bearley	d								07 44																			09 25									
Claverdon	d								07 50																			09 31									
Hatton	d																											09 41									
Warwick Parkway	d			07 37					08 00	08 18					08 34					09 02	09 21			09 40					10 16					10 38			
Warwick	d								08 03						08 37					09 06				09 44				09 48						10 42			
Leamington Spa 8	d			07 44					08 08	08 24					08 42					09 11	09 27			09 49				09 53	10 22					10 46			
Banbury	d		07 44	08 03				08 07	08 25						09 00			09 05		09 30				10 07				10 13	10 40					11 04			
Kings Sutton	d								08 31									09 10										10 18									
Bicester North 3	d		07 59					08 22	08 40					08 55	09 13			09 21		09 42			09 58	10 19				10 30					10 58	11 16			11 30
Haddenham & Thame Parkway	d		08 11					08 36	08 51					09 08				09 34		09 53			10 10					10 42					11 10				11 43
Aylesbury	d	08 00									08 47								09 30								10 33										
Little Kimble	d										08 56								09 39																		
Monks Risborough	d										09 00								09 43								10 44										
Princes Risborough 2	d		08 20				08 38	08 44			09a06			09 15				09 41	09 47				10 17			10 42	10a49	10 51					11 17			11 42	11 51
Saunderton	d						08 43							09 20				09 46										10 56					11 22				
High Wycombe 1	d		08 30			08 38	08 49	08 54					09 12	09 26			09 40	09 53	09 57	10 06			10 27	10 40	10 44	10 52		11 02					11 29	11 37	11 41	11 52	12 01
Beaconsfield	d					08 45		09 01					09 19				09 47		10 03				10 33		10 51			11 09					11 35		11 49	11 58	
Seer Green	d						08 57						09 22				09 50									10 59							11 38				
Gerrards Cross 1	d				08 45	08 51	09 02					09 19	09 27			09 44	09 55		10 09			10 20	10 39		10 57	11 04						11 20	11 42		11 55	12 04	
Denham Golf Club	d				08 48											09 48																11 23					
Denham	d					08 55						09 23				09 51						10 24										11 26					
West Ruislip 3 §	⊖ d					09 00						09 27				09 56						10 29										11 31					
South Ruislip §	⊖ d				08 55								09 34				10 03								11 04										12 03		
Northolt Park	d				08 59								09 38			10 02						10 35										11 36					
Sudbury Hill Harrow	d											09 34										10 38										11 39					
Sudbury & Harrow Road	d				09 03																	10 41															
Wembley Stadium	d		08 48			09 09						09 38					10 10					10 44			11 11							11 44			12 10		
London Paddington 15	⊖ a																																				
London Marylebone 10	⊖ a	08 59	09 02	09 03	09 16	09 21	09 25	09 28	09 32	09 36		09 52	09 55	09 58	09 59	10 18	10 23	10 26	10 32	10 36	10 39	10 57	11 00	11 11	11 24	11 27		11 29	11 34			11 57	12 00	12 08	12 23	12 26	12 31

§ London Underground Limited (Central Line) also operate services between South Ruislip and West Ruislip at frequent intervals

BZ Business Zone available offering greater comfort and an enhanced working environment. Supplement payable.

For complete service between Banbury and Leamington (Birmingham), please refer to table 71

Table 115R

Mondays to Fridays

9 December to 16 May

Kidderminster, Birmingham Snow Hill, Stratford-upon-Avon, Banbury, Aylesbury and High Wycombe - London

Network Diagram - see first Page of Table 114

		CH	CH	CH	CH	CH	CH	CH	CH	CH	LM	CH	LM
		◇ ⊥ BZ				◇			◇	◇			
Kidderminster	d												
Stourbridge Junction 2	d												
Cradley Heath	d												
Rowley Regis	d												
Birmingham Snow Hill	d					11 12							
Birmingham Moor Street	d	10 55				11 15				11 55			
Solihull	d	11 04				11 24				12 03			
Dorridge	d					11 29							
Lapworth	d												
Stratford-upon-Avon	d								11 35		12 03		13 03
Stratford-upon-Avon Parkway	d								11 39		12a06		13a06
Wilmcote	d								11 42				
Bearley	d								11 46				
Claverdon	d												
Hatton	d								11 56				
Warwick Parkway	d	11 16				11 38				12 15			
Warwick	d					11 42			12 02				
Leamington Spa 8	d	11 22				11 46			12 07	12 20			
Banbury	d	11 40				12 04			12 25	12 38			
Kings Sutton	d												
Bicester North 3	d				11 58	12 16			12 37				
Haddenham & Thame Parkway	d				12 10				12 48				
Aylesbury	d		11 51									12 51	
Little Kimble	d		12 00									13 00	
Monks Risborough	d		12 04									13 04	
Princes Risborough 2	d		12a10		12 17			12 42	12 56			13a10	
Saunderton	d				12 22								
High Wycombe 1	d				12 29	12 37	12 43	12 52	13 05				
Beaconsfield	d				12 35		12 50	12 58					
Seer Green	d				12 38								
Gerrards Cross 1	d			12 20	12 42		12 56	13 04					
Denham Golf Club	d			12 23									
Denham	d			12 26									
West Ruislip 3 § ⊖	d			12 31									
South Ruislip § ⊖	d						13 04						
Northolt Park	d			12 36									
Sudbury Hill Harrow	d			12 39									
Sudbury & Harrow Road	d												
Wembley Stadium	d			12 44			13 11						
London Paddington 15 ⊖	a												
London Marylebone 10 ⊖	a	12 34		12 57	13 00	13 08	13 24	13 27	13 33	13 34			

		CH	CH	CH	CH	CH	CH	CH	LM	CH	CH	CH	CH
				◇				◇ ⊥ BZ				◇ ⊥	
Kidderminster	d												
Stourbridge Junction 2	d												
Cradley Heath	d												
Rowley Regis	d												
Birmingham Snow Hill	d			12 12								13 12	
Birmingham Moor Street	d			12 15				12 55				13 15	
Solihull	d			12 24				13 04				13 24	
Dorridge	d			12 29								13 30	
Lapworth	d												
Stratford-upon-Avon	d								14 03				
Stratford-upon-Avon Parkway	d								14a06				
Wilmcote	d												
Bearley	d												
Claverdon	d												
Hatton	d												
Warwick Parkway	d			12 38				13 16				13 40	
Warwick	d			12 42								13 43	
Leamington Spa 8	d			12 46				13 22				13 48	
Banbury	d			13 04			13 13	13 40				14 06	
Kings Sutton	d						13 18						
Bicester North 3	d		12 58	13 16			13 30				13 58	14 18	
Haddenham & Thame Parkway	d		13 10				13 43				14 10		
Aylesbury	d					13 27							
Little Kimble	d												
Monks Risborough	d					13 38							
Princes Risborough 2	d		13 17			13 42	13 51				14 17		
Saunderton	d		13 22								14 22		
High Wycombe 1	d		13 29	13 37	13 41	13 52	14 01				14 29	14 39	14 43
Beaconsfield	d		13 35		13 49	13 58					14 35		14 50
Seer Green	d		13 38								14 38		
Gerrards Cross 1	d	13 20	13 42		13 55	14 04				14 20	14 42		14 56
Denham Golf Club	d	13 23								14 23			
Denham	d	13 26								14 26			
West Ruislip 3 § ⊖	d	13 31								14 31			
South Ruislip § ⊖	d				14 03								15 04
Northolt Park	d	13 36								14 36			
Sudbury Hill Harrow	d	13 39								14 39			
Sudbury & Harrow Road	d												
Wembley Stadium	d	13 44			14 10					14 44			15 11
London Paddington 15 ⊖	a												
London Marylebone 10 ⊖	a	13 57	14 00	14 08	14 23	14 26	14 31	14 34		14 57	15 00	15 08	15 24

		CH	CH	CH	CH	CH	CH	CH	CH	CH	CH	CH	LM
				◇				◇ ⊥			◇	◇ ⊥	
Kidderminster	d												
Stourbridge Junction 2	d												
Cradley Heath	d												
Rowley Regis	d												
Birmingham Snow Hill	d							14 12					
Birmingham Moor Street	d			13 55				14 15				14 55	
Solihull	d			14 04				14 24				15 04	
Dorridge	d							14 29					
Lapworth	d												
Stratford-upon-Avon	d										14 35		15 03
Stratford-upon-Avon Parkway	d										14 39		15a06
Wilmcote	d										14 42		
Bearley	d										14 46		
Claverdon	d										14 52		
Hatton	d										14 57		
Warwick Parkway	d			14 16				14 38				15 16	
Warwick	d							14 42			15 03		
Leamington Spa 8	d			14 22				14 46			15 08	15 22	
Banbury	d			14 40				15 04			15 26	15 40	
Kings Sutton	d												
Bicester North 3	d		14 30				14 58	15 16			15 38		
Haddenham & Thame Parkway	d		14 43				15 10				15 49		
Aylesbury	d	14 27			14 51								
Little Kimble	d				15 00								
Monks Risborough	d	14 38			15 04								
Princes Risborough 2	d	14 42	14 51		15a10		15 17			15 42	15 56		
Saunderton	d						15 22						
High Wycombe 1	d	14 52	15 01				15 29	15 37	15 41	15 52	16 05		
Beaconsfield	d	14 58					15 35		15 48	15 58			
Seer Green	d								15 51				
Gerrards Cross 1	d	15 04				15 20	15 41		15 56	16 04			
Denham Golf Club	d					15 23							
Denham	d					15 26							
West Ruislip 3 § ⊖	d					15 31							
South Ruislip § ⊖	d								16 04				
Northolt Park	d					15 36							
Sudbury Hill Harrow	d					15 39							
Sudbury & Harrow Road	d												
Wembley Stadium	d					15 44			16 11				
London Paddington 15 ⊖	a												
London Marylebone 10 ⊖	a	15 27	15 31	15 34		15 57	16 00	16 08	16 24	16 27	16 34	16 36	

§ London Underground Limited (Central Line) also operate services between South Ruislip and West Ruislip at frequent intervals

BZ Business Zone available offering greater comfort and an enhanced working environment. Supplement payable.

For complete service between Banbury and Leamington (Birmingham), please refer to table 71

Table 115R

Mondays to Fridays

9 December to 16 May

Kidderminster, Birmingham Snow Hill, Stratford-upon-Avon, Banbury, Aylesbury and High Wycombe - London

Network Diagram - see first Page of Table 114

Station		LM	CH	CH	CH	CH	CH	CH	CH	CH	CH	CH	CH
						◇					◇ BZ		
Kidderminster	d												
Stourbridge Junction 2	d												
Cradley Heath	d												
Rowley Regis	d												
Birmingham Snow Hill	d					15 12							
Birmingham Moor Street	d					15 15					15 55		
Solihull	d					15 24					16 04		
Dorridge	d					15 30							
Lapworth	d												
Stratford-upon-Avon	d	16 03											
Stratford-upon-Avon Parkway	d	16a06											
Wilmcote	d												
Bearley	d												
Claverdon	d												
Hatton	d												
Warwick Parkway	d					15 39					16 17		
Warwick	d					15 43							
Leamington Spa 8	d					15 47					16 23		
Banbury	d					16 05				16 12	16 41		
Kings Sutton	d									16 17			
Bicester North 3	d				15 58	16 17				16 30	16 54		
Haddenham & Thame Parkway	d				16 10					16 44			
Aylesbury	d								16 28				
Little Kimble	d								16 37				
Monks Risborough	d								16 41				
Princes Risborough 2	d				16 17				16 45	16 51			
Saunderton	d				16 22					16 56			
High Wycombe 1	d			16 20	16 29	16 38		16 45	16 55	17 03			17 20
Beaconsfield	d			16 27	16 35			16 52	17 01				17 27
Seer Green	d			16 30				16 56					17 30
Gerrards Cross 1	d		16 24	16 35	16 41		16 51	17 01	17 07	17 13			17 35
Denham Golf Club	d		16 27				16 54						
Denham	d		16 30	16 39			16 57						17 39
West Ruislip 3 § ⊖	d			16 49								17 26	17 49
South Ruislip § ⊖	d						17 03			17 21		17 31	
Northolt Park	d			16 55								17 35	
Sudbury Hill Harrow	d			16 58								17 38	
Sudbury & Harrow Road	d												
Wembley Stadium	d		16 40	17 02			17 10		17 20			17 43	17 58
London Paddington 15 ⊖	a												
London Marylebone 10 ⊖	a		16 55	17 16	17 00	17 08	17 23	17 26	17 33	17 39	17 42	17 55	18 16

Station		CH	CH	CH	CH	CH	CH	CH	CH	CH	CH	CH	CH
			◇						◇				◇
Kidderminster	d												
Stourbridge Junction 2	d												
Cradley Heath	d												
Rowley Regis	d												
Birmingham Snow Hill	d		16 12						16 52				17 07
Birmingham Moor Street	d		16 15						16 55				17 10
Solihull	d		16 24						17 03				17 18
Dorridge	d		16 29										17 26
Lapworth	d												
Stratford-upon-Avon	d												
Stratford-upon-Avon Parkway	d												
Wilmcote	d												
Bearley	d												
Claverdon	d												
Hatton	d												
Warwick Parkway	d		16 39						17 15				17 35
Warwick	d		16 43						17 18				17 39
Leamington Spa 8	d		16 48						17 23				17 43
Banbury	d		17 06					17 12	17 41				18 02
Kings Sutton	d							17 17					
Bicester North 3	d	17 02	17 18					17 32	17 54			18 02	18 15
Haddenham & Thame Parkway	d	17 13						17 46				18 13	18 26
Aylesbury	d					17 30							
Little Kimble	d					17 39							
Monks Risborough	d					17 43							
Princes Risborough 2	d	17 20			17 35	17a49		17 53				18 20	
Saunderton	d							17 58					
High Wycombe 1	d	17 29	17 39		17 45		17 54	18 05			18 20	18 29	18 39
Beaconsfield	d	17 35			17 52		18 01	18 11			18 27	18 35	
Seer Green	d				17 56						18 30		
Gerrards Cross 1	d	17 41		17 51	18 01		18 07				18 35	18 41	
Denham Golf Club	d			17 54									
Denham	d			17 57			18 12				18 39		
West Ruislip 3 § ⊖	d									18 26	18 49		
South Ruislip § ⊖	d						18 19			18 31			
Northolt Park	d									18 35			
Sudbury Hill Harrow	d									18 38			
Sudbury & Harrow Road	d												
Wembley Stadium	d			18 08			18 26			18 43	18 58		
London Paddington 15 ⊖	a												
London Marylebone 10 ⊖	a	18 00	18 10	18 21	18 26		18 41	18 44	18 47	18 55	19 13	19 00	19 11

Station		CH	CH	CH	CH	CH	CH	LM	CH	CH	CH	CH	CH
					◇	◇					◇		
Kidderminster	d												
Stourbridge Junction 2	d												
Cradley Heath	d												
Rowley Regis	d												
Birmingham Snow Hill	d					17 52					18 12		
Birmingham Moor Street	d					17 55					18 15		
Solihull	d					18 05					18 24		
Dorridge	d					18 12					18 29		
Lapworth	d										18 34		
Stratford-upon-Avon	d				17 35			19 05				19 12	
Stratford-upon-Avon Parkway	d				17 39			19a08				19 16	
Wilmcote	d				17 42							19 20	
Bearley	d											19 24	
Claverdon	d				17 51							19 29	
Hatton	d				17 56						18 40	19a36	
Warwick Parkway	d					18 22					18 45		
Warwick	d				18 02						18 49		
Leamington Spa 8	d				18 08	18 28					18 54		
Banbury	d				18 27	18 46					19 13		
Kings Sutton	d										19 18		
Bicester North 3	d				18 41	18 58				19 15	19 33		
Haddenham & Thame Parkway	d				18 54	19 09					19 44		
Aylesbury	d	18 18							19 13				
Little Kimble	d	18 27											
Monks Risborough	d	18 31							19 24				
Princes Risborough 2	d	18 36			19 01	19 16			19a32	19 34			
Saunderton	d				19 06								
High Wycombe 1	d	18 46	18 54		19 13	19 25	19 33			19 44	19 58		
Beaconsfield	d	18 52	19 01		19 19		19 40						
Seer Green	d		19 05				19 44						
Gerrards Cross 1	d	18 58	19 10		19 25		19 49						19 57
Denham Golf Club	d	19 02											20 00
Denham	d	19 05											20 03
West Ruislip 3 § ⊖	d			19 17									20 13
South Ruislip § ⊖	d	19 11		19 21			19 57						
Northolt Park	d			19 25									20 19
Sudbury Hill Harrow	d			19 28									20 22
Sudbury & Harrow Road	d												
Wembley Stadium	d	19 19	19 24	19 32			20 04						20 27
London Paddington 15 ⊖	a												
London Marylebone 10 ⊖	a	19 34	19 38	19 46	19 49	19 50	20 16			20 20	20 30		20 42

§ London Underground Limited (Central Line) also operate services between South Ruislip and West Ruislip at frequent intervals

BZ Business Zone available offering greater comfort and an enhanced working environment. Supplement payable.

For complete service between Banbury and Leamington (Birmingham), please refer to table 71

Table 115R

Mondays to Fridays

9 December to 16 May

Kidderminster, Birmingham Snow Hill, Stratford-upon-Avon, Banbury, Aylesbury and High Wycombe - London

Network Diagram - see first Page of Table 114

		CH	CH	CH	CH	CH	CH	CH	CH	CH	CH	CH	CH	CH	CH	CH	CH	CH	CH	CH	CH	LM
			◇		◇ ⚒						◇				◇		◇					
Kidderminster	d																					
Stourbridge Junction 2	d																					
Cradley Heath	d																					
Rowley Regis	d																					
Birmingham Snow Hill	d		18 40		19 14						20 15						21 15					
Birmingham Moor Street	d		18 43		19 17						20 18						21 18					
Solihull	d		18 52		19 26						20 27						21 27					
Dorridge	d		18 57		19 31						20 33						21 32					
Lapworth	d				19 35												21 37					
Stratford-upon-Avon	d														20 49						23 15	23 30
Stratford-upon-Avon Parkway	d														20 53							23a33
Wilmcote	d														20 56							
Bearley	d																					
Claverdon	d														21 03							
Hatton	d				19 41										21 09		21 43					
Warwick Parkway	d		19 06		19 46						20 43						21 48					
Warwick	d				19 49						20 47				21 16		21 51				23 34	
Leamington Spa 8	d		19 12		19 54						20 52				21 21		21 56				23 39	
Banbury	d		19 32		20 12				20 34		21 13				21 46		22 14		22 30		23a57	
Kings Sutton	d								20 39										22 35			
Bicester North 3	d		19 45	20 02	20 24			20 32	20 50		21 25			21 32	21 59		22 27		22 47			
Haddenham & Thame Parkway	d		19 57					20 45	21 01					21 45	22 10				22 59			
Aylesbury	d					20 18						21 30								23 03		
Little Kimble	d					20 27						21 39								23 11		
Monks Risborough	d					20 31						21 43								23 15		
Princes Risborough 2	d	19 57	20 05			20a42		20 52	21 08			21a49		21 52	22 17				23 06	23 19		
Saunderton	d	20 02						20 57						21 57						23 24		
High Wycombe 1	d	20 09	20 14	20 27	20 45			21 04	21 17	21 27	21 45			22 04	22 26	22 30	22 48	23 00	23 17	23 30		
Beaconsfield	d		20 20	20 34				21 11	21 23	21 34				22 11	22 33	22 37		23 07	23 23	23 37		
Seer Green	d			20 38						21 38						22 41		23 10		23 40		
Gerrards Cross 1	d		20 26	20 43			20 57	21 17	21 29	21 43			21 57	22 17	22 39	22 46		23 15	23 29	23 45		
Denham Golf Club	d						21 00						22 00			22 49		23 18				
Denham	d						21 03						22 03			22 52		23 21		23 49		
West Ruislip 3 § ⊖	d						21 08						22 08			23 00		23 25		23 53		
South Ruislip § ⊖	d			20 51						21 51						23 04		23 30	23 37			
Northolt Park	d						21 14						22 14			23 08		23 33		23 59		
Sudbury Hill Harrow	d																					
Sudbury & Harrow Road	d																					
Wembley Stadium	d			20 58			21 19	21 30		21 58			22 19	22 30		23 13		23 39		00 04		
London Paddington 15 ⊖	a																					
London Marylebone 10 ⊖	a	20 45	20 51	21 10	21 12		21 31	21 46	21 54	22 10	22 13		22 33	22 43	23 01	23 26	23 13	23 52	23 56	00 17		

§ London Underground Limited (Central Line) also operate services between South Ruislip and West Ruislip at frequent intervals

For complete service between Banbury and Leamington (Birmingham), please refer to table 71

Table 115R

Saturdays

14 December to 17 May

Kidderminster, Birmingham Snow Hill, Stratford-upon-Avon, Banbury, Aylesbury and High Wycombe - London

Network Diagram - see first Page of Table 114

		CH	CH	CH	CH	CH	CH	CH	CH	CH	CH	CH	CH
								◇	◇			◇	
Kidderminster	d											06 37	
Stourbridge Junction 2	d											06 45	
Cradley Heath	d											06 51	
Rowley Regis	d											06 57	
Birmingham Snow Hill	d											07 12	
Birmingham Moor Street	d							06 15	06 42			07 15	
Solihull	d							06 24	06 51			07 24	
Dorridge	d							06 29	06 56			07 30	
Lapworth	d							06 33					
Stratford-upon-Avon	d												
Stratford-upon-Avon Parkway	d												
Wilmcote	d												
Bearley	d												
Claverdon	d												
Hatton	d							06 39					
Warwick Parkway	d							06 44	07 05			07 40	
Warwick	d							06 47				07 43	
Leamington Spa 8	d							06 52	07 11			07 48	
Banbury	d				06 04	06 29		07 10	07 29			08 07	
Kings Sutton	d					06 34							
Bicester North 3	d				06 19	06 45		07 23	07 42			08 20	08 26
Haddenham & Thame Parkway	d				06 31	06 57		07 34	07 53			08 31	08 39
Aylesbury	d		05 15	05 55			06 55			07 46	08 04		
Little Kimble	d		05 23	06 03			07 03			07 55			
Monks Risborough	d		05 27	06 07			07 07			07 59			
Princes Risborough 2	d		05 31	06 11	06 39		07 11	07 42		08 03	08 18		08 46
Saunderton	d		05 36	06 16			07 16			08 08			08 51
High Wycombe 1	d		05 43	06 23	06 49	07 11	07 23	07 51		08 14	08 28		08 58
Beaconsfield	d		05 50	06 30	06 55		07 30	07 57		08 21	08 35		09 05
Seer Green	d		05 53	06 33			07 33			08 24			
Gerrards Cross 1	d		05 58	06 38	07 01		07 38	08 03		08 29	08 41		09 11
Denham Golf Club	d		06 01	06 41			07 41			08 32			
Denham	d		06 04	06 44			07 44			08 35			09 15
West Ruislip 3 § ⊖	d		06 09	06 49			07 49				08 48		
South Ruislip § ⊖	d		06 13	06 53			07 53			08 41			09 21
Northolt Park	d		06 17	06 57			07 57			08 45			09 25
Sudbury Hill Harrow	d												
Sudbury & Harrow Road	d												
Wembley Stadium	d	00 04	06 22	07 02	07 13		08 02			08 50			09 30
London Paddington 15 ⊖	a												
London Marylebone 10 ⊖	a	00 17	06 35	07 15	07 26	07 42	08 15	08 23	08 30	09 02	09 08	09 11	09 44

		CH	CH	CH	CH	CH	CH	LM	CH	CH	CH	CH	CH
		◇ BZ		◇	◇		◇				◇		
Kidderminster	d	07 12					08 13						
Stourbridge Junction 2	d	07 22					08 26						
Cradley Heath	d						08 32						
Rowley Regis	d	07 33					08 37						
Birmingham Snow Hill	d	07 51					08 52				09 12		
Birmingham Moor Street	d	07 55			08 15		08 55				09 15		
Solihull	d	08 05			08 24		09 05				09 24		
Dorridge	d				08 29						09 29		
Lapworth	d												
Stratford-upon-Avon	d			07 56				09 03					
Stratford-upon-Avon Parkway	d			08 00				09a06					
Wilmcote	d			08 03									
Bearley	d												
Claverdon	d			08 11									
Hatton	d			08 17									
Warwick Parkway	d	08 18			08 39		09 19				09 39		
Warwick	d			08 24	08 43						09 42		
Leamington Spa 8	d	08 24		08 29	08 48		09 25				09 48		
Banbury	d	08 44		08 50	09 10		09 45			09 25	10 06		
Kings Sutton	d			08 55						09 31			
Bicester North 3	d	08 57		09 06	09 23					09 42	10 19		
Haddenham & Thame Parkway	d	09 08		09 19	09 34					09 55	10 30		
Aylesbury	d		08 56						09 43				
Little Kimble	d		09 05						09 51				
Monks Risborough	d		09 09						09 55				
Princes Risborough 2	d		09 16	09 26	09 42				10a03	10 10	10 37		
Saunderton	d			09 31						10 15			
High Wycombe 1	d		09 26	09 38	09 51	09 54				10 22	10 46		10 54
Beaconsfield	d		09 33	09 45		10 01				10 29			11 01
Seer Green	d		09 36							10 32			
Gerrards Cross 1	d		09 41	09 51		10 07				10 37		10 42	11 07
Denham Golf Club	d		09 44									10 46	
Denham	d		09 47			10 11						10 49	11 11
West Ruislip 3 § ⊖	d		09 52									10 59	
South Ruislip § ⊖	d					10 16							11 16
Northolt Park	d					10 20							11 20
Sudbury Hill Harrow	d												
Sudbury & Harrow Road	d												
Wembley Stadium	d		10 01			10 25						11 08	11 25
London Paddington 15 ⊖	a												
London Marylebone 10 ⊖	a	09 47	10 14	10 17	10 20	10 37	10 42			11 02	11 14	11 24	11 38

		CH	CH	LM	CH	CH	CH	LM	CH	CH	CH	CH	CH
		◇	◇ BZ			◇				◇			◇
Kidderminster	d		09 10										
Stourbridge Junction 2	d		09 20										
Cradley Heath	d												
Rowley Regis	d		09 31										
Birmingham Snow Hill	d		09 51			10 12							11 12
Birmingham Moor Street	d		09 55			10 15				10 55			11 15
Solihull	d		10 05			10 24				11 04			11 24
Dorridge	d					10 30							11 29
Lapworth	d												
Stratford-upon-Avon	d	09 14		10 03				11 03					
Stratford-upon-Avon Parkway	d	09 18		10a06				11a06					
Wilmcote	d	09 22											
Bearley	d	09 25											
Claverdon	d	09 31											
Hatton	d	09 41											
Warwick Parkway	d		10 19			10 40				11 15			11 39
Warwick	d	09 48				10 44							11 42
Leamington Spa 8	d	09 53	10 25			10 49				11 21			11 48
Banbury	d	10 13	10 45			11 09				11 40			12 06
Kings Sutton	d	10 18											
Bicester North 3	d	10 33	10 58			11 23			11 33	11 54			12 21
Haddenham & Thame Parkway	d	10 46				11 34			11 46				12 32
Aylesbury	d				10 43						11 43		
Little Kimble	d										11 51		
Monks Risborough	d				10 54						11 55		
Princes Risborough 2	d	10 54			10 59	11 41			11 54		11 59		12 40
Saunderton	d	10 59							11 59				
High Wycombe 1	d	11 06			11 20	11 50	11 54		12 06		12a12	12 20	12 49
Beaconsfield	d	11 12			11 27		12 01		12 12			12 27	
Seer Green	d				11 30							12 30	
Gerrards Cross 1	d	11 18			11 35		12 07		12 18			12 35	
Denham Golf Club	d				11 38							12 38	
Denham	d				11 41		12 11					12 41	
West Ruislip 3 § ⊖	d				11 46							12 46	
South Ruislip § ⊖	d						12 16					12 50	
Northolt Park	d						12 20					12 54	
Sudbury Hill Harrow	d												
Sudbury & Harrow Road	d												
Wembley Stadium	d				11 55		12 25					12 59	
London Paddington 15 ⊖	a												
London Marylebone 10 ⊖	a	11 41	11 44		12 06	12 17	12 37		12 41	12 44		13 12	13 17

§ London Underground Limited (Central Line) also operate services between South Ruislip and West Ruislip at frequent intervals

BZ Business Zone available offering greater comfort and an enhanced working environment. Supplement payable.

For complete service between Banbury and Leamington (Birmingham), please refer to table 71

Table 115R

Saturdays

14 December to 17 May

Kidderminster, Birmingham Snow Hill, Stratford-upon-Avon, Banbury, Aylesbury and High Wycombe - London

Network Diagram - see first Page of Table 114

Station		CH	CH	CH	LM	LM	CH	CH	CH	CH
			◇	◇				◇		
Kidderminster	d									
Stourbridge Junction 2	d									
Cradley Heath	d									
Rowley Regis	d									
Birmingham Snow Hill	d							12 12		
Birmingham Moor Street	d			11 55				12 15		
Solihull	d			12 04				12 24		
Dorridge	d							12 29		
Lapworth	d									
Stratford-upon-Avon	d		11 37		12 03	12 52				
Stratford-upon-Avon Parkway	d		11 40		12a06	12a55				
Wilmcote	d		11 44							
Bearley	d									
Claverdon	d		11 52							
Hatton	d		11 58							
Warwick Parkway	d			12 21				12 39		
Warwick	d		12 04					12 42		
Leamington Spa 8	d		12 09	12 27				12 48		
Banbury	d		12 27	12 46				13 08		
Kings Sutton	d		12 32							
Bicester North 3	d		12 42	12 58				13 24		13 33
Haddenham & Thame Parkway	d		12 53					13 35		13 46
Aylesbury	d	12 30							13 30	
Little Kimble	d	12 39							13 39	
Monks Risborough	d	12 43							13 43	
Princes Risborough 2	d	12a50	13 00					13 43	13a50	13 54
Saunderton	d		13 05							13 59
High Wycombe 1	d		13 12				13 20	13 52		14 06
Beaconsfield	d		13 18				13 27			14 12
Seer Green	d						13 30			
Gerrards Cross 1	d		13 24				13 35			14 18
Denham Golf Club	d						13 38			
Denham	d						13 41			
West Ruislip 3 § ⊖	d						13 46			
South Ruislip § ⊖	d						13 50			
Northolt Park	d						13 54			
Sudbury Hill Harrow	d									
Sudbury & Harrow Road	d									
Wembley Stadium	d		13 34				13 59			14 30
London Paddington 15 ⊖	a									
London Marylebone 10 ⊖	a		13 47	13 50			14 12	14 18		14 43

Station		CH	CH	CH	CH	CH	CH	LM	LM	CH
		◇		◇		◇	◇ 🍴 BZ			
Kidderminster	d									
Stourbridge Junction 2	d									
Cradley Heath	d									
Rowley Regis	d									
Birmingham Snow Hill	d			13 12						
Birmingham Moor Street	d	12 55		13 15			13 55			
Solihull	d	13 04		13 24			14 05			
Dorridge	d			13 29						
Lapworth	d									
Stratford-upon-Avon	d					13 37		14 03	14 52	
Stratford-upon-Avon Parkway	d					13 40		14a06	14a55	
Wilmcote	d					13 44				
Bearley	d					13 48				
Claverdon	d									
Hatton	d					13 58				
Warwick Parkway	d	13 19		13 39			14 18			
Warwick	d			13 42		14 04				
Leamington Spa 8	d	13 25		13 48		14 09	14 25			
Banbury	d	13 44		14 10		14 27	14 43			
Kings Sutton	d					14 32				
Bicester North 3	d	13 56		14 22		14 42	14 56			
Haddenham & Thame Parkway	d			14 33		14 53				
Aylesbury	d				14 30					
Little Kimble	d				14 39					
Monks Risborough	d				14 43					
Princes Risborough 2	d			14 41	14a50	15 00				
Saunderton	d					15 05				
High Wycombe 1	d		14 20	14 50		15 12				15 20
Beaconsfield	d		14 27			15 18				15 27
Seer Green	d		14 30							15 30
Gerrards Cross 1	d		14 35			15 24				15 35
Denham Golf Club	d		14 38							15 38
Denham	d		14 41							15 41
West Ruislip 3 § ⊖	d		14 46							15 46
South Ruislip § ⊖	d		14 50							15 50
Northolt Park	d		14 54							15 54
Sudbury Hill Harrow	d									
Sudbury & Harrow Road	d									
Wembley Stadium	d		14 59			15 34				15 59
London Paddington 15 ⊖	a									
London Marylebone 10 ⊖	a	14 47	15 14	15 17		15 47	15 50			16 12

Station		CH	CH	CH	CH	CH	CH	CH	CH	CH
		◇			◇ 🍴		◇			◇
Kidderminster	d									
Stourbridge Junction 2	d									
Cradley Heath	d									
Rowley Regis	d									
Birmingham Snow Hill	d	14 12					15 12			
Birmingham Moor Street	d	14 15			14 55		15 15			
Solihull	d	14 24			15 04		15 24			
Dorridge	d	14 29					15 29			
Lapworth	d									
Stratford-upon-Avon	d									15 37
Stratford-upon-Avon Parkway	d									15 40
Wilmcote	d									15 44
Bearley	d									
Claverdon	d									15 52
Hatton	d									15 58
Warwick Parkway	d	14 39			15 16		15 39			
Warwick	d	14 42					15 42			16 04
Leamington Spa 8	d	14 48			15 23		15 48			16 09
Banbury	d	15 09			15 42		16 07			16 27
Kings Sutton	d									16 32
Bicester North 3	d	15 24		15 33	15 55		16 21			16 42
Haddenham & Thame Parkway	d	15 35		15 46			16 32			16 53
Aylesbury	d		15 30						16 30	
Little Kimble	d		15 39						16 39	
Monks Risborough	d		15 43						16 43	
Princes Risborough 2	d	15 43	15a50	15 54			16 40		16a50	17 00
Saunderton	d			15 59						17 05
High Wycombe 1	d	15 52		16 06		16 20	16 50	16 53		17 12
Beaconsfield	d			16 12		16 27		16 59		17 18
Seer Green	d					16 30		17 02		
Gerrards Cross 1	d			16 18		16 35		17 07		17 23
Denham Golf Club	d					16 38				
Denham	d			16 22		16 41		17 11		
West Ruislip 3 § ⊖	d					16 46				
South Ruislip § ⊖	d					16 50		17 16		
Northolt Park	d					16 54		17 20		
Sudbury Hill Harrow	d									
Sudbury & Harrow Road	d									
Wembley Stadium	d			16 32		16 59		17 25		
London Paddington 15 ⊖	a									
London Marylebone 10 ⊖	a	16 18		16 44	16 47	17 14	17 22	17 38		17 44

Station		CH	LM	LM	CH	CH	CH	CH	CH	CH
		◇				◇				◇
Kidderminster	d									
Stourbridge Junction 2	d									
Cradley Heath	d									
Rowley Regis	d									
Birmingham Snow Hill	d					16 12				
Birmingham Moor Street	d	15 55				16 15				16 55
Solihull	d	16 04				16 24				17 04
Dorridge	d					16 29				
Lapworth	d									
Stratford-upon-Avon	d		16 03	16 52						
Stratford-upon-Avon Parkway	d		16a06	16a55						
Wilmcote	d									
Bearley	d									
Claverdon	d									
Hatton	d									
Warwick Parkway	d	16 16				16 39				17 16
Warwick	d					16 42				
Leamington Spa 8	d	16 23				16 48				17 23
Banbury	d	16 44				17 08				17 45
Kings Sutton	d									
Bicester North 3	d	16 58				17 23			17 33	17 59
Haddenham & Thame Parkway	d					17 34			17 46	
Aylesbury	d							17 30		
Little Kimble	d							17 39		
Monks Risborough	d							17 43		
Princes Risborough 2	d					17 41		17a50	17 54	
Saunderton	d								18 00	
High Wycombe 1	d					17 50	17 53		18 07	
Beaconsfield	d						17 59		18 13	
Seer Green	d						18 02			
Gerrards Cross 1	d				17 40		18 07		18 19	
Denham Golf Club	d				17 43					
Denham	d				17 46		18 11			
West Ruislip 3 § ⊖	d				17 50					
South Ruislip § ⊖	d						18 16			
Northolt Park	d						18 20			
Sudbury Hill Harrow	d									
Sudbury & Harrow Road	d									
Wembley Stadium	d				17 59		18 25			
London Paddington 15 ⊖	a									
London Marylebone 10 ⊖	a	17 47			18 12	18 20	18 38		18 44	18 47

§ London Underground Limited (Central Line) also operate services between South Ruislip and West Ruislip at frequent intervals

BZ Business Zone available offering greater comfort and an enhanced working environment. Supplement payable.

For complete service between Banbury and Leamington (Birmingham), please refer to table 71

Table 115R

Saturdays

14 December to 17 May

Kidderminster, Birmingham Snow Hill, Stratford-upon-Avon, Banbury, Aylesbury and High Wycombe - London

Network Diagram - see first Page of Table 114

		CH	CH ◇	CH ◇	CH	CH	CH	CH ◇	CH	CH	CH ◇	CH	CH	CH	CH ◇	CH	CH ◇	CH	CH	CH ◇	CH	LM
Kidderminster	d																					
Stourbridge Junction 2	d																					
Cradley Heath	d																					
Rowley Regis	d																					
Birmingham Snow Hill	d		17 12					17 52			18 42				19 42					21 22		
Birmingham Moor Street	d		17 15					17 55			18 45				19 45		20 45			21 25		
Solihull	d		17 24					18 04			18 54				19 54		20 54			21 34		
Dorridge	d		17 29								18 59				19 59		20 59			21 42		
Lapworth	d														20 03		21 03			21 47		
Stratford-upon-Avon	d			17 35									19 37					21 35				23 30
Stratford-upon-Avon Parkway	d			17 38									19 40									23a33
Wilmcote	d			17 42									19 44									
Bearley	d			17 46									19 48									
Claverdon	d			17 52									19 54									
Hatton	d												20 00		20 09		21 09			21 52		
Warwick Parkway	d		17 39					18 16			19 08		20 06		20 14		21 14			21 57		
Warwick	d		17 42	18 03				18 19			19 11		20 09		20 17		21 17	21 55		22 01		
Leamington Spa 8	d		17 48	18 08				18 25			19 17		20a17		20 23		21 21	22a04		22 05		
Banbury	d		18 08	18 26				18 45			19 35			20 11	20 46		21 41			22 23		
Kings Sutton	d													20 16						22 28		
Bicester North 3	d		18 21	18 38			18 45	18 58			19 47			20 27	20 59		21 54			22 38		
Haddenham & Thame Parkway	d		18 32				18 58				19 58			20 39	21 10		22 05			22 49		
Aylesbury	d				18 35					19 20						21 20			22 25		22 45	
Little Kimble	d				18 44					19 28						21 28					22 53	
Monks Risborough	d				18 48					19 32						21 32					22 57	
Princes Risborough 2	d		18 40		18a55		19 05			19 36	20 05			20 46	21 17	21 36	22 13		22 39	22 56	23 01	
Saunderton	d						19 10			19 41				20 51		21 41					23 06	
High Wycombe 1	d		18 49			19 00	19 25		19 35	19 47	20 14	20 35		20 58	21 26	21 47	22 22		22 49	23 06	23 12	
Beaconsfield	d					19 07	19 32		19 42	19 54		20 42		21 04	21 32	21 54	22 28		22 55		23 19	
Seer Green	d					19 10			19 45			20 45		21 07		21 57			22 58		23 22	
Gerrards Cross 1	d	18 40				19 15	19 38		19 50	20 00		20 50		21 12	21 37	22 02	22 33		23 03		23 27	
Denham Golf Club	d	18 43							19 53			20 53		21 16		22 05			23 07		23 30	
Denham	d	18 46				19 19			19 56	20 04		20 56		21 18		22 08			23 10		23 33	
West Ruislip 3 § ⊖	d	18 50							20 00			21 00		21 23		22 12			23 19		23 37	
South Ruislip § ⊖	d					19 24				20 10				21 27		22 16			23 23		23 41	
Northolt Park	d					19 28				20 14		21 06		21 30		22 20			23 27		23 45	
Sudbury Hill Harrow	d																					
Sudbury & Harrow Road	d																					
Wembley Stadium	d	18 59				19 33			20 09	20 19		21 11		21 35		22 25			23 32	23 23	23 50	
London Paddington 15 ⊖	a																					
London Marylebone 10 ⊖	a	19 12	19 16	19 24		19 47	20 00	19 50	20 22	20 32	20 40	21 24		21 48	21 58	22 38	23 00		23 43	23 35	00 03	

§ London Underground Limited (Central Line) also operate services between South Ruislip and West Ruislip at frequent intervals

For complete service between Banbury and Leamington (Birmingham), please refer to table 71

Table 115R

Sundays

8 December to 11 May

Kidderminster, Birmingham Snow Hill, Stratford-upon-Avon, Banbury, Aylesbury and High Wycombe - London

Network Diagram - see first Page of Table 114

		CH	CH	CH	CH	CH	CH	CH	CH	CH
								◇		◇
Kidderminster	d									
Stourbridge Junction 2	d									
Cradley Heath	d									
Rowley Regis	d									
Birmingham Snow Hill	d									
Birmingham Moor Street	d							08 25		08 55
Solihull	d							08 34		09 04
Dorridge	d							08 39		09 09
Lapworth	d									
Stratford-upon-Avon	d									
Stratford-upon-Avon Parkway	d									
Wilmcote	d									
Bearley	d									
Claverdon	d									
Hatton	d									
Warwick Parkway	d							08 49		09 19
Warwick	d							08 52		
Leamington Spa 8	d							08 58		09 25
Banbury	d				08 40			09 16	09 22	09 43
Kings Sutton	d								09 27	
Bicester North 3	d			08 25	08 55			09 29	09 38	09 55
Haddenham & Thame Parkway	d			08 38	09 08			09 40		
Aylesbury	d	07 23	07 55			08 55				
Little Kimble	d	07 31	08 03			09 03				
Monks Risborough	d	07 35	08 07			09 07				
Princes Risborough 2	d	07 39	08 11	08 45		09a14	09 17		09 56	
Saunderton	d	07 44	08 16				09 22			
High Wycombe 1	d	07 51	08 23	08 55	09 22		09 28		10 06	
Beaconsfield	d	07 57	08 29	09 01	09 29		09 34		10 12	
Seer Green	d	08 00	08 32				09 37			
Gerrards Cross 1	d	08 05	08 37	09 07	09 35		09 42		10 18	
Denham Golf Club	d	08 08	08 40				09 45			
Denham	d	08 11	08 43				09 48			
West Ruislip 3 § ⊖	d	08 15	08 47				09 52			
South Ruislip § ⊖	d	08 19	08 51				09 56			
Northolt Park	d	08 23	08 55				10 00			
Sudbury Hill Harrow	d									
Sudbury & Harrow Road	d									
Wembley Stadium	d	08 28	09 00				10 05			
London Paddington 15 ⊖	a									
London Marylebone 10 ⊖	a	08 41	09 13	09 32	09 58		10 18	10 21	10 41	10 44

		CH	CH	CH	CH	CH	CH	CH	CH	CH
				◇	◇	◇			◇	
Kidderminster	d									
Stourbridge Junction 2	d									
Cradley Heath	d									
Rowley Regis	d									
Birmingham Snow Hill	d			09 12					10 12	
Birmingham Moor Street	d			09 15		09 55			10 15	
Solihull	d			09 24		10 04			10 24	
Dorridge	d			09 29		10 09			10 29	
Lapworth	d								10 33	
Stratford-upon-Avon	d				09 38					
Stratford-upon-Avon Parkway	d				09 41					
Wilmcote	d				09 44					
Bearley	d									
Claverdon	d									
Hatton	d				09 55				10 38	
Warwick Parkway	d			09 39		10 19			10 44	
Warwick	d			09 42	10 01				10 47	
Leamington Spa 8	d			09 48	10 06	10 25			10 52	
Banbury	d		09 50	10 06	10 24	10 43			11 10	
Kings Sutton	d				10 29					
Bicester North 3	d		10 06	10 19	10 39	10 55			11 22	11 33
Haddenham & Thame Parkway	d		10 19	10 30	10 50				11 33	11 46
Aylesbury	d	09 55					10 55			
Little Kimble	d	10 03					11 03			
Monks Risborough	d	10 07					11 07			
Princes Risborough 2	d	10 11	10 26	10 38	10 57		11 11		11 40	11 53
Saunderton	d	10 16					11 16			
High Wycombe 1	d	10 23	10 36	10 47	11 06		11 23	11 36	11 49	12 03
Beaconsfield	d	10 29	10 43		11 12		11 29	11 43		12 09
Seer Green	d	10 32					11 32			
Gerrards Cross 1	d	10 37	10 49		11 18		11 37	11 49		12 15
Denham Golf Club	d	10 40								
Denham	d	10 43					11 41			
West Ruislip 3 § ⊖	d						11 45			
South Ruislip § ⊖	d	10 49					11 49			
Northolt Park	d	10 53					11 53			
Sudbury Hill Harrow	d									
Sudbury & Harrow Road	d									
Wembley Stadium	d	10 58			11 28		11 58			12 27
London Paddington 15 ⊖	a									
London Marylebone 10 ⊖	a	11 11	11 14	11 17	11 41	11 44	12 11	12 14	12 17	12 41

		CH	CH	CH	CH	CH	CH	CH	CH	CH
		◇ BZ			◇	◇	◇			◇
Kidderminster	d									
Stourbridge Junction 2	d									
Cradley Heath	d									
Rowley Regis	d									
Birmingham Snow Hill	d				11 12					12 12
Birmingham Moor Street	d	10 55			11 15		11 55			12 15
Solihull	d	11 04			11 24		12 04			12 24
Dorridge	d	11 10			11 29		12 09			12 29
Lapworth	d									12 33
Stratford-upon-Avon	d					11 38				
Stratford-upon-Avon Parkway	d					11 41				
Wilmcote	d					11 44				
Bearley	d									
Claverdon	d									
Hatton	d					11 55				12 38
Warwick Parkway	d	11 20			11 39		12 19			12 44
Warwick	d				11 42	12 01				12 47
Leamington Spa 8	d	11 26			11 48	12 06	12 25			12 52
Banbury	d	11 44			12 06	12 24	12 43			13 10
Kings Sutton	d					12 29				
Bicester North 3	d	11 57			12 19	12 39	12 55			13 22
Haddenham & Thame Parkway	d				12 30	12 50				13 33
Aylesbury	d		11 55					12 55		
Little Kimble	d		12 03					13 03		
Monks Risborough	d		12 07					13 07		
Princes Risborough 2	d		12 11		12 38	12 57		13 11		13 40
Saunderton	d		12 16					13 16		
High Wycombe 1	d		12 23	12 36	12 47	13 06		13 23	13 36	13 49
Beaconsfield	d		12 29	12 43		13 12		13 29	13 43	
Seer Green	d		12 32					13 32		
Gerrards Cross 1	d		12 37	12 49		13 18		13 37	13 49	
Denham Golf Club	d		12 40							
Denham	d		12 43					13 41		
West Ruislip 3 § ⊖	d							13 45		
South Ruislip § ⊖	d		12 49					13 49		
Northolt Park	d		12 53					13 53		
Sudbury Hill Harrow	d									
Sudbury & Harrow Road	d									
Wembley Stadium	d		12 58			13 28		13 58		
London Paddington 15 ⊖	a									
London Marylebone 10 ⊖	a	12 44	13 11	13 14	13 17	13 41	13 44	14 10	14 14	14 17

		CH	CH	CH	CH	CH	CH	CH	CH	CH
			◇			◇	◇	◇		
Kidderminster	d									
Stourbridge Junction 2	d									
Cradley Heath	d									
Rowley Regis	d									
Birmingham Snow Hill	d					13 12				
Birmingham Moor Street	d		12 55			13 15		13 55		
Solihull	d		13 04			13 24		14 04		
Dorridge	d		13 09			13 29		14 09		
Lapworth	d									
Stratford-upon-Avon	d						13 38			
Stratford-upon-Avon Parkway	d						13 41			
Wilmcote	d						13 44			
Bearley	d									
Claverdon	d									
Hatton	d						13 55			
Warwick Parkway	d		13 19			13 39		14 19		
Warwick	d					13 42	14 01			
Leamington Spa 8	d		13 25			13 48	14 06	14 25		
Banbury	d		13 43			14 06	14 24	14 43		
Kings Sutton	d						14 29			
Bicester North 3	d	13 33	13 55			14 19	14 39	14 55		
Haddenham & Thame Parkway	d	13 46				14 30	14 50			
Aylesbury	d			13 55					14 55	
Little Kimble	d			14 03					15 03	
Monks Risborough	d			14 07					15 07	
Princes Risborough 2	d	13 53		14 11		14 38	14 57		15 11	
Saunderton	d			14 16					15 16	
High Wycombe 1	d	14 03		14 23	14 36	14 47	15 06		15 23	15 36
Beaconsfield	d	14 09		14 29	14 43		15 12		15 29	15 43
Seer Green	d			14 32					15 32	
Gerrards Cross 1	d	14 15		14 37	14 49		15 18		15 37	15 49
Denham Golf Club	d			14 40						
Denham	d			14 43					15 41	
West Ruislip 3 § ⊖	d								15 45	
South Ruislip § ⊖	d			14 49					15 49	
Northolt Park	d			14 53					15 53	
Sudbury Hill Harrow	d									
Sudbury & Harrow Road	d									
Wembley Stadium	d	14 27		14 58			15 28		15 58	
London Paddington 15 ⊖	a									
London Marylebone 10 ⊖	a	14 41	14 44	15 11	15 14	15 17	15 41	15 44	16 11	16 14

§ London Underground Limited (Central Line) also operate services between South Ruislip and West Ruislip at frequent intervals

BZ Business Zone available offering greater comfort and an enhanced working environment. Supplement payable.

For complete service between Banbury and Leamington (Birmingham), please refer to table 71

Table 115R

Sundays
8 December to 11 May

Kidderminster, Birmingham Snow Hill, Stratford-upon-Avon, Banbury, Aylesbury and High Wycombe - London

Network Diagram - see first Page of Table 114

		CH	CH	CH	CH	CH	CH	CH	CH	CH	CH	CH	CH	CH	CH	CH
		◇		◇			◇	◇	◇			◇		◇		
Kidderminster	d															
Stourbridge Junction 2	d															
Cradley Heath	d															
Rowley Regis	d															
Birmingham Snow Hill	d	14 12					15 12					16 12				
Birmingham Moor Street	d	14 15		14 55			15 15		15 55			16 15		16 55		
Solihull	d	14 24		15 04			15 24		16 04			16 24		17 04		
Dorridge	d	14 29		15 09			15 29		16 09			16 29		17 09		
Lapworth	d	14 33										16 33				
Stratford-upon-Avon	d							15 38								
Stratford-upon-Avon Parkway	d							15 41								
Wilmcote	d							15 44								
Bearley	d															
Claverdon	d															
Hatton	d	14 38						15 55				16 38				
Warwick Parkway	d	14 44		15 19			15 39		16 19			16 44		17 19		
Warwick	d	14 47					15 42	16 01				16 47				
Leamington Spa 8	d	14 52		15 25			15 48	16 06	16 25			16 52		17 25		
Banbury	d	15 10		15 43			16 06	16 24	16 43			17 10		17 43		
Kings Sutton	d							16 29								
Bicester North 3	d	15 22	15 33	15 55			16 19	16 39	16 55			17 22	17 33	17 55		
Haddenham & Thame Parkway	d	15 33	15 46				16 30	16 50				17 33	17 46			
Aylesbury	d				15 55					16 55					17 55	
Little Kimble	d				16 03					17 03					18 03	
Monks Risborough	d				16 07					17 07					18 07	
Princes Risborough 2	d	15 40	15 53		16 11		16 38	16 57		17 11		17 40	17 53		18 11	
Saunderton	d				16 16					17 16					18 16	
High Wycombe 1	d	15 49	16 03		16 23	16 36	16 47	17 06		17 23	17 36	17 49	18 03		18 23	18 36
Beaconsfield	d		16 09		16 29	16 43		17 12		17 29	17 43		18 09		18 29	18 43
Seer Green	d				16 32					17 32					18 32	
Gerrards Cross 1	d		16 15		16 37	16 49		17 18		17 37	17 49		18 15		18 37	18 49
Denham Golf Club	d				16 40										18 40	
Denham	d				16 43					17 41					18 43	
West Ruislip 3 § ⊖	d									17 45						
South Ruislip § ⊖	d				16 49					17 49					18 49	
Northolt Park	d				16 53					17 53					18 53	
Sudbury Hill Harrow	d															
Sudbury & Harrow Road	d															
Wembley Stadium	d		16 27		16 58			17 28		17 58			18 27		18 58	
London Paddington 15 ⊖	a															
London Marylebone 10 ⊖	a	16 17	16 41	16 44	17 11	17 14	17 17	17 40	17 43	18 11	18 14	18 17	18 41	18 44	19 11	19 14

		CH	CH	CH	CH	CH	CH	CH	CH	CH	CH	CH	CH	CH	CH
		◇	◇	◇			◇		◇		◇	◇	◇		◇
Kidderminster	d														
Stourbridge Junction 2	d														
Cradley Heath	d														
Rowley Regis	d														
Birmingham Snow Hill	d	17 12					18 12				19 15		20 15		21 15
Birmingham Moor Street	d	17 15		17 55			18 15		18 55		19 18		20 18		21 18
Solihull	d	17 24		18 04			18 24		19 04		19 26		20 27		21 27
Dorridge	d	17 29		18 09			18 29		19 09		19 34		20 33		21 34
Lapworth	d										19 38				
Stratford-upon-Avon	d		17 38									20 00			
Stratford-upon-Avon Parkway	d		17 41									20 03			
Wilmcote	d		17 44									20 06			
Bearley	d														
Claverdon	d														
Hatton	d		17 55								19 43	20 17			
Warwick Parkway	d	17 39		18 19			18 39		19 19		19 48		20 43		21 44
Warwick	d	17 42	18 01				18 42				19 51	20 23	20 46		21 47
Leamington Spa 8	d	17 48	18 06	18 25			18 48		19 25		19 57	20 28	20 51		21 52
Banbury	d	18 06	18 24	18 43			19 06		19 43		20 15	20 48	21 09		22 15
Kings Sutton	d		18 29								20 20		21 14		22 20
Bicester North 3	d	18 19	18 39	18 55			19 19	19 33	19 55		20 31	21 02	21 24		22 30
Haddenham & Thame Parkway	d	18 30	18 50				19 30	19 46			20 42	21 15	21 34		22 41
Aylesbury	d				18 55					19 55				22 21	
Little Kimble	d				19 03					20 03				22 29	
Monks Risborough	d				19 07					20 07				22 33	
Princes Risborough 2	d	18 38	18 57		19 11		19 38	19 53		20 11	20 49	21 22	21 41	22a40	22 49
Saunderton	d				19 16					20 16	20 54		21 46		22 54
High Wycombe 1	d	18 47	19 06		19 23	19 36	19 47	20 03		20 23	21 00	21 32	21 53		23 01
Beaconsfield	d		19 12		19 29	19 43		20 09		20 29	21 07	21 38	21 59		23 07
Seer Green	d				19 32					20 32	21 10		22 02		23 10
Gerrards Cross 1	d		19 18		19 37	19 49		20 15		20 37	21 15	21 44	22 06		23 14
Denham Golf Club	d									20 40			22 09		
Denham	d				19 41					20 43	21 19		22 12		23 18
West Ruislip 3 § ⊖	d				19 45						21 24		22 16		23 22
South Ruislip § ⊖	d				19 49					20 49	21 28		22 20		23 26
Northolt Park	d				19 53					20 53	21 31		22 24		23 30
Sudbury Hill Harrow	d														
Sudbury & Harrow Road	d														
Wembley Stadium	d		19 28		19 58			20 27		20 58	21 37		22 29		23 35
London Paddington 15 ⊖	a														
London Marylebone 10 ⊖	a	19 17	19 41	19 44	20 11	20 14	20 17	20 40	20 43	21 11	21 50	22 08	22 41		23 47

§ London Underground Limited (Central Line) also operate services between South Ruislip and West Ruislip at frequent intervals

For complete service between Banbury and Leamington (Birmingham), please refer to table 71

Table 115A

Mondays to Fridays

9 December to 16 May

Chinnor - Princes Risborough

Bus Service

Network Diagram - see first Page of Table 114

		CH	CH	CH		CH		CH	CH	CH
Chinnor, Lower Road	d	06 19	06 48	07 20		07 56		09 16	09 51	17 18
Chinnor, Estover Way	d	06 21	06 50	07 22		07 58		09 18	09 53	17 20
Chinnor, The Wheatsheaf	d	06 22	06 51	07 23		07 59		09 19	09 54	17 21
Chinnor, The Red Lion	d	06 25	06 54	07 26		08 02		09 22	09 57	17 24
Bledlow, Village Hall	d	06 28	06 57	07 29		08 05		09 25	10 00	17 27
Princes Risborough	a	06 35	07 04	07 36		08 12		09 32	10 07	17 41

No Saturday or Sunday service

Table 115A-R

Mondays to Fridays

9 December to 16 May

Princes Risborough - Chinnor

Bus Service

Network Diagram - see first Page of Table 114

		CH	CH		CH	CH		CH	CH		CH	CH	CH
Princes Risborough	d	07 38	08 15		16 35	17 08		18 08	18 35		19 10	20 00	21 00
Bledlow, Village Hall	d	07 52	08 30		16 42	17 15		18 15	18 42		19 17	20 07	21 07
Chinnor, Lower Road	d	07 55	08 33		16 45	17 18		18 18	18 45		19 20	20 10	21 10
Chinnor, Estover Way	d	07 58	08 35		16 47	17 20		18 20	18 47		19 22	20 12	21 12
Chinnor, The Wheatsheaf	d	07 59	08 36		16 48	17 21		18 21	18 48		19 23	20 13	21 13
Chinnor, The Red Lion	a	08 02	08 39		16 51	17 24		18 24	18 51		19 25	20 15	21 15

No Saturday or Sunday service

Network Diagram for Tables 116, 117, 118, 119, 120, 121, 122, 126

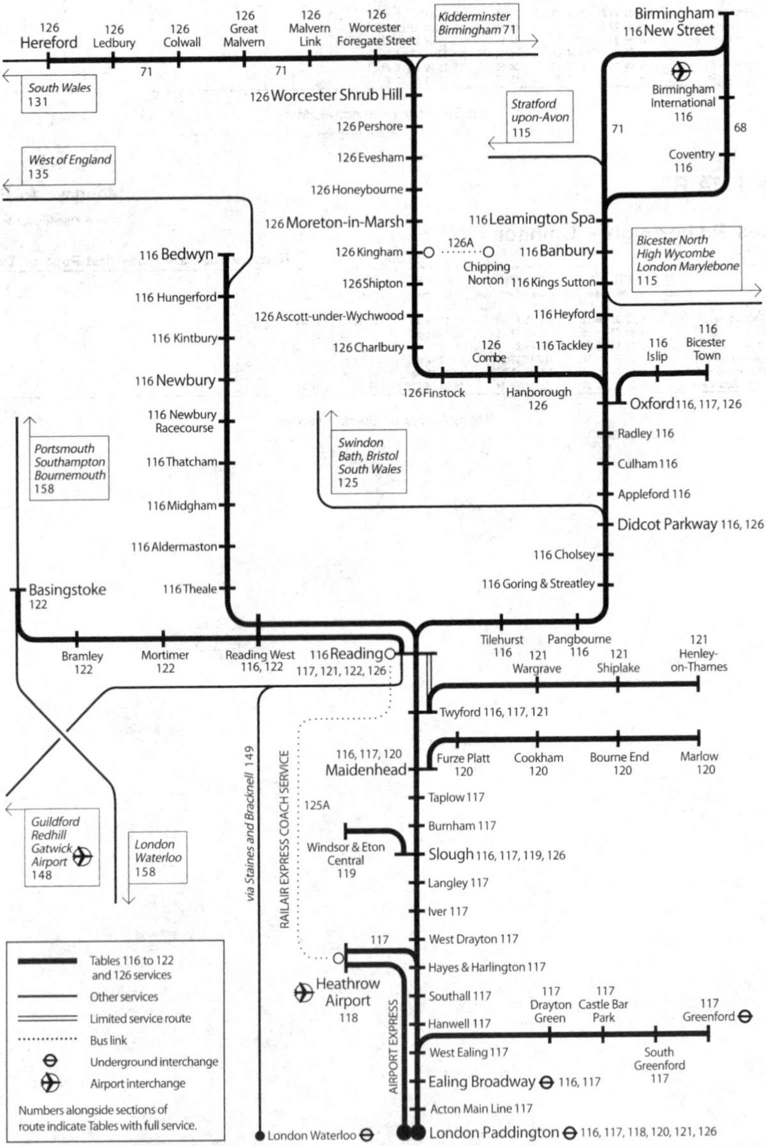

TOCs operating on this network - First Great Western (GW), Heathrow Connect (HC), Heathrow Express (HX), Chiltern Railways (CH), Cross Country (XC)

Table 116

Mondays to Fridays

9 December to 30 December

London and Reading - Bedwyn, Oxford, Bicester, Banbury and Birmingham

Network Diagram - refer to first Page of Table 116

Miles	Miles			GW MX	GW MO	GW MX	CH MX	GW MX	GW MO	GW MO	GW MX	GW MX	GW MX	GW	GW	CH	GW	GW	GW	GW	GW
				1	1	◇1		◇1	◇1		1	1	◇1	1	1		1	1	1	◇1	1
								☕	☕	🚌										☕	
0	—	**London Paddington 15** ⊖	d										00 22					05 12	05 17	05 19	
5¾	—	Ealing Broadway ⊖	d																05 25		
18½	—	Slough 3	d										00 41					05 30	05 51		
24¼	—	Maidenhead 3	d									00 05							05 59		
31	—	Twyford 3	d									00 13							06 07		
36	0	**Reading 7**	d			00 04		00 09	00 16		00 20	00 27	01 01		05 15			05 50	06 18	05 53	05 54
—	1	Reading West	d								00s23				05 17				→		
—	5¼	Theale	d								00s29				05 24						
—	8¾	Aldermaston	d								00s34				05 29						
—	10¾	Midgham	d								00s37				05 32						
—	13½	Thatcham	d								00s42				05 37						
—	16½	Newbury Racecourse	d								00s47				05 42						
—	17	**Newbury**	a								00 52				05 45						
—	—		d												05 45						
—	22½	Kintbury	d												05 51						
—	25½	Hungerford	d												05 56						
—	30½	**Bedwyn**	a												06 06						
38¾	—	Tilehurst	d									00 33									05 58
41½	—	Pangbourne	d		00 01							00 37									06 03
44¾	—	Goring & Streatley	d		00 07							00 41									06 08
48½	—	Cholsey	d		00 12							00 46									06 14
53¼	—	**Didcot Parkway**	a		00 21			00 29	00s33			00 56	01 19					06 05		06 08	06 21
—	—		d	00 07						00 45		00 56	01 19					06 06			06 25
55¼	—	Appleford	d									01 00									
56¼	—	Culham	d									01 03									06 31
58½	—	Radley	d	00 14						01 00		01 07									06 35
63½	0	**Oxford**	a	00 27		00 35				01 15		01 18	01 34					06 20			06 43
—	—		d				00 38							05 18		05 45	05 45				06 45
—	5¾	Islip	d													05 58					
—	11¾	**Bicester Town**	a													06 10					
72½	—	Tackley	d				00 48							05 27			05 54				06 53
75¼	—	Heyford	d				00 53							05 32			05 58				06 58
82¾	—	Kings Sutton	d				01 01							05 40			06 07				07 06
86¼	—	**Banbury**	a				01 11							05 47			06 14				07 14
106¼	—	Leamington Spa 8	a																		
115¾	—	Coventry	a																		
126½	—	Birmingham International	a																		
135	—	**Birmingham New Street 12**	a																		

Miles	Miles			XC	GW	GW	GW	XC	GW	GW	CH	GW	GW	GW	XC	GW	GW	GW	GW	GW
				◇1	1	◇1	1	◇1	1	◇1		1	1	◇1	◇1	1	1	1	◇1	◇1
																				A
				🛒				🛒						☕	🛒				☕	☕
0	—	**London Paddington 15** ⊖	d			05 45			05 57	06 20				06 30			06 48	06 57	07 00	07 06
5¾	—	Ealing Broadway ⊖	d						06 05									07 05		
18½	—	Slough 3	d			06 01			06 29	06 35							07 02	07 29		
24¼	—	Maidenhead 3	d						06 37									07 37		
31	—	Twyford 3	d				←		06 45				←					07 45		
36	0	**Reading 7**	d	06 10	06 13	06 17	06 18	06 40	06 53	06 51		06 52	06 53	06 56	07 09	07 10	07 19	07 53	07 28	07 33
—	1	Reading West	d		06 15				→			06 54				07 12		→		
—	5¼	Theale	d		06 21							07 00				07 18				
—	8¾	Aldermaston	d		06 26							07 05				07 23				
—	10¾	Midgham	d		06 30							07 09				07 27				
—	13½	Thatcham	d		06 35							07 14				07 32				
—	16½	Newbury Racecourse	d		06 39							07 18				07 36				
—	17	**Newbury**	a		06 45							07 21				07 42				07 47
—	—		d									07 21								
—	22½	Kintbury	d									07 28								
—	25½	Hungerford	d									07 32								
—	30½	**Bedwyn**	a									07 42								
38¾	—	Tilehurst	d				06 22						06 57				07 26			
41½	—	Pangbourne	d				06 27						07 01				07 30			
44¾	—	Goring & Streatley	d				06 33						07 06				07 36			
48½	—	Cholsey	d				06 39						07 11				07 41			
53¼	—	**Didcot Parkway**	a				06 47			07 06			07 19	07 10			07 48		07 43	
—	—		d				06 47			07 08			07 25				07 50			
55¼	—	Appleford	d										07 30							
56¼	—	Culham	d										07 32							
58½	—	Radley	d										07 36							
63½	0	**Oxford**	a	06 34		06 51	07 02	07 05		07 22			07 49		07 35		08 02			
—	—		d	06 36				07 08			07 33				07 36					
—	5¾	Islip	d								07 46									
—	11¾	**Bicester Town**	a								07 59									
72½	—	Tackley	d																	
75¼	—	Heyford	d																	
82¾	—	Kings Sutton	d																	
86¼	—	**Banbury**	a	06 52				07 25							07 55					
106¼	—	Leamington Spa 8	a	07 10				07 42							08 12					
115¾	—	Coventry	a	07 23											08 25					
126½	—	Birmingham International	a	07 37											08 37					
135	—	**Birmingham New Street 12**	a	07 48				08 14							08 48					

A The Devon Express

For complete service between Banbury and Leamington (Birmingham), please refer to table 71

Table 116

Mondays to Fridays

9 December to 30 December

London and Reading - Bedwyn, Oxford, Bicester, Banbury and Birmingham

Network Diagram - refer to first Page of Table 116

		GW	XC	GW	GW	GW	CH	GW	GW	GW	XC	GW	GW	GW	GW	GW	GW	GW	XC	GW
		1	◇1 🛒	◇1 ☕	1	1		1	1	◇1 ☕	◇1 🛒	1	1	1	1	1	◇1 ☕	1	◇1 🛒	◇1 ☕
London Paddington 15 ⊖	d			07 15	07 18	07 21			07 27	07 36			07 50	07 50		07 57	08 00			08 15
Ealing Broadway ⊖	d								07 35							08 05				
Slough 3	d					07 36			07 59				08 06	08 06		08 29				
Maidenhead 3	d								08 07							08 38				
Twyford 3	d							←	08 15						←	08 46				
Reading 7	d	07 33	07 41	07 42	07 48	07 52		07 53	08 24	08 02	08 09	08 12	08 22	08 22	08 24	08 55	08 27	08 34	08 40	08 45
Reading West	d								→			08 14				→				
Theale	d				07 56							08 20						08 41		
Aldermaston	d				08 01							08 25						08 46		
Midgham	d											08 29								
Thatcham	d				08 08							08 34						08 53		
Newbury Racecourse	d											08 38								
Newbury	a				08 13							08 44						08 59		
	d				08 13													08 59		
Kintbury	d				08 20													09 05		
Hungerford	d				08 24													09 09		
Bedwyn	a				08 34													09 21		
Tilehurst	d							07 57							08 27					
Pangbourne	d							08 01							08 31					
Goring & Streatley	d							08 06							08 36					
Cholsey	d							08 11							08 41					
Didcot Parkway	a	07 52		07 56				08 20		08 16					08 50		08 40			08 58
	d	08 08						08 25							08 55					
Appleford	d	08 13													09 00					
Culham	d	08 15													09 01					
Radley	d	08 19						08 33							09 06					
Oxford	a	08 31	08 07			08 19		08 44			08 34		08 49	08 49	09 16				09 04	
	d		08 09				08 35				08 36		08 53						09 07	
Islip	d						08 48													
Bicester Town	a						09 01													
Tackley	d												09 01							
Heyford	d												09 06							
Kings Sutton	d												09 15							
Banbury	a		08 26								08 52		09 22						09 25	
Leamington Spa 8	a		08 43								09 10								09 42	
Coventry	a										09 23									
Birmingham International	a										09 37									
Birmingham New Street 12	a		09 18								09 48								10 18	

		GW	GW	GW	GW	GW	XC	GW	GW	CH	GW	XC	GW	GW	GW	GW	GW	GW
		1	◇1 ☕	1	1	◇1 ☕	◇1 🛒	1	◇1		1	◇1 🛒	1	◇1 ☕	1	◇1 🛒	1	1
London Paddington 15 ⊖	d	08 18	08 22		08 27	08 30			08 51				08 55	09 15	09 18	09 21		09 27
Ealing Broadway ⊖	d				08 35								09 03					09 35
Slough 3	d		08 36		08 59				09 06				09 27			09 36		09 57
Maidenhead 3	d				09 06								09 35					10 04
Twyford 3	d			←	09 18						←		09 43				←	10 12
Reading 7	d	08 48	08 52	08 55	09 26	08 57	09 09	09 14	09 22		09 26	09 40	09 53	09 42	09 48	09 52	09 53	10 23
Reading West	d				→			09 16					→					→
Theale	d	08 56						09 22							09 56			
Aldermaston	d							09 27										
Midgham	d							09 31										
Thatcham	d	09 04						09 36							10 04			
Newbury Racecourse	d							09 40										
Newbury	a	09 14						09 46							10 10			
	d														10 10			
Kintbury	d														10 17			
Hungerford	d														10 21			
Bedwyn	a														10 32			
Tilehurst	d			08 59							09 30						09 57	
Pangbourne	d			09 03							09 34						10 01	
Goring & Streatley	d			09 08							09 39						10 06	
Cholsey	d			09 13							09 44						10 11	
Didcot Parkway	a			09 21		09 12			09 37		09 52			09 56			10 18	
	d			09 25					09 38		09 56						10 25	
Appleford	d																	
Culham	d										10 03							
Radley	d			09 33							10 05							
Oxford	a		09 20	09 45			09 34		09 53		10 18	10 04				10 20	10 43	
	d						09 36			10 00		10 07						
Islip	d									10 13								
Bicester Town	a									10 25								
Tackley	d																	
Heyford	d																	
Kings Sutton	d																	
Banbury	a						09 55					10 28						
Leamington Spa 8	a						10 11					10 46						
Coventry	a						10 24											
Birmingham International	a						10 37											
Birmingham New Street 12	a						10 48					11 18						

For complete service between Banbury and Leamington (Birmingham), please refer to table 71

Table 116

Mondays to Fridays

9 December to 30 December

London and Reading - Bedwyn, Oxford, Bicester, Banbury and Birmingham

Network Diagram - refer to first Page of Table 116

Station		GW	GW	XC	GW	GW	CH	GW	XC	GW	GW	GW	GW	GW	GW	GW	XC	GW	GW
		◇1	◇1	■ 1	1	◇1		1	◇1	1	◇1	1	◇1	1	1	◇1	◇1	1	1
		⊘	🍽	🛒					🛒		🍽		🍽			⊘	🛒		
London Paddington 15 ⊖	d	09 30	09 36			09 50				09 57	10 15	10 18	10 22		10 27	10 30			
Ealing Broadway ⊖	d									10 05					10 35				
Slough 3	d					10 06				10 27			10 36		10 57				
Maidenhead 3	d									10 34					11 04				
Twyford 3	d							←		10 42				←	11 12				
Reading 7	d	09 57	10 03	10 10	10 12	10 22		10 23	10 40	10 53	10 43	10 48	10 52	10 53	11 23	10 57	11 10		11 12
Reading West	d				10 14					→					→				11 14
Theale	d				10 20							10 56							11 20
Aldermaston	d				10 25														11 25
Midgham	d				10 29														11 29
Thatcham	d				10 34							11 04							11 34
Newbury Racecourse	d				10 38														11 38
Newbury	a				10 44							11 10							11 44
	d											11 10							
Kintbury	d											11 17							
Hungerford	d											11 21							
Bedwyn	a											11 32							
Tilehurst	d							10 27						10 57					
Pangbourne	d							10 31						11 01					
Goring & Streatley	d							10 36						11 06					
Cholsey	d							10 41						11 11					
Didcot Parkway	a	10 11	10 17					10 49			10 58			11 19		11 12			
	d							10 55						11 25					
Appleford	d																		
Culham	d																		
Radley	d							11 03											
Oxford	a			10 34		10 47		11 14	11 04				11 18	11 43			11 32		
	d			10 36			11 00		11 07								11 36	11 45	
Islip	d						11 13												
Bicester Town	a						11 25												
Tackley	d																	11 54	
Heyford	d																	11 58	
Kings Sutton	d																	12 07	
Banbury	a			10 52					11 24								11 51	12 13	
Leamington Spa 8	a			11 10					11 41								12 10		
Coventry	a			11 23													12 24		
Birmingham International	a			11 37													12 37		
Birmingham New Street 12	a			11 48					12 18								12 48		

Station		GW	GW	XC	GW	GW	GW	GW	GW	GW	GW	GW	XC	GW	GW	GW	XC	GW	GW
		◇1	1	◇1	1	◇1	1	◇1	1	1	◇1	◇1	◇1	1	◇1	1	■ 1	1	◇1
												A							
				🛒		🍽		🛒			🍽	🍽	🛒		🛒		🛒		🍽
London Paddington 15 ⊖	d	10 50			10 57	11 15	11 18	11 20		11 27	11 30	11 36			11 50			11 57	12 15
Ealing Broadway ⊖	d				11 05					11 35								12 05	
Slough 3	d	11 06			11 27			11 36		11 57					12 06			12 27	
Maidenhead 3	d				11 34					12 04								12 34	
Twyford 3	d		←		11 42				←	12 13						←		12 45	
Reading 7	d	11 21	11 23	11 40	11 53	11 44	11 48	11 52	11 53	12 23	11 57	12 03	12 10	12 12	12 22	12 23	12 40	12 53	12 42
Reading West	d				→					→				12 14				→	
Theale	d						11 56							12 20					
Aldermaston	d													12 25					
Midgham	d													12 29					
Thatcham	d						12 04							12 34					
Newbury Racecourse	d													12 38					
Newbury	a						12 10							12 44					
	d						12 10												
Kintbury	d						12 17												
Hungerford	d						12 21												
Bedwyn	a						12 31												
Tilehurst	d		11 27						11 57							12 27			
Pangbourne	d		11 31						12 01							12 31			
Goring & Streatley	d		11 36						12 06							12 36			
Cholsey	d		11 41						12 11							12 41			
Didcot Parkway	a	11 37	11 50			11 58			12 21		12 12	12 17				12 49			12 57
	d	11 38	11 55						12 25							12 55			
Appleford	d															13 00			
Culham	d																		
Radley	d		12 03													13 03			
Oxford	a	11 50	12 14	12 04				12 18	12 43				12 34		12 48	13 14	13 02		
	d			12 07									12 36				13 07		
Islip	d																		
Bicester Town	a																		
Tackley	d																		
Heyford	d																		
Kings Sutton	d																		
Banbury	a			12 24									12 52				13 25		
Leamington Spa 8	a			12 42									13 10				13 43		
Coventry	a												13 23						
Birmingham International	a												13 37						
Birmingham New Street 12	a			13 18									13 49				14 18		

A The Cheltenham Spa Express

For complete service between Banbury and Leamington (Birmingham), please refer to table 71

Table 116

Mondays to Fridays
9 December to 30 December

London and Reading - Bedwyn, Oxford, Bicester, Banbury and Birmingham

Network Diagram - refer to first Page of Table 116

		GW ◇1 🍽	GW ◇1 🛒	CH	GW 1	GW 1	GW ◇1 🍽	XC ◇1 🛒	GW 1	GW ◇1 🛒	GW 1	XC ◇1 🛒	GW 1	GW ◇1 🍽	GW 1	GW ◇1 🛒	GW 1	GW 1	GW 1
London Paddington 15 ⊖	d	12 18	12 21			12 27	12 30			12 50			12 57	13 15	13 18	13 21			13 27
Ealing Broadway ⊖	d					12 35							13 05						13 35
Slough 3	d		12 36			12 57				13 06			13 27			13 36			13 57
Maidenhead 3	d					13 04							13 34						14 04
Twyford 3	d				←	13 12					←		13 44					←	14 12
Reading 7	d	12 49	12 52		12 53	13 23	12 57	13 10	13 12	13 22	13 23	13 40	13 53	13 42	13 48	13 51		13 53	14 23
Reading West	d					→			13 14				→						→
Theale	d	12 57							13 20						13 56				
Aldermaston	d								13 25										
Midgham	d								13 29										
Thatcham	d	13 05							13 34						14 04				
Newbury Racecourse	d								13 38										
Newbury	a	13 13							13 44						14 10				
	d	13 13													14 10				
Kintbury	d														14 17				
Hungerford	d	13 22													14 21				
Bedwyn	a	13 30													14 32				
Tilehurst	d				12 57						13 27							13 57	
Pangbourne	d				13 01						13 31							14 01	
Goring & Streatley	d				13 06						13 36							14 06	
Cholsey	d				13 11						13 41							14 11	
Didcot Parkway	a				13 19		13 12			13 37	13 48			13 56				14 20	
	d				13 25					13 38	13 55							14 25	
Appleford	d																		
Culham	d										14 01								
Radley	d										14 03								
Oxford	a		13 20		13 43			13 34		13 50	14 14	14 04				14 18		14 43	
	d			13 30				13 36				14 07					14 24		
Islip	d			13 43															
Bicester Town	a			13 55															
Tackley	d																14 33		
Heyford	d																14 37		
Kings Sutton	d																14 46		
Banbury	a							13 52				14 25					14 52		
Leamington Spa 8	a							14 10				14 41							
Coventry	a							14 23											
Birmingham International	a							14 37											
Birmingham New Street 12	a							14 48				15 18							

		GW ◇1 🍽	GW ◇1 🍽	XC ◇1 🛒	GW 1	GW ◇1 🛒	CH	GW 1	XC ◇1 🛒	GW 1	GW ◇1 🍽	GW 1	GW ◇1 🛒	GW 1	GW 1	GW ◇1 🍽	XC ◇1 🛒	GW 1	GW ◇1 🛒
London Paddington 15 ⊖	d	13 30	13 36			13 50				13 57	14 15	14 18	14 21		14 27	14 30			14 50
Ealing Broadway ⊖	d									14 05					14 35				
Slough 3	d					14 06				14 27			14 36		14 57				15 06
Maidenhead 3	d									14 34					15 04				
Twyford 3	d							←		14 42				←	15 14				
Reading 7	d	13 57	14 03	14 10	14 12	14 22		14 23	14 40	14 55	14 44	14 48	14 52	14 55	15 23	14 57	15 09	15 12	15 22
Reading West	d				14 14					→					→			15 14	
Theale	d				14 20							14 56						15 20	
Aldermaston	d				14 25													15 25	
Midgham	d				14 29													15 29	
Thatcham	d				14 34							15 04						15 34	
Newbury Racecourse	d				14 38													15 38	
Newbury	a				14 44							15 10						15 44	
	d											15 10							
Kintbury	d											15 17							
Hungerford	d											15 21							
Bedwyn	a											15 33							
Tilehurst	d							14 27						14 59					
Pangbourne	d							14 31						15 04					
Goring & Streatley	d							14 36						15 09					
Cholsey	d							14 41						15 14					
Didcot Parkway	a	14 12	14 17					14 49			14 58			15 20		15 12			15 37
	d							14 55						15 25					15 38
Appleford	d																		
Culham	d																		
Radley	d							15 03											
Oxford	a			14 34		14 48		15 14	15 03				15 18	15 44			15 34		15 50
	d			14 36			15 00		15 07								15 36		
Islip	d						15 13												
Bicester Town	a						15 25												
Tackley	d																		
Heyford	d																		
Kings Sutton	d																		
Banbury	a			14 56					15 24								15 53		
Leamington Spa 8	a			15 13					15 42								16 10		
Coventry	a			15 25													16 23		
Birmingham International	a			15 37													16 37		
Birmingham New Street 12	a			15 48					16 18								16 48		

For complete service between Banbury and Leamington (Birmingham), please refer to table 71

Table 116

Mondays to Fridays

9 December to 30 December

London and Reading - Bedwyn, Oxford, Bicester, Banbury and Birmingham

Network Diagram - refer to first Page of Table 116

		GW	XC	GW	GW	GW	GW	GW	CH	GW	GW	GW	GW	XC FX	XC FO	GW	GW	GW	GW
		1	◇1 🛒	1	◇1 ☕	1	◇1 🛒	1		1	1	◇1 ☕	◇1 ☕	◇1 🛒	◇1 🛒	1	1	◇1 ☕	1
London Paddington 15 ⊖	d			14 57	15 15	15 18	15 22				15 27	15 30	15 36					15 52	
Ealing Broadway ⊖	d			15 05							15 35								
Slough 3	d			15 27			15 36				15 59								
Maidenhead 3	d			15 34							16 07								
Twyford 3	d	←		15 42						←	16 15								←
Reading 7	d	15 23	15 40	15 53	15 43	15 48	15 52			15 53	16 26	15 57	16 02	16 10	16 10	16 12		16u22	16 26
Reading West	d			→							→					16 14			
Theale	d					15 56										16 20			
Aldermaston	d															16 25			
Midgham	d															16 29			
Thatcham	d					16 04										16 34			
Newbury Racecourse	d															16 38			
Newbury	a					16 10										16 44			
	d					16 10											17 08		
Kintbury	d					16 17											17 14		
Hungerford	d					16 21											17 19		
Bedwyn	a					16 31											17 28		
Tilehurst	d	15 28								15 57									16 30
Pangbourne	d	15 31								16 01									16 34
Goring & Streatley	d	15 36								16 06									16 39
Cholsey	d	15 41								16 11									16 44
Didcot Parkway	a	15 49			15 57					16 19		16 11	16 16						16 50
	d	15 55								16 25									16 56
Appleford	d																		17 01
Culham	d	16 01																	17 04
Radley	d	16 03								16 33									17 08
Oxford	a	16 16	16 05				16 18			16 43				16 33	16 33			16 47	17 17
	d		16 07					16 23	16 26					16 35	16 36				
Islip	d								16 39										
Bicester Town	a								16 51										
Tackley	d							16 32											
Heyford	d							16 36											
Kings Sutton	d							16 45											
Banbury	a		16 23					16 51						16 53	16 53				
Leamington Spa 8	a		16 40											17 12	17 12				
Coventry	a													17 24	17 24				
Birmingham International	a													17 37	17 37				
Birmingham New Street 12	a		17 18											17 49	17 49				

		XC	GW	GW	GW	GW	GW	GW	GW	GW	GW	GW	XC	CH	GW	GW	GW	GW	GW
		◇1 🛒	1	1 ☕	1	◇1 🛒	1	1	1 ☕	1	◇1 ☕	1	◇1 🛒		1	1	◇1	1	1 ☕
London Paddington 15 ⊖	d		15 57	16 15	16 18	16 22		16 25	16 30		16 36						16 49		17 00
Ealing Broadway ⊖	d		16 05					16 33											
Slough 3	d		16 28			16 38		16 58									17 05		
Maidenhead 3	d		16 35					17 05											
Twyford 3	d		16 44				←	17 13										←	
Reading 7	d	16 40	16 55	16 44	16 48	16 52	16 55	17 23	16 57		17 04		17 09			17 12	17 21	17 23	17 26
Reading West	d		→					→								17 14			
Theale	d				16 56											17 20			
Aldermaston	d				17 01											17 25			
Midgham	d															17 29			
Thatcham	d				17 08											17 34			
Newbury Racecourse	d											←				17 38			
Newbury	a				17 14						17 18	17 14				17 44			
	d				17 24						17 19	17 24							
Kintbury	d				→							17 31							
Hungerford	d										17a28	17 35							
Bedwyn	a											17 46							
Tilehurst	d						16 58											17 27	
Pangbourne	d						17 03											17 32	
Goring & Streatley	d						17 08											17 37	
Cholsey	d						17 13								←			17 42	
Didcot Parkway	a			16 59			17 20		17 12						17 20		17 36	17 49	17 40
	d						17 26			17 15					17 26		17 38	18 05	
Appleford	d						→								17 31				
Culham	d														17 33			18 11	
Radley	d														17 37			18 15	
Oxford	a	17 04				17 22				17 30			17 34		17 44		17 51	18 23	
	d	17 07											17 36	17 45	17 46				
Islip	d													17 58					
Bicester Town	a													18 10					
Tackley	d														17 55				
Heyford	d														17 59				
Kings Sutton	d														18 08				
Banbury	a	17 28											17 54		18 15				
Leamington Spa 8	a	17 46											18 11						
Coventry	a												18 24						
Birmingham International	a												18 37						
Birmingham New Street 12	a	18 18											18 49						

For complete service between Banbury and Leamington (Birmingham), please refer to table 71

Table 116

Mondays to Fridays

9 December to 30 December

London and Reading - Bedwyn, Oxford, Bicester, Banbury and Birmingham

Network Diagram - refer to first Page of Table 116

Station		GW	GW	XC	GW	GW	GW	GW	GW	GW	GW
					R					R	
		◇1	◇1	◇1	1	1	◇1	1	1	1	◇1
					A						
		☕	☕	🛒	☕		☕			☕	☕
London Paddington 15 ⊖	d	17 03	17 06		17 15	17 18	17 22		17 24	17 30	17 33
Ealing Broadway ⊖	d								17 33		
Slough 3	d								17 58		
Maidenhead 3	d					17 41			18 10		
Twyford 3	d		17 30					←	18 17		
Reading 7	d	17u30	17 39	17 40	17 42	17 55	17 50	17 55	18 29	17 56	18 01
Reading West	d					→			→		
Theale	d		17 48								
Aldermaston	d										
Midgham	d										
Thatcham	d		17 58								
Newbury Racecourse	d										
Newbury	a	17 47	18 04								18 15
	d		18 05								
Kintbury	d		18 13								
Hungerford	d		18 19								
Bedwyn	a		18 26								
Tilehurst	d							17 59			
Pangbourne	d							18 04			
Goring & Streatley	d							18 10			
Cholsey	d							18 15			
Didcot Parkway	a				17 56			18 22		18 09	
	d							18 25			
Appleford	d										
Culham	d										
Radley	d							18 33			
Oxford	a			18 05			18 15	18 45			
	d			18 07							
Islip	d										
Bicester Town	a										
Tackley	d										
Heyford	d										
Kings Sutton	d										
Banbury	a			18 25							
Leamington Spa 8	a			18 45							
Coventry	a										
Birmingham International	a										
Birmingham New Street 12	a			19 18							

Station		GW	XC	GW	GW	GW	GW	GW	GW	GW
								R		
		1	◇1	1	1	◇1	◇1	1	1	◇1
								B		
			🛒			☕	☕	☕		☕
London Paddington 15 ⊖	d				17 35	17 42	17 49	18 00		18 05
Ealing Broadway ⊖	d									
Slough 3	d									
Maidenhead 3	d				17 58		18 09			
Twyford 3	d				18 07				←	18 28
Reading 7	d		18 10	18 12	18 20		18 22	18 27	18 29	18 37
Reading West	d			18 14						
Theale	d			18 20						18 46
Aldermaston	d			18 25						
Midgham	d			18 29						
Thatcham	d			18 34						18 56
Newbury Racecourse	d			18 38						
Newbury	a			18 44						19 02
	d	18 26								19 03
Kintbury	d	18 32								19 10
Hungerford	d	18 37								19 17
Bedwyn	a	18 46								19 24
Tilehurst	d				18 25				18 34	
Pangbourne	d				18 30				18 39	
Goring & Streatley	d				18 35				18 44	
Cholsey	d				18 41				18 50	
Didcot Parkway	a				18 47	18 19		18 41	18 58	
	d				18 47				19 03	
Appleford	d								19 08	
Culham	d									
Radley	d				18 55					
Oxford	a		18 34		19 07		18 47		19 18	
	d		18 36						19 19	
Islip	d									
Bicester Town	a									
Tackley	d								19 27	
Heyford	d								19 32	
Kings Sutton	d								19 44	
Banbury	a		18 54						19 50	
Leamington Spa 8	a		19 11							
Coventry	a		19 23							
Birmingham International	a		19 37							
Birmingham New Street 12	a		19 48							

Station		XC	GW	GW	GW	GW	CH	GW	GW	GW
								FO	FX	
			R							R
		◇1	1	1	1	◇1		1	1	1
						C				
		🛒	☕			☕				☕
London Paddington 15 ⊖	d		18 15	18 15	18 18	18 22		18 25	18 25	18 30
Ealing Broadway ⊖	d			18 23				18 33	18 33	
Slough 3	d			18 47				18 59	18 59	
Maidenhead 3	d			18 57	18 40			19 10	19 10	
Twyford 3	d			19 05	18 48			19 18	19 18	
Reading 7	d	18 40	18 42	19 19	18 57	18 51		19 27	19 27	18 55
Reading West	d			→	→			→	→	
Theale	d									
Aldermaston	d									
Midgham	d									
Thatcham	d									
Newbury Racecourse	d									
Newbury	a									
	d									
Kintbury	d									
Hungerford	d									
Bedwyn	a									
Tilehurst	d									
Pangbourne	d									
Goring & Streatley	d									
Cholsey	d									
Didcot Parkway	a		18 57							19 11
	d									
Appleford	d									
Culham	d									
Radley	d									
Oxford	a	19 11				19 20				
	d	19 13					19 30			
Islip	d						19 43			
Bicester Town	a						19 55			
Tackley	d									
Heyford	d									
Kings Sutton	d									
Banbury	a	19 30								
Leamington Spa 8	a	19 49								
Coventry	a									
Birmingham International	a									
Birmingham New Street 12	a	20 18								

Station		GW	GW	GW	XC	GW	GW	GW	GW
		1	◇1	1	◇1	1	◇1	1	1
			☕		🛒		☕		
London Paddington 15 ⊖	d		18 35				18 47		
Ealing Broadway ⊖	d								
Slough 3	d								
Maidenhead 3	d								
Twyford 3	d	←					19 10	←	
Reading 7	d	18 57	19 03		19 09	19 12	19 19	19 19	19 21
Reading West	d					19 15			
Theale	d					19 20			19 28
Aldermaston	d					19 25			
Midgham	d					19 29			
Thatcham	d					19 34			19 39
Newbury Racecourse	d					19 39			
Newbury	a		19 17			19 44			19 56
	d		19 19	19 27					19 56
Kintbury	d			19 33					20 03
Hungerford	d		19 29	19 38					20 08
Bedwyn	a		19 36	19 45					20 18
Tilehurst	d	19 01						19 24	
Pangbourne	d	19 06						19 28	
Goring & Streatley	d	19 12						19 33	
Cholsey	d	19 17						19 38	
Didcot Parkway	a	19 26					19 33	19 47	
	d	19 27						19 56	
Appleford	d								
Culham	d							20 03	
Radley	d	19 34							
Oxford	a	19 46			19 34			20 16	
	d				19 36				
Islip	d								
Bicester Town	a								
Tackley	d								
Heyford	d								
Kings Sutton	d								
Banbury	a				19 54				
Leamington Spa 8	a				20 12				
Coventry	a				20 24				
Birmingham International	a				20 37				
Birmingham New Street 12	a				20 48				

A The Red Dragon

B The Bristolian

C The Cathedrals Express

For complete service between Banbury and Leamington (Birmingham), please refer to table 71

Table 116

London and Reading - Bedwyn, Oxford, Bicester, Banbury and Birmingham

Mondays to Fridays

9 December to 30 December

Network Diagram - refer to first Page of Table 116

		GW	GW	GW FO	GW FX	GW	XC	GW	GW FO	GW FX	GW FO	GW	GW FX	GW FO	GW	GW	GW	XC	GW	GW
		◇1	1	1	1	1	◇1	1	1	1	1	1	◇1	◇1	1	1	1	◇1	◇1	◇1
		🚲	☕			A ✕				☕			☕	☕		☕			☕	☕
London Paddington 15 ⊖	d	18 50	19 00			19 03			19 12	19 15		19 18	19 22	19 22	19 27	19 30			19 45	19 48
Ealing Broadway ⊖	d														19 35					
Slough 3	d	19 07											19 36	19 36	19 59					
Maidenhead 3	d											19 40			20 09					20 06
Twyford 3	d			←	←						←	19 48			20 17		←			
Reading 7	d	19 23	19 27	19 27	19 27	19u33	19 40	19 42	19 43	19 42	19 43	19 57	19 52	19 52	20 25	19 57	19 57	20 10	20 12	20 18
Reading West	d							19 44	→			→			→					
Theale	d							19 50												
Aldermaston	d							19 55												
Midgham	d							19 59												
Thatcham	d							20 04												
Newbury Racecourse	d							20 08												
Newbury	a					19 50		20 11											20 28	
	d							20 33												
Kintbury	d							20 39												
Hungerford	d							20 43												
Bedwyn	a							20 53												
Tilehurst	d			19 31	19 31												20 01			
Pangbourne	d			19 35	19 35												20 06			
Goring & Streatley	d			19 40	19 40												20 11			
Cholsey	d			19 46	19 46												20 16			
Didcot Parkway	a		19 42	19 53	19 53					19 56	20 00					20 12	20 22			20 33
	d			20 01	20 08						20 09						20 25			
Appleford	d				20 13						20 13									
Culham	d																			
Radley	d				20 18						20 18						20 33			
Oxford	a	19 49		20 18	20 27		20 06				20 28		20 18	20 21			20 43	20 34		
	d						20 07											20 36		
Islip	d																			
Bicester Town	a																			
Tackley	d																			
Heyford	d																			
Kings Sutton	d																			
Banbury	a						20 27											20 52		
Leamington Spa 8	a						20 45											21 10		
Coventry	a																	21 23		
Birmingham International	a																	21 37		
Birmingham New Street 12	a						21 22											21 49		

		GW	CH	GW	GW	GW	XC	GW	GW	GW	GW	GW	GW	GW	GW	XC	GW	GW
		◇1		1	1	◇1	◇1	◇1	1	◇1	1	1	1	◇1	1	◇1	◇1	◇1
		🚲				☕		Ø		🚲				☕			☕	
London Paddington 15 ⊖	d	19 50			19 57	20 00		20 15		20 20			20 27	20 35			20 45	20 48
Ealing Broadway ⊖	d				20 05								20 35					
Slough 3	d	20 06			20 27					20 36			20 57					21 05
Maidenhead 3	d				20 34								21 04					
Twyford 3	d			←	20 42							←	21 12					
Reading 7	d	20 22		20 25	20 53	20 27	20 40	20 41	20 41	20 51		20 53	21 23	21 02		21 10	21 13	21 20
Reading West	d				→				20 44				→					
Theale	d								20 50									
Aldermaston	d								20 55									
Midgham	d								20 58									
Thatcham	d								21 03									
Newbury Racecourse	d								21 08									
Newbury	a								21 13					21 16				
	d														21 24			
Kintbury	d														21 30			
Hungerford	d														21 35			
Bedwyn	a														21 45			
Tilehurst	d			20 29								20 57						
Pangbourne	d			20 34								21 01						
Goring & Streatley	d			20 39								21 06						
Cholsey	d			20 44								21 11						
Didcot Parkway	a			20 51		20 41		20 56				21 19					21 27	
	d			20 57								21 25						
Appleford	d																	
Culham	d																	
Radley	d			21 04								21 33						
Oxford	a	20 52		21 15			21 05			21 17		21 44				21 34		21 51
	d	20 55	21 00				21 09				21 41					21 36		
Islip	d		21 13															
Bicester Town	a		21 25															
Tackley	d	21 04									21 50							
Heyford	d	21 08									21 54							
Kings Sutton	d	21 17									22 03							
Banbury	a	21 23					21 31				22 09					21 52		
Leamington Spa 8	a						21 51									22 10		
Coventry	a															22 22		
Birmingham International	a															22 33		
Birmingham New Street 12	a						22 17									22 45		

A Restaurant for customers joining at Pad, Reading + Newbury. The Armada

For complete service between Banbury and Leamington (Birmingham), please refer to table 71

Table 116

Mondays to Fridays
9 December to 30 December

London and Reading - Bedwyn, Oxford, Bicester, Banbury and Birmingham

Network Diagram - refer to first Page of Table 116

		GW	GW	GW	XC	GW	GW	GW	GW	GW	GW	GW	GW	CH	GW	GW	GW	GW	GW	GW
											FO	FX		FO		FO	FX	FO	FX	FO
		■1	■1	◇■1 ⊡	◇■1	◇■1	■1	■1	■1	◇■1 ⊡	◇■1 ⌶	◇■1 ⊡	■1		■1	■1	■1	◇■1 ⊡	◇■1 ⊡	◇■1
London Paddington 15 ⊖	d		20 57	21 15		21 18			21 27	21 45	21 48	21 48				21 57	21 57	22 15	22 15	22 18
Ealing Broadway ⊖	d		21 05						21 35							22 05	22 05			
Slough 3	d		21 27			21 35			22 07		22 04	22 04				22 30	22 42			22 35
Maidenhead 3	d		21 34						22 15							22 42	22 53			22 42
Twyford 3	d	←	21 42				←		22 23						←	22 50	23 01			
Reading 7	d	21 23	21 57	21 41	21 46	21 50	21 57	22 01	22 32	22 11	22 25	22 25			22 32	23 10	23 10	22 42	22 54	22 56
Reading West	d		→					22 03	→							→	→			
Theale	d							22 10												
Aldermaston	d							22 15												
Midgham	d							22 18												
Thatcham	d							22 23												
Newbury Racecourse	d							22 28												
Newbury	a							22 31												
	d							22 31												
Kintbury	d							22 37												
Hungerford	d							22 42												
Bedwyn	a							22 52												
Tilehurst	d	21 27					22 02								22 35					
Pangbourne	d	21 31					22 05								22 40					
Goring & Streatley	d	21 36					22 09								22 43					
Cholsey	d	21 41					22 14								22 48					
Didcot Parkway	a	21 52		22 01			22 24			22 31					22 58			23 02	23 13	
	d	21 52					22 25								22 58					
Appleford	d														23 03					
Culham	d														23 05					
Radley	d	21 59													23 09					
Oxford	a	22 12			22 28	22 18	22 41				22 47	22 47			23 22					23 27
	d				22 30								23 06	23 12						
Islip	d													23 25						
Bicester Town	a													23 37						
Tackley	d												23 15							
Heyford	d												23 19							
Kings Sutton	d												23 28							
Banbury	a				22 51								23 34							
Leamington Spa 8	a				23 09															
Coventry	a				23 24															
Birmingham International	a				23 34															
Birmingham New Street 12	a				00 02															

		GW	GW	GW	GW	GW	GW	GW	GW	GW	GW	GW	GW	GW	CH	GW	GW	GW	GW
		FX		FX	FO	FO	FX	FO	FX	FO	FX	FX	FO		MX			FO	
		◇■1	■1	■1	■1	■1	■1	◇■1 ⊡	◇■1 ⊡	◇■1	◇■1	■1	■1	◇■1		◇■1 ⊡	■1	■1	■1
London Paddington 15 ⊖	d	22 18				22 27	22 27	22 45	22 45	22 48	22 48			23 18		23 30	23 33	23 42	
Ealing Broadway ⊖	d					22 35	22 35										23 41		
Slough 3	d	22 39				23 11	23 11			23 05	23 08			23 38			23 57	00 01	
Maidenhead 3	d	22 47				23 23	23 23			23 12	23 17			23 46			00 05	00 10	
Twyford 3	d			←	←	23 31	23 31			23 20	23 26	←	←				00 13		←
Reading 7	d	23 01	23 03	23 10	23 10	23 41	23 40	23 11	23 23	23 28	23 34	23 40	23 41	00 04		00 09	00 27	00 25	00 27
Reading West	d		23 05			→	→										→		
Theale	d		23 11																
Aldermaston	d		23 16																
Midgham	d		23 20																
Thatcham	d		23 25																
Newbury Racecourse	d		23 29																
Newbury	a		23 32																
	d		23 32																
Kintbury	d		23 39																
Hungerford	d		23 43																
Bedwyn	a		23 53																
Tilehurst	d			23 14	23 14							23 44	23 44						00 33
Pangbourne	d			23 19	23 19							23 48	23 48						00 37
Goring & Streatley	d			23 22	23 22							23 52	23 52						00 41
Cholsey	d			23 27	23 27							23 57	23 57						00 46
Didcot Parkway	a			23 37	23 37			23 42	23 42			00 07	00 07			00 29		00 44	00 56
	d			23 38	23 38							00 07	00 08					00 44	00 56
Appleford	d																		01 00
Culham	d																		01 03
Radley	d											00 14	00 14						01 07
Oxford	a	23 29		23 54	23 56					23 56	00 01	00 27	00 27	00 35				01 02	01 18
	d														00 38				
Islip	d																		
Bicester Town	a																		
Tackley	d														00 48				
Heyford	d														00 53				
Kings Sutton	d														01 01				
Banbury	a														01 11				
Leamington Spa 8	a																		
Coventry	a																		
Birmingham International	a																		
Birmingham New Street 12	a																		

For complete service between Banbury and Leamington (Birmingham), please refer to table 71

Table 116

Mondays to Fridays

6 January to 10 February

London and Reading - Bedwyn, Oxford, Bicester, Banbury and Birmingham

Network Diagram - refer to first Page of Table 116

		GW MX	GW MO	GW MX	CH MX	GW MX	GW MO	GW MO	GW MX	GW MX	GW MX	GW	GW	CH	GW	GW	GW	GW	GW
		1	1	◇1		◇1	◇1		1	1	◇1	1	1		1	1	1	◇1	1
						(Catering)	(Catering)	(Bus)										(Catering)	
London Paddington 15	⊖ d										00 22					05 12	05 17	05 19	
Ealing Broadway	⊖ d																05 25		
Slough 3	d										00 41					05 30	05 51		
Maidenhead 3	d									00 05							05 59		
Twyford 3	d									00 13							06 07		
Reading 7	d			00 04		00 09	00 16		00 20	00 27	01 01		05 15			05 50	06 18	05 53	05 54
Reading West	d								00s23				05 17				→		
Theale	d								00s29				05 24						
Aldermaston	d								00s34				05 29						
Midgham	d								00s37				05 32						
Thatcham	d								00s42				05 37						
Newbury Racecourse	d								00s47				05 42						
Newbury	a								00 52				05 45						
	d												05 45						
Kintbury	d												05 51						
Hungerford	d												05 56						
Bedwyn	a												06 06						
Tilehurst	d									00 33									05 58
Pangbourne	d									00 37									06 03
Goring & Streatley	d		00 01							00 41									06 08
Cholsey	d		00 06							00 46									06 14
Didcot Parkway	a		00 21			00 29	00s33			00 56	01 19					06 05		06 08	06 21
	d	00 07						00 45		00 56	01 19					06 06			06 25
Appleford	d									01 00									
Culham	d									01 03									06 31
Radley	d	00 14						01 00		01 07									06 35
Oxford	a	00 27		00 35				01 15		01 18	01 34					06 20			06 43
	d				00 38							05 18		05 45	05 45				06 45
Islip	d													05 58					
Bicester Town	a													06 10					
Tackley	d				00 48							05 27			05 54				06 53
Heyford	d				00 53							05 32			05 58				06 58
Kings Sutton	d				01 01							05 40			06 07				07 06
Banbury	a				01 11							05 47			06 14				07 14
Leamington Spa 8	a																		
Coventry	a																		
Birmingham International	a																		
Birmingham New Street 12	a																		

		XC	GW	GW	GW	XC	GW	GW	CH	GW	GW	GW	XC	GW	GW	GW	GW	GW	GW
		◇1	1	◇1	1	◇1	1	◇1		1	1	◇1	◇1	1	1	1	◇1	◇1 A	1
		(Trolley)				(Trolley)						(Catering)	(Trolley)				(Catering)	(Catering)	
London Paddington 15	⊖ d			05 45			05 57	06 20				06 30			06 48	06 57	07 00	07 06	
Ealing Broadway	⊖ d						06 05									07 05			
Slough 3	d			06 01			06 29	06 35							07 02	07 29			
Maidenhead 3	d						06 37									07 37			
Twyford 3	d				←		06 45				←					07 45			
Reading 7	d	06 10	06 13	06 17	06 18	06 40	06 53	06 51		06 52	06 53	06 56	07 09	07 10	07 19	07 53	07 28	07 33	07 33
Reading West	d		06 15				→			06 54				07 12		→			
Theale	d		06 21							07 00				07 18					
Aldermaston	d		06 26							07 05				07 23					
Midgham	d		06 30							07 09				07 27					
Thatcham	d		06 35							07 14				07 32					
Newbury Racecourse	d		06 39							07 18				07 36					
Newbury	a		06 45							07 21				07 42				07 47	
	d									07 21									
Kintbury	d									07 28									
Hungerford	d									07 32									
Bedwyn	a									07 42									
Tilehurst	d				06 22						06 57				07 26				
Pangbourne	d				06 27						07 01				07 30				
Goring & Streatley	d				06 33						07 06				07 36				
Cholsey	d				06 39						07 11				07 41				
Didcot Parkway	a				06 47			07 06			07 19	07 10			07 48		07 43		07 52
	d				06 47			07 08			07 25				07 50				08 08
Appleford	d										07 30								08 13
Culham	d										07 32								08 15
Radley	d										07 36								08 19
Oxford	a	06 34		06 51	07 02	07 05		07 22			07 49		07 35		08 02				08 31
	d	06 36				07 08			07 33				07 36						
Islip	d								07 46										
Bicester Town	a								07 59										
Tackley	d																		
Heyford	d																		
Kings Sutton	d																		
Banbury	a	06 52				07 25							07 55						
Leamington Spa 8	a	07 10				07 42							08 12						
Coventry	a	07 23											08 25						
Birmingham International	a	07 37											08 37						
Birmingham New Street 12	a	07 48				08 14							08 48						

A The Devon Express

For complete service between Banbury and Leamington (Birmingham), please refer to table 71

Table 116

Mondays to Fridays

6 January to 10 February

London and Reading - Bedwyn, Oxford, Bicester, Banbury and Birmingham

Network Diagram - refer to first Page of Table 116

Station		XC	GW	GW	GW	CH	GW	GW	GW	XC
		◇1 🛒	◇1 🍽	1	1		1	1	◇1 🍽	◇1 🛒
London Paddington 15 ⊖	d		07 15	07 18	07 21			07 27	07 36	
Ealing Broadway ⊖	d							07 35		
Slough 3	d				07 36			07 59		
Maidenhead 3	d							08 07		
Twyford 3	d						←	08 15		
Reading 7	d	07 41	07 42	07 48	07 52		07 53	08 24	08 02	08 09
Reading West	d							→		
Theale	d			07 56						
Aldermaston	d			08 01						
Midgham	d									
Thatcham	d			08 08						
Newbury Racecourse	d									
Newbury	a			08 13						
	d			08 13						
Kintbury	d			08 20						
Hungerford	d			08 24						
Bedwyn	a			08 34						
Tilehurst	d						07 57			
Pangbourne	d						08 01			
Goring & Streatley	d						08 06			
Cholsey	d						08 11			
Didcot Parkway	a		07 56				08 20		08 16	
	d						08 25			
Appleford	d									
Culham	d									
Radley	d						08 33			
Oxford	a	08 07			08 19		08 44			08 34
	d	08 09				08 35				08 36
Islip	d					08 48				
Bicester Town	a					09 01				
Tackley	d									
Heyford	d									
Kings Sutton	d									
Banbury	a	08 26								08 52
Leamington Spa 8	a	08 43								09 10
Coventry	a									09 23
Birmingham International	a									09 37
Birmingham New Street 12	a	09 18								09 48

Station		GW	GW	GW	GW	GW	GW	GW	XC	GW
		1	1	1	1	1	◇1 🍽	1	◇1 🛒	◇1 🍽
London Paddington 15 ⊖	d		07 50	07 50		07 57	08 00			08 15
Ealing Broadway ⊖	d					08 05				
Slough 3	d		08 06	08 06		08 29				
Maidenhead 3	d					08 38				
Twyford 3	d				←	08 46				
Reading 7	d	08 12	08 22	08 22	08 24	08 55	08 27	08 34	08 40	08 45
Reading West	d	08 14				→				
Theale	d	08 20						08 41		
Aldermaston	d	08 25						08 46		
Midgham	d	08 29								
Thatcham	d	08 34						08 53		
Newbury Racecourse	d	08 38								
Newbury	a	08 44						08 59		
	d							08 59		
Kintbury	d							09 05		
Hungerford	d							09 09		
Bedwyn	a							09 21		
Tilehurst	d				08 27					
Pangbourne	d				08 31					
Goring & Streatley	d				08 36					
Cholsey	d				08 41					
Didcot Parkway	a				08 50		08 40			08 58
	d				08 55					
Appleford	d				09 00					
Culham	d				09 01					
Radley	d				09 06					
Oxford	a		08 49	08 49	09 16				09 04	
	d		08 53						09 07	
Islip	d									
Bicester Town	a									
Tackley	d		09 01							
Heyford	d		09 06							
Kings Sutton	d		09 15							
Banbury	a		09 22						09 25	
Leamington Spa 8	a								09 42	
Coventry	a									
Birmingham International	a									
Birmingham New Street 12	a								10 18	

Station		GW	GW	GW	GW	GW	XC	GW	GW	CH
		1	◇1 🍽	1	1	◇1 🍽	◇1 🛒	1	◇1	
London Paddington 15 ⊖	d	08 18	08 22		08 27	08 30			08 51	
Ealing Broadway ⊖	d				08 35					
Slough 3	d		08 36		08 59				09 06	
Maidenhead 3	d				09 06					
Twyford 3	d			←	09 18					
Reading 7	d	08 48	08 52	08 55	09 26	08 57	09 09	09 14	09 22	
Reading West	d				→			09 16		
Theale	d	08 56						09 22		
Aldermaston	d							09 27		
Midgham	d							09 31		
Thatcham	d	09 04						09 36		
Newbury Racecourse	d							09 40		
Newbury	a	09 14						09 46		
	d									
Kintbury	d									
Hungerford	d									
Bedwyn	a									
Tilehurst	d			08 59						
Pangbourne	d			09 03						
Goring & Streatley	d			09 08						
Cholsey	d			09 13						
Didcot Parkway	a			09 21		09 12			09 37	
	d			09 25					09 38	
Appleford	d									
Culham	d									
Radley	d			09 33						
Oxford	a		09 20	09 45			09 34		09 53	
	d						09 36			10 00
Islip	d									10 13
Bicester Town	a									10 25
Tackley	d									
Heyford	d									
Kings Sutton	d									
Banbury	a						09 55			
Leamington Spa 8	a						10 11			
Coventry	a						10 24			
Birmingham International	a						10 37			
Birmingham New Street 12	a						10 48			

Station		GW	XC	GW	GW	GW	GW	GW	GW	GW
		1	◇1 🛒	1	◇1 🍽	1	◇1 🛒	1	1	◇1 ∅
London Paddington 15 ⊖	d			08 55	09 15	09 18	09 21		09 27	09 30
Ealing Broadway ⊖	d			09 03					09 35	
Slough 3	d			09 27			09 36		09 57	
Maidenhead 3	d			09 35					10 04	
Twyford 3	d	←		09 43				←	10 12	
Reading 7	d	09 26	09 40	09 53	09 42	09 48	09 52	09 53	10 23	09 57
Reading West	d			→					→	
Theale	d					09 56				
Aldermaston	d									
Midgham	d									
Thatcham	d					10 04				
Newbury Racecourse	d									
Newbury	a					10 10				
	d					10 10				
Kintbury	d					10 17				
Hungerford	d					10 21				
Bedwyn	a					10 32				
Tilehurst	d	09 30						09 57		
Pangbourne	d	09 34						10 01		
Goring & Streatley	d	09 39						10 06		
Cholsey	d	09 44						10 11		
Didcot Parkway	a	09 52			09 56			10 18		10 11
	d	09 56						10 25		
Appleford	d									
Culham	d	10 03								
Radley	d	10 05								
Oxford	a	10 18	10 04				10 20	10 43		
	d		10 07							
Islip	d									
Bicester Town	a									
Tackley	d									
Heyford	d									
Kings Sutton	d									
Banbury	a		10 28							
Leamington Spa 8	a		10 46							
Coventry	a									
Birmingham International	a									
Birmingham New Street 12	a		11 18							

For complete service between Banbury and Leamington (Birmingham), please refer to table 71

Table 116

Mondays to Fridays

6 January to 10 February

London and Reading - Bedwyn, Oxford, Bicester, Banbury and Birmingham

Network Diagram - refer to first Page of Table 116

Station		GW	XC	GW	GW	CH	GW	XC	GW	GW
		◇1	1	1	◇1		1	◇1	1	◇1
London Paddington 15 ⊖	d	09 36			09 50				09 57	10 15
Ealing Broadway ⊖	d								10 05	
Slough 3	d				10 06				10 27	
Maidenhead 3	d								10 34	
Twyford 3	d						←		10 42	
Reading 7	d	10 03	10 10	10 12	10 22		10 23	10 40	10 53	10 43
Reading West	d			10 14					→	
Theale	d			10 20						
Aldermaston	d			10 25						
Midgham	d			10 29						
Thatcham	d			10 34						
Newbury Racecourse	d			10 38						
Newbury	a			10 44						
	d									
Kintbury	d									
Hungerford	d									
Bedwyn	a									
Tilehurst	d						10 27			
Pangbourne	d						10 31			
Goring & Streatley	d						10 36			
Cholsey	d						10 41			
Didcot Parkway	a	10 17					10 49			10 58
	d						10 55			
Appleford	d									
Culham	d									
Radley	d						11 03			
Oxford	a		10 34		10 47		11 14	11 04		
	d		10 36			11 00		11 07		
Islip	d					11 13				
Bicester Town	a					11 25				
Tackley	d									
Heyford	d									
Kings Sutton	d									
Banbury	a		10 52					11 24		
Leamington Spa 8	a		11 10					11 41		
Coventry	a		11 23							
Birmingham International	a		11 37							
Birmingham New Street 12	a		11 48					12 18		

Station		GW	GW	GW	GW	GW	XC	GW	GW	GW
		1	◇1	1	1	◇1	◇1	1	1	◇1
						Ø				
London Paddington 15 ⊖	d	10 18	10 22		10 27	10 30				10 50
Ealing Broadway ⊖	d				10 35					
Slough 3	d		10 36		10 57					11 06
Maidenhead 3	d				11 04					
Twyford 3	d			←	11 12					
Reading 7	d	10 48	10 52	10 53	11 23	10 57	11 10		11 12	11 21
Reading West	d				→				11 14	
Theale	d	10 56							11 20	
Aldermaston	d								11 25	
Midgham	d								11 29	
Thatcham	d	11 04							11 34	
Newbury Racecourse	d								11 38	
Newbury	a	11 10							11 44	
	d	11 10								
Kintbury	d	11 17								
Hungerford	d	11 21								
Bedwyn	a	11 32								
Tilehurst	d			10 57						
Pangbourne	d			11 01						
Goring & Streatley	d			11 06						
Cholsey	d			11 11						
Didcot Parkway	a			11 19		11 12				11 37
	d			11 25						11 38
Appleford	d									
Culham	d									
Radley	d									
Oxford	a		11 18	11 43			11 32			11 50
	d						11 36	11 45		
Islip	d									
Bicester Town	a									
Tackley	d							11 54		
Heyford	d							11 58		
Kings Sutton	d							12 07		
Banbury	a						11 51	12 13		
Leamington Spa 8	a						12 10			
Coventry	a						12 24			
Birmingham International	a						12 37			
Birmingham New Street 12	a						12 48			

Station		GW	XC	GW	GW	GW	GW	GW	GW	GW
		1	◇1	1	◇1	1	◇1	1	1	◇1
London Paddington 15 ⊖	d			10 57	11 15	11 18	11 20		11 27	11 30
Ealing Broadway ⊖	d			11 05					11 35	
Slough 3	d			11 27			11 36		11 57	
Maidenhead 3	d			11 34					12 04	
Twyford 3	d	←		11 42				←	12 13	
Reading 7	d	11 23	11 40	11 53	11 44	11 48	11 52	11 53	12 23	11 57
Reading West	d			→					→	
Theale	d					11 56				
Aldermaston	d									
Midgham	d									
Thatcham	d					12 04				
Newbury Racecourse	d									
Newbury	a					12 10				
	d					12 10				
Kintbury	d					12 17				
Hungerford	d					12 21				
Bedwyn	a					12 31				
Tilehurst	d	11 27						11 57		
Pangbourne	d	11 31						12 01		
Goring & Streatley	d	11 36						12 06		
Cholsey	d	11 41						12 11		
Didcot Parkway	a	11 50			11 58			12 21		12 12
	d	11 55						12 25		
Appleford	d									
Culham	d									
Radley	d	12 03								
Oxford	a	12 14	12 04				12 18	12 43		
	d		12 07							
Islip	d									
Bicester Town	a									
Tackley	d									
Heyford	d									
Kings Sutton	d									
Banbury	a		12 24							
Leamington Spa 8	a		12 42							
Coventry	a									
Birmingham International	a									
Birmingham New Street 12	a		13 18							

Station		GW	XC	GW	GW	GW	XC	GW	GW	GW
		◇1	◇1	1	◇1	1	1	1	◇1	◇1
		A								
London Paddington 15 ⊖	d	11 36			11 50			11 57	12 15	12 18
Ealing Broadway ⊖	d							12 05		
Slough 3	d				12 06			12 27		
Maidenhead 3	d							12 34		
Twyford 3	d					←		12 45		
Reading 7	d	12 03	12 10	12 12	12 22	12 23	12 40	12 53	12 42	12 49
Reading West	d			12 14				→		
Theale	d			12 20						12 57
Aldermaston	d			12 25						
Midgham	d			12 29						
Thatcham	d			12 34						13 05
Newbury Racecourse	d			12 38						
Newbury	a			12 44						13 13
	d									13 13
Kintbury	d									
Hungerford	d									13 22
Bedwyn	a									13 30
Tilehurst	d					12 27				
Pangbourne	d					12 31				
Goring & Streatley	d					12 36				
Cholsey	d					12 41				
Didcot Parkway	a	12 17				12 49			12 57	
	d					12 55				
Appleford	d					13 00				
Culham	d									
Radley	d					13 03				
Oxford	a		12 34		12 48	13 14	13 02			
	d		12 36				13 07			
Islip	d									
Bicester Town	a									
Tackley	d									
Heyford	d									
Kings Sutton	d									
Banbury	a		12 52				13 25			
Leamington Spa 8	a		13 10				13 43			
Coventry	a		13 23							
Birmingham International	a		13 37							
Birmingham New Street 12	a		13 49				14 18			

A The Cheltenham Spa Express

For complete service between Banbury and Leamington (Birmingham), please refer to table 71

Table 116

Mondays to Fridays

6 January to 10 February

London and Reading - Bedwyn, Oxford, Bicester, Banbury and Birmingham

Network Diagram - refer to first Page of Table 116

		GW	CH	GW	GW	GW	XC	GW	GW	GW	XC	GW	GW	GW	GW	GW	GW	GW	GW
		◇1		1	1	◇1	◇1	1	◇1	1	◇1	1	◇1	1	◇1	1	1	1	◇1
		✠				☕	✠		✠		✠		☕		✠				☕
London Paddington [15] ⊖	d	12 21			12 27	12 30			12 50			12 57	13 15	13 18	13 21			13 27	13 30
Ealing Broadway ⊖	d				12 35							13 05						13 35	
Slough [3]	d	12 36			12 57				13 06			13 27			13 36			13 57	
Maidenhead [3]	d				13 04							13 34						14 04	
Twyford [3]	d			←	13 12					←		13 44					←	14 12	
Reading [7]	d	12 52		12 53	13 23	12 57	13 10	13 12	13 22	13 23	13 40	13 53	13 42	13 48	13 51		13 53	14 23	13 57
Reading West	d				→			13 14				→						→	
Theale	d							13 20						13 56					
Aldermaston	d							13 25											
Midgham	d							13 29											
Thatcham	d							13 34						14 04					
Newbury Racecourse	d							13 38											
Newbury	a							13 44						14 10					
	d													14 10					
Kintbury	d													14 17					
Hungerford	d													14 21					
Bedwyn	a													14 32					
Tilehurst	d			12 57						13 27							13 57		
Pangbourne	d			13 01						13 31							14 01		
Goring & Streatley	d			13 06						13 36							14 06		
Cholsey	d			13 11						13 41							14 11		
Didcot Parkway	a			13 19		13 12			13 37	13 48			13 56				14 20		14 12
	d			13 25					13 38	13 55							14 25		
Appleford	d																		
Culham	d									14 01									
Radley	d									14 03									
Oxford	a	13 20		13 43			13 34		13 50	14 14	14 04				14 18		14 43		
	d		13 30				13 36				14 07					14 24			
Islip	d		13 43																
Bicester Town	a		13 55																
Tackley	d															14 33			
Heyford	d															14 37			
Kings Sutton	d															14 46			
Banbury	a						13 52				14 25					14 52			
Leamington Spa [8]	a						14 10				14 41								
Coventry	a						14 23												
Birmingham International	a						14 37												
Birmingham New Street [12]	a						14 48				15 18								

		GW	XC	GW	GW	CH	GW	XC	GW	GW	GW	GW	GW	GW	GW	XC	GW	GW	GW
		◇1	◇1	1	◇1		1	◇1	1	◇1	1	◇1	1	1	◇1	◇1	1	◇1	1
		☕	✠		✠			✠		☕		✠			☕	✠		✠	
London Paddington [15] ⊖	d	13 36			13 50				13 57	14 15	14 18	14 21		14 27	14 30			14 50	
Ealing Broadway ⊖	d								14 05					14 35					
Slough [3]	d				14 06				14 27			14 36		14 57				15 06	
Maidenhead [3]	d								14 34					15 04					
Twyford [3]	d						←		14 42				←	15 14					←
Reading [7]	d	14 03	14 10	14 12	14 22		14 23	14 40	14 55	14 44	14 48	14 52	14 55	15 23	14 57	15 09	15 12	15 22	15 23
Reading West	d			14 14					→					→			15 14		
Theale	d			14 20							14 56						15 20		
Aldermaston	d			14 25													15 25		
Midgham	d			14 29													15 29		
Thatcham	d			14 34							15 04						15 34		
Newbury Racecourse	d			14 38													15 38		
Newbury	a			14 44							15 10						15 44		
	d										15 10								
Kintbury	d										15 17								
Hungerford	d										15 21								
Bedwyn	a										15 33								
Tilehurst	d						14 27						14 59						15 28
Pangbourne	d						14 31						15 04						15 31
Goring & Streatley	d						14 36						15 09						15 36
Cholsey	d						14 41						15 14						15 41
Didcot Parkway	a	14 17					14 49			14 58			15 20		15 12			15 37	15 49
	d						14 55						15 25					15 38	15 55
Appleford	d																		
Culham	d																		16 01
Radley	d						15 03												16 03
Oxford	a		14 34		14 48		15 14	15 03				15 18	15 44			15 34		15 50	16 16
	d		14 36			15 00		15 07								15 36			
Islip	d					15 13													
Bicester Town	a					15 25													
Tackley	d																		
Heyford	d																		
Kings Sutton	d																		
Banbury	a		14 56					15 24								15 53			
Leamington Spa [8]	a		15 13					15 42								16 10			
Coventry	a		15 25													16 23			
Birmingham International	a		15 37													16 37			
Birmingham New Street [12]	a		15 48					16 18								16 48			

For complete service between Banbury and Leamington (Birmingham), please refer to table 71

Table 116

London and Reading - Bedwyn, Oxford, Bicester, Banbury and Birmingham

Mondays to Fridays

6 January to 10 February

Network Diagram - refer to first Page of Table 116

Station		XC	GW	GW	GW	GW	GW	CH	GW	GW
		◇1 🛒	1	◇1 🍽	1	◇1 🛒	1		1	1
London Paddington 15 ⊖	d		14 57	15 15	15 18	15 22				15 27
Ealing Broadway ⊖	d		15 05							15 35
Slough 3	d		15 27			15 36				15 59
Maidenhead 3	d		15 34							16 07
Twyford 3	d		15 42						←	16 15
Reading 7	d	15 40	15 53	15 43	15 48	15 52			15 53	16 26
Reading West	d		→							→
Theale	d				15 56					
Aldermaston	d									
Midgham	d									
Thatcham	d				16 04					
Newbury Racecourse	d									
Newbury	a				16 10					
	d				16 10					
Kintbury	d				16 17					
Hungerford	d				16 21					
Bedwyn	a				16 31					
Tilehurst	d								15 57	
Pangbourne	d								16 01	
Goring & Streatley	d								16 06	
Cholsey	d								16 11	
Didcot Parkway	a			15 57					16 19	
	d								16 25	
Appleford	d									
Culham	d									
Radley	d								16 33	
Oxford	a	16 05				16 18			16 43	
	d	16 07					16 23	16 26		
Islip	d							16 39		
Bicester Town	a							16 51		
Tackley	d						16 32			
Heyford	d						16 36			
Kings Sutton	d						16 45			
Banbury	a	16 23					16 51			
Leamington Spa 8	a	16 40								
Coventry	a									
Birmingham International	a									
Birmingham New Street 12	a	17 18								

Station		GW	GW	XC FX	XC FO	GW	GW	GW	GW	XC
		◇1 🍽	◇1 🍽	◇1 🛒	◇1 🛒	1	1	◇1 🍽	1	◇1 🛒
London Paddington 15 ⊖	d	15 30	15 36					15 52		
Ealing Broadway ⊖	d									
Slough 3	d									
Maidenhead 3	d									
Twyford 3	d								←	
Reading 7	d	15 57	16 02	16 10	16 10	16 12		16u22	16 26	16 40
Reading West	d					16 14				
Theale	d					16 20				
Aldermaston	d					16 25				
Midgham	d					16 29				
Thatcham	d					16 34				
Newbury Racecourse	d					16 38				
Newbury	a					16 44				
	d						17 08			
Kintbury	d						17 14			
Hungerford	d						17 19			
Bedwyn	a						17 28			
Tilehurst	d								16 30	
Pangbourne	d								16 34	
Goring & Streatley	d								16 39	
Cholsey	d								16 44	
Didcot Parkway	a	16 11	16 16						16 50	
	d								16 56	
Appleford	d								17 01	
Culham	d								17 04	
Radley	d								17 08	
Oxford	a			16 33	16 33			16 47	17 17	17 04
	d			16 35	16 36					17 07
Islip	d									
Bicester Town	a									
Tackley	d									
Heyford	d									
Kings Sutton	d									
Banbury	a			16 53	16 53					17 28
Leamington Spa 8	a			17 12	17 12					17 46
Coventry	a			17 24	17 24					
Birmingham International	a			17 37	17 37					
Birmingham New Street 12	a			17 49	17 49					18 18

Station		GW	GW	GW	GW	GW	GW	GW	GW	GW
		1	R 1 🍽	1	◇1 🛒	1	1	R 1 🍽	1	◇1 🍽
London Paddington 15 ⊖	d	15 57	16 15	16 18	16 22		16 25	16 30		16 36
Ealing Broadway ⊖	d	16 05					16 33			
Slough 3	d	16 28			16 38		16 58			
Maidenhead 3	d	16 35					17 05			
Twyford 3	d	16 44				←	17 13			
Reading 7	d	16 55	16 44	16 48	16 52	16 55	17 23	16 57		17 04
Reading West	d	→					→			
Theale	d			16 56						
Aldermaston	d			17 01						
Midgham	d									
Thatcham	d			17 08						
Newbury Racecourse	d									
Newbury	a			17 14						17 18
	d			17 24						17 19
Kintbury	d			→						
Hungerford	d									17a28
Bedwyn	a									
Tilehurst	d					16 58				
Pangbourne	d					17 03				
Goring & Streatley	d					17 08				
Cholsey	d					17 13				
Didcot Parkway	a		16 59			17 20		17 12		
	d					17 26			17 15	
Appleford	d					→				
Culham	d									
Radley	d									
Oxford	a				17 22				17 30	
	d									
Islip	d									
Bicester Town	a									
Tackley	d									
Heyford	d									
Kings Sutton	d									
Banbury	a									
Leamington Spa 8	a									
Coventry	a									
Birmingham International	a									
Birmingham New Street 12	a									

Station		GW	XC	CH	GW	GW	GW	GW	GW	GW
		1	◇1 🛒		1	1	◇1	1	R 1 🍽	◇1 🍽
London Paddington 15 ⊖	d						16 49		17 00	17 03
Ealing Broadway ⊖	d									
Slough 3	d						17 05			
Maidenhead 3	d									
Twyford 3	d							←		
Reading 7	d		17 09			17 12	17 21	17 23	17 26	17u30
Reading West	d					17 14				
Theale	d					17 20				
Aldermaston	d					17 25				
Midgham	d					17 29				
Thatcham	d					17 34				
Newbury Racecourse	d	←				17 38				
Newbury	a	17 14				17 44				17 47
	d	17 24								
Kintbury	d	17 31								
Hungerford	d	17 35								
Bedwyn	a	17 46								
Tilehurst	d							17 27		
Pangbourne	d							17 32		
Goring & Streatley	d							17 37		
Cholsey	d				←			17 42		
Didcot Parkway	a				17 20		17 36	17 49	17 40	
	d				17 26		17 38	18 05		
Appleford	d				17 31					
Culham	d				17 33			18 11		
Radley	d				17 37			18 15		
Oxford	a		17 34		17 44		17 51	18 23		
	d		17 36	17 45	17 46					
Islip	d			17 58						
Bicester Town	a			18 10						
Tackley	d				17 55					
Heyford	d				17 59					
Kings Sutton	d				18 08					
Banbury	a		17 54		18 15					
Leamington Spa 8	a		18 11							
Coventry	a		18 24							
Birmingham International	a		18 37							
Birmingham New Street 12	a		18 49							

For complete service between Banbury and Leamington (Birmingham), please refer to table 71

Table 116

Mondays to Fridays

6 January to 10 February

London and Reading - Bedwyn, Oxford, Bicester, Banbury and Birmingham

Network Diagram - refer to first Page of Table 116

Station		GW	XC	GW	GW	GW	GW	GW	GW	GW	GW	XC	GW	GW	GW	GW	GW	GW	GW	XC	GW	GW	GW	GW	CH	GW FO	GW FX	GW	GW	GW	GW	XC	GW	GW	GW	GW	GW
		◇1	◇1	■ 1 A	1	◇1	1	1	■ 1	◇1	1	◇1	1	1	◇1	◇1	■ 1 B	1	◇1	◇1	■ 1	1	1	◇1 C		1	1	■ 1	1	◇1	1	◇1	1	◇1	1	1	◇1
		⊐P	trolley	⊐P		⊐P			⊐P	⊐P		trolley			⊐P	⊐P	⊐P		⊐P	trolley	⊐P			⊐P				⊐P		⊐P		trolley		⊐P			trolley
London Paddington 15 ⊖	d	17 06		17 15	17 18	17 22		17 24	17 30	17 33				17 35	17 42	17 49	18 00		18 05		18 15	18 15	18 18	18 22		18 25	18 25	18 30		18 35				18 47			18 50
Ealing Broadway ⊖	d							17 33														18 23				18 33	18 33										
Slough 3	d							17 58														18 47				18 59	18 59										19 07
Maidenhead 3	d				17 41			18 10						17 58		18 09						18 57	18 40			19 10	19 10										
Twyford 3	d	17 30					←	18 17						18 07				←	18 28			19 05	18 48			19 18	19 18		←					19 10	←		
Reading 7	d	17 39	17 40	17 42	17 55	17 50	17 55	18 29	17 56	18 01		18 10	18 12	18 20		18 22	18 27	18 29	18 37	18 40	18 42	19 19	18 57	18 51		19 27	19 27	18 55	18 57	19 03		19 09	19 12	19 19	19 19	19 21	19 23
Reading West	d				→			→					18 14									→	→			→	→						19 15				
Theale	d	17 48											18 20						18 46														19 20			19 28	
Aldermaston	d												18 25																				19 25				
Midgham	d												18 29																				19 29				
Thatcham	d	17 58											18 34						18 56														19 34			19 39	
Newbury Racecourse	d												18 38																				19 39				
Newbury	a	18 04								18 15			18 44						19 02											19 17			19 44			19 56	
	d	18 05									18 26								19 03											19 19	19 27					19 56	
Kintbury	d	18 13									18 32								19 10												19 33					20 03	
Hungerford	d	18 19									18 37								19 17											19 29	19 38					20 08	
Bedwyn	a	18 26									18 46								19 24											19 36	19 45					20 18	
Tilehurst	d						17 59							18 25				18 34											19 01						19 24		
Pangbourne	d						18 04							18 30				18 39											19 06						19 28		
Goring & Streatley	d						18 10							18 35				18 44											19 12						19 33		
Cholsey	d						18 15							18 41				18 50											19 17						19 38		
Didcot Parkway	a			17 56			18 22		18 09					18 47	18 19		18 41	18 58			18 57							19 11	19 26					19 33	19 47		
	d						18 25							18 47				19 03											19 27						19 56		
Appleford	d																	19 08																			
Culham	d																																		20 03		
Radley	d						18 33							18 55															19 34								
Oxford	a		18 05			18 15	18 45					18 34		19 07		18 47		19 18		19 11				19 20					19 46			19 34			20 16		19 49
	d		18 07									18 36						19 19		19 13					19 30							19 36					
Islip	d																								19 43												
Bicester Town	a																								19 55												
Tackley	d																	19 27																			
Heyford	d																	19 32																			
Kings Sutton	d																	19 44																			
Banbury	a		18 25									18 54						19 50		19 30												19 54					
Leamington Spa 8	a		18 45									19 11								19 49												20 12					
Coventry	a											19 23																				20 24					
Birmingham International	a											19 37																				20 37					
Birmingham New Street 12	a		19 18									19 48								20 18												20 48					

A The Red Dragon
B The Bristolian
C The Cathedrals Express

For complete service between Banbury and Leamington (Birmingham), please refer to table 71

Table 116

Mondays to Fridays
6 January to 10 February

London and Reading - Bedwyn, Oxford, Bicester, Banbury and Birmingham

Network Diagram - refer to first Page of Table 116

		GW	GW FO	GW FX	GW	XC	GW	GW FO	GW FX	GW FO
		R			R				R	
		1	1	1	1	◇1	1	1	1	1
					A					
		☕			✕				☕	
London Paddington 15 ⊖	d	19 00			19 03			19 12	19 15	
Ealing Broadway ⊖	d									
Slough 3	d									
Maidenhead 3	d									
Twyford 3	d		←	←						←
Reading 7	d	19 27	19 27	19 27	19u33	19 40	19 42	19 43	19 42	19 43
Reading West	d						19 44	→		
Theale	d						19 50			
Aldermaston	d						19 55			
Midgham	d						19 59			
Thatcham	d						20 04			
Newbury Racecourse	d						20 08			
Newbury	a				19 50		20 11			
	d						20 33			
Kintbury	d						20 39			
Hungerford	d						20 43			
Bedwyn	a						20 53			
Tilehurst	d		19 31	19 31						
Pangbourne	d		19 35	19 35						
Goring & Streatley	d		19 40	19 40						
Cholsey	d		19 46	19 46						
Didcot Parkway	a	19 42	19 53	19 53					19 56	20 00
	d		20 01	20 08						20 09
Appleford	d			20 13						20 13
Culham	d									
Radley	d			20 18						20 18
Oxford	a		20 18	20 27		20 06				20 28
	d					20 07				
Islip	d									
Bicester Town	a									
Tackley	d									
Heyford	d									
Kings Sutton	d									
Banbury	a					20 27				
Leamington Spa 8	a					20 45				
Coventry	a									
Birmingham International	a									
Birmingham New Street 12	a					21 22				

		GW	GW FX	GW FO	GW	GW	GW	XC	GW	GW
						R				
		1	◇1	◇1	1	1	1	◇1	◇1	◇1
			☕	☕		☕			☕	☕
London Paddington 15 ⊖	d	19 18	19 22	19 22	19 27	19 30			19 45	19 48
Ealing Broadway ⊖	d				19 35					
Slough 3	d		19 36	19 36	19 59					
Maidenhead 3	d	19 40			20 09					20 06
Twyford 3	d	19 48			20 17		←			
Reading 7	d	19 57	19 52	19 52	20 25	19 57	19 57	20 10	20 12	20 18
Reading West	d	→			→					
Theale	d									
Aldermaston	d									
Midgham	d									
Thatcham	d									
Newbury Racecourse	d									
Newbury	a								20 28	
	d									
Kintbury	d									
Hungerford	d									
Bedwyn	a									
Tilehurst	d						20 01			
Pangbourne	d						20 06			
Goring & Streatley	d						20 11			
Cholsey	d						20 16			
Didcot Parkway	a					20 12	20 22			20 33
	d						20 25			
Appleford	d									
Culham	d									
Radley	d						20 33			
Oxford	a		20 18	20 21			20 43	20 34		
	d							20 36		
Islip	d									
Bicester Town	a									
Tackley	d									
Heyford	d									
Kings Sutton	d									
Banbury	a							20 52		
Leamington Spa 8	a							21 10		
Coventry	a							21 23		
Birmingham International	a							21 37		
Birmingham New Street 12	a							21 49		

		GW	CH	GW	GW	GW	XC	GW	GW	GW
		◇1		1	1	◇1	◇1	◇1	1	◇1
		⊤				☕		Ø		⊤
London Paddington 15 ⊖	d	19 50			19 57	20 00		20 15		20 20
Ealing Broadway ⊖	d				20 05					
Slough 3	d	20 06			20 27					20 36
Maidenhead 3	d				20 34					
Twyford 3	d			←	20 42					
Reading 7	d	20 22		20 25	20 53	20 27	20 40	20 41	20 41	20 51
Reading West	d				→				20 44	
Theale	d								20 50	
Aldermaston	d								20 55	
Midgham	d								20 58	
Thatcham	d								21 03	
Newbury Racecourse	d								21 08	
Newbury	a								21 13	
	d									
Kintbury	d									
Hungerford	d									
Bedwyn	a									
Tilehurst	d			20 29						
Pangbourne	d			20 34						
Goring & Streatley	d			20 39						
Cholsey	d			20 44						
Didcot Parkway	a			20 51		20 41		20 56		
	d			20 57						
Appleford	d									
Culham	d									
Radley	d			21 04						
Oxford	a	20 52		21 15			21 05			21 17
	d	20 55	21 00				21 09			
Islip	d		21 13							
Bicester Town	a		21 25							
Tackley	d	21 04								
Heyford	d	21 08								
Kings Sutton	d	21 17								
Banbury	a	21 23					21 31			
Leamington Spa 8	a						21 51			
Coventry	a									
Birmingham International	a									
Birmingham New Street 12	a						22 17			

		GW	GW	GW	GW	GW	XC	GW	GW	GW
		1	1	1	◇1	1	◇1	◇1	◇1	1
					☕			☕		
London Paddington 15 ⊖	d			20 27	20 35			20 45	20 48	
Ealing Broadway ⊖	d			20 35						
Slough 3	d			20 57					21 05	
Maidenhead 3	d			21 04						
Twyford 3	d		←	21 12						←
Reading 7	d		20 53	21 23	21 02		21 10	21 13	21 20	21 23
Reading West	d			→						
Theale	d									
Aldermaston	d									
Midgham	d									
Thatcham	d									
Newbury Racecourse	d									
Newbury	a				21 16					
	d					21 24				
Kintbury	d					21 30				
Hungerford	d					21 35				
Bedwyn	a					21 45				
Tilehurst	d		20 57							21 27
Pangbourne	d		21 01							21 31
Goring & Streatley	d		21 06							21 36
Cholsey	d		21 11							21 41
Didcot Parkway	a		21 19					21 27		21 52
	d		21 25							21 52
Appleford	d									
Culham	d									
Radley	d		21 33							21 59
Oxford	a		21 44				21 34		21 51	22 12
	d	21 41					21 36			
Islip	d									
Bicester Town	a									
Tackley	d	21 50								
Heyford	d	21 54								
Kings Sutton	d	22 03								
Banbury	a	22 09					21 52			
Leamington Spa 8	a						22 10			
Coventry	a						22 22			
Birmingham International	a						22 33			
Birmingham New Street 12	a						22 45			

A Restaurant for customers joining at Pad, Reading + Newbury. The Armada

For complete service between Banbury and Leamington (Birmingham), please refer to table 71

Table 116

Mondays to Fridays

6 January to 10 February

London and Reading - Bedwyn, Oxford, Bicester, Banbury and Birmingham

Network Diagram - refer to first Page of Table 116

Station		GW	GW	XC	GW	GW	GW	GW	GW	GW
										FO
		1	◇1 ☕	◇1	◇1	1	1	1	◇1 ☕	◇1 🍴
London Paddington 15 ⊖	d	20 57	21 15		21 18			21 27	21 45	21 48
Ealing Broadway ⊖	d	21 05						21 35		
Slough 3	d	21 27			21 35			22 07		22 04
Maidenhead 3	d	21 34						22 15		
Twyford 3	d	21 42				←		22 23		
Reading 7	d	21 57	21 41	21 46	21 50	21 57	22 01	22 32	22 11	22 25
Reading West	d	→					22 03	→		
Theale	d						22 10			
Aldermaston	d						22 15			
Midgham	d						22 18			
Thatcham	d						22 23			
Newbury Racecourse	d						22 28			
Newbury	a						22 31			
	d						22 31			
Kintbury	d						22 37			
Hungerford	d						22 42			
Bedwyn	a						22 52			
Tilehurst	d					22 02				
Pangbourne	d					22 05				
Goring & Streatley	d					22 09				
Cholsey	d					22 14				
Didcot Parkway	a		22 01			22 24			22 31	
	d					22 25				
Appleford	d									
Culham	d									
Radley	d									
Oxford	a			22 28	22 18	22 41				22 47
	d			22 30						
Islip	d									
Bicester Town	a									
Tackley	d									
Heyford	d									
Kings Sutton	d									
Banbury	a			22 51						
Leamington Spa 8	a			23 09						
Coventry	a			23 24						
Birmingham International	a			23 34						
Birmingham New Street 12	a			00 02						

Station		GW	GW	CH	GW	GW	GW	GW	GW	GW
		FX		FO		FO	FX	FO	FX	FO
		◇1 ☕	1		1	1	1	◇1 ☕	◇1 ☕	◇1
London Paddington 15 ⊖	d	21 48				21 57	21 57	22 15	22 15	22 18
Ealing Broadway ⊖	d					22 05	22 05			
Slough 3	d	22 04				22 30	22 42			22 35
Maidenhead 3	d					22 42	22 53			22 42
Twyford 3	d				←	22 50	23 01			
Reading 7	d	22 25			22 32	23 10	23 10	22 42	22 54	22 56
Reading West	d					→	→			
Theale	d									
Aldermaston	d									
Midgham	d									
Thatcham	d									
Newbury Racecourse	d									
Newbury	a									
	d									
Kintbury	d									
Hungerford	d									
Bedwyn	a									
Tilehurst	d				22 35					
Pangbourne	d				22 40					
Goring & Streatley	d				22 43					
Cholsey	d				22 48					
Didcot Parkway	a				22 58			23 02	23 13	
	d				22 58					
Appleford	d				23 03					
Culham	d				23 05					
Radley	d				23 09					
Oxford	a	22 47			23 22					23 27
	d		23 06	23 12						
Islip	d			23 25						
Bicester Town	a			23 37						
Tackley	d		23 15							
Heyford	d		23 19							
Kings Sutton	d		23 28							
Banbury	a		23 34							
Leamington Spa 8	a									
Coventry	a									
Birmingham International	a									
Birmingham New Street 12	a									

Station		GW	GW	GW	GW	GW	GW	GW	GW	GW
		FX		FX	FO	FO	FX	FO	FX	FO
		◇1	1	1	1	1	1	◇1 ☕	◇1 ☕	◇1
London Paddington 15 ⊖	d	22 18				22 27	22 27	22 45	22 45	22 48
Ealing Broadway ⊖	d					22 35	22 35			
Slough 3	d	22 39				23 11	23 11			23 05
Maidenhead 3	d	22 47				23 23	23 23			23 12
Twyford 3	d			←	←	23 31	23 31			23 20
Reading 7	d	23 01	23 03	23 10	23 10	23 41	23 40	23 11	23 23	23 28
Reading West	d		23 05			→	→			
Theale	d		23 11							
Aldermaston	d		23 16							
Midgham	d		23 20							
Thatcham	d		23 25							
Newbury Racecourse	d		23 29							
Newbury	a		23 32							
	d		23 32							
Kintbury	d		23 39							
Hungerford	d		23 43							
Bedwyn	a		23 53							
Tilehurst	d			23 14	23 14					
Pangbourne	d			23 19	23 19					
Goring & Streatley	d			23 22	23 22					
Cholsey	d			23 27	23 27					
Didcot Parkway	a			23 37	23 37			23 42	23 42	
	d			23 38	23 38					
Appleford	d									
Culham	d									
Radley	d									
Oxford	a	23 29		23 54	23 56					23 56
	d									
Islip	d									
Bicester Town	a									
Tackley	d									
Heyford	d									
Kings Sutton	d									
Banbury	a									
Leamington Spa 8	a									
Coventry	a									
Birmingham International	a									
Birmingham New Street 12	a									

Station		GW	GW	GW	GW	CH	GW	GW	GW	GW
		FX	FX	FO					FO	
		◇1	1	1	◇1		◇1 ☕	1	1	1
London Paddington 15 ⊖	d	22 48			23 18		23 30	23 33	23 42	
Ealing Broadway ⊖	d							23 41		
Slough 3	d	23 08			23 38			23 57	00 01	
Maidenhead 3	d	23 17			23 46			00 05	00 10	
Twyford 3	d	23 26	←	←				00 13		←
Reading 7	d	23 34	23 40	23 41	00 04		00 09	00 27	00 25	00 27
Reading West	d							→		
Theale	d									
Aldermaston	d									
Midgham	d									
Thatcham	d									
Newbury Racecourse	d									
Newbury	a									
	d									
Kintbury	d									
Hungerford	d									
Bedwyn	a									
Tilehurst	d		23 44	23 44						00 33
Pangbourne	d		23 48	23 48						00 37
Goring & Streatley	d		23 52	23 52						00 41
Cholsey	d		23 57	23 57						00 46
Didcot Parkway	a		00 07	00 07			00 29		00 44	00 56
	d		00 07	00 08					00 44	00 56
Appleford	d									01 00
Culham	d									01 03
Radley	d		00 14	00 14						01 07
Oxford	a	00 01	00 27	00 27	00 35				01 02	01 18
	d					00 38				
Islip	d									
Bicester Town	a									
Tackley	d					00 48				
Heyford	d					00 53				
Kings Sutton	d					01 01				
Banbury	a					01 11				
Leamington Spa 8	a									
Coventry	a									
Birmingham International	a									
Birmingham New Street 12	a									

For complete service between Banbury and Leamington (Birmingham), please refer to table 71

Table 116

Mondays to Fridays

17 February to 24 March

London and Reading - Bedwyn, Oxford, Bicester, Banbury and Birmingham

Network Diagram - refer to first Page of Table 116

		GW	GW	GW	CH	GW	GW	GW	GW	GW	GW	GW	GW	CH	GW	GW	GW	GW	GW
		MX	MO	MX	MX	MX	MO	MO	MX	MX	MX								
		1	1	◇1		◇1	◇1		1	1	◇1	1	1		1	1	1	◇1	1
						☕	☕	🚌										☕	
London Paddington 15 ⊖	d										00 22					05 12	05 17	05 19	
Ealing Broadway ⊖	d																05 25		
Slough 3	d										00 41					05 30	05 51		
Maidenhead 3	d									00 05							05 59		
Twyford 3	d									00 13							06 07		
Reading 7	d			00 04		00 09	00 16		00 20	00 27	01 01		05 15			05 50	06 18	05 53	05 54
Reading West	d								00s23				05 17				→		
Theale	d								00s29				05 24						
Aldermaston	d								00s34				05 29						
Midgham	d								00s37				05 32						
Thatcham	d								00s42				05 37						
Newbury Racecourse	d								00s47				05 42						
Newbury	a								00 52				05 45						
	d												05 45						
Kintbury	d												05 51						
Hungerford	d												05 56						
Bedwyn	a												06 06						
Tilehurst	d									00 33									05 58
Pangbourne	d		00 01							00 37									06 03
Goring & Streatley	d		00 07							00 41									06 08
Cholsey	d		00 12							00 46									06 14
Didcot Parkway	a		00 21			00 29	00s33			00 56	01 19					06 05		06 08	06 21
	d	00 07						00 45		00 56	01 19					06 06			06 25
Appleford	d									01 00									
Culham	d									01 03									06 31
Radley	d	00 14						01 00		01 07									06 35
Oxford	a	00 27		00 35				01 15		01 18	01 34					06 20			06 43
	d				00 38							05 18		05 45	05 45				06 45
Islip	d													05 58					
Bicester Town	a													06 10					
Tackley	d				00 48							05 27			05 54				06 53
Heyford	d				00 53							05 32			05 58				06 58
Kings Sutton	d				01 01							05 40			06 07				07 06
Banbury	a				01 11							05 47			06 14				07 14
Leamington Spa 8	a																		
Coventry	a																		
Birmingham International	a																		
Birmingham New Street 12	a																		

		XC	GW	GW	GW	XC	GW	GW	CH	GW	GW	GW	XC	GW	GW	GW	GW	GW	GW
		◇1	1	◇1	1	◇1	1	◇1		1	1	◇1	◇1	1	1	1	◇1	◇1	◇1
																	A	B	C
		🛒				🛒						☕	🛒				☕	☕	☕
London Paddington 15 ⊖	d			05 45			05 57	06 20				06 30			06 48	06 57	07 00	07 00	07 06
Ealing Broadway ⊖	d						06 05									07 05			
Slough 3	d			06 01			06 29	06 35							07 02	07 29			
Maidenhead 3	d						06 37									07 37			
Twyford 3	d				←		06 45				←					07 45			
Reading 7	d	06 10	06 13	06 17	06 18	06 40	06 53	06 51		06 52	06 53	06 56	07 09	07 10	07 19	07 53	07 28	07 29	07 33
Reading West	d		06 15				→			06 54				07 12		→			
Theale	d		06 21							07 00				07 18					
Aldermaston	d		06 26							07 05				07 23					
Midgham	d		06 30							07 09				07 27					
Thatcham	d		06 35							07 14				07 32					
Newbury Racecourse	d		06 39							07 18				07 36					
Newbury	a		06 45							07 21				07 42					07 47
	d									07 21									
Kintbury	d									07 28									
Hungerford	d									07 32									
Bedwyn	a									07 42									
Tilehurst	d				06 22						06 57				07 26				
Pangbourne	d				06 27						07 01				07 30				
Goring & Streatley	d				06 33						07 06				07 36				
Cholsey	d				06 39						07 11				07 41				
Didcot Parkway	a				06 47			07 06			07 19	07 10			07 48		07 43	07 43	
	d				06 47			07 08			07 25				07 50				
Appleford	d										07 30								
Culham	d										07 32								
Radley	d										07 36								
Oxford	a	06 34		06 51	07 02	07 05		07 22			07 49		07 35		08 02				
	d	06 36				07 08			07 33				07 36						
Islip	d								07 46										
Bicester Town	a								07 59										
Tackley	d																		
Heyford	d																		
Kings Sutton	d																		
Banbury	a	06 52				07 25							07 55						
Leamington Spa 8	a	07 10				07 42							08 12						
Coventry	a	07 23											08 25						
Birmingham International	a	07 37											08 37						
Birmingham New Street 12	a	07 48				08 14							08 48						

A until 23 March
B 24 March
C The Devon Express

For complete service between Banbury and Leamington (Birmingham), please refer to table 71

Table 116

Mondays to Fridays

17 February to 24 March

London and Reading - Bedwyn, Oxford, Bicester, Banbury and Birmingham

Network Diagram - refer to first Page of Table 116

		GW	XC	GW	GW	GW	CH	GW	GW	GW	XC	GW	GW	GW	GW	GW	GW	GW	XC	GW	GW	GW	GW	GW	GW	GW	XC	GW	GW	CH	GW	GW	XC	GW	GW	GW	GW
		1	◇1	◇1	1	1		1	1	◇1	◇1	1	1	1	1	1	◇1	1	◇1	◇1	1	◇1	1	1	1	◇1	◇1	1	◇1		1	1	◇1	1	◇1	1	◇1
																								A	B						A	B					
			🛒	🍴						🍴	🛒						🍴		🛒	🍴		🍴				🍴	🛒						🛒		🍴		🛒
London Paddington 15 ⊖	d			07 15	07 18	07 21			07 27	07 36			07 50	07 50		07 57	08 00			08 15	08 18	08 22		08 27	08 27	08 30			08 51					08 55	09 15	09 18	09 21
Ealing Broadway ⊖	d								07 35							08 05								08 35	08 35									09 03			
Slough 3	d					07 36			07 59				08 06	08 06		08 29						08 36		08 59	08 59				09 06					09 27			09 36
Maidenhead 3	d								08 07							08 38								09 06	09 06									09 35			
Twyford 3	d							←	08 15						←	08 46							←	09 17	09 18						←	←		09 43			
Reading 7	d	07 33	07 41	07 42	07 48	07 52		07 53	08 24	08 02	08 09	08 12	08 22	08 22	08 24	08 55	08 27	08 34	08 40	08 45	08 48	08 52	08 55	09 25	09 26	08 57	09 09	09 14	09 22		09 25	09 26	09 40	09 53	09 42	09 48	09 52
Reading West	d								→			08 14				→								→	→			09 16						→			
Theale	d				07 56							08 20						08 41			08 56							09 22								09 56	
Aldermaston	d				08 01							08 25						08 46										09 27									
Midgham	d											08 29																09 31									
Thatcham	d				08 08							08 34						08 53			09 04							09 36								10 04	
Newbury Racecourse	d											08 38																09 40									
Newbury	a				08 13							08 44						08 59			09 14							09 46								10 10	
	d				08 13													08 59																		10 10	
Kintbury	d				08 20													09 05																		10 17	
Hungerford	d				08 24													09 09																		10 21	
Bedwyn	a				08 34													09 21																		10 32	
Tilehurst	d							07 57							08 27								08 59								09 28	09 30					
Pangbourne	d							08 01							08 31								09 03								09 33	09 34					
Goring & Streatley	d							08 06							08 36								09 08								09 38	09 39					
Cholsey	d							08 11							08 41								09 13								09 43	09 44					
Didcot Parkway	a	07 52		07 56				08 20		08 16					08 50		08 40			08 58			09 21			09 12			09 37		09 50	09 52			09 56		
	d	08 08						08 25							08 55								09 25						09 38		09 56	09 56					
Appleford	d	08 13													09 00																						
Culham	d	08 15													09 01																10 03	10 03					
Radley	d	08 19						08 33							09 06								09 33								10 05	10 05					
Oxford	a	08 31	08 07			08 19		08 44			08 34		08 49	08 49	09 16				09 04			09 20	09 45				09 34		09 53		10 18	10 18	10 04				10 20
	d		08 09				08 35				08 36		08 53						09 07								09 36			10 00			10 07				
Islip	d						08 48																							10 13							
Bicester Town	a						09 01																							10 25							
Tackley	d												09 01																								
Heyford	d												09 06																								
Kings Sutton	d												09 15																								
Banbury	a		08 26								08 52		09 22						09 25								09 55						10 28				
Leamington Spa 3	a		08 43								09 10								09 42								10 11						10 46				
Coventry	a										09 23																10 24										
Birmingham International	a										09 37																10 37										
Birmingham New Street 12	a		09 18								09 48								10 18								10 48						11 18				

A from 10 March

B until 7 March

For complete service between Banbury and Leamington (Birmingham), please refer to table 71

Table 116

Mondays to Fridays

17 February to 24 March

London and Reading - Bedwyn, Oxford, Bicester, Banbury and Birmingham

Network Diagram - refer to first Page of Table 116

		GW	GW	GW	GW	XC	GW	GW	CH	GW
		1	1	◇1	◇1	▪ 1	1	◇1		1
				Ø	⊡	Ꮭ				
London Paddington 15 ⊖	d		09 27	09 30	09 36			09 50		
Ealing Broadway ⊖	d		09 35							
Slough 3	d		09 57					10 06		
Maidenhead 3	d		10 04							
Twyford 3	d	←	10 12							←
Reading 7	d	09 53	10 23	09 57	10 03	10 10	10 12	10 22		10 23
Reading West	d		→				10 14			
Theale	d						10 20			
Aldermaston	d						10 25			
Midgham	d						10 29			
Thatcham	d						10 34			
Newbury Racecourse	d						10 38			
Newbury	a						10 44			
	d									
Kintbury	d									
Hungerford	d									
Bedwyn	a									
Tilehurst	d	09 57								10 27
Pangbourne	d	10 01								10 31
Goring & Streatley	d	10 06								10 36
Cholsey	d	10 11								10 41
Didcot Parkway	a	10 18		10 11	10 17					10 49
	d	10 25								10 55
Appleford	d									
Culham	d									
Radley	d									11 03
Oxford	a	10 43				10 34		10 47		11 14
	d					10 36			11 00	
Islip	d								11 13	
Bicester Town	a								11 25	
Tackley	d									
Heyford	d									
Kings Sutton	d									
Banbury	a					10 52				
Leamington Spa 8	a					11 10				
Coventry	a					11 23				
Birmingham International	a					11 37				
Birmingham New Street 12	a					11 48				

		XC	GW	GW	GW	GW	GW	GW	GW	XC
		◇1	1	◇1	1	◇1	1	1	◇1	◇1
		Ꮭ		⊡		⊡			Ø	Ꮭ
London Paddington 15 ⊖	d		09 57	10 15	10 18	10 22		10 27	10 30	
Ealing Broadway ⊖	d		10 05					10 35		
Slough 3	d		10 27			10 36		10 57		
Maidenhead 3	d		10 34					11 04		
Twyford 3	d		10 42				←	11 12		
Reading 7	d	10 40	10 53	10 43	10 48	10 52	10 53	11 23	10 57	11 10
Reading West	d		→					→		
Theale	d				10 56					
Aldermaston	d									
Midgham	d									
Thatcham	d				11 04					
Newbury Racecourse	d									
Newbury	a				11 10					
	d				11 10					
Kintbury	d				11 17					
Hungerford	d				11 21					
Bedwyn	a				11 32					
Tilehurst	d						10 57			
Pangbourne	d						11 01			
Goring & Streatley	d						11 06			
Cholsey	d						11 11			
Didcot Parkway	a			10 58			11 19		11 12	
	d						11 25			
Appleford	d									
Culham	d									
Radley	d									
Oxford	a	11 04				11 18	11 43			11 32
	d	11 07								11 36
Islip	d									
Bicester Town	a									
Tackley	d									
Heyford	d									
Kings Sutton	d									
Banbury	a	11 24								11 51
Leamington Spa 8	a	11 41								12 10
Coventry	a									12 24
Birmingham International	a									12 37
Birmingham New Street 12	a	12 18								12 48

		GW	GW	GW	GW	XC	GW	GW	GW	GW
		1	1	◇1	1	◇1	1	◇1	1	◇1
						Ꮭ		⊡		Ꮭ
London Paddington 15 ⊖	d			10 50			10 57	11 15	11 18	11 20
Ealing Broadway ⊖	d						11 05			
Slough 3	d			11 06			11 27			11 36
Maidenhead 3	d						11 34			
Twyford 3	d				←		11 42			
Reading 7	d		11 12	11 21	11 23	11 40	11 53	11 44	11 48	11 52
Reading West	d		11 14				→			
Theale	d		11 20						11 56	
Aldermaston	d		11 25							
Midgham	d		11 29							
Thatcham	d		11 34						12 04	
Newbury Racecourse	d		11 38							
Newbury	a		11 44						12 10	
	d								12 10	
Kintbury	d								12 17	
Hungerford	d								12 21	
Bedwyn	a								12 31	
Tilehurst	d				11 27					
Pangbourne	d				11 31					
Goring & Streatley	d				11 36					
Cholsey	d				11 41					
Didcot Parkway	a			11 37	11 50			11 58		
	d			11 38	11 55					
Appleford	d									
Culham	d									
Radley	d				12 03					
Oxford	a			11 50	12 14	12 04				12 18
	d	11 45				12 07				
Islip	d									
Bicester Town	a									
Tackley	d	11 54								
Heyford	d	11 58								
Kings Sutton	d	12 07								
Banbury	a	12 13				12 24				
Leamington Spa 8	a					12 42				
Coventry	a									
Birmingham International	a									
Birmingham New Street 12	a					13 18				

		GW	GW	GW	GW	XC	GW	GW	GW	XC
		1	1	◇1	◇1	◇1	1	◇1	1	▪ 1
					A					
				⊡	⊡	Ꮭ		Ꮭ		Ꮭ
London Paddington 15 ⊖	d		11 27	11 30	11 36			11 50		
Ealing Broadway ⊖	d		11 35							
Slough 3	d		11 57					12 06		
Maidenhead 3	d		12 04							
Twyford 3	d	←	12 13						←	
Reading 7	d	11 53	12 23	11 57	12 03	12 10	12 12	12 22	12 23	12 40
Reading West	d		→				12 14			
Theale	d						12 20			
Aldermaston	d						12 25			
Midgham	d						12 29			
Thatcham	d						12 34			
Newbury Racecourse	d						12 38			
Newbury	a						12 44			
	d									
Kintbury	d									
Hungerford	d									
Bedwyn	a									
Tilehurst	d	11 57							12 27	
Pangbourne	d	12 01							12 31	
Goring & Streatley	d	12 06							12 36	
Cholsey	d	12 11							12 41	
Didcot Parkway	a	12 21		12 12	12 17				12 49	
	d	12 25							12 55	
Appleford	d								13 00	
Culham	d									
Radley	d								13 03	
Oxford	a	12 43				12 34		12 48	13 14	13 02
	d					12 36				13 07
Islip	d									
Bicester Town	a									
Tackley	d									
Heyford	d									
Kings Sutton	d									
Banbury	a					12 52				13 25
Leamington Spa 8	a					13 10				13 43
Coventry	a					13 23				
Birmingham International	a					13 37				
Birmingham New Street 12	a					13 49				14 18

A The Cheltenham Spa Express

For complete service between Banbury and Leamington (Birmingham), please refer to table 71

Table 116

Mondays to Fridays

17 February to 24 March

London and Reading - Bedwyn, Oxford, Bicester, Banbury and Birmingham

Network Diagram - refer to first Page of Table 116

		GW 1 A	GW 1 B	GW ◇1 ⊡	GW ◇1 ⊡	GW ◇1 ✕	CH	GW 1 A	GW 1 B	GW 1	GW ◇1 ⊡	XC ◇1 ✕	GW 1	GW ◇1 ✕	GW 1	XC ◇1 ✕	GW 1 A	GW 1 B	GW ◇1 ⊡	GW 1	GW ◇1 ✕	GW 1	GW 1 A	GW 1 B	GW 1	GW ◇1 ⊡	GW ◇1 ⊡	XC ◇1 ✕	GW 1	GW ◇1 ✕	CH	GW 1	XC ◇1 ✕	GW 1	GW ◇1 ⊡	GW 1	GW ◇1 ✕
London Paddington 15 ⊖	d	11 57	11 57	12 15	12 18	12 21				12 27	12 30			12 50			12 57	12 57	13 15	13 18	13 21				13 27	13 30	13 36			13 50				13 57	14 15	14 18	14 21
Ealing Broadway ⊖	d	12 05	12 05							12 35							13 05	13 05							13 35									14 05			
Slough 3	d	12 27	12 27			12 36				12 57				13 06			13 27	13 27			13 36				13 57					14 06				14 27			14 36
Maidenhead 3	d	12 34	12 34							13 04							13 34	13 34							14 04									14 34			
Twyford 3	d	12 42	12 45					←	←	13 12					←		13 42	13 44					←	←	14 12							←		14 42			
Reading 7	d	12 53	12 53	12 42	12 49	12 52		12 53	12 53	13 23	12 57	13 10	13 12	13 22	13 23	13 40	13 53	13 53	13 42	13 48	13 51		13 53	13 53	14 23	13 57	14 03	14 10	14 12	14 22		14 23	14 40	14 55	14 44	14 48	14 52
Reading West	d	→	→							→			13 14				→	→							→				14 14					→			
Theale	d				12 57								13 20							13 56									14 20							14 56	
Aldermaston	d												13 25																14 25								
Midgham	d												13 29																14 29								
Thatcham	d				13 05								13 34							14 04									14 34							15 04	
Newbury Racecourse	d												13 38																14 38								
Newbury	a				13 13								13 44							14 10									14 44							15 10	
	d				13 13															14 10																15 10	
Kintbury	d																			14 17																15 17	
Hungerford	d				13 22															14 21																15 21	
Bedwyn	a				13 30															14 32																15 33	
Tilehurst	d							12 57	12 57						13 27								13 57	13 57								14 27					
Pangbourne	d							13 01	13 01						13 31								14 01	14 01								14 31					
Goring & Streatley	d							13 06	13 06						13 36								14 06	14 06								14 36					
Cholsey	d							13 11	13 11						13 41								14 11	14 11								14 41					
Didcot Parkway	a			12 57				13 19	13 19		13 12			13 37	13 48				13 56				14 20	14 20		14 12	14 17					14 49			14 58		
	d							13 25	13 25					13 38	13 55								14 25	14 25								14 55					
Appleford	d																																				
Culham	d														14 01																						
Radley	d														14 03																	15 03					
Oxford	a					13 20		13 43	13 43			13 34		13 50	14 14	14 04					14 18		14 43	14 43				14 34		14 48		15 14	15 03				15 18
	d						13 30					13 36				14 07						14 24						14 36			15 00		15 07				
Islip	d						13 43																								15 13						
Bicester Town	a						13 55																								15 25						
Tackley	d																					14 33															
Heyford	d																					14 37															
Kings Sutton	d																					14 46															
Banbury	a											13 52				14 25						14 52						14 56					15 24				
Leamington Spa 8	a											14 10				14 41												15 13					15 42				
Coventry	a											14 23																15 25									
Birmingham International	a											14 37																15 37									
Birmingham New Street 12	a											14 48				15 18												15 48					16 18				

A from 10 March

B until 7 March

For complete service between Banbury and Leamington (Birmingham), please refer to table 71

Table 116

Mondays to Fridays

17 February to 24 March

London and Reading - Bedwyn, Oxford, Bicester, Banbury and Birmingham

Network Diagram - refer to first Page of Table 116

		GW	GW	GW	XC	GW	GW	GW	XC	GW
		1	1	◇1	◇1	1	◇1	1	◇1	1
				⊐P	⌶		⌶		⌶	
London Paddington 15 ⊖	d		14 27	14 30			14 50			14 57
Ealing Broadway ⊖	d		14 35							15 05
Slough 3	d		14 57				15 06			15 27
Maidenhead 3	d		15 04							15 34
Twyford 3	d	←	15 14					←		15 42
Reading 7	d	14 55	15 23	14 57	15 09	15 12	15 22	15 23	15 40	15 53
Reading West	d		→			15 14				→
Theale	d					15 20				
Aldermaston	d					15 25				
Midgham	d					15 29				
Thatcham	d					15 34				
Newbury Racecourse	d					15 38				
Newbury	a					15 44				
	d									
Kintbury	d									
Hungerford	d									
Bedwyn	a									
Tilehurst	d	14 59						15 28		
Pangbourne	d	15 04						15 31		
Goring & Streatley	d	15 09						15 36		
Cholsey	d	15 14						15 41		
Didcot Parkway	a	15 20		15 12			15 37	15 49		
	d	15 25					15 38	15 55		
Appleford	d									
Culham	d							16 01		
Radley	d							16 03		
Oxford	a	15 44			15 34		15 50	16 16	16 05	
	d				15 36				16 07	
Islip	d									
Bicester Town	a									
Tackley	d									
Heyford	d									
Kings Sutton	d									
Banbury	a				15 53				16 23	
Leamington Spa 8	a				16 10				16 40	
Coventry	a				16 23					
Birmingham International	a				16 37					
Birmingham New Street 12	a				16 48				17 18	

		GW	GW	GW	GW	CH	GW	GW	GW	GW
		◇1	1	◇1	1		1	1	◇1	◇1
		⊐P		⌶					⊐P	⊐P
London Paddington 15 ⊖	d	15 15	15 18	15 22				15 27	15 30	15 36
Ealing Broadway ⊖	d							15 35		
Slough 3	d			15 36				15 59		
Maidenhead 3	d							16 07		
Twyford 3	d						←	16 15		
Reading 7	d	15 43	15 48	15 52			15 53	16 26	15 57	16 02
Reading West	d							→		
Theale	d		15 56							
Aldermaston	d									
Midgham	d									
Thatcham	d		16 04							
Newbury Racecourse	d									
Newbury	a		16 10							
	d		16 10							
Kintbury	d		16 17							
Hungerford	d		16 21							
Bedwyn	a		16 31							
Tilehurst	d						15 57			
Pangbourne	d						16 01			
Goring & Streatley	d						16 06			
Cholsey	d						16 11			
Didcot Parkway	a	15 57					16 19		16 11	16 16
	d						16 25			
Appleford	d									
Culham	d									
Radley	d						16 33			
Oxford	a			16 18			16 43			
	d				16 23	16 26				
Islip	d					16 39				
Bicester Town	a					16 51				
Tackley	d				16 32					
Heyford	d				16 36					
Kings Sutton	d				16 45					
Banbury	a				16 51					
Leamington Spa 8	a									
Coventry	a									
Birmingham International	a									
Birmingham New Street 12	a									

		XC FX	XC FO	GW	GW	GW	GW	XC	GW	GW
		◇1	◇1	1	1	◇1	1	◇1	1	1
									A	B
		⌶	⌶			⊐P		⌶		
London Paddington 15 ⊖	d					15 52			15 57	15 57
Ealing Broadway ⊖	d								16 05	16 05
Slough 3	d								16 28	16 28
Maidenhead 3	d								16 35	16 35
Twyford 3	d						←		16 43	16 44
Reading 7	d	16 10	16 10	16 12		16u22	16 26	16 40	16 54	16 55
Reading West	d			16 14					→	→
Theale	d			16 20						
Aldermaston	d			16 25						
Midgham	d			16 29						
Thatcham	d			16 34						
Newbury Racecourse	d			16 38						
Newbury	a			16 44						
	d				17 08					
Kintbury	d				17 14					
Hungerford	d				17 19					
Bedwyn	a				17 28					
Tilehurst	d						16 30			
Pangbourne	d						16 34			
Goring & Streatley	d						16 39			
Cholsey	d						16 44			
Didcot Parkway	a						16 50			
	d						16 56			
Appleford	d						17 01			
Culham	d						17 04			
Radley	d						17 08			
Oxford	a	16 33	16 33			16 47	17 17	17 04		
	d	16 35	16 36					17 07		
Islip	d									
Bicester Town	a									
Tackley	d									
Heyford	d									
Kings Sutton	d									
Banbury	a	16 53	16 53					17 28		
Leamington Spa 8	a	17 12	17 12					17 46		
Coventry	a	17 24	17 24							
Birmingham International	a	17 37	17 37							
Birmingham New Street 12	a	17 49	17 49					18 18		

		GW	GW	GW	GW	GW	GW	GW	GW	GW
		R 1	1	◇1	1	1	1	R 1	1	◇1
					A	B				
		⊐P		⌶				⊐P		⊐P
London Paddington 15 ⊖	d	16 15	16 18	16 22			16 25	16 30		16 36
Ealing Broadway ⊖	d						16 33			
Slough 3	d			16 38			16 58			
Maidenhead 3	d						17 05			
Twyford 3	d				←	←	17 13			
Reading 7	d	16 44	16 48	16 52	16 54	16 55	17 23	16 57		17 04
Reading West	d						→			
Theale	d		16 56							
Aldermaston	d		17 01							
Midgham	d									
Thatcham	d		17 08							
Newbury Racecourse	d									
Newbury	a		17 14							17 18
	d		17 24							17 19
Kintbury	d		→							
Hungerford	d									
Bedwyn	a									17a28
Tilehurst	d				16 58	16 58				
Pangbourne	d				17 03	17 03				
Goring & Streatley	d				17 08	17 08				
Cholsey	d				17 14	17 13				
Didcot Parkway	a	16 59			17 20	17 20		17 12		
	d				17 26	17 26			17 15	
Appleford	d				→	→				
Culham	d									
Radley	d									
Oxford	a			17 22					17 30	
	d									
Islip	d									
Bicester Town	a									
Tackley	d									
Heyford	d									
Kings Sutton	d									
Banbury	a									
Leamington Spa 8	a									
Coventry	a									
Birmingham International	a									
Birmingham New Street 12	a									

A from 10 March

B until 7 March

For complete service between Banbury and Leamington (Birmingham), please refer to table 71

Table 116

Mondays to Fridays

17 February to 24 March

London and Reading - Bedwyn, Oxford, Bicester, Banbury and Birmingham

Network Diagram - refer to first Page of Table 116

Station		GW	XC	CH	GW	GW	GW	GW	GW	GW
		1	◇1		1	1	1	◇1	1	R 1
					A	B				
			🍴							🍴
London Paddington 15 ⊖	d							16 49		17 00
Ealing Broadway ⊖	d									
Slough 3	d							17 05		
Maidenhead 3	d									
Twyford 3	d								←	
Reading 7	d		17 09				17 12	17 21	17 23	17 26
Reading West	d						17 14			
Theale	d						17 20			
Aldermaston	d						17 25			
Midgham	d						17 29			
Thatcham	d						17 34			
Newbury Racecourse	d	←					17 38			
Newbury	a	17 14					17 44			
	d	17 24								
Kintbury	d	17 31								
Hungerford	d	17 35								
Bedwyn	a	17 46								
Tilehurst	d								17 27	
Pangbourne	d								17 32	
Goring & Streatley	d								17 37	
Cholsey	d				←	←			17 42	
Didcot Parkway	a				17 20	17 20		17 36	17 49	17 40
	d				17 26	17 26		17 38	18 05	
Appleford	d				17 31	17 31				
Culham	d				17 33	17 33			18 11	
Radley	d				17 37	17 37			18 15	
Oxford	a		17 34		17 44	17 44		17 51	18 23	
	d		17 36	17 45	17 46	17 46				
Islip	d			17 58						
Bicester Town	a			18 10						
Tackley	d				17 55	17 55				
Heyford	d				17 59	17 59				
Kings Sutton	d				18 08	18 08				
Banbury	a		17 54		18 15	18 15				
Leamington Spa 8	a		18 11							
Coventry	a		18 24							
Birmingham International	a		18 37							
Birmingham New Street 12	a		18 49							

Station		GW	GW	XC	GW	GW	GW	GW	GW	GW
		◇1	◇1	◇1	R 1	1	◇1	1	1	R 1
					C					
		🍴	🍴	🍴	🍴		🍴			🍴
London Paddington 15 ⊖	d	17 03	17 06		17 15	17 18	17 22		17 24	17 30
Ealing Broadway ⊖	d								17 33	
Slough 3	d								17 58	
Maidenhead 3	d					17 41			18 10	
Twyford 3	d		17 30					←	18 17	
Reading 7	d	17u30	17 39	17 40	17 42	17 55 →	17 50	17 55	18 29 →	17 56
Reading West	d									
Theale	d		17 48							
Aldermaston	d									
Midgham	d									
Thatcham	d		17 58							
Newbury Racecourse	d									
Newbury	a	17 47	18 04							
	d		18 05							
Kintbury	d		18 13							
Hungerford	d		18 19							
Bedwyn	a		18 26							
Tilehurst	d							17 59		
Pangbourne	d							18 04		
Goring & Streatley	d							18 10		
Cholsey	d							18 15		
Didcot Parkway	a				17 56			18 22		18 09
	d							18 25		
Appleford	d									
Culham	d									
Radley	d							18 33		
Oxford	a			18 05			18 15	18 45		
	d			18 07						
Islip	d									
Bicester Town	a									
Tackley	d									
Heyford	d									
Kings Sutton	d									
Banbury	a			18 25						
Leamington Spa 8	a			18 45						
Coventry	a									
Birmingham International	a									
Birmingham New Street 12	a			19 18						

Station		GW	GW	XC	GW	GW	GW	GW	GW	GW
		◇1	1	◇1	1	1	◇1	◇1	R 1	1
									D	
		🍴		🍴			🍴	🍴	🍴	
London Paddington 15 ⊖	d	17 33				17 35	17 42	17 49	18 00	
Ealing Broadway ⊖	d									
Slough 3	d									
Maidenhead 3	d					17 58		18 09		
Twyford 3	d					18 07				←
Reading 7	d	18 01		18 10	18 12	18 20		18 22	18 27	18 29
Reading West	d				18 14					
Theale	d				18 20					
Aldermaston	d				18 25					
Midgham	d				18 29					
Thatcham	d				18 34					
Newbury Racecourse	d				18 38					
Newbury	a	18 15			18 44					
	d		18 26							
Kintbury	d		18 32							
Hungerford	d		18 37							
Bedwyn	a		18 46							
Tilehurst	d					18 25				18 34
Pangbourne	d					18 30				18 39
Goring & Streatley	d					18 35				18 44
Cholsey	d					18 41				18 50
Didcot Parkway	a					18 47	18 19		18 41	18 58
	d					18 47				19 03
Appleford	d									19 08
Culham	d									
Radley	d					18 55				
Oxford	a			18 34		19 07		18 47		19 18
	d			18 36						19 19
Islip	d									
Bicester Town	a									
Tackley	d									19 27
Heyford	d									19 32
Kings Sutton	d									19 44
Banbury	a			18 54						19 50
Leamington Spa 8	a			19 11						
Coventry	a			19 23						
Birmingham International	a			19 37						
Birmingham New Street 12	a			19 48						

Station		GW	XC	GW	GW	GW	GW	CH	GW FO	GW FX
		◇1	◇1	R 1	1	1	◇1		1	1
							E			
		🍴	🍴	🍴			🍴			
London Paddington 15 ⊖	d	18 05		18 15	18 15	18 18	18 22		18 25	18 25
Ealing Broadway ⊖	d				18 23				18 33	18 33
Slough 3	d				18 47				18 59	18 59
Maidenhead 3	d				18 57	18 40			19 10	19 10
Twyford 3	d	18 28			19 05	18 48			19 18	19 18
Reading 7	d	18 37	18 40	18 42	19 19 →	18 57 →	18 51		19 27 →	19 27 →
Reading West	d									
Theale	d	18 46								
Aldermaston	d									
Midgham	d									
Thatcham	d	18 56								
Newbury Racecourse	d									
Newbury	a	19 02								
	d	19 03								
Kintbury	d	19 10								
Hungerford	d	19 17								
Bedwyn	a	19 24								
Tilehurst	d									
Pangbourne	d									
Goring & Streatley	d									
Cholsey	d									
Didcot Parkway	a			18 57						
	d									
Appleford	d									
Culham	d									
Radley	d									
Oxford	a		19 11				19 20			
	d		19 13					19 30		
Islip	d							19 43		
Bicester Town	a							19 55		
Tackley	d									
Heyford	d									
Kings Sutton	d									
Banbury	a		19 30							
Leamington Spa 8	a		19 49							
Coventry	a									
Birmingham International	a									
Birmingham New Street 12	a		20 18							

A from 10 March
B until 7 March
C The Red Dragon
D The Bristolian
E The Cathedrals Express

For complete service between Banbury and Leamington (Birmingham), please refer to table 71

Table 116

Mondays to Fridays

17 February to 24 March

London and Reading - Bedwyn, Oxford, Bicester, Banbury and Birmingham

Network Diagram - refer to first Page of Table 116

		GW	GW	GW	GW	XC	GW	GW	GW	GW
		R 1	1	◇1	1	◇1	1	◇1	1	1
London Paddington 15 ⊖	d	18 30		18 35				18 47		
Ealing Broadway ⊖	d									
Slough 3	d									
Maidenhead 3	d									
Twyford 3	d		←					19 10	←	
Reading 7	d	18 55	18 57	19 03		19 09	19 12	19 19	19 19	19 21
Reading West	d						19 15			
Theale	d						19 20			19 28
Aldermaston	d						19 25			
Midgham	d						19 29			
Thatcham	d						19 34			19 39
Newbury Racecourse	d						19 39			
Newbury	a			19 17			19 44			19 56
	d			19 19	19 27					19 56
Kintbury	d				19 33					20 03
Hungerford	d			19 29	19 38					20 08
Bedwyn	a			19 36	19 45					20 18
Tilehurst	d		19 01						19 24	
Pangbourne	d		19 06						19 28	
Goring & Streatley	d		19 12						19 33	
Cholsey	d		19 17						19 38	
Didcot Parkway	a	19 11	19 26					19 33	19 47	
	d		19 27						19 56	
Appleford	d									
Culham	d								20 03	
Radley	d		19 34							
Oxford	a		19 46			19 34			20 16	
	d					19 36				
Islip	d									
Bicester Town	a									
Tackley	d									
Heyford	d									
Kings Sutton	d									
Banbury	a					19 54				
Leamington Spa 8	a					20 12				
Coventry	a					20 24				
Birmingham International	a					20 37				
Birmingham New Street 12	a					20 48				

		GW	GW	GW FO	GW FX	GW	XC	GW	GW FO	GW FX
		◇1	R 1	1	1	R 1 A ✕	◇1	1	1	R 1
London Paddington 15 ⊖	d	18 50	19 00			19 03			19 12	19 15
Ealing Broadway ⊖	d									
Slough 3	d	19 07								
Maidenhead 3	d									
Twyford 3	d			←	←					
Reading 7	d	19 23	19 27	19 27	19 27	19u33	19 40	19 42	19 43	19 42
Reading West	d							19 44	→	
Theale	d							19 50		
Aldermaston	d							19 55		
Midgham	d							19 59		
Thatcham	d							20 04		
Newbury Racecourse	d							20 08		
Newbury	a					19 50		20 11		
	d							20 33		
Kintbury	d							20 39		
Hungerford	d							20 43		
Bedwyn	a							20 53		
Tilehurst	d			19 31	19 31					
Pangbourne	d			19 35	19 35					
Goring & Streatley	d			19 40	19 40					
Cholsey	d			19 46	19 46					
Didcot Parkway	a		19 42	19 53	19 53					19 56
	d			20 01	20 08					
Appleford	d				20 13					
Culham	d									
Radley	d				20 18					
Oxford	a	19 49		20 18	20 27		20 06			
	d						20 07			
Islip	d									
Bicester Town	a									
Tackley	d									
Heyford	d									
Kings Sutton	d									
Banbury	a						20 27			
Leamington Spa 8	a						20 45			
Coventry	a									
Birmingham International	a									
Birmingham New Street 12	a						21 22			

		GW FO	GW	GW FX	GW FO	GW	GW	GW	XC	GW
		1	1	◇1	◇1	1	R 1	1	◇1	◇1
London Paddington 15 ⊖	d		19 18	19 22	19 22	19 27	19 30			19 45
Ealing Broadway ⊖	d					19 35				
Slough 3	d			19 36	19 36	19 59				
Maidenhead 3	d		19 40			20 09				
Twyford 3	d	←	19 48			20 17		←		
Reading 7	d	19 43	19 57	19 52	19 52	20 25	19 57	19 57	20 10	20 12
Reading West	d		→			→				
Theale	d									
Aldermaston	d									
Midgham	d									
Thatcham	d									
Newbury Racecourse	d									
Newbury	a									20 28
	d									
Kintbury	d									
Hungerford	d									
Bedwyn	a									
Tilehurst	d							20 01		
Pangbourne	d							20 06		
Goring & Streatley	d							20 11		
Cholsey	d							20 16		
Didcot Parkway	a	20 00					20 12	20 22		
	d	20 09						20 25		
Appleford	d	20 13								
Culham	d									
Radley	d	20 18						20 33		
Oxford	a	20 28		20 18	20 21			20 43	20 34	
	d								20 36	
Islip	d									
Bicester Town	a									
Tackley	d									
Heyford	d									
Kings Sutton	d									
Banbury	a								20 52	
Leamington Spa 8	a								21 10	
Coventry	a								21 23	
Birmingham International	a								21 37	
Birmingham New Street 12	a								21 49	

		GW	GW	CH	GW	GW	GW	XC	GW	GW
		◇1	◇1		1	1	◇1	◇1	◇1 Ø	1
London Paddington 15 ⊖	d	19 48	19 50			19 57	20 00		20 15	
Ealing Broadway ⊖	d					20 05				
Slough 3	d		20 06			20 27				
Maidenhead 3	d	20 06				20 34				
Twyford 3	d				←	20 42				
Reading 7	d	20 18	20 22		20 25	20 53	20 27	20 40	20 41	20 41
Reading West	d					→				20 44
Theale	d									20 50
Aldermaston	d									20 55
Midgham	d									20 58
Thatcham	d									21 03
Newbury Racecourse	d									21 08
Newbury	a									21 13
	d									
Kintbury	d									
Hungerford	d									
Bedwyn	a									
Tilehurst	d				20 29					
Pangbourne	d				20 34					
Goring & Streatley	d				20 39					
Cholsey	d				20 44					
Didcot Parkway	a	20 33			20 51		20 41		20 56	
	d				20 57					
Appleford	d									
Culham	d									
Radley	d				21 04					
Oxford	a		20 52		21 15			21 05		
	d		20 55	21 00				21 09		
Islip	d			21 13						
Bicester Town	a			21 25						
Tackley	d		21 04							
Heyford	d		21 08							
Kings Sutton	d		21 17							
Banbury	a		21 23					21 31		
Leamington Spa 8	a							21 51		
Coventry	a									
Birmingham International	a									
Birmingham New Street 12	a							22 17		

A Restaurant for customers joining at Pad, Reading + Newbury. The Armada

For complete service between Banbury and Leamington (Birmingham), please refer to table 71

Table 116

Mondays to Fridays

17 February to 24 March

London and Reading - Bedwyn, Oxford, Bicester, Banbury and Birmingham

Network Diagram - refer to first Page of Table 116

		GW	GW	GW	GW	GW	GW	XC	GW	GW	GW	GW	GW	XC	GW	GW	GW	GW	GW
		◇1	1	1	1	◇1	1	◇1	◇1	◇1	1	1	◇1	◇1	◇1	1	1	1	◇1
		🚲				☕			☕				☕						☕
London Paddington 15 ⊖	d	20 20			20 27	20 35			20 45	20 48		20 57	21 15		21 18			21 27	21 45
Ealing Broadway ⊖	d				20 35							21 05						21 35	
Slough 3	d	20 36			20 57					21 05		21 27			21 35			22 07	
Maidenhead 3	d				21 04							21 34						22 15	
Twyford 3	d			←	21 12						←	21 42				←		22 23	
Reading 7	d	20 51		20 53	21 23	21 02		21 10	21 13	21 20	21 23	21 57	21 41	21 46	21 50	21 57	22 01	22 32	22 11
Reading West	d				→							→					22 03	→	
Theale	d																22 10		
Aldermaston	d																22 15		
Midgham	d																22 18		
Thatcham	d																22 23		
Newbury Racecourse	d																22 28		
Newbury	a					21 16											22 31		
	d						21 24										22 31		
Kintbury	d						21 30										22 37		
Hungerford	d						21 35										22 42		
Bedwyn	a						21 45										22 52		
Tilehurst	d			20 57							21 27					22 02			
Pangbourne	d			21 01							21 31					22 05			
Goring & Streatley	d			21 06							21 36					22 09			
Cholsey	d			21 11							21 41					22 14			
Didcot Parkway	a			21 19					21 27		21 52		22 01			22 24			22 31
	d			21 25							21 52					22 25			
Appleford	d																		
Culham	d																		
Radley	d			21 33							21 59								
Oxford	a	21 17		21 44				21 34		21 51	22 12			22 28	22 18	22 41			
	d		21 41					21 36						22 30					
Islip	d																		
Bicester Town	a																		
Tackley	d		21 50																
Heyford	d		21 54																
Kings Sutton	d		22 03																
Banbury	a		22 09					21 52						22 51					
Leamington Spa 8	a							22 10						23 09					
Coventry	a							22 22						23 24					
Birmingham International	a							22 33						23 34					
Birmingham New Street 12	a							22 45						00 02					

		GW FO	GW FX	GW	CH FO	GW	GW FO	GW FX	GW FO	GW FX	GW FO	GW FX	GW	GW FX	GW FO	GW FO	GW FX	GW FO	GW FX
		◇1	◇1	1		1	1	1	◇1	◇1	◇1	◇1	1	1	1	1	1	◇1	◇1
		🚲	☕						☕	☕								☕	☕
London Paddington 15 ⊖	d	21 48	21 48				21 57	21 57	22 15	22 15	22 18	22 18				22 27	22 27	22 45	22 45
Ealing Broadway ⊖	d						22 05	22 05								22 35	22 35		
Slough 3	d	22 04	22 04				22 30	22 42			22 35	22 39				23 11	23 11		
Maidenhead 3	d						22 42	22 53			22 42	22 47				23 23	23 23		
Twyford 3	d					←	22 50	23 01						←	←	23 31	23 31		
Reading 7	d	22 25	22 25			22 32	23 10	23 10	22 42	22 54	22 56	23 01	23 03	23 10	23 10	23 41	23 40	23 11	23 23
Reading West	d						→	→					23 05			→	→		
Theale	d												23 11						
Aldermaston	d												23 16						
Midgham	d												23 20						
Thatcham	d												23 25						
Newbury Racecourse	d												23 29						
Newbury	a												23 32						
	d												23 32						
Kintbury	d												23 39						
Hungerford	d												23 43						
Bedwyn	a												23 53						
Tilehurst	d					22 35								23 14	23 14				
Pangbourne	d					22 40								23 19	23 19				
Goring & Streatley	d					22 43								23 22	23 22				
Cholsey	d					22 48								23 27	23 27				
Didcot Parkway	a					22 58			23 02	23 13				23 37	23 37			23 42	23 42
	d					22 58								23 38	23 38				
Appleford	d					23 03													
Culham	d					23 05													
Radley	d					23 09													
Oxford	a	22 47	22 47			23 22					23 27	23 29		23 54	23 56				
	d			23 06	23 12														
Islip	d				23 25														
Bicester Town	a				23 37														
Tackley	d			23 15															
Heyford	d			23 19															
Kings Sutton	d			23 28															
Banbury	a			23 34															
Leamington Spa 8	a																		
Coventry	a																		
Birmingham International	a																		
Birmingham New Street 12	a																		

For complete service between Banbury and Leamington (Birmingham), please refer to table 71

Table 116

London and Reading - Bedwyn, Oxford, Bicester, Banbury and Birmingham

Mondays to Fridays

17 February to 24 March

Network Diagram - refer to first Page of Table 116

Station		GW FO ◇[1]	GW FX ◇[1]	GW FX [1]	GW FO [1]	GW ◇[1]	CH	GW ◇[1] ☕	GW [1]	GW FO [1]	GW [1]
London Paddington [15] ⊖	d	22 48	22 48			23 18		23 30	23 33	23 42	
Ealing Broadway ⊖	d								23 41		
Slough [3]	d	23 05	23 08			23 38			23 57	00 01	
Maidenhead [3]	d	23 12	23 17			23 46			00 05	00 10	
Twyford [3]	d	23 20	23 26	←	←				00 13		←
Reading [7]	d	23 28	23 34	23 40	23 41	00 04		00 09	00 27	00 25	00 27
Reading West	d								↦		
Theale	d										
Aldermaston	d										
Midgham	d										
Thatcham	d										
Newbury Racecourse	d										
Newbury	a										
	d										
Kintbury	d										
Hungerford	d										
Bedwyn	a										
Tilehurst	d			23 44	23 44						00 33
Pangbourne	d			23 48	23 48						00 37
Goring & Streatley	d			23 52	23 52						00 41
Cholsey	d			23 57	23 57						00 46
Didcot Parkway	a			00 07	00 07			00 29		00 44	00 56
	d			00 07	00 08					00 44	00 56
Appleford	d										01 00
Culham	d										01 03
Radley	d			00 14	00 14						01 07
Oxford	a	23 56	00 01	00 27	00 27	00 35				01 02	01 18
	d						00 38				
Islip	d										
Bicester Town	a										
Tackley	d						00 48				
Heyford	d						00 53				
Kings Sutton	d						01 01				
Banbury	a						01 11				
Leamington Spa [8]	a										
Coventry	a										
Birmingham International	a										
Birmingham New Street [12]	a										

For complete service between Banbury and Leamington (Birmingham), please refer to table 71

Table 116

London and Reading - Bedwyn, Oxford, Bicester, Banbury and Birmingham

Mondays to Fridays

31 March to 16 May

Network Diagram - refer to first Page of Table 116

		GW	GW	GW	CH	GW	GW	GW	GW	GW	GW	GW	GW	CH	GW	GW	GW	GW	GW
		MX	MO	MX	MX	MX	MO	MO	MX	MX	MX								
		1	1	◇1		◇1	◇1		1	1	◇1	1	1		1	1	1	◇1	1
						☕	☕	🚌										☕	
London Paddington 15 ⊖	d										00 22					05 12	05 17	05 19	
Ealing Broadway ⊖	d																05 25		
Slough 3	d										00 41					05 30	05 51		
Maidenhead 3	d									00 05							05 59		
Twyford 3	d									00 13							06 07		
Reading 7	d			00 04		00 09	00 16		00 20	00 27	01 01		05 15			05 50	06 18	05 53	05 54
Reading West	d								00s23				05 17				→		
Theale	d								00s29				05 24						
Aldermaston	d								00s34				05 29						
Midgham	d								00s37				05 32						
Thatcham	d								00s42				05 37						
Newbury Racecourse	d								00s47				05 42						
Newbury	a								00 52				05 45						
	d												05 45						
Kintbury	d												05 51						
Hungerford	d												05 56						
Bedwyn	a												06 06						
Tilehurst	d									00 33									05 58
Pangbourne	d									00 37									06 03
Goring & Streatley	d		00 04							00 41									06 08
Cholsey	d		00 09							00 46									06 14
Didcot Parkway	a		00 17			00 29	00s33			00 56	01 19					06 05		06 08	06 21
	d	00 07						00 45		00 56	01 19					06 06			06 25
Appleford	d									01 00									
Culham	d									01 03									06 31
Radley	d	00 14						01 00		01 07									06 35
Oxford	a	00 27		00 35				01 15		01 18	01 34					06 20			06 43
	d				00 38							05 18		05 45	05 45				06 45
Islip	d													05 58					
Bicester Town	a													06 10					
Tackley	d				00 48							05 27			05 54				06 53
Heyford	d				00 53							05 32			05 58				06 58
Kings Sutton	d				01 01							05 40			06 07				07 06
Banbury	a				01 11							05 47			06 14				07 14
Leamington Spa 8	a																		
Coventry	a																		
Birmingham International	a																		
Birmingham New Street 12	a																		

		XC	GW	GW	GW	XC	GW	GW	CH	GW	GW	GW	XC	GW	GW	GW	GW	GW	GW
		◇1	1	◇1	1	◇1	1	◇1		1	1	◇1	◇1	1	1	1	◇1	◇1	1
																		A	
		🍴				🍴						☕	🍴				☕	☕	
London Paddington 15 ⊖	d			05 45			05 57	06 20				06 30			06 48	06 57	07 00	07 06	
Ealing Broadway ⊖	d						06 05									07 05			
Slough 3	d			06 01			06 29	06 35							07 02	07 29			
Maidenhead 3	d						06 37									07 37			
Twyford 3	d				←		06 45				←					07 45			
Reading 7	d	06 10	06 13	06 17	06 18	06 40	06 53	06 51		06 52	06 53	06 56	07 09	07 10	07 19	07 53	07 29	07 33	07 33
Reading West	d		06 15				→			06 54				07 12		→			
Theale	d		06 21							07 00				07 18					
Aldermaston	d		06 26							07 05				07 23					
Midgham	d		06 30							07 09				07 27					
Thatcham	d		06 35							07 14				07 32					
Newbury Racecourse	d		06 39							07 18				07 36					
Newbury	a		06 45							07 21				07 42				07 47	
	d									07 21									
Kintbury	d									07 28									
Hungerford	d									07 32									
Bedwyn	a									07 42									
Tilehurst	d				06 22						06 57				07 26				
Pangbourne	d				06 27						07 01				07 30				
Goring & Streatley	d				06 33						07 06				07 36				
Cholsey	d				06 39						07 11				07 41				
Didcot Parkway	a				06 47			07 06			07 19	07 10			07 48		07 43		07 52
	d				06 47			07 08			07 25				07 50				08 08
Appleford	d										07 30								08 13
Culham	d										07 32								08 15
Radley	d										07 36								08 19
Oxford	a	06 34		06 51	07 02	07 05		07 22			07 49		07 35		08 02				08 31
	d	06 36				07 08			07 33				07 36						
Islip	d								07 46										
Bicester Town	a								07 59										
Tackley	d																		
Heyford	d																		
Kings Sutton	d																		
Banbury	a	06 52				07 25							07 55						
Leamington Spa 8	a	07 10				07 42							08 12						
Coventry	a	07 23											08 25						
Birmingham International	a	07 37											08 37						
Birmingham New Street 12	a	07 48				08 14							08 48						

A The Devon Express

For complete service between Banbury and Leamington (Birmingham), please refer to table 71

Table 116

Mondays to Fridays

31 March to 16 May

London and Reading - Bedwyn, Oxford, Bicester, Banbury and Birmingham

Network Diagram - refer to first Page of Table 116

		XC	GW	GW	GW	CH	GW	GW	GW	XC	GW	GW	GW	GW	GW	GW	GW	XC	GW
		◇1	◇1	1	1		1	1	◇1	◇1	1	1	1	1	1	◇1	1	◇1	◇1
		trolley	cup						cup	trolley						cup		trolley	cup
London Paddington 15 ⊖	d		07 15	07 18	07 21			07 27	07 36			07 50	07 50		07 57	08 00			08 15
Ealing Broadway ⊖	d							07 35							08 05				
Slough 3	d				07 36			07 59				08 06	08 06		08 29				
Maidenhead 3	d							08 07							08 38				
Twyford 3	d						←	08 15						←	08 46				
Reading 7	d	07 41	07 42	07 48	07 52		07 53	08 24	08 02	08 09	08 12	08 22	08 22	08 24	08 55	08 27	08 34	08 40	08 45
Reading West	d							→			08 14				→				
Theale	d			07 56							08 20						08 41		
Aldermaston	d			08 01							08 25						08 46		
Midgham	d										08 29								
Thatcham	d			08 08							08 34						08 53		
Newbury Racecourse	d										08 38								
Newbury	a			08 13							08 44						08 59		
	d			08 13													08 59		
Kintbury	d			08 20													09 05		
Hungerford	d			08 24													09 09		
Bedwyn	a			08 34													09 21		
Tilehurst	d						07 57							08 27					
Pangbourne	d						08 01							08 31					
Goring & Streatley	d						08 06							08 36					
Cholsey	d						08 11							08 41					
Didcot Parkway	a		07 56				08 20		08 16					08 50		08 40			08 58
	d						08 25							08 55					
Appleford	d													09 00					
Culham	d													09 01					
Radley	d						08 33							09 06					
Oxford	a	08 07			08 19		08 44			08 34		08 49	08 49	09 16				09 04	
	d	08 09				08 35				08 36		08 53						09 07	
Islip	d					08 48													
Bicester Town	a					09 01													
Tackley	d											09 01							
Heyford	d											09 06							
Kings Sutton	d											09 15							
Banbury	a	08 26								08 52		09 22						09 25	
Leamington Spa 8	a	08 43								09 10								09 42	
Coventry	a									09 23									
Birmingham International	a									09 37									
Birmingham New Street 12	a	09 18								09 48								10 18	

		GW	GW	GW	GW	GW	XC	GW	GW	CH	GW	XC	GW	GW	GW	GW	GW	GW	GW
		1	◇1	1	1	◇1	◇1	1	◇1		1	◇1	1	◇1	1	◇1	1	1	◇1
			cup			cup	trolley					trolley		cup		trolley			Ø
London Paddington 15 ⊖	d	08 18	08 22		08 27	08 30			08 51				08 55	09 15	09 18	09 21		09 27	09 30
Ealing Broadway ⊖	d				08 35								09 03					09 35	
Slough 3	d		08 36		08 59				09 06				09 27			09 36		09 57	
Maidenhead 3	d				09 06								09 35					10 04	
Twyford 3	d			←	09 17						←		09 43				←	10 12	
Reading 7	d	08 48	08 52	08 55	09 25	08 57	09 09	09 14	09 22		09 25	09 40	09 53	09 42	09 48	09 52	09 53	10 23	09 57
Reading West	d				→			09 16					→					→	
Theale	d	08 56						09 22							09 56				
Aldermaston	d							09 27											
Midgham	d							09 31											
Thatcham	d	09 04						09 36							10 04				
Newbury Racecourse	d							09 40											
Newbury	a	09 14						09 46							10 10				
	d														10 10				
Kintbury	d														10 17				
Hungerford	d														10 21				
Bedwyn	a														10 32				
Tilehurst	d			08 59							09 28						09 57		
Pangbourne	d			09 03							09 33						10 01		
Goring & Streatley	d			09 08							09 38						10 06		
Cholsey	d			09 13							09 43						10 11		
Didcot Parkway	a			09 21		09 12			09 37		09 50			09 56			10 18		10 11
	d			09 25					09 38		09 56						10 25		
Appleford	d																		
Culham	d										10 03								
Radley	d			09 33							10 05								
Oxford	a		09 20	09 45			09 34		09 53		10 18	10 04				10 20	10 43		
	d						09 36			10 00		10 07							
Islip	d									10 13									
Bicester Town	a									10 25									
Tackley	d																		
Heyford	d																		
Kings Sutton	d																		
Banbury	a						09 55					10 28							
Leamington Spa 8	a						10 11					10 46							
Coventry	a						10 24												
Birmingham International	a						10 37												
Birmingham New Street 12	a						10 48					11 18							

For complete service between Banbury and Leamington (Birmingham), please refer to table 71

Table 116

Mondays to Fridays

31 March to 16 May

London and Reading - Bedwyn, Oxford, Bicester, Banbury and Birmingham

Network Diagram - refer to first Page of Table 116

		GW	XC	GW	GW	CH	GW	XC	GW	GW
			■							
		◇1	1	1	◇1		1	◇1	1	◇1
		🍽	🛒					🛒		🍽
London Paddington 15 ⊖	d	09 36			09 50				09 57	10 15
Ealing Broadway ⊖	d								10 05	
Slough 3	d				10 06				10 27	
Maidenhead 3	d								10 34	
Twyford 3	d						←		10 42	
Reading 7	d	10 03	10 10	10 12	10 22		10 23	10 40	10 53	10 43
Reading West	d			10 14					→	
Theale	d			10 20						
Aldermaston	d			10 25						
Midgham	d			10 29						
Thatcham	d			10 34						
Newbury Racecourse	d			10 38						
Newbury	a			10 44						
	d									
Kintbury	d									
Hungerford	d									
Bedwyn	a									
Tilehurst	d						10 27			
Pangbourne	d						10 31			
Goring & Streatley	d						10 36			
Cholsey	d						10 41			
Didcot Parkway	a	10 17					10 49			10 58
	d						10 55			
Appleford	d									
Culham	d									
Radley	d						11 03			
Oxford	a		10 34		10 47		11 14	11 04		
	d		10 36			11 00		11 07		
Islip	d					11 13				
Bicester Town	a					11 25				
Tackley	d									
Heyford	d									
Kings Sutton	d									
Banbury	a		10 52					11 24		
Leamington Spa 8	a		11 10					11 41		
Coventry	a		11 23							
Birmingham International	a		11 37							
Birmingham New Street 12	a		11 48					12 18		

		GW	GW	GW	GW	GW	XC	GW	GW	GW
		1	◇1	1	1	◇1	◇1	1	1	◇1
			🍽			⊘	🛒			
London Paddington 15 ⊖	d	10 18	10 22		10 27	10 30				10 50
Ealing Broadway ⊖	d				10 35					
Slough 3	d		10 36		10 57					11 06
Maidenhead 3	d				11 04					
Twyford 3	d			←	11 12					
Reading 7	d	10 48	10 52	10 53	11 23	10 57	11 10		11 12	11 21
Reading West	d				→				11 14	
Theale	d	10 56							11 20	
Aldermaston	d								11 25	
Midgham	d								11 29	
Thatcham	d	11 04							11 34	
Newbury Racecourse	d								11 38	
Newbury	a	11 10							11 44	
	d	11 10								
Kintbury	d	11 17								
Hungerford	d	11 21								
Bedwyn	a	11 32								
Tilehurst	d			10 57						
Pangbourne	d			11 01						
Goring & Streatley	d			11 06						
Cholsey	d			11 11						
Didcot Parkway	a			11 19		11 12				11 37
	d			11 25						11 38
Appleford	d									
Culham	d									
Radley	d									
Oxford	a		11 18	11 43			11 32			11 50
	d						11 36	11 45		
Islip	d									
Bicester Town	a									
Tackley	d							11 54		
Heyford	d							11 58		
Kings Sutton	d							12 07		
Banbury	a						11 51	12 13		
Leamington Spa 8	a						12 10			
Coventry	a						12 24			
Birmingham International	a						12 37			
Birmingham New Street 12	a						12 48			

		GW	XC	GW	GW	GW	GW	GW	GW	GW
		1	◇1	1	◇1	1	◇1	1	1	◇1
			🛒		🍽		🛒			🍽
London Paddington 15 ⊖	d			10 57	11 15	11 18	11 20		11 27	11 30
Ealing Broadway ⊖	d			11 05					11 35	
Slough 3	d			11 27			11 36		11 57	
Maidenhead 3	d			11 34					12 04	
Twyford 3	d	←		11 42				←	12 13	
Reading 7	d	11 23	11 40	11 53	11 44	11 48	11 52	11 53	12 23	11 57
Reading West	d			→					→	
Theale	d					11 56				
Aldermaston	d									
Midgham	d									
Thatcham	d					12 04				
Newbury Racecourse	d									
Newbury	a					12 10				
	d					12 10				
Kintbury	d					12 17				
Hungerford	d					12 21				
Bedwyn	a					12 31				
Tilehurst	d	11 27						11 57		
Pangbourne	d	11 31						12 01		
Goring & Streatley	d	11 36						12 06		
Cholsey	d	11 41						12 11		
Didcot Parkway	a	11 50			11 58			12 21		12 12
	d	11 55						12 25		
Appleford	d									
Culham	d									
Radley	d	12 03								
Oxford	a	12 14	12 04				12 18	12 43		
	d		12 07							
Islip	d									
Bicester Town	a									
Tackley	d									
Heyford	d									
Kings Sutton	d									
Banbury	a		12 24							
Leamington Spa 8	a		12 42							
Coventry	a									
Birmingham International	a									
Birmingham New Street 12	a		13 18							

		GW	XC	GW	GW	GW	XC	GW	GW	GW
							■			
		◇1	◇1	1	◇1	1	1	1	◇1	◇1
		A								
		🍽	🛒		🛒		🛒		🍽	🍽
London Paddington 15 ⊖	d	11 36			11 50			11 57	12 15	12 18
Ealing Broadway ⊖	d							12 05		
Slough 3	d				12 06			12 27		
Maidenhead 3	d							12 34		
Twyford 3	d					←		12 42		
Reading 7	d	12 03	12 10	12 12	12 22	12 23	12 40	12 53	12 42	12 49
Reading West	d			12 14				→		
Theale	d			12 20						12 57
Aldermaston	d			12 25						
Midgham	d			12 29						
Thatcham	d			12 34						13 05
Newbury Racecourse	d			12 38						
Newbury	a			12 44						13 13
	d									13 13
Kintbury	d									
Hungerford	d									13 22
Bedwyn	a									13 30
Tilehurst	d					12 27				
Pangbourne	d					12 31				
Goring & Streatley	d					12 36				
Cholsey	d					12 41				
Didcot Parkway	a	12 17				12 49			12 57	
	d					12 55				
Appleford	d					13 00				
Culham	d									
Radley	d					13 03				
Oxford	a		12 34		12 48	13 14	13 02			
	d		12 36				13 07			
Islip	d									
Bicester Town	a									
Tackley	d									
Heyford	d									
Kings Sutton	d									
Banbury	a		12 52				13 25			
Leamington Spa 8	a		13 10				13 43			
Coventry	a		13 23							
Birmingham International	a		13 37							
Birmingham New Street 12	a		13 49				14 18			

A The Cheltenham Spa Express

For complete service between Banbury and Leamington (Birmingham), please refer to table 71

Table 116

Mondays to Fridays

31 March to 16 May

London and Reading - Bedwyn, Oxford, Bicester, Banbury and Birmingham

Network Diagram - refer to first Page of Table 116

Station		GW ◇1 ✠	CH	GW 1	GW 1	GW ◇1 ⊡	XC ◇1 ✠	GW 1	GW ◇1 ✠	GW 1
London Paddington 15 ⊖	d	12 21			12 27	12 30			12 50	
Ealing Broadway ⊖	d				12 35					
Slough 3	d	12 36			12 57				13 06	
Maidenhead 3	d				13 04					
Twyford 3	d			←	13 12					←
Reading 7	d	12 52		12 53	13 23	12 57	13 10	13 12	13 22	13 23
Reading West	d				↦			13 14		
Theale	d							13 20		
Aldermaston	d							13 25		
Midgham	d							13 29		
Thatcham	d							13 34		
Newbury Racecourse	d							13 38		
Newbury	a							13 44		
	d									
Kintbury	d									
Hungerford	d									
Bedwyn	a									
Tilehurst	d			12 57						13 27
Pangbourne	d			13 01						13 31
Goring & Streatley	d			13 06						13 36
Cholsey	d			13 11						13 41
Didcot Parkway	a			13 19		13 12			13 37	13 48
	d			13 25					13 38	13 55
Appleford	d									
Culham	d									14 01
Radley	d									14 03
Oxford	a	13 20		13 43			13 34		13 50	14 14
	d		13 30				13 36			
Islip	d		13 43							
Bicester Town	a		13 55							
Tackley	d									
Heyford	d									
Kings Sutton	d									
Banbury	a						13 52			
Leamington Spa 8	a						14 10			
Coventry	a						14 23			
Birmingham International	a						14 37			
Birmingham New Street 12	a						14 48			

Station		XC ◇1 ✠	GW 1	GW ◇1 ⊡	GW 1	GW ◇1 ✠	GW 1	GW 1	GW 1	GW ◇1 ⊡
London Paddington 15 ⊖	d		12 57	13 15	13 18	13 21			13 27	13 30
Ealing Broadway ⊖	d		13 05						13 35	
Slough 3	d		13 27			13 36			13 57	
Maidenhead 3	d		13 34						14 04	
Twyford 3	d		13 42					←	14 12	
Reading 7	d	13 40	13 53	13 42	13 48	13 51		13 53	14 23	13 57
Reading West	d		↦						↦	
Theale	d				13 56					
Aldermaston	d									
Midgham	d									
Thatcham	d				14 04					
Newbury Racecourse	d									
Newbury	a				14 10					
	d				14 10					
Kintbury	d				14 17					
Hungerford	d				14 21					
Bedwyn	a				14 32					
Tilehurst	d							13 57		
Pangbourne	d							14 01		
Goring & Streatley	d							14 06		
Cholsey	d							14 11		
Didcot Parkway	a			13 56				14 20		14 12
	d							14 25		
Appleford	d									
Culham	d									
Radley	d									
Oxford	a	14 04				14 18		14 43		
	d	14 07					14 24			
Islip	d									
Bicester Town	a									
Tackley	d						14 33			
Heyford	d						14 37			
Kings Sutton	d						14 46			
Banbury	a	14 25					14 52			
Leamington Spa 8	a	14 41								
Coventry	a									
Birmingham International	a									
Birmingham New Street 12	a	15 18								

Station		GW ◇1 ⊡	XC ◇1 ✠	GW 1	GW ◇1 ✠	CH	GW 1	XC ◇1 ✠	GW 1	GW ◇1 ⊡
London Paddington 15 ⊖	d	13 36			13 50				13 57	14 15
Ealing Broadway ⊖	d								14 05	
Slough 3	d				14 06				14 27	
Maidenhead 3	d								14 34	
Twyford 3	d						←		14 42	
Reading 7	d	14 03	14 10	14 12	14 22		14 23	14 40	14 55	14 44
Reading West	d			14 14					↦	
Theale	d			14 20						
Aldermaston	d			14 25						
Midgham	d			14 29						
Thatcham	d			14 34						
Newbury Racecourse	d			14 38						
Newbury	a			14 44						
	d									
Kintbury	d									
Hungerford	d									
Bedwyn	a									
Tilehurst	d						14 27			
Pangbourne	d						14 31			
Goring & Streatley	d						14 36			
Cholsey	d						14 41			
Didcot Parkway	a	14 17					14 49			14 58
	d						14 55			
Appleford	d									
Culham	d									
Radley	d						15 03			
Oxford	a		14 34		14 48		15 14	15 03		
	d		14 36			15 00		15 07		
Islip	d					15 13				
Bicester Town	a					15 25				
Tackley	d									
Heyford	d									
Kings Sutton	d									
Banbury	a		14 56					15 24		
Leamington Spa 8	a		15 13					15 42		
Coventry	a		15 25							
Birmingham International	a		15 37							
Birmingham New Street 12	a		15 48					16 18		

Station		GW 1	GW ◇1 ✠	GW 1	GW 1	GW ◇1 ⊡	XC ◇1 ✠	GW 1	GW ◇1 ✠	GW 1
London Paddington 15 ⊖	d	14 18	14 21		14 27	14 30			14 50	
Ealing Broadway ⊖	d				14 35					
Slough 3	d		14 36		14 57				15 06	
Maidenhead 3	d				15 04					
Twyford 3	d			←	15 14					←
Reading 7	d	14 48	14 52	14 55	15 23	14 57	15 09	15 12	15 22	15 23
Reading West	d				↦			15 14		
Theale	d	14 56						15 20		
Aldermaston	d							15 25		
Midgham	d							15 29		
Thatcham	d	15 04						15 34		
Newbury Racecourse	d							15 38		
Newbury	a	15 10						15 44		
	d	15 10								
Kintbury	d	15 17								
Hungerford	d	15 21								
Bedwyn	a	15 33								
Tilehurst	d			14 59						15 28
Pangbourne	d			15 04						15 31
Goring & Streatley	d			15 09						15 36
Cholsey	d			15 14						15 41
Didcot Parkway	a			15 20		15 12			15 37	15 49
	d			15 25					15 38	15 55
Appleford	d									
Culham	d									16 01
Radley	d									16 03
Oxford	a		15 18	15 44			15 34		15 50	16 16
	d						15 36			
Islip	d									
Bicester Town	a									
Tackley	d									
Heyford	d									
Kings Sutton	d									
Banbury	a						15 53			
Leamington Spa 8	a						16 10			
Coventry	a						16 23			
Birmingham International	a						16 37			
Birmingham New Street 12	a						16 48			

For complete service between Banbury and Leamington (Birmingham), please refer to table 71

Table 116

Mondays to Fridays

31 March to 16 May

London and Reading - Bedwyn, Oxford, Bicester, Banbury and Birmingham

Network Diagram - refer to first Page of Table 116

		XC	GW	GW	GW	GW	GW	CH	GW	GW	GW	GW	XC FX	XC FO	GW	GW	GW	GW	XC
		◇1 🍴	1	◇1 ☕	1	◇1 🍴	1		1	1	◇1 ☕	◇1 ☕	◇1 🍴	◇1 🍴	1	1	◇1 ☕	1	◇1 🍴
London Paddington 15 ⊖	d		14 57	15 15	15 18	15 22				15 27	15 30	15 36					15 52		
Ealing Broadway ⊖	d		15 05							15 35									
Slough 3	d		15 27			15 36				15 59									
Maidenhead 3	d		15 34							16 07									
Twyford 3	d		15 42						←	16 15								←	
Reading 7	d	15 40	15 53	15 43	15 48	15 52			15 53	16 26	15 57	16 02	16 10	16 10	16 12		16u22	16 26	16 40
Reading West	d		→							→					16 14				
Theale	d				15 56										16 20				
Aldermaston	d														16 25				
Midgham	d														16 29				
Thatcham	d				16 04										16 34				
Newbury Racecourse	d														16 38				
Newbury	a				16 10										16 44				
	d				16 10											17 08			
Kintbury	d				16 17											17 14			
Hungerford	d				16 21											17 19			
Bedwyn	a				16 31											17 28			
Tilehurst	d								15 57									16 30	
Pangbourne	d								16 01									16 34	
Goring & Streatley	d								16 06									16 39	
Cholsey	d								16 11									16 44	
Didcot Parkway	a			15 57					16 19		16 11	16 16						16 50	
	d								16 25									16 56	
Appleford	d																	17 01	
Culham	d																	17 04	
Radley	d								16 33									17 08	
Oxford	a	16 05				16 18			16 43				16 33	16 33			16 47	17 17	17 04
	d	16 07					16 23	16 26					16 35	16 36					17 07
Islip	d							16 39											
Bicester Town	a							16 51											
Tackley	d						16 32												
Heyford	d						16 36												
Kings Sutton	d						16 45												
Banbury	a	16 23					16 51						16 53	16 53					17 28
Leamington Spa 8	a	16 40											17 12	17 12					17 46
Coventry	a												17 24	17 24					
Birmingham International	a												17 37	17 37					
Birmingham New Street 12	a	17 18											17 49	17 49					18 18

		GW	GW	GW	GW	GW	GW	GW	GW	GW	GW	XC	CH	GW	GW	GW	GW	GW	GW
		1	R 1 ☕	1	◇1 🍴	1	1	R 1 ☕	1	◇1 ☕	1	◇1 🍴		1	1	◇1	1	R 1 ☕	◇1 ☕
London Paddington 15 ⊖	d	15 57	16 15	16 18	16 22		16 25	16 30		16 36						16 49		17 00	17 03
Ealing Broadway ⊖	d	16 05					16 33												
Slough 3	d	16 28			16 38		16 58									17 05			
Maidenhead 3	d	16 35					17 05												
Twyford 3	d	16 43				←	17 13										←		
Reading 7	d	16 54	16 44	16 48	16 52	16 54	17 23	16 57		17 04		17 09			17 12	17 21	17 23	17 26	17u30
Reading West	d	→					→								17 14				
Theale	d			16 56											17 20				
Aldermaston	d			17 01											17 25				
Midgham	d														17 29				
Thatcham	d			17 08											17 34				
Newbury Racecourse	d										←				17 38				
Newbury	a			17 14						17 18	17 14				17 44				17 47
	d			17 24						17 19	17 24								
Kintbury	d			→							17 31								
Hungerford	d									17a28	17 35								
Bedwyn	a										17 46								
Tilehurst	d					16 58											17 27		
Pangbourne	d					17 03											17 32		
Goring & Streatley	d					17 08											17 37		
Cholsey	d					17 14								←			17 42		
Didcot Parkway	a		16 59			17 20		17 12						17 20		17 36	17 49	17 40	
	d					17 26			17 15					17 26		17 38	18 05		
Appleford	d					→								17 31					
Culham	d													17 33			18 11		
Radley	d													17 37			18 15		
Oxford	a				17 22				17 30			17 34		17 44		17 51	18 23		
	d											17 36	17 45	17 46					
Islip	d												17 58						
Bicester Town	a												18 10						
Tackley	d													17 55					
Heyford	d													17 59					
Kings Sutton	d													18 08					
Banbury	a											17 54		18 15					
Leamington Spa 8	a											18 11							
Coventry	a											18 24							
Birmingham International	a											18 37							
Birmingham New Street 12	a											18 49							

For complete service between Banbury and Leamington (Birmingham), please refer to table 71

Table 116

Mondays to Fridays

31 March to 16 May

London and Reading - Bedwyn, Oxford, Bicester, Banbury and Birmingham

Network Diagram - refer to first Page of Table 116

		GW	XC	GW	GW	GW	GW	GW	GW	GW
				R					R	
		◇1	◇1	1	1	◇1	1	1	1	◇1
				A						
		☕	🛒	☕		☕			☕	☕
London Paddington 15 ⊖	d	17 06		17 15	17 18	17 22		17 24	17 30	17 33
Ealing Broadway ⊖	d							17 33		
Slough 3	d							17 58		
Maidenhead 3	d				17 41			18 10		
Twyford 3	d	17 30					←	18 17		
Reading 7	d	17 39	17 40	17 42	17 55	17 50	17 55	18 29	17 56	18 01
Reading West	d				→			→		
Theale	d	17 48								
Aldermaston	d									
Midgham	d									
Thatcham	d	17 58								
Newbury Racecourse	d									
Newbury	a	18 04								18 15
	d	18 05								
Kintbury	d	18 13								
Hungerford	d	18 19								
Bedwyn	a	18 26								
Tilehurst	d						17 59			
Pangbourne	d						18 04			
Goring & Streatley	d						18 10			
Cholsey	d						18 15			
Didcot Parkway	a			17 56			18 22		18 09	
	d						18 25			
Appleford	d									
Culham	d									
Radley	d						18 33			
Oxford	a		18 05			18 15	18 45			
	d		18 07							
Islip	d									
Bicester Town	a									
Tackley	d									
Heyford	d									
Kings Sutton	d									
Banbury	a		18 25							
Leamington Spa 8	a		18 45							
Coventry	a									
Birmingham International	a									
Birmingham New Street 12	a		19 18							

		GW	XC	GW	GW	GW	GW	GW	GW	GW
								R		
		1	◇1	1	1	◇1	◇1	1	1	◇1
								B		
			🛒			☕	☕	☕		☕
London Paddington 15 ⊖	d				17 35	17 42	17 49	18 00		18 05
Ealing Broadway ⊖	d									
Slough 3	d									
Maidenhead 3	d				17 58		18 09			
Twyford 3	d				18 07				←	18 28
Reading 7	d		18 10	18 12	18 20		18 22	18 27	18 29	18 37
Reading West	d			18 14						
Theale	d			18 20						18 46
Aldermaston	d			18 25						
Midgham	d			18 29						
Thatcham	d			18 34						18 56
Newbury Racecourse	d			18 38						
Newbury	a			18 44						19 02
	d	18 26								19 03
Kintbury	d	18 32								19 10
Hungerford	d	18 37								19 17
Bedwyn	a	18 46								19 24
Tilehurst	d				18 25				18 34	
Pangbourne	d				18 30				18 39	
Goring & Streatley	d				18 35				18 44	
Cholsey	d				18 41				18 50	
Didcot Parkway	a				18 47	18 19		18 41	18 58	
	d				18 47				19 03	
Appleford	d								19 08	
Culham	d									
Radley	d				18 55					
Oxford	a		18 34		19 07		18 47		19 18	
	d		18 36						19 19	
Islip	d									
Bicester Town	a									
Tackley	d								19 27	
Heyford	d								19 32	
Kings Sutton	d								19 44	
Banbury	a		18 54						19 50	
Leamington Spa 8	a		19 11							
Coventry	a		19 23							
Birmingham International	a		19 37							
Birmingham New Street 12	a		19 48							

		XC	GW	GW	GW	GW	CH	GW	GW	GW
								FO	FX	
			R							R
		◇1	1	1	1	◇1		1	1	1
						C				
		🛒	☕			☕				☕
London Paddington 15 ⊖	d		18 15	18 15	18 18	18 22		18 25	18 25	18 30
Ealing Broadway ⊖	d			18 23				18 33	18 33	
Slough 3	d			18 47				18 59	18 59	
Maidenhead 3	d			18 57	18 40			19 10	19 10	
Twyford 3	d			19 05	18 48			19 18	19 18	
Reading 7	d	18 40	18 42	19 19	18 57	18 51		19 27	19 27	18 55
Reading West	d			→	→			→	→	
Theale	d									
Aldermaston	d									
Midgham	d									
Thatcham	d									
Newbury Racecourse	d									
Newbury	a									
	d									
Kintbury	d									
Hungerford	d									
Bedwyn	a									
Tilehurst	d									
Pangbourne	d									
Goring & Streatley	d									
Cholsey	d									
Didcot Parkway	a		18 57							19 11
	d									
Appleford	d									
Culham	d									
Radley	d									
Oxford	a	19 11				19 20				
	d	19 13					19 30			
Islip	d						19 43			
Bicester Town	a						19 55			
Tackley	d									
Heyford	d									
Kings Sutton	d									
Banbury	a	19 30								
Leamington Spa 8	a	19 49								
Coventry	a									
Birmingham International	a									
Birmingham New Street 12	a	20 18								

		GW	GW	GW	XC	GW	GW	GW	GW	GW
		1	◇1	1	◇1	1	◇1	1	1	◇1
			☕		🛒		☕			🛒
London Paddington 15 ⊖	d		18 35				18 47			18 50
Ealing Broadway ⊖	d									
Slough 3	d									19 07
Maidenhead 3	d									
Twyford 3	d	←					19 10	←		
Reading 7	d	18 57	19 03		19 09	19 12	19 19	19 19	19 21	19 23
Reading West	d					19 15				
Theale	d					19 20			19 28	
Aldermaston	d					19 25				
Midgham	d					19 29				
Thatcham	d					19 34			19 39	
Newbury Racecourse	d					19 39				
Newbury	a		19 17			19 44			19 56	
	d		19 19	19 27					19 56	
Kintbury	d			19 33					20 03	
Hungerford	d		19 29	19 38					20 08	
Bedwyn	a		19 36	19 45					20 18	
Tilehurst	d	19 01						19 24		
Pangbourne	d	19 06						19 28		
Goring & Streatley	d	19 12						19 33		
Cholsey	d	19 17						19 38		
Didcot Parkway	a	19 26					19 33	19 47		
	d	19 27						19 56		
Appleford	d									
Culham	d							20 03		
Radley	d	19 34								
Oxford	a	19 46			19 34			20 16		19 49
	d				19 36					
Islip	d									
Bicester Town	a									
Tackley	d									
Heyford	d									
Kings Sutton	d									
Banbury	a				19 54					
Leamington Spa 8	a				20 12					
Coventry	a				20 24					
Birmingham International	a				20 37					
Birmingham New Street 12	a				20 48					

A The Red Dragon

B The Bristolian

C The Cathedrals Express

For complete service between Banbury and Leamington (Birmingham), please refer to table 71

Table 116

Mondays to Fridays

31 March to 16 May

London and Reading - Bedwyn, Oxford, Bicester, Banbury and Birmingham

Network Diagram - refer to first Page of Table 116

		GW	GW	GW	GW	XC	GW	GW	GW	GW	GW	GW	GW	GW	GW	GW	XC	GW	GW
			FO	FX				FO	FX	FO		FX	FO						
		R			R				R						R				
		1	1	1	1	◇1	1	1	1	1	1	◇1	◇1	1	1	1	◇1	◇1	◇1
					A														
		☕			✕				☕			☕	☕		☕			☕	☕
London Paddington 15 ⊖	d	19 00			19 03			19 12	19 15		19 18	19 22	19 22	19 27	19 30			19 45	19 48
Ealing Broadway ⊖	d													19 35					
Slough 3	d											19 36	19 36	19 59					
Maidenhead 3	d										19 40			20 09					20 06
Twyford 3	d		←	←						←	19 48			20 17		←			
Reading 7	d	19 27	19 27	19 27	19u33	19 40	19 42	19 43	19 42	19 43	19 57	19 52	19 52	20 25	19 57	19 57	20 10	20 12	20 18
Reading West	d						19 44	→			→			→					
Theale	d						19 50												
Aldermaston	d						19 55												
Midgham	d						19 59												
Thatcham	d						20 04												
Newbury Racecourse	d						20 08												
Newbury	a				19 50		20 11											20 28	
	d						20 33												
Kintbury	d						20 39												
Hungerford	d						20 43												
Bedwyn	a						20 53												
Tilehurst	d		19 31	19 31												20 01			
Pangbourne	d		19 35	19 35												20 06			
Goring & Streatley	d		19 40	19 40												20 11			
Cholsey	d		19 46	19 46												20 16			
Didcot Parkway	a	19 42	19 53	19 53					19 56	20 00					20 12	20 22			20 33
	d		20 01	20 08						20 09						20 25			
Appleford	d			20 13						20 13									
Culham	d																		
Radley	d			20 18						20 18						20 33			
Oxford	a		20 18	20 27		20 06				20 28		20 18	20 21			20 43	20 34		
	d					20 07											20 36		
Islip	d																		
Bicester Town	a																		
Tackley	d																		
Heyford	d																		
Kings Sutton	d																		
Banbury	a					20 27											20 52		
Leamington Spa 8	a					20 45											21 10		
Coventry	a																21 23		
Birmingham International	a																21 37		
Birmingham New Street 12	a					21 22											21 49		

		GW	CH	GW	GW	GW	XC	GW	GW	GW	GW	GW	GW	GW	GW	XC	GW	GW	GW
		◇1		1	1	◇1	◇1	◇1	1	◇1	1	1	1	◇1	1	◇1	◇1	◇1	1
		🛒				☕		Ø		🛒				☕			☕		
London Paddington 15 ⊖	d	19 50			19 57	20 00		20 15		20 20			20 27	20 35			20 45	20 48	
Ealing Broadway ⊖	d				20 05								20 35						
Slough 3	d	20 06			20 27					20 36			20 57					21 05	
Maidenhead 3	d				20 34								21 04						
Twyford 3	d			←	20 42							←	21 12						←
Reading 7	d	20 22		20 25	20 53	20 27	20 40	20 41	20 41	20 51		20 53	21 23	21 02		21 10	21 13	21 20	21 23
Reading West	d				→				20 44				→						
Theale	d								20 50										
Aldermaston	d								20 55										
Midgham	d								20 58										
Thatcham	d								21 03										
Newbury Racecourse	d								21 08										
Newbury	a								21 13					21 16					
	d														21 24				
Kintbury	d														21 30				
Hungerford	d														21 35				
Bedwyn	a														21 45				
Tilehurst	d			20 29								20 57							21 27
Pangbourne	d			20 34								21 01							21 31
Goring & Streatley	d			20 39								21 06							21 36
Cholsey	d			20 44								21 11							21 41
Didcot Parkway	a			20 51		20 41		20 56				21 19					21 27		21 52
	d			20 57								21 25							21 52
Appleford	d																		
Culham	d																		
Radley	d			21 04								21 33							21 59
Oxford	a	20 52		21 15			21 05			21 17		21 44				21 34		21 51	22 12
	d	20 55	21 00				21 09				21 41					21 36			
Islip	d		21 13																
Bicester Town	a		21 25																
Tackley	d	21 04									21 50								
Heyford	d	21 08									21 54								
Kings Sutton	d	21 17									22 03								
Banbury	a	21 23					21 31				22 09					21 52			
Leamington Spa 8	a						21 51									22 10			
Coventry	a															22 22			
Birmingham International	a															22 33			
Birmingham New Street 12	a						22 17									22 45			

A Restaurant for customers joining at Pad, Reading + Newbury. The Armada

For complete service between Banbury and Leamington (Birmingham), please refer to table 71

Table 116

Mondays to Fridays

31 March to 16 May

London and Reading - Bedwyn, Oxford, Bicester, Banbury and Birmingham

Network Diagram - refer to first Page of Table 116

		GW	GW	XC	GW	GW	GW	GW	GW	GW	GW	GW	CH	GW	GW	GW	GW	GW	GW
										FO	FX		FO		FO	FX	FO	FX	FO
		1	◇1	◇1	◇1	1	1	1	◇1	◇1	◇1	1		1	1	1	◇1	◇1	◇1
			☕						☕	🍴	☕						☕	☕	
London Paddington 15 ⊖	d	20 57	21 15		21 18			21 27	21 45	21 48	21 48				21 57	21 57	22 15	22 15	22 18
Ealing Broadway ⊖	d	21 05						21 35							22 05	22 05			
Slough 3	d	21 27			21 35			22 07		22 04	22 04				22 30	22 42			22 35
Maidenhead 3	d	21 34						22 15							22 42	22 53			22 42
Twyford 3	d	21 42				←		22 23						←	22 50	23 01			
Reading 7	d	21 57	21 41	21 46	21 50	21 57	22 01	22 32	22 11	22 25	22 25			22 32	23 10	23 10	22 42	22 54	22 56
Reading West	d	↪					22 03	↪							↪	↪			
Theale	d						22 10												
Aldermaston	d						22 15												
Midgham	d						22 18												
Thatcham	d						22 23												
Newbury Racecourse	d						22 28												
Newbury	a						22 31												
	d						22 31												
Kintbury	d						22 37												
Hungerford	d						22 42												
Bedwyn	a						22 52												
Tilehurst	d					22 02								22 35					
Pangbourne	d					22 05								22 40					
Goring & Streatley	d					22 09								22 43					
Cholsey	d					22 14								22 48					
Didcot Parkway	a		22 01			22 24			22 31					22 58			23 02	23 13	
	d					22 25								22 58					
Appleford	d													23 03					
Culham	d													23 05					
Radley	d													23 09					
Oxford	a			22 28	22 18	22 41				22 47	22 47			23 22					23 27
	d			22 30								23 06	23 12						
Islip	d												23 25						
Bicester Town	a												23 37						
Tackley	d											23 15							
Heyford	d											23 19							
Kings Sutton	d											23 28							
Banbury	a			22 51								23 34							
Leamington Spa 8	a			23 09															
Coventry	a			23 24															
Birmingham International	a			23 34															
Birmingham New Street 12	a			00 02															

		GW	GW	GW	GW	GW	GW	GW	GW	GW	GW	GW	GW	GW	CH	GW	GW	GW	GW
		FX		FX	FO	FO	FX	FO	FX	FO	FX	FX	FO					FO	
		◇1	1	1	1	1	1	◇1	◇1	◇1	◇1	1	1	◇1		◇1	1	1	1
								☕	☕							☕			
London Paddington 15 ⊖	d	22 18				22 27	22 27	22 45	22 45	22 48	22 48			23 18		23 30	23 33	23 42	
Ealing Broadway ⊖	d					22 35	22 35										23 41		
Slough 3	d	22 39				23 11	23 11			23 05	23 08			23 38			23 57	00 01	
Maidenhead 3	d	22 47				23 23	23 23			23 12	23 17			23 46			00 05	00 10	
Twyford 3	d			←	←	23 31	23 31			23 20	23 26	←	←				00 13		←
Reading 7	d	23 01	23 03	23 10	23 10	23 41	23 40	23 11	23 23	23 28	23 34	23 40	23 41	00 04		00 09	00 27	00 25	00 27
Reading West	d		23 05			↪	↪										↪		
Theale	d		23 11																
Aldermaston	d		23 16																
Midgham	d		23 20																
Thatcham	d		23 25																
Newbury Racecourse	d		23 29																
Newbury	a		23 32																
	d		23 32																
Kintbury	d		23 39																
Hungerford	d		23 43																
Bedwyn	a		23 53																
Tilehurst	d			23 14	23 14							23 44	23 44						00 33
Pangbourne	d			23 19	23 19							23 48	23 48						00 37
Goring & Streatley	d			23 22	23 22							23 52	23 52						00 41
Cholsey	d			23 27	23 27							23 57	23 57						00 46
Didcot Parkway	a			23 37	23 37			23 42	23 42			00 07	00 07			00 29		00 44	00 56
	d			23 38	23 38							00 07	00 08					00 44	00 56
Appleford	d																		01 00
Culham	d																		01 03
Radley	d											00 14	00 14						01 07
Oxford	a	23 29		23 54	23 56					23 56	00 01	00 27	00 27	00 35				01 02	01 18
	d														00 38				
Islip	d																		
Bicester Town	a																		
Tackley	d														00 48				
Heyford	d														00 53				
Kings Sutton	d														01 01				
Banbury	a														01 11				
Leamington Spa 8	a																		
Coventry	a																		
Birmingham International	a																		
Birmingham New Street 12	a																		

For complete service between Banbury and Leamington (Birmingham), please refer to table 71

Table 116

Saturdays

14 December to 28 December

London and Reading - Bedwyn, Oxford, Bicester, Banbury and Birmingham

Network Diagram - refer to first Page of Table 116

Station		GW 1	GW ◇1	CH	GW ◇1 🍴	GW 1	GW 1	GW 1	GW ◇1	GW 1	GW 1	GW 1	GW 1	GW ◇1	GW 1	XC ◇1 🛒	GW 1	GW 1	GW ◇1
London Paddington 15 ⊖	d								00 22					05 21				05 25	05 50
Ealing Broadway ⊖	d																	05 33	
Slough 3	d						00 01		00 41					05 38				05 51	06 06
Maidenhead 3	d						00 10	00 05										06 02	
Twyford 3	d							00 13										06 10	
Reading 7	d		00 04		00 09	00 20	00 25	00 27	01 01		04 54	05 41	05 46	05 54		06 10	06 12	06 21	06 22
Reading West	d					00s23					05 06	05 44					06 14		
Theale	d					00s29					05 12	05 50					06 20		
Aldermaston	d					00s34					05 17	05 55					06 25		
Midgham	d					00s37					05 20	05 58					06 29		
Thatcham	d					00s42					05 25	06 03					06 34		
Newbury Racecourse	d					00s47					05 30	06 08					06 38		
Newbury	a					00 52					05 32	06 10					06 44		
	d										05 33	06 10							
Kintbury	d										05 39	06 17							
Hungerford	d										05 44	06 21							
Bedwyn	a										05 52	06 31							
Tilehurst	d							00 33					05 52					06 25	
Pangbourne	d							00 37					05 56					06 29	
Goring & Streatley	d							00 41					06 01					06 34	
Cholsey	d							00 46					06 06		←			06 39	
Didcot Parkway	a				00 29		00 44	00 56	01 19				06 12	06 07	06 12			06 46	06 37
	d	00 08					00 44	00 56	01 19				06 13	06 08	06 13			06 47	06 38
Appleford	d							01 00					→		06 17			→	
Culham	d							01 03							06 20				
Radley	d	00 14						01 07							06 24				
Oxford	a	00 27	00 35				01 02	01 18	01 34					06 22	06 32	06 36			06 52
	d			00 38						06 16						06 38			
Islip	d																		
Bicester Town	a																		
Tackley	d			00 48						06 25									
Heyford	d			00 53						06 29									
Kings Sutton	d			01 01						06 38									
Banbury	a			01 11						06 46						06 54			
Leamington Spa 8	a															07 13			
Coventry	a															07 25			
Birmingham International	a															07 37			
Birmingham New Street 12	a															07 48			

Station		CH	GW 1	XC ◇1 🛒	GW 1	GW 1	GW ◇1	GW 1	GW 1	GW ◇1 🍴	XC ◇1 🛒	GW 1	GW ◇1	GW 1	CH	GW 1	XC ◇1 🛒	GW 1	GW 1
London Paddington 15 ⊖	d					05 57	06 21		06 27	06 30			06 50						06 57
Ealing Broadway ⊖	d					06 05			06 35										07 05
Slough 3	d					06 30	06 38		06 57				07 06						07 27
Maidenhead 3	d					06 41			07 04										07 34
Twyford 3	d					06 49		←	07 12							←			07 42
Reading 7	d			06 45	06 48	06 56	06 54	06 56	07 23	06 57	07 10	07 11	07 22			07 23	07 47	07 48	07 53
Reading West	d					→			→			07 14							
Theale	d				06 56							07 20						07 56	
Aldermaston	d											07 25							
Midgham	d											07 29							
Thatcham	d				07 04							07 34						08 04	
Newbury Racecourse	d											07 38							
Newbury	a				07 10							07 43						08 10	
	d				07 10													08 10	
Kintbury	d				07 17													08 17	
Hungerford	d				07 21													08 21	
Bedwyn	a				07 31													08 31	
Tilehurst	d							07 00								07 27			07 57
Pangbourne	d							07 04								07 31			08 01
Goring & Streatley	d							07 09								07 36			08 06
Cholsey	d		←					07 14								07 41			08 11
Didcot Parkway	a		06 46					07 30		07 12						07 49			08 19
	d		06 47					07 30								07 51			08 25
Appleford	d																		
Culham	d															07 56			
Radley	d		06 54													08 00			
Oxford	a		07 03	07 10			07 20	07 43			07 34		07 48			08 09	08 13		08 40
	d	07 00		07 12							07 36			07 53	08 07		08 15		
Islip	d	07 13													08 20				
Bicester Town	a	07 25													08 32				
Tackley	d													08 02					
Heyford	d													08 06					
Kings Sutton	d													08 15					
Banbury	a			07 32							07 53			08 23			08 32		
Leamington Spa 8	a			07 50							08 11						08 49		
Coventry	a										08 23								
Birmingham International	a										08 37								
Birmingham New Street 12	a			08 17							08 48						09 20		

For complete service between Banbury and Leamington (Birmingham), please refer to table 71

Table 116

Saturdays

14 December to 28 December

London and Reading - Bedwyn, Oxford, Bicester, Banbury and Birmingham

Network Diagram - refer to first Page of Table 116

Station		GW	GW	GW	XC	GW	GW	GW	GW	XC
		◇1	1	R 1 ⊏P	◇1 ⊼	1	1	◇1	1	◇1 ⊼
London Paddington 15 ⊖	d	07 21	07 27	07 30				07 50		
Ealing Broadway ⊖	d		07 35							
Slough 3	d	07 38	07 57					08 06		
Maidenhead 3	d		08 04							
Twyford 3	d		08 12						←	
Reading 7	d	07 54	08 23	07 57	08 10	08 21		08 22	08 23	08 40
Reading West	d		→			08 23				
Theale	d					08 31				
Aldermaston	d					08 36				
Midgham	d					08 41				
Thatcham	d					08 46				
Newbury Racecourse	d					08 49				
Newbury	a					08 54				
	d						09 00			
Kintbury	d						09 06			
Hungerford	d						09 11			
Bedwyn	a						09 19			
Tilehurst	d								08 27	
Pangbourne	d								08 31	
Goring & Streatley	d								08 36	
Cholsey	d								08 41	
Didcot Parkway	a			08 12					08 48	
	d								08 55	
Appleford	d								09 00	
Culham	d									
Radley	d								09 03	
Oxford	a	08 19			08 34			08 48	09 14	09 04
	d				08 36					09 07
Islip	d									
Bicester Town	a									
Tackley	d									
Heyford	d									
Kings Sutton	d									
Banbury	a				08 53					09 23
Leamington Spa 8	a				09 11					09 41
Coventry	a				09 23					
Birmingham International	a				09 37					
Birmingham New Street 12	a				09 48					10 18

Station		GW	GW	GW	GW	CH	GW	GW	GW	XC
		1	◇1 ⊏P	◇1 ⊏P	◇1 ⊏P		1	1	◇1 ⊏P	◇1 ⊼
London Paddington 15 ⊖	d	07 57	08 15	08 18	08 21			08 27	08 30	
Ealing Broadway ⊖	d	08 05						08 35		
Slough 3	d	08 27			08 39			08 57		
Maidenhead 3	d	08 34						09 04		
Twyford 3	d	08 42					←	09 12		
Reading 7	d	08 54	08 42	08 48	08 54		08 54	09 23	08 57	09 10
Reading West	d	→						→		
Theale	d			08 58						
Aldermaston	d									
Midgham	d									
Thatcham	d			09 07						
Newbury Racecourse	d									
Newbury	a			09 13						
	d			09 14						
Kintbury	d									
Hungerford	d			09 23						
Bedwyn	a			09 30						
Tilehurst	d						08 58			
Pangbourne	d						09 01			
Goring & Streatley	d						09 06			
Cholsey	d						09 11			
Didcot Parkway	a		08 55				09 19		09 12	
	d						09 25			
Appleford	d									
Culham	d									
Radley	d									
Oxford	a				09 18		09 40			09 34
	d					09 28				09 36
Islip	d					09 41				
Bicester Town	a					09 53				
Tackley	d									
Heyford	d									
Kings Sutton	d									
Banbury	a									09 52
Leamington Spa 8	a									10 11
Coventry	a									10 23
Birmingham International	a									10 37
Birmingham New Street 12	a									10 48

Station		GW	GW	GW	XC	GW	GW	GW	GW	GW
		1	◇1	1	◇1 ⊼	1	1	1	1	◇1
London Paddington 15 ⊖	d		08 50				08 57	09 18		09 21
Ealing Broadway ⊖	d						09 05			
Slough 3	d		09 06				09 27			09 39
Maidenhead 3	d						09 34			
Twyford 3	d			←			09 42		←	
Reading 7	d	09 12	09 22	09 23	09 40		09 53	09 48	09 53	09 54
Reading West	d	09 14					→			
Theale	d	09 20						09 56		
Aldermaston	d	09 25								
Midgham	d	09 29								
Thatcham	d	09 34						10 04		
Newbury Racecourse	d	09 38								
Newbury	a	09 44						10 10		
	d							10 10		
Kintbury	d							10 17		
Hungerford	d							10 21		
Bedwyn	a							10 32		
Tilehurst	d			09 27					09 57	
Pangbourne	d			09 31					10 01	
Goring & Streatley	d			09 36					10 06	
Cholsey	d			09 41					10 11	
Didcot Parkway	a			09 48					10 18	
	d			09 55					10 25	
Appleford	d									
Culham	d			10 01						
Radley	d			10 03						
Oxford	a		09 48	10 14	10 04				10 40	10 19
	d				10 07	10 16				
Islip	d									
Bicester Town	a									
Tackley	d					10 25				
Heyford	d					10 29				
Kings Sutton	d					10 39				
Banbury	a				10 23	10 46				
Leamington Spa 8	a				10 41					
Coventry	a									
Birmingham International	a									
Birmingham New Street 12	a				11 18					

Station		GW	GW	XC	GW	GW	CH	GW	XC	GW
		1	◇1 ⊏P	◇1 ⊼	1	◇1		1	◇1 ⊼	1
London Paddington 15 ⊖	d	09 27	09 30			09 50				09 57
Ealing Broadway ⊖	d	09 35								10 05
Slough 3	d	09 57				10 06				10 27
Maidenhead 3	d	10 04								10 34
Twyford 3	d	10 14						←		10 44
Reading 7	d	10 23	09 57	10 10	10 12	10 22		10 23	10 39	10 53
Reading West	d	→			10 14					→
Theale	d				10 20					
Aldermaston	d				10 25					
Midgham	d				10 29					
Thatcham	d				10 34					
Newbury Racecourse	d				10 38					
Newbury	a				10 44					
	d									
Kintbury	d									
Hungerford	d									
Bedwyn	a									
Tilehurst	d							10 27		
Pangbourne	d							10 31		
Goring & Streatley	d							10 36		
Cholsey	d							10 41		
Didcot Parkway	a		10 12					10 49		
	d							10 55		
Appleford	d							11 00		
Culham	d									
Radley	d							11 03		
Oxford	a			10 34		10 48		11 14	11 04	
	d			10 36			11 00		11 07	
Islip	d						11 13			
Bicester Town	a						11 25			
Tackley	d									
Heyford	d									
Kings Sutton	d									
Banbury	a			10 53					11 23	
Leamington Spa 8	a			11 11					11 41	
Coventry	a			11 23						
Birmingham International	a			11 37						
Birmingham New Street 12	a			11 48					12 18	

For complete service between Banbury and Leamington (Birmingham), please refer to table 71

Table 116

Saturdays

14 December to 28 December

London and Reading - Bedwyn, Oxford, Bicester, Banbury and Birmingham

Network Diagram - refer to first Page of Table 116

Station		GW ◇1 ☕	GW 1	GW 1	GW ◇1 ☕	GW 1	GW ◇1 ☕	XC ◇1 🛒	GW 1	GW ◇1 🛒	GW 1	XC ◇1 🛒	GW 1
London Paddington 15 ⊖	d	10 15	10 18		10 21	10 27	10 30			10 50			
Ealing Broadway ⊖	d					10 35							
Slough 3	d				10 39	10 57				11 06			
Maidenhead 3	d					11 04							
Twyford 3	d			←		11 12					←		
Reading 7	d	10 42	10 48	10 53	10 54	11 23	10 58	11 09	11 12	11 22	11 23	11 40	
Reading West	d					→			11 14				
Theale	d		10 56						11 20				
Aldermaston	d								11 25				
Midgham	d								11 29				
Thatcham	d		11 04						11 34				
Newbury Racecourse	d								11 38				
Newbury	a		11 10						11 44				
	d		11 10										
Kintbury	d		11 17										
Hungerford	d		11 21										
Bedwyn	a		11 32										
Tilehurst	d			10 57							11 27		
Pangbourne	d			11 01							11 31		
Goring & Streatley	d			11 06							11 36		
Cholsey	d			11 11							11 41		
Didcot Parkway	a	10 55		11 19			11 12				11 49		
	d			11 25							11 55		
Appleford	d												
Culham	d												
Radley	d										12 03		
Oxford	a			11 40	11 19			11 34		11 48	12 14	12 05	
	d							11 36				12 07	12 16
Islip	d												
Bicester Town	a												
Tackley	d												12 25
Heyford	d												12 29
Kings Sutton	d												12 39
Banbury	a							11 53				12 23	12 46
Leamington Spa 8	a							12 11				12 41	
Coventry	a							12 23					
Birmingham International	a							12 37					
Birmingham New Street 12	a							12 48				13 18	

Station		GW 1	GW 1	GW 1	GW ◇1 🛒	CH	GW 1	GW ◇1 Ø	XC ◇1 🛒	GW 1	GW ◇1	GW 1	XC ◇1 🛒
London Paddington 15 ⊖	d	10 57	11 18		11 21		11 27	11 30			11 50		
Ealing Broadway ⊖	d	11 05					11 35						
Slough 3	d	11 27			11 39		11 57				12 06		
Maidenhead 3	d	11 34					12 04						
Twyford 3	d	11 42		←			12 12					←	
Reading 7	d	11 53	11 48	11 53	11 54		12 23	11 57	12 09	12 12	12 22	12 23	12 39
Reading West	d	→					→			12 14			
Theale	d		11 56							12 20			
Aldermaston	d									12 25			
Midgham	d									12 29			
Thatcham	d		12 04							12 34			
Newbury Racecourse	d									12 38			
Newbury	a		12 10							12 44			
	d		12 10										
Kintbury	d		12 17										
Hungerford	d		12 21										
Bedwyn	a		12 32										
Tilehurst	d			11 57								12 27	
Pangbourne	d			12 01								12 31	
Goring & Streatley	d			12 06								12 36	
Cholsey	d			12 11								12 41	
Didcot Parkway	a			12 19				12 12				12 48	
	d			12 25								12 55	
Appleford	d											13 00	
Culham	d												
Radley	d											13 03	
Oxford	a			12 40	12 20				12 33		12 48	13 14	13 04
	d					12 30			12 36				13 07
Islip	d					12 43							
Bicester Town	a					12 55							
Tackley	d												
Heyford	d												
Kings Sutton	d												
Banbury	a								12 53				13 23
Leamington Spa 8	a								13 11				13 41
Coventry	a								13 23				
Birmingham International	a								13 37				
Birmingham New Street 12	a								13 48				14 18

Station		GW 1	GW ◇1 ☕	GW ◇1 ☕	GW 1	GW ◇1	GW 1	GW ◇1 ☕	XC ◇1 🛒	CH	GW 1	GW ◇1 🛒	GW 1
London Paddington 15 ⊖	d	11 57	12 15	12 18		12 21	12 27	12 30				12 50	
Ealing Broadway ⊖	d	12 05					12 35						
Slough 3	d	12 27				12 39	12 57					13 06	
Maidenhead 3	d	12 34					13 04						
Twyford 3	d	12 45			←		13 12						←
Reading 7	d	12 53	12 42	12 48	12 53	12 54	13 23	12 57	13 10		13 12	13 22	13 23
Reading West	d	→					→				13 14		
Theale	d			12 56							13 20		
Aldermaston	d										13 25		
Midgham	d										13 29		
Thatcham	d			13 05							13 34		
Newbury Racecourse	d										13 38		
Newbury	a			13 12							13 44		
	d			13 13									
Kintbury	d												
Hungerford	d			13 21									
Bedwyn	a			13 29									
Tilehurst	d				12 57								13 27
Pangbourne	d				13 01								13 31
Goring & Streatley	d				13 06								13 36
Cholsey	d				13 11								13 41
Didcot Parkway	a		12 55		13 19			13 12					13 48
	d				13 25								13 55
Appleford	d												
Culham	d												14 01
Radley	d												14 03
Oxford	a				13 40	13 19			13 34			13 48	14 14
	d								13 36	13 41			
Islip	d									13 54			
Bicester Town	a									14 06			
Tackley	d												
Heyford	d												
Kings Sutton	d												
Banbury	a								13 53				
Leamington Spa 8	a								14 11				
Coventry	a								14 23				
Birmingham International	a								14 37				
Birmingham New Street 12	a								14 48				

For complete service between Banbury and Leamington (Birmingham), please refer to table 71

Table 116

Saturdays

14 December to 28 December

London and Reading - Bedwyn, Oxford, Bicester, Banbury and Birmingham

Network Diagram - refer to first Page of Table 116

		XC	GW	GW	GW	GW	GW	GW	GW	XC
		◇1 [trolley]	1	1	1	1	◇1 [trolley]	1	◇1 [restaurant]	◇1 [trolley]
London Paddington 15 ⊖	d			12 57	13 18		13 21	13 27	13 30	
Ealing Broadway ⊖	d			13 05				13 35		
Slough 3	d			13 27			13 39	13 57		
Maidenhead 3	d			13 34				14 04		
Twyford 3	d			13 42		←		14 12		
Reading 7	d	13 40		13 53	13 48	13 53	13 54	14 23	13 57	14 10
Reading West	d			→				→		
Theale	d				13 56					
Aldermaston	d									
Midgham	d									
Thatcham	d				14 04					
Newbury Racecourse	d									
Newbury	a				14 10					
	d				14 10					
Kintbury	d				14 17					
Hungerford	d				14 21					
Bedwyn	a				14 32					
Tilehurst	d					13 57				
Pangbourne	d					14 01				
Goring & Streatley	d					14 06				
Cholsey	d					14 11				
Didcot Parkway	a					14 19			14 12	
	d					14 25				
Appleford	d									
Culham	d									
Radley	d									
Oxford	a	14 04				14 40	14 19			14 34
	d	14 07	14 16							14 36
Islip	d									
Bicester Town	a									
Tackley	d		14 25							
Heyford	d		14 29							
Kings Sutton	d		14 39							
Banbury	a	14 23	14 46							14 53
Leamington Spa 8	a	14 41								15 11
Coventry	a									15 23
Birmingham International	a									15 37
Birmingham New Street 12	a	15 18								15 48

		GW	GW	CH	GW	XC	GW	GW	GW	GW
		1	◇1 [trolley]		1	◇1 [trolley]	1	◇1 [restaurant]	1	1
London Paddington 15 ⊖	d		13 50				13 57	14 15	14 18	
Ealing Broadway ⊖	d						14 05			
Slough 3	d		14 06				14 27			
Maidenhead 3	d						14 34			
Twyford 3	d				←		14 45			←
Reading 7	d	14 12	14 22		14 23	14 39	14 53	14 42	14 49	14 53
Reading West	d	14 14					→			
Theale	d	14 20							14 56	
Aldermaston	d	14 25								
Midgham	d	14 29								
Thatcham	d	14 34							15 05	
Newbury Racecourse	d	14 38								
Newbury	a	14 44							15 10	
	d								15 11	
Kintbury	d								15 17	
Hungerford	d								15 22	
Bedwyn	a								15 32	
Tilehurst	d				14 27					14 57
Pangbourne	d				14 31					15 01
Goring & Streatley	d				14 36					15 06
Cholsey	d				14 41					15 12
Didcot Parkway	a				14 48			14 55		15 19
	d				14 55					15 25
Appleford	d				15 00					
Culham	d									
Radley	d				15 03					
Oxford	a		14 48		15 14	15 04				15 40
	d			14 57		15 07				
Islip	d			15 10						
Bicester Town	a			15 22						
Tackley	d									
Heyford	d									
Kings Sutton	d									
Banbury	a					15 23				
Leamington Spa 8	a					15 41				
Coventry	a									
Birmingham International	a									
Birmingham New Street 12	a					16 18				

		GW	GW	GW	XC	GW	GW	CH	GW	XC
		◇1 [trolley]	1	◇1 [restaurant]	◇1 [trolley]	1	◇1		1	◇1 [trolley]
London Paddington 15 ⊖	d	14 21	14 27	14 30			14 50			
Ealing Broadway ⊖	d		14 35							
Slough 3	d	14 39	14 57				15 06			
Maidenhead 3	d		15 04							
Twyford 3	d		15 12						←	
Reading 7	d	14 54	15 23	14 57	15 09	15 12	15 22		15 23	15 40
Reading West	d		→			15 14				
Theale	d					15 20				
Aldermaston	d					15 25				
Midgham	d					15 29				
Thatcham	d					15 34				
Newbury Racecourse	d					15 38				
Newbury	a					15 44				
	d									
Kintbury	d									
Hungerford	d									
Bedwyn	a									
Tilehurst	d								15 27	
Pangbourne	d								15 31	
Goring & Streatley	d								15 36	
Cholsey	d								15 41	
Didcot Parkway	a			15 12					15 48	
	d								15 55	
Appleford	d									
Culham	d								16 01	
Radley	d								16 03	
Oxford	a	15 18			15 34		15 48		16 14	16 04
	d				15 36			16 00		16 07
Islip	d							16 13		
Bicester Town	a							16 25		
Tackley	d									
Heyford	d									
Kings Sutton	d									
Banbury	a				15 53					16 23
Leamington Spa 8	a				16 11					16 41
Coventry	a				16 23					
Birmingham International	a				16 37					
Birmingham New Street 12	a				16 48					17 18

		GW	GW	GW	GW	GW	GW	GW	XC	GW
		1	1	1	1	◇1 [trolley]	1	◇1 [restaurant]	◇1 [trolley]	1
London Paddington 15 ⊖	d		14 57	15 18		15 21	15 27	15 30		
Ealing Broadway ⊖	d		15 05				15 35			
Slough 3	d		15 27			15 39	15 57			
Maidenhead 3	d		15 34				16 04			
Twyford 3	d		15 42		←		16 13			
Reading 7	d		15 53	15 48	15 53	15 54	16 24	15 57	16 10	16 12
Reading West	d		→				→			16 14
Theale	d			15 56						16 20
Aldermaston	d									16 25
Midgham	d									16 29
Thatcham	d			16 04						16 34
Newbury Racecourse	d									16 38
Newbury	a			16 09						16 44
	d			16 10						
Kintbury	d			16 16						
Hungerford	d			16 21						
Bedwyn	a			16 31						
Tilehurst	d				15 57					
Pangbourne	d				16 01					
Goring & Streatley	d				16 06					
Cholsey	d				16 11					
Didcot Parkway	a				16 19			16 12		
	d				16 25					
Appleford	d									
Culham	d									
Radley	d									
Oxford	a				16 40	16 19			16 34	
	d	16 16							16 36	
Islip	d									
Bicester Town	a									
Tackley	d	16 25								
Heyford	d	16 29								
Kings Sutton	d	16 39								
Banbury	a	16 46							16 53	
Leamington Spa 8	a								17 11	
Coventry	a								17 23	
Birmingham International	a								17 37	
Birmingham New Street 12	a								17 48	

For complete service between Banbury and Leamington (Birmingham), please refer to table 71

Table 116

Saturdays

14 December to 28 December

London and Reading - Bedwyn, Oxford, Bicester, Banbury and Birmingham

Network Diagram - refer to first Page of Table 116

Station		GW ◇1	CH	GW 1	XC ◇1 (trolley)	GW 1	GW ◇1 (restaurant)	GW 1	GW 1	GW ◇1 (restaurant)
London Paddington 15 ⊖	d	15 50				15 57	16 15	16 18		16 21
Ealing Broadway ⊖	d					16 05				
Slough 3	d	16 06				16 27				16 38
Maidenhead 3	d					16 34				
Twyford 3	d			←		16 45			←	
Reading 7	d	16 22		16 24	16 39	16 53	16 42	16 48	16 53	16 54
Reading West	d					→				
Theale	d							16 56		
Aldermaston	d									
Midgham	d									
Thatcham	d							17 04		
Newbury Racecourse	d									
Newbury	a							17 10		
	d							17 10		
Kintbury	d							17 17		
Hungerford	d							17 21		
Bedwyn	a							17 32		
Tilehurst	d			16 28					16 57	
Pangbourne	d			16 32					17 01	
Goring & Streatley	d			16 37					17 06	
Cholsey	d			16 42					17 11	
Didcot Parkway	a			16 49			16 55		17 19	
	d			16 55					17 25	
Appleford	d			17 00						
Culham	d									
Radley	d			17 03						
Oxford	a	16 48		17 14	17 04				17 40	17 18
	d		17 10		17 07					
Islip	d		17 23							
Bicester Town	a		17 35							
Tackley	d									
Heyford	d									
Kings Sutton	d									
Banbury	a				17 23					
Leamington Spa 8	a				17 41					
Coventry	a									
Birmingham International	a									
Birmingham New Street 12	a				18 18					

Station		GW 1	GW ◇1 (restaurant)	XC ◇1 (trolley)	GW 1	GW ◇1 (trolley)	GW 1	XC ◇1 (trolley)	GW 1	GW 1
London Paddington 15 ⊖	d	16 27	16 30			16 50				16 57
Ealing Broadway ⊖	d	16 35								17 05
Slough 3	d	16 57				17 06				17 27
Maidenhead 3	d	17 04								17 34
Twyford 3	d	17 12					←			17 42
Reading 7	d	17 23	16 57	17 09	17 12	17 22	17 23	17 40		17 53
Reading West	d	→			17 14					→
Theale	d				17 20					
Aldermaston	d				17 25					
Midgham	d				17 29					
Thatcham	d				17 34					
Newbury Racecourse	d				17 38					
Newbury	a				17 44					
	d									
Kintbury	d									
Hungerford	d									
Bedwyn	a									
Tilehurst	d						17 27			
Pangbourne	d						17 31			
Goring & Streatley	d						17 36			
Cholsey	d						17 41			
Didcot Parkway	a		17 12				17 48			
	d						17 55			
Appleford	d									
Culham	d						18 01			
Radley	d						18 03			
Oxford	a			17 34		17 48	18 14	18 04		
	d			17 36				18 07	18 16	
Islip	d									
Bicester Town	a									
Tackley	d								18 25	
Heyford	d								18 29	
Kings Sutton	d								18 39	
Banbury	a			17 53				18 23	18 46	
Leamington Spa 8	a			18 11				18 41		
Coventry	a			18 23						
Birmingham International	a			18 37						
Birmingham New Street 12	a			18 48				19 18		

Station		GW 1	GW 1	GW ◇1 (restaurant)	GW 1	GW ◇1 (restaurant)	XC ◇1 (trolley)	CH	GW 1	GW ◇1 (trolley)
London Paddington 15 ⊖	d	17 18		17 21	17 27	17 30				17 50
Ealing Broadway ⊖	d				17 35					
Slough 3	d			17 39	17 57					18 06
Maidenhead 3	d				18 04					
Twyford 3	d		←		18 12					
Reading 7	d	17 48	17 53	17 54	18 23	17 57	18 09		18 12	18 22
Reading West	d				→				18 14	
Theale	d	17 56							18 20	
Aldermaston	d								18 25	
Midgham	d								18 29	
Thatcham	d	18 04							18 34	
Newbury Racecourse	d								18 38	
Newbury	a	18 10							18 44	
	d	18 10								
Kintbury	d	18 17								
Hungerford	d	18 21								
Bedwyn	a	18 30								
Tilehurst	d		17 57							
Pangbourne	d		18 01							
Goring & Streatley	d		18 06							
Cholsey	d		18 11							
Didcot Parkway	a		18 19			18 12				
	d		18 25							
Appleford	d									
Culham	d									
Radley	d									
Oxford	a		18 40	18 18			18 34			18 48
	d						18 36	18 41		
Islip	d							18 54		
Bicester Town	a							19 06		
Tackley	d									
Heyford	d									
Kings Sutton	d									
Banbury	a						18 53			
Leamington Spa 8	a						19 11			
Coventry	a						19 23			
Birmingham International	a						19 37			
Birmingham New Street 12	a						19 48			

Station		GW 1	XC ◇1 (trolley)	GW 1	GW ◇1 (restaurant)	GW 1	GW 1	GW ◇1 (restaurant)	GW 1	GW ◇1 (restaurant)
London Paddington 15 ⊖	d			17 57	18 15	18 18		18 21	18 27	18 30
Ealing Broadway ⊖	d			18 05					18 35	
Slough 3	d			18 27				18 38	18 57	
Maidenhead 3	d			18 34					19 04	
Twyford 3	d	←		18 45			←		19 12	
Reading 7	d	18 23	18 39	18 53	18 42	18 48	18 53	18 54	19 23	18 57
Reading West	d			→					→	
Theale	d					18 56				
Aldermaston	d									
Midgham	d									
Thatcham	d					19 04				
Newbury Racecourse	d									
Newbury	a					19 10				
	d					19 10				
Kintbury	d					19 17				
Hungerford	d					19 21				
Bedwyn	a					19 32				
Tilehurst	d	18 27					18 57			
Pangbourne	d	18 31					19 01			
Goring & Streatley	d	18 36					19 06			
Cholsey	d	18 41					19 11			
Didcot Parkway	a	18 48			18 55		19 19			19 12
	d	18 55					19 25			
Appleford	d	19 00								
Culham	d									
Radley	d	19 03								
Oxford	a	19 14	19 04				19 40	19 18		
	d		19 07							
Islip	d									
Bicester Town	a									
Tackley	d									
Heyford	d									
Kings Sutton	d									
Banbury	a		19 23							
Leamington Spa 8	a		19 41							
Coventry	a									
Birmingham International	a									
Birmingham New Street 12	a		20 18							

For complete service between Banbury and Leamington (Birmingham), please refer to table 71

Table 116

Saturdays

14 December to 28 December

London and Reading - Bedwyn, Oxford, Bicester, Banbury and Birmingham

Network Diagram - refer to first Page of Table 116

Station		XC	CH	GW	GW	GW	GW	GW	XC	GW
		◇1		◇1	1	1	1	◇1	◇1	◇1
		✕						☕		☕
London Paddington 15 ⊖	d			18 50			18 57	19 06		19 15
Ealing Broadway ⊖	d						19 05			
Slough 3	d			19 06			19 27			
Maidenhead 3	d						19 34			
Twyford 3	d					←	19 42			
Reading 7	d	19 09		19 22		19 23	19 53	19 32	19 40	19 42
Reading West	d						→			
Theale	d									
Aldermaston	d									
Midgham	d									
Thatcham	d									
Newbury Racecourse	d									
Newbury	a							19 47		
	d									
Kintbury	d									
Hungerford	d									
Bedwyn	a									
Tilehurst	d					19 27				
Pangbourne	d					19 31				
Goring & Streatley	d					19 36				
Cholsey	d					19 41				
Didcot Parkway	a					19 49				19 55
	d					19 55				
Appleford	d									
Culham	d					20 01				
Radley	d					20 03				
Oxford	a	19 34		19 48		20 14			20 04	
	d	19 36	19 48		19 56				20 07	
Islip	d		20 01							
Bicester Town	a		20 13							
Tackley	d				20 05					
Heyford	d				20 09					
Kings Sutton	d				20 18					
Banbury	a	19 53			20 25				20 28	
Leamington Spa 8	a	20 10							20 45	
Coventry	a	20 23								
Birmingham International	a	20 37								
Birmingham New Street 12	a	20 48							21 15	

Station		GW	GW	GW	GW	GW	XC	GW	CH	GW
		1	1	◇1	1	◇1	◇1	◇1		1
						☕		✕		
London Paddington 15 ⊖	d			19 21	19 27	19 30		19 50		
Ealing Broadway ⊖	d				19 35					
Slough 3	d			19 38	19 57			20 06		
Maidenhead 3	d				20 04					
Twyford 3	d		←		20 12					←
Reading 7	d	19 49	19 53	19 54	20 23	19 57	20 09	20 22		20 23
Reading West	d	19 52			→					
Theale	d	19 58								
Aldermaston	d	20 03								
Midgham	d	20 06								
Thatcham	d	20 11								
Newbury Racecourse	d	20 16								
Newbury	a	20 18								
	d	20 19								
Kintbury	d	20 25								
Hungerford	d	20 30								
Bedwyn	a	20 38								
Tilehurst	d		19 57							20 27
Pangbourne	d		20 01							20 31
Goring & Streatley	d		20 06							20 36
Cholsey	d		20 11							20 41
Didcot Parkway	a		20 18			20 11				20 49
	d		20 25							20 55
Appleford	d									21 00
Culham	d									
Radley	d									21 03
Oxford	a		20 41	20 20			20 34	20 47		21 14
	d						20 36		21 00	
Islip	d								21 13	
Bicester Town	a								21 25	
Tackley	d									
Heyford	d									
Kings Sutton	d									
Banbury	a						20 53			
Leamington Spa 8	a						21 11			
Coventry	a						21 23			
Birmingham International	a						21 37			
Birmingham New Street 12	a						21 48			

Station		GW	GW	GW	XC	GW	GW	GW	GW	GW
		1	◇1	◇1	◇1	◇1	1	◇1	1	1
			☕	☕		☕				
London Paddington 15 ⊖	d	19 57	20 00	20 06		20 15		20 18		
Ealing Broadway ⊖	d	20 05								
Slough 3	d	20 27						20 35		
Maidenhead 3	d	20 34								
Twyford 3	d	20 42								←
Reading 7	d	20 53	20 27	20 35	20 40	20 42	20 49	20 51		20 53
Reading West	d	→					20 52			
Theale	d						20 58			
Aldermaston	d						21 03			
Midgham	d						21 06			
Thatcham	d						21 11			
Newbury Racecourse	d						21 16			
Newbury	a			20 49			21 18			
	d						21 32			
Kintbury	d						21 39			
Hungerford	d						21 43			
Bedwyn	a						21 52			
Tilehurst	d									20 57
Pangbourne	d									21 01
Goring & Streatley	d									21 06
Cholsey	d									21 11
Didcot Parkway	a		20 41			20 55				21 19
	d									21 25
Appleford	d									
Culham	d									
Radley	d									
Oxford	a				21 04			21 18		21 40
	d				21 07				21 20	
Islip	d									
Bicester Town	a									
Tackley	d								21 29	
Heyford	d								21 33	
Kings Sutton	d								21 42	
Banbury	a				21 24				21 49	
Leamington Spa 8	a				21 43					
Coventry	a				21 55					
Birmingham International	a				22 10					
Birmingham New Street 12	a				22 21					

Station		GW	GW	XC	GW	GW	XC	GW	GW	CH
		1	◇1	◇1	◇1	1	◇1	1	◇1	
			☕		✕					
London Paddington 15 ⊖	d	20 27	20 30		20 48			20 57	21 18	
Ealing Broadway ⊖	d	20 35						21 05		
Slough 3	d	20 57			21 05			21 27	21 35	
Maidenhead 3	d	21 04						21 34		
Twyford 3	d	21 12				←		21 46		
Reading 7	d	21 24	20 57	21 09	21 21	21 24	21 40	21 55	21 51	
Reading West	d	→						→		
Theale	d									
Aldermaston	d									
Midgham	d									
Thatcham	d									
Newbury Racecourse	d									
Newbury	a									
	d									
Kintbury	d									
Hungerford	d									
Bedwyn	a									
Tilehurst	d					21 27				
Pangbourne	d					21 32				
Goring & Streatley	d					21 37				
Cholsey	d					21 42				
Didcot Parkway	a		21 12		21 36	21 49			22 07	
	d				21 37	21 55			22 08	
Appleford	d									
Culham	d					22 01				
Radley	d					22 03				
Oxford	a			21 34	21 50	22 14	22 03		22 22	
	d			21 36			22 07			22 25
Islip	d									22 38
Bicester Town	a									22 50
Tackley	d									
Heyford	d									
Kings Sutton	d									
Banbury	a			21 54			22 28			
Leamington Spa 8	a			22 11			22 45			
Coventry	a			22 23						
Birmingham International	a			22 36						
Birmingham New Street 12	a			22 48			23 16			

For complete service between Banbury and Leamington (Birmingham), please refer to table 71

Table 116

Saturdays

14 December to 28 December

London and Reading - Bedwyn, Oxford, Bicester, Banbury and Birmingham

Network Diagram - refer to first Page of Table 116

		GW	GW	GW	GW	GW	GW	GW	GW	GW	GW	GW	GW	GW	GW	GW	GW
		1	◇1	1	1	◇1	◇1	◇1	1		◇1	1	1	◇1	1	◇1	◇1
			⊏⊐				⊏⊐			🚌	⊏⊐					⊏⊐	
London Paddington 15 ⊖	d		21 30		21 42	21 48	22 00	22 18			22 35		22 42	22 48		23 30	23 33
Ealing Broadway ⊖	d				21 52								22 52				
Slough 3	d				22 18	22 05		22 35					23 20	23 05			23 50
Maidenhead 3	d				22 29			22 42					23 32	23 13			23 58
Twyford 3	d	←			22 38				←				23 40		←		
Reading 7	d	21 55	21 57	22 03	22 58	22 21	22 28	22 54	22 58		23 03	23 12	23 48	23 25	23 48	00 03	00 11
Reading West	d			22 06	→							23 14	→				
Theale	d			22 12								23 20					
Aldermaston	d			22 17								23 25					
Midgham	d			22 20								23 29					
Thatcham	d			22 25								23 34					
Newbury Racecourse	d			22 30								23 38					
Newbury	a			22 32								23 41					
	d			22 32								23 41					
Kintbury	d			22 39								23 48					
Hungerford	d			22 43								23 52					
Bedwyn	a			22 52								00 01					
Tilehurst	d	22 01							23 02						23 52		
Pangbourne	d	22 06															
Goring & Streatley	d	22 11							23 08						00 01		
Cholsey	d	22 16							23 13						00 06		
Didcot Parkway	a	22 23	22 12			22 35	22 42	23 09	23 21		23 24			23 41	00 15	00 19	00 28
	d	22 25				22 36		23 10	23 21					23 41	00 15		00 29
Appleford	d																00s33
Culham	d																00s35
Radley	d	22 34							23 29						00s23		00s39
Oxford	a	22 43				22 48		23 22	23 40					23 57	00 32		00 50
	d									23 53							
Islip	d																
Bicester Town	a																
Tackley	d									00s13							
Heyford	d									00s28							
Kings Sutton	d																
Banbury	a									00 53							
Leamington Spa 8	a																
Coventry	a																
Birmingham International	a																
Birmingham New Street 12	a																

For complete service between Banbury and Leamington (Birmingham), please refer to table 71

Table 116

Saturdays

4 January to 8 February

London and Reading - Bedwyn, Oxford, Bicester, Banbury and Birmingham

Network Diagram - refer to first Page of Table 116

Station		GW 1	GW ◇1	CH	GW ◇1	GW 1	GW 1	GW 1	GW ◇1	GW 1
London Paddington 15 ⊖	d								00 22	
Ealing Broadway ⊖	d									
Slough 3	d						00 01		00 41	
Maidenhead 3	d						00 10	00 05		
Twyford 3	d							00 13		
Reading 7	d		00 04		00 09	00 20	00 25	00 27	01 01	
Reading West	d					00s23				
Theale	d					00s29				
Aldermaston	d					00s34				
Midgham	d					00s37				
Thatcham	d					00s42				
Newbury Racecourse	d					00s47				
Newbury	a					00 52				
	d									
Kintbury	d									
Hungerford	d									
Bedwyn	a									
Tilehurst	d							00 33		
Pangbourne	d							00 37		
Goring & Streatley	d							00 41		
Cholsey	d							00 46		
Didcot Parkway	a				00 29		00 44	00 56	01 19	
	d	00 08					00 44	00 56	01 19	
Appleford	d							01 00		
Culham	d							01 03		
Radley	d	00 14						01 07		
Oxford	a	00 27	00 35				01 02	01 18	01 34	
	d			00 38						06 16
Islip	d									
Bicester Town	a									
Tackley	d			00 48						06 25
Heyford	d			00 53						06 29
Kings Sutton	d			01 01						06 38
Banbury	a			01 11						06 46
Leamington Spa 8	a									
Coventry	a									
Birmingham International	a									
Birmingham New Street 12	a									

Station		GW 1	GW 1	GW 1	GW ◇1	GW 1	XC ◇1	GW 1	GW 1	GW ◇1
London Paddington 15 ⊖	d				05 14				05 21	05 45
Ealing Broadway ⊖	d								05 29	
Slough 3	d				05 38				05 51	06 09
Maidenhead 3	d								06 02	
Twyford 3	d								06 10	
Reading 7	d	04 54	05 41	05 46	05 54		06 10	06 12	06 21	06 25
Reading West	d	05 06	05 44					06 14		
Theale	d	05 12	05 50					06 20		
Aldermaston	d	05 17	05 55					06 25		
Midgham	d	05 20	05 58					06 29		
Thatcham	d	05 25	06 03					06 34		
Newbury Racecourse	d	05 30	06 08					06 38		
Newbury	a	05 32	06 10					06 44		
	d	05 33	06 10							
Kintbury	d	05 39	06 17							
Hungerford	d	05 44	06 21							
Bedwyn	a	05 52	06 31							
Tilehurst	d			05 52					06 25	
Pangbourne	d			05 56					06 29	
Goring & Streatley	d			06 01					06 34	
Cholsey	d			06 06		←			06 39	
Didcot Parkway	a			06 12	06 07	06 12			06 46	06 40
	d			06 13	06 08	06 13			06 47	06 41
Appleford	d			→		06 17			→	
Culham	d					06 20				
Radley	d					06 24				
Oxford	a				06 22	06 32	06 36			06 55
	d						06 38			
Islip	d									
Bicester Town	a									
Tackley	d									
Heyford	d									
Kings Sutton	d									
Banbury	a						06 54			
Leamington Spa 8	a						07 13			
Coventry	a						07 25			
Birmingham International	a						07 37			
Birmingham New Street 12	a						07 48			

Station		CH	GW 1	XC ◇1	GW 1	GW 1	GW ◇1	GW 1	GW 1	GW ◇1
London Paddington 15 ⊖	d					05 57	06 14		06 19	06 22
Ealing Broadway ⊖	d					06 05			06 27	
Slough 3	d					06 30	06 38		06 52	
Maidenhead 3	d					06 41			07 03	
Twyford 3	d					06 49		←	07 11	
Reading 7	d			06 45	06 48	06 56	06 54	06 56	07 18	06 59
Reading West	d					→			→	
Theale	d				06 56					
Aldermaston	d									
Midgham	d									
Thatcham	d				07 04					
Newbury Racecourse	d									
Newbury	a				07 10					
	d				07 10					
Kintbury	d				07 17					
Hungerford	d				07 21					
Bedwyn	a				07 31					
Tilehurst	d							07 00		
Pangbourne	d							07 04		
Goring & Streatley	d							07 09		
Cholsey	d		←					07 14		
Didcot Parkway	a		06 46					07 30		07 12
	d		06 47					07 30		
Appleford	d									
Culham	d									
Radley	d		06 54							
Oxford	a		07 03	07 10			07 20	07 43		
	d	07 00		07 12						
Islip	d	07 13								
Bicester Town	a	07 25								
Tackley	d									
Heyford	d									
Kings Sutton	d									
Banbury	a			07 32						
Leamington Spa 8	a			07 50						
Coventry	a									
Birmingham International	a									
Birmingham New Street 12	a			08 17						

Station		XC ◇1	GW 1	GW 1	GW ◇1	GW 1	CH	XC ◇1	GW 1	GW 1
London Paddington 15 ⊖	d				06 43					06 56
Ealing Broadway ⊖	d									07 04
Slough 3	d				07 06					07 29
Maidenhead 3	d									07 40
Twyford 3	d			←						07 48
Reading 7	d	07 10	07 11	07 18	07 22			07 47	07 48	07 56
Reading West	d		07 14							
Theale	d		07 20						07 56	
Aldermaston	d		07 25							
Midgham	d		07 29							
Thatcham	d		07 34						08 04	
Newbury Racecourse	d		07 38							
Newbury	a		07 43						08 10	
	d								08 10	
Kintbury	d								08 17	
Hungerford	d								08 21	
Bedwyn	a								08 31	
Tilehurst	d			07 22						08 01
Pangbourne	d			07 27						08 04
Goring & Streatley	d			07 32						08 09
Cholsey	d			07 37						08 14
Didcot Parkway	a			07 45						08 22
	d			07 50						08 25
Appleford	d									
Culham	d			07 56						
Radley	d			08 00						
Oxford	a	07 34		08 09	07 48			08 13		08 40
	d	07 36				07 53	08 07	08 15		
Islip	d						08 20			
Bicester Town	a						08 32			
Tackley	d					08 02				
Heyford	d					08 06				
Kings Sutton	d					08 15				
Banbury	a	07 53				08 23		08 32		
Leamington Spa 8	a	08 11						08 49		
Coventry	a	08 23								
Birmingham International	a	08 37								
Birmingham New Street 12	a	08 48						09 20		

For complete service between Banbury and Leamington (Birmingham), please refer to table 71

Table 116

Saturdays

4 January to 8 February

London and Reading - Bedwyn, Oxford, Bicester, Banbury and Birmingham

Network Diagram - refer to first Page of Table 116

		GW	GW	XC	GW	GW	GW	GW	XC	GW
		◇1	■ 1 ⊡	◇1 ⚒	1	1	1	◇1	◇1 ⚒	1
London Paddington 15 ⊖	d	07 17	07 22				07 25	07 46		07 57
Ealing Broadway ⊖	d						07 33			08 05
Slough 3	d	07 41					07 58	08 10		08 30
Maidenhead 3	d						08 09			08 41
Twyford 3	d						08 17			08 49
Reading 7	d	07 57	07 59	08 10	08 21		08 25	08 26	08 40	08 57
Reading West	d				08 23					→
Theale	d				08 31					
Aldermaston	d				08 36					
Midgham	d				08 41					
Thatcham	d				08 46					
Newbury Racecourse	d				08 49					
Newbury	a				08 54					
	d					09 00				
Kintbury	d					09 06				
Hungerford	d					09 11				
Bedwyn	a					09 19				
Tilehurst	d						08 29			
Pangbourne	d						08 34			
Goring & Streatley	d						08 39			
Cholsey	d						08 44			
Didcot Parkway	a		08 14				08 51			
	d						08 56			
Appleford	d						09 01			
Culham	d									
Radley	d						09 04			
Oxford	a	08 21		08 34			09 15	08 52	09 04	
	d			08 36					09 07	
Islip	d									
Bicester Town	a									
Tackley	d									
Heyford	d									
Kings Sutton	d									
Banbury	a			08 53					09 23	
Leamington Spa 8	a			09 11					09 41	
Coventry	a			09 23						
Birmingham International	a			09 37						
Birmingham New Street 12	a			09 48					10 18	

		GW	GW	CH	GW	GW	XC	GW	GW	GW
		◇1 ⊡	◇1 ⊡		◇1 ⊡	1	◇1 ⚒	1	1	◇1
London Paddington 15 ⊖	d	08 13	08 17		08 22				08 23	08 46
Ealing Broadway ⊖	d								08 31	
Slough 3	d		08 39						08 56	09 09
Maidenhead 3	d								09 07	
Twyford 3	d					←			09 15	
Reading 7	d	08 48	08 55		08 57	08 57	09 10	09 12	09 27	09 25
Reading West	d							09 14	→	
Theale	d	08 58						09 20		
Aldermaston	d							09 25		
Midgham	d							09 29		
Thatcham	d	09 07						09 34		
Newbury Racecourse	d							09 38		
Newbury	a	09 13						09 44		
	d	09 14								
Kintbury	d									
Hungerford	d	09 23								
Bedwyn	a	09 30								
Tilehurst	d					09 01				
Pangbourne	d					09 05				
Goring & Streatley	d					09 10				
Cholsey	d					09 15				
Didcot Parkway	a				09 12	09 23				
	d					09 25				
Appleford	d									
Culham	d									
Radley	d									
Oxford	a		09 19			09 40	09 34			09 51
	d			09 28			09 36			
Islip	d			09 41						
Bicester Town	a			09 53						
Tackley	d									
Heyford	d									
Kings Sutton	d									
Banbury	a						09 52			
Leamington Spa 8	a						10 11			
Coventry	a						10 23			
Birmingham International	a						10 37			
Birmingham New Street 12	a						10 48			

		GW	GW	XC	GW	GW	GW	GW	GW	XC
		1	1	◇1 ⚒	1	1	◇1	1	◇1 ⊡	◇1 ⚒
London Paddington 15 ⊖	d					08 56	09 17	09 21	09 22	
Ealing Broadway ⊖	d					09 04		09 29		
Slough 3	d					09 29	09 42	09 55		
Maidenhead 3	d					09 40		10 06		
Twyford 3	d		←			09 48		10 14		
Reading 7	d		09 27	09 40	09 48	09 57	09 57	10 23	10 00	10 10
Reading West	d							→		
Theale	d				09 56					
Aldermaston	d									
Midgham	d									
Thatcham	d				10 04					
Newbury Racecourse	d									
Newbury	a				10 10					
	d				10 10					
Kintbury	d				10 17					
Hungerford	d				10 21					
Bedwyn	a				10 32					
Tilehurst	d		09 31			10 01				
Pangbourne	d		09 36			10 05				
Goring & Streatley	d		09 41			10 10				
Cholsey	d		09 46			10 15				
Didcot Parkway	a		09 53			10 22			10 15	
	d		09 58			10 25				
Appleford	d									
Culham	d		10 04							
Radley	d		10 06							
Oxford	a		10 17	10 04		10 40	10 22			10 34
	d	10 16		10 07						10 36
Islip	d									
Bicester Town	a									
Tackley	d	10 25								
Heyford	d	10 29								
Kings Sutton	d	10 39								
Banbury	a	10 46		10 23						10 53
Leamington Spa 8	a			10 41						11 11
Coventry	a									11 23
Birmingham International	a									11 37
Birmingham New Street 12	a			11 18						11 48

		GW	GW	GW	CH	XC	GW	GW	GW	GW
		1	1	◇1		◇1 ⚒	1	1	◇1 ⊡	1
London Paddington 15 ⊖	d			09 46				09 57	10 17	
Ealing Broadway ⊖	d							10 05		
Slough 3	d			10 09				10 30	10 40	
Maidenhead 3	d							10 41		
Twyford 3	d		←					10 49		←
Reading 7	d	10 12	10 23	10 26		10 39	10 48	10 57	10 55	10 57
Reading West	d	10 14						→		
Theale	d	10 20					10 56			
Aldermaston	d	10 25								
Midgham	d	10 29								
Thatcham	d	10 34					11 04			
Newbury Racecourse	d	10 38								
Newbury	a	10 44					11 10			
	d						11 10			
Kintbury	d						11 17			
Hungerford	d						11 21			
Bedwyn	a						11 32			
Tilehurst	d		10 27							11 00
Pangbourne	d		10 31							11 05
Goring & Streatley	d		10 36							11 10
Cholsey	d		10 41							11 15
Didcot Parkway	a		10 49							11 23
	d		10 55							11 25
Appleford	d		11 00							
Culham	d									
Radley	d		11 03							
Oxford	a		11 14	10 51		11 04			11 20	11 40
	d				11 00	11 07				
Islip	d				11 13					
Bicester Town	a				11 25					
Tackley	d									
Heyford	d									
Kings Sutton	d									
Banbury	a					11 23				
Leamington Spa 8	a					11 41				
Coventry	a									
Birmingham International	a									
Birmingham New Street 12	a					12 18				

For complete service between Banbury and Leamington (Birmingham), please refer to table 71

Table 116

Saturdays

4 January to 8 February

London and Reading - Bedwyn, Oxford, Bicester, Banbury and Birmingham

Network Diagram - refer to first Page of Table 116

Station		GW	XC	GW	GW	GW	XC	GW	GW	GW
		◇1	◇1	1	1	◇1	◇1	1	1	1
		🍴	🛒			🛒	🛒			
London Paddington 15 ⊖	d	10 22			10 23	10 46				10 57
Ealing Broadway ⊖	d				10 31					11 05
Slough 3	d				10 56	11 10				11 31
Maidenhead 3	d				11 07					11 42
Twyford 3	d				11 15					11 50
Reading 7	d	10 59	11 09	11 12	11 23	11 26	11 40		11 48	11 59
Reading West	d			11 14						→
Theale	d			11 20					11 56	
Aldermaston	d			11 25						
Midgham	d			11 29						
Thatcham	d			11 34					12 04	
Newbury Racecourse	d			11 38						
Newbury	a			11 44					12 10	
	d								12 10	
Kintbury	d								12 17	
Hungerford	d								12 21	
Bedwyn	a								12 32	
Tilehurst	d				11 27					
Pangbourne	d				11 32					
Goring & Streatley	d				11 37					
Cholsey	d				11 42					
Didcot Parkway	a	11 13			11 50					
	d				11 55					
Appleford	d									
Culham	d									
Radley	d				12 03					
Oxford	a		11 34		12 14	11 53	12 05			
	d		11 36				12 07	12 16		
Islip	d									
Bicester Town	a									
Tackley	d							12 25		
Heyford	d							12 29		
Kings Sutton	d							12 39		
Banbury	a		11 53				12 23	12 46		
Leamington Spa 8	a		12 11				12 41			
Coventry	a		12 23							
Birmingham International	a		12 37							
Birmingham New Street 12	a		12 48				13 18			

Station		GW	CH	GW	GW	XC	GW	GW	GW	XC
		◇1		1	◇1	◇1	1	1	◇1	◇1
		🛒			Ø	🛒				🛒
London Paddington 15 ⊖	d	11 17			11 22			11 23	11 46	
Ealing Broadway ⊖	d							11 31		
Slough 3	d	11 42						11 56	12 09	
Maidenhead 3	d							12 07		
Twyford 3	d			←				12 15		
Reading 7	d	11 57		11 59	12 00	12 10	12 12	12 25	12 25	12 39
Reading West	d						12 14			
Theale	d						12 20			
Aldermaston	d						12 25			
Midgham	d						12 29			
Thatcham	d						12 34			
Newbury Racecourse	d						12 38			
Newbury	a						12 44			
	d									
Kintbury	d									
Hungerford	d									
Bedwyn	a									
Tilehurst	d			12 02				12 29		
Pangbourne	d			12 07				12 34		
Goring & Streatley	d			12 12				12 39		
Cholsey	d			12 17				12 44		
Didcot Parkway	a			12 25	12 15			12 51		
	d			12 25				12 55		
Appleford	d							13 00		
Culham	d									
Radley	d							13 03		
Oxford	a	12 23		12 40		12 33		13 14	12 51	13 04
	d		12 30			12 36				13 07
Islip	d		12 43							
Bicester Town	a		12 55							
Tackley	d									
Heyford	d									
Kings Sutton	d									
Banbury	a					12 53				13 23
Leamington Spa 8	a					13 11				13 41
Coventry	a					13 23				
Birmingham International	a					13 37				
Birmingham New Street 12	a					13 48				14 18

Station		GW	GW	GW	GW	GW	XC	CH	GW	GW
		1	◇1	◇1	1	◇1	◇1		1	1
			🍴			🍴	🛒			
London Paddington 15 ⊖	d	11 57	12 13	12 17		12 22				12 23
Ealing Broadway ⊖	d	12 05								12 31
Slough 3	d	12 31		12 41						12 56
Maidenhead 3	d	12 42								13 07
Twyford 3	d	12 50			←					13 15
Reading 7	d	12 58	12 48	12 57	12 58	12 59	13 10		13 12	13 25
Reading West	d	→							13 14	
Theale	d		12 56						13 20	
Aldermaston	d								13 25	
Midgham	d								13 29	
Thatcham	d		13 05						13 34	
Newbury Racecourse	d								13 38	
Newbury	a		13 12						13 44	
	d		13 13							
Kintbury	d									
Hungerford	d		13 21							
Bedwyn	a		13 29							
Tilehurst	d				13 01					13 29
Pangbourne	d				13 06					13 34
Goring & Streatley	d				13 11					13 39
Cholsey	d				13 16					13 44
Didcot Parkway	a				13 24	13 14				13 51
	d				13 25					13 57
Appleford	d									
Culham	d									14 03
Radley	d									14 05
Oxford	a			13 21	13 40		13 34			14 16
	d						13 36	13 41		
Islip	d							13 54		
Bicester Town	a							14 06		
Tackley	d									
Heyford	d									
Kings Sutton	d									
Banbury	a						13 53			
Leamington Spa 8	a						14 11			
Coventry	a						14 23			
Birmingham International	a						14 37			
Birmingham New Street 12	a						14 48			

Station		GW	XC	GW	GW	GW	GW	GW	GW	XC
		◇1	◇1	1	1	1	◇1	1	◇1	◇1
		🛒	🛒				🛒		🍴	🛒
London Paddington 15 ⊖	d	12 46				12 57	13 17		13 22	
Ealing Broadway ⊖	d					13 05				
Slough 3	d	13 09				13 31	13 42			
Maidenhead 3	d					13 42				
Twyford 3	d					13 50		←		
Reading 7	d	13 25	13 40		13 48	13 58	13 57	13 58	14 00	14 10
Reading West	d					→				
Theale	d				13 56					
Aldermaston	d									
Midgham	d									
Thatcham	d				14 04					
Newbury Racecourse	d									
Newbury	a				14 10					
	d				14 10					
Kintbury	d				14 17					
Hungerford	d				14 21					
Bedwyn	a				14 32					
Tilehurst	d							14 02		
Pangbourne	d							14 06		
Goring & Streatley	d							14 11		
Cholsey	d							14 16		
Didcot Parkway	a							14 24	14 15	
	d							14 25		
Appleford	d									
Culham	d									
Radley	d									
Oxford	a	13 51	14 04				14 22	14 40		14 34
	d		14 07	14 16						14 36
Islip	d									
Bicester Town	a									
Tackley	d			14 25						
Heyford	d			14 29						
Kings Sutton	d			14 39						
Banbury	a		14 23	14 46						14 53
Leamington Spa 8	a		14 41							15 11
Coventry	a									15 23
Birmingham International	a									15 37
Birmingham New Street 12	a		15 18							15 48

For complete service between Banbury and Leamington (Birmingham), please refer to table 71

Table 116

Saturdays

4 January to 8 February

London and Reading - Bedwyn, Oxford, Bicester, Banbury and Birmingham

Network Diagram - refer to first Page of Table 116

Station		GW 1	GW 1	GW ◇1 (trolley)	CH	XC ◇1 (trolley)	GW 1	GW 1	GW ◇1 (trolley)	GW 1
London Paddington 15 ⊖	d		13 23	13 46				13 57	14 17	
Ealing Broadway ⊖	d		13 31					14 05		
Slough 3	d		13 56	14 10				14 31	14 42	
Maidenhead 3	d		14 07					14 42		
Twyford 3	d		14 15					14 50		←
Reading 7	d	14 12	14 25	14 26		14 39	14 49	14 58	14 57	14 58
Reading West	d	14 14						→		
Theale	d	14 20					14 56			
Aldermaston	d	14 25								
Midgham	d	14 29								
Thatcham	d	14 34					15 05			
Newbury Racecourse	d	14 38								
Newbury	a	14 44					15 10			
	d						15 11			
Kintbury	d						15 17			
Hungerford	d						15 22			
Bedwyn	a						15 32			
Tilehurst	d		14 29							15 02
Pangbourne	d		14 34							15 06
Goring & Streatley	d		14 39							15 11
Cholsey	d		14 44							15 17
Didcot Parkway	a		14 51							15 24
	d		14 55							15 25
Appleford	d		15 01							
Culham	d									
Radley	d		15 04							
Oxford	a		15 15	14 52		15 04			15 21	15 40
	d				14 57	15 07				
Islip	d				15 10					
Bicester Town	a				15 22					
Tackley	d									
Heyford	d									
Kings Sutton	d									
Banbury	a					15 23				
Leamington Spa 8	a					15 41				
Coventry	a									
Birmingham International	a									
Birmingham New Street 12	a					16 18				

Station		GW 1	GW ◇1 (restaurant)	XC ◇1 (trolley)	GW 1	GW 1	GW ◇1	CH	XC ◇1 (trolley)	GW 1
London Paddington 15 ⊖	d	14 21	14 22				14 46			
Ealing Broadway ⊖	d	14 29								
Slough 3	d	14 54					15 09			
Maidenhead 3	d	15 05								
Twyford 3	d	15 13				←				
Reading 7	d	15 22	15 01	15 10	15 12	15 22	15 25		15 40	
Reading West	d	→			15 14					
Theale	d				15 20					
Aldermaston	d				15 25					
Midgham	d				15 29					
Thatcham	d				15 34					
Newbury Racecourse	d				15 38					
Newbury	a				15 44					
	d									
Kintbury	d									
Hungerford	d									
Bedwyn	a									
Tilehurst	d					15 26				
Pangbourne	d					15 31				
Goring & Streatley	d					15 36				
Cholsey	d					15 41				
Didcot Parkway	a		15 16			15 48				
	d					15 55				
Appleford	d									
Culham	d					16 01				
Radley	d					16 03				
Oxford	a			15 34		16 14	15 51		16 04	
	d			15 36				16 00	16 07	16 16
Islip	d							16 13		
Bicester Town	a							16 25		
Tackley	d									16 25
Heyford	d									16 29
Kings Sutton	d									16 39
Banbury	a			15 53					16 23	16 46
Leamington Spa 8	a			16 11					16 41	
Coventry	a			16 23						
Birmingham International	a			16 37						
Birmingham New Street 12	a			16 48					17 18	

Station		GW 1	GW 1	GW ◇1 (trolley)	GW ◇1 (restaurant)	XC ◇1 (trolley)	GW 1	GW 1	GW ◇1	CH
London Paddington 15 ⊖	d		14 55	15 17	15 22			15 23	15 46	
Ealing Broadway ⊖	d		15 03					15 31		
Slough 3	d		15 29	15 42				15 56	16 09	
Maidenhead 3	d		15 40					16 07		
Twyford 3	d		15 48					16 15		
Reading 7	d	15 48	15 57	15 57	16 00	16 10	16 12	16 26	16 25	
Reading West	d						16 14	→		
Theale	d	15 56					16 20			
Aldermaston	d						16 25			
Midgham	d						16 29			
Thatcham	d	16 04					16 34			
Newbury Racecourse	d						16 38			
Newbury	a	16 09					16 44			
	d	16 10								
Kintbury	d	16 16								
Hungerford	d	16 21								
Bedwyn	a	16 31								
Tilehurst	d		16 00							
Pangbourne	d		16 05							
Goring & Streatley	d		16 10							
Cholsey	d		16 15							
Didcot Parkway	a		16 23		16 15					
	d		16 25							
Appleford	d									
Culham	d									
Radley	d									
Oxford	a		16 40	16 22		16 34			16 51	
	d					16 36				17 10
Islip	d									17 23
Bicester Town	a									17 35
Tackley	d									
Heyford	d									
Kings Sutton	d									
Banbury	a					16 53				
Leamington Spa 8	a					17 11				
Coventry	a					17 23				
Birmingham International	a					17 37				
Birmingham New Street 12	a					17 48				

Station		GW 1	XC ◇1 (trolley)	GW 1	GW 1	GW ◇1 (restaurant)	GW 1	GW ◇1 (restaurant)	XC ◇1 (trolley)	GW 1
London Paddington 15 ⊖	d				15 57	16 17		16 22		
Ealing Broadway ⊖	d				16 05					
Slough 3	d				16 31	16 41				
Maidenhead 3	d				16 42					
Twyford 3	d	←			16 50		←			
Reading 7	d	16 26	16 39	16 48	16 58	16 57	16 58	16 59	17 10	17 12
Reading West	d				→					17 14
Theale	d			16 56						17 20
Aldermaston	d									17 25
Midgham	d									17 29
Thatcham	d			17 04						17 34
Newbury Racecourse	d									17 38
Newbury	a			17 10						17 44
	d			17 10						
Kintbury	d			17 17						
Hungerford	d			17 21						
Bedwyn	a			17 32						
Tilehurst	d	16 29					17 01			
Pangbourne	d	16 33					17 06			
Goring & Streatley	d	16 38					17 11			
Cholsey	d	16 43					17 16			
Didcot Parkway	a	16 50					17 24	17 15		
	d	16 58					17 25			
Appleford	d	17 03								
Culham	d									
Radley	d	17 06								
Oxford	a	17 17	17 04			17 21	17 40		17 33	
	d		17 07						17 36	
Islip	d									
Bicester Town	a									
Tackley	d									
Heyford	d									
Kings Sutton	d									
Banbury	a		17 23						17 53	
Leamington Spa 8	a		17 41						18 11	
Coventry	a								18 23	
Birmingham International	a								18 37	
Birmingham New Street 12	a		18 18						18 48	

For complete service between Banbury and Leamington (Birmingham), please refer to table 71

Table 116

Saturdays

4 January to 8 February

London and Reading - Bedwyn, Oxford, Bicester, Banbury and Birmingham

Network Diagram - refer to first Page of Table 116

		GW	GW	XC	GW	GW	GW	GW	GW	GW	GW	XC	CH	GW	GW	GW	XC	GW	GW	GW	GW	XC	CH	GW	GW	GW	GW	GW	XC	GW	GW	GW	GW	GW	XC	GW	GW
		1	◇1	◇1	1	1	1	◇1	1	1	◇1	◇1		1	◇1	1	◇1	1	1	◇1	◇1	◇1		1	◇1	1	1	◇1	◇1	◇1	1	1	◇1	◇1	◇1	1	◇1
			🛒	🛒				☕			☕	🛒			🛒		🛒			☕	☕	🛒						☕		☕				☕			🛒
London Paddington 15 ⊖	d	16 23	16 46				16 57	17 17		17 21	17 22				17 46				17 57	18 17	18 22			18 23	18 46		18 56	19 00		19 06			19 18	19 22		19 23	19 45
Ealing Broadway ⊖	d	16 31					17 05			17 29									18 05					18 31			19 04									19 31	
Slough 3	d	16 56	17 10				17 30	17 41		17 56					18 09				18 30	18 41				18 57	19 10		19 29						19 42			19 56	20 09
Maidenhead 3	d	17 07					17 41			18 07									18 41					19 08			19 40									20 07	
Twyford 3	d	17 15					17 49		←	18 15						←			18 49					19 16			19 48					←				20 15	
Reading 7	d	17 25	17 26	17 40		17 48	17 57	17 56	17 57	18 25	17 58	18 09		18 12	18 25	18 25	18 39	18 48	18 57	18 57	19 00	19 09		19 25	19 25		19 56	19 35	19 40	19 45	19 49	19 56	19 58	20 01	20 09	20 26	20 25
Reading West	d						→			→				18 14													→				19 52					→	
Theale	d					17 56								18 20				18 56													19 58						
Aldermaston	d													18 25																	20 03						
Midgham	d													18 29																	20 06						
Thatcham	d					18 04								18 34				19 04													20 11						
Newbury Racecourse	d													18 38																	20 16						
Newbury	a					18 10								18 44				19 10										19 50			20 18						
	d					18 10												19 10													20 19						
Kintbury	d					18 17												19 17													20 25						
Hungerford	d					18 21												19 21													20 30						
Bedwyn	a					18 30												19 32													20 38						
Tilehurst	d	17 29							18 00							18 29			19 00					19 29								20 00					
Pangbourne	d	17 34							18 05							18 34			19 05					19 34								20 05					
Goring & Streatley	d	17 39							18 10							18 39			19 10					19 39								20 10					
Cholsey	d	17 44							18 15							18 44			19 15					19 44								20 15					
Didcot Parkway	a	17 51							18 23		18 13					18 51			19 23		19 15			19 51						19 59		20 22		20 13			
	d	17 57							18 25							18 55			19 25					19 56								20 25					
Appleford	d															19 01																					
Culham	d	18 03																						20 02													
Radley	d	18 05														19 04								20 04													
Oxford	a	18 16	17 52	18 04				18 21	18 40			18 34			18 51	19 15	19 04		19 40	19 22		19 34		20 15	19 51				20 04			20 40	20 24		20 34		20 50
	d			18 07	18 16							18 36	18 41				19 07					19 36	19 48			19 56			20 07						20 36		
Islip	d												18 54										20 01														
Bicester Town	a												19 06										20 13														
Tackley	d				18 25																					20 05											
Heyford	d				18 29																					20 09											
Kings Sutton	d				18 39																					20 18											
Banbury	a			18 23	18 46							18 53					19 23					19 53				20 25			20 28						20 53		
Leamington Spa 8	a			18 41								19 11					19 41					20 10							20 45						21 11		
Coventry	a											19 23										20 23													21 23		
Birmingham International	a											19 37										20 37													21 37		
Birmingham New Street 12	a			19 18								19 48					20 18					20 48							21 15						21 48		

For complete service between Banbury and Leamington (Birmingham), please refer to table 71

Table 116

Saturdays
4 January to 8 February

London and Reading - Bedwyn, Oxford, Bicester, Banbury and Birmingham

Network Diagram - refer to first Page of Table 116

Station		CH	GW	GW	GW	GW	XC	GW	GW	GW	GW	GW	XC	GW	GW	GW	XC	CH	GW
			1	◇1	1	◇1	◇1	1	1	1	◇1	◇1	◇1	1	◇1	1	◇1		1
				☕		☕						☕			🍴				
London Paddington 15 ⊖	d			19 52	19 56	20 00					20 18	20 21		20 23	20 44				20 57
Ealing Broadway ⊖	d				20 04									20 31					21 05
Slough 3	d				20 29						20 42			20 56	21 08				21 30
Maidenhead 3	d				20 40									21 07					21 41
Twyford 3	d		←		20 48					←				21 15		←			21 49
Reading 7	d		20 26	20 29	20 56	20 36	20 40		20 49	20 56	20 58	21 02	21 09	21 25	21 24	21 25	21 40		21 57
Reading West	d				→				20 52					→					
Theale	d								20 58										
Aldermaston	d								21 03										
Midgham	d								21 06										
Thatcham	d								21 11										
Newbury Racecourse	d								21 16										
Newbury	a					20 50			21 18										
	d								21 32										
Kintbury	d								21 39										
Hungerford	d								21 43										
Bedwyn	a								21 52										
Tilehurst	d		20 30							20 59						21 28			22 03
Pangbourne	d		20 34							21 04						21 33			22 08
Goring & Streatley	d		20 40							21 09						21 38			22 13
Cholsey	d		20 44							21 14						21 43			22 18
Didcot Parkway	a		20 52	20 43						21 22		21 17			21 39	21 50			22 25
	d		20 57							21 26					21 40	21 56			22 25
Appleford	d		21 02																→
Culham	d															22 03			
Radley	d		21 05													22 05			
Oxford	a		21 16				21 04			21 41	21 23		21 34		21 53	22 16	22 03		
	d	21 00					21 07	21 20					21 36				22 07	22 25	
Islip	d	21 13																22 38	
Bicester Town	a	21 25																22 50	
Tackley	d							21 29											
Heyford	d							21 33											
Kings Sutton	d							21 42											
Banbury	a						21 24	21 49					21 54				22 28		
Leamington Spa 8	a						21 43						22 11				22 45		
Coventry	a						21 55						22 23						
Birmingham International	a						22 10						22 36						
Birmingham New Street 12	a						22 21						22 48				23 16		

Station		GW	GW	GW	GW	GW	GW	GW	GW	GW	GW	GW	GW	GW	GW	GW	GW	GW
		◇1	◇1	1	1	◇1	1	◇1	◇1	1		1	1	◇1	◇1	1	◇1	◇1
			☕					☕			🚌			☕			☕	
London Paddington 15 ⊖	d	21 18	21 22			21 44	21 45	21 52	22 14				22 27	22 35	22 48		23 21	23 30
Ealing Broadway ⊖	d						21 55						22 37					
Slough 3	d	21 43				22 08	22 20		22 38				23 03		23 11			23 54
Maidenhead 3	d						22 31		22 45				23 15		23 20			00 02
Twyford 3	d						22 40			←			23 23			←		
Reading 7	d	21 59	22 01		22 03	22 23	23 02	22 27	22 57	23 02		23 12	23 48	23 20	23 33	23 48	00 05	00 15
Reading West	d				22 06		→					23 14	→					
Theale	d				22 12							23 20						
Aldermaston	d				22 17							23 25						
Midgham	d				22 20							23 29						
Thatcham	d				22 25							23 34						
Newbury Racecourse	d				22 30							23 38						
Newbury	a				22 32							23 41						
	d				22 32							23 41						
Kintbury	d				22 39							23 48						
Hungerford	d				22 43							23 52						
Bedwyn	a				22 52							00 01						
Tilehurst	d									23 06						23 52		
Pangbourne	d																	
Goring & Streatley	d									23 12						00 01		
Cholsey	d			←						23 17						00 06		
Didcot Parkway	a	22 14	22 16	22 25		22 38		22 41	23 12	23 25				23 33	23 49	00 15	00 19	00 32
	d	22 15		22 25		22 38			23 13	23 25					23 49	00 15		00 33
Appleford	d																	00s37
Culham	d																	00s39
Radley	d			22 34						23 33						00s23		00s43
Oxford	a	22 29		22 43		22 50			23 25	23 44					00 05	00 32		00 54
	d										23 53							
Islip	d																	
Bicester Town	a																	
Tackley	d										00s13							
Heyford	d										00s28							
Kings Sutton	d																	
Banbury	a										00 53							
Leamington Spa 8	a																	
Coventry	a																	
Birmingham International	a																	
Birmingham New Street 12	a																	

For complete service between Banbury and Leamington (Birmingham), please refer to table 71

Table 116

Saturdays

15 February to 22 March

London and Reading - Bedwyn, Oxford, Bicester, Banbury and Birmingham

Network Diagram - refer to first Page of Table 116

		GW 1	GW ◇1	CH	GW ◇1	GW 1	GW 1	GW 1	GW ◇1	GW 1	GW 1	GW 1	GW 1	GW ◇1	GW 1	XC ◇1	GW 1	GW 1	GW ◇1
London Paddington 15 ⊖	d								00 22					05 21				05 25	05 50
Ealing Broadway ⊖	d																	05 33	
Slough 3	d						00 01		00 41					05 38				05 51	06 06
Maidenhead 3	d						00 10	00 05										06 02	
Twyford 3	d							00 13										06 10	
Reading 7	d		00 04		00 09	00 20	00 25	00 27	01 01		04 54	05 41	05 46	05 54		06 10	06 12	06 21	06 22
Reading West	d					00s23					05 06	05 44					06 14		
Theale	d					00s29					05 12	05 50					06 20		
Aldermaston	d					00s34					05 17	05 55					06 25		
Midgham	d					00s37					05 20	05 58					06 29		
Thatcham	d					00s42					05 25	06 03					06 34		
Newbury Racecourse	d					00s47					05 30	06 08					06 38		
Newbury	a					00 52					05 32	06 10					06 44		
	d										05 33	06 10							
Kintbury	d										05 39	06 17							
Hungerford	d										05 44	06 21							
Bedwyn	a										05 52	06 31							
Tilehurst	d							00 33					05 52					06 25	
Pangbourne	d							00 37					05 56					06 29	
Goring & Streatley	d							00 41					06 01					06 34	
Cholsey	d							00 46					06 06		←			06 39	
Didcot Parkway	a				00 29		00 44	00 56	01 19				06 12	06 07	06 12			06 46	06 37
	d	00 08					00 44	00 56	01 19				06 13	06 08	06 13			06 47	06 38
Appleford	d							01 00					→		06 17			→	
Culham	d							01 03							06 20				
Radley	d	00 14						01 07							06 24				
Oxford	a	00 27	00 35				01 02	01 18	01 34					06 22	06 32	06 36			06 52
	d			00 38						06 16						06 38			
Islip	d																		
Bicester Town	a																		
Tackley	d			00 48						06 25									
Heyford	d			00 53						06 29									
Kings Sutton	d			01 01						06 38									
Banbury	a			01 11						06 46						06 54			
Leamington Spa 8	a															07 13			
Coventry	a															07 25			
Birmingham International	a															07 37			
Birmingham New Street 12	a															07 48			

		CH	GW 1	XC ◇1	GW 1	GW 1	GW ◇1	GW 1	GW 1	GW ◇1	XC ◇1	GW 1	GW ◇1	GW 1	CH	GW 1	XC ◇1	GW 1	GW 1
London Paddington 15 ⊖	d					05 57	06 21		06 27	06 30			06 50						06 57
Ealing Broadway ⊖	d					06 05			06 35										07 05
Slough 3	d					06 30	06 38		06 57				07 06						07 27
Maidenhead 3	d					06 41			07 04										07 34
Twyford 3	d					06 49		←	07 12							←			07 42
Reading 7	d			06 45	06 48	06 56	06 54	06 56	07 23	06 57	07 10	07 11	07 22			07 23	07 47	07 48	07 53
Reading West	d					→			→			07 14							
Theale	d				06 56							07 20						07 56	
Aldermaston	d											07 25							
Midgham	d											07 29							
Thatcham	d				07 04							07 34						08 04	
Newbury Racecourse	d											07 38							
Newbury	a				07 10							07 43						08 10	
	d				07 10													08 10	
Kintbury	d				07 17													08 17	
Hungerford	d				07 21													08 21	
Bedwyn	a				07 31													08 31	
Tilehurst	d							07 00								07 27			07 57
Pangbourne	d							07 04								07 31			08 01
Goring & Streatley	d							07 09								07 36			08 06
Cholsey	d		←					07 14								07 41			08 11
Didcot Parkway	a		06 46					07 30		07 12						07 49			08 19
	d		06 47					07 30								07 51			08 25
Appleford	d																		
Culham	d															07 56			
Radley	d		06 54													08 00			
Oxford	a		07 03	07 10			07 20	07 43			07 34		07 48			08 09	08 13		08 40
	d	07 00		07 12							07 36			07 53	08 07		08 15		
Islip	d	07 13													08 20				
Bicester Town	a	07 25													08 32				
Tackley	d													08 02					
Heyford	d													08 06					
Kings Sutton	d													08 15					
Banbury	a			07 32							07 53			08 23			08 32		
Leamington Spa 8	a			07 50							08 11						08 49		
Coventry	a										08 23								
Birmingham International	a										08 37								
Birmingham New Street 12	a			08 17							08 48						09 20		

For complete service between Banbury and Leamington (Birmingham), please refer to table 71

Table 116

Saturdays

15 February to 22 March

London and Reading - Bedwyn, Oxford, Bicester, Banbury and Birmingham

Network Diagram - refer to first Page of Table 116

		GW	GW	GW	XC	GW	GW	GW	GW	XC	GW	GW	GW	GW	CH	GW	GW	GW	XC
		◇1	1	R 1 ☕	◇1 🛒	1	1	◇1	1	◇1 🛒	1	◇1 ☕	◇1 ☕	◇1 ☕		1	1	◇1 ☕	◇1 🛒
London Paddington 15 ⊖	d	07 21	07 27	07 30				07 50			07 57	08 15	08 18	08 21			08 27	08 30	
Ealing Broadway ⊖	d		07 35								08 05						08 35		
Slough 3	d	07 38	07 57					08 06			08 27			08 39			08 57		
Maidenhead 3	d		08 04								08 34						09 04		
Twyford 3	d		08 12						←		08 42					←	09 12		
Reading 7	d	07 54	08 23	07 57	08 10	08 21		08 22	08 23	08 40	08 54	08 42	08 48	08 54		08 54	09 23	08 57	09 10
Reading West	d		→			08 23					→						→		
Theale	d					08 31							08 58						
Aldermaston	d					08 36													
Midgham	d					08 41													
Thatcham	d					08 46							09 07						
Newbury Racecourse	d					08 49													
Newbury	a					08 54							09 13						
	d						09 00						09 14						
Kintbury	d						09 06												
Hungerford	d						09 11						09 23						
Bedwyn	a						09 19						09 30						
Tilehurst	d								08 27							08 58			
Pangbourne	d								08 31							09 01			
Goring & Streatley	d								08 36							09 06			
Cholsey	d								08 41							09 11			
Didcot Parkway	a			08 12					08 48			08 55				09 19		09 12	
	d								08 55							09 25			
Appleford	d								09 00										
Culham	d																		
Radley	d								09 03										
Oxford	a	08 19			08 34			08 48	09 14	09 04				09 18		09 40			09 34
	d				08 36					09 07					09 28				09 36
Islip	d														09 41				
Bicester Town	a														09 53				
Tackley	d																		
Heyford	d																		
Kings Sutton	d																		
Banbury	a				08 53					09 23									09 52
Leamington Spa 8	a				09 11					09 41									10 11
Coventry	a				09 23														10 23
Birmingham International	a				09 37														10 37
Birmingham New Street 12	a				09 48					10 18									10 48

		GW	GW	GW	XC	GW	GW	GW	GW	GW	GW	GW	XC	GW	GW	CH	GW	XC	GW
		1	◇1	1	◇1 🛒	1	1	1	1	◇1	1	◇1 ☕	◇1 🛒	1	◇1		1	◇1 🛒	1
London Paddington 15 ⊖	d		08 50				08 57	09 18		09 21	09 27	09 30			09 50				09 57
Ealing Broadway ⊖	d						09 05				09 35								10 05
Slough 3	d		09 06				09 27			09 39	09 57				10 06				10 27
Maidenhead 3	d						09 34				10 04								10 34
Twyford 3	d			←			09 42		←		10 14						←		10 44
Reading 7	d	09 12	09 22	09 23	09 40		09 53	09 48	09 53	09 54	10 23	09 57	10 10	10 12	10 22		10 23	10 39	10 53
Reading West	d	09 14					→				→			10 14					→
Theale	d	09 20						09 56						10 20					
Aldermaston	d	09 25												10 25					
Midgham	d	09 29												10 29					
Thatcham	d	09 34						10 04						10 34					
Newbury Racecourse	d	09 38												10 38					
Newbury	a	09 44						10 10						10 44					
	d							10 10											
Kintbury	d							10 17											
Hungerford	d							10 21											
Bedwyn	a							10 32											
Tilehurst	d			09 27					09 57								10 27		
Pangbourne	d			09 31					10 01								10 31		
Goring & Streatley	d			09 36					10 06								10 36		
Cholsey	d			09 41					10 11								10 41		
Didcot Parkway	a			09 48					10 18			10 12					10 49		
	d			09 55					10 25								10 55		
Appleford	d																11 00		
Culham	d			10 01															
Radley	d			10 03													11 03		
Oxford	a		09 48	10 14	10 04				10 40	10 19			10 34		10 48		11 14	11 04	
	d				10 07	10 16							10 36			11 00		11 07	
Islip	d															11 13			
Bicester Town	a															11 25			
Tackley	d					10 25													
Heyford	d					10 29													
Kings Sutton	d					10 39													
Banbury	a				10 23	10 46							10 53					11 23	
Leamington Spa 8	a				10 41								11 11					11 41	
Coventry	a												11 23						
Birmingham International	a												11 37						
Birmingham New Street 12	a				11 18								11 48					12 18	

For complete service between Banbury and Leamington (Birmingham), please refer to table 71

Table 116

Saturdays

15 February to 22 March

London and Reading - Bedwyn, Oxford, Bicester, Banbury and Birmingham

Network Diagram - refer to first Page of Table 116

Station		GW ◇1 trolley	GW 1	GW 1	GW ◇1 trolley	GW 1	GW ◇1 trolley	XC ◇1 buffet	GW 1	GW ◇1 buffet
London Paddington 15 ⊖	d	10 15	10 18		10 21	10 27	10 30			10 50
Ealing Broadway ⊖	d					10 35				
Slough 3	d				10 39	10 57				11 06
Maidenhead 3	d					11 04				
Twyford 3	d			←		11 12				
Reading 7	d	10 42	10 48	10 53	10 54	11 23	10 58	11 09	11 12	11 22
Reading West	d					→			11 14	
Theale	d		10 56						11 20	
Aldermaston	d								11 25	
Midgham	d								11 29	
Thatcham	d		11 04						11 34	
Newbury Racecourse	d								11 38	
Newbury	a		11 10						11 44	
	d		11 10							
Kintbury	d		11 17							
Hungerford	d		11 21							
Bedwyn	a		11 32							
Tilehurst	d			10 57						
Pangbourne	d			11 01						
Goring & Streatley	d			11 06						
Cholsey	d			11 11						
Didcot Parkway	a	10 55		11 19			11 12			
	d			11 25						
Appleford	d									
Culham	d									
Radley	d									
Oxford	a			11 40	11 19			11 34		11 48
	d							11 36		
Islip	d									
Bicester Town	a									
Tackley	d									
Heyford	d									
Kings Sutton	d									
Banbury	a							11 53		
Leamington Spa 8	a							12 11		
Coventry	a							12 23		
Birmingham International	a							12 37		
Birmingham New Street 12	a							12 48		

Station		GW 1	XC ◇1 buffet	GW 1	GW 1	GW 1	GW 1	GW ◇1 buffet	CH	GW 1
London Paddington 15 ⊖	d				10 57	11 18		11 21		11 27
Ealing Broadway ⊖	d				11 05					11 35
Slough 3	d				11 27			11 39		11 57
Maidenhead 3	d				11 34					12 04
Twyford 3	d	←			11 42		←			12 12
Reading 7	d	11 23	11 40		11 53	11 48	11 53	11 54		12 23
Reading West	d				→					→
Theale	d					11 56				
Aldermaston	d									
Midgham	d									
Thatcham	d					12 04				
Newbury Racecourse	d									
Newbury	a					12 10				
	d					12 10				
Kintbury	d					12 17				
Hungerford	d					12 21				
Bedwyn	a					12 32				
Tilehurst	d	11 27					11 57			
Pangbourne	d	11 31					12 01			
Goring & Streatley	d	11 36					12 06			
Cholsey	d	11 41					12 11			
Didcot Parkway	a	11 49					12 19			
	d	11 55					12 25			
Appleford	d									
Culham	d									
Radley	d	12 03								
Oxford	a	12 14	12 05				12 40	12 20		
	d		12 07	12 16					12 30	
Islip	d								12 43	
Bicester Town	a								12 55	
Tackley	d			12 25						
Heyford	d			12 29						
Kings Sutton	d			12 39						
Banbury	a		12 23	12 46						
Leamington Spa 8	a		12 41							
Coventry	a									
Birmingham International	a									
Birmingham New Street 12	a		13 18							

Station		GW ◇1 Ø	XC ◇1 buffet	GW 1	GW ◇1	GW 1	XC ◇1 buffet	GW 1	GW ◇1 trolley	GW ◇1 trolley
London Paddington 15 ⊖	d	11 30			11 50			11 57	12 15	12 18
Ealing Broadway ⊖	d							12 05		
Slough 3	d				12 06			12 27		
Maidenhead 3	d							12 34		
Twyford 3	d					←		12 45		
Reading 7	d	11 57	12 09	12 12	12 22	12 23	12 39	12 53	12 42	12 48
Reading West	d			12 14				→		
Theale	d			12 20						12 56
Aldermaston	d			12 25						
Midgham	d			12 29						
Thatcham	d			12 34						13 05
Newbury Racecourse	d			12 38						
Newbury	a			12 44						13 12
	d									13 13
Kintbury	d									
Hungerford	d									13 21
Bedwyn	a									13 29
Tilehurst	d					12 27				
Pangbourne	d					12 31				
Goring & Streatley	d					12 36				
Cholsey	d					12 41				
Didcot Parkway	a	12 12				12 48			12 55	
	d					12 55				
Appleford	d					13 00				
Culham	d									
Radley	d					13 03				
Oxford	a		12 33		12 48	13 14	13 04			
	d		12 36				13 07			
Islip	d									
Bicester Town	a									
Tackley	d									
Heyford	d									
Kings Sutton	d									
Banbury	a		12 53				13 23			
Leamington Spa 8	a		13 11				13 41			
Coventry	a		13 23							
Birmingham International	a		13 37							
Birmingham New Street 12	a		13 48				14 18			

Station		GW 1	GW ◇1	GW 1	GW ◇1 trolley	XC ◇1 buffet	CH	GW 1	GW ◇1 buffet	GW 1
London Paddington 15 ⊖	d		12 21	12 27	12 30				12 50	
Ealing Broadway ⊖	d			12 35						
Slough 3	d		12 39	12 57					13 06	
Maidenhead 3	d			13 04						
Twyford 3	d	←		13 12						←
Reading 7	d	12 53	12 54	13 23	12 57	13 10		13 12	13 22	13 23
Reading West	d			→				13 14		
Theale	d							13 20		
Aldermaston	d							13 25		
Midgham	d							13 29		
Thatcham	d							13 34		
Newbury Racecourse	d							13 38		
Newbury	a							13 44		
	d									
Kintbury	d									
Hungerford	d									
Bedwyn	a									
Tilehurst	d	12 57								13 27
Pangbourne	d	13 01								13 31
Goring & Streatley	d	13 06								13 36
Cholsey	d	13 11								13 41
Didcot Parkway	a	13 19			13 12					13 48
	d	13 25								13 55
Appleford	d									
Culham	d									14 01
Radley	d									14 03
Oxford	a	13 40	13 19			13 34			13 48	14 14
	d					13 36	13 41			
Islip	d						13 54			
Bicester Town	a						14 06			
Tackley	d									
Heyford	d									
Kings Sutton	d									
Banbury	a					13 53				
Leamington Spa 8	a					14 11				
Coventry	a					14 23				
Birmingham International	a					14 37				
Birmingham New Street 12	a					14 48				

For complete service between Banbury and Leamington (Birmingham), please refer to table 71

Table 116

Saturdays
15 February to 22 March

London and Reading - Bedwyn, Oxford, Bicester, Banbury and Birmingham

Network Diagram - refer to first Page of Table 116

		XC ◇1	GW 1	GW 1	GW 1	GW 1	GW ◇1	GW 1	GW ◇1	XC ◇1	GW 1	GW ◇1	CH	GW 1	XC ◇1	GW 1	GW ◇1	GW 1	GW 1
London Paddington 15 ⊖	d			12 57	13 18		13 21	13 27	13 30			13 50				13 57	14 15	14 18	
Ealing Broadway ⊖	d			13 05				13 35								14 05			
Slough 3	d			13 27			13 39	13 57				14 06				14 27			
Maidenhead 3	d			13 34				14 04								14 34			
Twyford 3	d			13 42		←		14 12						←		14 45			←
Reading 7	d	13 40		13 53	13 48	13 53	13 54	14 23	13 57	14 10	14 12	14 22		14 23	14 39	14 53	14 42	14 49	14 53
Reading West	d			→				→			14 14					→			
Theale	d				13 56						14 20							14 56	
Aldermaston	d										14 25								
Midgham	d										14 29								
Thatcham	d				14 04						14 34							15 05	
Newbury Racecourse	d										14 38								
Newbury	a				14 10						14 44							15 10	
	d				14 10													15 11	
Kintbury	d				14 17													15 17	
Hungerford	d				14 21													15 22	
Bedwyn	a				14 32													15 32	
Tilehurst	d					13 57								14 27					14 57
Pangbourne	d					14 01								14 31					15 01
Goring & Streatley	d					14 06								14 36					15 06
Cholsey	d					14 11								14 41					15 12
Didcot Parkway	a					14 19			14 12					14 48			14 55		15 19
	d					14 25								14 55					15 25
Appleford	d													15 00					
Culham	d																		
Radley	d													15 03					
Oxford	a	14 04				14 40	14 19			14 34		14 48		15 14	15 04				15 40
	d	14 07	14 16							14 36			14 57		15 07				
Islip	d												15 10						
Bicester Town	a												15 22						
Tackley	d		14 25																
Heyford	d		14 29																
Kings Sutton	d		14 39																
Banbury	a	14 23	14 46							14 53					15 23				
Leamington Spa 8	a	14 41								15 11					15 41				
Coventry	a									15 23									
Birmingham International	a									15 37									
Birmingham New Street 12	a	15 18								15 48					16 18				

		GW ◇1	GW 1	GW ◇1	XC ◇1	GW 1	GW ◇1	CH	GW 1	XC ◇1	GW 1	GW 1	GW 1	GW 1	GW ◇1	GW 1	GW ◇1	XC ◇1	GW 1
London Paddington 15 ⊖	d	14 21	14 27	14 30			14 50					14 57	15 18		15 21	15 27	15 30		
Ealing Broadway ⊖	d		14 35									15 05				15 35			
Slough 3	d	14 39	14 57				15 06					15 27			15 39	15 57			
Maidenhead 3	d		15 04									15 34				16 04			
Twyford 3	d		15 12						←			15 42		←		16 13			
Reading 7	d	14 54	15 23	14 57	15 09	15 12	15 22		15 23	15 40		15 53	15 48	15 53	15 54	16 24	15 57	16 10	16 12
Reading West	d		→			15 14						→				→			16 14
Theale	d					15 20							15 56						16 20
Aldermaston	d					15 25													16 25
Midgham	d					15 29													16 29
Thatcham	d					15 34							16 04						16 34
Newbury Racecourse	d					15 38													16 38
Newbury	a					15 44							16 09						16 44
	d												16 10						
Kintbury	d												16 16						
Hungerford	d												16 21						
Bedwyn	a												16 31						
Tilehurst	d								15 27					15 57					
Pangbourne	d								15 31					16 01					
Goring & Streatley	d								15 36					16 06					
Cholsey	d								15 41					16 11					
Didcot Parkway	a			15 12					15 48					16 19			16 12		
	d								15 55					16 25					
Appleford	d																		
Culham	d								16 01										
Radley	d								16 03										
Oxford	a	15 18			15 34		15 48		16 14	16 04				16 40	16 19			16 34	
	d				15 36			16 00		16 07	16 16							16 36	
Islip	d							16 13											
Bicester Town	a							16 25											
Tackley	d										16 25								
Heyford	d										16 29								
Kings Sutton	d										16 39								
Banbury	a				15 53					16 23	16 46							16 53	
Leamington Spa 8	a				16 11					16 41								17 11	
Coventry	a				16 23													17 23	
Birmingham International	a				16 37													17 37	
Birmingham New Street 12	a				16 48					17 18								17 48	

For complete service between Banbury and Leamington (Birmingham), please refer to table 71

Table 116

Saturdays
15 February to 22 March

London and Reading - Bedwyn, Oxford, Bicester, Banbury and Birmingham

Network Diagram - refer to first Page of Table 116

		GW	CH	GW	XC	GW	GW	GW	GW	GW	GW	GW	XC	GW	GW	GW	XC	GW	GW
		◇1		1	◇1	1	◇1	1	1	◇1	1	◇1	◇1	1	◇1	1	◇1	1	1
					🛒		☕			☕		☕	🛒		🛒		🛒		
London Paddington 15 ⊖	d	15 50				15 57	16 15	16 18		16 21	16 27	16 30			16 50				16 57
Ealing Broadway ⊖	d					16 05					16 35								17 05
Slough 3	d	16 06				16 27				16 38	16 57				17 06				17 27
Maidenhead 3	d					16 34					17 04								17 34
Twyford 3	d			←		16 45			←		17 12					←			17 42
Reading 7	d	16 22		16 24	16 39	16 53	16 42	16 48	16 53	16 54	17 23	16 57	17 09	17 12	17 22	17 23	17 40		17 53
Reading West	d					→					→			17 14					→
Theale	d							16 56						17 20					
Aldermaston	d													17 25					
Midgham	d													17 29					
Thatcham	d							17 04						17 34					
Newbury Racecourse	d													17 38					
Newbury	a							17 10						17 44					
	d							17 10											
Kintbury	d							17 17											
Hungerford	d							17 21											
Bedwyn	a							17 32											
Tilehurst	d			16 28					16 57							17 27			
Pangbourne	d			16 32					17 01							17 31			
Goring & Streatley	d			16 37					17 06							17 36			
Cholsey	d			16 42					17 11							17 41			
Didcot Parkway	a			16 49			16 55		17 19			17 12				17 48			
	d			16 55					17 25							17 55			
Appleford	d			17 00															
Culham	d															18 01			
Radley	d			17 03												18 03			
Oxford	a	16 48		17 14	17 04				17 40	17 18			17 34		17 48	18 14	18 04		
	d		17 10		17 07								17 36				18 07	18 16	
Islip	d		17 23																
Bicester Town	a		17 35																
Tackley	d																	18 25	
Heyford	d																	18 29	
Kings Sutton	d																	18 39	
Banbury	a				17 23								17 53				18 23	18 46	
Leamington Spa 8	a				17 41								18 11				18 41		
Coventry	a												18 23						
Birmingham International	a												18 37						
Birmingham New Street 12	a				18 18								18 48				19 18		

		GW	GW	GW	GW	GW	XC	CH	GW	GW	GW	XC	GW	GW	GW	GW	GW	GW	GW
		1	1	◇1	1	◇1	◇1		1	◇1	1	◇1	1	◇1	1	1	◇1	1	◇1
				☕		☕	🛒			🛒		🛒		☕			☕		☕
London Paddington 15 ⊖	d	17 18		17 21	17 27	17 30				17 50			17 57	18 15	18 18		18 21	18 27	18 30
Ealing Broadway ⊖	d				17 35								18 05					18 35	
Slough 3	d			17 39	17 57					18 06			18 27				18 38	18 57	
Maidenhead 3	d				18 04								18 34					19 04	
Twyford 3	d		←		18 12						←		18 45			←		19 12	
Reading 7	d	17 48	17 53	17 54	18 23	17 57	18 09		18 12	18 22	18 23	18 39	18 53	18 42	18 48	18 53	18 54	19 23	18 57
Reading West	d				→				18 14				→					→	
Theale	d	17 56							18 20						18 56				
Aldermaston	d								18 25										
Midgham	d								18 29										
Thatcham	d	18 04							18 34						19 04				
Newbury Racecourse	d								18 38										
Newbury	a	18 10							18 44						19 10				
	d	18 10													19 10				
Kintbury	d	18 17													19 17				
Hungerford	d	18 21													19 21				
Bedwyn	a	18 30													19 32				
Tilehurst	d		17 57								18 27					18 57			
Pangbourne	d		18 01								18 31					19 01			
Goring & Streatley	d		18 06								18 36					19 06			
Cholsey	d		18 11								18 41					19 11			
Didcot Parkway	a		18 19			18 12					18 48			18 55		19 19			19 12
	d		18 25								18 55					19 25			
Appleford	d										19 00								
Culham	d																		
Radley	d										19 03								
Oxford	a		18 40	18 18			18 34			18 48	19 14	19 04				19 40	19 18		
	d						18 36	18 41				19 07							
Islip	d							18 54											
Bicester Town	a							19 06											
Tackley	d																		
Heyford	d																		
Kings Sutton	d																		
Banbury	a						18 53					19 23							
Leamington Spa 8	a						19 11					19 41							
Coventry	a						19 23												
Birmingham International	a						19 37												
Birmingham New Street 12	a						19 48					20 18							

For complete service between Banbury and Leamington (Birmingham), please refer to table 71

Table 116

Saturdays

15 February to 22 March

London and Reading - Bedwyn, Oxford, Bicester, Banbury and Birmingham

Network Diagram - refer to first Page of Table 116

		XC	CH	GW	GW	GW	GW	GW	XC	GW	GW	GW	GW	GW	GW	XC	GW	CH	GW
		◇1 [trolley]		◇1	1	1	1	◇1 [buffet]	◇1	◇1 [buffet]	1	1	◇1	1	◇1 [buffet]	◇1	◇1 [trolley]		1
London Paddington 15 ⊖	d			18 50			18 57	19 06		19 15			19 21	19 27	19 30		19 50		
Ealing Broadway ⊖	d						19 05							19 35					
Slough 3	d			19 06			19 27						19 38	19 57			20 06		
Maidenhead 3	d						19 34							20 04					
Twyford 3	d					←	19 42					←		20 12					←
Reading 7	d	19 09		19 22		19 23	19 53	19 32	19 40	19 42	19 49	19 53	19 54	20 23	19 57	20 09	20 22		20 23
Reading West	d						→				19 52			→					
Theale	d										19 58								
Aldermaston	d										20 03								
Midgham	d										20 06								
Thatcham	d										20 11								
Newbury Racecourse	d										20 16								
Newbury	a							19 47			20 18								
	d										20 19								
Kintbury	d										20 25								
Hungerford	d										20 30								
Bedwyn	a										20 38								
Tilehurst	d					19 27						19 57							20 27
Pangbourne	d					19 31						20 01							20 31
Goring & Streatley	d					19 36						20 06							20 36
Cholsey	d					19 41						20 11							20 41
Didcot Parkway	a					19 49				19 55		20 18			20 11				20 49
	d					19 55						20 25							20 55
Appleford	d																		21 00
Culham	d					20 01													
Radley	d					20 03													21 03
Oxford	a	19 34		19 48		20 14			20 04			20 41	20 20			20 34	20 47		21 14
	d	19 36	19 48		19 56				20 07							20 36		21 00	
Islip	d		20 01															21 13	
Bicester Town	a		20 13															21 25	
Tackley	d				20 05														
Heyford	d				20 09														
Kings Sutton	d				20 18														
Banbury	a	19 53			20 25				20 28							20 53			
Leamington Spa 8	a	20 10							20 45							21 11			
Coventry	a	20 23														21 23			
Birmingham International	a	20 37														21 37			
Birmingham New Street 12	a	20 48							21 15							21 48			

		GW	GW	GW	XC	GW	GW	GW	GW	GW	GW	GW	XC	GW	GW	XC	GW	GW	CH
		1	◇1 [buffet]	◇1 [buffet]	◇1	◇1 [buffet]	1	◇1	1	1	1	◇1 [buffet]	◇1	◇1 [trolley]	1	◇1	1	◇1	
London Paddington 15 ⊖	d	19 57	20 00	20 06		20 15		20 18			20 27	20 30		20 48			20 57	21 18	
Ealing Broadway ⊖	d	20 05									20 35						21 05		
Slough 3	d	20 27						20 35			20 57			21 05			21 27	21 35	
Maidenhead 3	d	20 34									21 04						21 34		
Twyford 3	d	20 42								←	21 12				←		21 46		
Reading 7	d	20 53	20 27	20 35	20 40	20 42	20 49	20 51		20 53	21 24	20 57	21 09	21 21	21 24	21 40	21 55	21 51	
Reading West	d	→					20 52				→						→		
Theale	d						20 58												
Aldermaston	d						21 03												
Midgham	d						21 06												
Thatcham	d						21 11												
Newbury Racecourse	d						21 16												
Newbury	a			20 49			21 18												
	d						21 32												
Kintbury	d						21 39												
Hungerford	d						21 43												
Bedwyn	a						21 52												
Tilehurst	d									20 57					21 27				
Pangbourne	d									21 01					21 32				
Goring & Streatley	d									21 06					21 37				
Cholsey	d									21 11					21 42				
Didcot Parkway	a		20 41			20 55				21 19		21 12		21 36	21 49			22 07	
	d									21 25				21 37	21 55			22 08	
Appleford	d																		
Culham	d														22 01				
Radley	d														22 03				
Oxford	a				21 04			21 18		21 40			21 34	21 50	22 14	22 03		22 22	
	d				21 07				21 20				21 36			22 07			22 25
Islip	d																		22 38
Bicester Town	a																		22 50
Tackley	d								21 29										
Heyford	d								21 33										
Kings Sutton	d								21 42										
Banbury	a				21 24				21 49				21 54			22 28			
Leamington Spa 8	a				21 43								22 11			22 45			
Coventry	a				21 55								22 23						
Birmingham International	a				22 10								22 36						
Birmingham New Street 12	a				22 21								22 48			23 16			

For complete service between Banbury and Leamington (Birmingham), please refer to table 71

Table 116

Saturdays

15 February to 22 March

London and Reading - Bedwyn, Oxford, Bicester, Banbury and Birmingham

Network Diagram - refer to first Page of Table 116

		GW	GW	GW	GW	GW	GW	GW	GW	GW	GW	GW	GW	GW	GW	GW	GW
		1	◇1	1	1	◇1	◇1	◇1	1		◇1	1	1	◇1	1	◇1	◇1
			⊡				⊡			🚌	⊡					⊡	
London Paddington 15 ⊖	d		21 30		21 42	21 48	22 00	22 18			22 35		22 42	22 48		23 30	23 33
Ealing Broadway ⊖	d				21 52								22 52				
Slough 3	d				22 18	22 05		22 35					23 20	23 05			23 50
Maidenhead 3	d				22 29			22 42					23 32	23 13			23 58
Twyford 3	d	←			22 38				←				23 40		←		
Reading 7	d	21 55	21 57	22 03	22 58	22 21	22 28	22 54	22 58		23 03	23 12	23 48	23 25	23 48	00 03	00 11
Reading West	d			22 06	→							23 14	→				
Theale	d			22 12								23 20					
Aldermaston	d			22 17								23 25					
Midgham	d			22 20								23 29					
Thatcham	d			22 25								23 34					
Newbury Racecourse	d			22 30								23 38					
Newbury	a			22 32								23 41					
	d			22 32								23 41					
Kintbury	d			22 39								23 48					
Hungerford	d			22 43								23 52					
Bedwyn	a			22 52								00 01					
Tilehurst	d	22 01							23 03						23 52		
Pangbourne	d	22 06							23 07						23 56		
Goring & Streatley	d	22 11							23 11						00 01		
Cholsey	d	22 16							23 16						00 06		
Didcot Parkway	a	22 23	22 12			22 35	22 47	23 10	23 24		23 27			23 42	00 15	00 19	00 28
	d	22 25				22 36		23 11	23 25					23 42	00 15		00 29
Appleford	d																00s33
Culham	d																00s35
Radley	d	22 34							23 32						00s23		00s39
Oxford	a	22 43				22 48		23 23	23 43					23 58	00 32		00 50
	d									23 53							
Islip	d																
Bicester Town	a																
Tackley	d									00s13							
Heyford	d									00s28							
Kings Sutton	d																
Banbury	a									00 53							
Leamington Spa 8	a																
Coventry	a																
Birmingham International	a																
Birmingham New Street 12	a																

For complete service between Banbury and Leamington (Birmingham), please refer to table 71

Table 116

Saturdays
29 March to 17 May

London and Reading - Bedwyn, Oxford, Bicester, Banbury and Birmingham

Network Diagram - refer to first Page of Table 116

		GW	GW	CH	GW	GW	GW	GW	GW	GW	GW	GW	GW	GW	GW	XC	GW	GW	GW
		1	◇1		◇1	1	1	1	◇1	1	1	1	1	◇1	1	◇1	1	1	◇1
London Paddington 15 ⊖	d								00 22					05 21				05 25	05 50
Ealing Broadway ⊖	d																	05 33	
Slough 3	d						00 01		00 41					05 38				05 51	06 06
Maidenhead 3	d						00 10	00 05										06 02	
Twyford 3	d							00 13										06 10	
Reading 7	d		00 04		00 09	00 20	00 25	00 27	01 01		04 54	05 41	05 46	05 54		06 10	06 12	06 21	06 22
Reading West	d					00s23					05 06	05 44					06 14		
Theale	d					00s29					05 12	05 50					06 20		
Aldermaston	d					00s34					05 17	05 55					06 25		
Midgham	d					00s37					05 20	05 58					06 29		
Thatcham	d					00s42					05 25	06 03					06 34		
Newbury Racecourse	d					00s47					05 30	06 08					06 38		
Newbury	a					00 52					05 32	06 10					06 44		
	d										05 33	06 10							
Kintbury	d										05 39	06 17							
Hungerford	d										05 44	06 21							
Bedwyn	a										05 52	06 31							
Tilehurst	d							00 33					05 52					06 25	
Pangbourne	d							00 37					05 56					06 29	
Goring & Streatley	d							00 41					06 01					06 34	
Cholsey	d							00 46					06 06		←			06 39	
Didcot Parkway	a				00 29		00 44	00 56	01 19				06 12	06 07	06 12			06 46	06 37
	d	00 08					00 44	00 56	01 19				06 13	06 08	06 13			06 47	06 38
Appleford	d							01 00					→		06 17			→	
Culham	d							01 03							06 20				
Radley	d	00 14						01 07							06 24				
Oxford	a	00 27	00 35				01 02	01 18	01 34					06 22	06 32	06 36			06 52
	d			00 38						06 16						06 38			
Islip	d																		
Bicester Town	a																		
Tackley	d			00 48						06 25									
Heyford	d			00 53						06 29									
Kings Sutton	d			01 01						06 38									
Banbury	a			01 11						06 46						06 54			
Leamington Spa 8	a															07 13			
Coventry	a															07 25			
Birmingham International	a															07 37			
Birmingham New Street 12	a															07 48			

		CH	GW	XC	GW	GW	GW	GW	GW	GW	XC	GW	GW	GW	CH	GW	XC	GW	GW
			1	◇1	1	1	◇1	1	1	◇1	◇1	1	◇1	1		1	◇1	1	1
London Paddington 15 ⊖	d					05 57	06 21		06 27	06 30			06 50						06 57
Ealing Broadway ⊖	d					06 05			06 35										07 05
Slough 3	d					06 30	06 38		06 57				07 06						07 27
Maidenhead 3	d					06 41			07 04										07 34
Twyford 3	d					06 49		←	07 12							←			07 42
Reading 7	d			06 45	06 48	06 56	06 54	06 56	07 23	06 57	07 10	07 11	07 22			07 23	07 47	07 48	07 53
Reading West	d					→			→			07 14							
Theale	d				06 56							07 20						07 56	
Aldermaston	d											07 25							
Midgham	d											07 29							
Thatcham	d				07 04							07 34						08 04	
Newbury Racecourse	d											07 38							
Newbury	a				07 10							07 43						08 10	
	d				07 10													08 10	
Kintbury	d				07 17													08 17	
Hungerford	d				07 21													08 21	
Bedwyn	a				07 31													08 31	
Tilehurst	d							07 00								07 27			07 57
Pangbourne	d							07 04								07 31			08 01
Goring & Streatley	d							07 09								07 36			08 06
Cholsey	d		←					07 14								07 41			08 11
Didcot Parkway	a		06 46					07 30		07 12						07 49			08 19
	d		06 47					07 30								07 51			08 25
Appleford	d																		
Culham	d															07 56			
Radley	d		06 54													08 00			
Oxford	a		07 03	07 10			07 20	07 43			07 34		07 48			08 09	08 13		08 40
	d	07 00		07 12							07 36			07 53	08 07		08 15		
Islip	d	07 13													08 20				
Bicester Town	a	07 25													08 32				
Tackley	d													08 02					
Heyford	d													08 06					
Kings Sutton	d													08 15					
Banbury	a			07 32							07 53			08 23			08 32		
Leamington Spa 8	a			07 50							08 11						08 49		
Coventry	a										08 23								
Birmingham International	a										08 37								
Birmingham New Street 12	a			08 17							08 48						09 20		

For complete service between Banbury and Leamington (Birmingham), please refer to table 71

Table 116

Saturdays
29 March to 17 May

London and Reading - Bedwyn, Oxford, Bicester, Banbury and Birmingham

Network Diagram - refer to first Page of Table 116

Station		GW	GW	GW	XC	GW	GW	GW	GW	XC
		◇1	1	R 1 FP	◇1 T	1	1	◇1	1	◇1 T
London Paddington 15 ⊖	d	07 21	07 27	07 30				07 50		
Ealing Broadway ⊖	d		07 35							
Slough 3	d	07 38	07 57					08 06		
Maidenhead 3	d		08 04							
Twyford 3	d		08 12						←	
Reading 7	d	07 54	08 23	07 57	08 10	08 21		08 22	08 23	08 40
Reading West	d		→			08 23				
Theale	d					08 31				
Aldermaston	d					08 36				
Midgham	d					08 41				
Thatcham	d					08 46				
Newbury Racecourse	d					08 49				
Newbury	a					08 54				
	d						09 00			
Kintbury	d						09 06			
Hungerford	d						09 11			
Bedwyn	a						09 19			
Tilehurst	d								08 27	
Pangbourne	d								08 31	
Goring & Streatley	d								08 36	
Cholsey	d								08 41	
Didcot Parkway	a			08 12					08 48	
	d								08 55	
Appleford	d								09 00	
Culham	d									
Radley	d								09 03	
Oxford	a	08 19			08 34			08 48	09 14	09 04
	d				08 36					09 07
Islip	d									
Bicester Town	a									
Tackley	d									
Heyford	d									
Kings Sutton	d									
Banbury	a				08 53					09 23
Leamington Spa 8	a				09 11					09 41
Coventry	a				09 23					
Birmingham International	a				09 37					
Birmingham New Street 12	a				09 48					10 18

Station		GW	GW	GW	GW	CH	GW	GW	GW	XC
		1	◇1 FP	◇1 FP	◇1 FP		1	1	◇1 FP	◇1 T
London Paddington 15 ⊖	d	07 57	08 15	08 18	08 21			08 27	08 30	
Ealing Broadway ⊖	d	08 05						08 35		
Slough 3	d	08 27			08 39			08 57		
Maidenhead 3	d	08 34						09 04		
Twyford 3	d	08 42					←	09 12		
Reading 7	d	08 54	08 42	08 48	08 54		08 54	09 23	08 57	09 10
Reading West	d	→						→		
Theale	d			08 58						
Aldermaston	d									
Midgham	d									
Thatcham	d			09 07						
Newbury Racecourse	d									
Newbury	a			09 13						
	d			09 14						
Kintbury	d									
Hungerford	d			09 23						
Bedwyn	a			09 30						
Tilehurst	d						08 58			
Pangbourne	d						09 01			
Goring & Streatley	d						09 06			
Cholsey	d						09 11			
Didcot Parkway	a		08 55				09 19		09 12	
	d						09 25			
Appleford	d									
Culham	d									
Radley	d									
Oxford	a				09 18		09 40			09 34
	d					09 28				09 36
Islip	d					09 41				
Bicester Town	a					09 53				
Tackley	d									
Heyford	d									
Kings Sutton	d									
Banbury	a									09 52
Leamington Spa 8	a									10 11
Coventry	a									10 23
Birmingham International	a									10 37
Birmingham New Street 12	a									10 48

Station		GW	GW	GW	XC	GW	GW	GW	GW	GW
		1	◇1	1	◇1 T	1	1	1	1	◇1
London Paddington 15 ⊖	d		08 50				08 57	09 18		09 21
Ealing Broadway ⊖	d						09 05			
Slough 3	d		09 06				09 27			09 39
Maidenhead 3	d						09 34			
Twyford 3	d			←			09 42		←	
Reading 7	d	09 12	09 22	09 23	09 40		09 53	09 48	09 53	09 54
Reading West	d	09 14					→			
Theale	d	09 20						09 56		
Aldermaston	d	09 25								
Midgham	d	09 29								
Thatcham	d	09 34						10 04		
Newbury Racecourse	d	09 38								
Newbury	a	09 44						10 10		
	d							10 10		
Kintbury	d							10 17		
Hungerford	d							10 21		
Bedwyn	a							10 32		
Tilehurst	d			09 27					09 57	
Pangbourne	d			09 31					10 01	
Goring & Streatley	d			09 36					10 06	
Cholsey	d			09 41					10 11	
Didcot Parkway	a			09 48					10 18	
	d			09 55					10 25	
Appleford	d									
Culham	d			10 01						
Radley	d			10 03						
Oxford	a		09 48	10 14	10 04				10 40	10 19
	d				10 07	10 16				
Islip	d									
Bicester Town	a									
Tackley	d					10 25				
Heyford	d					10 29				
Kings Sutton	d					10 39				
Banbury	a				10 23	10 46				
Leamington Spa 8	a				10 41					
Coventry	a									
Birmingham International	a									
Birmingham New Street 12	a				11 18					

Station		GW	GW	XC	GW	GW	CH	GW	XC	GW
		1	◇1 FP	◇1 T	1	◇1		1	◇1 T	1
London Paddington 15 ⊖	d	09 27	09 30			09 50				09 57
Ealing Broadway ⊖	d	09 35								10 05
Slough 3	d	09 57				10 06				10 27
Maidenhead 3	d	10 04								10 34
Twyford 3	d	10 14						←		10 44
Reading 7	d	10 23	09 57	10 10	10 12	10 22		10 23	10 39	10 53
Reading West	d	→			10 14					→
Theale	d				10 20					
Aldermaston	d				10 25					
Midgham	d				10 29					
Thatcham	d				10 34					
Newbury Racecourse	d				10 38					
Newbury	a				10 44					
	d									
Kintbury	d									
Hungerford	d									
Bedwyn	a									
Tilehurst	d							10 27		
Pangbourne	d							10 31		
Goring & Streatley	d							10 36		
Cholsey	d							10 41		
Didcot Parkway	a		10 12					10 49		
	d							10 55		
Appleford	d							11 00		
Culham	d									
Radley	d							11 03		
Oxford	a			10 34		10 48		11 14	11 04	
	d			10 36			11 00		11 07	
Islip	d						11 13			
Bicester Town	a						11 25			
Tackley	d									
Heyford	d									
Kings Sutton	d									
Banbury	a			10 53					11 23	
Leamington Spa 8	a			11 11					11 41	
Coventry	a			11 23						
Birmingham International	a			11 37						
Birmingham New Street 12	a			11 48					12 18	

For complete service between Banbury and Leamington (Birmingham), please refer to table 71

Table 116

Saturdays
29 March to 17 May

London and Reading - Bedwyn, Oxford, Bicester, Banbury and Birmingham

Network Diagram - refer to first Page of Table 116

Station		GW ◇1 ⊐	GW 1	GW 1	GW ◇1 ⊐	GW 1	GW ◇1 ⊐	XC ◇1 ⚲	GW 1	GW ◇1 ⚲
London Paddington 15 ⊖	d	10 15	10 18		10 21	10 27	10 30			10 50
Ealing Broadway ⊖	d					10 35				
Slough 3	d				10 39	10 57				11 06
Maidenhead 3	d					11 04				
Twyford 3	d			←		11 12				
Reading 7	d	10 42	10 48	10 53	10 54	11 23	10 58	11 09	11 12	11 22
Reading West	d					→			11 14	
Theale	d		10 56						11 20	
Aldermaston	d								11 25	
Midgham	d								11 29	
Thatcham	d		11 04						11 34	
Newbury Racecourse	d								11 38	
Newbury	a		11 10						11 44	
	d		11 10							
Kintbury	d		11 17							
Hungerford	d		11 21							
Bedwyn	a		11 32							
Tilehurst	d			10 57						
Pangbourne	d			11 01						
Goring & Streatley	d			11 06						
Cholsey	d			11 11						
Didcot Parkway	a	10 55		11 19			11 12			
	d			11 25						
Appleford	d									
Culham	d									
Radley	d									
Oxford	a			11 40	11 19			11 34		11 48
	d							11 36		
Islip	d									
Bicester Town	a									
Tackley	d									
Heyford	d									
Kings Sutton	d									
Banbury	a							11 53		
Leamington Spa 8	a							12 11		
Coventry	a							12 23		
Birmingham International	a							12 37		
Birmingham New Street 12	a							12 48		

Station		GW 1	XC ◇1 ⚲	GW 1	GW 1	GW 1	GW 1	GW ◇1 ⚲	CH	GW 1
London Paddington 15 ⊖	d				10 57	11 18		11 21		11 27
Ealing Broadway ⊖	d				11 05					11 35
Slough 3	d				11 27			11 39		11 57
Maidenhead 3	d				11 34					12 04
Twyford 3	d	←			11 42		←			12 12
Reading 7	d	11 23	11 40		11 53	11 48	11 53	11 54		12 23
Reading West	d				→					→
Theale	d					11 56				
Aldermaston	d									
Midgham	d									
Thatcham	d					12 04				
Newbury Racecourse	d									
Newbury	a					12 10				
	d					12 10				
Kintbury	d					12 17				
Hungerford	d					12 21				
Bedwyn	a					12 32				
Tilehurst	d	11 27					11 57			
Pangbourne	d	11 31					12 01			
Goring & Streatley	d	11 36					12 06			
Cholsey	d	11 41					12 11			
Didcot Parkway	a	11 49					12 19			
	d	11 55					12 25			
Appleford	d									
Culham	d									
Radley	d	12 03								
Oxford	a	12 14	12 05				12 40	12 20		
	d		12 07	12 16					12 30	
Islip	d								12 43	
Bicester Town	a								12 55	
Tackley	d			12 25						
Heyford	d			12 29						
Kings Sutton	d			12 39						
Banbury	a		12 23	12 46						
Leamington Spa 8	a		12 41							
Coventry	a									
Birmingham International	a									
Birmingham New Street 12	a		13 18							

Station		GW ◇1 ⊘	XC ◇1 ⚲	GW 1	GW ◇1	GW 1	XC ◇1 ⚲	GW 1	GW ◇1 ⊐	GW ◇1 ⊐
London Paddington 15 ⊖	d	11 30			11 50			11 57	12 15	12 18
Ealing Broadway ⊖	d							12 05		
Slough 3	d				12 06			12 27		
Maidenhead 3	d							12 34		
Twyford 3	d					←		12 45		
Reading 7	d	11 57	12 09	12 12	12 22	12 23	12 39	12 53	12 42	12 48
Reading West	d			12 14				→		
Theale	d			12 20						12 56
Aldermaston	d			12 25						
Midgham	d			12 29						
Thatcham	d			12 34						13 05
Newbury Racecourse	d			12 38						
Newbury	a			12 44						13 12
	d									13 13
Kintbury	d									
Hungerford	d									13 21
Bedwyn	a									13 29
Tilehurst	d					12 27				
Pangbourne	d					12 31				
Goring & Streatley	d					12 36				
Cholsey	d					12 41				
Didcot Parkway	a	12 12				12 48			12 55	
	d					12 55				
Appleford	d					13 00				
Culham	d									
Radley	d					13 03				
Oxford	a		12 33		12 48	13 14	13 04			
	d		12 36				13 07			
Islip	d									
Bicester Town	a									
Tackley	d									
Heyford	d									
Kings Sutton	d									
Banbury	a		12 53				13 23			
Leamington Spa 8	a		13 11				13 41			
Coventry	a		13 23							
Birmingham International	a		13 37							
Birmingham New Street 12	a		13 48				14 18			

Station		GW 1	GW ◇1	GW 1	GW ◇1 ⊐	XC ◇1 ⚲	CH	GW 1	GW ◇1 ⚲	GW 1
London Paddington 15 ⊖	d		12 21	12 27	12 30				12 50	
Ealing Broadway ⊖	d			12 35						
Slough 3	d		12 39	12 57					13 06	
Maidenhead 3	d			13 04						
Twyford 3	d	←		13 12						←
Reading 7	d	12 53	12 54	13 23	12 57	13 10		13 12	13 22	13 23
Reading West	d			→				13 14		
Theale	d							13 20		
Aldermaston	d							13 25		
Midgham	d							13 29		
Thatcham	d							13 34		
Newbury Racecourse	d							13 38		
Newbury	a							13 44		
	d									
Kintbury	d									
Hungerford	d									
Bedwyn	a									
Tilehurst	d	12 57								13 27
Pangbourne	d	13 01								13 31
Goring & Streatley	d	13 06								13 36
Cholsey	d	13 11								13 41
Didcot Parkway	a	13 19			13 12					13 48
	d	13 25								13 55
Appleford	d									
Culham	d									14 01
Radley	d									14 03
Oxford	a	13 40	13 19			13 34			13 48	14 14
	d					13 36	13 41			
Islip	d						13 54			
Bicester Town	a						14 06			
Tackley	d									
Heyford	d									
Kings Sutton	d									
Banbury	a					13 53				
Leamington Spa 8	a					14 11				
Coventry	a					14 23				
Birmingham International	a					14 37				
Birmingham New Street 12	a					14 48				

For complete service between Banbury and Leamington (Birmingham), please refer to table 71

Table 116

Saturdays

29 March to 17 May

London and Reading - Bedwyn, Oxford, Bicester, Banbury and Birmingham

Network Diagram - refer to first Page of Table 116

		XC	GW	GW	GW	GW	GW	GW	GW	XC	GW	GW	CH	GW	XC	GW	GW	GW	GW
		◇1	1	1	1	1	◇1	1	◇1	◇1	1	◇1		1	◇1	1	◇1	1	1
		✠					✠		🍴	✠		✠			✠		🍴		
London Paddington 15 ⊖	d			12 57	13 18		13 21	13 27	13 30			13 50				13 57	14 15	14 18	
Ealing Broadway ⊖	d			13 05				13 35								14 05			
Slough 3	d			13 27			13 39	13 57				14 06				14 27			
Maidenhead 3	d			13 34				14 04								14 34			
Twyford 3	d			13 42		←		14 12						←		14 45			←
Reading 7	d	13 40		13 53	13 48	13 53	13 54	14 23	13 57	14 10	14 12	14 22		14 23	14 39	14 53	14 42	14 49	14 53
Reading West	d			↳				↳			14 14					↳			
Theale	d				13 56						14 20							14 56	
Aldermaston	d										14 25								
Midgham	d										14 29								
Thatcham	d				14 04						14 34							15 05	
Newbury Racecourse	d										14 38								
Newbury	a				14 10						14 44							15 10	
	d				14 10													15 11	
Kintbury	d				14 17													15 17	
Hungerford	d				14 21													15 22	
Bedwyn	a				14 32													15 32	
Tilehurst	d					13 57								14 27					14 57
Pangbourne	d					14 01								14 31					15 01
Goring & Streatley	d					14 06								14 36					15 06
Cholsey	d					14 11								14 41					15 12
Didcot Parkway	a					14 19			14 12					14 48			14 55		15 19
	d					14 25								14 55					15 25
Appleford	d													15 00					
Culham	d																		
Radley	d													15 03					
Oxford	a	14 04				14 40	14 19			14 34		14 48		15 14	15 04				15 40
	d	14 07	14 16							14 36			14 57		15 07				
Islip	d												15 10						
Bicester Town	a												15 22						
Tackley	d		14 25																
Heyford	d		14 29																
Kings Sutton	d		14 39																
Banbury	a	14 23	14 46							14 53					15 23				
Leamington Spa 8	a	14 41								15 11					15 41				
Coventry	a									15 23									
Birmingham International	a									15 37									
Birmingham New Street 12	a	15 18								15 48					16 18				

		GW	GW	GW	XC	GW	GW	CH	GW	XC	GW	GW	GW	GW	GW	GW	GW	XC	GW
		◇1	1	◇1	◇1	1	◇1		1	◇1	1	1	1	1	◇1	1	◇1	◇1	1
		✠		🍴	✠					✠					✠		🍴	✠	
London Paddington 15 ⊖	d	14 21	14 27	14 30			14 50					14 57	15 18		15 21	15 27	15 30		
Ealing Broadway ⊖	d		14 35									15 05				15 35			
Slough 3	d	14 39	14 57				15 06					15 27			15 39	15 57			
Maidenhead 3	d		15 04									15 34				16 04			
Twyford 3	d		15 12						←			15 42		←		16 13			
Reading 7	d	14 54	15 23	14 57	15 09	15 12	15 22		15 23	15 40		15 53	15 48	15 53	15 54	16 24	15 57	16 10	16 12
Reading West	d		↳			15 14						↳				↳			16 14
Theale	d					15 20							15 56						16 20
Aldermaston	d					15 25													16 25
Midgham	d					15 29													16 29
Thatcham	d					15 34							16 04						16 34
Newbury Racecourse	d					15 38													16 38
Newbury	a					15 44							16 09						16 44
	d												16 10						
Kintbury	d												16 16						
Hungerford	d												16 21						
Bedwyn	a												16 31						
Tilehurst	d								15 27					15 57					
Pangbourne	d								15 31					16 01					
Goring & Streatley	d								15 36					16 06					
Cholsey	d								15 41					16 11					
Didcot Parkway	a			15 12					15 48					16 19			16 12		
	d								15 55					16 25					
Appleford	d																		
Culham	d								16 01										
Radley	d								16 03										
Oxford	a	15 18			15 34		15 48		16 14	16 04				16 40	16 19			16 34	
	d				15 36			16 00		16 07	16 16							16 36	
Islip	d							16 13											
Bicester Town	a							16 25											
Tackley	d										16 25								
Heyford	d										16 29								
Kings Sutton	d										16 39								
Banbury	a				15 53					16 23	16 46							16 53	
Leamington Spa 8	a				16 11					16 41								17 11	
Coventry	a				16 23													17 23	
Birmingham International	a				16 37													17 37	
Birmingham New Street 12	a				16 48					17 18								17 48	

For complete service between Banbury and Leamington (Birmingham), please refer to table 71

Table 116

Saturdays
29 March to 17 May

London and Reading - Bedwyn, Oxford, Bicester, Banbury and Birmingham

Network Diagram - refer to first Page of Table 116

		GW	CH	GW	XC	GW	GW	GW	GW	GW	GW	GW	XC	GW	GW	GW	XC	GW	GW
		◇1		1	◇1	1	◇1	1	1	◇1	1	◇1	◇1	1	◇1	1	◇1	1	1
					🛒		☕			☕		☕	🛒		🛒		🛒		
London Paddington 15 ⊖	d	15 50				15 57	16 15	16 18		16 21	16 27	16 30			16 50				16 57
Ealing Broadway ⊖	d					16 05					16 35								17 05
Slough 3	d	16 06				16 27				16 38	16 57				17 06				17 27
Maidenhead 3	d					16 34					17 04								17 34
Twyford 3	d			←		16 45			←		17 12					←			17 42
Reading 7	d	16 22		16 24	16 39	16 53	16 42	16 48	16 53	16 54	17 23	16 57	17 09	17 12	17 22	17 23	17 40		17 53
Reading West	d					→					→			17 14					→
Theale	d							16 56						17 20					
Aldermaston	d													17 25					
Midgham	d													17 29					
Thatcham	d							17 04						17 34					
Newbury Racecourse	d													17 38					
Newbury	a							17 10						17 44					
	d							17 10											
Kintbury	d							17 17											
Hungerford	d							17 21											
Bedwyn	a							17 32											
Tilehurst	d			16 28					16 57							17 27			
Pangbourne	d			16 32					17 01							17 31			
Goring & Streatley	d			16 37					17 06							17 36			
Cholsey	d			16 42					17 11							17 41			
Didcot Parkway	a			16 49			16 55		17 19			17 12				17 48			
	d			16 55					17 25							17 55			
Appleford	d			17 00															
Culham	d															18 01			
Radley	d			17 03												18 03			
Oxford	a	16 48		17 14	17 04				17 40	17 18			17 34		17 48	18 14	18 04		
	d		17 10		17 07								17 36				18 07	18 16	
Islip	d		17 23																
Bicester Town	a		17 35																
Tackley	d																	18 25	
Heyford	d																	18 29	
Kings Sutton	d																	18 39	
Banbury	a				17 23								17 53				18 23	18 46	
Leamington Spa 8	a				17 41								18 11				18 41		
Coventry	a												18 23						
Birmingham International	a												18 37						
Birmingham New Street 12	a				18 18								18 48				19 18		

		GW	GW	GW	GW	GW	XC	CH	GW	GW	GW	XC	GW	GW	GW	GW	GW	GW	GW
		1	1	◇1	1	◇1	◇1		1	◇1	1	◇1	1	◇1	1	1	◇1	1	◇1
				☕		☕	🛒			🛒		🛒		☕			☕		☕
London Paddington 15 ⊖	d	17 18		17 21	17 27	17 30				17 50			17 57	18 15	18 18		18 21	18 27	18 30
Ealing Broadway ⊖	d				17 35								18 05					18 35	
Slough 3	d			17 39	17 57					18 06			18 27				18 38	18 57	
Maidenhead 3	d				18 04								18 34					19 04	
Twyford 3	d		←		18 12						←		18 45			←		19 12	
Reading 7	d	17 48	17 53	17 54	18 23	17 57	18 09		18 12	18 22	18 23	18 39	18 53	18 42	18 48	18 53	18 54	19 23	18 57
Reading West	d				→				18 14				→					→	
Theale	d	17 56							18 20						18 56				
Aldermaston	d								18 25										
Midgham	d								18 29										
Thatcham	d	18 04							18 34						19 04				
Newbury Racecourse	d								18 38										
Newbury	a	18 10							18 44						19 10				
	d	18 10													19 10				
Kintbury	d	18 17													19 17				
Hungerford	d	18 21													19 21				
Bedwyn	a	18 30													19 32				
Tilehurst	d		17 57								18 27					18 57			
Pangbourne	d		18 01								18 31					19 01			
Goring & Streatley	d		18 06								18 36					19 06			
Cholsey	d		18 11								18 41					19 11			
Didcot Parkway	a		18 19			18 12					18 48			18 55		19 19			19 12
	d		18 25								18 55					19 25			
Appleford	d										19 00								
Culham	d																		
Radley	d										19 03								
Oxford	a		18 40	18 18			18 34			18 48	19 14	19 04				19 40	19 18		
	d						18 36	18 41				19 07							
Islip	d							18 54											
Bicester Town	a							19 06											
Tackley	d																		
Heyford	d																		
Kings Sutton	d																		
Banbury	a						18 53					19 23							
Leamington Spa 8	a						19 11					19 41							
Coventry	a						19 23												
Birmingham International	a						19 37												
Birmingham New Street 12	a						19 48					20 18							

For complete service between Banbury and Leamington (Birmingham), please refer to table 71

Table 116

Saturdays

29 March to 17 May

London and Reading - Bedwyn, Oxford, Bicester, Banbury and Birmingham

Network Diagram - refer to first Page of Table 116

		XC	CH	GW	GW	GW	GW	GW	XC	GW
		◇1 🍴		◇1	1	1	1	◇1 ☕	◇1	◇1 ☕
London Paddington 15 ⊖	d			18 50			18 57	19 06		19 15
Ealing Broadway ⊖	d						19 05			
Slough 3	d			19 06			19 27			
Maidenhead 3	d						19 34			
Twyford 3	d					←	19 42			
Reading 7	d	19 09		19 22		19 23	19 53	19 32	19 40	19 42
Reading West	d						→			
Theale	d									
Aldermaston	d									
Midgham	d									
Thatcham	d									
Newbury Racecourse	d									
Newbury	a							19 47		
	d									
Kintbury	d									
Hungerford	d									
Bedwyn	a									
Tilehurst	d					19 27				
Pangbourne	d					19 31				
Goring & Streatley	d					19 36				
Cholsey	d					19 41				
Didcot Parkway	a					19 49				19 55
	d					19 55				
Appleford	d									
Culham	d					20 01				
Radley	d					20 03				
Oxford	a	19 34		19 48		20 14			20 04	
	d	19 36	19 48		19 56				20 07	
Islip	d		20 01							
Bicester Town	a		20 13							
Tackley	d				20 05					
Heyford	d				20 09					
Kings Sutton	d				20 18					
Banbury	a	19 53			20 25				20 28	
Leamington Spa 8	a	20 10							20 45	
Coventry	a	20 23								
Birmingham International	a	20 37								
Birmingham New Street 12	a	20 48							21 15	

		GW	GW	GW	GW	GW	XC	GW	CH	GW
		1	1	◇1	1	◇1 ☕	◇1	◇1 🍴		1
London Paddington 15 ⊖	d			19 21	19 27	19 30		19 50		
Ealing Broadway ⊖	d				19 35					
Slough 3	d			19 38	19 57			20 06		
Maidenhead 3	d				20 04					
Twyford 3	d		←		20 12					←
Reading 7	d	19 49	19 53	19 54	20 23	19 57	20 09	20 22		20 23
Reading West	d	19 52			→					
Theale	d	19 58								
Aldermaston	d	20 03								
Midgham	d	20 06								
Thatcham	d	20 11								
Newbury Racecourse	d	20 16								
Newbury	a	20 18								
	d	20 19								
Kintbury	d	20 25								
Hungerford	d	20 30								
Bedwyn	a	20 38								
Tilehurst	d		19 57							20 27
Pangbourne	d		20 01							20 31
Goring & Streatley	d		20 06							20 36
Cholsey	d		20 11							20 41
Didcot Parkway	a		20 18			20 11				20 49
	d		20 25							20 55
Appleford	d									21 00
Culham	d									
Radley	d									21 03
Oxford	a		20 41	20 20			20 34	20 47		21 14
	d						20 36		21 00	
Islip	d								21 13	
Bicester Town	a								21 25	
Tackley	d									
Heyford	d									
Kings Sutton	d									
Banbury	a						20 53			
Leamington Spa 8	a						21 11			
Coventry	a						21 23			
Birmingham International	a						21 37			
Birmingham New Street 12	a						21 48			

		GW	GW	GW	XC	GW	GW	GW	GW	GW
		1	◇1 ☕	◇1 ☕	◇1	◇1 ☕	1	◇1	1	1
London Paddington 15 ⊖	d	19 57	20 00	20 06		20 15		20 18		
Ealing Broadway ⊖	d	20 05								
Slough 3	d	20 27						20 35		
Maidenhead 3	d	20 34								
Twyford 3	d	20 42								←
Reading 7	d	20 53	20 27	20 35	20 40	20 42	20 49	20 51		20 53
Reading West	d	→					20 52			
Theale	d						20 58			
Aldermaston	d						21 03			
Midgham	d						21 06			
Thatcham	d						21 11			
Newbury Racecourse	d						21 16			
Newbury	a			20 49			21 18			
	d						21 32			
Kintbury	d						21 39			
Hungerford	d						21 43			
Bedwyn	a						21 52			
Tilehurst	d									20 57
Pangbourne	d									21 01
Goring & Streatley	d									21 06
Cholsey	d									21 11
Didcot Parkway	a		20 41			20 55				21 19
	d									21 25
Appleford	d									
Culham	d									
Radley	d									
Oxford	a				21 04			21 18		21 40
	d				21 07				21 20	
Islip	d									
Bicester Town	a									
Tackley	d								21 29	
Heyford	d								21 33	
Kings Sutton	d								21 42	
Banbury	a				21 24				21 49	
Leamington Spa 8	a				21 43					
Coventry	a				21 55					
Birmingham International	a				22 10					
Birmingham New Street 12	a				22 21					

		GW	GW	XC	GW	GW	XC	CH	GW	GW
		1	◇1 ☕	◇1	◇1 🍴	1	◇1		1	◇1
London Paddington 15 ⊖	d	20 27	20 30		20 48				20 57	21 18
Ealing Broadway ⊖	d	20 35							21 05	
Slough 3	d	20 57			21 05				21 27	21 35
Maidenhead 3	d	21 04							21 34	
Twyford 3	d	21 12				←			21 42	
Reading 7	d	21 24	20 57	21 09	21 21	21 24	21 40		22 01	21 58
Reading West	d	→							→	
Theale	d									
Aldermaston	d									
Midgham	d									
Thatcham	d									
Newbury Racecourse	d									
Newbury	a									
	d									
Kintbury	d									
Hungerford	d									
Bedwyn	a									
Tilehurst	d					21 27				
Pangbourne	d					21 32				
Goring & Streatley	d					21 37				
Cholsey	d					21 42				
Didcot Parkway	a		21 12		21 36	21 49				22 13
	d				21 37	21 55				22 13
Appleford	d									
Culham	d					22 01				
Radley	d					22 03				
Oxford	a			21 34	21 50	22 14	22 03			22 27
	d			21 36			22 07	22 25		
Islip	d							22 38		
Bicester Town	a							22 50		
Tackley	d									
Heyford	d									
Kings Sutton	d									
Banbury	a			21 54			22 28			
Leamington Spa 8	a			22 11			22 45			
Coventry	a			22 23						
Birmingham International	a			22 36						
Birmingham New Street 12	a			22 48			23 16			

For complete service between Banbury and Leamington (Birmingham), please refer to table 71

Table 116

Saturdays
29 March to 17 May

London and Reading - Bedwyn, Oxford, Bicester, Banbury and Birmingham

Network Diagram - refer to first Page of Table 116

		GW	GW	GW	GW	GW	GW	GW	GW	GW	GW	GW	GW	GW	GW	GW	GW
		◇1	1	1	1	◇1	◇1	◇1	1		◇1	1	1	◇1	1	◇1	◇1
										🚌							
		⊏P					⊏P				⊏P					⊏P	
London Paddington 15 ⊖	d	21 30			21 42	21 48	22 00	22 18			22 35		22 36	22 48		23 30	23 33
Ealing Broadway ⊖	d				21 52								22 46				
Slough 3	d				22 18	22 05		22 35					23 11	23 16			23 50
Maidenhead 3	d				22 29			22 42					23 19	23 24			23 58
Twyford 3	d		←		22 38				←				23 27		←		
Reading 7	d	22 01	22 01	22 03	22 58	22 21	22 29	22 55	22 58		23 04	23 12	23 48	23 37	23 48	00 03	00 11
Reading West	d			22 06	→							23 14	→				
Theale	d			22 12								23 20					
Aldermaston	d			22 17								23 25					
Midgham	d			22 20								23 29					
Thatcham	d			22 25								23 34					
Newbury Racecourse	d			22 30								23 38					
Newbury	a			22 32								23 41					
	d			22 32								23 41					
Kintbury	d			22 39								23 48					
Hungerford	d			22 43								23 52					
Bedwyn	a			22 52								00 01					
Tilehurst	d		22 05						23 03						23 52		
Pangbourne	d		22 10						23 07						23 56		
Goring & Streatley	d		22 15						23 11						00 01		
Cholsey	d		22 20						23 16						00 06		
Didcot Parkway	a	22 16	22 27			22 35	22 47	23 09	23 24		23 27			23 53	00 15	00 19	00 28
	d		22 27			22 36		23 10	23 25					23 53	00 15		00 29
Appleford	d																00s33
Culham	d																00s35
Radley	d		22 35						23 32						00s23		00s39
Oxford	a		22 44			22 48		23 22	23 43					00 09	00 32		00 50
	d									23 53							
Islip	d																
Bicester Town	a																
Tackley	d									00s13							
Heyford	d									00s28							
Kings Sutton	d																
Banbury	a									00 53							
Leamington Spa 8	a																
Coventry	a																
Birmingham International	a																
Birmingham New Street 12	a																

For complete service between Banbury and Leamington (Birmingham), please refer to table 71

Table 116

Sundays

8 December to 29 December

London and Reading - Bedwyn, Oxford, Bicester, Banbury and Birmingham

Network Diagram - refer to first Page of Table 116

		GW	GW	GW	GW	GW	GW	GW	GW	GW	GW	GW	CH	XC	GW	GW	GW	GW	GW
		1	◇1	◇1	1			1	◇1		◇1	1		◇1	◇1	◇1	1	◇1	◇1
		A	A	A															
			catering			bus			catering					trolley	catering			catering	catering
London Paddington 15 ⊖	d							07 29	08 00		08 03				08 33	08 42	08 43	08 57	09 03
Ealing Broadway ⊖	d							07 36									08 54		
Slough 3	d							08 03			08 23					09 01	09 16		
Maidenhead 3	d							08 13			08 29						09 28		
Twyford 3	d							08 21				←					09 36		
Reading 7	d		00 03	00 11	00 15		08 12	08 49	08 39	08 44	08 46	08 49		09 11	09 14	09 22	09 45	09 32	09 38
Reading West	d				00s18		08 15	→									→		
Theale	d				00s24		08 21			08 51									
Aldermaston	d				00s29		08 26												
Midgham	d				00s32		08 29												
Thatcham	d				00s37		08 34			09 00									
Newbury Racecourse	d				00s42														
Newbury	a				00 45		08 41			09 05								09 46	
	d									09 06									
Kintbury	d									09 12									
Hungerford	d									09 17									
Bedwyn	a									09 24									
Tilehurst	d					00 46						08 53							
Pangbourne	d					00 56						08 57							
Goring & Streatley	d	00 01				01 06						08 59							
Cholsey	d	00 06				01 21						09 04							
Didcot Parkway	a	00 15	00 19	00 28		01 41			08 55		09 01	09 14			09 29	09 37			09 54
	d	00 15		00 29		01 41					09 01	09 14				09 38			
Appleford	d			00s33		01s51													
Culham	d			00s35		02s01													
Radley	d	00s23		00s39		02s11						09 21							
Oxford	a	00 32		00 50		02 26					09 13	09 32		09 35		09 53			
	d												09 36	09 37					
Islip	d												09 49						
Bicester Town	a												10 01						
Tackley	d																		
Heyford	d																		
Kings Sutton	d																		
Banbury	a													09 54					
Leamington Spa 8	a													10 11					
Coventry	a													10 24					
Birmingham International	a													10 38					
Birmingham New Street 12	a													10 50					

		GW	GW	GW	XC	GW	CH	GW	GW	GW	GW	XC	GW	GW	GW	GW	GW	GW	CH
		1	1	◇1	◇1	◇1		1	◇1	1	1	◇1	◇1	◇1	1	◇1	1	1	
				catering	trolley	catering			catering			trolley	catering	catering		catering			
London Paddington 15 ⊖	d			09 30		09 35		09 43	10 03				10 33	10 42	10 43	11 03			
Ealing Broadway ⊖	d							09 50							10 53				
Slough 3	d					09 56		10 14						11 03	11 16				
Maidenhead 3	d							10 27							11 28				
Twyford 3	d		←					10 35		←					11 36			←	
Reading 7	d	09 44	09 45	10 06	10 11	10 14		10 44	10 38	10 44	10 44	11 11	11 13	11 20	11 45	11 38	11 44	11 45	
Reading West	d	09 47						→			10 47				→				
Theale	d	09 53									10 53						11 51		
Aldermaston	d	09 58									10 58								
Midgham	d	10 01									11 01								
Thatcham	d	10 06									11 06						12 00		
Newbury Racecourse	d										11 11								
Newbury	a	10 12									11 15						12 05		
	d	10 12															12 06		
Kintbury	d	10 18															12 12		
Hungerford	d	10 23															12 17		
Bedwyn	a	10 31															12 25		
Tilehurst	d		09 49							10 48								11 48	
Pangbourne	d		09 53							10 53								11 53	
Goring & Streatley	d		09 58							10 57								11 57	
Cholsey	d		10 03							11 02								12 02	
Didcot Parkway	a		10 10	10 20		10 30			10 51	11 10			11 27	11 36		11 52		12 10	
	d		10 10			10 30				11 11				11 37				12 11	
Appleford	d		10 15																
Culham	d																		
Radley	d		10 20							11 19								12 19	
Oxford	a		10 30		10 35	10 45				11 27		11 34		11 50				12 28	
	d				10 37		10 56					11 37							12 33
Islip	d						11 09												12 46
Bicester Town	a						11 21												12 58
Tackley	d																		
Heyford	d																		
Kings Sutton	d																		
Banbury	a				10 54							11 54							
Leamington Spa 8	a				11 11							12 11							
Coventry	a				11 24							12 24							
Birmingham International	a				11 38							12 38							
Birmingham New Street 12	a				11 51							12 50							

A not 8 December

For complete service between Banbury and Leamington (Birmingham), please refer to table 71

Table 116

Sundays

8 December to 29 December

London and Reading - Bedwyn, Oxford, Bicester, Banbury and Birmingham

Network Diagram - refer to first Page of Table 116

Station		XC	GW	GW	GW	GW	GW	GW	GW	XC
		◇1	◇1	◇1	1	◇1	◇1	1	1	◇1
London Paddington 15 ⊖	d		11 33	11 42	11 43	11 57	12 03			
Ealing Broadway ⊖	d				11 53					
Slough 3	d			12 03	12 16					
Maidenhead 3	d				12 27					
Twyford 3	d				12 35				←	
Reading 7	d	12 11	12 13	12 21	12 45	12 32	12 38	12 44	12 45	12 54
Reading West	d				→			12 47		
Theale	d							12 53		
Aldermaston	d							12 58		
Midgham	d							13 01		
Thatcham	d							13 06		
Newbury Racecourse	d							13 11		
Newbury	a					12 47		13 15		
	d									
Kintbury	d									
Hungerford	d									
Bedwyn	a									
Tilehurst	d								12 48	
Pangbourne	d								12 53	
Goring & Streatley	d								12 57	
Cholsey	d								13 02	
Didcot Parkway	a		12 27	12 37			12 52		13 10	
	d			12 38					13 11	
Appleford	d								13 16	
Culham	d									
Radley	d								13 20	
Oxford	a	12 33		12 53					13 30	13 15
	d	12 37								13 17
Islip	d									
Bicester Town	a									
Tackley	d									
Heyford	d									
Kings Sutton	d									
Banbury	a	12 54								13 34
Leamington Spa 8	a	13 11								13 50
Coventry	a	13 23								
Birmingham International	a	13 37								
Birmingham New Street 12	a	13 48								14 19

Station		GW	XC	GW	CH	GW	GW	XC	GW	GW
		◇1	◇1	◇1		1	◇1	◇1	1	1
London Paddington 15 ⊖	d	12 33		12 42		12 43	13 03			
Ealing Broadway ⊖	d					12 53				
Slough 3	d			13 00		13 16				
Maidenhead 3	d					13 27				
Twyford 3	d					13 36				←
Reading 7	d	13 11	13 11	13 21		13 45	13 38	13 41	13 44	13 45
Reading West	d					→				
Theale	d								13 51	
Aldermaston	d									
Midgham	d									
Thatcham	d								14 00	
Newbury Racecourse	d									
Newbury	a								14 05	
	d								14 06	
Kintbury	d								14 12	
Hungerford	d								14 17	
Bedwyn	a								14 25	
Tilehurst	d									13 48
Pangbourne	d									13 53
Goring & Streatley	d									13 57
Cholsey	d									14 02
Didcot Parkway	a	13 27		13 36			13 52			14 10
	d			13 37						14 11
Appleford	d									
Culham	d									
Radley	d									14 20
Oxford	a		13 35	13 51				14 04		14 30
	d		13 37		13 56			14 06		
Islip	d				14 09					
Bicester Town	a				14 21					
Tackley	d									
Heyford	d									
Kings Sutton	d									
Banbury	a		13 54					14 23		
Leamington Spa 8	a		14 11					14 40		
Coventry	a		14 23							
Birmingham International	a		14 37							
Birmingham New Street 12	a		14 48					15 09		

Station		XC	GW	GW	GW	GW	GW	XC	GW	GW
		◇1	◇1	◇1	1	◇1	1	◇1	1	1
London Paddington 15 ⊖	d		13 37	13 42	13 43	13 57	14 03			
Ealing Broadway ⊖	d				13 53					
Slough 3	d			14 04	14 16					
Maidenhead 3	d				14 27					
Twyford 3	d				14 35					←
Reading 7	d	14 09	14 13	14 22	14 45	14 32	14 38	14 40	14 44	14 45
Reading West	d				→				14 47	
Theale	d								14 53	
Aldermaston	d								14 58	
Midgham	d								15 01	
Thatcham	d								15 06	
Newbury Racecourse	d								15 11	
Newbury	a					14 47			15 15	
	d									
Kintbury	d									
Hungerford	d									
Bedwyn	a									
Tilehurst	d									14 48
Pangbourne	d									14 53
Goring & Streatley	d									14 57
Cholsey	d									15 03
Didcot Parkway	a		14 27	14 36			14 51			15 10
	d			14 37						15 12
Appleford	d									
Culham	d									
Radley	d									15 20
Oxford	a	14 35		14 51				15 04		15 30
	d	14 37						15 06		
Islip	d									
Bicester Town	a									
Tackley	d									
Heyford	d									
Kings Sutton	d									
Banbury	a	14 54						15 24		
Leamington Spa 8	a	15 11						15 41		
Coventry	a	15 23								
Birmingham International	a	15 35								
Birmingham New Street 12	a	15 48						16 09		

Station		CH	XC	GW	GW	GW	GW	XC	GW	GW
			◇1	◇1	◇1	1	1	◇1	1	1
London Paddington 15 ⊖	d			14 37	14 42	14 43	15 03			
Ealing Broadway ⊖	d					14 53				
Slough 3	d				15 03	15 16				
Maidenhead 3	d					15 27				
Twyford 3	d					15 36				←
Reading 7	d		15 09	15 13	15 20	15 45	15 38	15 40	15 44	15 45
Reading West	d					→				
Theale	d								15 51	
Aldermaston	d									
Midgham	d									
Thatcham	d								16 00	
Newbury Racecourse	d									
Newbury	a								16 05	
	d								16 06	
Kintbury	d								16 12	
Hungerford	d								16 17	
Bedwyn	a								16 25	
Tilehurst	d									15 48
Pangbourne	d									15 53
Goring & Streatley	d									15 57
Cholsey	d									16 03
Didcot Parkway	a			15 27	15 35		15 51			16 10
	d				15 36					16 15
Appleford	d									
Culham	d									
Radley	d									16 22
Oxford	a		15 35		15 49			16 04		16 31
	d	15 33	15 37					16 06		
Islip	d	15 46								
Bicester Town	a	15 58								
Tackley	d									
Heyford	d									
Kings Sutton	d									
Banbury	a		15 54					16 24		
Leamington Spa 8	a		16 11					16 41		
Coventry	a		16 23							
Birmingham International	a		16 35							
Birmingham New Street 12	a		16 48					17 10		

For complete service between Banbury and Leamington (Birmingham), please refer to table 71

Table 116

Sundays

8 December to 29 December

London and Reading - Bedwyn, Oxford, Bicester, Banbury and Birmingham

Network Diagram - refer to first Page of Table 116

Station		XC	GW	GW	CH	GW	GW	GW	XC	GW
		◇1	◇1	◇1		1	◇1	R 1	◇1	1
London Paddington 15 ⊖	d		15 37	15 42		15 43	15 57	16 03		
Ealing Broadway ⊖	d					15 53				
Slough 3	d			16 03		16 16				
Maidenhead 3	d					16 27				
Twyford 3	d					16 35				
Reading 7	d	16 09	16 13	16 21		16 45	16 32	16 38	16 41	16 44
Reading West	d					→				16 47
Theale	d									16 53
Aldermaston	d									16 58
Midgham	d									17 01
Thatcham	d									17 06
Newbury Racecourse	d									17 11
Newbury	a						16 47			17 15
	d									
Kintbury	d									
Hungerford	d									
Bedwyn	a									
Tilehurst	d									
Pangbourne	d									
Goring & Streatley	d									
Cholsey	d									
Didcot Parkway	a		16 27	16 36				16 51		
	d			16 37						
Appleford	d									
Culham	d									
Radley	d									
Oxford	a	16 35		16 49					17 04	
	d	16 37			16 56				17 06	
Islip	d				17 09					
Bicester Town	a				17 21					
Tackley	d									
Heyford	d									
Kings Sutton	d									
Banbury	a	16 54							17 24	
Leamington Spa 8	a	17 11							17 41	
Coventry	a	17 23								
Birmingham International	a	17 35								
Birmingham New Street 12	a	17 48							18 09	

Station		GW	XC	GW	GW	GW	GW	XC	GW	GW
		1	◇1	◇1	◇1	1	R 1	◇1	1	1
London Paddington 15 ⊖	d			16 37	16 42	16 43	17 03			
Ealing Broadway ⊖	d					16 53				
Slough 3	d				17 01	17 16				
Maidenhead 3	d				17 08	17 27				
Twyford 3	d	←				17 36				←
Reading 7	d	16 45	17 09	17 13	17 21	17 45	17 38	17 40	17 44	17 45
Reading West	d					→				
Theale	d								17 51	
Aldermaston	d									
Midgham	d									
Thatcham	d								18 00	
Newbury Racecourse	d									
Newbury	a								18 05	
	d								18 06	
Kintbury	d								18 12	
Hungerford	d								18 17	
Bedwyn	a								18 25	
Tilehurst	d	16 48								17 48
Pangbourne	d	16 53								17 53
Goring & Streatley	d	16 57								17 57
Cholsey	d	17 03								18 01
Didcot Parkway	a	17 10		17 27	17 36		17 51			18 10
	d	17 13			17 37					18 13
Appleford	d									18 17
Culham	d									
Radley	d	17 20								18 22
Oxford	a	17 29	17 34		17 50			18 05		18 30
	d		17 37					18 07		
Islip	d									
Bicester Town	a									
Tackley	d									
Heyford	d									
Kings Sutton	d									
Banbury	a		17 53					18 24		
Leamington Spa 8	a		18 11					18 41		
Coventry	a		18 23							
Birmingham International	a		18 35							
Birmingham New Street 12	a		18 48					19 11		

Station		CH	XC	GW	GW	GW	GW	GW	XC	GW
			◇1	◇1	◇1	1	◇1	R 1	◇1	1
London Paddington 15 ⊖	d			17 37	17 42	17 43	17 57	18 03		
Ealing Broadway ⊖	d					17 53				
Slough 3	d				18 04	18 16				
Maidenhead 3	d				18 12	18 27				
Twyford 3	d					18 36				
Reading 7	d		18 10	18 14	18 26	18 45	18 32	18 38	18 41	18 44
Reading West	d					→				18 47
Theale	d									18 53
Aldermaston	d									18 58
Midgham	d									19 01
Thatcham	d									19 06
Newbury Racecourse	d									19 11
Newbury	a						18 47			19 15
	d									
Kintbury	d									
Hungerford	d									
Bedwyn	a									
Tilehurst	d									
Pangbourne	d									
Goring & Streatley	d									
Cholsey	d									
Didcot Parkway	a			18 27	18 39			18 51		
	d				18 40					
Appleford	d									
Culham	d									
Radley	d									
Oxford	a		18 35		18 51				19 03	
	d	18 37	18 37						19 06	
Islip	d	18 50								
Bicester Town	a	19 02								
Tackley	d									
Heyford	d									
Kings Sutton	d									
Banbury	a		18 54						19 23	
Leamington Spa 8	a		19 11						19 41	
Coventry	a		19 24						19 53	
Birmingham International	a		19 37						20 03	
Birmingham New Street 12	a		19 48						20 15	

Station		GW	XC	GW	GW	CH	GW	GW	XC	GW
		1	◇1	◇1	◇1		1	◇1	◇1	1
London Paddington 15 ⊖	d			18 37	18 42		18 43	19 03		
Ealing Broadway ⊖	d						18 53			
Slough 3	d				19 01		19 16			
Maidenhead 3	d				19 08		19 27			
Twyford 3	d	←					19 35			
Reading 7	d	18 45	19 11	19 13	19 21		19 45	19 38	19 40	19 44
Reading West	d						→			
Theale	d									19 51
Aldermaston	d									
Midgham	d									
Thatcham	d									20 00
Newbury Racecourse	d									
Newbury	a									20 05
	d									20 06
Kintbury	d									20 12
Hungerford	d									20 17
Bedwyn	a									20 25
Tilehurst	d	18 48								
Pangbourne	d	18 53								
Goring & Streatley	d	18 57								
Cholsey	d	19 01								
Didcot Parkway	a	19 10		19 27	19 36			19 51		
	d	19 13			19 37					
Appleford	d									
Culham	d									
Radley	d	19 20								
Oxford	a	19 30	19 35		19 49				20 03	
	d		19 37			19 56			20 06	
Islip	d					20 09				
Bicester Town	a					20 21				
Tackley	d									
Heyford	d									
Kings Sutton	d									
Banbury	a		19 54						20 23	
Leamington Spa 8	a		20 11						20 40	
Coventry	a		20 23						20 53	
Birmingham International	a		20 35						21 03	
Birmingham New Street 12	a		20 48						21 15	

For complete service between Banbury and Leamington (Birmingham), please refer to table 71

Table 116

Sundays

8 December to 29 December

London and Reading - Bedwyn, Oxford, Bicester, Banbury and Birmingham

Network Diagram - refer to first Page of Table 116

		GW	XC	GW	GW	GW	GW	GW	XC	GW	GW	CH	XC	GW	GW	XC	GW	GW	GW
		1	◇1	◇1	◇1	1	◇1	◇1	◇1	1	1		◇1	◇1	◇1	◇1	1	◇1	1
			🛒	🍴	🍴		🍴	🍴						🍴				🍴	
London Paddington 15 ⊖	d			19 37	19 42	19 43	19 57	20 03						20 37	20 42		20 43	21 03	
Ealing Broadway ⊖	d					19 53											20 53		
Slough 3	d				20 05	20 16									21 01		21 16		
Maidenhead 3	d					20 27											21 27		
Twyford 3	d	←				20 36					←						21 36		
Reading 7	d	19 45	20 11	20 14	20 22	20 45	20 32	20 34	20 40	20 44	20 45		21 11	21 14	21 26	21 35	21 45	21 38	21 44
Reading West	d					→				20 47							→		
Theale	d									20 53									21 51
Aldermaston	d									20 58									
Midgham	d									21 01									
Thatcham	d									21 06									22 00
Newbury Racecourse	d									21 11									
Newbury	a						20 47			21 16									22 05
	d																		22 06
Kintbury	d																		22 12
Hungerford	d																		22 17
Bedwyn	a																		22 25
Tilehurst	d	19 48									20 48								
Pangbourne	d	19 53									20 53								
Goring & Streatley	d	19 57									20 57								
Cholsey	d	20 03									21 03								
Didcot Parkway	a	20 10		20 27	20 36			20 51			21 14			21 27	21 41			21 54	
	d	20 12			20 37						21 15				21 43				
Appleford	d																		
Culham	d																		
Radley	d	20 19									21 22								
Oxford	a	20 29	20 35		20 50				21 04		21 30		21 35		21 56	22 02			
	d		20 37						21 06			21 33	21 37			22 06			
Islip	d											21 46							
Bicester Town	a											21 58							
Tackley	d																		
Heyford	d																		
Kings Sutton	d																		
Banbury	a		20 54						21 23				21 53			22 22			
Leamington Spa 8	a		21 11						21 40				22 11			22 40			
Coventry	a		21 23						21 52				22 22			22 52			
Birmingham International	a		21 35						22 02				22 32			23 02			
Birmingham New Street 12	a		21 48						22 14				22 43			23 13			

		GW	GW	GW	GW	GW	GW	GW	GW	GW	GW	GW	GW	GW	GW	GW	GW
		1	◇1	◇1	1	1	◇1	1		1	◇1	◇1		1	◇1	1	◇1
										A							
			🍴				🍴		🚌		🍴		🚌		🍴		🍴
London Paddington 15 ⊖	d		21 37	21 42		21 43	22 03			22 15	22 37	22 42		22 43	23 03		23 37
Ealing Broadway ⊖	d					21 53				22 23				22 53			
Slough 3	d			22 02		22 16				22 46		23 02		23 15			23 54
Maidenhead 3	d					22 26				22 56				23 24			
Twyford 3	d	←				22 35		←		23 04				23 32		←	
Reading 7	d	21 45	22 18	22 19	22 44	22 56	22 46	22 56		23 12	23 15	23 21		23 53	23 45	23 53	00 16
Reading West	d				22 47	→				23 16				→			
Theale	d				22 53					23 22							
Aldermaston	d				22 58												
Midgham	d				23 01												
Thatcham	d				23 06					23 30							
Newbury Racecourse	d				23 11												
Newbury	a				23 15					23 37							
	d																
Kintbury	d																
Hungerford	d																
Bedwyn	a																
Tilehurst	d	21 50						23 00								23 57	
Pangbourne	d	21 53						23 05								00 01	
Goring & Streatley	d	21 58						23 09								00 07	
Cholsey	d	22 03						23 14								00 12	
Didcot Parkway	a	22 13	22 31	22 36			23 00	23 23			23s30	23 40			23s59	00 21	00s33
	d	22 13		22 37					23 30				23 45				
Appleford	d																
Culham	d																
Radley	d	22 20											23 59				
Oxford	a	22 29		22 50					23 55				00 15				
	d																
Islip	d																
Bicester Town	a																
Tackley	d																
Heyford	d																
Kings Sutton	d																
Banbury	a																
Leamington Spa 8	a																
Coventry	a																
Birmingham International	a																
Birmingham New Street 12	a																

A 1 to Reading

For complete service between Banbury and Leamington (Birmingham), please refer to table 71

Table 116

Sundays

5 January to 9 February

London and Reading - Bedwyn, Oxford, Bicester, Banbury and Birmingham

Network Diagram - refer to first Page of Table 116

Station		GW	GW	GW	GW	GW	GW	GW	GW	GW	GW	GW	CH
		1	◇1	◇1	1			1	◇1		◇1	1	
			☕			bus			☕				
London Paddington 15 ⊖	d							07 29	08 00		08 03		
Ealing Broadway ⊖	d							07 36					
Slough 3	d							08 03			08 23		
Maidenhead 3	d			00 02				08 13			08 29		
Twyford 3	d							08 21				←	
Reading 7	d		00 05	00 15	00 15		08 12	08 49	08 39	08 44	08 46	08 49	
Reading West	d				00s18		08 15	→					
Theale	d				00s24		08 21			08 51			
Aldermaston	d				00s29		08 26						
Midgham	d				00s32		08 29						
Thatcham	d				00s37		08 34			09 00			
Newbury Racecourse	d				00s42								
Newbury	a				00 45		08 41			09 05			
	d									09 06			
Kintbury	d									09 12			
Hungerford	d									09 17			
Bedwyn	a									09 24			
Tilehurst	d					00 23						08 53	
Pangbourne	d					00 33							
Goring & Streatley	d	00 01				00 43						08 59	
Cholsey	d	00 06				00 58						09 04	
Didcot Parkway	a	00 15	00 19	00 32		01 18			08 55		09 01	09 14	
	d	00 15		00 33		01 18					09 01	09 14	
Appleford	d			00s37		01s28							
Culham	d			00s39		01s38							
Radley	d	00s23		00s43		01s48						09 21	
Oxford	a	00 32		00 54		02 03					09 13	09 30	
	d												09 36
Islip	d												09 49
Bicester Town	a												10 01
Tackley	d												
Heyford	d												
Kings Sutton	d												
Banbury	a												
Leamington Spa 8	a												
Coventry	a												
Birmingham International	a												
Birmingham New Street 12	a												

Station		XC	GW	GW	GW	GW	GW	GW	GW	GW	XC	GW	CH
		◇1	◇1	◇1	1	◇1	◇1	1	1	◇1	◇1	◇1	
		trolley	☕			☕	☕			☕	trolley	☕	
London Paddington 15 ⊖	d		08 33	08 42	08 43	08 57	09 03			09 30		09 33	
Ealing Broadway ⊖	d				08 54								
Slough 3	d			09 05	09 16							09 56	
Maidenhead 3	d				09 28								
Twyford 3	d				09 36				←				
Reading 7	d	09 11	09 14	09 22	09 45	09 32	09 38	09 44	09 45	10 06	10 11	10 14	
Reading West	d				→			09 47					
Theale	d							09 53					
Aldermaston	d							09 58					
Midgham	d							10 01					
Thatcham	d							10 06					
Newbury Racecourse	d												
Newbury	a					09 46		10 12					
	d							10 12					
Kintbury	d							10 18					
Hungerford	d							10 23					
Bedwyn	a							10 31					
Tilehurst	d								09 49				
Pangbourne	d												
Goring & Streatley	d								09 53				
Cholsey	d								09 58				
Didcot Parkway	a		09 29	09 37			09 54		10 10	10 20		10 30	
	d			09 38					10 10			10 30	
Appleford	d								10 15				
Culham	d												
Radley	d								10 20				
Oxford	a	09 35		09 53					10 30		10 35	10 45	
	d	09 37									10 37		10 56
Islip	d												11 09
Bicester Town	a												11 21
Tackley	d												
Heyford	d												
Kings Sutton	d												
Banbury	a	09 54									10 54		
Leamington Spa 8	a	10 11									11 11		
Coventry	a	10 24									11 24		
Birmingham International	a	10 38									11 38		
Birmingham New Street 12	a	10 50									11 51		

Station		GW	GW	GW	GW	XC	GW	GW	GW	GW	GW	GW	CH
		1	◇1	1	1	◇1	◇1	◇1	1	◇1	1	1	
			☕			trolley	☕	☕		☕			
London Paddington 15 ⊖	d	09 43	10 03				10 33	10 42	10 43	11 03			
Ealing Broadway ⊖	d	09 50							10 53				
Slough 3	d	10 14						11 03	11 16				
Maidenhead 3	d	10 27							11 28				
Twyford 3	d	10 35		←					11 36			←	
Reading 7	d	10 44	10 38	10 44	10 44	11 11	11 13	11 20	11 45	11 38	11 44	11 45	
Reading West	d	→			10 47				→				
Theale	d				10 53						11 51		
Aldermaston	d				10 58								
Midgham	d				11 01								
Thatcham	d				11 06						12 00		
Newbury Racecourse	d				11 11								
Newbury	a				11 15						12 05		
	d										12 06		
Kintbury	d										12 12		
Hungerford	d										12 17		
Bedwyn	a										12 25		
Tilehurst	d			10 48								11 48	
Pangbourne	d												
Goring & Streatley	d			10 57								11 57	
Cholsey	d			11 02								12 02	
Didcot Parkway	a		10 51	11 10			11 27	11 36		11 52		12 10	
	d			11 11				11 36				12 11	
Appleford	d												
Culham	d												
Radley	d			11 19								12 19	
Oxford	a			11 27		11 34		11 50				12 28	
	d					11 37							12 33
Islip	d												12 46
Bicester Town	a												12 58
Tackley	d												
Heyford	d												
Kings Sutton	d												
Banbury	a					11 54							
Leamington Spa 8	a					12 11							
Coventry	a					12 24							
Birmingham International	a					12 38							
Birmingham New Street 12	a					12 50							

For complete service between Banbury and Leamington (Birmingham), please refer to table 71

Table 116

Sundays

5 January to 9 February

London and Reading - Bedwyn, Oxford, Bicester, Banbury and Birmingham

Network Diagram - refer to first Page of Table 116

		XC	GW	GW	GW	GW	GW	XC	GW	GW
		◇1	◇1	◇1	1	◇1	◇1	◇1	1	1
		🛒	☕			☕	☕	🛒		
London Paddington 15 ⊖	d		11 33	11 42	11 43	11 57	12 03			
Ealing Broadway ⊖	d				11 53					
Slough 3	d			12 03	12 16					
Maidenhead 3	d				12 27					
Twyford 3	d				12 35					←
Reading 7	d	12 11	12 13	12 21	12 45	12 32	12 38	12 43	12 44	12 45
Reading West	d				→				12 47	
Theale	d								12 53	
Aldermaston	d								12 58	
Midgham	d								13 01	
Thatcham	d								13 06	
Newbury Racecourse	d								13 11	
Newbury	a					12 47			13 15	
	d									
Kintbury	d									
Hungerford	d									
Bedwyn	a									
Tilehurst	d									12 48
Pangbourne	d									
Goring & Streatley	d									12 57
Cholsey	d									13 02
Didcot Parkway	a		12 27	12 37			12 52			13 10
	d			12 38						13 11
Appleford	d									13 18
Culham	d									
Radley	d									13 22
Oxford	a	12 33		12 53				13 06		13 32
	d	12 37						13 17		
Islip	d									
Bicester Town	a									
Tackley	d									
Heyford	d									
Kings Sutton	d									
Banbury	a	12 54						13 34		
Leamington Spa 8	a	13 11						13 50		
Coventry	a	13 23								
Birmingham International	a	13 37								
Birmingham New Street 12	a	13 48						14 19		

		GW	XC	GW	CH	XC	GW	GW	GW	GW
		◇1	◇1	◇1		◇1	1	◇1	1	1
		☕	🛒	☕		🛒		☕		
London Paddington 15 ⊖	d	12 33		12 42			12 43	13 03		
Ealing Broadway ⊖	d						12 53			
Slough 3	d			13 05			13 16			
Maidenhead 3	d						13 27			
Twyford 3	d						13 36			←
Reading 7	d	13 11	13 11	13 21		13 36	13 45	13 38	13 44	13 45
Reading West	d						→			
Theale	d								13 51	
Aldermaston	d									
Midgham	d									
Thatcham	d								14 00	
Newbury Racecourse	d									
Newbury	a								14 05	
	d								14 06	
Kintbury	d								14 12	
Hungerford	d								14 17	
Bedwyn	a								14 25	
Tilehurst	d									13 48
Pangbourne	d									
Goring & Streatley	d									13 57
Cholsey	d									14 02
Didcot Parkway	a	13 27		13 36				13 52		14 10
	d			13 37						14 11
Appleford	d									
Culham	d									
Radley	d									14 20
Oxford	a		13 35	13 51		14 04				14 30
	d		13 37		13 56	14 06				
Islip	d				14 09					
Bicester Town	a				14 21					
Tackley	d									
Heyford	d									
Kings Sutton	d									
Banbury	a		13 54			14 23				
Leamington Spa 8	a		14 11			14 40				
Coventry	a		14 23							
Birmingham International	a		14 37							
Birmingham New Street 12	a		14 48			15 09				

		XC	GW	GW	GW	GW	GW	XC	GW	GW
		◇1	◇1	◇1	1	◇1	■ 1	◇1	1	1
		🛒	☕	☕		☕	☕	🛒		
London Paddington 15 ⊖	d		13 33	13 42	13 43	13 57	14 03			
Ealing Broadway ⊖	d				13 53					
Slough 3	d			14 04	14 16					
Maidenhead 3	d				14 27					
Twyford 3	d				14 35					←
Reading 7	d	14 09	14 13	14 22	14 45	14 32	14 38	14 40	14 44	14 45
Reading West	d				→				14 47	
Theale	d								14 53	
Aldermaston	d								14 58	
Midgham	d								15 01	
Thatcham	d								15 06	
Newbury Racecourse	d								15 11	
Newbury	a					14 47			15 15	
	d									
Kintbury	d									
Hungerford	d									
Bedwyn	a									
Tilehurst	d									14 48
Pangbourne	d									
Goring & Streatley	d									14 57
Cholsey	d									15 03
Didcot Parkway	a		14 27	14 36			14 51			15 10
	d			14 37						15 12
Appleford	d									
Culham	d									
Radley	d									15 20
Oxford	a	14 35		14 51				15 04		15 30
	d	14 37						15 06		
Islip	d									
Bicester Town	a									
Tackley	d									
Heyford	d									
Kings Sutton	d									
Banbury	a	14 54						15 24		
Leamington Spa 8	a	15 11						15 41		
Coventry	a	15 23								
Birmingham International	a	15 35								
Birmingham New Street 12	a	15 48						16 09		

		CH	XC	GW	GW	XC	GW	GW	GW	GW
			◇1	◇1	◇1	◇1	1	■ 1	1	1
			🛒	☕		🛒		☕		
London Paddington 15 ⊖	d			14 33	14 42		14 43	15 03		
Ealing Broadway ⊖	d						14 53			
Slough 3	d				15 05		15 16			
Maidenhead 3	d						15 27			
Twyford 3	d						15 36			←
Reading 7	d		15 09	15 13	15 23	15 36	15 45	15 38	15 44	15 45
Reading West	d						→			
Theale	d								15 51	
Aldermaston	d									
Midgham	d									
Thatcham	d								16 00	
Newbury Racecourse	d									
Newbury	a								16 05	
	d								16 06	
Kintbury	d								16 12	
Hungerford	d								16 17	
Bedwyn	a								16 25	
Tilehurst	d									15 48
Pangbourne	d									
Goring & Streatley	d									15 57
Cholsey	d									16 03
Didcot Parkway	a			15 27	15 37			15 51		16 10
	d				15 39					16 15
Appleford	d									
Culham	d									
Radley	d									16 22
Oxford	a		15 35		15 51	16 04				16 31
	d	15 33	15 37			16 06				
Islip	d	15 46								
Bicester Town	a	15 58								
Tackley	d									
Heyford	d									
Kings Sutton	d									
Banbury	a		15 54			16 24				
Leamington Spa 8	a		16 11			16 41				
Coventry	a		16 23							
Birmingham International	a		16 35							
Birmingham New Street 12	a		16 48			17 10				

For complete service between Banbury and Leamington (Birmingham), please refer to table 71

Table 116

Sundays

5 January to 9 February

London and Reading - Bedwyn, Oxford, Bicester, Banbury and Birmingham

Network Diagram - refer to first Page of Table 116

Station		XC	GW	GW	CH	GW	GW	XC	GW	GW
		◇1	◇1	◇1		1	◇1	◇1	1	1
London Paddington 15 ⊖	d		15 33	15 42		15 43	15 57		16 03	
Ealing Broadway ⊖	d					15 53				
Slough 3	d			16 02		16 16				
Maidenhead 3	d					16 27				
Twyford 3	d					16 35				
Reading 7	d	16 09	16 13	16 21		16 45	16 32	16 36	16 38	16 44
Reading West	d					→				16 47
Theale	d									16 53
Aldermaston	d									16 58
Midgham	d									17 01
Thatcham	d									17 06
Newbury Racecourse	d									17 11
Newbury	a						16 47			17 15
	d									
Kintbury	d									
Hungerford	d									
Bedwyn	a									
Tilehurst	d									
Pangbourne	d									
Goring & Streatley	d									
Cholsey	d									
Didcot Parkway	a		16 27	16 36					16 51	
	d			16 37						
Appleford	d									
Culham	d									
Radley	d									
Oxford	a	16 35		16 49				17 04		
	d	16 37			16 56			17 06		
Islip	d				17 09					
Bicester Town	a				17 21					
Tackley	d									
Heyford	d									
Kings Sutton	d									
Banbury	a	16 54						17 24		
Leamington Spa 8	a	17 11						17 41		
Coventry	a	17 23								
Birmingham International	a	17 35								
Birmingham New Street 12	a	17 48						18 09		

Station		GW	XC	GW	GW	XC	GW	GW	GW	GW
		1	◇1	◇1	◇1	◇1	1	1	1	1
London Paddington 15 ⊖	d			16 33	16 42		16 43	17 03		
Ealing Broadway ⊖	d						16 53			
Slough 3	d				17 01		17 16			
Maidenhead 3	d				17 08		17 27			
Twyford 3	d	←					17 36			←
Reading 7	d	16 45	17 09	17 13	17 21	17 35	17 45	17 38	17 44	17 45
Reading West	d						→			
Theale	d								17 51	
Aldermaston	d									
Midgham	d									
Thatcham	d								18 00	
Newbury Racecourse	d									
Newbury	a								18 05	
	d								18 06	
Kintbury	d								18 12	
Hungerford	d								18 17	
Bedwyn	a								18 25	
Tilehurst	d	16 48								17 48
Pangbourne	d									
Goring & Streatley	d	16 57								17 57
Cholsey	d	17 03								18 01
Didcot Parkway	a	17 10		17 27	17 36			17 51		18 10
	d	17 13			17 37					18 13
Appleford	d									18 17
Culham	d									
Radley	d	17 20								18 22
Oxford	a	17 29	17 34		17 50	18 05				18 30
	d		17 37			18 07				
Islip	d									
Bicester Town	a									
Tackley	d									
Heyford	d									
Kings Sutton	d									
Banbury	a		17 53			18 24				
Leamington Spa 8	a		18 11			18 41				
Coventry	a		18 23							
Birmingham International	a		18 35							
Birmingham New Street 12	a		18 48			19 11				

Station		CH	XC	GW	GW	GW	GW	XC	GW	GW
			◇1	◇1	◇1	1	◇1	◇1	1	1
London Paddington 15 ⊖	d			17 33	17 42	17 43	17 57		18 03	
Ealing Broadway ⊖	d					17 53				
Slough 3	d				18 04	18 16				
Maidenhead 3	d				18 12	18 27				
Twyford 3	d					18 36				
Reading 7	d		18 10	18 14	18 26	18 45	18 32	18 36	18 38	18 44
Reading West	d					→				18 47
Theale	d									18 53
Aldermaston	d									18 58
Midgham	d									19 01
Thatcham	d									19 06
Newbury Racecourse	d									19 11
Newbury	a						18 47			19 15
	d									
Kintbury	d									
Hungerford	d									
Bedwyn	a									
Tilehurst	d									
Pangbourne	d									
Goring & Streatley	d									
Cholsey	d									
Didcot Parkway	a			18 27	18 39				18 51	
	d				18 40					
Appleford	d									
Culham	d									
Radley	d									
Oxford	a		18 35		18 52			19 03		
	d	18 37	18 37					19 06		
Islip	d	18 50								
Bicester Town	a	19 02								
Tackley	d									
Heyford	d									
Kings Sutton	d									
Banbury	a		18 54					19 23		
Leamington Spa 8	a		19 11					19 41		
Coventry	a		19 24					19 53		
Birmingham International	a		19 37					20 03		
Birmingham New Street 12	a		19 48					20 15		

Station		GW	XC	GW	GW	CH	XC	GW	GW	GW
		1	◇1	◇1	◇1		◇1	1	◇1	1
London Paddington 15 ⊖	d			18 33	18 42			18 43	19 03	
Ealing Broadway ⊖	d							18 53		
Slough 3	d				19 02			19 16		
Maidenhead 3	d				19 08			19 27		
Twyford 3	d	←						19 35		
Reading 7	d	18 45	19 11	19 14	19 21		19 36	19 45	19 38	19 44
Reading West	d							→		
Theale	d									19 51
Aldermaston	d									
Midgham	d									
Thatcham	d									20 00
Newbury Racecourse	d									
Newbury	a									20 05
	d									20 06
Kintbury	d									20 12
Hungerford	d									20 17
Bedwyn	a									20 25
Tilehurst	d	18 48								
Pangbourne	d									
Goring & Streatley	d	18 57								
Cholsey	d	19 01								
Didcot Parkway	a	19 10		19 27	19 36				19 51	
	d	19 13			19 37					
Appleford	d									
Culham	d									
Radley	d	19 20								
Oxford	a	19 30	19 35		19 49		20 04			
	d		19 37			19 56	20 06			
Islip	d					20 09				
Bicester Town	a					20 21				
Tackley	d									
Heyford	d									
Kings Sutton	d									
Banbury	a		19 54				20 23			
Leamington Spa 8	a		20 11				20 40			
Coventry	a		20 23				20 53			
Birmingham International	a		20 35				21 03			
Birmingham New Street 12	a		20 48				21 15			

For complete service between Banbury and Leamington (Birmingham), please refer to table 71

Table 116

Sundays
5 January to 9 February

London and Reading - Bedwyn, Oxford, Bicester, Banbury and Birmingham

Network Diagram - refer to first Page of Table 116

		GW	XC	GW	GW	GW	GW	XC	GW	GW	GW	CH	XC	GW	GW	XC	GW	GW	GW
		1	◇1	◇1	◇1	1	◇1	◇1	◇1	1	1		◇1	◇1	◇1	◇1	1	◇1	1
			trolley	☕	☕		☕		☕					☕				☕	
London Paddington 15 ⊖	d			19 33	19 42	19 43	19 57		20 03					20 33	20 42		20 43	21 03	
Ealing Broadway ⊖	d					19 53											20 53		
Slough 3	d				20 05	20 16									21 01		21 16		
Maidenhead 3	d					20 27											21 27		
Twyford 3	d	←				20 36					←						21 36		
Reading 7	d	19 45	20 11	20 14	20 22	20 45	20 32	20 36	20 38	20 44	20 45		21 11	21 14	21 26	21 36	21 45	21 38	21 44
Reading West	d					→				20 47							→		
Theale	d									20 53									21 51
Aldermaston	d									20 58									
Midgham	d									21 01									
Thatcham	d									21 06									22 00
Newbury Racecourse	d									21 11									
Newbury	a						20 47			21 16									22 05
	d																		22 06
Kintbury	d																		22 12
Hungerford	d																		22 17
Bedwyn	a																		22 25
Tilehurst	d	19 48									20 49								
Pangbourne	d																		
Goring & Streatley	d	19 57									20 53								
Cholsey	d	20 01									20 58								
Didcot Parkway	a	20 10		20 27	20 36				20 51		21 14			21 27	21 41			21 54	
	d	20 12			20 37						21 15				21 43				
Appleford	d																		
Culham	d																		
Radley	d	20 19									21 22								
Oxford	a	20 29	20 35		20 50			21 04			21 30		21 35		21 56	22 02			
	d		20 37					21 06				21 33	21 37			22 06			
Islip	d											21 46							
Bicester Town	a											21 58							
Tackley	d																		
Heyford	d																		
Kings Sutton	d																		
Banbury	a		20 54					21 23					21 53			22 22			
Leamington Spa 8	a		21 11					21 40					22 11			22 40			
Coventry	a		21 23					21 52					22 22			22 52			
Birmingham International	a		21 35					22 02					22 32			23 02			
Birmingham New Street 12	a		21 48					22 14					22 43			23 13			

		GW	GW	GW	GW	GW	GW	GW	GW	GW	GW	GW	GW	GW	GW	GW	GW
		1	◇1	◇1	1	1	◇1	1		1	◇1	◇1		1	◇1	1	◇1
										A							
			☕				☕		🚌		☕		🚌		☕		☕
London Paddington 15 ⊖	d		21 33	21 42		21 43	22 03			22 15	22 37	22 42		22 43	23 03		23 37
Ealing Broadway ⊖	d					21 53				22 22				22 53			
Slough 3	d			22 06		22 16				22 46		23 02		23 15			23 57
Maidenhead 3	d					22 27				22 56				23 24			
Twyford 3	d	←				22 35		←		23 04				23 32		←	
Reading 7	d	21 45	22 09	22 24	22 44	22 55	22 45	22 55		23 12	23 15	23 21		23 53	23 45	23 53	00 16
Reading West	d				22 47	→				23 16				→			
Theale	d				22 53					23 22							
Aldermaston	d				22 58												
Midgham	d				23 01												
Thatcham	d				23 06					23 30							
Newbury Racecourse	d				23 11												
Newbury	a				23 15					23 37							
	d																
Kintbury	d																
Hungerford	d																
Bedwyn	a																
Tilehurst	d	21 50						23 00								23 57	
Pangbourne	d																
Goring & Streatley	d	21 53						23 05								00 01	
Cholsey	d	21 58						23 10								00 06	
Didcot Parkway	a	22 13	22 23	22 42			23 00	23 23			23s30	23 40			23s59	00 21	00s33
	d	22 13		22 42					23 30				23 45				
Appleford	d																
Culham	d																
Radley	d	22 20											23 59				
Oxford	a	22 29		22 53					23 55				00 15				
	d																
Islip	d																
Bicester Town	a																
Tackley	d																
Heyford	d																
Kings Sutton	d																
Banbury	a																
Leamington Spa 8	a																
Coventry	a																
Birmingham International	a																
Birmingham New Street 12	a																

A 1 to Reading

For complete service between Banbury and Leamington (Birmingham), please refer to table 71

Table 116

Sundays

16 February to 23 March

London and Reading - Bedwyn, Oxford, Bicester, Banbury and Birmingham

Network Diagram - refer to first Page of Table 116

		GW	GW	GW	GW	GW	GW	GW	GW	GW	GW	GW	CH	XC	GW	GW	GW	GW	GW
		1	◇1	◇1	1			1	◇1		◇1	1		◇1	◇1	◇1	1	◇1	◇1
			☕			🚌			☕					🛒	☕			☕	☕
London Paddington 15 ⊖	d							07 29	08 00		08 03				08 33	08 42	08 43	08 57	09 03
Ealing Broadway ⊖	d							07 36									08 54		
Slough 3	d							08 03			08 23					09 05	09 16		
Maidenhead 3	d							08 13			08 29						09 28		
Twyford 3	d							08 21				←					09 36		
Reading 7	d		00 03	00 11	00 15		08 12	08 49	08 39	08 44	08 46	08 49		09 11	09 14	09 22	09 45	09 32	09 38
Reading West	d				00s18		08 15	→									→		
Theale	d				00s24		08 21			08 51									
Aldermaston	d				00s29		08 26												
Midgham	d				00s32		08 29												
Thatcham	d				00s37		08 34			09 00									
Newbury Racecourse	d				00s42														
Newbury	a				00 45		08 41			09 05								09 46	
	d									09 06									
Kintbury	d									09 12									
Hungerford	d									09 17									
Bedwyn	a									09 24									
Tilehurst	d					00 46						08 53							
Pangbourne	d					00 56						08 57							
Goring & Streatley	d	00 01				01 06						08 59							
Cholsey	d	00 06				01 21						09 04							
Didcot Parkway	a	00 15	00 19	00 28		01 41			08 55		09 01	09 14			09 29	09 37			09 54
	d	00 15		00 29		01 41					09 01	09 14				09 38			
Appleford	d			00s33		01s51													
Culham	d			00s35		02s01													
Radley	d	00s23		00s39		02s11						09 21							
Oxford	a	00 32		00 50		02 26					09 13	09 30		09 35		09 53			
	d												09 36	09 37					
Islip	d												09 49						
Bicester Town	a												10 01						
Tackley	d																		
Heyford	d																		
Kings Sutton	d																		
Banbury	a													09 54					
Leamington Spa 8	a													10 11					
Coventry	a													10 24					
Birmingham International	a													10 38					
Birmingham New Street 12	a													10 50					

		GW	GW	GW	XC	GW	CH	GW	GW	GW	GW	GW	XC	GW	GW	GW	GW	GW	CH
		1	1	◇1	◇1	◇1		1	◇1	1	1	◇1	◇1	◇1	1	◇1	1	1	
				☕	🛒	☕			☕			☕	🛒	☕		☕			
London Paddington 15 ⊖	d			09 30		09 33		09 43	10 03			10 33		10 42	10 43	11 03			
Ealing Broadway ⊖	d							09 50							10 53				
Slough 3	d					09 56		10 14						11 03	11 16				
Maidenhead 3	d							10 27							11 28				
Twyford 3	d		←					10 35		←					11 36			←	
Reading 7	d	09 44	09 45	10 06	10 16	10 20		10 44	10 38	10 44	10 44	11 13	11 16	11 20	11 45	11 38	11 44	11 45	
Reading West	d	09 47						→			10 47				→				
Theale	d	09 53									10 53						11 51		
Aldermaston	d	09 58									10 58								
Midgham	d	10 01									11 01								
Thatcham	d	10 06									11 06						12 00		
Newbury Racecourse	d										11 11								
Newbury	a	10 12									11 15						12 05		
	d	10 12															12 06		
Kintbury	d	10 18															12 12		
Hungerford	d	10 23															12 17		
Bedwyn	a	10 31															12 25		
Tilehurst	d		09 49							10 48								11 48	
Pangbourne	d		09 53							10 53								11 53	
Goring & Streatley	d		09 58							10 57								11 57	
Cholsey	d		10 04							11 02								12 02	
Didcot Parkway	a		10 10	10 20		10 34			10 51	11 10		11 27		11 36		11 52		12 10	
	d		10 10			10 34				11 11				11 37				12 11	
Appleford	d		10 15																
Culham	d																		
Radley	d		10 20							11 19								12 19	
Oxford	a		10 30		10 40	10 45				11 27			11 40	11 50				12 28	
	d				10 41		10 56						11 41						12 33
Islip	d						11 09												12 46
Bicester Town	a						11 21												12 58
Tackley	d																		
Heyford	d																		
Kings Sutton	d																		
Banbury	a				10 58								11 58						
Leamington Spa 8	a				11 15								12 14						
Coventry	a				11 27								12 26						
Birmingham International	a				11 38								12 37						
Birmingham New Street 12	a				11 51								12 49						

For complete service between Banbury and Leamington (Birmingham), please refer to table 71

Table 116

Sundays
16 February to 23 March

London and Reading - Bedwyn, Oxford, Bicester, Banbury and Birmingham

Network Diagram - refer to first Page of Table 116

		GW	XC	GW	GW	GW	GW	GW	XC	GW
		◇1 🍴	◇1 🛒	◇1	1	◇1 🍴	◇1 🍴	1	◇1 🛒	1
London Paddington 15 ⊖	d	11 33		11 42	11 43	11 57	12 03			
Ealing Broadway ⊖	d				11 53					
Slough 3	d			12 03	12 16					
Maidenhead 3	d				12 27					
Twyford 3	d				12 35					←
Reading 7	d	12 10	12 16	12 21	12 50	12 32	12 38	12 44	12 49	12 50
Reading West	d				→			12 47		
Theale	d							12 53		
Aldermaston	d							12 58		
Midgham	d							13 01		
Thatcham	d							13 06		
Newbury Racecourse	d							13 11		
Newbury	a					12 47		13 15		
	d									
Kintbury	d									
Hungerford	d									
Bedwyn	a									
Tilehurst	d									12 55
Pangbourne	d									12 58
Goring & Streatley	d									13 03
Cholsey	d									13 08
Didcot Parkway	a	12 27		12 37			12 56			13 15
	d			12 38						13 16
Appleford	d									13 21
Culham	d									
Radley	d									13 25
Oxford	a		12 40	12 53					13 12	13 35
	d		12 41						13 17	
Islip	d									
Bicester Town	a									
Tackley	d									
Heyford	d									
Kings Sutton	d									
Banbury	a		12 58						13 34	
Leamington Spa 8	a		13 14						13 50	
Coventry	a		13 26							
Birmingham International	a		13 37							
Birmingham New Street 12	a		13 50						14 19	

		GW	XC	GW	CH	XC	GW	GW	GW	GW
		◇1 🍴	◇1 🛒	◇1 🍴		◇1 🛒	1	◇1 🍴	1	1
London Paddington 15 ⊖	d	12 33		12 42			12 43	13 03		
Ealing Broadway ⊖	d						12 53			
Slough 3	d			13 05			13 16			
Maidenhead 3	d						13 27			
Twyford 3	d						13 36			←
Reading 7	d	13 11	13 17	13 21		13 36	13 45	13 38	13 44	13 45
Reading West	d						→			
Theale	d								13 51	
Aldermaston	d									
Midgham	d									
Thatcham	d								14 00	
Newbury Racecourse	d									
Newbury	a								14 05	
	d								14 06	
Kintbury	d								14 12	
Hungerford	d								14 17	
Bedwyn	a								14 25	
Tilehurst	d									13 48
Pangbourne	d									13 53
Goring & Streatley	d									13 57
Cholsey	d									14 02
Didcot Parkway	a	13 27		13 36				13 56		14 10
	d			13 37						14 11
Appleford	d									
Culham	d									
Radley	d									14 20
Oxford	a		13 40	13 53		14 04				14 30
	d		13 41		13 56	14 06				
Islip	d				14 09					
Bicester Town	a				14 21					
Tackley	d									
Heyford	d									
Kings Sutton	d									
Banbury	a		13 58			14 23				
Leamington Spa 8	a		14 14			14 40				
Coventry	a		14 26							
Birmingham International	a		14 37							
Birmingham New Street 12	a		14 48			15 09				

		GW	XC	GW	GW	GW	XC	GW	GW	GW
		◇1 🍴	◇1 🛒	◇1 🍴	1	◇1 🍴	◇1 🛒	▪ 1 🍴	1	1
London Paddington 15 ⊖	d	13 33		13 42	13 43	13 57		14 03		
Ealing Broadway ⊖	d				13 53					
Slough 3	d			14 04	14 16					
Maidenhead 3	d				14 27					
Twyford 3	d				14 35					←
Reading 7	d	14 09	14 17	14 22	14 45	14 34	14 36	14 38	14 44	14 45
Reading West	d				→				14 47	
Theale	d								14 53	
Aldermaston	d								14 58	
Midgham	d								15 01	
Thatcham	d								15 06	
Newbury Racecourse	d								15 11	
Newbury	a					14 47			15 15	
	d									
Kintbury	d									
Hungerford	d									
Bedwyn	a									
Tilehurst	d									14 48
Pangbourne	d									14 53
Goring & Streatley	d									14 57
Cholsey	d									15 03
Didcot Parkway	a	14 27		14 36				14 57		15 10
	d			14 37						15 12
Appleford	d									
Culham	d									
Radley	d									15 20
Oxford	a		14 40	14 51			15 04			15 30
	d		14 41				15 06			
Islip	d									
Bicester Town	a									
Tackley	d									
Heyford	d									
Kings Sutton	d									
Banbury	a		14 58				15 24			
Leamington Spa 8	a		15 14				15 41			
Coventry	a		15 26							
Birmingham International	a		15 37							
Birmingham New Street 12	a		15 50				16 09			

		CH	GW	XC	GW	XC	GW	GW	GW	GW
			◇1 🍴	◇1 🛒	◇1	◇1 🛒	1	▪ 1 🍴	1	1
London Paddington 15 ⊖	d		14 33		14 42		14 43	15 03		
Ealing Broadway ⊖	d						14 53			
Slough 3	d				15 05		15 16			
Maidenhead 3	d						15 27			
Twyford 3	d						15 36			←
Reading 7	d		15 09	15 17	15 21	15 36	15 45	15 38	15 44	15 45
Reading West	d						→			
Theale	d								15 51	
Aldermaston	d									
Midgham	d									
Thatcham	d								16 00	
Newbury Racecourse	d									
Newbury	a								16 05	
	d								16 06	
Kintbury	d								16 12	
Hungerford	d								16 17	
Bedwyn	a								16 25	
Tilehurst	d									15 48
Pangbourne	d									15 53
Goring & Streatley	d									15 57
Cholsey	d									16 03
Didcot Parkway	a		15 27		15 37			15 57		16 10
	d				15 38					16 15
Appleford	d									
Culham	d									
Radley	d									16 22
Oxford	a			15 40	15 51	16 04				16 31
	d	15 33		15 41		16 06				
Islip	d	15 46								
Bicester Town	a	15 58								
Tackley	d									
Heyford	d									
Kings Sutton	d									
Banbury	a			15 58		16 24				
Leamington Spa 8	a			16 14		16 41				
Coventry	a			16 26						
Birmingham International	a			16 37						
Birmingham New Street 12	a			16 50		17 10				

For complete service between Banbury and Leamington (Birmingham), please refer to table 71

Table 116

Sundays

16 February to 23 March

London and Reading - Bedwyn, Oxford, Bicester, Banbury and Birmingham

Network Diagram - refer to first Page of Table 116

Station		GW	XC	GW	CH	GW	GW	XC	GW	GW
		◇1	◇1	◇1		1	◇1	◇1	R 1	1
		☕	🛒				☕	🛒	☕	
London Paddington 15 ⊖	d	15 33		15 42		15 43	15 57		16 03	
Ealing Broadway ⊖	d					15 53				
Slough 3	d			16 02		16 16				
Maidenhead 3	d					16 27				
Twyford 3	d					16 35				
Reading 7	d	16 09	16 17	16 21		16 45	16 32	16 36	16 38	16 44
Reading West	d					→				16 47
Theale	d									16 53
Aldermaston	d									16 58
Midgham	d									17 01
Thatcham	d									17 06
Newbury Racecourse	d									17 11
Newbury	a						16 47			17 15
	d									
Kintbury	d									
Hungerford	d									
Bedwyn	a									
Tilehurst	d									
Pangbourne	d									
Goring & Streatley	d									
Cholsey	d									
Didcot Parkway	a	16 27		16 36					16 57	
	d			16 37						
Appleford	d									
Culham	d									
Radley	d									
Oxford	a		16 40	16 49				17 04		
	d		16 41		16 56			17 06		
Islip	d				17 09					
Bicester Town	a				17 21					
Tackley	d									
Heyford	d									
Kings Sutton	d									
Banbury	a		16 58					17 24		
Leamington Spa 8	a		17 14					17 41		
Coventry	a		17 26							
Birmingham International	a		17 37							
Birmingham New Street 12	a		17 50					18 09		

Station		GW	GW	XC	GW	XC	GW	GW	GW	GW
		1	◇1	◇1	◇1	◇1	1	R 1	1	1
			☕	🛒		🛒		☕		
London Paddington 15 ⊖	d		16 33		16 42		16 43	17 03		
Ealing Broadway ⊖	d						16 53			
Slough 3	d				17 01		17 16			
Maidenhead 3	d				17 08		17 27			
Twyford 3	d	←					17 36			←
Reading 7	d	16 45	17 09	17 17	17 24	17 36	17 45	17 38	17 44	17 45
Reading West	d						→			
Theale	d								17 51	
Aldermaston	d									
Midgham	d									
Thatcham	d								18 00	
Newbury Racecourse	d									
Newbury	a								18 05	
	d								18 06	
Kintbury	d								18 12	
Hungerford	d								18 17	
Bedwyn	a								18 25	
Tilehurst	d	16 48								17 52
Pangbourne	d	16 53								17 56
Goring & Streatley	d	16 57								18 01
Cholsey	d	17 03								18 06
Didcot Parkway	a	17 10	17 27		17 38			17 57		18 13
	d	17 13			17 39					18 16
Appleford	d									18 20
Culham	d									
Radley	d	17 20								18 25
Oxford	a	17 29		17 40	17 50	18 05				18 33
	d			17 41		18 07				
Islip	d									
Bicester Town	a									
Tackley	d									
Heyford	d									
Kings Sutton	d									
Banbury	a			17 58		18 24				
Leamington Spa 8	a			18 14		18 41				
Coventry	a			18 26						
Birmingham International	a			18 37						
Birmingham New Street 12	a			18 50		19 11				

Station		CH	GW	XC	GW	GW	GW	GW	XC	GW
			◇1	◇1	◇1	1	◇1	R 1	◇1	1
			☕	🛒	☕		☕	☕	🛒	
London Paddington 15 ⊖	d		17 33		17 42	17 43	17 57	18 00		
Ealing Broadway ⊖	d					17 53				
Slough 3	d				18 04	18 16				
Maidenhead 3	d				18 12	18 27				
Twyford 3	d					18 36				
Reading 7	d		18 09	18 17	18 26	18 45	18 32	18 37	18 41	18 44
Reading West	d					→				18 47
Theale	d									18 53
Aldermaston	d									18 58
Midgham	d									19 01
Thatcham	d									19 06
Newbury Racecourse	d									19 11
Newbury	a						18 47			19 15
	d									
Kintbury	d									
Hungerford	d									
Bedwyn	a									
Tilehurst	d									
Pangbourne	d									
Goring & Streatley	d									
Cholsey	d									
Didcot Parkway	a		18 27		18 39			18 51		
	d				18 40					
Appleford	d									
Culham	d									
Radley	d									
Oxford	a			18 40	18 52				19 03	
	d	18 37		18 41					19 06	
Islip	d	18 50								
Bicester Town	a	19 02								
Tackley	d									
Heyford	d									
Kings Sutton	d									
Banbury	a			18 58					19 23	
Leamington Spa 8	a			19 14					19 41	
Coventry	a			19 27					19 53	
Birmingham International	a			19 38					20 03	
Birmingham New Street 12	a			19 50					20 15	

Station		GW	GW	XC	GW	CH	XC	GW	GW	GW
		1	◇1	◇1	◇1		◇1	1	◇1	1
			☕	🛒			🛒		☕	
London Paddington 15 ⊖	d		18 33		18 42			18 43	19 03	
Ealing Broadway ⊖	d							18 53		
Slough 3	d				19 02			19 16		
Maidenhead 3	d				19 08			19 27		
Twyford 3	d	←						19 35		
Reading 7	d	18 45	19 09	19 17	19 21		19 36	19 45	19 38	19 44
Reading West	d							→		
Theale	d									19 51
Aldermaston	d									
Midgham	d									
Thatcham	d									20 00
Newbury Racecourse	d									
Newbury	a									20 05
	d									20 06
Kintbury	d									20 12
Hungerford	d									20 17
Bedwyn	a									20 25
Tilehurst	d	18 48								
Pangbourne	d	18 52								
Goring & Streatley	d	18 57								
Cholsey	d	19 01								
Didcot Parkway	a	19 10	19 26		19 36				19 57	
	d	19 13			19 37					
Appleford	d									
Culham	d									
Radley	d	19 20								
Oxford	a	19 30		19 40	19 49		20 04			
	d			19 41		19 56	20 07			
Islip	d					20 09				
Bicester Town	a					20 21				
Tackley	d									
Heyford	d									
Kings Sutton	d									
Banbury	a			19 58			20 25			
Leamington Spa 8	a			20 14			20 42			
Coventry	a			20 27			20 54			
Birmingham International	a			20 38			21 04			
Birmingham New Street 12	a			20 50			21 16			

For complete service between Banbury and Leamington (Birmingham), please refer to table 71

Table 116

Sundays

16 February to 23 March

London and Reading - Bedwyn, Oxford, Bicester, Banbury and Birmingham

Network Diagram - refer to first Page of Table 116

		GW	GW	XC	GW	GW	GW	XC	GW	GW
		1	◇1	◇1	◇1	1	◇1	◇1	◇1	1
			☕	🍴	☕		☕		☕	
London Paddington 15 ⊖	d		19 33		19 42	19 43	19 57		20 03	
Ealing Broadway ⊖	d					19 53				
Slough 3	d				20 05	20 16				
Maidenhead 3	d					20 27				
Twyford 3	d	←				20 36				
Reading 7	d	19 45	20 09	20 17	20 22	20 45	20 32	20 36	20 38	20 44
Reading West	d					→				20 47
Theale	d									20 53
Aldermaston	d									20 58
Midgham	d									21 01
Thatcham	d									21 06
Newbury Racecourse	d									21 11
Newbury	a						20 47			21 16
	d									
Kintbury	d									
Hungerford	d									
Bedwyn	a									
Tilehurst	d	19 48								
Pangbourne	d	19 53								
Goring & Streatley	d	19 57								
Cholsey	d	20 01								
Didcot Parkway	a	20 10	20 27		20 36				20 56	
	d	20 12			20 37					
Appleford	d									
Culham	d									
Radley	d	20 19								
Oxford	a	20 29		20 41	20 50			21 04		
	d			20 42				21 06		
Islip	d									
Bicester Town	a									
Tackley	d									
Heyford	d									
Kings Sutton	d									
Banbury	a			20 59				21 23		
Leamington Spa 8	a			21 16				21 40		
Coventry	a			21 27				21 52		
Birmingham International	a			21 38				22 02		
Birmingham New Street 12	a			21 50				22 14		

		GW	CH	GW	XC	GW	XC	GW	GW	GW
		1		◇1	◇1	◇1	◇1	1	◇1	1
				☕					☕	
London Paddington 15 ⊖	d			20 33		20 42		20 43	21 03	
Ealing Broadway ⊖	d							20 53		
Slough 3	d					21 01		21 16		
Maidenhead 3	d							21 28		
Twyford 3	d	←						21 36		
Reading 7	d	20 45		21 11	21 17	21 26	21 36	21 45	21 38	21 44
Reading West	d							→		
Theale	d									21 51
Aldermaston	d									
Midgham	d									
Thatcham	d									22 00
Newbury Racecourse	d									
Newbury	a									22 05
	d									22 06
Kintbury	d									22 12
Hungerford	d									22 17
Bedwyn	a									22 25
Tilehurst	d	20 52								
Pangbourne	d	20 56								
Goring & Streatley	d	21 02								
Cholsey	d	21 06								
Didcot Parkway	a	21 14		21 27		21 41			21 54	
	d	21 15				21 43				
Appleford	d									
Culham	d									
Radley	d	21 22								
Oxford	a	21 32			21 40	21 56	22 02			
	d		21 33		21 41		22 06			
Islip	d		21 46							
Bicester Town	a		21 58							
Tackley	d									
Heyford	d									
Kings Sutton	d									
Banbury	a				21 58		22 22			
Leamington Spa 8	a				22 15		22 40			
Coventry	a				22 26		22 52			
Birmingham International	a				22 38		23 02			
Birmingham New Street 12	a				22 49		23 13			

		GW	GW	GW	GW	GW	GW	GW	GW	GW
		1	◇1	◇1	1	1	◇1	1		1
										A
			☕				☕		🚌	
London Paddington 15 ⊖	d		21 37	21 42		21 43	22 03			22 15
Ealing Broadway ⊖	d					21 53				22 23
Slough 3	d			22 06		22 16				22 46
Maidenhead 3	d					22 27				22 54
Twyford 3	d	←				22 35		←		23 02
Reading 7	d	21 45	22 15	22 24	22 44	22 55	22 46	22 55		23 12
Reading West	d				22 47	→				23 16
Theale	d				22 53					23 22
Aldermaston	d				22 58					
Midgham	d				23 01					
Thatcham	d				23 06					23 30
Newbury Racecourse	d				23 11					
Newbury	a				23 15					23 37
	d									
Kintbury	d									
Hungerford	d									
Bedwyn	a									
Tilehurst	d	21 49						23 00		
Pangbourne	d	21 53						23 04		
Goring & Streatley	d	21 58						23 08		
Cholsey	d	22 03						23 13		
Didcot Parkway	a	22 13	22 28	22 42			23 00	23 22		
	d	22 13		22 42					23 30	
Appleford	d									
Culham	d									
Radley	d	22 20								
Oxford	a	22 29		22 53					23 55	
	d									
Islip	d									
Bicester Town	a									
Tackley	d									
Heyford	d									
Kings Sutton	d									
Banbury	a									
Leamington Spa 8	a									
Coventry	a									
Birmingham International	a									
Birmingham New Street 12	a									

		GW	GW	GW	GW	GW	GW	GW
		◇1	◇1		1	◇1	1	◇1
		☕		🚌		☕		☕
London Paddington 15 ⊖	d	22 37	22 42		22 43	23 03		23 37
Ealing Broadway ⊖	d				22 53			
Slough 3	d		23 04		23 15			23 57
Maidenhead 3	d				23 24			
Twyford 3	d				23 32		←	
Reading 7	d	23 15	23 22		23 53	23 45	23 53	00 16
Reading West	d				→			
Theale	d							
Aldermaston	d							
Midgham	d							
Thatcham	d							
Newbury Racecourse	d							
Newbury	a							
	d							
Kintbury	d							
Hungerford	d							
Bedwyn	a							
Tilehurst	d						23 57	
Pangbourne	d						00 01	
Goring & Streatley	d						00 07	
Cholsey	d						00 12	
Didcot Parkway	a	23s30	23 39			23s59	00 21	00s33
	d			23 45				
Appleford	d							
Culham	d							
Radley	d			23 59				
Oxford	a			00 15				
	d							
Islip	d							
Bicester Town	a							
Tackley	d							
Heyford	d							
Kings Sutton	d							
Banbury	a							
Leamington Spa 8	a							
Coventry	a							
Birmingham International	a							
Birmingham New Street 12	a							

A 1 to Reading

For complete service between Banbury and Leamington (Birmingham), please refer to table 71

Table 116

Sundays

30 March to 11 May

London and Reading - Bedwyn, Oxford, Bicester, Banbury and Birmingham

Network Diagram - refer to first Page of Table 116

		GW	GW	GW	GW	GW	GW	GW	GW	GW	GW	GW	CH
		1	◇1	◇1	1			1	◇1	◇1		1	
			☕			🚌			☕				
London Paddington 15 ⊖	d							07 29	08 00	08 03			
Ealing Broadway ⊖	d							07 36					
Slough 3	d							08 01		08 22			
Maidenhead 3	d							08 13		08 29			
Twyford 3	d							08 21				←	
Reading 7	d		00 03	00 11	00 15		08 12	08 49	08 34	08 43	08 44	08 49	
Reading West	d				00s18		08 15	→					
Theale	d				00s24		08 21				08 51		
Aldermaston	d				00s29		08 26						
Midgham	d				00s32		08 29						
Thatcham	d				00s37		08 34				09 00		
Newbury Racecourse	d				00s42								
Newbury	a				00 45		08 41				09 05		
	d										09 06		
Kintbury	d										09 12		
Hungerford	d										09 17		
Bedwyn	a										09 24		
Tilehurst	d					00 23						08 53	
Pangbourne	d					00 33						08 57	
Goring & Streatley	d	00 01				00 43						08 59	
Cholsey	d	00 06				00 58						09 04	
Didcot Parkway	a	00 15	00 19	00 28		01 18			08 52	08 57		09 14	
	d	00 15		00 29		01 18				08 58		09 14	
Appleford	d			00s33		01s28							
Culham	d			00s35		01s38							
Radley	d	00s23		00s39		01s48						09 21	
Oxford	a	00 32		00 50		02 03				09 10		09 30	
	d												09 36
Islip	d												09 49
Bicester Town	a												10 01
Tackley	d												
Heyford	d												
Kings Sutton	d												
Banbury	a												
Leamington Spa 8	a												
Coventry	a												
Birmingham International	a												
Birmingham New Street 12	a												

		GW	XC	GW	GW	GW	GW	GW	GW	GW	XC	GW	CH
		◇1	◇1	◇1	1	◇1	◇1	1	1	◇1	◇1	◇1	
		☕	🛒			☕	☕			☕	🛒	☕	
London Paddington 15 ⊖	d	08 30		08 42	08 43	08 57	09 03			09 30		09 35	
Ealing Broadway ⊖	d				08 51								
Slough 3	d			09 05	09 15							09 56	
Maidenhead 3	d				09 29								
Twyford 3	d				09 37				←				
Reading 7	d	09 02	09 11	09 22	09 45	09 32	09 38	09 44	09 45	10 03	10 11	10 14	
Reading West	d				→			09 47					
Theale	d							09 53					
Aldermaston	d							09 58					
Midgham	d							10 01					
Thatcham	d							10 06					
Newbury Racecourse	d												
Newbury	a					09 47		10 12					
	d							10 12					
Kintbury	d							10 18					
Hungerford	d							10 23					
Bedwyn	a							10 31					
Tilehurst	d								09 48				
Pangbourne	d								09 53				
Goring & Streatley	d								09 57				
Cholsey	d								10 02				
Didcot Parkway	a	09 19		09 37			09 54		10 10	10 21		10 30	
	d			09 38					10 10			10 30	
Appleford	d								10 16				
Culham	d												
Radley	d								10 19				
Oxford	a		09 35	09 53					10 31		10 35	10 45	
	d		09 37								10 37		10 56
Islip	d												11 09
Bicester Town	a												11 21
Tackley	d												
Heyford	d												
Kings Sutton	d												
Banbury	a		09 54								10 54		
Leamington Spa 8	a		10 11								11 11		
Coventry	a		10 24								11 24		
Birmingham International	a		10 38								11 38		
Birmingham New Street 12	a		10 50								11 51		

		GW	GW	GW	GW	GW	XC	GW	GW	GW	GW	GW	CH
		1	◇1	1	1	◇1	◇1	◇1	1	◇1	1	1	
			☕			☕	🛒	☕		☕			
London Paddington 15 ⊖	d	09 43	10 03			10 30		10 42	10 43	11 03			
Ealing Broadway ⊖	d	09 48							10 50				
Slough 3	d	10 14						11 03	11 14				
Maidenhead 3	d	10 27							11 28				
Twyford 3	d	10 35			←				11 36			←	
Reading 7	d	10 45	10 38	10 44	10 45	11 03	11 11	11 20	11 45	11 38	11 44	11 45	
Reading West	d	→		10 47					→				
Theale	d			10 53							11 51		
Aldermaston	d			10 58									
Midgham	d			11 01									
Thatcham	d			11 06							12 00		
Newbury Racecourse	d			11 11									
Newbury	a			11 15							12 05		
	d										12 06		
Kintbury	d										12 12		
Hungerford	d										12 17		
Bedwyn	a										12 25		
Tilehurst	d				10 48							11 48	
Pangbourne	d				10 53							11 53	
Goring & Streatley	d				10 57							11 57	
Cholsey	d				11 02							12 02	
Didcot Parkway	a		10 53		11 10	11 21		11 36		11 53		12 10	
	d				11 11			11 37				12 11	
Appleford	d												
Culham	d												
Radley	d				11 19							12 19	
Oxford	a				11 27		11 35	11 50				12 28	
	d						11 37						12 33
Islip	d												12 46
Bicester Town	a												12 58
Tackley	d												
Heyford	d												
Kings Sutton	d												
Banbury	a						11 54						
Leamington Spa 8	a						12 11						
Coventry	a						12 24						
Birmingham International	a						12 38						
Birmingham New Street 12	a						12 50						

For complete service between Banbury and Leamington (Birmingham), please refer to table 71

Table 116

Sundays

30 March to 11 May

London and Reading - Bedwyn, Oxford, Bicester, Banbury and Birmingham

Network Diagram - refer to first Page of Table 116

		GW	XC	GW	GW	GW	GW	GW	GW	XC	GW	XC	GW	CH	GW	GW	XC	GW	GW	GW	XC	GW	GW	GW	GW	XC	GW	GW	CH	GW	GW	XC	GW	GW	GW	XC	GW
		◇1 ⊡	◇1 ⊼	◇1	1	◇1 ⊡	◇1 ⊡	1	1	◇1 ⊼	◇1 ⊡	◇1 ⊼	◇1 ⊡		1	◇1 ⊡	◇1 ⊼	1	1	◇1 ⊡	◇1 ⊼	◇1 ⊡	1	◇1 ⊡	▪ 1 ⊡	◇1 ⊼	1	1		◇1	◇1 ⊡	◇1 ⊼	◇1	1	▪ 1 ⊡	◇1 ⊼	1
London Paddington 15 ⊖	d	11 30		11 42	11 43	11 57	12 03				12 30		12 42		12 43	13 03				13 30		13 42	13 43	13 57	14 03					14 30	14 33			14 43	15 03		
Ealing Broadway ⊖	d				11 50										12 50								13 50											14 50			
Slough 3	d			12 03	12 16								13 00		13 16							14 04	14 16							14 50				15 16			
Maidenhead 3	d				12 25										13 27								14 27											15 27			
Twyford 3	d				12 33			←							13 34				←				14 35					←					←	15 35			
Reading 7	d	12 03	12 11	12 21	12 41	12 32	12 38	12 41	12 44	12 54	13 03	13 11	13 21		13 45	13 34	13 41	13 44	13 45	13 59	14 09	14 22	14 45	14 32	14 34	14 40	14 44	14 45		15 14	15 03	15 09	15 14	15 45	15 34	15 40	15 44
Reading West	d				→				12 47						→								→				14 47			→				→			
Theale	d								12 53									13 51									14 53										15 51
Aldermaston	d								12 58																		14 58										
Midgham	d								13 01																		15 01										
Thatcham	d								13 06									14 00									15 06										16 00
Newbury Racecourse	d								13 11																		15 11										
Newbury	a					12 47			13 15									14 05						14 47			15 15										16 05
	d																	14 06																			16 06
Kintbury	d																	14 12																			16 12
Hungerford	d																	14 17																			16 17
Bedwyn	a																	14 25																			16 25
Tilehurst	d							12 45											13 48									14 48									
Pangbourne	d							12 48											13 53									14 53									
Goring & Streatley	d							12 55											13 57									14 57									
Cholsey	d							13 00											14 02									15 03									
Didcot Parkway	a	12 21		12 37			12 53	13 09			13 21		13 36			13 53			14 10	14 17		14 36			14 53			15 10			15 21		15 29		15 53		
	d			12 38				13 09					13 37						14 11			14 37						15 12					15 29				
Appleford	d							13 12																													
Culham	d																																				
Radley	d							13 17											14 20									15 20									
Oxford	a		12 34	12 53				13 27		13 17		13 34	13 51				14 04		14 30		14 35	14 51				15 04		15 30				15 35	15 49			16 04	
	d		12 37							13 19		13 37		13 56			14 06				14 37					15 06			15 33			15 37				16 06	
Islip	d													14 09															15 46								
Bicester Town	a													14 21															15 58								
Tackley	d																																				
Heyford	d																																				
Kings Sutton	d																																				
Banbury	a		12 54							13 36		13 54					14 23				14 54					15 24						15 54				16 24	
Leamington Spa 8	a		13 11							13 52		14 11					14 40				15 11					15 41						16 11				16 41	
Coventry	a		13 23									14 23									15 23											16 23					
Birmingham International	a		13 37									14 37									15 35											16 35					
Birmingham New Street 12	a		13 48							14 19		14 48					15 09				15 48					16 09						16 48				17 10	

For complete service between Banbury and Leamington (Birmingham), please refer to table 71

Table 116

Sundays
30 March to 11 May

London and Reading - Bedwyn, Oxford, Bicester, Banbury and Birmingham

Network Diagram - refer to first Page of Table 116

		GW	GW	XC	GW	CH	GW	GW	GW	XC
		1	◇1	◇1	◇1		1	◇1	1	◇1
London Paddington 15 ⊖	d		15 33		15 42		15 43	15 57	16 03	
Ealing Broadway ⊖	d						15 50			
Slough 3	d				16 02		16 16			
Maidenhead 3	d						16 27			
Twyford 3	d	←					16 35			
Reading 7	d	15 45	16 03	16 09	16 21		16 45	16 32	16 34	16 41
Reading West	d						→			
Theale	d									
Aldermaston	d									
Midgham	d									
Thatcham	d									
Newbury Racecourse	d									
Newbury	a							16 47		
	d									
Kintbury	d									
Hungerford	d									
Bedwyn	a									
Tilehurst	d	15 48								
Pangbourne	d	15 53								
Goring & Streatley	d	15 57								
Cholsey	d	16 03								
Didcot Parkway	a	16 10	16 21		16 36				16 53	
	d	16 15			16 37					
Appleford	d									
Culham	d									
Radley	d	16 22								
Oxford	a	16 31		16 35	16 49					17 04
	d			16 37		16 56				17 06
Islip	d					17 09				
Bicester Town	a					17 21				
Tackley	d									
Heyford	d									
Kings Sutton	d									
Banbury	a			16 54						17 24
Leamington Spa 8	a			17 11						17 41
Coventry	a			17 23						
Birmingham International	a			17 35						
Birmingham New Street 12	a			17 48						18 09

		GW	GW	GW	XC	GW	GW	GW	XC	GW
		1	1	◇1	◇1	◇1	1	1	◇1	1
London Paddington 15 ⊖	d			16 33		16 42	16 43	17 03		
Ealing Broadway ⊖	d						16 51			
Slough 3	d					17 01	17 16			
Maidenhead 3	d					17 08	17 27			
Twyford 3	d		←				17 35			
Reading 7	d	16 44	16 45	17 09	17 09	17 21	17 45	17 34	17 40	17 44
Reading West	d	16 47					→			
Theale	d	16 53								17 51
Aldermaston	d	16 58								
Midgham	d	17 01								
Thatcham	d	17 06								18 00
Newbury Racecourse	d	17 11								
Newbury	a	17 15								18 05
	d									18 06
Kintbury	d									18 12
Hungerford	d									18 17
Bedwyn	a									18 25
Tilehurst	d		16 48							
Pangbourne	d		16 53							
Goring & Streatley	d		16 57							
Cholsey	d		17 03							
Didcot Parkway	a		17 10	17 27		17 36		17 53		
	d		17 13			17 37				
Appleford	d									
Culham	d									
Radley	d		17 20							
Oxford	a		17 30		17 34	17 50			18 05	
	d				17 37				18 07	
Islip	d									
Bicester Town	a									
Tackley	d									
Heyford	d									
Kings Sutton	d									
Banbury	a				17 53				18 24	
Leamington Spa 8	a				18 11				18 41	
Coventry	a				18 23					
Birmingham International	a				18 35					
Birmingham New Street 12	a				18 48				19 11	

		GW	CH	GW	XC	GW	GW	GW	GW	XC
		1		◇1	◇1	◇1	1	◇1	1	◇1
London Paddington 15 ⊖	d			17 33		17 42	17 43	17 57	18 03	
Ealing Broadway ⊖	d						17 51			
Slough 3	d					18 04	18 16			
Maidenhead 3	d					18 12	18 27			
Twyford 3	d	←					18 36			
Reading 7	d	17 45		18 03	18 10	18 26	18 45	18 32	18 34	18 41
Reading West	d						→			
Theale	d									
Aldermaston	d									
Midgham	d									
Thatcham	d									
Newbury Racecourse	d									
Newbury	a							18 47		
	d									
Kintbury	d									
Hungerford	d									
Bedwyn	a									
Tilehurst	d	17 48								
Pangbourne	d	17 53								
Goring & Streatley	d	17 57								
Cholsey	d	18 03								
Didcot Parkway	a	18 10		18 21		18 40			18 53	
	d	18 13				18 41				
Appleford	d	18 17								
Culham	d									
Radley	d	18 20								
Oxford	a	18 32			18 35	18 54				19 03
	d		18 37		18 37					19 06
Islip	d		18 50							
Bicester Town	a		19 02							
Tackley	d									
Heyford	d									
Kings Sutton	d									
Banbury	a				18 54					19 23
Leamington Spa 8	a				19 11					19 41
Coventry	a				19 24					19 53
Birmingham International	a				19 37					20 03
Birmingham New Street 12	a				19 48					20 15

		GW	GW	GW	XC	GW	CH	GW	GW	XC
		1	1	◇1	◇1	◇1		1	◇1	◇1
London Paddington 15 ⊖	d			18 33		18 42		18 43	19 03	
Ealing Broadway ⊖	d							18 51		
Slough 3	d					19 01		19 16		
Maidenhead 3	d					19 08		19 27		
Twyford 3	d		←					19 35		
Reading 7	d	18 44	18 45	19 03	19 09	19 21		19 45	19 34	19 40
Reading West	d	18 47						→		
Theale	d	18 53								
Aldermaston	d	18 58								
Midgham	d	19 01								
Thatcham	d	19 06								
Newbury Racecourse	d	19 11								
Newbury	a	19 15								
	d									
Kintbury	d									
Hungerford	d									
Bedwyn	a									
Tilehurst	d		18 48							
Pangbourne	d		18 53							
Goring & Streatley	d		18 57							
Cholsey	d		19 03							
Didcot Parkway	a		19 11	19 20		19 36			19 53	
	d		19 15			19 37				
Appleford	d									
Culham	d									
Radley	d		19 22							
Oxford	a		19 32		19 35	19 49				20 03
	d				19 37		19 56			20 06
Islip	d						20 09			
Bicester Town	a						20 21			
Tackley	d									
Heyford	d									
Kings Sutton	d									
Banbury	a				19 54					20 23
Leamington Spa 8	a				20 11					20 40
Coventry	a				20 23					20 53
Birmingham International	a				20 35					21 03
Birmingham New Street 12	a				20 48					21 15

For complete service between Banbury and Leamington (Birmingham), please refer to table 71

Table 116

Sundays
30 March to 11 May

London and Reading - Bedwyn, Oxford, Bicester, Banbury and Birmingham

Network Diagram - refer to first Page of Table 116

Station		GW	GW	GW	XC	GW	GW	GW	GW	XC	GW	GW	CH	GW	XC	GW	XC	GW	GW
		1	1	◇1	◇1	◇1	1	◇1	◇1	◇1	1	1		◇1	◇1	◇1	◇1	1	◇1
				☕	🛒	☕		☕	☕					☕					☕
London Paddington 15 ⊖	d			19 33		19 42	19 43	19 57	20 03					20 33		20 42		20 43	21 03
Ealing Broadway ⊖	d						19 50											20 51	
Slough 3	d					20 05	20 16									21 01		21 16	
Maidenhead 3	d						20 27											21 28	
Twyford 3	d		←				20 35					←						21 35	
Reading 7	d	19 44	19 45	20 03	20 09	20 22	20 45	20 32	20 34	20 41	20 44	20 45		21 03	21 09	21 26	21 35	21 45	21 38
Reading West	d						→				20 47							→	
Theale	d	19 51									20 53								
Aldermaston	d										20 58								
Midgham	d										21 01								
Thatcham	d	20 00									21 06								
Newbury Racecourse	d										21 11								
Newbury	a	20 05						20 47			21 16								
	d	20 06																	
Kintbury	d	20 12																	
Hungerford	d	20 17																	
Bedwyn	a	20 25																	
Tilehurst	d		19 48									20 48							
Pangbourne	d		19 53									20 53							
Goring & Streatley	d		19 57									20 57							
Cholsey	d		20 03									21 03							
Didcot Parkway	a		20 10	20 21		20 36			20 53			21 10		21 21		21 41			21 54
	d		20 12			20 37						21 15				21 43			
Appleford	d																		
Culham	d																		
Radley	d		20 19									21 22							
Oxford	a		20 30		20 35	20 50				21 04		21 30			21 35	21 56	22 02		
	d				20 37					21 06			21 33		21 37		22 06		
Islip	d												21 46						
Bicester Town	a												21 58						
Tackley	d																		
Heyford	d																		
Kings Sutton	d																		
Banbury	a				20 54					21 23					21 53		22 22		
Leamington Spa 8	a				21 11					21 40					22 11		22 40		
Coventry	a				21 23					21 52					22 22		22 52		
Birmingham International	a				21 35					22 02					22 32		23 02		
Birmingham New Street 12	a				21 48					22 14					22 43		23 13		

Station		GW	GW	GW	GW	GW	GW	GW	GW	GW	GW	GW	GW	GW	GW	GW	GW	GW
		1	1	◇1	◇1	1	1	◇1	1	1	◇1		◇1		1	◇1	1	◇1
										A		🚌		🚌				
				☕				☕			☕					☕		☕
London Paddington 15 ⊖	d			21 37	21 42		21 43	22 03		22 14	22 37		22 42		22 43	23 03		23 37
Ealing Broadway ⊖	d						21 53			22 23					22 53			
Slough 3	d				22 02		22 16			22 46			23 02		23 16			23 57
Maidenhead 3	d						22 25			22 56					23 25			
Twyford 3	d		←				22 32		←	23 04					23 32		←	
Reading 7	d	21 44	21 45	22 09	22 19	22 44	22 50	22 44	22 50	23 12	23 15		23 21		23 50	23 45	23 50	00 16
Reading West	d					22 47	→			23 15					→			
Theale	d	21 51				22 53				23 21								
Aldermaston	d					22 58												
Midgham	d					23 01												
Thatcham	d	22 00				23 06				23 30								
Newbury Racecourse	d					23 11												
Newbury	a	22 05				23 15				23 37								
	d	22 06																
Kintbury	d	22 12																
Hungerford	d	22 17																
Bedwyn	a	22 25																
Tilehurst	d		21 48						22 53								23 54	
Pangbourne	d		21 53						22 58								23 59	
Goring & Streatley	d		21 57						23 02								00 04	
Cholsey	d		22 03						23 07								00 09	
Didcot Parkway	a		22 13	22 23	22 36			23 00	23 16		23s28		23 40			23s59	00 17	00s33
	d		22 13		22 37							23 30		23 45				
Appleford	d																	
Culham	d																	
Radley	d		22 22											23 59				
Oxford	a		22 32		22 50							23 55		00 15				
	d																	
Islip	d																	
Bicester Town	a																	
Tackley	d																	
Heyford	d																	
Kings Sutton	d																	
Banbury	a																	
Leamington Spa 8	a																	
Coventry	a																	
Birmingham International	a																	
Birmingham New Street 12	a																	

A 1 to Reading

For complete service between Banbury and Leamington (Birmingham), please refer to table 71

Table 116R

Mondays to Fridays

9 December to 30 December

Birmingham, Banbury, Bicester, Oxford and Bedwyn - Reading and London

Network Diagram - refer to first Page of Table 116

Miles	Miles	Station		GW MO	GW MO	GW MO	GW MX	GW MO	GW MX	GW MO	GW MO	GW MX
				1	1	🚌	◇1	◇1	1	🚌	1	1
0	—	**Birmingham New Street** 12	d									
8½	—	Birmingham International	d									
19¼	—	Coventry	d									
28¾	—	Leamington Spa 8	d									
48¾	—	**Banbury**	d									
52¼	—	Kings Sutton	d									
59¾	—	Heyford	d									
62½	—	Tackley	d						00 03			
—	0	**Bicester Town**	d									
—	6	Islip	d									
71½	11¾	**Oxford**	a						00 14			
—	—		d			00 05	00 07		00 27	03 38		04 00
76½	—	Radley	d						00 33			
78¾	—	Culham	d									
79¾	—	Appleford	d									
81½	—	**Didcot Parkway**	a			00 30	00 20		00 42	04 03		04 12
—	—		d				00 21	00 35	00 46		04 12	04 12
86¾	—	Cholsey	d						00 52		04 18	04 18
90¼	—	Goring & Streatley	d	00 01					00 57		04 23	04 23
93½	—	Pangbourne	d	00 06					01 01		04 28	04 28
96¼	—	Tilehurst	d	00 10					01 06		04 32	04 32
—	0	**Bedwyn**	d									
—	5	Hungerford	d									
—	8	Kintbury	d									
—	13½	**Newbury**	a									
—	—		d									
—	14	Newbury Racecourse	d									
—	17	Thatcham	d									
—	19¾	Midgham	d									
—	21¾	Aldermaston	d		00 01							
—	25¾	Theale	d		00 06							
—	29½	Reading West	d		00s13							
99	30½	**Reading** 7	a	00 15	00 17		00 38	00 52	01 13		04 38	04 38
—	—		d	00 15			00 39	00 53	01 17		04 40	04 40
104	—	Twyford 3	a	00 23				01 00	01 23		04 46	04 46
110¾	—	Maidenhead 3	a	00 31				01 07	01 31		04 54	04 54
116½	—	Slough 3	a	00 39			00 55	01 15	01 39		04 59	04 59
129¼	—	Ealing Broadway ⊖	a	01 02				01 31	01 55		05 25	05 25
135	—	**London Paddington** 15 ⊖	a	01 14			01 20	01 41	02 07		05 41	05 41

Miles	Miles	Station		GW	GW	GW	GW	GW	GW	GW	GW	GW
				1	◇1 ☕	1	1	1	1	◇1	1	1
0	—	**Birmingham New Street** 12	d									
8½	—	Birmingham International	d									
19¼	—	Coventry	d									
28¾	—	Leamington Spa 8	d									
48¾	—	**Banbury**	d									
52¼	—	Kings Sutton	d									
59¾	—	Heyford	d									
62½	—	Tackley	d									
—	0	**Bicester Town**	d									
—	6	Islip	d									
71½	11¾	**Oxford**	a									
—	—		d	05 03		05 24		05 43		05 59		
76½	—	Radley	d	05 09				05 49				
78¾	—	Culham	d									
79¾	—	Appleford	d									
81½	—	**Didcot Parkway**	a	05 17		05 36		05 58		06 12		
—	—		d	05 18	05 41	05 46		06 00		06 13		06 20
86¾	—	Cholsey	d	05 23		05 52						06 25
90¼	—	Goring & Streatley	d	05 28		05 57						06 30
93½	—	Pangbourne	d	05 33		06 02						06 35
96¼	—	Tilehurst	d	05 37		06 06						06 40
—	0	**Bedwyn**	d						05 40			
—	5	Hungerford	d						05 46			
—	8	Kintbury	d						05 50			
—	13½	**Newbury**	a						05 57			
—	—		d				05 40		05 58		06 09	
—	14	Newbury Racecourse	d				05 42					
—	17	Thatcham	d				05 47		06 02		06 15	
—	19¾	Midgham	d				05 51					
—	21¾	Aldermaston	d				05 55					
—	25¾	Theale	d				06 00		06 10		06 24	
—	29½	Reading West	d				06 07		06 17		06 32	
99	30½	**Reading** 7	a	05 43	05 56	06 12	06 12	06 16	06 21	06 26	06 35	06 46
—	—		d	05 44	05 57	06 15		06 16	06 21	06 28	06 35	06 46
104	—	Twyford 3	a	05 50		06 21		06 23			06 42	↦
110¾	—	Maidenhead 3	a	05 58		06 28		06 31		06 39		
116½	—	Slough 3	a	06 10		06 40			06 40	06 47		
129¼	—	Ealing Broadway ⊖	a	06 35		07 05						
135	—	**London Paddington** 15 ⊖	a	06 46	06 24	07 17		06 54	07 01	07 08	07 12	

Miles	Miles	Station		GW	GW	GW	GW	GW	GW	GW	GW	GW
				◇1 ☕	1	1	◇1 ☕	◇1 ☕	1	1	■ 1 ☕	◇1 ☕
0	—	**Birmingham New Street** 12	d									
8½	—	Birmingham International	d									
19¼	—	Coventry	d									
28¾	—	Leamington Spa 8	d									
48¾	—	**Banbury**	d									
52¼	—	Kings Sutton	d									
59¾	—	Heyford	d									
62½	—	Tackley	d									
—	0	**Bicester Town**	d									
—	6	Islip	d									
71½	11¾	**Oxford**	a									
—	—		d			06 04	06 30					
76½	—	Radley	d			06 10						
78¾	—	Culham	d			06 14						
79¾	—	Appleford	d			06 16						
81½	—	**Didcot Parkway**	a			06 23						
—	—		d	06 28		06 36		06 46			06 59	
86¾	—	Cholsey	d			06 42						
90¼	—	Goring & Streatley	d			06 47						
93½	—	Pangbourne	d			06 52						
96¼	—	Tilehurst	d			06 57						
—	0	**Bedwyn**	d							06 13		
—	5	Hungerford	d							06 18		06 37
—	8	Kintbury	d							06 23		
—	13½	**Newbury**	a							06 30		06 49
—	—		d							06 30		06 50
—	14	Newbury Racecourse	d							06 32		
—	17	Thatcham	d							06 37		06 58
—	19¾	Midgham	d							06 42		
—	21¾	Aldermaston	d							06 45		
—	25¾	Theale	d							06 50		07 08
—	29½	Reading West	d		↤				↤	06 57		
99	30½	**Reading** 7	a	06 41	06 46	07 00	06 53	06 59	07 00	07 02	07 13	07 20
—	—		d	06 43	06 46	07 05	06 55	07 01	07 05		07 15	07 21
104	—	Twyford 3	a		06 53	↦						
110¾	—	Maidenhead 3	a		07 01		07 06		07 16			
116½	—	Slough 3	a	06 57								
129¼	—	Ealing Broadway ⊖	a									
135	—	**London Paddington** 15 ⊖	a	07 16	07 27		07 27	07 32	07 43		07 44	07 53

Miles	Miles	Station		GW	CH	GW	GW	GW	GW	GW	GW
				1		◇1	◇1 ☕	1	1	◇1 ☕	◇1 ☕
0	—	**Birmingham New Street** 12	d								
8½	—	Birmingham International	d								
19¼	—	Coventry	d								
28¾	—	Leamington Spa 8	d								
48¾	—	**Banbury**	d	06 07							
52¼	—	Kings Sutton	d	06 13							
59¾	—	Heyford	d	06 21							
62½	—	Tackley	d	06 26							
—	0	**Bicester Town**	d		06 19						
—	6	Islip	d		06 30						
71½	11¾	**Oxford**	a	06 36	06 45						
—	—		d	06 36			06 55				
76½	—	Radley	d	06 42							
78¾	—	Culham	d	06 46							
79¾	—	Appleford	d	06 49							
81½	—	**Didcot Parkway**	a	06 56			07 08				
—	—		d	07 00		07 06	07 10			07 20	
86¾	—	Cholsey	d	07 08		07 20					
90¼	—	Goring & Streatley	d	07 13		07 26					
93½	—	Pangbourne	d	07 18		07 33					
96¼	—	Tilehurst	d	07 23		07 40					
—	0	**Bedwyn**	d								06 45
—	5	Hungerford	d								06 53
—	8	Kintbury	d								06 59
—	13½	**Newbury**	a								07 06
—	—		d					06 56			07 08
—	14	Newbury Racecourse	d					06 58			
—	17	Thatcham	d					07 03			07 15
—	19¾	Midgham	d					07 07			
—	21¾	Aldermaston	d					07 11			
—	25¾	Theale	d					07 16			07 25
—	29½	Reading West	d					07 23	↤		07 34
99	30½	**Reading** 7	a	07 29			07 25	07 27	07 29	07 35	07 37
—	—		d	07 30			07 26		07 30	07 36	07 40
104	—	Twyford 3	a	↦					07 37		
110¾	—	Maidenhead 3	a			07 56			07 45		
116½	—	Slough 3	a						07 55		
129¼	—	Ealing Broadway ⊖	a						08 20		
135	—	**London Paddington** 15 ⊖	a			08 26	07 59		08 32	08 07	08 09

For complete service between Banbury and Leamington (Birmingham), please refer to table 71

Table 116R

Mondays to Fridays

9 December to 30 December

Birmingham, Banbury, Bicester, Oxford and Bedwyn - Reading and London

Network Diagram - refer to first Page of Table 116

		GW	XC	GW	GW	GW	GW	GW	GW	GW	GW	XC	GW	GW	GW	GW	GW	GW	GW	XC	CH	GW	GW	GW	GW	GW	GW	GW	GW	GW	XC	GW	GW	GW	GW	GW	GW
		■1	◇1 ⊼	■ ◇1 A 🍴	■1	■1	■1	◇1 ⊼	■ ■1 🍴	◇1 B 🍴⊘	◇1 🍴	◇1	■ ◇1 A 🍴	■1	◇1 B 🍴⊘	■1	■1	■1	◇1	◇1 ⊼		■ ◇1 C 🍴	■1	◇1 🍴	■1	■ ◇1 D 🍴⊘	■1	◇1 🍴	◇1 🍴	■1	◇1	■1	◇1 E 🍴⊘	■1	■1	◇1	◇1 🍴
Birmingham New Street 12	d		06 04									06 33								07 04											07 33						
Birmingham International	d		06 14																	07 14																	
Coventry	d		06 25																	07 25																	
Leamington Spa 8	d		06 37									07 00								07 38											07 59						
Banbury	d	06 25	06 54									07 20						07 27		07 56											08 16						
Kings Sutton	d	06 31																07 33																			
Heyford	d	06 39																07 41																			
Tackley	d	06 44																07 46																			
Bicester Town	d																				08 03																
Islip	d																				08 14																
Oxford	a	06 57	07 14									07 41						07 56		08 14	08 29										08 39						
	d	07 02	07 16				07 21	07 34				07 43			07 52			07 56	08 07	08 16										08 35	08 43		08 51			09 01	
Radley	d	07 08					07 28											08 02												08 41							
Culham	d	07 12					07 32											08 06																			
Appleford	d	07 14					07 35																							08 46							
Didcot Parkway	a	07 21					07 42											08 14	08 19											08 52						09 14	
	d	07 27		07 29			07 47		07 47		07 56		08 02					08 17	08 20			08 29			08 34	08 47		08 53	08 59	09 03						09 15	09 29
Cholsey	d	07 33					07 53											08 23							08 39					09 08							
Goring & Streatley	d	07 38					07 59											08 29							08 44					09 13							
Pangbourne	d	07 44					08 05											08 34							08 49					09 18							
Tilehurst	d	07 49					08 10											08 39							08 53					09 22							
Bedwyn	d					07 07											07 56																	08 41			
Hungerford	d					07 12				07 34							08 01																	08 46			
Kintbury	d					07 17											08 06																	08 51			
Newbury	a					07 24				07 46							08 14																	08 58			
	d					07 24				07 50						07 53								08 29								08 38		08 58			
Newbury Racecourse	d					07 26										07 55																08 40					
Thatcham	d					07 32										08 00																08 45		09 03			
Midgham	d					07 36										08 05																08 49					
Aldermaston	d					07 40										08 08																08 53					
Theale	d					07 45										08 14																08 58		09 11			
Reading West	d				←	07 52								←		08 22							←				←					09 05			←		
Reading 7	a	07 52	07 41	07 43	07 52	07 56	08 17	07 56	08 00	08 06	08 11	08 13	08 16	08 17	08 22	08 26		08 47	08 35	08 39		08 43	08 47	08 50	09 00	09 00	09 00	09 07	09 14	09 28	09 08	09 10	09 14	09 20	09 28	09 32	09 44
	d	07 56		07 45	07 56		08 19	07 57	08 02	08 09	08 13		08 18	08 19	08 24			08 48	08 36			08 45	08 48	08 52	09 05	09 02	09 05	09 08	09 16	09 33			09 18	09 21	09 33	09 37	09 46
Twyford 3	a	→			08 02		→							08 25				→					08 54		→		09 11			→					09 39		
Maidenhead 3	a				08 10									08 33									09 02				09 19								09 47		
Slough 3	a				08 20																						09 30								09 54	09 53	
Ealing Broadway ⊖	a																										09 54								10 19		
London Paddington 15 ⊖	a			08 14	08 48			08 31	08 33	08 38	08 40		08 45	08 58	08 51				09 06			09 14	09 27	09 21		09 29	10 05	09 40	09 44				09 47	09 56	10 31	10 12	10 15

A ◇ from Reading ■ to Reading

B 🍴 from Reading ⊘ to Reading

C The Bristolian. ◇ from Reading ■ to Reading

D 🍴 ◇ from Reading ⊘ ■ to Reading

E The Cathedrals Express. 🍴 from Reading ⊘ to Reading

For complete service between Banbury and Leamington (Birmingham), please refer to table 71

Table 116R

Mondays to Fridays

9 December to 30 December

Birmingham, Banbury, Bicester, Oxford and Bedwyn - Reading and London

Network Diagram - refer to first Page of Table 116

Station		GW	XC	GW	GW	GW	CH	GW	GW	XC	GW	GW	GW	GW	GW	GW	GW	XC	GW
		1	◇1	1	◇1	1		◇1	1	◇1	1	◇1	1	◇1	1	◇1	1	◇1	1
Birmingham New Street 12	d		08 04							08 33								09 04	
Birmingham International	d		08 14															09 14	
Coventry	d		08 25															09 25	
Leamington Spa 8	d		08 38							09 00								09 38	
Banbury	d		08 55							09 19							09 35	09 55	
Kings Sutton	d																09 40		
Heyford	d																09 49		
Tackley	d																09 54		
Bicester Town	d						09 07												
Islip	d						09 18												
Oxford	a		09 14				09 32			09 41							10 06	10 13	
	d	09 07	09 16		09 31				09 37	09 43		10 01					10 08	10 16	
Radley	d	09 13															10 14		
Culham	d	09 17																	
Appleford	d																		
Didcot Parkway	a	09 24							09 49								10 23		
	d	09 33						09 55	10 01					10 16		10 29	10 31		
Cholsey	d	09 39							10 07								10 37		
Goring & Streatley	d	09 44							10 12								10 42		
Pangbourne	d	09 49							10 17								10 47		
Tilehurst	d	09 53							10 21								10 51		
Bedwyn	d										09 39								
Hungerford	d										09 44								
Kintbury	d										09 49								
Newbury	a										09 56								
	d			09 22							09 56								10 13
Newbury Racecourse	d			09 25															10 15
Thatcham	d			09 30							10 01								10 20
Midgham	d			09 34															10 24
Aldermaston	d			09 38															10 28
Theale	d			09 43							10 09								10 33
Reading West	d			09 50		←							←		←				10 40
Reading 7	a	09 58	09 39	09 54	09 54	09 58		10 08	10 27	10 12	10 22	10 25	10 27	10 31	10 27	10 43	10 57	10 39	10 45
	d	10 03			09 55	10 03		10 09	10 33		10 22	10 26	10 33	10 32	10 33	10 45	11 03		
Twyford 3	a	→				10 09			→				→		10 39		→		
Maidenhead 3	a					10 17									10 47				
Slough 3	a				10 10	10 24						10 40			10 53				
Ealing Broadway ⊖	a					10 49									11 18				
London Paddington 15 ⊖	a				10 29	11 01		10 37			10 56	11 00		11 07	11 32	11 14			

Station		GW	GW	GW	GW	GW	XC	CH	GW	GW	GW	GW	GW	GW	GW	XC	GW	GW	GW
		◇1	1	◇1	1	1	◇1		1	◇1	1	◇1	1	◇1	1	◇1	1	◇1	1
				A															
Birmingham New Street 12	d						09 33									10 04			
Birmingham International	d															10 14			
Coventry	d															10 25			
Leamington Spa 8	d						10 00									10 38			
Banbury	d						10 19									10 55			
Kings Sutton	d																		
Heyford	d																		
Tackley	d																		
Bicester Town	d							10 30											
Islip	d							10 41											
Oxford	a						10 41	10 56								11 14			
	d	10 31				10 37	10 43			11 01					11 07	11 16		11 31	
Radley	d														11 13				
Culham	d																		
Appleford	d																		
Didcot Parkway	a					10 57									11 22				
	d			10 47		11 01						11 16		11 29	11 31				
Cholsey	d					11 07									11 37				
Goring & Streatley	d					11 12									11 42				
Pangbourne	d					11 17									11 47				
Tilehurst	d					11 21									11 51				
Bedwyn	d								10 39										
Hungerford	d								10 44										
Kintbury	d								10 49										
Newbury	a								10 56										
	d								10 56								11 13		
Newbury Racecourse	d																11 15		
Thatcham	d								11 01								11 20		
Midgham	d																11 24		
Aldermaston	d																11 28		
Theale	d								11 09								11 33		
Reading West	d		←		←						←		←				11 40		←
Reading 7	a	10 55	10 57	11 00	10 57	11 27	11 09		11 20	11 24	11 27	11 30	11 27	11 43	11 57	11 39	11 45	11 55	11 57
	d	10 56	11 03	11 02	11 03	11 33			11 21	11 26	11 33	11 32	11 33	11 44	12 03			11 56	12 03
Twyford 3	a		→		11 09	→					→		11 39		→				12 09
Maidenhead 3	a				11 17								11 47						12 17
Slough 3	a	11 10			11 24					11 39			11 54					12 10	12 24
Ealing Broadway ⊖	a				11 49								12 19						12 49
London Paddington 15 ⊖	a	11 30		11 33	12 01				11 56	11 59		12 02	12 31	12 14				12 30	13 02

A The Red Dragon

For complete service between Banbury and Leamington (Birmingham), please refer to table 71

Table 116R

Mondays to Fridays

9 December to 30 December

Birmingham, Banbury, Bicester, Oxford and Bedwyn - Reading and London

Network Diagram - refer to first Page of Table 116

		GW	GW	XC	CH	GW	GW	GW	GW	GW	GW	GW	XC	XC	GW	GW	GW	GW	GW	GW	XC	GW	GW	GW	GW	GW	GW	GW	XC	GW	GW	GW	GW	GW	XC	GW	GW
													FX	FO																							
		◇1 ⊏	1	◇1 ✕		1	◇1 ✕	1	◇1 ⊏	1	◇1 ⊏	1	◇1 ✕	◇1 ✕	1	◇1 ✕	1	◇1 ⊏	1	1	◇1 ✕	◇1 ✕	1	1	◇1 ⊏	◇1 ⊏	1	1	◇1 ✕	1	◇1 ✕	1	◇1 ⊏	1	◇1 ✕	◇1 ⊏	◇1 ✕
Birmingham New Street 12	d			10 33									11 04	11 04							11 33								12 04						12 33		
Birmingham International	d												11 14	11 14															12 14								
Coventry	d												11 25	11 25															12 25								
Leamington Spa 6	d			11 00									11 38	11 38							12 01								12 38						13 00		
Banbury	d			11 19									11 55	11 57							12 19							12 42	12 55						13 22		
Kings Sutton	d																											12 48									
Heyford	d																											12 56									
Tackley	d																											13 01									
Bicester Town	d				11 30																																
Islip	d				11 41																																
Oxford	a			11 41	11 56								12 14	12 14							12 41							13 11	13 14						13 41		
	d		11 37	11 43			12 01					12 07	12 16	12 16		12 31				12 37	12 43	13 01					13 07		13 16		13 31			13 37	13 44		14 01
Radley	d											12 13															13 13										
Culham	d																										13 17										
Appleford	d											12 17																									
Didcot Parkway	a		11 51									12 24								12 49							13 30							13 49			
	d	11 55	12 01						12 16		12 29	12 31						12 47		13 01					13 16	13 29	13 31						13 53	14 01			
Cholsey	d		12 07									12 37								13 07							13 37							14 07			
Goring & Streatley	d		12 12									12 42								13 12							13 42							14 12			
Pangbourne	d		12 17									12 47								13 17							13 47							14 17			
Tilehurst	d		12 21									12 51								13 21							13 51							14 21			
Bedwyn	d					11 39																	12 38													13 32	
Hungerford	d					11 44																	12 43													13 40	
Kintbury	d					11 49																	12 48														
Newbury	a					11 56																	12 55													13 50	
	d					11 56									12 13								13 03							13 13						13 51	
Newbury Racecourse	d														12 15															13 15							
Thatcham	d					12 01									12 20								13 08							13 20						13 58	
Midgham	d														12 24															13 24							
Aldermaston	d														12 28															13 28							
Theale	d					12 09									12 33								13 16							13 33						14 07	
Reading West	d							←		←					12 40		←		←					←						13 40		←					
Reading 7	a	12 08	12 27	12 12		12 22	12 25	12 27	12 30	12 27	12 43	12 57	12 39	12 39	12 45	12 55	12 57	13 00	12 57	13 28	13 07	13 25	13 25	13 28	13 30	13 43	13 57		13 39	13 45	13 54	13 57	14 05	14 27	14 11	14 20	14 25
	d	12 09	12 33			12 22	12 27	12 33	12 32	12 33	12 45	13 03				12 56	13 03	13 02	13 03	13 33		13 26	13 30	13 33	13 35	13 44	14 03				13 56	14 03	14 07	14 33		14 22	14 26
Twyford 3	a		→					→		12 39		→					→		13 09	→				13 39			→					14 09		→			
Maidenhead 3	a									12 47									13 17					13 47								14 17					
Slough 3	a						12 41			12 54						13 10			13 24			13 41		13 54							14 10	14 24					14 40
Ealing Broadway	⊖ a									13 19									13 49					14 19								14 49					
London Paddington 15	⊖ a	12 37				12 54	13 09		13 00	13 31	13 14					13 30		13 33	14 01			14 01	14 09	14 31	14 06	14 14					14 30	15 01	14 37			14 54	15 01

For complete service between Banbury and Leamington (Birmingham), please refer to table 71

Table 116R

Mondays to Fridays

9 December to 30 December

Birmingham, Banbury, Bicester, Oxford and Bedwyn - Reading and London

Network Diagram - refer to first Page of Table 116

		GW	GW	GW	GW	XC	CH	GW	GW	GW	GW	GW	GW	XC	GW	GW	GW	GW	GW
		1	◇1	◇1	1	◇1		1	◇1	1	◇1	1	1	◇1	1	◇1	1	◇1	1
											A								
			⊡	⊡		✕					⊡⊘			✕		✕		⊡	
Birmingham New Street 12	d					13 04								13 33					
Birmingham International	d					13 14													
Coventry	d					13 25													
Leamington Spa 8	d					13 38								14 00					
Banbury	d					13 55								14 19					
Kings Sutton	d																		
Heyford	d																		
Tackley	d																		
Bicester Town	d						14 00												
Islip	d						14 11												
Oxford	a					14 13	14 28							14 40					
	d				14 07	14 16			14 31				14 37	14 43		15 01			
Radley	d				14 13														
Culham	d																		
Appleford	d																		
Didcot Parkway	a				14 22								14 51						
	d		14 15	14 29	14 31						14 47		15 01					15 16	
Cholsey	d				14 37								15 07						
Goring & Streatley	d				14 42								15 12						
Pangbourne	d				14 47								15 17						
Tilehurst	d				14 51								15 21						
Bedwyn	d														14 39				
Hungerford	d														14 44				
Kintbury	d														14 49				
Newbury	a														14 56				
	d							14 13							14 56				
Newbury Racecourse	d							14 15											
Thatcham	d							14 20							15 01				
Midgham	d							14 24											
Aldermaston	d							14 28											
Theale	d							14 33							15 09				
Reading West	d	←						14 40		←		←					←		
Reading 7	a	14 27	14 30	14 43	14 56	14 39		14 45	14 55	14 56	15 00	14 56	15 27	15 08	15 21	15 24	15 27	15 30	15 27
	d	14 33	14 36	14 44	15 03				14 56	15 03	15 02	15 03	15 33		15 22	15 26	15 33	15 31	15 33
Twyford 3	a	14 39			→					→		15 09	→				→		15 39
Maidenhead 3	a	14 47										15 17							15 47
Slough 3	a	14 54							15 10			15 24				15 39			15 54
Ealing Broadway ⊖	a	15 19										15 49							16 19
London Paddington 15 ⊖	a	15 32	15 08	15 14					15 30		15 33	16 01			15 54	16 01		16 08	16 31

		GW	GW	XC	GW	GW	GW	GW	GW	GW	XC	CH	GW	GW	GW	GW	GW	GW	XC
		◇1	1	◇1	1	◇1	1	◇1	1	1	◇1		1	◇1	1	◇1	◇1	1	◇1
								B											
		⊡		✕		⊡		⊡			✕			✕		⊡	⊡		✕
Birmingham New Street 12	d			14 04							14 33								15 04
Birmingham International	d			14 14															15 14
Coventry	d			14 24															15 24
Leamington Spa 8	d			14 38							15 00								15 38
Banbury	d			14 55						15 08	15 19								15 55
Kings Sutton	d									15 14									
Heyford	d									15 22									
Tackley	d									15 27									
Bicester Town	d											15 30							
Islip	d											15 41							
Oxford	a			15 13						15 39	15 41	15 56							16 13
	d		15 07	15 16		15 31			15 37		15 43			16 01				16 07	16 16
Radley	d		15 13						15 43									16 13	
Culham	d		15 17																
Appleford	d																	16 17	
Didcot Parkway	a		15 24						15 51									16 27	
	d	15 29	15 35					15 53	16 01							16 16	16 29	16 35	
Cholsey	d		15 41						16 07									16 41	
Goring & Streatley	d		15 46						16 12									16 46	
Pangbourne	d		15 51						16 17									16 51	
Tilehurst	d		15 55						16 21									16 55	
Bedwyn	d												15 40						
Hungerford	d												15 45						
Kintbury	d												15 50						
Newbury	a												15 57						
	d				15 13								15 57						
Newbury Racecourse	d				15 15														
Thatcham	d				15 20								16 02						
Midgham	d				15 24														
Aldermaston	d				15 28														
Theale	d				15 33								16 10						
Reading West	d				15 40		←								←				
Reading 7	a	15 43	16 01	15 40	15 45	15 55	16 01	16 05	16 27		16 11		16 21	16 25	16 27	16 29	16 43	17 01	16 39
	d	15 44	16 03			15 57	16 03	16 07	16 31				16 22	16 26	16 31	16 31	16 45	17 03	
Twyford 3	a		→				16 09		→						16 37			→	
Maidenhead 3	a						16 17								16 47				
Slough 3	a					16 10	16 24							16 41	16 54				
Ealing Broadway ⊖	a						16 49								17 21				
London Paddington 15 ⊖	a	16 14				16 29	17 01	16 39					16 57	17 00	17 31	17 09	17 14		

A ⊡ from Reading ⊘ to Reading

B The Cheltenham Spa Express

For complete service between Banbury and Leamington (Birmingham), please refer to table 71

Table 116R

Mondays to Fridays

9 December to 30 December

Birmingham, Banbury, Bicester, Oxford and Bedwyn - Reading and London

Network Diagram - refer to first Page of Table 116

Station		GW 1	GW ◇1	GW ◇1 ☕	GW 1	GW 1	XC ◇1 🛒	GW 1	GW ◇1 ☕	GW 1	GW ◇1 🛒	GW ◇1 ☕	GW 1
Birmingham New Street 12	d						15 33						
Birmingham International	d												
Coventry	d												
Leamington Spa 8	d						16 01						
Banbury	d						16 19						
Kings Sutton	d												
Heyford	d												
Tackley	d												
Bicester Town	d												
Islip	d												
Oxford	a						16 40						
	d		16 31			16 37	16 43	16 49			17 01		
Radley	d					16 43							
Culham	d												
Appleford	d												
Didcot Parkway	a					16 51		17 03					
	d			16 47		17 05						17 16	
Cholsey	d					17 11							
Goring & Streatley	d					17 16							
Pangbourne	d					17 20							
Tilehurst	d					17 25							
Bedwyn	d									16 44			
Hungerford	d								16 39	16 49			
Kintbury	d									16 54			
Newbury	a								16 48	17 03			
	d	16 13							16 49				
Newbury Racecourse	d	16 15											
Thatcham	d	16 20							16 55				
Midgham	d	16 24											
Aldermaston	d	16 28											
Theale	d	16 33							17 05				
Reading West	d	16 40			←								←
Reading 7	a	16 45	16 56	17 00	17 01	17 31	17 07		17 16		17 26	17 31	17 31
	d		16 57	17 02	17 03	17 33			17 18		17 27	17 32	17 33
Twyford 3	a				17 09	→							17 39
Maidenhead 3	a				17 17						17 39		17 47
Slough 3	a		17 13		17 24				17 32				17 54
Ealing Broadway ⊖	a				17 49								18 19
London Paddington 15 ⊖	a		17 34	17 30	18 01				17 52		17 59	18 02	18 31

Station		GW ◇1 ☕	GW 1	XC ◇1 🛒	CH	GW 1	GW ◇1 ☕	GW 1	GW ◇1 ☕	GW 1	XC ◇1 🛒	GW 1	GW 1
Birmingham New Street 12	d			16 04							16 33		
Birmingham International	d			16 14									
Coventry	d			16 24									
Leamington Spa 8	d			16 38							17 00		
Banbury	d			16 55							17 19	17 23	
Kings Sutton	d											17 27	
Heyford	d											17 36	
Tackley	d											17 40	
Bicester Town	d				16 57								
Islip	d				17 08								
Oxford	a			17 13	17 23						17 40	17 52	
	d		17 07	17 16			17 31			17 37	17 43		
Radley	d		17 13							17 43			
Culham	d		17 17										
Appleford	d									17 47			
Didcot Parkway	a		17 24							17 54			
	d	17 29	17 31						17 53	18 00			
Cholsey	d		17 37							18 07			
Goring & Streatley	d		17 42							18 12			
Pangbourne	d		17 47							18 17			
Tilehurst	d		17 51							18 21			
Bedwyn	d												17 38
Hungerford	d												17 43
Kintbury	d												17 48
Newbury	a												17 55
	d					17 13							17 55
Newbury Racecourse	d					17 15							
Thatcham	d					17 20							18 00
Midgham	d					17 24							
Aldermaston	d					17 28							18 06
Theale	d					17 33							18 11
Reading West	d					17 40		←					
Reading 7	a	17 43	17 57	17 39		17 45	17 54	17 57	18 06	18 27	18 08		18 22
	d	17 46	18 08				17 56	18 08	18 08	18 33			18 23
Twyford 3	a		→					18 14		→			
Maidenhead 3	a							18 22					
Slough 3	a						18 10	18 34					
Ealing Broadway ⊖	a							18 53					
London Paddington 15 ⊖	a	18 15					18 28	19 02	18 39				18 54

Station		GW ◇1 🛒	GW 1	GW ◇1 ☕	GW 1	GW ◇1 ☕	GW 1	XC ◇1 🛒	GW 1	GW ◇1	GW ◇1 A ☕∅	GW 1	GW 1
Birmingham New Street 12	d							17 04					
Birmingham International	d							17 14					
Coventry	d							17 24					
Leamington Spa 8	d							17 38					
Banbury	d							17 55					
Kings Sutton	d												
Heyford	d												
Tackley	d												
Bicester Town	d												
Islip	d												
Oxford	a							18 15					
	d	18 01					18 07	18 16		18 31			18 37
Radley	d						18 13						18 43
Culham	d						18 17						
Appleford	d												18 47
Didcot Parkway	a						18 24						18 56
	d			18 16		18 29	18 31				18 47		19 01
Cholsey	d						18 37						19 07
Goring & Streatley	d						18 42						19 12
Pangbourne	d						18 47						19 17
Tilehurst	d						18 51						19 21
Bedwyn	d								17 55				
Hungerford	d								18 00				
Kintbury	d								18 05				
Newbury	a								18 12				
	d								18 13				
Newbury Racecourse	d								18 15				
Thatcham	d								18 20				
Midgham	d								18 24				
Aldermaston	d								18 28				
Theale	d								18 33				
Reading West	d		←		←				18 40			←	
Reading 7	a	18 24	18 27	18 30	18 27	18 45	18 58	18 40	18 45	18 58	19 01	18 58	19 27
	d	18 27	18 33	18 32	18 33	18 47	19 08			18 59	19 03	19 08	19 33
Twyford 3	a		→		18 39		→					19 14	→
Maidenhead 3	a				18 47							19 22	
Slough 3	a	18 40			18 54					19 10		19 30	
Ealing Broadway ⊖	a				19 19							19 54	
London Paddington 15 ⊖	a	18 59		19 02	19 31	19 16				19 31	19 33	20 03	

A ☕ from Reading ∅ to Reading

For complete service between Banbury and Leamington (Birmingham), please refer to table 71

Table 116R

Birmingham, Banbury, Bicester, Oxford and Bedwyn - Reading and London

Mondays to Fridays

9 December to 30 December

Network Diagram - refer to first Page of Table 116

Station		XC	CH	GW	GW	GW	GW	GW	GW	XC	GW	GW	GW
		◇1		1	1	◇1	1	◇1	1	◇1	◇1	1	◇1
		trolley				trolley		refreshments		trolley			refreshments
Birmingham New Street 12	d	17 33								18 04			
Birmingham International	d									18 14			
Coventry	d									18 24			
Leamington Spa 8	d	18 00								18 37			
Banbury	d	18 19							18 37	18 55			
Kings Sutton	d								18 43				
Heyford	d								18 51				
Tackley	d								18 56				
Bicester Town	d		18 18										
Islip	d		18 29										
Oxford	a	18 40	18 44						19 08	19 13			
	d	18 43				19 06			19 10	19 16	19 31		
Radley	d								19 16				
Culham	d												
Appleford	d												
Didcot Parkway	a								19 25				
	d							19 29	19 32				19 47
Cholsey	d								19 37				
Goring & Streatley	d								19 42				
Pangbourne	d								19 47				
Tilehurst	d								19 51				
Bedwyn	d				19 03								
Hungerford	d				19 08								
Kintbury	d				19 13								
Newbury	a				19 22								
	d			18 53									
Newbury Racecourse	d												
Thatcham	d			18 58									
Midgham	d												
Aldermaston	d												
Theale	d			19 06									
Reading West	d						←					←	
Reading 7	a	19 10		19 16		19 31	19 27	19 44	19 57	19 41	19 54	19 57	20 00
	d			19 18		19 33	19 33	19 45	19 58		19 55	19 58	20 02
Twyford 3	a						19 42		→			20 04	
Maidenhead 3	a						19 50					20 12	
Slough 3	a					19 47	19 57				20 10	20 22	
Ealing Broadway ⊖	a						20 22					20 49	
London Paddington 15 ⊖	a			19 54		20 06	20 32	20 14			20 30	20 59	20 37

Station		GW	GW	GW	XC	GW	GW	GW	GW	GW	GW	XC	CH
		◇1	◇1	1	◇1	◇1	1	1	1	◇1	1	◇1	
		refreshments	refreshments		trolley					refreshments		trolley	
Birmingham New Street 12	d				18 33							19 04	
Birmingham International	d											19 14	
Coventry	d											19 24	
Leamington Spa 8	d				19 00							19 38	
Banbury	d				19 19							19 55	
Kings Sutton	d												
Heyford	d												
Tackley	d												
Bicester Town	d												20 02
Islip	d												20 13
Oxford	a				19 39							20 13	20 28
	d			19 37	19 42	20 01					20 07	20 16	
Radley	d										20 13		
Culham	d										20 17		
Appleford	d												
Didcot Parkway	a			19 49							20 24		
	d		20 00	20 01						20 29	20 31		
Cholsey	d			20 07							20 37		
Goring & Streatley	d			20 12							20 42		
Pangbourne	d			20 17							20 47		
Tilehurst	d			20 21							20 51		
Bedwyn	d								19 54				
Hungerford	d								19 59				
Kintbury	d								20 04				
Newbury	a								20 11				
	d	19 49						19 55	20 11				
Newbury Racecourse	d							19 57					
Thatcham	d							20 02	20 16				
Midgham	d							20 06					
Aldermaston	d							20 10					
Theale	d							20 15	20 24				
Reading West	d						←	20 21					
Reading 7	a	20 06	20 14	20 27	20 08	20 26	20 27	20 27	20 34	20 44	20 57	20 39	
	d	20 08	20 15	20 33		20 26	20 33		20 34	20 45	21 12		
Twyford 3	a			→			20 39				→		
Maidenhead 3	a						20 47						
Slough 3	a					20 40	20 54						
Ealing Broadway ⊖	a						21 19						
London Paddington 15 ⊖	a	20 39	20 46			21 01	21 30		21 07	21 14			

Station		GW	GW	GW	GW	GW	XC	GW	GW	GW	GW	XC	GW
		◇1	1	◇1	1	1	◇1	1	1	◇1	1	◇1	◇1
		refreshments		refreshments			trolley					trolley	refreshments
Birmingham New Street 12	d						19 33					20 04	
Birmingham International	d											20 14	
Coventry	d											20 24	
Leamington Spa 8	d						20 04					20 38	
Banbury	d					20 01	20 22					20 55	
Kings Sutton	d					20 07							
Heyford	d					20 15							
Tackley	d					20 20							
Bicester Town	d												
Islip	d												
Oxford	a					20 32	20 39					21 13	
	d	20 31				20 37	20 41			21 01		21 16	
Radley	d												
Culham	d												
Appleford	d												
Didcot Parkway	a					20 49							
	d			20 47		21 01							21 29
Cholsey	d					21 07							
Goring & Streatley	d					21 12							
Pangbourne	d					21 17							
Tilehurst	d					21 21							
Bedwyn	d							20 33	21 01				
Hungerford	d							20 38	21 07				
Kintbury	d							20 43	21 11				
Newbury	a								21 18				
	d												
Newbury Racecourse	d							20 52					
Thatcham	d							20 57					
Midgham	d							21 02					
Aldermaston	d							21 05					
Theale	d							21 10					
Reading West	d		←		←			21 17			←		
Reading 7	a	20 55	20 57	21 00	20 57	21 29	21 07	21 22		21 24	21 29	21 41	21 43
	d	20 56	21 12	21 03	21 12	21 33				21 26	21 33		21 44
Twyford 3	a		→		21 18	→					21 39		
Maidenhead 3	a				21 26						21 47		
Slough 3	a	21 11			21 38					21 40	21 58		
Ealing Broadway ⊖	a				22 02						22 21		
London Paddington 15 ⊖	a	21 29		21 32	22 14					22 00	22 32		22 16

For complete service between Banbury and Leamington (Birmingham), please refer to table 71

Table 116R

Mondays to Fridays

9 December to 30 December

Birmingham, Banbury, Bicester, Oxford and Bedwyn - Reading and London

Network Diagram - refer to first Page of Table 116

		GW	GW	GW FO	GW FX	GW FO	GW FX	GW FO	GW FX	XC	GW	CH	GW FX	GW FO	XC
		1	1	◇1	◇1	◇1	◇1	◇1	◇1	◇1	1		◇1	◇1	◇1
													A	A	
						🚲	🚲	🚲	🚲						trolley
Birmingham New Street 12	d									20 33					21 04
Birmingham International	d														21 14
Coventry	d														21 24
Leamington Spa 8	d									21 00					21 38
Banbury	d									21 19			21 38	21 38	21 55
Kings Sutton	d												21 44	21 44	
Heyford	d												21 52	21 52	
Tackley	d												21 57	21 57	
Bicester Town	d											21 31			
Islip	d											21 42			
Oxford	a									21 40		21 57	22 07	22 07	22 14
	d		21 21	21 32	21 32					21 43	21 51		22 11	22 11	22 16
Radley	d		21 27								21 57				
Culham	d														
Appleford	d														
Didcot Parkway	a		21 34								22 06		22 24	22 24	
	d		21 44					21 53	21 53		22 08		22 27	22 27	
Cholsey	d		21 50								22 14				
Goring & Streatley	d		21 55								22 19				
Pangbourne	d		21 58								22 24				
Tilehurst	d		22 02								22 27				
Bedwyn	d														
Hungerford	d														
Kintbury	d														
Newbury	a														
	d	21 23				21 42	21 42								
Newbury Racecourse	d	21 25													
Thatcham	d	21 30													
Midgham	d	21 34													
Aldermaston	d	21 38													
Theale	d	21 43													
Reading West	d	21 49													
Reading 7	a	21 54	22 11	21 55	21 55	21 59	21 59	22 11	22 11	22 17	22 37		22 43	22 44	22 41
	d			21 56	21 56	22 00	22 00	22 12	22 12				22 44	22 44	
Twyford 3	a														
Maidenhead 3	a														
Slough 3	a			22 14	22 14								23 01	23 01	
Ealing Broadway ⊖	a														
London Paddington 15 ⊖	a			22 38	22 41	22 30	22 38	22 44	22 47				23 24	23 24	

		GW	GW FX	GW FO	GW FX	GW FO	GW	GW	GW	XC	GW	GW FX	GW FO	CH FO	GW	CH
		1	◇1	◇1	◇1	◇1	1	1	◇1	◇1	1	◇1	◇1		1	
					🚲	🚲						🚲	🚲			
Birmingham New Street 12	d									22 04						
Birmingham International	d									22 14						
Coventry	d									22 25						
Leamington Spa 8	d									22 38						23 39
Banbury	d							22 25		22 55					23 45	23 58
Kings Sutton	d							22 31							23 50	
Heyford	d							22 39							23 58	
Tackley	d							22 44							00 03	
Bicester Town	d													23 42		
Islip	d													23 53		
Oxford	a							22 56		23 14				00 08	00 14	00 22
	d		22 30	22 30			22 52		23 09	23 15					00 27	
Radley	d						22 58								00 33	
Culham	d						23 02									
Appleford	d						23 04									
Didcot Parkway	a						23 11		23 23						00 42	
	d				22 52	22 52	23 13		23 23			23 35	23 35		00 46	
Cholsey	d						23 19								00 52	
Goring & Streatley	d						23 24								00 57	
Pangbourne	d						23 27								01 01	
Tilehurst	d						23 31								01 06	
Bedwyn	d	21 55									23 00					
Hungerford	d	22 00									23 05					
Kintbury	d	22 05									23 10					
Newbury	a	22 12									23 17					
	d	22 13									23 17					
Newbury Racecourse	d	22 15									23 19					
Thatcham	d	22 20									23 24					
Midgham	d	22 24									23 29					
Aldermaston	d	22 28									23 32					
Theale	d	22 33									23 37					
Reading West	d	22 40									23 44					
Reading 7	a	22 45	22 53	22 54	23 06	23 08	23 41		23 41	23 49	23 49	23 53	23 54		01 13	
	d		22 59	22 59	23 09	23 09			23 41			23 55	23 55		01 17	
Twyford 3	a														01 23	
Maidenhead 3	a								23 54						01 31	
Slough 3	a		23 14	23 14					00 02						01 39	
Ealing Broadway ⊖	a														01 55	
London Paddington 15 ⊖	a		23 38	23 37	23 44	23 42			00 27			00 33	00 33		02 07	

A 1 to Oxford

For complete service between Banbury and Leamington (Birmingham), please refer to table 71

Table 116R

Mondays to Fridays

6 January to 10 February

Birmingham, Banbury, Bicester, Oxford and Bedwyn - Reading and London

Network Diagram - refer to first Page of Table 116

Station		GW MO	GW MO	GW MO	GW MX	GW MO	GW MX	GW MO	GW MO	GW MX
		1	1	🚌	◇1	◇1	1	🚌	1	1
Birmingham New Street 12	d									
Birmingham International	d									
Coventry	d									
Leamington Spa 8	d									
Banbury	d									
Kings Sutton	d									
Heyford	d									
Tackley	d						00 03			
Bicester Town	d									
Islip	d									
Oxford	a						00 14			
	d			00 05	00 07		00 27	03 38		04 00
Radley	d						00 33			
Culham	d									
Appleford	d									
Didcot Parkway	a			00 30	00 20		00 42	04 03		04 12
	d				00 21	00 35	00 46		04 12	04 12
Cholsey	d						00 52		04 18	04 18
Goring & Streatley	d						00 57		04 23	04 23
Pangbourne	d						01 01			04 28
Tilehurst	d	00 04					01 06		04 32	04 32
Bedwyn	d									
Hungerford	d									
Kintbury	d									
Newbury	a									
	d									
Newbury Racecourse	d									
Thatcham	d									
Midgham	d									
Aldermaston	d		00 01							
Theale	d		00 06							
Reading West	d		00s13							
Reading 7	a	00 14	00 17		00 38	00 58	01 13		04 38	04 38
	d	00 15			00 39	00 58	01 17		04 40	04 40
Twyford 3	a	00 23				01 05	01 23		04 46	04 46
Maidenhead 3	a	00 31				01 13	01 31		04 54	04 54
Slough 3	a	00 38			00 55	01 20	01 39		04 59	04 59
Ealing Broadway ⊖	a	01 02				01 37	01 55		05 25	05 25
London Paddington 15 ⊖	a	01 14			01 20	01 46	02 07		05 41	05 41

Station		GW	GW	GW	GW	GW	GW	GW	GW	GW
		1	◇1 ☕	1	1	1	1	◇1	1	1
Birmingham New Street 12	d									
Birmingham International	d									
Coventry	d									
Leamington Spa 8	d									
Banbury	d									
Kings Sutton	d									
Heyford	d									
Tackley	d									
Bicester Town	d									
Islip	d									
Oxford	a									
	d	05 03		05 24		05 43		05 59		
Radley	d	05 09				05 49				
Culham	d									
Appleford	d									
Didcot Parkway	a	05 17		05 36		05 58		06 12		
	d	05 18	05 41	05 46		06 00		06 13		06 20
Cholsey	d	05 23		05 52						06 25
Goring & Streatley	d	05 28		05 57						06 30
Pangbourne	d	05 33		06 02						06 35
Tilehurst	d	05 37		06 06						06 40
Bedwyn	d						05 40			
Hungerford	d						05 46			
Kintbury	d						05 50			
Newbury	a						05 57			
	d				05 40		05 58		06 09	
Newbury Racecourse	d				05 42					
Thatcham	d				05 47		06 02		06 15	
Midgham	d				05 51					
Aldermaston	d				05 55					
Theale	d				06 00		06 10		06 24	
Reading West	d				06 07		06 17		06 32	
Reading 7	a	05 43	05 56	06 12	06 12	06 16	06 21	06 26	06 35	06 46
	d	05 44	05 57	06 15		06 16	06 21	06 28	06 35	06 46
Twyford 3	a	05 50		06 21		06 23			06 42	→
Maidenhead 3	a	05 58		06 28		06 31		06 39		
Slough 3	a	06 10		06 40			06 40	06 47		
Ealing Broadway ⊖	a	06 35		07 05						
London Paddington 15 ⊖	a	06 46	06 24	07 17		06 54	07 01	07 08	07 12	

Station		GW	GW	GW	GW	GW	GW	GW	GW	GW
		◇1 ☕	1	1	◇1 ☕	◇1 ☕	1	1	R 1 ☕	◇1 ☕
Birmingham New Street 12	d									
Birmingham International	d									
Coventry	d									
Leamington Spa 8	d									
Banbury	d									
Kings Sutton	d									
Heyford	d									
Tackley	d									
Bicester Town	d									
Islip	d									
Oxford	a									
	d			06 04	06 30					
Radley	d			06 10						
Culham	d			06 14						
Appleford	d			06 16						
Didcot Parkway	a			06 23						
	d	06 28		06 36		06 46			06 59	
Cholsey	d			06 42						
Goring & Streatley	d			06 47						
Pangbourne	d			06 52						
Tilehurst	d			06 57						
Bedwyn	d							06 13		
Hungerford	d							06 18		06 37
Kintbury	d							06 23		
Newbury	a							06 30		06 49
	d							06 30		06 50
Newbury Racecourse	d							06 32		
Thatcham	d							06 37		06 58
Midgham	d							06 42		
Aldermaston	d							06 45		
Theale	d							06 50		07 08
Reading West	d		←				←	06 57		
Reading 7	a	06 41	06 46	07 00	06 53	06 59	07 00	07 02	07 13	07 20
	d	06 43	06 46	07 05	06 55	07 01	07 05		07 15	07 21
Twyford 3	a		06 53	→						
Maidenhead 3	a		07 01		07 06		07 16			
Slough 3	a	06 57								
Ealing Broadway ⊖	a									
London Paddington 15 ⊖	a	07 16	07 27		07 27	07 32	07 43		07 44	07 53

Station		GW	CH	GW	GW	GW	GW	GW	GW	GW
		1		◇1	◇1 ☕	1	1	◇1 ☕	◇1 ☕	1
Birmingham New Street 12	d									
Birmingham International	d									
Coventry	d									
Leamington Spa 8	d									
Banbury	d	06 07								06 25
Kings Sutton	d	06 13								06 31
Heyford	d	06 21								06 39
Tackley	d	06 26								06 44
Bicester Town	d		06 19							
Islip	d		06 30							
Oxford	a	06 36	06 45							06 57
	d	06 36			06 55					07 02
Radley	d	06 42								07 08
Culham	d	06 46								07 12
Appleford	d	06 49								07 14
Didcot Parkway	a	06 56			07 08					07 21
	d	07 00		07 06	07 10			07 20		07 27
Cholsey	d	07 08		07 20						07 33
Goring & Streatley	d	07 13		07 26						07 38
Pangbourne	d	07 18		07 33						07 44
Tilehurst	d	07 23		07 40						07 49
Bedwyn	d								06 45	
Hungerford	d								06 53	
Kintbury	d								06 59	
Newbury	a								07 06	
	d					06 56			07 08	
Newbury Racecourse	d					06 58				
Thatcham	d					07 03			07 15	
Midgham	d					07 07				
Aldermaston	d					07 11				
Theale	d					07 16			07 25	
Reading West	d					07 23	←		07 34	
Reading 7	a	07 29			07 25	07 27	07 29	07 35	07 37	07 52
	d	07 30			07 26		07 30	07 36	07 40	07 56
Twyford 3	a	→					07 37			→
Maidenhead 3	a			07 56			07 45			
Slough 3	a						07 55			
Ealing Broadway ⊖	a						08 20			
London Paddington 15 ⊖	a			08 26	07 59		08 32	08 07	08 09	

For complete service between Banbury and Leamington (Birmingham), please refer to table 71

Table 116R

Mondays to Fridays

6 January to 10 February

Birmingham, Banbury, Bicester, Oxford and Bedwyn - Reading and London

Network Diagram - refer to first Page of Table 116

Station		XC	GW	GW	GW	GW	GW	GW	GW	GW
		◇1 T	■ ◇1 A ☕	1	1	1	◇1 T	■ 1 ☕	◇1 B ☕Ø	◇1 ☕
Birmingham New Street 12	d	06 04								
Birmingham International	d	06 14								
Coventry	d	06 25								
Leamington Spa 8	d	06 37								
Banbury	d	06 54								
Kings Sutton	d									
Heyford	d									
Tackley	d									
Bicester Town	d									
Islip	d									
Oxford	a	07 14								
	d	07 16				07 21	07 34			
Radley	d					07 28				
Culham	d					07 32				
Appleford	d					07 35				
Didcot Parkway	a					07 42				
	d		07 29			07 47		07 47		07 56
Cholsey	d					07 53				
Goring & Streatley	d					07 59				
Pangbourne	d					08 05				
Tilehurst	d					08 10				
Bedwyn	d				07 07					
Hungerford	d				07 12				07 34	
Kintbury	d				07 17					
Newbury	a				07 24				07 46	
	d				07 24				07 50	
Newbury Racecourse	d				07 26					
Thatcham	d				07 32					
Midgham	d				07 36					
Aldermaston	d				07 40					
Theale	d				07 45					
Reading West	d			←	07 52					
Reading 7	a	07 41	07 43	07 52	07 56	08 17	07 56	08 00	08 06	08 11
	d		07 45	07 56		08 19	07 57	08 02	08 09	08 13
Twyford 3	a			08 02		→				
Maidenhead 3	a			08 10						
Slough 3	a			08 20						
Ealing Broadway ⊖	a									
London Paddington 15 ⊖	a		08 14	08 48			08 31	08 33	08 38	08 40

Station		XC	GW	GW	GW	GW	GW	GW	GW	XC
		◇1	■ ◇1 A ☕	1	◇1 B ☕Ø	1	1	1	◇1	◇1 T
Birmingham New Street 12	d	06 33								07 04
Birmingham International	d									07 14
Coventry	d									07 25
Leamington Spa 8	d	07 00								07 38
Banbury	d	07 20						07 27		07 56
Kings Sutton	d							07 33		
Heyford	d							07 41		
Tackley	d							07 46		
Bicester Town	d									
Islip	d									
Oxford	a	07 41						07 56		08 14
	d	07 43			07 52			07 56	08 07	08 16
Radley	d							08 02		
Culham	d							08 06		
Appleford	d									
Didcot Parkway	a							08 14	08 19	
	d		08 02					08 17	08 20	
Cholsey	d							08 23		
Goring & Streatley	d							08 29		
Pangbourne	d							08 34		
Tilehurst	d							08 39		
Bedwyn	d						07 56			
Hungerford	d						08 01			
Kintbury	d						08 06			
Newbury	a						08 14			
	d					07 53				
Newbury Racecourse	d					07 55				
Thatcham	d					08 00				
Midgham	d					08 05				
Aldermaston	d					08 08				
Theale	d					08 14				
Reading West	d			←		08 22				
Reading 7	a	08 13	08 16	08 17	08 22	08 26		08 47	08 35	08 39
	d		08 18	08 19	08 24			08 48	08 36	
Twyford 3	a			08 25				→		
Maidenhead 3	a			08 33						
Slough 3	a									
Ealing Broadway ⊖	a									
London Paddington 15 ⊖	a		08 45	08 58	08 51				09 06	

Station		CH	GW	GW	GW	GW	GW	GW	GW	GW
			■ ◇1 C ☕	1	◇1 ☕	1	■ ◇1 D ☕Ø	1	◇1 ☕	◇1 ☕
Birmingham New Street 12	d									
Birmingham International	d									
Coventry	d									
Leamington Spa 8	d									
Banbury	d									
Kings Sutton	d									
Heyford	d									
Tackley	d									
Bicester Town	d	08 03								
Islip	d	08 14								
Oxford	a	08 29								
	d									
Radley	d									
Culham	d									
Appleford	d									
Didcot Parkway	a									
	d		08 29			08 34	08 47		08 53	08 59
Cholsey	d					08 39				
Goring & Streatley	d					08 44				
Pangbourne	d					08 49				
Tilehurst	d					08 53				
Bedwyn	d									
Hungerford	d									
Kintbury	d									
Newbury	a									
	d				08 29					
Newbury Racecourse	d									
Thatcham	d									
Midgham	d									
Aldermaston	d									
Theale	d									
Reading West	d			←				←		
Reading 7	a		08 43	08 47	08 50	09 00	09 00	09 00	09 07	09 14
	d		08 45	08 48	08 52	09 05	09 02	09 05	09 08	09 16
Twyford 3	a			08 54		→		09 11		
Maidenhead 3	a			09 02				09 19		
Slough 3	a							09 30		
Ealing Broadway ⊖	a							09 54		
London Paddington 15 ⊖	a		09 14	09 27	09 21		09 29	10 05	09 40	09 44

Station		GW	XC	GW	GW	GW	GW	GW	GW	GW
		1	◇1	1	◇1 E ☕Ø	1	1	◇1	◇1 ☕	1
Birmingham New Street 12	d		07 33							
Birmingham International	d									
Coventry	d									
Leamington Spa 8	d		07 59							
Banbury	d		08 16							
Kings Sutton	d									
Heyford	d									
Tackley	d									
Bicester Town	d									
Islip	d									
Oxford	a		08 39							
	d	08 35	08 43		08 51			09 01		09 07
Radley	d	08 41								09 13
Culham	d									09 17
Appleford	d	08 46								
Didcot Parkway	a	08 52						09 14		09 24
	d	09 03						09 15	09 29	09 33
Cholsey	d	09 08								09 39
Goring & Streatley	d	09 13								09 44
Pangbourne	d	09 18								09 49
Tilehurst	d	09 22								09 53
Bedwyn	d					08 41				
Hungerford	d					08 46				
Kintbury	d					08 51				
Newbury	a					08 58				
	d			08 38		08 58				
Newbury Racecourse	d			08 40						
Thatcham	d			08 45		09 03				
Midgham	d			08 49						
Aldermaston	d			08 53						
Theale	d			08 58		09 11				
Reading West	d			09 05			←			
Reading 7	a	09 28	09 08	09 10	09 14	09 20	09 28	09 32	09 44	09 58
	d	09 33			09 18	09 21	09 33	09 37	09 46	10 03
Twyford 3	a	→					09 39			→
Maidenhead 3	a						09 47			
Slough 3	a						09 54	09 53		
Ealing Broadway ⊖	a						10 19			
London Paddington 15 ⊖	a				09 47	09 56	10 31	10 12	10 15	

A ◇ from Reading ■ to Reading

B ☕ from Reading Ø to Reading

C The Bristolian. ◇ from Reading ■ to Reading

D ☕ ◇ from Reading Ø ■ to Reading

E The Cathedrals Express. ☕ from Reading Ø to Reading

For complete service between Banbury and Leamington (Birmingham), please refer to table 71

Table 116R

Mondays to Fridays

6 January to 10 February

Birmingham, Banbury, Bicester, Oxford and Bedwyn - Reading and London

Network Diagram - refer to first Page of Table 116

		XC	GW	GW	GW	CH	GW	GW	XC	GW	GW	GW	GW	GW	GW	GW	XC	GW	GW
		◇1	1	◇1	1		◇1	1	◇1	1	◇1	1	◇1	1	◇1	1	◇1	1	◇1
		trolley					buffet		trolley		trolley		buffet		buffet		trolley		
Birmingham New Street 12	d	08 04							08 33								09 04		
Birmingham International	d	08 14															09 14		
Coventry	d	08 25															09 25		
Leamington Spa 8	d	08 38							09 00								09 38		
Banbury	d	08 55							09 19							09 35	09 55		
Kings Sutton	d															09 40			
Heyford	d															09 49			
Tackley	d															09 54			
Bicester Town	d					09 07													
Islip	d					09 18													
Oxford	a	09 14				09 32			09 41							10 06	10 13		
	d	09 16		09 31				09 37	09 43		10 01					10 08	10 16		10 31
Radley	d															10 14			
Culham	d																		
Appleford	d																		
Didcot Parkway	a							09 49								10 23			
	d						09 55	10 01					10 16		10 29	10 31			
Cholsey	d							10 07								10 37			
Goring & Streatley	d							10 12								10 42			
Pangbourne	d							10 17								10 47			
Tilehurst	d							10 21								10 51			
Bedwyn	d									09 39									
Hungerford	d									09 44									
Kintbury	d									09 49									
Newbury	a									09 56									
	d		09 22							09 56								10 13	
Newbury Racecourse	d		09 25															10 15	
Thatcham	d		09 30							10 01								10 20	
Midgham	d		09 34															10 24	
Aldermaston	d		09 38															10 28	
Theale	d		09 43							10 09								10 33	
Reading West	d		09 50		←							←		←				10 40	
Reading 7	a	09 39	09 54	09 54	09 58		10 08	10 27	10 12	10 22	10 25	10 27	10 31	10 27	10 43	10 57	10 39	10 45	10 55
	d			09 55	10 03		10 09	10 33		10 22	10 26	10 33	10 32	10 33	10 45	11 03			10 56
Twyford 3	a				10 09			→				→		10 39		→			
Maidenhead 3	a				10 17									10 47					
Slough 3	a			10 10	10 24						10 40			10 53					11 10
Ealing Broadway ⊖	a				10 49									11 18					
London Paddington 15 ⊖	a			10 29	11 01		10 37			10 56	11 00		11 07	11 32	11 14				11 30

		GW	GW	GW	GW	XC	CH	GW	GW	GW	GW	GW	GW	GW	XC	GW	GW	GW	GW
		1	◇1	1	1	◇1		1	◇1	1	◇1	1	◇1	1	◇1	1	◇1	1	◇1
			A																
			buffet			trolley			trolley		buffet		buffet		trolley		trolley		buffet
Birmingham New Street 12	d					09 33									10 04				
Birmingham International	d														10 14				
Coventry	d														10 25				
Leamington Spa 8	d					10 00									10 38				
Banbury	d					10 19									10 55				
Kings Sutton	d																		
Heyford	d																		
Tackley	d																		
Bicester Town	d						10 30												
Islip	d						10 41												
Oxford	a					10 41	10 56								11 14				
	d				10 37	10 43			11 01					11 07	11 16		11 31		
Radley	d													11 13					
Culham	d																		
Appleford	d																		
Didcot Parkway	a				10 57									11 22					
	d		10 47		11 01						11 16		11 29	11 31					11 55
Cholsey	d				11 07									11 37					
Goring & Streatley	d				11 12									11 42					
Pangbourne	d				11 17									11 47					
Tilehurst	d				11 21									11 51					
Bedwyn	d							10 39											
Hungerford	d							10 44											
Kintbury	d							10 49											
Newbury	a							10 56											
	d							10 56								11 13			
Newbury Racecourse	d															11 15			
Thatcham	d							11 01								11 20			
Midgham	d															11 24			
Aldermaston	d															11 28			
Theale	d							11 09								11 33			
Reading West	d	←		←						←		←				11 40		←	
Reading 7	a	10 57	11 00	10 57	11 27	11 09		11 20	11 24	11 27	11 30	11 27	11 43	11 57	11 39	11 45	11 55	11 57	12 08
	d	11 03	11 02	11 03	11 33			11 21	11 26	11 33	11 32	11 33	11 44	12 03			11 56	12 03	12 09
Twyford 3	a	→		11 09	→					→		11 39		→				12 09	
Maidenhead 3	a			11 17								11 47						12 17	
Slough 3	a			11 24					11 39			11 54					12 10	12 24	
Ealing Broadway ⊖	a			11 49								12 19						12 49	
London Paddington 15 ⊖	a		11 33	12 01				11 56	11 59		12 02	12 31	12 14				12 30	13 02	12 37

A The Red Dragon

For complete service between Banbury and Leamington (Birmingham), please refer to table 71

Table 116R

Mondays to Fridays

6 January to 10 February

Birmingham, Banbury, Bicester, Oxford and Bedwyn - Reading and London

Network Diagram - refer to first Page of Table 116

		GW	XC	CH	GW	GW	GW	GW	GW	GW	GW	XC FX	XC FO	GW	GW	GW	GW	GW	GW
		1	◇1 🛒		1	◇1 🛒	1	◇1 ⊡	1	◇1 ⊡	1	◇1 🛒	◇1 🛒	1	◇1 🛒	1	◇1 ⊡	1	1
Birmingham New Street 12	d		10 33									11 04	11 04						
Birmingham International	d											11 14	11 14						
Coventry	d											11 25	11 25						
Leamington Spa 8	d		11 00									11 38	11 38						
Banbury	d		11 19									11 55	11 57						
Kings Sutton	d																		
Heyford	d																		
Tackley	d																		
Bicester Town	d			11 30															
Islip	d			11 41															
Oxford	a		11 41	11 56								12 14	12 14						
	d	11 37	11 43			12 01					12 07	12 16	12 16		12 31				12 37
Radley	d										12 13								
Culham	d																		
Appleford	d										12 17								
Didcot Parkway	a	11 51									12 24								12 49
	d	12 01						12 16		12 29	12 31						12 47		13 01
Cholsey	d	12 07									12 37								13 07
Goring & Streatley	d	12 12									12 42								13 12
Pangbourne	d	12 17									12 47								13 17
Tilehurst	d	12 21									12 51								13 21
Bedwyn	d				11 39														
Hungerford	d				11 44														
Kintbury	d				11 49														
Newbury	a				11 56														
	d				11 56									12 13					
Newbury Racecourse	d													12 15					
Thatcham	d				12 01									12 20					
Midgham	d													12 24					
Aldermaston	d													12 28					
Theale	d				12 09									12 33					
Reading West	d						←		←					12 40		←		←	
Reading 7	a	12 27	12 12		12 22	12 25	12 27	12 30	12 27	12 43	12 57	12 39	12 39	12 45	12 55	12 57	13 00	12 57	13 28
	d	12 33			12 22	12 27	12 33	12 32	12 33	12 45	13 03				12 56	13 03	13 02	13 03	13 33
Twyford 3	a	→					→		12 39		→					→		13 09	→
Maidenhead 3	a								12 47									13 17	
Slough 3	a					12 41			12 54						13 10			13 24	
Ealing Broadway ⊖	a								13 19									13 49	
London Paddington 15 ⊖	a				12 54	13 09		13 00	13 31	13 14					13 30		13 33	14 01	

		XC	GW	GW	GW	GW	GW	GW	GW	XC	GW	GW	GW	GW	GW	XC	GW	GW	GW
		◇1 🛒	◇1 🛒	1	1	◇1 ⊡	◇1 ⊡	1	1	◇1 🛒	1	◇1 🛒	1	◇1 ⊡	1	◇1 🛒	◇1 ⊡	◇1 🛒	1
Birmingham New Street 12	d	11 33								12 04						12 33			
Birmingham International	d									12 14									
Coventry	d									12 25									
Leamington Spa 8	d	12 01								12 38						13 00			
Banbury	d	12 19							12 42	12 55						13 22			
Kings Sutton	d								12 48										
Heyford	d								12 56										
Tackley	d								13 01										
Bicester Town	d																		
Islip	d																		
Oxford	a	12 41							13 11	13 14						13 41			
	d	12 43	13 01					13 07		13 16		13 31			13 37	13 44		14 01	
Radley	d							13 13											
Culham	d							13 17											
Appleford	d																		
Didcot Parkway	a							13 30							13 49				
	d					13 16	13 29	13 31						13 53	14 01				
Cholsey	d							13 37							14 07				
Goring & Streatley	d							13 42							14 12				
Pangbourne	d							13 47							14 17				
Tilehurst	d							13 51							14 21				
Bedwyn	d			12 38													13 32		
Hungerford	d			12 43													13 40		
Kintbury	d			12 48															
Newbury	a			12 55													13 50		
	d			13 03							13 13						13 51		
Newbury Racecourse	d										13 15								
Thatcham	d			13 08							13 20						13 58		
Midgham	d										13 24								
Aldermaston	d										13 28								
Theale	d			13 16							13 33						14 07		
Reading West	d				←						13 40		←						←
Reading 7	a	13 07	13 25	13 25	13 28	13 30	13 43	13 57		13 39	13 45	13 54	13 57	14 05	14 27	14 11	14 20	14 25	14 27
	d		13 26	13 30	13 33	13 35	13 44	14 03				13 56	14 03	14 07	14 33		14 22	14 26	14 33
Twyford 3	a				13 39			→					14 09		→				14 39
Maidenhead 3	a				13 47								14 17						14 47
Slough 3	a		13 41		13 54							14 10	14 24					14 40	14 54
Ealing Broadway ⊖	a				14 19								14 49						15 19
London Paddington 15 ⊖	a		14 01	14 09	14 31	14 06	14 14					14 30	15 01	14 37			14 54	15 01	15 32

For complete service between Banbury and Leamington (Birmingham), please refer to table 71

Table 116R

Mondays to Fridays

6 January to 10 February

Birmingham, Banbury, Bicester, Oxford and Bedwyn - Reading and London

Network Diagram - refer to first Page of Table 116

		GW	GW	GW	XC	CH	GW	GW	GW	GW	GW	GW	XC	GW	GW	GW	GW	GW	GW
		◇1	◇1	1	◇1		1	◇1	1	◇1	1	1	◇1	1	◇1	1	◇1	1	◇1
										A									
		☕	☕		🛒					☕⊘			🛒		🛒		☕		☕
Birmingham New Street 12	d				13 04								13 33						
Birmingham International	d				13 14														
Coventry	d				13 25														
Leamington Spa 8	d				13 38								14 00						
Banbury	d				13 55								14 19						
Kings Sutton	d																		
Heyford	d																		
Tackley	d																		
Bicester Town	d					14 00													
Islip	d					14 11													
Oxford	a				14 13	14 28							14 40						
	d			14 07	14 16			14 31				14 37	14 43		15 01				
Radley	d			14 13															
Culham	d																		
Appleford	d																		
Didcot Parkway	a			14 22								14 51							
	d	14 15	14 29	14 31						14 47		15 01					15 16		15 29
Cholsey	d			14 37								15 07							
Goring & Streatley	d			14 42								15 12							
Pangbourne	d			14 47								15 17							
Tilehurst	d			14 51								15 21							
Bedwyn	d													14 39					
Hungerford	d													14 44					
Kintbury	d													14 49					
Newbury	a													14 56					
	d						14 13							14 56					
Newbury Racecourse	d						14 15												
Thatcham	d						14 20							15 01					
Midgham	d						14 24												
Aldermaston	d						14 28												
Theale	d						14 33							15 09					
Reading West	d						14 40		←		←					←		←	
Reading 7	a	14 30	14 43	14 56	14 39		14 45	14 55	14 56	15 00	14 56	15 27	15 08	15 21	15 24	15 27	15 30	15 27	15 43
	d	14 36	14 44	15 03				14 56	15 03	15 02	15 03	15 33		15 22	15 26	15 33	15 31	15 33	15 44
Twyford 3	a			↪					↪		15 09	↪				↪		15 39	
Maidenhead 3	a										15 17							15 47	
Slough 3	a							15 10			15 24				15 39			15 54	
Ealing Broadway ⊖	a										15 49							16 19	
London Paddington 15 ⊖	a	15 08	15 14					15 30		15 33	16 01			15 54	16 01		16 08	16 31	16 14

		GW	XC	GW	GW	GW	GW	GW	GW	XC	CH	GW	GW	GW	GW	GW	GW	XC	GW
		1	◇1	1	◇1	1	◇1	1	1	◇1		1	◇1	1	◇1	◇1	1	◇1	1
							B												
			🛒		☕		☕			🛒			🛒		☕	☕		🛒	
Birmingham New Street 12	d		14 04							14 33								15 04	
Birmingham International	d		14 14															15 14	
Coventry	d		14 24															15 24	
Leamington Spa 8	d		14 38							15 00								15 38	
Banbury	d		14 55						15 08	15 19								15 55	
Kings Sutton	d								15 14										
Heyford	d								15 22										
Tackley	d								15 27										
Bicester Town	d										15 30								
Islip	d										15 41								
Oxford	a		15 13						15 39	15 41	15 56							16 13	
	d	15 07	15 16		15 31			15 37		15 43			16 01				16 07	16 16	
Radley	d	15 13						15 43									16 13		
Culham	d	15 17																	
Appleford	d																16 17		
Didcot Parkway	a	15 24						15 51									16 27		
	d	15 35					15 53	16 01							16 16	16 29	16 35		
Cholsey	d	15 41						16 07									16 41		
Goring & Streatley	d	15 46						16 12									16 46		
Pangbourne	d	15 51						16 17									16 51		
Tilehurst	d	15 55						16 21									16 55		
Bedwyn	d											15 40							
Hungerford	d											15 45							
Kintbury	d											15 50							
Newbury	a											15 57							
	d			15 13								15 57							16 13
Newbury Racecourse	d			15 15															16 15
Thatcham	d			15 20								16 02							16 20
Midgham	d			15 24															16 24
Aldermaston	d			15 28															16 28
Theale	d			15 33								16 10							16 33
Reading West	d			15 40		←								←					16 40
Reading 7	a	16 01	15 40	15 45	15 55	16 01	16 05	16 27		16 11		16 21	16 25	16 27	16 29	16 43	17 01	16 39	16 45
	d	16 03			15 57	16 03	16 07	16 31				16 22	16 26	16 31	16 31	16 45	17 03		
Twyford 3	a	↪				16 09		↪						16 37			↪		
Maidenhead 3	a					16 17								16 47					
Slough 3	a				16 10	16 24							16 41	16 54					
Ealing Broadway ⊖	a					16 49								17 21					
London Paddington 15 ⊖	a				16 29	17 01	16 39					16 57	17 00	17 31	17 09	17 14			

A ☕ from Reading ⊘ to Reading

B The Cheltenham Spa Express

For complete service between Banbury and Leamington (Birmingham), please refer to table 71

Table 116R

Mondays to Fridays

6 January to 10 February

Birmingham, Banbury, Bicester, Oxford and Bedwyn - Reading and London

Network Diagram - refer to first Page of Table 116

		GW	GW	GW	GW	XC	GW	GW	GW	GW	GW	GW	GW	GW	XC	CH	GW	GW	GW	GW	GW	XC	GW	GW	GW	GW	GW	GW	GW	GW	XC	GW	GW	GW	GW	GW	XC
		◇1	◇1	1	1	◇1	1	◇1	1	◇1	◇1	1	◇1	1	◇1		1	◇1	1	◇1	1	◇1	1	1	◇1	1	◇1	1	◇1	1	◇1	1	◇1	◇1	1	1	◇1
			⊐			⚯		⊐		⚯	⊐		⊐		⚯			⊐		⊐		⚯			⚯		⊐		⊐		⚯			A ⊐⊘			⚯
Birmingham New Street 12	d					15 33									16 04							16 33									17 04						17 33
Birmingham International	d														16 14																17 14						
Coventry	d														16 24																17 24						
Leamington Spa 8	d					16 01									16 38							17 00									17 38						18 00
Banbury	d					16 19									16 55							17 19	17 23								17 55						18 19
Kings Sutton	d																						17 27														
Heyford	d																						17 36														
Tackley	d																						17 40														
Bicester Town	d															16 57																					
Islip	d															17 08																					
Oxford	a					16 40									17 13	17 23						17 40	17 52								18 15						18 40
	d	16 31			16 37	16 43	16 49			17 01				17 07	17 16			17 31			17 37	17 43			18 01					18 07	18 16		18 31			18 37	18 43
Radley	d				16 43									17 13							17 43									18 13						18 43	
Culham	d													17 17																18 17							
Appleford	d																				17 47															18 47	
Didcot Parkway	a				16 51		17 03							17 24							17 54									18 24						18 56	
	d		16 47		17 05						17 16		17 29	17 31						17 53	18 00						18 16		18 29	18 31				18 47		19 01	
Cholsey	d				17 11									17 37							18 07									18 37						19 07	
Goring & Streatley	d				17 16									17 42							18 12									18 42						19 12	
Pangbourne	d				17 20									17 47							18 17									18 47						19 17	
Tilehurst	d				17 25									17 51							18 21									18 51						19 21	
Bedwyn	d								16 44															17 38								17 55					
Hungerford	d							16 39	16 49															17 43								18 00					
Kintbury	d								16 54															17 48								18 05					
Newbury	a							16 48	17 03															17 55								18 12					
	d							16 49									17 13							17 55								18 13					
Newbury Racecourse	d																17 15															18 15					
Thatcham	d							16 55									17 20							18 00								18 20					
Midgham	d																17 24															18 24					
Aldermaston	d																17 28							18 06								18 28					
Theale	d							17 05									17 33							18 11								18 33					
Reading West	d			←								←					17 40		←							←		←				18 40			←		
Reading 7	a	16 56	17 00	17 01	17 31	17 07		17 16		17 26	17 31	17 31	17 43	17 57	17 39		17 45	17 54	17 57	18 06	18 27	18 08		18 22	18 24	18 27	18 30	18 27	18 45	18 58	18 40	18 45	18 58	19 01	18 58	19 27	19 10
	d	16 57	17 02	17 03	17 33			17 18		17 27	17 32	17 33	17 46	18 08				17 56	18 08	18 08	18 33			18 23	18 27	18 33	18 32	18 33	18 47	19 08			18 59	19 03	19 08	19 33	
Twyford 3	a			17 09	→							17 39		→					18 14		→					→		18 39		→					19 14	→	
Maidenhead 3	a			17 17						17 39		17 47							18 22									18 47							19 22		
Slough 3	a	17 13		17 24				17 32				17 54						18 10	18 34						18 40			18 54					19 10		19 30		
Ealing Broadway ⊖	a			17 49								18 19							18 53									19 19							19 54		
London Paddington 15 ⊖	a	17 34	17 30	18 01				17 52		17 59	18 02	18 31	18 15					18 28	19 02	18 39				18 54	18 59		19 02	19 31	19 16				19 31	19 33	20 03		

A ⊐ from Reading ⊘ to Reading

For complete service between Banbury and Leamington (Birmingham), please refer to table 71

Table 116R

Mondays to Fridays

6 January to 10 February

Birmingham, Banbury, Bicester, Oxford and Bedwyn - Reading and London

Network Diagram - refer to first Page of Table 116

		CH	GW	GW	GW	GW	GW	GW	XC	GW
			1	1	◇1 ℸ	1	◇1 ⊐	1	◇1 ℸ	◇1
Birmingham New Street 12	d								18 04	
Birmingham International	d								18 14	
Coventry	d								18 24	
Leamington Spa 8	d								18 37	
Banbury	d							18 37	18 55	
Kings Sutton	d							18 43		
Heyford	d							18 51		
Tackley	d							18 56		
Bicester Town	d	18 18								
Islip	d	18 29								
Oxford	a	18 44						19 08	19 13	
	d				19 06			19 10	19 16	19 31
Radley	d							19 16		
Culham	d									
Appleford	d									
Didcot Parkway	a							19 25		
	d						19 29	19 32		
Cholsey	d							19 37		
Goring & Streatley	d							19 42		
Pangbourne	d							19 47		
Tilehurst	d							19 51		
Bedwyn	d			19 03						
Hungerford	d			19 08						
Kintbury	d			19 13						
Newbury	a			19 22						
	d		18 53							
Newbury Racecourse	d									
Thatcham	d		18 58							
Midgham	d									
Aldermaston	d									
Theale	d		19 06							
Reading West	d					←				
Reading 7	a		19 16		19 31	19 27	19 44	19 57	19 41	19 54
	d		19 18		19 33	19 33	19 45	19 58		19 55
Twyford 3	a					19 42		→		
Maidenhead 3	a					19 50				
Slough 3	a				19 47	19 57				20 10
Ealing Broadway	⊖ a					20 22				
London Paddington 15	⊖ a		19 54		20 06	20 32	20 14			20 30

		GW	GW	GW	GW	GW	XC	GW	GW	GW
		1	◇1 ⊐	◇1 ⊐	◇1 ⊐	1	◇1 ℸ	◇1	1	1
Birmingham New Street 12	d						18 33			
Birmingham International	d									
Coventry	d									
Leamington Spa 8	d						19 00			
Banbury	d						19 19			
Kings Sutton	d									
Heyford	d									
Tackley	d									
Bicester Town	d									
Islip	d									
Oxford	a						19 39			
	d					19 37	19 42	20 01		
Radley	d									
Culham	d									
Appleford	d									
Didcot Parkway	a					19 49				
	d		19 47		20 00	20 01				
Cholsey	d					20 07				
Goring & Streatley	d					20 12				
Pangbourne	d					20 17				
Tilehurst	d					20 21				
Bedwyn	d									
Hungerford	d									
Kintbury	d									
Newbury	a									
	d			19 49						19 55
Newbury Racecourse	d									19 57
Thatcham	d									20 02
Midgham	d									20 06
Aldermaston	d									20 10
Theale	d									20 15
Reading West	d	←							←	20 21
Reading 7	a	19 57	20 00	20 06	20 14	20 27	20 08	20 26	20 27	20 27
	d	19 58	20 02	20 08	20 15	20 33		20 26	20 33	
Twyford 3	a	20 04				→			20 39	
Maidenhead 3	a	20 12							20 47	
Slough 3	a	20 22						20 40	20 54	
Ealing Broadway	⊖ a	20 49							21 19	
London Paddington 15	⊖ a	20 59	20 37	20 39	20 46			21 01	21 30	

		GW	GW	GW	XC	CH	GW	GW	GW	GW
		1	◇1 ⊐	1	◇1 ℸ		◇1 ⊐	1	◇1 ⊐	1
Birmingham New Street 12	d				19 04					
Birmingham International	d				19 14					
Coventry	d				19 24					
Leamington Spa 8	d				19 38					
Banbury	d				19 55					
Kings Sutton	d									
Heyford	d									
Tackley	d									
Bicester Town	d					20 02				
Islip	d					20 13				
Oxford	a				20 13	20 28				
	d			20 07	20 16		20 31			
Radley	d			20 13						
Culham	d			20 17						
Appleford	d									
Didcot Parkway	a			20 24						
	d		20 29	20 31					20 47	
Cholsey	d			20 37						
Goring & Streatley	d			20 42						
Pangbourne	d			20 47						
Tilehurst	d			20 51						
Bedwyn	d	19 54								
Hungerford	d	19 59								
Kintbury	d	20 04								
Newbury	a	20 11								
	d	20 11								
Newbury Racecourse	d									
Thatcham	d	20 16								
Midgham	d									
Aldermaston	d									
Theale	d	20 24								
Reading West	d							←		←
Reading 7	a	20 34	20 44	20 57	20 39		20 55	20 57	21 00	20 57
	d	20 34	20 45	21 12			20 56	21 12	21 03	21 12
Twyford 3	a			→				→		21 18
Maidenhead 3	a									21 26
Slough 3	a						21 11			21 38
Ealing Broadway	⊖ a									22 02
London Paddington 15	⊖ a	21 07	21 14				21 29		21 32	22 14

		GW	XC	GW	GW	GW	GW	XC	GW	GW
		1	◇1 ℸ	1	1	◇1	1	◇1 ℸ	◇1 ⊐	1
Birmingham New Street 12	d		19 33					20 04		
Birmingham International	d							20 14		
Coventry	d							20 24		
Leamington Spa 8	d		20 04					20 38		
Banbury	d	20 01	20 22					20 55		
Kings Sutton	d	20 07								
Heyford	d	20 15								
Tackley	d	20 20								
Bicester Town	d									
Islip	d									
Oxford	a	20 32	20 39					21 13		
	d	20 37	20 41			21 01		21 16		
Radley	d									
Culham	d									
Appleford	d									
Didcot Parkway	a	20 49								
	d	21 01							21 29	
Cholsey	d	21 07								
Goring & Streatley	d	21 12								
Pangbourne	d	21 17								
Tilehurst	d	21 21								
Bedwyn	d			20 33	21 01					
Hungerford	d			20 38	21 07					
Kintbury	d			20 43	21 11					
Newbury	a				21 18					
	d									21 23
Newbury Racecourse	d			20 52						21 25
Thatcham	d			20 57						21 30
Midgham	d			21 02						21 34
Aldermaston	d			21 05						21 38
Theale	d			21 10						21 43
Reading West	d			21 17			←			21 49
Reading 7	a	21 29	21 07	21 22		21 24	21 29	21 41	21 43	21 54
	d	21 33				21 26	21 33		21 44	
Twyford 3	a	→					21 39			
Maidenhead 3	a						21 47			
Slough 3	a					21 40	21 58			
Ealing Broadway	⊖ a						22 21			
London Paddington 15	⊖ a					22 00	22 32		22 16	

For complete service between Banbury and Leamington (Birmingham), please refer to table 71

Table 116R

Mondays to Fridays

6 January to 10 February

Birmingham, Banbury, Bicester, Oxford and Bedwyn - Reading and London

Network Diagram - refer to first Page of Table 116

		GW	GW	GW	GW	GW	GW	GW	XC	GW	CH	GW	GW	XC	GW	GW	GW	GW	GW	GW	GW	GW	XC	GW	GW	GW	GW	GW	GW	CH	GW	CH
			FO	FX	FO	FX	FO	FX				FX	FO			FX	FO	FX	FO						FX		FX			FO		
		1	◇1	◇1	◇1	◇1	◇1	◇1	◇1	1		◇1	◇1	◇1	1	◇1	◇1	◇1	◇1	1	1	◇1	◇1	1	◇1	◇1	◇1	◇1	◇1		1	
												A	A												B	C	D	C	E			
					bus	bus	bus	bus						trolley				bus	bus						bus	bus	bus	bus	bus			
Birmingham New Street 12	d								20 33					21 04									22 04									
Birmingham International	d													21 14									22 14									
Coventry	d													21 24									22 25									
Leamington Spa 8	d								21 00					21 38									22 38									23 39
Banbury	d								21 19			21 38	21 38	21 55							22 25		22 55								23 45	23 58
Kings Sutton	d											21 44	21 44								22 31										23 50	
Heyford	d											21 52	21 52								22 39										23 58	
Tackley	d											21 57	21 57								22 44										00 03	
Bicester Town	d										21 31																			23 42		
Islip	d										21 42																			23 53		
Oxford	a								21 40		21 57	22 07	22 07	22 14							22 56		23 14							00 08	00 14	00 22
	d	21 21	21 32	21 32					21 43	21 51		22 11	22 11	22 16		22 30	22 30			22 52		23 09	23 15								00 27	
Radley	d	21 27								21 57										22 58											00 33	
Culham	d																			23 02												
Appleford	d																			23 04												
Didcot Parkway	a	21 34								22 06		22 24	22 24							23 11		23 23									00 42	
	d	21 44					21 53	21 53		22 08		22 27	22 27					22 52	22 52	23 13		23 23			23 35	23 35	23 37		23 37		00 46	
Cholsey	d	21 50								22 14										23 19											00 52	
Goring & Streatley	d	21 55								22 19										23 24											00 57	
Pangbourne	d	21 58								22 24										23 27											01 01	
Tilehurst	d	22 02								22 27										23 31											01 06	
Bedwyn	d														21 55									23 00								
Hungerford	d														22 00									23 05								
Kintbury	d														22 05									23 10								
Newbury	a														22 12									23 17								
	d				21 42	21 42									22 13									23 17								
Newbury Racecourse	d														22 15									23 19								
Thatcham	d														22 20									23 24								
Midgham	d														22 24									23 29								
Aldermaston	d														22 28									23 32								
Theale	d														22 33									23 37								
Reading West	d														22 40									23 44				←				
Reading 7	a	22 11	21 55	21 55	21 59	21 59	22 11	22 11	22 17	22 37		22 43	22 44	22 41	22 45	22 53	22 54	23 06	23 08	23 41		23 41	23 49	23 49	23 53	23 54	23 53	23 54	23 54		01 13	
	d		21 56	21 56	22 00	22 00	22 12	22 12				22 44	22 44			22 59	22 59	23 09	23 09			23 41			23 55	23 55	23 55	23 55	23 55		01 17	
Twyford 3	a																									→					01 23	
Maidenhead 3	a																					23 54									01 31	
Slough 3	a		22 14	22 14								23 01	23 01			23 14	23 14					00 02									01 39	
Ealing Broadway ⊖	a																														01 55	
London Paddington 15 ⊖	a		22 38	22 41	22 30	22 38	22 44	22 47				23 24	23 24			23 38	23 37	23 44	23 42			00 27			00 33		00 33	00 33	00 33		02 07	

A 1 to Oxford
B until 23 January
C 10 January, 17 January, 24 January
D from 27 January
E 31 January, 7 February

For complete service between Banbury and Leamington (Birmingham), please refer to table 71

Table 116R

Mondays to Fridays

17 February to 24 March

Birmingham, Banbury, Bicester, Oxford and Bedwyn - Reading and London

Network Diagram - refer to first Page of Table 116

Station		GW MO	GW MO	GW MO	GW MX	GW MO	GW MX	GW MO	GW MO	GW MX	GW	GW	GW	GW	GW	GW	GW	GW	GW
		1	1		◇1	◇1	1		1	1	1	◇1	1	1	1	1	◇1	1	1
				🚌				🚌				☕							
Birmingham New Street 12	d																		
Birmingham International	d																		
Coventry	d																		
Leamington Spa 8	d																		
Banbury	d																		
Kings Sutton	d																		
Heyford	d																		
Tackley	d						00 03												
Bicester Town	d																		
Islip	d																		
Oxford	a						00 14												
	d			00 05	00 07		00 27	03 38		04 00	05 03		05 24		05 43		05 59		
Radley	d						00 33				05 09				05 49				
Culham	d																		
Appleford	d																		
Didcot Parkway	a			00 30	00 20		00 42	04 03		04 12	05 17		05 36		05 58		06 12		
	d				00 21	00 35	00 46		04 12	04 12	05 18	05 41	05 46		06 00		06 13		06 20
Cholsey	d						00 52		04 18	04 18	05 23		05 52						06 25
Goring & Streatley	d	00 01					00 57		04 23	04 23	05 28		05 57						06 30
Pangbourne	d	00 06					01 01		04 28	04 28	05 33		06 02						06 35
Tilehurst	d	00 10					01 06		04 32	04 32	05 37		06 06						06 40
Bedwyn	d															05 40			
Hungerford	d															05 46			
Kintbury	d															05 50			
Newbury	a															05 57			
	d													05 40		05 58		06 09	
Newbury Racecourse	d													05 42					
Thatcham	d													05 47		06 02		06 15	
Midgham	d													05 51					
Aldermaston	d		00 01											05 55					
Theale	d		00 06											06 00		06 10		06 24	
Reading West	d		00s13											06 07		06 17		06 32	
Reading 7	a	00 15	00 17		00 38	00 52	01 13		04 38	04 38	05 43	05 56	06 12	06 12	06 16	06 21	06 26	06 35	06 46
	d	00 15			00 39	00 53	01 17		04 40	04 40	05 44	05 57	06 15		06 16	06 21	06 28	06 35	06 46
Twyford 3	a	00 23				01 00	01 23		04 46	04 46	05 50		06 21		06 23			06 42	→
Maidenhead 3	a	00 31				01 07	01 31		04 54	04 54	05 58		06 28		06 31		06 39		
Slough 3	a	00 38			00 55	01 15	01 39		04 59	04 59	06 10		06 40			06 40	06 47		
Ealing Broadway ⊖	a	01 02				01 31	01 55		05 25	05 25	06 35		07 05						
London Paddington 15 ⊖	a	01 14			01 20	01 40	02 07		05 41	05 41	06 46	06 24	07 17		06 54	07 01	07 08	07 12	

Station		GW	GW	GW	GW	GW	GW	GW	GW	GW	GW	GW	CH	GW	GW	GW	GW	GW	GW
		◇1	1	1	◇1	◇1	1	1	1	◇1	◇1	1		◇1	◇1	1	1	◇1	◇1
										A	B							C	D
		☕			☕	☕			☕	☕	☕				☕			☕	☕
Birmingham New Street 12	d																		
Birmingham International	d																		
Coventry	d																		
Leamington Spa 8	d																		
Banbury	d											06 07							
Kings Sutton	d											06 13							
Heyford	d											06 21							
Tackley	d											06 26							
Bicester Town	d												06 19						
Islip	d												06 30						
Oxford	a											06 36	06 45						
	d			06 04	06 30							06 36			06 55				
Radley	d			06 10								06 42							
Culham	d			06 14								06 46							
Appleford	d			06 16								06 49							
Didcot Parkway	a			06 23								06 56			07 08				
	d	06 28		06 36		06 46			06 59			07 00		07 06	07 10			07 20	07 20
Cholsey	d			06 42								07 08		07 20					
Goring & Streatley	d			06 47								07 13		07 26					
Pangbourne	d			06 52								07 18		07 33					
Tilehurst	d			06 57								07 23		07 40					
Bedwyn	d							06 13											
Hungerford	d							06 18		06 37	06 37								
Kintbury	d							06 23											
Newbury	a							06 30		06 48	06 49								
	d							06 30		06 50	06 50					06 56			
Newbury Racecourse	d							06 32								06 58			
Thatcham	d							06 37		06 57	06 58					07 03			
Midgham	d							06 42								07 07			
Aldermaston	d							06 45								07 11			
Theale	d							06 50		07 07	07 08					07 16			
Reading West	d		←				←	06 57								07 23	←		
Reading 7	a	06 41	06 46	07 00	06 53	06 59	07 00	07 02	07 13	07 15	07 20	07 29			07 25	07 27	07 29	07 34	07 35
	d	06 43	06 46	07 05	06 55	07 01	07 05		07 15	07 18	07 21	07 30			07 26		07 30	07 37	07 36
Twyford 3	a		06 53	→								→					07 37	→	
Maidenhead 3	a		07 01		07 06		07 16							07 56			07 45		
Slough 3	a	06 57															07 55		
Ealing Broadway ⊖	a																08 20		
London Paddington 15 ⊖	a	07 16	07 27		07 27	07 32	07 43		07 44	07 53	07 53			08 26	07 59		08 32		08 07

A 24 March
B until 23 March
C from 10 March
D until 7 March

For complete service between Banbury and Leamington (Birmingham), please refer to table 71

Table 116R

Mondays to Fridays

17 February to 24 March

Birmingham, Banbury, Bicester, Oxford and Bedwyn - Reading and London

Network Diagram - refer to first Page of Table 116

		GW	GW	GW	XC	GW	GW	GW	GW	GW	GW	GW	GW	XC	GW	GW	GW	GW	GW
						■					■				■				
		◇1	◇1	1	◇1	◇1	1	1	1	◇1	1	◇1	◇1	◇1	◇1	1	◇1	1	1
		A				B						C			B		C		
		🍴	🍴		🛒	🍴				🛒	🍴	🍴⊘	🍴		🍴		🍴⊘		
Birmingham New Street 12	d				06 04									06 33					
Birmingham International	d				06 14														
Coventry	d				06 25														
Leamington Spa 8	d				06 37									07 00					
Banbury	d			06 25	06 54									07 20					
Kings Sutton	d			06 31															
Heyford	d			06 39															
Tackley	d			06 44															
Bicester Town	d																		
Islip	d																		
Oxford	a			06 57	07 14									07 41					
	d			07 02	07 16				07 21	07 34				07 43			07 52		
Radley	d			07 08					07 28										
Culham	d			07 12					07 32										
Appleford	d			07 14					07 35										
Didcot Parkway	a			07 21					07 42										
	d			07 27		07 29			07 47		07 47		07 56		08 02				
Cholsey	d			07 33					07 53										
Goring & Streatley	d			07 38					07 59										
Pangbourne	d			07 44					08 05										
Tilehurst	d			07 49					08 10										
Bedwyn	d		06 45					07 07											07 56
Hungerford	d		06 53					07 12				07 34							08 01
Kintbury	d		06 59					07 17											08 06
Newbury	a		07 06					07 24				07 46							08 14
	d		07 08					07 24				07 50						07 53	
Newbury Racecourse	d							07 26										07 55	
Thatcham	d		07 15					07 32										08 00	
Midgham	d							07 36										08 05	
Aldermaston	d							07 40										08 08	
Theale	d		07 25					07 45										08 14	
Reading West	d	←	07 34				←	07 52								←		08 22	
Reading 7	a	07 34	07 37	07 52	07 41	07 43	07 52	07 56	08 17	07 56	08 00	08 06	08 11	08 13	08 16	08 17	08 22	08 26	
	d	07 37	07 40	07 56		07 45	07 56		08 19	07 57	08 02	08 09	08 13		08 18	08 19	08 24		
Twyford 3	a			→			08 02		→							08 25			
Maidenhead 3	a						08 10									08 33			
Slough 3	a						08 20												
Ealing Broadway ⊖	a																		
London Paddington 15 ⊖	a	08 07	08 09			08 14	08 48			08 31	08 33	08 38	08 40		08 45	08 58	08 51		

		GW	GW	GW	XC	CH	GW	GW	GW	GW	GW	GW	GW	GW	GW	XC	GW	GW	GW
							■				■								
		1	◇1	◇1	◇1		◇1	1	◇1	1	◇1	1	◇1	◇1	1	◇1	1	◇1	◇1
			D	A			E				F							G	H
					🛒		🍴		🍴		🍴⊘		🍴	🍴				🍴⊘	🍴⊘
Birmingham New Street 12	d				07 04											07 33			
Birmingham International	d				07 14														
Coventry	d				07 25														
Leamington Spa 8	d				07 38											07 59			
Banbury	d	07 27			07 56											08 16			
Kings Sutton	d	07 33																	
Heyford	d	07 41																	
Tackley	d	07 46																	
Bicester Town	d					08 03													
Islip	d					08 14													
Oxford	a	07 56			08 14	08 29										08 39			
	d	07 56	08 07	08 07	08 16										08 35	08 43		08 51	08 51
Radley	d	08 02													08 41				
Culham	d	08 06																	
Appleford	d														08 46				
Didcot Parkway	a	08 14	08 19	08 19											08 52				
	d	08 17	08 20	08 20			08 29			08 34	08 47		08 53	08 59	09 03				
Cholsey	d	08 23								08 39					09 08				
Goring & Streatley	d	08 29								08 44					09 13				
Pangbourne	d	08 34								08 49					09 18				
Tilehurst	d	08 39								08 53					09 22				
Bedwyn	d																		
Hungerford	d																		
Kintbury	d																		
Newbury	a																		
	d								08 29								08 38		
Newbury Racecourse	d																08 40		
Thatcham	d																08 45		
Midgham	d																08 49		
Aldermaston	d																08 53		
Theale	d																08 58		
Reading West	d							←				←					09 05		
Reading 7	a	08 47	08 35	08 35	08 39		08 43	08 47	08 50	09 00	09 00	09 00	09 07	09 14	09 28	09 08	09 10	09 14	09 16
	d	08 48	08 36	08 38			08 45	08 48	08 52	09 05	09 02	09 05	09 08	09 16	09 33			09 18	09 18
Twyford 3	a	→						08 54		→		09 11			→				
Maidenhead 3	a							09 02				09 19							
Slough 3	a											09 30							
Ealing Broadway ⊖	a											09 54							
London Paddington 15 ⊖	a		09 06	09 08			09 14	09 27	09 21		09 29	10 05	09 40	09 44				09 47	09 47

A from 10 March
B ◇ from Reading ■ to Reading
C 🍴 from Reading ⊘ to Reading
D until 7 March
E The Bristolian. ◇ from Reading ■ to Reading
F 🍴 ◇ from Reading ⊘ ■ to Reading
G until 7 March. The Cathedrals Express. 🍴 from Reading ⊘ to Reading
H from 10 March. The Cathedrals Express. 🍴 from Reading ⊘ to Reading

For complete service between Banbury and Leamington (Birmingham), please refer to table 71

Table 116R

Mondays to Fridays

17 February to 24 March

Birmingham, Banbury, Bicester, Oxford and Bedwyn - Reading and London

Network Diagram - refer to first Page of Table 116

		GW	GW	GW	GW	GW	GW	XC	GW	GW	GW	CH	GW
		1	1	◇1	◇1	◇1	1	◇1	1	◇1	1		◇1
				A	B								
						💺		☕					💺
Birmingham New Street 12	d							08 04					
Birmingham International	d							08 14					
Coventry	d							08 25					
Leamington Spa 8	d							08 38					
Banbury	d							08 55					
Kings Sutton	d												
Heyford	d												
Tackley	d												
Bicester Town	d											09 07	
Islip	d											09 18	
Oxford	a							09 14				09 32	
	d			09 01	09 01		09 07	09 16		09 31			
Radley	d						09 13						
Culham	d						09 17						
Appleford	d												
Didcot Parkway	a			09 14	09 14		09 24						
	d			09 15	09 15	09 29	09 33						09 55
Cholsey	d						09 39						
Goring & Streatley	d						09 44						
Pangbourne	d						09 49						
Tilehurst	d						09 53						
Bedwyn	d	08 41											
Hungerford	d	08 46											
Kintbury	d	08 51											
Newbury	a	08 58											
	d	08 58							09 22				
Newbury Racecourse	d								09 25				
Thatcham	d	09 03							09 30				
Midgham	d								09 34				
Aldermaston	d								09 38				
Theale	d	09 11							09 43				
Reading West	d		←						09 50		←		
Reading 7	a	09 20	09 28	09 32	09 36	09 44	09 58	09 39	09 54	09 54	09 58		10 08
	d	09 21	09 33	09 37	09 37	09 46	10 03			09 55	10 03		10 09
Twyford 3	a		09 39				→				10 09		
Maidenhead 3	a		09 47								10 17		
Slough 3	a		09 54	09 53	09 52					10 10	10 24		
Ealing Broadway ⊖	a		10 19								10 49		
London Paddington 15 ⊖	a	09 56	10 31	10 12	10 12	10 15				10 29	11 01		10 37

		GW	XC	GW	GW	GW	GW	GW	GW	GW	GW	XC	GW
		1	◇1	1	◇1	1	◇1	◇1	1	◇1	1	◇1	1
							B	A					
			☕		☕		💺	💺		💺		☕	
Birmingham New Street 12	d		08 33									09 04	
Birmingham International	d											09 14	
Coventry	d											09 25	
Leamington Spa 8	d		09 00									09 38	
Banbury	d		09 19								09 35	09 55	
Kings Sutton	d										09 40		
Heyford	d										09 49		
Tackley	d										09 54		
Bicester Town	d												
Islip	d												
Oxford	a		09 41								10 06	10 13	
	d	09 37	09 43		10 01						10 08	10 16	
Radley	d										10 14		
Culham	d												
Appleford	d												
Didcot Parkway	a	09 49									10 23		
	d	10 01					10 16	10 16		10 29	10 31		
Cholsey	d	10 07									10 37		
Goring & Streatley	d	10 12									10 42		
Pangbourne	d	10 17									10 47		
Tilehurst	d	10 21									10 51		
Bedwyn	d			09 39									
Hungerford	d			09 44									
Kintbury	d			09 49									
Newbury	a			09 56									
	d			09 56									10 13
Newbury Racecourse	d												10 15
Thatcham	d			10 01									10 20
Midgham	d												10 24
Aldermaston	d												10 28
Theale	d			10 09									10 33
Reading West	d					←			←				10 40
Reading 7	a	10 27	10 12	10 22	10 25	10 27	10 30	10 31	10 27	10 43	10 57	10 39	10 45
	d	10 33		10 22	10 26	10 33	10 32	10 32	10 33	10 45	11 03		
Twyford 3	a	→				→			10 39		→		
Maidenhead 3	a								10 47				
Slough 3	a				10 40				10 53				
Ealing Broadway ⊖	a								11 18				
London Paddington 15 ⊖	a			10 56	11 00		11 07	11 07	11 32	11 14			

		GW	GW	GW	GW	GW	GW	GW	XC	CH	GW	GW	GW
		◇1	◇1	1	◇1	◇1	1	1	◇1		1	◇1	1
		B	A		C	D							
					💺	💺			☕			☕	
Birmingham New Street 12	d								09 33				
Birmingham International	d												
Coventry	d												
Leamington Spa 8	d								10 00				
Banbury	d								10 19				
Kings Sutton	d												
Heyford	d												
Tackley	d												
Bicester Town	d									10 30			
Islip	d									10 41			
Oxford	a								10 41	10 56			
	d	10 31	10 31					10 37	10 43			11 01	
Radley	d												
Culham	d												
Appleford	d												
Didcot Parkway	a							10 57					
	d				10 47	10 47		11 01					
Cholsey	d							11 07					
Goring & Streatley	d							11 12					
Pangbourne	d							11 17					
Tilehurst	d							11 21					
Bedwyn	d										10 39		
Hungerford	d										10 44		
Kintbury	d										10 49		
Newbury	a										10 56		
	d										10 56		
Newbury Racecourse	d												
Thatcham	d										11 01		
Midgham	d												
Aldermaston	d												
Theale	d										11 09		
Reading West	d			←			←						←
Reading 7	a	10 54	10 55	10 57	11 00	11 00	10 57	11 27	11 09		11 20	11 24	11 27
	d	10 55	10 56	11 03	11 02	11 03	11 03	11 33			11 21	11 26	11 33
Twyford 3	a			→			11 09	→					→
Maidenhead 3	a						11 17						
Slough 3	a	11 09	11 10				11 24					11 39	
Ealing Broadway ⊖	a						11 49						
London Paddington 15 ⊖	a	11 29	11 30		11 33	11 32	12 01				11 56	11 59	

A until 7 March
B from 10 March
C until 7 March. The Red Dragon
D from 10 March. The Red Dragon

For complete service between Banbury and Leamington (Birmingham), please refer to table 71

Table 116R

Mondays to Fridays

17 February to 24 March

Birmingham, Banbury, Bicester, Oxford and Bedwyn - Reading and London

Network Diagram - refer to first Page of Table 116

		GW	GW	GW	GW	XC	GW	GW	GW	GW	GW	XC	CH	GW	GW	GW	GW	GW	GW
		◇1 ☕	1	◇1 ☕	1	◇1 🛒	1	◇1 🛒	1	◇1 ☕	1	◇1 🛒		1	◇1 A 🛒	◇1 B 🛒	1	◇1 ☕	1
Birmingham New Street 12	d					10 04						10 33							
Birmingham International	d					10 14													
Coventry	d					10 25													
Leamington Spa 8	d					10 38						11 00							
Banbury	d					10 55						11 19							
Kings Sutton	d																		
Heyford	d																		
Tackley	d																		
Bicester Town	d												11 30						
Islip	d												11 41						
Oxford	a					11 14						11 41	11 56						
	d				11 07	11 16		11 31			11 37	11 43			12 01	12 01			
Radley	d				11 13														
Culham	d																		
Appleford	d																		
Didcot Parkway	a				11 22						11 51								
	d	11 16		11 29	11 31					11 55	12 01							12 16	
Cholsey	d				11 37						12 07								
Goring & Streatley	d				11 42						12 12								
Pangbourne	d				11 47						12 17								
Tilehurst	d				11 51						12 21								
Bedwyn	d													11 39					
Hungerford	d													11 44					
Kintbury	d													11 49					
Newbury	a													11 56					
	d						11 13							11 56					
Newbury Racecourse	d						11 15												
Thatcham	d						11 20							12 01					
Midgham	d						11 24												
Aldermaston	d						11 28												
Theale	d						11 33							12 09					
Reading West	d		←				11 40		←								←		←
Reading 7	a	11 30	11 27	11 43	11 57	11 39	11 45	11 55	11 57	12 08	12 27	12 12		12 22	12 25	12 25	12 27	12 30	12 27
	d	11 32	11 33	11 44	12 03			11 56	12 03	12 09	12 33			12 22	12 26	12 27	12 33	12 32	12 33
Twyford 3	a		11 39		→				12 09		→						→		12 39
Maidenhead 3	a		11 47						12 17										12 47
Slough 3	a		11 54					12 10	12 24						12 41	12 41			12 54
Ealing Broadway ⊖	a		12 19						12 49										13 19
London Paddington 15 ⊖	a	12 02	12 31	12 14				12 30	13 02	12 37				12 54	13 09	13 09		13 00	13 31

		GW	GW	GW	XC FX	XC FO	GW	GW	GW	GW	GW	GW	GW	XC	GW	GW	GW	GW	GW
		◇1 A ☕	◇1 B ☕	1	◇1 🛒	◇1 🛒	1	◇1 🛒	1	◇1 B ☕	1	◇1 A ☕	1	◇1 🛒	◇1 A 🛒	◇1 B 🛒	1	1	◇1 ☕
Birmingham New Street 12	d				11 04	11 04								11 33					
Birmingham International	d				11 14	11 14													
Coventry	d				11 25	11 25													
Leamington Spa 8	d				11 38	11 38								12 01					
Banbury	d				11 55	11 57								12 19					
Kings Sutton	d																		
Heyford	d																		
Tackley	d																		
Bicester Town	d																		
Islip	d																		
Oxford	a				12 14	12 14								12 41					
	d			12 07	12 16	12 16		12 31					12 37	12 43	13 01	13 01			
Radley	d			12 13															
Culham	d																		
Appleford	d			12 17															
Didcot Parkway	a			12 24									12 49						
	d	12 29	12 29	12 31						12 47		12 47	13 01						13 16
Cholsey	d			12 37									13 07						
Goring & Streatley	d			12 42									13 12						
Pangbourne	d			12 47									13 17						
Tilehurst	d			12 51									13 21						
Bedwyn	d																12 38		
Hungerford	d																12 43		
Kintbury	d																12 48		
Newbury	a																12 55		
	d						12 13										13 03		
Newbury Racecourse	d						12 15												
Thatcham	d						12 20										13 08		
Midgham	d						12 24												
Aldermaston	d						12 28												
Theale	d						12 33										13 16		
Reading West	d						12 40		←		←							←	
Reading 7	a	12 43	12 43	12 57	12 39	12 39	12 45	12 55	12 57	13 00	12 57	13 00	13 28	13 07	13 25	13 25	13 25	13 28	13 30
	d	12 44	12 45	13 03				12 56	13 03	13 02	13 03	13 04	13 33		13 26	13 26	13 30	13 33	13 35
Twyford 3	a			→					→		13 09		→					13 39	
Maidenhead 3	a										13 17							13 47	
Slough 3	a							13 10			13 24				13 41	13 41		13 54	
Ealing Broadway ⊖	a										13 49							14 19	
London Paddington 15 ⊖	a	13 14	13 14					13 30		13 33	14 01	13 33			14 00	14 01	14 09	14 31	14 06

A from 10 March

B until 7 March

For complete service between Banbury and Leamington (Birmingham), please refer to table 71

Table 116R

Mondays to Fridays

17 February to 24 March

Birmingham, Banbury, Bicester, Oxford and Bedwyn - Reading and London

Network Diagram - refer to first Page of Table 116

		GW	GW	GW	GW	XC	GW	GW	GW	GW	GW	GW	XC	GW	GW	GW	GW	GW	GW
		◇1	◇1	1	1	◇1	1	◇1	1	◇1	◇1	1	◇1	◇1	◇1	◇1	1	◇1	◇1
		A	B							A	B			A	B				
		🍴	🍴			🛒		🛒		🍴	🍴		🛒	🍴	🍴	🛒		🍴	🍴
Birmingham New Street 12	d					12 04							12 33						
Birmingham International	d					12 14													
Coventry	d					12 25													
Leamington Spa 8	d					12 38							13 00						
Banbury	d				12 42	12 55							13 22						
Kings Sutton	d				12 48														
Heyford	d				12 56														
Tackley	d				13 01														
Bicester Town	d																		
Islip	d																		
Oxford	a				13 11	13 14							13 41						
	d			13 07		13 16		13 31				13 37	13 44			14 01			
Radley	d			13 13															
Culham	d			13 17															
Appleford	d																		
Didcot Parkway	a			13 30								13 49							
	d	13 29	13 29	13 31						13 53	13 53	14 01						14 15	14 29
Cholsey	d			13 37								14 07							
Goring & Streatley	d			13 42								14 12							
Pangbourne	d			13 47								14 17							
Tilehurst	d			13 51								14 21							
Bedwyn	d													13 32	13 32				
Hungerford	d													13 40	13 40				
Kintbury	d																		
Newbury	a													13 50	13 50				
	d						13 13							13 51	13 51				
Newbury Racecourse	d						13 15												
Thatcham	d						13 20							13 58	13 58				
Midgham	d						13 24												
Aldermaston	d						13 28												
Theale	d						13 33							14 07	14 07				
Reading West	d						13 40		←								←		
Reading 7	a	13 43	13 43	13 57		13 39	13 45	13 54	13 57	14 05	14 06	14 27	14 11	14 20	14 20	14 25	14 27	14 30	14 43
	d	13 44	13 45	14 03				13 56	14 03	14 07	14 08	14 33		14 22	14 23	14 26	14 33	14 36	14 44
Twyford 3	a			→					14 09			→					14 39		
Maidenhead 3	a								14 17								14 47		
Slough 3	a							14 10	14 24							14 40	14 54		
Ealing Broadway ⊖	a								14 49								15 19		
London Paddington 15 ⊖	a	14 14	14 14					14 30	15 01	14 37	14 37			14 54	14 54	15 01	15 32	15 08	15 14

		GW	XC	CH	GW	GW	GW	GW	GW	GW	GW	XC	GW	GW	GW	GW	GW	GW	GW
		1	◇1		1	◇1	1	◇1	1	◇1	1	◇1	1	1	◇1	1	◇1	◇1	1
								C		D			B	A			A	B	
			🛒					🍴⊘		🍴⊘		🛒			🛒		🍴	🍴	
Birmingham New Street 12	d		13 04									13 33							
Birmingham International	d		13 14																
Coventry	d		13 25																
Leamington Spa 8	d		13 38									14 00							
Banbury	d		13 55									14 19							
Kings Sutton	d																		
Heyford	d																		
Tackley	d																		
Bicester Town	d			14 00															
Islip	d			14 11															
Oxford	a		14 13	14 28								14 40							
	d	14 07	14 16			14 31					14 37	14 43			15 01				
Radley	d	14 13																	
Culham	d																		
Appleford	d																		
Didcot Parkway	a	14 22									14 51								
	d	14 31						14 47		14 47	15 01						15 16	15 16	
Cholsey	d	14 37									15 07								
Goring & Streatley	d	14 42									15 12								
Pangbourne	d	14 47									15 17								
Tilehurst	d	14 51									15 21								
Bedwyn	d												14 39	14 39					
Hungerford	d												14 44	14 44					
Kintbury	d												14 49	14 49					
Newbury	a												14 56	14 56					
	d				14 13								14 56	14 56					
Newbury Racecourse	d				14 15														
Thatcham	d				14 20								15 01	15 01					
Midgham	d				14 24														
Aldermaston	d				14 28														
Theale	d				14 33								15 09	15 09					
Reading West	d				14 40		←		←							←			←
Reading 7	a	14 56	14 39		14 45	14 55	14 56	15 00	14 56	15 00	15 27	15 08	15 20	15 21	15 24	15 27	15 30	15 30	15 27
	d	15 03				14 56	15 03	15 02	15 03	15 04	15 33		15 20	15 22	15 26	15 33	15 31	15 33	15 33
Twyford 3	a	→					→		15 09		→					→			15 39
Maidenhead 3	a								15 17										15 47
Slough 3	a					15 10			15 24						15 39				15 54
Ealing Broadway ⊖	a								15 49										16 19
London Paddington 15 ⊖	a					15 30		15 33	16 01	15 33			15 54	15 54	16 01		16 08	16 08	16 31

A until 7 March
B from 10 March
C until 7 March. 🍴 from Reading ⊘ to Reading
D from 10 March. 🍴 from Reading ⊘ to Reading

For complete service between Banbury and Leamington (Birmingham), please refer to table 71

Table 116R

Mondays to Fridays

17 February to 24 March

Birmingham, Banbury, Bicester, Oxford and Bedwyn - Reading and London

Network Diagram - refer to first Page of Table 116

		GW	GW	XC	GW	GW	GW	GW	GW	GW	GW	XC	CH	GW	GW	GW	GW	GW	GW
		◇1	1	◇1	1	◇1	1	◇1	◇1	1	1	◇1		1	◇1	1	◇1	◇1	◇1
								A	B								C	D	D
		☕		🛒		☕		☕	☕			🛒			🛒		☕	☕	☕
Birmingham New Street 12	d			14 04								14 33							
Birmingham International	d			14 14															
Coventry	d			14 24															
Leamington Spa 8	d			14 38								15 00							
Banbury	d			14 55							15 08	15 19							
Kings Sutton	d										15 14								
Heyford	d										15 22								
Tackley	d										15 27								
Bicester Town	d												15 30						
Islip	d												15 41						
Oxford	a			15 13							15 39	15 41	15 56						
	d		15 07	15 16		15 31				15 37		15 43			16 01				
Radley	d		15 13							15 43									
Culham	d		15 17																
Appleford	d																		
Didcot Parkway	a		15 24							15 51									
	d	15 29	15 35					15 53	15 53	16 01							16 16	16 16	16 29
Cholsey	d		15 41							16 07									
Goring & Streatley	d		15 46							16 12									
Pangbourne	d		15 51							16 17									
Tilehurst	d		15 55							16 21									
Bedwyn	d													15 40					
Hungerford	d													15 45					
Kintbury	d													15 50					
Newbury	a													15 57					
	d				15 13									15 57					
Newbury Racecourse	d				15 15														
Thatcham	d				15 20									16 02					
Midgham	d				15 24														
Aldermaston	d				15 28														
Theale	d				15 33									16 10					
Reading West	d				15 40		←									←			
Reading 7	a	15 43	16 01	15 40	15 45	15 55	16 01	16 05	16 06	16 27		16 11		16 21	16 25	16 27	16 29	16 29	16 43
	d	15 44	16 03			15 57	16 03	16 07	16 08	16 31				16 22	16 26	16 31	16 31	16 33	16 44
Twyford 3	a		→				16 09			→						16 37			
Maidenhead 3	a						16 17									16 47			
Slough 3	a					16 10	16 24								16 41	16 54			
Ealing Broadway ⊖	a						16 49									17 21			
London Paddington 15 ⊖	a	16 14				16 29	17 01	16 39	16 39					16 57	17 00	17 31	17 09	17 08	17 14

		GW	GW	XC	GW	GW	GW	GW	GW	XC	GW	GW	GW	GW	GW	GW	GW	GW	XC
		◇1	1	◇1	1	◇1	◇1	1	1	◇1	1	◇1	1	◇1	◇1	1	◇1	1	◇1
		C																	
		☕		🛒			☕			🛒		☕		🛒	☕		☕		🛒
Birmingham New Street 12	d			15 04						15 33									16 04
Birmingham International	d			15 14															16 14
Coventry	d			15 24															16 24
Leamington Spa 8	d			15 38						16 01									16 38
Banbury	d			15 55						16 19									16 55
Kings Sutton	d																		
Heyford	d																		
Tackley	d																		
Bicester Town	d																		
Islip	d																		
Oxford	a			16 13						16 40									17 13
	d		16 07	16 16		16 31			16 37	16 43	16 49			17 01				17 07	17 16
Radley	d		16 13						16 43									17 13	
Culham	d																	17 17	
Appleford	d		16 17																
Didcot Parkway	a		16 27						16 51		17 03							17 24	
	d	16 29	16 35				16 47		17 05						17 16		17 29	17 31	
Cholsey	d		16 41						17 11									17 37	
Goring & Streatley	d		16 46						17 16									17 42	
Pangbourne	d		16 51						17 20									17 47	
Tilehurst	d		16 55						17 25									17 51	
Bedwyn	d												16 44						
Hungerford	d											16 39	16 49						
Kintbury	d												16 54						
Newbury	a											16 48	17 03						
	d				16 13							16 49							
Newbury Racecourse	d				16 15														
Thatcham	d				16 20							16 55							
Midgham	d				16 24														
Aldermaston	d				16 28														
Theale	d				16 33							17 05							
Reading West	d				16 40			←								←			
Reading 7	a	16 43	17 01	16 39	16 45	16 56	17 00	17 01	17 31	17 07		17 16		17 26	17 31	17 31	17 43	17 57	17 39
	d	16 45	17 03			16 57	17 02	17 03	17 33			17 18		17 27	17 32	17 33	17 46	18 08	
Twyford 3	a		→					17 09	→							17 39		→	
Maidenhead 3	a							17 17						17 39		17 47			
Slough 3	a					17 13		17 24				17 32				17 54			
Ealing Broadway ⊖	a							17 49								18 19			
London Paddington 15 ⊖	a	17 14				17 34	17 30	18 01				17 52		17 59	18 02	18 31	18 15		

A until 7 March. The Cheltenham Spa Express
B from 10 March. The Cheltenham Spa Express
C until 7 March
D from 10 March

For complete service between Banbury and Leamington (Birmingham), please refer to table 71

Table 116R

Mondays to Fridays

17 February to 24 March

Birmingham, Banbury, Bicester, Oxford and Bedwyn - Reading and London

Network Diagram - refer to first Page of Table 116

		CH	GW	GW	GW	GW	GW	XC	GW	GW	GW	GW	GW	GW	GW	GW	GW	XC	GW
			■	◇■	■	◇■	■	◇■	■	■	◇■	■	◇■	■	◇■	◇■	■	◇■	■
															A	B			
				☕		☕		🛒			🛒		☕		☕	☕		🛒	
Birmingham New Street ■	d							16 33										17 04	
Birmingham International	d																	17 14	
Coventry	d																	17 24	
Leamington Spa ■	d							17 00										17 38	
Banbury	d							17 19	17 23									17 55	
Kings Sutton	d								17 27										
Heyford	d								17 36										
Tackley	d								17 40										
Bicester Town	d	16 57																	
Islip	d	17 08																	
Oxford	a	17 23						17 40	17 52									18 15	
	d			17 31			17 37	17 43			18 01						18 07	18 16	
Radley	d						17 43										18 13		
Culham	d																18 17		
Appleford	d						17 47												
Didcot Parkway	a						17 54										18 24		
	d					17 53	18 00						18 16		18 29	18 29	18 31		
Cholsey	d						18 07										18 37		
Goring & Streatley	d						18 12										18 42		
Pangbourne	d						18 17										18 47		
Tilehurst	d						18 21										18 51		
Bedwyn	d									17 38									17 55
Hungerford	d									17 43									18 00
Kintbury	d									17 48									18 05
Newbury	a									17 55									18 12
	d		17 13							17 55									18 13
Newbury Racecourse	d		17 15																18 15
Thatcham	d		17 20							18 00									18 20
Midgham	d		17 24																18 24
Aldermaston	d		17 28							18 06									18 28
Theale	d		17 33							18 11									18 33
Reading West	d		17 40		←							←		←					18 40
Reading ■	a		17 45	17 54	17 57	18 06	18 27	18 08		18 22	18 24	18 27	18 30	18 27	18 45	18 45	18 58	18 40	18 45
	d			17 56	18 08	18 08	18 33			18 23	18 27	18 33	18 32	18 33	18 46	18 47	19 08		
Twyford ■	a				18 14		→					→		18 39			→		
Maidenhead ■	a				18 22									18 47					
Slough ■	a			18 10	18 34						18 40			18 54					
Ealing Broadway ⊖	a				18 53									19 19					
London Paddington ■ ⊖	a			18 28	19 02	18 39				18 54	18 59		19 02	19 31	19 16	19 16			

		GW	GW	GW	GW	GW	GW	GW	XC	CH	GW	GW	GW	GW	GW	GW	GW	GW	XC
		◇■	■	◇■	◇■	◇■	■	■	◇■		■	■	■	◇■	■	◇■	◇■	■	◇■
		A		B	C	D					B	A				A	B		
					☕⊘	☕⊘			🛒					🛒		☕	☕		🛒
Birmingham New Street ■	d								17 33										18 04
Birmingham International	d																		18 14
Coventry	d																		18 24
Leamington Spa ■	d								18 00										18 37
Banbury	d								18 19									18 37	18 55
Kings Sutton	d																	18 43	
Heyford	d																	18 51	
Tackley	d																	18 56	
Bicester Town	d									18 18									
Islip	d									18 29									
Oxford	a								18 40	18 44								19 08	19 13
	d	18 31		18 31				18 37	18 43					19 06				19 10	19 16
Radley	d							18 43										19 16	
Culham	d																		
Appleford	d							18 47											
Didcot Parkway	a							18 56										19 25	
	d				18 47	18 47		19 01								19 29	19 29	19 32	
Cholsey	d							19 07										19 37	
Goring & Streatley	d							19 12										19 42	
Pangbourne	d							19 17										19 47	
Tilehurst	d							19 21										19 51	
Bedwyn	d												19 03						
Hungerford	d												19 08						
Kintbury	d												19 13						
Newbury	a												19 22						
	d										18 53	18 53							
Newbury Racecourse	d																		
Thatcham	d										18 58	18 58							
Midgham	d																		
Aldermaston	d																		
Theale	d										19 06	19 06							
Reading West	d		←				←								←				
Reading ■	a	18 55	18 58	18 58	18 59	19 01	18 58	19 27	19 10		19 16	19 17		19 31	19 27	19 43	19 44	19 57	19 41
	d	18 57	19 08	18 59	19 02	19 03	19 08	19 33			19 18	19 18		19 33	19 33	19 45	19 45	19 58	
Twyford ■	a		→				19 14	→							19 42			→	
Maidenhead ■	a						19 22								19 50				
Slough ■	a	19 09		19 10			19 30							19 47	19 57				
Ealing Broadway ⊖	a						19 54								20 22				
London Paddington ■ ⊖	a	19 30		19 31	19 32	19 33	20 03				19 54	19 54		20 06	20 32	20 14	20 14		

A from 10 March
B until 7 March
C from 10 March. ☕ from Reading ⊘ to Reading
D until 7 March. ☕ from Reading ⊘ to Reading

For complete service between Banbury and Leamington (Birmingham), please refer to table 71

Table 116R

Mondays to Fridays

17 February to 24 March

Birmingham, Banbury, Bicester, Oxford and Bedwyn - Reading and London

Network Diagram - refer to first Page of Table 116

		GW	GW	GW	GW	GW	GW	GW	GW	GW	XC	GW	GW	GW	GW	GW	GW	GW	XC	CH	GW	GW	GW	GW	GW	XC	GW	GW	GW	GW	XC	GW	GW	GW	GW	GW	GW
																																			FO	FX	FO
		◇1	1	◇1	◇1	◇1	◇1	◇1	◇1	1	◇1	◇1	1	1	1	◇1	◇1	1	◇1		◇1	1	◇1	1	1	◇1	1	1	◇1	1	◇1	◇1	1	1	◇1	◇1	◇1
				A	B	A	B	A	B							B	A																				
Birmingham New Street 12	d										18 33								19 04							19 33					20 04						
Birmingham International	d																		19 14												20 14						
Coventry	d																		19 24												20 24						
Leamington Spa 8	d										19 00								19 38							20 04					20 38						
Banbury	d										19 19								19 55						20 01	20 22					20 55						
Kings Sutton	d																								20 07												
Heyford	d																								20 15												
Tackley	d																								20 20												
Bicester Town	d																			20 02																	
Islip	d																			20 13																	
Oxford	a										19 39								20 13	20 28					20 32	20 39					21 13						
	d	19 31								19 37	19 42	20 01						20 07	20 16		20 31				20 37	20 41			21 01		21 16			21 21	21 32	21 32	
Radley	d																	20 13																21 27			
Culham	d																	20 17																			
Appleford	d																																				
Didcot Parkway	a									19 49								20 24							20 49									21 34			
	d			19 47	19 47			20 00	20 00	20 01						20 29	20 29	20 31					20 47		21 01							21 29		21 44			
Cholsey	d									20 07								20 37							21 07									21 50			
Goring & Streatley	d									20 12								20 42							21 12									21 55			
Pangbourne	d									20 17								20 47							21 17									21 58			
Tilehurst	d									20 21								20 51							21 21									22 02			
Bedwyn	d														19 54												20 33	21 01									
Hungerford	d														19 59												20 38	21 07									
Kintbury	d														20 04												20 43	21 11									
Newbury	a														20 11													21 18									
	d					19 49	19 49							19 55	20 11																		21 23				21 42
Newbury Racecourse	d													19 57													20 52						21 25				
Thatcham	d													20 02	20 16												20 57						21 30				
Midgham	d													20 06													21 02						21 34				
Aldermaston	d													20 10													21 05						21 38				
Theale	d													20 15	20 24												21 10						21 43				
Reading West	d		←										←	20 21								←		←			21 17			←			21 49				
Reading 7	a	19 54	19 57	20 00	20 00	20 06	20 06	20 14	20 14	20 27	20 08	20 26	20 27	20 27	20 34	20 43	20 44	20 57	20 39		20 55	20 57	21 00	20 57	21 29	21 07	21 22		21 24	21 29	21 41	21 43	21 54	22 11	21 55	21 55	21 59
	d	19 55	19 58	20 02	20 07	20 08	20 10	20 15	20 16	20 33		20 26	20 33		20 34	20 45	20 45	21 12			20 56	21 12	21 03	21 12	21 33				21 26	21 33		21 44			21 56	21 56	22 00
Twyford 3	a		20 04							→			20 39					→				→		21 18	→					21 39							
Maidenhead 3	a		20 12										20 47											21 26						21 47							
Slough 3	a	20 10	20 22									20 40	20 54								21 11			21 38					21 40	21 58					22 14	22 14	
Ealing Broadway ⊖	a		20 49										21 19											22 02						22 21							
London Paddington 15 ⊖	a	20 30	20 59	20 37	20 37	20 39	20 39	20 46	20 46			21 01	21 30		21 07	21 14	21 14				21 29		21 32	22 14					22 00	22 32		22 16			22 38	22 41	22 30

A until 7 March

B from 10 March

For complete service between Banbury and Leamington (Birmingham), please refer to table 71

Table 116R

Mondays to Fridays

17 February to 24 March

Birmingham, Banbury, Bicester, Oxford and Bedwyn - Reading and London

Network Diagram - refer to first Page of Table 116

		GW	GW	GW	XC	GW	CH	GW	GW	XC	GW	GW	GW	GW	GW	GW	GW	GW	XC	GW	GW	GW	CH	GW	CH
		FX	FO	FX				FX	FO			FX	FO	FX	FO						FX	FO	FO		
		◇1	◇1	◇1	◇1	1		◇1	◇1	◇1	1	◇1	◇1	◇1	◇1	1	1	◇1	◇1	1	◇1	◇1		1	
								A	A																
Birmingham New Street 12	d				20 33					21 04									22 04						
Birmingham International	d									21 14									22 14						
Coventry	d									21 24									22 25						
Leamington Spa 8	d				21 00					21 38									22 38						23 39
Banbury	d				21 19			21 38	21 38	21 55							22 25		22 55					23 45	23 58
Kings Sutton	d							21 44	21 44								22 31							23 50	
Heyford	d							21 52	21 52								22 39							23 58	
Tackley	d							21 57	21 57								22 44							00 03	
Bicester Town	d						21 31																23 42		
Islip	d						21 42																23 53		
Oxford	a				21 40		21 57	22 07	22 07	22 14							22 56		23 14				00 08	00 14	00 22
	d				21 43	21 51		22 11	22 11	22 16		22 30	22 30			22 52		23 09	23 15					00 27	
Radley	d					21 57										22 58								00 33	
Culham	d															23 02									
Appleford	d															23 04									
Didcot Parkway	a					22 06		22 24	22 24							23 11		23 23						00 42	
	d		21 53	21 53		22 08		22 27	22 27					22 52	22 52	23 13		23 23			23 37	23 37		00 46	
Cholsey	d					22 14										23 19								00 52	
Goring & Streatley	d					22 19										23 24								00 57	
Pangbourne	d					22 24										23 27								01 01	
Tilehurst	d					22 27										23 31								01 06	
Bedwyn	d										21 55									23 00					
Hungerford	d										22 00									23 05					
Kintbury	d										22 05									23 10					
Newbury	a										22 12									23 17					
	d	21 42									22 13									23 17					
Newbury Racecourse	d										22 15									23 19					
Thatcham	d										22 20									23 24					
Midgham	d										22 24									23 29					
Aldermaston	d										22 28									23 32					
Theale	d										22 33									23 37					
Reading West	d										22 40									23 44					
Reading 7	a	21 59	22 11	22 11	22 17	22 37		22 43	22 44	22 41	22 45	22 53	22 54	23 06	23 08	23 41		23 41	23 49	23 49	23 53	23 54		01 13	
	d	22 00	22 12	22 12				22 44	22 44			22 59	22 59	23 09	23 09			23 41			23 55	23 55		01 17	
Twyford 3	a																							01 23	
Maidenhead 3	a																	23 54						01 31	
Slough 3	a							23 01	23 01			23 14	23 14					00 02						01 39	
Ealing Broadway ⊖	a																							01 55	
London Paddington 15 ⊖	a	22 38	22 44	22 47				23 24	23 24			23 38	23 37	23 44	23 42			00 27			00 33	00 33		02 07	

A 1 to Oxford

For complete service between Banbury and Leamington (Birmingham), please refer to table 71

Table 116R

Mondays to Fridays

31 March to 16 May

Birmingham, Banbury, Bicester, Oxford and Bedwyn - Reading and London

Network Diagram - refer to first Page of Table 116

		GW MO	GW MO	GW MO	GW MX	GW MO	GW MX	GW MO	GW MO	GW MX
		1	1	🚌	◇1	◇1	1	🚌	1	1
Birmingham New Street 12	d									
Birmingham International	d									
Coventry	d									
Leamington Spa 8	d									
Banbury	d									
Kings Sutton	d									
Heyford	d									
Tackley	d						00 03			
Bicester Town	d									
Islip	d									
Oxford	a						00 14			
	d			00 05	00 07		00 27	03 38		04 00
Radley	d						00 33			
Culham	d									
Appleford	d									
Didcot Parkway	a			00 30	00 20		00 42	04 03		04 12
	d				00 21	00 35	00 46		04 12	04 12
Cholsey	d						00 52		04 18	04 18
Goring & Streatley	d	00 01					00 57		04 23	04 23
Pangbourne	d	00 06					01 01		04 28	04 28
Tilehurst	d	00 10					01 06		04 32	04 32
Bedwyn	d									
Hungerford	d									
Kintbury	d									
Newbury	a									
	d									
Newbury Racecourse	d									
Thatcham	d									
Midgham	d									
Aldermaston	d		00 01							
Theale	d		00 06							
Reading West	d		00s13							
Reading 7	a	00 15	00 17		00 38	00 52	01 13		04 38	04 38
	d	00 15			00 39	00 53	01 17		04 40	04 40
Twyford 3	a	00 23				01 00	01 23		04 45	04 46
Maidenhead 3	a	00 31				01 07	01 31		04 54	04 54
Slough 3	a	00 39			00 55	01 14	01 39		04 59	04 59
Ealing Broadway ⊖	a	01 02				01 29	01 55		05 25	05 25
London Paddington 15 ⊖	a	01 14			01 20	01 39	02 07		05 41	05 41

		GW	GW	GW	GW	GW	GW	GW	GW	GW
		1	◇1 ☕	1	1	1	1	◇1	1	1
Birmingham New Street 12	d									
Birmingham International	d									
Coventry	d									
Leamington Spa 8	d									
Banbury	d									
Kings Sutton	d									
Heyford	d									
Tackley	d									
Bicester Town	d									
Islip	d									
Oxford	a									
	d	05 03		05 24		05 43		05 59		
Radley	d	05 09				05 49				
Culham	d									
Appleford	d									
Didcot Parkway	a	05 17		05 36		05 58		06 12		
	d	05 18	05 41	05 46		06 00		06 13		06 20
Cholsey	d	05 23		05 52						06 25
Goring & Streatley	d	05 28		05 57						06 30
Pangbourne	d	05 33		06 02						06 35
Tilehurst	d	05 37		06 06						06 40
Bedwyn	d						05 40			
Hungerford	d						05 46			
Kintbury	d						05 50			
Newbury	a						05 57			
	d				05 40		05 58		06 09	
Newbury Racecourse	d				05 42					
Thatcham	d				05 47		06 02		06 15	
Midgham	d				05 51					
Aldermaston	d				05 55					
Theale	d				06 00		06 10		06 24	
Reading West	d				06 07		06 17		06 32	
Reading 7	a	05 43	05 56	06 12	06 12	06 16	06 21	06 26	06 35	06 46
	d	05 44	05 57	06 15		06 16	06 21	06 28	06 35	06 46
Twyford 3	a	05 50		06 21		06 23			06 42	→
Maidenhead 3	a	05 58		06 28		06 31		06 39		
Slough 3	a	06 10		06 40			06 40	06 47		
Ealing Broadway ⊖	a	06 35		07 05						
London Paddington 15 ⊖	a	06 46	06 24	07 17		06 54	07 01	07 08	07 12	

		GW	GW	GW	GW	GW	GW	GW	GW	GW
		◇1 ☕	1	1	◇1 ☕	◇1 ☕	1	1	R 1 ☕	◇1 ☕
Birmingham New Street 12	d									
Birmingham International	d									
Coventry	d									
Leamington Spa 8	d									
Banbury	d									
Kings Sutton	d									
Heyford	d									
Tackley	d									
Bicester Town	d									
Islip	d									
Oxford	a									
	d			06 04	06 30					
Radley	d			06 10						
Culham	d			06 14						
Appleford	d			06 16						
Didcot Parkway	a			06 23						
	d	06 28		06 36		06 46			06 59	
Cholsey	d			06 42						
Goring & Streatley	d			06 47						
Pangbourne	d			06 52						
Tilehurst	d			06 57						
Bedwyn	d							06 13		
Hungerford	d							06 18		06 37
Kintbury	d							06 23		
Newbury	a							06 30		06 48
	d							06 30		06 50
Newbury Racecourse	d							06 32		
Thatcham	d							06 37		06 57
Midgham	d							06 42		
Aldermaston	d							06 45		
Theale	d							06 50		07 07
Reading West	d		←				←	06 57		
Reading 7	a	06 41	06 46	07 00	06 53	06 59	07 00	07 02	07 13	07 15
	d	06 43	06 46	07 05	06 55	07 01	07 05		07 15	07 18
Twyford 3	a		06 53	→						
Maidenhead 3	a		07 01		07 06		07 16			
Slough 3	a	06 57								
Ealing Broadway ⊖	a									
London Paddington 15 ⊖	a	07 16	07 27		07 27	07 32	07 43		07 44	07 53

		GW	CH	GW	GW	GW	GW	GW	GW	GW
		1		◇1	◇1 ☕	1	1	◇1 ☕	◇1 ☕	1
Birmingham New Street 12	d									
Birmingham International	d									
Coventry	d									
Leamington Spa 8	d									
Banbury	d	06 07								06 25
Kings Sutton	d	06 13								06 31
Heyford	d	06 21								06 39
Tackley	d	06 26								06 44
Bicester Town	d		06 19							
Islip	d		06 30							
Oxford	a	06 36	06 45							06 57
	d	06 36			06 55					07 02
Radley	d	06 42								07 08
Culham	d	06 46								07 12
Appleford	d	06 49								07 14
Didcot Parkway	a	06 56			07 08					07 21
	d	07 00		07 06	07 10			07 20		07 27
Cholsey	d	07 08		07 20						07 33
Goring & Streatley	d	07 13		07 26						07 38
Pangbourne	d	07 18		07 33						07 44
Tilehurst	d	07 23		07 40						07 49
Bedwyn	d								06 45	
Hungerford	d								06 53	
Kintbury	d								06 59	
Newbury	a								07 06	
	d					06 56			07 08	
Newbury Racecourse	d					06 58				
Thatcham	d					07 03			07 15	
Midgham	d					07 07				
Aldermaston	d					07 11				
Theale	d					07 16			07 25	
Reading West	d					07 23	←		07 34	
Reading 7	a	07 29			07 25	07 27	07 29	07 34	07 37	07 52
	d	07 30			07 26		07 30	07 37	07 40	07 56
Twyford 3	a	→					07 37			→
Maidenhead 3	a			07 56			07 45			
Slough 3	a						07 55			
Ealing Broadway ⊖	a						08 20			
London Paddington 15 ⊖	a			08 26	07 59		08 32	08 07	08 09	

For complete service between Banbury and Leamington (Birmingham), please refer to table 71

Table 116R

Mondays to Fridays

31 March to 16 May

Birmingham, Banbury, Bicester, Oxford and Bedwyn - Reading and London

Network Diagram - refer to first Page of Table 116

		XC	GW	GW	GW	GW	GW	GW	GW	GW	XC	GW	GW	GW	GW	GW	GW	GW	XC
		◇1 ⊥	R ◇1 A ☕	1	1	1	◇1 ⊥	R 1 ☕	◇1 B ☕⊘	◇1 ☕	◇1	R ◇1 A ☕	1	◇1 B ☕⊘	1	1	1	◇1	◇1 ⊥
Birmingham New Street 12	d	06 04									06 33								07 04
Birmingham International	d	06 14																	07 14
Coventry	d	06 25																	07 25
Leamington Spa 8	d	06 37									07 00								07 38
Banbury	d	06 54									07 20						07 27		07 56
Kings Sutton	d																07 33		
Heyford	d																07 41		
Tackley	d																07 46		
Bicester Town	d																		
Islip	d																		
Oxford	a	07 14									07 41						07 56		08 14
	d	07 16				07 21	07 34				07 43			07 52			07 56	08 07	08 16
Radley	d					07 28											08 02		
Culham	d					07 32											08 06		
Appleford	d					07 35													
Didcot Parkway	a					07 42											08 14	08 19	
	d		07 29			07 47		07 47		07 56		08 02					08 17	08 20	
Cholsey	d					07 53											08 23		
Goring & Streatley	d					07 59											08 29		
Pangbourne	d					08 05											08 34		
Tilehurst	d					08 10											08 39		
Bedwyn	d				07 07											07 56			
Hungerford	d				07 12				07 34							08 01			
Kintbury	d				07 17											08 06			
Newbury	a				07 24				07 46							08 14			
	d				07 24				07 50						07 53				
Newbury Racecourse	d				07 26										07 55				
Thatcham	d				07 32										08 00				
Midgham	d				07 36										08 05				
Aldermaston	d				07 40										08 08				
Theale	d				07 45										08 14				
Reading West	d			←	07 52								←		08 22				
Reading 7	a	07 41	07 43	07 52	07 56	08 17	07 56	08 00	08 06	08 11	08 13	08 16	08 17	08 22	08 26		08 47	08 35	08 39
	d		07 45	07 56		08 19	07 57	08 02	08 09	08 13		08 18	08 19	08 24			08 48	08 38	
Twyford 3	a			08 02		→							08 25				→		
Maidenhead 3	a			08 10									08 33						
Slough 3	a			08 20															
Ealing Broadway ⊖	a																		
London Paddington 15 ⊖	a		08 14	08 48			08 31	08 33	08 38	08 40		08 45	08 58	08 51				09 08	

		CH	GW	GW	GW	GW	GW	GW	GW	GW	GW	XC	GW	GW	GW	GW	GW	GW	GW
			R ◇1 C ☕	1	◇1 ☕	1	R ◇1 D ☕⊘	1	◇1 ☕	◇1 ☕	1	◇1	1	◇1 E ☕⊘	1	1	◇1	◇1 ☕	1
Birmingham New Street 12	d											07 33							
Birmingham International	d																		
Coventry	d																		
Leamington Spa 8	d											07 59							
Banbury	d											08 16							
Kings Sutton	d																		
Heyford	d																		
Tackley	d																		
Bicester Town	d	08 03																	
Islip	d	08 14																	
Oxford	a	08 29										08 39							
	d										08 35	08 43		08 51			09 01		09 07
Radley	d										08 41								09 13
Culham	d																		09 17
Appleford	d										08 46								
Didcot Parkway	a										08 52						09 14		09 24
	d		08 29			08 34	08 47		08 53	08 59	09 03						09 15	09 29	09 33
Cholsey	d					08 39					09 08								09 39
Goring & Streatley	d					08 44					09 13								09 44
Pangbourne	d					08 49					09 18								09 49
Tilehurst	d					08 53					09 22								09 53
Bedwyn	d														08 41				
Hungerford	d														08 46				
Kintbury	d														08 51				
Newbury	a														08 58				
	d				08 29								08 38		08 58				
Newbury Racecourse	d												08 40						
Thatcham	d												08 45		09 03				
Midgham	d												08 49						
Aldermaston	d												08 53						
Theale	d												08 58		09 11				
Reading West	d			←				←					09 05			←			
Reading 7	a		08 43	08 47	08 50	09 00	09 00	09 00	09 07	09 14	09 28	09 08	09 10	09 16	09 20	09 28	09 36	09 44	09 58
	d		08 45	08 48	08 52	09 05	09 02	09 05	09 08	09 16	09 33			09 18	09 21	09 33	09 37	09 46	10 03
Twyford 3	a			08 54		→		09 11			→					09 39			→
Maidenhead 3	a			09 02				09 19								09 47			
Slough 3	a							09 30								09 54	09 52		
Ealing Broadway ⊖	a							09 54								10 19			
London Paddington 15 ⊖	a		09 14	09 27	09 21		09 29	10 05	09 40	09 44				09 47	09 56	10 31	10 12	10 15	

A ◇ from Reading R to Reading

B ☕ from Reading ⊘ to Reading

C The Bristolian. ◇ from Reading R to Reading

D ☕ ◇ from Reading ⊘ R to Reading

E The Cathedrals Express. ☕ from Reading ⊘ to Reading

For complete service between Banbury and Leamington (Birmingham), please refer to table 71

Table 116R

Mondays to Fridays

31 March to 16 May

Birmingham, Banbury, Bicester, Oxford and Bedwyn - Reading and London

Network Diagram - refer to first Page of Table 116

		XC	GW	GW	GW	CH	GW	GW	XC	GW	GW	GW	GW	GW	GW	GW	XC	GW	GW
		◇1	1	◇1	1		◇1	1	◇1	1	◇1	1	◇1	1	◇1	1	◇1	1	◇1
		🛒					☕		🛒		🛒		☕		☕		🛒		
Birmingham New Street 12	d	08 04							08 33								09 04		
Birmingham International	d	08 14															09 14		
Coventry	d	08 25															09 25		
Leamington Spa 8	d	08 38							09 00								09 38		
Banbury	d	08 55							09 19							09 35	09 55		
Kings Sutton	d															09 40			
Heyford	d															09 49			
Tackley	d															09 54			
Bicester Town	d					09 07													
Islip	d					09 18													
Oxford	a	09 14				09 32			09 41							10 06	10 13		
	d	09 16		09 31				09 37	09 43		10 01					10 08	10 16		10 31
Radley	d															10 14			
Culham	d																		
Appleford	d																		
Didcot Parkway	a							09 49								10 23			
	d						09 55	10 01					10 16		10 29	10 31			
Cholsey	d							10 07								10 37			
Goring & Streatley	d							10 12								10 42			
Pangbourne	d							10 17								10 47			
Tilehurst	d							10 21								10 51			
Bedwyn	d									09 39									
Hungerford	d									09 44									
Kintbury	d									09 49									
Newbury	a									09 56									
	d		09 22							09 56								10 13	
Newbury Racecourse	d		09 25															10 15	
Thatcham	d		09 30							10 01								10 20	
Midgham	d		09 34															10 24	
Aldermaston	d		09 38															10 28	
Theale	d		09 43							10 09								10 33	
Reading West	d		09 50		←							←		←				10 40	
Reading 7	a	09 39	09 54	09 54	09 58		10 08	10 27	10 12	10 22	10 25	10 27	10 30	10 27	10 43	10 57	10 39	10 45	10 54
	d			09 55	10 03		10 09	10 33		10 22	10 26	10 33	10 32	10 33	10 45	11 03			10 55
Twyford 3	a				10 09			→				→		10 39		→			
Maidenhead 3	a				10 17									10 47					
Slough 3	a			10 10	10 24						10 40			10 53					11 09
Ealing Broadway ⊖	a				10 49									11 18					
London Paddington 15 ⊖	a			10 29	11 01		10 37			10 56	11 00		11 07	11 32	11 14				11 29

		GW	GW	GW	XC	CH	GW	GW	GW	GW	GW	GW	GW	XC	GW	GW	GW	GW	GW
		1	◇1	1	◇1		1	◇1	1	◇1	1	◇1	1	◇1	1	◇1	1	◇1	1
			A																
			☕		🛒			🛒		☕		☕		🛒		🛒		☕	
Birmingham New Street 12	d				09 33									10 04					
Birmingham International	d													10 14					
Coventry	d													10 25					
Leamington Spa 8	d				10 00									10 38					
Banbury	d				10 19									10 55					
Kings Sutton	d																		
Heyford	d																		
Tackley	d																		
Bicester Town	d					10 30													
Islip	d					10 41													
Oxford	a				10 41	10 56								11 14					
	d			10 37	10 43			11 01					11 07	11 16		11 31			11 37
Radley	d												11 13						
Culham	d																		
Appleford	d																		
Didcot Parkway	a			10 57									11 22						11 51
	d		10 47	11 01						11 16		11 29	11 31					11 55	12 01
Cholsey	d			11 07									11 37						12 07
Goring & Streatley	d			11 12									11 42						12 12
Pangbourne	d			11 17									11 47						12 17
Tilehurst	d			11 21									11 51						12 21
Bedwyn	d						10 39												
Hungerford	d						10 44												
Kintbury	d						10 49												
Newbury	a						10 56												
	d						10 56								11 13				
Newbury Racecourse	d														11 15				
Thatcham	d						11 01								11 20				
Midgham	d														11 24				
Aldermaston	d														11 28				
Theale	d						11 09								11 33				
Reading West	d	←							←		←				11 40		←		
Reading 7	a	10 57	11 00	11 27	11 09		11 20	11 24	11 27	11 30	11 27	11 43	11 57	11 39	11 45	11 55	11 57	12 08	12 27
	d	11 03	11 03	11 33			11 21	11 26	11 33	11 32	11 33	11 44	12 03			11 56	12 03	12 09	12 33
Twyford 3	a	11 09		→					→		11 39		→				12 09		→
Maidenhead 3	a	11 17									11 47						12 17		
Slough 3	a	11 24						11 39			11 54					12 10	12 24		
Ealing Broadway ⊖	a	11 49									12 19						12 49		
London Paddington 15 ⊖	a	12 01	11 32				11 56	11 59		12 02	12 31	12 14				12 30	13 02	12 37	

A The Red Dragon

For complete service between Banbury and Leamington (Birmingham), please refer to table 71

Table 116R

Mondays to Fridays

31 March to 16 May

Birmingham, Banbury, Bicester, Oxford and Bedwyn - Reading and London

Network Diagram - refer to first Page of Table 116

		XC	CH	GW	GW	GW	GW	GW	GW	GW	XC FX	XC FO	GW	GW	GW	GW	GW	XC	GW	GW	GW	GW	GW	GW	GW	XC	GW	GW	GW	GW	GW	XC	GW	GW	GW	GW	GW
		◇1 ⊼		1	◇1 ⊼	1	◇1 ⊏	1	◇1 ⊏	1	◇1 ⊼	◇1 ⊼	1	◇1 ⊼	1	◇1 ⊏	1	◇1 ⊼	◇1 ⊼	1	1	◇1 ⊏	◇1 ⊏	1	1	◇1 ⊼	1	◇1 ⊼	1	◇1 ⊏	1	◇1 ⊼	◇1 ⊏	◇1 ⊼	1	◇1 ⊏	◇1 ⊏
Birmingham New Street 12	d	10 33									11 04	11 04						11 33								12 04						12 33					
Birmingham International	d										11 14	11 14														12 14											
Coventry	d										11 25	11 25														12 25											
Leamington Spa 8	d	11 00									11 38	11 38						12 01								12 38						13 00					
Banbury	d	11 19									11 55	11 57						12 19							12 42	12 55						13 22					
Kings Sutton	d																								12 48												
Heyford	d																								12 56												
Tackley	d																								13 01												
Bicester Town	d		11 30																																		
Islip	d		11 41																																		
Oxford	a	11 41	11 56								12 14	12 14						12 41							13 11	13 14						13 41					
	d	11 43			12 01					12 07	12 16	12 16		12 31			12 37	12 43	13 01					13 07		13 16		13 31			13 37	13 44		14 01			
Radley	d									12 13														13 13													
Culham	d																							13 17													
Appleford	d									12 17																											
Didcot Parkway	a									12 24							12 49							13 30							13 49						
	d						12 16		12 29	12 31						12 47	13 01					13 16	13 29	13 31						13 53	14 01					14 15	14 29
Cholsey	d									12 37							13 07							13 37							14 07						
Goring & Streatley	d									12 42							13 12							13 42							14 12						
Pangbourne	d									12 47							13 17							13 47							14 17						
Tilehurst	d									12 51							13 21							13 51							14 21						
Bedwyn	d			11 39																12 38													13 32				
Hungerford	d			11 44																12 43													13 40				
Kintbury	d			11 49																12 48																	
Newbury	a			11 56																12 55													13 50				
	d			11 56									12 13							13 03							13 13						13 51				
Newbury Racecourse	d												12 15														13 15										
Thatcham	d			12 01									12 20							13 08							13 20						13 58				
Midgham	d												12 24														13 24										
Aldermaston	d												12 28														13 28										
Theale	d			12 09									12 33							13 16							13 33						14 07				
Reading West	d					←		←					12 40		←						←						13 40		←						←		
Reading 7	a	12 12		12 22	12 25	12 27	12 30	12 27	12 43	12 57	12 39	12 39	12 45	12 55	12 57	13 00	13 28	13 07	13 25	13 25	13 28	13 30	13 43	13 57		13 39	13 45	13 54	13 57	14 06	14 27	14 11	14 20	14 25	14 27	14 30	14 43
	d			12 22	12 26	12 33	12 32	12 33	12 44	13 03				12 56	13 03	13 04	13 33		13 26	13 30	13 33	13 35	13 45	14 03				13 56	14 03	14 08	14 33		14 23	14 26	14 33	14 36	14 44
Twyford 3	a					→		12 39		→					13 09		→				13 39			→					14 09		→				14 39		
Maidenhead 3	a							12 47							13 17						13 47								14 17						14 47		
Slough 3	a				12 41			12 54						13 10	13 24				13 41		13 54							14 10	14 24					14 40	14 54		
Ealing Broadway ⊖	a							13 19							13 49						14 19								14 49						15 19		
London Paddington 15 ⊖	a			12 54	13 09		13 00	13 31	13 14					13 30	14 01	13 33			14 00	14 09	14 31	14 06	14 14					14 30	15 01	14 37			14 54	15 01	15 32	15 08	15 14

For complete service between Banbury and Leamington (Birmingham), please refer to table 71

Table 116R

Mondays to Fridays

31 March to 16 May

Birmingham, Banbury, Bicester, Oxford and Bedwyn - Reading and London

Network Diagram - refer to first Page of Table 116

		GW ■1	XC ◇■1 🛒	CH	GW ■1	GW ◇■1	GW ■1	GW ◇■1 A 🍴⊘	GW ■1	XC ◇■1 🛒	GW ■1	GW ◇■1 🛒	GW ■1	GW ◇■1 🍴	GW ◇■1 🍴	GW ■1	XC ◇■1 🛒	GW ■1	GW ◇■1 🍴
Birmingham New Street ■12	d		13 04							13 33							14 04		
Birmingham International	d		13 14														14 14		
Coventry	d		13 25														14 24		
Leamington Spa ■8	d		13 38							14 00							14 38		
Banbury	d		13 55							14 19							14 55		
Kings Sutton	d																		
Heyford	d																		
Tackley	d																		
Bicester Town	d			14 00															
Islip	d			14 11															
Oxford	a		14 13	14 28						14 40							15 13		
	d	14 07	14 16			14 31			14 37	14 43		15 01				15 07	15 16		15 31
Radley	d	14 13														15 13			
Culham	d															15 17			
Appleford	d																		
Didcot Parkway	a	14 22							14 51							15 24			
	d	14 31						14 47	15 01					15 16	15 29	15 35			
Cholsey	d	14 37							15 07							15 41			
Goring & Streatley	d	14 42							15 12							15 46			
Pangbourne	d	14 47							15 17							15 51			
Tilehurst	d	14 51							15 21							15 55			
Bedwyn	d										14 39								
Hungerford	d										14 44								
Kintbury	d										14 49								
Newbury	a										14 56								
	d				14 13						14 56							15 13	
Newbury Racecourse	d				14 15													15 15	
Thatcham	d				14 20						15 01							15 20	
Midgham	d				14 24													15 24	
Aldermaston	d				14 28													15 28	
Theale	d				14 33						15 09							15 33	
Reading West	d				14 40		←						←					15 40	
Reading ■7	a	14 56	14 39		14 45	14 55	14 56	15 00	15 27	15 08	15 20	15 24	15 27	15 30	15 43	16 01	15 40	15 45	15 55
	d	15 03				14 56	15 03	15 04	15 33		15 20	15 26	15 33	15 33	15 44	16 03			15 57
Twyford ■3	a	→					15 09		→				15 39			→			
Maidenhead ■3	a						15 17						15 47						
Slough ■3	a					15 10	15 24					15 39	15 54						16 10
Ealing Broadway ⊖	a						15 49						16 19						
London Paddington ■15 ⊖	a					15 30	16 01	15 33			15 54	16 01	16 31	16 08	16 14				16 29

		GW ■1	GW ◇■1 B 🍴	GW ■1	GW ■1	XC ◇■1 🛒	CH	GW ■1	GW ◇■1 🛒	GW ■1	GW ◇■1 🍴	GW ◇■1 🍴	GW ■1	XC ◇■1 🛒	GW ■1	GW ◇■1	GW ◇■1 🍴	GW ■1	GW ■1
Birmingham New Street ■12	d					14 33								15 04					
Birmingham International	d													15 14					
Coventry	d													15 24					
Leamington Spa ■8	d					15 00								15 38					
Banbury	d				15 08	15 19								15 55					
Kings Sutton	d				15 14														
Heyford	d				15 22														
Tackley	d				15 27														
Bicester Town	d						15 30												
Islip	d						15 41												
Oxford	a				15 39	15 41	15 56							16 13					
	d			15 37		15 43			16 01				16 07	16 16		16 31			16 37
Radley	d			15 43									16 13						16 43
Culham	d																		
Appleford	d												16 17						
Didcot Parkway	a			15 51									16 27						16 51
	d		15 53	16 01							16 16	16 29	16 35				16 47		17 05
Cholsey	d			16 07									16 41						17 11
Goring & Streatley	d			16 12									16 46						17 16
Pangbourne	d			16 17									16 51						17 20
Tilehurst	d			16 21									16 55						17 25
Bedwyn	d							15 40											
Hungerford	d							15 45											
Kintbury	d							15 50											
Newbury	a							15 57											
	d							15 57							16 13				
Newbury Racecourse	d														16 15				
Thatcham	d							16 02							16 20				
Midgham	d														16 24				
Aldermaston	d														16 28				
Theale	d							16 10							16 33				
Reading West	d	←								←					16 40			←	
Reading ■7	a	16 01	16 06	16 27		16 11		16 21	16 25	16 27	16 29	16 43	17 01	16 39	16 45	16 56	17 00	17 01	17 31
	d	16 03	16 08	16 31				16 22	16 26	16 31	16 33	16 44	17 03			16 57	17 02	17 03	17 33
Twyford ■3	a	16 09		→						16 37			→					17 09	→
Maidenhead ■3	a	16 17								16 47								17 17	
Slough ■3	a	16 24							16 41	16 54						17 13		17 24	
Ealing Broadway ⊖	a	16 49								17 21								17 49	
London Paddington ■15 ⊖	a	17 01	16 39					16 57	17 00	17 31	17 08	17 14				17 34	17 30	18 01	

A 🍴 from Reading ⊘ to Reading

B The Cheltenham Spa Express

For complete service between Banbury and Leamington (Birmingham), please refer to table 71

Table 116R

Mondays to Fridays

31 March to 16 May

Birmingham, Banbury, Bicester, Oxford and Bedwyn - Reading and London

Network Diagram - refer to first Page of Table 116

Station		XC	GW	GW	GW	GW	GW	GW	GW	GW	XC	CH	GW	GW	GW	GW	GW	XC	GW
		◇1	1	◇1	1	◇1	◇1	1	◇1	1	◇1		1	◇1	1	◇1	1	◇1	1
		🛒		ⓟ		🛒	ⓟ		ⓟ		🛒			ⓟ		ⓟ		🛒	
Birmingham New Street 12	d	15 33									16 04							16 33	
Birmingham International	d										16 14								
Coventry	d										16 24								
Leamington Spa 8	d	16 01									16 38							17 00	
Banbury	d	16 19									16 55							17 19	17 23
Kings Sutton	d																		17 27
Heyford	d																		17 36
Tackley	d																		17 40
Bicester Town	d											16 57							
Islip	d											17 08							
Oxford	a	16 40									17 13	17 23						17 40	17 52
	d	16 43	16 49			17 01				17 07	17 16			17 31			17 37	17 43	
Radley	d									17 13							17 43		
Culham	d									17 17									
Appleford	d																17 47		
Didcot Parkway	a		17 03							17 24							17 54		
	d						17 16		17 29	17 31						17 53	18 00		
Cholsey	d									17 37							18 07		
Goring & Streatley	d									17 42							18 12		
Pangbourne	d									17 47							18 17		
Tilehurst	d									17 51							18 21		
Bedwyn	d				16 44														
Hungerford	d			16 39	16 49														
Kintbury	d				16 54														
Newbury	a			16 48	17 03														
	d			16 49									17 13						
Newbury Racecourse	d												17 15						
Thatcham	d			16 55									17 20						
Midgham	d												17 24						
Aldermaston	d												17 28						
Theale	d			17 05									17 33						
Reading West	d							←					17 40		←				
Reading 7	a	17 07		17 16		17 26	17 31	17 31	17 43	17 57	17 39		17 45	17 54	17 57	18 06	18 27	18 08	
	d			17 18		17 27	17 32	17 33	17 46	18 08				17 56	18 08	18 08	18 33		
Twyford 3	a							17 39		→					18 14		→		
Maidenhead 3	a					17 39		17 47							18 22				
Slough 3	a			17 32				17 54						18 10	18 34				
Ealing Broadway ⊖	a							18 19							18 53				
London Paddington 15 ⊖	a			17 52		17 59	18 02	18 31	18 15					18 28	19 02	18 39			

Station		GW	GW	GW	GW	GW	GW	GW	XC	GW	GW	GW	GW	GW	GW	XC	CH	GW	GW
		1	◇1	1	◇1	1	◇1	1	◇1	1	◇1	1	◇1	1	1	◇1		1	1
													A						
			🛒		ⓟ		ⓟ		🛒				ⓟ⊘			🛒			
Birmingham New Street 12	d								17 04							17 33			
Birmingham International	d								17 14										
Coventry	d								17 24										
Leamington Spa 8	d								17 38							18 00			
Banbury	d								17 55							18 19			
Kings Sutton	d																		
Heyford	d																		
Tackley	d																		
Bicester Town	d																18 18		
Islip	d																18 29		
Oxford	a								18 15							18 40	18 44		
	d		18 01					18 07	18 16		18 31				18 37	18 43			
Radley	d							18 13							18 43				
Culham	d							18 17											
Appleford	d														18 47				
Didcot Parkway	a							18 24							18 56				
	d				18 16		18 29	18 31					18 47		19 01				
Cholsey	d							18 37							19 07				
Goring & Streatley	d							18 42							19 12				
Pangbourne	d							18 47							19 17				
Tilehurst	d							18 51							19 21				
Bedwyn	d	17 38								17 55									19 03
Hungerford	d	17 43								18 00									19 08
Kintbury	d	17 48								18 05									19 13
Newbury	a	17 55								18 12									19 22
	d	17 55								18 13									
Newbury Racecourse	d									18 15								18 53	
Thatcham	d	18 00								18 20								18 58	
Midgham	d									18 24									
Aldermaston	d	18 06								18 28									
Theale	d	18 11								18 33								19 06	
Reading West	d			←		←				18 40		←		←					
Reading 7	a	18 22	18 24	18 27	18 30	18 27	18 45	18 58	18 40	18 45	18 55	18 58	18 59	18 58	19 27	19 10		19 17	
	d	18 23	18 27	18 33	18 32	18 33	18 46	19 08			18 57	19 08	19 02	19 08	19 33			19 18	
Twyford 3	a			→		18 39		→				→		19 14	→				
Maidenhead 3	a					18 47								19 22					
Slough 3	a		18 40			18 54					19 09			19 30					
Ealing Broadway ⊖	a					19 19								19 54					
London Paddington 15 ⊖	a	18 54	18 59		19 02	19 31	19 16				19 30		19 32	20 03				19 54	

A ⓟ from Reading ⊘ to Reading

For complete service between Banbury and Leamington (Birmingham), please refer to table 71

Table 116R

Mondays to Fridays

31 March to 16 May

Birmingham, Banbury, Bicester, Oxford and Bedwyn - Reading and London

Network Diagram - refer to first Page of Table 116

Station		GW	GW	GW	GW	XC	GW	GW	GW	GW
		◇1	1	◇1	1	◇1	◇1	1	◇1	◇1
Birmingham New Street 12	d					18 04				
Birmingham International	d					18 14				
Coventry	d					18 24				
Leamington Spa 8	d					18 37				
Banbury	d				18 37	18 55				
Kings Sutton	d				18 43					
Heyford	d				18 51					
Tackley	d				18 56					
Bicester Town	d									
Islip	d									
Oxford	a				19 08	19 13				
	d	19 06			19 10	19 16	19 31			
Radley	d				19 16					
Culham	d									
Appleford	d									
Didcot Parkway	a				19 25					
	d			19 29	19 32				19 47	
Cholsey	d				19 37					
Goring & Streatley	d				19 42					
Pangbourne	d				19 47					
Tilehurst	d				19 51					
Bedwyn	d									
Hungerford	d									
Kintbury	d									
Newbury	a									
	d									19 49
Newbury Racecourse	d									
Thatcham	d									
Midgham	d									
Aldermaston	d									
Theale	d									
Reading West	d		←					←		
Reading 7	a	19 31	19 27	19 43	19 57	19 41	19 54	19 57	20 00	20 06
	d	19 33	19 33	19 45	19 58		19 55	19 58	20 07	20 10
Twyford 3	a		19 42		→			20 04		
Maidenhead 3	a		19 50					20 12		
Slough 3	a	19 47	19 57				20 10	20 22		
Ealing Broadway ⊖	a		20 22					20 49		
London Paddington 15 ⊖	a	20 06	20 32	20 14			20 30	20 59	20 37	20 39

Station		GW	GW	XC	GW	GW	GW	GW	GW	GW
		◇1	1	◇1	◇1	1	1	1	◇1	1
Birmingham New Street 12	d			18 33						
Birmingham International	d									
Coventry	d									
Leamington Spa 8	d			19 00						
Banbury	d			19 19						
Kings Sutton	d									
Heyford	d									
Tackley	d									
Bicester Town	d									
Islip	d									
Oxford	a			19 39						
	d		19 37	19 42	20 01					20 07
Radley	d									20 13
Culham	d									20 17
Appleford	d									
Didcot Parkway	a		19 49							20 24
	d	20 00	20 01						20 29	20 31
Cholsey	d		20 07							20 37
Goring & Streatley	d		20 12							20 42
Pangbourne	d		20 17							20 47
Tilehurst	d		20 21							20 51
Bedwyn	d							19 54		
Hungerford	d							19 59		
Kintbury	d							20 04		
Newbury	a							20 11		
	d						19 55	20 11		
Newbury Racecourse	d						19 57			
Thatcham	d						20 02	20 16		
Midgham	d						20 06			
Aldermaston	d						20 10			
Theale	d						20 15	20 24		
Reading West	d					←	20 21			
Reading 7	a	20 14	20 27	20 08	20 26	20 27	20 27	20 34	20 43	20 57
	d	20 16	20 33		20 26	20 33		20 34	20 45	21 12
Twyford 3	a		→			20 39				→
Maidenhead 3	a					20 47				
Slough 3	a				20 40	20 54				
Ealing Broadway ⊖	a					21 19				
London Paddington 15 ⊖	a	20 46			21 01	21 30		21 07	21 14	

Station		XC	CH	GW	GW	GW	GW	GW	XC	GW
		◇1		◇1	1	◇1	1	1	◇1	1
Birmingham New Street 12	d	19 04							19 33	
Birmingham International	d	19 14								
Coventry	d	19 24								
Leamington Spa 8	d	19 38							20 04	
Banbury	d	19 55						20 01	20 22	
Kings Sutton	d							20 07		
Heyford	d							20 15		
Tackley	d							20 20		
Bicester Town	d		20 02							
Islip	d		20 13							
Oxford	a	20 13	20 28					20 32	20 39	
	d	20 16		20 31				20 37	20 41	
Radley	d									
Culham	d									
Appleford	d									
Didcot Parkway	a							20 49		
	d					20 47		21 01		
Cholsey	d							21 07		
Goring & Streatley	d							21 12		
Pangbourne	d							21 17		
Tilehurst	d							21 21		
Bedwyn	d									20 33
Hungerford	d									20 38
Kintbury	d									20 43
Newbury	a									
	d									
Newbury Racecourse	d									20 52
Thatcham	d									20 57
Midgham	d									21 02
Aldermaston	d									21 05
Theale	d									21 10
Reading West	d				←		←			21 17
Reading 7	a	20 39		20 55	20 57	21 00	20 57	21 29	21 07	21 22
	d			20 56	21 12	21 03	21 12	21 33		
Twyford 3	a				→		21 18	→		
Maidenhead 3	a						21 26			
Slough 3	a			21 11			21 38			
Ealing Broadway ⊖	a						22 02			
London Paddington 15 ⊖	a			21 29		21 32	22 14			

Station		GW	GW	GW	XC	GW	GW	GW	GW FO	GW FX
		1	◇1	1	◇1	◇1	1	1	◇1	◇1
Birmingham New Street 12	d				20 04					
Birmingham International	d				20 14					
Coventry	d				20 24					
Leamington Spa 8	d				20 38					
Banbury	d				20 55					
Kings Sutton	d									
Heyford	d									
Tackley	d									
Bicester Town	d									
Islip	d									
Oxford	a				21 13					
	d		21 01		21 16			21 21	21 32	21 32
Radley	d							21 27		
Culham	d									
Appleford	d									
Didcot Parkway	a							21 34		
	d					21 29		21 44		
Cholsey	d							21 50		
Goring & Streatley	d							21 55		
Pangbourne	d							21 58		
Tilehurst	d							22 02		
Bedwyn	d	21 01								
Hungerford	d	21 07								
Kintbury	d	21 11								
Newbury	a	21 18								
	d						21 23			
Newbury Racecourse	d						21 25			
Thatcham	d						21 30			
Midgham	d						21 34			
Aldermaston	d						21 38			
Theale	d						21 43			
Reading West	d			←			21 49			
Reading 7	a		21 24	21 29	21 41	21 43	21 54	22 11	21 55	21 55
	d		21 26	21 33		21 44			21 56	21 56
Twyford 3	a			21 39						
Maidenhead 3	a			21 47						
Slough 3	a		21 40	21 58					22 14	22 14
Ealing Broadway ⊖	a			22 21						
London Paddington 15 ⊖	a		22 00	22 32		22 16			22 38	22 41

For complete service between Banbury and Leamington (Birmingham), please refer to table 71

Table 116R

Mondays to Fridays

31 March to 16 May

Birmingham, Banbury, Bicester, Oxford and Bedwyn - Reading and London

Network Diagram - refer to first Page of Table 116

		GW	GW	GW	GW	XC	GW	CH	GW	GW	XC	GW	GW	GW	GW	GW	GW	GW	GW	XC	GW	GW	GW	CH	GW	CH
		FO	FX	FO	FX				FX	FO			FX	FO	FX	FO						FX	FO	FO		
		◇1	◇1	◇1	◇1	◇1	1		◇1	◇1	◇1	1	◇1	◇1	◇1	◇1	1	1	◇1	◇1	1	◇1	◇1		1	
									A	A																
		☕	☕	☕	☕						🛒				☕	☕						☕	☕			
Birmingham New Street 12	d					20 33					21 04									22 04						
Birmingham International	d										21 14									22 14						
Coventry	d										21 24									22 25						
Leamington Spa 8	d					21 00					21 38									22 38						23 39
Banbury	d					21 19			21 38	21 38	21 55							22 25		22 55					23 45	23 58
Kings Sutton	d								21 44	21 44								22 31							23 50	
Heyford	d								21 52	21 52								22 39							23 58	
Tackley	d								21 57	21 57								22 44							00 03	
Bicester Town	d							21 31																23 42		
Islip	d							21 42																23 53		
Oxford	a					21 40		21 57	22 07	22 07	22 14							22 56		23 14				00 08	00 14	00 22
	d					21 43	21 51		22 11	22 11	22 16		22 30	22 30			22 52		23 09	23 15					00 27	
Radley	d						21 57										22 58								00 33	
Culham	d																23 02									
Appleford	d																23 04									
Didcot Parkway	a						22 06		22 24	22 24							23 11		23 23						00 42	
	d			21 53	21 53		22 08		22 27	22 27					22 52	22 52	23 13		23 23			23 37	23 37		00 46	
Cholsey	d						22 14										23 19								00 52	
Goring & Streatley	d						22 19										23 24								00 57	
Pangbourne	d						22 24										23 27								01 01	
Tilehurst	d						22 27										23 31								01 06	
Bedwyn	d											21 55									23 00					
Hungerford	d											22 00									23 05					
Kintbury	d											22 05									23 10					
Newbury	a											22 12									23 17					
	d	21 42	21 42									22 13									23 17					
Newbury Racecourse	d											22 15									23 19					
Thatcham	d											22 20									23 24					
Midgham	d											22 24									23 29					
Aldermaston	d											22 28									23 32					
Theale	d											22 33									23 37					
Reading West	d											22 40									23 44					
Reading 7	a	21 59	21 59	22 11	22 11	22 17	22 37		22 43	22 44	22 41	22 45	22 53	22 54	23 06	23 08	23 41		23 41	23 49	23 49	23 53	23 54		01 13	
	d	22 00	22 00	22 12	22 12				22 44	22 44			22 59	22 59	23 09	23 09			23 41			23 55	23 55		01 17	
Twyford 3	a																								01 23	
Maidenhead 3	a																		23 54						01 31	
Slough 3	a								23 01	23 01			23 14	23 14					00 02						01 39	
Ealing Broadway ⊖	a																								01 55	
London Paddington 15 ⊖	a	22 30	22 38	22 44	22 47				23 24	23 24			23 38	23 37	23 44	23 42			00 27			00 33	00 33		02 07	

A 1 to Oxford

For complete service between Banbury and Leamington (Birmingham), please refer to table 71

Table 116R

Saturdays

14 December to 28 December

Birmingham, Banbury, Bicester, Oxford and Bedwyn - Reading and London

Network Diagram - refer to first Page of Table 116

		GW	GW	GW	GW	GW	GW	GW	GW	GW	GW	GW	GW	GW	GW	GW	GW	GW	GW
		◇1	1	1	1	1	◇1	1	1	◇1	1	◇1	1	1	◇1	◇1	1	◇1	1
							☕					☕				☕		☕	
Birmingham New Street 12	d																		
Birmingham International	d																		
Coventry	d																		
Leamington Spa 8	d																		
Banbury	d																		
Kings Sutton	d																		
Heyford	d																		
Tackley	d		00 03																
Bicester Town	d																		
Islip	d																		
Oxford	a		00 14																
	d	00 07	00 27	03 59	05 14	05 49			06 07	06 31				06 42	07 01				07 07
Radley	d		00 33		05 20				06 13										07 13
Culham	d				05 24														07 17
Appleford	d								06 17										
Didcot Parkway	a	00 20	00 42	04 10	05 31	06 01			06 24					06 54					07 24
	d	00 21	00 46	04 10	05 31	06 01	06 29		06 31			06 59		07 01		07 17		07 29	07 31
Cholsey	d		00 52		05 37	06 07			06 37					07 07					07 37
Goring & Streatley	d		00 57		05 42	06 12			06 42					07 12					07 42
Pangbourne	d		01 01		05 47	06 17			06 47					07 17					07 47
Tilehurst	d		01 06		05 51	06 21			06 51					07 21					07 51
Bedwyn	d							06 05					06 39						
Hungerford	d							06 11					06 43						
Kintbury	d							06 15					06 48						
Newbury	a							06 22					06 55						
	d							06 22					06 55						
Newbury Racecourse	d							06 24											
Thatcham	d							06 29					07 00						
Midgham	d							06 34											
Aldermaston	d							06 37											
Theale	d							06 42					07 08						
Reading West	d							06 49			←						←		
Reading 7	a	00 41	01 13	04 29	05 57	06 27	06 43	06 52	06 58	06 57	06 58	07 14	07 20	07 27	07 27	07 31	07 27	07 44	07 58
	d	00 43	01 17	04 40	06 03	06 33	06 45	06 53	07 03	07 03	07 03	07 15	07 22	07 33	07 27	07 32	07 33	07 46	08 03
Twyford 3	a		01 23	04 46	06 09	06 39			↦		07 09			↦			07 39		↦
Maidenhead 3	a		01 31	04 54	06 17	06 47					07 17						07 47		
Slough 3	a	00 59	01 39	05 02	06 24	06 54				07 17	07 24				07 42		07 54		
Ealing Broadway ⊖	a		01 55	05 19	06 49	07 19					07 49						08 19		
London Paddington 15 ⊖	a	01 21	02 07	05 31	07 01	07 31	07 14	07 22		07 37	08 01	07 44	07 54		08 01	08 07	08 31	08 14	

		XC	GW	GW	GW	GW	GW	GW	GW	GW	XC	GW	GW	GW	CH	GW	GW	GW	XC
		◇1	1	◇1	1	1	◇1	1	◇1	1	◇1	1	◇1	1		◇1	◇1	1	◇1
		trolley		trolley			☕		☕							☕	☕		trolley
Birmingham New Street 12	d	06 04									06 33								07 04
Birmingham International	d	06 14																	07 14
Coventry	d	06 25																	07 25
Leamington Spa 8	d	06 38									07 00								07 38
Banbury	d	06 55				07 03					07 19								07 55
Kings Sutton	d					07 08													
Heyford	d					07 17													
Tackley	d					07 21													
Bicester Town	d														07 36				
Islip	d														07 47				
Oxford	a	07 14				07 32					07 40				08 02				08 14
	d	07 16		07 31						07 37	07 43		08 01					08 07	08 16
Radley	d																	08 13	
Culham	d																		
Appleford	d																	08 17	
Didcot Parkway	a									07 49								08 24	
	d						07 47		07 59	08 01						08 17	08 29	08 31	
Cholsey	d									08 07								08 37	
Goring & Streatley	d									08 12								08 42	
Pangbourne	d									08 17								08 47	
Tilehurst	d									08 21								08 51	
Bedwyn	d											07 39							
Hungerford	d											07 44							
Kintbury	d											07 49							
Newbury	a											07 56							
	d		07 13									07 56							
Newbury Racecourse	d		07 15																
Thatcham	d		07 20									08 01							
Midgham	d		07 24																
Aldermaston	d		07 28																
Theale	d		07 33									08 09							
Reading West	d		07 42		←			←						←					
Reading 7	a	07 39	07 45	07 55	07 58		08 00	07 58	08 15	08 28	08 06	08 21	08 25	08 28		08 33	08 44	08 55	08 39
	d			07 55	08 03		08 02	08 03	08 17	08 33		08 22	08 26	08 33		08 33	08 46	09 03	
Twyford 3	a				↦			08 09		↦				08 39				↦	
Maidenhead 3	a							08 17						08 47					
Slough 3	a			08 10				08 24					08 40	08 54					
Ealing Broadway ⊖	a							08 49						09 19					
London Paddington 15 ⊖	a			08 29			08 32	09 01	08 44			08 54	08 59	09 31		09 02	09 14		

For complete service between Banbury and Leamington (Birmingham), please refer to table 71

Table 116R

Saturdays

14 December to 28 December

Birmingham, Banbury, Bicester, Oxford and Bedwyn - Reading and London

Network Diagram - refer to first Page of Table 116

		GW	GW	GW	GW	GW	GW	GW	GW	XC	GW	GW	GW	GW	GW	GW	GW	CH	XC
		1	◇1	◇1	◇1	1	◇1	◇1	1	◇1	1	◇1	1	◇1	1	◇1	1		◇1
														A					
			☕	☕	☕		☕	☕		🛒		🛒		☕⊘		☕			🛒
Birmingham New Street 12	d									07 33									08 04
Birmingham International	d																		08 14
Coventry	d																		08 25
Leamington Spa 8	d									08 00									08 38
Banbury	d									08 19									08 55
Kings Sutton	d																		
Heyford	d																		
Tackley	d																		
Bicester Town	d																	08 45	
Islip	d																	08 56	
Oxford	a									08 40								09 11	09 14
	d			08 31					08 37	08 43		09 01					09 07		09 16
Radley	d																09 13		
Culham	d																09 17		
Appleford	d																		
Didcot Parkway	a								08 49								09 24		
	d				08 47		08 54	09 00	09 01					09 17		09 29	09 31		
Cholsey	d								09 07								09 37		
Goring & Streatley	d								09 12								09 42		
Pangbourne	d								09 17								09 47		
Tilehurst	d								09 21								09 51		
Bedwyn	d										08 38								
Hungerford	d										08 43								
Kintbury	d										08 48								
Newbury	a										08 57								
	d	08 13	08 34								08 57				09 03				
Newbury Racecourse	d	08 15													09 06				
Thatcham	d	08 20									09 02				09 11				
Midgham	d	08 24													09 16				
Aldermaston	d	08 28													09 19				
Theale	d	08 33									09 10				09 24				
Reading West	d	08 40				←							←		09 31				
Reading 7	a	08 44	08 51	08 56	09 01	08 55	09 08	09 14	09 27	09 07	09 20	09 24	09 27	09 31	09 35	09 47	09 57		09 39
	d		08 52	08 56	09 02	09 03	09 10	09 16	09 33		09 21	09 24	09 33	09 33		09 49	10 03		
Twyford 3	a					09 09			→				09 39				→		
Maidenhead 3	a					09 17							09 47						
Slough 3	a			09 10		09 24						09 40	09 54						
Ealing Broadway ⊖	a					09 49							10 19						
London Paddington 15 ⊖	a		09 21	09 29	09 38	10 01	09 41	09 44			09 52	09 59	10 31	10 02		10 15			

		GW	GW	GW	GW	GW	GW	XC	GW	GW	GW	GW	GW	GW	GW	XC	CH	GW	GW
		◇1	1	1	◇1	1	1	◇1	1	◇1	◇1	1	◇1	◇1	1	◇1		1	◇1
		A			A														
		☕⊘			☕⊘			🛒		🛒	☕		☕	☕		🛒			☕
Birmingham New Street 12	d							08 33								09 04			
Birmingham International	d															09 14			
Coventry	d															09 25			
Leamington Spa 8	d							09 00								09 38			
Banbury	d			09 02				09 19								09 55			
Kings Sutton	d			09 08															
Heyford	d			09 17															
Tackley	d			09 21															
Bicester Town	d																09 57		
Islip	d																10 08		
Oxford	a			09 32				09 40								10 14	10 23		
	d	09 31					09 37	09 43		10 01					10 07	10 16			10 32
Radley	d														10 13				
Culham	d																		
Appleford	d														10 17				
Didcot Parkway	a						09 49								10 23				
	d				09 47		10 01				10 17		10 22	10 29	10 31				
Cholsey	d						10 07								10 37				
Goring & Streatley	d						10 12								10 42				
Pangbourne	d						10 17								10 47				
Tilehurst	d						10 21								10 51				
Bedwyn	d								09 39										
Hungerford	d								09 44										
Kintbury	d								09 49										
Newbury	a								09 56										
	d								09 56									10 13	
Newbury Racecourse	d																	10 15	
Thatcham	d								10 01									10 20	
Midgham	d																	10 24	
Aldermaston	d																	10 28	
Theale	d								10 09									10 33	
Reading West	d		←			←						←						10 40	
Reading 7	a	09 54	09 57		10 00	09 57	10 27	10 06	10 21	10 28	10 30	10 27	10 34	10 46	10 58	10 41		10 44	10 56
	d	09 55	10 03		10 02	10 03	10 33		10 22	10 28	10 32	10 33	10 36	10 47	11 03				10 58
Twyford 3	a		→			10 09	→					10 39			→				
Maidenhead 3	a					10 17						10 47							
Slough 3	a	10 09				10 24				10 43		10 54							11 12
Ealing Broadway ⊖	a					10 49						11 19							
London Paddington 15 ⊖	a	10 29			10 32	11 01			10 52	11 02	11 04	11 31	11 08	11 14					11 30

A ☕ from Reading ⊘ to Reading

For complete service between Banbury and Leamington (Birmingham), please refer to table 71

Table 116R

Saturdays

14 December to 28 December

Birmingham, Banbury, Bicester, Oxford and Bedwyn - Reading and London

Network Diagram - refer to first Page of Table 116

		GW	GW	GW	GW	XC	GW	GW	GW	GW	GW	XC	GW	GW	GW	GW	GW	GW	XC
		■1	◇■1	■1	■1	◇■1	■1	◇■1	■1	◇■1	■1	◇■1	■1	◇■1	■1	◇■1	■1	■1	◇■1
			⊡			⊥o				⊡		⊥o		⊥o		⊡			⊥o
Birmingham New Street 12	d					09 33						10 04							10 33
Birmingham International	d											10 14							
Coventry	d											10 25							
Leamington Spa 8	d					10 00						10 38							11 00
Banbury	d					10 19						10 55			11 02				11 19
Kings Sutton	d														11 08				
Heyford	d														11 17				
Tackley	d														11 21				
Bicester Town	d																		
Islip	d																		
Oxford	a					10 40						11 14			11 32				11 40
	d				10 37	10 43		11 01			11 07	11 16		11 30				11 37	11 43
Radley	d										11 13								
Culham	d																		
Appleford	d																		
Didcot Parkway	a				10 49						11 24							11 49	
	d		10 47		11 01					11 29	11 31					11 47		12 01	
Cholsey	d				11 07						11 37							12 07	
Goring & Streatley	d				11 12						11 42							12 12	
Pangbourne	d				11 17						11 47							12 17	
Tilehurst	d				11 21						11 51							12 21	
Bedwyn	d						10 39												
Hungerford	d						10 45												
Kintbury	d						10 49												
Newbury	a						10 56												
	d						10 56						11 13						
Newbury Racecourse	d												11 15						
Thatcham	d						11 01						11 20						
Midgham	d												11 24						
Aldermaston	d												11 28						
Theale	d						11 09						11 33						
Reading West	d	←		←					←				11 40				←		
Reading 7	a	10 58	11 01	10 58	11 27	11 11	11 20	11 24	11 27	11 43	11 56	11 39	11 44	11 57		12 01	11 56	12 28	12 07
	d	11 03	11 02	11 03	11 33		11 21	11 25	11 33	11 45	12 03			11 58		12 03	12 03	12 33	
Twyford 3	a	→		11 09	→				11 39		→						12 09	→	
Maidenhead 3	a			11 17					11 47								12 17		
Slough 3	a			11 24				11 39	11 54					12 12			12 24		
Ealing Broadway ⊖	a			11 49					12 19								12 49		
London Paddington 15 ⊖	a		11 33	12 01			11 52	11 59	12 31	12 14				12 32		12 37	13 01		

		CH	GW	GW	GW	GW	GW	GW	XC	GW	GW	GW	GW	GW	XC	GW	GW	GW	GW
			■1	◇■1	■1	◇■1	◇■1	■1	◇■1	■1	◇■1	■1	◇■1	■1	◇■1	◇■1	■1	◇■1	■1
				⊥o		⊡	⊡		⊥o		⊥o		⊡		⊥o	⊥o		⊡	
Birmingham New Street 12	d								11 04						11 33				
Birmingham International	d								11 14										
Coventry	d								11 25										
Leamington Spa 8	d								11 38						12 00				
Banbury	d								11 55						12 19				
Kings Sutton	d																		
Heyford	d																		
Tackley	d																		
Bicester Town	d	11 30																	
Islip	d	11 41																	
Oxford	a	11 56							12 14						12 40				
	d			12 01				12 07	12 16		12 31			12 37	12 43	13 01			13 07
Radley	d							12 13											13 13
Culham	d																		13 17
Appleford	d							12 17											
Didcot Parkway	a							12 24						12 51					13 24
	d					12 23	12 29	12 31					12 47	13 01				13 29	13 31
Cholsey	d							12 37						13 07					13 37
Goring & Streatley	d							12 42						13 12					13 42
Pangbourne	d							12 47						13 17					13 47
Tilehurst	d							12 51						13 21					13 51
Bedwyn	d		11 39																
Hungerford	d		11 44																
Kintbury	d		11 49																
Newbury	a		11 56																
	d		11 56							12 13									
Newbury Racecourse	d									12 15									
Thatcham	d		12 01							12 20									
Midgham	d									12 24									
Aldermaston	d									12 28									
Theale	d		12 09							12 33									
Reading West	d				←					12 40		←					←		
Reading 7	a		12 21	12 26	12 28	12 38	12 45	12 56	12 40	12 44	12 56	12 56	13 01	13 27	13 07	13 26	13 27	13 44	13 59
	d		12 22	12 27	12 33	12 39	12 47	13 03			12 57	13 03	13 07	13 33		13 27	13 33	13 45	14 03
Twyford 3	a				12 39			→				13 09		→			13 39		→
Maidenhead 3	a				12 47							13 17					13 47		
Slough 3	a			12 41	12 54						13 11	13 24				13 41	13 54		
Ealing Broadway ⊖	a				13 19							13 49					14 19		
London Paddington 15 ⊖	a		12 53	12 59	13 31	13 06	13 15				13 32	14 01	13 38			13 59	14 31	14 14	

For complete service between Banbury and Leamington (Birmingham), please refer to table 71

Table 116R

Saturdays

Birmingham, Banbury, Bicester, Oxford and Bedwyn - Reading and London

14 December to 28 December

Network Diagram - refer to first Page of Table 116

		XC ◇1 🛒	CH	GW 1	GW 1	GW ◇1	GW 1	GW 1	GW ◇1 ☕	GW 1
Birmingham New Street 12	d	12 04								
Birmingham International	d	12 14								
Coventry	d	12 25								
Leamington Spa 8	d	12 38								
Banbury	d	12 55						13 02		
Kings Sutton	d							13 08		
Heyford	d							13 17		
Tackley	d							13 21		
Bicester Town	d		13 00							
Islip	d		13 11							
Oxford	a	13 14	13 26					13 32		
	d	13 16				13 31				
Radley	d									
Culham	d									
Appleford	d									
Didcot Parkway	a									
	d								13 47	
Cholsey	d									
Goring & Streatley	d									
Pangbourne	d									
Tilehurst	d									
Bedwyn	d				13 07					
Hungerford	d				13 13					
Kintbury	d				13 17					
Newbury	a				13 24					
	d			13 13	13 28					
Newbury Racecourse	d			13 15						
Thatcham	d			13 20	13 33					
Midgham	d			13 24						
Aldermaston	d			13 28						
Theale	d			13 33	13 41					
Reading West	d			13 40			←			←
Reading 7	a	13 39		13 44	13 51	13 54	13 59		14 00	13 59
	d				13 51	13 56	14 03		14 02	14 03
Twyford 3	a						→			14 09
Maidenhead 3	a									14 17
Slough 3	a					14 09				14 24
Ealing Broadway ⊖	a									14 49
London Paddington 15 ⊖	a				14 22	14 29			14 32	15 01

		GW 1	XC ◇1 🛒	GW ◇1 ☕	GW ◇1 🛒	GW 1	GW ◇1 ☕	GW ◇1 ☕	GW 1	XC ◇1 🛒
Birmingham New Street 12	d		12 33							13 04
Birmingham International	d									13 14
Coventry	d									13 25
Leamington Spa 8	d		13 02							13 38
Banbury	d		13 21							13 55
Kings Sutton	d									
Heyford	d									
Tackley	d									
Bicester Town	d									
Islip	d									
Oxford	a		13 40							14 14
	d	13 37	13 43		14 01				14 07	14 16
Radley	d								14 13	
Culham	d									
Appleford	d								14 17	
Didcot Parkway	a	13 51							14 24	
	d	14 01					14 24	14 29	14 31	
Cholsey	d	14 07							14 37	
Goring & Streatley	d	14 12							14 42	
Pangbourne	d	14 17							14 47	
Tilehurst	d	14 21							14 51	
Bedwyn	d			13 33						
Hungerford	d			13 40						
Kintbury	d									
Newbury	a			13 49						
	d			13 50						
Newbury Racecourse	d									
Thatcham	d			13 57						
Midgham	d									
Aldermaston	d									
Theale	d			14 06						
Reading West	d					←				
Reading 7	a	14 27	14 09	14 22	14 26	14 27	14 39	14 45	14 56	14 40
	d	14 33		14 23	14 27	14 33	14 41	14 47	15 03	
Twyford 3	a	→				14 39			→	
Maidenhead 3	a					14 47				
Slough 3	a				14 41	14 54				
Ealing Broadway ⊖	a					15 19				
London Paddington 15 ⊖	a			14 50	14 59	15 31	15 09	15 14		

		GW 1	GW ◇1 ☕	GW 1	GW ◇1 ☕	GW 1	XC ◇1 🛒	CH	GW 1	GW ◇1
Birmingham New Street 12	d						13 33			
Birmingham International	d									
Coventry	d									
Leamington Spa 8	d						14 00			
Banbury	d						14 18			
Kings Sutton	d									
Heyford	d									
Tackley	d									
Bicester Town	d							14 18		
Islip	d							14 29		
Oxford	a						14 40	14 44		
	d		14 31			14 37	14 43			15 01
Radley	d									
Culham	d									
Appleford	d									
Didcot Parkway	a					14 49				
	d				14 47	15 01				
Cholsey	d					15 07				
Goring & Streatley	d					15 12				
Pangbourne	d					15 17				
Tilehurst	d					15 21				
Bedwyn	d								14 39	
Hungerford	d								14 44	
Kintbury	d								14 49	
Newbury	a								14 56	
	d	14 13							14 56	
Newbury Racecourse	d	14 15								
Thatcham	d	14 20							15 01	
Midgham	d	14 24								
Aldermaston	d	14 28								
Theale	d	14 33							15 09	
Reading West	d	14 40		←						
Reading 7	a	14 44	14 56	14 56	15 02	15 27	15 08		15 19	15 25
	d		14 58	15 03	15 04	15 32			15 20	15 25
Twyford 3	a			15 09		→				
Maidenhead 3	a			15 17						
Slough 3	a		15 13	15 24						15 40
Ealing Broadway ⊖	a			15 49						
London Paddington 15 ⊖	a		15 30	16 01	15 37				15 54	15 59

		GW 1	GW ◇1 ☕	GW 1	XC ◇1 🛒	GW 1	GW ◇1 🛒	GW 1	GW 1	GW ◇1 ☕
Birmingham New Street 12	d				14 04					
Birmingham International	d				14 14					
Coventry	d				14 25					
Leamington Spa 8	d				14 38					
Banbury	d				14 55				15 02	
Kings Sutton	d								15 08	
Heyford	d								15 17	
Tackley	d								15 21	
Bicester Town	d									
Islip	d									
Oxford	a				15 14				15 32	
	d			15 07	15 16		15 31			
Radley	d			15 13						
Culham	d			15 17						
Appleford	d									
Didcot Parkway	a			15 24						
	d		15 29	15 31						15 47
Cholsey	d			15 37						
Goring & Streatley	d			15 42						
Pangbourne	d			15 47						
Tilehurst	d			15 51						
Bedwyn	d									
Hungerford	d									
Kintbury	d									
Newbury	a									
	d					15 13				
Newbury Racecourse	d					15 15				
Thatcham	d					15 20				
Midgham	d					15 24				
Aldermaston	d					15 28				
Theale	d					15 33				
Reading West	d	←				15 40		←		
Reading 7	a	15 27	15 44	15 59	15 39	15 44	15 55	15 59		16 00
	d	15 32	15 45	16 03			15 56	16 03		16 01
Twyford 3	a	15 39		→				→		
Maidenhead 3	a	15 47								
Slough 3	a	15 54					16 11			
Ealing Broadway ⊖	a	16 19								
London Paddington 15 ⊖	a	16 31	16 14				16 30			16 33

For complete service between Banbury and Leamington (Birmingham), please refer to table 71

Table 116R

Saturdays

14 December to 28 December

Birmingham, Banbury, Bicester, Oxford and Bedwyn - Reading and London

Network Diagram - refer to first Page of Table 116

Station		GW	GW	XC	CH	GW	GW	GW	GW	GW	GW	XC	GW	GW	GW	GW	GW	GW	XC
		1	1	◇1 ⊼		1	◇1	1	◇1 ⊡	◇1 ⊡	1	◇1 ⊼	1	◇1 ⊼	1	◇1 ⊡	1	1	◇1 ⊼
Birmingham New Street 12	d			14 33								15 04							15 33
Birmingham International	d											15 14							
Coventry	d											15 25							
Leamington Spa 8	d			15 00								15 38							16 02
Banbury	d			15 20								15 55							16 22
Kings Sutton	d																		
Heyford	d																		
Tackley	d																		
Bicester Town	d				15 28														
Islip	d				15 39														
Oxford	a			15 40	15 54							16 14							16 40
	d		15 37	15 43			16 01				16 07	16 16		16 31				16 37	16 43
Radley	d										16 13								
Culham	d																		
Appleford	d										16 17								
Didcot Parkway	a		15 49								16 24							16 49	
	d		16 01						16 23	16 29	16 31					16 47		17 01	
Cholsey	d		16 07								16 37							17 07	
Goring & Streatley	d		16 12								16 42							17 12	
Pangbourne	d		16 17								16 47							17 17	
Tilehurst	d		16 21								16 51							17 21	
Bedwyn	d					15 39													
Hungerford	d					15 44													
Kintbury	d					15 49													
Newbury	a					15 56													
	d					15 56							16 13						
Newbury Racecourse	d												16 15						
Thatcham	d					16 01							16 20						
Midgham	d												16 24						
Aldermaston	d												16 28						
Theale	d					16 09							16 33						
Reading West	d	←						←					16 40		←		←		
Reading 7	a	15 59	16 27	16 09		16 20	16 25	16 27	16 38	16 44	16 56	16 40	16 44	16 55	16 56	17 00	16 56	17 27	17 08
	d	16 03	16 33			16 21	16 26	16 33	16 40	16 46	17 03			16 56	17 03	17 02	17 03	17 32	
Twyford 3	a	16 09	→					16 39			→				→		17 09	→	
Maidenhead 3	a	16 17						16 47									17 17		
Slough 3	a	16 24					16 40	16 54						17 10			17 24		
Ealing Broadway ⊖	a	16 49						17 19									17 49		
London Paddington 15 ⊖	a	17 01				16 52	16 59	17 31	17 07	17 14				17 29		17 32	18 01		

Station		CH	GW	GW	GW	GW	GW	XC	GW	GW	GW	GW	GW	XC	GW	GW	GW	GW	GW
			◇1 ⊡	◇1	1	◇1 ⊡	1	◇1 ⊼	1	◇1 ⊡	◇1 ⊡	1	1	◇1 ⊼	1	1	◇1	1	◇1 ⊡
Birmingham New Street 12	d							16 04						16 33					
Birmingham International	d							16 14											
Coventry	d							16 25											
Leamington Spa 8	d							16 38						17 00					
Banbury	d							16 55						17 19	17 23				
Kings Sutton	d														17 29				
Heyford	d														17 38				
Tackley	d														17 42				
Bicester Town	d	16 30																	
Islip	d	16 41																	
Oxford	a	16 56						17 14						17 41	17 53				
	d			17 01			17 07	17 16		17 31			17 37	17 43			18 01		
Radley	d						17 13												
Culham	d						17 17												
Appleford	d																		
Didcot Parkway	a						17 24						17 49						
	d					17 29	17 31				17 47		18 01						18 23
Cholsey	d						17 37						18 07						
Goring & Streatley	d						17 42						18 12						
Pangbourne	d						17 47						18 17						
Tilehurst	d						17 51						18 21						
Bedwyn	d		16 35						16 56							17 39			
Hungerford	d		16 43						17 00							17 44			
Kintbury	d								17 05							17 49			
Newbury	a		16 52						17 13							17 56			
	d		16 54						17 13							17 56			
Newbury Racecourse	d								17 15										
Thatcham	d		17 00						17 20							18 01			
Midgham	d								17 24										
Aldermaston	d								17 28										
Theale	d		17 08						17 33							18 09			
Reading West	d				←				17 40			←						←	
Reading 7	a		17 20	17 25	17 27	17 43	17 56	17 39	17 44	17 56	17 58	17 56	18 27	18 08		18 20	18 25	18 27	18 38
	d		17 21	17 26	17 32	17 44	18 03			17 58	18 01	18 03	18 32			18 21	18 25	18 32	18 40
Twyford 3	a				17 39		→					18 09	→					18 39	
Maidenhead 3	a				17 47							18 17						18 47	
Slough 3	a			17 40	17 54					18 11		18 24					18 40	18 54	
Ealing Broadway ⊖	a				18 19							18 49						19 19	
London Paddington 15 ⊖	a		17 51	17 59	18 31	18 14				18 29	18 32	19 01				18 52	18 59	19 31	19 08

For complete service between Banbury and Leamington (Birmingham), please refer to table 71

Table 116R

Saturdays

14 December to 28 December

Birmingham, Banbury, Bicester, Oxford and Bedwyn - Reading and London

Network Diagram - refer to first Page of Table 116

Station		GW	GW	XC	CH	GW	GW	GW	GW	GW	GW	XC	GW	GW	GW	GW	GW	XC	GW
		◇1 ☕	1	◇1 🛒		1	◇1 🛒	1	◇1 ☕	1	1	◇1 🛒	1	◇1	1	◇1 ☕	1	◇1 🛒	1
Birmingham New Street 12	d			17 04								17 33						18 04	
Birmingham International	d			17 14														18 14	
Coventry	d			17 25														18 25	
Leamington Spa 8	d			17 38								18 02						18 38	
Banbury	d			17 55								18 19						18 55	
Kings Sutton	d																		
Heyford	d																		
Tackley	d																		
Bicester Town	d				18 04														
Islip	d				18 15														
Oxford	a			18 14	18 30							18 40						19 14	
	d		18 07	18 16			18 31				18 37	18 43		19 01			19 07	19 16	
Radley	d		18 13														19 13		
Culham	d																19 17		
Appleford	d		18 17																
Didcot Parkway	a		18 24								18 49						19 24		
	d	18 29	18 31						18 47		19 01					19 29	19 31		
Cholsey	d		18 37								19 07						19 37		
Goring & Streatley	d		18 42								19 12						19 42		
Pangbourne	d		18 47								19 17						19 47		
Tilehurst	d		18 51								19 21						19 51		
Bedwyn	d												18 41						
Hungerford	d												18 46						
Kintbury	d												18 51						
Newbury	a												18 58						
	d					18 13							18 58						19 13
Newbury Racecourse	d					18 15													19 15
Thatcham	d					18 20							19 03						19 20
Midgham	d					18 24													19 24
Aldermaston	d					18 28													19 28
Theale	d					18 33							19 11						19 33
Reading West	d					18 40		←		←					←				19 40
Reading 7	a	18 44	18 56	18 40		18 44	18 55	18 56	19 00	18 56	19 27	19 08	19 19	19 25	19 27	19 46	19 57	19 39	19 44
	d	18 46	19 03				18 56	19 03	19 02	19 03	19 33		19 21	19 25	19 33	19 47	20 02		
Twyford 3	a		→					→		19 09	→				19 39		→		
Maidenhead 3	a									19 17					19 47				
Slough 3	a						19 10			19 24				19 40	19 54				
Ealing Broadway ⊖	a									19 49					20 19				
London Paddington 15 ⊖	a	19 13					19 29		19 32	20 01			19 52	19 59	20 31	20 14			

Station		GW	GW	GW	GW	GW	GW	XC	CH	GW	GW	GW	GW	GW	GW	XC	GW	GW	GW
		◇1 🛒	1	1	◇1 ☕	◇1 ☕	1	◇1 🛒		◇1	1	1	◇1 ☕	◇1 ☕	1	◇1 🛒	◇1	1	◇1 ☕
Birmingham New Street 12	d							18 33								19 04			
Birmingham International	d															19 14			
Coventry	d															19 25			
Leamington Spa 8	d							19 00								19 38			
Banbury	d			19 02				19 19								19 55			
Kings Sutton	d			19 08															
Heyford	d			19 17															
Tackley	d			19 21															
Bicester Town	d								19 17										
Islip	d								19 28										
Oxford	a			19 32				19 40	19 43							20 14			
	d	19 31					19 37	19 43		20 01					20 07	20 16	20 31		
Radley	d														20 13				
Culham	d																		
Appleford	d														20 17				
Didcot Parkway	a						19 49								20 24				
	d				19 47		20 01						20 24	20 29	20 31				20 47
Cholsey	d						20 07								20 37				
Goring & Streatley	d						20 12								20 42				
Pangbourne	d						20 17								20 47				
Tilehurst	d						20 21								20 51				
Bedwyn	d											19 41							
Hungerford	d											19 47							
Kintbury	d											19 51							
Newbury	a											19 58							
	d					19 46						19 58							
Newbury Racecourse	d											20 00							
Thatcham	d											20 05							
Midgham	d											20 10							
Aldermaston	d											20 13							
Theale	d											20 18							
Reading West	d		←								←	20 25						←	
Reading 7	a	19 55	19 57		20 00	20 07	20 27	20 08		20 25	20 27	20 28	20 38	20 44	20 57	20 40	20 55	20 57	21 06
	d	19 55	20 02		20 03	20 09	20 33			20 25	20 33		20 40	20 46	21 03		20 56	21 03	21 08
Twyford 3	a		20 09				→				20 39				→			21 09	
Maidenhead 3	a		20 17								20 47							21 19	
Slough 3	a	20 10	20 24							20 40	20 54						21 10	21 27	
Ealing Broadway ⊖	a		20 49								21 19							21 52	
London Paddington 15 ⊖	a	20 29	21 01		20 32	20 37				20 59	21 31		21 07	21 14			21 29	22 02	21 37

For complete service between Banbury and Leamington (Birmingham), please refer to table 71

Table 116R

Saturdays

14 December to 28 December

Birmingham, Banbury, Bicester, Oxford and Bedwyn - Reading and London

Network Diagram - refer to first Page of Table 116

		GW	XC	CH	GW	GW	GW	GW	XC	GW	GW	GW	XC	GW	GW	GW	CH	XC	GW	GW	GW	GW	GW	GW	GW	GW	CH
		■1	◇■1		◇■1	■1	■1	■1	◇■1	◇■1	◇■1	◇■1	◇■1	■1	◇■1	■1		◇■1	■1	■1	◇■1	◇■1	◇■1	◇■1	■1	■1	
			trolley						trolley	☕		☕	trolley								☕			☕			
Birmingham New Street 12	d		19 33						20 04				20 33					21 04									
Birmingham International	d								20 14									21 14									
Coventry	d								20 25									21 25									
Leamington Spa 8	d		20 03						20 38				21 00					21 38									
Banbury	d		20 20				20 38		20 55				21 20					21 55	22 00								
Kings Sutton	d						20 44												22 06								
Heyford	d						20 53												22 15								
Tackley	d						20 57												22 19								
Bicester Town	d			20 28													21 37										22 55
Islip	d			20 39													21 48										23 06
Oxford	a		20 40	20 54			21 08		21 14				21 41				22 03	22 16	22 30								23 21
	d	20 37	20 43		21 01				21 16		21 31		21 43	21 50	22 01			22 18				22 35	23 01			23 07	
Radley	d													21 56												23 13	
Culham	d																									23 17	
Appleford	d																									23 20	
Didcot Parkway	a	20 49									21 43			22 04	22 12							22 47	23 13			23 25	
	d	21 01								21 34	21 45	21 47		22 04	22 13						22 49	22 51	23 13	23 30		23 36	
Cholsey	d	21 07												22 10												23 42	
Goring & Streatley	d	21 12												22 15												23 47	
Pangbourne	d	21 17												22 21													
Tilehurst	d	21 21												22 24												23 56	
Bedwyn	d							20 48												22 00					23 00		
Hungerford	d							20 54												22 06					23 06		
Kintbury	d							20 58												22 10					23 10		
Newbury	a							21 05												22 17					23 17		
	d							21 05												22 17					23 17		
Newbury Racecourse	d							21 08												22 19					23 19		
Thatcham	d							21 13												22 24					23 24		
Midgham	d							21 17												22 29					23 29		
Aldermaston	d							21 21												22 32					23 32		
Theale	d							21 26												22 37					23 37		
Reading West	d					←		21 33								←				22 44					23 44		
Reading 7	a	21 27	21 08		21 27	21 27		21 36	21 38	21 48	21 59	22 02	22 08	22 31	22 31	22 31		22 41		22 48	23 04	23 08	23 30	23 46	23 48	00 03	
	d	21 33			21 27	21 33				21 50	22 02	22 06		22 33	22 31	22 33					23 05	23 09	23 31	23 47		00 04	
Twyford 8	a	→				21 39								→		22 39										00 11	
Maidenhead 8	a					21 47										22 47										00 19	
Slough 8	a				21 42	21 58					22 15				22 46	22 58						23 27	23 49			00 30	
Ealing Broadway ⊖	a					22 23										23 23										00 54	
London Paddington 15 ⊖	a				22 01	22 32				22 16	22 38	22 40			23 08	23 32					23 37	23 45	00 17	00 33		01 05	

For complete service between Banbury and Leamington (Birmingham), please refer to table 71

Table 116R

Saturdays

4 January to 8 February

Birmingham, Banbury, Bicester, Oxford and Bedwyn - Reading and London

Network Diagram - refer to first Page of Table 116

		GW	GW	GW	GW	GW	GW	GW	GW	GW	GW	GW	GW	GW	GW	GW	GW	GW	XC
		◇1	1	1	1	1	◇1 bike	1	1	◇1	◇1 bike	1	1	◇1	1	◇1 bike	◇1 bike	1	◇1 trolley
Birmingham New Street 12	d																		06 04
Birmingham International	d																		06 14
Coventry	d																		06 25
Leamington Spa 8	d																		06 38
Banbury	d																		06 55
Kings Sutton	d																		
Heyford	d																		
Tackley	d		00 03																
Bicester Town	d																		
Islip	d																		
Oxford	a		00 14																07 14
	d	00 07	00 27	03 59	05 09	05 49			06 07	06 31			06 42	07 01				07 07	07 16
Radley	d		00 33		05 15				06 13									07 13	
Culham	d				05 19													07 17	
Appleford	d								06 17										
Didcot Parkway	a	00 20	00 42	04 10	05 26	06 01			06 24				06 54					07 24	
	d	00 21	00 46	04 10	05 31	06 01	06 29		06 31		06 59		07 01			07 17	07 29	07 31	
Cholsey	d		00 52		05 37	06 07			06 37				07 07					07 37	
Goring & Streatley	d		00 57		05 42	06 12			06 42				07 12					07 42	
Pangbourne	d		01 01		05 47	06 17			06 47				07 17					07 47	
Tilehurst	d		01 06		05 51	06 21			06 51				07 21					07 51	
Bedwyn	d							06 05				06 39							
Hungerford	d							06 11				06 43							
Kintbury	d							06 15				06 48							
Newbury	a							06 22				06 55							
	d							06 22				06 55							
Newbury Racecourse	d							06 24											
Thatcham	d							06 29				07 00							
Midgham	d							06 34											
Aldermaston	d							06 37											
Theale	d							06 42				07 08							
Reading West	d							06 49							←				
Reading 7	a	00 41	01 13	04 29	05 57	06 28	06 43	06 53	06 58	06 58	07 14	07 21	07 27	07 27	07 27	07 31	07 44	07 58	07 39
	d	00 43	01 17	04 40	05 59	06 33	06 45		06 59	07 03	07 15		07 29	07 27	07 29	07 32	07 46	07 59	
Twyford 3	a		01 23	04 46	06 05	06 39			07 05				→		07 35			→	
Maidenhead 3	a		01 31	04 54	06 13	06 47			07 13						07 43				
Slough 3	a	00 59	01 39	05 02	06 24	07 01			07 24	07 18				07 46	07 54				
Ealing Broadway ⊖	a		01 55	05 19	06 49	07 26			07 49						08 19				
London Paddington 15 ⊖	a	01 21	02 07	05 31	07 01	07 36	07 22		08 01	07 44	07 53			08 10	08 31	08 14	08 30		

		GW	GW	GW	GW	GW	GW	GW	XC	GW	GW	GW	CH	GW	GW	XC	GW	GW	GW
		1	◇1 trolley	1	1	◇1 bike	◇1 bike	1	◇1	1	◇1	1		◇1 bike	1	◇1 trolley	1	◇1 bike	◇1 bike
Birmingham New Street 12	d								06 33							07 04			
Birmingham International	d															07 14			
Coventry	d															07 25			
Leamington Spa 8	d								07 00							07 38			
Banbury	d				07 03				07 19							07 55			
Kings Sutton	d				07 08														
Heyford	d				07 17														
Tackley	d				07 21														
Bicester Town	d												07 36						
Islip	d												07 47						
Oxford	a				07 32				07 40				08 02			08 14			
	d		07 31					07 37	07 43		08 01				08 07	08 16			
Radley	d														08 13				
Culham	d																		
Appleford	d														08 17				
Didcot Parkway	a							07 49							08 24				
	d					07 47	07 59	08 01						08 17	08 27			08 29	
Cholsey	d							08 07							08 33				
Goring & Streatley	d							08 12							08 38				
Pangbourne	d							08 17							08 43				
Tilehurst	d							08 21							08 47				
Bedwyn	d									07 39									
Hungerford	d									07 44									
Kintbury	d									07 49									
Newbury	a									07 56									
	d	07 13								07 56							08 13		08 34
Newbury Racecourse	d	07 15															08 15		
Thatcham	d	07 20								08 01							08 20		
Midgham	d	07 24															08 24		
Aldermaston	d	07 28															08 28		
Theale	d	07 33								08 09							08 33		
Reading West	d	07 42		←								←					08 40		
Reading 7	a	07 45	07 55	07 58		08 00	08 15	08 28	08 06	08 20	08 24	08 28		08 36	08 54	08 39	08 44	08 44	08 53
	d		07 55	07 59		08 02	08 17	08 29			08 24	08 29		08 36	08 59			08 46	08 54
Twyford 3	a			08 05				→				08 35			→				
Maidenhead 3	a			08 13								08 43							
Slough 3	a		08 11	08 24							08 40	08 54							
Ealing Broadway ⊖	a			08 49								09 19							
London Paddington 15 ⊖	a		08 39	09 01		08 43	08 53				09 07	09 31		09 15				09 26	09 31

For complete service between Banbury and Leamington (Birmingham), please refer to table 71

Table 116R

Saturdays

4 January to 8 February

Birmingham, Banbury, Bicester, Oxford and Bedwyn - Reading and London

Network Diagram - refer to first Page of Table 116

		GW	GW	GW	GW	GW	GW	XC	GW	GW
		1	◇1	1	◇1	◇1	1	◇1	1	◇1
			☕		☕	☕		🛒		🛒
Birmingham New Street 12	d							07 33		
Birmingham International	d									
Coventry	d									
Leamington Spa 8	d							08 00		
Banbury	d							08 19		
Kings Sutton	d									
Heyford	d									
Tackley	d									
Bicester Town	d									
Islip	d									
Oxford	a							08 40		
	d		08 31				08 37	08 43		09 01
Radley	d									
Culham	d									
Appleford	d									
Didcot Parkway	a						08 49			
	d				08 47	09 00	09 01			
Cholsey	d						09 07			
Goring & Streatley	d						09 12			
Pangbourne	d						09 17			
Tilehurst	d						09 21			
Bedwyn	d								08 38	
Hungerford	d								08 43	
Kintbury	d								08 48	
Newbury	a								08 57	
	d								08 57	
Newbury Racecourse	d									
Thatcham	d								09 02	
Midgham	d									
Aldermaston	d									
Theale	d								09 10	
Reading West	d	←		←						
Reading 7	a	08 54	08 57	08 54	09 01	09 14	09 28	09 07	09 20	09 24
	d	08 59	08 57	08 59	09 02	09 16	09 33			09 24
Twyford 3	a	→		09 05			→			
Maidenhead 3	a			09 13						
Slough 3	a		09 13	09 24						09 41
Ealing Broadway ⊖	a			09 49						
London Paddington 15 ⊖	a		09 39	10 01	09 42	09 54				10 07

		GW	GW	GW	GW	GW	CH	XC	GW	GW
		1	◇1	1	◇1	1		◇1	◇1	1
			A						A	
			☕⊘		☕			🛒	☕⊘	
Birmingham New Street 12	d							08 04		
Birmingham International	d							08 14		
Coventry	d							08 25		
Leamington Spa 8	d							08 38		
Banbury	d							08 55		
Kings Sutton	d									
Heyford	d									
Tackley	d									
Bicester Town	d						08 45			
Islip	d						08 56			
Oxford	a						09 11	09 14		
	d					09 07		09 16	09 31	
Radley	d					09 13				
Culham	d					09 17				
Appleford	d									
Didcot Parkway	a					09 24				
	d		09 17		09 29	09 31				
Cholsey	d					09 37				
Goring & Streatley	d					09 42				
Pangbourne	d					09 47				
Tilehurst	d					09 51				
Bedwyn	d									
Hungerford	d									
Kintbury	d									
Newbury	a									
	d			09 03						
Newbury Racecourse	d			09 06						
Thatcham	d			09 11						
Midgham	d			09 16						
Aldermaston	d			09 19						
Theale	d			09 24						
Reading West	d	←		09 31						←
Reading 7	a	09 28	09 31	09 35	09 47	09 57		09 39	09 54	09 57
	d	09 33	09 33		09 49	09 59			09 55	09 59
Twyford 3	a	09 39				→				10 05
Maidenhead 3	a	09 47								10 13
Slough 3	a	10 00							10 10	10 24
Ealing Broadway ⊖	a	10 25								10 49
London Paddington 15 ⊖	a	10 34	10 13		10 29				10 39	11 01

		GW	GW	GW	XC	GW	GW	GW	GW	GW
		1	◇1	1	◇1	1	◇1	1	◇1	◇1
			A							
			☕⊘		🛒		🛒		☕	☕
Birmingham New Street 12	d				08 33					
Birmingham International	d									
Coventry	d									
Leamington Spa 8	d				09 00					
Banbury	d	09 02			09 19					
Kings Sutton	d	09 08								
Heyford	d	09 17								
Tackley	d	09 21								
Bicester Town	d									
Islip	d									
Oxford	a	09 32			09 40					
	d			09 37	09 43		10 01			
Radley	d									
Culham	d									
Appleford	d									
Didcot Parkway	a			09 49						
	d		09 47	10 00					10 17	10 22
Cholsey	d			10 06						
Goring & Streatley	d			10 11						
Pangbourne	d			10 16						
Tilehurst	d			10 20						
Bedwyn	d					09 39				
Hungerford	d					09 44				
Kintbury	d					09 49				
Newbury	a					09 56				
	d					09 56				
Newbury Racecourse	d									
Thatcham	d					10 01				
Midgham	d									
Aldermaston	d									
Theale	d					10 09				
Reading West	d							←		
Reading 7	a		10 00	10 27	10 06	10 21	10 28	10 27	10 31	10 34
	d		10 02	10 32			10 28	10 32	10 33	10 36
Twyford 3	a			→				10 38		
Maidenhead 3	a							10 46		
Slough 3	a						10 45	10 57		
Ealing Broadway ⊖	a							11 22		
London Paddington 15 ⊖	a		10 43				11 09	11 32	11 12	11 21

		GW	GW	XC	CH	GW	GW	GW	GW	GW
		◇1	1	◇1		1	◇1	1	◇1	1
		☕		🛒			☕		☕	
Birmingham New Street 12	d			09 04						
Birmingham International	d			09 14						
Coventry	d			09 25						
Leamington Spa 8	d			09 38						
Banbury	d			09 55						
Kings Sutton	d									
Heyford	d									
Tackley	d									
Bicester Town	d				09 57					
Islip	d				10 08					
Oxford	a			10 14	10 23					
	d		10 07	10 16			10 32			10 37
Radley	d		10 13							
Culham	d									
Appleford	d		10 17							
Didcot Parkway	a		10 23							10 49
	d	10 29	10 31						10 47	11 01
Cholsey	d		10 37							11 07
Goring & Streatley	d		10 42							11 12
Pangbourne	d		10 47							11 17
Tilehurst	d		10 51							11 21
Bedwyn	d									
Hungerford	d									
Kintbury	d									
Newbury	a									
	d					10 13				
Newbury Racecourse	d					10 15				
Thatcham	d					10 20				
Midgham	d					10 24				
Aldermaston	d					10 28				
Theale	d					10 33				
Reading West	d					10 40		←		
Reading 7	a	10 46	10 57	10 41		10 44	10 56	10 57	11 01	11 27
	d	10 47	10 59				10 58	10 59	11 02	11 29
Twyford 3	a		→					11 05		→
Maidenhead 3	a							11 13		
Slough 3	a						11 15	11 24		
Ealing Broadway ⊖	a							11 49		
London Paddington 15 ⊖	a	11 26					11 40	12 01	11 43	

A ☕ from Reading ⊘ to Reading

For complete service between Banbury and Leamington (Birmingham), please refer to table 71

Table 116R

Saturdays

4 January to 8 February

Birmingham, Banbury, Bicester, Oxford and Bedwyn - Reading and London

Network Diagram - refer to first Page of Table 116

		XC	GW	GW	GW	GW	GW	XC	GW	GW	GW	GW	GW	GW	XC	CH	GW	GW	GW
		◇1	1	◇1	1	◇1	1	◇1	1	◇1	1	1	◇1	1	◇1		1	◇1	1
Birmingham New Street 12	d	09 33						10 04							10 33				
Birmingham International	d							10 14											
Coventry	d							10 25											
Leamington Spa 8	d	10 00						10 38							11 00				
Banbury	d	10 19						10 55				11 02			11 19				
Kings Sutton	d											11 08							
Heyford	d											11 17							
Tackley	d											11 21							
Bicester Town	d															11 30			
Islip	d															11 41			
Oxford	a	10 40						11 14				11 32			11 40	11 56			
	d	10 43		11 01			11 07	11 16		11 30				11 37	11 43			12 01	
Radley	d						11 13												
Culham	d																		
Appleford	d																		
Didcot Parkway	a						11 24							11 49					
	d					11 29	11 31						11 47	12 01					
Cholsey	d						11 37							12 07					
Goring & Streatley	d						11 42							12 12					
Pangbourne	d						11 47							12 17					
Tilehurst	d						11 51							12 21					
Bedwyn	d		10 39														11 39		
Hungerford	d		10 45														11 44		
Kintbury	d		10 49														11 49		
Newbury	a		10 56														11 56		
	d		10 56						11 13								11 56		
Newbury Racecourse	d								11 15										
Thatcham	d		11 01						11 20								12 01		
Midgham	d								11 24										
Aldermaston	d								11 28										
Theale	d		11 09						11 33								12 09		
Reading West	d				←				11 40		←								←
Reading 7	a	11 11	11 20	11 26	11 27	11 43	11 56	11 39	11 44	11 57	11 56		12 01	12 27	12 07		12 21	12 26	12 27
	d			11 27	11 29	11 45	11 59			11 58	11 59		12 03	12 29				12 27	12 29
Twyford 3	a				11 35		→				12 05			→					12 35
Maidenhead 3	a				11 43						12 13								12 43
Slough 3	a			11 42	11 54					12 13	12 24							12 42	12 55
Ealing Broadway ⊖	a				12 19						12 49								13 20
London Paddington 15 ⊖	a			12 07	12 31	12 26				12 40	13 01		12 43					13 07	13 32

		GW	GW	XC	GW	GW	GW	GW	GW	XC	GW	GW	GW	GW	XC	CH	GW	GW	GW
		◇1	1	◇1	1	◇1	1	◇1	1	◇1	◇1	1	◇1	1	◇1		1	1	◇1
Birmingham New Street 12	d			11 04						11 33					12 04				
Birmingham International	d			11 14											12 14				
Coventry	d			11 25											12 25				
Leamington Spa 8	d			11 38						12 00					12 38				
Banbury	d			11 55						12 19					12 55				
Kings Sutton	d																		
Heyford	d																		
Tackley	d																		
Bicester Town	d															13 00			
Islip	d															13 11			
Oxford	a			12 14						12 40					13 14	13 26			
	d		12 07	12 16		12 31			12 37	12 43	13 01			13 07	13 16				13 31
Radley	d		12 13											13 13					
Culham	d													13 17					
Appleford	d		12 17																
Didcot Parkway	a		12 24						12 51					13 24					
	d	12 29	12 31					12 47	13 01				13 29	13 31					
Cholsey	d		12 37						13 07					13 37					
Goring & Streatley	d		12 42						13 12					13 42					
Pangbourne	d		12 47						13 17					13 47					
Tilehurst	d		12 51						13 21					13 51					
Bedwyn	d																	13 07	
Hungerford	d																	13 13	
Kintbury	d																	13 17	
Newbury	a																	13 24	
	d				12 13												13 13	13 28	
Newbury Racecourse	d				12 15												13 15		
Thatcham	d				12 20												13 20	13 33	
Midgham	d				12 24												13 24		
Aldermaston	d				12 28												13 28		
Theale	d				12 33												13 33	13 41	
Reading West	d				12 40		←					←					13 40		
Reading 7	a	12 45	12 56	12 40	12 44	12 56	12 56	13 01	13 27	13 07	13 26	13 27	13 44	13 59	13 39		13 44	13 54	13 54
	d	12 47	12 59			12 57	12 59	13 04	13 29		13 27	13 29	13 45	13 59					13 55
Twyford 3	a		→				13 05		→			13 35		→					
Maidenhead 3	a						13 13					13 43							
Slough 3	a					13 12	13 24				13 42	13 54							14 10
Ealing Broadway ⊖	a						13 49					14 19							
London Paddington 15 ⊖	a	13 26				13 39	14 01	13 42			14 07	14 31	14 26						14 39

For complete service between Banbury and Leamington (Birmingham), please refer to table 71

Table 116R

Saturdays

4 January to 8 February

Birmingham, Banbury, Bicester, Oxford and Bedwyn - Reading and London

Network Diagram - refer to first Page of Table 116

		GW	GW	GW	GW	XC	GW	GW	GW	GW	GW	XC	GW	GW	GW	GW	GW	XC	CH
		1	1	◇1	1	◇1	◇1	◇1	1	◇1	1	◇1	1	◇1	1	◇1	1	◇1	
				☕		🛒	☕	🛒		☕		🛒		☕		☕		🛒	
Birmingham New Street 12	d					12 33						13 04						13 33	
Birmingham International	d											13 14							
Coventry	d											13 25							
Leamington Spa 8	d					13 02						13 38						14 00	
Banbury	d		13 02			13 21						13 55						14 18	
Kings Sutton	d		13 08																
Heyford	d		13 17																
Tackley	d		13 21																
Bicester Town	d																		14 18
Islip	d																		14 29
Oxford	a		13 32			13 40						14 14						14 40	14 44
	d				13 37	13 43		14 01			14 07	14 16		14 31			14 37	14 43	
Radley	d										14 13								
Culham	d																		
Appleford	d										14 17								
Didcot Parkway	a				13 51						14 24						14 49		
	d			13 47	14 01					14 29	14 31					14 47	15 01		
Cholsey	d				14 07						14 37						15 07		
Goring & Streatley	d				14 12						14 42						15 12		
Pangbourne	d				14 17						14 47						15 17		
Tilehurst	d				14 21						14 51						15 21		
Bedwyn	d						13 33												
Hungerford	d						13 40												
Kintbury	d																		
Newbury	a						13 49												
	d						13 50						14 13						
Newbury Racecourse	d												14 15						
Thatcham	d						13 57						14 20						
Midgham	d												14 24						
Aldermaston	d												14 28						
Theale	d						14 06						14 33						
Reading West	d	←							←				14 40		←				
Reading 7	a	13 59		14 00	14 27	14 09	14 21	14 26	14 27	14 44	14 56	14 40	14 44	14 56	14 56	15 02	15 27	15 08	
	d	13 59		14 02	14 29		14 23	14 27	14 29	14 46	14 59			14 58	14 59	15 04	15 28		
Twyford 3	a	14 05			→				14 35		→				15 05		→		
Maidenhead 3	a	14 13							14 43						15 13				
Slough 3	a	14 29						14 42	14 54					15 14	15 24				
Ealing Broadway ⊖	a	14 54							15 19						15 49				
London Paddington 15 ⊖	a	15 05		14 42			14 59	15 07	15 31	15 26				15 39	16 01	15 42			

		GW	GW	GW	GW	GW	XC	GW	GW	GW	GW	GW	GW	XC	CH	GW	GW	GW	GW
		1	◇1	1	◇1	1	◇1	1	◇1	1	1	◇1	1	◇1		1	◇1	1	◇1
					☕		🛒		🛒			☕		🛒					☕
Birmingham New Street 12	d						14 04							14 33					
Birmingham International	d						14 14												
Coventry	d						14 25												
Leamington Spa 8	d						14 38							15 00					
Banbury	d						14 55				15 02			15 20					
Kings Sutton	d										15 08								
Heyford	d										15 17								
Tackley	d										15 21								
Bicester Town	d														15 28				
Islip	d														15 39				
Oxford	a						15 14				15 32			15 40	15 54				
	d		15 01			15 07	15 16		15 31				15 37	15 43			16 01		
Radley	d					15 13													
Culham	d					15 17													
Appleford	d																		
Didcot Parkway	a					15 24							15 49						
	d				15 29	15 31						15 47	16 01						16 29
Cholsey	d					15 37							16 07						
Goring & Streatley	d					15 42							16 12						
Pangbourne	d					15 47							16 17						
Tilehurst	d					15 51							16 21						
Bedwyn	d	14 39														15 39			
Hungerford	d	14 44														15 44			
Kintbury	d	14 49														15 49			
Newbury	a	14 56														15 56			
	d	14 56						15 13								15 56			
Newbury Racecourse	d							15 15											
Thatcham	d	15 01						15 20								16 01			
Midgham	d							15 24											
Aldermaston	d							15 28											
Theale	d	15 09						15 33								16 09			
Reading West	d			←				15 40		←								←	
Reading 7	a	15 24	15 25	15 27	15 44	15 59	15 39	15 44	15 54	15 59		16 00	16 27	16 09		16 21	16 25	16 27	16 44
	d		15 25	15 28	15 45	16 01			15 55	16 01		16 01	16 29				16 26	16 29	16 46
Twyford 3	a			15 35		→				16 07			→					16 35	
Maidenhead 3	a			15 43						16 15								16 43	
Slough 3	a		15 41	15 54					16 14	16 29							16 41	16 54	
Ealing Broadway ⊖	a			16 19						16 55								17 19	
London Paddington 15 ⊖	a		16 07	16 31	16 26				16 40	17 04		16 43					17 07	17 31	17 26

For complete service between Banbury and Leamington (Birmingham), please refer to table 71

Table 116R

Saturdays

4 January to 8 February

Birmingham, Banbury, Bicester, Oxford and Bedwyn - Reading and London

Network Diagram - refer to first Page of Table 116

Station		GW	XC	GW	GW	GW	GW	GW	XC	CH	GW	GW	GW	GW	GW	XC	GW	GW	GW
		1	◇1 🛒	1	◇1 🛒	1	◇1 ☕	1	◇1 🛒		◇1 ☕	◇1	1	◇1 ☕	1	◇1 🛒	1	◇1 ☕	1
Birmingham New Street 12	d		15 04						15 33							16 04			
Birmingham International	d		15 14													16 14			
Coventry	d		15 25													16 25			
Leamington Spa 8	d		15 38						16 02							16 38			
Banbury	d		15 55						16 22							16 55			
Kings Sutton	d																		
Heyford	d																		
Tackley	d																		
Bicester Town	d									16 30									
Islip	d									16 41									
Oxford	a		16 14						16 40	16 56						17 14			
	d	16 07	16 16		16 31			16 37	16 43			17 01			17 07	17 16		17 31	
Radley	d	16 13													17 13				
Culham	d														17 17				
Appleford	d	16 17																	
Didcot Parkway	a	16 24						16 49							17 24				
	d	16 31					16 47	17 01						17 29	17 31				
Cholsey	d	16 37						17 07							17 37				
Goring & Streatley	d	16 42						17 12							17 42				
Pangbourne	d	16 47						17 17							17 47				
Tilehurst	d	16 51						17 21							17 51				
Bedwyn	d										16 35						16 56		
Hungerford	d										16 43						17 00		
Kintbury	d																17 05		
Newbury	a										16 52						17 13		
	d			16 13							16 54						17 13		
Newbury Racecourse	d			16 15													17 15		
Thatcham	d			16 20							17 00						17 20		
Midgham	d			16 24													17 24		
Aldermaston	d			16 28													17 28		
Theale	d			16 33							17 08						17 33		
Reading West	d			16 40		←							←				17 40		←
Reading 7	a	16 56	16 40	16 44	16 55	16 56	17 00	17 27	17 08		17 20	17 25	17 27	17 43	17 56	17 39	17 44	17 56	17 56
	d	16 59			16 55	16 59	17 02	17 28			17 21	17 26	17 28	17 44	17 59			17 58	17 59
Twyford 3	a	→				17 05		→					17 35		→				18 05
Maidenhead 3	a					17 13							17 43						18 13
Slough 3	a				17 11	17 29						17 41	17 54					18 15	18 24
Ealing Broadway ⊖	a					17 54							18 19						18 49
London Paddington 15 ⊖	a				17 39	18 05	17 42				17 57	18 07	18 31	18 23				18 39	19 01

Station		GW	GW	XC	GW	GW	GW	GW	GW	GW	XC	CH	GW	GW	GW	GW	GW	XC	GW
		◇1 ☕	1	◇1 🛒	1	1	◇1	1	◇1 ☕	1	◇1 🛒		1	◇1 🛒	1	◇1 ☕	1	◇1 🛒	1
Birmingham New Street 12	d			16 33							17 04							17 33	
Birmingham International	d										17 14								
Coventry	d										17 25								
Leamington Spa 8	d			17 00							17 38							18 02	
Banbury	d			17 19	17 23						17 55							18 19	
Kings Sutton	d				17 29														
Heyford	d				17 38														
Tackley	d				17 42														
Bicester Town	d											18 04							
Islip	d											18 15							
Oxford	a			17 41	17 53						18 14	18 30						18 40	
	d		17 37	17 43			18 01			18 07	18 16			18 31			18 37	18 43	
Radley	d									18 13									
Culham	d																		
Appleford	d									18 17									
Didcot Parkway	a		17 49							18 24							18 49		
	d	17 47	18 01						18 29	18 31						18 47	19 01		
Cholsey	d		18 07							18 37							19 07		
Goring & Streatley	d		18 12							18 42							19 12		
Pangbourne	d		18 17							18 47							19 17		
Tilehurst	d		18 21							18 51							19 21		
Bedwyn	d					17 39													18 41
Hungerford	d					17 44													18 46
Kintbury	d					17 49													18 51
Newbury	a					17 56													18 58
	d					17 56							18 13						18 58
Newbury Racecourse	d												18 15						
Thatcham	d					18 01							18 20						19 03
Midgham	d												18 24						
Aldermaston	d												18 28						
Theale	d					18 09							18 33						19 11
Reading West	d							←					18 40		←				
Reading 7	a	17 58	18 27	18 08		18 21	18 25	18 27	18 44	18 56	18 40		18 44	18 55	18 56	19 00	19 27	19 08	19 22
	d	18 01	18 28				18 25	18 28	18 46	18 59				18 56	18 59	19 02	19 29		
Twyford 3	a		→					18 35		→					19 05		→		
Maidenhead 3	a							18 43							19 13				
Slough 3	a						18 41	18 54						19 11	19 29				
Ealing Broadway ⊖	a							19 19							19 54				
London Paddington 15 ⊖	a	18 42					19 07	19 31	19 26					19 38	20 05	19 41			

For complete service between Banbury and Leamington (Birmingham), please refer to table 71

Table 116R

Saturdays

4 January to 8 February

Birmingham, Banbury, Bicester, Oxford and Bedwyn - Reading and London

Network Diagram - refer to first Page of Table 116

		GW ◇1	GW 1	GW ◇1 ☕	GW 1	XC ◇1 🛒	GW 1	GW ◇1 🛒	GW 1	GW 1	GW ◇1 ☕	GW ◇1 ☕	GW 1	XC ◇1 🛒	CH	GW ◇1	GW 1	GW 1	GW ◇1 ☕
Birmingham New Street 12	d					18 04								18 33					
Birmingham International	d					18 14													
Coventry	d					18 25													
Leamington Spa 8	d					18 38								19 00					
Banbury	d					18 55				19 02				19 19					
Kings Sutton	d									19 08									
Heyford	d									19 17									
Tackley	d									19 21									
Bicester Town	d														19 17				
Islip	d														19 28				
Oxford	a					19 14				19 32				19 40	19 43				
	d	19 01			19 07	19 16		19 31					19 37	19 43		20 01			
Radley	d				19 13														
Culham	d				19 17														
Appleford	d																		
Didcot Parkway	a				19 24								19 49						
	d			19 29	19 31						19 47		20 01						20 29
Cholsey	d				19 37								20 07						
Goring & Streatley	d				19 42								20 12						
Pangbourne	d				19 47								20 17						
Tilehurst	d				19 51								20 21						
Bedwyn	d																	19 41	
Hungerford	d																	19 47	
Kintbury	d																	19 51	
Newbury	a																	19 58	
	d						19 13					19 46						19 58	
Newbury Racecourse	d						19 15											20 00	
Thatcham	d						19 20											20 05	
Midgham	d						19 24											20 10	
Aldermaston	d						19 28											20 13	
Theale	d						19 33											20 18	
Reading West	d		←				19 40		←								←	20 25	
Reading 7	a	19 25	19 27	19 46	19 57	19 39	19 44	19 55	19 57		20 00	20 07	20 27	20 08		20 25	20 27	20 28	20 44
	d	19 25	19 29	19 47	19 58			19 55	19 58		20 03	20 09	20 29			20 25	20 29		20 46
Twyford 3	a		19 35		→				20 05				→				20 35		
Maidenhead 3	a		19 43						20 13								20 43		
Slough 3	a	19 41	19 54					20 11	20 27							20 41	20 54		
Ealing Broadway ⊖	a		20 19						20 53								21 19		
London Paddington 15 ⊖	a	20 07	20 31	20 30				20 37	21 02		20 40	20 51				21 07	21 31		21 25

		GW 1	XC ◇1 🛒	GW ◇1	GW 1	GW ◇1 ☕	GW 1	XC ◇1 🛒	CH	GW ◇1	GW 1	GW 1	GW 1	XC ◇1 🛒	GW ◇1 ☕	GW ◇1	GW ◇1 ☕	XC ◇1 🛒	GW 1
Birmingham New Street 12	d		19 04					19 33						20 04				20 33	
Birmingham International	d		19 14											20 14					
Coventry	d		19 25											20 25					
Leamington Spa 8	d		19 38					20 03						20 38				21 00	
Banbury	d		19 55					20 20				20 38		20 55				21 20	
Kings Sutton	d											20 44							
Heyford	d											20 53							
Tackley	d											20 57							
Bicester Town	d								20 28										
Islip	d								20 39										
Oxford	a		20 14					20 40	20 54			21 08		21 14				21 41	
	d	20 07	20 16	20 31			20 37	20 43		21 01				21 16		21 31		21 43	21 50
Radley	d	20 13																	21 56
Culham	d																		
Appleford	d	20 17																	
Didcot Parkway	a	20 24					20 49									21 43			22 04
	d	20 31				20 47	21 01								21 34	21 45	21 47		22 04
Cholsey	d	20 37					21 07												22 10
Goring & Streatley	d	20 42					21 12												22 15
Pangbourne	d	20 47					21 17												22 21
Tilehurst	d	20 51					21 21												22 24
Bedwyn	d												20 48						
Hungerford	d												20 54						
Kintbury	d												20 58						
Newbury	a												21 05						
	d												21 05						
Newbury Racecourse	d												21 08						
Thatcham	d												21 13						
Midgham	d												21 17						
Aldermaston	d												21 21						
Theale	d												21 26						
Reading West	d				←						←		21 33						
Reading 7	a	20 57	20 40	20 55	20 57	21 06	21 27	21 08		21 27	21 27		21 36	21 38	21 48	21 59	22 02	22 08	22 31
	d	20 59		20 56	20 59	21 08	21 33			21 27	21 33				21 50	22 02	22 06		22 33
Twyford 3	a	→			21 05		→				21 39								→
Maidenhead 3	a				21 15						21 47								
Slough 3	a			21 13	21 27					21 43	21 58					22 17			
Ealing Broadway ⊖	a				21 53						22 23								
London Paddington 15 ⊖	a			21 38	22 03	21 51				22 07	22 32				22 26	22 42	22 45		

For complete service between Banbury and Leamington (Birmingham), please refer to table 71

Table 116R

Saturdays

4 January to 8 February

Birmingham, Banbury, Bicester, Oxford and Bedwyn - Reading and London

Network Diagram - refer to first Page of Table 116

		GW ◇1	GW 1	CH	XC ◇1	GW 1	GW 1	GW ◇1	GW ◇1	GW ◇1	GW 1	GW ◇1	GW 1	CH
Birmingham New Street 12	d				21 04									
Birmingham International	d				21 14									
Coventry	d				21 25									
Leamington Spa 8	d				21 38									
Banbury	d				21 55	22 00								
Kings Sutton	d					22 06								
Heyford	d					22 15								
Tackley	d					22 19								
Bicester Town	d			21 37										22 55
Islip	d			21 48										23 06
Oxford	a			22 03	22 16	22 30								23 21
	d	22 01			22 18				22 35	23 01			23 07	
Radley	d												23 13	
Culham	d												23 17	
Appleford	d												23 20	
Didcot Parkway	a	22 12							22 47	23 13			23 25	
	d	22 13						22 49	22 51	23 13		23 30	23 36	
Cholsey	d												23 42	
Goring & Streatley	d												23 47	
Pangbourne	d													
Tilehurst	d												23 56	
Bedwyn	d						22 00				23 00			
Hungerford	d						22 06				23 06			
Kintbury	d						22 10				23 10			
Newbury	a						22 17				23 17			
	d						22 17				23 17			
Newbury Racecourse	d						22 19				23 19			
Thatcham	d						22 24				23 24			
Midgham	d						22 29				23 29			
Aldermaston	d						22 32				23 32			
Theale	d						22 37				23 37			
Reading West	d		←				22 44				23 44			
Reading 7	a	22 31	22 31		22 47		22 48	23 11	23 14	23 37	23 48	23 53	00 06	
	d	22 31	22 33					23 12	23 15	23 38		23 54	00 08	
Twyford 3	a		22 39										00 14	
Maidenhead 3	a		22 47										00 22	
Slough 3	a	22 47	22 58						23 33	23 58			00 34	
Ealing Broadway ⊖	a		23 23										00 58	
London Paddington 15 ⊖	a	23 11	23 32					23 53	23 56	00 32		00 36	01 09	

For complete service between Banbury and Leamington (Birmingham), please refer to table 71

Table 116R

Saturdays

15 February to 22 March

Birmingham, Banbury, Bicester, Oxford and Bedwyn - Reading and London

Network Diagram - refer to first Page of Table 116

		GW	GW	GW	GW	GW	GW	GW	GW	GW	GW	GW	GW	GW	GW	GW	GW	GW	GW
		◇1	1	1	1	1	◇1 □P	1	1	◇1	1	◇1 □P	1	1	◇1	◇1 □P	1	◇1 □P	1
Birmingham New Street 12	d																		
Birmingham International	d																		
Coventry	d																		
Leamington Spa 8	d																		
Banbury	d																		
Kings Sutton	d																		
Heyford	d																		
Tackley	d		00 03																
Bicester Town	d																		
Islip	d																		
Oxford	a		00 14																
	d	00 07	00 27	03 59	05 14	05 49			06 07	06 31				06 42	07 01				07 07
Radley	d		00 33		05 20				06 13										07 13
Culham	d				05 24														07 17
Appleford	d								06 17										
Didcot Parkway	a	00 20	00 42	04 10	05 31	06 01			06 24					06 54					07 24
	d	00 21	00 46	04 10	05 31	06 01	06 29		06 31			06 59		07 01		07 17		07 29	07 31
Cholsey	d		00 52		05 37	06 07			06 37					07 07					07 37
Goring & Streatley	d		00 57		05 42	06 12			06 42					07 12					07 42
Pangbourne	d		01 01		05 47	06 17			06 47					07 17					07 47
Tilehurst	d		01 06		05 51	06 21			06 51					07 21					07 51
Bedwyn	d							06 05					06 39						
Hungerford	d							06 11					06 43						
Kintbury	d							06 15					06 48						
Newbury	a							06 22					06 55						
	d							06 22					06 55						
Newbury Racecourse	d							06 24											
Thatcham	d							06 29					07 00						
Midgham	d							06 34											
Aldermaston	d							06 37											
Theale	d							06 42					07 08						
Reading West	d							06 49			←						←		
Reading 7	a	00 41	01 13	04 29	05 57	06 27	06 43	06 52	06 58	06 57	06 58	07 14	07 20	07 27	07 27	07 31	07 27	07 44	07 58
	d	00 43	01 17	04 40	06 03	06 33	06 45	06 53	07 03	07 03	07 03	07 15	07 22	07 33	07 27	07 32	07 33	07 46	08 03
Twyford 3	a		01 23	04 46	06 09	06 39			→		07 09			→			07 39		→
Maidenhead 3	a		01 31	04 54	06 17	06 47					07 17						07 47		
Slough 3	a	00 59	01 39	05 02	06 24	06 54				07 17	07 24				07 42		07 54		
Ealing Broadway ⊖	a		01 55	05 19	06 49	07 19					07 49						08 19		
London Paddington 15 ⊖	a	01 21	02 07	05 31	07 01	07 31	07 14	07 22		07 37	08 01	07 44	07 54		08 01	08 07	08 31	08 14	

		XC	GW	GW	GW	GW	GW	GW	GW	GW	XC	GW	GW	GW	CH	GW	GW	GW	XC
		◇1 H	1	◇1 H	1	1	◇1 □P	1	◇1 □P	1	◇1	1	◇1	1		◇1 □P	◇1 □P	1	◇1 H
Birmingham New Street 12	d	06 04									06 33								07 04
Birmingham International	d	06 14																	07 14
Coventry	d	06 25																	07 25
Leamington Spa 8	d	06 38									07 00								07 38
Banbury	d	06 55				07 03					07 19								07 55
Kings Sutton	d					07 08													
Heyford	d					07 17													
Tackley	d					07 21													
Bicester Town	d														07 36				
Islip	d														07 47				
Oxford	a	07 14				07 32					07 40				08 02				08 14
	d	07 16		07 31						07 37	07 43		08 01					08 07	08 16
Radley	d																	08 13	
Culham	d																		
Appleford	d																	08 17	
Didcot Parkway	a									07 49								08 24	
	d						07 47		07 59	08 01						08 17	08 29	08 31	
Cholsey	d									08 07								08 37	
Goring & Streatley	d									08 12								08 42	
Pangbourne	d									08 17								08 47	
Tilehurst	d									08 21								08 51	
Bedwyn	d											07 39							
Hungerford	d											07 44							
Kintbury	d											07 49							
Newbury	a											07 56							
	d		07 13									07 56							
Newbury Racecourse	d		07 15																
Thatcham	d		07 20									08 01							
Midgham	d		07 24																
Aldermaston	d		07 28																
Theale	d		07 33									08 09							
Reading West	d		07 42		←			←						←					
Reading 7	a	07 39	07 45	07 55	07 58		08 00	07 58	08 15	08 28	08 06	08 21	08 25	08 28		08 33	08 44	08 55	08 39
	d			07 55	08 03		08 02	08 03	08 17	08 33		08 22	08 26	08 33		08 33	08 46	09 03	
Twyford 3	a				→			08 09		→				08 39				→	
Maidenhead 3	a							08 17						08 47					
Slough 3	a			08 10				08 24					08 40	08 54					
Ealing Broadway ⊖	a							08 49						09 19					
London Paddington 15 ⊖	a			08 29			08 32	09 01	08 44			08 54	08 59	09 31		09 02	09 14		

For complete service between Banbury and Leamington (Birmingham), please refer to table 71

Table 116R

Saturdays

15 February to 22 March

Birmingham, Banbury, Bicester, Oxford and Bedwyn - Reading and London

Network Diagram - refer to first Page of Table 116

		GW	GW	GW	GW	GW	GW	GW	GW	XC	GW	GW	GW
		1	◇1	◇1	◇1	1	◇1	◇1	1	◇1	1	◇1	1
			☕	☕	☕		☕	☕		🛒		🛒	
Birmingham New Street 12	d									07 33			
Birmingham International	d												
Coventry	d												
Leamington Spa 8	d									08 00			
Banbury	d									08 19			
Kings Sutton	d												
Heyford	d												
Tackley	d												
Bicester Town	d												
Islip	d												
Oxford	a									08 40			
	d			08 31					08 37	08 43		09 01	
Radley	d												
Culham	d												
Appleford	d												
Didcot Parkway	a								08 49				
	d				08 47		08 54	09 00	09 01				
Cholsey	d								09 07				
Goring & Streatley	d								09 12				
Pangbourne	d								09 17				
Tilehurst	d								09 21				
Bedwyn	d										08 38		
Hungerford	d										08 43		
Kintbury	d										08 48		
Newbury	a										08 57		
	d	08 13	08 34								08 57		
Newbury Racecourse	d	08 15											
Thatcham	d	08 20									09 02		
Midgham	d	08 24											
Aldermaston	d	08 28											
Theale	d	08 33									09 10		
Reading West	d	08 40				←							←
Reading 7	a	08 44	08 51	08 56	09 01	08 55	09 08	09 14	09 27	09 07	09 20	09 24	09 27
	d		08 52	08 56	09 02	09 03	09 10	09 16	09 33		09 21	09 24	09 33
Twyford 3	a					09 09			→				09 39
Maidenhead 3	a					09 17							09 47
Slough 3	a			09 10		09 24						09 40	09 54
Ealing Broadway ⊖	a					09 49							10 19
London Paddington 15 ⊖	a		09 21	09 29	09 38	10 01	09 41	09 44			09 52	09 59	10 31

		GW	GW	GW	GW	CH	XC	GW	GW	GW	GW	GW	GW
		◇1	1	◇1	1		◇1	◇1	1	1	◇1	1	1
		A ☕Ø		☕			🛒	A ☕Ø			A ☕Ø		
Birmingham New Street 12	d						08 04						
Birmingham International	d						08 14						
Coventry	d						08 25						
Leamington Spa 8	d						08 38						
Banbury	d						08 55			09 02			
Kings Sutton	d									09 08			
Heyford	d									09 17			
Tackley	d									09 21			
Bicester Town	d					08 45							
Islip	d					08 56							
Oxford	a					09 11	09 14			09 32			
	d				09 07		09 16	09 31					09 37
Radley	d				09 13								
Culham	d				09 17								
Appleford	d												
Didcot Parkway	a				09 24								09 49
	d	09 17		09 29	09 31						09 47		10 01
Cholsey	d				09 37								10 07
Goring & Streatley	d				09 42								10 12
Pangbourne	d				09 47								10 17
Tilehurst	d				09 51								10 21
Bedwyn	d												
Hungerford	d												
Kintbury	d												
Newbury	a												
	d		09 03										
Newbury Racecourse	d		09 06										
Thatcham	d		09 11										
Midgham	d		09 16										
Aldermaston	d		09 19										
Theale	d		09 24										
Reading West	d		09 31						←			←	
Reading 7	a	09 31	09 35	09 47	09 57		09 39	09 54	09 57		10 00	09 57	10 27
	d	09 33		09 49	10 03			09 55	10 03		10 02	10 03	10 33
Twyford 3	a				→				→			10 09	→
Maidenhead 3	a											10 17	
Slough 3	a							10 09				10 24	
Ealing Broadway ⊖	a											10 49	
London Paddington 15 ⊖	a	10 02		10 15				10 29			10 32	11 01	

		XC	GW	GW	GW	GW	GW	GW	GW	XC	CH	GW	GW
		◇1	1	◇1	◇1	1	◇1	◇1	1	◇1		1	◇1
		🛒		🛒	☕		☕	☕		🛒			☕
Birmingham New Street 12	d	08 33								09 04			
Birmingham International	d									09 14			
Coventry	d									09 25			
Leamington Spa 8	d	09 00								09 38			
Banbury	d	09 19								09 55			
Kings Sutton	d												
Heyford	d												
Tackley	d												
Bicester Town	d										09 57		
Islip	d										10 08		
Oxford	a	09 40								10 14	10 23		
	d	09 43		10 01					10 07	10 16			10 32
Radley	d								10 13				
Culham	d												
Appleford	d								10 17				
Didcot Parkway	a								10 23				
	d				10 17		10 22	10 29	10 31				
Cholsey	d								10 37				
Goring & Streatley	d								10 42				
Pangbourne	d								10 47				
Tilehurst	d								10 51				
Bedwyn	d		09 39										
Hungerford	d		09 44										
Kintbury	d		09 49										
Newbury	a		09 56										
	d		09 56									10 13	
Newbury Racecourse	d											10 15	
Thatcham	d		10 01									10 20	
Midgham	d											10 24	
Aldermaston	d											10 28	
Theale	d		10 09									10 33	
Reading West	d					←						10 40	
Reading 7	a	10 06	10 21	10 28	10 30	10 27	10 34	10 46	10 58	10 41		10 44	10 56
	d		10 22	10 28	10 32	10 33	10 36	10 47	11 03				10 58
Twyford 3	a					10 39			→				
Maidenhead 3	a					10 47							
Slough 3	a			10 43		10 54							11 12
Ealing Broadway ⊖	a					11 19							
London Paddington 15 ⊖	a		10 52	11 02	11 04	11 31	11 08	11 14					11 30

A ☕ from Reading Ø to Reading

For complete service between Banbury and Leamington (Birmingham), please refer to table 71

Table 116R

Saturdays

15 February to 22 March

Birmingham, Banbury, Bicester, Oxford and Bedwyn - Reading and London

Network Diagram - refer to first Page of Table 116

		GW 1	GW ◇1 🛋	GW 1	GW 1	XC ◇1 🛒	GW 1	GW ◇1	GW 1	GW ◇1 🛋	GW 1	XC ◇1 🛒	GW 1	GW ◇1 🛒	GW 1	GW ◇1 🛋	GW 1	GW 1	XC ◇1 🛒
Birmingham New Street 12	d					09 33						10 04							10 33
Birmingham International	d											10 14							
Coventry	d											10 25							
Leamington Spa 8	d					10 00						10 38							11 00
Banbury	d					10 19						10 55			11 02				11 19
Kings Sutton	d														11 08				
Heyford	d														11 17				
Tackley	d														11 21				
Bicester Town	d																		
Islip	d																		
Oxford	a					10 40						11 14			11 32				11 40
	d				10 37	10 43		11 01			11 07	11 16		11 30				11 37	11 43
Radley	d										11 13								
Culham	d																		
Appleford	d																		
Didcot Parkway	a				10 49						11 24							11 49	
	d		10 47		11 01					11 29	11 31					11 47		12 01	
Cholsey	d				11 07						11 37							12 07	
Goring & Streatley	d				11 12						11 42							12 12	
Pangbourne	d				11 17						11 47							12 17	
Tilehurst	d				11 21						11 51							12 21	
Bedwyn	d						10 39												
Hungerford	d						10 45												
Kintbury	d						10 49												
Newbury	a						10 56												
	d						10 56						11 13						
Newbury Racecourse	d												11 15						
Thatcham	d						11 01						11 20						
Midgham	d												11 24						
Aldermaston	d												11 28						
Theale	d						11 09						11 33						
Reading West	d	←		←					←				11 40				←		
Reading 7	a	10 58	11 01	10 58	11 27	11 11	11 20	11 24	11 27	11 43	11 56	11 39	11 44	11 57		12 01	11 56	12 28	12 07
	d	11 03	11 02	11 03	11 33		11 21	11 25	11 33	11 45	12 03			11 58		12 03	12 03	12 33	
Twyford 3	a	→		11 09	→				11 39		→						12 09	→	
Maidenhead 3	a			11 17					11 47								12 17		
Slough 3	a			11 24				11 39	11 54					12 12			12 24		
Ealing Broadway ⊖	a			11 49					12 19								12 49		
London Paddington 15 ⊖	a		11 33	12 01			11 52	11 59	12 31	12 14				12 32		12 37	13 01		

		CH	GW 1	GW ◇1 🛒	GW 1	GW ◇1 🛋	GW ◇1 🛋	GW 1	XC ◇1 🛒	GW 1	GW ◇1 🛒	GW 1	GW ◇1 🛋	GW 1	XC ◇1 🛒	GW ◇1 🛒	GW 1	GW ◇1 🛋	GW 1
Birmingham New Street 12	d								11 04						11 33				
Birmingham International	d								11 14										
Coventry	d								11 25										
Leamington Spa 8	d								11 38						12 00				
Banbury	d								11 55						12 19				
Kings Sutton	d																		
Heyford	d																		
Tackley	d																		
Bicester Town	d	11 30																	
Islip	d	11 41																	
Oxford	a	11 56							12 14						12 40				
	d			12 01				12 07	12 16		12 31			12 37	12 43	13 01			13 07
Radley	d							12 13											13 13
Culham	d																		13 17
Appleford	d							12 17											
Didcot Parkway	a							12 24						12 51					13 24
	d					12 23	12 29	12 31					12 47	13 01				13 29	13 31
Cholsey	d							12 37						13 07					13 37
Goring & Streatley	d							12 42						13 12					13 42
Pangbourne	d							12 47						13 17					13 47
Tilehurst	d							12 51						13 21					13 51
Bedwyn	d		11 39																
Hungerford	d		11 44																
Kintbury	d		11 49																
Newbury	a		11 56																
	d		11 56							12 13									
Newbury Racecourse	d									12 15									
Thatcham	d		12 01							12 20									
Midgham	d									12 24									
Aldermaston	d									12 28									
Theale	d		12 09							12 33									
Reading West	d				←					12 40		←					←		
Reading 7	a		12 21	12 26	12 28	12 38	12 45	12 56	12 40	12 44	12 56	12 56	13 01	13 27	13 07	13 26	13 27	13 44	13 59
	d		12 22	12 27	12 33	12 39	12 47	13 03			12 57	13 03	13 07	13 33		13 27	13 33	13 45	14 03
Twyford 3	a				12 39			→				13 09		→			13 39		→
Maidenhead 3	a				12 47							13 17					13 47		
Slough 3	a			12 41	12 54						13 11	13 24				13 41	13 54		
Ealing Broadway ⊖	a				13 19							13 49					14 19		
London Paddington 15 ⊖	a		12 53	12 59	13 31	13 06	13 15				13 32	14 01	13 38			13 59	14 31	14 14	

For complete service between Banbury and Leamington (Birmingham), please refer to table 71

Table 116R

Saturdays

15 February to 22 March

Birmingham, Banbury, Bicester, Oxford and Bedwyn - Reading and London

Network Diagram - refer to first Page of Table 116

		XC	CH	GW	GW	GW	GW	GW	GW	GW	GW	XC	GW	GW	GW	GW	GW	GW	XC
		◇1 trolley		1	1	◇1	1	1	◇1 buffet	1	1	◇1 trolley	◇1 buffet	◇1 trolley	1	◇1 buffet	◇1 buffet	1	◇1 trolley
Birmingham New Street 12	d	12 04										12 33							13 04
Birmingham International	d	12 14																	13 14
Coventry	d	12 25																	13 25
Leamington Spa 8	d	12 38										13 02							13 38
Banbury	d	12 55						13 02				13 21							13 55
Kings Sutton	d							13 08											
Heyford	d							13 17											
Tackley	d							13 21											
Bicester Town	d		13 00																
Islip	d		13 11																
Oxford	a	13 14	13 26					13 32				13 40							14 14
	d	13 16				13 31					13 37	13 43		14 01				14 07	14 16
Radley	d																	14 13	
Culham	d																		
Appleford	d																	14 17	
Didcot Parkway	a										13 51							14 24	
	d								13 47		14 01					14 24	14 29	14 31	
Cholsey	d										14 07							14 37	
Goring & Streatley	d										14 12							14 42	
Pangbourne	d										14 17							14 47	
Tilehurst	d										14 21							14 51	
Bedwyn	d				13 07								13 33						
Hungerford	d				13 13								13 40						
Kintbury	d				13 17														
Newbury	a				13 24								13 49						
	d			13 13	13 28								13 50						
Newbury Racecourse	d			13 15															
Thatcham	d			13 20	13 33								13 57						
Midgham	d			13 24															
Aldermaston	d			13 28															
Theale	d			13 33	13 41								14 06						
Reading West	d			13 40			←			←					←				
Reading 7	a	13 39		13 44	13 51	13 54	13 59		14 00	13 59	14 27	14 09	14 22	14 26	14 27	14 39	14 45	14 56	14 40
	d				13 51	13 56	14 03		14 02	14 03	14 33		14 23	14 27	14 33	14 41	14 47	15 03	
Twyford 3	a						→			14 09	→				14 39			→	
Maidenhead 3	a									14 17					14 47				
Slough 3	a					14 09				14 24				14 41	14 54				
Ealing Broadway ⊖	a									14 49					15 19				
London Paddington 15 ⊖	a				14 22	14 29			14 32	15 01			14 50	14 59	15 31	15 09	15 14		

		GW	GW	GW	GW	GW	XC	CH	GW	GW	GW	GW	GW	XC	GW	GW	GW	GW	GW
		1	◇1 buffet	1	◇1 buffet	1	◇1 trolley		1	◇1	1	◇1 buffet	1	◇1 trolley	1	◇1 trolley	1	1	◇1 buffet
Birmingham New Street 12	d						13 33							14 04					
Birmingham International	d													14 14					
Coventry	d													14 25					
Leamington Spa 8	d						14 00							14 38					
Banbury	d						14 18							14 55				15 02	
Kings Sutton	d																	15 08	
Heyford	d																	15 17	
Tackley	d																	15 21	
Bicester Town	d							14 18											
Islip	d							14 29											
Oxford	a						14 40	14 44						15 14				15 32	
	d		14 31			14 37	14 43			15 01			15 07	15 16		15 31			
Radley	d												15 13						
Culham	d												15 17						
Appleford	d																		
Didcot Parkway	a					14 49							15 24						
	d				14 47	15 01						15 29	15 31						15 47
Cholsey	d					15 07							15 37						
Goring & Streatley	d					15 12							15 42						
Pangbourne	d					15 17							15 47						
Tilehurst	d					15 21							15 51						
Bedwyn	d								14 39										
Hungerford	d								14 44										
Kintbury	d								14 49										
Newbury	a								14 56										
	d	14 13							14 56						15 13				
Newbury Racecourse	d	14 15													15 15				
Thatcham	d	14 20							15 01						15 20				
Midgham	d	14 24													15 24				
Aldermaston	d	14 28													15 28				
Theale	d	14 33							15 09						15 33				
Reading West	d	14 40		←							←				15 40		←		
Reading 7	a	14 44	14 56	14 56	15 02	15 27	15 08		15 19	15 25	15 27	15 44	15 59	15 39	15 44	15 55	15 59		16 00
	d		14 58	15 03	15 04	15 32			15 20	15 25	15 32	15 45	16 03			15 56	16 03		16 01
Twyford 3	a			15 09		→					15 39		→				→		
Maidenhead 3	a			15 17							15 47								
Slough 3	a		15 13	15 24						15 40	15 54					16 11			
Ealing Broadway ⊖	a			15 49							16 19								
London Paddington 15 ⊖	a		15 30	16 01	15 37				15 54	15 59	16 31	16 14				16 30			16 33

For complete service between Banbury and Leamington (Birmingham), please refer to table 71

Table 116R

Saturdays

15 February to 22 March

Birmingham, Banbury, Bicester, Oxford and Bedwyn - Reading and London

Network Diagram - refer to first Page of Table 116

Station		GW 1	GW 1	XC ◇1 🍴	CH	GW 1	GW ◇1	GW 1	GW ◇1 ☕	GW ◇1 ☕	GW 1	XC ◇1 🍴	GW 1	GW ◇1 🍴	GW 1	GW ◇1 ☕	GW 1	GW 1	XC ◇1 🍴
Birmingham New Street 12	d			14 33								15 04							15 33
Birmingham International	d											15 14							
Coventry	d											15 25							
Leamington Spa 8	d			15 00								15 38							16 02
Banbury	d			15 20								15 55							16 22
Kings Sutton	d																		
Heyford	d																		
Tackley	d																		
Bicester Town	d				15 28														
Islip	d				15 39														
Oxford	a			15 40	15 54							16 14							16 40
	d		15 37	15 43			16 01				16 07	16 16		16 31				16 37	16 43
Radley	d										16 13								
Culham	d																		
Appleford	d										16 17								
Didcot Parkway	a		15 49								16 24							16 49	
	d		16 01						16 23	16 29	16 31					16 47		17 01	
Cholsey	d		16 07								16 37							17 07	
Goring & Streatley	d		16 12								16 42							17 12	
Pangbourne	d		16 17								16 47							17 17	
Tilehurst	d		16 21								16 51							17 21	
Bedwyn	d					15 39													
Hungerford	d					15 44													
Kintbury	d					15 49													
Newbury	a					15 56													
	d					15 56							16 13						
Newbury Racecourse	d												16 15						
Thatcham	d					16 01							16 20						
Midgham	d												16 24						
Aldermaston	d												16 28						
Theale	d					16 09							16 33						
Reading West	d	←						←					16 40		←		←		
Reading 7	a	15 59	16 27	16 09		16 20	16 25	16 27	16 38	16 44	16 56	16 40	16 44	16 55	16 56	17 00	16 56	17 27	17 08
	d	16 03	16 33			16 21	16 26	16 33	16 40	16 46	17 03			16 56	17 03	17 02	17 03	17 32	
Twyford 3	a	16 09	→					16 39			→				→		17 09	→	
Maidenhead 3	a	16 17						16 47									17 17		
Slough 3	a	16 24					16 40	16 54						17 10			17 24		
Ealing Broadway ⊖	a	16 49						17 19									17 49		
London Paddington 15 ⊖	a	17 01				16 52	16 59	17 31	17 07	17 14				17 29		17 32	18 01		

Station		CH	GW ◇1 ☕	GW ◇1	GW 1	GW ◇1 ☕	GW 1	XC ◇1 🍴	GW 1	GW ◇1 ☕	GW ◇1 ☕	GW 1	GW 1	XC ◇1 🍴	GW 1	GW 1	GW ◇1	GW 1	GW ◇1 ☕
Birmingham New Street 12	d							16 04						16 33					
Birmingham International	d							16 14											
Coventry	d							16 25											
Leamington Spa 8	d							16 38						17 00					
Banbury	d							16 55						17 19	17 23				
Kings Sutton	d														17 29				
Heyford	d														17 38				
Tackley	d														17 42				
Bicester Town	d	16 30																	
Islip	d	16 41																	
Oxford	a	16 56						17 14						17 41	17 53				
	d			17 01			17 07	17 16		17 31			17 37	17 43			18 01		
Radley	d						17 13												
Culham	d						17 17												
Appleford	d																		
Didcot Parkway	a						17 24						17 49						
	d					17 29	17 31				17 47		18 01						18 23
Cholsey	d						17 37						18 07						
Goring & Streatley	d						17 42						18 12						
Pangbourne	d						17 47						18 17						
Tilehurst	d						17 51						18 21						
Bedwyn	d		16 35						16 56							17 39			
Hungerford	d		16 43						17 00							17 44			
Kintbury	d								17 05							17 49			
Newbury	a		16 52						17 13							17 56			
	d		16 54						17 13							17 56			
Newbury Racecourse	d								17 15										
Thatcham	d		17 00						17 20							18 01			
Midgham	d								17 24										
Aldermaston	d								17 28										
Theale	d		17 08						17 33							18 09			
Reading West	d				←				17 40			←						←	
Reading 7	a		17 20	17 25	17 27	17 43	17 56	17 39	17 44	17 56	17 58	17 56	18 27	18 08		18 20	18 25	18 27	18 38
	d		17 21	17 26	17 32	17 44	18 03			17 58	18 01	18 03	18 32			18 21	18 25	18 32	18 40
Twyford 3	a				17 39		→					18 09	→					18 39	
Maidenhead 3	a				17 47							18 17						18 47	
Slough 3	a			17 40	17 54					18 11		18 24					18 40	18 54	
Ealing Broadway ⊖	a				18 19							18 49						19 19	
London Paddington 15 ⊖	a		17 51	17 59	18 31	18 14				18 29	18 32	19 01				18 52	18 59	19 31	19 08

For complete service between Banbury and Leamington (Birmingham), please refer to table 71

Table 116R

Saturdays

15 February to 22 March

Birmingham, Banbury, Bicester, Oxford and Bedwyn - Reading and London

Network Diagram - refer to first Page of Table 116

		GW	GW	XC	CH	GW	GW	GW	GW	GW	GW	XC	GW	GW	GW	GW	GW	XC	GW
		◇1 ☕	1	◇1 🛒		1	◇1 🛒	1	◇1 ☕	1	1	◇1 🛒	1	◇1	1	◇1 ☕	1	◇1 🛒	1
Birmingham New Street 12	d			17 04								17 33						18 04	
Birmingham International	d			17 14														18 14	
Coventry	d			17 25														18 25	
Leamington Spa 8	d			17 38								18 02						18 38	
Banbury	d			17 55								18 19						18 55	
Kings Sutton	d																		
Heyford	d																		
Tackley	d																		
Bicester Town	d				18 04														
Islip	d				18 15														
Oxford	a			18 14	18 30							18 40						19 14	
	d		18 07	18 16			18 31				18 37	18 43		19 01			19 07	19 16	
Radley	d		18 13														19 13		
Culham	d																19 17		
Appleford	d		18 17																
Didcot Parkway	a		18 24								18 49						19 24		
	d	18 29	18 31						18 47		19 01					19 29	19 31		
Cholsey	d		18 37								19 07						19 37		
Goring & Streatley	d		18 42								19 12						19 42		
Pangbourne	d		18 47								19 17						19 47		
Tilehurst	d		18 51								19 21						19 51		
Bedwyn	d												18 41						
Hungerford	d												18 46						
Kintbury	d												18 51						
Newbury	a												18 58						
	d					18 13							18 58						19 13
Newbury Racecourse	d					18 15													19 15
Thatcham	d					18 20							19 03						19 20
Midgham	d					18 24													19 24
Aldermaston	d					18 28													19 28
Theale	d					18 33							19 11						19 33
Reading West	d					18 40		←		←					←				19 40
Reading 7	a	18 44	18 56	18 40		18 44	18 55	18 56	19 00	18 56	19 27	19 08	19 19	19 25	19 27	19 46	19 57	19 39	19 44
	d	18 46	19 03				18 56	19 03	19 02	19 03	19 33		19 21	19 25	19 33	19 47	20 02		
Twyford 3	a		→					→		19 09	→				19 39		→		
Maidenhead 3	a									19 17					19 47				
Slough 3	a						19 10			19 24				19 40	19 54				
Ealing Broadway ⊖	a									19 49					20 19				
London Paddington 15 ⊖	a	19 13					19 29		19 32	20 01			19 52	19 59	20 31	20 14			

		GW	GW	GW	GW	GW	GW	XC	CH	GW	GW	GW	GW	GW	GW	XC	GW	GW	GW
		◇1 🛒	1	1	◇1 ☕	◇1 ☕	1	◇1 🛒		◇1	1	1	◇1 ☕	◇1 ☕	1	◇1 🛒	◇1	1	◇1 ☕
Birmingham New Street 12	d							18 33								19 04			
Birmingham International	d															19 14			
Coventry	d															19 25			
Leamington Spa 8	d							19 00								19 38			
Banbury	d			19 02				19 19								19 55			
Kings Sutton	d			19 08															
Heyford	d			19 17															
Tackley	d			19 21															
Bicester Town	d								19 17										
Islip	d								19 28										
Oxford	a			19 32				19 40	19 43							20 14			
	d	19 31					19 37	19 43		20 01					20 07	20 16	20 31		
Radley	d														20 13				
Culham	d																		
Appleford	d														20 17				
Didcot Parkway	a						19 49								20 24				
	d				19 47		20 01						20 24	20 29	20 31				20 47
Cholsey	d						20 07								20 37				
Goring & Streatley	d						20 12								20 42				
Pangbourne	d						20 17								20 47				
Tilehurst	d						20 21								20 51				
Bedwyn	d											19 41							
Hungerford	d											19 47							
Kintbury	d											19 51							
Newbury	a											19 58							
	d					19 46						19 58							
Newbury Racecourse	d											20 00							
Thatcham	d											20 05							
Midgham	d											20 10							
Aldermaston	d											20 13							
Theale	d											20 18							
Reading West	d		←								←	20 25						←	
Reading 7	a	19 55	19 57		20 00	20 07	20 27	20 08		20 25	20 27	20 28	20 38	20 44	20 57	20 40	20 55	20 57	21 06
	d	19 55	20 02		20 03	20 09	20 33			20 25	20 33		20 40	20 46	21 03		20 56	21 03	21 08
Twyford 3	a		20 09				→				20 39				→			21 09	
Maidenhead 3	a		20 17								20 47							21 19	
Slough 3	a	20 10	20 24							20 40	20 54						21 10	21 27	
Ealing Broadway ⊖	a		20 49								21 19							21 52	
London Paddington 15 ⊖	a	20 29	21 01		20 32	20 37				20 59	21 31		21 07	21 14			21 29	22 02	21 37

For complete service between Banbury and Leamington (Birmingham), please refer to table 71

Table 116R

Saturdays

15 February to 22 March

Birmingham, Banbury, Bicester, Oxford and Bedwyn - Reading and London

Network Diagram - refer to first Page of Table 116

Station		GW	XC	CH	GW	GW	GW	GW	XC	GW	GW	GW	XC
		1	◇1		◇1	1	1	1	◇1	◇1	◇1	◇1	◇1
Birmingham New Street 12	d		19 33						20 04				20 33
Birmingham International	d								20 14				
Coventry	d								20 25				
Leamington Spa 8	d		20 03						20 38				21 00
Banbury	d		20 20				20 38		20 55				21 20
Kings Sutton	d						20 44						
Heyford	d						20 53						
Tackley	d						20 57						
Bicester Town	d			20 28									
Islip	d			20 39									
Oxford	a		20 40	20 54			21 08		21 14				21 41
	d	20 37	20 43		21 01				21 16		21 31		21 43
Radley	d												
Culham	d												
Appleford	d												
Didcot Parkway	a	20 49									21 43		
	d	21 01								21 34	21 45	21 47	
Cholsey	d	21 07											
Goring & Streatley	d	21 12											
Pangbourne	d	21 17											
Tilehurst	d	21 21											
Bedwyn	d							20 48					
Hungerford	d							20 54					
Kintbury	d							20 58					
Newbury	a							21 05					
	d							21 05					
Newbury Racecourse	d							21 08					
Thatcham	d							21 13					
Midgham	d							21 17					
Aldermaston	d							21 21					
Theale	d							21 26					
Reading West	d					←		21 33					
Reading 7	a	21 27	21 08		21 27	21 27		21 36	21 38	21 48	21 59	22 02	22 08
	d	21 33			21 27	21 33				21 50	22 02	22 06	
Twyford 3	a	→				21 39							
Maidenhead 3	a					21 47							
Slough 3	a				21 42	21 58					22 15		
Ealing Broadway ⊖	a					22 23							
London Paddington 15 ⊖	a				22 01	22 32				22 16	22 38	22 40	

Station		GW	GW	CH	XC	GW	GW	GW	GW	GW	GW	GW	GW	CH
		1	◇1		◇1	1	1	◇1	◇1	◇1	1	◇1	1	
Birmingham New Street 12	d				21 04									
Birmingham International	d				21 14									
Coventry	d				21 25									
Leamington Spa 8	d				21 38									
Banbury	d				21 55	22 00								
Kings Sutton	d					22 06								
Heyford	d					22 15								
Tackley	d					22 19								
Bicester Town	d			21 37										22 55
Islip	d			21 48										23 06
Oxford	a			22 03	22 16	22 30								23 21
	d	21 50	22 01		22 18				22 35	23 01			23 07	
Radley	d	21 56											23 13	
Culham	d												23 17	
Appleford	d												23 20	
Didcot Parkway	a	22 04	22 12						22 47	23 13			23 25	
	d	22 04	22 13					22 49	22 51	23 13		23 30	23 36	
Cholsey	d	22 10											23 42	
Goring & Streatley	d	22 15											23 47	
Pangbourne	d	22 21											23 51	
Tilehurst	d	22 24											23 56	
Bedwyn	d						22 00				23 00			
Hungerford	d						22 06				23 06			
Kintbury	d						22 10				23 10			
Newbury	a						22 17				23 17			
	d						22 17				23 17			
Newbury Racecourse	d						22 19				23 19			
Thatcham	d						22 24				23 24			
Midgham	d						22 29				23 29			
Aldermaston	d						22 32				23 32			
Theale	d						22 37				23 37			
Reading West	d						22 44				23 44			
Reading 7	a	22 31	22 35		22 44		22 48	23 07	23 09	23 31	23 48	23 48	00 03	
	d	22 33	22 35					23 08	23 10	23 31		23 48	00 04	
Twyford 3	a	22 39											00 11	
Maidenhead 3	a	22 47											00 19	
Slough 3	a	22 58	22 50						23 28	23 50			00 30	
Ealing Broadway ⊖	a	23 23											00 54	
London Paddington 15 ⊖	a	23 32	23 09					23 40	23 46	00 17		00 36	01 05	

For complete service between Banbury and Leamington (Birmingham), please refer to table 71

Table 116R

Saturdays

29 March to 17 May

Birmingham, Banbury, Bicester, Oxford and Bedwyn - Reading and London

Network Diagram - refer to first Page of Table 116

		GW	GW	GW	GW	GW	GW	GW	GW	GW
		◇1	1	1	1	1	◇1 ☕	1	1	◇1
Birmingham New Street 12	d									
Birmingham International	d									
Coventry	d									
Leamington Spa 8	d									
Banbury	d									
Kings Sutton	d									
Heyford	d									
Tackley	d		00 03							
Bicester Town	d									
Islip	d									
Oxford	a		00 14							
	d	00 07	00 27	03 59	05 14	05 49			06 07	06 31
Radley	d		00 33		05 20				06 13	
Culham	d				05 24					
Appleford	d								06 17	
Didcot Parkway	a	00 20	00 42	04 10	05 31	06 01			06 24	
	d	00 21	00 46	04 10	05 31	06 01	06 29		06 31	
Cholsey	d		00 52		05 37	06 07			06 37	
Goring & Streatley	d		00 57		05 42	06 12			06 42	
Pangbourne	d		01 01		05 47	06 17			06 47	
Tilehurst	d		01 06		05 51	06 21			06 51	
Bedwyn	d							06 05		
Hungerford	d							06 11		
Kintbury	d							06 15		
Newbury	a							06 22		
	d							06 22		
Newbury Racecourse	d							06 24		
Thatcham	d							06 29		
Midgham	d							06 34		
Aldermaston	d							06 37		
Theale	d							06 42		
Reading West	d							06 49		
Reading 7	a	00 41	01 13	04 29	05 57	06 27	06 43	06 52	06 58	06 57
	d	00 43	01 17	04 40	06 03	06 33	06 45	06 53	07 03	07 03
Twyford 3	a		01 23	04 46	06 09	06 39			→	
Maidenhead 3	a		01 31	04 54	06 17	06 47				
Slough 3	a	00 59	01 39	05 02	06 24	06 54				07 17
Ealing Broadway ⊖	a		01 55	05 19	06 49	07 19				
London Paddington 15 ⊖	a	01 21	02 07	05 31	07 01	07 31	07 14	07 22		07 37

		GW	GW	GW	GW	GW	GW	GW	GW	GW
		1	◇1 ☕	1	1	◇1	◇1 ☕	1	◇1 ☕	1
Birmingham New Street 12	d									
Birmingham International	d									
Coventry	d									
Leamington Spa 8	d									
Banbury	d									
Kings Sutton	d									
Heyford	d									
Tackley	d									
Bicester Town	d									
Islip	d									
Oxford	a									
	d				06 42	07 01				07 07
Radley	d									07 13
Culham	d									07 17
Appleford	d									
Didcot Parkway	a				06 54					07 24
	d		06 59		07 01		07 17		07 29	07 31
Cholsey	d				07 07					07 37
Goring & Streatley	d				07 12					07 42
Pangbourne	d				07 17					07 47
Tilehurst	d				07 21					07 51
Bedwyn	d			06 39						
Hungerford	d			06 43						
Kintbury	d			06 48						
Newbury	a			06 55						
	d			06 55						
Newbury Racecourse	d									
Thatcham	d			07 00						
Midgham	d									
Aldermaston	d									
Theale	d			07 08						
Reading West	d	←						←		
Reading 7	a	06 58	07 14	07 20	07 27	07 27	07 31	07 27	07 44	07 58
	d	07 03	07 15	07 22	07 33	07 27	07 32	07 33	07 46	08 03
Twyford 3	a	07 09			→			07 39		→
Maidenhead 3	a	07 17						07 47		
Slough 3	a	07 24				07 42		07 54		
Ealing Broadway ⊖	a	07 49						08 19		
London Paddington 15 ⊖	a	08 01	07 44	07 54		08 01	08 07	08 31	08 14	

		XC	GW	GW	GW	GW	GW	GW	GW	GW
		◇1 🛒	1	◇1 🛒	1	1	◇1 ☕	1	◇1 ☕	1
Birmingham New Street 12	d	06 04								
Birmingham International	d	06 14								
Coventry	d	06 25								
Leamington Spa 8	d	06 38								
Banbury	d	06 55				07 03				
Kings Sutton	d					07 08				
Heyford	d					07 17				
Tackley	d					07 21				
Bicester Town	d									
Islip	d									
Oxford	a	07 14				07 32				
	d	07 16		07 31						07 37
Radley	d									
Culham	d									
Appleford	d									
Didcot Parkway	a									07 49
	d						07 47		07 59	08 01
Cholsey	d									08 07
Goring & Streatley	d									08 12
Pangbourne	d									08 17
Tilehurst	d									08 21
Bedwyn	d									
Hungerford	d									
Kintbury	d									
Newbury	a									
	d		07 13							
Newbury Racecourse	d		07 15							
Thatcham	d		07 20							
Midgham	d		07 24							
Aldermaston	d		07 28							
Theale	d		07 33							
Reading West	d		07 42		←			←		
Reading 7	a	07 39	07 45	07 55	07 58		08 00	07 58	08 15	08 28
	d			07 55	08 03		08 02	08 03	08 17	08 33
Twyford 3	a				→			08 09		→
Maidenhead 3	a							08 17		
Slough 3	a			08 10				08 24		
Ealing Broadway ⊖	a							08 49		
London Paddington 15 ⊖	a			08 29			08 32	09 01	08 44	

		XC	GW	GW	GW	CH	GW	GW	GW	XC
		◇1	1	◇1	1		◇1 ☕	◇1 ☕	1	◇1 🛒
Birmingham New Street 12	d	06 33								07 04
Birmingham International	d									07 14
Coventry	d									07 25
Leamington Spa 8	d	07 00								07 38
Banbury	d	07 19								07 55
Kings Sutton	d									
Heyford	d									
Tackley	d									
Bicester Town	d					07 36				
Islip	d					07 47				
Oxford	a	07 40				08 02				08 14
	d	07 43		08 01					08 07	08 16
Radley	d								08 13	
Culham	d									
Appleford	d								08 17	
Didcot Parkway	a								08 24	
	d						08 17	08 29	08 31	
Cholsey	d								08 37	
Goring & Streatley	d								08 42	
Pangbourne	d								08 47	
Tilehurst	d								08 51	
Bedwyn	d		07 39							
Hungerford	d		07 44							
Kintbury	d		07 49							
Newbury	a		07 56							
	d		07 56							
Newbury Racecourse	d									
Thatcham	d		08 01							
Midgham	d									
Aldermaston	d									
Theale	d		08 09							
Reading West	d				←					
Reading 7	a	08 06	08 21	08 25	08 28		08 33	08 44	08 55	08 39
	d		08 22	08 26	08 33		08 33	08 46	09 03	
Twyford 3	a				08 39				→	
Maidenhead 3	a				08 47					
Slough 3	a			08 40	08 54					
Ealing Broadway ⊖	a				09 19					
London Paddington 15 ⊖	a		08 54	08 59	09 31		09 02	09 14		

For complete service between Banbury and Leamington (Birmingham), please refer to table 71

Table 116R

Saturdays

29 March to 17 May

Birmingham, Banbury, Bicester, Oxford and Bedwyn - Reading and London

Network Diagram - refer to first Page of Table 116

		GW	GW	GW	GW	GW	GW	GW	GW	XC	GW	GW	GW	GW	GW	GW	GW	CH	XC
		1	◇1	◇1	◇1	1	◇1	◇1	1	◇1	1	◇1	1	◇1	1	◇1	1		◇1
														A					
			⊡	⊡	⊡		⊡	⊡		⚲		⚲		⊡⊘		⊡			⚲
Birmingham New Street 12	d									07 33									08 04
Birmingham International	d																		08 14
Coventry	d																		08 25
Leamington Spa 8	d									08 00									08 38
Banbury	d									08 19									08 55
Kings Sutton	d																		
Heyford	d																		
Tackley	d																		
Bicester Town	d																	08 45	
Islip	d																	08 56	
Oxford	a									08 40								09 11	09 14
	d			08 31					08 37	08 43		09 01					09 07		09 16
Radley	d																09 13		
Culham	d																09 17		
Appleford	d																		
Didcot Parkway	a								08 49								09 24		
	d				08 47		08 54	09 00	09 01					09 17		09 29	09 31		
Cholsey	d								09 07								09 37		
Goring & Streatley	d								09 12								09 42		
Pangbourne	d								09 17								09 47		
Tilehurst	d								09 21								09 51		
Bedwyn	d										08 38								
Hungerford	d										08 43								
Kintbury	d										08 48								
Newbury	a										08 57								
	d	08 13	08 34								08 57				09 03				
Newbury Racecourse	d	08 15													09 06				
Thatcham	d	08 20									09 02				09 11				
Midgham	d	08 24													09 16				
Aldermaston	d	08 28													09 19				
Theale	d	08 33									09 10				09 24				
Reading West	d	08 40				←							←		09 31				
Reading 7	a	08 44	08 51	08 56	09 01	08 55	09 08	09 14	09 27	09 07	09 20	09 24	09 27	09 31	09 35	09 47	09 57		09 39
	d		08 52	08 56	09 02	09 03	09 10	09 16	09 33		09 21	09 24	09 33	09 33		09 49	10 03		
Twyford 3	a					09 09			→				09 39				→		
Maidenhead 3	a					09 17							09 47						
Slough 3	a			09 10		09 24						09 40	09 54						
Ealing Broadway ⊖	a					09 49							10 19						
London Paddington 15 ⊖	a		09 21	09 29	09 38	10 01	09 41	09 44			09 52	09 59	10 31	10 02		10 15			

		GW	GW	GW	GW	GW	GW	XC	GW	GW	GW	GW	GW	GW	GW	XC	CH	GW	GW
		◇1	1	1	◇1	1	1	◇1	1	◇1	◇1	1	◇1	◇1	1	◇1		1	◇1
		A			A														
		⊡⊘			⊡⊘			⚲		⚲	⊡		⊡	⊡		⚲			⊡
Birmingham New Street 12	d							08 33								09 04			
Birmingham International	d															09 14			
Coventry	d															09 25			
Leamington Spa 8	d							09 00								09 38			
Banbury	d			09 02				09 19								09 55			
Kings Sutton	d			09 08															
Heyford	d			09 17															
Tackley	d			09 21															
Bicester Town	d																09 57		
Islip	d																10 08		
Oxford	a			09 32				09 40								10 14	10 23		
	d	09 31					09 37	09 43		10 01					10 07	10 16			10 32
Radley	d														10 13				
Culham	d																		
Appleford	d														10 17				
Didcot Parkway	a						09 49								10 23				
	d				09 47		10 01				10 17		10 22	10 29	10 31				
Cholsey	d						10 07								10 37				
Goring & Streatley	d						10 12								10 42				
Pangbourne	d						10 17								10 47				
Tilehurst	d						10 21								10 51				
Bedwyn	d								09 39										
Hungerford	d								09 44										
Kintbury	d								09 49										
Newbury	a								09 56										
	d								09 56									10 13	
Newbury Racecourse	d																	10 15	
Thatcham	d								10 01									10 20	
Midgham	d																	10 24	
Aldermaston	d																	10 28	
Theale	d								10 09									10 33	
Reading West	d		←			←						←						10 40	
Reading 7	a	09 54	09 57		10 00	09 57	10 27	10 06	10 21	10 28	10 30	10 27	10 34	10 46	10 58	10 41		10 44	10 56
	d	09 55	10 03		10 02	10 03	10 33		10 22	10 28	10 32	10 33	10 36	10 47	11 03				10 58
Twyford 3	a		→			10 09	→					10 39			→				
Maidenhead 3	a					10 17						10 47							
Slough 3	a	10 09				10 24				10 43		10 54							11 12
Ealing Broadway ⊖	a					10 49						11 19							
London Paddington 15 ⊖	a	10 29			10 32	11 01			10 52	11 02	11 04	11 31	11 08	11 14					11 30

A ⊡ from Reading ⊘ to Reading

For complete service between Banbury and Leamington (Birmingham), please refer to table 71

Table 116R

Saturdays

29 March to 17 May

Birmingham, Banbury, Bicester, Oxford and Bedwyn - Reading and London

Network Diagram - refer to first Page of Table 116

Station		GW 1	GW ◇1 ☕	GW 1	GW 1	XC ◇1 🍴	GW 1	GW ◇1	GW 1	GW ◇1 ☕
Birmingham New Street 12	d					09 33				
Birmingham International	d									
Coventry	d									
Leamington Spa 8	d					10 00				
Banbury	d					10 19				
Kings Sutton	d									
Heyford	d									
Tackley	d									
Bicester Town	d									
Islip	d									
Oxford	a					10 40				
	d				10 37	10 43		11 01		
Radley	d									
Culham	d									
Appleford	d									
Didcot Parkway	a				10 49					
	d		10 47		11 01					11 29
Cholsey	d				11 07					
Goring & Streatley	d				11 12					
Pangbourne	d				11 17					
Tilehurst	d				11 21					
Bedwyn	d						10 39			
Hungerford	d						10 45			
Kintbury	d						10 49			
Newbury	a						10 56			
	d						10 56			
Newbury Racecourse	d									
Thatcham	d						11 01			
Midgham	d									
Aldermaston	d									
Theale	d						11 09			
Reading West	d	←		←					←	
Reading 7	a	10 58	11 01	10 58	11 27	11 11	11 20	11 24	11 27	11 43
	d	11 03	11 02	11 03	11 33		11 21	11 25	11 33	11 45
Twyford 3	a	→		11 09	→				11 39	
Maidenhead 3	a			11 17					11 47	
Slough 3	a			11 24				11 39	11 54	
Ealing Broadway ⊖	a			11 49					12 19	
London Paddington 15 ⊖	a		11 33	12 01			11 52	11 59	12 31	12 14

Station		GW 1	XC ◇1 🍴	GW 1	GW ◇1 🍴	GW 1	GW ◇1 ☕	GW 1	GW 1	XC ◇1 🍴
Birmingham New Street 12	d		10 04							10 33
Birmingham International	d		10 14							
Coventry	d		10 25							
Leamington Spa 8	d		10 38							11 00
Banbury	d		10 55			11 02				11 19
Kings Sutton	d					11 08				
Heyford	d					11 17				
Tackley	d					11 21				
Bicester Town	d									
Islip	d									
Oxford	a		11 14			11 32				11 40
	d	11 07	11 16		11 30				11 37	11 43
Radley	d	11 13								
Culham	d									
Appleford	d									
Didcot Parkway	a	11 24							11 49	
	d	11 31					11 47		12 01	
Cholsey	d	11 37							12 07	
Goring & Streatley	d	11 42							12 12	
Pangbourne	d	11 47							12 17	
Tilehurst	d	11 51							12 21	
Bedwyn	d									
Hungerford	d									
Kintbury	d									
Newbury	a									
	d			11 13						
Newbury Racecourse	d			11 15						
Thatcham	d			11 20						
Midgham	d			11 24						
Aldermaston	d			11 28						
Theale	d			11 33						
Reading West	d			11 40				←		
Reading 7	a	11 56	11 39	11 44	11 57		12 01	11 56	12 28	12 07
	d	12 03			11 58		12 03	12 03	12 33	
Twyford 3	a	→						12 09	→	
Maidenhead 3	a							12 17		
Slough 3	a				12 12			12 24		
Ealing Broadway ⊖	a							12 49		
London Paddington 15 ⊖	a				12 32		12 37	13 01		

Station		CH	GW 1	GW ◇1 🍴	GW 1	GW ◇1 ☕	GW ◇1 ☕	GW 1	XC ◇1 🍴	GW 1
Birmingham New Street 12	d								11 04	
Birmingham International	d								11 14	
Coventry	d								11 25	
Leamington Spa 8	d								11 38	
Banbury	d								11 55	
Kings Sutton	d									
Heyford	d									
Tackley	d									
Bicester Town	d	11 30								
Islip	d	11 41								
Oxford	a	11 56							12 14	
	d			12 01				12 07	12 16	
Radley	d							12 13		
Culham	d									
Appleford	d							12 17		
Didcot Parkway	a							12 24		
	d					12 23	12 29	12 31		
Cholsey	d							12 37		
Goring & Streatley	d							12 42		
Pangbourne	d							12 47		
Tilehurst	d							12 51		
Bedwyn	d		11 39							
Hungerford	d		11 44							
Kintbury	d		11 49							
Newbury	a		11 56							
	d		11 56							12 13
Newbury Racecourse	d									12 15
Thatcham	d		12 01							12 20
Midgham	d									12 24
Aldermaston	d									12 28
Theale	d		12 09							12 33
Reading West	d				←					12 40
Reading 7	a		12 21	12 26	12 28	12 38	12 45	12 56	12 40	12 44
	d		12 22	12 27	12 33	12 39	12 47	13 03		
Twyford 3	a				12 39			→		
Maidenhead 3	a				12 47					
Slough 3	a			12 41	12 54					
Ealing Broadway ⊖	a				13 19					
London Paddington 15 ⊖	a		12 53	12 59	13 31	13 06	13 15			

Station		GW ◇1 🍴	GW 1	GW ◇1 ☕	GW 1	XC ◇1 🍴	GW ◇1 🍴	GW 1	GW ◇1 ☕	GW 1
Birmingham New Street 12	d					11 33				
Birmingham International	d									
Coventry	d									
Leamington Spa 8	d					12 00				
Banbury	d					12 19				
Kings Sutton	d									
Heyford	d									
Tackley	d									
Bicester Town	d									
Islip	d									
Oxford	a					12 40				
	d	12 31			12 37	12 43	13 01			13 07
Radley	d									13 13
Culham	d									13 17
Appleford	d									
Didcot Parkway	a				12 51					13 24
	d			12 47	13 01				13 29	13 31
Cholsey	d				13 07					13 37
Goring & Streatley	d				13 12					13 42
Pangbourne	d				13 17					13 47
Tilehurst	d				13 21					13 51
Bedwyn	d									
Hungerford	d									
Kintbury	d									
Newbury	a									
	d									
Newbury Racecourse	d									
Thatcham	d									
Midgham	d									
Aldermaston	d									
Theale	d									
Reading West	d		←					←		
Reading 7	a	12 56	12 56	13 01	13 27	13 07	13 26	13 27	13 44	13 59
	d	12 57	13 03	13 07	13 33		13 27	13 33	13 45	14 03
Twyford 3	a		13 09		→			13 39		→
Maidenhead 3	a		13 17					13 47		
Slough 3	a	13 11	13 24				13 41	13 54		
Ealing Broadway ⊖	a		13 49					14 19		
London Paddington 15 ⊖	a	13 32	14 01	13 38			13 59	14 31	14 14	

For complete service between Banbury and Leamington (Birmingham), please refer to table 71

Table 116R

Saturdays

29 March to 17 May

Birmingham, Banbury, Bicester, Oxford and Bedwyn - Reading and London

Network Diagram - refer to first Page of Table 116

		XC	CH	GW	GW	GW	GW	GW	GW	GW	GW	XC	GW	GW	GW	GW	GW	GW	XC
		◇1		1	1	◇1	1	1	◇1	1	1	◇1	◇1	◇1	1	◇1	◇1	1	◇1
		[trolley]							[buffet]			[trolley]	[buffet]	[trolley]		[buffet]	[buffet]		[trolley]
Birmingham New Street 12	d	12 04										12 33							13 04
Birmingham International	d	12 14																	13 14
Coventry	d	12 25																	13 25
Leamington Spa 8	d	12 38										13 02							13 38
Banbury	d	12 55						13 02				13 21							13 55
Kings Sutton	d							13 08											
Heyford	d							13 17											
Tackley	d							13 21											
Bicester Town	d		13 00																
Islip	d		13 11																
Oxford	a	13 14	13 26					13 32				13 40							14 14
	d	13 16				13 31					13 37	13 43		14 01				14 07	14 16
Radley	d																	14 13	
Culham	d																		
Appleford	d																	14 17	
Didcot Parkway	a										13 51							14 24	
	d								13 47		14 01					14 24	14 29	14 31	
Cholsey	d										14 07							14 37	
Goring & Streatley	d										14 12							14 42	
Pangbourne	d										14 17							14 47	
Tilehurst	d										14 21							14 51	
Bedwyn	d				13 07								13 33						
Hungerford	d				13 13								13 40						
Kintbury	d				13 17														
Newbury	a				13 24								13 49						
	d			13 13	13 28								13 50						
Newbury Racecourse	d			13 15															
Thatcham	d			13 20	13 33								13 57						
Midgham	d			13 24															
Aldermaston	d			13 28															
Theale	d			13 33	13 41								14 06						
Reading West	d			13 40			←			←					←				
Reading 7	a	13 39		13 44	13 51	13 54	13 59		14 00	13 59	14 27	14 09	14 22	14 26	14 27	14 39	14 45	14 56	14 40
	d				13 51	13 56	14 03		14 02	14 03	14 33		14 23	14 27	14 33	14 41	14 47	15 03	
Twyford 3	a						→			14 09	→				14 39			→	
Maidenhead 3	a									14 17					14 47				
Slough 3	a					14 09				14 24				14 41	14 54				
Ealing Broadway	⊖ a									14 49					15 19				
London Paddington 15	⊖ a				14 22	14 29			14 32	15 01			14 50	14 59	15 31	15 09	15 14		

		GW	GW	GW	GW	GW	XC	CH	GW	GW	GW	GW	GW	XC	GW	GW	GW	GW	GW
		1	◇1	1	◇1	1	◇1		1	◇1	1	◇1	1	◇1	1	◇1	1	1	◇1
			[buffet]		[buffet]		[trolley]					[buffet]		[trolley]		[trolley]			[buffet]
Birmingham New Street 12	d						13 33							14 04					
Birmingham International	d													14 14					
Coventry	d													14 25					
Leamington Spa 8	d						14 00							14 38					
Banbury	d						14 18							14 55				15 02	
Kings Sutton	d																	15 08	
Heyford	d																	15 17	
Tackley	d																	15 21	
Bicester Town	d							14 18											
Islip	d							14 29											
Oxford	a						14 40	14 44						15 14				15 32	
	d		14 31			14 37	14 43			15 01			15 07	15 16		15 31			
Radley	d												15 13						
Culham	d												15 17						
Appleford	d																		
Didcot Parkway	a					14 49							15 24						
	d				14 47	15 01						15 29	15 31						15 47
Cholsey	d					15 07							15 37						
Goring & Streatley	d					15 12							15 42						
Pangbourne	d					15 17							15 47						
Tilehurst	d					15 21							15 51						
Bedwyn	d								14 39										
Hungerford	d								14 44										
Kintbury	d								14 49										
Newbury	a								14 56										
	d	14 13							14 56						15 13				
Newbury Racecourse	d	14 15													15 15				
Thatcham	d	14 20							15 01						15 20				
Midgham	d	14 24													15 24				
Aldermaston	d	14 28													15 28				
Theale	d	14 33							15 09						15 33				
Reading West	d	14 40		←							←				15 40		←		
Reading 7	a	14 44	14 56	14 56	15 02	15 27	15 08		15 19	15 25	15 27	15 44	15 59	15 39	15 44	15 55	15 59		16 00
	d		14 58	15 03	15 04	15 32			15 20	15 25	15 32	15 45	16 03			15 56	16 03		16 01
Twyford 3	a			15 09		→					15 39		→				→		
Maidenhead 3	a			15 17							15 47								
Slough 3	a		15 13	15 24						15 40	15 54					16 11			
Ealing Broadway	⊖ a			15 49							16 19								
London Paddington 15	⊖ a		15 30	16 01	15 37				15 54	15 59	16 31	16 14				16 30			16 33

For complete service between Banbury and Leamington (Birmingham), please refer to table 71

Table 116R

Saturdays

29 March to 17 May

Birmingham, Banbury, Bicester, Oxford and Bedwyn - Reading and London

Network Diagram - refer to first Page of Table 116

		GW 1	GW 1	XC ◇1 ✠	CH	GW 1	GW ◇1	GW 1	GW ◇1 ₽	GW ◇1 ₽	GW 1	XC ◇1 ✠	GW 1	GW ◇1 ✠	GW 1	GW ◇1 ₽	GW 1	GW 1	XC ◇1 ✠
Birmingham New Street 12	d			14 33								15 04							15 33
Birmingham International	d											15 14							
Coventry	d											15 25							
Leamington Spa 8	d			15 00								15 38							16 02
Banbury	d			15 20								15 55							16 22
Kings Sutton	d																		
Heyford	d																		
Tackley	d																		
Bicester Town	d				15 28														
Islip	d				15 39														
Oxford	a			15 40	15 54							16 14							16 40
	d		15 37	15 43			16 01				16 07	16 16		16 31				16 37	16 43
Radley	d										16 13								
Culham	d																		
Appleford	d										16 17								
Didcot Parkway	a		15 49								16 24							16 49	
	d		16 01						16 23	16 29	16 31					16 47		17 01	
Cholsey	d		16 07								16 37							17 07	
Goring & Streatley	d		16 12								16 42							17 12	
Pangbourne	d		16 17								16 47							17 17	
Tilehurst	d		16 21								16 51							17 21	
Bedwyn	d					15 39													
Hungerford	d					15 44													
Kintbury	d					15 49													
Newbury	a					15 56													
	d					15 56							16 13						
Newbury Racecourse	d												16 15						
Thatcham	d					16 01							16 20						
Midgham	d												16 24						
Aldermaston	d												16 28						
Theale	d					16 09							16 33						
Reading West	d	←						←					16 40		←		←		
Reading 7	a	15 59	16 27	16 09		16 20	16 25	16 27	16 38	16 44	16 56	16 40	16 44	16 55	16 56	17 00	16 56	17 27	17 08
	d	16 03	16 33			16 21	16 26	16 33	16 40	16 46	17 03			16 56	17 03	17 02	17 03	17 32	
Twyford 3	a	16 09	→					16 39			→				→		17 09	→	
Maidenhead 3	a	16 17						16 47									17 17		
Slough 3	a	16 24					16 40	16 54						17 10			17 24		
Ealing Broadway ⊖	a	16 49						17 19									17 49		
London Paddington 15 ⊖	a	17 01				16 52	16 59	17 31	17 07	17 14				17 29		17 32	18 01		

		CH	GW ◇1 ₽	GW ◇1	GW 1	GW ◇1 ₽	GW 1	XC ◇1 ✠	GW 1	GW ◇1 ₽	GW ◇1 ₽	GW 1	GW 1	XC ◇1 ✠	GW 1	GW 1	GW ◇1	GW 1	GW ◇1 ₽
Birmingham New Street 12	d							16 04						16 33					
Birmingham International	d							16 14											
Coventry	d							16 25											
Leamington Spa 8	d							16 38						17 00					
Banbury	d							16 55						17 19	17 23				
Kings Sutton	d														17 29				
Heyford	d														17 38				
Tackley	d														17 42				
Bicester Town	d	16 30																	
Islip	d	16 41																	
Oxford	a	16 56						17 14						17 41	17 53				
	d			17 01			17 07	17 16		17 31			17 37	17 43			18 01		
Radley	d						17 13												
Culham	d						17 17												
Appleford	d																		
Didcot Parkway	a						17 24						17 49						
	d					17 29	17 31				17 47		18 01						18 23
Cholsey	d						17 37						18 07						
Goring & Streatley	d						17 42						18 12						
Pangbourne	d						17 47						18 17						
Tilehurst	d						17 51						18 21						
Bedwyn	d		16 35						16 56							17 39			
Hungerford	d		16 43						17 00							17 44			
Kintbury	d								17 05							17 49			
Newbury	a		16 52						17 13							17 56			
	d		16 54						17 13							17 56			
Newbury Racecourse	d								17 15										
Thatcham	d		17 00						17 20							18 01			
Midgham	d								17 24										
Aldermaston	d								17 28										
Theale	d		17 08						17 33							18 09			
Reading West	d				←				17 40			←						←	
Reading 7	a		17 20	17 25	17 27	17 43	17 56	17 39	17 44	17 56	17 58	17 56	18 27	18 08		18 20	18 25	18 27	18 38
	d		17 21	17 26	17 32	17 44	18 03			17 58	18 01	18 03	18 32			18 21	18 25	18 32	18 40
Twyford 3	a				17 39		→					18 09	→					18 39	
Maidenhead 3	a				17 47							18 17						18 47	
Slough 3	a			17 40	17 54					18 11		18 24					18 40	18 54	
Ealing Broadway ⊖	a				18 19							18 49						19 19	
London Paddington 15 ⊖	a		17 51	17 59	18 31	18 14				18 29	18 32	19 01				18 52	18 59	19 31	19 08

For complete service between Banbury and Leamington (Birmingham), please refer to table 71

Table 116R

Saturdays

29 March to 17 May

Birmingham, Banbury, Bicester, Oxford and Bedwyn - Reading and London

Network Diagram - refer to first Page of Table 116

		GW	GW	XC	CH	GW	GW	GW	GW	GW	GW	XC	GW	GW	GW	GW	GW	XC	GW
		◇1	1	◇1		1	◇1	1	◇1	1	1	◇1	1	◇1	1	◇1	1	◇1	1
		☕		🍴			🍴		☕			🍴				☕		🍴	
Birmingham New Street 12	d			17 04								17 33						18 04	
Birmingham International	d			17 14														18 14	
Coventry	d			17 25														18 25	
Leamington Spa 8	d			17 38								18 02						18 38	
Banbury	d			17 55								18 19						18 55	
Kings Sutton	d																		
Heyford	d																		
Tackley	d																		
Bicester Town	d				18 04														
Islip	d				18 15														
Oxford	a			18 14	18 30							18 40						19 14	
	d		18 07	18 16			18 31				18 37	18 43		19 01			19 07	19 16	
Radley	d		18 13														19 13		
Culham	d																19 17		
Appleford	d		18 17																
Didcot Parkway	a		18 24								18 49						19 24		
	d	18 29	18 31						18 47		19 01					19 29	19 31		
Cholsey	d		18 37								19 07						19 37		
Goring & Streatley	d		18 42								19 12						19 42		
Pangbourne	d		18 47								19 17						19 47		
Tilehurst	d		18 51								19 21						19 51		
Bedwyn	d												18 41						
Hungerford	d												18 46						
Kintbury	d												18 51						
Newbury	a												18 58						
	d					18 13							18 58						19 13
Newbury Racecourse	d					18 15													19 15
Thatcham	d					18 20							19 03						19 20
Midgham	d					18 24													19 24
Aldermaston	d					18 28													19 28
Theale	d					18 33							19 11						19 33
Reading West	d					18 40		←		←					←				19 40
Reading 7	a	18 44	18 56	18 40		18 44	18 55	18 56	19 00	18 56	19 27	19 08	19 19	19 25	19 27	19 46	19 57	19 39	19 44
	d	18 46	19 03				18 56	19 03	19 02	19 03	19 33		19 21	19 25	19 33	19 47	20 02		
Twyford 3	a		→					→		19 09	→				19 39		→		
Maidenhead 3	a									19 17					19 47				
Slough 3	a						19 10			19 24				19 40	19 54				
Ealing Broadway ⊖	a									19 49					20 19				
London Paddington 15 ⊖	a	19 13					19 29		19 32	20 01			19 52	19 59	20 31	20 14			

		GW	GW	GW	GW	GW	GW	XC	CH	GW	GW	GW	GW	GW	GW	XC	GW	GW	GW
		◇1	1	1	◇1	◇1	1	◇1		◇1	1	1	◇1	◇1	1	◇1	◇1	1	◇1
		🍴			☕	☕		🍴					☕	☕		🍴			☕
Birmingham New Street 12	d							18 33								19 04			
Birmingham International	d															19 14			
Coventry	d															19 25			
Leamington Spa 8	d							19 00								19 38			
Banbury	d			19 02				19 19								19 55			
Kings Sutton	d			19 08															
Heyford	d			19 17															
Tackley	d			19 21															
Bicester Town	d								19 17										
Islip	d								19 28										
Oxford	a			19 32				19 40	19 43							20 14			
	d	19 31					19 37	19 43		20 01					20 07	20 16	20 31		
Radley	d														20 13				
Culham	d																		
Appleford	d														20 17				
Didcot Parkway	a						19 49								20 24				
	d				19 47		20 01						20 24	20 29	20 31				20 47
Cholsey	d						20 07								20 37				
Goring & Streatley	d						20 12								20 42				
Pangbourne	d						20 17								20 47				
Tilehurst	d						20 21								20 51				
Bedwyn	d											19 41							
Hungerford	d											19 47							
Kintbury	d											19 51							
Newbury	a											19 58							
	d					19 46						19 58							
Newbury Racecourse	d											20 00							
Thatcham	d											20 05							
Midgham	d											20 10							
Aldermaston	d											20 13							
Theale	d											20 18							
Reading West	d		←								←	20 25						←	
Reading 7	a	19 55	19 57		20 00	20 07	20 27	20 08		20 25	20 27	20 28	20 38	20 44	20 57	20 40	20 55	20 57	21 06
	d	19 55	20 02		20 03	20 09	20 33			20 25	20 33		20 40	20 46	21 03		20 56	21 03	21 08
Twyford 3	a		20 09				→				20 39				→			21 09	
Maidenhead 3	a		20 17								20 47							21 19	
Slough 3	a	20 10	20 24							20 40	20 54						21 10	21 27	
Ealing Broadway ⊖	a		20 49								21 19							21 52	
London Paddington 15 ⊖	a	20 29	21 01		20 32	20 37				20 59	21 31		21 07	21 14			21 29	22 02	21 37

For complete service between Banbury and Leamington (Birmingham), please refer to table 71

Table 116R

Saturdays

29 March to 17 May

Birmingham, Banbury, Bicester, Oxford and Bedwyn - Reading and London

Network Diagram - refer to first Page of Table 116

		GW	XC	CH	GW	GW	GW	GW	XC	GW	GW	GW	XC	GW	GW	CH	XC	GW	GW	GW	GW	GW	GW	GW	GW	CH
		1	◇1 trolley		◇1	1	1	1	◇1 trolley	◇1 buffet	◇1	◇1 buffet	◇1 trolley	1	◇1		◇1	1	1	◇1 buffet	◇1	◇1	1	◇1 buffet	1	
Birmingham New Street 12	d		19 33						20 04				20 33				21 04									
Birmingham International	d								20 14								21 14									
Coventry	d								20 25								21 25									
Leamington Spa 8	d		20 03						20 38				21 00				21 38									
Banbury	d		20 20				20 38		20 55				21 20				21 55	22 00								
Kings Sutton	d						20 44											22 06								
Heyford	d						20 53											22 15								
Tackley	d						20 57											22 19								
Bicester Town	d			20 28												21 37										22 55
Islip	d			20 39												21 48										23 06
Oxford	a		20 40	20 54			21 08		21 14				21 41			22 03	22 16	22 30								23 21
	d	20 37	20 43		21 01				21 16		21 31		21 43	21 50	22 01		22 18				22 35	23 01			23 07	
Radley	d													21 56											23 13	
Culham	d																								23 17	
Appleford	d																								23 20	
Didcot Parkway	a	20 49									21 43			22 04	22 12						22 47	23 13			23 25	
	d	21 01								21 34	21 45	21 47		22 04	22 13					22 49	22 51	23 13		23 30	23 36	
Cholsey	d	21 07												22 10											23 42	
Goring & Streatley	d	21 12												22 15											23 47	
Pangbourne	d	21 17												22 21											23 51	
Tilehurst	d	21 21												22 24											23 56	
Bedwyn	d							20 48											22 00				23 00			
Hungerford	d							20 54											22 06				23 06			
Kintbury	d							20 58											22 10				23 10			
Newbury	a							21 05											22 17				23 17			
	d							21 05											22 17				23 17			
Newbury Racecourse	d							21 08											22 19				23 19			
Thatcham	d							21 13											22 24				23 24			
Midgham	d							21 17											22 29				23 29			
Aldermaston	d							21 21											22 32				23 32			
Theale	d							21 26											22 37				23 37			
Reading West	d					←		21 33											22 44				23 44			
Reading 7	a	21 27	21 08		21 27	21 27		21 36	21 38	21 48	21 59	22 02	22 08	22 31	22 35		22 45		22 48	23 07	23 09	23 31	23 48	23 48	00 03	
	d	21 33			21 27	21 33				21 50	22 02	22 06		22 33	22 36					23 08	23 10	23 31		23 48	00 04	
Twyford 3	a	→				21 39								22 39											00 11	
Maidenhead 3	a					21 47								22 47											00 19	
Slough 3	a				21 42	21 58					22 15			23 00	22 51						23 28	23 50			00 28	
Ealing Broadway ⊖	a					22 23								23 25											00 54	
London Paddington 15 ⊖	a				22 01	22 32				22 16	22 38	22 40		23 34	23 10					23 42	23 46	00 17		00 36	01 06	

For complete service between Banbury and Leamington (Birmingham), please refer to table 71

Table 116R

Sundays

8 December to 29 December

Birmingham, Banbury, Bicester, Oxford and Bedwyn - Reading and London

Network Diagram - refer to first Page of Table 116

		GW	GW	GW	GW	GW	GW	GW	GW	GW	GW	XC	CH	GW	GW	GW	GW	GW	GW
		1	1	◇1	1	◇1	1	◇1	◇1	1	1	◇1		◇1	1	◇1	1	◇1	1
		A																	
				☕				☕				🛒		☕		☕			
Birmingham New Street 12	d											09 04							
Birmingham International	d											09 14							
Coventry	d											09 25							
Leamington Spa 8	d											09 38							
Banbury	d											09 55							
Kings Sutton	d																		
Heyford	d																		
Tackley	d																		
Bicester Town	d												10 05						
Islip	d												10 16						
Oxford	a											10 14	10 32						
	d					08 50	09 05		09 50		10 05	10 16						10 51	11 05
Radley	d						09 11				10 11								11 11
Culham	d																		
Appleford	d										10 16								
Didcot Parkway	a					09 02	09 20		10 02		10 21							11 06	11 20
	d		08 30	08 43		09 03	09 20	09 44	10 03		10 27					10 44		11 06	11 21
Cholsey	d		08 36				09 26				10 34								11 26
Goring & Streatley	d		08 42				09 32				10 40								11 32
Pangbourne	d		08 46				09 36				10 44								11 38
Tilehurst	d		08 51				09 41				10 48								11 42
Bedwyn	d									09 35							10 42		
Hungerford	d									09 41							10 48		
Kintbury	d									09 46							10 52		
Newbury	a									09 52							10 59		
	d				08 46					09 53				10 32			11 00		
Newbury Racecourse	d				08 48					09 55									
Thatcham	d				08 53					10 00							11 05		
Midgham	d				08 58					10 05									
Aldermaston	d				09 01					10 08									
Theale	d				09 06					10 13							11 13		
Reading West	d				09 14					10 21					←				
Reading 7	a		08 57	09 05	09 17	09 22	09 45	10 02	10 19	10 24	10 55	10 42		10 48	10 55	11 03	11 21	11 25	11 48
	d	00 04	08 58	09 05		09 24	09 52	10 03	10 20		10 56			10 51	10 56	11 04		11 25	11 51
Twyford 3	a	00 11	09 03				09 58				→				11 02				→
Maidenhead 3	a	00 19	09 12				10 06								11 10				
Slough 3	a	00 30	09 20			09 38	10 13		10 38						11 19			11 42	
Ealing Broadway ⊖	a	00 54	09 42				10 42								11 42				
London Paddington 15 ⊖	a	01 05	09 53	09 44		10 00	10 52	10 43	11 00					11 29	11 52	11 43		12 04	

		XC	GW	GW	GW	GW	GW	GW	CH	GW	GW	XC	GW	GW	GW	GW	GW	GW	GW
		◇1	◇1	◇1	1	◇1	◇1	◇1		1	1	◇1	◇1	1	◇1	◇1	1	◇1	1
		☕	☕	☕		☕	☕					☕	☕		☕	☕			
Birmingham New Street 12	d	10 04										11 04							
Birmingham International	d	10 14										11 14							
Coventry	d	10 25										11 25							
Leamington Spa 8	d	10 38										11 38							
Banbury	d	10 55										11 55							
Kings Sutton	d																		
Heyford	d																		
Tackley	d																		
Bicester Town	d								11 27										
Islip	d								11 38										
Oxford	a	11 14							11 54			12 14							
	d	11 16						11 50		12 05		12 16						12 51	13 05
Radley	d									12 11									13 11
Culham	d																		
Appleford	d									12 16									
Didcot Parkway	a							12 02		12 21								13 05	13 20
	d		11 30				11 47	12 03		12 21			12 29		12 47	12 59		13 06	13 29
Cholsey	d									12 26									13 34
Goring & Streatley	d									12 32									13 40
Pangbourne	d									12 38									13 44
Tilehurst	d									12 42									13 48
Bedwyn	d																12 42		
Hungerford	d																12 48		
Kintbury	d																12 52		
Newbury	a																12 59		
	d			11 26							11 53						13 00		
Newbury Racecourse	d										11 55								
Thatcham	d										12 00						13 05		
Midgham	d										12 05								
Aldermaston	d										12 08								
Theale	d										12 13						13 13		
Reading West	d				←	←					12 21			←					
Reading 7	a	11 39	11 43	11 45	11 48	11 45	12 02	12 18		12 48	12 24	12 42	12 44	12 48	13 02	13 14	13 21	13 22	13 51
	d		11 45	11 52	11 51	11 52	12 03	12 19		12 51			12 45	12 51	13 03	13 15		13 23	13 53
Twyford 3	a			→	11 57					→				12 57					→
Maidenhead 3	a				12 04									13 04					
Slough 3	a				12 15			12 34						13 15				13 37	
Ealing Broadway ⊖	a				12 42									13 42					
London Paddington 15 ⊖	a		12 22		12 51	12 29	12 42	12 56					13 23	13 51	13 42	13 59		14 01	

A not 8 December

For complete service between Banbury and Leamington (Birmingham), please refer to table 71

Table 116R

Sundays

8 December to 29 December

Birmingham, Banbury, Bicester, Oxford and Bedwyn - Reading and London

Network Diagram - refer to first Page of Table 116

Station		XC	CH	GW	GW	GW	GW	XC	GW	GW
		◇1		R 1	◇1	1	R 1	◇1	◇1	1
Birmingham New Street 12	d	12 04						12 33		
Birmingham International	d	12 14								
Coventry	d	12 25								
Leamington Spa 8	d	12 38						13 00		
Banbury	d	12 55						13 19		
Kings Sutton	d									
Heyford	d									
Tackley	d									
Bicester Town	d		13 03							
Islip	d		13 14							
Oxford	a	13 14	13 30					13 37		
	d	13 16						13 43	13 50	
Radley	d									
Culham	d									
Appleford	d									
Didcot Parkway	a								14 02	
	d			13 29			13 47		14 03	
Cholsey	d									
Goring & Streatley	d									
Pangbourne	d									
Tilehurst	d									
Bedwyn	d									
Hungerford	d									
Kintbury	d									
Newbury	a									
	d				13 31					13 53
Newbury Racecourse	d									13 55
Thatcham	d									14 00
Midgham	d									14 05
Aldermaston	d									14 08
Theale	d									14 13
Reading West	d					←				14 21
Reading 7	a	13 45		13 48	13 50	13 51	14 02	14 07	14 18	14 24
	d			13 48	13 52	13 53	14 03		14 19	
Twyford 3	a					13 58				
Maidenhead 3	a					14 05				
Slough 3	a					14 16			14 35	
Ealing Broadway ⊖	a					14 41				
London Paddington 15 ⊖	a			14 23	14 30	14 51	14 42		14 57	

Station		GW	XC	GW	GW	GW	XC	GW	GW	CH
		1	◇1	R 1	1	R 1	◇1	1	◇1	
Birmingham New Street 12	d		13 04				13 33			
Birmingham International	d		13 14							
Coventry	d		13 25							
Leamington Spa 8	d		13 38				13 59			
Banbury	d		13 55				14 19			
Kings Sutton	d									
Heyford	d									
Tackley	d									
Bicester Town	d									14 27
Islip	d									14 38
Oxford	a		14 14				14 37			14 54
	d	14 05	14 16				14 43		14 51	
Radley	d	14 11								
Culham	d									
Appleford	d									
Didcot Parkway	a	14 18							15 05	
	d	14 29		14 29		14 47			15 06	
Cholsey	d	14 34								
Goring & Streatley	d	14 40								
Pangbourne	d	14 44								
Tilehurst	d	14 48								
Bedwyn	d							14 42		
Hungerford	d							14 48		
Kintbury	d							14 52		
Newbury	a							14 59		
	d							15 00		
Newbury Racecourse	d									
Thatcham	d							15 05		
Midgham	d									
Aldermaston	d									
Theale	d							15 13		
Reading West	d				←					
Reading 7	a	14 50	14 39	14 45	14 50	15 02	15 07	15 21	15 22	
	d	14 53		14 45	14 53	15 03			15 23	
Twyford 3	a	→			14 59					
Maidenhead 3	a				15 06					
Slough 3	a				15 14				15 38	
Ealing Broadway ⊖	a				15 42					
London Paddington 15 ⊖	a			15 23	15 51	15 42			15 57	

Station		GW	XC	GW	GW	GW	XC	GW	GW	GW
		1	◇1	◇1	1	R 1	◇1	◇1	1	1
Birmingham New Street 12	d		14 04				14 33			
Birmingham International	d		14 14							
Coventry	d		14 25							
Leamington Spa 8	d		14 38				15 00			
Banbury	d		14 55				15 19			
Kings Sutton	d									
Heyford	d									
Tackley	d									
Bicester Town	d									
Islip	d									
Oxford	a		15 14				15 40			
	d	15 05	15 16				15 43	15 49		16 05
Radley	d	15 11								16 11
Culham	d									
Appleford	d	15 16								
Didcot Parkway	a	15 21						16 02		16 19
	d	15 29		15 29		15 47		16 08		16 29
Cholsey	d	15 34								16 34
Goring & Streatley	d	15 40								16 39
Pangbourne	d	15 44								16 40
Tilehurst	d	15 48								16 48
Bedwyn	d									
Hungerford	d									
Kintbury	d									
Newbury	a									
	d								15 53	
Newbury Racecourse	d								15 55	
Thatcham	d								16 00	
Midgham	d								16 05	
Aldermaston	d								16 08	
Theale	d								16 13	
Reading West	d				←				16 21	
Reading 7	a	15 51	15 39	15 44	15 51	16 02	16 07	16 23	16 24	16 53
	d	15 53		15 45	15 53	16 03		16 24		16 53
Twyford 3	a	→			15 59					→
Maidenhead 3	a				16 06					
Slough 3	a				16 17			16 38		
Ealing Broadway ⊖	a				16 42					
London Paddington 15 ⊖	a			16 22	16 53	16 42		16 58		

Station		XC	CH	GW	GW	GW	GW	XC	GW	GW
		◇1		R 1	◇1	1	R 1	◇1	◇1	1
Birmingham New Street 12	d	15 04						15 33		
Birmingham International	d	15 14								
Coventry	d	15 25								
Leamington Spa 8	d	15 38						16 00		
Banbury	d	15 55						16 19		
Kings Sutton	d									
Heyford	d									
Tackley	d									
Bicester Town	d		16 03							
Islip	d		16 14							
Oxford	a	16 14	16 30					16 37		
	d	16 16						16 43		
Radley	d									
Culham	d									
Appleford	d									
Didcot Parkway	a									
	d			16 29			16 47		16 59	
Cholsey	d									
Goring & Streatley	d									
Pangbourne	d									
Tilehurst	d									
Bedwyn	d									16 42
Hungerford	d									16 48
Kintbury	d									16 52
Newbury	a									16 59
	d				16 31					17 00
Newbury Racecourse	d									
Thatcham	d									17 05
Midgham	d									
Aldermaston	d									
Theale	d									17 13
Reading West	d					←				
Reading 7	a	16 39		16 44	16 49	16 53	17 02	17 08	17 16	17 21
	d			16 45	16 52	16 53	17 03		17 16	
Twyford 3	a					16 59				
Maidenhead 3	a					17 06				
Slough 3	a					17 15				
Ealing Broadway ⊖	a					17 42				
London Paddington 15 ⊖	a			17 23	17 30	17 52	17 43		17 57	

For complete service between Banbury and Leamington (Birmingham), please refer to table 71

Table 116R

Sundays

8 December to 29 December

Birmingham, Banbury, Bicester, Oxford and Bedwyn - Reading and London

Network Diagram - refer to first Page of Table 116

Station		GW	GW	XC	GW	GW	GW	XC	GW	GW
		◇1 ⊡	1	◇1 ⊡	◇1 ⊡	1	R 1 ⊡	◇1 ⊤	◇1 ⊡	◇1 ⊡
Birmingham New Street 12	d			16 04				16 33		
Birmingham International	d			16 14						
Coventry	d			16 25						
Leamington Spa 8	d			16 38				17 00		
Banbury	d			16 55				17 18		
Kings Sutton	d									
Heyford	d									
Tackley	d									
Bicester Town	d									
Islip	d									
Oxford	a			17 14				17 37		
	d	16 53	17 05	17 16				17 43		17 50
Radley	d		17 11							
Culham	d									
Appleford	d		17 16							
Didcot Parkway	a	17 06	17 22							18 03
	d	17 07	17 29		17 29		17 47		17 59	18 03
Cholsey	d		17 34							
Goring & Streatley	d		17 40							
Pangbourne	d		17 44							
Tilehurst	d		17 48							
Bedwyn	d									
Hungerford	d									
Kintbury	d									
Newbury	a									
	d									
Newbury Racecourse	d									
Thatcham	d									
Midgham	d									
Aldermaston	d									
Theale	d									
Reading West	d					←				
Reading 7	a	17 25	17 51	17 38	17 49	17 51	18 02	18 07	18 17	18 19
	d	17 27	17 53		17 50	17 53	18 03		18 17	18 20
Twyford 3	a		→			17 58				
Maidenhead 3	a					18 05				
Slough 3	a	17 44				18 15				18 36
Ealing Broadway ⊖	a					18 42				
London Paddington 15 ⊖	a	18 07			18 22	18 52	18 44		18 57	19 01

Station		CH	GW	GW	XC	GW	GW	GW	XC	GW
			1	1	◇1 ⊡	◇1 ⊡	1	◇1 ⊡	◇1 ⊤	◇1 ⊡
Birmingham New Street 12	d				17 04				17 33	
Birmingham International	d				17 14					
Coventry	d				17 25					
Leamington Spa 8	d				17 38				18 01	
Banbury	d				17 55				18 20	
Kings Sutton	d									
Heyford	d									
Tackley	d									
Bicester Town	d	17 27								
Islip	d	17 38								
Oxford	a	17 54			18 14				18 41	
	d			18 05	18 16				18 43	
Radley	d			18 11						
Culham	d									
Appleford	d									
Didcot Parkway	a			18 19						
	d			18 29				18 47		18 59
Cholsey	d			18 34						
Goring & Streatley	d			18 40						
Pangbourne	d			18 44						
Tilehurst	d			18 48						
Bedwyn	d									
Hungerford	d									
Kintbury	d									
Newbury	a									
	d		17 53			18 34				
Newbury Racecourse	d		17 55							
Thatcham	d		18 00							
Midgham	d		18 05							
Aldermaston	d		18 08							
Theale	d		18 13							
Reading West	d		18 21				←			
Reading 7	a		18 24	18 51	18 39	18 49	18 51	19 02	19 07	19 14
	d			18 53		18 52	18 53	19 03		19 20
Twyford 3	a			→			18 58			
Maidenhead 3	a						19 10			
Slough 3	a						19 17			
Ealing Broadway ⊖	a						19 42			
London Paddington 15 ⊖	a					19 29	19 52	19 44		19 58

Station		GW	GW	GW	GW	XC	CH	XC	GW	GW
		1	◇1 ⊡	R 1 ⊡	1	◇1 ⊡		◇1 ⊤	◇1 ⊡	◇1
Birmingham New Street 12	d					18 04		18 33		
Birmingham International	d					18 14				
Coventry	d					18 25				
Leamington Spa 8	d					18 38		19 00		
Banbury	d					18 55		19 19		
Kings Sutton	d									
Heyford	d									
Tackley	d									
Bicester Town	d						19 07			
Islip	d						19 18			
Oxford	a					19 14	19 34	19 37		
	d		18 50		19 05	19 16		19 43		19 50
Radley	d				19 11					
Culham	d									
Appleford	d				19 16					
Didcot Parkway	a		19 02		19 22					20 03
	d		19 08	19 16	19 29				19 59	20 04
Cholsey	d				19 34					
Goring & Streatley	d				19 40					
Pangbourne	d				19 44					
Tilehurst	d				19 48					
Bedwyn	d	18 42								
Hungerford	d	18 48								
Kintbury	d	18 52								
Newbury	a	18 59								
	d	19 00								
Newbury Racecourse	d									
Thatcham	d	19 05								
Midgham	d									
Aldermaston	d									
Theale	d	19 13								
Reading West	d									
Reading 7	a	19 21	19 28	19 33	19 51	19 39		20 07	20 16	20 22
	d		19 29	19 34	19 53				20 17	20 23
Twyford 3	a				19 58					
Maidenhead 3	a				20 05					
Slough 3	a		19 42		20 17					20 39
Ealing Broadway ⊖	a				20 42					
London Paddington 15 ⊖	a		20 02	20 13	20 53				20 57	21 00

Station		GW	GW	GW	XC	GW	GW	XC	GW	GW
		1	◇1 ⊡	1	◇1 ⊡	◇1 ⊡	1	◇1 ⊤	◇1 ⊡	◇1
Birmingham New Street 12	d				19 04			19 33		
Birmingham International	d				19 14					
Coventry	d				19 25					
Leamington Spa 8	d				19 38			20 00		
Banbury	d				19 55			20 19		
Kings Sutton	d									
Heyford	d									
Tackley	d									
Bicester Town	d									
Islip	d									
Oxford	a				20 14			20 40		
	d			20 05	20 16			20 43		20 50
Radley	d			20 11						
Culham	d									
Appleford	d									
Didcot Parkway	a			20 19						21 02
	d		20 16	20 29					20 59	21 03
Cholsey	d			20 34						
Goring & Streatley	d			20 40						
Pangbourne	d			20 44						
Tilehurst	d			20 48						
Bedwyn	d									
Hungerford	d									
Kintbury	d									
Newbury	a									
	d	19 53				20 25				
Newbury Racecourse	d	19 55								
Thatcham	d	20 00								
Midgham	d	20 05								
Aldermaston	d	20 08								
Theale	d	20 13								
Reading West	d	20 21					←			
Reading 7	a	20 24	20 33	20 51	20 39	20 49	20 51	21 07	21 16	21 20
	d		20 34	20 53		20 52	20 53		21 17	21 22
Twyford 3	a			→			20 58			
Maidenhead 3	a						21 05			21 35
Slough 3	a						21 17			21 39
Ealing Broadway ⊖	a						21 42			
London Paddington 15 ⊖	a		21 04			21 29	21 52		21 56	22 03

For complete service between Banbury and Leamington (Birmingham), please refer to table 71

Table 116R

Sundays

8 December to 29 December

Birmingham, Banbury, Bicester, Oxford and Bedwyn - Reading and London

Network Diagram - refer to first Page of Table 116

		CH	GW	GW	GW	XC	XC	GW	GW	GW	XC	GW	GW	CH	GW	GW	GW	GW	GW	GW	GW
			1	◇1	1	◇1	◇1	◇1	◇1	1	◇1	◇1	1		1	◇1	◇1			1	1
				☕		☕	🍴	☕			🍴	☕					☕	🚌			
Birmingham New Street 12	d					20 04	20 33				21 04										
Birmingham International	d					20 14					21 14										
Coventry	d					20 25					21 24										
Leamington Spa 8	d					20 38	21 00				21 35										
Banbury	d					20 55	21 19														
Kings Sutton	d																				
Heyford	d																				
Tackley	d																				
Bicester Town	d	20 27												22 03							
Islip	d	20 38												22 14							
Oxford	a	20 54				21 14	21 37				22 08			22 30							
	d				21 05	21 16	21 40		21 50		22 10		22 17			22 46		23 00			
Radley	d				21 11								22 23					23 15			
Culham	d																				
Appleford	d																				
Didcot Parkway	a				21 22				22 01				22 28			22 58		23 35			
	d			21 24	21 29			22 01	22 03				22 29			22 59	23 10			23 50	
Cholsey	d				21 34								22 34							23 56	
Goring & Streatley	d				21 40								22 40							00 01	
Pangbourne	d				21 44								22 44							00 06	
Tilehurst	d				21 48								22 48							00 10	
Bedwyn	d		20 54												22 35						
Hungerford	d		21 00												22 41						
Kintbury	d		21 04												22 45						
Newbury	a		21 11												22 52						
	d		21 12							21 53		22 19			22 53				23 23		23 45
Newbury Racecourse	d									21 55											23 47
Thatcham	d		21 17							22 00					22 58				23 28		23 52
Midgham	d									22 05											23 57
Aldermaston	d									22 08											00 01
Theale	d		21 25							22 13					23 06				23 36		00 06
Reading West	d									22 21											00s13
Reading 7	a		21 33	21 39	21 55	21 46	22 08	22 18	22 18	22 24	22 35	22 39	22 57		23 15	23 18	23 29		23 44	00 15	00 17
	d			21 47	21 56			22 19	22 22			22 40	23 03			23 18	23 31			00 15	
Twyford 3	a				22 02								23 09							00 23	
Maidenhead 3	a				22 10								23 17							00 31	
Slough 3	a				22 18				22 39				23 25			23 36				00 39	
Ealing Broadway ⊖	a				22 42								23 54							01 02	
London Paddington 15 ⊖	a			22 30	22 52			22 58	23 03			23 18	00 05			00 06	00 13			01 14	

For complete service between Banbury and Leamington (Birmingham), please refer to table 71

Table 116R

Sundays

5 January to 9 February

Birmingham, Banbury, Bicester, Oxford and Bedwyn - Reading and London

Network Diagram - refer to first Page of Table 116

Station		GW	GW	GW	GW	GW	GW	GW	GW	GW
		1	1	1	◇1	1	◇1	◇1	1	1
							☕			
Birmingham New Street 12	d									
Birmingham International	d									
Coventry	d									
Leamington Spa 8	d									
Banbury	d									
Kings Sutton	d									
Heyford	d									
Tackley	d									
Bicester Town	d									
Islip	d									
Oxford	a									
	d				08 43	08 56		09 43		10 05
Radley	d					09 02				10 11
Culham	d									
Appleford	d									10 16
Didcot Parkway	a				08 55	09 11		09 55		10 21
	d		08 30		08 56	09 11	09 40	09 56		10 27
Cholsey	d		08 36			09 18				10 34
Goring & Streatley	d		08 41			09 23				10 40
Pangbourne	d									
Tilehurst	d		08 51			09 30				10 48
Bedwyn	d								09 35	
Hungerford	d								09 41	
Kintbury	d								09 46	
Newbury	a								09 52	
	d			08 48					09 53	
Newbury Racecourse	d			08 50					09 55	
Thatcham	d			08 55					10 00	
Midgham	d			09 00					10 05	
Aldermaston	d			09 03					10 08	
Theale	d			09 08					10 13	
Reading West	d			09 16					10 21	
Reading 7	a		08 57	09 19	09 20	09 40	10 03	10 19	10 24	10 55
	d	00 08	08 59		09 26	09 48	10 03	10 20		10 56
Twyford 3	a	00 14	09 03			09 54				↪
Maidenhead 3	a	00 22	09 12			10 02				
Slough 3	a	00 34	09 20		09 40	10 21		10 38		
Ealing Broadway ⊖	a	00 58	09 43			10 43				
London Paddington 15 ⊖	a	01 09	09 54		10 03	10 53	10 43	11 00		

Station		XC	CH	GW	GW	GW	GW	GW	GW	GW
		◇1		◇1	1	◇1	1	◇1	◇1	◇1
		🍴		☕		☕			☕	☕
Birmingham New Street 12	d	09 04								
Birmingham International	d	09 14								
Coventry	d	09 25								
Leamington Spa 8	d	09 38								
Banbury	d	09 55								
Kings Sutton	d									
Heyford	d									
Tackley	d									
Bicester Town	d		10 05							
Islip	d		10 16							
Oxford	a	10 14	10 32							
	d	10 16						10 51		
Radley	d									
Culham	d									
Appleford	d									
Didcot Parkway	a							11 04		
	d					10 44		11 04	11 20	
Cholsey	d									
Goring & Streatley	d									
Pangbourne	d									
Tilehurst	d									
Bedwyn	d						10 42			
Hungerford	d						10 48			
Kintbury	d						10 52			
Newbury	a						10 59			
	d			10 32			11 00			11 26
Newbury Racecourse	d									
Thatcham	d						11 05			
Midgham	d									
Aldermaston	d									
Theale	d						11 13			
Reading West	d				←					
Reading 7	a	10 45		10 48	10 55	11 08	11 21	11 27	11 40	11 45
	d			10 51	10 56	11 09		11 27	11 45	11 52
Twyford 3	a				11 02					
Maidenhead 3	a				11 10					
Slough 3	a				11 27			11 42		
Ealing Broadway ⊖	a				11 50					
London Paddington 15 ⊖	a			11 29	12 00	11 46		12 06	12 25	12 29

Station		GW	XC	GW	GW	CH	GW	GW	GW	XC
		1	◇1	◇1	◇1		1	◇1	1	◇1
			☕	☕				☕		☕
Birmingham New Street 12	d		10 04							11 04
Birmingham International	d		10 14							11 14
Coventry	d		10 25							11 25
Leamington Spa 8	d		10 38							11 38
Banbury	d		10 55							11 55
Kings Sutton	d									
Heyford	d									
Tackley	d									
Bicester Town	d					11 27				
Islip	d					11 38				
Oxford	a		11 14			11 54				12 14
	d	11 05	11 16		11 47				12 05	12 16
Radley	d	11 11							12 11	
Culham	d									
Appleford	d								12 16	
Didcot Parkway	a	11 20			11 59				12 22	
	d	11 29		11 41	12 00			12 19	12 29	
Cholsey	d	11 34							12 34	
Goring & Streatley	d	11 40							12 40	
Pangbourne	d									
Tilehurst	d	11 48							12 48	
Bedwyn	d									
Hungerford	d									
Kintbury	d									
Newbury	a									
	d						11 53			
Newbury Racecourse	d						11 55			
Thatcham	d						12 00			
Midgham	d						12 05			
Aldermaston	d						12 08			
Theale	d						12 13			
Reading West	d						12 21			
Reading 7	a	11 54	11 45	12 02	12 18		12 24	12 41	12 54	12 45
	d	11 57		12 03	12 19			12 45	12 57	
Twyford 3	a	12 03							13 03	
Maidenhead 3	a	12 10							13 14	
Slough 3	a	12 21			12 40				13 21	
Ealing Broadway ⊖	a	12 42							13 42	
London Paddington 15 ⊖	a	12 53		12 42	13 00			13 23	13 55	

Station		GW	GW	GW	GW	GW	XC	CH	GW	GW
		◇1	1	◇1	B 1	1	◇1		◇1	1
		☕			☕		🍴		☕	
Birmingham New Street 12	d						12 04			
Birmingham International	d						12 14			
Coventry	d						12 25			
Leamington Spa 8	d						12 38			
Banbury	d						12 55			
Kings Sutton	d									
Heyford	d									
Tackley	d									
Bicester Town	d							13 03		
Islip	d							13 14		
Oxford	a						13 14	13 30		
	d			12 51		13 05	13 16			
Radley	d					13 11				
Culham	d									
Appleford	d									
Didcot Parkway	a			13 05		13 22				
	d	12 41		13 06	13 25	13 29				
Cholsey	d					13 34				
Goring & Streatley	d					13 40				
Pangbourne	d									
Tilehurst	d					13 48				
Bedwyn	d		12 42							
Hungerford	d		12 48							
Kintbury	d		12 52							
Newbury	a		12 59							
	d		13 00						13 31	
Newbury Racecourse	d									
Thatcham	d		13 05							
Midgham	d									
Aldermaston	d									
Theale	d		13 13							
Reading West	d									←
Reading 7	a	13 02	13 21	13 26	13 45	13 54	13 45		13 50	13 54
	d	13 03		13 27	13 45	13 57			13 52	13 57
Twyford 3	a					↪				14 03
Maidenhead 3	a									14 10
Slough 3	a			13 43						14 21
Ealing Broadway ⊖	a									14 42
London Paddington 15 ⊖	a	13 43		14 08	14 26				14 30	14 56

For complete service between Banbury and Leamington (Birmingham), please refer to table 71

Table 116R

Sundays

5 January to 9 February

Birmingham, Banbury, Bicester, Oxford and Bedwyn - Reading and London

Network Diagram - refer to first Page of Table 116

Station		GW	XC	GW	GW	GW	GW	XC	GW	XC
		R 1 ☕	◇1 🛒	1	◇1	R 1 ☕	1	◇1 ☕	R 1 ☕	◇1 🛒
Birmingham New Street 12	d		12 33					13 04		13 33
Birmingham International	d							13 14		
Coventry	d							13 25		
Leamington Spa 8	d		13 00					13 38		14 00
Banbury	d		13 19					13 55		14 19
Kings Sutton	d									
Heyford	d									
Tackley	d									
Bicester Town	d									
Islip	d									
Oxford	a		13 37					14 14		14 37
	d		13 43		13 50		14 05	14 16		14 43
Radley	d						14 11			
Culham	d									
Appleford	d									
Didcot Parkway	a				14 02		14 19			
	d	13 41			14 03	14 28	14 29		14 41	
Cholsey	d						14 34			
Goring & Streatley	d						14 40			
Pangbourne	d									
Tilehurst	d						14 48			
Bedwyn	d									
Hungerford	d									
Kintbury	d									
Newbury	a									
	d			13 53						
Newbury Racecourse	d			13 55						
Thatcham	d			14 00						
Midgham	d			14 05						
Aldermaston	d			14 08						
Theale	d			14 13						
Reading West	d			14 21						
Reading 7	a	14 02	14 14	14 24	14 25	14 49	14 56	14 45	15 02	15 13
	d	14 03			14 25	14 49	14 59		15 03	
Twyford 3	a						15 03			
Maidenhead 3	a						15 10			
Slough 3	a				14 42		15 21			
Ealing Broadway ⊖	a						15 46			
London Paddington 15 ⊖	a	14 42			15 03	15 26	15 56		15 42	

Station		GW	GW	CH	GW	XC	GW	GW	GW	XC
		1	◇1		1	◇1 ☕	◇1 ☕	1	R 1 ☕	◇1 🛒
Birmingham New Street 12	d					14 04				14 33
Birmingham International	d					14 14				
Coventry	d					14 25				
Leamington Spa 8	d					14 38				15 00
Banbury	d					14 55				15 19
Kings Sutton	d									
Heyford	d									
Tackley	d									
Bicester Town	d			14 27						
Islip	d			14 38						
Oxford	a			14 54		15 14				15 40
	d		14 51		15 05	15 16				15 43
Radley	d				15 11					
Culham	d									
Appleford	d				15 16					
Didcot Parkway	a		15 05		15 22					
	d		15 06		15 29		15 29		15 41	
Cholsey	d				15 34					
Goring & Streatley	d				15 40					
Pangbourne	d									
Tilehurst	d				15 48					
Bedwyn	d	14 42								
Hungerford	d	14 48								
Kintbury	d	14 52								
Newbury	a	14 59								
	d	15 00								
Newbury Racecourse	d									
Thatcham	d	15 05								
Midgham	d									
Aldermaston	d									
Theale	d	15 13								
Reading West	d							←		
Reading 7	a	15 21	15 26		15 56	15 45	15 50	15 56	16 02	16 13
	d		15 27		15 57		15 51	15 57	16 03	
Twyford 3	a				→			16 03		
Maidenhead 3	a							16 10		
Slough 3	a		15 44					16 23		
Ealing Broadway ⊖	a							16 46		
London Paddington 15 ⊖	a		16 06				16 28	16 58	16 44	

Station		GW	GW	GW	GW	XC	CH	GW	GW	GW
		◇1 ☕	1	R 1 ☕	1	◇1 ☕		◇1 ☕	1	R 1 ☕
Birmingham New Street 12	d					15 04				
Birmingham International	d					15 14				
Coventry	d					15 25				
Leamington Spa 8	d					15 38				
Banbury	d					15 55				
Kings Sutton	d									
Heyford	d									
Tackley	d									
Bicester Town	d						16 03			
Islip	d						16 14			
Oxford	a					16 14	16 30			
	d	15 49			16 05	16 16				
Radley	d				16 11					
Culham	d									
Appleford	d									
Didcot Parkway	a	16 02			16 19					
	d	16 04		16 21	16 29					16 41
Cholsey	d				16 34					
Goring & Streatley	d				16 40					
Pangbourne	d									
Tilehurst	d				16 48					
Bedwyn	d									
Hungerford	d									
Kintbury	d									
Newbury	a									
	d		15 53					16 31		
Newbury Racecourse	d		15 55							
Thatcham	d		16 00							
Midgham	d		16 05							
Aldermaston	d		16 08							
Theale	d		16 13							
Reading West	d		16 21						←	
Reading 7	a	16 23	16 24	16 44	16 56	16 46		16 49	16 56	17 02
	d	16 24		16 45	16 57			16 52	16 57	17 03
Twyford 3	a				→				17 03	
Maidenhead 3	a								17 10	
Slough 3	a	16 38							17 20	
Ealing Broadway ⊖	a								17 42	
London Paddington 15 ⊖	a	17 04		17 23				17 27	17 54	17 44

Station		XC	GW	GW	GW	GW	XC	GW	GW	GW
		◇1 🛒	◇1 ☕	1	◇1 ☕	1	◇1 ☕	◇1 ☕	1	R 1 ☕
Birmingham New Street 12	d	15 33					16 04			
Birmingham International	d						16 14			
Coventry	d						16 25			
Leamington Spa 8	d	15 59					16 38			
Banbury	d	16 19					16 55			
Kings Sutton	d									
Heyford	d									
Tackley	d									
Bicester Town	d									
Islip	d									
Oxford	a	16 37					17 14			
	d	16 43			16 53	17 05	17 16			
Radley	d					17 11				
Culham	d									
Appleford	d					17 16				
Didcot Parkway	a				17 06	17 22				
	d		16 55		17 07	17 29		17 29		17 41
Cholsey	d					17 34				
Goring & Streatley	d					17 40				
Pangbourne	d									
Tilehurst	d					17 48				
Bedwyn	d			16 42						
Hungerford	d			16 48						
Kintbury	d			16 52						
Newbury	a			16 59						
	d			17 00						
Newbury Racecourse	d									
Thatcham	d			17 05						
Midgham	d									
Aldermaston	d									
Theale	d			17 13						
Reading West	d								←	
Reading 7	a	17 14	17 16	17 21	17 30	17 57	17 44	17 49	17 57	18 02
	d		17 16		17 30	17 57		17 50	17 57	18 03
Twyford 3	a					→			18 03	
Maidenhead 3	a								18 12	
Slough 3	a				17 48				18 25	
Ealing Broadway ⊖	a								18 51	
London Paddington 15 ⊖	a		17 57		18 14			18 26	19 01	18 44

For complete service between Banbury and Leamington (Birmingham), please refer to table 71

Table 116R

Sundays

5 January to 9 February

Birmingham, Banbury, Bicester, Oxford and Bedwyn - Reading and London

Network Diagram - refer to first Page of Table 116

Station		XC	GW	GW	CH	GW	GW	XC	GW	GW	GW	XC	GW	GW	GW	GW	GW	XC	CH
		◇1	◇1	◇1		1	1	◇1	◇1	1	◇1	◇1	◇1	1	◇1	1	1	◇1	
Birmingham New Street 12	d	16 33						17 04				17 33						18 04	
Birmingham International	d							17 14										18 14	
Coventry	d							17 25										18 25	
Leamington Spa 8	d	17 00						17 38				18 00						18 38	
Banbury	d	17 19						17 55				18 19						18 55	
Kings Sutton	d																		
Heyford	d																		
Tackley	d																		
Bicester Town	d				17 27														19 07
Islip	d				17 38														19 18
Oxford	a	17 37			17 54			18 14				18 40						19 14	19 34
	d	17 43		17 50			18 05	18 16				18 42			18 50		19 05	19 16	
Radley	d						18 11										19 11		
Culham	d																		
Appleford	d																19 16		
Didcot Parkway	a			18 03			18 19								19 02		19 22		
	d		17 55	18 03			18 29				18 41		18 59		19 08	19 12	19 29		
Cholsey	d						18 35										19 34		
Goring & Streatley	d						18 40										19 40		
Pangbourne	d																		
Tilehurst	d						18 48										19 48		
Bedwyn	d													18 42					
Hungerford	d													18 48					
Kintbury	d													18 52					
Newbury	a													18 59					
	d					17 53			18 34					19 00					
Newbury Racecourse	d					17 55													
Thatcham	d					18 00								19 05					
Midgham	d					18 05													
Aldermaston	d					18 08													
Theale	d					18 13								19 13					
Reading West	d					18 21				←									
Reading 7	a	18 13	18 17	18 22		18 24	18 53	18 46	18 49	18 53	19 02	19 12	19 20	19 21	19 28	19 33	19 56	19 45	
	d		18 17	18 24			18 57		18 52	18 57	19 03		19 20		19 29	19 34	19 57		
Twyford 3	a						→			19 03							20 03		
Maidenhead 3	a									19 10							20 10		
Slough 3	a			18 43						19 22					19 46		20 21		
Ealing Broadway ⊖	a									19 42							20 47		
London Paddington 15 ⊖	a		19 03	19 06					19 29	19 55	19 43		19 58		20 11	20 13	20 57		

Station		XC	GW	GW	GW	GW	GW	XC	GW	GW	XC	GW	GW	CH	GW	GW	GW	XC	XC
		◇1	◇1	1	◇1	◇1	1	◇1	◇1	1	◇1	◇1	◇1		1	◇1	1	◇1	◇1
Birmingham New Street 12	d	18 33						19 04			19 33							20 04	20 33
Birmingham International	d							19 14										20 14	
Coventry	d							19 25										20 25	
Leamington Spa 8	d	19 00						19 38			20 00							20 38	21 00
Banbury	d	19 19						19 55			20 19							20 55	21 19
Kings Sutton	d																		
Heyford	d																		
Tackley	d																		
Bicester Town	d													20 27					
Islip	d													20 38					
Oxford	a	19 37						20 14			20 40			20 54				21 14	21 37
	d	19 43			19 50		20 05	20 16			20 43		20 50				21 05	21 16	21 40
Radley	d						20 11										21 11		
Culham	d																		
Appleford	d																		
Didcot Parkway	a				20 03		20 19						21 02				21 19		
	d		19 59		20 04	20 16	20 29					20 56	21 03			21 24	21 29		
Cholsey	d						20 34										21 34		
Goring & Streatley	d						20 40										21 40		
Pangbourne	d																		
Tilehurst	d						20 48										21 48		
Bedwyn	d														20 54				
Hungerford	d														21 00				
Kintbury	d														21 04				
Newbury	a														21 11				
	d			19 53					20 25						21 12				
Newbury Racecourse	d			19 55															
Thatcham	d			20 00											21 17				
Midgham	d			20 05															
Aldermaston	d			20 08															
Theale	d			20 13											21 25				
Reading West	d			20 21						←									
Reading 7	a	20 13	20 19	20 24	20 28	20 39	20 56	20 47	20 49	20 56	21 13	21 16	21 23		21 33	21 47	22 00	21 44	22 10
	d		20 21		20 29	20 40	20 57		20 52	20 57		21 17	21 26			21 47	22 01		
Twyford 3	a						→			21 01							22 07		
Maidenhead 3	a									21 10			21 39				22 15		
Slough 3	a				20 48					21 21			21 47				22 23		
Ealing Broadway ⊖	a									21 43							22 47		
London Paddington 15 ⊖	a		20 58		21 09	21 15			21 29	21 58		21 59	22 09			22 30	22 58		

For complete service between Banbury and Leamington (Birmingham), please refer to table 71

Table 116R

Sundays

5 January to 9 February

Birmingham, Banbury, Bicester, Oxford and Bedwyn - Reading and London

Network Diagram - refer to first Page of Table 116

		GW	GW	GW	XC	GW	GW	CH	GW	GW	GW	GW	GW	GW	GW
		◇1	◇1	1	◇1	◇1	1		1	◇1	◇1			1	1
		☕			✕	☕					☕	🚌			
Birmingham New Street [12]	d				21 04										
Birmingham International	d				21 14										
Coventry	d				21 24										
Leamington Spa [8]	d				21 35										
Banbury	d														
Kings Sutton	d														
Heyford	d														
Tackley	d														
Bicester Town	d							22 03							
Islip	d							22 14							
Oxford	a				22 08			22 30							
	d		21 44		22 10		22 17			22 46		23 00			
Radley	d						22 23					23 15			
Culham	d														
Appleford	d														
Didcot Parkway	a		21 56				22 28			22 58		23 35			
	d	21 55	21 58				22 29			22 59	23 10			23 46	
Cholsey	d						22 34							23 52	
Goring & Streatley	d						22 40							23 57	
Pangbourne	d														
Tilehurst	d						22 48							00 04	
Bedwyn	d								22 35						
Hungerford	d								22 41						
Kintbury	d								22 45						
Newbury	a								22 52						
	d			21 53		22 19			22 53				23 23		23 45
Newbury Racecourse	d			21 55											23 47
Thatcham	d			22 00					22 58				23 28		23 52
Midgham	d			22 05											23 57
Aldermaston	d			22 08											00 01
Theale	d			22 13					23 06				23 36		00 06
Reading West	d			22 21											00s13
Reading [7]	a	22 15	22 18	22 24	22 38	22 40	22 59		23 15	23 24	23 32		23 44	00 14	00 17
	d	22 17	22 22			22 41	23 03			23 25	23 33			00 15	
Twyford [3]	a						23 09							00 23	
Maidenhead [3]	a						23 17							00 31	
Slough [3]	a		22 42				23 25			23 42				00 38	
Ealing Broadway ⊖	a						23 54							01 02	
London Paddington [15] ⊖	a	23 02	23 06			23 22	00 05			00 11	00 13			01 14	

For complete service between Banbury and Leamington (Birmingham), please refer to table 71

Table 116R

Sundays

16 February to 23 March

Birmingham, Banbury, Bicester, Oxford and Bedwyn - Reading and London

Network Diagram - refer to first Page of Table 116

		GW	GW	GW	GW	GW	GW	GW	GW	GW	XC	CH	GW	GW
		1	1	1	◇1	1	◇1	◇1	1	1	◇1		◇1	1
Birmingham New Street 12	d										09 04			
Birmingham International	d										09 14			
Coventry	d										09 25			
Leamington Spa 8	d										09 38			
Banbury	d										09 55			
Kings Sutton	d													
Heyford	d													
Tackley	d													
Bicester Town	d											10 05		
Islip	d											10 16		
Oxford	a										10 14	10 32		
	d				08 50	09 05		09 50		10 05	10 16			
Radley	d					09 11				10 11				
Culham	d													
Appleford	d									10 16				
Didcot Parkway	a				09 02	09 20		10 02		10 21				
	d		08 30		09 03	09 20	09 44	10 03		10 28				
Cholsey	d		08 36			09 26				10 34				
Goring & Streatley	d		08 41			09 32				10 40				
Pangbourne	d		08 46			09 36				10 44				
Tilehurst	d		08 51			09 41				10 48				
Bedwyn	d								09 35					
Hungerford	d								09 41					
Kintbury	d								09 46					
Newbury	a								09 52					
	d			08 48					09 53				10 32	
Newbury Racecourse	d			08 50					09 55					
Thatcham	d			08 55					10 00					
Midgham	d			09 00					10 05					
Aldermaston	d			09 03					10 08					
Theale	d			09 08					10 13					
Reading West	d			09 16					10 21					←
Reading 7	a		08 57	09 19	09 20	09 45	10 02	10 19	10 24	10 55	10 40		10 48	10 55
	d	00 04	08 58		09 24	09 52	10 03	10 20		10 56			10 51	10 56
Twyford 3	a	00 11	09 03			09 58				→				11 02
Maidenhead 3	a	00 19	09 12			10 06								11 10
Slough 3	a	00 30	09 20		09 38	10 13		10 38						11 19
Ealing Broadway ⊖	a	00 54	09 42			10 42								11 42
London Paddington 15 ⊖	a	01 05	09 53		10 00	10 53	10 43	11 00					11 29	11 53

		GW	GW	GW	GW	GW	XC	GW	GW	GW	GW	CH	GW
		◇1	1	◇1	◇1	1	◇1	◇1	1	◇1	◇1		1
Birmingham New Street 12	d						10 04						
Birmingham International	d						10 14						
Coventry	d						10 25						
Leamington Spa 8	d						10 38						
Banbury	d						10 55						
Kings Sutton	d												
Heyford	d												
Tackley	d												
Bicester Town	d											11 27	
Islip	d											11 38	
Oxford	a						11 14					11 54	
	d			10 51		11 05	11 16				11 50		
Radley	d					11 11							
Culham	d												
Appleford	d												
Didcot Parkway	a			11 06		11 20					12 02		
	d	10 44		11 06	11 20	11 29				11 47	12 03		
Cholsey	d					11 34							
Goring & Streatley	d					11 40							
Pangbourne	d					11 45							
Tilehurst	d					11 49							
Bedwyn	d		10 42										
Hungerford	d		10 48										
Kintbury	d		10 52										
Newbury	a		10 59										
	d		11 00					11 26					11 53
Newbury Racecourse	d												11 55
Thatcham	d		11 05										12 00
Midgham	d												12 05
Aldermaston	d												12 08
Theale	d		11 13										12 13
Reading West	d								←				12 21
Reading 7	a	11 03	11 21	11 25	11 35	11 54	11 40	11 45	11 54	12 03	12 18		12 24
	d	11 04		11 25	11 45	11 57		11 52	11 57	12 03	12 19		
Twyford 3	a					→			12 03				
Maidenhead 3	a								12 10				
Slough 3	a			11 42					12 21		12 35		
Ealing Broadway ⊖	a								12 42				
London Paddington 15 ⊖	a	11 43		12 04	12 22			12 29	12 51	12 42	13 00		

		GW	GW	XC	GW	GW	GW	GW	GW	GW	XC	CH
		◇1	1	◇1	◇1	◇1	1	◇1	◇1	1	◇1	
Birmingham New Street 12	d			11 04							12 04	
Birmingham International	d			11 14							12 14	
Coventry	d			11 25							12 25	
Leamington Spa 8	d			11 38							12 38	
Banbury	d			11 55							12 55	
Kings Sutton	d											
Heyford	d											
Tackley	d											
Bicester Town	d											13 03
Islip	d											13 14
Oxford	a			12 14							13 14	13 30
	d		12 05	12 16				12 51		13 05	13 16	
Radley	d		12 11							13 11		
Culham	d											
Appleford	d		12 16									
Didcot Parkway	a		12 22					13 05		13 19		
	d	12 19	12 29		12 47	12 59		13 06	13 25	13 29		
Cholsey	d		12 34							13 34		
Goring & Streatley	d		12 40							13 40		
Pangbourne	d		12 45							13 44		
Tilehurst	d		12 49							13 48		
Bedwyn	d						12 42					
Hungerford	d						12 48					
Kintbury	d						12 52					
Newbury	a						12 59					
	d						13 00					
Newbury Racecourse	d											
Thatcham	d						13 05					
Midgham	d											
Aldermaston	d											
Theale	d						13 13					
Reading West	d											
Reading 7	a	12 36	12 54	12 40	13 04	13 19	13 21	13 22	13 44	13 51	13 40	
	d	12 45	12 57		13 04	13 19		13 23	13 45	13 53		
Twyford 3	a		13 03							→		
Maidenhead 3	a		13 12									
Slough 3	a		13 21					13 37				
Ealing Broadway ⊖	a		13 42									
London Paddington 15 ⊖	a	13 23	13 55		13 42	13 59		14 02	14 23			

For complete service between Banbury and Leamington (Birmingham), please refer to table 71

Table 116R

Sundays

16 February to 23 March

Birmingham, Banbury, Bicester, Oxford and Bedwyn - Reading and London

Network Diagram - refer to first Page of Table 116

		GW	GW	GW	XC	GW	GW	GW	XC	GW	XC	GW	GW	CH	GW	GW	XC	GW	XC
		◇1	1	R 1	◇1	◇1	1	1	◇1	R 1	◇1	1	◇1		◇1	1	◇1	R 1	◇1
Birmingham New Street 12	d				12 33				13 04		13 33						14 04		14 33
Birmingham International	d								13 14								14 14		
Coventry	d								13 25								14 25		
Leamington Spa 8	d				13 00				13 38		14 00						14 38		15 00
Banbury	d				13 19				13 55		14 19						14 55		15 19
Kings Sutton	d																		
Heyford	d																		
Tackley	d																		
Bicester Town	d													14 27					
Islip	d													14 38					
Oxford	a				13 37				14 14		14 37			14 54			15 14		15 40
	d				13 43	13 50		14 05	14 16		14 43		14 51			15 05	15 16		15 43
Radley	d							14 11								15 11			
Culham	d																		
Appleford	d															15 16			
Didcot Parkway	a					14 02		14 19					15 05			15 22			
	d			13 47		14 03		14 29		14 47			15 06		15 27	15 29		15 47	
Cholsey	d							14 34								15 34			
Goring & Streatley	d							14 40								15 40			
Pangbourne	d							14 44								15 44			
Tilehurst	d							14 48								15 48			
Bedwyn	d											14 42							
Hungerford	d											14 48							
Kintbury	d											14 52							
Newbury	a											14 59							
	d	13 31					13 53					15 00							
Newbury Racecourse	d						13 55												
Thatcham	d						14 00					15 05							
Midgham	d						14 05												
Aldermaston	d						14 08												
Theale	d						14 13					15 13							
Reading West	d		←				14 21												
Reading 7	a	13 50	13 51	14 02	14 07	14 18	14 24	14 51	14 40	15 02	15 07	15 21	15 22		15 43	15 51	15 40	16 04	16 07
	d	13 52	13 53	14 03		14 19		14 53		15 03			15 23		15 45	15 53		16 04	
Twyford 3	a		13 58					14 58								15 58			
Maidenhead 3	a		14 05					15 05								16 05			
Slough 3	a		14 16			14 35		15 16					15 37			16 16			
Ealing Broadway ⊖	a		14 42					15 42								16 42			
London Paddington 15 ⊖	a	14 30	14 51	14 42		14 57		15 51		15 43			16 00		16 22	16 54		16 43	

		GW	GW	GW	XC	CH	GW	GW	GW	XC	GW	GW	GW	GW	GW	XC	GW	XC	GW
		◇1	1	1	◇1		◇1	1	R 1	◇1	◇1	1	◇1	◇1	1	◇1	R 1	◇1	◇1
Birmingham New Street 12	d				15 04					15 33						16 04		16 33	
Birmingham International	d				15 14											16 14			
Coventry	d				15 25											16 25			
Leamington Spa 8	d				15 38					15 59						16 38		17 00	
Banbury	d				15 55					16 19						16 55		17 19	
Kings Sutton	d																		
Heyford	d																		
Tackley	d																		
Bicester Town	d					16 03													
Islip	d					16 14													
Oxford	a				16 14	16 30				16 37						17 14		17 37	
	d	15 49		16 05	16 16					16 43			16 53		17 05	17 16		17 43	
Radley	d			16 11											17 11				
Culham	d																		
Appleford	d														17 16				
Didcot Parkway	a	16 02		16 19									17 06		17 22				
	d	16 08		16 29					16 47		16 59		17 07	17 19	17 29		17 47		17 55
Cholsey	d			16 34											17 34				
Goring & Streatley	d			16 40											17 40				
Pangbourne	d			16 44											17 44				
Tilehurst	d			16 48											17 48				
Bedwyn	d											16 42							
Hungerford	d											16 48							
Kintbury	d											16 52							
Newbury	a											16 59							
	d		15 53				16 31					17 00							
Newbury Racecourse	d		15 55																
Thatcham	d		16 00									17 05							
Midgham	d		16 05																
Aldermaston	d		16 08																
Theale	d		16 13									17 13							
Reading West	d		16 21					←											
Reading 7	a	16 23	16 24	16 53	16 40		16 49	16 53	17 04	17 08	17 19	17 21	17 25	17 35	17 52	17 40	18 03	18 07	18 12
	d	16 24		16 53			16 52	16 53	17 04		17 19		17 27	17 45	17 53		18 04		18 12
Twyford 3	a			→				16 59							17 58				
Maidenhead 3	a							17 06							18 05				
Slough 3	a	16 38						17 15					17 44		18 16				
Ealing Broadway ⊖	a							17 42							18 42				
London Paddington 15 ⊖	a	17 04					17 30	17 53	17 44		17 57		18 07	18 26	18 52		18 43		18 57

For complete service between Banbury and Leamington (Birmingham), please refer to table 71

Table 116R

Sundays

16 February to 23 March

Birmingham, Banbury, Bicester, Oxford and Bedwyn - Reading and London

Network Diagram - refer to first Page of Table 116

		GW	CH	GW	GW	XC	GW	GW	GW	XC	GW	GW	GW	GW	XC	CH	GW	XC	GW	GW	GW	GW	GW	XC	GW	GW	XC	GW	GW	CH	GW	GW	GW	XC	XC	GW	GW
		◇1 ☕		1	1	◇1 ☕	◇1 ☕	1	◇1 ☕	◇1 🛒	◇1 ☕	1	◇1 ☕	1	◇1 ☕		1 ☕	◇1 🛒	◇1 ☕	◇1	1	◇1 ☕	1	◇1 ☕	◇1 ☕	1	◇1 🛒	◇1 ☕	◇1		1	◇1 ☕	1	◇1 ☕	◇1 🛒	◇1 ☕	◇1
Birmingham New Street 12	d					17 04				17 33					18 04			18 33						19 04			19 33							20 04	20 33		
Birmingham International	d					17 14									18 14									19 14										20 14			
Coventry	d					17 25									18 25									19 25										20 25			
Leamington Spa 8	d					17 38				18 00					18 38			19 00						19 38			20 00							20 38	21 00		
Banbury	d					17 55				18 19					18 55			19 19						19 55			20 19							20 55	21 19		
Kings Sutton	d																																				
Heyford	d																																				
Tackley	d																																				
Bicester Town	d		17 27													19 07														20 27							
Islip	d		17 38													19 18														20 38							
Oxford	a		17 54			18 14				18 40					19 14	19 34		19 37						20 14			20 40			20 54				21 14	21 37		
	d	17 50			18 05	18 16				18 42			18 50	19 05	19 16			19 43		19 50			20 05	20 16			20 43		20 50				21 05		21 40		21 50
Radley	d				18 11									19 11									20 11										21 11				
Culham	d																																				
Appleford	d													19 16																							
Didcot Parkway	a	18 03			18 18								19 02	19 22						20 03			20 19						21 02				21 19				22 01
	d	18 03			18 29				18 47		18 59		19 08	19 29			19 47		19 59	20 04		20 16	20 29					20 59	21 03			21 24	21 29			22 01	22 03
Cholsey	d				18 34									19 34									20 34										21 34				
Goring & Streatley	d				18 40									19 40									20 40										21 40				
Pangbourne	d				18 44									19 44									20 44										21 44				
Tilehurst	d				18 48									19 48									20 48										21 48				
Bedwyn	d											18 42																			20 54						
Hungerford	d											18 48																			21 00						
Kintbury	d											18 52																			21 04						
Newbury	a											18 59																			21 11						
	d			17 53			18 34					19 00									19 53				20 27						21 12						
Newbury Racecourse	d			17 55																	19 55																
Thatcham	d			18 00								19 05									20 00										21 17						
Midgham	d			18 05																	20 05																
Aldermaston	d			18 08																	20 08																
Theale	d			18 13								19 13									20 13										21 25						
Reading West	d			18 21				←													20 21					←											
Reading 7	a	18 19		18 24	18 51	18 40	18 49	18 51	19 03	19 06	19 20	19 21	19 28	19 51	19 40		20 04	20 07	20 14	20 22	20 24	20 33	20 51	20 40	20 49	20 51	21 07	21 16	21 23		21 33	21 42	21 56		22 04	22 18	22 18
	d	18 20			18 53		18 52	18 53	19 04		19 20		19 29	19 53			20 04		20 16	20 23		20 34	20 53		20 52	20 53		21 25	21 26			21 43	21 56			22 19	22 22
Twyford 3	a				→			18 58						19 58									→			20 58							22 02				
Maidenhead 3	a							19 05						20 05												21 05			21 39				22 10				
Slough 3	a	18 36						19 17					19 42	20 17						20 39						21 17			21 43				22 18				22 39
Ealing Broadway	⊖ a							19 42						20 42												21 42							22 42				
London Paddington 15	⊖ a	19 01					19 30	19 53	19 43		19 58		20 07	20 53			20 43		20 57	21 00		21 13			21 29	21 52		22 01	22 06			22 30	22 52			22 58	23 03

For complete service between Banbury and Leamington (Birmingham), please refer to table 71

Table 116R

Sundays

16 February to 23 March

Birmingham, Banbury, Bicester, Oxford and Bedwyn - Reading and London

Network Diagram - refer to first Page of Table 116

		GW	XC	GW	GW	CH	GW	GW	GW	GW	GW	GW	GW
		1	◇1	◇1	1		1	◇1	◇1			1	1
			trolley	first class					first class	bus			
Birmingham New Street 12	d		21 04										
Birmingham International	d		21 14										
Coventry	d		21 24										
Leamington Spa 8	d		21 35										
Banbury	d												
Kings Sutton	d												
Heyford	d												
Tackley	d												
Bicester Town	d					22 03							
Islip	d					22 14							
Oxford	a		22 08			22 30							
	d		22 10		22 17			22 46		23 00			
Radley	d				22 23					23 15			
Culham	d												
Appleford	d												
Didcot Parkway	a				22 28			22 58		23 35			
	d				22 29			22 59	23 10			23 50	
Cholsey	d				22 34							23 56	
Goring & Streatley	d				22 40							00 01	
Pangbourne	d				22 44							00 06	
Tilehurst	d				22 48							00 10	
Bedwyn	d						22 35						
Hungerford	d						22 41						
Kintbury	d						22 45						
Newbury	a						22 52						
	d	21 53		22 19			22 53				23 23		23 45
Newbury Racecourse	d	21 55											23 47
Thatcham	d	22 00					22 58				23 28		23 52
Midgham	d	22 05											23 57
Aldermaston	d	22 08											00 01
Theale	d	22 13					23 06				23 36		00 06
Reading West	d	22 21											00s13
Reading 7	a	22 24	22 33	22 37	22 57		23 15	23 18	23 29		23 44	00 15	00 17
	d			22 38	23 03			23 18	23 31			00 15	
Twyford 3	a				23 09							00 23	
Maidenhead 3	a				23 17							00 31	
Slough 3	a				23 25			23 36				00 38	
Ealing Broadway ⊖	a				23 54							01 02	
London Paddington 15 ⊖	a			23 17	00 05			00 12	00 13			01 14	

For complete service between Banbury and Leamington (Birmingham), please refer to table 71

Table 116R

Sundays

30 March to 11 May

Birmingham, Banbury, Bicester, Oxford and Bedwyn - Reading and London

Network Diagram - refer to first Page of Table 116

		GW	GW	GW	GW	GW	GW	GW	GW	GW	XC	CH	GW	GW	GW	GW	GW	GW	GW	XC	GW	GW	GW	GW	CH	GW	GW	GW	XC	GW	GW	GW	GW	GW	GW	XC	CH
		1	1	1	◇1	1	◇1 ⊏P	◇1	1	1	◇1 ⊼		◇1 ⊏P	1	◇1 ⊏P	1	◇1	◇1 ⊏P	1	◇1 ⊏P	◇1 ⊏P	1	◇1 ⊏P	◇1		1	◇1 ⊏P	1	◇1 ⊏P	◇1 ⊏P	◇1 ⊏P	1	◇1	1 ⊏P	1	◇1 ⊼	
Birmingham New Street 12	d										09 04									10 04									11 04							12 04	
Birmingham International	d										09 14									10 14									11 14							12 14	
Coventry	d										09 25									10 25									11 25							12 25	
Leamington Spa 8	d										09 38									10 38									11 38							12 38	
Banbury	d										09 55									10 55									11 55							12 55	
Kings Sutton	d																																				
Heyford	d																																				
Tackley	d																																				
Bicester Town	d											10 05													11 27												13 03
Islip	d											10 16													11 38												13 14
Oxford	a										10 14	10 32								11 14					11 54				12 14							13 14	13 30
	d				08 50	09 05		09 50		10 05	10 16						10 51		11 05	11 16				11 50				12 05	12 16				12 51		13 05	13 16	
Radley	d					09 11				10 11									11 11									12 11							13 11		
Culham	d																																				
Appleford	d									10 16																		12 16									
Didcot Parkway	a				09 02	09 20		10 02		10 21							11 06		11 20					12 02				12 22					13 05		13 22		
	d		08 30		09 03	09 20	09 44	10 03		10 29					10 44		11 06	11 20	11 29				11 43	12 03			12 19	12 29		12 43	12 59		13 06	13 25	13 29		
Cholsey	d		08 36			09 26				10 34									11 34									12 34							13 34		
Goring & Streatley	d		08 41			09 32				10 40									11 40									12 40							13 40		
Pangbourne	d		08 46			09 36				10 44									11 45									12 44							13 44		
Tilehurst	d		08 51			09 41				10 48									11 51									12 49							13 48		
Bedwyn	d								09 35							10 42																12 42					
Hungerford	d								09 41							10 48																12 48					
Kintbury	d								09 46							10 52																12 52					
Newbury	a								09 52							10 59																12 59					
	d			08 48					09 53				10 32			11 00					11 26					11 53						13 00					
Newbury Racecourse	d			08 50					09 55																	11 55											
Thatcham	d			08 55					10 00							11 05										12 00						13 05					
Midgham	d			09 00					10 05																	12 05											
Aldermaston	d			09 03					10 08																	12 08											
Theale	d			09 08					10 13							11 13										12 13						13 13					
Reading West	d			09 16					10 21					←								←				12 21											
Reading 7	a		08 57	09 19	09 20	09 45	10 02	10 19	10 24	10 55	10 43		10 48	10 55	11 03	11 21	11 25	11 35	11 54	11 44	11 45	11 54	12 01	12 18		12 24	12 35	12 54	12 43	13 01	13 15	13 21	13 22	13 44	13 53	13 44	
	d	00 04	08 58		09 24	09 52	10 03	10 20		10 56			10 51	10 56	11 04		11 25	11 44	11 57		11 52	11 57	12 05	12 19			12 45	12 57		13 03	13 18		13 23	13 45	13 53		
Twyford 3	a	00 11	09 03			09 58				→				11 02					→			12 03						13 03							→		
Maidenhead 3	a	00 19	09 12			10 06								11 10								12 12						13 11									
Slough 3	a	00 28	09 20		09 38	10 13		10 38						11 19			11 43					12 21		12 35				13 20					13 36				
Ealing Broadway ⊖	a	00 54	09 42			10 42								11 42								12 42						13 42									
London Paddington 15 ⊖	a	01 06	09 53		10 00	10 53	10 43	11 00					11 27	11 52	11 43		12 04	12 22			12 29	12 52	12 41	12 57			13 22	13 55		13 42	14 02		14 01	14 25			

For complete service between Banbury and Leamington (Birmingham), please refer to table 71

Table 116R

Sundays

30 March to 11 May

Birmingham, Banbury, Bicester, Oxford and Bedwyn - Reading and London

Network Diagram - refer to first Page of Table 116

		GW	GW	GW	XC	GW	GW	GW	XC	GW	XC	GW	GW	CH	GW	GW	XC	GW	XC
				R						R								R	
		◇1	1	1	◇1	◇1	1	1	◇1	1	◇1	1	◇1		◇1	1	◇1	1	◇1
		⊡		⊡	⊼				⊡	⊡	⊼				⊡		⊡	⊡	⊼
Birmingham New Street 12	d				12 33				13 04		13 33						14 04		14 33
Birmingham International	d								13 14								14 14		
Coventry	d								13 25								14 25		
Leamington Spa 8	d				13 00				13 38		13 59						14 38		15 00
Banbury	d				13 19				13 55		14 19						14 55		15 19
Kings Sutton	d																		
Heyford	d																		
Tackley	d																		
Bicester Town	d													14 27					
Islip	d													14 38					
Oxford	a				13 37				14 14		14 37			14 54			15 14		15 40
	d				13 43	13 50		14 05	14 16		14 43		14 51			15 05	15 16		15 43
Radley	d							14 11								15 11			
Culham	d																		
Appleford	d															15 16			
Didcot Parkway	a					14 02		14 19					15 05			15 22			
	d			13 43		14 03		14 29		14 43			15 06		15 28	15 29		15 43	
Cholsey	d							14 34								15 34			
Goring & Streatley	d							14 40								15 40			
Pangbourne	d							14 44								15 44			
Tilehurst	d							14 48								15 48			
Bedwyn	d											14 42							
Hungerford	d											14 48							
Kintbury	d											14 52							
Newbury	a											14 59							
	d	13 31					13 53					15 00							
Newbury Racecourse	d						13 55												
Thatcham	d						14 00					15 05							
Midgham	d						14 05												
Aldermaston	d						14 08												
Theale	d						14 13					15 13							
Reading West	d		←				14 21												
Reading 7	a	13 50	13 53	14 01	14 07	14 18	14 24	14 50	14 45	15 01	15 07	15 21	15 22		15 43	15 56	15 42	16 01	16 07
	d	13 52	13 53	14 03		14 19		14 53		15 03			15 23		15 45	15 57		16 03	
Twyford 3	a		13 58					14 58								16 03			
Maidenhead 3	a		14 05					15 05								16 12			
Slough 3	a		14 16			14 35		15 16					15 37			16 19			
Ealing Broadway ⊖	a		14 42					15 42								16 42			
London Paddington 15 ⊖	a	14 30	14 52	14 42		15 00		15 52		15 42			16 00		16 26	16 54		16 42	

		GW	GW	GW	XC	CH	GW	GW	GW	XC	GW	GW	GW	GW	GW	XC	GW	XC	GW
									R								R		
		◇1	1	1	◇1		◇1	1	1	◇1	◇1	1	◇1	◇1	1	◇1	1	◇1	◇1
		⊡			⊡		⊡		⊡	⊼	⊡		⊡	⊡		⊡	⊡	⊼	⊡
Birmingham New Street 12	d				15 04					15 33						16 04		16 33	
Birmingham International	d				15 14											16 14			
Coventry	d				15 25											16 25			
Leamington Spa 8	d				15 38					15 59						16 38		17 00	
Banbury	d				15 55					16 19						16 55		17 19	
Kings Sutton	d																		
Heyford	d																		
Tackley	d																		
Bicester Town	d					16 03													
Islip	d					16 14													
Oxford	a				16 14	16 30				16 37						17 14		17 37	
	d	15 49		16 05	16 16					16 43			16 53		17 05	17 16		17 43	
Radley	d			16 11											17 11				
Culham	d																		
Appleford	d														17 16				
Didcot Parkway	a	16 02		16 19									17 06		17 22				
	d	16 04		16 29					16 43		16 59		17 07	17 19	17 29		17 43		17 59
Cholsey	d			16 34											17 34				
Goring & Streatley	d			16 40											17 40				
Pangbourne	d			16 44											17 44				
Tilehurst	d			16 48											17 48				
Bedwyn	d											16 42							
Hungerford	d											16 48							
Kintbury	d											16 52							
Newbury	a											16 59							
	d		15 53				16 31					17 00							
Newbury Racecourse	d		15 55																
Thatcham	d		16 00									17 05							
Midgham	d		16 05																
Aldermaston	d		16 08																
Theale	d		16 13									17 13							
Reading West	d		16 21					←											
Reading 7	a	16 19	16 24	16 56	16 46		16 49	16 56	17 01	17 08	17 19	17 21	17 25	17 37	17 57	17 45	18 01	18 07	18 18
	d	16 25		16 57			16 52	16 57	17 03		17 19		17 27	17 38	17 57		18 04		18 18
Twyford 3	a			→				17 03							18 03				
Maidenhead 3	a							17 11							18 12				
Slough 3	a	16 38						17 20					17 44		18 20				
Ealing Broadway ⊖	a							17 42							18 42				
London Paddington 15 ⊖	a	17 03					17 30	17 53	17 42		17 57		18 07	18 22	18 53		18 42		18 57

For complete service between Banbury and Leamington (Birmingham), please refer to table 71

Table 116R

Sundays

30 March to 11 May

Birmingham, Banbury, Bicester, Oxford and Bedwyn - Reading and London

Network Diagram - refer to first Page of Table 116

		GW	CH	GW	GW	XC	GW	GW	GW	XC
		◇1 ☕		1	1	◇1 ☕	◇1 ☕	1	◇1 ☕	◇1 🍽
Birmingham New Street 12	d					17 04				17 33
Birmingham International	d					17 14				
Coventry	d					17 25				
Leamington Spa 8	d					17 38				18 00
Banbury	d					17 55				18 20
Kings Sutton	d									
Heyford	d									
Tackley	d									
Bicester Town	d		17 27							
Islip	d		17 38							
Oxford	a		17 54			18 14				18 41
	d	17 50			18 05	18 16				18 43
Radley	d				18 11					
Culham	d									
Appleford	d									
Didcot Parkway	a	18 03			18 19					
	d	18 03			18 29				18 43	
Cholsey	d				18 34					
Goring & Streatley	d				18 40					
Pangbourne	d				18 44					
Tilehurst	d				18 48					
Bedwyn	d									
Hungerford	d									
Kintbury	d									
Newbury	a									
	d			17 53			18 34			
Newbury Racecourse	d			17 55						
Thatcham	d			18 00						
Midgham	d			18 05						
Aldermaston	d			18 08						
Theale	d			18 13						
Reading West	d			18 21				←		
Reading 7	a	18 22		18 24	18 52	18 45	18 49	18 52	19 00	19 07
	d	18 24			18 53		18 52	18 53	19 03	
Twyford 3	a				→			18 58		
Maidenhead 3	a							19 10		
Slough 3	a	18 39						19 17		
Ealing Broadway ⊖	a							19 42		
London Paddington 15 ⊖	a	19 01					19 29	19 53	19 41	

		GW	GW	GW	GW	XC	CH	GW	XC	GW
		◇1 ☕	1	◇1 ☕	1	◇1 ☕		1 ☕	◇1 🍽	◇1 ☕
Birmingham New Street 12	d					18 04			18 33	
Birmingham International	d					18 14				
Coventry	d					18 25				
Leamington Spa 8	d					18 38			19 00	
Banbury	d					18 55			19 19	
Kings Sutton	d									
Heyford	d									
Tackley	d									
Bicester Town	d						19 07			
Islip	d						19 18			
Oxford	a					19 14	19 34		19 37	
	d			18 50	19 05	19 16			19 43	
Radley	d				19 11					
Culham	d									
Appleford	d				19 16					
Didcot Parkway	a			19 02	19 22					
	d	18 59		19 08	19 29			19 43		19 59
Cholsey	d				19 34					
Goring & Streatley	d				19 40					
Pangbourne	d				19 44					
Tilehurst	d				19 49					
Bedwyn	d		18 42							
Hungerford	d		18 48							
Kintbury	d		18 52							
Newbury	a		18 59							
	d		19 00							
Newbury Racecourse	d									
Thatcham	d		19 05							
Midgham	d									
Aldermaston	d									
Theale	d		19 13							
Reading West	d									
Reading 7	a	19 20	19 21	19 28	19 51	19 45		20 01	20 07	20 12
	d	19 20		19 29	19 53			20 02		20 16
Twyford 3	a				19 58					
Maidenhead 3	a				20 12					
Slough 3	a			19 43	20 17					
Ealing Broadway ⊖	a				20 42					
London Paddington 15 ⊖	a	19 57		20 04	20 53			20 42		20 57

		GW	GW	GW	GW	XC	GW	GW	XC	GW
		◇1	1	◇1 ☕	1	◇1 ☕	◇1 ☕	1	◇1 🍽	◇1 ☕
Birmingham New Street 12	d					19 04			19 33	
Birmingham International	d					19 14				
Coventry	d					19 25				
Leamington Spa 8	d					19 38			20 00	
Banbury	d					19 55			20 19	
Kings Sutton	d									
Heyford	d									
Tackley	d									
Bicester Town	d									
Islip	d									
Oxford	a					20 14			20 40	
	d	19 50			20 05	20 16			20 43	
Radley	d				20 11					
Culham	d									
Appleford	d									
Didcot Parkway	a	20 03			20 21					
	d	20 04		20 09	20 29					20 59
Cholsey	d				20 34					
Goring & Streatley	d				20 40					
Pangbourne	d				20 44					
Tilehurst	d				20 48					
Bedwyn	d									
Hungerford	d									
Kintbury	d									
Newbury	a									
	d		19 53				20 25			
Newbury Racecourse	d		19 55							
Thatcham	d		20 00							
Midgham	d		20 05							
Aldermaston	d		20 08							
Theale	d		20 13							
Reading West	d		20 21					←		
Reading 7	a	20 22	20 24	20 29	20 51	20 45	20 49	20 51	21 07	21 16
	d	20 23		20 30	20 53		20 52	20 53		21 17
Twyford 3	a				→			20 58		
Maidenhead 3	a							21 04		
Slough 3	a	20 39						21 19		
Ealing Broadway ⊖	a							21 40		
London Paddington 15 ⊖	a	21 01		21 03			21 29	21 50		21 57

		GW	CH	GW	GW	GW	XC	XC	GW	GW
		◇1		1	◇1 ☕	1	◇1 ☕	◇1 🍽	◇1 ☕	◇1
Birmingham New Street 12	d						20 04	20 33		
Birmingham International	d						20 14			
Coventry	d						20 25			
Leamington Spa 8	d						20 38	21 00		
Banbury	d						20 55	21 19		
Kings Sutton	d									
Heyford	d									
Tackley	d									
Bicester Town	d		20 27							
Islip	d		20 38							
Oxford	a		20 54				21 14	21 37		
	d	20 50				21 05	21 16	21 40		21 50
Radley	d					21 11				
Culham	d									
Appleford	d									
Didcot Parkway	a	21 05				21 19				22 01
	d	21 06			21 24	21 29			22 01	22 04
Cholsey	d					21 34				
Goring & Streatley	d					21 40				
Pangbourne	d					21 44				
Tilehurst	d					21 48				
Bedwyn	d			20 54						
Hungerford	d			21 00						
Kintbury	d			21 04						
Newbury	a			21 11						
	d			21 12						
Newbury Racecourse	d									
Thatcham	d			21 17						
Midgham	d									
Aldermaston	d									
Theale	d			21 25						
Reading West	d									
Reading 7	a	21 20		21 33	21 42	21 56	21 44	22 08	22 18	22 18
	d	21 22			21 43	21 57			22 19	22 20
Twyford 3	a					22 03				
Maidenhead 3	a	21 36				22 11				
Slough 3	a	21 41				22 20				22 39
Ealing Broadway ⊖	a					22 42				
London Paddington 15 ⊖	a	22 03			22 26	22 52			22 56	23 00

For complete service between Banbury and Leamington (Birmingham), please refer to table 71

Table 116R

Sundays
30 March to 11 May

Birmingham, Banbury, Bicester, Oxford and Bedwyn - Reading and London

Network Diagram - refer to first Page of Table 116

		GW	XC	GW	GW	CH	GW	GW	GW	GW	GW	GW	GW
		1	◇1	◇1	1		1	◇1	◇1			1	1
			(trolley)	(buffet)					(buffet)	(bus)			
Birmingham New Street 12	d		21 04										
Birmingham International	d		21 14										
Coventry	d		21 24										
Leamington Spa 8	d		21 35										
Banbury	d												
Kings Sutton	d												
Heyford	d												
Tackley	d												
Bicester Town	d					22 03							
Islip	d					22 14							
Oxford	a		22 08			22 30							
	d		22 10		22 15			22 46		23 00			
Radley	d				22 21					23 15			
Culham	d												
Appleford	d												
Didcot Parkway	a				22 28			22 58		23 35			
	d				22 29			22 59	23 10			23 50	
Cholsey	d				22 34							23 56	
Goring & Streatley	d				22 40							00 01	
Pangbourne	d				22 44							00 06	
Tilehurst	d				22 48							00 10	
Bedwyn	d						22 35						
Hungerford	d						22 41						
Kintbury	d						22 45						
Newbury	a						22 52						
	d	21 53		22 19			22 53				23 23		23 45
Newbury Racecourse	d	21 55											23 47
Thatcham	d	22 00					22 58				23 28		23 52
Midgham	d	22 05											23 57
Aldermaston	d	22 08											00 01
Theale	d	22 13					23 06				23 36		00 06
Reading West	d	22 21											00s13
Reading 7	a	22 24	22 33	22 40	22 57		23 15	23 18	23 29		23 44	00 15	00 17
	d			22 41	22 57			23 18	23 31			00 15	
Twyford 3	a				23 01							00 23	
Maidenhead 3	a				23 11							00 31	
Slough 3	a				23 21			23 36				00 39	
Ealing Broadway ⊖	a				23 44							01 02	
London Paddington 15 ⊖	a			23 23	23 54			00 01	00 06			01 14	

For complete service between Banbury and Leamington (Birmingham), please refer to table 71

Table 117

Mondays to Fridays

9 December to 3 January

Network Diagram - refer to first Page of Table 116

London - Greenford and Reading

Miles	Miles	Miles	Station		GW MO 1	GW MX 1	GW MX 1	GW MO ◇1	GW MO 1	GW MX 1	GW MX ◇1	GW MX 1	GW MO 1		GW 1	GW 1	HC	GW 1	HC	GW 1	HC	GW 1	GW 1		GW ◇1
0	0	0	**London Paddington 15** ⊖	d							00 22	00 34	00 34		01 34	03 34	04 42	05 12	05 13	05 17	05 33	05 42	05 45		05 45
4¼	4¼	4¼	Acton Main Line	d																			05 51		
5¾	5¾	5¾	**Ealing Broadway** ⊖	d					00 02			00 42	00 43		01 42	03 42	04 50		05 21	05 25	05 41	05 50	05 54		
6½	6½	6½	West Ealing	d																	05 43		05 57		
—	7¼	—	Drayton Green	d																			05 59		
—	7½	—	Castle Bar Park	d																			06 01		
—	8¼	—	South Greenford	d																			06 04		
—	9¼	—	**Greenford** ⊖	a																			06 09		
7¼	—	7¼	Hanwell	d																	05 45				
9	—	9	Southall	d					00 07	00 07		00 47	00 48		01 47	03 48	04 54		05 25	05 31	05 49	05 58			
10¾	—	10¾	Hayes & Harlington	d					00 11	00 12		00 51	00 52		01 51	03 52	04 58		05 29	05 36	05 53	06 02			
—	—	14¾	**Heathrow Terminal 1-2 2** ✈	a													05 04		05 35		06 05				
—	—	16½	**Heathrow Terminal 4** ✈	a													05 10		05 41						
13¼	—	—	West Drayton	d					00 15	00 16		00 55	00 56		01 55	03 56				05 41		06 06			
14¾	—	—	Iver	d						00 19												06 09			
16¼	—	—	Langley	d					00 20	00 22		01 00	01 01							05 46		06 13			
18½	—	—	**Slough 3**	a					00 24	00 28	00 40	01 05	01 05		02 04	04 04		05 29		05 50		06 17			06 01
—	—	—		d				00 11	00 24	00 28	00 41	01 05	01 05		02 04	04 05		05 30		05 51		06 17			06 01
21	—	—	Burnham	d					00 28	00 32		01 09	01 09									↪			
22½	—	—	Taplow	d						00 36		01 13													
24¼	—	—	**Maidenhead 3**	d			00 05	00 18	00 33	00 41		01 16	01 16		02 11	04 12				05 59					
31	—	—	**Twyford 3**	d	00 03	00 08	00 13		00 41	00 48		01 24	01 24		02 19	04 20				06 07					
36	—	—	**Reading 7**	a	00 12	00 16	00 22	00 33	00 49	00 56	01 01	01 35	01 32		02 29	04 30		05 48		06 15					06 17
—	—	—	Oxford	a			01 18				01 34							06 20		07 02					06 51

Station		GW 1	GW 1	HC	GW 1	GW 1	GW ◇1	GW 1	GW 1		HC	GW 1	GW 1	GW 1	GW 1	GW 1	HC	GW 1	GW 1		GW 1	GW 1	GW 1	GW 1	HC
London Paddington 15 ⊖	d		05 57	06 03	06 12	06 15	06 20		06 27		06 33	06 42	06 45	06 48		06 57	07 03	07 12	07 12		07 15	07 21		07 27	07 33
Acton Main Line	d					06 21							06 51								07 21				
Ealing Broadway ⊖	d		06 05	06 11	06 20	06 24			06 35		06 41	06 50	06 54			07 05	07 11		07 20		07 24			07 35	07 41
West Ealing	d			06 13		06 27					06 43		06 57				07 13				07 27				07 43
Drayton Green	d					06 29							06 59								07 29				
Castle Bar Park	d					06 31							07 01								07 31				
South Greenford	d					06 34							07 04								07 34				
Greenford ⊖	a					06 39							07 09								07 39				
Hanwell	d			06 15							06 45						07 15								07 45
Southall	d		06 10	06 19	06 28				06 41		06 49	06 58				07 10	07 19		07 28					07 40	07 49
Hayes & Harlington	d		06 14	06 23	06 32				06 45		06 53	07 02				07 14	07 23		07 32					07 44	07 53
Heathrow Terminal 1-2 2 ✈	a			06 35							07 05						07 35								08 05
Heathrow Terminal 4 ✈	a																								
West Drayton	d		06 18		06 40				06 49			07 06				07 18			07 36					07 48	
Iver	d		06 21						06 52							07 21								07 51	
Langley	d	←	06 25					←	06 56						←	07 25							←	07 55	
Slough 3	a	06 17	06 29		06 47		06 35	06 47	07 00			07 13		07 02	07 13	07 29			07 43			07 36	07 43	07 59	
	d	06 17	06 29		06 47		06 35	06 47	07 00			07 13		07 02	07 13	07 29			07 43			07 36	07 43	07 59	
Burnham	d	06 21			↪			06 51				↪			07 17				↪				07 47		
Taplow	d	06 25						06 54							07 21								07 51		
Maidenhead 3	d	06 29	06 37					06 58	07 08						07 25	07 37		07 43					07 55	08 07	
Twyford 3	d	06 38	06 45					07 06	07 16						07 37	07 45		07 51					08 03	08 15	
Reading 7	a	06 48	06 53				06 49	07 14	07 27					07 19	07 45	07 52		08 02				07 51	08 14	08 23	
Oxford	a		07 49				07 22							08 02		08 44						08 19		09 16	

Station		GW 1	GW 1	GW 1	GW 1		GW 1	HC	GW 1	GW 1	GW 1	GW ◇1 🛒	GW 1	GW 1	HC		GW 1	GW 1	GW 1	GW ◇1	GW 1	GW 1	GW 1	HC	GW 1
London Paddington 15 ⊖	d	07 42	07 45	07 50			07 57	08 03	08 09	08 12	08 15	08 22		08 27	08 33		08 38	08 46	08 47	08 51			08 55	09 03	09 12
Acton Main Line	d		07 51								08 21							08 51							
Ealing Broadway ⊖	d	07 50	07 54				08 05	08 11	08 17	08 20	08 24			08 35	08 41		08 47	08 54	08 59				09 03	09 11	09 20
West Ealing	d		07 57					08 13			08 27				08 43			08 57	09 01					09 13	
Drayton Green	d		07 59								08 29							08 59							
Castle Bar Park	d		08 01								08 31							09 01							
South Greenford	d		08 04								08 34							09 04							
Greenford ⊖	a		08 09								08 39							09 10							
Hanwell	d							08 15							08 45		08 50							09 15	
Southall	d	07 59					08 10	08 19		08 28				08 40	08 49								09 08	09 19	09 28
Hayes & Harlington	d	08 02					08 14	08 23		08 32				08 44	08 54		08 57		09 08				09 12	09 23	09 32
Heathrow Terminal 1-2 2 ✈	a							08 35							09 05									09 35	
Heathrow Terminal 4 ✈	a																								
West Drayton	d	08 06					08 18			08 36				08 48			09 01						09 16		09 36
Iver	d						08 21							08 51			09 04						09 19		
Langley	d				←		08 25						←	08 55			09 06				←	←	09 23		
Slough 3	a	08 13		08 06	08 13		08 29		08 34	08 43		08 36	08 43	08 59			09 11		09 16	09 06	09 11	09 16	09 27		09 43
	d	08 13		08 06	08 13		08 29		08 34	08 43		08 36	08 43	08 59			09 12		09 16	09 06	09 12	09 16	09 27		09 43
Burnham	d	↪			08 17					↪			08 47				↪		↪			09 20			↪
Taplow	d				08 21								08 51									09 24			
Maidenhead 3	d				08 25		08 38		08 42				08 55	09 06							09 18	09 28	09 35		
Twyford 3	d				08 33		08 46		08 50				09 03	09 18							09 27	09 37	09 43		
Reading 7	a			08 21	08 43		08 54		09 00			08 51	09 14	09 26						09 20	09 34	09 47	09 51		
Oxford	a			08 49			09 45					09 20		10 18						09 53			10 43		

For non-stop services between London and Reading please see table 116

Passengers who hold valid tickets for Acton Main Line, West Ealing and Hanwell will be able to use local Transport for London (TFL) bus services to reach these stations. Tel 0843 222 1234

Table 117

Mondays to Fridays

9 December to 3 January

Network Diagram - refer to first Page of Table 116

London - Greenford and Reading

Station			GW 1	GW ◇1 🛒	GW 1	GW 1	HC	GW 1	GW 1	GW ◇1	GW 1		GW 1	HC	GW 1	GW 1	GW ◇1 ⊡	GW 1	GW 1	HC	GW 1		GW 1	GW ◇1	GW 1
London Paddington 15 ⊖	d		09 15	09 21		09 27	09 33	09 42	09 45	09 50			09 57	10 03	10 12	10 15	10 22		10 27	10 33	10 42		10 45	10 50	
Acton Main Line	d		09 21						09 51							10 21							10 51		
Ealing Broadway ⊖	d		09 24			09 35	09 41	09 50	09 54				10 05	10 11	10 20	10 24			10 35	10 41	10 50		10 54		
West Ealing	d		09 27				09 43		09 57					10 13		10 27				10 43			10 57		
Drayton Green	d		09 29						09 59							10 29							10 59		
Castle Bar Park	d		09 31						10 01							10 31							11 01		
South Greenford	d		09 34						10 04							10 34							11 04		
Greenford ⊖	a		09 39						10 09							10 39							11 09		
Hanwell	d						09 45							10 15						10 45					
Southall	d						09 49	09 58						10 19	10 28					10 49	10 58				
Hayes & Harlington	d					09 42	09 53	10 02					10 12	10 23	10 32				10 42	10 53	11 02				
Heathrow Terminal 1-2 2 ✈	a						10 05							10 35						11 05					
Heathrow Terminal 4 ✈	a																								
West Drayton	d					09 46		10 06					10 16		10 36				10 46		11 06				
Iver	d					09 49							10 19						10 49						
Langley	d				←	09 52					←		10 22					←	10 52						←
Slough 3	a			09 36	09 43	09 57		10 13		10 06	10 13		10 27		10 43		10 36	10 43	10 57		11 13			11 06	11 13
	d			09 36	09 43	09 57		10 13		10 06	10 13		10 27		10 43		10 36	10 43	10 57		11 13			11 06	11 13
Burnham	d				09 45			→			10 17				→			10 47			→				11 17
Taplow	d				09 51						10 21							10 51							11 21
Maidenhead 3	d				09 55	10 04					10 25		10 34					10 55	11 04						11 25
Twyford 3	d				10 03	10 12					10 38		10 42					11 06	11 12						11 35
Reading 7	a			09 52	10 14	10 21				10 21	10 45		10 50				10 51	11 15	11 21					11 21	11 45
Oxford	a			10 20		11 14				10 47			11 43				11 18		12 14					11 50	

Station		GW 1	HC	GW 1	GW 1	GW ◇1 🛒	GW 1		GW 1	HC	GW 1	GW 1	GW ◇1 🛒	GW 1	GW 1	HC	GW 1		GW 1	GW ◇1 🛒	GW 1	GW 1	HC	GW 1	GW 1
London Paddington 15 ⊖	d	10 57	11 03	11 12	11 15	11 20			11 27	11 33	11 42	11 45	11 50		11 57	12 03	12 12		12 15	12 21		12 27	12 33	12 42	12 45
Acton Main Line	d				11 21							11 51							12 21						12 51
Ealing Broadway ⊖	d	11 05	11 11	11 20	11 24				11 35	11 41	11 50	11 54			12 05	12 11	12 20		12 24			12 35	12 41	12 50	12 54
West Ealing	d		11 13		11 27					11 43		11 57				12 13			12 27				12 43		12 57
Drayton Green	d				11 29							11 59							12 29						12 59
Castle Bar Park	d				11 31							12 01							12 31						13 01
South Greenford	d				11 34							12 04							12 34						13 04
Greenford ⊖	a				11 39							12 09							12 39						13 10
Hanwell	d		11 15							11 45						12 15							12 45		
Southall	d		11 19	11 28						11 49	11 58					12 19	12 28						12 49	12 58	
Hayes & Harlington	d	11 12	11 23	11 32					11 42	11 53	12 02				12 12	12 23	12 32					12 42	12 53	13 02	
Heathrow Terminal 1-2 2 ✈	a		11 35							12 05						12 35							13 05		
Heathrow Terminal 4 ✈	a																								
West Drayton	d	11 16		11 36					11 46		12 06				12 16		12 36					12 46		13 06	
Iver	d	11 19							11 49						12 19							12 49			
Langley	d	11 22					←		11 52					←	12 22						←	12 52			
Slough 3	a	11 27		11 43		11 36	11 43		11 57		12 13		12 06	12 13	12 27		12 43			12 36	12 43	12 57		13 13	
	d	11 27		11 43		11 36	11 43		11 57		12 13		12 06	12 13	12 27		12 43			12 36	12 43	12 57		13 13	
Burnham	d			→			11 47				→			12 17			→				12 47			→	
Taplow	d						11 51							12 21							12 51				
Maidenhead 3	d	11 34					11 55		12 04					12 25	12 34						12 55	13 04			
Twyford 3	d	11 42					12 03		12 13					12 37	12 45						13 06	13 12			
Reading 7	a	11 52				11 52	12 15		12 22				12 22	12 45	12 52					12 51	13 15	13 20			
Oxford	a	12 43				12 18			13 14				12 48		13 43					13 20		14 14			

Station		GW ◇1 🛒	GW 1		GW 1	HC	GW 1	GW 1	GW ◇1 🛒	GW 1	GW 1	HC	GW 1		GW 1	GW ◇1 🛒	GW 1	GW 1	HC	GW 1	GW 1	GW ◇1 🛒	GW 1		GW 1
London Paddington 15 ⊖	d	12 50			12 57	13 03	13 12	13 15	13 21		13 27	13 33	13 42		13 45	13 50		13 57	14 03	14 12	14 15	14 21			14 27
Acton Main Line	d							13 21							13 51						14 21				
Ealing Broadway ⊖	d				13 05	13 11	13 20	13 24			13 35	13 41	13 50		13 54			14 05	14 11	14 20	14 24				14 35
West Ealing	d					13 13		13 27				13 43			13 57				14 13		14 27				
Drayton Green	d							13 29							13 59						14 29				
Castle Bar Park	d							13 31							14 01						14 31				
South Greenford	d							13 34							14 04						14 34				
Greenford ⊖	a							13 39							14 09						14 39				
Hanwell	d					13 15						13 45							14 15						
Southall	d					13 19	13 28					13 49	13 58						14 19	14 28					
Hayes & Harlington	d				13 12	13 23	13 32				13 42	13 53	14 02					14 12	14 23	14 32					14 42
Heathrow Terminal 1-2 2 ✈	a					13 35						14 05							14 35						
Heathrow Terminal 4 ✈	a																								
West Drayton	d				13 16		13 36				13 46		14 06					14 16		14 36					14 46
Iver	d				13 19						13 49							14 19							14 49
Langley	d		←		13 22					←	13 52						←	14 22					←		14 52
Slough 3	a	13 06	13 13		13 27		13 43		13 36	13 43	13 57		14 13			14 06	14 13	14 27		14 43		14 36	14 43		14 57
	d	13 06	13 13		13 27		13 43		13 36	13 43	13 57		14 13			14 06	14 13	14 27		14 43		14 36	14 43		14 57
Burnham	d		13 17				→			13 47			→				14 17			→			14 47		
Taplow	d		13 21							13 51							14 21						14 51		
Maidenhead 3	d		13 25		13 34					13 55	14 04						14 25	14 34					14 55		15 04
Twyford 3	d		13 33		13 44					14 03	14 12						14 33	14 42					15 03		15 14
Reading 7	a	13 22	13 43		13 53				13 51	14 15	14 21					14 21	14 43	14 54				14 52	15 13		15 21
Oxford	a	13 50			14 43				14 18		15 14					14 48		15 44				15 18			16 16

For non-stop services between London and Reading please see table 116

Passengers who hold valid tickets for Acton Main Line, West Ealing and Hanwell will be able to use local Transport for London (TFL) bus services to reach these stations. Tel 0843 222 1234

Table 117

London - Greenford and Reading

Mondays to Fridays

9 December to 3 January

Network Diagram - refer to first Page of Table 116

		HC	GW	GW	GW	GW	GW	HC	GW		GW	GW	GW	GW	HC	GW	GW	GW	GW		HC	GW	GW	GW	GW
			1	1	◇1 🛒	1	1		1		1	◇1 🛒	1	1		1	1	1	1			1	1	◇1 🛒	1
London Paddington 15 ⊖	d	14 33	14 42	14 45	14 50		14 57	15 03	15 12		15 15	15 22		15 27	15 33	15 40	15 42	15 45	15 57		16 03	16 12	16 15	16 22	
Acton Main Line	d			14 51							15 21							15 51					16 21		
Ealing Broadway ⊖	d	14 41	14 50	14 54			15 05	15 11	15 20		15 24			15 35	15 41		15 50	15 54	16 05		16 11	16 20	16 24		
West Ealing	d	14 43		14 57				15 13			15 27				15 43			15 57			16 13		16 27		
Drayton Green	d			14 59							15 29							15 59					16 29		
Castle Bar Park	d			15 01							15 31							16 01					16 31		
South Greenford	d			15 04							15 34							16 04					16 34		
Greenford ⊖	a			15 09							15 39							16 09					16 39		
Hanwell	d	14 45						15 15							15 45						16 15				
Southall	d	14 49	14 58					15 19	15 28					15 40	15 49		15 58				16 19	16 28			
Hayes & Harlington	d	14 53	15 02				15 12	15 23	15 32					15 44	15 53		16 04		16 12		16 23	16 32			
Heathrow Terminal 1-2 2 ✈	a	15 05						15 35							16 05						16 35				
Heathrow Terminal 4 ✈	a																								
West Drayton	d		15 06				15 16		15 36					15 48			16 09		16 16			16 36			
Iver	d						15 19							15 51					16 19						
Langley	d					←	15 22						←	15 55					16 23						←
Slough 3	a		15 13		15 06	15 13	15 27		15 43			15 36	15 43	15 59		16 11	16 16		16 28			16 44		16 37	16 44
	d		15 13		15 06	15 13	15 27		15 43			15 36	15 43	15 59		16 11	16 16		16 28			16 45		16 38	16 45
Burnham	d		↪			15 17			↪				15 47				16 20					↪			16 50
Taplow	d					15 21							15 51				16 23								16 54
Maidenhead 3	d					15 25	15 34						15 55	16 07		16a22	16 27		16 35						16 59
Twyford 3	d					15 33	15 42						16 03	16 15			16 36		16 44						17 07
Reading 7	a				15 22	15 43	15 50					15 51	16 15	16 23			16 46		16 53					16 52	17 18
Oxford	a				15 50		16 43					16 18		17 17					17 44					17 22	

		GW	HC	GW	GW		GW	GW	GW	HC	GW	GW	GW	GW	GW		HC	GW	GW	GW	GW	GW	GW	GW	HC
		1		1	1		◇1	1	1		1	1	1	1	1			1	1	1	1	1	◇1 ☕	1	
London Paddington 15 ⊖	d	16 25	16 33	16 42	16 45		16 49		16 57	17 03	17 12	17 15	17 18	17 18	17 24		17 33	17 35		17 42	17 45	17 48	17 49	17 57	18 03
Acton Main Line	d				16 51								17 24									17 54			
Ealing Broadway ⊖	d	16 33	16 41	16 50	16 54				17 06	17 11		17 23	17 27		17 33		17 41				17 53	17 57		18 05	18 11
West Ealing	d		16 43		16 57					17 13			17 30				17 43					18 00			18 13
Drayton Green	d				16 59								17 32									18 02			
Castle Bar Park	d				17 01								17 34									18 04			
South Greenford	d				17 04								17 37									18 07			
Greenford ⊖	a				17 09								17 42									18 12			
Hanwell	d		16 45							17 15							17 45								18 15
Southall	d	16 38	16 49	16 58						17 19		17 29			17 37		17 49				17 59			18 10	18 19
Hayes & Harlington	d	16 42	16 53	17 02					17 13	17 23		17 33			17 41		17 53				18 03			18 14	18 23
Heathrow Terminal 1-2 2 ✈	a		17 05							17 35							18 05								18 35
Heathrow Terminal 4 ✈	a																								
West Drayton	d	16 47		17 07					17 18			17 38			17 47						18 08			18 19	
Iver	d	16 50							17 22						17 50									18 22	
Langley	d	16 53		17 12				←	17 26			17 44			17 54						18 12			18 26	
Slough 3	a	16 58		17 16			17 04	17 16	17 29		17 32	17 48			17 58					18 04	18 16			18 30	
	d	16 58		17 17			17 05	17 17	17 30		17 35	17 49			17 58					18 05	18 16			18 30	
Burnham	d			↪				17 21	17 35		17 40	17 54			18 02						18 21			18 35	
Taplow	d							17 25			17 43				18 06									18 39	
Maidenhead 3	d	17 05						17 30	17 44		17 48	18a05		17 41	18 10			17 58	←	18a13	18 26		18 09	18 45	
Twyford 3	d	17 13						17 38	17 52		17a58				18 17			18 07	18 17		18 34			18 52	
Reading 7	a	17 21					17 19	17 46	18 00					17 54	↪			18 14	18 26		18 44		18 20	↪	
Oxford	a	18 23					17 51							18 45				19 07	19 18				18 47		

			GW	GW	GW	GW	GW	GW	GW FO	GW FX	HC		GW	GW	GW	GW	GW	GW FO	GW FX	GW	GW		HC	GW	GW
			1	1	1	1	1	1	1	1			1	1	◇1 ☕	1	◇1 🛒	1	1	1	1			1	1
London Paddington 15 ⊖	d		18 12	18 15	18 18	18 18			18 25	18 25	18 33		18 42	18 45	18 47	18 48	18 50				18 58		19 03	19 05	19 12
Acton Main Line	d				18 24											18 54									
Ealing Broadway ⊖	d			18 23	18 27				18 33	18 33	18 41			18 53		18 57					19 07		19 11		19 20
West Ealing	d				18 30						18 43					19 00							19 13		
Drayton Green	d				18 32											19 02									
Castle Bar Park	d				18 34											19 04									
South Greenford	d				18 37											19 07									
Greenford ⊖	a				18 42											19 12									
Hanwell	d										18 45												19 15		
Southall	d			18 29					18 38	18 38	18 49			18 58							19 12		19 19		19 28
Hayes & Harlington	d			18 33					18 42	18 42	18 53			19 02							19 16		19 23		19 32
Heathrow Terminal 1-2 2 ✈	a										19 05												19 35		
Heathrow Terminal 4 ✈	a																								
West Drayton	d			18 38					18 46	18 46				19 07							19 21				19 36
Iver	d								18 49	18 49											19 24				
Langley	d			18 42					18 52	18 52										←	19 28				
Slough 3	a		18 35	18 47					18 59	18 59			19 05	19 14			19 06			19 14	19 32				19 42
	d		18 36	18 47					18 59	18 59			19 06	19 14			19 07			19 14	19 32				19 43
Burnham	d			18 51					19 03	19 03				↪						19 18	19 35				↪
Taplow	d								19 06	19 06											19 40				
Maidenhead 3	d		18 49	18 57		18 40	←	←	19 10	19 10			19a14					←	←	19 24	19 43			19 27	
Twyford 3	d		18a58	19 05		18 48	18 52	19 05	19 18	19 18					19 10			19 18	19 18	19 38	19 52			19a38	
Reading 7	a			↪		18 56	19 00	19 13	↪	↪					19 18		19 21	19 26	19 26	19 47	↪				
Oxford	a					19 46		20 16									19 49	20 18	20 27						

For non-stop services between London and Reading please see table 116

Passengers who hold valid tickets for Acton Main Line, West Ealing and Hanwell will be able to use local Transport for London (TFL) bus services to reach these stations. Tel 0843 222 1234

Table 117

London - Greenford and Reading

Mondays to Fridays

9 December to 3 January

Network Diagram - refer to first Page of Table 116

Station	GW	GW	GW	GW	GW	GW		GW	HC	GW	GW	GW	GW	GW	GW	HC		GW	GW	GW	GW	GW	HC	GW
			FX	FO																				
	1	1	◇1	◇1	1	1		1		1	1	◇1	◇1	1	1			1	1	◇1	1	1		1
			☕	☕								☕	🛒							🛒				
London Paddington 15 ⊖ d	19 15	19 18	19 22	19 22				19 27	19 33	19 42	19 45	19 48	19 50		19 57	20 03		20 12	20 15	20 20		20 27	20 33	20 42
Acton Main Line d	19 21										19 51								20 21					
Ealing Broadway ⊖ d	19 24							19 35	19 41	19 50	19 54				20 05	20 11		20 20	20 24			20 35	20 41	20 50
West Ealing d	19 27								19 43		19 57					20 13			20 27				20 43	
Drayton Green d	19 29										19 59								20 29					
Castle Bar Park d	19 31										20 01								20 31					
South Greenford d	19 34										20 04								20 34					
Greenford ⊖ a	19 39										20 09								20 39					
Hanwell d									19 45							20 15							20 45	
Southall d								19 40	19 49	19 58						20 19		20 28					20 49	20 58
Hayes & Harlington d								19 44	19 53	20 02					20 12	20 23		20 32				20 42	20 53	21 02
Heathrow Terminal 1-2 2 ✈ a									20 05							20 35							21 05	
Heathrow Terminal 4 ✈ a																								
West Drayton d								19 48		20 06					20 16			20 36				20 46		21 06
Iver d								19 51		20 09					20 19							20 49		
Langley d						←		19 55		20 13				←	20 22						←	20 52		
Slough 3 a			19 36	19 36		19 42		19 59		20 17			20 06	20 17	20 27			20 43		20 35	20 43	20 57		21 13
d			19 36	19 36		19 43		19 59		20 17			20 06	20 17	20 27			20 43		20 36	20 43	20 57		21 13
Burnham d						19 47		20 03		→				20 20				→			20 47			→
Taplow d						19 51								20 25							20 51			
Maidenhead 3 d		19 40			←	19 55		20 09				20 06		20 29	20 34						20 55	21 04		
Twyford 3 d		19 48			19 52	20 03		20 17						20 37	20 42						21 03	21 12		
Reading 7 a		19 56	19 51	19 51	20 00	20 13		20 25				20 18	20 21	20 45	20 50					20 49	21 13	21 20		
Oxford a		20 43	20 18	20 21				21 15					20 52		21 44					21 17		22 12		

Station	GW	GW		GW	GW	GW	HC	GW	GW	GW	GW	GW		HC	GW	GW	GW	GW	GW	GW	GW	GW		GW
					FX	FO								FO	FX	FO	FO	FX		FX	FO	FO		FX
	1	◇1		1	1	1		1	1	◇1	1	1			1	1	◇1	◇1	1	1	1	1		1
																	🛒	☕						
London Paddington 15 ⊖ d	20 45	20 48			20 57	20 57	21 03	21 12	21 15	21 18		21 27		21 33	21 36	21 42	21 48	21 48				21 57		21 57
Acton Main Line d	20 51								21 21						21 42	21 48								
Ealing Broadway ⊖ d	20 54				21 05	21 05	21 11	21 20	21 24			21 35		21 41	21 45	21 51						22 05		22 05
West Ealing d	20 57						21 13		21 27					21 43										
Drayton Green d	20 59								21 29															
Castle Bar Park d	21 01								21 31															
South Greenford d	21 04								21 34															
Greenford ⊖ a	21 09								21 39															
Hanwell d							21 15							21 45										
Southall d							21 19	21 28				21 42		21 49	21 52	21 58						22 10		22 10
Hayes & Harlington d					21 12	21 12	21 23	21 32				21 46		21 53	21 55	22 02						22 14		22 14
Heathrow Terminal 1-2 2 ✈ a							21 35							22 05										
Heathrow Terminal 4 ✈ a																								
West Drayton d					21 16	21 16		21 36				21 50			22 01	22 06						22 18		22 18
Iver d					21 19	21 19						21 53										22 21		22 21
Langley d				←	21 22	21 22					←	21 57							←	←	←	22 25		22 25
Slough 3 a		21 04		21 13	21 27	21 27		21 43		21 34	21 43	22 02			22 11	22 14	22 03	22 03	22 02	22 11	22 14	22 30		22 30
d		21 05		21 13	21 27	21 27		21 43		21 35	21 43	22 07			22 14	22 14	22 04	22 04	22 07	22 14	22 14	22 30		22 42
Burnham d				21 17				→			21 47	→			→	→				22 18	22 18	22 34		→
Taplow d				21 21							21 51									22 22	22 22	22 38		
Maidenhead 3 d				21 25	21 34	21 34					21 55								22 15	22 26	22 26	22 42		
Twyford 3 d				21 33	21 42	21 42					22 03								22 23	22 34	22 34	22 50		
Reading 7 a		21 20		21 43	21 51	21 54				21 50	22 14						22 23	22 23	22 30	22 45	22 45	22 59		
Oxford a		21 51			22 41	22 41				22 18							22 47	22 47	23 22			23 56		

Station	HC	HC	GW	GW	GW	GW	GW	HC		GW	GW	GW	GW	GW	GW	HC	HC	GW		GW	GW	GW	GW	GW
	FO	FX	FO	FX	FX	FO	FX	FO		FO	FX	FO	FX	FO	FX	FO	FX	FO		FX		FO	FX	FO
			◇1	◇1	1	1	1			◇1	◇1	1	1	1	1			◇1		◇1	1	1	1	1
London Paddington 15 ⊖ d	22 03	22 07	22 18	22 18		22 27	22 27	22 33		22 48	22 48			23 00	23 00	23 03	23 07	23 18		23 18	23 33	23 42	23 49	23 49
Acton Main Line d														23 06										23 55
Ealing Broadway ⊖ d	22 11	22 15				22 35	22 35	22 41						23 09	23 09	23 12	23 15				23 41		23 59	23 59
West Ealing d	22 13							22 43								23 14								00 01
Drayton Green d																								
Castle Bar Park d																								
South Greenford d																								
Greenford ⊖ a																								
Hanwell d	22 15							22 45								23 16								00 04
Southall d	22 19	22 19				22 40	22 40	22 49						23 15	23 15	23 20	23 20						00 07	00 07
Hayes & Harlington d	22 23	22 24				22 44	22 44	22 53						23 19	23 19	23 24	23 25				23 48		00 12	00 12
Heathrow Terminal 1-2 2 ✈ a	22 35	22 29						23 05								23 35	23 32							
Heathrow Terminal 4 ✈ a																23 41	23 38							
West Drayton d						22 48	22 48							23 23	23 23								00 16	00 16
Iver d						22 51	22 51							23 26	23 26								00 19	00 19
Langley d					←	22 55	22 55					←	←	23 29	23 29								00 22	00 22
Slough 3 a			22 34	22 39	22 30	22 59	23 00			23 04	23 08	22 59	23 00	23 34	23 34			23 36		23 38	23 57	00 01	00 28	00 28
d			22 35	22 39	22 42	23 11	23 11			23 05	23 08	23 11	23 11	23 34	23 34			23 38		23 38	23 57	00 01	00 28	00 28
Burnham d					22 46	→	→					23 15	23 15										00 32	00 32
Taplow d					22 49							23 19	23 19										00 36	00 36
Maidenhead 3 d			22 42	22 47	22 53					23 12	23 17	23 23	23 23	23 41	23 41			23 46		23 46	00 05	00 10	00 41	00 41
Twyford 3 d					23 01					23 20	23 26	23 31	23 31	23 49	23 49						00 13		00 48	00 48
Reading 7 a			22 54	23 01	23 10					23 27	23 33	23 40	23 40	23 59	23 59			00 04		00 04	00 22	00 25	00 56	00 58
Oxford a			23 27	23 29	23 54					23 56	00 01	00 27	00 27					00 35		00 35	01 18	01 02		

For non-stop services between London and Reading please see table 116

Passengers who hold valid tickets for Acton Main Line, West Ealing and Hanwell will be able to use local Transport for London (TFL) bus services to reach these stations. Tel 0843 222 1234

Table 117

Mondays to Fridays

6 January to 7 February

Network Diagram - refer to first Page of Table 116

London - Greenford and Reading

		GW MO 1	GW MX 1	GW MX 1	GW MO ◇1	GW MO 1	GW MX 1	GW MX ◇1	GW MO 1	GW MX 1	GW MO 1	GW MX 1	GW 1	HC	GW 1	HC	GW 1	HC	GW 1	GW 1	GW ◇1	GW 1	GW 1
London Paddington 15 ⊖	d							00 22	00 34	00 34	01 34	01 34	03 34	04 42	05 12	05 13	05 17	05 33	05 42	05 45	05 45		05 57
Acton Main Line	d																			05 51			
Ealing Broadway ⊖	d					00 02			00 42	00 42	01 42	01 42	03 42	04 50		05 21	05 25	05 41	05 50	05 54			06 05
West Ealing	d																	05 43		05 57			
Drayton Green	d																			05 59			
Castle Bar Park	d																			06 01			
South Greenford	d																			06 04			
Greenford ⊖	a																			06 09			
Hanwell	d																	05 45					
Southall	d					00 07	00 07		00 47	00 47	01 47	01 47	03 48	04 54		05 25	05 31	05 49	05 58				06 10
Hayes & Harlington	d					00 11	00 12		00 51	00 51	01 51	01 51	03 52	04 58		05 29	05 36	05 53	06 02				06 14
Heathrow Terminal 1-2 2 ✈	a													05 04		05 35		06 05					
Heathrow Terminal 4 ✈	a													05 10		05 41							
West Drayton	d					00 15	00 16		00 55	00 55	01 55	01 55	03 56				05 41		06 06				06 18
Iver	d						00 19												06 09				06 21
Langley	d					00 20	00 22		01 00	01 00							05 46		06 13			←	06 25
Slough 3	a					00 24	00 28	00 40	01 05	01 05	02 04	02 04	04 04		05 29		05 50		06 17		06 01	06 17	06 29
	d				00 07	00 24	00 28	00 41	01 05	01 05	02 04	02 04	04 05		05 30		05 51		06 17		06 01	06 17	06 29
Burnham	d					00 28	00 32		01 09	01 09									→			06 21	
Taplow	d						00 36			01 13												06 25	
Maidenhead 3	d			00 05	00 15	00 33	00 41		01 15	01 16	02 10	02 11	04 12				05 59					06 29	06 37
Twyford 3	d	00 03	00 08	00 13		00 41	00 48		01 23	01 24	02 19	02 19	04 20				06 07					06 38	06 45
Reading 7	a	00 12	00 16	00 22	00 30	00 49	00 56	01 01	01 32	01 35	02 29	02 29	04 30		05 48		06 15				06 17	06 48	06 53
Oxford	a			01 18				01 34							06 20		07 02				06 51		07 49

		HC	GW 1	GW 1	GW ◇1	GW 1	GW 1	HC	GW 1	GW 1	GW 1	GW 1	GW 1	HC	GW 1	GW 1	GW 1	GW 1	GW 1	GW 1	HC	GW 1	GW 1
London Paddington 15 ⊖	d	06 03	06 12	06 15	06 20		06 27	06 33	06 42	06 45	06 48		06 57	07 03	07 12	07 12	07 15	07 21		07 27	07 33	07 42	07 45
Acton Main Line	d			06 21						06 51							07 21						07 51
Ealing Broadway ⊖	d	06 11	06 20	06 24			06 35	06 41	06 50	06 54			07 05	07 11		07 20	07 24			07 35	07 41	07 50	07 54
West Ealing	d	06 13		06 27				06 43		06 57				07 13			07 27				07 43		07 57
Drayton Green	d			06 29						06 59							07 29						07 59
Castle Bar Park	d			06 31						07 01							07 31						08 01
South Greenford	d			06 34						07 04							07 34						08 04
Greenford ⊖	a			06 39						07 09							07 39						08 09
Hanwell	d	06 15						06 45						07 15							07 45		
Southall	d	06 19	06 28				06 41	06 49	06 58				07 10	07 19		07 28				07 40	07 49	07 59	
Hayes & Harlington	d	06 23	06 32				06 45	06 53	07 02				07 14	07 23		07 32				07 44	07 53	08 02	
Heathrow Terminal 1-2 2 ✈	a	06 35						07 05						07 35							08 05		
Heathrow Terminal 4 ✈	a																						
West Drayton	d		06 40				06 49		07 06				07 18			07 36				07 48		08 06	
Iver	d						06 52						07 21							07 51			
Langley	d					←	06 56					←	07 25						←	07 55			
Slough 3	a		06 47		06 35	06 47	07 00		07 13		07 02	07 13	07 29			07 43		07 36	07 43	07 59		08 13	
	d		06 47		06 35	06 47	07 00		07 13		07 02	07 13	07 29			07 43		07 36	07 43	07 59		08 13	
Burnham	d		→			06 51			→			07 17				→			07 47			→	
Taplow	d					06 54						07 21							07 51				
Maidenhead 3	d					06 58	07 08					07 25	07 37		07 43				07 55	08 07			
Twyford 3	d					07 06	07 16					07 37	07 45		07 51				08 03	08 15			
Reading 7	a				06 49	07 14	07 27				07 19	07 45	07 52		08 02			07 51	08 14	08 23			
Oxford	a				07 22						08 02		08 44					08 19		09 16			

		GW 1	GW 1	GW 1	HC	GW 1	GW 1	GW 1	GW ◇1 R	GW 1	GW 1	HC	GW 1	GW 1	GW 1	GW ◇1	GW 1	GW 1	GW 1	HC	GW 1	GW 1
London Paddington 15 ⊖	d	07 50		07 57	08 03	08 09	08 12	08 15	08 22		08 27	08 33	08 38	08 46	08 47	08 51			08 55	09 03	09 12	09 15
Acton Main Line	d							08 21						08 51								09 21
Ealing Broadway ⊖	d			08 05	08 11	08 17	08 20	08 24			08 35	08 41	08 47	08 54	08 59				09 03	09 11	09 20	09 24
West Ealing	d				08 13			08 27				08 43		08 57	09 01					09 13		09 27
Drayton Green	d							08 29						08 59								09 29
Castle Bar Park	d							08 31						09 01								09 31
South Greenford	d							08 34						09 04								09 34
Greenford ⊖	a							08 39						09 10								09 39
Hanwell	d				08 15							08 45	08 50							09 15		
Southall	d			08 10	08 19		08 28				08 40	08 49							09 08	09 19	09 28	
Hayes & Harlington	d			08 14	08 23		08 32				08 44	08 54	08 57		09 08				09 12	09 23	09 32	
Heathrow Terminal 1-2 2 ✈	a				08 35							09 05								09 35		
Heathrow Terminal 4 ✈	a																					
West Drayton	d			08 18			08 36				08 48		09 01						09 16		09 36	
Iver	d			08 21							08 51		09 04						09 19			
Langley	d		←	08 25						←	08 55		09 06				←	←	09 23			
Slough 3	a	08 06	08 13	08 29		08 34	08 43		08 36	08 43	08 59		09 11		09 16	09 06	09 11	09 16	09 27		09 43	
	d	08 06	08 13	08 29		08 34	08 43		08 36	08 43	08 59		09 12		09 16	09 06	09 12	09 16	09 27		09 43	
Burnham	d		08 17				→			08 47			→		→			09 20			→	
Taplow	d		08 21							08 51								09 24				
Maidenhead 3	d		08 25	08 38		08 42				08 55	09 06						09 18	09 28	09 35			
Twyford 3	d		08 33	08 46		08 50				09 03	09 18						09 27	09 37	09 43			
Reading 7	a	08 21	08 43	08 54		09 00			08 51	09 14	09 26					09 20	09 34	09 47	09 51			
Oxford	a	08 49		09 45					09 20		10 18					09 53			10 43			

For non-stop services between London and Reading please see table 116

Passengers who hold valid tickets for Acton Main Line, West Ealing and Hanwell will be able to use local Transport for London (TFL) bus services to reach these stations. Tel 0843 222 1234

Table 117

London - Greenford and Reading

Mondays to Fridays

6 January to 7 February

Network Diagram - refer to first Page of Table 116

		GW	GW	GW	HC	GW	GW	GW		GW	GW	HC	GW	GW	GW	GW	GW	HC		GW	GW	GW	GW	GW	HC
		◇1 ⊥	1	1		1	1	◇1		1	1		1	1	◇1 ⊏	1	1			1	1	◇1	1	1	
London Paddington 15 ⊖	d	09 21		09 27	09 33	09 42	09 45	09 50			09 57	10 03	10 12	10 15	10 22		10 27	10 33		10 42	10 45	10 50		10 57	11 03
Acton Main Line	d						09 51							10 21							10 51				
Ealing Broadway ⊖	d			09 35	09 41	09 50	09 54				10 05	10 11	10 20	10 24			10 35	10 41		10 50	10 54			11 05	11 11
West Ealing	d				09 43		09 57					10 13		10 27				10 43			10 57				11 13
Drayton Green	d						09 59							10 29							10 59				
Castle Bar Park	d						10 01							10 31							11 01				
South Greenford	d						10 04							10 34							11 04				
Greenford ⊖	a						10 09							10 39							11 09				
Hanwell	d				09 45							10 15						10 45							11 15
Southall	d				09 49	09 58						10 19	10 28					10 49		10 58					11 19
Hayes & Harlington	d			09 42	09 53	10 02					10 12	10 23	10 32				10 42	10 53		11 02				11 12	11 23
Heathrow Terminal 1-2 2 ✈	a				10 05							10 35						11 05							11 35
Heathrow Terminal 4 ✈	a																								
West Drayton	d			09 46		10 06					10 16		10 36				10 46			11 06				11 16	
Iver	d			09 49							10 19						10 49							11 19	
Langley	d		←	09 52						←	10 22					←	10 52						←	11 22	
Slough 3	a	09 36	09 43	09 57		10 13		10 06		10 13	10 27		10 43		10 36	10 43	10 57			11 13		11 06	11 13	11 27	
	d	09 36	09 43	09 57		10 13		10 06		10 13	10 27		10 43		10 36	10 43	10 57			11 13		11 06	11 13	11 27	
Burnham	d		09 45			→				10 17			→			10 47				→			11 17		
Taplow	d		09 51							10 21						10 51							11 21		
Maidenhead 3	d		09 55	10 04						10 25	10 34					10 55	11 04						11 25	11 34	
Twyford 3	d		10 03	10 12						10 38	10 42					11 06	11 12						11 35	11 42	
Reading 7	a	09 52	10 14	10 21				10 21		10 45	10 50				10 51	11 15	11 21					11 21	11 45	11 52	
Oxford	a	10 20		11 14				10 47			11 43				11 18		12 14					11 50		12 43	

		GW	GW	GW		GW	GW	HC	GW	GW	GW	GW	GW	HC		GW	GW	GW	GW	GW	HC	GW	GW	GW	
		1	1	◇1 ⊥		1	1		1	1	◇1 ⊥	1	1			1	1	◇1 ⊥	1	1		1	1	◇1 ⊥	
London Paddington 15 ⊖	d	11 12	11 15	11 20			11 27	11 33	11 42	11 45	11 50		11 57	12 03		12 12	12 15	12 21		12 27	12 33	12 42	12 45	12 50	
Acton Main Line	d		11 21							11 51							12 21						12 51		
Ealing Broadway ⊖	d	11 20	11 24				11 35	11 41	11 50	11 54			12 05	12 11		12 20	12 24			12 35	12 41	12 50	12 54		
West Ealing	d		11 27					11 43		11 57				12 13			12 27				12 43		12 57		
Drayton Green	d		11 29							11 59							12 29						12 59		
Castle Bar Park	d		11 31							12 01							12 31						13 01		
South Greenford	d		11 34							12 04							12 34						13 04		
Greenford ⊖	a		11 39							12 09							12 39						13 10		
Hanwell	d							11 45						12 15							12 45				
Southall	d	11 28						11 49	11 58					12 19		12 28					12 49	12 58			
Hayes & Harlington	d	11 32					11 42	11 53	12 02				12 12	12 23		12 32				12 42	12 53	13 02			
Heathrow Terminal 1-2 2 ✈	a							12 05						12 35							13 05				
Heathrow Terminal 4 ✈	a																								
West Drayton	d	11 36					11 46		12 06				12 16			12 36				12 46		13 06			
Iver	d						11 49						12 19							12 49					
Langley	d					←	11 52					←	12 22						←	12 52					
Slough 3	a	11 43		11 36		11 43	11 57		12 13		12 06	12 13	12 27			12 43		12 36	12 43	12 57		13 13		13 06	
	d	11 43		11 36		11 43	11 57		12 13		12 06	12 13	12 27			12 43		12 36	12 43	12 57		13 13		13 06	
Burnham	d	→				11 47			→			12 17				→			12 47			→			
Taplow	d					11 51						12 21							12 51						
Maidenhead 3	d					11 55	12 04					12 25	12 34						12 55	13 04					
Twyford 3	d					12 03	12 13					12 37	12 45						13 06	13 12					
Reading 7	a			11 52		12 15	12 22				12 22	12 45	12 52					12 51	13 15	13 20				13 22	
Oxford	a			12 18			13 14				12 48		13 43					13 20		14 14				13 50	

		GW	GW	HC	GW	GW	GW	GW	GW	HC		GW	GW	GW	GW	GW	HC	GW	GW	GW		GW	GW	HC	GW
		1	1		1	1	◇1 ⊥	1	1			1	1	◇1 ⊥	1	1		1	1	◇1 ⊥		1	1		1
London Paddington 15 ⊖	d		12 57	13 03	13 12	13 15	13 21		13 27	13 33		13 42	13 45	13 50		13 57	14 03	14 12	14 15	14 21			14 27	14 33	14 42
Acton Main Line	d					13 21							13 51						14 21						
Ealing Broadway ⊖	d		13 05	13 11	13 20	13 24			13 35	13 41		13 50	13 54			14 05	14 11	14 20	14 24				14 35	14 41	14 50
West Ealing	d			13 13		13 27				13 43			13 57				14 13		14 27					14 43	
Drayton Green	d					13 29							13 59						14 29						
Castle Bar Park	d					13 31							14 01						14 31						
South Greenford	d					13 34							14 04						14 34						
Greenford ⊖	a					13 39							14 09						14 39						
Hanwell	d			13 15						13 45							14 15							14 45	
Southall	d			13 19	13 28					13 49		13 58					14 19	14 28						14 49	14 58
Hayes & Harlington	d		13 12	13 23	13 32				13 42	13 53		14 02				14 12	14 23	14 32					14 42	14 53	15 02
Heathrow Terminal 1-2 2 ✈	a			13 35						14 05							14 35							15 05	
Heathrow Terminal 4 ✈	a																								
West Drayton	d		13 16		13 36				13 46			14 06				14 16		14 36					14 46		15 06
Iver	d		13 19						13 49							14 19							14 49		
Langley	d	←	13 22					←	13 52						←	14 22						←	14 52		
Slough 3	a	13 13	13 27		13 43		13 36	13 43	13 57			14 13		14 06	14 13	14 27		14 43		14 36		14 43	14 57		15 13
	d	13 13	13 27		13 43		13 36	13 43	13 57			14 13		14 06	14 13	14 27		14 43		14 36		14 43	14 57		15 13
Burnham	d	13 17			→			13 47				→			14 17			→				14 47			→
Taplow	d	13 21						13 51							14 21							14 51			
Maidenhead 3	d	13 25	13 34					13 55	14 04						14 25	14 34						14 55	15 04		
Twyford 3	d	13 33	13 44					14 03	14 12						14 33	14 42						15 03	15 14		
Reading 7	a	13 43	13 53				13 51	14 15	14 21					14 21	14 43	14 54				14 52		15 13	15 21		
Oxford	a		14 43				14 18		15 14					14 48		15 44				15 18			16 16		

For non-stop services between London and Reading please see table 116

Passengers who hold valid tickets for Acton Main Line, West Ealing and Hanwell will be able to use local Transport for London (TFL) bus services to reach these stations. Tel 0843 222 1234

Table 117

London - Greenford and Reading

Mondays to Fridays

6 January to 7 February

Network Diagram - refer to first Page of Table 116

	GW 1	GW ◇1 🚲	GW 1	GW 1	HC		GW 1	GW 1	GW ◇1 🚲	GW 1	GW 1	HC	GW 1	GW 1	GW 1		GW 1	HC	GW 1	GW 1	GW ◇1 🚲	GW 1	GW 1	HC
London Paddington 15 ⊖ d	14 45	14 50		14 57	15 03		15 12	15 15	15 22		15 27	15 33	15 40	15 42	15 45		15 57	16 03	16 12	16 15	16 22		16 25	16 33
Acton Main Line d	14 51							15 21							15 51					16 21				
Ealing Broadway ⊖ d	14 54			15 05	15 11		15 20	15 24			15 35	15 41		15 50	15 54		16 05	16 11	16 20	16 24			16 33	16 41
West Ealing d	14 57				15 13			15 27				15 43			15 57			16 13		16 27				16 43
Drayton Green d	14 59							15 29							15 59					16 29				
Castle Bar Park d	15 01							15 31							16 01					16 31				
South Greenford d	15 04							15 34							16 04					16 34				
Greenford ⊖ a	15 09							15 39							16 09					16 39				
Hanwell d					15 15							15 45						16 15						16 45
Southall d					15 19		15 28				15 40	15 49		15 58				16 19	16 28				16 38	16 49
Hayes & Harlington d				15 12	15 23		15 32				15 44	15 53		16 04			16 12	16 23	16 32				16 42	16 53
Heathrow Terminal 1-2 2 ✈ a					15 35							16 05						16 35						17 05
Heathrow Terminal 4 ✈ a																								
West Drayton d				15 16			15 36				15 48			16 09			16 16		16 36				16 47	
Iver d				15 19							15 51						16 19						16 50	
Langley d			←	15 22						←	15 55						16 23					←	16 53	
Slough 3 a		15 06	15 13	15 27			15 43		15 36	15 43	15 59		16 11	16 16			16 28		16 44		16 37	16 44	16 58	
d		15 06	15 13	15 27			15 43		15 36	15 43	15 59		16 11	16 16			16 28		16 45		16 38	16 45	16 58	
Burnham d			15 17				→			15 47				16 20					→			16 50		
Taplow d			15 21							15 51				16 23								16 54		
Maidenhead 3 d			15 25	15 34						15 55	16 07		16a22	16 27			16 35					16 59	17 05	
Twyford 3 d			15 33	15 42						16 03	16 15			16 36			16 44					17 07	17 13	
Reading 7 a		15 22	15 43	15 50					15 51	16 15	16 23			16 46			16 53				16 52	17 18	17 21	
Oxford a		15 50		16 43					16 18		17 17						17 44				17 22		18 23	

	GW 1		GW 1	GW ◇1	GW 1	GW 1	HC	GW 1	GW 1	GW 1	GW 1		GW 1	HC	GW 1	GW 1	GW 1	GW 1	GW 1	GW ◇1 ☕	GW 1		HC	GW 1
London Paddington 15 ⊖ d	16 42		16 45	16 49		16 57	17 03	17 12	17 15	17 18	17 18		17 24	17 33	17 35		17 42	17 45	17 48	17 49	17 57		18 03	18 12
Acton Main Line d			16 51							17 24									17 54					
Ealing Broadway ⊖ d	16 50		16 54			17 06	17 11		17 23	17 27			17 33	17 41				17 53	17 57		18 05		18 11	
West Ealing d			16 57				17 13			17 30				17 43					18 00				18 13	
Drayton Green d			16 59							17 32									18 02					
Castle Bar Park d			17 01							17 34									18 04					
South Greenford d			17 04							17 37									18 07					
Greenford ⊖ a			17 09							17 42									18 12					
Hanwell d							17 15							17 45									18 15	
Southall d	16 58						17 19		17 29				17 37	17 49				17 59			18 10		18 19	
Hayes & Harlington d	17 02					17 13	17 23		17 33				17 41	17 53				18 03			18 14		18 23	
Heathrow Terminal 1-2 2 ✈ a							17 35							18 05									18 35	
Heathrow Terminal 4 ✈ a																								
West Drayton d	17 07					17 18			17 38				17 47					18 08			18 19			
Iver d						17 22							17 50								18 22			
Langley d	17 12				←	17 26			17 44				17 54					18 12			18 26			
Slough 3 a	17 16			17 04	17 16	17 29		17 32	17 48				17 58				18 04	18 16			18 30			18 35
d	17 17			17 05	17 17	17 30		17 35	17 49				17 58				18 05	18 16			18 30			18 36
Burnham d	→				17 21	17 35		17 40	17 54				18 02					18 21			18 35			
Taplow d					17 25			17 43					18 06								18 39			
Maidenhead 3 d					17 30	17 44		17 48	18a05		17 41		18 10		17 58	←	18a13	18 26		18 09	18 45			18 49
Twyford 3 d					17 38	17 52		17a58					18 17		18 07	18 17		18 34			18 52			18a58
Reading 7 a				17 19	17 46	18 00					17 54		→		18 14	18 26		18 44		18 20	→			
Oxford a				17 51							18 45				19 07	19 18				18 47				

	GW 1	GW 1	GW 1	GW 1	GW 1	GW FO 1	GW FX 1		HC	GW 1	GW 1	GW ◇1 ☕	GW 1	GW ◇1 🚲	GW FO 1	GW FX 1	GW 1		GW 1	HC	GW 1	GW 1	GW 1	GW 1
London Paddington 15 ⊖ d	18 15	18 18	18 18			18 25	18 25		18 33	18 42	18 45	18 47	18 48	18 50					18 58	19 03	19 05	19 12	19 15	19 18
Acton Main Line d		18 24											18 54										19 21	
Ealing Broadway ⊖ d	18 23	18 27				18 33	18 33		18 41		18 53		18 57						19 07	19 11		19 20	19 24	
West Ealing d		18 30							18 43				19 00							19 13			19 27	
Drayton Green d		18 32											19 02										19 29	
Castle Bar Park d		18 34											19 04										19 31	
South Greenford d		18 37											19 07										19 34	
Greenford ⊖ a		18 42											19 12										19 39	
Hanwell d									18 45											19 15				
Southall d	18 29					18 38	18 38		18 49		18 58								19 12	19 19		19 28		
Hayes & Harlington d	18 33					18 42	18 42		18 53		19 02								19 16	19 23		19 32		
Heathrow Terminal 1-2 2 ✈ a									19 05											19 35				
Heathrow Terminal 4 ✈ a																								
West Drayton d	18 38					18 46	18 46				19 07								19 21			19 36		
Iver d						18 49	18 49												19 24					
Langley d	18 42					18 52	18 52										←		19 28					
Slough 3 a	18 47					18 59	18 59			19 05	19 14			19 06			19 14		19 32			19 42		
d	18 47					18 59	18 59			19 06	19 14			19 07			19 14		19 32			19 43		
Burnham d	18 51					19 03	19 03				→						19 18		19 35			→		
Taplow d						19 06	19 06												19 40					
Maidenhead 3 d	18 57		18 40	←	←	19 10	19 10			19a14					←	←	19 24		19 43		19 27			19 40
Twyford 3 d	19 05		18 48	18 52	19 05	19 18	19 18					19 10			19 18	19 18	19 38		19 52		19a38			19 48
Reading 7 a	→		18 56	19 00	19 13	→	→					19 18		19 21	19 26	19 26	19 47		→					19 56
Oxford a			19 46		20 16									19 49	20 18	20 27								20 43

For non-stop services between London and Reading please see table 116

Passengers who hold valid tickets for Acton Main Line, West Ealing and Hanwell will be able to use local Transport for London (TFL) bus services to reach these stations. Tel 0843 222 1234

Table 117

London - Greenford and Reading

Mondays to Fridays

6 January to 7 February

Network Diagram - refer to first Page of Table 116

		GW	GW	GW	GW	GW	HC	GW	GW	GW	GW	GW	GW	HC	GW	GW	GW	GW	GW	HC	GW	GW
		FX	FO																			
		◇1	◇1	1	1	1		1	1	◇1	◇1	1	1		1	1	◇1	1	1		1	1
		🍴	🍴							🍴	🛒						🛒					
London Paddington [15] ⊖	d	19 22	19 22			19 27	19 33	19 42	19 45	19 48	19 50		19 57	20 03	20 12	20 15	20 20		20 27	20 33	20 42	20 45
Acton Main Line	d								19 51							20 21						20 51
Ealing Broadway ⊖	d					19 35	19 41	19 50	19 54				20 05	20 11	20 20	20 24			20 35	20 41	20 50	20 54
West Ealing	d						19 43		19 57					20 13		20 27				20 43		20 57
Drayton Green	d								19 59							20 29						20 59
Castle Bar Park	d								20 01							20 31						21 01
South Greenford	d								20 04							20 34						21 04
Greenford ⊖	a								20 09							20 39						21 09
Hanwell	d						19 45							20 15						20 45		
Southall	d					19 40	19 49	19 58						20 19	20 28					20 49	20 58	
Hayes & Harlington	d					19 44	19 53	20 02					20 12	20 23	20 32				20 42	20 53	21 02	
Heathrow Terminal 1-2 [2] ✈	a						20 05							20 35						21 05		
Heathrow Terminal 4 ✈	a																					
West Drayton	d					19 48		20 06					20 16		20 36				20 46		21 06	
Iver	d					19 51		20 09					20 19						20 49			
Langley	d				←	19 55		20 13				←	20 22					←	20 52			
Slough [3]	a	19 36	19 36		19 42	19 59		20 17			20 06	20 17	20 27		20 43		20 35	20 43	20 57		21 13	
	d	19 36	19 36		19 43	19 59		20 17			20 06	20 17	20 27		20 43		20 36	20 43	20 57		21 13	
Burnham	d				19 47	20 03		→				20 20			→			20 47			→	
Taplow	d				19 51							20 25						20 51				
Maidenhead [3]	d			←	19 55	20 09				20 06		20 29	20 34					20 55	21 04			
Twyford [3]	d			19 52	20 03	20 17						20 37	20 42					21 03	21 12			
Reading [7]	a	19 51	19 51	20 00	20 13	20 25				20 18	20 21	20 45	20 50				20 49	21 13	21 20			
Oxford	a	20 18	20 21			21 15					20 52		21 44				21 17		22 12			

		GW	GW	GW	GW	HC	GW	GW	GW	GW	GW	HC	GW	GW	GW	GW	GW	GW	GW	GW	GW	HC	HC
				FX	FO							FO	FX	FO	FO	FX		FX	FO	FO	FX	FO	FX
		◇1	1	1	1		1	1	◇1	1	1		1	1	◇1	◇1	1	1	1	1	1		
															🛒	🍴							
London Paddington [15] ⊖	d	20 48		20 57	20 57	21 03	21 12	21 15	21 18		21 27	21 33	21 36	21 42	21 48	21 48				21 57	21 57	22 03	22 07
Acton Main Line	d							21 21					21 42	21 48									
Ealing Broadway ⊖	d			21 05	21 05	21 11	21 20	21 24			21 35	21 41	21 45	21 51						22 05	22 05	22 11	22 15
West Ealing	d					21 13		21 27				21 43										22 13	
Drayton Green	d							21 29															
Castle Bar Park	d							21 31															
South Greenford	d							21 34															
Greenford ⊖	a							21 39															
Hanwell	d					21 15						21 45										22 15	
Southall	d					21 19	21 28				21 42	21 49	21 52	21 58						22 10	22 10	22 19	22 19
Hayes & Harlington	d			21 12	21 12	21 23	21 32				21 46	21 53	21 55	22 02						22 14	22 14	22 23	22 24
Heathrow Terminal 1-2 [2] ✈	a					21 35						22 05										22 35	22 29
Heathrow Terminal 4 ✈	a																						
West Drayton	d			21 16	21 16		21 36				21 50		22 01	22 06						22 18	22 18		
Iver	d			21 19	21 19						21 53									22 21	22 21		
Langley	d		←	21 22	21 22					←	21 57						←	←	←	22 25	22 25		
Slough [3]	a	21 04	21 13	21 27	21 27		21 43		21 34	21 43	22 02		22 11	22 14	22 03	22 03	22 02	22 11	22 14	22 30	22 30		
	d	21 05	21 13	21 27	21 27		21 43		21 35	21 43	22 07		22 14	22 14	22 04	22 04	22 07	22 14	22 14	22 30	22 42		
Burnham	d		21 17				→			21 47	→		→	→				22 18	22 18	22 34	→		
Taplow	d		21 21							21 51								22 22	22 22	22 38			
Maidenhead [3]	d		21 25	21 34	21 34					21 55							22 15	22 26	22 26	22 42			
Twyford [3]	d		21 33	21 42	21 42					22 03							22 23	22 34	22 34	22 50			
Reading [7]	a	21 20	21 43	21 51	21 54				21 50	22 14					22 23	22 23	22 30	22 45	22 45	22 59			
Oxford	a	21 51		22 41	22 41				22 18						22 47	22 47	23 22			23 56			

		GW	GW	GW	GW	GW	HC	GW	GW	GW	GW	GW	GW	HC	HC	GW	GW	GW	GW	GW	GW
		FO	FX	FX	FO	FX	FO	FO	FX	FO	FX	FO	FX	FO	FX	FO	FX		FO	FX	FO
		◇1	◇1	1	1	1		◇1	◇1	1	1	1	1			◇1	◇1	1	1	1	1
London Paddington [15] ⊖	d	22 18	22 18		22 27	22 27	22 33	22 48	22 48			23 00	23 00	23 03	23 07	23 18	23 18	23 33	23 42	23 49	23 49
Acton Main Line	d											23 06									23 55
Ealing Broadway ⊖	d				22 35	22 35	22 41					23 09	23 09	23 12	23 15			23 41		23 59	23 59
West Ealing	d						22 43							23 14							00 01
Drayton Green	d																				
Castle Bar Park	d																				
South Greenford	d																				
Greenford ⊖	a																				
Hanwell	d						22 45							23 16							00 04
Southall	d				22 40	22 40	22 49					23 15	23 15	23 20	23 20					00 07	00 07
Hayes & Harlington	d				22 44	22 44	22 53					23 19	23 19	23 24	23 25			23 48		00 12	00 12
Heathrow Terminal 1-2 [2] ✈	a						23 05							23 35	23 32						
Heathrow Terminal 4 ✈	a													23 41	23 38						
West Drayton	d				22 48	22 48						23 23	23 23							00 16	00 16
Iver	d				22 51	22 51						23 26	23 26							00 19	00 19
Langley	d			←	22 55	22 55				←	←	23 29	23 29							00 22	00 22
Slough [3]	a	22 34	22 39	22 30	22 59	23 00		23 04	23 08	22 59	23 00	23 34	23 34			23 36	23 38	23 57	00 01	00 28	00 28
	d	22 35	22 39	22 42	23 11	23 11		23 05	23 08	23 11	23 11	23 34	23 34			23 38	23 38	23 57	00 01	00 28	00 28
Burnham	d			22 46	→	→				23 15	23 15									00 32	00 32
Taplow	d			22 49						23 19	23 19									00 36	00 36
Maidenhead [3]	d	22 42	22 47	22 53				23 12	23 17	23 23	23 23	23 41	23 41			23 46	23 46	00 05	00 10	00 41	00 41
Twyford [3]	d			23 01				23 20	23 26	23 31	23 31	23 49	23 49					00 13		00 48	00 48
Reading [7]	a	22 54	23 01	23 10				23 27	23 33	23 40	23 40	23 59	23 59			00 04	00 04	00 22	00 25	00 56	00 58
Oxford	a	23 27	23 29	23 54				23 56	00 01	00 27	00 27					00 35	00 35	01 18	01 02		

For non-stop services between London and Reading please see table 116

Passengers who hold valid tickets for Acton Main Line, West Ealing and Hanwell will be able to use local Transport for London (TFL) bus services to reach these stations. Tel 0843 222 1234

Table 117

London - Greenford and Reading

Mondays to Fridays

17 February to 24 March

Network Diagram - refer to first Page of Table 116

Station		GW	GW	GW	GW	GW	GW	GW	GW	GW		GW	GW	HC	GW	HC	GW	HC	GW	GW		GW	GW	GW	HC
		MO	MX	MX	MO	MO	MX	MX	MX	MO															
		1	1	1	◇1	1	1	◇1	1	1		1	1		1		1		1	1		◇1	1	1	
London Paddington 15 ⊖	d							00 22	00 34	00 34		01 34	03 34	04 42	05 12	05 13	05 17	05 33	05 42	05 45		05 45		05 57	06 03
Acton Main Line	d																			05 51					
Ealing Broadway ⊖	d					00 02			00 42	00 43		01 42	03 42	04 50		05 21	05 25	05 41	05 50	05 54				06 05	06 11
West Ealing	d																	05 43		05 57					06 13
Drayton Green	d																			05 59					
Castle Bar Park	d																			06 01					
South Greenford	d																			06 04					
Greenford ⊖	a																			06 09					
Hanwell	d																	05 45							06 15
Southall	d					00 07	00 07		00 47	00 48		01 47	03 48	04 54		05 25	05 31	05 49	05 58					06 10	06 19
Hayes & Harlington	d					00 11	00 12		00 51	00 52		01 51	03 52	04 58		05 29	05 36	05 53	06 02					06 14	06 23
Heathrow Terminal 1-2 2 ✈	a													05 04		05 35		06 05							06 35
Heathrow Terminal 4 ✈	a													05 10		05 41									
West Drayton	d					00 15	00 16		00 55	00 56		01 55	03 56				05 41		06 06					06 18	
Iver	d						00 19												06 09					06 21	
Langley	d					00 20	00 22		01 00	01 01							05 46		06 13				←	06 25	
Slough 3	a					00 24	00 28	00 40	01 05	01 05		02 04	04 04		05 29		05 50		06 17			06 01	06 17	06 29	
	d				00 11	00 24	00 28	00 41	01 05	01 05		02 04	04 05		05 30		05 51		06 17			06 01	06 17	06 29	
Burnham	d					00 28	00 32		01 09	01 09									→				06 21		
Taplow	d						00 36		01 13														06 25		
Maidenhead 3	d			00 05	00 18	00 33	00 41		01 16	01 16		02 11	04 12				05 59						06 29	06 37	
Twyford 3	d	00 03	00 08	00 13		00 41	00 48		01 24	01 24		02 19	04 20				06 07						06 38	06 45	
Reading 7	a	00 12	00 16	00 22	00 33	00 49	00 56	01 01	01 35	01 32		02 29	04 30		05 48		06 15					06 17	06 48	06 53	
Oxford	a			01 18				01 34							06 20		07 02					06 51		07 49	

Station		GW	GW	GW	GW	GW		HC	GW	GW	GW	GW	GW	HC	GW	GW		GW	GW	GW	GW	HC	GW	GW	GW
		1	1	◇1	1	1			1	1	1	1	1		1	1		1	1	1	1		1	1	1
London Paddington 15 ⊖	d	06 12	06 15	06 20		06 27		06 33	06 42	06 45	06 48		06 57	07 03	07 12	07 12		07 15	07 21		07 27	07 33	07 42	07 45	07 50
Acton Main Line	d		06 21							06 51								07 21						07 51	
Ealing Broadway ⊖	d	06 20	06 24			06 35		06 41	06 50	06 54			07 05	07 11		07 20		07 24			07 35	07 41	07 50	07 54	
West Ealing	d		06 27					06 43		06 57				07 13				07 27				07 43		07 57	
Drayton Green	d		06 29							06 59								07 29						07 59	
Castle Bar Park	d		06 31							07 01								07 31						08 01	
South Greenford	d		06 34							07 04								07 34						08 04	
Greenford ⊖	a		06 39							07 09								07 39						08 09	
Hanwell	d							06 45						07 15								07 45			
Southall	d	06 28				06 41		06 49	06 58				07 10	07 19		07 28					07 40	07 49	07 59		
Hayes & Harlington	d	06 32				06 45		06 53	07 02				07 14	07 23		07 32					07 44	07 53	08 02		
Heathrow Terminal 1-2 2 ✈	a							07 05						07 35								08 05			
Heathrow Terminal 4 ✈	a																								
West Drayton	d	06 40				06 49			07 06				07 18			07 36					07 48		08 06		
Iver	d					06 52							07 21								07 51				
Langley	d				←	06 56						←	07 25							←	07 55				
Slough 3	a	06 47		06 35	06 47	07 00			07 13		07 02	07 13	07 29			07 43			07 36	07 43	07 59		08 13		08 06
	d	06 47		06 35	06 47	07 00			07 13		07 02	07 13	07 29			07 43			07 36	07 43	07 59		08 13		08 06
Burnham	d	→			06 51				→			07 17				→				07 47			→		
Taplow	d				06 54							07 21								07 51					
Maidenhead 3	d				06 58	07 08						07 25	07 37		07 43					07 55	08 07				
Twyford 3	d				07 06	07 16						07 37	07 45		07 51					08 03	08 15				
Reading 7	a			06 49	07 14	07 27					07 19	07 45	07 52		08 02				07 51	08 14	08 23				08 21
Oxford	a			07 22							08 02		08 44						08 19		09 16				08 49

Station		GW		GW	HC	GW	GW	GW	GW	GW	GW	GW		HC	GW	GW	GW	GW	GW	GW	GW	GW		GW	HC
		1		1		1	1	1	◇1	1	1	1			1	1	1	1	◇1	1	1	1		1	
											A	B					A	B			A	B			
London Paddington 15 ⊖	d			07 57	08 03	08 09	08 12	08 15	08 22		08 27	08 27		08 33	08 38	08 46	08 47	08 47	08 51					08 55	09 03
Acton Main Line	d							08 21								08 51									
Ealing Broadway ⊖	d			08 05	08 11	08 17	08 20	08 24			08 35	08 35		08 41	08 47	08 54	08 59	08 59						09 03	09 11
West Ealing	d				08 13			08 27						08 43		08 57	09 01	09 01							09 13
Drayton Green	d							08 29								08 59									
Castle Bar Park	d							08 31								09 01									
South Greenford	d							08 34								09 04									
Greenford ⊖	a							08 39								09 10									
Hanwell	d				08 15									08 45	08 50										09 15
Southall	d			08 10	08 19		08 28				08 40	08 40		08 49										09 08	09 19
Hayes & Harlington	d			08 14	08 23		08 32				08 44	08 44		08 54	08 57		09 08	09 08						09 12	09 23
Heathrow Terminal 1-2 2 ✈	a				08 35									09 05											09 35
Heathrow Terminal 4 ✈	a																								
West Drayton	d			08 18			08 36				08 48	08 48			09 01									09 16	
Iver	d			08 21							08 51	08 51			09 04									09 19	
Langley	d	←		08 25						←	08 55	08 55			09 06					←	←	←		09 23	
Slough 3	a	08 13		08 29		08 34	08 43		08 36	08 43	08 59	08 59			09 11		09 16	09 16	09 06	09 11	09 16	09 16		09 27	
	d	08 13		08 29		08 34	08 43		08 36	08 43	08 59	08 59			09 12		09 16	09 16	09 06	09 12	09 16	09 16		09 27	
Burnham	d	08 17					→			08 47					→		→	→			09 20	09 20			
Taplow	d	08 21								08 51											09 24	09 24			
Maidenhead 3	d	08 25		08 38		08 42				08 55	09 06	09 06								09 18	09 28	09 28		09 35	
Twyford 3	d	08 33		08 46		08 50				09 03	09 17	09 18								09 27	09 36	09 37		09 43	
Reading 7	a	08 43		08 54		09 00			08 51	09 14	09 24	09 26							09 20	09 34	09 47	09 47		09 51	
Oxford	a			09 45					09 20		10 18	10 18							09 53					10 43	

A from 10 March

B until 7 March

For non-stop services between London and Reading please see table 116

Passengers who hold valid tickets for Acton Main Line, West Ealing and Hanwell will be able to use local Transport for London (TFL) bus services to reach these stations. Tel 0843 222 1234

Table 117

Mondays to Fridays

17 February to 24 March

Network Diagram - refer to first Page of Table 116

London - Greenford and Reading

Station		GW 1	GW 1	GW ◇1 trolley	GW 1	GW 1	HC	GW 1		GW 1	GW ◇1	GW 1	GW 1	HC	GW 1	GW 1	GW ◇1 restaurant	GW 1		GW 1	HC	GW 1	GW 1	GW ◇1	GW 1
London Paddington 15 ⊖	d	09 12	09 15	09 21		09 27	09 33	09 42		09 45	09 50		09 57	10 03	10 12	10 15	10 22			10 27	10 33	10 42	10 45	10 50	
Acton Main Line	d		09 21							09 51						10 21							10 51		
Ealing Broadway ⊖	d	09 20	09 24			09 35	09 41	09 50		09 54			10 05	10 11	10 20	10 24				10 35	10 41	10 50	10 54		
West Ealing	d		09 27				09 43			09 57				10 13		10 27					10 43		10 57		
Drayton Green	d		09 29							09 59						10 29							10 59		
Castle Bar Park	d		09 31							10 01						10 31							11 01		
South Greenford	d		09 34							10 04						10 34							11 04		
Greenford ⊖	a		09 39							10 09						10 39							11 09		
Hanwell	d						09 45							10 15							10 45				
Southall	d	09 28					09 49	09 58						10 19	10 28						10 49	10 58			
Hayes & Harlington	d	09 32				09 42	09 53	10 02					10 12	10 23	10 32					10 42	10 53	11 02			
Heathrow Terminal 1-2 2 ✈	a						10 05							10 35							11 05				
Heathrow Terminal 4 ✈	a																								
West Drayton	d	09 36				09 46		10 06					10 16		10 36					10 46		11 06			
Iver	d					09 49							10 19							10 49					
Langley	d				←	09 52						←	10 22					←		10 52					←
Slough 3	a	09 43		09 36	09 43	09 57		10 13			10 06	10 13	10 27		10 43		10 36	10 43		10 57		11 13		11 06	11 13
	d	09 43		09 36	09 43	09 57		10 13			10 06	10 13	10 27		10 43		10 36	10 43		10 57		11 13		11 06	11 13
Burnham	d	→			09 45			→				10 17			→			10 47				→			11 17
Taplow	d				09 51							10 21						10 51							11 21
Maidenhead 3	d				09 55	10 04						10 25	10 34					10 55		11 04					11 25
Twyford 3	d				10 03	10 12						10 38	10 42					11 06		11 12					11 35
Reading 7	a			09 52	10 14	10 21					10 21	10 45	10 50				10 51	11 15		11 21				11 21	11 45
Oxford	a			10 20		11 14					10 47		11 43				11 18			12 14				11 50	

Station		GW 1	HC	GW 1		GW 1	GW ◇1 trolley	GW 1	GW 1	HC	GW 1	GW 1	GW ◇1 trolley	GW 1		GW 1 A	GW 1 B	HC	GW 1	GW 1	GW ◇1 trolley	GW 1	GW 1	HC	
London Paddington 15 ⊖	d	10 57	11 03	11 12		11 15	11 20		11 27	11 33	11 42	11 45	11 50			11 57	11 57	12 03	12 12	12 15	12 21		12 27	12 33	
Acton Main Line	d					11 21						11 51								12 21					
Ealing Broadway ⊖	d	11 05	11 11	11 20		11 24			11 35	11 41	11 50	11 54				12 05	12 05	12 11	12 20	12 24			12 35	12 41	
West Ealing	d		11 13			11 27				11 43		11 57						12 13		12 27				12 43	
Drayton Green	d					11 29						11 59								12 29					
Castle Bar Park	d					11 31						12 01								12 31					
South Greenford	d					11 34						12 04								12 34					
Greenford ⊖	a					11 39						12 09								12 39					
Hanwell	d		11 15							11 45								12 15						12 45	
Southall	d		11 19	11 28						11 49	11 58							12 19	12 28					12 49	
Hayes & Harlington	d	11 12	11 23	11 32					11 42	11 53	12 02					12 12	12 12	12 23	12 32				12 42	12 53	
Heathrow Terminal 1-2 2 ✈	a		11 35							12 05								12 35						13 05	
Heathrow Terminal 4 ✈	a																								
West Drayton	d	11 16		11 36					11 46		12 06					12 16	12 16		12 36				12 46		
Iver	d	11 19							11 49							12 19	12 19						12 49		
Langley	d	11 22						←	11 52					←		12 22	12 22					←	12 52		
Slough 3	a	11 27		11 43			11 36	11 43	11 57		12 13		12 06	12 13		12 27	12 27		12 43		12 36	12 43	12 57		
	d	11 27		11 43			11 36	11 43	11 57		12 13		12 06	12 13		12 27	12 27		12 43		12 36	12 43	12 57		
Burnham	d			→				11 47			→			12 17					→			12 47			
Taplow	d							11 51						12 21								12 51			
Maidenhead 3	d	11 34						11 55	12 04					12 25		12 34	12 34					12 55	13 04		
Twyford 3	d	11 42						12 03	12 13					12 37		12 42	12 45					13 06	13 12		
Reading 7	a	11 52					11 52	12 15	12 22				12 22	12 45		12 49	12 52				12 51	13 15	13 20		
Oxford	a	12 43					12 18		13 14				12 48			13 43	13 43				13 20		14 14		

A from 10 March

B until 7 March

For non-stop services between London and Reading please see table 116

Passengers who hold valid tickets for Acton Main Line, West Ealing and Hanwell will be able to use local Transport for London (TFL) bus services to reach these stations. Tel 0843 222 1234

Table 117

London - Greenford and Reading

Mondays to Fridays

17 February to 24 March

Network Diagram - refer to first Page of Table 116

		GW	GW	GW	GW	GW		GW	HC	GW	GW	GW	GW	GW	HC	GW		GW	GW	GW	GW	HC	GW	GW	GW
		1	1	◇1	1	1		1		1	1	◇1	1	1		1		1	◇1	1	1		1	1	◇1
						A		B																	
				trolley								trolley							trolley						trolley
London Paddington 15 ⊖	d	12 42	12 45	12 50		12 57		12 57	13 03	13 12	13 15	13 21		13 27	13 33	13 42		13 45	13 50		13 57	14 03	14 12	14 15	14 21
Acton Main Line	d		12 51								13 21							13 51						14 21	
Ealing Broadway ⊖	d	12 50	12 54			13 05		13 05	13 11	13 20	13 24			13 35	13 41	13 50		13 54			14 05	14 11	14 20	14 24	
West Ealing	d		12 57						13 13		13 27				13 43			13 57				14 13		14 27	
Drayton Green	d		12 59								13 29							13 59						14 29	
Castle Bar Park	d		13 01								13 31							14 01						14 31	
South Greenford	d		13 04								13 34							14 04						14 34	
Greenford ⊖	a		13 10								13 39							14 09						14 39	
Hanwell	d								13 15						13 45							14 15			
Southall	d	12 58							13 19	13 28					13 49	13 58						14 19	14 28		
Hayes & Harlington	d	13 02				13 12		13 12	13 23	13 32				13 42	13 53	14 02					14 12	14 23	14 32		
Heathrow Terminal 1-2 2 ✈	a								13 35						14 05							14 35			
Heathrow Terminal 4 ✈	a																								
West Drayton	d	13 06				13 16		13 16		13 36				13 46		14 06					14 16		14 36		
Iver	d					13 19		13 19						13 49							14 19				
Langley	d				←	13 22		13 22					←	13 52						←	14 22				
Slough 3	a	13 13		13 06	13 13	13 27		13 27		13 43		13 36	13 43	13 57		14 13			14 06	14 13	14 27		14 43		14 36
	d	13 13		13 06	13 13	13 27		13 27		13 43		13 36	13 43	13 57		14 13			14 06	14 13	14 27		14 43		14 36
Burnham	d	→			13 17					→			13 47			→				14 17			→		
Taplow	d				13 21								13 51							14 21					
Maidenhead 3	d				13 25	13 34		13 34					13 55	14 04						14 25	14 34				
Twyford 3	d				13 33	13 42		13 44					14 03	14 12						14 33	14 42				
Reading 7	a			13 22	13 43	13 50		13 53				13 51	14 15	14 21					14 21	14 43	14 54				14 52
Oxford	a			13 50		14 43		14 43				14 18		15 14					14 48		15 44				15 18

		GW		GW	HC	GW	GW	GW	GW	GW	HC	GW		GW	GW	GW	GW	HC	GW	GW	GW	GW		GW	HC
		1		1		1	1	◇1	1	1		1		1	◇1	1	1		1	1	1	1		1	
																						A		B	
								trolley							trolley										
London Paddington 15 ⊖	d			14 27	14 33	14 42	14 45	14 50		14 57	15 03	15 12		15 15	15 22		15 27	15 33	15 40	15 42	15 45	15 57		15 57	16 03
Acton Main Line	d						14 51							15 21							15 51				
Ealing Broadway ⊖	d			14 35	14 41	14 50	14 54			15 05	15 11	15 20		15 24			15 35	15 41		15 50	15 54	16 05		16 05	16 11
West Ealing	d				14 43		14 57				15 13			15 27				15 43			15 57				16 13
Drayton Green	d						14 59							15 29							15 59				
Castle Bar Park	d						15 01							15 31							16 01				
South Greenford	d						15 04							15 34							16 04				
Greenford ⊖	a						15 09							15 39							16 09				
Hanwell	d				14 45						15 15							15 45							16 15
Southall	d				14 49	14 58					15 19	15 28					15 40	15 49		15 58					16 19
Hayes & Harlington	d			14 42	14 53	15 02				15 12	15 23	15 32					15 44	15 53		16 04		16 12		16 12	16 23
Heathrow Terminal 1-2 2 ✈	a				15 05						15 35							16 05							16 35
Heathrow Terminal 4 ✈	a																								
West Drayton	d			14 46		15 06				15 16		15 36					15 48			16 09		16 16		16 16	
Iver	d			14 49						15 19							15 51					16 19		16 19	
Langley	d	←		14 52					←	15 22						←	15 55					16 23		16 23	
Slough 3	a	14 43		14 57		15 13		15 06	15 13	15 27		15 43			15 36	15 43	15 59		16 11	16 16		16 28		16 28	
	d	14 43		14 57		15 13		15 06	15 13	15 27		15 43			15 36	15 43	15 59		16 11	16 16		16 28		16 28	
Burnham	d	14 47				→			15 17			→				15 47				16 20					
Taplow	d	14 51							15 21							15 51				16 23					
Maidenhead 3	d	14 55		15 04					15 25	15 34						15 55	16 07		16a22	16 27		16 35		16 35	
Twyford 3	d	15 03		15 14					15 33	15 42						16 03	16 15			16 36		16 43		16 44	
Reading 7	a	15 13		15 21				15 22	15 43	15 50					15 51	16 15	16 23			16 46		16 52		16 53	
Oxford	a			16 16				15 50		16 43					16 18		17 17					17 44		17 44	

A from 10 March

B until 7 March

For non-stop services between London and Reading please see table 116

Passengers who hold valid tickets for Acton Main Line, West Ealing and Hanwell will be able to use local Transport for London (TFL) bus services to reach these stations. Tel 0843 222 1234

Table 117

Mondays to Fridays

17 February to 24 March

London - Greenford and Reading

Network Diagram - refer to first Page of Table 116

		GW	GW	GW	GW	GW	HC	GW	GW	GW	GW	GW	HC	GW	GW	GW	GW	GW	HC	GW	GW	GW
		1	1	◇1	1	1		1	1	◇1	1	1		1	1	1	1	1		1	1	1
London Paddington 15 ⊖	d	16 12	16 15	16 22		16 25	16 33	16 42	16 45	16 49		16 57	17 03	17 12	17 15	17 18	17 18	17 24	17 33	17 35		17 42
Acton Main Line	d		16 21						16 51							17 24						
Ealing Broadway ⊖	d	16 20	16 24			16 33	16 41	16 50	16 54			17 06	17 11		17 23	17 27		17 33	17 41			
West Ealing	d		16 27				16 43		16 57				17 13			17 30			17 43			
Drayton Green	d		16 29						16 59							17 32						
Castle Bar Park	d		16 31						17 01							17 34						
South Greenford	d		16 34						17 04							17 37						
Greenford ⊖	a		16 39						17 09							17 42						
Hanwell	d						16 45						17 15						17 45			
Southall	d	16 28				16 38	16 49	16 58					17 19		17 29			17 37	17 49			
Hayes & Harlington	d	16 32				16 42	16 53	17 02				17 13	17 23		17 33			17 41	17 53			
Heathrow Terminal 1-2 2 ✈	a						17 05						17 35						18 05			
Heathrow Terminal 4 ✈	a																					
West Drayton	d	16 36				16 47		17 07				17 18			17 38			17 47				
Iver	d					16 50						17 22						17 50				
Langley	d				←	16 53		17 12			←	17 26			17 44			17 54				
Slough 3	a	16 44		16 37	16 44	16 58		17 16		17 04	17 16	17 29		17 32	17 48			17 58				18 04
	d	16 45		16 38	16 45	16 58		17 17		17 05	17 17	17 30		17 35	17 49			17 58				18 05
Burnham	d	→			16 50			→			17 21	17 35		17 40	17 54			18 02				
Taplow	d				16 54						17 25			17 43				18 06				
Maidenhead 3	d				16 59	17 05					17 30	17 44		17 48	18a05		17 41	18 10		17 58	←	18a13
Twyford 3	d				17 07	17 13					17 38	17 52		17a58				18 17		18 07	18 17	
Reading 7	a			16 52	17 18	17 21				17 19	17 46	18 00					17 54	→		18 14	18 26	
Oxford	a			17 22		18 23				17 51							18 45			19 07	19 18	

		GW	GW	GW	GW	HC	GW	GW	GW	GW	GW	GW	GW	GW	HC	GW	GW	GW	GW	GW	GW	GW	GW
													FO	FX							FO	FX	
		1	1	◇1	1		1	1	1	1	1	1	1	1		1	1	◇1	1	◇1	1	1	1
London Paddington 15 ⊖	d	17 45	17 48	17 49	17 57	18 03	18 12	18 15	18 18	18 18			18 25	18 25	18 33	18 42	18 45	18 47	18 48	18 50			
Acton Main Line	d		17 54						18 24										18 54				
Ealing Broadway ⊖	d	17 53	17 57		18 05	18 11		18 23	18 27				18 33	18 33	18 41		18 53		18 57				
West Ealing	d		18 00			18 13			18 30						18 43				19 00				
Drayton Green	d		18 02						18 32										19 02				
Castle Bar Park	d		18 04						18 34										19 04				
South Greenford	d		18 07						18 37										19 07				
Greenford ⊖	a		18 12						18 42										19 12				
Hanwell	d					18 15									18 45								
Southall	d	17 59			18 10	18 19		18 29					18 38	18 38	18 49		18 58						
Hayes & Harlington	d	18 03			18 14	18 23		18 33					18 42	18 42	18 53		19 02						
Heathrow Terminal 1-2 2 ✈	a					18 35									19 05								
Heathrow Terminal 4 ✈	a																						
West Drayton	d	18 08			18 19			18 38					18 46	18 46			19 07						
Iver	d				18 22								18 49	18 49									
Langley	d	18 12			18 26			18 42					18 52	18 52									←
Slough 3	a	18 16			18 30		18 35	18 47					18 59	18 59		19 05	19 14			19 06			19 14
	d	18 16			18 30		18 36	18 47					18 59	18 59		19 06	19 14			19 07			19 14
Burnham	d	18 21			18 35			18 51					19 03	19 03			→						19 18
Taplow	d				18 39								19 06	19 06									
Maidenhead 3	d	18 26		18 09	18 45		18 49	18 57		18 40	←	←	19 10	19 10		19a14					←	←	19 24
Twyford 3	d	18 34			18 52		18a58	19 05		18 48	18 52	19 05	19 18	19 18				19 10			19 18	19 18	19 38
Reading 7	a	18 44		18 20	→			→		18 56	19 00	19 13	→	→				19 18		19 21	19 26	19 26	19 47
Oxford	a			18 47						19 46		20 16								19 49	20 18	20 27	

For non-stop services between London and Reading please see table 116

Passengers who hold valid tickets for Acton Main Line, West Ealing and Hanwell will be able to use local Transport for London (TFL) bus services to reach these stations. Tel 0843 222 1234

Table 117

Mondays to Fridays

17 February to 24 March

Network Diagram - refer to first Page of Table 116

London - Greenford and Reading

	GW 1	HC	GW 1	GW 1	GW 1	GW 1	GW FX ◇1 ☕	GW FO ◇1 ☕	GW 1	GW 1	GW 1	HC	GW 1	GW 1	GW ◇1 ☕	GW ◇1 🛒	GW 1	GW 1	HC	GW 1	GW 1
London Paddington 15 ⊖ d	18 58	19 03	19 05	19 12	19 15	19 18	19 22	19 22			19 27	19 33	19 42	19 45	19 48	19 50		19 57	20 03	20 12	20 15
Acton Main Line d					19 21									19 51							20 21
Ealing Broadway ⊖ d	19 07	19 11		19 20	19 24						19 35	19 41	19 50	19 54				20 05	20 11	20 20	20 24
West Ealing d		19 13			19 27							19 43		19 57					20 13		20 27
Drayton Green d					19 29									19 59							20 29
Castle Bar Park d					19 31									20 01							20 31
South Greenford d					19 34									20 04							20 34
Greenford ⊖ a					19 39									20 09							20 39
Hanwell d		19 15										19 45							20 15		
Southall d	19 12	19 19		19 28							19 40	19 49	19 58						20 19	20 28	
Hayes & Harlington d	19 16	19 23		19 32							19 44	19 53	20 02					20 12	20 23	20 32	
Heathrow Terminal 1-2 2 ✈ a		19 35										20 05							20 35		
Heathrow Terminal 4 ✈ a																					
West Drayton d	19 21			19 36							19 48		20 06					20 16		20 36	
Iver d	19 24										19 51		20 09					20 19			
Langley d	19 28									←	19 55		20 13				←	20 22			
Slough 3 a	19 32			19 42			19 36	19 36		19 42	19 59		20 17			20 06	20 17	20 27		20 43	
d	19 32			19 43			19 36	19 36		19 43	19 59		20 17			20 06	20 17	20 27		20 43	
Burnham d	19 35			→						19 47	20 03		→				20 20			→	
Taplow d	19 40									19 51							20 25				
Maidenhead 3 d	19 43		19 27			19 40			←	19 55	20 09				20 06		20 29	20 34			
Twyford 3 d	19 52		19a38			19 48			19 52	20 03	20 17						20 37	20 42			
Reading 7 a	→					19 56	19 51	19 51	20 00	20 13	20 25				20 18	20 21	20 45	20 50			
Oxford a						20 43	20 18	20 21			21 15					20 52		21 44			

	GW ◇1 🛒	GW 1	GW 1	HC	GW 1	GW 1	GW ◇1	GW 1	GW FX 1	GW FO 1	HC	GW 1	GW 1	GW ◇1	GW 1	GW 1	HC FO	GW FX 1	GW FO 1	GW FO ◇1 🛒	GW FX ◇1 ☕	GW 1
London Paddington 15 ⊖ d	20 20		20 27	20 33	20 42	20 45	20 48		20 57	20 57	21 03	21 12	21 15	21 18		21 27	21 33	21 36	21 42	21 48	21 48	
Acton Main Line d						20 51							21 21					21 42	21 48			
Ealing Broadway ⊖ d			20 35	20 41	20 50	20 54			21 05	21 05	21 11	21 20	21 24			21 35	21 41	21 45	21 51			
West Ealing d				20 43		20 57					21 13		21 27				21 43					
Drayton Green d						20 59							21 29									
Castle Bar Park d						21 01							21 31									
South Greenford d						21 04							21 34									
Greenford ⊖ a						21 09							21 39									
Hanwell d				20 45							21 15						21 45					
Southall d				20 49	20 58						21 19	21 28				21 42	21 49	21 52	21 58			
Hayes & Harlington d			20 42	20 53	21 02				21 12	21 12	21 23	21 32				21 46	21 53	21 55	22 02			
Heathrow Terminal 1-2 2 ✈ a				21 05							21 35						22 05					
Heathrow Terminal 4 ✈ a																						
West Drayton d			20 46		21 06				21 16	21 16		21 36				21 50		22 01	22 06			
Iver d			20 49						21 19	21 19						21 53						
Langley d		←	20 52					←	21 22	21 22					←	21 57						←
Slough 3 a	20 35	20 43	20 57		21 13		21 04	21 13	21 27	21 27		21 43		21 34	21 43	22 02		22 11	22 14	22 03	22 03	22 02
d	20 36	20 43	20 57		21 13		21 05	21 13	21 27	21 27		21 43		21 35	21 43	22 07		22 14	22 14	22 04	22 04	22 07
Burnham d		20 47			→			21 17				→			21 47	→		→	→			
Taplow d		20 51						21 21							21 51							
Maidenhead 3 d		20 55	21 04					21 25	21 34	21 34					21 55							22 15
Twyford 3 d		21 03	21 12					21 33	21 42	21 42					22 03							22 23
Reading 7 a	20 49	21 13	21 20				21 20	21 43	21 51	21 54				21 50	22 14					22 23	22 23	22 30
Oxford a	21 17		22 12				21 51		22 41	22 41				22 18						22 47	22 47	23 22

	GW FX 1	GW FO 1	GW FO 1	GW FX 1	HC FO	HC FX	GW FO ◇1	GW FX ◇1	GW FX 1	GW FO 1	GW FX 1	HC FO	GW FO ◇1	GW FX ◇1	GW FO 1	GW FX 1	GW FO 1	GW FX 1	HC FO	HC FX	GW FO ◇1
London Paddington 15 ⊖ d			21 57	21 57	22 03	22 07	22 18	22 18		22 27	22 27	22 33	22 48	22 48			23 00	23 00	23 03	23 07	23 18
Acton Main Line d																	23 06				
Ealing Broadway ⊖ d			22 05	22 05	22 11	22 15				22 35	22 35	22 41					23 09	23 09	23 12	23 15	
West Ealing d					22 13							22 43							23 14		
Drayton Green d																					
Castle Bar Park d																					
South Greenford d																					
Greenford ⊖ a																					
Hanwell d					22 15							22 45							23 16		
Southall d			22 10	22 10	22 19	22 19				22 40	22 40	22 49					23 15	23 15	23 20	23 20	
Hayes & Harlington d			22 14	22 14	22 23	22 24				22 44	22 44	22 53					23 19	23 19	23 24	23 25	
Heathrow Terminal 1-2 2 ✈ a					22 35	22 29						23 05							23 35	23 32	
Heathrow Terminal 4 ✈ a																			23 41	23 38	
West Drayton d			22 18	22 18						22 48	22 48						23 23	23 23			
Iver d			22 21	22 21						22 51	22 51						23 26	23 26			
Langley d	←	←	22 25	22 25					←	22 55	22 55				←	←	23 29	23 29			
Slough 3 a	22 11	22 14	22 30	22 30			22 34	22 39	22 30	22 59	23 00		23 04	23 08	22 59	23 00	23 34	23 34			23 36
d	22 14	22 14	22 30	22 42			22 35	22 39	22 42	23 11	23 11		23 05	23 08	23 11	23 11	23 34	23 34			23 38
Burnham d	22 18	22 18	22 34	→					22 46	→	→				23 15	23 15					
Taplow d	22 22	22 22	22 38						22 49						23 19	23 19					
Maidenhead 3 d	22 26	22 26	22 42				22 42	22 47	22 53				23 12	23 17	23 23	23 23	23 41	23 41			23 46
Twyford 3 d	22 34	22 34	22 50						23 01				23 20	23 26	23 31	23 31	23 49	23 49			
Reading 7 a	22 45	22 45	22 59				22 54	23 01	23 10				23 27	23 33	23 40	23 40	23 59	23 59			00 04
Oxford a			23 56				23 27	23 29	23 54				23 56	00 01	00 27	00 27					00 35

For non-stop services between London and Reading please see table 116

Passengers who hold valid tickets for Acton Main Line, West Ealing and Hanwell will be able to use local Transport for London (TFL) bus services to reach these stations. Tel 0843 222 1234

Table 117

London - Greenford and Reading

Mondays to Fridays

17 February to 24 March

Network Diagram - refer to first Page of Table 116

Station		GW FX ◇1	GW 1	GW FO 1	GW FX 1	GW FO 1
London Paddington 15 ⊖	d	23 18	23 33	23 42	23 49	23 49
Acton Main Line	d					23 55
Ealing Broadway ⊖	d		23 41		23 59	23 59
West Ealing	d					00 01
Drayton Green	d					
Castle Bar Park	d					
South Greenford	d					
Greenford ⊖	a					
Hanwell	d					00 04
Southall	d				00 07	00 07
Hayes & Harlington	d		23 48		00 12	00 12
Heathrow Terminal 1-2 2 ✈	a					
Heathrow Terminal 4 ✈	a					
West Drayton	d				00 16	00 16
Iver	d				00 19	00 19
Langley	d				00 22	00 22
Slough 3	a	23 38	23 57	00 01	00 28	00 28
	d	23 38	23 57	00 01	00 28	00 28
Burnham	d				00 32	00 32
Taplow	d				00 36	00 36
Maidenhead 3	d	23 46	00 05	00 10	00 41	00 41
Twyford 3	d		00 13		00 48	00 48
Reading 7	a	00 04	00 22	00 25	00 56	00 58
Oxford	a	00 35	01 18	01 02		

Mondays to Fridays

31 March to 16 May

Station		GW MO 1	GW MX 1	GW MX 1	GW MO ◇1	GW MO 1	GW MX 1	GW MX ◇1	GW MX 1	GW MO 1	GW MX 1	GW 1
London Paddington 15 ⊖	d							00 22	00 34	00 34		01 34
Acton Main Line	d											
Ealing Broadway ⊖	d					00 02			00 42	00 42		01 42
West Ealing	d											
Drayton Green	d											
Castle Bar Park	d											
South Greenford	d											
Greenford ⊖	a											
Hanwell	d											
Southall	d					00 07	00 07		00 47	00 48		01 47
Hayes & Harlington	d					00 11	00 12		00 51	00 52		01 51
Heathrow Terminal 1-2 2 ✈	a											
Heathrow Terminal 4 ✈	a											
West Drayton	d					00 15	00 16		00 55	00 56		01 55
Iver	d						00 19					
Langley	d					00 20	00 22		01 00	01 00	←	
Slough 3	a					00 24	00 28	00 40	01 05	01 02	01 05	02 04
	d				00 07	00 24	00 28	00 41	01 05	01 04	01 05	02 04
Burnham	d						00 32		→		01 09	
Taplow	d						00 36				01 13	
Maidenhead 3	d			00 05	00 15	00 33	00 41			01 12	01 16	02 11
Twyford 3	d	00 03	00 08	00 13		00 41	00 48			01 21	01 24	02 19
Reading 7	a	00 13	00 16	00 22	00 30	00 49	00 56	01 01		01 29	01 35	02 29
Oxford	a			01 18				01 34				

Station		GW 1	HC	GW 1	HC	GW 1	HC	GW 1	GW 1	GW ◇1	GW 1	GW 1
London Paddington 15 ⊖	d	03 34	04 42	05 12	05 13	05 17	05 33	05 42	05 45	05 45		05 57
Acton Main Line	d								05 51			
Ealing Broadway ⊖	d	03 42	04 50		05 21	05 25	05 41	05 50	05 54			06 05
West Ealing	d						05 43		05 57			
Drayton Green	d								05 59			
Castle Bar Park	d								06 01			
South Greenford	d								06 04			
Greenford ⊖	a								06 09			
Hanwell	d						05 45					
Southall	d	03 48	04 54		05 25	05 31	05 49	05 58				06 10
Hayes & Harlington	d	03 52	04 58		05 29	05 36	05 53	06 02				06 14
Heathrow Terminal 1-2 2 ✈	a		05 04		05 35		06 05					
Heathrow Terminal 4 ✈	a		05 10		05 41							
West Drayton	d	03 56				05 41		06 06				06 18
Iver	d							06 09				06 21
Langley	d					05 46		06 13			←	06 25
Slough 3	a	04 04		05 29		05 50		06 17		06 01	06 17	06 29
	d	04 05		05 30		05 51		06 17		06 01	06 17	06 29
Burnham	d							→			06 21	
Taplow	d										06 25	
Maidenhead 3	d	04 12				05 59					06 29	06 37
Twyford 3	d	04 20				06 07					06 38	06 45
Reading 7	a	04 30		05 48		06 15				06 17	06 48	06 53
Oxford	a			06 20		07 02				06 51		07 49

For non-stop services between London and Reading please see table 116

Passengers who hold valid tickets for Acton Main Line, West Ealing and Hanwell will be able to use local Transport for London (TFL) bus services to reach these stations. Tel 0843 222 1234

Table 117

Mondays to Fridays

31 March to 16 May

Network Diagram - refer to first Page of Table 116

London - Greenford and Reading

		HC		GW 1	GW 1	GW ◇1	GW 1	GW 1	HC	GW 1	GW 1	GW 1		GW 1	GW 1	HC	GW 1	GW 1	GW 1	GW 1	GW 1	GW 1		HC	GW 1
London Paddington 15 ⊖	d	06 03		06 12	06 15	06 20		06 27	06 33	06 42	06 45	06 48			06 57	07 03	07 12	07 12	07 15	07 21		07 27		07 33	07 42
Acton Main Line	d				06 21						06 51								07 21						
Ealing Broadway ⊖	d	06 11		06 20	06 24			06 35	06 41	06 50	06 54				07 05	07 11		07 20	07 24			07 35		07 41	07 50
West Ealing	d	06 13			06 27				06 43		06 57					07 13			07 27					07 43	
Drayton Green	d				06 29						06 59								07 29						
Castle Bar Park	d				06 31						07 01								07 31						
South Greenford	d				06 34						07 04								07 34						
Greenford ⊖	a				06 39						07 09								07 39						
Hanwell	d	06 15							06 45							07 15								07 45	
Southall	d	06 19		06 28				06 41	06 49	06 58					07 10	07 19		07 28				07 40		07 49	07 59
Hayes & Harlington	d	06 23		06 32				06 45	06 53	07 02					07 14	07 23		07 32				07 44		07 53	08 02
Heathrow Terminal 1-2 2 ✈	a	06 35							07 05							07 35								08 05	
Heathrow Terminal 4 ✈	a																								
West Drayton	d			06 40				06 49		07 06					07 18			07 36				07 48			08 06
Iver	d							06 52							07 21							07 51			
Langley	d						←	06 56						←	07 25						←	07 55			
Slough 3	a			06 47		06 35	06 47	07 00		07 13		07 02		07 13	07 29			07 43		07 36	07 43	07 59			08 13
	d			06 47		06 35	06 47	07 00		07 13		07 02		07 13	07 29			07 43		07 36	07 43	07 59			08 13
Burnham	d			→			06 51			→				07 17				→			07 47				→
Taplow	d						06 54							07 21							07 51				
Maidenhead 3	d						06 58	07 08						07 25	07 37		07 43				07 55	08 07			
Twyford 3	d						07 06	07 16						07 37	07 45		07 51				08 03	08 15			
Reading 7	a					06 49	07 14	07 27				07 19		07 45	07 52		08 02			07 51	08 14	08 23			
Oxford	a					07 22						08 02			08 44					08 19		09 16			

		GW 1	GW 1	GW 1	GW 1	HC	GW 1	GW 1		GW 1	GW ◇1 ☕	GW 1	GW 1	HC	GW 1	GW 1	GW 1	GW ◇1		GW 1	GW 1	GW 1	HC	GW 1	GW 1
London Paddington 15 ⊖	d	07 45	07 50		07 57	08 03	08 09	08 12		08 15	08 22		08 27	08 33	08 38	08 46	08 47	08 51				08 55	09 03	09 12	09 15
Acton Main Line	d	07 51								08 21						08 51									09 21
Ealing Broadway ⊖	d	07 54			08 05	08 11	08 17	08 20		08 24			08 35	08 41	08 47	08 54	08 59					09 03	09 11	09 20	09 24
West Ealing	d	07 57				08 13				08 27				08 43		08 57	09 01						09 13		09 27
Drayton Green	d	07 59								08 29						08 59									09 29
Castle Bar Park	d	08 01								08 31						09 01									09 31
South Greenford	d	08 04								08 34						09 04									09 34
Greenford ⊖	a	08 09								08 39						09 10									09 39
Hanwell	d					08 15								08 45	08 50								09 15		
Southall	d				08 10	08 19		08 28					08 40	08 49								09 08	09 19	09 28	
Hayes & Harlington	d				08 14	08 23		08 32					08 44	08 54	08 57		09 08					09 12	09 23	09 32	
Heathrow Terminal 1-2 2 ✈	a					08 35								09 05									09 35		
Heathrow Terminal 4 ✈	a																								
West Drayton	d				08 18			08 36					08 48		09 01							09 16		09 36	
Iver	d				08 21								08 51		09 04							09 19			
Langley	d			←	08 25							←	08 55		09 06					←	←	09 23			
Slough 3	a		08 06	08 13	08 29		08 34	08 43			08 36	08 43	08 59		09 11		09 16	09 06		09 11	09 16	09 27		09 43	
	d		08 06	08 13	08 29		08 34	08 43			08 36	08 43	08 59		09 12		09 16	09 06		09 12	09 16	09 27		09 43	
Burnham	d			08 17				→				08 47			→		→				09 20			→	
Taplow	d			08 21								08 51									09 24				
Maidenhead 3	d			08 25	08 38		08 42					08 55	09 06							09 18	09 28	09 35			
Twyford 3	d			08 33	08 46		08 50					09 03	09 17							09 27	09 36	09 43			
Reading 7	a		08 21	08 43	08 54		09 00				08 51	09 14	09 24					09 20		09 34	09 47	09 51			
Oxford	a		08 49		09 45						09 20		10 18					09 53				10 43			

		GW ◇1 🛒	GW 1	GW 1		HC	GW 1	GW 1	GW ◇1	GW 1	GW 1	HC	GW 1	GW 1		GW ◇1 ☕	GW 1	GW 1	HC	GW 1	GW 1	GW ◇1	GW 1	GW 1	
London Paddington 15 ⊖	d	09 21		09 27		09 33	09 42	09 45	09 50		09 57	10 03	10 12	10 15		10 22		10 27	10 33	10 42	10 45	10 50		10 57	
Acton Main Line	d							09 51						10 21							10 51				
Ealing Broadway ⊖	d			09 35		09 41	09 50	09 54			10 05	10 11	10 20	10 24				10 35	10 41	10 50	10 54			11 05	
West Ealing	d					09 43		09 57				10 13		10 27					10 43		10 57				
Drayton Green	d							09 59						10 29							10 59				
Castle Bar Park	d							10 01						10 31							11 01				
South Greenford	d							10 04						10 34							11 04				
Greenford ⊖	a							10 09						10 39							11 09				
Hanwell	d					09 45						10 15							10 45						
Southall	d					09 49	09 58					10 19	10 28						10 49	10 58					
Hayes & Harlington	d			09 42		09 53	10 02				10 12	10 23	10 32					10 42	10 53	11 02				11 12	
Heathrow Terminal 1-2 2 ✈	a					10 05						10 35							11 05						
Heathrow Terminal 4 ✈	a																								
West Drayton	d			09 46			10 06				10 16		10 36					10 46		11 06				11 16	
Iver	d			09 49							10 19							10 49						11 19	
Langley	d		←	09 52						←	10 22						←	10 52					←	11 22	
Slough 3	a	09 36	09 43	09 57			10 13		10 06	10 13	10 27		10 43			10 36	10 43	10 57		11 13		11 06	11 13	11 27	
	d	09 36	09 43	09 57			10 13		10 06	10 13	10 27		10 43			10 36	10 43	10 57		11 13		11 06	11 13	11 27	
Burnham	d		09 45				→			10 17			→				10 47			→			11 17		
Taplow	d		09 51							10 21							10 51						11 21		
Maidenhead 3	d		09 55	10 04						10 25	10 34						10 55	11 04					11 25	11 34	
Twyford 3	d		10 03	10 12						10 38	10 42						11 06	11 12					11 35	11 42	
Reading 7	a	09 52	10 14	10 21					10 21	10 45	10 50					10 51	11 15	11 21				11 21	11 45	11 52	
Oxford	a	10 20		11 14					10 47		11 43					11 18		12 14				11 50		12 43	

For non-stop services between London and Reading please see table 116

Passengers who hold valid tickets for Acton Main Line, West Ealing and Hanwell will be able to use local Transport for London (TFL) bus services to reach these stations. Tel 0843 222 1234

Table 117

Mondays to Fridays

31 March to 16 May

Network Diagram - refer to first Page of Table 116

London - Greenford and Reading

		HC	GW 1	GW 1	GW ◇1	GW 1	GW 1	HC	GW 1	GW 1		GW ◇1	GW 1	GW 1	HC	GW 1	GW 1	GW ◇1	GW 1	GW 1		HC	GW 1	GW 1	GW ◇1
London Paddington 15 ⊖	d	11 03	11 12	11 15	11 20		11 27	11 33	11 42	11 45		11 50		11 57	12 03	12 12	12 15	12 21		12 27		12 33	12 42	12 45	12 50
Acton Main Line	d			11 21						11 51							12 21							12 51	
Ealing Broadway ⊖	d	11 11	11 20	11 24			11 35	11 41	11 50	11 54				12 05	12 11	12 20	12 24			12 35		12 41	12 50	12 54	
West Ealing	d	11 13		11 27				11 43		11 57					12 13		12 27					12 43		12 57	
Drayton Green	d			11 29						11 59							12 29							12 59	
Castle Bar Park	d			11 31						12 01							12 31							13 01	
South Greenford	d			11 34						12 04							12 34							13 04	
Greenford ⊖	a			11 39						12 09							12 39							13 10	
Hanwell	d	11 15						11 45							12 15							12 45			
Southall	d	11 19	11 28					11 49	11 58						12 19	12 28						12 49	12 58		
Hayes & Harlington	d	11 23	11 32				11 42	11 53	12 02					12 12	12 23	12 32				12 42		12 53	13 02		
Heathrow Terminal 1-2 2 ✈	a	11 35						12 05							12 35							13 05			
Heathrow Terminal 4 ✈	a																								
West Drayton	d		11 36				11 46		12 06					12 16		12 36				12 46			13 06		
Iver	d						11 49							12 19						12 49					
Langley	d					←	11 52						←	12 22					←	12 52					
Slough 3	a		11 43		11 36	11 43	11 57		12 13			12 06	12 13	12 27		12 43		12 36	12 43	12 57			13 13		13 06
	d		11 43		11 36	11 43	11 57		12 13			12 06	12 13	12 27		12 43		12 36	12 43	12 57			13 13		13 06
Burnham	d		→			11 47			→				12 17			→			12 47				→		
Taplow	d					11 51							12 21						12 51						
Maidenhead 3	d					11 55	12 04						12 25	12 34					12 55	13 04					
Twyford 3	d					12 03	12 13						12 37	12 42					13 06	13 12					
Reading 7	a				11 52	12 15	12 22					12 22	12 45	12 49				12 51	13 15	13 20					13 22
Oxford	a				12 18		13 14					12 48		13 43				13 20		14 14					13 50

		GW 1	GW 1	HC	GW 1	GW 1		GW ◇1	GW 1	GW 1	HC	GW 1	GW 1	GW ◇1	GW 1	GW 1		HC	GW 1	GW 1	GW ◇1	GW 1	GW 1	HC	GW 1
London Paddington 15 ⊖	d		12 57	13 03	13 12	13 15		13 21		13 27	13 33	13 42	13 45	13 50		13 57		14 03	14 12	14 15	14 21		14 27	14 33	14 42
Acton Main Line	d					13 21							13 51							14 21					
Ealing Broadway ⊖	d		13 05	13 11	13 20	13 24				13 35	13 41	13 50	13 54			14 05		14 11	14 20	14 24			14 35	14 41	14 50
West Ealing	d			13 13		13 27					13 43		13 57					14 13		14 27				14 43	
Drayton Green	d					13 29							13 59							14 29					
Castle Bar Park	d					13 31							14 01							14 31					
South Greenford	d					13 34							14 04							14 34					
Greenford ⊖	a					13 39							14 09							14 39					
Hanwell	d			13 15							13 45							14 15						14 45	
Southall	d			13 19	13 28						13 49	13 58						14 19	14 28					14 49	14 58
Hayes & Harlington	d		13 12	13 23	13 32					13 42	13 53	14 02				14 12		14 23	14 32				14 42	14 53	15 02
Heathrow Terminal 1-2 2 ✈	a			13 35							14 05							14 35						15 05	
Heathrow Terminal 4 ✈	a																								
West Drayton	d		13 16		13 36					13 46		14 06				14 16			14 36				14 46		15 06
Iver	d		13 19							13 49						14 19							14 49		
Langley	d	←	13 22						←	13 52					←	14 22						←	14 52		
Slough 3	a	13 13	13 27		13 43			13 36	13 43	13 57		14 13		14 06	14 13	14 27			14 43		14 36	14 43	14 57		15 13
	d	13 13	13 27		13 43			13 36	13 43	13 57		14 13		14 06	14 13	14 27			14 43		14 36	14 43	14 57		15 13
Burnham	d	13 17			→				13 47			→			14 17				→			14 47			→
Taplow	d	13 21							13 51						14 21							14 51			
Maidenhead 3	d	13 25	13 34						13 55	14 04					14 25	14 34						14 55	15 04		
Twyford 3	d	13 33	13 42						14 03	14 12					14 33	14 42						15 03	15 14		
Reading 7	a	13 43	13 50					13 51	14 15	14 21				14 21	14 43	14 54					14 52	15 13	15 21		
Oxford	a		14 43					14 18		15 14				14 48		15 44					15 18		16 16		

		GW 1		GW ◇1	GW 1	GW 1	HC	GW 1	GW 1	GW ◇1	GW 1	GW 1		HC	GW 1	GW 1	GW 1	GW 1	HC	GW 1	GW 1	GW ◇1		GW 1	GW 1
London Paddington 15 ⊖	d	14 45		14 50		14 57	15 03	15 12	15 15	15 22		15 27		15 33	15 40	15 42	15 45	15 57	16 03	16 12	16 15	16 22			16 25
Acton Main Line	d	14 51							15 21								15 51				16 21				
Ealing Broadway ⊖	d	14 54				15 05	15 11	15 20	15 24			15 35		15 41		15 50	15 54	16 05	16 11	16 20	16 24				16 33
West Ealing	d	14 57					15 13		15 27					15 43			15 57		16 13		16 27				
Drayton Green	d	14 59							15 29								15 59				16 29				
Castle Bar Park	d	15 01							15 31								16 01				16 31				
South Greenford	d	15 04							15 34								16 04				16 34				
Greenford ⊖	a	15 09							15 39								16 09				16 39				
Hanwell	d						15 15							15 45					16 15						
Southall	d						15 19	15 28				15 40		15 49		15 58			16 19	16 28					16 38
Hayes & Harlington	d					15 12	15 23	15 32				15 44		15 53		16 04		16 12	16 23	16 32					16 42
Heathrow Terminal 1-2 2 ✈	a						15 35							16 05					16 35						
Heathrow Terminal 4 ✈	a																								
West Drayton	d					15 16		15 36				15 48				16 09		16 16		16 36					16 47
Iver	d					15 19						15 51						16 19							16 50
Langley	d				←	15 22					←	15 55						16 23						←	16 53
Slough 3	a			15 06	15 13	15 27		15 43		15 36	15 43	15 59			16 11	16 16		16 28		16 44		16 37		16 44	16 58
	d			15 06	15 13	15 27		15 43		15 36	15 43	15 59			16 11	16 16		16 28		16 45		16 38		16 45	16 58
Burnham	d				15 17			→			15 47					16 20				→				16 50	
Taplow	d				15 21						15 51					16 23								16 54	
Maidenhead 3	d				15 25	15 34					15 55	16 07			16a22	16 27		16 35						16 59	17 05
Twyford 3	d				15 33	15 42					16 03	16 15				16 36		16 43						17 07	17 13
Reading 7	a			15 22	15 43	15 50				15 51	16 15	16 23				16 46		16 52				16 52		17 18	17 21
Oxford	a			15 50		16 43				16 18		17 17						17 44				17 22			18 23

For non-stop services between London and Reading please see table 116

Passengers who hold valid tickets for Acton Main Line, West Ealing and Hanwell will be able to use local Transport for London (TFL) bus services to reach these stations. Tel 0843 222 1234

Table 117

Mondays to Fridays

31 March to 16 May

Network Diagram - refer to first Page of Table 116

London - Greenford and Reading

		HC	GW 1	GW 1	GW ◇1	GW 1	GW 1	HC		GW 1	GW 1	GW 1	GW 1	GW 1	HC	GW 1	GW 1	GW 1		GW 1	GW 1	GW ◇1	GW 1	HC	GW 1
London Paddington 15 ⊖	d	16 33	16 42	16 45	16 49		16 57	17 03		17 12	17 15	17 18	17 18	17 24	17 33	17 35		17 42		17 45	17 48	17 49	17 57	18 03	18 12
Acton Main Line	d			16 51								17 24									17 54				
Ealing Broadway ⊖	d	16 41	16 50	16 54			17 06	17 11			17 23	17 27		17 33	17 41					17 53	17 57		18 05	18 11	
West Ealing	d	16 43		16 57				17 13				17 30			17 43						18 00			18 13	
Drayton Green	d			16 59								17 32									18 02				
Castle Bar Park	d			17 01								17 34									18 04				
South Greenford	d			17 04								17 37									18 07				
Greenford ⊖	a			17 09								17 42									18 12				
Hanwell	d	16 45						17 15							17 45									18 15	
Southall	d	16 49	16 58					17 19			17 29			17 37	17 49					17 59			18 10	18 19	
Hayes & Harlington	d	16 53	17 02				17 13	17 23			17 33			17 41	17 53					18 03			18 14	18 23	
Heathrow Terminal 1-2 2 ✈	a	17 05						17 35							18 05									18 35	
Heathrow Terminal 4 ✈	a																								
West Drayton	d		17 07				17 18				17 38			17 47						18 08			18 19		
Iver	d						17 22							17 50									18 22		
Langley	d		17 12			←	17 26				17 44			17 54						18 12			18 26		
Slough 3	a		17 16		17 04	17 16	17 29			17 32	17 48			17 58				18 04		18 16			18 30		18 35
	d		17 17		17 05	17 17	17 30			17 35	17 49			17 58				18 05		18 16			18 30		18 36
Burnham	d		→			17 21	17 35			17 40	17 54			18 02						18 21			18 35		
Taplow	d					17 25				17 43				18 06									18 39		
Maidenhead 3	d					17 30	17 44			17 48	18a05		17 41	18 10		17 58	←	18a13		18 26		18 09	18 45		18 49
Twyford 3	d					17 38	17 52			17a58				18 17		18 07	18 17			18 34			18 52		18a58
Reading 7	a				17 19	17 46	18 00						17 54	→		18 14	18 26			18 44		18 20	→		
Oxford	a				17 51								18 45			19 07	19 18					18 47			

		GW 1	GW 1	GW 1		GW 1	GW 1	GW FO 1	GW FX 1	HC	GW 1	GW 1	GW ◇1	GW 1		GW ◇1	GW FO 1	GW FX 1	GW 1	GW 1	HC	GW 1	GW 1	GW 1	
London Paddington 15 ⊖	d	18 15	18 18	18 18				18 25	18 25	18 33	18 42	18 45	18 47	18 48		18 50				18 58	19 03	19 05	19 12	19 15	
Acton Main Line	d		18 24											18 54										19 21	
Ealing Broadway ⊖	d	18 23	18 27					18 33	18 33	18 41		18 53		18 57						19 07	19 11		19 20	19 24	
West Ealing	d		18 30							18 43				19 00							19 13			19 27	
Drayton Green	d		18 32											19 02										19 29	
Castle Bar Park	d		18 34											19 04										19 31	
South Greenford	d		18 37											19 07										19 34	
Greenford ⊖	a		18 42											19 12										19 39	
Hanwell	d									18 45											19 15				
Southall	d	18 29						18 38	18 38	18 49		18 58								19 12	19 19		19 28		
Hayes & Harlington	d	18 33						18 42	18 42	18 53		19 02								19 16	19 23		19 32		
Heathrow Terminal 1-2 2 ✈	a									19 05											19 35				
Heathrow Terminal 4 ✈	a																								
West Drayton	d	18 38						18 46	18 46			19 07								19 21			19 36		
Iver	d							18 49	18 49											19 24					
Langley	d	18 42						18 52	18 52										←	19 28					
Slough 3	a	18 47						18 59	18 59		19 05	19 14				19 06			19 14	19 32			19 42		
	d	18 47						18 59	18 59		19 06	19 14				19 07			19 14	19 32			19 43		
Burnham	d	18 51						19 03	19 03			→							19 18	19 35			→		
Taplow	d							19 06	19 06											19 40					
Maidenhead 3	d	18 57		18 40		←	←	19 10	19 10		19a14						←	←	19 24	19 43		19 27			
Twyford 3	d	19 05		18 48		18 52	19 05	19 18	19 18				19 10				19 18	19 18	19 38	19 52		19a38			
Reading 7	a	→		18 56		19 00	19 13	→	→				19 18			19 21	19 26	19 26	19 47	→					
Oxford	a			19 46			20 16									19 49	20 18	20 27							

For non-stop services between London and Reading please see table 116

Passengers who hold valid tickets for Acton Main Line, West Ealing and Hanwell will be able to use local Transport for London (TFL) bus services to reach these stations. Tel 0843 222 1234

Table 117

Mondays to Fridays

31 March to 16 May

Network Diagram - refer to first Page of Table 116

London - Greenford and Reading

Station		GW [1]	GW FX ◇[1] [P]	GW FO ◇[1] [P]	GW [1]	GW [1]	GW [1]	HC	GW [1]	GW [1]	GW ◇[1] [P]	GW ◇[1] [trolley]	GW [1]	GW [1]	HC	GW [1]	GW [1]	GW ◇[1] [trolley]	GW [1]	GW [1]	HC	GW [1]	GW [1]
London Paddington [15] ⊖	d	19 18	19 22	19 22			19 27	19 33	19 42	19 45	19 48	19 50		19 57	20 03	20 12	20 15	20 20		20 27	20 33	20 42	20 45
Acton Main Line	d									19 51							20 21						20 51
Ealing Broadway ⊖	d						19 35	19 41	19 50	19 54				20 05	20 11	20 20	20 24			20 35	20 41	20 50	20 54
West Ealing	d							19 43		19 57					20 13		20 27				20 43		20 57
Drayton Green	d									19 59							20 29						20 59
Castle Bar Park	d									20 01							20 31						21 01
South Greenford	d									20 04							20 34						21 04
Greenford ⊖	a									20 09							20 39						21 09
Hanwell	d							19 45							20 15						20 45		
Southall	d						19 40	19 49	19 58						20 19	20 28					20 49	20 58	
Hayes & Harlington	d						19 44	19 53	20 02					20 12	20 23	20 32				20 42	20 53	21 02	
Heathrow Terminal 1-2 [2] ✈	a							20 05							20 35						21 05		
Heathrow Terminal 4 ✈	a																						
West Drayton	d						19 48		20 06					20 16		20 36				20 46		21 06	
Iver	d						19 51		20 09					20 19						20 49			
Langley	d					←	19 55		20 13				←	20 22					←	20 52			
Slough [3]	a		19 36	19 36		19 42	19 59		20 17			20 06	20 17	20 27		20 43		20 35	20 43	20 57		21 13	
	d		19 36	19 36		19 43	19 59		20 17			20 06	20 17	20 27		20 43		20 36	20 43	20 57		21 13	
Burnham	d					19 47	20 03		→				20 20			→			20 47			→	
Taplow	d					19 51							20 25						20 51				
Maidenhead [3]	d	19 40			←	19 55	20 09				20 06		20 29	20 34					20 55	21 04			
Twyford [3]	d	19 48			19 52	20 03	20 17						20 37	20 42					21 03	21 12			
Reading [7]	a	19 56	19 51	19 51	20 00	20 13	20 25				20 18	20 21	20 45	20 50				20 49	21 13	21 20			
Oxford	a	20 43	20 18	20 21			21 15					20 52		21 44				21 17		22 12			

Station		GW ◇[1]	GW [1]	GW FX [1]	GW FO [1]	HC	GW [1]	GW [1]	GW ◇[1]	GW [1]	GW [1]	HC FO	GW FX [1]	GW FO [1]	GW FO ◇[1] [trolley]	GW FX ◇[1] [P]	GW [1]	GW FX [1]	GW FO [1]	GW FO [1]	GW FX [1]	HC FO
London Paddington [15] ⊖	d	20 48		20 57	20 57	21 03	21 12	21 15	21 18		21 27	21 33	21 36	21 42	21 48	21 48				21 57	21 57	22 03
Acton Main Line	d							21 21					21 42	21 48								
Ealing Broadway ⊖	d			21 05	21 05	21 11	21 20	21 24			21 35	21 41	21 45	21 51						22 05	22 05	22 11
West Ealing	d					21 13		21 27				21 43										22 13
Drayton Green	d							21 29														
Castle Bar Park	d							21 31														
South Greenford	d							21 34														
Greenford ⊖	a							21 39														
Hanwell	d					21 15						21 45										22 15
Southall	d					21 19	21 28				21 42	21 49	21 52	21 58						22 10	22 10	22 19
Hayes & Harlington	d			21 12	21 12	21 23	21 32				21 46	21 53	21 55	22 02						22 14	22 14	22 23
Heathrow Terminal 1-2 [2] ✈	a					21 35						22 05										22 35
Heathrow Terminal 4 ✈	a																					
West Drayton	d			21 16	21 16		21 36				21 50		22 01	22 06						22 18	22 18	
Iver	d			21 19	21 19						21 53									22 21	22 21	
Langley	d		←	21 22	21 22					←	21 57						←	←	←	22 25	22 25	
Slough [3]	a	21 04	21 13	21 27	21 27		21 43		21 34	21 43	22 02		22 11	22 14	22 03	22 03	22 02	22 11	22 14	22 30	22 30	
	d	21 05	21 13	21 27	21 27		21 43		21 35	21 43	22 07		22 14	22 14	22 04	22 04	22 07	22 14	22 14	22 30	22 42	
Burnham	d		21 17				→			21 47	→		→	→				22 18	22 18	22 34	→	
Taplow	d		21 21							21 51								22 22	22 22	22 38		
Maidenhead [3]	d		21 25	21 34	21 34					21 55							22 15	22 26	22 26	22 42		
Twyford [3]	d		21 33	21 42	21 42					22 03							22 23	22 34	22 34	22 50		
Reading [7]	a	21 20	21 43	21 51	21 54				21 50	22 14					22 23	22 23	22 30	22 45	22 45	22 59		
Oxford	a	21 51		22 41	22 41				22 18						22 47	22 47	23 22			23 56		

Station		HC FX	GW FO ◇[1]	GW FX ◇[1]	GW FX [1]	GW FO [1]	GW FX [1]	HC FO	GW FO ◇[1]	GW FX ◇[1]	GW FO [1]	GW FX [1]	GW FO [1]	GW FX [1]	HC FO	HC FX	GW FO ◇[1]	GW FX ◇[1]	GW [1]	GW FO [1]	GW FX [1]	GW FO [1]
London Paddington [15] ⊖	d	22 07	22 18	22 18		22 27	22 27	22 33	22 48	22 48			23 00	23 00	23 03	23 07	23 18	23 18	23 33	23 42	23 49	23 49
Acton Main Line	d												23 06									23 55
Ealing Broadway ⊖	d	22 15				22 35	22 35	22 41					23 09	23 09	23 12	23 15			23 41		23 59	23 59
West Ealing	d							22 43							23 14							00 01
Drayton Green	d																					
Castle Bar Park	d																					
South Greenford	d																					
Greenford ⊖	a																					
Hanwell	d							22 45							23 16							00 04
Southall	d	22 19				22 40	22 40	22 49					23 15	23 15	23 20	23 20					00 07	00 07
Hayes & Harlington	d	22 24				22 44	22 44	22 53					23 19	23 19	23 24	23 25			23 48		00 12	00 12
Heathrow Terminal 1-2 [2] ✈	a	22 29						23 05							23 35	23 32						
Heathrow Terminal 4 ✈	a														23 41	23 38						
West Drayton	d					22 48	22 48						23 23	23 23							00 16	00 16
Iver	d					22 51	22 51						23 26	23 26							00 19	00 19
Langley	d				←	22 55	22 55				←	←	23 29	23 29							00 22	00 22
Slough [3]	a		22 34	22 39	22 30	22 59	23 00		23 04	23 08	22 59	23 00	23 34	23 34			23 36	23 38	23 57	00 01	00 28	00 28
	d		22 35	22 39	22 42	23 11	23 11		23 05	23 08	23 11	23 11	23 34	23 34			23 38	23 38	23 57	00 01	00 28	00 28
Burnham	d				22 46	→	→				23 15	23 15									00 32	00 32
Taplow	d				22 49						23 19	23 19									00 36	00 36
Maidenhead [3]	d		22 42	22 47	22 53				23 12	23 17	23 23	23 23	23 41	23 41			23 46	23 46	00 05	00 10	00 41	00 41
Twyford [3]	d				23 01				23 20	23 26	23 31	23 31	23 49	23 49					00 13		00 48	00 48
Reading [7]	a		22 54	23 01	23 10				23 27	23 33	23 40	23 40	23 59	23 59			00 04	00 04	00 22	00 25	00 56	00 58
Oxford	a		23 27	23 29	23 54				23 56	00 01	00 27	00 27					00 35	00 35	01 18	01 02		

For non-stop services between London and Reading please see table 116

Passengers who hold valid tickets for Acton Main Line, West Ealing and Hanwell will be able to use local Transport for London (TFL) bus services to reach these stations. Tel 0843 222 1234

Table 117

Saturdays

14 December to 28 December

Network Diagram - refer to first Page of Table 116

London - Greenford and Reading

		GW 1	GW 1	GW 1	GW 1	GW ◇1	GW 1	GW 1	GW 1	HC		HC	GW ◇1	GW 1	HC	GW 1	GW ◇1	GW 1	HC	GW 1		GW 1	GW ◇1	GW 1	GW 1
London Paddington 15 ⊖	d					00 22	00 34	01 44	03 34	04 42		05 13	05 21	05 25	05 33	05 45	05 50	05 57	06 03	06 12		06 15	06 21		06 27
Acton Main Line	d															05 51						06 21			
Ealing Broadway ⊖	d						00 42	01 52	03 42	04 50		05 21		05 33	05 41	05 54		06 05	06 11	06 20		06 24			06 35
West Ealing	d				00 01										05 43	05 57			06 13			06 27			
Drayton Green	d															05 59						06 29			
Castle Bar Park	d															06 01						06 31			
South Greenford	d															06 04						06 34			
Greenford ⊖	a															06 09						06 39			
Hanwell	d				00 04										05 45				06 15						
Southall	d				00 07		00 47	01 57	03 47	04 54		05 25		05 38	05 49			06 10	06 19	06 28					
Hayes & Harlington	d				00 12		00 51	02 01	03 51	04 58		05 29		05 42	05 53			06 14	06 23	06 32					06 42
Heathrow Terminal 1-2 2 ✈	a									05 04		05 35			06 05				06 35						
Heathrow Terminal 4 ✈	a									05 10		05 41													
West Drayton	d				00 16		00 55	02 05	03 55									06 18		06 36					06 46
Iver	d				00 19													06 21							06 49
Langley	d				00 22		01 00											06 25						←	06 52
Slough 3	a				00 28	00 41	01 05	02 13	04 03				05 37	05 50			06 06	06 29		06 43			06 37	06 43	06 57
	d			00 01	00 28	00 41	01 05	02 13	04 03				05 38	05 51			06 06	06 30		06 43			06 38	06 43	06 57
Burnham	d				00 32		01 09							05 55				06 34		→				06 47	
Taplow	d				00 36		01 13							05 58				06 37						06 51	
Maidenhead 3	d		00 05	00 10	00 41		01 16	02 21	04 11					06 02				06 41						06 55	07 04
Twyford 3	d	00 08	00 13		00 48		01 24	02 29	04 19					06 10				06 49						07 03	07 12
Reading 7	a	00 16	00 22	00 25	00 58	01 01	01 35	02 38	04 30				05 52	06 17			06 22	06 56					06 53	07 11	07 19
Oxford	a		01 18	01 02		01 34							06 22	07 03			06 52	07 43					07 20		08 09

		HC	GW 1	GW 1	GW ◇1	GW 1		GW 1	HC	GW 1	GW 1	GW ◇1	GW 1	GW 1	HC	GW 1		GW 1	GW ◇1	GW 1	GW 1	HC	GW 1	GW 1	GW ◇1
London Paddington 15 ⊖	d	06 33	06 42	06 45	06 50			06 57	07 03	07 12	07 15	07 21		07 27	07 33	07 42		07 45	07 50		07 57	08 03	08 12	08 15	08 21
Acton Main Line	d			06 51							07 21							07 51						08 21	
Ealing Broadway ⊖	d	06 41	06 50	06 54				07 05	07 11	07 20	07 24			07 35	07 41	07 50		07 54			08 05	08 11	08 20	08 24	
West Ealing	d	06 43		06 57					07 13		07 27				07 43			07 57				08 13		08 27	
Drayton Green	d			06 59							07 29							07 59						08 29	
Castle Bar Park	d			07 01							07 31							08 01						08 31	
South Greenford	d			07 04							07 34							08 04						08 34	
Greenford ⊖	a			07 09							07 39							08 09						08 39	
Hanwell	d	06 45							07 15						07 45							08 15			
Southall	d	06 49	06 58						07 19	07 28					07 49	07 58						08 19	08 28		
Hayes & Harlington	d	06 53	07 02					07 12	07 23	07 32				07 42	07 53	08 02					08 12	08 23	08 32		
Heathrow Terminal 1-2 2 ✈	a	07 05							07 35						08 05							08 35			
Heathrow Terminal 4 ✈	a																								
West Drayton	d		07 06					07 16		07 36				07 46		08 06					08 16		08 36		
Iver	d							07 19						07 49							08 19				
Langley	d					←		07 22					←	07 52						←	08 22				
Slough 3	a		07 13		07 06	07 13		07 27		07 43		07 37	07 43	07 57		08 13			08 06	08 13	08 27		08 43		08 38
	d		07 13		07 06	07 13		07 27		07 43		07 38	07 43	07 57		08 13			08 06	08 13	08 27		08 43		08 39
Burnham	d		→			07 17				→			07 47			→				08 17			→		
Taplow	d					07 21							07 51							08 21					
Maidenhead 3	d					07 25		07 34					07 55	08 04						08 25	08 34				
Twyford 3	d					07 33		07 42					08 05	08 12						08 34	08 42				
Reading 7	a				07 22	07 43		07 53				07 53	08 14	08 21					08 22	08 42	08 54				08 53
Oxford	a				07 48			08 40				08 19		09 14					08 48		09 40				09 18

		GW 1		GW 1	HC	GW 1	GW 1	GW ◇1	GW 1	GW 1	HC	GW 1		GW 1	GW ◇1	GW 1	GW 1	HC	GW 1	GW 1	GW ◇1	GW 1		GW 1	HC
London Paddington 15 ⊖	d			08 27	08 33	08 42	08 45	08 50		08 57	09 03	09 12		09 15	09 21		09 27	09 33	09 42	09 45	09 50			09 57	10 03
Acton Main Line	d						08 51							09 21						09 51					
Ealing Broadway ⊖	d			08 35	08 41	08 50	08 54			09 05	09 11	09 20		09 24			09 35	09 41	09 50	09 54				10 05	10 11
West Ealing	d				08 43		08 57				09 13			09 27				09 43		09 57					10 13
Drayton Green	d						08 59							09 29						09 59					
Castle Bar Park	d						09 01							09 31						10 01					
South Greenford	d						09 04							09 34						10 04					
Greenford ⊖	a						09 09							09 39						10 09					
Hanwell	d				08 45						09 15							09 45							10 15
Southall	d				08 49	08 58					09 19	09 28						09 49	09 58						10 19
Hayes & Harlington	d			08 42	08 53	09 02				09 12	09 23	09 32					09 42	09 53	10 02					10 12	10 23
Heathrow Terminal 1-2 2 ✈	a				09 05						09 35							10 05							10 35
Heathrow Terminal 4 ✈	a																								
West Drayton	d			08 46		09 06				09 16		09 36					09 46		10 06					10 16	
Iver	d			08 49						09 19							09 49							10 19	
Langley	d	←		08 52					←	09 22						←	09 52					←		10 22	
Slough 3	a	08 43		08 57		09 13		09 06	09 13	09 27		09 43			09 38	09 43	09 57		10 13		10 06	10 13		10 27	
	d	08 43		08 57		09 13		09 06	09 13	09 27		09 43			09 39	09 43	09 57		10 13		10 06	10 13		10 27	
Burnham	d	08 47				→			09 17			→				09 47			→			10 17			
Taplow	d	08 51							09 21							09 51						10 21			
Maidenhead 3	d	08 55		09 04					09 25	09 34						09 55	10 04					10 25		10 34	
Twyford 3	d	09 03		09 12					09 35	09 42						10 04	10 14					10 33		10 44	
Reading 7	a	09 12		09 23				09 22	09 45	09 52					09 54	10 13	10 23				10 22	10 41		10 53	
Oxford	a			10 14				09 48		10 40					10 19		11 14				10 48			11 40	

For non-stop services between London and Reading please see table 116

Passengers who hold valid tickets for Acton Main Line, West Ealing and Hanwell will be able to use local Transport for London (TFL) bus services to reach these stations. Tel 0843 222 1234

Table 117

Saturdays

14 December to 28 December

London - Greenford and Reading

Network Diagram - refer to first Page of Table 116

		GW 1	GW 1	GW ◇1 ☕	GW 1	GW 1	HC	GW 1		GW 1	GW ◇1 🛒	GW 1	GW 1	HC	GW 1	GW 1	GW ◇1 🛒	GW 1		GW 1	HC	GW 1	GW 1	GW ◇1	GW 1
London Paddington 15 ⊖	d	10 12	10 15	10 21		10 27	10 33	10 42		10 45	10 50		10 57	11 03	11 12	11 15	11 21			11 27	11 33	11 42	11 45	11 50	
Acton Main Line	d		10 21							10 51						11 21							11 51		
Ealing Broadway ⊖	d	10 20	10 24			10 35	10 41	10 52		10 54			11 05	11 11	11 20	11 24				11 35	11 41	11 50	11 54		
West Ealing	d		10 27				10 43			10 57				11 13		11 27					11 43		11 57		
Drayton Green	d		10 29							10 59						11 29							11 59		
Castle Bar Park	d		10 31							11 01						11 31							12 01		
South Greenford	d		10 34							11 04						11 34							12 04		
Greenford ⊖	a		10 39							11 09						11 39							12 09		
Hanwell	d						10 45							11 15							11 45				
Southall	d	10 28					10 49	10 58						11 19	11 28						11 49	11 58			
Hayes & Harlington	d	10 32				10 42	10 53	11 02					11 12	11 23	11 32					11 42	11 53	12 02			
Heathrow Terminal 1-2 2 ✈	a						11 05							11 35							12 05				
Heathrow Terminal 4 ✈	a																								
West Drayton	d	10 36				10 46		11 06					11 16		11 36					11 46		12 06			
Iver	d					10 49							11 19							11 49					
Langley	d				←	10 52						←	11 22					←		11 52					←
Slough 3	a	10 43		10 38	10 43	10 57		11 13			11 06	11 13	11 27		11 43		11 38	11 43		11 57		12 13		12 06	12 13
	d	10 43		10 39	10 43	10 57		11 13			11 06	11 13	11 27		11 43		11 39	11 43		11 57		12 13		12 06	12 13
Burnham	d	↦			10 47			↦				11 17			↦			11 47				↦			12 17
Taplow	d				10 51							11 21						11 51							12 21
Maidenhead 3	d				10 55	11 04						11 25	11 34					11 55		12 04					12 25
Twyford 3	d				11 03	11 12						11 33	11 42					12 03		12 12					12 33
Reading 7	a			10 53	11 14	11 21					11 22	11 41	11 52				11 54	12 11		12 21				12 22	12 41
Oxford	a			11 19		12 14					11 48		12 40				12 20			13 14				12 48	

		GW 1	HC	GW 1		GW 1	GW ◇1	GW 1	GW 1	HC	GW 1	GW 1	GW ◇1 🛒	GW 1		GW 1	HC	GW 1	GW 1	GW ◇1 🛒	GW 1	GW 1	HC	GW 1	
London Paddington 15 ⊖	d	11 57	12 03	12 12		12 15	12 21		12 27	12 33	12 42	12 45	12 50			12 57	13 03	13 12	13 15	13 21		13 27	13 33	13 42	
Acton Main Line	d					12 21						12 51							13 21						
Ealing Broadway ⊖	d	12 05	12 11	12 20		12 24			12 35	12 41	12 50	12 54				13 05	13 11	13 20	13 24			13 35	13 41	13 50	
West Ealing	d		12 13			12 27				12 43		12 57					13 13		13 27				13 43		
Drayton Green	d					12 29						12 59							13 29						
Castle Bar Park	d					12 31						13 01							13 31						
South Greenford	d					12 34						13 04							13 34						
Greenford ⊖	a					12 39						13 09							13 39						
Hanwell	d		12 15							12 45							13 15						13 45		
Southall	d		12 19	12 28						12 49	12 58						13 19	13 28					13 49	13 58	
Hayes & Harlington	d	12 12	12 23	12 32					12 42	12 53	13 02					13 12	13 23	13 32				13 42	13 53	14 02	
Heathrow Terminal 1-2 2 ✈	a		12 35							13 05							13 35						14 05		
Heathrow Terminal 4 ✈	a																								
West Drayton	d	12 16		12 36					12 46		13 06					13 16		13 36				13 46		14 06	
Iver	d	12 19							12 49							13 19						13 49			
Langley	d	12 22						←	12 52					←		13 22					←	13 52			
Slough 3	a	12 27		12 43			12 39	12 43	12 57		13 13		13 06	13 13		13 27		13 43		13 38	13 43	13 57		14 13	
	d	12 27		12 43			12 39	12 43	12 57		13 13		13 06	13 13		13 27		13 43		13 39	13 43	13 57		14 13	
Burnham	d			↦				12 47			↦			13 17				↦			13 47			↦	
Taplow	d							12 51						13 21							13 51				
Maidenhead 3	d	12 34						12 55	13 04					13 25		13 34					13 55	14 04			
Twyford 3	d	12 45						13 03	13 12					13 33		13 42					14 06	14 12			
Reading 7	a	12 53					12 54	13 11	13 21				13 22	13 43		13 51				13 54	14 14	14 21			
Oxford	a	13 40					13 19		14 14				13 48			14 40				14 19		15 14			

		GW 1	GW ◇1 🛒	GW 1	GW 1	HC	GW 1	GW 1	GW ◇1 🛒	GW 1		GW 1	HC	GW 1	GW 1	GW ◇1	GW 1	GW 1	HC	GW 1		GW 1	GW ◇1 🛒	GW 1	GW 1
London Paddington 15 ⊖	d	13 45	13 50		13 57	14 03	14 12	14 15	14 21			14 27	14 33	14 42	14 45	14 50		14 57	15 03	15 12		15 15	15 21		15 27
Acton Main Line	d	13 51						14 21							14 51							15 21			
Ealing Broadway ⊖	d	13 54			14 05	14 11	14 20	14 24				14 35	14 41	14 50	14 54			15 05	15 11	15 20		15 24			15 35
West Ealing	d	13 57				14 13		14 27					14 43		14 57				15 13			15 27			
Drayton Green	d	13 59						14 29							14 59							15 29			
Castle Bar Park	d	14 01						14 31							15 01							15 31			
South Greenford	d	14 04						14 34							15 04							15 34			
Greenford ⊖	a	14 09						14 39							15 09							15 39			
Hanwell	d					14 15							14 45						15 15						
Southall	d					14 19	14 28						14 49	14 58					15 19	15 28					
Hayes & Harlington	d				14 12	14 23	14 32					14 42	14 53	15 02				15 12	15 23	15 32					15 42
Heathrow Terminal 1-2 2 ✈	a					14 35							15 05						15 35						
Heathrow Terminal 4 ✈	a																								
West Drayton	d				14 16		14 36					14 46		15 06				15 16		15 36					15 46
Iver	d				14 19							14 49						15 19							15 49
Langley	d			←	14 22					←		14 52					←	15 22						←	15 52
Slough 3	a		14 06	14 13	14 27		14 43		14 38	14 43		14 57		15 13		15 06	15 13	15 27		15 43			15 38	15 43	15 57
	d		14 06	14 13	14 27		14 43		14 39	14 43		14 57		15 13		15 06	15 13	15 27		15 43			15 39	15 43	15 57
Burnham	d			14 17			↦			14 47				↦			15 17			↦				15 47	
Taplow	d			14 21						14 51							15 21							15 51	
Maidenhead 3	d			14 25	14 34					14 55		15 04					15 25	15 34						15 55	16 04
Twyford 3	d			14 37	14 45					15 03		15 12					15 33	15 42						16 06	16 13
Reading 7	a		14 22	14 46	14 53				14 53	15 13		15 22				15 22	15 43	15 52					15 54	16 14	16 22
Oxford	a		14 48		15 40				15 18			16 14				15 48		16 40					16 19		17 14

For non-stop services between London and Reading please see table 116

Passengers who hold valid tickets for Acton Main Line, West Ealing and Hanwell will be able to use local Transport for London (TFL) bus services to reach these stations. Tel 0843 222 1234

Table 117

Saturdays

14 December to 28 December

Network Diagram - refer to first Page of Table 116

London - Greenford and Reading

		HC	GW	GW	GW	GW		GW	HC	GW	GW	GW	GW	GW	HC	GW		GW	GW	GW	GW	HC	GW	GW	GW
			1	1	◇1	1		1		1	1	◇1 ☕	1	1		1		1	◇1 🛒	1	1		1	1	◇1 ☕
London Paddington 15 ⊖	d	15 33	15 42	15 45	15 50			15 57	16 03	16 12	16 15	16 21		16 27	16 33	16 42		16 45	16 50		16 57	17 03	17 12	17 15	17 21
Acton Main Line	d			15 51							16 21							16 51						17 21	
Ealing Broadway ⊖	d	15 41	15 50	15 54				16 05	16 11	16 20	16 24			16 35	16 41	16 50		16 54			17 05	17 11	17 20	17 24	
West Ealing	d	15 43		15 57					16 13		16 27				16 43			16 57				17 13		17 27	
Drayton Green	d			15 59							16 29							16 59						17 29	
Castle Bar Park	d			16 01							16 31							17 01						17 31	
South Greenford	d			16 04							16 34							17 04						17 34	
Greenford ⊖	a			16 09							16 39							17 09						17 39	
Hanwell	d	15 45							16 15						16 45							17 15			
Southall	d	15 49	15 58						16 19	16 28					16 49	16 58						17 19	17 28		
Hayes & Harlington	d	15 53	16 02					16 12	16 23	16 32				16 42	16 53	17 02					17 12	17 23	17 32		
Heathrow Terminal 1-2 2 ✈	a	16 05							16 35						17 05							17 35			
Heathrow Terminal 4 ✈	a																								
West Drayton	d		16 06					16 16		16 36				16 46		17 06					17 16		17 36		
Iver	d							16 19						16 49							17 19				
Langley	d					←		16 22					←	16 52						←	17 22				
Slough 3	a		16 13		16 06	16 13		16 27		16 43		16 37	16 43	16 57		17 13			17 06	17 13	17 27		17 43		17 38
	d		16 13		16 06	16 13		16 27		16 43		16 38	16 43	16 57		17 13			17 06	17 13	17 27		17 43		17 39
Burnham	d		→			16 17				→			16 47			→				17 17			→		
Taplow	d					16 21							16 51							17 21					
Maidenhead 3	d					16 25		16 34					16 55	17 04						17 25	17 34				
Twyford 3	d					16 33		16 45					17 03	17 12						17 33	17 42				
Reading 7	a				16 22	16 41		16 53				16 52	17 12	17 21					17 22	17 41	17 51				17 53
Oxford	a				16 48			17 40				17 18		18 14					17 48		18 40				18 18

		GW		GW	HC	GW	GW	GW	GW	GW	HC	GW		GW	GW	GW	GW	HC	GW	GW	GW	GW		GW	HC
		1		1		1	1	◇1 🛒	1	1		1		1	◇1 ☕	1	1		1	1	◇1	1		1	
London Paddington 15 ⊖	d			17 27	17 33	17 42	17 45	17 50		17 57	18 03	18 12		18 15	18 21		18 27	18 33	18 42	18 45	18 50			18 57	19 03
Acton Main Line	d						17 51							18 21						18 51					
Ealing Broadway ⊖	d			17 35	17 41	17 50	17 54			18 05	18 11	18 20		18 24			18 35	18 41	18 50	18 54				19 05	19 11
West Ealing	d				17 43		17 57				18 13			18 27				18 43		18 57					19 13
Drayton Green	d						17 59							18 29						18 59					
Castle Bar Park	d						18 01							18 31						19 01					
South Greenford	d						18 04							18 34						19 04					
Greenford ⊖	a						18 09							18 39						19 09					
Hanwell	d				17 45						18 15							18 45							19 15
Southall	d				17 49	17 58					18 19	18 28						18 49	18 58						19 19
Hayes & Harlington	d			17 42	17 53	18 02				18 12	18 23	18 32					18 42	18 53	19 02					19 12	19 23
Heathrow Terminal 1-2 2 ✈	a				18 05						18 35							19 05							19 35
Heathrow Terminal 4 ✈	a																								
West Drayton	d			17 46		18 06				18 16		18 36					18 46		19 06					19 16	
Iver	d			17 49						18 19							18 49							19 19	
Langley	d	←		17 52					←	18 22						←	18 52					←		19 22	
Slough 3	a	17 43		17 57		18 13		18 06	18 13	18 27		18 43			18 37	18 43	18 57		19 13		19 06	19 13		19 27	
	d	17 43		17 57		18 13		18 06	18 13	18 27		18 43			18 38	18 43	18 57		19 13		19 06	19 13		19 27	
Burnham	d	17 47				→			18 17			→				18 47			→			19 17			
Taplow	d	17 51							18 21							18 51						19 21			
Maidenhead 3	d	17 55		18 04					18 25	18 34						18 55	19 04					19 25		19 34	
Twyford 3	d	18 03		18 12					18 33	18 45						19 03	19 12					19 33		19 42	
Reading 7	a	18 11		18 22				18 22	18 41	18 53					18 52	19 12	19 21				19 22	19 43		19 51	
Oxford	a			19 14				18 48		19 40					19 18		20 14				19 48			20 41	

		GW	GW	GW	GW	GW	HC	GW		GW	GW	GW	GW	HC	GW	GW	GW	GW		GW	HC	GW	GW	GW	GW
		1	1	◇1	1	1		1		1	◇1 🛒	1	1		1	1	◇1	1		1		1	1	◇1 🛒	1
London Paddington 15 ⊖	d	19 12	19 15	19 21		19 27	19 33	19 42		19 45	19 50		19 57	20 03	20 12	20 15	20 18			20 27	20 33	20 42	20 45	20 48	
Acton Main Line	d		19 21							19 51						20 21							20 51		
Ealing Broadway ⊖	d	19 20	19 24			19 35	19 41	19 50		19 54			20 05	20 11	20 20	20 24				20 35	20 41	20 50	20 54		
West Ealing	d		19 27				19 43			19 57				20 13		20 27					20 43		20 57		
Drayton Green	d		19 29							19 59						20 29							20 59		
Castle Bar Park	d		19 31							20 01						20 31							21 01		
South Greenford	d		19 34							20 04						20 34							21 04		
Greenford ⊖	a		19 39							20 09						20 39							21 09		
Hanwell	d						19 45							20 15							20 45				
Southall	d	19 28					19 49	19 58						20 19	20 28						20 49	20 58			
Hayes & Harlington	d	19 32				19 42	19 53	20 02					20 12	20 23	20 32					20 42	20 53	21 02			
Heathrow Terminal 1-2 2 ✈	a						20 05							20 35							21 05				
Heathrow Terminal 4 ✈	a																								
West Drayton	d	19 36				19 46		20 06					20 16		20 36					20 46		21 06			
Iver	d					19 49							20 19							20 49					
Langley	d				←	19 52						←	20 22					←		20 52					←
Slough 3	a	19 43		19 37	19 43	19 57		20 13			20 06	20 13	20 27		20 43		20 34	20 43		20 57		21 13		21 04	21 13
	d	19 43		19 38	19 43	19 57		20 13			20 06	20 13	20 27		20 43		20 35	20 43		20 57		21 13		21 05	21 13
Burnham	d	→			19 47			→				20 17			→			20 47				→			21 17
Taplow	d				19 51							20 21						20 51							21 21
Maidenhead 3	d				19 55	20 04						20 25	20 34					20 55		21 04					21 25
Twyford 3	d				20 03	20 12						20 36	20 42					21 06		21 12					21 33
Reading 7	a			19 53	20 13	20 20					20 21	20 45	20 52				20 50	21 15		21 20				21 21	21 43
Oxford	a			20 20		21 14					20 47		21 40				21 18			22 14				21 50	

For non-stop services between London and Reading please see table 116

Passengers who hold valid tickets for Acton Main Line, West Ealing and Hanwell will be able to use local Transport for London (TFL) bus services to reach these stations. Tel 0843 222 1234

Table 117

Saturdays

14 December to 28 December

Network Diagram - refer to first Page of Table 116

London - Greenford and Reading

Station		GW [1]	HC	GW [1]		GW [1]	GW ◇[1]	GW [1]	HC	GW [1]	GW ◇[1]	GW [1]	HC	GW [1]		GW ◇[1]	GW [1]	HC	GW [1]	GW ◇[1]	GW [1]	HC	GW [1]	GW ◇[1]	
London Paddington [15] ⊖	d	20 57	21 03	21 12		21 15	21 18		21 33	21 42	21 48		22 03	22 12		22 18		22 33	22 42	22 48		23 03	23 15	23 33	
Acton Main Line	d					21 21				21 48									22 48						
Ealing Broadway ⊖	d	21 05	21 11	21 20		21 24			21 41	21 52			22 11	22 20				22 41	22 52			23 11	23 23		
West Ealing	d		21 13			21 27			21 43				22 13					22 43				23 13			
Drayton Green	d					21 29																			
Castle Bar Park	d					21 31																			
South Greenford	d					21 34																			
Greenford ⊖	a					21 39																			
Hanwell	d		21 15						21 45				22 15					22 45				23 15			
Southall	d		21 19	21 28					21 49	21 58			22 19	22 28				22 49	22 58			23 19	23 29		
Hayes & Harlington	d	21 12	21 23	21 32					21 53	22 02			22 23	22 32				22 53	23 02			23 23	23 33		
Heathrow Terminal 1-2 [2] ✈	a		21 35						22 05				22 35					23 05				23 35			
Heathrow Terminal 4 ✈	a																					23 41			
West Drayton	d	21 16		21 36						22 06				22 36					23 06				23 37		
Iver	d	21 19		21 40						22 10				22 40					23 10				23 40		
Langley	d	21 22		21 43				←		22 13		←		22 43			←		23 13		←		23 43		
Slough [3]	a	21 27		21 47			21 34	21 47		22 17	22 05	22 17		22 47		22 34	22 47		23 17	23 04	23 17		23 47	23 49	
	d	21 27		21 47			21 35	21 47		22 18	22 05	22 18		22 47		22 35	22 47		23 20	23 05	23 20		23 54	23 50	
Burnham	d			→				21 52		→		22 22		→			22 51		→		23 24		→		
Taplow	d							21 55				22 25					22 55				23 27				
Maidenhead [3]	d	21 34						21 59				22 29				22 42	22 59			23 13	23 32			23 58	
Twyford [3]	d	21 46						22 07				22 38					23 07				23 40				
Reading [7]	a	21 55					21 51	22 15			22 20	22 46				22 53	23 19			23 25	23 47			00 11	
Oxford	a	22 43					22 22				22 48	23 40				23 22				23 57	00 32			00 50	

Station		GW [1]	GW [1]
London Paddington [15] ⊖	d		23 42
Acton Main Line	d		
Ealing Broadway ⊖	d		23 50
West Ealing	d		
Drayton Green	d		
Castle Bar Park	d		
South Greenford	d		
Greenford ⊖	a		
Hanwell	d		
Southall	d		23 56
Hayes & Harlington	d		00 01
Heathrow Terminal 1-2 [2] ✈	a		
Heathrow Terminal 4 ✈	a		
West Drayton	d		00 05
Iver	d		
Langley	d	←	
Slough [3]	a	23 47	00 11
	d	23 54	00 12
Burnham	d	23 57	00 16
Taplow	d	00 01	00 20
Maidenhead [3]	d	00 05	00 24
Twyford [3]	d	00 13	00 31
Reading [7]	a	00 21	00 39
Oxford	a		

Saturdays

4 January to 8 February

Station		GW [1]	GW [1]	GW [1]	GW [1]	GW ◇[1]	GW [1]	GW [1]	GW [1]	HC		HC	GW ◇[1]	GW [1]	HC	GW [1]	GW ◇[1]	GW [1]	HC	GW [1]		GW ◇[1]	GW [1]	HC	GW ◇[1]
London Paddington [15] ⊖	d					00 22	00 34	01 44	03 34	04 42		05 13	05 14	05 21	05 33	05 45	05 45	05 57	06 03	06 13		06 14	06 19	06 33	06 43
Acton Main Line	d															05 51				06 19					
Ealing Broadway ⊖	d						00 42	01 52	03 42	04 50		05 21		05 29	05 41	05 54		06 05	06 11	06 22			06 27	06 41	
West Ealing	d				00 01										05 43	05 57			06 13	06 27				06 43	
Drayton Green	d															05 59				06 29					
Castle Bar Park	d															06 01				06 31					
South Greenford	d															06 04				06 34					
Greenford ⊖	a															06 09				06 39					
Hanwell	d				00 04										05 45				06 15					06 45	
Southall	d				00 07		00 47	01 57	03 47	04 54		05 25		05 34	05 49			06 10	06 19				06 33	06 49	
Hayes & Harlington	d				00 12		00 51	02 01	03 51	04 58		05 29		05 38	05 53			06 14	06 23				06 37	06 53	
Heathrow Terminal 1-2 [2] ✈	a									05 04		05 35			06 05				06 35					07 05	
Heathrow Terminal 4 ✈	a									05 10		05 41													
West Drayton	d				00 16		00 55	02 05	03 55									06 18					06 41		
Iver	d				00 19													06 21					06 44		
Langley	d				00 22		01 00											06 25					06 46		
Slough [3]	a				00 28	00 41	01 05	02 13	04 03				05 37	05 50			06 09	06 29				06 37	06 51		07 06
	d			00 01	00 28	00 41	01 05	02 13	04 03				05 38	05 51			06 09	06 30				06 38	06 52		07 06
Burnham	d				00 32		01 09							05 55				06 34					06 56		
Taplow	d				00 36		01 13							05 58				06 37					06 59		
Maidenhead [3]	d		00 05	00 10	00 41		01 16	02 21	04 11					06 02				06 41					07 03		
Twyford [3]	d	00 08	00 13		00 48		01 24	02 29	04 19					06 10				06 49					07 11		
Reading [7]	a	00 16	00 22	00 25	00 58	01 01	01 35	02 38	04 30				05 52	06 17			06 25	06 56				06 53	07 18		07 22
Oxford	a		01 18	01 02		01 34							06 22	07 03			06 55	07 43				07 20	08 09		07 48

For non-stop services between London and Reading please see table 116

Passengers who hold valid tickets for Acton Main Line, West Ealing and Hanwell will be able to use local Transport for London (TFL) bus services to reach these stations. Tel 0843 222 1234

Table 117

Saturdays

4 January to 8 February

Network Diagram - refer to first Page of Table 116

London - Greenford and Reading

		GW 1	GW 1	HC	GW 1	GW ◇1		GW 1	HC	GW 1	GW ◇1	GW 1	HC	GW 1	GW ◇1	GW 1		HC	GW 1	GW ◇1	GW 1	HC	GW 1	GW ◇1	GW 1
London Paddington 15 ⊖	d	06 45	06 56	07 03	07 15	07 17		07 25	07 33	07 45	07 46	07 57	08 03	08 15	08 17	08 23		08 33	08 45	08 46	08 56	09 03	09 15	09 17	09 21
Acton Main Line	d	06 51			07 21					07 51				08 21					08 51				09 21		
Ealing Broadway ⊖	d	06 54	07 04	07 11	07 24			07 33	07 41	07 54		08 05	08 11	08 24		08 31		08 41	08 54		09 04	09 11	09 24		09 29
West Ealing	d	06 57		07 13	07 27				07 43	07 57			08 13	08 27				08 43	08 57			09 13	09 27		
Drayton Green	d	06 59			07 29					07 59				08 29					08 59				09 29		
Castle Bar Park	d	07 01			07 31					08 01				08 31					09 01				09 31		
South Greenford	d	07 04			07 34					08 04				08 34					09 04				09 34		
Greenford ⊖	a	07 09			07 39					08 09				08 39					09 09				09 39		
Hanwell	d			07 15					07 45				08 15					08 45				09 15			
Southall	d		07 10	07 19				07 39	07 49			08 11	08 19			08 37		08 49			09 10	09 19			09 35
Hayes & Harlington	d		07 14	07 23				07 43	07 53			08 15	08 23			08 41		08 53			09 14	09 23			09 39
Heathrow Terminal 1-2 2 ✈	a			07 35					08 05				08 35					09 05				09 35			
Heathrow Terminal 4 ✈	a																								
West Drayton	d		07 18					07 47				08 19				08 45					09 18				09 43
Iver	d		07 21					07 50				08 22				08 48					09 21				09 46
Langley	d		07 23					07 52				08 24				08 50					09 23				09 48
Slough 3	a		07 28			07 40		07 57			08 09	08 29			08 38	08 55				09 09	09 28			09 41	09 53
	d		07 29			07 41		07 58			08 10	08 30			08 39	08 56				09 09	09 29			09 42	09 55
Burnham	d		07 33					08 02				08 34				09 00					09 33				09 59
Taplow	d		07 36					08 05				08 37				09 03					09 36				10 02
Maidenhead 3	d		07 40					08 09				08 41				09 07					09 40				10 06
Twyford 3	d		07 48					08 17				08 49				09 15					09 48				10 14
Reading 7	a		07 56			07 56		08 25			08 26	08 57			08 54	09 24				09 25	09 56			09 57	10 22
Oxford	a		08 40			08 21		09 15			08 52	09 40			09 19	10 17				09 51	10 40			10 22	11 14

		HC		GW 1	GW ◇1	GW 1	HC	GW 1	GW ◇1	GW 1	HC	GW 1		GW ◇1	GW 1	HC	GW 1	GW ◇1	GW 1	HC	GW 1	GW ◇1		GW 1	HC
London Paddington 15 ⊖	d	09 33		09 45	09 46	09 57	10 03	10 15	10 17	10 23	10 33	10 45		10 46	10 57	11 03	11 15	11 17	11 23	11 33	11 45	11 46		11 57	12 03
Acton Main Line	d			09 51				10 21				10 51					11 21				11 51				
Ealing Broadway ⊖	d	09 41		09 54		10 05	10 11	10 24		10 31	10 41	10 54			11 05	11 11	11 24		11 31	11 41	11 54			12 05	12 11
West Ealing	d	09 43		09 57			10 13	10 27			10 43	10 57				11 13	11 27			11 43	11 57				12 13
Drayton Green	d			09 59				10 29				10 59					11 29				11 59				
Castle Bar Park	d			10 01				10 31				11 01					11 31				12 01				
South Greenford	d			10 04				10 34				11 04					11 34				12 04				
Greenford ⊖	a			10 09				10 39				11 09					11 39				12 09				
Hanwell	d	09 45					10 15				10 45					11 15				11 45					12 15
Southall	d	09 49				10 11	10 19			10 37	10 49				11 11	11 19			11 37	11 49				12 11	12 19
Hayes & Harlington	d	09 53				10 15	10 23			10 41	10 53				11 15	11 23			11 41	11 53				12 15	12 23
Heathrow Terminal 1-2 2 ✈	a	10 05					10 35				11 05					11 35				12 05					12 35
Heathrow Terminal 4 ✈	a																								
West Drayton	d					10 19				10 45					11 20				11 45					12 20	
Iver	d					10 22				10 48					11 23				11 48					12 23	
Langley	d					10 24				10 50					11 25				11 50					12 25	
Slough 3	a				10 09	10 29			10 39	10 55				11 10	11 30			11 41	11 55			12 09		12 30	
	d				10 09	10 30			10 40	10 56				11 10	11 31			11 42	11 56			12 09		12 31	
Burnham	d					10 34				11 00					11 35				12 00					12 35	
Taplow	d					10 37				11 03					11 38				12 03					12 38	
Maidenhead 3	d					10 41				11 07					11 42				12 07					12 42	
Twyford 3	d					10 49				11 15					11 50				12 15					12 50	
Reading 7	a				10 25	10 57			10 54	11 23				11 26	11 58			11 57	12 24			12 25		12 58	
Oxford	a				10 51	11 40			11 20	12 14				11 53	12 40			12 23	13 14			12 51		13 40	

		GW 1	GW ◇1	GW 1	HC	GW 1	GW ◇1	GW 1		HC	GW 1	GW ◇1	GW 1	HC	GW 1	GW ◇1	GW 1	HC		GW 1	GW ◇1	GW 1	HC	GW 1	GW ◇1
London Paddington 15 ⊖	d	12 15	12 17	12 23	12 33	12 45	12 46	12 57		13 03	13 15	13 17	13 23	13 33	13 45	13 46	13 57	14 03		14 15	14 17	14 21	14 33	14 45	14 46
Acton Main Line	d	12 21				12 51					13 21				13 51					14 21				14 51	
Ealing Broadway ⊖	d	12 24		12 31	12 41	12 54		13 05		13 11	13 24		13 31	13 41	13 54		14 05	14 11		14 24		14 29	14 41	14 54	
West Ealing	d	12 27			12 43	12 57				13 13	13 27			13 43	13 57			14 13		14 27			14 43	14 57	
Drayton Green	d	12 29				12 59					13 29				13 59					14 29				14 59	
Castle Bar Park	d	12 31				13 01					13 31				14 01					14 31				15 01	
South Greenford	d	12 34				13 04					13 34				14 04					14 34				15 04	
Greenford ⊖	a	12 39				13 09					13 39				14 09					14 39				15 09	
Hanwell	d				12 45					13 15				13 45				14 15					14 45		
Southall	d			12 37	12 49			13 11		13 19			13 37	13 49			14 11	14 19				14 35	14 49		
Hayes & Harlington	d			12 41	12 53			13 15		13 23			13 41	13 53			14 15	14 23				14 39	14 53		
Heathrow Terminal 1-2 2 ✈	a				13 05					13 35				14 05				14 35					15 05		
Heathrow Terminal 4 ✈	a																								
West Drayton	d			12 45				13 20					13 45				14 20					14 43			
Iver	d			12 48				13 23					13 48				14 23					14 46			
Langley	d			12 50				13 25					13 50				14 25					14 48			
Slough 3	a		12 41	12 55			13 09	13 30				13 41	13 55			14 09	14 30				14 41	14 53			15 09
	d		12 41	12 56			13 09	13 31				13 42	13 56			14 10	14 31				14 42	14 54			15 09
Burnham	d			13 00				13 35					14 00				14 35					14 58			
Taplow	d			13 03				13 38					14 03				14 38					15 01			
Maidenhead 3	d			13 07				13 42					14 07				14 42					15 05			
Twyford 3	d			13 15				13 50					14 15				14 50					15 13			
Reading 7	a		12 56	13 24			13 25	13 58				13 57	14 23			14 26	14 58				14 56	15 22			15 25
Oxford	a		13 21	14 16			13 51	14 40				14 22	15 15			14 52	15 40				15 21	16 14			15 51

For non-stop services between London and Reading please see table 116

Passengers who hold valid tickets for Acton Main Line, West Ealing and Hanwell will be able to use local Transport for London (TFL) bus services to reach these stations. Tel 0843 222 1234

Table 117

Saturdays

4 January to 8 February

Network Diagram - refer to first Page of Table 116

London - Greenford and Reading

		GW 1	HC	GW 1	GW ◇1 🛒	GW 1	HC	GW 1	GW ◇1	GW 1	HC	GW 1	GW ◇1 ☕	GW 1	HC	GW 1	GW ◇1 🛒	GW 1	HC	GW 1	GW ◇1 ☕	GW 1
London Paddington 15 ⊖	d	14 55	15 03	15 15	15 17	15 23	15 33	15 45	15 46	15 57	16 03	16 15	16 17	16 23	16 33	16 45	16 46	16 57	17 03	17 15	17 17	17 21
Acton Main Line	d			15 21				15 51				16 21				16 51				17 21		
Ealing Broadway ⊖	d	15 03	15 11	15 24		15 31	15 41	15 54		16 05	16 11	16 24		16 31	16 41	16 54		17 05	17 11	17 24		17 29
West Ealing	d		15 13	15 27			15 43	15 57			16 13	16 27			16 43	16 57			17 13	17 27		
Drayton Green	d			15 29				15 59				16 29				16 59				17 29		
Castle Bar Park	d			15 31				16 01				16 31				17 01				17 31		
South Greenford	d			15 34				16 04				16 34				17 04				17 34		
Greenford ⊖	a			15 39				16 09				16 39				17 09				17 39		
Hanwell	d		15 15				15 45				16 15				16 45				17 15			
Southall	d	15 09	15 19			15 37	15 49			16 11	16 19			16 37	16 49			17 11	17 19			17 35
Hayes & Harlington	d	15 13	15 23			15 41	15 53			16 15	16 23			16 41	16 53			17 15	17 23			17 41
Heathrow Terminal 1-2 2 ✈	a		15 35				16 05				16 35				17 05				17 35			
Heathrow Terminal 4 ✈	a																					
West Drayton	d	15 18				15 45				16 20				16 45				17 19				17 45
Iver	d	15 21				15 48				16 23				16 48				17 22				17 48
Langley	d	15 23				15 50				16 25				16 50				17 24				17 50
Slough 3	a	15 28			15 41	15 55			16 09	16 30			16 39	16 55			17 09	17 29			17 39	17 55
	d	15 29			15 42	15 56			16 09	16 31			16 41	16 56			17 10	17 30			17 41	17 56
Burnham	d	15 33				16 00				16 35				17 00				17 34				18 00
Taplow	d	15 36				16 03				16 38				17 03				17 37				18 03
Maidenhead 3	d	15 40				16 07				16 42				17 07				17 41				18 07
Twyford 3	d	15 48				16 15				16 50				17 15				17 49				18 15
Reading 7	a	15 56			15 57	16 23			16 25	16 58			16 55	17 23			17 26	17 57			17 56	18 25
Oxford	a	16 40			16 22	17 17			16 51	17 40			17 21	18 16			17 52	18 40			18 21	19 15

		HC	GW 1	GW ◇1 🛒	GW 1	HC	GW 1	GW ◇1 ☕	GW 1	HC	GW 1	GW ◇1	GW 1	HC	GW 1	GW ◇1	GW 1	HC	GW 1	GW ◇1 🛒	GW 1	HC	GW 1
London Paddington 15 ⊖	d	17 33	17 45	17 46	17 57	18 03	18 15	18 17	18 23	18 33	18 45	18 46	18 56	19 03	19 15	19 18	19 23	19 33	19 45	19 45	19 56	20 03	20 15
Acton Main Line	d		17 51				18 21				18 51				19 21				19 51				20 21
Ealing Broadway ⊖	d	17 41	17 54		18 05	18 11	18 24		18 31	18 41	18 54		19 04	19 11	19 24		19 31	19 41	19 54		20 04	20 11	20 24
West Ealing	d	17 43	17 57			18 13	18 27			18 43	18 57			19 13	19 27			19 43	19 57			20 13	20 27
Drayton Green	d		17 59				18 29				18 59				19 29				19 59				20 29
Castle Bar Park	d		18 01				18 31				19 01				19 31				20 01				20 31
South Greenford	d		18 04				18 34				19 04				19 34				20 04				20 34
Greenford ⊖	a		18 09				18 39				19 09				19 39				20 09				20 39
Hanwell	d	17 45				18 15				18 45				19 15				19 45				20 15	
Southall	d	17 49			18 11	18 19			18 37	18 49			19 10	19 19			19 37	19 49			20 10	20 19	
Hayes & Harlington	d	17 53			18 15	18 23			18 41	18 53			19 14	19 23			19 41	19 53			20 14	20 23	
Heathrow Terminal 1-2 2 ✈	a	18 05				18 35				19 05				19 35				20 05				20 35	
Heathrow Terminal 4 ✈	a																						
West Drayton	d				18 19				18 46				19 18				19 45				20 18		
Iver	d				18 22				18 49				19 21				19 48				20 21		
Langley	d				18 24				18 51				19 23				19 50				20 23		
Slough 3	a			18 09	18 29			18 40	18 56			19 09	19 28			19 41	19 55			20 08	20 28		
	d			18 09	18 30			18 41	18 57			19 10	19 29			19 42	19 56			20 09	20 29		
Burnham	d				18 34				19 01				19 33				20 00				20 33		
Taplow	d				18 37				19 04				19 36				20 03				20 36		
Maidenhead 3	d				18 41				19 08				19 40				20 07				20 40		
Twyford 3	d				18 49				19 16				19 48				20 15				20 48		
Reading 7	a			18 25	18 57			18 55	19 25			19 25	19 56			19 57	20 23			20 24	20 56		
Oxford	a			18 51	19 40			19 22	20 15			19 51	20 40			20 24	21 16			20 50	21 41		

		GW ◇1	GW 1	HC	GW ◇1 🛒	GW 1	GW 1	HC	GW 1	GW ◇1	GW 1	HC	GW ◇1	GW 1	HC	GW 1	GW ◇1	GW 1	GW 1	HC	GW ◇1	GW 1	HC
London Paddington 15 ⊖	d	20 18	20 23	20 33	20 44	20 45	20 57	21 03	21 15	21 18	21 21	21 33	21 44	21 45	22 03	22 12	22 14		22 27	22 33	22 48	22 58	23 03
Acton Main Line	d					20 51			21 21					21 51					22 33				
Ealing Broadway ⊖	d		20 31	20 41		20 54	21 05	21 11	21 24		21 29	21 41		21 55	22 11	22 20			22 37	22 41		23 06	23 11
West Ealing	d			20 43		20 57		21 13	21 27			21 43			22 13					22 43			23 13
Drayton Green	d					20 59			21 29														
Castle Bar Park	d					21 01			21 31														
South Greenford	d					21 04			21 34														
Greenford ⊖	a					21 09			21 39														
Hanwell	d			20 45				21 15				21 45			22 15					22 45			23 15
Southall	d		20 37	20 49			21 11	21 19			21 36	21 49		22 00	22 19	22 28			22 42	22 49		23 12	23 19
Hayes & Harlington	d		20 41	20 53			21 15	21 23			21 39	21 53		22 04	22 23	22 32			22 47	22 53		23 16	23 23
Heathrow Terminal 1-2 2 ✈	a			21 05				21 35				22 05			22 35					23 05			23 35
Heathrow Terminal 4 ✈	a																						23 41
West Drayton	d		20 45				21 19				21 43			22 08		22 36			22 51			23 20	
Iver	d		20 48				21 22				21 47			22 12		22 40			22 55			23 23	
Langley	d		20 50				21 24				21 51			22 15		22 43		←	22 58			23 26	
Slough 3	a	20 41	20 55		21 07		21 29			21 41	21 54		22 07	22 19		22 47	22 37	22 47	23 02		23 11	23 30	
	d	20 42	20 56		21 08		21 30			21 43	21 54		22 08	22 20		22 47	22 38	22 47	23 03		23 11	23 31	
Burnham	d		21 00				21 34				21 59			22 24		→		22 51	23 07			23 34	
Taplow	d		21 03				21 37				22 03			22 27				22 55	23 10			23 38	
Maidenhead 3	d		21 07				21 41				22 07			22 31			22 45	22 59	23 15		23 20	23 42	
Twyford 3	d		21 15				21 49				22 15			22 40				23 07	23 23			23 50	
Reading 7	a	20 57	21 23		21 24		21 57			21 59	22 22		22 23	22 48			22 56	23 15	23 30		23 33	23 58	
Oxford	a	21 23	22 16		21 53		22 43			22 29			22 50	23 44			23 25		00 32		00 05		

For non-stop services between London and Reading please see table 116

Passengers who hold valid tickets for Acton Main Line, West Ealing and Hanwell will be able to use local Transport for London (TFL) bus services to reach these stations. Tel 0843 222 1234

Table 117

Saturdays

4 January to 8 February

Network Diagram - refer to first Page of Table 116

London - Greenford and Reading

		GW ◇1	GW 1
London Paddington 15 ⊖	d	23 30	23 42
Acton Main Line	d		
Ealing Broadway ⊖	d		23 50
West Ealing	d		
Drayton Green	d		
Castle Bar Park	d		
South Greenford	d		
Greenford ⊖	a		
Hanwell	d		
Southall	d		23 56
Hayes & Harlington	d		00 01
Heathrow Terminal 1-2 2 ✈	a		
Heathrow Terminal 4 ✈	a		
West Drayton	d		00 05
Iver	d		
Langley	d		
Slough 3	a	23 53	00 11
	d	23 54	00 12
Burnham	d		00 16
Taplow	d		00 20
Maidenhead 3	d	00 02	00a28
Twyford 3	d		
Reading 7	a	00 15	
Oxford	a	00 54	

Saturdays

15 February to 22 March

		GW 1	GW 1	GW 1	GW 1	GW ◇1	GW 1	GW 1	GW 1	HC		HC	GW ◇1	GW 1	HC	GW 1	GW ◇1	GW 1	HC	GW 1		GW 1	GW ◇1	GW 1	GW 1
London Paddington 15 ⊖	d					00 22	00 34	01 44	03 34	04 42		05 13	05 21	05 25	05 33	05 45	05 50	05 57	06 03	06 12		06 15	06 21		06 27
Acton Main Line	d															05 51						06 21			
Ealing Broadway ⊖	d						00 42	01 52	03 42	04 50		05 21		05 33	05 41	05 54		06 05	06 11	06 20		06 24			06 35
West Ealing	d				00 01										05 43	05 57			06 13			06 27			
Drayton Green	d															05 59						06 29			
Castle Bar Park	d															06 01						06 31			
South Greenford	d															06 04						06 34			
Greenford ⊖	a															06 09						06 39			
Hanwell	d				00 04										05 45				06 15						
Southall	d				00 07		00 47	01 57	03 47	04 54		05 25		05 38	05 49			06 10	06 19	06 28					
Hayes & Harlington	d				00 12		00 51	02 01	03 51	04 58		05 29		05 42	05 53			06 14	06 23	06 32					06 42
Heathrow Terminal 1-2 2 ✈	a									05 04		05 35			06 05				06 35						
Heathrow Terminal 4 ✈	a									05 10		05 41													
West Drayton	d				00 16		00 55	02 05	03 55									06 18		06 36					06 46
Iver	d				00 19													06 21							06 49
Langley	d				00 22		01 00											06 25						←	06 52
Slough 3	a				00 28	00 41	01 05	02 13	04 03				05 37	05 50			06 06	06 29		06 43			06 37	06 43	06 57
	d			00 01	00 28	00 41	01 05	02 13	04 03				05 38	05 51			06 06	06 30		06 43			06 38	06 43	06 57
Burnham	d				00 32		01 09							05 55				06 34		→				06 47	
Taplow	d				00 36		01 13							05 58				06 37						06 51	
Maidenhead 3	d		00 05	00 10	00 41		01 16	02 21	04 11					06 02				06 41						06 55	07 04
Twyford 3	d	00 08	00 13		00 48		01 24	02 29	04 19					06 10				06 49						07 03	07 12
Reading 7	a	00 16	00 22	00 25	00 58	01 01	01 35	02 38	04 30				05 52	06 17			06 22	06 56					06 53	07 11	07 19
Oxford	a		01 18	01 02		01 34							06 22	07 03			06 52	07 43					07 20		08 09

		HC	GW 1	GW 1	GW ◇1	GW 1		GW 1	HC	GW 1	GW 1	GW ◇1	GW 1	GW 1	HC	GW 1		GW 1	GW ◇1	GW 1	GW 1	HC	GW 1	GW 1	GW ◇1 ⊡P
London Paddington 15 ⊖	d	06 33	06 42	06 45	06 50			06 57	07 03	07 12	07 15	07 21		07 27	07 33	07 42		07 45	07 50		07 57	08 03	08 12	08 15	08 21
Acton Main Line	d			06 51							07 21							07 51						08 21	
Ealing Broadway ⊖	d	06 41	06 50	06 54				07 05	07 11	07 20	07 24			07 35	07 41	07 50		07 54			08 05	08 11	08 20	08 24	
West Ealing	d	06 43		06 57					07 13		07 27				07 43			07 57				08 13		08 27	
Drayton Green	d			06 59							07 29							07 59						08 29	
Castle Bar Park	d			07 01							07 31							08 01						08 31	
South Greenford	d			07 04							07 34							08 04						08 34	
Greenford ⊖	a			07 09							07 39							08 09						08 39	
Hanwell	d	06 45							07 15						07 45							08 15			
Southall	d	06 49	06 58						07 19	07 28					07 49	07 58						08 19	08 28		
Hayes & Harlington	d	06 53	07 02					07 12	07 23	07 32				07 42	07 53	08 02					08 12	08 23	08 32		
Heathrow Terminal 1-2 2 ✈	a	07 05							07 35						08 05							08 35			
Heathrow Terminal 4 ✈	a																								
West Drayton	d		07 06					07 16		07 36				07 46		08 06					08 16		08 36		
Iver	d							07 19						07 49							08 19				
Langley	d					←		07 22					←	07 52						←	08 22				
Slough 3	a		07 13		07 06	07 13		07 27		07 43		07 37	07 43	07 57		08 13			08 06	08 13	08 27		08 43		08 38
	d		07 13		07 06	07 13		07 27		07 43		07 38	07 43	07 57		08 13			08 06	08 13	08 27		08 43		08 39
Burnham	d		→			07 17				→			07 47			→				08 17			→		
Taplow	d					07 21							07 51							08 21					
Maidenhead 3	d					07 25		07 34					07 55	08 04						08 25	08 34				
Twyford 3	d					07 33		07 42					08 05	08 12						08 34	08 42				
Reading 7	a				07 22	07 43		07 53				07 53	08 14	08 21					08 22	08 42	08 54				08 53
Oxford	a				07 48			08 40				08 19		09 14					08 48		09 40				09 18

For non-stop services between London and Reading please see table 116

Passengers who hold valid tickets for Acton Main Line, West Ealing and Hanwell will be able to use local Transport for London (TFL) bus services to reach these stations. Tel 0843 222 1234

Table 117

Saturdays

15 February to 22 March

London - Greenford and Reading

Network Diagram - refer to first Page of Table 116

		GW		GW	HC	GW	GW	GW	GW	GW	HC	GW		GW	GW	GW	GW	HC	GW	GW	GW	GW		GW	HC
		1		1		1	1	◇1	1	1		1		1	◇1	1	1		1	1	◇1	1		1	
London Paddington 15 ⊖	d			08 27	08 33	08 42	08 45	08 50		08 57	09 03	09 12		09 15	09 21		09 27	09 33	09 42	09 45	09 50			09 57	10 03
Acton Main Line	d						08 51							09 21						09 51					
Ealing Broadway ⊖	d			08 35	08 41	08 50	08 54			09 05	09 11	09 20		09 24			09 35	09 41	09 50	09 54				10 05	10 11
West Ealing	d				08 43		08 57				09 13			09 27				09 43		09 57					10 13
Drayton Green	d						08 59							09 29						09 59					
Castle Bar Park	d						09 01							09 31						10 01					
South Greenford	d						09 04							09 34						10 04					
Greenford ⊖	a						09 09							09 39						10 09					
Hanwell	d				08 45						09 15							09 45							10 15
Southall	d				08 49	08 58					09 19	09 28						09 49	09 58						10 19
Hayes & Harlington	d			08 42	08 53	09 02				09 12	09 23	09 32					09 42	09 53	10 02					10 12	10 23
Heathrow Terminal 1-2 2 ✈	a				09 05						09 35							10 05							10 35
Heathrow Terminal 4 ✈	a																								
West Drayton	d			08 46		09 06				09 16		09 36					09 46		10 06					10 16	
Iver	d			08 49						09 19							09 49							10 19	
Langley	d	←		08 52					←	09 22						←	09 52					←		10 22	
Slough 3	a	08 43		08 57		09 13		09 06	09 13	09 27		09 43			09 38	09 43	09 57		10 13		10 06	10 13		10 27	
	d	08 43		08 57		09 13		09 06	09 13	09 27		09 43			09 39	09 43	09 57		10 13		10 06	10 13		10 27	
Burnham	d	08 47				→			09 17			→				09 47			→			10 17			
Taplow	d	08 51							09 21							09 51						10 21			
Maidenhead 3	d	08 55		09 04					09 25	09 34						09 55	10 04					10 25		10 34	
Twyford 3	d	09 03		09 12					09 35	09 42						10 04	10 14					10 33		10 44	
Reading 7	a	09 12		09 23				09 22	09 45	09 52					09 54	10 13	10 23				10 22	10 41		10 53	
Oxford	a			10 14				09 48		10 40					10 19		11 14				10 48			11 40	

		GW	GW	GW	GW	GW	HC	GW		GW	GW	GW	GW	HC	GW	GW	GW	GW		GW	HC	GW	GW	GW	GW
		1	1	◇1 ⊐	1	1		1		1	◇1 ⊥	1	1		1	1	◇1 ⊥	1		1		1	1	◇1	1
London Paddington 15 ⊖	d	10 12	10 15	10 21		10 27	10 33	10 42		10 45	10 50		10 57	11 03	11 12	11 15	11 21			11 27	11 33	11 42	11 45	11 50	
Acton Main Line	d		10 21							10 51						11 21							11 51		
Ealing Broadway ⊖	d	10 20	10 24			10 35	10 41	10 52		10 54			11 05	11 11	11 20	11 24				11 35	11 41	11 50	11 54		
West Ealing	d		10 27				10 43			10 57				11 13		11 27					11 43		11 57		
Drayton Green	d		10 29							10 59						11 29							11 59		
Castle Bar Park	d		10 31							11 01						11 31							12 01		
South Greenford	d		10 34							11 04						11 34							12 04		
Greenford ⊖	a		10 39							11 09						11 39							12 09		
Hanwell	d						10 45							11 15							11 45				
Southall	d	10 28					10 49	10 58						11 19	11 28						11 49	11 58			
Hayes & Harlington	d	10 32				10 42	10 53	11 02					11 12	11 23	11 32					11 42	11 53	12 02			
Heathrow Terminal 1-2 2 ✈	a						11 05							11 35							12 05				
Heathrow Terminal 4 ✈	a																								
West Drayton	d	10 36				10 46		11 06					11 16		11 36					11 46		12 06			
Iver	d					10 49							11 19							11 49					
Langley	d				←	10 52						←	11 22					←		11 52					←
Slough 3	a	10 43		10 38	10 43	10 57		11 13			11 06	11 13	11 27		11 43		11 38	11 43		11 57		12 13		12 06	12 13
	d	10 43		10 39	10 43	10 57		11 13			11 06	11 13	11 27		11 43		11 39	11 43		11 57		12 13		12 06	12 13
Burnham	d	→			10 47			→				11 17			→			11 47				→			12 17
Taplow	d				10 51							11 21						11 51							12 21
Maidenhead 3	d				10 55	11 04						11 25	11 34					11 55		12 04					12 25
Twyford 3	d				11 03	11 12						11 33	11 42					12 03		12 12					12 33
Reading 7	a			10 53	11 14	11 21					11 22	11 41	11 52				11 54	12 11		12 21				12 22	12 41
Oxford	a			11 19		12 14					11 48		12 40				12 20			13 14				12 48	

		GW	HC	GW		GW	GW	GW	GW	HC	GW	GW	GW	GW		GW	HC	GW	GW	GW	GW	GW	HC	GW	
		1		1		1	◇1	1	1		1	1	◇1 ⊥	1		1		1	1	◇1 ⊥	1	1		1	
London Paddington 15 ⊖	d	11 57	12 03	12 12		12 15	12 21		12 27	12 33	12 42	12 45	12 50			12 57	13 03	13 12	13 15	13 21		13 27	13 33	13 42	
Acton Main Line	d					12 21						12 51							13 21						
Ealing Broadway ⊖	d	12 05	12 11	12 20		12 24			12 35	12 41	12 50	12 54				13 05	13 11	13 20	13 24			13 35	13 41	13 50	
West Ealing	d		12 13			12 27				12 43		12 57					13 13		13 27				13 43		
Drayton Green	d					12 29						12 59							13 29						
Castle Bar Park	d					12 31						13 01							13 31						
South Greenford	d					12 34						13 04							13 34						
Greenford ⊖	a					12 39						13 09							13 39						
Hanwell	d		12 15							12 45							13 15						13 45		
Southall	d		12 19	12 28						12 49	12 58						13 19	13 28					13 49	13 58	
Hayes & Harlington	d	12 12	12 23	12 32					12 42	12 53	13 02					13 12	13 23	13 32				13 42	13 53	14 02	
Heathrow Terminal 1-2 2 ✈	a		12 35							13 05							13 35						14 05		
Heathrow Terminal 4 ✈	a																								
West Drayton	d	12 16		12 36					12 46		13 06					13 16		13 36				13 46		14 06	
Iver	d	12 19							12 49							13 19						13 49			
Langley	d	12 22						←	12 52					←		13 22					←	13 52			
Slough 3	a	12 27		12 43			12 39	12 43	12 57		13 13		13 06	13 13		13 27		13 43		13 38	13 43	13 57		14 13	
	d	12 27		12 43			12 39	12 43	12 57		13 13		13 06	13 13		13 27		13 43		13 39	13 43	13 57		14 13	
Burnham	d			→				12 47			→			13 17				→			13 47			→	
Taplow	d							12 51						13 21							13 51				
Maidenhead 3	d	12 34						12 55	13 04					13 25		13 34					13 55	14 04			
Twyford 3	d	12 45						13 03	13 12					13 33		13 42					14 06	14 12			
Reading 7	a	12 53					12 54	13 11	13 21				13 22	13 43		13 51				13 54	14 14	14 21			
Oxford	a	13 40					13 19		14 14				13 48			14 40				14 19		15 14			

For non-stop services between London and Reading please see table 116

Passengers who hold valid tickets for Acton Main Line, West Ealing and Hanwell will be able to use local Transport for London (TFL) bus services to reach these stations. Tel 0843 222 1234

Table 117

Saturdays

15 February to 22 March

Network Diagram - refer to first Page of Table 116

London - Greenford and Reading

		GW	GW	GW	GW	HC	GW	GW	GW	GW		GW	HC	GW	GW	GW	GW	GW	HC	GW		GW	GW	GW	GW
		1	◇1 🛒	1	1		1	1	◇1 🛒	1		1		1	1	◇1	1	1		1		1	◇1 🛒	1	1
London Paddington 15 ⊖	d	13 45	13 50		13 57	14 03	14 12	14 15	14 21			14 27	14 33	14 42	14 45	14 50		14 57	15 03	15 12		15 15	15 21		15 27
Acton Main Line	d	13 51						14 21							14 51							15 21			
Ealing Broadway ⊖	d	13 54			14 05	14 11	14 20	14 24				14 35	14 41	14 50	14 54			15 05	15 11	15 20		15 24			15 35
West Ealing	d	13 57				14 13		14 27					14 43		14 57				15 13			15 27			
Drayton Green	d	13 59						14 29							14 59							15 29			
Castle Bar Park	d	14 01						14 31							15 01							15 31			
South Greenford	d	14 04						14 34							15 04							15 34			
Greenford ⊖	a	14 09						14 39							15 09							15 39			
Hanwell	d					14 15							14 45						15 15						
Southall	d					14 19	14 28						14 49	14 58					15 19	15 28					
Hayes & Harlington	d				14 12	14 23	14 32					14 42	14 53	15 02				15 12	15 23	15 32					15 42
Heathrow Terminal 1-2 2 ✈	a					14 35							15 05						15 35						
Heathrow Terminal 4 ✈	a																								
West Drayton	d				14 16		14 36					14 46		15 06				15 16		15 36					15 46
Iver	d				14 19							14 49						15 19							15 49
Langley	d			←	14 22					←		14 52					←	15 22						←	15 52
Slough 3	a		14 06	14 13	14 27		14 43		14 38	14 43		14 57		15 13		15 06	15 13	15 27		15 43			15 38	15 43	15 57
	d		14 06	14 13	14 27		14 43		14 39	14 43		14 57		15 13		15 06	15 13	15 27		15 43			15 39	15 43	15 57
Burnham	d			14 17			→			14 47				→			15 17			→				15 47	
Taplow	d			14 21						14 51							15 21							15 51	
Maidenhead 3	d			14 25	14 34					14 55		15 04					15 25	15 34						15 55	16 04
Twyford 3	d			14 37	14 45					15 03		15 12					15 33	15 42						16 06	16 13
Reading 7	a		14 22	14 46	14 53				14 53	15 13		15 22				15 22	15 43	15 52					15 54	16 14	16 22
Oxford	a		14 48		15 40				15 18			16 14				15 48		16 40					16 19		17 14

		HC	GW	GW	GW	GW		GW	HC	GW	GW	GW	GW	GW	HC	GW		GW	GW	GW	GW	HC	GW	GW	GW
			1	1	◇1	1		1		1	1	◇1 ☕	1	1		1		1	◇1 🛒	1	1		1	1	◇1 ☕
London Paddington 15 ⊖	d	15 33	15 42	15 45	15 50			15 57	16 03	16 12	16 15	16 21		16 27	16 33	16 42		16 45	16 50		16 57	17 03	17 12	17 15	17 21
Acton Main Line	d			15 51							16 21							16 51						17 21	
Ealing Broadway ⊖	d	15 41	15 50	15 54				16 05	16 11	16 20	16 24			16 35	16 41	16 50		16 54			17 05	17 11	17 20	17 24	
West Ealing	d	15 43		15 57					16 13		16 27				16 43			16 57				17 13		17 27	
Drayton Green	d			15 59							16 29							16 59						17 29	
Castle Bar Park	d			16 01							16 31							17 01						17 31	
South Greenford	d			16 04							16 34							17 04						17 34	
Greenford ⊖	a			16 09							16 39							17 09						17 39	
Hanwell	d	15 45							16 15						16 45							17 15			
Southall	d	15 49	15 58						16 19	16 28					16 49	16 58						17 19	17 28		
Hayes & Harlington	d	15 53	16 02					16 12	16 23	16 32				16 42	16 53	17 02					17 12	17 23	17 32		
Heathrow Terminal 1-2 2 ✈	a	16 05							16 35						17 05							17 35			
Heathrow Terminal 4 ✈	a																								
West Drayton	d		16 06					16 16		16 36				16 46		17 06					17 16		17 36		
Iver	d							16 19						16 49							17 19				
Langley	d					←		16 22					←	16 52						←	17 22				
Slough 3	a		16 13		16 06	16 13		16 27		16 43		16 37	16 43	16 57		17 13			17 06	17 13	17 27		17 43		17 38
	d		16 13		16 06	16 13		16 27		16 43		16 38	16 43	16 57		17 13			17 06	17 13	17 27		17 43		17 39
Burnham	d		→			16 17				→			16 47			→				17 17			→		
Taplow	d					16 21							16 51							17 21					
Maidenhead 3	d					16 25		16 34					16 55	17 04						17 25	17 34				
Twyford 3	d					16 33		16 45					17 03	17 12						17 33	17 42				
Reading 7	a				16 22	16 41		16 53				16 52	17 12	17 21					17 22	17 41	17 51				17 53
Oxford	a				16 48			17 40				17 18		18 14					17 48		18 40				18 18

		GW		GW	HC	GW	GW	GW	GW	GW	HC	GW		GW	GW	GW	GW	HC	GW	GW	GW	GW		GW	HC
		1		1		1	1	◇1 🛒	1	1		1		1	◇1 ☕	1	1		1	1	◇1	1		1	
London Paddington 15 ⊖	d			17 27	17 33	17 42	17 45	17 50		17 57	18 03	18 12		18 15	18 21		18 27	18 33	18 42	18 45	18 50			18 57	19 03
Acton Main Line	d						17 51							18 21						18 51					
Ealing Broadway ⊖	d			17 35	17 41	17 50	17 54			18 05	18 11	18 20		18 24			18 35	18 41	18 50	18 54				19 05	19 11
West Ealing	d				17 43		17 57				18 13			18 27				18 43		18 57					19 13
Drayton Green	d						17 59							18 29						18 59					
Castle Bar Park	d						18 01							18 31						19 01					
South Greenford	d						18 04							18 34						19 04					
Greenford ⊖	a						18 09							18 39						19 09					
Hanwell	d				17 45						18 15							18 45							19 15
Southall	d				17 49	17 58					18 19	18 28						18 49	18 58						19 19
Hayes & Harlington	d			17 42	17 53	18 02				18 12	18 23	18 32					18 42	18 53	19 02					19 12	19 23
Heathrow Terminal 1-2 2 ✈	a				18 05						18 35							19 05							19 35
Heathrow Terminal 4 ✈	a																								
West Drayton	d			17 46		18 06				18 16		18 36					18 46		19 06					19 16	
Iver	d			17 49						18 19							18 49							19 19	
Langley	d	←		17 52					←	18 22						←	18 52					←		19 22	
Slough 3	a	17 43		17 57		18 13		18 06	18 13	18 27		18 43			18 37	18 43	18 57		19 13		19 06	19 13		19 27	
	d	17 43		17 57		18 13		18 06	18 13	18 27		18 43			18 38	18 43	18 57		19 13		19 06	19 13		19 27	
Burnham	d	17 47				→			18 17			→				18 47			→			19 17			
Taplow	d	17 51							18 21							18 51						19 21			
Maidenhead 3	d	17 55		18 04					18 25	18 34						18 55	19 04					19 25		19 34	
Twyford 3	d	18 03		18 12					18 33	18 45						19 03	19 12					19 33		19 42	
Reading 7	a	18 11		18 22				18 22	18 41	18 53					18 52	19 12	19 21				19 22	19 43		19 51	
Oxford	a			19 14				18 48		19 40					19 18		20 14				19 48			20 41	

For non-stop services between London and Reading please see table 116

Passengers who hold valid tickets for Acton Main Line, West Ealing and Hanwell will be able to use local Transport for London (TFL) bus services to reach these stations. Tel 0843 222 1234

Table 117

Saturdays

15 February to 22 March

London - Greenford and Reading

Network Diagram - refer to first Page of Table 116

		GW 1	GW 1	GW ◇1	GW 1	GW 1	HC	GW 1		GW 1	GW ◇1 ⌶	GW 1	GW 1	HC	GW 1	GW 1	GW ◇1	GW 1		GW 1	HC	GW 1	GW 1	GW ◇1 ⌶	GW 1
London Paddington 15 ⊖	d	19 12	19 15	19 21		19 27	19 33	19 42		19 45	19 50		19 57	20 03	20 12	20 15	20 18			20 27	20 33	20 42	20 45	20 48	
Acton Main Line	d		19 21							19 51						20 21							20 51		
Ealing Broadway ⊖	d	19 20	19 24			19 35	19 41	19 50		19 54			20 05	20 11	20 20	20 24				20 35	20 41	20 50	20 54		
West Ealing	d		19 27				19 43			19 57				20 13		20 27					20 43		20 57		
Drayton Green	d		19 29							19 59						20 29							20 59		
Castle Bar Park	d		19 31							20 01						20 31							21 01		
South Greenford	d		19 34							20 04						20 34							21 04		
Greenford ⊖	a		19 39							20 09						20 39							21 09		
Hanwell	d						19 45							20 15							20 45				
Southall	d	19 28					19 49	19 58						20 19	20 28						20 49	20 58			
Hayes & Harlington	d	19 32				19 42	19 53	20 02					20 12	20 23	20 32					20 42	20 53	21 02			
Heathrow Terminal 1-2 2 ✈	a						20 05							20 35							21 05				
Heathrow Terminal 4 ✈	a																								
West Drayton	d	19 36				19 46		20 06					20 16		20 36					20 46		21 06			
Iver	d					19 49							20 19							20 49					
Langley	d				←	19 52						←	20 22					←		20 52					←
Slough 3	a	19 43		19 37	19 43	19 57		20 13			20 06	20 13	20 27		20 43		20 34	20 43		20 57		21 13		21 04	21 13
	d	19 43		19 38	19 43	19 57		20 13			20 06	20 13	20 27		20 43		20 35	20 43		20 57		21 13		21 05	21 13
Burnham	d	→			19 47			→				20 17			→			20 47				→			21 17
Taplow	d				19 51							20 21						20 51							21 21
Maidenhead 3	d				19 55	20 04						20 25	20 34					20 55		21 04					21 25
Twyford 3	d				20 03	20 12						20 36	20 42					21 06		21 12					21 33
Reading 7	a			19 53	20 13	20 20					20 21	20 45	20 52				20 50	21 15		21 20				21 21	21 43
Oxford	a			20 20		21 14					20 47		21 40				21 18			22 14				21 50	

		GW 1	HC	GW 1		GW 1	GW ◇1	GW 1	HC	GW 1	GW ◇1	GW 1	HC	GW 1		GW ◇1	GW 1	HC	GW 1	GW ◇1	GW 1	HC	GW 1	GW ◇1	
London Paddington 15 ⊖	d	20 57	21 03	21 12		21 15	21 18		21 33	21 42	21 48		22 03	22 12		22 18		22 33	22 42	22 48		23 03	23 15	23 33	
Acton Main Line	d					21 21				21 48									22 48						
Ealing Broadway ⊖	d	21 05	21 11	21 20		21 24			21 41	21 52			22 11	22 20				22 41	22 52			23 11	23 23		
West Ealing	d		21 13			21 27			21 43				22 13					22 43				23 13			
Drayton Green	d					21 29																			
Castle Bar Park	d					21 31																			
South Greenford	d					21 34																			
Greenford ⊖	a					21 39																			
Hanwell	d		21 15						21 45				22 15					22 45				23 15			
Southall	d		21 19	21 28					21 49	21 58			22 19	22 28				22 49	22 58			23 19	23 29		
Hayes & Harlington	d	21 12	21 23	21 32					21 53	22 02			22 23	22 32				22 53	23 02			23 23	23 33		
Heathrow Terminal 1-2 2 ✈	a		21 35						22 05				22 35					23 05				23 35			
Heathrow Terminal 4 ✈	a																					23 41			
West Drayton	d	21 16		21 36						22 06				22 36					23 06				23 37		
Iver	d	21 19		21 40						22 10				22 40					23 10				23 40		
Langley	d	21 22		21 43				←		22 13		←		22 43			←		23 13		←		23 43		
Slough 3	a	21 27		21 47			21 34	21 47		22 17	22 05	22 17		22 47		22 34	22 47		23 17	23 04	23 17		23 47	23 49	
	d	21 27		21 47			21 35	21 47		22 18	22 05	22 18		22 47		22 35	22 47		23 20	23 05	23 20		23 54	23 50	
Burnham	d			→				21 52		→		22 22		→			22 51		→		23 24		→		
Taplow	d							21 55				22 25					22 55				23 27				
Maidenhead 3	d	21 34						21 59				22 29				22 42	22 59			23 13	23 32			23 58	
Twyford 3	d	21 46						22 07				22 38					23 07				23 40				
Reading 7	a	21 55					21 51	22 15			22 20	22 46				22 53	23 19			23 25	23 47			00 11	
Oxford	a	22 43					22 22				22 48	23 43				23 23				23 58	00 32			00 50	

		GW 1	GW 1
London Paddington 15 ⊖	d		23 42
Acton Main Line	d		
Ealing Broadway ⊖	d		23 50
West Ealing	d		
Drayton Green	d		
Castle Bar Park	d		
South Greenford	d		
Greenford ⊖	a		
Hanwell	d		
Southall	d		23 56
Hayes & Harlington	d		00 01
Heathrow Terminal 1-2 2 ✈	a		
Heathrow Terminal 4 ✈	a		
West Drayton	d		00 05
Iver	d		
Langley	d	←	
Slough 3	a	23 47	00 11
	d	23 54	00 12
Burnham	d	23 57	00 16
Taplow	d	00 01	00 20
Maidenhead 3	d	00 05	00a23
Twyford 3	d	00 13	
Reading 7	a	00 21	
Oxford	a		

For non-stop services between London and Reading please see table 116

Passengers who hold valid tickets for Acton Main Line, West Ealing and Hanwell will be able to use local Transport for London (TFL) bus services to reach these stations. Tel 0843 222 1234

Table 117

Saturdays

29 March to 17 May

Network Diagram - refer to first Page of Table 116

London - Greenford and Reading

		GW 1	GW 1	GW 1	GW 1	GW ◇1	GW 1	GW 1	GW 1	HC		HC	GW ◇1	GW 1	HC	GW 1	GW ◇1	GW 1	HC	GW 1		GW 1	GW ◇1	GW 1	GW 1
London Paddington 15 ⊖	d					00 22	00 34	01 44	03 34	04 42		05 13	05 21	05 25	05 33	05 45	05 50	05 57	06 03	06 12		06 15	06 21		06 27
Acton Main Line	d															05 51						06 21			
Ealing Broadway ⊖	d						00 42	01 52	03 42	04 50		05 21		05 33	05 41	05 54		06 05	06 11	06 20		06 24			06 35
West Ealing	d				00 01										05 43	05 57			06 13			06 27			
Drayton Green	d															05 59						06 29			
Castle Bar Park	d															06 01						06 31			
South Greenford	d															06 04						06 34			
Greenford ⊖	a															06 09						06 39			
Hanwell	d				00 04										05 45				06 15						
Southall	d				00 07		00 47	01 57	03 47	04 54		05 25		05 38	05 49			06 10	06 19	06 28					
Hayes & Harlington	d				00 12		00 51	02 01	03 51	04 58		05 29		05 42	05 53			06 14	06 23	06 32					06 42
Heathrow Terminal 1-2 2 ✈	a									05 04		05 35			06 05				06 35						
Heathrow Terminal 4 ✈	a									05 10		05 41													
West Drayton	d				00 16		00 55	02 05	03 55									06 18		06 36					06 46
Iver	d				00 19													06 21							06 49
Langley	d				00 22		01 00											06 25						←	06 52
Slough 3	a				00 28	00 41	01 05	02 13	04 03				05 37	05 50			06 06	06 29		06 43			06 37	06 43	06 57
	d			00 01	00 28	00 41	01 05	02 13	04 03				05 38	05 51			06 06	06 30		06 43			06 38	06 43	06 57
Burnham	d				00 32		01 09							05 55				06 34		→				06 47	
Taplow	d				00 36		01 13							05 58				06 37						06 51	
Maidenhead 3	d		00 05	00 10	00 41		01 16	02 21	04 11					06 02				06 41						06 55	07 04
Twyford 3	d	00 08	00 13		00 48		01 24	02 29	04 19					06 10				06 49						07 03	07 12
Reading 7	a	00 16	00 22	00 25	00 58	01 01	01 35	02 38	04 30				05 52	06 17			06 22	06 56					06 53	07 11	07 19
Oxford	a		01 18	01 02		01 34							06 22	07 03			06 52	07 43					07 20		08 09

		HC	GW 1	GW 1	GW ◇1	GW 1		GW 1	HC	GW 1	GW 1	GW ◇1	GW 1	GW 1	HC	GW 1		GW 1	GW ◇1	GW 1	GW 1	HC	GW 1	GW 1	GW ◇1 ⊡
London Paddington 15 ⊖	d	06 33	06 42	06 45	06 50			06 57	07 03	07 12	07 15	07 21		07 27	07 33	07 42		07 45	07 50		07 57	08 03	08 12	08 15	08 21
Acton Main Line	d			06 51							07 21							07 51						08 21	
Ealing Broadway ⊖	d	06 41	06 50	06 54				07 05	07 11	07 20	07 24			07 35	07 41	07 50		07 54			08 05	08 11	08 20	08 24	
West Ealing	d	06 43		06 57					07 13		07 27				07 43			07 57				08 13		08 27	
Drayton Green	d			06 59							07 29							07 59						08 29	
Castle Bar Park	d			07 01							07 31							08 01						08 31	
South Greenford	d			07 04							07 34							08 04						08 34	
Greenford ⊖	a			07 09							07 39							08 09						08 39	
Hanwell	d	06 45							07 15						07 45							08 15			
Southall	d	06 49	06 58						07 19	07 28					07 49	07 58						08 19	08 28		
Hayes & Harlington	d	06 53	07 02					07 12	07 23	07 32				07 42	07 53	08 02					08 12	08 23	08 32		
Heathrow Terminal 1-2 2 ✈	a	07 05							07 35						08 05							08 35			
Heathrow Terminal 4 ✈	a																								
West Drayton	d		07 06					07 16		07 36				07 46		08 06					08 16		08 36		
Iver	d							07 19						07 49							08 19				
Langley	d					←		07 22					←	07 52						←	08 22				
Slough 3	a		07 13		07 06	07 13		07 27		07 43		07 37	07 43	07 57		08 13			08 06	08 13	08 27		08 43		08 38
	d		07 13		07 06	07 13		07 27		07 43		07 38	07 43	07 57		08 13			08 06	08 13	08 27		08 43		08 39
Burnham	d		→			07 17				→			07 47			→				08 17			→		
Taplow	d					07 21							07 51							08 21					
Maidenhead 3	d					07 25		07 34					07 55	08 04						08 25	08 34				
Twyford 3	d					07 33		07 42					08 05	08 12						08 34	08 42				
Reading 7	a				07 22	07 43		07 53				07 53	08 14	08 21					08 22	08 42	08 54				08 53
Oxford	a				07 48			08 40				08 19		09 14					08 48		09 40				09 18

		GW 1		GW 1	HC	GW 1	GW 1	GW ◇1	GW 1	GW 1	HC	GW 1		GW 1	GW ◇1	GW 1	GW 1	HC	GW 1	GW 1	GW ◇1	GW 1		GW 1	HC
London Paddington 15 ⊖	d			08 27	08 33	08 42	08 45	08 50		08 57	09 03	09 12		09 15	09 21		09 27	09 33	09 42	09 45	09 50			09 57	10 03
Acton Main Line	d						08 51							09 21						09 51					
Ealing Broadway ⊖	d			08 35	08 41	08 50	08 54			09 05	09 11	09 20		09 24			09 35	09 41	09 50	09 54				10 05	10 11
West Ealing	d				08 43		08 57				09 13			09 27				09 43		09 57					10 13
Drayton Green	d						08 59							09 29						09 59					
Castle Bar Park	d						09 01							09 31						10 01					
South Greenford	d						09 04							09 34						10 04					
Greenford ⊖	a						09 09							09 39						10 09					
Hanwell	d				08 45						09 15							09 45							10 15
Southall	d				08 49	08 58					09 19	09 28						09 49	09 58						10 19
Hayes & Harlington	d			08 42	08 53	09 02				09 12	09 23	09 32					09 42	09 53	10 02					10 12	10 23
Heathrow Terminal 1-2 2 ✈	a				09 05						09 35							10 05							10 35
Heathrow Terminal 4 ✈	a																								
West Drayton	d			08 46		09 06				09 16		09 36					09 46		10 06					10 16	
Iver	d			08 49						09 19							09 49							10 19	
Langley	d	←		08 52					←	09 22						←	09 52					←		10 22	
Slough 3	a	08 43		08 57		09 13		09 06	09 13	09 27		09 43			09 38	09 43	09 57		10 13		10 06	10 13		10 27	
	d	08 43		08 57		09 13		09 06	09 13	09 27		09 43			09 39	09 43	09 57		10 13		10 06	10 13		10 27	
Burnham	d	08 47				→			09 17			→				09 47			→			10 17			
Taplow	d	08 51							09 21							09 51						10 21			
Maidenhead 3	d	08 55		09 04					09 25	09 34						09 55	10 04					10 25		10 34	
Twyford 3	d	09 03		09 12					09 35	09 42						10 04	10 14					10 33		10 44	
Reading 7	a	09 12		09 23				09 22	09 45	09 52					09 54	10 13	10 23				10 22	10 41		10 53	
Oxford	a			10 14				09 48		10 40					10 19		11 14				10 48			11 40	

For non-stop services between London and Reading please see table 116

Passengers who hold valid tickets for Acton Main Line, West Ealing and Hanwell will be able to use local Transport for London (TFL) bus services to reach these stations. Tel 0843 222 1234

Table 117

Saturdays

29 March to 17 May

London - Greenford and Reading

Network Diagram - refer to first Page of Table 116

		GW 1	GW 1	GW ◇1	GW 1	GW 1	HC	GW 1		GW 1	GW ◇1 ⚯	GW 1	GW 1	HC	GW 1	GW 1	GW ◇1 ⚯	GW 1		GW 1	HC	GW 1	GW 1	GW ◇1	GW 1
London Paddington 15 ⊖	d	10 12	10 15	10 21		10 27	10 33	10 42		10 45	10 50		10 57	11 03	11 12	11 15	11 21			11 27	11 33	11 42	11 45	11 50	
Acton Main Line	d		10 21							10 51						11 21							11 51		
Ealing Broadway ⊖	d	10 20	10 24			10 35	10 41	10 52		10 54			11 05	11 11	11 20	11 24				11 35	11 41	11 50	11 54		
West Ealing	d		10 27				10 43			10 57				11 13		11 27					11 43		11 57		
Drayton Green	d		10 29							10 59						11 29							11 59		
Castle Bar Park	d		10 31							11 01						11 31							12 01		
South Greenford	d		10 34							11 04						11 34							12 04		
Greenford ⊖	a		10 39							11 09						11 39							12 09		
Hanwell	d						10 45							11 15							11 45				
Southall	d	10 28					10 49	10 58						11 19	11 28						11 49	11 58			
Hayes & Harlington	d	10 32				10 42	10 53	11 02					11 12	11 23	11 32					11 42	11 53	12 02			
Heathrow Terminal 1-2 2 ✈	a						11 05							11 35							12 05				
Heathrow Terminal 4 ✈	a																								
West Drayton	d	10 36				10 46		11 06					11 16		11 36					11 46		12 06			
Iver	d					10 49							11 19							11 49					
Langley	d				←	10 52						←	11 22					←		11 52					←
Slough 3	a	10 43		10 38	10 43	10 57		11 13			11 06	11 13	11 27		11 43		11 38	11 43		11 57		12 13		12 06	12 13
	d	10 43		10 39	10 43	10 57		11 13			11 06	11 13	11 27		11 43		11 39	11 43		11 57		12 13		12 06	12 13
Burnham	d	→			10 47			→				11 17			→			11 47				→			12 17
Taplow	d				10 51							11 21						11 51							12 21
Maidenhead 3	d				10 55	11 04						11 25	11 34					11 55		12 04					12 25
Twyford 3	d				11 03	11 12						11 33	11 42					12 03		12 12					12 33
Reading 7	a			10 53	11 14	11 21					11 22	11 41	11 52				11 54	12 11		12 21				12 22	12 41
Oxford	a			11 19		12 14					11 48		12 40				12 20			13 14				12 48	

		GW 1	HC	GW 1		GW 1	GW ◇1	GW 1	GW 1	HC	GW 1	GW 1	GW ◇1 ⚯	GW 1		GW 1	HC	GW 1	GW 1	GW ◇1 ⚯	GW 1	GW 1	HC	GW 1	
London Paddington 15 ⊖	d	11 57	12 03	12 12		12 15	12 21		12 27	12 33	12 42	12 45	12 50			12 57	13 03	13 12	13 15	13 21		13 27	13 33	13 42	
Acton Main Line	d					12 21						12 51							13 21						
Ealing Broadway ⊖	d	12 05	12 11	12 20		12 24			12 35	12 41	12 50	12 54				13 05	13 11	13 20	13 24			13 35	13 41	13 50	
West Ealing	d		12 13			12 27				12 43		12 57					13 13		13 27				13 43		
Drayton Green	d					12 29						12 59							13 29						
Castle Bar Park	d					12 31						13 01							13 31						
South Greenford	d					12 34						13 04							13 34						
Greenford ⊖	a					12 39						13 09							13 39						
Hanwell	d		12 15							12 45							13 15						13 45		
Southall	d		12 19	12 28						12 49	12 58						13 19	13 28					13 49	13 58	
Hayes & Harlington	d	12 12	12 23	12 32					12 42	12 53	13 02					13 12	13 23	13 32				13 42	13 53	14 02	
Heathrow Terminal 1-2 2 ✈	a		12 35							13 05							13 35						14 05		
Heathrow Terminal 4 ✈	a																								
West Drayton	d	12 16		12 36					12 46		13 06					13 16		13 36				13 46		14 06	
Iver	d	12 19							12 49							13 19						13 49			
Langley	d	12 22						←	12 52					←		13 22					←	13 52			
Slough 3	a	12 27		12 43			12 39	12 43	12 57		13 13		13 06	13 13		13 27		13 43		13 38	13 43	13 57		14 13	
	d	12 27		12 43			12 39	12 43	12 57		13 13		13 06	13 13		13 27		13 43		13 39	13 43	13 57		14 13	
Burnham	d			→				12 47			→			13 17				→			13 47			→	
Taplow	d							12 51						13 21							13 51				
Maidenhead 3	d	12 34						12 55	13 04					13 25		13 34					13 55	14 04			
Twyford 3	d	12 45						13 03	13 12					13 33		13 42					14 06	14 12			
Reading 7	a	12 53					12 54	13 11	13 21				13 22	13 43		13 51				13 54	14 14	14 21			
Oxford	a	13 40					13 19		14 14				13 48			14 40				14 19		15 14			

		GW 1	GW ◇1 ⚯	GW 1	GW 1	HC	GW 1	GW 1	GW ◇1 ⚯	GW 1		GW 1	HC	GW 1	GW 1	GW ◇1	GW 1	GW 1	HC	GW 1		GW 1	GW ◇1 ⚯	GW 1	GW 1
London Paddington 15 ⊖	d	13 45	13 50		13 57	14 03	14 12	14 15	14 21			14 27	14 33	14 42	14 45	14 50		14 57	15 03	15 12		15 15	15 21		15 27
Acton Main Line	d	13 51						14 21							14 51							15 21			
Ealing Broadway ⊖	d	13 54			14 05	14 11	14 20	14 24				14 35	14 41	14 50	14 54			15 05	15 11	15 20		15 24			15 35
West Ealing	d	13 57				14 13		14 27					14 43		14 57				15 13			15 27			
Drayton Green	d	13 59						14 29							14 59							15 29			
Castle Bar Park	d	14 01						14 31							15 01							15 31			
South Greenford	d	14 04						14 34							15 04							15 34			
Greenford ⊖	a	14 09						14 39							15 09							15 39			
Hanwell	d					14 15							14 45						15 15						
Southall	d					14 19	14 28						14 49	14 58					15 19	15 28					
Hayes & Harlington	d				14 12	14 23	14 32					14 42	14 53	15 02				15 12	15 23	15 32					15 42
Heathrow Terminal 1-2 2 ✈	a					14 35							15 05						15 35						
Heathrow Terminal 4 ✈	a																								
West Drayton	d				14 16		14 36					14 46		15 06				15 16		15 36					15 46
Iver	d				14 19							14 49						15 19							15 49
Langley	d			←	14 22					←		14 52					←	15 22						←	15 52
Slough 3	a		14 06	14 13	14 27		14 43		14 38	14 43		14 57		15 13		15 06	15 13	15 27		15 43			15 38	15 43	15 57
	d		14 06	14 13	14 27		14 43		14 39	14 43		14 57		15 13		15 06	15 13	15 27		15 43			15 39	15 43	15 57
Burnham	d			14 17			→			14 47				→			15 17			→				15 47	
Taplow	d			14 21						14 51							15 21							15 51	
Maidenhead 3	d			14 25	14 34					14 55		15 04					15 25	15 34						15 55	16 04
Twyford 3	d			14 37	14 45					15 03		15 12					15 33	15 42						16 06	16 13
Reading 7	a		14 22	14 46	14 53				14 53	15 13		15 22				15 22	15 43	15 52					15 54	16 14	16 22
Oxford	a		14 48		15 40				15 18			16 14				15 48		16 40					16 19		17 14

For non-stop services between London and Reading please see table 116

Passengers who hold valid tickets for Acton Main Line, West Ealing and Hanwell will be able to use local Transport for London (TFL) bus services to reach these stations. Tel 0843 222 1234

Table 117

Saturdays

29 March to 17 May

Network Diagram - refer to first Page of Table 116

London - Greenford and Reading

Station		HC	GW	GW	GW	GW		GW	HC	GW	GW	GW	GW	GW	HC	GW		GW	GW	GW	GW	HC	GW	GW	GW
			1	1	◇1	1		1		1	1	◇1 bar	1	1		1		1	◇1 trolley	1	1		1	1	◇1 bar
London Paddington 15 ⊖	d	15 33	15 42	15 45	15 50			15 57	16 03	16 12	16 15	16 21		16 27	16 33	16 42		16 45	16 50		16 57	17 03	17 12	17 15	17 21
Acton Main Line	d			15 51							16 21							16 51						17 21	
Ealing Broadway ⊖	d	15 41	15 50	15 54				16 05	16 11	16 20	16 24			16 35	16 41	16 50		16 54			17 05	17 11	17 20	17 24	
West Ealing	d	15 43		15 57					16 13		16 27				16 43			16 57				17 13		17 27	
Drayton Green	d			15 59							16 29							16 59						17 29	
Castle Bar Park	d			16 01							16 31							17 01						17 31	
South Greenford	d			16 04							16 34							17 04						17 34	
Greenford ⊖	a			16 09							16 39							17 09						17 39	
Hanwell	d	15 45							16 15						16 45							17 15			
Southall	d	15 49	15 58						16 19	16 28					16 49	16 58						17 19	17 28		
Hayes & Harlington	d	15 53	16 02					16 12	16 23	16 32				16 42	16 53	17 02					17 12	17 23	17 32		
Heathrow Terminal 1-2 2 ✈	a	16 05							16 35						17 05							17 35			
Heathrow Terminal 4 ✈	a																								
West Drayton	d		16 06					16 16		16 36				16 46		17 06					17 16		17 36		
Iver	d							16 19						16 49							17 19				
Langley	d					←		16 22					←	16 52						←	17 22				
Slough 3	a		16 13		16 06	16 13		16 27		16 43		16 37	16 43	16 57		17 13			17 06	17 13	17 27		17 43		17 38
	d		16 13		16 06	16 13		16 27		16 43		16 38	16 43	16 57		17 13			17 06	17 13	17 27		17 43		17 39
Burnham	d		→			16 17				→			16 47			→				17 17			→		
Taplow	d					16 21							16 51							17 21					
Maidenhead 3	d					16 25		16 34					16 55	17 04						17 25	17 34				
Twyford 3	d					16 33		16 45					17 03	17 12						17 33	17 42				
Reading 7	a				16 22	16 41		16 53				16 52	17 12	17 21					17 22	17 41	17 51				17 53
Oxford	a				16 48			17 40				17 18		18 14					17 48		18 40				18 18

Station		GW		GW	HC	GW	GW	GW	GW	GW	HC	GW		GW	GW	GW	GW	HC	GW	GW	GW	GW		GW	HC
		1		1		1	1	◇1 trolley	1	1		1		1	◇1 bar	1	1		1	1	◇1	1		1	
London Paddington 15 ⊖	d			17 27	17 33	17 42	17 45	17 50		17 57	18 03	18 12		18 15	18 21		18 27	18 33	18 42	18 45	18 50			18 57	19 03
Acton Main Line	d						17 51							18 21						18 51					
Ealing Broadway ⊖	d			17 35	17 41	17 50	17 54			18 05	18 11	18 20		18 24			18 35	18 41	18 50	18 54				19 05	19 11
West Ealing	d				17 43		17 57				18 13			18 27				18 43		18 57					19 13
Drayton Green	d						17 59							18 29						18 59					
Castle Bar Park	d						18 01							18 31						19 01					
South Greenford	d						18 04							18 34						19 04					
Greenford ⊖	a						18 09							18 39						19 09					
Hanwell	d				17 45						18 15							18 45							19 15
Southall	d				17 49	17 58					18 19	18 28						18 49	18 58						19 19
Hayes & Harlington	d			17 42	17 53	18 02				18 12	18 23	18 32					18 42	18 53	19 02					19 12	19 23
Heathrow Terminal 1-2 2 ✈	a				18 05						18 35							19 05							19 35
Heathrow Terminal 4 ✈	a																								
West Drayton	d			17 46		18 06				18 16		18 36					18 46		19 06					19 16	
Iver	d			17 49						18 19							18 49							19 19	
Langley	d	←		17 52					←	18 22						←	18 52					←		19 22	
Slough 3	a	17 43		17 57		18 13		18 06	18 13	18 27		18 43			18 37	18 43	18 57		19 13		19 06	19 13		19 27	
	d	17 43		17 57		18 13		18 06	18 13	18 27		18 43			18 38	18 43	18 57		19 13		19 06	19 13		19 27	
Burnham	d	17 47				→			18 17			→				18 47			→			19 17			
Taplow	d	17 51							18 21							18 51						19 21			
Maidenhead 3	d	17 55		18 04					18 25	18 34						18 55	19 04					19 25		19 34	
Twyford 3	d	18 03		18 12					18 33	18 45						19 03	19 12					19 33		19 42	
Reading 7	a	18 11		18 22				18 22	18 41	18 53					18 52	19 12	19 21				19 22	19 43		19 51	
Oxford	a			19 14				18 48		19 40					19 18		20 14				19 48			20 41	

Station		GW	GW	GW	GW	GW	HC	GW		GW	GW	GW	GW	HC	GW	GW	GW	GW		GW	HC	GW	GW	GW	GW
		1	1	◇1	1	1		1		1	◇1 trolley	1	1		1	1	◇1	1		1		1	1	◇1 trolley	1
London Paddington 15 ⊖	d	19 12	19 15	19 21		19 27	19 33	19 42		19 45	19 50		19 57	20 03	20 12	20 15	20 18			20 27	20 33	20 42	20 45	20 48	
Acton Main Line	d		19 21							19 51						20 21							20 51		
Ealing Broadway ⊖	d	19 20	19 24			19 35	19 41	19 50		19 54			20 05	20 11	20 20	20 24				20 35	20 41	20 50	20 54		
West Ealing	d		19 27				19 43			19 57				20 13		20 27					20 43		20 57		
Drayton Green	d		19 29							19 59						20 29							20 59		
Castle Bar Park	d		19 31							20 01						20 31							21 01		
South Greenford	d		19 34							20 04						20 34							21 04		
Greenford ⊖	a		19 39							20 09						20 39							21 09		
Hanwell	d						19 45							20 15							20 45				
Southall	d	19 28					19 49	19 58						20 19	20 28						20 49	20 58			
Hayes & Harlington	d	19 32				19 42	19 53	20 02					20 12	20 23	20 32					20 42	20 53	21 02			
Heathrow Terminal 1-2 2 ✈	a						20 05							20 35							21 05				
Heathrow Terminal 4 ✈	a																								
West Drayton	d	19 36				19 46		20 06					20 16		20 36					20 46		21 06			
Iver	d					19 49							20 19							20 49					
Langley	d				←	19 52						←	20 22					←		20 52					←
Slough 3	a	19 43		19 37	19 43	19 57		20 13			20 06	20 13	20 27		20 43		20 34	20 43		20 57		21 13		21 04	21 13
	d	19 43		19 38	19 43	19 57		20 13			20 06	20 13	20 27		20 43		20 35	20 43		20 57		21 13		21 05	21 13
Burnham	d	→			19 47			→				20 17			→			20 47				→			21 17
Taplow	d				19 51							20 21						20 51							21 21
Maidenhead 3	d				19 55	20 04						20 25	20 34					20 55		21 04					21 25
Twyford 3	d				20 03	20 12						20 36	20 42					21 06		21 12					21 33
Reading 7	a			19 53	20 13	20 20					20 21	20 45	20 52				20 50	21 15		21 20				21 21	21 43
Oxford	a			20 20		21 14					20 47		21 40				21 18			22 14				21 50	

For non-stop services between London and Reading please see table 116

Passengers who hold valid tickets for Acton Main Line, West Ealing and Hanwell will be able to use local Transport for London (TFL) bus services to reach these stations. Tel 0843 222 1234

Table 117

Saturdays

29 March to 17 May

Network Diagram - refer to first Page of Table 116

London - Greenford and Reading

		GW 1	HC	GW 1	GW 1	GW ◇1	GW 1	HC	GW 1	GW ◇1	GW 1	HC	GW 1	GW ◇1	GW 1	HC	GW 1	GW ◇1	GW (bus)	GW 1	GW (bus)	HC
London Paddington 15 ⊖	d	20 57	21 03	21 12	21 15	21 18		21 33	21 42	21 48		22 03	22 12	22 18		22 33	22 36	22 48		22 58		23 03
Acton Main Line	d				21 21				21 48								22 42					
Ealing Broadway ⊖	d	21 05	21 11	21 20	21 24			21 41	21 52			22 11	22 20			22 41	22 46			23 06		23 11
West Ealing	d		21 13		21 27			21 43				22 13				22 43						23 13
Drayton Green	d				21 29																	
Castle Bar Park	d				21 31																	
South Greenford	d				21 34																	
Greenford ⊖	a				21 39																	
Hanwell	d		21 15					21 45				22 15				22 45						23 15
Southall	d		21 19	21 28				21 49	21 58			22 19	22 28			22 49	22 52			23 13		23 19
Hayes & Harlington	d	21 12	21 23	21 32				21 53	22 02			22 23	22 32			22 53	22 56			23 16		23 23
Heathrow Terminal 1-2 2 ✈	a		21 35					22 05				22 35				23 05						23 35
Heathrow Terminal 4 ✈	a																					23 41
West Drayton	d	21 16		21 36					22 06				22 36				22 59			23 20		
Iver	d	21 19		21 40					22 10				22 40				23 03			23 23		
Langley	d	21 22		21 43			←		22 13		←		22 43		←		23 06			23 26		
Slough 3	a	21 27		21 47		21 34	21 47		22 17	22 05	22 17		22 47	22 34	22 47		23 10	23 15		23 30		
	d	21 27		21 47		21 35	21 47		22 18	22 05	22 18		22 47	22 35	22 47		23 11	23 16	23 18	23 31	23 36	
Burnham	d			→			21 52		→		22 22		→		22 51				23 29		23 47	
Taplow	d						21 55				22 25				22 55				23a39		23a57	
Maidenhead 3	d	21 34					21 59				22 29			22 42	22 59		23 19	23 24		23 39		
Twyford 3	d	21 42					22 07				22 38				23 07		23 27			23 47		
Reading 7	a	21 50				21 58	22 15			22 20	22 46			22 54	23 19		23 34	23 37		23 54		
Oxford	a	22 44				22 27				22 48	23 43			23 22			00 32	00 09				

		GW ◇1	GW 1
London Paddington 15 ⊖	d	23 33	23 42
Acton Main Line	d		
Ealing Broadway ⊖	d		23 50
West Ealing	d		
Drayton Green	d		
Castle Bar Park	d		
South Greenford	d		
Greenford ⊖	a		
Hanwell	d		
Southall	d		23 56
Hayes & Harlington	d		00 01
Heathrow Terminal 1-2 2 ✈	a		
Heathrow Terminal 4 ✈	a		
West Drayton	d		00 05
Iver	d		
Langley	d		
Slough 3	a	23 49	00 12
	d	23 50	00 13
Burnham	d		
Taplow	d		
Maidenhead 3	d	23 58	00 21
Twyford 3	d		00a29
Reading 7	a	00 11	
Oxford	a	00 50	

For non-stop services between London and Reading please see table 116

Passengers who hold valid tickets for Acton Main Line, West Ealing and Hanwell will be able to use local Transport for London (TFL) bus services to reach these stations. Tel 0843 222 1234

Table 117

Sundays

8 December to 29 December

Network Diagram - refer to first Page of Table 116

London - Greenford and Reading

		GW	GW	GW	GW	GW		HC	HC	GW	HC	GW	GW	HC	GW	GW		GW	HC	GW	GW	GW	HC	GW	GW
		1	1	1	1	1				1		1	◇1		1	◇1		1		1	◇1	1		1	◇1
		A	A																		☕				☕
London Paddington 15 ⊖	d			00 05	00 30	01 00			06 12	06 43	07 12	07 29	08 03	08 12	08 15	08 42		08 43	09 12	09 15	09 35	09 43	10 12	10 15	10 42
Acton Main Line	d																								
Ealing Broadway ⊖	d			00 13	00 38	01 08		05 20	06 20	06 52	07 20	07 36		08 20	08 24			08 54	09 20	09 24		09 50	10 20	10 24	
West Ealing	d																								
Drayton Green	d																								
Castle Bar Park	d																								
South Greenford	d																								
Greenford ⊖	a																								
Hanwell	d																								
Southall	d			00 19	00 44	01 13		05 24	06 24	06 58	07 24	07 42		08 24	08 29			08 59	09 24	09 29		09 56	10 24	10 29	
Hayes & Harlington	d		00 01	00 23	00 48	01 17		05 28	06 28	07 02	07 28	07 46		08 28	08 33			09 02	09 28	09 33		10 01	10 28	10 33	
Heathrow Terminal 1-2 2 ✈	a							05 34	06 34		07 34			08 34					09 34				10 34		
Heathrow Terminal 4 ✈	a							05 40	06 41		07 41			08 41					09 41				10 41		
West Drayton	d		00 05	00 27	00 52					07 06		07 50			08 37			09 06		09 37		10 05		10 37	
Iver	d			00 30																					
Langley	d			00 33	00 56					07 11		07 55			08 42			09 11		09 42		10 09		10 42	
Slough 3	a		00 11	00 37	01 00	01 26				07 16		07 58	08 23		08 44	08 59		09 14		09 45	09 55	10 13		10 46	11 03
	d		00 12	00 37	01 01	01 27				07 16		08 03	08 23		08 45	09 01		09 16		09 46	09 56	10 14		10 46	11 03
Burnham	d		00 16	00 41						07 20		08 08						09 20				10 18			
Taplow	d	00 01	00 20	00 45																					
Maidenhead 3	d	00 05	00 24	00 49	01 08	01 34				07 24		08 13	08 29		08 53			09 28		09 54		10 27		10 54	
Twyford 3	d	00 13	00 31	00 57	01 16	01 42				07 34		08 21			09 02			09 36		10 02		10 35		11 02	
Reading 7	a	00 21	00 39	01 04	01 23	01 49				07 41		08 29	08 45		09 12	09 21		09 44		10 13	10 14	10 42		11 09	11 20
Oxford	a											09 32	09 13			09 53		10 30			10 45	11 27			11 50

		GW		HC	GW	GW	GW	HC	GW	GW	GW	HC		GW	GW	GW	HC	GW	GW	GW	HC	GW		GW	GW
		1			1	◇1	1		1	◇1	1			1	◇1	1		1	◇1	1		1		◇1	1
										☕					☕										
London Paddington 15 ⊖	d	10 43		11 12	11 15	11 42	11 43	12 12	12 15	12 42	12 43	13 12		13 15	13 42	13 43	14 12	14 15	14 42	14 43	15 12	15 15		15 42	15 43
Acton Main Line	d																								
Ealing Broadway ⊖	d	10 53		11 20	11 24		11 53	12 20	12 24		12 53	13 20		13 24		13 53	14 20	14 24		14 53	15 20	15 24			15 53
West Ealing	d																								
Drayton Green	d																								
Castle Bar Park	d																								
South Greenford	d																								
Greenford ⊖	a																								
Hanwell	d																								
Southall	d	10 59		11 24	11 29		11 59	12 24	12 29		12 59	13 24		13 29		13 59	14 24	14 29		14 59	15 24	15 29			15 59
Hayes & Harlington	d	11 02		11 28	11 33		12 02	12 28	12 33		13 02	13 28		13 33		14 02	14 28	14 33		15 02	15 28	15 33			16 02
Heathrow Terminal 1-2 2 ✈	a			11 34				12 34				13 34					14 34				15 34				
Heathrow Terminal 4 ✈	a			11 41				12 41				13 41					14 41				15 41				
West Drayton	d	11 06			11 37		12 06		12 37		13 06			13 37		14 06		14 37		15 06		15 37			16 06
Iver	d																								
Langley	d	11 11			11 42		12 11		12 42		13 11			13 42		14 11		14 42		15 11		15 42			16 11
Slough 3	a	11 14			11 46	12 02	12 14		12 46	13 00	13 14			13 46	14 04	14 14		14 46	15 03	15 14		15 46		16 02	16 14
	d	11 16			11 46	12 03	12 16		12 46	13 00	13 16			13 46	14 04	14 16		14 46	15 03	15 16		15 46		16 03	16 16
Burnham	d	11 20					12 20				13 20					14 20				15 20		15 50			16 20
Taplow	d																								
Maidenhead 3	d	11 28			11 54		12 27		12 54		13 27			13 54		14 27		14 54		15 27		15 56			16 27
Twyford 3	d	11 36			12 02		12 35		13 02		13 36			14 02		14 35		15 02		15 36		16 03			16 35
Reading 7	a	11 44			12 10	12 20	12 44		13 10	13 21	13 44			14 10	14 21	14 44		15 11	15 20	15 44		16 11		16 20	16 44
Oxford	a	12 28				12 53	13 30			13 51	14 30				14 51	15 30			15 49	16 31				16 49	17 29

A not 8 December

For non-stop services between London and Reading please see table 116

Passengers who hold valid tickets for Acton Main Line, West Ealing and Hanwell will be able to use local Transport for London (TFL) bus services to reach these stations. Tel 0843 222 1234

Table 117

Sundays

8 December to 29 December

Network Diagram - refer to first Page of Table 116

London - Greenford and Reading

Station		HC	GW 1	GW ◇1	GW 1	HC	GW 1	GW ◇1	GW 1	HC	GW 1	GW ◇1	GW 1
London Paddington 15 ⊖	d	16 12	16 15	16 42	16 43	17 12	17 15	17 42	17 43	18 12	18 15	18 42	18 43
Acton Main Line	d												
Ealing Broadway ⊖	d	16 20	16 24		16 53	17 20	17 24		17 53	18 20	18 24		18 53
West Ealing	d												
Drayton Green	d												
Castle Bar Park	d												
South Greenford	d												
Greenford ⊖	a												
Hanwell	d												
Southall	d	16 24	16 29		16 59	17 24	17 29		17 59	18 24	18 29		18 59
Hayes & Harlington	d	16 28	16 33		17 02	17 28	17 33		18 02	18 28	18 33		19 02
Heathrow Terminal 1-2 2 ✈	a	16 34				17 34				18 34			
Heathrow Terminal 4 ✈	a	16 41				17 41				18 41			
West Drayton	d		16 37		17 06		17 37		18 06		18 37		19 06
Iver	d												
Langley	d		16 42		17 11		17 42		18 11		18 42		19 11
Slough 3	a		16 46	17 00	17 14		17 46	18 03	18 14		18 46	19 00	19 14
	d		16 46	17 01	17 16		17 46	18 04	18 16		18 46	19 01	19 16
Burnham	d		16 50		17 20		17 50		18 20		18 50		19 20
Taplow	d												
Maidenhead 3	d		16 56	17 08	17 27		17 56	18 12	18 27		18 56	19 08	19 27
Twyford 3	d		17 03		17 36		18 03		18 36		19 03		19 35
Reading 7	a		17 12	17 20	17 44		18 12	18 25	18 44		19 12	19 20	19 44
Oxford	a			17 50	18 30			18 51	19 30			19 49	20 29

Station		HC	GW 1	GW ◇1	GW 1	HC	GW 1	GW ◇1	GW 1	HC
London Paddington 15 ⊖	d	19 12	19 15	19 42	19 43	20 12	20 15	20 42	20 43	21 12
Acton Main Line	d									
Ealing Broadway ⊖	d	19 20	19 24		19 53	20 20	20 24		20 53	21 20
West Ealing	d									
Drayton Green	d									
Castle Bar Park	d									
South Greenford	d									
Greenford ⊖	a									
Hanwell	d									
Southall	d	19 24	19 29		19 59	20 24	20 29		20 59	21 24
Hayes & Harlington	d	19 28	19 33		20 02	20 28	20 33		21 02	21 28
Heathrow Terminal 1-2 2 ✈	a	19 34				20 34				21 34
Heathrow Terminal 4 ✈	a	19 41				20 41				21 41
West Drayton	d		19 37		20 06		20 37		21 06	
Iver	d									
Langley	d		19 42		20 11		20 42		21 11	
Slough 3	a		19 46	20 04	20 14		20 46	21 00	21 14	
	d		19 46	20 05	20 16		20 46	21 01	21 16	
Burnham	d		19 50		20 20		20 50		21 20	
Taplow	d									
Maidenhead 3	d		19 56		20 27		20 56		21 27	
Twyford 3	d		20 03		20 36		21 04		21 36	
Reading 7	a		20 12	20 22	20 44		21 12	21 22	21 44	
Oxford	a			20 50	21 30			21 56	22 29	

Station		GW 1	GW ◇1	GW 1	HC	GW 1	GW ◇1	GW 1	HC	GW 1	GW ◇1	GW 1
London Paddington 15 ⊖	d	21 15	21 42	21 43	22 12	22 15	22 42	22 43	23 12	23 15	23 47	23 53
Acton Main Line	d											
Ealing Broadway ⊖	d	21 24		21 53	22 20	22 23		22 53	23 20	23 23	23 55	00 02
West Ealing	d											
Drayton Green	d											
Castle Bar Park	d											
South Greenford	d											
Greenford ⊖	a											
Hanwell	d											
Southall	d	21 29		21 59	22 24	22 28		22 59	23 24	23 29		00 07
Hayes & Harlington	d	21 33		22 02	22 28	22 33		23 02	23 28	23 33		00 11
Heathrow Terminal 1-2 2 ✈	a				22 34				23 34			
Heathrow Terminal 4 ✈	a				22 41				23 41			
West Drayton	d	21 37		22 06		22 37		23 06		23 37		00 15
Iver	d											
Langley	d	21 42		22 11		22 41		23 11		23 41		00 20
Slough 3	a	21 45	22 01	22 14		22 45	23 02	23 14		23 43	00 10	00 24
	d	21 46	22 02	22 16		22 46	23 02	23 15		23 45	00 11	00 24
Burnham	d	21 50		22 21		22 51		23 20		23 51		00 28
Taplow	d											
Maidenhead 3	d	21 56		22 26		22 56		23 24		23 56	00 18	00 33
Twyford 3	d	22 03		22 35		23 04		23 32		00 03		00 41
Reading 7	a	22 12	22 17	22 44		23 12	23 20	23 41		00 12	00 33	00 49
Oxford	a		22 50									

For non-stop services between London and Reading please see table 116

Passengers who hold valid tickets for Acton Main Line, West Ealing and Hanwell will be able to use local Transport for London (TFL) bus services to reach these stations. Tel 0843 222 1234

Table 117

Sundays

5 January to 9 February

Network Diagram - refer to first Page of Table 116

London - Greenford and Reading

		GW ◇1	GW 1	GW 🚌	GW 1	GW 🚌		GW 1	GW 🚌	GW 1	GW 🚌	HC	HC	GW 1	HC	GW 1		GW ◇1	HC	GW 1	GW ◇1	GW 1	HC	GW 1	GW ◇1 ☕
London Paddington 15 ⊖	d				00 05			00 30		01 00			06 12	06 43	07 12	07 29		08 03	08 12	08 15	08 42	08 43	09 12	09 15	09 33
Acton Main Line	d																								
Ealing Broadway ⊖	d				00 13			00 38		01 08		05 20	06 20	06 52	07 20	07 36			08 20	08 24		08 54	09 20	09 24	
West Ealing	d																								
Drayton Green	d																								
Castle Bar Park	d																								
South Greenford	d																								
Greenford ⊖	a																								
Hanwell	d																								
Southall	d				00 19			00 44		01 13		05 24	06 24	06 58	07 24	07 42			08 24	08 29		08 59	09 24	09 29	
Hayes & Harlington	d		00 01		00 23			00 48		01 17		05 28	06 28	07 02	07 28	07 46			08 28	08 33		09 02	09 28	09 33	
Heathrow Terminal 1-2 2 ✈	a											05 34	06 34		07 34				08 34				09 34		
Heathrow Terminal 4 ✈	a											05 40	06 41		07 41				08 41				09 41		
West Drayton	d		00 05		00 27			00 52						07 06		07 50				08 37		09 06		09 37	
Iver	d				00 30																				
Langley	d				00 33			00 56						07 11		07 55				08 42		09 11		09 42	
Slough 3	a		00 11		00 37			01 00		01 25				07 16		07 58		08 23		08 44	09 03	09 14		09 45	09 55
	d		00 12		00 38			01 01		01 26				07 16		08 03		08 23		08 45	09 05	09 16		09 46	09 56
Burnham	d		00 16		00 42									07 20		08 08						09 20			
Taplow	d		00 20		00 45																				
Maidenhead 3	d	00 02	00a28	00 35	00a49	00 56		01a08	01 15	01a33	01 40			07a27		08 13		08 29		08 53		09 28		09 54	
Twyford 3	d			01a00		01a21			01a40		02a05					08 21				09 02		09 36		10 02	
Reading 7	a	00 15														08 29		08 45		09 12	09 21	09 44		10 13	10 14
Oxford	a	00 54														09 30		09 13			09 53	10 30			10 45

		GW 1		HC	GW 1	GW ◇1 ☕	GW 1	HC	GW 1	GW ◇1	GW 1	HC		GW 1	GW ◇1 ☕	GW 1	HC	GW 1	GW ◇1 ☕	GW 1	HC	GW 1		GW ◇1	GW 1
London Paddington 15 ⊖	d	09 43		10 12	10 15	10 42	10 43	11 12	11 15	11 42	11 43	12 12		12 15	12 42	12 43	13 12	13 15	13 42	13 43	14 12	14 15		14 42	14 43
Acton Main Line	d																								
Ealing Broadway ⊖	d	09 50		10 20	10 24		10 53	11 20	11 24		11 53	12 20		12 24		12 53	13 20	13 24		13 53	14 20	14 24			14 53
West Ealing	d																								
Drayton Green	d																								
Castle Bar Park	d																								
South Greenford	d																								
Greenford ⊖	a																								
Hanwell	d																								
Southall	d	09 56		10 24	10 29		10 59	11 24	11 29		11 59	12 24		12 29		12 59	13 24	13 29		13 59	14 24	14 29			14 59
Hayes & Harlington	d	10 01		10 28	10 33		11 02	11 28	11 33		12 02	12 28		12 33		13 02	13 28	13 33		14 02	14 28	14 33			15 02
Heathrow Terminal 1-2 2 ✈	a			10 34				11 34				12 34					13 34				14 34				
Heathrow Terminal 4 ✈	a			10 41				11 41				12 41					13 41				14 41				
West Drayton	d	10 05			10 37		11 06		11 37		12 06			12 37		13 06		13 37		14 06		14 37			15 06
Iver	d																								
Langley	d	10 09			10 42		11 11		11 42		12 11			12 42		13 11		13 42		14 11		14 42			15 11
Slough 3	a	10 13			10 46	11 03	11 14		11 46	12 02	12 14			12 46	13 05	13 14		13 46	14 04	14 14		14 46		15 05	15 14
	d	10 14			10 46	11 03	11 16		11 46	12 03	12 16			12 46	13 05	13 16		13 46	14 04	14 16		14 46		15 05	15 16
Burnham	d	10 18					11 20				12 20					13 20				14 20					15 20
Taplow	d																								
Maidenhead 3	d	10 27			10 54		11 28		11 54		12 27			12 54		13 27		13 54		14 27		14 54			15 27
Twyford 3	d	10 35			11 02		11 36		12 02		12 35			13 02		13 36		14 02		14 35		15 02			15 36
Reading 7	a	10 42			11 09	11 20	11 44		12 10	12 20	12 44			13 10	13 21	13 44		14 10	14 21	14 44		15 11		15 22	15 44
Oxford	a	11 27				11 50	12 28			12 53	13 32				13 51	14 30			14 51	15 30				15 51	16 31

		HC	GW 1	GW ◇1	GW 1	HC	GW 1	GW ◇1		GW 1	HC	GW 1	GW ◇1 ☕	GW 1	HC	GW 1	GW ◇1	GW 1		HC	GW 1	GW ◇1 ☕	GW 1	HC	GW 1
London Paddington 15 ⊖	d	15 12	15 15	15 42	15 43	16 12	16 15	16 42		16 43	17 12	17 15	17 42	17 43	18 12	18 15	18 42	18 43		19 12	19 15	19 42	19 43	20 12	20 15
Acton Main Line	d																								
Ealing Broadway ⊖	d	15 20	15 24		15 53	16 20	16 24			16 53	17 20	17 24		17 53	18 20	18 24		18 53		19 20	19 24		19 53	20 20	20 24
West Ealing	d																								
Drayton Green	d																								
Castle Bar Park	d																								
South Greenford	d																								
Greenford ⊖	a																								
Hanwell	d																								
Southall	d	15 24	15 29		15 59	16 24	16 29			16 59	17 24	17 29		17 59	18 24	18 29		18 59		19 24	19 29		19 59	20 24	20 29
Hayes & Harlington	d	15 28	15 33		16 02	16 28	16 33			17 02	17 28	17 33		18 02	18 28	18 33		19 02		19 28	19 33		20 02	20 28	20 33
Heathrow Terminal 1-2 2 ✈	a	15 34				16 34					17 34				18 34					19 34				20 34	
Heathrow Terminal 4 ✈	a	15 41				16 41					17 41				18 41					19 41				20 41	
West Drayton	d		15 37		16 06		16 37			17 06		17 37		18 06		18 37		19 06			19 37		20 06		20 37
Iver	d																								
Langley	d		15 42		16 11		16 42			17 11		17 42		18 11		18 42		19 11			19 42		20 11		20 42
Slough 3	a		15 46	16 01	16 14		16 46	17 00		17 14		17 46	18 03	18 14		18 46	19 01	19 14			19 46	20 04	20 14		20 46
	d		15 46	16 02	16 16		16 46	17 01		17 16		17 46	18 04	18 16		18 46	19 02	19 16			19 46	20 05	20 16		20 46
Burnham	d		15 50		16 20		16 50			17 20		17 50		18 20		18 50		19 20			19 50		20 20		20 50
Taplow	d																								
Maidenhead 3	d		15 56		16 27		16 56	17 08		17 27		17 57	18 12	18 27		18 56	19 08	19 27			19 56		20 27		20 56
Twyford 3	d		16 03		16 35		17 03			17 36		18 04		18 36		19 03		19 35			20 03		20 36		21 04
Reading 7	a		16 11	16 20	16 44		17 12	17 20		17 44		18 12	18 25	18 44		19 12	19 20	19 44			20 12	20 22	20 44		21 12
Oxford	a			16 49	17 29			17 50		18 30			18 52	19 30			19 49	20 29				20 50	21 30		

For non-stop services between London and Reading please see table 116

Passengers who hold valid tickets for Acton Main Line, West Ealing and Hanwell will be able to use local Transport for London (TFL) bus services to reach these stations. Tel 0843 222 1234

Table 117

Sundays

5 January to 9 February

Network Diagram - refer to first Page of Table 116

London - Greenford and Reading

		GW ◇1	GW 1	HC	GW 1	GW ◇1	GW 1	HC	GW 1	GW ◇1	GW 1	HC	GW 1	GW ◇1	GW 1
London Paddington 15 ⊖	d	20 42	20 43	21 12	21 15	21 42	21 43	22 12	22 15	22 42	22 43	23 12	23 15	23 47	23 53
Acton Main Line	d														
Ealing Broadway ⊖	d		20 53	21 20	21 24		21 53	22 20	22 22		22 53	23 20	23 23	23 55	00 02
West Ealing	d														
Drayton Green	d														
Castle Bar Park	d														
South Greenford	d														
Greenford ⊖	a														
Hanwell	d														
Southall	d		20 59	21 24	21 29		21 59	22 24	22 28		22 59	23 24	23 29		00 07
Hayes & Harlington	d		21 02	21 28	21 33		22 02	22 28	22 33		23 02	23 28	23 33		00 11
Heathrow Terminal 1-2 2 ✈	a			21 34				22 34				23 34			
Heathrow Terminal 4 ✈	a			21 41				22 41				23 41			
West Drayton	d		21 06		21 37		22 06		22 37		23 06		23 37		00 15
Iver	d														
Langley	d		21 11		21 42		22 11		22 41		23 11		23 41		00 20
Slough 3	a	21 00	21 14		21 45	22 05	22 14		22 45	23 02	23 14		23 43	00 07	00 24
	d	21 01	21 16		21 46	22 06	22 16		22 46	23 02	23 15		23 45	00 07	00 24
Burnham	d		21 20		21 50		22 20		22 51		23 20		23 50		00 28
Taplow	d														
Maidenhead 3	d		21 27		21 56		22 27		22 56		23 24		23 56	00 15	00 33
Twyford 3	d		21 36		22 03		22 35		23 04		23 32		00 03		00 41
Reading 7	a	21 22	21 44		22 12	22 23	22 44		23 12	23 20	23 41		00 12	00 30	00 49
Oxford	a	21 56	22 29			22 53									

Sundays

16 February to 23 March

		GW 1	GW 1	GW (bus)	GW 1	GW (bus)	GW 1	GW (bus)	GW 1	GW (bus)	HC	HC	GW 1	HC	GW 1	GW ◇1	HC	GW 1	GW ◇1	GW 1	HC	GW 1	GW ◇1 (catering)
London Paddington 15 ⊖	d				00 05		00 30		01 00			06 12	06 43	07 12	07 29	08 03	08 12	08 15	08 42	08 43	09 12	09 15	09 33
Acton Main Line	d																						
Ealing Broadway ⊖	d				00 13		00 38		01 08		05 20	06 20	06 52	07 20	07 36		08 20	08 24		08 54	09 20	09 24	
West Ealing	d																						
Drayton Green	d																						
Castle Bar Park	d																						
South Greenford	d																						
Greenford ⊖	a																						
Hanwell	d																						
Southall	d				00 19		00 44		01 13		05 24	06 24	06 58	07 24	07 42		08 24	08 29		08 59	09 24	09 29	
Hayes & Harlington	d		00 01		00 23		00 48		01 17		05 28	06 28	07 02	07 28	07 46		08 28	08 33		09 02	09 28	09 33	
Heathrow Terminal 1-2 2 ✈	a										05 34	06 34		07 34			08 34				09 34		
Heathrow Terminal 4 ✈	a										05 40	06 41		07 41			08 41				09 41		
West Drayton	d		00 05		00 27		00 52						07 06		07 50			08 37		09 06		09 37	
Iver	d				00 30																		
Langley	d				00 33		00 56						07 11		07 55			08 42		09 11		09 42	
Slough 3	a		00 11		00 37		01 00		01 25				07 16		07 58	08 23		08 44	09 03	09 14		09 45	09 55
	d		00 12		00 38		01 01		01 26				07 16		08 03	08 23		08 45	09 05	09 16		09 46	09 56
Burnham	d		00 16		00 42								07 20		08 08					09 20			
Taplow	d	00 01	00 20		00 45																		
Maidenhead 3	d	00 05	00a23	00 30	00a49	00 56	01a08	01 15	01a33	01 40			07a27		08 13	08 29		08 53		09 28		09 54	
Twyford 3	d	00 13		00a55		01a21		01a40		02a05					08 21			09 02		09 36		10 02	
Reading 7	a	00 21													08 29	08 45		09 12	09 21	09 44		10 13	10 19
Oxford	a														09 30	09 13			09 53	10 30			10 45

For non-stop services between London and Reading please see table 116

Passengers who hold valid tickets for Acton Main Line, West Ealing and Hanwell will be able to use local Transport for London (TFL) bus services to reach these stations. Tel 0843 222 1234

Table 117

Sundays

16 February to 23 March

Network Diagram - refer to first Page of Table 116

London - Greenford and Reading

Station		GW [1]		HC	GW [1]	GW ◇[1] ⊏P	GW [1]	HC	GW [1]	GW ◇[1]	GW [1]	HC		GW [1]	GW ◇[1] ⊏P	GW [1]	HC	GW [1]	GW ◇[1] ⊏P	GW [1]	HC	GW [1]		GW ◇[1]	GW [1]
London Paddington [15] ⊖	d	09 43		10 12	10 15	10 42	10 43	11 12	11 15	11 42	11 43	12 12		12 15	12 42	12 43	13 12	13 15	13 42	13 43	14 12	14 15		14 42	14 43
Acton Main Line	d																								
Ealing Broadway ⊖	d	09 50		10 20	10 24		10 53	11 20	11 24		11 53	12 20		12 24		12 53	13 20	13 24		13 53	14 20	14 24			14 53
West Ealing	d																								
Drayton Green	d																								
Castle Bar Park	d																								
South Greenford	d																								
Greenford ⊖	a																								
Hanwell	d																								
Southall	d	09 56		10 24	10 29		10 59	11 24	11 29		11 59	12 24		12 29		12 59	13 24	13 29		13 59	14 24	14 29			14 59
Hayes & Harlington	d	10 01		10 28	10 33		11 02	11 28	11 33		12 02	12 28		12 33		13 02	13 28	13 33		14 02	14 28	14 33			15 02
Heathrow Terminal 1-2 [2] ✈	a			10 34				11 34				12 34					13 34				14 34				
Heathrow Terminal 4 ✈	a			10 41				11 41				12 41					13 41				14 41				
West Drayton	d	10 05			10 37		11 06		11 37		12 06			12 37		13 06		13 37		14 06		14 37			15 06
Iver	d																								
Langley	d	10 09			10 42		11 11		11 42		12 11			12 42		13 11		13 42		14 11		14 42			15 11
Slough [3]	a	10 13			10 46	11 03	11 14		11 46	12 02	12 14			12 46	13 05	13 14		13 46	14 04	14 14		14 46		15 05	15 14
	d	10 14			10 46	11 03	11 16		11 46	12 03	12 16			12 46	13 05	13 16		13 46	14 04	14 16		14 46		15 05	15 16
Burnham	d	10 18					11 20				12 20					13 20				14 20					15 20
Taplow	d																								
Maidenhead [3]	d	10 27			10 54		11 28		11 54		12 27			12 54		13 27		13 54		14 27		14 54			15 27
Twyford [3]	d	10 35			11 02		11 36		12 02		12 35			13 02		13 36		14 02		14 35		15 02			15 36
Reading [7]	a	10 42			11 09	11 20	11 44		12 13	12 20	12 44			13 12	13 21	13 44		14 12	14 21	14 44		15 12		15 21	15 44
Oxford	a	11 27				11 50	12 28			12 53	13 35				13 53	14 30			14 51	15 30				15 51	16 31

Station		HC	GW [1]	GW ◇[1]	GW [1]	HC	GW [1]	GW ◇[1]		GW [1]	HC	GW [1]	GW ◇[1] ⊏P	GW [1]	HC	GW [1]	GW ◇[1]	GW [1]		HC	GW [1]	GW ◇[1] ⊏P	GW [1]	HC	GW [1]
London Paddington [15] ⊖	d	15 12	15 15	15 42	15 43	16 12	16 15	16 42		16 43	17 12	17 15	17 42	17 43	18 12	18 15	18 42	18 43		19 12	19 15	19 42	19 43	20 12	20 15
Acton Main Line	d																								
Ealing Broadway ⊖	d	15 20	15 24		15 53	16 20	16 24			16 53	17 20	17 24		17 53	18 20	18 24		18 53		19 20	19 24		19 53	20 20	20 24
West Ealing	d																								
Drayton Green	d																								
Castle Bar Park	d																								
South Greenford	d																								
Greenford ⊖	a																								
Hanwell	d																								
Southall	d	15 24	15 29		15 59	16 24	16 29			16 59	17 24	17 29		17 59	18 24	18 29		18 59		19 24	19 29		19 59	20 24	20 29
Hayes & Harlington	d	15 28	15 33		16 02	16 28	16 33			17 02	17 28	17 33		18 02	18 28	18 33		19 02		19 28	19 33		20 02	20 28	20 33
Heathrow Terminal 1-2 [2] ✈	a	15 34				16 34					17 34				18 34					19 34				20 34	
Heathrow Terminal 4 ✈	a	15 41				16 41					17 41				18 41					19 41				20 41	
West Drayton	d		15 37		16 06		16 37			17 06		17 37		18 06		18 37		19 06			19 37		20 06		20 37
Iver	d																								
Langley	d		15 42		16 11		16 42			17 11		17 42		18 11		18 42		19 11			19 42		20 11		20 42
Slough [3]	a		15 46	16 01	16 15		16 46	17 00		17 14		17 46	18 03	18 14		18 46	19 01	19 14			19 46	20 04	20 14		20 46
	d		15 46	16 02	16 16		16 46	17 01		17 16		17 46	18 04	18 16		18 46	19 02	19 16			19 46	20 05	20 16		20 46
Burnham	d		15 50		16 20		16 50			17 20		17 50		18 20		18 50		19 20			19 50		20 20		20 50
Taplow	d																								
Maidenhead [3]	d		15 56		16 27		16 56	17 08		17 27		17 56	18 12	18 27		18 56	19 08	19 27			19 56		20 27		20 56
Twyford [3]	d		16 03		16 35		17 03			17 36		18 03		18 36		19 03		19 35			20 03		20 36		21 04
Reading [7]	a		16 12	16 20	16 44		17 12	17 24		17 44		18 12	18 25	18 44		19 12	19 20	19 44			20 12	20 22	20 44		21 12
Oxford	a			16 49	17 29			17 50		18 33			18 52	19 30			19 49	20 29				20 50	21 32		

Station		GW ◇[1]	GW [1]	HC		GW [1]	GW ◇[1]	GW [1]	HC	GW [1]	GW ◇[1]	GW [1]	HC	GW [1]		GW ◇[1]	GW [1]
London Paddington [15] ⊖	d	20 42	20 43	21 12		21 15	21 42	21 43	22 12	22 15	22 42	22 43	23 12	23 15		23 47	23 53
Acton Main Line	d																
Ealing Broadway ⊖	d		20 53	21 20		21 24		21 53	22 20	22 23		22 53	23 20	23 23		23 55	00 02
West Ealing	d																
Drayton Green	d																
Castle Bar Park	d																
South Greenford	d																
Greenford ⊖	a																
Hanwell	d																
Southall	d		20 59	21 24		21 29		21 59	22 24	22 28		22 59	23 24	23 29			00 07
Hayes & Harlington	d		21 02	21 28		21 33		22 02	22 28	22 33		23 02	23 28	23 33			00 11
Heathrow Terminal 1-2 [2] ✈	a			21 34					22 34				23 34				
Heathrow Terminal 4 ✈	a			21 41					22 41				23 41				
West Drayton	d		21 06			21 37		22 06		22 37		23 06		23 37			00 15
Iver	d																
Langley	d		21 11			21 42		22 11		22 41		23 12		23 41			00 20
Slough [3]	a	21 00	21 14			21 45	22 05	22 14		22 45	23 03	23 14		23 43		00 10	00 24
	d	21 01	21 16			21 46	22 06	22 16		22 46	23 04	23 15		23 45		00 11	00 24
Burnham	d		21 20			21 50		22 20		22 50		23 20		23 50			00 28
Taplow	d																
Maidenhead [3]	d		21 28			21 56		22 27		22 54		23 24		23 56		00 18	00 33
Twyford [3]	d		21 36			22 03		22 35		23 02		23 32		00 03			00 41
Reading [7]	a	21 22	21 44			22 12	22 23	22 44		23 09	23 21	23 41		00 12		00 33	00 49
Oxford	a	21 56	22 29				22 53										

For non-stop services between London and Reading please see table 116

Passengers who hold valid tickets for Acton Main Line, West Ealing and Hanwell will be able to use local Transport for London (TFL) bus services to reach these stations. Tel 0843 222 1234

Table 117

Sundays

30 March to 11 May

London - Greenford and Reading

Network Diagram - refer to first Page of Table 116

Station		GW 1	GW (bus)	GW 1	GW (bus)	GW 1	GW 1	HC	HC	GW 1		HC	GW 1	GW ◇1	HC	GW 1	GW ◇1	GW 1	HC	GW 1		GW ◇1 (catering)	GW 1	HC	GW 1
London Paddington 15 ⊖	d			00 05		00 30	01 00		06 12	06 43		07 12	07 29	08 03	08 12	08 15	08 42	08 43	09 12	09 15		09 35	09 43	10 12	10 15
Acton Main Line	d																								
Ealing Broadway ⊖	d			00 13		00 38	01 08	05 20	06 20	06 50		07 20	07 36		08 20	08 23		08 51	09 20	09 24			09 48	10 20	10 24
West Ealing	d																								
Drayton Green	d																								
Castle Bar Park	d																								
South Greenford	d																								
Greenford ⊖	a																								
Hanwell	d																								
Southall	d			00 19		00 44	01 13	05 24	06 24	06 56		07 24	07 42		08 24	08 28		08 59	09 24	09 29			09 56	10 24	10 29
Hayes & Harlington	d	00 01		00 23		00 48	01 17	05 28	06 28	07 00		07 28	07 46		08 28	08 32		09 03	09 28	09 33			10 00	10 28	10 33
Heathrow Terminal 1-2 2 ✈	a							05 34	06 34			07 34			08 34				09 34					10 34	
Heathrow Terminal 4 ✈	a							05 40	06 41			07 41			08 41				09 41					10 41	
West Drayton	d	00 05		00 27		00 52				07 04			07 50			08 36		09 07		09 37			10 05		10 37
Iver	d			00 30																					
Langley	d			00 33		00 56				07 10			07 55			08 41		09 12		09 42			10 10		10 42
Slough 3	a	00 12		00 37		01 00	01 24			07 15			07 59	08 20		08 43	09 03	09 15		09 45		09 55	10 13		10 45
	d	00 13	00 20	00 37	00 45	01 01	01 25			07 15			08 01	08 22		08 44	09 05	09 15		09 46		09 56	10 14		10 46
Burnham	d		00 31		00 56					07 19			08 07					09 20					10 19		
Taplow	d		00a41		01a06																				
Maidenhead 3	d	00 21		00 45		01 09	01 33			07 25			08 13	08 29		08 52		09 29		09 54			10 27		10 54
Twyford 3	d	00a29		00a53		01a16	01a40			07a35			08 21			09 02		09 37		10 02			10 35		11 02
Reading 7	a												08 29	08 41		09 10	09 22	09 45		10 13		10 12	10 43		11 10
Oxford	a												09 30	09 10			09 53	10 31				10 45	11 27		

Station		GW ◇1 (catering)	GW 1	HC	GW 1	GW ◇1		GW 1	HC	GW 1	GW ◇1 (catering)	GW 1	HC	GW 1	GW ◇1 (catering)	GW 1		HC	GW 1	GW ◇1	GW 1	HC	GW 1	GW ◇1	GW 1
London Paddington 15 ⊖	d	10 42	10 43	11 12	11 15	11 42		11 43	12 12	12 15	12 42	12 43	13 12	13 15	13 42	13 43		14 12	14 15	14 30	14 43	15 12	15 15	15 42	15 43
Acton Main Line	d																								
Ealing Broadway ⊖	d		10 50	11 20	11 23			11 50	12 20	12 24		12 50	13 20	13 24		13 50		14 20	14 24		14 50	15 20	15 24		15 50
West Ealing	d																								
Drayton Green	d																								
Castle Bar Park	d																								
South Greenford	d																								
Greenford ⊖	a																								
Hanwell	d																								
Southall	d		10 57	11 24	11 29			11 57	12 24	12 29		12 59	13 24	13 29		13 58		14 24	14 29		14 58	15 24	15 29		15 58
Hayes & Harlington	d		11 01	11 28	11 33			12 01	12 28	12 33		13 03	13 28	13 33		14 02		14 28	14 33		15 02	15 28	15 33		16 02
Heathrow Terminal 1-2 2 ✈	a			11 34					12 34				13 34					14 34				15 34			
Heathrow Terminal 4 ✈	a			11 41					12 41				13 41					14 41				15 41			
West Drayton	d		11 06		11 37			12 06		12 37		13 07		13 37		14 07			14 37		15 07		15 37		16 07
Iver	d																								
Langley	d		11 10		11 42			12 11		12 42		13 11		13 42		14 11			14 42		15 11		15 42		16 11
Slough 3	a	11 03	11 13		11 45	12 02		12 14		12 45	13 00	13 14		13 45	14 04	14 14			14 46	14 49	15 14		15 46	16 01	16 14
	d	11 03	11 14		11 46	12 03		12 16		12 46	13 00	13 16		13 46	14 04	14 16			14 46	14 50	15 16		15 46	16 02	16 16
Burnham	d		11 20					12 20				13 20				14 20					15 20		15 50		16 20
Taplow	d																								
Maidenhead 3	d		11 28		11 54			12 25		12 54		13 27		13 54		14 27			14 54		15 27		15 56		16 27
Twyford 3	d		11 36		12 02			12 33		13 02		13 34		14 02		14 35			15 02		15 35		16 04		16 35
Reading 7	a	11 20	11 44		12 10	12 20		12 41		13 09	13 16	13 44		14 10	14 21	14 44			15 09	15 06	15 44		16 11	16 20	16 44
Oxford	a	11 50	12 28			12 53		13 27			13 51	14 30			14 51	15 30				15 49	16 31			16 49	17 30

Station		HC		GW 1	GW ◇1	GW 1	HC	GW 1	GW ◇1 (catering)	GW 1	HC	GW 1		GW ◇1	GW 1	HC	GW 1	GW ◇1 (catering)	GW 1	HC	GW 1	GW ◇1		GW 1	HC
London Paddington 15 ⊖	d	16 12		16 15	16 42	16 43	17 12	17 15	17 42	17 43	18 12	18 15		18 42	18 43	19 12	19 15	19 42	19 43	20 12	20 15	20 42		20 43	21 12
Acton Main Line	d																								
Ealing Broadway ⊖	d	16 20		16 24		16 51	17 20	17 24		17 51	18 20	18 24			18 51	19 20	19 24		19 50	20 20	20 24			20 51	21 20
West Ealing	d																								
Drayton Green	d																								
Castle Bar Park	d																								
South Greenford	d																								
Greenford ⊖	a																								
Hanwell	d																								
Southall	d	16 24		16 29		16 59	17 24	17 29		17 59	18 24	18 29			18 59	19 24	19 29		19 58	20 24	20 29			20 59	21 24
Hayes & Harlington	d	16 28		16 33		17 02	17 28	17 33		18 03	18 28	18 33			19 02	19 28	19 33		20 02	20 28	20 33			21 03	21 28
Heathrow Terminal 1-2 2 ✈	a	16 34					17 34				18 34					19 34				20 34					21 34
Heathrow Terminal 4 ✈	a	16 41					17 41				18 41					19 41				20 41					21 41
West Drayton	d			16 37		17 06		17 37		18 07		18 37			19 06		19 37		20 06		20 37			21 07	
Iver	d																								
Langley	d			16 42		17 10		17 42		18 11		18 42			19 11		19 42		20 10		20 42			21 11	
Slough 3	a			16 46	17 00	17 14		17 46	18 03	18 14		18 46		19 00	19 14		19 46	20 04	20 14		20 46	21 00		21 14	
	d			16 46	17 01	17 16		17 46	18 04	18 16		18 46		19 01	19 16		19 46	20 05	20 16		20 46	21 01		21 16	
Burnham	d			16 50		17 20		17 50		18 20		18 50			19 20		19 50		20 20		20 50			21 20	
Taplow	d																								
Maidenhead 3	d			16 56	17 08	17 27		17 56	18 12	18 27		18 56		19 08	19 27		19 56		20 27		20 56			21 28	
Twyford 3	d			17 04		17 35		18 04		18 36		19 04			19 35		20 05		20 35		21 04			21 35	
Reading 7	a			17 11	17 20	17 44		18 11	18 25	18 42		19 12		19 20	19 44		20 14	20 22	20 44		21 12	21 17		21 44	
Oxford	a				17 50	18 32			18 54	19 32				19 49	20 30			20 50	21 30			21 56		22 32	

For non-stop services between London and Reading please see table 116

Passengers who hold valid tickets for Acton Main Line, West Ealing and Hanwell will be able to use local Transport for London (TFL) bus services to reach these stations. Tel 0843 222 1234

Table 117

Sundays

30 March to 11 May

Network Diagram - refer to first Page of Table 116

London - Greenford and Reading

		GW 1	GW ◇1	GW 1	HC	GW 1	GW ◇1	GW 1		HC	GW 1	GW ◇1	GW 1
London Paddington 15 ⊖	d	21 15	21 42	21 43	22 12	22 14	22 42	22 43		23 12	23 15	23 47	23 53
Acton Main Line	d												
Ealing Broadway ⊖	d	21 24		21 53	22 20	22 23		22 53		23 20	23 23	23 55	00 02
West Ealing	d												
Drayton Green	d												
Castle Bar Park	d												
South Greenford	d												
Greenford ⊖	a												
Hanwell	d												
Southall	d	21 29		21 59	22 24	22 28		22 59		23 24	23 29		00 07
Hayes & Harlington	d	21 33		22 02	22 28	22 33		23 02		23 28	23 33		00 11
Heathrow Terminal 1-2 2 ✈	a				22 34					23 34			
Heathrow Terminal 4 ✈	a				22 41					23 41			
West Drayton	d	21 37		22 06		22 37		23 06			23 37		00 15
Iver	d												
Langley	d	21 42		22 11		22 41		23 11			23 41		00 20
Slough 3	a	21 46	22 01	22 14		22 45	23 02	23 14			23 43	00 07	00 24
	d	21 46	22 02	22 16		22 46	23 02	23 16			23 45	00 07	00 24
Burnham	d	21 50		22 20		22 50		23 20			23 50		
Taplow	d												
Maidenhead 3	d	21 56		22 25		22 56		23 25			23 56	00 15	00 33
Twyford 3	d	22 04		22 32		23 04		23 32			00 03		00 41
Reading 7	a	22 11	22 17	22 39		23 12	23 20	23 42			00 13	00 30	00 49
Oxford	a		22 50										

For non-stop services between London and Reading please see table 116

Passengers who hold valid tickets for Acton Main Line, West Ealing and Hanwell will be able to use local Transport for London (TFL) bus services to reach these stations. Tel 0843 222 1234

Table 117R

Mondays to Fridays

9 December to 3 January

Network Diagram - refer to first Page of Table 116

Reading and Greenford - London

Miles	Miles	Miles			GW MX 1	GW MX ◇1	HC MX	HC MO	GW MO 1	GW MO 1	GW MX 1	GW MO 1	GW MX 1	GW MX ◇1	GW MO ◇1	GW MX 1	GW 1	GW 1	GW MX 1	GW MO 1	HC	GW 1	HC
—	—	—	Oxford	d										00 07		00 27			04 00				
0	—	—	**Reading 7**	d						00 15	00 17	←		00 39	00 53	01 17	02 24	03 54	04 40	04 40		05 14	
5	—	—	**Twyford 3**	d						00 24	00 23	00 24			01 00	01 23	02 30	04 00	04 46	04 46		05 20	
11¾	—	—	**Maidenhead 3**	d						→	00 31	00 32			01 08	01 31	02 38	04 08	04 54	04 54		05 28	
13½	—	—	Taplow	d							00 34											05 32	
15	—	—	Burnham	d							00 37		←									05 35	
17½	—	—	**Slough 3**	a							00 42	00 39	00 42	00 55	01 15	01 39	02 45	04 15	04 59	04 59		05 40	
—	—	—		d		00 02			00 02		00 42	00 40	00 42	00 56	01 15	01 39	02 45	04 15	05 00	05 00		05 40	
19¾	—	—	Langley	d					00 06		→	00 44	00 46						05 04	05 04		05 44	
21¼	—	—	Iver	d															05 07	05 07		05 47	
22¾	—	—	West Drayton	d					00 11			00 48	00 51				02 52	04 22	05 11	05 11		05 51	
—	—	0	**Heathrow Terminal 4** ✈	d			00 01	00 01													05 23		05 51
—	—	1¾	**Heathrow Terminal 1-2 2** ✈	d			00 07	00 07													05 29		05 57
25¼	—	5¾	Hayes & Harlington	d			00 13	00 14	00 17			00 54	00 56		01 25	01 48	02 57	04 27	05 17	05 17	05 35	05 56	06 03
27	—	7½	Southall	d			00 16	00 17	00 20			00 57	00 59				03 00	04 30	05 19	05 19	05 38	05 59	06 06
28¾	—	9¼	Hanwell	d																	05 41		06 09
—	0	—	**Greenford** ⊖	d																			
—	1	—	South Greenford	d																			
—	1¾	—	Castle Bar Park	d																			
—	2	—	Drayton Green	d																			
29½	2¾	10	West Ealing	d																	05 43		06 11
30¼	3½	11	**Ealing Broadway** ⊖	d	00 06		00 22	00 22	00 27			01 03	01 05		01 32	01 55	03 06	04 36	05 28	05 28	05 46	06 05	06 14
31¾	5	12¼	Acton Main Line	d															05 31	05 31		06 08	
36	9¼	16½	**London Paddington 15** ⊖	a	00 17	00 27	00 30	00 30	00 38			01 14	01 18	01 20	01 41	02 07	03 18	04 48	05 41	05 41	05 56	06 16	06 24

		GW 1	GW 1	GW 1	GW 1	HC	GW 1	GW 1	GW 1	GW 1	GW ◇1	HC	GW 1	GW 1	GW 1	GW 1	GW 1	GW ◇1 ⊡	GW 1	HC	GW 1	GW 1	GW 1
Oxford	d			05 03					05 24	05 43	05 59							06 30				06 04	
Reading 7	d	05 39		05 44	05 59		06 06		06 15	06 16	06 28		06 31	06 35		06 36	06 46	06 55	06 59		07 02	07 05	
Twyford 3	d	05 45		05 50			06 13		06 21	06 23			06 37	06 43		06 43	06 54		07 05		07 09		
Maidenhead 3	d	05 53		05 58	06 10		06 21		06 29	06 31	06 40		06 45			06 53	07 02	07 08	07 13		07 17	07 16	
Taplow	d			06 02			06 24		06 32							06 57							
Burnham	d			06 05			06 27		06 35				06 49			07 01					07 21		
Slough 3	a	06 01		06 10	06 17		06 32		06 40		06 47		06 54			07 06			07 20		07 26		
	d	06 01		06 10	06 17		06 32		06 40		06 48		06 56			07 06			07 21		07 27		
Langley	d			06 14			06 36		06 44				06 59			07 11					07 31		
Iver	d			06 17					06 47				07 03			07 14							
West Drayton	d			06 21			06 41		06 51				07 07			07 18					07 36		
Heathrow Terminal 4 ✈	d																						
Heathrow Terminal 1-2 2 ✈	d					06 27						06 57								07 27			
Hayes & Harlington	d	06 10		06 26		06 33	06 46		06 56			07 03	07 11			07 23				07 33	07 41		
Southall	d	06 13		06 29		06 36	06 50		07 00			07 06	07 15			07 27				07 36	07 45		
Hanwell	d					06 39						07 09								07 39			
Greenford ⊖	d		06 16					06 46							07 16								07 46
South Greenford	d		06 19					06 49							07 19								07 49
Castle Bar Park	d		06 22					06 52							07 22								07 52
Drayton Green	d		06 24					06 54							07 24								07 54
West Ealing	d		06 26			06 41		06 56				07 11			07 26					07 41			07 56
Ealing Broadway ⊖	d	06 19	06 29	06 35		06 44	06 55	06 59	07 05			07 14	07 21		07 29	07 33				07 44	07 52		07 59
Acton Main Line	d		06 33	06 38				07 03							07 33								08 03
London Paddington 15 ⊖	a	06 31	06 42	06 46	06 36	06 54	07 09	07 12	07 17	06 54	07 08	07 24	07 32	07 12	07 42	07 44	07 27	07 27	07 49	07 54	08 04	07 43	08 12

		GW 1	GW 1	GW 1	HC	GW 1	GW 1	GW ◇1	GW 1	GW 1	GW 1	GW 1	HC	GW 1	GW 1	GW 1	GW 1	GW 1	HC	GW 1	GW 1	GW 1
Oxford	d					06 36					07 02						07 21				07 56	
Reading 7	d	07 09				07 30	07 34				07 56	08 04				08 11	08 19			08 31	08 48	
Twyford 3	d	07 15	07 23			07 37	07 41		07 54		08 02	08a10				08 19	08 26			08 37	08 54	
Maidenhead 3	d	07 23	07 32	07 41		07 45	07 49	07 59	08 02		08 11					08 27	08 35	08 41		08 45	09 03	
Taplow	d	07 27					07 53									08 30				08 49		
Burnham	d	07 30				07 51	07 56				08 16					08 34				08 50		
Slough 3	a	07 35		07 49		07 55	08 01				08 20					08 39		08 49		08 57		
	d	07 36		07 50		07 56	08 01				08 21			08 29		08 39		08 50		08 57		
Langley	d	07 41				08 00	08 06							08 32		08 43				09 01		
Iver	d	07 44				08 03										08 46				09 04		
West Drayton	d	07 48				08 07	08 11							08 38		08 50				09 08		
Heathrow Terminal 4 ✈	d																					
Heathrow Terminal 1-2 2 ✈	d				07 57								08 27						08 57			
Hayes & Harlington	d	07 53			08 03	08 12	08 16						08 33	08 42		08 54			09 03	09 13		
Southall	d	07 57			08 06	08 16	08 20						08 36	08 46				09 01	09 06	09 17		
Hanwell	d				08 09								08 39						09 09			
Greenford ⊖	d									08 16					08 46							09 16
South Greenford	d									08 19					08 49							09 19
Castle Bar Park	d									08 22					08 52							09 22
Drayton Green	d									08 24					08 54							09 24
West Ealing	d				08 11					08 26			08 41		08 56				09 11			09 26
Ealing Broadway ⊖	d	08 03			08 14	08 21	08 25			08 29			08 44	08 52	08 59	09 04			09 14	09 23		09 29
Acton Main Line	d									08 33					09 03							09 33
London Paddington 15 ⊖	a	08 16	08 02	08 21	08 24	08 32	08 37	08 26	08 28	08 42	08 48		08 54	09 03	09 12	09 16	08 58	09 21	09 24	09 35	09 27	09 42

For non-stop services between London and Reading please see table 116

Passengers who hold valid tickets for Acton Main Line, West Ealing and Hanwell will be able to use local Transport for London (TFL) bus services to reach these stations. Tel 0843 222 1234

Table 117R

Mondays to Fridays

9 December to 3 January

Network Diagram - refer to first Page of Table 116

Reading and Greenford - London

		GW	HC	GW	GW	GW	GW	GW	HC	GW		GW	GW	GW	GW	HC	GW	GW	GW	GW		GW	HC	GW	GW
		■1		■1	■1	■1	■1	◇■1		■1		■1	◇■1	■1	■1		■1	■1	◇■1 🛒	■1		■1		■1	■1
Oxford	d						08 35	09 01					09 31				09 07		10 01					09 37	
Reading ■7	d			09 05		09 18	09 33	09 37				09 48	09 55				10 03	10 18	10 26					10 33	10 48
Twyford ■3	d			09 11		09 24	09 39					09 54					10 09	10 24						10 39	10 54
Maidenhead ■3	d			09 19		09 35	09 47					10 02					10 17	10 32						10 47	11 02
Taplow	d			09 22		09 36						10 06						10 36							11 06
Burnham	d			09 25		09 39				←		10 09			←			10 39				←			11 09
Slough ■3	a			09 30		09 44	09 54	09 53		09 54		10 14	10 10		10 14		10 24	10 44	10 40			10 44		10 53	11 14
	d	09 14		09 30		09 44	09 54	09 54		09 54		10 14	10 11		10 14		10 24	10 44	10 41			10 44		10 54	11 14
Langley	d			09 35			→			09 58		→					10 28	→						10 58	→
Iver	d			09 37						10 01							10 31							11 01	
West Drayton	d	09 21		09 41		09 51				10 05					10 21		10 35					10 51		11 05	
Heathrow Terminal 4 ✈	d																								
Heathrow Terminal 1-2 ■2 ✈	d		09 27						09 57							10 27							10 57		
Hayes & Harlington	d	09 26	09 34	09 46		09 56			10 03	10 10					10 26	10 33	10 40					10 56	11 03	11 09	
Southall	d	09 30	09 37	09 50					10 06	10 13						10 36	10 43						11 06	11 13	
Hanwell	d		09 41						10 09							10 39							11 09		
Greenford ⊖	d				09 46									10 16						10 46					
South Greenford	d				09 49									10 19						10 49					
Castle Bar Park	d				09 52									10 22						10 52					
Drayton Green	d				09 54									10 24						10 54					
West Ealing	d		09 42		09 56				10 11					10 26		10 41				10 56			11 11		
Ealing Broadway ⊖	d	09 36	09 46	09 55	09 59	10 08			10 14	10 19				10 29	10 33	10 44	10 49			10 59		11 03	11 14	11 19	
Acton Main Line	d				10 03									10 33						11 03					
London Paddington ■15 ⊖	a	09 48	09 54	10 05	10 12	10 18		10 12	10 24	10 31			10 29	10 42	10 46	10 54	11 01		11 00	11 12		11 16	11 24	11 32	

		GW	GW	GW	HC	GW		GW	GW	GW	GW	HC	GW	GW	GW	GW		GW	HC	GW	GW	GW	GW	GW	HC
		◇■1	■1	■1		■1		■1	◇■1 🛒	■1	■1		■1	■1	◇■1 🛒	■1		■1		■1	■1	◇■1 🛒	■1	■1	
Oxford	d	10 31				10 08			11 01				10 37		11 31					11 07		12 01			
Reading ■7	d	10 56				11 03		11 18	11 26				11 33	11 48	11 56					12 03	12 18	12 27			
Twyford ■3	d					11 09		11 24					11 39	11 54						12 09	12 24				
Maidenhead ■3	d					11 17		11 32					11 47	12 02						12 17	12 32				
Taplow	d							11 36						12 06							12 36				
Burnham	d			←				11 39			←			12 09				←			12 39			←	
Slough ■3	a	11 10		11 14		11 24		11 44	11 39		11 44		11 54	12 14	12 10			12 14		12 24	12 44	12 41		12 44	
	d	11 11		11 14		11 24		11 44	11 40		11 44		11 54	12 14	12 11			12 14		12 24	12 44	12 41		12 44	
Langley	d					11 28		→					11 58	→						12 28	→				
Iver	d					11 31							12 01							12 31					
West Drayton	d			11 21		11 35					11 51		12 05					12 21		12 35				12 51	
Heathrow Terminal 4 ✈	d																								
Heathrow Terminal 1-2 ■2 ✈	d				11 27							11 57							12 27						12 57
Hayes & Harlington	d			11 26	11 33	11 40					11 56	12 03	12 10					12 26	12 33	12 40				12 56	13 03
Southall	d				11 36	11 43						12 06	12 13						12 36	12 43					13 06
Hanwell	d				11 39							12 09							12 39						13 09
Greenford ⊖	d		11 16							11 46						12 16							12 46		
South Greenford	d		11 19							11 49						12 19							12 49		
Castle Bar Park	d		11 22							11 52						12 22							12 52		
Drayton Green	d		11 24							11 54						12 24							12 54		
West Ealing	d		11 26		11 41					11 56		12 11				12 26			12 41				12 56		13 11
Ealing Broadway ⊖	d		11 29	11 33	11 44	11 49				11 59	12 07	12 14	12 19			12 29		12 33	12 44	12 49			12 59	13 03	13 14
Acton Main Line	d		11 33							12 03						12 33							13 03		
London Paddington ■15 ⊖	a	11 30	11 42	11 46	11 54	12 01			11 59	12 12	12 18	12 24	12 31		12 30	12 42		12 46	12 54	13 02		13 09	13 12	13 16	13 24

		GW		GW	GW	GW	GW	HC	GW	GW	GW	GW		GW	HC	GW	GW	GW	GW	GW	HC	GW		GW	GW
		■1		■1	◇■1 🛒	■1	■1		■1	■1	◇■1 🛒	■1		■1		■1	■1	◇■1 🛒	■1	■1		■1		■1	◇■1 🛒
Oxford	d	11 37			12 31				12 07		13 01					12 37		13 31				13 07			14 01
Reading ■7	d	12 33		12 48	12 56				13 03	13 18	13 26					13 33	13 48	13 56				14 03		14 18	14 26
Twyford ■3	d	12 39		12 54					13 09	13 24						13 39	13 54					14 09		14 24	
Maidenhead ■3	d	12 47		13 02					13 17	13 32						13 47	14 02					14 17		14 32	
Taplow	d			13 06						13 36							14 06							14 36	
Burnham	d			13 09			←			13 39				←			14 09			←				14 39	
Slough ■3	a	12 54		13 14	13 10		13 14		13 24	13 44	13 41			13 44		13 54	14 13	14 10		14 13		14 24		14 44	14 40
	d	12 54		13 14	13 11		13 14		13 24	13 48	13 41			13 48		13 54	14 14	14 11		14 14		14 24		14 44	14 41
Langley	d	12 58		→					13 28	→						13 58	→					14 28		→	
Iver	d	13 01							13 31							14 01						14 31			
West Drayton	d	13 05					13 21		13 35					13 51		14 05				14 21		14 35			
Heathrow Terminal 4 ✈	d																								
Heathrow Terminal 1-2 ■2 ✈	d							13 27							13 57						14 27				
Hayes & Harlington	d	13 10					13 26	13 33	13 40					13 56	14 03	14 10				14 26	14 33	14 40			
Southall	d	13 13						13 36	13 43						14 06	14 13					14 36	14 43			
Hanwell	d							13 39							14 09						14 39				
Greenford ⊖	d					13 16						13 46							14 16						
South Greenford	d					13 19						13 49							14 19						
Castle Bar Park	d					13 22						13 52							14 22						
Drayton Green	d					13 24						13 54							14 24						
West Ealing	d					13 26		13 41				13 56			14 11				14 26		14 41				
Ealing Broadway ⊖	d	13 19				13 29	13 33	13 44	13 49			13 59		14 03	14 14	14 19			14 29	14 33	14 44	14 49			
Acton Main Line	d					13 33						14 03							14 33						
London Paddington ■15 ⊖	a	13 31			13 30	13 42	13 46	13 54	14 01		14 01	14 12		14 16	14 24	14 31		14 30	14 42	14 46	14 54	15 01			15 01

For non-stop services between London and Reading please see table 116

Passengers who hold valid tickets for Acton Main Line, West Ealing and Hanwell will be able to use local Transport for London (TFL) bus services to reach these stations. Tel 0843 222 1234

Table 117R

Mondays to Fridays

9 December to 3 January

Network Diagram - refer to first Page of Table 116

Reading and Greenford - London

		GW 1	GW 1	HC	GW 1	GW 1	GW ◇1	GW 1		GW 1	HC	GW 1	GW 1	GW ◇1 🛒	GW 1	GW 1	HC	GW 1		GW 1	GW ◇1 ☕	GW 1	GW 1	HC	GW 1
Oxford	d				13 37		14 31					14 07		15 01				14 37			15 31				15 07
Reading 7	d				14 33	14 48	14 56					15 03	15 18	15 26				15 33		15 48	15 57				16 03
Twyford 3	d				14 39	14 54						15 09	15 24					15 39		15 54					16 09
Maidenhead 3	d				14 47	15 02						15 17	15 32					15 47		16 02					16 17
Taplow	d					15 06							15 36							16 06					
Burnham	d		←			15 09				←			15 39			←				16 09			←		
Slough 3	a		14 44		14 54	15 14	15 10			15 14		15 24	15 44	15 39		15 44		15 54		16 14	16 10		16 14		16 24
	d		14 44		14 54	15 14	15 11			15 14		15 24	15 44	15 40		15 44		15 54		16 14	16 11		16 14		16 24
Langley	d				14 58	→						15 28	→					15 58		→					16 28
Iver	d				15 01							15 31						16 01							16 31
West Drayton	d		14 51		15 05					15 21		15 35				15 51		16 05					16 21		16 35
Heathrow Terminal 4 ✈	d																								
Heathrow Terminal 1-2 2 ✈	d			14 57							15 27						15 57							16 27	
Hayes & Harlington	d		14 56	15 03	15 10					15 26	15 33	15 40				15 56	16 03	16 10					16 26	16 33	16 40
Southall	d			15 06	15 13						15 36	15 43					16 06	16 13						16 36	16 43
Hanwell	d			15 09							15 39						16 09							16 39	
Greenford ⊖	d	14 46						15 16							15 46							16 16			
South Greenford	d	14 49						15 19							15 49							16 19			
Castle Bar Park	d	14 52						15 22							15 52							16 22			
Drayton Green	d	14 54						15 24							15 54							16 24			
West Ealing	d	14 56		15 11				15 26			15 41				15 56		16 11					16 26		16 41	
Ealing Broadway ⊖	d	14 59	15 03	15 14	15 19			15 29		15 33	15 44	15 49			15 59	16 03	16 14	16 19				16 29	16 33	16 44	16 49
Acton Main Line	d	15 03						15 33							16 03							16 33			
London Paddington 15 ⊖	a	15 12	15 16	15 24	15 32		15 30	15 42		15 46	15 54	16 01		16 01	16 12	16 16	16 24	16 31			16 29	16 42	16 46	16 54	17 01

		GW 1	GW ◇1 🛒	GW 1		GW 1	HC	GW 1	GW 1	GW ◇1	GW 1	GW 1	HC	GW 1		GW 1	GW ◇1 ☕	GW ◇1 🛒	GW 1	GW 1	HC	GW 1	GW 1	GW 1	
Oxford	d		16 01					15 37		16 31				16 07				17 01				16 37			
Reading 7	d	16 18	16 26					16 31	16 48	16 57				17 03		17 14	17 18	17 27				17 33	17 42	17 54	
Twyford 3	d	16 24						16 39	16 54					17 09		17 24						17 39	17 48		
Maidenhead 3	d	16 32						16 47	17 02					17 17		17 32		17 40				17 47	17 56	18 08	
Taplow	d	16 36							17 06							17 36							18 00		
Burnham	d	16 39				←			17 09			←				17 39				←			18 02		
Slough 3	a	16 44	16 41			16 44		16 54	17 16	17 13		17 16		17 24		17 44	17 32			17 44		17 54	18 07	18 16	
	d	16 44	16 41			16 44		16 54	17 17	17 14		17 17		17 24		17 44	17 33			17 44		17 54	18 07	18 16	
Langley	d	→						16 58	→					17 28		→						17 58		→	
Iver	d							17 01						17 31								18 01			
West Drayton	d					16 51		17 05				17 24		17 35						17 51		18 05	18 14		
Heathrow Terminal 4 ✈	d																								
Heathrow Terminal 1-2 2 ✈	d						16 57						17 27								17 57				
Hayes & Harlington	d					16 56	17 03	17 10				17 29	17 33	17 40						17 56	18 03	18 10	18 19		
Southall	d						17 06	17 13					17 36	17 43							18 06	18 13			
Hanwell	d						17 09						17 39								18 09				
Greenford ⊖	d			16 46							17 16								17 46						
South Greenford	d			16 49							17 19								17 49						
Castle Bar Park	d			16 52							17 22								17 52						
Drayton Green	d			16 54							17 24								17 54						
West Ealing	d			16 56			17 11				17 26		17 41						17 56		18 11				
Ealing Broadway ⊖	d			16 59		17 03	17 14	17 21			17 29	17 36	17 44	17 49					17 59	18 03	18 14	18 19	18 26		
Acton Main Line	d			17 03							17 33								18 03						
London Paddington 15 ⊖	a		17 00	17 12		17 17	17 24	17 31		17 34	17 42	17 46	17 54	18 01			17 52	17 59	18 12	18 14	18 24	18 31	18 37		

		GW ◇1 ☕	GW 1	GW 1	HC	GW 1	GW 1	GW 1	GW ◇1 🛒	GW 1		GW 1	HC	GW 1	GW 1	GW ◇1	GW 1	GW 1	HC	GW 1		GW 1	GW 1	GW ◇1 🛒	HC
Oxford	d	17 31					17 07		18 01					17 37		18 31				18 07				19 06	
Reading 7	d	17 56					18 08	18 18	18 27					18 33	18 48	18 59				19 08			19 20	19 33	
Twyford 3	d						18 14	18 24						18 39	18 54					19 14			19 26		
Maidenhead 3	d					18 15	18 27	18 32						18 48	19 05					19 22			19 34		
Taplow	d							18 35							19 09								19 37		
Burnham	d			←				18 39				←			19 12			←					19 40		
Slough 3	a	18 10		18 16		18 22	18 34	18 44	18 40			18 44		18 54	19 17	19 10		19 17		19 30			19 45	19 47	
	d	18 11		18 16		18 22	18 34	18 44	18 41			18 44		18 54	19 17	19 11		19 17		19 30			19 45	19 48	
Langley	d					18 26		→						18 58	→					19 34					
Iver	d					18 29								19 01						19 37					
West Drayton	d					18 33						18 51		19 05				19 24		19 40			19 52		
Heathrow Terminal 4 ✈	d																								
Heathrow Terminal 1-2 2 ✈	d				18 27								18 57						19 27						19 57
Hayes & Harlington	d			18 27	18 33	18 38	18 43					18 56	19 03	19 10				19 29	19 33	19 45			19 57		20 03
Southall	d				18 36	18 42							19 06	19 13					19 36	19 48					20 06
Hanwell	d				18 39								19 09						19 39						20 09
Greenford ⊖	d		18 16							18 46							19 16					19 46			
South Greenford	d		18 19							18 49							19 19					19 49			
Castle Bar Park	d		18 22							18 52							19 22					19 52			
Drayton Green	d		18 24							18 54							19 24					19 54			
West Ealing	d		18 26		18 41					18 56			19 11				19 26		19 41			19 56			20 11
Ealing Broadway ⊖	d		18 29	18 35	18 44	18 48	18 53			18 59		19 05	19 14	19 19			19 29	19 36	19 44	19 54		19 59	20 04		20 14
Acton Main Line	d		18 33							19 03							19 34					20 03			
London Paddington 15 ⊖	a	18 28	18 42	18 46	18 54	18 59	19 02		18 59	19 12		19 18	19 24	19 31		19 31	19 42	19 46	19 54	20 03		20 12	20 17	20 06	20 24

For non-stop services between London and Reading please see table 116

Passengers who hold valid tickets for Acton Main Line, West Ealing and Hanwell will be able to use local Transport for London (TFL) bus services to reach these stations. Tel 0843 222 1234

Table 117R

Mondays to Fridays

9 December to 3 January

Network Diagram - refer to first Page of Table 116

Reading and Greenford - London

		GW	GW	GW	GW	GW		GW	GW	HC	GW	GW	GW	GW	GW	HC		GW	GW	GW	GW	GW	HC	GW	GW
			FX	FO				FO	FX																
		1	1	1	◇1	1		1	1		1	1	◇1	1	1			1	1	◇1	1	1		1	1
Oxford	d	18 37			19 31						19 10		20 01					19 37		20 31					20 07
Reading 7	d	19 33	19 48	19 48	19 55						19 58	20 18	20 26					20 33	20 48	20 56					21 12
Twyford 3	d	19 42	19 54	19 54							20 04	20 24						20 39	20 54						21 18
Maidenhead 3	d	19 50	20 02	20 02							20 12	20 32						20 47	21 02						21 26
Taplow	d		20 05	20 05								20 36							21 06						21 30
Burnham	d		20 09	20 09				←	←			20 39			←				21 09			←			21 33
Slough 3	a	19 57	20 14	20 14	20 10			20 14	20 14		20 22	20 44	20 40		20 44			20 54	21 13	21 11		21 13			21 38
	d	19 57	20 14	20 14	20 11			20 14	20 14		20 24	20 44	20 41		20 44			20 54	21 14	21 12		21 14			21 38
Langley	d	20 01	→	→							20 28	→						20 58	→			21 17			21 42
Iver	d	20 04									20 31							21 01				21 20			21 45
West Drayton	d	20 08						20 21	20 21		20 35				20 51			21 05				21 24			21 49
Heathrow Terminal 4 ✈	d																								
Heathrow Terminal 1-2 2 ✈	d									20 27						20 57							21 27		
Hayes & Harlington	d	20 13						20 26	20 26	20 33	20 40				20 56	21 03		21 10				21 28	21 33		21 54
Southall	d	20 16								20 36	20 43					21 06		21 13					21 36		21 57
Hanwell	d									20 39						21 09							21 39		
Greenford ⊖	d					20 16								20 46							21 16			21 45	
South Greenford	d					20 19								20 49							21 19			21 48	
Castle Bar Park	d					20 22								20 52							21 22			21 51	
Drayton Green	d					20 24								20 54							21 24			21 53	
West Ealing	d					20 26				20 41				20 56		21 11					21 26		21 41	21 55	
Ealing Broadway ⊖	d	20 22				20 29		20 32	20 33	20 44	20 49			20 59	21 03	21 14		21 19			21 29	21 35	21 44	21 58	22 03
Acton Main Line	d					20 33								21 03							21 33			22 01	
London Paddington 15 ⊖	a	20 32			20 30	20 42		20 49	20 49	20 54	20 59		21 01	21 12	21 16	21 24		21 30		21 29	21 42	21 47	21 54	22 11	22 14

		GW		HC	GW	GW	GW	HC	HC	GW	GW	GW		HC	GW	GW	HC	HC	GW	GW	GW				
				FO		FO	FX	FO	FX					FO	FO	FX	FO	FX							
		◇1			1	◇1	◇1			1	◇	1			◇1	◇1			1	1	◇1				
Oxford	d	21 01			20 37	21 32	21 32				22 11				22 30	22 30					23 09				
Reading 7	d	21 26			21 33	21 56	21 56			22 17	22 44	22 48			22 59	22 59				23 15	23 41				
Twyford 3	d				21 39					22 23		22 54								23 22					
Maidenhead 3	d				21 47					22 32		23 02								23 29	23 55				
Taplow	d				21 50					22 34		23 05								23 33					
Burnham	d				21 53					22 37		23 08							←	23 36					
Slough 3	a	21 40			21 58	22 14	22 14			22 42	23 01	23 14			23 14	23 14			23 14	23 41	00 02				
	d	21 41			21 59	22 14	22 14			22 42	23 01	23 27			23 14	23 14			23 27	23 41	00 02				
Langley	d				22 02					22 46		→							23 32	23 45					
Iver	d				22 05					22 49									23 35	23 48					
West Drayton	d				22 09					22 53									23 39	23 51					
Heathrow Terminal 4 ✈	d																								
Heathrow Terminal 1-2 2 ✈	d			21 57				22 27	22 39					22 57			23 27	23 30							
Hayes & Harlington	d			22 03	22 14			22 33	22 45	22 59				23 03			23 33	23 36	23 43	23 56					
Southall	d			22 06				22 36	22 48	23 02				23 06			23 36	23 39	23 47	23 59					
Hanwell	d			22 09				22 39						23 09			23 39								
Greenford ⊖	d																								
South Greenford	d																								
Castle Bar Park	d																								
Drayton Green	d																								
West Ealing	d			22 11				22 41						23 11			23 41								
Ealing Broadway ⊖	d			22 14	22 21			22 44	22 55	23 08				23 14			23 44	23 44	23 52	00 06					
Acton Main Line	d									23 11								23 47							
London Paddington 15 ⊖	a	22 00		22 24	22 32	22 38	22 41	22 54	23 02	23 19	23 24			23 24	23 37	23 38	23 54	23 55	00 02	00 17	00 27				

For non-stop services between London and Reading please see table 116

Passengers who hold valid tickets for Acton Main Line, West Ealing and Hanwell will be able to use local Transport for London (TFL) bus services to reach these stations. Tel 0843 222 1234

Table 117R

Mondays to Fridays

6 January to 7 February

Network Diagram - refer to first Page of Table 116

Reading and Greenford - London

		GW	GW	HC	HC	GW		GW	GW	GW	GW	GW	GW	GW	GW	GW		GW	HC	GW	HC	GW	GW	GW	GW
		MX	MX	MX	MO	MO		MO	MX	MX	MO	MX	MX	MO		MX		MO							
		1	◇1			1		1	1	◇1	◇1	1	1	1	1	1		1		1		1	1	1	1
Oxford	d									00 07		00 27				04 00								05 03	
Reading 7	d							00 15	00 17	00 39	00 58	01 17	02 24	02 24	03 54	04 40		04 40		05 14		05 39		05 44	05 59
Twyford 3	d							00 23	00 23		01 05	01 23	02 30	02 30	04 00	04 46		04 46		05 20		05 45		05 50	
Maidenhead 3	d							00 31	00 31		01 13	01 31	02 38	02 38	04 08	04 54		04 54		05 28		05 53		05 58	06 10
Taplow	d								00 34											05 32				06 02	
Burnham	d								00 37											05 35				06 05	
Slough 3	a							00 38	00 42	00 55	01 20	01 39	02 45	02 50	04 15	04 59		04 59		05 40		06 01		06 10	06 17
	d		00 02			00 02		00 39	00 42	00 56	01 21	01 39	02 45	02 50	04 15	05 00		05 00		05 40		06 01		06 10	06 17
Langley	d					00 06		00 43	00 46							05 04		05 04		05 44				06 14	
Iver	d															05 07		05 07		05 47				06 17	
West Drayton	d					00 11		00 48	00 51				02 52	02 57	04 22	05 11		05 11		05 51				06 21	
Heathrow Terminal 4 ✈	d			00 01	00 01														05 23		05 51				
Heathrow Terminal 1-2 2 ✈	d			00 07	00 07														05 29		05 57				
Hayes & Harlington	d			00 13	00 14	00 17		00 54	00 56		01 30	01 48	02 57	03 02	04 27	05 17		05 17	05 35	05 56	06 03	06 10		06 26	
Southall	d			00 16	00 17	00 20		00 57	00 59				03 00	03 04	04 30	05 19		05 19	05 38	05 59	06 06	06 13		06 29	
Hanwell	d																		05 41		06 09				
Greenford ⊖	d																						06 16		
South Greenford	d																						06 19		
Castle Bar Park	d																						06 22		
Drayton Green	d																						06 24		
West Ealing	d																		05 43		06 11		06 26		
Ealing Broadway ⊖	d	00 06		00 22	00 22	00 27		01 03	01 05		01 37	01 55	03 06	03 10	04 36	05 28		05 28	05 46	06 05	06 14	06 19	06 29	06 35	
Acton Main Line	d															05 31		05 31		06 08			06 33	06 38	
London Paddington 15 ⊖	a	00 17	00 27	00 30	00 30	00 38		01 14	01 18	01 20	01 46	02 07	03 18	03 22	04 48	05 41		05 41	05 56	06 16	06 24	06 31	06 42	06 46	06 36

		HC		GW	GW	GW	GW	GW	HC	GW	GW	GW		GW	GW	GW	GW	HC	GW	GW	GW	GW		GW	GW
				1	1	1	1	◇1		1	1	1		1	1	◇1	1		1	1	1	1		1	1
Oxford	d					05 24	05 43	05 59								06 30				06 04					
Reading 7	d			06 06		06 15	06 16	06 28		06 31	06 35			06 36	06 46	06 55	06 59		07 02	07 05		07 09			
Twyford 3	d			06 13		06 21	06 23			06 37	06 43			06 43	06 54		07 05		07 09			07 15		07 23	
Maidenhead 3	d			06 21		06 29	06 31	06 40		06 45				06 53	07 02	07 08	07 13		07 17	07 16		07 23		07 32	07 41
Taplow	d			06 24		06 32								06 57								07 27			
Burnham	d			06 27		06 35				06 49				07 01					07 21			07 30			
Slough 3	a			06 32		06 40		06 47		06 54				07 06			07 20		07 26			07 35			07 49
	d			06 32		06 40		06 48		06 56				07 06			07 21		07 27			07 36			07 50
Langley	d			06 36		06 44				06 59				07 11					07 31			07 41			
Iver	d					06 47				07 03				07 14								07 44			
West Drayton	d			06 41		06 51				07 07				07 18					07 36			07 48			
Heathrow Terminal 4 ✈	d																								
Heathrow Terminal 1-2 2 ✈	d	06 27							06 57									07 27							
Hayes & Harlington	d	06 33		06 46		06 56			07 03	07 11				07 23				07 33	07 41			07 53			
Southall	d	06 36		06 50		07 00			07 06	07 15				07 27				07 36	07 45			07 57			
Hanwell	d	06 39							07 09									07 39							
Greenford ⊖	d				06 46							07 16									07 46				
South Greenford	d				06 49							07 19									07 49				
Castle Bar Park	d				06 52							07 22									07 52				
Drayton Green	d				06 54							07 24									07 54				
West Ealing	d	06 41			06 56				07 11			07 26						07 41			07 56				
Ealing Broadway ⊖	d	06 44		06 55	06 59	07 05			07 14	07 21		07 29		07 33				07 44	07 52		07 59	08 03			
Acton Main Line	d				07 03							07 33									08 03				
London Paddington 15 ⊖	a	06 54		07 09	07 12	07 17	06 54	07 08	07 24	07 32	07 12	07 42		07 44	07 27	07 27	07 49	07 54	08 04	07 43	08 12	08 16		08 02	08 21

		HC	GW	GW	GW	GW	GW	GW		GW	HC	GW	GW	GW	GW	GW	HC	GW		GW	GW	GW	HC	GW	GW
			1	1	◇1	1	1	1		1		1	1	1	1	1		1		1	1	1		1	1
Oxford	d		06 36					07 02							07 21					07 56					
Reading 7	d		07 30	07 34				07 56		08 04				08 11	08 19			08 31		08 48				09 05	
Twyford 3	d		07 37	07 41		07 54		08 02		08a10				08 19	08 26			08 37		08 54				09 11	
Maidenhead 3	d		07 45	07 49	07 59	08 02		08 11						08 27	08 35	08 41		08 45		09 03				09 19	
Taplow	d			07 53										08 30				08 49						09 22	
Burnham	d		07 51	07 56				08 16						08 34				08 50						09 25	
Slough 3	a		07 55	08 01				08 20						08 39		08 49		08 57						09 30	
	d		07 56	08 01				08 21				08 29		08 39		08 50		08 57				09 14		09 30	
Langley	d		08 00	08 06								08 32		08 43				09 01						09 35	
Iver	d		08 03											08 46				09 04						09 37	
West Drayton	d		08 07	08 11								08 38		08 50				09 08				09 21		09 41	
Heathrow Terminal 4 ✈	d																								
Heathrow Terminal 1-2 2 ✈	d	07 57									08 27						08 57						09 27		
Hayes & Harlington	d	08 03	08 12	08 16							08 33	08 42		08 54			09 03	09 13				09 26	09 34	09 46	
Southall	d	08 06	08 16	08 20							08 36	08 46				09 01	09 06	09 17				09 30	09 37	09 50	
Hanwell	d	08 09									08 39						09 09						09 41		
Greenford ⊖	d						08 16						08 46								09 16				09 46
South Greenford	d						08 19						08 49								09 19				09 49
Castle Bar Park	d						08 22						08 52								09 22				09 52
Drayton Green	d						08 24						08 54								09 24				09 54
West Ealing	d	08 11					08 26				08 41		08 56				09 11				09 26		09 42		09 56
Ealing Broadway ⊖	d	08 14	08 21	08 25			08 29				08 44	08 52	08 59	09 04			09 14	09 23			09 29	09 36	09 46	09 55	09 59
Acton Main Line	d						08 33						09 03								09 33				10 03
London Paddington 15 ⊖	a	08 24	08 32	08 37	08 26	08 28	08 42	08 48			08 54	09 03	09 12	09 16	08 58	09 21	09 24	09 35		09 27	09 42	09 48	09 54	10 05	10 12

For non-stop services between London and Reading please see table 116

Passengers who hold valid tickets for Acton Main Line, West Ealing and Hanwell will be able to use local Transport for London (TFL) bus services to reach these stations. Tel 0843 222 1234

Table 117R

Mondays to Fridays

6 January to 7 February

Network Diagram - refer to first Page of Table 116

Reading and Greenford - London

		GW 1	GW 1	GW ◇1	HC	GW 1	GW 1	GW ◇1	GW 1	GW 1	HC	GW 1	GW 1	GW ◇1 (bus)	GW 1	GW 1	HC	GW 1	GW 1	GW ◇1	GW 1	GW 1
Oxford	d		08 35	09 01				09 31				09 07		10 01				09 37		10 31		
Reading 7	d	09 18	09 33	09 37			09 48	09 55				10 03	10 18	10 26				10 33	10 48	10 56		
Twyford 3	d	09 24	09 39				09 54					10 09	10 24					10 39	10 54			
Maidenhead 3	d	09 35	09 47				10 02					10 17	10 32					10 47	11 02			
Taplow	d	09 36					10 06						10 36						11 06			
Burnham	d	09 39				←	10 09			←			10 39			←			11 09			←
Slough 3	a	09 44	09 54	09 53		09 54	10 14	10 10		10 14		10 24	10 44	10 40		10 44		10 53	11 14	11 10		11 14
	d	09 44	09 55	09 54		09 55	10 14	10 11		10 14		10 24	10 44	10 41		10 44		10 54	11 14	11 11		11 14
Langley	d		→			09 58	→					10 28	→					10 58	→			
Iver	d					10 01						10 31						11 01				
West Drayton	d	09 51				10 05				10 21		10 35				10 51		11 05				11 21
Heathrow Terminal 4 ✈	d																					
Heathrow Terminal 1-2 2 ✈	d				09 57						10 27						10 57					
Hayes & Harlington	d	09 56			10 03	10 10				10 26	10 33	10 40				10 56	11 03	11 09				11 26
Southall	d				10 06	10 13					10 36	10 43					11 06	11 13				
Hanwell	d				10 09						10 39						11 09					
Greenford ⊖	d								10 16						10 46						11 16	
South Greenford	d								10 19						10 49						11 19	
Castle Bar Park	d								10 22						10 52						11 22	
Drayton Green	d								10 24						10 54						11 24	
West Ealing	d				10 11				10 26		10 41				10 56		11 11				11 26	
Ealing Broadway ⊖	d	10 08			10 14	10 19			10 29	10 33	10 44	10 49			10 59	11 03	11 14	11 19			11 29	11 33
Acton Main Line	d								10 33						11 03						11 33	
London Paddington 15 ⊖	a	10 18		10 12	10 24	10 31		10 29	10 42	10 46	10 54	11 01		11 00	11 12	11 16	11 24	11 32		11 30	11 42	11 46

		HC	GW 1	GW 1	GW ◇1 (bus)	GW 1	GW 1	HC	GW 1	GW 1	GW ◇1 (bus)	GW 1	GW 1	HC	GW 1	GW 1	GW ◇1 (bus)	GW 1	GW 1	HC	GW 1	GW 1	GW ◇1 (bus)
Oxford	d		10 08		11 01				10 37		11 31				11 07		12 01				11 37		12 31
Reading 7	d		11 03	11 18	11 26				11 33	11 48	11 56				12 03	12 18	12 27				12 33	12 48	12 56
Twyford 3	d		11 09	11 24					11 39	11 54					12 09	12 24					12 39	12 54	
Maidenhead 3	d		11 17	11 32					11 47	12 02					12 17	12 32					12 47	13 02	
Taplow	d			11 36						12 06						12 36						13 06	
Burnham	d			11 39			←			12 09			←			12 39			←			13 09	
Slough 3	a		11 24	11 44	11 39		11 44		11 54	12 14	12 10		12 14		12 24	12 44	12 41		12 44		12 54	13 14	13 10
	d		11 24	11 44	11 40		11 44		11 54	12 14	12 11		12 14		12 24	12 44	12 41		12 44		12 54	13 14	13 11
Langley	d		11 28	→					11 58	→					12 28	→					12 58	→	
Iver	d		11 31						12 01						12 31						13 01		
West Drayton	d		11 35				11 51		12 05				12 21		12 35				12 51		13 05		
Heathrow Terminal 4 ✈	d																						
Heathrow Terminal 1-2 2 ✈	d	11 27						11 57						12 27						12 57			
Hayes & Harlington	d	11 33	11 40				11 56	12 03	12 10				12 26	12 33	12 40				12 56	13 03	13 10		
Southall	d	11 36	11 43					12 06	12 13					12 36	12 43					13 06	13 13		
Hanwell	d	11 39						12 09						12 39						13 09			
Greenford ⊖	d					11 46						12 16						12 46					
South Greenford	d					11 49						12 19						12 49					
Castle Bar Park	d					11 52						12 22						12 52					
Drayton Green	d					11 54						12 24						12 54					
West Ealing	d	11 41				11 56		12 11				12 26		12 41				12 56		13 11			
Ealing Broadway ⊖	d	11 44	11 49			11 59	12 07	12 14	12 19			12 29	12 33	12 44	12 49			12 59	13 03	13 14	13 19		
Acton Main Line	d					12 03						12 33						13 03					
London Paddington 15 ⊖	a	11 54	12 01		11 59	12 12	12 18	12 24	12 31		12 30	12 42	12 46	12 54	13 02		13 09	13 12	13 16	13 24	13 31		13 30

		GW 1	GW 1	HC	GW 1	GW 1	GW ◇1 (bus)	GW 1	GW 1	HC	GW 1	GW 1	GW ◇1 (bus)	GW 1	GW 1	HC	GW 1	GW 1	GW ◇1 (bus)	GW 1	GW 1	HC	GW 1
Oxford	d				12 07		13 01				12 37		13 31				13 07		14 01				13 37
Reading 7	d				13 03	13 18	13 26				13 33	13 48	13 56				14 03	14 18	14 26				14 33
Twyford 3	d				13 09	13 24					13 39	13 54					14 09	14 24					14 39
Maidenhead 3	d				13 17	13 32					13 47	14 02					14 17	14 32					14 47
Taplow	d					13 36						14 06						14 36					
Burnham	d		←			13 39			←			14 09			←			14 39			←		
Slough 3	a		13 14		13 24	13 44	13 41		13 44		13 54	14 13	14 10		14 13		14 24	14 44	14 40		14 44		14 54
	d		13 14		13 24	13 48	13 41		13 48		13 54	14 14	14 11		14 14		14 24	14 44	14 41		14 44		14 54
Langley	d				13 28	→					13 58	→					14 28	→					14 58
Iver	d				13 31						14 01						14 31						15 01
West Drayton	d		13 21		13 35				13 51		14 05				14 21		14 35				14 51		15 05
Heathrow Terminal 4 ✈	d																						
Heathrow Terminal 1-2 2 ✈	d			13 27						13 57						14 27						14 57	
Hayes & Harlington	d		13 26	13 33	13 40				13 56	14 03	14 10				14 26	14 33	14 40				14 56	15 03	15 10
Southall	d			13 36	13 43					14 06	14 13					14 36	14 43					15 06	15 13
Hanwell	d			13 39						14 09						14 39						15 09	
Greenford ⊖	d	13 16						13 46						14 16						14 46			
South Greenford	d	13 19						13 49						14 19						14 49			
Castle Bar Park	d	13 22						13 52						14 22						14 52			
Drayton Green	d	13 24						13 54						14 24						14 54			
West Ealing	d	13 26		13 41				13 56		14 11				14 26		14 41				14 56		15 11	
Ealing Broadway ⊖	d	13 29	13 33	13 44	13 49			13 59	14 03	14 14	14 19			14 29	14 33	14 44	14 49			14 59	15 03	15 14	15 19
Acton Main Line	d	13 33						14 03						14 33						15 03			
London Paddington 15 ⊖	a	13 42	13 46	13 54	14 01		14 01	14 12	14 16	14 24	14 31		14 30	14 42	14 46	14 54	15 01		15 01	15 12	15 16	15 24	15 32

For non-stop services between London and Reading please see table 116

Passengers who hold valid tickets for Acton Main Line, West Ealing and Hanwell will be able to use local Transport for London (TFL) bus services to reach these stations. Tel 0843 222 1234

Table 117R

Reading and Greenford - London

Mondays to Fridays

6 January to 7 February

Network Diagram - refer to first Page of Table 116

		GW 1		GW ◇1	GW 1	GW 1	HC	GW 1	GW 1	GW ◇1 🛒	GW 1	GW 1		HC	GW 1	GW 1	GW ◇1 ☕	GW 1	GW 1	HC	GW 1	GW 1		GW ◇1 🛒	GW 1
Oxford	d			14 31				14 07		15 01					14 37		15 31				15 07			16 01	
Reading 7	d	14 48		14 56				15 03	15 18	15 26					15 33	15 48	15 57				16 03	16 18		16 26	
Twyford 3	d	14 54						15 09	15 24						15 39	15 54					16 09	16 24			
Maidenhead 3	d	15 02						15 17	15 32						15 47	16 02					16 17	16 32			
Taplow	d	15 06							15 36							16 06						16 36			
Burnham	d	15 09				←			15 39			←				16 09			←			16 39			
Slough 3	a	15 14		15 10		15 14		15 24	15 44	15 39		15 44			15 54	16 14	16 10		16 14		16 24	16 44		16 41	
	d	15 14		15 11		15 14		15 24	15 44	15 40		15 44			15 54	16 14	16 11		16 14		16 24	16 44		16 41	
Langley	d	→						15 28	→						15 58	→					16 28	→			
Iver	d							15 31							16 01						16 31				
West Drayton	d					15 21		15 35				15 51			16 05				16 21		16 35				
Heathrow Terminal 4 ✈	d																								
Heathrow Terminal 1-2 2 ✈	d						15 27							15 57						16 27					
Hayes & Harlington	d					15 26	15 33	15 40				15 56		16 03	16 10				16 26	16 33	16 40				
Southall	d						15 36	15 43						16 06	16 13					16 36	16 43				
Hanwell	d						15 39							16 09						16 39					
Greenford ⊖	d				15 16						15 46							16 16							16 46
South Greenford	d				15 19						15 49							16 19							16 49
Castle Bar Park	d				15 22						15 52							16 22							16 52
Drayton Green	d				15 24						15 54							16 24							16 54
West Ealing	d				15 26		15 41				15 56			16 11				16 26		16 41					16 56
Ealing Broadway ⊖	d				15 29	15 33	15 44	15 49			15 59	16 03		16 14	16 19			16 29	16 33	16 44	16 49				16 59
Acton Main Line	d				15 33						16 03							16 33							17 03
London Paddington 15 ⊖	a			15 30	15 42	15 46	15 54	16 01		16 01	16 12	16 16		16 24	16 31		16 29	16 42	16 46	16 54	17 01			17 00	17 12

		GW 1	HC	GW 1	GW 1	GW ◇1	GW 1	GW 1		HC	GW 1	GW 1	GW ◇1 ☕	GW ◇1 🛒	GW 1	GW 1	HC	GW 1		GW 1	GW 1	GW ◇1 ☕	GW 1	GW 1	HC
Oxford	d			15 37		16 31					16 07			17 01				16 37				17 31			
Reading 7	d			16 31	16 48	16 57					17 03	17 14	17 18	17 27				17 33		17 42	17 54	17 56			
Twyford 3	d			16 39	16 54						17 09	17 24						17 39		17 48					
Maidenhead 3	d			16 47	17 02						17 17	17 32		17 40				17 47		17 56	18 08				
Taplow	d				17 06							17 36								18 00					
Burnham	d	←			17 09			←				17 39				←				18 02				←	
Slough 3	a	16 44		16 54	17 16	17 13		17 16			17 24	17 44	17 32			17 44		17 54		18 07	18 16	18 10		18 16	
	d	16 44		16 54	17 17	17 14		17 17			17 24	17 44	17 33			17 44		17 54		18 07	18 16	18 11		18 16	
Langley	d			16 58	→						17 28	→						17 58			→				
Iver	d			17 01							17 31							18 01							
West Drayton	d	16 51		17 05				17 24			17 35					17 51		18 05		18 14					
Heathrow Terminal 4 ✈	d																								
Heathrow Terminal 1-2 2 ✈	d		16 57							17 27							17 57								18 27
Hayes & Harlington	d	16 56	17 03	17 10				17 29		17 33	17 40					17 56	18 03	18 10		18 19				18 27	18 33
Southall	d		17 06	17 13						17 36	17 43						18 06	18 13							18 36
Hanwell	d		17 09							17 39							18 09								18 39
Greenford ⊖	d						17 16								17 46								18 16		
South Greenford	d						17 19								17 49								18 19		
Castle Bar Park	d						17 22								17 52								18 22		
Drayton Green	d						17 24								17 54								18 24		
West Ealing	d		17 11				17 26			17 41					17 56		18 11						18 26		18 41
Ealing Broadway ⊖	d	17 03	17 14	17 21			17 29	17 36		17 44	17 49				17 59	18 03	18 14	18 19		18 26			18 29	18 35	18 44
Acton Main Line	d						17 33								18 03								18 33		
London Paddington 15 ⊖	a	17 17	17 24	17 31		17 34	17 42	17 46		17 54	18 01		17 52	17 59	18 12	18 14	18 24	18 31		18 37		18 28	18 42	18 46	18 54

		GW 1	GW 1	GW 1		GW ◇1 🛒	GW 1	GW 1	HC	GW 1	GW 1	GW ◇1	GW 1	GW 1		HC	GW 1	GW 1	GW 1	GW ◇1 🛒	HC	GW 1	GW FX 1	GW FO 1	
Oxford	d		17 07			18 01				17 37		18 31					18 07			19 06		18 37			
Reading 7	d		18 08	18 18		18 27				18 33	18 48	18 59					19 08		19 20	19 33		19 33	19 48	19 48	
Twyford 3	d		18 14	18 24						18 39	18 54						19 14		19 26			19 42	19 54	19 54	
Maidenhead 3	d	18 15	18 27	18 32						18 48	19 05						19 22		19 34			19 50	20 02	20 02	
Taplow	d			18 35							19 09								19 37				20 05	20 05	
Burnham	d			18 39				←			19 12			←					19 40				20 09	20 09	
Slough 3	a	18 22	18 34	18 44		18 40		18 44		18 54	19 17	19 10		19 17			19 30		19 45	19 47		19 57	20 14	20 14	
	d	18 22	18 34	18 44		18 41		18 44		18 54	19 17	19 11		19 17			19 30		19 45	19 48		19 57	20 14	20 14	
Langley	d	18 26		→						18 58	→						19 34					20 01	→	→	
Iver	d	18 29								19 01							19 37					20 04			
West Drayton	d	18 33						18 51		19 05				19 24			19 40		19 52			20 08			
Heathrow Terminal 4 ✈	d																								
Heathrow Terminal 1-2 2 ✈	d								18 57							19 27					19 57				
Hayes & Harlington	d	18 38	18 43					18 56	19 03	19 10				19 29		19 33	19 45		19 57		20 03	20 13			
Southall	d	18 42							19 06	19 13						19 36	19 48				20 06	20 16			
Hanwell	d								19 09							19 39					20 09				
Greenford ⊖	d						18 46						19 16					19 46							
South Greenford	d						18 49						19 19					19 49							
Castle Bar Park	d						18 52						19 22					19 52							
Drayton Green	d						18 54						19 24					19 54							
West Ealing	d						18 56		19 11				19 26			19 41		19 56			20 11				
Ealing Broadway ⊖	d	18 48	18 53				18 59	19 05	19 14	19 19			19 29	19 36		19 44	19 54	19 59	20 04		20 14	20 22			
Acton Main Line	d						19 03						19 34					20 03							
London Paddington 15 ⊖	a	18 59	19 02			18 59	19 12	19 18	19 24	19 31		19 31	19 42	19 46		19 54	20 03	20 12	20 17	20 06	20 24	20 32			

For non-stop services between London and Reading please see table 116

Passengers who hold valid tickets for Acton Main Line, West Ealing and Hanwell will be able to use local Transport for London (TFL) bus services to reach these stations. Tel 0843 222 1234

Table 117R

Mondays to Fridays

6 January to 7 February

Network Diagram - refer to first Page of Table 116

Reading and Greenford - London

		GW	GW	GW	GW	HC	GW	GW	GW	GW		GW	HC	GW	GW	GW	GW	GW	HC	GW		GW	GW	HC	GW
				FO	FX																			FO	
		◇ 1	1	1	1		1	1	◇ 1	1		1		1	1	◇ 1	1	1		1		1	◇ 1		1
Oxford	d	19 31					19 10		20 01					19 37		20 31						20 07	21 01		20 37
Reading 7	d	19 55					19 58	20 18	20 26					20 33	20 48	20 56						21 12	21 26		21 33
Twyford 3	d						20 04	20 24						20 39	20 54							21 18			21 39
Maidenhead 3	d						20 12	20 32						20 47	21 02							21 26			21 47
Taplow	d							20 36							21 06							21 30			21 50
Burnham	d			←	←			20 39				←			21 09			←				21 33			21 53
Slough 3	a	20 10		20 14	20 14		20 22	20 44	20 40			20 44		20 54	21 13	21 11		21 13				21 38	21 40		21 58
	d	20 11		20 14	20 14		20 24	20 44	20 41			20 44		20 54	21 14	21 12		21 14				21 38	21 41		21 59
Langley	d						20 28	→						20 58	→			21 17				21 42			22 02
Iver	d						20 31							21 01				21 20				21 45			22 05
West Drayton	d			20 21	20 21		20 35					20 51		21 05				21 24				21 49			22 09
Heathrow Terminal 4 ✈	d																								
Heathrow Terminal 1-2 2 ✈	d					20 27							20 57						21 27					21 57	
Hayes & Harlington	d			20 26	20 26	20 33	20 40					20 56	21 03	21 10				21 28	21 33			21 54		22 03	22 14
Southall	d					20 36	20 43						21 06	21 13					21 36			21 57		22 06	
Hanwell	d					20 39							21 09						21 39					22 09	
Greenford ⊖	d		20 16							20 46							21 16			21 45					
South Greenford	d		20 19							20 49							21 19			21 48					
Castle Bar Park	d		20 22							20 52							21 22			21 51					
Drayton Green	d		20 24							20 54							21 24			21 53					
West Ealing	d		20 26			20 41				20 56			21 11				21 26		21 41	21 55				22 11	
Ealing Broadway ⊖	d		20 29	20 32	20 33	20 44	20 49			20 59		21 03	21 14	21 19			21 29	21 35	21 44	21 58		22 03		22 14	22 21
Acton Main Line	d		20 33							21 03							21 33			22 01					
London Paddington 15 ⊖	a	20 30	20 42	20 49	20 49	20 54	20 59		21 01	21 12		21 16	21 24	21 30		21 29	21 42	21 47	21 54	22 11		22 14	22 00	22 24	22 32

		GW	GW	HC	HC	GW		GW	GW	HC	GW	GW	HC	HC	GW	GW		GW
		FO	FX	FO	FX					FO	FO	FX	FO	FX				
		◇ 1	◇ 1			1		◇	1		◇ 1	◇ 1			1	1		◇ 1
Oxford	d	21 32	21 32					22 11			22 30	22 30						23 09
Reading 7	d	21 56	21 56			22 17		22 44	22 48		22 59	22 59				23 15		23 41
Twyford 3	d					22 23			22 54							23 22		
Maidenhead 3	d					22 32			23 02							23 29		23 55
Taplow	d					22 34			23 05							23 33		
Burnham	d					22 37			23 08						←	23 36		
Slough 3	a	22 14	22 14			22 42		23 01	23 14		23 14	23 14			23 14	23 41		00 02
	d	22 14	22 14			22 42		23 01	23 27		23 14	23 14			23 27	23 41		00 02
Langley	d					22 46			→						23 32	23 45		
Iver	d					22 49									23 35	23 48		
West Drayton	d					22 53									23 39	23 51		
Heathrow Terminal 4 ✈	d																	
Heathrow Terminal 1-2 2 ✈	d			22 27	22 39					22 57			23 27	23 30				
Hayes & Harlington	d			22 33	22 45	22 59				23 03			23 33	23 36	23 43	23 56		
Southall	d			22 36	22 48	23 02				23 06			23 36	23 39	23 47	23 59		
Hanwell	d			22 39						23 09			23 39					
Greenford ⊖	d																	
South Greenford	d																	
Castle Bar Park	d																	
Drayton Green	d																	
West Ealing	d			22 41						23 11			23 41					
Ealing Broadway ⊖	d			22 44	22 55	23 08				23 14			23 44	23 44	23 52	00 06		
Acton Main Line	d					23 11								23 47				
London Paddington 15 ⊖	a	22 38	22 41	22 54	23 02	23 19		23 24		23 24	23 37	23 38	23 54	23 55	00 02	00 17		00 27

For non-stop services between London and Reading please see table 116

Passengers who hold valid tickets for Acton Main Line, West Ealing and Hanwell will be able to use local Transport for London (TFL) bus services to reach these stations. Tel 0843 222 1234

Table 117R

Reading and Greenford - London

Mondays to Fridays

17 February to 24 March

Network Diagram - refer to first Page of Table 116

		GW MX 1	GW MX ◇1	HC MX	HC MO	GW MO 1		GW MO 1	GW MX 1	GW MX ◇1	GW MO ◇1	GW MX 1	GW 1	GW 1	GW MX 1	GW MO 1		HC	GW 1	HC	GW 1	GW 1	GW 1	GW 1	HC
Oxford	d									00 07		00 27			04 00								05 03		
Reading 7	d							00 15	00 17	00 39	00 53	01 17	02 24	03 54	04 40	04 40			05 14		05 39		05 44	05 59	
Twyford 3	d							00 23	00 23		01 00	01 23	02 30	04 00	04 46	04 46			05 20		05 45		05 50		
Maidenhead 3	d							00 31	00 31		01 08	01 31	02 38	04 08	04 54	04 54			05 28		05 53		05 58	06 10	
Taplow	d								00 34										05 32				06 02		
Burnham	d								00 37										05 35				06 05		
Slough 3	a							00 38	00 42	00 55	01 15	01 39	02 45	04 15	04 59	04 59			05 40		06 01		06 10	06 17	
	d		00 02			00 02		00 39	00 42	00 56	01 15	01 39	02 45	04 15	05 00	05 00			05 40		06 01		06 10	06 17	
Langley	d					00 06		00 44	00 46						05 04	05 04			05 44				06 14		
Iver	d														05 07	05 07			05 47				06 17		
West Drayton	d					00 11		00 48	00 51				02 52	04 22	05 11	05 11			05 51				06 21		
Heathrow Terminal 4 ✈	d			00 01	00 01													05 23		05 51					
Heathrow Terminal 1-2 2 ✈	d			00 07	00 07													05 29		05 57					06 27
Hayes & Harlington	d			00 13	00 14	00 17		00 54	00 56		01 24	01 48	02 57	04 27	05 17	05 17		05 35	05 56	06 03	06 10		06 26		06 33
Southall	d			00 16	00 17	00 20		00 57	00 59				03 00	04 30	05 19	05 19		05 38	05 59	06 06	06 13		06 29		06 36
Hanwell	d																	05 41		06 09					06 39
Greenford ⊖	d																					06 16			
South Greenford	d																					06 19			
Castle Bar Park	d																					06 22			
Drayton Green	d																					06 24			
West Ealing	d																	05 43		06 11		06 26			06 41
Ealing Broadway ⊖	d	00 06		00 22	00 22	00 27		01 03	01 05		01 31	01 55	03 06	04 36	05 28	05 28		05 46	06 05	06 14	06 19	06 29	06 35		06 44
Acton Main Line	d														05 31	05 31			06 08			06 33	06 38		
London Paddington 15 ⊖	a	00 17	00 27	00 30	00 30	00 38		01 14	01 18	01 20	01 40	02 07	03 18	04 48	05 41	05 41		05 56	06 16	06 24	06 31	06 42	06 46	06 36	06 54

		GW 1		GW 1	GW 1	GW 1	GW ◇1	HC	GW 1	GW 1	GW 1	GW 1		GW 1	GW ◇1 🍴	GW 1	HC	GW 1	GW 1	GW 1	GW 1	GW 1 A		GW 1 B	GW 1
Oxford	d				05 24	05 43	05 59								06 30				06 04						
Reading 7	d	06 06			06 15	06 16	06 28		06 31	06 35		06 36		06 46	06 55	06 59		07 02	07 05		07 09				
Twyford 3	d	06 13			06 21	06 23			06 37	06 43		06 43		06 54		07 05		07 09			07 15	07 20		07 23	
Maidenhead 3	d	06 21			06 29	06 31	06 40		06 45			06 53		07 02	07 08	07 13		07 17	07 16		07 23	07 29		07 32	07 41
Taplow	d	06 24			06 32							06 57									07 27				
Burnham	d	06 27			06 35				06 49			07 01						07 21			07 30				
Slough 3	a	06 32			06 40		06 47		06 54			07 06				07 20		07 26			07 35				07 49
	d	06 32			06 40		06 48		06 56			07 06				07 21		07 27			07 36				07 50
Langley	d	06 36			06 44				06 59			07 11						07 31			07 41				
Iver	d				06 47				07 03			07 14									07 44				
West Drayton	d	06 41			06 51				07 07			07 18						07 36			07 48				
Heathrow Terminal 4 ✈	d																								
Heathrow Terminal 1-2 2 ✈	d							06 57									07 27								
Hayes & Harlington	d	06 46			06 56			07 03	07 11			07 23					07 33	07 41			07 53				
Southall	d	06 50			07 00			07 06	07 15			07 27					07 36	07 45			07 57				
Hanwell	d							07 09									07 39								
Greenford ⊖	d			06 46							07 16									07 46					
South Greenford	d			06 49							07 19									07 49					
Castle Bar Park	d			06 52							07 22									07 52					
Drayton Green	d			06 54							07 24									07 54					
West Ealing	d			06 56				07 11			07 26						07 41			07 56					
Ealing Broadway ⊖	d	06 55		06 59	07 05			07 14	07 21		07 29	07 33					07 44	07 52		07 59	08 03				
Acton Main Line	d			07 03							07 33									08 03					
London Paddington 15 ⊖	a	07 09		07 12	07 17	06 54	07 08	07 24	07 32	07 12	07 42	07 44		07 27	07 27	07 49	07 54	08 04	07 43	08 12	08 16	07 57		08 02	08 21

		HC	GW 1	GW 1	GW ◇1	GW 1	GW 1	GW 1		GW 1	HC	GW 1	GW 1	GW 1	GW 1	GW 1	HC	GW 1		GW 1	GW 1	GW 1	HC	GW 1	GW 1
Oxford	d		06 36					07 02							07 21					07 56					
Reading 7	d		07 30	07 34				07 56		08 04				08 11	08 19			08 31		08 48				09 05	
Twyford 3	d		07 37	07 41		07 54		08 02		08a10				08 19	08 26			08 37		08 54				09 11	
Maidenhead 3	d		07 45	07 49	07 59	08 02		08 11						08 27	08 35	08 41		08 45		09 03				09 19	
Taplow	d			07 53										08 30				08 49						09 22	
Burnham	d		07 51	07 56				08 16						08 34				08 50						09 25	
Slough 3	a		07 55	08 01				08 20						08 39		08 49		08 57						09 30	
	d		07 56	08 01				08 21				08 29		08 39		08 50		08 57				09 14		09 30	
Langley	d		08 00	08 06								08 32		08 43				09 01						09 35	
Iver	d		08 03											08 46				09 04						09 37	
West Drayton	d		08 07	08 11								08 38		08 50				09 08				09 21		09 41	
Heathrow Terminal 4 ✈	d																								
Heathrow Terminal 1-2 2 ✈	d	07 57									08 27						08 57						09 27		
Hayes & Harlington	d	08 03	08 12	08 16							08 33	08 42		08 54			09 03	09 13				09 26	09 34	09 46	
Southall	d	08 06	08 16	08 20							08 36	08 46				09 01	09 06	09 17				09 30	09 37	09 50	
Hanwell	d	08 09									08 39						09 09						09 41		
Greenford ⊖	d						08 16						08 46								09 16				09 46
South Greenford	d						08 19						08 49								09 19				09 49
Castle Bar Park	d						08 22						08 52								09 22				09 52
Drayton Green	d						08 24						08 54								09 24				09 54
West Ealing	d	08 11					08 26				08 41		08 56				09 11				09 26		09 42		09 56
Ealing Broadway ⊖	d	08 14	08 21	08 25			08 29				08 44	08 52	08 59	09 04			09 14	09 23			09 29	09 36	09 46	09 55	09 59
Acton Main Line	d						08 33						09 03								09 33				10 03
London Paddington 15 ⊖	a	08 24	08 32	08 37	08 26	08 28	08 42	08 48			08 54	09 03	09 12	09 16	08 58	09 21	09 24	09 35		09 27	09 42	09 48	09 54	10 05	10 12

A 24 March

B until 23 March

For non-stop services between London and Reading please see table 116

Passengers who hold valid tickets for Acton Main Line, West Ealing and Hanwell will be able to use local Transport for London (TFL) bus services to reach these stations. Tel 0843 222 1234

Table 117R

Mondays to Fridays

17 February to 24 March

Network Diagram - refer to first Page of Table 116

Reading and Greenford - London

		GW 1	GW 1	GW ◇1 A	GW ◇1 B	HC	GW 1	GW 1	GW ◇1	GW 1	GW 1	HC	GW 1	GW 1	GW ◇1 🚲	GW 1	GW 1	HC	GW 1	GW 1	GW ◇1 A	GW ◇1 B
Oxford	d		08 35	09 01	09 01				09 31				09 07		10 01				09 37		10 31	10 31
Reading 7	d	09 18	09 33	09 37	09 37			09 48	09 55				10 03	10 18	10 26				10 33	10 48	10 55	10 56
Twyford 3	d	09 24	09 39					09 54					10 09	10 24					10 39	10 54		
Maidenhead 3	d	09 35	09 47					10 02					10 17	10 32					10 47	11 02		
Taplow	d	09 36						10 06						10 36						11 06		
Burnham	d	09 39					←	10 09			←			10 39			←			11 09		
Slough 3	a	09 44	09 54	09 52	09 53		09 54	10 14	10 10		10 14		10 24	10 44	10 40		10 44		10 53	11 14	11 09	11 10
	d	09 44	09 54	09 53	09 54		09 54	10 14	10 11		10 14		10 24	10 44	10 41		10 44		10 54	11 14	11 10	11 11
Langley	d		→				09 58	→					10 28	→					10 58	→		
Iver	d						10 01						10 31						11 01			
West Drayton	d	09 51					10 05				10 21		10 35				10 51		11 05			
Heathrow Terminal 4 ✈	d																					
Heathrow Terminal 1-2 2 ✈	d					09 57						10 27						10 57				
Hayes & Harlington	d	09 56				10 03	10 10				10 26	10 33	10 40				10 56	11 03	11 09			
Southall	d					10 06	10 13					10 36	10 43					11 06	11 13			
Hanwell	d					10 09						10 39						11 09				
Greenford ⊖	d									10 16						10 46						
South Greenford	d									10 19						10 49						
Castle Bar Park	d									10 22						10 52						
Drayton Green	d									10 24						10 54						
West Ealing	d					10 11				10 26		10 41				10 56		11 11				
Ealing Broadway ⊖	d	10 08				10 14	10 19			10 29	10 33	10 44	10 49			10 59	11 03	11 14	11 19			
Acton Main Line	d									10 33						11 03						
London Paddington 15 ⊖	a	10 18		10 12	10 12	10 24	10 31		10 29	10 42	10 46	10 54	11 01		11 00	11 12	11 16	11 24	11 32		11 29	11 30

		GW 1	GW 1	HC	GW 1	GW 1	GW ◇1 🚲	GW 1	GW 1	HC	GW 1	GW 1	GW ◇1 🚲	GW 1	GW 1	HC	GW 1	GW 1	GW ◇1 A 🚲	GW ◇1 B 🚲	GW 1	GW 1	HC
Oxford	d				10 08		11 01				10 37		11 31				11 07		12 01	12 01			
Reading 7	d				11 03	11 18	11 26				11 33	11 48	11 56				12 03	12 18	12 26	12 27			
Twyford 3	d				11 09	11 24					11 39	11 54					12 09	12 24					
Maidenhead 3	d				11 17	11 32					11 47	12 02					12 17	12 32					
Taplow	d					11 36						12 06						12 36					
Burnham	d		←			11 39			←			12 09			←			12 39				←	
Slough 3	a		11 14		11 24	11 44	11 39		11 44		11 54	12 14	12 10		12 14		12 24	12 44	12 41	12 41		12 44	
	d		11 14		11 24	11 44	11 40		11 44		11 54	12 14	12 11		12 14		12 24	12 44	12 41	12 41		12 44	
Langley	d				11 28	→					11 58	→					12 28	→					
Iver	d				11 31						12 01						12 31						
West Drayton	d		11 21		11 35				11 51		12 05				12 21		12 35					12 51	
Heathrow Terminal 4 ✈	d																						
Heathrow Terminal 1-2 2 ✈	d			11 27						11 57						12 27							12 57
Hayes & Harlington	d		11 26	11 33	11 40				11 56	12 03	12 10				12 26	12 33	12 40					12 56	13 03
Southall	d			11 36	11 43					12 06	12 13					12 36	12 43						13 06
Hanwell	d			11 39						12 09						12 39							13 09
Greenford ⊖	d	11 16						11 46						12 16							12 46		
South Greenford	d	11 19						11 49						12 19							12 49		
Castle Bar Park	d	11 22						11 52						12 22							12 52		
Drayton Green	d	11 24						11 54						12 24							12 54		
West Ealing	d	11 26		11 41				11 56		12 11				12 26		12 41					12 56		13 11
Ealing Broadway ⊖	d	11 29	11 33	11 44	11 49			11 59	12 07	12 14	12 19			12 29	12 33	12 44	12 49				12 59	13 03	13 14
Acton Main Line	d	11 33						12 03						12 33							13 03		
London Paddington 15 ⊖	a	11 42	11 46	11 54	12 01		11 59	12 12	12 18	12 24	12 31		12 30	12 42	12 46	12 54	13 02		13 09	13 09	13 12	13 16	13 24

A from 10 March **B** until 7 March

For non-stop services between London and Reading please see table 116

Passengers who hold valid tickets for Acton Main Line, West Ealing and Hanwell will be able to use local Transport for London (TFL) bus services to reach these stations. Tel 0843 222 1234

Table 117R

Reading and Greenford - London

Mondays to Fridays

17 February to 24 March

Network Diagram - refer to first Page of Table 116

		GW		GW	GW	GW	GW	HC	GW	GW	GW	GW		GW	GW	GW	GW	HC	GW	GW	GW	GW		GW	HC
		1		1	◇1	1	1		1	1	1	◇1		◇1	1	1	1		1	1	◇1	1		1	
										A	B	A		B		A	B								
					trolley							trolley		trolley							trolley				
Oxford	d	11 37			12 31				12 07			13 01		13 01					12 37		13 31				
Reading 7	d	12 33		12 48	12 56				13 03	13 18	13 18	13 26		13 26					13 33	13 48	13 56				
Twyford 3	d	12 39		12 54					13 09	13 24	13 24								13 39	13 54					
Maidenhead 3	d	12 47		13 02					13 17	13 32	13 32								13 47	14 02					
Taplow	d			13 06						13 36	13 36									14 06					
Burnham	d			13 09			←			13 39	13 39					←	←			14 09				←	
Slough 3	a	12 54		13 14	13 10		13 14		13 24	13 44	13 44	13 41		13 41		13 44	13 44		13 54	14 13	14 10			14 13	
	d	12 54		13 14	13 11		13 14		13 24	13 47	13 48	13 41		13 41		13 47	13 48		13 54	14 14	14 11			14 14	
Langley	d	12 58		→					13 28	→	→								13 58	→					
Iver	d	13 01							13 31										14 01						
West Drayton	d	13 05					13 21		13 35							13 51	13 51		14 05					14 21	
Heathrow Terminal 4	✈ d																								
Heathrow Terminal 1-2 2	✈ d							13 27										13 57							14 27
Hayes & Harlington	d	13 10					13 26	13 33	13 40							13 56	13 56	14 03	14 10					14 26	14 33
Southall	d	13 13						13 36	13 43									14 06	14 13						14 36
Hanwell	d							13 39										14 09							14 39
Greenford	⊖ d					13 16									13 46							14 16			
South Greenford	d					13 19									13 49							14 19			
Castle Bar Park	d					13 22									13 52							14 22			
Drayton Green	d					13 24									13 54							14 24			
West Ealing	d					13 26		13 41							13 56			14 11				14 26			14 41
Ealing Broadway	⊖ d	13 19				13 29	13 33	13 44	13 49						13 59	14 03	14 03	14 14	14 19			14 29		14 33	14 44
Acton Main Line	d					13 33									14 03							14 33			
London Paddington 15	⊖ a	13 31			13 30	13 42	13 46	13 54	14 01			14 00		14 01	14 12	14 16	14 16	14 24	14 31		14 30	14 42		14 46	14 54

		GW	GW	GW	GW	GW	HC	GW		GW	GW	GW	GW	HC	GW	GW	GW	GW		GW	HC	GW	GW	GW	GW
		1	1	◇1	1	1		1		1	◇1	1	1		1	1	◇1	1		1		1	1	◇1	1
				trolley													trolley							☕	
Oxford	d	13 07		14 01				13 37			14 31				14 07		15 01					14 37		15 31	
Reading 7	d	14 03	14 18	14 26				14 33		14 48	14 56				15 03	15 18	15 26					15 33	15 48	15 57	
Twyford 3	d	14 09	14 24					14 39		14 54					15 09	15 24						15 39	15 54		
Maidenhead 3	d	14 17	14 32					14 47		15 02					15 17	15 32						15 47	16 02		
Taplow	d		14 36							15 06						15 36							16 06		
Burnham	d		14 39			←				15 09			←			15 39				←			16 09		
Slough 3	a	14 24	14 44	14 40		14 44		14 54		15 14	15 10		15 14		15 24	15 44	15 39			15 44		15 54	16 14	16 10	
	d	14 24	14 44	14 41		14 44		14 54		15 14	15 11		15 14		15 24	15 44	15 40			15 44		15 54	16 14	16 11	
Langley	d	14 28	→					14 58		→					15 28	→						15 58	→		
Iver	d	14 31						15 01							15 31							16 01			
West Drayton	d	14 35				14 51		15 05					15 21		15 35					15 51		16 05			
Heathrow Terminal 4	✈ d																								
Heathrow Terminal 1-2 2	✈ d						14 57							15 27							15 57				
Hayes & Harlington	d	14 40				14 56	15 03	15 10					15 26	15 33	15 40					15 56	16 03	16 10			
Southall	d	14 43					15 06	15 13						15 36	15 43						16 06	16 13			
Hanwell	d						15 09							15 39							16 09				
Greenford	⊖ d				14 46							15 16						15 46							16 16
South Greenford	d				14 49							15 19						15 49							16 19
Castle Bar Park	d				14 52							15 22						15 52							16 22
Drayton Green	d				14 54							15 24						15 54							16 24
West Ealing	d				14 56		15 11					15 26		15 41				15 56			16 11				16 26
Ealing Broadway	⊖ d	14 49			14 59	15 03	15 14	15 19				15 29	15 33	15 44	15 49			15 59		16 03	16 14	16 19			16 29
Acton Main Line	d				15 03							15 33						16 03							16 33
London Paddington 15	⊖ a	15 01		15 01	15 12	15 16	15 24	15 32			15 30	15 42	15 46	15 54	16 01		16 01	16 12		16 16	16 24	16 31		16 29	16 42

A from 10 March

B until 7 March

For non-stop services between London and Reading please see table 116

Passengers who hold valid tickets for Acton Main Line, West Ealing and Hanwell will be able to use local Transport for London (TFL) bus services to reach these stations. Tel 0843 222 1234

Table 117R

Mondays to Fridays

17 February to 24 March

Network Diagram - refer to first Page of Table 116

Reading and Greenford - London

		GW	HC	GW	GW	GW	GW	GW	HC	GW		GW	GW	GW	GW	HC	GW	GW	GW	GW		GW	GW	HC	GW
		1		1	1	◇1	1	1		1		1	◇1	1	1		1	1	◇1	◇1		1	1		1
Oxford	d			15 07		16 01				15 37			16 31				16 07			17 01					16 37
Reading 7	d			16 03	16 18	16 26				16 31		16 48	16 57				17 03	17 14	17 18	17 27					17 33
Twyford 3	d			16 09	16 24					16 39		16 54					17 09	17 24							17 39
Maidenhead 3	d			16 17	16 32					16 47		17 02					17 17	17 32		17 40					17 47
Taplow	d				16 36							17 06						17 36							
Burnham	d	←			16 39			←				17 09			←			17 39					←		
Slough 3	a	16 14		16 24	16 44	16 41		16 44		16 54		17 16	17 13		17 16		17 24	17 44	17 32				17 44		17 54
	d	16 14		16 24	16 44	16 41		16 44		16 54		17 17	17 14		17 17		17 24	17 44	17 33				17 44		17 54
Langley	d			16 28	→					16 58		→					17 28	→							17 58
Iver	d			16 31						17 01							17 31								18 01
West Drayton	d	16 21		16 35				16 51		17 05					17 24		17 35						17 51		18 05
Heathrow Terminal 4 ✈	d																								
Heathrow Terminal 1-2 2 ✈	d		16 27						16 57							17 27								17 57	
Hayes & Harlington	d	16 26	16 33	16 40				16 56	17 03	17 10					17 29	17 33	17 40						17 56	18 03	18 10
Southall	d		16 36	16 43					17 06	17 13						17 36	17 43							18 06	18 13
Hanwell	d		16 39						17 09							17 39								18 09	
Greenford ⊖	d						16 46							17 16								17 46			
South Greenford	d						16 49							17 19								17 49			
Castle Bar Park	d						16 52							17 22								17 52			
Drayton Green	d						16 54							17 24								17 54			
West Ealing	d		16 41				16 56		17 11					17 26		17 41						17 56		18 11	
Ealing Broadway ⊖	d	16 33	16 44	16 49			16 59	17 03	17 14	17 21				17 29	17 36	17 44	17 49					17 59	18 03	18 14	18 19
Acton Main Line	d						17 03							17 33								18 03			
London Paddington 15 ⊖	a	16 46	16 54	17 01		17 00	17 12	17 17	17 24	17 31			17 34	17 42	17 46	17 54	18 01		17 52	17 59		18 12	18 14	18 24	18 31

		GW	GW	GW	GW	GW		HC	GW	GW	GW	GW	GW	GW	HC	GW		GW	GW	GW	GW	GW	HC	GW	GW
		1	1	◇1	1	1			1	1	1	◇1	1	1		1		1	◇1	◇1	1	1		1	1
																			A	B					
Oxford	d			17 31						17 07		18 01				17 37			18 31	18 31				18 07	
Reading 7	d	17 42	17 54	17 56						18 08	18 18	18 27				18 33		18 48	18 57	18 59				19 08	
Twyford 3	d	17 48								18 14	18 24					18 39		18 54						19 14	
Maidenhead 3	d	17 56	18 08						18 15	18 27	18 32					18 48		19 05						19 22	
Taplow	d	18 00									18 35							19 09							
Burnham	d	18 02				←					18 39			←				19 12				←			
Slough 3	a	18 07	18 16	18 10		18 16			18 22	18 34	18 44	18 40		18 44		18 54		19 17	19 09	19 10		19 17		19 30	
	d	18 07	18 16	18 11		18 16			18 22	18 34	18 44	18 41		18 44		18 54		19 17	19 10	19 11		19 17		19 30	
Langley	d		→						18 26		→					18 58		→						19 34	
Iver	d								18 29							19 01								19 37	
West Drayton	d	18 14							18 33					18 51		19 05						19 24		19 40	
Heathrow Terminal 4 ✈	d																								
Heathrow Terminal 1-2 2 ✈	d							18 27							18 57								19 27		
Hayes & Harlington	d	18 19				18 27		18 33	18 38	18 43				18 56	19 03	19 10						19 29	19 33	19 45	
Southall	d							18 36	18 42						19 06	19 13							19 36	19 48	
Hanwell	d							18 39							19 09								19 39		
Greenford ⊖	d				18 16								18 46								19 16				19 46
South Greenford	d				18 19								18 49								19 19				19 49
Castle Bar Park	d				18 22								18 52								19 22				19 52
Drayton Green	d				18 24								18 54								19 24				19 54
West Ealing	d				18 26			18 41					18 56		19 11						19 26		19 41		19 56
Ealing Broadway ⊖	d	18 26			18 29	18 35		18 44	18 48	18 53			18 59	19 05	19 14	19 19					19 29	19 36	19 44	19 54	19 59
Acton Main Line	d				18 33								19 03								19 34				20 03
London Paddington 15 ⊖	a	18 37		18 28	18 42	18 46		18 54	18 59	19 02		18 59	19 12	19 18	19 24	19 31			19 30	19 31	19 42	19 46	19 54	20 03	20 12

A from 10 March

B until 7 March

For non-stop services between London and Reading please see table 116

Passengers who hold valid tickets for Acton Main Line, West Ealing and Hanwell will be able to use local Transport for London (TFL) bus services to reach these stations. Tel 0843 222 1234

Table 117R

Mondays to Fridays

17 February to 24 March

Network Diagram - refer to first Page of Table 116

Reading and Greenford - London

		GW	GW	HC	GW	GW FX	GW FO	GW	GW	GW FO	GW FX	HC	GW	GW	GW	GW	GW	HC	GW	GW	GW	GW	GW
		[1]	◇[1]		[1]	[1]	[1]	◇[1]	[1]	[1]	[1]		[1]	[1]	◇[1]	[1]	[1]		[1]	[1]	◇[1]	[1]	[1]
Oxford	d		19 06		18 37			19 31					19 10		20 01				19 37		20 31		
Reading [7]	d	19 20	19 33		19 33	19 48	19 48	19 55					19 58	20 18	20 26				20 33	20 48	20 56		
Twyford [3]	d	19 26			19 42	19 54	19 54						20 04	20 24					20 39	20 54			
Maidenhead [3]	d	19 34			19 50	20 02	20 02						20 12	20 32					20 47	21 02			
Taplow	d	19 37				20 05	20 05							20 36						21 06			
Burnham	d	19 40				20 09	20 09			←	←			20 39			←			21 09			←
Slough [3]	a	19 45	19 47		19 57	20 14	20 14	20 10		20 14	20 14		20 22	20 44	20 40		20 44		20 54	21 13	21 11		21 13
	d	19 45	19 48		19 57	20 14	20 14	20 11		20 14	20 14		20 24	20 44	20 41		20 44		20 54	21 14	21 12		21 14
Langley	d				20 01	↪	↪						20 28	↪					20 58	↪			21 17
Iver	d				20 04								20 31						21 01				21 20
West Drayton	d	19 52			20 08					20 21	20 21		20 35				20 51		21 05				21 24
Heathrow Terminal 4 ✈	d																						
Heathrow Terminal 1-2 [2] ✈	d			19 57								20 27						20 57					
Hayes & Harlington	d	19 57		20 03	20 13					20 26	20 26	20 33	20 40				20 56	21 03	21 10				21 28
Southall	d			20 06	20 16							20 36	20 43					21 06	21 13				
Hanwell	d			20 09								20 39						21 09					
Greenford ⊖	d								20 16							20 46						21 16	
South Greenford	d								20 19							20 49						21 19	
Castle Bar Park	d								20 22							20 52						21 22	
Drayton Green	d								20 24							20 54						21 24	
West Ealing	d			20 11					20 26			20 41				20 56		21 11				21 26	
Ealing Broadway ⊖	d	20 04		20 14	20 22				20 29	20 32	20 33	20 44	20 49			20 59	21 03	21 14	21 19			21 29	21 35
Acton Main Line	d								20 33							21 03						21 33	
London Paddington [15] ⊖	a	20 17	20 06	20 24	20 32			20 30	20 42	20 49	20 49	20 54	20 59		21 01	21 12	21 16	21 24	21 30		21 29	21 42	21 47

		HC	GW	GW	GW	HC FO	GW	GW FO	GW FX	HC FO	HC FX	GW	GW	GW	HC FO	GW FO	GW FX	HC FO	HC FX	GW	GW	GW
			[1]	[1]	◇[1]		[1]	◇[1]	◇[1]			[1]	◇	[1]		◇[1]	◇[1]			[1]	[1]	◇[1]
Oxford	d			20 07	21 01		20 37	21 32	21 32				22 11			22 30	22 30					23 09
Reading [7]	d			21 12	21 26		21 33	21 56	21 56			22 17	22 44	22 48		22 59	22 59				23 15	23 41
Twyford [3]	d			21 18			21 39					22 23		22 54							23 22	
Maidenhead [3]	d			21 26			21 47					22 32		23 02							23 29	23 55
Taplow	d			21 30			21 50					22 34		23 05							23 33	
Burnham	d			21 33			21 53					22 37		23 08						←	23 36	
Slough [3]	a			21 38	21 40		21 58	22 14	22 14			22 42	23 01	23 14		23 14	23 14			23 14	23 41	00 02
	d			21 38	21 41		21 59	22 14	22 14			22 42	23 01	23 27		23 14	23 14			23 27	23 41	00 02
Langley	d			21 42			22 02					22 46		↪						23 32	23 45	
Iver	d			21 45			22 05					22 49								23 35	23 48	
West Drayton	d			21 49			22 09					22 53								23 39	23 51	
Heathrow Terminal 4 ✈	d																					
Heathrow Terminal 1-2 [2] ✈	d	21 27				21 57				22 27	22 39				22 57			23 27	23 30			
Hayes & Harlington	d	21 33		21 54		22 03	22 14			22 33	22 45	22 59			23 03			23 33	23 36	23 43	23 56	
Southall	d	21 36		21 57		22 06				22 36	22 48	23 02			23 06			23 36	23 39	23 47	23 59	
Hanwell	d	21 39				22 09				22 39					23 09			23 39				
Greenford ⊖	d		21 45																			
South Greenford	d		21 48																			
Castle Bar Park	d		21 51																			
Drayton Green	d		21 53																			
West Ealing	d	21 41	21 55			22 11				22 41					23 11			23 41				
Ealing Broadway ⊖	d	21 44	21 58	22 03		22 14	22 21			22 44	22 55	23 08			23 14			23 44	23 44	23 52	00 06	
Acton Main Line	d		22 01									23 11							23 47			
London Paddington [15] ⊖	a	21 54	22 11	22 14	22 00	22 24	22 32	22 38	22 41	22 54	23 02	23 19	23 24		23 24	23 37	23 38	23 54	23 55	00 02	00 17	00 27

For non-stop services between London and Reading please see table 116

Passengers who hold valid tickets for Acton Main Line, West Ealing and Hanwell will be able to use local Transport for London (TFL) bus services to reach these stations. Tel 0843 222 1234

Table 117R

Mondays to Fridays

31 March to 16 May

Network Diagram - refer to first Page of Table 116

Reading and Greenford - London

		GW MX 1	GW MX ◇1	HC MX	HC MO	GW MO 1	GW MO 1	GW MX 1	GW MO 1	GW MX 1	GW MX ◇1	GW MO ◇1	GW MX 1	GW 1	GW 1	GW MX 1	GW MO 1	HC	GW 1	HC	GW 1	GW 1	GW 1
Oxford	d										00 07		00 27			04 00							05 03
Reading 7	d						00 15	00 17	←		00 39	00 53	01 17	02 24	03 54	04 40	04 40		05 14		05 39		05 44
Twyford 3	d						00 24	00 23	00 24			01 00	01 23	02 30	04 00	04 46	04 46		05 20		05 45		05 50
Maidenhead 3	d						→	00 31	00 32			01 08	01 31	02 38	04 08	04 54	04 54		05 28		05 53		05 58
Taplow	d							00 34											05 32				06 02
Burnham	d							00 37		←									05 35				06 05
Slough 3	a							00 42	00 39	00 42	00 55	01 14	01 39	02 45	04 15	04 59	04 59		05 40		06 01		06 10
	d		00 02			00 02		00 42	00 40	00 42	00 56	01 15	01 39	02 45	04 15	05 00	05 00		05 40		06 01		06 10
Langley	d					00 06		→	00 44	00 46						05 04	05 04		05 44				06 14
Iver	d															05 07	05 07		05 47				06 17
West Drayton	d					00 11			00 48	00 51				02 52	04 22	05 11	05 11		05 51				06 21
Heathrow Terminal 4 ✈	d			00 01	00 01													05 23		05 51			
Heathrow Terminal 1-2 2 ✈	d			00 07	00 07													05 29		05 57			
Hayes & Harlington	d			00 13	00 14	00 17			00 54	00 56		01 23	01 48	02 57	04 27	05 17	05 17	05 35	05 56	06 03	06 10		06 26
Southall	d			00 16	00 17	00 20			00 57	00 59				03 00	04 30	05 19	05 19	05 38	05 59	06 06	06 13		06 29
Hanwell	d																	05 41		06 09			
Greenford ⊖	d																					06 16	
South Greenford	d																					06 19	
Castle Bar Park	d																					06 22	
Drayton Green	d																					06 24	
West Ealing	d																	05 43		06 11		06 26	
Ealing Broadway ⊖	d	00 06		00 22	00 22	00 27			01 03	01 05		01 30	01 55	03 06	04 36	05 28	05 28	05 46	06 05	06 14	06 19	06 29	06 35
Acton Main Line	d															05 31	05 31		06 08			06 33	06 38
London Paddington 15 ⊖	a	00 17	00 27	00 30	00 30	00 35			01 14	01 18	01 20	01 39	02 07	03 18	04 48	05 41	05 41	05 56	06 16	06 24	06 31	06 42	06 46

		GW 1	HC	GW 1	GW 1	GW 1	GW 1	GW ◇1	HC	GW 1	GW 1	GW 1	GW 1	GW 1	GW ◇1 ☕	GW 1	HC	GW 1	GW 1	GW 1	GW 1	GW 1
Oxford	d					05 24	05 43	05 59							06 30				06 04			
Reading 7	d	05 59		06 06		06 15	06 16	06 28		06 31	06 35		06 36	06 46	06 55	06 59		07 02	07 05		07 09	
Twyford 3	d			06 13		06 21	06 23			06 37	06 43		06 43	06 54		07 05		07 09			07 15	07 20
Maidenhead 3	d	06 10		06 21		06 29	06 31	06 40		06 45			06 53	07 02	07 08	07 13		07 17	07 16		07 23	07 29
Taplow	d			06 24		06 32							06 57								07 27	
Burnham	d			06 27		06 35				06 49			07 01					07 21			07 30	
Slough 3	a	06 17		06 32		06 40		06 47		06 54			07 06			07 20		07 26			07 35	
	d	06 17		06 32		06 40		06 48		06 56			07 06			07 21		07 27			07 36	
Langley	d			06 36		06 44				06 59			07 11					07 31			07 41	
Iver	d					06 47				07 03			07 14								07 44	
West Drayton	d			06 41		06 51				07 07			07 18					07 36			07 48	
Heathrow Terminal 4 ✈	d																					
Heathrow Terminal 1-2 2 ✈	d		06 27						06 57								07 27					
Hayes & Harlington	d		06 33	06 46		06 56			07 03	07 11			07 23				07 33	07 41			07 53	
Southall	d		06 36	06 50		07 00			07 06	07 15			07 27				07 36	07 45			07 57	
Hanwell	d		06 39						07 09								07 39					
Greenford ⊖	d				06 46							07 16								07 46		
South Greenford	d				06 49							07 19								07 49		
Castle Bar Park	d				06 52							07 22								07 52		
Drayton Green	d				06 54							07 24								07 54		
West Ealing	d		06 41		06 56				07 11			07 26					07 41			07 56		
Ealing Broadway ⊖	d		06 44	06 55	06 59	07 05			07 14	07 21		07 29	07 33				07 44	07 52		07 59	08 03	
Acton Main Line	d				07 03							07 33								08 03		
London Paddington 15 ⊖	a	06 36	06 54	07 09	07 12	07 17	06 54	07 08	07 24	07 32	07 12	07 42	07 44	07 27	07 27	07 49	07 54	08 04	07 43	08 12	08 16	07 57

		GW 1	HC	GW 1	GW 1	GW ◇1	GW 1	GW 1	GW 1	GW 1	HC	GW 1	GW 1	GW 1	GW 1	GW 1	HC	GW 1	GW 1	GW 1	GW 1	HC	GW 1
Oxford	d			06 36					07 02						07 21				07 56				
Reading 7	d			07 30	07 34				07 56	08 04				08 11	08 19			08 31	08 48				09 05
Twyford 3	d			07 37	07 41		07 54		08 02	08a10				08 19	08 26			08 37	08 54				09 11
Maidenhead 3	d	07 41		07 45	07 49	07 59	08 02		08 11					08 27	08 35	08 41		08 45	09 03				09 19
Taplow	d				07 53									08 30				08 49					09 22
Burnham	d			07 51	07 56				08 16					08 34				08 50					09 25
Slough 3	a	07 49		07 55	08 01				08 20					08 39		08 49		08 57					09 30
	d	07 50		07 56	08 01				08 21			08 29		08 39		08 50		08 57			09 14		09 30
Langley	d			08 00	08 06							08 32		08 43				09 01					09 35
Iver	d			08 03										08 46				09 04					09 37
West Drayton	d			08 07	08 11							08 38		08 50				09 08			09 21		09 41
Heathrow Terminal 4 ✈	d																						
Heathrow Terminal 1-2 2 ✈	d		07 57								08 27						08 57					09 27	
Hayes & Harlington	d		08 03	08 12	08 16						08 33	08 42		08 54			09 03	09 13			09 26	09 34	09 46
Southall	d		08 06	08 16	08 20						08 36	08 46				09 01	09 06	09 17			09 30	09 37	09 50
Hanwell	d		08 09								08 39						09 09					09 41	
Greenford ⊖	d							08 16					08 46							09 16			
South Greenford	d							08 19					08 49							09 19			
Castle Bar Park	d							08 22					08 52							09 22			
Drayton Green	d							08 24					08 54							09 24			
West Ealing	d		08 11					08 26			08 41		08 56				09 11			09 26		09 42	
Ealing Broadway ⊖	d		08 14	08 21	08 25			08 29			08 44	08 52	08 59	09 04			09 14	09 23		09 29	09 36	09 46	09 55
Acton Main Line	d							08 33					09 03							09 33			
London Paddington 15 ⊖	a	08 21	08 24	08 32	08 37	08 26	08 28	08 42	08 48		08 54	09 03	09 12	09 16	08 58	09 21	09 24	09 35	09 27	09 42	09 48	09 54	10 05

For non-stop services between London and Reading please see table 116

Passengers who hold valid tickets for Acton Main Line, West Ealing and Hanwell will be able to use local Transport for London (TFL) bus services to reach these stations. Tel 0843 222 1234

Table 117R

Mondays to Fridays

31 March to 16 May

Reading and Greenford - London

Network Diagram - refer to first Page of Table 116

		GW	GW	GW		GW	HC	GW	GW	GW	GW	GW	HC	GW		GW	GW	GW	GW	HC	GW	GW	GW	GW	
		[1]	[1]	[1]		◇[1]		[1]	[1]	◇[1]	[1]	[1]		[1]		[1]	◇[1] 🚲	[1]	[1]		[1]	[1]	◇[1]	[1]	
Oxford	d			08 35		09 01				09 31				09 07			10 01				09 37		10 31		
Reading [7]	d		09 18	09 33		09 37			09 48	09 55				10 03		10 18	10 26				10 33	10 48	10 55		
Twyford [3]	d		09 24	09 39					09 54					10 09		10 24					10 39	10 54			
Maidenhead [3]	d		09 35	09 47					10 02					10 17		10 32					10 47	11 02			
Taplow	d		09 36						10 06							10 36						11 06			
Burnham	d		09 39					←	10 09			←				10 39			←			11 09			
Slough [3]	a		09 44	09 54		09 52		09 54	10 14	10 10		10 14		10 24		10 44	10 40		10 44		10 53	11 14	11 09		
	d		09 44	09 54		09 53		09 54	10 14	10 11		10 14		10 24		10 44	10 41		10 44		10 54	11 14	11 10		
Langley	d			→				09 58	→					10 28		→					10 58	→			
Iver	d							10 01						10 31							11 01				
West Drayton	d		09 51					10 05				10 21		10 35					10 51		11 05				
Heathrow Terminal 4 ✈	d																								
Heathrow Terminal 1-2 [2] ✈	d						09 57						10 27							10 57					
Hayes & Harlington	d		09 56				10 03	10 10				10 26	10 33	10 40					10 56	11 03	11 09				
Southall	d						10 06	10 13					10 36	10 43						11 06	11 13				
Hanwell	d						10 09						10 39							11 09					
Greenford ⊖	d	09 46									10 16							10 46						11 16	
South Greenford	d	09 49									10 19							10 49						11 19	
Castle Bar Park	d	09 52									10 22							10 52						11 22	
Drayton Green	d	09 54									10 24							10 54						11 24	
West Ealing	d	09 56					10 11				10 26		10 41					10 56		11 11				11 26	
Ealing Broadway ⊖	d	09 59	10 08				10 14	10 19			10 29	10 33	10 44	10 49				10 59	11 03	11 14	11 19			11 29	
Acton Main Line	d	10 03									10 33							11 03						11 33	
London Paddington [15] ⊖	a	10 12	10 18			10 12	10 24	10 31		10 29	10 42	10 46	10 54	11 01			11 00	11 12	11 16	11 24	11 32		11 29	11 42	

		GW	HC	GW	GW	GW	GW	GW	HC	GW		GW	GW	GW	GW	HC	GW	GW	GW	GW		GW	HC	GW	GW
		[1]		[1]	[1]	◇[1] 🚲	[1]	[1]		[1]		[1]	◇[1] 🚲	[1]	[1]		[1]	[1]	◇[1] 🚲	[1]		[1]		[1]	[1]
Oxford	d			10 08		11 01				10 37			11 31				11 07		12 01					11 37	
Reading [7]	d			11 03	11 18	11 26				11 33		11 48	11 56				12 03	12 18	12 26					12 33	12 48
Twyford [3]	d			11 09	11 24					11 39		11 54					12 09	12 24						12 39	12 54
Maidenhead [3]	d			11 17	11 32					11 47		12 02					12 17	12 32						12 47	13 02
Taplow	d				11 36							12 06						12 36							13 06
Burnham	d	←			11 39			←				12 09			←			12 39				←			13 09
Slough [3]	a	11 14		11 24	11 44	11 39		11 44		11 54		12 14	12 10		12 14		12 24	12 44	12 41			12 44		12 54	13 14
	d	11 14		11 24	11 44	11 40		11 44		11 54		12 14	12 11		12 14		12 24	12 44	12 41			12 44		12 54	13 14
Langley	d			11 28	→					11 58		→					12 28	→						12 58	→
Iver	d			11 31						12 01							12 31							13 01	
West Drayton	d	11 21		11 35				11 51		12 05					12 21		12 35					12 51		13 05	
Heathrow Terminal 4 ✈	d																								
Heathrow Terminal 1-2 [2] ✈	d		11 27						11 57							12 27							12 57		
Hayes & Harlington	d	11 26	11 33	11 40				11 56	12 03	12 10					12 26	12 33	12 40					12 56	13 03	13 10	
Southall	d		11 36	11 43					12 06	12 13						12 36	12 43						13 06	13 13	
Hanwell	d		11 39						12 09							12 39							13 09		
Greenford ⊖	d						11 46							12 16						12 46					
South Greenford	d						11 49							12 19						12 49					
Castle Bar Park	d						11 52							12 22						12 52					
Drayton Green	d						11 54							12 24						12 54					
West Ealing	d		11 41				11 56		12 11					12 26		12 41				12 56			13 11		
Ealing Broadway ⊖	d	11 33	11 44	11 49			11 59	12 07	12 14	12 19				12 29	12 33	12 44	12 49			12 59		13 03	13 14	13 19	
Acton Main Line	d						12 03							12 33						13 03					
London Paddington [15] ⊖	a	11 46	11 54	12 01		11 59	12 12	12 18	12 24	12 31			12 30	12 42	12 46	12 54	13 02		13 09	13 12		13 16	13 24	13 31	

		GW	GW	GW	HC	GW		GW	GW	GW	GW	HC	GW	GW	GW	GW		GW	HC	GW	GW	GW	GW	GW	HC
		◇[1] 🚲	[1]	[1]		[1]		[1]	◇[1] 🚲	[1]	[1]		[1]	[1]	◇[1] 🚲	[1]		[1]		[1]	[1]	◇[1] 🚲	[1]	[1]	
Oxford	d	12 31				12 07			13 01				12 37		13 31					13 07		14 01			
Reading [7]	d	12 56				13 03		13 18	13 26				13 33	13 48	13 56					14 03	14 18	14 26			
Twyford [3]	d					13 09		13 24					13 39	13 54						14 09	14 24				
Maidenhead [3]	d					13 17		13 32					13 47	14 02						14 17	14 32				
Taplow	d							13 36						14 06							14 36				
Burnham	d			←				13 39			←			14 09				←			14 39			←	
Slough [3]	a	13 10		13 14		13 24		13 44	13 41		13 44		13 54	14 13	14 10			14 13		14 24	14 44	14 40		14 44	
	d	13 11		13 14		13 24		13 47	13 41		13 47		13 54	14 14	14 11			14 14		14 24	14 44	14 41		14 44	
Langley	d					13 28		→					13 58	→						14 28	→				
Iver	d					13 31							14 01							14 31					
West Drayton	d			13 21		13 35					13 51		14 05					14 21		14 35				14 51	
Heathrow Terminal 4 ✈	d																								
Heathrow Terminal 1-2 [2] ✈	d				13 27							13 57							14 27						14 57
Hayes & Harlington	d			13 26	13 33	13 40					13 56	14 03	14 10					14 26	14 33	14 40				14 56	15 03
Southall	d				13 36	13 43						14 06	14 13						14 36	14 43					15 06
Hanwell	d				13 39							14 09							14 39						15 09
Greenford ⊖	d		13 16							13 46						14 16							14 46		
South Greenford	d		13 19							13 49						14 19							14 49		
Castle Bar Park	d		13 22							13 52						14 22							14 52		
Drayton Green	d		13 24							13 54						14 24							14 54		
West Ealing	d		13 26		13 41					13 56		14 11				14 26			14 41				14 56		15 11
Ealing Broadway ⊖	d		13 29	13 33	13 44	13 49				13 59	14 03	14 14	14 19			14 29		14 33	14 44	14 49			14 59	15 03	15 14
Acton Main Line	d		13 33							14 03						14 33							15 03		
London Paddington [15] ⊖	a	13 30	13 42	13 46	13 54	14 01			14 00	14 12	14 16	14 24	14 31		14 30	14 42		14 46	14 54	15 01		15 01	15 12	15 16	15 24

For non-stop services between London and Reading please see table 116

Passengers who hold valid tickets for Acton Main Line, West Ealing and Hanwell will be able to use local Transport for London (TFL) bus services to reach these stations. Tel 0843 222 1234

Table 117R

Mondays to Fridays

31 March to 16 May

Network Diagram - refer to first Page of Table 116

Reading and Greenford - London

		GW 1		GW 1	GW ◇1	GW 1	GW 1	HC	GW 1	GW 1	GW ◇1	GW 1		GW 1	HC	GW 1	GW 1	GW ◇1	GW 1	GW 1	HC	GW 1		GW 1	GW ◇1
Oxford	d	13 37			14 31				14 07		15 01					14 37		15 31				15 07			16 01
Reading 7	d	14 33		14 48	14 56				15 03	15 18	15 26					15 33	15 48	15 57				16 03		16 18	16 26
Twyford 3	d	14 39		14 54					15 09	15 24						15 39	15 54					16 09		16 24	
Maidenhead 3	d	14 47		15 02					15 17	15 32						15 47	16 02					16 17		16 32	
Taplow	d			15 06						15 36							16 06							16 36	
Burnham	d			15 09			←			15 39				←			16 09			←				16 39	
Slough 3	a	14 54		15 14	15 10		15 14		15 24	15 44	15 39			15 44		15 54	16 14	16 10		16 14		16 24		16 44	16 41
	d	14 54		15 14	15 11		15 14		15 24	15 44	15 40			15 44		15 54	16 14	16 11		16 14		16 24		16 44	16 41
Langley	d	14 58		→					15 28	→						15 58	→					16 28		→	
Iver	d	15 01							15 31							16 01						16 31			
West Drayton	d	15 05					15 21		15 35					15 51		16 05				16 21		16 35			
Heathrow Terminal 4	d																								
Heathrow Terminal 1-2 2	d							15 27							15 57						16 27				
Hayes & Harlington	d	15 10					15 26	15 33	15 40					15 56	16 03	16 10				16 26	16 33	16 40			
Southall	d	15 13						15 36	15 43						16 06	16 13					16 36	16 43			
Hanwell	d							15 39							16 09						16 39				
Greenford	d					15 16						15 46							16 16						
South Greenford	d					15 19						15 49							16 19						
Castle Bar Park	d					15 22						15 52							16 22						
Drayton Green	d					15 24						15 54							16 24						
West Ealing	d					15 26		15 41				15 56			16 11				16 26		16 41				
Ealing Broadway	d	15 19				15 29	15 33	15 44	15 49			15 59		16 03	16 14	16 19			16 29	16 33	16 44	16 49			
Acton Main Line	d					15 33						16 03							16 33						
London Paddington 15	a	15 32			15 30	15 42	15 46	15 54	16 01		16 01	16 12		16 16	16 24	16 31		16 29	16 42	16 46	16 54	17 01			17 00

		GW 1	GW 1	HC	GW 1	GW 1	GW ◇1	GW 1		GW 1	HC	GW 1	GW 1	GW ◇1	GW ◇1	GW 1	GW 1	HC		GW 1	GW 1	GW 1	GW ◇1	GW 1	GW 1
Oxford	d				15 37		16 31					16 07			17 01					16 37			17 31		
Reading 7	d				16 31	16 48	16 57					17 03	17 14	17 18	17 27					17 33	17 42	17 54	17 56		
Twyford 3	d				16 39	16 54						17 09	17 24							17 39	17 48				
Maidenhead 3	d				16 47	17 02						17 17	17 32		17 40					17 47	17 56	18 08			
Taplow	d					17 06							17 36								18 00				
Burnham	d		←			17 09				←			17 39				←				18 02				←
Slough 3	a		16 44		16 54	17 16	17 13			17 16		17 24	17 44	17 32			17 44			17 54	18 07	18 16	18 10		18 16
	d		16 44		16 54	17 17	17 14			17 17		17 24	17 44	17 33			17 44			17 54	18 07	18 16	18 11		18 16
Langley	d				16 58	→						17 28	→							17 58		→			
Iver	d				17 01							17 31								18 01					
West Drayton	d		16 51		17 05					17 24		17 35					17 51			18 05	18 14				
Heathrow Terminal 4	d																								
Heathrow Terminal 1-2 2	d			16 57							17 27							17 57							
Hayes & Harlington	d		16 56	17 03	17 10					17 29	17 33	17 40					17 56	18 03		18 10	18 19				18 27
Southall	d			17 06	17 13						17 36	17 43						18 06		18 13					
Hanwell	d			17 09							17 39							18 09							
Greenford	d	16 46						17 16								17 46								18 16	
South Greenford	d	16 49						17 19								17 49								18 19	
Castle Bar Park	d	16 52						17 22								17 52								18 22	
Drayton Green	d	16 54						17 24								17 54								18 24	
West Ealing	d	16 56		17 11				17 26			17 41					17 56		18 11						18 26	
Ealing Broadway	d	16 59	17 03	17 14	17 21			17 29		17 36	17 44	17 49				17 59	18 03	18 14		18 19	18 26			18 29	18 35
Acton Main Line	d	17 03						17 33								18 03								18 33	
London Paddington 15	a	17 12	17 17	17 24	17 31		17 34	17 42		17 46	17 54	18 01		17 52	17 59	18 12	18 14	18 24		18 31	18 37		18 28	18 42	18 46

		HC	GW 1	GW 1		GW 1	GW ◇1	GW 1	GW 1	HC	GW 1	GW 1	GW ◇1	GW 1		GW 1	HC	GW 1	GW 1	GW 1	GW ◇1	HC	GW 1	GW FX 1	
Oxford	d			17 07			18 01				17 37		18 31					18 07			19 06		18 37		
Reading 7	d			18 08		18 18	18 27				18 33	18 48	18 57					19 08		19 20	19 33		19 33	19 48	
Twyford 3	d			18 14		18 24					18 39	18 54						19 14		19 26			19 42	19 54	
Maidenhead 3	d		18 15	18 27		18 32					18 48	19 05						19 22		19 34			19 50	20 02	
Taplow	d					18 35						19 09								19 37				20 05	
Burnham	d					18 39			←			19 12				←				19 40				20 09	
Slough 3	a		18 22	18 34		18 44	18 40		18 44		18 54	19 17	19 09			19 17		19 30		19 45	19 47		19 57	20 14	
	d		18 22	18 34		18 44	18 41		18 44		18 54	19 17	19 10			19 17		19 30		19 45	19 48		19 57	20 14	
Langley	d		18 26			→					18 58	→						19 34					20 01	→	
Iver	d		18 29								19 01							19 37					20 04		
West Drayton	d		18 33						18 51		19 05					19 24		19 40		19 52			20 08		
Heathrow Terminal 4	d																								
Heathrow Terminal 1-2 2	d	18 27								18 57							19 27					19 57			
Hayes & Harlington	d	18 33	18 38	18 43					18 56	19 03	19 10					19 29	19 33	19 45		19 57		20 03	20 13		
Southall	d	18 36	18 42							19 06	19 13						19 36	19 48				20 06	20 16		
Hanwell	d	18 39								19 09							19 39					20 09			
Greenford	d							18 46						19 16					19 46						
South Greenford	d							18 49						19 19					19 49						
Castle Bar Park	d							18 52						19 22					19 52						
Drayton Green	d							18 54						19 24					19 54						
West Ealing	d	18 41						18 56		19 11				19 26			19 41		19 56			20 11			
Ealing Broadway	d	18 44	18 48	18 53				18 59	19 05	19 14	19 19			19 29		19 36	19 44	19 54	19 59	20 04		20 14	20 22		
Acton Main Line	d							19 03						19 34					20 03						
London Paddington 15	a	18 54	18 59	19 02			18 59	19 12	19 18	19 24	19 31		19 30	19 42		19 46	19 54	20 03	20 12	20 17	20 06	20 24	20 32		

For non-stop services between London and Reading please see table 116

Passengers who hold valid tickets for Acton Main Line, West Ealing and Hanwell will be able to use local Transport for London (TFL) bus services to reach these stations. Tel 0843 222 1234

Table 117R

Mondays to Fridays

31 March to 16 May

Network Diagram - refer to first Page of Table 116

Reading and Greenford - London

		GW FO	GW	GW	GW FO	GW FX	HC	GW	GW	GW		GW	GW	HC	GW	GW	GW	GW	GW	HC		GW	GW	GW	HC FO
		1	◇1	1	1	1		1	1	◇1		1	1		1	1	◇1 🚲	1	1			1	1	◇1	
Oxford	d		19 31					19 10		20 01					19 37		20 31						20 07	21 01	
Reading 7	d	19 48	19 55					19 58	20 18	20 26					20 33	20 48	20 56						21 12	21 26	
Twyford 3	d	19 54						20 04	20 24						20 39	20 54							21 18		
Maidenhead 3	d	20 02						20 12	20 32						20 47	21 02							21 26		
Taplow	d	20 05							20 36							21 06							21 30		
Burnham	d	20 09			←	←			20 39				←			21 09			←				21 33		
Slough 3	a	20 14	20 10		20 14	20 14		20 22	20 44	20 40			20 44		20 54	21 13	21 11		21 13				21 38	21 40	
	d	20 14	20 11		20 14	20 14		20 24	20 44	20 41			20 44		20 54	21 14	21 12		21 14				21 38	21 41	
Langley	d	→						20 28	→						20 58	→			21 17				21 42		
Iver	d							20 31							21 01				21 20				21 45		
West Drayton	d				20 21	20 21		20 35					20 51		21 05				21 24				21 49		
Heathrow Terminal 4 ✈	d																								
Heathrow Terminal 1-2 2 ✈	d						20 27							20 57						21 27					21 57
Hayes & Harlington	d				20 26	20 26	20 33	20 40					20 56	21 03	21 10				21 28	21 33			21 54		22 03
Southall	d						20 36	20 43						21 06	21 13					21 36			21 57		22 06
Hanwell	d						20 39							21 09						21 39					22 09
Greenford ⊖	d			20 16								20 46						21 16				21 45			
South Greenford	d			20 19								20 49						21 19				21 48			
Castle Bar Park	d			20 22								20 52						21 22				21 51			
Drayton Green	d			20 24								20 54						21 24				21 53			
West Ealing	d			20 26			20 41					20 56		21 11				21 26		21 41		21 55			22 11
Ealing Broadway ⊖	d			20 29	20 32	20 33	20 44	20 49				20 59	21 03	21 14	21 19			21 29	21 35	21 44		21 58	22 03		22 14
Acton Main Line	d			20 33								21 03						21 33				22 01			
London Paddington 15 ⊖	a		20 30	20 42	20 49	20 49	20 54	20 59		21 01		21 12	21 16	21 24	21 30		21 29	21 42	21 47	21 54		22 11	22 14	22 00	22 24

		GW	GW FO	GW FX	HC FO	HC FX		GW	GW	GW	HC FO	GW FO	GW FX	HC FO	HC FX	GW		GW	GW						
		1	◇1	◇1				1	◇	1		◇1	◇1			1		1	◇1						
Oxford	d	20 37	21 32	21 32					22 11			22 30	22 30						23 09						
Reading 7	d	21 33	21 56	21 56				22 17	22 44	22 48		22 59	22 59					23 15	23 41						
Twyford 3	d	21 39						22 23		22 54								23 22							
Maidenhead 3	d	21 47						22 32		23 02								23 29	23 55						
Taplow	d	21 50						22 34		23 05								23 33							
Burnham	d	21 53						22 37		23 08						←		23 36							
Slough 3	a	21 58	22 14	22 14				22 42	23 01	23 14		23 14	23 14			23 14		23 41	00 02						
	d	21 59	22 14	22 14				22 42	23 01	23 27		23 14	23 14			23 27		23 41	00 02						
Langley	d	22 02						22 46		→						23 32		23 45							
Iver	d	22 05						22 49								23 35		23 48							
West Drayton	d	22 09						22 53								23 39		23 51							
Heathrow Terminal 4 ✈	d																								
Heathrow Terminal 1-2 2 ✈	d				22 27	22 39					22 57			23 27	23 30										
Hayes & Harlington	d	22 14			22 33	22 45		22 59			23 03			23 33	23 36	23 43		23 56							
Southall	d				22 36	22 48		23 02			23 06			23 36	23 39	23 47		23 59							
Hanwell	d				22 39						23 09			23 39											
Greenford ⊖	d																								
South Greenford	d																								
Castle Bar Park	d																								
Drayton Green	d																								
West Ealing	d				22 41						23 11			23 41											
Ealing Broadway ⊖	d	22 21			22 44	22 55		23 08			23 14			23 44	23 44	23 52		00 06							
Acton Main Line	d							23 11							23 47										
London Paddington 15 ⊖	a	22 32	22 38	22 41	22 54	23 02		23 19	23 24		23 24	23 37	23 38	23 54	23 55	00 02		00 17	00 27						

For non-stop services between London and Reading please see table 116

Passengers who hold valid tickets for Acton Main Line, West Ealing and Hanwell will be able to use local Transport for London (TFL) bus services to reach these stations. Tel 0843 222 1234

Table 117R

Saturdays

14 December to 28 December

Network Diagram - refer to first Page of Table 116

Reading and Greenford - London

		GW 1	GW ◇1	HC	GW 1	GW ◇1		GW 1	GW 1	GW 1	HC	GW 1	HC	GW 1	GW 1	GW 1		HC	GW 1	GW 1	GW 1	HC	GW 1	GW 1	GW 1
Oxford	d					00 07		00 27		03 59									05 14				05 49		
Reading 7	d				00 17	00 43		01 17	04 10	04 40		05 10		05 30		05 48			06 03		06 18		06 33		06 48
Twyford 3	d				00 23			01 23	04 16	04 47		05 16		05 39		05 54			06 09		06 24		06 39		06 54
Maidenhead 3	d				00 31			01 31	04 24	04 55		05 24		05 47		06 02			06 17		06 32		06 47		07 02
Taplow	d				00 34							05 28				06 06					06 36				07 06
Burnham	d				00 37							05 31				06 09					06 39				07 09
Slough 3	a				00 42	00 59		01 39	04 32	05 02		05 35		05 54		06 14			06 24		06 44		06 54		07 14
	d		00 02		00 42	01 00		01 39	04 32	05 02		05 36		05 54		06 14			06 24		06 44		06 54		07 14
Langley	d				00 46							05 40		05 58					06 28				06 58		
Iver	d											05 43		06 01					06 31				07 01		
West Drayton	d				00 51				04 38			05 45		06 05		06 21			06 35		06 51		07 05		07 21
Heathrow Terminal 4 ✈	d			00 01							05 23		05 51												
Heathrow Terminal 1-2 2 ✈	d			00 07							05 29		05 57					06 27				06 57			
Hayes & Harlington	d			00 14	00 56			01 48	04 43	05 11	05 35	05 51	06 03	06 10		06 26		06 33	06 40		06 56	07 03	07 10		07 26
Southall	d			00 17	00 59				04 46	05 14	05 38	05 54	06 06	06 13				06 36	06 43			07 06	07 13		
Hanwell	d										05 41		06 09					06 39				07 09			
Greenford ⊖	d														06 16					06 46				07 16	
South Greenford	d														06 19					06 49				07 19	
Castle Bar Park	d														06 22					06 52				07 22	
Drayton Green	d														06 24					06 54				07 24	
West Ealing	d										05 43		06 11		06 26			06 41		06 56		07 11		07 26	
Ealing Broadway ⊖	d	00 06		00 22	01 05			01 55	04 52	05 19	05 46	06 00	06 14	06 19	06 29	06 33		06 44	06 49	06 59	07 03	07 14	07 19	07 29	07 33
Acton Main Line	d									05 24		06 03			06 33					07 03				07 33	
London Paddington 15 ⊖	a	00 17	00 27	00 30	01 18	01 21		02 07	05 01	05 31	05 56	06 11	06 24	06 31	06 42	06 46		06 54	07 01	07 12	07 16	07 24	07 31	07 42	07 46

		GW ◇1		HC	GW 1	GW 1	GW ◇1	GW 1	GW 1	HC	GW 1	GW 1		GW ◇1 🚲	GW 1	GW 1	HC	GW 1	GW 1	GW ◇1	GW 1	GW 1		HC	GW 1
Oxford	d	06 31			06 07		07 01				06 42			07 31				07 07		08 01					07 37
Reading 7	d	07 03			07 03	07 18	07 27				07 33	07 48		07 55				08 03	08 18	08 26					08 33
Twyford 3	d				07 09	07 24					07 39	07 54						08 09	08 24						08 39
Maidenhead 3	d				07 17	07 32					07 47	08 02						08 17	08 32						08 47
Taplow	d					07 36						08 06							08 36						
Burnham	d					07 39			←			08 09				←			08 39			←			
Slough 3	a	07 17			07 24	07 44	07 42		07 44		07 54	08 14		08 10		08 14		08 24	08 44	08 40		08 44			08 54
	d	07 18			07 24	07 44	07 42		07 44		07 54	08 14		08 10		08 14		08 24	08 44	08 41		08 44			08 54
Langley	d				07 28	→					07 58	→						08 28	→						08 58
Iver	d				07 31						08 01							08 31							09 01
West Drayton	d				07 35				07 51		08 05					08 21		08 35				08 52			09 05
Heathrow Terminal 4 ✈	d																								
Heathrow Terminal 1-2 2 ✈	d			07 27						07 57							08 27							08 57	
Hayes & Harlington	d			07 33	07 40				07 56	08 03	08 10					08 26	08 33	08 40				08 58		09 03	09 10
Southall	d			07 36	07 43					08 06	08 13						08 36	08 43						09 06	09 13
Hanwell	d			07 39						08 09							08 39							09 09	
Greenford ⊖	d							07 46							08 16						08 46				
South Greenford	d							07 49							08 19						08 49				
Castle Bar Park	d							07 52							08 22						08 52				
Drayton Green	d							07 54							08 24						08 54				
West Ealing	d			07 41				07 56		08 11					08 26		08 41				08 56			09 11	
Ealing Broadway ⊖	d			07 44	07 49			07 59	08 03	08 14	08 19				08 29	08 33	08 44	08 49			08 59	09 05		09 14	09 19
Acton Main Line	d							08 03							08 33						09 03				
London Paddington 15 ⊖	a	07 37		07 54	08 01		08 01	08 12	08 16	08 24	08 31			08 29	08 42	08 46	08 54	09 01		08 59	09 12	09 16		09 24	09 31

		GW 1	GW ◇1 ⊏P	GW 1	GW 1	HC	GW 1	GW 1		GW ◇1 🚲	GW 1	GW 1	HC	GW 1	GW 1	GW ◇1 A ⊏P⊘	GW 1	GW 1		HC	GW 1	GW 1	GW ◇1 🚲	GW 1	GW 1
Oxford	d		08 31				08 07			09 01				08 37		09 31					09 07		10 01		
Reading 7	d	08 48	08 56				09 03	09 18		09 24				09 33	09 48	09 55					10 03	10 18	10 28		
Twyford 3	d	08 54					09 09	09 24						09 39	09 54						10 09	10 24			
Maidenhead 3	d	09 02					09 17	09 32						09 47	10 02						10 17	10 32			
Taplow	d	09 06						09 36							10 06							10 36			
Burnham	d	09 09			←			09 39				←			10 09			←				10 39			←
Slough 3	a	09 14	09 10		09 14		09 24	09 44		09 40		09 44		09 54	10 14	10 09		10 14			10 24	10 44	10 43		10 44
	d	09 14	09 12		09 14		09 24	09 44		09 40		09 44		09 54	10 14	10 10		10 14			10 24	10 44	10 43		10 44
Langley	d	→					09 28	→						09 58	→						10 28	→			
Iver	d						09 31							10 01							10 31				
West Drayton	d				09 21		09 35					09 51		10 05				10 21			10 35				10 51
Heathrow Terminal 4 ✈	d																								
Heathrow Terminal 1-2 2 ✈	d					09 27							09 57							10 27					
Hayes & Harlington	d				09 26	09 33	09 40					09 56	10 03	10 10				10 26		10 33	10 40				10 56
Southall	d					09 36	09 43						10 06	10 13						10 36	10 43				
Hanwell	d					09 39							10 09							10 39					
Greenford ⊖	d			09 16							09 46						10 16							10 46	
South Greenford	d			09 19							09 49						10 19							10 49	
Castle Bar Park	d			09 22							09 52						10 22							10 52	
Drayton Green	d			09 24							09 54						10 24							10 54	
West Ealing	d			09 26		09 41					09 56		10 11				10 26			10 41				10 56	
Ealing Broadway ⊖	d			09 29	09 33	09 44	09 49				09 59	10 03	10 14	10 19			10 29	10 33		10 44	10 49			10 59	11 03
Acton Main Line	d			09 33							10 03						10 33							11 03	
London Paddington 15 ⊖	a		09 29	09 42	09 46	09 54	10 01			09 59	10 12	10 16	10 24	10 31		10 29	10 42	10 46		10 54	11 01		11 02	11 12	11 16

A ⊏P from Reading ⊘ to Reading

For non-stop services between London and Reading please see table 116

Passengers who hold valid tickets for Acton Main Line, West Ealing and Hanwell will be able to use local Transport for London (TFL) bus services to reach these stations. Tel 0843 222 1234

Table 117R

Saturdays

14 December to 28 December

Reading and Greenford - London

Network Diagram - refer to first Page of Table 116

		HC	GW	GW		GW	GW	GW	HC	GW	GW	GW	GW	GW		HC	GW	GW	GW	GW	GW	HC	GW	GW	
			1	1		◇1	1	1		1	1	◇1	1	1			1	1	◇1	1	1		1	1	
Oxford	d		09 37			10 32				10 07		11 01					10 37		11 30				11 07		
Reading 7	d		10 33	10 48		10 58				11 03	11 18	11 25					11 33	11 48	11 58				12 03	12 18	
Twyford 3	d		10 39	10 54						11 09	11 24						11 39	11 54					12 09	12 24	
Maidenhead 3	d		10 47	11 02						11 17	11 32						11 47	12 02					12 17	12 32	
Taplow	d			11 06							11 36							12 06						12 36	
Burnham	d			11 09				←			11 39			←				12 09			←			12 39	
Slough 3	a		10 54	11 14		11 12		11 14		11 24	11 44	11 39		11 44			11 54	12 14	12 12		12 14		12 24	12 44	
	d		10 54	11 14		11 13		11 14		11 24	11 44	11 40		11 44			11 54	12 14	12 14		12 14		12 24	12 44	
Langley	d		10 58	→						11 28	→						11 58	→					12 28	→	
Iver	d		11 01							11 31							12 01						12 31		
West Drayton	d		11 05					11 21		11 35				11 51			12 05				12 21		12 35		
Heathrow Terminal 4 ✈	d																								
Heathrow Terminal 1-2 2 ✈	d	10 57							11 27							11 57						12 27			
Hayes & Harlington	d	11 03	11 10					11 26	11 33	11 40				11 56		12 03	12 10				12 26	12 33	12 40		
Southall	d	11 06	11 13						11 36	11 43						12 06	12 13					12 36	12 43		
Hanwell	d	11 09							11 39							12 09						12 39			
Greenford ⊖	d						11 16						11 46							12 16					
South Greenford	d						11 19						11 49							12 19					
Castle Bar Park	d						11 22						11 52							12 22					
Drayton Green	d						11 24						11 54							12 24					
West Ealing	d	11 11					11 26		11 41				11 56			12 11				12 26		12 41			
Ealing Broadway ⊖	d	11 14	11 19				11 29	11 33	11 44	11 49			11 59	12 03		12 14	12 19			12 29	12 33	12 44	12 49		
Acton Main Line	d						11 33						12 03							12 33					
London Paddington 15 ⊖	a	11 24	11 31			11 30	11 42	11 46	11 54	12 01		11 59	12 12	12 16		12 24	12 31		12 32	12 42	12 46	12 54	13 01		

		GW	GW	GW	HC	GW	GW	GW	GW	GW		HC	GW	GW	GW	GW	GW	HC	GW	GW		GW	GW	GW	HC
		◇1	1	1		1	1	◇1	1	1			1	1	◇1	1	1		1	1		◇1	1	1	
Oxford	d	12 01				11 37		12 31					12 07		13 01				12 37			13 31			
Reading 7	d	12 27				12 33	12 48	12 57					13 03	13 18	13 27				13 33	13 48		13 56			
Twyford 3	d					12 39	12 54						13 09	13 24					13 39	13 54					
Maidenhead 3	d					12 47	13 02						13 17	13 32					13 47	14 02					
Taplow	d						13 06							13 36						14 06					
Burnham	d			←			13 09			←				13 39			←			14 09				←	
Slough 3	a	12 41		12 44		12 54	13 14	13 11		13 14			13 24	13 44	13 41		13 44		13 54	14 14		14 09		14 14	
	d	12 42		12 44		12 54	13 14	13 13		13 14			13 24	13 44	13 42		13 44		13 54	14 14		14 11		14 14	
Langley	d					12 58	→						13 28	→					13 58	→					
Iver	d					13 01							13 31						14 01						
West Drayton	d			12 51		13 05				13 21			13 35				13 51		14 05					14 21	
Heathrow Terminal 4 ✈	d																								
Heathrow Terminal 1-2 2 ✈	d				12 57							13 27						13 57							14 27
Hayes & Harlington	d			12 56	13 03	13 10				13 26		13 33	13 40				13 56	14 03	14 10					14 26	14 33
Southall	d				13 06	13 13						13 36	13 43					14 06	14 13						14 36
Hanwell	d				13 09							13 39						14 09							14 39
Greenford ⊖	d		12 46						13 16							13 46							14 16		
South Greenford	d		12 49						13 19							13 49							14 19		
Castle Bar Park	d		12 52						13 22							13 52							14 22		
Drayton Green	d		12 54						13 24							13 54							14 24		
West Ealing	d		12 56		13 11				13 26			13 41				13 56		14 11					14 26		14 41
Ealing Broadway ⊖	d		12 59	13 03	13 14	13 19			13 29	13 33		13 44	13 49			13 59	14 03	14 14	14 19				14 29	14 33	14 44
Acton Main Line	d		13 03						13 33							14 03							14 33		
London Paddington 15 ⊖	a	12 59	13 12	13 16	13 24	13 31		13 32	13 42	13 46		13 54	14 01		13 59	14 12	14 16	14 24	14 31			14 29	14 42	14 46	14 54

		GW	GW	GW	GW	GW		HC	GW	GW	GW	GW	GW	HC	GW	GW		GW	GW	GW	HC	GW	GW	GW	GW
		1	1	◇1	1	1			1	1	◇1	1	1		1	1		◇1	1	1		1	1	◇1	1
Oxford	d	13 07		14 01					13 37		14 31				14 07			15 01				14 37		15 31	
Reading 7	d	14 03	14 18	14 27					14 33	14 48	14 58				15 03	15 18		15 25				15 32	15 48	15 56	
Twyford 3	d	14 09	14 24						14 39	14 54					15 09	15 24						15 39	15 54		
Maidenhead 3	d	14 17	14 32						14 47	15 02					15 17	15 32						15 47	16 02		
Taplow	d		14 36							15 06						15 36							16 06		
Burnham	d		14 39			←				15 09			←			15 39				←			16 09		
Slough 3	a	14 24	14 44	14 41		14 44			14 54	15 14	15 13		15 14		15 24	15 44		15 40		15 44		15 54	16 14	16 11	
	d	14 24	14 44	14 42		14 44			14 54	15 14	15 13		15 14		15 24	15 44		15 40		15 44		15 54	16 14	16 12	
Langley	d	14 28	→						14 58	→					15 28	→						15 58	→		
Iver	d	14 31							15 01						15 31							16 01			
West Drayton	d	14 35				14 51			15 05				15 21		15 35					15 51		16 05			
Heathrow Terminal 4 ✈	d																								
Heathrow Terminal 1-2 2 ✈	d							14 57						15 27							15 57				
Hayes & Harlington	d	14 40				14 56		15 03	15 10				15 26	15 33	15 40					15 56	16 03	16 10			
Southall	d	14 43						15 06	15 13					15 36	15 43						16 06	16 13			
Hanwell	d							15 09						15 39							16 09				
Greenford ⊖	d				14 46							15 16							15 46						16 16
South Greenford	d				14 49							15 19							15 49						16 19
Castle Bar Park	d				14 52							15 22							15 52						16 22
Drayton Green	d				14 54							15 24							15 54						16 24
West Ealing	d				14 56			15 11				15 26		15 41					15 56		16 11				16 26
Ealing Broadway ⊖	d	14 49			14 59	15 03		15 14	15 19			15 29	15 33	15 44	15 49				15 59	16 03	16 14	16 19			16 29
Acton Main Line	d				15 03							15 33							16 03						16 33
London Paddington 15 ⊖	a	15 01		14 59	15 12	15 16		15 24	15 31		15 30	15 42	15 46	15 54	16 01			15 59	16 12	16 16	16 24	16 31		16 30	16 42

For non-stop services between London and Reading please see table 116

Passengers who hold valid tickets for Acton Main Line, West Ealing and Hanwell will be able to use local Transport for London (TFL) bus services to reach these stations. Tel 0843 222 1234

Table 117R

Saturdays

14 December to 28 December

Network Diagram - refer to first Page of Table 116

Reading and Greenford - London

		GW 1		HC	GW 1	GW 1	GW ◇1	GW 1	GW 1	HC	GW 1	GW 1		GW ◇1	GW 1	GW 1	HC	GW 1	GW 1	GW ◇1	GW 1	GW 1		HC	GW 1
Oxford	d				15 07		16 01				15 37			16 31				16 07		17 01					16 37
Reading 7	d				16 03	16 18	16 26				16 33	16 48		16 56				17 03	17 18	17 26					17 32
Twyford 3	d				16 09	16 24					16 39	16 54						17 09	17 24						17 39
Maidenhead 3	d				16 17	16 32					16 47	17 02						17 17	17 32						17 47
Taplow	d					16 36						17 06							17 36						
Burnham	d	←				16 39			←			17 09				←			17 39			←			
Slough 3	a	16 14			16 24	16 44	16 40		16 44		16 54	17 14		17 10		17 14		17 24	17 44	17 40		17 44			17 54
	d	16 14			16 24	16 44	16 41		16 44		16 54	17 14		17 11		17 14		17 24	17 44	17 41		17 44			17 54
Langley	d				16 28	→					16 58	→						17 28	→						17 58
Iver	d				16 31						17 01							17 31							18 01
West Drayton	d	16 21			16 35				16 51		17 05					17 21		17 35				17 51			18 05
Heathrow Terminal 4 ✈	d																								
Heathrow Terminal 1-2 2 ✈	d			16 27						16 57							17 27							17 57	
Hayes & Harlington	d	16 26		16 33	16 40				16 56	17 03	17 10					17 26	17 33	17 40				17 56		18 03	18 10
Southall	d			16 36	16 43					17 06	17 13						17 36	17 43						18 06	18 13
Hanwell	d			16 39						17 09							17 39							18 09	
Greenford ⊖	d							16 46							17 16						17 46				
South Greenford	d							16 49							17 19						17 49				
Castle Bar Park	d							16 52							17 22						17 52				
Drayton Green	d							16 54							17 24						17 54				
West Ealing	d			16 41				16 56		17 11					17 26		17 41				17 56			18 11	
Ealing Broadway ⊖	d	16 33		16 44	16 49			16 59	17 03	17 14	17 19				17 29	17 33	17 44	17 49			17 59	18 03		18 14	18 19
Acton Main Line	d							17 03							17 33						18 03				
London Paddington 15 ⊖	a	16 46		16 54	17 01		16 59	17 12	17 16	17 24	17 31			17 29	17 42	17 46	17 54	18 01		17 59	18 12	18 16		18 24	18 31

		GW 1	GW ◇1	GW 1	GW 1	HC	GW 1	GW 1		GW ◇1	GW 1	GW 1	HC	GW 1	GW 1	GW ◇1	GW 1	GW 1		HC	GW 1	GW 1	GW ◇1	GW 1	GW 1
Oxford	d		17 31				17 07			18 01				17 37		18 31					18 07		19 01		
Reading 7	d	17 48	17 58				18 03	18 18		18 25				18 32	18 48	18 56					19 03	19 18	19 25		
Twyford 3	d	17 54					18 09	18 24						18 39	18 54						19 09	19 24			
Maidenhead 3	d	18 02					18 17	18 32						18 47	19 02						19 17	19 32			
Taplow	d	18 06						18 36							19 06							19 36			
Burnham	d	18 09			←			18 39				←			19 09			←				19 39			←
Slough 3	a	18 14	18 11		18 14		18 24	18 44		18 40		18 44		18 54	19 14	19 10		19 14			19 24	19 44	19 40		19 44
	d	18 14	18 12		18 14		18 24	18 44		18 40		18 44		18 54	19 14	19 11		19 14			19 24	19 44	19 40		19 44
Langley	d	→					18 28	→						18 58	→						19 28	→			
Iver	d						18 31							19 01							19 31				
West Drayton	d				18 21		18 35					18 51		19 05				19 21			19 35				19 51
Heathrow Terminal 4 ✈	d																								
Heathrow Terminal 1-2 2 ✈	d					18 27							18 57							19 27					
Hayes & Harlington	d				18 26	18 33	18 40					18 56	19 03	19 10				19 26		19 33	19 40				19 56
Southall	d					18 36	18 43						19 06	19 13						19 36	19 43				
Hanwell	d					18 39							19 09							19 39					
Greenford ⊖	d			18 16							18 46						19 16							19 46	
South Greenford	d			18 19							18 49						19 19							19 49	
Castle Bar Park	d			18 22							18 52						19 22							19 52	
Drayton Green	d			18 24							18 54						19 24							19 54	
West Ealing	d			18 26		18 41					18 56		19 11				19 26			19 41				19 56	
Ealing Broadway ⊖	d			18 29	18 33	18 44	18 49				18 59	19 03	19 14	19 19			19 29	19 33		19 44	19 49			19 59	20 03
Acton Main Line	d			18 33							19 03						19 33							20 03	
London Paddington 15 ⊖	a		18 29	18 42	18 46	18 54	19 01			18 59	19 12	19 16	19 24	19 31		19 29	19 42	19 46		19 54	20 01		19 59	20 12	20 16

		HC	GW 1	GW 1		GW ◇1	GW 1	GW 1	HC	GW 1	GW 1	GW ◇1	GW 1	GW 1		HC	GW 1	GW 1	GW ◇1	GW 1	GW 1	HC	GW 1	GW 1	
Oxford	d		18 37			19 31				19 07		20 01					19 37		20 31				20 07		
Reading 7	d		19 33	19 48		19 55				20 02	20 18	20 25					20 33	20 48	20 56				21 03	21 18	
Twyford 3	d		19 39	19 54						20 09	20 24						20 39	20 54					21 12	21 24	
Maidenhead 3	d		19 47	20 02						20 17	20 32						20 47	21 02					21 19	21 32	
Taplow	d			20 06							20 36							21 06						21 36	
Burnham	d			20 09				←			20 39			←				21 09			←			21 39	
Slough 3	a		19 54	20 14		20 10		20 14		20 24	20 44	20 40		20 44			20 54	21 14	21 10		21 14		21 27	21 44	
	d		19 54	20 14		20 10		20 14		20 24	20 44	20 40		20 44			20 54	21 14	21 11		21 14		21 27	21 44	
Langley	d		19 58	→						20 28	→						20 58	→					21 31	→	
Iver	d		20 01							20 31							21 01						21 34		
West Drayton	d		20 05					20 21		20 35				20 51			21 05				21 21		21 38		
Heathrow Terminal 4 ✈	d																								
Heathrow Terminal 1-2 2 ✈	d	19 57							20 27							20 57						21 27			
Hayes & Harlington	d	20 03	20 10					20 26	20 33	20 40				20 56		21 03	21 10				21 26	21 33	21 43		
Southall	d	20 06	20 13						20 36	20 43						21 06	21 13					21 36	21 46		
Hanwell	d	20 09							20 39							21 09						21 39			
Greenford ⊖	d						20 16						20 46							21 16					
South Greenford	d						20 19						20 49							21 19					
Castle Bar Park	d						20 22						20 52							21 22					
Drayton Green	d						20 24						20 54							21 24					
West Ealing	d	20 11					20 26		20 41				20 56			21 11				21 26		21 41			
Ealing Broadway ⊖	d	20 14	20 19				20 29	20 33	20 44	20 49			20 59	21 03		21 14	21 19			21 29	21 33	21 44	21 52		
Acton Main Line	d						20 33						21 03							21 33					
London Paddington 15 ⊖	a	20 24	20 31			20 29	20 42	20 46	20 54	21 01		20 59	21 12	21 16		21 24	21 31		21 29	21 42	21 46	21 54	22 02		

For non-stop services between London and Reading please see table 116

Passengers who hold valid tickets for Acton Main Line, West Ealing and Hanwell will be able to use local Transport for London (TFL) bus services to reach these stations. Tel 0843 222 1234

Table 117R

Saturdays

14 December to 28 December

Reading and Greenford - London

Network Diagram - refer to first Page of Table 116

Station		GW ◇1	GW 1	GW 1	HC	GW 1	GW ◇1	HC	GW 1	GW ◇1	HC	GW 1	GW 1	GW ◇1	HC	GW 1	GW ◇1	GW 1
Oxford	d	21 01				20 37	21 31			22 01		21 50		22 35			23 01	23 07
Reading 7	d	21 27				21 33	22 02		22 03	22 31		22 33	22 48	23 09		23 19	23 31	00 04
Twyford 3	d					21 39			22 09			22 39	22 55			23 24		00 11
Maidenhead 3	d					21 47			22 17			22 47	23 03			23 32		00 19
Taplow	d					21 51			22 21			22 51	23 07			23 36		00 23
Burnham	d			←		21 54			22 24			22 54	23 10			23 39		00 26
Slough 3	a	21 42		21 44		21 58	22 15		22 28	22 46		22 58	23 15	23 27		23 45	23 49	00 30
	d	21 42		21 44		21 59	22 16		22 29	22 46		22 59	23 15	23 28		23 45	23 50	00 31
Langley	d					22 03						23 03						00 35
Iver	d					22 06						23 06						00 38
West Drayton	d			21 51		22 10			22 36			23 10	23 22			23 52		00 41
Heathrow Terminal 4 ✈	d																	
Heathrow Terminal 1-2 2 ✈	d				21 57			22 27			22 57				23 27			
Hayes & Harlington	d			21 56	22 03	22 14		22 33	22 40		23 03	23 14	23 27		23 33	23 57		00 46
Southall	d				22 06	22 18		22 36	22 44		23 06	23 18	23 31		23 36			00 49
Hanwell	d				22 09			22 39			23 09				23 39			
Greenford ⊖	d		21 46															
South Greenford	d		21 49															
Castle Bar Park	d		21 52															
Drayton Green	d		21 54															
West Ealing	d		21 56		22 11			22 41			23 11				23 41			
Ealing Broadway ⊖	d		21 59	22 03	22 14	22 23		22 44	22 49		23 14	23 23	23 36		23 44	00 04		00 55
Acton Main Line	d		22 03															
London Paddington 15 ⊖	a	22 01	22 12	22 15	22 24	22 32	22 38	22 54	22 58	23 08	23 24	23 32	23 45	23 45	23 54	00 14	00 17	01 05

Saturdays

4 January to 8 February

Station		GW 1	GW ◇1	HC	GW 1	GW ◇1	GW 1	GW 1	GW 1	HC	GW 1	HC	GW 1	HC	GW 1	GW 1	HC	GW 1	GW 1	GW 1	GW ◇1	HC	GW 1
Oxford	d					00 07	00 27		03 59						05 09			05 49		06 07	06 31		
Reading 7	d				00 17	00 43	01 17	04 10	04 40		05 10				05 59			06 33		06 59	07 03		
Twyford 3	d				00 23		01 23	04 16	04 47		05 16				06 05			06 39		07 05			
Maidenhead 3	d				00 31		01 31	04 24	04 55		05 24				06 13			06 47		07 13			
Taplow	d				00 34						05 28				06 17			06 51		07 17			
Burnham	d				00 37						05 31				06 20			06 54		07 20			←
Slough 3	a				00 42	00 59	01 39	04 32	05 02		05 35				06 24			07 01		07 24	07 18		07 24
	d		00 02		00 42	01 00	01 39	04 32	05 02		05 36				06 25			07 02		07 25	07 19		07 25
Langley	d				00 46						05 40				06 28			07 05		→			07 28
Iver	d										05 43				06 31			07 08					07 31
West Drayton	d				00 51			04 38			05 45				06 35			07 12					07 36
Heathrow Terminal 4 ✈	d			00 01						05 23		05 51											
Heathrow Terminal 1-2 2 ✈	d			00 07						05 29		05 57		06 27			06 57					07 27	
Hayes & Harlington	d			00 14	00 56		01 48	04 43	05 11	05 35	05 51	06 03		06 33	06 40		07 03	07 17				07 33	07 40
Southall	d			00 17	00 59			04 46	05 14	05 38	05 54	06 06		06 36	06 43		07 06	07 20				07 36	07 43
Hanwell	d									05 41		06 09		06 39			07 09					07 39	
Greenford ⊖	d												06 16			06 46			07 16				
South Greenford	d												06 19			06 49			07 19				
Castle Bar Park	d												06 22			06 52			07 22				
Drayton Green	d												06 24			06 54			07 24				
West Ealing	d									05 43		06 11	06 26	06 41		06 56	07 11		07 26			07 41	
Ealing Broadway ⊖	d	00 06		00 22	01 05		01 55	04 52	05 19	05 46	06 00	06 14	06 29	06 44	06 49	06 59	07 14	07 26	07 29			07 44	07 49
Acton Main Line	d								05 24		06 03		06 33			07 03			07 33				
London Paddington 15 ⊖	a	00 17	00 27	00 30	01 18	01 21	02 07	05 01	05 31	05 56	06 11	06 24	06 42	06 54	07 01	07 12	07 24	07 36	07 42		07 44	07 54	08 01

For non-stop services between London and Reading please see table 116

Passengers who hold valid tickets for Acton Main Line, West Ealing and Hanwell will be able to use local Transport for London (TFL) bus services to reach these stations. Tel 0843 222 1234

Table 117R

Saturdays

4 January to 8 February

Network Diagram - refer to first Page of Table 116

Reading and Greenford - London

		GW		GW	HC	GW	GW	GW	HC	GW	GW	GW		HC	GW	GW	GW	HC	GW	GW	GW	HC		GW	GW
		◇1		1		1	◇1 trolley	1		1	◇1	1			1	◇1 buffet	1		1	◇1 trolley	1			1	◇1 A buffet/⊘
Oxford	d	07 01				06 42	07 31			07 07	08 01				07 37	08 31			08 07	09 01				08 37	09 31
Reading 7	d	07 27				07 29	07 55			07 59	08 24				08 29	08 57			08 59	09 24				09 33	09 55
Twyford 3	d					07 35				08 05					08 35				09 05					09 39	
Maidenhead 3	d					07 43				08 13					08 43				09 13					09 49	
Taplow	d					07 47				08 17					08 47				09 17					09 53	
Burnham	d					07 50				08 20					08 50				09 20					09 56	
Slough 3	a	07 46				07 54	08 11			08 24	08 40				08 54	09 13			09 24	09 41				10 00	10 10
	d	07 46				07 55	08 11			08 24	08 40				08 54	09 15			09 24	09 41				10 00	10 11
Langley	d					07 58				08 28					08 58				09 28					10 04	
Iver	d					08 01				08 31					09 01				09 31					10 07	
West Drayton	d					08 05				08 35					09 05				09 35					10 11	
Heathrow Terminal 4 ✈	d																								
Heathrow Terminal 1-2 2 ✈	d				07 57				08 27					08 57				09 27				09 57			
Hayes & Harlington	d				08 03	08 10			08 33	08 40				09 03	09 10			09 33	09 40			10 03		10 16	
Southall	d				08 06	08 13			08 36	08 43				09 06	09 13			09 36	09 43			10 06		10 19	
Hanwell	d				08 09				08 39					09 09				09 39				10 09			
Greenford ⊖	d			07 46				08 16				08 46					09 16				09 46				
South Greenford	d			07 49				08 19				08 49					09 19				09 49				
Castle Bar Park	d			07 52				08 22				08 52					09 22				09 52				
Drayton Green	d			07 54				08 24				08 54					09 24				09 54				
West Ealing	d			07 56	08 11			08 26	08 41			08 56		09 11			09 26	09 41			09 56	10 11			
Ealing Broadway ⊖	d			07 59	08 14	08 19		08 29	08 44	08 49		08 59		09 14	09 19		09 29	09 44	09 49		09 59	10 14		10 25	
Acton Main Line	d			08 03				08 33				09 03					09 33				10 03				
London Paddington 15 ⊖	a	08 10		08 12	08 24	08 31	08 39	08 42	08 54	09 01	09 07	09 12		09 24	09 31	09 39	09 42	09 54	10 01	10 07	10 12	10 24		10 34	10 39

		GW	HC	GW	GW	GW	HC	GW		GW	GW	HC	GW	GW	GW	HC	GW	GW		GW	HC	GW	GW	GW	HC
		1		1	◇1 trolley	1		1		◇1 buffet	1		1	◇1	1		1	◇1 trolley		1		1	◇1 trolley	1	
Oxford	d			09 07	10 01			09 37		10 32			10 07	11 01			10 37	11 30				11 07	12 01		
Reading 7	d			09 59	10 28			10 32		10 58			10 59	11 27			11 29	11 58				11 59	12 27		
Twyford 3	d			10 05				10 38					11 05				11 35					12 05			
Maidenhead 3	d			10 13				10 46					11 13				11 43					12 13			
Taplow	d			10 17				10 50					11 17				11 47					12 17			
Burnham	d			10 20				10 53					11 20				11 50					12 20			
Slough 3	a			10 24	10 45			10 57		11 15			11 24	11 42			11 54	12 13				12 24	12 42		
	d			10 24	10 45			10 57		11 16			11 24	11 43			11 54	12 15				12 24	12 43		
Langley	d			10 28				11 01					11 28				11 58					12 28			
Iver	d			10 31				11 04					11 31				12 01					12 31			
West Drayton	d			10 35				11 08					11 35				12 05					12 35			
Heathrow Terminal 4 ✈	d																								
Heathrow Terminal 1-2 2 ✈	d		10 27				10 57					11 27				11 57					12 27				12 57
Hayes & Harlington	d		10 33	10 40			11 03	11 14				11 33	11 40			12 03	12 10				12 33	12 40			13 03
Southall	d		10 36	10 43			11 06	11 16				11 36	11 43			12 06	12 13				12 36	12 43			13 06
Hanwell	d		10 39				11 09					11 39				12 09					12 39				13 09
Greenford ⊖	d	10 16				10 46					11 16				11 46					12 16				12 46	
South Greenford	d	10 19				10 49					11 19				11 49					12 19				12 49	
Castle Bar Park	d	10 22				10 52					11 22				11 52					12 22				12 52	
Drayton Green	d	10 24				10 54					11 24				11 54					12 24				12 54	
West Ealing	d	10 26	10 41			10 56	11 11				11 26	11 41			11 56	12 11				12 26	12 41			12 56	13 11
Ealing Broadway ⊖	d	10 29	10 44	10 49		10 59	11 14	11 23			11 29	11 44	11 49		11 59	12 14	12 19			12 29	12 44	12 49		12 59	13 14
Acton Main Line	d	10 33				11 03					11 33				12 03					12 33				13 03	
London Paddington 15 ⊖	a	10 42	10 54	11 01	11 09	11 12	11 24	11 32		11 40	11 42	11 54	12 01	12 07	12 12	12 24	12 31	12 40		12 42	12 54	13 01	13 07	13 12	13 24

		GW	GW	GW		HC	GW	GW	GW	HC	GW	GW	GW	HC		GW	GW	GW	HC	GW	GW	GW	HC	GW	
		1	◇1 trolley	1			1	◇1 trolley	1		1	◇1	1			1	◇1 trolley	1		1	◇1 buffet	1		1	
Oxford	d	11 37	12 31				12 07	13 01			12 37	13 31				13 07	14 01			13 37	14 31			14 07	
Reading 7	d	12 29	12 57				12 59	13 27			13 29	13 55				13 59	14 27			14 29	14 58			14 59	
Twyford 3	d	12 35					13 05				13 35					14 06				14 35				15 05	
Maidenhead 3	d	12 43					13 13				13 43					14 19				14 43				15 13	
Taplow	d	12 48					13 17				13 47					14 22				14 47				15 17	
Burnham	d	12 51					13 20				13 50					14 25				14 50				15 20	
Slough 3	a	12 55	13 12				13 24	13 42			13 54	14 10				14 29	14 42			14 54	15 14			15 24	
	d	12 55	13 14				13 24	13 43			13 54	14 11				14 29	14 43			14 54	15 15			15 24	
Langley	d	12 59					13 28				13 58					14 33				14 58				15 28	
Iver	d	13 02					13 31				14 01					14 36				15 01				15 31	
West Drayton	d	13 06					13 35				14 05					14 40				15 05				15 35	
Heathrow Terminal 4 ✈	d																								
Heathrow Terminal 1-2 2 ✈	d					13 27				13 57				14 27					14 57				15 27		
Hayes & Harlington	d	13 11				13 33	13 40			14 03	14 10			14 33		14 46			15 03	15 10			15 33	15 40	
Southall	d	13 14				13 36	13 43			14 06	14 13			14 36		14 48			15 06	15 13			15 36	15 43	
Hanwell	d					13 39				14 09				14 39					15 09				15 39		
Greenford ⊖	d			13 16					13 46				14 16					14 46				15 16			
South Greenford	d			13 19					13 49				14 19					14 49				15 19			
Castle Bar Park	d			13 22					13 52				14 22					14 52				15 22			
Drayton Green	d			13 24					13 54				14 24					14 54				15 24			
West Ealing	d			13 26		13 41			13 56	14 11			14 26	14 41				14 56	15 11			15 26	15 41		
Ealing Broadway ⊖	d	13 20		13 29		13 44	13 49		13 59	14 14	14 19		14 29	14 44		14 55		14 59	15 14	15 19		15 29	15 44	15 49	
Acton Main Line	d			13 33					14 03				14 33					15 03				15 33			
London Paddington 15 ⊖	a	13 32	13 39	13 42		13 54	14 01	14 07	14 12	14 24	14 31	14 39	14 42	14 54		15 05	15 07	15 12	15 24	15 31	15 39	15 42	15 54	16 01	

A buffet from Reading ⊘ to Reading

For non-stop services between London and Reading please see table 116

Passengers who hold valid tickets for Acton Main Line, West Ealing and Hanwell will be able to use local Transport for London (TFL) bus services to reach these stations. Tel 0843 222 1234

Table 117R

Saturdays

4 January to 8 February

Network Diagram - refer to first Page of Table 116

Reading and Greenford - London

Station		GW	GW	HC	GW	GW	GW	HC	GW	GW		GW	HC	GW	GW	GW	HC	GW	GW	GW		HC	GW	GW	GW
		◇1	1		1	◇1 ⊼	1		1	◇1		1		1	◇1 ⊼	1		1	◇1	1			1	◇1 ⊡	1
Oxford	d	15 01			14 37	15 31			15 07	16 01				15 37	16 31			16 07	17 01				16 37	17 31	
Reading 7	d	15 25			15 28	15 55			16 01	16 26				16 29	16 55			16 59	17 26				17 28	17 58	
Twyford 3	d				15 35				16 07					16 35				17 05					17 35		
Maidenhead 3	d				15 43				16 18					16 43				17 18					17 43		
Taplow	d				15 47				16 22					16 47				17 22					17 47		
Burnham	d				15 50				16 25					16 50				17 25					17 50		
Slough 3	a	15 41			15 54	16 14			16 29	16 41				16 54	17 11			17 29	17 41				17 54	18 15	
	d	15 41			15 54	16 15			16 29	16 42				16 54	17 12			17 29	17 42				17 54	18 16	
Langley	d				15 58				16 33					16 58				17 33					17 58		
Iver	d				16 01				16 36					17 01				17 36					18 01		
West Drayton	d				16 05				16 40					17 05				17 40					18 05		
Heathrow Terminal 4 ✈	d																								
Heathrow Terminal 1-2 2 ✈	d			15 57				16 27					16 57				17 27					17 57			
Hayes & Harlington	d			16 03	16 10			16 33	16 45				17 03	17 10			17 33	17 45				18 03	18 10		
Southall	d			16 06	16 13			16 36	16 48				17 06	17 13			17 36	17 48				18 06	18 13		
Hanwell	d			16 09				16 39					17 09				17 39					18 09			
Greenford ⊖	d		15 46				16 16					16 46				17 16				17 46					18 16
South Greenford	d		15 49				16 19					16 49				17 19				17 49					18 19
Castle Bar Park	d		15 52				16 22					16 52				17 22				17 52					18 22
Drayton Green	d		15 54				16 24					16 54				17 24				17 54					18 24
West Ealing	d		15 56	16 11			16 26	16 41				16 56	17 11			17 26	17 41			17 56		18 11			18 26
Ealing Broadway ⊖	d		15 59	16 14	16 19		16 29	16 44	16 55			16 59	17 14	17 19		17 29	17 44	17 54		17 59		18 14	18 19		18 29
Acton Main Line	d		16 03				16 33					17 03				17 33				18 03					18 33
London Paddington 15 ⊖	a	16 07	16 12	16 24	16 31	16 40	16 42	16 54	17 04	17 07		17 12	17 24	17 31	17 39	17 42	17 54	18 05	18 07	18 12		18 24	18 31	18 39	18 42

Station		HC	GW	GW	GW	HC		GW	GW	GW	HC	GW	GW	GW	HC	GW		GW	GW	HC	GW	GW	GW	HC	GW
			1	◇1	1			1	◇1 ⊼	1		1	◇1	1		1		◇1 ⊼	1		1	◇1	1		1
Oxford	d		17 07	18 01				17 37	18 31			18 07	19 01			18 37		19 31			19 07	20 01			19 37
Reading 7	d		17 59	18 25				18 28	18 56			18 59	19 25			19 29		19 55			19 58	20 25			20 29
Twyford 3	d		18 05					18 35				19 05				19 35					20 05				20 35
Maidenhead 3	d		18 13					18 43				19 18				19 43					20 16				20 43
Taplow	d		18 17					18 47				19 22				19 47					20 20				20 47
Burnham	d		18 20					18 50				19 25				19 50					20 23				20 50
Slough 3	a		18 24	18 41				18 54	19 11			19 29	19 41			19 54		20 11			20 27	20 41			20 54
	d		18 24	18 41				18 54	19 12			19 29	19 41			19 54		20 11			20 27	20 41			20 54
Langley	d		18 28					18 58				19 33				19 58					20 31				20 58
Iver	d		18 31					19 01				19 36				20 01					20 34				21 01
West Drayton	d		18 35					19 05				19 40				20 05					20 38				21 05
Heathrow Terminal 4 ✈	d																								
Heathrow Terminal 1-2 2 ✈	d	18 27				18 57					19 27				19 57					20 27				20 57	
Hayes & Harlington	d	18 33	18 40			19 03		19 10			19 33	19 45			20 03	20 10				20 33	20 44			21 03	21 10
Southall	d	18 36	18 43			19 06		19 13			19 36	19 48			20 06	20 13				20 36	20 47			21 06	21 13
Hanwell	d	18 39				19 09					19 39				20 09					20 39				21 09	
Greenford ⊖	d				18 46					19 16				19 46					20 16				20 46		
South Greenford	d				18 49					19 19				19 49					20 19				20 49		
Castle Bar Park	d				18 52					19 22				19 52					20 22				20 52		
Drayton Green	d				18 54					19 24				19 54					20 24				20 54		
West Ealing	d	18 41			18 56	19 11				19 26	19 41			19 56	20 11				20 26	20 41			20 56	21 11	
Ealing Broadway ⊖	d	18 44	18 49		18 59	19 14		19 19		19 29	19 44	19 54		19 59	20 14	20 19			20 29	20 44	20 53		20 59	21 14	21 19
Acton Main Line	d				19 03					19 33				20 03					20 33				21 03		
London Paddington 15 ⊖	a	18 54	19 01	19 07	19 12	19 24		19 31	19 38	19 42	19 54	20 05	20 07	20 12	20 24	20 31		20 37	20 42	20 54	21 02	21 07	21 12	21 24	21 31

Station		GW		GW	HC	GW	GW	GW	HC	GW	GW	HC		GW	GW	HC	GW	GW	HC	GW	GW	GW		GW	
		◇1		1		1	◇1	1		1	◇1			1	◇1		1	1		◇1	1	◇1		1	
Oxford	d	20 31				20 07	21 01			20 37	21 31				22 01		21 50			22 35		23 01		23 07	
Reading 7	d	20 56				20 59	21 27			21 33	22 02			22 03	22 31		22 33	22 48		23 15	23 19	23 38		00 08	
Twyford 3	d					21 08				21 39				22 09			22 39	22 55			23 24			00 15	
Maidenhead 3	d					21 15				21 47				22 17			22 47	23 03			23 32			00 23	
Taplow	d					21 20				21 51				22 21			22 51	23 07			23 36			00 26	
Burnham	d					21 23				21 54				22 24			22 54	23 10			23 39			00 29	
Slough 3	a	21 13				21 27	21 43			21 58	22 17			22 28	22 47		22 58	23 15		23 33	23 44	23 58		00 34	
	d	21 14				21 27	21 43			21 59	22 18			22 29	22 47		22 59	23 15		23 34	23 45	23 59		00 34	
Langley	d					21 31				22 03							23 03							00 39	
Iver	d					21 34				22 06							23 06							00 42	
West Drayton	d					21 38				22 10				22 36			23 10	23 22			23 52			00 45	
Heathrow Terminal 4 ✈	d																								
Heathrow Terminal 1-2 2 ✈	d				21 27				21 57			22 27				22 57			23 27						
Hayes & Harlington	d				21 33	21 44			22 03	22 14		22 33		22 40		23 03	23 14	23 27	23 33		23 57			00 50	
Southall	d				21 36	21 47			22 06	22 18		22 36		22 44		23 06	23 18	23 31	23 36					00 53	
Hanwell	d				21 39				22 09			22 39				23 09			23 39						
Greenford ⊖	d			21 16				21 46																	
South Greenford	d			21 19				21 49																	
Castle Bar Park	d			21 22				21 52																	
Drayton Green	d			21 24				21 54																	
West Ealing	d			21 26	21 41			21 56	22 11			22 41				23 11			23 41						
Ealing Broadway ⊖	d			21 29	21 44	21 53		21 59	22 14	22 23		22 44		22 49		23 14	23 23	23 36	23 44		00 04			00 59	
Acton Main Line	d			21 33				22 03																	
London Paddington 15 ⊖	a	21 38		21 42	21 54	22 03	22 07	22 12	22 24	22 32	22 42	22 54		22 58	23 11	23 24	23 32	23 47	23 54	23 56	00 14	00 32		01 09	

For non-stop services between London and Reading please see table 116

Passengers who hold valid tickets for Acton Main Line, West Ealing and Hanwell will be able to use local Transport for London (TFL) bus services to reach these stations. Tel 0843 222 1234

Table 117R

Saturdays

15 February to 22 March

Network Diagram - refer to first Page of Table 116

Reading and Greenford - London

	GW	GW	HC	GW	GW	GW	GW	GW	HC		GW	HC
	1	◇1		1	◇1	1	1	1			1	
Oxford d					00 07	00 27		03 59				
Reading 7 d				00 17	00 43	01 17	04 10	04 40			05 10	
Twyford 3 d				00 23		01 23	04 16	04 47			05 16	
Maidenhead 3 d				00 31		01 31	04 24	04 55			05 24	
Taplow d				00 34							05 28	
Burnham d				00 37							05 31	
Slough 3 a				00 42	00 59	01 39	04 32	05 02			05 35	
d		00 02		00 42	01 00	01 39	04 32	05 02			05 36	
Langley d				00 46							05 40	
Iver d											05 43	
West Drayton d				00 51			04 38				05 45	
Heathrow Terminal 4 ✈ d			00 01						05 23			05 51
Heathrow Terminal 1-2 2 ✈ d			00 07						05 29			05 57
Hayes & Harlington d			00 14	00 56		01 48	04 43	05 11	05 35		05 51	06 03
Southall d			00 17	00 59			04 46	05 14	05 38		05 54	06 06
Hanwell d									05 41			06 09
Greenford ⊖ d												
South Greenford d												
Castle Bar Park d												
Drayton Green d												
West Ealing d									05 43			06 11
Ealing Broadway ⊖ d	00 06		00 22	01 05		01 55	04 52	05 19	05 46		06 00	06 14
Acton Main Line d								05 24			06 03	
London Paddington 15 ⊖ a	00 17	00 27	00 30	01 18	01 21	02 07	05 01	05 31	05 56		06 11	06 24

	GW	GW	GW	HC	GW	GW	GW		HC	GW	GW	GW
	1	1	1		1	1	1			1	1	1
Oxford d					05 14					05 49		
Reading 7 d	05 30		05 48		06 03		06 18			06 33		06 48
Twyford 3 d	05 39		05 54		06 09		06 24			06 39		06 54
Maidenhead 3 d	05 47		06 02		06 17		06 32			06 47		07 02
Taplow d			06 06				06 36					07 06
Burnham d			06 09				06 39					07 09
Slough 3 a	05 54		06 14		06 24		06 44			06 54		07 14
d	05 54		06 14		06 24		06 44			06 54		07 14
Langley d	05 58				06 28					06 58		
Iver d	06 01				06 31					07 01		
West Drayton d	06 05		06 21		06 35		06 51			07 05		07 21
Heathrow Terminal 4 ✈ d												
Heathrow Terminal 1-2 2 ✈ d				06 27					06 57			
Hayes & Harlington d	06 10		06 26	06 33	06 40		06 56		07 03	07 10		07 26
Southall d	06 13			06 36	06 43				07 06	07 13		
Hanwell d				06 39					07 09			
Greenford ⊖ d		06 16				06 46					07 16	
South Greenford d		06 19				06 49					07 19	
Castle Bar Park d		06 22				06 52					07 22	
Drayton Green d		06 24				06 54					07 24	
West Ealing d		06 26		06 41		06 56			07 11		07 26	
Ealing Broadway ⊖ d	06 19	06 29	06 33	06 44	06 49	06 59	07 03		07 14	07 19	07 29	07 33
Acton Main Line d		06 33				07 03					07 33	
London Paddington 15 ⊖ a	06 31	06 42	06 46	06 54	07 01	07 12	07 16		07 24	07 31	07 42	07 46

	GW	HC	GW	GW	GW		GW	GW	HC	GW	GW	GW
	◇1		1	1	◇1		1	1		1	1	◇1 [trolley]
Oxford d	06 31		06 07		07 01					06 42		07 31
Reading 7 d	07 03		07 03	07 18	07 27					07 33	07 48	07 55
Twyford 3 d			07 09	07 24						07 39	07 54	
Maidenhead 3 d			07 17	07 32						07 47	08 02	
Taplow d				07 36							08 06	
Burnham d				07 39				←			08 09	
Slough 3 a	07 17		07 24	07 44	07 42			07 44		07 54	08 14	08 10
d	07 18		07 24	07 44	07 42			07 44		07 54	08 14	08 10
Langley d			07 28	→						07 58	→	
Iver d			07 31							08 01		
West Drayton d			07 35					07 51		08 05		
Heathrow Terminal 4 ✈ d												
Heathrow Terminal 1-2 2 ✈ d		07 27							07 57			
Hayes & Harlington d		07 33	07 40					07 56	08 03	08 10		
Southall d		07 36	07 43						08 06	08 13		
Hanwell d		07 39							08 09			
Greenford ⊖ d							07 46					
South Greenford d							07 49					
Castle Bar Park d							07 52					
Drayton Green d							07 54					
West Ealing d		07 41					07 56		08 11			
Ealing Broadway ⊖ d		07 44	07 49				07 59	08 03	08 14	08 19		
Acton Main Line d							08 03					
London Paddington 15 ⊖ a	07 37	07 54	08 01		08 01		08 12	08 16	08 24	08 31		08 29

	GW	GW	HC		GW	GW	GW	GW	GW	HC	GW	GW
	1	1			1	1	◇1	1	1		1	1
Oxford d					07 07		08 01				07 37	
Reading 7 d					08 03	08 18	08 26				08 33	08 48
Twyford 3 d					08 09	08 24					08 39	08 54
Maidenhead 3 d					08 17	08 32					08 47	09 02
Taplow d						08 36						09 06
Burnham d		←				08 39			←			09 09
Slough 3 a		08 14			08 24	08 44	08 40		08 44		08 54	09 14
d		08 14			08 24	08 44	08 41		08 44		08 54	09 14
Langley d					08 28	→					08 58	→
Iver d					08 31						09 01	
West Drayton d		08 21			08 35				08 52		09 05	
Heathrow Terminal 4 ✈ d												
Heathrow Terminal 1-2 2 ✈ d			08 27							08 57		
Hayes & Harlington d		08 26	08 33		08 40				08 58	09 03	09 10	
Southall d			08 36		08 43					09 06	09 13	
Hanwell d			08 39							09 09		
Greenford ⊖ d	08 16							08 46				
South Greenford d	08 19							08 49				
Castle Bar Park d	08 22							08 52				
Drayton Green d	08 24							08 54				
West Ealing d	08 26		08 41					08 56		09 11		
Ealing Broadway ⊖ d	08 29	08 33	08 44		08 49			08 59	09 05	09 14	09 19	
Acton Main Line d	08 33							09 03				
London Paddington 15 ⊖ a	08 42	08 46	08 54		09 01		08 59	09 12	09 16	09 24	09 31	

	GW		GW	GW	HC	GW	GW	GW	GW	GW	HC	
	◇1 [restaurant]		1	1		1	1	◇1 [trolley]	1	1		
Oxford d	08 31					08 07		09 01				
Reading 7 d	08 56					09 03	09 18	09 24				
Twyford 3 d						09 09	09 24					
Maidenhead 3 d						09 17	09 32					
Taplow d							09 36					
Burnham d				←			09 39			←		
Slough 3 a	09 10			09 14		09 24	09 44	09 40		09 44		
d	09 12			09 14		09 24	09 44	09 40		09 44		
Langley d						09 28	→					
Iver d						09 31						
West Drayton d				09 21		09 35				09 51		
Heathrow Terminal 4 ✈ d												
Heathrow Terminal 1-2 2 ✈ d					09 27						09 57	
Hayes & Harlington d				09 26	09 33	09 40				09 56	10 03	
Southall d					09 36	09 43					10 06	
Hanwell d					09 39						10 09	
Greenford ⊖ d			09 16						09 46			
South Greenford d			09 19						09 49			
Castle Bar Park d			09 22						09 52			
Drayton Green d			09 24						09 54			
West Ealing d			09 26		09 41				09 56		10 11	
Ealing Broadway ⊖ d			09 29	09 33	09 44	09 49			09 59	10 03	10 14	
Acton Main Line d			09 33						10 03			
London Paddington 15 ⊖ a	09 29		09 42	09 46	09 54	10 01		09 59	10 12	10 16	10 24	

	GW	GW	GW	GW	GW	HC	GW	GW	GW		GW	GW
	1	1	◇1 A [restaurant ⊘]	1	1		1	1	◇1 [trolley]		1	1
Oxford d	08 37		09 31				09 07		10 01			
Reading 7 d	09 33	09 48	09 55				10 03	10 18	10 28			
Twyford 3 d	09 39	09 54					10 09	10 24				
Maidenhead 3 d	09 47	10 02					10 17	10 32				
Taplow d		10 06						10 36				
Burnham d		10 09			←			10 39				←
Slough 3 a	09 54	10 14	10 09		10 14		10 24	10 44	10 43			10 44
d	09 54	10 14	10 10		10 14		10 24	10 44	10 43			10 44
Langley d	09 58	→					10 28	→				
Iver d	10 01						10 31					
West Drayton d	10 05				10 21		10 35					10 51
Heathrow Terminal 4 ✈ d												
Heathrow Terminal 1-2 2 ✈ d						10 27						
Hayes & Harlington d	10 10				10 26	10 33	10 40					10 56
Southall d	10 13					10 36	10 43					
Hanwell d						10 39						
Greenford ⊖ d				10 16							10 46	
South Greenford d				10 19							10 49	
Castle Bar Park d				10 22							10 52	
Drayton Green d				10 24							10 54	
West Ealing d				10 26		10 41					10 56	
Ealing Broadway ⊖ d	10 19			10 29	10 33	10 44	10 49				10 59	11 03
Acton Main Line d				10 33							11 03	
London Paddington 15 ⊖ a	10 31		10 29	10 42	10 46	10 54	11 01		11 02		11 12	11 16

A [restaurant] from Reading ⊘ to Reading

For non-stop services between London and Reading please see table 116

Passengers who hold valid tickets for Acton Main Line, West Ealing and Hanwell will be able to use local Transport for London (TFL) bus services to reach these stations. Tel 0843 222 1234

Table 117R

Saturdays

15 February to 22 March

Reading and Greenford - London

Network Diagram - refer to first Page of Table 116

		HC	GW 1	GW 1	GW ◇1 ☕	GW 1	GW 1	HC		GW 1	GW 1	GW ◇1	GW 1	GW 1	HC	GW 1	GW 1	GW ◇1 trolley		GW 1	GW 1	HC	GW 1	GW 1	GW ◇1 trolley
Oxford	d		09 37		10 32					10 07		11 01				10 37		11 30					11 07		12 01
Reading 7	d		10 33	10 48	10 58					11 03	11 18	11 25				11 33	11 48	11 58					12 03	12 18	12 27
Twyford 3	d		10 39	10 54						11 09	11 24					11 39	11 54						12 09	12 24	
Maidenhead 3	d		10 47	11 02						11 17	11 32					11 47	12 02						12 17	12 32	
Taplow	d			11 06							11 36						12 06							12 36	
Burnham	d			11 09			←				11 39			←			12 09				←			12 39	
Slough 3	a		10 54	11 14	11 12		11 14			11 24	11 44	11 39		11 44		11 54	12 14	12 12			12 14		12 24	12 44	12 41
	d		10 54	11 14	11 13		11 14			11 24	11 44	11 40		11 44		11 54	12 14	12 14			12 14		12 24	12 44	12 42
Langley	d		10 58	→						11 28	→					11 58	→						12 28	→	
Iver	d		11 01							11 31						12 01							12 31		
West Drayton	d		11 05				11 21			11 35				11 51		12 05					12 21		12 35		
Heathrow Terminal 4 ✈	d																								
Heathrow Terminal 1-2 2 ✈	d	10 57						11 27							11 57							12 27			
Hayes & Harlington	d	11 03	11 10				11 26	11 33		11 40				11 56	12 03	12 10					12 26	12 33	12 40		
Southall	d	11 06	11 13					11 36		11 43					12 06	12 13						12 36	12 43		
Hanwell	d	11 09						11 39							12 09							12 39			
Greenford ⊖	d					11 16							11 46							12 16					
South Greenford	d					11 19							11 49							12 19					
Castle Bar Park	d					11 22							11 52							12 22					
Drayton Green	d					11 24							11 54							12 24					
West Ealing	d	11 11				11 26		11 41					11 56		12 11					12 26		12 41			
Ealing Broadway ⊖	d	11 14	11 19			11 29	11 33	11 44		11 49			11 59	12 03	12 14	12 19				12 29	12 33	12 44	12 49		
Acton Main Line	d					11 33							12 03							12 33					
London Paddington 15 ⊖	a	11 24	11 31		11 30	11 42	11 46	11 54		12 01		11 59	12 12	12 16	12 24	12 31		12 32		12 42	12 46	12 54	13 01		12 59

		GW 1	GW 1	HC		GW 1	GW 1	GW ◇1 trolley	GW 1	GW 1	HC	GW 1	GW 1	GW ◇1 trolley		GW 1	GW 1	HC	GW 1	GW 1	GW ◇1	GW 1	GW 1	HC	
Oxford	d					11 37		12 31				12 07		13 01					12 37		13 31				
Reading 7	d					12 33	12 48	12 57				13 03	13 18	13 27					13 33	13 48	13 56				
Twyford 3	d					12 39	12 54					13 09	13 24						13 39	13 54					
Maidenhead 3	d					12 47	13 02					13 17	13 32						13 47	14 02					
Taplow	d						13 06						13 36							14 06					
Burnham	d		←				13 09			←			13 39				←			14 09			←		
Slough 3	a		12 44			12 54	13 14	13 11		13 14		13 24	13 44	13 41			13 44		13 54	14 14	14 09		14 14		
	d		12 44			12 54	13 14	13 13		13 14		13 24	13 44	13 42			13 44		13 54	14 14	14 11		14 14		
Langley	d					12 58	→					13 28	→						13 58	→					
Iver	d					13 01						13 31							14 01						
West Drayton	d		12 51			13 05				13 21		13 35					13 51		14 05				14 21		
Heathrow Terminal 4 ✈	d																								
Heathrow Terminal 1-2 2 ✈	d			12 57							13 27							13 57						14 27	
Hayes & Harlington	d		12 56	13 03		13 10				13 26	13 33	13 40					13 56	14 03	14 10				14 26	14 33	
Southall	d			13 06		13 13					13 36	13 43						14 06	14 13					14 36	
Hanwell	d			13 09							13 39							14 09						14 39	
Greenford ⊖	d	12 46							13 16							13 46						14 16			
South Greenford	d	12 49							13 19							13 49						14 19			
Castle Bar Park	d	12 52							13 22							13 52						14 22			
Drayton Green	d	12 54							13 24							13 54						14 24			
West Ealing	d	12 56		13 11					13 26		13 41					13 56		14 11				14 26		14 41	
Ealing Broadway ⊖	d	12 59	13 03	13 14		13 19			13 29	13 33	13 44	13 49				13 59	14 03	14 14	14 19			14 29	14 33	14 44	
Acton Main Line	d	13 03							13 33							14 03						14 33			
London Paddington 15 ⊖	a	13 12	13 16	13 24		13 31		13 32	13 42	13 46	13 54	14 01		13 59		14 12	14 16	14 24	14 31		14 29	14 42	14 46	14 54	

		GW 1	GW 1	GW ◇1 trolley	GW 1	GW 1	HC	GW 1	GW 1	GW ◇1 ☕		GW 1	GW 1	HC	GW 1	GW 1	GW ◇1	GW 1	GW 1	HC		GW 1	GW 1	GW ◇1 trolley	GW 1
Oxford	d	13 07		14 01				13 37		14 31					14 07		15 01					14 37		15 31	
Reading 7	d	14 03	14 18	14 27				14 33	14 48	14 58					15 03	15 18	15 25					15 32	15 48	15 56	
Twyford 3	d	14 09	14 24					14 39	14 54						15 09	15 24						15 39	15 54		
Maidenhead 3	d	14 17	14 32					14 47	15 02						15 17	15 32						15 47	16 02		
Taplow	d		14 36						15 06							15 36							16 06		
Burnham	d		14 39			←			15 09				←			15 39			←				16 09		
Slough 3	a	14 24	14 44	14 41		14 44		14 54	15 14	15 13			15 14		15 24	15 44	15 40		15 44			15 54	16 14	16 11	
	d	14 24	14 44	14 42		14 44		14 54	15 14	15 13			15 14		15 24	15 44	15 40		15 44			15 54	16 14	16 12	
Langley	d	14 28	→					14 58	→						15 28	→						15 58	→		
Iver	d	14 31						15 01							15 31							16 01			
West Drayton	d	14 35				14 51		15 05					15 21		15 35				15 51			16 05			
Heathrow Terminal 4 ✈	d																								
Heathrow Terminal 1-2 2 ✈	d						14 57							15 27						15 57					
Hayes & Harlington	d	14 40				14 56	15 03	15 10					15 26	15 33	15 40				15 56	16 03		16 10			
Southall	d	14 43					15 06	15 13						15 36	15 43					16 06		16 13			
Hanwell	d						15 09							15 39						16 09					
Greenford ⊖	d				14 46							15 16						15 46							16 16
South Greenford	d				14 49							15 19						15 49							16 19
Castle Bar Park	d				14 52							15 22						15 52							16 22
Drayton Green	d				14 54							15 24						15 54							16 24
West Ealing	d				14 56		15 11					15 26		15 41				15 56		16 11					16 26
Ealing Broadway ⊖	d	14 49			14 59	15 03	15 14	15 19				15 29	15 33	15 44	15 49			15 59	16 03	16 14		16 19			16 29
Acton Main Line	d				15 03							15 33						16 03							16 33
London Paddington 15 ⊖	a	15 01		14 59	15 12	15 16	15 24	15 31		15 30		15 42	15 46	15 54	16 01		15 59	16 12	16 16	16 24		16 31		16 30	16 42

For non-stop services between London and Reading please see table 116

Passengers who hold valid tickets for Acton Main Line, West Ealing and Hanwell will be able to use local Transport for London (TFL) bus services to reach these stations. Tel 0843 222 1234

Table 117R

Saturdays

15 February to 22 March

Network Diagram - refer to first Page of Table 116

Reading and Greenford - London

		GW 1	HC	GW 1	GW 1	GW ◇1		GW 1	GW 1	HC	GW 1	GW 1	GW ◇1 [trolley]	GW 1	GW 1	HC		GW 1	GW 1	GW ◇1	GW 1	GW 1	HC	GW 1	GW 1
Oxford	d			15 07		16 01					15 37		16 31					16 07		17 01				16 37	
Reading 7	d			16 03	16 18	16 26					16 33	16 48	16 56					17 03	17 18	17 26				17 32	17 48
Twyford 3	d			16 09	16 24						16 39	16 54						17 09	17 24					17 39	17 54
Maidenhead 3	d			16 17	16 32						16 47	17 02						17 17	17 32					17 47	18 02
Taplow	d				16 36							17 06							17 36						18 06
Burnham	d	←			16 39				←			17 09			←				17 39			←			18 09
Slough 3	a	16 14		16 24	16 44	16 40			16 44		16 54	17 14	17 10		17 14			17 24	17 44	17 40		17 44		17 54	18 14
	d	16 14		16 24	16 44	16 41			16 44		16 54	17 14	17 11		17 14			17 24	17 44	17 41		17 44		17 54	18 14
Langley	d			16 28	→						16 58	→						17 28	→					17 58	→
Iver	d			16 31							17 01							17 31						18 01	
West Drayton	d	16 21		16 35					16 51		17 05				17 21			17 35				17 51		18 05	
Heathrow Terminal 4 ✈	d																								
Heathrow Terminal 1-2 2 ✈	d		16 27							16 57						17 27							17 57		
Hayes & Harlington	d	16 26	16 33	16 40					16 56	17 03	17 10				17 26	17 33		17 40				17 56	18 03	18 10	
Southall	d		16 36	16 43						17 06	17 13					17 36		17 43					18 06	18 13	
Hanwell	d		16 39							17 09						17 39							18 09		
Greenford ⊖	d							16 46						17 16							17 46				
South Greenford	d							16 49						17 19							17 49				
Castle Bar Park	d							16 52						17 22							17 52				
Drayton Green	d							16 54						17 24							17 54				
West Ealing	d		16 41					16 56		17 11				17 26		17 41					17 56		18 11		
Ealing Broadway ⊖	d	16 33	16 44	16 49				16 59	17 03	17 14	17 19			17 29	17 33	17 44		17 49			17 59	18 03	18 14	18 19	
Acton Main Line	d							17 03						17 33							18 03				
London Paddington 15 ⊖	a	16 46	16 54	17 01		16 59		17 12	17 16	17 24	17 31		17 29	17 42	17 46	17 54		18 01		17 59	18 12	18 16	18 24	18 31	

		GW ◇1 [restaurant]		GW 1	GW 1	HC	GW 1	GW 1	GW ◇1	GW 1	GW 1	HC		GW 1	GW 1	GW ◇1 [trolley]	GW 1	GW 1	HC	GW 1	GW 1	GW ◇1		GW 1	GW 1
Oxford	d	17 31					17 07		18 01					17 37		18 31				18 07		19 01			
Reading 7	d	17 58					18 03	18 18	18 25					18 32	18 48	18 56				19 03	19 18	19 25			
Twyford 3	d						18 09	18 24						18 39	18 54					19 09	19 24				
Maidenhead 3	d						18 17	18 32						18 47	19 02					19 17	19 32				
Taplow	d							18 36							19 06						19 36				
Burnham	d				←			18 39			←				19 09			←			19 39				←
Slough 3	a	18 11			18 14		18 24	18 44	18 40		18 44			18 54	19 14	19 10		19 14		19 24	19 44	19 40			19 44
	d	18 12			18 14		18 24	18 44	18 40		18 44			18 54	19 14	19 11		19 14		19 24	19 44	19 40			19 44
Langley	d						18 28	→						18 58	→					19 28	→				
Iver	d						18 31							19 01						19 31					
West Drayton	d				18 21		18 35				18 51			19 05				19 21		19 35					19 51
Heathrow Terminal 4 ✈	d																								
Heathrow Terminal 1-2 2 ✈	d					18 27						18 57							19 27						
Hayes & Harlington	d				18 26	18 33	18 40				18 56	19 03		19 10				19 26	19 33	19 40					19 56
Southall	d					18 36	18 43					19 06		19 13					19 36	19 43					
Hanwell	d					18 39						19 09							19 39						
Greenford ⊖	d			18 16						18 46							19 16							19 46	
South Greenford	d			18 19						18 49							19 19							19 49	
Castle Bar Park	d			18 22						18 52							19 22							19 52	
Drayton Green	d			18 24						18 54							19 24							19 54	
West Ealing	d			18 26		18 41				18 56		19 11					19 26		19 41					19 56	
Ealing Broadway ⊖	d			18 29	18 33	18 44	18 49			18 59	19 03	19 14		19 19			19 29	19 33	19 44	19 49				19 59	20 03
Acton Main Line	d			18 33						19 03							19 33							20 03	
London Paddington 15 ⊖	a	18 29		18 42	18 46	18 54	19 01		18 59	19 12	19 16	19 24		19 31		19 29	19 42	19 46	19 54	20 01		19 59		20 12	20 16

		HC	GW 1	GW 1	GW ◇1 [trolley]	GW 1	GW 1	HC		GW 1	GW 1	GW ◇1	GW 1	GW 1	HC	GW 1	GW 1	GW ◇1		GW 1	GW 1	HC	GW 1	GW 1	GW ◇1
Oxford	d		18 37		19 31					19 07		20 01				19 37		20 31					20 07		21 01
Reading 7	d		19 33	19 48	19 55					20 02	20 18	20 25				20 33	20 48	20 56					21 03	21 18	21 27
Twyford 3	d		19 39	19 54						20 09	20 24					20 39	20 54						21 12	21 24	
Maidenhead 3	d		19 47	20 02						20 17	20 32					20 47	21 02						21 19	21 32	
Taplow	d			20 06							20 36						21 06							21 36	
Burnham	d			20 09			←				20 39			←			21 09				←			21 39	
Slough 3	a		19 54	20 14	20 10		20 14			20 24	20 44	20 40		20 44		20 54	21 14	21 10			21 14		21 27	21 44	21 42
	d		19 54	20 14	20 10		20 14			20 24	20 44	20 40		20 44		20 54	21 14	21 11			21 14		21 27	21 44	21 42
Langley	d		19 58	→						20 28	→					20 58	→						21 31	→	
Iver	d		20 01							20 31						21 01							21 34		
West Drayton	d		20 05				20 21			20 35				20 51		21 05					21 21		21 38		
Heathrow Terminal 4 ✈	d																								
Heathrow Terminal 1-2 2 ✈	d	19 57						20 27							20 57							21 27			
Hayes & Harlington	d	20 03	20 10				20 26	20 33		20 40				20 56	21 03	21 10					21 26	21 33	21 43		
Southall	d	20 06	20 13					20 36		20 43					21 06	21 13						21 36	21 46		
Hanwell	d	20 09						20 39							21 09							21 39			
Greenford ⊖	d					20 16							20 46							21 16					
South Greenford	d					20 19							20 49							21 19					
Castle Bar Park	d					20 22							20 52							21 22					
Drayton Green	d					20 24							20 54							21 24					
West Ealing	d	20 11				20 26		20 41					20 56		21 11					21 26		21 41			
Ealing Broadway ⊖	d	20 14	20 19			20 29	20 33	20 44		20 49			20 59	21 03	21 14	21 19				21 29	21 33	21 44	21 52		
Acton Main Line	d					20 33							21 03							21 33					
London Paddington 15 ⊖	a	20 24	20 31		20 29	20 42	20 46	20 54		21 01		20 59	21 12	21 16	21 24	21 31		21 29		21 42	21 46	21 54	22 02		22 01

For non-stop services between London and Reading please see table 116

Passengers who hold valid tickets for Acton Main Line, West Ealing and Hanwell will be able to use local Transport for London (TFL) bus services to reach these stations. Tel 0843 222 1234

Table 117R

Saturdays

15 February to 22 March

Network Diagram - refer to first Page of Table 116

Reading and Greenford - London

		GW 1	GW 1	HC		GW 1	GW ◇1	HC	GW 1	GW 1	GW ◇1	HC	GW 1	GW 1		GW ◇1	HC	GW 1	GW ◇1	GW 1
Oxford	d					20 37	21 31			21 50	22 01					22 35			23 01	23 07
Reading 7	d					21 33	22 02		22 03	22 33	22 35			22 48		23 10		23 19	23 31	00 04
Twyford 3	d					21 39			22 09	22 39				22 55				23 24		00 11
Maidenhead 3	d					21 47			22 17	22 47				23 03				23 32		00 19
Taplow	d					21 51			22 21	22 51				23 07				23 36		00 23
Burnham	d		←			21 54			22 24	22 54			←	23 10				23 39		00 26
Slough 3	a		21 44			21 58	22 15		22 28	22 58	22 50		22 58	23 15		23 28		23 45	23 50	00 30
	d		21 44			21 59	22 16		22 29	22 59	22 50		22 59	23 15		23 29		23 45	23 50	00 31
Langley	d					22 03				→			23 03							00 35
Iver	d					22 06							23 06							00 38
West Drayton	d		21 51			22 10			22 36				23 10	23 22				23 52		00 41
Heathrow Terminal 4 ✈	d																			
Heathrow Terminal 1-2 2 ✈	d			21 57				22 27				22 57					23 27			
Hayes & Harlington	d		21 56	22 03		22 14		22 33	22 40			23 03	23 14	23 27			23 33	23 57		00 46
Southall	d			22 06		22 18		22 36	22 44			23 06	23 18	23 31			23 36			00 49
Hanwell	d			22 09				22 39				23 09					23 39			
Greenford ⊖	d	21 46																		
South Greenford	d	21 49																		
Castle Bar Park	d	21 52																		
Drayton Green	d	21 54																		
West Ealing	d	21 56		22 11				22 41				23 11					23 41			
Ealing Broadway ⊖	d	21 59	22 03	22 14		22 23		22 44	22 49			23 14	23 23	23 36			23 44	00 04		00 55
Acton Main Line	d	22 03																		
London Paddington 15 ⊖	a	22 12	22 15	22 24		22 32	22 38	22 54	22 58		23 09	23 24	23 32	23 47		23 46	23 54	00 14	00 17	01 05

Saturdays

29 March to 17 May

		GW 1	GW ◇1	HC	GW 1	GW ◇1	GW 1	GW 1	GW 1	HC		GW 1	HC	GW 1	GW 1	GW 1	HC	GW 1	GW 1	GW 1		HC	GW 1	GW 1	GW 1
Oxford	d					00 07	00 27		03 59									05 14					05 49		
Reading 7	d				00 17	00 43	01 17	04 10	04 40			05 10		05 30		05 48		06 03		06 18			06 33		06 48
Twyford 3	d				00 23		01 23	04 16	04 47			05 16		05 39		05 54		06 09		06 24			06 39		06 54
Maidenhead 3	d				00 31		01 31	04 24	04 55			05 24		05 47		06 02		06 17		06 32			06 47		07 02
Taplow	d				00 34							05 28				06 06				06 36					07 06
Burnham	d				00 37							05 31				06 09				06 39					07 09
Slough 3	a				00 42	00 59	01 39	04 32	05 02			05 35		05 54		06 14		06 24		06 44			06 54		07 14
	d		00 02		00 42	01 00	01 39	04 32	05 02			05 36		05 54		06 14		06 24		06 44			06 54		07 14
Langley	d				00 46							05 40		05 58				06 28					06 58		
Iver	d											05 43		06 01				06 31					07 01		
West Drayton	d				00 51			04 38				05 45		06 05		06 21		06 35		06 51			07 05		07 21
Heathrow Terminal 4 ✈	d			00 01						05 23			05 51												
Heathrow Terminal 1-2 2 ✈	d			00 07						05 29			05 57				06 27					06 57			
Hayes & Harlington	d			00 14	00 56		01 48	04 43	05 11	05 35		05 51	06 03	06 10		06 26	06 33	06 40		06 56		07 03	07 10		07 26
Southall	d			00 17	00 59			04 46	05 14	05 38		05 54	06 06	06 13			06 36	06 43				07 06	07 13		
Hanwell	d									05 41			06 09				06 39					07 09			
Greenford ⊖	d														06 16				06 46					07 16	
South Greenford	d														06 19				06 49					07 19	
Castle Bar Park	d														06 22				06 52					07 22	
Drayton Green	d														06 24				06 54					07 24	
West Ealing	d									05 43			06 11		06 26		06 41		06 56			07 11		07 26	
Ealing Broadway ⊖	d	00 06		00 22	01 05		01 55	04 52	05 19	05 46		06 00	06 14	06 19	06 29	06 33	06 44	06 49	06 59	07 03		07 14	07 19	07 29	07 33
Acton Main Line	d								05 24			06 03			06 33				07 03					07 33	
London Paddington 15 ⊖	a	00 17	00 27	00 30	01 18	01 21	02 07	05 01	05 31	05 56		06 11	06 24	06 31	06 42	06 46	06 54	07 01	07 12	07 16		07 24	07 31	07 42	07 46

		GW ◇1	HC	GW 1	GW 1	GW ◇1		GW 1	GW 1	HC	GW 1	GW 1	GW ◇1 🍴	GW 1	GW 1	HC		GW 1	GW 1	GW ◇1	GW 1	GW 1	HC	GW 1	GW 1
Oxford	d	06 31		06 07		07 01					06 42		07 31					07 07		08 01				07 37	
Reading 7	d	07 03		07 03	07 18	07 27					07 33	07 48	07 55					08 03	08 18	08 26				08 33	08 48
Twyford 3	d			07 09	07 24						07 39	07 54						08 09	08 24					08 39	08 54
Maidenhead 3	d			07 17	07 32						07 47	08 02						08 17	08 32					08 47	09 02
Taplow	d				07 36							08 06							08 36						09 06
Burnham	d				07 39				←			08 09			←				08 39			←			09 09
Slough 3	a	07 17		07 24	07 44	07 42			07 44		07 54	08 14	08 10		08 14			08 24	08 44	08 40		08 44		08 54	09 14
	d	07 18		07 24	07 44	07 42			07 44		07 54	08 14	08 10		08 14			08 24	08 44	08 41		08 44		08 54	09 14
Langley	d			07 28	→						07 58	→						08 28	→					08 58	→
Iver	d			07 31							08 01							08 31						09 01	
West Drayton	d			07 35					07 51		08 05				08 21			08 35				08 52		09 05	
Heathrow Terminal 4 ✈	d																								
Heathrow Terminal 1-2 2 ✈	d		07 27							07 57						08 27							08 57		
Hayes & Harlington	d		07 33	07 40					07 56	08 03	08 10				08 26	08 33		08 40				08 58	09 03	09 10	
Southall	d		07 36	07 43						08 06	08 13					08 36		08 43					09 06	09 13	
Hanwell	d		07 39							08 09						08 39							09 09		
Greenford ⊖	d							07 46						08 16							08 46				
South Greenford	d							07 49						08 19							08 49				
Castle Bar Park	d							07 52						08 22							08 52				
Drayton Green	d							07 54						08 24							08 54				
West Ealing	d		07 41					07 56		08 11				08 26		08 41					08 56		09 11		
Ealing Broadway ⊖	d		07 44	07 49				07 59	08 03	08 14	08 19			08 29	08 33	08 44		08 49			08 59	09 05	09 14	09 19	
Acton Main Line	d							08 03						08 33							09 03				
London Paddington 15 ⊖	a	07 37	07 54	08 01		08 01		08 12	08 16	08 24	08 31		08 29	08 42	08 46	08 54		09 01		08 59	09 12	09 16	09 24	09 31	

For non-stop services between London and Reading please see table 116

Passengers who hold valid tickets for Acton Main Line, West Ealing and Hanwell will be able to use local Transport for London (TFL) bus services to reach these stations. Tel 0843 222 1234

Table 117R

Saturdays

29 March to 17 May

Network Diagram - refer to first Page of Table 116

Reading and Greenford - London

		GW		GW	GW	HC	GW	GW	GW	GW	GW	HC		GW	GW	GW	GW	GW	HC	GW	GW	GW		GW	GW
		◇1		1	1		1	1	◇1	1	1			1	1	◇1	1	1		1	1	◇1		1	1
																A									
		⊡							⌶							⊡⊘						⌶			
Oxford	d	08 31					08 07		09 01					08 37		09 31				09 07		10 01			
Reading 7	d	08 56					09 03	09 18	09 24					09 33	09 48	09 55				10 03	10 18	10 28			
Twyford 3	d						09 09	09 24						09 39	09 54					10 09	10 24				
Maidenhead 3	d						09 17	09 32						09 47	10 02					10 17	10 32				
Taplow	d							09 36							10 06						10 36				
Burnham	d				←			09 39			←				10 09			←			10 39				←
Slough 3	a	09 10			09 14		09 24	09 44	09 40		09 44			09 54	10 14	10 09		10 14		10 24	10 44	10 43			10 44
	d	09 12			09 14		09 24	09 44	09 40		09 44			09 54	10 14	10 10		10 14		10 24	10 44	10 43			10 44
Langley	d						09 28	→						09 58	→					10 28	→				
Iver	d						09 31							10 01						10 31					
West Drayton	d				09 21		09 35				09 51			10 05				10 21		10 35					10 51
Heathrow Terminal 4 ✈	d																								
Heathrow Terminal 1-2 2 ✈	d					09 27						09 57							10 27						
Hayes & Harlington	d				09 26	09 33	09 40				09 56	10 03		10 10				10 26	10 33	10 40					10 56
Southall	d					09 36	09 43					10 06		10 13					10 36	10 43					
Hanwell	d					09 39						10 09							10 39						
Greenford ⊖	d			09 16						09 46							10 16							10 46	
South Greenford	d			09 19						09 49							10 19							10 49	
Castle Bar Park	d			09 22						09 52							10 22							10 52	
Drayton Green	d			09 24						09 54							10 24							10 54	
West Ealing	d			09 26		09 41				09 56		10 11					10 26		10 41					10 56	
Ealing Broadway ⊖	d			09 29	09 33	09 44	09 49			09 59	10 03	10 14		10 19			10 29	10 33	10 44	10 49				10 59	11 03
Acton Main Line	d			09 33						10 03							10 33							11 03	
London Paddington 15 ⊖	a	09 29		09 42	09 46	09 54	10 01		09 59	10 12	10 16	10 24		10 31		10 29	10 42	10 46	10 54	11 01		11 02		11 12	11 16

		HC	GW	GW	GW	GW	GW	HC		GW	GW	GW	GW	GW	HC	GW	GW	GW		GW	GW	HC	GW	GW	GW
			1	1	◇1	1	1			1	1	◇1	1	1		1	1	◇1		1	1		1	1	◇1
					⊡													⌶							⌶
Oxford	d		09 37		10 32					10 07		11 01				10 37		11 30					11 07		12 01
Reading 7	d		10 33	10 48	10 58					11 03	11 18	11 25				11 33	11 48	11 58					12 03	12 18	12 27
Twyford 3	d		10 39	10 54						11 09	11 24					11 39	11 54						12 09	12 24	
Maidenhead 3	d		10 47	11 02						11 17	11 32					11 47	12 02						12 17	12 32	
Taplow	d			11 06							11 36						12 06							12 36	
Burnham	d			11 09			←				11 39			←			12 09				←			12 39	
Slough 3	a		10 54	11 14	11 12		11 14			11 24	11 44	11 39		11 44		11 54	12 14	12 12			12 14		12 24	12 44	12 41
	d		10 54	11 14	11 13		11 14			11 24	11 44	11 40		11 44		11 54	12 14	12 14			12 14		12 24	12 44	12 42
Langley	d		10 58	→						11 28	→					11 58	→						12 28	→	
Iver	d		11 01							11 31						12 01							12 31		
West Drayton	d		11 05				11 21			11 35				11 51		12 05					12 21		12 35		
Heathrow Terminal 4 ✈	d																								
Heathrow Terminal 1-2 2 ✈	d	10 57						11 27							11 57							12 27			
Hayes & Harlington	d	11 03	11 10				11 26	11 33		11 40				11 56	12 03	12 10					12 26	12 33	12 40		
Southall	d	11 06	11 13					11 36		11 43					12 06	12 13						12 36	12 43		
Hanwell	d	11 09						11 39							12 09							12 39			
Greenford ⊖	d					11 16							11 46							12 16					
South Greenford	d					11 19							11 49							12 19					
Castle Bar Park	d					11 22							11 52							12 22					
Drayton Green	d					11 24							11 54							12 24					
West Ealing	d	11 11				11 26		11 41					11 56		12 11					12 26		12 41			
Ealing Broadway ⊖	d	11 14	11 19			11 29	11 33	11 44		11 49			11 59	12 03	12 14	12 19				12 29	12 33	12 44	12 49		
Acton Main Line	d					11 33							12 03							12 33					
London Paddington 15 ⊖	a	11 24	11 31		11 30	11 42	11 46	11 54		12 01		11 59	12 12	12 16	12 24	12 31		12 32		12 42	12 46	12 54	13 01		12 59

		GW	GW	HC		GW	GW	GW	GW	GW	HC	GW	GW	GW		GW	GW	HC	GW	GW	GW	GW	GW	HC	
		1	1			1	1	◇1	1	1		1	1	◇1		1	1		1	1	◇1	1	1		
								⌶						⌶											
Oxford	d					11 37		12 31				12 07		13 01					12 37		13 31				
Reading 7	d					12 33	12 48	12 57				13 03	13 18	13 27					13 33	13 48	13 56				
Twyford 3	d					12 39	12 54					13 09	13 24						13 39	13 54					
Maidenhead 3	d					12 47	13 02					13 17	13 32						13 47	14 02					
Taplow	d						13 06						13 36							14 06					
Burnham	d		←				13 09			←			13 39				←			14 09			←		
Slough 3	a		12 44			12 54	13 14	13 11		13 14		13 24	13 44	13 41			13 44		13 54	14 14	14 09		14 14		
	d		12 44			12 54	13 14	13 13		13 14		13 24	13 44	13 42			13 44		13 54	14 14	14 11		14 14		
Langley	d					12 58	→					13 28	→						13 58	→					
Iver	d					13 01						13 31							14 01						
West Drayton	d		12 51			13 05				13 21		13 35					13 51		14 05				14 21		
Heathrow Terminal 4 ✈	d																								
Heathrow Terminal 1-2 2 ✈	d			12 57							13 27							13 57						14 27	
Hayes & Harlington	d		12 56	13 03		13 10				13 26	13 33	13 40					13 56	14 03	14 10				14 26	14 33	
Southall	d			13 06		13 13					13 36	13 43						14 06	14 13					14 36	
Hanwell	d			13 09							13 39							14 09						14 39	
Greenford ⊖	d	12 46							13 16							13 46						14 16			
South Greenford	d	12 49							13 19							13 49						14 19			
Castle Bar Park	d	12 52							13 22							13 52						14 22			
Drayton Green	d	12 54							13 24							13 54						14 24			
West Ealing	d	12 56		13 11					13 26		13 41					13 56		14 11				14 26		14 41	
Ealing Broadway ⊖	d	12 59	13 03	13 14		13 19			13 29	13 33	13 44	13 49				13 59	14 03	14 14	14 19			14 29	14 33	14 44	
Acton Main Line	d	13 03							13 33							14 03						14 33			
London Paddington 15 ⊖	a	13 12	13 16	13 24		13 31		13 32	13 42	13 46	13 54	14 01		13 59		14 12	14 16	14 24	14 31		14 29	14 42	14 46	14 54	

A ⊡ from Reading ⊘ to Reading

For non-stop services between London and Reading please see table 116

Passengers who hold valid tickets for Acton Main Line, West Ealing and Hanwell will be able to use local Transport for London (TFL) bus services to reach these stations. Tel 0843 222 1234

Table 117R

Saturdays

29 March to 17 May

Reading and Greenford - London

Network Diagram - refer to first Page of Table 116

		GW 1	GW 1	GW ◇1 🚲	GW 1	GW 1	HC	GW 1	GW 1	GW ◇1 ☕		GW 1	GW 1	HC	GW 1	GW 1	GW ◇1	GW 1	GW 1	HC		GW 1	GW 1	GW ◇1 🚲	GW 1
Oxford	d	13 07		14 01				13 37		14 31					14 07		15 01					14 37		15 31	
Reading 7	d	14 03	14 18	14 27				14 33	14 48	14 58					15 03	15 18	15 25					15 32	15 48	15 56	
Twyford 3	d	14 09	14 24					14 39	14 54						15 09	15 24						15 39	15 54		
Maidenhead 3	d	14 17	14 32					14 47	15 02						15 17	15 32						15 47	16 02		
Taplow	d		14 36						15 06							15 36							16 06		
Burnham	d		14 39			←			15 09				←			15 39			←				16 09		
Slough 3	a	14 24	14 44	14 41		14 44		14 54	15 14	15 13			15 14		15 24	15 44	15 40		15 44			15 54	16 14	16 11	
	d	14 24	14 44	14 42		14 44		14 54	15 14	15 13			15 14		15 24	15 44	15 40		15 44			15 54	16 14	16 12	
Langley	d	14 28	→					14 58	→						15 28	→						15 58	→		
Iver	d	14 31						15 01							15 31							16 01			
West Drayton	d	14 35				14 51		15 05					15 21		15 35				15 51			16 05			
Heathrow Terminal 4 ✈	d																								
Heathrow Terminal 1-2 2 ✈	d						14 57							15 27						15 57					
Hayes & Harlington	d	14 40				14 56	15 03	15 10					15 26	15 33	15 40				15 56	16 03		16 10			
Southall	d	14 43					15 06	15 13						15 36	15 43					16 06		16 13			
Hanwell	d						15 09							15 39						16 09					
Greenford ⊖	d				14 46							15 16						15 46							16 16
South Greenford	d				14 49							15 19						15 49							16 19
Castle Bar Park	d				14 52							15 22						15 52							16 22
Drayton Green	d				14 54							15 24						15 54							16 24
West Ealing	d				14 56		15 11					15 26		15 41				15 56		16 11					16 26
Ealing Broadway ⊖	d	14 49			14 59	15 03	15 14	15 19				15 29	15 33	15 44	15 49			15 59	16 03	16 14		16 19			16 29
Acton Main Line	d				15 03							15 33						16 03							16 33
London Paddington 15 ⊖	a	15 01		14 59	15 12	15 16	15 24	15 31		15 30		15 42	15 46	15 54	16 01		15 59	16 12	16 16	16 24		16 31		16 30	16 42

		GW 1	HC	GW 1	GW 1	GW ◇1		GW 1	GW 1	HC	GW 1	GW 1	GW ◇1 🚲	GW 1	GW 1	HC		GW 1	GW 1	GW ◇1	GW 1	GW 1	HC	GW 1	GW 1
Oxford	d			15 07		16 01					15 37		16 31					16 07		17 01				16 37	
Reading 7	d			16 03	16 18	16 26					16 33	16 48	16 56					17 03	17 18	17 26				17 32	17 48
Twyford 3	d			16 09	16 24						16 39	16 54						17 09	17 24					17 39	17 54
Maidenhead 3	d			16 17	16 32						16 47	17 02						17 17	17 32					17 47	18 02
Taplow	d				16 36							17 06							17 36						18 06
Burnham	d	←			16 39				←			17 09			←				17 39			←			18 09
Slough 3	a	16 14		16 24	16 44	16 40			16 44		16 54	17 14	17 10		17 14			17 24	17 44	17 40		17 44		17 54	18 14
	d	16 14		16 24	16 44	16 41			16 44		16 54	17 14	17 11		17 14			17 24	17 44	17 41		17 44		17 54	18 14
Langley	d			16 28	→						16 58	→						17 28	→					17 58	→
Iver	d			16 31							17 01							17 31						18 01	
West Drayton	d	16 21		16 35					16 51		17 05				17 21			17 35				17 51		18 05	
Heathrow Terminal 4 ✈	d																								
Heathrow Terminal 1-2 2 ✈	d		16 27							16 57						17 27							17 57		
Hayes & Harlington	d	16 26	16 33	16 40					16 56	17 03	17 10				17 26	17 33		17 40				17 56	18 03	18 10	
Southall	d		16 36	16 43						17 06	17 13					17 36		17 43					18 06	18 13	
Hanwell	d		16 39							17 09						17 39							18 09		
Greenford ⊖	d							16 46						17 16							17 46				
South Greenford	d							16 49						17 19							17 49				
Castle Bar Park	d							16 52						17 22							17 52				
Drayton Green	d							16 54						17 24							17 54				
West Ealing	d		16 41					16 56		17 11				17 26		17 41					17 56		18 11		
Ealing Broadway ⊖	d	16 33	16 44	16 49				16 59	17 03	17 14	17 19			17 29	17 33	17 44		17 49			17 59	18 03	18 14	18 19	
Acton Main Line	d							17 03						17 33							18 03				
London Paddington 15 ⊖	a	16 46	16 54	17 01		16 59		17 12	17 16	17 24	17 31		17 29	17 42	17 46	17 54		18 01		17 59	18 12	18 16	18 24	18 31	

		GW ◇1 ☕		GW 1	GW 1	HC	GW 1	GW 1	GW ◇1	GW 1	GW 1	HC		GW 1	GW 1	GW ◇1 🚲	GW 1	GW 1	HC	GW 1	GW 1	GW ◇1		GW 1	GW 1
Oxford	d	17 31					17 07		18 01					17 37		18 31				18 07		19 01			
Reading 7	d	17 58					18 03	18 18	18 25					18 32	18 48	18 56				19 03	19 18	19 25			
Twyford 3	d						18 09	18 24						18 39	18 54					19 09	19 24				
Maidenhead 3	d						18 17	18 32						18 47	19 02					19 17	19 32				
Taplow	d							18 36							19 06						19 36				
Burnham	d				←			18 39			←				19 09			←			19 39				←
Slough 3	a	18 11			18 14		18 24	18 44	18 40		18 44			18 54	19 14	19 10		19 14		19 24	19 44	19 40			19 44
	d	18 12			18 14		18 24	18 44	18 40		18 44			18 54	19 14	19 11		19 14		19 24	19 44	19 40			19 44
Langley	d						18 28	→						18 58	→					19 28	→				
Iver	d						18 31							19 01						19 31					
West Drayton	d				18 21		18 35				18 51			19 05				19 21		19 35					19 51
Heathrow Terminal 4 ✈	d																								
Heathrow Terminal 1-2 2 ✈	d					18 27						18 57							19 27						
Hayes & Harlington	d				18 26	18 33	18 40				18 56	19 03		19 10				19 26	19 33	19 40					19 56
Southall	d					18 36	18 43					19 06		19 13					19 36	19 43					
Hanwell	d					18 39						19 09							19 39						
Greenford ⊖	d			18 16						18 46							19 16							19 46	
South Greenford	d			18 19						18 49							19 19							19 49	
Castle Bar Park	d			18 22						18 52							19 22							19 52	
Drayton Green	d			18 24						18 54							19 24							19 54	
West Ealing	d			18 26		18 41				18 56		19 11					19 26		19 41					19 56	
Ealing Broadway ⊖	d			18 29	18 33	18 44	18 49			18 59	19 03	19 14		19 19			19 29	19 33	19 44	19 49				19 59	20 03
Acton Main Line	d			18 33						19 03							19 33							20 03	
London Paddington 15 ⊖	a	18 29		18 42	18 46	18 54	19 01		18 59	19 12	19 16	19 24		19 31		19 29	19 42	19 46	19 54	20 01		19 59		20 12	20 16

For non-stop services between London and Reading please see table 116

Passengers who hold valid tickets for Acton Main Line, West Ealing and Hanwell will be able to use local Transport for London (TFL) bus services to reach these stations. Tel 0843 222 1234

Table 117R

Saturdays

29 March to 17 May

Network Diagram - refer to first Page of Table 116

Reading and Greenford - London

Station		HC	GW 1	GW 1	GW ◇1 (bicycle)	GW 1	GW 1	HC		GW 1	GW 1	GW ◇1	GW 1	GW 1	HC	GW 1	GW 1	GW ◇1		GW 1	GW 1	HC	GW 1	GW 1	GW ◇1
Oxford	d		18 37		19 31					19 07		20 01				19 37		20 31					20 07		21 01
Reading 7	d		19 33	19 48	19 55					20 02	20 18	20 25				20 33	20 48	20 56					21 03	21 18	21 27
Twyford 3	d		19 39	19 54						20 09	20 24					20 39	20 54						21 12	21 24	
Maidenhead 3	d		19 47	20 02						20 17	20 32					20 47	21 02						21 19	21 32	
Taplow	d			20 06							20 36						21 06							21 36	
Burnham	d			20 09			←				20 39			←			21 09				←			21 39	
Slough 3	a		19 54	20 14	20 10		20 14			20 24	20 44	20 40		20 44		20 54	21 14	21 10			21 14		21 27	21 44	21 42
	d		19 54	20 14	20 10		20 14			20 24	20 44	20 40		20 44		20 54	21 14	21 11			21 14		21 27	21 44	21 42
Langley	d		19 58	↪						20 28	↪					20 58	↪						21 31	↪	
Iver	d		20 01							20 31						21 01							21 34		
West Drayton	d		20 05				20 21			20 35				20 51		21 05					21 21		21 38		
Heathrow Terminal 4 ✈	d																								
Heathrow Terminal 1-2 2 ✈	d	19 57						20 27							20 57							21 27			
Hayes & Harlington	d	20 03	20 10				20 26	20 33		20 40				20 56	21 03	21 10					21 26	21 33	21 43		
Southall	d	20 06	20 13					20 36		20 43					21 06	21 13						21 36	21 46		
Hanwell	d	20 09						20 39							21 09							21 39			
Greenford ⊖	d					20 16							20 46							21 16					
South Greenford	d					20 19							20 49							21 19					
Castle Bar Park	d					20 22							20 52							21 22					
Drayton Green	d					20 24							20 54							21 24					
West Ealing	d	20 11				20 26		20 41					20 56		21 11					21 26		21 41			
Ealing Broadway ⊖	d	20 14	20 19			20 29	20 33	20 44		20 49			20 59	21 03	21 14	21 19				21 29	21 33	21 44	21 52		
Acton Main Line	d					20 33							21 03							21 33					
London Paddington 15 ⊖	a	20 24	20 31		20 29	20 42	20 46	20 54		21 01		20 59	21 12	21 16	21 24	21 31		21 29		21 42	21 46	21 54	22 02		22 01

Station		GW 1	GW 1	HC		GW 1	GW ◇1	HC	GW 1	GW 1	GW ◇1	HC	GW 1	GW 1		GW (bus)	GW ◇1	HC	GW 1	GW ◇1	GW (bus)	GW 1			
Oxford	d					20 37	21 31			21 50	22 01						22 35			23 01		23 07			
Reading 7	d					21 33	22 02		22 03	22 33	22 36			22 48			23 10		23 19	23 31		00 04			
Twyford 3	d					21 39			22 09	22 39				22 55					23 24			00 11			
Maidenhead 3	d					21 47			22 17	22 48				23 03					23 33			00 21			
Taplow	d					21 51			22 21	22 52						23 02					23 44				
Burnham	d		←			21 54			22 24	22 55			←			23 13					23 55				
Slough 3	a		21 44			21 58	22 15		22 28	23 00	22 51		23 00	23 10		23 23	23 28		23 39	23 50	00 05	00 28			
	d		21 44			21 59	22 16		22 29	23 00	22 51		23 00	23 11			23 29		23 46	23 50		00 31			
Langley	d					22 03				↪			23 04									00 35			
Iver	d					22 06							23 07									00 38			
West Drayton	d		21 51			22 10			22 36				23 11	23 18					23 51			00 41			
Heathrow Terminal 4 ✈	d																								
Heathrow Terminal 1-2 2 ✈	d			21 57				22 27				22 57						23 27							
Hayes & Harlington	d		21 56	22 03		22 14		22 33	22 40			23 03	23 15	23 26				23 33	23 57			00 45			
Southall	d			22 06		22 18		22 36	22 44			23 06	23 20	23 30				23 36				00 49			
Hanwell	d			22 09				22 39				23 09						23 39							
Greenford ⊖	d	21 46																							
South Greenford	d	21 49																							
Castle Bar Park	d	21 52																							
Drayton Green	d	21 54																							
West Ealing	d	21 56		22 11				22 41				23 11						23 41							
Ealing Broadway ⊖	d	21 59	22 03	22 14		22 23		22 44	22 49			23 14	23 25	23 36				23 44	00 04			00 55			
Acton Main Line	d	22 03																							
London Paddington 15 ⊖	a	22 12	22 15	22 24		22 32	22 38	22 54	22 58		23 10	23 24	23 34	23 47			23 46	23 54	00 14	00 17		01 06			

For non-stop services between London and Reading please see table 116

Passengers who hold valid tickets for Acton Main Line, West Ealing and Hanwell will be able to use local Transport for London (TFL) bus services to reach these stations. Tel 0843 222 1234

Table 117R

Sundays

8 December to 29 December

Network Diagram - refer to first Page of Table 116

Reading and Greenford - London

		GW 1 A	HC	GW 1 A	HC	GW 1		HC	GW 1	HC	GW 1	GW 1	HC	GW 1	GW 1	GW ◇1		GW 1	HC	GW 1	GW 1	GW ◇1	GW 1	HC	GW 1
Oxford	d															08 50				09 05		09 50			10 05
Reading 7	d			00 04		06 23			07 23		08 20	08 25		08 58	09 18	09 24				09 52	10 18	10 20			10 56
Twyford 3	d			00 11		06 29			07 29			08 31		09 03	09 24					09 58	10 24				11 03
Maidenhead 3	d			00 19		06 36			07 36			08 36		09 12	09 36					10 06	10 36				11 11
Taplow	d			00 23																					
Burnham	d			00 26		06 40			07 40			08 40			09 40			←			10 40		←		
Slough 3	a			00 30		06 45			07 45		08 38	08 47		09 20	09 45	09 38		09 45		10 13	10 45	10 38	10 45		11 19
	d			00 31		06 47			07 47		08 39	08 48		09 21	09 47	09 38		09 47		10 20	10 46	10 39	10 46		11 21
Langley	d			00 35		06 50			07 50			08 50		09 26	→			09 50		10 25	→		10 50		11 25
Iver	d			00 38																					
West Drayton	d			00 41		06 56			07 56			08 56		09 30				09 56		10 29			10 55		11 29
Heathrow Terminal 4 ✈	d		00 01		06 07			07 07		08 07			09 07						10 07					11 07	
Heathrow Terminal 1-2 2 ✈	d		00 07		06 13			07 13		08 13			09 13						10 13					11 13	
Hayes & Harlington	d		00 13	00 46	06 19	07 01		07 19	08 01	08 19		09 01	09 19	09 33				10 01	10 19	10 33			11 00	11 19	11 33
Southall	d		00 16	00 49	06 22	07 05		07 22	08 05	08 22		09 06	09 22	09 37				10 05	10 22	10 37				11 22	11 37
Hanwell	d																								
Greenford ⊖	d																								
South Greenford	d																								
Castle Bar Park	d																								
Drayton Green	d																								
West Ealing	d																								
Ealing Broadway ⊖	d	00 04	00 21	00 55	06 27	07 11		07 27	08 10	08 27		09 10	09 27	09 42				10 11	10 27	10 42			11 09	11 27	11 42
Acton Main Line	d																								
London Paddington 15 ⊖	a	00 14	00 30	01 05	06 36	07 22		07 36	08 20	08 36	09 00	09 21	09 36	09 53		10 00		10 20	10 36	10 52		11 00	11 19	11 36	11 52

		GW 1		GW ◇1	GW 1	HC	GW 1	GW 1	GW ◇1	GW 1	HC	GW 1		GW 1	GW ◇1	GW 1	HC	GW 1	GW 1	GW ◇1	GW 1	HC		GW 1	GW 1
Oxford	d			10 51			11 05		11 50			12 05			12 51			13 05		13 50				14 05	
Reading 7	d	11 18		11 25			11 51	12 18	12 19			12 51		13 18	13 23			13 53	14 18	14 19				14 53	15 18
Twyford 3	d	11 24					11 57	12 24				12 57		13 24				13 59	14 24					14 59	15 24
Maidenhead 3	d	11 36					12 06	12 36				13 06		13 36				14 06	14 36					15 06	15 36
Taplow	d																								
Burnham	d	11 40			←			12 40		←				13 40		←			14 40		←				15 40
Slough 3	a	11 45		11 42	11 45		12 15	12 44	12 34	12 44		13 15		13 44	13 37	13 44		14 16	14 44	14 35	14 44			15 14	15 44
	d	11 48		11 42	11 48		12 17	12 47	12 35	12 47		13 17		13 47	13 39	13 47		14 17	14 47	14 35	14 47			15 17	15 47
Langley	d	→			11 50		12 22	→		12 50		13 22		→		13 50		14 25	→		14 50			15 22	→
Iver	d																								
West Drayton	d				11 57		12 29			12 56		13 29				13 56		14 29			14 56			15 29	
Heathrow Terminal 4 ✈	d					12 07					13 07						14 07					15 07			
Heathrow Terminal 1-2 2 ✈	d					12 13					13 13						14 13					15 13			
Hayes & Harlington	d				12 01	12 19	12 33			13 01	13 19	13 33				14 01	14 19	14 33			15 01	15 19		15 33	
Southall	d					12 22	12 37				13 22	13 37					14 22	14 37				15 22		15 37	
Hanwell	d																								
Greenford ⊖	d																								
South Greenford	d																								
Castle Bar Park	d																								
Drayton Green	d																								
West Ealing	d																								
Ealing Broadway ⊖	d				12 08	12 27	12 42			13 08	13 27	13 42				14 08	14 27	14 41			15 08	15 27		15 42	
Acton Main Line	d																								
London Paddington 15 ⊖	a			12 04	12 18	12 36	12 51		12 56	13 19	13 36	13 51			14 01	14 19	14 36	14 51		14 57	15 20	15 36		15 51	

		GW ◇1	GW 1	HC	GW 1	GW 1	GW ◇1 ⊏P	GW 1		HC	GW 1	GW 1	GW ◇1 ⊏P	GW 1	HC	GW 1	GW 1	GW ◇1 ⊏P		GW 1	HC	GW 1	GW 1	GW ◇1 ⊏P	GW 1
Oxford	d	14 51			15 05		15 49				16 05		16 53			17 05		17 50				18 05		18 50	
Reading 7	d	15 23			15 53	16 18	16 24				16 53	17 18	17 27			17 53	18 18	18 20				18 53	19 18	19 29	
Twyford 3	d				15 59	16 24					16 59	17 24				17 59	18 24					18 59	19 24		
Maidenhead 3	d				16 06	16 36					17 06	17 36				18 06	18 36					19 10	19 36		
Taplow	d																								
Burnham	d		←		16 11	16 40		←			17 13	17 40		←		18 11	18 40			←		19 11	19 40		←
Slough 3	a	15 38	15 44		16 17	16 44	16 38	16 44			17 15	17 44	17 44	17 44		18 15	18 44	18 36		18 44		19 17	19 44	19 42	19 44
	d	15 38	15 47		16 17	16 47	16 38	16 47			17 19	17 47	17 45	17 47		18 17	18 47	18 37		18 47		19 17	19 47	19 43	19 47
Langley	d		15 50		16 22	→		16 50			17 25	→		17 50		18 22	→			18 50		19 25	→		19 50
Iver	d																								
West Drayton	d		15 56		16 29			16 56			17 29			17 56		18 29				18 56		19 29			19 56
Heathrow Terminal 4 ✈	d			16 07						17 07					18 07						19 07				
Heathrow Terminal 1-2 2 ✈	d			16 13						17 13					18 13						19 13				
Hayes & Harlington	d		16 01	16 19	16 33			17 01		17 19	17 33			18 01	18 19	18 33				19 01	19 19	19 33			20 01
Southall	d			16 22	16 37					17 22	17 37				18 22	18 37					19 22	19 37			
Hanwell	d																								
Greenford ⊖	d																								
South Greenford	d																								
Castle Bar Park	d																								
Drayton Green	d																								
West Ealing	d																								
Ealing Broadway ⊖	d		16 08	16 27	16 42			17 08		17 27	17 42			18 08	18 27	18 42				19 08	19 27	19 42			20 08
Acton Main Line	d																								
London Paddington 15 ⊖	a	15 57	16 20	16 36	16 53		16 58	17 19		17 36	17 52		18 07	18 19	18 36	18 52		19 01		19 20	19 36	19 52		20 02	20 19

A not 8 December

For non-stop services between London and Reading please see table 116

Passengers who hold valid tickets for Acton Main Line, West Ealing and Hanwell will be able to use local Transport for London (TFL) bus services to reach these stations. Tel 0843 222 1234

Table 117R

Sundays

8 December to 29 December

Network Diagram - refer to first Page of Table 116

Reading and Greenford - London

Station		HC	GW [1]	GW [1]		GW ◇[1]	GW [1]	HC	GW [1]	GW ◇[1]	GW [1]	HC	GW [1]	GW ◇[1]		HC	GW [1]	GW [1]	GW ◇[1]	GW [1]					
Oxford	d		19 05			19 50			20 05	20 50			21 05	21 50				22 17	22 46						
Reading [7]	d		19 53	20 18		20 23			20 53	21 22	21 23		21 56	22 22			22 45	23 03	23 18	23 36					
Twyford [3]	d		19 59	20 24					20 59		21 30		22 03				22 54	23 09		23 42					
Maidenhead [3]	d		20 06	20 36					21 06	21 36	21 36		22 11				23 03	23 17		23 50					
Taplow	d																								
Burnham	d		20 11	20 40			←		21 11		21 40		22 15				23 07			23 55					
Slough [3]	a		20 17	20 44		20 39	20 44		21 17	21 39	21 47		22 18	22 39			23 12	23 25	23 36	00 01					
	d		20 17	20 47		20 39	20 47		21 17	21 42	21 47		22 20	22 40			23 12	23 25	23 36	00 02					
Langley	d		20 22	→			20 50		21 25		21 50		22 22				23 15	23 33		00 06					
Iver	d																								
West Drayton	d		20 29				20 56		21 29		21 57		22 29				23 26	23 37		00 11					
Heathrow Terminal 4 ✈	d	20 07						21 07				22 07				23 07									
Heathrow Terminal 1-2 [2] ✈	d	20 13						21 13				22 13				23 13									
Hayes & Harlington	d	20 19	20 33				21 01	21 19	21 33		22 01	22 19	22 33			23 19	23 30	23 46		00 17					
Southall	d	20 22	20 37				21 06	21 22	21 37		22 05	22 22	22 37			23 22	23 33	23 49		00 20					
Hanwell	d																								
Greenford ⊖	d																								
South Greenford	d																								
Castle Bar Park	d																								
Drayton Green	d																								
West Ealing	d																								
Ealing Broadway ⊖	d	20 27	20 42				21 11	21 27	21 42		22 12	22 27	22 42			23 27	23 38	23 54		00 27					
Acton Main Line	d																								
London Paddington [15] ⊖	a	20 36	20 53			21 00	21 22	21 36	21 52	22 03	22 22	22 36	22 52	23 03		23 36	23 49	00 05	00 06	00 38					

Sundays

5 January to 9 February

Station		GW [1]	HC	GW [1]	GW 🚌	HC	GW [1]	GW 🚌	HC	GW [1]		HC	GW [1]	GW [1]	HC	GW [1]	GW [1]	GW ◇[1]	GW [1]	HC		GW [1]	GW [1]	GW ◇[1]	GW [1]
Oxford	d																	08 43				08 56		09 43	
Reading [7]	d			00 08									08 20	08 25		08 59	09 18	09 26				09 48	10 18	10 20	
Twyford [3]	d			00 15	06 00			07 00						08 31		09 03	09 24					09 54	10 24		
Maidenhead [3]	d			00 23	06a30		06 36	07a30		07 36				08 36		09 12	09 36					10 14	10 36		
Taplow	d			00 26																					
Burnham	d			00 29			06 40			07 40				08 40			09 40		←				10 40		←
Slough [3]	a			00 34			06 45			07 45			08 38	08 47		09 20	09 45	09 40	09 45			10 21	10 45	10 38	10 45
	d			00 34			06 47			07 47			08 39	08 48		09 21	09 47	09 41	09 47			10 21	10 46	10 39	10 46
Langley	d			00 39			06 52			07 50				08 50		09 26	→		09 50			10 25	→		10 50
Iver	d			00 42																					
West Drayton	d			00 45			06 56			07 56				08 56		09 30			09 56			10 29			10 55
Heathrow Terminal 4 ✈	d		00 01			06 07			07 07			08 07			09 07					10 07					
Heathrow Terminal 1-2 [2] ✈	d		00 07			06 13			07 13			08 13			09 13					10 13					
Hayes & Harlington	d		00 13	00 50		06 19	07 01		07 19	08 01		08 19		09 01	09 19	09 33			10 01	10 19		10 33			11 00
Southall	d		00 16	00 53		06 22	07 05		07 22	08 05		08 22		09 06	09 22	09 37			10 05	10 22		10 37			11 04
Hanwell	d																								
Greenford ⊖	d																								
South Greenford	d																								
Castle Bar Park	d																								
Drayton Green	d																								
West Ealing	d																								
Ealing Broadway ⊖	d	00 04	00 21	00 59		06 27	07 11		07 27	08 10		08 27		09 10	09 27	09 43			10 12	10 27		10 43			11 08
Acton Main Line	d																								
London Paddington [15] ⊖	a	00 14	00 30	01 09		06 36	07 22		07 36	08 20		08 36	09 02	09 22	09 36	09 54		10 03	10 21	10 36		10 53		11 00	11 20

Station		HC	GW [1]	GW [1]	GW ◇[1]	GW [1]		HC	GW [1]	GW [1]	GW ◇[1]	GW [1]	HC	GW [1]	GW [1]	GW ◇[1]		GW [1]	HC	GW [1]	GW [1]	GW ◇[1]	GW [1]	HC	GW [1]
Oxford	d		10 05		10 51				11 05		11 47			12 05		12 51				13 05		13 50			14 05
Reading [7]	d		10 56	11 18	11 27				11 57	12 18	12 19			12 57	13 18	13 27				13 57	14 18	14 25			14 59
Twyford [3]	d		11 03	11 24					12 03	12 24				13 03	13 24					14 03	14 24				15 03
Maidenhead [3]	d		11 17	11 36					12 15	12 36				13 15	13 36					14 15	14 36				15 15
Taplow	d																								
Burnham	d			11 40		←				12 40		←			13 40			←			14 40		←		
Slough [3]	a		11 27	11 46	11 42	11 46			12 21	12 45	12 40	12 45		13 21	13 50	13 43		13 50		14 21	14 44	14 42	14 44		15 21
	d		11 29	11 49	11 42	11 49			12 21	12 47	12 40	12 47		13 21	13 51	13 45		13 51		14 21	14 47	14 42	14 47		15 23
Langley	d		11 31	→		11 52			12 25	→		12 50		13 25	→			13 54		14 25	→		14 50		15 29
Iver	d																								
West Drayton	d		11 37			11 58			12 29			12 56		13 29				14 00		14 29			14 56		15 33
Heathrow Terminal 4 ✈	d	11 07						12 07					13 07						14 07					15 07	
Heathrow Terminal 1-2 [2] ✈	d	11 13						12 13					13 13						14 13					15 13	
Hayes & Harlington	d	11 19	11 41			12 02		12 19	12 33			13 01	13 19	13 33				14 03	14 19	14 33			15 01	15 19	15 37
Southall	d	11 22	11 45			12 06		12 22	12 37			13 04	13 22	13 37				14 08	14 22	14 37			15 04	15 22	15 41
Hanwell	d																								
Greenford ⊖	d																								
South Greenford	d																								
Castle Bar Park	d																								
Drayton Green	d																								
West Ealing	d																								
Ealing Broadway ⊖	d	11 27	11 50			12 10		12 27	12 42			13 09	13 27	13 42				14 12	14 27	14 42			15 10	15 27	15 46
Acton Main Line	d																								
London Paddington [15] ⊖	a	11 36	12 00		12 06	12 21		12 36	12 53		13 00	13 20	13 36	13 55		14 08		14 23	14 36	14 56		15 03	15 20	15 36	15 56

For non-stop services between London and Reading please see table 116

Passengers who hold valid tickets for Acton Main Line, West Ealing and Hanwell will be able to use local Transport for London (TFL) bus services to reach these stations. Tel 0843 222 1234

Table 117R

Sundays

5 January to 9 February

Network Diagram - refer to first Page of Table 116

Reading and Greenford - London

		GW 1		GW ◇1	GW 1	HC	GW 1	GW 1	GW ◇1 🍴	GW 1	HC	GW 1		GW 1	GW ◇1 🍴	GW 1	HC	GW 1	GW 1	GW ◇1 🍴	GW 1	HC		GW 1	GW 1
Oxford	d			14 51			15 05		15 49			16 05			16 53			17 05		17 50				18 05	
Reading 7	d	15 18		15 27			15 57	16 18	16 24			16 57		17 18	17 30			17 57	18 18	18 24				18 57	19 18
Twyford 3	d	15 24					16 03	16 24				17 03		17 24				18 03	18 24					19 03	19 24
Maidenhead 3	d	15 36					16 15	16 36				17 14		17 39				18 15	18 36					19 12	19 45
Taplow	d																								
Burnham	d	15 40			←		16 17	16 40		←		17 17		17 42		←		18 18	18 40		←			19 15	19 53
Slough 3	a	15 44		15 44	15 44		16 23	16 44	16 38	16 44		17 20		17 49	17 48	17 49		18 25	18 44	18 43	18 44			19 22	19 58
	d	15 47		15 45	15 47		16 24	16 47	16 38	16 47		17 21		17 51	17 48	17 51		18 28	18 47	18 44	18 47			19 22	19 59
Langley	d	→			15 50		16 29	→		16 52		17 25		→		17 56		18 33	→		18 50			19 25	→
Iver	d																								
West Drayton	d				15 56		16 33			16 56		17 29				18 00		18 38			18 56			19 29	
Heathrow Terminal 4 ✈	d					16 07					17 07						18 07					19 07			
Heathrow Terminal 1-2 2 ✈	d					16 13					17 13						18 13					19 13			
Hayes & Harlington	d				16 01	16 19	16 37			17 01	17 19	17 33				18 05	18 19	18 41			19 01	19 20		19 33	
Southall	d				16 04	16 22	16 41			17 04	17 22	17 37				18 08	18 22	18 46			19 05	19 23		19 37	
Hanwell	d																								
Greenford ⊖	d																								
South Greenford	d																								
Castle Bar Park	d																								
Drayton Green	d																								
West Ealing	d																								
Ealing Broadway ⊖	d				16 11	16 27	16 46			17 10	17 27	17 42				18 13	18 27	18 51			19 10	19 28		19 42	
Acton Main Line	d																								
London Paddington 15 ⊖	a			16 06	16 20	16 36	16 58		17 04	17 19	17 36	17 54			18 14	18 24	18 36	19 01		19 06	19 20	19 36		19 55	

		GW ◇1 🍴	GW 1	HC	GW 1	GW 1	GW ◇1	GW 1		HC	GW 1	GW 1	GW ◇1	GW 1	HC	GW 1	GW ◇1	GW 1		HC	GW 1	GW ◇1	GW 1		
Oxford	d	18 50			19 05		19 50				20 05		20 50			21 05	21 44				22 17	22 46			
Reading 7	d	19 29			19 57	20 18	20 29				20 57	21 23	21 26			22 01	22 22	22 24			23 03	23 25	23 36		
Twyford 3	d				20 03	20 24					21 03	21 30				22 08		22 33			23 09		23 42		
Maidenhead 3	d				20 12	20 45					21 12	21 43	21 39			22 16		22 42			23 17		23 50		
Taplow	d																								
Burnham	d		←		20 16	20 50		←			21 15	21 46		←		22 20		22 46					23 55		
Slough 3	a	19 46	19 58		20 21	20 59	20 48	20 59			21 21	21 50	21 47	21 50		22 23	22 42	22 49			23 25	23 42	00 01		
	d	19 47	19 59		20 21	20 59	20 49	20 59			21 22	21 51	21 47	21 51		22 24	22 43	22 49			23 25	23 43	00 02		
Langley	d		20 01		20 25	→		21 02			21 26	→		21 55		22 28		22 53			23 33		00 06		
Iver	d																								
West Drayton	d		20 06		20 29			21 06			21 31			21 59		22 35		22 57			23 37		00 11		
Heathrow Terminal 4 ✈	d			20 07						21 07					22 07					23 07					
Heathrow Terminal 1-2 2 ✈	d			20 13						21 13					22 13					23 13					
Hayes & Harlington	d		20 09	20 20	20 38			21 08		21 19	21 35			22 04	22 19	22 39		23 02		23 19	23 46		00 17		
Southall	d		20 16	20 23	20 42			21 13		21 22	21 38			22 10	22 22	22 42				23 22	23 49		00 20		
Hanwell	d																								
Greenford ⊖	d																								
South Greenford	d																								
Castle Bar Park	d																								
Drayton Green	d																								
West Ealing	d																								
Ealing Broadway ⊖	d		20 20	20 28	20 47			21 20		21 27	21 44			22 15	22 27	22 48		23 13		23 27	23 54		00 27		
Acton Main Line	d																								
London Paddington 15 ⊖	a	20 11	20 29	20 36	20 57		21 09	21 29		21 36	21 58		22 09	22 25	22 36	22 58	23 06	23 22		23 36	00 05	00 11	00 38		

For non-stop services between London and Reading please see table 116

Passengers who hold valid tickets for Acton Main Line, West Ealing and Hanwell will be able to use local Transport for London (TFL) bus services to reach these stations. Tel 0843 222 1234

Table 117R

Sundays

16 February to 23 March

Network Diagram - refer to first Page of Table 116

Reading and Greenford - London

		GW 1	HC	GW 1	GW 🚌	HC		GW 1	GW 🚌	HC	GW 1	HC	GW 1	GW 1	HC	GW 1		GW 1	GW ◇1	GW 1	HC	GW 1	GW 1	GW ◇1	GW 1
Oxford	d																		08 50			09 05		09 50	
Reading 7	d			00 04									08 20	08 25		08 58		09 18	09 24			09 52	10 18	10 20	
Twyford 3	d			00 11	06 00				07 00					08 31		09 03		09 24				09 58	10 24		
Maidenhead 3	d			00 19	06a30			06 36	07a30		07 36			08 36		09 12		09 36				10 06	10 36		
Taplow	d			00 23																					
Burnham	d			00 26				06 40			07 40			08 40				09 40		←			10 40		←
Slough 3	a			00 30				06 45			07 45		08 38	08 47		09 20		09 45	09 38	09 45		10 13	10 45	10 38	10 45
	d			00 31				06 47			07 47		08 39	08 48		09 21		09 47	09 38	09 47		10 21	10 47	10 39	10 47
Langley	d			00 35				06 52			07 50			08 50		09 26		→		09 50		10 25	→		10 50
Iver	d			00 38																					
West Drayton	d			00 41				06 56			07 56			08 57		09 30				09 56		10 29			10 56
Heathrow Terminal 4 ✈	d		00 01			06 07				07 07		08 07			09 07						10 07				
Heathrow Terminal 1-2 2 ✈	d		00 07			06 13				07 13		08 13			09 13						10 13				
Hayes & Harlington	d		00 13	00 46		06 19		07 01		07 19	08 01	08 19		09 01	09 19	09 33				10 01	10 19	10 33			11 01
Southall	d		00 16	00 49		06 22		07 05		07 22	08 05	08 22		09 06	09 22	09 37				10 05	10 22	10 37			11 04
Hanwell	d																								
Greenford ⊖	d																								
South Greenford	d																								
Castle Bar Park	d																								
Drayton Green	d																								
West Ealing	d																								
Ealing Broadway ⊖	d	00 04	00 21	00 55		06 27		07 11		07 27	08 10	08 27		09 10	09 27	09 42				10 11	10 27	10 42			11 11
Acton Main Line	d																								
London Paddington 15 ⊖	a	00 14	00 30	01 05		06 36		07 22		07 36	08 20	08 36	09 00	09 22	09 36	09 53			10 00	10 20	10 36	10 53		11 00	11 20

		HC		GW 1	GW 1	GW ◇1	GW 1	HC	GW 1	GW 1	GW ◇1	GW 1		HC	GW 1	GW 1	GW ◇1	GW 1	HC	GW 1	GW 1	GW ◇1		GW 1	HC
Oxford	d			10 05		10 51			11 05		11 50				12 05		12 51			13 05		13 50			
Reading 7	d			10 56	11 18	11 25			11 57	12 18	12 19				12 57	13 18	13 23			13 53	14 18	14 19			
Twyford 3	d			11 03	11 24				12 03	12 24					13 03	13 24				13 59	14 24				
Maidenhead 3	d			11 11	11 36				12 12	12 36					13 12	13 36				14 06	14 36				
Taplow	d																								
Burnham	d				11 40		←			12 40		←				13 40		←			14 40			←	
Slough 3	a			11 19	11 47	11 42	11 47		12 21	12 44	12 35	12 44			13 21	13 44	13 37	13 44		14 16	14 44	14 35		14 44	
	d			11 21	11 47	11 42	11 47		12 21	12 47	12 35	12 47			13 21	13 47	13 39	13 47		14 17	14 47	14 35		14 47	
Langley	d			11 25	→		11 52		12 25	→		12 50			13 25	→		13 50		14 25	→			14 50	
Iver	d																								
West Drayton	d			11 29			11 58		12 29			12 56			13 29			13 56		14 29				14 56	
Heathrow Terminal 4 ✈	d	11 07						12 07						13 07					14 07						15 07
Heathrow Terminal 1-2 2 ✈	d	11 13						12 13						13 13					14 13						15 13
Hayes & Harlington	d	11 19		11 33			12 00	12 19	12 33			13 01		13 19	13 33			14 01	14 19	14 33				15 01	15 19
Southall	d	11 22		11 37			12 06	12 22	12 37			13 04		13 22	13 37			14 04	14 22	14 37				15 04	15 22
Hanwell	d																								
Greenford ⊖	d																								
South Greenford	d																								
Castle Bar Park	d																								
Drayton Green	d																								
West Ealing	d																								
Ealing Broadway ⊖	d	11 27		11 42			12 10	12 27	12 42			13 11		13 27	13 42			14 11	14 27	14 42				15 11	15 27
Acton Main Line	d																								
London Paddington 15 ⊖	a	11 36		11 53		12 04	12 20	12 36	12 51		13 00	13 20		13 36	13 55		14 02	14 21	14 36	14 51		14 57		15 21	15 36

		GW 1	GW 1	GW ◇1	GW 1	HC	GW 1	GW 1		GW ◇1 ☕	GW 1	HC	GW 1	GW 1	GW ◇1 ☕	GW 1	HC	GW 1		GW 1	GW ◇1 ☕	GW 1	HC	GW 1	GW 1
Oxford	d	14 05		14 51			15 05			15 49			16 05		16 53			17 05			17 50			18 05	
Reading 7	d	14 53	15 18	15 23			15 53	16 18		16 24			16 53	17 18	17 27			17 53		18 18	18 20			18 53	19 18
Twyford 3	d	14 59	15 24				15 59	16 24					16 59	17 24				17 59		18 24				18 59	19 24
Maidenhead 3	d	15 06	15 36				16 06	16 36					17 06	17 39				18 06		18 36				19 06	19 36
Taplow	d																								
Burnham	d		15 40		←		16 12	16 40			←		17 13	17 44		←		18 11		18 40		←		19 11	19 40
Slough 3	a	15 16	15 44	15 37	15 44		16 16	16 44		16 38	16 44		17 15	17 48	17 44	17 48		18 16		18 44	18 36	18 44		19 17	19 44
	d	15 17	15 47	15 38	15 47		16 17	16 52		16 38	16 52		17 19	17 49	17 45	17 49		18 17		18 47	18 37	18 47		19 17	19 47
Langley	d	15 22	→		15 50		16 22	→			16 56		17 25	→		17 52		18 22		→		18 50		19 25	→
Iver	d																								
West Drayton	d	15 29			15 56		16 29				17 00		17 29			17 58		18 29				18 56		19 29	
Heathrow Terminal 4 ✈	d					16 07						17 07					18 07						19 07		
Heathrow Terminal 1-2 2 ✈	d					16 13						17 13					18 13						19 13		
Hayes & Harlington	d	15 33			16 01	16 19	16 33				17 04	17 19	17 33			18 03	18 19	18 33				19 01	19 19	19 33	
Southall	d	15 37			16 04	16 22	16 37				17 07	17 22	17 37			18 07	18 22	18 37				19 05	19 22	19 37	
Hanwell	d																								
Greenford ⊖	d																								
South Greenford	d																								
Castle Bar Park	d																								
Drayton Green	d																								
West Ealing	d																								
Ealing Broadway ⊖	d	15 42			16 11	16 27	16 42				17 14	17 27	17 42			18 12	18 27	18 42				19 11	19 27	19 42	
Acton Main Line	d																								
London Paddington 15 ⊖	a	15 51		16 00	16 20	16 36	16 54			17 04	17 23	17 36	17 53		18 07	18 22	18 36	18 52			19 01	19 20	19 36	19 53	

For non-stop services between London and Reading please see table 116

Passengers who hold valid tickets for Acton Main Line, West Ealing and Hanwell will be able to use local Transport for London (TFL) bus services to reach these stations. Tel 0843 222 1234

Table 117R

Reading and Greenford - London

Sundays

16 February to 23 March

Network Diagram - refer to first Page of Table 116

		GW	GW	HC	GW	GW	GW	GW	HC	GW	GW	GW	GW	HC	GW	GW	HC	GW	GW	GW	GW
		◇1 ☕	1		1	1	◇1	1		1	1	◇1	1		1	◇1		1	1	◇1	1
Oxford	d	18 50			19 05		19 50			20 05		20 50			21 05	21 50			22 17	22 46	
Reading 7	d	19 29			19 53	20 20	20 23			20 53	21 23	21 26			21 56	22 22		22 46	23 03	23 18	23 36
Twyford 3	d				19 59	20 26				20 59	21 30				22 02			22 52	23 09		23 42
Maidenhead 3	d				20 06	20 36				21 06	21 36	21 40			22 11			23 00	23 17		23 50
Taplow	d																				
Burnham	d		←		20 11	20 40		←		21 11	21 40		←		22 15			23 05			23 55
Slough 3	a	19 42	19 44		20 17	20 44	20 39	20 44		21 17	21 47	21 43	21 47		22 18	22 39		23 09	23 25	23 36	00 01
	d	19 43	19 47		20 17	20 47	20 39	20 47		21 17	21 47	21 46	21 47		22 20	22 40		23 10	23 25	23 36	00 02
Langley	d		19 50		20 22	→		20 50		21 25	→		21 50		22 24			23 14	23 33		00 06
Iver	d																				
West Drayton	d		19 56		20 29			20 56		21 29			21 57		22 29			23 17	23 37		00 11
Heathrow Terminal 4 ✈	d			20 07					21 07					22 07			23 07				
Heathrow Terminal 1-2 2 ✈	d			20 13					21 13					22 13			23 13				
Hayes & Harlington	d		20 01	20 19	20 33			21 01	21 19	21 33			22 01	22 19	22 33		23 19	23 21	23 46		00 17
Southall	d		20 06	20 22	20 37			21 06	21 22	21 37			22 05	22 22	22 37		23 22	23 25	23 49		00 20
Hanwell	d																				
Greenford ⊖	d																				
South Greenford	d																				
Castle Bar Park	d																				
Drayton Green	d																				
West Ealing	d																				
Ealing Broadway ⊖	d		20 11	20 27	20 42			21 11	21 27	21 42			22 12	22 27	22 42		23 27	23 31	23 54		00 27
Acton Main Line	d																				
London Paddington 15 ⊖	a	20 07	20 21	20 36	20 53		21 00	21 22	21 36	21 52		22 06	22 22	22 36	22 52	23 03	23 36	23 40	00 05	00 12	00 38

Sundays

30 March to 11 May

		GW	GW	HC	GW	HC	GW	HC	GW	HC	GW	GW	HC	GW	GW	GW	HC	GW	GW	GW	GW	HC	GW
		🚌	1		1		1		1		1	1		1	◇1	1		1	1	◇1	1		1
Oxford	d														08 50			09 05		09 50			10 05
Reading 7	d				00 04						08 20	08 25		08 58	09 24	09 27		09 52	10 19	10 20			10 56
Twyford 3	d				00 11		06 29		07 29			08 31		09 03		09 32		09 58	10 26				11 03
Maidenhead 3	d				00 21		06 36		07 36			08 36		09 12		09 36		10 06	10 36				11 11
Taplow	d	00 02																					
Burnham	d	00 13					06 40		07 40			08 40				09 40			10 40		←		
Slough 3	a	00 23			00 28		06 45		07 45		08 38	08 45		09 20	09 38	09 45		10 13	10 46	10 38	10 46		11 19
	d				00 31		06 47		07 47		08 39	08 47		09 21	09 38	09 47		10 20	10 48	10 39	10 48		11 21
Langley	d				00 35		06 53		07 50			08 50		09 25		09 50		10 25	→		10 50		11 25
Iver	d				00 38																		
West Drayton	d				00 41		06 56		07 56			08 56		09 30		09 56		10 29			10 56		11 29
Heathrow Terminal 4 ✈	d			00 01		06 07		07 07		08 07			09 07				10 07					11 07	
Heathrow Terminal 1-2 2 ✈	d			00 07		06 13		07 13		08 13			09 13				10 13					11 13	
Hayes & Harlington	d			00 13	00 45	06 19	07 01	07 19	08 01	08 19		09 01	09 19	09 33		10 01	10 19	10 33			11 01	11 19	11 33
Southall	d			00 16	00 49	06 22	07 05	07 22	08 05	08 22		09 06	09 22	09 37		10 06	10 22	10 37			11 04	11 22	11 37
Hanwell	d																						
Greenford ⊖	d																						
South Greenford	d																						
Castle Bar Park	d																						
Drayton Green	d																						
West Ealing	d																						
Ealing Broadway ⊖	d		00 04	00 21	00 55	06 27	07 11	07 27	08 10	08 27		09 10	09 27	09 42		10 12	10 27	10 42			11 10	11 27	11 42
Acton Main Line	d																						
London Paddington 15 ⊖	a		00 14	00 30	01 06	06 36	07 22	07 36	08 21	08 36	09 00	09 22	09 36	09 53	10 00	10 21	10 36	10 53		11 00	11 20	11 36	11 52

For non-stop services between London and Reading please see table 116

Passengers who hold valid tickets for Acton Main Line, West Ealing and Hanwell will be able to use local Transport for London (TFL) bus services to reach these stations. Tel 0843 222 1234

Table 117R

Sundays

30 March to 11 May

Network Diagram - refer to first Page of Table 116

Reading and Greenford - London

Station		GW 1	GW ◇1	GW 1	HC	GW 1	GW 1	GW ◇1	GW 1	HC	GW 1	GW 1	GW ◇1	GW 1	HC	GW 1	GW 1	GW ◇1	GW 1	HC	GW 1	GW 1
Oxford	d		10 51			11 05		11 50			12 05		12 51			13 05		13 50			14 05	
Reading 7	d	11 18	11 25			11 57	12 18	12 19			12 57	13 18	13 23			13 53	14 18	14 19			14 53	15 18
Twyford 3	d	11 24				12 03	12 24				13 03	13 24				13 59	14 24				14 59	15 24
Maidenhead 3	d	11 36				12 12	12 36				13 11	13 36				14 06	14 36				15 06	15 36
Taplow	d																					
Burnham	d	11 40		←			12 40		←			13 40		←			14 40		←			15 40
Slough 3	a	11 44	11 43	11 44		12 21	12 44	12 35	12 44		13 20	13 44	13 36	13 44		14 16	14 44	14 35	14 44		15 16	15 44
	d	11 48	11 43	11 48		12 21	12 48	12 35	12 48		13 21	13 47	13 38	13 47		14 17	14 47	14 35	14 47		15 17	15 47
Langley	d	→		11 50		12 25	→		12 50		13 25	→		13 50		14 25	→		14 50		15 22	→
Iver	d																					
West Drayton	d			11 56		12 29			12 56		13 29			13 56		14 29			14 56		15 29	
Heathrow Terminal 4 ✈	d				12 07					13 07					14 07					15 07		
Heathrow Terminal 1-2 2 ✈	d				12 13					13 13					14 13					15 13		
Hayes & Harlington	d			12 01	12 19	12 33			13 01	13 19	13 33			14 01	14 19	14 33			15 01	15 19	15 33	
Southall	d			12 04	12 22	12 37			13 04	13 22	13 37			14 04	14 22	14 37			15 04	15 22	15 37	
Hanwell	d																					
Greenford ⊖	d																					
South Greenford	d																					
Castle Bar Park	d																					
Drayton Green	d																					
West Ealing	d																					
Ealing Broadway ⊖	d			12 10	12 27	12 42			13 10	13 27	13 42			14 10	14 27	14 42			15 11	15 27	15 42	
Acton Main Line	d																					
London Paddington 15 ⊖	a		12 04	12 20	12 36	12 52		12 57	13 20	13 36	13 55		14 01	14 20	14 36	14 52		15 00	15 20	15 36	15 52	

Station		GW ◇1	GW 1	HC	GW 1	GW 1	GW ◇1 ☕	GW 1	HC	GW 1	GW 1	GW ◇1 ☕	GW 1	HC	GW 1	GW 1	GW ◇1 ☕	GW 1	HC	GW 1	GW 1	GW ◇1 ☕	GW 1
Oxford	d	14 51			15 05		15 49			16 05		16 53			17 05		17 50			18 05		18 50	
Reading 7	d	15 23			15 57	16 18	16 25			16 57	17 18	17 27			17 57	18 18	18 24			18 53	19 18	19 29	
Twyford 3	d				16 03	16 24				17 03	17 24				18 03	18 24				18 59	19 24		
Maidenhead 3	d				16 12	16 36				17 12	17 36				18 12	18 36				19 10	19 36		
Taplow	d																						
Burnham	d		←		16 15	16 40		←		17 15	17 40		←		18 15	18 40		←		19 15	19 40		←
Slough 3	a	15 37	15 44		16 19	16 44	16 38	16 44		17 20	17 44	17 44	17 44		18 20	18 44	18 39	18 44		19 17	19 44	19 43	19 44
	d	15 38	15 47		16 19	16 47	16 38	16 47		17 21	17 47	17 45	17 47		18 21	18 47	18 40	18 47		19 17	19 47	19 44	19 47
Langley	d		15 50		16 26	→		16 50		17 25	→		17 50		18 26	→		18 50		19 25	→		19 50
Iver	d																						
West Drayton	d		15 56		16 29			16 56		17 29			17 56		18 29			18 56		19 29			19 56
Heathrow Terminal 4 ✈	d			16 07					17 07					18 07					19 07				
Heathrow Terminal 1-2 2 ✈	d			16 13					17 13					18 13					19 13				
Hayes & Harlington	d		16 01	16 19	16 33			17 01	17 19	17 33			18 01	18 19	18 33			19 01	19 19	19 33			20 01
Southall	d		16 04	16 22	16 37			17 04	17 22	17 37			18 04	18 22	18 37			19 04	19 22	19 37			20 04
Hanwell	d																						
Greenford ⊖	d																						
South Greenford	d																						
Castle Bar Park	d																						
Drayton Green	d																						
West Ealing	d																						
Ealing Broadway ⊖	d		16 11	16 27	16 42			17 10	17 27	17 42			18 10	18 27	18 42			19 10	19 27	19 42			20 11
Acton Main Line	d																						
London Paddington 15 ⊖	a	16 00	16 21	16 36	16 54		17 03	17 23	17 36	17 53		18 07	18 19	18 36	18 53		19 01	19 20	19 36	19 53		20 04	20 19

Station		HC	GW 1	GW 1	GW ◇1	GW 1	HC	GW 1	GW ◇1	GW 1	HC	GW 1	GW ◇1	GW 1	HC	GW 1	GW ◇1	GW 1
Oxford	d		19 05		19 50			20 05	20 50			21 05	21 50			22 15	22 46	
Reading 7	d		19 53	20 18	20 23			20 53	21 22	21 23		21 57	22 20	22 24		22 57	23 18	23 36
Twyford 3	d		19 59	20 24				20 59		21 31		22 03		22 33		23 02		23 42
Maidenhead 3	d		20 12	20 36				21 10	21 36	21 41		22 11		22 41		23 12		23 50
Taplow	d																	
Burnham	d		20 15	20 40		←		21 14		21 46		22 15		22 46		23 16		23 56
Slough 3	a		20 17	20 44	20 39	20 44		21 19	21 41	21 51		22 20	22 39	22 49		23 21	23 36	00 01
	d		20 17	20 47	20 39	20 47		21 19	21 43	21 51		22 21	22 40	22 49		23 22	23 36	00 02
Langley	d		20 25	→		20 50		21 23		21 54		22 24		22 55		23 26		00 06
Iver	d																	
West Drayton	d		20 29			20 56		21 27		21 58		22 29		22 59		23 30		00 11
Heathrow Terminal 4 ✈	d	20 07					21 07				22 07				23 07			
Heathrow Terminal 1-2 2 ✈	d	20 13					21 13				22 13				23 13			
Hayes & Harlington	d	20 19	20 33			21 01	21 19	21 31		22 01	22 19	22 33		23 03	23 19	23 35		00 17
Southall	d	20 22	20 37			21 06	21 22	21 34		22 05	22 22	22 37			23 22	23 39		00 20
Hanwell	d																	
Greenford ⊖	d																	
South Greenford	d																	
Castle Bar Park	d																	
Drayton Green	d																	
West Ealing	d																	
Ealing Broadway ⊖	d	20 27	20 42			21 11	21 27	21 41		22 12	22 27	22 42		23 11	23 27	23 44		00 27
Acton Main Line	d																	
London Paddington 15 ⊖	a	20 36	20 53		21 01	21 21	21 36	21 50	22 03	22 23	22 36	22 52	23 00	23 21	23 36	23 54	00 01	00 35

For non-stop services between London and Reading please see table 116

Passengers who hold valid tickets for Acton Main Line, West Ealing and Hanwell will be able to use local Transport for London (TFL) bus services to reach these stations. Tel 0843 222 1234

Table 118

London - Heathrow Airport

Mondays to Fridays

9 December to 16 May

Network Diagram - refer to first Page of Table 116

Miles			HC	HX	HX 1	HC	HX 1	HX	HX 1	HX	HX 1	HX	HX 1	HX	HX 1	HX		HX 1	HX	HX 1	HX	HX 1	HX	HX 1
0	London Paddington 15 ⊖	d	04 42		05 10	05 13	05 25		05 40		05 55		06 10		06 25		and at the same minutes past each hour until	20 40		20 55		21 10		21 25
14¾	Heathrow Terminal 1-2 2 ✈	a	05 04		05 26	05 35	05 40		05 55		06 10		06 25		06 40			20 55		21 10		21 25		21 40
—		d	05 05	05 16	05 29	05 36	05 41	05 44	05 56	06 03	06 11	06 18	06 26	06 33	06 41	06 48		20 56	21 03	21 11	21 18	21 26	21 33	21 41
—	Heathrow Terminal 4 ✈	a	05 10	05 20		05 41		05 48		06 07		06 22		06 37		06 52			21 07		21 22		21 37	
16¼	Heathrow Terminal 5 ✈	a			05 33		05 46		06 01		06 16		06 31		06 46			21 01		21 16		21 31		21 46

		HX		HX 1	HX	HX 1	HX	HX FO 1	HX FX	HC FX	HX FO	HX FO 1		HX FX	HX FX 1	HX FO	HX FO 1	HX	HX FX	HX FO 1	HX FX 1	HX		HX FO 1	HX FX
London Paddington 15 ⊖	d			21 40		21 55		22 10		22 07		22 25			22 25		22 40			22 55	22 55			23 10	
Heathrow Terminal 1-2 2 ✈	a			21 55		22 10		22 25		22 29		22 40			22 43		22 55			23 10	23 11			23 25	
	d	21 48		21 56	22 03	22 11	22 18	22 26	22 31	22 33	22 33	22 41		22 45	22 47	22 48	22 56	23 03	23 06	23 11	23 12	23 18		23 26	23 30
Heathrow Terminal 4 ✈	a	21 52			22 07		22 22		22 35		22 37			22 49		22 52		23 07				23 22			23 34
Heathrow Terminal 5 ✈	a			22 01		22 16		22 31		22 37		22 46			22 51		23 01		23 10	23 16	23 17			23 31	

		HX FO	HC FX	HC FO	HX FO 1	HX FX 1	HX
London Paddington 15 ⊖	d		23 07	23 03	23 25	23 25	
Heathrow Terminal 1-2 2 ✈	a		23 32	23 35	23 40	23 41	
	d	23 33	23 34	23 37	23 41	23 42	23 48
Heathrow Terminal 4 ✈	a	23 37	23 38	23 41			23 52
Heathrow Terminal 5 ✈	a				23 46	23 47	

Saturdays

14 December to 17 May

		HC	HX	HX 1	HC	HX 1	HX	HX 1	HX	HX 1	HX	HX 1	HX	HX 1	HX		HX 1	HX	HX 1	HX	HX 1	HX	HX 1	HX
London Paddington 15 ⊖	d	04 42		05 10	05 13	05 25		05 40		05 55		06 10		06 25		and at the same minutes past each hour until	10 40		10 55		11 10		11 25	
Heathrow Terminal 1-2 2 ✈	a	05 04		05 26	05 35	05 40		05 55		06 10		06 25		06 40			10 55		11 10		11 25		11 40	
	d	05 05	05 16	05 29	05 36	05 41	05 44	05 56	06 03	06 11	06 18	06 26	06 33	06 41	06 48		10 56	11 03	11 11	11 18	11 26	11 33	11 41	11 48
Heathrow Terminal 4 ✈	a	05 10	05 20		05 41		05 48		06 07		06 22		06 37		06 52			11 07		11 22		11 37		11 52
Heathrow Terminal 5 ✈	a			05 33		05 46		06 01		06 16		06 31		06 46			11 01		11 16		11 31		11 46	

			HX 1	HX	HX 1	HX	HX 1	HX	HX 1	HX	HX 1	HX	HX 1	HX	HX 1	HX	HX 1		HX	HX 1	HX	HX 1	HX	HX 1
London Paddington 15 ⊖	d		11 40		11 55		12 10		12 25		12 40		12 55		13 10		13 25	and at the same minutes past each hour until		21 40		21 55		22 10
Heathrow Terminal 1-2 2 ✈	a		11 55		12 10		12 25		12 40		12 55		13 10		13 25		13 40			21 55		22 10		22 25
	d		11 56	12 03	12 11	12 18	12 26	12 33	12 42	12 48	12 56	13 03	13 11	13 18	13 26	13 33	13 41		21 48	21 56	22 03	22 11	22 18	22 26
Heathrow Terminal 4 ✈	a			12 07		12 22		12 37		12 52		13 07		13 22		13 37			21 52		22 07		22 22	
Heathrow Terminal 5 ✈	a		12 01		12 16		12 31		12 46		13 01		13 16		13 31		13 46			22 01		22 16		22 31

		HX	HX 1		HX	HX 1	HX	HX 1	HX	HX 1	HX	HC	HX 1		HX
London Paddington 15 ⊖	d		22 25			22 40		22 55		23 10		23 03	23 25		
Heathrow Terminal 1-2 2 ✈	a		22 40			22 55		23 10		23 25		23 35	23 40		
	d	22 33	22 41		22 48	22 56	23 03	23 11	23 18	23 26	23 33	23 37	23 41		23 48
Heathrow Terminal 4 ✈	a	22 37			22 52		23 07		23 22		23 37	23 41			23 52
Heathrow Terminal 5 ✈	a		22 46			23 01		23 16		23 31			23 46		

Sundays

8 December to 11 May

		HX 1	HC	HX 1	HC	HX 1	HX	HX 1	HX	HX	HX	HC	HX 1	HX		HX 1	HX	HX 1	HX	HX 1	HX	HC	HX 1	HX
London Paddington 15 ⊖	d	05 10		05 25		05 40		05 55		06 10		06 12	06 25		and at the same minutes past each hour until	13 40		13 55		14 10		14 12	14 25	
Heathrow Terminal 1-2 2 ✈	a	05 26		05 41		05 56		06 11		06 26		06 34	06 41			13 56		14 11		14 26		14 34	14 41	
	d	05 27	05 36	05 42	05 47	05 59	06 01	06 13	06 19	06 31	06 33	06 37	06 47	06 49		13 59	14 01	14 13	14 19	14 31	14 33	14 37	14 47	14 49
Heathrow Terminal 4 ✈	a		05 40		05 51		06 05		06 23		06 37	06 41		06 53			14 05		14 23		14 37	14 41		14 53
Heathrow Terminal 5 ✈	a	05 32		05 47		06 03		06 17		06 35			06 51			14 03		14 17		14 35			14 51	

			HX 1	HX	HX 1	HX	HX 1	HX	HC	HX 1	HX		HX 1	HX	HX 1	HX	HX 1	HX	HC	HX 1	HX		HX 1 A
London Paddington 15 ⊖	d		14 40		14 55		15 10		15 12	15 25			15 40		15 55		16 10		16 12	16 25			16 40
Heathrow Terminal 1-2 2 ✈	a		14 56		15 12		15 26		15 34	15 41			15 56		16 11		16 26		16 34	16 41			16 56
	d		14 59	15 01	15 13	15 19	15 31	15 33	15 37	15 47	15 49		15 59	16 01	16 13	16 19	16 31	16 33	16 37	16 47	16 49		16 59
Heathrow Terminal 4 ✈	a			15 05		15 23		15 37	15 41		15 53			16 05		16 23		16 37	16 41		16 53		
Heathrow Terminal 5 ✈	a		15 03		15 17		15 35			15 51			16 03		16 17		16 35			16 51			17 03

		HX	HX 1	HX	HX	HX	HC	HX	HX	HX		HX	HX	HX	HX	HX	HC	HX	HX	HX		HX	HX	HX
London Paddington 15 ⊖	d		16 55		17 10		17 12	17 25		17 40	and at the same minutes past each hour until		21 55		22 10		22 12	22 25		22 40			22 55	
Heathrow Terminal 1-2 2 ✈	a		17 11		17 26		17 34	17 41		17 56			22 11		22 26		22 34	22 41		22 56			23 11	
	d	17 01	17 13	17 19	17 31	17 33	17 37	17 47	17 49	17 59		22 01	22 13	22 19	22 31	22 33	22 37	22 47	22 49	22 59		23 01	23 13	23 19
Heathrow Terminal 4 ✈	a	17 05		17 23		17 37	17 41		17 53			22 05		22 23		22 37	22 41		22 53			23 05		23 23
Heathrow Terminal 5 ✈	a		17 17		17 35			17 51		18 03			22 17		22 35			22 51		23 03			23 17	

A until 23 March

Table 118

Sundays

8 December to 11 May

Network Diagram - refer to first Page of Table 116

London - Heathrow Airport

	HX		HX	HC	HX	HX
London Paddington 15 ⊖ d	23 10			23 12	23 25	
Heathrow Terminal 1-2 2 ✈ a	23 26			23 34	23 41	
d	23 31		23 33	23 37	23 47	23 49
Heathrow Terminal 4 ✈ a			23 37	23 41		23 53
Heathrow Terminal 5 ✈ a	23 35				23 51	

Table 118R

Mondays to Fridays

9 December to 16 May

Network Diagram - refer to first Page of Table 116

Heathrow Airport - London

Miles		HC	HX	HC	HX	HX	HX		HC	HX	HX	HX	HX	HX	HX	HX	HX		HX	HX	HX	HX	HX	HX
			1		1		1				1		1		1		1			1		1		1
0	Heathrow Terminal 5 ✈ d		05 07		05 27		05 42				05 57		06 12		06 27		06 42			06 57		07 12		07 27
—	Heathrow Terminal 4 ✈ d	00 01		05 23		05 32			05 51	05 56		06 11		06 26		06 41			06 56		07 11		07 26	
1½	Heathrow Terminal 1-2 2 ✈ a	00 05	05 11	05 27	05 31	05 36	05 46		05 55	06 00	06 01	06 15	06 16	06 30	06 31	06 45	06 46		07 00	07 01	07 15	07 16	07 30	07 31
—	d	00 07	05 12	05 29	05 33		05 48		05 57		06 03		06 18		06 33		06 48			07 03		07 18		07 33
16¼	London Paddington 15 ⊖ a	00 30	05 28	05 56	05 49		06 04		06 24		06 19		06 34		06 49		07 05			07 19		07 35		07 49

	HX	HX	HX		HX	HX	HX	HX	HX	HX	HX	HX	HX		HX	HX	HX	HX	HX	HX	HX	HX	HX	
		1			1		1		1		1		1			1		1		1		1		
Heathrow Terminal 5 ✈ d		07 42			07 57		08 12		08 27		08 42		08 57			09 12		09 27		09 42		09 57		
Heathrow Terminal 4 ✈ d	07 41		07 56			08 11		08 26		08 41		08 56			09 11		09 26		09 41		09 56		10 11	
Heathrow Terminal 1-2 2 ✈ a	07 45	07 46	08 00		08 01	08 15	08 16	08 30	08 31	08 45	08 46	09 00	09 01		09 15	09 16	09 30	09 31	09 45	09 46	10 00	10 01	10 15	
d		07 48			08 03		08 18		08 33		08 48		09 03			09 18		09 33		09 48		10 03		
London Paddington 15 ⊖ a		08 04			08 19		08 35		08 49		09 04		09 19			09 35		09 49		10 05		10 19		

	HX	HX	HX	HX	HX	HX	HX	HX	HX		HX	HX	HX	HX	HX	HX	HX	HX	HX		HX	HX	HX	HX
	1		1		1		1		1			1		1		1		1			1		1	
Heathrow Terminal 5 ✈ d	10 12		10 27		10 42		10 57		11 12			11 27		11 42		11 57		12 12			12 27		12 42	
Heathrow Terminal 4 ✈ d		10 26		10 41		10 56		11 11			11 26		11 41		11 56		12 11		12 26			12 41		12 56
Heathrow Terminal 1-2 2 ✈ a	10 16	10 30	10 31	10 45	10 46	11 00	11 01	11 15	11 16		11 30	11 31	11 45	11 46	12 00	12 01	12 15	12 16	12 30		12 31	12 45	12 46	13 00
d	10 18		10 33		10 48		11 03		11 18			11 33		11 48		12 03		12 18			12 33		12 48	
London Paddington 15 ⊖ a	10 34		10 49		11 04		11 19		11 35			11 49		12 04		12 19		12 34			12 49		13 04	

	HX	HX	HX	HX	HX		HX	HX	HX	HX	HX	HX	HX	HX	HX		HX	HX	HX	HX	HX	HX	HX	HX
	1		1		1			1		1		1		1			1		1		1		1	
Heathrow Terminal 5 ✈ d	12 57		13 12		13 27			13 42		13 57		14 12		14 27			14 42		14 57		15 12		15 27	
Heathrow Terminal 4 ✈ d		13 11		13 26			13 41		13 56		14 11		14 26		14 41			14 56		15 11		15 26		15 41
Heathrow Terminal 1-2 2 ✈ a	13 01	13 15	13 16	13 30	13 31		13 45	13 46	14 00	14 01	14 15	14 16	14 30	14 31	14 45		14 46	15 00	15 01	15 15	15 16	15 30	15 31	15 45
d	13 03		13 18		13 33			13 48		14 03		14 18		14 33			14 48		15 03		15 18		15 33	
London Paddington 15 ⊖ a	13 19		13 35		13 49			14 04		14 19		14 35		14 49			15 04		15 19		15 35		15 49	

	HX	and at the same minutes past each hour until		HX	HX	HX	HX	HX	HX	HX	HX		HX	HX	HX	HX	HX	HX	HX	HX	HX		HX	HX
	1				1		1		1		1			1		1		1		1			1	
Heathrow Terminal 5 ✈ d	15 42				17 57		18 12		18 27		18 42			18 57		19 12		19 27		19 42			19 57	
Heathrow Terminal 4 ✈ d				17 56		18 11		18 26		18 41			18 56		19 11		19 26		19 41		19 56			20 11
Heathrow Terminal 1-2 2 ✈ a	15 46			18 00	18 01	18 15	18 16	18 30	18 31	18 45	18 46		19 00	19 01	19 15	19 16	19 30	19 31	19 45	19 46	20 00		20 01	20 15
d	15 48				18 03		18 18		18 33		18 48			19 03		19 18		19 33		19 48			20 03	
London Paddington 15 ⊖ a	16 05				18 19		18 35		18 49		19 05			19 19		19 35		19 49		20 04			20 19	

	HX	HX	HX	HX	HX	HX	HX		HX	HX	HX	HX	HX	HX	HX	HX	HX		HX FO	HX FX	HX FX	HX FO	HX FO	HC FX
	1		1		1		1			1		1		1		1			1	1			1	
Heathrow Terminal 5 ✈ d	20 12		20 27		20 42		20 57			21 12		21 27		21 42		21 57			22 12	22 12			22 27	22 33
Heathrow Terminal 4 ✈ d		20 26		20 41		20 56			21 11		21 26		21 41		21 56		22 11				22 25	22 26		
Heathrow Terminal 1-2 2 ✈ a	20 16	20 30	20 31	20 45	20 46	21 00	21 01		21 15	21 16	21 30	21 31	21 45	21 46	22 00	22 01	22 15		22 16	22 16	22 29	22 30	22 31	22 37
d	20 18		20 33		20 48		21 03			21 18		21 33		21 48		22 03			22 18	22 18			22 33	22 39
London Paddington 15 ⊖ a	20 34		20 49		21 04		21 19			21 34		21 49		22 04		22 19			22 34	22 36			22 49	23 02

	HX FX	HX FO	HX FO		HX FX	HX	HX FX	HX FO	HX	HX FO	HX FX	HX FX	HC FX		HX FO	HX FO	HX	HX	HX FO	HX FX				
			1		1			1		1	1					1		1						
Heathrow Terminal 5 ✈ d			22 42		22 42		22 57	22 57		23 12	23 12		23 24			23 27		23 42	23 53	23 54				
Heathrow Terminal 4 ✈ d	22 38	22 41				22 56			23 11			23 24			23 26		23 41							
Heathrow Terminal 1-2 2 ✈ a	22 42	22 45	22 46		22 47	23 00	23 01	23 01	23 15	23 16	23 16	23 28	23 28		23 30	23 31	23 45	23 46	23 57	23 58				
d			22 48		22 48			23 03		23 18	23 18		23 30			23 33		23 48						
London Paddington 15 ⊖ a			23 04		23 06			23 19		23 34	23 35		23 55			23 49		00 05						

Saturdays

14 December to 17 May

	HC	HX	HC	HX	HX	HX	HC	HX	HX	HX	HX	HX	HX	HX	HX	and at the same minutes past each hour until		HX	HX	HX	HX	HX	HX	HX
		1		1		1			1		1		1		1				1		1		1	
Heathrow Terminal 5 ✈ d		05 07		05 27		05 42			05 57		06 12		06 27		06 42				08 57		09 12		09 27	
Heathrow Terminal 4 ✈ d	00 01		05 23		05 32		05 51	05 56		06 11		06 26		06 41				08 56		09 11		09 26		09 41
Heathrow Terminal 1-2 2 ✈ a	00 05	05 11	05 27	05 31	05 36	05 46	05 55	06 00	06 01	06 15	06 16	06 30	06 31	06 45	06 46			09 00	09 01	09 15	09 16	09 30	09 31	09 45
d	00 07	05 12	05 29	05 33		05 48	05 57		06 03		06 18		06 33		06 48				09 03		09 18		09 33	
London Paddington 15 ⊖ a	00 30	05 28	05 56	05 49		06 04	06 24		06 19		06 34		06 49		07 04				09 19		09 34		09 49	

		HX 1		HX	HX 1	HX	HX 1	HX	HX 1	HX	HX 1	HX		HX 1	HX	HX 1	HX	HX 1	HX	HX 1	HX	HX 1		HX	HX 1
Heathrow Terminal 5	d	09 42			09 57		10 12		10 27		10 42			10 57		11 12		11 27		11 42		11 57			12 12
Heathrow Terminal 4	d			09 56		10 11		10 26		10 41		10 56			11 11		11 26		11 41		11 56			12 11	
Heathrow Terminal 1-2 2	a	09 46		10 00	10 01	10 15	10 16	10 30	10 31	10 45	10 46	11 00		11 01	11 15	11 16	11 30	11 31	11 45	11 46	12 00	12 01		12 15	12 16
	d	09 48			10 03		10 18		10 33		10 48			11 03		11 18		11 33		11 48		12 03			12 18
London Paddington 15	a	10 04			10 19		10 34		10 49		11 05			11 19		11 35		11 49		12 04		12 19			12 34

		HX	HX 1	HX	HX 1	HX	HX 1	HX		HX 1	HX	HX 1	HX	HX 1	HX	HX 1	HX	HX 1		HX	HX 1	HX	HX 1	HX	HX 1
Heathrow Terminal 5	d		12 27		12 42		12 57			13 12		13 27		13 42		13 57		14 12			14 27		14 42		14 57
Heathrow Terminal 4	d	12 26		12 41		12 56		13 11			13 26		13 41		13 56		14 11			14 26		14 41		14 56	
Heathrow Terminal 1-2 2	a	12 30	12 31	12 45	12 46	13 00	13 01	13 15		13 16	13 30	13 31	13 45	13 46	14 00	14 01	14 15	14 16		14 30	14 31	14 45	14 46	15 00	15 01
	d		12 33		12 48		13 03			13 18		13 33		13 48		14 03		14 18			14 33		14 48		15 03
London Paddington 15	a		12 49		13 04		13 19			13 35		13 49		14 04		14 19		14 34			14 49		15 04		15 19

Table 118R

Saturdays

14 December to 17 May

Network Diagram - refer to first Page of Table 116

Heathrow Airport - London

			HX	HX 1	HX	HX 1	HX	HX 1	HX	HX 1	HX		HX 1	HX	HX 1	HX	HX 1	HX	HX 1	HX	HX 1	and at the same minutes past each hour until			
Heathrow Terminal 5	d			15 12		15 27		15 42		15 57			16 12		16 27		16 42		16 57		17 12				
Heathrow Terminal 4	d		15 11		15 26		15 41		15 56		16 11			16 26		16 41		16 56		17 11					
Heathrow Terminal 1-2 2	a		15 15	15 16	15 30	15 31	15 45	15 46	16 00	16 01	16 15		16 16	16 30	16 31	16 45	16 46	17 00	17 01	17 15	17 16				
	d			15 18		15 33		15 48		16 03			16 18		16 33		16 48		17 03		17 18				
London Paddington 15	a			15 34		15 49		16 04		16 19			16 35		16 49		17 04		17 19		17 34				

		HX	HX 1	HX	HX 1	HX	HX 1	HX	HX 1		HX	HX 1	HX	HX 1	HX	HX 1	HX	HX 1	HX		HX 1	HX	HX 1	HX	HX 1
Heathrow Terminal 5	d		20 27		20 42		20 57		21 12			21 27		21 42		21 57		22 12			22 27		22 42		22 57
Heathrow Terminal 4	d	20 26		20 41		20 56		21 11			21 26		21 41		21 56		22 11		22 26			22 41		22 56	
Heathrow Terminal 1-2 2	a	20 30	20 31	20 45	20 46	21 00	21 01	21 15	21 16		21 30	21 31	21 45	21 46	22 00	22 01	22 15	22 16	22 30		22 31	22 45	22 46	23 00	23 01
	d		20 33		20 48		21 03		21 18			21 33		21 48		22 03		22 18			22 33		22 48		23 03
London Paddington 15	a		20 49		21 04		21 19		21 34			21 49		22 04		22 19		22 35			22 49		23 05		23 19

		HX	HX 1	HX	HX 1		HX	HX 1	HX
Heathrow Terminal 5	d		23 12		23 27			23 42	23 53
Heathrow Terminal 4	d	23 11		23 26			23 41		
Heathrow Terminal 1-2 2	a	23 15	23 16	23 30	23 31		23 45	23 46	23 57
	d		23 18		23 33			23 48	
London Paddington 15	a		23 34		23 49			00 04	

Sundays

8 December to 11 May

		HC	HX 1	and every 15 minutes until		HX 1		HX	HX 1	HC	HX	HX 1	HX	HX 1	HX	HX 1	and at the same minutes past each hour until		HX	HX 1	HC	HX	HX 1	HX	HX 1
Heathrow Terminal 5	d		05 03			05 48			06 03			06 18		06 33		06 48				22 03			22 18		22 33
Heathrow Terminal 4	d	00 01						05 53		06 07	06 13		06 25		06 41				21 53		22 07	22 13		22 25	
Heathrow Terminal 1-2 2	a	00 05	05 07			05 52		05 57	06 07	06 11	06 17	06 22	06 29	06 37	06 45	06 52			21 57	22 07	22 11	22 17	22 22	22 29	22 37
	d	00 07	05 08			05 53			06 08	06 13		06 23		06 38		06 53				22 08	22 13		22 23		22 38
London Paddington 15	a	00 30	05 24			06 09			06 24	06 36		06 39		06 54		07 09				22 24	22 36		22 39		22 54

		HX	HX 1		HX	HX 1 A	HX 1 B	HC	HX	HX 1	HX	HX 1	HX		HX 1	HX
Heathrow Terminal 5	d		22 48			23 03	23 03			23 18		23 33			23 48	23 58
Heathrow Terminal 4	d	22 41			22 53			23 07	23 13		23 25		23 41			
Heathrow Terminal 1-2 2	a	22 45	22 52		22 57	23 07	23 07	23 11	23 17	23 22	23 29	23 37	23 45		23 52	00 02
	d		22 53			23 08	23 08	23 13		23 23		23 38			23 53	
London Paddington 15	a		23 09			23 24	23 25	23 36		23 43		23 56			00 09	

A from 5 January

B until 29 December

Table 119

Slough - Windsor & Eton

Mondays to Fridays

9 December to 16 May

Network Diagram - refer to first Page of Table 116

Miles			GW 1	GW 1	GW 1	GW 1	GW 1	GW 1	GW 1	GW 1	GW 1		GW 1	GW 1	GW 1	GW 1	GW 1	GW 1	GW 1	GW 1	GW 1	and at the same minutes past each hour until		
0	Slough 3	d	05 38	05 58	06 18	06 37	06 55	07 13	07 31	07 54	08 13		08 31	08 54	09 14	09 33	09 53	10 11	10 30	10 50	11 10			
2¾	Windsor & Eton Central	a	05 44	06 04	06 24	06 43	07 01	07 19	07 37	08 00	08 19		08 37	09 00	09 20	09 39	09 59	10 17	10 36	10 56	11 16			

		GW 1	GW 1	GW 1		GW 1	GW 1	GW 1	GW 1	GW 1	GW 1	GW 1	GW 1	GW 1		GW 1	GW 1	GW 1	GW 1	GW 1	GW 1	and at the same minutes past each hour until		
Slough 3	d	14 30	14 50	15 10		15 30	15 50	16 21	16 43	17 01	17 21	17 40	17 58	18 16		18 40	18 58	19 16	19 40	20 00	20 20			
Windsor & Eton Central	a	14 36	14 56	15 16		15 36	15 56	16 27	16 49	17 07	17 27	17 46	18 04	18 22		18 46	19 04	19 22	19 46	20 06	20 26			

		GW 1	GW 1	GW 1
Slough 3	d	22 40	23 00	23 20
Windsor & Eton Central	a	22 46	23 06	23 26

Saturdays

14 December to 17 May

		GW 1	and every 30 minutes until	GW 1		GW 1	GW 1	GW 1	and at the same minutes past each hour until	GW 1	GW 1	GW 1			GW 1	and every 30 minutes until	GW 1		GW 1	and every 30 minutes until	GW 1
Slough 3	d	06 17		10 17		10 37	10 57	11 17		18 37	18 57	19 17			19 47		21 17		21 52		23 22
Windsor & Eton Central	a	06 23		10 23		10 43	11 03	11 23		18 43	19 03	19 23			19 53		21 23		21 58		23 28

		GW 1
Slough 3	d	23 56
Windsor & Eton Central	a	00 02

Sundays

8 December to 11 May

		GW 1	and every 30 minutes until	GW 1		GW 1	GW 1	GW 1	and at the same minutes past each hour until	GW 1	GW 1	GW 1		GW 1	GW 1	GW 1	GW 1	GW 1	GW 1	and every 30 minutes until	GW 1
Slough 3	d	08 22		09 52		10 12	10 32	10 52		18 12	18 32	18 52		19 23	19 52	20 23	20 52	21 23	21 52		23 22
Windsor & Eton Central	a	08 28		09 58		10 18	10 38	10 58		18 18	18 38	18 58		19 30	19 58	20 29	20 58	21 30	21 58		23 28

Table 119R

Windsor & Eton - Slough

Mondays to Fridays

9 December to 16 May

Network Diagram - refer to first Page of Table 116

Miles			GW 1	GW 1	GW 1	GW 1	GW 1	GW 1	GW 1	GW 1	GW 1	GW 1	GW 1	GW 1	GW 1	GW 1	GW 1	GW 1	GW 1	and at the same minutes past each hour until
0	Windsor & Eton Central	d	05 48	06 08	06 28	06 46	07 04	07 22	07 40	08 04	08 22	08 40	09 04	09 24	09 42	10 02	10 20	10 40	11 00	
2¾	Slough 3	a	05 54	06 14	06 34	06 52	07 10	07 28	07 46	08 10	08 28	08 46	09 10	09 30	09 48	10 08	10 26	10 46	11 06	

		GW 1	GW 1	GW 1	GW 1	GW 1	GW 1	GW 1	GW 1	GW 1	GW 1	GW 1	GW 1	GW 1	GW 1	GW 1	GW 1	and at the same minutes past each hour until	GW 1	GW 1	GW 1
Windsor & Eton Central	d	15 20	15 40	16 00	16 30	16 52	17 10	17 30	17 49	18 07	18 28	18 49	19 07	19 27	19 50	20 10	20 30		22 50	23 10	23 30
Slough 3	a	15 26	15 46	16 06	16 36	16 58	17 16	17 36	17 55	18 13	18 34	18 55	19 13	19 33	19 56	20 16	20 36		22 56	23 16	23 36

Saturdays

14 December to 17 May

		GW 1	and every 30 minutes until	GW 1	GW 1	GW 1	GW 1	and at the same minutes past each hour until	GW 1	GW 1	GW 1	GW 1	GW 1	GW 1	GW 1	GW 1	GW 1	GW 1	GW 1
Windsor & Eton Central	d	06 27		10 27	10 47	11 07	11 27		18 47	19 07	19 27	19 57	20 26	20 56	21 26	22 01	22 32	23 02	23 32
Slough 3	a	06 33		10 33	10 53	11 13	11 33		18 53	19 13	19 33	20 03	20 32	21 02	21 32	22 07	22 38	23 08	23 38

Sundays

8 December to 11 May

		GW 1	GW 1	and every 30 minutes until	GW 1	GW 1	GW 1	GW 1	and at the same minutes past each hour until	GW 1	GW 1	GW 1	GW 1	and every 30 minutes until	GW 1
Windsor & Eton Central	d	00 05	08 32		10 02	10 22	10 42	11 02		18 22	18 42	19 02	19 32		23 32
Slough 3	a	00 11	08 38		10 08	10 28	10 48	11 08		18 28	18 48	19 08	19 38		23 38

Table 120

Maidenhead - Marlow

Mondays to Fridays

9 December to 16 May

Network Diagram - refer to first Page of Table 116

Miles			GW MX 1	GW 1	GW 1	GW 1	GW 1	GW 1	GW 1	GW 1	GW 1		GW 1	GW 1	GW 1	GW 1	GW 1	GW 1	GW 1	GW 1	GW 1		GW 1	GW 1	GW 1
—	London Paddington 15 ⊖	d																							
0	**Maidenhead 3**	d		05 25	05 49		06 31		07 09		07 41			08 11		09 02	09 38	10 38	11 38	12 38	13 38		14 38	15 38	16 40
1¼	Furze Platt	d		05 29	05 53		06 35		07 13		07 45			08 15		09 06	09 42	10 42	11 42	12 42	13 42		14 42	15 42	16 44
3	Cookham	d		05 32							07 48			08 18		09 09	09 45	10 45	11 45	12 45	13 45		14 45	15 45	16 47
4½	Bourne End 3	a		05 36	06 01		06 43		07 21		07 52			08 22		09 13	09 49	10 49	11 49	12 49	13 49		14 49	15 49	16 51
—		d	00 04	05 40		06 18		06 49		07 28			07 57		08 25		09 53	10 53	11 53	12 53	13 53		14 53	15 53	16 55
7¼	**Marlow**	a	00 12	05 48		06 25		06 56		07 35			08 04		08 32		10 01	11 01	12 01	13 01	14 01		15 01	16 01	17 03

		GW 1	GW 1	GW 1	GW 1	GW 1	GW 1		GW 1	GW 1	GW 1	GW 1	GW 1	GW 1	GW 1
London Paddington 15 ⊖	d		17 42				18 42								
Maidenhead 3	d	17 47	18 14		18 47		19 17			19 49		20 42	21 40	22 50	23 49
Furze Platt	d	17 51	18 18		18 50		19 21			19 53		20 46	21 44	22 54	23 53
Cookham	d	17 54	18 22		18 54		19 25			19 56		20 49	21 47	22 57	23 56
Bourne End 3	a	17 58	18 28		18 58		19 29			20 00		20 53	21 51	23 01	23 59
	d	18 02		18 31		19 03			19 34		20 03	20 57	21 55	23 05	00 04
Marlow	a	18 10		18 38		19 10			19 41		20 10	21 05	22 03	23 13	00 12

Saturdays

14 December to 28 December

		GW 1	GW 1	GW 1	GW 1	GW 1	GW 1	GW 1	GW 1	GW 1		GW 1	GW 1	GW 1	GW 1	GW 1	GW 1	GW 1	GW 1	GW 1		GW 1
London Paddington 15 ⊖	d																					
Maidenhead 3	d		06 38	07 38	08 38	09 38	10 38	11 38	12 38	13 38		14 38	15 38	16 38	17 38	18 38	19 38	20 40	21 50	22 50		23 42
Furze Platt	d		06 42	07 42	08 42	09 42	10 42	11 42	12 42	13 42		14 42	15 42	16 42	17 42	18 42	19 42	20 44	21 54	22 54		23 46
Cookham	d		06 45	07 45	08 45	09 45	10 45	11 45	12 45	13 45		14 45	15 45	16 45	17 45	18 45	19 45	20 47	21 57	22 57		23 49
Bourne End 3	a		06 49	07 49	08 49	09 49	10 49	11 49	12 49	13 49		14 49	15 49	16 49	17 49	18 49	19 49	20 51	22 01	23 01		23 53
	d	00 04	06 53	07 53	08 53	09 53	10 53	11 53	12 53	13 53		14 53	15 53	16 53	17 53	18 53	19 53	20 55	22 05	23 05		23 58
Marlow	a	00 12	07 01	08 01	09 01	10 01	11 01	12 01	13 01	14 01		15 01	16 01	17 01	18 01	19 01	20 01	21 03	22 13	23 13		00 05

Saturdays

4 January to 8 February

		GW 1	GW 1	GW 1	GW 1	GW 1	GW 1	GW 1	GW 1	GW 1		GW 1	GW 1	GW 1	GW 1	GW 1	GW 1	GW 1	GW 1	GW 1		GW 1
London Paddington 15 ⊖	d																					
Maidenhead 3	d		06 38	07 46	08 46	09 46	10 49	11 46	12 47	13 46		14 46	15 46	16 46	17 46	18 46	19 46	20 46	21 50	22 50		23 42
Furze Platt	d		06 42	07 50	08 50	09 50	10 53	11 50	12 51	13 50		14 50	15 50	16 50	17 50	18 50	19 50	20 50	21 54	22 54		23 46
Cookham	d		06 45	07 53	08 53	09 53	10 56	11 53	12 54	13 53		14 53	15 53	16 53	17 53	18 53	19 53	20 53	21 57	22 57		23 49
Bourne End 3	a		06 49	07 57	08 57	09 57	11 00	11 57	12 58	13 57		14 57	15 57	16 57	17 57	18 57	19 57	20 57	22 01	23 01		23 53
	d	00 04	06 53	08 01	09 01	10 01	11 04	12 01	13 02	14 01		15 01	16 01	17 01	18 01	19 01	20 01	21 01	22 05	23 05		23 58
Marlow	a	00 12	07 01	08 09	09 09	10 09	11 12	12 09	13 10	14 09		15 09	16 09	17 09	18 09	19 09	20 09	21 09	22 13	23 13		00 05

Saturdays

15 February to 17 May

		GW 1	GW 1	GW 1	GW 1	GW 1	GW 1	GW 1	GW 1	GW 1		GW 1	GW 1	GW 1	GW 1	GW 1	GW 1	GW 1	GW 1	GW 1		GW 1
London Paddington 15 ⊖	d																					
Maidenhead 3	d		06 38	07 38	08 38	09 38	10 38	11 38	12 38	13 38		14 38	15 38	16 38	17 38	18 38	19 38	20 40	21 50	22 50		23 42
Furze Platt	d		06 42	07 42	08 42	09 42	10 42	11 42	12 42	13 42		14 42	15 42	16 42	17 42	18 42	19 42	20 44	21 54	22 54		23 46
Cookham	d		06 45	07 45	08 45	09 45	10 45	11 45	12 45	13 45		14 45	15 45	16 45	17 45	18 45	19 45	20 47	21 57	22 57		23 49
Bourne End 3	a		06 49	07 49	08 49	09 49	10 49	11 49	12 49	13 49		14 49	15 49	16 49	17 49	18 49	19 49	20 51	22 01	23 01		23 53
	d	00 04	06 53	07 53	08 53	09 53	10 53	11 53	12 53	13 53		14 53	15 53	16 53	17 53	18 53	19 53	20 55	22 05	23 05		23 58
Marlow	a	00 12	07 01	08 01	09 01	10 01	11 01	12 01	13 01	14 01		15 01	16 01	17 01	18 01	19 01	20 01	21 03	22 13	23 13		00 05

Sundays

8 December to 11 May

		GW 1	GW 1	GW 1	GW 1	GW 1	GW 1	GW 1	GW 1	GW 1		GW 1	GW 1	GW 1	GW 1 A	GW 1 B	GW 1
London Paddington 15 ⊖	d																
Maidenhead 3	d	08 35	09 35	10 35	11 35	12 35	13 35	14 35	15 35	16 35		17 35	18 35	19 35	20 35	20 36	21 45
Furze Platt	d	08 39	09 39	10 39	11 39	12 39	13 39	14 39	15 39	16 39		17 39	18 39	19 39	20 39	20 40	21 49
Cookham	d	08 42	09 42	10 42	11 42	12 42	13 42	14 42	15 42	16 42		17 42	18 42	19 42	20 42	20 43	21 52
Bourne End 3	a	08 47	09 47	10 47	11 47	12 47	13 47	14 47	15 47	16 47		17 47	18 47	19 47	20 47	20 48	21 57
	d	08 51	09 51	10 51	11 51	12 51	13 51	14 51	15 51	16 51		17 51	18 51	19 51	20 51	20 52	22 01
Marlow	a	08 58	09 58	10 58	11 58	12 58	13 58	14 58	15 58	16 58		17 58	18 58	19 58	20 58	20 59	22 08

A until 9 February

B from 16 February

Table 120R

Mondays to Fridays

9 December to 16 May

Network Diagram - refer to first Page of Table 116

Marlow - Maidenhead

Miles			GW MX 1	GW 1	GW 1	GW 1	GW 1	GW 1	GW 1	GW 1	GW 1	GW 1	GW 1	GW 1	GW 1	GW 1	GW 1	GW 1	GW 1	GW 1	GW 1	GW 1	GW 1
0	**Marlow**	d	00 15	06 04		06 38		07 17		07 46		08 15		08 35		10 05	11 06	12 06	13 06	14 06	15 06	16 06	17 06
2¾	Bourne End 3	a	00 22	06 11		06 45		07 24		07 53		08 22		08 42		10 12	11 13	12 13	13 13	14 13	15 13	16 13	17 13
—		d	00 26		06 14		06 48		07 27		07 56		08 28	08 46	09 17	10 16	11 17	12 17	13 17	14 17	15 17	16 17	17 17
4¼	Cookham	d	00 30		06 17		06 51		07 30		07 59		08 31	08 50	09 20	10 20	11 21	12 21	13 21	14 21	15 21	16 21	17 21
6	Furze Platt	d	00 33		06 21		06 55		07 34		08 03		08 35	08 53	09 24	10 23	11 24	12 24	13 24	14 24	15 24	16 24	17 24
7¼	**Maidenhead** 3	a	00 38		06 25		06 59		07 38		08 07		08 39	08 58	09 28	10 28	11 29	12 29	13 29	14 29	15 29	16 29	17 29
—	London Paddington 15 ⊖	a							08 21				09 21										

		GW 1	GW 1	GW 1	GW 1	GW 1	GW 1	GW 1	GW 1	GW 1	GW 1	GW 1	GW 1
Marlow	d	18 21		18 52		19 24		19 53		20 15	21 08	22 06	23 16
Bourne End 3	a	18 28		18 59		19 31		20 00		20 22	21 15	22 13	23 23
	d		18 31		19 02		19 34		20 05	20 26	21 19	22 17	23 27
Cookham	d		18 34		19 05		19 37		20 08	20 30	21 23	22 21	23 31
Furze Platt	d		18 37		19 08		19 40		20 12	20 33	21 26	22 24	23 34
Maidenhead 3	a		18 42		19 13		19 45		20 16	20 38	21 31	22 29	23 39
London Paddington 15 ⊖	a												

Saturdays

14 December to 28 December

		GW 1	GW 1	GW 1	GW 1	GW 1	GW 1	GW 1	GW 1	GW 1	GW 1	GW 1	GW 1	GW 1	GW 1	GW 1	GW 1	GW 1	GW 1
Marlow	d	00 15	07 06	08 06	09 06	10 06	11 06	12 06	13 06	14 06	15 06	16 06	17 06	18 06	19 06	20 06	21 06	22 16	23 16
Bourne End 3	a	00 22	07 13	08 13	09 13	10 13	11 13	12 13	13 13	14 13	15 13	16 13	17 13	18 13	19 13	20 13	21 13	22 23	23 23
	d	00 26	07 17	08 17	09 17	10 17	11 17	12 17	13 17	14 17	15 17	16 17	17 17	18 17	19 17	20 17	21 17	22 27	23 27
Cookham	d	00 30	07 21	08 21	09 21	10 21	11 21	12 21	13 21	14 21	15 21	16 21	17 21	18 21	19 21	20 21	21 21	22 31	23 31
Furze Platt	d	00 33	07 24	08 24	09 24	10 24	11 24	12 24	13 24	14 24	15 24	16 24	17 24	18 24	19 24	20 24	21 24	22 34	23 34
Maidenhead 3	a	00 38	07 29	08 29	09 29	10 29	11 29	12 29	13 29	14 29	15 29	16 29	17 29	18 29	19 29	20 29	21 29	22 39	23 39
London Paddington 15 ⊖	a																		

Saturdays

4 January to 8 February

		GW 1	GW 1	GW 1	GW 1	GW 1	GW 1	GW 1	GW 1	GW 1	GW 1	GW 1	GW 1	GW 1	GW 1	GW 1	GW 1	GW 1	GW 1
Marlow	d	00 15	07 06	08 13	09 13	10 13	11 15	12 13	13 13	14 13	15 13	16 13	17 13	18 13	19 13	20 13	21 13	22 16	23 16
Bourne End 3	a	00 22	07 13	08 20	09 20	10 20	11 22	12 20	13 20	14 20	15 20	16 20	17 20	18 20	19 20	20 20	21 20	22 23	23 23
	d	00 26	07 17	08 24	09 24	10 24	11 26	12 24	13 24	14 24	15 24	16 24	17 24	18 24	19 24	20 24	21 24	22 27	23 27
Cookham	d	00 30	07 21	08 28	09 28	10 28	11 30	12 28	13 28	14 28	15 28	16 28	17 28	18 28	19 28	20 28	21 28	22 31	23 31
Furze Platt	d	00 33	07 24	08 31	09 31	10 31	11 33	12 31	13 31	14 31	15 31	16 31	17 31	18 31	19 31	20 31	21 31	22 34	23 34
Maidenhead 3	a	00 38	07 29	08 36	09 36	10 36	11 38	12 36	13 36	14 36	15 36	16 36	17 36	18 36	19 36	20 36	21 36	22 39	23 39
London Paddington 15 ⊖	a																		

Saturdays

15 February to 17 May

		GW 1	GW 1	GW 1	GW 1	GW 1	GW 1	GW 1	GW 1	GW 1	GW 1	GW 1	GW 1	GW 1	GW 1	GW 1	GW 1	GW 1	GW 1
Marlow	d	00 15	07 06	08 06	09 06	10 06	11 06	12 06	13 06	14 06	15 06	16 06	17 06	18 06	19 06	20 06	21 06	22 16	23 16
Bourne End 3	a	00 22	07 13	08 13	09 13	10 13	11 13	12 13	13 13	14 13	15 13	16 13	17 13	18 13	19 13	20 13	21 13	22 23	23 23
	d	00 26	07 17	08 17	09 17	10 17	11 17	12 17	13 17	14 17	15 17	16 17	17 17	18 17	19 17	20 17	21 17	22 27	23 27
Cookham	d	00 30	07 21	08 21	09 21	10 21	11 21	12 21	13 21	14 21	15 21	16 21	17 21	18 21	19 21	20 21	21 21	22 31	23 31
Furze Platt	d	00 33	07 24	08 24	09 24	10 24	11 24	12 24	13 24	14 24	15 24	16 24	17 24	18 24	19 24	20 24	21 24	22 34	23 34
Maidenhead 3	a	00 38	07 29	08 29	09 29	10 29	11 29	12 29	13 29	14 29	15 29	16 29	17 29	18 29	19 29	20 29	21 29	22 39	23 39
London Paddington 15 ⊖	a																		

Sundays

8 December to 11 May

		GW 1	GW 1	GW 1	GW 1	GW 1	GW 1	GW 1	GW 1	GW 1	GW 1	GW 1	GW 1	GW 1	GW 1 A	GW 1 B	GW 1
Marlow	d	00 08	09 01	10 01	11 01	12 01	13 01	14 01	15 01	16 01	17 01	18 01	19 01	20 01	21 01	21 02	22 11
Bourne End 3	a	00 15	09 08	10 08	11 08	12 08	13 08	14 08	15 08	16 08	17 08	18 08	19 08	20 08	21 08	21 09	22 18
	d	00 19	09 12	10 12	11 12	12 12	13 12	14 12	15 12	16 12	17 12	18 12	19 12	20 12	21 12	21 13	22 22
Cookham	d	00 23	09 16	10 16	11 16	12 16	13 16	14 16	15 16	16 16	17 16	18 16	19 16	20 16	21 16	21 17	22 25
Furze Platt	d	00 26	09 20	10 20	11 20	12 20	13 20	14 20	15 20	16 20	17 20	18 20	19 20	20 20	21 20	21 21	22 29
Maidenhead 3	a	00 31	09 24	10 24	11 24	12 24	13 24	14 24	15 24	16 24	17 24	18 24	19 24	20 24	21 24	21 25	22 33
London Paddington 15 ⊖	a																

A until 9 February

B from 16 February

Table 121

Twyford - Henley-on-Thames

Mondays to Fridays

9 December to 16 May

Network Diagram - refer to first Page of Table 116

Miles			GW 1	GW 1	GW 1	GW 1	GW 1	GW 1	GW 1	GW 1	GW 1	GW 1	GW 1	GW 1	GW 1	GW 1	GW 1	GW 1	GW 1	GW 1	GW 1	GW 1	GW 1
—	London Paddington 15 ⊖	d																			17 12		18 12
—	Reading 7	d					08 04																
0	**Twyford 3**	d	05 42	06 21	06 50	07 25	08 12	08 45	09 21	09 53	10 36	11 21	12 06	12 51	13 36	14 21	15 06	15 48	16 48	17 31	17 58	18 31	18 58
1¾	Wargrave	d	05 46	06 25	06 54	07 29	08 17	08 49	09 25	09 57	10 40	11 25	12 10	12 55	13 40	14 25	15 10	15 52	16 52	17 35	18 03	18 35	19 03
2¾	Shiplake	d	05 49	06 28	06 57	07 32	08 20	08 52	09 28	10 00	10 43	11 28	12 13	12 58	13 43	14 28	15 13	15 55	16 55	17 38	18 06	18 38	19 06
4½	**Henley-on-Thames**	a	05 54	06 33	07 02	07 37	08 24	08 57	09 33	10 05	10 48	11 33	12 18	13 03	13 48	14 33	15 18	16 00	17 00	17 43	18 13	18 43	19 13

		GW 1	GW 1	GW 1	GW 1	GW 1	GW 1
London Paddington 15 ⊖	d	19 05					
Reading 7	d						
Twyford 3	d	19 38	20 09	20 47	21 50	22 40	23 37
Wargrave	d	19 42	20 13	20 51	21 54	22 44	23 41
Shiplake	d	19 45	20 16	20 54	21 57	22 47	23 44
Henley-on-Thames	a	19 52	20 21	20 59	22 02	22 52	23 49

Saturdays

14 December to 28 December

		GW 1	GW 1		GW 1	GW 1
London Paddington 15 ⊖	d			and hourly until		
Reading 7	d					
Twyford 3	d	06 57	07 50		22 50	23 40
Wargrave	d	07 01	07 54		22 54	23 44
Shiplake	d	07 04	07 57		22 57	23 47
Henley-on-Thames	a	07 09	08 02		23 02	23 52

Saturdays

4 January to 8 February

		GW 1	GW 1	GW 1	GW 1	GW 1	GW 1		GW 1	GW 1	GW 1	GW 1	GW 1	GW 1	GW 1	GW 1	GW 1	GW 1
London Paddington 15 ⊖	d							and hourly until										
Reading 7	d																	
Twyford 3	d	06 57	07 53	08 54	09 53	10 53	11 55		14 55	15 53	16 55	17 54	18 54	19 53	20 53	21 54	22 50	23 40
Wargrave	d	07 01	07 57	08 58	09 57	10 57	11 59		14 59	15 57	16 59	17 58	18 58	19 57	20 57	21 58	22 54	23 44
Shiplake	d	07 04	08 00	09 01	10 00	11 00	12 02		15 02	16 00	17 02	18 01	19 01	20 00	21 00	22 01	22 57	23 47
Henley-on-Thames	a	07 09	08 05	09 06	10 05	11 05	12 07		15 07	16 05	17 07	18 06	19 06	20 05	21 05	22 06	23 02	23 52

Saturdays

15 February to 17 May

		GW 1	GW 1		GW 1	GW 1
London Paddington 15 ⊖	d			and hourly until		
Reading 7	d					
Twyford 3	d	06 57	07 50		22 50	23 40
Wargrave	d	07 01	07 54		22 54	23 44
Shiplake	d	07 04	07 57		22 57	23 47
Henley-on-Thames	a	07 09	08 02		23 02	23 52

Sundays

8 December to 11 May

		GW 1		GW 1
London Paddington 15 ⊖	d		and hourly until	
Reading 7	d			
Twyford 3	d	09 43		21 43
Wargrave	d	09 47		21 47
Shiplake	d	09 50		21 50
Henley-on-Thames	a	09 55		21 55

Table 121R

Henley-on-Thames - Twyford

Mondays to Fridays

9 December to 16 May

Network Diagram - refer to first Page of Table 116

Miles			GW 1	GW 1	GW 1 A	GW 1 B	GW 1	GW 1	GW 1	GW 1	GW 1	GW 1	GW 1	GW 1	GW 1	GW 1	GW 1
0	**Henley-on-Thames**	d	06 06	06 36	07 07	07 09	07 42	08 27	09 01	09 36	10 09	10 54	11 39	12 24	13 09	13 54	14 39
1¾	Shiplake	d	06 10	06 40	07 11	07 13	07 46	08 31	09 05	09 40	10 13	10 58	11 43	12 28	13 13	13 58	14 43
2¾	Wargrave	d	06 13	06 43	07 14	07 16	07 49	08 34	09 08	09 43	10 16	11 01	11 46	12 31	13 16	14 01	14 46
4½	**Twyford** 3	a	06 18	06 48	07 19	07 21	07 54	08 39	09 13	09 48	10 21	11 06	11 51	12 36	13 21	14 06	14 51
—	Reading 7	a															
—	London Paddington 15 ⊖	a			07 57	08 02	08 28										

		GW 1	GW 1	GW 1	GW 1	GW 1	GW 1
Henley-on-Thames	d	15 24	16 20	17 09	17 46	18 17	18 46
Shiplake	d	15 28	16 24	17 13	17 50	18 21	18 50
Wargrave	d	15 31	16 27	17 16	17 53	18 24	18 53
Twyford 3	a	15 36	16 32	17 21	17 58	18 29	18 58
Reading 7	a						
London Paddington 15 ⊖	a						

		GW 1	GW 1	GW 1	GW 1	GW 1	GW 1	GW 1
Henley-on-Thames	d	19 18	19 55	20 24	21 02	22 06	23 03	23 53
Shiplake	d	19 22	19 59	20 28	21 06	22 10	23 07	23 57
Wargrave	d	19 25	20 02	20 31	21 09	22 13	23 10	23 59
Twyford 3	a	19 30	20 07	20 36	21 14	22 18	23 15	00 05
Reading 7	a							00 16
London Paddington 15 ⊖	a							

Saturdays

14 December to 28 December

		GW 1		GW 1	GW 1	GW 1	GW 1
Henley-on-Thames	d	07 24	and hourly until	21 24	22 21	23 11	23 55
Shiplake	d	07 28		21 28	22 25	23 15	23 59
Wargrave	d	07 31		21 31	22 28	23 18	00 02
Twyford 3	a	07 36		21 36	22 33	23 23	00 07
Reading 7	a						
London Paddington 15 ⊖	a						

Saturdays

4 January to 8 February

		GW 1	GW 1	GW 1	GW 1	GW 1	GW 1	GW 1		GW 1	GW 1	GW 1	GW 1	GW 1
Henley-on-Thames	d	07 19	08 18	09 22	10 21	11 18	12 19	13 18	and hourly until	20 18	21 22	22 21	23 06	23 55
Shiplake	d	07 23	08 22	09 26	10 25	11 22	12 23	13 22		20 22	21 26	22 25	23 10	23 59
Wargrave	d	07 26	08 25	09 29	10 28	11 25	12 26	13 25		20 25	21 29	22 28	23 13	00 02
Twyford 3	a	07 31	08 30	09 34	10 33	11 30	12 31	13 30		20 30	21 34	22 33	23 18	00 07
Reading 7	a													
London Paddington 15 ⊖	a													

Saturdays

15 February to 17 May

		GW 1		GW 1	GW 1	GW 1	GW 1
Henley-on-Thames	d	07 24	and hourly until	21 24	22 21	23 11	23 55
Shiplake	d	07 28		21 28	22 25	23 15	23 59
Wargrave	d	07 31		21 31	22 28	23 18	00 02
Twyford 3	a	07 36		21 36	22 33	23 23	00 07
Reading 7	a						
London Paddington 15 ⊖	a						

Sundays

8 December to 11 May

		GW 1 C	GW 1		GW 1
Henley-on-Thames	d		10 07	and hourly until	22 07
Shiplake	d		10 11		22 11
Wargrave	d	00 02	10 14		22 14
Twyford 3	a	00 07	10 19		22 19
Reading 7	a				
London Paddington 15 ⊖	a				

A from 24 March

B until 21 March

C not 8 December

Table 122

Reading - Basingstoke

Mondays to Fridays

9 December to 16 May

Network Diagram - refer to first Page of Table 116

Miles			GW	GW	GW	GW	GW	XC ◇1 🛒	GW	XC ◇1	GW		XC ◇1 🛒	GW	GW	XC ◇1 🛒	GW	XC ◇1 🛒	GW	XC ◇1 🛒	GW		GW	XC ◇1 🛒	GW
0	**Reading 7**	d	05 39	06 05	06 39	07 07	07 37	07 46	08 08	08 18	08 38		08 46	09 05	09 39	09 46	10 07	10 16	10 40	10 46	11 07		11 39	11 46	12 07
1	Reading West	d	05 42	06 08	06 42	07 10	07 40		08 11		08 41			09 08	09 42		10 10		10 43		11 10		11 42		12 10
7¼	Mortimer	d	05 50	06 16	06 50	07 18	07 48		08 19		08 49			09 16	09 50		10 18		10 51		11 18		11 50		12 18
10½	Bramley (Hants)	d	05 55	06 21	06 55	07 23	07 53		08 24		08 54			09 21	09 55		10 23		10 56		11 23		11 55		12 23
15½	**Basingstoke**	a	06 04	06 30	07 04	07 32	08 02	08 08	08 33	08 40	09 03		09 09	09 30	10 04	10 08	10 32	10 38	11 05	11 08	11 32		12 04	12 08	12 32

		XC ◇1 🛒	GW	XC ◇1 🛒	GW	GW	XC ◇1 🛒		GW	XC ◇1 🛒	GW	XC ◇1 🛒	GW	GW	XC ◇1 🛒	GW	XC ◇1 🛒		GW	XC ◇1 🛒	GW	GW	XC ◇1 🛒	GW	GW
Reading 7	d	12 16	12 40	12 45	13 07	13 39	13 46		14 07	14 16	14 39	14 46	15 07	15 39	15 46	16 07	16 16		16 36	16 45	17 07	17 33	17 46	18 07	18 34
Reading West	d		12 43		13 10	13 42			14 10		14 42		15 10	15 42		16 10			16 39		17 10	17 36		18 10	18 37
Mortimer	d		12 51		13 18	13 50			14 18		14 50		15 18	15 50		16 18			16 47		17 18	17 44		18 18	18 45
Bramley (Hants)	d		12 56		13 23	13 55			14 23		14 55		15 23	15 55		16 23			16 52		17 23	17 49		18 23	18 50
Basingstoke	a	12 39	13 05	13 08	13 32	14 03	14 08		14 32	14 39	15 04	15 08	15 32	16 04	16 08	16 32	16 39		17 01	17 08	17 32	17 58	18 08	18 32	18 59

		XC ◇1 🛒	GW		GW	XC ◇1 🛒	GW	GW	XC ◇1	GW 1	GW 1	XC ◇1	GW 1		XC ◇1	XC ◇1	GW 1	GW 1
Reading 7	d	18 46	19 07		19 38	19 47	20 07	20 37	20 46	21 07	21 39	21 46	22 10		22 22	22 48	22 55	23 34
Reading West	d		19 10		19 41		20 10	20 40		21 10	21 42		22 13				22 58	23 37
Mortimer	d		19 18		19 49		20 18	20 48		21 18	21 50		22 21				23 06	23 45
Bramley (Hants)	d		19 23		19 54		20 23	20 53		21 23	21 55		22 26				23 11	23 50
Basingstoke	a	19 08	19 32		20 03	20 09	20 32	21 02	21 09	21 31	22 03	22 09	22 34		22 39	23 05	23 19	23 58

Saturdays

14 December to 28 December

		GW 1	GW 1	GW 1	GW 1	XC ◇1 🛒	GW 1	XC ◇1	GW 1	XC ◇1 🛒		GW 1	GW 1	XC ◇1 🛒	GW 1	XC ◇1 🛒	GW 1	XC ◇1 🛒	GW 1	GW 1		XC ◇1 🛒	GW 1	XC ◇1 🛒	GW 1
Reading 7	d	06 07	06 39	07 07	07 39	07 46	08 07	08 16	08 39	08 46		09 07	09 39	09 46	10 07	10 18	10 39	10 46	11 07	11 39		11 46	12 07	12 16	12 39
Reading West	d	06 10	06 42	07 10	07 42		08 10		08 42			09 10	09 42		10 10		10 42		11 10	11 42			12 10		12 42
Mortimer	d	06 18	06 50	07 18	07 50		08 18		08 50			09 18	09 50		10 18		10 50		11 18	11 50			12 18		12 50
Bramley (Hants)	d	06 23	06 55	07 23	07 55		08 23		08 55			09 23	09 55		10 23		10 55		11 23	11 55			12 23		12 55
Basingstoke	a	06 32	07 03	07 32	08 03	08 08	08 31	08 40	09 04	09 08		09 31	10 04	10 08	10 31	10 39	11 03	11 08	11 31	12 03		12 08	12 31	12 40	13 04

		XC ◇1 🛒	GW 1	GW 1	XC ◇1 🛒	GW 1		XC ◇1 🛒	GW 1	XC ◇1 🛒	GW 1	GW 1	XC ◇1 🛒	GW 1	XC ◇1 🛒	GW 1		XC ◇1 🛒	GW 1	GW 1	XC ◇1 🛒	GW 1	XC ◇1 🛒	GW 1	XC ◇1 🛒
Reading 7	d	12 46	13 07	13 39	13 46	14 07		14 16	14 39	14 46	15 07	15 39	15 46	16 07	16 15	16 39		16 46	17 07	17 39	17 45	18 07	18 15	18 39	18 45
Reading West	d		13 10	13 42		14 10			14 42		15 10	15 42		16 10		16 42			17 10	17 42		18 10		18 42	
Mortimer	d		13 18	13 50		14 18			14 50		15 18	15 50		16 18		16 50			17 18	17 50		18 18		18 50	
Bramley (Hants)	d		13 23	13 55		14 23			14 55		15 23	15 55		16 23		16 55			17 23	17 55		18 23		18 55	
Basingstoke	a	13 08	13 31	14 03	14 08	14 31		14 40	15 03	15 08	15 31	16 03	16 08	16 31	16 40	17 03		17 08	17 31	18 03	18 08	18 31	18 40	19 03	19 08

		GW 1		GW 1	XC ◇1 🛒	GW 1	GW 1	XC ◇1	GW 1	GW 1	XC ◇1	GW 1		GW 1	XC ◇1	GW 1
Reading 7	d	19 07		19 39	19 46	20 07	20 39	20 46	21 07	21 39	21 45	22 07		22 39	22 49	23 07
Reading West	d	19 10		19 42		20 10	20 42		21 10	21 42		22 10		22 42		23 10
Mortimer	d	19 18		19 50		20 18	20 50		21 18	21 50		22 18		22 50		23 18
Bramley (Hants)	d	19 23		19 55		20 23	20 55		21 23	21 55		22 23		22 55		23 23
Basingstoke	a	19 31		20 03	20 08	20 31	21 03	21 08	21 31	22 03	22 09	22 31		23 03	23 07	23 31

Saturdays

4 January to 8 February

		GW 1	GW 1	GW 1	GW 1	XC ◇1 🛒	GW 1	XC ◇1	GW 1	XC ◇1 🛒		GW 1	GW 1	XC ◇1 🛒	GW 1	XC ◇1 🛒	GW 1	XC ◇1 🛒	GW 1	GW 1		XC ◇1 🛒	GW 1	XC ◇1 🛒	GW 1
Reading 7	d	06 07	06 39	07 07	07 39	07 46	08 07	08 16	08 39	08 46		09 07	09 39	09 46	10 07	10 18	10 39	10 46	11 07	11 39		11 46	12 07	12 16	12 39
Reading West	d	06 10	06 42	07 10	07 42		08 10		08 42			09 10	09 42		10 10		10 42		11 10	11 42			12 10		12 42
Mortimer	d	06 18	06 50	07 18	07 50		08 18		08 50			09 18	09 50		10 18		10 50		11 18	11 50			12 18		12 50
Bramley (Hants)	d	06 23	06 55	07 23	07 55		08 23		08 55			09 23	09 55		10 23		10 55		11 23	11 55			12 23		12 55
Basingstoke	a	06 32	07 03	07 32	08 03	08 08	08 31	08 40	09 04	09 08		09 31	10 04	10 08	10 31	10 39	11 03	11 08	11 31	12 03		12 08	12 31	12 40	13 04

		XC ◇1 🛒	GW 1	GW 1	XC ◇1 🛒	GW 1		XC ◇1 🛒	GW 1	XC ◇1 🛒	GW 1	GW 1	XC ◇1 🛒	GW 1	XC ◇1 🛒	GW 1		XC ◇1 🛒	GW 1	GW 1	XC ◇1 🛒	GW 1	XC ◇1 🛒	GW 1	XC ◇1 🛒
Reading 7	d	12 46	13 07	13 39	13 46	14 07		14 16	14 39	14 46	15 07	15 39	15 46	16 07	16 16	16 39		16 46	17 07	17 39	17 45	18 07	18 15	18 39	18 45
Reading West	d		13 10	13 42		14 10			14 42		15 10	15 42		16 10		16 42			17 10	17 42		18 10		18 42	
Mortimer	d		13 18	13 50		14 18			14 50		15 18	15 50		16 18		16 50			17 18	17 50		18 18		18 50	
Bramley (Hants)	d		13 23	13 55		14 23			14 55		15 23	15 55		16 23		16 55			17 23	17 55		18 23		18 55	
Basingstoke	a	13 08	13 31	14 03	14 08	14 31		14 40	15 03	15 08	15 31	16 03	16 08	16 31	16 40	17 03		17 08	17 31	18 03	18 08	18 31	18 40	19 03	19 08

Table 122

Reading - Basingstoke

Saturdays

4 January to 8 February

Network Diagram - refer to first Page of Table 116

		GW	GW	XC	GW	GW	XC		GW	GW	XC	GW	GW	XC	GW
		■1	■1	◇■1 🛒	■1	■1	◇■1		■1	■1	◇■1	■1	■1	◇■1	■1
Reading ■7	d	19 07	19 39	19 46	20 07	20 39	20 46		21 07	21 39	21 45	22 07	22 39	22 53	23 07
Reading West	d	19 10	19 42		20 10	20 42			21 10	21 42		22 10	22 42		23 10
Mortimer	d	19 18	19 50		20 18	20 50			21 18	21 50		22 18	22 50		23 18
Bramley (Hants)	d	19 23	19 55		20 23	20 55			21 23	21 55		22 23	22 55		23 23
Basingstoke	a	19 31	20 03	20 08	20 31	21 03	21 08		21 31	22 03	22 09	22 31	23 03	23 12	23 31

Saturdays

15 February to 22 March

		GW	GW	GW	GW	XC	GW	XC	GW	XC		GW	GW	XC	GW	XC	GW	XC	GW	GW		XC	GW	XC	GW
		■1	■1	■1	■1	◇■1 🛒	■1	◇■1	■1	◇■1 🛒		■1	■1	◇■1 🛒	■1	◇■1 🛒	■1	◇■1 🛒	■1	■1		◇■1 🛒	■1	◇■1 🛒	■1
Reading ■7	d	06 07	06 39	07 07	07 39	07 46	08 07	08 16	08 39	08 46		09 07	09 39	09 46	10 07	10 18	10 39	10 46	11 07	11 39		11 46	12 07	12 16	12 39
Reading West	d	06 10	06 42	07 10	07 42		08 10		08 42			09 10	09 42		10 10		10 42		11 10	11 42			12 10		12 42
Mortimer	d	06 18	06 50	07 18	07 50		08 18		08 50			09 18	09 50		10 18		10 50		11 18	11 50			12 18		12 50
Bramley (Hants)	d	06 23	06 55	07 23	07 55		08 23		08 55			09 23	09 55		10 23		10 55		11 23	11 55			12 23		12 55
Basingstoke	a	06 32	07 03	07 32	08 03	08 08	08 31	08 40	09 04	09 08		09 31	10 04	10 08	10 31	10 39	11 03	11 08	11 31	12 03		12 08	12 31	12 40	13 04

		XC	GW	GW	XC	GW		XC	GW	XC	GW	GW	XC	GW	XC	GW		XC	GW	GW	XC	GW	XC	GW	XC
		◇■1 🛒	■1	■1	◇■1 🛒	■1		◇■1 🛒	■1	◇■1 🛒	■1	■1	◇■1 🛒	■1	◇■1 🛒	■1		◇■1 🛒	■1	■1	◇■1 🛒	■1	◇■1 🛒	■1	◇■1 🛒
Reading ■7	d	12 46	13 07	13 39	13 46	14 07		14 16	14 39	14 46	15 07	15 39	15 46	16 07	16 15	16 39		16 46	17 07	17 39	17 45	18 07	18 15	18 39	18 45
Reading West	d		13 10	13 42		14 10			14 42		15 10	15 42		16 10		16 42			17 10	17 42		18 10		18 42	
Mortimer	d		13 18	13 50		14 18			14 50		15 18	15 50		16 18		16 50			17 18	17 50		18 18		18 50	
Bramley (Hants)	d		13 23	13 55		14 23			14 55		15 23	15 55		16 23		16 55			17 23	17 55		18 23		18 55	
Basingstoke	a	13 08	13 31	14 03	14 08	14 31		14 40	15 03	15 08	15 31	16 03	16 08	16 31	16 40	17 03		17 08	17 31	18 03	18 08	18 31	18 40	19 03	19 08

		GW		GW	XC	GW	GW	XC	GW	GW	XC	GW		GW	XC	GW
		■1		■1	◇■1 🛒	■1	■1	◇■1	■1	■1	◇■1	■1		■1	◇■1	■1
Reading ■7	d	19 07		19 39	19 46	20 07	20 39	20 46	21 07	21 39	21 45	22 07		22 39	22 46	23 07
Reading West	d	19 10		19 42		20 10	20 42		21 10	21 42		22 10		22 42		23 10
Mortimer	d	19 18		19 50		20 18	20 50		21 18	21 50		22 18		22 50		23 18
Bramley (Hants)	d	19 23		19 55		20 23	20 55		21 23	21 55		22 23		22 55		23 23
Basingstoke	a	19 31		20 03	20 08	20 31	21 03	21 08	21 31	22 03	22 09	22 31		23 03	23 13	23 31

Saturdays

29 March to 17 May

		GW	GW	GW	GW	XC	GW	XC	GW	XC		GW	GW	XC	GW	XC	GW	XC	GW	GW		XC	GW	XC	GW
		■1	■1	■1	■1	◇■1 🛒	■1	◇■1	■1	◇■1 🛒		■1	■1	◇■1 🛒	■1	◇■1 🛒	■1	◇■1 🛒	■1	■1		◇■1 🛒	■1	◇■1 🛒	■1
Reading ■7	d	06 07	06 39	07 07	07 39	07 46	08 07	08 16	08 39	08 46		09 07	09 39	09 46	10 07	10 18	10 39	10 46	11 07	11 39		11 46	12 07	12 16	12 39
Reading West	d	06 10	06 42	07 10	07 42		08 10		08 42			09 10	09 42		10 10		10 42		11 10	11 42			12 10		12 42
Mortimer	d	06 18	06 50	07 18	07 50		08 18		08 50			09 18	09 50		10 18		10 50		11 18	11 50			12 18		12 50
Bramley (Hants)	d	06 23	06 55	07 23	07 55		08 23		08 55			09 23	09 55		10 23		10 55		11 23	11 55			12 23		12 55
Basingstoke	a	06 32	07 03	07 32	08 03	08 08	08 31	08 40	09 04	09 08		09 31	10 04	10 08	10 31	10 39	11 03	11 08	11 31	12 03		12 08	12 31	12 40	13 04

		XC	GW	GW	XC	GW		XC	GW	XC	GW	GW	XC	GW	XC	GW		XC	GW	GW	XC	GW	XC	GW	XC
		◇■1 🛒	■1	■1	◇■1 🛒	■1		◇■1 🛒	■1	◇■1 🛒	■1	■1	◇■1 🛒	■1	◇■1 🛒	■1		◇■1 🛒	■1	■1	◇■1 🛒	■1	◇■1 🛒	■1	◇■1 🛒
Reading ■7	d	12 46	13 07	13 39	13 46	14 07		14 16	14 39	14 46	15 07	15 39	15 46	16 07	16 15	16 39		16 46	17 07	17 39	17 45	18 07	18 15	18 39	18 45
Reading West	d		13 10	13 42		14 10			14 42		15 10	15 42		16 10		16 42			17 10	17 42		18 10		18 42	
Mortimer	d		13 18	13 50		14 18			14 50		15 18	15 50		16 18		16 50			17 18	17 50		18 18		18 50	
Bramley (Hants)	d		13 23	13 55		14 23			14 55		15 23	15 55		16 23		16 55			17 23	17 55		18 23		18 55	
Basingstoke	a	13 08	13 31	14 03	14 08	14 31		14 40	15 03	15 08	15 31	16 03	16 08	16 31	16 40	17 03		17 08	17 31	18 03	18 08	18 31	18 40	19 03	19 08

		GW		GW	XC	GW	GW	XC	GW	GW	XC	GW		GW	XC	GW
		■1		■1	◇■1 🛒	■1	■1	◇■1	■1	■1	◇■1	■1		■1	◇■1	■1
Reading ■7	d	19 07		19 39	19 46	20 07	20 39	20 46	21 07	21 39	21 45	22 07		22 39	22 53	23 07
Reading West	d	19 10		19 42		20 10	20 42		21 10	21 42		22 10		22 42		23 10
Mortimer	d	19 18		19 50		20 18	20 50		21 18	21 50		22 18		22 50		23 18
Bramley (Hants)	d	19 23		19 55		20 23	20 55		21 23	21 55		22 23		22 55		23 23
Basingstoke	a	19 31		20 03	20 08	20 31	21 03	21 08	21 31	22 03	22 09	22 31		23 03	23 12	23 31

Table 122

Sundays

8 December to 9 February

Network Diagram - refer to first Page of Table 116

Reading - Basingstoke

		GW 1 A	GW 1	GW 1	XC ◇1	and at the same minutes past each hour until	GW 1	XC ◇1	GW 1	GW 1
Reading 7	d	07 37	08 37	09 37	09 53		21 37	21 53	22 37	23 37
Reading West	d	07 40	08 40	09 40	.		21 40	.	22 41	23 40
Mortimer	d	07 48	08 48	09 48	.		21 48	.	22 49	23 48
Bramley (Hants)	d	07 53	08 53	09 53	.		21 53	.	22 54	23 53
Basingstoke	a	08 01	09 01	10 01	10 09		22 01	22 09	23 02	00 01

Sundays

16 February to 23 March

		GW 1	GW 1	GW 1	XC ◇1	GW 1	XC ◇1	GW 1	XC ◇1	GW 1	XC ◇1	and at the same minutes past each hour until	GW 1	XC ◇1	GW 1	XC ◇1	GW 1	XC ◇1	GW 1	XC ◇1	GW 1	XC ◇1	GW 1
Reading 7	d	07 37	08 37	09 37	09 53	10 37	10 41	11 37	11 42	12 37	12 41		15 37	15 41	16 37	16 44	17 37	17 41	18 37	18 41	19 37	19 43	20 37
Reading West	d	07 40	08 40	09 40	.	10 40	.	11 40	.	12 40	.		15 40	.	16 40	.	17 40	.	18 40	.	19 40	.	20 40
Mortimer	d	07 48	08 48	09 48	.	10 48	.	11 48	.	12 48	.		15 48	.	16 48	.	17 48	.	18 48	.	19 48	.	20 48
Bramley (Hants)	d	07 53	08 53	09 53	.	10 53	.	11 53	.	12 53	.		15 53	.	16 53	.	17 53	.	18 53	.	19 53	.	20 53
Basingstoke	a	08 01	09 01	10 01	10 09	11 01	11 09	12 01	12 10	13 01	13 09		16 01	16 09	17 01	17 09	18 01	18 09	19 01	19 09	20 01	20 09	21 01

		XC ◇1	GW 1	GW 1	GW 1
Reading 7	d	20 41	21 37	22 37	23 37
Reading West	d	.	21 40	22 41	23 40
Mortimer	d	.	21 48	22 49	23 48
Bramley (Hants)	d	.	21 53	22 54	23 53
Basingstoke	a	21 09	22 01	23 02	00 01

Sundays

30 March to 11 May

		GW 1	GW 1	GW 1	XC ◇1	and at the same minutes past each hour until	GW 1	XC ◇1	GW 1	GW 1
Reading 7	d	07 37	08 37	09 37	09 53		21 37	21 53	22 37	23 37
Reading West	d	07 40	08 40	09 40	.		21 40	.	22 41	23 40
Mortimer	d	07 48	08 48	09 48	.		21 48	.	22 49	23 48
Bramley (Hants)	d	07 53	08 53	09 53	.		21 53	.	22 54	23 53
Basingstoke	a	08 01	09 01	10 01	10 09		22 01	22 09	23 02	00 01

A from 5 January

Table 122R

Basingstoke - Reading

Mondays to Fridays

9 December to 16 May

Network Diagram - refer to first Page of Table 116

Miles			GW MX [1]	GW MO [1]	XC ◇[1]	GW	GW	XC ◇[1]		GW	GW	XC ◇[1] 🛒	GW	XC ◇[1]	GW	XC ◇[1] 🛒	GW	GW		XC [R] [1] 🛒	GW	XC ◇[1] 🛒	GW	XC ◇[1] 🛒	GW
0	**Basingstoke**	d	00 02	00 07	05 47	06 07	06 33	06 47		07 08	07 36	07 47	08 05	08 18	08 36	08 47	09 06	09 36		09 47	10 06	10 19	10 36	10 47	11 07
5	Bramley (Hants)	d	00 09	00 14		06 14	06 40			07 14	07 43		08 12		08 43		09 13	09 43			10 13		10 43		11 14
8¼	Mortimer	d	00 14	00 19		06 19	06 45			07 19	07 48		08 17		08 48		09 18	09 48			10 18		10 48		11 19
14½	Reading West	d	00 22	00 26		06 28	06 54			07 28	07 57		08 26		08 57		09 27	09 57			10 27		10 57		11 28
15½	**Reading [7]**	a	00 26	00 30	06 04	06 32	06 57	07 04		07 32	08 00	08 03	08 29	08 36	09 00	09 03	09 30	10 00		10 03	10 30	10 34	11 00	11 03	11 31

		GW	XC ◇[1] 🛒	GW		XC [R] [1] 🛒	GW	XC ◇[1] 🛒	GW	GW	XC ◇[1] 🛒	GW	XC ◇[1] 🛒	GW		XC ◇[1] 🛒	GW	GW	XC ◇[1] 🛒	GW	XC ◇[1] 🛒	GW	XC ◇[1] 🛒	GW	
Basingstoke	d	11 36	11 47	12 06		12 18	12 36	12 47	13 07	13 36	13 47	14 06	14 19	14 37		14 47	15 07	15 36	15 47	16 06	16 18	16 36	16 47	17 04	
Bramley (Hants)	d	11 43		12 13			12 43		13 14	13 43		14 13		14 44			15 14	15 43		16 13		16 43		17 11	
Mortimer	d	11 48		12 18			12 48		13 19	13 48		14 18		14 49			15 19	15 48		16 18		16 48		17 16	
Reading West	d	11 57		12 27			12 57		13 28	13 57		14 27		14 58			15 28	15 57		16 27		16 57		17 25	
Reading [7]	a	12 00	12 03	12 30		12 33	13 00	13 03	13 31	14 00	14 03	14 30	14 34	15 01		15 03	15 31	16 00	16 03	16 30	16 33	17 00	17 03	17 28	

		GW	XC ◇[1] 🛒	GW	XC ◇[1] 🛒	GW	XC ◇[1] 🛒	GW	GW	XC ◇[1] 🛒		GW	GW	XC ◇[1]	GW	GW [1]	GW [1]	GW [1]	GW [1]					
Basingstoke	d	17 36	17 47	18 04	18 18	18 36	18 47	19 08	19 36	19 47		20 06	20 36	20 47	21 06	21 42	22 24	22 55	23 30					
Bramley (Hants)	d	17 43		18 11		18 43		19 15	19 43			20 13	20 43		21 13	21 49	22 31	23 02	23 37					
Mortimer	d	17 48		18 16		18 48		19 20	19 48			20 18	20 48		21 18	21 54	22 36	23 07	23 42					
Reading West	d	17 57		18 25		18 57		19 29	19 57			20 27	20 58		21 27	22 02	22 44	23 15	23 50					
Reading [7]	a	18 00	18 03	18 28	18 33	19 00	19 03	19 32	20 00	20 03		20 30	21 01	21 04	21 30	22 05	22 47	23 18	23 53					

Saturdays

14 December to 28 December

		GW [1]	XC ◇[1]	GW [1]	XC ◇[1] 🛒	GW [1]	XC ◇[1]	GW [1]	XC ◇[1] 🛒	GW [1]		XC ◇[1]	GW [1]	XC ◇[1] 🛒	GW [1]	GW [1]	XC ◇[1] 🛒	GW [1]	XC ◇[1] 🛒	GW [1]		XC ◇[1] 🛒	GW [1]	GW [1]	XC ◇[1] 🛒
Basingstoke	d	00 02	05 41	06 37	06 47	07 07	07 25	07 37	07 47	08 07		08 19	08 37	08 47	09 07	09 37	09 47	10 07	10 19	10 37		10 47	11 07	11 37	11 47
Bramley (Hants)	d	00 09		06 44		07 14		07 44		08 14			08 44		09 14	09 44		10 14		10 44			11 14	11 44	
Mortimer	d	00 14		06 49		07 19		07 49		08 19			08 49		09 19	09 49		10 19		10 49			11 19	11 49	
Reading West	d	00 22		06 57		07 27		07 57		08 27			08 57		09 27	09 57		10 27		10 57			11 27	11 57	
Reading [7]	a	00 26	05 58	07 00	07 04	07 31	07 42	08 00	08 03	08 31		08 35	09 00	09 04	09 31	10 00	10 03	10 31	10 34	11 00		11 03	11 31	12 00	12 03

		GW [1]	XC ◇[1] 🛒	GW [1]	XC ◇[1] 🛒	GW [1]		GW [1]	XC ◇[1] 🛒	GW [1]	XC ◇[1] 🛒	GW [1]	XC ◇[1] 🛒	GW [1]	GW [1]	XC ◇[1] 🛒		GW [1]	XC ◇[1] 🛒	GW [1]	XC ◇[1] 🛒	GW [1]	GW [1]	XC ◇[1] 🛒	GW [1]
Basingstoke	d	12 07	12 19	12 37	12 47	13 07		13 37	13 47	14 07	14 19	14 37	14 47	15 07	15 37	15 47		16 07	16 18	16 37	16 47	17 07	17 37	17 47	18 07
Bramley (Hants)	d	12 14		12 44		13 14		13 44		14 14		14 44		15 14	15 44			16 14		16 44		17 14	17 44		18 14
Mortimer	d	12 19		12 49		13 19		13 49		14 19		14 49		15 19	15 49			16 19		16 49		17 19	17 49		18 19
Reading West	d	12 27		12 57		13 27		13 57		14 27		14 57		15 27	15 57			16 27		16 57		17 27	17 57		18 27
Reading [7]	a	12 31	12 34	13 00	13 04	13 31		14 00	14 04	14 31	14 34	15 00	15 03	15 31	16 00	16 03		16 31	16 34	17 00	17 03	17 31	18 00	18 03	18 31

		XC ◇[1] 🛒		GW [1]	XC ◇[1] 🛒	GW [1]	GW [1]	XC ◇[1] 🛒	GW [1]	GW [1]	XC ◇[1]	GW [1]		GW [1]	GW [1]	GW [1]	GW [1]	GW [1]							
Basingstoke	d	18 18		18 37	18 47	19 07	19 37	19 47	20 08	20 37	20 47	21 07		21 37	22 07	22 37	23 07	23 37							
Bramley (Hants)	d			18 44		19 14	19 44		20 14	20 44		21 14		21 44	22 14	22 44	23 14	23 44							
Mortimer	d			18 49		19 19	19 49		20 19	20 49		21 19		21 49	22 19	22 49	23 19	23 49							
Reading West	d			18 57		19 27	19 57		20 27	20 57		21 27		21 57	22 27	22 57	23 27	23 57							
Reading [7]	a	18 34		19 00	19 03	19 31	20 01	20 03	20 32	21 01	21 03	21 31		22 00	22 31	23 00	23 31	00 01							

Saturdays

4 January to 8 February

		GW [1]	XC ◇[1]	GW [1]	XC ◇[1] 🛒	GW [1]	XC ◇[1]	GW [1]	XC ◇[1] 🛒	GW [1]		XC ◇[1]	GW [1]	XC ◇[1] 🛒	GW [1]	GW [1]	XC ◇[1] 🛒	GW [1]	XC ◇[1] 🛒	GW [1]		XC ◇[1] 🛒	GW [1]	GW [1]	XC ◇[1] 🛒
Basingstoke	d	00 02	05 41	06 37	06 47	07 07	07 25	07 37	07 47	08 07		08 19	08 37	08 47	09 07	09 37	09 47	10 07	10 19	10 37		10 47	11 07	11 37	11 47
Bramley (Hants)	d	00 09		06 44		07 14		07 44		08 14			08 44		09 14	09 44		10 14		10 44			11 14	11 44	
Mortimer	d	00 14		06 49		07 19		07 49		08 19			08 49		09 19	09 49		10 19		10 49			11 19	11 49	
Reading West	d	00 22		06 57		07 27		07 57		08 27			08 57		09 27	09 57		10 27		10 57			11 27	11 57	
Reading [7]	a	00 26	05 58	07 00	07 04	07 31	07 42	08 00	08 03	08 31		08 35	09 00	09 04	09 31	10 00	10 04	10 31	10 34	11 00		11 03	11 31	12 00	12 04

		GW [1]	XC ◇[1] 🛒	GW [1]	XC ◇[1] 🛒	GW [1]		GW [1]	XC ◇[1] 🛒	GW [1]	XC ◇[1] 🛒	GW [1]	XC ◇[1] 🛒	GW [1]	GW [1]	XC ◇[1] 🛒		GW [1]	XC ◇[1] 🛒	GW [1]	XC ◇[1] 🛒	GW [1]	GW [1]	XC ◇[1] 🛒	GW [1]
Basingstoke	d	12 07	12 19	12 37	12 47	13 07		13 37	13 47	14 07	14 19	14 37	14 47	15 07	15 37	15 47		16 07	16 18	16 37	16 47	17 07	17 37	17 47	18 07
Bramley (Hants)	d	12 14		12 44		13 14		13 44		14 14		14 44		15 14	15 44			16 14		16 44		17 14	17 44		18 14
Mortimer	d	12 19		12 49		13 19		13 49		14 19		14 49		15 19	15 49			16 19		16 49		17 19	17 49		18 19
Reading West	d	12 27		12 57		13 27		13 57		14 27		14 57		15 27	15 57			16 27		16 57		17 27	17 57		18 27
Reading [7]	a	12 31	12 34	13 00	13 04	13 31		14 00	14 03	14 31	14 34	15 00	15 04	15 31	16 00	16 03		16 31	16 34	17 00	17 03	17 31	18 00	18 03	18 31

Table 122R

Saturdays

4 January to 8 February

Network Diagram - refer to first Page of Table 116

Basingstoke - Reading

		XC	GW	XC	GW		GW	XC	GW	GW	XC	GW	GW	GW	GW		GW	GW							
		◇1	1	◇1	1		1	◇1	1	1	◇1	1	1	1	1		1	1							
		🛒		🛒				🛒																	
Basingstoke	d	18 18	18 37	18 47	19 07		19 37	19 47	20 08	20 37	20 47	21 07	21 37	22 07	22 37		23 07	23 37							
Bramley (Hants)	d		18 44		19 14		19 44		20 14	20 44		21 14	21 44	22 14	22 44		23 14	23 44							
Mortimer	d		18 49		19 19		19 49		20 19	20 49		21 19	21 49	22 19	22 49		23 19	23 49							
Reading West	d		18 57		19 27		19 57		20 27	20 57		21 27	21 57	22 27	22 57		23 27	23 57							
Reading 7	a	18 34	19 00	19 03	19 31		20 01	20 03	20 32	21 01	21 03	21 31	22 00	22 31	23 00		23 31	00 01							

Saturdays

15 February to 22 March

		GW	XC	GW	XC	GW	XC	GW	XC	GW		XC	GW	XC	GW	GW	XC	GW	XC	GW		XC	GW	GW	XC
		1	◇1	1	◇1	1	◇1	1	◇1	1		◇1	1	◇1	1	1	◇1	1	◇1	1		◇1	1	1	◇1
					🛒				🛒					🛒			🛒		🛒			🛒			🛒
Basingstoke	d	00 02	05 41	06 37	06 47	07 07	07 25	07 37	07 47	08 07		08 19	08 37	08 47	09 07	09 37	09 47	10 07	10 19	10 37		10 47	11 07	11 37	11 47
Bramley (Hants)	d	00 09		06 44		07 14		07 44		08 14			08 44		09 14	09 44		10 14		10 44			11 14	11 44	
Mortimer	d	00 14		06 49		07 19		07 49		08 19			08 49		09 19	09 49		10 19		10 49			11 19	11 49	
Reading West	d	00 22		06 57		07 27		07 57		08 27			08 57		09 27	09 57		10 27		10 57			11 27	11 57	
Reading 7	a	00 26	05 58	07 00	07 04	07 31	07 42	08 00	08 03	08 31		08 35	09 00	09 04	09 31	10 00	10 03	10 31	10 34	11 00		11 03	11 31	12 00	12 03

		GW	XC	GW	XC	GW		GW	XC	GW	XC	GW	XC	GW	GW	XC		GW	XC	GW	XC	GW	GW	XC	GW
		1	◇1	1	◇1	1		1	◇1	1	◇1	1	◇1	1	1	◇1		1	◇1	1	◇1	1	1	◇1	1
			🛒		🛒				🛒		🛒		🛒			🛒			🛒		🛒			🛒	
Basingstoke	d	12 07	12 19	12 37	12 47	13 07		13 37	13 47	14 07	14 19	14 37	14 47	15 07	15 37	15 47		16 07	16 18	16 37	16 47	17 07	17 37	17 47	18 07
Bramley (Hants)	d	12 14		12 44		13 14		13 44		14 14		14 44		15 14	15 44			16 14		16 44		17 14	17 44		18 14
Mortimer	d	12 19		12 49		13 19		13 49		14 19		14 49		15 19	15 49			16 19		16 49		17 19	17 49		18 19
Reading West	d	12 27		12 57		13 27		13 57		14 27		14 57		15 27	15 57			16 27		16 57		17 27	17 57		18 27
Reading 7	a	12 31	12 34	13 00	13 04	13 31		14 00	14 04	14 31	14 34	15 00	15 03	15 31	16 00	16 03		16 31	16 34	17 00	17 03	17 31	18 00	18 03	18 31

		XC		GW	XC	GW	GW	XC	GW	GW	XC	GW		GW	GW	GW	GW	GW							
		◇1		1	◇1	1	1	◇1	1	1	◇1	1		1	1	1	1	1							
		🛒			🛒			🛒																	
Basingstoke	d	18 18		18 37	18 47	19 07	19 37	19 47	20 08	20 37	20 47	21 07		21 37	22 07	22 37	23 07	23 37							
Bramley (Hants)	d			18 44		19 14	19 44		20 14	20 44		21 14		21 44	22 14	22 44	23 14	23 44							
Mortimer	d			18 49		19 19	19 49		20 19	20 49		21 19		21 49	22 19	22 49	23 19	23 49							
Reading West	d			18 57		19 27	19 57		20 27	20 57		21 27		21 57	22 27	22 57	23 27	23 57							
Reading 7	a	18 34		19 00	19 03	19 31	20 01	20 03	20 32	21 01	21 03	21 31		22 00	22 31	23 00	23 31	00 01							

Saturdays

29 March to 17 May

		GW	XC	GW	XC	GW	XC	GW	XC	GW		XC	GW	XC	GW	GW	XC	GW	XC	GW		XC	GW	GW	XC
		1	◇1	1	◇1	1	◇1	1	◇1	1		◇1	1	◇1	1	1	◇1	1	◇1	1		◇1	1	1	◇1
					🛒				🛒					🛒			🛒		🛒			🛒			🛒
Basingstoke	d	00 02	05 41	06 37	06 47	07 07	07 25	07 37	07 47	08 07		08 19	08 37	08 47	09 07	09 37	09 47	10 07	10 19	10 37		10 47	11 07	11 37	11 47
Bramley (Hants)	d	00 09		06 44		07 14		07 44		08 14			08 44		09 14	09 44		10 14		10 44			11 14	11 44	
Mortimer	d	00 14		06 49		07 19		07 49		08 19			08 49		09 19	09 49		10 19		10 49			11 19	11 49	
Reading West	d	00 22		06 57		07 27		07 57		08 27			08 57		09 27	09 57		10 27		10 57			11 27	11 57	
Reading 7	a	00 26	05 58	07 00	07 04	07 31	07 42	08 00	08 03	08 31		08 35	09 00	09 04	09 31	10 00	10 03	10 31	10 34	11 00		11 03	11 31	12 00	12 03

		GW	XC	GW	XC	GW		GW	XC	GW	XC	GW	XC	GW	GW	XC		GW	XC	GW	XC	GW	GW	XC	GW
		1	◇1	1	◇1	1		1	◇1	1	◇1	1	◇1	1	1	◇1		1	◇1	1	◇1	1	1	◇1	1
			🛒		🛒				🛒		🛒		🛒			🛒			🛒		🛒			🛒	
Basingstoke	d	12 07	12 19	12 37	12 47	13 07		13 37	13 47	14 07	14 19	14 37	14 47	15 07	15 37	15 47		16 07	16 18	16 37	16 47	17 07	17 37	17 47	18 07
Bramley (Hants)	d	12 14		12 44		13 14		13 44		14 14		14 44		15 14	15 44			16 14		16 44		17 14	17 44		18 14
Mortimer	d	12 19		12 49		13 19		13 49		14 19		14 49		15 19	15 49			16 19		16 49		17 19	17 49		18 19
Reading West	d	12 27		12 57		13 27		13 57		14 27		14 57		15 27	15 57			16 27		16 57		17 27	17 57		18 27
Reading 7	a	12 31	12 34	13 00	13 04	13 31		14 00	14 04	14 31	14 34	15 00	15 03	15 31	16 00	16 03		16 31	16 34	17 00	17 03	17 31	18 00	18 03	18 31

		XC		GW	XC	GW	GW	XC	GW	GW	XC	GW		GW	GW	GW	GW	GW							
		◇1		1	◇1	1	1	◇1	1	1	◇1	1		1	1	1	1	1							
		🛒			🛒			🛒																	
Basingstoke	d	18 18		18 37	18 47	19 07	19 37	19 47	20 08	20 37	20 47	21 07		21 37	22 07	22 37	23 07	23 37							
Bramley (Hants)	d			18 44		19 14	19 44		20 14	20 44		21 14		21 44	22 14	22 44	23 14	23 44							
Mortimer	d			18 49		19 19	19 49		20 19	20 49		21 19		21 49	22 19	22 49	23 19	23 49							
Reading West	d			18 57		19 27	19 57		20 27	20 57		21 27		21 57	22 27	22 57	23 27	23 57							
Reading 7	a	18 34		19 00	19 03	19 31	20 01	20 03	20 32	21 01	21 03	21 31		22 00	22 31	23 00	23 31	00 01							

Table 122R

Sundays

8 December to 9 February

Basingstoke - Reading

Network Diagram - refer to first Page of Table 116

		GW	GW	XC	GW	XC		GW	XC	GW	XC	GW	XC	GW	XC	GW		XC	GW	XC	GW	XC	GW	XC	GW
		1	1	◇1	1	◇1		1	◇1	1	◇1	1	◇1	1	◇1	1		◇1	1	◇1	1	◇1	1	◇1	1
		A																							
				[trolley]		[trolley]			[trolley]		[trolley]		[trolley]		[trolley]			[trolley]		[trolley]		[trolley]		[trolley]	
Basingstoke	d	08 07	09 07	09 47	10 07	10 47		11 07	11 47	12 07	12 47	13 07	13 47	14 07	14 47	15 07		15 47	16 07	16 47	17 07	17 47	18 07	18 47	19 07
Bramley (Hants)	d	08 14	09 14		10 14			11 14		12 14		13 14		14 14		15 14			16 14		17 14		18 14		19 14
Mortimer	d	08 19	09 19		10 19			11 19		12 19		13 19		14 19		15 19			16 19		17 19		18 19		19 19
Reading West	d	08 27	09 27		10 27			11 27		12 27		13 27		14 27		15 27			16 27		17 27		18 27		19 27
Reading 7	a	08 30	09 30	10 04	10 30	11 03		11 30	12 02	12 30	13 03	13 30	14 02	14 30	15 03	15 30		16 02	16 30	17 02	17 30	18 04	18 30	19 02	19 30

		XC		GW	XC	GW	GW	GW
		◇1		1	◇1	1	1	1
		[trolley]						
Basingstoke	d	19 47		20 07	20 47	21 07	22 07	23 07
Bramley (Hants)	d			20 14		21 14	22 15	23 14
Mortimer	d			20 19		21 19	22 20	23 19
Reading West	d			20 27		21 27	22 30	23 27
Reading 7	a	20 03		20 30	21 02	21 30	22 33	23 30

Sundays

16 February to 23 March

		GW	GW	XC		GW	XC	GW	GW	GW
		1	1	◇1	and at the same minutes past each hour until	1	◇1	1	1	1
				[trolley]						
Basingstoke	d	08 07	09 07	09 47		20 07	20 47	21 07	22 07	23 07
Bramley (Hants)	d	08 14	09 14			20 14		21 14	22 15	23 14
Mortimer	d	08 19	09 19			20 19		21 19	22 20	23 19
Reading West	d	08 27	09 27			20 27		21 27	22 30	23 27
Reading 7	a	08 30	09 30	10 15		20 30	21 15	21 30	22 33	23 30

Sundays

30 March to 11 May

		GW	GW	XC	GW	XC	GW	XC	GW	XC		GW	XC	GW	XC	GW	XC	GW	XC	GW		XC	GW	XC	GW
		1	1	◇1	1	◇1	1	◇1	1	◇1		1	◇1	1	◇1	1	◇1	1	◇1	1		◇1	1	◇1	1
				[trolley]		[trolley]		[trolley]		[trolley]			[trolley]		[trolley]		[trolley]		[trolley]			[trolley]		[trolley]	
Basingstoke	d	08 07	09 07	09 47	10 07	10 47	11 07	11 47	12 07	12 47		13 07	13 47	14 07	14 47	15 07	15 47	16 07	16 47	17 07		17 47	18 07	18 47	19 07
Bramley (Hants)	d	08 14	09 14		10 14		11 14		12 14			13 14		14 14		15 14		16 14		17 14			18 14		19 14
Mortimer	d	08 19	09 19		10 19		11 19		12 19			13 19		14 19		15 19		16 19		17 19			18 19		19 19
Reading West	d	08 27	09 27		10 27		11 27		12 27			13 27		14 27		15 27		16 27		17 27			18 27		19 27
Reading 7	a	08 30	09 30	10 04	10 30	11 03	11 30	12 02	12 30	13 03		13 30	14 02	14 30	15 03	15 30	16 02	16 30	17 03	17 30		18 04	18 30	19 02	19 30

		XC	GW	XC	GW	GW		GW
		◇1	1	◇1	1	1		1
		[trolley]						
Basingstoke	d	19 47	20 07	20 47	21 07	22 07		23 07
Bramley (Hants)	d		20 14		21 14	22 15		23 14
Mortimer	d		20 19		21 19	22 20		23 19
Reading West	d		20 27		21 27	22 30		23 27
Reading 7	a	20 03	20 30	21 02	21 30	22 33		23 30

A from 5 January

Network Diagram for Table 123

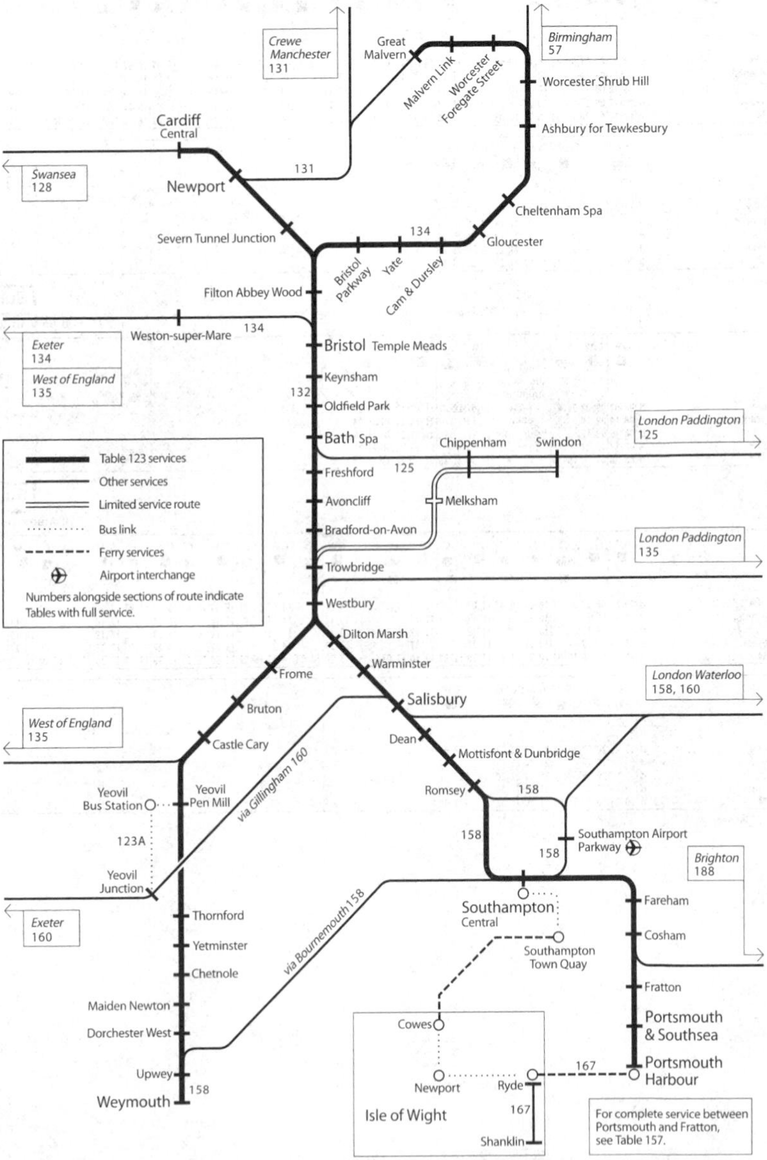

Crewe
Manchester
131
Great Malvern
Malvern Link
Worcester Foregate Street
Birmingham
57
Worcester Shrub Hill
Ashbury for Tewkesbury
Cardiff
Central
Swansea
128
131
Newport
Cheltenham Spa
134
Severn Tunnel Junction
Gloucester
Bristol Parkway
Yate
Cam & Dursley
Filton Abbey Wood
134
Weston-super-Mare
Exeter
134
West of England
135
Bristol Temple Meads
Keynsham
132
Oldfield Park
London Paddington
125
Bath Spa
Chippenham
Swindon
Table 123 services
Other services
Limited service route
Bus link
Ferry services
Airport interchange
Numbers alongside sections of route indicate Tables with full service.
Freshford
125
Avoncliff
Melksham
Bradford-on-Avon
London Paddington
135
Trowbridge
Westbury
Dilton Marsh
Frome
Warminster
London Waterloo
158, 160
Salisbury
Bruton
West of England
135
Castle Cary
Dean
Mottisfont & Dunbridge
via Gillingham 160
Yeovil
Bus Station
Yeovil
Pen Mill
Romsey
158
158
Southampton Airport Parkway
123A
158
Brighton
188
Yeovil
Junction
via Bournemouth 158
Fareham
Southampton
Central
Exeter
160
Thornford
Cosham
Yetminster
Southampton
Town Quay
Chetnole
Fratton
Maiden Newton
Cowes
Portsmouth
& Southsea
Dorchester West
Portsmouth
Harbour
167
Upwey
Newport
Ryde
158
Weymouth
167
Isle of Wight
Shanklin
For complete service between Portsmouth and Fratton, see Table 157.

TOCs operating on this network - First Great Western (GW), South West Trains (SW)

Table 123

Mondays to Fridays

9 December to 16 May

Brighton, Portsmouth and Weymouth - Bristol, Cardiff, Gloucester and Great Malvern

Network Diagram - see first Page of Table 123

Miles	Miles	Miles	Miles	Miles			GW	GW	GW	GW	GW	GW	GW	GW	SW		GW	GW	GW	GW	GW	GW	GW	GW	GW
								◇1	◇1			◇	◇1		1		◇			◇1	R	◇		◇	◇
								A					B							C					
								⊏P	⊏P				Ø							⊏P	⌶			⌶	
—	—	0	—	—	Brighton 10	d																			
—	—	1½	—	—	Hove 2	d																			
—	—	6	—	—	Shoreham-by-Sea	d																			
—	—	10½	—	—	Worthing 4	d																			
—	—	22½	—	—	Barnham	d																			
—	—	28¾	—	—	**Chichester 4**	d																			
—	—	37½	—	—	Havant	d																			
0	—	—	—	—	**Portsmouth Harbour** ⛴	d															06 00			07 05	
0¾	—	—	—	—	Portsmouth & Southsea	d															06 04			07 09	
1¾	—	—	—	—	Fratton	d															06 08			07 13	
5½	—	41¾	—	—	Cosham	d															06 15			07 21	
11¼	—	47½	—	—	Fareham	a															06 23			07 28	
—	—	—	—	—		d															06 24			07 29	
25¾	—	62¼	—	—	**Southampton Central** ⛴	d															06 46			07 52	08 23
34	—	70¼	—	—	Romsey	d															07 00			08 11	08 35
50½	—	86¾	—	—	**Salisbury**	a															07 18			08 29	09 00
—	—	—	—	—		d				06 02					06 40						07 19			08 30	09 03
70¼	—	106½	—	—	Warminster	d				06 24					07 00				07 23		07 39			08 52	09 25
73½	—	109¾	—	—	Dilton Marsh	d				06x28									07x27		07x43				09x29
—	0	—	0	—	**Weymouth**	d											05 33					06 40			
—	2½	—	2½	—	Upwey	d											05 37					06 45			
—	7	—	7	—	Dorchester West	d											05 45					06 53			
—	14¾	—	14¾	—	Maiden Newton	d											05 57					07 05			
—	21¼	—	21¼	—	Chetnole	d											06x06					07x13			
—	23¼	—	23¼	—	Yetminster	d											06x08					07x16			
—	24¼	—	24¼	—	Thornford	d											06x10					07x18			
—	27½	—	27½	—	Yeovil Pen Mill	d											06 20					07 30			
—	39¼	—	39¼	—	Castle Cary	a											06 33					07 43			
—	—	—	—	—		d							06 39				06 45			07 27		07 44			
—	42¾	—	42¾	—	Bruton	d											06 51					07 49			
—	53¼	—	53¼	—	Frome	d			06 05			06 45					07 04					08 02			
75	59	111¼	59	—	**Westbury**	a			06 15	06 33		06 54	06 59		07 08		07 12		07 32	07 45	07 47	08 09		09 01	09 35
—	—	—	—	—		d	05 58	06 03	06 16		06 38	06 55	07 01	07 04	07 09		07 18	07 28	07 38	07 51	07 53	08 17	08 45	09 10	09 38
79	63	115¼	63	5	Trowbridge	d	06 04				06 44	07 02		07 10	07 15		07 24	07 38	07 44		08 00	08 23	08 51	09 16	09 44
82¼	66¼	118½	66¼	—	Bradford-on-Avon	d	06 10				06 50	07 08			07 21		07 30		07 50		08 06	08 29	08 57	09 22	09 50
83½	67¾	119¾	67¾	—	Avoncliff	d	06 13				06 53	07 11					07 33		07 53			08 32	09 00		09 53
84½	68½	120¾	68½	—	Freshford	d	06 16				06 56	07 13					07 36		07 56		08 10	08 35	09 03		09 56
91½	75¾	128	75¾	—	Bath Spa 7	a	06 26				07 06	07 24			07 33		07 46		08 06		08 21	08 45	09 13	09 35	10 06
—	—	—	—	9½	Melksham	d								07 20				07 48							
—	—	—	—	15¾	Chippenham	a								07 30				07 59							
—	—	—	—	32½	Swindon	a								07 48				08 18							
—	—	—	—	—	London Paddington 15 ⊖	a		07 53	08 09				08 38							09 21					
92½	76¾	129	76¾	—	Oldfield Park	a	06 30				07 10	07 28			07 37		07 50		08 10		08 25	08 49	09 17		10 10
98½	82¾	134¾	82¾	—	Keynsham	a	06 37				07 18	07 35			07 44		07 58		08 18		08 32	08 56	09 25	09 44	10 18
103	87¼	139½	87¼	—	**Bristol Temple Meads 10**	a	06 46				07 27	07 46			07 52		08 06		08 29		08 41	09 05	09 36	09 52	10 28
107½	91¾	144	91¾	—	Filton Abbey Wood	a	07 01				07 42	08 00					08 21		08 48		09 01	09 22	09 48	10 03	10 48
—	—	145½	93¼	—	Bristol Parkway	d					07 48						08a29		08 52			09a28	09 52		10 55
—	—	151¾	99½	—	Yate	d					07 57								09 02				10 01		11 04
—	—	162¼	110	—	Cam & Dursley	d					08 10								09 14				10 14		11 18
—	—	175¼	123	—	Gloucester	d					08a29			08 54					09 36				10a32		11 36
—	—	181¾	129½	—	Cheltenham Spa	d								09a05					09 48						11 48
—	—	189	137	—	Ashchurch for Tewkesbury	d													09 56						11 56
—	—	203¾	151½	—	Worcester Shrub Hill	d													10 14						12 14
—	—	204½	152¼	—	Worcester Foregate Street	d													10 17						12 17
—	—	211¼	159	—	Malvern Link	d													10 26						12 26
—	—	212½	160¼	—	Great Malvern	a													10 32						12 33
119½	119½	—	—	—	Severn Tunnel Jn	a	07 14																		
129½	113½	—	—	—	Newport (South Wales)	a	07 25					08 27									09 24			10 26	
141¼	125¼	—	—	—	**Cardiff Central 7**	a	07 44					08 44									09 43			10 43	

A From Bristol Temple Meads B From Exeter St Davids. Ø to Westbury C From Plymouth

For connections from Bristol Parkway and Cardiff Central to Swansea please see Table 128

For connections from Castle Cary, Westbury and Bristol Temple Meads to Exeter and Plymouth please see Table 135

For connections from Salisbury to Yeovil Junction and Exeter please see Table 160

For connections from Bournemouth to Southampton Central, Weymouth and Upwey please see Table 158

For Bus Connections between Yeovil Junction and Yeovil Pen Mill please see Table 123A

Table 123

Mondays to Fridays

9 December to 16 May

Brighton, Portsmouth and Weymouth - Bristol, Cardiff, Gloucester and Great Malvern

Network Diagram - see first Page of Table 123

		GW	GW	GW	GW	GW	GW	GW	SW	GW	GW	GW	GW	GW	GW	GW	GW	GW	SW	GW	GW	GW
			◇1	◇	◇		◇1	◇	◇1	◇		◇	◇	◇1	◇	◇	◇		◇1		◇	◇1
			A				B			C				D					E			F
			Ø	🛒			☕	🛒		🛒		🛒		☕	🛒		🛒					✕☕
Brighton 10	d									08 59												
Hove 2	d									09 03												
Shoreham-by-Sea	d									09 13												
Worthing 4	d									09 22												
Barnham	d									09 37												
Chichester 4	d									09 46												
Havant	d									09 58												
Portsmouth Harbour ⛴	d			08 23				09 23				10 23			11 23		12 23					
Portsmouth & Southsea	d			08 27				09 27				10 27			11 27		12 27					
Fratton	d			08 31				09 31				10 31			11 31		12 31					
Cosham	d			08 39				09 39		10 05		10 39			11 39		12 39					
Fareham	a			08 46				09 46		10 12		10 46			11 46		12 46					
	d			08 47				09 47		10 13		10 47			11 47		12 47					
Southampton Central ⛴	d			09 10				10 10		10 42		11 10			12 10	12 27	13 10					
Romsey	d			09 21				10 21		10 54		11 21			12 21	12 39	13 21					
Salisbury	a			09 39				10 39		11 13		11 39			12 39	13 02	13 39					
	d			09 40				10 40	10 52	11 14		11 40			12 40	13 06	13 40		13 52			
Warminster	d			10 01		10 25		11 01	11 12	11 33		12 01			13 01	13 34	14 01		14 12			
Dilton Marsh	d					10x29										13x38						
Weymouth	d				08 53								11 10								13 10	
Upwey	d				08 58								11 15								13 15	
Dorchester West	d				09 06								11 23								13 23	
Maiden Newton	d				09 18								11 43								13 46	
Chetnole	d				09x26								11x50								13x53	
Yetminster	d				09x29								11x53								13x56	
Thornford	d				09x31								11x55								13x59	
Yeovil Pen Mill	d				09 41								12 05								14 08	
Castle Cary	a				09 54								12 19								14 22	
	d		09 42		09 55								12 23	12 45							14 22	14 45
Bruton	d				10 01								12 29								14 28	
Frome	d				10 15								12 42								14 41	
Westbury	a		10 00	10 09	10 24	10 33		11 09	11 20	11 41		12 09	12 48	13 04	13 09	13 42	14 09		14 20		14 48	15 02
	d	09 48	10 01	10 10	10 38		11 05	11 10	11 21	11 42	11 47	12 10	12 52	13 06	13 10	13 44	14 10	14 14	14 21	14 38	14 51	15 04
Trowbridge	d	09 54		10 16	10 44			11 16	11 27	11 49	11 53	12 16	12 58		13 16	13 50	14 16	14 20	14 27	14 44	14 57	
Bradford-on-Avon	d			10 22	10 50			11 22	11 33	11 55		12 22	13 04		13 22	13 56	14 22		14 33	14 50	15 03	
Avoncliff	d				10 53					11 58			13 07			13 59				14 53	15 06	
Freshford	d				10 56					12 00			13 10			14 02				14 56	15 09	
Bath Spa 7	a			10 34	11 06			11 34	11 46	12 11		12 34	13 20		13 34	14 12	14 34		14 46	15 06	15 19	
Melksham	d	10 04									12 03							14 30				
Chippenham	a	10 14									12 12							14 41				
Swindon	a	10 34									12 36							15 03				
London Paddington 15 ⊖	a		11 24				12 23							14 54								16 22
Oldfield Park	a				11 10					12 15			13 24			14 16				15 10		
Keynsham	a				11 18				11 54	12 22			13 32			14 24			14 54	15 18		
Bristol Temple Meads 10	a			10 48	11 28			11 48	12 05	12 33		12 48	13 41		13 48	14 35	14 48		15 05	15 28	15 34	
Filton Abbey Wood	a			11 01				12 01		12 48		13 01			14 01	14 47	15 01				15 48	
Bristol Parkway	d									12 52						14 52				15a46	15 52	
Yate	d									13 01						15 01					16 01	
Cam & Dursley	d									13 14						15 14					16 14	
Gloucester	d									13 37						15 36					16a33	
Cheltenham Spa	d									13 48						15 48						
Ashchurch for Tewkesbury	d									13 56						15 56						
Worcester Shrub Hill	d									14 14						16 14						
Worcester Foregate Street	d									14 17						16 17						
Malvern Link	d									14 26						16 26						
Great Malvern	a									14 35						16 32						
Severn Tunnel Jn.	a																					
Newport (South Wales)	a			11 26				12 26				13 26			14 26		15 26					
Cardiff Central 7	a			11 43				12 43				13 43			14 43		15 43					

A From Penzance. Ø to Westbury
B From Penzance
C 🛒 to Southampton Central
D From Paignton
E From London Waterloo
F From Plymouth. Restaurant available for customers joining until Castle Cary. ☕ from Westbury ✕ to Westbury

For connections from Bristol Parkway and Cardiff Central to Swansea please see Table 128

For connections from Castle Cary, Westbury and Bristol Temple Meads to Exeter and Plymouth please see Table 135

For connections from Salisbury to Yeovil Junction and Exeter please see Table 160

For connections from Bournemouth to Southampton Central, Weymouth and Upwey please see Table 158

For Bus Connections between Yeovil Junction and Yeovil Pen Mill please see Table 123A

Table 123

Mondays to Fridays

9 December to 16 May

Brighton, Portsmouth and Weymouth - Bristol, Cardiff, Gloucester and Great Malvern

Network Diagram - see first Page of Table 123

		GW	GW	GW	GW	GW	GW	GW	GW	GW	GW	GW	GW	GW	GW	GW	GW	GW	GW	GW	GW	GW	GW	GW
								R			R		R											
		◇	A		◇1	◇1 B	◇1 C			◇							◇	◇ D	◇1 E	◇ F	◇	◇	◇	1
		🛒			🍽	🍽	🍽	🛒			🛒		🛒				🛒		🍽			🛒	🛒	
Brighton 10	d																					16 59		
Hove 2	d																					17 03		
Shoreham-by-Sea	d																					17 13		
Worthing 4	d																					17 22		
Barnham	d																					17 39		
Chichester 4	d																					17 47		
Havant	d																					17 58		
Portsmouth Harbour ⛴	d	13 23						14 23			15 23		16 23				17 23						18 23	
Portsmouth & Southsea	d	13 27						14 27			15 27		16 27				17 27						18 27	
Fratton	d	13 31						14 31			15 31		16 31				17 31						18 31	
Cosham	d	13 39						14 39			15 39		16 39				17 39					18 05	18 39	
Fareham	a	13 46						14 46			15 46		16 46				17 46					18 12	18 46	
	d	13 47						14 47			15 47		16 47				17 47					18 13	18 47	
Southampton Central ⛴	d	14 10						15 10			16 10		17 10				18 10					18 42	19 10	
Romsey	d	14 21						15 21			16 21		17 21				18 21					18 54	19 21	
Salisbury	a	14 39						15 39			16 39		17 39				18 39					19 12	19 39	
	d	14 40						15 40			16 40		17 40				18 40					19 13	19 40	
Warminster	d	15 01		15 28				16 01			17 01	17 28	18 01	18 18			19 01					19 32	20 01	
Dilton Marsh	d			15x32								17x32		18x22								19x37		
Weymouth	d									15 08								17 30						
Upwey	d									15 13								17 35						
Dorchester West	d									15 21								17 43						
Maiden Newton	d									15 33								17 54						
Chetnole	d									15x42								18x03						
Yetminster	d									15x45								18x06						
Thornford	d									15x47								18x08						
Yeovil Pen Mill	d									15 56								18 23						
Castle Cary	a									16 09								18 36						
	d					15 52				16 10								18 37	18 54					
Bruton	d									16 16								18 43						
Frome	d		14 59				15 55			16 29								19 06		←				20 15
Westbury	a	15 09	15 09	15 36			16 05	16 09		16 38	17 09	17 36	18 09	18 28			19 09	19 17	19 12	19 17		19 40	20 09	20 26
	d	15 10		15 38			16 08	16 10	16 15	16 38	17 10	17 38	18 10		18 32	18 38	19 10	19 19	19 13	19 19	19 32	19 41	20 10	
Trowbridge	d	15 16		15 44				16 16	16 21	16 44	17 16	17 44	18 16		18 38	18 44	19 16	→		19 25	19 38	19 48	20 16	
Bradford-on-Avon	d	15 22		15 50				16 22		16 50	17 22	17 50	18 22			18 50	19 22			19 31		19 54	20 22	
Avoncliff	d			15 53						16 53		17 53				18 53				19 34				
Freshford	d			15 56						16 56		17 56				18 56				19 37				
Bath Spa 7	a	15 34		16 06				16 34		17 06	17 34	18 06	18 34			19 06	19 34			19 47		20 07	20 34	
Melksham	d								16 31						18 48						19 47			
Chippenham	a								16 41						18 59						20 00			
Swindon	a								17 03						19 23						20 21			
London Paddington 15 ⊖	a				17d06	17 24	17 52												20 39					
Oldfield Park	a			16 10						17 10		18 10				19 10				19 51		20 11		
Keynsham	a			16 18						17 18		18 18				19 18				19 59		20 18		
Bristol Temple Meads 10	a	15 48		16 29	19 41			16 48		17 29	17 48	18 28	18 48			19 29	19 48			20 08		20 26	20 48	
Filton Abbey Wood	a	16 01		16 48				17 01		17 48	18 01	18 48	19 01			19 48	20 01						21 01	
Bristol Parkway	d			16 52						17 53		18 52				19 52								
Yate	d			17 01						18 01		19 01				20 01								
Cam & Dursley	d			17 14						18 14		19 13				20 14								
Gloucester	d			17 36						18a33		19 38				20 36					21 23			
Cheltenham Spa	d			17 48								19 50				20a48					21a33			
Ashchurch for Tewkesbury	d			17 56								19 59												
Worcester Shrub Hill	d			18 19								20 20												
Worcester Foregate Street	d			18 22								20 24												
Malvern Link	d			18 31								20 34												
Great Malvern	a			18 36								20 40												
Severn Tunnel Jn.	a							17 13			18 13		19 13				20 16						21 13	
Newport (South Wales)	a	16 25						17 25			18 25		19 26				20 27						21 26	
Cardiff Central 7	a	16 43						17 44			18 43		19 46				20 43						21 45	

A To Warminster
B From Paignton. The Torbay Express
C From Taunton
D To Bristol Temple Meads
E From Plymouth
F From Weymouth

For connections from Bristol Parkway and Cardiff Central to Swansea please see Table 128

For connections from Castle Cary, Westbury and Bristol Temple Meads to Exeter and Plymouth please see Table 135

For connections from Salisbury to Yeovil Junction and Exeter please see Table 160

For connections from Bournemouth to Southampton Central, Weymouth and Upwey please see Table 158

For Bus Connections between Yeovil Junction and Yeovil Pen Mill please see Table 123A

Table 123

Mondays to Fridays

9 December to 16 May

Brighton, Portsmouth and Weymouth - Bristol, Cardiff, Gloucester and Great Malvern

Network Diagram - see first Page of Table 123

		GW	GW FO ◇[1] A		GW FX ◇[1] B	GW FO ◇	GW FX ◇	GW	SW ◇[1] C	GW	GW FX ◇	GW FO ◇	GW		GW	GW
Brighton [10]	d															
Hove [2]	d															
Shoreham-by-Sea	d															
Worthing [4]	d															
Barnham	d															
Chichester [4]	d															
Havant	d															
Portsmouth Harbour	d					19 23	19 23				20 23	20 23				21 23
Portsmouth & Southsea	d					19 27	19 27				20 27	20 27				21 27
Fratton	d					19 31	19 31				20 31	20 31				21 31
Cosham	d					19 38	19 38									
Fareham	a					19 46	19 46				20 46	20 46				21 47
	d					19 47	19 47				20 47	20 47				21 48
Southampton Central	d					20 10	20 10				21 10	21 10	21 20			22 22
Romsey	d					20 21	20 21				21 21	21 21	21 31			22 34
Salisbury	a					20 39	20 39				21 39	21 39	21 51			22 58
	d					20 40	20 40		20 57		21 40	21 40	21 53			23 00
Warminster	d					21 01	21 01		21 17		22 01	22 01	22 15			23 20
Dilton Marsh	d												22x19			23x24
Weymouth	d									20 21						
Upwey	d									20 26						
Dorchester West	d									20 34						
Maiden Newton	d									20 45						
Chetnole	d									20x52						
Yetminster	d									20x56						
Thornford	d									20x58						
Yeovil Pen Mill	d									21 06						
Castle Cary	a									21 18						
	d		20 46		20 46					21 18						
Bruton	d									21 24						
Frome	d							21 02		21 37						
Westbury	a		21 04		21 04	21 08	21 08	21 12	21 25	21 46	22 09	22 09	22 26			23 31
	d	20 38	21 05		21 05	21 10	21 10		21 25	21 55	22 10	22 10			22 32	
Trowbridge	d	20 44				21 17	21 17		21 31	22 02	22 16	22 16			22 38	
Bradford-on-Avon	d	20 50				21 23	21 23		21 37	22 08	22 22	22 22			22 44	
Avoncliff	d	20 53								22 11					22 46	
Freshford	d	20 56								22 13					22 50	
Bath Spa [7]	a	21 06				21 34	21 34		21 50	22 24	22 34	22 34			23 00	
Melksham	d															
Chippenham	a															
Swindon	a															
London Paddington [15] ⊖	a		22 30		22 38											
Oldfield Park	a	21 10								22 28					23 04	
Keynsham	a	21 18							21 58	22 35					23 12	
Bristol Temple Meads [10]	a	21 28				21 48	21 48		22 06	22 43	22 48	22 50			23 23	
Filton Abbey Wood	a					22 01	22 01				23 01	23 01				
Bristol Parkway	d															
Yate	d															
Cam & Dursley	d															
Gloucester	d															
Cheltenham Spa	d															
Ashchurch for Tewkesbury	d															
Worcester Shrub Hill	d															
Worcester Foregate Street	d															
Malvern Link	d															
Great Malvern	a															
Severn Tunnel Jn.	a					22 17	22 17				23 16	23 16				
Newport (South Wales)	a					22 29	22 36				23 34	23 34				
Cardiff Central [7]	a					22 52	23 00				23 56	23 56				

A From Taunton

B From Exeter St Davids

C From London Waterloo

For connections from Bristol Parkway and Cardiff Central to Swansea please see Table 128

For connections from Castle Cary, Westbury and Bristol Temple Meads to Exeter and Plymouth please see Table 135

For connections from Salisbury to Yeovil Junction and Exeter please see Table 160

For connections from Bournemouth to Southampton Central, Weymouth and Upwey please see Table 158

For Bus Connections between Yeovil Junction and Yeovil Pen Mill please see Table 123A

Table 123

Saturdays

14 December to 28 December

Brighton, Portsmouth and Weymouth - Bristol, Cardiff, Gloucester and Great Malvern

Network Diagram - see first Page of Table 123

		GW	GW	GW	SW	GW	GW	GW	GW	GW	GW	GW	GW	GW	GW	GW	GW	GW	GW	GW	GW	SW	GW
					1			◇1 A	◇	◇			◇ B		◇	◇1 A	◇ B	◇		1 C	◇ B	◇1 D	
Brighton 10	d																						
Hove 2	d																						
Shoreham-by-Sea	d																						
Worthing 4	d																						
Barnham	d																						
Chichester 4	d																						
Havant	d																						
Portsmouth Harbour	d								06 00				07 23				08 23				09 23		
Portsmouth & Southsea	d								06 04				07 27				08 27				09 27		
Fratton	d								06 08				07 31				08 31				09 31		
Cosham	d								06 19				07 39				08 39				09 39		
Fareham	a								06 27				07 46				08 46				09 46		
	d								06 28				07 47				08 47				09 47		
Southampton Central	d								06 53				08 10		08 27		09 10				10 10		
Romsey	d								07 11				08 21		08 38		09 21				10 21		
Salisbury	a								07 29				08 40		09 02		09 39				10 39		
	d	06 03			06 40				07 30				08 40		09 03		09 40				10 40	10 52	
Warminster	d	06 25			07 00		07 23		07 50				09 01		09 25		10 01		10 25		11 01	11 12	
Dilton Marsh	d	06x29					07x27		07x54						09x29				10x29				
Weymouth	d									06 38								08 46					
Upwey	d									06 43								08 51					
Dorchester West	d									06 51								08 59					
Maiden Newton	d									07 03								09 11					
Chetnole	d									07x11								09x19					
Yetminster	d									07x14								09x22					
Thornford	d									07x16								09x24					
Yeovil Pen Mill	d									07 30								09 34					
Castle Cary	a									07 43								09 47					
	d							07 33		07 44						09 40		09 48					
Bruton	d									07 49								09 54					
Frome	d			06 49						08 02								10 07					
Westbury	a	06 33		06 58	07 08		07 31	07 51	07 59	08 11			09 09		09 35	09 58	10 09	10 16	10 33		11 09	11 20	
	d		06 38		07 09	07 32	07 38	07 56	08 02	08 17	08 22	08 38	09 10	09 32	09 38	09 59	10 10	10 38		11 02	11 10	11 21	11 32
Trowbridge	d		06 44		07 15	07 38	07 44		08 08	08 23	08 28	08 44	09 16	09 38	09 44		10 16	10 44			11 16	11 27	11 38
Bradford-on-Avon	d		06 50		07 21		07 50		08 14	08 29		08 50	09 22		09 50		10 22	10 50			11 22	11 33	
Avoncliff	d		06 53				07 53			08 32		08 53			09 53			10 53					
Freshford	d		06 56				07 56			08 35		08 56			09 56			10 56					
Bath Spa 7	a		07 06		07 33		08 06		08 30	08 45		09 06	09 34		10 06		10 34	11 06			11 34	11 46	
Melksham	d					07 48					08 37			09 48									11 48
Chippenham	a					08 00					08 47			10 00									12 00
Swindon	a					08 20					09 06			10 20									12 20
London Paddington 15 ⊖	a							09 21								11 24				12 23			
Oldfield Park	a		07 10		07 37		08 11			08 49		09 10			10 10			11 10					
Keynsham	a		07 18		07 44		08 18			08 57		09 18			10 18			11 18				11 54	
Bristol Temple Meads 10	a		07 27		07 52		08 29		08 44	09 05		09 27	09 48		10 29		10 48	11 29			11 48	12 05	
Filton Abbey Wood	a		07 48				08 48		09 01			09 48	10 01		10 48		11 01	11 48			12 01		
Bristol Parkway	d		07 52				08 52					09 52			10 52			11 52					
Yate	d		08 01				09 01					10 01			11 01			12 01					
Cam & Dursley	d		08 14				09 14					10 14			11 14			12 14					
Gloucester	d		08a33				09 37					10a33			11 36			12a33					
Cheltenham Spa	d						09 48								11 48								
Ashchurch for Tewkesbury	d						09 57								11 57								
Worcester Shrub Hill	d						10 15								12 16								
Worcester Foregate Street	d						10 18								12a18								
Malvern Link	d						10 27																
Great Malvern	a						10 32																
Severn Tunnel Jn.	a																						
Newport (South Wales)	a								09 25				10 24				11 24				12 24		
Cardiff Central 7	a								09 43				10 43				11 43				12 43		

A From Plymouth
B to Bristol Temple Meads
C From Penzance
D From London Waterloo

For connections from Bristol Parkway and Cardiff Central to Swansea please see Table 128

For connections from Castle Cary, Westbury and Bristol Temple Meads to Exeter and Plymouth please see Table 135

For connections from Salisbury to Yeovil Junction and Exeter please see Table 160

For connections from Bournemouth to Southampton Central, Weymouth and Upwey please see Table 158

For Bus Connections between Yeovil Junction and Yeovil Pen Mill please see Table 123A

No full service avaiable from/to Brighton between 14 Dec - 28 Dec

Table 123

Saturdays

14 December to 28 December

Brighton, Portsmouth and Weymouth - Bristol, Cardiff, Gloucester and Great Malvern

Network Diagram - see first Page of Table 123

Station		GW	GW	GW	GW	GW		GW	GW	GW	SW	GW	GW	GW	GW	GW		GW	GW	GW	GW	GW	GW	GW	GW
		◇	◇	◇	◇1	◇			◇	◇	◇1	◇	◇1			◇			◇1	◇1	◇		◇	◇	
					A						B		C Ø		D				E	F					
Brighton 10	d	09 00																							
Hove 2	d	09 04																							
Shoreham-by-Sea	d	09 13																							
Worthing 4	d	09 22																							
Barnham	d	09 41																							
Chichester 4	d	09 49																							
Havant	d	10 00																							
Portsmouth Harbour	d		10 23			11 23				12 23						13 23					14 23			15 23	
Portsmouth & Southsea	d		10 27			11 27				12 27						13 27					14 27			15 27	
Fratton	d		10 31			11 31				12 31						13 31					14 31			15 31	
Cosham	d	10 06	10 39			11 39				12 39						13 39					14 39			15 39	
Fareham	a	10 15	10 46			11 46				12 46						13 46					14 46			15 46	
	d	10 16	10 47			11 47				12 47						13 47					14 47			15 47	
Southampton Central	d	10 42	11 10			12 10			12 27	13 10						14 10					15 10			16 10	
Romsey	d	10 53	11 21			12 21			12 38	13 21						14 21					15 21			16 21	
Salisbury	a	11 12	11 39			12 39			13 02	13 39						14 39					15 39			16 39	
	d	11 13	11 40			12 40			13 04	13 40	13 52					14 40					15 40			16 40	
Warminster	d	11 35	12 01			13 01			13 26	14 01	14 12					15 01		15 28			16 01			17 01	17 28
Dilton Marsh	d								13x30									15x33							17 32
Weymouth	d			11 10								13 10											15 08		
Upwey	d			11 15								13 15											15 13		
Dorchester West	d			11 26								13 23											15 21		
Maiden Newton	d			11 43								13 43											15 33		
Chetnole	d			11x50								13x51											15x42		
Yetminster	d			11x53								13x54											15x45		
Thornford	d			11x56								13x56											15x47		
Yeovil Pen Mill	d			12 05								14 06											15 56		
Castle Cary	a			12 19								14 19											16 09		
	d			12 22	12 45							14 20	14 44						15 50				16 10		
Bruton	d			12 27								14 26											16 16		
Frome	d			12 39								14 39			14 59					15 55			16 29		
Westbury	a	11 43	12 09	12 48	13 03	13 09			13 34	14 09	14 20	14 48	15 01		15 08	15 09		15 36		16 05	16 09		16 38	17 09	17 36
	d	11 47	12 10	12 49	13 05	13 10		13 32	13 38	14 10	14 21	14 48	15 03	15 06		15 10		15 38		16 07	16 10	16 32	16 38	17 10	17 38
Trowbridge	d	11 53	12 16	12 56		13 16		13 38	13 44	14 16	14 27	14 55		15 12		15 16		15 44			16 16	16 38	16 44	17 16	17 44
Bradford-on-Avon	d	11 59	12 22	13 02		13 22			13 50	14 22	14 33	15 01				15 22		15 50			16 22		16 48	17 22	17 50
Avoncliff	d	12 02		13 05					13 53			15 04						15 53					16 51		17 53
Freshford	d	12 05		13 07					13 56			15 06						15 56					16 54		17 56
Bath Spa 7	a	12 15	12 34	13 18		13 34			14 06	14 34	14 46	15 17				15 35		16 06			16 34		17 06	17 34	18 06
Melksham	d							13 48						15 21								16 48			
Chippenham	a							14 00						15 29								17 00			
Swindon	a							14 20						15 50								17 22			
London Paddington 15 ⊖	a				14 50								16 23						17 21	17 51					
Oldfield Park	a	12 19		13 22					14 10			15 21						16 10					17 10		18 10
Keynsham	a	12 26		13 28					14 18		14 54	15 28						16 18					17 18		18 18
Bristol Temple Meads 10	a	12 35	12 48	13 37		13 48			14 29	14 48	15 05	15 36				15 49		16 29			16 48		17 27	17 48	18 29
Filton Abbey Wood	a	12 48	13 01	13 48		14 01			14 48	15 01		15 48				16 01		16 48			17 01		17 48	18 01	18 48
Bristol Parkway	d	12 52		13 52					14 52			15 52						16 52					17 52		18 52
Yate	d	13 01		14 01					15 01			16 01						17 01					18 01		19 01
Cam & Dursley	d	13 14		14 14					15 14			16 14						17 14					18 14		19 14
Gloucester	d	13 37		14a33					15 37			16a33						17 37					18a33		19 37
Cheltenham Spa	d	13 48							15 48									17 48							19 48
Ashchurch for Tewkesbury	d	13 57							15 57									17 57							19 57
Worcester Shrub Hill	d	14 15							16 14									18 18							20 20
Worcester Foregate Street	d	14 18							16 17									18 21							20 25
Malvern Link	d	14 27							16 26									18 30							20 34
Great Malvern	a	14 32							16 32									18 36							20 40
Severn Tunnel Jn	a																				17 14			18 13	
Newport (South Wales)	a		13 25			14 24				15 24						16 24					17 26			18 25	
Cardiff Central 7	a		13 43			14 43				15 43						16 43					17 43			18 43	

A From Exeter St Davids
B From London Waterloo
C From Penzance. Ø to Westbury
D To Warminster
E From Plymouth
F From Taunton

For connections from Bristol Parkway and Cardiff Central to Swansea please see Table 128

For connections from Castle Cary, Westbury and Bristol Temple Meads to Exeter and Plymouth please see Table 135

For connections from Salisbury to Yeovil Junction and Exeter please see Table 160

For connections from Bournemouth to Southampton Central, Weymouth and Upwey please see Table 158

For Bus Connections between Yeovil Junction and Yeovil Pen Mill please see Table 123A

No full service avaiable from/to Brighton between 14 Dec - 28 Dec

Table 123

Saturdays

14 December to 28 December

Brighton, Portsmouth and Weymouth - Bristol, Cardiff, Gloucester and Great Malvern

Network Diagram - see first Page of Table 123

		GW		GW	GW	GW	GW	GW	GW	GW	GW	GW		GW	GW	GW	SW	GW	GW	GW
						◇	◇	◇1	◇	◇	◇1	◇				◇	◇1		◇	
						A		B	C		D						E			
Brighton 10	d									17 00										
Hove 2	d									17 04										
Shoreham-by-Sea	d									17 13										
Worthing 4	d									17 22										
Barnham	d									17 38										
Chichester 4	d									17 46										
Havant	d									18 00										
Portsmouth Harbour	d	16 23					17 23					18 23				19 23			20 23	
Portsmouth & Southsea	d	16 27					17 27					18 27				19 27			20 27	
Fratton	d	16 31					17 31					18 31				19 31			20 31	
Cosham	d	16 39					17 39			18 06		18 39				19 39				
Fareham	a	16 46					17 46			18 14		18 46				19 46			20 45	
	d	16 47					17 47			18 15		18 47				19 47			20 47	
Southampton Central	d	17 10					18 10			18 45		19 10				20 10			21 10	21 27
Romsey	d	17 21					18 21			18 56		19 21				20 21			21 21	21 38
Salisbury	a	17 39					18 39			19 14		19 39				20 39			21 40	22 02
	d	17 40					18 40			19 15		19 40				20 40	20 57		21 40	22 04
Warminster	d	18 01					19 01			19 36		20 01				21 01	21 17		22 01	22 26
Dilton Marsh	d									19x41										22x30
Weymouth	d					17 28												20 21		
Upwey	d					17 33												20 26		
Dorchester West	d					17 41												20 34		
Maiden Newton	d					17 52												20 45		
Chetnole	d					18x01												20x54		
Yetminster	d					18x04												20x57		
Thornford	d					18x06												20x59		
Yeovil Pen Mill	d					18 18												21 09		
Castle Cary	a					18 31												21 22		
	d					18 32		18 53			19 47							21 23		
Bruton	d					18 38												21 29		
Frome	d					18 56			←						20 53			21 42		
Westbury	a	18 09				19 05	19 09	19 11	19 05	19 45	20 05	20 09			21 02	21 09	21 25	21 51	22 10	22 34
	d	18 10		18 32	18 38	19 17	19 10	19 12	19 17	19 46	20 06	20 10		20 38		21 10	21 25	21 55	22 10	22 38
Trowbridge	d	18 16		18 38	18 44	→	19 16		19 23	19 52		20 16		20 44		21 16	21 31	22 02	22 16	22 44
Bradford-on-Avon	d	18 22			18 50		19 22		19 29	19 58		20 22		20 50		21 22	21 37	22 08	22 22	22 50
Avoncliff	d				18 53				19 32					20 53				22 11		22 53
Freshford	d				18 56				19 35					20 56				22 13		22 56
Bath Spa 7	a	18 34			19 07		19 34		19 45	20 10		20 34		21 06		21 37	21 50	22 24	22 34	23 07
Melksham	d			18 48																
Chippenham	a			19 00																
Swindon	a			19 22																
London Paddington 15 ⊖	a							20 37			21 32									
Oldfield Park	a				19 11				19 49	20 14				21 11				22 28		23 11
Keynsham	a				19 18				19 57	20 21				21 18			21 58	22 35		23 18
Bristol Temple Meads 10	a	18 48			19 29		19 48		20 05	20 29		20 48		21 28		21 51	22 06	22 44	22 50	23 28
Filton Abbey Wood	a	19 01			19 48		20 01					21 01				22 01			23 01	
Bristol Parkway	d				19 52															
Yate	d				20 01															
Cam & Dursley	d				20 14															
Gloucester	d				20 37															
Cheltenham Spa	d				20a49															
Ashchurch for Tewkesbury	d																			
Worcester Shrub Hill	d																			
Worcester Foregate Street	d																			
Malvern Link	d																			
Great Malvern	a																			
Severn Tunnel Jn.	a															22 17			23 17	
Newport (South Wales)	a	19 24					20 25					21 25				22 40			23 35	
Cardiff Central 7	a	19 41					20 43					21 43				23 00			23 55	

A To Bristol Temple Meads
B From Plymouth
C From Weymouth
D From Penzance
E From Basingstoke

For connections from Bristol Parkway and Cardiff Central to Swansea please see Table 128

For connections from Castle Cary, Westbury and Bristol Temple Meads to Exeter and Plymouth please see Table 135

For connections from Salisbury to Yeovil Junction and Exeter please see Table 160

For connections from Bournemouth to Southampton Central, Weymouth and Upwey please see Table 158

For Bus Connections between Yeovil Junction and Yeovil Pen Mill please see Table 123A

No full service avaiable from/to Brighton between 14 Dec - 28 Dec

Table 123

Saturdays

4 January to 8 February

Brighton, Portsmouth and Weymouth - Bristol, Cardiff, Gloucester and Great Malvern

Network Diagram - see first Page of Table 123

		GW	GW	GW	SW	GW	GW	GW	GW	GW	GW	GW	GW	GW	GW	GW	GW	GW	GW	GW	GW	SW	GW
					1			◇1 A ☕	◇	◇			◇ B 🛒	◇		◇1 A ☕	◇ B 🛒	◇		R 1 C ☕	◇ B 🛒	◇1 D	
Brighton 10	d																						
Hove 2	d																						
Shoreham-by-Sea	d																						
Worthing 4	d																						
Barnham	d																						
Chichester 4	d																						
Havant	d																						
Portsmouth Harbour ⛴	d								06 00				07 23				08 23				09 23		
Portsmouth & Southsea	d								06 04				07 27				08 27				09 27		
Fratton	d								06 08				07 31				08 31				09 31		
Cosham	d								06 19				07 39				08 39				09 39		
Fareham	a								06 27				07 46				08 46				09 46		
	d								06 28				07 47				08 47				09 47		
Southampton Central ⛴	d								06 53				08 10	08 27			09 10				10 10		
Romsey	d								07 11				08 21	08 38			09 21				10 21		
Salisbury	a								07 29				08 40	09 02			09 39				10 39		
	d	06 03			06 40				07 30				08 40	09 03			09 40				10 40	10 52	
Warminster	d	06 25			07 00		07 23		07 50				09 01	09 25			10 01		10 25		11 01	11 12	
Dilton Marsh	d	06x29					07x27		07x54					09x29					10x29				
Weymouth	d									06 38								08 46					
Upwey	d									06 43								08 51					
Dorchester West	d									06 51								08 59					
Maiden Newton	d									07 03								09 11					
Chetnole	d									07x11								09x19					
Yetminster	d									07x14								09x22					
Thornford	d									07x16								09x24					
Yeovil Pen Mill	d									07 30								09 34					
Castle Cary	a									07 43								09 47					
	d							07 33		07 44						09 40		09 48					
Bruton	d									07 49								09 54					
Frome	d			06 49						08 02								10 07					
Westbury	a	06 33		06 58	07 08		07 31	07 51	07 59	08 11			09 09	09 35		09 58	10 09	10 16	10 33		11 09	11 20	
	d		06 38		07 09	07 32	07 38	07 56	08 02	08 17	08 22	08 38	09 10	09 38	09 48	09 59	10 10	10 38		11 02	11 10	11 21	11 38
Trowbridge	d		06 44		07 15	07 38	07 44		08 08	08 23	08 28	08 44	09 16	09 44	09 54		10 16	10 44			11 16	11 27	11 44
Bradford-on-Avon	d		06 50		07 21		07 50		08 14	08 29		08 50	09 22	09 50			10 22	10 50			11 22	11 33	
Avoncliff	d		06 53				07 53			08 32		08 53		09 53				10 53					
Freshford	d		06 56				07 56			08 35		08 56		09 56				10 56					
Bath Spa 7	a		07 06		07 33		08 06		08 30	08 45		09 06	09 34	10 06			10 34	11 07			11 34	11 46	
Melksham	d					07 48					08 37				10 04								11 54
Chippenham	a					08 00					08 47				10 14								12 04
Swindon	a					08 20					09 06				10 34								12 24
London Paddington 15 ⊖	a							09 31								11 32				12 30			
Oldfield Park	a		07 10		07 37		08 11			08 49		09 10		10 10				11 11					
Keynsham	a		07 18		07 44		08 18			08 57		09 18		10 18				11 19				11 54	
Bristol Temple Meads 10	a		07 27		07 52		08 29		08 44	09 05		09 27	09 48	10 29			10 48	11 29			11 48	12 05	
Filton Abbey Wood	a		07 48				08 48		09 01			09 48	10 01	10 48			11 01	11 48			12 01		
Bristol Parkway	d		07 52				08 52					09 52		10 52				11 52					
Yate	d		08 01				09 01					10 01		11 01				12 01					
Cam & Dursley	d		08 14				09 14					10 14		11 14				12 14					
Gloucester	d		08a33				09 37					10a33		11 36				12a33					
Cheltenham Spa	d						09 48							11 48									
Ashchurch for Tewkesbury	d						09 57							11 57									
Worcester Shrub Hill	d						10 15							12 16									
Worcester Foregate Street	d						10 18							12a18									
Malvern Link	d						10 27																
Great Malvern	a						10 32																
Severn Tunnel Jn.	a																						
Newport (South Wales)	a								09 25				10 24				11 24				12 24		
Cardiff Central 7	a								09 43				10 43				11 43				12 43		

A From Plymouth
B 🛒 to Bristol Temple Meads
C From Penzance
D From London Waterloo

For connections from Bristol Parkway and Cardiff Central to Swansea please see Table 128

For connections from Castle Cary, Westbury and Bristol Temple Meads to Exeter and Plymouth please see Table 135

For connections from Salisbury to Yeovil Junction and Exeter please see Table 160

For connections from Bournemouth to Southampton Central, Weymouth and Upwey please see Table 158

For Bus Connections between Yeovil Junction and Yeovil Pen Mill please see Table 123A

Table 123

Saturdays

4 January to 8 February

Brighton, Portsmouth and Weymouth - Bristol, Cardiff, Gloucester and Great Malvern

Network Diagram - see first Page of Table 123

		GW	GW	GW	GW	GW		GW	GW	GW	SW	GW	GW
		◇	◇	◇	◇1	◇		◇		◇	◇1	◇	◇1
					A ☕						B		C ⊘
Brighton 10	d	09 00											
Hove 2	d	09 04											
Shoreham-by-Sea	d	09 13											
Worthing 4	d	09 22											
Barnham	d	09 41											
Chichester 4	d	09 49											
Havant	d	10 00											
Portsmouth Harbour ⛴	d		10 23			11 23				12 23			
Portsmouth & Southsea	d		10 27			11 27				12 27			
Fratton	d		10 31			11 31				12 31			
Cosham	d	10 06	10 39			11 39				12 39			
Fareham	a	10 15	10 46			11 46				12 46			
	d	10 16	10 47			11 47				12 47			
Southampton Central ⛴	d	10 42	11 10			12 10		12 27		13 10			
Romsey	d	10 53	11 21			12 21		12 38		13 21			
Salisbury	a	11 12	11 39			12 39		13 02		13 39			
	d	11 13	11 40			12 40		13 04		13 40	13 52		
Warminster	d	11 35	12 01			13 01		13 26		14 01	14 12		
Dilton Marsh	d							13x30					
Weymouth	d			11 10								13 10	
Upwey	d			11 15								13 15	
Dorchester West	d			11 26								13 23	
Maiden Newton	d			11 43								13 43	
Chetnole	d			11x50								13x51	
Yetminster	d			11x53								13x54	
Thornford	d			11x56								13x56	
Yeovil Pen Mill	d			12 05								14 06	
Castle Cary	a			12 19								14 19	
	d			12 22	12 45							14 20	14 44
Bruton	d			12 27								14 26	
Frome	d			12 39								14 39	
Westbury	a	11 43	12 09	12 48	13 03	13 09		13 34		14 09	14 20	14 48	15 01
	d	11 47	12 10	12 49	13 05	13 10		13 38	13 48	14 10	14 21	14 48	15 03
Trowbridge	d	11 53	12 16	12 56		13 16		13 44	13 54	14 16	14 27	14 55	
Bradford-on-Avon	d	11 59	12 22	13 02		13 22		13 50		14 22	14 33	15 01	
Avoncliff	d	12 02		13 05				13 53				15 04	
Freshford	d	12 05		13 07				13 56				15 06	
Bath Spa 7	a	12 15	12 34	13 18		13 34		14 08		14 34	14 46	15 17	
Melksham	d								14 04				
Chippenham	a								14 14				
Swindon	a								14 34				
London Paddington 15 ⊖	a				14 59								16 30
Oldfield Park	a	12 19		13 22				14 12				15 21	
Keynsham	a	12 26		13 28				14 20			14 54	15 28	
Bristol Temple Meads 10	a	12 35	12 48	13 37		13 48		14 31		14 48	15 05	15 36	
Filton Abbey Wood	a	12 48	13 01	13 48		14 01		14 48		15 01		15 48	
Bristol Parkway	d	12 52		13 52				14 52				15 52	
Yate	d	13 01		14 01				15 01				16 01	
Cam & Dursley	d	13 14		14 14				15 14				16 14	
Gloucester	d	13 37		14a33				15 37				16a33	
Cheltenham Spa	d	13 48						15 48					
Ashchurch for Tewkesbury	d	13 57						15 57					
Worcester Shrub Hill	d	14 15						16 14					
Worcester Foregate Street	d	14 18						16 17					
Malvern Link	d	14 27						16 26					
Great Malvern	a	14 32						16 32					
Severn Tunnel Jn.	a												
Newport (South Wales)	a		13 25			14 24				15 24			
Cardiff Central 7	a		13 43			14 43				15 43			

		GW	GW	GW		GW	GW	GW	GW	GW	GW	GW	GW
				◇			◇1	◇1	◇	◇		◇	
			D				E	F ☕					
Brighton 10	d												
Hove 2	d												
Shoreham-by-Sea	d												
Worthing 4	d												
Barnham	d												
Chichester 4	d												
Havant	d												
Portsmouth Harbour ⛴	d			13 23					14 23			15 23	
Portsmouth & Southsea	d			13 27					14 27			15 27	
Fratton	d			13 31					14 31			15 31	
Cosham	d			13 39					14 39			15 39	
Fareham	a			13 46					14 46			15 46	
	d			13 47					14 47			15 47	
Southampton Central ⛴	d			14 10					15 10			16 10	
Romsey	d			14 21					15 21			16 21	
Salisbury	a			14 39					15 39			16 39	
	d			14 40					15 40			16 40	
Warminster	d			15 01		15 28			16 01			17 01	17 28
Dilton Marsh	d					15x33							17 32
Weymouth	d									15 08			
Upwey	d									15 13			
Dorchester West	d									15 21			
Maiden Newton	d									15 33			
Chetnole	d									15x42			
Yetminster	d									15x45			
Thornford	d									15x47			
Yeovil Pen Mill	d									15 56			
Castle Cary	a									16 09			
	d						15 50			16 10			
Bruton	d									16 16			
Frome	d		14 59					15 55		16 29			
Westbury	a		15 08	15 09		15 36		16 05	16 09	16 38		17 09	17 36
	d	15 06		15 10		15 38		16 07	16 10	16 38	16 48	17 10	17 38
Trowbridge	d	15 12		15 16		15 44			16 16	16 44	16 54	17 16	17 44
Bradford-on-Avon	d			15 22		15 50			16 22	16 48		17 22	17 50
Avoncliff	d					15 53				16 51			17 53
Freshford	d					15 56				16 54			17 56
Bath Spa 7	a			15 35		16 06			16 34	17 08		17 34	18 06
Melksham	d	15 21									17 04		
Chippenham	a	15 29									17 14		
Swindon	a	15 50									17 34		
London Paddington 15 ⊖	a						17 30	17 57					
Oldfield Park	a					16 10				17 12			18 10
Keynsham	a					16 18				17 20			18 18
Bristol Temple Meads 10	a			15 49		16 29			16 48	17 29		17 48	18 29
Filton Abbey Wood	a			16 01		16 48			17 01	17 48		18 01	18 48
Bristol Parkway	d					16 52				17 52			18 52
Yate	d					17 01				18 01			19 01
Cam & Dursley	d					17 14				18 14			19 14
Gloucester	d					17 37				18a33			19 37
Cheltenham Spa	d					17 48							19 48
Ashchurch for Tewkesbury	d					17 57							19 57
Worcester Shrub Hill	d					18 18							20 20
Worcester Foregate Street	d					18 21							20 25
Malvern Link	d					18 30							20 34
Great Malvern	a					18 36							20 40
Severn Tunnel Jn.	a								17 14			18 13	
Newport (South Wales)	a			16 24					17 26			18 25	
Cardiff Central 7	a			16 43					17 43			18 43	

A From Exeter St Davids
B From London Waterloo
C From Penzance. ⊘ to Westbury
D To Warminster
E From Plymouth
F From Taunton

For connections from Bristol Parkway and Cardiff Central to Swansea please see Table 128

For connections from Castle Cary, Westbury and Bristol Temple Meads to Exeter and Plymouth please see Table 135

For connections from Salisbury to Yeovil Junction and Exeter please see Table 160

For connections from Bournemouth to Southampton Central, Weymouth and Upwey please see Table 158

For Bus Connections between Yeovil Junction and Yeovil Pen Mill please see Table 123A

Table 123

Saturdays

4 January to 8 February

Brighton, Portsmouth and Weymouth - Bristol, Cardiff, Gloucester and Great Malvern

Network Diagram - see first Page of Table 123

		GW	GW	GW	GW	GW	GW	GW	GW	GW	GW	GW	GW	GW	SW	GW	GW	GW
		R			◇ A	◇	◇1 B ☕	◇ C	◇	◇1 D ☕	◇			◇	◇1 E		◇	
Brighton 10	d								17 00									
Hove 2	d								17 04									
Shoreham-by-Sea	d								17 13									
Worthing 4	d								17 22									
Barnham	d								17 38									
Chichester 4	d								17 46									
Havant	d								18 00									
Portsmouth Harbour ⛴	d	16 23				17 23					18 23			19 23			20 23	
Portsmouth & Southsea	d	16 27				17 27					18 27			19 27			20 27	
Fratton	d	16 31				17 31					18 31			19 31			20 31	
Cosham	d	16 39				17 39			18 06		18 39			19 39				
Fareham	a	16 46				17 46			18 14		18 46			19 46			20 45	
	d	16 47				17 47			18 15		18 47			19 47			20 47	
Southampton Central ⛴	d	17 10				18 10			18 45		19 10			20 10			21 10	21 27
Romsey	d	17 21				18 21			18 56		19 21			20 21			21 21	21 38
Salisbury	a	17 39				18 39			19 14		19 39			20 39			21 40	22 02
	d	17 40				18 40			19 15		19 40			20 40	20 57		21 40	22 04
Warminster	d	18 01				19 01			19 36		20 01			21 01	21 17		22 01	22 26
Dilton Marsh	d								19x41									22x30
Weymouth	d				17 28											20 21		
Upwey	d				17 33											20 26		
Dorchester West	d				17 41											20 34		
Maiden Newton	d				17 52											20 45		
Chetnole	d				18x01											20x54		
Yetminster	d				18x04											20x57		
Thornford	d				18x06											20x59		
Yeovil Pen Mill	d				18 18											21 09		
Castle Cary	a				18 31											21 22		
	d				18 32		18 53			19 47						21 23		
Bruton	d				18 38											21 29		
Frome	d				18 56			←					20 53			21 42		
Westbury	a	18 09			19 05	19 09	19 11	19 05	19 45	20 05	20 09		21 02	21 09	21 25	21 51	22 10	22 34
	d	18 10	18 38	18 48	19 17	19 10	19 12	19 17	19 46	20 06	20 10	20 38		21 10	21 25	21 55	22 10	22 38
Trowbridge	d	18 16	18 44	18 54	↪	19 16		19 23	19 52		20 16	20 44		21 16	21 31	22 02	22 16	22 44
Bradford-on-Avon	d	18 22	18 50			19 22		19 29	19 58		20 22	20 50		21 22	21 37	22 08	22 22	22 50
Avoncliff	d		18 53					19 32				20 53				22 11		22 53
Freshford	d		18 56					19 35				20 56				22 13		22 56
Bath Spa 7	a	18 34	19 07			19 34		19 45	20 10		20 34	21 07		21 38	21 50	22 24	22 34	23 10
Melksham	d			19 04														
Chippenham	a			19 14														
Swindon	a			19 34														
London Paddington 15 ⊖	a						20 51			21 41								
Oldfield Park	a		19 11					19 49	20 14			21 12				22 28		23 14
Keynsham	a		19 18					19 57	20 21			21 20			21 58	22 35		23 22
Bristol Temple Meads 10	a	18 48	19 29			19 48		20 05	20 29		20 48	21 29		21 52	22 06	22 44	22 50	23 30
Filton Abbey Wood	a	19 01	19 48			20 01					21 01			22 01			23 01	
Bristol Parkway	d		19 52														23a07	
Yate	d		20 01															
Cam & Dursley	d		20 14															
Gloucester	d		20 37															
Cheltenham Spa	d		20a49															
Ashchurch for Tewkesbury	d																	
Worcester Shrub Hill	d																	
Worcester Foregate Street	d																	
Malvern Link	d																	
Great Malvern	a																	
Severn Tunnel Jn	a													22 17				
Newport (South Wales)	a	19 24				20 25					21 25			22 40				
Cardiff Central 7	a	19 41				20 43					21 43			23 00				

A To Bristol Temple Meads
B From Plymouth
C From Weymouth
D From Penzance
E From Basingstoke

For connections from Bristol Parkway and Cardiff Central to Swansea please see Table 128

For connections from Castle Cary, Westbury and Bristol Temple Meads to Exeter and Plymouth please see Table 135

For connections from Salisbury to Yeovil Junction and Exeter please see Table 160

For connections from Bournemouth to Southampton Central, Weymouth and Upwey please see Table 158

For Bus Connections between Yeovil Junction and Yeovil Pen Mill please see Table 123A

Table 123

Saturdays

15 February to 22 March

Brighton, Portsmouth and Weymouth - Bristol, Cardiff, Gloucester and Great Malvern

Network Diagram - see first Page of Table 123

		GW	GW	GW	SW	GW	GW	GW	GW	GW	GW	GW	GW	GW	GW	GW	GW	GW	GW	GW	GW	SW	GW
					1			◇1	◇	◇			◇		◇	◇1	◇	◇		R 1	◇	◇1	
								A ⊡					B ⊤			A ⊡	B ⊤			C ⊡	B ⊤	D	
Brighton 10	d																						
Hove 2	d																						
Shoreham-by-Sea	d																						
Worthing 4	d																						
Barnham	d																						
Chichester 4	d																						
Havant	d																						
Portsmouth Harbour ⛴	d								06 00				07 23				08 23				09 23		
Portsmouth & Southsea	d								06 04				07 27				08 27				09 27		
Fratton	d								06 08				07 31				08 31				09 31		
Cosham	d								06 19				07 39				08 39				09 39		
Fareham	a								06 27				07 46				08 46				09 46		
	d								06 28				07 47				08 47				09 47		
Southampton Central ⛴	d								06 53				08 10		08 27		09 10				10 10		
Romsey	d								07 11				08 21		08 38		09 21				10 21		
Salisbury	a								07 29				08 40		09 02		09 39				10 39		
	d	06 03			06 40				07 30				08 40		09 03		09 40				10 40	10 52	
Warminster	d	06 25			07 00		07 23		07 50				09 01		09 25		10 01		10 25		11 01	11 12	
Dilton Marsh	d	06x29					07x27		07x54						09x29				10x29				
Weymouth	d									06 38								08 46					
Upwey	d									06 43								08 51					
Dorchester West	d									06 51								08 59					
Maiden Newton	d									07 03								09 11					
Chetnole	d									07x11								09x19					
Yetminster	d									07x14								09x22					
Thornford	d									07x16								09x24					
Yeovil Pen Mill	d									07 30								09 34					
Castle Cary	a									07 43								09 47					
	d							07 33		07 44						09 40		09 48					
Bruton	d									07 49								09 54					
Frome	d			06 49						08 02								10 07					
Westbury	a	06 33		06 58	07 08		07 31	07 51	07 59	08 11			09 09		09 35	09 58	10 09	10 16	10 33		11 09	11 20	
	d		06 38		07 09	07 32	07 38	07 56	08 02	08 17	08 22	08 38	09 10	09 32	09 38	09 59	10 10	10 38		11 02	11 10	11 21	11 32
Trowbridge	d		06 44		07 15	07 38	07 44		08 08	08 23	08 28	08 44	09 16	09 38	09 44		10 16	10 44			11 16	11 27	11 38
Bradford-on-Avon	d		06 50		07 21		07 50		08 14	08 29		08 50	09 22		09 50		10 22	10 50			11 22	11 33	
Avoncliff	d		06 53				07 53			08 32		08 53			09 53			10 53					
Freshford	d		06 56				07 56			08 35		08 56			09 56			10 56					
Bath Spa 7	a		07 06		07 33		08 06		08 30	08 45		09 06	09 34		10 06		10 34	11 06			11 34	11 46	
Melksham	d					07 48					08 37			09 48									11 48
Chippenham	a					08 00					08 47			10 00									12 00
Swindon	a					08 20					09 06			10 20									12 20
London Paddington 15 ⊖	a							09 21								11 24				12 23			
Oldfield Park	a		07 10		07 37		08 11			08 49		09 10			10 10			11 10					
Keynsham	a		07 18		07 44		08 18			08 57		09 18			10 18			11 18				11 54	
Bristol Temple Meads 10	a		07 27		07 52		08 29		08 44	09 05		09 27	09 48		10 29		10 48	11 29			11 48	12 05	
Filton Abbey Wood	a		07 48				08 48		09 01			09 48	10 01		10 48		11 01	11 48			12 01		
Bristol Parkway	d		07 52				08 52					09 52			10 52			11 52					
Yate	d		08 01				09 01					10 01			11 01			12 01					
Cam & Dursley	d		08 14				09 14					10 14			11 14			12 14					
Gloucester	d		08a33				09 37					10a33			11 36			12a33					
Cheltenham Spa	d						09 48								11 48								
Ashchurch for Tewkesbury	d						09 57								11 57								
Worcester Shrub Hill	d						10 15								12 16								
Worcester Foregate Street	d						10 18								12a18								
Malvern Link	d						10 27																
Great Malvern	a						10 32																
Severn Tunnel Jn.	a																						
Newport (South Wales)	a								09 25				10 24				11 24				12 24		
Cardiff Central 7	a								09 43				10 43				11 43				12 43		

A From Plymouth
B ⊤ to Bristol Temple Meads
C From Penzance
D From London Waterloo

For connections from Bristol Parkway and Cardiff Central to Swansea please see Table 128

For connections from Castle Cary, Westbury and Bristol Temple Meads to Exeter and Plymouth please see Table 135

For connections from Salisbury to Yeovil Junction and Exeter please see Table 160

For connections from Bournemouth to Southampton Central, Weymouth and Upwey please see Table 158

For Bus Connections between Yeovil Junction and Yeovil Pen Mill please see Table 123A

Table 123

Saturdays

15 February to 22 March

Brighton, Portsmouth and Weymouth - Bristol, Cardiff, Gloucester and Great Malvern

Network Diagram - see first Page of Table 123

		GW ◇	GW ◇	GW ◇	GW ◇1 A ☕	GW ◇	GW	GW ◇	GW ◇	SW ◇1 B	GW ◇	GW ◇1 C ⌀	GW	GW D	GW ◇	GW	GW ◇1 E	GW ◇1 F ☕	GW ◇	GW	GW ◇	GW ◇	GW
Brighton 10	d	09 00																					
Hove 2	d	09 04																					
Shoreham-by-Sea	d	09 13																					
Worthing 4	d	09 22																					
Barnham	d	09 41																					
Chichester 4	d	09 49																					
Havant	d	10 00																					
Portsmouth Harbour ⛴	d		10 23			11 23			12 23						13 23				14 23			15 23	
Portsmouth & Southsea	d		10 27			11 27			12 27						13 27				14 27			15 27	
Fratton	d		10 31			11 31			12 31						13 31				14 31			15 31	
Cosham	d	10 06	10 39			11 39			12 39						13 39				14 39			15 39	
Fareham	a	10 15	10 46			11 46			12 46						13 46				14 46			15 46	
	d	10 16	10 47			11 47			12 47						13 47				14 47			15 47	
Southampton Central ⛴	d	10 42	11 10			12 10		12 27	13 10						14 10				15 10			16 10	
Romsey	d	10 53	11 21			12 21		12 38	13 21						14 21				15 21			16 21	
Salisbury	a	11 12	11 39			12 39		13 02	13 39						14 39				15 39			16 39	
	d	11 13	11 40			12 40		13 04	13 40	13 52					14 40				15 40			16 40	
Warminster	d	11 35	12 01			13 01		13 26	14 01	14 12					15 01	15 28			16 01			17 01	17 28
Dilton Marsh	d							13x30								15x33							17 32
Weymouth	d			11 10							13 10										15 08		
Upwey	d			11 15							13 15										15 13		
Dorchester West	d			11 26							13 23										15 21		
Maiden Newton	d			11 43							13 43										15 33		
Chetnole	d			11x50							13x51										15x42		
Yetminster	d			11x53							13x54										15x45		
Thornford	d			11x56							13x56										15x47		
Yeovil Pen Mill	d			12 05							14 06										15 56		
Castle Cary	a			12 19							14 19										16 09		
	d			12 22	12 45						14 20	14 44					15 50				16 10		
Bruton	d			12 27							14 26										16 16		
Frome	d			12 39							14 39			14 59				15 55			16 29		
Westbury	a	11 43	12 09	12 48	13 03	13 09		13 34	14 09	14 20	14 48	15 01		15 08	15 09	15 36		16 05	16 09		16 38	17 09	17 36
	d	11 47	12 10	12 49	13 05	13 10	13 32	13 38	14 10	14 21	14 48	15 03	15 06		15 10	15 38		16 07	16 10	16 32	16 38	17 10	17 38
Trowbridge	d	11 53	12 16	12 56		13 16	13 38	13 44	14 16	14 27	14 55		15 12		15 16	15 44			16 16	16 38	16 44	17 16	17 44
Bradford-on-Avon	d	11 59	12 22	13 02		13 22		13 50	14 22	14 33	15 01				15 22	15 50			16 22		16 48	17 22	17 50
Avoncliff	d	12 02		13 05				13 53			15 04					15 53					16 51		17 53
Freshford	d	12 05		13 07				13 56			15 06					15 56					16 54		17 56
Bath Spa 7	a	12 15	12 34	13 18		13 34		14 06	14 34	14 46	15 17				15 35	16 06			16 34		17 06	17 34	18 06
Melksham	d						13 48						15 21							16 48			
Chippenham	a						14 00						15 29							17 00			
Swindon	a						14 20						15 50							17 22			
London Paddington 15 ⊖	a				14 50							16 23					17 21	17 51					
Oldfield Park	a	12 19		13 22				14 10			15 21					16 10					17 10		18 10
Keynsham	a	12 26		13 28				14 18		14 54	15 28					16 18					17 18		18 18
Bristol Temple Meads 10	a	12 35	12 48	13 37		13 48		14 29	14 48	15 05	15 36				15 49	16 29			16 48		17 27	17 48	18 29
Filton Abbey Wood	a	12 48	13 01	13 48		14 01		14 48	15 01		15 48				16 01	16 48			17 01		17 48	18 01	18 48
Bristol Parkway	d	12 52		13 52				14 52			15 52					16 52					17 52		18 52
Yate	d	13 01		14 01				15 01			16 01					17 01					18 01		19 01
Cam & Dursley	d	13 14		14 14				15 14			16 14					17 14					18 14		19 14
Gloucester	d	13 37		14a33				15 37			16a33					17 37					18a33		19 37
Cheltenham Spa	d	13 48						15 48								17 48							19 48
Ashchurch for Tewkesbury	d	13 57						15 57								17 57							19 57
Worcester Shrub Hill	d	14 15						16 14								18 18							20 20
Worcester Foregate Street	d	14 18						16 17								18 21							20 25
Malvern Link	d	14 27						16 26								18 30							20 34
Great Malvern	a	14 32						16 32								18 36							20 40
Severn Tunnel Jn.	a																		17 14			18 13	
Newport (South Wales)	a		13 25			14 24			15 24						16 24				17 26			18 25	
Cardiff Central 7	a		13 43			14 43			15 43						16 43				17 43			18 43	

A From Exeter St Davids
B From London Waterloo
C From Penzance. ⌀ to Westbury
D To Warminster
E From Plymouth
F From Taunton

For connections from Bristol Parkway and Cardiff Central to Swansea please see Table 128

For connections from Castle Cary, Westbury and Bristol Temple Meads to Exeter and Plymouth please see Table 135

For connections from Salisbury to Yeovil Junction and Exeter please see Table 160

For connections from Bournemouth to Southampton Central, Weymouth and Upwey please see Table 158

For Bus Connections between Yeovil Junction and Yeovil Pen Mill please see Table 123A

Table 123

Saturdays

15 February to 22 March

Brighton, Portsmouth and Weymouth - Bristol, Cardiff, Gloucester and Great Malvern

Network Diagram - see first Page of Table 123

		GW		GW	GW	GW	GW	GW	GW	GW	GW	GW		GW	GW	GW	SW	GW	GW	GW
		■																		
						◇	◇	◇■1	◇	◇	◇■1	◇				◇	◇■1		◇	
						A		B	C		D						E			
								🛏			🛏									
Brighton ■10	d									17 00										
Hove ■2	d									17 04										
Shoreham-by-Sea	d									17 13										
Worthing ■4	d									17 22										
Barnham	d									17 38										
Chichester ■4	d									17 46										
Havant	d									18 00										
Portsmouth Harbour ⛴	d	16 23					17 23					18 23				19 23			20 23	
Portsmouth & Southsea	d	16 27					17 27					18 27				19 27			20 27	
Fratton	d	16 31					17 31					18 31				19 31			20 31	
Cosham	d	16 39					17 39			18 06		18 39				19 39				
Fareham	a	16 46					17 46			18 14		18 46				19 46			20 45	
	d	16 47					17 47			18 15		18 47				19 47			20 47	
Southampton Central ⛴	d	17 10					18 10			18 45		19 10				20 10			21 10	21 27
Romsey	d	17 21					18 21			18 56		19 21				20 21			21 21	21 38
Salisbury	a	17 39					18 39			19 14		19 39				20 39			21 40	22 02
	d	17 40					18 40			19 15		19 40				20 40	20 57		21 40	22 04
Warminster	d	18 01					19 01			19 36		20 01				21 01	21 17		22 01	22 26
Dilton Marsh	d									19x41										22x30
Weymouth	d					17 28												20 21		
Upwey	d					17 33												20 26		
Dorchester West	d					17 41												20 34		
Maiden Newton	d					17 52												20 45		
Chetnole	d					18x01												20x54		
Yetminster	d					18x04												20x57		
Thornford	d					18x06												20x59		
Yeovil Pen Mill	d					18 18												21 09		
Castle Cary	a					18 31												21 22		
	d					18 32		18 53			19 47							21 23		
Bruton	d					18 38												21 29		
Frome	d					18 56			←						20 53			21 42		
Westbury	a	18 09				19 05	19 09	19 11	19 05	19 45	20 05	20 09			21 02	21 09	21 25	21 51	22 10	22 34
	d	18 10		18 32	18 38	19 17	19 10	19 12	19 17	19 46	20 06	20 10		20 38		21 10	21 25	21 55	22 10	22 38
Trowbridge	d	18 16		18 38	18 44	→	19 16		19 23	19 52		20 16		20 44		21 16	21 31	22 02	22 16	22 44
Bradford-on-Avon	d	18 22			18 50		19 22		19 29	19 58		20 22		20 50		21 22	21 37	22 08	22 22	22 50
Avoncliff	d				18 53				19 32					20 53				22 11		22 53
Freshford	d				18 56				19 35					20 56				22 13		22 56
Bath Spa ■7	a	18 34			19 07		19 34		19 45	20 10		20 34		21 06		21 37	21 50	22 24	22 34	23 07
Melksham	d			18 48																
Chippenham	a			19 00																
Swindon	a			19 22																
London Paddington ■15 ⊖	a							20 37			21 32									
Oldfield Park	a				19 11				19 49	20 14				21 11				22 28		23 11
Keynsham	a				19 18				19 57	20 21				21 18			21 58	22 35		23 18
Bristol Temple Meads ■10	a	18 48			19 29		19 48		20 05	20 29		20 48		21 28		21 51	22 06	22 44	22 50	23 28
Filton Abbey Wood	a	19 01			19 48		20 01					21 01				22 01			23 01	
Bristol Parkway	d				19 52															
Yate	d				20 01															
Cam & Dursley	d				20 14															
Gloucester	d				20 37															
Cheltenham Spa	d				20a49															
Ashchurch for Tewkesbury	d																			
Worcester Shrub Hill	d																			
Worcester Foregate Street	d																			
Malvern Link	d																			
Great Malvern	a																			
Severn Tunnel Jn.	a															22 17			23 17	
Newport (South Wales)	a	19 24					20 25					21 25				22 40			23 35	
Cardiff Central ■7	a	19 41					20 43					21 43				23 00			23 55	

A To Bristol Temple Meads
B From Plymouth
C From Weymouth
D From Penzance
E From Basingstoke

For connections from Bristol Parkway and Cardiff Central to Swansea please see Table 128

For connections from Castle Cary, Westbury and Bristol Temple Meads to Exeter and Plymouth please see Table 135

For connections from Salisbury to Yeovil Junction and Exeter please see Table 160

For connections from Bournemouth to Southampton Central, Weymouth and Upwey please see Table 158

For Bus Connections between Yeovil Junction and Yeovil Pen Mill please see Table 123A

Table 123

Saturdays
29 March to 17 May

Brighton, Portsmouth and Weymouth - Bristol, Cardiff, Gloucester and Great Malvern

Network Diagram - see first Page of Table 123

		GW	GW	GW	SW	GW	GW	GW	GW	GW		GW	GW	GW	GW	GW	GW	GW	GW	GW		GW	GW	SW	GW
					1			◇1 A 🍴	◇	◇				◇ B 🛒		◇	◇1 A 🍴	◇ B 🛒	◇			R 1 C 🍴	◇ B 🛒	◇1 D	
Brighton 10	d																								
Hove 2	d																								
Shoreham-by-Sea	d																								
Worthing 4	d																								
Barnham	d																								
Chichester 4	d																								
Havant	d																								
Portsmouth Harbour ⛴	d								06 00					07 23				08 23					09 23		
Portsmouth & Southsea	d								06 04					07 27				08 27					09 27		
Fratton	d								06 08					07 31				08 31					09 31		
Cosham	d								06 19					07 39				08 39					09 39		
Fareham	a								06 27					07 46				08 46					09 46		
	d								06 28					07 47				08 47					09 47		
Southampton Central ⛴	d								06 53					08 10		08 27		09 10					10 10		
Romsey	d								07 11					08 21		08 38		09 21					10 21		
Salisbury	a								07 29					08 40		09 02		09 39					10 39		
	d	06 03			06 40				07 30					08 40		09 03		09 40					10 40	10 52	
Warminster	d	06 25			07 00		07 23		07 50					09 01		09 25		10 01		10 25			11 01	11 12	
Dilton Marsh	d	06x29					07x27		07x54							09x29				10x29					
Weymouth	d									06 38									08 46						
Upwey	d									06 43									08 51						
Dorchester West	d									06 51									08 59						
Maiden Newton	d									07 03									09 11						
Chetnole	d									07x11									09x19						
Yetminster	d									07x14									09x22						
Thornford	d									07x16									09x24						
Yeovil Pen Mill	d									07 30									09 34						
Castle Cary	a									07 43									09 47						
	d							07 33		07 44							09 40		09 48						
Bruton	d									07 49									09 54						
Frome	d			06 49						08 02									10 07						
Westbury	a	06 33		06 58	07 08		07 31	07 51	07 59	08 11				09 09		09 35	09 58	10 09	10 16	10 33			11 09	11 20	
	d		06 38		07 09	07 32	07 38	07 56	08 02	08 17		08 22	08 38	09 10	09 32	09 38	09 59	10 10	10 38			11 02	11 10	11 21	11 32
Trowbridge	d		06 44		07 15	07 38	07 44		08 08	08 23		08 28	08 44	09 16	09 38	09 44		10 16	10 44				11 16	11 27	11 38
Bradford-on-Avon	d		06 50		07 21		07 50		08 14	08 29			08 50	09 22		09 50		10 22	10 50				11 22	11 33	
Avoncliff	d		06 53				07 53			08 32			08 53			09 53			10 53						
Freshford	d		06 56				07 56			08 35			08 56			09 56			10 56						
Bath Spa 7	a		07 06		07 33		08 06		08 30	08 45			09 06	09 34		10 06		10 34	11 06				11 34	11 46	
Melksham	d					07 48						08 37			09 48										11 48
Chippenham	a					08 00						08 47			10 00										12 00
Swindon	a					08 20						09 06			10 20										12 20
London Paddington 15 ⊖	a							09 21									11 24					12 23			
Oldfield Park	a		07 10		07 37		08 11			08 49			09 10			10 10			11 10						
Keynsham	a		07 18		07 44		08 18			08 57			09 18			10 18			11 18					11 54	
Bristol Temple Meads 10	a		07 27		07 52		08 29		08 44	09 05			09 27	09 48		10 29		10 48	11 29				11 48	12 05	
Filton Abbey Wood	a		07 48				08 48		09 01				09 48	10 01		10 48		11 01	11 48				12 01		
Bristol Parkway	d		07 52				08 52						09 52			10 52			11 52						
Yate	d		08 01				09 01						10 01			11 01			12 01						
Cam & Dursley	d		08 14				09 14						10 14			11 14			12 14						
Gloucester	d		08a33				09 37						10a33			11 36			12a33						
Cheltenham Spa	d						09 48									11 48									
Ashchurch for Tewkesbury	d						09 57									11 57									
Worcester Shrub Hill	d						10 15									12 16									
Worcester Foregate Street	d						10 18									12a18									
Malvern Link	d						10 27																		
Great Malvern	a						10 32																		
Severn Tunnel Jn.	a																								
Newport (South Wales)	a								09 25					10 24				11 24					12 24		
Cardiff Central 7	a								09 43					10 43				11 43					12 43		

A From Plymouth
B 🛒 to Bristol Temple Meads
C From Penzance
D From London Waterloo

For connections from Bristol Parkway and Cardiff Central to Swansea please see Table 128

For connections from Castle Cary, Westbury and Bristol Temple Meads to Exeter and Plymouth please see Table 135

For connections from Salisbury to Yeovil Junction and Exeter please see Table 160

For connections from Bournemouth to Southampton Central, Weymouth and Upwey please see Table 158

For Bus Connections between Yeovil Junction and Yeovil Pen Mill please see Table 123A

Table 123

Saturdays
29 March to 17 May

Brighton, Portsmouth and Weymouth - Bristol, Cardiff, Gloucester and Great Malvern

Network Diagram - see first Page of Table 123

		GW	GW	GW	GW	GW	GW	GW	GW	SW	GW	GW	GW	GW	GW	GW	GW	GW	GW	GW	GW	GW	GW
		◇	◇	◇	◇1	◇		◇	◇	◇1	◇	◇1			◇		◇1	◇1	◇		◇	◇	
					A ☕					B		C ⊘		D			E	F ☕					
Brighton 10	d	09 00																					
Hove 2	d	09 04																					
Shoreham-by-Sea	d	09 13																					
Worthing 4	d	09 22																					
Barnham	d	09 41																					
Chichester 4	d	09 49																					
Havant	d	10 00																					
Portsmouth Harbour ⛴	d		10 23			11 23			12 23						13 23				14 23			15 23	
Portsmouth & Southsea	d		10 27			11 27			12 27						13 27				14 27			15 27	
Fratton	d		10 31			11 31			12 31						13 31				14 31			15 31	
Cosham	d	10 06	10 39			11 39			12 39						13 39				14 39			15 39	
Fareham	a	10 15	10 46			11 46			12 46						13 46				14 46			15 46	
	d	10 16	10 47			11 47			12 47						13 47				14 47			15 47	
Southampton Central ⛴	d	10 42	11 10			12 10		12 27	13 10						14 10				15 10			16 10	
Romsey	d	10 53	11 21			12 21		12 38	13 21						14 21				15 21			16 21	
Salisbury	a	11 12	11 39			12 39		13 02	13 39						14 39				15 39			16 39	
	d	11 13	11 40			12 40		13 04	13 40	13 52					14 40				15 40			16 40	
Warminster	d	11 35	12 01			13 01		13 26	14 01	14 12					15 01	15 28			16 01			17 01	17 28
Dilton Marsh	d							13x30								15x33							17 32
Weymouth	d			11 10							13 10										15 08		
Upwey	d			11 15							13 15										15 13		
Dorchester West	d			11 26							13 23										15 21		
Maiden Newton	d			11 43							13 43										15 33		
Chetnole	d			11x50							13x51										15x42		
Yetminster	d			11x53							13x54										15x45		
Thornford	d			11x56							13x56										15x47		
Yeovil Pen Mill	d			12 05							14 06										15 56		
Castle Cary	a			12 19							14 19										16 09		
	d			12 22	12 45						14 20	14 44					15 50				16 10		
Bruton	d			12 27							14 26										16 16		
Frome	d			12 39							14 39			14 59				15 55			16 29		
Westbury	a	11 43	12 09	12 48	13 03	13 09		13 34	14 09	14 20	14 48	15 01		15 08	15 09	15 36		16 05	16 09		16 38	17 09	17 36
	d	11 47	12 10	12 49	13 05	13 10	13 32	13 38	14 10	14 21	14 48	15 03	15 06		15 10	15 38		16 07	16 10	16 32	16 38	17 10	17 38
Trowbridge	d	11 53	12 16	12 56		13 16	13 38	13 44	14 16	14 27	14 55		15 12		15 16	15 44			16 16	16 38	16 44	17 16	17 44
Bradford-on-Avon	d	11 59	12 22	13 02		13 22		13 50	14 22	14 33	15 01				15 22	15 50			16 22		16 48	17 22	17 50
Avoncliff	d	12 02		13 05				13 53			15 04					15 53					16 51		17 53
Freshford	d	12 05		13 07				13 56			15 06					15 56					16 54		17 56
Bath Spa 7	a	12 15	12 34	13 18		13 34		14 06	14 34	14 46	15 17				15 35	16 06			16 34		17 06	17 34	18 06
Melksham	d						13 48						15 21							16 48			
Chippenham	a						14 00						15 29							17 00			
Swindon	a						14 20						15 50							17 22			
London Paddington 15 ⊖	a				14 50							16 23					17 21	17 51					
Oldfield Park	a	12 19		13 22				14 10			15 21					16 10					17 10		18 10
Keynsham	a	12 26		13 28				14 18		14 54	15 28					16 18					17 18		18 18
Bristol Temple Meads 10	a	12 35	12 48	13 37		13 48		14 29	14 48	15 05	15 36				15 49	16 29			16 48		17 27	17 48	18 29
Filton Abbey Wood	a	12 48	13 01	13 48		14 01		14 48	15 01		15 48				16 01	16 48			17 01		17 48	18 01	18 48
Bristol Parkway	d	12 52		13 52				14 52			15 52					16 52					17 52		18 52
Yate	d	13 01		14 01				15 01			16 01					17 01					18 01		19 01
Cam & Dursley	d	13 14		14 14				15 14			16 14					17 14					18 14		19 14
Gloucester	d	13 37		14a33				15 37			16a33					17 37					18a33		19 37
Cheltenham Spa	d	13 48						15 48								17 48							19 48
Ashchurch for Tewkesbury	d	13 57						15 57								17 57							19 57
Worcester Shrub Hill	d	14 15						16 14								18 18							20 20
Worcester Foregate Street	d	14 18						16 17								18 21							20 25
Malvern Link	d	14 27						16 26								18 30							20 34
Great Malvern	a	14 32						16 32								18 36							20 40
Severn Tunnel Jn	a																		17 14			18 13	
Newport (South Wales)	a		13 25			14 24			15 24						16 24				17 26			18 25	
Cardiff Central 7	a		13 43			14 43			15 43						16 43				17 43			18 43	

A From Exeter St Davids
B From London Waterloo
C From Penzance. ⊘ to Westbury
D To Warminster
E From Plymouth
F From Taunton

For connections from Bristol Parkway and Cardiff Central to Swansea please see Table 128

For connections from Castle Cary, Westbury and Bristol Temple Meads to Exeter and Plymouth please see Table 135

For connections from Salisbury to Yeovil Junction and Exeter please see Table 160

For connections from Bournemouth to Southampton Central, Weymouth and Upwey please see Table 158

For Bus Connections between Yeovil Junction and Yeovil Pen Mill please see Table 123A

Table 123

Saturdays

29 March to 17 May

Brighton, Portsmouth and Weymouth - Bristol, Cardiff, Gloucester and Great Malvern

Network Diagram - see first Page of Table 123

		GW	GW	GW	GW	GW	GW	GW	GW	GW	GW	GW	GW	GW	SW	GW	GW	GW
		■			◇	◇	◇■	◇	◇	◇■	◇			◇	◇■		◇	
					A		B	C		D					E			
							🍴			🍴								
Brighton ■	d								17 00									
Hove ■	d								17 04									
Shoreham-by-Sea	d								17 13									
Worthing ■	d								17 22									
Barnham	d								17 38									
Chichester ■	d								17 46									
Havant	d								18 00									
Portsmouth Harbour ⛴	d	16 23				17 23					18 23			19 23			20 23	
Portsmouth & Southsea	d	16 27				17 27					18 27			19 27			20 27	
Fratton	d	16 31				17 31					18 31			19 31			20 31	
Cosham	d	16 39				17 39			18 06		18 39			19 39				
Fareham	a	16 46				17 46			18 14		18 46			19 46			20 45	
	d	16 47				17 47			18 15		18 47			19 47			20 47	
Southampton Central ⛴	d	17 10				18 10			18 45		19 10			20 10			21 10	21 27
Romsey	d	17 21				18 21			18 56		19 21			20 21			21 21	21 38
Salisbury	a	17 39				18 39			19 14		19 39			20 39			21 40	22 02
	d	17 40				18 40			19 15		19 40			20 40	20 57		21 40	22 04
Warminster	d	18 01				19 01			19 36		20 01			21 01	21 17		22 01	22 26
Dilton Marsh	d								19x41									22x30
Weymouth	d				17 28											20 21		
Upwey	d				17 33											20 26		
Dorchester West	d				17 41											20 34		
Maiden Newton	d				17 52											20 45		
Chetnole	d				18x01											20x54		
Yetminster	d				18x04											20x57		
Thornford	d				18x06											20x59		
Yeovil Pen Mill	d				18 18											21 09		
Castle Cary	a				18 31											21 22		
	d				18 32		18 53			19 47						21 23		
Bruton	d				18 38											21 29		
Frome	d				18 56			←					20 53			21 42		
Westbury	a	18 09			19 05	19 09	19 11	19 05	19 45	20 05	20 09		21 02	21 09	21 25	21 51	22 10	22 34
	d	18 10	18 32	18 38	19 17	19 10	19 12	19 17	19 46	20 06	20 10	20 38		21 10	21 25	21 55	22 10	22 38
Trowbridge	d	18 16	18 38	18 44	→	19 16		19 23	19 52		20 16	20 44		21 16	21 31	22 02	22 16	22 44
Bradford-on-Avon	d	18 22		18 50		19 22		19 29	19 58		20 22	20 50		21 22	21 37	22 08	22 22	22 50
Avoncliff	d			18 53				19 32				20 53				22 11		22 53
Freshford	d			18 56				19 35				20 56				22 13		22 56
Bath Spa ■	a	18 34		19 07		19 34		19 45	20 10		20 34	21 06		21 37	21 50	22 24	22 34	23 11
Melksham	d		18 48															
Chippenham	a		19 00															
Swindon	a		19 22															
London Paddington ■ ⊖	a						20 37			21 32								
Oldfield Park	a			19 11				19 49	20 14			21 11				22 28		23 15
Keynsham	a			19 18				19 57	20 21			21 18			21 58	22 35		23 22
Bristol Temple Meads ■	a	18 48		19 29		19 48		20 05	20 29		20 48	21 28		21 51	22 06	22 44	22 50	23 32
Filton Abbey Wood	a	19 01		19 48		20 01					21 01			22 01			23 01	
Bristol Parkway	d			19 52														
Yate	d			20 01														
Cam & Dursley	d			20 14														
Gloucester	d			20 37														
Cheltenham Spa	d			20a49														
Ashchurch for Tewkesbury	d																	
Worcester Shrub Hill	d																	
Worcester Foregate Street	d																	
Malvern Link	d																	
Great Malvern	a																	
Severn Tunnel Jn.	a													22 17			23 17	
Newport (South Wales)	a	19 24				20 25					21 25			22 40			23 35	
Cardiff Central ■	a	19 41				20 43					21 43			23 00			23 55	

A To Bristol Temple Meads
B From Plymouth
C From Weymouth
D From Penzance
E From Basingstoke

For connections from Bristol Parkway and Cardiff Central to Swansea please see Table 128

For connections from Castle Cary, Westbury and Bristol Temple Meads to Exeter and Plymouth please see Table 135

For connections from Salisbury to Yeovil Junction and Exeter please see Table 160

For connections from Bournemouth to Southampton Central, Weymouth and Upwey please see Table 158

For Bus Connections between Yeovil Junction and Yeovil Pen Mill please see Table 123A

Table 123

Sundays

8 December to 29 December

Brighton, Portsmouth and Weymouth - Bristol, Cardiff, Gloucester and Great Malvern

Network Diagram - see first Page of Table 123

Station		GW	GW	GW	GW	GW	GW	GW	GW	GW		GW	GW	GW	SW	GW	GW	GW	GW	GW		GW	GW	GW	GW
		A	◇1 B	C		◇1 D	R		◇1 E	◇			◇	R 1 E	◇1 F	◇	◇	◇1 D	◇			R		◇1 D	◇
Brighton 10	d												11 10												
Hove 2	d												11 14												
Shoreham-by-Sea	d												11 20												
Worthing 4	d												11 29												
Barnham	d												11 53												
Chichester 4	d												12 01												
Havant	d												12 12												
Portsmouth Harbour	d						09 08			11 08						13 08			14 08			15 08			16 08
Portsmouth & Southsea	d						09 12			11 12						13 12			14 12			15 12			16 12
Fratton	d						09 16			11 16						13 16			14 16			15 16			16 16
Cosham	d						09 23			11 23			12 23			13 23			14 23			15 23			16 23
Fareham	a						09 31			11 31			12 31			13 31			14 31			15 31			16 31
	d						09 32			11 32			12 32			13 32			14 32			15 32			16 32
Southampton Central	d						09 54			11 54			12 54			13 54			14 54			15 54			16 54
Romsey	d						10 06			12 06			13 06			14 06			15 06			16 06			17 06
Salisbury	a						10 24			12 24			13 24			14 24			15 24			16 24			17 24
	d						10 26			12 27			13 26		13 55	14 27			15 27			16 27			17 27
Warminster	d						10 46			12 46			13 46		14 15	14 48			15 48			16 48			17 48
Dilton Marsh	d						10x51									14x53			15x53			16x53			
Weymouth	d																14 00								
Upwey	d																14 05								
Dorchester West	d																14 13								
Maiden Newton	d																14 25								
Chetnole	d																14x33								
Yetminster	d																14x36								
Thornford	d																14x38								
Yeovil Pen Mill	d																14 48								
Castle Cary	a																15 00								
	d		09 34						12 33								15 03	15 34						17 37	
Bruton	d																15 08								
Frome	d	09 39		←													15 21								
Westbury	a	09 48	09 51	09 48			10 56		12 52	12 56			13 56		14 23	14 56	15 30	15 51	15 56			16 56		17 54	17 56
	d	09 58	09 54	09 58	10 32	10 52	10 59	11 50	12 53	12 56		13 32	13 56	13 59	14 24	15 00	15 31	15 52	16 00	16 29		17 00	17 16	17 56	18 00
Trowbridge	d	→		10 04	10 37		11 05	11 56		13 02		13 37	14 02		14 30	15 06	15 37		16 06	16 34		17 06	17 21		18 06
Bradford-on-Avon	d			10 10			11 11	12 02		13 08			14 08		14 36	15 12	15 43		16 12			17 12			18 12
Avoncliff	d			10 13				12 05					14 11				15 46								18 16
Freshford	d			10 15				12 07					14 14				15 49								18 19
Bath Spa 7	a			10 26			11 24	12 19		13 22			14 24		14 50	15 24	15 59		16 24			17 24			18 30
Melksham	d				10 47							13 47								16 44			17 31		
Chippenham	a				11 00							14 00								17 00			17 41		
Swindon	a				11 19							14 19								17 17			18 00		
London Paddington 15 ⊖	a		11 29			12 29			14 30					15 30				17 30						19 29	
Oldfield Park	a			10 30			11 27	12 23		13 25			14 27				16 02					17 28			
Keynsham	a			10 37			11 35	12 30		13 32			14 35		14 58		16 10					17 35			
Bristol Temple Meads 10	a			10 45			11 44	12 38		13 41			14 44		15 06	15 40	16 19		16 37			17 44			18 43
Filton Abbey Wood	a						11 55			13 55			14 55			15 55			16 55			17 55			18 55
Bristol Parkway	d																								
Yate	d																								
Cam & Dursley	d																								
Gloucester	d																								
Cheltenham Spa	d																								
Ashchurch for Tewkesbury	d																								
Worcester Shrub Hill	d																								
Worcester Foregate Street	d																								
Malvern Link	d																								
Great Malvern	a																								
Severn Tunnel Jn.	a						12 11			14 08			15 05			16 08			17 10			18 08			19 08
Newport (South Wales)	a						12 30			14 26			15 24			16 26			17 29			18 26			19 26
Cardiff Central 7	a						12 45			14 46			15 41			16 44			17 46			18 44			19 42

A To Bristol Temple Meads
B From Exeter St Davids
C From Frome
D From Plymouth
E From Penzance
F From London Waterloo

For connections from Bristol Parkway and Cardiff Central to Swansea please see Table 128

For connections from Castle Cary, Westbury and Bristol Temple Meads to Exeter and Plymouth please see Table 135

For connections from Salisbury to Yeovil Junction and Exeter please see Table 160

For connections from Bournemouth to Southampton Central, Weymouth and Upwey please see Table 158

For Bus Connections between Yeovil Junction and Yeovil Pen Mill please see Table 123A

Table 123

Sundays

8 December to 29 December

Brighton, Portsmouth and Weymouth - Bristol, Cardiff, Gloucester and Great Malvern

Network Diagram - see first Page of Table 123

		GW	GW	GW	GW	GW	GW	GW	SW	GW	GW	GW	GW	GW	GW	GW	GW
		◇		◇	◇		◇1	◇	◇1	◇1	◇	◇		◇1		◇	
							A		B	C			D	C	E		
							⊡			⊡				⊡			
Brighton 10	d	15 46									17 46						
Hove 2	d	15 50									17 50						
Shoreham-by-Sea	d	15 56									17 56						
Worthing 4	d	16 08									18 08						
Barnham	d	16 23									18 23						
Chichester 4	d	16 37									18 32						
Havant	d	16 48									18 50						
Portsmouth Harbour ⛴	d			17 08				18 08				19 08				20 08	22 05
Portsmouth & Southsea	d			17 12				18 12				19 12				20 12	22 12
Fratton	d			17 16				18 16				19 16				20 16	22 16
Cosham	d	16 55		17 23				18 23			18 57	19 23					
Fareham	a	17 03		17 31				18 31			19 04	19 31				20 31	22 31
	d	17 03		17 32				18 32			19 05	19 32				20 32	22 32
Southampton Central ⛴	d	17 26		17 54				18 54			19 28	19 54				20 54	22 57
Romsey	d	17 39		18 06				19 06			19 40	20 06				21 06	23 09
Salisbury	a	18 00		18 24				19 24			19 58	20 24				21 24	23 27
	d	18 01		18 27				19 25	19 55		20 01	20 27				21 27	23 28
Warminster	d	18 21		18 48				19 48	20 15		20 21	20 48				21 48	23 48
Dilton Marsh	d	18x26									20x26					21x53	23x53
Weymouth	d				17 56								20 09				
Upwey	d				18 01								20 14				
Dorchester West	d				18 09								20 22				
Maiden Newton	d				18 21								20 34				
Chetnole	d				18x29								20x42				
Yetminster	d				18x32								20x45				
Thornford	d				18x34								20x47				
Yeovil Pen Mill	d				18 44								20 57				
Castle Cary	a				18 56								21 09				
	d				18 59					20 07			21 10	21 19			
Bruton	d				19 05								21 16				
Frome	d				19 18								21 34		←		
Westbury	a	18 29		18 56	19 27			19 55	20 23	20 26	20 30	20 56	21 43	21 39	21 43	21 56	23 57
	d	18 32	18 50	18 57	19 30	19 40	19 51	20 00	20 23	20 27	20 39	21 00	21 48	21 40	21 48	22 00	
Trowbridge	d	18 38	18 56	19 02	19 36	19 45		20 06	20 29		20 45	21 06	→		21 54	22 06	
Bradford-on-Avon	d	18 44		19 08	19 42			20 12	20 35		20 51	21 12			22 00	22 12	
Avoncliff	d				19 45						20 54				22 03		
Freshford	d				19 48						20 57				22 06		
Bath Spa 7	a	18 55		19 22	19 58			20 26	20 49		21 08	21 26			22 17	22 26	
Melksham	d		19 05			19 56											
Chippenham	a		19 15			20 06											
Swindon	a		19 33			20 24											
London Paddington 15 ⊖	a						21 29			22 00				23 18			
Oldfield Park	a	19 00			20 01						21 11				22 20		
Keynsham	a	19 07			20 09				20 58		21 19				22 28		
Bristol Temple Meads 10	a	19 17		19 35	20 18			20 39	21 06		21 27	21 39			22 36	22 40	
Filton Abbey Wood	a			19 55				20 55				21 55				22 55	
Bristol Parkway	d																
Yate	d																
Cam & Dursley	d																
Gloucester	d					21 25											
Cheltenham Spa	d					21a33											
Ashchurch for Tewkesbury	d																
Worcester Shrub Hill	d																
Worcester Foregate Street	d																
Malvern Link	d																
Great Malvern	a																
Severn Tunnel Jn.	a			20 10				21 07				22 12				23 07	
Newport (South Wales)	a			20 28				21 26				22 31				23 25	
Cardiff Central 7	a			20 46				21 42				22 53				23 47	

A From Plymouth
B From London Waterloo
C From Penzance
D To Bristol Temple Meads
E From Weymouth

For connections from Bristol Parkway and Cardiff Central to Swansea please see Table 128

For connections from Castle Cary, Westbury and Bristol Temple Meads to Exeter and Plymouth please see Table 135

For connections from Salisbury to Yeovil Junction and Exeter please see Table 160

For connections from Bournemouth to Southampton Central, Weymouth and Upwey please see Table 158

For Bus Connections between Yeovil Junction and Yeovil Pen Mill please see Table 123A

Table 123

Sundays

5 January to 9 February

Brighton, Portsmouth and Weymouth - Bristol, Cardiff, Gloucester and Great Malvern

Network Diagram - see first Page of Table 123

		GW	GW	GW	GW	GW	GW	GW	GW	GW	GW	GW	GW	SW	GW	GW	GW	GW	GW	GW	GW	GW	GW
			◇1			◇1	R		◇1	◇		◇	R 1	◇1	◇	◇	◇1	◇		R		◇1	◇
		A	B	C		D			E				E	F			D					D	
			☕			☕			☕				☕				☕					☕	
Brighton 10	d											11 10											
Hove 2	d											11 14											
Shoreham-by-Sea	d											11 20											
Worthing 4	d											11 29											
Barnham	d											11 53											
Chichester 4	d											12 01											
Havant	d											12 12											
Portsmouth Harbour ⛴	d						09 08			11 08					13 08			14 08		15 08			16 08
Portsmouth & Southsea	d						09 12			11 12					13 12			14 12		15 12			16 12
Fratton	d						09 16			11 16					13 16			14 16		15 16			16 16
Cosham	d						09 23			11 23		12 23			13 23			14 23		15 23			16 23
Fareham	a						09 31			11 31		12 31			13 31			14 31		15 31			16 31
	d						09 32			11 32		12 32			13 32			14 32		15 32			16 32
Southampton Central ⛴	d						09 54			11 54		12 54			13 54			14 54		15 54			16 54
Romsey	d						10 06			12 06		13 06			14 06			15 06		16 06			17 06
Salisbury	a						10 24			12 24		13 24			14 24			15 24		16 24			17 24
	d						10 26			12 27		13 26		13 55	14 27			15 27		16 27			17 27
Warminster	d						10 46			12 46		13 46		14 15	14 48			15 48		16 48			17 48
Dilton Marsh	d						10x51								14x53			15x53		16x53			
Weymouth	d															14 00							
Upwey	d															14 05							
Dorchester West	d															14 13							
Maiden Newton	d															14 25							
Chetnole	d															14x33							
Yetminster	d															14x36							
Thornford	d															14x38							
Yeovil Pen Mill	d															14 48							
Castle Cary	a															15 00							
	d		09 34						12 33							15 03	15 34					17 37	
Bruton	d															15 08							
Frome	d	09 39		←												15 21							
Westbury	a	09 48	09 51	09 48			10 56		12 52	12 56		13 56		14 23	14 56	15 30	15 51	15 56		16 56		17 54	17 56
	d	09 58	09 54	09 58	10 30	10 52	10 59	11 50	12 53	12 56	13 32	13 56	13 59	14 24	15 00	15 31	15 52	16 00	16 29	17 00	17 16	17 56	18 00
Trowbridge	d	→		10 04	10 35		11 05	11 56		13 02	13 37	14 02		14 30	15 06	15 37		16 06	16 34	17 06	17 21		18 06
Bradford-on-Avon	d			10 10			11 11	12 02		13 08		14 08		14 36	15 12	15 43		16 12		17 12			18 12
Avoncliff	d			10 13				12 05				14 11				15 46							18 16
Freshford	d			10 15				12 07				14 14				15 49							18 19
Bath Spa 7	a			10 26			11 24	12 19		13 22		14 24		14 50	15 24	15 59		16 24		17 24			18 30
Melksham	d				10 46						13 48								16 44		17 31		
Chippenham	a				10 55						13 57								17 00		17 41		
Swindon	a				11 15						14 17								17 17		18 00		
London Paddington 15 ⊖	a		11 29			12 29			14 30				15 30				17 27					19 29	
Oldfield Park	a			10 30			11 27	12 23		13 25		14 27				16 02				17 28			
Keynsham	a			10 37			11 35	12 30		13 32		14 35		14 58		16 10				17 35			
Bristol Temple Meads 10	a			10 45			11 44	12 38		13 41		14 44		15 06	15 40	16 19		16 37		17 44			18 43
Filton Abbey Wood	a						11 55			13 55		14 55			15 55			16 55		17 55			18 55
Bristol Parkway	d																						
Yate	d																						
Cam & Dursley	d																						
Gloucester	d																						
Cheltenham Spa	d																						
Ashchurch for Tewkesbury	d																						
Worcester Shrub Hill	d																						
Worcester Foregate Street	d																						
Malvern Link	d																						
Great Malvern	a																						
Severn Tunnel Jn.	a						12 11			14 08		15 05			16 08			17 10		18 08			19 08
Newport (South Wales)	a						12 30			14 26		15 24			16 26			17 29		18 26			19 26
Cardiff Central 7	a						12 45			14 46		15 41			16 44			17 46		18 44			19 42

A To Bristol Temple Meads
B From Exeter St Davids
C From Frome
D From Plymouth
E From Penzance
F From London Waterloo

For connections from Bristol Parkway and Cardiff Central to Swansea please see Table 128

For connections from Castle Cary, Westbury and Bristol Temple Meads to Exeter and Plymouth please see Table 135

For connections from Salisbury to Yeovil Junction and Exeter please see Table 160

For connections from Bournemouth to Southampton Central, Weymouth and Upwey please see Table 158

For Bus Connections between Yeovil Junction and Yeovil Pen Mill please see Table 123A

Table 123

Sundays

5 January to 9 February

Brighton, Portsmouth and Weymouth - Bristol, Cardiff, Gloucester and Great Malvern

Network Diagram - see first Page of Table 123

		GW	GW	GW	GW	GW	GW	GW	SW	GW	GW	GW	GW	GW	GW	GW	GW
		◇		◇	◇		◇1	◇	◇1	◇1	◇	◇		◇1		◇	
							A		B	C			D	C	E		
							🍴			🍴				🍴			
Brighton 10	d	15 46									17 46						
Hove 2	d	15 50									17 50						
Shoreham-by-Sea	d	15 56									17 56						
Worthing 4	d	16 08									18 08						
Barnham	d	16 23									18 23						
Chichester 4	d	16 37									18 32						
Havant	d	16 48									18 50						
Portsmouth Harbour ⛴	d			17 08				18 08				19 08				20 08	22 05
Portsmouth & Southsea	d			17 12				18 12				19 12				20 12	22 12
Fratton	d			17 16				18 16				19 16				20 16	22 16
Cosham	d	16 55		17 23				18 23			18 57	19 23					
Fareham	a	17 03		17 31				18 31			19 04	19 31				20 31	22 31
	d	17 03		17 32				18 32			19 05	19 32				20 32	22 32
Southampton Central ⛴	d	17 26		17 54				18 54			19 28	19 54				20 54	22 57
Romsey	d	17 39		18 06				19 06			19 40	20 06				21 06	23 09
Salisbury	a	18 00		18 24				19 24			19 58	20 24				21 24	23 27
	d	18 01		18 27				19 25	19 55		20 01	20 27				21 27	23 28
Warminster	d	18 21		18 48				19 48	20 15		20 21	20 48				21 48	23 48
Dilton Marsh	d	18x26									20x26					21x53	23x53
Weymouth	d				17 56								20 09				
Upwey	d				18 01								20 14				
Dorchester West	d				18 09								20 22				
Maiden Newton	d				18 21								20 34				
Chetnole	d				18x29								20x42				
Yetminster	d				18x32								20x45				
Thornford	d				18x34								20x47				
Yeovil Pen Mill	d				18 44								20 57				
Castle Cary	a				18 56								21 09				
	d				18 59					20 07			21 10	21 19			
Bruton	d				19 05								21 16				
Frome	d				19 18								21 34		←		
Westbury	a	18 29		18 56	19 27			19 55	20 23	20 26	20 30	20 56	21 43	21 39	21 43	21 56	23 57
	d	18 32	18 50	18 57	19 30	19 40	19 51	20 00	20 23	20 27	20 39	21 00	21 48	21 40	21 48	22 00	
Trowbridge	d	18 38	18 56	19 02	19 36	19 45		20 06	20 29		20 45	21 06	→		21 54	22 06	
Bradford-on-Avon	d	18 44		19 08	19 42			20 12	20 35		20 51	21 12			22 00	22 12	
Avoncliff	d				19 45						20 54				22 03		
Freshford	d				19 48						20 57				22 06		
Bath Spa 7	a	18 55		19 22	19 58			20 26	20 49		21 08	21 26			22 17	22 26	
Melksham	d		19 05			19 56											
Chippenham	a		19 15			20 06											
Swindon	a		19 33			20 24											
London Paddington 15 ⊖	a						21 29			22 03				23 22			
Oldfield Park	a	19 00			20 01						21 11				22 20		
Keynsham	a	19 07			20 09				20 58		21 19				22 28		
Bristol Temple Meads 10	a	19 17		19 35	20 18			20 39	21 06		21 27	21 39			22 36	22 40	
Filton Abbey Wood	a			19 55				20 55				21 55				22 55	
Bristol Parkway	d																
Yate	d																
Cam & Dursley	d																
Gloucester	d					21 25											
Cheltenham Spa	d					21a33											
Ashchurch for Tewkesbury	d																
Worcester Shrub Hill	d																
Worcester Foregate Street	d																
Malvern Link	d																
Great Malvern	a																
Severn Tunnel Jn.	a			20 10				21 07				22 12				23 07	
Newport (South Wales)	a			20 28				21 26				22 31				23 25	
Cardiff Central 7	a			20 46				21 42				22 53				23 47	

A From Plymouth
B From London Waterloo
C From Penzance
D To Bristol Temple Meads
E From Weymouth

For connections from Bristol Parkway and Cardiff Central to Swansea please see Table 128

For connections from Castle Cary, Westbury and Bristol Temple Meads to Exeter and Plymouth please see Table 135

For connections from Salisbury to Yeovil Junction and Exeter please see Table 160

For connections from Bournemouth to Southampton Central, Weymouth and Upwey please see Table 158

For Bus Connections between Yeovil Junction and Yeovil Pen Mill please see Table 123A

Table 123

Sundays

16 February to 23 March

Brighton, Portsmouth and Weymouth - Bristol, Cardiff, Gloucester and Great Malvern

Network Diagram - see first Page of Table 123

		GW	GW	GW	GW	GW	GW	GW	GW	GW		GW	GW	GW	SW	GW	GW	GW	GW	GW		GW	GW	GW	GW
							[R]															[R]			
			◇1			◇1			◇1	◇			◇	◇1	◇1	◇	◇	◇1	◇					◇1	◇
		A	B	C		B			B					B	D			B						B	
			☕			☕			☕					☕				☕						☕	
Brighton 10	d												11 10												
Hove 2	d												11 14												
Shoreham-by-Sea	d												11 20												
Worthing 4	d												11 29												
Barnham	d												11 53												
Chichester 4	d												12 01												
Havant	d												12 12												
Portsmouth Harbour ⛴	d						09 08			11 08						13 08			14 08			15 08			16 08
Portsmouth & Southsea	d						09 12			11 12						13 12			14 12			15 12			16 12
Fratton	d						09 16			11 16						13 16			14 16			15 16			16 16
Cosham	d						09 23			11 23			12 23			13 23			14 23			15 23			16 23
Fareham	a						09 31			11 31			12 31			13 31			14 31			15 31			16 31
	d						09 32			11 32			12 32			13 32			14 32			15 32			16 32
Southampton Central ⛴	d						09 54			11 54			12 54			13 54			14 54			15 54			16 54
Romsey	d						10 06			12 06			13 06			14 06			15 06			16 06			17 06
Salisbury	a						10 24			12 24			13 24			14 24			15 24			16 24			17 24
	d						10 26			12 27			13 26		13 55	14 27			15 27			16 27			17 27
Warminster	d						10 46			12 46			13 46		14 15	14 48			15 48			16 48			17 48
Dilton Marsh	d						10x51									14x53			15x53			16x53			
Weymouth	d																14 00								
Upwey	d																14 05								
Dorchester West	d																14 13								
Maiden Newton	d																14 25								
Chetnole	d																14x33								
Yetminster	d																14x36								
Thornford	d																14x38								
Yeovil Pen Mill	d																14 48								
Castle Cary	a																15 00								
	d		09 34						12 33								15 03	15 34						17 37	
Bruton	d																15 08								
Frome	d	09 39		←													15 21								
Westbury	a	09 48	09 51	09 48			10 56		12 52	12 56			13 56		14 23	14 56	15 30	15 51	15 56			16 56		17 54	17 56
	d	09 58	09 54	09 58	10 30	10 52	10 59	11 50	12 53	12 56		13 32	13 56	13 59	14 24	15 00	15 31	15 52	16 00	16 29		17 00	17 16	17 56	18 00
Trowbridge	d	→		10 04	10 35		11 05	11 56		13 02		13 37	14 02		14 30	15 06	15 37		16 06	16 34		17 06	17 21		18 06
Bradford-on-Avon	d			10 10			11 11	12 02		13 08			14 08		14 36	15 12	15 43		16 12			17 12			18 12
Avoncliff	d			10 13				12 05					14 11				15 46								18 16
Freshford	d			10 15				12 07					14 14				15 49								18 19
Bath Spa 7	a			10 26			11 24	12 19		13 22			14 24		14 50	15 24	15 59		16 24			17 24			18 30
Melksham	d				10 46							13 48								16 44			17 31		
Chippenham	a				10 55							13 57								16 54			17 41		
Swindon	a				11 15							14 17								17 13			18 00		
London Paddington 15 ⊖	a		11 29			12 29			14 30					15 30				17 30						19 30	
Oldfield Park	a			10 30			11 27	12 23		13 25			14 27				16 02					17 28			
Keynsham	a			10 37			11 35	12 30		13 32			14 35		14 58		16 10					17 35			
Bristol Temple Meads 10	a			10 45			11 44	12 38		13 41			14 44		15 06	15 40	16 19		16 37			17 44			18 43
Filton Abbey Wood	a						11 55			13 55			14 55			15 55			16 55			17 55			18 55
Bristol Parkway	d																								
Yate	d																								
Cam & Dursley	d																								
Gloucester	d																								
Cheltenham Spa	d																								
Ashchurch for Tewkesbury	d																								
Worcester Shrub Hill	d																								
Worcester Foregate Street	d																								
Malvern Link	d																								
Great Malvern	a																								
Severn Tunnel Jn.	a						12 11			14 08			15 05			16 08			17 10			18 08			19 08
Newport (South Wales)	a						12 30			14 26			15 24			16 26			17 29			18 26			19 26
Cardiff Central 7	a						12 45			14 46			15 41			16 44			17 46			18 44			19 42

A To Bristol Temple Meads
B From Exeter St Davids
C From Frome
D From London Waterloo

For connections from Bristol Parkway and Cardiff Central to Swansea please see Table 128

For connections from Castle Cary, Westbury and Bristol Temple Meads to Exeter and Plymouth please see Table 135

For connections from Salisbury to Yeovil Junction and Exeter please see Table 160

For connections from Bournemouth to Southampton Central, Weymouth and Upwey please see Table 158

For Bus Connections between Yeovil Junction and Yeovil Pen Mill please see Table 123A

Table 123

Sundays

16 February to 23 March

Brighton, Portsmouth and Weymouth - Bristol, Cardiff, Gloucester and Great Malvern

Network Diagram - see first Page of Table 123

		GW	GW	GW	GW	GW	GW	GW	SW	GW	GW	GW	GW	GW	GW	GW	GW
		◇		◇	◇		◇1	◇	◇1	◇1	◇	◇		◇1		◇	
							A		B	A			C	A	D		
							☕			☕				☕			
Brighton 10	d	15 46									17 46						
Hove 2	d	15 50									17 50						
Shoreham-by-Sea	d	15 56									17 56						
Worthing 4	d	16 08									18 08						
Barnham	d	16 23									18 23						
Chichester 4	d	16 37									18 32						
Havant	d	16 48									18 50						
Portsmouth Harbour ⛴	d			17 08				18 08				19 08				20 08	22 05
Portsmouth & Southsea	d			17 12				18 12				19 12				20 12	22 12
Fratton	d			17 16				18 16				19 16				20 16	22 16
Cosham	d	16 55		17 23				18 23			18 57	19 23					
Fareham	a	17 03		17 31				18 31			19 04	19 31				20 31	22 31
	d	17 03		17 32				18 32			19 05	19 32				20 32	22 32
Southampton Central ⛴	d	17 26		17 54				18 54			19 28	19 54				20 54	22 57
Romsey	d	17 39		18 06				19 06			19 40	20 06				21 06	23 09
Salisbury	a	18 00		18 24				19 24			19 58	20 24				21 24	23 27
	d	18 01		18 27				19 25	19 55		20 01	20 27				21 27	23 28
Warminster	d	18 21		18 48				19 48	20 15		20 21	20 48				21 48	23 48
Dilton Marsh	d	18x26									20x26					21x53	23x53
Weymouth	d				17 56								20 09				
Upwey	d				18 01								20 14				
Dorchester West	d				18 09								20 22				
Maiden Newton	d				18 21								20 34				
Chetnole	d				18x29								20x42				
Yetminster	d				18x32								20x45				
Thornford	d				18x34								20x47				
Yeovil Pen Mill	d				18 44								20 57				
Castle Cary	a				18 56								21 09				
	d				18 59					20 07			21 10	21 19			
Bruton	d				19 05								21 16				
Frome	d				19 18								21 34		←		
Westbury	a	18 29		18 56	19 27			19 55	20 23	20 26	20 30	20 56	21 43	21 39	21 43	21 56	23 57
	d	18 32	18 50	18 57	19 30	19 40	19 54	20 00	20 23	20 27	20 39	21 00	21 48	21 40	21 48	22 00	
Trowbridge	d	18 38	18 56	19 02	19 36	19 45		20 06	20 29		20 45	21 06	→		21 54	22 06	
Bradford-on-Avon	d	18 44		19 08	19 42			20 12	20 35		20 51	21 12			22 00	22 12	
Avoncliff	d				19 45						20 54				22 03		
Freshford	d				19 48						20 57				22 06		
Bath Spa 7	a	18 55		19 22	19 58			20 26	20 49		21 11	21 26			22 17	22 26	
Melksham	d		19 05			19 56											
Chippenham	a		19 15			20 06											
Swindon	a		19 33			20 24											
London Paddington 15 ⊖	a						21 29			21 59				23 17			
Oldfield Park	a	19 00			20 01						21 14				22 20		
Keynsham	a	19 07			20 09				20 58		21 22				22 28		
Bristol Temple Meads 10	a	19 17		19 35	20 18			20 39	21 06		21 30	21 39			22 36	22 40	
Filton Abbey Wood	a			19 55				20 55				21 55				22 55	
Bristol Parkway	d																
Yate	d																
Cam & Dursley	d																
Gloucester	d					21 25											
Cheltenham Spa	d					21a33											
Ashchurch for Tewkesbury	d																
Worcester Shrub Hill	d																
Worcester Foregate Street	d																
Malvern Link	d																
Great Malvern	a																
Severn Tunnel Jn.	a			20 10				21 07				22 12				23 07	
Newport (South Wales)	a			20 28				21 26				22 31				23 25	
Cardiff Central 7	a			20 46				21 42				22 53				23 47	

A From Exeter St Davids
B From London Waterloo
C To Bristol Temple Meads
D From Weymouth

For connections from Bristol Parkway and Cardiff Central to Swansea please see Table 128

For connections from Castle Cary, Westbury and Bristol Temple Meads to Exeter and Plymouth please see Table 135

For connections from Salisbury to Yeovil Junction and Exeter please see Table 160

For connections from Bournemouth to Southampton Central, Weymouth and Upwey please see Table 158

For Bus Connections between Yeovil Junction and Yeovil Pen Mill please see Table 123A

Table 123

Sundays

30 March to 11 May

Brighton, Portsmouth and Weymouth - Bristol, Cardiff, Gloucester and Great Malvern

Network Diagram - see first Page of Table 123

		GW	GW	GW	GW	GW	GW	GW	GW	GW	GW	GW	GW	SW	GW	GW	GW	GW	GW	GW	GW	GW	GW
		A	◇1 B	C		◇1 D	■		◇1 E	◇		◇	■ 1 E	◇1 F	◇	◇	◇1 D	◇		■		◇1 D	◇
Brighton 10	d											11 10											
Hove 2	d											11 14											
Shoreham-by-Sea	d											11 20											
Worthing 4	d											11 29											
Barnham	d											11 53											
Chichester 4	d											12 01											
Havant	d											12 12											
Portsmouth Harbour	d						09 08			11 08					13 08			14 08		15 08			16 08
Portsmouth & Southsea	d						09 12			11 12					13 12			14 12		15 12			16 12
Fratton	d						09 16			11 16					13 16			14 16		15 16			16 16
Cosham	d						09 23			11 23		12 23			13 23			14 23		15 23			16 23
Fareham	a						09 31			11 31		12 31			13 31			14 31		15 31			16 31
	d						09 32			11 32		12 32			13 32			14 32		15 32			16 32
Southampton Central	d						09 54			11 54		12 54			13 54			14 54		15 54			16 54
Romsey	d						10 06			12 06		13 06			14 06			15 06		16 06			17 06
Salisbury	a						10 24			12 24		13 24			14 24			15 24		16 24			17 24
	d						10 26			12 27		13 26		13 55	14 27			15 27		16 27			17 27
Warminster	d						10 46			12 46		13 46		14 15	14 48			15 48		16 48			17 48
Dilton Marsh	d						10x51								14x53			15x53		16x53			
Weymouth	d															14 00							
Upwey	d															14 05							
Dorchester West	d															14 13							
Maiden Newton	d															14 25							
Chetnole	d															14x33							
Yetminster	d															14x36							
Thornford	d															14x38							
Yeovil Pen Mill	d															14 48							
Castle Cary	a															15 00							
	d		09 34						12 33							15 03	15 34					17 37	
Bruton	d															15 08							
Frome	d	09 39		←												15 21							
Westbury	a	09 48	09 51	09 48			10 56		12 52	12 56		13 56		14 23	14 56	15 30	15 51	15 56		16 56		17 54	17 56
	d	09 58	09 54	09 58	10 30	10 52	10 59	11 50	12 53	12 56	13 32	13 56	13 59	14 24	15 00	15 31	15 52	16 00	16 29	17 00	17 16	17 56	18 00
Trowbridge	d	→		10 04	10 35		11 05	11 56		13 02	13 37	14 02		14 30	15 06	15 37		16 06	16 34	17 06	17 21		18 06
Bradford-on-Avon	d			10 10			11 11	12 02		13 08		14 08		14 36	15 12	15 43		16 12		17 12			18 12
Avoncliff	d			10 13				12 05				14 11				15 46							18 16
Freshford	d			10 15				12 07				14 14				15 49							18 19
Bath Spa 7	a			10 26			11 24	12 19		13 22		14 24		14 50	15 24	15 59		16 24		17 24			18 30
Melksham	d				10 46						13 48								16 44		17 31		
Chippenham	a				10 55						13 57								16 54		17 41		
Swindon	a				11 15						14 17								17 13		18 00		
London Paddington 15 ⊖	a		11 27			12 29			14 30				15 29				17 30					19 29	
Oldfield Park	a			10 30			11 27	12 23		13 25		14 27				16 02				17 28			
Keynsham	a			10 37			11 35	12 30		13 32		14 35		14 58		16 10				17 35			
Bristol Temple Meads 10	a			10 45			11 44	12 38		13 41		14 44		15 06	15 40	16 19		16 37		17 44			18 43
Filton Abbey Wood	a						11 55			13 55		14 55			15 55			16 55		17 55			18 55
Bristol Parkway	d																						
Yate	d																						
Cam & Dursley	d																						
Gloucester	d																						
Cheltenham Spa	d																						
Ashchurch for Tewkesbury	d																						
Worcester Shrub Hill	d																						
Worcester Foregate Street	d																						
Malvern Link	d																						
Great Malvern	a																						
Severn Tunnel Jn.	a						12 11			14 08		15 05			16 08			17 10		18 08			19 08
Newport (South Wales)	a						12 30			14 26		15 24			16 26			17 29		18 26			19 26
Cardiff Central 7	a						12 45			14 46		15 41			16 44			17 46		18 44			19 42

A To Bristol Temple Meads
B From Exeter St Davids
C From Frome
D From Plymouth
E From Penzance
F From London Waterloo

For connections from Bristol Parkway and Cardiff Central to Swansea please see Table 128

For connections from Castle Cary, Westbury and Bristol Temple Meads to Exeter and Plymouth please see Table 135

For connections from Salisbury to Yeovil Junction and Exeter please see Table 160

For connections from Bournemouth to Southampton Central, Weymouth and Upwey please see Table 158

For Bus Connections between Yeovil Junction and Yeovil Pen Mill please see Table 123A

Table 123

Sundays

30 March to 11 May

Brighton, Portsmouth and Weymouth - Bristol, Cardiff, Gloucester and Great Malvern

Network Diagram - see first Page of Table 123

		GW ◇	GW	GW ◇	GW ◇	GW	GW ◇1 A	GW ◇	SW ◇1 B	GW ◇1 C	GW ◇	GW ◇	GW D	GW ◇1 C	GW E	GW ◇	GW
Brighton 10	d	15 46									17 46						
Hove 2	d	15 50									17 50						
Shoreham-by-Sea	d	15 56									17 56						
Worthing 4	d	16 08									18 08						
Barnham	d	16 23									18 23						
Chichester 4	d	16 37									18 32						
Havant	d	16 48									18 50						
Portsmouth Harbour ⛴	d			17 08				18 08				19 08				20 08	22 05
Portsmouth & Southsea	d			17 12				18 12				19 12				20 12	22 12
Fratton	d			17 16				18 16				19 16				20 16	22 16
Cosham	d	16 55		17 23				18 23			18 57	19 23					
Fareham	a	17 03		17 31				18 31			19 04	19 31				20 31	22 31
	d	17 03		17 32				18 32			19 05	19 32				20 32	22 32
Southampton Central ⛴	d	17 26		17 54				18 54			19 28	19 54				20 54	22 57
Romsey	d	17 39		18 06				19 06			19 40	20 06				21 06	23 09
Salisbury	a	18 00		18 24				19 24			19 58	20 24				21 24	23 27
	d	18 01		18 27				19 25	19 55		20 01	20 27				21 27	23 28
Warminster	d	18 21		18 48				19 48	20 15		20 21	20 48				21 48	23 48
Dilton Marsh	d	18x26									20x26					21x53	23x53
Weymouth	d				17 56								20 09				
Upwey	d				18 01								20 14				
Dorchester West	d				18 09								20 22				
Maiden Newton	d				18 21								20 34				
Chetnole	d				18x29								20x42				
Yetminster	d				18x32								20x45				
Thornford	d				18x34								20x47				
Yeovil Pen Mill	d				18 44								20 57				
Castle Cary	a				18 56								21 09				
	d				18 59					20 07			21 10	21 19			
Bruton	d				19 05								21 16				
Frome	d				19 18								21 34		←		
Westbury	a	18 29		18 56	19 27			19 55	20 23	20 26	20 30	20 56	21 43	21 39	21 43	21 56	23 57
	d	18 32	18 50	18 57	19 30	19 40	19 51	20 00	20 23	20 27	20 39	21 00	21 48	21 40	21 48	22 00	
Trowbridge	d	18 38	18 56	19 02	19 36	19 45		20 06	20 29		20 45	21 06	→		21 54	22 06	
Bradford-on-Avon	d	18 44		19 08	19 42			20 12	20 35		20 51	21 12			22 00	22 12	
Avoncliff	d				19 45						20 54				22 03		
Freshford	d				19 48						20 57				22 06		
Bath Spa 7	a	18 55		19 22	19 58			20 26	20 49		21 08	21 27			22 17	22 26	
Melksham	d		19 05			19 56											
Chippenham	a		19 15			20 06											
Swindon	a		19 33			20 24											
London Paddington 15 ⊖	a						21 29			21 52				23 23			
Oldfield Park	a	19 00			20 01						21 11				22 20		
Keynsham	a	19 07			20 09				20 58		21 19				22 28		
Bristol Temple Meads 10	a	19 17		19 35	20 18			20 39	21 06		21 27	21 40			22 36	22 40	
Filton Abbey Wood	a			19 55				20 55				21 55				22 55	
Bristol Parkway	d																
Yate	d																
Cam & Dursley	d																
Gloucester	d					21 25											
Cheltenham Spa	d					21a33											
Ashchurch for Tewkesbury	d																
Worcester Shrub Hill	d																
Worcester Foregate Street	d																
Malvern Link	d																
Great Malvern	a																
Severn Tunnel Jn.	a			20 10				21 07				22 12				23 07	
Newport (South Wales)	a			20 28				21 26				22 27				23 25	
Cardiff Central 7	a			20 46				21 42				22 49				23 47	

A From Plymouth
B From London Waterloo
C From Penzance
D To Bristol Temple Meads
E From Weymouth

For connections from Bristol Parkway and Cardiff Central to Swansea please see Table 128

For connections from Castle Cary, Westbury and Bristol Temple Meads to Exeter and Plymouth please see Table 135

For connections from Salisbury to Yeovil Junction and Exeter please see Table 160

For connections from Bournemouth to Southampton Central, Weymouth and Upwey please see Table 158

For Bus Connections between Yeovil Junction and Yeovil Pen Mill please see Table 123A

Table 123R

Mondays to Fridays

9 December to 16 May

Great Malvern, Gloucester, Cardiff and Bristol - Weymouth, Portsmouth and Brighton

Network Diagram - see first Page of Table 123

Miles	Miles	Miles	Miles	Miles			GW MX	GW	GW	GW	GW	GW	GW	GW	GW		GW	GW	GW	GW	GW	SW	GW	GW	GW
																				[R]					
										◇■1		◇					◇	◇■1			◇	◇■1			◇
							A			B								C				D			
										🍽							🛒	🍽		🛒					🛒
0	0	—	—	—	**Cardiff Central ■7**	d											06 28			07 30					08 30
11¾	11¾	—	—	—	Newport (South Wales)	d											06 42			07 44					08 44
21¾	21¾	—	—	—	Severn Tunnel Jn	d											06 53			07 55					08 55
—	—	0	0	—	Great Malvern	d																			
—	—	1¼	1¼	—	Malvern Link	d																			
—	—	8	8	—	Worcester Foregate Street	d																			
—	—	8½	8½	—	Worcester Shrub Hill	d															06 49				
—	—	23¼	23¼	—	Ashchurch for Tewkesbury	d															07 05				
—	—	30½	30½	—	Cheltenham Spa	d													06 24		07 16				
—	—	37	37	—	Gloucester	d								05 18					06 42		07 39				
—	—	50	50	—	Cam & Dursley	d													06 57		07 53				
—	—	60¾	60¾	—	Yate	d													07 12		08 08				
—	—	67	67	—	Bristol Parkway	d													07 23		08 19				
33¾	33¾	68½	68½	—	Filton Abbey Wood	d											07 09		07 28	08 09	08 23				09 09
38¼	38¼	73	73	—	**Bristol Temple Meads ■10**	d				05 18		05 44			06 48		07 22		07 49	08 22	08 41	08 51		09 05	09 22
42¾	42¾	77½	77½	—	Keynsham	d						05 51			06 55				07 56		08 48	08 58			
48¾	48¾	83½	83½	—	Oldfield Park	d						05 59			07 02				08 03		08 55			09 17	
—	—	—	—	—	London Paddington ■15 ⊖	d												07 06							
—	—	—	—	0	Swindon	d								06 12									08 49		
—	—	—	—	16¾	Chippenham	d								06 29									09 06		
—	—	—	—	23	Melksham	d								06 38									09 15		
49¾	49¾	84½	84½	—	**Bath Spa ■7**	d						06 03			07 06		07 35		08 07	08 36	08 59	09 07		09 21	09 36
56¾	56¾	91¾	91¾	—	Freshford	d						06 12			07 15				08 16		09 08				
57¾	57¾	92½	92½	—	Avoncliff	d						06 15			07 18				08 19		09 11				
59	59	94	94	—	Bradford-on-Avon	d				05 42		06 19			07 22		07 47		08 23	08 47	09 15	09 20		09 33	
62¼	62¼	97¼	97¼	28½	Trowbridge	d				05 49		06 26		06 47	07 28		07 53		08 29	08 53	09 21	09 27	09 31	09 39	09 51
66¼	66¼	101¼	101¼	32½	**Westbury**	a				05 57		06 31		06 55	07 35		08 00	08 25	08 36	09 00	09 28	09 33	09 42	09 49	09 58
—	—	—	—	—		d	00 08	05 24	05 49		06 25	06 40	06 47	07 01			08 01			09 01	09 32	09 39			09 59
—	72	—	107	—	Frome	d	00a19				06a35		06 56								09 41				
—	82½	—	117½	—	Bruton	d							07 08								09 53				
—	86	—	121	—	Castle Cary	a							07 13								09 59				
—	—	—	—	—		d							07 14								10 00				
—	97¾	—	132¾	—	Yeovil Pen Mill	d							07 35								10 14				
—	101	—	135¾	—	Thornford	d							07x39								10x18				
—	102	—	137	—	Yetminster	d							07x42								10x21				
—	104	—	139	—	Chetnole	d							07x46								10x25				
—	110½	—	145½	—	Maiden Newton	d							07 58								10 37				
—	118¼	—	153¼	—	Dorchester West	d							08 09								10 48				
—	122¾	—	157¾	—	Upwey	a							08 16								10 55				
—	125¼	—	160¼	—	**Weymouth**	a							08 24								11 03				
67¾	—	102½	—	—	Dilton Marsh	d								07x03											
71	—	105¾	—	—	Warminster	d		05 32	05 57			06 48		07 12			08 09			09 09		09 46			10 07
90¾	—	125½	—	—	**Salisbury**	a		05 55	06 18			07 10		07 36			08 32			09 32		10 09			10 29
—	—	—	—	—		d			06 19			07 11		07 36			08 32			09 32					10 30
107¼	—	142¼	—	—	Romsey	d			06 38			07 30		07 56			08 50			09 50					10 50
115½	—	150¼	—	—	**Southampton Central**	a			06 49			07 40		08 09			09 04			10 04					11 04
130	—	165	—	—	Fareham	a			07 15			08 05					09 27			10 27					11 27
—	—	—	—	—		d			07 16			08 06					09 27			10 28					11 27
135¾	—	170¾	—	—	Cosham	a			07 25			08 13					09 35			10 36					11 35
139½	—	—	—	—	Fratton	a			07 34			08 20					09 42			10 43					11 42
140½	—	—	—	—	Portsmouth & Southsea	a			07 38			08 24					09 46			10 47					11 46
141¼	—	—	—	—	**Portsmouth Harbour**	a			07 45			08 30					09 52			10 54					11 54
—	—	174¾	—	—	Havant	a																			
—	—	183¾	—	—	**Chichester ■4**	a																			
—	—	190	—	—	Barnham	a																			
—	—	201¾	—	—	Worthing ■4	a																			
—	—	206½	—	—	Shoreham-by-Sea	a																			
—	—	211	—	—	Hove ■2	a																			
—	—	212½	—	—	Brighton ■10	a																			

A From Bristol Temple Meads
B To London Paddington
C To Paignton. The Devon Express
D To London Waterloo

For connections from Swansea to Cardiff Central and Bristol Parkway please see Table 128

For connections from Plymouth and Exeter to Bristol Temple Meads, Westbury and Castle Cary, please see Table 135

For connections from Exeter and Yeovil Junction to Salisbury please see Table 160

For connections from Upwey, Weymouth and Southampton Central to Bournemouth please see Table 158

For Bus Connections between Yeovil Junction and Yeovil Pen Mill please see Table 123A

Table 123R

Mondays to Fridays

9 December to 16 May

Great Malvern, Gloucester, Cardiff and Bristol - Weymouth, Portsmouth and Brighton

Network Diagram - see first Page of Table 123

		GW	GW	GW	GW	GW	GW	GW	GW	GW		GW	GW	GW	GW	SW	GW	GW	GW	GW		GW	GW FO	GW
														■										
			◇1	◇	◇				◇	◇1		◇	◇			◇1	◇1	◇		◇			◇	◇
			A							B				C		D	E					F	G	
			🍴		🛒				🛒	Ø			🛒	🛒		🛒	🍴	🛒		🛒				
Cardiff Central 7	d				09 30				10 30				11 30					12 30		13 30				
Newport (South Wales)	d				09 44				10 44				11 44					12 44		13 44				
Severn Tunnel Jn.	d				09 55																			
Great Malvern	d							08 50						10 50										12 50
Malvern Link	d							08 53						10 53										12 53
Worcester Foregate Street	d							09 03						11 03										13 03
Worcester Shrub Hill	d							09 06						11 06										13 06
Ashchurch for Tewkesbury	d							09 24						11 24										13 24
Cheltenham Spa	d							09 33						11 33										13 33
Gloucester	d			08 41				09 45				10 41		11 47					12 41					13 46
Cam & Dursley	d			08 56				10 00				10 56		12 00					12 56					14 00
Yate	d			09 10				10 14				11 10		12 14					13 10					14 14
Bristol Parkway	d			09 20				10 23				11 20		12 23					13 19					14 23
Filton Abbey Wood	d			09 23	10 09			10 26	11 09			11 23	12 09	12 26				13 09	13 23	14 09				14 26
Bristol Temple Meads 10	d			09 49	10 22			10 49	11 22			11 49	12 22	12 39		12 51		13 22	13 49	14 22				14 48
Keynsham	d			09 56				10 56				11 56		12 46		12 58			13 56					14 55
Oldfield Park	d			10 03				11 03				12 03		12 53					14 03					15 02
London Paddington 15 ⊖	d		09 06							11 06							12 18							
Swindon	d						10 47								12 47									
Chippenham	d						11 04								13 04									
Melksham	d						11 13								13 13									
Bath Spa 7	d			10 07	10 35			11 07	11 35			12 07	12 35	12 57		13 07		13 35	14 07	14 35				15 06
Freshford	d			10 16				11 16				12 16		13 06					14 16					15 15
Avoncliff	d			10 19				11 19				12 19		13 08					14 19					15 18
Bradford-on-Avon	d			10 23	10 47			11 23	11 47			12 23	12 47	13 12		13 20		13 47	14 23	14 47				15 22
Trowbridge	d			10 29	10 53		11 24	11 29	11 53			12 29	12 53	13 19	13 23	13 27		13 53	14 29	14 53				15 28
Westbury	a			10 36	11 00		11 33	11 36	12 00	12 20		12 36	13 00	13 26	13 33	13 35	13 58	14 00	14 36	15 00				15 35
	d	10 08		10 37	11 01	11 11			12 01	12 21		12 37	13 01	13 27		13 39	13 58	14 01	14 37	15 01		15 12	15 20	15 38
Frome	d			10 47								12 49							14a50				15 31	15 47
Bruton	d			10 58								13 01											15 44	15 58
Castle Cary	a		10 31	11 03						12 40		13 06					14 16						15 49	16 04
	d			11 04								13 06												16 09
Yeovil Pen Mill	d			11 18								13 20												16 24
Thornford	d			11x22								13x25												16x28
Yetminster	d			11x25								13x28												16x31
Chetnole	d			11x29								13x32												16x35
Maiden Newton	d			11 41								13 44												16 47
Dorchester West	d			11 54								13 54												16 58
Upwey	a			12 02								14 02												17 05
Weymouth	a			12 09								14 09												17 10
Dilton Marsh	d	10x10				11x13								13x29								15x14		
Warminster	d	10a19			11 09	11 21			12 09				13 09	13 36		13 46		14 09		15 09		15a23		
Salisbury	a				11 32	11 42			12 32				13 32	13 58		14 10		14 32		15 32				
	d				11 32	11 43			12 32				13 32	13 59				14 32		15 32				
Romsey	d				11 50	12 04			12 50				13 50	14 19				14 50		15 50				
Southampton Central	a				12 04	12 21			13 04				14 04	14 32				15 04		16 04				
Fareham	a				12 27				13 27				14 27	14 58				15 27		16 27				
	d				12 27				13 27				14 27	14 59				15 27		16 27				
Cosham	a				12 35				13 35				14 35	15 07				15 35		16 35				
Fratton	a				12 42				13 42				14 42					15 42		16 42				
Portsmouth & Southsea	a				12 46				13 46				14 46					15 46		16 46				
Portsmouth Harbour	a				12 54				13 54				14 54					15 54		16 54				
Havant	a													15 14										
Chichester 4	a													15 25										
Barnham	a													15 36										
Worthing 4	a													15 54										
Shoreham-by-Sea	a													16 01										
Hove 2	a													16 07										
Brighton 10	a													16 14										

A To Plymouth
B To Plymouth. The Mayflower
C 🛒 from Bristol Temple Meads
D To London Waterloo
E To Taunton
F From Frome
G To Exeter St Davids

For connections from Swansea to Cardiff Central and Bristol Parkway please see Table 128

For connections from Plymouth and Exeter to Bristol Temple Meads, Westbury and Castle Cary, please see Table 135

For connections from Exeter and Yeovil Junction to Salisbury please see Table 160

For connections from Upwey, Weymouth and Southampton Central to Bournemouth please see Table 158

For Bus Connections between Yeovil Junction and Yeovil Pen Mill please see Table 123A

Table 123R

Mondays to Fridays

9 December to 16 May

Great Malvern, Gloucester, Cardiff and Bristol - Weymouth, Portsmouth and Brighton

Network Diagram - see first Page of Table 123

		GW	GW	GW	GW	SW	GW	GW	GW	GW	GW	GW	GW	GW	GW	GW	GW	GW	GW	GW	GW	GW	GW
		◇ 🛒		◇[1] A Ø		◇[1] B	◇ 🛒		◇			◇[1] C ⊡	[R] 🛒		◇		◇[1] D ⊡	[R] 🛒	◇		◇[1] ⊡	◇ 🛒	◇[1] C ⊡
Cardiff Central [7]	d	14 30					15 30						16 30					17 30				18 30	
Newport (South Wales)	d	14 44					15 44						16 44					17 44				18 44	
Severn Tunnel Jn.	d												16 55					17 55				18 55	
Great Malvern	d								14 50											16 48			
Malvern Link	d								14 53											16 51			
Worcester Foregate Street	d								15 03											17 02			
Worcester Shrub Hill	d								15 06											17 06			
Ashchurch for Tewkesbury	d								15 24											17 24			
Cheltenham Spa	d								15 33										17 39	17 33			
Gloucester	d				14 41				15 46						16 40				17 54	17 46			
Cam & Dursley	d				14 56				16 00						16 56					18 00			
Yate	d				15 10				16 14						17 10					18 14			
Bristol Parkway	d				15 20				16 23	16 46					17 20	17 48				18 23			
Filton Abbey Wood	d	15 09			15 23		16 09		16 26	16 50	16 55		17 09		17 23	17 52		18 09		18 27		19 09	
Bristol Temple Meads [10]	d	15 22			15 44	15 51	16 22		16 49	17 05	17 14		17 22		17 49	18 07		18 22		18 52		19 22	
Keynsham	d				15 51	15 58			16 56	17 12					17 56	18 14				18 59			
Oldfield Park	d				15 58				17 03	17 19	17 26				18 03	18 22				19 06			
London Paddington [15] ⊖	d			15 06								16 36					17 33				18 05		18 35
Swindon	d		15 14											17 36					18 50				
Chippenham	d		15 39											17 53					19 07				
Melksham	d		15 53											18 03					19 17				
Bath Spa [7]	d	15 35			16 02	16 07	16 35		17 07	17 23	17 30		17 37		18 07	18 26		18 35		19 10		19 35	
Freshford	d				16 11				17 17		17 39				18 16	18 35				19 19			
Avoncliff	d				16 14				17 19						18 19	18 37				19 22			
Bradford-on-Avon	d	15 47			16 18	16 24	16 47		17 24	17 35	17 44		17 50		18 23	18 41		18 47		19 26		19 47	
Trowbridge	d	15 53	16 02		16 24	16 30	16 53		17 31	17 42	17 50		17 57	18 13	18 29	18 48		18 53	19 26	19 32		19 53	
Westbury	a	16 00	16 10	16 22	16 33	16 37	17 00		17 36	17 49	17 58	18 02	18 05	18 21	18 36	18 56	18 59	19 00	19 33	19 39	19 53	20 00	20 05
	d	16 01		16 23		16 39	17 01	17 11	17 39	17 50		18 03	18 05		18 40		19 01	19 02	19 41		19 55	20 01	20 06
Frome	d								17 49						18 49						20a06		
Bruton	d								18 01						19 01								
Castle Cary	a			16 41					18 06			18 21			19 06		19 18						20 24
	d								18 06						19 06								
Yeovil Pen Mill	d								18 22						19 19								
Thornford	d								18x26						19x25								
Yetminster	d								18x29						19x28								
Chetnole	d								18x33						19x32								
Maiden Newton	d								18 45						19 44								
Dorchester West	d								18 58						19 54								
Upwey	a								19 06						20 02								
Weymouth	a								19 12						20 10								
Dilton Marsh	d							17x13		17x53									19x43				
Warminster	d	16 09				16 47	17 09	17a22		18a01			18 13					19 09	19 51			20 09	
Salisbury	a	16 32				17 09	17 32						18 35					19 32	20 13			20 32	
	d	16 32					17 32						18 35					19 32	20 14			20 32	
Romsey	d	16 50					17 50						18 54					19 50	20 35			20 50	
Southampton Central	a	17 04					18 04						19 04					20 04	20 48			21 04	
Fareham	a	17 27					18 27						19 27					20 27				21 27	
	d	17 27					18 27						19 27					20 27				21 27	
Cosham	a	17 35					18 35						19 34										
Fratton	a	17 42					18 48						19 42					20 42				21 41	
Portsmouth & Southsea	a	17 46					18 52						19 46					20 46				21 45	
Portsmouth Harbour	a	17 54					19 00						19 54					20 54				21 52	
Havant	a																						
Chichester [4]	a																						
Barnham	a																						
Worthing [4]	a																						
Shoreham-by-Sea	a																						
Hove [2]	a																						
Brighton [10]	a																						

A To Penzance. The Cornishman
B To London Waterloo
C To Exeter St Davids
D To Paignton

For connections from Swansea to Cardiff Central and Bristol Parkway please see Table 128

For connections from Plymouth and Exeter to Bristol Temple Meads, Westbury and Castle Cary, please see Table 135

For connections from Exeter and Yeovil Junction to Salisbury please see Table 160

For connections from Upwey, Weymouth and Southampton Central to Bournemouth please see Table 158

For Bus Connections between Yeovil Junction and Yeovil Pen Mill please see Table 123A

Table 123R

Mondays to Fridays

9 December to 16 May

Great Malvern, Gloucester, Cardiff and Bristol - Weymouth, Portsmouth and Brighton

Network Diagram - see first Page of Table 123

		GW	GW		GW	GW	GW	GW	GW	GW	SW	GW
					◇	◇ 1		◇ 1	◇		1	
						A		A				
						☕		☕				
Cardiff Central 7	d				19 30				20 30	21 00		
Newport (South Wales)	d				19 44				20 44	21 15		
Severn Tunnel Jn.	d									21 25		
Great Malvern	d											
Malvern Link	d											
Worcester Foregate Street	d											
Worcester Shrub Hill	d											
Ashchurch for Tewkesbury	d											
Cheltenham Spa	d											
Gloucester	d	18 41										
Cam & Dursley	d	18 56										
Yate	d	19 10										
Bristol Parkway	d	19 20										
Filton Abbey Wood	d	19 24			20 09				21 08	21 42		
Bristol Temple Meads 10	d	19 49			20 22		20 49		21 23	22 04	22 23	23 20
Keynsham	d	19 56					20 56			22 11		23 27
Oldfield Park	d	20 03					21 03			22 18		23 34
London Paddington 15 ⊖	d					19 45		20 35				
Swindon	d		20 12									
Chippenham	d		20 29									
Melksham	d		20 38									
Bath Spa 7	d	20 07			20 36		21 07		21 36	22 21	22 36	23 38
Freshford	d	20 16					21 16			22 30		23 47
Avoncliff	d	20 19					21 19			22 33		23 50
Bradford-on-Avon	d	20 23			20 47		21 23		21 48	22 37	22 47	23 54
Trowbridge	d	20 29	20 48		20 53		21 29		21 55	22 43	22 53	23 59
Westbury	a	20 36	20 55		21 00	21 06	21 36	21 56	22 03	22 50	23 00	00 07
	d	20 37			21 01	21 06	21 40	21 56	22 03		23 05	00 08
Frome	d	20a48					21 50					00a19
Bruton	d						22 02					
Castle Cary	a					21 24	22 07	22 14				
	d						22 08					
Yeovil Pen Mill	d						22 23					
Thornford	d						22x28					
Yetminster	d						22x31					
Chetnole	d						22x35					
Maiden Newton	d						22 47					
Dorchester West	d						22 58					
Upwey	a						23 05					
Weymouth	a						23 13					
Dilton Marsh	d								22x06			
Warminster	d				21 09				22 11		23 12	
Salisbury	a				21 32				22 32		23 35	
	d				21 32				22 32			
Romsey	d				21 50				22 53			
Southampton Central	a				22 02				23 04			
Fareham	a				22 42				23 27			
	d				22 42				23 27			
Cosham	a											
Fratton	a				22 56				23 44			
Portsmouth & Southsea	a				22 59				23 48			
Portsmouth Harbour	a				23 04				23 54			
Havant	a											
Chichester 4	a											
Barnham	a											
Worthing 4	a											
Shoreham-by-Sea	a											
Hove 2	a											
Brighton 10	a											

A To Plymouth

For connections from Swansea to Cardiff Central and Bristol Parkway please see Table 128

For connections from Plymouth and Exeter to Bristol Temple Meads, Westbury and Castle Cary, please see Table 135

For connections from Exeter and Yeovil Junction to Salisbury please see Table 160

For connections from Upwey, Weymouth and Southampton Central to Bournemouth please see Table 158

For Bus Connections between Yeovil Junction and Yeovil Pen Mill please see Table 123A

Table 123R

Saturdays

14 December to 28 December

Great Malvern, Gloucester, Cardiff and Bristol - Weymouth, Portsmouth and Brighton

Network Diagram - see first Page of Table 123

		GW	GW	GW	GW	GW	GW	GW	GW	GW	GW	GW	GW	SW	GW	GW	GW	GW	GW	GW	GW	GW	GW
		A			◇				◇		◇		◇	◇1 B	◇1 C	◇		◇	◇ D				◇ D
Cardiff Central 7	d								06 30		07 30					08 30			09 30				10 30
Newport (South Wales)	d								06 44		07 44					08 44			09 44				10 44
Severn Tunnel Jn.	d								06 55		07 55					08 55			09 55				
Great Malvern	d																						
Malvern Link	d																						
Worcester Foregate Street	d																						
Worcester Shrub Hill	d												06 47										
Ashchurch for Tewkesbury	d												07 03									09 08	
Cheltenham Spa	d												07 13									09 24	
Gloucester	d												07 40									09 34	
Cam & Dursley	d												07 55					08 41				09 46	
Yate	d												08 10					08 56				10 02	
Bristol Parkway	d												08 20					09 11				10 16	
Filton Abbey Wood	d								07 09		08 09		08 23			09 09		09 20				10 25	
Bristol Temple Meads 10	d				05 49			06 49	07 22	07 49	08 22		08 39	08 51		09 22		09 23	10 09			10 28	11 09
Keynsham	d				05 56			06 56		07 56			08 46	08 58				09 49	10 22			10 49	11 22
Oldfield Park	d				06 03			07 03		08 03			08 53					09 56				10 56	
London Paddington 15 ⊖	d														08 18			10 03				11 03	
Swindon	d											08 36									10 36		
Chippenham	d											08 53									10 53		
Melksham	d											09 02									11 02		
Bath Spa 7	d				06 07			07 07	07 35	08 07	08 35		08 57	09 07		09 35		10 07	10 35			11 07	11 35
Freshford	d				06 16			07 16		08 16			09 06					10 16				11 16	
Avoncliff	d				06 19			07 19		08 19			09 09					10 19				11 19	
Bradford-on-Avon	d				06 23			07 23	07 47	08 23	08 47		09 13	09 20		09 47		10 23	10 47			11 23	11 47
Trowbridge	d				06 29			07 29	07 53	08 29	08 53	09 12	09 19	09 27		09 53		10 29	10 53		11 12	11 29	11 53
Westbury	a				06 36			07 36	08 01	08 36	09 01	09 20	09 26	09 34	09 57	10 00		10 36	11 01		11 20	11 36	12 01
	d	00 08	05 26	06 01	06 43	06 47	07 03		08 01		09 01		09 27	09 39	09 57	10 00	10 10	10 37	11 01	11 11			12 01
Frome	d	00a19				06 56							09 36					10 46					
Bruton	d					07 08							09 48					10 58					
Castle Cary	a					07 14							09 53		10 16			11 03					
	d					07 15							09 53					11 03					
Yeovil Pen Mill	d					07 29							10 07					11 17					
Thornford	d					07x33							10x12					11x22					
Yetminster	d					07x36							10x15					11x25					
Chetnole	d					07x40							10x19					11x29					
Maiden Newton	d					07 52							10 31					11 41					
Dorchester West	d					08 03							10 38					11 54					
Upwey	a					08 10							10 49					12 02					
Weymouth	a					08 17							10 57					12 09					
Dilton Marsh	d						07x06										10x13			11x13			
Warminster	d		05 34	06 09	06 51		07 13		08 09		09 09			09 46		10 09	10a19		11 09	11 21			12 09
Salisbury	a		05 58	06 31	07 12		07 34		08 32		09 31			10 09		10 31			11 32	11 42			12 32
	d			06 32	07 24		07 36		08 32		09 32					10 32			11 32	11 43			12 32
Romsey	d			06 50	07 44		07 55		08 50		09 50					10 50			11 50	12 04			12 50
Southampton Central	a			07 02	08 02		08 07		09 03		10 03					11 03			12 03	12 21			13 03
Fareham	a			07 27	08 27				09 27		10 27					11 27			12 27				13 27
	d			07 27	08 27				09 27		10 27					11 27			12 27				13 27
Cosham	a			07 35	08 35				09 35		10 35					11 35			12 35				13 35
Fratton	a			07 42	08 42				09 42		10 42					11 42			12 42				13 42
Portsmouth & Southsea	a			07 46	08 46				09 46		10 46					11 46			12 46				13 46
Portsmouth Harbour	a			07 52	08 52				09 52		10 52					11 52			12 52				13 52
Havant	a																						
Chichester 4	a																						
Barnham	a																						
Worthing 4	a																						
Shoreham-by-Sea	a																						
Hove 2	a																						
Brighton 10	a																						

A From Bristol Temple Meads
B To London Waterloo
C To Exeter St Davids
D from Bristol Temple Meads

For connections from Swansea to Cardiff Central and Bristol Parkway please see Table 128

For connections from Plymouth and Exeter to Bristol Temple Meads, Westbury and Castle Cary, please see Table 135

For connections from Exeter and Yeovil Junction to Salisbury please see Table 160

For connections from Upwey, Weymouth and Southampton Central to Bournemouth please see Table 158

For Bus Connections between Yeovil Junction and Yeovil Pen Mill please see Table 123A

No full service avaiable from/to Brighton between 14 Dec - 28 Dec

Table 123R

Saturdays

14 December to 28 December

Great Malvern, Gloucester, Cardiff and Bristol - Weymouth, Portsmouth and Brighton

Network Diagram - see first Page of Table 123

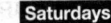

		GW	GW	GW	GW	GW		SW	GW	GW	GW	GW	GW	GW	GW	GW		GW	GW	GW	SW	GW	GW	GW	GW
						■																			■
		◇1	◇	◇		◇		◇1	◇1	◇		◇			◇	◇			◇1		◇1	◇		◇	
		A		B		C		D	E				F						G		D				
		⌀		⊼				⊼	⊏										⊏						
Cardiff Central 7	d			11 30						12 30		13 30				14 30						15 30			16 30
Newport (South Wales)	d			11 44						12 44		13 44				14 44						15 44			16 44
Severn Tunnel Jn.	d																								16 55
Great Malvern	d					10 46																		14 50	
Malvern Link	d					10 48																		14 52	
Worcester Foregate Street	d					10 58									12 41									15 04	
Worcester Shrub Hill	d					11 06									12 54									15 06	
Ashchurch for Tewkesbury	d					11 24									13 10									15 24	
Cheltenham Spa	d					11 34									13 20									15 34	
Gloucester	d		10 41			11 46					12 41				13 42					14 41				15 46	
Cam & Dursley	d		10 56			12 02					12 56				13 58					14 56				16 02	
Yate	d		11 11			12 16					13 11				14 13					15 11				16 16	
Bristol Parkway	d		11 21			12 25					13 20				14 22					15 20				16 25	
Filton Abbey Wood	d		11 24	12 09		12 28				13 09	13 23	14 09			14 25	15 09				15 23		16 09		16 28	17 09
Bristol Temple Meads 10	d		11 49	12 22		12 43		12 51		13 22	13 49	14 22			14 49	15 22				15 39	15 51	16 22		16 49	17 22
Keynsham	d		11 56			12 50		12 58			13 56				14 56					15 46	15 58			16 56	
Oldfield Park	d		12 03			12 57					14 03				15 03					15 53				17 03	
London Paddington 15 ⊖	d	11 06							12 18										15 06						
Swindon	d				12 36									14 36				15 22							
Chippenham	d				12 53									14 53				15 39							
Melksham	d				13 02									15 02				15 48							
Bath Spa 7	d		12 07	12 35		13 00		13 07		13 35	14 07	14 35			15 07	15 35				15 57	16 07	16 35		17 07	17 35
Freshford	d		12 16								14 16				15 16					16 06				17 16	
Avoncliff	d		12 19								14 19				15 19					16 09				17 19	
Bradford-on-Avon	d		12 23	12 47		13 13		13 20		13 47	14 23	14 47			15 23	15 47				16 13	16 24	16 47		17 23	17 47
Trowbridge	d		12 29	12 53	13 12	13 20		13 27		13 53	14 29	14 53		15 12	15 29	15 53		15 58		16 19	16 30	16 53		17 29	17 53
Westbury	a	12 21	12 36	13 01	13 20	13 27		13 33	13 57	14 01	14 36	15 01		15 20	15 36	16 01		16 05	16 21	16 26	16 37	17 01		17 36	18 01
	d	12 21	12 37	13 01		13 28		13 39	13 58	14 01	14 40	15 01	15 11		15 37	16 01			16 22		16 39	17 01	17 08	17 38	18 01
Frome	d		12 47								14a51				15 46									17 47	
Bruton	d		12 57												15 57									17 59	
Castle Cary	a	12 39	13 03						14 15						16 03				16 40					18 04	
	d		13 04												16 09									18 05	
Yeovil Pen Mill	d		13 17												16 24									18 21	
Thornford	d		13x22												16x28									18x26	
Yetminster	d		13x25												16x31									18x29	
Chetnole	d		13x29												16x35									18x33	
Maiden Newton	d		13 41												16 47									18 44	
Dorchester West	d		13 54												16 58									18 54	
Upwey	a		14 02												17 05									19 02	
Weymouth	a		14 08												17 10									19 10	
Dilton Marsh	d					13x31							15x14										17x10		
Warminster	d			13 09		13 37		13 46		14 09		15 09	15a23			16 09					16 47	17 09	17a19		18 09
Salisbury	a			13 32		13 59		14 10		14 32		15 32				16 32					17 09	17 32			18 32
	d			13 32		14 00				14 32		15 32				16 32						17 32			18 32
Romsey	d			13 50		14 20				14 50		15 50				16 50						17 51			18 50
Southampton Central	a			14 03		14 32				15 03		16 03				17 03						18 03			19 03
Fareham	a			14 27		14 54				15 27		16 27				17 27						18 27			19 27
	d			14 27		14 55				15 27		16 27				17 27						18 27			19 27
Cosham	a			14 35		15 03				15 35		16 35				17 35						18 35			19 35
Fratton	a			14 42						15 42		16 42				17 42						18 42			19 42
Portsmouth & Southsea	a			14 46						15 46		16 46				17 46						18 45			19 46
Portsmouth Harbour	a			14 52						15 52		16 52				17 52						18 53			19 52
Havant	a					15 10																			
Chichester 4	a					15 21																			
Barnham	a					15 29																			
Worthing 4	a					15 44																			
Shoreham-by-Sea	a					15 55																			
Hove 2	a					16 07																			
Brighton 10	a					16 14																			

A To Plymouth
B ⊼ from Bristol Temple Meads
C ■ from Bristol Temple Meads ◇ to Bristol Temple Meads
D To London Waterloo
E To Taunton
F From Frome
G To Penzance

For connections from Swansea to Cardiff Central and Bristol Parkway please see Table 128

For connections from Plymouth and Exeter to Bristol Temple Meads, Westbury and Castle Cary, please see Table 135

For connections from Exeter and Yeovil Junction to Salisbury please see Table 160

For connections from Upwey, Weymouth and Southampton Central to Bournemouth please see Table 158

For Bus Connections between Yeovil Junction and Yeovil Pen Mill please see Table 123A

No full service avaiable from/to Brighton between 14 Dec - 28 Dec

Table 123R

Saturdays

14 December to 28 December

Great Malvern, Gloucester, Cardiff and Bristol - Weymouth, Portsmouth and Brighton

Network Diagram - see first Page of Table 123

		GW		GW	GW	GW	GW	GW	GW	GW	GW	GW		GW	GW	GW	GW	GW	GW	SW	GW
				◇1	◇	◇			◇		◇1			◇	◇1			◇		1	
				A							B				B						
				🍴							🍴				🍴						
Cardiff Central 7	d					17 30			18 30					19 30				20 30			
Newport (South Wales)	d					17 44			18 44					19 44				20 44			
Severn Tunnel Jn.	d					17 55															
Great Malvern	d							16 50													
Malvern Link	d							16 52													
Worcester Foregate Street	d							17 04													
Worcester Shrub Hill	d							17 06													
Ashchurch for Tewkesbury	d							17 24													
Cheltenham Spa	d							17 34									20 01				
Gloucester	d				16 41			17 46				18 41					20 13				
Cam & Dursley	d				16 56			18 02				18 56									
Yate	d				17 11			18 16				19 11									
Bristol Parkway	d				17 20			18 25				19 20									
Filton Abbey Wood	d				17 24	18 09		18 28	19 09			19 23		20 09				21 08			
Bristol Temple Meads 10	d				17 49	18 22		18 49	19 22			19 49		20 22		20 49		21 22	22 00	22 23	23 11
Keynsham	d				17 56			18 56				19 56				20 56			22 07		23 18
Oldfield Park	d				18 03			19 03				20 03				21 03			22 14		23 25
London Paddington 15 ⊖	d			17 06							19 06				20 06						
Swindon	d	17 36								19 36							21 08				
Chippenham	d	17 53								19 53							21 25				
Melksham	d	18 02								20 02							21 34				
Bath Spa 7	d				18 07	18 35		19 07	19 35			20 07		20 35		21 07		21 35	22 18	22 36	23 29
Freshford	d				18 16			19 16				20 16				21 16			22 27		23 38
Avoncliff	d				18 19			19 19				20 19				21 19			22 30		23 40
Bradford-on-Avon	d				18 23	18 47		19 23	19 47			20 23		20 47		21 23		21 47	22 34	22 47	23 44
Trowbridge	d	18 12			18 29	18 53		19 29	19 53	20 12		20 29		20 53		21 29	21 44	21 53	22 40	22 53	23 50
Westbury	a	18 18		18 21	18 36	19 01		19 36	20 01	20 20	20 26	20 36		21 01	21 27	21 36	21 52	22 01	22 47	23 00	23 57
	d			18 23	18 39	19 01	19 18		20 01		20 27	20 37		21 01	21 29	21 41		22 01		23 05	23 58
Frome	d				18 49							20a48				21 50					00a08
Bruton	d				19 00											22 02					
Castle Cary	a			18 40	19 05						20 44				21 46	22 07					
	d				19 06											22 08					
Yeovil Pen Mill	d				19 19											22 23					
Thornford	d				19x24											22x28					
Yetminster	d				19x27											22x31					
Chetnole	d				19x31											22x35					
Maiden Newton	d				19 43											22 47					
Dorchester West	d				19 54											22 58					
Upwey	a				20 01											23 05					
Weymouth	a				20 09											23 13					
Dilton Marsh	d						19x21											22x05			
Warminster	d					19 09	19 28		20 09					21 09				22 10		23 12	
Salisbury	a					19 32	19 49		20 32					21 32				22 32		23 35	
	d					19 32	19 50		20 32					21 32				22 32			
Romsey	d					19 50	20 11		20 50					21 50				22 50			
Southampton Central	a					20 02	20 21		21 03					22 03				23 03			
Fareham	a					20 27			21 27					22 26				23 26			
	d					20 27			21 27					22 27				23 27			
Cosham	a																				
Fratton	a					20 42			21 42					22 42				23 40			
Portsmouth & Southsea	a					20 46			21 46					22 46				23 44			
Portsmouth Harbour	a					20 52			21 52					22 52				23 52			
Havant	a																				
Chichester 4	a																				
Barnham	a																				
Worthing 4	a																				
Shoreham-by-Sea	a																				
Hove 2	a																				
Brighton 10	a																				

A To Penzance

B To Plymouth

For connections from Swansea to Cardiff Central and Bristol Parkway please see Table 128

For connections from Plymouth and Exeter to Bristol Temple Meads, Westbury and Castle Cary, please see Table 135

For connections from Exeter and Yeovil Junction to Salisbury please see Table 160

For connections from Upwey, Weymouth and Southampton Central to Bournemouth please see Table 158

For Bus Connections between Yeovil Junction and Yeovil Pen Mill please see Table 123A

No full service avaiable from/to Brighton between 14 Dec - 28 Dec

Table 123R

Saturdays

4 January to 8 February

Great Malvern, Gloucester, Cardiff and Bristol - Weymouth, Portsmouth and Brighton

Network Diagram - see first Page of Table 123

		GW	GW	GW	GW	GW	GW	GW	GW	GW		GW	GW	SW	GW	GW	GW	GW	GW	GW		GW	GW	GW	GW
		A			◇				◇			◇	◇	◇[1] B		◇[1] C	◇		◇	◇ D 🛒					◇ D 🛒
Cardiff Central [7]	d								06 30			07 30					08 30			09 30					10 30
Newport (South Wales)	d								06 44			07 44					08 44			09 44					10 44
Severn Tunnel Jn	d								06 55			07 55					08 55			09 55					
Great Malvern	d																								
Malvern Link	d																								
Worcester Foregate Street	d																								
Worcester Shrub Hill	d												06 47											09 08	
Ashchurch for Tewkesbury	d												07 03											09 24	
Cheltenham Spa	d												07 13											09 34	
Gloucester	d												07 40						08 41					09 46	
Cam & Dursley	d												07 55						08 56					10 02	
Yate	d												08 10						09 11					10 16	
Bristol Parkway	d												08 20						09 20					10 25	
Filton Abbey Wood	d								07 09			08 09	08 23				09 09		09 23	10 09				10 28	11 09
Bristol Temple Meads [10]	d				05 49			06 49	07 22	07 49		08 22	08 39	08 51			09 22		09 49	10 22				10 49	11 22
Keynsham	d				05 56			06 56		07 56			08 46	08 58					09 56					10 56	
Oldfield Park	d				06 03			07 03		08 03			08 53						10 03					11 03	
London Paddington [15] ⊖	d															08 13									
Swindon	d														08 50								10 46		
Chippenham	d														09 07								11 03		
Melksham	d														09 16								11 12		
Bath Spa [7]	d				06 07			07 07	07 35	08 07		08 35	08 57	09 07			09 35		10 07	10 35				11 07	11 35
Freshford	d				06 16			07 16		08 16			09 06						10 16					11 16	
Avoncliff	d				06 19			07 19		08 19			09 09						10 19					11 19	
Bradford-on-Avon	d				06 23			07 23	07 47	08 23		08 47	09 13	09 20			09 47		10 23	10 47				11 23	11 47
Trowbridge	d				06 29			07 29	07 53	08 29		08 53	09 19	09 27	09 32		09 53		10 29	10 53			11 22	11 29	11 53
Westbury	a				06 36			07 36	08 01	08 36		09 01	09 26	09 34	09 38	09 57	10 00		10 36	11 01			11 33	11 36	12 01
	d	00 08	05 26	06 01	06 43	06 47	07 03		08 01			09 01	09 27	09 39		09 57	10 00	10 10	10 37	11 01		11 11			12 01
Frome	d	00a19				06 56							09 36						10 46						
Bruton	d					07 08							09 48						10 58						
Castle Cary	a					07 14							09 53			10 16			11 03						
	d					07 15							09 53						11 03						
Yeovil Pen Mill	d					07 29							10 07						11 17						
Thornford	d					07x33							10x12						11x22						
Yetminster	d					07x36							10x15						11x25						
Chetnole	d					07x40							10x19						11x29						
Maiden Newton	d					07 52							10 31						11 41						
Dorchester West	d					08 03							10 38						11 54						
Upwey	a					08 10							10 49						12 02						
Weymouth	a					08 17							10 57						12 09						
Dilton Marsh	d						07x06											10x13				11x13			
Warminster	d		05 34	06 09	06 51		07 13		08 09			09 09		09 46			10 09	10a19		11 09		11 21			12 09
Salisbury	a		05 58	06 31	07 12		07 34		08 32			09 31		10 09			10 31			11 32		11 42			12 32
	d			06 32	07 24		07 36		08 32			09 32					10 32			11 32		11 43			12 32
Romsey	d			06 50	07 44		07 55		08 50			09 50					10 50			11 50		12 04			12 50
Southampton Central	a			07 02	08 02		08 07		09 03			10 03					11 03			12 03		12 21			13 03
Fareham	a			07 27	08 27				09 27			10 27					11 27			12 27					13 27
	d			07 27	08 27				09 27			10 27					11 27			12 27					13 27
Cosham	a			07 35	08 35				09 35			10 35					11 35			12 35					13 35
Fratton	a			07 42	08 42				09 42			10 42					11 42			12 42					13 42
Portsmouth & Southsea	a			07 46	08 46				09 46			10 46					11 46			12 46					13 46
Portsmouth Harbour	a			07 52	08 52				09 52			10 52					11 52			12 52					13 52
Havant	a																								
Chichester [4]	a																								
Barnham	a																								
Worthing [4]	a																								
Shoreham-by-Sea	a																								
Hove [2]	a																								
Brighton [10]	a																								

A From Bristol Temple Meads
B To London Waterloo
C To Exeter St Davids
D 🛒 from Bristol Temple Meads

For connections from Swansea to Cardiff Central and Bristol Parkway please see Table 128

For connections from Plymouth and Exeter to Bristol Temple Meads, Westbury and Castle Cary, please see Table 135

For connections from Exeter and Yeovil Junction to Salisbury please see Table 160

For connections from Upwey, Weymouth and Southampton Central to Bournemouth please see Table 158

For Bus Connections between Yeovil Junction and Yeovil Pen Mill please see Table 123A

Table 123R

Saturdays

4 January to 8 February

Great Malvern, Gloucester, Cardiff and Bristol - Weymouth, Portsmouth and Brighton

Network Diagram - see first Page of Table 123

		GW	GW	GW	GW	SW	GW	GW	GW	GW	GW	GW	GW	GW	GW	GW	GW	SW	GW	GW	GW	GW	GW
		◇1 A ⌀	◇	◇ B 🛒	R ◇ C	◇1 D 🛒		◇1 E ☕	◇		◇	F	◇		◇	◇1 G ☕		◇1 D		◇		◇	R
Cardiff Central 7	d			11 30					12 30		13 30				14 30					15 30			16 30
Newport (South Wales)	d			11 44					12 44		13 44				14 44					15 44			16 44
Severn Tunnel Jn.	d																						16 55
Great Malvern	d				10 46																	14 50	
Malvern Link	d				10 48																	14 52	
Worcester Foregate Street	d				10 58								12 41									15 04	
Worcester Shrub Hill	d				11 06								12 54									15 06	
Ashchurch for Tewkesbury	d				11 24								13 10									15 24	
Cheltenham Spa	d				11 34								13 20						15 00			15 34	
Gloucester	d		10 41		11 46					12 41			13 42				14 41		15 13			15 46	
Cam & Dursley	d		10 56		12 02					12 56			13 58				14 56					16 02	
Yate	d		11 11		12 16					13 11			14 13				15 11					16 16	
Bristol Parkway	d		11 21		12 25					13 20			14 22				15 20					16 25	
Filton Abbey Wood	d		11 24	12 09	12 28				13 09	13 23	14 09		14 25		15 09		15 23			16 09		16 28	17 09
Bristol Temple Meads 10	d		11 49	12 22	12 43	12 51			13 22	13 49	14 22		14 49		15 22		15 39	15 51		16 22		16 49	17 22
Keynsham	d		11 56		12 50	12 58				13 56			14 56				15 46	15 58				16 56	
Oldfield Park	d		12 03		12 57					14 03			15 03				15 53					17 03	
London Paddington 15 ⊖	d	11 00						12 13								15 00							
Swindon	d						12 50							15 12					16 06				
Chippenham	d						13 07							15 29					16 23				
Melksham	d						13 16							15 38					16 33				
Bath Spa 7	d		12 07	12 35	13 00	13 07			13 35	14 07	14 35		15 07		15 35		15 57	16 07		16 35		17 07	17 35
Freshford	d		12 16							14 16			15 16				16 06					17 16	
Avoncliff	d		12 19							14 19			15 19				16 09					17 19	
Bradford-on-Avon	d		12 23	12 47	13 13	13 20			13 47	14 23	14 47		15 23		15 47		16 13	16 24		16 47		17 23	17 47
Trowbridge	d		12 29	12 53	13 20	13 27	13 32		13 53	14 29	14 53		15 29	15 48	15 53		16 19	16 30	16 41	16 53		17 29	17 53
Westbury	a	12 24	12 36	13 01	13 27	13 33	13 38	13 57	14 01	14 36	15 01		15 36	15 56	16 01	16 23	16 26	16 37	16 48	17 01		17 36	18 01
	d	12 24	12 37	13 01	13 28	13 39		13 58	14 01	14 40	15 01	15 11	15 37		16 01	16 24		16 39		17 01	17 08	17 38	18 01
Frome	d		12 47							14a51			15 46									17 47	
Bruton	d		12 57										15 57									17 59	
Castle Cary	a	12 42	13 03					14 15					16 03			16 42						18 04	
	d		13 04										16 09									18 05	
Yeovil Pen Mill	d		13 17										16 24									18 21	
Thornford	d		13x22										16x28									18x26	
Yetminster	d		13x25										16x31									18x29	
Chetnole	d		13x29										16x35									18x33	
Maiden Newton	d		13 41										16 47									18 44	
Dorchester West	d		13 54										16 58									18 54	
Upwey	a		14 02										17 05									19 02	
Weymouth	a		14 08										17 10									19 10	
Dilton Marsh	d				13x31							15x14									17x10		
Warminster	d			13 09	13 37	13 46			14 09		15 09	15a23			16 09			16 47		17 09	17a19		18 09
Salisbury	a			13 32	13 59	14 10			14 32		15 32				16 32			17 09		17 32			18 32
	d			13 32	14 00				14 32		15 32				16 32					17 32			18 32
Romsey	d			13 50	14 20				14 50		15 50				16 50					17 51			18 50
Southampton Central	a			14 03	14 32				15 03		16 03				17 03					18 03			19 03
Fareham	a			14 27	14 54				15 27		16 27				17 27					18 27			19 27
	d			14 27	14 55				15 27		16 27				17 27					18 27			19 27
Cosham	a			14 35	15 03				15 35		16 35				17 35					18 35			19 35
Fratton	a			14 42					15 42		16 42				17 42					18 42			19 42
Portsmouth & Southsea	a			14 46					15 46		16 46				17 46					18 45			19 46
Portsmouth Harbour	a			14 52					15 52		16 52				17 52					18 53			19 52
Havant	a				15 10																		
Chichester 4	a				15 21																		
Barnham	a				15 29																		
Worthing 4	a				15 44																		
Shoreham-by-Sea	a				15 55																		
Hove 2	a				16 07																		
Brighton 10	a				16 14																		

A To Plymouth
B 🛒 from Bristol Temple Meads
C R from Bristol Temple Meads ◇ to Bristol Temple Meads
D To London Waterloo
E To Taunton
F From Frome
G To Penzance

For connections from Swansea to Cardiff Central and Bristol Parkway please see Table 128

For connections from Plymouth and Exeter to Bristol Temple Meads, Westbury and Castle Cary, please see Table 135

For connections from Exeter and Yeovil Junction to Salisbury please see Table 160

For connections from Upwey, Weymouth and Southampton Central to Bournemouth please see Table 158

For Bus Connections between Yeovil Junction and Yeovil Pen Mill please see Table 123A

Table 123R

Saturdays

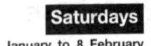

4 January to 8 February

Great Malvern, Gloucester, Cardiff and Bristol - Weymouth, Portsmouth and Brighton

Network Diagram - see first Page of Table 123

		GW	GW	GW	GW	GW	GW	GW	GW	GW	GW	GW	GW	GW	GW	GW	GW	SW	GW
		◇1 A ☕		◇	◇			◇	◇1 B ☕			◇	◇1 B ☕			◇		1	
Cardiff Central 7	d				17 30			18 30				19 30				20 30			
Newport (South Wales)	d				17 44			18 44				19 44				20 44			
Severn Tunnel Jn.	d				17 55														
Great Malvern	d						16 50												
Malvern Link	d						16 52												
Worcester Foregate Street	d						17 04												
Worcester Shrub Hill	d						17 06												
Ashchurch for Tewkesbury	d						17 24												
Cheltenham Spa	d						17 34												
Gloucester	d			16 41			17 46				18 41								
Cam & Dursley	d			16 56			18 02				18 56								
Yate	d			17 11			18 16				19 11								
Bristol Parkway	d			17 20			18 25				19 20								
Filton Abbey Wood	d			17 24	18 09		18 28	19 09			19 23	20 09				21 08			
Bristol Temple Meads 10	d			17 49	18 22		18 49	19 22			19 49	20 22		20 49		21 22	22 00	22 23	23 11
Keynsham	d			17 56			18 56				19 56			20 56			22 07		23 18
Oldfield Park	d			18 03			19 03				20 03			21 03			22 14		23 25
London Paddington 15 ⊖	d	17 00							19 00				20 00						
Swindon	d		17 46							19 47					21 14				
Chippenham	d		18 03							20 04					21 31				
Melksham	d		18 12							20 13					21 40				
Bath Spa 7	d			18 07	18 35		19 07	19 35			20 07	20 35		21 07		21 35	22 18	22 36	23 29
Freshford	d			18 16			19 16				20 16			21 16			22 27		23 38
Avoncliff	d			18 19			19 19				20 19			21 19			22 30		23 40
Bradford-on-Avon	d			18 23	18 47		19 23	19 47			20 23	20 47		21 23		21 47	22 34	22 47	23 44
Trowbridge	d		18 22	18 29	18 53		19 29	19 53		20 23	20 29	20 53		21 29	21 49	21 53	22 40	22 53	23 50
Westbury	a	18 24	18 30	18 36	19 01		19 36	20 01	20 29	20 31	20 36	21 01	21 28	21 36	21 56	22 01	22 47	23 00	23 57
	d	18 25		18 39	19 01	19 18		20 01	20 30		20 37	21 01	21 30	21 41		22 01		23 05	23 58
Frome	d			18 49							20a48			21 50					00a08
Bruton	d			19 00										22 02					
Castle Cary	a	18 43		19 05					20 47				21 47	22 07					
	d			19 06										22 08					
Yeovil Pen Mill	d			19 19										22 23					
Thornford	d			19x24										22x28					
Yetminster	d			19x27										22x31					
Chetnole	d			19x31										22x35					
Maiden Newton	d			19 43										22 47					
Dorchester West	d			19 54										22 58					
Upwey	a			20 01										23 05					
Weymouth	a			20 09										23 13					
Dilton Marsh	d					19x21										22x05			
Warminster	d				19 09	19 28		20 09				21 09				22 10		23 12	
Salisbury	a				19 32	19 49		20 32				21 32				22 32		23 35	
	d				19 32	19 50		20 32				21 32				22 32			
Romsey	d				19 50	20 11		20 50				21 50				22 50			
Southampton Central	a				20 02	20 21		21 03				22 03				23 03			
Fareham	a				20 27			21 27				22 26				23 26			
	d				20 27			21 27				22 27				23 27			
Cosham	a																		
Fratton	a				20 42			21 42				22 42				23 40			
Portsmouth & Southsea	a				20 46			21 46				22 46				23 44			
Portsmouth Harbour	a				20 52			21 52				22 52				23 52			
Havant	a																		
Chichester 4	a																		
Barnham	a																		
Worthing 4	a																		
Shoreham-by-Sea	a																		
Hove 2	a																		
Brighton 10	a																		

A To Penzance

B To Plymouth

For connections from Swansea to Cardiff Central and Bristol Parkway please see Table 128

For connections from Plymouth and Exeter to Bristol Temple Meads, Westbury and Castle Cary, please see Table 135

For connections from Exeter and Yeovil Junction to Salisbury please see Table 160

For connections from Upwey, Weymouth and Southampton Central to Bournemouth please see Table 158

For Bus Connections between Yeovil Junction and Yeovil Pen Mill please see Table 123A

Table 123R

Saturdays

15 February to 22 March

Great Malvern, Gloucester, Cardiff and Bristol - Weymouth, Portsmouth and Brighton

Network Diagram - see first Page of Table 123

		GW	GW	GW	GW	GW	GW	GW	GW	GW		GW	GW	GW	SW	GW	GW	GW	GW	GW		GW	GW	GW	GW
					◇				◇			◇		◇	◇1	◇1	◇		◇	◇					◇
		A													B	C				D					D
Cardiff Central 7	d								06 30			07 30					08 30			09 30					10 30
Newport (South Wales)	d								06 44			07 44					08 44			09 44					10 44
Severn Tunnel Jn	d								06 55			07 55					08 55			09 55					
Great Malvern	d																								
Malvern Link	d																								
Worcester Foregate Street	d																								
Worcester Shrub Hill	d													06 47										09 08	
Ashchurch for Tewkesbury	d													07 03										09 24	
Cheltenham Spa	d													07 13										09 34	
Gloucester	d													07 40					08 41					09 46	
Cam & Dursley	d													07 55					08 56					10 02	
Yate	d													08 10					09 11					10 16	
Bristol Parkway	d													08 20					09 20					10 25	
Filton Abbey Wood	d								07 09			08 09		08 23			09 09		09 23	10 09				10 28	11 09
Bristol Temple Meads 10	d				05 49			06 49	07 22	07 49		08 22		08 39	08 51		09 22		09 49	10 22				10 49	11 22
Keynsham	d				05 56			06 56		07 56				08 46	08 58				09 56					10 56	
Oldfield Park	d				06 03			07 03		08 03				08 53					10 03					11 03	
London Paddington 15 ⊖	d															08 18									
Swindon	d												08 36										10 36		
Chippenham	d												08 53										10 53		
Melksham	d												09 02										11 02		
Bath Spa 7	d				06 07			07 07	07 35	08 07		08 35		08 57	09 07		09 35		10 07	10 35				11 07	11 35
Freshford	d				06 16			07 16		08 16				09 06					10 16					11 16	
Avoncliff	d				06 19			07 19		08 19				09 09					10 19					11 19	
Bradford-on-Avon	d				06 23			07 23	07 47	08 23		08 47		09 13	09 20		09 47		10 23	10 47				11 23	11 47
Trowbridge	d				06 29			07 29	07 53	08 29		08 53	09 12	09 19	09 27		09 53		10 29	10 53			11 12	11 29	11 53
Westbury	a				06 36			07 36	08 01	08 36		09 01	09 20	09 26	09 34	09 57	10 00		10 36	11 01			11 20	11 36	12 01
	d	00 08	05 26	06 01	06 43	06 47	07 03		08 01			09 01		09 27	09 39	09 57	10 00	10 10	10 37	11 01		11 11			12 01
Frome	d	00a19				06 56								09 36					10 46						
Bruton	d					07 08								09 48					10 58						
Castle Cary	a					07 14								09 53		10 16			11 03						
	d					07 15								09 53					11 03						
Yeovil Pen Mill	d					07 29								10 07					11 17						
Thornford	d					07x33								10x12					11x22						
Yetminster	d					07x36								10x15					11x25						
Chetnole	d					07x40								10x19					11x29						
Maiden Newton	d					07 52								10 31					11 41						
Dorchester West	d					08 03								10 38					11 54						
Upwey	a					08 10								10 49					12 02						
Weymouth	a					08 17								10 57					12 09						
Dilton Marsh	d						07x06											10x13				11x13			
Warminster	d		05 34	06 09	06 51		07 13		08 09			09 09			09 46		10 09	10a19		11 09		11 21			12 09
Salisbury	a		05 58	06 31	07 12		07 34		08 32			09 31			10 09		10 31			11 32		11 42			12 32
	d			06 32	07 24		07 36		08 32			09 32					10 32			11 32		11 43			12 32
Romsey	d			06 50	07 44		07 55		08 50			09 50					10 50			11 50		12 04			12 50
Southampton Central	a			07 02	08 02		08 07		09 03			10 03					11 03			12 03		12 21			13 03
Fareham	a			07 27	08 27				09 27			10 27					11 27			12 27					13 27
	d			07 27	08 27				09 27			10 27					11 27			12 27					13 27
Cosham	a			07 35	08 35				09 35			10 35					11 35			12 35					13 35
Fratton	a			07 42	08 42				09 42			10 42					11 42			12 42					13 42
Portsmouth & Southsea	a			07 46	08 46				09 46			10 46					11 46			12 46					13 46
Portsmouth Harbour	a			07 52	08 52				09 52			10 52					11 52			12 52					13 52
Havant	a																								
Chichester 4	a																								
Barnham	a																								
Worthing 4	a																								
Shoreham-by-Sea	a																								
Hove 2	a																								
Brighton 10	a																								

A From Bristol Temple Meads
B To London Waterloo
C To Exeter St Davids
D from Bristol Temple Meads

For connections from Swansea to Cardiff Central and Bristol Parkway please see Table 128

For connections from Plymouth and Exeter to Bristol Temple Meads, Westbury and Castle Cary, please see Table 135

For connections from Exeter and Yeovil Junction to Salisbury please see Table 160

For connections from Upwey, Weymouth and Southampton Central to Bournemouth please see Table 158

For Bus Connections between Yeovil Junction and Yeovil Pen Mill please see Table 123A

Table 123R

Saturdays

15 February to 22 March

Great Malvern, Gloucester, Cardiff and Bristol - Weymouth, Portsmouth and Brighton

Network Diagram - see first Page of Table 123

		GW	GW	GW	GW	GW		SW	GW	GW	GW	GW	GW	GW	GW	GW		GW	GW	GW	SW	GW	GW	GW	GW
		◇1 A	◇	◇ B		◇ C		◇1 D	◇1 E	◇		◇	F		◇	◇			◇1 G		◇1 D	◇		◇	
Cardiff Central 7	d			11 30						12 30		13 30				14 30						15 30			16 30
Newport (South Wales)	d			11 44						12 44		13 44				14 44						15 44			16 44
Severn Tunnel Jn.	d																								16 55
Great Malvern	d					10 46																		14 50	
Malvern Link	d					10 48																		14 52	
Worcester Foregate Street	d					10 58									12 41									15 04	
Worcester Shrub Hill	d					11 06									12 54									15 06	
Ashchurch for Tewkesbury	d					11 24									13 10									15 24	
Cheltenham Spa	d					11 34									13 20									15 34	
Gloucester	d		10 41			11 46					12 41				13 42					14 41				15 46	
Cam & Dursley	d		10 56			12 02					12 56				13 58					14 56				16 02	
Yate	d		11 11			12 16					13 11				14 13					15 11				16 16	
Bristol Parkway	d		11 21			12 25					13 20				14 22					15 20				16 25	
Filton Abbey Wood	d		11 24	12 09		12 28				13 09	13 23	14 09			14 25	15 09				15 23		16 09		16 28	17 09
Bristol Temple Meads 10	d		11 49	12 22		12 43		12 51		13 22	13 49	14 22			14 49	15 22				15 39	15 51	16 22		16 49	17 22
Keynsham	d		11 56			12 50		12 58			13 56				14 56					15 46	15 58			16 56	
Oldfield Park	d		12 03			12 57					14 03				15 03					15 53				17 03	
London Paddington 15 ⊖	d	11 06							12 18										15 06						
Swindon	d				12 36									14 36				15 22							
Chippenham	d				12 53									14 53				15 39							
Melksham	d				13 02									15 02				15 48							
Bath Spa 7	d		12 07	12 35		13 00		13 07		13 35	14 07	14 35			15 07	15 35				15 57	16 07	16 35		17 07	17 35
Freshford	d		12 16								14 16				15 16					16 06				17 16	
Avoncliff	d		12 19								14 19				15 19					16 09				17 19	
Bradford-on-Avon	d		12 23	12 47		13 13		13 20		13 47	14 23	14 47			15 23	15 47				16 13	16 24	16 47		17 23	17 47
Trowbridge	d		12 29	12 53	13 12	13 20		13 27		13 53	14 29	14 53		15 12	15 29	15 53		15 58		16 19	16 30	16 53		17 29	17 53
Westbury	a	12 21	12 36	13 01	13 20	13 27		13 33	13 57	14 01	14 36	15 01		15 20	15 36	16 01		16 05	16 21	16 26	16 37	17 01		17 36	18 01
	d	12 21	12 37	13 01		13 28		13 39	13 58	14 01	14 40	15 01	15 11		15 37	16 01			16 22		16 39	17 01	17 08	17 38	18 01
Frome	d		12 47								14a51				15 46									17 47	
Bruton	d		12 57												15 57									17 59	
Castle Cary	a	12 39	13 03						14 15						16 03				16 40					18 04	
	d		13 04												16 09									18 05	
Yeovil Pen Mill	d		13 17												16 24									18 21	
Thornford	d		13x22												16x28									18x26	
Yetminster	d		13x25												16x31									18x29	
Chetnole	d		13x29												16x35									18x33	
Maiden Newton	d		13 41												16 47									18 44	
Dorchester West	d		13 54												16 58									18 54	
Upwey	a		14 02												17 05									19 02	
Weymouth	a		14 08												17 10									19 10	
Dilton Marsh	d					13x31							15x14										17x10		
Warminster	d			13 09		13 37		13 46		14 09		15 09	15a23			16 09					16 47	17 09	17a19		18 09
Salisbury	a			13 32		13 59		14 10		14 32		15 32				16 32					17 09	17 32			18 32
	d			13 32		14 00				14 32		15 32				16 32						17 32			18 32
Romsey	d			13 50		14 20				14 50		15 50				16 50						17 51			18 50
Southampton Central	a			14 03		14 32				15 03		16 03				17 03						18 03			19 03
Fareham	a			14 27		14 54				15 27		16 27				17 27						18 27			19 27
	d			14 27		14 55				15 27		16 27				17 27						18 27			19 27
Cosham	a			14 35		15 03				15 35		16 35				17 35						18 35			19 35
Fratton	a			14 42						15 42		16 42				17 42						18 42			19 42
Portsmouth & Southsea	a			14 46						15 46		16 46				17 46						18 45			19 46
Portsmouth Harbour	a			14 52						15 52		16 52				17 52						18 53			19 52
Havant	a					15 10																			
Chichester 4	a					15 21																			
Barnham	a					15 29																			
Worthing 4	a					15 44																			
Shoreham-by-Sea	a					15 55																			
Hove 2	a					16 07																			
Brighton 10	a					16 14																			

A To Plymouth

B from Bristol Temple Meads

C ◇ from Bristol Temple Meads to Bristol Temple Meads

D To London Waterloo

E To Taunton

F From Frome

G To Penzance

For connections from Swansea to Cardiff Central and Bristol Parkway please see Table 128

For connections from Plymouth and Exeter to Bristol Temple Meads, Westbury and Castle Cary, please see Table 135

For connections from Exeter and Yeovil Junction to Salisbury please see Table 160

For connections from Upwey, Weymouth and Southampton Central to Bournemouth please see Table 158

For Bus Connections between Yeovil Junction and Yeovil Pen Mill please see Table 123A

Table 123R

Saturdays

15 February to 22 March

Great Malvern, Gloucester, Cardiff and Bristol - Weymouth, Portsmouth and Brighton

Network Diagram - see first Page of Table 123

		GW		GW	GW	GW	GW	GW	GW	GW	GW	GW		GW	GW	GW	GW	GW	GW	SW	GW
				◇1	◇	◇			◇		◇1			◇	◇1			◇		1	
				A							B				C						
				⊡							⊡				⊡						
Cardiff Central 7	d					17 30			18 30					19 30				20 30			
Newport (South Wales)	d					17 44			18 44					19 44				20 44			
Severn Tunnel Jn.	d					17 55															
Great Malvern	d							16 50													
Malvern Link	d							16 52													
Worcester Foregate Street	d							17 04													
Worcester Shrub Hill	d							17 06													
Ashchurch for Tewkesbury	d							17 24													
Cheltenham Spa	d							17 34									20 01				
Gloucester	d				16 41			17 46				18 41					20 13				
Cam & Dursley	d				16 56			18 02				18 56									
Yate	d				17 11			18 16				19 11									
Bristol Parkway	d				17 20			18 25				19 20									
Filton Abbey Wood	d				17 24	18 09		18 28	19 09			19 23		20 09				21 08			
Bristol Temple Meads 10	d				17 49	18 22		18 49	19 22			19 49		20 22		20 49		21 22	22 00	22 23	23 11
Keynsham	d				17 56			18 56				19 56				20 56			22 07		23 18
Oldfield Park	d				18 03			19 03				20 03				21 03			22 14		23 25
London Paddington 15 ⊖	d			17 06							19 06				20 06						
Swindon	d	17 36								19 36							21 08				
Chippenham	d	17 53								19 53							21 25				
Melksham	d	18 02								20 02							21 34				
Bath Spa 7	d				18 07	18 35		19 07	19 35			20 07		20 35		21 07		21 35	22 18	22 36	23 29
Freshford	d				18 16			19 16				20 16				21 16			22 27		23 38
Avoncliff	d				18 19			19 19				20 19				21 19			22 30		23 40
Bradford-on-Avon	d				18 23	18 47		19 23	19 47			20 23		20 47		21 23		21 47	22 34	22 47	23 44
Trowbridge	d	18 12			18 29	18 53		19 29	19 53	20 12		20 29		20 53		21 29	21 44	21 53	22 40	22 53	23 50
Westbury	a	18 18		18 21	18 36	19 01		19 36	20 01	20 20	20 26	20 36		21 01	21 27	21 36	21 52	22 01	22 47	23 00	23 57
	d			18 23	18 39	19 01	19 18		20 01		20 27	20 37		21 01	21 29	21 41		22 01		23 05	23 58
Frome	d				18 49							20a48				21 50					00a08
Bruton	d				19 00											22 02					
Castle Cary	a			18 40	19 05						20 44				21 46	22 07					
	d				19 06											22 08					
Yeovil Pen Mill	d				19 19											22 23					
Thornford	d				19x24											22x28					
Yetminster	d				19x27											22x31					
Chetnole	d				19x31											22x35					
Maiden Newton	d				19 43											22 47					
Dorchester West	d				19 54											22 58					
Upwey	a				20 01											23 05					
Weymouth	a				20 09											23 13					
Dilton Marsh	d						19x21											22x05			
Warminster	d					19 09	19 28		20 09					21 09				22 10		23 12	
Salisbury	a					19 32	19 49		20 32					21 32				22 32		23 35	
	d					19 32	19 50		20 32					21 32				22 32			
Romsey	d					19 50	20 11		20 50					21 50				22 50			
Southampton Central	a					20 02	20 21		21 03					22 03				23 03			
Fareham	a					20 27			21 27					22 26				23 26			
	d					20 27			21 27					22 27				23 27			
Cosham	a																				
Fratton	a					20 42			21 42					22 42				23 40			
Portsmouth & Southsea	a					20 46			21 46					22 46				23 44			
Portsmouth Harbour	a					20 52			21 52					22 52				23 52			
Havant	a																				
Chichester 4	a																				
Barnham	a																				
Worthing 4	a																				
Shoreham-by-Sea	a																				
Hove 2	a																				
Brighton 10	a																				

A To Penzance
B To Plymouth
C To Exeter St Davids

For connections from Swansea to Cardiff Central and Bristol Parkway please see Table 128

For connections from Plymouth and Exeter to Bristol Temple Meads, Westbury and Castle Cary, please see Table 135

For connections from Exeter and Yeovil Junction to Salisbury please see Table 160

For connections from Upwey, Weymouth and Southampton Central to Bournemouth please see Table 158

For Bus Connections between Yeovil Junction and Yeovil Pen Mill please see Table 123A

Table 123R

Saturdays

29 March to 17 May

Great Malvern, Gloucester, Cardiff and Bristol - Weymouth, Portsmouth and Brighton

Network Diagram - see first Page of Table 123

		GW	GW	GW	GW	GW	GW	GW	GW	GW	GW	GW	GW	SW	GW	GW	GW	GW	GW	GW	GW	GW	GW
					◇				◇		◇		◇	◇1	◇1	◇		◇	◇				◇
		A												B	C				D				D
															⊡				🚲				🚲
Cardiff Central 7	d								06 30		07 30					08 30			09 30				10 30
Newport (South Wales)	d								06 44		07 44					08 44			09 44				10 44
Severn Tunnel Jn.	d								06 55		07 55					08 55			09 55				
Great Malvern	d																						
Malvern Link	d																						
Worcester Foregate Street	d																						
Worcester Shrub Hill	d												06 47									09 08	
Ashchurch for Tewkesbury	d												07 03									09 24	
Cheltenham Spa	d												07 13									09 34	
Gloucester	d												07 40					08 41				09 46	
Cam & Dursley	d												07 55					08 56				10 02	
Yate	d												08 10					09 11				10 16	
Bristol Parkway	d												08 20					09 20				10 25	
Filton Abbey Wood	d								07 09		08 09		08 23			09 09		09 23	10 09			10 28	11 09
Bristol Temple Meads 10	d				05 49			06 49	07 22	07 49	08 22		08 39	08 51		09 22		09 49	10 22			10 49	11 22
Keynsham	d				05 56			06 56		07 56			08 46	08 58				09 56				10 56	
Oldfield Park	d				06 03			07 03		08 03			08 53					10 03				11 03	
London Paddington 15 ⊖	d														08 18								
Swindon	d											08 36									10 36		
Chippenham	d											08 53									10 53		
Melksham	d											09 02									11 02		
Bath Spa 7	d				06 07			07 07	07 35	08 07	08 35		08 57	09 07		09 35		10 07	10 35			11 07	11 35
Freshford	d				06 16			07 16		08 16			09 06					10 16				11 16	
Avoncliff	d				06 19			07 19		08 19			09 09					10 19				11 19	
Bradford-on-Avon	d				06 23			07 23	07 47	08 23	08 47		09 13	09 20		09 47		10 23	10 47			11 23	11 47
Trowbridge	d				06 29			07 29	07 53	08 29	08 53	09 12	09 19	09 27		09 53		10 29	10 53		11 12	11 29	11 53
Westbury	a				06 36			07 36	08 01	08 36	09 01	09 20	09 26	09 34	09 57	10 00		10 36	11 01		11 20	11 36	12 01
	d	00 08	05 26	06 01	06 43	06 47	07 03		08 01		09 01		09 27	09 39	09 57	10 00	10 10	10 37	11 01	11 11			12 01
Frome	d	00a19				06 56							09 36					10 46					
Bruton	d					07 08							09 48					10 58					
Castle Cary	a					07 14							09 53		10 16			11 03					
	d					07 15							09 53					11 03					
Yeovil Pen Mill	d					07 29							10 07					11 17					
Thornford	d					07x33							10x12					11x22					
Yetminster	d					07x36							10x15					11x25					
Chetnole	d					07x40							10x19					11x29					
Maiden Newton	d					07 52							10 31					11 41					
Dorchester West	d					08 03							10 38					11 54					
Upwey	a					08 10							10 49					12 02					
Weymouth	a					08 17							10 57					12 09					
Dilton Marsh	d						07x06										10x13			11x13			
Warminster	d		05 34	06 09	06 51		07 13		08 09		09 09			09 46		10 09	10a19		11 09	11 21			12 09
Salisbury	a		05 58	06 31	07 12		07 34		08 32		09 31			10 09		10 31			11 32	11 42			12 32
	d			06 32	07 24		07 36		08 32		09 32					10 32			11 32	11 43			12 32
Romsey	d			06 50	07 44		07 55		08 50		09 50					10 50			11 50	12 04			12 50
Southampton Central	a			07 02	08 02		08 07		09 03		10 03					11 03			12 03	12 21			13 03
Fareham	a			07 27	08 27				09 27		10 27					11 27			12 27				13 27
	d			07 27	08 27				09 27		10 27					11 27			12 27				13 27
Cosham	a			07 35	08 35				09 35		10 35					11 35			12 35				13 35
Fratton	a			07 42	08 42				09 42		10 42					11 42			12 42				13 42
Portsmouth & Southsea	a			07 46	08 46				09 46		10 46					11 46			12 46				13 46
Portsmouth Harbour	a			07 52	08 52				09 52		10 52					11 52			12 52				13 52
Havant	a																						
Chichester 4	a																						
Barnham	a																						
Worthing 4	a																						
Shoreham-by-Sea	a																						
Hove 2	a																						
Brighton 10	a																						

A From Bristol Temple Meads
B To London Waterloo
C To Exeter St Davids
D 🚲 from Bristol Temple Meads

For connections from Swansea to Cardiff Central and Bristol Parkway please see Table 128

For connections from Plymouth and Exeter to Bristol Temple Meads, Westbury and Castle Cary, please see Table 135

For connections from Exeter and Yeovil Junction to Salisbury please see Table 160

For connections from Upwey, Weymouth and Southampton Central to Bournemouth please see Table 158

For Bus Connections between Yeovil Junction and Yeovil Pen Mill please see Table 123A

Table 123R

Saturdays

29 March to 17 May

Great Malvern, Gloucester, Cardiff and Bristol - Weymouth, Portsmouth and Brighton

Network Diagram - see first Page of Table 123

		GW	GW	GW	GW	GW		SW	GW	GW	GW	GW	GW	GW	GW	GW		GW	GW	GW	SW	GW	GW	GW	GW
						■																			■
		◇1	◇	◇		◇		◇1	◇1	◇		◇			◇	◇			◇1		◇1	◇		◇	
		A Ø		B ⚲		C		D ⚲	E ☕				F						G ☕		D				
Cardiff Central 7	d			11 30						12 30		13 30				14 30						15 30			16 30
Newport (South Wales)	d			11 44						12 44		13 44				14 44						15 44			16 44
Severn Tunnel Jn.	d																								16 55
Great Malvern	d					10 46																		14 50	
Malvern Link	d					10 48																		14 52	
Worcester Foregate Street	d					10 58									12 41									15 04	
Worcester Shrub Hill	d					11 06									12 54									15 06	
Ashchurch for Tewkesbury	d					11 24									13 10									15 24	
Cheltenham Spa	d					11 34									13 20									15 34	
Gloucester	d		10 41			11 46					12 41				13 42					14 41				15 46	
Cam & Dursley	d		10 56			12 02					12 56				13 58					14 56				16 02	
Yate	d		11 11			12 16					13 11				14 13					15 11				16 16	
Bristol Parkway	d		11 21			12 25					13 20				14 22					15 20				16 25	
Filton Abbey Wood	d		11 24	12 09		12 28				13 09	13 23	14 09			14 25	15 09				15 23		16 09		16 28	17 09
Bristol Temple Meads 10	d		11 49	12 22		12 43		12 51		13 22	13 49	14 22			14 49	15 22				15 39	15 51	16 22		16 49	17 22
Keynsham	d		11 56			12 50		12 58			13 56				14 56					15 46	15 58			16 56	
Oldfield Park	d		12 03			12 57					14 03				15 03					15 53				17 03	
London Paddington 15 ⊖	d	11 06							12 18										15 06						
Swindon	d				12 36									14 36				15 22							
Chippenham	d				12 53									14 53				15 39							
Melksham	d				13 02									15 02				15 48							
Bath Spa 7	d		12 07	12 35		13 00		13 07		13 35	14 07	14 35			15 07	15 35				15 57	16 07	16 35		17 07	17 35
Freshford	d		12 16								14 16				15 16					16 06				17 16	
Avoncliff	d		12 19								14 19				15 19					16 09				17 19	
Bradford-on-Avon	d		12 23	12 47		13 13		13 20		13 47	14 23	14 47			15 23	15 47				16 13	16 24	16 47		17 23	17 47
Trowbridge	d		12 29	12 53	13 12	13 20		13 27		13 53	14 29	14 53		15 12	15 29	15 53		15 58		16 19	16 30	16 53		17 29	17 53
Westbury	a	12 21	12 36	13 01	13 20	13 27		13 33	13 57	14 01	14 36	15 01		15 20	15 36	16 01		16 05	16 21	16 26	16 37	17 01		17 36	18 01
	d	12 21	12 37	13 01		13 28		13 39	13 58	14 01	14 40	15 01	15 11		15 37	16 01			16 22		16 39	17 01	17 08	17 38	18 01
Frome	d		12 47								14a51				15 46									17 47	
Bruton	d		12 57												15 57									17 59	
Castle Cary	a	12 39	13 03						14 15						16 03				16 40					18 04	
	d		13 04												16 09									18 05	
Yeovil Pen Mill	d		13 17												16 24									18 21	
Thornford	d		13x22												16x28									18x26	
Yetminster	d		13x25												16x31									18x29	
Chetnole	d		13x29												16x35									18x33	
Maiden Newton	d		13 41												16 47									18 44	
Dorchester West	d		13 54												16 58									18 54	
Upwey	a		14 02												17 05									19 02	
Weymouth	a		14 08												17 10									19 10	
Dilton Marsh	d					13x31							15x14										17x10		
Warminster	d			13 09		13 37		13 46		14 09		15 09	15a23			16 09					16 47	17 09	17a19		18 09
Salisbury	a			13 32		13 59		14 10		14 32		15 32				16 32					17 09	17 32			18 32
	d			13 32		14 00				14 32		15 32				16 32						17 32			18 32
Romsey	d			13 50		14 20				14 50		15 50				16 50						17 51			18 50
Southampton Central	a			14 03		14 32				15 03		16 03				17 03						18 03			19 03
Fareham	a			14 27		14 54				15 27		16 27				17 27						18 27			19 27
	d			14 27		14 55				15 27		16 27				17 27						18 27			19 27
Cosham	a			14 35		15 03				15 35		16 35				17 35						18 35			19 35
Fratton	a			14 42						15 42		16 42				17 42						18 42			19 42
Portsmouth & Southsea	a			14 46						15 46		16 46				17 46						18 45			19 46
Portsmouth Harbour	a			14 52						15 52		16 52				17 52						18 53			19 52
Havant	a					15 10																			
Chichester 4	a					15 21																			
Barnham	a					15 29																			
Worthing 4	a					15 44																			
Shoreham-by-Sea	a					15 55																			
Hove 2	a					16 07																			
Brighton 10	a					16 14																			

A To Plymouth
B ⚲ from Bristol Temple Meads
C ◇ from Bristol Temple Meads ■ to Bristol Temple Meads
D To London Waterloo
E To Taunton
F From Frome
G To Penzance

For connections from Swansea to Cardiff Central and Bristol Parkway please see Table 128

For connections from Plymouth and Exeter to Bristol Temple Meads, Westbury and Castle Cary, please see Table 135

For connections from Exeter and Yeovil Junction to Salisbury please see Table 160

For connections from Upwey, Weymouth and Southampton Central to Bournemouth please see Table 158

For Bus Connections between Yeovil Junction and Yeovil Pen Mill please see Table 123A

Table 123R

Saturdays

29 March to 17 May

Great Malvern, Gloucester, Cardiff and Bristol - Weymouth, Portsmouth and Brighton

Network Diagram - see first Page of Table 123

		GW	GW	GW	GW	GW	GW	GW	GW	GW	GW	GW	GW	GW	GW	GW	GW	SW	GW
			◇1	◇	◇			◇		◇1		◇	◇1			◇		1	
			A							B			B						
			☕							☕			☕						
Cardiff Central 7	d				17 30			18 30				19 30				20 30			
Newport (South Wales)	d				17 44			18 44				19 44				20 44			
Severn Tunnel Jn	d				17 55														
Great Malvern	d						16 50												
Malvern Link	d						16 52												
Worcester Foregate Street	d						17 04												
Worcester Shrub Hill	d						17 06												
Ashchurch for Tewkesbury	d						17 24												
Cheltenham Spa	d						17 34								20 01				
Gloucester	d			16 41			17 46				18 41				20 13				
Cam & Dursley	d			16 56			18 02				18 56								
Yate	d			17 11			18 16				19 11								
Bristol Parkway	d			17 20			18 25				19 20								
Filton Abbey Wood	d			17 24	18 09		18 28	19 09			19 23	20 09				21 08			
Bristol Temple Meads 10	d			17 49	18 22		18 49	19 22			19 49	20 22		20 49		21 22	22 00	22 23	23 11
Keynsham	d			17 56			18 56				19 56			20 56			22 07		23 18
Oldfield Park	d			18 03			19 03				20 03			21 03			22 14		23 25
London Paddington 15 ⊖	d		17 06							19 06			20 06						
Swindon	d	17 36							19 36						21 08				
Chippenham	d	17 53							19 53						21 25				
Melksham	d	18 02							20 02						21 34				
Bath Spa 7	d			18 07	18 35		19 07	19 35			20 07	20 35		21 07		21 35	22 18	22 36	23 29
Freshford	d			18 16			19 16				20 16			21 16			22 27		23 38
Avoncliff	d			18 19			19 19				20 19			21 19			22 30		23 40
Bradford-on-Avon	d			18 23	18 47		19 23	19 47			20 23	20 47		21 23		21 47	22 34	22 47	23 44
Trowbridge	d	18 12		18 29	18 53		19 29	19 53	20 12		20 29	20 53		21 29	21 44	21 53	22 40	22 53	23 50
Westbury	a	18 18	18 21	18 36	19 01		19 36	20 01	20 20	20 26	20 36	21 01	21 27	21 36	21 52	22 01	22 47	23 00	23 57
	d		18 23	18 39	19 01	19 18		20 01		20 27	20 37	21 01	21 29	21 41		22 01		23 05	23 58
Frome	d			18 49							20a48			21 50					00a08
Bruton	d			19 00										22 02					
Castle Cary	a		18 40	19 05						20 44			21 46	22 07					
	d			19 06										22 08					
Yeovil Pen Mill	d			19 19										22 23					
Thornford	d			19x24										22x28					
Yetminster	d			19x27										22x31					
Chetnole	d			19x31										22x35					
Maiden Newton	d			19 43										22 47					
Dorchester West	d			19 54										22 58					
Upwey	a			20 01										23 05					
Weymouth	a			20 09										23 13					
Dilton Marsh	d					19x21										22x05			
Warminster	d				19 09	19 28		20 09				21 09				22 10		23 12	
Salisbury	a				19 32	19 49		20 32				21 32				22 32		23 35	
	d				19 32	19 50		20 32				21 32				22 32			
Romsey	d				19 50	20 11		20 50				21 50				22 50			
Southampton Central	a				20 02	20 21		21 03				22 03				23 03			
Fareham	a				20 27			21 27				22 26				23 26			
	d				20 27			21 27				22 27				23 27			
Cosham	a																		
Fratton	a				20 42			21 42				22 42				23 40			
Portsmouth & Southsea	a				20 46			21 46				22 46				23 44			
Portsmouth Harbour	a				20 52			21 52				22 52				23 52			
Havant	a																		
Chichester 4	a																		
Barnham	a																		
Worthing 4	a																		
Shoreham-by-Sea	a																		
Hove 2	a																		
Brighton 10	a																		

A To Penzance

B To Plymouth

For connections from Swansea to Cardiff Central and Bristol Parkway please see Table 128

For connections from Plymouth and Exeter to Bristol Temple Meads, Westbury and Castle Cary, please see Table 135

For connections from Exeter and Yeovil Junction to Salisbury please see Table 160

For connections from Upwey, Weymouth and Southampton Central to Bournemouth please see Table 158

For Bus Connections between Yeovil Junction and Yeovil Pen Mill please see Table 123A

Table 123R

Sundays

8 December to 29 December

Great Malvern, Gloucester, Cardiff and Bristol - Weymouth, Portsmouth and Brighton

Network Diagram - see first Page of Table 123

		GW ◇	GW ◇1 A ☕	GW ◇	GW ◇1 B ☕	GW ◇	GW	GW R ◇ C	GW ◇1 D ☕	GW ◇	GW ◇1 A ☕	GW	GW ◇	GW ◇1 B ☕	GW	GW ◇	SW ◇1 E	GW ◇	GW ◇1 B ☕	GW ◇	GW	GW ◇	GW ◇ F
Cardiff Central 7	d	08 05		09 15		10 08		11 08		12 08			13 08			14 08		15 08		16 08		16 35	
Newport (South Wales)	d	08 23		09 29		10 22		11 22		12 21			13 22			14 22		15 22		16 22		16 49	
Severn Tunnel Jn.	d	08 41		09 47		10 39		11 39		12 39			13 39			14 39		15 39		16 32			
Great Malvern	d																						
Malvern Link	d																						
Worcester Foregate Street	d																						
Worcester Shrub Hill	d																						
Ashchurch for Tewkesbury	d																						
Cheltenham Spa	d																						
Gloucester	d																						
Cam & Dursley	d																						
Yate	d																						
Bristol Parkway	d																						
Filton Abbey Wood	d	08 55		10 03		10 54		11 54		12 56			13 54			14 54		15 54		16 46		17 19	
Bristol Temple Meads 10	d	09 10		10 15		11 09		12 15		13 10		13 55	14 15			15 10	16 04	16 14		17 14		17 40	17 43
Keynsham	d	09 17				11 15				13 17		14 02				15 17	16 11			17 21			17 50
Oldfield Park	d	09 24				11 22				13 24		14 10				15 25				17 28			17 58
London Paddington 15 ⊖	d		08 57		09 57				11 27		12 57			13 57					15 57				
Swindon	d						11 36								14 39						17 28		
Chippenham	d						11 53								14 56						17 45		
Melksham	d						12 02								15 05						17 54		
Bath Spa 7	d	09 27		10 29		11 25		12 27		13 27		14 14	14 27			15 28	16 20	16 26		17 32		17 52	18 01
Freshford	d			10 38				12 38				14 23	14 38					16 37					18 11
Avoncliff	d			10 40				12 40				14 26	14 40					16 39					18 13
Bradford-on-Avon	d	09 40		10 44		11 38		12 44		13 40		14 30	14 44			15 41	16 31	16 43		17 44		18 05	18 17
Trowbridge	d	09 47		10 51		11 47	12 11	12 51		13 48		14 36	14 51		15 14	15 47	16 37	16 50		17 51	18 03	18 12	18 24
Westbury	a	09 54	10 20	10 59		11 54	12 18	12 58	13 04	13 54	14 18	14 42	14 58		15 21	15 57	16 44	16 58	17 23	18 00	18 10	18 19	18 31
	d	09 59		10 59		12 01		13 01	13 05	14 01		14 46	15 01			16 05	16 46	17 01	17 24	18 01		18 20	18 31
Frome	d											14 54											18 39
Bruton	d											15 06											18 52
Castle Cary	a				11 33				13 24			15 10		15 34					17 42				18 57
	d											15 11											18 58
Yeovil Pen Mill	d											15 26											19 12
Thornford	d											15 32											19x17
Yetminster	d											15 35											19x20
Chetnole	d											15 39											19x24
Maiden Newton	d											15 50											19 36
Dorchester West	d											16 01											19 47
Upwey	a											16 10											19 55
Weymouth	a											16 15											20 01
Dilton Marsh	d	10x02				12x04				14x04						16x08		17x04				18x23	
Warminster	d	10 08		11 07		12 10		13 08		14 10			15 08			16 14	16 53	17 10		18 08		18 29	
Salisbury	a	10 32		11 32		12 32		13 32		14 34			15 32			16 35	17 16	17 32		18 32		18 52	
	d	10 32		11 32		12 36		13 32		14 44			15 32			16 35		17 32		18 32		18 56	
Romsey	d	10 50		11 50		12 50		13 50		15 02			15 50			16 51		17 50		18 50		19 14	
Southampton Central	a	11 03		12 03		13 05		14 03		15 13			16 03			17 03		18 03		19 03		19 25	
Fareham	a	11 26		12 26		13 29		14 26		15 50			16 26			17 26		18 26		19 26		19 48	
	d	11 26		12 26		13 30		14 26		15 51			16 26			17 26		18 26		19 26		19 49	
Cosham	a	11 33		12 34		13 37		14 33		16 01			16 33			17 33		18 33		19 33		19 57	
Fratton	a	11 40		12 41				14 40					16 40			17 40		18 40		19 40			
Portsmouth & Southsea	a	11 45		12 45				14 45					16 45			17 45		18 45		19 45			
Portsmouth Harbour	a	11 52		12 52				14 52					16 52			17 52		18 53		19 52			
Havant	a					13 46				16 11												20 09	
Chichester 4	a					13 57				16 22												20 20	
Barnham	a					14 10				16 30												20 28	
Worthing 4	a					14 28				16 46												20 46	
Shoreham-by-Sea	a					14 38				16 52												20 52	
Hove 2	a					14 49				16 59												20 59	
Brighton 10	a					14 55				17 05												21 04	

A To Penzance
B To Plymouth
C ◇ from Bristol Temple Meads R to Bristol Temple Meads
D To Paignton
E To London Waterloo
F From Weston-super-Mare

For connections from Swansea to Cardiff Central and Bristol Parkway please see Table 128

For connections from Plymouth and Exeter to Bristol Temple Meads, Westbury and Castle Cary, please see Table 135

For connections from Exeter and Yeovil Junction to Salisbury please see Table 160

For connections from Upwey, Weymouth and Southampton Central to Bournemouth please see Table 158

For Bus Connections between Yeovil Junction and Yeovil Pen Mill please see Table 123A

Table 123R

Sundays

8 December to 29 December

Great Malvern, Gloucester, Cardiff and Bristol - Weymouth, Portsmouth and Brighton

Network Diagram - see first Page of Table 123

		GW	GW	GW	GW	GW		GW	GW	GW	GW	GW	GW	SW	GW	GW
		◇		◇ 1	◇	◇		◇ 1		◇	◇ 1		◇	1		
				A				B			B					
Cardiff Central 7	d	17 08			17 40	18 08				19 08			20 18			22 00
Newport (South Wales)	d	17 22			17 54	18 22				19 22			20 31			22 19
Severn Tunnel Jn.	d	17 39				18 39				19 39			20 48			22 36
Great Malvern	d															
Malvern Link	d															
Worcester Foregate Street	d															
Worcester Shrub Hill	d															
Ashchurch for Tewkesbury	d															
Cheltenham Spa	d															
Gloucester	d															
Cam & Dursley	d															
Yate	d															
Bristol Parkway	d															
Filton Abbey Wood	d	17 54			18 23	18 54				19 54			21 02			22 52
Bristol Temple Meads 10	d	18 09			18 50	19 10				20 15		20 49	21 25	21 35	22 15	23 10
Keynsham	d	18 16				19 17						20 56			22 22	
Oldfield Park	d	18 23				19 24						21 04			22 30	
London Paddington 15 ⊖	d			17 57				18 57			19 57					
Swindon	d		18 24						19 53							
Chippenham	d		18 41						20 10							
Melksham	d		18 50						20 19							
Bath Spa 7	d	18 26			19 02	19 27				20 27		21 07	21 38	21 49	22 33	23 22
Freshford	d									20 38		21 17			22 43	
Avoncliff	d									20 40		21 20			22 46	
Bradford-on-Avon	d	18 39			19 15	19 40				20 44		21 24	21 50	22 00	22 50	23 35
Trowbridge	d	18 46	19 00		19 22	19 47			20 29	20 51		21 30	21 57	22 06	22 56	23 42
Westbury	a	18 53	19 07	19 24	19 29	19 55			20 36	20 58	21 25	21 37	22 04	22 13	23 03	23 49
	d	19 01			19 31	19 59				21 01	21 27	21 38	22 05	22 15		23 50
Frome	d											21 48				
Bruton	d											21 59				
Castle Cary	a							20 29			21 43	22 04				
	d											22 05				
Yeovil Pen Mill	d											22 19				
Thornford	d											22x23				
Yetminster	d											22x26				
Chetnole	d											22x30				
Maiden Newton	d											22 42				
Dorchester West	d											22 53				
Upwey	a											23 00				
Weymouth	a											23 06				
Dilton Marsh	d					20x02										23x53
Warminster	d	19 08			19 38	20 08				21 08			22 13	22 22		23a59
Salisbury	a	19 29			20 00	20 30				21 32			22 34	22 46		
	d	19 32			20 01	20 32				21 32			22 36			
Romsey	d	19 50			20 19	20 50				21 50			22 54			
Southampton Central	a	20 03			20 29	21 03				22 03			23 05			
Fareham	a	20 26			20 54	21 26				22 26			23 29			
	d	20 26			20 55	21 26				22 26			23 30			
Cosham	a															
Fratton	a	20 40			21 09	21 40				22 40			23 43			
Portsmouth & Southsea	a	20 47			21 15	21 43				22 43			23 46			
Portsmouth Harbour	a	20 52			21 26	21 49				22 52			23 54			
Havant	a															
Chichester 4	a															
Barnham	a															
Worthing 4	a															
Shoreham-by-Sea	a															
Hove 2	a															
Brighton 10	a															

A To Penzance

B To Plymouth

For connections from Swansea to Cardiff Central and Bristol Parkway please see Table 128

For connections from Plymouth and Exeter to Bristol Temple Meads, Westbury and Castle Cary, please see Table 135

For connections from Exeter and Yeovil Junction to Salisbury please see Table 160

For connections from Upwey, Weymouth and Southampton Central to Bournemouth please see Table 158

For Bus Connections between Yeovil Junction and Yeovil Pen Mill please see Table 123A

Table 123R

Sundays

5 January to 9 February

Great Malvern, Gloucester, Cardiff and Bristol - Weymouth, Portsmouth and Brighton

Network Diagram - see first Page of Table 123

		GW	GW	GW	GW	GW	GW	GW	GW	GW	GW	GW	GW	GW	GW	GW	SW	GW	GW	GW	GW	GW	GW
								■															
		◇	◇1	◇	◇1	◇		◇	◇1	◇	◇1		◇	◇1		◇	◇1	◇	◇1	◇		◇	◇
			A		B			C	D		A			B			E		B				F
			🍴		🍴				🍴		🍴			🍴					🍴				
Cardiff Central 7	d			09 15		10 08		11 08		12 08			13 08			14 08		15 08		16 08		16 35	
Newport (South Wales)	d			09 29		10 22		11 22		12 21			13 22			14 22		15 22		16 22		16 49	
Severn Tunnel Jn	d			09 47		10 33		11 33		12 33			13 33			14 33		15 32		16 32			
Great Malvern	d																						
Malvern Link	d																						
Worcester Foregate Street	d																						
Worcester Shrub Hill	d																						
Ashchurch for Tewkesbury	d																						
Cheltenham Spa	d																						
Gloucester	d																						
Cam & Dursley	d																						
Yate	d																						
Bristol Parkway	d	08 52																					
Filton Abbey Wood	d	08 55		10 03		10 48		11 48		12 50			13 48			14 48		15 47		16 46		17 19	
Bristol Temple Meads 10	d	09 10		10 15		11 09		12 15		13 10		13 55	14 15			15 10	16 04	16 14		17 14		17 40	17 43
Keynsham	d	09 17				11 15				13 17		14 02				15 17	16 11			17 21			17 50
Oldfield Park	d	09 24				11 22				13 24		14 10				15 25				17 28			17 58
London Paddington 15 ⊖	d		08 57		09 57				11 27		12 57			13 57					15 57				
Swindon	d						11 36								14 39						17 28		
Chippenham	d						11 53								14 56						17 45		
Melksham	d						12 02								15 05						17 54		
Bath Spa 7	d	09 27		10 27		11 25		12 27		13 27		14 14	14 27			15 28	16 20	16 26		17 32		17 52	18 01
Freshford	d			10 38				12 38				14 23	14 38					16 37					18 11
Avoncliff	d			10 40				12 40				14 26	14 40					16 39					18 13
Bradford-on-Avon	d	09 40		10 44		11 38		12 44		13 40		14 30	14 44			15 41	16 31	16 43		17 44		18 05	18 17
Trowbridge	d	09 47		10 51		11 47	12 11	12 51		13 48		14 36	14 51		15 14	15 47	16 37	16 50		17 51	18 03	18 12	18 24
Westbury	a	09 54	10 20	10 59		11 54	12 18	12 58	13 04	13 54	14 18	14 42	14 58		15 21	15 57	16 44	16 58	17 23	18 00	18 10	18 19	18 31
	d	09 59		11 01		12 01		13 01	13 05	14 01		14 46	15 01			16 05	16 46	17 01	17 24	18 01		18 20	18 31
Frome	d											14 54											18 39
Bruton	d											15 06											18 52
Castle Cary	a				11 33				13 24			15 10		15 34					17 42				18 57
	d											15 11											18 58
Yeovil Pen Mill	d											15 26											19 12
Thornford	d											15 32											19x17
Yetminster	d											15 35											19x20
Chetnole	d											15 39											19x24
Maiden Newton	d											15 50											19 36
Dorchester West	d											16 01											19 47
Upwey	a											16 10											19 55
Weymouth	a											16 15											20 01
Dilton Marsh	d	10x02				12x04				14x04						16x08		17x04				18x23	
Warminster	d	10 08		11 08		12 10		13 08		14 10			15 08			16 14	16 53	17 10		18 08		18 29	
Salisbury	a	10 32		11 32		12 32		13 32		14 34			15 32			16 35	17 16	17 32		18 32		18 52	
	d	10 32		11 32		12 36		13 32		14 44			15 32			16 35		17 32		18 32		18 56	
Romsey	d	10 50		11 50		12 50		13 50		15 02			15 50			16 51		17 50		18 50		19 14	
Southampton Central	a	11 03		12 03		13 05		14 03		15 13			16 03			17 03		18 03		19 03		19 25	
Fareham	a	11 26		12 26		13 29		14 26		15 50			16 26			17 26		18 26		19 26		19 48	
	d	11 26		12 26		13 30		14 26		15 51			16 26			17 26		18 26		19 26		19 49	
Cosham	a	11 33		12 33		13 37		14 33		16 01			16 33			17 33		18 33		19 33		19 57	
Fratton	a	11 40		12 40				14 40					16 40			17 40		18 40		19 40			
Portsmouth & Southsea	a	11 45		12 45				14 45					16 45			17 44		18 45		19 45			
Portsmouth Harbour	a	11 52		12 52				14 52					16 52			17 52		18 53		19 52			
Havant	a					13 46				16 11												20 09	
Chichester 4	a					13 57				16 22												20 20	
Barnham	a					14 10				16 30												20 28	
Worthing 4	a					14 28				16 46												20 46	
Shoreham-by-Sea	a					14 38				16 52												20 52	
Hove 2	a					14 49				16 59												20 59	
Brighton 10	a					14 55				17 05												21 04	

A To Penzance
B To Plymouth
C ◇ from Bristol Temple Meads ■ to Bristol Temple Meads
D To Paignton
E To London Waterloo
F From Weston-super-Mare

For connections from Swansea to Cardiff Central and Bristol Parkway please see Table 128

For connections from Plymouth and Exeter to Bristol Temple Meads, Westbury and Castle Cary, please see Table 135

For connections from Exeter and Yeovil Junction to Salisbury please see Table 160

For connections from Upwey, Weymouth and Southampton Central to Bournemouth please see Table 158

For Bus Connections between Yeovil Junction and Yeovil Pen Mill please see Table 123A

Table 123R

Sundays

5 January to 9 February

Great Malvern, Gloucester, Cardiff and Bristol - Weymouth, Portsmouth and Brighton

Network Diagram - see first Page of Table 123

		GW	GW	GW	GW	GW		GW	GW	GW	GW	GW	GW	SW	GW	GW
		◇		◇1	◇	◇		◇1		◇	◇1		◇	1		
				A				B			B					
				⊡				⊡			⊡					
Cardiff Central 7	d	17 08			17 40	18 08				19 08			20 18			22 00
Newport (South Wales)	d	17 22			17 54	18 22				19 22			20 31			22 19
Severn Tunnel Jn.	d	17 36				18 39				19 39			20 48			22 36
Great Malvern	d															
Malvern Link	d															
Worcester Foregate Street	d															
Worcester Shrub Hill	d															
Ashchurch for Tewkesbury	d															
Cheltenham Spa	d															
Gloucester	d															
Cam & Dursley	d															
Yate	d															
Bristol Parkway	d															
Filton Abbey Wood	d	17 51			18 23	18 54				19 54			21 02			22 52
Bristol Temple Meads 10	d	18 09			18 50	19 10				20 15		21 00	21 25	21 35	22 15	23 10
Keynsham	d	18 16				19 17						21 07			22 22	
Oldfield Park	d	18 23				19 24						21 15			22 30	
London Paddington 15 ⊖	d			17 57				18 57			19 57					
Swindon	d		18 24						19 53							
Chippenham	d		18 41						20 10							
Melksham	d		18 50						20 19							
Bath Spa 7	d	18 26			19 02	19 27				20 27		21 18	21 38	21 49	22 33	23 22
Freshford	d									20 38		21 28			22 43	
Avoncliff	d									20 40		21 31			22 46	
Bradford-on-Avon	d	18 39			19 15	19 40				20 44		21 35	21 50	22 00	22 50	23 35
Trowbridge	d	18 46	19 00		19 22	19 47			20 29	20 51		21 41	21 57	22 06	22 56	23 42
Westbury	a	18 53	19 07	19 24	19 29	19 55			20 36	20 58	21 25	21 48	22 04	22 13	23 03	23 49
	d	19 01			19 31	19 59				21 01	21 27	21 49	22 05	22 15		23 50
Frome	d											21 59				
Bruton	d											22 10				
Castle Cary	a							20 29			21 43	22 15				
	d											22 16				
Yeovil Pen Mill	d											22 30				
Thornford	d											22x34				
Yetminster	d											22x37				
Chetnole	d											22x41				
Maiden Newton	d											22 53				
Dorchester West	d											23 04				
Upwey	a											23 18				
Weymouth	a											23 24				
Dilton Marsh	d					20x02										23x53
Warminster	d	19 08			19 38	20 08				21 08			22 13	22 22		23a59
Salisbury	a	19 29			20 00	20 30				21 32			22 34	22 46		
	d	19 32			20 01	20 32				21 32			22 36			
Romsey	d	19 50			20 19	20 50				21 50			22 54			
Southampton Central	a	20 03			20 29	21 03				22 03			23 05			
Fareham	a	20 26			20 54	21 26				22 26			23 29			
	d	20 26			20 55	21 26				22 26			23 30			
Cosham	a															
Fratton	a	20 40			21 09	21 40				22 40			23 43			
Portsmouth & Southsea	a	20 47			21 15	21 43				22 43			23 46			
Portsmouth Harbour	a	20 52			21 26	21 49				22 52			23 54			
Havant	a															
Chichester 4	a															
Barnham	a															
Worthing 4	a															
Shoreham-by-Sea	a															
Hove 2	a															
Brighton 10	a															

A To Penzance

B To Plymouth

For connections from Swansea to Cardiff Central and Bristol Parkway please see Table 128

For connections from Plymouth and Exeter to Bristol Temple Meads, Westbury and Castle Cary, please see Table 135

For connections from Exeter and Yeovil Junction to Salisbury please see Table 160

For connections from Upwey, Weymouth and Southampton Central to Bournemouth please see Table 158

For Bus Connections between Yeovil Junction and Yeovil Pen Mill please see Table 123A

Table 123R

Sundays

16 February to 23 March

Great Malvern, Gloucester, Cardiff and Bristol - Weymouth, Portsmouth and Brighton

Network Diagram - see first Page of Table 123

		GW	GW	GW	GW	GW	GW	GW	GW	GW	GW	GW	GW	GW	GW	GW	SW	GW	GW	GW	GW	GW	GW
								■															
		◇	◇■1	◇	◇■1	◇		◇	◇■1	◇	◇■1		◇	◇■1		◇	◇■1	◇	◇■1	◇		◇	◇
			A		A			B	A		A			A			C		A				D
			🛒		🛒				🛒		🛒			🛒					🛒				
Cardiff Central [7]	d	08 05		09 13		10 08		11 08		12 08			13 08			14 08		15 08		16 08		16 35	
Newport (South Wales)	d	08 23		09 27		10 22		11 22		12 21			13 22			14 22		15 22		16 22		16 49	
Severn Tunnel Jn.	d	08 41		09 45		10 39		11 39		12 39			13 39			14 39		15 39		16 38			
Great Malvern	d																						
Malvern Link	d																						
Worcester Foregate Street	d																						
Worcester Shrub Hill	d																						
Ashchurch for Tewkesbury	d																						
Cheltenham Spa	d																						
Gloucester	d																						
Cam & Dursley	d																						
Yate	d																						
Bristol Parkway	d																						
Filton Abbey Wood	d	08 55		10 01		10 54		11 54		12 56			13 54			14 54		15 54		16 53		17 19	
Bristol Temple Meads [10]	d	09 10		10 13		11 09		12 15		13 10		13 55	14 15			15 10	16 04	16 14		17 14		17 40	17 43
Keynsham	d	09 17				11 15				13 17		14 02				15 17	16 11			17 21			17 50
Oldfield Park	d	09 24				11 22				13 24		14 10				15 25				17 28			17 58
London Paddington [15] ⊖	d		08 57		09 57				11 27		12 57			13 57					15 57				
Swindon	d						11 36								14 39						17 28		
Chippenham	d						11 53								14 56						17 45		
Melksham	d						12 02								15 05						17 54		
Bath Spa [7]	d	09 27		10 24		11 25		12 27		13 27		14 14	14 27			15 28	16 20	16 26		17 32		17 52	18 01
Freshford	d			10 34				12 38				14 23	14 38					16 37					18 11
Avoncliff	d			10 37				12 40				14 26	14 40					16 39					18 13
Bradford-on-Avon	d	09 40		10 41		11 38		12 44		13 40		14 30	14 44			15 41	16 31	16 43		17 44		18 05	18 17
Trowbridge	d	09 47		10 48		11 47	12 11	12 51		13 48		14 36	14 51		15 14	15 47	16 37	16 50		17 51	18 03	18 12	18 24
Westbury	a	09 54	10 20	10 55		11 54	12 18	12 58	13 04	13 54	14 18	14 42	14 58		15 21	15 57	16 44	16 57	17 23	18 00	18 10	18 19	18 31
	d	09 59		11 01		12 01		13 01	13 05	14 01		14 46	15 01			16 05	16 46	17 01	17 24	18 01		18 20	18 31
Frome	d											14 54											18 39
Bruton	d											15 06											18 52
Castle Cary	a				11 33				13 24			15 10		15 34					17 42				18 57
	d											15 11											18 58
Yeovil Pen Mill	d											15 26											19 12
Thornford	d											15 32											19x17
Yetminster	d											15 35											19x20
Chetnole	d											15 39											19x24
Maiden Newton	d											15 50											19 36
Dorchester West	d											16 01											19 47
Upwey	a											16 10											19 55
Weymouth	a											16 15											20 01
Dilton Marsh	d	10x02				12x04				14x04						16x08		17x04				18x23	
Warminster	d	10 08		11 08		12 10		13 08		14 10			15 08			16 14	16 53	17 10		18 08		18 29	
Salisbury	a	10 32		11 32		12 32		13 32		14 34			15 32			16 35	17 16	17 32		18 32		18 52	
	d	10 32		11 32		12 36		13 32		14 44			15 32			16 35		17 32		18 32		18 56	
Romsey	d	10 50		11 50		12 53		13 50		15 02			15 50			16 51		17 50		18 50		19 14	
Southampton Central	a	11 03		12 03		13 05		14 03		15 13			16 03			17 03		18 03		19 03		19 25	
Fareham	a	11 26		12 26		13 29		14 26		15 50			16 26			17 26		18 26		19 26		19 48	
	d	11 26		12 26		13 30		14 26		15 51			16 26			17 26		18 26		19 26		19 49	
Cosham	a	11 33		12 33		13 37		14 33		16 01			16 33			17 34		18 33		19 33		19 57	
Fratton	a	11 40		12 40				14 40					16 40			17 40		18 40		19 40			
Portsmouth & Southsea	a	11 45		12 45				14 45					16 45			17 44		18 45		19 45			
Portsmouth Harbour	a	11 52		12 52				14 52					16 52			17 52		18 53		19 52			
Havant	a					13 46				16 11												20 09	
Chichester [4]	a					13 57				16 22												20 20	
Barnham	a					14 10				16 30												20 28	
Worthing [4]	a					14 28				16 46												20 46	
Shoreham-by-Sea	a					14 38				16 52												20 52	
Hove [2]	a					14 49				16 59												20 59	
Brighton [10]	a					14 55				17 05												21 04	

A To Exeter St Davids

B ◇ from Bristol Temple Meads ■ to Bristol Temple Meads

C To London Waterloo

D From Weston-super-Mare

For connections from Swansea to Cardiff Central and Bristol Parkway please see Table 128

For connections from Plymouth and Exeter to Bristol Temple Meads, Westbury and Castle Cary, please see Table 135

For connections from Exeter and Yeovil Junction to Salisbury please see Table 160

For connections from Upwey, Weymouth and Southampton Central to Bournemouth please see Table 158

For Bus Connections between Yeovil Junction and Yeovil Pen Mill please see Table 123A

Table 123R

Sundays

16 February to 23 March

Great Malvern, Gloucester, Cardiff and Bristol - Weymouth, Portsmouth and Brighton

Network Diagram - see first Page of Table 123

		GW	GW	GW	GW	GW	GW	GW	GW	GW	GW	GW	SW	GW	GW
		◇		◇1	◇	◇	◇1		◇	◇1		◇	1		
				A			A			A					
				☕			☕			☕					
Cardiff Central 7	d	17 08			17 40	18 08			19 08			20 18			22 00
Newport (South Wales)	d	17 22			17 54	18 22			19 22			20 31			22 19
Severn Tunnel Jn	d	17 39				18 39			19 39			20 48			22 36
Great Malvern	d														
Malvern Link	d														
Worcester Foregate Street	d														
Worcester Shrub Hill	d														
Ashchurch for Tewkesbury	d														
Cheltenham Spa	d														
Gloucester	d														
Cam & Dursley	d														
Yate	d														
Bristol Parkway	d														
Filton Abbey Wood	d	17 54			18 23	18 54			19 54			21 02			22 52
Bristol Temple Meads 10	d	18 09			18 50	19 10			20 15		20 49	21 21	21 35	22 15	23 10
Keynsham	d	18 16				19 17					20 56			22 22	
Oldfield Park	d	18 23				19 24					21 04			22 30	
London Paddington 15 ⊖	d			17 57			18 57			19 57					
Swindon	d		18 24					19 53							
Chippenham	d		18 41					20 10							
Melksham	d		18 50					20 19							
Bath Spa 7	d	18 26			19 02	19 27			20 27		21 07	21 34	21 49	22 33	23 22
Freshford	d								20 38		21 17			22 43	
Avoncliff	d								20 40		21 20			22 46	
Bradford-on-Avon	d	18 39			19 15	19 40			20 44		21 24	21 46	22 00	22 50	23 35
Trowbridge	d	18 46	19 00		19 22	19 47		20 29	20 51		21 30	21 53	22 06	22 56	23 42
Westbury	a	18 53	19 07	19 24	19 29	19 55		20 36	20 58	21 24	21 37	22 00	22 13	23 03	23 49
	d	19 01			19 31	19 59			21 01	21 27	21 38	22 05	22 15		23 50
Frome	d										21 48				
Bruton	d										21 59				
Castle Cary	a						20 29			21 43	22 04				
	d										22 05				
Yeovil Pen Mill	d										22 19				
Thornford	d										22x23				
Yetminster	d										22x26				
Chetnole	d										22x30				
Maiden Newton	d										22 42				
Dorchester West	d										22 53				
Upwey	a										23 00				
Weymouth	a										23 06				
Dilton Marsh	d					20x02									23x53
Warminster	d	19 08			19 38	20 08			21 08			22 13	22 22		23a59
Salisbury	a	19 29			20 00	20 30			21 32			22 34	22 46		
	d	19 32			20 01	20 32			21 32			22 36			
Romsey	d	19 50			20 19	20 50			21 50			22 54			
Southampton Central	a	20 03			20 29	21 03			22 03			23 05			
Fareham	a	20 26			20 54	21 26			22 26			23 29			
	d	20 26			20 55	21 26			22 26			23 30			
Cosham	a														
Fratton	a	20 40			21 09	21 40			22 40			23 43			
Portsmouth & Southsea	a	20 47			21 15	21 43			22 43			23 46			
Portsmouth Harbour	a	20 52			21 26	21 49			22 52			23 54			
Havant	a														
Chichester 4	a														
Barnham	a														
Worthing 4	a														
Shoreham-by-Sea	a														
Hove 2	a														
Brighton 10	a														

A To Exeter St Davids

For connections from Swansea to Cardiff Central and Bristol Parkway please see Table 128

For connections from Plymouth and Exeter to Bristol Temple Meads, Westbury and Castle Cary, please see Table 135

For connections from Exeter and Yeovil Junction to Salisbury please see Table 160

For connections from Upwey, Weymouth and Southampton Central to Bournemouth please see Table 158

For Bus Connections between Yeovil Junction and Yeovil Pen Mill please see Table 123A

Table 123R

Sundays

30 March to 11 May

Great Malvern, Gloucester, Cardiff and Bristol - Weymouth, Portsmouth and Brighton

Network Diagram - see first Page of Table 123

		GW	GW	GW	GW	GW	GW	GW	GW	GW	GW	GW	GW	GW	GW	GW	SW	GW	GW	GW	GW	GW	GW
		◇	◇[1]	◇	◇[1]	◇		[R] ◇	◇[1]	◇	◇[1]		◇	◇[1]		◇	◇[1]	◇	◇[1]	◇		◇	◇
			A ☕		B ☕			C	D ☕		A ☕			B ☕			E		B ☕				F
Cardiff Central [7]	d	08 05		09 13		10 08		11 08		12 08			13 08			14 08		15 08		16 08		16 35	
Newport (South Wales)	d	08 23		09 27		10 22		11 22		12 21			13 22			14 22		15 22		16 22		16 49	
Severn Tunnel Jn.	d	08 41		09 45		10 39		11 39		12 33			13 33			14 33		15 32		16 38			
Great Malvern	d																						
Malvern Link	d																						
Worcester Foregate Street	d																						
Worcester Shrub Hill	d																						
Ashchurch for Tewkesbury	d																						
Cheltenham Spa	d																						
Gloucester	d																						
Cam & Dursley	d																						
Yate	d																						
Bristol Parkway	d																						
Filton Abbey Wood	d	08 55		10 01		10 54		11 54		12 50			13 48			14 50		15 47		16 53		17 19	
Bristol Temple Meads [10]	d	09 10		10 13		11 09		12 15		13 10		13 55	14 15			15 10	16 04	16 14		17 14		17 40	17 43
Keynsham	d	09 17				11 15				13 17		14 02				15 17	16 11			17 21			17 50
Oldfield Park	d	09 24				11 22				13 24		14 10				15 25				17 28			17 58
London Paddington [15] ⊖	d		08 57		09 57				11 33		12 57			13 57					15 57				
Swindon	d						11 36								14 42						17 28		
Chippenham	d						11 53								14 59						17 45		
Melksham	d						12 02								15 08						17 54		
Bath Spa [7]	d	09 27		10 24		11 25		12 27		13 27		14 14	14 27			15 28	16 20	16 26		17 32		17 52	18 01
Freshford	d			10 35				12 38				14 23	14 38					16 37					18 11
Avoncliff	d			10 37				12 40				14 26	14 40					16 39					18 13
Bradford-on-Avon	d	09 40		10 41		11 38		12 44		13 40		14 30	14 44			15 41	16 31	16 43		17 44		18 05	18 17
Trowbridge	d	09 47		10 48		11 47	12 11	12 51		13 48		14 36	14 51		15 17	15 47	16 37	16 50		17 51	18 03	18 12	18 24
Westbury	a	09 54	10 20	10 55		11 54	12 18	12 58	13 04	13 54	14 18	14 42	14 58		15 24	15 57	16 44	16 58	17 23	18 00	18 10	18 19	18 31
	d	09 59		11 01		12 01		13 01	13 05	14 01		14 46	15 01			16 05	16 46	17 01	17 24	18 01		18 20	18 31
Frome	d											14 54											18 39
Bruton	d											15 06											18 52
Castle Cary	a				11 33				13 24			15 10		15 35					17 42				18 57
	d											15 11											18 58
Yeovil Pen Mill	d											15 26											19 12
Thornford	d											15 32											19x17
Yetminster	d											15 35											19x20
Chetnole	d											15 39											19x24
Maiden Newton	d											15 50											19 36
Dorchester West	d											16 01											19 47
Upwey	a											16 10											19 55
Weymouth	a											16 15											20 01
Dilton Marsh	d	10x02				12x04				14x04						16x08		17x04				18x23	
Warminster	d	10 08		11 08		12 10		13 08		14 10			15 08			16 14	16 53	17 10		18 08		18 29	
Salisbury	a	10 32		11 32		12 32		13 32		14 34			15 32			16 35	17 16	17 32		18 32		18 52	
	d	10 32		11 32		12 35		13 32		14 44			15 32			16 35		17 32		18 32		18 56	
Romsey	d	10 50		11 50		12 53		13 50		15 02			15 50			16 51		17 50		18 50		19 14	
Southampton Central	a	11 03		12 03		13 05		14 03		15 13			16 03			17 03		18 03		19 03		19 25	
Fareham	a	11 26		12 26		13 29		14 26		15 50			16 26			17 26		18 26		19 26		19 48	
	d	11 26		12 26		13 30		14 26		15 51			16 26			17 26		18 26		19 26		19 49	
Cosham	a	11 33		12 33		13 37		14 33		16 01			16 33			17 33		18 33		19 33		19 57	
Fratton	a	11 40		12 40				14 40					16 40			17 40		18 40		19 40			
Portsmouth & Southsea	a	11 45		12 45				14 45					16 45			17 44		18 45		19 45			
Portsmouth Harbour	a	11 52		12 52				14 52					16 52			17 52		18 53		19 52			
Havant	a					13 46				16 11												20 09	
Chichester [4]	a					13 57				16 22												20 20	
Barnham	a					14 10				16 30												20 28	
Worthing [4]	a					14 28				16 46												20 46	
Shoreham-by-Sea	a					14 38				16 52												20 52	
Hove [2]	a					14 49				16 59												20 59	
Brighton [10]	a					14 55				17 05												21 04	

A To Penzance
B To Plymouth
C ◇ from Bristol Temple Meads [R] to Bristol Temple Meads
D To Paignton
E To London Waterloo
F From Weston-super-Mare

For connections from Swansea to Cardiff Central and Bristol Parkway please see Table 128

For connections from Plymouth and Exeter to Bristol Temple Meads, Westbury and Castle Cary, please see Table 135

For connections from Exeter and Yeovil Junction to Salisbury please see Table 160

For connections from Upwey, Weymouth and Southampton Central to Bournemouth please see Table 158

For Bus Connections between Yeovil Junction and Yeovil Pen Mill please see Table 123A

Table 123R

Sundays
30 March to 11 May

Great Malvern, Gloucester, Cardiff and Bristol - Weymouth, Portsmouth and Brighton

Network Diagram - see first Page of Table 123

		GW	GW	GW	GW	GW		GW	GW	GW	GW	GW	GW	SW	GW	GW
		◇		◇1	◇	◇		◇1		◇	◇1		◇	1		
				A				B			B					
				☕				☕			☕					
Cardiff Central 7	d	17 08			17 40	18 08				19 08			20 18			22 00
Newport (South Wales)	d	17 22			17 54	18 22				19 22			20 31			22 19
Severn Tunnel Jn.	d	17 36				18 39				19 39			20 48			22 36
Great Malvern	d															
Malvern Link	d															
Worcester Foregate Street	d															
Worcester Shrub Hill	d															
Ashchurch for Tewkesbury	d															
Cheltenham Spa	d															
Gloucester	d															
Cam & Dursley	d															
Yate	d															
Bristol Parkway	d															
Filton Abbey Wood	d	17 51			18 23	18 54				19 54			21 02			22 52
Bristol Temple Meads 10	d	18 09			18 50	19 10				20 15		20 49	21 25	21 35	22 15	23 10
Keynsham	d	18 16				19 17						20 56			22 22	
Oldfield Park	d	18 23				19 24						21 04			22 30	
London Paddington 15 ⊖	d			17 57				18 57			19 57					
Swindon	d		18 24						19 53							
Chippenham	d		18 41						20 10							
Melksham	d		18 50						20 19							
Bath Spa 7	d	18 26			19 02	19 27				20 27		21 07	21 38	21 49	22 33	23 22
Freshford	d									20 38		21 17			22 43	
Avoncliff	d									20 40		21 20			22 46	
Bradford-on-Avon	d	18 39			19 15	19 40				20 44		21 24	21 50	22 00	22 50	23 35
Trowbridge	d	18 46	19 00		19 22	19 47			20 29	20 51		21 30	21 57	22 06	22 56	23 42
Westbury	a	18 53	19 07	19 24	19 29	19 55			20 36	20 58	21 25	21 37	22 04	22 13	23 03	23 49
	d	19 01			19 31	19 59				21 01	21 27	21 38	22 05	22 15		23 50
Frome	d											21 48				
Bruton	d											21 59				
Castle Cary	a							20 29			21 43	22 04				
	d											22 05				
Yeovil Pen Mill	d											22 19				
Thornford	d											22x23				
Yetminster	d											22x26				
Chetnole	d											22x30				
Maiden Newton	d											22 42				
Dorchester West	d											22 53				
Upwey	a											23 00				
Weymouth	a											23 06				
Dilton Marsh	d					20x02										23x53
Warminster	d	19 08			19 38	20 08				21 08			22 13	22 22		23a59
Salisbury	a	19 29			20 00	20 30				21 32			22 34	22 46		
	d	19 32			20 01	20 32				21 32			22 36			
Romsey	d	19 50			20 19	20 50				21 50			22 54			
Southampton Central	a	20 03			20 29	21 03				22 03			23 05			
Fareham	a	20 26			20 54	21 26				22 26			23 29			
	d	20 26			20 55	21 26				22 26			23 30			
Cosham	a															
Fratton	a	20 40			21 09	21 40				22 40			23 43			
Portsmouth & Southsea	a	20 47			21 15	21 43				22 43			23 46			
Portsmouth Harbour	a	20 52			21 26	21 49				22 52			23 54			
Havant	a															
Chichester 4	a															
Barnham	a															
Worthing 4	a															
Shoreham-by-Sea	a															
Hove 2	a															
Brighton 10	a															

A To Penzance
B To Plymouth

For connections from Swansea to Cardiff Central and Bristol Parkway please see Table 128

For connections from Plymouth and Exeter to Bristol Temple Meads, Westbury and Castle Cary, please see Table 135

For connections from Exeter and Yeovil Junction to Salisbury please see Table 160

For connections from Upwey, Weymouth and Southampton Central to Bournemouth please see Table 158

For Bus Connections between Yeovil Junction and Yeovil Pen Mill please see Table 123A

Table 123A

Yeovil Pen Mill - Yeovil Junction

Mondays to Fridays

9 December to 16 May

Network Diagram - see first Page of Table 123

		GW	GW	GW	GW	GW	GW	GW	GW	GW	GW	GW	GW	GW	GW	GW	GW	GW	GW	GW	GW	GW	GW
		BHX	BHX	BHX	BHX	BHX	BHX	BHX	BHX	BHX	BHX	BHX	BHX	BHX	BHX	BHX	BHX	BHX	BHX	BHX	BHX	BHX	
		A	A	A	A	A	A	A	A	A	A	A	A	A	A	A	A	A	A	A	A	A	A
		Bus	Bus	Bus	Bus	Bus	Bus	Bus	Bus	Bus	Bus	Bus	Bus	Bus	Bus	Bus	Bus	Bus	Bus	Bus	Bus	Bus	Bus
Yeovil Pen Mill	d	07 20	07 50	08 20	08 50	09 20	09 50	10 20	10 50	11 20	11 50	12 20	12 50	13 20	13 50	14 20	14 50	15 20	15 50	16 20	16 50	17 33	18 22
Yeovil Bus Station	d	07 30	08 00	08 30	09 00	09 30	10 00	10 30	11 00	11 30	12 00	12 30	13 00	13 30	14 00	14 30	15 00	15 30	16 00	16 30	17a00	17b43	18 30
Yeovil Junction	a	07 35	08 05	08 35	09 05	09 35	10 05	10 35	11 05	11 35	12 05	12 35	13 05	13 35	14 05	14 35	15 05	15 35	16 05	16 35			18 35

		GW
		A
		Bus
Yeovil Pen Mill	d	19 22
Yeovil Bus Station	d	19 30
Yeovil Junction	a	19 35

Saturdays

14 December to 17 May

		GW	GW	GW	GW	GW	GW	GW	GW	GW	GW	GW	GW	GW	GW	GW	GW	GW	GW	GW	GW	GW	GW
		Bus	Bus	Bus	Bus	Bus	Bus	Bus	Bus	Bus	Bus	Bus	Bus	Bus	Bus	Bus	Bus	Bus	Bus	Bus	Bus	Bus	Bus
Yeovil Pen Mill	d	07 20	07 50	08 20	08 50	09 20	09 50	10 20	10 50	11 20	11 50	12 20	12 50	13 20	13 50	14 20	14 50	15 20	15 50	16 20	16 50	17 33	18 22
Yeovil Bus Station	d	07 30	08 00	08 30	09 00	09 30	10 00	10 30	11 00	11 30	12 00	12 30	13 00	13 30	14 00	14 30	15 00	15 30	16 00	16 30	17a00	17b43	18 30
Yeovil Junction	a	07 35	08 05	08 35	09 05	09 35	10 05	10 35	11 05	11 35	12 05	12 35	13 05	13 35	14 05	14 35	15 05	15 35	16 05	16 35			18 35

		GW
		Bus
Yeovil Pen Mill	d	19 22
Yeovil Bus Station	d	19 30
Yeovil Junction	a	19 35

A not 25 December, 26 December, 1 January, 18 April, 21 April, 5 May

b Arrival time, stops on request

No Sunday Service

Table 123A-R

Yeovil Junction - Yeovil Pen Mill

Mondays to Fridays

9 December to 16 May

Network Diagram - see first Page of Table 123

		GW	GW	GW	GW	GW	GW	GW	GW	GW	GW	GW	GW	GW	GW	GW	GW	GW	GW	GW	GW	GW	GW
		BHX	BHX	BHX	BHX	BHX	BHX	BHX	BHX	BHX	BHX	BHX	BHX	BHX	BHX	BHX	BHX	BHX	BHX	BHX	BHX	BHX	BHX
		A	A	A	A	A	A	A	A	A	A	A	A	A	A	A	A	A	A	A	A	A	A
		Bus	Bus	Bus	Bus	Bus	Bus	Bus	Bus	Bus	Bus	Bus	Bus	Bus	Bus	Bus	Bus	Bus	Bus	Bus	Bus	Bus	Bus
Yeovil Junction	d	07 20	07 50	08 20	08 50	09 20	09 50	10 20	10 50	11 20	11 50	12 20	12 50	13 20	13 50	14 20	14 50	15 20	15 50	16 20	16 50	17 50	18 50
Yeovil Bus Station	d	07 27	07 57	08 27	08 57	09 27	09 57	10 27	10 57	11 27	11 57	12 27	12 57	13 27	13 57	14 27	14 57	15 27	15 57	16 27	17 10	17 57	18 57
Yeovil Pen Mill	a	07 32	08 02	08 32	09 02	09 32	10 02	10 32	11 02	11 32	12 02	12 32	13 02	13 32	14 02	14 32	15 02	15 32	16 02	16 32	17 15	18 02	19 02

		GW
		BHX
		A
		Bus
Yeovil Junction	d	19 50
Yeovil Bus Station	d	19 57
Yeovil Pen Mill	a	20 02

Saturdays

14 December to 17 May

		GW	GW	GW	GW	GW	GW	GW	GW	GW	GW	GW	GW	GW	GW	GW	GW	GW	GW	GW	GW	GW	GW
		Bus	Bus	Bus	Bus	Bus	Bus	Bus	Bus	Bus	Bus	Bus	Bus	Bus	Bus	Bus	Bus	Bus	Bus	Bus	Bus	Bus	Bus
Yeovil Junction	d	07 20	07 50	08 20	08 50	09 20	09 50	10 20	10 50	11 20	11 50	12 20	12 50	13 20	13 50	14 20	14 50	15 20	15 50	16 20	16 50	17 50	18 50
Yeovil Bus Station	d	07 27	07 57	08 27	08 57	09 27	09 57	10 27	10 57	11 27	11 57	12 27	12 57	13 27	13 57	14 27	14 57	15 27	15 57	16 27	17 10	17 57	18 57
Yeovil Pen Mill	a	07 32	08 02	08 32	09 02	09 32	10 02	10 32	11 02	11 32	12 02	12 32	13 02	13 32	14 02	14 32	15 02	15 32	16 02	16 32	17 15	18 02	19 02

		GW
		Bus
Yeovil Junction	d	19 50
Yeovil Bus Station	d	19 57
Yeovil Pen Mill	a	20 02

A not 25 December, 26 December, 1 January, 18 April, 21 April, 5 May

No Sunday Service

Route Diagram for Table 125

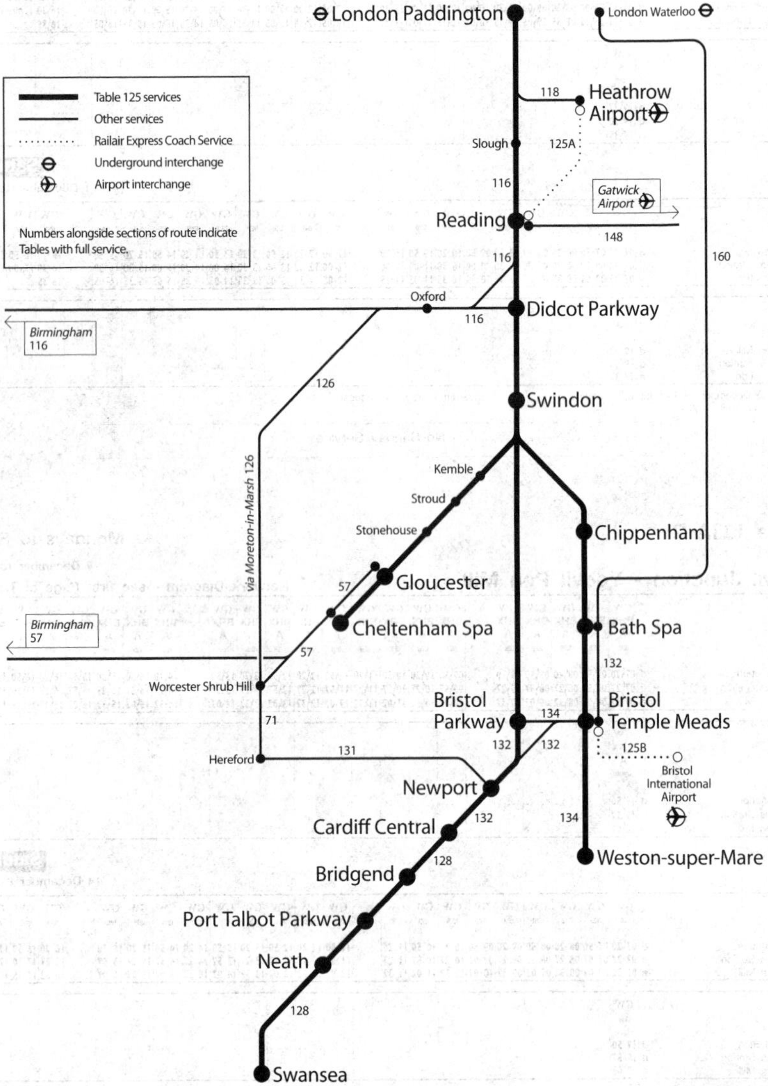

TOCs operating on this network - First Great Western (GW)

Table 125

Mondays to Fridays

9 December to 16 May

London - Swindon, Cheltenham Spa, Bristol, Weston-super-Mare and South Wales

Route Diagram - see first Page of Table 125

Miles	Miles	Miles			GW	GW	GW	GW	GW	GW	GW	GW	GW		GW	GW	GW		GW	GW	GW	GW	GW		GW
					MX	MX	MX	MX	MO	MO															
					◇1		◇1		◇1	◇1		◇1	◇1		◇1	◇1			◇1	◇1	◇1	◇1	◇1		
					A	B	A	C	D	E	F						G				J		K		L
					☕		☕	🚌	☕	☕		☕	☕		☕	☕			☕	☕	Ø	☕	☕		
—	—	—	**London Paddington** 15 ⊖	d								05 19			06 30	06 45			07 00	07 15	07 30	07 36	07 45		
18½	18½	18½	Slough 3	d																					
36	36	36	**Reading** 7	d			00 09		00ʃ16	00ʃ16		05 53			06 56	07 12			07 29	07 42	07 57	08 02	08 12		
53¼	53¼	53¼	Didcot Parkway	d			00 29		00s33	00s33		06 09			07 12				07 44	07 57		08 17			
77¼	77¼	77¼	**Swindon**	a			00 47		00s50	00s53		06 25			07 28	07 41			08 01	08 14	08 27	08 37	08 40		
—	—	—		d	00 01		00 48				06 12	06 27	06 51		07 30	07 42	07 54		08 01	08 15	08 27	08 41	08 42		08 49
—	—	91	Kemble	d				00ʃ11					07 07				08 07					09 01			
—	—	102¼	Stroud	d		00ʃ06		00ʃ41					07 22				08 22					09 16			
—	—	105	Stonehouse	d		00ʃ11							07 28				08 28					09 22			
—	—	113¾	Gloucester 7	a		00ʃ27		01s16					07 44				08 45					09 44			
—	—	120¼	**Cheltenham Spa**	a				01ʃ36					08 01				09 05					10 01			
—	—	—	Worcester Shrub Hill	a																					
—	94	—	Chippenham	d			01 03		01s06	01s08	06a28	06 41			07 44				08 17		08 42				09a05
—	107	—	Bath Spa 7	a			01 15		01s20	01s23		06 54			07 57				08 29		08 55				
111¾	—	—	Bristol Parkway 7	a	00 25											08 06				08 40			09 06		
—	—	—		d	00 27											08 08				08 41			09 08		
117¾	118½	—	**Bristol Temple Meads** 10	a			01 30		01ʃ36	01ʃ37		07 09			08 17				08 45		09 10				
—	137½	—	Weston-super-Mare	a																					
133½	—	—	Newport (South Wales)	a	00 55		02s11					07 46				08 32				09 07			09 29		
145¼	—	—	**Cardiff Central** 7	a	01 15		02 32					08 01				08 46				09 24			09 48		
165½	—	—	Bridgend	a	01 40							08 24				09 09							10 09		
177¾	—	—	Port Talbot Parkway	a	01 54							08 37				09 22							10 22		
183¼	—	—	Neath	a	02 02							08 45				09 30							10 30		
192¾	—	—	**Swansea**	a	02 16							08 58				09 45							10 44		

		GW	GW	GW	GW	GW	GW	GW	GW		GW	GW	GW	GW	GW	GW	GW	GW	GW		GW	GW	GW	GW	GW
		◇1	◇1	◇1		◇1	◇1	◇1	◇1		◇1	◇1		◇1	◇1	◇1		◇1	◇1		◇1	◇1	◇1	◇1	
						M			N			M	L	O		N		M					P	M	L
		☕	☕	☕		☕Ø	☕	☕	☕Ø		☕	☕Ø		☕	☕	☕Ø		☕Ø	☕		☕	☕	☕	☕Ø	
London Paddington 15 ⊖	d	08 00	08 15	08 30		08 45	09 00	09 15	09 30		09 36	09 45		10 00	10 15	10 30		10 45	11 00		11 15	11 30	11 36	11 45	
Slough 3	d																								
Reading 7	d	08 27	08 45	08 57		09 12	09 27	09 42	09 57		10 03	10 12		10 27	10 43	10 57		11 12	11 27		11 44	11 57	12 03	12 12	
Didcot Parkway	d	08 41	08 58	09 12				09 57	10 12		10 18				10 58	11 12					11 58	12 12	12 18		
Swindon	a	08 59	09 15	09 30		09 41	09 54	10 14	10 30		10 36	10 41		10 55	11 14	11 30		11 40	11 55		12 15	12 30	12 36	12 41	
	d	09 00	09 16	09 30	09 38	09 42	09 55	10 15	10 30		10 38	10 42	10 47	10 55	11 15	11 30	11 38	11 42	11 55		12 15	12 30	12 38	12 42	12 47
Kemble	d				09 52						10 52						11 52						12 52		
Stroud	d				10 07						11 07						12 07						13 07		
Stonehouse	d				10 12						11 12						12 12						13 12		
Gloucester 7	a				10 29						11 30						12 28						13 30		
Cheltenham Spa	a				10 48						11 52						12 46						13 52		
Worcester Shrub Hill	a																								
Chippenham	d	09 15		09 45			10 09		10 44				11a03	11 09		11 44			12 09			12 44			13a03
Bath Spa 7	a	09 29		09 59			10 24		10 59					11 24		11 59			12 23			12 59			
Bristol Parkway 7	a		09 42			10 06		10 40				11 06			11 42			12 06			12 42			13 06	
	d		09 43			10 08		10 41				11 08			11 43			12 08			12 43			13 08	
Bristol Temple Meads 10	a	09 45		10 15			10 39		11 15					11 40		12 15			12 39			13 15			
Weston-super-Mare	a													12 06											
Newport (South Wales)	a		10 06			10 31		11 06				11 31			12 04			12 31			13 05			13 31	
Cardiff Central 7	a		10 23			10 46		11 23				11 46			12 21			12 46			13 22			13 46	
Bridgend	a					11 09						12 09						13 09						14 09	
Port Talbot Parkway	a					11 22						12 22						13 22						14 22	
Neath	a					11 30						12 30						13 30						14 30	
Swansea	a					11 43						12 43						13 44						14 43	

- **A** From London Paddington
- **B** from 31 December. From Swindon
- **C** until 27 December. From Swindon
- **D** from 6 January. From London Paddington
- **E** until 30 December. From London Paddington
- **F** From Gloucester to Southampton Central
- **G** From Westbury
- **J** To Penzance. The Merchant Venturer
- **K** The St. David
- **L** To Westbury
- **M** ☕ from Bridgend Ø to Bridgend
- **N** ☕ from Chippenham Ø to Chippenham
- **O** To Paignton. The Torbay Express
- **P** The Cheltenham Spa Express

For connections from Heathrow Airport, Gatwick Airport and Oxford please see Tables 125A, 148 and 116. For connections to Birmingham New Street and Hereford please see Tables 57 and 131

For other services between London and Worcester refer to table 126

Table 125

Mondays to Fridays

9 December to 16 May

London - Swindon, Cheltenham Spa, Bristol, Weston-super-Mare and South Wales

Route Diagram - see first Page of Table 125

		GW ◇1 ☕	GW ◇1 ☕	GW ◇1 ☕	GW	GW ◇1 A ☕⊘	GW ◇1 ☕	GW ◇1 ☕	GW ◇1 ☕	GW ◇1 ☕	GW ◇1 ☕	GW ◇1 ☕	GW B	GW ◇1 ☕	GW ◇1 ☕	GW	GW ◇1 ☕	GW ◇1 ☕	GW ◇1 ☕	GW ◇1 ☕	GW ◇1 ☕	GW ◇1 ☕
London Paddington 15 ⊖	d	12 00	12 15	12 30		12 45	13 00	13 15	13 30	13 36	13 45	14 00		14 15	14 30		14 45	15 00	15 15	15 30	15 36	15 45
Slough 3	d																					
Reading 7	d	12 27	12 42	12 57		13 12	13 27	13 42	13 57	14 03	14 12	14 27		14 44	14 57		15 12	15 27	15 43	15 57	16 02	16 12
Didcot Parkway	d		12 58	13 12				13 57	14 12	14 18				14 58	15 12				15 58	16 12	16 17	
Swindon	a	12 55	13 15	13 30		13 40	13 54	14 14	14 30	14 36	14 41	14 55		15 15	15 30		15 41	15 55	16 15	16 29	16 36	16 41
	d	12 55	13 15	13 30	13 38	13 40	13 55	14 15	14 30	14 38	14 42	14 55	15 14	15 17	15 30	15 38	15 41	15 55	16 17	16 29	16 38	16 42
Kemble	d				13 52					14 52						15 52					16 52	
Stroud	d				14 07					15 07						16 07					17 07	
Stonehouse	d				14 12					15 12						16 12					17 12	
Gloucester 7	a				14 28					15 30						16 29					17 29	
Cheltenham Spa	a				14 47					15 52						16 47					17 52	
Worcester Shrub Hill	a																					
Chippenham	d	13 09		13 44			14 09		14 44			15 09	15a30		15 44			16 10		16 44		
Bath Spa 7	a	13 24		13 59			14 23		14 59			15 24			16 00			16 24		16 58		
Bristol Parkway 7	a		13 42			14 06		14 40			15 06			15 42			16 06		16 40			17 06
	d		13 43			14 08		14 41			15 08			15 43			16 08		16 41			17 08
Bristol Temple Meads 10	a	13 44		14 15			14 39		15 15			15 40			16 15			16 39		17 14		
Weston-super-Mare	a														16 52					17 52		
Newport (South Wales)	a		14 04			14 30		15 05			15 31			16 06			16 30		17 06			17 31
Cardiff Central 7	a		14 22			14 46		15 22			15 46			16 22			16 46		17 22			17 46
Bridgend	a					15 09					16 09						17 09					18 09
Port Talbot Parkway	a					15 22					16 22						17 22					18 22
Neath	a					15 30					16 30						17 30					18 30
Swansea	a					15 43					16 43						17 43					18 44

		GW ◇1 ☕	GW R 1 ☕	GW R 1 C ☕	GW B	GW R 1 D ☕	GW ◇	GW R 1 ☕	GW R ◇1 E ☕	GW R 1 C ☕	GW ◇1 ☕	GW R 1 ☕	GW ◇ F	GW R 1 G ☕	GW R 1 ☕	GW R 1 ☕	GW R 1 ☕	GW ◇1 ☕	GW R 1 ☕	GW B	GW FX R 1 ☕	GW FO R 1 ☕	GW ◇ H
London Paddington 15 ⊖	d	16 00	16 15	16 30		16 45		17 00	17 15	17 30	17 42	17 45		18 00	18 15	18 30	18 45	18 47	19 00		19 15	19 15	
Slough 3	d																						
Reading 7	d	16 27	16 44	16 57		17 12		17 26	17 42	17 56		18 12		18 27	18 42	18 55	19 12	19 19	19 27		19 42	19u48	
Didcot Parkway	d		17 01	17 12				17 42	17 58	18 11	18 21			18 42	18 58	19 12		19 34	19 42		19 57		
Swindon	a	16 55	17 17	17 30		17 39		17 58	18 13	18 28	18 40	18 44		18 59	19 14	19 29	19 40	19 54	20 01		20 14	20 15	
	d	16 56	17 19	17 30	17 36	17 41	17 54	18 00	18 15	18 30	18 45	18 45	18 50	19 00	19 16	19 29	19 41	19 55	20 01	20 12	20 16	20 16	20 25
Kemble	d						18 07				19 00							20 09					20 38
Stroud	d						18 22				19 17							20 25					20 53
Stonehouse	d						18 28				19 24							20 30					20 59
Gloucester 7	a						18 49				19 45							20 46					21 15
Cheltenham Spa	a						19 05				20 02							21 02					21 33
Worcester Shrub Hill	a																						
Chippenham	d	17 12		17 45	17a52			18 14		18 44			19a07	19 14		19 45			20 16	20a28			
Bath Spa 7	a	17 26		17 59				18 27		18 57				19 28		19 58			20 29				
Bristol Parkway 7	a		17 43			18 06			18 40			19 09			19 41		20 05				20 40	20 42	
	d		17 45			18 08			18 42			19 10			19 42		20 08				20 42	20 43	
Bristol Temple Meads 10	a	17 41		18 14				18 44		19 12				19 43		20 13			20 44				
Weston-super-Mare	a			18 51						19 48						20 53							
Newport (South Wales)	a		18 07			18 30			19 11			19 33			20 05		20 31				21 04	21 05	
Cardiff Central 7	a		18 22			18 48			19 26			19 49			20 22		20 48				21 19	21 19	
Bridgend	a		18 48			19 09			19 50			20 11			20 45		21 15				21 45	21 45	
Port Talbot Parkway	a		19 01			19 22			20 03			20 26			20 58		21 28				21 58	21 58	
Neath	a		19 09			19 30			20 10			20 34			21 05		21 36				22 06	22 06	
Swansea	a		19 22			19 45			20 22			20 47			21 19		21 49				22 20	22 20	

- **A** ☕ from Bridgend ⊘ to Bridgend
- **B** To Westbury
- **C** To Taunton
- **D** The Capitals United
- **E** To Carmarthen. The Red Dragon. ◇ from Bridgend R to Bridgend
- **F** From Cheltenham Spa to Southampton Central
- **G** The Bristolian
- **H** From Westbury

For connections from Heathrow Airport, Gatwick Airport and Oxford please see Tables 125A, 148 and 116. For connections to Birmingham New Street and Hereford please see Tables 57 and 131

For other services between London and Worcester refer to table 126

Table 125

Mondays to Fridays

9 December to 16 May

London - Swindon, Cheltenham Spa, Bristol, Weston-super-Mare and South Wales

Route Diagram - see first Page of Table 125

		GW	GW FO		GW FX	GW	GW	GW	GW	GW	GW	GW FO	GW FX		GW	GW FX	GW FX	GW FO	GW FX	GW FO	GW FX
		R 1	◇1		◇1	◇1	◇1	◇1		◇1	◇1	◇1	◇1					◇1	◇1	◇1	◇1
							A				B				C	D	D				
																🚌	🚌				
		☕	☕		☕	☕	☕⊘	☕		☕	☕	☕	☕					☕	☕	☕	☕
London Paddington 15 ⊖	d	19 30	19 48		19 48	20 00	20 15	20 45		21 15	21 45	22 15	22 15					22 45	22 45	23 30	23 30
Slough 3	d																				
Reading 7	d	19 57	20 18		20 18	20 27	20 41	21 13		21 41	22 11	22 42	22 54					23 11	23 23	00 09	00 09
Didcot Parkway	d	20 12	20 34		20 34	20 42	20 57	21 28		22 01	22 31	23 03	23 14					23 43	23 43	00 29	00 29
Swindon	a	20 30	20 48		20 52	21 00	21 14	21 45		22 19	22 48	23 21	23 31					23 59	23 59	00 47	00 47
	d	20 30	20 54		20 54	21 00	21 15	21 45	22 04	22 19	22 49	23 22	23 33		23 36	23 41	23 41	00 01	00 01	00 48	00 48
Kemble	d		21 11		21 11				22 21						23 50		00 11				
Stroud	d		21 26		21 26				22 36						00 06		00 41				
Stonehouse	d		21 31		21 31				22 41						00 11						
Gloucester 7	a		21 46		21 46				22 56						00 27	00s41	01s16				
Cheltenham Spa	a		22 02		22 02				23 10							01 01	01 36				
Worcester Shrub Hill	a		22 24		22 24																
Chippenham	d	20 44				21 16		22 00			23 03	23 36	23 46							01 03	01 03
Bath Spa 7	a	20 59				21 29		22 14			23 17	23 49	23 58							01 15	01 15
Bristol Parkway 7	a						21 40			22 46								00 25	00 25		
	d						21 41			22 47								00 27	00 27		
Bristol Temple Meads 10	a	21 15				21 44		22 29			23 32	00 04	00 14							01 30	01 30
Weston-super-Mare	a	21 50									00s05										
Newport (South Wales)	a						22 03			23 19								00 49	00 55	02s03	02s11
Cardiff Central 7	a						22 23			23 40								01 04	01 15	02 20	02 32
Bridgend	a						22 46			00 03								01 30	01 40		
Port Talbot Parkway	a						23 00			00 17								01 43	01 54		
Neath	a						23 08			00 25								01 51	02 02		
Swansea	a						23 22			00 39								02 05	02 16		

Saturdays

14 December to 28 December

		GW	GW	GW	GW	GW	GW	GW	GW	GW		GW	GW	GW	GW	GW	GW	GW	GW	GW		GW	GW	GW	GW
		◇1		◇1		◇1	◇1	R 1		◇1		◇1	◇1	◇1	◇1	◇1		◇1		◇1		◇1	◇1	◇1	◇1
		E	F	E				G	H										H						A
		☕		☕		☕	☕	☕		☕		☕	☕	☕	☕	☕		☕		☕		☕	☕	☕	☕⊘
London Paddington 15 ⊖	d					06 30	07 00	07 30		07 45		08 00	08 15	08 30	08 45	09 00		09 30		09 45		10 00	10 15	10 30	10 45
Slough 3	d																								
Reading 7	d			00 09		06 57	07 27	07 57		08 12		08 27	08 42	08 57	09 13	09 27		09 57		10 14		10 27	10 42	10 58	11 12
Didcot Parkway	d			00 29		07 12		08 12					08 56	09 12				10 12					10 56	11 12	
Swindon	a			00 47		07 30	07 55	08 30		08 41		08 55	09 15	09 30	09 40	09 54		10 30		10 40		10 54	11 15	11 30	11 39
	d	00 01		00 48	07 16	07 30	07 55	08 30	08 36	08 41		08 55	09 15	09 30	09 40	09 55	10 14	10 30	10 36	10 41		10 55	11 15	11 30	11 39
Kemble	d				07 30								09 31				10 28						11 31		
Stroud	d		00 06		07 45								09 46				10 43						11 46		
Stonehouse	d		00 11		07 50								09 51				10 48						11 51		
Gloucester 7	a		00 27		08 06								10 06				11 05						12 06		
Cheltenham Spa	a				08 24								10 22				11 23						12 22		
Worcester Shrub Hill	a																								
Chippenham	d			01 03		07 45	08 09	08 44	08a52			09 09		09 44		10 09		10 44	10a52			11 09		11 45	
Bath Spa 7	a			01 15		08 00	08 24	09 00				09 24		10 00		10 24		11 00				11 24		12 00	
Bristol Parkway 7	a	00 25								09 06					10 06					11 06					12 05
	d	00 27								09 08					10 08					11 08					12 08
Bristol Temple Meads 10	a			01 30		08 16	08 39	09 15				09 39		10 15		10 39		11 15				11 39		12 15	
Weston-super-Mare	a																								
Newport (South Wales)	a	00 49		02s03						09 30					10 31					11 31					12 31
Cardiff Central 7	a	01 04		02 20						09 47					10 46					11 46					12 46
Bridgend	a	01 30								10 09					11 09					12 09					13 09
Port Talbot Parkway	a	01 43								10 22					11 22					12 22					13 22
Neath	a	01 51								10 30					11 30					12 30					13 30
Swansea	a	02 05								10 43					11 43					12 43					13 43

A ☕ from Bridgend ⊘ to Bridgend
B To Exeter St Davids
C from 27 December
D until 26 December
E From London Paddington
F From Swindon
G To Penzance
H To Westbury

For connections from Heathrow Airport, Gatwick Airport and Oxford please see Tables 125A, 148 and 116. For connections to Birmingham New Street and Hereford please see Tables 57 and 131

For other services between London and Worcester refer to table 126

Table 125

Saturdays

14 December to 28 December

London - Swindon, Cheltenham Spa, Bristol, Weston-super-Mare and South Wales

Route Diagram - see first Page of Table 125

		GW		GW	GW	GW	GW	GW	GW	GW	GW	GW		GW	GW	GW	GW	GW	GW	GW	GW	GW		GW	GW
		◇1			◇1		◇1	◇1	◇1	◇1	◇1	◇1			◇1		◇1	◇1	◇1		◇1	◇1		◇1	
					A	B	C									B				B					
		🍽			🍽⊘		🍽⊘	🍽	🍽	🍽	🍽	🍽			🍽		🍽	🍽	🍽		🍽	🍽		🍽	
London Paddington 15 ⊖	d	11 00			11 30		11 45	12 00	12 15	12 30	12 45	13 00			13 30		13 45	14 00	14 15		14 30	14 45		15 00	
Slough 3	d																								
Reading 7	d	11 27			11 57		12 12	12 27	12 42	12 57	13 14	13 27			13 57		14 12	14 27	14 42		14 57	15 12		15 27	
Didcot Parkway	d				12 12				12 56	13 12					14 12				14 56		15 12				
Swindon	a	11 54			12 30		12 39	12 54	13 15	13 30	13 41	13 55			14 30		14 41	14 54	15 15		15 30	15 39		15 54	
	d	11 55		12 14	12 30	12 36	12 41	12 55	13 15	13 30	13 41	13 55		14 14	14 30	14 36	14 41	14 55	15 15	15 22	15 30	15 39		15 55	16 14
Kemble	d			12 28					13 31					14 28					15 31						16 28
Stroud	d			12 43					13 46					14 43					15 46						16 43
Stonehouse	d			12 48					13 51					14 48					15 51						16 48
Gloucester 7	a			13 03					14 06					15 03					16 06						17 03
Cheltenham Spa	a			13 24					14 22					15 25					16 22						17 25
Worcester Shrub Hill	a																								
Chippenham	d	12 09			12 44	12a52		13 09		13 44		14 09			14 44	14a52		15 09		15a38	15 44			16 09	
Bath Spa 7	a	12 24			12 59			13 24		14 00		14 24			15 00			15 24			16 00			16 24	
Bristol Parkway 7	a						13 06				14 06						15 06					16 05			
	d						13 08				14 08						15 08					16 08			
Bristol Temple Meads 10	a	12 39			13 14			13 42		14 15		14 39			15 15			15 41			16 15			16 39	
Weston-super-Mare	a																								
Newport (South Wales)	a						13 31				14 31						15 31					16 30			
Cardiff Central 7	a						13 47				14 46						15 45					16 46			
Bridgend	a						14 09				15 09						16 09					17 09			
Port Talbot Parkway	a						14 22				15 22						16 22					17 22			
Neath	a						14 30				15 30						16 30					17 30			
Swansea	a						14 43				15 43						16 43					17 43			

		GW	GW	GW	GW	GW	GW	GW		GW	GW	GW	GW	GW	GW	GW	GW	GW		GW	GW	GW	GW	GW	GW
		◇1	◇1	◇1	◇1	◇1		◇1		◇1		◇1	◇1	◇1	◇1	◇1		◇1		◇1		◇1	◇1	◇1	◇1
						D	B						E			F	B			F					
		🍽	🍽	🍽	🍽	🍽		🍽		🍽		🍽	🍽	🍽	🍽	🍽		🍽		🍽		🍽	🍽	🍽	🍽
London Paddington 15 ⊖	d	15 30	15 45	16 00	16 15	16 30		16 45		17 00		17 30	17 45	18 00	18 15	18 30		18 45		19 00		19 15	19 30	19 45	20 00
Slough 3	d																								
Reading 7	d	15 57	16 12	16 27	16 42	16 57		17 12		17 27		17 57	18 12	18 27	18 42	18 57		19 12		19 27		19 42	19 57	20 12	20 27
Didcot Parkway	d	16 12			16 56	17 12						18 12			18 56	19 12						19 56	20 12		20 42
Swindon	a	16 30	16 41	16 54	17 15	17 30		17 40		17 54		18 30	18 40	18 54	19 15	19 30		19 39		19 54		20 14	20 30	20 40	21 00
	d	16 30	16 41	16 55	17 15	17 30	17 36	17 40		17 55	18 14	18 30	18 40	18 55	19 15	19 30	19 36	19 39		19 55	20 00	20 14	20 30	20 40	21 00
Kemble	d				17 31						18 28				19 31						20 15				
Stroud	d				17 46						18 43				19 46						20 30				
Stonehouse	d				17 51						18 48				19 51						20 35				
Gloucester 7	a				18 06						19 03				20 06						20 50				
Cheltenham Spa	a				18 22						19 25				20 22						21 03				
Worcester Shrub Hill	a																								
Chippenham	d	16 44		17 09		17 44	17a52			18 09		18 44		19 09		19 44	19a52			20 09			20 45		21 14
Bath Spa 7	a	17 00		17 24		18 00				18 24		19 00		19 24		20 00				20 24			21 00		21 30
Bristol Parkway 7	a		17 06					18 06					19 07					20 06				20 40		21 06	
	d		17 08					18 08					19 08					20 08				20 40		21 08	
Bristol Temple Meads 10	a	17 15		17 39		18 15				18 39		19 15		19 38		20 15				20 40			21 16		21 45
Weston-super-Mare	a					18 36						19 50				20 36				21 26					
Newport (South Wales)	a		17 29					18 30					19 30					20 30				21 03		21 31	
Cardiff Central 7	a		17 46					18 46					19 46					20 44				21 20		21 47	
Bridgend	a		18 09					19 09					20 09					21 09				21 46		22 09	
Port Talbot Parkway	a		18 22					19 22					20 22					21 22				21 59		22 23	
Neath	a		18 30					19 30					20 30					21 30				22 07		22 31	
Swansea	a		18 46					19 43					20 43					21 43				22 20		22 45	

A 🍽 from Chippenham ⊘ to Chippenham
B To Westbury
C 🍽 from Bridgend ⊘ to Bridgend
D To Paignton
E To Carmarthen
F To Taunton

For connections from Heathrow Airport, Gatwick Airport and Oxford please see Tables 125A, 148 and 116. For connections to Birmingham New Street and Hereford please see Tables 57 and 131

For other services between London and Worcester refer to table 126

Table 125

Saturdays

14 December to 28 December

London - Swindon, Cheltenham Spa, Bristol, Weston-super-Mare and South Wales

Route Diagram - see first Page of Table 125

		GW	GW	GW	GW	GW	GW	GW	GW	GW
			◇1	◇1	◇1	◇1		◇1	◇1	◇1
		A		B						
			☕	☕	☕	☕		☕	☕	☕
London Paddington 15 ⊖	d		20 15	20 30	20 45	21 30		22 00	22 35	23 30
Slough 3	d									
Reading 7	d		20 42	20 57	21 13	21 57		22 28	23 03	00 03
Didcot Parkway	d		20 56	21 12		22 12		22 43	23 26	00 19
Swindon	a		21 15	21 30	21 40	22 30		22 59	23 42	00 36
	d	21 08	21 15	21 30	21 42	22 32	22 40	23 00	23 43	00 38
Kemble	d		21 31				22 54			
Stroud	d		21 46				23 09			
Stonehouse	d		21 51				23 14			
Gloucester 7	a		22 06				23 30			
Cheltenham Spa	a		22 21							
Worcester Shrub Hill	a									
Chippenham	d	21a24		21 44		22 46			23 57	00 52
Bath Spa 7	a			22 00		23 01			00 15	01 06
Bristol Parkway 7	a				22 06			23 28		
	d				22 11			23 29		
Bristol Temple Meads 10	a			22 14		23 15			00 27	01 20
Weston-super-Mare	a			22s47						
Newport (South Wales)	a				22 46			23 58		
Cardiff Central 7	a				23 07			00 18		
Bridgend	a				23 29					
Port Talbot Parkway	a				23 43					
Neath	a				23 51					
Swansea	a				00 05					

Saturdays

4 January to 8 February

		GW	GW	GW	GW	GW	GW	GW	GW	GW	GW	GW
								R				
		◇1		◇1		◇1	◇1	1	◇1		◇1	
		C	D	C				E		F		
		☕		☕		☕	☕	☕	☕		☕	
London Paddington 15 ⊖	d					06 22	06 52	07 22	07 36		07 52	
Slough 3	d											
Reading 7	d			00 09		06 59	07 28	07 59	08 14		08 30	
Didcot Parkway	d			00 29		07 12		08 14				
Swindon	a			00 47		07 30	07 55	08 32	08 41		08 58	
	d	00 01		00 48	07 16	07 30	07 55	08 32	08 42	08 50	08 59	09 15
Kemble	d				07 30							09 31
Stroud	d		00 06		07 45							09 46
Stonehouse	d		00 11		07 50							09 51
Gloucester 7	a		00 27		08 06							10 06
Cheltenham Spa	a				08 24							10 22
Worcester Shrub Hill	a											
Chippenham	d			01 03		07 45	08 09	08 47		09a06	09 12	
Bath Spa 7	a			01 15		08 00	08 24	09 01			09 27	
Bristol Parkway 7	a	00 25							09 06			
	d	00 27							09 08			
Bristol Temple Meads 10	a			01 30		08 16	08 39	09 15			09 43	
Weston-super-Mare	a											
Newport (South Wales)	a	00 49		02s03					09 30			
Cardiff Central 7	a	01 04		02 20					09 47			
Bridgend	a	01 30							10 09			
Port Talbot Parkway	a	01 43							10 22			
Neath	a	01 51							10 30			
Swansea	a	02 05							10 44			

		GW	GW	GW	GW	GW	GW	GW	GW	GW	GW	GW
		◇1	◇1	◇1		◇1	◇1		◇1		◇1	◇1
								F				G
		☕	☕	☕		☕	☕		☕		☕	☕⊘
London Paddington 15 ⊖	d	08 22	08 36	08 52		09 22	09 36		09 52		10 22	10 36
Slough 3	d											
Reading 7	d	08 57	09 13	09 29		10 00	10 14		10 29		10 59	11 13
Didcot Parkway	d	09 12				10 15					11 13	
Swindon	a	09 30	09 40	09 56		10 32	10 40		10 56		11 31	11 40
	d	09 30	09 41	09 58	10 14	10 33	10 41	10 46	10 58	11 14	11 31	11 41
Kemble	d				10 28					11 30		
Stroud	d				10 43					11 45		
Stonehouse	d				10 48					11 50		
Gloucester 7	a				11 05					12 05		
Cheltenham Spa	a				11 23					12 18		
Worcester Shrub Hill	a											
Chippenham	d	09 44		10 11		10 46		11a02	11 11		11 46	
Bath Spa 7	a	10 00		10 26		11 02			11 26		12 01	
Bristol Parkway 7	a		10 06				11 06					12 06
	d		10 08				11 08					12 08
Bristol Temple Meads 10	a	10 15		10 42		11 18			11 42		12 16	
Weston-super-Mare	a											
Newport (South Wales)	a		10 31				11 31					12 31
Cardiff Central 7	a		10 46				11 46					12 46
Bridgend	a		11 09				12 09					13 09
Port Talbot Parkway	a		11 22				12 22					13 22
Neath	a		11 30				12 30					13 30
Swansea	a		11 43				12 43					13 43

A From Cheltenham Spa to Westbury
B To Exeter St Davids
C From London Paddington
D From Swindon
E To Penzance
F To Westbury
G ☕ from Bridgend ⊘ to Bridgend

For connections from Heathrow Airport, Gatwick Airport and Oxford please see Tables 125A, 148 and 116. For connections to Birmingham New Street and Hereford please see Tables 57 and 131

For other services between London and Worcester refer to table 126

Table 125

Saturdays

4 January to 8 February

London - Swindon, Cheltenham Spa, Bristol, Weston-super-Mare and South Wales

Route Diagram - see first Page of Table 125

		GW		GW	GW	GW	GW	GW	GW	GW	GW	GW		GW	GW	GW	GW	GW	GW	GW	GW	GW		GW	GW
		◇1		1	◇1	◇1		◇1		◇1	◇1	◇1			◇1	◇1	◇1		◇1	◇1	◇1	◇1			
					A	B	C											C						D	
		☕			☕⊘	☕⊘		☕		☕	☕	☕			☕	☕	☕		☕	☕	☕	☕			
London Paddington 15 ⊖	d	10 52			11 22	11 36		11 52		12 22	12 36	12 52			13 22	13 36	13 52			14 22	14 36	14 52			
Slough 3	d																								
Reading 7	d	11 31			12 00	12 14		12 30		12 59	13 13	13 29			14 00	14 14	14 30			15 01	15 16	15 29			
Didcot Parkway	d				12 15					13 14					14 15					15 16					
Swindon	a	11 58			12 33	12 40		12 57		13 32	13 40	13 57			14 33	14 41	14 57			15 33	15 43	15 56			
	d	11 59		12 14	12 33	12 41	12 50	12 58	13 14	13 32	13 41	13 58		14 14	14 33	14 41	14 59	15 12	15 15	15 34	15 44	15 58		16 06	16 14
Kemble	d			12 27					13 30					14 28					15 31						16 28
Stroud	d			12 42					13 45					14 43					15 46						16 43
Stonehouse	d			12 48					13 50					14 48					15 51						16 48
Gloucester 7	a			13 04					14 06					15 03					16 06						17 03
Cheltenham Spa	a			13 23					14 22					15 25					16 22						17 25
Worcester Shrub Hill	a																								
Chippenham	d	12 13			12 47		13a06	13 12		13 46		14 11			14 47		15 12	15a28		15 48		16 11		16a23	
Bath Spa 7	a	12 28			13 02			13 27		14 02		14 26			15 03		15 28			16 03		16 26			
Bristol Parkway 7	a					13 06					14 06					15 06					16 09				
	d					13 08					14 08					15 08					16 11				
Bristol Temple Meads 10	a	12 43			13 17			13 45		14 18		14 42			15 18		15 45			16 19		16 42			
Weston-super-Mare	a																								
Newport (South Wales)	a					13 31					14 31					15 31					16 33				
Cardiff Central 7	a					13 47					14 46					15 45					16 48				
Bridgend	a					14 09					15 09					16 09					17 09				
Port Talbot Parkway	a					14 22					15 22					16 22					17 22				
Neath	a					14 30					15 30					16 30					17 30				
Swansea	a					14 43					15 43					16 43					17 43				

		GW	GW	GW	GW	GW	GW	GW		GW	GW	GW	GW	GW	GW	GW	GW	GW		GW	GW	GW	GW	GW	GW
		◇1	◇1	◇1		◇1	◇1			◇1	1	◇1	◇1	◇1		◇1	◇1			◇1		◇1	◇1	◇1	◇1
						E		C					F			G		C		G					
		☕	☕	☕		☕	☕			☕		☕	☕	☕		☕	☕			☕		☕	☕	☕	☕
London Paddington 15 ⊖	d	15 22	15 36	15 52		16 22	16 36			16 52		17 22	17 36	17 52		18 22	18 36			18 52		19 06	19 22	19 36	19 52
Slough 3	d																								
Reading 7	d	16 00	16 14	16 29		16 59	17 13			17 31		17 58	18 14	18 29		19 00	19 14			19 30		19 45	20 01	20 13	20 29
Didcot Parkway	d	16 15				17 15						18 13				19 15						20 00	20 14		20 45
Swindon	a	16 33	16 41	16 56		17 32	17 40			17 58		18 31	18 41	18 56		19 33	19 40			19 57		20 17	20 32	20 40	21 02
	d	16 33	16 41	16 58	17 14	17 33	17 41	17 46		17 59	18 14	18 31	18 41	18 57	19 14	19 33	19 41	19 47		19 58	20 02	20 18	20 32	20 41	21 03
Kemble	d				17 30						18 27				19 30						20 16				
Stroud	d				17 45						18 42				19 45						20 31				
Stonehouse	d				17 50						18 48				19 50						20 36				
Gloucester 7	a				18 06						19 04				20 06						20 51				
Cheltenham Spa	a				18 19						19 25				20 19						21 04				
Worcester Shrub Hill	a																								
Chippenham	d	16 47		17 11		17 48		18a02		18 13		18 45		19 11		19 47		20a03		20 12			20 47		21 17
Bath Spa 7	a	17 03		17 26		18 02				18 28		19 01		19 26		20 03				20 27			21 02		21 32
Bristol Parkway 7	a		17 06				18 06						19 08				20 06					20 43		21 06	
	d		17 08				18 08						19 08				20 08					20 43		21 08	
Bristol Temple Meads 10	a	17 18		17 42		18 18				18 43		19 16		19 40		20 18				20 43			21 18		21 47
Weston-super-Mare	a					18 38						19 51				20 39				21 26					
Newport (South Wales)	a		17 29				18 30						19 30				20 30					21 06		21 31	
Cardiff Central 7	a		17 46				18 46						19 46				20 45					21 23		21 47	
Bridgend	a		18 09				19 09						20 09				21 09					21 49		22 09	
Port Talbot Parkway	a		18 22				19 22						20 22				21 22					22 02		22 23	
Neath	a		18 30				19 30						20 30				21 30					22 10		22 31	
Swansea	a		18 46				19 43						20 43				21 43					22 23		22 45	

A ☕ from Chippenham ⊘ to Chippenham
B ☕ from Bridgend ⊘ to Bridgend
C To Westbury
D From Cheltenham Spa to Westbury
E To Paignton
F To Carmarthen
G To Taunton

For connections from Heathrow Airport, Gatwick Airport and Oxford please see Tables 125A, 148 and 116. For connections to Birmingham New Street and Hereford please see Tables 57 and 131

For other services between London and Worcester refer to table 126

Table 125

Saturdays

4 January to 8 February

London - Swindon, Cheltenham Spa, Bristol, Weston-super-Mare and South Wales

Route Diagram - see first Page of Table 125

		GW	GW	GW	GW	GW	GW	GW	GW	GW
			◇1	◇1	◇1	◇1		◇1	◇1	◇1
		A		B						
			☕	☕	☕	☕		☕	☕	☕
London Paddington 15 ⊖	d			20 21	20 36	21 22		21 52	22 35	23 21
Slough 3	d									
Reading 7	d			21 02	21 13	22 01		22 27	23 20	00 05
Didcot Parkway	d			21 17		22 16		22 42	23 35	00 19
Swindon	a			21 35	21 40	22 34		22 58	23 51	00 36
	d	21 14	21 15	21 35	21 42	22 35	22 40	22 59	23 52	00 38
Kemble	d		21 31				22 54			
Stroud	d		21 46				23 09			
Stonehouse	d		21 51				23 14			
Gloucester 7	a		22 06				23 30			
Cheltenham Spa	a		22 21							
Worcester Shrub Hill	a									
Chippenham	d	21a30		21 49		22 50			00 06	00 52
Bath Spa 7	a			22 05		23 05			00 23	01 06
Bristol Parkway 7	a				22 06			23 25		
	d				22 11			23 27		
Bristol Temple Meads 10	a			22 19		23 19			00 35	01 20
Weston-super-Mare	a			22s51						
Newport (South Wales)	a				22 46			00 01		
Cardiff Central 7	a				23 07					
Bridgend	a				23 29					
Port Talbot Parkway	a				23 43					
Neath	a				23 51					
Swansea	a				00 05					

Saturdays

15 February to 22 March

		GW	GW	GW	GW	GW	GW	GW	GW	GW	GW	GW	GW	GW	GW	GW	GW	GW	GW	GW	GW	GW	GW
								R															
		◇1		◇1		◇1	◇1	1		◇1	◇1	◇1	◇1	◇1	◇1		◇1		◇1	◇1	◇1	◇1	◇1
		C	D	C				E	A									A					F
		☕		☕		☕	☕	☕		☕	☕	☕	☕	☕	☕		☕		☕	☕	☕	☕	☕⊘
London Paddington 15 ⊖	d					06 30	07 00	07 30		07 45	08 00	08 15	08 30	08 45	09 00		09 30		09 45	10 00	10 15	10 30	10 45
Slough 3	d																						
Reading 7	d			00 09		06 57	07 27	07 57		08 12	08 27	08 42	08 57	09 13	09 27		09 57		10 14	10 27	10 42	10 58	11 12
Didcot Parkway	d			00 29		07 12		08 12				08 56	09 12				10 12				10 56	11 12	
Swindon	a			00 47		07 30	07 55	08 30		08 41	08 55	09 15	09 30	09 40	09 54		10 30		10 40	10 54	11 15	11 30	11 39
	d	00 01		00 48	07 16	07 30	07 55	08 30	08 36	08 41	08 55	09 15	09 30	09 40	09 55	10 14	10 30	10 36	10 41	10 55	11 15	11 30	11 39
Kemble	d				07 30							09 31				10 28					11 31		
Stroud	d		00 06		07 45							09 46				10 43					11 46		
Stonehouse	d		00 11		07 50							09 51				10 48					11 51		
Gloucester 7	a		00 27		08 06							10 06				11 05					12 06		
Cheltenham Spa	a				08 24							10 22				11 23					12 22		
Worcester Shrub Hill	a																						
Chippenham	d			01 03		07 45	08 09	08 44	08a52		09 09		09 44		10 09		10 44	10a52		11 09		11 45	
Bath Spa 7	a			01 15		08 00	08 24	09 00			09 24		10 00		10 24		11 00			11 24		12 00	
Bristol Parkway 7	a	00 25								09 06				10 06					11 06				12 05
	d	00 27								09 08				10 08					11 08				12 08
Bristol Temple Meads 10	a			01 30		08 16	08 39	09 15			09 39		10 15		10 39		11 15			11 39		12 15	
Weston-super-Mare	a																						
Newport (South Wales)	a	00 49		02s03						09 30				10 31					11 31				12 31
Cardiff Central 7	a	01 04		02 20						09 47				10 46					11 46				12 46
Bridgend	a	01 30								10 09				11 09					12 09				13 09
Port Talbot Parkway	a	01 43								10 22				11 22					12 22				13 22
Neath	a	01 51								10 30				11 30					12 30				13 30
Swansea	a	02 05								10 43				11 43					12 43				13 43

A To Westbury
B To Exeter St Davids
C From London Paddington
D From Swindon
E To Penzance
F ☕ from Bridgend ⊘ to Bridgend

For connections from Heathrow Airport, Gatwick Airport and Oxford please see Tables 125A, 148 and 116. For connections to Birmingham New Street and Hereford please see Tables 57 and 131

For other services between London and Worcester refer to table 126

Table 125

Saturdays

15 February to 22 March

London - Swindon, Cheltenham Spa, Bristol, Weston-super-Mare and South Wales

Route Diagram - see first Page of Table 125

		GW		GW	GW	GW	GW	GW	GW	GW	GW	GW		GW	GW	GW	GW	GW	GW	GW	GW	GW		GW	GW
		◇1			◇1		◇1	◇1	◇1	◇1	◇1	◇1			◇1		◇1	◇1	◇1		◇1	◇1		◇1	
					A	B	C									B				B					
		R			R⊘		R⊘	R	R	R	R	R			R		R	R	R		R	R		R	
London Paddington 15 ⊖	d	11 00			11 30		11 45	12 00	12 15	12 30	12 45	13 00			13 30		13 45	14 00	14 15		14 30	14 45		15 00	
Slough 3	d																								
Reading 7	d	11 27			11 57		12 12	12 27	12 42	12 57	13 14	13 27			13 57		14 12	14 27	14 42		14 57	15 12		15 27	
Didcot Parkway	d				12 12				12 56	13 12					14 12				14 56		15 12				
Swindon	a	11 54			12 30		12 39	12 54	13 15	13 30	13 41	13 55			14 30		14 41	14 54	15 15		15 30	15 39		15 54	
	d	11 55		12 14	12 30	12 36	12 41	12 55	13 15	13 30	13 41	13 55		14 14	14 30	14 36	14 41	14 55	15 15	15 22	15 30	15 39		15 55	16 14
Kemble	d			12 28					13 31					14 28					15 31						16 28
Stroud	d			12 43					13 46					14 43					15 46						16 43
Stonehouse	d			12 48					13 51					14 48					15 51						16 48
Gloucester 7	a			13 03					14 06					15 03					16 06						17 03
Cheltenham Spa	a			13 24					14 22					15 25					16 22						17 25
Worcester Shrub Hill	a																								
Chippenham	d	12 09			12 44	12a52		13 09		13 44		14 09			14 44	14a52		15 09		15a38	15 44			16 09	
Bath Spa 7	a	12 24			12 59			13 24		14 00		14 24			15 00			15 24			16 00			16 24	
Bristol Parkway 7	a						13 06				14 06						15 06					16 05			
	d						13 08				14 08						15 08					16 08			
Bristol Temple Meads 10	a	12 39			13 14			13 42		14 15		14 39			15 15			15 41			16 15			16 39	
Weston-super-Mare	a																								
Newport (South Wales)	a						13 31				14 31						15 31					16 30			
Cardiff Central 7	a						13 47				14 46						15 45					16 46			
Bridgend	a						14 09				15 09						16 09					17 09			
Port Talbot Parkway	a						14 22				15 22						16 22					17 22			
Neath	a						14 30				15 30						16 30					17 30			
Swansea	a						14 43				15 43						16 43					17 43			

		GW	GW	GW	GW	GW	GW	GW		GW	GW	GW	GW	GW	GW	GW	GW	GW		GW	GW	GW	GW	GW	GW
		◇1	◇1	◇1	◇1	◇1		◇1		◇1		◇1	◇1	◇1	◇1	◇1		◇1		◇1		◇1	◇1	◇1	◇1
						D	B						E			F	B			F					
		R	R	R	R	R		R		R		R	R	R	R	R		R		R		R	R	R	R
London Paddington 15 ⊖	d	15 30	15 45	16 00	16 15	16 30		16 45		17 00		17 30	17 45	18 00	18 15	18 30		18 45		19 00		19 15	19 30	19 45	20 00
Slough 3	d																								
Reading 7	d	15 57	16 12	16 27	16 42	16 57		17 12		17 27		17 57	18 12	18 27	18 42	18 57		19 12		19 27		19 42	19 57	20 12	20 27
Didcot Parkway	d	16 12			16 56	17 12						18 12			18 56	19 12						19 56	20 12		20 42
Swindon	a	16 30	16 41	16 54	17 15	17 30		17 40		17 54		18 30	18 40	18 54	19 15	19 30		19 39		19 54		20 14	20 30	20 40	21 00
	d	16 30	16 41	16 55	17 15	17 30	17 36	17 40		17 55	18 14	18 30	18 40	18 55	19 15	19 30	19 36	19 39		19 55	20 00	20 14	20 30	20 40	21 00
Kemble	d				17 31						18 28				19 31						20 15				
Stroud	d				17 46						18 43				19 46						20 30				
Stonehouse	d				17 51						18 48				19 51						20 35				
Gloucester 7	a				18 06						19 03				20 06						20 50				
Cheltenham Spa	a				18 22						19 25				20 22						21 03				
Worcester Shrub Hill	a																								
Chippenham	d	16 44		17 09		17 44	17a52			18 09		18 44		19 09		19 44	19a52			20 09			20 45		21 14
Bath Spa 7	a	17 00		17 24		18 00				18 24		19 00		19 24		20 00				20 24			21 00		21 30
Bristol Parkway 7	a		17 06					18 06					19 07					20 06				20 40		21 06	
	d		17 08					18 08					19 08					20 08				20 40		21 08	
Bristol Temple Meads 10	a	17 15		17 39		18 15				18 39		19 15		19 38		20 15				20 40			21 16		21 45
Weston-super-Mare	a					18 36						19 50				20 36				21 26					
Newport (South Wales)	a		17 29					18 30					19 30					20 30				21 03		21 31	
Cardiff Central 7	a		17 46					18 46					19 46					20 44				21 20		21 47	
Bridgend	a		18 09					19 09					20 09					21 09				21 46		22 09	
Port Talbot Parkway	a		18 22					19 22					20 22					21 22				21 59		22 23	
Neath	a		18 30					19 30					20 30					21 30				22 07		22 31	
Swansea	a		18 46					19 43					20 43					21 43				22 20		22 45	

A R from Chippenham ⊘ to Chippenham
B To Westbury
C R from Bridgend ⊘ to Bridgend
D To Paignton
E To Carmarthen
F To Taunton

For connections from Heathrow Airport, Gatwick Airport and Oxford please see Tables 125A, 148 and 116. For connections to Birmingham New Street and Hereford please see Tables 57 and 131

For other services between London and Worcester refer to table 126

Table 125

Saturdays

15 February to 22 March

London - Swindon, Cheltenham Spa, Bristol, Weston-super-Mare and South Wales

Route Diagram - see first Page of Table 125

		GW	GW	GW	GW	GW	GW	GW	GW	GW
			◇1	◇1	◇1	◇1		◇1	◇1	◇1
		A		B						
			☕	☕	☕	☕		☕	☕	☕
London Paddington 15 ⊖	d		20 15	20 30	20 45	21 30		22 00	22 35	23 30
Slough 3	d									
Reading 7	d		20 42	20 57	21 13	21 57		22 28	23 03	00 03
Didcot Parkway	d		20 56	21 12		22 12		22 48	23 29	00 19
Swindon	a		21 15	21 30	21 40	22 30		23 04	23 45	00 37
	d	21 08	21 15	21 30	21 42	22 32	22 40	23 05	23 46	00 38
Kemble	d		21 31				22 54			
Stroud	d		21 46				23 09			
Stonehouse	d		21 51				23 14			
Gloucester 7	a		22 06				23 30			
Cheltenham Spa	a		22 21							
Worcester Shrub Hill	a									
Chippenham	d	21a24		21 44		22 46			00 01	00 53
Bath Spa 7	a			22 00		23 01			00 17	01 07
Bristol Parkway 7	a				22 06			23 31		
	d				22 11			23 33		
Bristol Temple Meads 10	a			22 14		23 15			00 29	01 21
Weston-super-Mare	a			22s47						
Newport (South Wales)	a				22 46			00 01		
Cardiff Central 7	a				23 07			00 21		
Bridgend	a				23 29					
Port Talbot Parkway	a				23 43					
Neath	a				23 51					
Swansea	a				00 05					

Saturdays

29 March to 17 May

		GW	GW	GW	GW	GW	GW	GW	GW	GW	GW	GW	GW	GW	GW	GW	GW	GW	GW	GW	GW	GW	GW
		◇1		◇1		◇1	◇1	R 1		◇1	◇1	◇1	◇1	◇1	◇1		◇1		◇1	◇1	◇1	◇1	◇1
		C	D	C				E	F									F					G
		☕		☕		☕	☕	☕		☕	☕	☕	☕	☕	☕		☕		☕	☕	☕	☕	☕⊘
London Paddington 15 ⊖	d					06 30	07 00	07 30		07 45	08 00	08 15	08 30	08 45	09 00		09 30		09 45	10 00	10 15	10 30	10 45
Slough 3	d																						
Reading 7	d			00 09		06 57	07 27	07 57		08 12	08 27	08 42	08 57	09 13	09 27		09 57		10 14	10 27	10 42	10 58	11 12
Didcot Parkway	d			00 29		07 12		08 12				08 56	09 12				10 12				10 56	11 12	
Swindon	a			00 47		07 30	07 55	08 30		08 41	08 55	09 15	09 30	09 40	09 54		10 30		10 40	10 54	11 15	11 30	11 39
	d	00 01		00 48	07 16	07 30	07 55	08 30	08 36	08 41	08 55	09 15	09 30	09 40	09 55	10 14	10 30	10 36	10 41	10 55	11 15	11 30	11 39
Kemble	d				07 30							09 31				10 28					11 31		
Stroud	d		00 06		07 45							09 46				10 43					11 46		
Stonehouse	d		00 11		07 50							09 51				10 48					11 51		
Gloucester 7	a		00 27		08 06							10 06				11 05					12 06		
Cheltenham Spa	a				08 24							10 22				11 23					12 22		
Worcester Shrub Hill	a																						
Chippenham	d			01 03		07 45	08 09	08 44	08a52		09 09		09 44		10 09		10 44	10a52		11 09		11 45	
Bath Spa 7	a			01 15		08 00	08 24	09 00			09 24		10 00		10 24		11 00			11 24		12 00	
Bristol Parkway 7	a	00 25								09 06				10 06					11 06				12 05
	d	00 27								09 08				10 08					11 08				12 08
Bristol Temple Meads 10	a			01 30		08 16	08 39	09 15			09 39		10 15		10 39		11 15			11 39		12 15	
Weston-super-Mare	a																						
Newport (South Wales)	a	00 49		02s03						09 30				10 31					11 31				12 31
Cardiff Central 7	a	01 04		02 20						09 47				10 46					11 46				12 46
Bridgend	a	01 30								10 09				11 09					12 09				13 09
Port Talbot Parkway	a	01 43								10 22				11 22					12 22				13 22
Neath	a	01 51								10 30				11 30					12 30				13 30
Swansea	a	02 05								10 43				11 43					12 43				13 43

A From Cheltenham Spa to Westbury
B To Exeter St Davids
C From London Paddington
D From Swindon
E To Penzance
F To Westbury
G ☕ from Bridgend ⊘ to Bridgend

For connections from Heathrow Airport, Gatwick Airport and Oxford please see Tables 125A, 148 and 116. For connections to Birmingham New Street and Hereford please see Tables 57 and 131

For other services between London and Worcester refer to table 126

Table 125

Saturdays

29 March to 17 May

London - Swindon, Cheltenham Spa, Bristol, Weston-super-Mare and South Wales

Route Diagram - see first Page of Table 125

		GW		GW	GW	GW	GW	GW	GW	GW	GW	GW		GW	GW	GW	GW	GW	GW	GW	GW	GW		GW	GW
		◇1			◇1		◇1	◇1	◇1	◇1	◇1	◇1			◇1		◇1	◇1	◇1		◇1	◇1		◇1	
					A	B	C									B				B					
		☕			☕⊘		☕⊘	☕	☕	☕	☕	☕			☕		☕	☕	☕		☕	☕		☕	
London Paddington 15 ⊖	d	11 00			11 30		11 45	12 00	12 15	12 30	12 45	13 00			13 30		13 45	14 00	14 15		14 30	14 45		15 00	
Slough 3	d																								
Reading 7	d	11 27			11 57		12 12	12 27	12 42	12 57	13 14	13 27			13 57		14 12	14 27	14 42		14 57	15 12		15 27	
Didcot Parkway	d				12 12				12 56	13 12					14 12				14 56		15 12				
Swindon	a	11 54			12 30		12 39	12 54	13 15	13 30	13 41	13 55			14 30		14 41	14 54	15 15		15 30	15 39		15 54	
	d	11 55		12 14	12 30	12 36	12 41	12 55	13 15	13 30	13 41	13 55		14 14	14 30	14 36	14 41	14 55	15 15	15 22	15 30	15 39		15 55	16 14
Kemble	d			12 28					13 31					14 28					15 31						16 28
Stroud	d			12 43					13 46					14 43					15 46						16 43
Stonehouse	d			12 48					13 51					14 48					15 51						16 48
Gloucester 7	a			13 03					14 06					15 03					16 06						17 03
Cheltenham Spa	a			13 24					14 22					15 25					16 22						17 25
Worcester Shrub Hill	a																								
Chippenham	d	12 09			12 44	12a52		13 09		13 44		14 09			14 44	14a52		15 09		15a38	15 44			16 09	
Bath Spa 7	a	12 24			12 59			13 24		14 00		14 24			15 00			15 24			16 00			16 24	
Bristol Parkway 7	a						13 06				14 06						15 06					16 05			
	d						13 08				14 08						15 08					16 08			
Bristol Temple Meads 10	a	12 39			13 14			13 42		14 15		14 39			15 15			15 41			16 15			16 39	
Weston-super-Mare	a																								
Newport (South Wales)	a						13 31				14 31						15 31					16 30			
Cardiff Central 7	a						13 47				14 46						15 45					16 46			
Bridgend	a						14 09				15 09						16 09					17 09			
Port Talbot Parkway	a						14 22				15 22						16 22					17 22			
Neath	a						14 30				15 30						16 30					17 30			
Swansea	a						14 43				15 43						16 43					17 43			

		GW	GW	GW	GW	GW	GW	GW		GW	GW	GW	GW	GW	GW	GW	GW	GW		GW	GW	GW	GW	GW	GW
		◇1	◇1	◇1	◇1	◇1		◇1		◇1		◇1	◇1	◇1	◇1	◇1		◇1		◇1		◇1	◇1	◇1	◇1
						D	B						E			F	B			F					
		☕	☕	☕	☕	☕		☕		☕		☕	☕	☕	☕	☕		☕		☕		☕	☕	☕	☕
London Paddington 15 ⊖	d	15 30	15 45	16 00	16 15	16 30		16 45		17 00		17 30	17 45	18 00	18 15	18 30		18 45		19 00		19 15	19 30	19 45	20 00
Slough 3	d																								
Reading 7	d	15 57	16 12	16 27	16 42	16 57		17 12		17 27		17 57	18 12	18 27	18 42	18 57		19 12		19 27		19 42	19 57	20 12	20 27
Didcot Parkway	d	16 12			16 56	17 12						18 12			18 56	19 12						19 56	20 12		20 42
Swindon	a	16 30	16 41	16 54	17 15	17 30		17 40		17 54		18 30	18 40	18 54	19 15	19 30		19 39		19 54		20 14	20 30	20 40	21 00
	d	16 30	16 41	16 55	17 15	17 30	17 36	17 40		17 55	18 14	18 30	18 40	18 55	19 15	19 30	19 36	19 39		19 55	20 00	20 14	20 30	20 40	21 00
Kemble	d				17 31						18 28				19 31						20 15				
Stroud	d				17 46						18 43				19 46						20 30				
Stonehouse	d				17 51						18 48				19 51						20 35				
Gloucester 7	a				18 06						19 03				20 06						20 50				
Cheltenham Spa	a				18 22						19 25				20 22						21 03				
Worcester Shrub Hill	a																								
Chippenham	d	16 44		17 09		17 44	17a52			18 09		18 44		19 09		19 44	19a52			20 09			20 45		21 14
Bath Spa 7	a	17 00		17 24		18 00				18 24		19 00		19 24		20 00				20 24			21 00		21 30
Bristol Parkway 7	a		17 06					18 06					19 07					20 06				20 40		21 06	
	d		17 08					18 08					19 08					20 08				20 40		21 08	
Bristol Temple Meads 10	a	17 15		17 39		18 15				18 39		19 15		19 38		20 15				20 40			21 16		21 45
Weston-super-Mare	a					18 36						19 50				20 36				21 26					
Newport (South Wales)	a		17 29					18 30					19 30					20 30				21 03		21 31	
Cardiff Central 7	a		17 46					18 46					19 46					20 44				21 20		21 47	
Bridgend	a		18 09					19 09					20 09					21 09				21 46		22 09	
Port Talbot Parkway	a		18 22					19 22					20 22					21 22				21 59		22 23	
Neath	a		18 30					19 30					20 30					21 30				22 07		22 31	
Swansea	a		18 46					19 43					20 43					21 43				22 20		22 45	

A ☕ from Chippenham ⊘ to Chippenham
B To Westbury
C ☕ from Bridgend ⊘ to Bridgend
D To Paignton
E To Carmarthen
F To Taunton

For connections from Heathrow Airport, Gatwick Airport and Oxford please see Tables 125A, 148 and 116. For connections to Birmingham New Street and Hereford please see Tables 57 and 131

For other services between London and Worcester refer to table 126

Table 125

Saturdays
29 March to 17 May

London - Swindon, Cheltenham Spa, Bristol, Weston-super-Mare and South Wales

Route Diagram - see first Page of Table 125

		GW	GW	GW	GW	GW	GW	GW	GW	GW
			◇1	◇1	◇1	◇1		◇1	◇1	◇1
		A		B						
			☕	☕	☕	☕		☕	☕	☕
London Paddington [15] ⊖	d		20 15	20 30	20 45	21 30		22 00	22 35	23 30
Slough [3]	d									
Reading [7]	d		20 42	20 57	21 13	22 01		22 29	23 04	00 03
Didcot Parkway	d		20 56	21 12		22 16		22 48	23 29	00 19
Swindon	a		21 15	21 30	21 40	22 35		23 04	23 45	00 37
	d	21 08	21 15	21 30	21 42	22 36	22 40	23 05	23 46	00 38
Kemble	d		21 31				22 54			
Stroud	d		21 46				23 09			
Stonehouse	d		21 51				23 14			
Gloucester [7]	a		22 06				23 30			
Cheltenham Spa	a		22 21							
Worcester Shrub Hill	a									
Chippenham	d	21a24		21 44		22 51			00 01	00 53
Bath Spa [7]	a			22 00		23 06			00 17	01 07
Bristol Parkway [7]	a				22 06			23 31		
	d				22 11			23 33		
Bristol Temple Meads [10]	a			22 14		23 20			00 29	01 21
Weston-super-Mare	a			22s47						
Newport (South Wales)	a				22 46			00 01		
Cardiff Central [7]	a				23 07			00 21		
Bridgend	a				23 29					
Port Talbot Parkway	a				23 43					
Neath	a				23 51					
Swansea	a				00 05					

Sundays
8 December to 29 December

		GW	GW	GW	GW	GW	GW	GW	GW	GW
		◇1	◇1	◇1	◇1	◇1	◇1		◇1	
		C	D				E			F
		☕	☕	☕		☕	☕		☕	
London Paddington [15] ⊖	d		08 00	08 33		09 03	09 30		10 03	
Slough [3]	d									
Reading [7]	d	00 03	08 39	09 14		09 38	10 06		10 38	
Didcot Parkway	d	00 19	08 55	09 29		09 54	10 21		10 52	
Swindon	a	00 36	09 17	09 47		10 12	10 39		11 10	
	d	00 38	09 18	09 49	09 52	10 14	10 40	10 44	11 11	11 36
Kemble	d				10 05			10 58		
Stroud	d				10 21			11 13		
Stonehouse	d				10 26			11 18		
Gloucester [7]	a				10 41			11 33		
Cheltenham Spa	a				10 57			11 45		
Worcester Shrub Hill	a									
Chippenham	d	00 52	09 33			10 29			11 26	11a52
Bath Spa [7]	a	01 06	09 46			10 42			11 40	
Bristol Parkway [7]	a			10 14			11 07			
	d			10 15			11 09			
Bristol Temple Meads [10]	a	01 20	10 00			10 57			11 56	
Weston-super-Mare	a								12 31	
Newport (South Wales)	a			10 42			11 35			
Cardiff Central [7]	a			10 58			11 54			
Bridgend	a			11 20			12 17			
Port Talbot Parkway	a			11 33			12 30			
Neath	a			11 42			12 38			
Swansea	a			11 55			12 51			

		GW	GW	GW	GW	GW	GW	GW	GW	GW
		◇1		◇1		◇1	◇1	◇1	◇1	
						E			D	
		☕		☕		☕	☕	☕	☕	
London Paddington [15] ⊖	d	10 33		11 03		11 33	12 03	12 33	13 03	
Slough [3]	d									
Reading [7]	d	11 13		11 38		12 13	12 38	13 11	13 38	
Didcot Parkway	d	11 28		11 53		12 28	12 53	13 27	13 53	
Swindon	a	11 45		12 11		12 46	13 10	13 45	14 10	
	d	11 47	11 50	12 12	12 44	12 47	13 11	13 46	14 11	14 26
Kemble	d		12 04		12 58					14 41
Stroud	d		12 19		13 13					14 56
Stonehouse	d		12 24		13 18					15 01
Gloucester [7]	a		12 39		13 33					15 15
Cheltenham Spa	a		12 51		13 45					15 33
Worcester Shrub Hill	a									
Chippenham	d			12 27			13 27		14 26	
Bath Spa [7]	a			12 40			13 40		14 39	
Bristol Parkway [7]	a	12 12				13 13		14 12		
	d	12 13				13 14		14 13		
Bristol Temple Meads [10]	a			12 55			13 55		14 53	
Weston-super-Mare	a						14 28			
Newport (South Wales)	a	12 38				13 38		14 38		
Cardiff Central [7]	a	12 58				13 58		14 58		
Bridgend	a	13 19				14 17		15 20		
Port Talbot Parkway	a	13 32				14 32		15 32		
Neath	a	13 41				14 40		15 41		
Swansea	a	13 54				14 54		15 53		

		GW	GW	GW	GW
				R	
			◇1	1	◇1
		F	E		
			☕	☕	☕
London Paddington [15] ⊖	d		13 37	14 03	14 37
Slough [3]	d				
Reading [7]	d		14 13	14 38	15 13
Didcot Parkway	d		14 28	14 52	15 28
Swindon	a		14 45	15 10	15 45
	d	14 39	14 46	15 11	15 46
Kemble	d				
Stroud	d				
Stonehouse	d				
Gloucester [7]	a				
Cheltenham Spa	a				
Worcester Shrub Hill	a				
Chippenham	d	14a55		15 26	
Bath Spa [7]	a			15 40	
Bristol Parkway [7]	a		15 12		16 12
	d		15 13		16 13
Bristol Temple Meads [10]	a			15 55	
Weston-super-Mare	a				
Newport (South Wales)	a		15 40		16 38
Cardiff Central [7]	a		15 59		16 58
Bridgend	a		16 21		17 20
Port Talbot Parkway	a		16 33		17 32
Neath	a		16 42		17 41
Swansea	a		16 54		17 54

A From Cheltenham Spa to Westbury
B To Exeter St Davids
C not 8 December. From London Paddington
D To Plymouth
E To Carmarthen
F To Westbury

For connections from Heathrow Airport, Gatwick Airport and Oxford please see Tables 125A, 148 and 116. For connections to Birmingham New Street and Hereford please see Tables 57 and 131

For other services between London and Worcester refer to table 126

Table 125

Sundays

8 December to 29 December

London - Swindon, Cheltenham Spa, Bristol, Weston-super-Mare and South Wales

Route Diagram - see first Page of Table 125

		GW		GW	GW	GW	GW	GW	GW	GW	GW	GW		GW	GW	GW	GW	GW	GW	GW	GW	GW		GW	GW
				R 1	◇1	R 1		◇1	◇1	R 1				R 1	◇1	R 1	◇1	◇1		◇1		◇1		◇1	◇1
				A			B					B							B	C	D				
				☕	☕	☕		☕	☕	☕				☕	☕	☕	☕	☕		☕		☕		☕	☕
London Paddington 15 ⊖	d			15 03	15 37	16 03		16 27	16 37	17 03				17 30	17 37	18 03	18 30	18 37		19 03		19 30		19 37	20 03
Slough 3	d																								
Reading 7	d			15 38	16 13	16 38		17 03	17 13	17 38				18 04	18 14	18 38	19 03	19 13		19 38		20 05		20 14	20 34
Didcot Parkway	d			15 52	16 28	16 52			17 28	17 52					18 28	18 52		19 28		19 52				20 28	20 52
Swindon	a			16 10	16 45	17 10		17 32	17 45	18 10				18 37	18 45	19 10	19 34	19 45		20 10		20 34		20 45	21 10
	d	16 01		16 11	16 46	17 11	17 28	17 33	17 46	18 11	18 18	18 24		18 38	18 46	19 11	19 35	19 46	19 53	20 11	20 30	20 34		20 46	21 11
Kemble	d	16 16						17 47			18 32						19 49				20 45				
Stroud	d	16 31						18 02			18 46						20 04				21 00				
Stonehouse	d	16 36						18 08			18 51						20 09				21 04				
Gloucester 7	a	16 49						18 23			19 14						20 26				21 19				
Cheltenham Spa	a	17 03						18 44									20 45				21 33				
Worcester Shrub Hill	a																								
Chippenham	d			16 26		17 26	17a44			18 26		18a40		18 51		19 26			20a09	20 26		20 49			21 26
Bath Spa 7	a			16 40		17 40				18 40				19 06		19 40				20 39		21 01			21 40
Bristol Parkway 7	a				17 12				18 12						19 12			20 12						21 12	
	d				17 13				18 13						19 13			20 13						21 13	
Bristol Temple Meads 10	a			16 55		17 56				18 56				19 18		19 56				20 55		21 17			21 55
Weston-super-Mare	a			17 29										19 56						21 27					22 28
Newport (South Wales)	a				17 38				18 38						19 43			20 40						21 40	
Cardiff Central 7	a				17 58				18 58						20 02			20 59						22 01	
Bridgend	a				18 20				19 20						20 23			21 20						22 23	
Port Talbot Parkway	a				18 32				19 32						20 37			21 33						22 37	
Neath	a				18 41				19 41						20 45			21 41						22 45	
Swansea	a				18 58				19 58						20 58			21 55						22 58	

		GW	GW	GW	GW	GW	GW	GW		GW	GW
		◇1	◇1	◇1	◇1		◇1	◇1		◇1	◇1
		☕	☕	☕	☕		☕	☕		☕	☕
London Paddington 15 ⊖	d	20 30	20 37	21 03	21 37		22 03	22 37		23 03	23 37
Slough 3	d										23 54
Reading 7	d	21 03	21 14	21 38	22 18		22 46	23 15		23 45	00 16
Didcot Parkway	d		21 28	21 54	22 32		23 00	23s30		23s59	00s33
Swindon	a	21 32	21 45	22 15	22 51		23 18	23s51		00s19	00s53
	d	21 34	21 46	22 15	22 53	22 56	23 19				
Kemble	d	21 48				23 10					
Stroud	d	22 04				23 25					
Stonehouse	d	22 09				23 30					
Gloucester 7	a	22 24				23 45					
Cheltenham Spa	a	22 40				00 04					
Worcester Shrub Hill	a										
Chippenham	d			22 30			23 34			00s34	01s08
Bath Spa 7	a			22 44			23 48			00s49	01s23
Bristol Parkway 7	a		22 12		23 18			00s21			
	d		22 13		23 19						
Bristol Temple Meads 10	a			23 01			00 04	00 32		01 06	01 37
Weston-super-Mare	a										
Newport (South Wales)	a		22 40		23 43						
Cardiff Central 7	a		23 00		00 08						
Bridgend	a		23 22		00 31						
Port Talbot Parkway	a		23 36		00 43						
Neath	a		23 44		00 52						
Swansea	a		00 01		01 05						

A To Taunton
B To Westbury
C To Exeter St Davids
D From Westbury

For connections from Heathrow Airport, Gatwick Airport and Oxford please see Tables 125A, 148 and 116. For connections to Birmingham New Street and Hereford please see Tables 57 and 131

For other services between London and Worcester refer to table 126

Table 125

Sundays

5 January to 9 February

London - Swindon, Cheltenham Spa, Bristol, Weston-super-Mare and South Wales

Route Diagram - see first Page of Table 125

		GW	GW	GW	GW	GW	GW	GW	GW	GW	GW	GW	GW	GW	GW	GW	GW	GW	GW	GW	GW	GW	GW
		◇1	◇1	◇1	◇1	◇1	◇1	◇1		◇1			◇1	◇1		◇1	◇1	◇1	◇1			◇1	R 1
		A	A	B				C			D					C			B		D	C	
		☕	☕	☕	☕		☕	☕		☕			☕	☕		☕	☕	☕	☕			☕	☕
London Paddington 15 ⊖	d			08 00	08 33		09 03	09 30		10 03			10 33	11 03		11 33	12 03	12 33	13 03			13 33	14 03
Slough 3	d																						
Reading 7	d		00 05	08 39	09 14		09 38	10 06		10 38			11 13	11 38		12 13	12 38	13 11	13 38			14 13	14 38
Didcot Parkway	d		00 19	08 55	09 29		09 54	10 21		10 52			11 28	11 53		12 28	12 53	13 27	13 53			14 28	14 52
Swindon	a		00 36	09 12	09 47		10 11	10 39		11 10			11 45	12 11		12 46	13 11	13 45	14 10			14 45	15 10
	d		00 38	09 13	09 49	09 52	10 12	10 40	10 44	11 11	11 36	11 39	11 47	12 12	12 44	12 47	13 12	13 46	14 11	14 26	14 39	14 46	15 11
Kemble	d					10 05			10 58			11 54			12 58					14 41			
Stroud	d					10 21			11 13			12 09			13 13					14 56			
Stonehouse	d					10 26			11 18			12 14			13 18					15 01			
Gloucester 7	a					10 41			11 33			12 32			13 33					15 16			
Cheltenham Spa	a					10 57			11 45			12 44			13 45					15 33			
Worcester Shrub Hill	a																						
Chippenham	d	00 06	00 52	09 28			10 27			11 26	11a52			12 27			13 27		14 27		14a55		15 26
Bath Spa 7	a	00 23	01 06	09 41			10 40			11 40				12 40			13 40		14 40				15 40
Bristol Parkway 7	a				10 14			11 05					12 12			13 13		14 12				15 12	
	d				10 15			11 06					12 13			13 14		14 13				15 13	
Bristol Temple Meads 10	a	00 35	01 20	09 57			10 55			11 56				12 55			13 55		14 55				15 55
Weston-super-Mare	a									12 31							14 28						
Newport (South Wales)	a				10 42			11 32					12 38			13 38		14 38				15 40	
Cardiff Central 7	a				10 58			11 50					12 58			13 58		14 58				15 59	
Bridgend	a				11 20			12 13					13 19			14 17		15 20				16 21	
Port Talbot Parkway	a				11 33			12 26					13 32			14 32		15 32				16 33	
Neath	a				11 42			12 34					13 41			14 40		15 41				16 42	
Swansea	a				11 55			12 47					13 54			14 54		15 53				16 54	

		GW	GW	GW	GW	GW	GW	GW	GW	GW	GW	GW	GW	GW	GW	GW	GW	GW	GW	GW	GW	GW
		◇1		R 1	◇1	R 1		◇1	◇1	R 1			R 1	◇1	R 1	◇1	◇1		◇1		◇1	◇1
				E			D					D						D	F	G		
		☕		☕	☕	☕		☕	☕	☕			☕	☕	☕	☕	☕		☕		☕	☕
London Paddington 15 ⊖	d	14 33		15 03	15 33	16 03		16 27	16 33	17 03			17 30	17 33	18 03	18 30	18 33		19 03		19 30	19 33
Slough 3	d																					
Reading 7	d	15 13		15 38	16 13	16 38		17 03	17 13	17 38			18 04	18 14	18 38	19 03	19 14		19 38		20 05	20 14
Didcot Parkway	d	15 28		15 52	16 28	16 52			17 28	17 52				18 28	18 52		19 28		19 52			20 28
Swindon	a	15 45		16 10	16 45	17 10		17 32	17 45	18 10			18 37	18 45	19 10	19 34	19 45		20 10		20 34	20 45
	d	15 46	16 01	16 11	16 46	17 11	17 28	17 33	17 46	18 11	18 18	18 24	18 38	18 46	19 11	19 35	19 46	19 53	20 11	20 30	20 34	20 46
Kemble	d		16 16					17 47			18 32					19 49				20 45		
Stroud	d		16 31					18 02			18 46					20 04				21 00		
Stonehouse	d		16 36					18 08			18 51					20 10				21 04		
Gloucester 7	a		16 49					18 23			19 14					20 26				21 19		
Cheltenham Spa	a		17 03					18 44								20 45				21 33		
Worcester Shrub Hill	a																					
Chippenham	d			16 26		17 26	17a44			18 26		18a40	18 51		19 26			20a09	20 26		20 49	
Bath Spa 7	a			16 40		17 40				18 40			19 06		19 40				20 39		21 01	
Bristol Parkway 7	a	16 12			17 12				18 12					19 12			20 12					21 12
	d	16 13			17 13				18 13					19 13			20 13					21 13
Bristol Temple Meads 10	a			16 55		17 56				18 56			19 18		19 56				20 55		21 17	
Weston-super-Mare	a			17 29									19 56						21 28			
Newport (South Wales)	a	16 38			17 38				18 38					19 43			20 40					21 40
Cardiff Central 7	a	16 58			17 58				18 58					20 02			20 59					22 01
Bridgend	a	17 20			18 20				19 20					20 23			21 20					22 23
Port Talbot Parkway	a	17 32			18 32				19 32					20 37			21 33					22 37
Neath	a	17 41			18 41				19 41					20 45			21 41					22 45
Swansea	a	17 54			18 58				19 58					20 58			21 55					22 58

A From London Paddington
B To Plymouth
C To Carmarthen
D To Westbury
E To Taunton
F To Exeter St Davids
G From Westbury

For connections from Heathrow Airport, Gatwick Airport and Oxford please see Tables 125A, 148 and 116. For connections to Birmingham New Street and Hereford please see Tables 57 and 131

For other services between London and Worcester refer to table 126

Table 125

Sundays

5 January to 9 February

London - Swindon, Cheltenham Spa, Bristol, Weston-super-Mare and South Wales

Route Diagram - see first Page of Table 125

		GW	GW	GW	GW	GW	GW	GW	GW	GW	GW
		◇1	◇1	◇1	◇1	◇1		◇1	◇1	◇1	◇1
		☕	☕	☕	☕	☕		☕	☕	☕	☕
London Paddington 15 ⊖	d	20 03	20 30	20 33	21 03	21 33		22 03	22 37	23 03	23 37
Slough 3	d										23 57
Reading 7	d	20 38	21 07	21 14	21 38	22 09		22 45	23 15	23 45	00 16
Didcot Parkway	d	20 52		21 28	21 54	22 24		23 00	23s30	23s59	00s33
Swindon	a	21 10	21 34	21 45	22 15	22 44		23 18	23s51	00s19	00s50
	d	21 11	21 34	21 46	22 15	22 45	22 56	23 19			
Kemble	d		21 48				23 10				
Stroud	d		22 04				23 25				
Stonehouse	d		22 09				23 30				
Gloucester 7	a		22 24				23 45				
Cheltenham Spa	a		22 42				00 04				
Worcester Shrub Hill	a										
Chippenham	d	21 26			22 30			23 34		00s34	01s06
Bath Spa 7	a	21 40			22 44			23 48		00s49	01s20
Bristol Parkway 7	a			22 12		23 11			00s20		
	d			22 13		23 12					
Bristol Temple Meads 10	a	21 55			23 01			00 04	00 32	01 04	01 36
Weston-super-Mare	a	22 28									
Newport (South Wales)	a			22 40		23 40					
Cardiff Central 7	a			23 00		00 05					
Bridgend	a			23 22		00 27					
Port Talbot Parkway	a			23 36		00 39					
Neath	a			23 44		00 47					
Swansea	a			00 01		01 02					

Sundays

16 February to 23 March

		GW	GW	GW	GW	GW	GW	GW	GW	GW	GW	GW	GW	GW	GW	GW	GW	GW	GW	GW	GW	GW	GW
																							R
		◇1	◇1	◇1	◇1	◇1	◇1	◇1		◇1		◇1		◇1		◇1	◇1	◇1	◇1			◇1	1
		A	A	B				C			D					C			B		D	C	
		☕	☕	☕	☕		☕	☕		☕		☕		☕		☕	☕	☕	☕			☕	☕
London Paddington 15 ⊖	d			08 00	08 33		09 03	09 30		10 03		10 33		11 03		11 33	12 03	12 33	13 03			13 33	14 03
Slough 3	d																						
Reading 7	d		00 03	08 39	09 14		09 38	10 06		10 38		11 13		11 38		12 10	12 38	13 11	13 38			14 09	14 38
Didcot Parkway	d		00 19	08 55	09 29		09 54	10 21		10 52		11 28		11 53		12 28	12 57	13 27	13 57			14 28	14 57
Swindon	a		00 37	09 12	09 47		10 12	10 39		11 10		11 45		12 11		12 46	13 14	13 45	14 14			14 45	15 15
	d		00 38	09 12	09 49	09 54	10 14	10 40	10 46	11 11	11 36	11 47	11 50	12 12	12 44	12 47	13 15	13 46	14 15	14 26	14 39	14 46	15 15
Kemble	d					10 07			11 00				12 04		12 58					14 41			
Stroud	d					10 23			11 15				12 19		13 13					14 56			
Stonehouse	d					10 28			11 20				12 24		13 18					15 01			
Gloucester 7	a					10 43			11 35				12 39		13 33					15 16			
Cheltenham Spa	a					10 59			11 46				12 51		13 45					15 33			
Worcester Shrub Hill	a																						
Chippenham	d	00 01	00 53	09 28			10 29			11 26	11a52			12 27			13 30		14 30		14a55		15 31
Bath Spa 7	a	00 17	01 07	09 41			10 42			11 40				12 40			13 43		14 43				15 45
Bristol Parkway 7	a				10 14			11 07				12 13				13 13		14 12				15 12	
	d				10 15			11 09				12 14				13 14		14 13				15 13	
Bristol Temple Meads 10	a	00 29	01 21	09 57			10 58			12 00				12 58			13 58		14 58				15 59
Weston-super-Mare	a									12 31							14 31						
Newport (South Wales)	a				10 42			11 35				12 41				13 38		14 38				15 40	
Cardiff Central 7	a				11 00			11 54				13 00				13 58		14 58				15 59	
Bridgend	a				11 23			12 17				13 22				14 17		15 20				16 21	
Port Talbot Parkway	a				11 36			12 30				13 35				14 32		15 32				16 33	
Neath	a				11 44			12 38				13 44				14 40		15 41				16 42	
Swansea	a				11 58			12 51				13 57				14 54		15 53				16 54	

A From London Paddington
B To Exeter St Davids
C To Carmarthen
D To Westbury

For connections from Heathrow Airport, Gatwick Airport and Oxford please see Tables 125A, 148 and 116. For connections to Birmingham New Street and Hereford please see Tables 57 and 131

For other services between London and Worcester refer to table 126

Table 125

Sundays

16 February to 23 March

London - Swindon, Cheltenham Spa, Bristol, Weston-super-Mare and South Wales

Route Diagram - see first Page of Table 125

		GW	GW	GW	GW	GW	GW	GW	GW	GW	GW	GW	GW	GW	GW	GW	GW	GW	GW	GW	GW	GW
		◇1		R 1	◇1	R 1		◇1	◇1	R 1			R 1	◇1	R 1	◇1	◇1		◇1		◇1	◇1
				A			B					B						B	C	D		
		☕		☕	☕	☕		☕	☕	☕			☕	☕	☕	☕	☕		☕		☕	☕
London Paddington 15 ⊖	d	14 33		15 03	15 33	16 03		16 27	16 33	17 03			17 27	17 33	18 00	18 27	18 33		19 03		19 27	19 33
Slough 3	d																					
Reading 7	d	15 09		15 38	16 09	16 38		17 03	17 09	17 38			18 04	18 09	18 37	19 03	19 09		19 38		20 03	20 09
Didcot Parkway	d	15 28		15 57	16 28	16 57			17 28	17 57				18 28	18 52		19 27		19 57			20 28
Swindon	a	15 45		16 15	16 45	17 15		17 34	17 45	18 15			18 37	18 45	19 10	19 40	19 45		20 14		20 34	20 45
	d	15 46	16 01	16 15	16 46	17 15	17 28	17 36	17 46	18 15	18 18	18 24	18 38	18 46	19 11	19 42	19 46	19 53	20 16	20 30	20 34	20 46
Kemble	d		16 16					17 49			18 32					19 55				20 45		
Stroud	d		16 31					18 05			18 46					20 11				21 00		
Stonehouse	d		16 36					18 10			18 51					20 15				21 04		
Gloucester 7	a		16 49					18 27			19 14					20 31				21 19		
Cheltenham Spa	a		17 03					18 44								20 49				21 33		
Worcester Shrub Hill	a																					
Chippenham	d			16 31		17 31	17a44			18 31		18a40	18 51		19 26			20a09	20 30		20 49	
Bath Spa 7	a			16 45		17 45				18 45			19 06		19 40				20 43		21 04	
Bristol Parkway 7	a	16 12			17 12				18 12					19 12			20 12					21 12
	d	16 13			17 13				18 13					19 13			20 13					21 13
Bristol Temple Meads 10	a			16 59		17 59				18 59			19 18		19 56				20 58		21 19	
Weston-super-Mare	a			17 31									19 56						21 31			
Newport (South Wales)	a	16 38			17 38				18 38					19 43			20 40					21 40
Cardiff Central 7	a	16 58			17 58				18 58					20 02			20 59					22 01
Bridgend	a	17 20			18 20				19 20					20 23			21 20					22 23
Port Talbot Parkway	a	17 32			18 32				19 32					20 37			21 33					22 37
Neath	a	17 41			18 41				19 41					20 45			21 41					22 45
Swansea	a	17 54			18 58				19 58					20 58			21 55					22 58

		GW	GW	GW	GW	GW	GW	GW	GW	GW	GW
		◇1	◇1	◇1	◇1	◇1		◇1	◇1	◇1	◇1
		☕	☕	☕	☕	☕		☕	☕	☕	☕
London Paddington 15 ⊖	d	20 03	20 27	20 33	21 03	21 37		22 03	22 37	23 03	23 37
Slough 3	d										23 57
Reading 7	d	20 38	21 03	21 11	21 38	22 15		22 46	23 15	23 45	00 16
Didcot Parkway	d	20 57		21 28	21 54	22 29		23 00	23s30	23s59	00s33
Swindon	a	21 14	21 34	21 49	22 15	22 49		23 18	23s51	00s19	00s50
	d	21 16	21 35	21 50	22 15	22 50	22 56	23 19			
Kemble	d		21 48				23 10				
Stroud	d		22 04				23 25				
Stonehouse	d		22 09				23 30				
Gloucester 7	a		22 24				23 45				
Cheltenham Spa	a		22 42				00 04				
Worcester Shrub Hill	a										
Chippenham	d	21 30			22 30			23 34		00s34	01s06
Bath Spa 7	a	21 43			22 44			23 47		00s49	01s20
Bristol Parkway 7	a			22 16		23 15			00s20		
	d			22 17		23 16					
Bristol Temple Meads 10	a	21 59			23 01			00 04	00 32	01 04	01 36
Weston-super-Mare	a	22 34									
Newport (South Wales)	a			22 44		23 40					
Cardiff Central 7	a			23 04		00 05					
Bridgend	a			23 26		00 27					
Port Talbot Parkway	a			23 40		00 39					
Neath	a			23 48		00 47					
Swansea	a			00 05		01 02					

A To Taunton
B To Westbury
C To Exeter St Davids
D From Westbury

For connections from Heathrow Airport, Gatwick Airport and Oxford please see Tables 125A, 148 and 116. For connections to Birmingham New Street and Hereford please see Tables 57 and 131

For other services between London and Worcester refer to table 126

Table 125

Sundays

30 March to 11 May

London - Swindon, Cheltenham Spa, Bristol, Weston-super-Mare and South Wales

Route Diagram - see first Page of Table 125

		GW ◇1 A 🍴	GW ◇1 A 🍴	GW ◇1 B 🍴	GW ◇1 🍴	GW ◇1	GW ◇1 🍴	GW ◇1 C 🍴	GW	GW ◇1 🍴	GW D	GW ◇1 🍴	GW	GW ◇1 🍴	GW ◇1 C 🍴	GW	GW ◇1 🍴	GW ◇1 🍴	GW ◇1 B 🍴	GW	GW ◇1 C 🍴	GW D	GW R 1 🍴
London Paddington 15 ⊖	d			08 00	08 30		09 03	09 30		10 03		10 30		11 03	11 30		12 03	12 30	13 03		13 30		14 03
Slough 3	d																						
Reading 7	d		00 03	08 34	09 02		09 38	10 03		10 38		11 03		11 38	12 03		12 38	13 03	13 34		13 59		14 34
Didcot Parkway	d		00 19	08 52	09 20		09 54	10 22		10 54		11 22		11 54	12 22		12 54	13 22	13 54		14 18		14 54
Swindon	a		00 37	09 10	09 36		10 12	10 39		11 13		11 39		12 13	12 39		13 13	13 39	14 13		14 36		15 13
	d		00 38	09 11	09 38	09 52	10 14	10 40	10 45	11 13	11 36	11 47	11 50	12 13	12 40	12 44	13 13	13 40	14 13	14 26	14 37	14 42	15 13
Kemble	d					10 05			10 59				12 04			12 58				14 41			
Stroud	d					10 21			11 14				12 19			13 13				14 56			
Stonehouse	d					10 26			11 19				12 24			13 18				15 01			
Gloucester 7	a					10 41			11 34				12 39			13 33				15 15			
Cheltenham Spa	a					10 57			11 46				12 51			13 45				15 33			
Worcester Shrub Hill	a																						
Chippenham	d	00 01	00 53	09 26			10 29			11 28	11a52			12 28			13 28		14 28			14a58	15 28
Bath Spa 7	a	00 17	01 07	09 39			10 42			11 42				12 42			13 42		14 42				15 42
Bristol Parkway 7	a				10 02			11 07				12 14			13 07			14 07			15 02		
	d				10 04			11 08				12 14			13 08			14 08			15 03		
Bristol Temple Meads 10	a	00 29	01 21	09 53			10 57			11 58				12 58			14 00		14 58				15 59
Weston-super-Mare	a									12 31							14 30						
Newport (South Wales)	a				10 29			11 35				12 38			13 35			14 35			15 35		
Cardiff Central 7	a				10 46			11 54				12 58			13 56			14 53			15 56		
Bridgend	a				11 09			12 17				13 19			14 17			15 15			16 21		
Port Talbot Parkway	a				11 22			12 30				13 32			14 32			15 27			16 33		
Neath	a				11 31			12 38				13 41			14 40			15 36			16 42		
Swansea	a				11 44			12 51				13 54			14 52			15 48			16 54		

		GW ◇1 🍴	GW	GW R 1 E 🍴	GW ◇1 🍴	GW R 1 🍴	GW D	GW ◇1 🍴	GW ◇1 🍴	GW R 1 🍴	GW	GW D	GW R 1 🍴	GW ◇1 🍴	GW R 1 🍴	GW ◇1 🍴	GW ◇1 🍴	GW D	GW ◇1 F 🍴	GW G	GW ◇1 🍴	GW ◇1 🍴
London Paddington 15 ⊖	d	14 33		15 03	15 33	16 03		16 27	16 33	17 03			17 27	17 33	18 03	18 27	18 33		19 03		19 27	19 33
Slough 3	d																					
Reading 7	d	15 03		15 34	16 03	16 34		16 59	17 09	17 34			18 00	18 03	18 34	19 00	19 03		19 34		20 00	20 03
Didcot Parkway	d	15 22		15 54	16 22	16 54			17 28	17 54				18 22	18 54		19 22		19 54			20 22
Swindon	a	15 39		16 13	16 39	17 13		17 34	17 47	18 13			18 37	18 39	19 13	19 34	19 38		20 10		20 34	20 39
	d	15 40	16 01	16 13	16 40	17 13	17 28	17 36	17 48	18 13	18 18	18 24	18 38	18 40	19 13	19 36	19 45	19 53	20 11	20 30	20 34	20 40
Kemble	d		16 16					17 49			18 32					19 49				20 45		
Stroud	d		16 31					18 05			18 46					20 05				21 00		
Stonehouse	d		16 36					18 10			18 51					20 09				21 04		
Gloucester 7	a		16 49					18 27			19 14					20 25				21 19		
Cheltenham Spa	a		17 03					18 44								20 43				21 33		
Worcester Shrub Hill	a																					
Chippenham	d			16 28		17 28	17a44			18 28		18a40	18 51		19 28			20a09	20 26		20 49	
Bath Spa 7	a			16 42		17 42				18 42			19 06		19 42				20 40		21 01	
Bristol Parkway 7	a	16 07			17 06				18 14					19 07			20 13					21 07
	d	16 08			17 08				18 15					19 08			20 13					21 08
Bristol Temple Meads 10	a			16 55		17 59				18 56			19 20		19 56				20 54		21 17	
Weston-super-Mare	a			17 28									19 56						21 28			
Newport (South Wales)	a	16 35			17 38				18 38					19 35			20 40					21 35
Cardiff Central 7	a	16 53			17 58				18 58					19 52			20 59					21 56
Bridgend	a	17 18			18 20				19 20					20 14			21 20					22 18
Port Talbot Parkway	a	17 30			18 32				19 32					20 28			21 33					22 32
Neath	a	17 39			18 41				19 41					20 35			21 41					22 40
Swansea	a	17 52			18 58				19 58					20 49			21 55					22 53

A From London Paddington
B To Plymouth
C To Carmarthen
D To Westbury
E To Taunton
F To Exeter St Davids
G From Westbury

For connections from Heathrow Airport, Gatwick Airport and Oxford please see Tables 125A, 148 and 116. For connections to Birmingham New Street and Hereford please see Tables 57 and 131

For other services between London and Worcester refer to table 126

Table 125

Sundays

30 March to 11 May

London - Swindon, Cheltenham Spa, Bristol, Weston-super-Mare and South Wales

Route Diagram - see first Page of Table 125

		GW	GW	GW	GW	GW	GW		GW	GW	GW	GW
		◇1	◇1	◇1	◇1	◇1			◇1	◇1	◇1	◇1
London Paddington 15 ⊖	d	20 03	20 27	20 33	21 03	21 37			22 03	22 37	23 03	23 37
Slough 3	d											23 57
Reading 7	d	20 34	21 00	21 03	21 38	22 09			22 44	23 15	23 45	00 16
Didcot Parkway	d	20 54		21 22	21 54	22 24			23 00	23s28	23s59	00s33
Swindon	a	21 10	21 34	21 39	22 15	22 49			23 18	23s49	00s19	00s50
	d	21 11	21 34	21 40	22 15	22 50	22 56		23 19			
Kemble	d		21 48				23 10					
Stroud	d		22 04				23 25					
Stonehouse	d		22 09				23 30					
Gloucester 7	a		22 24				23 45					
Cheltenham Spa	a		22 42				00 04					
Worcester Shrub Hill	a											
Chippenham	d	21 26			22 30				23 34		00s34	01s06
Bath Spa 7	a	21 40			22 44				23 48		00s49	01s20
Bristol Parkway 7	a			22 07		23 15				00s19		
	d			22 08		23 16						
Bristol Temple Meads 10	a	21 55			23 01				00 04	00 32	01 04	01 36
Weston-super-Mare	a	22 28										
Newport (South Wales)	a			22 40		23 40						
Cardiff Central 7	a			23 00		00 05						
Bridgend	a			23 22		00 27						
Port Talbot Parkway	a			23 36		00 39						
Neath	a			23 44		00 47						
Swansea	a			00 01		01 02						

For connections from Heathrow Airport, Gatwick Airport and Oxford please see Tables 125A, 148 and 116. For connections to Birmingham New Street and Hereford please see Tables 57 and 131

For other services between London and Worcester refer to table 126

Table 125R

Mondays to Fridays

9 December to 20 December

South Wales, Weston-super-Mare, Bristol, Cheltenham Spa and Swindon - London

Route Diagram - see first Page of Table 125

Miles	Miles	Miles			GW	GW	GW	GW	GW	GW	GW	GW	GW	GW	GW	GW	GW	GW	GW	GW	GW	GW	GW
									R	R		R	R		R		R	R		R			
					◇1		◇1	◇1	1	1	◇1	◇1	1	◇1	◇1		1	◇1		◇1	◇1	◇1	◇1
						A						B			B	C	D	E	F	G		H	I
					☕		☕	☕	☕	☕	☕	☕	☕	☕	☕		⊘	☕		☕⊘	☕	☕	☕⊘
0	—	—	**Swansea**	d				03 57		04 58			05 27				05 58			06 28			06 58
9½	—	—	Neath	d				04 09		05 10			05 39				06 10			06 40			07 10
15	—	—	Port Talbot Parkway	d				04 17		05 18			05 47				06 18			06 48			07 18
27¼	—	—	Bridgend	d				04 29		05 31			06 00				06 31			07 01			07 31
47½	—	—	**Cardiff Central** 7	d				05 14		05 55			06 24				06 55			07 25			07 55
59¼	—	—	Newport (South Wales)	d				05 32		06 09			06 38				07 09			07 39			08 09
—	0	—	Weston-super-Mare	d											06 20			06 48				07 25	
—	19	—	**Bristol Temple Meads** 10	d	04 47		05 29		06 00			06 30			07 00			07 30				08 00	
81	—	—	Bristol Parkway 7	a				05 59		06 29			06 58				07 29			07 59			08 30
—	—	—		d	04u57			06 00		06 31			07 01				07 31			08 01			08 31
—	30½	—	Bath Spa 7	d			05 41		06 13			06 43			07 13			07 43				08 13	
—	43½	—	Chippenham	d			05 54		06 25			06 55			07 25	07 31		07 55	07 59			08 25	
—	—	—	Worcester Shrub Hill	d							05 21										07 08		
—	—	0	**Cheltenham Spa**	d							05 53			06 30							07 29		
—	—	6½	Gloucester 7	d		05 18					06 08			06 45							07 45		
—	—	15½	Stonehouse	d		05 32					06 23			06 59							07 58		
—	—	18	Stroud	d		05 37					06 29			07 05							08 04		
—	—	29¼	Kemble	d		05 51					06 43			07 19							08 19		
115½	60¼	43	**Swindon**	a	05 22	06 06	06 08	06 26	06 40	06 57	06 58	07 10	07 27	07 35	07 40	07 48	07 57	08 10	08 18	08 27	08 33	08 40	08 57
—	—	—		d	05 23		06 10	06 27	06 41	06 58	07 01	07 11	07 28	07 35	07 41		07 58	08 11		08 28	08 35	08 41	08 59
139½	84¼	67	Didcot Parkway	a	05 41		06 27	06 45	06 58		07 19	07 28	07 45	07 53	08 01			08 28		08 45	08 52	08 58	
156¾	101½	84½	**Reading** 7	a	05 56		06 41	06 59	07 13	07 30	07 35	07 43	08 00	08 11	08 16			08 43		09 00	09 07	09 14	09 25
174¼	119	101¾	Slough 3	a			06 57																
192¾	137½	120¼	**London Paddington** 15 ⊖	a	06 24		07 16	07 32	07 44	08 02	08 07	08 14	08 33	08 40	08 45		08 54	09 14		09 29	09 40	09 44	09 58

		GW	GW	GW	GW	GW	GW	GW	GW	GW	GW	GW	GW	GW	GW	GW	GW	GW	GW	GW	GW	GW	GW
			◇1	◇1	◇1	◇1	◇1	◇1		◇1		◇1	◇1	◇1	◇1	◇1	◇1	◇1	◇1		◇1		◇1
		J	K	I						L	F	M										F	N
			☕	☕⊘	☕	☕	☕	☕		☕		☕	☕	☕	☕	☕	☕	☕	☕		☕		☕
Swansea	d			07 28			07 58			08 28					09 28						10 28		
Neath	d			07 40			08 10			08 40					09 40						10 40		
Port Talbot Parkway	d			07 48			08 18			08 48					09 48						10 48		
Bridgend	d			08 01			08 31			09 01					10 01						11 01		
Cardiff Central 7	d			08 25			08 55			09 25			09 55		10 25			10 55			11 25		
Newport (South Wales)	d			08 39			09 09			09 39			10 09		10 39			11 09			11 39		
Weston-super-Mare	d		07 49									09 29											
Bristol Temple Meads 10	d	08 12	08 30			09 00		09 30				10 00		10 30			11 00		11 30				12 00
Bristol Parkway 7	a			08 59			09 30			09 59			10 30		11 00			11 30			11 59		
	d			09 01			09 31			10 01			10 31		11 01			11 31			12 01		
Bath Spa 7	d	08 30	08 43			09 13		09 43				10 13		10 43			11 13		11 43				12 13
Chippenham	d	08 45	08 55			09 25		09 55			10 14	10 25		10 55			11 25		11 55			12 13	12 25
Worcester Shrub Hill	d																						
Cheltenham Spa	d				08 31				09 20							10 31				11 20			
Gloucester 7	d				08 46				09 33							10 46				11 33			
Stonehouse	d				09 00				09 47							11 00				11 47			
Stroud	d				09 07				09 52							11 07				11 52			
Kemble	d				09 21				10 07							11 21				12 07			
Swindon	a	09 04	09 10	09 27	09 35	09 40	09 57	10 10	10 24	10 27	10 34	10 40	10 57	11 10	11 27	11 35	11 40	11 57	12 10	12 24	12 27	12 36	12 40
	d		09 11	09 29	09 37	09 41	09 59	10 11		10 29		10 41	10 59	11 11	11 29	11 37	11 41	11 59	12 11		12 29		12 41
Didcot Parkway	a		09 28		09 54		10 16	10 28		10 46			11 16	11 28		11 54		12 16	12 28		12 46		
Reading 7	a		09 44	09 59	10 08	10 12	10 31	10 43		11 00		11 08	11 30	11 43	11 59	12 08	12 12	12 30	12 43		13 00		13 09
Slough 3	a																						
London Paddington 15 ⊖	a		10 15	10 32	10 37	10 42	11 07	11 14		11 33		11 38	12 02	12 14	12 33	12 37	12 44	13 00	13 14		13 33		13 38

A To Southampton Central
B ◇ from Reading R to Reading
C From Westbury to Cheltenham Spa
D The Capitals United
E The Bristolian. ◇ from Reading R to Reading
F From Westbury
G ☕ ◇ from Reading ⊘ R to Reading
H From Plymouth
I ☕ from Reading ⊘ to Reading
J From Gloucester
K From Taunton
L From Carmarthen. The Red Dragon
M From Paignton
N From Penzance

For connections from Hereford and Birmingham New Street please see Tables 131 and 57. For connections to Oxford, Gatwick Airport and Heathrow Airport please see Tables 116, 148 and 125A

For other services between London and Worcester refer to table 126

Table 125R

Mondays to Fridays

9 December to 20 December

South Wales, Weston-super-Mare, Bristol, Cheltenham Spa and Swindon - London

Route Diagram - see first Page of Table 125

		GW	GW	GW	GW	GW	GW	GW	GW	GW		GW	GW	GW	GW	GW	GW	GW	GW	GW		GW	GW	GW	GW
		◇1	◇1	◇1	◇1	◇1	◇1	◇1		◇1		◇1	◇1		◇1	◇1	◇1	◇1	◇1	◇1			◇1	◇1	◇1
				A						B				C			D							E	
		☕	☕	☕	☕	☕	☕	☕		☕⊘		☕	☕		☕	☕	☕	☕	☕	☕			☕	☕	☕
Swansea	d			11 28						12 28						13 28							14 28		
Neath	d			11 40						12 40						13 40							14 40		
Port Talbot Parkway	d			11 48						12 48						13 48							14 48		
Bridgend	d			12 01						13 01						14 01							15 01		
Cardiff Central 7	d	11 55		12 25			12 55			13 25			13 55			14 25			14 55				15 25		15 55
Newport (South Wales)	d	12 09		12 39			13 09			13 39			14 09			14 39			15 09				15 39		16 09
Weston-super-Mare	d																								
Bristol Temple Meads 10	d		12 30			13 00		13 30				14 00			14 30			15 00		15 30				16 00	
Bristol Parkway 7	a	12 30		12 59			13 30			13 59			14 30			15 00			15 30				15 59		16 30
	d	12 31		13 01			13 31			14 01			14 31			15 01			15 31				16 01		16 31
Bath Spa 7	d		12 43			13 13		13 43				14 13			14 43			15 13		15 43				16 13	
Chippenham	d		12 55			13 25		13 55				14 25		14 41	14 55			15 25		15 55				16 25	
Worcester Shrub Hill	d																								
Cheltenham Spa	d				12 20				13 20								14 20					15 20			
Gloucester 7	d				12 44				13 33								14 44					15 33			
Stonehouse	d				12 59				13 47								14 59					15 47			
Stroud	d				13 05				13 52								15 05					15 52			
Kemble	d				13 19				14 07								15 19					16 07			
Swindon	a	12 57	13 10	13 27	13 33	13 40	13 57	14 10	14 24	14 27		14 40	14 57	15 03	15 10	15 27	15 33	15 39	15 57	16 10		16 24	16 27	16 40	16 57
	d	12 59	13 11	13 29	13 35	13 41	13 59	14 11		14 29		14 41	14 59		15 11	15 29	15 35	15 41	15 59	16 11			16 29	16 41	16 59
Didcot Parkway	a	13 16	13 28		13 52		14 15	14 28		14 46			15 16		15 28		15 52		16 16	16 28			16 46		17 16
Reading 7	a	13 30	13 43	13 59	14 05	14 11	14 30	14 43		15 00		15 09	15 30		15 43	16 00	16 05	16 12	16 29	16 43			17 00	17 08	17 31
Slough 3	a																								
London Paddington 15 ⊖	a	14 06	14 14	14 33	14 37	14 40	15 08	15 14		15 33		15 44	16 08		16 14	16 32	16 39	16 44	17 09	17 14			17 30	17 38	18 02

		GW	GW	GW	GW	GW		GW	GW	GW	GW	GW	GW	GW	GW	GW		GW	GW	GW	GW	GW	GW	GW	GW
																								FO	FX
			◇1	◇1	◇1	◇1		◇1	◇1	◇1	◇1	◇	◇1	◇1		◇1		◇1	◇1	◇	◇1		◇1	◇1	◇1
		C								B		F			C					G					
			☕	☕	☕	☕		☕	☕	☕⊘	☕		☕	☕		☕		☕	☕		☕		☕	☕	☕
Swansea	d			15 28						16 28						17 28					18 28			19 29	19 29
Neath	d			15 40						16 40						17 40					18 40			19 40	19 40
Port Talbot Parkway	d			15 48						16 48						17 48					18 48			19 48	19 48
Bridgend	d			16 01						17 01						18 01					19 01			20 01	20 01
Cardiff Central 7	d			16 25				16 55		17 25			17 55			18 25					19 25			20 25	20 25
Newport (South Wales)	d			16 39				17 09		17 39			18 09			18 39					19 39			20 39	20 39
Weston-super-Mare	d								17 10					18 08											
Bristol Temple Meads 10	d		16 30			17 00			17 30		18 00			18 30					19 30				20 30		
Bristol Parkway 7	a			16 59				17 30		17 59			18 30			18 59					19 59			21 01	21 01
	d			17 01				17 31		18 01			18 31			19 01					20 01			21 01	21 01
Bath Spa 7	d		16 43			17 13			17 43		18 13			18 43					19 43				20 43		
Chippenham	d	16 42	16 55			17 25			17 55		18 25			18 55	19 00				19 55	20 01			20 55		
Worcester Shrub Hill	d																								
Cheltenham Spa	d				16 20							17 39						18 34				20 01			
Gloucester 7	d				16 43							17 54						18 49				20 12			
Stonehouse	d				16 58							18 07						19 05				20 25			
Stroud	d				17 04							18 12						19 11				20 30			
Kemble	d				17 19							18 27						19 25				20 46			
Swindon	a	17 03	17 10	17 27	17 33	17 40		17 57	18 10	18 27	18 40	18 44	18 57	19 10	19 23	19 27		19 39	20 10	20 21	20 27	21 04	21 10	21 29	21 29
	d		17 11	17 29	17 35	17 41		17 59	18 11	18 29	18 41		18 59	19 11		19 29		19 41	20 11		20 29		21 11	21 33	21 33
Didcot Parkway	a		17 28		17 52			18 16	18 28	18 46				19 28		19 46		19 58	20 28		20 46		21 28	21 52	21 52
Reading 7	a		17 43	18 00	18 06	18 12		18 30	18 45	19 01	19 10		19 25	19 44		20 00		20 14	20 44		21 00		21 43	22 11	22 11
Slough 3	a																								
London Paddington 15 ⊖	a		18 15	18 30	18 39	18 44		19 02	19 16	19 33	19 39		19 54	20 14		20 37		20 46	21 14		21 32		22 16	22 44	22 47

A The St. David
B ☕ from Reading ⊘ to Reading
C From Westbury
D The Cheltenham Spa Express
E The Merchant Venturer
F To Southampton Central
G From Westbury to Cheltenham Spa

For connections from Hereford and Birmingham New Street please see Tables 131 and 57. For connections to Oxford, Gatwick Airport and Heathrow Airport please see Tables 116, 148 and 125A

For other services between London and Worcester refer to table 126

Table 125R

Mondays to Fridays

9 December to 20 December

South Wales, Weston-super-Mare, Bristol, Cheltenham Spa and Swindon - London

Route Diagram - see first Page of Table 125

		GW	GW	GW	GW	GW	GW	GW		GW	GW	GW	GW	LM
			FO	FX	FX	FO	FX	FX		FO	FX	FO	FX	FO
			◇1	◇1	◇1	◇1					◇1	◇1		
					A	A					B	B		C
							🚌	🚌					🚌	
			☕	☕	☕	☕					☕	☕		
Swansea	d		20 28	20 28										
Neath	d		20 40	20 40										
Port Talbot Parkway	d		20 48	20 48										
Bridgend	d		21 01	21 01										
Cardiff Central 7	d		21 25	21 25										
Newport (South Wales)	d		21 39	21 39										
Weston-super-Mare	d										22 01	22 01		
Bristol Temple Meads 10	d				21 50	21 50					22 35	22 35		
Bristol Parkway 7	a		21 59	21 59										
	d		22 01	22 01										
Bath Spa 7	d				22 02	22 02					22 47	22 47		
Chippenham	d				22 15	22 15					23 00	23 00		
Worcester Shrub Hill	d													23 46
Cheltenham Spa	d	21 00								22 01				00 09
Gloucester 7	d	21 21					21 31	22 06		22 14			22 21	00a20
Stonehouse	d	21 33								22 28				
Stroud	d	21 39					22 01			22 33			22 51	
Kemble	d	21 54					22 31			22 46			23 21	
Swindon	a	22 09	22 27	22 27	22 33	22 33	23 06	23 06		23 05	23 14	23 14	23 56	
	d		22 28	22 28	22 34	22 34					23 16	23 16		
Didcot Parkway	a				22 50	22 50					23 33	23 33		
Reading 7	a		23 02	23 02	23 06	23 08					23 53	23 54		
Slough 3	a													
London Paddington 15 ⊖	a		23 40	23 41	23 44	23 42					00 33	00 33		

Mondays to Fridays

23 December to 16 May

		GW	GW	GW	GW	GW		GW		GW		GW	GW	GW	GW	GW	GW	GW	GW	GW		GW	GW	GW	GW
						R		R				R	R		R		R	R		R					
		◇1		◇1	◇1	1		1		◇1		◇1	1	◇1	◇1		1	◇1		◇1		◇1	◇1	◇1	
			D									G			G	H	I	J	K	L			M	N	O
		☕		☕	☕	☕		☕		☕		☕	☕	☕	☕		⊘	☕		☕⊘		☕	☕	☕⊘	
Swansea	d				03 57			04 58					05 27				05 58			06 28				06 58	
Neath	d				04 09			05 10					05 39				06 10			06 40				07 10	
Port Talbot Parkway	d				04 17			05 18					05 47				06 18			06 48				07 18	
Bridgend	d				04 29			05 31					06 00				06 31			07 01				07 31	
Cardiff Central 7	d				05 14			05 55					06 24				06 55			07 25				07 55	
Newport (South Wales)	d				05 32			06 09					06 38				07 09			07 39				08 09	
Weston-super-Mare	d														06 20			06 48					07 25		
Bristol Temple Meads 10	d	04 47		05 29		06 00						06 30			07 00			07 30					08 00		08 12
Bristol Parkway 7	a				05 59			06 29					06 58				07 29			07 59				08 30	
	d	04u57			06 00			06 31					07 01				07 31			08 01				08 31	
Bath Spa 7	d			05 41		06 13						06 43			07 13			07 43					08 13		08 30
Chippenham	d			05 54		06 25						06 55			07 25	07 31		07 55	07 59				08 25		08 45
Worcester Shrub Hill	d									05 21												07 08			
Cheltenham Spa	d									05 53				06 30								07 29			
Gloucester 7	d		05 18							06 08				06 45								07 45			
Stonehouse	d		05 32							06 23				06 59								07 58			
Stroud	d		05 37							06 29				07 05								08 04			
Kemble	d		05 51							06 43				07 19								08 19			
Swindon	a	05 22	06 06	06 08	06 26	06 40		06 57		06 58		07 10	07 27	07 35	07 40	07 48	07 57	08 10	08 18	08 27		08 33	08 40	08 57	09 04
	d	05 23		06 10	06 27	06 41		06 58		07 01		07 11	07 28	07 35	07 41		07 58	08 11		08 28		08 35	08 41	08 59	
Didcot Parkway	a	05 41		06 27	06 45	06 58				07 19		07 28	07 45	07 53	08 01			08 28		08 45		08 52	08 58		
Reading 7	a	05 56		06 41	06 59	07 13		07 30		07 35		07 43	08 00	08 11	08 16			08 43		09 00		09 07	09 14	09 25	
Slough 3	a			06 57																					
London Paddington 15 ⊖	a	06 24		07 16	07 32	07 44		08 02		08 07		08 14	08 33	08 40	08 45		08 54	09 14		09 29		09 40	09 44	09 58	

A From Penzance
B From Taunton
C From Birmingham New Street
D To Southampton Central
G ◇ from Reading R to Reading
H From Westbury to Cheltenham Spa
I The Capitals United
J The Bristolian. ◇ from Reading R to Reading
K From Westbury
L ☕ ◇ from Reading ⊘ R to Reading
M From Plymouth
N ☕ from Reading ⊘ to Reading
O From Gloucester

For connections from Hereford and Birmingham New Street please see Tables 131 and 57. For connections to Oxford, Gatwick Airport and Heathrow Airport please see Tables 116, 148 and 125A

For other services between London and Worcester refer to table 126

Table 125R

Mondays to Fridays

23 December to 16 May

South Wales, Weston-super-Mare, Bristol, Cheltenham Spa and Swindon - London

Route Diagram - see first Page of Table 125

		GW	GW	GW	GW	GW	GW	GW	GW	GW	GW	GW	GW	GW	GW	GW	GW	GW	GW	GW
		◇1	◇1	◇1	◇1	◇1	◇1		◇1		◇1	◇1	◇1	◇1	◇1	◇1	◇1	◇1		◇1
		A	B						F	G	H									
		☕	☕⊘	☕	☕	☕	☕		☕		☕	☕	☕	☕	☕	☕	☕	☕		☕
Swansea	d		07 28			07 58			08 28					09 28						10 28
Neath	d		07 40			08 10			08 40					09 40						10 40
Port Talbot Parkway	d		07 48			08 18			08 48					09 48						10 48
Bridgend	d		08 01			08 31			09 01					10 01						11 01
Cardiff Central 7	d		08 25			08 55			09 25			09 55		10 25			10 55			11 25
Newport (South Wales)	d		08 39			09 09			09 39			10 09		10 39			11 09			11 39
Weston-super-Mare	d	07 49									09 29									
Bristol Temple Meads 10	d	08 30			09 00		09 30				10 00		10 30			11 00		11 30		
Bristol Parkway 7	a		08 59			09 30			09 59			10 30		11 00			11 30			11 59
	d		09 01			09 31			10 01			10 31		11 01			11 31			12 01
Bath Spa 7	d	08 43			09 13		09 43				10 13		10 43			11 13		11 43		
Chippenham	d	08 55			09 25		09 55			10 14	10 25		10 55			11 25		11 55		
Worcester Shrub Hill	d																			
Cheltenham Spa	d			08 31				09 20							10 31				11 20	
Gloucester 7	d			08 46				09 33							10 46				11 33	
Stonehouse	d			09 00				09 47							11 00				11 47	
Stroud	d			09 07				09 52							11 07				11 52	
Kemble	d			09 21				10 07							11 21				12 07	
Swindon	a	09 10	09 27	09 35	09 40	09 57	10 10	10 24	10 27	10 34	10 40	10 57	11 10	11 27	11 35	11 40	11 57	12 10	12 24	12 27
	d	09 11	09 29	09 37	09 41	09 59	10 11		10 29		10 41	10 59	11 11	11 29	11 37	11 41	11 59	12 11		12 29
Didcot Parkway	a	09 28		09 54		10 16	10 28		10 46			11 16	11 28		11 54		12 16	12 28		12 46
Reading 7	a	09 44	09 59	10 08	10 12	10 31	10 43		11 00		11 08	11 30	11 43	11 59	12 08	12 12	12 30	12 43		13 00
Slough 3	a																			
London Paddington 15 ⊖	a	10 15	10 32	10 37	10 42	11 07	11 14		11 33		11 38	12 02	12 14	12 33	12 37	12 44	13 00	13 14		13 33

		GW	GW	GW	GW	GW	GW	GW	GW	GW	GW	GW	GW	GW	GW	GW	GW	GW	GW
			◇1	◇1	◇1	◇1	◇1	◇1	◇1	◇1		◇1	◇1	◇1		◇1	◇1	◇1	◇1
		G	I			K						B			G			M	
			☕	☕	☕	☕	☕	☕	☕	☕		☕⊘	☕	☕		☕	☕	☕	☕
Swansea	d					11 28						12 28					13 28		
Neath	d					11 40						12 40					13 40		
Port Talbot Parkway	d					11 48						12 48					13 48		
Bridgend	d					12 01						13 01					14 01		
Cardiff Central 7	d			11 55		12 25			12 55			13 25		13 55			14 25		
Newport (South Wales)	d			12 09		12 39			13 09			13 39		14 09			14 39		
Weston-super-Mare	d																		
Bristol Temple Meads 10	d		12 00		12 30			13 00		13 30			14 00			14 30			15 00
Bristol Parkway 7	a			12 30		12 59			13 30			13 59		14 30			15 00		
	d			12 31		13 01			13 31			14 01		14 31			15 01		
Bath Spa 7	d		12 13		12 43			13 13		13 43			14 13			14 43			15 13
Chippenham	d	12 13	12 25		12 55			13 25		13 55			14 25		14 41	14 55			15 25
Worcester Shrub Hill	d																		
Cheltenham Spa	d						12 20				13 20							14 20	
Gloucester 7	d						12 44				13 33							14 44	
Stonehouse	d						12 59				13 47							14 59	
Stroud	d						13 05				13 52							15 05	
Kemble	d						13 19				14 07							15 19	
Swindon	a	12 36	12 40	12 57	13 10	13 27	13 33	13 40	13 57	14 10	14 24	14 27	14 40	14 57	15 03	15 10	15 27	15 33	15 39
	d		12 41	12 59	13 11	13 29	13 35	13 41	13 59	14 11		14 29	14 41	14 59		15 11	15 29	15 35	15 41
Didcot Parkway	a			13 16	13 28		13 52		14 15	14 28		14 46		15 16		15 28		15 52	
Reading 7	a		13 09	13 30	13 43	13 59	14 06	14 11	14 30	14 43		15 00	15 09	15 30		15 43	16 00	16 06	16 12
Slough 3	a																		
London Paddington 15 ⊖	a		13 38	14 06	14 14	14 33	14 37	14 40	15 08	15 14		15 33	15 44	16 08		16 14	16 32	16 39	16 44

A From Taunton
B ☕ from Reading ⊘ to Reading
F The Red Dragon
G From Westbury
H From Paignton
I From Penzance
K The St. David
M The Cheltenham Spa Express

For connections from Hereford and Birmingham New Street please see Tables 131 and 57. For connections to Oxford, Gatwick Airport and Heathrow Airport please see Tables 116, 148 and 125A

For other services between London and Worcester refer to table 126

Table 125R

Mondays to Fridays

23 December to 16 May

South Wales, Weston-super-Mare, Bristol, Cheltenham Spa and Swindon - London

Route Diagram - see first Page of Table 125

		GW	GW	GW	GW	GW	GW	GW	GW	GW	GW	GW	GW	GW	GW	GW	GW	GW	GW	GW	GW	GW
		◇1	◇1		◇1	◇1	◇1		◇1	◇1	◇1	◇1	◇1	◇1	◇1	◇1	◇1	◇1	◇1	◇	◇1	◇1
						C		D		A	B		A	B			E	F		G		A
		☕	☕		☕	☕	☕		☕	☕	☕	☕	☕	☕	☕	☕	☕⊘	☕⊘	☕		☕	☕
Swansea	d				14 28					15 28	15 28						16 28	16 28				
Neath	d				14 40					15 40	15 40						16 40	16 40				
Port Talbot Parkway	d				14 48					15 48	15 48						16 48	16 48				
Bridgend	d				15 01					16 01	16 01						17 01	17 01				
Cardiff Central 7	d	14 55			15 25		15 55			16 25	16 25				16 55		17 25	17 25			17 55	
Newport (South Wales)	d	15 09			15 39		16 09			16 39	16 39				17 09		17 39	17 39			18 09	
Weston-super-Mare	d															17 10						18 08
Bristol Temple Meads 10	d		15 30			16 00			16 30				17 00	17 00		17 30			18 00			18 30
Bristol Parkway 7	a	15 30			15 59		16 30			16 59	16 59				17 30		17 59	17 59			18 30	
	d	15 31			16 01		16 31			17 01	17 01				17 31		18 01	18 01			18 31	
Bath Spa 7	d		15 43			16 13			16 43				17 13	17 13		17 43			18 13			18 43
Chippenham	d		15 55			16 25		16 42	16 55				17 25	17 25		17 55			18 25			18 55
Worcester Shrub Hill	d																					
Cheltenham Spa	d			15 20								16 20								17 39		
Gloucester 7	d			15 33								16 43								17 54		
Stonehouse	d			15 47								16 58								18 07		
Stroud	d			15 52								17 04								18 12		
Kemble	d			16 07								17 19								18 27		
Swindon	a	15 57	16 10	16 24	16 27	16 40	16 57	17 03	17 10	17 27	17 27	17 33	17 40	17 40	17 57	18 10	18 27	18 27	18 40	18 44	18 57	19 10
	d	15 59	16 11		16 29	16 41	16 59		17 11	17 29	17 29	17 35	17 41	17 41	17 59	18 11	18 29	18 29	18 41		18 59	19 11
Didcot Parkway	a	16 16	16 28		16 46		17 16		17 28			17 52			18 16	18 28	18 46	18 46				19 28
Reading 7	a	16 29	16 43		17 00	17 08	17 31		17 43	17 58	18 00	18 06	18 10	18 12	18 30	18 45	18 59	19 01	19 10		19 25	19 43
Slough 3	a																					
London Paddington 15 ⊖	a	17 09	17 14		17 30	17 38	18 02		18 15	18 30	18 30	18 39	18 44	18 44	19 02	19 16	19 32	19 33	19 39		19 54	20 14

		GW	GW	GW	GW	GW	GW	GW	GW	GW	GW	GW	GW	GW	GW	GW	GW	GW	GW	GW	GW
											FO	FX		FO	FX	FX	FO				FO
		◇1		◇1	◇1	◇1	◇	◇1		◇1	◇1	◇1		◇1	◇1	◇1	◇1				◇1
		B	D				H									I	I	J	J	K	M
		☕		☕	☕	☕		☕		☕	☕	☕		☕	☕	☕	☕	🚌	🚌		☕
Swansea	d			17 28				18 28			19 29	19 29		20 28	20 28						
Neath	d			17 40				18 40			19 40	19 40		20 40	20 40						
Port Talbot Parkway	d			17 48				18 48			19 48	19 48		20 48	20 48						
Bridgend	d			18 01				19 01			20 01	20 01		21 01	21 01						
Cardiff Central 7	d			18 25				19 25			20 25	20 25		21 25	21 25						
Newport (South Wales)	d			18 39				19 39			20 39	20 39		21 39	21 39						
Weston-super-Mare	d	18 08																			22 01
Bristol Temple Meads 10	d	18 30				19 30				20 30						21 50	21 50				22 35
Bristol Parkway 7	a			18 59				19 59			21 01	21 01		21 59	21 59						
	d			19 01				20 01			21 01	21 01		22 01	22 01						
Bath Spa 7	d	18 43				19 43				20 43						22 02	22 02				22 47
Chippenham	d	18 55	19 00			19 55	20 01			20 55						22 15	22 15				23 00
Worcester Shrub Hill	d																				
Cheltenham Spa	d				18 34				20 01				21 00							22 01	
Gloucester 7	d				18 49				20 12				21 21					21 31	22 06	22 14	
Stonehouse	d				19 05				20 25				21 33							22 28	
Stroud	d				19 11				20 30				21 39					22 01		22 33	
Kemble	d				19 25				20 46				21 54					22 31		22 46	
Swindon	a	19 10	19 23	19 27	19 39	20 10	20 21	20 27	21 04	21 10	21 29	21 29	22 09	22 27	22 27	22 33	22 33	23 06	23 06	23 05	23 14
	d	19 11		19 29	19 41	20 11		20 29		21 11	21 33	21 33		22 28	22 28	22 34	22 34				23 16
Didcot Parkway	a	19 28		19 46	19 58	20 28		20 46		21 28	21 52	21 52				22 50	22 50				23 33
Reading 7	a	19 44		20 00	20 14	20 44		21 00		21 43	22 11	22 11		23 02	23 02	23 06	23 08				23 54
Slough 3	a																				
London Paddington 15 ⊖	a	20 14		20 37	20 46	21 14		21 32		22 16	22 44	22 47		23 40	23 41	23 44	23 42				00 33

A from 10 March
B until 7 March
C The Merchant Venturer
D From Westbury
E from 10 March. ☕ from Reading ⊘ to Reading
F until 7 March. ☕ from Reading ⊘ to Reading
G To Southampton Central
H From Westbury to Cheltenham Spa
I From Penzance
J until 26 December
K from 27 December
M From Taunton

For connections from Hereford and Birmingham New Street please see Tables 131 and 57. For connections to Oxford, Gatwick Airport and Heathrow Airport please see Tables 116, 148 and 125A

For other services between London and Worcester refer to table 126

Table 125R

South Wales, Weston-super-Mare, Bristol, Cheltenham Spa and Swindon - London

Mondays to Fridays

23 December to 16 May

Route Diagram - see first Page of Table 125

		GW FO ◇1 A 🛒	GW C 🚌	LM FO D
Swansea	d			
Neath	d			
Port Talbot Parkway	d			
Bridgend	d			
Cardiff Central 7	d			
Newport (South Wales)	d			
Weston-super-Mare	d	22 01		
Bristol Temple Meads 10	d	22 35		
Bristol Parkway 7	a			
	d			
Bath Spa 7	d	22 47		
Chippenham	d	23 00		
Worcester Shrub Hill	d			23 46
Cheltenham Spa	d			00 09
Gloucester 7	d		22 21	00a20
Stonehouse	d			
Stroud	d		22 51	
Kemble	d		23 21	
Swindon	a	23 14	23 56	
	d	23 16		
Didcot Parkway	a	23 35		
Reading 7	a	23 54		
Slough 3	a			
London Paddington 15 ⊖	a	00 33		

Saturdays

14 December to 28 December

		LM D	GW ◇1 🛒	GW	GW ◇1 🛒	GW ◇1 🛒	GW ◇1 🛒	GW ◇1 🛒	GW ◇1 🛒	GW ◇1 🛒	GW ◇1 🛒	GW E	GW ◇1 🛒	GW ◇1 🛒	GW ◇1 F 🛒	GW ◇1 G 🛒Ø	GW E	GW ◇1 🛒	GW ◇1 G 🛒Ø	GW ◇1 H 🛒	GW ◇1 🛒	GW ◇1 🛒	GW ◇1 🛒
Swansea	d				03 58	04 58		05 28		05 58			06 28			06 58			07 28		07 58		
Neath	d				04 10	05 10		05 40		06 10			06 40			07 10			07 40		08 10		
Port Talbot Parkway	d				04 18	05 18		05 48		06 18			06 48			07 18			07 48		08 18		
Bridgend	d				04 30	05 31		06 01		06 31			07 01			07 31			08 01		08 31		
Cardiff Central 7	d				04 55	05 55		06 25		06 55			07 25			07 55			08 25		08 55		
Newport (South Wales)	d				05 09	06 09		06 39		07 09			07 39			08 09			08 39		09 09		
Weston-super-Mare	d								06 24						07 24					08 30			
Bristol Temple Meads 10	d		05 30		06 00		06 30		07 00		07 30				08 00			08 30		09 00			09 30
Bristol Parkway 7	a					06 29		06 59		07 29			07 59			08 30			08 59		09 30		
	d					06 31		07 01		07 31			08 01			08 31			09 01		09 31		
Bath Spa 7	d		05 43		06 13		06 43		07 13		07 43				08 13			08 43		09 13			09 43
Chippenham	d		05 55		06 25		06 55		07 25		07 55	08 00			08 25		08 48	08 55		09 25			09 55
Worcester Shrub Hill	d																					08 36	
Cheltenham Spa	d	00 09		05 30										07 30								08 59	
Gloucester 7	d	00a20		05 42										07 46								09 14	
Stonehouse	d			05 56										07 59								09 29	
Stroud	d			06 01										08 04								09 34	
Kemble	d			06 16										08 19								09 49	
Swindon	a		06 09	06 32	06 40	06 57	07 09	07 27	07 40	07 57	08 09	08 20	08 27	08 35	08 40	08 58	09 06	09 09	09 27	09 40	09 56	10 03	10 10
	d		06 11		06 41	06 59	07 11	07 29	07 41	07 59	08 11		08 29	08 36	08 41	08 59		09 11	09 29	09 41	09 59	10 04	10 11
Didcot Parkway	a		06 28		06 58	07 16	07 28	07 46	07 59	08 16	08 28		08 46	08 52	08 59	09 16		09 28	09 46		10 16	10 21	10 28
Reading 7	a		06 43		07 14	07 31	07 44	08 00	08 15	08 33	08 44		09 01	09 08	09 14	09 31		09 47	10 00	10 11	10 30	10 34	10 46
Slough 3	a																						
London Paddington 15 ⊖	a		07 14		07 44	08 07	08 14	08 32	08 44	09 02	09 14		09 38	09 41	09 44	10 02		10 15	10 32	10 39	11 04	11 08	11 14

A From Taunton
C until 26 December
D From Birmingham New Street
E From Westbury
F From Taunton
G 🛒 from Reading Ø to Reading
H From Exeter St Davids

For connections from Hereford and Birmingham New Street please see Tables 131 and 57. For connections to Oxford, Gatwick Airport and Heathrow Airport please see Tables 116, 148 and 125A

For other services between London and Worcester refer to table 126

Table 125R

Saturdays

14 December to 28 December

South Wales, Weston-super-Mare, Bristol, Cheltenham Spa and Swindon - London

Route Diagram - see first Page of Table 125

		GW	GW	GW	GW	GW	GW	GW	GW	GW	GW	GW	GW	GW	GW	GW	GW	GW	GW	GW	GW	GW
			◇1	◇1		◇1	◇1	◇1	◇1	◇1		◇1	◇1		◇1	◇1	◇1	◇1	◇1		◇1	◇1
		A								B	A	C								A		
			☕	☕		☕	☕	☕	☕	☕		☕	☕		☕	☕	☕	☕	☕		☕	☕
Swansea	d		08 28				09 28					10 28				11 28					12 28	
Neath	d		08 40				09 40					10 40				11 40					12 40	
Port Talbot Parkway	d		08 48				09 48					10 48				11 48					12 48	
Bridgend	d		09 01				10 01					11 01				12 01					13 01	
Cardiff Central 7	d		09 25				10 25					11 25				12 25					13 25	
Newport (South Wales)	d		09 39				10 39					11 39				12 39					13 39	
Weston-super-Mare	d																					
Bristol Temple Meads 10	d			10 00		10 30		11 00		11 30			12 00		12 30		13 00		13 30			14 00
Bristol Parkway 7	a		09 59				10 59					11 59				12 59					13 59	
	d		10 01				11 01					12 01				13 01					14 01	
Bath Spa 7	d			10 13		10 43		11 13		11 43			12 13		12 43		13 13		13 43			14 13
Chippenham	d	10 00		10 25		10 55		11 25		11 55	12 00		12 25		12 55		13 25		13 55	14 00		14 25
Worcester Shrub Hill	d																					
Cheltenham Spa	d				10 01				11 00					12 01				13 00				
Gloucester 7	d				10 13				11 15					12 13				13 15				
Stonehouse	d				10 27				11 29					12 27				13 30				
Stroud	d				10 32				11 35					12 32				13 36				
Kemble	d				10 47				11 49					12 47				13 50				
Swindon	a	10 20	10 28	10 39	11 04	11 10	11 27	11 39	12 03	12 09	12 20	12 27	12 40	13 04	13 09	13 27	13 39	14 04	14 10	14 20	14 27	14 39
	d		10 29	10 41		11 11	11 29	11 41	12 05	12 11		12 29	12 41		13 11	13 29	13 41	14 06	14 11		14 29	14 41
Didcot Parkway	a		10 47			11 28	11 46		12 22	12 28		12 46			13 28	13 46		14 23	14 28		14 46	
Reading 7	a		11 01	11 12		11 43	12 01	12 11	12 38	12 45		13 01	13 11		13 44	14 00	14 12	14 39	14 45		15 02	15 10
Slough 3	a																					
London Paddington 15 ⊖	a		11 33	11 40		12 14	12 37	12 41	13 06	13 15		13 38	13 42		14 14	14 32	14 39	15 09	15 14		15 37	15 41

		GW	GW	GW	GW	GW	GW	GW	GW	GW	GW	GW	GW	GW	GW	GW	GW	GW	GW	GW	GW	GW	GW
			◇1	◇1	◇1		◇1	◇1	◇1	◇1		◇1		◇1	◇1	◇1	◇1	◇1	◇1		◇1		◇1
						A							A									A	
			☕	☕	☕		☕	☕	☕	☕		☕		☕	☕	☕	☕	☕	☕		☕		☕
Swansea	d			13 28					14 28					15 28				16 28					17 28
Neath	d			13 40					14 40					15 40				16 40					17 40
Port Talbot Parkway	d			13 48					14 48					15 48				16 48					17 48
Bridgend	d			14 01					15 01					16 01				17 01					18 01
Cardiff Central 7	d			14 25					15 25					16 25				17 25					18 25
Newport (South Wales)	d			14 39					15 39					16 39				17 39					18 39
Weston-super-Mare	d																						
Bristol Temple Meads 10	d		14 30		15 00			15 30		16 00		16 30			17 00		17 30		18 00		18 30		
Bristol Parkway 7	a			14 59					15 59					16 59				17 59					18 59
	d			15 01					16 01					17 01				18 01					19 01
Bath Spa 7	d		14 43		15 13			15 43		16 13		16 43			17 13		17 43		18 13		18 43		
Chippenham	d		14 55		15 25	15 30		15 55		16 25		16 55	17 00		17 25		17 55		18 25		18 55	19 00	
Worcester Shrub Hill	d																						
Cheltenham Spa	d	14 01					15 00				16 01					17 00				18 01			
Gloucester 7	d	14 13					15 15				16 13					17 15				18 13			
Stonehouse	d	14 27					15 29				16 27					17 29				18 27			
Stroud	d	14 32					15 35				16 32					17 35				18 32			
Kemble	d	14 47					15 49				16 47					17 49				18 47			
Swindon	a	15 04	15 09	15 27	15 39	15 50	16 03	16 09	16 27	16 39	17 04	17 10	17 22	17 27	17 39	18 03	18 09	18 27	18 39	19 04	19 09	19 22	19 27
	d		15 11	15 29	15 41		16 05	16 11	16 29	16 41		17 11		17 29	17 41	18 05	18 11	18 29	18 41		19 11		19 29
Didcot Parkway	a		15 28	15 46			16 22	16 28	16 46			17 28		17 46		18 22	18 28	18 46			19 28		19 46
Reading 7	a		15 44	16 00	16 12		16 38	16 44	17 00	17 10		17 43		17 58	18 12	18 38	18 44	19 00	19 10		19 46		20 00
Slough 3	a																						
London Paddington 15 ⊖	a		16 14	16 33	16 39		17 07	17 14	17 32	17 38		18 14		18 32	18 40	19 08	19 13	19 32	19 39		20 14		20 32

A From Westbury **B** From Paignton **C** From Carmarthen

For connections from Hereford and Birmingham New Street please see Tables 131 and 57. For connections to Oxford, Gatwick Airport and Heathrow Airport please see Tables 116, 148 and 125A

For other services between London and Worcester refer to table 126

Table 125R

South Wales, Weston-super-Mare, Bristol, Cheltenham Spa and Swindon - London

Saturdays

14 December to 28 December

Route Diagram - see first Page of Table 125

		GW	GW	GW	GW	GW	GW	GW	GW	GW	GW
		◇1	◇1	◇1		◇1	◇1		◇1	◇1
					A				B	C
		☕	☕	☕		☕	☕		☕	☕
Swansea	d			18 28			19 28			
Neath	d			18 40			19 40			
Port Talbot Parkway	d			18 48			19 48			
Bridgend	d			19 01			20 01			
Cardiff Central 7	d			19 25			20 25			
Newport (South Wales)	d			19 39			20 39			
Weston-super-Mare	d					20 10				21 53
Bristol Temple Meads 10	d		19 30			20 33			21 47	22 30
Bristol Parkway 7	a			19 59			21 01			
	d			20 01			21 01			
Bath Spa 7	d		19 43			20 46			22 02	22 43
Chippenham	d		19 55			20 58			22 15	22 55
Worcester Shrub Hill	d									
Cheltenham Spa	d	19 00			20 01			21 20		
Gloucester 7	d	19 15			20 13			21 34		
Stonehouse	d	19 30			20 27			21 48		
Stroud	d	19 36			20 32			21 53		
Kemble	d	19 50			20 47			22 08		
Swindon	a	20 04	20 09	20 27	21 03	21 13	21 29	22 25	22 29	23 10
	d	20 06	20 11	20 29		21 14	21 29		22 31	23 11
Didcot Parkway	a	20 23	20 28	20 46		21 31	21 47		22 48	23 28
Reading 7	a	20 38	20 44	21 06		21 48	22 02		23 04	23 46
Slough 3	a									
London Paddington 15 ⊖	a	21 07	21 14	21 37		22 16	22 40		23 37	00 33

Saturdays

4 January to 8 February

		LM	GW	GW	GW	GW	GW	GW	GW	GW	GW	GW
			◇1		◇1	◇1	◇1	◇1	◇1	◇1	◇1	
		D										E
			☕		☕	☕	☕	☕	☕	☕	☕	
Swansea	d				03 58	04 58		05 28		05 58		
Neath	d				04 10	05 10		05 40		06 10		
Port Talbot Parkway	d				04 18	05 18		05 48		06 18		
Bridgend	d				04 30	05 31		06 01		06 31		
Cardiff Central 7	d				04 55	05 55		06 25		06 55		
Newport (South Wales)	d				05 09	06 09		06 39		07 09		
Weston-super-Mare	d								06 24			
Bristol Temple Meads 10	d		05 30		06 00		06 30		07 00		07 30	
Bristol Parkway 7	a					06 29		06 59		07 29		
	d					06 31		07 01		07 31		
Bath Spa 7	d		05 43		06 13		06 43		07 13		07 43	
Chippenham	d		05 55		06 25		06 55		07 25		07 55	08 00
Worcester Shrub Hill	d											
Cheltenham Spa	d	00 09		05 30								
Gloucester 7	d	00a20		05 42								
Stonehouse	d			05 56								
Stroud	d			06 01								
Kemble	d			06 16								
Swindon	a		06 09	06 32	06 40	06 57	07 09	07 27	07 40	07 57	08 09	08 20
	d		06 11		06 41	06 59	07 11	07 29	07 41	07 59	08 11	
Didcot Parkway	a		06 28		06 58	07 16	07 28	07 46	07 59	08 16	08 28	
Reading 7	a		06 43		07 14	07 31	07 44	08 00	08 15	08 36	08 44	
Slough 3	a											
London Paddington 15 ⊖	a		07 22		07 53	08 14	08 30	08 43	08 53	09 15	09 26	

		GW	GW	GW	GW	GW	GW	GW	GW	GW	GW	GW
		◇1	◇1	◇1	◇1		◇1	◇1	◇1	◇1	◇1	◇1
				C	F	E		F	G			
		☕	☕	☕	☕⊘		☕	☕⊘	☕	☕	☕	☕
Swansea	d	06 28			06 58			07 28		07 58		
Neath	d	06 40			07 10			07 40		08 10		
Port Talbot Parkway	d	06 48			07 18			07 48		08 18		
Bridgend	d	07 01			07 31			08 01		08 31		
Cardiff Central 7	d	07 25			07 55			08 25		08 55		
Newport (South Wales)	d	07 39			08 09			08 39		09 09		
Weston-super-Mare	d			07 24					08 30			
Bristol Temple Meads 10	d			08 00			08 30		09 00			09 30
Bristol Parkway 7	a	07 59			08 30			08 59		09 30		
	d	08 01			08 31			09 01		09 31		
Bath Spa 7	d			08 13			08 43		09 13			09 43
Chippenham	d			08 25		08 48	08 55		09 25			09 55
Worcester Shrub Hill	d										08 36	
Cheltenham Spa	d		07 30								08 59	
Gloucester 7	d		07 46								09 14	
Stonehouse	d		07 59								09 29	
Stroud	d		08 05								09 34	
Kemble	d		08 19								09 49	
Swindon	a	08 27	08 37	08 40	08 58	09 06	09 09	09 27	09 40	09 56	10 03	10 10
	d	08 29		08 41	08 59		09 11	09 29	09 41	09 59	10 04	10 11
Didcot Parkway	a	08 46		08 59	09 16		09 28	09 46		10 16	10 21	10 28
Reading 7	a	09 01		09 14	09 31		09 47	10 00	10 11	10 31	10 34	10 46
Slough 3	a											
London Paddington 15 ⊖	a	09 42		09 54	10 13		10 29	10 43	10 52	11 12	11 21	11 26

A To Westbury
B From Penzance
C From Taunton
D From Birmingham New Street
E From Westbury
F ☕ from Reading ⊘ to Reading
G From Exeter St Davids

For connections from Hereford and Birmingham New Street please see Tables 131 and 57. For connections to Oxford, Gatwick Airport and Heathrow Airport please see Tables 116, 148 and 125A

For other services between London and Worcester refer to table 126

Table 125R

Saturdays

4 January to 8 February

South Wales, Weston-super-Mare, Bristol, Cheltenham Spa and Swindon - London

Route Diagram - see first Page of Table 125

		GW		GW	GW	GW	GW	GW	GW	GW	GW	GW		GW	GW	GW	GW	GW	GW	GW	GW	GW		GW	GW
		◇1			◇1		◇1	◇1	◇1	◇1	◇1			◇1	◇1		◇1	◇1	◇1		◇1	◇1			◇1
				A							B	A		C										A	
		🍴			🍴		🍴	🍴	🍴	🍴	🍴			🍴	🍴		🍴	🍴	🍴		🍴	🍴			🍴
Swansea	d	08 28						09 28						10 28				11 28				12 28			
Neath	d	08 40						09 40						10 40				11 40				12 40			
Port Talbot Parkway	d	08 48						09 48						10 48				11 48				12 48			
Bridgend	d	09 01						10 01						11 01				12 01				13 01			
Cardiff Central 7	d	09 25						10 25						11 25				12 25				13 25			
Newport (South Wales)	d	09 39						10 39						11 39				12 39				13 39			
Weston-super-Mare	d																								
Bristol Temple Meads 10	d				10 00		10 30		11 00		11 30				12 00		12 30		13 00		13 30				14 00
Bristol Parkway 7	a	09 59						10 59						11 59				12 59				13 59			
	d	10 01						11 01						12 01				13 01				14 01			
Bath Spa 7	d				10 13		10 43		11 13		11 43				12 13		12 43		13 13		13 43				14 13
Chippenham	d			10 14	10 25		10 55		11 25		11 55	12 04			12 25		12 55		13 25		13 55			14 14	14 25
Worcester Shrub Hill	d																								
Cheltenham Spa	d					10 01				11 00						12 01				13 00					
Gloucester 7	d					10 13				11 15						12 13				13 13					
Stonehouse	d					10 27				11 29						12 27				13 26					
Stroud	d					10 32				11 35						12 32				13 31					
Kemble	d					10 47				11 49						12 47				13 46					
Swindon	a	10 28		10 34	10 39	11 04	11 10	11 27	11 39	12 04	12 09	12 24		12 27	12 40	13 04	13 09	13 27	13 39	14 02	14 10	14 27		14 34	14 39
	d	10 29			10 41		11 11	11 29	11 41		12 11			12 29	12 41		13 11	13 29	13 41		14 11	14 29			14 41
Didcot Parkway	a	10 47					11 28	11 46			12 28			12 46			13 28	13 46			14 28	14 46			
Reading 7	a	11 01			11 12		11 43	12 01	12 11		12 45			13 01	13 11		13 44	14 00	14 12		14 44	15 02			15 10
Slough 8	a																								
London Paddington 15 ⊖	a	11 43			11 53		12 26	12 43	12 53		13 26			13 42	13 53		14 26	14 42	14 53		15 26	15 42			15 53

		GW	GW	GW	GW	GW	GW	GW		GW	GW	GW	GW	GW	GW	GW	GW	GW		GW	GW	GW	GW	GW	GW
		1	◇1	◇1	◇1			◇1		◇1	◇1		◇1	◇1		◇1	◇1	◇1		◇1	◇1		◇1	◇1	
						A	D								A										A
			🍴	🍴	🍴			🍴		🍴	🍴		🍴	🍴		🍴	🍴	🍴		🍴	🍴		🍴	🍴	
Swansea	d			13 28						14 28				15 28						16 28				17 28	
Neath	d			13 40						14 40				15 40						16 40				17 40	
Port Talbot Parkway	d			13 48						14 48				15 48						16 48				17 48	
Bridgend	d			14 01						15 01				16 01						17 01				18 01	
Cardiff Central 7	d			14 25						15 25				16 25						17 25				18 25	
Newport (South Wales)	d			14 39						15 39				16 39						17 39				18 39	
Weston-super-Mare	d																								
Bristol Temple Meads 10	d		14 30		15 00			15 30			16 00		16 30			17 00		17 30			18 00		18 30		
Bristol Parkway 7	a			14 59						15 59				16 59						17 59				18 59	
	d			15 01						16 01				17 01						18 01				19 01	
Bath Spa 7	d		14 43		15 13			15 43			16 13		16 43			17 13		17 43			18 13		18 43		
Chippenham	d		14 55		15 25	15 30		15 55			16 25		16 55		17 14	17 25		17 55			18 25		18 55		19 14
Worcester Shrub Hill	d																								
Cheltenham Spa	d	14 01					15 00					16 01					17 00					18 01			
Gloucester 7	d	14 17					15 13					16 13					17 15					18 13			
Stonehouse	d	14 32					15 27					16 27					17 29					18 27			
Stroud	d	14 37					15 32					16 32					17 35					18 32			
Kemble	d	14 52					15 47					16 47					17 49					18 47			
Swindon	a	15 08	15 09	15 27	15 39	15 50	16 03	16 09		16 27	16 39	17 04	17 10	17 27	17 34	17 39	18 04	18 09		18 27	18 39	19 04	19 09	19 27	19 34
	d		15 11	15 29	15 41			16 11		16 29	16 41		17 11	17 29		17 41		18 11		18 29	18 41		19 11	19 29	
Didcot Parkway	a		15 28	15 46				16 28		16 46			17 28	17 46				18 28		18 46			19 28	19 46	
Reading 7	a		15 44	16 00	16 12			16 44		17 00	17 10		17 43	17 58		18 12		18 44		19 00	19 10		19 46	20 00	
Slough 8	a																								
London Paddington 15 ⊖	a		16 26	16 43	16 52			17 26		17 42	17 51		18 23	18 42		18 54		19 26		19 41	19 51		20 30	20 40	

A From Westbury
B From Paignton
C From Carmarthen
D To Westbury

For connections from Hereford and Birmingham New Street please see Tables 131 and 57. For connections to Oxford, Gatwick Airport and Heathrow Airport please see Tables 116, 148 and 125A

For other services between London and Worcester refer to table 126

Table 125R

Saturdays
4 January to 8 February

South Wales, Weston-super-Mare, Bristol, Cheltenham Spa and Swindon - London

Route Diagram - see first Page of Table 125

		GW	GW	GW	GW	GW	GW	GW	GW	GW
			◇1	◇1	1	◇1	◇1		◇1	◇1
									A	B
			🍴	🍴		🍴	🍴		🍴	🍴
Swansea	d			18 28			19 28			
Neath	d			18 40			19 40			
Port Talbot Parkway	d			18 48			19 48			
Bridgend	d			19 01			20 01			
Cardiff Central 7	d			19 25			20 25			
Newport (South Wales)	d			19 39			20 39			
Weston-super-Mare	d					20 10				21 53
Bristol Temple Meads 10	d		19 30			20 33			21 47	22 30
Bristol Parkway 7	a			19 59			21 01			
	d			20 01			21 01			
Bath Spa 7	d		19 43			20 46			22 02	22 43
Chippenham	d		19 55			20 58			22 15	22 55
Worcester Shrub Hill	d									
Cheltenham Spa	d	19 00			20 01			21 20		
Gloucester 7	d	19 12			20 17			21 34		
Stonehouse	d	19 26			20 30			21 48		
Stroud	d	19 31			20 36			21 53		
Kemble	d	19 46			20 50			22 08		
Swindon	a	20 02	20 09	20 27	21 06	21 13	21 29	22 25	22 29	23 10
	d		20 11	20 29		21 14	21 29		22 31	23 11
Didcot Parkway	a		20 28	20 46		21 31	21 47		22 48	23 28
Reading 7	a		20 44	21 06		21 48	22 02		23 11	23 53
Slough 3	a									
London Paddington 15 ⊖	a		21 25	21 51		22 26	22 45		23 53	00 36

Saturdays
15 February to 22 March

		LM	GW	GW	GW	GW	GW	GW	GW	GW	GW	GW	GW	GW	GW	GW	GW	GW	GW	GW	GW	GW	GW
			◇1		◇1	◇1	◇1	◇1	◇1	◇1	◇1		◇1	◇1	◇1	◇1		◇1	◇1	◇1	◇1	◇1	◇1
		C										D			B	E	D		E	F			
			🍴		🍴	🍴	🍴	🍴	🍴	🍴	🍴		🍴	🍴	🍴	🍴⊘		🍴	🍴⊘	🍴	🍴	🍴	🍴
Swansea	d				03 58	04 58		05 28		05 58			06 28			06 58			07 28		07 58		
Neath	d				04 10	05 10		05 40		06 10			06 40			07 10			07 40		08 10		
Port Talbot Parkway	d				04 18	05 18		05 48		06 18			06 48			07 18			07 48		08 18		
Bridgend	d				04 30	05 31		06 01		06 31			07 01			07 31			08 01		08 31		
Cardiff Central 7	d				04 55	05 55		06 25		06 55			07 25			07 55			08 25		08 55		
Newport (South Wales)	d				05 09	06 09		06 39		07 09			07 39			08 09			08 39		09 09		
Weston-super-Mare	d								06 24						07 24					08 30			
Bristol Temple Meads 10	d		05 30		06 00		06 30		07 00		07 30				08 00			08 30		09 00			09 30
Bristol Parkway 7	a					06 29		06 59		07 29			07 59			08 30			08 59		09 30		
	d					06 31		07 01		07 31			08 01			08 31			09 01		09 31		
Bath Spa 7	d		05 43		06 13		06 43		07 13		07 43				08 13			08 43		09 13			09 43
Chippenham	d		05 55		06 25		06 55		07 25		07 55	08 00			08 25		08 48	08 55		09 25			09 55
Worcester Shrub Hill	d																					08 36	
Cheltenham Spa	d	00 09		05 30										07 30								08 59	
Gloucester 7	d	00a20		05 42										07 46								09 14	
Stonehouse	d			05 56										07 59								09 29	
Stroud	d			06 01										08 04								09 34	
Kemble	d			06 16										08 19								09 49	
Swindon	a		06 09	06 32	06 40	06 57	07 09	07 27	07 40	07 57	08 09	08 20	08 27	08 35	08 40	08 58	09 06	09 09	09 27	09 40	09 56	10 03	10 10
	d		06 11		06 41	06 59	07 11	07 29	07 41	07 59	08 11		08 29	08 36	08 41	08 59		09 11	09 29	09 41	09 59	10 04	10 11
Didcot Parkway	a		06 28		06 58	07 16	07 28	07 46	07 59	08 16	08 28		08 46	08 52	08 59	09 16		09 28	09 46		10 16	10 21	10 28
Reading 7	a		06 43		07 14	07 31	07 44	08 00	08 15	08 33	08 44		09 01	09 08	09 14	09 31		09 47	10 00	10 11	10 30	10 34	10 46
Slough 3	a																						
London Paddington 15 ⊖	a		07 14		07 44	08 07	08 14	08 32	08 44	09 02	09 14		09 38	09 41	09 44	10 02		10 15	10 32	10 39	11 04	11 08	11 14

A From Penzance
B From Taunton
C From Birmingham New Street
D From Westbury
E 🍴 from Reading ⊘ to Reading
F From Exeter St Davids

For connections from Hereford and Birmingham New Street please see Tables 131 and 57. For connections to Oxford, Gatwick Airport and Heathrow Airport please see Tables 116, 148 and 125A

For other services between London and Worcester refer to table 126

Table 125R

Saturdays

15 February to 22 March

South Wales, Weston-super-Mare, Bristol, Cheltenham Spa and Swindon - London

Route Diagram - see first Page of Table 125

		GW	GW	GW	GW	GW	GW	GW	GW	GW	GW	GW	GW	GW	GW	GW	GW	GW	GW	GW	GW	GW
			◇1	◇1		◇1	◇1	◇1	◇1	◇1		◇1	◇1		◇1	◇1	◇1	◇1	◇1		◇1	◇1
		A								B	A	C								A		
			☕	☕		☕	☕	☕	☕	☕		☕	☕		☕	☕	☕	☕	☕		☕	☕
Swansea	d		08 28				09 28					10 28				11 28					12 28	
Neath	d		08 40				09 40					10 40				11 40					12 40	
Port Talbot Parkway	d		08 48				09 48					10 48				11 48					12 48	
Bridgend	d		09 01				10 01					11 01				12 01					13 01	
Cardiff Central 7	d		09 25				10 25					11 25				12 25					13 25	
Newport (South Wales)	d		09 39				10 39					11 39				12 39					13 39	
Weston-super-Mare	d																					
Bristol Temple Meads 10	d			10 00		10 30		11 00		11 30			12 00		12 30		13 00		13 30			14 00
Bristol Parkway 7	a		09 59				10 59					11 59				12 59					13 59	
	d		10 01				11 01					12 01				13 01					14 01	
Bath Spa 7	d			10 13		10 43		11 13		11 43			12 13		12 43		13 13		13 43			14 13
Chippenham	d	10 00		10 25		10 55		11 25		11 55	12 00		12 25		12 55		13 25		13 55	14 00		14 25
Worcester Shrub Hill	d																					
Cheltenham Spa	d				10 01				11 00					12 01				13 00				
Gloucester 7	d				10 13				11 15					12 13				13 15				
Stonehouse	d				10 27				11 29					12 27				13 30				
Stroud	d				10 32				11 35					12 32				13 36				
Kemble	d				10 47				11 49					12 47				13 50				
Swindon	a	10 20	10 28	10 39	11 04	11 10	11 27	11 39	12 03	12 09	12 20	12 27	12 40	13 04	13 09	13 27	13 39	14 04	14 10	14 20	14 27	14 39
	d		10 29	10 41		11 11	11 29	11 41	12 05	12 11		12 29	12 41		13 11	13 29	13 41	14 06	14 11		14 29	14 41
Didcot Parkway	a		10 47			11 28	11 46		12 22	12 28		12 46			13 28	13 46		14 23	14 28		14 46	
Reading 7	a		11 01	11 12		11 43	12 01	12 11	12 38	12 45		13 01	13 11		13 44	14 00	14 12	14 39	14 45		15 02	15 10
Slough 3	a																					
London Paddington 15 ⊖	a		11 33	11 40		12 14	12 37	12 41	13 06	13 15		13 38	13 42		14 14	14 32	14 39	15 09	15 14		15 37	15 41

		GW	GW	GW	GW	GW	GW	GW	GW	GW	GW	GW	GW	GW	GW	GW	GW	GW	GW	GW	GW	GW	GW
			◇1	◇1	◇1		◇1	◇1	◇1	◇1		◇1		◇1	◇1	◇1	◇1	◇1	◇1		◇1		◇1
						A							A									A	
			☕	☕	☕		☕	☕	☕	☕		☕		☕	☕	☕	☕	☕	☕		☕		☕
Swansea	d			13 28					14 28					15 28				16 28					17 28
Neath	d			13 40					14 40					15 40				16 40					17 40
Port Talbot Parkway	d			13 48					14 48					15 48				16 48					17 48
Bridgend	d			14 01					15 01					16 01				17 01					18 01
Cardiff Central 7	d			14 25					15 25					16 25				17 25					18 25
Newport (South Wales)	d			14 39					15 39					16 39				17 39					18 39
Weston-super-Mare	d																						
Bristol Temple Meads 10	d		14 30		15 00			15 30		16 00		16 30			17 00		17 30		18 00		18 30		
Bristol Parkway 7	a			14 59					15 59					16 59				17 59					18 59
	d			15 01					16 01					17 01				18 01					19 01
Bath Spa 7	d		14 43		15 13			15 43		16 13		16 43			17 13		17 43		18 13		18 43		
Chippenham	d		14 55		15 25	15 30		15 55		16 25		16 55	17 00		17 25		17 55		18 25		18 55	19 00	
Worcester Shrub Hill	d																						
Cheltenham Spa	d	14 01					15 00				16 01					17 00				18 01			
Gloucester 7	d	14 13					15 15				16 13					17 15				18 13			
Stonehouse	d	14 27					15 29				16 27					17 29				18 27			
Stroud	d	14 32					15 35				16 32					17 35				18 32			
Kemble	d	14 47					15 49				16 47					17 49				18 47			
Swindon	a	15 04	15 09	15 27	15 39	15 50	16 03	16 09	16 27	16 39	17 04	17 10	17 22	17 27	17 39	18 03	18 09	18 27	18 39	19 04	19 09	19 22	19 27
	d		15 11	15 29	15 41		16 05	16 11	16 29	16 41		17 11		17 29	17 41	18 05	18 11	18 29	18 41		19 11		19 29
Didcot Parkway	a		15 28	15 46			16 22	16 28	16 46			17 28		17 46		18 22	18 28	18 46			19 28		19 46
Reading 7	a		15 44	16 00	16 12		16 38	16 44	17 00	17 10		17 43		17 58	18 12	18 38	18 44	19 00	19 10		19 46		20 00
Slough 3	a																						
London Paddington 15 ⊖	a		16 14	16 33	16 39		17 07	17 14	17 32	17 38		18 14		18 32	18 40	19 08	19 13	19 32	19 39		20 14		20 32

A From Westbury **B** From Paignton **C** From Carmarthen

For connections from Hereford and Birmingham New Street please see Tables 131 and 57. For connections to Oxford, Gatwick Airport and Heathrow Airport please see Tables 116, 148 and 125A

For other services between London and Worcester refer to table 126

Table 125R

Saturdays
15 February to 22 March

South Wales, Weston-super-Mare, Bristol, Cheltenham Spa and Swindon - London

Route Diagram - see first Page of Table 125

		GW	GW	GW	GW	GW	GW	GW	GW	GW
		◇1	◇1	◇1		◇1	◇1		◇1	◇1
					A				B	C
		(P)	(P)	(P)		(P)	(P)		(P)	(P)
Swansea	d			18 28			19 28			
Neath	d			18 40			19 40			
Port Talbot Parkway	d			18 48			19 48			
Bridgend	d			19 01			20 01			
Cardiff Central [7]	d			19 25			20 25			
Newport (South Wales)	d			19 39			20 39			
Weston-super-Mare	d					20 10				21 53
Bristol Temple Meads [10]	d		19 30			20 33			21 47	22 30
Bristol Parkway [7]	a			19 59			21 01			
	d			20 01			21 01			
Bath Spa [7]	d		19 43			20 46			22 02	22 43
Chippenham	d		19 55			20 58			22 15	22 55
Worcester Shrub Hill	d									
Cheltenham Spa	d	19 00			20 01			21 20		
Gloucester [7]	d	19 15			20 13			21 34		
Stonehouse	d	19 30			20 27			21 48		
Stroud	d	19 36			20 32			21 53		
Kemble	d	19 50			20 47			22 08		
Swindon	a	20 04	20 09	20 27	21 03	21 13	21 29	22 25	22 29	23 10
	d	20 06	20 11	20 29		21 14	21 29		22 31	23 11
Didcot Parkway	a	20 23	20 28	20 46		21 31	21 47		22 48	23 28
Reading [7]	a	20 38	20 44	21 06		21 48	22 02		23 07	23 48
Slough [3]	a									
London Paddington [15] ⊖	a	21 07	21 14	21 37		22 16	22 40		23 40	00 36

Saturdays
29 March to 17 May

		LM	GW	GW	GW	GW	GW	GW	GW	GW
			◇1		◇1	◇1	◇1	◇1	◇1	◇1
		D								
			(P)		(P)	(P)	(P)	(P)	(P)	(P)
Swansea	d				03 58	04 58		05 28		05 58
Neath	d				04 10	05 10		05 40		06 10
Port Talbot Parkway	d				04 18	05 18		05 48		06 18
Bridgend	d				04 30	05 31		06 01		06 31
Cardiff Central [7]	d				04 55	05 55		06 25		06 55
Newport (South Wales)	d				05 09	06 09		06 39		07 09
Weston-super-Mare	d								06 24	
Bristol Temple Meads [10]	d		05 30		06 00		06 30		07 00	
Bristol Parkway [7]	a					06 29		06 59		07 29
	d					06 31		07 01		07 31
Bath Spa [7]	d		05 43		06 13		06 43		07 13	
Chippenham	d		05 55		06 25		06 55		07 25	
Worcester Shrub Hill	d									
Cheltenham Spa	d	00 09		05 30						
Gloucester [7]	d	00a20		05 42						
Stonehouse	d			05 56						
Stroud	d			06 01						
Kemble	d			06 16						
Swindon	a		06 09	06 32	06 40	06 57	07 09	07 27	07 40	07 57
	d		06 11		06 41	06 59	07 11	07 29	07 41	07 59
Didcot Parkway	a		06 28		06 58	07 16	07 28	07 46	07 59	08 16
Reading [7]	a		06 43		07 14	07 31	07 44	08 00	08 15	08 33
Slough [3]	a									
London Paddington [15] ⊖	a		07 14		07 44	08 07	08 14	08 32	08 44	09 02

		GW	GW	GW	GW	GW	GW	GW	GW	GW	GW	GW	GW	GW
		◇1		◇1	◇1	◇1	◇1		◇1	◇1	◇1	◇1	◇1	◇1
			E			C	F	E		F	G			
		(P)		(P)	(P)	(P)	(P)⊘		(P)	(P)⊘	(P)	(P)	(P)	(P)
Swansea	d			06 28			06 58			07 28		07 58		
Neath	d			06 40			07 10			07 40		08 10		
Port Talbot Parkway	d			06 48			07 18			07 48		08 18		
Bridgend	d			07 01			07 31			08 01		08 31		
Cardiff Central [7]	d			07 25			07 55			08 25		08 55		
Newport (South Wales)	d			07 39			08 09			08 39		09 09		
Weston-super-Mare	d					07 24					08 30			
Bristol Temple Meads [10]	d	07 30				08 00			08 30		09 00			09 30
Bristol Parkway [7]	a			07 59			08 30			08 59		09 30		
	d			08 01			08 31			09 01		09 31		
Bath Spa [7]	d	07 43				08 13			08 43		09 13			09 43
Chippenham	d	07 55	08 00			08 25		08 48	08 55		09 25			09 55
Worcester Shrub Hill	d												08 36	
Cheltenham Spa	d				07 30								08 59	
Gloucester [7]	d				07 46								09 14	
Stonehouse	d				07 59								09 29	
Stroud	d				08 04								09 34	
Kemble	d				08 19								09 49	
Swindon	a	08 09	08 20	08 27	08 35	08 40	08 58	09 06	09 09	09 27	09 40	09 56	10 03	10 10
	d	08 11		08 29	08 36	08 41	08 59		09 11	09 29	09 41	09 59	10 04	10 11
Didcot Parkway	a	08 28		08 46	08 52	08 59	09 16		09 28	09 46		10 16	10 21	10 28
Reading [7]	a	08 44		09 01	09 08	09 14	09 31		09 47	10 00	10 11	10 30	10 34	10 46
Slough [3]	a													
London Paddington [15] ⊖	a	09 14		09 38	09 41	09 44	10 02		10 15	10 32	10 39	11 04	11 08	11 14

A To Westbury
B From Penzance
C From Taunton
D From Birmingham New Street
E From Westbury
F (P) from Reading ⊘ to Reading
G From Exeter St Davids

For connections from Hereford and Birmingham New Street please see Tables 131 and 57. For connections to Oxford, Gatwick Airport and Heathrow Airport please see Tables 116, 148 and 125A

For other services between London and Worcester refer to table 126

Table 125R

Saturdays

29 March to 17 May

South Wales, Weston-super-Mare, Bristol, Cheltenham Spa and Swindon - London

Route Diagram - see first Page of Table 125

		GW		GW	GW	GW	GW	GW	GW	GW	GW	GW		GW	GW	GW	GW	GW	GW	GW	GW	GW		GW	GW
				◇1	◇1		◇1	◇1	◇1	◇1	◇1			◇1	◇1		◇1	◇1	◇1	◇1	◇1			◇1	◇1
		A									B	A		C								A			
				☕	☕		☕	☕	☕	☕	☕			☕	☕		☕	☕	☕	☕	☕			☕	☕
Swansea	d			08 28				09 28						10 28				11 28						12 28	
Neath	d			08 40				09 40						10 40				11 40						12 40	
Port Talbot Parkway	d			08 48				09 48						10 48				11 48						12 48	
Bridgend	d			09 01				10 01						11 01				12 01						13 01	
Cardiff Central 7	d			09 25				10 25						11 25				12 25						13 25	
Newport (South Wales)	d			09 39				10 39						11 39				12 39						13 39	
Weston-super-Mare	d																								
Bristol Temple Meads 10	d				10 00		10 30		11 00		11 30				12 00		12 30		13 00		13 30				14 00
Bristol Parkway 7	a			09 59				10 59						11 59				12 59						13 59	
	d			10 01				11 01						12 01				13 01						14 01	
Bath Spa 7	d				10 13		10 43		11 13		11 43				12 13		12 43		13 13		13 43				14 13
Chippenham	d	10 00			10 25		10 55		11 25		11 55	12 00			12 25		12 55		13 25		13 55	14 00			14 25
Worcester Shrub Hill	d																								
Cheltenham Spa	d					10 01				11 00						12 01				13 00					
Gloucester 7	d					10 13				11 15						12 13				13 15					
Stonehouse	d					10 27				11 29						12 27				13 30					
Stroud	d					10 32				11 35						12 32				13 36					
Kemble	d					10 47				11 49						12 47				13 50					
Swindon	a	10 20		10 28	10 39	11 04	11 10	11 27	11 39	12 03	12 09	12 20		12 27	12 40	13 04	13 09	13 27	13 39	14 04	14 10	14 20		14 27	14 39
	d			10 29	10 41		11 11	11 29	11 41	12 05	12 11			12 29	12 41		13 11	13 29	13 41	14 06	14 11			14 29	14 41
Didcot Parkway	a			10 47			11 28	11 46		12 22	12 28			12 46			13 28	13 46		14 23	14 28			14 46	
Reading 7	a			11 01	11 12		11 43	12 01	12 11	12 38	12 45			13 01	13 11		13 44	14 00	14 12	14 39	14 45			15 02	15 10
Slough 3	a																								
London Paddington 15 ⊖	a			11 33	11 40		12 14	12 37	12 41	13 06	13 15			13 38	13 42		14 14	14 32	14 39	15 09	15 14			15 37	15 41

		GW	GW	GW	GW	GW	GW	GW		GW	GW	GW	GW	GW	GW	GW	GW	GW		GW	GW	GW	GW	GW	GW
			◇1	◇1	◇1		◇1	◇1		◇1	◇1		◇1		◇1	◇1	◇1	◇1		◇1	◇1		◇1		◇1
						A								A										A	
			☕	☕	☕		☕	☕		☕	☕		☕		☕	☕	☕	☕		☕	☕		☕		☕
Swansea	d			13 28						14 28					15 28					16 28					17 28
Neath	d			13 40						14 40					15 40					16 40					17 40
Port Talbot Parkway	d			13 48						14 48					15 48					16 48					17 48
Bridgend	d			14 01						15 01					16 01					17 01					18 01
Cardiff Central 7	d			14 25						15 25					16 25					17 25					18 25
Newport (South Wales)	d			14 39						15 39					16 39					17 39					18 39
Weston-super-Mare	d																								
Bristol Temple Meads 10	d		14 30		15 00			15 30			16 00		16 30			17 00		17 30			18 00		18 30		
Bristol Parkway 7	a			14 59						15 59					16 59					17 59					18 59
	d			15 01						16 01					17 01					18 01					19 01
Bath Spa 7	d		14 43		15 13			15 43			16 13		16 43			17 13		17 43			18 13		18 43		
Chippenham	d		14 55		15 25	15 30		15 55			16 25		16 55	17 00		17 25		17 55			18 25		18 55	19 00	
Worcester Shrub Hill	d																								
Cheltenham Spa	d	14 01					15 00					16 01					17 00					18 01			
Gloucester 7	d	14 13					15 15					16 13					17 15					18 13			
Stonehouse	d	14 27					15 29					16 27					17 29					18 27			
Stroud	d	14 32					15 35					16 32					17 35					18 32			
Kemble	d	14 47					15 49					16 47					17 49					18 47			
Swindon	a	15 04	15 09	15 27	15 39	15 50	16 03	16 09		16 27	16 39	17 04	17 10	17 22	17 27	17 39	18 03	18 09		18 27	18 39	19 04	19 09	19 22	19 27
	d		15 11	15 29	15 41		16 05	16 11		16 29	16 41		17 11		17 29	17 41	18 05	18 11		18 29	18 41		19 11		19 29
Didcot Parkway	a		15 28	15 46			16 22	16 28		16 46			17 28		17 46		18 22	18 28		18 46			19 28		19 46
Reading 7	a		15 44	16 00	16 12		16 38	16 44		17 00	17 10		17 43		17 58	18 12	18 38	18 44		19 00	19 10		19 46		20 00
Slough 3	a																								
London Paddington 15 ⊖	a		16 14	16 33	16 39		17 07	17 14		17 32	17 38		18 14		18 32	18 40	19 08	19 13		19 32	19 39		20 14		20 32

A From Westbury **B** From Paignton **C** From Carmarthen

For connections from Hereford and Birmingham New Street please see Tables 131 and 57. For connections to Oxford, Gatwick Airport and Heathrow Airport please see Tables 116, 148 and 125A

For other services between London and Worcester refer to table 126

Table 125R

Saturdays

29 March to 17 May

South Wales, Weston-super-Mare, Bristol, Cheltenham Spa and Swindon - London

Route Diagram - see first Page of Table 125

		GW	GW	GW	GW	GW	GW	GW	GW	GW
		◇1	◇1	◇1		◇1	◇1		◇1	◇1
					A				B	C
		⊐	⊐	⊐		⊐	⊐		⊐	⊐
Swansea	d			18 28			19 28			
Neath	d			18 40			19 40			
Port Talbot Parkway	d			18 48			19 48			
Bridgend	d			19 01			20 01			
Cardiff Central 7	d			19 25			20 25			
Newport (South Wales)	d			19 39			20 39			
Weston-super-Mare	d					20 10				21 53
Bristol Temple Meads 10	d		19 30			20 33			21 47	22 30
Bristol Parkway 7	a			19 59			21 01			
	d			20 01			21 01			
Bath Spa 7	d		19 43			20 46			22 02	22 43
Chippenham	d		19 55			20 58			22 15	22 55
Worcester Shrub Hill	d									
Cheltenham Spa	d	19 00			20 01			21 20		
Gloucester 7	d	19 15			20 13			21 34		
Stonehouse	d	19 30			20 27			21 48		
Stroud	d	19 36			20 32			21 53		
Kemble	d	19 50			20 47			22 08		
Swindon	a	20 04	20 09	20 27	21 03	21 13	21 29	22 25	22 29	23 10
	d	20 06	20 11	20 29		21 14	21 29		22 31	23 11
Didcot Parkway	a	20 23	20 28	20 46		21 31	21 47		22 48	23 28
Reading 7	a	20 38	20 44	21 06		21 48	22 02		23 07	23 48
Slough 3	a									
London Paddington 15 ⊖	a	21 07	21 14	21 37		22 16	22 40		23 42	00 36

Sundays

8 December to 29 December

		GW	GW	GW	GW	GW	GW	GW	GW	GW	GW	GW	GW	GW	GW	GW	GW	GW	GW	GW	GW	GW
		◇1	1	◇1	◇1	◇1		◇1	◇1			◇1	◇1		◇1	R 1	R 1		R 1		R 1	◇1
										D						E				D		
		⊐	⊐	⊐	⊐	⊐		⊐	⊐			⊐	⊐		⊐	⊐	⊐		⊐		⊐	⊐
Swansea	d					08 07						09 21			10 21		11 21				12 21	
Neath	d					08 19						09 33			10 33		11 33				12 33	
Port Talbot Parkway	d					08 26						09 40			10 40		11 40				12 40	
Bridgend	d					08 39						09 53			10 53		11 53				12 53	
Cardiff Central 7	d			07 45		09 05						10 15			11 15		12 15				13 15	
Newport (South Wales)	d			08 03		09 19						10 32			11 32		12 32				13 32	
Weston-super-Mare	d				08 12				09 56										12 51			
Bristol Temple Meads 10	d	07 45	08 15		08 45			09 48	10 30				11 30			12 30			13 30			14 30
Bristol Parkway 7	a			08 31		09 46						10 59			11 59		12 59				13 59	
	d			08 32		09 48						11 01			12 01		13 01				14 01	
Bath Spa 7	d	07 58	08 28		08 58			10 01	10 43				11 43			12 43			13 43			14 43
Chippenham	d	08 10	08 40		09 10			10 13	10 55	11 01			11 55			12 55			13 55	14 01		14 55
Worcester Shrub Hill	d																					
Cheltenham Spa	d						09 24				10 24			11 20				13 03				
Gloucester 7	d						09 37				10 37			11 33				13 15				
Stonehouse	d						09 50				10 50			11 46				13 28				
Stroud	d						09 55				10 55			11 51				13 33				
Kemble	d						10 09				11 09			12 05				13 47				
Swindon	a	08 24	08 55	08 58	09 24	10 13	10 24	10 27	11 10	11 19	11 24	11 26	12 10	12 20	12 26	13 10	13 26	14 02	14 10	14 19	14 26	15 10
	d	08 26		09 00	09 29	10 14		10 29	11 11			11 29	12 11		12 29	13 11	13 29		14 11		14 29	15 11
Didcot Parkway	a	08 43			09 44			10 44	11 29			11 46	12 29		12 46	13 28	13 46		14 28		14 46	15 28
Reading 7	a	09 05		09 30	10 02	10 42		11 03	11 43			12 02	12 44		13 02	13 48	14 02		14 45		15 02	15 44
Slough 3	a																					
London Paddington 15 ⊖	a	09 44		10 08	10 43	11 22		11 43	12 22			12 42	13 23		13 42	14 23	14 42		15 23		15 42	16 22

A To Westbury
B From Penzance
C From Taunton
D From Westbury
E From Plymouth

For connections from Hereford and Birmingham New Street please see Tables 131 and 57. For connections to Oxford, Gatwick Airport and Heathrow Airport please see Tables 116, 148 and 125A

For other services between London and Worcester refer to table 126

Table 125R

Sundays

8 December to 29 December

South Wales, Weston-super-Mare, Bristol, Cheltenham Spa and Swindon - London

Route Diagram - see first Page of Table 125

		GW		GW	GW	GW	GW	GW	GW	GW	GW	GW		GW	GW	GW	GW	GW	GW	GW	GW	GW		GW	GW
				R 1	R 1	R 1	◇1	◇1	◇1		R 1			◇1		R 1	◇1	◇1	◇1	R 1	◇1			◇1	◇1
										A					A	B	C	D			B	A			C
				☕	☕	☕	☕	☕	☕		☕			☕		☕	☕	☕	☕	☕	☕			☕	☕
Swansea	d			13 21		14 21					15 21						16 21			16 51					17 51
Neath	d			13 33		14 33					15 33						16 33			17 03					18 03
Port Talbot Parkway	d			13 40		14 40					15 40						16 40			17 10					18 10
Bridgend	d			13 53		14 53					15 53						16 53			17 23					18 23
Cardiff Central 7	d			14 15		15 15					16 15						17 15			17 50					18 50
Newport (South Wales)	d			14 32		15 32					16 32						17 32			18 04					19 04
Weston-super-Mare	d				14 51											17 02		17 29							
Bristol Temple Meads 10	d				15 30		16 00		16 30					17 00		17 30		18 00			18 30			19 00	
Bristol Parkway 7	a			14 59		15 59					16 59						17 59			18 31					19 31
	d			15 01		16 01					17 01						18 01			18 33					19 33
Bath Spa 7	d				15 43		16 13		16 43					17 13		17 43		18 13			18 43			19 13	
Chippenham	d				15 55		16 25		16 55	17 00				17 25	17 42	17 55		18 25			18 55	19 15		19 25	
Worcester Shrub Hill	d																								
Cheltenham Spa	d	14 05						15 46				16 32							17 46						
Gloucester 7	d	14 21						16 02				16 45							18 00						
Stonehouse	d	14 34						16 17				16 57							18 15						
Stroud	d	14 40						16 22				17 02							18 21						
Kemble	d	14 57						16 37				17 17							18 35						
Swindon	a	15 12		15 26	16 10	16 26	16 41	16 52	17 10	17 17	17 26	17 33		17 40	18 00	18 10	18 26	18 40	18 50	18 57	19 10	19 33		19 40	19 57
	d			15 29	16 11	16 29	16 41	16 54	17 11		17 29			17 41		18 11	18 29	18 41	18 51	18 59	19 11			19 41	19 59
Didcot Parkway	a			15 46	16 28	16 46	16 58		17 28		17 46			17 58			18 46	18 58		19 15				19 58	20 15
Reading 7	a			16 02	16 44	17 02	17 16	17 21	17 49		18 02			18 17		18 46	19 02	19 14	19 23	19 33	19 42			20 16	20 33
Slough 3	a																								
London Paddington 15 ⊖	a			16 42	17 23	17 43	17 57	18 01	18 22		18 44			18 57		19 22	19 44	19 58	20 01	20 13	20 23			20 57	21 04

		GW	GW	GW	GW	GW	GW	GW		GW	GW
				◇1	◇1	◇1	◇1	◇1			◇1
			E	F				C			B
				☕	☕	☕	☕	☕			☕
Swansea	d				18 51			19 55			
Neath	d				19 03			20 07			
Port Talbot Parkway	d				19 10			20 14			
Bridgend	d				19 23			20 28			
Cardiff Central 7	d				19 50			20 55			
Newport (South Wales)	d				20 04			21 09			
Weston-super-Mare	d			19 27			20 26				
Bristol Temple Meads 10	d			20 00			21 00				22 10
Bristol Parkway 7	a				20 31			21 36			
	d				20 33			21 38			
Bath Spa 7	d			20 13			21 13				22 23
Chippenham	d		20 07	20 25			21 25				22 35
Worcester Shrub Hill	d										
Cheltenham Spa	d					19 59				21 46	
Gloucester 7	d	19 34				20 13				21 58	
Stonehouse	d	19 48				20 27				22 11	
Stroud	d	19 53				20 33				22 16	
Kemble	d	20 07				20 48				22 31	
Swindon	a	20 23	20 24	20 40	20 57	21 02	21 40	22 04		22 46	22 50
	d			20 41	20 59	21 02	21 41	22 05			22 52
Didcot Parkway	a			20 58		21 24	22 00				23 09
Reading 7	a			21 16	21 33	21 39	22 18	22 42			23 29
Slough 3	a										
London Paddington 15 ⊖	a			21 56	22 06	22 30	22 58	23 20			00 13

A From Westbury
B From Plymouth
C From Carmarthen
D From Paignton
E From Westbury to Cheltenham Spa
F From Taunton

For connections from Hereford and Birmingham New Street please see Tables 131 and 57. For connections to Oxford, Gatwick Airport and Heathrow Airport please see Tables 116, 148 and 125A

For other services between London and Worcester refer to table 126

Table 125R

Sundays

5 January to 9 February

South Wales, Weston-super-Mare, Bristol, Cheltenham Spa and Swindon - London

Route Diagram - see first Page of Table 125

		GW	GW	GW	GW	GW		GW	GW	GW	GW	GW	GW	GW	GW	GW		GW	GW	GW	GW	GW	GW	GW	GW
		A 🚌	1 ☕	◇1 ☕	◇1 ☕	◇1 ☕			◇1 ☕	◇1 ☕	B		◇1 ☕	◇1 ☕		◇1 ☕		R 1 C ☕	R 1 ☕		R 1 ☕	B	R 1 ☕	◇1 ☕	
Swansea	d					08 03							09 21			10 21			11 21				12 21		
Neath	d					08 15							09 33			10 33			11 33				12 33		
Port Talbot Parkway	d					08 22							09 40			10 40			11 40				12 40		
Bridgend	d					08 35							09 53			10 53			11 53				12 53		
Cardiff Central 7	d					09 00							10 15			11 15			12 15				13 15		
Newport (South Wales)	d			08 08		09 14							10 32			11 32			12 32				13 32		
Weston-super-Mare	d				08 10					09 47											12 51				
Bristol Temple Meads 10	d		08 25		08 40				09 48	10 20				11 20				12 25			13 25			14 30	
Bristol Parkway 7	a			08 41		09 34							10 53			11 53			12 53				13 53		
	d			08 42		09 36							10 55			11 55			12 55				13 55		
Bath Spa 7	d		08 38		08 56				10 01	10 33				11 33				12 38			13 39			14 43	
Chippenham	d	07 15	08 50		09 08				10 13	10 45	10 57			11 45				12 50			13 51	13 58		14 55	
Worcester Shrub Hill	d																								
Cheltenham Spa	d							09 24				10 18			11 18					13 03					14 05
Gloucester 7	d							09 37				10 31			11 31					13 16					14 21
Stonehouse	d							09 50				10 44			11 44					13 29					14 34
Stroud	d							09 55				10 49			11 49					13 34					14 40
Kemble	d							10 09				11 03			12 03					13 48					14 57
Swindon	a	07 50	09 05	09 08	09 22	10 01		10 24	10 27	11 01	11 15	11 18	11 20	12 00	12 18	12 20		13 05	13 20	14 03	14 06	14 17	14 20	15 10	15 12
	d			09 11	09 24	10 02			10 29	11 02			11 23	12 01		12 23		13 06	13 23		14 09		14 23	15 11	
Didcot Parkway	a				09 39				10 44	11 19			11 40	12 19		12 40		13 24	13 40		14 27		14 40	15 28	
Reading 7	a			09 43	10 03	10 34			11 08	11 40			12 02	12 41		13 02		13 45	14 02		14 49		15 02	15 50	
Slough 3	a																								
London Paddington 15 ⊖	a			10 22	10 43	11 19			11 46	12 25			12 42	13 23		13 43		14 26	14 42		15 26		15 42	16 28	

		GW		GW	GW	GW	GW	GW	GW	GW	GW	GW		GW	GW	GW	GW	GW	GW	GW	GW	GW		GW	GW
		R 1 ☕		R 1 ☕	R 1 ☕	◇1 ☕	◇1 ☕	◇1 ☕	B	R 1 ☕		◇1 ☕		B	R 1 C ☕	◇1 D ☕	◇1 E ☕	◇1 ☕	R 1 ☕	◇1 C ☕	B	◇1 ☕		◇1 D ☕	
Swansea	d	13 21			14 21					15 21						16 21			16 51					17 51	
Neath	d	13 33			14 33					15 33						16 33			17 03					18 03	
Port Talbot Parkway	d	13 40			14 40					15 40						16 40			17 10					18 10	
Bridgend	d	13 53			14 53					15 53						16 53			17 23					18 23	
Cardiff Central 7	d	14 15			15 15					16 15						17 15			17 50					18 50	
Newport (South Wales)	d	14 32			15 32					16 32						17 31			18 04					19 04	
Weston-super-Mare	d			14 48											17 02		17 29								
Bristol Temple Meads 10	d			15 20		15 55		16 30				16 55			17 25		18 00			18 20		19 00			
Bristol Parkway 7	a	14 53			15 53					16 53						17 53			18 27					19 31	
	d	14 55			15 55					16 55						17 55			18 29					19 33	
Bath Spa 7	d			15 34		16 08		16 43				17 08			17 38		18 13			18 33		19 13			
Chippenham	d			15 46		16 20		16 55	17 00			17 20		17 42	17 50		18 25			18 45	19 15	19 25			
Worcester Shrub Hill	d																								
Cheltenham Spa	d						15 42				16 32							17 42							
Gloucester 7	d						15 56				16 45							17 56							19 34
Stonehouse	d						16 11				16 57							18 11							19 48
Stroud	d						16 16				17 02							18 17							19 53
Kemble	d						16 31				17 17							18 32							20 07
Swindon	a	15 20		16 01	16 20	16 36	16 46	17 10	17 17	17 20	17 33	17 35		18 00	18 05	18 20	18 40	18 48	18 53	18 59	19 33	19 40		19 57	20 23
	d	15 23		16 02	16 23	16 36	16 51	17 11		17 23		17 38			18 06	18 23	18 41	18 49	18 55	19 01		19 41		19 59	
Didcot Parkway	a	15 40		16 21	16 40	16 55		17 28		17 40		17 54				18 40	18 58		19 11			19 58		20 15	
Reading 7	a	16 02		16 44	17 02	17 16	17 24	17 49		18 02		18 17			18 46	19 02	19 20	19 23	19 33	19 42		20 19		20 39	
Slough 3	a																								
London Paddington 15 ⊖	a	16 44		17 23	17 44	17 57	18 05	18 26		18 44		19 03			19 27	19 43	19 58	20 03	20 13	20 19		20 58		21 15	

A To Reading Bus
B From Westbury
C From Plymouth
D From Carmarthen
E From Paignton

For connections from Hereford and Birmingham New Street please see Tables 131 and 57. For connections to Oxford, Gatwick Airport and Heathrow Airport please see Tables 116, 148 and 125A

For other services between London and Worcester refer to table 126

Table 125R

Sundays

5 January to 9 February

South Wales, Weston-super-Mare, Bristol, Cheltenham Spa and Swindon - London

Route Diagram - see first Page of Table 125

		GW	GW	GW	GW	GW	GW	GW	GW
			◇1	◇1	◇1	◇1	◇1		◇1
		A	B				C		D
Swansea	d			18 51			19 55		
Neath	d			19 03			20 07		
Port Talbot Parkway	d			19 10			20 14		
Bridgend	d			19 23			20 28		
Cardiff Central 7	d			19 50			20 55		
Newport (South Wales)	d			20 04			21 09		
Weston-super-Mare	d		19 27			20 21			
Bristol Temple Meads 10	d		19 55			20 55			22 10
Bristol Parkway 7	a			20 31			21 36		
	d			20 33			21 38		
Bath Spa 7	d		20 09			21 08			22 23
Chippenham	d	20 07	20 21			21 20			22 35
Worcester Shrub Hill	d								
Cheltenham Spa	d				19 59			21 46	
Gloucester 7	d				20 13			21 58	
Stonehouse	d				20 27			22 11	
Stroud	d				20 33			22 16	
Kemble	d				20 48			22 31	
Swindon	a	20 24	20 36	20 57	21 02	21 34	22 04	22 46	22 50
	d		20 37	20 59	21 02	21 35	22 05		22 52
Didcot Parkway	a		20 55		21 24	21 54			23 09
Reading 7	a		21 16	21 33	21 47	22 15	22 44		23 32
Slough 3	a								
London Paddington 15 ⊖	a		21 59	22 14	22 30	23 02	23 27		00 13

Sundays

16 February to 23 March

		GW	GW	GW	GW	GW	GW	GW	GW	GW	GW	GW	GW	GW	GW	GW	GW	GW	GW	GW	GW	GW
																	R	R			R	
			1	◇1	◇1	◇1		◇1	◇1			◇1	◇1		◇1	◇1	1	1			1	◇1
		E								F						G				F		
Swansea	d					07 58						09 21			10 21		11 21				12 21	
Neath	d					08 10						09 33			10 33		11 33				12 33	
Port Talbot Parkway	d					08 17						09 40			10 40		11 40				12 40	
Bridgend	d					08 31						09 53			10 53		11 53				12 53	
Cardiff Central 7	d			07 45		08 55						10 15			11 15		12 15				13 15	
Newport (South Wales)	d			08 03		09 10						10 32			11 32		12 32				13 32	
Weston-super-Mare	d				08 12				09 47									12 51				
Bristol Temple Meads 10	d		08 15		08 45			09 48	10 20				11 20			12 25		13 25				14 25
Bristol Parkway 7	a			08 31		09 37						10 59			11 59		12 59				13 59	
	d			08 32		09 39						11 01			12 01		13 01				14 01	
Bath Spa 7	d		08 28		08 58			10 01	10 33				11 33			12 38		13 38				14 38
Chippenham	d	07 15	08 40		09 10			10 13	10 45	10 57			11 45			12 50		13 50		13 58		14 50
Worcester Shrub Hill	d																					
Cheltenham Spa	d						09 24				10 24			11 20					13 03			
Gloucester 7	d						09 37				10 37			11 33					13 27			
Stonehouse	d						09 50				10 50			11 46					13 40			
Stroud	d						09 55				10 55			11 51					13 45			
Kemble	d						10 09				11 09			12 05					13 59			
Swindon	a	07 50	08 55	08 58	09 24	10 04	10 24	10 27	11 00	11 15	11 24	11 26	12 00	12 20	12 26	13 05	13 26	14 05	14 14	14 17	14 26	15 05
	d			09 00	09 29	10 05		10 29	11 02			11 29	12 01		12 29	13 06	13 29	14 06			14 29	15 06
Didcot Parkway	a				09 44			10 44	11 19			11 46	12 19		12 46	13 24	13 46				14 46	15 26
Reading 7	a			09 30	10 02	10 37		11 03	11 35			12 03	12 36		13 04	13 44	14 02	14 37			15 02	15 43
Slough 3	a																					
London Paddington 15 ⊖	a			10 08	10 43	11 23		11 43	12 22			12 42	13 23		13 42	14 23	14 42	15 23			15 43	16 22

A From Westbury to Cheltenham Spa
B From Taunton
C From Carmarthen
D From Plymouth
E To Reading Bus
F From Westbury
G From Exeter St Davids

For connections from Hereford and Birmingham New Street please see Tables 131 and 57. For connections to Oxford, Gatwick Airport and Heathrow Airport please see Tables 116, 148 and 125A

For other services between London and Worcester refer to table 126

Table 125R

Sundays

16 February to 23 March

South Wales, Weston-super-Mare, Bristol, Cheltenham Spa and Swindon - London

Route Diagram - see first Page of Table 125

		GW	GW	GW	GW	GW	GW	GW	GW	GW	GW	GW	GW	GW	GW	GW	GW	GW	GW	GW	GW	GW
			R [1]	R [1]	R [1]	◇[1]	◇[1]	◇[1]		R [1]		◇[1]		◇[1]	◇[1]	◇[1]	◇[1]	◇[1]	R [1]		◇[1]	◇[1]
									A				A	B	C	B		B		A		C
			☕	☕	☕	☕	☕	☕		☕		☕		☕	☕	☕	☕	☕	☕		☕	☕
Swansea	d		13 21		14 21					15 21					16 21				17 17			17 51
Neath	d		13 33		14 33					15 33					16 33				17 29			18 03
Port Talbot Parkway	d		13 40		14 40					15 40					16 40				17 36			18 10
Bridgend	d		13 53		14 53					15 53					16 53				17 49			18 23
Cardiff Central 7	d		14 15		15 15					16 15					17 15				18 15			18 50
Newport (South Wales)	d		14 32		15 32					16 32					17 32				18 32			19 04
Weston-super-Mare	d			14 51										17 02		17 29						
Bristol Temple Meads 10	d			15 24		16 00		16 20				16 55		17 25		18 00		18 20			19 00	
Bristol Parkway 7	a		14 59		15 59					16 59					17 59				18 59			19 31
	d		15 01		16 01					17 01					18 01				19 01			19 33
Bath Spa 7	d			15 37		16 13		16 33				17 08		17 38		18 13		18 33			19 13	
Chippenham	d			15 49		16 25		16 45	16 55			17 20	17 42	17 50		18 25		18 45		19 15	19 25	
Worcester Shrub Hill	d																					
Cheltenham Spa	d	14 05					15 46				16 32						17 46					
Gloucester 7	d	14 21					16 02				16 45						18 00					
Stonehouse	d	14 34					16 17				16 57						18 15					
Stroud	d	14 40					16 22				17 02						18 21					
Kemble	d	14 57					16 37				17 17						18 35					
Swindon	a	15 12	15 26	16 04	16 26	16 41	16 52	17 00	17 13	17 26	17 32	17 35	18 00	18 05	18 26	18 40	18 50	18 59	19 27	19 33	19 40	19 57
	d		15 29	16 05	16 29	16 41	16 54	17 01		17 29		17 38		18 06	18 29	18 41	18 51	19 01	19 29		19 41	19 59
Didcot Parkway	a		15 46		16 46	16 59		17 18		17 46		17 54			18 46	18 58			19 46		19 58	20 15
Reading 7	a		16 04	16 35	17 04	17 19	17 23	17 35		18 03		18 12		18 39	19 03	19 20	19 23	19 32	20 04		20 14	20 33
Slough 3	a																					
London Paddington 15 ⊖	a		16 43	17 13	17 44	17 57	18 03	18 26		18 43		18 57		19 22	19 43	19 58	20 04	20 13	20 43		20 57	21 13

		GW	GW	GW	GW	GW	GW	GW	GW	GW
				◇[1]	◇[1]	◇[1]	◇[1]	◇[1]		◇[1]
			D					C		B
				☕	☕	☕	☕	☕		☕
Swansea	d				18 51			19 55		
Neath	d				19 03			20 07		
Port Talbot Parkway	d				19 10			20 14		
Bridgend	d				19 23			20 28		
Cardiff Central 7	d				19 50			20 55		
Newport (South Wales)	d				20 04			21 09		
Weston-super-Mare	d						20 26			
Bristol Temple Meads 10	d			20 00			21 00			22 10
Bristol Parkway 7	a				20 31			21 36		
	d				20 33			21 38		
Bath Spa 7	d			20 13			21 13			22 23
Chippenham	d		20 07	20 25			21 24			22 35
Worcester Shrub Hill	d									
Cheltenham Spa	d					19 59			21 46	
Gloucester 7	d	19 34				20 13			21 58	
Stonehouse	d	19 48				20 27			22 11	
Stroud	d	19 53				20 33			22 16	
Kemble	d	20 07				20 48			22 31	
Swindon	a	20 23	20 24	20 40	20 57	21 02	21 40	22 04	22 46	22 50
	d			20 41	20 59	21 02	21 41	22 05		22 52
Didcot Parkway	a			20 58		21 24	22 00			23 09
Reading 7	a			21 16	21 33	21 42	22 18	22 38		23 29
Slough 3	a									
London Paddington 15 ⊖	a			22 01	22 14	22 30	22 58	23 19		00 13

A From Westbury
B From Exeter St Davids
C From Carmarthen
D From Westbury to Cheltenham Spa

For connections from Hereford and Birmingham New Street please see Tables 131 and 57. For connections to Oxford, Gatwick Airport and Heathrow Airport please see Tables 116, 148 and 125A

For other services between London and Worcester refer to table 126

Table 125R

Sundays

30 March to 11 May

South Wales, Weston-super-Mare, Bristol, Cheltenham Spa and Swindon - London

Route Diagram - see first Page of Table 125

		GW	GW	GW	GW	GW		GW	GW	GW	GW	GW	GW	GW	GW	GW		GW	GW	GW	GW	GW	GW	GW	
																		R	R		R		R		
			1	◇1	◇1	◇1			◇1	◇1			◇1	◇1		◇1		1	1		1		1	◇1	
		A									B							C				B			
		🚌	☕	☕	☕	☕			☕	☕			☕	☕		☕		☕	☕		☕		☕	☕	
Swansea	d					07 58							09 21			10 21			11 21				12 21		
Neath	d					08 10							09 33			10 33			11 33				12 33		
Port Talbot Parkway	d					08 17							09 40			10 40			11 40				12 40		
Bridgend	d					08 31							09 53			10 53			11 53				12 53		
Cardiff Central 7	d			07 45		08 55							10 15			11 15			12 15				13 15		
Newport (South Wales)	d			08 03		09 10							10 32			11 32			12 32				13 32		
Weston-super-Mare	d				08 12					09 47											12 51				
Bristol Temple Meads 10	d		08 15		08 45				09 48	10 20				11 20				12 25			13 25			14 25	
Bristol Parkway 7	a			08 32		09 37							10 56			11 56			12 56				13 56		
	d			08 34		09 39							10 57			11 57			12 57				13 57		
Bath Spa 7	d		08 28		08 58				10 01	10 33				11 33				12 38			13 38			14 38	
Chippenham	d	07 15	08 40		09 10				10 13	10 45	10 57			11 45				12 50			13 50	13 58		14 50	
Worcester Shrub Hill	d																								
Cheltenham Spa	d							09 24				10 18			11 20					13 03					
Gloucester 7	d							09 37				10 31			11 33					13 15					
Stonehouse	d							09 50				10 44			11 46					13 28					
Stroud	d							09 55				10 49			11 51					13 33					
Kemble	d							10 09				11 03			12 05					13 47					
Swindon	a	07 50	08 55	08 59	09 24	10 04		10 24	10 27	11 00	11 15	11 18	11 22	12 00	12 20	12 22		13 05	13 22	14 02	14 05	14 17	14 22	15 05	
	d			09 02	09 29	10 05			10 29	11 02			11 25	12 01		12 25		13 06	13 25		14 07		14 25	15 06	
Didcot Parkway	a				09 44				10 44	11 19			11 42	12 19		12 42		13 24	13 42				14 42	15 26	
Reading 7	a			09 32	10 02	10 37			11 03	11 35			12 01	12 35		13 01		13 44	14 01		14 40		15 01	15 43	
Slough 3	a																								
London Paddington 15 ⊖	a			10 08	10 43	11 24			11 43	12 22			12 41	13 22		13 42		14 25	14 42		15 22		15 42	16 26	

		GW		GW	GW	GW	GW	GW	GW	GW	GW	GW		GW	GW	GW	GW	GW	GW	GW	GW	GW		GW	GW
				R	R	R					R					R					R				
				1	1	1	◇1	◇1	◇1		1			◇1		1	◇1	◇1	◇1	◇1	1			◇1	◇1
										B					B	C	D	E		C		B			D
				☕	☕	☕	☕	☕	☕		☕			☕		☕	☕	☕	☕	☕	☕			☕	☕
Swansea	d			13 21		14 21					15 21						16 21				17 17				17 51
Neath	d			13 33		14 33					15 33						16 33				17 29				18 03
Port Talbot Parkway	d			13 40		14 40					15 40						16 40				17 36				18 10
Bridgend	d			13 53		14 53					15 53						16 53				17 49				18 23
Cardiff Central 7	d			14 15		15 15					16 15						17 15				18 15				18 50
Newport (South Wales)	d			14 32		15 32					16 32						17 32				18 32				19 04
Weston-super-Mare	d				14 51											17 02		17 29							
Bristol Temple Meads 10	d				15 23		16 00		16 20					17 00		17 25		18 00		18 20				19 00	
Bristol Parkway 7	a			14 56		15 56					16 55						17 55				18 55				19 24
	d			14 57		15 57					16 57						17 57				18 57				19 26
Bath Spa 7	d				15 36		16 13		16 33					17 13		17 38		18 13		18 33				19 13	
Chippenham	d				15 48		16 25		16 45	16 55				17 25	17 42	17 50		18 25		18 45		19 15		19 25	
Worcester Shrub Hill	d																								
Cheltenham Spa	d	14 05						15 42				16 32							17 46						
Gloucester 7	d	14 21						15 56				16 45							18 00						
Stonehouse	d	14 34						16 11				16 57							18 15						
Stroud	d	14 40						16 16				17 02							18 21						
Kemble	d	14 57						16 31				17 17							18 35						
Swindon	a	15 12		15 22	16 03	16 22	16 41	16 46	17 00	17 13	17 22	17 33		17 40	18 00	18 05	18 22	18 40	18 50	18 59	19 22	19 33		19 40	19 50
	d			15 25	16 04	16 25	16 41	16 51	17 01		17 25			17 41		18 06	18 25	18 41	18 51	19 00	19 25			19 41	19 52
Didcot Parkway	a			15 42		16 42	16 58		17 18		17 42			17 58			18 42	18 58			19 42			19 58	20 08
Reading 7	a			16 01	16 36	17 01	17 19	17 21	17 37		18 01			18 18		18 39	19 00	19 20	19 23	19 33	20 01			20 12	20 29
Slough 3	a																								
London Paddington 15 ⊖	a			16 42	17 12	17 42	17 57	18 01	18 22		18 42			18 57		19 25	19 41	19 57	20 03	20 22	20 42			20 57	21 03

A To Reading Bus
B From Westbury
C From Plymouth
D From Carmarthen
E From Paignton

For connections from Hereford and Birmingham New Street please see Tables 131 and 57. For connections to Oxford, Gatwick Airport and Heathrow Airport please see Tables 116, 148 and 125A

For other services between London and Worcester refer to table 126

Table 125R

Sundays

30 March to 11 May

South Wales, Weston-super-Mare, Bristol, Cheltenham Spa and Swindon - London

Route Diagram - see first Page of Table 125

		GW	GW	GW	GW	GW	GW	GW		GW	GW
				◇1	◇1	◇1	◇1	◇1			◇1
			A	B				C			D
				🍴	🍴	🍴	🍴	🍴			🍴
Swansea	d				18 51			19 55			
Neath	d				19 03			20 07			
Port Talbot Parkway	d				19 10			20 14			
Bridgend	d				19 23			20 28			
Cardiff Central 7	d				19 50			20 55			
Newport (South Wales)	d				20 04			21 09			
Weston-super-Mare	d			19 27			20 26				
Bristol Temple Meads 10	d			20 00			21 00				22 10
Bristol Parkway 7	a				20 25			21 36			
	d				20 27			21 38			
Bath Spa 7	d			20 13			21 13				22 23
Chippenham	d		20 07	20 25			21 24				22 35
Worcester Shrub Hill	d										
Cheltenham Spa	d					19 59				21 46	
Gloucester 7	d	19 34				20 13				21 58	
Stonehouse	d	19 48				20 27				22 11	
Stroud	d	19 53				20 33				22 16	
Kemble	d	20 07				20 48				22 31	
Swindon	a	20 23	20 24	20 40	20 50	21 02	21 40	22 04		22 46	22 50
	d			20 41	20 52	21 02	21 41	22 05			22 52
Didcot Parkway	a			20 58		21 24	22 00				23 09
Reading 7	a			21 16	21 29	21 42	22 18	22 44			23 29
Slough 3	a										
London Paddington 15 ⊖	a			21 57	22 05	22 26	22 56	23 27			00 06

A From Westbury to Cheltenham Spa
B From Taunton
C From Carmarthen
D From Plymouth

For connections from Hereford and Birmingham New Street please see Tables 131 and 57. For connections to Oxford, Gatwick Airport and Heathrow Airport please see Tables 116, 148 and 125A

For other services between London and Worcester refer to table 126

Table 125A

Mondays to Fridays

9 December to 16 May

Reading - Heathrow Railair Link

Express Coach Service

Route Diagram - see first Page of Table 125

		GW	GW	GW	GW	GW	GW	GW	GW	GW	GW	GW	GW	GW	GW	GW	GW	GW	GW	GW	GW	GW	GW
				A	B	A	A	B	A	A	B	A	B	A	A	B	A	B	A	A	B	A	B
Reading 7	d	04 00	05 00	05 30	05 45	05 55	06 08	06 15	06 20	06 40	06 45	07 00	07 15	07 20	07 40	07 45	08 00	08 15	08 20	08 40	08 45	09 05	09 15
Heathrow Terminal 5 Bus	a	04 38	05 38	06 08	06 25	06 33	06 48	06 55	07 15	07 35	07 25	07 55	07 55	08 15	08 35	08 25	08 55	08 55	09 15	09 35	09 25	09 45	09 55
Heathrow Terminal 1 Bus	a	04 46	05 46	06 16	06 35	06 41	06 58	07 05	07 25	07 45	07 35	08 05	08 05	08 25	08 45	08 35	09 05	09 05	09 25	09 45	09 35	09 55	10 05
Heathrow Terminal 2 Bus	a																						
Heathrow Terminal 3 Bus	a	04 51	05 51	06 21	06 41	06 46	07 04	07 11	07 31	07 51	07 41	08 11	08 11	08 31	08 51	08 41	09 11	09 11	09 31	09 51	09 41	10 01	10 11

		GW	GW	GW	GW	GW	GW	GW	GW	GW	GW	GW	GW	GW	GW	GW	GW	GW	GW	GW	GW	GW	GW
		A		A	B	A		A	B	A		A	B	A		A	B	A		A	B	A	
Reading 7	d	09 25	09 45	10 05	10 15	10 25	10 45	11 05	11 15	11 25	11 45	12 05	12 15	12 25	12 45	13 05	13 15	13 25	13 45	14 05	14 15	14 25	14 45
Heathrow Terminal 5 Bus	a	10 05	10 25	10 45	10 55	11 05	11 25	11 45	11 55	12 05	12 25	12 45	12 55	13 05	13 25	13 45	13 55	14 05	14 25	14 45	14 55	15 05	15 25
Heathrow Terminal 1 Bus	a	10 15	10 35	10 55	11 05	11 15	11 35	11 55	12 05	12 15	12 35	12 55	13 05	13 15	13 35	13 55	14 05	14 15	14 35	14 55	15 05	15 15	15 35
Heathrow Terminal 2 Bus	a																						
Heathrow Terminal 3 Bus	a	10 21	10 41	11 01	11 11	11 21	11 41	12 01	12 11	12 21	12 41	13 01	13 11	13 21	13 41	14 01	14 11	14 21	14 41	15 01	15 11	15 21	15 41

		GW	GW	GW	GW	GW	GW	GW	GW	GW	GW	GW	GW	GW	GW	GW	GW	GW	GW	GW	GW	GW
		A	B	A		A	B	A		A	B	A		A	B	A	B	A	B	A	B	A
Reading 7	d	15 05	15 15	15 25	15 45	16 05	16 15	16 25	16 45	17 05	17 15	17 25	17 45	18 05	18 15	18 35	18 45	19 05	19 15	19 35	19 45	20 05
Heathrow Terminal 5 Bus	a	15 45	15 55	16 05	16 25	16 45	16 55	17 05	17 25	17 45	17 55	18 05	18 25	18 45	18 55	19 15	19 25	19 45	19 55	20 15	20 25	20 43
Heathrow Terminal 1 Bus	a	15 55	16 05	16 15	16 35	16 55	17 05	17 15	17 35	17 55	18 05	18 15	18 35	18 55	19 05	19 25	19 35	19 55	20 05	20 25	20 35	20 51
Heathrow Terminal 2 Bus	a																					
Heathrow Terminal 3 Bus	a	16 01	16 11	16 21	16 41	17 01	17 11	17 21	17 41	18 01	18 11	18 21	18 41	19 01	19 11	19 31	19 41	20 01	20 11	20 31	20 41	20 56

		GW	GW	GW	GW	GW	GW
		B	A	B	A		
Reading 7	d	20 25	20 35	20 55	21 05	22 05	23 05
Heathrow Terminal 5 Bus	a	21 05	21 13	21 35	21 43	22 43	23 43
Heathrow Terminal 1 Bus	a	21 15	21 21	21 45	21 51	22 51	23 51
Heathrow Terminal 2 Bus	a						
Heathrow Terminal 3 Bus	a	21 21	21 26	21 51	21 56	22 56	23 56

Saturdays

14 December to 17 May

		GW	GW	GW	GW	GW	GW	GW	GW	GW	GW	GW	GW	GW	GW	GW	GW	GW	GW	GW	GW	GW	GW
Reading 7	d	04 00	05 00	05 45	06 15	06 45	07 15	07 45	08 15	08 45	09 15	09 45	10 15	10 45	11 15	11 45	12 15	12 45	13 15	13 45	14 15	14 45	15 15
Heathrow Terminal 5 Bus	a	04 38	05 38	06 25	06 55	07 25	07 55	08 25	08 55	09 25	09 55	10 25	10 55	11 25	11 55	12 25	12 55	13 25	13 55	14 25	14 55	15 25	15 55
Heathrow Terminal 1 Bus	a	04 46	05 46	06 35	07 05	07 35	08 05	08 35	09 05	09 35	10 05	10 35	11 05	11 35	12 05	12 35	13 05	13 35	14 05	14 35	15 05	15 35	16 05
Heathrow Terminal 2 Bus	a																						
Heathrow Terminal 3 Bus	a	04 51	05 51	06 41	07 11	07 41	08 11	08 41	09 11	09 41	10 11	10 41	11 11	11 41	12 11	12 41	13 11	13 41	14 11	14 41	15 11	15 41	16 11

		GW	GW	GW	GW	GW	GW	GW	GW	GW	GW	GW	GW	GW
Reading 7	d	15 45	16 15	16 45	17 15	17 45	18 15	18 45	19 15	19 45	20 25	20 55	22 05	23 05
Heathrow Terminal 5 Bus	a	16 25	16 55	17 25	17 55	18 25	18 55	19 25	19 55	20 25	21 05	21 35	22 43	23 43
Heathrow Terminal 1 Bus	a	16 35	17 05	17 35	18 05	18 35	19 05	19 35	20 05	20 35	21 15	21 45	22 51	23 51
Heathrow Terminal 2 Bus	a													
Heathrow Terminal 3 Bus	a	16 41	17 11	17 41	18 11	18 41	19 11	19 41	20 11	20 41	21 21	21 51	22 56	23 56

Sundays

8 December to 11 May

		GW	GW	GW	GW	GW	GW	GW	GW	GW	GW	GW	GW	GW	GW	GW	GW	GW	GW	GW	GW	GW	GW
Reading 7	d	04 00	05 00	05 45	06 15	06 45	07 15	07 45	08 15	08 45	09 15	09 45	10 15	10 45	11 15	11 45	12 15	12 45	13 15	13 45	14 15	14 45	15 15
Heathrow Terminal 5 Bus	a	04 38	05 38	06 25	06 55	07 25	07 55	08 25	08 55	09 25	09 55	10 25	10 55	11 25	11 55	12 25	12 55	13 25	13 55	14 25	14 55	15 25	15 55
Heathrow Terminal 1 Bus	a	04 46	05 46	06 35	07 05	07 35	08 05	08 35	09 05	09 35	10 05	10 35	11 05	11 35	12 05	12 35	13 05	13 35	14 05	14 35	15 05	15 35	16 05
Heathrow Terminal 2 Bus	a																						
Heathrow Terminal 3 Bus	a	04 51	05 51	06 41	07 11	07 41	08 11	08 41	09 11	09 41	10 11	10 41	11 11	11 41	12 11	12 41	13 11	13 41	14 11	14 41	15 11	15 41	16 11

		GW	GW	GW	GW	GW	GW	GW	GW	GW	GW	GW	GW	GW
Reading 7	d	15 45	16 15	16 45	17 15	17 45	18 15	18 45	19 15	19 45	20 25	20 55	22 05	23 05
Heathrow Terminal 5 Bus	a	16 25	16 55	17 25	17 55	18 25	18 55	19 25	19 55	20 25	21 05	21 35	22 43	23 43
Heathrow Terminal 1 Bus	a	16 35	17 05	17 35	18 05	18 35	19 05	19 35	20 05	20 35	21 15	21 45	22 51	23 51
Heathrow Terminal 2 Bus	a													
Heathrow Terminal 3 Bus	a	16 41	17 11	17 41	18 11	18 41	19 11	19 41	20 11	20 41	21 21	21 51	22 56	23 56

A not 18 April, 21 April, 5 May

B 18 April, 21 April, 5 May

On Bank Holidays bus times may vary; please check before you travel

Table 125A-R

Mondays to Fridays

9 December to 16 May

Heathrow - Reading Railair Link

Express Coach Service

Route Diagram - see first Page of Table 125

		GW	GW	GW	GW	GW		GW	GW	GW	GW	GW	GW	GW	GW	GW		GW	GW	GW	GW	GW	GW	GW	GW
					A	A		B	A	B	A	B	A	B	A	A		B	A	A	B	A		A	B
Heathrow Central Bus Stn	d	00 05	05 00	06 00	06 30	06 57		07 00	07 20	07 30	07 40	08 00	08 00	08 30	08 20	08 40		09 00	09 00	09 20	09 30	09 40	10 00	10 15	10 30
Heathrow Terminal 5 Bus	d	00 13	05 08	06 08	06 38	07 05		07 10	07 28	07 40	07 50	08 10	08 10	08 40	08 30	08 50		09 10	09 10	09 30	09 40	09 50	10 10	10 25	10 40
Reading 7	a	00 51	05 46	06 46	07 21	07 48		07 53	08 21	08 23	08 46	08 53	09 06	09 23	09 26	09 39		09 53	09 59	10 13	10 23	10 33	10 53	11 08	11 23

		GW		GW	GW	GW	GW	GW	GW	GW	GW	GW		GW	GW	GW	GW	GW	GW	GW	GW	GW		GW	GW
		A		A	B	A	B	A	A	B	A	B		A	A	B	A	B	A	A	B	A		B	A
Heathrow Central Bus Stn	d	10 35		10 55	11 00	11 15	11 30	11 35	11 55	12 00	12 15	12 30		12 35	12 55	13 00	13 15	13 30	13 35	13 55	14 00	14 15		14 30	14 35
Heathrow Terminal 5 Bus	d	10 45		11 05	11 10	11 25	11 40	11 45	12 05	12 10	12 25	12 40		12 45	13 05	13 10	13 25	13 40	13 45	14 05	14 10	14 25		14 40	14 45
Reading 7	a	11 28		11 48	11 53	12 08	12 23	12 28	12 48	12 53	13 08	13 23		13 28	13 48	13 53	14 08	14 23	14 28	14 48	14 53	15 08		15 23	15 28

		GW	GW	GW	GW	GW	GW	GW		GW	GW	GW	GW	GW	GW	GW	GW	GW		GW	GW	GW	GW	GW	GW
		A	B	A	B	A	A	B		A	B	A	B	A	A	B	A	A		B	A	B	A	B	A
Heathrow Central Bus Stn	d	14 55	15 00	15 15	15 30	15 35	15 55	16 00		16 15	16 30	16 35	17 00	16 55	17 15	17 30	17 35	17 55		18 00	18 15	18 30	18 35	19 00	18 55
Heathrow Terminal 5 Bus	d	15 05	15 10	15 25	15 40	15 45	16 05	16 10		16 25	16 40	16 45	17 10	17 05	17 25	17 40	17 45	18 05		18 10	18 25	18 40	18 45	19 10	19 05
Reading 7	a	15 48	15 53	16 08	16 23	16 28	16 48	16 53		17 14	17 23	17 34	17 53	17 54	18 14	18 23	18 34	18 34		18 53	19 14	19 23	19 34	19 53	19 54

		GW	GW	GW		GW	GW	GW	GW	GW	GW	GW	GW	GW		GW	GW								
		B	A	A		B	A	B	A	B	A	B	A	B		A									
Heathrow Central Bus Stn	d	19 20	19 15	19 40		19 50	20 10	20 20	20 40	20 50	21 10	21 30	21 40	22 00		22 15	23 05								
Heathrow Terminal 5 Bus	d	19 30	19 25	19 50		20 00	20 20	20 30	20 50	21 00	21 20	21 38	21 50	22 08		22 23	23 13								
Reading 7	a	20 13	20 14	20 31		20 43	21 01	21 13	21 31	21 43	22 01	22 19	22 31	22 49		23 01	23 51								

Saturdays

14 December to 17 May

		GW	GW	GW	GW	GW	GW	GW	GW	GW		GW	GW	GW	GW	GW	GW	GW	GW	GW		GW	GW	GW	GW
Heathrow Central Bus Stn	d	00 05	05 00	06 00	07 00	07 30	08 00	08 30	09 00	09 30		10 00	10 30	11 00	11 30	12 00	12 30	13 00	13 30	14 00		14 30	15 00	15 30	16 00
Heathrow Terminal 5 Bus	d	00 13	05 08	06 08	07 10	07 40	08 10	08 40	09 10	09 40		10 10	10 40	11 10	11 40	12 10	12 40	13 10	13 40	14 10		14 40	15 10	15 40	16 10
Reading 7	a	00 51	05 46	06 46	07 53	08 53	08 53	09 23	09 53	10 23		10 53	11 23	11 53	12 23	12 53	13 23	13 53	14 23	14 53		15 23	15 53	16 23	16 53

		GW	GW	GW	GW	GW		GW	GW	GW	GW	GW	GW	GW	GW										
Heathrow Central Bus Stn	d	16 30	17 00	17 30	18 00	18 30		19 00	19 20	19 50	20 20	20 50	21 30	22 00	23 05										
Heathrow Terminal 5 Bus	d	16 40	17 10	17 40	18 10	18 40		19 10	19 30	20 00	20 30	21 00	21 38	22 08	23 13										
Reading 7	a	17 23	17 53	18 23	18 53	19 23		19 53	20 13	20 43	21 13	21 43	22 19	22 49	23 51										

Sundays

8 December to 11 May

		GW	GW	GW	GW	GW	GW	GW	GW	GW		GW	GW	GW	GW	GW	GW	GW	GW	GW		GW	GW	GW	GW
Heathrow Central Bus Stn	d	00 05	05 00	06 00	07 00	07 30	08 00	08 30	09 00	09 30		10 00	10 30	11 00	11 30	12 00	12 30	13 00	13 30	14 00		14 30	15 00	15 30	16 00
Heathrow Terminal 5 Bus	d	00 13	05 08	06 08	07 10	07 40	08 10	08 40	09 10	09 40		10 10	10 40	11 10	11 40	12 10	12 40	13 10	13 40	14 10		14 40	15 10	15 40	16 10
Reading 7	a	00 51	05 46	06 46	07 53	08 23	08 53	09 23	09 53	10 23		10 53	11 23	11 53	12 23	12 53	13 23	13 53	14 23	14 53		15 23	15 53	16 23	16 53

		GW	GW	GW	GW	GW		GW	GW	GW	GW	GW	GW	GW	GW										
Heathrow Central Bus Stn	d	16 30	17 00	17 30	18 00	18 30		19 00	19 20	19 50	20 20	20 50	21 30	22 00	23 05										
Heathrow Terminal 5 Bus	d	16 40	17 10	17 40	18 10	18 40		19 10	19 30	20 00	20 30	21 00	21 38	22 08	23 13										
Reading 7	a	17 23	17 53	18 53	18 53	19 23		19 53	20 13	20 43	21 13	21 43	22 19	22 49	23 51										

A not 18 April, 21 April, 5 May

B 18 April, 21 April, 5 May

On Bank Holidays bus times may vary; please check before you travel

Table 125B

Mondays to Fridays

9 December to 16 May

Bristol - Bristol International Airport

Bus Service

Route Diagram - see first Page of Table 125

	GW	GW	GW	GW	and hourly until	GW	GW	GW	GW		GW	GW	GW	GW	GW	GW	GW	GW	GW		GW	GW	GW
	BHX	BHX	BHX	BHX		BHX	BHX	BHX	BHX		BHX	BHX	BHX	BHX	BHX	BHX	BHX	BHX	BHX		BHX	BHX	BHX
																		A	B		A	B	A
Bristol Temple Meads d	00 09	00 29	00 59	01 29		04 29	04 59	05 32	05 52	....	06 12	06 22	06 32	06 42	06 52	07 02	07 12	07 22	07 22	....	07 32	07 32	07 42
Bristol Internatl Airport a	00 27	00 47	01 17	01 47		04 47	05 17	05 51	06 11	.	06 31	06 41	06 51	07 01	07 11	07 21	07 31	07 42	07 43	.	07 52	07 56	08 02

	GW	GW	GW	GW	GW	GW		GW	GW	GW	GW	GW	GW	GW	GW	GW		GW	GW	GW	GW	GW	GW	GW
	BHX	BHX	BHX	BHX	BHX	BHX		BHX	BHX	BHX	BHX	BHX	BHX	BHX	BHX	BHX		BHX	BHX	BHX	BHX	BHX	BHX	BHX
	B	A	B	A	B	A		B	A	B	A	B	A	B	A	B		A	B	A	B	A	B	A
Bristol Temple Meads d	07 46	07 52	07 56	08 02	08 06	08 12	....	08 16	08 22	08 26	08 32	08 36	08 42	08 46	08 52	08 56	....	09 02	09 06	09 12	09 16	09 22	09 26	09 32
Bristol Internatl Airport a	08 10	08 12	08 20	08 22	08 30	08 32	.	08 40	08 42	08 50	08 52	09 00	09 02	09 10	09 12	09 20	.	09 22	09 30	09 32	09 40	09 42	09 49	09 53

	GW	GW		GW	GW	GW	GW	GW	GW	GW	GW	GW		GW	GW	GW	GW	GW	GW	GW	GW	GW		GW
	BHX	BHX		BHX	BHX	BHX	BHX	BHX	BHX	BHX	BHX	BHX		BHX	BHX	BHX	BHX	BHX	BHX	BHX	BHX	BHX		BHX
	B	A		B	A	B	A	B	A	B	A	B		A	B	A	B	A	B	A	B	A		B
Bristol Temple Meads d	09 36	09 44	....	09 45	09 54	09 55	10 04	10 05	10 14	10 15	10 24	10 25	....	10 34	10 35	10 44	10 45	10 54	10 55	11 04	11 05	11 14	....	11 15
Bristol Internatl Airport a	09 58	10 05	.	10 07	10 15	10 17	10 25	10 27	10 35	10 37	10 45	10 47	.	10 55	10 57	11 05	11 07	11 15	11 17	11 25	11 27	11 35	.	11 37

	GW	GW	GW	GW	GW	GW	GW	GW		GW	GW	GW	GW	GW	GW	GW	GW	GW		GW	GW	GW	GW	GW
	BHX	BHX	BHX	BHX	BHX	BHX	BHX	BHX		BHX	BHX	BHX	BHX	BHX	BHX	BHX	BHX	BHX		BHX	BHX	BHX	BHX	BHX
	A	B	A	B	A	B	A	B		A	B	A	B	A	B	A	B	A		B	A	B	A	B
Bristol Temple Meads d	11 24	11 25	11 34	11 35	11 44	11 45	11 54	11 55	....	12 04	12 05	12 14	12 15	12 24	12 25	12 34	12 35	12 44	....	12 45	12 54	12 55	13 04	13 05
Bristol Internatl Airport a	11 45	11 47	11 55	11 57	12 05	12 07	12 15	12 17	.	12 25	12 27	12 35	12 37	12 45	12 47	12 55	12 57	13 05	.	13 07	13 15	13 17	13 25	13 27

	GW	GW	GW	GW		GW	GW	GW	GW	GW	GW	GW	GW	GW		GW	GW	GW	GW	GW	GW	GW	GW	GW
	BHX	BHX	BHX	BHX		BHX	BHX	BHX	BHX	BHX	BHX	BHX	BHX	BHX		BHX	BHX	BHX	BHX	BHX	BHX	BHX	BHX	BHX
	A	B	A	B		A	B	A	B	A	B	A	B	A		B	A	B	A	B	A	B	A	B
Bristol Temple Meads d	13 14	13 15	13 24	13 25	....	13 34	13 35	13 44	13 45	13 54	13 55	14 04	14 05	14 14	....	14 15	14 24	14 25	14 34	14 35	14 44	14 45	14 54	14 55
Bristol Internatl Airport a	13 35	13 37	13 45	13 47	.	13 55	13 57	14 05	14 07	14 15	14 17	14 25	14 27	14 35	.	14 37	14 45	14 47	14 55	14 57	15 05	15 07	15 15	15 17

		GW	GW	GW	GW	GW	GW	GW	GW	GW		GW	GW	GW	GW	GW	GW	GW	GW	GW		GW	GW	GW
		BHX	BHX	BHX	BHX	BHX	BHX	BHX	BHX	BHX		BHX	BHX	BHX	BHX	BHX	BHX	BHX	BHX	BHX		BHX	BHX	BHX
		A	B	A	B	A	B	A	B	A		B	A	B	A	B	A	B	A	B		A	B	A
Bristol Temple Meads d	....	15 04	15 05	15 14	15 15	15 24	15 25	15 34	15 35	15 44	....	15 47	15 54	15 57	16 04	16 07	16 14	16 17	16 24	16 27	....	16 34	16 37	16 44
Bristol Internatl Airport a	.	15 25	15 27	15 35	15 37	15 45	15 49	15 55	16 01	16 05	.	16 13	16 15	16 23	16 25	16 33	16 35	16 43	16 45	16 53	.	16 55	17 03	17 05

	GW	GW	GW	GW	GW	GW		GW	GW	GW	GW	GW	GW	GW	GW	GW		GW	GW	GW	GW	GW	GW	GW
	BHX	BHX	BHX	BHX	BHX	BHX		BHX	BHX	BHX	BHX	BHX	BHX	BHX	BHX	BHX		BHX	BHX	BHX	BHX	BHX	BHX	BHX
	B	A	B	A	B	A		B	A	B	A	B	A	B	A	B		A	B	A	B	A	B	A
Bristol Temple Meads d	16 47	16 54	16 57	17 04	17 07	17 14	....	17 17	17 24	17 27	17 34	17 37	17 44	17 47	17 54	17 57	....	18 04	18 07	18 14	18 15	18 24	18 25	18 34
Bristol Internatl Airport a	17 13	17 15	17 23	17 25	17 33	17 35	.	17 43	17 45	17 53	17 55	18 03	18 05	18 13	18 15	18 21	.	18 25	18 29	18 35	18 37	18 45	18 47	18 55

	GW	GW		GW	GW	GW	GW	GW	GW	and at the same minutes past each hour until	GW	GW	GW									
	BHX	BHX		BHX	BHX	BHX	BHX	BHX	BHX		BHX	BHX	BHX									
	B	A		B	A	B																
Bristol Temple Meads d	18 35	18 44	....	18 45	18 54	18 55	19 11	19 31	19 51		23 11	23 31	23 51	....	....	....	....	....	....	....	....	....
Bristol Internatl Airport a	18 57	19 05	.	19 07	19 15	19 17	19 30	19 50	20 10		23 30	23 50	00 10	.	.	.	.	.	.	.	.	.

Saturdays

14 December to 17 May

	GW	GW	GW	GW	and hourly until	GW	GW	GW	GW		GW	GW	GW	GW	GW	GW	GW	GW	GW		GW	GW	GW
Bristol Temple Meads d	00 09	00 29	00 59	01 29		04 29	04 59	05 32	05 52	....	06 12	06 22	06 32	06 42	06 52	07 02	07 12	07 22	07 32	....	07 42	07 52	08 02
Bristol Internatl Airport a	00 27	00 47	01 17	01 47		04 47	05 17	05 51	06 11	.	06 31	06 41	06 51	07 01	07 11	07 21	07 31	07 42	07 52	.	08 02	08 12	08 22

	GW	GW	GW	GW	GW	GW		GW	GW	GW	GW	GW	GW	GW	GW	GW	and at the same minutes past each hour until	GW	GW	GW	GW	GW	GW
Bristol Temple Meads d	08 12	08 22	08 32	08 42	08 52	09 02	....	09 12	09 22	09 32	09 45	09 55	10 05	10 15	10 25	10 35		13 45	13 55	14 05	14 15	14 25	14 35
Bristol Internatl Airport a	08 32	08 42	08 52	09 02	09 12	09 22	.	09 32	09 42	09 54	10 07	10 17	10 27	10 37	10 47	10 57		14 07	14 17	14 27	14 37	14 47	14 57

		GW	GW	GW	GW	and every 15 minutes until	GW		GW	and every 15 minutes until	GW		GW	GW	GW	GW	and at the same minutes past each hour until	GW	GW	GW	
Bristol Temple Meads d	....	14 45	15 00	15 15	15 30		17 45	....	18 00		18 45	....	19 00	19 11	19 31	19 51		23 11	23 31	23 51	....
Bristol Internatl Airport a	.	15 07	15 22	15 37	15 51		18 06	.	18 22		19 07	.	19 19	19 30	19 50	20 10		23 30	23 50	00 10	.

A 25 December, 26 December, 1 January, 18 April, 21 April, 5 May

B not 25 December, 26 December, 1 January, 18 April, 21 April, 5 May

Table 125B

Sundays

8 December to 11 May

Bristol - Bristol International Airport

Bus Service

Route Diagram - see first Page of Table 125

			GW 🚌	GW 🚌	GW 🚌	GW 🚌	and hourly until	GW 🚌	GW 🚌	GW 🚌	and every 15 minutes until	GW 🚌			GW 🚌	and every 15 minutes until	GW 🚌		GW 🚌	and every 15 minutes until	GW 🚌
Bristol Temple Meads 10	d	.....	00 09	00 29	00 59	01 29		04 29	04 59	05 27		07 12	.....	.....	07 27		09 27	.....	09 44		18 59
Bristol Internatl Airport ✈	a	.	00 27	00 47	01 17	01 47		04 47	05 17	05 46		07 31	.	.	07 47		09 47	.	10 05		19 20

			GW 🚌	GW 🚌	GW 🚌	and at the same minutes past each hour until	GW 🚌	GW 🚌	GW 🚌														
Bristol Temple Meads 10	d	.....	19 11	19 31	19 51		23 11	23 31	23 51	.....	.....	.....	.....	.....	.....	.....	.....	.....	.....	.....	.....	.....	.....
Bristol Internatl Airport ✈	a	.	19 30	19 50	20 10		23 30	23 50	00 10	.	.	.	.	.	.	.	.	.	.	.	.	.	.

Table 125B-R

Mondays to Fridays

9 December to 16 May

Bristol International Airport - Bristol

Bus Service

Route Diagram - see first Page of Table 125

		GW BHX 🚌	GW BHX 🚌	GW BHX 🚌	GW BHX 🚌	GW BHX 🚌		GW BHX 🚌	GW BHX 🚌	GW BHX 🚌	GW BHX A 🚌	GW BHX B 🚌	GW BHX 🚌	GW BHX 🚌	GW BHX 🚌	GW BHX 🚌		GW BHX 🚌	GW BHX 🚌	GW BHX 🚌	GW BHX A 🚌	GW BHX B 🚌	GW BHX A 🚌	GW BHX B 🚌	GW BHX A 🚌
Bristol Internatl Airport ✈	d	00 10	00 30	00 50	01 20	01 50	.....	02 50	03 50	04 50	05 20	05 30	05 40	06 00	06 20	06 40	.....	06 50	07 00	07 10	07 20	07 20	07 30	07 30	07 40
Bristol Temple Meads 10	a	00 30	00 50	01 10	01 40	02 10	.	03 10	04 10	05 11	05 42	05 52	06 02	06 22	06 42	07 02	.	07 12	07 22	07 32	07 44	07 48	07 54	08 02	08 04

		GW BHX B 🚌		GW BHX A 🚌	GW BHX B 🚌	GW BHX A 🚌	GW BHX B 🚌	GW BHX A 🚌	GW BHX B 🚌	GW BHX A 🚌	GW BHX B 🚌	GW BHX A 🚌		GW BHX B 🚌	GW BHX A 🚌	GW BHX B 🚌	GW BHX A 🚌	GW BHX B 🚌	GW BHX A 🚌	GW BHX B 🚌	GW BHX A 🚌	GW BHX B 🚌		GW BHX A 🚌	GW BHX B 🚌
Bristol Internatl Airport ✈	d	07 40	.....	07 50	07 50	08 00	08 00	08 10	08 10	08 20	08 20	08 30	.....	08 30	08 40	08 40	08 50	08 50	09 00	09 00	09 10	09 10	.....	09 20	09 20
Bristol Temple Meads 10	a	08 12	.	08 14	08 22	08 24	08 32	08 34	08 42	08 44	08 52	08 54	.	09 02	09 04	09 12	09 14	09 22	09 24	09 32	09 34	09 42	.	09 46	09 51

		GW BHX A 🚌	GW BHX B 🚌	GW BHX A 🚌	GW BHX B 🚌	GW BHX A 🚌	GW BHX B 🚌	GW BHX A 🚌		GW BHX B 🚌	GW BHX A 🚌	GW BHX B 🚌	GW BHX A 🚌	GW BHX B 🚌	GW BHX A 🚌	GW BHX B 🚌	GW BHX A 🚌	GW BHX B 🚌		GW BHX A 🚌	GW BHX B 🚌	GW BHX A 🚌	GW BHX B 🚌	GW BHX A 🚌	GW BHX B 🚌
Bristol Internatl Airport ✈	d	09 30	09 30	09 40	09 40	09 50	09 50	10 00	.....	10 00	10 10	10 10	10 20	10 20	10 30	10 30	10 40	10 40	.....	10 50	10 50	11 00	11 00	11 10	11 10
Bristol Temple Meads 10	a	09 57	09 59	10 07	10 09	10 17	10 19	10 27	.	10 29	10 37	10 39	10 47	10 49	10 57	10 59	11 07	11 09	.	11 17	11 19	11 27	11 29	11 37	11 39

		GW BHX A 🚌	GW BHX B 🚌	GW BHX A 🚌		GW BHX B 🚌	GW BHX A 🚌	GW BHX B 🚌	GW BHX A 🚌	GW BHX B 🚌	GW BHX A 🚌	GW BHX B 🚌	GW BHX A 🚌	GW BHX B 🚌		GW BHX A 🚌	GW BHX B 🚌	GW BHX A 🚌	GW BHX B 🚌	GW BHX A 🚌	GW BHX B 🚌	GW BHX A 🚌	GW BHX B 🚌	GW BHX A 🚌	
Bristol Internatl Airport ✈	d	11 20	11 20	11 30	.....	11 30	11 40	11 40	11 50	11 50	12 00	12 00	12 10	12 10	.....	12 20	12 20	12 30	12 30	12 40	12 40	12 50	12 50	13 00	.....
Bristol Temple Meads 10	a	11 47	11 49	11 57	.	11 59	12 07	12 09	12 17	12 19	12 27	12 29	12 37	12 39	.	12 47	12 49	12 57	12 59	13 07	13 09	13 17	13 19	13 27	.

		GW BHX B 🚌	GW BHX A 🚌	GW BHX B 🚌	GW BHX A 🚌	GW BHX B 🚌	GW BHX A 🚌	GW BHX B 🚌	GW BHX A 🚌	GW BHX B 🚌		GW BHX A 🚌	GW BHX B 🚌	GW BHX A 🚌	GW BHX B 🚌	GW BHX A 🚌	GW BHX B 🚌	GW BHX A 🚌	GW BHX B 🚌	GW BHX A 🚌		GW BHX B 🚌	GW BHX A 🚌	GW BHX B 🚌	GW BHX A 🚌
Bristol Internatl Airport ✈	d	13 00	13 10	13 10	13 20	13 20	13 30	13 30	13 40	13 40	.....	13 50	13 50	14 00	14 00	14 10	14 10	14 20	14 20	14 30	.....	14 30	14 40	14 40	14 50
Bristol Temple Meads 10	a	13 29	13 37	13 39	13 47	13 49	13 57	13 59	14 07	14 09	.	14 17	14 19	14 27	14 29	14 37	14 39	14 47	14 49	14 57	.	14 59	15 07	15 09	15 17

		GW BHX B 🚌	GW BHX A 🚌	GW BHX B 🚌	GW BHX A 🚌	GW BHX B 🚌		GW BHX A 🚌	GW BHX B 🚌	GW BHX A 🚌	GW BHX B 🚌	GW BHX A 🚌	GW BHX B 🚌	GW BHX A 🚌	GW BHX B 🚌	GW BHX A 🚌		GW BHX B 🚌	GW BHX A 🚌	GW BHX B 🚌	GW BHX A 🚌	GW BHX B 🚌	GW BHX A 🚌	GW BHX B 🚌	GW BHX A 🚌
Bristol Internatl Airport ✈	d	14 50	15 00	15 00	15 10	15 10	.....	15 20	15 20	15 30	15 30	15 40	15 40	15 50	15 50	16 00	.....	16 00	16 10	16 10	16 20	16 20	16 30	16 30	16 40
Bristol Temple Meads 10	a	15 19	15 27	15 29	15 37	15 39	.	15 47	15 50	15 57	16 01	16 07	16 11	16 17	16 21	16 27	.	16 31	16 37	16 41	16 47	16 51	16 57	17 01	17 07

		GW BHX B 🚌		GW BHX A 🚌	GW BHX B 🚌	GW BHX A 🚌	GW BHX B 🚌	GW BHX A 🚌	GW BHX B 🚌	GW BHX A 🚌	GW BHX B 🚌	GW BHX A 🚌		GW BHX B 🚌	GW BHX A 🚌	GW BHX B 🚌	GW BHX A 🚌	GW BHX B 🚌	GW BHX A 🚌	GW BHX B 🚌	GW BHX A 🚌	GW BHX B 🚌		GW BHX A 🚌	GW BHX B 🚌
Bristol Internatl Airport ✈	d	16 40	.....	16 50	16 50	17 00	17 00	17 10	17 10	17 20	17 20	17 30	.....	17 30	17 40	17 40	17 50	17 50	18 00	18 00	18 10	18 10	.....	18 20	18 20
Bristol Temple Meads 10	a	17 11	.	17 17	17 21	17 27	17 31	17 37	17 41	17 47	17 51	17 57	.	18 01	18 07	18 11	18 17	18 20	18 27	18 29	18 37	18 39	.	18 47	18 49

		GW BHX A 🚌	GW BHX B 🚌	GW BHX A 🚌	GW BHX B 🚌	GW BHX A 🚌	GW BHX B 🚌	GW BHX 🚌		GW BHX 🚌	GW BHX 🚌	GW BHX 🚌	GW BHX 🚌	GW BHX 🚌	and at the same minutes past each hour until	GW BHX 🚌	GW BHX 🚌	GW BHX 🚌		GW BHX 🚌	GW BHX 🚌			
Bristol Internatl Airport ✈	d	18 30	18 30	18 40	18 40	18 50	18 50	19 00	.....	19 10	19 20	19 30	19 50	20 10		22 30	22 50	23 10	.....	23 30	23 50	.....	.....	.....
Bristol Temple Meads 10	a	18 57	18 59	19 07	19 09	19 14	19 15	19 23	.	19 33	19 43	19 53	20 13	20 33		22 53	23 13	23 33	.	23 53	00 11	.	.	.

Saturdays

14 December to 17 May

		GW	GW	GW	GW	GW	GW	GW	GW	GW		GW	GW	GW	GW	GW	GW	GW	GW	GW		GW	GW	GW	GW
		🚌	🚌	🚌	🚌	🚌	🚌	🚌	🚌	🚌		🚌	🚌	🚌	🚌	🚌	🚌	🚌	🚌	🚌		🚌	🚌	🚌	🚌
Bristol Internatl Airport	✈ d	00 10	00 30	00 50	01 20	01 50	02 50	03 50	04 50	05 30	.....	05 40	06 00	06 20	06 40	06 50	07 00	07 10	07 20	07 30	.....	07 40	07 50	08 00	08 10
Bristol Temple Meads 10	a	00 30	00 50	01 10	01 40	02 10	03 10	04 10	05 11	05 52	.	06 02	06 22	06 42	07 02	07 12	07 22	07 32	07 44	07 54	.	08 04	08 14	08 24	08 34

		GW	GW	GW	GW	GW		GW	GW	GW	GW	GW	GW	GW	GW	and at the same minutes past each hour until	GW	GW	GW	GW	GW	GW		GW
		🚌	🚌	🚌	🚌	🚌		🚌	🚌	🚌	🚌	🚌	🚌	🚌	🚌		🚌	🚌	🚌	🚌	🚌	🚌		🚌
Bristol Internatl Airport	✈ d	08 20	08 30	08 40	08 50	09 00	.....	09 10	09 20	09 30	09 40	09 50	10 00	10 10	10 20		12 30	12 40	12 50	13 00	13 10	13 20	.....	13 30
Bristol Temple Meads 10	a	08 44	08 54	09 04	09 14	09 24	.	09 34	09 47	09 58	10 08	10 18	10 28	10 38	10 48		12 58	13 08	13 18	13 28	13 38	13 48	.	13 58

		GW	GW	GW	and every 15 minutes until	GW	GW	GW	GW	GW	GW	and at the same minutes past each hour until	GW	GW	GW		GW	GW					
		🚌	🚌	🚌		🚌	🚌	🚌	🚌	🚌	🚌		🚌	🚌	🚌		🚌	🚌					
Bristol Internatl Airport	✈ d	13 40	13 50	14 00		18 45	19 00	19 15	19 30	19 50	20 10		22 30	22 50	23 10	.....	23 30	23 50	.....	.....	.....	.....	.....
Bristol Temple Meads 10	a	14 08	14 18	14 28		19 13	19 23	19 38	19 53	20 13	20 33		22 53	23 13	23 33	.	23 53	00 11	.	.	.	.	.

A 25 December, 26 December, 1 January, 18 April, 21 April, 5 May

B not 25 December, 26 December, 1 January, 18 April, 21 April, 5 May

Table 125B-R

Sundays

8 December to 11 May

Bristol International Airport - Bristol

Bus Service

Route Diagram - see first Page of Table 125

			GW	GW	GW	GW	GW	GW	GW	GW	GW	and every 15 minutes until	GW			GW	and every 15 minutes until	GW		GW	and every 15 minutes until	GW
			🚌	🚌	🚌	🚌	🚌	🚌	🚌	🚌	🚌		🚌			🚌		🚌		🚌		🚌
Bristol Internatl Airport	✈ d	.....	00 10	00 30	00 50	01 20	01 50	02 50	03 50	04 50	05 30		07 15	.....	.....	07 30		09 15	.....	09 30		18 45
Bristol Temple Meads 10	a	.	00 30	00 50	01 10	01 40	02 10	03 10	04 10	05 11	05 52		07 37	.	.	07 54		09 39	.	09 57		19 12

		GW		GW	GW	GW	GW	and at the same minutes past each hour until	GW	GW	GW	GW		GW										
		🚌		🚌	🚌	🚌	🚌		🚌	🚌	🚌	🚌		🚌										
Bristol Internatl Airport	✈ d	19 00	.....	19 15	19 30	19 50	20 10		22 30	22 50	23 10	23 30	.....	23 50	.....	.....	.....	.....	.....	.....	.....	.....	.....	.....
Bristol Temple Meads 10	a	19 23	.	19 38	19 53	20 13	20 33		22 53	23 13	23 33	23 53	.	00 11	.	.	.	.	.	.	.	.	.	.

Table 126

Mondays to Fridays

9 December to 16 May

London and Oxford - Worcester and Hereford

Network Diagram - refer to first Page of Table 116

Miles	Station		GW MO	GW MX	GW	GW	GW	GW	GW	GW	GW	GW	GW
			◇1	◇1	1	◇1	1	1	◇1	◇1	◇1	◇1	◇1
						A	A						
				☕		🛒	🛒		☕	🛒		☕	🛒
0	**London Paddington** 15 ⊖	d				05 45	06 48	07 50	08 22	09 21	09 50	10 22	11 20
18½	Slough 3	d				06 01	07 02	08 06	08 36	09 36	10 06	10 36	11 36
36	Reading 7	d				06 17	07 19	08 22	08 52	09 52	10 22	10 52	11 52
53¼	Didcot Parkway	d					07 50						
63½	**Oxford**	d				06 51	08 04	08 58	09 21	10 25	10 48	11 19	12 19
70½	Hanborough	d				07 03	08 14	09 07	09 31	10 35	10 57	11 29	12 29
71½	Combe	d											
75	Finstock	d											
76¾	Charlbury	a				07 10	08 22	09 14	09 39	10 42	11 04	11 37	12 36
—		d				07 10	08 22	09 14	09 39	10 42	11 04	11 37	12 36
80½	Ascott-under-Wychwood	d											
81¾	Shipton	d											
84¾	Kingham	d				07 19	08 31	09 23	09 49	10 51	11 13	11 47	12 45
91¾	Moreton-in-Marsh	a				07 28	08 38	09 35	09 58	11 00	11 22	11 56	12 54
—		d			05 45	07 28	08 39		09 58	11 00		11 56	12 54
101¾	Honeybourne	d				07 39	08 49		10 10			12 08	13 05
106¾	Evesham	a			05 59	07 46	08 56		10 18	11 15		12 16	13 12
—		d			05 59	07 47	08 56		10 25	11 15		12 25	13 12
112¾	Pershore	d	00 01	00 02	06 07	07 55	09 03		10 33	11 22		12 32	13 19
120½	**Worcester Shrub Hill** 7	a	00 12	00 13	06 19	08 07	09 15		10 45	11 35		12 44	13 32
121¼	**Worcester Foregate Street** 7	a			06 25	08 16	09 19		10 49	11 41		12 49	13 36
128	Malvern Link	a					09 28		11 04			12 58	13 51
128¾	Great Malvern	a					09 33		11 08			13 03	13 56
131¾	Colwall	a							11 14			13 15	
136	Ledbury	a							11 22			13 24	
149¾	**Hereford** 7	a							11 43			13 48	

Miles	Station		GW	GW	GW	GW	GW	GW	GW	GW	GW FX	GW FO
			◇1	◇1	◇1	◇1	1	◇1	◇1	◇1	◇1	◇1
					B					C		
			🛒	🛒	🛒	☕		☕	☕	☕	☕	☕
0	**London Paddington** 15 ⊖	d	12 21	13 21	14 21	15 52		17 22	17 49	18 22	19 22	19 22
18½	Slough 3	d	12 36	13 36	14 36						19 36	19 36
36	Reading 7	d	12 52	13 51	14 52	16u22		17 50	18 22	18 51	19 52	19 52
53¼	Didcot Parkway	d					17 15					
63½	**Oxford**	d	13 25	14 19	15 20	16 49	17 32	18 17	18 49	19 23	20 20	20 24
70½	Hanborough	d	13 34	14 29	15 29	16 59	17 41	18 26		19 33	20 30	20 34
71½	Combe	d					17 45					
75	Finstock	d					17 51					
76¾	Charlbury	a	13 41	14 36	15 36	17 06	17 55	18 34	19 02	19 41	20 38	20 42
—		d	13 41	14 36	15 36	17 07	17 56	18 35	19 03	19 42	20 38	20 42
80½	Ascott-under-Wychwood	d					18 02					
81¾	Shipton	d					18 06		19 11			
84¾	Kingham	d	13 50	14 45	15 45	17 17	18 11	18 45	19 18	19 52	20 48	20 52
91¾	Moreton-in-Marsh	a	13 59	14 54	15 54	17 26	18 20	18 54	19 27	20 01	20 57	21 01
—		d	13 59		15 54	17 27	18 20	18 55	19 28	20 02	20 57	21 01
101¾	Honeybourne	d	14 10		16 05	17 39	18 32	19 06		20 13	21 09	21 13
106¾	Evesham	a	14 17		16 12	17 48	18 39	19 15	19 44	20 21	21 17	21 21
—		d	14 26		16 21	17 49	18 40	19 15	19 45	20 22	21 21	21 21
112¾	Pershore	d	14 34		16 29	17 56	18 48	19 23	19 53	20 29	21 28	21 28
120½	**Worcester Shrub Hill** 7	a	14 46		16 40	18 09	18 59	19 35	20 05	20 41	21 47	21 47
121¼	**Worcester Foregate Street** 7	a	14 52		16 44		19 11	19 39		20 45	21 51	21 51
128	Malvern Link	a	15 07				19 20	19 49		20 54	22 03	22 03
128¾	Great Malvern	a	15 10				19 24	19 53		20 59	22 07	22 07
131¾	Colwall	a						20 00		21 05	22 26	22 26
136	Ledbury	a						20 08		21 14	22 35	22 35
149¾	**Hereford** 7	a						20 29		21 34	22 55	22 55

Station		GW	GW FX	GW FO
		◇1	◇1	◇1
		B		
		🛒	☕	🛒
London Paddington 15 ⊖	d	20 20	21 48	21 48
Slough 3	d	20 36	22 04	22 04
Reading 7	d	20 51	22 25	22 25
Didcot Parkway	d			
Oxford	d	21 21	22 53	22 53
Hanborough	d	21 31	23 03	23 03
Combe	d			
Finstock	d			
Charlbury	a	21 38	23 10	23 10
	d	21 38	23 11	23 11
Ascott-under-Wychwood	d			
Shipton	d		23 18	23 18
Kingham	d	21 48	23 24	23 24
Moreton-in-Marsh	a	21 57	23 33	23 33
	d	21 57	23 34	23 34
Honeybourne	d	22 09	23 45	23 45
Evesham	a	22 17	23 53	23 53
	d	22 18	23 54	23 54
Pershore	d	22 25	00 02	00 02
Worcester Shrub Hill 7	a	22 40	00 13	00 13
Worcester Foregate Street 7	a	22 44		
Malvern Link	a	22 53		
Great Malvern	a	22 59		
Colwall	a			
Ledbury	a			
Hereford 7	a			

A 🛒 from Oxford

B 🛒 to Oxford

C The Cathedrals Express

For other services between London and Worcester refer to table 125

Table 126

Saturdays

14 December to 28 December

Network Diagram - refer to first Page of Table 116

London and Oxford - Worcester and Hereford

		GW	GW	GW	GW	GW	GW	GW	GW	GW	GW	GW	GW	GW	GW	GW
		◇1	◇1	◇1	◇1	◇1	◇1	◇1	◇1	◇1	◇1	◇1	◇1	◇1	◇1	◇1
				A	A						B				B	
		⊼		⊼	⊼	⊡	⊡	⊼	⊼	⊼	⊼	⊡	⊡	⊡	⊼	
London Paddington 15 ⊖	d		05 21	06 21	07 21	08 21	10 21	11 21	13 21	14 21	15 21	16 21	17 21	18 21	19 50	21 48
Slough 3	d		05 38	06 38	07 38	08 39	10 39	11 39	13 39	14 39	15 39	16 38	17 39	18 38	20 06	22 05
Reading 7	d		05 54	06 54	07 54	08 54	10 54	11 54	13 54	14 54	15 54	16 54	17 54	18 54	20 22	22 21
Didcot Parkway	d		06 08													22 36
Oxford	d		06 23	07 23	08 23	09 23	11 23	12 23	14 23	15 23	16 23	17 23	18 23	19 23	20 49	22 50
Hanborough	d		06 33	07 32	08 32	09 33	11 32	12 34	14 32	15 32	16 32	17 32	18 32	19 32	20 58	23 00
Combe	d															
Finstock	d															
Charlbury	a		06 41	07 39	08 39	09 41	11 40	12 41	14 39	15 39	16 39	17 40	18 40	19 40	21 05	23 07
	d		06 41	07 39	08 39	09 41	11 40	12 41	14 39	15 39	16 39	17 40	18 40	19 40	21 05	23 07
Ascott-under-Wychwood	d															
Shipton	d								14 46			17 48			21 12	23 14
Kingham	d		06 51	07 48	08 48	09 51	11 50	12 50	14 51	15 48	16 48	17 54	18 50	19 50	21 17	23 19
Moreton-in-Marsh	a		07 00	07 57	08 57	10 00	11 59	12 59	14 59	15 57	16 57	18 03	18 59	19 59	21 25	23 27
	d		07 00	07 57	08 57	10 00	11 59	12 59	14 59	15 57	16 57	18 03	18 59	19 59	21 25	23 27
Honeybourne	d		07 12	08 08	09 08	10 12	12 11	13 10	15 10	16 08	17 08	18 15	19 11	20 11	21 36	23 38
Evesham	a		07 20	08 16	09 16	10 20	12 19	13 17	15 18	16 16	17 16	18 23	19 19	20 19	21 43	23 45
	d		07 25	08 21	09 21	10 25	12 20	13 21	15 21	16 21	17 21	18 24	19 21	20 23	21 43	23 45
Pershore	d	00 02	07 32	08 28	09 28	10 32	12 27	13 28	15 28	16 28	17 28	18 31	19 28	20 30	21 50	23 53
Worcester Shrub Hill 7	a	00 13	07 44	08 40	09 40	10 44	12 40	13 40	15 40	16 40	17 40	18 44	19 41	20 43	22 02	00 07
Worcester Foregate Street 7	a		07 49	08 44	09 44	10 49	12 49	13 44	15 44	16 44	17 44	18 55	19 45	20 49	22 06	
Malvern Link	a		07 58	08 54	09 54	10 58	12 58	13 54	15 54	16 55	17 54	19 05		20 58	22 16	
Great Malvern	a		08 03	09 00	10 00	11 02	13 03	14 00	16 00	17 00	18 00	19 09		21 02	22 22	
Colwall	a					11 12	13 13					19 15		21 08		
Ledbury	a					11 20	13 21					19 23		21 16		
Hereford 7	a					11 39	13 39					19 45		21 35		

Saturdays

4 January to 8 February

		GW	GW	GW	GW	GW	GW	GW	GW	GW	GW	GW	GW	GW	GW	GW
		◇1	◇1	◇1	◇1	◇1	◇1	◇1	◇1	◇1	◇1	◇1	◇1	◇1	◇1	◇1
				A	A						B				B	
		⊼		⊼	⊼	⊡	⊡	⊼	⊼	⊼	⊼	⊡	⊡	⊡	⊼	
London Paddington 15 ⊖	d		05 14	06 14	07 17	08 17	10 17	11 17	13 17	14 17	15 17	16 17	17 17	18 17	19 45	21 44
Slough 3	d		05 38	06 38	07 41	08 39	10 40	11 42	13 42	14 42	15 42	16 41	17 41	18 41	20 09	22 08
Reading 7	d		05 54	06 54	07 57	08 55	10 55	11 57	13 57	14 57	15 57	16 57	17 56	18 57	20 25	22 23
Didcot Parkway	d		06 08													22 38
Oxford	d		06 23	07 23	08 23	09 23	11 23	12 27	14 26	15 25	16 25	17 23	18 23	19 23	20 52	22 52
Hanborough	d		06 33	07 32	08 32	09 33	11 32	12 36	14 35	15 35	16 35	17 32	18 32	19 32	21 01	23 01
Combe	d															
Finstock	d															
Charlbury	a		06 41	07 39	08 39	09 41	11 40	12 43	14 42	15 42	16 42	17 40	18 40	19 40	21 08	23 08
	d		06 41	07 39	08 39	09 41	11 40	12 44	14 42	15 42	16 42	17 40	18 40	19 40	21 08	23 09
Ascott-under-Wychwood	d															
Shipton	d								14 49			17 48			21 15	23 15
Kingham	d		06 51	07 48	08 48	09 51	11 50	12 53	14 54	15 51	16 51	17 54	18 50	19 50	21 20	23 20
Moreton-in-Marsh	a		07 00	07 57	08 57	10 00	11 59	13 01	15 02	15 59	16 59	18 03	18 59	19 59	21 28	23 28
	d		07 00	07 57	08 57	10 00	11 59	13 01	15 02	16 00	17 00	18 03	18 59	19 59	21 28	23 29
Honeybourne	d		07 12	08 08	09 08	10 12	12 11	13 12	15 13	16 11	17 11	18 15	19 11	20 11	21 39	23 40
Evesham	a		07 20	08 16	09 16	10 20	12 19	13 20	15 21	16 18	17 18	18 23	19 19	20 20	21 46	23 46
	d		07 25	08 21	09 21	10 25	12 20	13 21	15 22	16 21	17 21	18 24	19 21	20 23	21 46	23 47
Pershore	d	00 02	07 32	08 28	09 28	10 32	12 27	13 28	15 29	16 28	17 28	18 31	19 28	20 30	21 53	23 54
Worcester Shrub Hill 7	a	00 13	07 44	08 40	09 40	10 44	12 40	13 40	15 41	16 40	17 40	18 44	19 41	20 43	22 05	00 10
Worcester Foregate Street 7	a		07 49	08 44	09 44	10 49	12 49	13 44	15 44	16 44	17 44	18 55	19 45	20 49	22 08	
Malvern Link	a		07 58	08 54	09 54	10 58	12 58	13 54	15 54	16 55	17 54	19 05		20 58	22 17	
Great Malvern	a		08 03	09 00	10 00	11 02	13 03	14 00	16 00	17 00	18 00	19 09		21 02	22 23	
Colwall	a					11 12	13 13					19 15		21 08		
Ledbury	a					11 20	13 21					19 23		21 16		
Hereford 7	a					11 39	13 39					19 45		21 35		

A ⊼ from Oxford

B ⊼ to Oxford

For other services between London and Worcester refer to table 125

Table 126

Saturdays

15 February to 17 May

Network Diagram - refer to first Page of Table 116

London and Oxford - Worcester and Hereford

		GW	GW	GW	GW	GW	GW	GW	GW	GW	GW	GW	GW	GW	GW	GW
		◇1	◇1	◇1	◇1	◇1	◇1	◇1	◇1	◇1	◇1	◇1	◇1	◇1	◇1	◇1
				A	A						B				B	
		🛒		🛒	🛒	☕	☕	🛒	🛒	🛒	🛒	☕	☕	☕	🛒	
London Paddington 15 ⊖	d		05 21	06 21	07 21	08 21	10 21	11 21	13 21	14 21	15 21	16 21	17 21	18 21	19 50	21 48
Slough 3	d		05 38	06 38	07 38	08 39	10 39	11 39	13 39	14 39	15 39	16 38	17 39	18 38	20 06	22 05
Reading 7	d		05 54	06 54	07 54	08 54	10 54	11 54	13 54	14 54	15 54	16 54	17 54	18 54	20 22	22 21
Didcot Parkway	d		06 08													22 36
Oxford	d		06 23	07 23	08 23	09 23	11 23	12 23	14 23	15 23	16 23	17 23	18 23	19 23	20 49	22 50
Hanborough	d		06 33	07 32	08 32	09 33	11 32	12 34	14 32	15 32	16 32	17 32	18 32	19 32	20 58	23 00
Combe	d															
Finstock	d															
Charlbury	a		06 41	07 39	08 39	09 41	11 40	12 41	14 39	15 39	16 39	17 40	18 40	19 40	21 05	23 07
	d		06 41	07 39	08 39	09 41	11 40	12 41	14 39	15 39	16 39	17 40	18 40	19 40	21 05	23 07
Ascott-under-Wychwood	d															
Shipton	d								14 46			17 48			21 12	23 14
Kingham	d		06 51	07 48	08 48	09 51	11 50	12 50	14 51	15 48	16 48	17 54	18 50	19 50	21 17	23 19
Moreton-in-Marsh	a		07 00	07 57	08 57	10 00	11 59	12 59	14 59	15 57	16 57	18 03	18 59	19 59	21 25	23 27
	d		07 00	07 57	08 57	10 00	11 59	12 59	14 59	15 57	16 57	18 03	18 59	19 59	21 25	23 27
Honeybourne	d		07 12	08 08	09 08	10 12	12 11	13 10	15 10	16 08	17 08	18 15	19 11	20 11	21 36	23 38
Evesham	a		07 20	08 16	09 16	10 20	12 19	13 17	15 18	16 16	17 16	18 23	19 19	20 19	21 43	23 45
	d		07 25	08 21	09 21	10 25	12 20	13 21	15 21	16 21	17 21	18 24	19 21	20 23	21 43	23 45
Pershore	d	00 02	07 32	08 28	09 28	10 32	12 27	13 28	15 28	16 28	17 28	18 31	19 28	20 30	21 50	23 53
Worcester Shrub Hill 7	a	00 13	07 44	08 40	09 40	10 44	12 40	13 40	15 40	16 40	17 40	18 44	19 41	20 43	22 02	00 07
Worcester Foregate Street 7	a		07 49	08 44	09 44	10 49	12 49	13 44	15 44	16 44	17 44	18 55	19 45	20 49	22 06	
Malvern Link	a		07 58	08 54	09 54	10 58	12 58	13 54	15 54	16 55	17 54	19 05		20 58	22 16	
Great Malvern	a		08 03	09 00	10 00	11 02	13 03	14 00	16 00	17 00	18 00	19 09		21 02	22 22	
Colwall	a					11 12	13 13					19 15		21 08		
Ledbury	a					11 20	13 21					19 23		21 16		
Hereford 7	a					11 39	13 39					19 45		21 35		

Sundays

8 December to 29 December

		GW	GW	GW	GW	GW	GW	GW	GW	GW	GW	GW	GW
		◇1	◇1	◇1	◇1	◇1	◇1	◇1	◇1	◇1	◇1	◇1	◇1
			☕	☕	☕	☕				☕		☕	
London Paddington 15 ⊖	d	08 03	09 35	10 42	12 42	13 42	14 42	15 42	16 42	17 42	18 42	19 42	21 42
Slough 3	d	08 23	09 56	11 03	13 00	14 04	15 03	16 03	17 01	18 04	19 01	20 05	22 02
Reading 7	d	08 46	10 14	11 20	13 21	14 22	15 20	16 21	17 21	18 26	19 21	20 22	22 19
Didcot Parkway	d	09 01	10 30	11 37	13 37	14 37	15 36	16 37	17 37	18 40	19 37	20 37	22 37
Oxford	d	09 18	10 49	11 52	13 54	14 52	15 58	16 57	17 55	18 57	19 58	20 54	22 57
Hanborough	d	09 28	11 00	12 02	14 02		16 07		18 08	19 07	20 08	21 04	23 07
Combe	d												
Finstock	d												
Charlbury	a	09 35	11 07	12 10	14 09	15 06	16 14	17 10	18 15	19 14	20 15	21 11	23 14
	d	09 35	11 08	12 10	14 10	15 07	16 15	17 11	18 15	19 15	20 16	21 12	23 15
Ascott-under-Wychwood	d												
Shipton	d												
Kingham	d	09 44	11 18	12 19	14 19	15 16	16 24	17 20	18 24	19 25	20 25	21 21	23 24
Moreton-in-Marsh	a	09 52	11 26	12 27	14 28	15 26	16 32	17 28	18 32	19 33	20 33	21 30	23 33
	d	09 53	11 27	12 28	14 29	15 26	16 32	17 28	18 33	19 34	20 33	21 31	23 34
Honeybourne	d	10 04	11 39	12 40		15 40	16 43		18 44	19 46	20 44	21 42	23 45
Evesham	a	10 10	11 47	12 47	14 47	15 49	16 51	17 44	18 50	19 54	20 52	21 50	23 52
	d	10 13	11 49	12 48	14 48	15 49	16 51	17 45	18 51	19 55	20 52	21 51	23 53
Pershore	d	10 20	11 56	12 56	14 55	15 57	16 59	17 53	18 58	20 02	21 00	21 59	00 01
Worcester Shrub Hill 7	a	10 32	12 08	13 08	15 07	16 09	17 10	18 04	19 10	20 14	21 11	22 10	00 12
Worcester Foregate Street 7	a	10 36	12 11	13 12	15 11		17 13	18 07	19 13	20 19		22 14	
Malvern Link	a	10 51	12 20	13 22	15 20		17 22		19 22	20 28		22 24	
Great Malvern	a	10 54	12 24	13 26	15 24		17 25		19 25	20 32		22 28	
Colwall	a		12 32	13 33	15 30		17 31			20 38			
Ledbury	a		12 40	13 41	15 38		17 38			20 46			
Hereford 7	a		12 59	14 08	15 57		17 55			21 04			

A 🛒 from Oxford

B 🛒 to Oxford

For other services between London and Worcester refer to table 125

Table 126

Sundays

5 January to 9 February

Network Diagram - refer to first Page of Table 116

London and Oxford - Worcester and Hereford

		GW	GW	GW	GW	GW	GW		GW	GW	GW	GW	GW	GW
		◇1	◇1	◇1	◇1	◇1	◇1		◇1	◇1	◇1	◇1	◇1	◇1
			☕	☕	☕	☕					☕		☕	
London Paddington 15 ⊖	d	08 03	09 33	10 42	12 42	13 42	14 42		15 42	16 42	17 42	18 42	19 42	21 42
Slough 3	d	08 23	09 56	11 03	13 05	14 04	15 05		16 02	17 01	18 04	19 02	20 05	22 06
Reading 7	d	08 46	10 14	11 20	13 21	14 22	15 23		16 21	17 21	18 26	19 21	20 22	22 24
Didcot Parkway	d	09 01	10 30	11 36	13 37	14 37	15 39		16 37	17 37	18 40	19 37	20 37	22 42
Oxford	d	09 18	10 49	11 52	13 54	14 52	15 58		16 57	17 55	18 57	19 58	20 54	22 57
Hanborough	d	09 28	11 00	12 02	14 02		16 07			18 08	19 07	20 08	21 04	23 07
Combe	d													
Finstock	d													
Charlbury	a	09 35	11 07	12 10	14 09	15 06	16 14		17 10	18 15	19 14	20 15	21 11	23 14
	d	09 35	11 08	12 10	14 10	15 07	16 15		17 11	18 15	19 15	20 16	21 12	23 15
Ascott-under-Wychwood	d													
Shipton	d													
Kingham	d	09 44	11 18	12 19	14 19	15 16	16 24		17 20	18 24	19 25	20 25	21 21	23 24
Moreton-in-Marsh	a	09 52	11 26	12 27	14 28	15 26	16 32		17 28	18 32	19 33	20 33	21 30	23 33
	d	09 53	11 27	12 28	14 29	15 26	16 32		17 28	18 33	19 34	20 33	21 31	23 34
Honeybourne	d	10 04	11 39	12 39		15 40	16 43			18 44	19 46	20 44	21 42	23 45
Evesham	a	10 10	11 47	12 47	14 47	15 49	16 51		17 44	18 50	19 54	20 52	21 50	23 52
	d	10 13	11 49	12 48	14 48	15 49	16 51		17 45	18 51	19 55	20 52	21 51	23 53
Pershore	d	10 20	11 56	12 56	14 55	15 57	16 59		17 53	18 58	20 02	21 00	21 59	00 01
Worcester Shrub Hill 7	a	10 32	12 08	13 08	15 07	16 09	17 10		18 04	19 10	20 14	21 11	22 10	00 12
Worcester Foregate Street 7	a	10 36	12 11	13 12	15 11		17 13		18 07	19 13	20 18		22 14	
Malvern Link	a	10 51	12 20	13 22	15 20		17 22			19 22	20 28		22 24	
Great Malvern	a	10 54	12 24	13 26	15 24		17 25			19 25	20 32		22 28	
Colwall	a		12 32	13 33	15 30		17 31				20 38			
Ledbury	a		12 40	13 41	15 38		17 38				20 46			
Hereford 7	a		12 59	14 08	15 57		17 55				21 04			

Sundays

16 February to 23 March

		GW	GW	GW	GW	GW	GW	GW	GW	GW		GW	GW	GW
		◇1	◇1	◇1	◇1	◇1	◇1	◇1	◇1	◇1		◇1	◇1	◇1
			☕	☕	☕	☕				☕			☕	
London Paddington 15 ⊖	d	08 03	09 33	10 42	12 42	13 42	14 42	15 42	16 42	17 42		18 42	19 42	21 42
Slough 3	d	08 23	09 56	11 03	13 05	14 04	15 05	16 02	17 01	18 04		19 02	20 05	22 06
Reading 7	d	08 46	10 20	11 20	13 21	14 22	15 21	16 21	17 24	18 26		19 21	20 22	22 24
Didcot Parkway	d	09 01	10 34	11 37	13 37	14 37	15 38	16 37	17 39	18 40		19 37	20 37	22 42
Oxford	d	09 18	10 49	11 52	13 54	14 52	15 58	16 57	17 58	18 57		19 58	20 54	22 57
Hanborough	d	09 28	11 00	12 02	14 02		16 07		18 08	19 07		20 08	21 04	23 07
Combe	d													
Finstock	d													
Charlbury	a	09 35	11 07	12 10	14 09	15 06	16 14	17 10	18 15	19 14		20 15	21 11	23 14
	d	09 35	11 08	12 10	14 10	15 07	16 15	17 11	18 15	19 15		20 16	21 12	23 15
Ascott-under-Wychwood	d													
Shipton	d													
Kingham	d	09 44	11 18	12 19	14 19	15 16	16 24	17 20	18 24	19 25		20 25	21 21	23 24
Moreton-in-Marsh	a	09 52	11 26	12 27	14 28	15 26	16 32	17 28	18 32	19 33		20 33	21 30	23 33
	d	09 53	11 27	12 28	14 29	15 26	16 32	17 28	18 33	19 34		20 33	21 31	23 34
Honeybourne	d	10 04	11 39	12 40		15 40	16 43		18 44	19 46		20 44	21 42	23 45
Evesham	a	10 10	11 47	12 47	14 47	15 49	16 51	17 44	18 50	19 54		20 52	21 50	23 52
	d	10 13	11 49	12 48	14 48	15 49	16 51	17 45	18 51	19 55		20 52	21 51	23 53
Pershore	d	10 20	11 56	12 56	14 55	15 57	16 59	17 53	18 58	20 02		21 00	21 59	00 01
Worcester Shrub Hill 7	a	10 32	12 08	13 08	15 07	16 09	17 10	18 04	19 10	20 14		21 11	22 10	00 12
Worcester Foregate Street 7	a	10 36	12 11	13 12	15 11		17 13	18 07	19 13	20 18			22 14	
Malvern Link	a	10 51	12 20	13 22	15 20		17 22		19 22	20 28			22 24	
Great Malvern	a	10 54	12 24	13 26	15 24		17 25		19 25	20 32			22 28	
Colwall	a		12 32	13 32	15 30		17 31			20 38				
Ledbury	a		12 40	13 41	15 38		17 38			20 46				
Hereford 7	a		12 59	14 08	15 57		17 55			21 04				

For other services between London and Worcester refer to table 125

Table 126

Sundays

30 March to 11 May

Network Diagram - refer to first Page of Table 116

London and Oxford - Worcester and Hereford

		GW	GW	GW	GW	GW	GW	GW	GW	GW	GW	GW	GW
		◇1	◇1	◇1	◇1	◇1	◇1	◇1	◇1	◇1	◇1	◇1	◇1
			⊡	⊡	⊡	⊡				⊡		⊡	
London Paddington 15 ⊖	d	08 03	09 35	10 42	12 42	13 42	14 30	15 42	16 42	17 42	18 42	19 42	21 42
Slough 3	d	08 22	09 56	11 03	13 00	14 04	14 50	16 02	17 01	18 04	19 01	20 05	22 02
Reading 7	d	08 43	10 14	11 20	13 21	14 22	15 14	16 21	17 21	18 26	19 21	20 22	22 19
Didcot Parkway	d	08 58	10 30	11 37	13 37	14 37	15 29	16 37	17 37	18 41	19 37	20 37	22 37
Oxford	d	09 18	10 49	11 53	13 54	14 52	15 56	16 57	17 55	18 57	19 58	20 54	22 57
Hanborough	d	09 28	11 00	12 03	14 02	.	16 05	.	18 08	19 07	20 08	21 04	23 07
Combe	d												
Finstock	d												
Charlbury	a	09 35	11 07	12 10	14 09	15 06	16 12	17 10	18 15	19 14	20 15	21 11	23 14
	d	09 35	11 08	12 11	14 10	15 07	16 13	17 11	18 15	19 15	20 16	21 12	23 15
Ascott-under-Wychwood	d												
Shipton	d												
Kingham	d	09 44	11 18	12 19	14 19	15 16	16 22	17 20	18 24	19 25	20 25	21 22	23 24
Moreton-in-Marsh	a	09 52	11 26	12 27	14 28	15 26	16 30	17 28	18 32	19 33	20 33	21 30	23 33
	d	09 53	11 27	12 28	14 29	15 26	16 30	17 28	18 33	19 34	20 33	21 31	23 34
Honeybourne	d	10 04	11 39	12 40	.	15 40	16 41	.	18 44	19 46	20 44	21 43	23 45
Evesham	a	10 10	11 47	12 47	14 47	15 49	16 49	17 44	18 50	19 54	20 52	21 51	23 52
	d	10 13	11 49	12 48	14 48	15 49	16 49	17 45	18 51	19 55	20 52	21 52	23 53
Pershore	d	10 20	11 56	12 56	14 55	15 57	16 57	17 53	18 58	20 02	21 00	21 59	00 01
Worcester Shrub Hill 7	a	10 32	12 08	13 09	15 07	16 09	17 08	18 04	19 10	20 14	21 11	22 11	00 12
Worcester Foregate Street 7	a	10 36	12 11	13 13	15 11		17 11	18 07	19 13	20 18		22 14	
Malvern Link	a	10 51	12 20	13 22	15 20	.	17 20	.	19 22	20 28	.	22 24	.
Great Malvern	a	10 54	12 24	13 26	15 24		17 23		19 25	20 32		22 28	
Colwall	a	.	12 32	13 33	15 30	.	17 29	.	.	20 38	.	.	.
Ledbury	a		12 40	13 41	15 38		17 36			20 46			
Hereford 7	a	.	12 59	14 08	15 57	.	17 53	.	.	21 04	.	.	.

For other services between London and Worcester refer to table 125

Table 126R

Mondays to Fridays

9 December to 16 May

Network Diagram - refer to first Page of Table 116

Hereford and Worcester - Oxford and London

Miles			GW	GW	GW	GW	GW	GW	GW	GW	GW	GW	GW	GW	GW	GW	GW	GW	GW	GW	GW	GW	GW FO
			◇1	◇1	◇1	◇1	1	◇1	◇1	◇1	◇1	◇1	◇1	◇1	◇1	◇1	◇1	◇1	1	◇1	◇1	◇1	◇1
						A		B	C		D	E											
			🍴	🍴	🛒	🍴⊘		🍴⊘	🍴⊘	🛒			🛒	🛒	🛒	🍴	🛒			🍴	🛒	🍴	
0	**Hereford 7**	d		04 50		05 28		06 42	06 42							13 14				15 14			
13¾	Ledbury	d				05 45		06 59	06 59							13 31				15 31			
18	Colwall	d				05 53		07 06	07 06							13 39				15 39			
20¾	Great Malvern	d		05 17		05 59		07 12	07 12				09 54			13 45	14 26		15 32	15 45			19 44
21¾	Malvern Link	d		05 20		06 03		07 17	07 17				09 56			13 50	14 28			15 49			19 46
28½	**Worcester Foregate Street 7**	d		05 31		06 14	06 52	07 28	07 28	08 26			10 06		12 06	14 01	14 38		15 42	16 01	17 28	18 49	19 56
29¼	**Worcester Shrub Hill 7**	d	05 11	05 36		06 30	06 55	07 32	07 32	08 39			10 09		12 08	14 09	14 41		15 45	16 05	17 31	18 55	20 04
37	Pershore	d		05 45		06 38	07 04	07 41	07 41	08 48			10 18		12 17	14 18	14 50		15 54	16 14	17 40	19 04	20 12
43	Evesham	a	05 25	05 53		06 46	07 12	07 49	07 49	08 56			10 26		12 25	14 26	14 58		16 01	16 22	17 48	19 12	20 20
—		d	05 27	05 53		06 49	07 12	07 50	07 50	09 04			10 30		12 31	14 28	15 05		16 02	16 23	17 48	19 12	20 20
48	Honeybourne	d	05 34			06 56		07 58	07 58	09 11			10 37		12 38	14 35	15 12			16 30	17 55	19 20	20 27
58	Moreton-in-Marsh	a	05 46	06 09		07 08	07 27	08 10	08 10	09 23			10 49		12 50	14 47	15 24		16 16	16 42	18 07	19 32	20 39
—		d	05 47	06 09		07 09	07 27	08 11	08 11	09 23	09 50	09 50	10 49	11 50	12 50	14 48	15 24	15 53	16 17	16 45	18 07	19 46	20 47
65	Kingham	d	05 55	06 18		07 18	07 35	08 20	08 20	09 31	09 58	09 58	10 57	11 58	12 58	14 56	15 32	16 00	16 25	16 53	18 15	19 55	20 55
68	Shipton	d					07 40														18 20		
69¼	Ascott-under-Wychwood	d					07 43																
73	Charlbury	a	06 05	06 28		07 28	07 49	08 30	08 30	09 41	10 08	10 08	11 06	12 08	13 08	15 06	15 41	16 10	16 34	17 03	18 27	20 04	21 05
—		d	06 06	06 28	07 12	07 30	07 49	08 31	08 31	09 41	10 08	10 08	11 06	12 08	13 08	15 07	15 41	16 10	16 34	17 10	18 37	20 05	21 05
74¾	Finstock	d					07 52																
78¼	Combe	d					07 57																
79¼	Hanborough	d	06 14	06 36	07 21	07 39	08 01	08 39	08 39	09 48	10 16	10 16	11 14	12 15	13 15	15 15	15 49	16 17		17 18	18 44	20 13	21 12
86¼	**Oxford**	a	06 24	06 49	07 30	07 47	08 12	08 49	08 49	09 59	10 28	10 28	11 28	12 29	13 26	15 25	15 59	16 28	16 48	17 29	18 55	20 24	21 27
96½	Didcot Parkway	a		07 08															17 03				
113¾	Reading 7	a	06 53	07 25	07 56	08 22		09 14	09 16	10 25	10 54	10 55	11 55	12 55	13 54	15 55	16 25	16 56		17 54	19 31	20 55	21 55
131¼	Slough 3	a								10 40	11 09	11 10	12 10	13 10	14 10	16 10	16 41	17 13		18 10	19 47	21 11	22 14
149¾	**London Paddington 15** ⊖	a	07 27	07 59	08 31	08 51		09 47	09 47	11 00	11 29	11 30	12 30	13 30	14 30	16 29	17 00	17 34		18 28	20 06	21 29	22 38

		GW FX	GW FX	GW FO	GW FX	GW FO
		◇1	◇1	◇1	◇1	◇1
Hereford 7	d				21 51	21 51
Ledbury	d				22 09	22 09
Colwall	d				22 17	22 17
Great Malvern	d	19 44			22 22	22 22
Malvern Link	d	19 46				
Worcester Foregate Street 7	d	19 56	20 59	20 59	22 34	22 34
Worcester Shrub Hill 7	d	20 04	21 03	21 03	22 43	22 43
Pershore	d	20 12	21 12	21 12	22 52	22 52
Evesham	a	20 20	21 20	21 20	23 00	23 00
	d	20 20	21 21	21 21	23 01	23 01
Honeybourne	d	20 27	21 28	21 28	23 08	23 08
Moreton-in-Marsh	a	20 39	21 40	21 40	23 20	23 20
	d	20 47	21 41	21 41	23 26	23 26
Kingham	d	20 55	21 49	21 49	23 35	23 35
Shipton	d					
Ascott-under-Wychwood	d					
Charlbury	a	21 05	21 59	21 59	23 45	23 45
	d	21 05	22 07	22 07	23 45	23 45
Finstock	d					
Combe	d					
Hanborough	d	21 12	22 15	22 15		
Oxford	a	21 27	22 27	22 27	23 58	23 58
Didcot Parkway	a				00 20	00 20
Reading 7	a	21 55	22 53	22 54	00 38	00 41
Slough 3	a	22 14	23 14	23 14	00 55	00 59
London Paddington 15 ⊖	a	22 41	23 38	23 37	01 20	01 21

A 🍴 from Reading ⊘ to Reading

B until 7 March. The Cathedrals Express. 🍴 from Reading ⊘ to Reading

C from 10 March. The Cathedrals Express. 🍴 from Reading ⊘ to Reading

D from 10 March

E until 7 March

For other services between London and Worcester refer to table 125

Table 126R

Saturdays

14 December to 28 December

Network Diagram - refer to first Page of Table 116

Hereford and Worcester - Oxford and London

		GW	GW	GW	GW	GW	GW	GW	GW	GW	GW	GW	GW	GW	GW	GW
		◇1	◇1	◇1	◇1	◇1	◇1	◇1	◇1	◇1	◇1	◇1	◇1	◇1	◇1	1
				A												
		⊤	⊏	⊏⊘	⊏	⊤	⊤	⊏	⊤	⊏	⊤	⊤				
Hereford 7	d		06 17	07 10				12 13		15 13					20 20	
Ledbury	d		06 34	07 30				12 31		15 31					20 40	
Colwall	d		06 41	07 37				12 38		15 38					20 47	
Great Malvern	d	05 56	06 49	07 44	08 43	09 51	10 58	12 44	14 34	15 44	16 34	17 49	18 35		20 53	22 41
Malvern Link	d	05 59	06 53	07 48	08 47	09 54	11 01	12 48	14 37	15 48	16 37	17 52	18 38		20 57	22 44
Worcester Foregate Street 7	d	06 09	07 04	07 59	08 58	10 04	11 11	12 59	14 57	15 59	16 55	18 02	18 49	20 02	21 11	22 53
Worcester Shrub Hill 7	d	06 12	07 08	08 04	09 02	10 08	11 15	13 04	15 01	16 04	17 02	18 06	19 02	20 06	21 15	22 57
Pershore	d	06 21	07 17	08 13	09 11	10 16	11 23	13 13	15 10	16 12	17 10	18 15	19 10	20 15	21 24	23 06
Evesham	a	06 29	07 25	08 21	09 19	10 24	11 31	13 21	15 18	16 20	17 18	18 23	19 18	20 23	21 32	23 14
	d	06 29	07 26	08 25	09 32	10 31	11 32	13 30	15 26	16 21	17 26	18 27	19 27	20 24	21 33	
Honeybourne	d	06 36	07 33	08 32	09 39	10 38	11 38	13 37	15 33	16 28	17 32	18 33	19 33	20 31	21 40	
Moreton-in-Marsh	a	06 48	07 45	08 44	09 51	10 49	11 50	13 49	15 45	16 40	17 44	18 45	19 45	20 43	21 52	
	d	06 48	07 45	08 45	09 51	10 50	11 50	13 49	15 45	16 41	17 44	18 45	19 45	20 43	21 52	
Kingham	d	06 56	07 54	08 53	10 00	10 58	11 58	13 58	15 53	16 49	17 52	18 53	19 53	20 52	22 01	
Shipton	d		07 59	08 59						16 55					22 06	
Ascott-under-Wychwood	d															
Charlbury	a	07 05	08 07	09 06	10 10	11 07	12 08	14 08	16 02	17 02	18 02	19 03	20 03	21 02	22 14	
	d	07 05	08 07	09 07	10 10	11 07	12 08	14 08	16 02	17 03	18 02	19 03	20 03	21 07	22 14	
Finstock	d															
Combe	d															
Hanborough	d	07 13	08 15	09 15	10 18	11 15	12 15	14 16	16 10	17 11	18 09	19 10	20 10	21 15	22 22	
Oxford	a	07 23	08 26	09 25	10 28	11 26	12 28	14 27	16 21	17 21	18 21	19 21	20 21	21 26	22 34	
Didcot Parkway	a													21 43	22 47	
Reading 7	a	07 55	08 56	09 54	10 56	11 57	12 56	14 56	16 55	17 56	18 55	19 55	20 55	21 59	23 08	
Slough 3	a	08 10	09 10	10 09	11 12	12 12	13 11	15 13	17 10	18 11	19 10	20 10	21 10	22 15	23 27	
London Paddington 15 ⊖	a	08 29	09 29	10 29	11 30	12 32	13 32	15 30	17 29	18 29	19 29	20 29	21 29	22 38	23 45	

Saturdays

4 January to 8 February

		GW	GW	GW	GW	GW	GW	GW	GW	GW	GW	GW	GW	GW	GW	GW
		◇1	◇1	◇1	◇1	◇1	◇1	◇1	◇1	◇1	◇1	◇1	◇1	◇1	◇1	1
				A												
		⊤	⊏	⊏⊘	⊏	⊤	⊤	⊏	⊤	⊏	⊤	⊤				
Hereford 7	d		06 17	07 10				12 13		15 13					20 20	
Ledbury	d		06 34	07 30				12 31		15 31					20 40	
Colwall	d		06 41	07 37				12 38		15 38					20 47	
Great Malvern	d	05 56	06 49	07 44	08 43	09 51	10 58	12 44	14 34	15 44	16 34	17 49	18 35		20 53	22 41
Malvern Link	d	05 59	06 53	07 48	08 47	09 54	11 01	12 48	14 37	15 48	16 37	17 52	18 38		20 57	22 44
Worcester Foregate Street 7	d	06 09	07 04	07 59	08 58	10 04	11 11	12 59	14 57	15 59	16 55	18 02	18 49	20 02	21 11	22 53
Worcester Shrub Hill 7	d	06 12	07 08	08 04	09 02	10 08	11 15	13 04	15 01	16 04	17 02	18 06	19 02	20 06	21 15	22 57
Pershore	d	06 21	07 17	08 13	09 11	10 16	11 23	13 13	15 10	16 12	17 10	18 15	19 10	20 15	21 24	23 06
Evesham	a	06 29	07 25	08 21	09 19	10 24	11 31	13 21	15 18	16 20	17 18	18 23	19 18	20 23	21 32	23 14
	d	06 29	07 26	08 25	09 32	10 31	11 32	13 30	15 26	16 21	17 26	18 27	19 27	20 24	21 33	
Honeybourne	d	06 36	07 33	08 32	09 39	10 38	11 38	13 37	15 33	16 28	17 32	18 33	19 33	20 31	21 40	
Moreton-in-Marsh	a	06 48	07 45	08 44	09 51	10 49	11 50	13 49	15 45	16 40	17 44	18 45	19 45	20 43	21 52	
	d	06 48	07 45	08 45	09 51	10 50	11 50	13 49	15 45	16 41	17 44	18 45	19 45	20 43	21 52	
Kingham	d	06 56	07 54	08 53	10 00	10 58	11 58	13 58	15 53	16 49	17 52	18 53	19 53	20 52	22 01	
Shipton	d		07 59	08 59						16 55					22 06	
Ascott-under-Wychwood	d															
Charlbury	a	07 05	08 07	09 06	10 10	11 07	12 08	14 08	16 02	17 02	18 02	19 03	20 03	21 02	22 14	
	d	07 05	08 07	09 07	10 10	11 07	12 08	14 08	16 02	17 03	18 02	19 03	20 03	21 07	22 14	
Finstock	d															
Combe	d															
Hanborough	d	07 13	08 15	09 15	10 18	11 15	12 15	14 16	16 10	17 11	18 09	19 10	20 10	21 15	22 22	
Oxford	a	07 23	08 26	09 25	10 28	11 26	12 28	14 27	16 21	17 21	18 21	19 21	20 21	21 26	22 34	
Didcot Parkway	a													21 43	22 47	
Reading 7	a	07 55	08 57	09 54	10 56	11 57	12 56	14 56	16 55	17 56	18 55	19 55	20 55	21 59	23 14	
Slough 3	a	08 11	09 13	10 10	11 15	12 13	13 12	15 14	17 11	18 15	19 11	20 11	21 13	22 17	23 33	
London Paddington 15 ⊖	a	08 39	09 39	10 39	11 40	12 40	13 39	15 39	17 39	18 39	19 38	20 37	21 38	22 42	23 56	

A ⊏ from Reading ⊘ to Reading

For other services between London and Worcester refer to table 125

Table 126R

Saturdays

15 February to 17 May

Network Diagram - refer to first Page of Table 116

Hereford and Worcester - Oxford and London

		GW	GW	GW	GW	GW	GW	GW	GW	GW	GW	GW	GW	GW	GW	GW
		◇**1**	◇**1**	◇**1**	◇**1**	◇**1**	◇**1**	◇**1**	◇**1**	◇**1**	◇**1**	◇**1**	◇**1**	◇**1**	◇**1**	**1**
				A												
		🛒	🍽	🍽⊘	🍽	🛒	🛒	🍽	🛒	🍽	🛒	🛒				
Hereford 7	d		06 17	07 10				12 13		15 13					20 20	
Ledbury	d		06 34	07 30				12 31		15 31					20 40	
Colwall	d		06 41	07 37				12 38		15 38					20 47	
Great Malvern	d	05 56	06 49	07 44	08 43	09 51	10 58	12 44	14 34	15 44	16 34	17 49	18 35		20 53	22 41
Malvern Link	d	05 59	06 53	07 48	08 47	09 54	11 01	12 48	14 37	15 48	16 37	17 52	18 38		20 57	22 44
Worcester Foregate Street 7	d	06 09	07 04	07 59	08 58	10 04	11 11	12 59	14 57	15 59	16 55	18 02	18 49	20 02	21 11	22 53
Worcester Shrub Hill 7	d	06 12	07 08	08 04	09 02	10 08	11 15	13 04	15 01	16 04	17 02	18 06	19 02	20 06	21 15	22 57
Pershore	d	06 21	07 17	08 13	09 11	10 16	11 23	13 13	15 10	16 12	17 10	18 15	19 10	20 15	21 24	23 06
Evesham	a	06 29	07 25	08 21	09 19	10 24	11 31	13 21	15 18	16 20	17 18	18 23	19 18	20 23	21 32	23 14
	d	06 29	07 26	08 25	09 32	10 31	11 32	13 30	15 26	16 21	17 26	18 27	19 27	20 24	21 33	
Honeybourne	d	06 36	07 33	08 32	09 39	10 38	11 38	13 37	15 33	16 28	17 32	18 33	19 33	20 31	21 40	
Moreton-in-Marsh	a	06 48	07 45	08 44	09 51	10 49	11 50	13 49	15 45	16 40	17 44	18 45	19 45	20 43	21 52	
	d	06 48	07 45	08 45	09 51	10 50	11 50	13 49	15 45	16 41	17 44	18 45	19 45	20 43	21 52	
Kingham	d	06 56	07 54	08 53	10 00	10 58	11 58	13 58	15 53	16 49	17 52	18 53	19 53	20 52	22 01	
Shipton	d		07 59	08 59						16 55					22 06	
Ascott-under-Wychwood	d															
Charlbury	a	07 05	08 07	09 06	10 10	11 07	12 08	14 08	16 02	17 02	18 02	19 03	20 03	21 02	22 14	
	d	07 05	08 07	09 07	10 10	11 07	12 08	14 08	16 02	17 03	18 02	19 03	20 03	21 07	22 14	
Finstock	d															
Combe	d															
Hanborough	d	07 13	08 15	09 15	10 18	11 15	12 15	14 16	16 10	17 11	18 09	19 10	20 10	21 15	22 22	
Oxford	a	07 23	08 26	09 25	10 28	11 26	12 28	14 27	16 21	17 21	18 21	19 21	20 21	21 26	22 34	
Didcot Parkway	a													21 43	22 47	
Reading 7	a	07 55	08 56	09 54	10 56	11 57	12 56	14 56	16 55	17 56	18 55	19 55	20 55	21 59	23 09	
Slough 3	a	08 10	09 10	10 09	11 12	12 12	13 11	15 13	17 10	18 11	19 10	20 10	21 10	22 15	23 28	
London Paddington 15 ⊖	a	08 29	09 29	10 29	11 30	12 32	13 32	15 30	17 29	18 29	19 29	20 29	21 29	22 38	23 46	

Sundays

8 December to 29 December

		GW	GW	GW	GW	GW	GW	GW	GW	GW	GW	GW
		◇**1**	◇**1**	◇**1**	◇**1**	◇**1**	◇**1**	◇**1**	◇**1**	◇**1**	◇**1**	◇**1**
					🍽	🍽	🍽	🍽				
Hereford 7	d				13 33	14 35		16 34		18 30		
Ledbury	d				13 52	14 55		16 52		18 48		
Colwall	d				13 59	15 02		17 00		18 55		
Great Malvern	d	09 20	11 15	13 15	14 11	15 07		17 05		19 11	20 15	
Malvern Link	d	09 23	11 18	13 18	14 15	15 11		17 09		19 14	20 18	
Worcester Foregate Street 7	d	09 32	11 28	13 27	14 26	15 22		17 22	18 26	19 29	20 28	
Worcester Shrub Hill 7	d	09 35	11 31	13 31	14 30	15 26	16 28	17 28	18 30	19 33	20 31	21 28
Pershore	d	09 44	11 40	13 40	14 40	15 35	16 38	17 37	18 40	19 42	20 41	21 37
Evesham	a	09 51	11 48	13 47	14 47	15 44	16 45	17 44	18 48	19 50	20 48	21 45
	d	09 52	11 50	13 49	14 50	15 47	16 48	17 49	18 49	19 51	20 49	21 48
Honeybourne	d	09 59	11 57	13 56		15 54	16 56	17 56	18 57	19 58	20 56	21 55
Moreton-in-Marsh	a	10 10	12 08	14 07	15 05	16 06	17 07	18 08	19 08	20 09	21 07	22 07
	d	10 11	12 09	14 08	15 08	16 07	17 09	18 10	19 10	20 12	21 08	22 07
Kingham	d	10 19	12 17	14 16	15 16	16 16	17 18	18 19	19 19	20 20	21 16	22 15
Shipton	d											
Ascott-under-Wychwood	d											
Charlbury	a	10 28	12 26	14 25	15 26	16 26	17 27	18 29	19 28	20 29	21 25	22 24
	d	10 28	12 26	14 25	15 27	16 27	17 28	18 30	19 29	20 30	21 25	22 25
Finstock	d											
Combe	d											
Hanborough	d	10 36	12 34	14 33	15 35	16 35	17 36		19 37	20 38	21 33	22 33
Oxford	a	10 49	12 49	14 49	15 48	16 50	17 49	18 49	19 49	20 49	21 49	22 42
Didcot Parkway	a	11 06	13 05	15 05	16 02	17 06	18 03	19 02	20 03	21 02	22 01	22 58
Reading 7	a	11 25	13 22	15 22	16 23	17 25	18 19	19 28	20 22	21 20	22 18	23 18
Slough 3	a	11 42	13 37	15 38	16 38	17 44	18 36	19 42	20 39	21 39	22 39	23 36
London Paddington 15 ⊖	a	12 04	14 01	15 57	16 58	18 07	19 01	20 02	21 00	22 03	23 03	00 06

A 🍽 from Reading ⊘ to Reading

For other services between London and Worcester refer to table 125

Table 126R

Sundays

5 January to 9 February

Hereford and Worcester - Oxford and London

Network Diagram - refer to first Page of Table 116

		GW ◇1	GW ◇1	GW ◇1	GW ◇1 ☕	GW ◇1 ☕	GW ◇1 ☕	GW ◇1 ☕	GW ◇1	GW ◇1	GW ◇1	GW ◇1
Hereford 7	d				13 33	14 35		16 34		18 30		
Ledbury	d				13 52	14 55		16 52		18 48		
Colwall	d				13 59	15 02		17 00		18 55		
Great Malvern	d	09 20	11 15	13 15	14 11	15 07		17 05		19 11	20 15	
Malvern Link	d	09 23	11 18	13 18	14 15	15 11		17 09		19 14	20 18	
Worcester Foregate Street 7	d	09 32	11 28	13 27	14 26	15 22		17 22	18 26	19 29	20 28	
Worcester Shrub Hill 7	d	09 35	11 31	13 31	14 30	15 26	16 28	17 28	18 30	19 33	20 31	21 28
Pershore	d	09 44	11 40	13 40	14 40	15 35	16 38	17 37	18 40	19 42	20 41	21 37
Evesham	a	09 51	11 48	13 47	14 47	15 44	16 45	17 44	18 48	19 50	20 48	21 45
	d	09 52	11 50	13 49	14 50	15 47	16 48	17 49	18 49	19 51	20 49	21 48
Honeybourne	d	09 59	11 57	13 56		15 54	16 56	17 56	18 57	19 58	20 56	21 55
Moreton-in-Marsh	a	10 10	12 08	14 07	15 05	16 06	17 07	18 08	19 08	20 09	21 07	22 07
	d	10 11	12 09	14 08	15 08	16 07	17 09	18 10	19 10	20 12	21 08	22 07
Kingham	d	10 19	12 17	14 16	15 16	16 16	17 18	18 19	19 19	20 20	21 16	22 15
Shipton	d											
Ascott-under-Wychwood	d											
Charlbury	a	10 28	12 26	14 25	15 26	16 25	17 27	18 29	19 28	20 29	21 25	22 24
	d	10 28	12 26	14 25	15 27	16 26	17 28	18 30	19 29	20 30	21 25	22 25
Finstock	d											
Combe	d											
Hanborough	d	10 36	12 34	14 33	15 35	16 34	17 36		19 37	20 38	21 33	22 33
Oxford	a	10 49	12 49	14 50	15 48	16 50	17 49	18 49	19 49	20 49	21 43	22 42
Didcot Parkway	a	11 04	13 05	15 05	16 02	17 06	18 03	19 02	20 03	21 02	21 56	22 58
Reading 7	a	11 27	13 26	15 26	16 23	17 30	18 22	19 28	20 28	21 23	22 18	23 24
Slough 3	a	11 42	13 43	15 44	16 38	17 48	18 43	19 46	20 48	21 47	22 42	23 42
London Paddington 15 ⊖	a	12 06	14 08	16 06	17 04	18 14	19 06	20 11	21 09	22 09	23 06	00 11

Sundays

16 February to 23 March

		GW ◇1	GW ◇1	GW ◇1	GW ◇1 ☕	GW ◇1 ☕	GW ◇1 ☕	GW ◇1 ☕	GW ◇1	GW ◇1	GW ◇1	GW ◇1
Hereford 7	d				13 33	14 35		16 34		18 30		
Ledbury	d				13 52	14 55		16 52		18 48		
Colwall	d				13 59	15 02		17 00		18 55		
Great Malvern	d	09 20	11 15	13 15	14 11	15 07		17 05		19 11	20 15	
Malvern Link	d	09 23	11 18	13 18	14 15	15 11		17 09		19 14	20 18	
Worcester Foregate Street 7	d	09 32	11 28	13 27	14 26	15 22		17 22	18 26	19 29	20 28	
Worcester Shrub Hill 7	d	09 35	11 31	13 31	14 30	15 26	16 28	17 28	18 30	19 33	20 31	21 28
Pershore	d	09 44	11 40	13 40	14 40	15 35	16 38	17 37	18 40	19 42	20 41	21 37
Evesham	a	09 51	11 48	13 47	14 47	15 43	16 45	17 44	18 48	19 50	20 48	21 45
	d	09 52	11 50	13 49	14 50	15 47	16 48	17 49	18 49	19 51	20 49	21 48
Honeybourne	d	09 59	11 57	13 56		15 54	16 56	17 56	18 57	19 58	20 56	21 55
Moreton-in-Marsh	a	10 10	12 08	14 07	15 05	16 06	17 07	18 08	19 08	20 09	21 07	22 07
	d	10 11	12 09	14 08	15 08	16 07	17 09	18 10	19 10	20 12	21 08	22 07
Kingham	d	10 19	12 17	14 16	15 16	16 16	17 18	18 19	19 19	20 20	21 16	22 15
Shipton	d											
Ascott-under-Wychwood	d											
Charlbury	a	10 28	12 26	14 25	15 26	16 25	17 27	18 29	19 28	20 29	21 25	22 24
	d	10 28	12 26	14 25	15 27	16 26	17 28	18 30	19 29	20 30	21 25	22 25
Finstock	d											
Combe	d											
Hanborough	d	10 36	12 34	14 33	15 35	16 34	17 36		19 37	20 38	21 33	22 33
Oxford	a	10 49	12 49	14 49	15 48	16 50	17 49	18 49	19 49	20 49	21 49	22 42
Didcot Parkway	a	11 06	13 05	15 05	16 02	17 06	18 03	19 02	20 03	21 02	22 01	22 58
Reading 7	a	11 25	13 22	15 22	16 23	17 25	18 19	19 28	20 22	21 23	22 18	23 18
Slough 3	a	11 42	13 37	15 37	16 38	17 44	18 36	19 42	20 39	21 43	22 39	23 36
London Paddington 15 ⊖	a	12 04	14 02	16 00	17 04	18 07	19 01	20 07	21 00	22 06	23 03	00 12

For other services between London and Worcester refer to table 125

Table 126R

Sundays

30 March to 11 May

Network Diagram - refer to first Page of Table 116

Hereford and Worcester - Oxford and London

		GW	GW	GW	GW	GW	GW	GW		GW	GW	GW	GW
		◇1	◇1	◇1	◇1	◇1	◇1	◇1		◇1	◇1	◇1	◇1
					🍴	🍴	🍴	🍴					
Hereford 7	d				13 33	14 35		16 34			18 30		
Ledbury	d				13 52	14 55		16 52			18 48		
Colwall	d				13 59	15 02		17 00			18 55		
Great Malvern	d	09 20	11 15	13 15	14 11	15 07		17 05			19 11	20 15	
Malvern Link	d	09 23	11 18	13 18	14 15	15 11		17 09			19 14	20 18	
Worcester Foregate Street 7	d	09 32	11 28	13 27	14 26	15 22		17 22		18 26	19 29	20 28	
Worcester Shrub Hill 7	d	09 35	11 31	13 31	14 30	15 26	16 28	17 28		18 30	19 33	20 31	21 28
Pershore	d	09 44	11 40	13 40	14 40	15 35	16 38	17 37		18 40	19 42	20 41	21 37
Evesham	a	09 51	11 48	13 47	14 47	15 44	16 45	17 44		18 48	19 50	20 48	21 45
	d	09 52	11 50	13 49	14 50	15 47	16 48	17 51		18 49	19 51	20 49	21 48
Honeybourne	d	09 59	11 57	13 56		15 54	16 56	17 59		18 57	19 58	20 56	21 55
Moreton-in-Marsh	a	10 10	12 08	14 07	15 05	16 06	17 07	18 10		19 08	20 09	21 07	22 07
	d	10 11	12 09	14 08	15 08	16 07	17 09	18 13		19 10	20 12	21 08	22 07
Kingham	d	10 19	12 17	14 16	15 16	16 16	17 18	18 22		19 19	20 20	21 16	22 15
Shipton	d												
Ascott-under-Wychwood	d												
Charlbury	a	10 28	12 26	14 25	15 26	16 25	17 27	18 31		19 28	20 29	21 25	22 24
	d	10 28	12 26	14 25	15 27	16 26	17 28	18 33		19 29	20 30	21 25	22 25
Finstock	d												
Combe	d												
Hanborough	d	10 36	12 34	14 33	15 35	16 35	17 36			19 37	20 38	21 33	22 33
Oxford	a	10 49	12 49	14 49	15 48	16 50	17 49	18 48		19 48	20 49	21 48	22 42
Didcot Parkway	a	11 06	13 05	15 05	16 02	17 06	18 03	19 02		20 03	21 05	22 01	22 58
Reading 7	a	11 25	13 22	15 22	16 19	17 25	18 22	19 28		20 22	21 20	22 18	23 18
Slough 3	a	11 43	13 36	15 37	16 38	17 44	18 39	19 43		20 39	21 41	22 39	23 36
London Paddington 15 ⊖	a	12 04	14 01	16 00	17 03	18 07	19 01	20 04		21 01	22 03	23 00	00 01

For other services between London and Worcester refer to table 125

Table 126A

Mondays to Fridays

9 December to 16 May

Kingham - Chipping Norton

Network Diagram - refer to first Page of Table 116

Bus Service

		GW	GW	GW	GW	GW	GW	GW	GW	GW	GW	GW	GW	GW	GW	GW	GW	GW	GW	GW	GW
		BHX	BHX	BHX	BHX	BHX	BHX	BHX	BHX		BHX	BHX	BHX	BHX		BHX	BHX		BHX	BHX	BHX
		A	A	A	A	A	A	A	A	B	A	A	A	A	B	A	A	B	A	A	A
		🚌	🚌	🚌	🚌	🚌	🚌	🚌	🚌	🚌	🚌	🚌	🚌	🚌	🚌	🚌	🚌	🚌	🚌	🚌	🚌
Kingham	d	06 30	07 00	07 30	08 35	09 55	10 55	11 55	12 55	13 23	13 55	14 55	15 50	16 40	17 17	17 20	18 10	18 22	18 50	19 20	19 52
Chipping Norton West St.	a	06 43	07 13	07 43	08 48	10 08	11 08	12 08	13 08	13 35	14 08	15 08	16 03	16 53	17 29	17 33	18 23	18 34	19 03	19x33	20x05

Saturdays

14 December to 17 May

		GW	GW	GW	GW	GW	GW	GW	GW	GW	GW	GW	GW	GW
		🚌	🚌	🚌	🚌	🚌	🚌	🚌	🚌	🚌	🚌	🚌	🚌	🚌
Kingham	d	08 15	08 55	09 55	10 55	11 55	12 55	13 55	14 55	15 50	16 50	17 55	18 50	19 50
Chipping Norton West St.	a	08 28	09 08	10 08	11 08	12 08	13 08	14 08	15 08	16 03	17 03	18 08	19 03	20x03

Sundays

8 December to 11 May

		GW	GW	GW
		🚌	🚌	🚌
Kingham	d	13 23	17 17	18 22
Chipping Norton West St.	a	13 35	17 29	18 34

A not 25 December, 26 December, 1 January, 18 April, 21 April, 5 May

B 18 April, 21 April, 5 May

Table 126A-R

Mondays to Fridays

9 December to 16 May

Chipping Norton - Kingham

Network Diagram - refer to first Page of Table 116

Bus Service

		GW	GW	GW	GW	GW	GW	GW	GW	GW	GW	GW	GW	GW	GW	GW	GW	GW	GW
		BHX	BHX	BHX	BHX		BHX	BHX	BHX	BHX	BHX		BHX	BHX	BHX	BHX	BHX		BHX	BHX
		A	A	A	A	B	A	A	A	A	A	B	A	A	A	A	A	B	A	A
		🚌	🚌	🚌	🚌	🚌	🚌	🚌	🚌	🚌	🚌	🚌	🚌	🚌	🚌	🚌	🚌	🚌	🚌	🚌
Chipping Norton West St	d	06 00	06 45	07 15	08 00	09 25	09 30	10 35	11 35	12 35	13 35	13 39	14 35	15 30	16 20	16 55	17 45	18 03	18 25	19 05
Kingham	a	06 12	06 58	07 28	08 14	09 37	09 44	10 50	11 50	12 50	13 50	13 51	14 50	15 44	16 35	17 10	18 00	18 15	18 40	19 20

Saturdays

14 December to 17 May

		GW	GW	GW	GW	GW	GW	GW	GW	GW	GW	GW	GW	GW
		🚌	🚌	🚌	🚌	🚌	🚌	🚌	🚌	🚌	🚌	🚌	🚌	🚌
Chipping Norton West St	d	08 00	08 30	09 30	10 35	11 35	12 35	13 35	14 35	15 30	16 30	17 30	18 25	19 10
Kingham	a	08 14	08 44	09 44	10 50	11 50	12 50	13 50	14 50	15 44	16 45	17 45	18 40	19 25

Sundays

8 December to 11 May

		GW	GW	GW
		🚌	🚌	🚌
Chipping Norton West St	d	09 25	13 39	18 03
Kingham	a	09 37	13 51	18 15

A not 25 December, 26 December, 1 January, 18 April, 21 April, 5 May

B 18 April, 21 April, 5 May

Route Diagram for Tables 127, 128

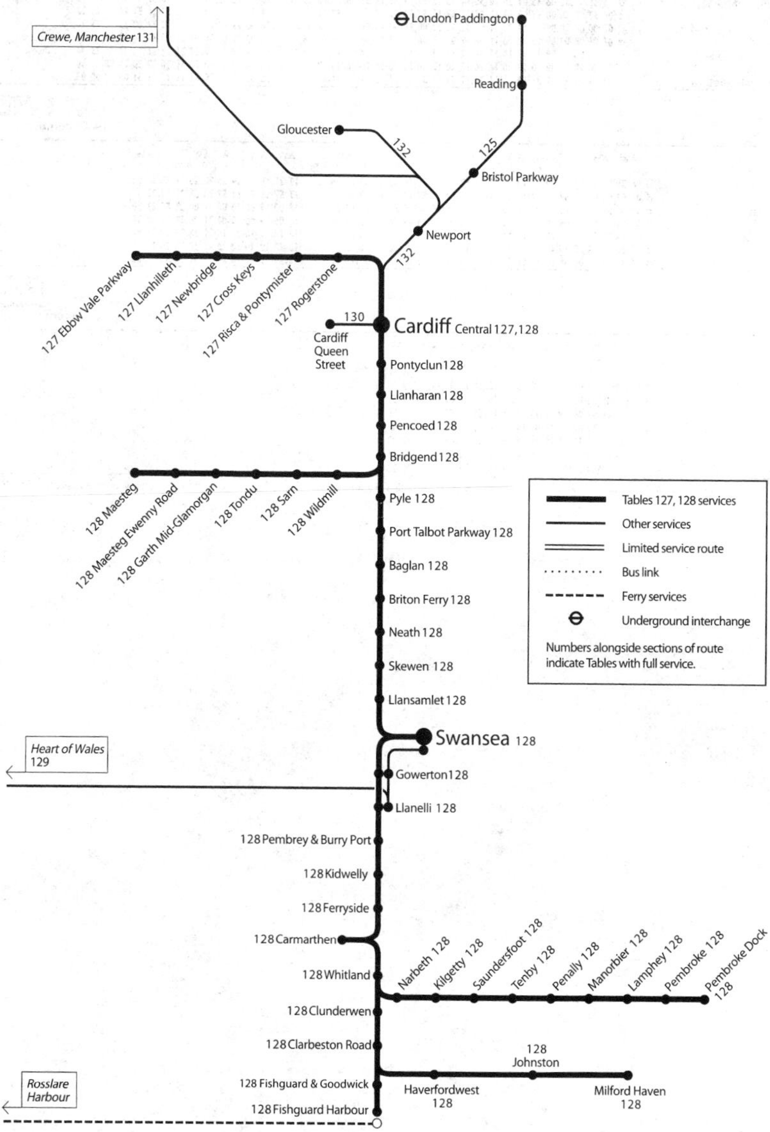

Crewe, Manchester 131
London Paddington
Reading
Gloucester
132
125
Bristol Parkway
Newport
132
127 Ebbw Vale Parkway
127 Llanhilleth
127 Newbridge
127 Cross Keys
127 Risca & Pontymister
127 Rogerstone
130
Cardiff Queen Street
Cardiff Central 127,128
Pontyclun 128
Llanharan 128
Pencoed 128
Bridgend 128
128 Maesteg
128 Maesteg Ewenny Road
128 Garth Mid-Glamorgan
128 Tondu
128 Sarn
128 Wildmill
Pyle 128
Port Talbot Parkway 128
Baglan 128
Briton Ferry 128
Neath 128
Skewen 128
Llansamlet 128
Swansea 128
Heart of Wales 129
Gowerton 128
Llanelli 128
128 Pembrey & Burry Port
128 Kidwelly
128 Ferryside
128 Carmarthen
128 Whitland
128 Clunderwen
128 Clarbeston Road
128 Fishguard & Goodwick
128 Fishguard Harbour
Rosslare Harbour
Narbeth 128
Kilgetty 128
Saundersfoot 128
Tenby 128
Penally 128
Manorbier 128
Lamphey 128
Pembroke 128
Pembroke Dock 128
Haverfordwest 128
128 Johnston
Milford Haven 128
Tables 127, 128 services
Other services
Limited service route
Bus link
Ferry services
Underground interchange
Numbers alongside sections of route indicate Tables with full service.

TOCs operating on this network - Arriva Trains Wales (AW), First Great Western (GW)

Table 127

Mondays to Fridays

9 December to 16 May

Cardiff Central - Ebbw Vale Parkway

Route Diagram - see first Page of Table 127

Miles			AW	AW	AW	AW	AW	AW	AW	AW	AW	AW	AW	AW	AW	AW	AW	AW	AW FX	AW FO
0	**Cardiff Central** 7	d	06 35	07 35	08 35	09 35	10 35	11 35	12 35	13 35	14 35	15 35	16 35	17 35	18 35	19 35	20 35	21 35	23 05	23 05
14	Rogerstone	d	06 57	07 58	08 57	09 57	10 57	11 57	12 57	13 57	14 57	15 57	16 57	17 57	18 57	19 57	20 57	21 57	23 27	23 27
15¼	Risca & Pontymister	d	07 00	08 00	09 00	10 00	11 00	12 00	13 00	14 00	15 00	16 00	17 00	18 00	19 00	20 00	21 00	22 00	23 30	23 30
17¼	Cross Keys	d	07 06	08 07	09 06	10 06	11 06	12 06	13 06	14 06	15 06	16 06	17 06	18 06	19 06	20 06	21 06	22 06	23 36	23 36
20¾	Newbridge (Ebbw Vale)	d	07 14	08 15	09 14	10 14	11 14	12 14	13 14	14 14	15 14	16 14	17 14	18 14	19 14	20 14	21 14	22 14	23 44	23 44
23½	Llanhilleth	d	07 20	08 21	09 20	10 20	11 20	12 20	13 20	14 20	15 20	16 20	17 20	18 20	19 20	20 20	21 20	22 20	23 50	23 50
28¾	**Ebbw Vale Parkway**	a	07 31	08 31	09 31	10 31	11 31	12 31	13 31	14 31	15 31	16 31	17 31	18 31	19 31	20 31	21 31	22 31	00 02	00 05

Saturdays

14 December to 17 May

		AW	AW	AW	AW	AW	AW	AW	AW	AW	AW	AW	AW	AW	AW	AW	AW	AW
Cardiff Central 7	d	06 35	07 39	08 35	09 35	10 35	11 35	12 35	13 35	14 35	15 35	16 35	17 35	18 35	19 35	20 35	21 35	23 05
Rogerstone	d	06 57	08 00	08 57	09 57	10 57	11 57	12 57	13 57	14 57	15 57	16 57	17 57	18 57	19 57	20 57	21 57	23 27
Risca & Pontymister	d	07 00	08 04	09 00	10 00	11 00	12 00	13 00	14 00	15 00	16 00	17 00	18 00	19 00	20 00	21 00	22 00	23 30
Cross Keys	d	07 06	08 09	09 06	10 06	11 06	12 06	13 06	14 06	15 06	16 06	17 06	18 06	19 06	20 06	21 06	22 06	23 36
Newbridge (Ebbw Vale)	d	07 14	08 17	09 14	10 14	11 14	12 14	13 14	14 14	15 14	16 14	17 14	18 14	19 14	20 14	21 14	22 14	23 44
Llanhilleth	d	07 20	08 23	09 20	10 20	11 20	12 20	13 20	14 20	15 20	16 20	17 20	18 20	19 20	20 20	21 20	22 20	23 50
Ebbw Vale Parkway	a	07 31	08 35	09 31	10 31	11 31	12 31	13 31	14 31	15 31	16 31	17 31	18 31	19 31	20 34	21 31	22 31	00 02

Sundays

8 December to 11 May

		AW A	AW B	AW	AW	AW	AW	AW	AW C	AW
Cardiff Central 7	d	07 40		09 24	11 30	13 30	15 30	17 30	19 16	19 30
Rogerstone	d	08 03	08 03	09 45	11 51	13 51	15 51	17 51	19 54	19 51
Risca & Pontymister	d	08 07	08 07	09 49	11 55	13 55	15 55	17 55		19 55
Cross Keys	d	08 13	08 13	09 55	12 01	14 01	16 01	18 01		20 01
Newbridge (Ebbw Vale)	d	08 21	08 21	10 03	12 09	14 09	16 09	18 09		20 09
Llanhilleth	d	08 28	08 28	10 10	12 16	14 16	16 16	18 16		20 16
Ebbw Vale Parkway	a	08 39	08 39	10 21	12 27	14 27	16 27	18 27		20 27

A until 29 December, from 16 February **B** from 5 January until 9 February **C** from 5 January until 9 February, not 26 January

Table 127R

Ebbw Vale Parkway - Cardiff Central

Mondays to Fridays

9 December to 16 May

Route Diagram - see first Page of Table 127

Miles			AW	AW	AW	AW	AW	AW	AW	AW	AW	AW	AW	AW	AW	AW	AW	AW FX	AW FO	AW
0	**Ebbw Vale Parkway**	d	06 40	07 40	08 40	09 40	10 40	11 40	12 40	13 40	14 40	15 40	16 40	17 40	18 40	19 40	20 40	21 40	21 40	22 40
5¼	Llanhilleth	d	06 48	07 48	08 48	09 48	10 48	11 48	12 48	13 48	14 48	15 48	16 48	17 48	18 48	19 48	20 48	21 48	21 48	22 48
8	Newbridge (Ebbw Vale)	d	06 54	07 54	08 54	09 54	10 54	11 54	12 54	13 54	14 54	15 54	16 54	17 54	18 54	19 54	20 54	21 54	21 54	22 54
11½	Cross Keys	d	07 02	08 02	09 02	10 02	11 02	12 02	13 02	14 02	15 02	16 02	17 02	18 02	19 02	20 02	21 02	22 02	22 02	23 02
13½	Risca & Pontymister	d	07 07	08 07	09 07	10 07	11 07	12 07	13 07	14 07	15 07	16 07	17 07	18 07	19 07	20 07	21 07	22 07	22 07	23 07
14¾	Rogerstone	d	07 11	08 11	09 11	10 11	11 11	12 11	13 11	14 11	15 11	16 11	17 11	18 11	19 11	20 11	21 11	22 11	22 11	23 11
28¾	**Cardiff Central 7**	a	07 37	08 37	09 38	10 37	11 37	12 36	13 37	14 37	15 36	16 37	17 37	18 37	19 39	20 39	21 38	22 40	22 41	23 37

Saturdays

14 December to 17 May

		AW	AW	AW	AW	AW	AW	AW	AW	AW	AW	AW	AW	AW	AW	AW	AW	AW
Ebbw Vale Parkway	d	06 40	07 40	08 40	09 40	10 40	11 40	12 40	13 40	14 40	15 40	16 40	17 40	18 40	19 40	20 40	21 40	22 40
Llanhilleth	d	06 48	07 48	08 48	09 48	10 48	11 48	12 48	13 48	14 48	15 48	16 48	17 48	18 48	19 48	20 48	21 48	22 48
Newbridge (Ebbw Vale)	d	06 54	07 54	08 54	09 54	10 54	11 54	12 54	13 54	14 54	15 54	16 54	17 54	18 54	19 54	20 54	21 54	22 54
Cross Keys	d	07 02	08 02	09 02	10 02	11 02	12 02	13 02	14 02	15 02	16 02	17 02	18 02	19 02	20 02	21 02	22 02	23 02
Risca & Pontymister	d	07 07	08 07	09 07	10 07	11 07	12 07	13 07	14 07	15 07	16 07	17 07	18 07	19 07	20 07	21 07	22 07	23 07
Rogerstone	d	07 11	08 11	09 11	10 11	11 11	12 11	13 11	14 11	15 11	16 11	17 11	18 11	19 11	20 11	21 11	22 11	23 11
Cardiff Central 7	a	07 37	08 37	09 37	10 37	11 37	12 37	13 37	14 37	15 37	16 37	17 37	18 37	19 37	20 37	21 37	22 44	23 37

Sundays

8 December to 11 May

		AW	AW	AW	AW	AW	AW	AW
Ebbw Vale Parkway	d	08 40	10 27	12 27	14 30	16 30	18 30	20 40
Llanhilleth	d	08 48	10 35	12 35	14 38	16 38	18 38	20 48
Newbridge (Ebbw Vale)	d	08 54	10 41	12 41	14 44	16 44	18 44	20 54
Cross Keys	d	09 02	10 49	12 49	14 52	16 52	18 52	21 02
Risca & Pontymister	d	09 07	10 54	12 54	14 57	16 57	18 57	21 07
Rogerstone	d	09 11	10 58	12 58	15 01	17 01	19 01	21 11
Cardiff Central 7	a	09 33	11 24	13 25	15 23	17 25	19 23	21 37

Table 128

Mondays to Fridays

9 December to 16 May

Cardiff - Maesteg, Swansea and West Wales

Route Diagram - see first Page of Table 127

Miles	Miles			AW MX	AW MO	AW	AW MX	GW MX	GW MO	AW MX	GW MO	GW MX		AW	AW	AW	AW	AW	AW	AW	AW	AW		AW	
				◇	◇	R	◇	◇1	◇1 A	◇	◇1 B	◇1		◇							◇			◇	
								☕	☕		☕	☕									🛒				
—	—	London Paddington 15 ⊖	d																						
—	—	Reading 7	d																						
—	—	Manchester Piccadilly 10	d																						
—	—	Gloucester 7	d																						
—	—	Bristol Parkway 7	d									00 27													
—	—	Newport (South Wales)	d									00 56													
0	—	**Cardiff Central 7**	d						00 05		00 09	01 17									05 39	05 53		06 42	
11	—	Pontyclun	d																		05 51				
14	—	Llanharan	d																		05 56				
16¼	—	Pencoed	d																		06 01				
20¼	0	Bridgend	d					00 05	00 27		00 31	01 42									06 07	06 15		07 02	
—	1	Wildmill	d																			06 17			
—	2¼	Sarn	d																			06 20			
—	3	Tondu	d																			06 24			
—	7	Garth (Mid Glamorgan)	d																			06 33			
—	7¾	Maesteg (Ewenny Road)	d																			06 36			
—	8¼	Maesteg	a																			06 41			
26¼	—	Pyle	d																		06 15			07 10	
32½	—	Port Talbot Parkway	d				00 01	00 18	00 40		00 44	01 55									06 23			07 18	
34½	—	Baglan	d				00 05														06 27			07 22	
36¼	—	Briton Ferry	d				00 09														06 30			07 25	
38	—	Neath	d				00 13	00 26	00 48		00 53	02 03									06 34			07 29	
41¼	—	Skewen	d				00 16														06 38			07 33	
43½	—	Llansamlet	d				00 20														06 42			07 37	
47½	—	**Swansea**	a				00 28	00 39	01 02		01 05	02 16									06 51			07 45	
—	—		d				00 45							04 31					05 45		06 53			07 50	
53	—	Gowerton	d				00s55							04 42					05 55		07 03			08 00	
58¾	—	Llanelli	a				01s02							04 49					06 02		07 11			08 07	
—	—		d	00 03															06 04		07 11			08 08	
62¾	—	Pembrey & Burry Port	d	00 08	00 04		01s09												06 10		07 17			08 14	
68	—	Kidwelly	d		00x11		01b16												06x17		07x23			08x20	
72¼	—	Ferryside	d		00x17		01b22												06x23		07x29			08x26	
79¼	—	**Carmarthen**	a	00 28	00 30		01 40												06 37		07 43			08 40	
—	—		d	00 31	00 34										04 58	05 30	05 50	05 58	06 38		07 46			08 43	
93¼	—	Whitland	a	00 46	00 50										05 11	05 46	06 05	06 13	06 56		08 00			08 59	
—	—		d	00 46	00 50										05 11	05 47	06 05	06 13	06 56		08 00			09 02	09 07
—	5¼	Narberth	d													05x56			07x05					09x11	
—	10¾	Kilgetty	d													06x05			07x15					09x21	
—	11½	Saundersfoot	d													06x07			07x17					09x23	
—	15¾	**Tenby**	a													06 14			07 24					09 30	
—	—		d													06 24			07 32					09 43	
—	17	Penally	d													06x27			07x35					09x46	
—	20¼	Manorbier	d													06 33			07 42					09 53	
—	23¾	Lamphey	d													06x41			07x49					10x00	
—	25¼	Pembroke	d													06 44			07 52					10 03	
—	27¼	**Pembroke Dock**	a													06 54			08 07					10 18	
98¾	—	Clunderwen	d												05x18		06x12	06x19			08x07				09x14
105¼	0	Clarbeston Road	d	01x00	01x03										05x26		06x20	06x27		07 34	08x14				09x22
—	5¼	Haverfordwest	d												05 37			06 35			08 23				
—	10	Johnston	d							00x06					05x45			06x43			08x31				
—	14	**Milford Haven**	a							00 21					06 00			06 58			08 43				
—	—	Fishguard & Goodwick	a	01 20	01 22												06 38			07 52					09 41
121	—	**Fishguard Harbour 30** ⛴	a	01 28	01 27												06 44			07 58					09 47
—	—		d			02 45																			
—	—	Rosslare Harbour ⛴	a			06 15																			

A from 6 January

B until 30 December

b Stops to set down only, stops on request

When events are being held at the Millenium Stadium, services are subject to alteration. Please check times before travelling.

Ferry service between Fishguard Harbour and Rosslare Harbour is operated by Stena Line

Table 128

Mondays to Fridays

9 December to 16 May

Cardiff - Maesteg, Swansea and West Wales

Route Diagram - see first Page of Table 127

		AW	AW	AW	GW	AW	AW	GW		AW	AW	AW	AW	GW	AW	AW	AW	GW		AW	AW	AW	AW	AW	AW
																					⊟				
				◇	◇1	◇	◇	◇1		◇				◇1	◇		◇	◇1		◇					◇
														A				B							
				🛒	☕	🛒		☕		🛒				☕	🛒		🛒	☕⊘		🛒					🛒
London Paddington 15 ⊖	d				05 19			06 45						07 45				08 45							
Reading 7	d				05 53			07 12						08 12				09 12							
Manchester Piccadilly 10	d														06 30		07 30								08 30
Gloucester 7	d	05 50											07 58			08 58									
Bristol Parkway 7	d							08 08						09 08				10 08							
Newport (South Wales)	d	06 44		07 31	07 46		08 01	08 32		08 38			08 52	09 30	09 37	09 52	10 22	10 31		10 40					11 22
Cardiff Central 7	d	07 03	07 14	07 50	08 03		08 21	08 48		09 04		09 14	09 18	09 48	10 04	10 18	10 40	10 48		10 57			11 14	11 18	11 38
Pontyclun	d	07 15					08 33						09 30			10 30								11 30	
Llanharan	d	07 20					08 38						09 35			10 35								11 35	
Pencoed	d	07 24					08 42						09 39			10 39								11 39	
Bridgend	d	07 33	07 41	08 09	08 24		08 50	09 09		09 23		09 34	09 46	10 09	10 23	10 46	10 59	11 09		11 19			11 34	11 46	11 59
Wildmill	d	07 35					08 52						09 49			10 49								11 49	
Sarn	d	07 38					08 55						09 52			10 52								11 52	
Tondu	d	07 42					08 59						09 55			10 55								11 55	
Garth (Mid Glamorgan)	d	07 51					09 08						10 05			11 05								12 04	
Maesteg (Ewenny Road)	d	07 54					09 11						10 07			11 07								12 07	
Maesteg	a	07 56					09 16						10 12			11 12								12 14	
Pyle	d		07 51	08 17								09 43											11 42		
Port Talbot Parkway	d		08 00	08 25	08 37			09 22		09 36		09 52		10 22	10 36		11 11	11 22					11 50		12 11
Baglan	d		08 03	08 27								09 55											11 54		
Briton Ferry	d		08 07	08 31								09 59											11 57		
Neath	d		08 11	08 35	08 45			09 30		09 43		10 03		10 30	10 43		11 18	11 30					12 01		12 18
Skewen	d		08 14	08 38								10 06											12 05		
Llansamlet	d		08 18	08 42								10 10											12 09		
Swansea	a		08 30	08 51	08 58			09 45		09 55		10 21		10 44	10 55		11 33	11 43					12 20		12 34
	d			09 07		09 14				10 00					11 00		11 36					12 00			12 40
Gowerton	d			09 18		09 26				10 11					11 12							12 10			12 51
Llanelli	a			09 24		09 32				10 17					11 18		11 52			11 59		12 17			12 57
	d			09 26						10 19					11 18		11 54			12 03		12 19			12 59
Pembrey & Burry Port	d			09 32						10 25					11 24		12 00					12 25			13 05
Kidwelly	d			09x38						10x31							12x06								
Ferryside	d			09x43						10x36							12x11								
Carmarthen	a			09 56						10 51					11 44		12 26					12 48			13 22
	d			09 59							10 58				11 48							12 51			13 30
Whitland	a			10 13							11 12				12 01					12 45		13 06			13 45
	d			10 14							11 13				12 01					12 45		13 06			13 45
Narberth	d										11x22											13x15			
Kilgetty	d										11x32											13x25			
Saundersfoot	d										11x34											13x27			
Tenby	a										11 41											13 34			
	d										11 49											13 45			
Penally	d										11x52											13x48			
Manorbier	d										11 58											13 54			
Lamphey	d										12x06											14x02			
Pembroke	d										12 09											14 05			
Pembroke Dock	a										12 23											14 19			
Clunderwen	d			10x20											12x07										13x52
Clarbeston Road	d			10x28											12x15										13x59
Haverfordwest	d			10 36											12 23										14 08
Johnston	d			10x44											12x31										14x16
Milford Haven	a			10 57											12 48										14 31
Fishguard & Goodwick	a																			13 17					
Fishguard Harbour 30 ⛴	a																			13 27					
	d																				14 30				
Rosslare Harbour ⛴	a																				18 00				

A The St. David

B ☕ from Bridgend ⊘ to Bridgend

When events are being held at the Millenium Stadium, services are subject to alteration. Please check times before travelling.

Ferry service between Fishguard Harbour and Rosslare Harbour is operated by Stena Line

Table 128

Mondays to Fridays

9 December to 16 May

Cardiff - Maesteg, Swansea and West Wales

Route Diagram - see first Page of Table 127

		GW	AW	AW	AW	GW	AW	AW	AW	AW	GW	AW	AW	GW	AW	AW	AW	AW	GW	AW	AW	AW
																■		■				
		◇1	◇		◇	◇1				◇	◇1		◇	◇1					◇1	◇		
		A				A					A			A								
		🍽Ø			🛒	🍽Ø				🛒	🍽Ø		🛒	🍽Ø		🛒		🛒	🍽	🛒		
London Paddington 15 ⊖	d	09 45				10 45					11 45			12 45					13 45			
Reading 7	d	10 12				11 12					12 12			13 12					14 12			
Manchester Piccadilly 10	d				09 30					10 30			11 30					12 30				
Gloucester 7	d			10 58													13 58			14 45		
Bristol Parkway 7	d	11 08				12 08					13 08			14 08					15 08			
Newport (South Wales)	d	11 31		11 52	12 23	12 31				13 23	13 31		14 22	14 31		14 55	14 59	15 22	15 31	15 42		
Cardiff Central 7	d	11 48		12 18	12 39	12 48		13 13	13 18	13 41	13 48	14 21	14 43	14 48		15 13	15 18	15 39	15 48	16 04	16 18	16 37
Pontyclun	d			12 30					13 30			14 33					15 30				16 30	16 49
Llanharan	d			12 35					13 35			14 38					15 35				16 35	
Pencoed	d			12 39					13 39			14 42					15 39				16 39	16 56
Bridgend	d	12 09		12 46	12 58	13 09		13 34	13 46	14 04	14 09	14 49	15 02	15 09		15 32	15 46	16 01	16 09	16 25	16 46	17a03
Wildmill	d			12 49					13 49			14 52					15 49				16 49	
Sarn	d			12 52					13 52			14 55					15 52				16 52	
Tondu	d			12 55					13 55			14 58									16 55	
Garth (Mid Glamorgan)	d			13 05					14 05			15 08					16 05				17 05	
Maesteg (Ewenny Road)	d			13 07					14 07			15 10					16 07				17 07	
Maesteg	a			13 12					14 12			15 15					16 12				17 12	
Pyle	d							13 42								15 40				16 33		
Port Talbot Parkway	d	12 22			13 11	13 22		13 50		14 18	14 22		15 15	15 22		15 49		16 14	16 22	16 41		
Baglan	d							13 54								15 52						
Briton Ferry	d							13 57								15 55						
Neath	d	12 30			13 18	13 30		14 01		14 25	14 30		15 22	15 30		15 59		16 21	16 30	16 49		
Skewen	d							14 05								16 03						
Llansamlet	d							14 09								16 07						
Swansea	a	12 43			13 33	13 44		14 20		14 34	14 43		15 34	15 43		16 15		16 33	16 43	17 02		
	d		13 14		13 37		14 00			14 37			15 37		16 00	16 23		16 40		17 05		
Gowerton	d		13 26		13 48					14 51			15 48		16 11	16x34		16 51		17 16		
Llanelli	a		13 33		13 54		14 15			14 55			15 54		16 17	16 41		16 57		17 23		
	d				13 56		14 16			14 56			15 56		16 18			16 59		17 24		
Pembrey & Burry Port	d				14 02		14 22			15 02			16 02		16 24			17 05		17 30		
Kidwelly	d				14x08								16x08					17x11		17x36		
Ferryside	d				14x13								16x13					17x16		17x42		
Carmarthen	a				14 30		14 45			15 22			16 30		16 47			17 28		17 55		
	d						14 51			15 28					16 51			17 31		17 57		
Whitland	a						15 05			15 43					17 05			17 45		18 12		
	d						15 06			15 43					17 06			17 46		18 13		
Narberth	d						15x15								17x15							
Kilgetty	d						15x25								17x25							
Saundersfoot	d						15x27								17x27							
Tenby	a						15 34								17 34							
	d						15 45								17 45							
Penally	d						15x48								17x48							
Manorbier	d						15 54								17 54							
Lamphey	d						16x02								18x02							
Pembroke	d						16 05								18 05							
Pembroke Dock	a						16 19								18 19							
Clunderwen	d									15x50								17x52		18x20		
Clarbeston Road	d									15x57								18x00		18x27		
Haverfordwest	d									16 06								18 08				
Johnston	d									16x14								18x16				
Milford Haven	a									16 29								18 31				
Fishguard & Goodwick	a																			18 46		
Fishguard Harbour 30 ⛴	a																			18 56		
	d																					
Rosslare Harbour ⛴	a																					

A 🍽 from Bridgend Ø to Bridgend

When events are being held at the Millenium Stadium, services are subject to alteration. Please check times before travelling.

Ferry service between Fishguard Harbour and Rosslare Harbour is operated by Stena Line

Table 128

Mondays to Fridays

Cardiff - Maesteg, Swansea and West Wales

9 December to 16 May

Route Diagram - see first Page of Table 127

		AW	GW	AW	AW	AW	AW	AW	GW	AW	AW	GW	AW	GW	AW	AW	AW	GW	AW	AW	GW	AW	GW
				■				■				■		■	■			■		■	■		■
			◇1			◇	◇		◇1			1		1				◇1			1		1
														A				B					
			☕	🛒		🛒		🛒	☕			☕		☕	🛒	🛒		☕		🛒	☕		☕
London Paddington 15 ⊖	d		14 45						15 45			16 15		16 45				17 15			17 45		18 15
Reading 7	d		15 12						16 12			16 44		17 12				17 42			18 12		18 42
Manchester Piccadilly 10	d			13 30				14 30							15 30					16 30			
Gloucester 7	d										16 58						17 58					19 00	
Bristol Parkway 7	d		16 08						17 08			17 45		18 08				18 42			19 10		19 42
Newport (South Wales)	d		16 31	16 40		17 01		17 22	17 31		17 52	18 08		18 31	18 41		18 53	19 12		19 22	19 33	19 54	20 06
Cardiff Central 7	d		16 48	17 04		17 18		17 40	17 48	18 04	18 12	18 27		18 50	19 04		19 10	19 29		19 46	19 52	20 13	20 25
Pontyclun	d					17 32				18 16	18 24						19 26					20 25	
Llanharan	d					17 36					18 29						19 31					20 30	
Pencoed	d					17 40					18 33						19 35					20 34	
Bridgend	d		17 09	17 25		17 46		18 00	18 09	18 25	18 44	18 49		19 09	19 23		19 46	19 51		20 05	20 11	20 41	20 46
Wildmill	d					17 48					18 47						19 49					20 44	
Sarn	d					17 51					18 50						19 52					20 47	
Tondu	d					17 55					18 53						19 55					20 50	
Garth (Mid Glamorgan)	d					18 04					19 03						20 05					21 00	
Maesteg (Ewenny Road)	d					18 07					19 05						20 07					21 02	
Maesteg	a					18 15					19 10						20 12					21 07	
Pyle	d			17 32				18 08		18 35					19 30								
Port Talbot Parkway	d		17 22	17 40				18 17	18 22	18 42		19 02		19 22	19 38			20 04		20 21	20 26		20 59
Baglan	d			17 42						18 47					19 41								
Briton Ferry	d			17 46						18 49					19 44								
Neath	d		17 30	17 50				18 25	18 30	18 53		19 10		19 30	19 48			20 11		20 28	20 34		21 07
Skewen	d			17 54						18 58					19 53								
Llansamlet	d			17 58						19 02					19 57								
Swansea	a		17 43	18 05				18 38	18 44	19 10		19 22		19 45	20 04			20 22		20 42	20 47		21 19
	d	17 35		18 09			18 21	18 41					19 34		20 11			20 33		20 52			
Gowerton	d	17 45		18 20			18 32	18 52					19 45		20 22					21 03			
Llanelli	a	17 52		18 26			18 37	18 59					19 52		20 28			20 49		21 09			
	d	17 54		18 28				19 00					19 54		20 30			20 50		21 11			
Pembrey & Burry Port	d	18 00		18 33				19 06					20 00		20 35			20 57		21 16			
Kidwelly	d	18x08		18 39									20x07										
Ferryside	d	18x14		18 45									20x13										
Carmarthen	a	18 30		18 57				19 27					20 29		20 55			21 22		21 36			
	d			19 02				19 30								21 00				21 38			
Whitland	a			19 18				19 45								21 15				21 53			
	d			19 18				19 46								21 15				21 53			
Narberth	d			19x28												21x24							
Kilgetty	d			19x38												21x33							
Saundersfoot	d			19x40												21x35							
Tenby	a			19 52												21 42							
	d				20 00											21 44							
Penally	d				20x03											21x47							
Manorbier	d				20 09											21 53							
Lamphey	d				20x17											22x00							
Pembroke	d				20 20											22 03							
Pembroke Dock	a				20 35											22 16							
Clunderwen	d							19x53												22x00			
Clarbeston Road	d							20x00											20 05	22x07			
Haverfordwest	d							20 09												22 20			
Johnston	d							20x17												22x28			
Milford Haven	a							20 32												22 43			
Fishguard & Goodwick	a																		20 23				
Fishguard Harbour 30 ⛴	a																		20 29				
	d																						
Rosslare Harbour ⛴	a																						

A The Capitals United

B The Red Dragon. ◇ from Bridgend ■ to Bridgend

When events are being held at the Millenium Stadium, services are subject to alteration. Please check times before travelling.

Ferry service between Fishguard Harbour and Rosslare Harbour is operated by Stena Line

Table 128

Mondays to Fridays

9 December to 16 May

Cardiff - Maesteg, Swansea and West Wales

Route Diagram - see first Page of Table 127

		GW	AW	AW	GW	GW	AW	AW	GW	AW	AW	AW	AW	GW	GW	GW
					FX	FO	FX	FO				FO	FX		FO	FX
		R 1	◇		R 1	R 1	◇	◇	◇1	◇		◇	◇	◇1	◇1	◇1
							A	B	C							
		⊡			⊡	⊡	⚲	⚲	⊡⊘					⊡	⊡	⊡
London Paddington 15 ⊖	d	18 45			19 15	19 15			20 15					21 15	22 45	22 45
Reading 7	d	19 12			19 42	19u48			20 41					21 41	23 11	23 23
Manchester Piccadilly 10	d						18 30	18 30				19 30	19 30			
Gloucester 7	d			19 58												
Bristol Parkway 7	d	20 08			20 42	20 43			21 41					22 47	00 27	00 27
Newport (South Wales)	d	20 33		20 52	21 05	21 07	21 52	21 52	22 05			22 41	22 42	23 19	00 49	00 56
Cardiff Central 7	d	20 54	21 04	21 10	21 24	21 24	22 09	22 09	22 26		22 35	23 15	23 15	23 43	01 06	01 17
Pontyclun	d			21 22			22 21	22 21				23 29	23 29			
Llanharan	d			21 27			22 25	22 25				23 34	23 34			
Pencoed	d			21 32			22 29	22 29				23 39	23 39			
Bridgend	d	21 15	21 27	21 41	21 46	21 46	22 35	22 35	22 48		22 59	23 45	23 45	00 05	01 31	01 42
Wildmill	d			21 43							23 01					
Sarn	d			21 46							23 04					
Tondu	d			21 50							23 08					
Garth (Mid Glamorgan)	d			21 59							23 17					
Maesteg (Ewenny Road)	d			22 02							23 20					
Maesteg	a			22 06							23 24					
Pyle	d		21 34									23 53	23 53			
Port Talbot Parkway	d	21 28	21 45		21 59	21 59	22 47	22 47	23 01			00 01	00 01	00 18	01 45	01 55
Baglan	d											00 05	00 05			
Briton Ferry	d											00 09	00 09			
Neath	d	21 36	21 52		22 07	22 07		22 54	23 09			00 13	00 13	00 26	01 53	02 03
Skewen	d											00 16	00 16			
Llansamlet	d											00 20	00 20			
Swansea	a	21 49	22 04		22 20	22 20		23 07	23 22			00 28	00 28	00 39	02 05	02 16
	d		22 27					23 11		23 45		00 45	00 45			
Gowerton	d		22 38					23 22		23 56		00s55	00s55			
Llanelli	a		22 44				23 20	23 29		00 01		01s02	01s02			
	d		22 46				23 21	23 31		00 03						
Pembrey & Burry Port	d		22 51				23 27	23 37		00 08		01b10	01s09			
Kidwelly	d		22x57				23x33	23x43				01b16	01b16			
Ferryside	d		23x03				23x38	23x48				01b22	01b22			
Carmarthen	a		23 15				23 57	00 07		00 28		01 40	01 40			
	d		23 20							00 31						
Whitland	a		23 34							00 46						
	d		23 35							00 46						
Narberth	d															
Kilgetty	d															
Saundersfoot	d															
Tenby	a															
	d															
Penally	d															
Manorbier	d															
Lamphey	d															
Pembroke	d															
Pembroke Dock	a															
Clunderwen	d		23x41													
Clarbeston Road	d		23x50							01x00						
Haverfordwest	d		23 58													
Johnston	d		00x06													
Milford Haven	a		00 21													
Fishguard & Goodwick	a									01 20						
Fishguard Harbour 30 ⛴	a									01 28						
	d															
Rosslare Harbour ⛴	a															

A ⚲ from Llanelli

B ⚲ from Swansea

C ⊡ from Bridgend ⊘ to Bridgend

b Stops to set down only, stops on request

When events are being held at the Millenium Stadium, services are subject to alteration. Please check times before travelling.

Ferry service between Fishguard Harbour and Rosslare Harbour is operated by Stena Line

Table 128

Saturdays

Cardiff - Maesteg, Swansea and West Wales

14 December to 28 December

Route Diagram - see first Page of Table 127

		AW	AW	AW	AW	GW	AW	GW	AW	AW		AW	AW	AW	AW	AW	AW	AW	AW			AW	GW	AW	GW
		◇	🚌		◇	◇1 ☕	◇	◇1 ☕	◇								◇ 🚲		◇				1		◇1
London Paddington 15 ⊖	d																								
Reading 7	d																								
Manchester Piccadilly 10	d																								
Gloucester 7	d																					05 50			
Bristol Parkway 7	d							00 27																	07 11
Newport (South Wales)	d							00 49														06 44			07 31
Cardiff Central 7	d							01 06									05 39	05 51	06 42			07 04		07 14	07 48
Pontyclun	d																05 51	06 03				07 16			
Llanharan	d																05 56	06 08				07 21			
Pencoed	d																06 01	06 12				07 25			
Bridgend	d					00 05		01 31									06 07	06 20	07 02			07 32		07 34	08 09
Wildmill	d																	06 22				07 35			
Sarn	d																	06 25				07 38			
Tondu	d																	06 29				07 41			
Garth (Mid Glamorgan)	d																	06 38				07 51			
Maesteg (Ewenny Road)	d																	06 41				07 53			
Maesteg	a																	06 45				07 58			
Pyle	d																06 15		07 10					07 43	
Port Talbot Parkway	d				00 01	00 18		01 45									06 23		07 18					07 52	08 22
Baglan	d				00 05												06 27		07 22					07 55	
Briton Ferry	d				00 09												06 30		07 25					07 59	
Neath	d				00 13	00 26		01 53									06 34		07 29					08 03	08 30
Skewen	d				00 16												06 38		07 33					08 06	
Llansamlet	d				00 20												06 42		07 37					08 10	
Swansea	a				00 28	00 39		02 05									06 51		07 45					08 21	08 44
	d			00 05	00 45				04 31						05 45		06 53		07 50				08 15		
Gowerton	d			00 16	00s55				04 42						05 55		07 03		08 00						
Llanelli	a			00 23	01s02				04 49						06 02		07 11		08 07				08 31		
	d	00 03		00 25											06 04		07 11		08 08				08 36		
Pembrey & Burry Port	d	00 08		00 31	01b10										06 10		07 17		08 14				08 43		
Kidwelly	d			00x38	01b16										06x17		07x23		08x20						
Ferryside	d			00x44	01b22										06x23		07x29		08x26						
Carmarthen	a	00 28		01 00	01 40										06 37		07 43		08 40				09 08		
	d	00 31								04 54		05 30	05 50	05 58	06 38		07 46		08 43						
Whitland	a	00 46								05 07		05 46	06 05	06 13	06 56		08 00		08 59						
	d	00 46								05 07		05 46	06 06	06 13	06 56		08 00		09 01	09 07					
Narberth	d											05x55			07x05				09x10						
Kilgetty	d											06x05			07x15				09x20						
Saundersfoot	d											06x07			07x17				09x22						
Tenby	a											06 14			07 24				09 29						
	d											06 24			07 32				09 43						
Penally	d											06x27			07x35				09x46						
Manorbier	d											06 33			07 42				09 53						
Lamphey	d											06x41			07x49				10x00						
Pembroke	d											06 44			07 52				10 03						
Pembroke Dock	a											06 59			08 07				10 17						
Clunderwen	d									05x14			06x13	06x19			08x07			09x14					
Clarbeston Road	d	01x00								05x22			06x21	06x27		07 34	08x15			09x22					
Haverfordwest	d									05 34				06 35			08 23								
Johnston	d						00x06			05x42				06x43			08x31								
Milford Haven	a						00 21			05 57				06 58			08 49								
Fishguard & Goodwick	a	01 20											06 39			07 52				09 41					
Fishguard Harbour 30 ⛴	a	01 28											06 46			07 58				09 47					
	d		02 45																						
Rosslare Harbour ⛴🚌	a		06 15																						

b Stops to set down only, stops on request

When events are being held at the Millenium Stadium, services are subject to alteration. Please check times before travelling.

Ferry service between Fishguard Harbour and Rosslare Harbour is operated by Stena Line

Table 128

Saturdays

14 December to 28 December

Cardiff - Maesteg, Swansea and West Wales

Route Diagram - see first Page of Table 127

		AW	AW	AW	AW	AW		AW	AW	GW	AW	AW	GW	AW	AW	AW		AW	AW	AW	GW	AW	AW	AW	GW
															B										
		◇		◇	◇					◇1	◇		◇1	◇				◇			◇1	◇		◇	◇1 A
		🛒		🛒	🛒					🍴	🛒		🍴	🛒				🛒			🍴	🛒			🍴⊘
London Paddington 15 ⊖	d									07 45			08 45								09 45				10 45
Reading 7	d									08 12			09 13								10 14				11 12
Manchester Piccadilly 10	d										06 30							07 30				08 30			
Gloucester 7	d								07 58			08 58											10 58		
Bristol Parkway 7	d									09 08			10 08								11 08				12 08
Newport (South Wales)	d	07 38	08 01		08 33				08 52	09 31	09 38	09 52	10 31	10 40				10 40			11 31	11 37	11 52		12 31
Cardiff Central 7	d	07 58	08 23		09 04			09 14	09 18	09 48	10 04	10 18	10 48	10 57				11 04	11 14	11 21	11 48	12 04	12 18		12 48
Pontyclun	d		08 35						09 30			10 30								11 33			12 30		
Llanharan	d		08 39						09 35			10 35								11 38			12 35		
Pencoed	d		08 43						09 39			10 39								11 42			12 39		
Bridgend	d	08 17	08 51		09 23			09 34	09 46	10 09	10 23	10 46	11 09	11 20				11 25	11 34	11 49	12 09	12 23	12 46		13 09
Wildmill	d		08 53						09 49			10 49								11 52			12 49		
Sarn	d		08 56						09 52			10 52								11 55			12 52		
Tondu	d		09 00						09 55			10 55								11 58			12 55		
Garth (Mid Glamorgan)	d		09 09						10 05			11 05								12 08			13 05		
Maesteg (Ewenny Road)	d		09 12						10 07			11 07								12 10			13 07		
Maesteg	a		09 16						10 12			11 12								12 15			13 12		
Pyle	d							09 43											11 42						
Port Talbot Parkway	d	08 30			09 38			09 52		10 22	10 35		11 22					11 37	11 50		12 22	12 36			13 22
Baglan	d							09 55											11 54						
Briton Ferry	d							09 59											11 57						
Neath	d	08 37			09 45			10 03		10 30	10 42		11 30					11 44	12 01		12 30	12 43			13 30
Skewen	d							10 06											12 05						
Llansamlet	d							10 10											12 09						
Swansea	a	08 54			09 57			10 21		10 43	10 55		11 43					11 59	12 21		12 43	12 55			13 43
	d	09 00		09 14	10 04						11 00					11 50		12 05				13 03		13 15	
Gowerton	d	09 11		09 26	10 15						11 12							12 16				13 14		13 26	
Llanelli	a	09 17		09 33	10 21						11 17			12 00		12 05		12 22				13 20		13 33	
	d	09 19			10 22						11 18			12 01		12 06		12 24				13 22			
Pembrey & Burry Port	d	09 25			10 28						11 26					12 12		12 30				13 28			
Kidwelly	d	09x31			10x34													12x36							
Ferryside	d	09x36			10x40													12x41							
Carmarthen	a	09 48			10 51						11 45					12 36		12 53				13 47			
	d	09 57				10 56					11 48					12 58						13 51			
Whitland	a	10 13				11 10					12 02			12 36		13 13						14 06			
	d	10 14				11 11					12 03			12 37		13 14						14 06			
Narberth	d					11x20										13x21									
Kilgetty	d					11x30										13x31									
Saundersfoot	d					11x32										13x33									
Tenby	a					11 39										13 40									
	d					11 45										13 45									
Penally	d					11x48										13x48									
Manorbier	d					11 54										13 54									
Lamphey	d					12x02										14x02									
Pembroke	d					12 05										14 05									
Pembroke Dock	a					12 20										14 19									
Clunderwen	d	10x20									12x09											14x13			
Clarbeston Road	d	10x28									12x17											14x20			
Haverfordwest	d	10 36									12 25											14 29			
Johnston	d	10x44									12x33											14x37			
Milford Haven	a	10 58									12 48											14 52			
Fishguard & Goodwick	a													13 09											
Fishguard Harbour 30 ⛴	a													13 19											
	d														14 30										
Rosslare Harbour ⛴	a														18 00										

A 🍴 from Bridgend ⊘ to Bridgend

When events are being held at the Millenium Stadium, services are subject to alteration. Please check times before travelling.

Ferry service between Fishguard Harbour and Rosslare Harbour is operated by Stena Line

Table 128

Saturdays

Cardiff - Maesteg, Swansea and West Wales

14 December to 28 December

Route Diagram - see first Page of Table 127

		AW		AW	AW	AW	GW	AW	AW	GW	AW	AW		AW	AW	AW	GW	AW	AW	GW	AW	AW		AW	AW
				◇			◇1 A	◇		◇1	◇					R	◇1	◇		◇1		R		◇	◇
London Paddington 15 ⊖	d						11 45			12 45							13 45			14 45					
Reading 7	d						12 12			13 14							14 12			15 12					
Manchester Piccadilly 10	d			09 30				10 30			11 30					12 30						13 30			
Gloucester 7	d														13 58			14 35							
Bristol Parkway 7	d						13 08			14 08							15 08			16 08					
Newport (South Wales)	d			12 37			13 31	13 37		14 31	14 39			14 57	14 52	15 22	15 31	15 37		16 31		16 37		16 56	
Cardiff Central 7	d			13 04	13 14	13 18	13 48	14 04	14 21	14 48	15 04			15 14	15 18	15 40	15 48	16 04	16 18	16 48		17 04		17 18	
Pontyclun	d					13 30			14 33						15 30				16 30					17 30	
Llanharan	d					13 35			14 38						15 35				16 35					17 35	
Pencoed	d					13 39			14 42						15 39				16 39					17 39	
Bridgend	d			13 23	13 34	13 46	14 09	14 23	14 49	15 09	15 23			15 34	15 46	15 59	16 09	16 24	16 46	17 09		17 25		17 46	
Wildmill	d					13 49			14 52						15 49				16 49					17 48	
Sarn	d					13 52			14 55						15 52				16 52					17 51	
Tondu	d					13 55			14 58						15 55				16 55					17 55	
Garth (Mid Glamorgan)	d					14 05			15 08						16 05				17 05					18 04	
Maesteg (Ewenny Road)	d					14 07			15 10						16 07				17 07					18 07	
Maesteg	a					14 12			15 15						16 12				17 12					18 15	
Pyle	d				13 42									15 42				16 32				17 32			
Port Talbot Parkway	d			13 36	13 50		14 22	14 36		15 22	15 36			15 50		16 16	16 22	16 40		17 22		17 40			
Baglan	d				13 54									15 54								17 42			
Briton Ferry	d				13 57									15 57								17 46			
Neath	d			13 43	14 01		14 30	14 43		15 30	15 43			16 01		16 23	16 30	16 48		17 30		17 50			
Skewen	d				14 05									16 05								17 54			
Llansamlet	d				14 09									16 09								17 58			
Swansea	a			13 55	14 20		14 43	14 55		15 43	15 55			16 17		16 35	16 43	17 01		17 43		18 05			
	d	13 50		14 05				15 00			16 00	16 05		16 23		16 40		17 06			17 50	18 09			18 21
Gowerton	d			14 16				15 12			16 11	16 21		16 34		16 51		17 16			18 00	18 20			18 32
Llanelli	a	14 05		14 22				15 18			16 17	16 27		16 41		16 57		17 23			18 07	18 26			18 39
	d	14 06		14 24				15 20			16 19	16 29				16 59		17 24			18 09	18 28			
Pembrey & Burry Port	d	14 12		14 30				15 26			16 25	16 35				17 05		17 30			18 15	18 33			
Kidwelly	d			14x36							16x31					17x11		17x36			18x23	18x39			
Ferryside	d			14x41							16x36					17x16		17x42			18x29	18x45			
Carmarthen	a	14 40		14 53				15 45			16 53	16 58				17 28		17 55			18 47	18 58			
	d	14 58						15 49				17 01				17 31		17 57				19 02			
Whitland	a	15 12						16 03				17 15				17 45		18 12				19 18			
	d	15 12						16 04				17 15				17 46		18 13				19 18			
Narberth	d	15x21										17x24										19x28			
Kilgetty	d	15x31										17x34										19x38			
Saundersfoot	d	15x33										17x36										19x40			
Tenby	a	15 40										17 43										19 50			
	d	15 45										17 47										19 50			
Penally	d	15x48										17x50										19x53			
Manorbier	d	15 54										17 57										20 00			
Lamphey	d	16x02										18x04										20x07			
Pembroke	d	16 05										18 07										20 10			
Pembroke Dock	a	16 19										18 22										20 20			
Clunderwen	d							16x10								17x52		18x20							
Clarbeston Road	d							16x18								18x00		18x27							
Haverfordwest	d							16 26								18 08									
Johnston	d							16x34								18x16									
Milford Haven	a							16 49								18 31									
Fishguard & Goodwick	a																	18 46							
Fishguard Harbour 30 ⛴	a																	18 51							
	d																								
Rosslare Harbour ⛴	a																								

A from Bridgend ⊘ to Bridgend

When events are being held at the Millenium Stadium, services are subject to alteration. Please check times before travelling.

Ferry service between Fishguard Harbour and Rosslare Harbour is operated by Stena Line

Table 128

Saturdays

14 December to 28 December

Cardiff - Maesteg, Swansea and West Wales

Route Diagram - see first Page of Table 127

		AW	GW	AW	AW	AW	GW	AW	AW	AW	GW	AW	GW	AW	GW	AW	AW	GW	GW	AW	AW	AW	GW
				■				■				■											
			◇1				◇1				◇1		◇1		◇1	◇		◇1	◇1	◇			◇1
			🍴	🛒			🍴	🛒			🍴	🛒	🍴		🍴			🍴	🍴	🛒			🍴
London Paddington 15 ⊖	d		15 45				16 45				17 45				18 45			19 15	19 45				20 45
Reading 7	d		16 12				17 12				18 12				19 12			19 42	20 12				21 13
Manchester Piccadilly 10	d			14 30				15 30				16 30								18 30			
Gloucester 7	d				16 58				17 58					18 58			19 58						
Bristol Parkway 7	d		17 08				18 08				19 08				20 08			20 40	21 08				22 11
Newport (South Wales)	d		17 31	17 37	17 52		18 31	18 37	18 52		19 31	19 41		19 52	20 31		20 52	21 04	21 31	21 45			22 47
Cardiff Central 7	d	17 38	17 48	18 04	18 18		18 48	19 04	19 15		19 48	20 04		20 13	20 48	21 04	21 10	21 22	21 48	22 07		22 44	23 08
Pontyclun	d				18 30				19 28					20 25			21 22			22 19		22 58	
Llanharan	d				18 35				19 33					20 30			21 27			22 23		23 03	
Pencoed	d				18 39				19 37					20 34			21 30			22 27		23 08	
Bridgend	d	17 58	18 09	18 25	18 46		19 09	19 24	19 45		20 09	20 23		20 41	21 09	21 23	21 41	21 46	22 10	22 33		23 14	23 30
Wildmill	d				18 49				19 48					20 44			21 43						
Sarn	d				18 52				19 51					20 47			21 46						
Tondu	d				18 55				19 54					20 50			21 50						
Garth (Mid Glamorgan)	d				19 05				20 04					21 00			21 59						
Maesteg (Ewenny Road)	d				19 07				20 06					21 02			22 02						
Maesteg	a				19 13				20 11					21 07			22 06						
Pyle	d	18 06		18 33				19 31								21 31						23 22	
Port Talbot Parkway	d	18 14	18 22	18 41			19 22	19 39			20 22	20 36			21 22	21 39		21 59	22 23	22 45		23 31	23 43
Baglan	d	18 18						19 42														23 35	
Briton Ferry	d	18 21						19 45														23 38	
Neath	d	18 25	18 30	18 49			19 30	19 49			20 30				21 30	21 46		22 07	22 31	22 52		23 42	23 51
Skewen	d	18 29						19 54														23 46	
Llansamlet	d	18 33						19 58														23 50	
Swansea	a	18 44	18 46	19 02			19 43	20 05			20 43				21 43	21 57		22 20	22 45	23 05		23 58	00 05
	d			19 05		19 34		20 13			21 00					22 25				23 10	23 45	00 10	
Gowerton	d			19 16		19 45		20 24					←			22 36				23 21		00s21	
Llanelli	a			19 23		19 52		20 30			21 16	21 05	21 16			22 42				23 27	00 01	00s29	
	d			19 24		19 54		20 32			21 16	21 06	21 16			22 44				23 29	00 02		
Pembrey & Burry Port	d			19 30		20 00		20 37			→	21 12	21 23			22 50				23 34	00 07	00s35	
Kidwelly	d					20x07										22x56				23x40		00x41	
Ferryside	d					20x13										23x01				23x46		00x47	
Carmarthen	a			19 51		20 29		20 57				21 31	21 48			23 18				00 03	00 28	01 05	
	d			19 55				21 00				22 05									00 31		
Whitland	a			20 10				21 15				22 19									00 46		
	d			20 10				21 15				22 20									00 46		
Narberth	d							21x24															
Kilgetty	d							21x33															
Saundersfoot	d							21x35															
Tenby	a							21 42															
	d							21 43															
Penally	d							21x46															
Manorbier	d							21 52															
Lamphey	d							22x00															
Pembroke	d							22 03															
Pembroke Dock	a							22 18															
Clunderwen	d			20x17								22x26											
Clarbeston Road	d			20x25						20 30		22x34									01x00		
Haverfordwest	d			20 33								22 42											
Johnston	d			20x41								22x50											
Milford Haven	a			20 56								23 05											
Fishguard & Goodwick	a									20 48											01 18		
Fishguard Harbour 30 ⛴	a									20 54											01 28		
	d																						
Rosslare Harbour ⛴	a																						

When events are being held at the Millenium Stadium, services are subject to alteration. Please check times before travelling.

Ferry service between Fishguard Harbour and Rosslare Harbour is operated by Stena Line

Table 128

Saturdays

4 January to 8 February

Cardiff - Maesteg, Swansea and West Wales

Route Diagram - see first Page of Table 127

		AW	AW	AW	AW	GW	AW	GW	AW	AW		AW	AW	AW	AW	AW	AW	AW	AW			AW	GW	AW	GW
		◇	R		◇	◇ 1	◇	◇ 1	◇								◇		◇				1		◇ 1
London Paddington 15 ⊖	d																								
Reading 7	d																								
Manchester Piccadilly 10	d																								
Gloucester 7	d																					05 50			
Bristol Parkway 7	d							00 27																	07 11
Newport (South Wales)	d							00 49														06 44			07 31
Cardiff Central 7	d							01 06									05 39	05 51	06 42			07 04		07 14	07 48
Pontyclun	d																05 51	06 03				07 16			
Llanharan	d																05 56	06 08				07 21			
Pencoed	d																06 01	06 12				07 25			
Bridgend	d					00 05		01 31									06 07	06 20	07 02			07 32		07 34	08 09
Wildmill	d																	06 22				07 35			
Sarn	d																	06 25				07 38			
Tondu	d																					07 41			
Garth (Mid Glamorgan)	d																	06 38				07 51			
Maesteg (Ewenny Road)	d																	06 41				07 53			
Maesteg	a																	06 45				07 58			
Pyle	d																06 15		07 10					07 43	
Port Talbot Parkway	d				00 01	00 18		01 45									06 23		07 18					07 52	08 22
Baglan	d				00 05												06 27		07 22					07 55	
Briton Ferry	d				00 09												06 30		07 25					07 59	
Neath	d				00 13	00 26		01 53									06 34		07 29					08 03	08 30
Skewen	d				00 16												06 38		07 33					08 06	
Llansamlet	d				00 20												06 42		07 37					08 10	
Swansea	a				00 28	00 39		02 05									06 51		07 45					08 21	08 44
	d			00 05	00 45				04 31						05 45		06 53		07 50				08 15		
Gowerton	d			00 16	00s55				04 42						05 55		07 03		08 00						
Llanelli	a			00 23	01s02				04 49						06 02		07 11		08 07				08 31		
	d	00 03		00 25											06 04		07 11		08 08				08 36		
Pembrey & Burry Port	d	00 08		00 31	01b10										06 10		07 17		08 14				08 43		
Kidwelly	d			00x38	01b16										06x17		07x23		08x20						
Ferryside	d			00x44	01b22										06x23		07x29		08x26						
Carmarthen	a	00 28		01 00	01 40										06 37		07 43		08 40				09 08		
	d	00 31								04 54		05 30	05 50	05 58	06 38		07 46		08 43						
Whitland	a	00 46								05 07		05 46	06 05	06 13	06 56		08 00		08 59						
	d	00 46								05 07		05 46	06 06	06 13	06 56		08 00		09 01	09 07					
Narberth	d											05x55			07x05				09x10						
Kilgetty	d											06x05			07x15				09x20						
Saundersfoot	d											06x07			07x17				09x22						
Tenby	a											06 14			07 24				09 29						
	d											06 24			07 32				09 43						
Penally	d											06x27			07x35				09x46						
Manorbier	d											06 33			07 42				09 53						
Lamphey	d											06x41			07x49				10x00						
Pembroke	d											06 44			07 52				10 03						
Pembroke Dock	a											06 59			08 07				10 17						
Clunderwen	d									05x14			06x13	06x19			08x07			09x14					
Clarbeston Road	d	01x00								05x22			06x21	06x27		07 34	08x15			09x22					
Haverfordwest	d									05 34				06 35			08 23								
Johnston	d						00x06			05x42				06x43			08x31								
Milford Haven	a						00 21			05 57				06 58			08 49								
Fishguard & Goodwick	a	01 20											06 39			07 52				09 41					
Fishguard Harbour 30 ⛴	a	01 28											06 46			07 58				09 47					
	d		02 45																						
Rosslare Harbour ⛴	a		06 15																						

b Stops to set down only, stops on request

When events are being held at the Millenium Stadium, services are subject to alteration. Please check times before travelling.

Ferry service between Fishguard Harbour and Rosslare Harbour is operated by Stena Line

Table 128

Saturdays

4 January to 8 February

Cardiff - Maesteg, Swansea and West Wales

Route Diagram - see first Page of Table 127

		AW	AW	AW	AW	AW	AW	AW	GW	AW	AW	GW	AW	AW	AW	AW	AW	AW	GW	AW	AW	AW	GW
														B									
		◇		◇	◇				◇1	◇		◇1	◇			◇			◇1	◇		◇	◇1 A
		🛒		🛒	🛒				🍽	🛒		🍽	🛒			🛒			🍽	🛒			🍽Ø
London Paddington 15 ⊖	d								07 36			08 36							09 36				10 36
Reading 7	d								08 14			09 13							10 14				11 13
Manchester Piccadilly 10	d									06 30						07 30				08 30			
Gloucester 7	d							07 58			08 58										10 58		
Bristol Parkway 7	d								09 08			10 08							11 08				12 08
Newport (South Wales)	d	07 38	08 01		08 33			08 52	09 31	09 38	09 52	10 31	10 40			10 40			11 31	11 37	11 52		12 31
Cardiff Central 7	d	07 58	08 23		09 04		09 14	09 18	09 48	10 04	10 18	10 48	10 57			11 04	11 14	11 21	11 48	12 04	12 18		12 48
Pontyclun	d		08 35					09 30			10 30							11 33			12 30		
Llanharan	d		08 39					09 35			10 35							11 38			12 35		
Pencoed	d		08 43					09 39			10 39							11 42			12 39		
Bridgend	d	08 17	08 51		09 23		09 34	09 46	10 09	10 23	10 46	11 09	11 20			11 25	11 34	11 49	12 09	12 23	12 46		13 09
Wildmill	d		08 53					09 49			10 49							11 52			12 49		
Sarn	d		08 56					09 52			10 52							11 55			12 52		
Tondu	d		09 00					09 55			10 55							11 58			12 55		
Garth (Mid Glamorgan)	d		09 09					10 05			11 05							12 08			13 05		
Maesteg (Ewenny Road)	d		09 12					10 07			11 07							12 10			13 07		
Maesteg	a		09 16					10 12			11 12							12 15			13 12		
Pyle	d						09 43										11 42						
Port Talbot Parkway	d	08 30			09 38		09 52		10 22	10 35		11 22				11 37	11 50		12 22	12 36			13 22
Baglan	d						09 55										11 54						
Briton Ferry	d						09 59										11 57						
Neath	d	08 37			09 45		10 03		10 30	10 42		11 30				11 44	12 01		12 30	12 43			13 30
Skewen	d						10 06										12 05						
Llansamlet	d						10 10										12 09						
Swansea	a	08 54			09 57		10 21		10 44	10 55		11 43				11 59	12 21		12 43	12 55			13 43
	d	09 00		09 14	10 04					11 00					11 50	12 05				13 03		13 15	
Gowerton	d	09 11		09 26	10 15					11 12						12 16				13 14		13 26	
Llanelli	a	09 17		09 33	10 21					11 17			12 00		12 05	12 22				13 20		13 33	
	d	09 19			10 22					11 18			12 01		12 06	12 24				13 22			
Pembrey & Burry Port	d	09 25			10 28					11 26					12 12	12 30				13 28			
Kidwelly	d	09x31			10x34											12x36							
Ferryside	d	09x36			10x40											12x41							
Carmarthen	a	09 48			10 51					11 45					12 36	12 53				13 47			
	d	09 57				10 56				11 48					12 58					13 51			
Whitland	a	10 13				11 10				12 02			12 36		13 13					14 06			
	d	10 14				11 11				12 03			12 37		13 14					14 06			
Narberth	d					11x20									13x21								
Kilgetty	d					11x30									13x31								
Saundersfoot	d					11x32									13x33								
Tenby	a					11 39									13 40								
	d					11 45									13 45								
Penally	d					11x48									13x48								
Manorbier	d					11 54									13 54								
Lamphey	d					12x02									14x02								
Pembroke	d					12 05									14 05								
Pembroke Dock	a					12 20									14 19								
Clunderwen	d	10x20								12x09										14x13			
Clarbeston Road	d	10x28								12x17										14x20			
Haverfordwest	d	10 36								12 25										14 29			
Johnston	d	10x44								12x33										14x37			
Milford Haven	a	10 58								12 48										14 52			
Fishguard & Goodwick	a												13 09										
Fishguard Harbour 30 ⛴	a												13 19										
	d													14 30									
Rosslare Harbour ⛴	a													18 00									

A 🍽 from Bridgend Ø to Bridgend

When events are being held at the Millenium Stadium, services are subject to alteration. Please check times before travelling.

Ferry service between Fishguard Harbour and Rosslare Harbour is operated by Stena Line

Table 128

Saturdays

Cardiff - Maesteg, Swansea and West Wales

4 January to 8 February

Route Diagram - see first Page of Table 127

Station		AW		AW	AW	AW	GW	AW	AW	GW	AW	AW		AW	AW	AW	GW	AW	AW	GW	AW	AW		AW	AW
																■						■			
				◇			◇1	◇		◇1	◇						◇1	◇		◇1				◇	◇
							A																		
				⊼			⊡⊘	⊼		⊡	⊼					⊼	⊡	⊼	⊼	⊡		⊼		⊼	
London Paddington 15 ⊖	d						11 36			12 36							13 36			14 36					
Reading 7	d						12 14			13 13							14 14			15 16					
Manchester Piccadilly 10	d			09 30				10 30			11 30					12 30						13 30			
Gloucester 7	d														13 58			14 35							
Bristol Parkway 7	d						13 08			14 08							15 08			16 11					
Newport (South Wales)	d			12 37			13 31	13 37		14 31	14 39			14 57	14 52	15 22	15 31	15 37		16 34		16 37		16 56	
Cardiff Central 7	d			13 04	13 14	13 18	13 48	14 04	14 21	14 48	15 04			15 14	15 18	15 40	15 48	16 04	16 18	16 48		17 04		17 18	
Pontyclun	d					13 30			14 33						15 30				16 30					17 30	
Llanharan	d					13 35			14 38						15 35				16 35					17 35	
Pencoed	d					13 39			14 42						15 39				16 39					17 39	
Bridgend	d			13 23	13 34	13 46	14 09	14 23	14 49	15 09	15 23			15 34	15 46	15 59	16 09	16 24	16 46	17 09		17 25		17 46	
Wildmill	d					13 49			14 52						15 49				16 49					17 48	
Sarn	d					13 52			14 55						15 52				16 52					17 51	
Tondu	d					13 55			14 58										16 55						
Garth (Mid Glamorgan)	d					14 05			15 08						16 05				17 05					18 04	
Maesteg (Ewenny Road)	d					14 07			15 10						16 07				17 07					18 07	
Maesteg	a					14 12			15 15						16 12				17 12					18 15	
Pyle	d				13 42									15 42				16 32				17 32			
Port Talbot Parkway	d			13 36	13 50		14 22	14 36		15 22	15 36			15 50		16 16	16 22	16 40		17 22		17 40			
Baglan	d				13 54									15 54								17 42			
Briton Ferry	d				13 57									15 57								17 46			
Neath	d			13 43	14 01		14 30	14 43		15 30	15 43			16 01		16 23	16 30	16 48		17 30		17 50			
Skewen	d				14 05									16 05								17 54			
Llansamlet	d				14 09									16 09								17 58			
Swansea	a			13 55	14 20		14 43	14 55		15 43	15 55			16 17		16 35	16 43	17 01		17 43		18 05			
	d	13 50		14 05				15 00			16 00	16 05		16 23		16 40		17 06			17 50	18 09			18 21
Gowerton	d			14 16				15 12			16 11	16 21		16 34		16 51		17 16			18 00	18 20			18 32
Llanelli	a	14 05		14 22				15 18			16 17	16 27		16 41		16 57		17 23			18 07	18 26			18 39
	d	14 06		14 24				15 20			16 19	16 29				16 59		17 24			18 09	18 28			
Pembrey & Burry Port	d	14 12		14 30				15 26			16 25	16 35				17 05		17 30			18 15	18 33			
Kidwelly	d			14x36							16x31					17x11		17x36			18x23	18x39			
Ferryside	d			14x41							16x36					17x16		17x42			18x29	18x45			
Carmarthen	a	14 40		14 53				15 45			16 53	16 58				17 28		17 55			18 47	18 58			
	d	14 58						15 49				17 01				17 31		17 57				19 02			
Whitland	a	15 12						16 03				17 15				17 45		18 12				19 18			
	d	15 12						16 04				17 15				17 46		18 13				19 18			
Narberth	d	15x21										17x24										19x28			
Kilgetty	d	15x31										17x34										19x38			
Saundersfoot	d	15x33										17x36										19x40			
Tenby	a	15 40										17 43										19 50			
	d	15 45										17 47										19 50			
Penally	d	15x48										17x50										19x53			
Manorbier	d	15 54										17 57										20 00			
Lamphey	d	16x02										18x04										20x07			
Pembroke	d	16 05										18 07										20 10			
Pembroke Dock	a	16 19										18 22										20 20			
Clunderwen	d							16x10								17x52		18x20							
Clarbeston Road	d							16x18								18x00		18x27							
Haverfordwest	d							16 26								18 08									
Johnston	d							16x34								18x16									
Milford Haven	a							16 49								18 31									
Fishguard & Goodwick	a																	18 46							
Fishguard Harbour 30 ⛴	a																	18 51							
	d																								
Rosslare Harbour ⛴	a																								

A ⊡ from Bridgend ⊘ to Bridgend

When events are being held at the Millenium Stadium, services are subject to alteration. Please check times before travelling.

Ferry service between Fishguard Harbour and Rosslare Harbour is operated by Stena Line

Table 128

Saturdays

4 January to 8 February

Cardiff - Maesteg, Swansea and West Wales

Route Diagram - see first Page of Table 127

		AW	GW	AW	AW	AW	GW	AW		AW	AW	GW	AW	GW	AW	GW	AW	AW		GW	GW	AW	AW	AW	GW
				■				■					■												
			◇1				◇1					◇1		◇1		◇1	◇			◇1	◇1	◇			◇1
			☕	🛒			☕	🛒				☕	🛒	☕		☕				☕	☕	🛒			☕
London Paddington 15 ⊖	d		15 36				16 36					17 36				18 36				19 06	19 36				20 36
Reading 7	d		16 14				17 13					18 14				19 14				19 45	20 13				21 13
Manchester Piccadilly 10	d			14 30				15 30					16 30									18 30			
Gloucester 7	d				16 58					17 58					18 58			19 58							
Bristol Parkway 7	d		17 08				18 08					19 08				20 08				20 43	21 08				22 11
Newport (South Wales)	d		17 31	17 37	17 52		18 31	18 37		18 52		19 31	19 41		19 52	20 31		20 52		21 07	21 31	21 45			22 47
Cardiff Central 7	d	17 38	17 48	18 04	18 18		18 48	19 04		19 15		19 48	20 04		20 13	20 48	21 04	21 10		21 25	21 48	22 07		22 44	23 08
Pontyclun	d				18 30					19 28					20 25			21 22				22 19		22 58	
Llanharan	d				18 35					19 33					20 30			21 27				22 23		23 03	
Pencoed	d				18 39					19 37					20 34			21 30				22 27		23 08	
Bridgend	d	17 58	18 09	18 25	18 46		19 09	19 24		19 45		20 09	20 23		20 41	21 09	21 23	21 41		21 49	22 10	22 33		23 14	23 30
Wildmill	d				18 49					19 48					20 44			21 43							
Sarn	d				18 52					19 51					20 47			21 46							
Tondu	d				18 55										20 50			21 50							
Garth (Mid Glamorgan)	d				19 05					20 04					21 00			21 59							
Maesteg (Ewenny Road)	d				19 07					20 06					21 02			22 02							
Maesteg	a				19 13					20 11					21 07			22 06							
Pyle	d	18 06		18 33				19 31									21 31							23 22	
Port Talbot Parkway	d	18 14	18 22	18 41			19 22	19 39				20 22	20 36			21 22	21 39			22 02	22 23	22 45		23 31	23 43
Baglan	d	18 18						19 42																23 35	
Briton Ferry	d	18 21						19 45																23 38	
Neath	d	18 25	18 30	18 49			19 30	19 49				20 30				21 30	21 46			22 10	22 31	22 52		23 42	23 51
Skewen	d	18 29						19 54																23 46	
Llansamlet	d	18 33						19 58																23 50	
Swansea	a	18 44	18 46	19 02			19 43	20 05				20 43				21 43	21 57			22 23	22 45	23 05		23 58	00 05
	d			19 05		19 34		20 13				21 00					22 25					23 10	23 45	00 10	
Gowerton	d			19 16		19 45		20 24						←			22 36					23 21		00s21	
Llanelli	a			19 23		19 52		20 30				21 16	21 05	21 16			22 42					23 27	00 01	00s29	
	d			19 24		19 54		20 32				21 16	21 06	21 16			22 44					23 29	00 02		
Pembrey & Burry Port	d			19 30		20 00		20 37				→	21 12	21 23			22 50					23 34	00 07	00s35	
Kidwelly	d					20x07											22x56					23x40		00x41	
Ferryside	d					20x13											23x01					23x46		00x47	
Carmarthen	a			19 51		20 29		20 57					21 31	21 48			23 18					00 03	00 28	01 05	
	d			19 55				21 00					22 05										00 31		
Whitland	a			20 10				21 15					22 19										00 46		
	d			20 10				21 15					22 20										00 46		
Narberth	d							21x24																	
Kilgetty	d							21x33																	
Saundersfoot	d							21x35																	
Tenby	a							21 42																	
	d							21 43																	
Penally	d							21x46																	
Manorbier	d							21 52																	
Lamphey	d							22x00																	
Pembroke	d							22 03																	
Pembroke Dock	a							22 18																	
Clunderwen	d			20x17									22x26												
Clarbeston Road	d			20x25							20 30		22x34										01x00		
Haverfordwest	d			20 33									22 42												
Johnston	d			20x41									22x50												
Milford Haven	a			20 56									23 05												
Fishguard & Goodwick	a										20 48												01 18		
Fishguard Harbour 30 ⛴	a										20 54												01 28		
	d																								
Rosslare Harbour ⛴	a																								

When events are being held at the Millenium Stadium, services are subject to alteration. Please check times before travelling.

Ferry service between Fishguard Harbour and Rosslare Harbour is operated by Stena Line

Table 128

Saturdays

15 February to 17 May

Cardiff - Maesteg, Swansea and West Wales

Route Diagram - see first Page of Table 127

		AW	AW	AW	AW	GW	AW	GW	AW	AW		AW	AW	AW	AW	AW	AW	AW	AW			AW	GW	AW	GW
		◇	B		◇	◇1 ✉	◇	◇1 ✉	◇								◇ ⚲		◇				1		◇1
London Paddington 15 ⊖	d																								
Reading 7	d																								
Manchester Piccadilly 10	d																								
Gloucester 7	d																					05 50			
Bristol Parkway 7	d							00 27																	07 11
Newport (South Wales)	d							00 49														06 44			07 31
Cardiff Central 7	d							01 06									05 39	05 51	06 42			07 04		07 14	07 48
Pontyclun	d																05 51	06 03				07 16			
Llanharan	d																05 56	06 08				07 21			
Pencoed	d																06 01	06 12				07 25			
Bridgend	d					00 05		01 31									06 07	06 20	07 02			07 32		07 34	08 09
Wildmill	d																	06 22				07 35			
Sarn	d																	06 25				07 38			
Tondu	d																					07 41			
Garth (Mid Glamorgan)	d																	06 38				07 51			
Maesteg (Ewenny Road)	d																	06 41				07 53			
Maesteg	a																	06 45				07 58			
Pyle	d																06 15		07 10					07 43	
Port Talbot Parkway	d				00 01	00 18		01 45									06 23		07 18					07 52	08 22
Baglan	d				00 05												06 27		07 22					07 55	
Briton Ferry	d				00 09												06 30		07 25					07 59	
Neath	d				00 13	00 26		01 53									06 34		07 29					08 03	08 30
Skewen	d				00 16												06 38		07 33					08 06	
Llansamlet	d				00 20												06 42		07 37					08 10	
Swansea	a				00 28	00 39		02 05									06 51		07 45					08 21	08 44
	d			00 05	00 45				04 31						05 45		06 53		07 50				08 15		
Gowerton	d			00 16	00s55				04 42						05 55		07 03		08 00						
Llanelli	a			00 23	01s02				04 49						06 02		07 11		08 07				08 31		
	d	00 03		00 25											06 04		07 11		08 08				08 36		
Pembrey & Burry Port	d	00 08		00 31	01b10										06 10		07 17		08 14				08 43		
Kidwelly	d			00x38	01b16										06x17		07x23		08x20						
Ferryside	d			00x44	01b22										06x23		07x29		08x26						
Carmarthen	a	00 28		01 00	01 40										06 37		07 43		08 40				09 08		
	d	00 31								04 54		05 30	05 50	05 58	06 38		07 46		08 43						
Whitland	a	00 46								05 07		05 46	06 05	06 13	06 56		08 00		08 59						
	d	00 46								05 07		05 46	06 06	06 13	06 56		08 00		09 01	09 07					
Narberth	d											05x55			07x05				09x10						
Kilgetty	d											06x05			07x15				09x20						
Saundersfoot	d											06x07			07x17				09x22						
Tenby	a											06 14			07 24				09 29						
	d											06 24			07 32				09 43						
Penally	d											06x27			07x35				09x46						
Manorbier	d											06 33			07 42				09 53						
Lamphey	d											06x41			07x49				10x00						
Pembroke	d											06 44			07 52				10 03						
Pembroke Dock	a											06 59			08 07				10 17						
Clunderwen	d									05x14			06x13	06x19			08x07			09x14					
Clarbeston Road	d	01x00								05x22			06x21	06x27		07 34	08x15			09x22					
Haverfordwest	d									05 34				06 35			08 23								
Johnston	d						00x06			05x42				06x43			08x31								
Milford Haven	a						00 21			05 57				06 58			08 49								
Fishguard & Goodwick	a	01 20											06 39			07 52				09 41					
Fishguard Harbour 30 ⛴	a	01 28											06 46			07 58				09 47					
	d		02 45																						
Rosslare Harbour ⛴	a		06 15																						

b Stops to set down only, stops on request

When events are being held at the Millenium Stadium, services are subject to alteration. Please check times before travelling.

Ferry service between Fishguard Harbour and Rosslare Harbour is operated by Stena Line

Table 128

Saturdays

15 February to 17 May

Cardiff - Maesteg, Swansea and West Wales

Route Diagram - see first Page of Table 127

		AW	AW	AW	AW	AW		AW	AW	GW	AW	AW	GW	AW	AW	AW		AW	AW	AW	GW	AW	AW	AW	GW
															R										
		◇		◇	◇					◇1	◇		◇1	◇				◇			◇1	◇		◇	◇1 A
		trolley		trolley	trolley					restaurant	trolley		restaurant	trolley				trolley			restaurant	trolley			restaurant ∅
London Paddington 15 ⊖	d									07 45			08 45								09 45				10 45
Reading 7	d									08 12			09 13								10 14				11 12
Manchester Piccadilly 10	d										06 30							07 30				08 30			
Gloucester 7	d								07 58			08 58											10 58		
Bristol Parkway 7	d									09 08			10 08								11 08				12 08
Newport (South Wales)	d	07 38	08 01		08 33				08 52	09 31	09 38	09 52	10 31	10 40				10 40			11 31	11 37	11 52		12 31
Cardiff Central 7	d	07 58	08 23		09 04			09 14	09 18	09 48	10 04	10 18	10 48	10 57				11 04	11 14	11 21	11 48	12 04	12 18		12 48
Pontyclun	d		08 35						09 30			10 30								11 33			12 30		
Llanharan	d		08 39						09 35			10 35								11 38			12 35		
Pencoed	d		08 43						09 39			10 39								11 42			12 39		
Bridgend	d	08 17	08 51		09 23			09 34	09 46	10 09	10 23	10 46	11 09	11 20				11 25	11 34	11 49	12 09	12 23	12 46		13 09
Wildmill	d		08 53						09 49			10 49								11 52			12 49		
Sarn	d		08 56						09 52			10 52								11 55			12 52		
Tondu	d		09 00						09 55			10 55								11 58			12 55		
Garth (Mid Glamorgan)	d		09 09						10 05			11 05								12 08			13 05		
Maesteg (Ewenny Road)	d		09 12						10 07			11 07								12 10			13 07		
Maesteg	a		09 16						10 12			11 12								12 15			13 12		
Pyle	d							09 43											11 42						
Port Talbot Parkway	d	08 30			09 38			09 52		10 22	10 35		11 22					11 37	11 50		12 22	12 36			13 22
Baglan	d							09 55											11 54						
Briton Ferry	d							09 59											11 57						
Neath	d	08 37			09 45			10 03		10 30	10 42		11 30					11 44	12 01		12 30	12 43			13 30
Skewen	d							10 06											12 05						
Llansamlet	d							10 10											12 09						
Swansea	a	08 54			09 57			10 21		10 43	10 55		11 43					11 59	12 21		12 43	12 55			13 43
	d	09 00		09 14	10 04						11 00					11 50		12 05				13 03		13 15	
Gowerton	d	09 11		09 26	10 15						11 12							12 16				13 14		13 26	
Llanelli	a	09 17		09 33	10 21						11 17			12 00		12 05		12 22				13 20		13 33	
	d	09 19			10 22						11 18			12 01		12 06		12 24				13 22			
Pembrey & Burry Port	d	09 25			10 28						11 26					12 12		12 30				13 28			
Kidwelly	d	09x31			10x34													12x36							
Ferryside	d	09x36			10x40													12x41							
Carmarthen	a	09 48			10 51						11 45					12 36		12 53				13 47			
	d	09 57				10 56					11 48					12 58						13 51			
Whitland	a	10 13				11 10					12 02			12 36		13 13						14 06			
	d	10 14				11 11					12 03			12 37		13 14						14 06			
Narberth	d					11x20										13x21									
Kilgetty	d					11x30										13x31									
Saundersfoot	d					11x32										13x33									
Tenby	a					11 39										13 40									
	d					11 45										13 45									
Penally	d					11x48										13x48									
Manorbier	d					11 54										13 54									
Lamphey	d					12x02										14x02									
Pembroke	d					12 05										14 05									
Pembroke Dock	a					12 20										14 19									
Clunderwen	d	10x20									12x09											14x13			
Clarbeston Road	d	10x28									12x17											14x20			
Haverfordwest	d	10 36									12 25											14 29			
Johnston	d	10x44									12x33											14x37			
Milford Haven	a	10 58									12 48											14 52			
Fishguard & Goodwick	a													13 09											
Fishguard Harbour 30 ferry	a													13 19											
	d														14 30										
Rosslare Harbour ferry	a														18 00										

A restaurant from Bridgend ∅ to Bridgend

When events are being held at the Millenium Stadium, services are subject to alteration. Please check times before travelling.

Ferry service between Fishguard Harbour and Rosslare Harbour is operated by Stena Line

Table 128

Saturdays

15 February to 17 May

Cardiff - Maesteg, Swansea and West Wales

Route Diagram - see first Page of Table 127

		AW		AW	AW	AW	GW	AW	AW	GW	AW	AW		AW	AW	AW	GW	AW	AW	GW	AW	AW		AW	AW
																■R						■R			
				◇			◇■1	◇		◇■1	◇						◇■1	◇		◇■1				◇	◇
							A																		
				🛒			🍽⊘	🛒		🍽	🛒					🛒	🍽	🛒	🛒	🍽		🛒		🛒	
London Paddington [15] ⊖	d						11 45			12 45							13 45			14 45					
Reading [7]	d						12 12			13 14							14 12			15 12					
Manchester Piccadilly [10]	d			09 30				10 30			11 30					12 30						13 30			
Gloucester [7]	d														13 58			14 35							
Bristol Parkway [7]	d						13 08			14 08							15 08			16 08					
Newport (South Wales)	d			12 37			13 31	13 37		14 31	14 39			14 57	14 52	15 22	15 31	15 37		16 31		16 37		16 56	
Cardiff Central [7]	d			13 04	13 14	13 18	13 48	14 04	14 21	14 48	15 04			15 14	15 18	15 40	15 48	16 04	16 18	16 48		17 04		17 18	
Pontyclun	d					13 30			14 33						15 30				16 30					17 30	
Llanharan	d					13 35			14 38						15 35				16 35					17 35	
Pencoed	d					13 39			14 42						15 39				16 39					17 39	
Bridgend	d			13 23	13 34	13 46	14 09	14 23	14 49	15 09	15 23			15 34	15 46	15 59	16 09	16 24	16 46	17 09		17 25		17 46	
Wildmill	d					13 49			14 52						15 49				16 49					17 48	
Sarn	d					13 52			14 55						15 52				16 52					17 51	
Tondu	d					13 55			14 58										16 55						
Garth (Mid Glamorgan)	d					14 05			15 08						16 05				17 05					18 04	
Maesteg (Ewenny Road)	d					14 07			15 10						16 07				17 07					18 07	
Maesteg	a					14 12			15 15						16 12				17 12					18 15	
Pyle	d				13 42									15 42				16 32				17 32			
Port Talbot Parkway	d			13 36	13 50		14 22	14 36		15 22	15 36			15 50		16 16	16 22	16 40		17 22		17 40			
Baglan	d				13 54									15 54								17 42			
Briton Ferry	d				13 57									15 57								17 46			
Neath	d			13 43	14 01		14 30	14 43		15 30	15 43			16 01		16 23	16 30	16 48		17 30		17 50			
Skewen	d				14 05									16 05								17 54			
Llansamlet	d				14 09									16 09								17 58			
Swansea	a			13 55	14 20		14 43	14 55		15 43	15 55			16 17		16 35	16 43	17 01		17 43		18 05			
	d	13 50		14 05				15 00			16 00	16 05		16 23		16 40		17 06			17 50	18 09			18 21
Gowerton	d			14 16				15 12			16 11	16 21		16 34		16 51		17 16			18 00	18 20			18 32
Llanelli	a	14 05		14 22				15 18			16 17	16 27		16 41		16 57		17 23			18 07	18 26			18 39
	d	14 06		14 24				15 20			16 19	16 29				16 59		17 24			18 09	18 28			
Pembrey & Burry Port	d	14 12		14 30				15 26			16 25	16 35				17 05		17 30			18 15	18 33			
Kidwelly	d			14x36							16x31					17x11		17x36			18x23	18x39			
Ferryside	d			14x41							16x36					17x16		17x42			18x29	18x45			
Carmarthen	a	14 40		14 53				15 45			16 53	16 58				17 28		17 55			18 47	18 58			
	d	14 58						15 49				17 01				17 31		17 57				19 02			
Whitland	a	15 12						16 03				17 15				17 45		18 12				19 18			
	d	15 12						16 04				17 15				17 46		18 13				19 18			
Narberth	d	15x21										17x24										19x28			
Kilgetty	d	15x31										17x34										19x38			
Saundersfoot	d	15x33										17x36										19x40			
Tenby	a	15 40										17 43										19 50			
	d	15 45										17 47										19 50			
Penally	d	15x48										17x50										19x53			
Manorbier	d	15 54										17 57										20 00			
Lamphey	d	16x02										18x04										20x07			
Pembroke	d	16 05										18 07										20 10			
Pembroke Dock	a	16 19										18 22										20 20			
Clunderwen	d							16x10								17x52		18x20							
Clarbeston Road	d							16x18								18x00		18x27							
Haverfordwest	d							16 26								18 08									
Johnston	d							16x34								18x16									
Milford Haven	a							16 49								18 31									
Fishguard & Goodwick	a																	18 46							
Fishguard Harbour [30] ⛴	a																	18 51							
	d																								
Rosslare Harbour ⛴	a																								

A 🍽 from Bridgend ⊘ to Bridgend

When events are being held at the Millenium Stadium, services are subject to alteration. Please check times before travelling.

Ferry service between Fishguard Harbour and Rosslare Harbour is operated by Stena Line

Table 128

Saturdays

15 February to 17 May

Cardiff - Maesteg, Swansea and West Wales

Route Diagram - see first Page of Table 127

		AW	GW	AW	AW	AW	GW	AW	AW	AW	GW	AW	GW	AW	GW	AW	AW	GW	GW	AW	AW	AW	GW
				R				R				R											
			◇1				◇1				◇1		◇1		◇1	◇		◇1	◇1	◇			◇1
			☕	🛒			☕	🛒			☕	🛒	☕		☕			☕	☕	🛒			☕
London Paddington 15 ⊖	d		15 45				16 45				17 45				18 45			19 15	19 45				20 45
Reading 7	d		16 12				17 12				18 12				19 12			19 42	20 12				21 13
Manchester Piccadilly 10	d			14 30				15 30				16 30								18 30			
Gloucester 7	d				16 58				17 58					18 58			19 58						
Bristol Parkway 7	d		17 08				18 08				19 08				20 08			20 40	21 08				22 11
Newport (South Wales)	d		17 31	17 37	17 52		18 31	18 37	18 52		19 31	19 41		19 52	20 31		20 52	21 04	21 31	21 45			22 47
Cardiff Central 7	d	17 38	17 48	18 04	18 18		18 48	19 04	19 15		19 48	20 04		20 13	20 48	21 04	21 10	21 22	21 48	22 07		22 44	23 08
Pontyclun	d				18 30				19 28					20 25			21 22			22 19		22 58	
Llanharan	d				18 35				19 33					20 30			21 27			22 23		23 03	
Pencoed	d				18 39				19 37					20 34			21 30			22 27		23 08	
Bridgend	d	17 58	18 09	18 25	18 46		19 09	19 24	19 45		20 09	20 23		20 41	21 09	21 23	21 41	21 46	22 10	22 33		23 14	23 30
Wildmill	d				18 49				19 48					20 44			21 43						
Sarn	d				18 52				19 51					20 47			21 46						
Tondu	d				18 55									20 50			21 50						
Garth (Mid Glamorgan)	d				19 05				20 04					21 00			21 59						
Maesteg (Ewenny Road)	d				19 07				20 06					21 02			22 02						
Maesteg	a				19 13				20 11					21 07			22 06						
Pyle	d	18 06		18 33				19 31								21 31						23 22	
Port Talbot Parkway	d	18 14	18 22	18 41			19 22	19 39			20 22	20 36			21 22	21 39		21 59	22 23	22 45		23 31	23 43
Baglan	d	18 18						19 42														23 35	
Briton Ferry	d	18 21						19 45														23 38	
Neath	d	18 25	18 30	18 49			19 30	19 49			20 30				21 30	21 46		22 07	22 31	22 52		23 42	23 51
Skewen	d	18 29						19 54														23 46	
Llansamlet	d	18 33						19 58														23 50	
Swansea	a	18 44	18 46	19 02			19 43	20 05			20 43				21 43	21 57		22 20	22 45	23 05		23 58	00 05
	d			19 05		19 34		20 13			21 00					22 25				23 10	23 45	00 10	
Gowerton	d			19 16		19 45		20 24					←			22 36				23 21		00s21	
Llanelli	a			19 23		19 52		20 30			21 16	21 05	21 16			22 42				23 27	00 01	00s29	
	d			19 24		19 54		20 32			21 16	21 06	21 16			22 44				23 29	00 02		
Pembrey & Burry Port	d			19 30		20 00		20 37			→	21 12	21 23			22 50				23 34	00 07	00s35	
Kidwelly	d					20x07										22x56				23x40		00x41	
Ferryside	d					20x13										23x01				23x46		00x47	
Carmarthen	a			19 51		20 29		20 57				21 31	21 48			23 18				00 03	00 28	01 05	
	d			19 55				21 00				22 05									00 31		
Whitland	a			20 10				21 15				22 19									00 46		
	d			20 10				21 15				22 20									00 46		
Narberth	d							21x24															
Kilgetty	d							21x33															
Saundersfoot	d							21x35															
Tenby	a							21 42															
	d							21 43															
Penally	d							21x46															
Manorbier	d							21 52															
Lamphey	d							22x00															
Pembroke	d							22 03															
Pembroke Dock	a							22 18															
Clunderwen	d			20x17								22x26											
Clarbeston Road	d			20x25						20 30		22x34									01x00		
Haverfordwest	d			20 33								22 42											
Johnston	d			20x41								22x50											
Milford Haven	a			20 56								23 05											
Fishguard & Goodwick	a									20 48											01 18		
Fishguard Harbour 30 ⛴	a									20 54											01 28		
	d																						
Rosslare Harbour ⛴	a																						

When events are being held at the Millenium Stadium, services are subject to alteration. Please check times before travelling.

Ferry service between Fishguard Harbour and Rosslare Harbour is operated by Stena Line

Table 128

Sundays

Cardiff - Maesteg, Swansea and West Wales

8 December to 29 December

Route Diagram - see first Page of Table 127

		AW	AW	AW	AW	AW	AW	AW	GW	AW	AW	GW	AW	GW	AW	GW	AW	AW	GW	AW	GW	AW	GW
			R				◇	◇	◇1	◇	R	◇1	◇	◇1		◇1	R	◇	◇1		◇1	R	◇1
							🛒		☕			☕	🛒	☕		☕	🛒		☕		☕	🛒	☕
London Paddington 15 ⊖	d								08 33			09 30		10 33		11 33			12 33		13 37		14 37
Reading 7	d								09 14			10 06		11 13		12 13			13 11		14 13		15 13
Manchester Piccadilly 10	d																						
Gloucester 7	d																10 30					12 30	
Bristol Parkway 7	d								10 15			11 09		12 13		13 14			14 13		15 13		16 13
Newport (South Wales)	d						09 30		10 43	11 00		11 36		12 38		13 38	13 29		14 38		15 40	15 49	16 38
Cardiff Central 7	d						09 50		11 01	11 18		11 58	12 16	12 59		13 59	14 05		14 59		16 00	16 16	16 59
Pontyclun	d						10 03										14 18						
Llanharan	d						10 08										14 23						
Pencoed	d						10 13										14 28						
Bridgend	d						10 20		11 21	11 38		12 18	12 37	13 20		14 19	14 35		15 20		16 21	16 37	17 20
Wildmill	d																						
Sarn	d																						
Tondu	d																						
Garth (Mid Glamorgan)	d																						
Maesteg (Ewenny Road)	d																						
Maesteg	a																						
Pyle	d						10 28						12 45				14 43					16 45	
Port Talbot Parkway	d						10 37		11 34	11 52		12 31	12 54	13 33		14 32	14 51		15 33		16 34	16 54	17 33
Baglan	d																						
Briton Ferry	d																						
Neath	d						10 45		11 43	12 00		12 39		13 41		14 40	14 59		15 41		16 42	17 02	17 41
Skewen	d																						
Llansamlet	d																						
Swansea	a						10 58		11 55	12 13		12 51		13 54		14 54	15 12		15 53		16 54	17 14	17 54
	d			00 10			11 02	11 08		12 15		12 58			14 13	15 01	15 15	15 29		16 36	17 05	17 26	
Gowerton	d			00s21			11 13	11 17		12 26					14 24		15 26	15 39		16 47		17 37	
Llanelli	a			00s29			11 20	11 24		12 33		13 15	13 23		14 31	15 17	15 33	15 46		16 54	17 21	17 44	
	d	00 02					11 22			12 35		13 16	13 24		14 33	15 18	15 34			16 56	17 22	17 45	
Pembrey & Burry Port	d	00 07		00s35			11 28			12 40		13 23	13 30		14 39	15 25	15 40			17 02	17 29	17 51	
Kidwelly	d			00x41			11x35			12x47					14x45					17x09			
Ferryside	d			00x47			11x41			12x53					14x51					17x15			
Carmarthen	a	00 28		01 05			11 54			13 05		13 44	13 56		15 06	15 46	16 03			17 28	17 50	18 14	
	d	00 31			09 55	10 19	12 06			13 08			14 05		15 08		16 09			17 33		18 20	
Whitland	a	00 46			10 11	10 34	12 22			13 23			14 21		15 22		16 25			17 48		18 36	
	d	00 46			10 11	10 34	12 22			13 24			14 21		15 23		16 27			17 48		18 37	
Narberth	d					10x43									15x32					17x57			
Kilgetty	d					10x52									15x42					18x07			
Saundersfoot	d					10x54									15x44					18x09			
Tenby	a					11 01									15 51					18 16			
	d					11 11									15 55					18 19			
Penally	d					11x14									15x58					18x22			
Manorbier	d					11 20									16 04					18 29			
Lamphey	d					11x28									16x12					18x36			
Pembroke	d					11 31									16 15					18 40			
Pembroke Dock	a					11 44									16 30					18 55			
Clunderwen	d				10x19		12x30						14x29				16x34					18x45	
Clarbeston Road	d	01x00			10x27		12x38						14x37				16x42					18x53	
Haverfordwest	d				10 35		12 46						14 45				16 51					19 01	
Johnston	d				10x44		12x55						14x54				16x59					19x10	
Milford Haven	a				10 55		13 06						15 09				17 11					19 25	
Fishguard & Goodwick	a	01 18								13 55													
Fishguard Harbour 30 ⛴	a	01 28								14 00													
	d		02 45								14 30												
Rosslare Harbour ⛴	a		06 15								18 00												

When events are being held at the Millenium Stadium, services are subject to alteration. Please check times before travelling.

Ferry service between Fishguard Harbour and Rosslare Harbour is operated by Stena Line

Table 128

Sundays

8 December to 29 December

Cardiff - Maesteg, Swansea and West Wales

Route Diagram - see first Page of Table 127

		AW	GW	AW	AW	GW	AW	GW	AW	GW	GW	AW	GW	GW
				■										
			◇■			◇■		◇■	◇	◇■	◇■	◇	◇■	◇■
			⊡	⊼		⊡		⊡	⊼	⊡	⊡		⊡	⊡
London Paddington ■ ⊖	d		15 37			16 37		17 37		18 37	19 37		20 37	21 37
Reading ■	d		16 13			17 13		18 14		19 13	20 14		21 14	22 18
Manchester Piccadilly ■	d			14 30										
Gloucester ■	d													
Bristol Parkway ■	d		17 13			18 13		19 13		20 13	21 13		22 13	23 19
Newport (South Wales)	d		17 38	17 34		18 38		19 44		20 40	21 40		22 40	23 47
Cardiff Central ■	d		17 59	18 06		18 59		20 03	20 15	20 59	22 03	22 30	23 01	00 09
Pontyclun	d			18 21										
Llanharan	d			18 26										
Pencoed	d			18 30										
Bridgend	d		18 20	18 38		19 20		20 24	20 37	21 20	22 24	22 51	23 23	00 31
Wildmill	d													
Sarn	d													
Tondu	d													
Garth (Mid Glamorgan)	d													
Maesteg (Ewenny Road)	d													
Maesteg	a													
Pyle	d			18 46					20 45					
Port Talbot Parkway	d		18 33	18 54		19 32		20 37	20 54	21 33	22 37	23 05	23 37	00 44
Baglan	d													
Briton Ferry	d													
Neath	d		18 41	19 02		19 41		20 45	21 02	21 41	22 45	23 13	23 45	00 53
Skewen	d													
Llansamlet	d													
Swansea	a		18 58	19 15		19 58		20 58	21 14	21 55	22 58	23 25	00 01	01 05
	d	18 10		19 20			20 35		21 18			23 38		
Gowerton	d	18 21		19 31			20 46		21 29			23 49		
Llanelli	a	18 28		19 38			20 54		21 36			23 56		
	d	18 30		19 39			20 55		21 37			23 58		
Pembrey & Burry Port	d	18 36		19 45			21 01		21 43			00 04		
Kidwelly	d	18x43					21x08					00x11		
Ferryside	d	18x49					21x14					00x17		
Carmarthen	a	19 02		20 07			21 32		22 06			00 30		
	d	19 06		20 08					22 10			00 34		
Whitland	a	19 22		20 24					22 26			00 50		
	d	19 22		20 30	20 37				22 26			00 50		
Narberth	d				20x44									
Kilgetty	d				20x53									
Saundersfoot	d				20x55									
Tenby	a				21 02									
	d				21 06									
Penally	d				21x09									
Manorbier	d				21 15									
Lamphey	d				21x23									
Pembroke	d				21 26									
Pembroke Dock	a				21 36									
Clunderwen	d	19x30		20x38					22x34					
Clarbeston Road	d	19x38		20x46					22x42			01x03		
Haverfordwest	d	19a46		20 54					22 50					
Johnston	d			21x03					22x59					
Milford Haven	a			21 20					23 10					
Fishguard & Goodwick	a											01 22		
Fishguard Harbour ■ ⛴	a											01 27		
	d													
Rosslare Harbour ⛴	a													

When events are being held at the Millenium Stadium, services are subject to alteration. Please check times before travelling.

Ferry service between Fishguard Harbour and Rosslare Harbour is operated by Stena Line

Table 128

Sundays

5 January to 9 February

Cardiff - Maesteg, Swansea and West Wales

Route Diagram - see first Page of Table 127

		AW	AW	AW	AW	AW	AW	AW	GW	AW	AW	GW	AW	GW	AW	GW	AW	AW	GW	AW	GW	AW	GW
							◇	◇	◇1	◇		◇1	◇	◇1		◇1		◇	◇1		◇1		◇1
London Paddington 15 ⊖	d								08 33			09 30		10 33		11 33			12 33		13 33		14 33
Reading 7	d								09 14			10 06		11 13		12 13			13 11		14 13		15 13
Manchester Piccadilly 10	d																						
Gloucester 7	d																10 30					12 30	
Bristol Parkway 7	d								10 15			11 06		12 13		13 14			14 13		15 13		16 13
Newport (South Wales)	d						09 30		10 43	11 00		11 32		12 38		13 38	13 29		14 38		15 40	15 49	16 38
Cardiff Central 7	d						09 50		11 01	11 18		11 54	12 16	12 59		13 59	14 05		14 59		16 00	16 16	16 59
Pontyclun	d						10 03										14 18						
Llanharan	d						10 08										14 23						
Pencoed	d						10 13										14 28						
Bridgend	d						10 20		11 21	11 38		12 14	12 37	13 20		14 19	14 35		15 20		16 21	16 37	17 20
Wildmill	d																						
Sarn	d																						
Tondu	d																						
Garth (Mid Glamorgan)	d																						
Maesteg (Ewenny Road)	d																						
Maesteg	a																						
Pyle	d						10 28						12 45				14 43					16 45	
Port Talbot Parkway	d						10 37		11 34	11 52		12 27	12 54	13 33		14 32	14 51		15 33		16 34	16 54	17 33
Baglan	d																						
Briton Ferry	d																						
Neath	d						10 45		11 43	12 00		12 35		13 41		14 40	14 59		15 41		16 42	17 02	17 41
Skewen	d																						
Llansamlet	d																						
Swansea	a						10 58		11 55	12 13		12 47		13 54		14 54	15 12		15 53		16 54	17 14	17 54
	d			00 10			11 02	11 08		12 15		12 58			14 13	15 01	15 15	15 29		16 36	17 05	17 26	
Gowerton	d			00s21			11 13	11 17		12 26					14 24		15 26	15 39		16 47		17 37	
Llanelli	a			00s29			11 20	11 24		12 33		13 15	13 23		14 31	15 17	15 33	15 46		16 54	17 21	17 44	
	d	00 02					11 22			12 35		13 16	13 24		14 33	15 18	15 34			16 56	17 22	17 45	
Pembrey & Burry Port	d	00 07		00s35			11 28			12 40		13 23	13 30		14 39	15 25	15 40			17 02	17 29	17 51	
Kidwelly	d			00x41			11x35			12x47					14x45					17x09			
Ferryside	d			00x47			11x41			12x53					14x51					17x15			
Carmarthen	a	00 28		01 05			11 54			13 05		13 44	13 56		15 06	15 46	16 03			17 28	17 50	18 14	
	d	00 31			09 55	10 19	12 06			13 08			14 05		15 08		16 09			17 33		18 20	
Whitland	a	00 46			10 11	10 34	12 22			13 23			14 21		15 22		16 25			17 48		18 36	
	d	00 46			10 11	10 34	12 22			13 24			14 21		15 23		16 27			17 48		18 37	
Narberth	d					10x43									15x32					17x57			
Kilgetty	d					10x52									15x42					18x07			
Saundersfoot	d					10x54									15x44					18x09			
Tenby	a					11 01									15 51					18 16			
	d					11 11									15 55					18 19			
Penally	d					11x14									15x58					18x22			
Manorbier	d					11 20									16 04					18 29			
Lamphey	d					11x28									16x12					18x36			
Pembroke	d					11 31									16 15					18 40			
Pembroke Dock	a					11 44									16 30					18 55			
Clunderwen	d				10x19		12x30						14x29				16x34					18x45	
Clarbeston Road	d	01x00			10x27		12x38						14x37				16x42					18x53	
Haverfordwest	d				10 35		12 46						14 45				16 51					19 01	
Johnston	d				10x44		12x55						14x54				16x59					19x10	
Milford Haven	a				10 55		13 06						15 09				17 11					19 25	
Fishguard & Goodwick	a	01 18								13 55													
Fishguard Harbour 30	a	01 28								14 00													
	d		02 45								14 30												
Rosslare Harbour	a		06 15								18 00												

When events are being held at the Millenium Stadium, services are subject to alteration. Please check times before travelling.

Ferry service between Fishguard Harbour and Rosslare Harbour is operated by Stena Line

Table 128

Sundays

5 January to 9 February

Cardiff - Maesteg, Swansea and West Wales

Route Diagram - see first Page of Table 127

		AW	GW	AW	AW	GW	AW	GW	AW	GW	GW	AW	GW	GW
			◇1			◇1		◇1	◇	◇1	◇1	◇	◇1	◇1
London Paddington 15 ⊖	d		15 33			16 33		17 33		18 33	19 33		20 33	21 33
Reading 7	d		16 13			17 13		18 14		19 14	20 14		21 14	22 09
Manchester Piccadilly 10	d			14 30										
Gloucester 7	d													
Bristol Parkway 7	d		17 13			18 13		19 13		20 13	21 13		22 13	23 12
Newport (South Wales)	d		17 38	17 34		18 38		19 44		20 40	21 40		22 40	23 44
Cardiff Central 7	d		17 59	18 06		18 59		20 03	20 15	20 59	22 03	22 30	23 01	00 05
Pontyclun	d			18 21										
Llanharan	d			18 26										
Pencoed	d			18 30										
Bridgend	d		18 20	18 38		19 20		20 24	20 37	21 20	22 24	22 51	23 23	00 27
Wildmill	d													
Sarn	d													
Tondu	d													
Garth (Mid Glamorgan)	d													
Maesteg (Ewenny Road)	d													
Maesteg	a													
Pyle	d			18 46					20 45					
Port Talbot Parkway	d		18 33	18 54		19 32		20 37	20 54	21 33	22 37	23 05	23 37	00 40
Baglan	d													
Briton Ferry	d													
Neath	d		18 41	19 02		19 41		20 45	21 02	21 41	22 45	23 13	23 45	00 48
Skewen	d													
Llansamlet	d													
Swansea	a		18 58	19 15		19 58		20 58	21 14	21 55	22 58	23 25	00 01	01 02
	d	18 10		19 20			20 35		21 18			23 38		
Gowerton	d	18 21		19 31			20 46		21 29			23 49		
Llanelli	a	18 28		19 38			20 54		21 36			23 56		
	d	18 30		19 39			20 55		21 37			23 58		
Pembrey & Burry Port	d	18 36		19 45			21 01		21 43			00 04		
Kidwelly	d	18x43					21x08					00x11		
Ferryside	d	18x49					21x14					00x17		
Carmarthen	a	19 02		20 07			21 32		22 06			00 30		
	d	19 06		20 08					22 10			00 34		
Whitland	a	19 22		20 24					22 26			00 50		
	d	19 22		20 30	20 37				22 26			00 50		
Narberth	d				20x44									
Kilgetty	d				20x53									
Saundersfoot	d				20x55									
Tenby	a				21 02									
	d				21 06									
Penally	d				21x09									
Manorbier	d				21 15									
Lamphey	d				21x23									
Pembroke	d				21 26									
Pembroke Dock	a				21 36									
Clunderwen	d	19x30		20x38					22x34					
Clarbeston Road	d	19x38		20x46					22x42			01x03		
Haverfordwest	d	19a46		20 54					22 50					
Johnston	d			21x03					22x59					
Milford Haven	a			21 20					23 10					
Fishguard & Goodwick	a											01 22		
Fishguard Harbour 30	a											01 27		
	d													
Rosslare Harbour	a													

When events are being held at the Millenium Stadium, services are subject to alteration. Please check times before travelling.

Ferry service between Fishguard Harbour and Rosslare Harbour is operated by Stena Line

Table 128

Sundays

16 February to 23 March

Cardiff - Maesteg, Swansea and West Wales

Route Diagram - see first Page of Table 127

		AW	AW	AW	AW	AW	AW	AW	GW	AW	AW	GW	AW	GW	AW	GW	AW	AW	GW	AW	GW	AW	GW
			B								B						■					■	
							◇	◇	◇1	◇		◇1	◇	◇1		◇1		◇	◇1		◇1		◇1
							🛒		🍽			🍽	🛒	🍽		🍽	🛒		🍽		🍽	🛒	🍽
London Paddington 15 ⊖	d								08 33			09 30		10 33		11 33			12 33		13 33		14 33
Reading 7	d								09 14			10 06		11 13		12 10			13 11		14 09		15 09
Manchester Piccadilly 10	d																10 30					12 30	
Gloucester 7	d																						
Bristol Parkway 7	d								10 15			11 09		12 14		13 14			14 13		15 13		16 13
Newport (South Wales)	d						09 30		10 43	11 00		11 36		12 41		13 38	13 29		14 38		15 40	15 49	16 38
Cardiff Central 7	d						09 50		11 03	11 18		11 58	12 16	13 02		13 59	14 05		14 59		16 00	16 16	16 59
Pontyclun	d						10 03										14 18						
Llanharan	d						10 08										14 23						
Pencoed	d						10 13										14 28						
Bridgend	d						10 20		11 24	11 38		12 18	12 37	13 23		14 19	14 35		15 20		16 21	16 37	17 20
Wildmill	d																						
Sarn	d																						
Tondu	d																						
Garth (Mid Glamorgan)	d																						
Maesteg (Ewenny Road)	d																						
Maesteg	a																						
Pyle	d						10 28						12 45				14 43					16 45	
Port Talbot Parkway	d						10 37		11 37	11 52		12 31	12 54	13 36		14 32	14 51		15 33		16 34	16 54	17 33
Baglan	d																						
Briton Ferry	d																						
Neath	d						10 45		11 45	12 00		12 39		13 44		14 40	14 59		15 41		16 42	17 02	17 41
Skewen	d																						
Llansamlet	d																						
Swansea	a						10 58		11 58	12 13		12 51		13 57		14 54	15 12		15 53		16 54	17 14	17 54
	d			00 10			11 02	11 08		12 15		12 58			14 13	15 01	15 15	15 29		16 36	17 05	17 26	
Gowerton	d			00s21			11 13	11 17		12 26					14 24		15 26	15 39		16 47		17 37	
Llanelli	a			00s29			11 20	11 24		12 33		13 15	13 23		14 31	15 17	15 33	15 46		16 54	17 21	17 44	
	d	00 02					11 22			12 35		13 16	13 24		14 33	15 18	15 34			16 56	17 22	17 45	
Pembrey & Burry Port	d	00 07		00s35			11 28			12 40		13 23	13 30		14 39	15 25	15 40			17 02	17 29	17 51	
Kidwelly	d			00x41			11x35			12x47					14x45					17x09			
Ferryside	d			00x47			11x41			12x53					14x51					17x15			
Carmarthen	a	00 28		01 05			11 54			13 05		13 44	13 56		15 06	15 46	16 03			17 28	17 50	18 14	
	d	00 31			09 55	10 19	12 06			13 08			14 05		15 08		16 09			17 33		18 20	
Whitland	a	00 46			10 11	10 34	12 22			13 23			14 21		15 22		16 25			17 48		18 36	
	d	00 46			10 11	10 34	12 22			13 24			14 21		15 23		16 27			17 48		18 37	
Narberth	d					10x43									15x32					17x57			
Kilgetty	d					10x52									15x42					18x07			
Saundersfoot	d					10x54									15x44					18x09			
Tenby	a					11 01									15 51					18 16			
	d					11 11									15 55					18 19			
Penally	d					11x14									15x58					18x22			
Manorbier	d					11 20									16 04					18 29			
Lamphey	d					11x28									16x12					18x36			
Pembroke	d					11 31									16 15					18 40			
Pembroke Dock	a					11 44									16 30					18 55			
Clunderwen	d				10x19		12x30						14x29				16x34					18x45	
Clarbeston Road	d	01x00			10x27		12x38						14x37				16x42					18x53	
Haverfordwest	d				10 35		12 46						14 45				16 51					19 01	
Johnston	d				10x44		12x55						14x54				16x59					19x10	
Milford Haven	a				10 55		13 06						15 09				17 11					19 25	
Fishguard & Goodwick	a	01 18								13 55													
Fishguard Harbour 30 ⛴	a	01 28								14 00													
	d		02 45								14 30												
Rosslare Harbour ⛴	a		06 15								18 00												

When events are being held at the Millenium Stadium, services are subject to alteration. Please check times before travelling.

Ferry service between Fishguard Harbour and Rosslare Harbour is operated by Stena Line

Table 128

Sundays

16 February to 23 March

Cardiff - Maesteg, Swansea and West Wales

Route Diagram - see first Page of Table 127

		AW	GW	AW	AW	GW		AW	GW	AW	GW	GW	AW	GW	GW
				B											
			◇1			◇1			◇1	◇	◇1	◇1	◇	◇1	◇1
			☕	🛒		☕			☕	🛒	☕	☕		☕	☕
London Paddington 15 ⊖	d		15 33			16 33			17 33		18 33	19 33		20 33	21 37
Reading 7	d		16 09			17 09			18 09		19 09	20 09		21 11	22 15
Manchester Piccadilly 10	d			14 30											
Gloucester 7	d														
Bristol Parkway 7	d		17 13			18 13			19 13		20 13	21 13		22 17	23 16
Newport (South Wales)	d		17 38	17 34		18 38			19 44		20 40	21 40		22 45	23 44
Cardiff Central 7	d		17 59	18 06		18 59			20 03	20 15	20 59	22 03	22 30	23 05	00 05
Pontyclun	d			18 21											
Llanharan	d			18 26											
Pencoed	d			18 30											
Bridgend	d		18 20	18 38		19 20			20 24	20 37	21 20	22 24	22 51	23 27	00 27
Wildmill	d														
Sarn	d														
Tondu	d														
Garth (Mid Glamorgan)	d														
Maesteg (Ewenny Road)	d														
Maesteg	a														
Pyle	d			18 46						20 45					
Port Talbot Parkway	d		18 33	18 54		19 32			20 37	20 54	21 33	22 37	23 05	23 41	00 40
Baglan	d														
Briton Ferry	d														
Neath	d		18 41	19 02		19 41			20 45	21 02	21 41	22 45	23 13	23 49	00 48
Skewen	d														
Llansamlet	d														
Swansea	a		18 58	19 15		19 58			20 58	21 14	21 55	22 58	23 25	00 05	01 02
	d	18 10		19 20				20 35		21 18			23 38		
Gowerton	d	18 21		19 31				20 46		21 29			23 49		
Llanelli	a	18 28		19 38				20 54		21 36			23 56		
	d	18 30		19 39				20 55		21 37			23 58		
Pembrey & Burry Port	d	18 36		19 45				21 01		21 43			00 04		
Kidwelly	d	18x43						21x08					00x11		
Ferryside	d	18x49						21x14					00x17		
Carmarthen	a	19 02		20 07				21 32		22 06			00 30		
	d	19 06		20 08						22 10			00 34		
Whitland	a	19 22		20 24						22 26			00 50		
	d	19 22		20 30	20 37					22 26			00 50		
Narberth	d				20x44										
Kilgetty	d				20x53										
Saundersfoot	d				20x55										
Tenby	a				21 02										
	d				21 06										
Penally	d				21x09										
Manorbier	d				21 15										
Lamphey	d				21x23										
Pembroke	d				21 26										
Pembroke Dock	a				21 36										
Clunderwen	d	19x30		20x38						22x34					
Clarbeston Road	d	19x38		20x46						22x42			01x03		
Haverfordwest	d	19a46		20 54						22 50					
Johnston	d			21x03						22x59					
Milford Haven	a			21 20						23 10					
Fishguard & Goodwick	a												01 22		
Fishguard Harbour 30 ⛴	a												01 27		
	d														
Rosslare Harbour ⛴🚌	a														

When events are being held at the Millenium Stadium, services are subject to alteration. Please check times before travelling.

Ferry service between Fishguard Harbour and Rosslare Harbour is operated by Stena Line

Table 128

Sundays

30 March to 11 May

Cardiff - Maesteg, Swansea and West Wales

Route Diagram - see first Page of Table 127

		AW	AW	AW	AW	AW	AW	AW	GW	AW		AW	GW	AW	GW	AW	GW	AW	AW	GW		AW	GW	AW	GW
			R									R						R						R	
							◇	◇	◇1	◇			◇1	◇	◇1		◇1		◇	◇1			◇1		◇1
							trolley		buffet				buffet	trolley	buffet		buffet	trolley		buffet			buffet	trolley	buffet
London Paddington 15 ⊖	d								08 30				09 30		10 30		11 30			12 30			13 30		14 33
Reading 7	d								09 02				10 03		11 03		12 03			13 03			13 59		15 03
Manchester Piccadilly 10	d																	10 30						12 30	
Gloucester 7	d																								
Bristol Parkway 7	d								10 04				11 08		12 14		13 08			14 08			15 03		16 08
Newport (South Wales)	d						09 30		10 29	11 00			11 35		12 38		13 35	13 29		14 35			15 35	15 49	16 35
Cardiff Central 7	d						09 50		10 50	11 18			11 58	12 16	12 59		13 59	14 05		14 54			16 00	16 16	16 57
Pontyclun	d						10 03											14 18							
Llanharan	d						10 08											14 23							
Pencoed	d						10 13											14 28							
Bridgend	d						10 20		11 10	11 38			12 18	12 37	13 20		14 19	14 35		15 15			16 21	16 37	17 18
Wildmill	d																								
Sarn	d																								
Tondu	d																								
Garth (Mid Glamorgan)	d																								
Maesteg (Ewenny Road)	d																								
Maesteg	a																								
Pyle	d						10 28							12 45				14 43						16 45	
Port Talbot Parkway	d						10 37		11 23	11 52			12 31	12 54	13 33		14 32	14 51		15 28			16 34	16 54	17 31
Baglan	d																								
Briton Ferry	d																								
Neath	d						10 45		11 32	12 00			12 39		13 41		14 40	14 59		15 36			16 42	17 02	17 39
Skewen	d																								
Llansamlet	d																								
Swansea	a						10 58		11 44	12 13			12 51		13 54		14 52	15 12		15 48			16 54	17 14	17 52
	d			00 10			11 02	11 08		12 15			12 58			14 13	15 01	15 15	15 29			16 36	17 05	17 26	
Gowerton	d			00s21			11 13	11 17		12 26						14 24		15 26	15 39			16 47		17 37	
Llanelli	a			00s29			11 20	11 24		12 33			13 15	13 23		14 31	15 17	15 33	15 46			16 54	17 21	17 44	
	d	00 02					11 22			12 35			13 16	13 24		14 33	15 18	15 34				16 56	17 22	17 45	
Pembrey & Burry Port	d	00 07		00s35			11 28			12 40			13 23	13 30		14 39	15 25	15 40				17 02	17 29	17 51	
Kidwelly	d			00x41			11x35			12x47						14x45						17x09			
Ferryside	d			00x47			11x41			12x53						14x51						17x15			
Carmarthen	a	00 28		01 05			11 54			13 05			13 44	13 56		15 06	15 46	16 03				17 28	17 50	18 14	
	d	00 31			09 55	10 19	12 06			13 08				14 05		15 08		16 09				17 33		18 20	
Whitland	a	00 46			10 11	10 34	12 22			13 23				14 21		15 22		16 25				17 48		18 36	
	d	00 46			10 11	10 34	12 22			13 24				14 21		15 23		16 27				17 48		18 37	
Narberth	d					10x43										15x32						17x57			
Kilgetty	d					10x52										15x42						18x07			
Saundersfoot	d					10x54										15x44						18x09			
Tenby	a					11 01										15 51						18 16			
	d					11 11										15 55						18 19			
Penally	d					11x14										15x58						18x22			
Manorbier	d					11 20										16 04						18 29			
Lamphey	d					11x28										16x12						18x36			
Pembroke	d					11 31										16 15						18 40			
Pembroke Dock	a					11 44										16 30						18 55			
Clunderwen	d				10x19		12x30							14x29				16x34						18x45	
Clarbeston Road	d	01x00			10x27		12x38							14x37				16x42						18x53	
Haverfordwest	d				10 35		12 46							14 45				16 51						19 01	
Johnston	d				10x44		12x55							14x54				16x59						19x10	
Milford Haven	a				10 55		13 06							15 09				17 11						19 25	
Fishguard & Goodwick	a	01 18								13 55															
Fishguard Harbour 30 ⛴	a	01 28								14 00															
	d		02 45									14 30													
Rosslare Harbour ⛴	a		06 15									18 00													

When events are being held at the Millenium Stadium, services are subject to alteration. Please check times before travelling.

Ferry service between Fishguard Harbour and Rosslare Harbour is operated by Stena Line

Table 128

Sundays

30 March to 11 May

Cardiff - Maesteg, Swansea and West Wales

Route Diagram - see first Page of Table 127

		AW	GW	AW	AW	GW	AW	GW	AW	GW	GW	AW	GW	GW
				■										
			◇1			◇1		◇1	◇	◇1	◇1	◇	◇1	◇1
			🍴	🛒		🍴		🍴	🛒	🍴	🍴		🍴	🍴
London Paddington 15 ⊖	d		15 33			16 33		17 33		18 33	19 33		20 33	21 37
Reading 7	d		16 03			17 09		18 03		19 03	20 03		21 03	22 09
Manchester Piccadilly 10	d			14 30										
Gloucester 7	d													
Bristol Parkway 7	d		17 08			18 15		19 08		20 13	21 08		22 08	23 16
Newport (South Wales)	d		17 38	17 34		18 38		19 35		20 40	21 35		22 40	23 44
Cardiff Central 7	d		17 59	18 06		18 59		19 53	20 15	20 59	21 58	22 30	23 01	00 05
Pontyclun	d			18 21										
Llanharan	d			18 26										
Pencoed	d			18 30										
Bridgend	d		18 20	18 38		19 20		20 15	20 37	21 20	22 19	22 51	23 23	00 27
Wildmill	d													
Sarn	d													
Tondu	d													
Garth (Mid Glamorgan)	d													
Maesteg (Ewenny Road)	d													
Maesteg	a													
Pyle	d			18 46					20 45					
Port Talbot Parkway	d		18 33	18 54		19 32		20 28	20 54	21 33	22 32	23 05	23 37	00 40
Baglan	d													
Briton Ferry	d													
Neath	d		18 41	19 02		19 41		20 35	21 02	21 41	22 40	23 13	23 45	00 48
Skewen	d													
Llansamlet	d													
Swansea	a		18 58	19 15		19 58		20 49	21 14	21 55	22 53	23 25	00 01	01 02
	d	18 10		19 20			20 35		21 18			23 38		
Gowerton	d	18 21		19 31			20 46		21 29			23 49		
Llanelli	a	18 28		19 38			20 54		21 36			23 56		
	d	18 30		19 39			20 55		21 37			23 58		
Pembrey & Burry Port	d	18 36		19 45			21 01		21 43			00 04		
Kidwelly	d	18x43					21x08					00x11		
Ferryside	d	18x49					21x14					00x17		
Carmarthen	a	19 02		20 07			21 32		22 06			00 30		
	d	19 06		20 08					22 10			00 34		
Whitland	a	19 22		20 24					22 26			00 50		
	d	19 22		20 30	20 37				22 26			00 50		
Narberth	d				20x44									
Kilgetty	d				20x53									
Saundersfoot	d				20x55									
Tenby	a				21 02									
	d				21 06									
Penally	d				21x09									
Manorbier	d				21 15									
Lamphey	d				21x23									
Pembroke	d				21 26									
Pembroke Dock	a				21 36									
Clunderwen	d	19x30		20x38					22x34					
Clarbeston Road	d	19x38		20x46					22x42			01x03		
Haverfordwest	d	19a46		20 54					22 50					
Johnston	d			21x03					22x59					
Milford Haven	a			21 20					23 10					
Fishguard & Goodwick	a											01 22		
Fishguard Harbour 30 ⛴	a											01 27		
	d													
Rosslare Harbour ⛴🚌	a													

When events are being held at the Millenium Stadium, services are subject to alteration. Please check times before travelling.

Ferry service between Fishguard Harbour and Rosslare Harbour is operated by Stena Line

Table 128R

Mondays to Fridays

9 December to 16 May

West Wales, Swansea and Maesteg - Cardiff

Route Diagram - see first Page of Table 127

Miles	Miles			AW MO	AW MX	AW MO	AW MX	GW	GW	GW	GW	AW		GW	GW	AW	AW	GW	AW	GW	AW	AW		AW	AW
				◇		◇	◇	◇[1] 🍴	R [1] A 🍴	R [1] B 🍴	R [1] 🍴	◇ 🛒		R [1] C ⊘	R ◇[1] D 🍴⊘		◇ 🛒	◇[1] E 🍴⊘	◇ 🛒	◇[1] E 🍴⊘		◇ 🛒			
—	—	Rosslare Harbour	d																						
0	—	**Fishguard Harbour**	a																						
—	—		d			01 50	01 50																	06 53	
—	—	Fishguard & Goodwick	d			01 53	01 53																	06 56	
—	0	**Milford Haven**	d		00 18																	06 00			
—	4	Johnston	d		00x26																	06x08			
—	8¾	Haverfordwest	d		00 33																	06 15			
15¾	14	Clarbeston Road	d		00x41	02x12	02x12															06x23		07a17	
22¼	—	Clunderwen	d		00x48																	06x30			
—	0	**Pembroke Dock**	d																						
—	2	Pembroke	d																						
—	3½	Lamphey	d																						
—	7	Manorbier	d																						
—	10¼	Penally	d																						
—	11½	**Tenby**	a																						
—	—		d																						
—	15¾	Saundersfoot	d																						
—	16½	Kilgetty	d																						
—	22	Narberth	d																						
27¾	27¼	Whitland	a		00 54	02 24	02 24															06 36			
—	—		d		00 54	02 24	02 24															06 36			
41¾	—	**Carmarthen**	a		01 16	02 41	02 41															06 52			
—	—		d			02 44	03 03					05 03					05 50		06 15			06 57			
48¾	—	Ferryside	d														06x00		06x25						
53	—	Kidwelly	d														06x05		06x30						
58¼	—	Pembrey & Burry Port	d									05 21					06 12		06 37			07 15			
62¼	—	Llanelli	a			03 06	03 25					05 26					06 17		06 42			07 20			
—	—		d			03 06	03 25					05 28					06 18		06 44			07 22			
68	—	Gowerton	d														06 24		06 50			07 28			
73½	—	**Swansea**	a			03 29	03 48										06 38		07 04			07 41			
—	—		d					03 57	04 58	04 58	05 27			05 58	06 28		06 42	06 58	07 06	07 28		07 45			
77½	—	Llansamlet	d														06 46								
79¼	—	Skewen	d														06 50								
83	—	Neath	d					04 09	05 10	05 10	05 39			06 10	06 40		06 54	07 10	07 17	07 40		07 56			
84¾	—	Briton Ferry	d														06 58								
86½	—	Baglan	d														07 01								
88½	—	Port Talbot Parkway	d					04 17	05 18	05 18	05 47	06 01		06 18	06 48		07 05	07 18	07 24	07 48		08 03			
94¾	—	Pyle	d									06 09					07 13		07 32			08 10			
—	0	Maesteg	d													06 44									07 59
—	0½	Maesteg (Ewenny Road)	d													06 46									08 01
—	1¼	Garth (Mid Glamorgan)	d													06 49									08 04
—	5¼	Tondu	d													06 57									08 13
—	6	Sarn	d													07 00									08 16
—	7¼	Wildmill	d													07 03									08 18
100¾	8¼	Bridgend	d	00 06				04 29	05 31	05 31	06 00	06 16		06 31	07 01	07 07	07 21	07 31	07 40	08 01	08 08	08 18			08 22
104¾	—	Pencoed	d									06 22				07 13	07 27				08 14				08 28
107	—	Llanharan	d									06 26				07 17			07 47			08 25			
110	—	Pontyclun	d									06 31				07 21	07 34				08 22				08 35
121	—	**Cardiff Central**	a	00 30				05 02	05 52	05 52	06 21	06 43		06 52	07 22	07 35	07 48	07 52	08 02	08 22	08 34	08 43			08 48
—	—	Newport (South Wales)	a					05 31	06 09	06 09	06 37	07 02		07 09	07 39			08 09	08 17	08 39		09 03			09 25
—	—	Bristol Parkway	a					05 59	06 29	06 29	06 58			07 29	07 59			08 30		08 59					
—	—	Gloucester	a																						10 20
—	—	Manchester Piccadilly	a									10 14							11 15			12 15			
—	—	Reading	a					06 59	07 28	07 30	08 00				09 00			09 25		09 59					
—	—	London Paddington ⊖	a					07 32	08 02	08 02	08 33			08 54	09 29			09 58		10 32					

A from 10 March
B until 7 March
C The Capitals United
D 🍴 ◇ from Reading ⊘ R to Reading
E 🍴 from Reading ⊘ to Reading

When events are being held at the Millenium Stadium, services are subject to alteration. Please check times before travelling.

Ferry service between Fishguard Harbour and Rosslare Harbour is operated by Stena Line

Table 128R

Mondays to Fridays

9 December to 16 May

West Wales, Swansea and Maesteg - Cardiff

Route Diagram - see first Page of Table 127

		GW	GW	GW	GW	AW	AW	AW		GW	AW	AW	AW	GW	AW	AW	AW	AW		GW	GW	AW	AW	AW	AW
																								[B]	
		◇1	◇1	◇1	◇1	◇				◇1	◇	◇		◇1	◇					◇1	◇1		◇		
		A	B	C	D															E	F				
		☕	☕	☕	☕	🛒				☕		🛒		☕	🛒					☕	☕		🛒		🛒
Rosslare Harbour ⛴🚌	d																							09 00	
Fishguard Harbour 30 ⛴	a																							12 30	
	d											08 04										09 54			
Fishguard & Goodwick	d											08 07										09 57			
Milford Haven	d					07 05									09 08										
Johnston	d					07x13									09x16										
Haverfordwest	d					07 20									09 23										
Clarbeston Road	d					07x28						08x25			09x31							10x17			
Clunderwen	d					07x35						08x33			09x38							10x25			
Pembroke Dock	d							06 59										09 09							
Pembroke	d							07 07										09 17							
Lamphey	d							07x10										09x20							
Manorbier	d							07 18										09 29							
Penally	d							07x24										09x34							
Tenby	a							07 27										09 37							
	d							07 29										09 38							
Saundersfoot	d							07x35										09x46							
Kilgetty	d							07x37										09x48							
Narberth	d							07x47										09x58							
Whitland	a					07 41		07 55				08 37			09 44			10 06				10 31			
	d					07 41		07 56				08 38			09 44			10 07				10 32			
Carmarthen	a					07 55		08 15				08 57			10 03			10 24				10 49			
	d			07 30	07 30	08 01		08 18				09 00			10 06			10 31					11 03		
Ferryside	d			07 43	07 43	08x11		08x28				09x10											11x13		
Kidwelly	d			07 50	07 50	08x16		08x34				09x15											11x18		
Pembrey & Burry Port	d			07 58	07 58	08 23		08 41				09 18			10 25			10 50					11 24		
Llanelli	a			08 03	08 03	08 28		08 46				09 24			10 31			10 56					11 30		
	d			08 05	08 05	08 30		08 48			08 55	09 25			10 32			10 57					11 31		
Gowerton	d					08 36					09 04	09 35						11 04					11 38		
Swansea	a			08 21	08 21	08 49		09 07			09 18	09 51			10 49			11 23					11 52		
	d	07 58	07 58	08 28	08 28	08 55		09 10		09 28	09 34	09 55		10 28	10 55		11 10			11 28	11 28		11 55		
Llansamlet	d							09 17									11 17								
Skewen	d							09 21									11 21								
Neath	d	08 10	08 10	08 40	08 40	09 06		09 25		09 40	09 45	10 06		10 40	11 06		11 25			11 40	11 40		12 06		
Briton Ferry	d							09 29									11 28								
Baglan	d							09 32									11 32								
Port Talbot Parkway	d	08 18	08 18	08 48	08 48	09 13		09 36		09 48	09 52	10 13		10 48	11 13		11 36			11 48	11 48		12 13		
Pyle	d							09 45			10 05						11 44								
Maesteg	d						09 16						10 16			11 15									12 15
Maesteg (Ewenny Road)	d						09 18						10 18			11 17									12 17
Garth (Mid Glamorgan)	d						09 21						10 21			11 20									12 20
Tondu	d						09 30						10 30			11 29									12 29
Sarn	d						09 33						10 33			11 32									12 32
Wildmill	d						09 35						10 35			11 34									12 34
Bridgend	d	08 31	08 31	09 01	09 01	09 26	09 39	09 53		10 01	10 14	10 26	10 39	11 01	11 26	11 38	11 55			12 01	12 01		12 26		12 38
Pencoed	d						09 45						10 45			11 44									12 44
Llanharan	d						09 49						10 49			11 48									12 48
Pontyclun	d						09 53						10 53			11 52									12 52
Cardiff Central 7	a	08 52	08 52	09 22	09 22	09 46	10 07	10 17		10 22	10 44	10 48	11 10	11 22	11 46	12 08	12 18			12 22	12 22		12 48		13 06
Newport (South Wales)	a	09 09	09 09	09 39	09 39	10 17	10 25	10 35		10 39		11 02		11 39	12 17	12 25				12 39	12 39		13 02		13 27
Bristol Parkway 7	a	09 30	09 30	09 59	09 59					11 00				11 59						12 59	12 59				
Gloucester 7	a						11 20									13 20									14 21
Manchester Piccadilly 10	a					13 15						14 15			15 15								16 15		
Reading 7	a	10 30	10 31	11 00	11 00					11 59				13 00						13 58	13 59				
London Paddington 15 ⊖	a	11 07	11 07	11 32	11 33					12 33				13 33						14 33	14 33				

A from 10 March
B until 7 March
C from 10 March. The Red Dragon
D until 7 March. The Red Dragon
E from 10 March. The St. David
F until 7 March. The St. David

When events are being held at the Millenium Stadium, services are subject to alteration. Please check times before travelling.

Ferry service between Fishguard Harbour and Rosslare Harbour is operated by Stena Line

Table 128R

Mondays to Fridays

9 December to 16 May

West Wales, Swansea and Maesteg - Cardiff

Route Diagram - see first Page of Table 127

		GW	AW	AW	AW	AW	GW	GW	AW	AW	GW	AW	AW	AW	AW	AW	GW	GW	AW	AW	GW	GW
												🔲	🔲		🔲				🔲			
		◇1	◇		◇		◇1	◇1	◇		◇1						◇1	◇1			◇1	◇1
		A					B	C									B	C			D	E
		🍽⊘	🛒		🛒		🍽	🍽	🛒		🍽	🛒	🛒				🍽	🍽	🛒		🍽⊘	🍽⊘
Rosslare Harbour ⛴	d																					
Fishguard Harbour 30 ⛴	a																					
	d												13 29									
Fishguard & Goodwick	d												13 32									
Milford Haven	d		11 08									13 08										
Johnston	d		11x16									13x16										
Haverfordwest	d		11 23									13 23										
Clarbeston Road	d		11x31									13x31										
Clunderwen	d		11x38									13x38										
Pembroke Dock	d					11 09										13 09						
Pembroke	d					11 17										13 17						
Lamphey	d					11x20										13x20						
Manorbier	d					11 29										13 29						
Penally	d					11x34										13x34						
Tenby	a					11 37										13 37						
	d					11 43										13 41						
Saundersfoot	d					11x51										13x49						
Kilgetty	d					11x53										13x51						
Narberth	d					12x03										14x01						
Whitland	a		11 44			12 11						13 44	14 04			14 09						
	d		11 44			12 11						13 44	14 04			14 09						
Carmarthen	a		12 00			12 29						14 00	14 21			14 31						
	d		12 05			12 33			13 02			14 05	14 28			14 37			15 03			
Ferryside	d								13x12										15x13			
Kidwelly	d								13x17										15x18			
Pembrey & Burry Port	d		12 23			12 52			13 23			14 23				14 56			15 25			
Llanelli	a		12 28			12 58			13 29			14 28	14 50			15 02			15 30			
	d		12 30		12 42	12 59			13 30			14 30	14 50			15 02			15 32			
Gowerton	d		12 36						13 37			14 36							15 38			
Swansea	a		12 49		13 04	13 22			13 51			14 49				15 23			15 51			
	d	12 28	12 54		13 10		13 28	13 28	13 55		14 28	14 55			15 10		15 28	15 28	15 55		16 28	16 28
Llansamlet	d				13 17										15 17							
Skewen	d				13 21										15 21							
Neath	d	12 40	13 05		13 25		13 40	13 40	14 06		14 40	15 06			15 25		15 40	15 40	16 06		16 40	16 40
Briton Ferry	d				13 28										15 28							
Baglan	d				13 32										15 32							
Port Talbot Parkway	d	12 48	13 12		13 36		13 48	13 48	14 13		14 48	15 13			15 36		15 48	15 48	16 13		16 48	16 48
Pyle	d				13 44										15 44							
Maesteg	d			13 15						14 15				15 15						16 15		
Maesteg (Ewenny Road)	d			13 17						14 17				15 17						16 17		
Garth (Mid Glamorgan)	d			13 20						14 20				15 20						16 20		
Tondu	d			13 29						14 29				15 29						16 29		
Sarn	d			13 32						14 32				15 32						16 32		
Wildmill	d			13 34						14 34				15 34						16 34		
Bridgend	d	13 01	13 25	13 38	13 53		14 01	14 01	14 26	14 38	15 01	15 26	15 37	15 39	15 53		16 01	16 01	16 26	16 38	17 01	17 01
Pencoed	d			13 44						14 44				15 45						16 44		
Llanharan	d			13 48						14 48				15 49						16 48		
Pontyclun	d			13 52						14 52				15 53						16 52		
Cardiff Central 7	a	13 22	13 47	14 07	14 15		14 22	14 22	14 47	15 06	15 22	15 47	15 58	16 07	16 13		16 22	16 22	16 46	17 06	17 22	17 22
Newport (South Wales)	a	13 39	14 17				14 39	14 39	15 02	15 27	15 39	16 02		16 25	16 33		16 39	16 39	17 02	17 25	17 39	17 39
Bristol Parkway 7	a	13 59					15 00	15 00			15 59						16 59	16 59			17 59	17 59
Gloucester 7	a									16 21				17 20						18 21		
Manchester Piccadilly 10	a		17 14						18 13			19 15							20 15			
Reading 7	a	15 00					15 59	16 00			17 00						17 58	18 00			18 59	19 01
London Paddington 15 ⊖	a	15 33					16 32	16 32			17 30						18 30	18 30			19 32	19 33

A 🍽 from Reading ⊘ to Reading
B from 10 March
C until 7 March
D from 10 March. 🍽 from Reading ⊘ to Reading
E until 7 March. 🍽 from Reading ⊘ to Reading

When events are being held at the Millenium Stadium, services are subject to alteration. Please check times before travelling.

Ferry service between Fishguard Harbour and Rosslare Harbour is operated by Stena Line

Table 128R

Mondays to Fridays

9 December to 16 May

West Wales, Swansea and Maesteg - Cardiff

Route Diagram - see first Page of Table 127

		AW	AW	AW	AW	GW	AW	AW	AW	GW		AW	AW	AW	AW	AW	GW FO	GW FX	AW	AW		GW FO	GW FX	AW	AW
		■		■																					
						◇1	◇	◇		◇1		◇					◇1	◇1	◇			◇1	◇1	◇	
		[trolley]		[trolley]		[buffet]	[trolley]			[buffet]							[buffet]	[buffet]				[buffet]	[buffet]		
Rosslare Harbour [ferry]	d																								
Fishguard Harbour 30 [ferry]	a																								
	d													19 00											
Fishguard & Goodwick	d													19 03											
Milford Haven	d	15 08										17 08												19 08	
Johnston	d	15x16										17x16												19x16	
Haverfordwest	d	15 23										17 23												19 23	
Clarbeston Road	d	15x31										17x31		19a22										19x31	
Clunderwen	d	15x38										17x38												19x38	
Pembroke Dock	d				15 09								17 09		19 19										
Pembroke	d				15 17								17 17		19 27										
Lamphey	d				15x20								17x20		19x31										
Manorbier	d				15 29								17 29		19 39										
Penally	d				15x34								17x34		19x44										
Tenby	a				15 37								17 37		19 47										
	d				15 41								17 38												
Saundersfoot	d				15x49								17x46												
Kilgetty	d				15x51								17x48												
Narberth	d				16x01								17x58												
Whitland	a	15 44			16 09							17 44	18 06											19 44	
	d	15 44			16 09							17 45	18 07											19 44	
Carmarthen	a	16 00			16 27							18 02	18 24											20 00	
	d	16 05			16 31		17 02					18 06	18 31						18 50					20 05	
Ferryside	d						17x12					18x16							19x00						
Kidwelly	d						17x17					18x22							19x06						
Pembrey & Burry Port	d	16 23			16 50		17 23					18 29	18 50						19 14					20 23	
Llanelli	a	16 28			16 56		17 29					18 34	18 56						19 20					20 28	
	d	16 30		16 45	16 57		17 30	17 48				18 35	18 57						19 21					20 29	
Gowerton	d	16 36			17 04		17 37	17 55				18 43	19 05						19 29					20 36	
Swansea	a	16 49		17 02	17 22		17 49	18 17				18 55	19 22						19 43					20 49	
	d	16 55		17 10		17 28	17 55			18 28		18 58					19 29	19 29	19 51			20 28	20 28	20 56	
Llansamlet	d			17 16								19 05													
Skewen	d			17 20								19 09													
Neath	d	17 06		17 24		17 40	18 06			18 40		19 13					19 40	19 40	20 02			20 40	20 40	21 07	
Briton Ferry	d			17 28								19 16													
Baglan	d			17 31								19 20													
Port Talbot Parkway	d	17 13		17 35		17 48	18 13			18 48		19 24					19 48	19 48	20 09			20 48	20 48	21 14	
Pyle	d			17 43								19 32													
Maesteg	d		17 15						18 20							19 20				20 15					21 15
Maesteg (Ewenny Road)	d		17 17						18 22							19 22				20 17					21 17
Garth (Mid Glamorgan)	d		17 20						18 25							19 25				20 20					21 20
Tondu	d		17 29						18 34							19 34				20 29					21 29
Sarn	d		17 32						18 37							19 37				20 32					21 32
Wildmill	d		17 34						18 39							19 39				20 34					21 34
Bridgend	d	17 26	17 38	17 55		18 01	18 26		18 43	19 01		19 40				19 43	20 01	20 01	20 23	20 38		21 01	21 01	21 27	21 38
Pencoed	d		17 44						18 49							19 49				20 44					21 44
Llanharan	d		17 48						18 52							19 52				20 48					21 48
Pontyclun	d		17 52						18 57							19 58				20 52					21 52
Cardiff Central 7	a	17 46	18 06	18 14		18 22	18 46		19 13	19 22		20 03				20 13	20 22	20 22	20 46	21 06		21 22	21 22	21 50	22 10
Newport (South Wales)	a	18 02	18 25	18 33		18 39	19 03			19 39							20 38	20 38		21 25		21 38	21 38		
Bristol Parkway 7	a					18 59				19 59							21 01	21 01				21 59	21 59		
Gloucester 7	a		19 20																	22 21					
Manchester Piccadilly 10	a	21 06					22 13																		
Reading 7	a					20 00				21 00							22 11	22 11				23 02	23 02		
London Paddington 15 ⊖	a					20 37				21 32							22 44	22 47				23 40	23 41		

When events are being held at the Millenium Stadium, services are subject to alteration. Please check times before travelling.

Ferry service between Fishguard Harbour and Rosslare Harbour is operated by Stena Line

Table 128R

Mondays to Fridays

9 December to 16 May

West Wales, Swansea and Maesteg - Cardiff

Route Diagram - see first Page of Table 127

		AW ◇	AW	AW	AW 🅁	AW ◇	AW FO	AW FX	AW	AW	AW	AW
Rosslare Harbour ⛴	d				21 00							
Fishguard Harbour 30 ⛴	a				00 30							
	d			20 50								
Fishguard & Goodwick	d			20 53								
Milford Haven	d		20 36									23 18
Johnston	d		20x44									23x26
Haverfordwest	d		20 51									23 33
Clarbeston Road	d		20x59	21x12								23x41
Clunderwen	d		21x06	21x19								23x48
Pembroke Dock	d									21 09	22 18	
Pembroke	d									21 17	22 26	
Lamphey	d									21x20	22x29	
Manorbier	d									21 29	22 37	
Penally	d									21x34	22x43	
Tenby	a									21 37	22 45	
	d	19 57								21 42	22 45	
Saundersfoot	d	20x05								21x50	22x53	
Kilgetty	d	20x07								21x52	22x55	
Narberth	d	20x17								22x02	23x04	
Whitland	a	20 25	21 12	21 26						22 10	23 12	23 54
	d	20 27	21 12	21 26						22 10	23 15	23 54
Carmarthen	a	20 45	21 34	21 46						22 28	23 34	00 16
	d	20 47								22 35		
Ferryside	d	20x58								22x45		
Kidwelly	d	21x04								22x51		
Pembrey & Burry Port	d	21 11								22 58		
Llanelli	a	21 17								23 04		
	d	21 17				21 43				23 05		
Gowerton	d	21 26				21 50				23 12		
Swansea	a	21 42				22 08				23 34		
	d	21 45							22 32			
Llansamlet	d	21 52							22 39			
Skewen	d	21 56							22 43			
Neath	d	22 00							22 47			
Briton Ferry	d	22 03							22 50			
Baglan	d	22 07							22 54			
Port Talbot Parkway	d	22 11							22 58			
Pyle	d	22 19							23 06			
Maesteg	d						22 15	22 15				
Maesteg (Ewenny Road)	d						22 17	22 17				
Garth (Mid Glamorgan)	d						22 20	22 20				
Tondu	d						22 29	22 29				
Sarn	d						22 32	22 32				
Wildmill	d						22 34	22 34				
Bridgend	d	22 27					22 38	22 38	23 14			
Pencoed	d						22 44	22 44				
Llanharan	d						22 48	22 48				
Pontyclun	d						22 52	22 52				
Cardiff Central 7	a	22 49					23 09	23 09	23 38			
Newport (South Wales)	a						23 38	23 39				
Bristol Parkway 7	a											
Gloucester 7	a						00 39	00 39				
Manchester Piccadilly 10	a											
Reading 7	a											
London Paddington 15 ⊖	a											

When events are being held at the Millenium Stadium, services are subject to alteration. Please check times before travelling.

Ferry service between Fishguard Harbour and Rosslare Harbour is operated by Stena Line

Table 128R

Saturdays

14 December to 28 December

West Wales, Swansea and Maesteg - Cardiff

Route Diagram - see first Page of Table 127

		AW	AW	GW	GW	GW	AW	GW	GW	AW		AW	GW	AW	GW	AW	AW	AW	GW	GW		AW	AW	AW	GW
			◇	◇1	◇1	◇1	◇	◇1	◇1			◇	◇1	◇	◇1	◇			◇1	◇1		◇			◇1
													A		A										
				☕	☕	☕	🛒	☕	☕			🛒	☕⊘	🛒	☕⊘	🛒			☕	☕		🛒			☕
Rosslare Harbour ⛴	d																								
Fishguard Harbour 30 ⛴	a																								
	d		01 50														06 53								
Fishguard & Goodwick	d		01 53														06 56								
Milford Haven	d	00 18														06 00						07 05			
Johnston	d	00x26														06x08						07x13			
Haverfordwest	d	00 33														06 15						07 20			
Clarbeston Road	d	00x41	02x12													06x23	07a17					07x28			
Clunderwen	d	00x48														06x30						07x35			
Pembroke Dock	d																							06 59	
Pembroke	d																							07 07	
Lamphey	d																							07x10	
Manorbier	d																							07 18	
Penally	d																							07x24	
Tenby	a																							07 27	
	d																							07 29	
Saundersfoot	d																							07x35	
Kilgetty	d																							07x37	
Narberth	d																							07x47	
Whitland	a	00 54	02 24													06 36						07 41		07 55	
	d	00 54	02 24													06 36						07 41		07 56	
Carmarthen	a	01 16	02 41													06 52						07 55		08 15	
	d		02 44				05 04					05 55		06 20		06 57						08 01		08 18	
Ferryside	d											06x05		06x30								08x11		08x28	
Kidwelly	d											06x10		06x35								08x16		08x34	
Pembrey & Burry Port	d						05 22					06 17		06 42		07 15						08 23		08 41	
Llanelli	a		03 06				05 27					06 22		06 47		07 20						08 28		08 46	
	d		03 06				05 29					06 24		06 48		07 22						08 30		08 48	
Gowerton	d											06 30		06 55		07 28						08 36			
Swansea	a		03 29									06 43		07 08		07 41						08 49		09 07	
	d			03 58	04 58	05 28		05 58	06 28			06 47	06 58	07 11	07 28	07 45			07 58	08 28		08 55		09 10	09 28
Llansamlet	d													07 18										09 17	
Skewen	d													07 22										09 21	
Neath	d			04 10	05 10	05 40		06 10	06 40			06 58	07 10	07 26	07 40	07 56			08 10	08 40		09 06		09 25	09 40
Briton Ferry	d													07 29										09 29	
Baglan	d													07 33										09 32	
Port Talbot Parkway	d			04 18	05 18	05 48	06 02	06 18	06 48			07 05	07 18	07 37	07 48	08 03			08 18	08 48		09 13		09 36	09 48
Pyle	d						06 09					07 12		07 45		08 09						09 21		09 45	
Maesteg	d									06 46								08 00					09 17		
Maesteg (Ewenny Road)	d									06 48								08 02					09 19		
Garth (Mid Glamorgan)	d									06 51								08 05					09 22		
Tondu	d									07 00								08 14					09 31		
Sarn	d									07 03								08 17					09 34		
Wildmill	d									07 05								08 19					09 36		
Bridgend	d			04 30	05 31	06 01	06 17	06 31	07 01	07 09		07 20	07 31	07 53	08 01	08 17		08 23	08 31	09 01		09 28	09 40	09 53	10 01
Pencoed	d						06 23			07 15				08 07		08 23							09 46		
Llanharan	d						06 26					07 27		08 11				08 30					09 50		
Pontyclun	d						06 31			07 22				08 15		08 30							09 54		
Cardiff Central 7	a			04 52	05 52	06 22	06 43	06 52	07 22	07 36		07 42	07 52	08 34	08 22	08 42		08 47	08 52	09 22		09 48	10 09	10 17	10 22
Newport (South Wales)	a			05 09	06 09	06 38	07 02	07 08	07 39			08 02	08 08		08 38	09 02		09 24	09 08	09 39		10 07	10 25	10 35	10 39
Bristol Parkway 7	a			05 36	06 29	06 59		07 29	07 59				08 30		08 59				09 30	09 59					10 59
Gloucester 7	a																	10 19					11 21		
Manchester Piccadilly 10	a						10 14					11 15				12 15						13 15			
Reading 7	a			07 14	07 31	08 00		08 33	09 01				09 31		10 00				10 30	11 01					12 01
London Paddington 15 ⊖	a			07 44	08 07	08 32		09 02	09 38				10 02		10 32				11 04	11 33					12 37

A ☕ from Reading ⊘ to Reading

When events are being held at the Millenium Stadium, services are subject to alteration. Please check times before travelling.

Ferry service between Fishguard Harbour and Rosslare Harbour is operated by Stena Line

Table 128R

Saturdays

West Wales, Swansea and Maesteg - Cardiff

14 December to 28 December

Route Diagram - see first Page of Table 127

Station		AW	AW	AW	GW	AW	AW	AW	AW	GW	AW	AW	AW	AW	GW	AW	AW	AW	AW	GW	AW	AW	GW
													R										
		◇	◇		◇1	◇				◇1		◇			◇1	◇		◇		◇1	◇		◇1
			🛒		☕	🛒				☕		🛒		🛒	☕	🛒		🛒		☕	🛒		☕
Rosslare Harbour ⛴	d												09 00										
Fishguard Harbour 30 ⛴	a												12 30										
	d		08 04								09 53												
Fishguard & Goodwick	d		08 07								09 56												
Milford Haven	d					09 08										11 08							
Johnston	d					09x16										11x16							
Haverfordwest	d					09 23										11 23							
Clarbeston Road	d		08x25			09x31					10x14					11x31							
Clunderwen	d		08x33			09x38					10x22					11x38							
Pembroke Dock	d								09 09										11 09				
Pembroke	d								09 17										11 17				
Lamphey	d								09x20										11x20				
Manorbier	d								09 29										11 29				
Penally	d								09x34										11x34				
Tenby	a								09 37										11 37				
	d								09 37										11 41				
Saundersfoot	d								09x45										11x49				
Kilgetty	d								09x47										11x51				
Narberth	d								09x57										12x01				
Whitland	a		08 37			09 44			10 05		10 28					11 44			12 09				
	d		08 38			09 44			10 05		10 29					11 44			12 09				
Carmarthen	a		08 57			10 02			10 23		10 46					12 00			12 27				
	d		09 00		09 35	10 04			10 27			11 09				12 05			12 31		13 02		
Ferryside	d		09x10									11x19									13x12		
Kidwelly	d		09x15									11x24									13x17		
Pembrey & Burry Port	d		09 21		09 56	10 24			10 47			11 30				12 23			12 50		13 23		
Llanelli	a		09 27		10 01	10 29			10 53			11 36				12 28			12 56		13 29		
	d	08 55	09 28		10 03	10 31			10 53			11 37				12 30		12 37	12 57		13 30		
Gowerton	d	09 04	09 35						11 01			11 44				12 36					13 37		
Swansea	a	09 18	09 47		10 21	10 48			11 23			11 56				12 49		13 00	13 23		13 49		
	d	09 34	09 55		10 28	10 55		11 10		11 28		12 00			12 28	12 53		13 10		13 28	14 00		14 28
Llansamlet	d							11 17										13 17					
Skewen	d							11 21										13 21					
Neath	d	09 45	10 06		10 40	11 06		11 25		11 40		12 11			12 40	13 04		13 25		13 40	14 11		14 40
Briton Ferry	d							11 28										13 28					
Baglan	d							11 32										13 32					
Port Talbot Parkway	d	09 52	10 13		10 48	11 13		11 36		11 48		12 18			12 48	13 11		13 36		13 48	14 18		14 48
Pyle	d	10 05	10 20			11 21		11 44								13 19		13 44					
Maesteg	d			10 15			11 15							12 17			13 15					14 15	
Maesteg (Ewenny Road)	d			10 17			11 17							12 19			13 17					14 17	
Garth (Mid Glamorgan)	d			10 20			11 20							12 22			13 20					14 20	
Tondu	d			10 29			11 29							12 31			13 29					14 29	
Sarn	d			10 32			11 32							12 34			13 32					14 32	
Wildmill	d			10 34			11 34							12 36			13 34					14 34	
Bridgend	d	10 14	10 28	10 38	11 01	11 28	11 38	11 56		12 01		12 31		12 40	13 01	13 26	13 38	13 53		14 01	14 31	14 38	15 01
Pencoed	d			10 44			11 44							12 46			13 44					14 44	
Llanharan	d			10 48			11 48							12 50			13 48					14 48	
Pontyclun	d			10 52			11 52							12 54			13 52					14 52	
Cardiff Central 7	a	10 44	10 48	11 13	11 22	11 48	12 07	12 18		12 22		12 52		13 09	13 22	13 48	14 09	14 15		14 22	14 52	15 07	15 22
Newport (South Wales)	a		11 07		11 39	12 07	12 25			12 39		13 07		13 26	13 38	14 07		14 34		14 39	15 07	15 25	15 39
Bristol Parkway 7	a				11 59					12 59					13 59					14 59			15 59
Gloucester 7	a						13 21							14 19								16 19	
Manchester Piccadilly 10	a		14 15			15 15						16 15				17 14					18 15		
Reading 7	a				13 01					14 00					15 02					16 00			17 00
London Paddington 15 ⊖	a				13 38					14 32					15 37					16 33			17 32

When events are being held at the Millenium Stadium, services are subject to alteration. Please check times before travelling.

Ferry service between Fishguard Harbour and Rosslare Harbour is operated by Stena Line

Table 128R

Saturdays

14 December to 28 December

West Wales, Swansea and Maesteg - Cardiff

Route Diagram - see first Page of Table 127

		AW		AW	AW	AW	AW	GW	AW	AW	GW	AW		AW	AW	AW	GW	AW	AW	AW	GW	AW		AW	AW
		R		R					R			R													
								◇1			◇1						◇1	◇	◇		◇1	◇			◇
		🛒		🛒				🍴	🛒		🍴	🛒					🍴	🛒			🍴				
Rosslare Harbour ⛴	d																								
Fishguard Harbour 30 ⛴	a																								
	d			13 29																				19 00	
Fishguard & Goodwick	d			13 32																				19 03	
Milford Haven	d	13 08										15 08										17 08			
Johnston	d	13x16										15x16										17x16			
Haverfordwest	d	13 23										15 23										17 23			
Clarbeston Road	d	13x31										15x31										17x31		19a22	
Clunderwen	d	13x38										15x38										17x38			
Pembroke Dock	d						13 09									15 09									
Pembroke	d						13 17									15 17									
Lamphey	d						13x20									15x20									
Manorbier	d						13 29									15 29									
Penally	d						13x34									15x34									
Tenby	a						13 37									15 37									
	d						13 42									15 40									
Saundersfoot	d						13x50									15x48									
Kilgetty	d						13x52									15x50									
Narberth	d						14x02									16x00									
Whitland	a	13 44		14 04			14 10					15 44				16 08						17 44			
	d	13 44		14 04			14 11					15 44				16 09						17 45			
Carmarthen	a	14 00		14 20			14 28					16 00				16 26						18 03			
	d	14 05		14 24			14 33		15 03			16 05				16 31		17 03				18 07			
Ferryside	d								15x13									17x13				18x17			
Kidwelly	d								15x18									17x18				18x23			
Pembrey & Burry Port	d	14 23					14 52		15 25			16 23				16 50		17 24				18 30			
Llanelli	a	14 28		14 47			14 58		15 30			16 28				16 56		17 30				18 35			
	d	14 30		14 47			14 58		15 32			16 30			16 47	16 57		17 31	17 41			18 36			
Gowerton	d	14 36							15 38			16 36				17 04		17 38	17 48			18 44			
Swansea	a	14 49					15 22		15 51			16 49			17 04	17 22		17 50	18 10			18 56			
	d	14 55				15 10		15 28	15 55		16 28	16 58			17 10		17 28	17 54			18 28	19 00			
Llansamlet	d					15 17									17 17										
Skewen	d					15 21									17 21										
Neath	d	15 06				15 25		15 40	16 06		16 40	17 09			17 25		17 40	18 05			18 40	19 11			
Briton Ferry	d					15 28									17 28										
Baglan	d					15 32									17 32										
Port Talbot Parkway	d	15 13				15 36		15 48	16 13		16 48	17 16			17 36		17 48	18 12			18 48	19 19			
Pyle	d					15 44			16 21			17 24			17 44										
Maesteg	d				15 17					16 15				17 15						18 20					19 15
Maesteg (Ewenny Road)	d				15 19					16 17				17 17						18 22					19 17
Garth (Mid Glamorgan)	d				15 22					16 20				17 20						18 25					19 20
Tondu	d				15 31					16 29				17 29						18 34					19 29
Sarn	d				15 34					16 32				17 32						18 37					19 32
Wildmill	d				15 36					16 34				17 34						18 39					19 34
Bridgend	d	15 26		15 31	15 40	15 53		16 01	16 28	16 38	17 01	17 31		17 38	17 55		18 01	18 25		18 43	19 01	19 33			19 38
Pencoed	d				15 46					16 44				17 44						18 49					19 44
Llanharan	d				15 50					16 48				17 48						18 53					19 47
Pontyclun	d				15 54					16 52				17 52						18 57					19 52
Cardiff Central 7	a	15 51		15 58	16 09	16 16		16 22	16 48	17 07	17 22	17 51		18 07	18 20		18 22	18 45		19 13	19 22	19 56			20 05
Newport (South Wales)	a	16 07			16 23	16 32		16 39	17 07	17 27	17 39	18 07		18 25			18 39	19 03			19 39				20 24
Bristol Parkway 7	a							16 59			17 59						18 59				19 59				
Gloucester 7	a				17 19					18 20				19 20											
Manchester Piccadilly 10	a	19 15							20 15			21 16						22 13							23 49
Reading 7	a							17 58			19 00						20 00				21 06				
London Paddington 15 ⊖	a							18 32			19 32						20 32				21 37				

When events are being held at the Millenium Stadium, services are subject to alteration. Please check times before travelling.

Ferry service between Fishguard Harbour and Rosslare Harbour is operated by Stena Line

Table 128R

Saturdays

West Wales, Swansea and Maesteg - Cardiff

14 December to 28 December

Route Diagram - see first Page of Table 127

		AW	AW	GW	AW	AW	AW	AW	AW	AW	AW	AW	AW	AW	AW	AW	AW	AW
											R							
				◇1 ☕	◇		◇		◇				◇					
Rosslare Harbour	d										21 00							
Fishguard Harbour [30]	a										00 30							
	d									21 00								
Fishguard & Goodwick	d									21 03								
Milford Haven	d						19 08					21 16						23 18
Johnston	d						19x16					21x24						23x26
Haverfordwest	d						19 23					21 31						23 33
Clarbeston Road	d						19x31			21x22		21x39						23x41
Clunderwen	d						19x38			21x29		21x46						23x48
Pembroke Dock	d		17 12						19 09							21 09	22 18	
Pembroke	d		17 20						19 17							21 17	22 26	
Lamphey	d		17x23						19x21							21x20	22x29	
Manorbier	d		17 32						19 29							21 29	22 37	
Penally	d		17x37						19x34							21x34	22x43	
Tenby	a		17 40						19 37							21 37	22 45	
	d		17 46						19 49							21 42	22 45	
Saundersfoot	d		17x54						19x57							21x50	22x53	
Kilgetty	d		17x56						19x59							21x52	22x55	
Narberth	d		18x06						20x09							22x02	23x04	
Whitland	a		18 14				19 44		20 17	21 36		21 52				22 10	23 12	23 54
	d		18 15				19 44		20 19	21 36		21 52				22 11	23 15	23 54
Carmarthen	a		18 32				20 04		20 37	21 57		22 14				22 28	23 34	00 16
	d		18 37		18 51		20 07		20 47							22 35		
Ferryside	d				19x01				20x58							22x45		
Kidwelly	d				19x07				21x04							22x51		
Pembrey & Burry Port	d		18 56		19 15		20 25		21 11							22 58		
Llanelli	a		19 02		19 21		20 30		21 17							23 04		
	d		19 02		19 22		20 31		21 17				21 40			23 05		
Gowerton	d		19 11		19 30		20 38		21 26				21 47			23 12		
Swansea	a		19 25		19 44		20 51		21 42				22 10			23 30		
	d	19 10		19 28	19 52		20 55		21 43						22 20			
Llansamlet	d	19 17							21 50						22 27			
Skewen	d	19 21							21 54						22 31			
Neath	d	19 25		19 40	20 03		21 06		21 59						22 35			
Briton Ferry	d	19 28							22 02						22 38			
Baglan	d	19 32							22 06						22 42			
Port Talbot Parkway	d	19 36		19 48	20 10		21 13		22 10						22 46			
Pyle	d	19 44							22 18						22 54			
Maesteg	d					20 15		21 15						22 15				
Maesteg (Ewenny Road)	d					20 17		21 17						22 17				
Garth (Mid Glamorgan)	d					20 20		21 20						22 20				
Tondu	d					20 29		21 29						22 29				
Sarn	d					20 32		21 32						22 32				
Wildmill	d					20 34		21 34						22 34				
Bridgend	d	19 52		20 01	20 24	20 38	21 26	21 38	22 26					22 38	23 02			
Pencoed	d					20 44		21 44						22 44				
Llanharan	d					20 48		21 48						22 48				
Pontyclun	d					20 52		21 52						22 52				
Cardiff Central [7]	a	20 17		20 23	20 47	21 07	21 46	22 09	22 50					23 08	23 26			
Newport (South Wales)	a			20 39		21 25	22 10							23 37				
Bristol Parkway [7]	a			21 01														
Gloucester [7]	a					22 22								00 38				
Manchester Piccadilly [10]	a																	
Reading [7]	a			22 02														
London Paddington [15] ⊖	a			22 40														

When events are being held at the Millenium Stadium, services are subject to alteration. Please check times before travelling.

Ferry service between Fishguard Harbour and Rosslare Harbour is operated by Stena Line

Table 128R

Saturdays

4 January to 8 February

West Wales, Swansea and Maesteg - Cardiff

Route Diagram - see first Page of Table 127

		AW	AW	GW	GW	GW	AW	GW	GW	AW		AW	GW	AW	GW	AW	AW	AW	GW	GW		AW	AW	AW	GW
			◇	◇1	◇1	◇1	◇	◇1	◇1			◇	◇1	◇	◇1	◇			◇1	◇1		◇			◇1
													A		A										
				🍴	🍴	🍴	🛒	🍴	🍴			🛒	🍴Ø	🛒	🍴Ø	🛒			🍴	🍴		🛒			🍴
Rosslare Harbour ⛴	d																								
Fishguard Harbour 30 ⛴	a																								
	d		01 50														06 53								
Fishguard & Goodwick	d		01 53														06 56								
Milford Haven	d	00 18														06 00						07 05			
Johnston	d	00x26														06x08						07x13			
Haverfordwest	d	00 33														06 15						07 20			
Clarbeston Road	d	00x41	02x12													06x23	07a17					07x28			
Clunderwen	d	00x48														06x30						07x35			
Pembroke Dock	d																							06 59	
Pembroke	d																							07 07	
Lamphey	d																							07x10	
Manorbier	d																							07 18	
Penally	d																							07x24	
Tenby	a																							07 27	
	d																							07 29	
Saundersfoot	d																							07x35	
Kilgetty	d																							07x37	
Narberth	d																							07x47	
Whitland	a	00 54	02 24													06 36						07 41		07 55	
	d	00 54	02 24													06 36						07 41		07 56	
Carmarthen	a	01 16	02 41													06 52						07 55		08 15	
	d		02 44				05 04					05 55		06 20		06 57						08 01		08 18	
Ferryside	d											06x05		06x30								08x11		08x28	
Kidwelly	d											06x10		06x35								08x16		08x34	
Pembrey & Burry Port	d						05 22					06 17		06 42		07 15						08 23		08 41	
Llanelli	a		03 06				05 27					06 22		06 47		07 20						08 28		08 46	
	d		03 06				05 29					06 24		06 48		07 22						08 30		08 48	
Gowerton	d											06 30		06 55		07 28						08 36			
Swansea	a		03 29									06 43		07 08		07 41						08 49		09 07	
	d			03 58	04 58	05 28		05 58	06 28			06 47	06 58	07 11	07 28	07 45			07 58	08 28		08 55		09 10	09 28
Llansamlet	d													07 18										09 17	
Skewen	d													07 22										09 21	
Neath	d			04 10	05 10	05 40		06 10	06 40			06 58	07 10	07 26	07 40	07 56			08 10	08 40		09 06		09 25	09 40
Briton Ferry	d													07 29										09 29	
Baglan	d													07 33										09 32	
Port Talbot Parkway	d			04 18	05 18	05 48	06 02	06 18	06 48			07 05	07 18	07 37	07 48	08 03			08 18	08 48		09 13		09 36	09 48
Pyle	d						06 09					07 12		07 45		08 09						09 21		09 45	
Maesteg	d									06 46								08 00					09 17		
Maesteg (Ewenny Road)	d									06 48								08 02					09 19		
Garth (Mid Glamorgan)	d									06 51								08 05					09 22		
Tondu	d									07 00								08 14					09 31		
Sarn	d									07 03								08 17					09 34		
Wildmill	d									07 05								08 19					09 36		
Bridgend	d			04 30	05 31	06 01	06 17	06 31	07 01	07 09		07 20	07 31	07 53	08 01	08 17		08 23	08 31	09 01		09 28	09 40	09 53	10 01
Pencoed	d						06 23			07 15				08 07		08 23							09 46		
Llanharan	d						06 26					07 27		08 11				08 30					09 50		
Pontyclun	d						06 31			07 22				08 15		08 30							09 54		
Cardiff Central 7	a			04 52	05 52	06 22	06 43	06 52	07 22	07 36		07 42	07 52	08 34	08 22	08 42		08 47	08 52	09 22		09 48	10 09	10 17	10 22
Newport (South Wales)	a			05 09	06 09	06 38	07 02	07 08	07 39			08 02	08 08		08 38	09 02		09 24	09 08	09 39		10 07	10 25	10 35	10 39
Bristol Parkway 7	a			05 36	06 29	06 59		07 29	07 59				08 30		08 59				09 30	09 59					10 59
Gloucester 7	a																	10 19					11 21		
Manchester Piccadilly 10	a						10 14					11 15				12 15						13 15			
Reading 7	a			07 14	07 31	08 00		08 36	09 01				09 31		10 00				10 31	11 01					12 01
London Paddington 15 ⊖	a			07 53	08 14	08 43		09 15	09 42				10 13		10 43				11 12	11 43					12 43

A 🍴 from Reading Ø to Reading

When events are being held at the Millenium Stadium, services are subject to alteration. Please check times before travelling.

Ferry service between Fishguard Harbour and Rosslare Harbour is operated by Stena Line

Table 128R

Saturdays

West Wales, Swansea and Maesteg - Cardiff

4 January to 8 February

Route Diagram - see first Page of Table 127

		AW	AW	AW	GW	AW	AW	AW	AW	GW	AW	AW	AW	AW	GW	AW	AW	AW	AW	GW	AW	AW	GW
													R										
		◇	◇		◇1	◇				◇1		◇			◇1	◇		◇		◇1	◇		◇1
			🛒		🍴	🛒				🍴		🛒		🛒	🍴	🛒		🛒		🍴	🛒		🍴
Rosslare Harbour (ferry)	d												09 00										
Fishguard Harbour 30 (ferry)	a												12 30										
	d		08 04								09 53												
Fishguard & Goodwick	d		08 07								09 56												
Milford Haven	d					09 08										11 08							
Johnston	d					09x16										11x16							
Haverfordwest	d					09 23										11 23							
Clarbeston Road	d		08x25			09x31					10x14					11x31							
Clunderwen	d		08x33			09x38					10x22					11x38							
Pembroke Dock	d								09 09										11 09				
Pembroke	d								09 17										11 17				
Lamphey	d								09x20										11x20				
Manorbier	d								09 29										11 29				
Penally	d								09x34										11x34				
Tenby	a								09 37										11 37				
	d								09 37										11 41				
Saundersfoot	d								09x45										11x49				
Kilgetty	d								09x47										11x51				
Narberth	d								09x57										12x01				
Whitland	a		08 37			09 44			10 05		10 28					11 44			12 09				
	d		08 38			09 44			10 05		10 29					11 44			12 09				
Carmarthen	a		08 57			10 02			10 23		10 46					12 00			12 27				
	d		09 00		09 35	10 04			10 27			11 09				12 05			12 31		13 02		
Ferryside	d		09x10									11x19									13x12		
Kidwelly	d		09x15									11x24									13x17		
Pembrey & Burry Port	d		09 21		09 56	10 24			10 47			11 30				12 23			12 50		13 23		
Llanelli	a		09 27		10 01	10 29			10 53			11 36				12 28			12 56		13 29		
	d	08 55	09 28		10 03	10 31			10 53			11 37				12 30		12 37	12 57		13 30		
Gowerton	d	09 04	09 35						11 01			11 44				12 36					13 37		
Swansea	a	09 18	09 47		10 21	10 48			11 23			11 56				12 49		13 00	13 23		13 49		
	d	09 34	09 55		10 28	10 55		11 10		11 28		12 00			12 28	12 53		13 10		13 28	14 00		14 28
Llansamlet	d							11 17										13 17					
Skewen	d							11 21										13 21					
Neath	d	09 45	10 06		10 40	11 06		11 25		11 40		12 11			12 40	13 04		13 25		13 40	14 11		14 40
Briton Ferry	d							11 28										13 28					
Baglan	d							11 32										13 32					
Port Talbot Parkway	d	09 52	10 13		10 48	11 13		11 36		11 48		12 18			12 48	13 11		13 36		13 48	14 18		14 48
Pyle	d	10 05	10 20			11 21		11 44								13 19		13 44					
Maesteg	d			10 15			11 15							12 17			13 15					14 15	
Maesteg (Ewenny Road)	d			10 17			11 17							12 19			13 17					14 17	
Garth (Mid Glamorgan)	d			10 20			11 20							12 22			13 20					14 20	
Tondu	d			10 29			11 29							12 31			13 29					14 29	
Sarn	d			10 32			11 32							12 34			13 32					14 32	
Wildmill	d			10 34			11 34							12 36			13 34					14 34	
Bridgend	d	10 14	10 28	10 38	11 01	11 28	11 38	11 56		12 01		12 31		12 40	13 01	13 26	13 38	13 53		14 01	14 31	14 38	15 01
Pencoed	d			10 44			11 44							12 46			13 44					14 44	
Llanharan	d			10 48			11 48							12 50			13 48					14 48	
Pontyclun	d			10 52			11 52							12 54			13 52					14 52	
Cardiff Central 7	a	10 44	10 48	11 13	11 22	11 48	12 07	12 18		12 22		12 52		13 09	13 22	13 48	14 09	14 15		14 22	14 52	15 07	15 22
Newport (South Wales)	a		11 07		11 39	12 07	12 25			12 39		13 07		13 26	13 38	14 07		14 34		14 39	15 07	15 25	15 39
Bristol Parkway 7	a				11 59					12 59					13 59					14 59			15 59
Gloucester 7	a						13 21							14 19								16 19	
Manchester Piccadilly 10	a		14 15			15 15						16 15				17 14					18 15		
Reading 7	a				13 01					14 00					15 02					16 00			17 00
London Paddington 15 ⊖	a				13 42					14 42					15 42					16 43			17 42

When events are being held at the Millenium Stadium, services are subject to alteration. Please check times before travelling.

Ferry service between Fishguard Harbour and Rosslare Harbour is operated by Stena Line

Table 128R

Saturdays

4 January to 8 February

West Wales, Swansea and Maesteg - Cardiff

Route Diagram - see first Page of Table 127

		AW		AW	AW	AW	AW	GW	AW	AW	GW	AW		AW	AW	AW	GW	AW	AW	AW	GW	AW		AW	AW
		■		■					■			■													
								◇1			◇1						◇1	◇	◇		◇1	◇			◇
		🛒		🛒				🍽	🛒		🍽	🛒					🍽	🛒			🍽				
Rosslare Harbour ⛴	d																								
Fishguard Harbour 30 ⛴	a																								
	d			13 29																				19 00	
Fishguard & Goodwick	d			13 32																				19 03	
Milford Haven	d	13 08										15 08										17 08			
Johnston	d	13x16										15x16										17x16			
Haverfordwest	d	13 23										15 23										17 23			
Clarbeston Road	d	13x31										15x31										17x31		19a22	
Clunderwen	d	13x38										15x38										17x38			
Pembroke Dock	d						13 09									15 09									
Pembroke	d						13 17									15 17									
Lamphey	d						13x20									15x20									
Manorbier	d						13 29									15 29									
Penally	d						13x34									15x34									
Tenby	a						13 37									15 37									
	d						13 42									15 40									
Saundersfoot	d						13x50									15x48									
Kilgetty	d						13x52									15x50									
Narberth	d						14x02									16x00									
Whitland	a	13 44		14 04			14 10					15 44				16 08						17 44			
	d	13 44		14 04			14 11					15 44				16 09						17 45			
Carmarthen	a	14 00		14 20			14 28					16 00				16 26						18 03			
	d	14 05		14 24			14 33		15 03			16 05				16 31		17 03				18 07			
Ferryside	d								15x13									17x13				18x17			
Kidwelly	d								15x18									17x18				18x23			
Pembrey & Burry Port	d	14 23					14 52		15 25			16 23				16 50		17 24				18 30			
Llanelli	a	14 28		14 47			14 58		15 30			16 28				16 56		17 30				18 35			
	d	14 30		14 47			14 58		15 32			16 30			16 47	16 57		17 31	17 41			18 36			
Gowerton	d	14 36							15 38			16 36				17 04		17 38	17 48			18 44			
Swansea	a	14 49					15 22		15 51			16 49			17 04	17 22		17 50	18 10			18 56			
	d	14 55				15 10		15 28	15 55		16 28	16 58			17 10		17 28	17 54			18 28	19 00			
Llansamlet	d					15 17									17 17										
Skewen	d					15 21									17 21										
Neath	d	15 06				15 25		15 40	16 06		16 40	17 09			17 25		17 40	18 05			18 40	19 11			
Briton Ferry	d					15 28									17 28										
Baglan	d					15 32									17 32										
Port Talbot Parkway	d	15 13				15 36		15 48	16 13		16 48	17 16			17 36		17 48	18 12			18 48	19 19			
Pyle	d					15 44			16 21			17 24			17 44										
Maesteg	d				15 17					16 15				17 15						18 20					19 15
Maesteg (Ewenny Road)	d				15 19					16 17				17 17						18 22					19 17
Garth (Mid Glamorgan)	d				15 22					16 20				17 20						18 25					19 20
Tondu	d				15 31					16 29				17 29						18 34					19 29
Sarn	d				15 34					16 32				17 32						18 37					19 32
Wildmill	d				15 36					16 34				17 34						18 39					19 34
Bridgend	d	15 26		15 31	15 40	15 53		16 01	16 28	16 38	17 01	17 31		17 38	17 55		18 01	18 25		18 43	19 01	19 33			19 38
Pencoed	d				15 46					16 44				17 44						18 49					19 44
Llanharan	d				15 50					16 48				17 48						18 53					19 47
Pontyclun	d				15 54					16 52				17 52						18 57					19 52
Cardiff Central 7	a	15 51		15 58	16 09	16 16		16 22	16 48	17 07	17 22	17 51		18 07	18 20		18 22	18 45		19 13	19 22	19 56			20 05
Newport (South Wales)	a	16 07			16 23	16 32		16 39	17 07	17 27	17 39	18 07		18 25			18 39	19 03			19 39				20 24
Bristol Parkway 7	a							16 59			17 59						18 59				19 59				
Gloucester 7	a				17 19					18 20				19 20											
Manchester Piccadilly 10	a	19 15							20 15			21 16						22 13							23 49
Reading 7	a							17 58			19 00						20 00				21 06				
London Paddington 15 ⊖	a							18 42			19 41						20 40				21 51				

When events are being held at the Millenium Stadium, services are subject to alteration. Please check times before travelling.

Ferry service between Fishguard Harbour and Rosslare Harbour is operated by Stena Line

Table 128R

Saturdays

4 January to 8 February

West Wales, Swansea and Maesteg - Cardiff

Route Diagram - see first Page of Table 127

		AW	AW	GW	AW	AW	AW	AW		AW	AW	AW	AW	AW	AW	AW	AW	AW		AW
				◇1 ⊡	◇		◇			◇		R		◇						
Rosslare Harbour	d											21 00								
Fishguard Harbour 30	a											00 30								
	d										21 00									
Fishguard & Goodwick	d										21 03									
Milford Haven	d						19 08						21 16							23 18
Johnston	d						19x16						21x24							23x26
Haverfordwest	d						19 23						21 31							23 33
Clarbeston Road	d						19x31				21x22		21x39							23x41
Clunderwen	d						19x38				21x29		21x46							23x48
Pembroke Dock	d		17 12							19 09							21 09	22 18		
Pembroke	d		17 20							19 17							21 17	22 26		
Lamphey	d		17x23							19x21							21x20	22x29		
Manorbier	d		17 32							19 29							21 29	22 37		
Penally	d		17x37							19x34							21x34	22x43		
Tenby	a		17 40							19 37							21 37	22 45		
	d		17 46							19 49							21 42	22 45		
Saundersfoot	d		17x54							19x57							21x50	22x53		
Kilgetty	d		17x56							19x59							21x52	22x55		
Narberth	d		18x06							20x09							22x02	23x04		
Whitland	a		18 14				19 44			20 17	21 36		21 52				22 10	23 12		23 54
	d		18 15				19 44			20 19	21 36		21 52				22 11	23 15		23 54
Carmarthen	a		18 32				20 04			20 37	21 57		22 14				22 28	23 34		00 16
	d		18 37		18 51		20 07			20 47							22 35			
Ferryside	d				19x01					20x58							22x45			
Kidwelly	d				19x07					21x04							22x51			
Pembrey & Burry Port	d		18 56		19 15		20 25			21 11							22 58			
Llanelli	a		19 02		19 21		20 30			21 17							23 04			
	d		19 02		19 22		20 31			21 17				21 40			23 05			
Gowerton	d		19 11		19 30		20 38			21 26				21 47			23 12			
Swansea	a		19 25		19 44		20 51			21 42				22 10			23 30			
	d	19 10		19 28	19 52		20 55			21 43						22 20				
Llansamlet	d	19 17								21 50						22 27				
Skewen	d	19 21								21 54						22 31				
Neath	d	19 25		19 40	20 03		21 06			21 59						22 35				
Briton Ferry	d	19 28								22 02						22 38				
Baglan	d	19 32								22 06						22 42				
Port Talbot Parkway	d	19 36		19 48	20 10		21 13			22 10						22 46				
Pyle	d	19 44								22 18						22 54				
Maesteg	d					20 15		21 15							22 15					
Maesteg (Ewenny Road)	d					20 17		21 17							22 17					
Garth (Mid Glamorgan)	d					20 20		21 20							22 20					
Tondu	d					20 29		21 29							22 29					
Sarn	d					20 32		21 32							22 32					
Wildmill	d					20 34		21 34							22 34					
Bridgend	d	19 52		20 01	20 24	20 38	21 26	21 38		22 26					22 38	23 02				
Pencoed	d					20 44		21 44							22 44					
Llanharan	d					20 48		21 48							22 48					
Pontyclun	d					20 52		21 52							22 52					
Cardiff Central 7	a	20 17		20 23	20 47	21 07	21 46	22 09		22 50					23 08	23 26				
Newport (South Wales)	a			20 39		21 25	22 10								23 37					
Bristol Parkway 7	a			21 01																
Gloucester 7	a					22 22									00 38					
Manchester Piccadilly 10	a																			
Reading 7	a			22 02																
London Paddington 15 ⊖	a			22 45																

When events are being held at the Millenium Stadium, services are subject to alteration. Please check times before travelling.

Ferry service between Fishguard Harbour and Rosslare Harbour is operated by Stena Line

Table 128R

Saturdays

15 February to 17 May

West Wales, Swansea and Maesteg - Cardiff

Route Diagram - see first Page of Table 127

		AW	AW	GW	GW	GW	AW	GW	GW	AW		AW	GW	AW	GW	AW	AW	AW	GW	GW		AW	AW	AW	GW
			◇	◇1	◇1	◇1	◇	◇1	◇1			◇	◇1	◇	◇1	◇			◇1	◇1		◇			◇1
													A		A										
				☕	☕	☕	🛒	☕	☕			🛒	☕⊘	🛒	☕⊘	🛒			☕	☕		🛒			☕
Rosslare Harbour ⛴	d																								
Fishguard Harbour 30 ⛴	a																								
	d		01 50														06 53								
Fishguard & Goodwick	d		01 53														06 56								
Milford Haven	d	00 18														06 00						07 05			
Johnston	d	00x26														06x08						07x13			
Haverfordwest	d	00 33														06 15						07 20			
Clarbeston Road	d	00x41	02x12													06x23	07a17					07x28			
Clunderwen	d	00x48														06x30						07x35			
Pembroke Dock	d																							06 59	
Pembroke	d																							07 07	
Lamphey	d																							07x10	
Manorbier	d																							07 18	
Penally	d																							07x24	
Tenby	a																							07 27	
	d																							07 29	
Saundersfoot	d																							07x35	
Kilgetty	d																							07x37	
Narberth	d																							07x47	
Whitland	a	00 54	02 24													06 36						07 41		07 55	
	d	00 54	02 24													06 36						07 41		07 56	
Carmarthen	a	01 16	02 41													06 52						07 55		08 15	
	d		02 44				05 04					05 55		06 20		06 57						08 01		08 18	
Ferryside	d											06x05		06x30								08x11		08x28	
Kidwelly	d											06x10		06x35								08x16		08x34	
Pembrey & Burry Port	d						05 22					06 17		06 42		07 15						08 23		08 41	
Llanelli	a		03 06				05 27					06 22		06 47		07 20						08 28		08 46	
	d		03 06				05 29					06 24		06 48		07 22						08 30		08 48	
Gowerton	d											06 30		06 55		07 28						08 36			
Swansea	a		03 29									06 43		07 08		07 41						08 49		09 07	
	d			03 58	04 58	05 28		05 58	06 28			06 47	06 58	07 11	07 28	07 45			07 58	08 28		08 55		09 10	09 28
Llansamlet	d													07 18										09 17	
Skewen	d													07 22										09 21	
Neath	d			04 10	05 10	05 40		06 10	06 40			06 58	07 10	07 26	07 40	07 56			08 10	08 40		09 06		09 25	09 40
Briton Ferry	d													07 29										09 29	
Baglan	d													07 33										09 32	
Port Talbot Parkway	d			04 18	05 18	05 48	06 02	06 18	06 48			07 05	07 18	07 37	07 48	08 03			08 18	08 48		09 13		09 36	09 48
Pyle	d						06 09					07 12		07 45		08 09						09 21		09 45	
Maesteg	d									06 46								08 00					09 17		
Maesteg (Ewenny Road)	d									06 48								08 02					09 19		
Garth (Mid Glamorgan)	d									06 51								08 05					09 22		
Tondu	d									07 00								08 14					09 31		
Sarn	d									07 03								08 17					09 34		
Wildmill	d									07 05								08 19					09 36		
Bridgend	d			04 30	05 31	06 01	06 17	06 31	07 01	07 09		07 20	07 31	07 53	08 01	08 17		08 23	08 31	09 01		09 28	09 40	09 53	10 01
Pencoed	d						06 23			07 15				08 07		08 23							09 46		
Llanharan	d						06 26					07 27		08 11				08 30					09 50		
Pontyclun	d						06 31			07 22				08 15		08 30							09 54		
Cardiff Central 7	a			04 52	05 52	06 22	06 43	06 52	07 22	07 36		07 42	07 52	08 34	08 22	08 42		08 47	08 52	09 22		09 48	10 09	10 17	10 22
Newport (South Wales)	a			05 09	06 09	06 38	07 02	07 08	07 39			08 02	08 08		08 38	09 02		09 24	09 08	09 39		10 07	10 25	10 35	10 39
Bristol Parkway 7	a			05 36	06 29	06 59		07 29	07 59				08 30		08 59				09 30	09 59					10 59
Gloucester 7	a																	10 19					11 21		
Manchester Piccadilly 10	a						10 14					11 15				12 15						13 15			
Reading 7	a			07 14	07 31	08 00		08 33	09 01				09 31		10 00				10 30	11 01					12 01
London Paddington 15 ⊖	a			07 44	08 07	08 32		09 02	09 38				10 02		10 32				11 04	11 33					12 37

A ☕ from Reading ⊘ to Reading

When events are being held at the Millenium Stadium, services are subject to alteration. Please check times before travelling.

Ferry service between Fishguard Harbour and Rosslare Harbour is operated by Stena Line

Table 128R

Saturdays

15 February to 17 May

West Wales, Swansea and Maesteg - Cardiff

Route Diagram - see first Page of Table 127

Station		AW	AW	AW	GW	AW		AW	AW	AW	GW	AW	AW
		◇	◇ 🚲		◇[1] ☕	◇ 🚲					◇[1] ☕		◇ 🚲
Rosslare Harbour ⛴🚌	d												
Fishguard Harbour [30] ⛴	a												
	d		08 04									09 53	
Fishguard & Goodwick	d		08 07									09 56	
Milford Haven	d					09 08							
Johnston	d					09x16							
Haverfordwest	d					09 23							
Clarbeston Road	d		08x25			09x31						10x14	
Clunderwen	d		08x33			09x38						10x22	
Pembroke Dock	d									09 09			
Pembroke	d									09 17			
Lamphey	d									09x20			
Manorbier	d									09 29			
Penally	d									09x34			
Tenby	a									09 37			
	d									09 37			
Saundersfoot	d									09x45			
Kilgetty	d									09x47			
Narberth	d									09x57			
Whitland	a		08 37			09 44				10 05		10 28	
	d		08 38			09 44				10 05		10 29	
Carmarthen	a		08 57			10 02				10 23		10 46	
	d		09 00		09 35	10 04				10 27			11 09
Ferryside	d		09x10										11x19
Kidwelly	d		09x15										11x24
Pembrey & Burry Port	d		09 21		09 56	10 24				10 47			11 30
Llanelli	a		09 27		10 01	10 29				10 53			11 36
	d	08 55	09 28		10 03	10 31				10 53			11 37
Gowerton	d	09 04	09 35							11 01			11 44
Swansea	a	09 18	09 47		10 21	10 48				11 23			11 56
	d	09 34	09 55		10 28	10 55			11 10		11 28		12 00
Llansamlet	d								11 17				
Skewen	d								11 21				
Neath	d	09 45	10 06		10 40	11 06			11 25		11 40		12 11
Briton Ferry	d								11 28				
Baglan	d								11 32				
Port Talbot Parkway	d	09 52	10 13		10 48	11 13			11 36		11 48		12 18
Pyle	d	10 05	10 20			11 21			11 44				
Maesteg	d			10 15				11 15					
Maesteg (Ewenny Road)	d			10 17				11 17					
Garth (Mid Glamorgan)	d			10 20				11 20					
Tondu	d			10 29				11 29					
Sarn	d			10 32				11 32					
Wildmill	d			10 34				11 34					
Bridgend	d	10 14	10 28	10 38	11 01	11 28		11 38	11 56		12 01		12 31
Pencoed	d			10 44				11 44					
Llanharan	d			10 48				11 48					
Pontyclun	d			10 52				11 52					
Cardiff Central [7]	a	10 44	10 48	11 13	11 22	11 48		12 07	12 18		12 22		12 52
Newport (South Wales)	a		11 07		11 39	12 07		12 25			12 39		13 07
Bristol Parkway [7]	a				11 59						12 59		
Gloucester [7]	a							13 21					
Manchester Piccadilly [10]	a		14 15			15 15							16 15
Reading [7]	a				13 01						14 00		
London Paddington [15] ⊖	a				13 38						14 32		

Station		AW	AW	GW		AW	AW	AW	AW	GW	AW	AW	GW
		R	🚲	◇[1] ☕		◇ 🚲		◇ 🚲		◇[1] ☕	◇ 🚲		◇[1] ☕
Rosslare Harbour ⛴🚌	d	09 00											
Fishguard Harbour [30] ⛴	a	12 30											
	d												
Fishguard & Goodwick	d												
Milford Haven	d					11 08							
Johnston	d					11x16							
Haverfordwest	d					11 23							
Clarbeston Road	d					11x31							
Clunderwen	d					11x38							
Pembroke Dock	d								11 09				
Pembroke	d								11 17				
Lamphey	d								11x20				
Manorbier	d								11 29				
Penally	d								11x34				
Tenby	a								11 37				
	d								11 41				
Saundersfoot	d								11x49				
Kilgetty	d								11x51				
Narberth	d								12x01				
Whitland	a					11 44			12 09				
	d					11 44			12 09				
Carmarthen	a					12 00			12 27				
	d					12 05			12 31		13 02		
Ferryside	d										13x12		
Kidwelly	d										13x17		
Pembrey & Burry Port	d					12 23			12 50		13 23		
Llanelli	a					12 28			12 56		13 29		
	d					12 30		12 37	12 57		13 30		
Gowerton	d					12 36					13 37		
Swansea	a					12 49		13 00	13 23		13 49		
	d			12 28		12 53		13 10		13 28	14 00		14 28
Llansamlet	d							13 17					
Skewen	d							13 21					
Neath	d			12 40		13 04		13 25		13 40	14 11		14 40
Briton Ferry	d							13 28					
Baglan	d							13 32					
Port Talbot Parkway	d			12 48		13 11		13 36		13 48	14 18		14 48
Pyle	d					13 19		13 44					
Maesteg	d		12 17				13 15					14 15	
Maesteg (Ewenny Road)	d		12 19				13 17					14 17	
Garth (Mid Glamorgan)	d		12 22				13 20					14 20	
Tondu	d		12 31				13 29					14 29	
Sarn	d		12 34				13 32					14 32	
Wildmill	d		12 36				13 34					14 34	
Bridgend	d		12 40	13 01		13 26	13 38	13 53		14 01	14 31	14 38	15 01
Pencoed	d		12 46				13 44					14 44	
Llanharan	d		12 50				13 48					14 48	
Pontyclun	d		12 54				13 52					14 52	
Cardiff Central [7]	a		13 09	13 22		13 48	14 09	14 15		14 22	14 52	15 07	15 22
Newport (South Wales)	a		13 26	13 38		14 07		14 34		14 39	15 07	15 25	15 39
Bristol Parkway [7]	a			13 59						14 59			15 59
Gloucester [7]	a		14 19									16 19	
Manchester Piccadilly [10]	a					17 14					18 15		
Reading [7]	a			15 02						16 00			17 00
London Paddington [15] ⊖	a			15 37						16 33			17 32

When events are being held at the Millenium Stadium, services are subject to alteration. Please check times before travelling.

Ferry service between Fishguard Harbour and Rosslare Harbour is operated by Stena Line

Table 128R

Saturdays

15 February to 17 May

West Wales, Swansea and Maesteg - Cardiff

Route Diagram - see first Page of Table 127

		AW	AW	AW	AW	AW	GW	AW	AW	GW	AW	AW	AW	AW	GW	AW	AW	AW	GW	AW	AW	AW
		■	■					■			■											
							◇1			◇1					◇1	◇	◇		◇1	◇		◇ A
		⊥	⊥				⊡	⊥		⊡	⊥				⊡	⊥			⊡			
Rosslare Harbour ⛴	d																					
Fishguard Harbour 30 ⛴	a																					
	d		13 29																		19 00	
Fishguard & Goodwick	d		13 32																		19 03	
Milford Haven	d	13 08									15 08									17 08		
Johnston	d	13x16									15x16									17x16		
Haverfordwest	d	13 23									15 23									17 23		
Clarbeston Road	d	13x31									15x31									17x31	19a22	
Clunderwen	d	13x38									15x38									17x38		
Pembroke Dock	d					13 09								15 09								
Pembroke	d					13 17								15 17								
Lamphey	d					13x20								15x20								
Manorbier	d					13 29								15 29								
Penally	d					13x34								15x34								
Tenby	a					13 37								15 37								
	d					13 42								15 40								
Saundersfoot	d					13x50								15x48								
Kilgetty	d					13x52								15x50								
Narberth	d					14x02								16x00								
Whitland	a	13 44	14 04			14 10					15 44			16 08						17 44		
	d	13 44	14 04			14 11					15 44			16 09						17 45		
Carmarthen	a	14 00	14 20			14 28					16 00			16 26						18 03		
	d	14 05	14 24			14 33		15 03			16 05			16 31		17 03				18 07		
Ferryside	d							15x13								17x13				18x17		
Kidwelly	d							15x18								17x18				18x23		
Pembrey & Burry Port	d	14 23				14 52		15 25			16 23			16 50		17 24				18 30		
Llanelli	a	14 28	14 47			14 58		15 30			16 28			16 56		17 30				18 35		
	d	14 30	14 47			14 58		15 32			16 30		16 47	16 57		17 31	17 41			18 36		
Gowerton	d	14 36						15 38			16 36			17 04		17 38	17 48			18 44		
Swansea	a	14 49				15 22		15 51			16 49		17 04	17 22		17 50	18 10			18 56		
	d	14 55			15 10		15 28	15 55		16 28	16 58		17 10		17 28	17 54			18 28	19 00		
Llansamlet	d				15 17								17 17									
Skewen	d				15 21								17 21									
Neath	d	15 06			15 25		15 40	16 06		16 40	17 09		17 25		17 40	18 05			18 40	19 11		
Briton Ferry	d				15 28								17 28									
Baglan	d				15 32								17 32									
Port Talbot Parkway	d	15 13			15 36		15 48	16 13		16 48	17 16		17 36		17 48	18 12			18 48	19 19		
Pyle	d				15 44			16 21			17 24		17 44									
Maesteg	d			15 17					16 15			17 15						18 20				19 15
Maesteg (Ewenny Road)	d			15 19					16 17			17 17						18 22				19 17
Garth (Mid Glamorgan)	d			15 22					16 20			17 20						18 25				19 20
Tondu	d			15 31					16 29			17 29						18 34				19 29
Sarn	d			15 34					16 32			17 32						18 37				19 32
Wildmill	d			15 36					16 34			17 34						18 39				19 34
Bridgend	d	15 26	15 31	15 40	15 53		16 01	16 28	16 38	17 01	17 31	17 38	17 55		18 01	18 25		18 43	19 01	19 33		19 38
Pencoed	d			15 46					16 44			17 44						18 49				19 44
Llanharan	d			15 50					16 48			17 48						18 53				19 47
Pontyclun	d			15 54					16 52			17 52						18 57				19 52
Cardiff Central 7	a	15 51	15 58	16 09	16 16		16 22	16 48	17 07	17 22	17 51	18 07	18 20		18 22	18 45		19 13	19 22	19 56		20 05
Newport (South Wales)	a	16 07		16 23	16 32		16 39	17 07	17 27	17 39	18 07	18 25			18 39	19 03			19 39			20 24
Bristol Parkway 7	a						16 59			17 59					18 59				19 59			
Gloucester 7	a			17 19					18 20			19 20										
Manchester Piccadilly 10	a	19 15						20 15			21 16					22 13						
Reading 7	a						17 58			19 00					20 00				21 06			
London Paddington 15 ⊖	a						18 32			19 32					20 32				21 37			

A until 22 March

When events are being held at the Millenium Stadium, services are subject to alteration. Please check times before travelling.

Ferry service between Fishguard Harbour and Rosslare Harbour is operated by Stena Line

Table 128R

Saturdays

15 February to 17 May

West Wales, Swansea and Maesteg - Cardiff

Route Diagram - see first Page of Table 127

		AW	AW	AW	GW	AW	AW	AW	AW	AW	AW	AW	AW	AW	AW	AW	AW	AW	AW
												□							
		◇			◇1	◇		◇		◇				◇					
		A																	
					☕														
Rosslare Harbour	d											21 00							
Fishguard Harbour 30	a											00 30							
	d										21 00								
Fishguard & Goodwick	d										21 03								
Milford Haven	d							19 08					21 16						23 18
Johnston	d							19x16					21x24						23x26
Haverfordwest	d							19 23					21 31						23 33
Clarbeston Road	d							19x31			21x22		21x39						23x41
Clunderwen	d							19x38			21x29		21x46						23x48
Pembroke Dock	d			17 12						19 09							21 09	22 18	
Pembroke	d			17 20						19 17							21 17	22 26	
Lamphey	d			17x23						19x21							21x20	22x29	
Manorbier	d			17 32						19 29							21 29	22 37	
Penally	d			17x37						19x34							21x34	22x43	
Tenby	a			17 40						19 37							21 37	22 45	
	d			17 46						19 49							21 42	22 45	
Saundersfoot	d			17x54						19x57							21x50	22x53	
Kilgetty	d			17x56						19x59							21x52	22x55	
Narberth	d			18x06						20x09							22x02	23x04	
Whitland	a			18 14				19 44		20 17	21 36		21 52				22 10	23 12	23 54
	d			18 15				19 44		20 19	21 36		21 52				22 11	23 15	23 54
Carmarthen	a			18 32				20 04		20 37	21 57		22 14				22 28	23 34	00 16
	d			18 37		18 51		20 07		20 47							22 35		
Ferryside	d					19x01				20x58							22x45		
Kidwelly	d					19x07				21x04							22x51		
Pembrey & Burry Port	d			18 56		19 15		20 25		21 11							22 58		
Llanelli	a			19 02		19 21		20 30		21 17							23 04		
	d			19 02		19 22		20 31		21 17				21 40			23 05		
Gowerton	d			19 11		19 30		20 38		21 26				21 47			23 12		
Swansea	a			19 25		19 44		20 51		21 42				22 10			23 30		
	d		19 10		19 28	19 52		20 55		21 43						22 20			
Llansamlet	d		19 17							21 50						22 27			
Skewen	d		19 21							21 54						22 31			
Neath	d		19 25		19 40	20 03		21 06		21 59						22 35			
Briton Ferry	d		19 28							22 02						22 38			
Baglan	d		19 32							22 06						22 42			
Port Talbot Parkway	d		19 36		19 48	20 10		21 13		22 10						22 46			
Pyle	d		19 44							22 18						22 54			
Maesteg	d	19 15					20 15		21 15						22 15				
Maesteg (Ewenny Road)	d	19 17					20 17		21 17						22 17				
Garth (Mid Glamorgan)	d	19 20					20 20		21 20						22 20				
Tondu	d	19 29					20 29		21 29						22 29				
Sarn	d	19 32					20 32		21 32						22 32				
Wildmill	d	19 34					20 34		21 34						22 34				
Bridgend	d	19 38	19 52		20 01	20 24	20 38	21 26	21 38	22 26					22 38	23 02			
Pencoed	d	19 44					20 44		21 44						22 44				
Llanharan	d	19 47					20 48		21 48						22 48				
Pontyclun	d	19 52					20 52		21 52						22 52				
Cardiff Central 7	a	20 05	20 17		20 23	20 47	21 07	21 46	22 09	22 50					23 08	23 26			
Newport (South Wales)	a	20 24			20 39		21 25	22 10							23 37				
Bristol Parkway 7	a				21 01														
Gloucester 7	a						22 22								00 38				
Manchester Piccadilly 10	a	23 49																	
Reading 7	a				22 02														
London Paddington 15 ⊖	a				22 40														

A from 29 March

When events are being held at the Millenium Stadium, services are subject to alteration. Please check times before travelling.

Ferry service between Fishguard Harbour and Rosslare Harbour is operated by Stena Line

Table 128R

Sundays

8 December to 29 December

West Wales, Swansea and Maesteg - Cardiff

Route Diagram - see first Page of Table 127

		AW	AW	GW	AW	GW	GW	AW	GW	AW	AW	GW	GW	AW	AW	GW	GW	AW	AW	GW	AW	GW	AW
		◇	🚌	◇1 ☕	R	◇1 ☕	◇1 ☕		R 1 ☕	◇ 🛒		R 1 ☕	R 1 ☕	R 🛒		R 1 ☕	R 1 ☕	R 🛒	◇	◇1 ☕	🛒	R 1 ☕	R 🛒
Rosslare Harbour ⛴🚌	d				09 00																		
Fishguard Harbour 30 ⛴	a				12 30																		
	d	01 48																			14 23		
Fishguard & Goodwick	d	01 51																			14 26		
Milford Haven	d													11 28				13 25					15 28
Johnston	d													11x36				13x31					15x36
Haverfordwest	d													11 43				13 38					15 43
Clarbeston Road	d													11x52				13x47					15x52
Clunderwen	d													11x59				13x54					15x59
Pembroke Dock	d														11 57								
Pembroke	d														12 05								
Lamphey	d														12x08								
Manorbier	d														12 17								
Penally	d														12x22								
Tenby	a														12 25								
	d														12 25								
Saundersfoot	d														12x33								
Kilgetty	d														12x35								
Narberth	d														12x45								
Whitland	a	02s22												12 06	12 53			14 01			14 57		16 06
	d													12 08	12 57			14 04			14 58		16 09
Carmarthen	a	02 40												12 26	13 14			14 22			15 15		16 26
	d	02 43	02 50					09 40		10 30	11 07			12 29	13 17			14 39		15 27	15 38		16 31
Ferryside	d							09x50			11x17				13x27						15x49		16x41
Kidwelly	d							09x56			11x23				13x33						15x55		16x47
Pembrey & Burry Port	d							10 03		10 49	11 31			12 49	13 40			14 58		15 47	16 02		16 55
Llanelli	a	03s06						10 09		10 54	11 37			12 55	13 46			15 04		15 56	16 08		17 01
	d							10 10		10 56	11 37			12 55	13 47			15 05	15 41	15 59	16 08		17 01
Gowerton	d							10 17			11 45			13 04	13 54			15 13	15 49		16 16		17 10
Swansea	a		03 50					10 35		11 15	12 01			13 18	14 12			15 27	16 07	16 14	16 34		17 23
	d			08 07		09 21	10 21		11 21	11 32		12 21	13 21	13 43		14 21	15 21	15 34		16 21		16 51	17 30
Llansamlet	d																						
Skewen	d																						
Neath	d			08 19		09 33	10 33		11 33	11 43		12 33	13 33	13 54		14 33	15 33	15 45		16 33		17 03	17 41
Briton Ferry	d																						
Baglan	d																						
Port Talbot Parkway	d			08 26		09 40	10 40		11 40	11 50		12 40	13 40	14 01		14 40	15 40	15 52		16 40		17 10	17 48
Pyle	d									11 59				14 10				16 00					17 56
Maesteg	d																						
Maesteg (Ewenny Road)	d																						
Garth (Mid Glamorgan)	d																						
Tondu	d																						
Sarn	d																						
Wildmill	d																						
Bridgend	d			08 39		09 53	10 53		11 53	12 06		12 53	13 53	14 18		14 53	15 53	16 08		16 53		17 23	18 04
Pencoed	d									12 12								16 14					18 10
Llanharan	d									12 16								16 18					18 14
Pontyclun	d									12 21								16 23					18 19
Cardiff Central 7	a	04 10		09 00		10 14	11 14		12 14	12 35		13 14	14 14	14 40		15 14	16 14	16 37		17 15		17 45	18 32
Newport (South Wales)	a			09 18		10 31	11 31		12 31	12 52		13 31	14 31	15 05		15 31	16 31	16 53		17 31		18 03	18 52
Bristol Parkway 7	a			09 46		10 59	11 59		12 59			13 59	14 59			15 59	16 59			17 59		18 31	
Gloucester 7	a																						
Manchester Piccadilly 10	a									16 15				18 17				20 17					22 19
Reading 7	a			10 42		12 02	13 02		14 02			15 02	16 02			17 02	18 02			19 02		19 33	
London Paddington 15 ⊖	a			11 22		12 42	13 42		14 42			15 42	16 42			17 43	18 44			19 44		20 13	

When events are being held at the Millenium Stadium, services are subject to alteration. Please check times before travelling.

Ferry service between Fishguard Harbour and Rosslare Harbour is operated by Stena Line

Table 128R

Sundays

West Wales, Swansea and Maesteg - Cardiff

8 December to 29 December

Route Diagram - see first Page of Table 127

		GW	GW	AW	AW	GW	AW	AW	AW	AW	AW	AW	AW	AW
											R			
		◇1	◇1			◇1	◇			◇		◇		
Rosslare Harbour	d										21 00			
Fishguard Harbour 30	a										00 30			
	d													
Fishguard & Goodwick	d													
Milford Haven	d				17 30				19 38			21 35		23 15
Johnston	d				17x38				19x46			21x43		23x23
Haverfordwest	d				17 45				19 53			21 51		23 30
Clarbeston Road	d				17x53				20x01			21x59		23x39
Clunderwen	d				18x00				20x08			22x07		23x46
Pembroke Dock	d			16 45				19 00					21 45	
Pembroke	d			16 53				19 08					21 53	
Lamphey	d			16x56				19x11					21x56	
Manorbier	d			17 05				19 20					22 05	
Penally	d			17x10				19x25					22x10	
Tenby	a			17 13				19 28					22 13	
	d			17 13				19 28					22 13	
Saundersfoot	d			17x21				19x36					22x21	
Kilgetty	d			17x23				19x38					22x23	
Narberth	d			17x33				19x48					22x33	
Whitland	a			17 41	18 06			19 56	20 14			22 13	22 41	23 53
	d			17 44	18 08			19 59	20 17			22 14	22 44	23 53
Carmarthen	a			18 02	18 29			20 16	20 36			22 31	23 05	00 14
	d	16 55		18 07		19 05		20 19		21 00		22 34		
Ferryside	d			18x17				20x30				22x44		
Kidwelly	d			18x23				20x36				22x50		
Pembrey & Burry Port	d	17 15		18 31		19 25		20 43		21 19		22 58		
Llanelli	a	17 21		18 37		19 31		20 49		21 25		23 04		
	d	17 22		18 38		19 32	19 55	20 51		21 26		23 04		
Gowerton	d			18 46			20 02	20 58		21 33		23 12		
Swansea	a	17 39		19 08		19 49	20 16	21 17		21 46		23 27		
	d	17 51	18 51			19 55	20 40			21 52		23 31		
Llansamlet	d													
Skewen	d													
Neath	d	18 03	19 03			20 07	20 51			22 03		23 43		
Briton Ferry	d													
Baglan	d													
Port Talbot Parkway	d	18 10	19 10			20 14	20 58			22 10		23 50		
Pyle	d									22 18		23 58		
Maesteg	d													
Maesteg (Ewenny Road)	d													
Garth (Mid Glamorgan)	d													
Tondu	d													
Sarn	d													
Wildmill	d													
Bridgend	d	18 23	19 23			20 28	21 12			22 26		00 06		
Pencoed	d													
Llanharan	d													
Pontyclun	d													
Cardiff Central 7	a	18 45	19 45			20 50	21 36			22 49		00 30		
Newport (South Wales)	a	19 03	20 03			21 08				23 18				
Bristol Parkway 7	a	19 31	20 31			21 36								
Gloucester 7	a													
Manchester Piccadilly 10	a													
Reading 7	a	20 33	21 33			22 42								
London Paddington 15 ⊖	a	21 04	22 06			23 20								

When events are being held at the Millenium Stadium, services are subject to alteration. Please check times before travelling.

Ferry service between Fishguard Harbour and Rosslare Harbour is operated by Stena Line

Table 128R

Sundays

5 January to 9 February

West Wales, Swansea and Maesteg - Cardiff

Route Diagram - see first Page of Table 127

		AW	AW	GW	AW	GW	GW	AW	GW	AW	AW	GW	GW	AW	AW	GW	GW	AW	AW	GW	AW	GW	AW
					R				R			R	R	R		R	R	R				R	R
		◇	🚌	◇1		◇1	◇1		1	◇		1	1			1	1		◇	◇1		1	
				☕		☕	☕		☕	🛒		☕	☕	🛒		☕	☕	🛒		☕	🛒	☕	🛒
Rosslare Harbour ⛴🚌	d				09 00																		
Fishguard Harbour 30 ⛴	a				12 30																		
	d	01 48																			14 23		
Fishguard & Goodwick	d	01 51																			14 26		
Milford Haven	d													11 28				13 25					15 28
Johnston	d													11x36				13x31					15x36
Haverfordwest	d													11 43				13 38					15 43
Clarbeston Road	d													11x52				13x47					15x52
Clunderwen	d													11x59				13x54					15x59
Pembroke Dock	d														11 57								
Pembroke	d														12 05								
Lamphey	d														12x08								
Manorbier	d														12 17								
Penally	d														12x22								
Tenby	a														12 25								
	d														12 25								
Saundersfoot	d														12x33								
Kilgetty	d														12x35								
Narberth	d														12x45								
Whitland	a	02s22												12 06	12 53			14 01			14 57		16 06
	d													12 08	12 57			14 04			14 58		16 09
Carmarthen	a	02 40												12 26	13 14			14 22			15 15		16 26
	d	02 43	02 50					09 40		10 30	11 07			12 29	13 17			14 39		15 27	15 38		16 31
Ferryside	d							09x50			11x17				13x27						15x49		16x41
Kidwelly	d							09x56			11x23				13x33						15x55		16x47
Pembrey & Burry Port	d							10 03		10 49	11 31			12 49	13 40			14 58		15 47	16 02		16 55
Llanelli	a	03s06						10 09		10 54	11 37			12 55	13 46			15 04		15 56	16 08		17 01
	d							10 10		10 56	11 37			12 55	13 47			15 05	15 41	15 59	16 08		17 01
Gowerton	d							10 17			11 45			13 04	13 54			15 13	15 49		16 16		17 10
Swansea	a		03 50					10 35		11 15	12 01			13 18	14 12			15 27	16 07	16 14	16 34		17 23
	d			08 03		09 21	10 21		11 21	11 32		12 21	13 21	13 43		14 21	15 21	15 34		16 21		16 51	17 30
Llansamlet	d																						
Skewen	d																						
Neath	d			08 15		09 33	10 33		11 33	11 43		12 33	13 33	13 54		14 33	15 33	15 45		16 33		17 03	17 41
Briton Ferry	d																						
Baglan	d																						
Port Talbot Parkway	d			08 22		09 40	10 40		11 40	11 50		12 40	13 40	14 01		14 40	15 40	15 52		16 40		17 10	17 48
Pyle	d									11 59				14 10				16 00					17 56
Maesteg	d																						
Maesteg (Ewenny Road)	d																						
Garth (Mid Glamorgan)	d																						
Tondu	d																						
Sarn	d																						
Wildmill	d																						
Bridgend	d			08 35		09 53	10 53		11 53	12 06		12 53	13 53	14 18		14 53	15 53	16 08		16 53		17 23	18 04
Pencoed	d									12 12								16 14					18 10
Llanharan	d									12 16								16 18					18 14
Pontyclun	d									12 21								16 23					18 19
Cardiff Central 7	a	04 10		08 56		10 14	11 14		12 14	12 35		13 14	14 14	14 40		15 14	16 14	16 37		17 14		17 45	18 32
Newport (South Wales)	a			09 13		10 31	11 31		12 31	12 52		13 31	14 31	15 05		15 31	16 31	16 53		17 31		18 03	18 52
Bristol Parkway 7	a			09 34		10 53	11 53		12 53			13 53	14 53			15 53	16 53			17 53		18 27	
Gloucester 7	a																						
Manchester Piccadilly 10	a									16 15				18 17				20 17					22 19
Reading 7	a			10 34		12 02	13 02		14 02			15 02	16 02			17 02	18 02			19 02		19 33	
London Paddington 15 ⊖	a			11 19		12 42	13 43		14 42			15 42	16 44			17 44	18 44			19 43		20 13	

When events are being held at the Millenium Stadium, services are subject to alteration. Please check times before travelling.

Ferry service between Fishguard Harbour and Rosslare Harbour is operated by Stena Line

Table 128R

Sundays

5 January to 9 February

West Wales, Swansea and Maesteg - Cardiff

Route Diagram - see first Page of Table 127

		GW	GW	AW	AW	GW		AW	AW	AW	AW	AW	AW	AW	AW
												R			
		◇1	◇1			◇1		◇			◇		◇		
		☕	☕			☕									
Rosslare Harbour	d											21 00			
Fishguard Harbour 30	a											00 30			
	d														
Fishguard & Goodwick	d														
Milford Haven	d				17 30					19 38			21 35		23 15
Johnston	d				17x38					19x46			21x43		23x23
Haverfordwest	d				17 45					19 53			21 51		23 30
Clarbeston Road	d				17x53					20x01			21x59		23x39
Clunderwen	d				18x00					20x08			22x07		23x46
Pembroke Dock	d			16 45					19 00					21 45	
Pembroke	d			16 53					19 08					21 53	
Lamphey	d			16x56					19x11					21x56	
Manorbier	d			17 05					19 20					22 05	
Penally	d			17x10					19x25					22x10	
Tenby	a			17 13					19 28					22 13	
	d			17 13					19 28					22 13	
Saundersfoot	d			17x21					19x36					22x21	
Kilgetty	d			17x23					19x38					22x23	
Narberth	d			17x33					19x48					22x33	
Whitland	a			17 41	18 06				19 56	20 14			22 13	22 41	23 53
	d			17 44	18 08				19 59	20 17			22 14	22 44	23 53
Carmarthen	a			18 02	18 29				20 16	20 36			22 31	23 05	00 14
	d	16 55		18 07		19 05			20 19		21 00		22 34		
Ferryside	d			18x17					20x30				22x44		
Kidwelly	d			18x23					20x36				22x50		
Pembrey & Burry Port	d	17 15		18 31		19 25			20 43		21 19		22 58		
Llanelli	a	17 21		18 37		19 31			20 49		21 25		23 04		
	d	17 22		18 38		19 32		19 55	20 51		21 26		23 04		
Gowerton	d			18 46				20 02	20 58		21 33		23 12		
Swansea	a	17 39		19 08		19 49		20 16	21 17		21 46		23 27		
	d	17 51	18 51			19 55		20 40			21 52		23 31		
Llansamlet	d														
Skewen	d														
Neath	d	18 03	19 03			20 07		20 51			22 03		23 43		
Briton Ferry	d														
Baglan	d														
Port Talbot Parkway	d	18 10	19 10			20 14		20 58			22 10		23 50		
Pyle	d										22 18		23 58		
Maesteg	d														
Maesteg (Ewenny Road)	d														
Garth (Mid Glamorgan)	d														
Tondu	d														
Sarn	d														
Wildmill	d														
Bridgend	d	18 23	19 23			20 28		21 12			22 26		00 06		
Pencoed	d														
Llanharan	d														
Pontyclun	d														
Cardiff Central 7	a	18 45	19 45			20 50		21 36			22 49		00 30		
Newport (South Wales)	a	19 03	20 03			21 08					23 18				
Bristol Parkway 7	a	19 31	20 31			21 36									
Gloucester 7	a														
Manchester Piccadilly 10	a														
Reading 7	a	20 39	21 33			22 44									
London Paddington 15 ⊖	a	21 15	22 14			23 27									

When events are being held at the Millenium Stadium, services are subject to alteration. Please check times before travelling.

Ferry service between Fishguard Harbour and Rosslare Harbour is operated by Stena Line

Table 128R

Sundays

16 February to 23 March

West Wales, Swansea and Maesteg - Cardiff

Route Diagram - see first Page of Table 127

		AW	AW	GW	AW	GW	GW	AW	GW	AW		AW	GW	GW	AW	AW	GW	GW	AW	AW		GW	AW	GW	AW
					B				R				R	R	R		R	R	R					R	R
		◇		◇1		◇1	◇1		1	◇			1	1			1	1		◇		◇1		1	
			🚌																						
				☕		☕	☕		☕	🛒			☕	☕	🛒		☕	☕	🛒			☕	🛒	☕	🛒
Rosslare Harbour	d				09 00																				
Fishguard Harbour 30	a				12 30																				
	d	01 48																					14 23		
Fishguard & Goodwick	d	01 51																					14 26		
Milford Haven	d														11 28				13 25						15 28
Johnston	d														11x36				13x31						15x36
Haverfordwest	d														11 43				13 38						15 43
Clarbeston Road	d														11x52				13x47						15x52
Clunderwen	d														11x59				13x54						15x59
Pembroke Dock	d															11 57									
Pembroke	d															12 05									
Lamphey	d															12x08									
Manorbier	d															12 17									
Penally	d															12x22									
Tenby	a															12 25									
	d															12 25									
Saundersfoot	d															12x33									
Kilgetty	d															12x35									
Narberth	d															12x45									
Whitland	a	02s22													12 06	12 53			14 01				14 57		16 06
	d														12 08	12 57			14 04				14 58		16 09
Carmarthen	a	02 40													12 26	13 14			14 22				15 15		16 26
	d	02 43	02 50					09 40		10 30		11 07			12 29	13 17			14 39			15 27	15 38		16 31
Ferryside	d							09x50				11x17				13x27							15x49		16x41
Kidwelly	d							09x56				11x23				13x33							15x55		16x47
Pembrey & Burry Port	d							10 03		10 49		11 31			12 49	13 40			14 58			15 47	16 02		16 55
Llanelli	a	03s06						10 09		10 54		11 37			12 55	13 46			15 04			15 56	16 08		17 01
	d							10 10		10 56		11 37			12 55	13 47			15 05	15 41		15 59	16 08		17 01
Gowerton	d							10 17				11 45			13 04	13 54			15 13	15 49			16 16		17 10
Swansea	a		03 50					10 35		11 15		12 01			13 18	14 12			15 27	16 07		16 14	16 34		17 23
	d			07 58		09 21	10 21		11 21	11 32			12 21	13 21	13 43		14 21	15 21	15 34			16 21		17 17	17 30
Llansamlet	d																								
Skewen	d																								
Neath	d			08 10		09 33	10 33		11 33	11 43			12 33	13 33	13 54		14 33	15 33	15 45			16 33		17 29	17 41
Briton Ferry	d																								
Baglan	d																								
Port Talbot Parkway	d			08 17		09 40	10 40		11 40	11 50			12 40	13 40	14 01		14 40	15 40	15 52			16 40		17 36	17 48
Pyle	d									11 59					14 10				16 00						17 56
Maesteg	d																								
Maesteg (Ewenny Road)	d																								
Garth (Mid Glamorgan)	d																								
Tondu	d																								
Sarn	d																								
Wildmill	d																								
Bridgend	d			08 31		09 53	10 53		11 53	12 06			12 53	13 53	14 18		14 53	15 53	16 08			16 53		17 49	18 04
Pencoed	d									12 12									16 14						18 10
Llanharan	d									12 16									16 18						18 14
Pontyclun	d									12 21									16 23						18 19
Cardiff Central 7	a	04 10		08 52		10 14	11 14		12 14	12 35			13 14	14 14	14 40		15 14	16 14	16 37			17 14		18 10	18 32
Newport (South Wales)	a			09 08		10 31	11 31		12 31	12 52			13 31	14 31	15 05		15 31	16 31	16 53			17 31		18 31	18 52
Bristol Parkway 7	a			09 37		10 59	11 59		12 59				13 59	14 59			15 59	16 59				17 59		18 59	
Gloucester 7	a																								
Manchester Piccadilly 10	a									16 15					18 17				20 17						22 19
Reading 7	a			10 37		12 03	13 04		14 02				15 02	16 04			17 04	18 03				19 03		20 04	
London Paddington 15 ⊖	a			11 23		12 42	13 42		14 42				15 43	16 43			17 44	18 43				19 43		20 43	

When events are being held at the Millenium Stadium, services are subject to alteration. Please check times before travelling.

Ferry service between Fishguard Harbour and Rosslare Harbour is operated by Stena Line

Table 128R

Sundays

16 February to 23 March

West Wales, Swansea and Maesteg - Cardiff

Route Diagram - see first Page of Table 127

		GW	GW	AW	AW	GW		AW	AW	AW	AW	AW	AW	AW	AW
												R			
		◇1	◇1			◇1		◇			◇		◇		
		⊡	⊡			⊡									
Rosslare Harbour	d											21 00			
Fishguard Harbour 30	a											00 30			
	d														
Fishguard & Goodwick	d														
Milford Haven	d				17 30					19 38			21 35		23 15
Johnston	d				17x38					19x46			21x43		23x23
Haverfordwest	d				17 45					19 53			21 51		23 30
Clarbeston Road	d				17x53					20x01			21x59		23x39
Clunderwen	d				18x00					20x08			22x07		23x46
Pembroke Dock	d			16 45					19 00					21 45	
Pembroke	d			16 53					19 08					21 53	
Lamphey	d			16x56					19x11					21x56	
Manorbier	d			17 05					19 20					22 05	
Penally	d			17x10					19x25					22x10	
Tenby	a			17 13					19 28					22 13	
	d			17 13					19 28					22 13	
Saundersfoot	d			17x21					19x36					22x21	
Kilgetty	d			17x23					19x38					22x23	
Narberth	d			17x33					19x48					22x33	
Whitland	a			17 41	18 06				19 56	20 14			22 13	22 41	23 53
	d			17 44	18 08				19 59	20 17			22 14	22 44	23 53
Carmarthen	a			18 02	18 29				20 16	20 36			22 31	23 05	00 14
	d	16 55		18 07		19 05			20 19		21 00		22 34		
Ferryside	d			18x17					20x30				22x44		
Kidwelly	d			18x23					20x36				22x50		
Pembrey & Burry Port	d	17 15		18 31		19 25			20 43		21 19		22 58		
Llanelli	a	17 21		18 37		19 31			20 49		21 25		23 04		
	d	17 22		18 38		19 32		19 55	20 51		21 26		23 04		
Gowerton	d			18 46				20 02	20 58		21 33		23 12		
Swansea	a	17 39		19 08		19 49		20 16	21 17		21 46		23 27		
	d	17 51	18 51			19 55		20 40			21 52		23 31		
Llansamlet	d														
Skewen	d														
Neath	d	18 03	19 03			20 07		20 51			22 03		23 43		
Briton Ferry	d														
Baglan	d														
Port Talbot Parkway	d	18 10	19 10			20 14		20 58			22 10		23 50		
Pyle	d										22 18		23 58		
Maesteg	d														
Maesteg (Ewenny Road)	d														
Garth (Mid Glamorgan)	d														
Tondu	d														
Sarn	d														
Wildmill	d														
Bridgend	d	18 23	19 23			20 28		21 12			22 26		00 06		
Pencoed	d														
Llanharan	d														
Pontyclun	d														
Cardiff Central 7	a	18 45	19 45			20 50		21 36			22 49		00 30		
Newport (South Wales)	a	19 03	20 03			21 08					23 18				
Bristol Parkway 7	a	19 31	20 31			21 36									
Gloucester 7	a														
Manchester Piccadilly 10	a														
Reading 7	a	20 33	21 33			22 38									
London Paddington 15 ⊖	a	21 13	22 14			23 19									

When events are being held at the Millenium Stadium, services are subject to alteration. Please check times before travelling.

Ferry service between Fishguard Harbour and Rosslare Harbour is operated by Stena Line

Table 128R

Sundays

30 March to 11 May

West Wales, Swansea and Maesteg - Cardiff

Route Diagram - see first Page of Table 127

		AW	AW	GW	AW	GW	GW	AW	GW	AW	AW	GW	GW	AW	AW	GW	GW	AW	AW	GW	AW	GW	AW
					R				R			R	R	R		R	R	R				R	R
		◇		◇1		◇1	◇1		1	◇		1	1			1	1		◇	◇1		1	
			🚌																				
				☕		☕	☕		☕	🛒		☕	☕	🛒		☕	☕	🛒		☕	🛒	☕	🛒
Rosslare Harbour ⛴🚌	d				09 00																		
Fishguard Harbour 30 ⛴	a				12 30																		
	d	01 48																			14 23		
Fishguard & Goodwick	d	01 51																			14 26		
Milford Haven	d													11 28				13 25					15 28
Johnston	d													11x36				13x31					15x36
Haverfordwest	d													11 43				13 38					15 43
Clarbeston Road	d													11x52				13x47					15x52
Clunderwen	d													11x59				13x54					15x59
Pembroke Dock	d														11 57								
Pembroke	d														12 05								
Lamphey	d														12x08								
Manorbier	d														12 17								
Penally	d														12x22								
Tenby	a														12 25								
	d														12 25								
Saundersfoot	d														12x33								
Kilgetty	d														12x35								
Narberth	d														12x45								
Whitland	a	02s22												12 06	12 53			14 01			14 57		16 06
	d													12 08	12 57			14 04			14 58		16 09
Carmarthen	a	02 40												12 26	13 14			14 22			15 15		16 26
	d	02 43	02 50					09 40		10 30	11 07			12 29	13 17			14 39		15 27	15 38		16 31
Ferryside	d							09x50			11x17				13x27						15x49		16x41
Kidwelly	d							09x56			11x23				13x33						15x55		16x47
Pembrey & Burry Port	d							10 03		10 49	11 31			12 49	13 40			14 58		15 47	16 02		16 55
Llanelli	a	03s06						10 09		10 54	11 37			12 55	13 46			15 04		15 56	16 08		17 01
	d							10 10		10 56	11 37			12 55	13 47			15 05	15 41	15 59	16 08		17 01
Gowerton	d							10 17			11 45			13 04	13 54			15 13	15 49		16 16		17 10
Swansea	a		03 50					10 35		11 15	12 01			13 18	14 12			15 27	16 07	16 14	16 34		17 23
	d			07 58		09 21	10 21		11 21	11 32		12 21	13 21	13 43		14 21	15 21	15 34		16 21		17 17	17 30
Llansamlet	d																						
Skewen	d																						
Neath	d			08 10		09 33	10 33		11 33	11 43		12 33	13 33	13 54		14 33	15 33	15 45		16 33		17 29	17 41
Briton Ferry	d																						
Baglan	d																						
Port Talbot Parkway	d			08 17		09 40	10 40		11 40	11 50		12 40	13 40	14 01		14 40	15 40	15 52		16 40		17 36	17 48
Pyle	d									11 59				14 10				16 00					17 56
Maesteg	d																						
Maesteg (Ewenny Road)	d																						
Garth (Mid Glamorgan)	d																						
Tondu	d																						
Sarn	d																						
Wildmill	d																						
Bridgend	d			08 31		09 53	10 53		11 53	12 06		12 53	13 53	14 18		14 53	15 53	16 08		16 53		17 49	18 04
Pencoed	d									12 12								16 14					18 10
Llanharan	d									12 16								16 18					18 14
Pontyclun	d									12 21								16 23					18 19
Cardiff Central 7	a	04 10		08 52		10 14	11 14		12 14	12 35		13 14	14 14	14 40		15 14	16 14	16 37		17 14		18 10	18 32
Newport (South Wales)	a			09 08		10 31	11 31		12 31	12 52		13 31	14 31	15 05		15 31	16 31	16 53		17 31		18 31	18 52
Bristol Parkway 7	a			09 37		10 56	11 56		12 56			13 56	14 56			15 56	16 55			17 55		18 55	
Gloucester 7	a																						
Manchester Piccadilly 10	a									16 15				18 17				20 17					22 19
Reading 7	a			10 37		12 01	13 01		14 01			15 01	16 01			17 01	18 01			19 00		20 01	
London Paddington 15 ⊖	a			11 24		12 41	13 42		14 42			15 42	16 42			17 42	18 42			19 41		20 42	

When events are being held at the Millenium Stadium, services are subject to alteration. Please check times before travelling.

Ferry service between Fishguard Harbour and Rosslare Harbour is operated by Stena Line

Table 128R

Sundays

30 March to 11 May

West Wales, Swansea and Maesteg - Cardiff

Route Diagram - see first Page of Table 127

		GW	GW	AW	AW	GW		AW	AW	AW	AW	AW	AW	AW	AW
												R			
		◇1	◇1			◇1		◇			◇		◇		
		☕	☕			☕									
Rosslare Harbour ⛴🚌	d											21 00			
Fishguard Harbour 30 ⛴	a											00 30			
	d														
Fishguard & Goodwick	d														
Milford Haven	d				17 30					19 38			21 35		23 15
Johnston	d				17x38					19x46			21x43		23x23
Haverfordwest	d				17 45					19 53			21 51		23 30
Clarbeston Road	d				17x53					20x01			21x59		23x39
Clunderwen	d				18x00					20x08			22x07		23x46
Pembroke Dock	d			16 45					19 00					21 45	
Pembroke	d			16 53					19 08					21 53	
Lamphey	d			16x56					19x11					21x56	
Manorbier	d			17 05					19 20					22 05	
Penally	d			17x10					19x25					22x10	
Tenby	a			17 13					19 28					22 13	
	d			17 13					19 28					22 13	
Saundersfoot	d			17x21					19x36					22x21	
Kilgetty	d			17x23					19x38					22x23	
Narberth	d			17x33					19x48					22x33	
Whitland	a			17 41	18 06				19 56	20 14			22 13	22 41	23 53
	d			17 44	18 08				19 59	20 17			22 14	22 44	23 53
Carmarthen	a			18 02	18 29				20 16	20 36			22 31	23 05	00 14
	d	16 55		18 07		19 05			20 19		21 00		22 34		
Ferryside	d			18x17					20x30				22x44		
Kidwelly	d			18x23					20x36				22x50		
Pembrey & Burry Port	d	17 15		18 31		19 25			20 43		21 19		22 58		
Llanelli	a	17 21		18 37		19 31			20 49		21 25		23 04		
	d	17 22		18 38		19 32		19 55	20 51		21 26		23 04		
Gowerton	d			18 46				20 02	20 58		21 33		23 12		
Swansea	a	17 39		19 08		19 49		20 16	21 17		21 46		23 27		
	d	17 51	18 51			19 55		20 40			21 52		23 31		
Llansamlet	d														
Skewen	d														
Neath	d	18 03	19 03			20 07		20 51			22 03		23 43		
Briton Ferry	d														
Baglan	d														
Port Talbot Parkway	d	18 10	19 10			20 14		20 58			22 10		23 50		
Pyle	d										22 18		23 58		
Maesteg	d														
Maesteg (Ewenny Road)	d														
Garth (Mid Glamorgan)	d														
Tondu	d														
Sarn	d														
Wildmill	d														
Bridgend	d	18 23	19 23			20 28		21 12			22 26		00 06		
Pencoed	d														
Llanharan	d														
Pontyclun	d														
Cardiff Central 7	a	18 45	19 45			20 50		21 36			22 49		00 30		
Newport (South Wales)	a	19 03	20 03			21 08					23 18				
Bristol Parkway 7	a	19 24	20 25			21 36									
Gloucester 7	a														
Manchester Piccadilly 10	a														
Reading 7	a	20 29	21 29			22 44									
London Paddington 15 ⊖	a	21 03	22 05			23 27									

When events are being held at the Millenium Stadium, services are subject to alteration. Please check times before travelling.

Ferry service between Fishguard Harbour and Rosslare Harbour is operated by Stena Line

Network Diagram for Tables 129, 131

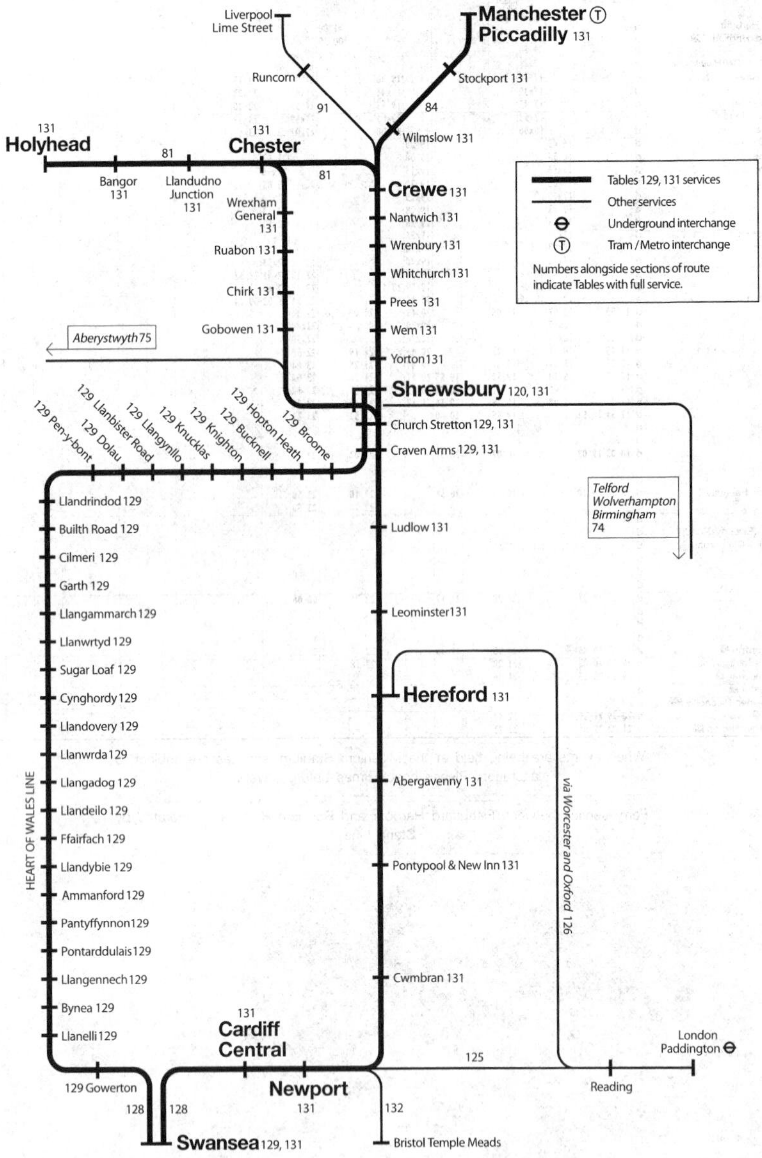

TOC operating on this network - Arriva Trains Wales (AW)

Table 129

Mondays to Saturdays

9 December to 17 May

Shrewsbury - Swansea

HEART OF WALES LINE

Route Diagram - see first Page of Table 129

Miles			AW	AW	AW	AW	AW	AW	AW
				SX	SO	SX	SO	SX	SO
			◇	◇ 🛒	◇ 🛒	◇	◇	◇	◇
0	**Shrewsbury**	d	05 16	09 00	09 00	14 04	14 05	18 05	18 05
12¾	Church Stretton	d	05 33	09 18	09 17	14 22	14 23	18 22	18 23
20	Craven Arms	d	05 47	09 28	09 30	14 33	14 36	18 35	18 36
22½	Broome	d	05x52	09x34	09x35	14x39	14x42	18x40	18x42
25	Hopton Heath	d	05x56	09x38	09x39	14x43	14x45	18x44	18x45
28	Bucknell	d	06x00	09x43	09x43	14x48	14x50	18x48	18x50
32¼	Knighton	a	06 07	09 50	09 50	14 55	14 56	18 55	18 56
—		d	06 09	09 52	09 52	14 57	14 59	18 57	18 59
34¾	Knucklas	d	06x14	09x58	09x57	15x03	15x04	19x02	19x04
38¾	Llangynllo	d	06x22	10x06	10x05	15x11	15x11	19x10	19x11
41¾	Llanbister Road	d	06x27	10x11	10x10	15x16	15x16	19x15	19x16
45¼	Dolau	d	06x32	10x17	10x15	15x22	15x21	19x20	19x22
48½	Pen-y-bont	d	06x36	10x21	10x20	15x26	15x25	19x24	19x26
51¾	Llandrindod	a	06 43	10 28	10 29	15 35	15 35	19 31	19 35
—		d	06 52	10 31	10 29	15 42	15 42	19 34	19 35
57½	Builth Road	d	07x01	10x40	10x39	15x51	15x51	19x43	19x45
59½	Cilmeri	d	07x04	10x44	10x42	15x55	15x55	19x46	19x48
63	Garth (Powys)	d	07x09	10x49	10x47	16x00	16x00	19x52	19x53
64¾	Llangammarch	d	07x12	10x53	10x51	16x04	16x04	19x55	19x57
68	Llanwrtyd	a	07 18	10 59	10 57	16 10	16 10	20 01	20 03
—		d	07 21	11 07	11 06	16 13	16 13	20 10	20 10
70¾	Sugar Loaf	d	07x27	11x13	11x13	16x19	16x19	20x16	20x16
74¾	Cynghordy	d	07x33	11x20	11x20	16x26	16x26	20x23	20x23
79½	Llandovery	a	07 43	11 30	11 29	16 36	16 36	20 33	20 33
—		d	07 45	11 32	11 32	16 38	16 38	20 35	20 35
83¼	Llanwrda	d	07x51	11x38	11x37	16x44	16x44	20x41	20x41
85	Llangadog	d	07x54	11x42	11x41	16x48	16x48	20x45	20x45
90¾	Llandeilo	a	08 03	11 51	11 50	16 57	16 57	20 54	20 54
—		d	08 06	11 54	11 53	17 00	17 00	20 57	20 57
91½	Ffairfach	d	08 08	11 56	11 55	17 02	17 02	20 59	20 59
95½	Llandybie	d	08x16	12x04	12x02	17x10	17x10	21x07	21x07
97¼	Ammanford	d	08x20	12x08	12x07	17x14	17x14	21x11	21x11
98½	Pantyffynnon	d	08 23	12 11	12 10	17 17	17 17	21 14	21 14
103¼	Pontarddulais	d	08x30	12x18	12x17	17x24	17x24	21x21	21x21
105½	Llangennech	d	08x35	12x23	12x21	17x29	17x29	21x26	21x26
107½	Bynea	d	08x38	12x26	12x24	17x32	17x32	21x29	21x29
110¼	Llanelli	a	08 43	12 35	12 29	17 38	17 37	21 34	21 34
116	Gowerton	a	09 04			17 55	17 48	21 50	21 47
121½	**Swansea**	a	09 18	13 04	13 00	18 17	18 10	22 08	22 10

Sundays

8 December to 11 May

		AW	AW
		◇	◇
Shrewsbury	d	12 04	16 18
Church Stretton	d	12 22	16 36
Craven Arms	d	12 33	16 47
Broome	d	12x39	16x53
Hopton Heath	d	12x43	16x57
Bucknell	d	12x48	17x02
Knighton	a	12 55	17 08
	d	12 57	17 11
Knucklas	d	13x03	17x16
Llangynllo	d	13x11	17x24
Llanbister Road	d	13x16	17x29
Dolau	d	13x22	17x35
Pen-y-bont	d	13x26	17x40
Llandrindod	a	13 35	17 49
	d	13 41	17 54
Builth Road	d	13x50	18x04
Cilmeri	d	13x54	18x07
Garth (Powys)	d	13x59	18x13
Llangammarch	d	14x03	18x17
Llanwrtyd	a	14 09	18 23
	d	14 12	18 25
Sugar Loaf	d	14x18	18x32
Cynghordy	d	14x25	18x39
Llandovery	a	14 35	18 48
	d	14 37	18 51
Llanwrda	d	14x43	18x57
Llangadog	d	14x47	19x01
Llandeilo	a	14 56	19 10
	d	14 59	19 12
Ffairfach	d	15 01	19 15
Llandybie	d	15x09	19x22
Ammanford	d	15x13	19x27
Pantyffynnon	d	15 16	19 30
Pontarddulais	d	15x23	19x37
Llangennech	d	15x28	19x41
Bynea	d	15x31	19x45
Llanelli	a	15 36	19 50
Gowerton	a	15 49	20 02
Swansea	a	16 07	20 16

When events are being held at the Millenium Stadium, services are subject to alteration. Please check times before travelling.

Table 129R

Mondays to Saturdays

9 December to 17 May

Swansea - Shrewsbury

HEART OF WALES LINE

Route Diagram - see first Page of Table 129

Miles			AW SO ◇	AW SX ◇	AW SO ◇ 🛒	AW SX ◇ 🛒	AW SO ◇	AW SX ◇	AW SX ◇	AW SO ◇
0	**Swansea**	d	04 31	04 31	09 14	09 14	13 15	13 14	18 21	18 21
5½	Gowerton	d	04 42	04 42	09 26	09 26	13 26	13 26	18 32	18 32
11¼	Llanelli	d	04 50	04 50	09 34	09 34	13 35	13 35	18 40	18 40
14	Bynea	d	04x55	04x55	09x39	09x39	13x40	13x40	18x44	18x44
16	Llangennech	d	04x58	04x58	09x43	09x43	13x44	13x44	18x48	18x48
18¼	Pontarddulais	d	05x02	05x02	09x47	09x47	13x48	13x48	18x52	18x52
23	Pantyffynnon	d	05 10	05 10	09 55	09 55	13 56	13 56	18 59	18 59
24¼	Ammanford	d	05 13	05 13	09 58	09 58	13 59	13 59	19 02	19 02
26	Llandybie	d	05 17	05 17	10 02	10 02	14 03	14 03	19 07	19 07
30	Ffairfach	d	05x24	05x24	10x10	10x10	14x11	14x11	19x14	19x14
30¾	Llandeilo	a	05 27	05 27	10 12	10 12	14 13	14 13	19 16	19 16
—		d	05 29	05 29	10 15	10 15	14 16	14 16	19 19	19 19
36½	Llangadog	d	05 39	05 39	10 24	10 24	14 25	14 25	19 28	19 28
38¼	Llanwrda	d	05 42	05 42	10 28	10 28	14 29	14 29	19 32	19 32
42	Llandovery	a	05 49	05 49	10 34	10 34	14 35	14 35	19 38	19 38
—		d	05 51	05 51	10 37	10 37	14 38	14 38	19 41	19 41
46¾	Cynghordy	d	05x59	05x59	10x45	10x45	14x46	14x46	19x49	19x49
49½	Sugar Loaf	d	06x07	06x07	10x54	10x54	14x55	14x55	19x57	19x57
53½	Llanwrtyd	a	06 13	06 13	11 00	11 00	15 01	15 01	20 03	20 03
—		d	06 16	06 16	11 05	11 05	15 03	15 03	20 07	20 07
56¾	Llangammarch	d	06x21	06x21	11x11	11x11	15x09	15x09	20x12	20x13
58½	Garth (Powys)	d	06x25	06x25	11x15	11x17	15x13	15x13	20x16	20x16
62	Cilmeri	d	06x30	06x30	11x20	11x21	15x19	15x19	20x21	20x21
64	Builth Road	d	06x33	06x33	11x23	11x24	15x22	15x22	20x24	20x24
69¾	Llandrindod	a	06 44	06 44	11 35	11 36	15 34	15 34	20 36	20 36
—		d	06 55	06 55	11 39	11 40	15 43	15 43	20 40	20 40
73¼	Pen-y-bont	d	07x02	07x02	11x46	11x48	15x50	15x51	20x47	20x47
76¼	Dolau	d	07x07	07 07	11 51	11 53	15 55	15 56	20 52	20 52
79¾	Llanbister Road	d	07x12	07x13	11x57	11x59	16x01	16x02	20x58	20x58
82¾	Llangynllo	d	07x17	07x18	12x02	12x05	16x06	16x07	21x03	21x03
86¾	Knucklas	d	07x23	07x24	12x08	12x11	16x12	16x14	21x09	21x09
89¼	Knighton	a	07 29	07 30	12 13	12 16	16 17	16 19	21 14	21 14
—		d	07 32	07 32	12 16	12 18	16 20	16 22	21 17	21 17
93½	Bucknell	d	07 38	07 38	12 22	12 24	16 26	16 28	21 23	21 23
96½	Hopton Heath	d	07x42	07x42	12x26	12x28	16x30	16x32	21x27	21x27
99	Broome	d	07x46	07x46	12x30	12x32	16x35	16x37	21x31	21x31
101½	Craven Arms	a	07 53	07 53	12 37	12 39	16 42	16 43	21 38	21 38
108¾	Church Stretton	a	08 06	08 06	12 51	12 52	16 55	16 56	21 51	21 51
121½	**Shrewsbury**	a	08 22	08 22	13 09	13 08	17 16	17 12	22 08	22 08

Sundays

8 December to 11 May

		AW ◇	AW ◇
Swansea	d	11 08	15 29
Gowerton	d	11 17	15 39
Llanelli	d	11 29	15 51
Bynea	d	11x34	15x56
Llangennech	d	11x38	16x00
Pontarddulais	d	11x42	16x04
Pantyffynnon	d	11 50	16 11
Ammanford	d	11 53	16 14
Llandybie	d	11 57	16 19
Ffairfach	d	12x05	16x26
Llandeilo	a	12 07	16 29
	d	12 10	16 31
Llangadog	d	12 19	16 41
Llanwrda	d	12 23	16 44
Llandovery	a	12 29	16 51
	d	12 32	16 53
Cynghordy	d	12x40	17x02
Sugar Loaf	d	12x49	17x10
Llanwrtyd	a	12 55	17 16
	d	12 57	17 19
Llangammarch	d	13x03	17x25
Garth (Powys)	d	13x07	17x29
Cilmeri	d	13x13	17x34
Builth Road	d	13x16	17x38
Llandrindod	a	13 28	17 49
	d	13 43	18 00
Pen-y-bont	d	13x51	18x08
Dolau	d	13 56	18 13
Llanbister Road	d	14x02	18x19
Llangynllo	d	14x07	18x24
Knucklas	d	14x14	18x31
Knighton	a	14 19	18 36
	d	14 22	18 39
Bucknell	d	14 28	18 45
Hopton Heath	d	14x32	18x49
Broome	d	14x37	18x54
Craven Arms	a	14 44	19 01
Church Stretton	a	14 57	19 16
Shrewsbury	a	15 15	19 31

When events are being held at the Millenium Stadium, services are subject to alteration. Please check times before travelling.

Network Diagram for Table 130

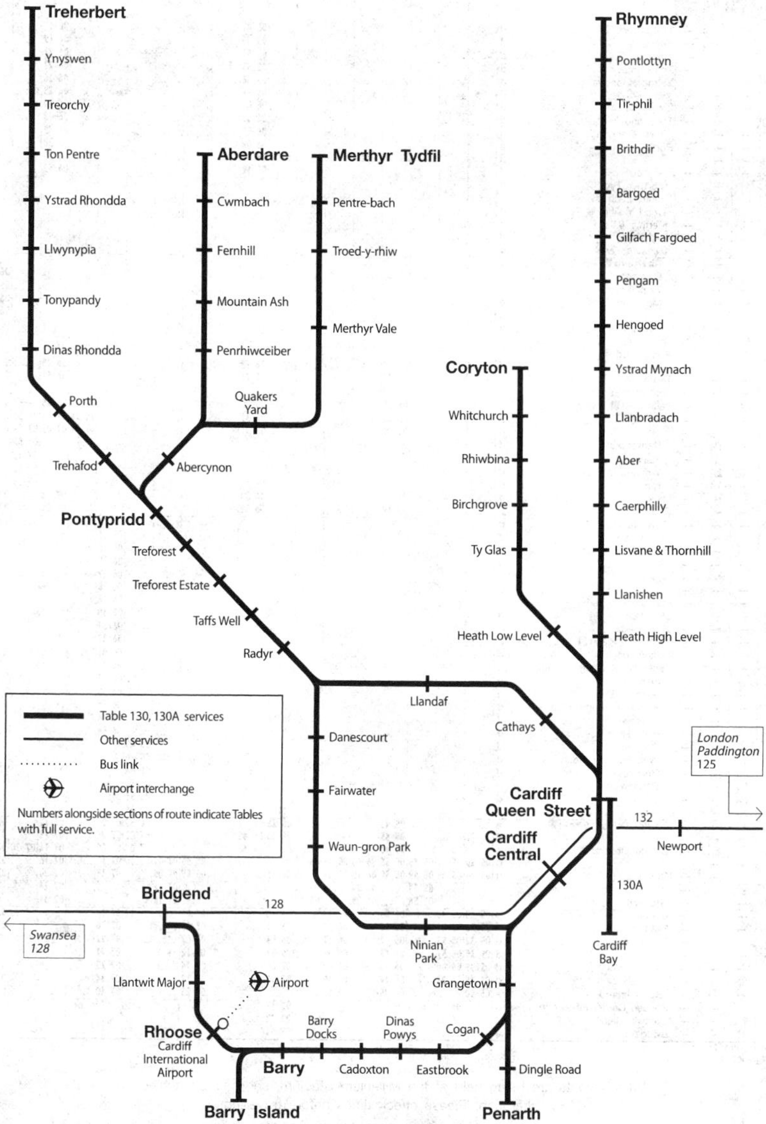

Treherbert
Ynyswen
Treorchy
Ton Pentre
Ystrad Rhondda
Llwynypia
Tonypandy
Dinas Rhondda
Porth
Trehafod
Aberdare
Cwmbach
Fernhill
Mountain Ash
Penrhiwceiber
Merthyr Tydfil
Pentre-bach
Troed-y-rhiw
Merthyr Vale
Quakers Yard
Abercynon
Pontypridd
Treforest
Treforest Estate
Taffs Well
Radyr
Rhymney
Pontlottyn
Tir-phil
Brithdir
Bargoed
Gilfach Fargoed
Pengam
Hengoed
Ystrad Mynach
Llanbradach
Aber
Caerphilly
Lisvane & Thornhill
Llanishen
Heath High Level
Coryton
Whitchurch
Rhiwbina
Birchgrove
Ty Glas
Heath Low Level
Llandaf
Cathays
Danescourt
Fairwater
Waun-gron Park
Table 130, 130A services
Other services
Bus link
Airport interchange
Numbers alongside sections of route indicate Tables with full service.
London Paddington 125
Cardiff Queen Street
Cardiff Central
132
Newport
130A
Cardiff Bay
Bridgend
128
Swansea 128
Ninian Park
Llantwit Major
Airport
Grangetown
Rhoose Cardiff International Airport
Barry Docks
Dinas Powys
Cogan
Barry
Cadoxton
Eastbrook
Dingle Road
Barry Island
Penarth

TOCs operating on this network - Arriva Trains Wales (AW)

Table 130

Mondays to Fridays

9 December to 16 May

Treherbert, Aberdare, Merthyr, Pontypridd, Rhymney and Coryton - Cardiff, Penarth, Barry, Barry Island and Bridgend

Network Diagram - see first Page of Table 130

Miles	Miles	Miles	Miles	Miles			AW	AW	AW	AW	AW	AW	AW	AW	AW		AW A	AW	AW B	AW	AW C	AW	AW D	AW	AW
0	—	—	—	—	**Treherbert**	d									05 47							06 17			
0½	—	—	—	—	Ynyswen	d									05 49							06 19			
1¼	—	—	—	—	Treorchy	d									05 51							06 21			
2¾	—	—	—	—	Ton Pentre	d									05 53							06 23			
3¼	—	—	—	—	Ystrad Rhondda	a									05 56							06 26			
—	—	—	—	—		d									05 58							06 28			
4½	—	—	—	—	Llwynypia	d									06 00							06 30			
5½	—	—	—	—	Tonypandy	d									06 03							06 33			
6	—	—	—	—	Dinas Rhondda	d									06 05							06 35			
7½	—	—	—	—	Porth	a									06 08							06 38			
—	—	—	—	—		d									06 09							06 39			
8¾	—	—	—	—	Trehafod	d									06 12							06 42			
—	—	0	—	—	**Merthyr Tydfil**	d																			
—	—	1½	—	—	Pentre-bach	d																			
—	—	2¾	—	—	Troed Y Rhiw	d																			
—	—	4½	—	—	Merthyr Vale	a																			
—	—	—	—	—		d																			
—	—	6¾	—	—	Quakers Yard	d																			
—	—	—	—	0	**Aberdare** [3]	d																		06 22	
—	—	—	—	1½	Cwmbach	d																		06 25	
—	—	—	—	2¾	Fernhill	d																		06 28	
—	—	—	—	3¾	Mountain Ash	a																		06 31	
—	—	—	—	—		d																		06 34	
—	—	—	—	5	Penrhiwceiber	d																		06 37	
—	—	8¼	—	7¾	Abercynon	d																		06 43	
10¾	—	11½	—	11	**Pontypridd** [3]	a									06 17							06 47		06 52	
—	—	—	—	—		d				05 18					06 18							06 48		06 54	
11½	—	—	—	—	Trefforest	d				05 21					06 21							06 51		06 57	
14	—	—	—	—	Trefforest Estate	d				05 25															
16¼	—	—	—	—	Taffs Well [3]	d				05 28					06 28						06 53	06 58	←	07 04	
18¼	—	—	0	—	Radyr [3]	a				05 31					06 31						06 56	07 01	06 56	07 07	
—	—	—	—	—		d				05 31					06 31						07 04	07 01	07 04	07 07	
—	—	—	1½	—	Danescourt	d															→		07 08		
—	—	—	2	—	Fairwater	d																	07 10		
—	—	—	2¼	—	Waun-gron Park	d																	07 12		
—	—	—	3¾	—	Ninian Park	d																	07 15		
19¼	—	—	—	—	Llandaf	d				05 34					06 34							07 04		07 10	
21¾	—	—	—	—	Cathays	d				05 39					06 39							07 09		07 15	
—	0	—	—	—	**Rhymney** [3]	d														06 08					06 32
—	1	—	—	—	Pontlottyn	d														06 11					06 35
—	3½	—	—	—	Tir-phil	d														06 16					06 40
—	4½	—	—	—	Brithdir	d														06 18					06 42
—	6	—	—	—	Bargoed	a														06 22					06 46
—	—	—	—	—		d														06 25					06 46
—	6½	—	—	—	Gilfach Fargoed	d														06 28					
—	7½	—	—	—	Pengam	d														06 30					06 51
—	9¼	—	—	—	Hengoed	d														06 34					06 54
—	10½	—	—	—	Ystrad Mynach [3]	d														06 37					06 57
—	13	—	—	—	Llanbradach	d														06 41					07 01
—	—	—	—	—	Energlyn & Churchill Park	d														06 45					07 05
—	15	—	—	—	Aber	d														06 47					07 07
—	15¾	—	—	—	Caerphilly [3]	d								06 10						06 50					07 10
—	18¼	—	—	—	Lisvane & Thornhill	d								06 14						06 54					07 14
—	19¼	—	—	—	Llanishen	d								06 16						06 56					07 16
—	20¼	—	—	—	Heath High Level	d								06 19						06 59					07 19
—	—	0	—	—	**Coryton**	d													06 45						
—	—	0½	—	—	Whitchurch (Cardiff)	d													06 46						
—	—	0¾	—	—	Rhiwbina	d													06 48						
—	—	1¼	—	—	Birchgrove	d													06 50						
—	—	1½	—	—	Ty Glas	d													06 51						
—	—	2¼	—	—	Heath Low Level	d													06 54						
22½	22¾	4¾	—	—	**Cardiff Queen Street** [3]	a				05 43				06 25	06 43				06 59	07 04		07 12		07 19	07 24
—	—	—	—	—		d				05 45				06 26	06 43				07 01	07 06		07 13		07 21	07 26
23	23¼	—	4¾	—	**Cardiff Central** [7]	a				05 48				06 29	06 48				07 04	07 09		07 16	07 20	07 24	07 29
—	—	—	—	—		d	05 20	05 41	05 45	05 55	06 16	06 25	06 36	06 41			06 55	07 01		07 10		07 16		07 25	07 31
24	24¼	—	—	—	Grangetown	d	05 24	05 45	05 49	05 59	06 20	06 29	06 40	06 45			06 59	07 05		07 14		07 20		07 29	07 35
—	26¾	—	—	—	Dingle Road	d			05 53		06 24		06 44					07 11				07 26			07 41
—	27	—	—	—	**Penarth**	a			05 58		06 29		06 49					07 16				07 31			07 46
25¾	—	—	—	—	Cogan	d	05 28	05 48		06 03		06 33		06 48			07 03			07 18				07 33	
26½	—	—	—	—	Eastbrook	d	05 30	05 51		06 05		06 35		06 51			07 05			07 20				07 35	
27½	—	—	—	—	Dinas Powys	d	05 32	05 53		06 07		06 37		06 53			07 07			07 22				07 37	
29½	—	—	—	—	Cadoxton	d	05 37	05 57		06 12		06 42		06 57			07 12			07 27				07 42	
30¼	—	—	—	—	Barry Docks	d	05 39	06 00		06 14		06 44		07 00			07 14			07 29				07 44	
31½	—	0	—	—	**Barry** [3]	d	05 44	06 05		06 19		06 49		07 05			07 19			07 34				07 49	
32¼	—	—	—	—	**Barry Island**	a	05 50			06 25		06 55					07 25			07 40				07 55	
—	—	3¼	—	—	Rhoose Cardiff Int Airport ✈	d		06 12						07 12											
—	—	9¾	—	—	Llantwit Major	d		06 23						07 22											
—	—	19	—	—	**Bridgend**	a		06 40						07 39											

A From Hereford
B To Radyr
C To Coryton
D From Taffs Well to Coryton

When events are being held at the Millenium Stadium, services are subject to alteration. Please check times before travelling.

For connections to Cardiff Bay please refer to Table 130A

Table 130

Mondays to Fridays

9 December to 16 May

Treherbert, Aberdare, Merthyr, Pontypridd, Rhymney and Coryton - Cardiff, Penarth, Barry, Barry Island and Bridgend

Network Diagram - see first Page of Table 130

		AW	AW	AW	AW	AW	AW	AW	AW	AW	AW	AW	AW	AW	AW	AW	AW	AW	AW	AW	AW	AW
		A				B			A				B			A				B		
Treherbert	d				06 47							07 17							07 45			
Ynyswen	d				06 49							07 19							07 47			
Treorchy	d				06 51							07 21							07 49			
Ton Pentre	d				06 53							07 23							07 51			
Ystrad Rhondda	a				06 56							07 26							07 54			
	d				06 58							07 28							07 58			
Llwynypia	d				07 00							07 30							08 00			
Tonypandy	d				07 03							07 33							08 03			
Dinas Rhondda	d				07 05							07 35							08 05			
Porth	a				07 08							07 38							08 08			
	d				07 09							07 39							08 09			
Trehafod	d				07 12							07 42							08 12			
Merthyr Tydfil	d		06 38							07 08							07 38					
Pentre-bach	d		06 42							07 12							07 42					
Troed Y Rhiw	d		06 45							07 15							07 45					
Merthyr Vale	a		06 48							07 18							07 48					
	d		06 50							07 20							07 50					
Quakers Yard	d		06 55							07 25							07 55					
Aberdare 3	d						06 52							07 22							07 52	
Cwmbach	d						06 55							07 25							07 55	
Fernhill	d						06 58							07 28							07 58	
Mountain Ash	a						07 01							07 31							08 01	
	d						07 04							07 34							08 04	
Penrhiwceiber	d						07 07							07 37							08 07	
Abercynon	d		06 59				07 13			07 29				07 43			07 59				08 13	
Pontypridd 3	a		07 07		07 17		07 22			07 37		07 47		07 52			08 07		08 17		08 22	
	d		07 09		07 18		07 24			07 39		07 48		07 54			08 09		08 18		08 24	
Trefforest	d		07 12		07 21		07 27			07 42		07 51		07 57			08 12		08 21		08 27	
Trefforest Estate	d		07 16							07 46							08 16					
Taffs Well 3	d		07 20		07 28		07 34			07 50		07 58		08 04			08 20		08 28		08 34	
Radyr 3	a		07 23		07 31		07 37			07 53		08 01		08 07			08 23		08 31		08 37	
	d		07 23		07 31	07 34	07 37			07 53		08 01	08 04	08 07			08 23		08 31	08 34	08 37	
Danescourt	d					07 38							08 08							08 38		
Fairwater	d					07 40							08 10							08 40		
Waun-gron Park	d					07 42							08 12							08 42		
Ninian Park	d					07 45							08 15							08 45		
Llandaf	d		07 26		07 34		07 40			07 56		08 04		08 10			08 26		08 34		08 40	
Cathays	d		07 31		07 39		07 45			08 01		08 09		08 15			08 31		08 39		08 45	
Rhymney 3	d							07 00							07 24			07 42				
Pontlottyn	d							07 03							07 27			07 45				
Tir-phil	d							07 08							07 32			07 50				
Brithdir	d							07 10							07 34			07 52				
Bargoed	a							07 14							07 38			07 59				
	d			07 02				07 15			07 32				07 43			08 00				08 15
Gilfach Fargoed	d			07 04				07 18							07 46							08 18
Pengam	d			07 07				07 20			07 37				07 48			08 05				08 20
Hengoed	d			07 10				07 24			07 40				07 52			08 09				08 24
Ystrad Mynach 3	d			07 13				07 27			07 43				07 55			08 12				08 27
Llanbradach	d			07 18				07 31			07 48				08 00			08 16				08 31
Energlyn & Churchill Park	d							07 35							08 04			08 20				08 35
Aber	d			07 22				07 37			07 52				08 07			08 22				08 37
Caerphilly 3	d			07 25				07 40			07 55				08 10			08 25				08 40
Lisvane & Thornhill	d			07 29				07 44			07 59				08 14			08 29				08 44
Llanishen	d			07 31				07 46			08 01				08 16			08 31				08 46
Heath High Level	d			07 34				07 49			08 04				08 19			08 34				08 49
Coryton	d	07 15							07 45							08 15						
Whitchurch (Cardiff)	d	07 16							07 46							08 16						
Rhiwbina	d	07 18							07 48							08 18						
Birchgrove	d	07 20							07 50							08 20						
Ty Glas	d	07 21							07 51							08 21						
Heath Low Level	d	07 24							07 54							08 24						
Cardiff Queen Street 3	a	07 30	07 34	07 39	07 44		07 49	07 54	07 59	08 04	08 09	08 14		08 19	08 24	08 29	08 34	08 39	08 44		08 49	08 54
	d	07 31	07 36	07 41	07 46		07 51	07 56	08 01	08 06	08 11	08 16		08 21	08 26	08 31	08 36	08 41	08 46		08 51	08 56
Cardiff Central 7	a	07 34	07 38	07 44	07 52	07 50	07 54	07 59	08 04	08 09	08 14	08 22	08 20	08 24	08 29	08 34	08 39	08 47	08 52	08 50	08 54	08 59
	d		07 41	07 46			07 55	08 01		08 10	08 16			08 25	08 31		08 41				08 55	09 01
Grangetown	d		07 45	07 50			07 59	08 05		08 14	08 20			08 29	08 35		08 45				08 59	09 05
Dingle Road	d			07 56				08 11			08 26				08 41							09 11
Penarth	a			08 01				08 16			08 31				08 46							09 16
Cogan	d		07 48				08 03			08 18				08 33			08 48				09 03	
Eastbrook	d		07 51				08 05			08 20				08 35			08 51				09 05	
Dinas Powys	d		07 53				08 07			08 22				08 37			08 53				09 07	
Cadoxton	d		07 57				08 12			08 27				08 42			08 57				09 12	
Barry Docks	d		08 00				08 14			08 29				08 44			08 59				09 14	
Barry 3	d		08 05				08 19			08 34				08 49			09 03				09 19	
Barry Island	a						08 25			08 40				08 55							09 25	
Rhoose Cardiff Int Airport ✈	d		08 12														09 10					
Llantwit Major	d		08 22														09 19					
Bridgend	a		08 39														09 36					

A To Radyr

B To Coryton

When events are being held at the Millenium Stadium, services are subject to alteration. Please check times before travelling.

For connections to Cardiff Bay please refer to Table 130A

Table 130

Mondays to Fridays

9 December to 16 May

Treherbert, Aberdare, Merthyr, Pontypridd, Rhymney and Coryton - Cardiff, Penarth, Barry, Barry Island and Bridgend

Network Diagram - see first Page of Table 130

		AW A	AW	AW	AW	AW B	AW	AW	AW A	AW	AW	AW	AW B	AW	AW	AW A	AW	AW	AW	AW B	AW	AW	AW A
Treherbert	d				08 17							08 47							09 17				
Ynyswen	d				08 19							08 49							09 19				
Treorchy	d				08 21							08 51							09 21				
Ton Pentre	d				08 23							08 53							09 23				
Ystrad Rhondda	a				08 26							08 56							09 26				
	d				08 28							08 58							09 28				
Llwynypia	d				08 30							09 00							09 30				
Tonypandy	d				08 33							09 03							09 33				
Dinas Rhondda	d				08 35							09 05							09 35				
Porth	a				08 38							09 08							09 38				
	d				08 39							09 09							09 39				
Trehafod	d				08 42							09 12							09 42				
Merthyr Tydfil	d		08 08							08 38							09 08						
Pentre-bach	d		08 12							08 42							09 12						
Troed Y Rhiw	d		08 15							08 45							09 15						
Merthyr Vale	a		08 18							08 48							09 18						
	d		08 20							08 50							09 20						
Quakers Yard	d		08 25							08 55							09 25						
Aberdare 3	d						08 22							08 52							09 22		
Cwmbach	d						08 25							08 55							09 25		
Fernhill	d						08 28							08 58							09 28		
Mountain Ash	a						08 31							09 01							09 31		
	d						08 34							09 04							09 34		
Penrhiwceiber	d						08 37							09 07							09 37		
Abercynon	d		08 29				08 43			08 59				09 13			09 29				09 43		
Pontypridd 3	a		08 37		08 47		08 52			09 07		09 17		09 22			09 37		09 47		09 52		
	d		08 39		08 48		08 54			09 09		09 18		09 24			09 39		09 48		09 54		
Trefforest	d		08 42		08 51		08 57			09 12		09 21		09 27			09 42		09 51		09 57		
Trefforest Estate	d		08 46							09 16							09 46						
Taffs Well 3	d		08 50		08 58		09 04			09 20		09 28		09 34			09 50		09 58		10 04		
Radyr 3	a		08 53		09 01		09 07			09 23		09 31		09 37			09 53		10 01		10 07		
	d		08 53		09 01	09 04	09 07			09 23		09 31	09 34	09 37			09 53		10 01	10 04	10 07		
Danescourt	d					09 08							09 38							10 08			
Fairwater	d					09 10							09 40							10 10			
Waun-gron Park	d					09 12							09 42							10 12			
Ninian Park	d					09 15							09 45							10 15			
Llandaf	d		08 56		09 04		09 10			09 26		09 34		09 40			09 56		10 04		10 10		
Cathays	d		09 01		09 09		09 15			09 31		09 39		09 45			10 01		10 09		10 15		
Rhymney 3	d							08 30														09 27	
Pontlottyn	d							08 33														09 30	
Tir-phil	d							08 37														09 35	
Brithdir	d							08 40														09 37	
Bargoed	a							08 44														09 41	
	d			08 32				08 47			09 00				09 17			09 32				09 45	
Gilfach Fargoed	d														09 19								
Pengam	d			08 37				08 52			09 05				09 22			09 37				09 50	
Hengoed	d			08 40				08 55			09 09				09 25			09 40				09 54	
Ystrad Mynach 3	d			08 43				08 58			09 12				09 28			09 43				09 57	
Llanbradach	d			08 48				09 03			09 16				09 33			09 48				10 01	
Energlyn & Churchill Park	d										09 20											10 05	
Aber	d			08 52				09 07			09 22				09 37			09 52				10 07	
Caerphilly 3	d			08 55				09 10			09 25				09 40			09 55				10 10	
Lisvane & Thornhill	d			08 59				09 14			09 29				09 44			09 59				10 14	
Llanishen	d			09 01				09 16			09 31				09 46			10 01				10 16	
Heath High Level	d			09 04				09 19			09 34				09 49			10 04				10 19	
Coryton	d	08 45							09 15							09 45							10 15
Whitchurch (Cardiff)	d	08 46							09 16							09 46							10 16
Rhiwbina	d	08 48							09 18							09 48							10 18
Birchgrove	d	08 50							09 20							09 50							10 20
Ty Glas	d	08 51							09 21							09 51							10 21
Heath Low Level	d	08 54							09 24							09 54							10 24
Cardiff Queen Street 3	a	08 59	09 04	09 09	09 14		09 19	09 24	09 29	09 34	09 39	09 44		09 49	09 54	09 59	10 04	10 09	10 14		10 19	10 24	10 29
	d	09 01	09 06	09 11	09 16		09 21	09 26	09 31	09 36	09 41	09 46		09 51	09 56	10 01	10 06	10 11	10 16		10 21	10 26	10 31
Cardiff Central 7	a	09 04	09 09	09 14	09 22	09 20	09 24	09 29	09 34	09 39	09 44	09 52	09 50	09 54	09 59	10 04	10 09	10 14	10 22	10 20	10 24	10 29	10 34
	d		09 10	09 16			09 25	09 31		09 41	09 46			09 55	10 01		10 10	10 16			10 25	10 31	
Grangetown	d		09 14	09 20			09 29	09 35		09 45	09 50			09 59	10 05		10 14	10 20			10 29	10 35	
Dingle Road	d			09 26				09 41			09 56				10 11			10 26				10 41	
Penarth	a			09 31				09 46			10 01				10 16			10 31				10 46	
Cogan	d		09 18				09 33			09 48				10 03			10 18				10 33		
Eastbrook	d		09 20				09 35			09 51				10 05			10 20				10 35		
Dinas Powys	d		09 22				09 37			09 53				10 07			10 22				10 37		
Cadoxton	d		09 27				09 42			09 57				10 12			10 27				10 42		
Barry Docks	d		09 29				09 44			09 59				10 14			10 29				10 44		
Barry 3	d		09 34				09 49			10 03				10 19			10 34				10 49		
Barry Island	a		09 40				09 55							10 25			10 40				10 55		
Rhoose Cardiff Int Airport ✈	d									10 10													
Llantwit Major	d									10 19													
Bridgend	a									10 36													

A To Radyr

B To Coryton

When events are being held at the Millenium Stadium, services are subject to alteration. Please check times before travelling.

For connections to Cardiff Bay please refer to Table 130A

Table 130

Mondays to Fridays

9 December to 16 May

Treherbert, Aberdare, Merthyr, Pontypridd, Rhymney and Coryton - Cardiff, Penarth, Barry, Barry Island and Bridgend

Network Diagram - see first Page of Table 130

		AW	AW	AW	AW A	AW	AW	AW	AW B	AW	AW	AW A	AW	AW	AW	AW B	AW	AW	AW	AW A	AW	AW
Treherbert	d			09 47											10 17				10 47			
Ynyswen	d			09 49											10 19				10 49			
Treorchy	d			09 51											10 21				10 51			
Ton Pentre	d			09 53											10 23				10 53			
Ystrad Rhondda	a			09 56											10 26				10 56			
	d			09 58											10 28				10 58			
Llwynypia	d			10 00											10 30				11 00			
Tonypandy	d			10 03											10 33				11 03			
Dinas Rhondda	d			10 05											10 35				11 05			
Porth	a			10 08											10 38				11 08			
	d			10 09											10 52				11 09			
Trehafod	d			10 12											10 55				11 12			
Merthyr Tydfil	d	09 38					10 04										10 38					
Pentre-bach	d	09 42					10 08										10 42					
Troed Y Rhiw	d	09 45					10 11										10 45					
Merthyr Vale	a	09 48					10 14										10 48					
	d	09 50					10 16										10 50					
Quakers Yard	d	09 55					10 22										10 55					
Aberdare 3	d					09 52							10 22								10 52	
Cwmbach	d					09 55							10 25								10 55	
Fernhill	d					09 58							10 28								10 58	
Mountain Ash	a					10 01							10 31								11 01	
	d					10 04							10 34								11 04	
Penrhiwceiber	d					10 07							10 37								11 07	
Abercynon	d	09 59				10 13	10 26						10 43				10 59				11 13	
Pontypridd 3	a	10 07		10 17		10 22	10 32						10 52		11 00		11 07		11 17		11 22	
	d	10 09		10 18		10 24				10 39			10 54		11 04		11 09		11 18		11 24	
Trefforest	d	10 12		10 21		10 27				10 42			10 57		11 07		11 12		11 21		11 27	
Trefforest Estate	d	10 16															11 16					
Taffs Well 3	d	10 20		10 28		10 34				10 50			11 04		11 13		11 20		11 28		11 34	
Radyr 3	a	10 23		10 31		10 37				10 53			11 07		11 17		11 23		11 31		11 37	
	d	10 23		10 31	10 34	10 37				10 53		11 04	11 07		11 17		11 23		11 31	11 34	11 37	
Danescourt	d				10 38							11 08								11 38		
Fairwater	d				10 40							11 10								11 40		
Waun-gron Park	d				10 42							11 12								11 42		
Ninian Park	d				10 45							11 15								11 45		
Llandaf	d	10 26		10 34		10 40				10 56			11 10				11 26		11 34		11 40	
Cathays	d	10 31		10 39		10 45				11 01			11 15				11 31		11 39		11 45	
Rhymney 3	d													10 27								
Pontlottyn	d													10 30								
Tir-phil	d													10 35								
Brithdir	d													10 37								
Bargoed	a													10 41								
	d		10 00					10 17			10 32			10 45				11 00				11 17
Gilfach Fargoed	d							10 19														11 19
Pengam	d		10 05					10 22			10 37			10 50				11 05				11 22
Hengoed	d		10 09					10 25			10 40			10 54				11 09				11 25
Ystrad Mynach 3	d		10 12					10 28			10 43			10 57				11 12				11 28
Llanbradach	d		10 16					10 33			10 48			11 01				11 16				11 33
Energlyn & Churchill Park	d		10 20											11 05				11 20				
Aber	d		10 22					10 37			10 52			11 07				11 22				11 37
Caerphilly 3	d		10 25					10 40			10 55			11 10				11 25				11 40
Lisvane & Thornhill	d		10 29					10 44			10 59			11 14				11 29				11 44
Llanishen	d		10 31					10 46			11 01			11 16				11 31				11 46
Heath High Level	d		10 34					10 49			11 04			11 19				11 34				11 49
Coryton	d								10 45							11 15						
Whitchurch (Cardiff)	d								10 46							11 16						
Rhiwbina	d								10 48							11 18						
Birchgrove	d								10 50							11 20						
Ty Glas	d								10 51							11 21						
Heath Low Level	d								10 54							11 24						
Cardiff Queen Street 3	a	10 34	10 39	10 44		10 49		10 54	10 59	11 04	11 09		11 19	11 24		11 29	11 34	11 39	11 44		11 49	11 54
	d	10 36	10 41	10 46		10 51		10 56	11 01	11 06	11 11		11 21	11 26		11 31	11 36	11 41	11 46		11 51	11 56
Cardiff Central 7	a	10 39	10 44	10 52	10 50	10 54		10 59	11 04	11 09	11 14	11 20	11 24	11 29	11 34	11 34	11 39	11 44	11 52	11 50	11 54	11 59
	d	10 41	10 46			10 55		11 01		11 10	11 16		11 25	11 31			11 41	11 46			11 55	12 01
Grangetown	d	10 45	10 50			10 59		11 05		11 14	11 20		11 29	11 35			11 45	11 50			11 59	12 05
Dingle Road	d		10 56					11 11			11 26			11 41				11 56				12 11
Penarth	a		11 01					11 16			11 31			11 46				12 01				12 16
Cogan	d	10 48				11 03				11 18			11 33				11 48				12 03	
Eastbrook	d	10 51				11 05				11 20			11 35				11 51				12 05	
Dinas Powys	d	10 53				11 07				11 22			11 37				11 53				12 07	
Cadoxton	d	10 57				11 12				11 27			11 42				11 57				12 12	
Barry Docks	d	11 00				11 14				11 29			11 44				12 00				12 14	
Barry 3	d	11 05				11 19				11 34			11 49				12 05				12 19	
Barry Island	a					11 25				11 40			11 55								12 25	
Rhoose Cardiff Int Airport ✈	d	11 12															12 12					
Llantwit Major	d	11 22															12 22					
Bridgend	a	11 39															12 37					

A To Coryton

B To Radyr

When events are being held at the Millenium Stadium, services are subject to alteration. Please check times before travelling.

For connections to Cardiff Bay please refer to Table 130A

Table 130

Mondays to Fridays

9 December to 16 May

Treherbert, Aberdare, Merthyr, Pontypridd, Rhymney and Coryton - Cardiff, Penarth, Barry, Barry Island and Bridgend

Network Diagram - see first Page of Table 130

		AW A	AW	AW	AW	AW B	AW	AW	AW A	AW	AW	AW	AW B	AW	AW	AW A	AW	AW	AW	AW B	AW	AW	AW A
Treherbert	d				11 17							11 47							12 17				
Ynyswen	d				11 19							11 49							12 19				
Treorchy	d				11 21							11 51							12 21				
Ton Pentre	d				11 23							11 53							12 23				
Ystrad Rhondda	a				11 26							11 56							12 26				
	d				11 28							11 58							12 28				
Llwynypia	d				11 30							12 00							12 30				
Tonypandy	d				11 33							12 03							12 33				
Dinas Rhondda	d				11 35							12 05							12 35				
Porth	a				11 38							12 08							12 38				
	d				11 39							12 09							12 39				
Trehafod	d				11 42							12 12							12 42				
Merthyr Tydfil	d		11 08							11 38							12 08						
Pentre-bach	d		11 12							11 42							12 12						
Troed Y Rhiw	d		11 15							11 45							12 15						
Merthyr Vale	a		11 18							11 48							12 18						
	d		11 20							11 50							12 20						
Quakers Yard	d		11 25							11 55							12 25						
Aberdare 3	d						11 22														12 22		
Cwmbach	d						11 25														12 25		
Fernhill	d						11 28														12 28		
Mountain Ash	a						11 31														12 31		
	d						11 34														12 34		
Penrhiwceiber	d						11 37														12 37		
Abercynon	d		11 29				11 43			11 59							12 29				12 43		
Pontypridd 3	a		11 37		11 47		11 52			12 07		12 17					12 37		12 48		12 52		
	d		11 39		11 48		11 54			12 09		12 18					12 39		12 48		12 54		
Trefforest	d		11 42		11 51		11 57			12 12		12 21					12 42		12 51		12 57		
Trefforest Estate	d		11 46							12 16							12 46						
Taffs Well 3	d		11 50		11 58		12 04			12 20		12 28					12 50		12 58		13 04		
Radyr 3	a		11 53		12 01		12 07			12 23		12 31					12 53		13 01		13 07		
	d		11 53		12 01	12 04	12 07			12 23		12 31	12 34				12 53		13 01	13 04	13 07		
Danescourt	d					12 08							12 38							13 08			
Fairwater	d					12 10							12 40							13 10			
Waun-gron Park	d					12 12							12 42							13 12			
Ninian Park	d					12 15							12 45							13 15			
Llandaf	d		11 56		12 04		12 10			12 26		12 34					12 56		13 04		13 10		
Cathays	d		12 01		12 09		12 15			12 31		12 39					13 01		13 09		13 15		
Rhymney 3	d							11 27														12 27	
Pontlottyn	d							11 30														12 30	
Tir-phil	d							11 35														12 35	
Brithdir	d							11 37														12 37	
Bargoed	a							11 41														12 41	
	d			11 32				11 45			12 00				12 17			12 32				12 45	
Gilfach Fargoed	d														12 19								
Pengam	d			11 37				11 50			12 05				12 22			12 37				12 50	
Hengoed	d			11 40				11 54			12 09				12 25			12 40				12 54	
Ystrad Mynach 3	d			11 43				11 57			12 12				12 28			12 43				12 57	
Llanbradach	d			11 48				12 01			12 16				12 33			12 48				13 01	
Energlyn & Churchill Park	d							12 05			12 20											13 05	
Aber	d			11 52				12 07			12 22				12 37			12 52				13 07	
Caerphilly 3	d			11 55				12 10			12 25				12 40			12 55				13 10	
Lisvane & Thornhill	d			11 59				12 14			12 29				12 44			12 59				13 14	
Llanishen	d			12 01				12 16			12 31				12 46			13 01				13 16	
Heath High Level	d			12 04				12 19			12 34				12 49			13 04				13 19	
Coryton	d	11 45							12 15							12 45							13 15
Whitchurch (Cardiff)	d	11 46							12 16							12 46							13 16
Rhiwbina	d	11 48							12 18							12 48							13 18
Birchgrove	d	11 50							12 20							12 50							13 20
Ty Glas	d	11 51							12 21							12 51							13 21
Heath Low Level	d	11 54							12 24							12 54							13 24
Cardiff Queen Street 3	a	11 59	12 04	12 09	12 14		12 19	12 24	12 29	12 34	12 39	12 44			12 54	12 59	13 04	13 09	13 14		13 19	13 24	13 29
	d	12 01	12 06	12 11	12 16		12 21	12 26	12 31	12 36	12 41	12 46			12 56	13 01	13 06	13 11	13 16		13 21	13 26	13 31
Cardiff Central 7	a	12 04	12 09	12 14	12 22	12 20	12 24	12 29	12 34	12 39	12 44	12 52	12 50		12 59	13 04	13 09	13 14	13 22	13 20	13 24	13 29	13 34
	d		12 10	12 16			12 25	12 31		12 41	12 46			12 55	13 01		13 10	13 16			13 25	13 31	
Grangetown	d		12 14	12 20			12 29	12 35		12 45	12 50			12 59	13 05		13 14	13 20			13 29	13 35	
Dingle Road	d			12 26				12 41			12 56				13 11			13 26				13 41	
Penarth	a			12 31				12 46			13 01				13 16			13 31				13 46	
Cogan	d		12 18				12 33			12 48				13 03			13 18				13 33		
Eastbrook	d		12 20				12 35			12 51				13 05			13 20				13 35		
Dinas Powys	d		12 22				12 37			12 53				13 07			13 22				13 37		
Cadoxton	d		12 27				12 42			12 57				13 12			13 27				13 42		
Barry Docks	d		12 29				12 44			13 00				13 14			13 29				13 44		
Barry 3	d		12 34				12 49			13 05				13 19			13 34				13 49		
Barry Island	a		12 40				12 55							13 25			13 40				13 55		
Rhoose Cardiff Int Airport ✈	d									13 12													
Llantwit Major	d									13 22													
Bridgend	a									13 39													

A To Radyr **B** To Coryton

When events are being held at the Millenium Stadium, services are subject to alteration. Please check times before travelling.

For connections to Cardiff Bay please refer to Table 130A

Table 130

Mondays to Fridays

9 December to 16 May

Treherbert, Aberdare, Merthyr, Pontypridd, Rhymney and Coryton - Cardiff, Penarth, Barry, Barry Island and Bridgend

Network Diagram - see first Page of Table 130

		AW	AW	AW	AW A	AW	AW	AW B	AW	AW	AW	AW A	AW	AW	AW B	AW	AW	AW	AW A	AW	AW	AW B	AW
Treherbert	d			12 47							13 17							13 47					
Ynyswen	d			12 49							13 19							13 49					
Treorchy	d			12 51							13 21							13 51					
Ton Pentre	d			12 53							13 23							13 53					
Ystrad Rhondda	a			12 56							13 26							13 56					
	d			12 58							13 28							13 58					
Llwynypia	d			13 00							13 30							14 00					
Tonypandy	d			13 03							13 33							14 03					
Dinas Rhondda	d			13 05							13 35							14 05					
Porth	a			13 08							13 38							14 08					
	d			13 09							13 39							14 09					
Trehafod	d			13 12							13 42							14 12					
Merthyr Tydfil	d	12 38							13 08							13 38							14 08
Pentre-bach	d	12 42							13 12							13 42							14 12
Troed Y Rhiw	d	12 45							13 15							13 45							14 15
Merthyr Vale	a	12 48							13 18							13 48							14 18
	d	12 50							13 20							13 50							14 20
Quakers Yard	d	12 55							13 25							13 55							14 25
Aberdare 3	d					12 52														13 52			
Cwmbach	d					12 55														13 55			
Fernhill	d					12 58														13 58			
Mountain Ash	a					13 01														14 01			
	d					13 04														14 04			
Penrhiwceiber	d					13 07														14 07			
Abercynon	d	12 59				13 13			13 29				13 45			13 59				14 13			14 29
Pontypridd 3	a	13 07		13 17		13 22			13 37		13 47		13 52			14 07		14 17		14 22			14 37
	d	13 09		13 18		13 24			13 39		13 48		13 54			14 09		14 18		14 24			14 39
Trefforest	d	13 12		13 21		13 27			13 42		13 51		13 57			14 12		14 21		14 27			14 42
Trefforest Estate	d	13 16							13 46							14 16							14 46
Taffs Well 3	d	13 20		13 28		13 34			13 50		13 58		14 04			14 20		14 28		14 34			14 50
Radyr 3	a	13 23		13 31		13 37			13 53		14 01		14 07			14 23		14 31		14 37			14 53
	d	13 23		13 31	13 34	13 37			13 53		14 01	14 04	14 07			14 23		14 31	14 34	14 37			14 53
Danescourt	d				13 38							14 08							14 38				
Fairwater	d				13 40							14 10							14 40				
Waun-gron Park	d				13 42							14 12							14 42				
Ninian Park	d				13 45							14 15							14 45				
Llandaf	d	13 26		13 34		13 40			13 56		14 04		14 10			14 26		14 34		14 40			14 56
Cathays	d	13 31		13 39		13 45			14 01		14 09		14 15			14 31		14 39		14 45			15 01
Rhymney 3	d													13 27									
Pontlottyn	d													13 30									
Tir-phil	d													13 35									
Brithdir	d													13 37									
Bargoed	a													13 41									
	d		13 00				13 17			13 32				13 45			14 00				14 17		
Gilfach Fargoed	d						13 19														14 19		
Pengam	d		13 05				13 22			13 37				13 50			14 05				14 22		
Hengoed	d		13 09				13 25			13 40				13 54			14 09				14 25		
Ystrad Mynach 3	d		13 12				13 28			13 43				13 57			14 12				14 28		
Llanbradach	d		13 16				13 33			13 48				14 01			14 16				14 33		
Energlyn & Churchill Park	d		13 20											14 05			14 20						
Aber	d		13 22				13 37			13 52				14 07			14 22				14 37		
Caerphilly 3	d		13 25				13 40			13 55				14 10			14 25				14 40		
Lisvane & Thornhill	d		13 29				13 44			13 59				14 14			14 29				14 44		
Llanishen	d		13 31				13 46			14 01				14 16			14 31				14 46		
Heath High Level	d		13 34				13 49			14 04				14 19			14 34				14 49		
Coryton	d							13 45							14 15							14 45	
Whitchurch (Cardiff)	d							13 46							14 16							14 46	
Rhiwbina	d							13 48							14 18							14 48	
Birchgrove	d							13 50							14 20							14 50	
Ty Glas	d							13 51							14 21							14 51	
Heath Low Level	d							13 54							14 24							14 54	
Cardiff Queen Street 3	a	13 34	13 39	13 44		13 49	13 54	13 59	14 04	14 09	14 14		14 19	14 24	14 29	14 34	14 39	14 44		14 49	14 54	14 59	15 04
	d	13 36	13 41	13 46		13 51	13 56	14 01	14 06	14 11	14 16		14 21	14 26	14 31	14 36	14 41	14 46		14 51	14 56	15 01	15 06
Cardiff Central 7	a	13 39	13 44	13 52	13 50	13 54	13 59	14 04	14 09	14 14	14 22	14 20	14 24	14 29	14 34	14 39	14 44	14 52	14 50	14 54	14 57	15 05	15 09
	d	13 41	13 46			13 55	14 01		14 10	14 16			14 25	14 31		14 41	14 46			14 55	15 01		15 10
Grangetown	d	13 45	13 50			13 59	14 05		14 14	14 20			14 29	14 35		14 45	14 50			14 59	15 05		15 14
Dingle Road	d		13 56				14 11			14 26				14 41			14 56				15 11		
Penarth	a		14 01				14 16			14 31				14 46			15 01				15 16		
Cogan	d	13 48				14 03			14 18				14 33			14 48				15 03			15 18
Eastbrook	d	13 51				14 05			14 20				14 35			14 51				15 05			15 20
Dinas Powys	d	13 53				14 07			14 22				14 37			14 53				15 07			15 22
Cadoxton	d	13 57				14 12			14 27				14 42			14 57				15 12			15 27
Barry Docks	d	14 00				14 14			14 29				14 44			15 00				15 14			15 29
Barry 3	d	14 05				14 19			14 34				14 49			15 05				15 19			15 34
Barry Island	a					14 25			14 40				14 55							15 25			15 40
Rhoose Cardiff Int Airport ✈	d	14 12														15 12							
Llantwit Major	d	14 22														15 22							
Bridgend	a	14 39														15 39							

A To Coryton

B To Radyr

When events are being held at the Millenium Stadium, services are subject to alteration. Please check times before travelling.

For connections to Cardiff Bay please refer to Table 130A

Table 130

Mondays to Fridays

9 December to 16 May

Treherbert, Aberdare, Merthyr, Pontypridd, Rhymney and Coryton - Cardiff, Penarth, Barry, Barry Island and Bridgend

Network Diagram - see first Page of Table 130

		AW	AW A	AW	AW	AW	AW B	AW	AW	AW	AW A	AW	AW	AW B	AW	AW	AW	AW A	AW	AW	AW B	AW
Treherbert	d					14 17				14 47							15 13					
Ynyswen	d					14 19				14 49							15 15					
Treorchy	d					14 21				14 51							15 21					
Ton Pentre	d					14 23				14 53							15 23					
Ystrad Rhondda	a					14 26				14 56							15 26					
	d					14 28				14 58							15 28					
Llwynypia	d					14 30				15 00							15 30					
Tonypandy	d					14 33				15 03							15 33					
Dinas Rhondda	d					14 35				15 05							15 35					
Porth	a					14 38				15 08							15 38					
	d					14 52				15 09							15 39					
Trehafod	d					14 55				15 12							15 42					
Merthyr Tydfil	d							14 38							15 08							15 38
Pentre-bach	d							14 42							15 12							15 42
Troed Y Rhiw	d							14 45							15 15							15 45
Merthyr Vale	a							14 48							15 18							15 48
	d							14 50							15 20							15 50
Quakers Yard	d							14 55							15 25							15 55
Aberdare 3	d			14 22								14 52							15 22			
Cwmbach	d			14 25								14 55							15 25			
Fernhill	d			14 28								14 58							15 28			
Mountain Ash	a			14 31								15 01							15 31			
	d			14 34								15 04							15 34			
Penrhiwceiber	d			14 37								15 07							15 37			
Abercynon	d			14 43				14 59				15 13			15 29				15 43			15 59
Pontypridd 3	a			14 52		15 00		15 07		15 17		15 22			15 37		15 47		15 52			16 07
	d			14 54		15 04		15 09		15 18		15 24			15 39		15 48		15 54			16 09
Trefforest	d			14 57		15 07		15 12		15 21		15 27			15 42		15 51		15 57			16 12
Trefforest Estate	d							15 16							15 46							16 16
Taffs Well 3	d			15 04		15 13		15 20		15 28		15 34			15 50		15 58		16 04			16 20
Radyr 3	a			15 07		15 17		15 23		15 31		15 37			15 53		16 01		16 07			16 23
	d		15 04	15 07		15 17		15 23		15 31	15 34	15 37			15 53		16 01	16 04	16 07			16 23
Danescourt	d		15 08								15 38							16 08				
Fairwater	d		15 10								15 40							16 10				
Waun-gron Park	d		15 12								15 42							16 12				
Ninian Park	d		15 15								15 45							16 15				
Llandaf	d			15 10				15 26		15 34		15 40			15 56		16 04		16 10			16 26
Cathays	d			15 15				15 31		15 39		15 45			16 01		16 09		16 15			16 31
Rhymney 3	d				14 27															15 27		
Pontlottyn	d				14 30															15 30		
Tir-phil	d				14 35															15 35		
Brithdir	d				14 37															15 37		
Bargoed	a				14 41															15 41		
	d	14 32			14 45				15 00				15 17			15 32				15 45		
Gilfach Fargoed	d												15 19									
Pengam	d	14 37			14 50				15 05				15 22			15 37				15 50		
Hengoed	d	14 40			14 54				15 09				15 25			15 40				15 54		
Ystrad Mynach 3	d	14 43			14 57				15 12				15 28			15 43				15 57		
Llanbradach	d	14 48			15 01				15 16				15 33			15 48				16 01		
Energlyn & Churchill Park	d				15 05				15 20											16 05		
Aber	d	14 52			15 07				15 22				15 37			15 52				16 07		
Caerphilly 3	d	14 55			15 10				15 25				15 40			15 55				16 10		
Lisvane & Thornhill	d	14 59			15 14				15 29				15 44			15 59				16 14		
Llanishen	d	15 01			15 16				15 31				15 46			16 01				16 16		
Heath High Level	d	15 04			15 19				15 34				15 49			16 04				16 19		
Coryton	d						15 15							15 45							16 15	
Whitchurch (Cardiff)	d						15 16							15 46							16 16	
Rhiwbina	d						15 18							15 48							16 18	
Birchgrove	d						15 20							15 50							16 20	
Ty Glas	d						15 21							15 51							16 21	
Heath Low Level	d						15 24							15 54							16 24	
Cardiff Queen Street 3	a	15 09		15 19	15 24		15 29	15 34	15 39	15 44		15 49	15 54	15 59	16 04	16 09	16 14		16 19	16 24	16 29	16 34
	d	15 11		15 21	15 26		15 31	15 36	15 41	15 46		15 51	15 56	16 01	16 06	16 11	16 16		16 21	16 26	16 31	16 36
Cardiff Central 7	a	15 14	15 20	15 24	15 29	15 34	15 34	15 39	15 44	15 52	15 50	15 54	15 59	16 04	16 09	16 14	16 22	16 20	16 24	16 32	16 34	16 39
	d	15 16		15 25	15 31			15 41	15 46			15 55	16 01		16 10	16 16			16 25			16 41
Grangetown	d	15 20		15 29	15 35			15 45	15 50			15 59	16 05		16 14	16 20			16 29			16 45
Dingle Road	d	15 26			15 41				15 56				16 11			16 26						
Penarth	a	15 31			15 46				16 01				16 16			16 31						
Cogan	d			15 33				15 48				16 03			16 18				16 33			16 48
Eastbrook	d			15 35				15 51				16 05			16 20				16 35			16 51
Dinas Powys	d			15 37				15 53				16 07			16 22				16 37			16 53
Cadoxton	d			15 42				15 57				16 12			16 27				16 42			16 57
Barry Docks	d			15 44				16 00				16 14			16 29				16 44			17 00
Barry 3	d			15 49				16 05				16 19			16 34				16 49			17 05
Barry Island	a			15 55								16 25			16 40				16 55			
Rhoose Cardiff Int Airport ✈	d							16 12														17 12
Llantwit Major	d							16 22														17 22
Bridgend	a							16 37														17 37

A To Coryton

B To Radyr

When events are being held at the Millenium Stadium, services are subject to alteration. Please check times before travelling.

For connections to Cardiff Bay please refer to Table 130A

Table 130

Mondays to Fridays

9 December to 16 May

Treherbert, Aberdare, Merthyr, Pontypridd, Rhymney and Coryton - Cardiff, Penarth, Barry, Barry Island and Bridgend

Network Diagram - see first Page of Table 130

		AW	AW	AW A	AW	AW	AW B	AW	AW	AW	AW A	AW	AW	AW B	AW	AW	AW	AW A	AW	AW	AW B	AW	AW
Treherbert	d		15 47							16 17							16 47						
Ynyswen	d		15 49							16 19							16 49						
Treorchy	d		15 51							16 21							16 51						
Ton Pentre	d		15 53							16 23							16 53						
Ystrad Rhondda	a		15 56							16 26							16 56						
	d		15 58							16 28							16 58						
Llwynypia	d		16 00							16 30							17 00						
Tonypandy	d		16 03							16 33							17 03						
Dinas Rhondda	d		16 05							16 35							17 05						
Porth	a		16 08							16 38							17 08						
	d		16 09							16 39							17 09						
Trehafod	d		16 12							16 42							17 12						
Merthyr Tydfil	d							16 08							16 38							17 08	
Pentre-bach	d							16 12							16 42							17 12	
Troed Y Rhiw	d							16 15							16 45							17 15	
Merthyr Vale	a							16 18							16 48							17 18	
	d							16 20							16 50							17 20	
Quakers Yard	d							16 25							16 55							17 25	
Aberdare Ⓑ	d				15 52							16 22							16 52				
Cwmbach	d				15 55							16 25							16 55				
Fernhill	d				15 58							16 28							16 58				
Mountain Ash	a				16 01							16 31							17 01				
	d				16 04							16 34							17 04				
Penrhiwceiber	d				16 07							16 37							17 07				
Abercynon	d				16 13			16 29				16 43			16 59				17 13			17 29	
Pontypridd Ⓑ	a		16 17		16 22			16 37		16 47		16 52			17 07		17 17		17 22			17 37	
	d		16 18		16 24			16 39		16 48		16 54			17 09		17 18		17 24			17 39	
Trefforest	d		16 21		16 27			16 42		16 51		16 57			17 12		17 21		17 27			17 42	
Trefforest Estate	d							16 46							17 16							17 46	
Taffs Well Ⓑ	d		16 28		16 34			16 50		16 58		17 04			17 20		17 28		17 34			17 50	
Radyr Ⓑ	a		16 31		16 37			16 53		17 01		17 07			17 23		17 31		17 37			17 53	
	d		16 31	16 34	16 37			16 53		17 01	17 04	17 07			17 23		17 31	17 34	17 37			17 53	
Danescourt	d			16 38							17 08							17 38					
Fairwater	d			16 40							17 10							17 40					
Waun-gron Park	d			16 42							17 12							17 42					
Ninian Park	d			16 45							17 15							17 45					
Llandaf	d		16 34		16 40			16 56		17 04		17 10			17 26		17 34		17 40			17 56	
Cathays	d		16 39		16 45			17 01		17 09		17 15			17 31		17 39		17 45			18 01	
Rhymney Ⓑ	d												16 27										
Pontlottyn	d												16 30										
Tir-phil	d												16 35										
Brithdir	d												16 37										
Bargoed	a												16 41										
	d	16 00				16 17			16 32				16 45			17 00				17 17			17 32
Gilfach Fargoed	d					16 19														17 19			
Pengam	d	16 05				16 22			16 37				16 50			17 05				17 22			17 37
Hengoed	d	16 09				16 25			16 40				16 54			17 09				17 25			17 40
Ystrad Mynach Ⓑ	d	16 12				16 28			16 43				16 57			17 12				17 28			17 43
Llanbradach	d	16 16				16 33			16 48				17 01			17 16				17 33			17 48
Energlyn & Churchill Park	d	16 20											17 05			17 20							
Aber	d	16 22				16 37			16 52				17 07			17 22				17 37			17 52
Caerphilly Ⓑ	d	16 25				16 40			16 55				17 10			17 25				17 40			17 55
Lisvane & Thornhill	d	16 29				16 44			16 59				17 14			17 29				17 44			17 59
Llanishen	d	16 31				16 46			17 01				17 16			17 31				17 46			18 01
Heath High Level	d	16 34				16 49			17 04				17 19			17 34				17 49			18 04
Coryton	d						16 45							17 15							17 45		
Whitchurch (Cardiff)	d						16 46							17 16							17 46		
Rhiwbina	d						16 48							17 18							17 48		
Birchgrove	d						16 50							17 20							17 50		
Ty Glas	d						16 51							17 21							17 51		
Heath Low Level	d						16 54							17 24							17 54		
Cardiff Queen Street Ⓑ	a	16 39	16 44		16 49	16 54	16 59	17 04	17 09	17 14		17 19	17 24	17 29	17 34	17 39	17 44		17 49	17 54	17 59	18 04	18 09
	d	16 41	16 46		16 51	16 56	17 01	17 06	17 11	17 16		17 21	17 26	17 31	17 36	17 41	17 46		17 51	17 56	18 01	18 06	18 11
Cardiff Central Ⓑ	a	16 44	16 52	16 50	16 54	16 59	17 04	17 09	17 14	17 22	17 20	17 24	17 29	17 34	17 39	17 44	17 52	17 50	17 54	17 59	18 04	18 09	18 14
	d	16 46			16 55	17 01		17 10	17 16			17 25	17 31		17 41	17 46			17 55	18 01		18 10	18 16
Grangetown	d	16 50			16 59	17 05		17 14	17 20			17 29	17 35		17 45	17 50			17 59	18 05		18 14	18 20
Dingle Road	d	16 56				17 11			17 26				17 41			17 56				18 11			18 26
Penarth	a	17 01				17 16			17 31				17 46			18 01				18 16			18 31
Cogan	d				17 03			17 18				17 33			17 48				18 03			18 18	
Eastbrook	d				17 05			17 20				17 35			17 51				18 05			18 20	
Dinas Powys	d				17 07			17 22				17 37			17 53				18 07			18 22	
Cadoxton	d				17 12			17 27				17 42			17 57				18 12			18 27	
Barry Docks	d				17 14			17 29				17 44			18 00				18 14			18 29	
Barry Ⓑ	d				17 19			17 34				17 49			18 05				18 19			18 34	
Barry Island	a				17 25			17 40				17 55							18 25			18 40	
Rhoose Cardiff Int Airport ✈	d														18 12								
Llantwit Major	d														18 22								
Bridgend	a														18 37								

A To Coryton **B** To Radyr

When events are being held at the Millenium Stadium, services are subject to alteration. Please check times before travelling.

For connections to Cardiff Bay please refer to Table 130A

Table 130

Mondays to Fridays

9 December to 16 May

Treherbert, Aberdare, Merthyr, Pontypridd, Rhymney and Coryton - Cardiff, Penarth, Barry, Barry Island and Bridgend

Network Diagram - see first Page of Table 130

		AW	AW		AW	AW	AW	AW	AW	AW	AW	AW	AW		AW	AW	AW	AW	AW	AW	AW	AW	AW		AW
			A				B			A										B					
Treherbert	d	17 17							17 47							18 17						18 47			
Ynyswen	d	17 19							17 49							18 19						18 49			
Treorchy	d	17 21							17 51							18 21						18 51			
Ton Pentre	d	17 23							17 53							18 23						18 53			
Ystrad Rhondda	a	17 26							17 56							18 26						18 56			
	d	17 28							17 58							18 28						18 58			
Llwynypia	d	17 30							18 00							18 30						19 00			
Tonypandy	d	17 33							18 03							18 33						19 03			
Dinas Rhondda	d	17 35							18 05							18 35						19 05			
Porth	a	17 38							18 08							18 38						19 08			
	d	17 39							18 09							18 39						19 09			
Trehafod	d	17 42							18 12							18 42						19 12			
Merthyr Tydfil	d							17 38							18 08						18 38				
Pentre-bach	d							17 42							18 12						18 42				
Troed Y Rhiw	d							17 45							18 15						18 45				
Merthyr Vale	a							17 48							18 18						18 48				
	d							17 50							18 20						18 50				
Quakers Yard	d							17 55							18 25						18 55				
Aberdare 3	d				17 22						17 52							18 22					18 52		
Cwmbach	d				17 25						17 55							18 25					18 55		
Fernhill	d				17 28						17 58							18 28					18 58		
Mountain Ash	a				17 31						18 01							18 31					19 01		
	d				17 34						18 04							18 34					19 04		
Penrhiwceiber	d				17 37						18 07							18 37					19 07		
Abercynon	d				17 43			17 59			18 13				18 29			18 43			18 59		19 13		
Pontypridd 3	a	17 47			17 52			18 07	18 17		18 22				18 37	18 47		18 52			19 07	19 17	19 22		
	d	17 48			17 54			18 09	18 18		18 24				18 39	18 48		18 54			19 09	19 18	19 24		
Trefforest	d	17 51			17 57			18 12	18 21		18 27				18 42	18 51		18 57			19 12	19 21	19 27		
Trefforest Estate	d							18 16							18 46						19 16				
Taffs Well 3	d	17 58			18 04			18 20	18 28		18 34				18 50	18 58		19 04			19 20	19 28	19 34		
Radyr 3	a	18 01			18 07			18 23	18 31		18 37				18 53	19 01		19 07			19 23	19 31	19 37		
	d	18 01	18 04		18 07			18 23	18 31	18 34	18 37				18 53	19 01	19 04	19 07			19 23	19 31	19 37		
Danescourt	d		18 08							18 38							19 08								
Fairwater	d		18 10							18 40							19 10								
Waun-gron Park	d		18 12							18 42							19 12								
Ninian Park	d		18 15							18 45							19 15								
Llandaf	d	18 04			18 10			18 26	18 34		18 40				18 56	19 04		19 10			19 26	19 34	19 40		
Cathays	d	18 09			18 15			18 31	18 39		18 45				19 01	19 09		19 15			19 31	19 39	19 45		
Rhymney 3	d					17 27																			
Pontlottyn	d					17 30																			
Tir-phil	d					17 35																			
Brithdir	d					17 37																			
Bargoed	a					17 41																			
	d					17 45						18 15							18 48						
Gilfach Fargoed	d											18 18							18 50						
Pengam	d					17 50						18 20							18 53						
Hengoed	d					17 54						18 24							18 56						
Ystrad Mynach 3	d					17 57						18 27							18 59						
Llanbradach	d					18 01						18 31							19 04						
Energlyn & Churchill Park	d					18 05						18 35													
Aber	d					18 07						18 37							19 08						
Caerphilly 3	d					18 10						18 40							19 11						19 40
Lisvane & Thornhill	d					18 14						18 44							19 15						19 44
Llanishen	d					18 16						18 46							19 17						19 46
Heath High Level	d					18 19						18 49							19 20						19 49
Coryton	d						18 15						18 45							19 15					
Whitchurch (Cardiff)	d						18 16						18 46							19 16					
Rhiwbina	d						18 18						18 48							19 18					
Birchgrove	d						18 20						18 50							19 20					
Ty Glas	d						18 21						18 51							19 21					
Heath Low Level	d						18 24						18 54							19 24					
Cardiff Queen Street 3	a	18 14			18 19	18 24	18 29	18 34	18 44		18 49	18 54	18 59		19 04	19 14		19 19	19 24	19 29	19 34	19 44	19 49		19 54
	d	18 16			18 21	18 26	18 31	18 36	18 46		18 51	18 56	19 01		19 06	19 16		19 21	19 26	19 31	19 36	19 46	19 51		19 56
Cardiff Central 7	a	18 21	18 20		18 24	18 29	18 34	18 39	18 52	18 50	18 54	18 59	19 06		19 10	19 22	19 22	19 24	19 29	19 34	19 39	19 52	19 57		19 59
	d				18 25	18 31		18 41			18 55	19 01						19 25	19 31		19 41				20 06
Grangetown	d				18 29	18 35		18 45			18 59	19 05						19 29	19 35		19 45				20 10
Dingle Road	d					18 41						19 11							19 41						20 14
Penarth	a					18 46						19 16							19 46						20 19
Cogan	d				18 33			18 48			19 03							19 33			19 48				
Eastbrook	d				18 35			18 51			19 05							19 35			19 51				
Dinas Powys	d				18 37			18 53			19 07							19 37			19 53				
Cadoxton	d				18 42			18 57			19 12							19 42			19 57				
Barry Docks	d				18 44			19 00			19 14							19 44			20 00				
Barry 3	d				18 49			19 05			19 19							19 49			20 05				
Barry Island	a				18 55						19 25							19 55							
Rhoose Cardiff Int Airport ✈	d							19 12													20 12				
Llantwit Major	d							19 22													20 22				
Bridgend	a							19 39													20 39				

A To Coryton **B** To Radyr

When events are being held at the Millenium Stadium, services are subject to alteration. Please check times before travelling.

For connections to Cardiff Bay please refer to Table 130A

Table 130

Mondays to Fridays

9 December to 16 May

Treherbert, Aberdare, Merthyr, Pontypridd, Rhymney and Coryton - Cardiff, Penarth, Barry, Barry Island and Bridgend

Network Diagram - see first Page of Table 130

		AW	AW	AW	AW	AW A	AW	AW	AW	AW	AW	AW	AW	AW	AW	AW A	AW	AW	AW	AW	AW	AW B	AW
Treherbert	d		19 17						19 47			20 17									21 17		
Ynyswen	d		19 19						19 49			20 19									21 19		
Treorchy	d		19 21						19 51			20 21									21 21		
Ton Pentre	d		19 23						19 53			20 23									21 23		
Ystrad Rhondda	a		19 26						19 56			20 26									21 26		
	d		19 28						19 58			20 28									21 28		
Llwynypia	d		19 30						20 00			20 30									21 30		
Tonypandy	d		19 33						20 03			20 33									21 33		
Dinas Rhondda	d		19 35						20 05			20 35									21 35		
Porth	a		19 38						20 08			20 38									21 38		
	d		19 39						20 09			20 39									21 39		
Trehafod	d		19 42						20 12			20 42									21 42		
Merthyr Tydfil	d	19 08					19 38										20 38						
Pentre-bach	d	19 12					19 42										20 42						
Troed Y Rhiw	d	19 15					19 45										20 45						
Merthyr Vale	a	19 18					19 48										20 48						
	d	19 20					19 50										20 50						
Quakers Yard	d	19 25					19 55										20 55						
Aberdare 3	d									19 52				20 22					20 54				
Cwmbach	d									19 55				20 25					20 57				
Fernhill	d									19 58				20 28					21 00				
Mountain Ash	a									20 01				20 31					21 03				
	d									20 04				20 34					21 04				
Penrhiwceiber	d									20 07				20 37					21 07				
Abercynon	d	19 29			19 43		19 59			20 13				20 43			20 59		21 13				
Pontypridd 3	a	19 37	19 47		19 52		20 07		20 18	20 22		20 47		20 52			21 07		21 22		21 47		
	d	19 39	19 48		19 54		20 09		20 18	20 24		20 48		20 54			21 09		21 24		21 48		
Trefforest	d	19 42	19 51		19 57		20 12		20 21	20 27		20 51		20 57			21 12		21 27		21 51		
Trefforest Estate	d	19 46					20 16										21 16						
Taffs Well 3	d	19 50	19 58		20 04		20 20		20 28	20 34		20 58		21 04			21 20		21 34		21 58		
Radyr 3	a	19 53	20 01		20 07		20 23		20 31	20 37		21 01		21 07			21 23		21 37		22 01		
	d	19 53	20 01	20 04	20 07		20 23		20 31	20 37		21 01	21 04	21 07			21 23		21 37		22 01	22 04	
Danescourt	d			20 08									21 08									22 08	
Fairwater	d			20 10									21 10									22 10	
Waun-gron Park	d			20 12									21 12									22 12	
Ninian Park	d			20 15									21 15									22 15	
Llandaf	d	19 56	20 04		20 10		20 26		20 34	20 40		21 04		21 10			21 26		21 40		22 04		
Cathays	d	20 01	20 09		20 15		20 31		20 39	20 45		21 09		21 15			21 31		21 45		22 09		
Rhymney 3	d							19 43										20 46					21 36
Pontlottyn	d							19 46										20 49					21 39
Tir-phil	d							19 51										20 54					21 44
Brithdir	d							19 53										20 56					21 46
Bargoed	a							19 57										21 00					21 50
	d							19 57										21 00					21 50
Gilfach Fargoed	d							20 00										21 03					21 53
Pengam	d							20 02										21 05					21 55
Hengoed	d							20 06										21 09					21 59
Ystrad Mynach 3	d							20 09										21 12		21 39			22 02
Llanbradach	d							20 13										21 16		21 44			22 06
Energlyn & Churchill Park	d							20 17										21 20					22 10
Aber	d							20 19										21 22		21 48			22 12
Caerphilly 3	d							20 22			20 40							21 25		21 51			22 15
Lisvane & Thornhill	d							20 26			20 44							21 29		21 55			22 19
Llanishen	d							20 28			20 46							21 31		21 57			22 21
Heath High Level	d							20 31			20 49							21 34		22 00			22 24
Coryton	d					20 15										21 15							
Whitchurch (Cardiff)	d					20 16										21 16							
Rhiwbina	d					20 18										21 18							
Birchgrove	d					20 20										21 20							
Ty Glas	d					20 21										21 21							
Heath Low Level	d					20 24										21 24							
Cardiff Queen Street 3	a	20 04	20 14		20 19	20 29	20 34	20 39	20 44	20 49	20 54	21 14		21 19		21 29	21 34	21 42	21 49	22 05	22 14		22 29
	d	20 06	20 16		20 21	20 31	20 36	20 41	20 46	20 51	20 56	21 16		21 21		21 31	21 36	21 44	21 51	22 06	22 16		22 31
Cardiff Central 7	a	20 09	20 22	20 24	20 25	20 34	20 39	20 47	20 52	20 57	20 59	21 22	21 25	21 27		21 34	21 39	21 47	21 54	22 09	22 22	22 20	22 34
	d	20 10			20 31		20 41			21 06	21 10				21 31		21 41		21 56	22 10			22 36
Grangetown	d	20 14			20 35		20 45			21 10	21 14				21 35		21 45		22 00	22 14			22 40
Dingle Road	d				20 41					21 14					21 41				22 04				22 44
Penarth	a				20 46					21 19					21 46				22 09				22 47
Cogan	d	20 18					20 48				21 18						21 48			22 18			
Eastbrook	d	20 20					20 51				21 20						21 51			22 20			
Dinas Powys	d	20 22					20 53				21 22						21 53			22 22			
Cadoxton	d	20 27					20 57				21 27						21 57			22 27			
Barry Docks	d	20 29					21 00				21 29						22 00			22 29			
Barry 3	d	20 34					21 05				21 34						22 05			22 34			
Barry Island	a	20 40									21 40									22 40			
Rhoose Cardiff Int Airport ✈	d						21 12										22 12						
Llantwit Major	d						21 22										22 22						
Bridgend	a						21 39										22 37						

A To Radyr

B To Coryton

When events are being held at the Millenium Stadium, services are subject to alteration. Please check times before travelling.

For connections to Cardiff Bay please refer to Table 130A

Table 130

Mondays to Fridays

9 December to 16 May

Treherbert, Aberdare, Merthyr, Pontypridd, Rhymney and Coryton - Cardiff, Penarth, Barry, Barry Island and Bridgend

Network Diagram - see first Page of Table 130

		AW	AW	AW	AW		AW	AW	AW
Treherbert	d								
Ynyswen	d								
Treorchy	d								
Ton Pentre	d								
Ystrad Rhondda	a								
	d								
Llwynypia	d								
Tonypandy	d								
Dinas Rhondda	d								
Porth	a								
	d								
Trehafod	d								
Merthyr Tydfil	d	21 38						22 38	
Pentre-bach	d	21 42						22 42	
Troed Y Rhiw	d	21 45						22 45	
Merthyr Vale	a	21 48						22 48	
	d	21 50						22 50	
Quakers Yard	d	21 55						22 55	
Aberdare 3	d			21 54					22 54
Cwmbach	d			21 57					22 57
Fernhill	d			22 00					23 00
Mountain Ash	a			22 03					23 03
	d			22 04					23 04
Penrhiwceiber	d			22 07					23 07
Abercynon	d	21 59		22 13				22 59	23 13
Pontypridd 3	a	22 07		22 22				23 07	23 22
	d	22 09		22 24				23 09	
Trefforest	d	22 12		22 27				23 12	
Trefforest Estate	d	22 16						23 16	
Taffs Well 3	d	22 20		22 34				23 20	
Radyr 3	a	22 23		22 37				23 23	
	d	22 23		22 37			23 14	23 23	
Danescourt	d								
Fairwater	d								
Waun-gron Park	d								
Ninian Park	d								
Llandaf	d	22 26		22 40			23 16	23 26	
Cathays	d	22 31		22 45			23 20	23 31	
Rhymney 3	d								
Pontlottyn	d								
Tir-phil	d								
Brithdir	d								
Bargoed	a								
	d								
Gilfach Fargoed	d								
Pengam	d								
Hengoed	d								
Ystrad Mynach 3	d								
Llanbradach	d								
Energlyn & Churchill Park	d								
Aber	d								
Caerphilly 3	d		22 28						
Lisvane & Thornhill	d								
Llanishen	d								
Heath High Level	d								
Coryton	d				22 45				
Whitchurch (Cardiff)	d				22 46				
Rhiwbina	d				22 48				
Birchgrove	d				22 50				
Ty Glas	d				22 51				
Heath Low Level	d				22 54				
Cardiff Queen Street 3	a	22 34	22 39	22 49	22 59		23 24	23 34	
	d	22 36	22 41	22 54	23 01		23 25	23 36	
Cardiff Central 7	a	22 39	22 43	23 00	23 06		23 28	23 42	
	d	22 41		23 12			23 31		
Grangetown	d	22 45		23 16			23 35		
Dingle Road	d			23 20					
Penarth	a			23 25					
Cogan	d	22 49					23 38		
Eastbrook	d	22 51					23 41		
Dinas Powys	d	22 53					23 43		
Cadoxton	d	22 58					23 47		
Barry Docks	d	23 00					23 50		
Barry 3	d	23 05					23 54		
Barry Island	a						00 01		
Rhoose Cardiff Int Airport	d	23 12							
Llantwit Major	d	23 22							
Bridgend	a	23 39							

When events are being held at the Millenium Stadium, services are subject to alteration. Please check times before travelling.

For connections to Cardiff Bay please refer to Table 130A

Table 130

Saturdays

14 December to 28 December

Treherbert, Aberdare, Merthyr, Pontypridd, Rhymney and Coryton - Cardiff, Penarth, Barry, Barry Island and Bridgend

Network Diagram - see first Page of Table 130

		AW	AW	AW	AW	AW	AW	AW	AW	AW	AW A	AW	AW B	AW	AW C	AW	AW D	AW	AW	AW B	AW	AW	AW
Treherbert	d									05 47						06 17							06 47
Ynyswen	d									05 49						06 19							06 49
Treorchy	d									05 51						06 21							06 51
Ton Pentre	d									05 53						06 23							06 53
Ystrad Rhondda	a									05 56						06 26							06 56
	d									05 58						06 28							06 58
Llwynypia	d									06 00						06 30							07 00
Tonypandy	d									06 03						06 33							07 03
Dinas Rhondda	d									06 05						06 35							07 05
Porth	a									06 08						06 38							07 08
	d									06 09						06 39							07 09
Trehafod	d									06 12						06 42							07 12
Merthyr Tydfil	d																				06 38		
Pentre-bach	d																				06 42		
Troed Y Rhiw	d																				06 45		
Merthyr Vale	a																				06 48		
	d																				06 50		
Quakers Yard	d																				06 55		
Aberdare ■	d																	06 22					
Cwmbach	d																	06 25					
Fernhill	d																	06 28					
Mountain Ash	a																	06 31					
	d																	06 34					
Penrhiwceiber	d																	06 37					
Abercynon	d																	06 43			06 59		
Pontypridd ■	a									06 17						06 47		06 52			07 07		07 17
	d				05 18					06 18						06 48		06 54			07 09		07 18
Trefforest	d				05 21					06 21						06 51		06 57			07 12		07 21
Trefforest Estate	d				05 25																07 16		
Taffs Well ■	d				05 28					06 28					06 53	06 58	←	07 04			07 20		07 28
Radyr ■	a				05 31					06 31					06 56	07 01	06 56	07 07			07 23		07 31
	d				05 31					06 31					07 04	07 01	07 04	07 07			07 23		07 31
Danescourt	d														→		07 08						
Fairwater	d																07 10						
Waun-gron Park	d																07 12						
Ninian Park	d																07 15						
Llandaf	d				05 34					06 34						07 04		07 10			07 26		07 34
Cathays	d				05 39					06 39						07 09		07 15			07 31		07 39
Rhymney ■	d													06 08					06 32				
Pontlottyn	d													06 11					06 35				
Tir-phil	d													06 16					06 40				
Brithdir	d													06 18					06 42				
Bargoed	a													06 22					06 46				
	d													06 25					06 46			07 02	
Gilfach Fargoed	d													06 28								07 04	
Pengam	d													06 30					06 51			07 07	
Hengoed	d													06 34					06 54			07 10	
Ystrad Mynach ■	d													06 37					06 57			07 13	
Llanbradach	d													06 41					07 01			07 18	
Energlyn & Churchill Park	d													06 45					07 05				
Aber	d													06 47					07 07			07 22	
Caerphilly ■	d								06 10					06 50					07 10			07 25	
Lisvane & Thornhill	d								06 14					06 54					07 14			07 29	
Llanishen	d								06 16					06 56					07 16			07 31	
Heath High Level	d								06 19					06 59					07 19			07 34	
Coryton	d												06 45							07 15			
Whitchurch (Cardiff)	d												06 46							07 16			
Rhiwbina	d												06 48							07 18			
Birchgrove	d												06 50							07 20			
Ty Glas	d												06 51							07 21			
Heath Low Level	d												06 54							07 24			
Cardiff Queen Street ■	a				05 43				06 25	06 42			06 59	07 04		07 12		07 19	07 24	07 30	07 34	07 39	07 44
	d				05 45				06 26	06 43			07 01	07 06		07 13		07 21	07 26	07 31	07 36	07 41	07 46
Cardiff Central ■	a				05 48				06 29	06 48			07 04	07 09		07 16	07 20	07 24	07 29	07 34	07 39	07 44	07 52
	d	05 20	05 41	05 46	05 55	06 16	06 25	06 36	06 41		06 55	07 01		07 10		07 16		07 25	07 31		07 41	07 46	
Grangetown	d	05 24	05 45	05 50	05 59	06 20	06 29	06 40	06 45		06 59	07 05		07 14		07 20		07 29	07 35		07 45	07 50	
Dingle Road	d			05 54		06 24		06 44				07 11				07 26			07 41			07 56	
Penarth	a			05 59		06 29		06 49				07 16				07 31			07 46			08 01	
Cogan	d	05 28	05 48		06 03		06 33		06 48		07 03			07 18				07 33			07 48		
Eastbrook	d	05 30	05 51		06 05		06 35		06 51		07 05			07 20				07 35			07 51		
Dinas Powys	d	05 32	05 53		06 07		06 37		06 53		07 07			07 22				07 37			07 53		
Cadoxton	d	05 37	05 57		06 12		06 42		06 57		07 12			07 27				07 42			07 57		
Barry Docks	d	05 39	06 00		06 14		06 44		07 00		07 14			07 29				07 44			08 00		
Barry ■	d	05 44	06 05		06 19		06 49		07 05		07 19			07 34				07 49			08 05		
Barry Island	a	05 50			06 25		06 55				07 25			07 40				07 55					
Rhoose Cardiff Int Airport ✈	d		06 12						07 12												08 12		
Llantwit Major	d		06 22						07 22												08 22		
Bridgend	a		06 39						07 39												08 39		

A From Hereford
B To Radyr
C To Coryton
D From Taffs Well to Coryton

When events are being held at the Millenium Stadium, services are subject to alteration. Please check times before travelling.

For connections to Cardiff Bay please refer to Table 130A

Table 130

Saturdays

14 December to 28 December

Treherbert, Aberdare, Merthyr, Pontypridd, Rhymney and Coryton - Cardiff, Penarth, Barry, Barry Island and Bridgend

Network Diagram - see first Page of Table 130

		AW A	AW	AW	AW B	AW		AW	AW	AW A	AW	AW	AW B	AW	AW	AW		AW A	AW	AW	AW B	AW	AW	AW	AW A
Treherbert	d								07 17							07 45								08 17	
Ynyswen	d								07 19							07 47								08 19	
Treorchy	d								07 21							07 49								08 21	
Ton Pentre	d								07 23							07 51								08 23	
Ystrad Rhondda	a								07 26							07 54								08 26	
	d								07 28							07 58								08 28	
Llwynypia	d								07 30							08 00								08 30	
Tonypandy	d								07 33							08 03								08 33	
Dinas Rhondda	d								07 35							08 05								08 35	
Porth	a								07 38							08 08								08 38	
	d								07 39							08 09								08 39	
Trehafod	d								07 42							08 12								08 42	
Merthyr Tydfil	d					07 08								07 38								08 08			
Pentre-bach	d					07 12								07 42								08 12			
Troed Y Rhiw	d					07 15								07 45								08 15			
Merthyr Vale	a					07 18								07 48								08 18			
	d					07 20								07 50								08 20			
Quakers Yard	d					07 25								07 55								08 25			
Aberdare 3	d		06 52								07 22								07 52						
Cwmbach	d		06 55								07 25								07 55						
Fernhill	d		06 58								07 28								07 58						
Mountain Ash	a		07 01								07 31								08 01						
	d		07 04								07 34								08 04						
Penrhiwceiber	d		07 07								07 37								08 07						
Abercynon	d		07 13			07 29					07 43			07 59					08 13			08 29			
Pontypridd 3	a		07 22			07 37			07 47		07 52			08 07		08 17			08 22			08 37		08 47	
	d		07 24			07 39			07 48		07 54			08 09		08 18			08 24			08 39		08 48	
Trefforest	d		07 27			07 42			07 51		07 57			08 12		08 21			08 27			08 42		08 51	
Trefforest Estate	d					07 46								08 16								08 46			
Taffs Well 3	d		07 34			07 50			07 58		08 04			08 20		08 28			08 34			08 50		08 58	
Radyr 3	a		07 37			07 53			08 01		08 07			08 23		08 31			08 37			08 53		09 01	
	d	07 34	07 37			07 53			08 01	08 04	08 07			08 23		08 31		08 34	08 37			08 53		09 01	09 04
Danescourt	d	07 38								08 08								08 38							09 08
Fairwater	d	07 40								08 10								08 40							09 10
Waun-gron Park	d	07 42								08 12								08 42							09 12
Ninian Park	d	07 45								08 15								08 45							09 15
Llandaf	d		07 40			07 56			08 04		08 10			08 26		08 34			08 40			08 56		09 04	
Cathays	d		07 45			08 01			08 09		08 15			08 31		08 39			08 45			09 01		09 09	
Rhymney 3	d			07 00								07 24			07 42										
Pontlottyn	d			07 03								07 27			07 45										
Tir-phil	d			07 08								07 32			07 50										
Brithdir	d			07 10								07 34			07 52										
Bargoed	a			07 14								07 38			07 59										
	d			07 15				07 32				07 43			08 00					08 15			08 32		
Gilfach Fargoed	d			07 18								07 46								08 18					
Pengam	d			07 20				07 37				07 48			08 05					08 20			08 37		
Hengoed	d			07 24				07 40				07 52			08 09					08 24			08 40		
Ystrad Mynach 3	d			07 27				07 43				07 55			08 12					08 27			08 43		
Llanbradach	d			07 31				07 48				08 00			08 16					08 31			08 48		
Energlyn & Churchill Park	d			07 35								08 04			08 20					08 35					
Aber	d			07 37				07 52				08 07			08 22					08 37			08 52		
Caerphilly 3	d			07 40				07 55				08 10			08 25					08 40			08 55		
Lisvane & Thornhill	d			07 44				07 59				08 14			08 29					08 44			08 59		
Llanishen	d			07 46				08 01				08 16			08 31					08 46			09 01		
Heath High Level	d			07 49				08 04				08 19			08 34					08 49			09 04		
Coryton	d				07 45								08 15								08 45				
Whitchurch (Cardiff)	d				07 46								08 16								08 46				
Rhiwbina	d				07 48								08 18								08 48				
Birchgrove	d				07 50								08 20								08 50				
Ty Glas	d				07 51								08 21								08 51				
Heath Low Level	d				07 54								08 24								08 54				
Cardiff Queen Street 3	a		07 49	07 54	07 59	08 04		08 09	08 14		08 19	08 24	08 29	08 34	08 39	08 44			08 49	08 54	08 59	09 04	09 09	09 14	
	d		07 51	07 56	08 01	08 06		08 11	08 16		08 21	08 26	08 31	08 36	08 41	08 46			08 51	08 56	09 01	09 06	09 11	09 16	
Cardiff Central 7	a	07 50	07 54	07 59	08 04	08 09		08 14	08 22	08 19	08 24	08 29	08 34	08 39	08 47	08 52		08 50	08 54	08 59	09 04	09 09	09 14	09 22	09 20
	d		07 55	08 01		08 10		08 16			08 25	08 31		08 41					08 55	09 01		09 10	09 16		
Grangetown	d		07 59	08 05		08 14		08 20			08 29	08 35		08 45					08 59	09 05		09 14	09 20		
Dingle Road	d			08 11				08 26				08 41								09 11			09 26		
Penarth	a			08 16				08 31				08 46								09 16			09 31		
Cogan	d		08 03			08 18					08 33			08 48					09 03			09 18			
Eastbrook	d		08 05			08 20					08 35			08 51					09 05			09 20			
Dinas Powys	d		08 07			08 22					08 37			08 53					09 07			09 22			
Cadoxton	d		08 12			08 27					08 42			08 57					09 12			09 27			
Barry Docks	d		08 14			08 29					08 44			09 00					09 14			09 29			
Barry 3	d		08 19			08 34					08 49			09 05					09 19			09 34			
Barry Island	a		08 25			08 40					08 55								09 25			09 40			
Rhoose Cardiff Int Airport ✈	d													09 12											
Llantwit Major	d													09 22											
Bridgend	a													09 39											

A To Coryton

B To Radyr

When events are being held at the Millenium Stadium, services are subject to alteration. Please check times before travelling.

For connections to Cardiff Bay please refer to Table 130A

Table 130

Saturdays

14 December to 28 December

Treherbert, Aberdare, Merthyr, Pontypridd, Rhymney and Coryton - Cardiff, Penarth, Barry, Barry Island and Bridgend

Network Diagram - see first Page of Table 130

		AW		AW	AW A	AW	AW	AW	AW B	AW	AW	AW A		AW	AW	AW	AW B	AW	AW	AW A	AW	AW		AW	AW B
Treherbert	d							08 47								09 17								09 47	
Ynyswen	d							08 49								09 19								09 49	
Treorchy	d							08 51								09 21								09 51	
Ton Pentre	d							08 53								09 23								09 53	
Ystrad Rhondda	a							08 56								09 26								09 56	
	d							08 58								09 28								09 58	
Llwynypia	d							09 00								09 30								10 00	
Tonypandy	d							09 03								09 33								10 03	
Dinas Rhondda	d							09 05								09 35								10 05	
Porth	a							09 08								09 38								10 08	
	d							09 09								09 39								10 09	
Trehafod	d							09 12								09 42								10 12	
Merthyr Tydfil	d					08 38								09 08							09 38				
Pentre-bach	d					08 42								09 12							09 42				
Troed Y Rhiw	d					08 45								09 15							09 45				
Merthyr Vale	a					08 48								09 18							09 48				
	d					08 50								09 20							09 50				
Quakers Yard	d					08 55								09 25							09 55				
Aberdare 3	d	08 22								08 52								09 22							
Cwmbach	d	08 25								08 55								09 25							
Fernhill	d	08 28								08 58								09 28							
Mountain Ash	a	08 31								09 01								09 31							
	d	08 34								09 04								09 34							
Penrhiwceiber	d	08 37								09 07								09 37							
Abercynon	d	08 43				08 59				09 13				09 29				09 43			09 59				
Pontypridd 3	a	08 52				09 07		09 17		09 22				09 37		09 47		09 52			10 07			10 17	
	d	08 54				09 09		09 18		09 24				09 39		09 48		09 54			10 09			10 18	
Trefforest	d	08 57				09 12		09 21		09 27				09 42		09 51		09 57			10 12			10 21	
Trefforest Estate	d					09 16								09 46							10 16				
Taffs Well 3	d	09 04				09 20		09 28		09 34				09 50		09 58		10 04			10 20			10 28	
Radyr 3	a	09 07				09 23		09 31		09 37				09 53		10 01		10 07			10 23			10 31	
	d	09 07				09 23		09 31	09 34	09 37				09 53		10 01	10 04	10 07			10 23			10 31	10 34
Danescourt	d								09 38								10 08								10 38
Fairwater	d								09 40								10 10								10 40
Waun-gron Park	d								09 42								10 12								10 42
Ninian Park	d								09 45								10 15								10 45
Llandaf	d	09 10				09 26		09 34		09 40				09 56		10 04		10 10			10 26			10 34	
Cathays	d	09 15				09 31		09 39		09 45				10 01		10 09		10 15			10 31			10 39	
Rhymney 3	d			08 30															09 27						
Pontlottyn	d			08 33															09 30						
Tir-phil	d			08 37															09 35						
Brithdir	d			08 40															09 37						
Bargoed	a			08 44															09 41						
	d			08 47			09 00				09 17				09 32				09 45			10 00			
Gilfach Fargoed	d										09 19														
Pengam	d			08 52			09 05				09 22				09 37				09 50			10 05			
Hengoed	d			08 55			09 09				09 25				09 40				09 54			10 09			
Ystrad Mynach 3	d			08 58			09 12				09 28				09 43				09 57			10 12			
Llanbradach	d			09 03			09 16				09 33				09 48				10 01			10 16			
Energlyn & Churchill Park	d						09 20												10 05			10 20			
Aber	d			09 07			09 22				09 37				09 52				10 07			10 22			
Caerphilly 3	d			09 10			09 25				09 40				09 55				10 10			10 25			
Lisvane & Thornhill	d			09 14			09 29				09 44				09 59				10 14			10 29			
Llanishen	d			09 16			09 31				09 46				10 01				10 16			10 31			
Heath High Level	d			09 19			09 34				09 49				10 04				10 19			10 34			
Coryton	d				09 15							09 45								10 15					
Whitchurch (Cardiff)	d				09 16							09 46								10 16					
Rhiwbina	d				09 18							09 48								10 18					
Birchgrove	d				09 20							09 50								10 20					
Ty Glas	d				09 21							09 51								10 21					
Heath Low Level	d				09 24							09 54								10 24					
Cardiff Queen Street 3	a	09 19		09 24	09 29	09 34	09 39	09 44		09 49	09 54	09 59		10 04	10 09	10 14		10 19	10 24	10 29	10 34	10 39		10 44	
	d	09 21		09 26	09 31	09 36	09 41	09 46		09 51	09 56	10 01		10 06	10 11	10 16		10 21	10 26	10 31	10 36	10 41		10 46	
Cardiff Central 7	a	09 24		09 29	09 34	09 39	09 44	09 52	09 50	09 54	09 59	10 04		10 09	10 14	10 22	10 20	10 24	10 29	10 34	10 39	10 44		10 52	10 50
	d	09 25		09 31		09 41	09 46			09 55	10 01			10 10	10 16			10 25	10 31		10 41	10 46			
Grangetown	d	09 29		09 35		09 45	09 50			09 59	10 05			10 14	10 20			10 29	10 35		10 45	10 50			
Dingle Road	d			09 41			09 56				10 11				10 26				10 41			10 56			
Penarth	a			09 46			10 01				10 16				10 31				10 46			11 01			
Cogan	d	09 33				09 48				10 03				10 18				10 33			10 48				
Eastbrook	d	09 35				09 51				10 05				10 20				10 35			10 51				
Dinas Powys	d	09 37				09 53				10 07				10 22				10 37			10 53				
Cadoxton	d	09 42				09 57				10 12				10 27				10 42			10 57				
Barry Docks	d	09 44				10 00				10 14				10 29				10 44			11 00				
Barry 3	d	09 49				10 05				10 19				10 34				10 49			11 05				
Barry Island	a	09 55								10 25				10 40				10 55							
Rhoose Cardiff Int Airport ✈	d					10 12															11 12				
Llantwit Major	d					10 22															11 22				
Bridgend	a					10 39															11 39				

A To Radyr

B To Coryton

When events are being held at the Millenium Stadium, services are subject to alteration. Please check times before travelling.

For connections to Cardiff Bay please refer to Table 130A

Table 130

Saturdays

14 December to 28 December

Treherbert, Aberdare, Merthyr, Pontypridd, Rhymney and Coryton - Cardiff, Penarth, Barry, Barry Island and Bridgend

Network Diagram - see first Page of Table 130

		AW	AW	AW	AW A	AW	AW	AW B	AW	AW	AW	AW A	AW	AW	AW	AW B	AW	AW	AW A	AW	AW	AW	AW B
Treherbert	d										10 17				10 47							11 17	
Ynyswen	d										10 19				10 49							11 19	
Treorchy	d										10 21				10 51							11 21	
Ton Pentre	d										10 23				10 53							11 23	
Ystrad Rhondda	a										10 26				10 56							11 26	
	d										10 28				10 58							11 28	
Llwynypia	d										10 30				11 00							11 30	
Tonypandy	d										10 33				11 03							11 33	
Dinas Rhondda	d										10 35				11 05							11 35	
Porth	a										10 38				11 08							11 38	
	d										10 52				11 09							11 39	
Trehafod	d										10 55				11 12							11 42	
Merthyr Tydfil	d		10 04										10 38							11 08			
Pentre-bach	d		10 08										10 42							11 12			
Troed Y Rhiw	d		10 11										10 45							11 15			
Merthyr Vale	a		10 14										10 48							11 18			
	d		10 16										10 50							11 20			
Quakers Yard	d		10 22										10 55							11 25			
Aberdare 3	d	09 52							10 22								10 52						
Cwmbach	d	09 55							10 25								10 55						
Fernhill	d	09 58							10 28								10 58						
Mountain Ash	a	10 01							10 31								11 01						
	d	10 04							10 34								11 04						
Penrhiwceiber	d	10 07							10 37								11 07						
Abercynon	d	10 13	10 26						10 43				10 59				11 13			11 29			
Pontypridd 3	a	10 22	10 32						10 52		11 00		11 07		11 17		11 22			11 37		11 47	
	d	10 24				10 39			10 54		11 04		11 09		11 18		11 24			11 39		11 48	
Trefforest	d	10 27				10 42			10 57		11 07		11 12		11 21		11 27			11 42		11 51	
Trefforest Estate	d												11 16							11 46			
Taffs Well 3	d	10 34				10 50			11 04		11 13		11 20		11 28		11 34			11 50		11 58	
Radyr 3	a	10 37				10 53			11 07		11 17		11 23		11 31		11 37			11 53		12 01	
	d	10 37				10 53		11 04	11 07		11 17		11 23		11 31	11 34	11 37			11 53		12 01	12 04
Danescourt	d							11 08								11 38							12 08
Fairwater	d							11 10								11 40							12 10
Waun-gron Park	d							11 12								11 42							12 12
Ninian Park	d							11 15								11 45							12 15
Llandaf	d	10 40				10 56			11 10				11 26		11 34		11 40			11 56		12 04	
Cathays	d	10 45				11 01			11 15				11 31		11 39		11 45			12 01		12 09	
Rhymney 3	d									10 27													
Pontlottyn	d									10 30													
Tir-phil	d									10 35													
Brithdir	d									10 37													
Bargoed	a									10 41													
	d			10 17			10 32			10 45				11 00				11 17			11 32		
Gilfach Fargoed	d			10 19														11 19					
Pengam	d			10 22			10 37			10 50				11 05				11 22			11 37		
Hengoed	d			10 25			10 40			10 54				11 09				11 25			11 40		
Ystrad Mynach 3	d			10 28			10 43			10 57				11 12				11 28			11 43		
Llanbradach	d			10 33			10 48			11 01				11 16				11 33			11 48		
Energlyn & Churchill Park	d									11 05				11 20									
Aber	d			10 37			10 52			11 07				11 22				11 37			11 52		
Caerphilly 3	d			10 40			10 55			11 10				11 25				11 40			11 55		
Lisvane & Thornhill	d			10 44			10 59			11 14				11 29				11 44			11 59		
Llanishen	d			10 46			11 01			11 16				11 31				11 46			12 01		
Heath High Level	d			10 49			11 04			11 19				11 34				11 49			12 04		
Coryton	d				10 45							11 15							11 45				
Whitchurch (Cardiff)	d				10 46							11 16							11 46				
Rhiwbina	d				10 48							11 18							11 48				
Birchgrove	d				10 50							11 20							11 50				
Ty Glas	d				10 51							11 21							11 51				
Heath Low Level	d				10 54							11 24							11 54				
Cardiff Queen Street 3	a	10 49		10 54	10 59	11 04	11 09		11 19	11 24		11 29	11 34	11 39	11 44		11 49	11 54	11 59	12 04	12 09	12 14	
	d	10 51		10 56	11 01	11 06	11 11		11 21	11 26		11 31	11 36	11 41	11 46		11 51	11 56	12 01	12 06	12 11	12 16	
Cardiff Central 7	a	10 54		10 59	11 04	11 09	11 14	11 20	11 24	11 29	11 34	11 34	11 39	11 44	11 52	11 50	11 54	11 59	12 04	12 09	12 14	12 22	12 20
	d	10 55		11 01		11 10	11 16		11 25	11 31			11 41	11 46			11 55	12 01		12 10	12 16		
Grangetown	d	10 59		11 05		11 14	11 20		11 29	11 35			11 45	11 50			11 59	12 05		12 14	12 20		
Dingle Road	d			11 11			11 26			11 41				11 56				12 11			12 26		
Penarth	a			11 16			11 31			11 46				12 01				12 16			12 31		
Cogan	d	11 03				11 18			11 33				11 48				12 03			12 18			
Eastbrook	d	11 05				11 20			11 35				11 51				12 05			12 20			
Dinas Powys	d	11 07				11 22			11 37				11 53				12 07			12 22			
Cadoxton	d	11 12				11 27			11 42				11 57				12 12			12 27			
Barry Docks	d	11 14				11 29			11 44				12 00				12 14			12 29			
Barry 3	d	11 19				11 34			11 49				12 05				12 19			12 34			
Barry Island	a	11 25				11 40			11 55								12 25			12 40			
Rhoose Cardiff Int Airport ✈	d												12 12										
Llantwit Major	d												12 22										
Bridgend	a												12 39										

A To Radyr **B** To Coryton

When events are being held at the Millenium Stadium, services are subject to alteration. Please check times before travelling.

For connections to Cardiff Bay please refer to Table 130A

Table 130

Saturdays

14 December to 28 December

Treherbert, Aberdare, Merthyr, Pontypridd, Rhymney and Coryton - Cardiff, Penarth, Barry, Barry Island and Bridgend

Network Diagram - see first Page of Table 130

		AW	AW	AW A	AW	AW	AW	AW B	AW	AW A	AW	AW	AW	AW B	AW	AW	AW A	AW	AW	AW	AW B	AW
Treherbert	d						11 47						12 17							12 47		
Ynyswen	d						11 49						12 19							12 49		
Treorchy	d						11 51						12 21							12 51		
Ton Pentre	d						11 53						12 23							12 53		
Ystrad Rhondda	a						11 56						12 26							12 56		
	d						11 58						12 28							12 58		
Llwynypia	d						12 00						12 30							13 00		
Tonypandy	d						12 03						12 33							13 03		
Dinas Rhondda	d						12 05						12 35							13 05		
Porth	a						12 08						12 38							13 08		
	d						12 09						12 39							13 09		
Trehafod	d						12 12						12 42							13 12		
Merthyr Tydfil	d				11 38						12 08							12 38				
Pentre-bach	d				11 42						12 12							12 42				
Troed Y Rhiw	d				11 45						12 15							12 45				
Merthyr Vale	a				11 48						12 18							12 48				
	d				11 50						12 20							12 50				
Quakers Yard	d				11 55						12 25							12 55				
Aberdare 3	d	11 22													12 22							12 52
Cwmbach	d	11 25													12 25							12 55
Fernhill	d	11 28													12 28							12 58
Mountain Ash	a	11 31													12 31							13 01
	d	11 34													12 34							13 04
Penrhiwceiber	d	11 37													12 37							13 07
Abercynon	d	11 43			11 59						12 29				12 43			12 59				13 13
Pontypridd 3	a	11 52			12 07		12 17				12 37		12 48		12 52			13 07		13 17		13 22
	d	11 54			12 09		12 18				12 39		12 48		12 54			13 09		13 18		13 24
Trefforest	d	11 57			12 12		12 21				12 42		12 51		12 57			13 12		13 21		13 27
Trefforest Estate	d				12 16						12 46							13 16				
Taffs Well 3	d	12 04			12 20		12 28				12 50		12 58		13 04			13 20		13 28		13 34
Radyr 3	a	12 07			12 23		12 31				12 53		13 01		13 07			13 23		13 31		13 37
	d	12 07			12 23		12 31	12 34			12 53		13 01	13 04	13 07			13 23		13 31	13 34	13 37
Danescourt	d							12 38						13 08							13 38	
Fairwater	d							12 40						13 10							13 40	
Waun-gron Park	d							12 42						13 12							13 42	
Ninian Park	d							12 45						13 15							13 45	
Llandaf	d	12 10			12 26		12 34				12 56		13 04		13 10			13 26		13 34		13 40
Cathays	d	12 15			12 31		12 39				13 01		13 09		13 15			13 31		13 39		13 45
Rhymney 3	d		11 27													12 27						
Pontlottyn	d		11 30													12 30						
Tir-phil	d		11 35													12 35						
Brithdir	d		11 37													12 37						
Bargoed	a		11 41													12 41						
	d		11 45			12 00			12 17			12 32				12 45			13 00			
Gilfach Fargoed	d								12 19													
Pengam	d		11 50			12 05			12 22			12 37				12 50			13 05			
Hengoed	d		11 54			12 09			12 25			12 40				12 54			13 09			
Ystrad Mynach 3	d		11 57			12 12			12 28			12 43				12 57			13 12			
Llanbradach	d		12 01			12 16			12 33			12 48				13 01			13 16			
Energlyn & Churchill Park	d		12 05			12 20										13 05			13 20			
Aber	d		12 07			12 22			12 37			12 52				13 07			13 22			
Caerphilly 3	d		12 10			12 25			12 40			12 55				13 10			13 25			
Lisvane & Thornhill	d		12 14			12 29			12 44			12 59				13 14			13 29			
Llanishen	d		12 16			12 31			12 46			13 01				13 16			13 31			
Heath High Level	d		12 19			12 34			12 49			13 04				13 19			13 34			
Coryton	d			12 15						12 45							13 15					
Whitchurch (Cardiff)	d			12 16						12 46							13 16					
Rhiwbina	d			12 18						12 48							13 18					
Birchgrove	d			12 20						12 50							13 20					
Ty Glas	d			12 21						12 51							13 21					
Heath Low Level	d			12 24						12 54							13 24					
Cardiff Queen Street 3	a	12 19	12 24	12 29	12 34	12 39	12 44		12 54	12 59	13 04	13 09	13 14		13 19	13 24	13 29	13 34	13 39	13 44		13 49
	d	12 21	12 26	12 31	12 36	12 41	12 46		12 56	13 01	13 06	13 11	13 16		13 21	13 26	13 31	13 36	13 41	13 46		13 51
Cardiff Central 7	a	12 24	12 29	12 34	12 39	12 44	12 52	12 50	12 59	13 04	13 09	13 14	13 22	13 20	13 24	13 29	13 34	13 39	13 44	13 52	13 50	13 54
	d	12 25	12 31		12 41	12 46	12 55		13 01		13 10	13 16			13 25	13 31		13 41	13 46			13 55
Grangetown	d	12 29	12 35		12 45	12 50	12 59		13 05		13 14	13 20			13 29	13 35		13 45	13 50			13 59
Dingle Road	d		12 41			12 56			13 11			13 26				13 41			13 56			
Penarth	a		12 46			13 01			13 16			13 31				13 46			14 01			
Cogan	d	12 33			12 48		13 03				13 18				13 33			13 48				14 03
Eastbrook	d	12 35			12 51		13 05				13 20				13 35			13 51				14 05
Dinas Powys	d	12 37			12 53		13 07				13 22				13 37			13 53				14 07
Cadoxton	d	12 42			12 57		13 12				13 27				13 42			13 57				14 12
Barry Docks	d	12 44			13 00		13 14				13 29				13 44			14 00				14 14
Barry 3	d	12 49			13 05		13 19				13 34				13 49			14 05				14 19
Barry Island	a	12 55					13 25				13 40				13 55							14 25
Rhoose Cardiff Int Airport ✈	d				13 12													14 12				
Llantwit Major	d				13 22													14 22				
Bridgend	a				13 39													14 39				

A To Radyr

B To Coryton

When events are being held at the Millenium Stadium, services are subject to alteration. Please check times before travelling.

For connections to Cardiff Bay please refer to Table 130A

Table 130

Saturdays

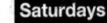

14 December to 28 December

Treherbert, Aberdare, Merthyr, Pontypridd, Rhymney and Coryton - Cardiff, Penarth, Barry, Barry Island and Bridgend

Network Diagram - see first Page of Table 130

		AW	AW A	AW	AW	AW	AW B	AW	AW	AW A	AW	AW	AW	AW B	AW	AW	AW A	AW	AW	AW B	AW	AW	AW
Treherbert	d					13 17							13 47										14 17
Ynyswen	d					13 19							13 49										14 19
Treorchy	d					13 21							13 51										14 21
Ton Pentre	d					13 23							13 53										14 23
Ystrad Rhondda	a					13 26							13 56										14 26
	d					13 28							13 58										14 28
Llwynypia	d					13 30							14 00										14 30
Tonypandy	d					13 33							14 03										14 33
Dinas Rhondda	d					13 35							14 05										14 35
Porth	a					13 38							14 08										14 38
	d					13 39							14 09										14 52
Trehafod	d					13 42							14 12										14 55
Merthyr Tydfil	d			13 08							13 38							14 08					
Pentre-bach	d			13 12							13 42							14 12					
Troed Y Rhiw	d			13 15							13 45							14 15					
Merthyr Vale	a			13 18							13 48							14 18					
	d			13 20							13 50							14 20					
Quakers Yard	d			13 25							13 55							14 25					
Aberdare 3	d														13 52						14 22		
Cwmbach	d														13 55						14 25		
Fernhill	d														13 58						14 28		
Mountain Ash	a														14 01						14 31		
	d														14 04						14 34		
Penrhiwceiber	d														14 07						14 37		
Abercynon	d			13 29				13 45			13 59				14 13			14 29			14 43		
Pontypridd 3	a			13 37		13 47		13 52			14 07		14 17		14 22			14 37			14 52		15 00
	d			13 39		13 48		13 54			14 09		14 18		14 24			14 39			14 54		15 04
Trefforest	d			13 42		13 51		13 57			14 12		14 21		14 27			14 42			14 57		15 07
Trefforest Estate	d			13 46							14 16							14 46					
Taffs Well 3	d			13 50		13 58		14 04			14 20		14 28		14 34			14 50			15 04		15 13
Radyr 3	a			13 53		14 01		14 07			14 23		14 31		14 37			14 53			15 07		15 17
	d			13 53		14 01	14 04	14 07			14 23		14 31	14 34	14 37			14 53		15 04	15 07		15 17
Danescourt	d						14 08							14 38						15 08			
Fairwater	d						14 10							14 40						15 10			
Waun-gron Park	d						14 12							14 42						15 12			
Ninian Park	d						14 15							14 45						15 15			
Llandaf	d			13 56		14 04		14 10			14 26		14 34		14 40			14 56			15 10		
Cathays	d			14 01		14 09		14 15			14 31		14 39		14 45			15 01			15 15		
Rhymney 3	d								13 27													14 27	
Pontlottyn	d								13 30													14 30	
Tir-phil	d								13 35													14 35	
Brithdir	d								13 37													14 37	
Bargoed	a								13 41													14 41	
	d	13 17			13 32				13 45			14 00				14 17			14 32			14 45	
Gilfach Fargoed	d	13 19														14 19							
Pengam	d	13 22			13 37				13 50			14 05				14 22			14 37			14 50	
Hengoed	d	13 25			13 40				13 54			14 09				14 25			14 40			14 54	
Ystrad Mynach 3	d	13 28			13 43				13 57			14 12				14 28			14 43			14 57	
Llanbradach	d	13 33			13 48				14 01			14 16				14 33			14 48			15 01	
Energlyn & Churchill Park	d								14 05			14 20										15 05	
Aber	d	13 37			13 52				14 07			14 22				14 37			14 52			15 07	
Caerphilly 3	d	13 40			13 55				14 10			14 25				14 40			14 55			15 10	
Lisvane & Thornhill	d	13 44			13 59				14 14			14 29				14 44			14 59			15 14	
Llanishen	d	13 46			14 01				14 16			14 31				14 46			15 01			15 16	
Heath High Level	d	13 49			14 04				14 19			14 34				14 49			15 04			15 19	
Coryton	d		13 45							14 15							14 45						
Whitchurch (Cardiff)	d		13 46							14 16							14 46						
Rhiwbina	d		13 48							14 18							14 48						
Birchgrove	d		13 50							14 20							14 50						
Ty Glas	d		13 51							14 21							14 51						
Heath Low Level	d		13 54							14 24							14 54						
Cardiff Queen Street 3	a	13 54	13 59	14 04	14 09	14 14		14 19	14 24	14 29	14 34	14 39	14 44		14 49	14 54	14 59	15 04	15 09		15 19	15 24	
	d	13 56	14 01	14 06	14 11	14 16		14 21	14 26	14 31	14 36	14 41	14 46		14 51	14 56	15 01	15 06	15 11		15 21	15 26	
Cardiff Central 7	a	13 59	14 04	14 09	14 14	14 22	14 20	14 24	14 29	14 34	14 39	14 44	14 52	14 50	14 54	14 59	15 04	15 09	15 14	15 20	15 24	15 29	15 34
	d	14 01		14 10	14 16			14 25	14 31		14 41	14 46			14 55	15 01		15 10	15 16		15 25	15 31	
Grangetown	d	14 05		14 14	14 20			14 29	14 35		14 45	14 50			14 59	15 05		15 14	15 20		15 29	15 35	
Dingle Road	d	14 11			14 26				14 41			14 56				15 11			15 26			15 41	
Penarth	a	14 16			14 31				14 46			15 01				15 16			15 31			15 46	
Cogan	d			14 18				14 33			14 48				15 03			15 18			15 33		
Eastbrook	d			14 20				14 35			14 51				15 05			15 20			15 35		
Dinas Powys	d			14 22				14 37			14 53				15 07			15 22			15 37		
Cadoxton	d			14 27				14 42			14 57				15 12			15 27			15 42		
Barry Docks	d			14 29				14 44			15 00				15 14			15 29			15 44		
Barry 3	d			14 34				14 49			15 05				15 19			15 34			15 49		
Barry Island	a			14 40				14 55							15 25			15 40			15 55		
Rhoose Cardiff Int Airport ✈	d										15 12												
Llantwit Major	d										15 22												
Bridgend	a										15 39												

A To Radyr

B To Coryton

When events are being held at the Millenium Stadium, services are subject to alteration. Please check times before travelling.

For connections to Cardiff Bay please refer to Table 130A

Table 130

Saturdays

14 December to 28 December

Treherbert, Aberdare, Merthyr, Pontypridd, Rhymney and Coryton - Cardiff, Penarth, Barry, Barry Island and Bridgend

Network Diagram - see first Page of Table 130

		AW A	AW	AW	AW	AW B	AW	AW	AW A	AW	AW	AW	AW B	AW	AW	AW A	AW	AW	AW	AW B	AW	AW	AW A
Treherbert	d				14 47							15 13							15 47				
Ynyswen	d				14 49							15 15							15 49				
Treorchy	d				14 51							15 21							15 51				
Ton Pentre	d				14 53							15 23							15 53				
Ystrad Rhondda	a				14 56							15 26							15 56				
	d				14 58							15 28							15 58				
Llwynypia	d				15 00							15 30							16 00				
Tonypandy	d				15 03							15 33							16 03				
Dinas Rhondda	d				15 05							15 35							16 05				
Porth	a				15 08							15 38							16 08				
	d				15 09							15 39							16 09				
Trehafod	d				15 12							15 42							16 12				
Merthyr Tydfil	d		14 38							15 08							15 38						
Pentre-bach	d		14 42							15 12							15 42						
Troed Y Rhiw	d		14 45							15 15							15 45						
Merthyr Vale	a		14 48							15 18							15 48						
	d		14 50							15 20							15 50						
Quakers Yard	d		14 55							15 25							15 55						
Aberdare 3	d						14 52							15 22							15 52		
Cwmbach	d						14 55							15 25							15 55		
Fernhill	d						14 58							15 28							15 58		
Mountain Ash	a						15 01							15 31							16 01		
	d						15 04							15 34							16 04		
Penrhiwceiber	d						15 07							15 37							16 07		
Abercynon	d		14 59				15 13			15 29				15 43			15 59				16 13		
Pontypridd 3	a		15 07		15 17		15 22			15 37		15 47		15 52			16 07		16 17		16 22		
	d		15 09		15 18		15 24			15 39		15 48		15 54			16 09		16 18		16 24		
Trefforest	d		15 12		15 21		15 27			15 42		15 51		15 57			16 12		16 21		16 27		
Trefforest Estate	d		15 16							15 46							16 16						
Taffs Well 3	d		15 20		15 28		15 34			15 50		15 58		16 04			16 20		16 28		16 34		
Radyr 3	a		15 23		15 31		15 37			15 53		16 01		16 07			16 23		16 31		16 37		
	d		15 23		15 31	15 34	15 37			15 53		16 01	16 04	16 07			16 23		16 31	16 34	16 37		
Danescourt	d					15 38							16 08							16 38			
Fairwater	d					15 40							16 10							16 40			
Waun-gron Park	d					15 42							16 12							16 42			
Ninian Park	d					15 45							16 15							16 45			
Llandaf	d		15 26		15 34		15 40			15 56		16 04		16 10			16 26		16 34		16 40		
Cathays	d		15 31		15 39		15 45			16 01		16 09		16 15			16 31		16 39		16 45		
Rhymney 3	d														15 27								
Pontlottyn	d														15 30								
Tir-phil	d														15 35								
Brithdir	d														15 37								
Bargoed	a														15 41								
	d			15 00				15 17			15 32				15 45			16 00				16 17	
Gilfach Fargoed	d							15 19														16 19	
Pengam	d			15 05				15 22			15 37				15 50			16 05				16 22	
Hengoed	d			15 09				15 25			15 40				15 54			16 09				16 25	
Ystrad Mynach 3	d			15 12				15 28			15 43				15 57			16 12				16 28	
Llanbradach	d			15 16				15 33			15 48				16 01			16 16				16 33	
Energlyn & Churchill Park	d			15 20											16 05			16 20					
Aber	d			15 22				15 37			15 52				16 07			16 22				16 37	
Caerphilly 3	d			15 25				15 40			15 55				16 10			16 25				16 40	
Lisvane & Thornhill	d			15 29				15 44			15 59				16 14			16 29				16 44	
Llanishen	d			15 31				15 46			16 01				16 16			16 31				16 46	
Heath High Level	d			15 34				15 49			16 04				16 19			16 34				16 49	
Coryton	d	15 15							15 45							16 15							16 45
Whitchurch (Cardiff)	d	15 16							15 46							16 16							16 46
Rhiwbina	d	15 18							15 48							16 18							16 48
Birchgrove	d	15 20							15 50							16 20							16 50
Ty Glas	d	15 21							15 51							16 21							16 51
Heath Low Level	d	15 24							15 54							16 24							16 54
Cardiff Queen Street 3	a	15 29	15 34	15 39	15 44		15 49	15 54	15 59	16 04	16 09	16 14		16 19	16 24	16 29	16 34	16 39	16 44		16 49	16 54	16 59
	d	15 31	15 36	15 41	15 46		15 51	15 56	16 01	16 06	16 11	16 16		16 21	16 26	16 31	16 36	16 41	16 46		16 51	16 56	17 01
Cardiff Central 7	a	15 34	15 39	15 44	15 52	15 50	15 54	15 59	16 04	16 09	16 14	16 22	16 20	16 24	16 32	16 34	16 39	16 44	16 52	16 50	16 54	16 59	17 04
	d		15 41	15 46			15 55	16 01		16 10	16 16			16 25			16 41	16 46			16 55	17 01	
Grangetown	d		15 45	15 50			15 59	16 05		16 14	16 20			16 29			16 45	16 50			16 59	17 05	
Dingle Road	d			15 56				16 11			16 26							16 56				17 11	
Penarth	a			16 01				16 16			16 31							17 01				17 16	
Cogan	d		15 48				16 03			16 18				16 33			16 48				17 03		
Eastbrook	d		15 51				16 05			16 20				16 35			16 51				17 05		
Dinas Powys	d		15 53				16 07			16 22				16 37			16 53				17 07		
Cadoxton	d		15 57				16 12			16 27				16 42			16 57				17 12		
Barry Docks	d		16 00				16 14			16 29				16 44			17 00				17 14		
Barry 3	d		16 05				16 19			16 34				16 49			17 05				17 19		
Barry Island	a						16 25			16 40				16 55							17 25		
Rhoose Cardiff Int Airport ✈	d		16 12														17 12						
Llantwit Major	d		16 22														17 22						
Bridgend	a		16 39														17 39						

A To Radyr

B To Coryton

When events are being held at the Millenium Stadium, services are subject to alteration. Please check times before travelling.

For connections to Cardiff Bay please refer to Table 130A

Table 130

Saturdays

14 December to 28 December

Treherbert, Aberdare, Merthyr, Pontypridd, Rhymney and Coryton - Cardiff, Penarth, Barry, Barry Island and Bridgend

Network Diagram - see first Page of Table 130

		AW		AW	AW	AW A	AW	AW	AW B	AW	AW	AW		AW A	AW	AW	AW B	AW	AW	AW	AW A	AW		AW	AW B
Treherbert	d				16 17							16 47								17 17					
Ynyswen	d				16 19							16 49								17 19					
Treorchy	d				16 21							16 51								17 21					
Ton Pentre	d				16 23							16 53								17 23					
Ystrad Rhondda	a				16 26							16 56								17 26					
	d				16 28							16 58								17 28					
Llwynypia	d				16 30							17 00								17 30					
Tonypandy	d				16 33							17 03								17 33					
Dinas Rhondda	d				16 35							17 05								17 35					
Porth	a				16 38							17 08								17 38					
	d				16 39							17 09								17 39					
Trehafod	d				16 42							17 12								17 42					
Merthyr Tydfil	d	16 08								16 38								17 08							
Pentre-bach	d	16 12								16 42								17 12							
Troed Y Rhiw	d	16 15								16 45								17 15							
Merthyr Vale	a	16 18								16 48								17 18							
	d	16 20								16 50								17 20							
Quakers Yard	d	16 25								16 55								17 25							
Aberdare 3	d						16 22								16 52							17 22			
Cwmbach	d						16 25								16 55							17 25			
Fernhill	d						16 28								16 58							17 28			
Mountain Ash	a						16 31								17 01							17 31			
	d						16 34								17 04							17 34			
Penrhiwceiber	d						16 37								17 07							17 37			
Abercynon	d	16 29					16 43			16 59					17 13			17 29				17 43			
Pontypridd 3	a	16 37			16 47		16 52			17 07		17 17			17 22			17 37		17 47		17 52			
	d	16 39			16 48		16 54			17 09		17 18			17 24			17 39		17 48		17 54			
Trefforest	d	16 42			16 51		16 57			17 12		17 21			17 27			17 42		17 51		17 57			
Trefforest Estate	d	16 46								17 16								17 46							
Taffs Well 3	d	16 50			16 58		17 04			17 20		17 28			17 34			17 50		17 58		18 04			
Radyr 3	a	16 53			17 01		17 07			17 23		17 31			17 37			17 53		18 01		18 07			
	d	16 53			17 01	17 04	17 07			17 23		17 31		17 34	17 37			17 53		18 01	18 04	18 07			
Danescourt	d					17 08								17 38							18 08				
Fairwater	d					17 10								17 40							18 10				
Waun-gron Park	d					17 12								17 42							18 12				
Ninian Park	d					17 15								17 45							18 15				
Llandaf	d	16 56			17 04		17 10			17 26		17 34			17 40			17 56		18 04		18 10			
Cathays	d	17 01			17 09		17 15			17 31		17 39			17 45			18 01		18 09		18 15			
Rhymney 3	d							16 27																17 27	
Pontlottyn	d							16 30																17 30	
Tir-phil	d							16 35																17 35	
Brithdir	d							16 37																17 37	
Bargoed	a							16 41																17 41	
	d			16 32				16 45			17 00					17 17			17 32					17 45	
Gilfach Fargoed	d															17 19									
Pengam	d			16 37				16 50			17 05					17 22			17 37					17 50	
Hengoed	d			16 40				16 54			17 09					17 25			17 40					17 54	
Ystrad Mynach 3	d			16 43				16 57			17 12					17 28			17 43					17 57	
Llanbradach	d			16 48				17 01			17 16					17 33			17 48					18 01	
Energlyn & Churchill Park	d							17 05			17 20													18 05	
Aber	d			16 52				17 07			17 22					17 37			17 52					18 07	
Caerphilly 3	d			16 55				17 10			17 25					17 40			17 55					18 10	
Lisvane & Thornhill	d			16 59				17 14			17 29					17 44			17 59					18 14	
Llanishen	d			17 01				17 16			17 31					17 46			18 01					18 16	
Heath High Level	d			17 04				17 19			17 34					17 49			18 04					18 19	
Coryton	d								17 15								17 45								18 15
Whitchurch (Cardiff)	d								17 16								17 46								18 16
Rhiwbina	d								17 18								17 48								18 18
Birchgrove	d								17 20								17 50								18 20
Ty Glas	d								17 21								17 51								18 21
Heath Low Level	d								17 24								17 54								18 24
Cardiff Queen Street 3	a	17 04		17 09	17 14		17 19	17 24	17 29	17 34	17 39	17 44			17 49	17 54	17 59	18 04	18 09	18 14		18 19		18 24	18 29
	d	17 06		17 11	17 16		17 21	17 26	17 31	17 36	17 41	17 46			17 51	17 56	18 01	18 06	18 11	18 16		18 21		18 26	18 31
Cardiff Central 7	a	17 09		17 14	17 22	17 20	17 24	17 29	17 34	17 39	17 44	17 52		17 50	17 54	17 59	18 04	18 09	18 14	18 22	18 20	18 24		18 29	18 34
	d	17 10		17 16			17 25	17 31		17 41	17 46				17 55	18 01		18 10	18 16			18 25		18 31	
Grangetown	d	17 14		17 20			17 29	17 35		17 45	17 50				17 59	18 05		18 14	18 20			18 29		18 35	
Dingle Road	d			17 26				17 41			17 56					18 11			18 26					18 41	
Penarth	a			17 31				17 46			18 01					18 16			18 31					18 46	
Cogan	d	17 18					17 33			17 48					18 03			18 18				18 33			
Eastbrook	d	17 20					17 35			17 51					18 05			18 20				18 35			
Dinas Powys	d	17 22					17 37			17 53					18 07			18 22				18 37			
Cadoxton	d	17 27					17 42			17 57					18 12			18 27				18 42			
Barry Docks	d	17 29					17 44			18 00					18 14			18 29				18 44			
Barry 3	d	17 34					17 49			18 05					18 19			18 34				18 49			
Barry Island	a	17 40					17 55								18 25			18 40				18 55			
Rhoose Cardiff Int Airport ✈	d									18 12															
Llantwit Major	d									18 22															
Bridgend	a									18 39															

A To Coryton **B** To Radyr

When events are being held at the Millenium Stadium, services are subject to alteration. Please check times before travelling.

For connections to Cardiff Bay please refer to Table 130A

Table 130

Saturdays

14 December to 28 December

Treherbert, Aberdare, Merthyr, Pontypridd, Rhymney and Coryton - Cardiff, Penarth, Barry, Barry Island and Bridgend

Network Diagram - see first Page of Table 130

		AW	AW	AW	AW	AW	AW	AW	AW	AW	AW	AW	AW	AW	AW	AW	AW	AW	AW	AW	AW	AW	AW
				A									B									B	
Treherbert	d		17 47						18 17						18 47				19 17				
Ynyswen	d		17 49						18 19						18 49				19 19				
Treorchy	d		17 51						18 21						18 51				19 21				
Ton Pentre	d		17 53						18 23						18 53				19 23				
Ystrad Rhondda	a		17 56						18 26						18 56				19 26				
	d		17 58						18 28						18 58				19 28				
Llwynypia	d		18 00						18 30						19 00				19 30				
Tonypandy	d		18 03						18 33						19 03				19 33				
Dinas Rhondda	d		18 05						18 35						19 05				19 35				
Porth	a		18 08						18 38						19 08				19 38				
	d		18 09						18 39						19 09				19 39				
Trehafod	d		18 12						18 42						19 12				19 42				
Merthyr Tydfil	d	17 38						18 08						18 38				19 08					19 38
Pentre-bach	d	17 42						18 12						18 42				19 12					19 42
Troed Y Rhiw	d	17 45						18 15						18 45				19 15					19 45
Merthyr Vale	a	17 48						18 18						18 48				19 18					19 48
	d	17 50						18 20						18 50				19 20					19 50
Quakers Yard	d	17 55						18 25						18 55				19 25					19 55
Aberdare 3	d				17 52						18 22					18 52							
Cwmbach	d				17 55						18 25					18 55							
Fernhill	d				17 58						18 28					18 58							
Mountain Ash	a				18 01						18 31					19 01							
	d				18 04						18 34					19 04							
Penrhiwceiber	d				18 07						18 37					19 07							
Abercynon	d	17 59			18 13			18 29			18 43			18 59		19 13		19 29			19 43		19 59
Pontypridd 3	a	18 07	18 17		18 22			18 37	18 47		18 52			19 07	19 17	19 22		19 37	19 47		19 52		20 07
	d	18 09	18 18		18 24			18 39	18 48		18 54			19 09	19 18	19 24		19 39	19 48		19 54		20 09
Trefforest	d	18 12	18 21		18 27			18 42	18 51		18 57			19 12	19 21	19 27		19 42	19 51		19 57		20 12
Trefforest Estate	d	18 16						18 46						19 16				19 46					20 16
Taffs Well 3	d	18 20	18 28		18 34			18 50	18 58		19 04			19 20	19 28	19 34		19 50	19 58		20 04		20 20
Radyr 3	a	18 23	18 31		18 37			18 53	19 01		19 07			19 23	19 31	19 37		19 53	20 01		20 07		20 23
	d	18 23	18 31	18 34	18 37			18 53	19 01	19 04	19 07			19 23	19 31	19 37		19 53	20 01	20 04	20 07		20 23
Danescourt	d			18 38						19 08										20 08			
Fairwater	d			18 40						19 10										20 10			
Waun-gron Park	d			18 42						19 12										20 12			
Ninian Park	d			18 45						19 15										20 15			
Llandaf	d	18 26	18 34		18 40			18 56	19 04		19 10			19 26	19 34	19 40		19 56	20 04		20 10		20 26
Cathays	d	18 31	18 39		18 45			19 01	19 09		19 15			19 31	19 39	19 45		20 01	20 09		20 15		20 31
Rhymney 3	d																						
Pontlottyn	d																						
Tir-phil	d																						
Brithdir	d																						
Bargoed	a																						
	d					18 15						18 48											
Gilfach Fargoed	d					18 18						18 50											
Pengam	d					18 20						18 53											
Hengoed	d					18 24						18 56											
Ystrad Mynach 3	d					18 27						18 59											
Llanbradach	d					18 31						19 04											
Energlyn & Churchill Park	d					18 35																	
Aber	d					18 37						19 08											
Caerphilly 3	d					18 40						19 11					19 40						
Lisvane & Thornhill	d					18 44						19 15					19 44						
Llanishen	d					18 46						19 17					19 46						
Heath High Level	d					18 49						19 20					19 49						
Coryton	d						18 45						19 15									20 15	
Whitchurch (Cardiff)	d						18 46						19 16									20 16	
Rhiwbina	d						18 48						19 18									20 18	
Birchgrove	d						18 50						19 20									20 20	
Ty Glas	d						18 51						19 21									20 21	
Heath Low Level	d						18 54						19 24									20 24	
Cardiff Queen Street 3	a	18 34	18 44		18 49	18 54	18 59	19 04	19 14		19 19	19 24	19 29	19 34	19 44	19 49	19 54	20 04	20 14		20 19	20 29	20 34
	d	18 36	18 46		18 51	18 56	19 01	19 06	19 16		19 21	19 26	19 31	19 36	19 46	19 51	19 56	20 06	20 16		20 21	20 31	20 36
Cardiff Central 7	a	18 39	18 52	18 50	18 54	18 59	19 06	19 10	19 22	19 22	19 24	19 29	19 34	19 39	19 52	19 57	19 59	20 09	20 22	20 24	20 24	20 34	20 39
	d	18 41			18 55	19 01					19 25	19 31		19 41			20 06	20 10			20 31		20 41
Grangetown	d	18 45			18 59	19 05					19 29	19 35		19 45			20 10	20 14			20 35		20 45
Dingle Road	d					19 11						19 41					20 14				20 41		
Penarth	a					19 16						19 46					20 19				20 46		
Cogan	d	18 48			19 03						19 33			19 48				20 18					20 48
Eastbrook	d	18 51			19 05						19 35			19 51				20 20					20 51
Dinas Powys	d	18 53			19 07						19 37			19 53				20 22					20 53
Cadoxton	d	18 57			19 12						19 42			19 57				20 27					20 57
Barry Docks	d	19 00			19 14						19 44			20 00				20 29					21 00
Barry 3	d	19 05			19 19						19 49			20 05				20 34					21 05
Barry Island	a				19 25						19 55							20 40					
Rhoose Cardiff Int Airport ✈	d	19 12												20 12									21 12
Llantwit Major	d	19 22												20 22									21 22
Bridgend	a	19 39												20 39									21 39

A To Coryton

B To Radyr

When events are being held at the Millenium Stadium, services are subject to alteration. Please check times before travelling.

For connections to Cardiff Bay please refer to Table 130A

Table 130

Saturdays

14 December to 28 December

Treherbert, Aberdare, Merthyr, Pontypridd, Rhymney and Coryton - Cardiff, Penarth, Barry, Barry Island and Bridgend

Network Diagram - see first Page of Table 130

		AW	AW	AW	AW	AW	AW	AW	AW	AW A	AW	AW	AW	AW	AW	AW B	AW	AW	AW	AW	AW	AW
Treherbert	d		19 47			20 17									21 17							
Ynyswen	d		19 49			20 19									21 19							
Treorchy	d		19 51			20 21									21 21							
Ton Pentre	d		19 53			20 23									21 23							
Ystrad Rhondda	a		19 56			20 26									21 26							
	d		19 58			20 28									21 28							
Llwynypia	d		20 00			20 30									21 30							
Tonypandy	d		20 03			20 33									21 33							
Dinas Rhondda	d		20 05			20 35									21 35							
Porth	a		20 08			20 38									21 38							
	d		20 09			20 39									21 39							
Trehafod	d		20 12			20 42									21 42							
Merthyr Tydfil	d										20 38							21 38				
Pentre-bach	d										20 42							21 42				
Troed Y Rhiw	d										20 45							21 45				
Merthyr Vale	a										20 48							21 48				
	d										20 50							21 50				
Quakers Yard	d										20 55							21 55				
Aberdare 3	d			19 52				20 22					20 54							21 54		
Cwmbach	d			19 55				20 25					20 57							21 57		
Fernhill	d			19 58				20 28					21 00							22 00		
Mountain Ash	a			20 01				20 31					21 03							22 03		
	d			20 04				20 34					21 04							22 04		
Penrhiwceiber	d			20 07				20 37					21 07							22 07		
Abercynon	d			20 13				20 43			20 59		21 13					21 59		22 13		
Pontypridd 3	a		20 18	20 22		20 47		20 52			21 07		21 22		21 47			22 07		22 22		
	d		20 18	20 24		20 48		20 54			21 09		21 24		21 48			22 09		22 24		
Trefforest	d		20 21	20 27		20 51		20 57			21 12		21 27		21 51			22 12		22 27		
Trefforest Estate	d										21 16							22 16				
Taffs Well 3	d		20 28	20 34		20 58		21 04			21 20		21 34		21 58			22 20		22 33		
Radyr 3	a		20 31	20 37		21 01		21 07			21 23		21 37		22 01			22 23		22 37		
	d		20 31	20 37		21 01	21 04	21 07			21 23		21 37		22 01	22 04		22 23		22 37		23 14
Danescourt	d						21 08									22 08						
Fairwater	d						21 10									22 10						
Waun-gron Park	d						21 12									22 12						
Ninian Park	d						21 15									22 15						
Llandaf	d		20 34	20 40		21 04		21 10			21 26		21 40		22 04			22 26		22 40		23 16
Cathays	d		20 39	20 45		21 09		21 15			21 31		21 45		22 09			22 31		22 44		23 20
Rhymney 3	d	19 43										20 46					21 36					
Pontlottyn	d	19 46										20 49					21 39					
Tir-phil	d	19 51										20 54					21 44					
Brithdir	d	19 53										20 56					21 46					
Bargoed	a	19 57										21 00					21 50					
	d	19 57										21 00					21 50					
Gilfach Fargoed	d	20 00										21 03					21 53					
Pengam	d	20 02										21 05					21 55					
Hengoed	d	20 06										21 09					21 59					
Ystrad Mynach 3	d	20 09										21 12		21 39			22 02					
Llanbradach	d	20 13										21 16		21 44			22 06					
Energlyn & Churchill Park	d	20 17										21 20					22 10					
Aber	d	20 19										21 22		21 48			22 12					
Caerphilly 3	d	20 22			20 40							21 25		21 51			22 15		22 28			
Lisvane & Thornhill	d	20 26			20 44							21 29		21 55			22 19					
Llanishen	d	20 28			20 46							21 31		21 57			22 21					
Heath High Level	d	20 31			20 49							21 34		22 00			22 24					
Coryton	d									21 15											22 45	
Whitchurch (Cardiff)	d									21 16											22 46	
Rhiwbina	d									21 18											22 48	
Birchgrove	d									21 20											22 50	
Ty Glas	d									21 21											22 51	
Heath Low Level	d									21 24											22 54	
Cardiff Queen Street 3	a	20 39	20 44	20 49	20 54	21 14		21 19		21 29	21 34	21 42	21 49	22 05	22 14		22 29	22 34	22 39	22 49	22 59	23 24
	d	20 41	20 46	20 51	20 56	21 16		21 21		21 31	21 36	21 44	21 51	22 06	22 16		22 31	22 36	22 40	22 54	23 01	23 25
Cardiff Central 7	a	20 47	20 52	20 57	20 59	21 22	21 25	21 27		21 34	21 39	21 47	21 54	22 09	22 22	22 20	22 34	22 41	22 43	23 00	23 06	23 28
	d			21 06	21 10				21 31		21 41		22 06	22 11			22 36			23 12		23 30
Grangetown	d			21 10	21 14				21 35		21 45		22 10	22 15			22 40			23 16		23 34
Dingle Road	d			21 14					21 41				22 14				22 44			23 20		
Penarth	a			21 19					21 46				22 19				22 47			23 25		
Cogan	d				21 18						21 48			22 18								23 37
Eastbrook	d				21 20						21 51			22 21								23 40
Dinas Powys	d				21 22						21 53			22 23								23 42
Cadoxton	d				21 27						21 57			22 27								23 46
Barry Docks	d				21 29						22 00			22 30								23 49
Barry 3	d				21 34						22 05			22 34								23 53
Barry Island	a				21 40									22 40								23 58
Rhoose Cardiff Int Airport ✈	d										22 12											
Llantwit Major	d										22 22											
Bridgend	a										22 39											

A To Radyr

B To Coryton

When events are being held at the Millenium Stadium, services are subject to alteration. Please check times before travelling.

For connections to Cardiff Bay please refer to Table 130A

Table 130

Saturdays

14 December to 28 December

Treherbert, Aberdare, Merthyr, Pontypridd, Rhymney and Coryton - Cardiff, Penarth, Barry, Barry Island and Bridgend

Network Diagram - see first Page of Table 130

		AW	AW
Treherbert	d		
Ynyswen	d		
Treorchy	d		
Ton Pentre	d		
Ystrad Rhondda	a		
	d		
Llwynypia	d		
Tonypandy	d		
Dinas Rhondda	d		
Porth	a		
	d		
Trehafod	d		
Merthyr Tydfil	d	22 38	
Pentre-bach	d	22 42	
Troed Y Rhiw	d	22 45	
Merthyr Vale	a	22 48	
	d	22 50	
Quakers Yard	d	22 55	
Aberdare 3	d		22 54
Cwmbach	d		22 57
Fernhill	d		23 00
Mountain Ash	a		23 03
	d		23 04
Penrhiwceiber	d		23 07
Abercynon	d	22 59	23 13
Pontypridd 3	a	23 07	23 22
	d	23 09	
Trefforest	d	23 12	
Trefforest Estate	d	23 16	
Taffs Well 3	d	23 20	
Radyr 3	a	23 23	
	d	23 23	
Danescourt	d		
Fairwater	d		
Waun-gron Park	d		
Ninian Park	d		
Llandaf	d	23 26	
Cathays	d	23 31	
Rhymney 3	d		
Pontlottyn	d		
Tir-phil	d		
Brithdir	d		
Bargoed	a		
	d		
Gilfach Fargoed	d		
Pengam	d		
Hengoed	d		
Ystrad Mynach 3	d		
Llanbradach	d		
Energlyn & Churchill Park	d		
Aber	d		
Caerphilly 3	d		
Lisvane & Thornhill	d		
Llanishen	d		
Heath High Level	d		
Coryton	d		
Whitchurch (Cardiff)	d		
Rhiwbina	d		
Birchgrove	d		
Ty Glas	d		
Heath Low Level	d		
Cardiff Queen Street 3	a	23 34	
	d	23 36	
Cardiff Central 7	a	23 42	
	d		
Grangetown	d		
Dingle Road	d		
Penarth	a		
Cogan	d		
Eastbrook	d		
Dinas Powys	d		
Cadoxton	d		
Barry Docks	d		
Barry 3	d		
Barry Island	a		
Rhoose Cardiff Int Airport ✈	d		
Llantwit Major	d		
Bridgend	a		

When events are being held at the Millenium Stadium, services are subject to alteration. Please check times before travelling.

For connections to Cardiff Bay please refer to Table 130A

Table 130

Saturdays

4 January to 8 February

Treherbert, Aberdare, Merthyr, Pontypridd, Rhymney and Coryton - Cardiff, Penarth, Barry, Barry Island and Bridgend

Network Diagram - see first Page of Table 130

		AW	AW	AW	AW	AW	AW	AW	AW	AW	AW	AW	AW	AW	AW	AW	AW	AW	AW	AW	AW	AW	AW
											A		B		C		D			B			
Treherbert	d									05 47						06 17							06 47
Ynyswen	d									05 49						06 19							06 49
Treorchy	d									05 51						06 21							06 51
Ton Pentre	d									05 53						06 23							06 53
Ystrad Rhondda	a									05 56						06 26							06 56
	d									05 58						06 28							06 58
Llwynypia	d									06 00						06 30							07 00
Tonypandy	d									06 03						06 33							07 03
Dinas Rhondda	d									06 05						06 35							07 05
Porth	a									06 08						06 38							07 08
	d									06 09						06 39							07 09
Trehafod	d									06 12						06 42							07 12
Merthyr Tydfil	d																				06 38		
Pentre-bach	d																				06 42		
Troed Y Rhiw	d																				06 45		
Merthyr Vale	a																				06 48		
	d																				06 50		
Quakers Yard	d																				06 55		
Aberdare 3	d																	06 22					
Cwmbach	d																	06 25					
Fernhill	d																	06 28					
Mountain Ash	a																	06 31					
	d																	06 34					
Penrhiwceiber	d																	06 37					
Abercynon	d																	06 43			06 59		
Pontypridd 3	a									06 17						06 47		06 52			07 07		07 17
	d				05 18					06 18						06 48		06 54			07 09		07 18
Trefforest	d				05 21					06 21						06 51		06 57			07 12		07 21
Trefforest Estate	d				05 25																07 16		
Taffs Well 3	d				05 28					06 28					06 53	06 58	←	07 04			07 20		07 28
Radyr 3	a				05 31					06 31					06 56	07 01	06 56	07 07			07 23		07 31
	d				05 31					06 31					07 04	07 01	07 04	07 07			07 23		07 31
Danescourt	d														→		07 08						
Fairwater	d																07 10						
Waun-gron Park	d																07 12						
Ninian Park	d																07 15						
Llandaf	d				05 34					06 34						07 04		07 10			07 26		07 34
Cathays	d				05 39					06 39						07 09		07 15			07 31		07 39
Rhymney 3	d													06 08					06 32				
Pontlottyn	d													06 11					06 35				
Tir-phil	d													06 16					06 40				
Brithdir	d													06 18					06 42				
Bargoed	a													06 22					06 46				
	d													06 25					06 46			07 02	
Gilfach Fargoed	d													06 28								07 04	
Pengam	d													06 30					06 51			07 07	
Hengoed	d													06 34					06 54			07 10	
Ystrad Mynach 3	d													06 37					06 57			07 13	
Llanbradach	d													06 41					07 01			07 18	
Energlyn & Churchill Park	d													06 45					07 05				
Aber	d													06 47					07 07			07 22	
Caerphilly 3	d								06 10					06 50					07 10			07 25	
Lisvane & Thornhill	d								06 14					06 54					07 14			07 29	
Llanishen	d								06 16					06 56					07 16			07 31	
Heath High Level	d								06 19					06 59					07 19			07 34	
Coryton	d												06 45							07 15			
Whitchurch (Cardiff)	d												06 46							07 16			
Rhiwbina	d												06 48							07 18			
Birchgrove	d												06 50							07 20			
Ty Glas	d												06 51							07 21			
Heath Low Level	d												06 54							07 24			
Cardiff Queen Street 3	a				05 43				06 25	06 42			06 59	07 04		07 12		07 19	07 24	07 30	07 34	07 39	07 44
	d				05 45				06 26	06 43			07 01	07 06		07 13		07 21	07 26	07 31	07 36	07 41	07 46
Cardiff Central 7	a				05 48				06 29	06 48			07 04	07 09		07 16	07 20	07 24	07 29	07 34	07 39	07 44	07 52
	d	05 20	05 41	05 46	05 55	06 16	06 25	06 36	06 41		06 55	07 01		07 10		07 16		07 25	07 31		07 41	07 46	
Grangetown	d	05 24	05 45	05 50	05 59	06 20	06 29	06 40	06 45		06 59	07 05		07 14		07 20		07 29	07 35		07 45	07 50	
Dingle Road	d			05 54		06 24		06 44				07 11				07 26			07 41			07 56	
Penarth	a			05 59		06 29		06 49				07 16				07 31			07 46			08 01	
Cogan	d	05 28	05 48		06 03		06 33		06 48		07 03			07 18				07 33			07 48		
Eastbrook	d	05 30	05 51		06 05		06 35		06 51		07 05			07 20				07 35			07 51		
Dinas Powys	d	05 32	05 53		06 07		06 37		06 53		07 07			07 22				07 37			07 53		
Cadoxton	d	05 37	05 57		06 12		06 42		06 57		07 12			07 27				07 42			07 57		
Barry Docks	d	05 39	06 00		06 14		06 44		07 00		07 14			07 29				07 44			08 00		
Barry 3	d	05 44	06 05		06 19		06 49		07 05		07 19			07 34				07 49			08 05		
Barry Island	a	05 50			06 25		06 55				07 25			07 40				07 55					
Rhoose Cardiff Int Airport ✈	d		06 12						07 12												08 12		
Llantwit Major	d		06 22						07 22												08 22		
Bridgend	a		06 39						07 39												08 39		

A From Hereford
B To Radyr
C To Coryton
D From Taffs Well to Coryton

When events are being held at the Millenium Stadium, services are subject to alteration. Please check times before travelling.

For connections to Cardiff Bay please refer to Table 130A

Table 130

Saturdays
4 January to 8 February

Treherbert, Aberdare, Merthyr, Pontypridd, Rhymney and Coryton - Cardiff, Penarth, Barry, Barry Island and Bridgend

Network Diagram - see first Page of Table 130

		AW A	AW	AW	AW B	AW		AW	AW	AW A	AW	AW	AW B	AW	AW	AW		AW A	AW	AW	AW B	AW	AW	AW	AW A
Treherbert	d								07 17							07 45								08 17	
Ynyswen	d								07 19							07 47								08 19	
Treorchy	d								07 21							07 49								08 21	
Ton Pentre	d								07 23							07 51								08 23	
Ystrad Rhondda	a								07 26							07 54								08 26	
	d								07 28							07 58								08 28	
Llwynypia	d								07 30							08 00								08 30	
Tonypandy	d								07 33							08 03								08 33	
Dinas Rhondda	d								07 35							08 05								08 35	
Porth	a								07 38							08 08								08 38	
	d								07 39							08 09								08 39	
Trehafod	d								07 42							08 12								08 42	
Merthyr Tydfil	d					07 08								07 38								08 08			
Pentre-bach	d					07 12								07 42								08 12			
Troed Y Rhiw	d					07 15								07 45								08 15			
Merthyr Vale	a					07 18								07 48								08 18			
	d					07 20								07 50								08 20			
Quakers Yard	d					07 25								07 55								08 25			
Aberdare	d		06 52								07 22								07 52						
Cwmbach	d		06 55								07 25								07 55						
Fernhill	d		06 58								07 28								07 58						
Mountain Ash	a		07 01								07 31								08 01						
	d		07 04								07 34								08 04						
Penrhiwceiber	d		07 07								07 37								08 07						
Abercynon	d		07 13			07 29					07 43			07 59					08 13			08 29			
Pontypridd	a		07 22			07 37			07 47		07 52			08 07		08 17			08 22			08 37		08 47	
	d		07 24			07 39			07 48		07 54			08 09		08 18			08 24			08 39		08 48	
Trefforest	d		07 27			07 42			07 51		07 57			08 12		08 21			08 27			08 42		08 51	
Trefforest Estate	d					07 46								08 16								08 46			
Taffs Well	d		07 34			07 50			07 58		08 04			08 20		08 28			08 34			08 50		08 58	
Radyr	a		07 37			07 53			08 01		08 07			08 23		08 31			08 37			08 53		09 01	
	d	07 34	07 37			07 53			08 01	08 04	08 07			08 23		08 31		08 34	08 37			08 53		09 01	09 04
Danescourt	d	07 38								08 08								08 38							09 08
Fairwater	d	07 40								08 10								08 40							09 10
Waun-gron Park	d	07 42								08 12								08 42							09 12
Ninian Park	d	07 45								08 15								08 45							09 15
Llandaf	d		07 40			07 56			08 04		08 10			08 26		08 34			08 40			08 56		09 04	
Cathays	d		07 45			08 01			08 09		08 15			08 31		08 39			08 45			09 01		09 09	
Rhymney	d			07 00								07 24			07 42										
Pontlottyn	d			07 03								07 27			07 45										
Tir-phil	d			07 08								07 32			07 50										
Brithdir	d			07 10								07 34			07 52										
Bargoed	a			07 14								07 38			07 59										
	d			07 15				07 32				07 43			08 00					08 15			08 32		
Gilfach Fargoed	d			07 18								07 46								08 18					
Pengam	d			07 20				07 37				07 48			08 05					08 20			08 37		
Hengoed	d			07 24				07 40				07 52			08 09					08 24			08 40		
Ystrad Mynach	d			07 27				07 43				07 55			08 12					08 27			08 43		
Llanbradach	d			07 31				07 48				08 00			08 16					08 31			08 48		
Energlyn & Churchill Park	d			07 35								08 04			08 20					08 35					
Aber	d			07 37				07 52				08 07			08 22					08 37			08 52		
Caerphilly	d			07 40				07 55				08 10			08 25					08 40			08 55		
Lisvane & Thornhill	d			07 44				07 59				08 14			08 29					08 44			08 59		
Llanishen	d			07 46				08 01				08 16			08 31					08 46			09 01		
Heath High Level	d			07 49				08 04				08 19			08 34					08 49			09 04		
Coryton	d				07 45								08 15								08 45				
Whitchurch (Cardiff)	d				07 46								08 16								08 46				
Rhiwbina	d				07 48								08 18								08 48				
Birchgrove	d				07 50								08 20								08 50				
Ty Glas	d				07 51								08 21								08 51				
Heath Low Level	d				07 54								08 24								08 54				
Cardiff Queen Street	a		07 49	07 54	07 59	08 04		08 09	08 14		08 19	08 24	08 29	08 34	08 39	08 44			08 49	08 54	08 59	09 04	09 09	09 14	
	d		07 51	07 56	08 01	08 06		08 11	08 16		08 21	08 26	08 31	08 36	08 41	08 46			08 51	08 56	09 01	09 06	09 11	09 16	
Cardiff Central	a	07 50	07 54	07 59	08 04	08 09		08 14	08 22	08 19	08 24	08 29	08 34	08 39	08 47	08 52		08 50	08 54	08 59	09 04	09 09	09 14	09 22	09 20
	d		07 55	08 01		08 10		08 16			08 25	08 31		08 41					08 55	09 01		09 10	09 16		
Grangetown	d		07 59	08 05		08 14		08 20			08 29	08 35		08 45					08 59	09 05		09 14	09 20		
Dingle Road	d			08 11				08 26				08 41								09 11			09 26		
Penarth	a			08 16				08 31				08 46								09 16			09 31		
Cogan	d		08 03			08 18					08 33			08 48					09 03			09 18			
Eastbrook	d		08 05			08 20					08 35			08 51					09 05			09 20			
Dinas Powys	d		08 07			08 22					08 37			08 53					09 07			09 22			
Cadoxton	d		08 12			08 27					08 42			08 57					09 12			09 27			
Barry Docks	d		08 14			08 29					08 44			09 00					09 14			09 29			
Barry	d		08 19			08 34					08 49			09 05					09 19			09 34			
Barry Island	a		08 25			08 40					08 55								09 25			09 40			
Rhoose Cardiff Int Airport ✈	d													09 12											
Llantwit Major	d													09 22											
Bridgend	a													09 39											

A To Coryton
B To Radyr

When events are being held at the Millenium Stadium, services are subject to alteration. Please check times before travelling.

For connections to Cardiff Bay please refer to Table 130A

Table 130

Saturdays

4 January to 8 February

Treherbert, Aberdare, Merthyr, Pontypridd, Rhymney and Coryton - Cardiff, Penarth, Barry, Barry Island and Bridgend

Network Diagram - see first Page of Table 130

		AW	AW	AW A	AW	AW	AW	AW B	AW	AW	AW A	AW	AW	AW	AW B	AW	AW	AW A	AW	AW	AW	AW B
Treherbert	d						08 47							09 17							09 47	
Ynyswen	d						08 49							09 19							09 49	
Treorchy	d						08 51							09 21							09 51	
Ton Pentre	d						08 53							09 23							09 53	
Ystrad Rhondda	a						08 56							09 26							09 56	
	d						08 58							09 28							09 58	
Llwynypia	d						09 00							09 30							10 00	
Tonypandy	d						09 03							09 33							10 03	
Dinas Rhondda	d						09 05							09 35							10 05	
Porth	a						09 08							09 38							10 08	
	d						09 09							09 39							10 09	
Trehafod	d						09 12							09 42							10 12	
Merthyr Tydfil	d				08 38							09 08							09 38			
Pentre-bach	d				08 42							09 12							09 42			
Troed Y Rhiw	d				08 45							09 15							09 45			
Merthyr Vale	a				08 48							09 18							09 48			
	d				08 50							09 20							09 50			
Quakers Yard	d				08 55							09 25							09 55			
Aberdare 3	d	08 22							08 52							09 22						
Cwmbach	d	08 25							08 55							09 25						
Fernhill	d	08 28							08 58							09 28						
Mountain Ash	a	08 31							09 01							09 31						
	d	08 34							09 04							09 34						
Penrhiwceiber	d	08 37							09 07							09 37						
Abercynon	d	08 43			08 59				09 13			09 29				09 43			09 59			
Pontypridd 3	a	08 52			09 07		09 17		09 22			09 37		09 47		09 52			10 07		10 17	
	d	08 54			09 09		09 18		09 24			09 39		09 48		09 54			10 09		10 18	
Trefforest	d	08 57			09 12		09 21		09 27			09 42		09 51		09 57			10 12		10 21	
Trefforest Estate	d				09 16							09 46							10 16			
Taffs Well 3	d	09 04			09 20		09 28		09 34			09 50		09 58		10 04			10 20		10 28	
Radyr 3	a	09 07			09 23		09 31		09 37			09 53		10 01		10 07			10 23		10 31	
	d	09 07			09 23		09 31	09 34	09 37			09 53		10 01	10 04	10 07			10 23		10 31	10 34
Danescourt	d							09 38							10 08							10 38
Fairwater	d							09 40							10 10							10 40
Waun-gron Park	d							09 42							10 12							10 42
Ninian Park	d							09 45							10 15							10 45
Llandaf	d	09 10			09 26		09 34		09 40			09 56		10 04		10 10			10 26		10 34	
Cathays	d	09 15			09 31		09 39		09 45			10 01		10 09		10 15			10 31		10 39	
Rhymney 3	d		08 30														09 27					
Pontlottyn	d		08 33														09 30					
Tir-phil	d		08 37														09 35					
Brithdir	d		08 40														09 37					
Bargoed	a		08 44														09 41					
	d		08 47			09 00				09 17			09 32				09 45			10 00		
Gilfach Fargoed	d									09 19												
Pengam	d		08 52			09 05				09 22			09 37				09 50			10 05		
Hengoed	d		08 55			09 09				09 25			09 40				09 54			10 09		
Ystrad Mynach 3	d		08 58			09 12				09 28			09 43				09 57			10 12		
Llanbradach	d		09 03			09 16				09 33			09 48				10 01			10 16		
Energlyn & Churchill Park	d					09 20											10 05			10 20		
Aber	d		09 07			09 22				09 37			09 52				10 07			10 22		
Caerphilly 3	d		09 10			09 25				09 40			09 55				10 10			10 25		
Lisvane & Thornhill	d		09 14			09 29				09 44			09 59				10 14			10 29		
Llanishen	d		09 16			09 31				09 46			10 01				10 16			10 31		
Heath High Level	d		09 19			09 34				09 49			10 04				10 19			10 34		
Coryton	d			09 15							09 45							10 15				
Whitchurch (Cardiff)	d			09 16							09 46							10 16				
Rhiwbina	d			09 18							09 48							10 18				
Birchgrove	d			09 20							09 50							10 20				
Ty Glas	d			09 21							09 51							10 21				
Heath Low Level	d			09 24							09 54							10 24				
Cardiff Queen Street 3	a	09 19	09 24	09 29	09 34	09 39	09 44		09 49	09 54	09 59	10 04	10 09	10 14		10 19	10 24	10 29	10 34	10 39	10 44	
	d	09 21	09 26	09 31	09 36	09 41	09 46		09 51	09 56	10 01	10 06	10 11	10 16		10 21	10 26	10 31	10 36	10 41	10 46	
Cardiff Central 7	a	09 24	09 29	09 34	09 39	09 44	09 52	09 50	09 54	09 59	10 04	10 09	10 14	10 22	10 20	10 24	10 29	10 34	10 39	10 44	10 52	10 50
	d	09 25	09 31		09 41	09 46			09 55	10 01		10 10	10 16			10 25	10 31		10 41	10 46		
Grangetown	d	09 29	09 35		09 45	09 50			09 59	10 05		10 14	10 20			10 29	10 35		10 45	10 50		
Dingle Road	d		09 41			09 56				10 11			10 26				10 41			10 56		
Penarth	a		09 46			10 01				10 16			10 31				10 46			11 01		
Cogan	d	09 33			09 48				10 03			10 18				10 33			10 48			
Eastbrook	d	09 35			09 51				10 05			10 20				10 35			10 51			
Dinas Powys	d	09 37			09 53				10 07			10 22				10 37			10 53			
Cadoxton	d	09 42			09 57				10 12			10 27				10 42			10 57			
Barry Docks	d	09 44			10 00				10 14			10 29				10 44			11 00			
Barry 3	d	09 49			10 05				10 19			10 34				10 49			11 05			
Barry Island	a	09 55							10 25			10 40				10 55						
Rhoose Cardiff Int Airport ✈	d				10 12														11 12			
Llantwit Major	d				10 22														11 22			
Bridgend	a				10 39														11 39			

A To Radyr **B** To Coryton

When events are being held at the Millenium Stadium, services are subject to alteration. Please check times before travelling.

For connections to Cardiff Bay please refer to Table 130A

Table 130

Saturdays

4 January to 8 February

Treherbert, Aberdare, Merthyr, Pontypridd, Rhymney and Coryton - Cardiff, Penarth, Barry, Barry Island and Bridgend

Network Diagram - see first Page of Table 130

		AW	AW	AW	AW A	AW	AW	AW B	AW	AW	AW	AW A	AW	AW	AW	AW B	AW	AW	AW A	AW	AW	AW	AW B
Treherbert	d										10 17				10 47							11 17	
Ynyswen	d										10 19				10 49							11 19	
Treorchy	d										10 21				10 51							11 21	
Ton Pentre	d										10 23				10 53							11 23	
Ystrad Rhondda	a										10 26				10 56							11 26	
	d										10 28				10 58							11 28	
Llwynypia	d										10 30				11 00							11 30	
Tonypandy	d										10 33				11 03							11 33	
Dinas Rhondda	d										10 35				11 05							11 35	
Porth	a										10 38				11 08							11 38	
	d										10 52				11 09							11 39	
Trehafod	d										10 55				11 12							11 42	
Merthyr Tydfil	d		10 04										10 38							11 08			
Pentre-bach	d		10 08										10 42							11 12			
Troed Y Rhiw	d		10 11										10 45							11 15			
Merthyr Vale	a		10 14										10 48							11 18			
	d		10 16										10 50							11 20			
Quakers Yard	d		10 22										10 55							11 25			
Aberdare 3	d	09 52							10 22								10 52						
Cwmbach	d	09 55							10 25								10 55						
Fernhill	d	09 58							10 28								10 58						
Mountain Ash	a	10 01							10 31								11 01						
	d	10 04							10 34								11 04						
Penrhiwceiber	d	10 07							10 37								11 07						
Abercynon	d	10 13	10 26						10 43				10 59				11 13			11 29			
Pontypridd 3	a	10 22	10 32						10 52		11 00		11 07		11 17		11 22			11 37		11 47	
	d	10 24				10 39			10 54		11 04		11 09		11 18		11 24			11 39		11 48	
Trefforest	d	10 27				10 42			10 57		11 07		11 12		11 21		11 27			11 42		11 51	
Trefforest Estate	d												11 16							11 46			
Taffs Well 3	d	10 34				10 50			11 04		11 13		11 20		11 28		11 34			11 50		11 58	
Radyr 3	a	10 37				10 53			11 07		11 17		11 23		11 31		11 37			11 53		12 01	
	d	10 37				10 53		11 04	11 07		11 17		11 23		11 31	11 34	11 37			11 53		12 01	12 04
Danescourt	d							11 08								11 38							12 08
Fairwater	d							11 10								11 40							12 10
Waun-gron Park	d							11 12								11 42							12 12
Ninian Park	d							11 15								11 45							12 15
Llandaf	d	10 40				10 56			11 10				11 26		11 34		11 40			11 56		12 04	
Cathays	d	10 45				11 01			11 15				11 31		11 39		11 45			12 01		12 09	
Rhymney 3	d									10 27													
Pontlottyn	d									10 30													
Tir-phil	d									10 35													
Brithdir	d									10 37													
Bargoed	a									10 41													
	d			10 17			10 32			10 45				11 00				11 17			11 32		
Gilfach Fargoed	d			10 19														11 19					
Pengam	d			10 22			10 37			10 50				11 05				11 22			11 37		
Hengoed	d			10 25			10 40			10 54				11 09				11 25			11 40		
Ystrad Mynach 3	d			10 28			10 43			10 57				11 12				11 28			11 43		
Llanbradach	d			10 33			10 48			11 01				11 16				11 33			11 48		
Energlyn & Churchill Park	d									11 05				11 20									
Aber	d			10 37			10 52			11 07				11 22				11 37			11 52		
Caerphilly 3	d			10 40			10 55			11 10				11 25				11 40			11 55		
Lisvane & Thornhill	d			10 44			10 59			11 14				11 29				11 44			11 59		
Llanishen	d			10 46			11 01			11 16				11 31				11 46			12 01		
Heath High Level	d			10 49			11 04			11 19				11 34				11 49			12 04		
Coryton	d				10 45							11 15							11 45				
Whitchurch (Cardiff)	d				10 46							11 16							11 46				
Rhiwbina	d				10 48							11 18							11 48				
Birchgrove	d				10 50							11 20							11 50				
Ty Glas	d				10 51							11 21							11 51				
Heath Low Level	d				10 54							11 24							11 54				
Cardiff Queen Street 3	a	10 49		10 54	10 59	11 04	11 09		11 19	11 24		11 29	11 34	11 39	11 44		11 49	11 54	11 59	12 04	12 09	12 14	
	d	10 51		10 56	11 01	11 06	11 11		11 21	11 26		11 31	11 36	11 41	11 46		11 51	11 56	12 01	12 06	12 11	12 16	
Cardiff Central 7	a	10 54		10 59	11 04	11 09	11 14	11 20	11 24	11 29	11 34	11 34	11 39	11 44	11 52	11 50	11 54	11 59	12 04	12 09	12 14	12 22	12 20
	d	10 55		11 01		11 10	11 16		11 25	11 31			11 41	11 46			11 55	12 01		12 10	12 16		
Grangetown	d	10 59		11 05		11 14	11 20		11 29	11 35			11 45	11 50			11 59	12 05		12 14	12 20		
Dingle Road	d			11 11			11 26			11 41				11 56				12 11			12 26		
Penarth	a			11 16			11 31			11 46				12 01				12 16			12 31		
Cogan	d	11 03				11 18			11 33				11 48				12 03			12 18			
Eastbrook	d	11 05				11 20			11 35				11 51				12 05			12 20			
Dinas Powys	d	11 07				11 22			11 37				11 53				12 07			12 22			
Cadoxton	d	11 12				11 27			11 42				11 57				12 12			12 27			
Barry Docks	d	11 14				11 29			11 44				12 00				12 14			12 29			
Barry 3	d	11 19				11 34			11 49				12 05				12 19			12 34			
Barry Island	a	11 25				11 40			11 55								12 25			12 40			
Rhoose Cardiff Int Airport ✈	d												12 12										
Llantwit Major	d												12 22										
Bridgend	a												12 39										

A To Radyr

B To Coryton

When events are being held at the Millenium Stadium, services are subject to alteration. Please check times before travelling.

For connections to Cardiff Bay please refer to Table 130A

Table 130

Saturdays

4 January to 8 February

Treherbert, Aberdare, Merthyr, Pontypridd, Rhymney and Coryton - Cardiff, Penarth, Barry, Barry Island and Bridgend

Network Diagram - see first Page of Table 130

		AW	AW	AW A	AW	AW	AW	AW B	AW	AW A	AW	AW	AW	AW B	AW	AW	AW A	AW	AW	AW	AW B	AW
Treherbert	d						11 47						12 17							12 47		
Ynyswen	d						11 49						12 19							12 49		
Treorchy	d						11 51						12 21							12 51		
Ton Pentre	d						11 53						12 23							12 53		
Ystrad Rhondda	a						11 56						12 26							12 56		
	d						11 58						12 28							12 58		
Llwynypia	d						12 00						12 30							13 00		
Tonypandy	d						12 03						12 33							13 03		
Dinas Rhondda	d						12 05						12 35							13 05		
Porth	a						12 08						12 38							13 08		
	d						12 09						12 39							13 09		
Trehafod	d						12 12						12 42							13 12		
Merthyr Tydfil	d				11 38						12 08							12 38				
Pentre-bach	d				11 42						12 12							12 42				
Troed Y Rhiw	d				11 45						12 15							12 45				
Merthyr Vale	a				11 48						12 18							12 48				
	d				11 50						12 20							12 50				
Quakers Yard	d				11 55						12 25							12 55				
Aberdare 3	d	11 22													12 22							12 52
Cwmbach	d	11 25													12 25							12 55
Fernhill	d	11 28													12 28							12 58
Mountain Ash	a	11 31													12 31							13 01
	d	11 34													12 34							13 04
Penrhiwceiber	d	11 37													12 37							13 07
Abercynon	d	11 43			11 59						12 29				12 43			12 59				13 13
Pontypridd 3	a	11 52			12 07		12 17				12 37		12 48		12 52			13 07		13 17		13 22
	d	11 54			12 09		12 18				12 39		12 48		12 54			13 09		13 18		13 24
Trefforest	d	11 57			12 12		12 21				12 42		12 51		12 57			13 12		13 21		13 27
Trefforest Estate	d				12 16						12 46							13 16				
Taffs Well 3	d	12 04			12 20		12 28				12 50		12 58		13 04			13 20		13 28		13 34
Radyr 3	a	12 07			12 23		12 31				12 53		13 01		13 07			13 23		13 31		13 37
	d	12 07			12 23		12 31	12 34			12 53		13 01	13 04	13 07			13 23		13 31	13 34	13 37
Danescourt	d							12 38						13 08							13 38	
Fairwater	d							12 40						13 10							13 40	
Waun-gron Park	d							12 42						13 12							13 42	
Ninian Park	d							12 45						13 15							13 45	
Llandaf	d	12 10			12 26		12 34				12 56		13 04		13 10			13 26		13 34		13 40
Cathays	d	12 15			12 31		12 39				13 01		13 09		13 15			13 31		13 39		13 45
Rhymney 3	d		11 27													12 27						
Pontlottyn	d		11 30													12 30						
Tir-phil	d		11 35													12 35						
Brithdir	d		11 37													12 37						
Bargoed	a		11 41													12 41						
	d		11 45			12 00			12 17			12 32				12 45			13 00			
Gilfach Fargoed	d								12 19													
Pengam	d		11 50			12 05			12 22			12 37				12 50			13 05			
Hengoed	d		11 54			12 09			12 25			12 40				12 54			13 09			
Ystrad Mynach 3	d		11 57			12 12			12 28			12 43				12 57			13 12			
Llanbradach	d		12 01			12 16			12 33			12 48				13 01			13 16			
Energlyn & Churchill Park	d		12 05			12 20										13 05			13 20			
Aber	d		12 07			12 22			12 37			12 52				13 07			13 22			
Caerphilly 3	d		12 10			12 25			12 40			12 55				13 10			13 25			
Lisvane & Thornhill	d		12 14			12 29			12 44			12 59				13 14			13 29			
Llanishen	d		12 16			12 31			12 46			13 01				13 16			13 31			
Heath High Level	d		12 19			12 34			12 49			13 04				13 19			13 34			
Coryton	d			12 15						12 45							13 15					
Whitchurch (Cardiff)	d			12 16						12 46							13 16					
Rhiwbina	d			12 18						12 48							13 18					
Birchgrove	d			12 20						12 50							13 20					
Ty Glas	d			12 21						12 51							13 21					
Heath Low Level	d			12 24						12 54							13 24					
Cardiff Queen Street 3	a	12 19	12 24	12 29	12 34	12 39	12 44		12 54	12 59	13 04	13 09	13 14		13 19	13 24	13 29	13 34	13 39	13 44		13 49
	d	12 21	12 26	12 31	12 36	12 41	12 46		12 56	13 01	13 06	13 11	13 16		13 21	13 26	13 31	13 36	13 41	13 46		13 51
Cardiff Central 7	a	12 24	12 29	12 34	12 39	12 44	12 52	12 50	12 59	13 04	13 09	13 14	13 22	13 20	13 24	13 29	13 34	13 39	13 44	13 52	13 50	13 54
	d	12 25	12 31		12 41	12 46	12 55		13 01		13 10	13 16			13 25	13 31		13 41	13 46			13 55
Grangetown	d	12 29	12 35		12 45	12 50	12 59		13 05		13 14	13 20			13 29	13 35		13 45	13 50			13 59
Dingle Road	d		12 41			12 56			13 11			13 26				13 41			13 56			
Penarth	a		12 46			13 01			13 16			13 31				13 46			14 01			
Cogan	d	12 33			12 48		13 03				13 18				13 33			13 48				14 03
Eastbrook	d	12 35			12 51		13 05				13 20				13 35			13 51				14 05
Dinas Powys	d	12 37			12 53		13 07				13 22				13 37			13 53				14 07
Cadoxton	d	12 42			12 57		13 12				13 27				13 42			13 57				14 12
Barry Docks	d	12 44			13 00		13 14				13 29				13 44			14 00				14 14
Barry 3	d	12 49			13 05		13 19				13 34				13 49			14 05				14 19
Barry Island	a	12 55					13 25				13 40				13 55							14 25
Rhoose Cardiff Int Airport ✈	d				13 12													14 12				
Llantwit Major	d				13 22													14 22				
Bridgend	a				13 39													14 39				

A To Radyr

B To Coryton

When events are being held at the Millenium Stadium, services are subject to alteration. Please check times before travelling.

For connections to Cardiff Bay please refer to Table 130A

Table 130

Saturdays

4 January to 8 February

Treherbert, Aberdare, Merthyr, Pontypridd, Rhymney and Coryton - Cardiff, Penarth, Barry, Barry Island and Bridgend

Network Diagram - see first Page of Table 130

		AW	AW A	AW	AW	AW	AW B	AW	AW	AW A		AW	AW	AW	AW B	AW	AW	AW A	AW	AW		AW B	AW	AW	AW
Treherbert	d					13 17								13 47											14 17
Ynyswen	d					13 19								13 49											14 19
Treorchy	d					13 21								13 51											14 21
Ton Pentre	d					13 23								13 53											14 23
Ystrad Rhondda	a					13 26								13 56											14 26
	d					13 28								13 58											14 28
Llwynypia	d					13 30								14 00											14 30
Tonypandy	d					13 33								14 03											14 33
Dinas Rhondda	d					13 35								14 05											14 35
Porth	a					13 38								14 08											14 38
	d					13 39								14 09											14 52
Trehafod	d					13 42								14 12											14 55
Merthyr Tydfil	d			13 08								13 38							14 08						
Pentre-bach	d			13 12								13 42							14 12						
Troed Y Rhiw	d			13 15								13 45							14 15						
Merthyr Vale	a			13 18								13 48							14 18						
	d			13 20								13 50							14 20						
Quakers Yard	d			13 25								13 55							14 25						
Aberdare 3	d															13 52							14 22		
Cwmbach	d															13 55							14 25		
Fernhill	d															13 58							14 28		
Mountain Ash	a															14 01							14 31		
	d															14 04							14 34		
Penrhiwceiber	d															14 07							14 37		
Abercynon	d			13 29				13 45				13 59				14 13			14 29				14 43		
Pontypridd 3	a			13 37		13 47		13 52				14 07		14 17		14 22			14 37				14 52		15 00
	d			13 39		13 48		13 54				14 09		14 18		14 24			14 39				14 54		15 04
Trefforest	d			13 42		13 51		13 57				14 12		14 21		14 27			14 42				14 57		15 07
Trefforest Estate	d			13 46								14 16							14 46						
Taffs Well 3	d			13 50		13 58		14 04				14 20		14 28		14 34			14 50				15 04		15 13
Radyr 3	a			13 53		14 01		14 07				14 23		14 31		14 37			14 53				15 07		15 17
	d			13 53		14 01	14 04	14 07				14 23		14 31	14 34	14 37			14 53			15 04	15 07		15 17
Danescourt	d						14 08								14 38							15 08			
Fairwater	d						14 10								14 40							15 10			
Waun-gron Park	d						14 12								14 42							15 12			
Ninian Park	d						14 15								14 45							15 15			
Llandaf	d			13 56		14 04		14 10				14 26		14 34		14 40			14 56				15 10		
Cathays	d			14 01		14 09		14 15				14 31		14 39		14 45			15 01				15 15		
Rhymney 3	d								13 27															14 27	
Pontlottyn	d								13 30															14 30	
Tir-phil	d								13 35															14 35	
Brithdir	d								13 37															14 37	
Bargoed	a								13 41															14 41	
	d	13 17			13 32				13 45				14 00				14 17			14 32				14 45	
Gilfach Fargoed	d	13 19															14 19								
Pengam	d	13 22			13 37				13 50				14 05				14 22			14 37				14 50	
Hengoed	d	13 25			13 40				13 54				14 09				14 25			14 40				14 54	
Ystrad Mynach 3	d	13 28			13 43				13 57				14 12				14 28			14 43				14 57	
Llanbradach	d	13 33			13 48				14 01				14 16				14 33			14 48				15 01	
Energlyn & Churchill Park	d								14 05				14 20											15 05	
Aber	d	13 37			13 52				14 07				14 22				14 37			14 52				15 07	
Caerphilly 3	d	13 40			13 55				14 10				14 25				14 40			14 55				15 10	
Lisvane & Thornhill	d	13 44			13 59				14 14				14 29				14 44			14 59				15 14	
Llanishen	d	13 46			14 01				14 16				14 31				14 46			15 01				15 16	
Heath High Level	d	13 49			14 04				14 19				14 34				14 49			15 04				15 19	
Coryton	d		13 45							14 15								14 45							
Whitchurch (Cardiff)	d		13 46							14 16								14 46							
Rhiwbina	d		13 48							14 18								14 48							
Birchgrove	d		13 50							14 20								14 50							
Ty Glas	d		13 51							14 21								14 51							
Heath Low Level	d		13 54							14 24								14 54							
Cardiff Queen Street 3	a	13 54	13 59	14 04	14 09	14 14		14 19	14 24	14 29		14 34	14 39	14 44		14 49	14 54	14 59	15 04	15 09			15 19	15 24	
	d	13 56	14 01	14 06	14 11	14 16		14 21	14 26	14 31		14 36	14 41	14 46		14 51	14 56	15 01	15 06	15 11			15 21	15 26	
Cardiff Central 7	a	13 59	14 04	14 09	14 14	14 22	14 20	14 24	14 29	14 34		14 39	14 44	14 52	14 50	14 54	14 59	15 04	15 09	15 14		15 20	15 24	15 29	15 34
	d	14 01		14 10	14 16			14 25	14 31			14 41	14 46			14 55	15 01		15 10	15 16			15 25	15 31	
Grangetown	d	14 05		14 14	14 20			14 29	14 35			14 45	14 50			14 59	15 05		15 14	15 20			15 29	15 35	
Dingle Road	d	14 11			14 26				14 41				14 56				15 11			15 26				15 41	
Penarth	a	14 16			14 31				14 46				15 01				15 16			15 31				15 46	
Cogan	d			14 18				14 33				14 48				15 03			15 18				15 33		
Eastbrook	d			14 20				14 35				14 51				15 05			15 20				15 35		
Dinas Powys	d			14 22				14 37				14 53				15 07			15 22				15 37		
Cadoxton	d			14 27				14 42				14 57				15 12			15 27				15 42		
Barry Docks	d			14 29				14 44				15 00				15 14			15 29				15 44		
Barry 3	d			14 34				14 49				15 05				15 19			15 34				15 49		
Barry Island	a			14 40				14 55								15 25			15 40				15 55		
Rhoose Cardiff Int Airport ✈	d											15 12													
Llantwit Major	d											15 22													
Bridgend	a											15 39													

A To Radyr

B To Coryton

When events are being held at the Millenium Stadium, services are subject to alteration. Please check times before travelling.

For connections to Cardiff Bay please refer to Table 130A

Table 130

Saturdays

4 January to 8 February

Treherbert, Aberdare, Merthyr, Pontypridd, Rhymney and Coryton - Cardiff, Penarth, Barry, Barry Island and Bridgend

Network Diagram - see first Page of Table 130

		AW A	AW	AW	AW	AW B	AW	AW	AW A	AW	AW	AW	AW B	AW	AW	AW A	AW	AW	AW	AW B	AW	AW	AW A
Treherbert	d				14 47							15 13							15 47				
Ynyswen	d				14 49							15 15							15 49				
Treorchy	d				14 51							15 21							15 51				
Ton Pentre	d				14 53							15 23							15 53				
Ystrad Rhondda	a				14 56							15 26							15 56				
	d				14 58							15 28							15 58				
Llwynypia	d				15 00							15 30							16 00				
Tonypandy	d				15 03							15 33							16 03				
Dinas Rhondda	d				15 05							15 35							16 05				
Porth	a				15 08							15 38							16 08				
	d				15 09							15 39							16 09				
Trehafod	d				15 12							15 42							16 12				
Merthyr Tydfil	d		14 38							15 08							15 38						
Pentre-bach	d		14 42							15 12							15 42						
Troed Y Rhiw	d		14 45							15 15							15 45						
Merthyr Vale	a		14 48							15 18							15 48						
	d		14 50							15 20							15 50						
Quakers Yard	d		14 55							15 25							15 55						
Aberdare ■	d						14 52							15 22							15 52		
Cwmbach	d						14 55							15 25							15 55		
Fernhill	d						14 58							15 28							15 58		
Mountain Ash	a						15 01							15 31							16 01		
	d						15 04							15 34							16 04		
Penrhiwceiber	d						15 07							15 37							16 07		
Abercynon	d		14 59				15 13			15 29				15 43			15 59				16 13		
Pontypridd ■	a		15 07		15 17		15 22			15 37		15 47		15 52			16 07		16 17		16 22		
	d		15 09		15 18		15 24			15 39		15 48		15 54			16 09		16 18		16 24		
Trefforest	d		15 12		15 21		15 27			15 42		15 51		15 57			16 12		16 21		16 27		
Trefforest Estate	d		15 16							15 46							16 16						
Taffs Well ■	d		15 20		15 28		15 34			15 50		15 58		16 04			16 20		16 28		16 34		
Radyr ■	a		15 23		15 31		15 37			15 53		16 01		16 07			16 23		16 31		16 37		
	d		15 23		15 31	15 34	15 37			15 53		16 01	16 04	16 07			16 23		16 31	16 34	16 37		
Danescourt	d					15 38							16 08							16 38			
Fairwater	d					15 40							16 10							16 40			
Waun-gron Park	d					15 42							16 12							16 42			
Ninian Park	d					15 45							16 15							16 45			
Llandaf	d		15 26		15 34		15 40			15 56		16 04		16 10			16 26		16 34		16 40		
Cathays	d		15 31		15 39		15 45			16 01		16 09		16 15			16 31		16 39		16 45		
Rhymney ■	d														15 27								
Pontlottyn	d														15 30								
Tir-phil	d														15 35								
Brithdir	d														15 37								
Bargoed	a														15 41								
	d			15 00				15 17			15 32				15 45			16 00				16 17	
Gilfach Fargoed	d							15 19														16 19	
Pengam	d			15 05				15 22			15 37				15 50			16 05				16 22	
Hengoed	d			15 09				15 25			15 40				15 54			16 09				16 25	
Ystrad Mynach ■	d			15 12				15 28			15 43				15 57			16 12				16 28	
Llanbradach	d			15 16				15 33			15 48				16 01			16 16				16 33	
Energlyn & Churchill Park	d			15 20											16 05			16 20					
Aber	d			15 22				15 37			15 52				16 07			16 22				16 37	
Caerphilly ■	d			15 25				15 40			15 55				16 10			16 25				16 40	
Lisvane & Thornhill	d			15 29				15 44			15 59				16 14			16 29				16 44	
Llanishen	d			15 31				15 46			16 01				16 16			16 31				16 46	
Heath High Level	d			15 34				15 49			16 04				16 19			16 34				16 49	
Coryton	d	15 15							15 45							16 15							16 45
Whitchurch (Cardiff)	d	15 16							15 46							16 16							16 46
Rhiwbina	d	15 18							15 48							16 18							16 48
Birchgrove	d	15 20							15 50							16 20							16 50
Ty Glas	d	15 21							15 51							16 21							16 51
Heath Low Level	d	15 24							15 54							16 24							16 54
Cardiff Queen Street ■	a	15 29	15 34	15 39	15 44		15 49	15 54	15 59	16 04	16 09	16 14		16 19	16 24	16 29	16 34	16 39	16 44		16 49	16 54	16 59
	d	15 31	15 36	15 41	15 46		15 51	15 56	16 01	16 06	16 11	16 16		16 21	16 26	16 31	16 36	16 41	16 46		16 51	16 56	17 01
Cardiff Central ■	a	15 34	15 39	15 44	15 52	15 50	15 54	15 59	16 04	16 09	16 14	16 22	16 20	16 24	16 32	16 34	16 39	16 44	16 52	16 50	16 54	16 59	17 04
	d		15 41	15 46			15 55	16 01		16 10	16 16			16 25			16 41	16 46			16 55	17 01	
Grangetown	d		15 45	15 50			15 59	16 05		16 14	16 20			16 29			16 45	16 50			16 59	17 05	
Dingle Road	d			15 56				16 11			16 26							16 56				17 11	
Penarth	a			16 01				16 16			16 31							17 01				17 16	
Cogan	d		15 48				16 03			16 18				16 33			16 48				17 03		
Eastbrook	d		15 51				16 05			16 20				16 35			16 51				17 05		
Dinas Powys	d		15 53				16 07			16 22				16 37			16 53				17 07		
Cadoxton	d		15 57				16 12			16 27				16 42			16 57				17 12		
Barry Docks	d		16 00				16 14			16 29				16 44			17 00				17 14		
Barry ■	d		16 05				16 19			16 34				16 49			17 05				17 19		
Barry Island	a						16 25			16 40				16 55							17 25		
Rhoose Cardiff Int Airport ✈	d		16 12														17 12						
Llantwit Major	d		16 22														17 22						
Bridgend	a		16 39														17 39						

A To Radyr **B** To Coryton

When events are being held at the Millenium Stadium, services are subject to alteration. Please check times before travelling.

For connections to Cardiff Bay please refer to Table 130A

Table 130

Saturdays

4 January to 8 February

Treherbert, Aberdare, Merthyr, Pontypridd, Rhymney and Coryton - Cardiff, Penarth, Barry, Barry Island and Bridgend

Network Diagram - see first Page of Table 130

		AW	AW	AW	AW A	AW	AW	AW B	AW	AW	AW	AW A	AW	AW	AW B	AW	AW	AW	AW A	AW	AW	AW B
Treherbert	d			16 17							16 47							17 17				
Ynyswen	d			16 19							16 49							17 19				
Treorchy	d			16 21							16 51							17 21				
Ton Pentre	d			16 23							16 53							17 23				
Ystrad Rhondda	a			16 26							16 56							17 26				
	d			16 28							16 58							17 28				
Llwynypia	d			16 30							17 00							17 30				
Tonypandy	d			16 33							17 03							17 33				
Dinas Rhondda	d			16 35							17 05							17 35				
Porth	a			16 38							17 08							17 38				
	d			16 39							17 09							17 39				
Trehafod	d			16 42							17 12							17 42				
Merthyr Tydfil	d	16 08							16 38							17 08						
Pentre-bach	d	16 12							16 42							17 12						
Troed Y Rhiw	d	16 15							16 45							17 15						
Merthyr Vale	a	16 18							16 48							17 18						
	d	16 20							16 50							17 20						
Quakers Yard	d	16 25							16 55							17 25						
Aberdare 3	d					16 22							16 52							17 22		
Cwmbach	d					16 25							16 55							17 25		
Fernhill	d					16 28							16 58							17 28		
Mountain Ash	a					16 31							17 01							17 31		
	d					16 34							17 04							17 34		
Penrhiwceiber	d					16 37							17 07							17 37		
Abercynon	d	16 29				16 43			16 59				17 13			17 29				17 43		
Pontypridd 3	a	16 37		16 47		16 52			17 07		17 17		17 22			17 37		17 47		17 52		
	d	16 39		16 48		16 54			17 09		17 18		17 24			17 39		17 48		17 54		
Trefforest	d	16 42		16 51		16 57			17 12		17 21		17 27			17 42		17 51		17 57		
Trefforest Estate	d	16 46							17 16							17 46						
Taffs Well 3	d	16 50		16 58		17 04			17 20		17 28		17 34			17 50		17 58		18 04		
Radyr 3	a	16 53		17 01		17 07			17 23		17 31		17 37			17 53		18 01		18 07		
	d	16 53		17 01	17 04	17 07			17 23		17 31	17 34	17 37			17 53		18 01	18 04	18 07		
Danescourt	d				17 08							17 38							18 08			
Fairwater	d				17 10							17 40							18 10			
Waun-gron Park	d				17 12							17 42							18 12			
Ninian Park	d				17 15							17 45							18 15			
Llandaf	d	16 56		17 04		17 10			17 26		17 34		17 40			17 56		18 04		18 10		
Cathays	d	17 01		17 09		17 15			17 31		17 39		17 45			18 01		18 09		18 15		
Rhymney 3	d						16 27														17 27	
Pontlottyn	d						16 30														17 30	
Tir-phil	d						16 35														17 35	
Brithdir	d						16 37														17 37	
Bargoed	a						16 41														17 41	
	d		16 32				16 45			17 00				17 17			17 32				17 45	
Gilfach Fargoed	d													17 19								
Pengam	d		16 37				16 50			17 05				17 22			17 37				17 50	
Hengoed	d		16 40				16 54			17 09				17 25			17 40				17 54	
Ystrad Mynach 3	d		16 43				16 57			17 12				17 28			17 43				17 57	
Llanbradach	d		16 48				17 01			17 16				17 33			17 48				18 01	
Energlyn & Churchill Park	d						17 05			17 20											18 05	
Aber	d		16 52				17 07			17 22				17 37			17 52				18 07	
Caerphilly 3	d		16 55				17 10			17 25				17 40			17 55				18 10	
Lisvane & Thornhill	d		16 59				17 14			17 29				17 44			17 59				18 14	
Llanishen	d		17 01				17 16			17 31				17 46			18 01				18 16	
Heath High Level	d		17 04				17 19			17 34				17 49			18 04				18 19	
Coryton	d							17 15							17 45							18 15
Whitchurch (Cardiff)	d							17 16							17 46							18 16
Rhiwbina	d							17 18							17 48							18 18
Birchgrove	d							17 20							17 50							18 20
Ty Glas	d							17 21							17 51							18 21
Heath Low Level	d							17 24							17 54							18 24
Cardiff Queen Street 3	a	17 04	17 09	17 14		17 19	17 24	17 29	17 34	17 39	17 44		17 49	17 54	17 59	18 04	18 09	18 14		18 19	18 24	18 29
	d	17 06	17 11	17 16		17 21	17 26	17 31	17 36	17 41	17 46		17 51	17 56	18 01	18 06	18 11	18 16		18 21	18 26	18 31
Cardiff Central 7	a	17 09	17 14	17 22	17 20	17 24	17 29	17 34	17 39	17 44	17 52	17 50	17 54	17 59	18 04	18 09	18 14	18 22	18 20	18 24	18 29	18 34
	d	17 10	17 16			17 25	17 31		17 41	17 46			17 55	18 01		18 10	18 16			18 25	18 31	
Grangetown	d	17 14	17 20			17 29	17 35		17 45	17 50			17 59	18 05		18 14	18 20			18 29	18 35	
Dingle Road	d		17 26				17 41			17 56				18 11			18 26				18 41	
Penarth	a		17 31				17 46			18 01				18 16			18 31				18 46	
Cogan	d	17 18				17 33			17 48				18 03			18 18				18 33		
Eastbrook	d	17 20				17 35			17 51				18 05			18 20				18 35		
Dinas Powys	d	17 22				17 37			17 53				18 07			18 22				18 37		
Cadoxton	d	17 27				17 42			17 57				18 12			18 27				18 42		
Barry Docks	d	17 29				17 44			18 00				18 14			18 29				18 44		
Barry 3	d	17 34				17 49			18 05				18 19			18 34				18 49		
Barry Island	a	17 40				17 55							18 25			18 40				18 55		
Rhoose Cardiff Int Airport ✈	d								18 12													
Llantwit Major	d								18 22													
Bridgend	a								18 39													

A To Coryton

B To Radyr

When events are being held at the Millenium Stadium, services are subject to alteration. Please check times before travelling.

For connections to Cardiff Bay please refer to Table 130A

Table 130

Saturdays
4 January to 8 February

Treherbert, Aberdare, Merthyr, Pontypridd, Rhymney and Coryton - Cardiff, Penarth, Barry, Barry Island and Bridgend

Network Diagram - see first Page of Table 130

		AW	AW	AW A	AW	AW	AW	AW	AW	AW	AW	AW	AW B	AW	AW	AW	AW	AW	AW	AW	AW	AW B	AW
Treherbert	d		17 47						18 17						18 47				19 17				
Ynyswen	d		17 49						18 19						18 49				19 19				
Treorchy	d		17 51						18 21						18 51				19 21				
Ton Pentre	d		17 53						18 23						18 53				19 23				
Ystrad Rhondda	a		17 56						18 26						18 56				19 26				
	d		17 58						18 28						18 58				19 28				
Llwynypia	d		18 00						18 30						19 00				19 30				
Tonypandy	d		18 03						18 33						19 03				19 33				
Dinas Rhondda	d		18 05						18 35						19 05				19 35				
Porth	a		18 08						18 38						19 08				19 38				
	d		18 09						18 39						19 09				19 39				
Trehafod	d		18 12						18 42						19 12				19 42				
Merthyr Tydfil	d	17 38						18 08						18 38				19 08					19 38
Pentre-bach	d	17 42						18 12						18 42				19 12					19 42
Troed Y Rhiw	d	17 45						18 15						18 45				19 15					19 45
Merthyr Vale	a	17 48						18 18						18 48				19 18					19 48
	d	17 50						18 20						18 50				19 20					19 50
Quakers Yard	d	17 55						18 25						18 55				19 25					19 55
Aberdare 3	d				17 52						18 22					18 52							
Cwmbach	d				17 55						18 25					18 55							
Fernhill	d				17 58						18 28					18 58							
Mountain Ash	a				18 01						18 31					19 01							
	d				18 04						18 34					19 04							
Penrhiwceiber	d				18 07						18 37					19 07							
Abercynon	d	17 59			18 13			18 29			18 43			18 59		19 13		19 29			19 43		19 59
Pontypridd 3	a	18 07	18 17		18 22			18 37	18 47		18 52			19 07	19 17	19 22		19 37	19 47		19 52		20 07
	d	18 09	18 18		18 24			18 39	18 48		18 54			19 09	19 18	19 24		19 39	19 48		19 54		20 09
Trefforest	d	18 12	18 21		18 27			18 42	18 51		18 57			19 12	19 21	19 27		19 42	19 51		19 57		20 12
Trefforest Estate	d	18 16						18 46						19 16				19 46					20 16
Taffs Well 3	d	18 20	18 28		18 34			18 50	18 58		19 04			19 20	19 28	19 34		19 50	19 58		20 04		20 20
Radyr 3	a	18 23	18 31		18 37			18 53	19 01		19 07			19 23	19 31	19 37		19 53	20 01		20 07		20 23
	d	18 23	18 31	18 34	18 37			18 53	19 01	19 04	19 07			19 23	19 31	19 37		19 53	20 01	20 04	20 07		20 23
Danescourt	d			18 38						19 08										20 08			
Fairwater	d			18 40						19 10										20 10			
Waun-gron Park	d			18 42						19 12										20 12			
Ninian Park	d			18 45						19 15										20 15			
Llandaf	d	18 26	18 34		18 40			18 56	19 04		19 10			19 26	19 34	19 40		19 56	20 04		20 10		20 26
Cathays	d	18 31	18 39		18 45			19 01	19 09		19 15			19 31	19 39	19 45		20 01	20 09		20 15		20 31
Rhymney 3	d																						
Pontlottyn	d																						
Tir-phil	d																						
Brithdir	d																						
Bargoed	a																						
	d					18 15						18 48											
Gilfach Fargoed	d					18 18						18 50											
Pengam	d					18 20						18 53											
Hengoed	d					18 24						18 56											
Ystrad Mynach 3	d					18 27						18 59											
Llanbradach	d					18 31						19 04											
Energlyn & Churchill Park	d					18 35																	
Aber	d					18 37						19 08											
Caerphilly 3	d					18 40						19 11					19 40						
Lisvane & Thornhill	d					18 44						19 15					19 44						
Llanishen	d					18 46						19 17					19 46						
Heath High Level	d					18 49						19 20					19 49						
Coryton	d						18 45						19 15									20 15	
Whitchurch (Cardiff)	d						18 46						19 16									20 16	
Rhiwbina	d						18 48						19 18									20 18	
Birchgrove	d						18 50						19 20									20 20	
Ty Glas	d						18 51						19 21									20 21	
Heath Low Level	d						18 54						19 24									20 24	
Cardiff Queen Street 3	a	18 34	18 44		18 49	18 54	18 59	19 04	19 14		19 19	19 24	19 29	19 34	19 44	19 49	19 54	20 04	20 14		20 19	20 29	20 34
	d	18 36	18 46		18 51	18 56	19 01	19 06	19 16		19 21	19 26	19 31	19 36	19 46	19 51	19 56	20 06	20 16		20 21	20 31	20 36
Cardiff Central 7	a	18 39	18 52	18 50	18 54	18 59	19 06	19 10	19 22	19 22	19 24	19 29	19 34	19 39	19 52	19 57	19 59	20 09	20 22	20 24	20 24	20 34	20 39
	d	18 41			18 55	19 01					19 25	19 31		19 41			20 06	20 10			20 31		20 41
Grangetown	d	18 45			18 59	19 05					19 29	19 35		19 45			20 10	20 14			20 35		20 45
Dingle Road	d					19 11						19 41					20 14				20 41		
Penarth	a					19 16						19 46					20 19				20 46		
Cogan	d	18 48			19 03						19 33			19 48				20 18					20 48
Eastbrook	d	18 51			19 05						19 35			19 51				20 20					20 51
Dinas Powys	d	18 53			19 07						19 37			19 53				20 22					20 53
Cadoxton	d	18 57			19 12						19 42			19 57				20 27					20 57
Barry Docks	d	19 00			19 14						19 44			20 00				20 29					21 00
Barry 3	d	19 05			19 19						19 49			20 05				20 34					21 05
Barry Island	a				19 25						19 55							20 40					
Rhoose Cardiff Int Airport ✈	d	19 12												20 12									21 12
Llantwit Major	d	19 22												20 22									21 22
Bridgend	a	19 39												20 39									21 39

A To Coryton
B To Radyr

When events are being held at the Millenium Stadium, services are subject to alteration. Please check times before travelling.

For connections to Cardiff Bay please refer to Table 130A

Table 130

Saturdays
4 January to 8 February

Treherbert, Aberdare, Merthyr, Pontypridd, Rhymney and Coryton - Cardiff, Penarth, Barry, Barry Island and Bridgend

Network Diagram - see first Page of Table 130

		AW	AW	AW	AW	AW	AW	AW	AW	AW	AW	AW	AW	AW	AW	AW	AW	AW	AW	AW	AW	AW
										A				B				Bus			Bus	
Treherbert	d		19 47			20 17											21 17					
Ynyswen	d		19 49			20 19											21 19					
Treorchy	d		19 51			20 21											21 21					
Ton Pentre	d		19 53			20 23											2! 23					
Ystrad Rhondda	a		19 56			20 26											21 26					
	d		19 58			20 28											21 28					
Llwynypia	d		20 00			20 30											21 30					
Tonypandy	d		20 03			20 33											21 33					
Dinas Rhondda	d		20 05			20 35											21 35					
Porth	a		20 08			20 38											21 38					
	d		20 09			20 39											21 39					
Trehafod	d		20 12			20 42											21 42					
Merthyr Tydfil	d										20 38											21 38
Pentre-bach	d										20 42											21 42
Troed Y Rhiw	d										20 45											21 45
Merthyr Vale	a										20 48											21 48
	d										20 50											21 50
Quakers Yard	d										20 55											21 55
Aberdare 3	d			19 52				20 22							20 54							
Cwmbach	d			19 55				20 25							20 57							
Fernhill	d			19 58				20 28							21 00							
Mountain Ash	a			20 01				20 31							21 03							
	d			20 04				20 34							21 04							
Penrhiwceiber	d			20 07				20 37							21 07							
Abercynon	d			20 13				20 43			20 59				21 13							21 59
Pontypridd 3	a		20 18	20 22		20 47		20 52			21 07				21 22		21 47					22 07
	d		20 18	20 24		20 48		20 54			21 09				21 24		21 48					22 09
Trefforest	d		20 21	20 27		20 51		20 57			21 12				21 27		21 51					22 12
Trefforest Estate	d										21 16											22 16
Taffs Well 3	d		20 28	20 34		20 58		21 04			21 20				21 34		21 58					22 20
Radyr 3	a		20 31	20 37		21 01		21 07			21 23				21 37		22 01					22 23
	d		20 31	20 37		21 01	21 04	21 07			21 23				21 37	21 58	22 05				22 11	22 24
Danescourt	d						21 08										22 09					
Fairwater	d						21 10										22 11					
Waun-gron Park	d						21 12										22 13					
Ninian Park	d						21 15										22 16					
Llandaf	d		20 34	20 40		21 04		21 10			21 26				21 40						22 21	
Cathays	d		20 39	20 45		21 09		21 15			21 31				21 45						22 36	
Rhymney 3	d	19 43										20 46							21 36			
Pontlottyn	d	19 46										20 49							21 39			
Tir-phil	d	19 51										20 54							21 44			
Brithdir	d	19 53										20 56							21 46			
Bargoed	a	19 57										21 00							21 50			
	d	19 57										21 00							21 50			
Gilfach Fargoed	d	20 00										21 03							21 53			
Pengam	d	20 02										21 05							21 55			
Hengoed	d	20 06										21 09							21 59			
Ystrad Mynach 3	d	20 09										21 12	21 39						22 02			
Llanbradach	d	20 13										21 16	21 44						22 06			
Energlyn & Churchill Park	d	20 17										21 20							22 10			
Aber	d	20 19										21 22	21 48						22 12			
Caerphilly 3	d	20 22			20 40							21 25	21 51						22 15			
Lisvane & Thornhill	d	20 26			20 44							21 29	21 55						22 19			
Llanishen	d	20 28			20 46							21 31	21 57						22 21			
Heath High Level	d	20 31			20 49							21 34	22a00					22 10	22a28			
Coryton	d									21 15												
Whitchurch (Cardiff)	d									21 16												
Rhiwbina	d									21 18												
Birchgrove	d									21 20												
Ty Glas	d									21 21												
Heath Low Level	d									21 24												
Cardiff Queen Street 3	a	20 39	20 44	20 49	20 54	21 14		21 19		21 29	21 34	21 42			21 49			22 25			22 41	
	d	20 41	20 46	20 51	20 56	21 16		21 21		21 31	21 36	21 44		21 49	21 51			22 25			22 41	
Cardiff Central 7	a	20 47	20 52	20 57	20 59	21 22	21 25	21 27		21 34	21 39	21 47		21 52	21 54	22 14	22 23	22 33			22 49	22 43
	d			21 06	21 10				21 31		21 41				22 06			22 33		22 36		
Grangetown	d			21 10	21 14				21 35		21 45				22 10			22 38		22 40		
Dingle Road	d			21 14					21 41						22 14					22 44		
Penarth	a			21 19					21 46						22 19					22 47		
Cogan	d				21 18						21 48							22 43				
Eastbrook	d				21 20						21 51							22 48				
Dinas Powys	d				21 22						21 53							22 53				
Cadoxton	d				21 27						21 57							23 03				
Barry Docks	d				21 29						22 00							23 08				
Barry 3	d				21 34						22 05							23 13				
Barry Island	a				21 40													23 18				
Rhoose Cardiff Int Airport ✈	d										22 12											
Llantwit Major	d										22 22											
Bridgend	a										22 39											

A To Radyr
B From Cardiff Bay

When events are being held at the Millenium Stadium, services are subject to alteration. Please check times before travelling.

For connections to Cardiff Bay please refer to Table 130A

Table 130

Saturdays

4 January to 8 February

Treherbert, Aberdare, Merthyr, Pontypridd, Rhymney and Coryton - Cardiff, Penarth, Barry, Barry Island and Bridgend

Network Diagram - see first Page of Table 130

		AW 🚌	AW	AW 🚌	AW 🚌	AW	AW	AW 🚌	AW	AW		AW 🚌	AW
Treherbert	d												
Ynyswen	d												
Treorchy	d												
Ton Pentre	d												
Ystrad Rhondda	a												
	d												
Llwynypia	d												
Tonypandy	d												
Dinas Rhondda	d												
Porth	a												
	d												
Trehafod	d												
Merthyr Tydfil	d									22 38			
Pentre-bach	d									22 42			
Troed Y Rhiw	d									22 45			
Merthyr Vale	a									22 48			
	d									22 50			
Quakers Yard	d									22 55			
Aberdare 3	d					21 54							22 54
Cwmbach	d					21 57							22 57
Fernhill	d					22 00							23 00
Mountain Ash	a					22 03							23 03
	d					22 04							23 04
Penrhiwceiber	d					22 07							23 07
Abercynon	d					22 13				22 59			23 13
Pontypridd 3	a					22 22				23 07			23 22
	d					22 24				23 09			
Trefforest	d					22 27				23 12			
Trefforest Estate	d									23 16			
Taffs Well 3	d					22 33				23 20			
Radyr 3	a					22 37				23 23			
	d				22 33	22 37		22 47	23 14	23 24		23 34	
Danescourt	d												
Fairwater	d												
Waun-gron Park	d												
Ninian Park	d												
Llandaf	d				22 43			22 57				23 44	
Cathays	d				22 58			23 12				23 59	
Rhymney 3	d												
Pontlottyn	d												
Tir-phil	d												
Brithdir	d												
Bargoed	a												
	d												
Gilfach Fargoed	d												
Pengam	d												
Hengoed	d												
Ystrad Mynach 3	d												
Llanbradach	d												
Energlyn & Churchill Park	d												
Aber	d												
Caerphilly 3	d		22 28										
Lisvane & Thornhill	d												
Llanishen	d												
Heath High Level	d	22 34	22a37	22 47									
Coryton	d												
Whitchurch (Cardiff)	d												
Rhiwbina	d												
Birchgrove	d												
Ty Glas	d												
Heath Low Level	d												
Cardiff Queen Street 3	a	22 49		23 02	23 03			23 17				00 04	
	d	22 49		23 02	23 03			23 17				00 04	
Cardiff Central 7	a	22 57		23 10	23 11	22 53		23 25	23 25	23 38		00 12	
	d						23 12		23 30				
Grangetown	d						23 16		23 34				
Dingle Road	d						23 20						
Penarth	a						23 25						
Cogan	d								23 37				
Eastbrook	d								23 40				
Dinas Powys	d								23 42				
Cadoxton	d								23 46				
Barry Docks	d								23 49				
Barry 3	d								23 53				
Barry Island	a								23 58				
Rhoose Cardiff Int Airport ✈	d												
Llantwit Major	d												
Bridgend	a												

When events are being held at the Millenium Stadium, services are subject to alteration. Please check times before travelling.

For connections to Cardiff Bay please refer to Table 130A

Table 130

Saturdays

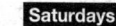

15 February to 17 May

Treherbert, Aberdare, Merthyr, Pontypridd, Rhymney and Coryton - Cardiff, Penarth, Barry, Barry Island and Bridgend

Network Diagram - see first Page of Table 130

		AW	AW	AW	AW	AW	AW	AW	AW	AW		AW	AW	AW	AW	AW	AW	AW	AW	AW		AW	AW	AW	AW
												A		B		C		D				B			
Treherbert	d									05 47							06 17								06 47
Ynyswen	d									05 49							06 19								06 49
Treorchy	d									05 51							06 21								06 51
Ton Pentre	d									05 53							06 23								06 53
Ystrad Rhondda	a									05 56							06 26								06 56
	d									05 58							06 28								06 58
Llwynypia	d									06 00							06 30								07 00
Tonypandy	d									06 03							06 33								07 03
Dinas Rhondda	d									06 05							06 35								07 05
Porth	a									06 08							06 38								07 08
	d									06 09							06 39								07 09
Trehafod	d									06 12							06 42								07 12
Merthyr Tydfil	d																						06 38		
Pentre-bach	d																						06 42		
Troed Y Rhiw	d																						06 45		
Merthyr Vale	a																						06 48		
	d																						06 50		
Quakers Yard	d																						06 55		
Aberdare [3]	d																		06 22						
Cwmbach	d																		06 25						
Fernhill	d																		06 28						
Mountain Ash	a																		06 31						
	d																		06 34						
Penrhiwceiber	d																		06 37						
Abercynon	d																		06 43				06 59		
Pontypridd [3]	a									06 17							06 47		06 52				07 07		07 17
	d				05 18					06 18							06 48		06 54				07 09		07 18
Trefforest	d				05 21					06 21							06 51		06 57				07 12		07 21
Trefforest Estate	d				05 25																		07 16		
Taffs Well [3]	d				05 28					06 28						06 53	06 58	←	07 04				07 20		07 28
Radyr [3]	a				05 31					06 31						06 56	07 01	06 56	07 07				07 23		07 31
	d				05 31					06 31						07 04	07 01	07 04	07 07				07 23		07 31
Danescourt	d															↪		07 08							
Fairwater	d																	07 10							
Waun-gron Park	d																	07 12							
Ninian Park	d																	07 15							
Llandaf	d				05 34					06 34							07 04		07 10				07 26		07 34
Cathays	d				05 39					06 39							07 09		07 15				07 31		07 39
Rhymney [3]	d														06 08					06 32					
Pontlottyn	d														06 11					06 35					
Tir-phil	d														06 16					06 40					
Brithdir	d														06 18					06 42					
Bargoed	a														06 22					06 46					
	d														06 25					06 46				07 02	
Gilfach Fargoed	d														06 28									07 04	
Pengam	d														06 30					06 51				07 07	
Hengoed	d														06 34					06 54				07 10	
Ystrad Mynach [3]	d														06 37					06 57				07 13	
Llanbradach	d														06 41					07 01				07 18	
Energlyn & Churchill Park	d														06 45					07 05					
Aber	d														06 47					07 07				07 22	
Caerphilly [3]	d								06 10						06 50					07 10				07 25	
Lisvane & Thornhill	d								06 14						06 54					07 14				07 29	
Llanishen	d								06 16						06 56					07 16				07 31	
Heath High Level	d								06 19						06 59					07 19				07 34	
Coryton	d													06 45								07 15			
Whitchurch (Cardiff)	d													06 46								07 16			
Rhiwbina	d													06 48								07 18			
Birchgrove	d													06 50								07 20			
Ty Glas	d													06 51								07 21			
Heath Low Level	d													06 54								07 24			
Cardiff Queen Street [3]	a				05 43				06 25	06 42				06 59	07 04		07 12		07 19	07 24		07 30	07 34	07 39	07 44
	d				05 45				06 26	06 43				07 01	07 06		07 13		07 21	07 26		07 31	07 36	07 41	07 46
Cardiff Central [7]	a				05 48				06 29	06 48				07 04	07 09		07 16	07 20	07 24	07 29		07 34	07 39	07 44	07 52
	d	05 20	05 41	05 46	05 55	06 16	06 25	06 36	06 41			06 55	07 01		07 10		07 16		07 25	07 31			07 41	07 46	
Grangetown	d	05 24	05 45	05 50	05 59	06 20	06 29	06 40	06 45			06 59	07 05		07 14		07 20		07 29	07 35			07 45	07 50	
Dingle Road	d			05 54		06 24		06 44					07 11				07 26			07 41				07 56	
Penarth	a			05 59		06 29		06 49					07 16				07 31			07 46				08 01	
Cogan	d	05 28	05 48		06 03		06 33		06 48			07 03			07 18				07 33				07 48		
Eastbrook	d	05 30	05 51		06 05		06 35		06 51			07 05			07 20				07 35				07 51		
Dinas Powys	d	05 32	05 53		06 07		06 37		06 53			07 07			07 22				07 37				07 53		
Cadoxton	d	05 37	05 57		06 12		06 42		06 57			07 12			07 27				07 42				07 57		
Barry Docks	d	05 39	06 00		06 14		06 44		07 00			07 14			07 29				07 44				08 00		
Barry [3]	d	05 44	06 05		06 19		06 49		07 05			07 19			07 34				07 49				08 05		
Barry Island	a	05 50			06 25		06 55					07 25			07 40				07 55						
Rhoose Cardiff Int Airport ✈	d		06 12						07 12														08 12		
Llantwit Major	d		06 22						07 22														08 22		
Bridgend	a		06 39						07 39														08 39		

A From Hereford
B To Radyr
C To Coryton
D From Taffs Well to Coryton

When events are being held at the Millenium Stadium, services are subject to alteration. Please check times before travelling.

For connections to Cardiff Bay please refer to Table 130A

Table 130

Saturdays

15 February to 17 May

Treherbert, Aberdare, Merthyr, Pontypridd, Rhymney and Coryton - Cardiff, Penarth, Barry, Barry Island and Bridgend

Network Diagram - see first Page of Table 130

		AW A	AW	AW	AW B	AW		AW	AW	AW A	AW	AW	AW B	AW	AW	AW		AW A	AW	AW	AW B	AW	AW	AW	AW A
Treherbert	d								07 17							07 45								08 17	
Ynyswen	d								07 19							07 47								08 19	
Treorchy	d								07 21							07 49								08 21	
Ton Pentre	d								07 23							07 51								08 23	
Ystrad Rhondda	a								07 26							07 54								08 26	
	d								07 28							07 58								08 28	
Llwynypia	d								07 30							08 00								08 30	
Tonypandy	d								07 33							08 03								08 33	
Dinas Rhondda	d								07 35							08 05								08 35	
Porth	a								07 38							08 08								08 38	
	d								07 39							08 09								08 39	
Trehafod	d								07 42							08 12								08 42	
Merthyr Tydfil	d					07 08								07 38								08 08			
Pentre-bach	d					07 12								07 42								08 12			
Troed Y Rhiw	d					07 15								07 45								08 15			
Merthyr Vale	a					07 18								07 48								08 18			
	d					07 20								07 50								08 20			
Quakers Yard	d					07 25								07 55								08 25			
Aberdare 3	d		06 52								07 22								07 52						
Cwmbach	d		06 55								07 25								07 55						
Fernhill	d		06 58								07 28								07 58						
Mountain Ash	a		07 01								07 31								08 01						
	d		07 04								07 34								08 04						
Penrhiwceiber	d		07 07								07 37								08 07						
Abercynon	d		07 13			07 29					07 43			07 59					08 13			08 29			
Pontypridd 3	a		07 22			07 37			07 47		07 52			08 07		08 17			08 22			08 37		08 47	
	d		07 24			07 39			07 48		07 54			08 09		08 18			08 24			08 39		08 48	
Trefforest	d		07 27			07 42			07 51		07 57			08 12		08 21			08 27			08 42		08 51	
Trefforest Estate	d					07 46								08 16								08 46			
Taffs Well 3	d		07 34			07 50			07 58		08 04			08 20		08 28			08 34			08 50		08 58	
Radyr 3	a		07 37			07 53			08 01		08 07			08 23		08 31			08 37			08 53		09 01	
	d	07 34	07 37			07 53			08 01	08 04	08 07			08 23		08 31		08 34	08 37			08 53		09 01	09 04
Danescourt	d	07 38								08 08								08 38							09 08
Fairwater	d	07 40								08 10								08 40							09 10
Waun-gron Park	d	07 42								08 12								08 42							09 12
Ninian Park	d	07 45								08 15								08 45							09 15
Llandaf	d		07 40			07 56			08 04		08 10			08 26		08 34			08 40			08 56		09 04	
Cathays	d		07 45			08 01			08 09		08 15			08 31		08 39			08 45			09 01		09 09	
Rhymney 3	d			07 00								07 24			07 42										
Pontlottyn	d			07 03								07 27			07 45										
Tir-phil	d			07 08								07 32			07 50										
Brithdir	d			07 10								07 34			07 52										
Bargoed	a			07 14								07 38			07 59										
	d			07 15				07 32				07 43			08 00					08 15			08 32		
Gilfach Fargoed	d			07 18								07 46								08 18					
Pengam	d			07 20				07 37				07 48			08 05					08 20			08 37		
Hengoed	d			07 24				07 40				07 52			08 09					08 24			08 40		
Ystrad Mynach 3	d			07 27				07 43				07 55			08 12					08 27			08 43		
Llanbradach	d			07 31				07 48				08 00			08 16					08 31			08 48		
Energlyn & Churchill Park	d			07 35								08 04			08 20					08 35					
Aber	d			07 37				07 52				08 07			08 22					08 37			08 52		
Caerphilly 3	d			07 40				07 55				08 10			08 25					08 40			08 55		
Lisvane & Thornhill	d			07 44				07 59				08 14			08 29					08 44			08 59		
Llanishen	d			07 46				08 01				08 16			08 31					08 46			09 01		
Heath High Level	d			07 49				08 04				08 19			08 34					08 49			09 04		
Coryton	d				07 45								08 15								08 45				
Whitchurch (Cardiff)	d				07 46								08 16								08 46				
Rhiwbina	d				07 48								08 18								08 48				
Birchgrove	d				07 50								08 20								08 50				
Ty Glas	d				07 51								08 21								08 51				
Heath Low Level	d				07 54								08 24								08 54				
Cardiff Queen Street 3	a		07 49	07 54	07 59	08 04		08 09	08 14		08 19	08 24	08 29	08 34	08 39	08 44			08 49	08 54	08 59	09 04	09 09	09 14	
	d		07 51	07 56	08 01	08 06		08 11	08 16		08 21	08 26	08 31	08 36	08 41	08 46			08 51	08 56	09 01	09 06	09 11	09 16	
Cardiff Central 7	a	07 50	07 54	07 59	08 04	08 09		08 14	08 22	08 19	08 24	08 29	08 34	08 39	08 47	08 52		08 50	08 54	08 59	09 04	09 09	09 14	09 22	09 20
	d		07 55	08 01		08 10		08 16			08 25	08 31		08 41					08 55	09 01		09 10	09 16		
Grangetown	d		07 59	08 05		08 14		08 20			08 29	08 35		08 45					08 59	09 05		09 14	09 20		
Dingle Road	d			08 11				08 26				08 41								09 11			09 26		
Penarth	a			08 16				08 31				08 46								09 16			09 31		
Cogan	d		08 03			08 18					08 33			08 48					09 03			09 18			
Eastbrook	d		08 05			08 20					08 35			08 51					09 05			09 20			
Dinas Powys	d		08 07			08 22					08 37			08 53					09 07			09 22			
Cadoxton	d		08 12			08 27					08 42			08 57					09 12			09 27			
Barry Docks	d		08 14			08 29					08 44			09 00					09 14			09 29			
Barry 3	d		08 19			08 34					08 49			09 05					09 19			09 34			
Barry Island	a		08 25			08 40					08 55								09 25			09 40			
Rhoose Cardiff Int Airport ✈	d													09 12											
Llantwit Major	d													09 22											
Bridgend	a													09 39											

A To Coryton   **B** To Radyr

When events are being held at the Millenium Stadium, services are subject to alteration. Please check times before travelling.

For connections to Cardiff Bay please refer to Table 130A

Table 130

Saturdays

15 February to 17 May

Treherbert, Aberdare, Merthyr, Pontypridd, Rhymney and Coryton - Cardiff, Penarth, Barry, Barry Island and Bridgend

Network Diagram - see first Page of Table 130

		AW	AW	AW A	AW	AW	AW	AW B	AW	AW	AW A	AW	AW	AW	AW B	AW	AW	AW A	AW	AW	AW	AW B
Treherbert	d						08 47							09 17							09 47	
Ynyswen	d						08 49							09 19							09 49	
Treorchy	d						08 51							09 21							09 51	
Ton Pentre	d						08 53							09 23							09 53	
Ystrad Rhondda	a						08 56							09 26							09 56	
	d						08 58							09 28							09 58	
Llwynypia	d						09 00							09 30							10 00	
Tonypandy	d						09 03							09 33							10 03	
Dinas Rhondda	d						09 05							09 35							10 05	
Porth	a						09 08							09 38							10 08	
	d						09 09							09 39							10 09	
Trehafod	d						09 12							09 42							10 12	
Merthyr Tydfil	d				08 38							09 08							09 38			
Pentre-bach	d				08 42							09 12							09 42			
Troed Y Rhiw	d				08 45							09 15							09 45			
Merthyr Vale	a				08 48							09 18							09 48			
	d				08 50							09 20							09 50			
Quakers Yard	d				08 55							09 25							09 55			
Aberdare 3	d	08 22							08 52							09 22						
Cwmbach	d	08 25							08 55							09 25						
Fernhill	d	08 28							08 58							09 28						
Mountain Ash	a	08 31							09 01							09 31						
	d	08 34							09 04							09 34						
Penrhiwceiber	d	08 37							09 07							09 37						
Abercynon	d	08 43			08 59				09 13			09 29				09 43			09 59			
Pontypridd 3	a	08 52			09 07		09 17		09 22			09 37		09 47		09 52			10 07		10 17	
	d	08 54			09 09		09 18		09 24			09 39		09 48		09 54			10 09		10 18	
Trefforest	d	08 57			09 12		09 21		09 27			09 42		09 51		09 57			10 12		10 21	
Trefforest Estate	d				09 16							09 46							10 16			
Taffs Well 3	d	09 04			09 20		09 28		09 34			09 50		09 58		10 04			10 20		10 28	
Radyr 3	a	09 07			09 23		09 31		09 37			09 53		10 01		10 07			10 23		10 31	
	d	09 07			09 23		09 31	09 34	09 37			09 53		10 01	10 04	10 07			10 23		10 31	10 34
Danescourt	d							09 38							10 08							10 38
Fairwater	d							09 40							10 10							10 40
Waun-gron Park	d							09 42							10 12							10 42
Ninian Park	d							09 45							10 15							10 45
Llandaf	d	09 10			09 26		09 34		09 40			09 56		10 04		10 10			10 26		10 34	
Cathays	d	09 15			09 31		09 39		09 45			10 01		10 09		10 15			10 31		10 39	
Rhymney 3	d		08 30														09 27					
Pontlottyn	d		08 33														09 30					
Tir-phil	d		08 37														09 35					
Brithdir	d		08 40														09 37					
Bargoed	a		08 44														09 41					
	d		08 47			09 00				09 17			09 32				09 45			10 00		
Gilfach Fargoed	d									09 19												
Pengam	d		08 52			09 05				09 22			09 37				09 50			10 05		
Hengoed	d		08 55			09 09				09 25			09 40				09 54			10 09		
Ystrad Mynach 3	d		08 58			09 12				09 28			09 43				09 57			10 12		
Llanbradach	d		09 03			09 16				09 33			09 48				10 01			10 16		
Energlyn & Churchill Park	d					09 20											10 05			10 20		
Aber	d		09 07			09 22				09 37			09 52				10 07			10 22		
Caerphilly 3	d		09 10			09 25				09 40			09 55				10 10			10 25		
Lisvane & Thornhill	d		09 14			09 29				09 44			09 59				10 14			10 29		
Llanishen	d		09 16			09 31				09 46			10 01				10 16			10 31		
Heath High Level	d		09 19			09 34				09 49			10 04				10 19			10 34		
Coryton	d			09 15							09 45							10 15				
Whitchurch (Cardiff)	d			09 16							09 46							10 16				
Rhiwbina	d			09 18							09 48							10 18				
Birchgrove	d			09 20							09 50							10 20				
Ty Glas	d			09 21							09 51							10 21				
Heath Low Level	d			09 24							09 54							10 24				
Cardiff Queen Street 3	a	09 19	09 24	09 29	09 34	09 39	09 44		09 49	09 54	09 59	10 04	10 09	10 14		10 19	10 24	10 29	10 34	10 39	10 44	
	d	09 21	09 26	09 31	09 36	09 41	09 46		09 51	09 56	10 01	10 06	10 11	10 16		10 21	10 26	10 31	10 36	10 41	10 46	
Cardiff Central 7	a	09 24	09 29	09 34	09 39	09 44	09 52	09 50	09 54	09 59	10 04	10 09	10 14	10 22	10 20	10 24	10 29	10 34	10 39	10 44	10 52	10 50
	d	09 25	09 31		09 41	09 46			09 55	10 01		10 10	10 16			10 25	10 31		10 41	10 46		
Grangetown	d	09 29	09 35		09 45	09 50			09 59	10 05		10 14	10 20			10 29	10 35		10 45	10 50		
Dingle Road	d		09 41			09 56				10 11			10 26				10 41			10 56		
Penarth	a		09 46			10 01				10 16			10 31				10 46			11 01		
Cogan	d	09 33			09 48				10 03			10 18				10 33			10 48			
Eastbrook	d	09 35			09 51				10 05			10 20				10 35			10 51			
Dinas Powys	d	09 37			09 53				10 07			10 22				10 37			10 53			
Cadoxton	d	09 42			09 57				10 12			10 27				10 42			10 57			
Barry Docks	d	09 44			10 00				10 14			10 29				10 44			11 00			
Barry 3	d	09 49			10 05				10 19			10 34				10 49			11 05			
Barry Island	a	09 55							10 25			10 40				10 55						
Rhoose Cardiff Int Airport ✈	d				10 12														11 12			
Llantwit Major	d				10 22														11 22			
Bridgend	a				10 39														11 39			

A To Radyr

B To Coryton

When events are being held at the Millenium Stadium, services are subject to alteration. Please check times before travelling.

For connections to Cardiff Bay please refer to Table 130A

Table 130

Saturdays

15 February to 17 May

Treherbert, Aberdare, Merthyr, Pontypridd, Rhymney and Coryton - Cardiff, Penarth, Barry, Barry Island and Bridgend

Network Diagram - see first Page of Table 130

		AW	AW	AW	AW A	AW	AW	AW B	AW	AW	AW	AW A	AW	AW	AW	AW B	AW	AW	AW A	AW	AW	AW	AW B
Treherbert	d										10 17				10 47							11 17	
Ynyswen	d										10 19				10 49							11 19	
Treorchy	d										10 21				10 51							11 21	
Ton Pentre	d										10 23				10 53							11 23	
Ystrad Rhondda	a										10 26				10 56							11 26	
	d										10 28				10 58							11 28	
Llwynypia	d										10 30				11 00							11 30	
Tonypandy	d										10 33				11 03							11 33	
Dinas Rhondda	d										10 35				11 05							11 35	
Porth	a										10 38				11 08							11 38	
	d										10 52				11 09							11 39	
Trehafod	d										10 55				11 12							11 42	
Merthyr Tydfil	d		10 04										10 38							11 08			
Pentre-bach	d		10 08										10 42							11 12			
Troed Y Rhiw	d		10 11										10 45							11 15			
Merthyr Vale	a		10 14										10 48							11 18			
	d		10 16										10 50							11 20			
Quakers Yard	d		10 22										10 55							11 25			
Aberdare [3]	d	09 52							10 22								10 52						
Cwmbach	d	09 55							10 25								10 55						
Fernhill	d	09 58							10 28								10 58						
Mountain Ash	a	10 01							10 31								11 01						
	d	10 04							10 34								11 04						
Penrhiwceiber	d	10 07							10 37								11 07						
Abercynon	d	10 13	10 26						10 43				10 59				11 13			11 29			
Pontypridd [3]	a	10 22	10 32						10 52		11 00		11 07		11 17		11 22			11 37		11 47	
	d	10 24				10 39			10 54		11 04		11 09		11 18		11 24			11 39		11 48	
Trefforest	d	10 27				10 42			10 57		11 07		11 12		11 21		11 27			11 42		11 51	
Trefforest Estate	d												11 16							11 46			
Taffs Well [3]	d	10 34				10 50			11 04		11 13		11 20		11 28		11 34			11 50		11 58	
Radyr [3]	a	10 37				10 53			11 07		11 17		11 23		11 31		11 37			11 53		12 01	
	d	10 37				10 53		11 04	11 07		11 17		11 23		11 31	11 34	11 37			11 53		12 01	12 04
Danescourt	d							11 08								11 38							12 08
Fairwater	d							11 10								11 40							12 10
Waun-gron Park	d							11 12								11 42							12 12
Ninian Park	d							11 15								11 45							12 15
Llandaf	d	10 40				10 56			11 10				11 26		11 34		11 40			11 56		12 04	
Cathays	d	10 45				11 01			11 15				11 31		11 39		11 45			12 01		12 09	
Rhymney [3]	d									10 27													
Pontlottyn	d									10 30													
Tir-phil	d									10 35													
Brithdir	d									10 37													
Bargoed	a									10 41													
	d			10 17			10 32			10 45				11 00				11 17			11 32		
Gilfach Fargoed	d			10 19														11 19					
Pengam	d			10 22			10 37			10 50				11 05				11 22			11 37		
Hengoed	d			10 25			10 40			10 54				11 09				11 25			11 40		
Ystrad Mynach [3]	d			10 28			10 43			10 57				11 12				11 28			11 43		
Llanbradach	d			10 33			10 48			11 01				11 16				11 33			11 48		
Energlyn & Churchill Park	d									11 05				11 20									
Aber	d			10 37			10 52			11 07				11 22				11 37			11 52		
Caerphilly [3]	d			10 40			10 55			11 10				11 25				11 40			11 55		
Lisvane & Thornhill	d			10 44			10 59			11 14				11 29				11 44			11 59		
Llanishen	d			10 46			11 01			11 16				11 31				11 46			12 01		
Heath High Level	d			10 49			11 04			11 19				11 34				11 49			12 04		
Coryton	d				10 45							11 15							11 45				
Whitchurch (Cardiff)	d				10 46							11 16							11 46				
Rhiwbina	d				10 48							11 18							11 48				
Birchgrove	d				10 50							11 20							11 50				
Ty Glas	d				10 51							11 21							11 51				
Heath Low Level	d				10 54							11 24							11 54				
Cardiff Queen Street [3]	a	10 49		10 54	10 59	11 04	11 09		11 19	11 24		11 29	11 34	11 39	11 44		11 49	11 54	11 59	12 04	12 09	12 14	
	d	10 51		10 56	11 01	11 06	11 11		11 21	11 26		11 31	11 36	11 41	11 46		11 51	11 56	12 01	12 06	12 11	12 16	
Cardiff Central [7]	a	10 54		10 59	11 04	11 09	11 14	11 20	11 24	11 29	11 34	11 34	11 39	11 44	11 52	11 50	11 54	11 59	12 04	12 09	12 14	12 22	12 20
	d	10 55		11 01		11 10	11 16		11 25	11 31			11 41	11 46			11 55	12 01		12 10	12 16		
Grangetown	d	10 59		11 05		11 14	11 20		11 29	11 35			11 45	11 50			11 59	12 05		12 14	12 20		
Dingle Road	d			11 11			11 26			11 41				11 56				12 11			12 26		
Penarth	a			11 16			11 31			11 46				12 01				12 16			12 31		
Cogan	d	11 03				11 18			11 33				11 48				12 03			12 18			
Eastbrook	d	11 05				11 20			11 35				11 51				12 05			12 20			
Dinas Powys	d	11 07				11 22			11 37				11 53				12 07			12 22			
Cadoxton	d	11 12				11 27			11 42				11 57				12 12			12 27			
Barry Docks	d	11 14				11 29			11 44				12 00				12 14			12 29			
Barry [3]	d	11 19				11 34			11 49				12 05				12 19			12 34			
Barry Island	a	11 25				11 40			11 55								12 25			12 40			
Rhoose Cardiff Int Airport ✈	d												12 12										
Llantwit Major	d												12 22										
Bridgend	a												12 39										

A To Radyr

B To Coryton

When events are being held at the Millenium Stadium, services are subject to alteration. Please check times before travelling.

For connections to Cardiff Bay please refer to Table 130A

Table 130

Saturdays

15 February to 17 May

Treherbert, Aberdare, Merthyr, Pontypridd, Rhymney and Coryton - Cardiff, Penarth, Barry, Barry Island and Bridgend

Network Diagram - see first Page of Table 130

		AW	AW	AW A	AW	AW	AW	AW B	AW	AW A	AW	AW	AW	AW B	AW	AW	AW A	AW	AW	AW	AW B	AW
Treherbert	d						11 47						12 17							12 47		
Ynyswen	d						11 49						12 19							12 49		
Treorchy	d						11 51						12 21							12 51		
Ton Pentre	d						11 53						12 23							12 53		
Ystrad Rhondda	a						11 56						12 26							12 56		
	d						11 58						12 28							12 58		
Llwynypia	d						12 00						12 30							13 00		
Tonypandy	d						12 03						12 33							13 03		
Dinas Rhondda	d						12 05						12 35							13 05		
Porth	a						12 08						12 38							13 08		
	d						12 09						12 39							13 09		
Trehafod	d						12 12						12 42							13 12		
Merthyr Tydfil	d				11 38						12 08							12 38				
Pentre-bach	d				11 42						12 12							12 42				
Troed Y Rhiw	d				11 45						12 15							12 45				
Merthyr Vale	a				11 48						12 18							12 48				
	d				11 50						12 20							12 50				
Quakers Yard	d				11 55						12 25							12 55				
Aberdare 3	d	11 22													12 22							12 52
Cwmbach	d	11 25													12 25							12 55
Fernhill	d	11 28													12 28							12 58
Mountain Ash	a	11 31													12 31							13 01
	d	11 34													12 34							13 04
Penrhiwceiber	d	11 37													12 37							13 07
Abercynon	d	11 43			11 59						12 29				12 43			12 59				13 13
Pontypridd 3	a	11 52			12 07		12 17				12 37		12 48		12 52			13 07		13 17		13 22
	d	11 54			12 09		12 18				12 39		12 48		12 54			13 09		13 18		13 24
Trefforest	d	11 57			12 12		12 21				12 42		12 51		12 57			13 12		13 21		13 27
Trefforest Estate	d				12 16						12 46							13 16				
Taffs Well 3	d	12 04			12 20		12 28				12 50		12 58		13 04			13 20		13 28		13 34
Radyr 3	a	12 07			12 23		12 31				12 53		13 01		13 07			13 23		13 31		13 37
	d	12 07			12 23		12 31	12 34			12 53		13 01	13 04	13 07			13 23		13 31	13 34	13 37
Danescourt	d							12 38						13 08							13 38	
Fairwater	d							12 40						13 10							13 40	
Waun-gron Park	d							12 42						13 12							13 42	
Ninian Park	d							12 45						13 15							13 45	
Llandaf	d	12 10			12 26		12 34				12 56		13 04		13 10			13 26		13 34		13 40
Cathays	d	12 15			12 31		12 39				13 01		13 09		13 15			13 31		13 39		13 45
Rhymney 3	d		11 27													12 27						
Pontlottyn	d		11 30													12 30						
Tir-phil	d		11 35													12 35						
Brithdir	d		11 37													12 37						
Bargoed	a		11 41													12 41						
	d		11 45			12 00			12 17			12 32				12 45			13 00			
Gilfach Fargoed	d								12 19													
Pengam	d		11 50			12 05			12 22			12 37				12 50			13 05			
Hengoed	d		11 54			12 09			12 25			12 40				12 54			13 09			
Ystrad Mynach 3	d		11 57			12 12			12 28			12 43				12 57			13 12			
Llanbradach	d		12 01			12 16			12 33			12 48				13 01			13 16			
Energlyn & Churchill Park	d		12 05			12 20										13 05			13 20			
Aber	d		12 07			12 22			12 37			12 52				13 07			13 22			
Caerphilly 3	d		12 10			12 25			12 40			12 55				13 10			13 25			
Lisvane & Thornhill	d		12 14			12 29			12 44			12 59				13 14			13 29			
Llanishen	d		12 16			12 31			12 46			13 01				13 16			13 31			
Heath High Level	d		12 19			12 34			12 49			13 04				13 19			13 34			
Coryton	d			12 15						12 45							13 15					
Whitchurch (Cardiff)	d			12 16						12 46							13 16					
Rhiwbina	d			12 18						12 48							13 18					
Birchgrove	d			12 20						12 50							13 20					
Ty Glas	d			12 21						12 51							13 21					
Heath Low Level	d			12 24						12 54							13 24					
Cardiff Queen Street 3	a	12 19	12 24	12 29	12 34	12 39	12 44		12 54	12 59	13 04	13 09	13 14		13 19	13 24	13 29	13 34	13 39	13 44		13 49
	d	12 21	12 26	12 31	12 36	12 41	12 46		12 56	13 01	13 06	13 11	13 16		13 21	13 26	13 31	13 36	13 41	13 46		13 51
Cardiff Central 7	a	12 24	12 29	12 34	12 39	12 44	12 52	12 50	12 59	13 04	13 09	13 14	13 22	13 20	13 24	13 29	13 34	13 39	13 44	13 52	13 50	13 54
	d	12 25	12 31		12 41	12 46	12 55		13 01		13 10	13 16			13 25	13 31		13 41	13 46			13 55
Grangetown	d	12 29	12 35		12 45	12 50	12 59		13 05		13 14	13 20			13 29	13 35		13 45	13 50			13 59
Dingle Road	d		12 41			12 56			13 11			13 26				13 41			13 56			
Penarth	a		12 46			13 01			13 16			13 31				13 46			14 01			
Cogan	d	12 33			12 48		13 03				13 18				13 33			13 48				14 03
Eastbrook	d	12 35			12 51		13 05				13 20				13 35			13 51				14 05
Dinas Powys	d	12 37			12 53		13 07				13 22				13 37			13 53				14 07
Cadoxton	d	12 42			12 57		13 12				13 27				13 42			13 57				14 12
Barry Docks	d	12 44			13 00		13 14				13 29				13 44			14 00				14 14
Barry 3	d	12 49			13 05		13 19				13 34				13 49			14 05				14 19
Barry Island	a	12 55					13 25				13 40				13 55							14 25
Rhoose Cardiff Int Airport ✈	d				13 12													14 12				
Llantwit Major	d				13 22													14 22				
Bridgend	a				13 39													14 39				

A To Radyr

B To Coryton

When events are being held at the Millenium Stadium, services are subject to alteration. Please check times before travelling.

For connections to Cardiff Bay please refer to Table 130A

Table 130

Saturdays

15 February to 17 May

Treherbert, Aberdare, Merthyr, Pontypridd, Rhymney and Coryton - Cardiff, Penarth, Barry, Barry Island and Bridgend

Network Diagram - see first Page of Table 130

Station		AW	AW A	AW	AW	AW	AW B	AW	AW	AW A		AW	AW	AW	AW B	AW	AW	AW A	AW	AW		AW B	AW	AW	AW
Treherbert	d					13 17								13 47											14 17
Ynyswen	d					13 19								13 49											14 19
Treorchy	d					13 21								13 51											14 21
Ton Pentre	d					13 23								13 53											14 23
Ystrad Rhondda	a					13 26								13 56											14 26
	d					13 28								13 58											14 28
Llwynypia	d					13 30								14 00											14 30
Tonypandy	d					13 33								14 03											14 33
Dinas Rhondda	d					13 35								14 05											14 35
Porth	a					13 38								14 08											14 38
	d					13 39								14 09											14 52
Trehafod	d					13 42								14 12											14 55
Merthyr Tydfil	d			13 08								13 38							14 08						
Pentre-bach	d			13 12								13 42							14 12						
Troed Y Rhiw	d			13 15								13 45							14 15						
Merthyr Vale	a			13 18								13 48							14 18						
	d			13 20								13 50							14 20						
Quakers Yard	d			13 25								13 55							14 25						
Aberdare 3	d															13 52							14 22		
Cwmbach	d															13 55							14 25		
Fernhill	d															13 58							14 28		
Mountain Ash	a															14 01							14 31		
	d															14 04							14 34		
Penrhiwceiber	d															14 07							14 37		
Abercynon	d			13 29				13 45				13 59				14 13			14 29				14 43		
Pontypridd 3	a			13 37		13 47		13 52				14 07		14 17		14 22			14 37				14 52		15 00
	d			13 39		13 48		13 54				14 09		14 18		14 24			14 39				14 54		15 04
Trefforest	d			13 42		13 51		13 57				14 12		14 21		14 27			14 42				14 57		15 07
Trefforest Estate	d			13 46								14 16							14 46						
Taffs Well 3	d			13 50		13 58		14 04				14 20		14 28		14 34			14 50				15 04		15 13
Radyr 3	a			13 53		14 01		14 07				14 23		14 31		14 37			14 53				15 07		15 17
	d			13 53		14 01	14 04	14 07				14 23		14 31	14 34	14 37			14 53			15 04	15 07		15 17
Danescourt	d						14 08								14 38							15 08			
Fairwater	d						14 10								14 40							15 10			
Waun-gron Park	d						14 12								14 42							15 12			
Ninian Park	d						14 15								14 45							15 15			
Llandaf	d			13 56		14 04		14 10				14 26		14 34		14 40			14 56				15 10		
Cathays	d			14 01		14 09		14 15				14 31		14 39		14 45			15 01				15 15		
Rhymney 3	d								13 27															14 27	
Pontlottyn	d								13 30															14 30	
Tir-phil	d								13 35															14 35	
Brithdir	d								13 37															14 37	
Bargoed	a								13 41															14 41	
	d	13 17			13 32				13 45				14 00				14 17			14 32				14 45	
Gilfach Fargoed	d	13 19															14 19								
Pengam	d	13 22			13 37				13 50				14 05				14 22			14 37				14 50	
Hengoed	d	13 25			13 40				13 54				14 09				14 25			14 40				14 54	
Ystrad Mynach 3	d	13 28			13 43				13 57				14 12				14 28			14 43				14 57	
Llanbradach	d	13 33			13 48				14 01				14 16				14 33			14 48				15 01	
Energlyn & Churchill Park	d								14 05				14 20											15 05	
Aber	d	13 37			13 52				14 07				14 22				14 37			14 52				15 07	
Caerphilly 3	d	13 40			13 55				14 10				14 25				14 40			14 55				15 10	
Lisvane & Thornhill	d	13 44			13 59				14 14				14 29				14 44			14 59				15 14	
Llanishen	d	13 46			14 01				14 16				14 31				14 46			15 01				15 16	
Heath High Level	d	13 49			14 04				14 19				14 34				14 49			15 04				15 19	
Coryton	d		13 45							14 15								14 45							
Whitchurch (Cardiff)	d		13 46							14 16								14 46							
Rhiwbina	d		13 48							14 18								14 48							
Birchgrove	d		13 50							14 20								14 50							
Ty Glas	d		13 51							14 21								14 51							
Heath Low Level	d		13 54							14 24								14 54							
Cardiff Queen Street 3	a	13 54	13 59	14 04	14 09	14 14		14 19	14 24	14 29		14 34	14 39	14 44		14 49	14 54	14 59	15 04	15 09			15 19	15 24	
	d	13 56	14 01	14 06	14 11	14 16		14 21	14 26	14 31		14 36	14 41	14 46		14 51	14 56	15 01	15 06	15 11			15 21	15 26	
Cardiff Central 7	a	13 59	14 04	14 09	14 14	14 22	14 20	14 24	14 29	14 34		14 39	14 44	14 52	14 50	14 54	14 59	15 04	15 09	15 14		15 20	15 24	15 29	15 34
	d	14 01		14 10	14 16			14 25	14 31			14 41	14 46			14 55	15 01		15 10	15 16			15 25	15 31	
Grangetown	d	14 05		14 14	14 20			14 29	14 35			14 45	14 50			14 59	15 05		15 14	15 20			15 29	15 35	
Dingle Road	d	14 11			14 26				14 41				14 56				15 11			15 26				15 41	
Penarth	a	14 16			14 31				14 46				15 01				15 16			15 31				15 46	
Cogan	d			14 18				14 33				14 48				15 03			15 18				15 33		
Eastbrook	d			14 20				14 35				14 51				15 05			15 20				15 35		
Dinas Powys	d			14 22				14 37				14 53				15 07			15 22				15 37		
Cadoxton	d			14 27				14 42				14 57				15 12			15 27				15 42		
Barry Docks	d			14 29				14 44				15 00				15 14			15 29				15 44		
Barry 3	d			14 34				14 49				15 05				15 19			15 34				15 49		
Barry Island	a			14 40				14 55								15 25			15 40				15 55		
Rhoose Cardiff Int Airport ✈	d											15 12													
Llantwit Major	d											15 22													
Bridgend	a											15 39													

A To Radyr **B** To Coryton

When events are being held at the Millenium Stadium, services are subject to alteration. Please check times before travelling.

For connections to Cardiff Bay please refer to Table 130A

Table 130

Saturdays

15 February to 17 May

Treherbert, Aberdare, Merthyr, Pontypridd, Rhymney and Coryton - Cardiff, Penarth, Barry, Barry Island and Bridgend

Network Diagram - see first Page of Table 130

		AW A	AW	AW	AW	AW B	AW	AW	AW A	AW	AW	AW	AW B	AW	AW	AW A	AW	AW	AW	AW B	AW	AW	AW A
Treherbert	d				14 47							15 13							15 47				
Ynyswen	d				14 49							15 15							15 49				
Treorchy	d				14 51							15 21							15 51				
Ton Pentre	d				14 53							15 23							15 53				
Ystrad Rhondda	a				14 56							15 26							15 56				
	d				14 58							15 28							15 58				
Llwynypia	d				15 00							15 30							16 00				
Tonypandy	d				15 03							15 33							16 03				
Dinas Rhondda	d				15 05							15 35							16 05				
Porth	a				15 08							15 38							16 08				
	d				15 09							15 39							16 09				
Trehafod	d				15 12							15 42							16 12				
Merthyr Tydfil	d		14 38							15 08							15 38						
Pentre-bach	d		14 42							15 12							15 42						
Troed Y Rhiw	d		14 45							15 15							15 45						
Merthyr Vale	a		14 48							15 18							15 48						
	d		14 50							15 20							15 50						
Quakers Yard	d		14 55							15 25							15 55						
Aberdare 3	d						14 52							15 22							15 52		
Cwmbach	d						14 55							15 25							15 55		
Fernhill	d						14 58							15 28							15 58		
Mountain Ash	a						15 01							15 31							16 01		
	d						15 04							15 34							16 04		
Penrhiwceiber	d						15 07							15 37							16 07		
Abercynon	d		14 59				15 13			15 29				15 43			15 59				16 13		
Pontypridd 3	a		15 07		15 17		15 22			15 37		15 47		15 52			16 07		16 17		16 22		
	d		15 09		15 18		15 24			15 39		15 48		15 54			16 09		16 18		16 24		
Trefforest	d		15 12		15 21		15 27			15 42		15 51		15 57			16 12		16 21		16 27		
Trefforest Estate	d		15 16							15 46							16 16						
Taffs Well 3	d		15 20		15 28		15 34			15 50		15 58		16 04			16 20		16 28		16 34		
Radyr 3	a		15 23		15 31		15 37			15 53		16 01		16 07			16 23		16 31		16 37		
	d		15 23		15 31	15 34	15 37			15 53		16 01	16 04	16 07			16 23		16 31	16 34	16 37		
Danescourt	d					15 38							16 08							16 38			
Fairwater	d					15 40							16 10							16 40			
Waun-gron Park	d					15 42							16 12							16 42			
Ninian Park	d					15 45							16 15							16 45			
Llandaf	d		15 26		15 34		15 40			15 56		16 04		16 10			16 26		16 34		16 40		
Cathays	d		15 31		15 39		15 45			16 01		16 09		16 15			16 31		16 39		16 45		
Rhymney 3	d														15 27								
Pontlottyn	d														15 30								
Tir-phil	d														15 35								
Brithdir	d														15 37								
Bargoed	a														15 41								
	d			15 00				15 17			15 32				15 45			16 00				16 17	
Gilfach Fargoed	d							15 19														16 19	
Pengam	d			15 05				15 22			15 37				15 50			16 05				16 22	
Hengoed	d			15 09				15 25			15 40				15 54			16 09				16 25	
Ystrad Mynach 3	d			15 12				15 28			15 43				15 57			16 12				16 28	
Llanbradach	d			15 16				15 33			15 48				16 01			16 16				16 33	
Energlyn & Churchill Park	d			15 20											16 05			16 20					
Aber	d			15 22				15 37			15 52				16 07			16 22				16 37	
Caerphilly 3	d			15 25				15 40			15 55				16 10			16 25				16 40	
Lisvane & Thornhill	d			15 29				15 44			15 59				16 14			16 29				16 44	
Llanishen	d			15 31				15 46			16 01				16 16			16 31				16 46	
Heath High Level	d			15 34				15 49			16 04				16 19			16 34				16 49	
Coryton	d	15 15							15 45							16 15							16 45
Whitchurch (Cardiff)	d	15 16							15 46							16 16							16 46
Rhiwbina	d	15 18							15 48							16 18							16 48
Birchgrove	d	15 20							15 50							16 20							16 50
Ty Glas	d	15 21							15 51							16 21							16 51
Heath Low Level	d	15 24							15 54							16 24							16 54
Cardiff Queen Street 3	a	15 29	15 34	15 39	15 44		15 49	15 54	15 59	16 04	16 09	16 14		16 19	16 24	16 29	16 34	16 39	16 44		16 49	16 54	16 59
	d	15 31	15 36	15 41	15 46		15 51	15 56	16 01	16 06	16 11	16 16		16 21	16 26	16 31	16 36	16 41	16 46		16 51	16 56	17 01
Cardiff Central 7	a	15 34	15 39	15 44	15 52	15 50	15 54	15 59	16 04	16 09	16 14	16 22	16 20	16 24	16 32	16 34	16 39	16 44	16 52	16 50	16 54	16 59	17 04
	d		15 41	15 46			15 55	16 01		16 10	16 16			16 25			16 41	16 46			16 55	17 01	
Grangetown	d		15 45	15 50			15 59	16 05		16 14	16 20			16 29			16 45	16 50			16 59	17 05	
Dingle Road	d			15 56				16 11			16 26							16 56				17 11	
Penarth	a			16 01				16 16			16 31							17 01				17 16	
Cogan	d		15 48				16 03			16 18				16 33			16 48				17 03		
Eastbrook	d		15 51				16 05			16 20				16 35			16 51				17 05		
Dinas Powys	d		15 53				16 07			16 22				16 37			16 53				17 07		
Cadoxton	d		15 57				16 12			16 27				16 42			16 57				17 12		
Barry Docks	d		16 00				16 14			16 29				16 44			17 00				17 14		
Barry 3	d		16 05				16 19			16 34				16 49			17 05				17 19		
Barry Island	a						16 25			16 40				16 55							17 25		
Rhoose Cardiff Int Airport ✈	d		16 12														17 12						
Llantwit Major	d		16 22														17 22						
Bridgend	a		16 39														17 39						

A To Radyr
B To Coryton

When events are being held at the Millenium Stadium, services are subject to alteration. Please check times before travelling.

For connections to Cardiff Bay please refer to Table 130A

Table 130

Saturdays

15 February to 17 May

Treherbert, Aberdare, Merthyr, Pontypridd, Rhymney and Coryton - Cardiff, Penarth, Barry, Barry Island and Bridgend

Network Diagram - see first Page of Table 130

		AW	AW	AW	AW A	AW	AW	AW B	AW	AW	AW	AW A	AW	AW	AW B	AW	AW	AW	AW A	AW	AW	AW B
Treherbert	d			16 17							16 47							17 17				
Ynyswen	d			16 19							16 49							17 19				
Treorchy	d			16 21							16 51							17 21				
Ton Pentre	d			16 23							16 53							17 23				
Ystrad Rhondda	a			16 26							16 56							17 26				
	d			16 28							16 58							17 28				
Llwynypia	d			16 30							17 00							17 30				
Tonypandy	d			16 33							17 03							17 33				
Dinas Rhondda	d			16 35							17 05							17 35				
Porth	a			16 38							17 08							17 38				
	d			16 39							17 09							17 39				
Trehafod	d			16 42							17 12							17 42				
Merthyr Tydfil	d	16 08							16 38							17 08						
Pentre-bach	d	16 12							16 42							17 12						
Troed Y Rhiw	d	16 15							16 45							17 15						
Merthyr Vale	a	16 18							16 48							17 18						
	d	16 20							16 50							17 20						
Quakers Yard	d	16 25							16 55							17 25						
Aberdare 3	d					16 22							16 52							17 22		
Cwmbach	d					16 25							16 55							17 25		
Fernhill	d					16 28							16 58							17 28		
Mountain Ash	a					16 31							17 01							17 31		
	d					16 34							17 04							17 34		
Penrhiwceiber	d					16 37							17 07							17 37		
Abercynon	d	16 29				16 43			16 59				17 13			17 29				17 43		
Pontypridd 3	a	16 37		16 47		16 52			17 07		17 17		17 22			17 37		17 47		17 52		
	d	16 39		16 48		16 54			17 09		17 18		17 24			17 39		17 48		17 54		
Trefforest	d	16 42		16 51		16 57			17 12		17 21		17 27			17 42		17 51		17 57		
Trefforest Estate	d	16 46							17 16							17 46						
Taffs Well 3	d	16 50		16 58		17 04			17 20		17 28		17 34			17 50		17 58		18 04		
Radyr 3	a	16 53		17 01		17 07			17 23		17 31		17 37			17 53		18 01		18 07		
	d	16 53		17 01	17 04	17 07			17 23		17 31	17 34	17 37			17 53		18 01	18 04	18 07		
Danescourt	d				17 08							17 38							18 08			
Fairwater	d				17 10							17 40							18 10			
Waun-gron Park	d				17 12							17 42							18 12			
Ninian Park	d				17 15							17 45							18 15			
Llandaf	d	16 56		17 04		17 10			17 26		17 34		17 40			17 56		18 04		18 10		
Cathays	d	17 01		17 09		17 15			17 31		17 39		17 45			18 01		18 09		18 15		
Rhymney 3	d						16 27														17 27	
Pontlottyn	d						16 30														17 30	
Tir-phil	d						16 35														17 35	
Brithdir	d						16 37														17 37	
Bargoed	a						16 41														17 41	
	d		16 32				16 45			17 00				17 17			17 32				17 45	
Gilfach Fargoed	d													17 19								
Pengam	d		16 37				16 50			17 05				17 22			17 37				17 50	
Hengoed	d		16 40				16 54			17 09				17 25			17 40				17 54	
Ystrad Mynach 3	d		16 43				16 57			17 12				17 28			17 43				17 57	
Llanbradach	d		16 48				17 01			17 16				17 33			17 48				18 01	
Energlyn & Churchill Park	d						17 05			17 20											18 05	
Aber	d		16 52				17 07			17 22				17 37			17 52				18 07	
Caerphilly 3	d		16 55				17 10			17 25				17 40			17 55				18 10	
Lisvane & Thornhill	d		16 59				17 14			17 29				17 44			17 59				18 14	
Llanishen	d		17 01				17 16			17 31				17 46			18 01				18 16	
Heath High Level	d		17 04				17 19			17 34				17 49			18 04				18 19	
Coryton	d							17 15							17 45							18 15
Whitchurch (Cardiff)	d							17 16							17 46							18 16
Rhiwbina	d							17 18							17 48							18 18
Birchgrove	d							17 20							17 50							18 20
Ty Glas	d							17 21							17 51							18 21
Heath Low Level	d							17 24							17 54							18 24
Cardiff Queen Street 3	a	17 04	17 09	17 14		17 19	17 24	17 29	17 34	17 39	17 44		17 49	17 54	17 59	18 04	18 09	18 14		18 19	18 24	18 29
	d	17 06	17 11	17 16		17 21	17 26	17 31	17 36	17 41	17 46		17 51	17 56	18 01	18 06	18 11	18 16		18 21	18 26	18 31
Cardiff Central 7	a	17 09	17 14	17 22	17 20	17 24	17 29	17 34	17 39	17 44	17 52	17 50	17 54	17 59	18 04	18 09	18 14	18 22	18 20	18 24	18 29	18 34
	d	17 10	17 16			17 25	17 31		17 41	17 46			17 55	18 01		18 10	18 16			18 25	18 31	
Grangetown	d	17 14	17 20			17 29	17 35		17 45	17 50			17 59	18 05		18 14	18 20			18 29	18 35	
Dingle Road	d		17 26				17 41			17 56				18 11			18 26				18 41	
Penarth	a		17 31				17 46			18 01				18 16			18 31				18 46	
Cogan	d	17 18				17 33			17 48				18 03			18 18				18 33		
Eastbrook	d	17 20				17 35			17 51				18 05			18 20				18 35		
Dinas Powys	d	17 22				17 37			17 53				18 07			18 22				18 37		
Cadoxton	d	17 27				17 42			17 57				18 12			18 27				18 42		
Barry Docks	d	17 29				17 44			18 00				18 14			18 29				18 44		
Barry 3	d	17 34				17 49			18 05				18 19			18 34				18 49		
Barry Island	a	17 40				17 55							18 25			18 40				18 55		
Rhoose Cardiff Int Airport ✈	d								18 12													
Llantwit Major	d								18 22													
Bridgend	a								18 39													

A To Coryton **B** To Radyr

When events are being held at the Millenium Stadium, services are subject to alteration. Please check times before travelling.

For connections to Cardiff Bay please refer to Table 130A

Table 130

Saturdays

15 February to 17 May

Treherbert, Aberdare, Merthyr, Pontypridd, Rhymney and Coryton - Cardiff, Penarth, Barry, Barry Island and Bridgend

Network Diagram - see first Page of Table 130

		AW	AW	AW	AW	AW	AW	AW	AW	AW	AW	AW	AW	AW	AW	AW	AW	AW	AW	AW	AW	AW	AW
				A									B									B	
Treherbert	d		17 47						18 17						18 47				19 17				
Ynyswen	d		17 49						18 19						18 49				19 19				
Treorchy	d		17 51						18 21						18 51				19 21				
Ton Pentre	d		17 53						18 23						18 53				19 23				
Ystrad Rhondda	a		17 56						18 26						18 56				19 26				
	d		17 58						18 28						18 58				19 28				
Llwynypia	d		18 00						18 30						19 00				19 30				
Tonypandy	d		18 03						18 33						19 03				19 33				
Dinas Rhondda	d		18 05						18 35						19 05				19 35				
Porth	a		18 08						18 38						19 08				19 38				
	d		18 09						18 39						19 09				19 39				
Trehafod	d		18 12						18 42						19 12				19 42				
Merthyr Tydfil	d	17 38						18 08						18 38				19 08					19 38
Pentre-bach	d	17 42						18 12						18 42				19 12					19 42
Troed Y Rhiw	d	17 45						18 15						18 45				19 15					19 45
Merthyr Vale	a	17 48						18 18						18 48				19 18					19 48
	d	17 50						18 20						18 50				19 20					19 50
Quakers Yard	d	17 55						18 25						18 55				19 25					19 55
Aberdare 3	d				17 52						18 22					18 52							
Cwmbach	d				17 55						18 25					18 55							
Fernhill	d				17 58						18 28					18 58							
Mountain Ash	a				18 01						18 31					19 01							
	d				18 04						18 34					19 04							
Penrhiwceiber	d				18 07						18 37					19 07							
Abercynon	d	17 59			18 13			18 29			18 43			18 59		19 13		19 29			19 43		19 59
Pontypridd 3	a	18 07	18 17		18 22			18 37	18 47		18 52			19 07	19 17	19 22		19 37	19 47		19 52		20 07
	d	18 09	18 18		18 24			18 39	18 48		18 54			19 09	19 18	19 24		19 39	19 48		19 54		20 09
Trefforest	d	18 12	18 21		18 27			18 42	18 51		18 57			19 12	19 21	19 27		19 42	19 51		19 57		20 12
Trefforest Estate	d	18 16						18 46						19 16				19 46					20 16
Taffs Well 3	d	18 20	18 28		18 34			18 50	18 58		19 04			19 20	19 28	19 34		19 50	19 58		20 04		20 20
Radyr 3	a	18 23	18 31		18 37			18 53	19 01		19 07			19 23	19 31	19 37		19 53	20 01		20 07		20 23
	d	18 23	18 31	18 34	18 37			18 53	19 01	19 04	19 07			19 23	19 31	19 37		19 53	20 01	20 04	20 07		20 23
Danescourt	d			18 38						19 08										20 08			
Fairwater	d			18 40						19 10										20 10			
Waun-gron Park	d			18 42						19 12										20 12			
Ninian Park	d			18 45						19 15										20 15			
Llandaf	d	18 26	18 34		18 40			18 56	19 04		19 10			19 26	19 34	19 40		19 56	20 04		20 10		20 26
Cathays	d	18 31	18 39		18 45			19 01	19 09		19 15			19 31	19 39	19 45		20 01	20 09		20 15		20 31
Rhymney 3	d																						
Pontlottyn	d																						
Tir-phil	d																						
Brithdir	d																						
Bargoed	a																						
	d					18 15						18 48											
Gilfach Fargoed	d					18 18						18 50											
Pengam	d					18 20						18 53											
Hengoed	d					18 24						18 56											
Ystrad Mynach 3	d					18 27						18 59											
Llanbradach	d					18 31						19 04											
Energlyn & Churchill Park	d					18 35																	
Aber	d					18 37						19 08											
Caerphilly 3	d					18 40						19 11					19 40						
Lisvane & Thornhill	d					18 44						19 15					19 44						
Llanishen	d					18 46						19 17					19 46						
Heath High Level	d					18 49						19 20					19 49						
Coryton	d						18 45						19 15									20 15	
Whitchurch (Cardiff)	d						18 46						19 16									20 16	
Rhiwbina	d						18 48						19 18									20 18	
Birchgrove	d						18 50						19 20									20 20	
Ty Glas	d						18 51						19 21									20 21	
Heath Low Level	d						18 54						19 24									20 24	
Cardiff Queen Street 3	a	18 34	18 44		18 49	18 54	18 59	19 04	19 14		19 19	19 24	19 29	19 34	19 44	19 49	19 54	20 04	20 14		20 19	20 29	20 34
	d	18 36	18 46		18 51	18 56	19 01	19 06	19 16		19 21	19 26	19 31	19 36	19 46	19 51	19 56	20 06	20 16		20 21	20 31	20 36
Cardiff Central 7	a	18 39	18 52	18 50	18 54	18 59	19 06	19 10	19 22	19 22	19 24	19 29	19 34	19 39	19 52	19 57	19 59	20 09	20 22	20 24	20 24	20 34	20 39
	d	18 41			18 55	19 01					19 25	19 31		19 41			20 06	20 10			20 31		20 41
Grangetown	d	18 45			18 59	19 05					19 29	19 35		19 45			20 10	20 14			20 35		20 45
Dingle Road	d					19 11						19 41					20 14				20 41		
Penarth	a					19 16						19 46					20 19				20 46		
Cogan	d	18 48			19 03						19 33			19 48				20 18					20 48
Eastbrook	d	18 51			19 05						19 35			19 51				20 20					20 51
Dinas Powys	d	18 53			19 07						19 37			19 53				20 22					20 53
Cadoxton	d	18 57			19 12						19 42			19 57				20 27					20 57
Barry Docks	d	19 00			19 14						19 44			20 00				20 29					21 00
Barry 3	d	19 05			19 19						19 49			20 05				20 34					21 05
Barry Island	a				19 25						19 55							20 40					
Rhoose Cardiff Int Airport ✈	d	19 12												20 12									21 12
Llantwit Major	d	19 22												20 22									21 22
Bridgend	a	19 39												20 39									21 39

A To Coryton

B To Radyr

When events are being held at the Millenium Stadium, services are subject to alteration. Please check times before travelling.

For connections to Cardiff Bay please refer to Table 130A

Table 130

Saturdays

15 February to 17 May

Treherbert, Aberdare, Merthyr, Pontypridd, Rhymney and Coryton - Cardiff, Penarth, Barry, Barry Island and Bridgend

Network Diagram - see first Page of Table 130

		AW	AW	AW	AW	AW	AW	AW	AW	AW	AW	AW	AW	AW	AW	AW	AW	AW	AW	AW	AW	AW
										A						B						
Treherbert	d		19 47			20 17									21 17							
Ynyswen	d		19 49			20 19									21 19							
Treorchy	d		19 51			20 21									21 21							
Ton Pentre	d		19 53			20 23									21 23							
Ystrad Rhondda	a		19 56			20 26									21 26							
	d		19 58			20 28									21 28							
Llwynypia	d		20 00			20 30									21 30							
Tonypandy	d		20 03			20 33									21 33							
Dinas Rhondda	d		20 05			20 35									21 35							
Porth	a		20 08			20 38									21 38							
	d		20 09			20 39									21 39							
Trehafod	d		20 12			20 42									21 42							
Merthyr Tydfil	d										20 38							21 38				
Pentre-bach	d										20 42							21 42				
Troed Y Rhiw	d										20 45							21 45				
Merthyr Vale	a										20 48							21 48				
	d										20 50							21 50				
Quakers Yard	d										20 55							21 55				
Aberdare 3	d			19 52				20 22					20 54							21 54		
Cwmbach	d			19 55				20 25					20 57							21 57		
Fernhill	d			19 58				20 28					21 00							22 00		
Mountain Ash	a			20 01				20 31					21 03							22 03		
	d			20 04				20 34					21 04							22 04		
Penrhiwceiber	d			20 07				20 37					21 07							22 07		
Abercynon	d			20 13				20 43			20 59		21 13					21 59		22 13		
Pontypridd 3	a		20 18	20 22		20 47		20 52			21 07		21 22		21 47			22 07		22 22		
	d		20 18	20 24		20 48		20 54			21 09		21 24		21 48			22 09		22 24		
Trefforest	d		20 21	20 27		20 51		20 57			21 12		21 27		21 51			22 12		22 27		
Trefforest Estate	d										21 16							22 16				
Taffs Well 3	d		20 28	20 34		20 58		21 04			21 20		21 34		21 58			22 20		22 33		
Radyr 3	a		20 31	20 37		21 01		21 07			21 23		21 37		22 01			22 23		22 37		
	d		20 31	20 37		21 01	21 04	21 07			21 23		21 37		22 01	22 04		22 23		22 37		23 14
Danescourt	d						21 08									22 08						
Fairwater	d						21 10									22 10						
Waun-gron Park	d						21 12									22 12						
Ninian Park	d						21 15									22 15						
Llandaf	d		20 34	20 40		21 04		21 10			21 26		21 40		22 04			22 26		22 40		23 16
Cathays	d		20 39	20 45		21 09		21 15			21 31		21 45		22 09			22 31		22 44		23 20
Rhymney 3	d	19 43										20 46					21 36					
Pontlottyn	d	19 46										20 49					21 39					
Tir-phil	d	19 51										20 54					21 44					
Brithdir	d	19 53										20 56					21 46					
Bargoed	a	19 57										21 00					21 50					
	d	19 57										21 00					21 50					
Gilfach Fargoed	d	20 00										21 03					21 53					
Pengam	d	20 02										21 05					21 55					
Hengoed	d	20 06										21 09					21 59					
Ystrad Mynach 3	d	20 09										21 12		21 39			22 02					
Llanbradach	d	20 13										21 16		21 44			22 06					
Energlyn & Churchill Park	d	20 17										21 20					22 10					
Aber	d	20 19										21 22		21 48			22 12					
Caerphilly 3	d	20 22			20 40							21 25		21 51			22 15		22 28			
Lisvane & Thornhill	d	20 26			20 44							21 29		21 55			22 19					
Llanishen	d	20 28			20 46							21 31		21 57			22 21					
Heath High Level	d	20 31			20 49							21 34		22 00			22 24					
Coryton	d									21 15											22 45	
Whitchurch (Cardiff)	d									21 16											22 46	
Rhiwbina	d									21 18											22 48	
Birchgrove	d									21 20											22 50	
Ty Glas	d									21 21											22 51	
Heath Low Level	d									21 24											22 54	
Cardiff Queen Street 3	a	20 39	20 44	20 49	20 54	21 14		21 19		21 29	21 34	21 42	21 49	22 05	22 14		22 29	22 34	22 39	22 49	22 59	23 24
	d	20 41	20 46	20 51	20 56	21 16		21 21		21 31	21 36	21 44	21 51	22 06	22 16		22 31	22 36	22 40	22 54	23 01	23 25
Cardiff Central 7	a	20 47	20 52	20 57	20 59	21 22	21 25	21 27		21 34	21 39	21 47	21 54	22 09	22 22	22 20	22 34	22 41	22 43	23 00	23 06	23 28
	d			21 06	21 10				21 31		21 41		22 06	22 11			22 36			23 12		23 30
Grangetown	d			21 10	21 14				21 35		21 45		22 10	22 15			22 40			23 16		23 34
Dingle Road	d			21 14					21 41				22 14				22 44			23 20		
Penarth	a			21 19					21 46				22 19				22 47			23 25		
Cogan	d				21 18						21 48			22 18								23 37
Eastbrook	d				21 20						21 51			22 21								23 40
Dinas Powys	d				21 22						21 53			22 23								23 42
Cadoxton	d				21 27						21 57			22 27								23 46
Barry Docks	d				21 29						22 00			22 30								23 49
Barry 3	d				21 34						22 05			22 34								23 53
Barry Island	a				21 40									22 40								23 58
Rhoose Cardiff Int Airport ✈	d										22 12											
Llantwit Major	d										22 22											
Bridgend	a										22 39											

A To Radyr

B To Coryton

When events are being held at the Millenium Stadium, services are subject to alteration. Please check times before travelling.

For connections to Cardiff Bay please refer to Table 130A

Table 130

Saturdays

15 February to 17 May

Treherbert, Aberdare, Merthyr, Pontypridd, Rhymney and Coryton - Cardiff, Penarth, Barry, Barry Island and Bridgend

Network Diagram - see first Page of Table 130

		AW	AW
Treherbert	d		
Ynyswen	d		
Treorchy	d		
Ton Pentre	d		
Ystrad Rhondda	a		
	d		
Llwynypia	d		
Tonypandy	d		
Dinas Rhondda	d		
Porth	a		
	d		
Trehafod	d		
Merthyr Tydfil	d	22 38	
Pentre-bach	d	22 42	
Troed Y Rhiw	d	22 45	
Merthyr Vale	a	22 48	
	d	22 50	
Quakers Yard	d	22 55	
Aberdare 3	d		22 54
Cwmbach	d		22 57
Fernhill	d		23 00
Mountain Ash	a		23 03
	d		23 04
Penrhiwceiber	d		23 07
Abercynon	d	22 59	23 13
Pontypridd 3	a	23 07	23 22
	d	23 09	
Trefforest	d	23 12	
Trefforest Estate	d	23 16	
Taffs Well 3	d	23 20	
Radyr 3	a	23 23	
	d	23 23	
Danescourt	d		
Fairwater	d		
Waun-gron Park	d		
Ninian Park	d		
Llandaf	d	23 26	
Cathays	d	23 31	
Rhymney 3	d		
Pontlottyn	d		
Tir-phil	d		
Brithdir	d		
Bargoed	a		
	d		
Gilfach Fargoed	d		
Pengam	d		
Hengoed	d		
Ystrad Mynach 3	d		
Llanbradach	d		
Energlyn & Churchill Park	d		
Aber	d		
Caerphilly 3	d		
Lisvane & Thornhill	d		
Llanishen	d		
Heath High Level	d		
Coryton	d		
Whitchurch (Cardiff)	d		
Rhiwbina	d		
Birchgrove	d		
Ty Glas	d		
Heath Low Level	d		
Cardiff Queen Street 3	a	23 34	
	d	23 36	
Cardiff Central 7	a	23 42	
	d		
Grangetown	d		
Dingle Road	d		
Penarth	a		
Cogan	d		
Eastbrook	d		
Dinas Powys	d		
Cadoxton	d		
Barry Docks	d		
Barry 3	d		
Barry Island	a		
Rhoose Cardiff Int Airport ✈	d		
Llantwit Major	d		
Bridgend	a		

When events are being held at the Millenium Stadium, services are subject to alteration. Please check times before travelling.

For connections to Cardiff Bay please refer to Table 130A

Table 130

Sundays

8 December to 29 December

Treherbert, Aberdare, Merthyr, Pontypridd, Rhymney and Coryton - Cardiff, Penarth, Barry, Barry Island and Bridgend

Network Diagram - see first Page of Table 130

		AW	AW	AW	AW	AW	AW	AW	AW	AW	AW	AW	AW	AW	AW	AW	AW	AW	AW	AW	AW	AW	AW
Treherbert	d			08 17					10 07						12 07						14 17		
Ynyswen	d			08 19					10 09						12 09						14 19		
Treorchy	d			08 21					10 11						12 11						14 21		
Ton Pentre	d			08 23					10 13						12 13						14 23		
Ystrad Rhondda	a			08 26					10 16						12 16						14 26		
	d			08 28					10 18						12 18						14 28		
Llwynypia	d			08 30					10 20						12 20						14 30		
Tonypandy	d			08 33					10 23						12 23						14 33		
Dinas Rhondda	d			08 35					10 25						12 25						14 35		
Porth	a			08 38					10 28						12 28						14 38		
	d			08 39					10 29						12 29						14 39		
Trehafod	d			08 42					10 32						12 32						14 42		
Merthyr Tydfil	d						09 38						11 38						13 38				
Pentre-bach	d						09 42						11 42						13 42				
Troed Y Rhiw	d						09 45						11 45						13 45				
Merthyr Vale	a						09 48						11 48						13 48				
	d						09 50						11 50						13 50				
Quakers Yard	d						09 55						11 55						13 55				
Aberdare 3	d							09 54		10 54						12 54						14 54	
Cwmbach	d							09 57		10 57						12 57						14 57	
Fernhill	d							10 00		11 00						13 00						15 00	
Mountain Ash	a							10 03		11 03						13 03						15 03	
	d							10 04		11 04						13 04						15 04	
Penrhiwceiber	d							10 07		11 07						13 07						15 07	
Abercynon	d						09 59	10 13		11 13			11 59			13 13			13 59			15 13	
Pontypridd 3	a			08 47			10 07	10 22	10 37	11 22			12 07		12 37	13 22			14 07		14 47	15 22	
	d			08 48			10 09	10 24	10 38	11 24			12 09		12 38	13 24			14 09		14 48	15 24	
Trefforest	d			08 51			10 12	10 27	10 41	11 27			12 12		12 41	13 27			14 12		14 51	15 27	
Trefforest Estate	d																						
Taffs Well 3	d			08 58			10 20	10 34	10 48	11 34			12 20		12 48	13 34			14 20		14 58	15 34	
Radyr 3	a			09 01			10 23	10 37	10 51	11 37			12 23		12 51	13 37			14 23		15 01	15 37	
	d			09 01			10 23	10 37	10 51	11 37			12 23		12 51	13 37			14 23		15 01	15 37	
Danescourt	d																						
Fairwater	d																						
Waun-gron Park	d																						
Ninian Park	d																						
Llandaf	d			09 04			10 26	10 40	10 54	11 40			12 26		12 54	13 40			14 26		15 04	15 40	
Cathays	d			09 09			10 31	10 45	10 59	11 45			12 31		12 59	13 45			14 31		15 09	15 45	
Rhymney 3	d				09 08						11 09						13 09						15 20
Pontlottyn	d				09 11						11 12						13 12						15 23
Tir-phil	d				09 16						11 17						13 17						15 28
Brithdir	d				09 18						11 19						13 19						15 30
Bargoed	a				09 22						11 23						13 23						15 34
	d				09 23						11 23						13 23						15 35
Gilfach Fargoed	d				09 26						11 26						13 26						15 38
Pengam	d				09 28						11 28						13 28						15 40
Hengoed	d				09 32						11 32						13 32						15 44
Ystrad Mynach 3	d				09 35						11 35						13 35						15 47
Llanbradach	d				09 39						11 39						13 39						15 51
Energlyn & Churchill Park	d				09 43						11 43						13 43						15 55
Aber	d				09 45						11 45						13 45						15 57
Caerphilly 3	d				09 48						11 48						13 48						16 00
Lisvane & Thornhill	d				09 52						11 52						13 52						16 04
Llanishen	d				09 54						11 54						13 54						16 06
Heath High Level	d				09 57						11 57						13 57						16 09
Coryton	d																						
Whitchurch (Cardiff)	d																						
Rhiwbina	d																						
Birchgrove	d																						
Ty Glas	d																						
Heath Low Level	d																						
Cardiff Queen Street 3	a			09 12	10 02		10 34	10 49	11 02	11 49	12 02		12 34		13 02	13 49	14 02		14 34		15 14	15 49	16 14
	d			09 14	10 04		10 36	10 51	11 04	11 51	12 04		12 36		13 04	13 51	14 04		14 36		15 16	15 51	16 16
Cardiff Central 7	a			09 17	10 07		10 39	10 54	11 07	11 57	12 07		12 39		13 06	13 57	14 07		14 39		15 18	15 57	16 18
	d	08 25	08 41	09 25	10 25	10 31	10 41	10 55	11 25		12 25	12 31	12 41	12 55	13 25		14 25	14 31	14 41	14 55	15 25		16 25
Grangetown	d	08 29	08 45	09 29	10 29	10 35	10 45	10 59	11 29		12 29	12 35	12 45	12 59	13 29		14 29	14 35	14 45	14 59	15 29		16 29
Dingle Road	d					10 41						12 41						14 41					
Penarth	a					10 46						12 46						14 46					
Cogan	d	08 33	08 48	09 33	10 33		10 48	11 03	11 33		12 33		12 48	13 03	13 33		14 33		14 48	15 03	15 32		16 33
Eastbrook	d	08 35	08 51	09 35	10 35		10 51	11 05	11 35		12 35		12 51	13 05	13 35		14 35		14 51	15 05	15 35		16 35
Dinas Powys	d	08 37	08 53	09 37	10 37		10 53	11 07	11 37		12 37		12 53	13 07	13 37		14 37		14 53	15 07	15 37		16 37
Cadoxton	d	08 42	08 57	09 42	10 42		10 57	11 12	11 42		12 42		12 57	13 12	13 42		14 42		14 57	15 12	15 41		16 42
Barry Docks	d	08 44	09 00	09 44	10 44		11 00	11 14	11 44		12 44		13 00	13 14	13 44		14 44		15 00	15 14	15 44		16 44
Barry 3	d	08 49	09 05	09 49	10 49		11 05	11 19	11 49		12 49		13 05	13 19	13 49		14 49		15 05	15 19	15 48		16 49
Barry Island	a	08 55		09 55	10 55			11 25	11 55		12 55			13 25	13 55		14 55			15 25	15 54		16 55
Rhoose Cardiff Int Airport ✈	d		09 12				11 12						13 12						15 12				
Llantwit Major	d		09 22				11 22						13 22						15 22				
Bridgend	a		09 40				11 40						13 40						15 40				

When events are being held at the Millenium Stadium, services are subject to alteration. Please check times before travelling.

For connections to Cardiff Bay please refer to Table 130A

Table 130

Sundays

8 December to 29 December

Treherbert, Aberdare, Merthyr, Pontypridd, Rhymney and Coryton - Cardiff, Penarth, Barry, Barry Island and Bridgend

Network Diagram - see first Page of Table 130

		AW	AW	AW	AW	AW		AW	AW	AW	AW	AW	AW	AW	AW	AW		AW	AW	AW	AW	AW			
Treherbert	d				16 17							18 17							20 17						
Ynyswen	d				16 19							18 19							20 19						
Treorchy	d				16 21							18 21							20 21						
Ton Pentre	d				16 23							18 23							20 23						
Ystrad Rhondda	a				16 26							18 26							20 26						
	d				16 28							18 28							20 28						
Llwynypia	d				16 30							18 30							20 30						
Tonypandy	d				16 33							18 33							20 33						
Dinas Rhondda	d				16 35							18 35							20 35						
Porth	a				16 38							18 38							20 38						
	d				16 39							18 39							20 39						
Trehafod	d				16 42							18 42							20 42						
Merthyr Tydfil	d		15 38						17 38						19 38						21 38				
Pentre-bach	d		15 42						17 42						19 42						21 42				
Troed Y Rhiw	d		15 45						17 45						19 45						21 45				
Merthyr Vale	a		15 48						17 48						19 48						21 48				
	d		15 50						17 50						19 50						21 50				
Quakers Yard	d		15 55						17 55						19 55						21 55				
Aberdare 3	d					16 54							18 54							20 54					
Cwmbach	d					16 57							18 57							20 57					
Fernhill	d					17 00							19 00							21 00					
Mountain Ash	a					17 03							19 03							21 03					
	d					17 04							19 04							21 04					
Penrhiwceiber	d					17 07							19 07							21 07					
Abercynon	d		15 59			17 13				17 59			19 13			19 59				21 13		21 59			
Pontypridd 3	a		16 07		16 47	17 22				18 07		18 47	19 22			20 07			20 47	21 22		22 07			
	d		16 09		16 48	17 24				18 09		18 48	19 24			20 09			20 48	21 24		22 09			
Trefforest	d		16 12		16 51	17 27				18 12		18 51	19 27			20 12			20 51	21 27		22 12			
Trefforest Estate	d																								
Taffs Well 3	d		16 20		16 58	17 34				18 20		18 58	19 34			20 20			20 58	21 34		22 20			
Radyr 3	a		16 23		17 01	17 37				18 23		19 01	19 37			20 23			21 01	21 37		22 23			
	d		16 23		17 01	17 37				18 23		19 01	19 37			20 23			21 01	21 37		22 23			
Danescourt	d																								
Fairwater	d																								
Waun-gron Park	d																								
Ninian Park	d																								
Llandaf	d		16 26		17 04	17 40				18 26		19 04	19 40			20 26			21 04	21 40		22 26			
Cathays	d		16 31		17 09	17 45				18 31		19 09	19 45			20 31			21 09	21 45		22 31			
Rhymney 3	d							17 20						19 20											
Pontlottyn	d							17 23						19 23											
Tir-phil	d							17 28						19 28											
Brithdir	d							17 30						19 30											
Bargoed	a							17 34						19 34											
	d							17 35						19 35											
Gilfach Fargoed	d							17 38						19 38											
Pengam	d							17 40						19 40											
Hengoed	d							17 44						19 44											
Ystrad Mynach 3	d							17 47						19 47											
Llanbradach	d							17 51						19 51											
Energlyn & Churchill Park	d							17 55						19 55											
Aber	d							17 57						19 57											
Caerphilly 3	d							18 00						20 00											
Lisvane & Thornhill	d							18 04						20 04											
Llanishen	d							18 06						20 06											
Heath High Level	d							18 09						20 09											
Coryton	d																								
Whitchurch (Cardiff)	d																								
Rhiwbina	d																								
Birchgrove	d																								
Ty Glas	d																								
Heath Low Level	d																								
Cardiff Queen Street 3	a		16 34		17 14	17 49		18 14		18 34		19 14	19 49	20 14		20 34			21 14	21 49		22 34			
	d		16 36		17 16	17 51		18 16		18 36		19 16	19 51	20 16		20 36			21 16	21 51		22 36			
Cardiff Central 7	a		16 39		17 18	17 57		18 18		18 39		19 18	19 54	20 18		20 39			21 18	21 56		22 42			
	d	16 31	16 41	16 55	17 25			18 25	18 31	18 41	18 55	19 25	19 55	20 25	20 31	20 41		20 55	21 25		22 25				
Grangetown	d	16 35	16 45	16 59	17 29			18 29	18 35	18 45	18 59	19 29	19 59	20 29	20 35	20 45		20 59	21 29		22 29				
Dingle Road	d	16 41							18 41						20 41										
Penarth	a	16 46							18 46						20 46										
Cogan	d		16 48	17 03	17 33			18 33		18 48	19 03	19 33	20 03	20 33		20 48		21 03	21 33		22 33				
Eastbrook	d		16 51	17 05	17 35			18 35		18 51	19 05	19 35	20 05	20 35		20 51		21 05	21 35		22 35				
Dinas Powys	d		16 53	17 07	17 37			18 37		18 53	19 07	19 37	20 07	20 37		20 53		21 07	21 37		22 37				
Cadoxton	d		16 57	17 12	17 42			18 42		18 57	19 12	19 42	20 12	20 42		20 57		21 12	21 42		22 42				
Barry Docks	d		17 00	17 14	17 44			18 44		19 00	19 14	19 44	20 14	20 44		21 00		21 14	21 44		22 44				
Barry 3	d		17 05	17 19	17 49			18 49		19 05	19 19	19 49	20 19	20 49		21 05		21 19	21 49		22 49				
Barry Island	a			17 25	17 55			18 55			19 25	19 55	20 25	20 55				21 25	21 55		22 55				
Rhoose Cardiff Int Airport ✈	d		17 12							19 12						21 12									
Llantwit Major	d		17 22							19 22						21 22									
Bridgend	a		17 40							19 40						21 40									

When events are being held at the Millenium Stadium, services are subject to alteration. Please check times before travelling.

For connections to Cardiff Bay please refer to Table 130A

Table 130

Sundays

5 January to 9 February

Treherbert, Aberdare, Merthyr, Pontypridd, Rhymney and Coryton - Cardiff, Penarth, Barry, Barry Island and Bridgend

Network Diagram - see first Page of Table 130

		AW A 🚌	AW	AW	AW	AW 🚌	AW	AW	AW	AW	AW	AW	AW	AW	AW	AW	AW	AW	AW	AW	AW	AW	AW
Treherbert	d				08 17						10 07						12 07						14 17
Ynyswen	d				08 19						10 09						12 09						14 19
Treorchy	d				08 21						10 11						12 11						14 21
Ton Pentre	d				08 23						10 13						12 13						14 23
Ystrad Rhondda	a				08 26						10 16						12 16						14 26
	d				08 28						10 18						12 18						14 28
Llwynypia	d				08 30						10 20						12 20						14 30
Tonypandy	d				08 33						10 23						12 23						14 33
Dinas Rhondda	d				08 35						10 25						12 25						14 35
Porth	a				08 38						10 28						12 28						14 38
	d				08 39						10 29						12 29						14 39
Trehafod	d				08 42						10 32						12 32						14 42
Merthyr Tydfil	d								09 38						11 38						13 38		
Pentre-bach	d								09 42						11 42						13 42		
Troed Y Rhiw	d								09 45						11 45						13 45		
Merthyr Vale	a								09 48						11 48						13 48		
	d								09 50						11 50						13 50		
Quakers Yard	d								09 55						11 55						13 55		
Aberdare 3	d									09 54		10 54						12 54					
Cwmbach	d									09 57		10 57						12 57					
Fernhill	d									10 00		11 00						13 00					
Mountain Ash	a									10 03		11 03						13 03					
	d									10 04		11 04						13 04					
Penrhiwceiber	d									10 07		11 07						13 07					
Abercynon	d								09 59	10 13		11 13			11 59			13 13			13 59		
Pontypridd 3	a				08 47				10 07	10 22	10 37	11 22			12 07		12 37	13 22			14 07		14 47
	d				08 48				10 09	10 24	10 38	11 24			12 09		12 38	13 24			14 09		14 48
Trefforest	d				08 51				10 12	10 27	10 41	11 27			12 12		12 41	13 27			14 12		14 51
Trefforest Estate	d																						
Taffs Well 3	d				08 58				10 20	10 34	10 48	11 34			12 20		12 48	13 34			14 20		14 58
Radyr 3	a				09 01				10 23	10 37	10 51	11 37			12 23		12 51	13 37			14 23		15 01
	d				09 02	09 11			10 23	10 37	10 51	11 37			12 23		12 51	13 37			14 23		15 01
Danescourt	d																						
Fairwater	d																						
Waun-gron Park	d																						
Ninian Park	d																						
Llandaf	d					09 21			10 26	10 40	10 54	11 40			12 26		12 54	13 40			14 26		15 04
Cathays	d					09 36			10 31	10 45	10 59	11 45			12 31		12 59	13 45			14 31		15 09
Rhymney 3	d						09 20						11 21						13 09				
Pontlottyn	d						09 23						11 24						13 12				
Tir-phil	d						09 28						11 29						13 17				
Brithdir	d						09 30						11 31						13 19				
Bargoed	a						09 34						11 35						13 23				
	d						09 35						11 36						13 23				
Gilfach Fargoed	d						09 38						11 39						13 26				
Pengam	d						09 40						11 41						13 28				
Hengoed	d						09 44						11 45						13 32				
Ystrad Mynach 3	d						09 47						11 48						13 35				
Llanbradach	d						09 51						11 52						13 39				
Energlyn & Churchill Park	d						09 55						11 56						13 43				
Aber	d						09 57						11 58						13 45				
Caerphilly 3	d						10 00						12 01						13 48				
Lisvane & Thornhill	d						10 04						12 05						13 52				
Llanishen	d						10 06						12 07						13 54				
Heath High Level	d						10 09						12 10						13 57				
Coryton	d																						
Whitchurch (Cardiff)	d																						
Rhiwbina	d																						
Birchgrove	d																						
Ty Glas	d																						
Heath Low Level	d																						
Cardiff Queen Street 3	a					09 41	10 14		10 34	10 49	11 02	11 49	12 15		12 34		13 02	13 49	14 02		14 34		15 14
	d	00 04				09 41	10 16		10 36	10 51	11 04	11 51	12 17		12 36		13 04	13 51	14 04		14 36		15 16
Cardiff Central 7	a	00 12			09 18	09 49	10 19		10 39	10 54	11 07	11 57	12 20		12 39		13 06	13 57	14 07		14 39		15 18
	d		08 25	08 41	09 25		10 25	10 31	10 41	10 55	11 25		12 25	12 31	12 41	12 55	13 25		14 25	14 31	14 41	14 55	15 25
Grangetown	d		08 29	08 45	09 29		10 29	10 35	10 45	10 59	11 29		12 29	12 35	12 45	12 59	13 29		14 29	14 35	14 45	14 59	15 29
Dingle Road	d							10 41						12 41						14 41			
Penarth	a							10 46						12 46						14 46			
Cogan	d		08 33	08 48	09 33		10 33		10 48	11 03	11 33		12 33		12 48	13 03	13 33		14 33		14 48	15 03	15 32
Eastbrook	d		08 35	08 51	09 35		10 35		10 51	11 05	11 35		12 35		12 51	13 05	13 35		14 35		14 51	15 05	15 35
Dinas Powys	d		08 37	08 53	09 37		10 37		10 53	11 07	11 37		12 37		12 53	13 07	13 37		14 37		14 53	15 07	15 37
Cadoxton	d		08 42	08 57	09 42		10 42		10 57	11 12	11 42		12 42		12 57	13 12	13 42		14 42		14 57	15 12	15 41
Barry Docks	d		08 44	09 00	09 44		10 44		11 00	11 14	11 44		12 44		13 00	13 14	13 44		14 44		15 00	15 14	15 44
Barry 3	d		08 49	09 05	09 49		10 49		11 05	11 19	11 49		12 49		13 05	13 19	13 49		14 49		15 05	15 19	15 48
Barry Island	a		08 55		09 55		10 55			11 25	11 55		12 55			13 25	13 55		14 55			15 25	15 54
Rhoose Cardiff Int Airport ✈	d			09 12					11 12						13 12						15 12		
Llantwit Major	d			09 22					11 22						13 22						15 22		
Bridgend	a			09 40					11 40						13 40						15 40		

A From Radyr

When events are being held at the Millenium Stadium, services are subject to alteration. Please check times before travelling.

For connections to Cardiff Bay please refer to Table 130A

Table 130

Sundays

5 January to 9 February

Treherbert, Aberdare, Merthyr, Pontypridd, Rhymney and Coryton - Cardiff, Penarth, Barry, Barry Island and Bridgend

Network Diagram - see first Page of Table 130

		AW	AW	AW	AW	AW	AW	AW	AW	AW	AW	AW	AW	AW	AW	AW	AW	AW	AW	AW	AW	AW
Treherbert	d						16 17						18 17						20 17			
Ynyswen	d						16 19						18 19						20 19			
Treorchy	d						16 21						18 21						20 21			
Ton Pentre	d						16 23						18 23						20 23			
Ystrad Rhondda	a						16 26						18 26						20 26			
	d						16 28						18 28						20 28			
Llwynypia	d						16 30						18 30						20 30			
Tonypandy	d						16 33						18 33						20 33			
Dinas Rhondda	d						16 35						18 35						20 35			
Porth	a						16 38						18 38						20 38			
	d						16 39						18 39						20 39			
Trehafod	d						16 42						18 42						20 42			
Merthyr Tydfil	d				15 38						17 38						19 38					21 38
Pentre-bach	d				15 42						17 42						19 42					21 42
Troed Y Rhiw	d				15 45						17 45						19 45					21 45
Merthyr Vale	a				15 48						17 48						19 48					21 48
	d				15 50						17 50						19 50					21 50
Quakers Yard	d				15 55						17 55						19 55					21 55
Aberdare 3	d	14 54						16 54						18 54						20 54		
Cwmbach	d	14 57						16 57						18 57						20 57		
Fernhill	d	15 00						17 00						19 00						21 00		
Mountain Ash	a	15 03						17 03						19 03						21 03		
	d	15 04						17 04						19 04						21 04		
Penrhiwceiber	d	15 07						17 07						19 07						21 07		
Abercynon	d	15 13			15 59			17 13			17 59			19 13			19 59			21 13		21 59
Pontypridd 3	a	15 22			16 07		16 47	17 22			18 07		18 47	19 22			20 07		20 47	21 22		22 07
	d	15 24			16 09		16 48	17 24			18 09		18 48	19 24			20 09		20 48	21 24		22 09
Trefforest	d	15 27			16 12		16 51	17 27			18 12		18 51	19 27			20 12		20 51	21 27		22 12
Trefforest Estate	d																					
Taffs Well 3	d	15 34			16 20		16 58	17 34			18 20		18 58	19 34			20 20		20 58	21 34		22 20
Radyr 3	a	15 37			16 23		17 01	17 37			18 23		19 01	19 37			20 23		21 01	21 37		22 23
	d	15 37			16 23		17 01	17 37			18 23		19 01	19 37			20 23		21 01	21 37		22 23
Danescourt	d																					
Fairwater	d																					
Waun-gron Park	d																					
Ninian Park	d																					
Llandaf	d	15 40			16 26		17 04	17 40			18 26		19 04	19 40			20 26		21 04	21 40		22 26
Cathays	d	15 45			16 31		17 09	17 45			18 31		19 09	19 45			20 31		21 09	21 45		22 31
Rhymney 3	d		15 20						17 20						19 20							
Pontlottyn	d		15 23						17 23						19 23							
Tir-phil	d		15 28						17 28						19 28							
Brithdir	d		15 30						17 30						19 30							
Bargoed	a		15 34						17 34						19 34							
	d		15 35						17 35						19 35							
Gilfach Fargoed	d		15 38						17 38						19 38							
Pengam	d		15 40						17 40						19 40							
Hengoed	d		15 44						17 44						19 44							
Ystrad Mynach 3	d		15 47						17 47						19 47							
Llanbradach	d		15 51						17 51						19 51							
Energlyn & Churchill Park	d		15 55						17 55						19 55							
Aber	d		15 57						17 57						19 57							
Caerphilly 3	d		16 00						18 00						20 00							
Lisvane & Thornhill	d		16 04						18 04						20 04							
Llanishen	d		16 06						18 06						20 06							
Heath High Level	d		16 09						18 09						20 09							
Coryton	d																					
Whitchurch (Cardiff)	d																					
Rhiwbina	d																					
Birchgrove	d																					
Ty Glas	d																					
Heath Low Level	d																					
Cardiff Queen Street 3	a	15 49	16 14		16 34		17 14	17 49	18 14		18 34		19 14	19 49	20 14		20 34		21 14	21 49		22 34
	d	15 51	16 16		16 36		17 16	17 51	18 16		18 36		19 16	19 51	20 16		20 36		21 16	21 51		22 36
Cardiff Central 7	a	15 57	16 18		16 39		17 18	17 57	18 18		18 39		19 18	19 54	20 18		20 39		21 18	21 56		22 42
	d		16 25	16 31	16 41	16 55	17 25		18 25	18 31	18 41	18 55	19 25	19 55	20 25	20 31	20 41	20 55	21 25		22 25	
Grangetown	d		16 29	16 35	16 45	16 59	17 29		18 29	18 35	18 45	18 59	19 29	19 59	20 29	20 35	20 45	20 59	21 29		22 29	
Dingle Road	d			16 41						18 41						20 41						
Penarth	a			16 46						18 46						20 46						
Cogan	d		16 33		16 48	17 03	17 33		18 33		18 48	19 03	19 33	20 03	20 33		20 48	21 03	21 33		22 33	
Eastbrook	d		16 35		16 51	17 05	17 35		18 35		18 51	19 05	19 35	20 05	20 35		20 51	21 05	21 35		22 35	
Dinas Powys	d		16 37		16 53	17 07	17 37		18 37		18 53	19 07	19 37	20 07	20 37		20 53	21 07	21 37		22 37	
Cadoxton	d		16 42		16 57	17 12	17 42		18 42		18 57	19 12	19 42	20 12	20 42		20 57	21 12	21 42		22 42	
Barry Docks	d		16 44		17 00	17 14	17 44		18 44		19 00	19 14	19 44	20 14	20 44		21 00	21 14	21 44		22 44	
Barry 3	d		16 49		17 05	17 19	17 49		18 49		19 05	19 19	19 49	20 19	20 49		21 05	21 19	21 49		22 49	
Barry Island	a		16 55			17 25	17 55		18 55			19 25	19 55	20 25	20 55			21 25	21 55		22 55	
Rhoose Cardiff Int Airport ✈	d				17 12						19 12						21 12					
Llantwit Major	d				17 22						19 22						21 22					
Bridgend	a				17 40						19 40						21 40					

When events are being held at the Millenium Stadium, services are subject to alteration. Please check times before travelling.

For connections to Cardiff Bay please refer to Table 130A

Table 130

Sundays

16 February to 11 May

Treherbert, Aberdare, Merthyr, Pontypridd, Rhymney and Coryton - Cardiff, Penarth, Barry, Barry Island and Bridgend

Network Diagram - see first Page of Table 130

		AW	AW	AW	AW	AW	AW	AW	AW	AW	AW	AW	AW	AW	AW	AW	AW	AW	AW	AW	AW	AW	AW
Treherbert	d			08 17					10 07						12 07						14 17		
Ynyswen	d			08 19					10 09						12 09						14 19		
Treorchy	d			08 21					10 11						12 11						14 21		
Ton Pentre	d			08 23					10 13						12 13						14 23		
Ystrad Rhondda	a			08 26					10 16						12 16						14 26		
	d			08 28					10 18						12 18						14 28		
Llwynypia	d			08 30					10 20						12 20						14 30		
Tonypandy	d			08 33					10 23						12 23						14 33		
Dinas Rhondda	d			08 35					10 25						12 25						14 35		
Porth	a			08 38					10 28						12 28						14 38		
	d			08 39					10 29						12 29						14 39		
Trehafod	d			08 42					10 32						12 32						14 42		
Merthyr Tydfil	d						09 38						11 38						13 38				
Pentre-bach	d						09 42						11 42						13 42				
Troed Y Rhiw	d						09 45						11 45						13 45				
Merthyr Vale	a						09 48						11 48						13 48				
	d						09 50						11 50						13 50				
Quakers Yard	d						09 55						11 55						13 55				
Aberdare 3	d							09 54		10 54						12 54						14 54	
Cwmbach	d							09 57		10 57						12 57						14 57	
Fernhill	d							10 00		11 00						13 00						15 00	
Mountain Ash	a							10 03		11 03						13 03						15 03	
	d							10 04		11 04						13 04						15 04	
Penrhiwceiber	d							10 07		11 07						13 07						15 07	
Abercynon	d						09 59	10 13		11 13			11 59			13 13			13 59			15 13	
Pontypridd 3	a			08 47			10 07	10 22	10 37	11 22			12 07		12 37	13 22			14 07		14 47	15 22	
	d			08 48			10 09	10 24	10 38	11 24			12 09		12 38	13 24			14 09		14 48	15 24	
Trefforest	d			08 51			10 12	10 27	10 41	11 27			12 12		12 41	13 27			14 12		14 51	15 27	
Trefforest Estate	d																						
Taffs Well 3	d			08 58			10 20	10 34	10 48	11 34			12 20		12 48	13 34			14 20		14 58	15 34	
Radyr 3	a			09 01			10 23	10 37	10 51	11 37			12 23		12 51	13 37			14 23		15 01	15 37	
	d			09 01			10 23	10 37	10 51	11 37			12 23		12 51	13 37			14 23		15 01	15 37	
Danescourt	d																						
Fairwater	d																						
Waun-gron Park	d																						
Ninian Park	d																						
Llandaf	d			09 04			10 26	10 40	10 54	11 40			12 26		12 54	13 40			14 26		15 04	15 40	
Cathays	d			09 09			10 31	10 45	10 59	11 45			12 31		12 59	13 45			14 31		15 09	15 45	
Rhymney 3	d				09 08						11 09						13 09						15 20
Pontlottyn	d				09 11						11 12						13 12						15 23
Tir-phil	d				09 16						11 17						13 17						15 28
Brithdir	d				09 18						11 19						13 19						15 30
Bargoed	a				09 22						11 23						13 23						15 34
	d				09 23						11 23						13 23						15 35
Gilfach Fargoed	d				09 26						11 26						13 26						15 38
Pengam	d				09 28						11 28						13 28						15 40
Hengoed	d				09 32						11 32						13 32						15 44
Ystrad Mynach 3	d				09 35						11 35						13 35						15 47
Llanbradach	d				09 39						11 39						13 39						15 51
Energlyn & Churchill Park	d				09 43						11 43						13 43						15 55
Aber	d				09 45						11 45						13 45						15 57
Caerphilly 3	d				09 48						11 48						13 48						16 00
Lisvane & Thornhill	d				09 52						11 52						13 52						16 04
Llanishen	d				09 54						11 54						13 54						16 06
Heath High Level	d				09 57						11 57						13 57						16 09
Coryton	d																						
Whitchurch (Cardiff)	d																						
Rhiwbina	d																						
Birchgrove	d																						
Ty Glas	d																						
Heath Low Level	d																						
Cardiff Queen Street 3	a			09 12	10 02		10 34	10 49	11 02	11 49	12 02		12 34		13 02	13 49	14 02		14 34		15 14	15 49	16 14
	d			09 14	10 04		10 36	10 51	11 04	11 51	12 04		12 36		13 04	13 51	14 04		14 36		15 16	15 51	16 16
Cardiff Central 7	a			09 17	10 07		10 39	10 54	11 07	11 57	12 07		12 39		13 06	13 57	14 07		14 39		15 18	15 57	16 18
	d	08 25	08 41	09 25	10 25	10 31	10 41	10 55	11 25		12 25	12 31	12 41	12 55	13 25		14 25	14 31	14 41	14 55	15 25		16 25
Grangetown	d	08 29	08 45	09 29	10 29	10 35	10 45	10 59	11 29		12 29	12 35	12 45	12 59	13 29		14 29	14 35	14 45	14 59	15 29		16 29
Dingle Road	d					10 41						12 41						14 41					
Penarth	a					10 46						12 46						14 46					
Cogan	d	08 33	08 48	09 33	10 33		10 48	11 03	11 33		12 33		12 48	13 03	13 33		14 33		14 48	15 03	15 32		16 33
Eastbrook	d	08 35	08 51	09 35	10 35		10 51	11 05	11 35		12 35		12 51	13 05	13 35		14 35		14 51	15 05	15 35		16 35
Dinas Powys	d	08 37	08 53	09 37	10 37		10 53	11 07	11 37		12 37		12 53	13 07	13 37		14 37		14 53	15 07	15 37		16 37
Cadoxton	d	08 42	08 57	09 42	10 42		10 57	11 12	11 42		12 42		12 57	13 12	13 42		14 42		14 57	15 12	15 41		16 42
Barry Docks	d	08 44	09 00	09 44	10 44		11 00	11 14	11 44		12 44		13 00	13 14	13 44		14 44		15 00	15 14	15 44		16 44
Barry 3	d	08 49	09 05	09 49	10 49		11 05	11 19	11 49		12 49		13 05	13 19	13 49		14 49		15 05	15 19	15 48		16 49
Barry Island	a	08 55		09 55	10 55			11 25	11 55		12 55			13 25	13 55		14 55			15 25	15 54		16 55
Rhoose Cardiff Int Airport ✈	d		09 12				11 12						13 12						15 12				
Llantwit Major	d		09 22				11 22						13 22						15 22				
Bridgend	a		09 40				11 40						13 40						15 40				

When events are being held at the Millenium Stadium, services are subject to alteration. Please check times before travelling.

For connections to Cardiff Bay please refer to Table 130A

Table 130

Sundays

16 February to 11 May

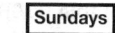

Treherbert, Aberdare, Merthyr, Pontypridd, Rhymney and Coryton - Cardiff, Penarth, Barry, Barry Island and Bridgend

Network Diagram - see first Page of Table 130

		AW	AW	AW	AW	AW		AW	AW	AW	AW	AW	AW	AW	AW	AW		AW	AW	AW	AW	AW			
Treherbert	d				16 17							18 17							20 17						
Ynyswen	d				16 19							18 19							20 19						
Treorchy	d				16 21							18 21							20 21						
Ton Pentre	d				16 23							18 23							20 23						
Ystrad Rhondda	a				16 26							18 26							20 26						
	d				16 28							18 28							20 28						
Llwynypia	d				16 30							18 30							20 30						
Tonypandy	d				16 33							18 33							20 33						
Dinas Rhondda	d				16 35							18 35							20 35						
Porth	a				16 38							18 38							20 38						
	d				16 39							18 39							20 39						
Trehafod	d				16 42							18 42							20 42						
Merthyr Tydfil	d		15 38						17 38						19 38						21 38			
Pentre-bach	d		15 42						17 42						19 42						21 42			
Troed Y Rhiw	d		15 45						17 45						19 45						21 45			
Merthyr Vale	a		15 48						17 48						19 48						21 48			
	d		15 50						17 50						19 50						21 50			
Quakers Yard	d		15 55						17 55						19 55						21 55			
Aberdare 3	d					16 54							18 54							20 54					
Cwmbach	d					16 57							18 57							20 57					
Fernhill	d					17 00							19 00							21 00					
Mountain Ash	a					17 03							19 03							21 03					
	d					17 04							19 04							21 04					
Penrhiwceiber	d					17 07							19 07							21 07					
Abercynon	d		15 59			17 13				17 59			19 13			19 59				21 13		21 59			
Pontypridd 3	a		16 07		16 47	17 22				18 07		18 47	19 22			20 07			20 47	21 22		22 07			
	d		16 09		16 48	17 24				18 09		18 48	19 24			20 09			20 48	21 24		22 09			
Trefforest	d		16 12		16 51	17 27				18 12		18 51	19 27			20 12			20 51	21 27		22 12			
Trefforest Estate	d																								
Taffs Well 3	d		16 20		16 58	17 34				18 20		18 58	19 34			20 20			20 58	21 34		22 20			
Radyr 3	a		16 23		17 01	17 37				18 23		19 01	19 37			20 23			21 01	21 37		22 23			
	d		16 23		17 01	17 37				18 23		19 01	19 37			20 23			21 01	21 37		22 23			
Danescourt	d																								
Fairwater	d																								
Waun-gron Park	d																								
Ninian Park	d																								
Llandaf	d		16 26		17 04	17 40				18 26		19 04	19 40			20 26			21 04	21 40		22 26			
Cathays	d		16 31		17 09	17 45				18 31		19 09	19 45			20 31			21 09	21 45		22 31			
Rhymney 3	d							17 20						19 20											
Pontlottyn	d							17 23						19 23											
Tir-phil	d							17 28						19 28											
Brithdir	d							17 30						19 30											
Bargoed	a							17 34						19 34											
	d							17 35						19 35											
Gilfach Fargoed	d							17 38						19 38											
Pengam	d							17 40						19 40											
Hengoed	d							17 44						19 44											
Ystrad Mynach 3	d							17 47						19 47											
Llanbradach	d							17 51						19 51											
Energlyn & Churchill Park	d							17 55						19 55											
Aber	d							17 57						19 57											
Caerphilly 3	d							18 00						20 00											
Lisvane & Thornhill	d							18 04						20 04											
Llanishen	d							18 06						20 06											
Heath High Level	d							18 09						20 09											
Coryton	d																								
Whitchurch (Cardiff)	d																								
Rhiwbina	d																								
Birchgrove	d																								
Ty Glas	d																								
Heath Low Level	d																								
Cardiff Queen Street 3	a		16 34		17 14	17 49		18 14		18 34		19 14	19 49	20 14		20 34			21 14	21 49		22 34			
	d		16 36		17 16	17 51		18 16		18 36		19 16	19 51	20 16		20 36			21 16	21 51		22 36			
Cardiff Central 7	a		16 39		17 18	17 57		18 18		18 39		19 18	19 54	20 18		20 39			21 18	21 56		22 42			
	d	16 31	16 41	16 55	17 25			18 25	18 31	18 41	18 55	19 25	19 55	20 25	20 31	20 41		20 55	21 25		22 25				
Grangetown	d	16 35	16 45	16 59	17 29			18 29	18 35	18 45	18 59	19 29	19 59	20 29	20 35	20 45		20 59	21 29		22 29				
Dingle Road	d	16 41							18 41						20 41										
Penarth	a	16 46							18 46						20 46										
Cogan	d		16 48	17 03	17 33			18 33		18 48	19 03	19 33	20 03	20 33		20 48		21 03	21 33		22 33				
Eastbrook	d		16 51	17 05	17 35			18 35		18 51	19 05	19 35	20 05	20 35		20 51		21 05	21 35		22 35				
Dinas Powys	d		16 53	17 07	17 37			18 37		18 53	19 07	19 37	20 07	20 37		20 53		21 07	21 37		22 37				
Cadoxton	d		16 57	17 12	17 42			18 42		18 57	19 12	19 42	20 12	20 42		20 57		21 12	21 42		22 42				
Barry Docks	d		17 00	17 14	17 44			18 44		19 00	19 14	19 44	20 14	20 44		21 00		21 14	21 44		22 44				
Barry 3	d		17 05	17 19	17 49			18 49		19 05	19 19	19 49	20 19	20 49		21 05		21 19	21 49		22 49				
Barry Island	a			17 25	17 55			18 55			19 25	19 55	20 25	20 55				21 25	21 55		22 55				
Rhoose Cardiff Int Airport ✈	d		17 12							19 12						21 12									
Llantwit Major	d		17 22							19 22						21 22									
Bridgend	a		17 40							19 40						21 40									

When events are being held at the Millenium Stadium, services are subject to alteration. Please check times before travelling.

For connections to Cardiff Bay please refer to Table 130A

Table 130R

Mondays to Fridays

9 December to 16 May

Bridgend, Barry Island, Barry, Penarth and Cardiff - Coryton, Rhymney, Pontypridd, Merthyr, Aberdare and Treherbert

Network Diagram - see first Page of Table 130

Miles	Miles	Miles	Miles	Miles			AW		AW	AW	AW	AW	AW	AW	AW	AW	AW	AW	AW	AW	AW	AW	AW	AW
—	—	0	—	—	**Bridgend**	d										05 42								
—	—	9¼	—	—	Llantwit Major	d										05 56								
—	—	15¾	—	—	Rhoose Cardiff Int Airport ✈	d										06 06								
0	—	—	—	—	**Barry Island**	d			05 15				05 50						06 25					
0¾	—	19	—	—	**Barry** [3]	d			05 20				05 55			06 15			06 30					
2	—	—	—	—	Barry Docks	d			05 23				05 58			06 18			06 33					
2¾	—	—	—	—	Cadoxton	d			05 26				06 01			06 21			06 36					
4¾	—	—	—	—	Dinas Powys	d			05 30				06 05			06 25			06 40					
5¾	—	—	—	—	Eastbrook	d			05 33				06 08			06 28			06 43					
6½	—	—	—	—	Cogan	d			05 35				06 10			06 30			06 45					
—	0	—	—	—	**Penarth**	d						06 02					06 32						07 02	
—	0¼	—	—	—	Dingle Road	d						06 04					06 34						07 04	
8¼	2¾	—	—	—	Grangetown	d			05 39			06 08	06 14			06 34	06 38		06 49				07 08	
9¼	3¾	—	—	—	**Cardiff Central** [7]	a			05 44			06 13	06 19			06 39	06 44		06 54				07 14	
—	—	—	—	—		d	05 26		05 46	05 56	06 11	06 15	06 21	06 26	06 36	06 41	06 46	06 51	06 56	07 06	07 06	07 11	07 16	07 21
9¾	4¼	1	—	—	**Cardiff Queen Street** [3]	a	05 29		05 49	05 59	06 14	06 19	06 24	06 29	06 39	06 44	06 49	06 54	06 59	07 09		07 14	07 19	07 24
—	—	—	—	—		d	05 30		05 50	06 00	06 15	06 20	06 25	06 30	06 40	06 45	06 50	06 55	07 00	07 10		07 15	07 20	07 25
—	—	3½	—	—	Heath Low Level	d							06 30					07 00						07 30
—	4½	—	—	—	Ty Glas	d							06 33					07 03						07 33
—	—	4¾	—	—	Birchgrove	d							06 34					07 04						07 34
—	—	5¼	—	—	Rhiwbina	d							06 36					07 06						07 36
—	—	5½	—	—	Whitchurch (Cardiff)	d							06 38					07 08						07 38
—	—	6	0	—	**Coryton**	a							06 43					07 13						07 43
—	6¾	—	—	—	Heath High Level	d			05 55			06 25					06 55						07 25	
—	7¾	—	—	—	Llanishen	d			05 58			06 28					06 58						07 28	
—	8¾	—	—	—	Lisvane & Thornhill	d			06 00			06 30					07 00						07 30	
—	11¼	—	—	—	Caerphilly [3]	d			06a08			06 36					07 06						07 36	
—	12	—	—	—	Aber	d						06 38					07 08						07 38	
—	—	—	—	—	Energlyn & Churchill Park	d																	07 40	
—	14	—	—	—	Llanbradach	d						06 42					07 12						07 44	
—	16¾	—	—	—	Ystrad Mynach [3]	d						06 47					07 17						07 49	
—	17¾	—	—	—	Hengoed	d						06 50					07 20						07 52	
—	19½	—	—	—	Pengam	d						06 53					07 23						07 55	
—	20½	—	—	—	Gilfach Fargoed	d																		
—	21	—	—	—	Bargoed	a						07 01					07 31						08 04	
—	—	—	—	—		d																		
—	22½	—	—	—	Brithdir	d																		
—	23½	—	—	—	Tir-phil	d																		
—	26	—	—	—	Pontlottyn	d																		
—	27	—	—	—	**Rhymney** [3]	a																		
10½	—	—	—	—	Cathays	d	05 33			06 03	06 18			06 33	06 43	06 48			07 03	07 13		07 18		
13	—	—	—	—	Llandaf	d	05 37			06 07	06 22			06 37	06 47	06 52			07 07	07 17		07 22		
—	—	—	7	—	Ninian Park	d															07 10			
—	—	—	8½	—	Waun-gron Park	d															07 13			
—	—	—	9	—	Fairwater	d															07 15			
—	—	—	9½	—	Danescourt	d															07 17			
14	—	—	10¼	—	Radyr [3]	a	05 40			06 10	06 24			06 40	06 50	06 54			07 10	07 20	07 24	07 25		
—	—	—	—	—		d	05 40			06 10	06 24			06 40	06 50	06 55			07 10	07 20		07 25		
16	—	—	—	—	Taffs Well [3]	d	05 44			06 14	06 28			06 44	06 54	06 59			07 14	07 24		07 29		
18¼	—	—	—	—	Trefforest Estate	d	05 48			06 18				06 48					07 18					
20¾	—	—	—	—	Trefforest	d	05 52			06 22	06 35			06 52	07 01	07 06			07 22	07 31		07 36		
21¾	—	0	—	0	**Pontypridd** [3]	a	05 55			06 25	06 38			06 55	07 04	07 09			07 25	07 34		07 39		
—	—	—	—	—		d	05 57	06 11		06 27	06 41			06 57	07 06	07 11			07 27	07 36		07 41		
—	—	3¼	—	3¼	Abercynon	d	06 04	06 19		06 34	06 49			07 04		07 19			07 34			07 49		
—	—	—	—	6	Penrhiwceiber	d		06 24			06 54					07 24						07 54		
—	—	—	—	7¼	Mountain Ash	a		06 28			06 58					07 28						07 58		
—	—	—	—	—		d		06 33			07 03					07 33						08 03		
—	—	—	—	8¼	Fernhill	d		06 35			07 05					07 35						08 05		
—	—	—	—	9½	Cwmbach	d		06 39			07 09					07 39						08 09		
—	—	—	—	11	**Aberdare** [3]	a		06 46			07 16					07 46						08 16		
—	—	4¾	—	—	Quakers Yard	d	06 09			06 39				07 09					07 39					
—	—	7	—	—	Merthyr Vale	a	06 14			06 44				07 14					07 44					
—	—	—	—	—		d	06 17			06 47				07 17					07 47					
—	—	8¾	—	—	Troed Y Rhiw	d	06 20			06 50				07 20					07 50					
—	—	10	—	—	Pentre-bach	d	06 23			06 53				07 23					07 53					
—	—	11½	—	—	**Merthyr Tydfil**	a	06 31			07 01				07 31					08 01					
23½	—	—	—	—	Trehafod	d									07 11					07 41				
24¾	—	—	—	—	Porth	a									07 14					07 44				
—	—	—	—	—		d									07 15					07 45				
26¼	—	—	—	—	Dinas Rhondda	d									07 19					07 49				
26¾	—	—	—	—	Tonypandy	d									07 21					07 51				
27¾	—	—	—	—	Llwynypia	d									07 23					07 53				
29	—	—	—	—	Ystrad Rhondda	a									07 26					07 56				
—	—	—	—	—		d									07 29					07 59				
29½	—	—	—	—	Ton Pentre	d									07 31					08 01				
30¾	—	—	—	—	Treorchy	d									07 34					08 04				
31¾	—	—	—	—	Ynyswen	d									07 37					08 07				
32¼	—	—	—	—	**Treherbert**	a									07 43					08 13				

When events are being held at the Millenium Stadium, services are subject to alteration. Please check times before travelling.

For connections to Cardiff Bay please refer to Table 130A

Table 130R

Mondays to Fridays

9 December to 16 May

Bridgend, Barry Island, Barry, Penarth and Cardiff - Coryton, Rhymney, Pontypridd, Merthyr, Aberdare and Treherbert

Network Diagram - see first Page of Table 130

		AW	AW	AW	AW	AW	AW	AW	AW	AW	AW	AW	AW	AW	AW	AW	AW	AW	AW	AW	AW	AW
Bridgend	d					06 42														07 42		
Llantwit Major	d					06 56														07 56		
Rhoose Cardiff Int Airport ✈	d					07 06														08 06		
Barry Island	d	06 55							07 25				07 40			07 55						
Barry 3	d	07 00				07 15			07 30				07 45			08 00				08 15		
Barry Docks	d	07 03				07 18			07 33				07 48			08 03				08 18		
Cadoxton	d	07 06				07 21			07 36				07 51			08 06				08 21		
Dinas Powys	d	07 10				07 25			07 40				07 55			08 10				08 25		
Eastbrook	d	07 13				07 28			07 43				07 58			08 13				08 28		
Cogan	d	07 15				07 30			07 45				08 00			08 15				08 30		
Penarth	d		07 17				07 32			07 47				08 02			08 17				08 32	
Dingle Road	d		07 19				07 34			07 49				08 04			08 19				08 34	
Grangetown	d	07 19	07 23			07 34	07 38		07 49	07 53			08 04	08 08		08 19	08 23			08 34	08 38	
Cardiff Central 7	a	07 24	07 29			07 39	07 44		07 54	07 59			08 09	08 14		08 24	08 29			08 39	08 44	
	d	07 26	07 31	07 36	07 36	07 41	07 46	07 51	07 56	08 01	08 06	08 06	08 11	08 16	08 21	08 26	08 31	08 36	08 36	08 41	08 46	08 51
Cardiff Queen Street 3	a	07 29	07 34	07 39		07 44	07 49	07 54	07 59	08 04	08 09		08 14	08 19	08 24	08 29	08 34	08 39		08 44	08 49	08 54
	d	07 30	07 35	07 40		07 45	07 50	07 55	08 00	08 05	08 10		08 15	08 20	08 25	08 30	08 35	08 40		08 45	08 50	08 55
Heath Low Level	d							08 00							08 30							09 00
Ty Glas	d							08 03							08 33							09 03
Birchgrove	d							08 04							08 34							09 04
Rhiwbina	d							08 06							08 36							09 06
Whitchurch (Cardiff)	d							08 08							08 38							09 08
Coryton	a							08 13							08 43							09 13
Heath High Level	d		07 40				07 55			08 10				08 25			08 40				08 55	
Llanishen	d		07 43				07 58			08 13				08 28			08 43				08 58	
Lisvane & Thornhill	d		07 45				08 00			08 15				08 30			08 45				09 00	
Caerphilly 3	d		07 51				08 06			08 21				08 36			08 51				09 06	
Aber	d		07 53				08 08			08 23				08 38			08 53				09 08	
Energlyn & Churchill Park	d									08 25				08 40								
Llanbradach	d		07 57				08 12			08 29				08 44			08 57				09 12	
Ystrad Mynach 3	d		08 02				08 17			08 34				08 49			09 02				09 17	
Hengoed	d		08 05				08 20			08 37				08 52			09 05				09 20	
Pengam	d		08 08				08 23			08 40				08 55			09 08				09 23	
Gilfach Fargoed	d									08 43												
Bargoed	a		08 13				08 31			08 50				09 00			09 16				09 31	
	d		08 14											09 01								
Brithdir	d		08 18											09 05								
Tir-phil	d		08 21											09 08								
Pontlottyn	d		08 25											09 12								
Rhymney 3	a		08 31											09 18								
Cathays	d	07 33		07 43		07 48			08 03		08 13		08 18			08 33		08 43		08 48		
Llandaf	d	07 37		07 47		07 52			08 07		08 17		08 22			08 37		08 47		08 52		
Ninian Park	d				07 40							08 10							08 40			
Waun-gron Park	d				07 43							08 13							08 43			
Fairwater	d				07 45							08 15							08 45			
Danescourt	d				07 47							08 17							08 47			
Radyr 3	a	07 40		07 50	07 54	07 55			08 10		08 20	08 24	08 25			08 40		08 50	08 54	08 55		
	d	07 40		07 50		07 55			08 10		08 20		08 25			08 40		08 50		08 55		
Taffs Well 3	d	07 44		07 54		07 59			08 14		08 24		08 29			08 44		08 54		08 59		
Trefforest Estate	d	07 48							08 18							08 48						
Trefforest	d	07 52		08 01		08 06			08 22		08 31		08 36			08 52		09 01		09 06		
Pontypridd 3	a	07 55		08 04		08 09			08 25		08 34		08 39			08 55		09 04		09 09		
	d	07 57		08 06		08 11			08 27		08 36		08 41			08 57		09 06		09 11		
Abercynon	d	08 04				08 19			08 34				08 49			09 04				09 19		
Penrhiwceiber	d					08 24							08 54							09 24		
Mountain Ash	a					08 28							08 58							09 28		
	d					08 33							09 03							09 33		
Fernhill	d					08 35							09 05							09 35		
Cwmbach	d					08 39							09 09							09 39		
Aberdare 3	a					08 46							09 16							09 46		
Quakers Yard	d	08 09							08 39							09 09						
Merthyr Vale	a	08 14							08 44							09 14						
	d	08 17							08 47							09 17						
Troed Y Rhiw	d	08 20							08 50							09 20						
Pentre-bach	d	08 23							08 53							09 23						
Merthyr Tydfil	a	08 31							09 01							09 31						
Trehafod	d			08 11							08 41							09 11				
Porth	a			08 14							08 44							09 14				
	d			08 15							08 45							09 15				
Dinas Rhondda	d			08 19							08 49							09 19				
Tonypandy	d			08 21							08 51							09 21				
Llwynypia	d			08 23							08 53							09 23				
Ystrad Rhondda	a			08 26							08 56							09 26				
	d			08 29							08 59							09 29				
Ton Pentre	d			08 31							09 01							09 31				
Treorchy	d			08 34							09 04							09 34				
Ynyswen	d			08 37							09 07							09 37				
Treherbert	a			08 43							09 13							09 43				

When events are being held at the Millenium Stadium, services are subject to alteration. Please check times before travelling.

For connections to Cardiff Bay please refer to Table 130A

Table 130R

Mondays to Fridays

9 December to 16 May

Bridgend, Barry Island, Barry, Penarth and Cardiff - Coryton, Rhymney, Pontypridd, Merthyr, Aberdare and Treherbert

Network Diagram - see first Page of Table 130

		AW	AW	AW	AW	AW	AW	AW	AW	AW	AW	AW	AW	AW	AW	AW	AW	AW	AW	AW	AW	AW	AW
Bridgend	d												08 42										
Llantwit Major	d												08 56										
Rhoose Cardiff Int Airport ✈	d												09 06										
Barry Island	d	08 25				08 40			08 55							09 25					09 40		
Barry 3	d	08 30				08 45			09 00				09 15			09 30					09 45		
Barry Docks	d	08 33				08 48			09 03				09 18			09 33					09 48		
Cadoxton	d	08 36				08 51			09 06				09 21			09 36					09 51		
Dinas Powys	d	08 40				08 55			09 10				09 25			09 40					09 55		
Eastbrook	d	08 43				08 58			09 13				09 28			09 43					09 58		
Cogan	d	08 45				09 00			09 15				09 30			09 45					10 00		
Penarth	d		08 47							09 17				09 32				09 47				10 02	
Dingle Road	d		08 49							09 19				09 34				09 49				10 04	
Grangetown	d	08 49	08 53			09 04			09 19	09 23			09 34	09 38		09 49		09 53			10 04	10 08	
Cardiff Central 7	a	08 54	08 59			09 09			09 24	09 29			09 39	09 44		09 54		09 59			10 09	10 14	
	d	08 56	09 01	09 06	09 06	09 11	09 16	09 21	09 26	09 31	09 36	09 36	09 41	09 46	09 51	09 56		10 01	10 06	10 06	10 11	10 16	10 21
Cardiff Queen Street 3	a	08 59	09 04	09 09		09 14	09 19	09 24	09 29	09 34	09 39		09 44	09 49	09 54	09 59		10 04	10 09		10 14	10 19	10 24
	d	09 00	09 05	09 10		09 15	09 20	09 25	09 30	09 35	09 40		09 45	09 50	09 55	10 00		10 05	10 10		10 15	10 20	10 25
Heath Low Level	d							09 30							10 00								10 30
Ty Glas	d							09 33							10 03								10 33
Birchgrove	d							09 34							10 04								10 34
Rhiwbina	d							09 36							10 06								10 36
Whitchurch (Cardiff)	d							09 38							10 08								10 38
Coryton	a							09 43							10 13								10 43
Heath High Level	d		09 10				09 25			09 40				09 55				10 10				10 25	
Llanishen	d		09 13				09 28			09 43				09 58				10 13				10 28	
Lisvane & Thornhill	d		09 15				09 30			09 45				10 00				10 15				10 30	
Caerphilly 3	d		09 21				09 36			09 51				10 06				10 21				10 36	
Aber	d		09 23				09 38			09 53				10 08				10 23				10 38	
Energlyn & Churchill Park	d		09 25				09 40											10 25				10 40	
Llanbradach	d		09 29				09 44			09 57				10 12				10 29				10 44	
Ystrad Mynach 3	d		09 34				09 49			10 02				10 17				10 34				10 49	
Hengoed	d		09 37				09 52			10 05				10 20				10 37				10 52	
Pengam	d		09 40				09 55			10 08				10 23				10 40				10 55	
Gilfach Fargoed	d		09 43															10 43					
Bargoed	a		09 50				10 00			10 16				10 31				10 50				11 00	
	d						10 01															11 01	
Brithdir	d						10 05															11 05	
Tir-phil	d						10 08															11 08	
Pontlottyn	d						10 12															11 12	
Rhymney 3	a						10 18															11 18	
Cathays	d	09 03		09 13		09 18			09 33		09 43		09 48			10 03			10 13		10 18		
Llandaf	d	09 07		09 17		09 22			09 37		09 47		09 52			10 07			10 17		10 22		
Ninian Park	d				09 10							09 40								10 10			
Waun-gron Park	d				09 13							09 43								10 13			
Fairwater	d				09 15							09 45								10 15			
Danescourt	d				09 17							09 47								10 17			
Radyr 3	a	09 10		09 20	09 24	09 25			09 40		09 50	09 54	09 55			10 10			10 20	10 24	10 25		
	d	09 10		09 20		09 25			09 40		09 50		09 55			10 10			10 20		10 25		
Taffs Well 3	d	09 14		09 24		09 29			09 44		09 54		09 59			10 14			10 24		10 29		
Trefforest Estate	d	09 18							09 48														
Trefforest	d	09 22		09 31		09 36			09 52		10 01		10 06			10 22			10 31		10 36		
Pontypridd 3	a	09 25		09 34		09 39			09 55		10 04		10 09			10 30			10 34		10 39		
	d	09 27		09 36		09 41			09 57		10 06		10 11				10 35		10 36		10 41		
Abercynon	d	09 34				09 49			10 04				10 19				10 41				10 49		
Penrhiwceiber	d					09 54							10 24								10 54		
Mountain Ash	a					09 58							10 28								10 58		
	d					10 03							10 33								11 03		
Fernhill	d					10 05							10 35								11 05		
Cwmbach	d					10 09							10 39								11 09		
Aberdare 3	a					10 16							10 46								11 16		
Quakers Yard	d	09 39							10 09								10 45						
Merthyr Vale	a	09 44							10 14								10 50						
	d	09 47							10 17								10 52						
Troed Y Rhiw	d	09 50							10 20								10 55						
Pentre-bach	d	09 53							10 23								10 58						
Merthyr Tydfil	a	10 01							10 31								11 06						
Trehafod	d			09 41							10 11								10 41				
Porth	a			09 44							10 14								10 44				
	d			09 45							10 15								10 45				
Dinas Rhondda	d			09 49							10 19								10 49				
Tonypandy	d			09 51							10 21								10 51				
Llwynypia	d			09 53							10 23								10 53				
Ystrad Rhondda	a			09 56							10 26								10 56				
	d			09 59							10 29								10 59				
Ton Pentre	d			10 01							10 31								11 01				
Treorchy	d			10 04							10 34								11 04				
Ynyswen	d			10 07							10 37								11 07				
Treherbert	a			10 13							10 43								11 13				

When events are being held at the Millenium Stadium, services are subject to alteration. Please check times before travelling.

For connections to Cardiff Bay please refer to Table 130A

Table 130R

Mondays to Fridays

9 December to 16 May

Bridgend, Barry Island, Barry, Penarth and Cardiff - Coryton, Rhymney, Pontypridd, Merthyr, Aberdare and Treherbert

Network Diagram - see first Page of Table 130

Station		AW	AW		AW	AW	AW	AW	AW	AW	AW	AW	AW		AW	AW	AW	AW	AW	AW	AW	AW	AW		AW
Bridgend	d						09 45																10 45		
Llantwit Major	d						09 58																10 58		
Rhoose Cardiff Int Airport ✈	d						10 08																11 08		
Barry Island	d	09 55									10 25					10 40			10 55						
Barry 3	d	10 00					10 16				10 30					10 45			11 00				11 16		
Barry Docks	d	10 03					10 19				10 33					10 48			11 03				11 19		
Cadoxton	d	10 06					10 22				10 36					10 51			11 06				11 22		
Dinas Powys	d	10 10					10 26				10 40					10 55			11 10				11 26		
Eastbrook	d	10 13					10 28				10 43					10 58			11 13				11 28		
Cogan	d	10 15					10 30				10 45					11 00			11 15				11 30		
Penarth	d		10 17					10 32					10 47				11 02			11 17					11 32
Dingle Road	d		10 19					10 34					10 49				11 04			11 19					11 34
Grangetown	d	10 19	10 23				10 34	10 38			10 49		10 53			11 04	11 08		11 19	11 23			11 34		11 38
Cardiff Central 7	a	10 24	10 29				10 42	10 44			10 54		10 59			11 09	11 14		11 24	11 29			11 39		11 44
	d	10 26	10 31		10 36	10 36		10 46	10 51	10 54	10 56		11 01		11 06	11 11	11 16	11 21	11 26	11 31	11 36	11 36	11 41		11 46
Cardiff Queen Street 3	a	10 29	10 34		10 39			10 49	10 54		10 59		11 04			11 14	11 19	11 24	11 29	11 34	11 39		11 44		11 49
	d	10 30	10 35		10 40			10 50	10 55		11 00		11 05			11 15	11 20	11 25	11 30	11 35	11 40		11 45		11 50
Heath Low Level	d								11 00									11 30							
Ty Glas	d								11 03									11 33							
Birchgrove	d								11 04									11 34							
Rhiwbina	d								11 06									11 36							
Whitchurch (Cardiff)	d								11 08									11 38							
Coryton	a								11 13									11 43							
Heath High Level	d		10 40					10 55					11 10				11 25			11 40					11 55
Llanishen	d		10 43					10 58					11 13				11 28			11 43					11 58
Lisvane & Thornhill	d		10 45					11 00					11 15				11 30			11 45					12 00
Caerphilly 3	d		10 51					11 06					11 21				11 36			11 51					12 06
Aber	d		10 53					11 08					11 23				11 38			11 53					12 08
Energlyn & Churchill Park	d												11 25				11 40								
Llanbradach	d		10 57					11 12					11 29				11 44			11 57					12 12
Ystrad Mynach 3	d		11 02					11 17					11 34				11 49			12 02					12 17
Hengoed	d		11 05					11 20					11 37				11 52			12 05					12 20
Pengam	d		11 08					11 23					11 40				11 55			12 08					12 23
Gilfach Fargoed	d												11 43												
Bargoed	a		11 16					11 31					11 50				12 00			12 16					12 31
	d																12 01								
Brithdir	d																12 05								
Tir-phil	d																12 08								
Pontlottyn	d																12 12								
Rhymney 3	a																12 18								
Cathays	d	10 33			10 43						11 03					11 18			11 33		11 43		11 48		
Llandaf	d	10 37			10 47						11 07					11 22			11 37		11 47		11 52		
Ninian Park	d					10 40									11 10							11 40			
Waun-gron Park	d					10 43									11 13							11 43			
Fairwater	d					10 45									11 15							11 45			
Danescourt	d					10 47						←			11 17							11 47			
Radyr 3	a	10 40			10 50	10 54				11 02	11 10	11 02			11 24	11 25			11 40		11 50	11 54	11 55		
	d	10 40			10 50					11 20	11 10	11 20				11 25			11 40		11 50		11 55		
Taffs Well 3	d	10 44			10 54					↪	11 14	11 24				11 29			11 44		11 54		11 59		
Trefforest Estate	d	10 48									11 18								11 48						
Trefforest	d	10 52			11 01						11 22	11 31				11 36			11 52		12 01		12 06		
Pontypridd 3	a	10 55			11 04						11 25	11 34				11 39			11 55		12 04		12 09		
	d	10 57			11 06						11 27	11 36				11 41			11 57		12 06		12 11		
Abercynon	d	11 04									11 34					11 49			12 04				12 19		
Penrhiwceiber	d															11 54							12 24		
Mountain Ash	a															11 58							12 28		
	d															12 03							12 33		
Fernhill	d															12 05							12 35		
Cwmbach	d															12 09							12 39		
Aberdare 3	a															12 16							12 46		
Quakers Yard	d	11 09									11 39								12 09						
Merthyr Vale	a	11 14									11 44								12 14						
	d	11 17									11 47								12 17						
Troed Y Rhiw	d	11 20									11 50								12 20						
Pentre-bach	d	11 23									11 53								12 23						
Merthyr Tydfil	a	11 31									12 01								12 31						
Trehafod	d				11 11							11 41									12 11				
Porth	a				11 14							11 44									12 14				
	d				11 15							11 45									12 15				
Dinas Rhondda	d				11 19							11 49									12 19				
Tonypandy	d				11 21							11 51									12 21				
Llwynypia	d				11 23							11 53									12 23				
Ystrad Rhondda	a				11 26							11 56									12 26				
	d				11 29							11 59									12 29				
Ton Pentre	d				11 31							12 01									12 31				
Treorchy	d				11 34							12 04									12 34				
Ynyswen	d				11 37							12 07									12 37				
Treherbert	a				11 43							12 13									12 43				

When events are being held at the Millenium Stadium, services are subject to alteration. Please check times before travelling.

For connections to Cardiff Bay please refer to Table 130A

Table 130R

Mondays to Fridays

9 December to 16 May

Bridgend, Barry Island, Barry, Penarth and Cardiff - Coryton, Rhymney, Pontypridd, Merthyr, Aberdare and Treherbert

Network Diagram - see first Page of Table 130

		AW	AW	AW	AW	AW	AW	AW	AW		AW	AW	AW	AW	AW	AW	AW	AW	AW		AW	AW	AW	AW	AW
Bridgend	d																11 42								
Llantwit Major	d																11 56								
Rhoose Cardiff Int Airport ✈	d																12 06								
Barry Island	d		11 25				11 40				11 55								12 25					12 40	
Barry 3	d		11 30				11 45				12 00						12 15		12 30					12 45	
Barry Docks	d		11 33				11 48				12 03						12 18		12 33					12 48	
Cadoxton	d		11 36				11 51				12 06						12 21		12 36					12 51	
Dinas Powys	d		11 40				11 55				12 10						12 25		12 40					12 55	
Eastbrook	d		11 43				11 58				12 13						12 28		12 43					12 58	
Cogan	d		11 45				12 00				12 15						12 30		12 45					13 00	
Penarth	d			11 47				12 02				12 17				12 32					12 47				13 02
Dingle Road	d			11 49				12 04				12 19				12 34					12 49				13 04
Grangetown	d		11 49	11 53			12 04	12 08			12 19	12 23				12 38	12 34		12 49		12 53			13 04	13 08
Cardiff Central 7	a		11 54	11 58			12 09	12 14			12 24	12 29				12 44	12 46		12 54		12 59			13 09	13 14
	d	11 51	11 56	12 01	12 06	12 06	12 11	12 16	12 21		12 26	12 31	12 36	12 36	12 41	12 46		12 51	12 56		13 01	13 06	13 06	13 11	13 16
Cardiff Queen Street 3	a	11 54	11 59	12 04	12 09		12 14	12 19	12 24		12 29	12 34	12 39		12 44	12 49		12 54	12 59		13 04	13 09		13 14	13 19
	d	11 55	12 00	12 05	12 10		12 15	12 20	12 25		12 30	12 35	12 40		12 45	12 50		12 55	13 00		13 05	13 10		13 15	13 20
Heath Low Level	d	12 00							12 30									13 00							
Ty Glas	d	12 03							12 33									13 03							
Birchgrove	d	12 04							12 34									13 04							
Rhiwbina	d	12 06							12 36									13 06							
Whitchurch (Cardiff)	d	12 08							12 38									13 08							
Coryton	a	12 13							12 43									13 13							
Heath High Level	d			12 10				12 25				12 40				12 55					13 10				13 25
Llanishen	d			12 13				12 28				12 43				12 58					13 13				13 28
Lisvane & Thornhill	d			12 15				12 30				12 45				13 00					13 15				13 30
Caerphilly 3	d			12 21				12 36				12 51				13 06					13 21				13 36
Aber	d			12 23				12 38				12 53				13 08					13 23				13 38
Energlyn & Churchill Park	d			12 25				12 40													13 25				13 40
Llanbradach	d			12 29				12 44				12 57				13 12					13 29				13 44
Ystrad Mynach 3	d			12 34				12 49				13 02				13 17					13 34				13 49
Hengoed	d			12 37				12 52				13 05				13 20					13 37				13 52
Pengam	d			12 40				12 55				13 08				13 23					13 40				13 55
Gilfach Fargoed	d			12 43																	13 43				
Bargoed	a			12 50				13 00				13 16				13 31					13 50				14 00
	d							13 01																	14 01
Brithdir	d							13 05																	14 05
Tir-phil	d							13 08																	14 08
Pontlottyn	d							13 12																	14 12
Rhymney 3	a							13 18																	14 18
Cathays	d		12 03		12 13		12 18				12 33		12 43		12 48				13 03			13 13		13 18	
Llandaf	d		12 07		12 17		12 22				12 37		12 47		12 52				13 07			13 17		13 22	
Ninian Park	d					12 10								12 40									13 10		
Waun-gron Park	d					12 13								12 43									13 13		
Fairwater	d					12 15								12 45									13 15		
Danescourt	d					12 17								12 47									13 17		
Radyr 3	a		12 10		12 20	12 24	12 25				12 40		12 50	12 54	12 55				13 10			13 20	13 24	13 25	
	d		12 10		12 20		12 25				12 40		12 50		12 55				13 10			13 20		13 25	
Taffs Well 3	d		12 14		12 24		12 29				12 44		12 54		12 59				13 14			13 24		13 29	
Trefforest Estate	d		12 18								12 48								13 18						
Trefforest	d		12 22		12 31		12 36				12 52		13 01		13 06				13 22			13 31		13 36	
Pontypridd 3	a		12 25		12 34		12 42				12 55		13 04		13 09				13 25			13 34		13 39	
	d		12 27		12 36						12 57		13 06		13 11				13 27			13 36		13 41	
Abercynon	d		12 34								13 04				13 19				13 34					13 49	
Penrhiwceiber	d														13 24									13 54	
Mountain Ash	a														13 28									13 58	
	d														13 33									14 03	
Fernhill	d														13 35									14 05	
Cwmbach	d														13 39									14 09	
Aberdare 3	a														13 46									14 16	
Quakers Yard	d		12 39								13 09								13 39						
Merthyr Vale	a		12 44								13 14								13 44						
	d		12 47								13 17								13 47						
Troed Y Rhiw	d		12 50								13 20								13 50						
Pentre-bach	d		12 53								13 23								13 53						
Merthyr Tydfil	a		13 01								13 31								14 01						
Trehafod	d				12 41								13 11									13 41			
Porth	a				12 44								13 14									13 44			
	d				12 45								13 15									13 45			
Dinas Rhondda	d				12 49								13 19									13 49			
Tonypandy	d				12 51								13 21									13 51			
Llwynypia	d				12 53								13 23									13 53			
Ystrad Rhondda	a				12 56								13 26									13 56			
	d				12 59								13 29									13 59			
Ton Pentre	d				13 01								13 31									14 01			
Treorchy	d				13 04								13 34									14 04			
Ynyswen	d				13 07								13 37									14 07			
Treherbert	a				13 13								13 43									14 13			

When events are being held at the Millenium Stadium, services are subject to alteration. Please check times before travelling.

For connections to Cardiff Bay please refer to Table 130A

Table 130R

Mondays to Fridays

9 December to 16 May

Bridgend, Barry Island, Barry, Penarth and Cardiff - Coryton, Rhymney, Pontypridd, Merthyr, Aberdare and Treherbert

Network Diagram - see first Page of Table 130

		AW	AW	AW	AW	AW	AW	AW	AW	AW	AW	AW	AW	AW	AW	AW	AW	AW	AW	AW	AW	AW	AW
Bridgend	d						12 42														13 42		
Llantwit Major	d						12 56														13 56		
Rhoose Cardiff Int Airport ✈	d						13 06														14 06		
Barry Island	d		12 55							13 25				13 40			13 55						
Barry 3	d		13 00				13 15			13 30				13 45			14 00				14 15		
Barry Docks	d		13 03				13 18			13 33				13 48			14 03				14 18		
Cadoxton	d		13 06				13 21			13 36				13 51			14 06				14 21		
Dinas Powys	d		13 10				13 25			13 40				13 55			14 10				14 25		
Eastbrook	d		13 13				13 28			13 43				13 58			14 13				14 28		
Cogan	d		13 15				13 30			13 45				14 00			14 15				14 30		
Penarth	d			13 17				13 32			13 47				14 02			14 17				14 32	
Dingle Road	d			13 19				13 34			13 49				14 04			14 19				14 34	
Grangetown	d		13 19	13 23			13 34	13 38		13 49	13 53			14 04	14 08		14 19	14 23			14 34	14 38	
Cardiff Central 7	a		13 24	13 29			13 39	13 44		13 54	13 59			14 09	14 14		14 24	14 29			14 39	14 44	
	d	13 21	13 26	13 31	13 36	13 36	13 41	13 46	13 51	13 56	14 01	14 06	14 06	14 11	14 16	14 21	14 26	14 31	14 36	14 36	14 41	14 46	14 51
Cardiff Queen Street 3	a	13 24	13 29	13 34	13 39		13 44	13 49	13 54	13 59	14 04	14 09		14 14	14 19	14 24	14 29	14 34	14 39		14 44	14 49	14 54
	d	13 25	13 30	13 35	13 40		13 45	13 50	13 55	14 00	14 05	14 10		14 15	14 20	14 25	14 30	14 35	14 40		14 45	14 50	14 55
Heath Low Level	d	13 30							14 00							14 30							15 00
Ty Glas	d	13 33							14 03							14 33							15 03
Birchgrove	d	13 34							14 04							14 34							15 04
Rhiwbina	d	13 36							14 06							14 36							15 06
Whitchurch (Cardiff)	d	13 38							14 08							14 38							15 08
Coryton	a	13 43							14 13							14 43							15 13
Heath High Level	d			13 40				13 55			14 10				14 25			14 40				14 55	
Llanishen	d			13 43				13 58			14 13				14 28			14 43				14 58	
Lisvane & Thornhill	d			13 45				14 00			14 15				14 30			14 45				15 00	
Caerphilly 3	d			13 51				14 06			14 21				14 36			14 51				15 06	
Aber	d			13 53				14 08			14 23				14 38			14 53				15 08	
Energlyn & Churchill Park	d										14 25				14 40								
Llanbradach	d			13 57				14 12			14 29				14 44			14 57				15 12	
Ystrad Mynach 3	d			14 02				14 17			14 34				14 49			15 02				15 17	
Hengoed	d			14 05				14 20			14 37				14 52			15 05				15 20	
Pengam	d			14 08				14 23			14 40				14 55			15 08				15 23	
Gilfach Fargoed	d										14 43												
Bargoed	a			14 16				14 31			14 50				15 00			15 16				15 31	
	d														15 01								
Brithdir	d														15 05								
Tir-phil	d														15 08								
Pontlottyn	d														15 12								
Rhymney 3	a														15 18								
Cathays	d		13 33		13 43		13 48			14 03		14 13		14 18			14 33		14 43		14 48		
Llandaf	d		13 37		13 47		13 52			14 07		14 17		14 22			14 37		14 47		14 52		
Ninian Park	d					13 40							14 10							14 40			
Waun-gron Park	d					13 43							14 13							14 43			
Fairwater	d					13 45							14 15							14 45			
Danescourt	d					13 47							14 17							14 47			
Radyr 3	a		13 40		13 50	13 54	13 55			14 10		14 20	14 24	14 25			14 40		14 50	14 54	14 55		
	d		13 40		13 50		13 55			14 10		14 20		14 25			14 40		14 50		14 55		
Taffs Well 3	d		13 44		13 54		13 59			14 14		14 24		14 29			14 44		14 54		14 59		
Trefforest Estate	d		13 48							14 18							14 48						
Trefforest	d		13 52		14 01		14 06			14 22		14 31		14 36			14 52		15 01		15 06		
Pontypridd 3	a		13 55		14 04		14 09			14 25		14 34		14 39			14 55		15 04		15 09		
	d		13 57		14 06		14 11			14 27		14 36		14 41			14 57		15 06		15 11		
Abercynon	d		14 04				14 19			14 34				14 49			15 04				15 19		
Penrhiwceiber	d						14 24							14 54							15 24		
Mountain Ash	a						14 28							14 58							15 28		
	d						14 33							15 03							15 33		
Fernhill	d						14 35							15 05							15 35		
Cwmbach	d						14 39							15 09							15 39		
Aberdare 3	a						14 46							15 16							15 46		
Quakers Yard	d		14 09							14 39							15 09						
Merthyr Vale	a		14 14							14 44							15 14						
	d		14 17							14 47							15 17						
Troed Y Rhiw	d		14 20							14 50							15 20						
Pentre-bach	d		14 23							14 53							15 23						
Merthyr Tydfil	a		14 31							15 01							15 31						
Trehafod	d				14 11							14 41							15 11				
Porth	a				14 14							14 44							15 14				
	d				14 15							14 45							15 15				
Dinas Rhondda	d				14 19							14 49							15 19				
Tonypandy	d				14 21							14 51							15 21				
Llwynypia	d				14 23							14 53							15 23				
Ystrad Rhondda	a				14 26							14 56							15 26				
	d				14 29							14 59							15 29				
Ton Pentre	d				14 31							15 01							15 31				
Treorchy	d				14 34							15 04							15 34				
Ynyswen	d				14 37							15 07							15 37				
Treherbert	a				14 43							15 13							15 43				

When events are being held at the Millenium Stadium, services are subject to alteration. Please check times before travelling.

For connections to Cardiff Bay please refer to Table 130A

Table 130R

Mondays to Fridays

9 December to 16 May

Bridgend, Barry Island, Barry, Penarth and Cardiff - Coryton, Rhymney, Pontypridd, Merthyr, Aberdare and Treherbert

Network Diagram - see first Page of Table 130

		AW	AW	AW	AW	AW	AW	AW	AW	AW	AW	AW	AW	AW	AW	AW	AW	AW	AW	AW	AW	AW
Bridgend	d													14 42								
Llantwit Major	d													14 56								
Rhoose Cardiff Int Airport ✈	d													15 06								
Barry Island	d		14 25				14 40			14 55							15 25				15 40	
Barry [3]	d		14 30				14 45			15 00				15 15			15 30				15 45	
Barry Docks	d		14 33				14 48			15 04				15 18			15 33				15 48	
Cadoxton	d		14 36				14 51			15 07				15 21			15 36				15 51	
Dinas Powys	d		14 40				14 55			15 11				15 25			15 40				15 55	
Eastbrook	d		14 43				14 58			15 13				15 28			15 43				15 58	
Cogan	d		14 45				15 00			15 15				15 30			15 45				16 00	
Penarth	d				14 47			15 02			15 17				15 32			15 47				16 02
Dingle Road	d				14 49			15 04			15 19				15 34			15 49				16 04
Grangetown	d		14 49		14 53		15 04	15 08		15 19	15 23			15 34	15 38		15 49	15 53			16 04	16 08
Cardiff Central [7]	a		14 54		14 59		15 10	15 14		15 24	15 29			15 39	15 44		15 54	15 59			16 09	16 14
	d	14 51	14 56		15 01	15 06	15 11	15 16	15 21	15 26	15 31	15 36	15 36	15 41	15 46	15 51	15 56	16 01	16 06	16 06	16 11	16 16
Cardiff Queen Street [3]	a		14 59		15 04		15 14	15 19	15 24	15 29	15 34	15 39		15 44	15 49	15 54	15 59	16 04	16 09		16 14	16 19
	d		15 00		15 05		15 15	15 20	15 25	15 30	15 35	15 40		15 45	15 50	15 55	16 00	16 05	16 10		16 15	16 20
Heath Low Level	d								15 30							16 00						
Ty Glas	d								15 33							16 03						
Birchgrove	d								15 34							16 04						
Rhiwbina	d								15 36							16 06						
Whitchurch (Cardiff)	d								15 38							16 08						
Coryton	a								15 43							16 13						
Heath High Level	d				15 10			15 25			15 40				15 55			16 10				16 25
Llanishen	d				15 13			15 28			15 43				15 58			16 13				16 28
Lisvane & Thornhill	d				15 15			15 30			15 45				16 00			16 15				16 30
Caerphilly [3]	d				15 21			15 36			15 51				16 06			16 21				16 36
Aber	d				15 23			15 38			15 53				16 08			16 23				16 38
Energlyn & Churchill Park	d				15 25			15 40										16 25				16 40
Llanbradach	d				15 29			15 44			15 57				16 12			16 29				16 44
Ystrad Mynach [3]	d				15 34			15 49			16 02				16 17			16 34				16 49
Hengoed	d				15 37			15 52			16 05				16 20			16 37				16 52
Pengam	d				15 40			15 55			16 08				16 23			16 40				16 55
Gilfach Fargoed	d				15 43													16 43				
Bargoed	a				15 50			16 00			16 16				16 31			16 50				17 00
	d							16 01														17 01
Brithdir	d							16 05														17 05
Tir-phil	d							16 08														17 08
Pontlottyn	d							16 12														17 12
Rhymney [3]	a							16 18														17 18
Cathays	d		15 03				15 18			15 33		15 43		15 48			16 03		16 13		16 18	
Llandaf	d		15 07				15 22			15 37		15 47		15 52			16 07		16 17		16 22	
Ninian Park	d					15 10							15 40							16 10		
Waun-gron Park	d					15 13							15 43							16 13		
Fairwater	d					15 15							15 45							16 15		
Danescourt	d			←		15 17							15 47							16 17		
Radyr [3]	a	15 08	15 10	15 08		15 24	15 25			15 40		15 50	15 54	15 55			16 10		16 20	16 24	16 25	
	d	15 20	15 10	15 20			15 25			15 40		15 50		15 55			16 10		16 20		16 25	
Taffs Well [3]	d	→	15 14	15 24			15 29			15 44		15 54		15 59			16 14		16 24		16 29	
Trefforest Estate	d		15 18							15 48							16 18					
Trefforest	d		15 22	15 31			15 36			15 52		16 01		16 06			16 22		16 31		16 36	
Pontypridd [3]	a		15 25	15 34			15 39			15 55		16 04		16 09			16 25		16 34		16 39	
	d		15 27	15 36			15 41			15 57		16 06		16 11			16 27		16 36		16 41	
Abercynon	d		15 34				15 49			16 04				16 19			16 34				16 49	
Penrhiwceiber	d						15 54							16 24							16 54	
Mountain Ash	a						15 58							16 28							16 58	
	d						16 03							16 33							17 03	
Fernhill	d						16 05							16 35							17 05	
Cwmbach	d						16 09							16 39							17 09	
Aberdare [3]	a						16 16							16 46							17 16	
Quakers Yard	d		15 39							16 09							16 39					
Merthyr Vale	a		15 44							16 14							16 44					
	d		15 47							16 17							16 47					
Troed Y Rhiw	d		15 50							16 20							16 50					
Pentre-bach	d		15 53							16 23							16 53					
Merthyr Tydfil	a		16 01							16 31							17 01					
Trehafod	d			15 41								16 11							16 41			
Porth	a			15 44								16 14							16 44			
	d			15 45								16 15							16 45			
Dinas Rhondda	d			15 49								16 19							16 49			
Tonypandy	d			15 51								16 21							16 51			
Llwynypia	d			15 53								16 23							16 53			
Ystrad Rhondda	a			15 56								16 26							16 56			
	d			15 59								16 29							16 59			
Ton Pentre	d			16 01								16 31							17 01			
Treorchy	d			16 04								16 34							17 04			
Ynyswen	d			16 07								16 37							17 07			
Treherbert	a			16 13								16 43							17 13			

When events are being held at the Millenium Stadium, services are subject to alteration. Please check times before travelling.

For connections to Cardiff Bay please refer to Table 130A

Table 130R

Mondays to Fridays

9 December to 16 May

Bridgend, Barry Island, Barry, Penarth and Cardiff - Coryton, Rhymney, Pontypridd, Merthyr, Aberdare and Treherbert

Network Diagram - see first Page of Table 130

Station		AW	AW	AW	AW	AW	AW	AW	AW	AW	AW	AW	AW	AW	AW	AW	AW	AW	AW	AW	AW	AW	AW
Bridgend	d						15 42														16 42		
Llantwit Major	d						15 56														16 56		
Rhoose Cardiff Int Airport ✈	d						16 06														17 06		
Barry Island	d		15 55							16 25				16 40			16 55						
Barry 3	d		16 00				16 15			16 30				16 45			17 00				17 15		
Barry Docks	d		16 03				16 18			16 33				16 48			17 03				17 18		
Cadoxton	d		16 06				16 21			16 36				16 51			17 06				17 21		
Dinas Powys	d		16 10				16 25			16 40				16 55			17 10				17 25		
Eastbrook	d		16 13				16 28			16 43				16 58			17 13				17 28		
Cogan	d		16 15				16 30			16 45				17 00			17 15				17 30		
Penarth	d			16 17				16 32							17 02			17 17				17 32	
Dingle Road	d			16 19				16 34							17 04			17 19				17 34	
Grangetown	d		16 19	16 23			16 34	16 38		16 49				17 04	17 08		17 19	17 23			17 34	17 38	
Cardiff Central 7	a		16 24	16 29			16 39	16 44		16 54				17 09	17 14		17 24	17 29			17 39	17 44	
	d	16 21	16 26	16 31	16 36	16 36	16 41	16 46	16 51	16 56	17 01	17 06	17 06	17 11	17 16	17 21	17 26	17 31	17 36	17 36	17 41	17 46	17 51
Cardiff Queen Street 3	a	16 24	16 29	16 34	16 39		16 44	16 49	16 54	16 59	17 04	17 09		17 14	17 19	17 24	17 29	17 34	17 39		17 44	17 49	17 54
	d	16 25	16 30	16 35	16 40		16 45	16 50	16 55	17 00	17 05	17 10		17 15	17 20	17 25	17 30	17 35	17 40		17 45	17 50	17 55
Heath Low Level	d	16 30							17 00							17 30							18 00
Ty Glas	d	16 33							17 03							17 33							18 03
Birchgrove	d	16 34							17 04							17 34							18 04
Rhiwbina	d	16 36							17 06							17 36							18 06
Whitchurch (Cardiff)	d	16 38							17 08							17 38							18 08
Coryton	a	16 43							17 13							17 43							18 13
Heath High Level	d			16 40				16 55			17 10				17 25			17 40				17 55	
Llanishen	d			16 43				16 58			17 13				17 28			17 43				17 59	
Lisvane & Thornhill	d			16 45				17 00			17 15				17 30			17 45				18 02	
Caerphilly 3	d			16 51				17 06			17 21				17 36			17 51				18 07	
Aber	d			16 53				17 08			17 23				17 38			17 53				18 10	
Energlyn & Churchill Park	d										17 26				17 40			17 55				18 13	
Llanbradach	d			16 57				17 12			17 29				17 44			17 59				18 17	
Ystrad Mynach 3	d			17 02				17 17			17 35				17 49			18 04				18 22	
Hengoed	d			17 05				17 20			17 37				17 52			18 07				18 25	
Pengam	d			17 08				17 23			17 41				17 55			18 10				18 29	
Gilfach Fargoed	d										17 44							18 13				18 33	
Bargoed	a			17 16				17 31			17 47				18 03			18 16				18 36	
	d										17 49							18 18				18 44	
Brithdir	d										17 52							18 22				18 48	
Tir-phil	d										17 55							18 25				18 51	
Pontlottyn	d										18 00							18 29				18 55	
Rhymney 3	a										18 06							18 35				19 01	
Cathays	d		16 33		16 43		16 48			17 03		17 13		17 18			17 33		17 43		17 48		
Llandaf	d		16 37		16 47		16 52			17 07		17 17		17 22			17 37		17 47		17 52		
Ninian Park	d					16 40							17 10							17 40			
Waun-gron Park	d					16 43							17 13							17 43			
Fairwater	d					16 45							17 15							17 45			
Danescourt	d					16 47							17 17							17 47			
Radyr 3	a		16 40		16 50	16 54	16 55			17 10		17 20	17 24	17 25			17 40		17 50	17 54	17 55		
	d		16 40		16 50		16 55			17 10		17 20		17 25			17 40		17 50		17 55		
Taffs Well 3	d		16 44		16 54		16 59			17 14		17 24		17 29			17 44		17 54		17 59		
Trefforest Estate	d		16 48							17 18							17 48						
Trefforest	d		16 52		17 01		17 06			17 22		17 31		17 36			17 52		18 01		18 06		
Pontypridd 3	a		16 55		17 04		17 09			17 25		17 34		17 39			17 55		18 04		18 09		
	d		16 57		17 06		17 11			17 27		17 36		17 41			17 57		18 06		18 11		
Abercynon	d		17 04				17 19			17 34				17 49			18 04				18 19		
Penrhiwceiber	d						17 24							17 54							18 24		
Mountain Ash	a						17 28							17 58							18 28		
	d						17 33							18 03							18 33		
Fernhill	d						17 35							18 05							18 35		
Cwmbach	d						17 39							18 09							18 39		
Aberdare 3	a						17 46							18 16							18 46		
Quakers Yard	d		17 09							17 39							18 09						
Merthyr Vale	a		17 14							17 44							18 14						
	d		17 17							17 47							18 17						
Troed Y Rhiw	d		17 20							17 50							18 20						
Pentre-bach	d		17 23							17 53							18 23						
Merthyr Tydfil	a		17 31							18 01							18 31						
Trehafod	d				17 11							17 41							18 11				
Porth	a				17 14							17 44							18 14				
	d				17 15							17 45							18 15				
Dinas Rhondda	d				17 19							17 49							18 19				
Tonypandy	d				17 21							17 51							18 21				
Llwynypia	d				17 23							17 53							18 23				
Ystrad Rhondda	a				17 26							17 56							18 26				
	d				17 29							17 59							18 29				
Ton Pentre	d				17 31							18 01							18 31				
Treorchy	d				17 34							18 04							18 34				
Ynyswen	d				17 37							18 07							18 37				
Treherbert	a				17 43							18 13							18 43				

When events are being held at the Millenium Stadium, services are subject to alteration. Please check times before travelling.

For connections to Cardiff Bay please refer to Table 130A

Table 130R

Mondays to Fridays

9 December to 16 May

Bridgend, Barry Island, Barry, Penarth and Cardiff - Coryton, Rhymney, Pontypridd, Merthyr, Aberdare and Treherbert

Network Diagram - see first Page of Table 130

		AW	AW		AW	AW	AW	AW	AW	AW	AW		AW		AW	AW	AW	AW	AW		AW	AW	AW		AW
Bridgend	d														17 42										
Llantwit Major	d														17 56										
Rhoose Cardiff Int Airport ✈	d														18 06										
Barry Island	d	17 25					17 40			17 55								18 25			18 40	18 55			
Barry ■	d	17 30					17 45			18 00					18 15			18 30			18 45	19 00			
Barry Docks	d	17 33					17 48			18 03					18 18			18 33			18 48	19 03			
Cadoxton	d	17 36					17 51			18 06					18 21			18 36			18 51	19 06			
Dinas Powys	d	17 40					17 55			18 10					18 25			18 40			18 55	19 10			
Eastbrook	d	17 43					17 58			18 13					18 28			18 43			18 58	19 13			
Cogan	d	17 45					18 00			18 15					18 30			18 45			19 00	19 15			
Penarth	d		17 47					18 02			18 17					18 32			18 47				19 17		
Dingle Road	d		17 49					18 04			18 19					18 34			18 49				19 19		
Grangetown	d	17 49	17 53				18 04	18 08		18 19	18 23				18 34	18 38		18 49	18 53		19 04	19 19	19 23		
Cardiff Central ■	a	17 54	17 59				18 09	18 14		18 24	18 29				18 39	18 47		18 55	18 59		19 09	19 24	19 29		
	d	17 56	18 01		18 06	18 06	18 11	18 16	18 21	18 26	18 31	18 36	18 36		18 41		18 51		19 01	19 06	19 11	19 26	19 31		19 36
Cardiff Queen Street ■	a	17 59	18 04		18 09		18 14	18 19	18 24	18 29	18 34	18 38			18 44		18 54		19 04	19 09	19 14	19 29	19 34		
	d	18 00	18 05		18 10		18 15	18 20	18 25	18 30	18 35	18 40			18 50		18 55		19 05	19 10	19 15	19 30	19 35		
Heath Low Level	d								18 30								19 00								
Ty Glas	d								18 33								19 03								
Birchgrove	d								18 34								19 04								
Rhiwbina	d								18 36								19 06								
Whitchurch (Cardiff)	d								18 38								19 08								
Coryton	a								18 43								19 13								
Heath High Level	d		18 10					18 25			18 40								19 10				19 40		
Llanishen	d		18 13					18 28			18 43								19 13				19 43		
Lisvane & Thornhill	d		18 15					18 30			18 45								19 15				19 45		
Caerphilly ■	d		18 21					18 36			18 51								19a23				19 51		
Aber	d		18 23					18 38			18 53												19 53		
Energlyn & Churchill Park	d										18 56												19 56		
Llanbradach	d		18 27					18 42			18 59												19 59		
Ystrad Mynach ■	d		18 32					18a51			19 04												20 04		
Hengoed	d		18 35								19 07												20 07		
Pengam	d		18 38								19 10												20 10		
Gilfach Fargoed	d		18 41								19 13												20 13		
Bargoed	a		18 48								19 16												20 17		
	d										19 18												20 18		
Brithdir	d										19 22												20 22		
Tir-phil	d										19 25												20 25		
Pontlottyn	d										19 29												20 29		
Rhymney ■	a										19 36												20 35		
Cathays	d	18 03			18 13		18 18			18 33		18 43			18 52					19 13	19 18	19 33			
Llandaf	d	18 07			18 17		18 22			18 37		18 47			18 56					19 17	19 22	19 37			
Ninian Park	d					18 10							18 40												19 40
Waun-gron Park	d					18 13							18 43												19 43
Fairwater	d					18 15							18 45												19 45
Danescourt	d					18 17							18 47												19 47
Radyr ■	a	18 10			18 20	18 24	18 25			18 40		18 50	18 54		18 58					19 20	19 25	19 40			19 54
	d	18 10			18 20		18 25			18 40		18 50			18 58					19 20	19 25	19 40			
Taffs Well ■	d	18 14			18 24		18 29			18 44		18 54			19 03					19 24	19 29	19 44			
Trefforest Estate	d	18 18								18 48												19 48			
Trefforest	d	18 22			18 31		18 36			18 52		19 01			19 10					19 31	19 36	19 52			
Pontypridd ■	a	18 25			18 34		18 42			18 55		19 04			19 13					19 34	19 39	19 55			
	d	18 27			18 36					18 57		19 06			19 14					19 36	19 41	19 57			
Abercynon	d	18 34								19 04					19 21						19 49	20 04			
Penrhiwceiber	d														19 26						19 54				
Mountain Ash	a														19 30						19 56				
	d														19 33						20 03				
Fernhill	d														19 35						20 05				
Cwmbach	d														19 39						20 09				
Aberdare ■	a														19 46						20 16				
Quakers Yard	d	18 39								19 09												20 08			
Merthyr Vale	a	18 44								19 14												20 13			
	d	18 47								19 17												20 15			
Troed Y Rhiw	d	18 50								19 20												20 19			
Pentre-bach	d	18 53								19 23												20 22			
Merthyr Tydfil	a	19 01								19 31												20 30			
Trehafod	d				18 41							19 11								19 41					
Porth	a				18 44							19 14								19 44					
	d				18 45							19 15								19 45					
Dinas Rhondda	d				18 49							19 19								19 49					
Tonypandy	d				18 51							19 21								19 51					
Llwynypia	d				18 53							19 23								19 53					
Ystrad Rhondda	a				18 56							19 26								19 56					
	d				18 59							19 29								19 59					
Ton Pentre	d				19 01							19 31								20 01					
Treorchy	d				19 04							19 34								20 04					
Ynyswen	d				19 07							19 37								20 07					
Treherbert	a				19 13							19 43								20 13					

When events are being held at the Millenium Stadium, services are subject to alteration. Please check times before travelling.

For connections to Cardiff Bay please refer to Table 130A

Table 130R

Mondays to Fridays

9 December to 16 May

Bridgend, Barry Island, Barry, Penarth and Cardiff - Coryton, Rhymney, Pontypridd, Merthyr, Aberdare and Treherbert

Network Diagram - see first Page of Table 130

		AW	AW	AW	AW	AW	AW	AW	AW	AW	AW	AW	AW	AW	AW	AW	AW	AW	AW	AW	AW	AW	AW
Bridgend	d	18 42							19 42								20 42						21 42
Llantwit Major	d	18 56							19 56								20 56						21 56
Rhoose Cardiff Int Airport ✈	d	19 06							20 06								21 06						22 06
Barry Island	d			19 25		19 55							20 55								21 55		
Barry [3]	d	19 15		19 30		20 00			20 15				21 00				21 15				22 00		22 15
Barry Docks	d	19 18		19 33		20 03			20 18				21 03				21 18				22 03		22 18
Cadoxton	d	19 21		19 36		20 06			20 21				21 06				21 21				22 06		22 21
Dinas Powys	d	19 25		19 40		20 10			20 25				21 10				21 25				22 10		22 25
Eastbrook	d	19 28		19 43		20 13			20 28				21 13				21 28				22 13		22 28
Cogan	d	19 30		19 45		20 15			20 30				21 15				21 30				22 15		22 30
Penarth	d				19 47		20 20				20 47					21 20		21 47				22 20	
Dingle Road	d				19 49		20 22				20 49					21 22		21 49				22 22	
Grangetown	d	19 34		19 49	19 53	20 19	20 26		20 34		20 53		21 19			21 26	21 34	21 53			22 19	22 26	22 34
Cardiff Central [7]	a	19 39		19 56	19 59	20 24	20 31		20 39		21 00		21 24			21 38	21 39	21 59			22 24	22 33	22 39
	d	19 41	19 51	20 01	20 06	20 26	20 31	20 36	20 41	20 51	21 01	21 06	21 27	21 31	21 36		21 41	22 01	22 06	22 21	22 26	22 35	22 41
Cardiff Queen Street [3]	a	19 44	19 54	20 04	20 09	20 29	20 34		20 44	20 54	21 04	21 09	21 30	21 34			21 44	22 04	22 09	22 24	22 29	22 38	22 44
	d	19 45	19 55	20 05	20 10	20 30	20 35		20 45	20 55	21 05	21 10	21 31	21 35			21 45	22 05	22 10	22 25	22 30	22 39	22 45
Heath Low Level	d		20 00							21 00										22 30			
Ty Glas	d		20 03							21 03										22 33			
Birchgrove	d		20 04							21 04										22 34			
Rhiwbina	d		20 06							21 06										22 36			
Whitchurch (Cardiff)	d		20 08							21 08										22 38			
Coryton	a		20 13							21 13										22 43			
Heath High Level	d			20 10			20 40				21 10			21 40				22 10				22 44	
Llanishen	d			20 13			20 43				21 13			21 43				22 13				22 47	
Lisvane & Thornhill	d			20 15			20 45				21 15			21 45				22 15				22 49	
Caerphilly [3]	d			20a27			20 51				21 21			21 51				22a23				22 55	
Aber	d						20 53				21 23			21 53								22 57	
Energlyn & Churchill Park	d						20 56							21 56								22 59	
Llanbradach	d						20 59				21 27			21 59								23 03	
Ystrad Mynach [3]	d						21 04				21a36			22 04								23 08	
Hengoed	d						21 07							22 07								23 11	
Pengam	d						21 10							22 10								23 14	
Gilfach Fargoed	d						21 13							22 13								23 17	
Bargoed	a						21 17							22 17								23 21	
	d						21 18							22 18								23 22	
Brithdir	d						21 22							22 22								23 26	
Tir-phil	d						21 25							22 25								23 29	
Pontlottyn	d						21 29							22 29								23 33	
Rhymney [3]	a						21 36							22 36								23 39	
Cathays	d	19 48			20 13	20 33			20 48			21 13	21 34				21 48		22 13		22 33		22 48
Llandaf	d	19 52			20 17	20 37			20 52			21 17	21 38				21 52		22 17		22 37		22 52
Ninian Park	d							20 40							21 40								
Waun-gron Park	d							20 43							21 43								
Fairwater	d							20 45							21 45								
Danescourt	d							20 47							21 47								
Radyr [3]	a	19 55			20 20	20 40		20 54	20 55			21 20	21 41		21 54		21 55		22 20		22 40		22 55
	d	19 55			20 20	20 40			20 55			21 20	21 41				21 55		22 20		22 40		22 55
Taffs Well [3]	d	19 59			20 24	20 44			20 59			21 24	21 45				21 59		22 24		22 44		22 59
Trefforest Estate	d					20 48							21 49								22 48		
Trefforest	d	20 06			20 31	20 52			21 06			21 31	21 53				22 06		22 31		22 52		23 06
Pontypridd [3]	a	20 09			20 34	20 55			21 09			21 34	21 56				22 09		22 34		22 55		23 09
	d	20 11			20 36	20 57			21 11			21 36	21 58				22 11		22 36		22 57		23 11
Abercynon	d	20 21				21 04			21 19				22 05				22 19				23 04		23 19
Penrhiwceiber	d	20 26							21 24								22 24						23 24
Mountain Ash	a	20 30							21 28								22 28						23 28
	d	20 33							21 29								22 29						23 29
Fernhill	d	20 35							21 31								22 31						23 31
Cwmbach	d	20 39							21 35								22 35						23 35
Aberdare [3]	a	20 46							21 42								22 42						23 42
Quakers Yard	d					21 08							22 09								23 08		
Merthyr Vale	a					21 13							22 14								23 13		
	d					21 15							22 16								23 15		
Troed Y Rhiw	d					21 19							22 20								23 19		
Pentre-bach	d					21 22							22 23								23 22		
Merthyr Tydfil	a					21 30							22 31								23 30		
Trehafod	d				20 41							21 41							22 41				
Porth	a				20 44							21 44							22 44				
	d				20 45							21 45							22 45				
Dinas Rhondda	d				20 49							21 49							22 49				
Tonypandy	d				20 51							21 51							22 51				
Llwynypia	d				20 53							21 53							22 53				
Ystrad Rhondda	a				20 56							21 56							22 56				
	d				20 59							21 59							22 59				
Ton Pentre	d				21 01							22 01							23 01				
Treorchy	d				21 04							22 04							23 04				
Ynyswen	d				21 07							22 07							23 07				
Treherbert	a				21 13							22 13							23 13				

When events are being held at the Millenium Stadium, services are subject to alteration. Please check times before travelling.

For connections to Cardiff Bay please refer to Table 130A

Table 130R

Mondays to Fridays

9 December to 16 May

Bridgend, Barry Island, Barry, Penarth and Cardiff - Coryton, Rhymney, Pontypridd, Merthyr, Aberdare and Treherbert

Network Diagram - see first Page of Table 130

		AW	AW	AW	AW		AW	AW
Bridgend	d							22 42
Llantwit Major	d							22 56
Rhoose Cardiff Int Airport ✈	d							23 06
Barry Island	d				22 44			
Barry ■	d				22 49			23 15
Barry Docks	d				22 52			23 18
Cadoxton	d				22 55			23 21
Dinas Powys	d				22 59			23 25
Eastbrook	d				23 02			23 28
Cogan	d				23 04			23 30
Penarth	d			22 48			23 26	
Dingle Road	d			22 50			23 28	
Grangetown	d			22 54	23 08		23 32	23 34
Cardiff Central ■	a			23 01	23 13		23 40	23 43
	d	22 46	22 55	23 16	23 26			
Cardiff Queen Street ■	a	22 49		23 19	23 29			
	d	22 50		23 20	23 30			
Heath Low Level	d							
Ty Glas	d							
Birchgrove	d							
Rhiwbina	d							
Whitchurch (Cardiff)	d							
Coryton	a							
Heath High Level	d			23 25				
Llanishen	d			23 28				
Lisvane & Thornhill	d			23 30				
Caerphilly ■	d			23 36				
Aber	d			23 38				
Energlyn & Churchill Park	d							
Llanbradach	d			23 42				
Ystrad Mynach ■	d			23a51				
Hengoed	d							
Pengam	d							
Gilfach Fargoed	d							
Bargoed	a							
	d							
Brithdir	d							
Tir-phil	d							
Pontlottyn	d							
Rhymney ■	a							
Cathays	d	22 53			23 33			
Llandaf	d	22 57			23 37			
Ninian Park	d		22 59					
Waun-gron Park	d		23 02					
Fairwater	d		23 04					
Danescourt	d		23 06					
Radyr ■	a	22 59	23 14		23 40			
	d	22 59			23 40			
Taffs Well ■	d	23 03			23 44			
Trefforest Estate	d							
Trefforest	d	23 10			23 52			
Pontypridd ■	a	23 14			23 58			
	d	23 15						
Abercynon	d							
Penrhiwceiber	d							
Mountain Ash	a							
	d							
Fernhill	d							
Cwmbach	d							
Aberdare ■	a							
Quakers Yard	d							
Merthyr Vale	a							
	d							
Troed Y Rhiw	d							
Pentre-bach	d							
Merthyr Tydfil	a							
Trehafod	d	23 20						
Porth	a	23 23						
	d	23 24						
Dinas Rhondda	d	23 28						
Tonypandy	d	23 30						
Llwynypia	d	23 32						
Ystrad Rhondda	a	23 35						
	d	23 38						
Ton Pentre	d	23 40						
Treorchy	d	23 43						
Ynyswen	d	23 46						
Treherbert	a	23 52						

When events are being held at the Millenium Stadium, services are subject to alteration. Please check times before travelling.

For connections to Cardiff Bay please refer to Table 130A

Table 130R

Saturdays

14 December to 28 December

Bridgend, Barry Island, Barry, Penarth and Cardiff - Coryton, Rhymney, Pontypridd, Merthyr, Aberdare and Treherbert

Network Diagram - see first Page of Table 130

		AW		AW	AW	AW	AW	AW	AW	AW	AW	AW	AW	AW	AW	AW	AW	AW	AW	AW	AW	AW	AW
Bridgend	d										05 42												
Llantwit Major	d										05 56												
Rhoose Cardiff Int Airport ✈	d										06 06												
Barry Island	d			05 15				05 50						06 25						06 55			
Barry 3	d			05 20				05 55			06 15			06 30						07 00			
Barry Docks	d			05 23				05 58			06 18			06 33						07 03			
Cadoxton	d			05 26				06 01			06 21			06 36						07 06			
Dinas Powys	d			05 30				06 05			06 25			06 40						07 10			
Eastbrook	d			05 33				06 08			06 28			06 43						07 13			
Cogan	d			05 35				06 10			06 30			06 45						07 15			
Penarth	d						06 02					06 32						07 02			07 17		
Dingle Road	d						06 04					06 34						07 04			07 19		
Grangetown	d			05 39			06 08	06 14			06 34	06 38		06 49				07 08		07 19	07 23		
Cardiff Central 7	a			05 44			06 13	06 19			06 39	06 44		06 54				07 14		07 24	07 29		
	d	05 26		05 46	05 56	06 11	06 15	06 21	06 26	06 36	06 41	06 46	06 51	06 56	07 06	07 06	07 11	07 16	07 21	07 26	07 31	07 36	07 36
Cardiff Queen Street 3	a	05 29		05 49	05 59	06 14	06 19	06 24	06 29	06 39	06 44	06 49	06 54	06 59	07 09		07 14	07 19	07 24	07 29	07 34	07 39	
	d	05 30		05 50	06 00	06 15	06 20	06 25	06 30	06 40	06 45	06 50	06 55	07 00	07 10		07 15	07 20	07 25	07 30	07 35	07 40	
Heath Low Level	d							06 30					07 00						07 30				
Ty Glas	d							06 33					07 03						07 33				
Birchgrove	d							06 34					07 04						07 34				
Rhiwbina	d							06 36					07 06						07 36				
Whitchurch (Cardiff)	d							06 38					07 08						07 38				
Coryton	a							06 43					07 13						07 43				
Heath High Level	d			05 55			06 25					06 55						07 25			07 40		
Llanishen	d			05 58			06 28					06 58						07 28			07 43		
Lisvane & Thornhill	d			06 00			06 30					07 00						07 30			07 45		
Caerphilly 3	d			06a08			06 36					07 06						07 36			07 51		
Aber	d						06 38					07 08						07 38			07 53		
Energlyn & Churchill Park	d																	07 40					
Llanbradach	d						06 42					07 12						07 44			07 57		
Ystrad Mynach 3	d						06 47					07 17						07 49			08 02		
Hengoed	d						06 50					07 20						07 52			08 05		
Pengam	d						06 53					07 23						07 55			08 08		
Gilfach Fargoed	d																						
Bargoed	a						07 01					07 31						08 04			08 13		
	d																				08 14		
Brithdir	d																				08 18		
Tir-phil	d																				08 21		
Pontlottyn	d																				08 25		
Rhymney 3	a																				08 31		
Cathays	d	05 33			06 03	06 18			06 33	06 43	06 48			07 03	07 13		07 18			07 33		07 43	
Llandaf	d	05 37			06 07	06 22			06 37	06 47	06 52			07 07	07 17		07 22			07 37		07 47	
Ninian Park	d															07 10							07 40
Waun-gron Park	d															07 13							07 43
Fairwater	d															07 15							07 45
Danescourt	d															07 17							07 47
Radyr 3	a	05 40			06 10	06 24			06 40	06 50	06 54			07 10	07 20	07 24	07 25			07 40		07 50	07 54
	d	05 40			06 10	06 24			06 40	06 50	06 55			07 10	07 20		07 25			07 40		07 50	
Taffs Well 3	d	05 44			06 14	06 28			06 44	06 54	06 59			07 14	07 24		07 29			07 44		07 54	
Trefforest Estate	d	05 48			06 18				06 48					07 18						07 48			
Trefforest	d	05 52			06 22	06 35			06 52	07 01	07 06			07 22	07 31		07 36			07 52		08 01	
Pontypridd 3	a	05 55			06 25	06 38			06 55	07 04	07 09			07 25	07 34		07 39			07 55		08 04	
	d	05 57	06 11		06 27	06 41			06 57	07 06	07 11			07 27	07 36		07 41			07 57		08 06	
Abercynon	d	06 04	06 19		06 34	06 49			07 04		07 19			07 34			07 49			08 04			
Penrhiwceiber	d		06 24			06 54					07 24						07 54						
Mountain Ash	a		06 28			06 58					07 28						07 58						
	d		06 33			07 03					07 33						08 03						
Fernhill	d		06 35			07 05					07 35						08 05						
Cwmbach	d		06 39			07 09					07 39						08 09						
Aberdare 3	a		06 46			07 16					07 46						08 16						
Quakers Yard	d	06 09			06 39				07 09					07 39						08 09			
Merthyr Vale	a	06 14			06 44				07 14					07 44						08 14			
	d	06 17			06 47				07 17					07 47						08 17			
Troed Y Rhiw	d	06 20			06 50				07 20					07 50						08 20			
Pentre-bach	d	06 23			06 53				07 23					07 53						08 23			
Merthyr Tydfil	a	06 31			07 01				07 31					08 01						08 31			
Trehafod	d									07 11					07 41							08 11	
Porth	a									07 14					07 44							08 14	
	d									07 15					07 45							08 15	
Dinas Rhondda	d									07 19					07 49							08 19	
Tonypandy	d									07 21					07 51							08 21	
Llwynypia	d									07 23					07 53							08 23	
Ystrad Rhondda	a									07 26					07 56							08 26	
	d									07 29					07 59							08 29	
Ton Pentre	d									07 31					08 01							08 31	
Treorchy	d									07 34					08 04							08 34	
Ynyswen	d									07 37					08 07							08 37	
Treherbert	a									07 43					08 13							08 43	

When events are being held at the Millenium Stadium, services are subject to alteration. Please check times before travelling.

For connections to Cardiff Bay please refer to Table 130A

Table 130R

Saturdays

14 December to 28 December

Bridgend, Barry Island, Barry, Penarth and Cardiff - Coryton, Rhymney, Pontypridd, Merthyr, Aberdare and Treherbert

Network Diagram - see first Page of Table 130

		AW	AW	AW	AW	AW	AW	AW	AW	AW	AW	AW	AW	AW	AW	AW	AW	AW	AW	AW	AW	AW	AW
Bridgend	d	06 42														07 42							
Llantwit Major	d	06 56														07 56							
Rhoose Cardiff Int Airport ✈	d	07 06														08 06							
Barry Island	d				07 25				07 40			07 55							08 25				08 40
Barry [3]	d	07 15			07 30				07 45			08 00				08 15			08 30				08 45
Barry Docks	d	07 18			07 33				07 48			08 03				08 18			08 33				08 48
Cadoxton	d	07 21			07 36				07 51			08 06				08 21			08 36				08 51
Dinas Powys	d	07 25			07 40				07 55			08 10				08 25			08 40				08 55
Eastbrook	d	07 28			07 43				07 58			08 13				08 28			08 43				08 58
Cogan	d	07 30			07 45				08 00			08 15				08 30			08 45				09 00
Penarth	d		07 32			07 47				08 02			08 17				08 32			08 47			
Dingle Road	d		07 34			07 49				08 04			08 19				08 34			08 49			
Grangetown	d	07 34	07 38		07 49	07 53			08 05	08 08		08 19	08 23			08 34	08 38		08 49	08 53			09 04
Cardiff Central [7]	a	07 39	07 44		07 54	07 59			08 09	08 14		08 24	08 29			08 39	08 44		08 54	08 59			09 09
	d	07 41	07 46	07 51	07 56	08 01	08 06	08 06	08 11	08 16	08 21	08 26	08 31	08 36	08 36	08 41	08 46	08 51	08 56	09 01	09 06	09 06	09 11
Cardiff Queen Street [3]	a	07 44	07 49	07 54	07 59	08 04	08 09		08 14	08 19	08 24	08 29	08 34	08 39		08 44	08 49	08 54	08 59	09 04	09 09		09 14
	d	07 45	07 50	07 55	08 00	08 05	08 10		08 15	08 20	08 25	08 30	08 35	08 40		08 45	08 50	08 55	09 00	09 05	09 10		09 15
Heath Low Level	d			08 00							08 30							09 00					
Ty Glas	d			08 03							08 33							09 03					
Birchgrove	d			08 04							08 34							09 04					
Rhiwbina	d			08 06							08 36							09 06					
Whitchurch (Cardiff)	d			08 08							08 38							09 08					
Coryton	a			08 13							08 43							09 13					
Heath High Level	d		07 55			08 10				08 25			08 40				08 55			09 10			
Llanishen	d		07 58			08 13				08 28			08 43				08 58			09 13			
Lisvane & Thornhill	d		08 00			08 15				08 30			08 45				09 00			09 15			
Caerphilly [3]	d		08 06			08 21				08 36			08 51				09 06			09 21			
Aber	d		08 08			08 23				08 38			08 53				09 08			09 23			
Energlyn & Churchill Park	d					08 25				08 40										09 25			
Llanbradach	d		08 12			08 29				08 44			08 57				09 12			09 29			
Ystrad Mynach [3]	d		08 17			08 34				08 49			09 02				09 17			09 34			
Hengoed	d		08 20			08 37				08 52			09 05				09 20			09 37			
Pengam	d		08 23			08 40				08 55			09 08				09 23			09 40			
Gilfach Fargoed	d					08 43														09 43			
Bargoed	a		08 31			08 50				09 00			09 16				09 31			09 50			
	d									09 01													
Brithdir	d									09 05													
Tir-phil	d									09 08													
Pontlottyn	d									09 12													
Rhymney [3]	a									09 18													
Cathays	d	07 48			08 03		08 13		08 18			08 33		08 43		08 48			09 03		09 13		09 18
Llandaf	d	07 52			08 07		08 17		08 22			08 37		08 47		08 52			09 07		09 17		09 22
Ninian Park	d							08 10							08 40							09 10	
Waun-gron Park	d							08 13							08 43							09 13	
Fairwater	d							08 15							08 45							09 15	
Danescourt	d							08 17							08 47							09 17	
Radyr [3]	a	07 55			08 10		08 20	08 24	08 25			08 40		08 50	08 54	08 55			09 10		09 20	09 24	09 25
	d	07 55			08 10		08 20		08 25			08 40		08 50		08 55			09 10		09 20		09 25
Taffs Well [3]	d	07 59			08 14		08 24		08 29			08 44		08 54		08 59			09 14		09 24		09 29
Trefforest Estate	d				08 18							08 48							09 18				
Trefforest	d	08 06			08 22		08 31		08 36			08 52		09 01		09 06			09 22		09 31		09 36
Pontypridd [3]	a	08 09			08 25		08 34		08 39			08 55		09 04		09 09			09 25		09 34		09 39
	d	08 11			08 27		08 36		08 41			08 57		09 06		09 11			09 27		09 36		09 41
Abercynon	d	08 19			08 34				08 49			09 04				09 19			09 34				09 49
Penrhiwceiber	d	08 24							08 54							09 24							09 54
Mountain Ash	a	08 28							08 58							09 28							09 58
	d	08 33							09 03							09 33							10 03
Fernhill	d	08 35							09 05							09 35							10 05
Cwmbach	d	08 39							09 09							09 39							10 09
Aberdare [3]	a	08 46							09 16							09 46							10 16
Quakers Yard	d				08 39							09 09							09 39				
Merthyr Vale	a				08 44							09 14							09 44				
	d				08 47							09 17							09 47				
Troed Y Rhiw	d				08 50							09 20							09 50				
Pentre-bach	d				08 53							09 23							09 53				
Merthyr Tydfil	a				09 01							09 31							10 01				
Trehafod	d						08 41							09 11							09 41		
Porth	a						08 44							09 14							09 44		
	d						08 45							09 15							09 45		
Dinas Rhondda	d						08 49							09 19							09 49		
Tonypandy	d						08 51							09 21							09 51		
Llwynypia	d						08 53							09 23							09 53		
Ystrad Rhondda	a						08 56							09 26							09 56		
	d						08 59							09 29							09 59		
Ton Pentre	d						09 01							09 31							10 01		
Treorchy	d						09 04							09 34							10 04		
Ynyswen	d						09 07							09 37							10 07		
Treherbert	a						09 13							09 43							10 13		

When events are being held at the Millenium Stadium, services are subject to alteration. Please check times before travelling.

For connections to Cardiff Bay please refer to Table 130A

Table 130R

Saturdays

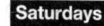

14 December to 28 December

Bridgend, Barry Island, Barry, Penarth and Cardiff - Coryton, Rhymney, Pontypridd, Merthyr, Aberdare and Treherbert

Network Diagram - see first Page of Table 130

		AW	AW	AW	AW	AW	AW	AW	AW	AW	AW	AW	AW	AW	AW	AW	AW	AW	AW	AW	AW	AW
Bridgend	d							08 42														
Llantwit Major	d							08 56														
Rhoose Cardiff Int Airport ✈	d							09 06														
Barry Island	d			08 55							09 25					09 40			09 55			
Barry 3	d			09 00				09 15			09 30					09 45			10 00			
Barry Docks	d			09 03				09 18			09 33					09 48			10 03			
Cadoxton	d			09 06				09 21			09 36					09 51			10 06			
Dinas Powys	d			09 10				09 25			09 40					09 55			10 10			
Eastbrook	d			09 13				09 28			09 43					09 58			10 13			
Cogan	d			09 15				09 30			09 45					10 00			10 15			
Penarth	d				09 17				09 32				09 47				10 02			10 17		
Dingle Road	d				09 19				09 34				09 49				10 04			10 19		
Grangetown	d			09 19	09 23			09 34	09 38		09 49		09 53			10 04	10 08		10 19	10 23		
Cardiff Central 7	a			09 24	09 29			09 39	09 44		09 54		09 59			10 09	10 14		10 24	10 29		
	d	09 16	09 21	09 26	09 31	09 36	09 36	09 41	09 46	09 51	09 56		10 01	10 06	10 06	10 11	10 16	10 21	10 26	10 31	10 36	10 36
Cardiff Queen Street 3	a	09 19	09 24	09 29	09 34	09 39		09 44	09 49	09 54	09 59		10 04	10 09		10 14	10 19	10 24	10 29	10 34	10 39	
	d	09 20	09 25	09 30	09 35	09 40		09 45	09 50	09 55	10 00		10 05	10 10		10 15	10 20	10 25	10 30	10 35	10 40	
Heath Low Level	d		09 30							10 00								10 30				
Ty Glas	d		09 33							10 03								10 33				
Birchgrove	d		09 34							10 04								10 34				
Rhiwbina	d		09 36							10 06								10 36				
Whitchurch (Cardiff)	d		09 38							10 08								10 38				
Coryton	a		09 43							10 13								10 43				
Heath High Level	d	09 25			09 40				09 55				10 10				10 25			10 40		
Llanishen	d	09 28			09 43				09 58				10 13				10 28			10 43		
Lisvane & Thornhill	d	09 30			09 45				10 00				10 15				10 30			10 45		
Caerphilly 3	d	09 36			09 51				10 06				10 21				10 36			10 51		
Aber	d	09 38			09 53				10 08				10 23				10 38			10 53		
Energlyn & Churchill Park	d	09 40											10 25				10 40					
Llanbradach	d	09 44			09 57				10 12				10 29				10 44			10 57		
Ystrad Mynach 3	d	09 49			10 02				10 17				10 34				10 49			11 02		
Hengoed	d	09 52			10 05				10 20				10 37				10 52			11 05		
Pengam	d	09 55			10 08				10 23				10 40				10 55			11 08		
Gilfach Fargoed	d												10 43									
Bargoed	a	10 00			10 16				10 31				10 50				11 00			11 16		
	d	10 01															11 01					
Brithdir	d	10 05															11 05					
Tir-phil	d	10 08															11 08					
Pontlottyn	d	10 12															11 12					
Rhymney 3	a	10 18															11 18					
Cathays	d			09 33		09 43		09 48			10 03			10 13		10 18			10 33		10 43	
Llandaf	d			09 37		09 47		09 52			10 07			10 17		10 22			10 37		10 47	
Ninian Park	d						09 40								10 10							10 40
Waun-gron Park	d						09 43								10 13							10 43
Fairwater	d						09 45								10 15							10 45
Danescourt	d						09 47								10 17							10 47
Radyr 3	a			09 40		09 50	09 54	09 55			10 10			10 20	10 24	10 25			10 40		10 50	10 54
	d			09 40		09 50		09 55			10 10			10 20		10 25			10 40		10 50	
Taffs Well 3	d			09 44		09 54		09 59			10 14			10 24		10 29			10 44		10 54	
Trefforest Estate	d			09 48															10 48			
Trefforest	d			09 52		10 01		10 06			10 22			10 31		10 36			10 52		11 01	
Pontypridd 3	a			09 55		10 04		10 09			10 30			10 34		10 39			10 55		11 04	
	d			09 57		10 06		10 11				10 35		10 36		10 41			10 57		11 06	
Abercynon	d			10 04				10 19				10 41				10 49			11 04			
Penrhiwceiber	d							10 24								10 54						
Mountain Ash	a							10 28								10 58						
	d							10 33								11 03						
Fernhill	d							10 35								11 05						
Cwmbach	d							10 39								11 09						
Aberdare 3	a							10 46								11 16						
Quakers Yard	d			10 09								10 45							11 09			
Merthyr Vale	a			10 14								10 50							11 14			
	d			10 17								10 52							11 17			
Troed Y Rhiw	d			10 20								10 55							11 20			
Pentre-bach	d			10 23								10 58							11 23			
Merthyr Tydfil	a			10 31								11 06							11 31			
Trehafod	d					10 11								10 41							11 11	
Porth	a					10 14								10 44							11 14	
	d					10 15								10 45							11 15	
Dinas Rhondda	d					10 19								10 49							11 19	
Tonypandy	d					10 21								10 51							11 21	
Llwynypia	d					10 23								10 53							11 23	
Ystrad Rhondda	a					10 26								10 56							11 26	
	d					10 29								10 59							11 29	
Ton Pentre	d					10 31								11 01							11 31	
Treorchy	d					10 34								11 04							11 34	
Ynyswen	d					10 37								11 07							11 37	
Treherbert	a					10 43								11 13							11 43	

When events are being held at the Millenium Stadium, services are subject to alteration. Please check times before travelling.

For connections to Cardiff Bay please refer to Table 130A

Table 130R

Saturdays

14 December to 28 December

Bridgend, Barry Island, Barry, Penarth and Cardiff - Coryton, Rhymney, Pontypridd, Merthyr, Aberdare and Treherbert

Network Diagram - see first Page of Table 130

		AW	AW	AW	AW	AW	AW	AW		AW	AW	AW	AW	AW	AW	AW	AW	AW		AW	AW	AW	AW	AW	AW
Bridgend	d	09 42																10 42							
Llantwit Major	d	09 56																10 56							
Rhoose Cardiff Int Airport ✈	d	10 06																11 06							
Barry Island	d					10 25					10 40			10 55								11 25			
Barry 3	d	10 15				10 30					10 45			11 00				11 15				11 30			
Barry Docks	d	10 18				10 33					10 48			11 03				11 18				11 33			
Cadoxton	d	10 21				10 36					10 51			11 06				11 21				11 36			
Dinas Powys	d	10 25				10 40					10 55			11 10				11 25				11 40			
Eastbrook	d	10 28				10 43					10 58			11 13				11 28				11 43			
Cogan	d	10 30				10 45					11 00			11 15				11 30				11 45			
Penarth	d		10 32					10 47				11 02			11 17					11 32			11 47		
Dingle Road	d		10 34					10 49				11 04			11 19					11 34			11 49		
Grangetown	d	10 34	10 38			10 49		10 53			11 04	11 08		11 19	11 23			11 34		11 38		11 49	11 53		
Cardiff Central 7	a	10 42	10 44			10 54		10 59			11 09	11 14		11 24	11 29			11 39		11 44		11 54	11 59		
	d		10 46	10 51	10 51	10 56		11 01		11 06	11 11	11 16	11 21	11 26	11 31	11 36	11 36	11 41		11 46	11 51	11 56	12 01	12 06	12 06
Cardiff Queen Street 3	a		10 49	10 54		10 59		11 04			11 14	11 19	11 24	11 29	11 34	11 39		11 44		11 49	11 54	11 59	12 04	12 09	
	d		10 50	10 55		11 00		11 05			11 15	11 20	11 25	11 30	11 35	11 40		11 45		11 50	11 55	12 00	12 05	12 10	
Heath Low Level	d			11 00									11 30								12 00				
Ty Glas	d			11 03									11 33								12 03				
Birchgrove	d			11 04									11 34								12 04				
Rhiwbina	d			11 06									11 36								12 06				
Whitchurch (Cardiff)	d			11 08									11 38								12 08				
Coryton	a			11 13									11 43								12 13				
Heath High Level	d		10 55					11 10				11 25			11 40					11 55			12 10		
Llanishen	d		10 58					11 13				11 28			11 43					11 58			12 13		
Lisvane & Thornhill	d		11 00					11 15				11 30			11 45					12 00			12 15		
Caerphilly 3	d		11 06					11 21				11 36			11 51					12 06			12 21		
Aber	d		11 08					11 23				11 38			11 53					12 08			12 23		
Energlyn & Churchill Park	d							11 25				11 40											12 25		
Llanbradach	d		11 12					11 29				11 44			11 57					12 12			12 29		
Ystrad Mynach 3	d		11 17					11 34				11 49			12 02					12 17			12 34		
Hengoed	d		11 20					11 37				11 52			12 05					12 20			12 37		
Pengam	d		11 23					11 40				11 55			12 08					12 23			12 40		
Gilfach Fargoed	d							11 43															12 43		
Bargoed	a		11 31					11 50				12 00			12 16					12 31			12 50		
	d											12 01													
Brithdir	d											12 05													
Tir-phil	d											12 08													
Pontlottyn	d											12 12													
Rhymney 3	a											12 18													
Cathays	d					11 03					11 18			11 33		11 43		11 48				12 03		12 13	
Llandaf	d					11 07					11 22			11 37		11 47		11 52				12 07		12 17	
Ninian Park	d									11 10							11 40								12 10
Waun-gron Park	d									11 13							11 43								12 13
Fairwater	d									11 15							11 45								12 15
Danescourt	d						←			11 17							11 47								12 17
Radyr 3	a				11 02	11 10	11 02			11 24	11 25			11 40		11 50	11 54	11 55				12 10		12 20	12 24
	d				11 20	11 10	11 20				11 25			11 40		11 50		11 55				12 10		12 20	
Taffs Well 3	d				→	11 14	11 24				11 29			11 44		11 54		11 59				12 14		12 24	
Trefforest Estate	d					11 18								11 48								12 18			
Trefforest	d					11 22	11 31				11 36			11 52		12 01		12 06				12 22		12 31	
Pontypridd 3	a					11 25	11 34				11 39			11 55		12 04		12 09				12 25		12 34	
	d					11 27	11 36				11 41			11 57		12 06		12 11				12 27		12 36	
Abercynon	d					11 34					11 49			12 04				12 19				12 34			
Penrhiwceiber	d										11 54							12 24							
Mountain Ash	a										11 58							12 28							
	d										12 03							12 33							
Fernhill	d										12 05							12 35							
Cwmbach	d										12 09							12 39							
Aberdare 3	a										12 16							12 46							
Quakers Yard	d					11 39								12 09								12 39			
Merthyr Vale	a					11 44								12 14								12 44			
	d					11 47								12 17								12 47			
Troed Y Rhiw	d					11 50								12 20								12 50			
Pentre-bach	d					11 53								12 23								12 53			
Merthyr Tydfil	a					12 01								12 31								13 01			
Trehafod	d						11 41									12 11								12 41	
Porth	a						11 44									12 14								12 44	
	d						11 45									12 15								12 45	
Dinas Rhondda	d						11 49									12 19								12 49	
Tonypandy	d						11 51									12 21								12 51	
Llwynypia	d						11 53									12 23								12 53	
Ystrad Rhondda	a						11 56									12 26								12 56	
	d						11 59									12 29								12 59	
Ton Pentre	d						12 01									12 31								13 01	
Treorchy	d						12 04									12 34								13 04	
Ynyswen	d						12 07									12 37								13 07	
Treherbert	a						12 13									12 43								13 13	

When events are being held at the Millenium Stadium, services are subject to alteration. Please check times before travelling.

For connections to Cardiff Bay please refer to Table 130A

Table 130R

Saturdays

14 December to 28 December

Bridgend, Barry Island, Barry, Penarth and Cardiff - Coryton, Rhymney, Pontypridd, Merthyr, Aberdare and Treherbert

Network Diagram - see first Page of Table 130

		AW	AW	AW	AW	AW	AW	AW	AW	AW	AW	AW	AW	AW	AW	AW	AW	AW	AW	AW	AW	AW
Bridgend	d								11 42													
Llantwit Major	d								11 56													
Rhoose Cardiff Int Airport ✈	d								12 06													
Barry Island	d	11 40			11 55							12 25				12 40			12 55			
Barry 3	d	11 45			12 00				12 15			12 30				12 45			13 00			
Barry Docks	d	11 48			12 03				12 18			12 33				12 48			13 03			
Cadoxton	d	11 51			12 06				12 21			12 36				12 51			13 06			
Dinas Powys	d	11 55			12 10				12 25			12 40				12 55			13 10			
Eastbrook	d	11 58			12 13				12 28			12 43				12 58			13 13			
Cogan	d	12 00			12 15				12 30			12 45				13 00			13 15			
Penarth	d		12 02			12 17				12 32			12 47				13 02			13 17		
Dingle Road	d		12 04			12 19				12 34			12 49				13 04			13 19		
Grangetown	d	12 04	12 08		12 19	12 23			12 34	12 38		12 49	12 53			13 04	13 08		13 19	13 23		
Cardiff Central 7	a	12 09	12 14		12 24	12 29			12 39	12 44		12 54	12 59			13 09	13 14		13 24	13 29		
	d	12 11	12 16	12 21	12 26	12 31	12 36	12 36	12 41	12 46	12 51	12 56	13 01	13 06	13 06	13 11	13 16	13 21	13 26	13 31	13 36	13 36
Cardiff Queen Street 3	a	12 14	12 19	12 24	12 29	12 34	12 39		12 44	12 49	12 54	12 59	13 04	13 09		13 14	13 19	13 24	13 29	13 34	13 39	
	d	12 15	12 20	12 25	12 30	12 35	12 40		12 45	12 50	12 55	13 00	13 05	13 10		13 15	13 20	13 25	13 30	13 35	13 40	
Heath Low Level	d			12 30							13 00							13 30				
Ty Glas	d			12 33							13 03							13 33				
Birchgrove	d			12 34							13 04							13 34				
Rhiwbina	d			12 36							13 06							13 36				
Whitchurch (Cardiff)	d			12 38							13 08							13 38				
Coryton	a			12 43							13 13							13 43				
Heath High Level	d		12 25			12 40				12 55			13 10				13 25			13 40		
Llanishen	d		12 28			12 43				12 58			13 13				13 28			13 43		
Lisvane & Thornhill	d		12 30			12 45				13 00			13 15				13 30			13 45		
Caerphilly 3	d		12 36			12 51				13 06			13 21				13 36			13 51		
Aber	d		12 38			12 53				13 08			13 23				13 38			13 53		
Energlyn & Churchill Park	d		12 40										13 25				13 40					
Llanbradach	d		12 44			12 57				13 12			13 29				13 44			13 57		
Ystrad Mynach 3	d		12 49			13 02				13 17			13 34				13 49			14 02		
Hengoed	d		12 52			13 05				13 20			13 37				13 52			14 05		
Pengam	d		12 55			13 08				13 23			13 40				13 55			14 08		
Gilfach Fargoed	d												13 43									
Bargoed	a		13 00			13 16				13 31			13 50				14 00			14 16		
	d		13 01														14 01					
Brithdir	d		13 05														14 05					
Tir-phil	d		13 08														14 08					
Pontlottyn	d		13 12														14 12					
Rhymney 3	a		13 18														14 18					
Cathays	d	12 18			12 33		12 43		12 48			13 03		13 13		13 18			13 33		13 43	
Llandaf	d	12 22			12 37		12 47		12 52			13 07		13 17		13 22			13 37		13 47	
Ninian Park	d							12 40							13 10							13 40
Waun-gron Park	d							12 43							13 13							13 43
Fairwater	d							12 45							13 15							13 45
Danescourt	d							12 47							13 17							13 47
Radyr 3	a	12 25			12 40		12 50	12 54	12 55			13 10		13 20	13 24	13 25			13 40		13 50	13 54
	d	12 25			12 40		12 50		12 55			13 10		13 20		13 25			13 40		13 50	
Taffs Well 3	d	12 29			12 44		12 54		12 59			13 14		13 24		13 29			13 44		13 54	
Trefforest Estate	d				12 48							13 18							13 48			
Trefforest	d	12 36			12 52		13 01		13 06			13 22		13 31		13 36			13 52		14 01	
Pontypridd 3	a	12 42			12 55		13 04		13 09			13 25		13 34		13 39			13 55		14 04	
	d				12 57		13 06		13 11			13 27		13 36		13 41			13 57		14 06	
Abercynon	d				13 04				13 19			13 34				13 49			14 04			
Penrhiwceiber	d								13 24							13 54						
Mountain Ash	a								13 28							13 58						
	d								13 33							14 03						
Fernhill	d								13 35							14 05						
Cwmbach	d								13 39							14 09						
Aberdare 3	a								13 46							14 16						
Quakers Yard	d				13 09							13 39							14 09			
Merthyr Vale	a				13 14							13 44							14 14			
	d				13 17							13 47							14 17			
Troed Y Rhiw	d				13 20							13 50							14 20			
Pentre-bach	d				13 23							13 53							14 23			
Merthyr Tydfil	a				13 31							14 01							14 31			
Trehafod	d						13 11							13 41							14 11	
Porth	a						13 14							13 44							14 14	
	d						13 15							13 45							14 15	
Dinas Rhondda	d						13 19							13 49							14 19	
Tonypandy	d						13 21							13 51							14 21	
Llwynypia	d						13 23							13 53							14 23	
Ystrad Rhondda	a						13 26							13 56							14 26	
	d						13 29							13 59							14 29	
Ton Pentre	d						13 31							14 01							14 31	
Treorchy	d						13 34							14 04							14 34	
Ynyswen	d						13 37							14 07							14 37	
Treherbert	a						13 43							14 13							14 43	

When events are being held at the Millenium Stadium, services are subject to alteration. Please check times before travelling.

For connections to Cardiff Bay please refer to Table 130A

Table 130R

Saturdays

14 December to 28 December

Bridgend, Barry Island, Barry, Penarth and Cardiff - Coryton, Rhymney, Pontypridd, Merthyr, Aberdare and Treherbert

Network Diagram - see first Page of Table 130

		AW	AW	AW	AW	AW	AW	AW	AW	AW		AW	AW	AW	AW	AW	AW	AW	AW	AW		AW	AW	AW	AW
Bridgend	d	12 42															13 42								
Llantwit Major	d	12 56															13 56								
Rhoose Cardiff Int Airport ✈	d	13 06															14 06								
Barry Island	d				13 25				13 40				13 55									14 25			
Barry 3	d	13 15			13 30				13 45				14 00				14 15					14 30			
Barry Docks	d	13 18			13 34				13 48				14 03				14 18					14 33			
Cadoxton	d	13 21			13 37				13 51				14 06				14 21					14 36			
Dinas Powys	d	13 25			13 41				13 55				14 10				14 25					14 40			
Eastbrook	d	13 28			13 43				13 58				14 13				14 28					14 43			
Cogan	d	13 30			13 45				14 00				14 15				14 30					14 45			
Penarth	d		13 32			13 47				14 02				14 17				14 32						14 47	
Dingle Road	d		13 34			13 49				14 04				14 19				14 34						14 49	
Grangetown	d	13 34	13 38		13 49	13 53			14 04	14 08			14 19	14 23			14 34	14 38				14 49		14 53	
Cardiff Central 7	a	13 39	13 44		13 54	13 59			14 09	14 14			14 24	14 29			14 39	14 44				14 54		14 59	
	d	13 41	13 46	13 51	13 56	14 01	14 06	14 06	14 11	14 16		14 21	14 26	14 31	14 36	14 36	14 41	14 46	14 51	14 51		14 56		15 01	15 06
Cardiff Queen Street 3	a	13 44	13 49	13 54	13 59	14 04	14 09		14 14	14 19		14 24	14 29	14 34	14 39		14 44	14 49	14 54			14 59		15 04	
	d	13 45	13 50	13 55	14 00	14 05	14 10		14 15	14 20		14 25	14 30	14 35	14 40		14 45	14 50	14 55			15 00		15 05	
Heath Low Level	d			14 00								14 30							15 00						
Ty Glas	d			14 03								14 33							15 03						
Birchgrove	d			14 04								14 34							15 04						
Rhiwbina	d			14 06								14 36							15 06						
Whitchurch (Cardiff)	d			14 08								14 38							15 08						
Coryton	a			14 13								14 43							15 13						
Heath High Level	d		13 55			14 10				14 25				14 40				14 55						15 10	
Llanishen	d		13 58			14 13				14 28				14 43				14 58						15 13	
Lisvane & Thornhill	d		14 00			14 15				14 30				14 45				15 00						15 15	
Caerphilly 3	d		14 06			14 21				14 36				14 51				15 06						15 21	
Aber	d		14 08			14 23				14 38				14 53				15 08						15 23	
Energlyn & Churchill Park	d					14 25				14 40														15 25	
Llanbradach	d		14 12			14 29				14 44				14 57				15 12						15 29	
Ystrad Mynach 3	d		14 17			14 34				14 49				15 02				15 17						15 34	
Hengoed	d		14 20			14 37				14 52				15 05				15 20						15 37	
Pengam	d		14 23			14 40				14 55				15 08				15 23						15 40	
Gilfach Fargoed	d					14 43																		15 43	
Bargoed	a		14 31			14 50				15 00				15 16				15 31						15 50	
	d									15 01															
Brithdir	d									15 05															
Tir-phil	d									15 08															
Pontlottyn	d									15 12															
Rhymney 3	a									15 18															
Cathays	d	13 48			14 03		14 13		14 18				14 33		14 43		14 48					15 03			
Llandaf	d	13 52			14 07		14 17		14 22				14 37		14 47		14 52					15 07			
Ninian Park	d							14 10								14 40									15 10
Waun-gron Park	d							14 13								14 43									15 13
Fairwater	d							14 15								14 45									15 15
Danescourt	d							14 17								14 47							←		15 17
Radyr 3	a	13 55			14 10		14 20	14 24	14 25				14 40		14 50	14 54	14 55			15 08		15 10	15 08		15 24
	d	13 55			14 10		14 20		14 25				14 40		14 50		14 55			15 20		15 10	15 20		
Taffs Well 3	d	13 59			14 14		14 24		14 29				14 44		14 54		14 59			→		15 14	15 24		
Trefforest Estate	d				14 18								14 48									15 18			
Trefforest	d	14 06			14 22		14 31		14 36				14 52		15 01		15 06					15 22	15 31		
Pontypridd 3	a	14 09			14 25		14 34		14 39				14 55		15 04		15 09					15 25	15 34		
	d	14 11			14 27		14 36		14 41				14 57		15 06		15 11					15 27	15 36		
Abercynon	d	14 19			14 34				14 49				15 04				15 19					15 34			
Penrhiwceiber	d	14 24							14 54								15 24								
Mountain Ash	a	14 28							14 58								15 28								
	d	14 33							15 03								15 33								
Fernhill	d	14 35							15 05								15 35								
Cwmbach	d	14 39							15 09								15 39								
Aberdare 3	a	14 46							15 16								15 46								
Quakers Yard	d				14 39								15 09									15 39			
Merthyr Vale	a				14 44								15 14									15 44			
	d				14 47								15 17									15 47			
Troed Y Rhiw	d				14 50								15 20									15 50			
Pentre-bach	d				14 53								15 23									15 53			
Merthyr Tydfil	a				15 01								15 31									16 01			
Trehafod	d						14 41								15 11								15 41		
Porth	a						14 44								15 14								15 44		
	d						14 45								15 15								15 45		
Dinas Rhondda	d						14 49								15 19								15 49		
Tonypandy	d						14 51								15 21								15 51		
Llwynypia	d						14 53								15 23								15 53		
Ystrad Rhondda	a						14 56								15 26								15 56		
	d						14 59								15 29								15 59		
Ton Pentre	d						15 01								15 31								16 01		
Treorchy	d						15 04								15 34								16 04		
Ynyswen	d						15 07								15 37								16 07		
Treherbert	a						15 13								15 43								16 13		

When events are being held at the Millenium Stadium, services are subject to alteration. Please check times before travelling.

For connections to Cardiff Bay please refer to Table 130A

Table 130R

Saturdays

14 December to 28 December

Bridgend, Barry Island, Barry, Penarth and Cardiff - Coryton, Rhymney, Pontypridd, Merthyr, Aberdare and Treherbert

Network Diagram - see first Page of Table 130

		AW	AW	AW	AW	AW	AW	AW	AW	AW	AW	AW	AW	AW	AW	AW	AW	AW	AW	AW	AW	AW	AW
Bridgend	d								14 42														15 42
Llantwit Major	d								14 56														15 56
Rhoose Cardiff Int Airport ✈	d								15 06														16 06
Barry Island	d	14 40			14 55							15 25				15 40			15 55				
Barry 3	d	14 45			15 00				15 15			15 30				15 45			16 00				16 15
Barry Docks	d	14 48			15 03				15 18			15 33				15 48			16 03				16 18
Cadoxton	d	14 51			15 06				15 21			15 36				15 51			16 06				16 21
Dinas Powys	d	14 55			15 10				15 25			15 40				15 55			16 10				16 25
Eastbrook	d	14 58			15 13				15 28			15 43				15 58			16 13				16 28
Cogan	d	15 00			15 15				15 30			15 45				16 00			16 15				16 30
Penarth	d		15 02			15 17				15 32			15 47				16 02			16 17			
Dingle Road	d		15 04			15 19				15 34			15 49				16 04			16 19			
Grangetown	d	15 04	15 08		15 19	15 23			15 34	15 38		15 49	15 53			16 04	16 08		16 19	16 23			16 34
Cardiff Central 7	a	15 09	15 14		15 24	15 29			15 39	15 44		15 54	15 59			16 09	16 14		16 24	16 29			16 39
	d	15 11	15 16	15 21	15 26	15 31	15 36	15 36	15 41	15 46	15 51	15 56	16 01	16 06	16 06	16 11	16 16	16 21	16 26	16 31	16 36	16 36	16 41
Cardiff Queen Street 3	a	15 14	15 19	15 24	15 29	15 34	15 39		15 44	15 49	15 54	15 59	16 04	16 09		16 14	16 19	16 24	16 29	16 34	16 39		16 44
	d	15 15	15 20	15 25	15 30	15 35	15 40		15 45	15 50	15 55	16 00	16 05	16 10		16 15	16 20	16 25	16 30	16 35	16 40		16 45
Heath Low Level	d			15 30							16 00							16 30					
Ty Glas	d			15 33							16 03							16 33					
Birchgrove	d			15 34							16 04							16 34					
Rhiwbina	d			15 36							16 06							16 36					
Whitchurch (Cardiff)	d			15 38							16 08							16 38					
Coryton	a			15 43							16 13							16 43					
Heath High Level	d		15 25			15 40				15 55			16 10				16 25			16 40			
Llanishen	d		15 28			15 43				15 58			16 13				16 28			16 43			
Lisvane & Thornhill	d		15 30			15 45				16 00			16 15				16 30			16 45			
Caerphilly 3	d		15 36			15 51				16 06			16 21				16 36			16 51			
Aber	d		15 38			15 53				16 08			16 23				16 38			16 53			
Energlyn & Churchill Park	d		15 40										16 25				16 40						
Llanbradach	d		15 44			15 57				16 12			16 29				16 44			16 57			
Ystrad Mynach 3	d		15 49			16 02				16 17			16 34				16 49			17 02			
Hengoed	d		15 52			16 05				16 20			16 37				16 52			17 05			
Pengam	d		15 55			16 08				16 23			16 40				16 55			17 08			
Gilfach Fargoed	d												16 43										
Bargoed	a		16 00			16 16				16 31			16 50				17 00			17 16			
	d		16 01														17 01						
Brithdir	d		16 05														17 05						
Tir-phil	d		16 08														17 08						
Pontlottyn	d		16 12														17 12						
Rhymney 3	a		16 18														17 18						
Cathays	d	15 18			15 33		15 43		15 48			16 03		16 13		16 18			16 33		16 43		16 48
Llandaf	d	15 22			15 37		15 47		15 52			16 07		16 17		16 22			16 37		16 47		16 52
Ninian Park	d							15 40							16 10							16 40	
Waun-gron Park	d							15 43							16 13							16 43	
Fairwater	d							15 45							16 15							16 45	
Danescourt	d							15 47							16 17							16 47	
Radyr 3	a	15 25			15 40		15 50	15 54	15 55			16 10		16 20	16 24	16 25			16 40		16 50	16 54	16 55
	d	15 25			15 40		15 50		15 55			16 10		16 20		16 25			16 40		16 50		16 55
Taffs Well 3	d	15 29			15 44		15 54		15 59			16 14		16 24		16 29			16 44		16 54		16 59
Trefforest Estate	d				15 48							16 18							16 48				
Trefforest	d	15 36			15 52		16 01		16 06			16 22		16 31		16 36			16 52		17 01		17 06
Pontypridd 3	a	15 39			15 55		16 04		16 09			16 25		16 34		16 39			16 55		17 04		17 09
	d	15 41			15 57		16 06		16 11			16 27		16 36		16 41			16 57		17 06		17 11
Abercynon	d	15 49			16 04				16 19			16 34				16 49			17 04				17 19
Penrhiwceiber	d	15 54							16 24							16 54							17 24
Mountain Ash	a	15 58							16 28							16 58							17 28
	d	16 03							16 33							17 03							17 33
Fernhill	d	16 05							16 35							17 05							17 35
Cwmbach	d	16 09							16 39							17 09							17 39
Aberdare 3	a	16 16							16 46							17 16							17 46
Quakers Yard	d				16 09							16 39							17 09				
Merthyr Vale	a				16 14							16 44							17 14				
	d				16 17							16 47							17 17				
Troed Y Rhiw	d				16 20							16 50							17 20				
Pentre-bach	d				16 23							16 53							17 23				
Merthyr Tydfil	a				16 31							17 01							17 31				
Trehafod	d						16 11							16 41							17 11		
Porth	a						16 14							16 44							17 14		
	d						16 15							16 45							17 15		
Dinas Rhondda	d						16 19							16 49							17 19		
Tonypandy	d						16 21							16 51							17 21		
Llwynypia	d						16 23							16 53							17 23		
Ystrad Rhondda	a						16 26							16 56							17 26		
	d						16 29							16 59							17 29		
Ton Pentre	d						16 31							17 01							17 31		
Treorchy	d						16 34							17 04							17 34		
Ynyswen	d						16 37							17 07							17 37		
Treherbert	a						16 43							17 13							17 43		

When events are being held at the Millenium Stadium, services are subject to alteration. Please check times before travelling.

For connections to Cardiff Bay please refer to Table 130A

Table 130R

Saturdays

14 December to 28 December

Bridgend, Barry Island, Barry, Penarth and Cardiff - Coryton, Rhymney, Pontypridd, Merthyr, Aberdare and Treherbert

Network Diagram - see first Page of Table 130

		AW		AW	AW	AW	AW	AW	AW	AW	AW	AW		AW	AW	AW	AW	AW	AW	AW	AW	AW		AW	AW
Bridgend	d																16 42								
Llantwit Major	d																16 56								
Rhoose Cardiff Int Airport ✈	d																17 06								
Barry Island	d				16 25				16 40			16 55								17 25					17 40
Barry 3	d				16 30				16 45			17 00					17 15			17 30					17 45
Barry Docks	d				16 33				16 48			17 03					17 18			17 33					17 48
Cadoxton	d				16 36				16 51			17 06					17 21			17 36					17 51
Dinas Powys	d				16 40				16 55			17 10					17 25			17 40					17 55
Eastbrook	d				16 43				16 58			17 13					17 28			17 43					17 58
Cogan	d				16 45				17 00			17 15					17 30			17 45					18 00
Penarth	d	16 32								17 02				17 17				17 32			17 47				
Dingle Road	d	16 34								17 04				17 19				17 34			17 49				
Grangetown	d	16 38			16 49				17 04	17 08		17 19		17 23			17 34	17 38		17 49	17 53				18 04
Cardiff Central 7	a	16 44			16 54				17 09	17 14		17 24		17 29			17 39	17 44		17 54	17 59				18 09
	d	16 46		16 51	16 56	17 01	17 06	17 06	17 11	17 16	17 21	17 26		17 31	17 36	17 36	17 41	17 46	17 51	17 56	18 01	18 06		18 06	18 11
Cardiff Queen Street 3	a	16 49		16 54	16 59	17 04	17 09		17 14	17 19	17 24	17 29		17 34	17 39		17 44	17 49	17 54	17 59	18 04	18 09			18 14
	d	16 50		16 55	17 00	17 05	17 10		17 15	17 20	17 25	17 30		17 35	17 40		17 45	17 50	17 55	18 00	18 05	18 10			18 15
Heath Low Level	d			17 00							17 30								18 00						
Ty Glas	d			17 03							17 33								18 03						
Birchgrove	d			17 04							17 34								18 04						
Rhiwbina	d			17 06							17 36								18 06						
Whitchurch (Cardiff)	d			17 08							17 38								18 08						
Coryton	a			17 13							17 43								18 13						
Heath High Level	d	16 55				17 10				17 25				17 40				17 55			18 10				
Llanishen	d	16 58				17 13				17 28				17 43				17 59			18 13				
Lisvane & Thornhill	d	17 00				17 15				17 30				17 45				18 02			18 15				
Caerphilly 3	d	17 06				17 21				17 36				17 51				18 07			18 21				
Aber	d	17 08				17 23				17 38				17 53				18 10			18 23				
Energlyn & Churchill Park	d					17 26				17 40				17 55				18 13							
Llanbradach	d	17 12				17 29				17 44				17 59				18 17			18 27				
Ystrad Mynach 3	d	17 17				17 35				17 49				18 04				18 22			18 32				
Hengoed	d	17 20				17 37				17 52				18 07				18 25			18 35				
Pengam	d	17 23				17 41				17 55				18 10				18 29			18 38				
Gilfach Fargoed	d					17 44								18 13				18 33			18 41				
Bargoed	a	17 31				17 47				18 03				18 16				18 36			18 48				
	d					17 49								18 18				18 44							
Brithdir	d					17 52								18 22				18 48							
Tir-phil	d					17 55								18 25				18 51							
Pontlottyn	d					18 00								18 29				18 55							
Rhymney 3	a					18 06								18 35				19 01							
Cathays	d				17 03		17 13		17 18			17 33			17 43		17 48			18 03		18 13			18 18
Llandaf	d				17 07		17 17		17 22			17 37			17 47		17 52			18 07		18 17			18 22
Ninian Park	d							17 10								17 40								18 10	
Waun-gron Park	d							17 13								17 43								18 13	
Fairwater	d							17 15								17 45								18 15	
Danescourt	d							17 17								17 47								18 17	
Radyr 3	a				17 10		17 20	17 24	17 25			17 40			17 50	17 54	17 55			18 10		18 20		18 24	18 25
	d				17 10		17 20		17 25			17 40			17 50		17 55			18 10		18 20			18 25
Taffs Well 3	d				17 14		17 24		17 29			17 44			17 54		17 59			18 14		18 24			18 29
Trefforest Estate	d				17 18							17 48								18 18					
Trefforest	d				17 22		17 31		17 36			17 52			18 01		18 06			18 22		18 31			18 36
Pontypridd 3	a				17 25		17 34		17 39			17 55			18 04		18 09			18 25		18 34			18 42
	d				17 27		17 36		17 41			17 57			18 06		18 11			18 27		18 36			
Abercynon	d				17 34				17 49			18 04					18 19			18 34					
Penrhiwceiber	d								17 54								18 24								
Mountain Ash	a								17 58								18 28								
	d								18 03								18 33								
Fernhill	d								18 05								18 35								
Cwmbach	d								18 09								18 39								
Aberdare 3	a								18 16								18 46								
Quakers Yard	d				17 39							18 09								18 39					
Merthyr Vale	a				17 44							18 14								18 44					
	d				17 47							18 17								18 47					
Troed Y Rhiw	d				17 50							18 20								18 50					
Pentre-bach	d				17 53							18 23								18 53					
Merthyr Tydfil	a				18 01							18 31								19 01					
Trehafod	d						17 41								18 11							18 41			
Porth	a						17 44								18 14							18 44			
	d						17 45								18 15							18 45			
Dinas Rhondda	d						17 49								18 19							18 49			
Tonypandy	d						17 51								18 21							18 51			
Llwynypia	d						17 53								18 23							18 53			
Ystrad Rhondda	a						17 56								18 26							18 56			
	d						17 59								18 29							18 59			
Ton Pentre	d						18 01								18 31							19 01			
Treorchy	d						18 04								18 34							19 04			
Ynyswen	d						18 07								18 37							19 07			
Treherbert	a						18 13								18 43							19 13			

When events are being held at the Millenium Stadium, services are subject to alteration. Please check times before travelling.

For connections to Cardiff Bay please refer to Table 130A

Table 130R

Saturdays

14 December to 28 December

Bridgend, Barry Island, Barry, Penarth and Cardiff - Coryton, Rhymney, Pontypridd, Merthyr, Aberdare and Treherbert

Network Diagram - see first Page of Table 130

		AW	AW	AW	AW		AW	AW	AW	AW	AW	AW		AW	AW	AW	AW	AW	AW	AW	AW	AW	AW
Bridgend	d							17 42										18 42					
Llantwit Major	d							17 56										18 56					
Rhoose Cardiff Int Airport ✈	d							18 06										19 06					
Barry Island	d			17 55							18 25			18 40	18 55					19 25		19 55	
Barry 3	d			18 00				18 15			18 30			18 45	19 00			19 15		19 30		20 00	
Barry Docks	d			18 03				18 18			18 33			18 48	19 03			19 18		19 33		20 03	
Cadoxton	d			18 06				18 21			18 36			18 51	19 06			19 21		19 36		20 06	
Dinas Powys	d			18 10				18 25			18 40			18 55	19 10			19 25		19 40		20 10	
Eastbrook	d			18 13				18 28			18 43			18 58	19 13			19 28		19 43		20 13	
Cogan	d			18 15				18 30			18 45			19 00	19 15			19 30		19 45		20 15	
Penarth	d	18 02			18 17				18 32			18 47				19 17					19 47		20 20
Dingle Road	d	18 04			18 19				18 34			18 49				19 19					19 49		20 22
Grangetown	d	18 08		18 19	18 23			18 34	18 38		18 49	18 53		19 04	19 19	19 23		19 34		19 49	19 53	20 19	20 26
Cardiff Central 7	a	18 14		18 25	18 29			18 39	18 47		18 55	18 59		19 09	19 24	19 29		19 39		19 56	19 59	20 24	20 31
	d	18 16	18 21	18 26	18 31	18 36	18 36	18 41		18 51		19 01	19 06	19 11	19 26	19 31	19 36	19 41	19 51	20 01	20 06	20 26	20 31
Cardiff Queen Street 3	a	18 19	18 24	18 29	18 34	18 38		18 44		18 54		19 04	19 09	19 14	19 29	19 34		19 44	19 54	20 04	20 09	20 29	20 34
	d	18 20	18 25	18 30	18 35	18 40		18 50		18 55		19 05	19 10	19 15	19 30	19 35		19 45	19 55	20 05	20 10	20 30	20 35
Heath Low Level	d		18 30							19 00									20 00				
Ty Glas	d		18 33							19 03									20 03				
Birchgrove	d		18 34							19 04									20 04				
Rhiwbina	d		18 36							19 06									20 06				
Whitchurch (Cardiff)	d		18 38							19 08									20 08				
Coryton	a		18 43							19 13									20 13				
Heath High Level	d	18 25			18 40							19 10				19 40				20 10			20 40
Llanishen	d	18 28			18 43							19 13				19 43				20 13			20 43
Lisvane & Thornhill	d	18 30			18 45							19 15				19 45				20 15			20 45
Caerphilly 3	d	18 36			18 51							19a23				19 51				20a27			20 51
Aber	d	18 38			18 53											19 53							20 53
Energlyn & Churchill Park	d				18 56											19 56							20 56
Llanbradach	d	18 42			18 59											19 59							20 59
Ystrad Mynach 3	d	18a51			19 04											20 04							21 04
Hengoed	d				19 07											20 07							21 07
Pengam	d				19 10											20 10							21 10
Gilfach Fargoed	d				19 13											20 13							21 13
Bargoed	a				19 16											20 17							21 17
	d				19 18											20 18							21 18
Brithdir	d				19 22											20 22							21 22
Tir-phil	d				19 25											20 25							21 25
Pontlottyn	d				19 29											20 29							21 29
Rhymney 3	a				19 36											20 35							21 36
Cathays	d			18 33		18 43		18 52					19 13	19 18	19 33			19 48			20 13	20 33	
Llandaf	d			18 37		18 47		18 56					19 17	19 22	19 37			19 52			20 17	20 37	
Ninian Park	d						18 40										19 40						
Waun-gron Park	d						18 43										19 43						
Fairwater	d						18 45										19 45						
Danescourt	d						18 47										19 47						
Radyr 3	a			18 40		18 50	18 54	18 58					19 20	19 25	19 40		19 54	19 55			20 20	20 40	
	d			18 40		18 50		18 58					19 20	19 25	19 40			19 55			20 20	20 40	
Taffs Well 3	d			18 44		18 54		19 03					19 24	19 29	19 44			19 59			20 24	20 44	
Trefforest Estate	d			18 48											19 48							20 48	
Trefforest	d			18 52		19 01		19 10					19 31	19 36	19 52			20 06			20 31	20 52	
Pontypridd 3	a			18 55		19 04		19 13					19 34	19 39	19 55			20 09			20 34	20 55	
	d			18 57		19 06		19 14					19 36	19 41	19 57			20 11			20 36	20 57	
Abercynon	d			19 04				19 21						19 49	20 04			20 21				21 04	
Penrhiwceiber	d							19 26						19 54				20 26					
Mountain Ash	a							19 30						19 56				20 30					
	d							19 33						20 03				20 33					
Fernhill	d							19 35						20 05				20 35					
Cwmbach	d							19 39						20 09				20 39					
Aberdare 3	a							19 46						20 16				20 46					
Quakers Yard	d			19 09											20 08							21 08	
Merthyr Vale	a			19 14											20 13							21 13	
	d			19 17											20 15							21 16	
Troed Y Rhiw	d			19 20											20 19							21 20	
Pentre-bach	d			19 23											20 22							21 23	
Merthyr Tydfil	a			19 31											20 30							21 31	
Trehafod	d					19 11							19 41								20 41		
Porth	a					19 14							19 44								20 44		
	d					19 15							19 45								20 45		
Dinas Rhondda	d					19 19							19 49								20 49		
Tonypandy	d					19 21							19 51								20 51		
Llwynypia	d					19 23							19 53								20 53		
Ystrad Rhondda	a					19 26							19 56								20 56		
	d					19 29							19 59								20 59		
Ton Pentre	d					19 31							20 01								21 01		
Treorchy	d					19 34							20 04								21 04		
Ynyswen	d					19 37							20 07								21 07		
Treherbert	a					19 43							20 13								21 13		

When events are being held at the Millenium Stadium, services are subject to alteration. Please check times before travelling.

For connections to Cardiff Bay please refer to Table 130A

Table 130R

Saturdays

14 December to 28 December

Bridgend, Barry Island, Barry, Penarth and Cardiff - Coryton, Rhymney, Pontypridd, Merthyr, Aberdare and Treherbert

Network Diagram - see first Page of Table 130

		AW	AW	AW	AW	AW	AW	AW	AW	AW	AW	AW	AW	AW	AW	AW	AW	AW	AW	AW	AW	AW
Bridgend	d		19 42								20 42						21 42					
Llantwit Major	d		19 56								20 56						21 56					
Rhoose Cardiff Int Airport ✈	d		20 06								21 06						22 06					
Barry Island	d						20 55								21 55						22 44	
Barry [3]	d		20 15				21 00				21 15				22 00		22 15				22 49	
Barry Docks	d		20 18				21 03				21 18				22 03		22 18				22 52	
Cadoxton	d		20 21				21 06				21 21				22 06		22 21				22 55	
Dinas Powys	d		20 25				21 10				21 25				22 10		22 25				22 59	
Eastbrook	d		20 28				21 13				21 28				22 13		22 28				23 02	
Cogan	d		20 30				21 15				21 30				22 15		22 30				23 04	
Penarth	d				20 47					21 20		21 47				22 20				22 47		23 26
Dingle Road	d				20 49					21 22		21 49				22 22				22 49		23 28
Grangetown	d		20 34		20 53		21 19			21 26	21 34	21 53			22 19	22 26	22 34			22 53	23 08	23 32
Cardiff Central [7]	a		20 39		20 59		21 24			21 37	21 39	21 59			22 24	22 33	22 39			23 03	23 13	23 40
	d	20 36	20 41	20 51	21 00	21 06	21 27	21 31	21 36		21 41	22 01	22 06	22 21	22 26	22 35	22 41	22 46	22 55	23 16	23 26	
Cardiff Queen Street [3]	a		20 44	20 54	21 03	21 09	21 30	21 34			21 44	22 04	22 09	22 24	22 29	22 38	22 44	22 49		23 19	23 29	
	d		20 45	20 55	21 04	21 10	21 31	21 35			21 45	22 05	22 10	22 25	22 30	22 39	22 45	22 50		23 20	23 30	
Heath Low Level	d			21 00										22 30								
Ty Glas	d			21 03										22 33								
Birchgrove	d			21 04										22 34								
Rhiwbina	d			21 06										22 36								
Whitchurch (Cardiff)	d			21 08										22 38								
Coryton	a			21 13										22 43								
Heath High Level	d				21 09			21 40				22 10				22 44				23 25		
Llanishen	d				21 12			21 43				22 13				22 47				23 28		
Lisvane & Thornhill	d				21 14			21 45				22 15				22 49				23 30		
Caerphilly [3]	d				21 19			21 51				22a23				22 55				23 36		
Aber	d				21 21			21 53								22 57				23 38		
Energlyn & Churchill Park	d							21 56								22 59						
Llanbradach	d				21 25			21 59								23 03				23 42		
Ystrad Mynach [3]	d				21a35			22 04								23 08				23a51		
Hengoed	d							22 07								23 11						
Pengam	d							22 10								23 14						
Gilfach Fargoed	d							22 13								23 17						
Bargoed	a							22 17								23 21						
	d							22 18								23 22						
Brithdir	d							22 22								23 26						
Tir-phil	d							22 25								23 29						
Pontlottyn	d							22 29								23 33						
Rhymney [3]	a							22 36								23 39						
Cathays	d		20 48			21 13	21 34				21 48		22 13		22 33		22 48	22 53			23 33	
Llandaf	d		20 52			21 17	21 38				21 52		22 17		22 37		22 52	22 57			23 37	
Ninian Park	d	20 40							21 40										22 59			
Waun-gron Park	d	20 43							21 43										23 02			
Fairwater	d	20 45							21 45										23 04			
Danescourt	d	20 47							21 47										23 06			
Radyr [3]	a	20 54	20 55			21 20	21 41		21 54		21 55		22 20		22 40		22 55	22 59	23 13		23 40	
	d		20 55			21 20	21 41				21 55		22 20		22 40		22 55	22 59			23 40	
Taffs Well [3]	d		20 59			21 24	21 45				21 59		22 24		22 44		22 59	23 03			23 44	
Trefforest Estate	d						21 49								22 48							
Trefforest	d		21 06			21 31	21 53				22 06		22 31		22 52		23 06	23 10			23 52	
Pontypridd [3]	a		21 09			21 34	21 56				22 09		22 34		22 55		23 09	23 14			23 58	
	d		21 11			21 36	21 58				22 11		22 36		22 57		23 11	23 15				
Abercynon	d		21 19				22 05				22 19				23 04		23 19					
Penrhiwceiber	d		21 24								22 24						23 24					
Mountain Ash	a		21 28								22 28						23 28					
	d		21 29								22 29						23 29					
Fernhill	d		21 31								22 31						23 31					
Cwmbach	d		21 35								22 35						23 35					
Aberdare [3]	a		21 42								22 42						23 42					
Quakers Yard	d						22 09								23 08							
Merthyr Vale	a						22 14								23 13							
	d						22 16								23 15							
Troed Y Rhiw	d						22 20								23 19							
Pentre-bach	d						22 23								23 22							
Merthyr Tydfil	a						22 31								23 30							
Trehafod	d					21 41							22 41					23 20				
Porth	a					21 44							22 44					23 23				
	d					21 45							22 45					23 24				
Dinas Rhondda	d					21 49							22 49					23 28				
Tonypandy	d					21 51							22 51					23 30				
Llwynypia	d					21 53							22 53					23 32				
Ystrad Rhondda	a					21 56							22 56					23 35				
	d					21 59							22 59					23 38				
Ton Pentre	d					22 01							23 01					23 40				
Treorchy	d					22 04							23 04					23 43				
Ynyswen	d					22 07							23 07					23 46				
Treherbert	a					22 13							23 13					23 52				

When events are being held at the Millenium Stadium, services are subject to alteration. Please check times before travelling.

For connections to Cardiff Bay please refer to Table 130A

Table 130R

Saturdays

14 December to 28 December

Bridgend, Barry Island, Barry, Penarth and Cardiff - Coryton, Rhymney, Pontypridd, Merthyr, Aberdare and Treherbert

Network Diagram - see first Page of Table 130

		AW
Bridgend	d	22 42
Llantwit Major	d	22 56
Rhoose Cardiff Int Airport ✈	d	23 06
Barry Island	d	
Barry 3	d	23 15
Barry Docks	d	23 18
Cadoxton	d	23 21
Dinas Powys	d	23 25
Eastbrook	d	23 28
Cogan	d	23 30
Penarth	d	
Dingle Road	d	
Grangetown	d	23 34
Cardiff Central 7	a	23 42
	d	
Cardiff Queen Street 3	a	
	d	
Heath Low Level	d	
Ty Glas	d	
Birchgrove	d	
Rhiwbina	d	
Whitchurch (Cardiff)	d	
Coryton	a	
Heath High Level	d	
Llanishen	d	
Lisvane & Thornhill	d	
Caerphilly 3	d	
Aber	d	
Energlyn & Churchill Park	d	
Llanbradach	d	
Ystrad Mynach 3	d	
Hengoed	d	
Pengam	d	
Gilfach Fargoed	d	
Bargoed	a	
	d	
Brithdir	d	
Tir-phil	d	
Pontlottyn	d	
Rhymney 3	a	
Cathays	d	
Llandaf	d	
Ninian Park	d	
Waun-gron Park	d	
Fairwater	d	
Danescourt	d	
Radyr 3	a	
	d	
Taffs Well 3	d	
Trefforest Estate	d	
Trefforest	d	
Pontypridd 3	a	
	d	
Abercynon	d	
Penrhiwceiber	d	
Mountain Ash	a	
	d	
Fernhill	d	
Cwmbach	d	
Aberdare 3	a	
Quakers Yard	d	
Merthyr Vale	a	
	d	
Troed Y Rhiw	d	
Pentre-bach	d	
Merthyr Tydfil	a	
Trehafod	d	
Porth	a	
	d	
Dinas Rhondda	d	
Tonypandy	d	
Llwynypia	d	
Ystrad Rhondda	a	
	d	
Ton Pentre	d	
Treorchy	d	
Ynyswen	d	
Treherbert	a	

When events are being held at the Millenium Stadium, services are subject to alteration. Please check times before travelling.

For connections to Cardiff Bay please refer to Table 130A

Table 130R

Saturdays

4 January to 8 February

Bridgend, Barry Island, Barry, Penarth and Cardiff - Coryton, Rhymney, Pontypridd, Merthyr, Aberdare and Treherbert

Network Diagram - see first Page of Table 130

		AW		AW	AW	AW	AW	AW	AW	AW	AW	AW	AW	AW	AW	AW	AW	AW	AW	AW	AW	AW	AW
Bridgend	d										05 42												
Llantwit Major	d										05 56												
Rhoose Cardiff Int Airport ✈	d										06 06												
Barry Island	d			05 15				05 50						06 25						06 55			
Barry 3	d			05 20				05 55			06 15			06 30						07 00			
Barry Docks	d			05 23				05 58			06 18			06 33						07 03			
Cadoxton	d			05 26				06 01			06 21			06 36						07 06			
Dinas Powys	d			05 30				06 05			06 25			06 40						07 10			
Eastbrook	d			05 33				06 08			06 28			06 43						07 13			
Cogan	d			05 35				06 10			06 30			06 45						07 15			
Penarth	d						06 02					06 32						07 02			07 17		
Dingle Road	d						06 04					06 34						07 04			07 19		
Grangetown	d			05 39			06 08	06 14			06 34	06 38		06 49				07 08		07 19	07 23		
Cardiff Central 7	a			05 44			06 13	06 19			06 39	06 44		06 54				07 14		07 24	07 29		
	d	05 26		05 46	05 56	06 11	06 15	06 21	06 26	06 36	06 41	06 46	06 51	06 56	07 06	07 06	07 11	07 16	07 21	07 26	07 31	07 36	07 36
Cardiff Queen Street 3	a	05 29		05 49	05 59	06 14	06 19	06 24	06 29	06 39	06 44	06 49	06 54	06 59	07 09		07 14	07 19	07 24	07 29	07 34	07 39	
	d	05 30		05 50	06 00	06 15	06 20	06 25	06 30	06 40	06 45	06 50	06 55	07 00	07 10		07 15	07 20	07 25	07 30	07 35	07 40	
Heath Low Level	d							06 30					07 00						07 30				
Ty Glas	d							06 33					07 03						07 33				
Birchgrove	d							06 34					07 04						07 34				
Rhiwbina	d							06 36					07 06						07 36				
Whitchurch (Cardiff)	d							06 38					07 08						07 38				
Coryton	a							06 43					07 13						07 43				
Heath High Level	d			05 55			06 25					06 55						07 25			07 40		
Llanishen	d			05 58			06 28					06 58						07 28			07 43		
Lisvane & Thornhill	d			06 00			06 30					07 00						07 30			07 45		
Caerphilly 3	d			06a08			06 36					07 06						07 36			07 51		
Aber	d						06 38					07 08						07 38			07 53		
Energlyn & Churchill Park	d																	07 40					
Llanbradach	d						06 42					07 12						07 44			07 57		
Ystrad Mynach 3	d						06 47					07 17						07 49			08 02		
Hengoed	d						06 50					07 20						07 52			08 05		
Pengam	d						06 53					07 23						07 55			08 08		
Gilfach Fargoed	d																						
Bargoed	a						07 01					07 31						08 04			08 13		
	d																				08 14		
Brithdir	d																				08 18		
Tir-phil	d																				08 21		
Pontlottyn	d																				08 25		
Rhymney 3	a																				08 31		
Cathays	d	05 33			06 03	06 18			06 33	06 43	06 48			07 03	07 13		07 18			07 33		07 43	
Llandaf	d	05 37			06 07	06 22			06 37	06 47	06 52			07 07	07 17		07 22			07 37		07 47	
Ninian Park	d															07 10							07 40
Waun-gron Park	d															07 13							07 43
Fairwater	d															07 15							07 45
Danescourt	d															07 17							07 47
Radyr 3	a	05 40			06 10	06 24			06 40	06 50	06 54			07 10	07 20	07 24	07 25			07 40		07 50	07 54
	d	05 40			06 10	06 24			06 40	06 50	06 55			07 10	07 20		07 25			07 40		07 50	
Taffs Well 3	d	05 44			06 14	06 28			06 44	06 54	06 59			07 14	07 24		07 29			07 44		07 54	
Trefforest Estate	d	05 48			06 18				06 48					07 18						07 48			
Trefforest	d	05 52			06 22	06 35			06 52	07 01	07 06			07 22	07 31		07 36			07 52		08 01	
Pontypridd 3	a	05 55			06 25	06 38			06 55	07 04	07 09			07 25	07 34		07 39			07 55		08 04	
	d	05 57	06 11		06 27	06 41			06 57	07 06	07 11			07 27	07 36		07 41			07 57		08 06	
Abercynon	d	06 04	06 19		06 34	06 49			07 04		07 19			07 34			07 49			08 04			
Penrhiwceiber	d		06 24			06 54					07 24						07 54						
Mountain Ash	a		06 28			06 58					07 28						07 58						
	d		06 33			07 03					07 33						08 03						
Fernhill	d		06 35			07 05					07 35						08 05						
Cwmbach	d		06 39			07 09					07 39						08 09						
Aberdare 3	a		06 46			07 16					07 46						08 16						
Quakers Yard	d	06 09			06 39				07 09					07 39						08 09			
Merthyr Vale	a	06 14			06 44				07 14					07 44						08 14			
	d	06 17			06 47				07 17					07 47						08 17			
Troed Y Rhiw	d	06 20			06 50				07 20					07 50						08 20			
Pentre-bach	d	06 23			06 53				07 23					07 53						08 23			
Merthyr Tydfil	a	06 31			07 01				07 31					08 01						08 31			
Trehafod	d									07 11					07 41							08 11	
Porth	a									07 14					07 44							08 14	
	d									07 15					07 45							08 15	
Dinas Rhondda	d									07 19					07 49							08 19	
Tonypandy	d									07 21					07 51							08 21	
Llwynypia	d									07 23					07 53							08 23	
Ystrad Rhondda	a									07 26					07 56							08 26	
	d									07 29					07 59							08 29	
Ton Pentre	d									07 31					08 01							08 31	
Treorchy	d									07 34					08 04							08 34	
Ynyswen	d									07 37					08 07							08 37	
Treherbert	a									07 43					08 13							08 43	

When events are being held at the Millenium Stadium, services are subject to alteration. Please check times before travelling.

For connections to Cardiff Bay please refer to Table 130A

Table 130R

Saturdays
4 January to 8 February

Bridgend, Barry Island, Barry, Penarth and Cardiff - Coryton, Rhymney, Pontypridd, Merthyr, Aberdare and Treherbert

Network Diagram - see first Page of Table 130

		AW	AW	AW	AW	AW	AW	AW	AW	AW	AW	AW	AW	AW	AW	AW	AW	AW	AW	AW	AW	AW	AW
Bridgend	d	06 42														07 42							
Llantwit Major	d	06 56														07 56							
Rhoose Cardiff Int Airport ✈	d	07 06														08 06							
Barry Island	d				07 25				07 40			07 55							08 25				08 40
Barry 3	d	07 15			07 30				07 45			08 00				08 15			08 30				08 45
Barry Docks	d	07 18			07 33				07 48			08 03				08 18			08 33				08 48
Cadoxton	d	07 21			07 36				07 51			08 06				08 21			08 36				08 51
Dinas Powys	d	07 25			07 40				07 55			08 10				08 25			08 40				08 55
Eastbrook	d	07 28			07 43				07 58			08 13				08 28			08 43				08 58
Cogan	d	07 30			07 45				08 00			08 15				08 30			08 45				09 00
Penarth	d		07 32			07 47				08 02			08 17				08 32			08 47			
Dingle Road	d		07 34			07 49				08 04			08 19				08 34			08 49			
Grangetown	d	07 34	07 38		07 49	07 53			08 05	08 08		08 19	08 23			08 34	08 38		08 49	08 53			09 04
Cardiff Central 7	a	07 39	07 44		07 54	07 59			08 09	08 14		08 24	08 29			08 39	08 44		08 54	08 59			09 09
	d	07 41	07 46	07 51	07 56	08 01	08 06	08 06	08 11	08 16	08 21	08 26	08 31	08 36	08 36	08 41	08 46	08 51	08 56	09 01	09 06	09 06	09 11
Cardiff Queen Street 3	a	07 44	07 49	07 54	07 59	08 04	08 09		08 14	08 19	08 24	08 29	08 34	08 39		08 44	08 49	08 54	08 59	09 04	09 09		09 14
	d	07 45	07 50	07 55	08 00	08 05	08 10		08 15	08 20	08 25	08 30	08 35	08 40		08 45	08 50	08 55	09 00	09 05	09 10		09 15
Heath Low Level	d			08 00							08 30							09 00					
Ty Glas	d			08 03							08 33							09 03					
Birchgrove	d			08 04							08 34							09 04					
Rhiwbina	d			08 06							08 36							09 06					
Whitchurch (Cardiff)	d			08 08							08 38							09 08					
Coryton	a			08 13							08 43							09 13					
Heath High Level	d		07 55			08 10				08 25			08 40				08 55			09 10			
Llanishen	d		07 58			08 13				08 28			08 43				08 58			09 13			
Lisvane & Thornhill	d		08 00			08 15				08 30			08 45				09 00			09 15			
Caerphilly 3	d		08 06			08 21				08 36			08 51				09 06			09 21			
Aber	d		08 08			08 23				08 38			08 53				09 08			09 23			
Energlyn & Churchill Park	d					08 25				08 40										09 25			
Llanbradach	d		08 12			08 29				08 44			08 57				09 12			09 29			
Ystrad Mynach 3	d		08 17			08 34				08 49			09 02				09 17			09 34			
Hengoed	d		08 20			08 37				08 52			09 05				09 20			09 37			
Pengam	d		08 23			08 40				08 55			09 08				09 23			09 40			
Gilfach Fargoed	d					08 43														09 43			
Bargoed	a		08 31			08 50				09 00			09 16				09 31			09 50			
	d									09 01													
Brithdir	d									09 05													
Tir-phil	d									09 08													
Pontlottyn	d									09 12													
Rhymney 3	a									09 18													
Cathays	d	07 48			08 03		08 13		08 18			08 33		08 43		08 48			09 03		09 13		09 18
Llandaf	d	07 52			08 07		08 17		08 22			08 37		08 47		08 52			09 07		09 17		09 22
Ninian Park	d							08 10							08 40							09 10	
Waun-gron Park	d							08 13							08 43							09 13	
Fairwater	d							08 15							08 45							09 15	
Danescourt	d							08 17							08 47							09 17	
Radyr 3	a	07 55			08 10		08 20	08 24	08 25			08 40		08 50	08 54	08 55			09 10		09 20	09 24	09 25
	d	07 55			08 10		08 20		08 25			08 40		08 50		08 55			09 10		09 20		09 25
Taffs Well 3	d	07 59			08 14		08 24		08 29			08 44		08 54		08 59			09 14		09 24		09 29
Trefforest Estate	d				08 18							08 48							09 18				
Trefforest	d	08 06			08 22		08 31		08 36			08 52		09 01		09 06			09 22		09 31		09 36
Pontypridd 3	a	08 09			08 25		08 34		08 39			08 55		09 04		09 09			09 25		09 34		09 39
	d	08 11			08 27		08 36		08 41			08 57		09 06		09 11			09 27		09 36		09 41
Abercynon	d	08 19			08 34				08 49			09 04				09 19			09 34				09 49
Penrhiwceiber	d	08 24							08 54							09 24							09 54
Mountain Ash	a	08 28							08 58							09 28							09 58
	d	08 33							09 03							09 33							10 03
Fernhill	d	08 35							09 05							09 35							10 05
Cwmbach	d	08 39							09 09							09 39							10 09
Aberdare 3	a	08 46							09 16							09 46							10 16
Quakers Yard	d				08 39							09 09							09 39				
Merthyr Vale	a				08 44							09 14							09 44				
	d				08 47							09 17							09 47				
Troed Y Rhiw	d				08 50							09 20							09 50				
Pentre-bach	d				08 53							09 23							09 53				
Merthyr Tydfil	a				09 01							09 31							10 01				
Trehafod	d						08 41							09 11							09 41		
Porth	a						08 44							09 14							09 44		
	d						08 45							09 15							09 45		
Dinas Rhondda	d						08 49							09 19							09 49		
Tonypandy	d						08 51							09 21							09 51		
Llwynypia	d						08 53							09 23							09 53		
Ystrad Rhondda	a						08 56							09 26							09 56		
	d						08 59							09 29							09 59		
Ton Pentre	d						09 01							09 31							10 01		
Treorchy	d						09 04							09 34							10 04		
Ynyswen	d						09 07							09 37							10 07		
Treherbert	a						09 13							09 43							10 13		

When events are being held at the Millenium Stadium, services are subject to alteration. Please check times before travelling.

For connections to Cardiff Bay please refer to Table 130A

Table 130R

Saturdays

4 January to 8 February

Bridgend, Barry Island, Barry, Penarth and Cardiff - Coryton, Rhymney, Pontypridd, Merthyr, Aberdare and Treherbert

Network Diagram - see first Page of Table 130

		AW		AW	AW	AW	AW	AW	AW	AW	AW	AW		AW	AW	AW	AW	AW	AW	AW	AW	AW		AW	AW
Bridgend	d								08 42																
Llantwit Major	d								08 56																
Rhoose Cardiff Int Airport ✈	d								09 06																
Barry Island	d				08 55							09 25						09 40			09 55				
Barry 3	d				09 00				09 15			09 30						09 45			10 00				
Barry Docks	d				09 03				09 18			09 33						09 48			10 03				
Cadoxton	d				09 06				09 21			09 36						09 51			10 06				
Dinas Powys	d				09 10				09 25			09 40						09 55			10 10				
Eastbrook	d				09 13				09 28			09 43						09 58			10 13				
Cogan	d				09 15				09 30			09 45						10 00			10 15				
Penarth	d					09 17				09 32					09 47				10 02			10 17			
Dingle Road	d					09 19				09 34					09 49				10 04			10 19			
Grangetown	d				09 19	09 23			09 34	09 38		09 49			09 53			10 04	10 08		10 19	10 23			
Cardiff Central 7	a				09 24	09 29			09 39	09 44		09 54			09 59			10 09	10 14		10 24	10 29			
	d	09 16		09 21	09 26	09 31	09 36	09 36	09 41	09 46	09 51	09 56			10 01	10 06	10 06	10 11	10 16	10 21	10 26	10 31		10 36	10 36
Cardiff Queen Street 3	a	09 19		09 24	09 29	09 34	09 39		09 44	09 49	09 54	09 59			10 04	10 09		10 14	10 19	10 24	10 29	10 34		10 39	
	d	09 20		09 25	09 30	09 35	09 40		09 45	09 50	09 55	10 00			10 05	10 10		10 15	10 20	10 25	10 30	10 35		10 40	
Heath Low Level	d			09 30							10 00									10 30					
Ty Glas	d			09 33							10 03									10 33					
Birchgrove	d			09 34							10 04									10 34					
Rhiwbina	d			09 36							10 06									10 36					
Whitchurch (Cardiff)	d			09 38							10 08									10 38					
Coryton	a			09 43							10 13									10 43					
Heath High Level	d	09 25				09 40				09 55					10 10				10 25			10 40			
Llanishen	d	09 28				09 43				09 58					10 13				10 28			10 43			
Lisvane & Thornhill	d	09 30				09 45				10 00					10 15				10 30			10 45			
Caerphilly 3	d	09 36				09 51				10 06					10 21				10 36			10 51			
Aber	d	09 38				09 53				10 08					10 23				10 38			10 53			
Energlyn & Churchill Park	d	09 40													10 25				10 40						
Llanbradach	d	09 44				09 57				10 12					10 29				10 44			10 57			
Ystrad Mynach 3	d	09 49				10 02				10 17					10 34				10 49			11 02			
Hengoed	d	09 52				10 05				10 20					10 37				10 52			11 05			
Pengam	d	09 55				10 08				10 23					10 40				10 55			11 08			
Gilfach Fargoed	d														10 43										
Bargoed	a	10 00				10 16				10 31					10 50				11 00			11 16			
	d	10 01																	11 01						
Brithdir	d	10 05																	11 05						
Tir-phil	d	10 08																	11 08						
Pontlottyn	d	10 12																	11 12						
Rhymney 3	a	10 18																	11 18						
Cathays	d				09 33		09 43		09 48			10 03				10 13		10 18			10 33			10 43	
Llandaf	d				09 37		09 47		09 52			10 07				10 17		10 22			10 37			10 47	
Ninian Park	d							09 40									10 10								10 40
Waun-gron Park	d							09 43									10 13								10 43
Fairwater	d							09 45									10 15								10 45
Danescourt	d							09 47									10 17								10 47
Radyr 3	a				09 40		09 50	09 54	09 55			10 10				10 20	10 24	10 25			10 40			10 50	10 54
	d				09 40		09 50		09 55			10 10				10 20		10 25			10 40			10 50	
Taffs Well 3	d				09 44		09 54		09 59			10 14				10 24		10 29			10 44			10 54	
Trefforest Estate	d				09 48																10 48				
Trefforest	d				09 52		10 01		10 06			10 22				10 31		10 36			10 52			11 01	
Pontypridd 3	a				09 55		10 04		10 09			10 30				10 34		10 39			10 55			11 04	
	d				09 57		10 06		10 11					10 35		10 36		10 41			10 57			11 06	
Abercynon	d				10 04				10 19					10 41				10 49			11 04				
Penrhiwceiber	d								10 24									10 54							
Mountain Ash	a								10 28									10 58							
	d								10 33									11 03							
Fernhill	d								10 35									11 05							
Cwmbach	d								10 39									11 09							
Aberdare 3	a								10 46									11 16							
Quakers Yard	d				10 09									10 45							11 09				
Merthyr Vale	a				10 14									10 50							11 14				
	d				10 17									10 52							11 17				
Troed Y Rhiw	d				10 20									10 55							11 20				
Pentre-bach	d				10 23									10 58							11 23				
Merthyr Tydfil	a				10 31									11 06							11 31				
Trehafod	d						10 11									10 41								11 11	
Porth	a						10 14									10 44								11 14	
	d						10 15									10 45								11 15	
Dinas Rhondda	d						10 19									10 49								11 19	
Tonypandy	d						10 21									10 51								11 21	
Llwynypia	d						10 23									10 53								11 23	
Ystrad Rhondda	a						10 26									10 56								11 26	
	d						10 29									10 59								11 29	
Ton Pentre	d						10 31									11 01								11 31	
Treorchy	d						10 34									11 04								11 34	
Ynyswen	d						10 37									11 07								11 37	
Treherbert	a						10 43									11 13								11 43	

When events are being held at the Millenium Stadium, services are subject to alteration. Please check times before travelling.

For connections to Cardiff Bay please refer to Table 130A

Table 130R

Saturdays
4 January to 8 February

Bridgend, Barry Island, Barry, Penarth and Cardiff - Coryton, Rhymney, Pontypridd, Merthyr, Aberdare and Treherbert

Network Diagram - see first Page of Table 130

		AW	AW	AW	AW	AW	AW	AW		AW	AW	AW	AW	AW	AW	AW	AW	AW		AW	AW	AW	AW	AW	AW
Bridgend	d	09 42																10 42							
Llantwit Major	d	09 56																10 56							
Rhoose Cardiff Int Airport ✈	d	10 06																11 06							
Barry Island	d					10 25					10 40			10 55								11 25			
Barry 3	d	10 15				10 30					10 45			11 00				11 15				11 30			
Barry Docks	d	10 18				10 33					10 48			11 03				11 18				11 33			
Cadoxton	d	10 21				10 36					10 51			11 06				11 21				11 36			
Dinas Powys	d	10 25				10 40					10 55			11 10				11 25				11 40			
Eastbrook	d	10 28				10 43					10 58			11 13				11 28				11 43			
Cogan	d	10 30				10 45					11 00			11 15				11 30				11 45			
Penarth	d		10 32					10 47				11 02			11 17					11 32			11 47		
Dingle Road	d		10 34					10 49				11 04			11 19					11 34			11 49		
Grangetown	d	10 34	10 38			10 49		10 53			11 04	11 08		11 19	11 23			11 34		11 38		11 49	11 53		
Cardiff Central 7	a	10 42	10 44			10 54		10 59			11 09	11 14		11 24	11 29			11 39		11 44		11 54	11 59		
	d		10 46	10 51	10 51	10 56		11 01		11 06	11 11	11 16	11 21	11 26	11 31	11 36	11 36	11 41		11 46	11 51	11 56	12 01	12 06	12 06
Cardiff Queen Street 3	a		10 49	10 54		10 59		11 04			11 14	11 19	11 24	11 29	11 34	11 39		11 44		11 49	11 54	11 59	12 04	12 09	
	d		10 50	10 55		11 00		11 05			11 15	11 20	11 25	11 30	11 35	11 40		11 45		11 50	11 55	12 00	12 05	12 10	
Heath Low Level	d			11 00									11 30								12 00				
Ty Glas	d			11 03									11 33								12 03				
Birchgrove	d			11 04									11 34								12 04				
Rhiwbina	d			11 06									11 36								12 06				
Whitchurch (Cardiff)	d			11 08									11 38								12 08				
Coryton	a			11 13									11 43								12 13				
Heath High Level	d		10 55					11 10				11 25			11 40					11 55			12 10		
Llanishen	d		10 58					11 13				11 28			11 43					11 58			12 13		
Lisvane & Thornhill	d		11 00					11 15				11 30			11 45					12 00			12 15		
Caerphilly 3	d		11 06					11 21				11 36			11 51					12 06			12 21		
Aber	d		11 08					11 23				11 38			11 53					12 08			12 23		
Energlyn & Churchill Park	d							11 25				11 40											12 25		
Llanbradach	d		11 12					11 29				11 44			11 57					12 12			12 29		
Ystrad Mynach 3	d		11 17					11 34				11 49			12 02					12 17			12 34		
Hengoed	d		11 20					11 37				11 52			12 05					12 20			12 37		
Pengam	d		11 23					11 40				11 55			12 08					12 23			12 40		
Gilfach Fargoed	d							11 43															12 43		
Bargoed	a		11 31					11 50				12 00			12 16					12 31			12 50		
	d											12 01													
Brithdir	d											12 05													
Tir-phil	d											12 08													
Pontlottyn	d											12 12													
Rhymney 3	a											12 18													
Cathays	d					11 03					11 18			11 33		11 43		11 48				12 03		12 13	
Llandaf	d					11 07					11 22			11 37		11 47		11 52				12 07		12 17	
Ninian Park	d									11 10							11 40								12 10
Waun-gron Park	d									11 13							11 43								12 13
Fairwater	d									11 15							11 45								12 15
Danescourt	d						←			11 17							11 47								12 17
Radyr 3	a				11 02	11 10	11 02			11 24	11 25			11 40		11 50	11 54	11 55				12 10		12 20	12 24
	d				11 20	11 10	11 20				11 25			11 40		11 50		11 55				12 10		12 20	
Taffs Well 3	d				→	11 14	11 24				11 29			11 44		11 54		11 59				12 14		12 24	
Trefforest Estate	d					11 18								11 48								12 18			
Trefforest	d					11 22	11 31				11 36			11 52		12 01		12 06				12 22		12 31	
Pontypridd 3	a					11 25	11 34				11 39			11 55		12 04		12 09				12 25		12 34	
	d					11 27	11 36				11 41			11 57		12 06		12 11				12 27		12 36	
Abercynon	d					11 34					11 49			12 04				12 19				12 34			
Penrhiwceiber	d										11 54							12 24							
Mountain Ash	a										11 58							12 28							
	d										12 03							12 33							
Fernhill	d										12 05							12 35							
Cwmbach	d										12 09							12 39							
Aberdare 3	a										12 16							12 46							
Quakers Yard	d					11 39								12 09								12 39			
Merthyr Vale	a					11 44								12 14								12 44			
	d					11 47								12 17								12 47			
Troed Y Rhiw	d					11 50								12 20								12 50			
Pentre-bach	d					11 53								12 23								12 53			
Merthyr Tydfil	a					12 01								12 31								13 01			
Trehafod	d						11 41									12 11								12 41	
Porth	a						11 44									12 14								12 44	
	d						11 45									12 15								12 45	
Dinas Rhondda	d						11 49									12 19								12 49	
Tonypandy	d						11 51									12 21								12 51	
Llwynypia	d						11 53									12 23								12 53	
Ystrad Rhondda	a						11 56									12 26								12 56	
	d						11 59									12 29								12 59	
Ton Pentre	d						12 01									12 31								13 01	
Treorchy	d						12 04									12 34								13 04	
Ynyswen	d						12 07									12 37								13 07	
Treherbert	a						12 13									12 43								13 13	

When events are being held at the Millenium Stadium, services are subject to alteration. Please check times before travelling.

For connections to Cardiff Bay please refer to Table 130A

Table 130R

Saturdays

4 January to 8 February

Bridgend, Barry Island, Barry, Penarth and Cardiff - Coryton, Rhymney, Pontypridd, Merthyr, Aberdare and Treherbert

Network Diagram - see first Page of Table 130

		AW	AW	AW	AW	AW	AW	AW	AW	AW	AW	AW	AW	AW	AW	AW	AW	AW	AW	AW	AW	AW
Bridgend	d								11 42													
Llantwit Major	d								11 56													
Rhoose Cardiff Int Airport ✈	d								12 06													
Barry Island	d	11 40			11 55							12 25				12 40			12 55			
Barry 3	d	11 45			12 00				12 15			12 30				12 45			13 00			
Barry Docks	d	11 48			12 03				12 18			12 33				12 48			13 03			
Cadoxton	d	11 51			12 06				12 21			12 36				12 51			13 06			
Dinas Powys	d	11 55			12 10				12 25			12 40				12 55			13 10			
Eastbrook	d	11 58			12 13				12 28			12 43				12 58			13 13			
Cogan	d	12 00			12 15				12 30			12 45				13 00			13 15			
Penarth	d		12 02			12 17				12 32			12 47				13 02			13 17		
Dingle Road	d		12 04			12 19				12 34			12 49				13 04			13 19		
Grangetown	d	12 04	12 08		12 19	12 23			12 34	12 38		12 49	12 53			13 04	13 08		13 19	13 23		
Cardiff Central 7	a	12 09	12 14		12 24	12 29			12 39	12 44		12 54	12 59			13 09	13 14		13 24	13 29		
	d	12 11	12 16	12 21	12 26	12 31	12 36	12 36	12 41	12 46	12 51	12 56	13 01	13 06	13 06	13 11	13 16	13 21	13 26	13 31	13 36	13 36
Cardiff Queen Street 3	a	12 14	12 19	12 24	12 29	12 34	12 39		12 44	12 49	12 54	12 59	13 04	13 09		13 14	13 19	13 24	13 29	13 34	13 39	
	d	12 15	12 20	12 25	12 30	12 35	12 40		12 45	12 50	12 55	13 00	13 05	13 10		13 15	13 20	13 25	13 30	13 35	13 40	
Heath Low Level	d			12 30							13 00							13 30				
Ty Glas	d			12 33							13 03							13 33				
Birchgrove	d			12 34							13 04							13 34				
Rhiwbina	d			12 36							13 06							13 36				
Whitchurch (Cardiff)	d			12 38							13 08							13 38				
Coryton	a			12 43							13 13							13 43				
Heath High Level	d		12 25			12 40				12 55			13 10				13 25			13 40		
Llanishen	d		12 28			12 43				12 58			13 13				13 28			13 43		
Lisvane & Thornhill	d		12 30			12 45				13 00			13 15				13 30			13 45		
Caerphilly 3	d		12 36			12 51				13 06			13 21				13 36			13 51		
Aber	d		12 38			12 53				13 08			13 23				13 38			13 53		
Energlyn & Churchill Park	d		12 40										13 25				13 40					
Llanbradach	d		12 44			12 57				13 12			13 29				13 44			13 57		
Ystrad Mynach 3	d		12 49			13 02				13 17			13 34				13 49			14 02		
Hengoed	d		12 52			13 05				13 20			13 37				13 52			14 05		
Pengam	d		12 55			13 08				13 23			13 40				13 55			14 08		
Gilfach Fargoed	d												13 43									
Bargoed	a		13 00			13 16				13 31			13 50				14 00			14 16		
	d		13 01														14 01					
Brithdir	d		13 05														14 05					
Tir-phil	d		13 08														14 08					
Pontlottyn	d		13 12														14 12					
Rhymney 3	a		13 18														14 18					
Cathays	d	12 18			12 33		12 43		12 48			13 03		13 13		13 18			13 33		13 43	
Llandaf	d	12 22			12 37		12 47		12 52			13 07		13 17		13 22			13 37		13 47	
Ninian Park	d							12 40							13 10							13 40
Waun-gron Park	d							12 43							13 13							13 43
Fairwater	d							12 45							13 15							13 45
Danescourt	d							12 47							13 17							13 47
Radyr 3	a	12 25			12 40		12 50	12 54	12 55			13 10		13 20	13 24	13 25			13 40		13 50	13 54
	d	12 25			12 40		12 50		12 55			13 10		13 20		13 25			13 40		13 50	
Taffs Well 3	d	12 29			12 44		12 54		12 59			13 14		13 24		13 29			13 44		13 54	
Trefforest Estate	d				12 48							13 18							13 48			
Trefforest	d	12 36			12 52		13 01		13 06			13 22		13 31		13 36			13 52		14 01	
Pontypridd 3	a	12 42			12 55		13 04		13 09			13 25		13 34		13 39			13 55		14 04	
	d				12 57		13 06		13 11			13 27		13 36		13 41			13 57		14 06	
Abercynon	d				13 04				13 19			13 34				13 49			14 04			
Penrhiwceiber	d								13 24							13 54						
Mountain Ash	a								13 28							13 58						
	d								13 33							14 03						
Fernhill	d								13 35							14 05						
Cwmbach	d								13 39							14 09						
Aberdare 3	a								13 46							14 16						
Quakers Yard	d				13 09							13 39							14 09			
Merthyr Vale	a				13 14							13 44							14 14			
	d				13 17							13 47							14 17			
Troed Y Rhiw	d				13 20							13 50							14 20			
Pentre-bach	d				13 23							13 53							14 23			
Merthyr Tydfil	a				13 31							14 01							14 31			
Trehafod	d						13 11							13 41							14 11	
Porth	a						13 14							13 44							14 14	
	d						13 15							13 45							14 15	
Dinas Rhondda	d						13 19							13 49							14 19	
Tonypandy	d						13 21							13 51							14 21	
Llwynypia	d						13 23							13 53							14 23	
Ystrad Rhondda	a						13 26							13 56							14 26	
	d						13 29							13 59							14 29	
Ton Pentre	d						13 31							14 01							14 31	
Treorchy	d						13 34							14 04							14 34	
Ynyswen	d						13 37							14 07							14 37	
Treherbert	a						13 43							14 13							14 43	

When events are being held at the Millenium Stadium, services are subject to alteration. Please check times before travelling.

For connections to Cardiff Bay please refer to Table 130A

Table 130R

Saturdays

4 January to 8 February

Bridgend, Barry Island, Barry, Penarth and Cardiff - Coryton, Rhymney, Pontypridd, Merthyr, Aberdare and Treherbert

Network Diagram - see first Page of Table 130

		AW	AW	AW	AW	AW	AW	AW	AW	AW
Bridgend	d	12 42								
Llantwit Major	d	12 56								
Rhoose Cardiff Int Airport ✈	d	13 06								
Barry Island	d				13 25				13 40	
Barry 3	d	13 15			13 30				13 45	
Barry Docks	d	13 18			13 34				13 48	
Cadoxton	d	13 21			13 37				13 51	
Dinas Powys	d	13 25			13 41				13 55	
Eastbrook	d	13 28			13 43				13 58	
Cogan	d	13 30			13 45				14 00	
Penarth	d		13 32			13 47				14 02
Dingle Road	d		13 34			13 49				14 04
Grangetown	d	13 34	13 38		13 49	13 53			14 04	14 08
Cardiff Central 7	a	13 39	13 44		13 54	13 59			14 09	14 14
	d	13 41	13 46	13 51	13 56	14 01	14 06	14 06	14 11	14 16
Cardiff Queen Street 3	a	13 44	13 49	13 54	13 59	14 04	14 09		14 14	14 19
	d	13 45	13 50	13 55	14 00	14 05	14 10		14 15	14 20
Heath Low Level	d			14 00						
Ty Glas	d			14 03						
Birchgrove	d			14 04						
Rhiwbina	d			14 06						
Whitchurch (Cardiff)	d			14 08						
Coryton	a			14 13						
Heath High Level	d		13 55			14 10				14 25
Llanishen	d		13 58			14 13				14 28
Lisvane & Thornhill	d		14 00			14 15				14 30
Caerphilly 3	d		14 06			14 21				14 36
Aber	d		14 08			14 23				14 38
Energlyn & Churchill Park	d					14 25				14 40
Llanbradach	d		14 12			14 29				14 44
Ystrad Mynach 3	d		14 17			14 34				14 49
Hengoed	d		14 20			14 37				14 52
Pengam	d		14 23			14 40				14 55
Gilfach Fargoed	d					14 43				
Bargoed	a		14 31			14 50				15 00
	d									15 01
Brithdir	d									15 05
Tir-phil	d									15 08
Pontlottyn	d									15 12
Rhymney 3	a									15 18
Cathays	d	13 48			14 03		14 13		14 18	
Llandaf	d	13 52			14 07		14 17		14 22	
Ninian Park	d							14 10		
Waun-gron Park	d							14 13		
Fairwater	d							14 15		
Danescourt	d							14 17		
Radyr 3	a	13 55			14 10		14 20	14 24	14 25	
	d	13 55			14 10		14 20		14 25	
Taffs Well 3	d	13 59			14 14		14 24		14 29	
Trefforest Estate	d				14 18					
Trefforest	d	14 06			14 22		14 31		14 36	
Pontypridd 3	a	14 09			14 25		14 34		14 39	
	d	14 11			14 27		14 36		14 41	
Abercynon	d	14 19			14 34				14 49	
Penrhiwceiber	d	14 24							14 54	
Mountain Ash	a	14 28							14 58	
	d	14 33							15 03	
Fernhill	d	14 35							15 05	
Cwmbach	d	14 39							15 09	
Aberdare 3	a	14 46							15 16	
Quakers Yard	d				14 39					
Merthyr Vale	a				14 44					
	d				14 47					
Troed Y Rhiw	d				14 50					
Pentre-bach	d				14 53					
Merthyr Tydfil	a				15 01					
Trehafod	d						14 41			
Porth	a						14 44			
	d						14 45			
Dinas Rhondda	d						14 49			
Tonypandy	d						14 51			
Llwynypia	d						14 53			
Ystrad Rhondda	a						14 56			
	d						14 59			
Ton Pentre	d						15 01			
Treorchy	d						15 04			
Ynyswen	d						15 07			
Treherbert	a						15 13			

		AW	AW	AW	AW	AW	AW	AW	AW	AW	AW	AW	AW	AW
Bridgend	d						13 42							
Llantwit Major	d						13 56							
Rhoose Cardiff Int Airport ✈	d						14 06							
Barry Island	d		13 55								14 25			
Barry 3	d		14 00				14 15				14 30			
Barry Docks	d		14 03				14 18				14 33			
Cadoxton	d		14 06				14 21				14 36			
Dinas Powys	d		14 10				14 25				14 40			
Eastbrook	d		14 13				14 28				14 43			
Cogan	d		14 15				14 30				14 45			
Penarth	d			14 17				14 32					14 47	
Dingle Road	d			14 19				14 34					14 49	
Grangetown	d		14 19	14 23			14 34	14 38			14 49		14 53	
Cardiff Central 7	a		14 24	14 29			14 39	14 44			14 54		14 59	
	d	14 21	14 26	14 31	14 36	14 36	14 41	14 46	14 51	14 51	14 56		15 01	15 06
Cardiff Queen Street 3	a	14 24	14 29	14 34	14 39		14 44	14 49	14 54		14 59		15 04	
	d	14 25	14 30	14 35	14 40		14 45	14 50	14 55		15 00		15 05	
Heath Low Level	d	14 30							15 00					
Ty Glas	d	14 33							15 03					
Birchgrove	d	14 34							15 04					
Rhiwbina	d	14 36							15 06					
Whitchurch (Cardiff)	d	14 38							15 08					
Coryton	a	14 43							15 13					
Heath High Level	d			14 40				14 55					15 10	
Llanishen	d			14 43				14 58					15 13	
Lisvane & Thornhill	d			14 45				15 00					15 15	
Caerphilly 3	d			14 51				15 06					15 21	
Aber	d			14 53				15 08					15 23	
Energlyn & Churchill Park	d												15 25	
Llanbradach	d			14 57				15 12					15 29	
Ystrad Mynach 3	d			15 02				15 17					15 34	
Hengoed	d			15 05				15 20					15 37	
Pengam	d			15 08				15 23					15 40	
Gilfach Fargoed	d												15 43	
Bargoed	a			15 16				15 31					15 50	
	d													
Brithdir	d													
Tir-phil	d													
Pontlottyn	d													
Rhymney 3	a													
Cathays	d		14 33		14 43		14 48				15 03			
Llandaf	d		14 37		14 47		14 52				15 07			
Ninian Park	d					14 40								15 10
Waun-gron Park	d					14 43								15 13
Fairwater	d					14 45								15 15
Danescourt	d					14 47						←		15 17
Radyr 3	a		14 40		14 50	14 54	14 55			15 08	15 10	15 08		15 24
	d		14 40		14 50		14 55			15 20	15 10	15 20		
Taffs Well 3	d		14 44		14 54		14 59			→	15 14	15 24		
Trefforest Estate	d		14 48								15 18			
Trefforest	d		14 52		15 01		15 06				15 22	15 31		
Pontypridd 3	a		14 55		15 04		15 09				15 25	15 34		
	d		14 57		15 06		15 11				15 27	15 36		
Abercynon	d		15 04				15 19				15 34			
Penrhiwceiber	d						15 24							
Mountain Ash	a						15 28							
	d						15 33							
Fernhill	d						15 35							
Cwmbach	d						15 39							
Aberdare 3	a						15 46							
Quakers Yard	d		15 09								15 39			
Merthyr Vale	a		15 14								15 44			
	d		15 17								15 47			
Troed Y Rhiw	d		15 20								15 50			
Pentre-bach	d		15 23								15 53			
Merthyr Tydfil	a		15 31								16 01			
Trehafod	d				15 11							15 41		
Porth	a				15 14							15 44		
	d				15 15							15 45		
Dinas Rhondda	d				15 19							15 49		
Tonypandy	d				15 21							15 51		
Llwynypia	d				15 23							15 53		
Ystrad Rhondda	a				15 26							15 56		
	d				15 29							15 59		
Ton Pentre	d				15 31							16 01		
Treorchy	d				15 34							16 04		
Ynyswen	d				15 37							16 07		
Treherbert	a				15 43							16 13		

When events are being held at the Millenium Stadium, services are subject to alteration. Please check times before travelling.

For connections to Cardiff Bay please refer to Table 130A

Table 130R

Saturdays

4 January to 8 February

Bridgend, Barry Island, Barry, Penarth and Cardiff - Coryton, Rhymney, Pontypridd, Merthyr, Aberdare and Treherbert

Network Diagram - see first Page of Table 130

		AW	AW	AW	AW	AW	AW	AW	AW	AW	AW	AW	AW	AW	AW	AW	AW	AW	AW	AW	AW	AW	AW
Bridgend	d								14 42														15 42
Llantwit Major	d								14 56														15 56
Rhoose Cardiff Int Airport ✈	d								15 06														16 06
Barry Island	d	14 40			14 55							15 25				15 40			15 55				
Barry 3	d	14 45			15 00				15 15			15 30				15 45			16 00				16 15
Barry Docks	d	14 48			15 03				15 18			15 33				15 48			16 03				16 18
Cadoxton	d	14 51			15 06				15 21			15 36				15 51			16 06				16 21
Dinas Powys	d	14 55			15 10				15 25			15 40				15 55			16 10				16 25
Eastbrook	d	14 58			15 13				15 28			15 43				15 58			16 13				16 28
Cogan	d	15 00			15 15				15 30			15 45				16 00			16 15				16 30
Penarth	d		15 02			15 17				15 32			15 47				16 02			16 17			
Dingle Road	d		15 04			15 19				15 34			15 49				16 04			16 19			
Grangetown	d	15 04	15 08		15 19	15 23			15 34	15 38		15 49	15 53			16 04	16 08		16 19	16 23			16 34
Cardiff Central 7	a	15 09	15 14		15 24	15 29			15 39	15 44		15 54	15 59			16 09	16 14		16 24	16 29			16 39
	d	15 11	15 16	15 21	15 26	15 31	15 36	15 36	15 41	15 46	15 51	15 56	16 01	16 06	16 06	16 11	16 16	16 21	16 26	16 31	16 36	16 36	16 41
Cardiff Queen Street 3	a	15 14	15 19	15 24	15 29	15 34	15 39		15 44	15 49	15 54	15 59	16 04	16 09		16 14	16 19	16 24	16 29	16 34	16 39		16 44
	d	15 15	15 20	15 25	15 30	15 35	15 40		15 45	15 50	15 55	16 00	16 05	16 10		16 15	16 20	16 25	16 30	16 35	16 40		16 45
Heath Low Level	d			15 30							16 00							16 30					
Ty Glas	d			15 33							16 03							16 33					
Birchgrove	d			15 34							16 04							16 34					
Rhiwbina	d			15 36							16 06							16 36					
Whitchurch (Cardiff)	d			15 38							16 08							16 38					
Coryton	a			15 43							16 13							16 43					
Heath High Level	d		15 25			15 40				15 55			16 10				16 25			16 40			
Llanishen	d		15 28			15 43				15 58			16 13				16 28			16 43			
Lisvane & Thornhill	d		15 30			15 45				16 00			16 15				16 30			16 45			
Caerphilly 3	d		15 36			15 51				16 06			16 21				16 36			16 51			
Aber	d		15 38			15 53				16 08			16 23				16 38			16 53			
Energlyn & Churchill Park	d		15 40										16 25				16 40						
Llanbradach	d		15 44			15 57				16 12			16 29				16 44			16 57			
Ystrad Mynach 3	d		15 49			16 02				16 17			16 34				16 49			17 02			
Hengoed	d		15 52			16 05				16 20			16 37				16 52			17 05			
Pengam	d		15 55			16 08				16 23			16 40				16 55			17 08			
Gilfach Fargoed	d												16 43										
Bargoed	a		16 00			16 16				16 31			16 50				17 00			17 16			
	d		16 01														17 01						
Brithdir	d		16 05														17 05						
Tir-phil	d		16 08														17 08						
Pontlottyn	d		16 12														17 12						
Rhymney 3	a		16 18														17 18						
Cathays	d	15 18			15 33		15 43		15 48			16 03		16 13		16 18			16 33		16 43		16 48
Llandaf	d	15 22			15 37		15 47		15 52			16 07		16 17		16 22			16 37		16 47		16 52
Ninian Park	d							15 40							16 10							16 40	
Waun-gron Park	d							15 43							16 13							16 43	
Fairwater	d							15 45							16 15							16 45	
Danescourt	d							15 47							16 17							16 47	
Radyr 3	a	15 25			15 40		15 50	15 54	15 55			16 10		16 20	16 24	16 25			16 40		16 50	16 54	16 55
	d	15 25			15 40		15 50		15 55			16 10		16 20		16 25			16 40		16 50		16 55
Taffs Well 3	d	15 29			15 44		15 54		15 59			16 14		16 24		16 29			16 44		16 54		16 59
Trefforest Estate	d				15 48							16 18							16 48				
Trefforest	d	15 36			15 52		16 01		16 06			16 22		16 31		16 36			16 52		17 01		17 06
Pontypridd 3	a	15 39			15 55		16 04		16 09			16 25		16 34		16 39			16 55		17 04		17 09
	d	15 41			15 57		16 06		16 11			16 27		16 36		16 41			16 57		17 06		17 11
Abercynon	d	15 49			16 04				16 19			16 34				16 49			17 04				17 19
Penrhiwceiber	d	15 54							16 24							16 54							17 24
Mountain Ash	a	15 58							16 28							16 58							17 28
	d	16 03							16 33							17 03							17 33
Fernhill	d	16 05							16 35							17 05							17 35
Cwmbach	d	16 09							16 39							17 09							17 39
Aberdare 3	a	16 16							16 46							17 16							17 46
Quakers Yard	d				16 09							16 39							17 09				
Merthyr Vale	a				16 14							16 44							17 14				
	d				16 17							16 47							17 17				
Troed Y Rhiw	d				16 20							16 50							17 20				
Pentre-bach	d				16 23							16 53							17 23				
Merthyr Tydfil	a				16 31							17 01							17 31				
Trehafod	d						16 11							16 41							17 11		
Porth	a						16 14							16 44							17 14		
	d						16 15							16 45							17 15		
Dinas Rhondda	d						16 19							16 49							17 19		
Tonypandy	d						16 21							16 51							17 21		
Llwynypia	d						16 23							16 53							17 23		
Ystrad Rhondda	a						16 26							16 56							17 26		
	d						16 29							16 59							17 29		
Ton Pentre	d						16 31							17 01							17 31		
Treorchy	d						16 34							17 04							17 34		
Ynyswen	d						16 37							17 07							17 37		
Treherbert	a						16 43							17 13							17 43		

When events are being held at the Millenium Stadium, services are subject to alteration. Please check times before travelling.

For connections to Cardiff Bay please refer to Table 130A

Table 130R

Saturdays
4 January to 8 February

Bridgend, Barry Island, Barry, Penarth and Cardiff - Coryton, Rhymney, Pontypridd, Merthyr, Aberdare and Treherbert

Network Diagram - see first Page of Table 130

		AW	AW	AW	AW	AW	AW	AW	AW	AW	AW	AW	AW	AW	AW	AW	AW	AW	AW	AW	AW	AW
Bridgend	d														16 42							
Llantwit Major	d														16 56							
Rhoose Cardiff Int Airport ✈	d														17 06							
Barry Island	d			16 25				16 40			16 55							17 25				17 40
Barry 3	d			16 30				16 45			17 00				17 15			17 30				17 45
Barry Docks	d			16 33				16 48			17 03				17 18			17 33				17 48
Cadoxton	d			16 36				16 51			17 06				17 21			17 36				17 51
Dinas Powys	d			16 40				16 55			17 10				17 25			17 40				17 55
Eastbrook	d			16 43				16 58			17 13				17 28			17 43				17 58
Cogan	d			16 45				17 00			17 15				17 30			17 45				18 00
Penarth	d	16 32							17 02			17 17				17 32			17 47			
Dingle Road	d	16 34							17 04			17 19				17 34			17 49			
Grangetown	d	16 38		16 49				17 04	17 08		17 19	17 23			17 34	17 38		17 49	17 53			18 04
Cardiff Central 7	a	16 44		16 54				17 09	17 14		17 24	17 29			17 39	17 44		17 54	17 59			18 09
	d	16 46	16 51	16 56	17 01	17 06	17 06	17 11	17 16	17 21	17 26	17 31	17 36	17 36	17 41	17 46	17 51	17 56	18 01	18 06	18 06	18 11
Cardiff Queen Street 3	a	16 49	16 54	16 59	17 04	17 09		17 14	17 19	17 24	17 29	17 34	17 39		17 44	17 49	17 54	17 59	18 04	18 09		18 14
	d	16 50	16 55	17 00	17 05	17 10		17 15	17 20	17 25	17 30	17 35	17 40		17 45	17 50	17 55	18 00	18 05	18 10		18 15
Heath Low Level	d		17 00							17 30							18 00					
Ty Glas	d		17 03							17 33							18 03					
Birchgrove	d		17 04							17 34							18 04					
Rhiwbina	d		17 06							17 36							18 06					
Whitchurch (Cardiff)	d		17 08							17 38							18 08					
Coryton	a		17 13							17 43							18 13					
Heath High Level	d	16 55			17 10				17 25			17 40				17 55			18 10			
Llanishen	d	16 58			17 13				17 28			17 43				17 59			18 13			
Lisvane & Thornhill	d	17 00			17 15				17 30			17 45				18 02			18 15			
Caerphilly 3	d	17 06			17 21				17 36			17 51				18 07			18 21			
Aber	d	17 08			17 23				17 38			17 53				18 10			18 23			
Energlyn & Churchill Park	d				17 26				17 40			17 55				18 13						
Llanbradach	d	17 12			17 29				17 44			17 59				18 17			18 27			
Ystrad Mynach 3	d	17 17			17 35				17 49			18 04				18 22			18 32			
Hengoed	d	17 20			17 37				17 52			18 07				18 25			18 35			
Pengam	d	17 23			17 41				17 55			18 10				18 29			18 38			
Gilfach Fargoed	d				17 44							18 13				18 33			18 41			
Bargoed	a	17 31			17 47				18 03			18 16				18 36			18 48			
	d				17 49							18 18				18 44						
Brithdir	d				17 52							18 22				18 48						
Tir-phil	d				17 55							18 25				18 51						
Pontlottyn	d				18 00							18 29				18 55						
Rhymney 3	a				18 06							18 35				19 01						
Cathays	d			17 03		17 13		17 18			17 33		17 43		17 48			18 03		18 13		18 18
Llandaf	d			17 07		17 17		17 22			17 37		17 47		17 52			18 07		18 17		18 22
Ninian Park	d						17 10							17 40							18 10	
Waun-gron Park	d						17 13							17 43							18 13	
Fairwater	d						17 15							17 45							18 15	
Danescourt	d						17 17							17 47							18 17	
Radyr 3	a			17 10		17 20	17 24	17 25			17 40		17 50	17 54	17 55			18 10		18 20	18 24	18 25
	d			17 10		17 20		17 25			17 40		17 50		17 55			18 10		18 20		18 25
Taffs Well 3	d			17 14		17 24		17 29			17 44		17 54		17 59			18 14		18 24		18 29
Trefforest Estate	d			17 18							17 48							18 18				
Trefforest	d			17 22		17 31		17 36			17 52		18 01		18 06			18 22		18 31		18 36
Pontypridd 3	a			17 25		17 34		17 39			17 55		18 04		18 09			18 25		18 34		18 42
	d			17 27		17 36		17 41			17 57		18 06		18 11			18 27		18 36		
Abercynon	d			17 34				17 49			18 04				18 19			18 34				
Penrhiwceiber	d							17 54							18 24							
Mountain Ash	a							17 58							18 28							
	d							18 03							18 33							
Fernhill	d							18 05							18 35							
Cwmbach	d							18 09							18 39							
Aberdare 3	a							18 16							18 46							
Quakers Yard	d			17 39							18 09							18 39				
Merthyr Vale	a			17 44							18 14							18 44				
	d			17 47							18 17							18 47				
Troed Y Rhiw	d			17 50							18 20							18 50				
Pentre-bach	d			17 53							18 23							18 53				
Merthyr Tydfil	a			18 01							18 31							19 01				
Trehafod	d					17 41							18 11							18 41		
Porth	a					17 44							18 14							18 44		
	d					17 45							18 15							18 45		
Dinas Rhondda	d					17 49							18 19							18 49		
Tonypandy	d					17 51							18 21							18 51		
Llwynypia	d					17 53							18 23							18 53		
Ystrad Rhondda	a					17 56							18 26							18 56		
	d					17 59							18 29							18 59		
Ton Pentre	d					18 01							18 31							19 01		
Treorchy	d					18 04							18 34							19 04		
Ynyswen	d					18 07							18 37							19 07		
Treherbert	a					18 13							18 43							19 13		

When events are being held at the Millenium Stadium, services are subject to alteration. Please check times before travelling.

For connections to Cardiff Bay please refer to Table 130A

Table 130R

Saturdays

4 January to 8 February

Bridgend, Barry Island, Barry, Penarth and Cardiff - Coryton, Rhymney, Pontypridd, Merthyr, Aberdare and Treherbert

Network Diagram - see first Page of Table 130

		AW	AW	AW	AW		AW	AW		AW	AW	AW	AW		AW	AW	AW	AW		AW	AW	AW	AW	AW	AW
Bridgend	d							17 42												18 42					
Llantwit Major	d							17 56												18 56					
Rhoose Cardiff Int Airport ✈	d							18 06												19 06					
Barry Island	d			17 55								18 25			18 40	18 55						19 25		19 55	
Barry 3	d			18 00				18 15				18 30			18 45	19 00				19 15		19 30		20 00	
Barry Docks	d			18 03				18 18				18 33			18 48	19 03				19 18		19 33		20 03	
Cadoxton	d			18 06				18 21				18 36			18 51	19 06				19 21		19 36		20 06	
Dinas Powys	d			18 10				18 25				18 40			18 55	19 10				19 25		19 40		20 10	
Eastbrook	d			18 13				18 28				18 43			18 58	19 13				19 28		19 43		20 13	
Cogan	d			18 15				18 30				18 45			19 00	19 15				19 30		19 45		20 15	
Penarth	d	18 02			18 17					18 32			18 47				19 17						19 47		20 20
Dingle Road	d	18 04			18 19					18 34			18 49				19 19						19 49		20 22
Grangetown	d	18 08		18 19	18 23			18 34		18 38		18 49	18 53		19 04	19 19	19 23			19 34		19 49	19 53	20 19	20 26
Cardiff Central 7	a	18 14		18 25	18 29			18 39		18 47		18 55	18 59		19 09	19 24	19 29			19 39		19 56	19 59	20 24	20 31
	d	18 16	18 21	18 26	18 31	18 36	18 36	18 41			18 51		19 01	19 06	19 11	19 26	19 31	19 36		19 41	19 51	20 01	20 06	20 26	20 31
Cardiff Queen Street 3	a	18 19	18 24	18 29	18 34	18 38		18 44			18 54		19 04	19 09	19 14	19 29	19 34			19 44	19 54	20 04	20 09	20 29	20 34
	d	18 20	18 25	18 30	18 35	18 40		18 50			18 55		19 05	19 10	19 15	19 30	19 35			19 45	19 55	20 05	20 10	20 30	20 35
Heath Low Level	d		18 30								19 00										20 00				
Ty Glas	d		18 33								19 03										20 03				
Birchgrove	d		18 34								19 04										20 04				
Rhiwbina	d		18 36								19 06										20 06				
Whitchurch (Cardiff)	d		18 38								19 08										20 08				
Coryton	a		18 43								19 13										20 13				
Heath High Level	d	18 25			18 40								19 10				19 40					20 10			20 40
Llanishen	d	18 28			18 43								19 13				19 43					20 13			20 43
Lisvane & Thornhill	d	18 30			18 45								19 15				19 45					20 15			20 45
Caerphilly 3	d	18 36			18 51								19a23				19 51					20a27			20 51
Aber	d	18 38			18 53												19 53								20 53
Energlyn & Churchill Park	d				18 56												19 56								20 56
Llanbradach	d	18 42			18 59												19 59								20 59
Ystrad Mynach 3	d	18a51			19 04												20 04								21 04
Hengoed	d				19 07												20 07								21 07
Pengam	d				19 10												20 10								21 10
Gilfach Fargoed	d				19 13												20 13								21 13
Bargoed	a				19 16												20 17								21 17
	d				19 18												20 18								21 18
Brithdir	d				19 22												20 22								21 22
Tir-phil	d				19 25												20 25								21 25
Pontlottyn	d				19 29												20 29								21 29
Rhymney 3	a				19 36												20 35								21 36
Cathays	d			18 33		18 43		18 52						19 13	19 18	19 33				19 48			20 13	20 33	
Llandaf	d			18 37		18 47		18 56						19 17	19 22	19 37				19 52			20 17	20 37	
Ninian Park	d						18 40											19 40							
Waun-gron Park	d						18 43											19 43							
Fairwater	d						18 45											19 45							
Danescourt	d						18 47											19 47							
Radyr 3	a			18 40		18 50	18 54	18 58						19 20	19 25	19 40		19 54		19 55			20 20	20 40	
	d			18 40		18 50		18 58						19 20	19 25	19 40				19 55			20 20	20 40	
Taffs Well 3	d			18 44		18 54		19 03						19 24	19 29	19 44				19 59			20 24	20 44	
Trefforest Estate	d			18 48												19 48								20 48	
Trefforest	d			18 52		19 01		19 10						19 31	19 36	19 52				20 06			20 31	20 52	
Pontypridd 3	a			18 55		19 04		19 13						19 34	19 39	19 55				20 09			20 34	20 55	
	d			18 57		19 06		19 14						19 36	19 41	19 57				20 11			20 36	20 57	
Abercynon	d			19 04				19 21							19 49	20 04				20 21				21 04	
Penrhiwceiber	d							19 26							19 54					20 26					
Mountain Ash	a							19 30							19 56					20 30					
	d							19 33							20 03					20 33					
Fernhill	d							19 35							20 05					20 35					
Cwmbach	d							19 39							20 09					20 39					
Aberdare 3	a							19 46							20 16					20 46					
Quakers Yard	d			19 09												20 08								21 08	
Merthyr Vale	a			19 14												20 13								21 13	
	d			19 17												20 15								21 16	
Troed Y Rhiw	d			19 20												20 19								21 20	
Pentre-bach	d			19 23												20 22								21 23	
Merthyr Tydfil	a			19 31												20 30								21 31	
Trehafod	d					19 11								19 41									20 41		
Porth	a					19 14								19 44									20 44		
	d					19 15								19 45									20 45		
Dinas Rhondda	d					19 19								19 49									20 49		
Tonypandy	d					19 21								19 51									20 51		
Llwynypia	d					19 23								19 53									20 53		
Ystrad Rhondda	a					19 26								19 56									20 56		
	d					19 29								19 59									20 59		
Ton Pentre	d					19 31								20 01									21 01		
Treorchy	d					19 34								20 04									21 04		
Ynyswen	d					19 37								20 07									21 07		
Treherbert	a					19 43								20 13									21 13		

When events are being held at the Millenium Stadium, services are subject to alteration. Please check times before travelling.

For connections to Cardiff Bay please refer to Table 130A

Table 130R

Saturdays

4 January to 8 February

Bridgend, Barry Island, Barry, Penarth and Cardiff - Coryton, Rhymney, Pontypridd, Merthyr, Aberdare and Treherbert

Network Diagram - see first Page of Table 130

		AW	AW	AW	AW	AW	AW	AW	AW	AW	AW	AW	AW	AW	AW	AW	AW	AW	AW	AW	AW	AW
									bus				bus			bus	bus					bus
Bridgend	d		19 42									20 42									21 42	
Llantwit Major	d		19 56									20 56									21 56	
Rhoose Cardiff Int Airport ✈	d		20 06									21 06									22 06	
Barry Island	d						20 55												21 55			
Barry [3]	d		20 15				21 00					21 15							22 00		22 15	
Barry Docks	d		20 18				21 03					21 18							22 03		22 18	
Cadoxton	d		20 21				21 06					21 21							22 06		22 21	
Dinas Powys	d		20 25				21 10					21 25							22 10		22 25	
Eastbrook	d		20 28				21 13					21 28							22 13		22 28	
Cogan	d		20 30				21 15					21 30							22 15		22 30	
Penarth	d				20 47						21 20			21 47						22 20		
Dingle Road	d				20 49						21 22			21 49						22 22		
Grangetown	d		20 34		20 53		21 19				21 26	21 34		21 53					22 19	22 26	22 34	
Cardiff Central [7]	a		20 39		20 59		21 24				21 37	21 39		21 59					22 24	22 33	22 43	
	d	20 36	20 41	20 51	21 00	21 06	21 27	21 31	21 32	21 36		21 41	21 52	22 01	22 06	22 10	22 11		22 29		22 45	22 52
Cardiff Queen Street [3]	a		20 44	20 54	21 03	21 09	21 30	21 34	21 40			21 44	22 00	22 04		22 18	22 19					23 00
	d		20 45	20 55	21 04	21 10	21 31	21 35	21 40			21 45	22 00	22 05		22 18	22 19					23 00
Heath Low Level	d			21 00																		
Ty Glas	d			21 03																		
Birchgrove	d			21 04																		
Rhiwbina	d			21 06																		
Whitchurch (Cardiff)	d			21 08																		
Coryton	a			21 13																		
Heath High Level	d				21 09			21 40						22 10			22a34	22 44				
Llanishen	d				21 12			21 43						22 13				22 47				
Lisvane & Thornhill	d				21 14			21 45						22 15				22 49				
Caerphilly [3]	d				21 19			21 51						22a23				22 55				
Aber	d				21 21			21 53										22 57				
Energlyn & Churchill Park	d							21 56										22 59				
Llanbradach	d				21 25			21 59										23 03				
Ystrad Mynach [3]	d				21a35			22 04										23 08				
Hengoed	d							22 07										23 11				
Pengam	d							22 10										23 14				
Gilfach Fargoed	d							22 13										23 17				
Bargoed	a							22 17										23 21				
	d							22 18										23 22				
Brithdir	d							22 22										23 26				
Tir-phil	d							22 25										23 29				
Pontlottyn	d							22 29										23 33				
Rhymney [3]	a							22 36										23 39				
Cathays	d		20 48			21 13	21 34		21 45			21 48	22 05			22 23						23 05
Llandaf	d		20 52			21 17	21 38		22 00			21 52	22 20			22 38						23 20
Ninian Park	d	20 40								21 40												
Waun-gron Park	d	20 43								21 43												
Fairwater	d	20 45								21 45												
Danescourt	d	20 47								21 47												
Radyr [3]	a	20 54	20 55			21 20	21 41		22 10	21 54		21 55	22 30		22 20	22 48			22 40		22 57	23 30
	d		20 55			21 20	21 41					21 55			22 20				22 40		22 58	
Taffs Well [3]	d		20 59			21 24	21 45					21 59			22 24				22 44		23 02	
Trefforest Estate	d						21 49												22 48			
Trefforest	d		21 06			21 31	21 53					22 06			22 31				22 52		23 09	
Pontypridd [3]	a		21 09			21 34	21 56					22 09			22 34				22 55		23 12	
	d		21 11			21 36	21 58					22 11			22 36				22 57		23 14	
Abercynon	d		21 19				22 05					22 19							23 04		23 21	
Penrhiwceiber	d		21 24									22 24									23 27	
Mountain Ash	a		21 28									22 28									23 30	
	d		21 29									22 29									23 31	
Fernhill	d		21 31									22 31									23 34	
Cwmbach	d		21 35									22 35									23 37	
Aberdare [3]	a		21 42									22 42									23 45	
Quakers Yard	d						22 09												23 08			
Merthyr Vale	a						22 14												23 13			
	d						22 16												23 15			
Troed Y Rhiw	d						22 20												23 19			
Pentre-bach	d						22 23												23 22			
Merthyr Tydfil	a						22 31												23 32			
Trehafod	d					21 41									22 41							
Porth	a					21 44									22 44							
	d					21 45									22 45							
Dinas Rhondda	d					21 49									22 49							
Tonypandy	d					21 51									22 51							
Llwynypia	d					21 53									22 53							
Ystrad Rhondda	a					21 56									22 56							
	d					21 59									22 59							
Ton Pentre	d					22 01									23 01							
Treorchy	d					22 04									23 04							
Ynyswen	d					22 07									23 07							
Treherbert	a					22 13									23 13							

When events are being held at the Millenium Stadium, services are subject to alteration. Please check times before travelling.

For connections to Cardiff Bay please refer to Table 130A

Table 130R

Saturdays

4 January to 8 February

Bridgend, Barry Island, Barry, Penarth and Cardiff - Coryton, Rhymney, Pontypridd, Merthyr, Aberdare and Treherbert

Network Diagram - see first Page of Table 130

		AW	AW	AW	AW	AW	AW	AW	AW
Bridgend	d								22 42
Llantwit Major	d								22 56
Rhoose Cardiff Int Airport ✈	d								23 06
Barry Island	d						22 44		
Barry ■	d						22 49		23 15
Barry Docks	d						22 52		23 18
Cadoxton	d						22 55		23 21
Dinas Powys	d						22 59		23 25
Eastbrook	d						23 02		23 28
Cogan	d						23 04		23 30
Penarth	d		22 47					23 26	
Dingle Road	d		22 49					23 28	
Grangetown	d		22 53				23 08	23 32	23 34
Cardiff Central ■	a		23 03				23 16	23 41	23 46
	d	22 55		23 14			23 21		
Cardiff Queen Street ■	a			23 22					
	d			23 22					
Heath Low Level	d								
Ty Glas	d								
Birchgrove	d								
Rhiwbina	d								
Whitchurch (Cardiff)	d								
Coryton	a								
Heath High Level	d			23a37	23 47				
Llanishen	d				23 50				
Lisvane & Thornhill	d				23 52				
Caerphilly ■	d				23 58				
Aber	d				23 59				
Energlyn & Churchill Park	d								
Llanbradach	d				00 04				
Ystrad Mynach ■	d				00a11				
Hengoed	d								
Pengam	d								
Gilfach Fargoed	d								
Bargoed	a								
	d								
Brithdir	d								
Tir-phil	d								
Pontlottyn	d								
Rhymney ■	a								
Cathays	d								
Llandaf	d								
Ninian Park	d	22 59							
Waun-gron Park	d	23 02							
Fairwater	d	23 04							
Danescourt	d	23 06							
Radyr ■	a	23 12					23 34		
	d						23 40		
Taffs Well ■	d						23 44		
Trefforest Estate	d								
Trefforest	d						23 52		
Pontypridd ■	a						23 58		
	d					23 18			
Abercynon	d								
Penrhiwceiber	d								
Mountain Ash	a								
	d								
Fernhill	d								
Cwmbach	d								
Aberdare ■	a								
Quakers Yard	d								
Merthyr Vale	a								
	d								
Troed Y Rhiw	d								
Pentre-bach	d								
Merthyr Tydfil	a								
Trehafod	d					23 23			
Porth	a					23 26			
	d					23 27			
Dinas Rhondda	d					23 31			
Tonypandy	d					23 33			
Llwynypia	d					23 35			
Ystrad Rhondda	a					23 38			
	d					23 40			
Ton Pentre	d					23 42			
Treorchy	d					23 45			
Ynyswen	d					23 48			
Treherbert	a					23 54			

When events are being held at the Millenium Stadium, services are subject to alteration. Please check times before travelling.

For connections to Cardiff Bay please refer to Table 130A

Table 130R

Saturdays

15 February to 17 May

Bridgend, Barry Island, Barry, Penarth and Cardiff - Coryton, Rhymney, Pontypridd, Merthyr, Aberdare and Treherbert

Network Diagram - see first Page of Table 130

		AW		AW	AW	AW	AW	AW	AW	AW	AW	AW	AW	AW	AW	AW	AW	AW	AW	AW	AW	AW
Bridgend	d										05 42											
Llantwit Major	d										05 56											
Rhoose Cardiff Int Airport ✈	d										06 06											
Barry Island	d			05 15				05 50						06 25						06 55			
Barry 3	d			05 20				05 55			06 15			06 30						07 00			
Barry Docks	d			05 23				05 58			06 18			06 33						07 03			
Cadoxton	d			05 26				06 01			06 21			06 36						07 06			
Dinas Powys	d			05 30				06 05			06 25			06 40						07 10			
Eastbrook	d			05 33				06 08			06 28			06 43						07 13			
Cogan	d			05 35				06 10			06 30			06 45						07 15			
Penarth	d						06 02					06 32						07 02			07 17		
Dingle Road	d						06 04					06 34						07 04			07 19		
Grangetown	d			05 39			06 08	06 14			06 34	06 38		06 49				07 08		07 19	07 23		
Cardiff Central 7	a			05 44			06 13	06 19			06 39	06 44		06 54				07 14		07 24	07 29		
	d	05 26		05 46	05 56	06 11	06 15	06 21	06 26	06 36	06 41	06 46	06 51	06 56	07 06	07 06	07 11	07 16	07 21	07 26	07 31	07 36	07 36
Cardiff Queen Street 3	a	05 29		05 49	05 59	06 14	06 19	06 24	06 29	06 39	06 44	06 49	06 54	06 59	07 09		07 14	07 19	07 24	07 29	07 34	07 39	
	d	05 30		05 50	06 00	06 15	06 20	06 25	06 30	06 40	06 45	06 50	06 55	07 00	07 10		07 15	07 20	07 25	07 30	07 35	07 40	
Heath Low Level	d							06 30					07 00						07 30				
Ty Glas	d							06 33					07 03						07 33				
Birchgrove	d							06 34					07 04						07 34				
Rhiwbina	d							06 36					07 06						07 36				
Whitchurch (Cardiff)	d							06 38					07 08						07 38				
Coryton	a							06 43					07 13						07 43				
Heath High Level	d			05 55			06 25					06 55						07 25			07 40		
Llanishen	d			05 58			06 28					06 58						07 28			07 43		
Lisvane & Thornhill	d			06 00			06 30					07 00						07 30			07 45		
Caerphilly 3	d			06a08			06 36					07 06						07 36			07 51		
Aber	d						06 38					07 08						07 38			07 53		
Energlyn & Churchill Park	d																	07 40					
Llanbradach	d						06 42					07 12						07 44			07 57		
Ystrad Mynach 3	d						06 47					07 17						07 49			08 02		
Hengoed	d						06 50					07 20						07 52			08 05		
Pengam	d						06 53					07 23						07 55			08 08		
Gilfach Fargoed	d																						
Bargoed	a						07 01					07 31						08 04			08 13		
	d																				08 14		
Brithdir	d																				08 18		
Tir-phil	d																				08 21		
Pontlottyn	d																				08 25		
Rhymney 3	a																				08 31		
Cathays	d	05 33			06 03	06 18			06 33	06 43	06 48			07 03	07 13		07 18			07 33		07 43	
Llandaf	d	05 37			06 07	06 22			06 37	06 47	06 52			07 07	07 17		07 22			07 37		07 47	
Ninian Park	d															07 10							07 40
Waun-gron Park	d															07 13							07 43
Fairwater	d															07 15							07 45
Danescourt	d															07 17							07 47
Radyr 3	a	05 40			06 10	06 24			06 40	06 50	06 54			07 10	07 20	07 24	07 25			07 40		07 50	07 54
	d	05 40			06 10	06 24			06 40	06 50	06 55			07 10	07 20		07 25			07 40		07 50	
Taffs Well 3	d	05 44			06 14	06 28			06 44	06 54	06 59			07 14	07 24		07 29			07 44		07 54	
Trefforest Estate	d	05 48			06 18				06 48					07 18						07 48			
Trefforest	d	05 52			06 22	06 35			06 52	07 01	07 06			07 22	07 31		07 36			07 52		08 01	
Pontypridd 3	a	05 55			06 25	06 38			06 55	07 04	07 09			07 25	07 34		07 39			07 55		08 04	
	d	05 57	06 11		06 27	06 41			06 57	07 06	07 11			07 27	07 36		07 41			07 57		08 06	
Abercynon	d	06 04	06 19		06 34	06 49			07 04		07 19			07 34			07 49			08 04			
Penrhiwceiber	d		06 24			06 54					07 24						07 54						
Mountain Ash	a		06 28			06 58					07 28						07 58						
	d		06 33			07 03					07 33						08 03						
Fernhill	d		06 35			07 05					07 35						08 05						
Cwmbach	d		06 39			07 09					07 39						08 09						
Aberdare 3	a		06 46			07 16					07 46						08 16						
Quakers Yard	d	06 09			06 39				07 09					07 39						08 09			
Merthyr Vale	a	06 14			06 44				07 14					07 44						08 14			
	d	06 17			06 47				07 17					07 47						08 17			
Troed Y Rhiw	d	06 20			06 50				07 20					07 50						08 20			
Pentre-bach	d	06 23			06 53				07 23					07 53						08 23			
Merthyr Tydfil	a	06 31			07 01				07 31					08 01						08 31			
Trehafod	d									07 11					07 41							08 11	
Porth	a									07 14					07 44							08 14	
	d									07 15					07 45							08 15	
Dinas Rhondda	d									07 19					07 49							08 19	
Tonypandy	d									07 21					07 51							08 21	
Llwynypia	d									07 23					07 53							08 23	
Ystrad Rhondda	a									07 26					07 56							08 26	
	d									07 29					07 59							08 29	
Ton Pentre	d									07 31					08 01							08 31	
Treorchy	d									07 34					08 04							08 34	
Ynyswen	d									07 37					08 07							08 37	
Treherbert	a									07 43					08 13							08 43	

When events are being held at the Millenium Stadium, services are subject to alteration. Please check times before travelling.

For connections to Cardiff Bay please refer to Table 130A

Table 130R

Saturdays

15 February to 17 May

Bridgend, Barry Island, Barry, Penarth and Cardiff - Coryton, Rhymney, Pontypridd, Merthyr, Aberdare and Treherbert

Network Diagram - see first Page of Table 130

		AW	AW	AW	AW	AW	AW	AW	AW	AW	AW	AW	AW	AW	AW	AW	AW	AW	AW	AW	AW	AW	AW
Bridgend	d	06 42														07 42							
Llantwit Major	d	06 56														07 56							
Rhoose Cardiff Int Airport ✈	d	07 06														08 06							
Barry Island	d				07 25				07 40			07 55							08 25				08 40
Barry [3]	d	07 15			07 30				07 45			08 00				08 15			08 30				08 45
Barry Docks	d	07 18			07 33				07 48			08 03				08 18			08 33				08 48
Cadoxton	d	07 21			07 36				07 51			08 06				08 21			08 36				08 51
Dinas Powys	d	07 25			07 40				07 55			08 10				08 25			08 40				08 55
Eastbrook	d	07 28			07 43				07 58			08 13				08 28			08 43				08 58
Cogan	d	07 30			07 45				08 00			08 15				08 30			08 45				09 00
Penarth	d		07 32			07 47				08 02			08 17				08 32			08 47			
Dingle Road	d		07 34			07 49				08 04			08 19				08 34			08 49			
Grangetown	d	07 34	07 38		07 49	07 53			08 05	08 08		08 19	08 23			08 34	08 38		08 49	08 53			09 04
Cardiff Central [7]	a	07 39	07 44		07 54	07 59			08 09	08 14		08 24	08 29			08 39	08 44		08 54	08 59			09 09
	d	07 41	07 46	07 51	07 56	08 01	08 06	08 06	08 11	08 16	08 21	08 26	08 31	08 36	08 36	08 41	08 46	08 51	08 56	09 01	09 06	09 06	09 11
Cardiff Queen Street [3]	a	07 44	07 49	07 54	07 59	08 04	08 09		08 14	08 19	08 24	08 29	08 34	08 39		08 44	08 49	08 54	08 59	09 04	09 09		09 14
	d	07 45	07 50	07 55	08 00	08 05	08 10		08 15	08 20	08 25	08 30	08 35	08 40		08 45	08 50	08 55	09 00	09 05	09 10		09 15
Heath Low Level	d			08 00							08 30							09 00					
Ty Glas	d			08 03							08 33							09 03					
Birchgrove	d			08 04							08 34							09 04					
Rhiwbina	d			08 06							08 36							09 06					
Whitchurch (Cardiff)	d			08 08							08 38							09 08					
Coryton	a			08 13							08 43							09 13					
Heath High Level	d		07 55			08 10				08 25			08 40				08 55			09 10			
Llanishen	d		07 58			08 13				08 28			08 43				08 58			09 13			
Lisvane & Thornhill	d		08 00			08 15				08 30			08 45				09 00			09 15			
Caerphilly [3]	d		08 06			08 21				08 36			08 51				09 06			09 21			
Aber	d		08 08			08 23				08 38			08 53				09 08			09 23			
Energlyn & Churchill Park	d					08 25				08 40										09 25			
Llanbradach	d		08 12			08 29				08 44			08 57				09 12			09 29			
Ystrad Mynach [3]	d		08 17			08 34				08 49			09 02				09 17			09 34			
Hengoed	d		08 20			08 37				08 52			09 05				09 20			09 37			
Pengam	d		08 23			08 40				08 55			09 08				09 23			09 40			
Gilfach Fargoed	d					08 43														09 43			
Bargoed	a		08 31			08 50				09 00			09 16				09 31			09 50			
	d									09 01													
Brithdir	d									09 05													
Tir-phil	d									09 08													
Pontlottyn	d									09 12													
Rhymney [3]	a									09 18													
Cathays	d	07 48			08 03		08 13		08 18			08 33		08 43		08 48			09 03		09 13		09 18
Llandaf	d	07 52			08 07		08 17		08 22			08 37		08 47		08 52			09 07		09 17		09 22
Ninian Park	d							08 10							08 40							09 10	
Waun-gron Park	d							08 13							08 43							09 13	
Fairwater	d							08 15							08 45							09 15	
Danescourt	d							08 17							08 47							09 17	
Radyr [3]	a	07 55			08 10		08 20	08 24	08 25			08 40		08 50	08 54	08 55			09 10		09 20	09 24	09 25
	d	07 55			08 10		08 20		08 25			08 40		08 50		08 55			09 10		09 20		09 25
Taffs Well [3]	d	07 59			08 14		08 24		08 29			08 44		08 54		08 59			09 14		09 24		09 29
Trefforest Estate	d				08 18							08 48							09 18				
Trefforest	d	08 06			08 22		08 31		08 36			08 52		09 01		09 06			09 22		09 31		09 36
Pontypridd [3]	a	08 09			08 25		08 34		08 39			08 55		09 04		09 09			09 25		09 34		09 39
	d	08 11			08 27		08 36		08 41			08 57		09 06		09 11			09 27		09 36		09 41
Abercynon	d	08 19			08 34				08 49			09 04				09 19			09 34				09 49
Penrhiwceiber	d	08 24							08 54							09 24							09 54
Mountain Ash	a	08 28							08 58							09 28							09 58
	d	08 33							09 03							09 33							10 03
Fernhill	d	08 35							09 05							09 35							10 05
Cwmbach	d	08 39							09 09							09 39							10 09
Aberdare [3]	a	08 46							09 16							09 46							10 16
Quakers Yard	d				08 39							09 09							09 39				
Merthyr Vale	a				08 44							09 14							09 44				
	d				08 47							09 17							09 47				
Troed Y Rhiw	d				08 50							09 20							09 50				
Pentre-bach	d				08 53							09 23							09 53				
Merthyr Tydfil	a				09 01							09 31							10 01				
Trehafod	d						08 41							09 11							09 41		
Porth	a						08 44							09 14							09 44		
	d						08 45							09 15							09 45		
Dinas Rhondda	d						08 49							09 19							09 49		
Tonypandy	d						08 51							09 21							09 51		
Llwynypia	d						08 53							09 23							09 53		
Ystrad Rhondda	a						08 56							09 26							09 56		
	d						08 59							09 29							09 59		
Ton Pentre	d						09 01							09 31							10 01		
Treorchy	d						09 04							09 34							10 04		
Ynyswen	d						09 07							09 37							10 07		
Treherbert	a						09 13							09 43							10 13		

When events are being held at the Millenium Stadium, services are subject to alteration. Please check times before travelling.

For connections to Cardiff Bay please refer to Table 130A

Table 130R

Saturdays

15 February to 17 May

Bridgend, Barry Island, Barry, Penarth and Cardiff - Coryton, Rhymney, Pontypridd, Merthyr, Aberdare and Treherbert

Network Diagram - see first Page of Table 130

		AW		AW	AW	AW	AW	AW	AW	AW	AW	AW		AW	AW	AW	AW	AW	AW	AW	AW	AW		AW	AW
Bridgend	d								08 42																
Llantwit Major	d								08 56																
Rhoose Cardiff Int Airport ✈	d								09 06																
Barry Island	d				08 55							09 25						09 40			09 55				
Barry 3	d				09 00				09 15			09 30						09 45			10 00				
Barry Docks	d				09 03				09 18			09 33						09 48			10 03				
Cadoxton	d				09 06				09 21			09 36						09 51			10 06				
Dinas Powys	d				09 10				09 25			09 40						09 55			10 10				
Eastbrook	d				09 13				09 28			09 43						09 58			10 13				
Cogan	d				09 15				09 30			09 45						10 00			10 15				
Penarth	d					09 17				09 32					09 47				10 02			10 17			
Dingle Road	d					09 19				09 34					09 49				10 04			10 19			
Grangetown	d				09 19	09 23			09 34	09 38		09 49			09 53			10 04	10 08		10 19	10 23			
Cardiff Central 7	a				09 24	09 29			09 39	09 44		09 54			09 59			10 09	10 14		10 24	10 29			
	d	09 16		09 21	09 26	09 31	09 36	09 36	09 41	09 46	09 51	09 56			10 01	10 06	10 06	10 11	10 16	10 21	10 26	10 31		10 36	10 36
Cardiff Queen Street 3	a	09 19		09 24	09 29	09 34	09 39		09 44	09 49	09 54	09 59			10 04	10 09		10 14	10 19	10 24	10 29	10 34		10 39	
	d	09 20		09 25	09 30	09 35	09 40		09 45	09 50	09 55	10 00			10 05	10 10		10 15	10 20	10 25	10 30	10 35		10 40	
Heath Low Level	d			09 30							10 00									10 30					
Ty Glas	d			09 33							10 03									10 33					
Birchgrove	d			09 34							10 04									10 34					
Rhiwbina	d			09 36							10 06									10 36					
Whitchurch (Cardiff)	d			09 38							10 08									10 38					
Coryton	a			09 43							10 13									10 43					
Heath High Level	d	09 25				09 40				09 55					10 10				10 25			10 40			
Llanishen	d	09 28				09 43				09 58					10 13				10 28			10 43			
Lisvane & Thornhill	d	09 30				09 45				10 00					10 15				10 30			10 45			
Caerphilly 3	d	09 36				09 51				10 06					10 21				10 36			10 51			
Aber	d	09 38				09 53				10 08					10 23				10 38			10 53			
Energlyn & Churchill Park	d	09 40													10 25				10 40						
Llanbradach	d	09 44				09 57				10 12					10 29				10 44			10 57			
Ystrad Mynach 3	d	09 49				10 02				10 17					10 34				10 49			11 02			
Hengoed	d	09 52				10 05				10 20					10 37				10 52			11 05			
Pengam	d	09 55				10 08				10 23					10 40				10 55			11 08			
Gilfach Fargoed	d														10 43										
Bargoed	a	10 00				10 16				10 31					10 50				11 00			11 16			
	d	10 01																	11 01						
Brithdir	d	10 05																	11 05						
Tir-phil	d	10 08																	11 08						
Pontlottyn	d	10 12																	11 12						
Rhymney 3	a	10 18																	11 18						
Cathays	d				09 33		09 43		09 48			10 03				10 13		10 18			10 33			10 43	
Llandaf	d				09 37		09 47		09 52			10 07				10 17		10 22			10 37			10 47	
Ninian Park	d							09 40									10 10								10 40
Waun-gron Park	d							09 43									10 13								10 43
Fairwater	d							09 45									10 15								10 45
Danescourt	d							09 47									10 17								10 47
Radyr 3	a				09 40		09 50	09 54	09 55			10 10				10 20	10 24	10 25			10 40			10 50	10 54
	d				09 40		09 50		09 55			10 10				10 20		10 25			10 40			10 50	
Taffs Well 3	d				09 44		09 54		09 59			10 14				10 24		10 29			10 44			10 54	
Trefforest Estate	d				09 48																10 48				
Trefforest	d				09 52		10 01		10 06			10 22				10 31		10 36			10 52			11 01	
Pontypridd 3	a				09 55		10 04		10 09			10 30				10 34		10 39			10 55			11 04	
	d				09 57		10 06		10 11					10 35		10 36		10 41			10 57			11 06	
Abercynon	d				10 04				10 19					10 41				10 49			11 04				
Penrhiwceiber	d								10 24									10 54							
Mountain Ash	a								10 28									10 58							
	d								10 33									11 03							
Fernhill	d								10 35									11 05							
Cwmbach	d								10 39									11 09							
Aberdare 3	a								10 46									11 16							
Quakers Yard	d				10 09									10 45							11 09				
Merthyr Vale	a				10 14									10 50							11 14				
	d				10 17									10 52							11 17				
Troed Y Rhiw	d				10 20									10 55							11 20				
Pentre-bach	d				10 23									10 58							11 23				
Merthyr Tydfil	a				10 31									11 06							11 31				
Trehafod	d						10 11									10 41								11 11	
Porth	a						10 14									10 44								11 14	
	d						10 15									10 45								11 15	
Dinas Rhondda	d						10 19									10 49								11 19	
Tonypandy	d						10 21									10 51								11 21	
Llwynypia	d						10 23									10 53								11 23	
Ystrad Rhondda	a						10 26									10 56								11 26	
	d						10 29									10 59								11 29	
Ton Pentre	d						10 31									11 01								11 31	
Treorchy	d						10 34									11 04								11 34	
Ynyswen	d						10 37									11 07								11 37	
Treherbert	a						10 43									11 13								11 43	

When events are being held at the Millenium Stadium, services are subject to alteration. Please check times before travelling.

For connections to Cardiff Bay please refer to Table 130A

Table 130R

Saturdays

15 February to 17 May

Bridgend, Barry Island, Barry, Penarth and Cardiff - Coryton, Rhymney, Pontypridd, Merthyr, Aberdare and Treherbert

Network Diagram - see first Page of Table 130

		AW	AW	AW	AW	AW	AW	AW	AW	AW	AW	AW	AW	AW	AW	AW	AW	AW	AW	AW	AW	AW	AW
Bridgend	d	09 42															10 42						
Llantwit Major	d	09 56															10 56						
Rhoose Cardiff Int Airport ✈	d	10 06															11 06						
Barry Island	d					10 25				10 40			10 55							11 25			
Barry 3	d	10 15				10 30				10 45			11 00				11 15			11 30			
Barry Docks	d	10 18				10 33				10 48			11 03				11 18			11 33			
Cadoxton	d	10 21				10 36				10 51			11 06				11 21			11 36			
Dinas Powys	d	10 25				10 40				10 55			11 10				11 25			11 40			
Eastbrook	d	10 28				10 43				10 58			11 13				11 28			11 43			
Cogan	d	10 30				10 45				11 00			11 15				11 30			11 45			
Penarth	d		10 32					10 47			11 02			11 17				11 32			11 47		
Dingle Road	d		10 34					10 49			11 04			11 19				11 34			11 49		
Grangetown	d	10 34	10 38			10 49		10 53		11 04	11 08		11 19	11 23			11 34	11 38		11 49	11 53		
Cardiff Central 7	a	10 42	10 44			10 54		10 59		11 09	11 14		11 24	11 29			11 39	11 44		11 54	11 59		
	d		10 46	10 51	10 51	10 56		11 01	11 06	11 11	11 16	11 21	11 26	11 31	11 36	11 36	11 41	11 46	11 51	11 56	12 01	12 06	12 06
Cardiff Queen Street 3	a		10 49	10 54		10 59		11 04		11 14	11 19	11 24	11 29	11 34	11 39		11 44	11 49	11 54	11 59	12 04	12 09	
	d		10 50	10 55		11 00		11 05		11 15	11 20	11 25	11 30	11 35	11 40		11 45	11 50	11 55	12 00	12 05	12 10	
Heath Low Level	d			11 00								11 30							12 00				
Ty Glas	d			11 03								11 33							12 03				
Birchgrove	d			11 04								11 34							12 04				
Rhiwbina	d			11 06								11 36							12 06				
Whitchurch (Cardiff)	d			11 08								11 38							12 08				
Coryton	a			11 13								11 43							12 13				
Heath High Level	d		10 55					11 10			11 25			11 40				11 55			12 10		
Llanishen	d		10 58					11 13			11 28			11 43				11 58			12 13		
Lisvane & Thornhill	d		11 00					11 15			11 30			11 45				12 00			12 15		
Caerphilly 3	d		11 06					11 21			11 36			11 51				12 06			12 21		
Aber	d		11 08					11 23			11 38			11 53				12 08			12 23		
Energlyn & Churchill Park	d							11 25			11 40										12 25		
Llanbradach	d		11 12					11 29			11 44			11 57				12 12			12 29		
Ystrad Mynach 3	d		11 17					11 34			11 49			12 02				12 17			12 34		
Hengoed	d		11 20					11 37			11 52			12 05				12 20			12 37		
Pengam	d		11 23					11 40			11 55			12 08				12 23			12 40		
Gilfach Fargoed	d							11 43													12 43		
Bargoed	a		11 31					11 50			12 00			12 16				12 31			12 50		
	d										12 01												
Brithdir	d										12 05												
Tir-phil	d										12 08												
Pontlottyn	d										12 12												
Rhymney 3	a										12 18												
Cathays	d					11 03				11 18			11 33		11 43		11 48			12 03		12 13	
Llandaf	d					11 07				11 22			11 37		11 47		11 52			12 07		12 17	
Ninian Park	d								11 10							11 40							12 10
Waun-gron Park	d								11 13							11 43							12 13
Fairwater	d								11 15							11 45							12 15
Danescourt	d						←		11 17							11 47							12 17
Radyr 3	a				11 02	11 10	11 02		11 24	11 25			11 40		11 50	11 54	11 55			12 10		12 20	12 24
	d				11 20	11 10	11 20			11 25			11 40		11 50		11 55			12 10		12 20	
Taffs Well 3	d				→	11 14	11 24			11 29			11 44		11 54		11 59			12 14		12 24	
Trefforest Estate	d					11 18							11 48							12 18			
Trefforest	d					11 22	11 31			11 36			11 52		12 01		12 06			12 22		12 31	
Pontypridd 3	a					11 25	11 34			11 39			11 55		12 04		12 09			12 25		12 34	
	d					11 27	11 36			11 41			11 57		12 06		12 11			12 27		12 36	
Abercynon	d					11 34				11 49			12 04				12 19			12 34			
Penrhiwceiber	d									11 54							12 24						
Mountain Ash	a									11 58							12 28						
	d									12 03							12 33						
Fernhill	d									12 05							12 35						
Cwmbach	d									12 09							12 39						
Aberdare 3	a									12 16							12 46						
Quakers Yard	d					11 39							12 09							12 39			
Merthyr Vale	a					11 44							12 14							12 44			
	d					11 47							12 17							12 47			
Troed Y Rhiw	d					11 50							12 20							12 50			
Pentre-bach	d					11 53							12 23							12 53			
Merthyr Tydfil	a					12 01							12 31							13 01			
Trehafod	d						11 41								12 11							12 41	
Porth	a						11 44								12 14							12 44	
	d						11 45								12 15							12 45	
Dinas Rhondda	d						11 49								12 19							12 49	
Tonypandy	d						11 51								12 21							12 51	
Llwynypia	d						11 53								12 23							12 53	
Ystrad Rhondda	a						11 56								12 26							12 56	
	d						11 59								12 29							12 59	
Ton Pentre	d						12 01								12 31							13 01	
Treorchy	d						12 04								12 34							13 04	
Ynyswen	d						12 07								12 37							13 07	
Treherbert	a						12 13								12 43							13 13	

When events are being held at the Millenium Stadium, services are subject to alteration. Please check times before travelling.

For connections to Cardiff Bay please refer to Table 130A

Table 130R

Saturdays

15 February to 17 May

Bridgend, Barry Island, Barry, Penarth and Cardiff - Coryton, Rhymney, Pontypridd, Merthyr, Aberdare and Treherbert

Network Diagram - see first Page of Table 130

		AW	AW	AW	AW	AW	AW	AW	AW	AW	AW	AW	AW	AW	AW	AW	AW	AW	AW	AW	AW	AW
Bridgend	d								11 42													
Llantwit Major	d								11 56													
Rhoose Cardiff Int Airport ✈	d								12 06													
Barry Island	d	11 40			11 55							12 25				12 40			12 55			
Barry 3	d	11 45			12 00				12 15			12 30				12 45			13 00			
Barry Docks	d	11 48			12 03				12 18			12 33				12 48			13 03			
Cadoxton	d	11 51			12 06				12 21			12 36				12 51			13 06			
Dinas Powys	d	11 55			12 10				12 25			12 40				12 55			13 10			
Eastbrook	d	11 58			12 13				12 28			12 43				12 58			13 13			
Cogan	d	12 00			12 15				12 30			12 45				13 00			13 15			
Penarth	d		12 02			12 17				12 32			12 47				13 02			13 17		
Dingle Road	d		12 04			12 19				12 34			12 49				13 04			13 19		
Grangetown	d	12 04	12 08		12 19	12 23			12 34	12 38		12 49	12 53			13 04	13 08		13 19	13 23		
Cardiff Central 7	a	12 09	12 14		12 24	12 29			12 39	12 44		12 54	12 59			13 09	13 14		13 24	13 29		
	d	12 11	12 16	12 21	12 26	12 31	12 36	12 36	12 41	12 46	12 51	12 56	13 01	13 06	13 06	13 11	13 16	13 21	13 26	13 31	13 36	13 36
Cardiff Queen Street 3	a	12 14	12 19	12 24	12 29	12 34	12 39		12 44	12 49	12 54	12 59	13 04	13 09		13 14	13 19	13 24	13 29	13 34	13 39	
	d	12 15	12 20	12 25	12 30	12 35	12 40		12 45	12 50	12 55	13 00	13 05	13 10		13 15	13 20	13 25	13 30	13 35	13 40	
Heath Low Level	d			12 30							13 00							13 30				
Ty Glas	d			12 33							13 03							13 33				
Birchgrove	d			12 34							13 04							13 34				
Rhiwbina	d			12 36							13 06							13 36				
Whitchurch (Cardiff)	d			12 38							13 08							13 38				
Coryton	a			12 43							13 13							13 43				
Heath High Level	d		12 25			12 40				12 55			13 10				13 25			13 40		
Llanishen	d		12 28			12 43				12 58			13 13				13 28			13 43		
Lisvane & Thornhill	d		12 30			12 45				13 00			13 15				13 30			13 45		
Caerphilly 3	d		12 36			12 51				13 06			13 21				13 36			13 51		
Aber	d		12 38			12 53				13 08			13 23				13 38			13 53		
Energlyn & Churchill Park	d		12 40										13 25				13 40					
Llanbradach	d		12 44			12 57				13 12			13 29				13 44			13 57		
Ystrad Mynach 3	d		12 49			13 02				13 17			13 34				13 49			14 02		
Hengoed	d		12 52			13 05				13 20			13 37				13 52			14 05		
Pengam	d		12 55			13 08				13 23			13 40				13 55			14 08		
Gilfach Fargoed	d												13 43									
Bargoed	a		13 00			13 16				13 31			13 50				14 00			14 16		
	d		13 01														14 01					
Brithdir	d		13 05														14 05					
Tir-phil	d		13 08														14 08					
Pontlottyn	d		13 12														14 12					
Rhymney 3	a		13 18														14 18					
Cathays	d	12 18			12 33		12 43		12 48			13 03		13 13		13 18			13 33		13 43	
Llandaf	d	12 22			12 37		12 47		12 52			13 07		13 17		13 22			13 37		13 47	
Ninian Park	d							12 40							13 10							13 40
Waun-gron Park	d							12 43							13 13							13 43
Fairwater	d							12 45							13 15							13 45
Danescourt	d							12 47							13 17							13 47
Radyr 3	a	12 25			12 40		12 50	12 54	12 55			13 10		13 20	13 24	13 25			13 40		13 50	13 54
	d	12 25			12 40		12 50		12 55			13 10		13 20		13 25			13 40		13 50	
Taffs Well 3	d	12 29			12 44		12 54		12 59			13 14		13 24		13 29			13 44		13 54	
Trefforest Estate	d				12 48							13 18							13 48			
Trefforest	d	12 36			12 52		13 01		13 06			13 22		13 31		13 36			13 52		14 01	
Pontypridd 3	a	12 42			12 55		13 04		13 09			13 25		13 34		13 39			13 55		14 04	
	d				12 57		13 06		13 11			13 27		13 36		13 41			13 57		14 06	
Abercynon	d				13 04				13 19			13 34				13 49			14 04			
Penrhiwceiber	d								13 24							13 54						
Mountain Ash	a								13 28							13 58						
	d								13 33							14 03						
Fernhill	d								13 35							14 05						
Cwmbach	d								13 39							14 09						
Aberdare 3	a								13 46							14 16						
Quakers Yard	d				13 09							13 39							14 09			
Merthyr Vale	a				13 14							13 44							14 14			
	d				13 17							13 47							14 17			
Troed Y Rhiw	d				13 20							13 50							14 20			
Pentre-bach	d				13 23							13 53							14 23			
Merthyr Tydfil	a				13 31							14 01							14 31			
Trehafod	d						13 11							13 41							14 11	
Porth	a						13 14							13 44							14 14	
	d						13 15							13 45							14 15	
Dinas Rhondda	d						13 19							13 49							14 19	
Tonypandy	d						13 21							13 51							14 21	
Llwynypia	d						13 23							13 53							14 23	
Ystrad Rhondda	a						13 26							13 56							14 26	
	d						13 29							13 59							14 29	
Ton Pentre	d						13 31							14 01							14 31	
Treorchy	d						13 34							14 04							14 34	
Ynyswen	d						13 37							14 07							14 37	
Treherbert	a						13 43							14 13							14 43	

When events are being held at the Millenium Stadium, services are subject to alteration. Please check times before travelling.

For connections to Cardiff Bay please refer to Table 130A

Table 130R

Saturdays

15 February to 17 May

Bridgend, Barry Island, Barry, Penarth and Cardiff - Coryton, Rhymney, Pontypridd, Merthyr, Aberdare and Treherbert

Network Diagram - see first Page of Table 130

		AW	AW	AW	AW	AW	AW	AW	AW	AW	AW	AW	AW	AW	AW	AW	AW	AW	AW	AW	AW	AW	AW
Bridgend	d	12 42														13 42							
Llantwit Major	d	12 56														13 56							
Rhoose Cardiff Int Airport ✈	d	13 06														14 06							
Barry Island	d				13 25				13 40			13 55								14 25			
Barry 3	d	13 15			13 30				13 45			14 00				14 15				14 30			
Barry Docks	d	13 18			13 34				13 48			14 03				14 18				14 33			
Cadoxton	d	13 21			13 37				13 51			14 06				14 21				14 36			
Dinas Powys	d	13 25			13 41				13 55			14 10				14 25				14 40			
Eastbrook	d	13 28			13 43				13 58			14 13				14 28				14 43			
Cogan	d	13 30			13 45				14 00			14 15				14 30				14 45			
Penarth	d		13 32			13 47				14 02			14 17				14 32					14 47	
Dingle Road	d		13 34			13 49				14 04			14 19				14 34					14 49	
Grangetown	d	13 34	13 38		13 49	13 53			14 04	14 08		14 19	14 23			14 34	14 38			14 49		14 53	
Cardiff Central 7	a	13 39	13 44		13 54	13 59			14 09	14 14		14 24	14 29			14 39	14 44			14 54		14 59	
	d	13 41	13 46	13 51	13 56	14 01	14 06	14 06	14 11	14 16	14 21	14 26	14 31	14 36	14 36	14 41	14 46	14 51	14 51	14 56		15 01	15 06
Cardiff Queen Street 3	a	13 44	13 49	13 54	13 59	14 04	14 09		14 14	14 19	14 24	14 29	14 34	14 39		14 44	14 49	14 54		14 59		15 04	
	d	13 45	13 50	13 55	14 00	14 05	14 10		14 15	14 20	14 25	14 30	14 35	14 40		14 45	14 50	14 55		15 00		15 05	
Heath Low Level	d			14 00							14 30							15 00					
Ty Glas	d			14 03							14 33							15 03					
Birchgrove	d			14 04							14 34							15 04					
Rhiwbina	d			14 06							14 36							15 06					
Whitchurch (Cardiff)	d			14 08							14 38							15 08					
Coryton	a			14 13							14 43							15 13					
Heath High Level	d		13 55			14 10				14 25			14 40				14 55					15 10	
Llanishen	d		13 58			14 13				14 28			14 43				14 58					15 13	
Lisvane & Thornhill	d		14 00			14 15				14 30			14 45				15 00					15 15	
Caerphilly 3	d		14 06			14 21				14 36			14 51				15 06					15 21	
Aber	d		14 08			14 23				14 38			14 53				15 08					15 23	
Energlyn & Churchill Park	d					14 25				14 40												15 25	
Llanbradach	d		14 12			14 29				14 44			14 57				15 12					15 29	
Ystrad Mynach 3	d		14 17			14 34				14 49			15 02				15 17					15 34	
Hengoed	d		14 20			14 37				14 52			15 05				15 20					15 37	
Pengam	d		14 23			14 40				14 55			15 08				15 23					15 40	
Gilfach Fargoed	d					14 43																15 43	
Bargoed	a		14 31			14 50				15 00			15 16				15 31					15 50	
	d									15 01													
Brithdir	d									15 05													
Tir-phil	d									15 08													
Pontlottyn	d									15 12													
Rhymney 3	a									15 18													
Cathays	d	13 48			14 03		14 13		14 18			14 33		14 43		14 48				15 03			
Llandaf	d	13 52			14 07		14 17		14 22			14 37		14 47		14 52				15 07			
Ninian Park	d							14 10							14 40								15 10
Waun-gron Park	d							14 13							14 43								15 13
Fairwater	d							14 15							14 45								15 15
Danescourt	d							14 17							14 47						←		15 17
Radyr 3	a	13 55			14 10		14 20	14 24	14 25			14 40		14 50	14 54	14 55			15 08	15 10	15 08		15 24
	d	13 55			14 10		14 20		14 25			14 40		14 50		14 55			15 20	15 10	15 20		
Taffs Well 3	d	13 59			14 14		14 24		14 29			14 44		14 54		14 59			→	15 14	15 24		
Trefforest Estate	d				14 18							14 48								15 18			
Trefforest	d	14 06			14 22		14 31		14 36			14 52		15 01		15 06				15 22	15 31		
Pontypridd 3	a	14 09			14 25		14 34		14 39			14 55		15 04		15 09				15 25	15 34		
	d	14 11			14 27		14 36		14 41			14 57		15 06		15 11				15 27	15 36		
Abercynon	d	14 19			14 34				14 49			15 04				15 19				15 34			
Penrhiwceiber	d	14 24							14 54							15 24							
Mountain Ash	a	14 28							14 58							15 28							
	d	14 33							15 03							15 33							
Fernhill	d	14 35							15 05							15 35							
Cwmbach	d	14 39							15 09							15 39							
Aberdare 3	a	14 46							15 16							15 46							
Quakers Yard	d				14 39							15 09								15 39			
Merthyr Vale	a				14 44							15 14								15 44			
	d				14 47							15 17								15 47			
Troed Y Rhiw	d				14 50							15 20								15 50			
Pentre-bach	d				14 53							15 23								15 53			
Merthyr Tydfil	a				15 01							15 31								16 01			
Trehafod	d						14 41							15 11							15 41		
Porth	a						14 44							15 14							15 44		
	d						14 45							15 15							15 45		
Dinas Rhondda	d						14 49							15 19							15 49		
Tonypandy	d						14 51							15 21							15 51		
Llwynypia	d						14 53							15 23							15 53		
Ystrad Rhondda	a						14 56							15 26							15 56		
	d						14 59							15 29							15 59		
Ton Pentre	d						15 01							15 31							16 01		
Treorchy	d						15 04							15 34							16 04		
Ynyswen	d						15 07							15 37							16 07		
Treherbert	a						15 13							15 43							16 13		

When events are being held at the Millenium Stadium, services are subject to alteration. Please check times before travelling.

For connections to Cardiff Bay please refer to Table 130A

Table 130R

Saturdays
15 February to 17 May

Bridgend, Barry Island, Barry, Penarth and Cardiff - Coryton, Rhymney, Pontypridd, Merthyr, Aberdare and Treherbert

Network Diagram - see first Page of Table 130

		AW	AW	AW	AW	AW	AW	AW	AW	AW	AW	AW	AW	AW	AW	AW	AW	AW	AW	AW	AW	AW	AW
Bridgend	d								14 42														15 42
Llantwit Major	d								14 56														15 56
Rhoose Cardiff Int Airport ✈	d								15 06														16 06
Barry Island	d	14 40			14 55							15 25				15 40			15 55				
Barry 3	d	14 45			15 00				15 15			15 30				15 45			16 00				16 15
Barry Docks	d	14 48			15 03				15 18			15 33				15 48			16 03				16 18
Cadoxton	d	14 51			15 06				15 21			15 36				15 51			16 06				16 21
Dinas Powys	d	14 55			15 10				15 25			15 40				15 55			16 10				16 25
Eastbrook	d	14 58			15 13				15 28			15 43				15 58			16 13				16 28
Cogan	d	15 00			15 15				15 30			15 45				16 00			16 15				16 30
Penarth	d		15 02			15 17				15 32			15 47				16 02			16 17			
Dingle Road	d		15 04			15 19				15 34			15 49				16 04			16 19			
Grangetown	d	15 04	15 08		15 19	15 23			15 34	15 38		15 49	15 53			16 04	16 08		16 19	16 23			16 34
Cardiff Central 7	a	15 09	15 14		15 24	15 29			15 39	15 44		15 54	15 59			16 09	16 14		16 24	16 29			16 39
	d	15 11	15 16	15 21	15 26	15 31	15 36	15 36	15 41	15 46	15 51	15 56	16 01	16 06	16 06	16 11	16 16	16 21	16 26	16 31	16 36	16 36	16 41
Cardiff Queen Street 3	a	15 14	15 19	15 24	15 29	15 34	15 39		15 44	15 49	15 54	15 59	16 04	16 09		16 14	16 19	16 24	16 29	16 34	16 39		16 44
	d	15 15	15 20	15 25	15 30	15 35	15 40		15 45	15 50	15 55	16 00	16 05	16 10		16 15	16 20	16 25	16 30	16 35	16 40		16 45
Heath Low Level	d			15 30							16 00							16 30					
Ty Glas	d			15 33							16 03							16 33					
Birchgrove	d			15 34							16 04							16 34					
Rhiwbina	d			15 36							16 06							16 36					
Whitchurch (Cardiff)	d			15 38							16 08							16 38					
Coryton	a			15 43							16 13							16 43					
Heath High Level	d		15 25			15 40				15 55			16 10				16 25			16 40			
Llanishen	d		15 28			15 43				15 58			16 13				16 28			16 43			
Lisvane & Thornhill	d		15 30			15 45				16 00			16 15				16 30			16 45			
Caerphilly 3	d		15 36			15 51				16 06			16 21				16 36			16 51			
Aber	d		15 38			15 53				16 08			16 23				16 38			16 53			
Energlyn & Churchill Park	d		15 40										16 25				16 40						
Llanbradach	d		15 44			15 57				16 12			16 29				16 44			16 57			
Ystrad Mynach 3	d		15 49			16 02				16 17			16 34				16 49			17 02			
Hengoed	d		15 52			16 05				16 20			16 37				16 52			17 05			
Pengam	d		15 55			16 08				16 23			16 40				16 55			17 08			
Gilfach Fargoed	d												16 43										
Bargoed	a		16 00			16 16				16 31			16 50				17 00			17 16			
	d		16 01														17 01						
Brithdir	d		16 05														17 05						
Tir-phil	d		16 08														17 08						
Pontlottyn	d		16 12														17 12						
Rhymney 3	a		16 18														17 18						
Cathays	d	15 18			15 33		15 43		15 48			16 03		16 13		16 18			16 33		16 43		16 48
Llandaf	d	15 22			15 37		15 47		15 52			16 07		16 17		16 22			16 37		16 47		16 52
Ninian Park	d							15 40							16 10							16 40	
Waun-gron Park	d							15 43							16 13							16 43	
Fairwater	d							15 45							16 15							16 45	
Danescourt	d							15 47							16 17							16 47	
Radyr 3	a	15 25			15 40		15 50	15 54	15 55			16 10		16 20	16 24	16 25			16 40		16 50	16 54	16 55
	d	15 25			15 40		15 50		15 55			16 10		16 20		16 25			16 40		16 50		16 55
Taffs Well 3	d	15 29			15 44		15 54		15 59			16 14		16 24		16 29			16 44		16 54		16 59
Trefforest Estate	d				15 48							16 18							16 48				
Trefforest	d	15 36			15 52		16 01		16 06			16 22		16 31		16 36			16 52		17 01		17 06
Pontypridd 3	a	15 39			15 55		16 04		16 09			16 25		16 34		16 39			16 55		17 04		17 09
	d	15 41			15 57		16 06		16 11			16 27		16 36		16 41			16 57		17 06		17 11
Abercynon	d	15 49			16 04				16 19			16 34				16 49			17 04				17 19
Penrhiwceiber	d	15 54							16 24							16 54							17 24
Mountain Ash	a	15 58							16 28							16 58							17 28
	d	16 03							16 33							17 03							17 33
Fernhill	d	16 05							16 35							17 05							17 35
Cwmbach	d	16 09							16 39							17 09							17 39
Aberdare 3	a	16 16							16 46							17 16							17 46
Quakers Yard	d				16 09							16 39							17 09				
Merthyr Vale	a				16 14							16 44							17 14				
	d				16 17							16 47							17 17				
Troed Y Rhiw	d				16 20							16 50							17 20				
Pentre-bach	d				16 23							16 53							17 23				
Merthyr Tydfil	a				16 31							17 01							17 31				
Trehafod	d						16 11							16 41							17 11		
Porth	a						16 14							16 44							17 14		
	d						16 15							16 45							17 15		
Dinas Rhondda	d						16 19							16 49							17 19		
Tonypandy	d						16 21							16 51							17 21		
Llwynypia	d						16 23							16 53							17 23		
Ystrad Rhondda	a						16 26							16 56							17 26		
	d						16 29							16 59							17 29		
Ton Pentre	d						16 31							17 01							17 31		
Treorchy	d						16 34							17 04							17 34		
Ynyswen	d						16 37							17 07							17 37		
Treherbert	a						16 43							17 13							17 43		

When events are being held at the Millenium Stadium, services are subject to alteration. Please check times before travelling.

For connections to Cardiff Bay please refer to Table 130A

Table 130R

Saturdays

15 February to 17 May

Bridgend, Barry Island, Barry, Penarth and Cardiff - Coryton, Rhymney, Pontypridd, Merthyr, Aberdare and Treherbert

Network Diagram - see first Page of Table 130

		AW	AW	AW	AW	AW	AW	AW	AW	AW	AW	AW	AW	AW	AW	AW	AW	AW	AW	AW	AW	AW
Bridgend	d														16 42							
Llantwit Major	d														16 56							
Rhoose Cardiff Int Airport ✈	d														17 06							
Barry Island	d			16 25				16 40			16 55							17 25				17 40
Barry 3	d			16 30				16 45			17 00				17 15			17 30				17 45
Barry Docks	d			16 33				16 48			17 03				17 18			17 33				17 48
Cadoxton	d			16 36				16 51			17 06				17 21			17 36				17 51
Dinas Powys	d			16 40				16 55			17 10				17 25			17 40				17 55
Eastbrook	d			16 43				16 58			17 13				17 28			17 43				17 58
Cogan	d			16 45				17 00			17 15				17 30			17 45				18 00
Penarth	d	16 32							17 02			17 17				17 32			17 47			
Dingle Road	d	16 34							17 04			17 19				17 34			17 49			
Grangetown	d	16 38		16 49				17 04	17 08		17 19	17 23			17 34	17 38		17 49	17 53			18 04
Cardiff Central 7	a	16 44		16 54				17 09	17 14		17 24	17 29			17 39	17 44		17 54	17 59			18 09
	d	16 46	16 51	16 56	17 01	17 06	17 06	17 11	17 16	17 21	17 26	17 31	17 36	17 36	17 41	17 46	17 51	17 56	18 01	18 06	18 06	18 11
Cardiff Queen Street 3	a	16 49	16 54	16 59	17 04	17 09		17 14	17 19	17 24	17 29	17 34	17 39		17 44	17 49	17 54	17 59	18 04	18 09		18 14
	d	16 50	16 55	17 00	17 05	17 10		17 15	17 20	17 25	17 30	17 35	17 40		17 45	17 50	17 55	18 00	18 05	18 10		18 15
Heath Low Level	d		17 00							17 30							18 00					
Ty Glas	d		17 03							17 33							18 03					
Birchgrove	d		17 04							17 34							18 04					
Rhiwbina	d		17 06							17 36							18 06					
Whitchurch (Cardiff)	d		17 08							17 38							18 08					
Coryton	a		17 13							17 43							18 13					
Heath High Level	d	16 55			17 10				17 25			17 40				17 55			18 10			
Llanishen	d	16 58			17 13				17 28			17 43				17 59			18 13			
Lisvane & Thornhill	d	17 00			17 15				17 30			17 45				18 02			18 15			
Caerphilly 3	d	17 06			17 21				17 36			17 51				18 07			18 21			
Aber	d	17 08			17 23				17 38			17 53				18 10			18 23			
Energlyn & Churchill Park	d				17 26				17 40			17 55				18 13						
Llanbradach	d	17 12			17 29				17 44			17 59				18 17			18 27			
Ystrad Mynach 3	d	17 17			17 35				17 49			18 04				18 22			18 32			
Hengoed	d	17 20			17 37				17 52			18 07				18 25			18 35			
Pengam	d	17 23			17 41				17 55			18 10				18 29			18 38			
Gilfach Fargoed	d				17 44							18 13				18 33			18 41			
Bargoed	a	17 31			17 47				18 03			18 16				18 36			18 48			
	d				17 49							18 18				18 44						
Brithdir	d				17 52							18 22				18 48						
Tir-phil	d				17 55							18 25				18 51						
Pontlottyn	d				18 00							18 29				18 55						
Rhymney 3	a				18 06							18 35				19 01						
Cathays	d			17 03		17 13		17 18			17 33		17 43		17 48			18 03		18 13		18 18
Llandaf	d			17 07		17 17		17 22			17 37		17 47		17 52			18 07		18 17		18 22
Ninian Park	d						17 10							17 40							18 10	
Waun-gron Park	d						17 13							17 43							18 13	
Fairwater	d						17 15							17 45							18 15	
Danescourt	d						17 17							17 47							18 17	
Radyr 3	a			17 10		17 20	17 24	17 25			17 40		17 50	17 54	17 55			18 10		18 20	18 24	18 25
	d			17 10		17 20		17 25			17 40		17 50		17 55			18 10		18 20		18 25
Taffs Well 3	d			17 14		17 24		17 29			17 44		17 54		17 59			18 14		18 24		18 29
Trefforest Estate	d			17 18							17 48							18 18				
Trefforest	d			17 22		17 31		17 36			17 52		18 01		18 06			18 22		18 31		18 36
Pontypridd 3	a			17 25		17 34		17 39			17 55		18 04		18 09			18 25		18 34		18 42
	d			17 27		17 36		17 41			17 57		18 06		18 11			18 27		18 36		
Abercynon	d			17 34				17 49			18 04				18 19			18 34				
Penrhiwceiber	d							17 54							18 24							
Mountain Ash	a							17 58							18 28							
	d							18 03							18 33							
Fernhill	d							18 05							18 35							
Cwmbach	d							18 09							18 39							
Aberdare 3	a							18 16							18 46							
Quakers Yard	d			17 39							18 09							18 39				
Merthyr Vale	a			17 44							18 14							18 44				
	d			17 47							18 17							18 47				
Troed Y Rhiw	d			17 50							18 20							18 50				
Pentre-bach	d			17 53							18 23							18 53				
Merthyr Tydfil	a			18 01							18 31							19 01				
Trehafod	d					17 41							18 11							18 41		
Porth	a					17 44							18 14							18 44		
	d					17 45							18 15							18 45		
Dinas Rhondda	d					17 49							18 19							18 49		
Tonypandy	d					17 51							18 21							18 51		
Llwynypia	d					17 53							18 23							18 53		
Ystrad Rhondda	a					17 56							18 26							18 56		
	d					17 59							18 29							18 59		
Ton Pentre	d					18 01							18 31							19 01		
Treorchy	d					18 04							18 34							19 04		
Ynyswen	d					18 07							18 37							19 07		
Treherbert	a					18 13							18 43							19 13		

When events are being held at the Millenium Stadium, services are subject to alteration. Please check times before travelling.

For connections to Cardiff Bay please refer to Table 130A

Table 130R

Saturdays

15 February to 17 May

Bridgend, Barry Island, Barry, Penarth and Cardiff - Coryton, Rhymney, Pontypridd, Merthyr, Aberdare and Treherbert

Network Diagram - see first Page of Table 130

		AW	AW	AW	AW		AW	AW	AW	AW	AW	AW		AW	AW	AW	AW	AW	AW	AW	AW	AW	AW
Bridgend	d							17 42										18 42					
Llantwit Major	d							17 56										18 56					
Rhoose Cardiff Int Airport ✈	d							18 06										19 06					
Barry Island	d			17 55							18 25			18 40	18 55					19 25		19 55	
Barry 3	d			18 00				18 15			18 30			18 45	19 00			19 15		19 30		20 00	
Barry Docks	d			18 03				18 18			18 33			18 48	19 03			19 18		19 33		20 03	
Cadoxton	d			18 06				18 21			18 36			18 51	19 06			19 21		19 36		20 06	
Dinas Powys	d			18 10				18 25			18 40			18 55	19 10			19 25		19 40		20 10	
Eastbrook	d			18 13				18 28			18 43			18 58	19 13			19 28		19 43		20 13	
Cogan	d			18 15				18 30			18 45			19 00	19 15			19 30		19 45		20 15	
Penarth	d	18 02			18 17				18 32			18 47				19 17					19 47		20 20
Dingle Road	d	18 04			18 19				18 34			18 49				19 19					19 49		20 22
Grangetown	d	18 08		18 19	18 23			18 34	18 38		18 49	18 53		19 04	19 19	19 23		19 34		19 49	19 53	20 19	20 26
Cardiff Central 7	a	18 14		18 25	18 29			18 39	18 47		18 55	18 59		19 09	19 24	19 29		19 39		19 56	19 59	20 24	20 31
	d	18 16	18 21	18 26	18 31	18 36	18 36	18 41		18 51		19 01	19 06	19 11	19 26	19 31	19 36	19 41	19 51	20 01	20 06	20 26	20 31
Cardiff Queen Street 3	a	18 19	18 24	18 29	18 34	18 38		18 44		18 54		19 04	19 09	19 14	19 29	19 34		19 44	19 54	20 04	20 09	20 29	20 34
	d	18 20	18 25	18 30	18 35	18 40		18 50		18 55		19 05	19 10	19 15	19 30	19 35		19 45	19 55	20 05	20 10	20 30	20 35
Heath Low Level	d		18 30							19 00									20 00				
Ty Glas	d		18 33							19 03									20 03				
Birchgrove	d		18 34							19 04									20 04				
Rhiwbina	d		18 36							19 06									20 06				
Whitchurch (Cardiff)	d		18 38							19 08									20 08				
Coryton	a		18 43							19 13									20 13				
Heath High Level	d	18 25			18 40							19 10				19 40				20 10			20 40
Llanishen	d	18 28			18 43							19 13				19 43				20 13			20 43
Lisvane & Thornhill	d	18 30			18 45							19 15				19 45				20 15			20 45
Caerphilly 3	d	18 36			18 51							19a23				19 51				20a27			20 51
Aber	d	18 38			18 53											19 53							20 53
Energlyn & Churchill Park	d				18 56											19 56							20 56
Llanbradach	d	18 42			18 59											19 59							20 59
Ystrad Mynach 3	d	18a51			19 04											20 04							21 04
Hengoed	d				19 07											20 07							21 07
Pengam	d				19 10											20 10							21 10
Gilfach Fargoed	d				19 13											20 13							21 13
Bargoed	a				19 16											20 17							21 17
	d				19 18											20 18							21 18
Brithdir	d				19 22											20 22							21 22
Tir-phil	d				19 25											20 25							21 25
Pontlottyn	d				19 29											20 29							21 29
Rhymney 3	a				19 36											20 35							21 36
Cathays	d			18 33		18 43		18 52					19 13	19 18	19 33			19 48			20 13	20 33	
Llandaf	d			18 37		18 47		18 56					19 17	19 22	19 37			19 52			20 17	20 37	
Ninian Park	d						18 40										19 40						
Waun-gron Park	d						18 43										19 43						
Fairwater	d						18 45										19 45						
Danescourt	d						18 47										19 47						
Radyr 3	a			18 40		18 50	18 54	18 58					19 20	19 25	19 40		19 54	19 55			20 20	20 40	
	d			18 40		18 50		18 58					19 20	19 25	19 40			19 55			20 20	20 40	
Taffs Well 3	d			18 44		18 54		19 03					19 24	19 29	19 44			19 59			20 24	20 44	
Trefforest Estate	d			18 48											19 48							20 48	
Trefforest	d			18 52		19 01		19 10					19 31	19 36	19 52			20 06			20 31	20 52	
Pontypridd 3	a			18 55		19 04		19 13					19 34	19 39	19 55			20 09			20 34	20 55	
	d			18 57		19 06		19 14					19 36	19 41	19 57			20 11			20 36	20 57	
Abercynon	d			19 04				19 21						19 49	20 04			20 21				21 04	
Penrhiwceiber	d							19 26						19 54				20 26					
Mountain Ash	a							19 30						19 56				20 30					
	d							19 33						20 03				20 33					
Fernhill	d							19 35						20 05				20 35					
Cwmbach	d							19 39						20 09				20 39					
Aberdare 3	a							19 46						20 16				20 46					
Quakers Yard	d			19 09											20 08							21 08	
Merthyr Vale	a			19 14											20 13							21 13	
	d			19 17											20 15							21 16	
Troed Y Rhiw	d			19 20											20 19							21 20	
Pentre-bach	d			19 23											20 22							21 23	
Merthyr Tydfil	a			19 31											20 30							21 31	
Trehafod	d					19 11							19 41								20 41		
Porth	a					19 14							19 44								20 44		
	d					19 15							19 45								20 45		
Dinas Rhondda	d					19 19							19 49								20 49		
Tonypandy	d					19 21							19 51								20 51		
Llwynypia	d					19 23							19 53								20 53		
Ystrad Rhondda	a					19 26							19 56								20 56		
	d					19 29							19 59								20 59		
Ton Pentre	d					19 31							20 01								21 01		
Treorchy	d					19 34							20 04								21 04		
Ynyswen	d					19 37							20 07								21 07		
Treherbert	a					19 43							20 13								21 13		

When events are being held at the Millenium Stadium, services are subject to alteration. Please check times before travelling.

For connections to Cardiff Bay please refer to Table 130A

Table 130R

Saturdays

15 February to 17 May

Bridgend, Barry Island, Barry, Penarth and Cardiff - Coryton, Rhymney, Pontypridd, Merthyr, Aberdare and Treherbert

Network Diagram - see first Page of Table 130

		AW	AW	AW	AW	AW	AW	AW	AW	AW	AW	AW	AW	AW	AW	AW	AW	AW	AW	AW	AW	AW
Bridgend	d		19 42								20 42						21 42					
Llantwit Major	d		19 56								20 56						21 56					
Rhoose Cardiff Int Airport ✈	d		20 06								21 06						22 06					
Barry Island	d						20 55								21 55						22 44	
Barry 3	d		20 15				21 00				21 15				22 00		22 15				22 49	
Barry Docks	d		20 18				21 03				21 18				22 03		22 18				22 52	
Cadoxton	d		20 21				21 06				21 21				22 06		22 21				22 55	
Dinas Powys	d		20 25				21 10				21 25				22 10		22 25				22 59	
Eastbrook	d		20 28				21 13				21 28				22 13		22 28				23 02	
Cogan	d		20 30				21 15				21 30				22 15		22 30				23 04	
Penarth	d				20 47					21 20		21 47				22 20				22 47		23 26
Dingle Road	d				20 49					21 22		21 49				22 22				22 49		23 28
Grangetown	d		20 34		20 53		21 19			21 26	21 34	21 53			22 19	22 26	22 34			22 53	23 08	23 32
Cardiff Central 7	a		20 39		20 59		21 24			21 37	21 39	21 59			22 24	22 33	22 39			23 03	23 13	23 40
	d	20 36	20 41	20 51	21 00	21 06	21 27	21 31	21 36		21 41	22 01	22 06	22 21	22 26	22 35	22 41	22 46	22 55	23 16	23 26	
Cardiff Queen Street 3	a		20 44	20 54	21 03	21 09	21 30	21 34			21 44	22 04	22 09	22 24	22 29	22 38	22 44	22 49		23 19	23 29	
	d		20 45	20 55	21 04	21 10	21 31	21 35			21 45	22 05	22 10	22 25	22 30	22 39	22 45	22 50		23 20	23 30	
Heath Low Level	d			21 00										22 30								
Ty Glas	d			21 03										22 33								
Birchgrove	d			21 04										22 34								
Rhiwbina	d			21 06										22 36								
Whitchurch (Cardiff)	d			21 08										22 38								
Coryton	a			21 13										22 43								
Heath High Level	d				21 09			21 40				22 10				22 44				23 25		
Llanishen	d				21 12			21 43				22 13				22 47				23 28		
Lisvane & Thornhill	d				21 14			21 45				22 15				22 49				23 30		
Caerphilly 3	d				21 19			21 51				22a23				22 55				23 36		
Aber	d				21 21			21 53								22 57				23 38		
Energlyn & Churchill Park	d							21 56								22 59						
Llanbradach	d				21 25			21 59								23 03				23 42		
Ystrad Mynach 3	d				21a35			22 04								23 08				23a51		
Hengoed	d							22 07								23 11						
Pengam	d							22 10								23 14						
Gilfach Fargoed	d							22 13								23 17						
Bargoed	a							22 17								23 21						
	d							22 18								23 22						
Brithdir	d							22 22								23 26						
Tir-phil	d							22 25								23 29						
Pontlottyn	d							22 29								23 33						
Rhymney 3	a							22 36								23 39						
Cathays	d		20 48			21 13	21 34				21 48		22 13		22 33		22 48	22 53			23 33	
Llandaf	d		20 52			21 17	21 38				21 52		22 17		22 37		22 52	22 57			23 37	
Ninian Park	d	20 40							21 40										22 59			
Waun-gron Park	d	20 43							21 43										23 02			
Fairwater	d	20 45							21 45										23 04			
Danescourt	d	20 47							21 47										23 06			
Radyr 3	a	20 54	20 55			21 20	21 41		21 54		21 55		22 20		22 40		22 55	22 59	23 13		23 40	
	d		20 55			21 20	21 41				21 55		22 20		22 40		22 55	22 59			23 40	
Taffs Well 3	d		20 59			21 24	21 45				21 59		22 24		22 44		22 59	23 03			23 44	
Trefforest Estate	d						21 49								22 48							
Trefforest	d		21 06			21 31	21 53				22 06		22 31		22 52		23 06	23 10			23 52	
Pontypridd 3	a		21 09			21 34	21 56				22 09		22 34		22 55		23 09	23 14			23 58	
	d		21 11			21 36	21 58				22 11		22 36		22 57		23 11	23 15				
Abercynon	d		21 19				22 05				22 19				23 04		23 19					
Penrhiwceiber	d		21 24								22 24						23 24					
Mountain Ash	a		21 28								22 28						23 28					
	d		21 29								22 29						23 29					
Fernhill	d		21 31								22 31						23 31					
Cwmbach	d		21 35								22 35						23 35					
Aberdare 3	a		21 42								22 42						23 42					
Quakers Yard	d						22 09								23 08							
Merthyr Vale	a						22 14								23 13							
	d						22 16								23 15							
Troed Y Rhiw	d						22 20								23 19							
Pentre-bach	d						22 23								23 22							
Merthyr Tydfil	a						22 31								23 30							
Trehafod	d					21 41							22 41					23 20				
Porth	a					21 44							22 44					23 23				
	d					21 45							22 45					23 24				
Dinas Rhondda	d					21 49							22 49					23 28				
Tonypandy	d					21 51							22 51					23 30				
Llwynypia	d					21 53							22 53					23 32				
Ystrad Rhondda	a					21 56							22 56					23 35				
	d					21 59							22 59					23 38				
Ton Pentre	d					22 01							23 01					23 40				
Treorchy	d					22 04							23 04					23 43				
Ynyswen	d					22 07							23 07					23 46				
Treherbert	a					22 13							23 13					23 52				

When events are being held at the Millenium Stadium, services are subject to alteration. Please check times before travelling.

For connections to Cardiff Bay please refer to Table 130A

Table 130R

Saturdays

15 February to 17 May

Bridgend, Barry Island, Barry, Penarth and Cardiff - Coryton, Rhymney, Pontypridd, Merthyr, Aberdare and Treherbert

Network Diagram - see first Page of Table 130

		AW
Bridgend	d	22 42
Llantwit Major	d	22 56
Rhoose Cardiff Int Airport ✈	d	23 06
Barry Island	d	
Barry 3	d	23 15
Barry Docks	d	23 18
Cadoxton	d	23 21
Dinas Powys	d	23 25
Eastbrook	d	23 28
Cogan	d	23 30
Penarth	d	
Dingle Road	d	
Grangetown	d	23 34
Cardiff Central 7	a	23 42
	d	
Cardiff Queen Street 3	a	
	d	
Heath Low Level	d	
Ty Glas	d	
Birchgrove	d	
Rhiwbina	d	
Whitchurch (Cardiff)	d	
Coryton	a	
Heath High Level	d	
Llanishen	d	
Lisvane & Thornhill	d	
Caerphilly 3	d	
Aber	d	
Energlyn & Churchill Park	d	
Llanbradach	d	
Ystrad Mynach 3	d	
Hengoed	d	
Pengam	d	
Gilfach Fargoed	d	
Bargoed	a	
	d	
Brithdir	d	
Tir-phil	d	
Pontlottyn	d	
Rhymney 3	a	
Cathays	d	
Llandaf	d	
Ninian Park	d	
Waun-gron Park	d	
Fairwater	d	
Danescourt	d	
Radyr 3	a	
	d	
Taffs Well 3	d	
Trefforest Estate	d	
Trefforest	d	
Pontypridd 3	a	
	d	
Abercynon	d	
Penrhiwceiber	d	
Mountain Ash	a	
	d	
Fernhill	d	
Cwmbach	d	
Aberdare 3	a	
Quakers Yard	d	
Merthyr Vale	a	
	d	
Troed Y Rhiw	d	
Pentre-bach	d	
Merthyr Tydfil	a	
Trehafod	d	
Porth	a	
	d	
Dinas Rhondda	d	
Tonypandy	d	
Llwynypia	d	
Ystrad Rhondda	a	
	d	
Ton Pentre	d	
Treorchy	d	
Ynyswen	d	
Treherbert	a	

When events are being held at the Millenium Stadium, services are subject to alteration. Please check times before travelling.

For connections to Cardiff Bay please refer to Table 130A

Table 130R

Sundays

8 December to 29 December

Bridgend, Barry Island, Barry, Penarth and Cardiff - Coryton, Rhymney, Pontypridd, Merthyr, Aberdare and Treherbert

Network Diagram - see first Page of Table 130

		AW	AW	AW	AW	AW	AW	AW	AW	AW	AW	AW	AW	AW	AW	AW	AW	AW	AW	AW	AW	AW	AW
Bridgend	d								09 42						11 42						13 42		
Llantwit Major	d								09 56						11 56						13 56		
Rhoose Cardiff Int Airport ✈	d								10 06						12 06						14 06		
Barry Island	d					08 55		09 55				10 55	11 25	11 55				12 55	13 25	13 55			
Barry 3	d					09 00		10 00	10 15			11 00	11 30	12 00	12 15			13 00	13 30	14 00	14 15		
Barry Docks	d					09 03		10 03	10 18			11 03	11 33	12 03	12 18			13 03	13 33	14 03	14 18		
Cadoxton	d					09 06		10 06	10 21			11 06	11 36	12 06	12 21			13 06	13 36	14 06	14 21		
Dinas Powys	d					09 10		10 10	10 25			11 10	11 40	12 10	12 25			13 10	13 40	14 10	14 25		
Eastbrook	d					09 13		10 13	10 28			11 13	11 43	12 13	12 28			13 13	13 43	14 13	14 28		
Cogan	d					09 15		10 15	10 30			11 15	11 45	12 15	12 30			13 15	13 45	14 15	14 30		
Penarth	d									10 47						12 47						14 47	
Dingle Road	d									10 49						12 49						14 49	
Grangetown	d					09 19		10 19	10 34	10 53		11 19	11 49	12 19	12 34	12 53		13 19	13 49	14 19	14 34	14 53	
Cardiff Central 7	a					09 24		10 24	10 42	10 59		11 24	11 54	12 24	12 42	12 59		13 24	13 54	14 24	14 42	14 59	
	d	08 26	08 41	08 54	09 00	09 41	10 06	10 26			11 00	11 41	12 06	12 26			13 06	13 41	14 06	14 26			15 06
Cardiff Queen Street 3	a	08 29	08 44	08 57	09 03	09 44	10 09	10 29			11 03	11 44	12 09	12 29			13 09	13 44	14 09	14 29			15 09
	d	08 30	08 45		09 04	09 45	10 10	10 30			11 04	11 45	12 10	12 30			13 10	13 45	14 10	14 30			15 10
Heath Low Level	d																						
Ty Glas	d																						
Birchgrove	d																						
Rhiwbina	d																						
Whitchurch (Cardiff)	d																						
Coryton	a																						
Heath High Level	d						10 15						12 15						14 15				
Llanishen	d						10 18						12 18						14 18				
Lisvane & Thornhill	d						10 20						12 20						14 20				
Caerphilly 3	d						10 26						12 26						14 26				
Aber	d						10 28						12 28						14 28				
Energlyn & Churchill Park	d						10 30						12 30						14 30				
Llanbradach	d						10 34						12 34						14 34				
Ystrad Mynach 3	d						10 39						12 39						14 39				
Hengoed	d						10 42						12 42						14 42				
Pengam	d						10 45						12 45						14 45				
Gilfach Fargoed	d						10 48						12 48						14 48				
Bargoed	a						10 51						12 51						14 51				
	d						10 51						12 51						14 51				
Brithdir	d						10 55						12 55						14 55				
Tir-phil	d						10 58						12 58						14 58				
Pontlottyn	d						11 02						13 02						15 02				
Rhymney 3	a						11 09						13 09						15 09				
Cathays	d	08 33	08 48		09 07	09 48		10 33			11 07	11 48		12 33			13 13	13 48		14 33			15 13
Llandaf	d	08 37	08 52		09 11	09 52		10 37			11 11	11 52		12 37			13 17	13 52		14 37			15 17
Ninian Park	d																						
Waun-gron Park	d																						
Fairwater	d																						
Danescourt	d																						
Radyr 3	a	08 40	08 55		09 14	09 55		10 40			11 14	11 55		12 40			13 20	13 55		14 40			15 20
	d	08 40	08 55		09 14	09 55		10 40			11 14	11 55		12 40			13 20	13 55		14 40			15 20
Taffs Well 3	d	08 44	08 59		09 18	09 59		10 44			11 18	11 59		12 44			13 24	13 59		14 44			15 24
Trefforest Estate	d																						
Trefforest	d	08 52	09 06		09 25	10 06		10 52			11 25	12 06		12 52			13 31	14 06		14 52			15 31
Pontypridd 3	a	08 55	09 09		09 28	10 09		10 55			11 28	12 09		12 55			13 34	14 09		14 55			15 34
	d	08 57	09 11		09 30	10 11		10 57			11 30	12 11		12 57			13 36	14 11		14 57			15 36
Abercynon	d	09 05	09 19			10 19		11 05				12 19		13 05				14 19		15 05			
Penrhiwceiber	d		09 24			10 24						12 24						14 24					
Mountain Ash	a		09 28			10 28						12 28						14 28					
	d		09 29			10 29						12 29						14 29					
Fernhill	d		09 31			10 31						12 31						14 31					
Cwmbach	d		09 35			10 35						12 35						14 35					
Aberdare 3	a		09 42			10 42						12 42						14 42					
Quakers Yard	d	09 09						11 09						13 09						15 09			
Merthyr Vale	a	09 14						11 14						13 14						15 14			
	d	09 16						11 16						13 16						15 16			
Troed Y Rhiw	d	09 20						11 20						13 20						15 20			
Pentre-bach	d	09 23						11 23						13 23						15 23			
Merthyr Tydfil	a	09 31						11 31						13 31						15 31			
Trehafod	d				09 35						11 35						13 41						15 41
Porth	a				09 38						11 38						13 44						15 44
	d				09 39						11 39						13 45						15 45
Dinas Rhondda	d				09 43						11 43						13 49						15 49
Tonypandy	d				09 45						11 45						13 51						15 51
Llwynypia	d				09 47						11 47						13 53						15 53
Ystrad Rhondda	a				09 50						11 50						13 56						15 56
	d				09 53						11 53						13 59						15 59
Ton Pentre	d				09 55						11 55						14 01						16 01
Treorchy	d				09 58						11 58						14 04						16 04
Ynyswen	d				10 01						12 01						14 07						16 07
Treherbert	a				10 07						12 07						14 13						16 13

When events are being held at the Millenium Stadium, services are subject to alteration. Please check times before travelling.

For connections to Cardiff Bay please refer to Table 130A

Table 130R

Sundays

8 December to 29 December

Bridgend, Barry Island, Barry, Penarth and Cardiff - Coryton, Rhymney, Pontypridd, Merthyr, Aberdare and Treherbert

Network Diagram - see first Page of Table 130

		AW	AW	AW	AW	AW		AW	AW	AW	AW	AW	AW	AW	AW	AW		AW	AW	AW	AW	AW	AW	AW	AW
Bridgend	d				15 42							17 42							19 42						
Llantwit Major	d				15 56							17 56							19 56						
Rhoose Cardiff Int Airport ✈	d				16 06							18 06							20 06						
Barry Island	d	14 55	15 25	15 55					16 55	17 25	17 55				18 55	19 25		19 55		20 25			20 55	21 25	21 55
Barry 3	d	15 00	15 30	16 00	16 15				17 00	17 30	18 00	18 15			19 00	19 30		20 00	20 15	20 30			21 00	21 30	22 00
Barry Docks	d	15 03	15 33	16 03	16 18				17 03	17 33	18 03	18 18			19 03	19 33		20 03	20 18	20 33			21 03	21 33	22 03
Cadoxton	d	15 06	15 36	16 06	16 21				17 06	17 36	18 06	18 21			19 06	19 36		20 06	20 21	20 36			21 06	21 36	22 06
Dinas Powys	d	15 10	15 40	16 10	16 25				17 10	17 40	18 10	18 25			19 10	19 40		20 10	20 25	20 40			21 10	21 40	22 10
Eastbrook	d	15 13	15 43	16 13	16 28				17 13	17 43	18 13	18 28			19 13	19 43		20 13	20 28	20 43			21 13	21 43	22 13
Cogan	d	15 15	15 45	16 15	16 30				17 15	17 45	18 15	18 30			19 15	19 45		20 15	20 30	20 45			21 15	21 45	22 15
Penarth	d					16 47							18 47								20 47				
Dingle Road	d					16 49							18 49								20 49				
Grangetown	d	15 19	15 49	16 19	16 34	16 53			17 19	17 49	18 19	18 34	18 53		19 19	19 49		20 19	20 34	20 49	20 53		21 19	21 49	22 19
Cardiff Central 7	a	15 25	15 54	16 24	16 42	16 59			17 24	17 54	18 24	18 42	19 00		19 24	19 54		20 24	20 42	20 54	21 00		21 26	21 54	22 26
	d	15 41	16 06	16 26				17 06	17 41	18 06	18 26			19 06	19 41	20 06		20 26		21 06		21 16		22 06	
Cardiff Queen Street 3	a	15 44	16 09	16 29				17 09	17 44	18 09	18 29			19 09	19 44	20 09		20 29		21 09		21 19		22 09	
	d	15 45	16 10	16 30				17 10	17 45	18 10	18 30			19 10	19 45	20 10		20 30		21 10		21 20		22 10	
Heath Low Level	d																								
Ty Glas	d																								
Birchgrove	d																								
Rhiwbina	d																								
Whitchurch (Cardiff)	d																								
Coryton	a																								
Heath High Level	d		16 15							18 15						20 15						21 25			
Llanishen	d		16 18							18 18						20 18						21 28			
Lisvane & Thornhill	d		16 20							18 20						20 20						21 30			
Caerphilly 3	d		16 26							18 26						20 26						21 36			
Aber	d		16 28							18 28						20 28						21 38			
Energlyn & Churchill Park	d		16 30							18 30						20 30						21 40			
Llanbradach	d		16 34							18 34						20 34						21 44			
Ystrad Mynach 3	d		16 39							18 39						20 39						21 49			
Hengoed	d		16 42							18 42						20 42						21 52			
Pengam	d		16 45							18 45						20 45						21 55			
Gilfach Fargoed	d		16 48							18 48						20 48						21 58			
Bargoed	a		16 51							18 51						20 51						22 01			
	d		16 51							18 51						20 51						22 01			
Brithdir	d		16 55							18 55						20 55						22 05			
Tir-phil	d		16 58							18 58						20 58						22 08			
Pontlottyn	d		17 02							19 02						21 02						22 12			
Rhymney 3	a		17 09							19 09						21 09						22 19			
Cathays	d	15 48		16 33				17 13	17 48		18 33			19 13	19 48			20 33		21 13				22 13	
Llandaf	d	15 52		16 37				17 17	17 52		18 37			19 17	19 52			20 37		21 17				22 17	
Ninian Park	d																								
Waun-gron Park	d																								
Fairwater	d																								
Danescourt	d																								
Radyr 3	a	15 55		16 40				17 20	17 55		18 40			19 20	19 55			20 40		21 20				22 20	
	d	15 55		16 40				17 20	17 55		18 40			19 20	19 55			20 40		21 20				22 20	
Taffs Well 3	d	15 59		16 44				17 24	17 59		18 44			19 24	19 59			20 44		21 24				22 24	
Trefforest Estate	d																								
Trefforest	d	16 06		16 52				17 31	18 06		18 52			19 31	20 06			20 52		21 31				22 31	
Pontypridd 3	a	16 09		16 55				17 34	18 09		18 55			19 34	20 09			20 55		21 34				22 34	
	d	16 11		16 57				17 36	18 11		18 57			19 36	20 11			20 57		21 36				22 36	
Abercynon	d	16 19		17 05					18 19		19 05				20 19			21 05							
Penrhiwceiber	d	16 24							18 24						20 24										
Mountain Ash	a	16 28							18 28						20 28										
	d	16 29							18 29						20 29										
Fernhill	d	16 31							18 31						20 31										
Cwmbach	d	16 35							18 35						20 35										
Aberdare 3	a	16 42							18 42						20 42										
Quakers Yard	d			17 09							19 09							21 09							
Merthyr Vale	a			17 14							19 14							21 14							
	d			17 16							19 16							21 16							
Troed Y Rhiw	d			17 20							19 20							21 20							
Pentre-bach	d			17 23							19 23							21 23							
Merthyr Tydfil	a			17 31							19 31							21 31							
Trehafod	d							17 41						19 41						21 41				22 41	
Porth	a							17 44						19 44						21 44				22 44	
	d							17 45						19 45						21 45				22 45	
Dinas Rhondda	d							17 49						19 49						21 49				22 49	
Tonypandy	d							17 51						19 51						21 51				22 51	
Llwynypia	d							17 53						19 53						21 53				22 53	
Ystrad Rhondda	a							17 56						19 56						21 56				22 56	
	d							17 59						19 59						21 59				22 59	
Ton Pentre	d							18 01						20 01						22 01				23 01	
Treorchy	d							18 04						20 04						22 04				23 04	
Ynyswen	d							18 07						20 07						22 07				23 07	
Treherbert	a							18 13						20 13						22 13				23 13	

When events are being held at the Millenium Stadium, services are subject to alteration. Please check times before travelling.

For connections to Cardiff Bay please refer to Table 130A

Table 130R

Sundays

8 December to 29 December

Bridgend, Barry Island, Barry, Penarth and Cardiff - Coryton, Rhymney, Pontypridd, Merthyr, Aberdare and Treherbert

Network Diagram - see first Page of Table 130

		AW	AW
Bridgend	d	21 42	
Llantwit Major	d	21 56	
Rhoose Cardiff Int Airport ✈	d	22 06	
Barry Island	d		22 55
Barry ■	d	22 15	23 00
Barry Docks	d	22 18	23 03
Cadoxton	d	22 21	23 06
Dinas Powys	d	22 25	23 10
Eastbrook	d	22 28	23 13
Cogan	d	22 30	23 15
Penarth	d		
Dingle Road	d		
Grangetown	d	22 34	23 19
Cardiff Central ■	a	22 42	23 26
	d		
Cardiff Queen Street ■	a		
	d		
Heath Low Level	d		
Ty Glas	d		
Birchgrove	d		
Rhiwbina	d		
Whitchurch (Cardiff)	d		
Coryton	a		
Heath High Level	d		
Llanishen	d		
Lisvane & Thornhill	d		
Caerphilly ■	d		
Aber	d		
Energlyn & Churchill Park	d		
Llanbradach	d		
Ystrad Mynach ■	d		
Hengoed	d		
Pengam	d		
Gilfach Fargoed	d		
Bargoed	a		
	d		
Brithdir	d		
Tir-phil	d		
Pontlottyn	d		
Rhymney ■	a		
Cathays	d		
Llandaf	d		
Ninian Park	d		
Waun-gron Park	d		
Fairwater	d		
Danescourt	d		
Radyr ■	a		
	d		
Taffs Well ■	d		
Trefforest Estate	d		
Trefforest	d		
Pontypridd ■	a		
	d		
Abercynon	d		
Penrhiwceiber	d		
Mountain Ash	a		
	d		
Fernhill	d		
Cwmbach	d		
Aberdare ■	a		
Quakers Yard	d		
Merthyr Vale	a		
	d		
Troed Y Rhiw	d		
Pentre-bach	d		
Merthyr Tydfil	a		
Trehafod	d		
Porth	a		
	d		
Dinas Rhondda	d		
Tonypandy	d		
Llwynypia	d		
Ystrad Rhondda	a		
	d		
Ton Pentre	d		
Treorchy	d		
Ynyswen	d		
Treherbert	a		

When events are being held at the Millenium Stadium, services are subject to alteration. Please check times before travelling.

For connections to Cardiff Bay please refer to Table 130A

Table 130R

Sundays

5 January to 9 February

Bridgend, Barry Island, Barry, Penarth and Cardiff - Coryton, Rhymney, Pontypridd, Merthyr, Aberdare and Treherbert

Network Diagram - see first Page of Table 130

		AW	AW 🚌	AW 🚌	AW 🚌	AW	AW	AW	AW 🚌	AW		AW	AW	AW	AW	AW	AW	AW	AW	AW		AW	AW	AW	AW
Bridgend	d														09 42							11 42			
Llantwit Major	d														09 56							11 56			
Rhoose Cardiff Int Airport ✈	d														10 06							12 06			
Barry Island	d									08 55				09 55				10 55	11 25	11 55					12 55
Barry 3	d									09 00				10 00	10 15			11 00	11 30	12 00		12 15			13 00
Barry Docks	d									09 03				10 03	10 18			11 03	11 33	12 03		12 18			13 03
Cadoxton	d									09 06				10 06	10 21			11 06	11 36	12 06		12 21			13 06
Dinas Powys	d									09 10				10 10	10 25			11 10	11 40	12 10		12 25			13 10
Eastbrook	d									09 13				10 13	10 28			11 13	11 43	12 13		12 28			13 13
Cogan	d									09 15				10 15	10 30			11 15	11 45	12 15		12 30			13 15
Penarth	d															10 47							12 47		
Dingle Road	d															10 49							12 49		
Grangetown	d									09 19				10 19	10 34	10 53		11 19	11 49	12 19		12 34	12 53		13 19
Cardiff Central 7	a									09 29				10 23	10 42	10 59		11 24	11 54	12 24		12 42	12 59		13 24
	d		07 52	08 07	08 26	08 29	08 44	09 02	09 07	09 41		10 15	10 18	10 26			11 00	11 41	12 06	12 26				13 06	13 41
Cardiff Queen Street 3	a		08 00	08 15	08 34				09 15			10 18	10 21	10 29			11 03	11 44	12 09	12 29				13 09	13 44
	d		08 00	08 15	08 34				09 15			10 19		10 30			11 04	11 45	12 10	12 30				13 10	13 45
Heath Low Level	d																								
Ty Glas	d																								
Birchgrove	d																								
Rhiwbina	d																								
Whitchurch (Cardiff)	d																								
Coryton	a																								
Heath High Level	d											10 23							12 15						
Llanishen	d											10 26							12 18						
Lisvane & Thornhill	d											10 29							12 20						
Caerphilly 3	d											10 34							12 26						
Aber	d											10 36							12 28						
Energlyn & Churchill Park	d											10 39							12 30						
Llanbradach	d	00 04										10 42							12 34						
Ystrad Mynach 3	d	00a11										10 48							12 39						
Hengoed	d											10 50							12 42						
Pengam	d											10 54							12 45						
Gilfach Fargoed	d											10 57							12 48						
Bargoed	a											10 59							12 51						
	d											11 00							12 51						
Brithdir	d											11 03							12 55						
Tir-phil	d											11 06							12 58						
Pontlottyn	d											11 11							13 02						
Rhymney 3	a											11 18							13 09						
Cathays	d		08 05	08 20	08 39				09 20					10 33			11 07	11 48		12 33				13 13	13 48
Llandaf	d		08 20	08 35	08 54				09 35					10 37			11 11	11 52		12 37				13 17	13 52
Ninian Park	d																								
Waun-gron Park	d																								
Fairwater	d																								
Danescourt	d																								
Radyr 3	a		08 30	08 45	09 04	08 40	08 55	09 13	09 45	09 52				10 40			11 14	11 55		12 40				13 20	13 55
	d					08 40	08 55	09 14		09 55				10 40			11 14	11 55		12 40				13 20	13 55
Taffs Well 3	d					08 44	08 59	09 18		09 59				10 44			11 18	11 59		12 44				13 24	13 59
Trefforest Estate	d																								
Trefforest	d					08 52	09 06	09 25		10 06				10 52			11 25	12 06		12 52				13 31	14 06
Pontypridd 3	a					08 55	09 09	09 28		10 09				10 55			11 28	12 09		12 55				13 34	14 09
	d					08 57	09 11	09 30		10 11				10 57			11 30	12 11		12 57				13 36	14 11
Abercynon	d					09 05	09 19			10 19				11 05				12 19		13 05					14 19
Penrhiwceiber	d						09 24			10 24								12 24							14 24
Mountain Ash	a						09 28			10 28								12 28							14 28
	d						09 29			10 29								12 29							14 29
Fernhill	d						09 31			10 31								12 31							14 31
Cwmbach	d						09 35			10 35								12 35							14 35
Aberdare 3	a						09 42			10 42								12 42							14 42
Quakers Yard	d					09 09								11 09						13 09					
Merthyr Vale	a					09 14								11 14						13 14					
	d					09 16								11 16						13 16					
Troed Y Rhiw	d					09 20								11 20						13 20					
Pentre-bach	d					09 23								11 23						13 23					
Merthyr Tydfil	a					09 31								11 31						13 31					
Trehafod	d							09 35									11 35							13 41	
Porth	a							09 38									11 38							13 44	
	d							09 39									11 39							13 45	
Dinas Rhondda	d							09 43									11 43							13 49	
Tonypandy	d							09 45									11 45							13 51	
Llwynypia	d							09 47									11 47							13 53	
Ystrad Rhondda	a							09 50									11 50							13 56	
	d							09 53									11 53							13 59	
Ton Pentre	d							09 55									11 55							14 01	
Treorchy	d							09 58									11 58							14 04	
Ynyswen	d							10 01									12 01							14 07	
Treherbert	a							10 07									12 07							14 13	

When events are being held at the Millenium Stadium, services are subject to alteration. Please check times before travelling.

For connections to Cardiff Bay please refer to Table 130A

Table 130R

Sundays

5 January to 9 February

Bridgend, Barry Island, Barry, Penarth and Cardiff - Coryton, Rhymney, Pontypridd, Merthyr, Aberdare and Treherbert

Network Diagram - see first Page of Table 130

		AW	AW	AW	AW	AW		AW	AW	AW	AW	AW	AW	AW	AW	AW		AW	AW	AW	AW	AW	AW	AW	AW
Bridgend	d			13 42							15 42							17 42						19 42	
Llantwit Major	d			13 56							15 56							17 56						19 56	
Rhoose Cardiff Int Airport ✈	d			14 06							16 06							18 06						20 06	
Barry Island	d	13 25	13 55					14 55	15 25	15 55				16 55	17 25	17 55					18 55	19 25	19 55		20 25
Barry 3	d	13 30	14 00	14 15				15 00	15 30	16 00	16 15			17 00	17 30	18 00		18 15			19 00	19 30	20 00	20 15	20 30
Barry Docks	d	13 33	14 03	14 18				15 03	15 33	16 03	16 18			17 03	17 33	18 03		18 18			19 03	19 33	20 03	20 18	20 33
Cadoxton	d	13 36	14 06	14 21				15 06	15 36	16 06	16 21			17 06	17 36	18 06		18 21			19 06	19 36	20 06	20 21	20 36
Dinas Powys	d	13 40	14 10	14 25				15 10	15 40	16 10	16 25			17 10	17 40	18 10		18 25			19 10	19 40	20 10	20 25	20 40
Eastbrook	d	13 43	14 13	14 28				15 13	15 43	16 13	16 28			17 13	17 43	18 13		18 28			19 13	19 43	20 13	20 28	20 43
Cogan	d	13 45	14 15	14 30				15 15	15 45	16 15	16 30			17 15	17 45	18 15		18 30			19 15	19 45	20 15	20 30	20 45
Penarth	d				14 47							16 47							18 47						
Dingle Road	d				14 49							16 49							18 49						
Grangetown	d	13 49	14 19	14 34	14 53			15 19	15 49	16 19	16 34	16 53		17 19	17 49	18 19		18 34	18 53		19 19	19 49	20 19	20 34	20 49
Cardiff Central 7	a	13 54	14 24	14 42	14 59			15 25	15 54	16 24	16 42	16 59		17 24	17 54	18 24		18 42	19 00		19 24	19 54	20 24	20 42	20 54
	d	14 06	14 26			15 06		15 41	16 06	16 26			17 06	17 41	18 06	18 26				19 06	19 41	20 06	20 26		21 06
Cardiff Queen Street 3	a	14 09	14 29			15 09		15 44	16 09	16 29			17 09	17 44	18 09	18 29				19 09	19 44	20 09	20 29		21 09
	d	14 10	14 30			15 10		15 45	16 10	16 30			17 10	17 45	18 10	18 30				19 10	19 45	20 10	20 30		21 10
Heath Low Level	d																								
Ty Glas	d																								
Birchgrove	d																								
Rhiwbina	d																								
Whitchurch (Cardiff)	d																								
Coryton	a																								
Heath High Level	d	14 15							16 15						18 15							20 15			
Llanishen	d	14 18							16 18						18 18							20 18			
Lisvane & Thornhill	d	14 20							16 20						18 20							20 20			
Caerphilly 3	d	14 26							16 26						18 26							20 26			
Aber	d	14 28							16 28						18 28							20 28			
Energlyn & Churchill Park	d	14 30							16 30						18 30							20 30			
Llanbradach	d	14 34							16 34						18 34							20 34			
Ystrad Mynach 3	d	14 39							16 39						18 39							20 39			
Hengoed	d	14 42							16 42						18 42							20 42			
Pengam	d	14 45							16 45						18 45							20 45			
Gilfach Fargoed	d	14 48							16 48						18 48							20 48			
Bargoed	a	14 51							16 51						18 51							20 51			
	d	14 51							16 51						18 51							20 51			
Brithdir	d	14 55							16 55						18 55							20 55			
Tir-phil	d	14 58							16 58						18 58							20 58			
Pontlottyn	d	15 02							17 02						19 02							21 02			
Rhymney 3	a	15 09							17 09						19 09							21 09			
Cathays	d		14 33			15 13		15 48		16 33			17 13	17 48		18 33				19 13	19 48		20 33		21 13
Llandaf	d		14 37			15 17		15 52		16 37			17 17	17 52		18 37				19 17	19 52		20 37		21 17
Ninian Park	d																								
Waun-gron Park	d																								
Fairwater	d																								
Danescourt	d																								
Radyr 3	a		14 40			15 20		15 55		16 40			17 20	17 55		18 40				19 20	19 55		20 40		21 20
	d		14 40			15 20		15 55		16 40			17 20	17 55		18 40				19 20	19 55		20 40		21 20
Taffs Well 3	d		14 44			15 24		15 59		16 44			17 24	17 59		18 44				19 24	19 59		20 44		21 24
Trefforest Estate	d																								
Trefforest	d		14 52			15 31		16 06		16 52			17 31	18 06		18 52				19 31	20 06		20 52		21 31
Pontypridd 3	a		14 55			15 34		16 09		16 55			17 34	18 09		18 55				19 34	20 09		20 55		21 34
	d		14 57			15 36		16 11		16 57			17 36	18 11		18 57				19 36	20 11		20 57		21 36
Abercynon	d		15 05					16 19		17 05				18 19		19 05					20 19		21 05		
Penrhiwceiber	d							16 24						18 24							20 24				
Mountain Ash	a							16 28						18 28							20 28				
	d							16 29						18 29							20 29				
Fernhill	d							16 31						18 31							20 31				
Cwmbach	d							16 35						18 35							20 35				
Aberdare 3	a							16 42						18 42							20 42				
Quakers Yard	d		15 09							17 09						19 09							21 09		
Merthyr Vale	a		15 14							17 14						19 14							21 14		
	d		15 16							17 16						19 16							21 16		
Troed Y Rhiw	d		15 20							17 20						19 20							21 20		
Pentre-bach	d		15 23							17 23						19 23							21 23		
Merthyr Tydfil	a		15 31							17 31						19 31							21 31		
Trehafod	d					15 41							17 41							19 41					21 41
Porth	a					15 44							17 44							19 44					21 44
	d					15 45							17 45							19 45					21 45
Dinas Rhondda	d					15 49							17 49							19 49					21 49
Tonypandy	d					15 51							17 51							19 51					21 51
Llwynypia	d					15 53							17 53							19 53					21 53
Ystrad Rhondda	a					15 56							17 56							19 56					21 56
	d					15 59							17 59							19 59					21 59
Ton Pentre	d					16 01							18 01							20 01					22 01
Treorchy	d					16 04							18 04							20 04					22 04
Ynyswen	d					16 07							18 07							20 07					22 07
Treherbert	a					16 13							18 13							20 13					22 13

When events are being held at the Millenium Stadium, services are subject to alteration. Please check times before travelling.

For connections to Cardiff Bay please refer to Table 130A

Table 130R

Sundays

5 January to 9 February

Bridgend, Barry Island, Barry, Penarth and Cardiff - Coryton, Rhymney, Pontypridd, Merthyr, Aberdare and Treherbert

Network Diagram - see first Page of Table 130

		AW		AW	AW	AW	AW	AW	AW
Bridgend	d							21 42	
Llantwit Major	d							21 56	
Rhoose Cardiff Int Airport ✈	d							22 06	
Barry Island	d				20 55	21 25	21 55		22 55
Barry 3	d				21 00	21 30	22 00	22 15	23 00
Barry Docks	d				21 03	21 33	22 03	22 18	23 03
Cadoxton	d				21 06	21 36	22 06	22 21	23 06
Dinas Powys	d				21 10	21 40	22 10	22 25	23 10
Eastbrook	d				21 13	21 43	22 13	22 28	23 13
Cogan	d				21 15	21 45	22 15	22 30	23 15
Penarth	d	20 47							
Dingle Road	d	20 49							
Grangetown	d	20 53			21 19	21 49	22 19	22 34	23 19
Cardiff Central 7	a	21 00			21 26	21 54	22 26	22 42	23 26
	d			21 16		22 06			
Cardiff Queen Street 3	a			21 19		22 09			
	d			21 20		22 10			
Heath Low Level	d								
Ty Glas	d								
Birchgrove	d								
Rhiwbina	d								
Whitchurch (Cardiff)	d								
Coryton	a								
Heath High Level	d			21 25					
Llanishen	d			21 28					
Lisvane & Thornhill	d			21 30					
Caerphilly 3	d			21 36					
Aber	d			21 38					
Energlyn & Churchill Park	d			21 40					
Llanbradach	d			21 44					
Ystrad Mynach 3	d			21 49					
Hengoed	d			21 52					
Pengam	d			21 55					
Gilfach Fargoed	d			21 58					
Bargoed	a			22 01					
	d			22 01					
Brithdir	d			22 05					
Tir-phil	d			22 08					
Pontlottyn	d			22 12					
Rhymney 3	a			22 19					
Cathays	d					22 13			
Llandaf	d					22 17			
Ninian Park	d								
Waun-gron Park	d								
Fairwater	d								
Danescourt	d								
Radyr 3	a					22 20			
	d					22 20			
Taffs Well 3	d					22 24			
Trefforest Estate	d								
Trefforest	d					22 31			
Pontypridd 3	a					22 34			
	d					22 36			
Abercynon	d								
Penrhiwceiber	d								
Mountain Ash	a								
	d								
Fernhill	d								
Cwmbach	d								
Aberdare 3	a								
Quakers Yard	d								
Merthyr Vale	a								
	d								
Troed Y Rhiw	d								
Pentre-bach	d								
Merthyr Tydfil	a								
Trehafod	d					22 41			
Porth	a					22 44			
	d					22 45			
Dinas Rhondda	d					22 49			
Tonypandy	d					22 51			
Llwynypia	d					22 53			
Ystrad Rhondda	a					22 56			
	d					22 59			
Ton Pentre	d					23 01			
Treorchy	d					23 04			
Ynyswen	d					23 07			
Treherbert	a					23 13			

When events are being held at the Millenium Stadium, services are subject to alteration. Please check times before travelling.

For connections to Cardiff Bay please refer to Table 130A

Table 130R

Sundays

16 February to 11 May

Bridgend, Barry Island, Barry, Penarth and Cardiff - Coryton, Rhymney, Pontypridd, Merthyr, Aberdare and Treherbert

Network Diagram - see first Page of Table 130

		AW	AW	AW	AW	AW	AW	AW	AW	AW	AW	AW	AW	AW	AW	AW	AW	AW	AW	AW	AW	AW	AW
Bridgend	d								09 42						11 42						13 42		
Llantwit Major	d								09 56						11 56						13 56		
Rhoose Cardiff Int Airport ✈	d								10 06						12 06						14 06		
Barry Island	d					08 55		09 55				10 55	11 25	11 55				12 55	13 25	13 55			
Barry 3	d					09 00		10 00	10 15			11 00	11 30	12 00	12 15			13 00	13 30	14 00	14 15		
Barry Docks	d					09 03		10 03	10 18			11 03	11 33	12 03	12 18			13 03	13 33	14 03	14 18		
Cadoxton	d					09 06		10 06	10 21			11 06	11 36	12 06	12 21			13 06	13 36	14 06	14 21		
Dinas Powys	d					09 10		10 10	10 25			11 10	11 40	12 10	12 25			13 10	13 40	14 10	14 25		
Eastbrook	d					09 13		10 13	10 28			11 13	11 43	12 13	12 28			13 13	13 43	14 13	14 28		
Cogan	d					09 15		10 15	10 30			11 15	11 45	12 15	12 30			13 15	13 45	14 15	14 30		
Penarth	d									10 47						12 47						14 47	
Dingle Road	d									10 49						12 49						14 49	
Grangetown	d					09 19		10 19	10 34	10 53		11 19	11 49	12 19	12 34	12 53		13 19	13 49	14 19	14 34	14 53	
Cardiff Central 7	a					09 24		10 24	10 42	10 59		11 24	11 54	12 24	12 42	12 59		13 24	13 54	14 24	14 42	14 59	
	d	08 26	08 41	08 54	09 00	09 41	10 06	10 26			11 00	11 41	12 06	12 26			13 06	13 41	14 06	14 26			15 06
Cardiff Queen Street 3	a	08 29	08 44	08 57	09 03	09 44	10 09	10 29			11 03	11 44	12 09	12 29			13 09	13 44	14 09	14 29			15 09
	d	08 30	08 45		09 04	09 45	10 10	10 30			11 04	11 45	12 10	12 30			13 10	13 45	14 10	14 30			15 10
Heath Low Level	d																						
Ty Glas	d																						
Birchgrove	d																						
Rhiwbina	d																						
Whitchurch (Cardiff)	d																						
Coryton	a																						
Heath High Level	d						10 15						12 15						14 15				
Llanishen	d						10 18						12 18						14 18				
Lisvane & Thornhill	d						10 20						12 20						14 20				
Caerphilly 3	d						10 26						12 26						14 26				
Aber	d						10 28						12 28						14 28				
Energlyn & Churchill Park	d						10 30						12 30						14 30				
Llanbradach	d						10 34						12 34						14 34				
Ystrad Mynach 3	d						10 39						12 39						14 39				
Hengoed	d						10 42						12 42						14 42				
Pengam	d						10 45						12 45						14 45				
Gilfach Fargoed	d						10 48						12 48						14 48				
Bargoed	a						10 51						12 51						14 51				
	d						10 51						12 51						14 51				
Brithdir	d						10 55						12 55						14 55				
Tir-phil	d						10 58						12 58						14 58				
Pontlottyn	d						11 02						13 02						15 02				
Rhymney 3	a						11 09						13 09						15 09				
Cathays	d	08 33	08 48		09 07	09 48		10 33			11 07	11 48		12 33			13 13	13 48		14 33			15 13
Llandaf	d	08 37	08 52		09 11	09 52		10 37			11 11	11 52		12 37			13 17	13 52		14 37			15 17
Ninian Park	d																						
Waun-gron Park	d																						
Fairwater	d																						
Danescourt	d																						
Radyr 3	a	08 40	08 55		09 14	09 55		10 40			11 14	11 55		12 40			13 20	13 55		14 40			15 20
	d	08 40	08 55		09 14	09 55		10 40			11 14	11 55		12 40			13 20	13 55		14 40			15 20
Taffs Well 3	d	08 44	08 59		09 18	09 59		10 44			11 18	11 59		12 44			13 24	13 59		14 44			15 24
Trefforest Estate	d																						
Trefforest	d	08 52	09 06		09 25	10 06		10 52			11 25	12 06		12 52			13 31	14 06		14 52			15 31
Pontypridd 3	a	08 55	09 09		09 28	10 09		10 55			11 28	12 09		12 55			13 34	14 09		14 55			15 34
	d	08 57	09 11		09 30	10 11		10 57			11 30	12 11		12 57			13 36	14 11		14 57			15 36
Abercynon	d	09 05	09 19			10 19		11 05				12 19		13 05				14 19		15 05			
Penrhiwceiber	d		09 24			10 24						12 24						14 24					
Mountain Ash	a		09 28			10 28						12 28						14 28					
	d		09 29			10 29						12 29						14 29					
Fernhill	d		09 31			10 31						12 31						14 31					
Cwmbach	d		09 35			10 35						12 35						14 35					
Aberdare 3	a		09 42			10 42						12 42						14 42					
Quakers Yard	d	09 09						11 09						13 09						15 09			
Merthyr Vale	a	09 14						11 14						13 14						15 14			
	d	09 16						11 16						13 16						15 16			
Troed Y Rhiw	d	09 20						11 20						13 20						15 20			
Pentre-bach	d	09 23						11 23						13 23						15 23			
Merthyr Tydfil	a	09 31						11 31						13 31						15 31			
Trehafod	d				09 35						11 35						13 41						15 41
Porth	a				09 38						11 38						13 44						15 44
	d				09 39						11 39						13 45						15 45
Dinas Rhondda	d				09 43						11 43						13 49						15 49
Tonypandy	d				09 45						11 45						13 51						15 51
Llwynypia	d				09 47						11 47						13 53						15 53
Ystrad Rhondda	a				09 50						11 50						13 56						15 56
	d				09 53						11 53						13 59						15 59
Ton Pentre	d				09 55						11 55						14 01						16 01
Treorchy	d				09 58						11 58						14 04						16 04
Ynyswen	d				10 01						12 01						14 07						16 07
Treherbert	a				10 07						12 07						14 13						16 13

When events are being held at the Millenium Stadium, services are subject to alteration. Please check times before travelling.

For connections to Cardiff Bay please refer to Table 130A

Table 130R

Sundays

16 February to 11 May

Bridgend, Barry Island, Barry, Penarth and Cardiff - Coryton, Rhymney, Pontypridd, Merthyr, Aberdare and Treherbert

Network Diagram - see first Page of Table 130

		AW	AW	AW	AW	AW	AW	AW	AW	AW	AW	AW	AW	AW	AW	AW	AW	AW	AW	AW	AW	AW	AW
Bridgend	d				15 42						17 42						19 42						
Llantwit Major	d				15 56						17 56						19 56						
Rhoose Cardiff Int Airport ✈	d				16 06						18 06						20 06						
Barry Island	d	14 55	15 25	15 55				16 55	17 25	17 55				18 55	19 25	19 55		20 25			20 55	21 25	21 55
Barry 3	d	15 00	15 30	16 00	16 15			17 00	17 30	18 00	18 15			19 00	19 30	20 00	20 15	20 30			21 00	21 30	22 00
Barry Docks	d	15 03	15 33	16 03	16 18			17 03	17 33	18 03	18 18			19 03	19 33	20 03	20 18	20 33			21 03	21 33	22 03
Cadoxton	d	15 06	15 36	16 06	16 21			17 06	17 36	18 06	18 21			19 06	19 36	20 06	20 21	20 36			21 06	21 36	22 06
Dinas Powys	d	15 10	15 40	16 10	16 25			17 10	17 40	18 10	18 25			19 10	19 40	20 10	20 25	20 40			21 10	21 40	22 10
Eastbrook	d	15 13	15 43	16 13	16 28			17 13	17 43	18 13	18 28			19 13	19 43	20 13	20 28	20 43			21 13	21 43	22 13
Cogan	d	15 15	15 45	16 15	16 30			17 15	17 45	18 15	18 30			19 15	19 45	20 15	20 30	20 45			21 15	21 45	22 15
Penarth	d					16 47						18 47							20 47				
Dingle Road	d					16 49						18 49							20 49				
Grangetown	d	15 19	15 49	16 19	16 34	16 53		17 19	17 49	18 19	18 34	18 53		19 19	19 49	20 19	20 34	20 49	20 53		21 19	21 49	22 19
Cardiff Central 7	a	15 25	15 54	16 24	16 42	16 59		17 24	17 54	18 24	18 42	19 00		19 24	19 54	20 24	20 42	20 54	21 00		21 26	21 54	22 26
	d	15 41	16 06	16 26			17 06	17 41	18 06	18 26			19 06	19 41	20 06	20 26		21 06		21 16		22 06	
Cardiff Queen Street 3	a	15 44	16 09	16 29			17 09	17 44	18 09	18 29			19 09	19 44	20 09	20 29		21 09		21 19		22 09	
	d	15 45	16 10	16 30			17 10	17 45	18 10	18 30			19 10	19 45	20 10	20 30		21 10		21 20		22 10	
Heath Low Level	d																						
Ty Glas	d																						
Birchgrove	d																						
Rhiwbina	d																						
Whitchurch (Cardiff)	d																						
Coryton	a																						
Heath High Level	d		16 15						18 15						20 15					21 25			
Llanishen	d		16 18						18 18						20 18					21 28			
Lisvane & Thornhill	d		16 20						18 20						20 20					21 30			
Caerphilly 3	d		16 26						18 26						20 26					21 36			
Aber	d		16 28						18 28						20 28					21 38			
Energlyn & Churchill Park	d		16 30						18 30						20 30					21 40			
Llanbradach	d		16 34						18 34						20 34					21 44			
Ystrad Mynach 3	d		16 39						18 39						20 39					21 49			
Hengoed	d		16 42						18 42						20 42					21 52			
Pengam	d		16 45						18 45						20 45					21 55			
Gilfach Fargoed	d		16 48						18 48						20 48					21 58			
Bargoed	a		16 51						18 51						20 51					22 01			
	d		16 51						18 51						20 51					22 01			
Brithdir	d		16 55						18 55						20 55					22 05			
Tir-phil	d		16 58						18 58						20 58					22 08			
Pontlottyn	d		17 02						19 02						21 02					22 12			
Rhymney 3	a		17 09						19 09						21 09					22 19			
Cathays	d	15 48		16 33			17 13	17 48		18 33			19 13	19 48		20 33		21 13				22 13	
Llandaf	d	15 52		16 37			17 17	17 52		18 37			19 17	19 52		20 37		21 17				22 17	
Ninian Park	d																						
Waun-gron Park	d																						
Fairwater	d																						
Danescourt	d																						
Radyr 3	a	15 55		16 40			17 20	17 55		18 40			19 20	19 55		20 40		21 20				22 20	
	d	15 55		16 40			17 20	17 55		18 40			19 20	19 55		20 40		21 20				22 20	
Taffs Well 3	d	15 59		16 44			17 24	17 59		18 44			19 24	19 59		20 44		21 24				22 24	
Trefforest Estate	d																						
Trefforest	d	16 06		16 52			17 31	18 06		18 52			19 31	20 06		20 52		21 31				22 31	
Pontypridd 3	a	16 09		16 55			17 34	18 09		18 55			19 34	20 09		20 55		21 34				22 34	
	d	16 11		16 57			17 36	18 11		18 57			19 36	20 11		20 57		21 36				22 36	
Abercynon	d	16 19		17 05				18 19		19 05				20 19		21 05							
Penrhiwceiber	d	16 24						18 24						20 24									
Mountain Ash	a	16 28						18 28						20 28									
	d	16 29						18 29						20 29									
Fernhill	d	16 31						18 31						20 31									
Cwmbach	d	16 35						18 35						20 35									
Aberdare 3	a	16 42						18 42						20 42									
Quakers Yard	d			17 09						19 09						21 09							
Merthyr Vale	a			17 14						19 14						21 14							
	d			17 16						19 16						21 16							
Troed Y Rhiw	d			17 20						19 20						21 20							
Pentre-bach	d			17 23						19 23						21 23							
Merthyr Tydfil	a			17 31						19 31						21 31							
Trehafod	d						17 41						19 41					21 41				22 41	
Porth	a						17 44						19 44					21 44				22 44	
	d						17 45						19 45					21 45				22 45	
Dinas Rhondda	d						17 49						19 49					21 49				22 49	
Tonypandy	d						17 51						19 51					21 51				22 51	
Llwynypia	d						17 53						19 53					21 53				22 53	
Ystrad Rhondda	a						17 56						19 56					21 56				22 56	
	d						17 59						19 59					21 59				22 59	
Ton Pentre	d						18 01						20 01					22 01				23 01	
Treorchy	d						18 04						20 04					22 04				23 04	
Ynyswen	d						18 07						20 07					22 07				23 07	
Treherbert	a						18 13						20 13					22 13				23 13	

When events are being held at the Millenium Stadium, services are subject to alteration. Please check times before travelling.

For connections to Cardiff Bay please refer to Table 130A

Table 130R

Sundays

16 February to 11 May

Bridgend, Barry Island, Barry, Penarth and Cardiff - Coryton, Rhymney, Pontypridd, Merthyr, Aberdare and Treherbert

Network Diagram - see first Page of Table 130

Station		AW	AW
Bridgend	d	21 42	
Llantwit Major	d	21 56	
Rhoose Cardiff Int Airport ✈	d	22 06	
Barry Island	d		22 55
Barry 3	d	22 15	23 00
Barry Docks	d	22 18	23 03
Cadoxton	d	22 21	23 06
Dinas Powys	d	22 25	23 10
Eastbrook	d	22 28	23 13
Cogan	d	22 30	23 15
Penarth	d		
Dingle Road	d		
Grangetown	d	22 34	23 19
Cardiff Central 7	a	22 42	23 26
	d		
Cardiff Queen Street 3	a		
	d		
Heath Low Level	d		
Ty Glas	d		
Birchgrove	d		
Rhiwbina	d		
Whitchurch (Cardiff)	d		
Coryton	a		
Heath High Level	d		
Llanishen	d		
Lisvane & Thornhill	d		
Caerphilly 3	d		
Aber	d		
Energlyn & Churchill Park	d		
Llanbradach	d		
Ystrad Mynach 3	d		
Hengoed	d		
Pengam	d		
Gilfach Fargoed	d		
Bargoed	a		
	d		
Brithdir	d		
Tir-phil	d		
Pontlottyn	d		
Rhymney 3	a		
Cathays	d		
Llandaf	d		
Ninian Park	d		
Waun-gron Park	d		
Fairwater	d		
Danescourt	d		
Radyr 3	a		
	d		
Taffs Well 3	d		
Trefforest Estate	d		
Trefforest	d		
Pontypridd 3	a		
	d		
Abercynon	d		
Penrhiwceiber	d		
Mountain Ash	a		
	d		
Fernhill	d		
Cwmbach	d		
Aberdare 3	a		
Quakers Yard	d		
Merthyr Vale	a		
	d		
Troed Y Rhiw	d		
Pentre-bach	d		
Merthyr Tydfil	a		
Trehafod	d		
Porth	a		
	d		
Dinas Rhondda	d		
Tonypandy	d		
Llwynypia	d		
Ystrad Rhondda	a		
	d		
Ton Pentre	d		
Treorchy	d		
Ynyswen	d		
Treherbert	a		

When events are being held at the Millenium Stadium, services are subject to alteration. Please check times before travelling.

For connections to Cardiff Bay please refer to Table 130A

Table 130A

Cardiff Queen Street to Cardiff Bay

Mondays to Saturdays

9 December to 3 January

Network Diagram - see first Page of Table 130

Miles			AW	AW	AW	AW	AW	and at the same minutes past each hour until	AW	AW	AW	AW	AW	AW	AW
—	Cardiff Queen Street 3	d	06 36	06 48	07 00	07 12	07 24		22 36	22 48	23 00	23 12	23 24	23 36	23 48
1	Cardiff Bay	a	06 40	06 52	07 04	07 16	07 28		22 40	22 52	23 04	23 16	23 28	23 40	23 52

Mondays to Saturdays

6 January to 7 February

		AW	AW	AW	AW	AW	and at the same minutes past each hour until	AW	AW	AW	AW	AW	AW	AW SX	AW SX	AW SX	AW SX	AW SX	AW SX	AW SX	AW SX	AW SX
Cardiff Queen Street 3	d	06 36	06 48	07 00	07 12	07 24		20 36	20 48	21 00	21 12	21 24	21 36	21 48	22 00	22 12	22 24	22 36	22 48	23 00	23 12	23 24
Cardiff Bay	a	06 40	06 52	07 04	07 16	07 28		20 40	20 52	21 04	21 16	21 28	21 40	21 52	22 04	22 16	22 28	22 40	22 52	23 04	23 16	23 28

		AW SX	AW SX
Cardiff Queen Street 3	d	23 36	23 48
Cardiff Bay	a	23 40	23 52

Mondays to Saturdays

10 February to 17 May

		AW	AW	AW	AW	AW	and at the same minutes past each hour until	AW	AW	AW	AW	AW	AW	AW
Cardiff Queen Street 3	d	06 36	06 48	07 00	07 12	07 24		22 36	22 48	23 00	23 12	23 24	23 36	23 48
Cardiff Bay	a	06 40	06 52	07 04	07 16	07 28		22 40	22 52	23 04	23 16	23 28	23 40	23 52

Sundays

8 December to 29 December

		AW	AW	AW	AW	AW	and at the same minutes past each hour until	AW	AW	AW	AW	AW
Cardiff Queen Street 3	d	09 00	09 12	09 24	09 36	09 48		18 00	18 12	18 24	18 36	18 48
Cardiff Bay	a	09 04	09 16	09 28	09 40	09 52		18 04	18 16	18 28	18 40	18 52

Sundays

16 February to 11 May

		AW	AW	AW	AW	AW	and at the same minutes past each hour until	AW	AW	AW	AW	AW
Cardiff Queen Street 3	d	09 00	09 12	09 24	09 36	09 48		18 00	18 12	18 24	18 36	18 48
Cardiff Bay	a	09 04	09 16	09 28	09 40	09 52		18 04	18 16	18 28	18 40	18 52

When events are being held at the Millenium Stadium, services are subject to alteration. Please check times before travelling.

Table 130A-R

Cardiff Bay to Cardiff Queen Street

Mondays to Saturdays

9 December to 3 January

Network Diagram - see first Page of Table 130

Miles			AW	AW	AW	AW	AW	and at the same minutes past each hour until	AW	AW	AW	AW	AW		AW	AW
—	Cardiff Bay	d	06 42	06 54	07 06	07 18	07 30		22 42	22 54	23 06	23 18	23 30		23 42	23 54
1	Cardiff Queen Street 3	a	06 46	06 58	07 10	07 22	07 34		22 46	22 58	23 10	23 22	23 34		23 46	23 58

Mondays to Saturdays

6 January to 7 February

		AW	AW	AW	AW	AW	and at the same minutes past each hour until	AW	AW	AW	AW	AW		AW	AW SX	AW SX	AW SX	AW SX	AW SX	AW SX	AW SX	AW SX		AW SX
Cardiff Bay	d	06 42	06 54	07 06	07 18	07 30		20 42	20 54	21 06	21 18	21 30		21 42	21 54	22 06	22 18	22 30	22 42	22 54	23 06	23 18		23 30
Cardiff Queen Street 3	a	06 46	06 58	07 10	07 22	07 34		20 46	20 58	21 10	21 22	21 34		21 46	21 58	22 10	22 22	22 34	22 46	22 58	23 10	23 22		23 34

		AW SX	AW SX
Cardiff Bay	d	23 42	23 54
Cardiff Queen Street 3	a	23 46	23 58

Mondays to Saturdays

10 February to 17 May

		AW	AW	AW	AW	AW	and at the same minutes past each hour until	AW	AW	AW	AW	AW		AW	AW
Cardiff Bay	d	06 42	06 54	07 06	07 18	07 30		22 42	22 54	23 06	23 18	23 30		23 42	23 54
Cardiff Queen Street 3	a	06 46	06 58	07 10	07 22	07 34		22 46	22 58	23 10	23 22	23 34		23 46	23 58

Sundays

8 December to 29 December

		AW	AW	AW	AW	AW	and at the same minutes past each hour until	AW	AW	AW	AW	AW
Cardiff Bay	d	09 06	09 18	09 30	09 42	09 54		18 06	18 18	18 30	18 42	18 54
Cardiff Queen Street 3	a	09 10	09 22	09 34	09 46	09 58		18 10	18 22	18 34	18 46	18 58

Sundays

16 February to 11 May

		AW	AW	AW	AW	AW	and at the same minutes past each hour until	AW	AW	AW	AW	AW
Cardiff Bay	d	09 06	09 18	09 30	09 42	09 54		18 06	18 18	18 30	18 42	18 54
Cardiff Queen Street 3	a	09 10	09 22	09 34	09 46	09 58		18 10	18 22	18 34	18 46	18 58

When events are being held at the Millenium Stadium, services are subject to alteration. Please check times before travelling.

Table 131

Mondays to Fridays

Manchester, Liverpool and Crewe - Cardiff

9 December to 16 May

Route Diagram - see first Page of Table 129

Miles	Miles	Station		AW	AW	AW	AW	AW	AW	AW	AW	AW		AW	AW	AW	AW	AW	AW	AW	AW	AW		AW	AW
				MO		MX						BHX			BHX	BHX									
					◇	◇		◇	◇	◇	◇ A			◇	[1]	◇ C	D	◇	◇	◇	◇			◇	◇
								⊥		⊥	⊥			⊥	⊠	⊥		⊥	⊥	⊥	⊥			⊥	⊥
0	—	**Manchester Piccadilly [10]**	d											06 30				07 30			08 30				09 30
6	—	Stockport	d											06 39				07 39			08 39				09 39
12	—	Wilmslow	d											06 46				07 46			08 46				09 46
—	1	Holyhead	d								04 25				05 33	05⌇14				06 28				07 15	
—	25	Bangor (Gwynedd)	d								04 57				06 01	05⌇43				07 06				08 02	
—	40	Llandudno Junction	d								05 15				06 19	06⌇07				07 24				08 25	
—	85	Chester	d								06 18				07 15	07⌇02				08 19				09 19	
—	97	Wrexham General	d								06 37				07 32	⌇				08 34					
—	102	Ruabon	d								06 44					⌇				08 41					
—	106	Chirk	d								06 50					⌇				08 47					
—	109	Gobowen	d								06 56					⌇				08 53					
31	—	**Crewe [10]**	d					04 54		05 55		06 40		07 08		07⌇34	07⌇34	08 08			09 08	09 20		09 47	10 08
35½	—	Nantwich	d					05 02		06 03		06 46		07 17		07⌇40	07⌇40					09 29		09 55	
40	—	Wrenbury	d							06x09						07x46	07x46					09x36			
44¾	—	Whitchurch (Shrops)	d					05 13		06 16		06 58				07⌇54	07⌇54					09 43		10 06	
49¾	—	Prees	d							06x22						07x59	07x59					09x50			
53	—	Wem	d					05 22		06 27		07 08				08⌇05	08⌇05					09 56		10 15	
56½	—	Yorton	d	00x02						06x32						08x10	08x10					10x01			
63¾	127	**Shrewsbury**	a	00 14				05 33		06 42	07 16	07 25		07 42	08 07	08⌇25	08⌇25	08 37		09 13	09 37	10 16		10 26	10 37
—	—		d		05 16			05 40	06 09	06 44	07 18			07 44	08 10			08 40	09 00	09 14	09 40				10 39
76½	140	Church Stretton	d		05 33			05 55	06 26	06 59				07 59					09 18	09 30					10 54
83¾	146	Craven Arms	d		05 47			06 03	06 34	07 07				08 07					09 28	09 38					
91	154	Ludlow	d					06 10	06 43	07 14	07 44			08 15				09 06		09 45	10 06				11 08
102	—	Leominster	d					06 21	06 54	07 25	07 54			08 26				09 16			10 16				11 18
114½	178	**Hereford [7]**	a					06 35	07 09	07 43	08 10			08 40	08 54			09 32		10 09	10 32				11 34
—	—		d			00 09	05 26	06 41	07 10	07 45	08 11			08 42	08 56			09 33		10 10	10 33				11 35
138½	202	Abergavenny	d			00 33	05 51	07 04	07 34	08 08	08 34			09 05				09 56		10 33	10 56				11 58
148	211	Pontypool and New Inn	d				06 02	07 14	07 45	08 17	08 44									10 43					
151	214	Cwmbran	d			00 46	06 07	07 19	07 50	08 22	08 49			09 17				10 09		10 48	11 09				12 11
158	221	**Newport (South Wales)**	a			01 00	06 19	07 29	08 00	08 37	09 00			09 36	09 41			10 20		11 01	11 20				12 22
169¾	233	**Cardiff Central [7]**	a			01 20	06 40	07 49	08 18	08 53	09 21			09 57	09 58			10 37		11 15	11 37				12 37
—	—	Swansea	a		09 18			08 51		09 55				10 55				11 33	13 04		12 34				13 33

A ⊥ from Chester

C not 21 April, 5 May

D 21 April, 5 May

For connections from Liverpool Lime Street and Runcorn please see Table 91.
For connections to Bristol Temple Meads please see Table 132

When events are being held at the Millenium Stadium, services are subject to alteration. Please check times before travelling.

For other services between Shrewsbury and Chester see table 75

For other stations served by AW trains from and to Cardiff between Chester and Holyhead see table 81

For connections to Reading and London Paddington via Newport see table 125

Table 131

Mondays to Fridays

9 December to 16 May

Manchester, Liverpool and Crewe - Cardiff

Route Diagram - see first Page of Table 129

		AW	AW	AW	AW	AW	AW	AW	AW	AW	AW	AW	AW
						R	R			R		R	
		◇	◇		◇			◇			◇		
		trolley	trolley		trolley	trolley	trolley			trolley	trolley	trolley	
Manchester Piccadilly 10	d		10 30		11 30		12 30			13 30		14 30	
Stockport	d		10 39		11 39		12 39			13 39		14 39	
Wilmslow	d		10 46		11 46		12 46			13 46		14 46	
Holyhead	d	08 05				10 40					12 32		
Bangor (Gwynedd)	d	09 02				11 07					13 07		
Llandudno Junction	d	09 25				11 25					13 25		
Chester	d	10 20				12 19					14 19		
Wrexham General	d	10 36				12 34					14 34		
Ruabon	d	10 42				12 41					14 41		
Chirk	d	10 48				12 48					14 47		
Gobowen	d	10 54				12 53					14 53		
Crewe 10	d		11 08	11 20	12 08		13 08		13 20	14 08		15 08	15 20
Nantwich	d			11 28					13 28	14 17			15 28
Wrenbury	d			11x35					13x35				15x35
Whitchurch (Shrops)	d			11 43					13 43	14 28			15 43
Prees	d			11x49					13x49				15x49
Wem	d			11 55					13 55				15 55
Yorton	d			12x01					14x01				16x01
Shrewsbury	a	11 14	11 37	12 11	12 37	13 14	13 37		14 11	14 45	15 13	15 37	16 11
	d	11 16	11 39		12 39	13 15	13 40	14 04		14 50	15 15	15 40	
Church Stretton	d		11 54			13 30		14 22		15 05	15 30		
Craven Arms	d	11 37				13 38		14 33		15 13	15 38		
Ludlow	d	11 44	12 08		13 05	13 45	14 06			15 20	15 46	16 06	
Leominster	d		12 18		13 15		14 16			15 31		16 16	
Hereford 7	a	12 06	12 34		13 31	14 09	14 32			15 49	16 09	16 32	
	d	12 08	12 35		13 32	14 11	14 33			15 51	16 11	16 33	
Abergavenny	d	12 31	12 58		13 55	14 33	14 56			16 14	16 34	16 56	
Pontypool and New Inn	d	12 42			14 05					16 23	16 44		
Cwmbran	d	12 47	13 11		14 10		15 09			16 28	16 49	17 09	
Newport (South Wales)	a	12 56	13 22		14 20	14 53	15 21			16 39	16 59	17 21	
Cardiff Central 7	a	13 22	13 39		14 37	15 11	15 36			16 57	17 15	17 38	
Swansea	a		14 34		15 34	16 15	16 33	18 17		18 05		18 38	

		AW	AW	AW	AW	AW	AW	AW	AW FO	AW FX
		R		R			R			
			◇		◇			◇	◇	◇
		trolley	trolley	trolley			trolley	trolley		
Manchester Piccadilly 10	d	15 30		16 30			17 30		18 30	18 30
Stockport	d	15 39		16 39			17 39		18 39	18 39
Wilmslow	d	15 46		16 46			17 46		18 46	18 46
Holyhead	d		14 34					16 50		
Bangor (Gwynedd)	d		15 04					17 18		
Llandudno Junction	d		15 27					17 37		
Chester	d		16 19					18 28		
Wrexham General	d		16 35					18 45		
Ruabon	d		16 42					18 51		
Chirk	d		16 48					18 58		
Gobowen	d		16 54					19 03		
Crewe 10	d	16 08		17 08		17 20	18 09		19 08	19 08
Nantwich	d	16 17				17 28	18 18		19 17	19 17
Wrenbury	d					17x35			19x23	19x23
Whitchurch (Shrops)	d	16 28				17 43	18 29		19 29	19 29
Prees	d					17x49			19x35	19x35
Wem	d	16 36				17 55	18 37		19 40	19 40
Yorton	d					18x01			19x45	19x45
Shrewsbury	a	16 47	17 14	17 37		18 11	18 48	19 24	19 55	19 55
	d	16 50	17 16	17 40	18 05		18 50	19 25	19 56	19 56
Church Stretton	d	17 06	17 31		18 22		19 05		20 11	20 11
Craven Arms	d	17 14	17 39		18 35		19 13		20 19	20 19
Ludlow	d	17 21	17 46	18 06			19 20	19 51	20 27	20 27
Leominster	d	17 32	17 57	18 16			19 31		20 37	20 37
Hereford 7	a	17 49	18 12	18 32			19 46	20 15	20 53	20 53
	d	17 51	18 14	18 33			19 48	20 17	20 54	20 54
Abergavenny	d	18 14	18 37	18 56			20 11	20 40	21 22	21 22
Pontypool and New Inn	d	18 24					20 21		21 32	21 32
Cwmbran	d	18 29	18 49	19 09			20 26	20 53	21 37	21 37
Newport (South Wales)	a	18 39	19 00	19 22			20 37	21 15	21 50	21 50
Cardiff Central 7	a	18 55	19 21	19 43			21 01	21 42	22 06	22 06
Swansea	a	20 04		20 42	22 08				23 07	

		AW FO	AW FX	AW FO	AW FX	AW	AW FO	AW FX	AW
		◇	◇	◇	◇	◇	◇	◇	◇
Manchester Piccadilly 10	d	19 30	19 30	20 30	20 30	21 35			22 36
Stockport	d	19 39	19 39	20 39	20 39	21 44			22 44
Wilmslow	d	19 46	19 46	20 46	20 46	21 51			22 52
Holyhead	d								
Bangor (Gwynedd)	d								
Llandudno Junction	d								
Chester	d								
Wrexham General	d								
Ruabon	d								
Chirk	d								
Gobowen	d								
Crewe 10	d	20 09	20 09	21 08	21 21	22 12			23 14
Nantwich	d	20 18	20 18	21 17	21 29	22 20			23 22
Wrenbury	d			21x23	21x35	22x26			23x27
Whitchurch (Shrops)	d	20 29	20 29	21 30	21 42	22 33			23 34
Prees	d			21x36	21x48	22x39			23x40
Wem	d	20 37	20 37	21 41	21 53	22 44			23 45
Yorton	d			21x46	21x58	22x49			23x50
Shrewsbury	a	20 48	20 48	21 55	22 08	23 01			00 04
	d	20 50	20 50	21 57	22 09		23 08	23 08	
Church Stretton	d	21 05	21 05	22 12	22 24		23 24	23 24	
Craven Arms	d	21 13	21 13	22 20	22 32		23 32	23 32	
Ludlow	d	21 20	21 20	22 27	22 40		23 41	23 41	
Leominster	d	21 31	21 31	22 38	22 50		23 52	23 52	
Hereford 7	a	21 46	21 46	22 56	23 09		00 07	00 07	
	d	21 50	21 50	22 58	23 11		00 09	00 09	
Abergavenny	d	22 16	22 16	23 21	23 34		00 33	00 33	
Pontypool and New Inn	d			23 30	23 43				
Cwmbran	d	22 28	22 28	23 35	23 48		00 46	00 46	
Newport (South Wales)	a	22 39	22 41	23 46	23 59		00 57	01 00	
Cardiff Central 7	a	22 56	23 03	00 02	00 22		01 18	01 20	
Swansea	a	00 28	00 28						

For connections from Liverpool Lime Street and Runcorn please see Table 91.
For connections to Bristol Temple Meads please see Table 132

When events are being held at the Millenium Stadium, services are subject to alteration. Please check times before travelling.

For other services between Shrewsbury and Chester see table 75

For other stations served by AW trains from and to Cardiff between Chester and Holyhead see table 81

For connections to Reading and London Paddington via Newport see table 125

Table 131

Saturdays

Manchester, Liverpool and Crewe - Cardiff

14 December to 17 May

Route Diagram - see first Page of Table 129

		AW	AW	AW	AW	AW	AW	AW	AW	AW	AW	AW	AW	AW	AW	AW	AW	AW	AW	AW	AW	AW	AW
																					■	■	
		◇	◇		◇ ⊼		◇ ⊼	◇ ⊼	◇ ⊼		◇ ⊼	◇ ⊼	◇ ⊼	◇ ⊼		◇ ⊼	◇ ⊼	◇ ⊼		◇ ⊼	⊼	⊼	◇
Manchester Piccadilly 10 ⛴	d								06 30		07 30			08 30		09 30		10 30		11 30		12 30	
Stockport	d								06 39		07 39			08 39		09 39		10 39		11 39		12 39	
Wilmslow	d								06 46		07 46			08 46		09 46		10 46		11 46		12 46	
Holyhead	d							04 25					06 35				08 20				10 33		
Bangor (Gwynedd)	d							04 57					07 07				09 02				11 05		
Llandudno Junction	d							05 15					07 25				09 25				11 25		
Chester	d							06 12					08 19				10 19				12 19		
Wrexham General	d							06 38					08 34				10 35				12 34		
Ruabon	d							06 45					08 41				10 42				12 41		
Chirk	d							06 51					08 47				10 48				12 47		
Gobowen	d							06 57					08 53				10 54				12 53		
Crewe 10	d				04 54		05 55		07 08	07 20	08 08			09 08	09 20	10 08		11 08	11 20	12 08		13 08	
Nantwich	d				05 02		06 03		07 17	07 27	08 17				09 28				11 31	12 17			
Wrenbury	d						06x09			07x34					09x34				11x42				
Whitchurch (Shrops)	d				05 13		06 16		07 28	07 41	08 27				09 42				11 49	12 27			
Prees	d						06x22			07x47					09x48				11x56				
Wem	d				05 22		06 27		07 36	07 53					09 54				12 02				
Yorton	d						06x32			07x58					10x00				12x08				
Shrewsbury	a				05 33		06 42	07 17	07 47	08 08	08 45		09 13	09 37	10 12	10 36	11 14	11 37	12 18	12 45	13 13	13 37	
	d		05 16		05 40	06 13	06 44	07 19	07 50		08 50	09 00	09 15	09 40		10 38	11 15	11 40		12 50	13 15	13 40	14 05
Church Stretton	d		05 33		05 55	06 28	06 59		08 05		09 05	09 17		09 55		10 54		11 55		13 05	13 30		14 23
Craven Arms	d		05 47		06 03	06 36	07 07		08 13		09 13	09 30		10 03		11 02		12 03		13 13	13 38		14 36
Ludlow	d				06 10	06 44	07 14	07 45	08 20		09 20		09 42	10 10		11 09	11 41	12 10		13 20	13 44	14 06	
Leominster	d				06 21	06 55	07 25	07 55	08 31		09 31			10 21		11 20		12 21		13 31		14 16	
Hereford 7	a				06 37	07 09	07 40	08 11	08 49		09 49		10 05	10 36		11 44	12 04	12 36		13 49	14 09	14 32	
	d	00 09		05 42	06 42	07 11	07 44	08 12	08 51		09 51		10 07	10 38		11 46	12 06	12 38		13 51	14 10	14 33	
Abergavenny	d	00 33		06 07	07 05	07 34	08 07	08 35	09 14		10 14		10 30	11 01		12 09	12 29	13 01		14 14	14 32	14 56	
Pontypool and New Inn	d			06 18	07 15	07 44	08 16	08 45					10 40				12 39				14 43		
Cwmbran	d	00 46		06 23	07 20	07 49	08 21	08 50	09 26		10 26		10 45	11 13		12 21	12 44	13 13		14 26	14 48	15 09	
Newport (South Wales)	a	00 57		06 34	07 37	08 00	08 31	09 01	09 37		10 38		10 55	11 27		12 35	12 54	13 28		14 36	15 04	15 21	
Cardiff Central 7	a	01 18		06 54	07 54	08 20	08 50	09 22	09 59		10 54		11 14	11 53		12 53	13 15	13 53		14 53	15 24	15 37	
Swansea	a		09 18		08 54		09 57		10 55		11 59	13 00		12 55		13 55		14 55		15 55		16 35	18 10

For connections from Liverpool Lime Street and Runcorn please see Table 91.
For connections to Bristol Temple Meads please see Table 132

When events are being held at the Millenium Stadium, services are subject to alteration. Please check times before travelling.

For other services between Shrewsbury and Chester see table 75

For other stations served by AW trains from and to Cardiff between Chester and Holyhead see table 81

For connections to Reading and London Paddington via Newport see table 125

Table 131

Saturdays

14 December to 17 May

Manchester, Liverpool and Crewe - Cardiff

Route Diagram - see first Page of Table 129

		AW		AW	AW	AW	AW	AW	AW	AW	AW	AW		AW	AW	AW	AW	AW	AW	AW	AW	AW		AW	AW
				■	■		■		■		■				■										
						◇				◇		◇				◇	◇	◇	◇	◇	◇	◇			
				A	B													A	C	A	B				D
				⚲	⚲	⚲	⚲		⚲	⚲	⚲				⚲	⚲	⚲								
Manchester Piccadilly 10	d			13 30	13 30		14 30		15 30		16 30				17 30		18 30	19 30	19 30	20 30	20 30	21 35		22 35	
Stockport	d			13 39	13 39		14 39		15 39		16 39				17 39		18 39	19 39	19 39	20 39	20 39	21 44		22 44	
Wilmslow	d			13 46	13 46		14 46		15 46		16 46				17 46		18 46	19 46	19 46	20 46	20 46	21 51		22 52	
Holyhead	d					12 38				14 23						16 50									
Bangor (Gwynedd)	d					13 07				14 53						17 18									
Llandudno Junction	d					13 25				15 16						17 36									
Chester	d					14 19				16 19						18 29									
Wrexham General	d					14 34				16 35						18 45									
Ruabon	d					14 41				16 42						18 52									
Chirk	d					14 47				16 48						18 58									
Gobowen	d					14 53				16 54						19 04									
Crewe 10	d	13 20		14 08	14 08		15 08	15 20	16 08		17 08			17 20	18 09		19 10	20 09	20 09	21 09	21 09	22 12		23 14	
Nantwich	d	13 28		14 17	14 17			15 28	16 17		17 17			17 28	18 17		19 18	20 17	20 18	21 17	21 17	22 20		23 22	
Wrenbury	d	13x35						15x38						17x35			19x24			21x23	21x23	22x26		23x27	
Whitchurch (Shrops)	d	13 43		14 27	14 27			15 45	16 27		17 27			17 43	18 28		19 31	20 27	20 29	21 30	21 30	22 33		23 34	
Prees	d	13x49						15x52						17x49			19x37			21x36	21x36	22x39		23x40	
Wem	d	13 55						15 58						17 55			19 42	20 36	20 37	21 41	21 41	22 44		23 45	
Yorton	d	14x01						16x03						18x01			19x47			21x46	21x46	22x49		23x50	
Shrewsbury	a	14 11		14 43	14 43	15 13	15 37	16 14	16 43	17 14	17 43			18 11	18 46	19 24	19 56	20 47	20 48	21 54	21 54	23 01		00 04	
	d			14 45	14 45	15 15	15 40		16 45	17 16	17 45	18 05			18 47	19 26	19 58	20 49	20 50	21 55	21 55				
Church Stretton	d			15 00	15 00		15 55		17 00		18 00	18 23			19 02		20 13	21 04	21 05	22 10	22 10				
Craven Arms	d			15 08	15 08		16 03		17 08		18 08	18 36			19 10		20 21	21 12	21 13	22 18	22 18				
Ludlow	d			15 15	15 15	15 41	16 10		17 15	17 42	18 15				19 18	19 51	20 28	21 19	21 20	22 26	22 26				
Leominster	d			15 26	15 26		16 21		17 26		18 26				19 28		20 39	21 30	21 31	22 37	22 37				
Hereford 7	a			15 41	15 41	16 03	16 36		17 41	18 05	18 41				19 47	20 15	20 54	21 45	21 46	22 51	22 51				
	d			15 46	15 46	16 06	16 38		17 46	18 07	18 43				19 48	20 17	20 56	21 47	21 48	22 53	22 53				23 18
Abergavenny	d			16 09	16 09	16 29	17 01		18 09	18 30	19 06				20 11	20 40	21 19	22 10	22 11	23 16	23 16				23 41
Pontypool and New Inn	d					16 39				18 40					20 21		21 28			23 25	23 25				
Cwmbran	d			16 21	16 21	16 44	17 13		18 21	18 45	19 18				20 26	20 52	21 33	22 22	22 23	23 30	23 30				23 53
Newport (South Wales)	a			16 33	16 33	16 54	17 33		18 33	18 55	19 34				20 36	21 14	21 44	22 35	22 35	23 46	23 46				00 04
Cardiff Central 7	a			16 53	16 55	17 08	17 53		18 53	19 15	19 58				20 58	21 43	22 04	22 55	22 55	00 06					00 28
Swansea	a			18 05	18 05		19 02		20 05			22 10					23 05								

		AW	AW
		B	A
Manchester Piccadilly 10	d		
Stockport	d		
Wilmslow	d		
Holyhead	d		
Bangor (Gwynedd)	d		
Llandudno Junction	d		
Chester	d		
Wrexham General	d		
Ruabon	d		
Chirk	d		
Gobowen	d		
Crewe 10	d		
Nantwich	d		
Wrenbury	d		
Whitchurch (Shrops)	d		
Prees	d		
Wem	d		
Yorton	d		
Shrewsbury	a		
	d		
Church Stretton	d		
Craven Arms	d		
Ludlow	d		
Leominster	d		
Hereford 7	a		
	d	23 18	23 18
Abergavenny	d	23 41	23 41
Pontypool and New Inn	d		
Cwmbran	d	23 53	23 53
Newport (South Wales)	a	00 06	00 06
Cardiff Central 7	a		00 29
Swansea	a		

A from 15 February
B from 4 January until 8 February
C until 8 February
D 14 December, 21 December, 28 December

For connections from Liverpool Lime Street and Runcorn please see Table 91.
For connections to Bristol Temple Meads please see Table 132

When events are being held at the Millenium Stadium, services are subject to alteration. Please check times before travelling.

For other services between Shrewsbury and Chester see table 75

For other stations served by AW trains from and to Cardiff between Chester and Holyhead see table 81

For connections to Reading and London Paddington via Newport see table 125

Table 131

Sundays

8 December to 11 May

Manchester, Liverpool and Crewe - Cardiff

Route Diagram - see first Page of Table 129

		AW	AW	AW	AW	AW	AW	AW	AW	AW
					■		■		■	■
			◇	◇		◇		◇		
		🚌								
				🛒	🛒		🛒	🛒	🛒	🛒
Manchester Piccadilly 10	d			09 30	10 30		11 24		12 30	13 30
Stockport	d			09 39	10 39		11 40		12 40	13 40
Wilmslow	d			09 47	10 48		11 47		12 48	13 47
Holyhead	d							10 20		
Bangor (Gwynedd)	d							10 59		
Llandudno Junction	d							11 22		
Chester	d							12 21		
Wrexham General	d							12 38		
Ruabon	d							12 45		
Chirk	d							12 52		
Gobowen	d							12 57		
Crewe 10	d			10 11	11 11		12 11		13 11	14 11
Nantwich	d			10 22					13 21	
Wrenbury	d			10x27					13x26	
Whitchurch (Shrops)	d			10 35					13 34	
Prees	d			10x40					13x39	
Wem	d			10 46					13 45	
Yorton	d			10x50					13x49	
Shrewsbury	a			11 01	11 41		12 43	13 18	13 59	14 41
	d	07 50		11 03	11 45	12 04	12 44	13 19	14 01	14 44
Church Stretton	d	08 15		11 19		12 22		13 35		15 00
Craven Arms	d	08 35		11 27		12 33		13 43		15 08
Ludlow	d	08 55		11 36	12 13		13 12	13 51	14 28	15 16
Leominster	d	09 20		11 47	12 23		13 22	14 02	14 39	15 26
Hereford 7	a	09 50		12 02	12 38		13 37	14 17	14 53	15 41
	d		10 09	12 03	12 39		13 39	14 19	14 56	15 43
Abergavenny	d		10 33	12 27	13 02		14 02	14 42	15 19	16 06
Pontypool and New Inn	d		10 43		13 12			14 52		16 16
Cwmbran	d		10 48	12 40	13 17		14 14	14 57	15 31	16 21
Newport (South Wales)	a		10 59	12 51	13 28		14 31	15 07	15 49	16 31
Cardiff Central 7	a		11 16	13 13	13 44		14 52	15 31	16 04	16 52
Swansea	a		12 13		15 12	16 07			17 14	

		AW	AW	AW	AW	AW	AW	AW	AW	AW	AW
		■		■	■	■	■	■			
			◇						◇	◇	
		🛒		🛒	🛒	🛒	🛒	🛒			
Manchester Piccadilly 10	d	14 30		15 30	16 30	17 30		18 30	19 30	20 30	
Stockport	d	14 39		15 39	16 39	17 39		18 39	19 39	20 39	
Wilmslow	d	14 47		15 47	16 47	17 47		18 47	19 47	20 47	
Holyhead	d						16 25				
Bangor (Gwynedd)	d						17 04				
Llandudno Junction	d						17 25				
Chester	d						18 24				23 00
Wrexham General	d						18 41				
Ruabon	d						18 47				
Chirk	d						18 54				
Gobowen	d						18 59				
Crewe 10	d	15 10		16 11	17 11	18 11		19 11	20 10	21 13	23 23
Nantwich	d				17 21			19 21		21 21	23 31
Wrenbury	d				17x26			19x26		21x26	23x37
Whitchurch (Shrops)	d				17 34			19 34		21 35	23 45
Prees	d				17x39			19x39		21x40	23x51
Wem	d				17 45			19 45		21 47	23 57
Yorton	d				17x49			19x49		21x51	00x02
Shrewsbury	a	15 44		16 43	18 00	18 43	19 20	20 00	20 44	22 03	00 14
	d	15 47	16 18	16 44	18 01	18 44	19 21	20 01	20 45	22 04	
Church Stretton	d		16 36	17 00			19 37		21 01	22 20	
Craven Arms	d		16 47	17 08			19 45		21 10	22 29	
Ludlow	d	16 17		17 16	18 29	19 12	19 53	20 29	21 18	22 37	
Leominster	d	16 28		17 26	18 39		20 04	20 39	21 30	22 49	
Hereford 7	a	16 43		17 41	18 54	19 34	20 18	20 54	21 44	23 03	
	d	16 44		17 43	18 55	19 36	20 21	20 55	21 46	23 05	
Abergavenny	d	17 08		18 06	19 18	19 59	20 46	21 18	22 10	23 29	
Pontypool and New Inn	d			18 16			20 56		22 21	23 39	
Cwmbran	d	17 21		18 21	19 31	20 11	21 01	21 31	22 26	23 44	
Newport (South Wales)	a	17 33		18 31	19 41	20 22	21 14	21 43	22 36	23 54	
Cardiff Central 7	a	17 50		18 50	19 58	20 43	21 36	22 12	23 02	00 20	
Swansea	a	19 15	20 16								

For connections from Liverpool Lime Street and Runcorn please see Table 91.
For connections to Bristol Temple Meads please see Table 132

When events are being held at the Millenium Stadium, services are subject to alteration. Please check times before travelling.

For other services between Shrewsbury and Chester see table 75

For other stations served by AW trains from and to Cardiff between Chester and Holyhead see table 81

For connections to Reading and London Paddington via Newport see table 125

Table 131R

Mondays to Fridays

9 December to 16 May

Cardiff - Crewe, Liverpool and Manchester

Route Diagram - see first Page of Table 129

Miles	Miles			AW MX ◇	AW MX	AW	AW ◇	AW ◇ 🛒	AW ◇ 🛒	AW	AW ◇	AW ◇ 🛒	AW ◇ 🛒	AW ◇ 🛒	AW	AW ◇ 🛒	AW ◇ 🛒	AW ◇ 🛒	AW	AW ◇ 🛒	AW ◇ 🛒	AW ◇ 🛒	AW ◇ 🛒
—	—	Swansea	d								04 31			07 06		07 45		08 55		09 55	09 14		10 55
0	0	**Cardiff Central 7**	d		00 30		04 35	05 10	05 40			06 50	07 21	08 05		08 50	09 21	10 05		10 50		11 21	12 05
11¾	11¾	**Newport (South Wales)**	d		01 00		04 53	05 28	05 58			07 04	07 36	08 19		09 05	09 36	10 19		11 04		11 36	12 19
18¾	18¾	Cwmbran	d		01 11		05 05	05 38	06 08			07 14	07 46	08 29		09 15	09 46	10 29		11 14		11 46	12 29
21¾	21¾	Pontypool and New Inn	d		01 17		05 11	05 44	06 14				07 52				09 52					11 52	
31¼	31¼	Abergavenny	d		01 28		05 18	05 53	06 23			07 27	08 01	08 42		09 28	10 01	10 42		11 27		12 01	12 42
55¼	55¼	**Hereford 7**	a		01 58		05 46	06 17	06 47			07 51	08 25	09 07		09 52	10 25	11 06		11 51		12 25	13 06
—	—		d				05 47	06 25	06 49			07 53	08 27	09 08		09 54	10 27	11 08		11 53		12 27	13 08
67¾	—	Leominster	d				06 00	06 38	07 02			08 06		09 21		10 07		11 21		12 06			13 21
78¾	78¾	Ludlow	d				06 11	06 49	07 13			08 17	08 48	09 32		10 18	10 48	11 32		12 17		12 48	13 32
86	86	Craven Arms	d				06 20	06 57	07 21		07 54	08 25	08 56			10 26	10 56			12 25	12 39	12 56	
93¼	93¼	Church Stretton	d				06 29	07 06	07 30		08 07	08 34	09 05			10 39	11 05			12 38	12 52	13 05	
106	106	**Shrewsbury**	a				06 43	07 20	07 44		08 22	08 48	09 19	09 58		10 52	11 19	11 58		12 52	13 08	13 19	13 58
—	—		d	00 12		05 44	06 44	07 24	07 46	07 57		08 50	09 24	10 00	10 18	10 53	11 24	11 59	12 24	12 54		13 24	13 59
113¼	—	Yorton	d	00x21		05x52				08x06					10x28				12x34				
116¾	—	Wem	d	00 26		05 58	06 56		07 57	08 09					10 31				12 37				
120	—	Prees	d	00x31		06x03				08x17					10x39				12x45				
125	—	Whitchurch (Shrops)	d	00 38		06 10	07 04		08 06	08 25		09 06			10 46	11 12			12 52	13 10			
129¾	—	Wrenbury	d	00x44		06x17				08x31					10x53				12x59				
134¼	—	Nantwich	d	00 51		06 23	07 13		08 15	08 38		09 16			10 59	11 20			13 05	13 20			
138¾	—	**Crewe 10**	a	01 06		06 35	07 24		08 24	08 49		09 27		10 29	11 09	11 29		12 29	13 15	13 28			14 29
—	124	Gobowen	a					07 42					09 42				11 42					13 42	
—	127	Chirk	a					07 47					09 47				11 47					13 47	
—	131	Ruabon	a					07 54					09 54				11 54					13 54	
—	136	Wrexham General	a					08 01					10 01				12 01					14 01	
—	148	Chester	a					08 20					10 19				12 19					14 19	
—	193	Llandudno Junction	a					09 16					11 14				13 11					15 11	
—	208	Bangor (Gwynedd)	a										11 38				13 29					15 29	
—	233	Holyhead	a										12 23				14 13					16 15	
157¾	—	Wilmslow	a				07 45		08 45			09 47		10 49		11 48		12 48		13 48			14 48
163¾	—	Stockport	a				07 54		08 59			09 57		10 58		11 58		12 58		13 58			14 58
169¾	—	**Manchester Piccadilly 10**	a				08 10		09 14			10 14		11 15		12 15		13 15		14 15			15 15

For connections from Bristol Temple Meads please see Table 132. For connections to Runcorn and Liverpool Lime Street please see Table 91

When events are being held at the Millenium Stadium, services are subject to alteration. Please check times before travelling.

For other services between Shrewsbury and Chester see table 75

For other stations served by AW trains from and to Cardiff between Chester and Holyhead see table 81

For connections to Reading and London Paddington via Newport see table 125

Table 131R

Cardiff - Crewe, Liverpool and Manchester

Mondays to Fridays

9 December to 16 May

Route Diagram - see first Page of Table 129

		AW		AW	AW	AW	AW	AW	AW	AW	AW	AW		AW	AW	AW BHX	AW	AW	AW	AW	AW	AW		AW	AW
										R	R	R			R	R	R	R							
																1									
				◇	◇	◇		◇	◇											◇	◇	◇		◇	◇
				🛒	🛒	🛒		🛒		🛒	🛒				🛒	☒	🛒	🛒		🛒					
Swansea	d			11 55		12 54		13 55	13 14		14 55	15 10			15 55		16 55	17 10		17 55		18 21			
Cardiff Central 7	d			12 50	13 21	14 05		14 50		15 21	15 50	16 21			16 50	17 16	17 50	18 21		18 50	19 34			20 17	20 55
Newport (South Wales)	d			13 04	13 36	14 19		15 04		15 36	16 04	16 35			17 04	17 31	18 04	18 35		19 05	19 48			20 31	21 12
Cwmbran	d			13 14	13 46	14 29		15 14		15 46	16 14	16 44			17 14	17 42	18 14			19 15	19 58			20 41	21 22
Pontypool and New Inn	d				13 52					15 52	16 19					17 49	18 19			19 20	20 03			20 47	
Abergavenny	d			13 26	14 01	14 43		15 27		16 01	16 29	16 57			17 27	18 00	18 29	18 57		19 30	20 12			20 56	21 35
Hereford 7	a			13 53	14 25	15 06		15 51		16 25	16 53	17 22			17 51	18 24	18 53	19 21		19 54	20 38			21 21	21 59
	d			13 55	14 27	15 08		15 53		16 27	16 54	17 24			17 53	18 25	18 54	19 22		19 55	20 39			21 22	22 01
Leominster	d			14 08		15 21		16 06		16 40	17 07				18 06		19 07			20 08	20 52			21 35	22 14
Ludlow	d			14 19	14 48	15 32		16 17		16 51	17 18				18 17		19 18	19 43		20 19	21 03			21 46	22 25
Craven Arms	d			14 27	14 56			16 25	16 43		17 27				18 25		19 27			20 28	21 12	21 38		21 54	22 33
Church Stretton	d			14 36	15 05				16 56	17 05	17 36				18 34		19 36			20 37	21 21	21 51		22 03	22 42
Shrewsbury	a			14 50	15 19	15 58		16 48	17 12	17 19	17 50	18 09			18 48	19 08	19 50	20 09		20 51	21 37	22 08		22 17	22 56
	d	14 24		14 52	15 24	15 59	16 24	16 50		17 24	17 51	18 10		18 25	18 50	19 09	19 51	20 10	20 32	20 52	21 39			22 19	23 06
Yorton	d	14x34					16x34							18x35					20x39					22x27	23x15
Wem	d	14 37					16 37	17 01						18 38					20 44					22 31	23 20
Prees	d	14x45					16x45							18x46					20x49					22x35	23x25
Whitchurch (Shrops)	d	14 52		15 08			16 52	17 10			18 09			18 53	19 06				20 56	21 10				22 42	23 32
Wrenbury	d	14x57					16x59							19x00					21x02					22x48	23x38
Nantwich	d	15 05		15 18			17 05	17 19			18 19			19 06	19 16				21 08	21 20				22 53	23 44
Crewe 10	a	15 15		15 27		16 29	17 15	17 28			18 28	18 43		19 16	19 25		20 22	20 40	21 19	21 29				23 03	23 53
Gobowen	a				15 42					17 42											21 57				
Chirk	a				15 47					17 47											22 02				
Ruabon	a				15 54					17 54											22 09				
Wrexham General	a				16 01					18 01						19 41					22 13				
Chester	a				16 20					18 20		19 05				20 01		21 01			22 34				00 27
Llandudno Junction	a				17 13					19 12						20 53					23 49				
Bangor (Gwynedd)	a				17 35					19 32						21 09					00 13				
Holyhead	a				18 19					20 18						21 45					00 48				
Wilmslow	a			15 47		16 48		17 47			18 48				19 48		20 40			21 48				23 22	
Stockport	a			15 58		16 58		17 57			18 58				19 58		20 51			21 58				23 30	
Manchester Piccadilly 10	a			16 15		17 14		18 13			19 15				20 15		21 06			22 13				23 48	

		AW MWFO	AW TThO
		◇	◇
Swansea	d		
Cardiff Central 7	d	21 55	21 55
Newport (South Wales)	d	22 12	22 12
Cwmbran	d	22 24	22 24
Pontypool and New Inn	d	22 30	22 30
Abergavenny	d	22 40	22 40
Hereford 7	a	23 06	23 06
	d	23 08	23 09
Leominster	d	23 21	23 22
Ludlow	d	23 32	23 33
Craven Arms	d	23 42	23 43
Church Stretton	d	23 51	23 52
Shrewsbury	a	00 07	00 07
	d	00 12	00 12
Yorton	d	00x21	00x21
Wem	d	00 26	00 26
Prees	d	00x31	00x31
Whitchurch (Shrops)	d	00 38	00 38
Wrenbury	d	00x44	00x44
Nantwich	d	00 51	00 51
Crewe 10	a	01 06	01 06
Gobowen	a		
Chirk	a		
Ruabon	a		
Wrexham General	a		
Chester	a		
Llandudno Junction	a		
Bangor (Gwynedd)	a		
Holyhead	a		
Wilmslow	a		
Stockport	a		
Manchester Piccadilly 10	a		

For connections from Bristol Temple Meads please see Table 132. For connections to Runcorn and Liverpool Lime Street please see Table 91

When events are being held at the Millenium Stadium, services are subject to alteration. Please check times before travelling.

For other services between Shrewsbury and Chester see table 75

For other stations served by AW trains from and to Cardiff between Chester and Holyhead see table 81

For connections to Reading and London Paddington via Newport see table 125

Table 131R

Saturdays

14 December to 17 May

Cardiff - Crewe, Liverpool and Manchester

Route Diagram - see first Page of Table 129

		AW	AW	AW	AW	AW	AW	AW	AW	AW		AW	AW	AW	AW	AW	AW	AW	AW	AW		AW	AW	AW	AW
		◇			◇	◇	◇		◇	◇		◇	◇		◇	◇	◇		◇	◇		◇	◇		◇
						🍴	🍴			🍴		🍴	🍴		🍴	🍴	🍴		🍴	🍴		🍴	🍴		🍴
Swansea	d								04 31				06 47		07 45		08 55		09 55	09 14			10 55		12 00
Cardiff Central 7	d		00 30		04 35	05 20	05 40			06 50		07 21	07 50		08 50	09 21	09 55		10 55			11 21	11 55		12 55
Newport (South Wales)	d		00 46		04 52	05 35	05 57			07 04		07 36	08 04		09 04	09 36	10 09		11 09			11 36	12 09		13 09
Cwmbran	d		00 56		05 03	05 45	06 08			07 14		07 46	08 14		09 14	09 46	10 19		11 19			11 46	12 19		13 19
Pontypool and New Inn	d		01 02		05 09	05 51	06 13					07 51				09 51						11 50			
Abergavenny	d		01 13		05 18	06 00	06 23			07 27		08 01	08 27		09 27	10 01	10 32		11 32			12 00	12 32		13 32
Hereford 7	a		01 43		05 46	06 24	06 46			07 51		08 26	08 51		09 51	10 26	10 56		11 56			12 26	12 56		13 56
	d				05 47	06 26	06 49			07 53		08 27	08 53		09 53	10 28	10 58		11 58			12 28	12 58		13 58
Leominster	d				06 00	06 40	07 02			08 06			09 06		10 06		11 11		12 11				13 11		14 11
Ludlow	d				06 11	06 51	07 13			08 17		08 48	09 17		10 17	10 49	11 22		12 22			12 49	13 22		14 22
Craven Arms	d				06 20	06 59	07 21		07 54	08 25		08 56			10 25	10 57			12 30	12 37		12 57			14 30
Church Stretton	d				06 29	07 08	07 30		08 07	08 34		09 05			10 34	11 06			12 39	12 51		13 06			14 40
Shrewsbury	a				06 43	07 22	07 44		08 22	08 51		09 19	09 43		10 48	11 20	11 48		12 53	13 09		13 20	13 48		14 53
	d	00 12		05 44	06 44	07 24	07 46	07 57		08 52		09 24	09 44	10 18	10 50	11 24	11 49	12 24	12 55			13 24	13 49	14 24	14 55
Yorton	d	00x21		05x52				08x06						10x28				12x34						14x34	
Wem	d	00 26		05 58	06 56		07 57	08 09						10 31				12 37						14 37	
Prees	d	00x31		06x03				08x17						10x39				12x45						14x45	
Whitchurch (Shrops)	d	00 38		06 10	07 04		08 06	08 25		09 09			10 01	10 46	11 06		12 06	12 52					14 06	14 52	
Wrenbury	d	00x44		06x17				08x31						10x53				12x59						14x57	
Nantwich	d	00 51		06 23	07 13		08 15	08 38		09 18			10 10	10 59	11 16		12 15	13 05					14 15	15 05	
Crewe 10	a	01 06		06 35	07 22		08 24	08 47		09 27			10 20	11 09	11 25		12 24	13 15	13 26				14 29	15 15	15 25
Gobowen	a					07 42						09 42				11 42						13 42			
Chirk	a					07 47						09 47				11 47						13 47			
Ruabon	a					07 54						09 54				11 54						13 54			
Wrexham General	a					08 00						10 01				12 01						14 01			
Chester	a					08 18						10 19				12 19						14 19			
Llandudno Junction	a					09 11						11 11				13 11						15 11			
Bangor (Gwynedd)	a					09 34						11 34				13 29						15 29			
Holyhead	a					10 14						12 09				14 13						16 13			
Wilmslow	a				07 44		08 45			09 47			10 48		11 48		12 48		13 48				14 48		15 45
Stockport	a				07 54		08 58			09 57			10 58		11 58		12 58		13 58				14 58		15 58
Manchester Piccadilly 10	a				08 10		09 15			10 14			11 15		12 15		13 15		14 15				15 15		16 15

		AW	AW	AW	AW	AW		AW	AW	AW	AW	AW	AW	AW	AW	AW		AW	AW	AW	AW	AW	AW	AW	
								R	R			R	R	R											
		◇	◇		◇	◇										◇		◇	◇	◇	◇	◇	◇		
																				A	B				
		🍴	🍴		🍴			🍴	🍴			🍴		🍴		🍴									
Swansea	d		12 53		14 00	13 15			14 55		15 10	15 55		16 58		17 54			18 21				20 55		
Cardiff Central 7	d	13 21	13 55		14 55			15 21	15 55		16 19	16 55	17 21	17 55		18 50		19 34		20 10	20 10	20 55	21 54		
Newport (South Wales)	d	13 36	14 09		15 09			15 36	16 09		16 34	17 09	17 35	18 09		19 04		19 48		20 26	20 26	21 10	22 12		
Cwmbran	d	13 46	14 19		15 19			15 46	16 19		16 44	17 19	17 46	18 19		19 15		19 58		20 37	20 37	21 21	22 24		
Pontypool and New Inn	d	13 50						15 52	16 24		16 50		17 52	18 24		19 20		20 03		20 42	20 42		22 29		
Abergavenny	d	14 01	14 32		15 32			16 01	16 34		17a02	17 32	18 01	18 34		19 29		20 12		20 52	20 52	21 34	22 39		
Hereford 7	a	14 26	14 56		15 56			16 25	16 58			17 56	18 25	18 58		19 53		20 38		21 17	21 17	21 58	23 03		
	d	14 26	14 58		15 58			16 27	16 59			17 58	18 27	18 59		19 55		20 39		21 20	21 20	22 00			
Leominster	d		15 11		16 11			16 40	17 12			18 11		19 12		20 08		20 52		21 33	21 33	22 14			
Ludlow	d	14 47	15 22		16 22			16 51	17 23			18 22	18 48	19 23		20 19		21 03		21 44	21 44	22 25			
Craven Arms	d	14 55			16 30	16 42						18 30	18 56			20 27		21 12	21 38	21 53	21 53	22 33			
Church Stretton	d	15 04			16 39	16 56		17 05				18 39	19 05			20 36		21 21	21 51	22 03	22 03	22 42			
Shrewsbury	a	15 18	15 48		16 53	17 16		17 19	17 49			18 53	19 19	19 49		20 53		21 35	22 08	22 17	22 17	22 57			
	d	15 24	15 49	16 24	16 55			17 24	17 51	18 25		18 55	19 24	19 52	20 32	20 57		21 37		22 19	22 19	23 06		23 50	
Yorton	d			16x34						18x35					20x39					22x27	22x27	23x14		23x58	
Wem	d			16 37						18 38					20 44					22 32	22 32	23 20		00 04	
Prees	d			16x45						18x46					20x49					22x36	22x36	23x24		00x07	
Whitchurch (Shrops)	d		16 06	16 52					18 07	18 53				20 08	20 56					22 44	22 44	23 31		00 15	
Wrenbury	d			16x59						19x00					21x02					22x49	22x49	23x36		00x20	
Nantwich	d		16 15	17 05					18 17	19 06				20 18	21 08					22 55	22 55	23 42		00 26	
Crewe 10	a		16 24	17 15	17 26				18 28	19 16		19 26		20 27	21 19	21 28				23 04	23 04	23 53		00 38	
Gobowen	a	15 42						17 42					19 42					21 55							
Chirk	a	15 47						17 47					19 47					22 00							
Ruabon	a	15 54						17 54					19 54					22 07							
Wrexham General	a	16 01						18 01					20 01					22 13							
Chester	a	16 22						18 21					20 21					22 31				00 24			
Llandudno Junction	a	17 14						19 14					21 24					23 38							
Bangor (Gwynedd)	a	17 36						19 32					21 42												
Holyhead	a	18 20						20 18					22 25												
Wilmslow	a		16 48		17 45				18 48			19 48		20 46		21 48				23 24	23 24				
Stockport	a		16 58		17 58				18 58			19 58		20 59		21 58				23 32	23 40				
Manchester Piccadilly 10	a		17 14		18 15				19 15			20 15		21 16		22 13				23 49					

A until 8 February, from 29 March

B from 15 February until 22 March

For connections from Bristol Temple Meads please see Table 132. For connections to Runcorn and Liverpool Lime Street please see Table 91

When events are being held at the Millenium Stadium, services are subject to alteration. Please check times before travelling.

For other services between Shrewsbury and Chester see table 75

For other stations served by AW trains from and to Cardiff between Chester and Holyhead see table 81

For connections to Reading and London Paddington via Newport see table 125

Table 131R

Sundays

Cardiff - Crewe, Liverpool and Manchester

8 December to 11 May

Route Diagram - see first Page of Table 129

		AW	AW	AW	AW	AW	AW	AW	AW	AW
										■
		A	◇	◇	◇	◇	◇	◇	◇	
				trolley	trolley	trolley	trolley	trolley		
Swansea	d							11 32	11 08	
Cardiff Central [7]	d			08 30	09 20	10 35	11 35	12 40		13 22
Newport (South Wales)	d			08 49	09 41	10 51	11 51	12 54		13 36
Cwmbran	d			09 00	09 51	11 02	12 05	13 09		13 47
Pontypool and New Inn	d			09 06	09 57	11 08	12 11	13 15		
Abergavenny	d			09 15	10 08	11 18	12 22	13 25		14 00
Hereford [7]	a			09 40	10 34	11 44	12 48	13 49		14 26
	d			09 41	10 36	11 50	12 54	13 55		14 26
Leominster	d			09 55	10 50	12 03	13 08	14 08		
Ludlow	d			10 06	11 01	12 14	13 19	14 19		14 48
Craven Arms	d			10 14		12 24		14 28	14 44	
Church Stretton	d			10 23		12 33		14 37	14 57	
Shrewsbury	a			10 37	11 30	12 48	13 48	14 51	15 15	15 21
	d		09 55	10 39	11 31	12 51	13 50	14 53		15 22
Yorton	d				11x40					
Wem	d	00 04		10 51	11 43					
Prees	d	00x07			11x50					
Whitchurch (Shrops)	d	00 15		11 00	11 58					
Wrenbury	d	00x20			12x04					
Nantwich	d	00 26		11 09	12 11					
Crewe [10]	a	00 38	10 25	11 22	12 22	13 26	14 25	15 25		
Gobowen	a									15 41
Chirk	a									15 47
Ruabon	a									15 53
Wrexham General	a									16 00
Chester	a									16 18
Llandudno Junction	a									17 29
Bangor (Gwynedd)	a									17 52
Holyhead	a									18 37
Wilmslow	a		10 46	11 41	12 48	13 49	14 48	15 46		
Stockport	a		10 58		12 58	14 00	15 00	15 58		
Manchester Piccadilly [10] ⛴	a		11 14	12 02	13 15	14 19	15 15	16 15		

		AW	AW	AW	AW	AW	AW	AW	AW	AW	AW	AW	AW
		■	■	■	■	■		■	■				
							◇			◇	◇	◇	◇
		trolley	trolley	trolley	trolley	trolley			trolley				
Swansea	d		13 43			15 34	15 29		17 30				21 52
Cardiff Central [7]	d	13 40	14 53	15 22	15 56	16 41		17 35	18 40	19 40		21 04	23 00
Newport (South Wales)	d	13 54	15 09	15 36	16 10	16 55		17 49	18 54	19 55		21 19	23 20
Cwmbran	d	14 09	15 23	15 47	16 24	17 10		18 04	19 09	20 10		21 30	23 29
Pontypool and New Inn	d			15 52		17 16		18 10		20 16		21 36	23 35
Abergavenny	d	14 22	15 37	16 02	16 37	17 26		18 20	19 22	20 26		21 46	23 45
Hereford [7]	a	14 47	16 01	16 27	17 02	17 50		18 44	19 47	20 52		22 12	00 17
	d	14 48	16 04	16 28	17 04	17 53		18 49	19 49	20 54		22 14	
Leominster	d	15 01		16 41		18 07		19 03	20 03	21 08		22 27	
Ludlow	d	15 12	16 25	16 52	17 26	18 18		19 14	20 14	21 19		22 38	
Craven Arms	d			17 00		18 26	19 03		20 22	21 29		22 48	
Church Stretton	d			17 09		18 35	19 16		20 31	21 38		22 57	
Shrewsbury	a	15 38	16 51	17 23	17 52	18 49	19 31	19 40	20 46	21 55		23 14	
	d	15 40	16 53	17 30	17 54	18 54		19 41	20 48		22 32	23 19	
Yorton	d	15x48						19x49				23x28	
Wem	d	15 51						19 52				23 34	
Prees	d	15x58						19x59				23x39	
Whitchurch (Shrops)	d	16 06						20 06				23 46	
Wrenbury	d	16x11						20x11				23x52	
Nantwich	d	16 18						20 18				23 59	
Crewe [10]	a	16 27	17 25		18 25	19 24		20 27	21 21		23 03	00 09	
Gobowen	a			17 49									
Chirk	a			17 54									
Ruabon	a			18 01									
Wrexham General	a			18 07									
Chester	a			18 25							23 31	00 33	
Llandudno Junction	a			19 22									
Bangor (Gwynedd)	a			19 47									
Holyhead	a			20 18									
Wilmslow	a	16 46	17 45		18 46	19 46		20 45	21 45				
Stockport	a	16 58	17 58		18 58	19 58		20 57	21 58				
Manchester Piccadilly [10] ⛴	a	17 15	18 17		19 15	20 17		21 14	22 19				

A not 8 December

For connections from Bristol Temple Meads please see Table 132. For connections to Runcorn and Liverpool Lime Street please see Table 91

When events are being held at the Millenium Stadium, services are subject to alteration. Please check times before travelling.

For other services between Shrewsbury and Chester see table 75

For other stations served by AW trains from and to Cardiff between Chester and Holyhead see table 81

For connections to Reading and London Paddington via Newport see table 125

Network Diagram for Tables 132, 133 ,134

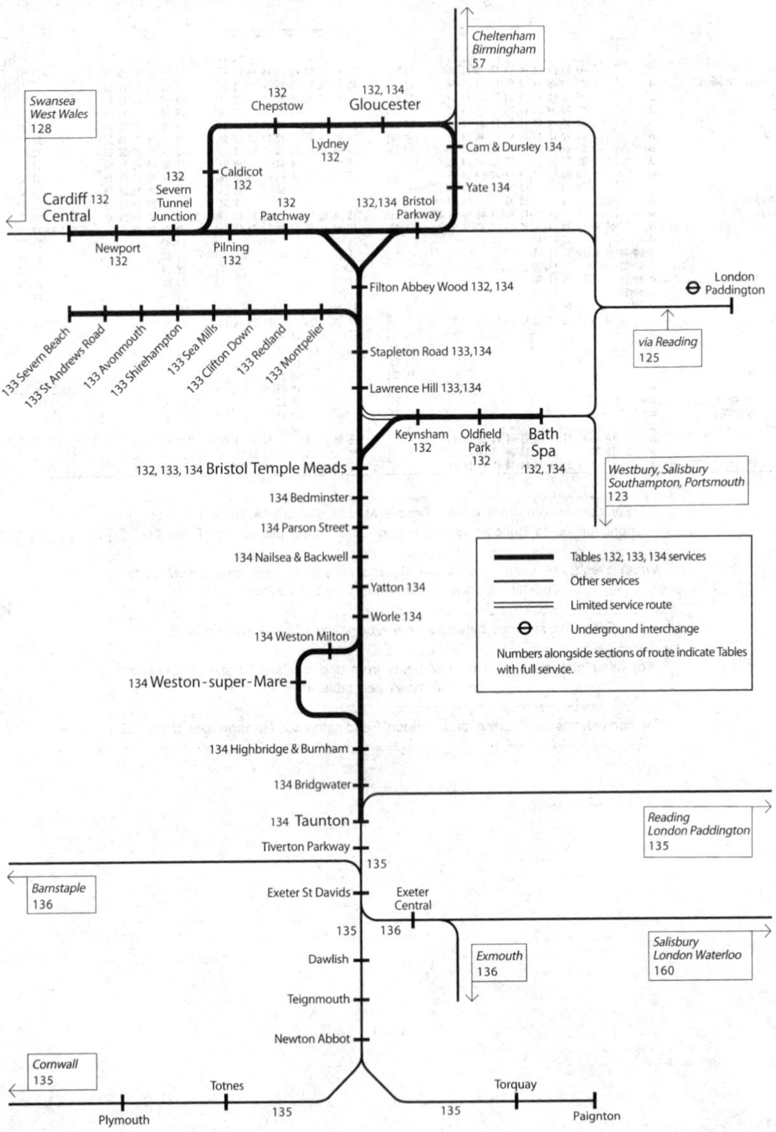

TOCs operating on this network - First Great Western (GW)
Arriva Trains Wales (AW), Cross Country (XC), South West Trains (SW)

Table 132

Mondays to Fridays

9 December to 16 May

Bath Spa, Bristol and Gloucester - Cardiff

Network Diagram - see first Page of Table 132

Miles	Miles	Miles			AW	GW	AW	GW	AW	GW	XC	XC	AW		GW	AW	GW	XC	XC	GW	AW	GW	XC		AW
					MX	MX	MX	MX	MX	MX	MX	MO													
					◇	◇1		◇1	◇	◇1	◇1	◇1						◇1	◇1		◇	◇1	◇1		◇
																		A							
						☕		☕		☕								🛒			🛒	☕			
0	—	—	**Bath Spa [7]**	d		00 01				01 16								06 09		06 28		06 56			
1	—	—	Oldfield Park	d																06 31					
7	—	—	Keynsham	d																06 38					
11½	—	—	**Bristol Temple Meads [10]**	a		00 14				01 30								06 20		06 46		07 09			
—	—	—		d						01 37	05 20	05 20			05 54		06 19	06 27		06 50		07 16			
16	—	—	Filton Abbey Wood	d											06 01		06 31			07 02		07 23			
—	0	—	**Bristol Parkway [7]**	a							05 29	05 29						06 37							
—	—	—		d				00 27			05 38	05 38													
17½	—	—	Patchway	d											06 06		06 35								
21	4¾	—	Pilning	d																					
—	—	0	**Gloucester [7]**	d												05 50			06 17				07 01		
—	—	19½	Lydney	d												06 09			06 36				07 20		
—	—	27¼	Chepstow	d												06 19			06 46				07 29		
—	—	34	Caldicot	d												06 26			06 54				07 38		
28	11¾	34¾	Severn Tunnel Jn	d											06 17	06 29	06 48		06 57	07 14			07 41		
38	21¾	44¾	Newport (South Wales)	a				00 55		02s11	05 58	06 08			06 28	06 41	06 59		07 08	07 25		07 46	07 52		
—	—	—		d	00 01		00 07	00 56	01 01		06 00	06 10	06 23		06 29	06 44	07 01		07 10	07 27	07 31	07 46	07 53		08 01
49¾	33½	56½	**Cardiff Central [7]**	a	00 22		00 35	01 15	01 20	02 32	06 18	06 24	06 40		06 48	07 00	07 18		07 26	07 44	07 49	08 01	08 08		08 18

		GW	GW	GW	SW	GW	GW	GW	AW		AW	AW	GW	GW	XC	GW	GW	GW	GW		GW	GW	AW	AW	AW
																								BHX	
																	R							R	
				◇	1	◇1	◇	◇1	◇			◇		◇1	◇1			◇1	◇1		◇	◇1	◇		
															B				C			D			
						☕		☕	🛒			🛒		☕	🛒		🛒	☕	☕			Ø	🛒	⊠	
Bath Spa [7]	d		07 08	07 25	07 35		07 48	07 59								08 08	08 22	08 31			08 47	08 57			
Oldfield Park	d		07 11	07 28	07 38		07 51									08 11	08 25				08 49				
Keynsham	d		07 18	07 35	07 45		07 58	08 09								08 18	08 34				08 57				
Bristol Temple Meads [10]	a		07 27	07 46	07 52		08 06	08 17								08 29	08 41	08 45			09 05	09 10			
	d	07 19	07 34	07 54			08 10						08 24			08 41	08 54				09 10				
Filton Abbey Wood	d	07 30	07 43	08 00			08 22						08 33			08 48	09 01				09 23				
Bristol Parkway [7]	a	07 33	07 47				08 29									08 52					09 28				
	d	07 40	07 48			08 08								08 41		08 52			09 08						
Patchway	d	07 44		08 06									08 37												
Pilning	d																								
Gloucester [7]	d		08a29								07 58				08 25	09a32									08 58
Lydney	d										08 17														09 17
Chepstow	d										08 27				08 51										09 27
Caldicot	d										08 35														09 35
Severn Tunnel Jn.	d	07 56									08 38		08 49												09 38
Newport (South Wales)	a	08 07		08 27		08 32					08 50		09 02	09 07	09 12		09 24		09 29						09 51
	d	08 09		08 27		08 32			08 38		08 52	09 01	09 03	09 08	09 13		09 25		09 30				09 37	09 41	09 52
Cardiff Central [7]	a	08 24		08 44		08 46			08 53		09 07	09 21	09 24	09 24	09 30		09 43		09 48				09 57	09 58	10 11

		GW	GW	XC	GW		GW	AW	GW	GW	GW	AW	AW	GW	GW		XC	GW	GW	AW	GW	GW	GW	AW	AW
																									R
			◇1	◇1			◇1	◇	◇	◇1	◇1	◇	◇		◇1		◇1	◇	◇1	◇	◇	◇1	◇1		
			☕				☕	🛒	🛒	☕	Ø	🛒	🛒		☕		🛒		☕	🛒	🛒	☕	Ø		🛒
Bath Spa [7]	d				09 15		09 30		09 36	10 00								10 08	10 26		10 36	11 00			
Oldfield Park	d				09 18													10 11							
Keynsham	d				09 25				09 44									10 18							
Bristol Temple Meads [10]	a				09 36		09 45		09 52	10 15								10 28	10 39		10 48	11 15			
	d	09 21			09 41				09 56					10 21				10 41			10 54				
Filton Abbey Wood	d	09 30			09 48				10 03					10 30				10 48			11 01				
Bristol Parkway [7]	a				09 52													10 54							
	d		09 43		09 52						10 08				10 41			10 55					11 08		
Patchway	d	09 35												10 35											
Pilning	d																								
Gloucester [7]	d			09 25	10a32												10 25	11a34						10 58	
Lydney	d																10 44							11 17	
Chepstow	d			09 51																				11 27	
Caldicot	d																							11 35	
Severn Tunnel Jn.	d	09 46												10 46										11 38	
Newport (South Wales)	a	09 58	10 06	10 11					10 26		10 31			11 02	11 06		11 11				11 26		11 31	11 50	
	d	10 00	10 06	10 13				10 22	10 26		10 31	10 40	11 01	11 02	11 06		11 12			11 22	11 27		11 31	11 52	11 55
Cardiff Central [7]	a	10 18	10 23	10 27				10 37	10 43		10 46	10 55	11 15	11 23	11 23		11 27			11 37	11 43		11 46	12 10	12 09

A 🛒 from Bristol Temple Meads
B 🛒 to Newport (South Wales)
C The St. David
D The Merchant Venturer

When events are being held at the Millenium Stadium, services are subject to alteration. Please check times before travelling.

Table 132

Mondays to Fridays

9 December to 16 May

Bath Spa, Bristol and Gloucester - Cardiff

Network Diagram - see first Page of Table 132

		GW	GW	GW	GW	XC	AW	GW	SW	GW	GW	AW	AW	GW	GW	XC	GW	GW	AW	GW	GW	GW	GW
		◇	◇	◇1	◇1	◇1	◇	◇	◇1	◇1	◇1		◇		◇1	◇1	◇	◇1	◇	◇	◇1	◇1	
				A																			
				☕	☕	T	T	T		☕	Ø		T		☕	T		☕	T	T	☕	Ø	
Bath Spa 7	d		11 08	11 24				11 36	11 47	12 00							12 12	12 24		12 36	13 00		
Oldfield Park	d		11 11														12 15						
Keynsham	d		11 18						11 55								12 22						
Bristol Temple Meads 10	a		11 28	11 40				11 48	12 05	12 15							12 33	12 39		12 48	13 15		
	d	11 21						11 54						12 21			12 41			12 54			13 21
Filton Abbey Wood	d	11 30						12 01						12 30			12 48			13 01			13 30
Bristol Parkway 7	a																12 52						
	d				11 43						12 08				12 43		12 52					13 08	
Patchway	d	11 35												12 35									13 35
Pilning	d																						
Gloucester 7	d					11 25						11 58				12 25	13a34						
Lydney	d											12 17											
Chepstow	d					11 51						12 27				12 51							
Caldicot	d											12 35											
Severn Tunnel Jn.	d	11 46										12 38		12 46									13 46
Newport (South Wales)	a	11 58			12 04	12 10		12 26			12 31	12 50		13 00	13 05	13 11				13 26		13 31	13 58
	d	12 00			12 06	12 12	12 23	12 27			12 31	12 52	12 57	13 01	13 06	13 12			13 23	13 26		13 31	14 00
Cardiff Central 7	a	12 18			12 21	12 26	12 37	12 43			12 46	13 07	13 22	13 22	13 22	13 29			13 39	13 43		13 46	14 18

		GW	GW	GW	XC	AW	GW	GW	GW	AW	AW	GW	GW	XC	GW	GW	AW	GW	SW	GW	GW	AW
										R							R					
		◇	◇1	◇1	◇1	◇	◇	◇1	◇1				◇1	◇1	◇	◇1		◇	◇1	◇1	◇1	◇
			☕	☕	T	T	T	☕	Ø	T			☕	T		☕	T	T		☕	☕	T
Bath Spa 7	d	13 22	13 24				13 36	14 00							14 14	14 24		14 36	14 47	15 00		
Oldfield Park	d	13 25													14 17							
Keynsham	d	13 32													14 24				14 55			
Bristol Temple Meads 10	a	13 41	13 44				13 48	14 15							14 35	14 39		14 48	15 05	15 15		
	d						13 54					14 21			14 41			14 54				
Filton Abbey Wood	d						14 01					14 30			14 48			15 01				
Bristol Parkway 7	a														14 51							
	d			13 43					14 08				14 41		14 52						15 08	
Patchway	d											14 35										
Pilning	d																					
Gloucester 7	d				13 25						13 58			14 25	15a34							14 45
Lydney	d				13 44						14 17											15 04
Chepstow	d										14 27			14 51								15 14
Caldicot	d										14 35											15 22
Severn Tunnel Jn.	d										14 38	14 46										15 25
Newport (South Wales)	a			14 04	14 10		14 26		14 30		14 50	15 02	15 05	15 10				15 26			15 31	15 37
	d			14 06	14 12	14 22	14 27		14 31	14 55	14 59	15 03	15 06	15 12			15 22	15 27			15 31	15 42
Cardiff Central 7	a			14 22	14 27	14 37	14 43		14 46	15 11	15 14	15 24	15 22	15 30			15 36	15 43			15 46	15 57

		GW	GW	GW	XC	GW	GW	GW	GW	GW	AW	AW	GW	GW	XC	GW	GW	AW	GW	GW	GW	AW	GW
											R							R	R				
			◇1		◇1	◇	◇1	◇	◇1	◇1		◇		◇1	◇1		◇1			◇1			◇1
			☕		T		☕	T	☕	☕	T	T		☕	T		☕	T	T	☕			☕
Bath Spa 7	d			15 08		15 21	15 24	15 36	16 02							16 08	16 24		16 36		16 43		16 59
Oldfield Park	d			15 11												16 11							
Keynsham	d			15 18												16 18					16 51		
Bristol Temple Meads 10	a			15 28		15 34	15 40	15 48	16 15							16 29	16 39		16 48		16 59		17 14
	d	15 21		15 34		15 41		15 54					16 24			16 41			16 54		17 10		
Filton Abbey Wood	d	15 30				15 48		16 01					16 30			16 48			17 01		17 22		
Bristol Parkway 7	a			15 46		15 52										16 52					17 27		
	d		15 43			15 52				16 08				16 41		16 52				17 08			
Patchway	d	15 35											16 35										
Pilning	d																						
Gloucester 7	d				15 25	16a33									16 25	17a34						16 58	
Lydney	d														16 44							17 17	
Chepstow	d				15 51										16 53							17 27	
Caldicot	d																					17 35	
Severn Tunnel Jn.	d	15 46											16 46						17 14			17 38	
Newport (South Wales)	a	15 58	16 06		16 11			16 25		16 30			17 00	17 06	17 11				17 25	17 31		17 50	
	d	16 00	16 06		16 12			16 25		16 31	16 40	17 01	17 01	17 06	17 12			17 22	17 27	17 31		17 52	
Cardiff Central 7	a	16 19	16 22		16 29			16 43		16 46	16 57	17 15	17 25	17 22	17 28			17 38	17 44	17 46		18 10	

A The Torbay Express

When events are being held at the Millenium Stadium, services are subject to alteration. Please check times before travelling.

Table 132

Mondays to Fridays

9 December to 16 May

Bath Spa, Bristol and Gloucester - Cardiff

Network Diagram - see first Page of Table 132

		GW	GW	XC	GW	GW	GW	GW	GW	AW	AW	AW	GW	GW	XC	GW	GW	AW	GW	GW	GW	AW
			■ 1	◇1	◇	◇1	■	■ 1	■ 1	■		◇		■ 1	◇1		■ 1	■	■	■ 1	■ 1	
									A					B								
			⊐P	⊥		⊐P	⊥	⊐P	⊐P	⊥		⊥		⊐P			⊐P	⊥	⊥	⊐P	⊐P	
Bath Spa ■	d				17 08	17 27	17 36	18 00								18 08	18 29		18 36	18 59		
Oldfield Park	d				17 11											18 11						
Keynsham	d				17 18											18 18						
Bristol Temple Meads ■	a				17 29	17 41	17 48	18 14								18 28	18 44		18 48	19 12		
	d	17 21			17 41		17 54						18 21			18 41			18 54			
Filton Abbey Wood	d	17 30			17 48		18 01						18 30			18 48			19 01			
Bristol Parkway ■	a				17 53											18 52						
	d		17 45		17 53				18 08					18 42		18 52					19 10	
Patchway	d	17 35											18 35									
Pilning	d																					
Gloucester ■	d			17 25	18a33						17 58				18 31	19a30						19 00
Lydney	d			17 44							18 17											19 20
Chepstow	d										18 27											19 29
Caldicot	d										18 35											19 37
Severn Tunnel Jn.	d	17 46					18 14				18 38		18 50						19 14			19 40
Newport (South Wales)	a	17 58	18 07	18 12			18 25		18 30		18 49		19 06	19 11	19 16				19 26		19 33	19 53
	d	18 00	18 08	18 13			18 26		18 31	18 41	18 53	19 01	19 06	19 12	19 17			19 22	19 26		19 33	19 54
Cardiff Central ■	a	18 17	18 22	18 28			18 43		18 48	18 55	19 09	19 21	19 24	19 26	19 33			19 43	19 46		19 49	20 12

		GW	GW	XC	GW	GW	GW	GW	GW	GW	GW	AW	XC	AW	GW	GW	GW	GW	XC	AW	GW	GW	AW
																	FX	FO					
			■ 1	◇1		◇1	■ 1	◇	◇	■ 1	■ 1	■	◇1		◇	■ 1	■ 1	■ 1	◇1	◇	◇	■ 1	◇
							C																
			⊐P			⊐P	⊐P	⊥		⊐P	⊐P	⊥			⊥	⊐P	⊐P	⊐P		⊥	⊥	⊐P	
Bath Spa ■	d				19 08	19 24	19 30	19 36	19 49	19 59					20 08	20 30					20 36	21 00	
Oldfield Park	d				19 11				19 52						20 11								
Keynsham	d				19 18				19 59						20 18								
Bristol Temple Meads ■	a				19 29	19 41	19 43	19 48	20 08	20 13					20 26	20 44					20 48	21 15	
	d	19 21			19 41			19 54					20 15								20 54		
Filton Abbey Wood	d	19 30			19 48			20 01					20 22								21 01		
Bristol Parkway ■	a				19 52																		
	d		19 42		19 52						20 08						20 42	20 43					
Patchway	d	19 35											20 25										
Pilning	d																						
Gloucester ■	d			19 26	20a32									19 58					20 25				
Lydney	d													20 17									
Chepstow	d													20 27									
Caldicot	d													20 35									
Severn Tunnel Jn.	d	19 46						20 16					20 37	20 38							21 14		
Newport (South Wales)	a	20 01	20 05	20 11				20 27			20 31		20 47	20 50			21 04	21 05	21 10		21 26		
	d	20 02	20 06	20 13				20 28			20 33	20 39	20 49	20 52			21 05	21 07	21 12	21 17	21 26		21 52
Cardiff Central ■	a	20 20	20 22	20 27				20 43			20 48	21 01	21 02	21 10			21 19	21 19	21 28	21 42	21 45		22 06

		GW	GW	GW	GW	XC	GW	GW	SW	GW	GW	AW	AW	GW	GW	GW	GW	GW	AW	AW	GW
							FO	FX				FO	FX		FX	FO			FO		FO
				◇1	◇1	◇1	◇	◇	◇1	◇1		◇	◇	◇1	◇	◇		◇1	◇		◇1
				⊐P	Ø					⊐P				⊐P				⊐P			⊐P
Bath Spa ■	d		21 08	21 30			21 36	21 36	21 51	22 15	22 25				22 36	22 36	23 02	23 19			23 50
Oldfield Park	d		21 11								22 28						23 05				
Keynsham	d		21 18						21 59		22 35						23 12				
Bristol Temple Meads ■	a		21 28	21 44			21 48	21 48	22 06	22 29	22 43				22 48	22 50	23 23	23 32			00 04
	d	21 19					21 54	21 54							22 54	22 54					
Filton Abbey Wood	d	21 30					22 01	22 01							23 01	23 01					
Bristol Parkway ■	a																				
	d				21 41									22 47							
Patchway	d	21 34					22 06	22 06							23 06	23 06					
Pilning	d																				
Gloucester ■	d					21 23														23 13	
Lydney	d					21 42														23 33	
Chepstow	d					21 51														23 42	
Caldicot	d					22 00														23 51	
Severn Tunnel Jn.	d	21 46				22 03	22 18	22 18							23 17	23 17				23 54	
Newport (South Wales)	a	21 58			22 03	22 14	22 29	22 36						23 19	23 34	23 34				00 06	
	d	21 59			22 05	22 15	22 30	22 37				22 41	22 42	23 19	23 35	23 35			23 47	00 07	
Cardiff Central ■	a	22 18			22 23	22 35	22 52	23 00				22 56	23 03	23 40	23 56	23 56			00 02	00 35	

A The Capitals United
B The Red Dragon
C The Bristolian

When events are being held at the Millenium Stadium, services are subject to alteration. Please check times before travelling.

Table 132

Saturdays

14 December to 28 December

Bath Spa, Bristol and Gloucester - Cardiff

Network Diagram - see first Page of Table 132

		AW	GW	AW	GW	AW		AW	XC	GW	GW	AW	XC	GW	GW	SW		AW	GW	GW	AW	AW	GW	AW	XC
			◇1	◇	◇1				◇1	◇1		◇	◇1			1				◇1	◇			◇	◇1
																									A
			☕		☕							🛒								☕	🛒			🛒	🛒
Bath Spa [7]	d				01 16										07 08	07 35				08 00					
Oldfield Park	d														07 11	07 38									
Keynsham	d														07 18	07 45									
Bristol Temple Meads [10]	a				01 30										07 27	07 52				08 16					
	d				01 37					06 46	06 50			07 21	07 41				07 54				08 20		
Filton Abbey Wood	d									06 54	07 02			07 30	07 48				08 01				08 30		
Bristol Parkway [7]	a									06 58					07 52										
	d		00 27							07 11					07 52										
Patchway	d													07 34									08 35		
Pilning	d																								
Gloucester [7]	d							05 50	06 14				06 57		08a33							07 58			08 22
Lydney	d							06 09	06 33				07 16									08 17			
Chepstow	d							06 19	06 42				07 26									08 27			08 48
Caldicot	d							06 27	06 51				07 34									08 35			
Severn Tunnel Jn.	d							06 30	06 54		07 14		07 37	07 46								08 38	08 46		
Newport (South Wales)	a		00 49		02s03			06 42	07 05	07 31	07 25		07 48	07 58					08 26			08 50	09 01		09 06
	d	00 07	00 49	00 59		06 38		06 44	07 06	07 31	07 26	07 38	07 50	07 58				08 01	08 27		08 33	08 52	09 01	09 02	09 07
Cardiff Central [7]	a	00 35	01 04	01 18	02 20	06 54		07 00	07 21	07 47	07 44	07 54	08 04	08 17				08 20	08 43		08 50	09 10	09 21	09 22	09 22

		GW		GW	GW	GW	GW	GW	AW	AW	GW	XC		GW	GW	GW	GW	GW	AW	AW	AW	GW		XC	GW
							R																		
				◇1	◇	◇	1	◇1	◇			◇1			◇1	◇	◇1	◇1	◇	◇	◇			◇1	◇
																B									
				☕			☕	☕	🛒						☕	🛒	☕	☕	🛒	🛒	🛒			🛒	
Bath Spa [7]	d	08 08		08 24	08 30	08 47	09 00							09 08	09 24	09 36	10 00								10 08
Oldfield Park	d	08 11				08 50								09 11											10 11
Keynsham	d	08 18				08 57								09 18											10 18
Bristol Temple Meads [10]	a	08 29		08 39	08 44	09 05	09 15							09 27	09 39	09 48	10 15								10 29
	d	08 41			08 54						09 21			09 41		09 54						10 21			10 41
Filton Abbey Wood	d	08 48			09 01						09 30			09 48		10 01						10 30			10 48
Bristol Parkway [7]	a	08 52												09 52											10 52
	d	08 52						09 08						09 52				10 08							10 52
Patchway	d										09 35											10 35			
Pilning	d																								
Gloucester [7]	d	09a33								08 58		09 22		10a33										10 22	11a32
Lydney	d									09 17														10 41	
Chepstow	d									09 27		09 48													
Caldicot	d									09 35															
Severn Tunnel Jn.	d									09 38	09 46											10 46			
Newport (South Wales)	a				09 25			09 30		09 50	09 58	10 05				10 24		10 31				11 00		11 06	
	d				09 25			09 31	09 38	09 52	09 59	10 07				10 24		10 31	10 40	10 40	10 57	11 01		11 07	
Cardiff Central [7]	a				09 43			09 47	09 59	10 07	10 18	10 21				10 43		10 46	10 54	10 55	11 14	11 21		11 24	

		GW	GW	GW	GW	AW	AW	GW		XC	GW	GW	GW	SW	GW	GW	AW	AW		AW	GW	XC	GW	GW	GW
		◇1	◇	◇1	◇1	◇				◇1	◇	◇1	◇	◇1	◇1	◇1	◇			◇		◇1	◇	◇1	◇
			B										B												
		☕	🛒	☕	☕	🛒				🛒		☕	🛒		☕	Ø	🛒			🛒		🛒		☕	
Bath Spa [7]	d	10 24	10 36	11 00							11 08	11 24	11 36	11 47	12 00								12 17	12 24	12 36
Oldfield Park	d										11 11												12 19		
Keynsham	d										11 18			11 55									12 27		
Bristol Temple Meads [10]	a	10 39	10 48	11 15							11 29	11 39	11 48	12 05	12 15								12 35	12 39	12 48
	d		10 54					11 21			11 41		11 54								12 21		12 41		12 54
Filton Abbey Wood	d		11 01					11 30			11 48		12 01								12 30		12 48		13 01
Bristol Parkway [7]	a										11 52												12 52		
	d				11 08						11 52					12 08							12 52		
Patchway	d							11 35													12 35				
Pilning	d																								
Gloucester [7]	d						10 58			11 22	12a33							11 57				12 22	13a35		
Lydney	d						11 17											12 16							
Chepstow	d						11 27			11 48								12 26				12 48			
Caldicot	d						11 35											12 34							
Severn Tunnel Jn.	d						11 38	11 46										12 37			12 46				
Newport (South Wales)	a		11 24		11 31		11 50	11 58		12 05			12 24			12 31		12 49			13 00	13 05			13 25
	d		11 24		11 31	11 37	11 52	11 59		12 07			12 25			12 31	12 37	12 51		12 56	13 01	13 07			13 25
Cardiff Central [7]	a		11 43		11 46	11 53	12 06	12 18		12 23			12 43			12 46	12 53	13 06		13 15	13 18	13 21			13 43

A 🛒 to Newport (South Wales)

B 🛒 to Bristol Temple Meads

When events are being held at the Millenium Stadium, services are subject to alteration. Please check times before travelling.

Table 132

Saturdays

14 December to 28 December

Bath Spa, Bristol and Gloucester - Cardiff

Network Diagram - see first Page of Table 132

		GW	GW	AW	GW	XC	GW	GW	GW	GW		GW	AW	AW	AW	GW	AW	XC	GW	GW		AW	GW	SW	GW
																	R					R			
		◇1 ☕	◇1 Ø	◇ 🛒		◇1 🛒	◇	◇1 ☕	◇	◇1 ☕		◇1 ☕	◇ 🛒				🛒	◇1 🛒	◇	◇1 ☕		🛒	◇	◇1	◇1 ☕
Bath Spa 7	d	13 00					13 19	13 24	13 36	14 00									14 08	14 24			14 36	14 47	15 00
Oldfield Park	d						13 22												14 11						
Keynsham	d						13 29												14 18					14 55	
Bristol Temple Meads 10	a	13 14					13 37	13 42	13 48	14 15									14 29	14 39			14 48	15 05	15 15
	d				13 21		13 41		13 54							14 21			14 41				14 54		
Filton Abbey Wood	d				13 30		13 48		14 01							14 30			14 48				15 01		
Bristol Parkway 7	a						13 52												14 52						
	d		13 08				13 52					14 08							14 52						
Patchway	d				13 35											14 35									
Pilning	d																								
Gloucester 7	d					13 22	14a33							13 58				14 22	15a33						
Lydney	d					13 41								14 17											
Chepstow	d													14 27				14 48							
Caldicot	d													14 35											
Severn Tunnel Jn.	d				13 46									14 38		14 46									
Newport (South Wales)	a		13 31		13 58	14 06			14 24			14 31		14 50		14 59		15 10					15 24		
	d		13 31	13 37	13 59	14 07			14 25			14 31	14 39	14 52	14 57	15 00	15 06	15 12				15 22	15 24		
Cardiff Central 7	a		13 47	13 53	14 18	14 22			14 43			14 46	14 53	15 09	15 12	15 18	15 24	15 26				15 37	15 43		

		GW	AW	GW	XC	GW		GW	GW	GW	GW	AW	AW	GW	XC	GW		GW	GW	GW	GW	AW	AW	GW	XC
												R										R			
		◇1 ☕	◇ 🛒		◇1 🛒	◇		◇1 ☕	◇	◇1 ☕	◇1 ☕	🛒	◇ 🛒		◇1 🛒			◇1 ☕	◇	◇1 ☕	◇1 ☕	🛒			◇1 🛒
Bath Spa 7	d					15 18		15 24	15 36	16 00						16 08		16 24	16 36	17 00					
Oldfield Park	d					15 21										16 11									
Keynsham	d					15 28										16 18									
Bristol Temple Meads 10	a					15 36		15 41	15 49	16 15						16 29		16 39	16 48	17 15					
	d			15 21		15 41			15 54					16 21		16 41			16 54					17 21	
Filton Abbey Wood	d			15 30		15 48			16 01					16 30		16 48			17 01					17 30	
Bristol Parkway 7	a					15 52										16 52									
	d	15 08				15 52					16 08					16 52					17 08				
Patchway	d			15 35										16 35										17 35	
Pilning	d			15 41																					
Gloucester 7	d		14 35		15 22	16a33									16 22	17a33							16 58		17 22
Lydney	d		14 54												16 41								17 17		17 41
Chepstow	d		15 04		15 48										16 50								17 27		
Caldicot	d		15 12																				17 35		
Severn Tunnel Jn.	d		15 15	15 46										16 46					17 14				17 38	17 46	
Newport (South Wales)	a	15 31	15 35	16 01	16 06				16 24		16 30			17 00	17 08				17 26		17 29		17 50	17 58	18 06
	d	15 31	15 37	16 01	16 07				16 24		16 31	16 37	16 56	17 01	17 09				17 26		17 31	17 37	17 52	18 00	18 07
Cardiff Central 7	a	15 45	15 53	16 18	16 25				16 43		16 46	16 53	17 08	17 18	17 24				17 43		17 46	17 53	18 10	18 18	18 22

		GW		GW	GW	GW	GW	AW	AW	AW	GW	XC		GW	GW	GW	GW	GW	AW	AW	GW	XC		GW	GW
								R								R			R						
		◇		◇1 ☕	◇	◇1 ☕	◇1 ☕	🛒		◇ 🛒		◇1			◇1 ☕		◇1 ☕	◇1 ☕	🛒			◇1			◇1 ☕
Bath Spa 7	d	17 08		17 24	17 36	18 00								18 08	18 24	18 36	19 00							19 08	19 24
Oldfield Park	d	17 11												18 11										19 11	
Keynsham	d	17 18												18 18										19 18	
Bristol Temple Meads 10	a	17 27		17 39	17 48	18 15								18 29	18 39	18 48	19 15							19 29	19 38
	d	17 41			17 54						18 21			18 41		18 54					19 21			19 41	
Filton Abbey Wood	d	17 48			18 01						18 30			18 48		19 01					19 28			19 48	
Bristol Parkway 7	a	17 52												18 52										19 52	
	d	17 52					18 08							18 52				19 08						19 52	
Patchway	d										18 35										19 33				
Pilning	d																								
Gloucester 7	d	18a33							17 58			18 27		19a33						18 58		19 22		20a33	
Lydney	d								18 17											19 17					
Chepstow	d								18 27											19 27					
Caldicot	d								18 35											19 34					
Severn Tunnel Jn.	d				18 14				18 38		18 47									19 37	19 44				
Newport (South Wales)	a				18 25		18 30		18 50		19 01	19 11				19 24		19 30		19 50	19 56	20 03			
	d				18 25		18 31	18 37	18 52	18 57	19 02	19 13				19 24		19 31	19 41	19 52	19 56	20 05			
Cardiff Central 7	a				18 43		18 46	18 53	19 10	19 15	19 18	19 30				19 41		19 46	19 58	20 11	20 16	20 20			

When events are being held at the Millenium Stadium, services are subject to alteration. Please check times before travelling.

Table 132

Saturdays

14 December to 28 December

Bath Spa, Bristol and Gloucester - Cardiff

Network Diagram - see first Page of Table 132

		GW	GW	GW		AW	XC	AW	GW	GW	GW	GW	XC	AW		GW	GW	GW	GW	AW	GW	XC	GW	AW
						■																		
		◇	◇	◇1			◇1		◇1	◇	◇1	◇1	◇1	◇		◇	◇1		◇1	◇		◇1	◇1	◇
				[catering]		[trolley]			[catering]		[catering]	[catering]		[trolley]			[catering]		[catering]	[trolley]			[catering]	
Bath Spa 7	d	19 36	19 47						20 00	20 12	20 24					20 36	21 00	21 07					21 30	
Oldfield Park	d		19 50							20 14								21 11						
Keynsham	d		19 57							20 21								21 18						
Bristol Temple Meads 10	a	19 48	20 05						20 15	20 29	20 40					20 48	21 16	21 28					21 45	
	d	19 54					20 10									20 54					21 29			
Filton Abbey Wood	d	20 01					20 17									21 01					21 36			
Bristol Parkway 7	a																							
	d			20 08								20 40							21 08					
Patchway	d						20 21														21 41			
Pilning	d																							
Gloucester 7	d							19 58					20 22									21 22		
Lydney	d							20 17														21 41		
Chepstow	d							20 27														21 50		
Caldicot	d							20 35														21 59		
Severn Tunnel Jn.	d						20 31	20 38													21 52	22 02		
Newport (South Wales)	a	20 25		20 30			20 44	20 50				21 03	21 09			21 25			21 31		22 09	22 19		
	d	20 25		20 31		20 38	20 46	20 52				21 04	21 10	21 15		21 25			21 31	21 45	22 11	22 23		22 36
Cardiff Central 7	a	20 43		20 44		20 58	21 00	21 09				21 20	21 26	21 43		21 43			21 47	22 04	22 30	22 45		22 55

		GW	SW	GW	GW	GW	GW	GW	GW	AW		GW	AW
		◇	◇1	◇1	◇1		◇	◇1		◇		◇1	
				[catering]	[catering]			[catering]				[catering]	
Bath Spa 7	d	21 39	21 51	22 00		22 25	22 36	23 02	23 08				
Oldfield Park	d					22 28			23 11				
Keynsham	d		21 59			22 36			23 18				
Bristol Temple Meads 10	a	21 51	22 06	22 14		22 44	22 50	23 15	23 28				
	d	21 54					22 54						
Filton Abbey Wood	d	22 01					23 01						
Bristol Parkway 7	a												
	d				22 11							23 29	
Patchway	d	22 06					23 06						
Pilning	d												
Gloucester 7	d												23 09
Lydney	d												23 28
Chepstow	d												23 38
Caldicot	d												23 46
Severn Tunnel Jn.	d	22 18					23 18						23 49
Newport (South Wales)	a	22 40			22 46		23 35					23 58	00 09
	d	22 40			22 47		23 36			23 47		23 58	00 11
Cardiff Central 7	a	23 00			23 07		23 55			00 06		00 18	00 36

Saturdays

4 January to 8 February

		AW	GW	AW	GW	AW	AW	XC	GW	GW		AW	XC	GW	GW	SW	AW	GW	GW	AW		AW	GW	AW	XC
			◇1	◇	◇1			◇1	◇1			◇	◇1			1			◇1	◇				◇	◇1
																									A
			[catering]		[catering]							[trolley]							[catering]	[trolley]				[trolley]	[trolley]
Bath Spa 7	d				01 16										07 08	07 35			08 00						
Oldfield Park	d														07 11	07 38									
Keynsham	d														07 18	07 45									
Bristol Temple Meads 10	a				01 30										07 27	07 52			08 16						
	d				01 37				06 46	06 50				07 21	07 41			07 54					08 20		
Filton Abbey Wood	d								06 54	07 02				07 30	07 48			08 01					08 30		
Bristol Parkway 7	a								06 58						07 52										
	d		00 27						07 11						07 52										
Patchway	d													07 34									08 35		
Pilning	d																								
Gloucester 7	d						05 50	06 14					06 57		08a33							07 58			08 22
Lydney	d						06 09	06 33					07 16									08 17			
Chepstow	d						06 19	06 42					07 26									08 27			08 48
Caldicot	d						06 27	06 51					07 34									08 35			
Severn Tunnel Jn.	d						06 30	06 54		07 14			07 37	07 46								08 38	08 46		
Newport (South Wales)	a		00 49		02s03		06 42	07 05	07 31	07 25			07 48	07 58				08 26				08 50	09 01		09 06
	d	00 07	00 49	00 59		06 38	06 44	07 06	07 31	07 26		07 38	07 50	07 58			08 01	08 27		08 33		08 52	09 01	09 02	09 07
Cardiff Central 7	a	00 35	01 04	01 18	02 20	06 54	07 00	07 21	07 47	07 44		07 54	08 04	08 17			08 20	08 43		08 50		09 10	09 21	09 22	09 22

A [trolley] to Newport (South Wales)

When events are being held at the Millenium Stadium, services are subject to alteration. Please check times before travelling.

Table 132

Saturdays

4 January to 8 February

Bath Spa, Bristol and Gloucester - Cardiff

Network Diagram - see first Page of Table 132

		GW		GW	GW	GW	GW	GW	AW	AW	GW	XC		GW	GW	GW	GW	GW	AW	AW	AW	GW		XC	GW
				◇1 ⊡	◇	◇	■ 1 ⊡	◇1 ⊡	◇ ⊼			◇1			◇1 ⊡	◇ A ⊼	◇1 ⊡	◇1 ⊡	◇ ⊼	◇ ⊼	◇ ⊼			◇1 ⊼	◇
Bath Spa 7	d	08 08		08 24	08 30	08 47	09 01							09 08	09 28	09 36	10 00								10 08
Oldfield Park	d	08 11				08 50								09 11											10 11
Keynsham	d	08 18				08 57								09 18											10 18
Bristol Temple Meads 10	a	08 29		08 39	08 44	09 05	09 15							09 27	09 43	09 48	10 15								10 29
	d	08 41			08 54						09 21			09 41		09 54						10 21			10 41
Filton Abbey Wood	d	08 48			09 01						09 30			09 48		10 01						10 30			10 48
Bristol Parkway 7	a	08 52												09 52											10 52
	d	08 52						09 08						09 52				10 08							10 52
Patchway	d										09 35											10 35			
Pilning	d																								
Gloucester 7	d	09a33								08 58		09 22		10a33										10 22	11a32
Lydney	d									09 17														10 41	
Chepstow	d									09 27		09 48													
Caldicot	d									09 35															
Severn Tunnel Jn.	d									09 38	09 46											10 46			
Newport (South Wales)	a				09 25			09 30		09 50	09 58	10 05				10 24		10 31				11 00		11 06	
	d				09 25			09 31	09 38	09 52	09 59	10 07				10 24		10 31	10 40	10 40	10 57	11 01		11 07	
Cardiff Central 7	a				09 43			09 47	09 59	10 07	10 18	10 21				10 43		10 46	10 54	10 55	11 14	11 21		11 24	

		GW	GW	GW	GW	AW	AW	GW		XC	GW	GW	GW	SW	GW	GW	AW	AW		AW	GW	XC	GW	GW	GW
		◇1 ⊡	◇ A ⊼	◇1 ⊡	◇1 ⊡	◇ ⊼				◇1 ⊼	◇	◇1 ⊡	◇ A ⊼	◇1	◇1 ⊡	◇1 Ø	◇ ⊼			◇ ⊼		◇1 ⊼	◇	◇1 ⊡	◇
Bath Spa 7	d	10 27	10 36	11 03							11 09	11 27	11 36	11 47	12 01								12 17	12 28	12 36
Oldfield Park	d										11 12												12 19		
Keynsham	d										11 19			11 55									12 27		
Bristol Temple Meads 10	a	10 42	10 48	11 18							11 29	11 42	11 48	12 05	12 16								12 35	12 43	12 48
	d		10 54					11 21			11 41		11 54								12 21		12 41		12 54
Filton Abbey Wood	d		11 01					11 30			11 48		12 01								12 30		12 48		13 01
Bristol Parkway 7	a										11 52												12 52		
	d				11 08						11 52					12 08							12 52		
Patchway	d							11 35													12 35				
Pilning	d																								
Gloucester 7	d						10 58			11 22	12a33							11 57				12 22	13a35		
Lydney	d						11 17											12 16							
Chepstow	d						11 27			11 48								12 26				12 48			
Caldicot	d						11 35											12 34							
Severn Tunnel Jn.	d						11 38	11 46										12 37			12 46				
Newport (South Wales)	a		11 24		11 31		11 50	11 58		12 05			12 24			12 31		12 49			13 00	13 05			13 25
	d		11 24		11 31	11 37	11 52	11 59		12 07			12 25			12 31	12 37	12 51		12 56	13 01	13 07			13 25
Cardiff Central 7	a		11 43		11 46	11 53	12 06	12 18		12 23			12 43			12 46	12 53	13 06		13 15	13 18	13 21			13 43

		GW	GW	AW		GW	XC	GW	GW	GW	GW	GW	AW	AW		AW	GW	AW	XC	GW	GW	AW	GW	SW	
		◇1 ⊡	◇1 Ø	◇ ⊼			◇1 ⊼	◇	◇1 ⊡	◇	◇1 ⊡	◇1 ⊡	◇ ⊼					■ ⊼	◇1 ⊼	◇	◇1 ⊡	■ ⊼	◇	◇1	
Bath Spa 7	d	13 03						13 19	13 27	13 36	14 02									14 10	14 27		14 36	14 47	
Oldfield Park	d							13 22												14 13					
Keynsham	d							13 29												14 20				14 55	
Bristol Temple Meads 10	a	13 17						13 37	13 45	13 48	14 18									14 31	14 42		14 48	15 05	
	d					13 21		13 41		13 54							14 21			14 41			14 54		
Filton Abbey Wood	d					13 30		13 48		14 01							14 30			14 48			15 01		
Bristol Parkway 7	a							13 52												14 52					
	d		13 08					13 52				14 08								14 52					
Patchway	d					13 35											14 35								
Pilning	d																								
Gloucester 7	d						13 22	14a33						13 58					14 22	15a33					
Lydney	d						13 41							14 17											
Chepstow	d													14 27					14 48						
Caldicot	d													14 35											
Severn Tunnel Jn.	d					13 46								14 38			14 46								
Newport (South Wales)	a		13 31			13 58	14 06			14 24		14 31		14 50			14 59		15 10				15 24		
	d		13 31	13 37		13 59	14 07			14 25		14 31	14 39	14 52		14 57	15 00	15 06	15 12			15 22	15 24		
Cardiff Central 7	a		13 47	13 53		14 18	14 22			14 43		14 46	14 53	15 09		15 12	15 18	15 24	15 26			15 37	15 43		

A ⊼ to Bristol Temple Meads

When events are being held at the Millenium Stadium, services are subject to alteration. Please check times before travelling.

Table 132

Saturdays

4 January to 8 February

Bath Spa, Bristol and Gloucester - Cardiff

Network Diagram - see first Page of Table 132

		GW	GW	AW	GW	XC		GW	GW	GW	GW	GW	AW	AW	GW	XC		GW	GW	GW	GW	GW	AW	AW	GW
													R										R		
		◇**1**	◇**1**	◇		◇**1**		◇	◇**1**	◇	◇**1**	◇**1**		◇		◇**1**			◇**1**	◇	◇**1**	◇**1**			
		☕	☕	🛒		🛒			☕		☕	☕	🛒	🛒		🛒			☕		☕	☕	🛒		
Bath Spa 7	d	15 03						15 18	15 28	15 36	16 04							16 08	16 27	16 36	17 03				
Oldfield Park	d							15 21										16 11							
Keynsham	d							15 28										16 18							
Bristol Temple Meads 10	a	15 18						15 36	15 45	15 49	16 19							16 29	16 42	16 48	17 18				
	d				15 21			15 41		15 54					16 21			16 41		16 54					17 21
Filton Abbey Wood	d				15 30			15 48		16 01					16 30			16 48		17 01					17 30
Bristol Parkway 7	a							15 52										16 52							
	d		15 08					15 52				16 11						16 52				17 08			
Patchway	d				15 35										16 35										17 35
Pilning	d				15 41																				
Gloucester 7	d			14 35		15 22		16a33								16 22		17a33						16 58	
Lydney	d			14 54												16 41								17 17	
Chepstow	d			15 04		15 48										16 50								17 27	
Caldicot	d			15 12																				17 35	
Severn Tunnel Jn.	d			15 15	15 46										16 46					17 14				17 38	17 46
Newport (South Wales)	a		15 31	15 35	16 01	16 06				16 24		16 33			17 00	17 08				17 26		17 29		17 50	17 58
	d		15 31	15 37	16 01	16 07				16 24		16 34	16 37	16 56	17 01	17 09				17 26		17 31	17 37	17 52	18 00
Cardiff Central 7	a		15 45	15 53	16 18	16 25				16 43		16 48	16 55	17 08	17 18	17 24				17 43		17 46	17 53	18 10	18 18

		XC		GW	GW	GW	GW	GW	AW	AW	AW	GW		XC	GW	GW	GW	GW	GW	AW	AW	GW		XC	GW
									R								R			R					
		◇**1**		◇	◇**1**	◇	◇**1**	◇**1**			◇			◇**1**		◇**1**		◇**1**	◇**1**					◇**1**	
		🛒			☕		☕	☕	🛒		🛒					☕		☕	☕	🛒					
Bath Spa 7	d			17 10	17 27	17 36	18 03								18 08	18 28	18 36	19 01							19 08
Oldfield Park	d			17 13											18 11										19 11
Keynsham	d			17 20											18 18										19 18
Bristol Temple Meads 10	a			17 29	17 42	17 48	18 18								18 29	18 43	18 48	19 16							19 29
	d			17 41		17 54						18 21			18 41		18 54					19 21			19 41
Filton Abbey Wood	d			17 48		18 01						18 30			18 48		19 01					19 28			19 48
Bristol Parkway 7	a			17 52											18 52										19 52
	d			17 52				18 08							18 52				19 08						19 52
Patchway	d											18 35										19 33			
Pilning	d																								
Gloucester 7	d	17 22		18a33						17 58				18 27	19a33						18 58			19 22	20a33
Lydney	d	17 41								18 17											19 17				
Chepstow	d									18 27											19 27				
Caldicot	d									18 35											19 34				
Severn Tunnel Jn.	d					18 14				18 38		18 47									19 37	19 44			
Newport (South Wales)	a	18 06				18 25		18 30		18 50		19 01		19 11			19 24		19 30		19 50	19 56		20 03	
	d	18 07				18 25		18 31	18 37	18 52	18 57	19 02		19 13			19 24		19 31	19 41	19 52	19 56		20 05	
Cardiff Central 7	a	18 22				18 43		18 46	18 53	19 10	19 15	19 18		19 30			19 41		19 46	19 58	20 11	20 16		20 20	

		GW	GW	GW	GW	AW	XC	AW		GW	GW	GW	GW	XC	AW	GW	GW	GW		GW	AW	GW	XC	GW	AW
						R																			
		◇**1**	◇	◇	◇**1**		◇**1**			◇**1**	◇	◇**1**	◇**1**	◇**1**	◇	◇	◇**1**	◇**1**			◇		◇**1**	◇**1**	◇
		☕			☕	🛒				☕		☕	☕		🛒		☕	☕			🛒			☕	
Bath Spa 7	d	19 26	19 36	19 47						20 03	20 12	20 27				20 36	21 02			21 09				21 33	
Oldfield Park	d			19 50							20 14									21 13					
Keynsham	d			19 57							20 21									21 20					
Bristol Temple Meads 10	a	19 40	19 48	20 05						20 18	20 29	20 43				20 48	21 18			21 29				21 47	
	d		19 54				20 10									20 54						21 29			
Filton Abbey Wood	d		20 01				20 17									21 01						21 36			
Bristol Parkway 7	a																								
	d				20 08								20 43					21 08							
Patchway	d						20 21															21 41			
Pilning	d																								
Gloucester 7	d							19 58						20 22									21 22		
Lydney	d							20 17															21 41		
Chepstow	d							20 27															21 50		
Caldicot	d							20 35															21 59		
Severn Tunnel Jn.	d						20 31	20 38														21 52	22 02		
Newport (South Wales)	a		20 25		20 30		20 44	20 50					21 06	21 12		21 25		21 31				22 09	22 19		
	d		20 25		20 31	20 38	20 46	20 52					21 07	21 14	21 15	21 25		21 31			21 45	22 11	22 23		22 36
Cardiff Central 7	a		20 43		20 45	20 58	21 00	21 09					21 23	21 29	21 43	21 43		21 47			22 04	22 30	22 45		22 55

When events are being held at the Millenium Stadium, services are subject to alteration. Please check times before travelling.

Table 132

Saturdays

4 January to 8 February

Bath Spa, Bristol and Gloucester - Cardiff

Network Diagram - see first Page of Table 132

		GW		SW	GW	GW	GW	GW	GW	GW	AW	GW		AW
		◇		◇1	◇1 ☕	◇1 ☕		◇	◇1 ☕		🚌	◇1 ☕		
Bath Spa 7	d	21 40		21 51	22 05		22 25	22 36	23 05	23 12				
Oldfield Park	d						22 28			23 15				
Keynsham	d			21 59			22 36			23 22				
Bristol Temple Meads 10	a	21 52		22 06	22 19		22 44	22 50	23 19	23 30				
	d	21 54						22 54						
Filton Abbey Wood	d	22 01						23 01						
Bristol Parkway 7	a							23 07						
	d					22 11						23 27		
Patchway	d	22 06										23 31		
Pilning	d													
Gloucester 7	d													23 09
Lydney	d													23 28
Chepstow	d													23 38
Caldicot	d													23 46
Severn Tunnel Jn.	d	22 18										23 42		23 49
Newport (South Wales)	a	22 40				22 46						00 01		00 10
	d	22 40				22 47					23 55			
Cardiff Central 7	a	23 00				23 07					00 25			

Saturdays

15 February to 22 March

		AW	GW	AW	GW	AW	AW	XC	GW	GW		AW	XC	GW	GW	SW	AW	GW	GW	AW		AW	GW	AW	XC
			◇1 ☕	◇	◇1 ☕			◇1	◇1			◇ 🛒	◇1			1			◇1 ☕	◇ 🛒				◇ 🛒	◇1 A 🛒
Bath Spa 7	d				01 16										07 08	07 35			08 00						
Oldfield Park	d														07 11	07 38									
Keynsham	d														07 18	07 45									
Bristol Temple Meads 10	a				01 30										07 27	07 52			08 16						
	d				01 37				06 46	06 50				07 21	07 41			07 54					08 20		
Filton Abbey Wood	d								06 54	07 02				07 30	07 48			08 01					08 30		
Bristol Parkway 7	a								06 58						07 52										
	d		00 27						07 11						07 52										
Patchway	d													07 34									08 35		
Pilning	d																								
Gloucester 7	d						05 50	06 14					06 57		08a33							07 58			08 22
Lydney	d						06 09	06 33					07 16									08 17			
Chepstow	d						06 19	06 42					07 26									08 27			08 48
Caldicot	d						06 27	06 51					07 34									08 35			
Severn Tunnel Jn.	d						06 30	06 54		07 14			07 37	07 46								08 38	08 46		
Newport (South Wales)	a		00 49		02s03		06 42	07 05	07 31	07 25			07 48	07 58				08 26				08 50	09 01		09 06
	d	00 07	00 49	00 59		06 38	06 44	07 06	07 31	07 26		07 38	07 50	07 58			08 01	08 27		08 33		08 52	09 01	09 02	09 07
Cardiff Central 7	a	00 35	01 04	01 18	02 20	06 54	07 00	07 21	07 47	07 44		07 54	08 04	08 17			08 20	08 43		08 50		09 10	09 21	09 22	09 22

		GW	GW	GW	GW	GW		GW	AW	AW	GW	XC	GW	GW	GW	GW		GW	AW	AW	AW	GW	XC	GW	GW
			◇1 ☕	◇	◇	R 1 ☕		◇1 ☕	◇ 🛒			◇1		◇1 ☕	◇ B 🛒	◇1 ☕		◇1 ☕	◇ 🛒	◇ 🛒	◇ 🛒		◇1 🛒	◇	◇1 ☕
Bath Spa 7	d	08 08	08 24	08 30	08 47	09 00							09 08	09 24	09 36	10 00								10 08	10 24
Oldfield Park	d	08 11			08 50								09 11											10 11	
Keynsham	d	08 18			08 57								09 18											10 18	
Bristol Temple Meads 10	a	08 29	08 39	08 44	09 05	09 15							09 27	09 39	09 48	10 15								10 29	10 39
	d	08 41		08 54							09 21		09 41		09 54							10 21		10 41	
Filton Abbey Wood	d	08 48		09 01							09 30		09 48		10 01							10 30		10 48	
Bristol Parkway 7	a	08 52											09 52											10 52	
	d	08 52						09 08					09 52					10 08						10 52	
Patchway	d										09 35											10 35			
Pilning	d																								
Gloucester 7	d	09a33								08 58		09 22	10a33										10 22	11a32	
Lydney	d									09 17													10 41		
Chepstow	d									09 27		09 48													
Caldicot	d									09 35															
Severn Tunnel Jn.	d									09 38	09 46											10 46			
Newport (South Wales)	a			09 25				09 30		09 50	09 58	10 05			10 24			10 31				11 00	11 06		
	d			09 25				09 31	09 38	09 52	09 59	10 07			10 24			10 31	10 40	10 40	10 57	11 01	11 07		
Cardiff Central 7	a			09 43				09 47	09 59	10 07	10 18	10 21			10 43			10 46	10 54	10 55	11 14	11 21	11 24		

A 🛒 to Newport (South Wales)

B 🛒 to Bristol Temple Meads

When events are being held at the Millenium Stadium, services are subject to alteration. Please check times before travelling.

Table 132

Saturdays

15 February to 22 March

Bath Spa, Bristol and Gloucester - Cardiff

Network Diagram - see first Page of Table 132

		GW	GW	GW	AW	AW	GW	XC		GW	GW	GW	SW	GW	GW	AW	AW	AW		GW	XC	GW	GW	GW	GW
		◇ A 🛒	◇1 ☕	◇1 ☕	◇ 🛒			◇1 🛒		◇	◇1 ☕	◇ A 🛒	◇1	◇1 ☕	◇1 Ø	◇ 🛒		◇ 🛒			◇1 🛒	◇	◇1 ☕	◇	◇1 ☕
Bath Spa 7	d	10 36	11 00							11 08	11 24	11 36	11 47	12 00								12 17	12 24	12 36	13 00
Oldfield Park	d									11 11												12 19			
Keynsham	d									11 18			11 55									12 27			
Bristol Temple Meads 10	a	10 48	11 15							11 29	11 39	11 48	12 05	12 15								12 35	12 39	12 48	13 14
	d	10 54					11 21			11 41		11 54								12 21		12 41		12 54	
Filton Abbey Wood	d	11 01					11 30			11 48		12 01								12 30		12 48		13 01	
Bristol Parkway 7	a									11 52												12 52			
	d			11 08						11 52					12 08							12 52			
Patchway	d						11 35													12 35					
Pilning	d																								
Gloucester 7	d					10 58		11 22		12a33							11 57				12 22	13a35			
Lydney	d					11 17											12 16								
Chepstow	d					11 27		11 48									12 26				12 48				
Caldicot	d					11 35											12 34								
Severn Tunnel Jn.	d					11 38	11 46										12 37			12 46					
Newport (South Wales)	a	11 24		11 31		11 50	11 58	12 05				12 24			12 31		12 49			13 00	13 05			13 25	
	d	11 24		11 31	11 37	11 52	11 59	12 07				12 25			12 31	12 37	12 51	12 56		13 01	13 07			13 25	
Cardiff Central 7	a	11 43		11 46	11 53	12 06	12 18	12 23				12 43			12 46	12 53	13 06	13 15		13 18	13 21			13 43	

		GW	AW	GW		XC	GW	GW	GW	GW	GW	AW	AW	AW		GW	AW	XC	GW	GW	AW	GW	SW	GW	
		◇1 Ø	◇ 🛒			◇1 🛒	◇	◇1 ☕	◇	◇1 ☕	◇1 ☕	◇ 🛒					■ 🛒	◇1 🛒	◇	◇1 ☕	■ 🛒	◇	◇1	◇1 ☕	
Bath Spa 7	d						13 19	13 24	13 36	14 00									14 08	14 24		14 36	14 47	15 00	
Oldfield Park	d						13 22												14 11						
Keynsham	d						13 29												14 18				14 55		
Bristol Temple Meads 10	a						13 37	13 42	13 48	14 15									14 29	14 39		14 48	15 05	15 15	
	d			13 21			13 41		13 54							14 21			14 41			14 54			
Filton Abbey Wood	d			13 30			13 48		14 01							14 30			14 48			15 01			
Bristol Parkway 7	a						13 52												14 52						
	d	13 08					13 52				14 08								14 52						
Patchway	d			13 35												14 35									
Pilning	d																								
Gloucester 7	d					13 22	14a33						13 58					14 22	15a33						
Lydney	d					13 41							14 17												
Chepstow	d												14 27					14 48							
Caldicot	d												14 35												
Severn Tunnel Jn.	d			13 46									14 38			14 46									
Newport (South Wales)	a	13 31		13 58		14 06			14 24		14 31		14 50			14 59		15 10				15 24			
	d	13 31	13 37	13 59		14 07			14 25		14 31	14 39	14 52	14 57		15 00	15 06	15 12			15 22	15 24			
Cardiff Central 7	a	13 47	13 53	14 18		14 22			14 43		14 46	14 53	15 09	15 12		15 18	15 24	15 26			15 37	15 43			

		GW	AW	GW	XC	GW	GW	GW	GW	GW		AW	AW	GW	XC	GW	GW	GW	GW	GW		AW	AW	GW	XC
		◇1 ☕	◇ 🛒		◇1 🛒	◇	◇1 ☕	◇	◇1 ☕	◇1 ☕		■ 🛒	◇ 🛒		◇1 🛒		◇1 ☕	◇	◇1 ☕	◇1 ☕		■ 🛒			◇1 🛒
Bath Spa 7	d					15 18	15 24	15 36	16 00							16 08	16 24	16 36	17 00						
Oldfield Park	d					15 21										16 11									
Keynsham	d					15 28										16 18									
Bristol Temple Meads 10	a					15 36	15 41	15 49	16 15							16 29	16 39	16 48	17 15						
	d			15 21		15 41		15 54						16 21		16 41		16 54						17 21	
Filton Abbey Wood	d			15 30		15 48		16 01						16 30		16 48		17 01						17 30	
Bristol Parkway 7	a					15 52										16 52									
	d	15 08				15 52				16 08						16 52				17 08					
Patchway	d			15 35										16 35										17 35	
Pilning	d			15 41																					
Gloucester 7	d		14 35		15 22	16a33									16 22	17a33							16 58		17 22
Lydney	d		14 54												16 41								17 17		17 41
Chepstow	d		15 04		15 48										16 50								17 27		
Caldicot	d		15 12																				17 35		
Severn Tunnel Jn.	d		15 15	15 46										16 46				17 14					17 38	17 46	
Newport (South Wales)	a	15 31	15 35	16 01	16 06			16 24		16 30				17 00	17 08			17 26		17 29			17 50	17 58	18 06
	d	15 31	15 37	16 01	16 07			16 24		16 31		16 37	16 56	17 01	17 09			17 26		17 31		17 37	17 52	18 00	18 07
Cardiff Central 7	a	15 45	15 53	16 18	16 25			16 43		16 46		16 53	17 08	17 18	17 24			17 43		17 46		17 53	18 10	18 18	18 22

A 🛒 to Bristol Temple Meads

When events are being held at the Millenium Stadium, services are subject to alteration. Please check times before travelling.

Table 132

Saturdays

15 February to 22 March

Bath Spa, Bristol and Gloucester - Cardiff

Network Diagram - see first Page of Table 132

		GW		GW	GW	GW	GW	AW	AW	AW	GW	XC		GW	GW	GW	GW	GW	AW	AW	GW	XC		GW	GW
								R								R			R						
		◇		◇1	◇	◇1	◇1			◇		◇1			◇1		◇1	◇1				◇1			◇1
				☕		☕	☕	🛒		🛒					☕		☕	☕	🛒						☕
Bath Spa 7	d	17 08		17 24	17 36	18 00								18 08	18 24	18 36	19 00							19 08	19 24
Oldfield Park	d	17 11												18 11										19 11	
Keynsham	d	17 18												18 18										19 18	
Bristol Temple Meads 10	a	17 27		17 39	17 48	18 15								18 29	18 39	18 48	19 15							19 29	19 38
	d	17 41			17 54						18 21			18 41		18 54					19 21			19 41	
Filton Abbey Wood	d	17 48			18 01						18 30			18 48		19 01					19 28			19 48	
Bristol Parkway 7	a	17 52												18 52										19 52	
	d	17 52					18 08							18 52				19 08						19 52	
Patchway	d										18 35										19 33				
Pilning	d																								
Gloucester 7	d	18a33							17 58			18 27		19a33						18 58		19 22		20a33	
Lydney	d								18 17											19 17					
Chepstow	d								18 27											19 27					
Caldicot	d								18 35											19 34					
Severn Tunnel Jn.	d				18 14				18 38		18 47									19 37	19 44				
Newport (South Wales)	a				18 25		18 30		18 50		19 01	19 11				19 24		19 30		19 50	19 56	20 03			
	d				18 25		18 31	18 37	18 52	18 57	19 02	19 13				19 24		19 31	19 41	19 52	19 56	20 05			
Cardiff Central 7	a				18 43		18 46	18 53	19 10	19 15	19 18	19 30				19 41		19 46	19 58	20 11	20 16	20 20			

		GW	GW	GW	AW	XC	AW	GW		GW	GW	GW	XC	AW	GW	GW	GW	GW		AW	GW	XC	GW	AW	GW
					R																				
		◇	◇	◇1		◇1		◇1		◇	◇1	◇1	◇1	◇	◇	◇1		◇1		◇		◇1	◇1	◇	◇
				☕	🛒			☕			☕	☕		🛒		☕		☕		🛒			☕		
Bath Spa 7	d	19 36	19 47					20 00		20 12	20 24				20 36	21 00	21 07						21 30		21 39
Oldfield Park	d		19 50							20 14							21 11								
Keynsham	d		19 57							20 21							21 18								
Bristol Temple Meads 10	a	19 48	20 05					20 15		20 29	20 40				20 48	21 16	21 28						21 45		21 51
	d	19 54				20 10									20 54						21 29				21 54
Filton Abbey Wood	d	20 01				20 17									21 01						21 36				22 01
Bristol Parkway 7	a																								
	d			20 08								20 40						21 08							
Patchway	d					20 21															21 41				22 06
Pilning	d																								
Gloucester 7	d						19 58						20 22									21 22			
Lydney	d						20 17															21 41			
Chepstow	d						20 27															21 50			
Caldicot	d						20 35															21 59			
Severn Tunnel Jn.	d					20 31	20 38														21 52	22 02			22 18
Newport (South Wales)	a	20 25		20 30		20 44	20 50					21 03	21 09		21 25			21 31			22 09	22 19			22 40
	d	20 25		20 31	20 38	20 46	20 52					21 04	21 10	21 15	21 25			21 31		21 45	22 11	22 23		22 36	22 40
Cardiff Central 7	a	20 43		20 44	20 58	21 00	21 09					21 20	21 26	21 43	21 43			21 47		22 04	22 30	22 45		22 55	23 00

		SW	GW	GW		GW	GW	GW	GW	AW	GW	AW
		◇1	◇1	◇1			◇	◇1		◇	◇1	
			☕	☕				☕			☕	
Bath Spa 7	d	21 51	22 00			22 25	22 36	23 02	23 08			
Oldfield Park	d					22 28			23 11			
Keynsham	d	21 59				22 36			23 18			
Bristol Temple Meads 10	a	22 06	22 14			22 44	22 50	23 15	23 28			
	d						22 54					
Filton Abbey Wood	d						23 01					
Bristol Parkway 7	a											
	d			22 11							23 33	
Patchway	d						23 06					
Pilning	d											
Gloucester 7	d											23 09
Lydney	d											23 28
Chepstow	d											23 38
Caldicot	d											23 46
Severn Tunnel Jn.	d						23 18					23 49
Newport (South Wales)	a			22 46			23 35				00 01	00 11
	d			22 47			23 36			23 47	00 01	00 12
Cardiff Central 7	a			23 07			23 55			00 06	00 21	00 38

When events are being held at the Millenium Stadium, services are subject to alteration. Please check times before travelling.

Table 132

Saturdays

29 March to 17 May

Bath Spa, Bristol and Gloucester - Cardiff

Network Diagram - see first Page of Table 132

		AW	GW	AW	GW	AW		AW	XC	GW	GW	AW	XC	GW	GW	SW		AW	GW	GW	AW	AW	GW	AW	XC
			◇1	◇	◇1				◇1	◇1		◇	◇1			1				◇1	◇			◇	◇1 A
			🍴		🍴							🛒								🍴	🛒			🛒	🛒
Bath Spa 7	d				01 16										07 08	07 35				08 00					
Oldfield Park	d														07 11	07 38									
Keynsham	d														07 18	07 45									
Bristol Temple Meads 10	a				01 30										07 27	07 52				08 16					
	d				01 37					06 46	06 50			07 21	07 41				07 54				08 20		
Filton Abbey Wood	d									06 54	07 02			07 30	07 48				08 01				08 30		
Bristol Parkway 7	a									06 58					07 52										
	d		00 27							07 11					07 52										
Patchway	d													07 34									08 35		
Pilning	d																								
Gloucester 7	d							05 50	06 14				06 57		08a33							07 58			08 22
Lydney	d							06 09	06 33				07 16									08 17			
Chepstow	d							06 19	06 42				07 26									08 27			08 48
Caldicot	d							06 27	06 51				07 34									08 35			
Severn Tunnel Jn.	d							06 30	06 54		07 14		07 37	07 46								08 38	08 46		
Newport (South Wales)	a		00 49		02s03			06 42	07 05	07 31	07 25		07 48	07 58					08 26			08 50	09 01		09 06
	d	00 07	00 49	00 59		06 38		06 44	07 06	07 31	07 26	07 38	07 50	07 58				08 01	08 27		08 33	08 52	09 01	09 02	09 07
Cardiff Central 7	a	00 35	01 04	01 18	02 20	06 54		07 00	07 21	07 47	07 44	07 54	08 04	08 17				08 20	08 43		08 50	09 10	09 21	09 22	09 22

		GW		GW	GW	GW	GW	GW	AW	AW	GW	XC		GW	GW	GW	GW	GW	AW	AW	AW	GW		XC	GW
				◇1	◇	◇	R 1	◇1	◇			◇1			◇1	◇ B	◇1	◇1	◇	◇	◇			◇1	◇
				🍴			🍴	🍴	🛒						🍴	🛒	🍴	🍴	🛒	🛒	🛒			🛒	
Bath Spa 7	d	08 08		08 24	08 30	08 47	09 00							09 08	09 24	09 36	10 00								10 08
Oldfield Park	d	08 11				08 50								09 11											10 11
Keynsham	d	08 18				08 57								09 18											10 18
Bristol Temple Meads 10	a	08 29		08 39	08 44	09 05	09 15							09 27	09 39	09 48	10 15								10 29
	d	08 41			08 54						09 21			09 41		09 54						10 21			10 41
Filton Abbey Wood	d	08 48			09 01						09 30			09 48		10 01						10 30			10 48
Bristol Parkway 7	a	08 52												09 52											10 52
	d	08 52						09 08						09 52				10 08							10 52
Patchway	d										09 35											10 35			
Pilning	d																								
Gloucester 7	d	09a33								08 58		09 22		10a33										10 22	11a32
Lydney	d									09 17														10 41	
Chepstow	d									09 27		09 48													
Caldicot	d									09 35															
Severn Tunnel Jn.	d									09 38	09 46											10 46			
Newport (South Wales)	a				09 25			09 30		09 50	09 58	10 05				10 24		10 31				11 00		11 06	
	d				09 25			09 31	09 38	09 52	09 59	10 07				10 24		10 31	10 40	10 40	10 57	11 01		11 07	
Cardiff Central 7	a				09 43			09 47	09 59	10 07	10 18	10 21				10 43		10 46	10 54	10 55	11 14	11 21		11 24	

		GW	GW	GW	GW	AW	AW	GW		XC	GW	GW	GW	SW	GW	GW	AW	AW		AW	GW	XC	GW	GW	GW
		◇1	◇ B	◇1	◇1	◇				◇1	◇	◇1	◇ B	◇1	◇1	◇1	◇			◇		◇1	◇	◇1	◇
		🍴	🛒	🍴	🍴	🛒				🛒		🍴	🛒		🍴	⌀	🛒			🛒		🛒		🍴	
Bath Spa 7	d	10 24	10 36	11 00							11 08	11 24	11 36	11 47	12 00								12 17	12 24	12 36
Oldfield Park	d										11 11												12 19		
Keynsham	d										11 18			11 55									12 27		
Bristol Temple Meads 10	a	10 39	10 48	11 15							11 29	11 39	11 48	12 05	12 15								12 35	12 39	12 48
	d		10 54					11 21			11 41		11 54								12 21		12 41		12 54
Filton Abbey Wood	d		11 01					11 30			11 48		12 01								12 30		12 48		13 01
Bristol Parkway 7	a										11 52												12 52		
	d				11 08						11 52					12 08							12 52		
Patchway	d							11 35													12 35				
Pilning	d																								
Gloucester 7	d						10 58			11 22	12a33							11 57				12 22	13a35		
Lydney	d						11 17											12 16							
Chepstow	d						11 27			11 48								12 26				12 48			
Caldicot	d						11 35											12 34							
Severn Tunnel Jn.	d						11 38	11 46										12 37			12 46				
Newport (South Wales)	a		11 24		11 31		11 50	11 58		12 05			12 24			12 31		12 49			13 00	13 05			13 25
	d		11 24		11 31	11 37	11 52	11 59		12 07			12 25			12 31	12 37	12 51		12 56	13 01	13 07			13 25
Cardiff Central 7	a		11 43		11 46	11 53	12 06	12 18		12 23			12 43			12 46	12 53	13 06		13 15	13 18	13 21			13 43

A 🛒 to Newport (South Wales)

B 🛒 to Bristol Temple Meads

When events are being held at the Millenium Stadium, services are subject to alteration. Please check times before travelling.

Table 132

Saturdays

29 March to 17 May

Bath Spa, Bristol and Gloucester - Cardiff

Network Diagram - see first Page of Table 132

		GW	GW	AW	GW	XC	GW	GW	GW	GW	GW	AW	AW	AW	GW	AW	XC	GW	GW	AW	GW	SW	GW
																R				R			
		◇1	◇1	◇		◇1	◇	◇1	◇	◇1	◇1	◇					◇1	◇	◇1		◇	◇1	◇1
		☕	⊘	🛒		🛒		☕		☕	☕	🛒				🛒	🛒		☕	🛒			☕
Bath Spa 7	d	13 00					13 19	13 24	13 36	14 00								14 08	14 24		14 36	14 47	15 00
Oldfield Park	d						13 22											14 11					
Keynsham	d						13 29											14 18				14 55	
Bristol Temple Meads 10	a	13 14					13 37	13 42	13 48	14 15								14 29	14 39		14 48	15 05	15 15
	d				13 21		13 41		13 54						14 21			14 41			14 54		
Filton Abbey Wood	d				13 30		13 48		14 01						14 30			14 48			15 01		
Bristol Parkway 7	a						13 52											14 52					
	d		13 08				13 52				14 08							14 52					
Patchway	d				13 35										14 35								
Pilning	d																						
Gloucester 7	d					13 22	14a33						13 58				14 22	15a33					
Lydney	d					13 41							14 17										
Chepstow	d												14 27				14 48						
Caldicot	d												14 35										
Severn Tunnel Jn.	d				13 46								14 38		14 46								
Newport (South Wales)	a		13 31		13 58	14 06			14 24		14 31		14 50		14 59		15 10				15 24		
	d		13 31	13 37	13 59	14 07			14 25		14 31	14 39	14 52	14 57	15 00	15 06	15 12			15 22	15 24		
Cardiff Central 7	a		13 47	13 53	14 18	14 22			14 43		14 46	14 53	15 09	15 12	15 18	15 24	15 26			15 37	15 43		

		GW	AW	GW	XC	GW	GW	GW	GW	GW	AW	AW	GW	XC	GW	GW	GW	GW	GW	AW	AW	GW	XC
											R									R			
		◇1	◇		◇1	◇	◇1	◇	◇1	◇1		◇		◇1		◇1	◇	◇1	◇1				◇1
		☕	🛒		🛒		☕		☕	☕	🛒	🛒		🛒		☕		☕	☕	🛒			🛒
Bath Spa 7	d					15 18	15 24	15 36	16 00						16 08	16 24	16 36	17 00					
Oldfield Park	d					15 21									16 11								
Keynsham	d					15 28									16 18								
Bristol Temple Meads 10	a					15 36	15 41	15 49	16 15						16 29	16 39	16 48	17 15					
	d			15 21		15 41		15 54					16 21		16 41		16 54					17 21	
Filton Abbey Wood	d			15 30		15 48		16 01					16 30		16 48		17 01					17 30	
Bristol Parkway 7	a					15 52									16 52								
	d	15 08				15 52				16 08					16 52				17 08				
Patchway	d			15 35									16 35									17 35	
Pilning	d			15 41																			
Gloucester 7	d		14 35		15 22	16a33								16 22	17a33						16 58		17 22
Lydney	d		14 54											16 41							17 17		17 41
Chepstow	d		15 04		15 48									16 50							17 27		
Caldicot	d		15 12																		17 35		
Severn Tunnel Jn.	d		15 15	15 46									16 46				17 14				17 38	17 46	
Newport (South Wales)	a	15 31	15 35	16 01	16 06			16 24		16 30			17 00	17 08			17 26		17 29		17 50	17 58	18 06
	d	15 31	15 37	16 01	16 07			16 24		16 31	16 37	16 56	17 01	17 09			17 26		17 31	17 37	17 52	18 00	18 07
Cardiff Central 7	a	15 45	15 53	16 18	16 25			16 43		16 46	16 53	17 08	17 18	17 24			17 43		17 46	17 53	18 10	18 18	18 22

		GW	GW	GW	GW	GW	AW	AW	AW	GW	XC	GW	GW	GW	GW	GW	AW	AW	GW	XC	GW	GW
							R							R			R					
		◇	◇1	◇	◇1	◇1			◇		◇1		◇1		◇1	◇1				◇1		◇1
			☕		☕	☕	🛒		🛒				☕		☕	☕	🛒					☕
Bath Spa 7	d	17 08	17 24	17 36	18 00							18 08	18 24	18 36	19 00						19 08	19 24
Oldfield Park	d	17 11										18 11									19 11	
Keynsham	d	17 18										18 18									19 18	
Bristol Temple Meads 10	a	17 27	17 39	17 48	18 15							18 29	18 39	18 48	19 15						19 29	19 38
	d	17 41		17 54						18 21		18 41		18 54					19 21		19 41	
Filton Abbey Wood	d	17 48		18 01						18 30		18 48		19 01					19 28		19 48	
Bristol Parkway 7	a	17 52										18 52									19 52	
	d	17 52				18 08						18 52				19 08					19 52	
Patchway	d									18 35									19 33			
Pilning	d																					
Gloucester 7	d	18a33						17 58			18 27	19a33						18 58		19 22	20a33	
Lydney	d							18 17										19 17				
Chepstow	d							18 27										19 27				
Caldicot	d							18 35										19 34				
Severn Tunnel Jn.	d			18 14				18 38		18 47								19 37	19 44			
Newport (South Wales)	a			18 25		18 30		18 50		19 01	19 11			19 24		19 30		19 50	19 56	20 03		
	d			18 25		18 31	18 37	18 52	18 57	19 02	19 13			19 24		19 31	19 41	19 52	19 56	20 05		
Cardiff Central 7	a			18 43		18 46	18 53	19 10	19 15	19 18	19 30			19 41		19 46	19 58	20 11	20 16	20 20		

When events are being held at the Millenium Stadium, services are subject to alteration. Please check times before travelling.

Table 132

Saturdays

29 March to 17 May

Bath Spa, Bristol and Gloucester - Cardiff

Network Diagram - see first Page of Table 132

		GW	GW	GW		AW	XC	AW	GW	GW	GW	GW	XC	AW		GW	GW	GW	GW	AW	GW	XC	GW	AW	
						R																			
		◇	◇	◇1			◇1		◇1	◇	◇1	◇1	◇1	◇		◇	◇1		◇1	◇		◇1	◇1	◇	
				⊡		🛒			⊡		⊡	⊡		🛒			⊡		⊡	🛒			⊡		
Bath Spa 7	d	19 36	19 47						20 00	20 12	20 24					20 36	21 00	21 07					21 30		
Oldfield Park	d		19 50							20 14								21 11							
Keynsham	d		19 57							20 21								21 18							
Bristol Temple Meads 10	a	19 48	20 05						20 15	20 29	20 40					20 48	21 16	21 28					21 45		
	d	19 54					20 10									20 54					21 29				
Filton Abbey Wood	d	20 01					20 17									21 01					21 36				
Bristol Parkway 7	a																								
	d			20 08								20 40							21 08						
Patchway	d						20 21														21 41				
Pilning	d																								
Gloucester 7	d							19 58					20 22									21 22			
Lydney	d							20 17														21 41			
Chepstow	d							20 27														21 50			
Caldicot	d							20 35														21 59			
Severn Tunnel Jn.	d						20 31	20 38													21 52	22 02			
Newport (South Wales)	a	20 25		20 30			20 44	20 50				21 03	21 09			21 25			21 31		22 09	22 19			
	d	20 25		20 31		20 38	20 46	20 52				21 04	21 10	21 15		21 25			21 31	21 45	22 11	22 23		22 36	
Cardiff Central 7	a	20 43		20 44		20 58	21 00	21 09				21 20	21 26	21 43		21 43			21 47	22 04	22 30	22 45		22 55	

		GW	SW	GW	GW	GW	GW	GW	GW	AW		GW	AW
		◇	◇1	◇1	◇1		◇	◇1		◇		◇1	
				⊡	⊡			⊡				⊡	
Bath Spa 7	d	21 39	21 51	22 00		22 25	22 36	23 06	23 13				
Oldfield Park	d					22 28			23 15				
Keynsham	d		21 59			22 36			23 22				
Bristol Temple Meads 10	a	21 51	22 06	22 14		22 44	22 50	23 20	23 32				
	d	21 54					22 54						
Filton Abbey Wood	d	22 01					23 01						
Bristol Parkway 7	a												
	d				22 11							23 33	
Patchway	d	22 06					23 06						
Pilning	d												
Gloucester 7	d												23 09
Lydney	d												23 28
Chepstow	d												23 38
Caldicot	d												23 46
Severn Tunnel Jn.	d	22 18					23 18						23 49
Newport (South Wales)	a	22 40			22 46		23 35					00 01	00 11
	d	22 40			22 47		23 36			23 47		00 01	00 12
Cardiff Central 7	a	23 00			23 07		23 55			00 06		00 21	00 38

Sundays

8 December to 29 December

		AW	AW	GW	GW	AW	GW	GW	GW	GW		GW	AW	GW	AW	XC	GW	GW	GW	GW		GW	AW	XC	AW
																	R								R
				◇1	◇1	◇		◇1	◇1			◇1	◇	◇1		◇1		◇1	◇1			◇1	◇	◇1	
		A	A	A	A																				
				⊡	⊡	🛒		⊡	⊡			⊡		⊡		🛒		⊡	⊡			⊡	🛒	🛒	🛒
Bath Spa 7	d			00 15	01 08			09 47		10 27		10 42					11 25	11 41		12 20		12 41			
Oldfield Park	d									10 30							11 28			12 23					
Keynsham	d									10 37							11 35			12 30					
Bristol Temple Meads 10	a			00 27	01 20			10 00		10 45		10 57					11 44	11 56		12 38		12 55			
	d						09 48										11 48								
Filton Abbey Wood	d						09 55										11 55								
Bristol Parkway 7	a																								
	d								10 15					11 09					12 13						
Patchway	d																12 01								
Pilning	d																								
Gloucester 7	d														10 48	11 05								12 05	
Lydney	d														11 07										
Chepstow	d														11 17										
Caldicot	d														11 25										
Severn Tunnel Jn.	d						10 08								11 27		12 12								
Newport (South Wales)	a						10 25		10 42					11 35	11 45	11 48	12 30		12 38					12 52	
	d	00 06	00 11			09 30	10 26		10 43				11 00	11 36	11 47	11 50	12 30		12 38				12 52	12 53	13 29
Cardiff Central 7	a	00 28	00 36			09 45	10 41		10 58				11 16	11 54	12 05	12 08	12 45		12 58				13 13	13 12	13 44

A not 8 December

When events are being held at the Millenium Stadium, services are subject to alteration. Please check times before travelling.

Table 132

Sundays

8 December to 29 December

Bath Spa, Bristol and Gloucester - Cardiff

Network Diagram - see first Page of Table 132

		AW		GW	XC	GW	GW	AW	GW	AW	XC	GW		AW	GW	SW	GW	AW	XC	GW	GW	GW		AW	GW
				◇1 ☕	◇1	◇	◇1 ☕	R 🛒	◇1 ☕	◇ 🛒	◇1	◇			◇1 ☕	◇1	◇1 ☕	R 🛒	◇1	◇	R 1 ☕	◇		R 🛒	◇1 ☕
Bath Spa 7	d					13 23	13 41					14 25			14 40	14 51				15 25	15 41	16 01			
Oldfield Park	d					13 26						14 28										16 02			
Keynsham	d					13 33						14 36				14 59						16 11			
Bristol Temple Meads 10	a					13 41	13 55					14 44			14 53	15 06				15 40	15 55	16 19			
	d					13 48						14 48								15 48					
Filton Abbey Wood	d					13 55						14 55								15 55					
Bristol Parkway 7	a																								
	d			13 14					14 13								15 13								16 13
Patchway	d																								
Pilning	d																								
Gloucester 7	d	12 30			13 23						14 24			14 33					15 23						
Lydney	d	12 49												14 52											
Chepstow	d	12 59												15 02											
Caldicot	d	13 07												15 10											
Severn Tunnel Jn.	d	13 10				14 08						15 06		15 13						16 08					
Newport (South Wales)	a	13 33		13 38	14 06	14 26			14 38		15 08	15 24		15 31			15 40		16 06	16 26					16 38
	d	13 34		13 38	14 08	14 26		14 32	14 38	15 07	15 09	15 24		15 33			15 40	15 49	16 08	16 26				16 31	16 38
Cardiff Central 7	a	13 52		13 58	14 26	14 46		14 52	14 58	15 31	15 31	15 41		15 47			15 59	16 04	16 26	16 44				16 52	16 58

		XC	GW	GW	AW	AW	GW	XC		GW	GW	AW	GW	XC	GW	GW	GW	GW		AW	GW	AW	XC	AW	GW
		◇1 🛒	◇	R 1 ☕	R 🛒		◇1 ☕	◇1 🛒		R	R 1 ☕	R 🛒	◇1 ☕	◇1	◇	R 1 ☕	◇	R 1 ☕		R 🛒	◇1 ☕		◇1	R 🛒	◇
Bath Spa 7	d		16 25	16 41						17 25	17 41				18 30	18 41	18 56	19 06							19 23
Oldfield Park	d									17 28							19 00								
Keynsham	d									17 36							19 07								
Bristol Temple Meads 10	a		16 37	16 55						17 44	17 56				18 43	18 56	19 17	19 18							19 35
	d		16 48							17 48					18 48										19 48
Filton Abbey Wood	d		16 55							17 55					18 55										19 55
Bristol Parkway 7	a																								
	d						17 13						18 13								19 13				
Patchway	d		17 00																						20 00
Pilning	d																								
Gloucester 7	d	16 23				16 37		17 23						18 23								18 48	19 28		
Lydney	d					16 56																19 07			
Chepstow	d					17 07																19 17			
Caldicot	d					17 13																19 25			
Severn Tunnel Jn.	d		17 11			17 16				18 08					19 08							19 32			20 11
Newport (South Wales)	a	17 06	17 29			17 37	17 38	18 06		18 26			18 38	19 06	19 26						19 43	19 51	20 11		20 28
	d	17 08	17 29		17 34	17 38	17 38	18 08		18 26		18 33	18 38	19 08	19 26					19 43	19 44	19 53	20 13	20 23	20 29
Cardiff Central 7	a	17 27	17 46		17 50	17 57	17 58	18 28		18 44		18 50	18 58	19 27	19 42					19 58	20 02	20 09	20 31	20 43	20 46

		GW	GW	GW		XC	AW	GW	AW	GW	SW	GW	GW	GW		AW	GW	GW	GW	AW	GW	GW	AW	GW	
		R 1 ☕	◇	◇1 ☕		◇1	R 🛒	◇		◇1 ☕	◇1	◇1 ☕	◇	◇1 ☕		R 🛒	◇	◇1 ☕		◇	◇1 ☕	◇		◇1 ☕	
Bath Spa 7	d	19 41	20 00					20 27		20 40	20 51	21 02	21 09				21 27	21 41	22 18			22 27		22 46	
Oldfield Park	d		20 01										21 11						22 20						
Keynsham	d		20 10								20 58		21 19						22 28						
Bristol Temple Meads 10	a	19 56	20 18					20 39		20 55	21 06	21 17	21 27				21 39	21 55	22 36			22 40		23 01	
	d							20 48									21 48					22 48			
Filton Abbey Wood	d							20 55									21 55					22 55			
Bristol Parkway 7	a																								
	d			20 13										21 13							22 13				
Patchway	d																22 02								
Pilning	d																								
Gloucester 7	d					20 23			20 31														22 33		
Lydney	d								20 50														22 52		
Chepstow	d								21 00														23 02		
Caldicot	d								21 10														23 09		
Severn Tunnel Jn.	d							21 08	21 13								22 13					23 07	23 13		
Newport (South Wales)	a			20 40		21 06		21 26	21 31					21 40			22 31				22 40	23 25	23 30		
	d			20 40		21 08	21 14	21 26	21 33					21 40		21 45	22 31			22 36	22 40	23 25	23 30		
Cardiff Central 7	a			20 59		21 26	21 36	21 42	21 49					22 01		22 12	22 53			23 02	23 00	23 47	23 50		

When events are being held at the Millenium Stadium, services are subject to alteration. Please check times before travelling.

Table 132

Sundays

8 December to 29 December

Bath Spa, Bristol and Gloucester - Cardiff

Network Diagram - see first Page of Table 132

		GW	GW	AW
		◇1	◇1	◇
		☕	☕	
Bath Spa 7	d		23 49	
Oldfield Park	d			
Keynsham	d			
Bristol Temple Meads 10	a		00 04	
	d			
Filton Abbey Wood	d			
Bristol Parkway 7	a			
	d	23 19		
Patchway	d			
Pilning	d			
Gloucester 7	d			
Lydney	d			
Chepstow	d			
Caldicot	d			
Severn Tunnel Jn.	d			
Newport (South Wales)	a	23 43		
	d	23 47		23 55
Cardiff Central 7	a	00 08		00 20

Sundays

5 January to 9 February

		GW	AW	GW	GW	AW	GW	GW	GW	GW		GW	AW	GW	AW	XC	GW	GW	GW	GW		GW	AW	XC	AW
																	R								R
				◇1	◇1	◇		◇1	◇1			◇1	◇	◇1		◇1		◇1	◇1			◇1	◇	◇1	
		🚌	🚌	☕	☕	trolley		☕	☕			☕		☕		trolley		☕	☕			☕	trolley	trolley	trolley
Bath Spa 7	d			00 23	01 08			09 42		10 27		10 41					11 25	11 41		12 20		12 41			
Oldfield Park	d									10 30							11 28			12 23					
Keynsham	d									10 37							11 35			12 30					
Bristol Temple Meads 10	a			00 35	01 20			09 57		10 45		10 55					11 44	11 56		12 38		12 55			
	d						09 48										11 48								
Filton Abbey Wood	d						09 55										11 55								
Bristol Parkway 7	a																								
	d								10 15					11 06					12 13						
Patchway	d																12 01								
Pilning	d																								
Gloucester 7	d														10 48	11 05								12 05	
Lydney	d														11 07										
Chepstow	d														11 17										
Caldicot	d														11 25										
Severn Tunnel Jn.	d						10 08								11 27		12 12								
Newport (South Wales)	a						10 25		10 42					11 32	11 45	11 48	12 30		12 38					12 52	
	d	00 15	00 20			09 30	10 26		10 43				11 00	11 32	11 47	11 50	12 30		12 38				12 52	12 53	13 29
Cardiff Central 7	a	00 45	00 50			09 44	10 41		10 58				11 16	11 50	12 05	12 08	12 45		12 58				13 13	13 12	13 44

		AW	GW	XC	GW	GW		AW	GW	AW	XC	GW	AW	GW	SW	GW		AW	XC	GW	GW	GW	AW	GW	XC
								R										R			R		R		
			◇1	◇1	◇	◇1			◇1	◇	◇1	◇		◇1	◇1	◇1			◇1	◇	1	◇		◇1	◇1
			☕			☕		trolley	☕	trolley				☕		☕		trolley			☕		trolley	☕	trolley
Bath Spa 7	d				13 23	13 41						14 25		14 41	14 51					15 25	15 41	16 01			
Oldfield Park	d				13 26							14 28										16 02			
Keynsham	d				13 33							14 36			14 59							16 11			
Bristol Temple Meads 10	a				13 41	13 55						14 44		14 55	15 06					15 40	15 55	16 19			
	d				13 48							14 48								15 48					
Filton Abbey Wood	d				13 55							14 55								15 55					
Bristol Parkway 7	a																								
	d		13 14						14 13							15 13								16 13	
Patchway	d																								
Pilning	d																								
Gloucester 7	d	12 30		13 25							14 24		14 33						15 27						16 21
Lydney	d	12 49											14 52												
Chepstow	d	12 59											15 02												
Caldicot	d	13 07											15 10												
Severn Tunnel Jn.	d	13 10			14 08							15 06	15 13							16 08					
Newport (South Wales)	a	13 33	13 38	14 08	14 26				14 38		15 08	15 24	15 31			15 40			16 10	16 26				16 38	17 06
	d	13 34	13 38	14 10	14 26			14 32	14 38	15 07	15 09	15 24	15 33			15 40		15 49	16 12	16 26			16 31	16 38	17 08
Cardiff Central 7	a	13 52	13 58	14 28	14 46			14 52	14 58	15 31	15 31	15 41	15 47			15 59		16 04	16 30	16 44			16 52	16 58	17 27

When events are being held at the Millenium Stadium, services are subject to alteration. Please check times before travelling.

Table 132

Sundays

5 January to 9 February

Bath Spa, Bristol and Gloucester - Cardiff

Network Diagram - see first Page of Table 132

		GW	GW	AW	AW	GW	XC	GW		GW	AW	GW	XC	GW	GW	GW	GW	AW		GW	AW	XC	AW	GW	GW
		◇	R 1 ☕	R 🛒		◇1 ☕	◇1 🛒	R		R 1 ☕	R 🛒	◇1 ☕	◇1 🛒	◇	R 1 ☕	◇	R 1 ☕	R 🛒		◇1 ☕		◇1 🛒	R 🛒	◇	R 1 ☕
Bath Spa 7	d	16 25	16 41					17 25		17 41				18 30	18 41	18 56	19 06							19 23	19 41
Oldfield Park	d							17 28								19 00									
Keynsham	d							17 36								19 07									
Bristol Temple Meads 10	a	16 37	16 55					17 44		17 56				18 43	18 56	19 17	19 18							19 35	19 56
	d	16 48						17 48						18 48										19 48	
Filton Abbey Wood	d	16 55						17 55						18 55										19 55	
Bristol Parkway 7	a																								
	d					17 13						18 13								19 13					
Patchway	d	17 00																						20 00	
Pilning	d																								
Gloucester 7	d				16 37		17 23						18 22								18 48	19 28			
Lydney	d				16 56																19 07				
Chepstow	d				17 07																19 17				
Caldicot	d				17 13																19 25				
Severn Tunnel Jn.	d	17 11			17 16			18 08						19 08							19 32			20 11	
Newport (South Wales)	a	17 29			17 37	17 38	18 06	18 26				18 38	19 06	19 26						19 43	19 51	20 11		20 28	
	d	17 29		17 34	17 38	17 38	18 08	18 26			18 33	18 38	19 07	19 26				19 43		19 44	19 53	20 13	20 23	20 29	
Cardiff Central 7	a	17 46		17 50	17 57	17 58	18 28	18 44			18 50	18 58	19 27	19 42				19 58		20 02	20 09	20 31	20 43	20 46	

		GW	GW	XC		AW	GW	AW	GW	SW	GW	GW	GW	AW		GW	GW	GW	AW	GW	GW	AW	GW	GW	
		◇	◇1 ☕	◇1 🛒		R 🛒	◇		◇1 ☕	◇1	◇1 ☕	◇	◇1 ☕	R 🛒		◇	◇1 ☕		◇	◇1 ☕	◇		◇1 ☕	◇1 ☕	
Bath Spa 7	d	20 00					20 27		20 40	20 51	21 02	21 09				21 27	21 41	22 18			22 27		22 46		
Oldfield Park	d	20 01										21 11						22 20							
Keynsham	d	20 10								20 58		21 19						22 28							
Bristol Temple Meads 10	a	20 18					20 39		20 55	21 06	21 17	21 27				21 39	21 55	22 36			22 40		23 01		
	d						20 48									21 48					22 48				
Filton Abbey Wood	d						20 55									21 55					22 55				
Bristol Parkway 7	a																								
	d		20 13										21 13							22 13				23 12	
Patchway	d															22 02									
Pilning	d																								
Gloucester 7	d			20 23				20 31														22 33			
Lydney	d							20 50														22 52			
Chepstow	d							21 00														23 02			
Caldicot	d							21 10														23 09			
Severn Tunnel Jn.	d						21 08	21 13								22 13					23 07	23 13			
Newport (South Wales)	a		20 40	21 06			21 26	21 31					21 40			22 31				22 40	23 25	23 30		23 40	
	d		20 40	21 08		21 14	21 26	21 33					21 40	21 45		22 31			22 36	22 40	23 25	23 30		23 44	
Cardiff Central 7	a		20 59	21 26		21 36	21 42	21 49					22 01	22 12		22 53			23 02	23 00	23 47	23 50		00 05	

		GW	AW
		◇1 ☕	◇
Bath Spa 7	d	23 49	
Oldfield Park	d		
Keynsham	d		
Bristol Temple Meads 10	a	00 04	
	d		
Filton Abbey Wood	d		
Bristol Parkway 7	a		
	d		
Patchway	d		
Pilning	d		
Gloucester 7	d		
Lydney	d		
Chepstow	d		
Caldicot	d		
Severn Tunnel Jn.	d		
Newport (South Wales)	a		
	d		23 55
Cardiff Central 7	a		00 20

When events are being held at the Millenium Stadium, services are subject to alteration. Please check times before travelling.

Table 132

Sundays

16 February to 23 March

Bath Spa, Bristol and Gloucester - Cardiff

Network Diagram - see first Page of Table 132

		GW	AW	AW	GW	GW		AW	GW	GW	GW	GW	GW	AW	GW	AW		XC	GW	GW	GW	GW	GW	AW	XC
		◇1 ☕			◇1 ☕	◇1 ☕		◇ 🛒		◇1 ☕	◇1 ☕		◇1 ☕	◇	◇1 ☕			◇1 🛒	R	◇1 ☕	◇1 ☕		◇1 ☕	◇ 🛒	◇1 🛒
Bath Spa 7	d				00 17	01 08				09 42		10 27	10 42						11 25	11 41		12 20	12 41		
Oldfield Park	d											10 30							11 28			12 23			
Keynsham	d											10 37							11 35			12 30			
Bristol Temple Meads 10	a				00 29	01 21				09 57		10 45	10 58						11 44	12 00		12 38	12 58		
	d								09 48										11 48						
Filton Abbey Wood	d								09 55										11 55						
Bristol Parkway 7	a																								
	d										10 15				11 09						12 14				
Patchway	d																		12 01						
Pilning	d																								
Gloucester 7	d															10 48		11 05							12 05
Lydney	d															11 07									
Chepstow	d															11 17									
Caldicot	d															11 25									
Severn Tunnel Jn.	d								10 08							11 27			12 12						
Newport (South Wales)	a								10 25		10 42				11 35	11 45		11 48	12 30		12 41				12 52
	d	00 01	00 07	00 12				09 30	10 26		10 43			11 00	11 36	11 47		11 50	12 30		12 41			12 52	12 53
Cardiff Central 7	a	00 21	00 29	00 38				09 45	10 41		11 00			11 16	11 54	12 05		12 08	12 45		13 00			13 13	13 12

		AW		AW	GW	XC	GW	GW	AW	GW	AW	XC		GW	AW	GW	SW	GW	AW	XC	GW	GW		GW	AW
		R 🛒			◇1 ☕	◇1	◇	◇1 ☕	R 🛒	◇1 ☕	◇ 🛒	◇1		◇		◇1 ☕	◇1	◇1 ☕	R 🛒	◇1	◇	R 1 ☕		◇	R 🛒
Bath Spa 7	d						13 23	13 44						14 25		14 44	14 51				15 25	15 45		16 01	
Oldfield Park	d						13 26							14 28										16 02	
Keynsham	d						13 33							14 36			14 59							16 11	
Bristol Temple Meads 10	a						13 41	13 58						14 44		14 58	15 06				15 40	15 59		16 19	
	d						13 48							14 48							15 48				
Filton Abbey Wood	d						13 55							14 55							15 55				
Bristol Parkway 7	a																								
	d				13 14					14 13								15 13							
Patchway	d																								
Pilning	d																								
Gloucester 7	d			12 30		13 25						14 24			14 33					15 27					
Lydney	d			12 49											14 52										
Chepstow	d			12 59											15 02										
Caldicot	d			13 07											15 10										
Severn Tunnel Jn.	d			13 10			14 08							15 06	15 13						16 08				
Newport (South Wales)	a			13 33	13 38	14 08	14 26			14 38		15 08		15 24	15 31			15 40		16 10	16 26				
	d	13 29		13 34	13 38	14 10	14 26		14 32	14 38	15 07	15 09		15 24	15 33			15 40	15 49	16 12	16 26				16 31
Cardiff Central 7	a	13 44		13 52	13 58	14 28	14 46		14 52	14 58	15 31	15 31		15 41	15 47			15 59	16 04	16 30	16 44				16 52

		GW	XC	GW	GW	AW	AW	GW		XC	GW	GW	AW	GW	XC	GW	GW	GW		GW	AW	GW	AW	XC	AW
		◇1 ☕	◇1 🛒	◇	R 1 ☕	R 🛒		◇1 ☕		◇1 🛒	R	R 1 ☕	R 🛒	◇1 ☕	◇1 🛒	◇	R 1 ☕	◇		R 1 ☕	R 🛒	◇1 ☕		◇1 🛒	R 🛒
Bath Spa 7	d			16 25	16 45						17 25	17 45				18 30	18 45	18 56		19 06					
Oldfield Park	d										17 28							19 00							
Keynsham	d										17 36							19 07							
Bristol Temple Meads 10	a			16 37	16 59						17 44	17 59				18 43	18 59	19 17		19 18					
	d			16 48							17 48					18 48									
Filton Abbey Wood	d			16 55							17 55					18 55									
Bristol Parkway 7	a																								
	d	16 13						17 13						18 13								19 13			
Patchway	d			17 00																					
Pilning	d																								
Gloucester 7	d		16 21				16 37			17 23					18 22								18 48	19 28	
Lydney	d						16 56																19 07		
Chepstow	d						17 07																19 17		
Caldicot	d						17 13																19 25		
Severn Tunnel Jn.	d			17 11			17 16				18 08					19 08							19 32		
Newport (South Wales)	a	16 38	17 06	17 29			17 37	17 38		18 06	18 26			18 38	19 06	19 26						19 43	19 51	20 11	
	d	16 38	17 08	17 29		17 34	17 38	17 38		18 08	18 26		18 33	18 38	19 07	19 26					19 43	19 44	19 53	20 13	20 23
Cardiff Central 7	a	16 58	17 27	17 46		17 50	17 57	17 58		18 28	18 44		18 50	18 58	19 27	19 42					19 58	20 02	20 09	20 31	20 43

When events are being held at the Millenium Stadium, services are subject to alteration. Please check times before travelling.

Table 132

Bath Spa, Bristol and Gloucester - Cardiff

Sundays

16 February to 23 March

Network Diagram - see first Page of Table 132

		GW	GW	GW	GW	XC	AW	GW	AW	GW
			[R]				[R]			
		◇	[1]	◇	◇[1]	◇[1]		◇		◇[1]
			☕		☕	🛒	🛒			☕
Bath Spa [7]	d	19 23	19 41	20 00				20 27		20 45
Oldfield Park	d			20 01						
Keynsham	d			20 10						
Bristol Temple Meads [10]	a	19 35	19 56	20 18				20 39		20 58
	d	19 48						20 48		
Filton Abbey Wood	d	19 55						20 55		
Bristol Parkway [7]	a									
	d				20 13					
Patchway	d	20 00								
Pilning	d									
Gloucester [7]	d					20 23			20 31	
Lydney	d								20 50	
Chepstow	d								21 00	
Caldicot	d								21 10	
Severn Tunnel Jn.	d	20 11						21 08	21 13	
Newport (South Wales)	a	20 28			20 40	21 06		21 26	21 31	
	d	20 29			20 40	21 08	21 14	21 26	21 33	
Cardiff Central [7]	a	20 46			20 59	21 26	21 36	21 42	21 49	

		SW	GW	GW	GW	AW	GW	GW	GW	AW	GW	GW	AW	GW
						[R]								
		◇[1]	◇[1]	◇	◇[1]		◇	◇[1]		◇	◇[1]	◇		◇[1]
			☕		☕	🛒		☕			☕			☕
Bath Spa [7]	d	20 51	21 05	21 12			21 27	21 45	22 18			22 27		22 46
Oldfield Park	d			21 14					22 20					
Keynsham	d	20 58		21 22					22 28					
Bristol Temple Meads [10]	a	21 06	21 19	21 30			21 39	21 59	22 36			22 40		23 01
	d						21 48					22 48		
Filton Abbey Wood	d						21 55					22 55		
Bristol Parkway [7]	a													
	d				21 13						22 17			
Patchway	d						22 02							
Pilning	d													
Gloucester [7]	d												22 33	
Lydney	d												22 52	
Chepstow	d												23 02	
Caldicot	d												23 09	
Severn Tunnel Jn.	d						22 13					23 07	23 13	
Newport (South Wales)	a				21 40		22 31				22 44	23 25	23 30	
	d				21 40	21 45	22 31			22 36	22 45	23 25	23 30	
Cardiff Central [7]	a				22 01	22 12	22 53			23 02	23 04	23 47	23 50	

		GW	GW	AW
		◇[1]	◇[1]	◇
		☕	☕	
Bath Spa [7]	d		23 48	
Oldfield Park	d			
Keynsham	d			
Bristol Temple Meads [10]	a		00 04	
	d			
Filton Abbey Wood	d			
Bristol Parkway [7]	a			
	d	23 16		
Patchway	d			
Pilning	d			
Gloucester [7]	d			
Lydney	d			
Chepstow	d			
Caldicot	d			
Severn Tunnel Jn.	d			
Newport (South Wales)	a	23 40		
	d	23 44		23 55
Cardiff Central [7]	a	00 05		00 20

Sundays

30 March to 11 May

		GW	AW	AW	GW	GW	AW	GW	GW	GW
		◇[1]			◇[1]	◇[1]	◇		◇[1]	◇[1]
		☕			☕	☕	🛒		☕	☕
Bath Spa [7]	d				00 17	01 08			09 40	
Oldfield Park	d									
Keynsham	d									
Bristol Temple Meads [10]	a				00 29	01 21			09 53	
	d							09 48		
Filton Abbey Wood	d							09 55		
Bristol Parkway [7]	a									
	d									10 04
Patchway	d									
Pilning	d									
Gloucester [7]	d									
Lydney	d									
Chepstow	d									
Caldicot	d									
Severn Tunnel Jn.	d							10 08		
Newport (South Wales)	a							10 25		10 29
	d	00 01	00 07	00 12			09 30	10 26		10 29
Cardiff Central [7]	a	00 21	00 29	00 38			09 45	10 41		10 46

		GW	GW	AW	GW	AW	XC	GW	GW	GW	GW	GW	AW	XC
								[R]						
			◇[1]	◇	◇[1]		◇[1]		◇[1]	◇[1]		◇[1]	◇	◇[1]
			☕		☕		🛒		☕	☕		☕	🛒	🛒
Bath Spa [7]	d	10 27	10 42					11 25	11 42		12 20	12 42		
Oldfield Park	d	10 30						11 28			12 23			
Keynsham	d	10 37						11 35			12 30			
Bristol Temple Meads [10]	a	10 45	10 57					11 44	11 58		12 38	12 58		
	d							11 48						
Filton Abbey Wood	d							11 55						
Bristol Parkway [7]	a													
	d				11 08					12 14				
Patchway	d							12 01						
Pilning	d													
Gloucester [7]	d					10 48	11 05							12 05
Lydney	d					11 07								
Chepstow	d					11 17								
Caldicot	d					11 25								
Severn Tunnel Jn.	d					11 27		12 12						
Newport (South Wales)	a				11 35	11 45	11 48	12 30		12 38				12 52
	d			11 00	11 35	11 47	11 50	12 30		12 38			12 52	12 53
Cardiff Central [7]	a			11 16	11 54	12 05	12 08	12 45		12 58			13 13	13 12

When events are being held at the Millenium Stadium, services are subject to alteration. Please check times before travelling.

Table 132

Sundays

30 March to 11 May

Bath Spa, Bristol and Gloucester - Cardiff

Network Diagram - see first Page of Table 132

		AW		AW	GW	XC	GW	GW	AW	GW	AW	XC		GW	AW	GW	SW	GW	AW	XC	GW	GW		GW	AW
		R 🛒			◇1 ☕	◇1	◇	◇1 ☕	R 🛒	◇1 ☕	◇ 🛒	◇1		◇		◇1 ☕	◇1	◇1 ☕	R 🛒	◇1	◇	R 1 ☕		◇	R 🛒
Bath Spa 7	d						13 23	13 42						14 25		14 42	14 51				15 25	15 42		16 01	
Oldfield Park	d						13 26							14 28										16 02	
Keynsham	d						13 33							14 36			14 59							16 11	
Bristol Temple Meads 10	a						13 41	14 00						14 44		14 58	15 06				15 40	15 59		16 19	
	d						13 48							14 48							15 48				
Filton Abbey Wood	d						13 55							14 55							15 55				
Bristol Parkway 7	a																								
	d				13 08					14 08								15 03							
Patchway	d																								
Pilning	d																								
Gloucester 7	d			12 30		13 23						14 24			14 33					15 23					
Lydney	d			12 49											14 52										
Chepstow	d			12 59											15 02										
Caldicot	d			13 07											15 10										
Severn Tunnel Jn.	d			13 10			14 08							15 06	15 13						16 08				
Newport (South Wales)	a			13 33	13 35	14 06	14 26			14 35		15 08		15 24	15 31			15 35		16 06	16 26				
	d	13 29		13 34	13 35	14 08	14 26		14 32	14 35	15 07	15 09		15 24	15 33			15 35	15 49	16 08	16 26				16 31
Cardiff Central 7	a	13 44		13 52	13 56	14 26	14 46		14 52	14 53	15 31	15 31		15 41	15 47			15 56	16 04	16 26	16 44				16 52

		GW	XC	GW	GW	AW	AW	GW		XC	GW	GW	AW	GW	XC	GW	GW	GW		GW	GW	AW	AW	XC	AW
		◇1 ☕	◇1 🛒	◇	R 1 ☕	R 🛒		◇1 ☕		◇1 🛒	R	R 1 ☕	R 🛒	◇1 ☕	◇1	◇	R 1 ☕	◇		R 1 ☕	◇1 ☕	R 🛒		◇1	R 🛒
Bath Spa 7	d			16 25	16 42						17 25	17 42				18 30	18 42	18 56		19 06					
Oldfield Park	d										17 28							19 00							
Keynsham	d										17 36							19 07							
Bristol Temple Meads 10	a			16 37	16 55						17 44	17 59				18 43	18 56	19 17		19 20					
	d			16 48							17 48					18 48									
Filton Abbey Wood	d			16 55							17 55					18 55									
Bristol Parkway 7	a																								
	d	16 08						17 08						18 15							19 08				
Patchway	d			17 00																					
Pilning	d																								
Gloucester 7	d		16 23				16 37			17 23					18 23								18 48	19 28	
Lydney	d						16 56																19 07		
Chepstow	d						17 07																19 17		
Caldicot	d						17 13																19 25		
Severn Tunnel Jn.	d			17 11			17 16				18 08					19 08							19 32		
Newport (South Wales)	a	16 35	17 06	17 29			17 37	17 38		18 06	18 26			18 38	19 06	19 26					19 35		19 51	20 11	
	d	16 35	17 08	17 29		17 34	17 38	17 38		18 08	18 26		18 33	18 38	19 08	19 26					19 35	19 43	19 53	20 13	20 23
Cardiff Central 7	a	16 53	17 27	17 46		17 50	17 57	17 58		18 28	18 44		18 50	18 58	19 27	19 42					19 52	19 58	20 09	20 31	20 43

		GW	GW	GW		GW	XC	AW	GW	AW	GW	SW	GW	GW		GW	AW	GW	GW	GW	AW	GW	GW	AW	
		◇	R 1 ☕	◇		◇1 ☕	◇1	R 🛒	◇		◇1 ☕	◇1	◇1 ☕	◇1 ☕		◇	R 🛒	◇	◇1 ☕		◇	◇1 ☕	◇		
Bath Spa 7	d	19 23	19 42	20 00					20 27		20 41	20 51	21 02			21 09		21 27	21 41	22 18			22 27		
Oldfield Park	d			20 01												21 11				22 20					
Keynsham	d			20 10								20 58				21 19				22 28					
Bristol Temple Meads 10	a	19 35	19 56	20 18					20 39		20 54	21 06	21 17			21 27		21 40	21 55	22 36			22 40		
	d	19 48							20 48									21 48					22 48		
Filton Abbey Wood	d	19 55							20 55									21 55					22 55		
Bristol Parkway 7	a																								
	d					20 13								21 08								22 08			
Patchway	d	20 00																22 02							
Pilning	d																								
Gloucester 7	d						20 23			20 31														22 33	
Lydney	d									20 50														22 52	
Chepstow	d									21 00														23 02	
Caldicot	d									21 10														23 09	
Severn Tunnel Jn.	d	20 11							21 08	21 13								22 13					23 07	23 13	
Newport (South Wales)	a	20 28				20 40	21 06		21 26	21 31				21 35				22 27				22 40	23 25	23 30	
	d	20 29				20 40	21 08	21 14	21 26	21 33				21 35			21 45	22 27			22 36	22 40	23 25	23 30	
Cardiff Central 7	a	20 46				20 59	21 26	21 36	21 42	21 49				21 56			22 12	22 49			23 02	23 00	23 47	23 50	

When events are being held at the Millenium Stadium, services are subject to alteration. Please check times before travelling.

Table 132

Sundays

30 March to 11 May

Bath Spa, Bristol and Gloucester - Cardiff

Network Diagram - see first Page of Table 132

		GW	GW	GW	AW
		◇1	◇1	◇1	◇
		☕	☕	☕	
Bath Spa 7	d	22 46		23 49	
Oldfield Park	d				
Keynsham	d				
Bristol Temple Meads 10	a	23 01		00 04	
	d				
Filton Abbey Wood	d				
Bristol Parkway 7	a				
	d		23 16		
Patchway	d				
Pilning	d				
Gloucester 7	d				
Lydney	d				
Chepstow	d				
Caldicot	d				
Severn Tunnel Jn.	d				
Newport (South Wales)	a		23 40		
	d		23 44		23 55
Cardiff Central 7	a		00 05		00 20

When events are being held at the Millenium Stadium, services are subject to alteration. Please check times before travelling.

Table 132R

Mondays to Fridays

9 December to 16 May

Cardiff - Gloucester, Bristol and Bath Spa

Network Diagram - see first Page of Table 132

Miles	Miles	Miles			AW MX	GW MX	GW	AW MX	AW	AW	GW	AW	GW	GW	GW	AW	GW	GW	GW	GW	GW	XC	AW
							◇1 ⊡		◇	◇ ⊤	◇1 ⊡	◇ ⊤	◇	R 1 ⊡	R 1 ⊡		R 1 ⊡	R 1 ⊡		R 1 ⊡	◇ ⊤	◇1	◇ ⊤
0	0	0	**Cardiff Central 7**	d				00 30	04 35	05 10	05 14	05 40		05 55		06 12	06 24				06 28	06 40	06 50
11¾	11¾	11¾	Newport (South Wales)	a				00 48	04 51	05 25	05 31	05 56		06 09		06 26	06 37				06 41	06 53	07 02
—	—	—		d							05 32			06 09		06 28	06 38				06 42	06 55	
21¾	21¾	21¾	Severn Tunnel Jn	d		00 03										06 38					06 53	07 05	
—	—	22½	Caldicot	d	00 01											06 40						07 08	
—	—	29¼	Chepstow	d	00 10											06 49						07 16	
—	—	37	Lydney	d	00 19											06 58						07 25	
—	—	56½	**Gloucester 7**	a	00 39											07 20						07 44	
28¾	28¾	—	Pilning	d																			
32¼	32¼	—	Patchway	d		00 16															07 06		
—	33½	—	**Bristol Parkway 7**	a							05 59			06 29			06 58						
—	—	—		d																			
33¾	—	—	Filton Abbey Wood	d		00 20															07 09		
38¼	—	—	**Bristol Temple Meads 10**	a		00 33															07 18		
—	—	—		d			05 29						05 44		06 00			06 30	06 48	07 00	07 22		
42¾	—	—	Keynsham	d									05 51						06 55				
48¾	—	—	Oldfield Park	d									05 59						07 02				
49¾	—	—	**Bath Spa 7**	a			05 40						06 01		06 11			06 41	07 05	07 11	07 34		

		GW	GW	GW	XC	GW	AW	AW	GW	GW	GW	XC	GW	GW	GW	SW	GW	GW	AW	GW	GW	GW	XC
		R 1 A ⊡		R 1 B Ø	◇1	◇1 ⊡		◇ ⊤		R 1 Ø	R ⊤	◇1	◇1 ⊡	◇	◇1 Ø	◇1	◇	◇1 ⊡	◇ ⊤	◇1 Ø		◇ ⊤	◇1
Cardiff Central 7	d			06 55	07 00		07 06	07 21		07 25	07 30	07 45			07 55		08 00		08 05	08 25		08 30	08 45
Newport (South Wales)	a			07 09	07 13		07 19	07 34		07 39	07 44	07 59			08 09		08 13		08 17	08 39		08 42	08 58
	d			07 09	07 15		07 23			07 39	07 44	08 02			08 09		08 15			08 39		08 44	09 00
Severn Tunnel Jn	d				07 25		07 38				07 55						08 26					08 55	
Caldicot	d						07 40																
Chepstow	d						07 49																09 18
Lydney	d						07 58					08 25											
Gloucester 7	a						08 20					08 47											09 44
Pilning	d																						
Patchway	d				07 37												08 39						
Bristol Parkway 7	a			07 29						07 59					08 30					08 59			
	d		07 23						07 49					08 19									
Filton Abbey Wood	d		07 28		07 41				07 53		08 09			08 23			08 42					09 09	
Bristol Temple Meads 10	a		07 40		07 51				08 02		08 18			08 36			08 53					09 18	
	d	07 30	07 49			08 00			08 12		08 22		08 30	08 41		08 51		09 00			09 05	09 22	
Keynsham	d		07 56						08 19					08 48		08 58							
Oldfield Park	d		08 03						08 26					08 55							09 17		
Bath Spa 7	a	07 41	08 06			08 11			08 29		08 34		08 41	08 58		09 05		09 11			09 19	09 34	

		AW	GW	GW	GW	GW	GW	AW	AW	GW	GW	XC	GW	GW	GW	GW	GW	AW	AW	AW	GW	GW
		◇ ⊤	◇1 ⊡	◇	◇1 ⊡	◇	◇1 ⊡		◇ ⊤	◇1 C ⊡	◇ ⊤	◇1 ⊤	◇1 ⊡		◇1 ⊡		◇1 ⊡	◇ ⊤			◇1 ⊡	◇ ⊤
Cardiff Central 7	d	08 50			08 55	09 00		09 12	09 21	09 25	09 30	09 45			09 55	10 00		10 05	10 12	10 20	10 25	10 30
Newport (South Wales)	a	09 03			09 09	09 13		09 25	09 34	09 39	09 42	09 58			10 08	10 13		10 17	10 25	10 35	10 39	10 42
	d				09 09	09 15		09 27		09 39	09 44	10 00			10 09	10 15			10 27		10 39	10 44
Severn Tunnel Jn	d					09 26		09 37			09 55					10 26			10 38			
Caldicot	d							09 39											10 40			
Chepstow	d							09 48				10 18							10 49			
Lydney	d							09 57											10 58			
Gloucester 7	a							10 20				10 44							11 20			
Pilning	d																					
Patchway	d					09 39										10 39						
Bristol Parkway 7	a				09 30					09 59					10 30						11 00	
	d			09 20										10 23								
Filton Abbey Wood	d			09 23		09 42					10 09			10 26		10 42						11 09
Bristol Temple Meads 10	a			09 35		09 53					10 19			10 39		10 51						11 18
	d		09 30	09 49			10 00				10 22		10 30	10 49			11 00					11 22
Keynsham	d			09 56										10 56								
Oldfield Park	d			10 03										11 03								
Bath Spa 7	a		09 41	10 06			10 11				10 34		10 41	11 06			11 11					11 34

A The Bristolian

B The Capitals United

C The Red Dragon

When events are being held at the Millenium Stadium, services are subject to alteration. Please check times before travelling.

Table 132R

Mondays to Fridays

9 December to 16 May

Cardiff - Gloucester, Bristol and Bath Spa

Network Diagram - see first Page of Table 132

		XC	AW	GW	GW	GW		GW	GW	AW	GW	GW	XC	GW	GW	GW		GW	SW	AW	AW	GW	GW	GW	XC
															■										
		◇[1]	◇	◇[1]	◇	◇[1]			◇[1]	◇	◇[1]	◇	◇[1]	◇[1]	A	◇[1]			◇[1]	◇		◇[1] B	◇[1]	◇	◇[1]
			trolley	buffet		buffet			buffet	trolley	buffet	trolley	trolley	buffet	trolley	buffet			trolley	trolley		buffet	buffet	trolley	trolley
Cardiff Central [7]	d	10 45	10 50			10 55		11 00		11 21	11 25	11 30	11 45			11 55		12 00		12 05	12 12	12 25		12 30	12 45
Newport (South Wales)	a	10 58	11 02			11 08		11 13		11 34	11 39	11 42	11 59			12 08		12 13		12 17	12 25	12 39		12 42	12 59
	d	11 00				11 09		11 15			11 39	11 44	12 02			12 09		12 15			12 28	12 39		12 44	13 01
Severn Tunnel Jn	d							11 26										12 26			12 39				
Caldicot	d																				12 42				
Chepstow	d												12 18								12 51				13 18
Lydney	d	11 25																			13 00				
Gloucester [7]	a	11 44											12 44								13 20				13 44
Pilning	d																								
Patchway	d							11 39										12 39							
Bristol Parkway [7]	a					11 30					11 59					12 30						12 59			
	d				11 20										12 23										
Filton Abbey Wood	d				11 23			11 42				12 09			12 26			12 42						13 09	
Bristol Temple Meads [10]	a				11 35			11 51				12 19			12 35			12 51						13 19	
	d			11 30	11 49				12 00			12 22		12 30	12 39				12 51				13 00	13 22	
Keynsham	d				11 56										12 46				12 58						
Oldfield Park	d				12 03										12 53										
Bath Spa [7]	a			11 41	12 06				12 12			12 34		12 41	12 55				13 05				13 11	13 34	

		AW		GW	GW	GW	GW	GW	AW	AW	GW	GW		XC	GW	GW	GW	GW	GW	AW	GW	GW		XC	AW
		◇		◇[1]		◇[1]	◇	◇[1]		◇	◇[1]	◇		◇[1]	◇[1]	◇	◇[1]		◇[1]	◇	◇[1]	◇		◇[1]	◇
		trolley		buffet		buffet		buffet	trolley	trolley	⊘	trolley		trolley	buffet		buffet		buffet	trolley	buffet	trolley		trolley	trolley
Cardiff Central [7]	d	12 50				12 55	13 00		13 12	13 21	13 25	13 30		13 45			13 55	14 00		14 05	14 25	14 30		14 45	14 50
Newport (South Wales)	a	13 02				13 08	13 13		13 27	13 34	13 39	13 42		13 58			14 08	14 13		14 17	14 39	14 42		14 59	15 02
	d					13 09	13 15		13 28		13 39	13 44		14 00			14 09	14 15			14 39	14 44		15 01	
Severn Tunnel Jn	d						13 26		13 39									14 26							
Caldicot	d								13 42																
Chepstow	d								13 51															15 18	
Lydney	d								14 00					14 25											
Gloucester [7]	a								14 21					14 44										15 44	
Pilning	d																								
Patchway	d						13 39											14 39							
Bristol Parkway [7]	a					13 30					13 59						14 30				15 00				
	d				13 19											14 23									
Filton Abbey Wood	d				13 23		13 42					14 09				14 26		14 42				15 09			
Bristol Temple Meads [10]	a				13 35		13 52					14 18				14 39		14 51				15 17			
	d			13 30	13 49			14 00				14 22			14 30	14 48			15 00			15 22			
Keynsham	d				13 56											14 55									
Oldfield Park	d				14 03											15 02									
Bath Spa [7]	a			13 41	14 06			14 11				14 34			14 41	15 05			15 11			15 34			

		GW	GW	GW	SW	GW	GW	AW		AW	GW	GW	GW	XC	AW	GW	GW	GW		GW	GW	AW	AW	GW	GW
										■					■								■		
		◇[1]		◇[1]	◇[1]		◇[1] C					◇[1]	◇	◇[1]		◇[1]	◇	◇[1]			◇[1]				◇[1]
		buffet		buffet			buffet			trolley		buffet	trolley	trolley	trolley	buffet		buffet			buffet				buffet
Cardiff Central [7]	d			14 55		15 00		15 12		15 21		15 25	15 30	15 45	15 50			15 55		16 00		16 10	16 21		16 25
Newport (South Wales)	a			15 08		15 13		15 27		15 34		15 39	15 43	15 58	16 02			16 08		16 13		16 25	16 33		16 39
	d			15 09		15 15		15 28				15 39	15 44	16 00				16 09		16 15		16 27			16 39
Severn Tunnel Jn	d					15 26		15 37												16 26		16 38			
Caldicot	d							15 41														16 40			
Chepstow	d							15 50						16 18								16 49			
Lydney	d							15 59														16 58			
Gloucester [7]	a							16 21						16 44								17 20			
Pilning	d																								
Patchway	d					15 39														16 38					
Bristol Parkway [7]	a			15 30								15 59						16 30							16 59
	d		15 20								15 53						16 23							16 46	
Filton Abbey Wood	d		15 23			15 42					15 57		16 09				16 26			16 42				16 50	
Bristol Temple Meads [10]	a		15 36			15 52							16 18				16 38			16 51				17 01	
	d	15 30	15 44		15 51		16 00						16 22			16 30	16 49				17 00			17 05	
Keynsham	d		15 51		15 58						16 11						16 56							17 12	
Oldfield Park	d		15 58								16 19						17 03							17 19	
Bath Spa [7]	a	15 41	16 00		16 05		16 11				16 21		16 34			16 41	17 06				17 11			17 22	

A trolley from Bristol Temple Meads

B The St. David

C The Merchant Venturer

When events are being held at the Millenium Stadium, services are subject to alteration. Please check times before travelling.

Table 132R

Mondays to Fridays

9 December to 16 May

Cardiff - Gloucester, Bristol and Bath Spa

Network Diagram - see first Page of Table 132

		GW	GW	XC	AW	GW	GW	GW	GW	GW		AW	AW	GW	GW	GW	XC	AW	GW	GW		GW	GW	AW	AW BHX
			R		R								R			R		R							R
				◇1		◇1	◇	◇1		◇1			1		◇1		◇1		◇1			◇1			
			[trolley]	[trolley]	[trolley]	[buffet]		[buffet]		[buffet]			⊠		Ø	[trolley]	[trolley]	[trolley]	[buffet]			[buffet]			[trolley]
Cardiff Central 7	d		16 30	16 45	16 50			16 55	17 00			17 12	17 16		17 25	17 30	17 45	17 50				17 55	18 00	18 12	18 21
Newport (South Wales)	a		16 42	16 58	17 02			17 08	17 13			17 25	17 30		17 39	17 42	17 58	18 02				18 08	18 13	18 25	18 33
	d		16 44	17 00				17 09	17 15			17 28			17 39	17 44	18 00					18 09	18 15	18 27	
Severn Tunnel Jn	d		16 55						17 26			17 39				17 55							18 26	18 38	
Caldicot	d											17 41												18 40	
Chepstow	d											17 50					18 18							18 49	
Lydney	d			17 25								17 59												18 58	
Gloucester 7	a			17 44								18 21					18 44							19 20	
Pilning	d																								
Patchway	d								17 39														18 39		
Bristol Parkway 7	a							17 30							17 59							18 30			
	d						17 20							17 48						18 23					
Filton Abbey Wood	d	16 55	17 09				17 23		17 43					17 52		18 09				18 27			18 43		
Bristol Temple Meads 10	a	17 04	17 18				17 36		17 53					18 04		18 18				18 38			18 51		
	d	17 14	17 22			17 30	17 49			18 00				18 07		18 22			18 30	18 52					
Keynsham	d						17 56							18 14						18 59					
Oldfield Park	d	17 26					18 03							18 22						19 06					
Bath Spa 7	a	17 28	17 33			17 41	18 06			18 11				18 24		18 34			18 41	19 09					

		GW	GW	XC	AW	GW		GW	GW	GW	GW	AW	XC	GW	GW	GW		AW	GW	GW	AW	GW	GW	XC	AW
		◇1	◇	◇1	◇	◇1				◇1	◇	◇	◇1	◇1				◇	◇1	◇	◇	◇1		◇1	
		[buffet]	[trolley]	[trolley]	[trolley]	[buffet]				[buffet]				[buffet]					[buffet]			[buffet]			
Cardiff Central 7	d	18 25	18 30	18 45	18 50				19 00	19 25	19 30	19 34	19 50			20 00		20 17	20 25	20 30	20 55		21 00	21 05	21 12
Newport (South Wales)	a	18 39	18 42	18 59	19 03				19 13	19 39	19 42	19 46	20 03			20 13		20 29	20 38	20 44	21 09		21 13	21 18	21 25
	d	18 39	18 44	19 01					19 15	19 39	19 44		20 05			20 15			20 39	20 44			21 15	21 21	21 27
Severn Tunnel Jn	d		18 55						19 26				20 15			20 26							21 25		21 38
Caldicot	d												20 18												21 40
Chepstow	d			19 18									20 26												21 49
Lydney	d												20 35												21 58
Gloucester 7	a			19 44									20 53											22 02	22 21
Pilning	d																								
Patchway	d								19 39							20 39							21 39		
Bristol Parkway 7	a	18 59								19 59									21 01						
	d							19 20																	
Filton Abbey Wood	d		19 09					19 24	19 42		20 09					20 42				21 08			21 42		
Bristol Temple Meads 10	a		19 18					19 35	19 51		20 17					20 53				21 19			21 52		
	d		19 22			19 30		19 49			20 22			20 30	20 49					21 23		21 50	22 04		
Keynsham	d							19 56							20 56								22 11		
Oldfield Park	d							20 03							21 03								22 18		
Bath Spa 7	a		19 34			19 41		20 06			20 34			20 41	21 06					21 36		22 01	22 21		

		GW		GW	SW	XC	GW	XC	AW	GW	GW	GW		AW FO	AW FX	GW
		◇1			1	◇	◇1	◇1	◇							
		[buffet]					[buffet]									
Cardiff Central 7	d	21 25		21 30		21 40		21 50	21 55	22 04		22 35		23 20	23 20	23 27
Newport (South Wales)	a	21 38		21 43		21 55		22 03	22 08	22 16		22 52		23 38	23 39	23 44
	d	21 39		21 43		21 56		22 05		22 18		22 52		23 40	23 40	23 45
Severn Tunnel Jn	d			21 54						22 35		23 10		23 58	23 58	00 03
Caldicot	d													00 01	00 01	
Chepstow	d													00 10	00 10	
Lydney	d													00 19	00 19	
Gloucester 7	a							22 46						00 39	00 39	
Pilning	d															
Patchway	d									22 48						00 16
Bristol Parkway 7	a	21 59														
	d															
Filton Abbey Wood	d			22 09						22 52		23 26				00 20
Bristol Temple Meads 10	a			22 22		22 29				23 05		23 37				00 33
	d				22 23		22 35				23 20					
Keynsham	d										23 27					
Oldfield Park	d										23 34					
Bath Spa 7	a				22 34		22 46				23 37					

When events are being held at the Millenium Stadium, services are subject to alteration. Please check times before travelling.

Table 132R

Saturdays

Cardiff - Gloucester, Bristol and Bath Spa

14 December to 28 December

Network Diagram - see first Page of Table 132

		AW	GW	GW ◇1 🍽	AW	AW ◇		GW ◇	GW ◇1 🍽	AW ◇ 🛒	AW ◇ 🛒	GW ◇1 🍽	AW	GW ◇1 🍽	GW ◇1 🍽	GW		GW ◇1 🍽	GW ◇	XC ◇1	AW ◇ 🛒	GW ◇1 🍽	GW ◇1 🍽	GW	XC ◇1
Cardiff Central [7]	d				00 30	04 35			04 55	05 20	05 40	05 55	06 12	06 25					06 30	06 40	06 50	06 55			07 00
Newport (South Wales)	a				00 43	04 50			05 09	05 33	05 55	06 09	06 25	06 38					06 43	06 53	07 02	07 08			07 13
	d								05 09			06 09	06 28	06 39					06 44	06 55		07 09			07 15
Severn Tunnel Jn	d		00 03										06 39						06 55	07 05					07 25
Caldicot	d	00 01											06 41							07 08					
Chepstow	d	00 10											06 50							07 16					
Lydney	d	00 19											06 59							07 25					
Gloucester [7]	a	00 39											07 20							07 44					
Pilning	d																								
Patchway	d		00 16																						07 37
Bristol Parkway [7]	a								05 36			06 29		06 59								07 29			
	d								05 42																
Filton Abbey Wood	d		00 20																07 09						07 41
Bristol Temple Meads [10]	a		00 33						05 54										07 19						07 51
	d			05 30				05 49	06 00						06 30	06 49		07 00	07 22				07 30	07 49	
Keynsham	d							05 56								06 56								07 56	
Oldfield Park	d							06 03								07 03								08 03	
Bath Spa [7]	a			05 41				06 05	06 11						06 41	07 05		07 11	07 34				07 41	08 05	

		GW ◇1 🍽		AW	AW ◇ 🛒	GW ◇1 🍽	GW ◇	XC ◇1	AW ◇ 🛒	GW ◇1 🍽	GW ◇	GW ◇1 ⊘		SW ◇1	GW	GW ◇1 🍽	GW ◇1 ⊘	GW ◇	XC ◇1	AW ◇ 🛒	GW ◇1 🍽	GW ◇		GW ◇1 🍽	GW
Cardiff Central [7]	d			07 12	07 21	07 25	07 30	07 45	07 50			07 55			08 00		08 25	08 30	08 45	08 50				08 55	09 00
Newport (South Wales)	a			07 25	07 34	07 39	07 42	07 59	08 02			08 08			08 13		08 38	08 42	08 58	09 02				09 08	09 13
	d			07 27		07 39	07 44	08 00				08 09			08 15		08 39	08 44	09 00					09 09	09 15
Severn Tunnel Jn	d			07 38			07 55								08 26			08 55							09 26
Caldicot	d			07 40																					
Chepstow	d			07 49															09 19						
Lydney	d			07 58				08 25																	
Gloucester [7]	a			08 21				08 44											09 46						
Pilning	d														08 32										
Patchway	d														08 39										09 39
Bristol Parkway [7]	a					07 59						08 30					08 59							09 30	
	d										08 20											09 20			
Filton Abbey Wood	d						08 09				08 23				08 42			09 09				09 23			09 42
Bristol Temple Meads [10]	a						08 19				08 34				08 53			09 19				09 36			09 51
	d	08 00					08 22			08 30	08 39			08 51		09 00		09 22			09 30	09 49			
Keynsham	d										08 46			08 58								09 56			
Oldfield Park	d										08 53											10 03			
Bath Spa [7]	a	08 11					08 34			08 41	08 56			09 05		09 11		09 34			09 41	10 05			

		GW ◇1 🍽	AW	AW ◇ 🛒	GW ◇1 🍽	GW ◇ A 🛒	XC ◇1 🛒	AW ◇ 🛒		GW ◇1 🍽	GW	GW	GW ◇1 🍽	AW	AW	GW ◇1 🍽	GW ◇ A 🛒	XC ◇1		AW ◇ 🛒	GW ◇1 🍽	GW ◇	GW	GW ◇1 🍽	AW ◇ 🛒
Cardiff Central [7]	d		09 12	09 21	09 25	09 30	09 45	09 55				10 00		10 12	10 20	10 25	10 30	10 45		10 55			11 00		11 21
Newport (South Wales)	a		09 24	09 34	09 39	09 42	09 58	10 07				10 13		10 25	10 35	10 39	10 42	10 58		11 07			11 13		11 34
	d		09 26		09 39	09 44	10 00					10 15		10 27		10 39	10 44	11 00					11 15		
Severn Tunnel Jn	d		09 36			09 55						10 26		10 38									11 26		
Caldicot	d		09 38											10 40											
Chepstow	d		09 48				10 18							10 49											
Lydney	d		09 56											10 58				11 25							
Gloucester [7]	a		10 19				10 44							11 21				11 44							
Pilning	d																								
Patchway	d											10 39											11 39		
Bristol Parkway [7]	a				09 59											10 59									
	d										10 25											11 21			
Filton Abbey Wood	d					10 09					10 28	10 42					11 09					11 24	11 42		
Bristol Temple Meads [10]	a					10 18					10 39	10 52					11 19					11 35	11 51		
	d	10 00				10 22				10 30	10 49		11 00				11 22				11 30	11 49		12 00	
Keynsham	d										10 56											11 56			
Oldfield Park	d										11 03											12 03			
Bath Spa [7]	a	10 11				10 34				10 41	11 05		11 11				11 34				11 41	12 05		12 11	

A 🛒 from Bristol Temple Meads

When events are being held at the Millenium Stadium, services are subject to alteration. Please check times before travelling.

Table 132R

Saturdays

14 December to 28 December

Cardiff - Gloucester, Bristol and Bath Spa

Network Diagram - see first Page of Table 132

		GW	GW	XC	AW	GW	GW	GW	SW	AW		GW	GW	GW	XC	AW	GW	GW	GW	GW		AW	AW	GW	GW
							R																		
		◇1	◇	◇1	◇	◇1	◇		◇1			◇1	◇1	◇	◇1	◇	◇1			◇1			◇	◇1	◇
			A				B																		
		☕	🛒	🛒	🛒	☕			🛒			☕	☕		🛒	🛒	☕			☕		🛒	🛒	☕	
Cardiff Central 7	d	11 25	11 30	11 45	11 55			12 00		12 12		12 25		12 30	12 45	12 55			13 00			13 12	13 21	13 25	13 30
Newport (South Wales)	a	11 39	11 42	11 58	12 07			12 13		12 25		12 39		12 42	12 59	13 07			13 13			13 26	13 34	13 38	13 42
	d	11 39	11 44	12 00				12 15		12 27		12 39		12 44	13 00				13 15			13 27		13 39	13 44
Severn Tunnel Jn	d							12 26		12 38									13 26			13 37			
Caldicot	d									12 40												13 39			
Chepstow	d			12 18						12 49					13 18							13 48			
Lydney	d									12 58												13 57			
Gloucester 7	a			12 44						13 21					13 44							14 19			
Pilning	d																								
Patchway	d							12 39											13 39						
Bristol Parkway 7	a	11 59										12 59												13 59	
	d						12 25											13 20							
Filton Abbey Wood	d		12 09				12 28	12 42						13 09				13 23	13 42						14 09
Bristol Temple Meads 10	a		12 19				12 39	12 51						13 19				13 34	13 53						14 19
	d		12 22			12 30	12 43		12 51				13 00	13 22			13 30	13 49		14 00					14 22
Keynsham	d						12 50		12 58									13 56							
Oldfield Park	d						12 57											14 03							
Bath Spa 7	a		12 34			12 41	13 00		13 05				13 11	13 34			13 41	14 05		14 11					14 34

		XC	AW	GW	GW	GW		GW	AW	GW	GW	XC	AW	GW	GW	GW		SW	AW	AW	GW	GW	GW	XC	AW
																				R					R
		◇1	◇	◇1	◇			◇1	◇	◇1	◇	◇1	◇	◇1				◇1			◇1	◇1	◇	◇1	
		🛒	🛒	☕				☕	🛒	☕		🛒	🛒	☕						🛒	☕	☕		🛒	🛒
Cardiff Central 7	d	13 45	13 55			14 00			14 18	14 25	14 30	14 45	14 55			15 00			15 12	15 21	15 25		15 30	15 45	15 55
Newport (South Wales)	a	13 58	14 07			14 13			14 34	14 39	14 42	14 58	15 07			15 13			15 25	15 34	15 39		15 42	15 58	16 07
	d	14 00				14 15				14 39	14 44	15 00				15 15			15 27		15 39		15 44	16 00	
Severn Tunnel Jn	d					14 26										15 26			15 37						
Caldicot	d																		15 38						
Chepstow	d											15 18							15 47					16 18	
Lydney	d	14 25																	15 56						
Gloucester 7	a	14 44										15 44							16 19					16 44	
Pilning	d																								
Patchway	d					14 39										15 39									
Bristol Parkway 7	a									14 59											15 59				
	d				14 22										15 20										
Filton Abbey Wood	d				14 25	14 42					15 09				15 23	15 42							16 09		
Bristol Temple Meads 10	a				14 38	14 51					15 19				15 35	15 51							16 19		
	d			14 30	14 49			15 00			15 22			15 30	15 39			15 51				16 00	16 22		
Keynsham	d				14 56										15 46			15 58							
Oldfield Park	d				15 03										15 53										
Bath Spa 7	a			14 41	15 05			15 11			15 34			15 41	15 56			16 05				16 11	16 34		

		GW		GW	GW	GW	AW	AW	GW	GW	XC	AW		GW	GW	GW	GW	AW	AW	GW	GW	XC		AW	GW
										R		R							R					R	
		◇1		◇		◇1			◇1		◇1			◇1	◇		◇1			◇1	◇	◇1			◇1
		☕				☕			☕		🛒	🛒		☕			☕			☕		🛒		🛒	☕
Cardiff Central 7	d				16 00		16 12	16 19	16 25	16 30	16 45	16 55				17 00		17 12	17 21	17 25	17 30	17 45		17 55	
Newport (South Wales)	a				16 13		16 23	16 32	16 39	16 42	16 58	17 07				17 13		17 27	17 33	17 39	17 42	17 58		18 07	
	d				16 15		16 26		16 39	16 44	17 00					17 15		17 27		17 39	17 44	18 00			
Severn Tunnel Jn	d				16 26		16 38			16 55						17 26		17 38			17 55				
Caldicot	d						16 40											17 40							
Chepstow	d						16 49											17 49				18 18			
Lydney	d						16 58				17 25							17 58							
Gloucester 7	a						17 19				17 44							18 20				18 44			
Pilning	d																								
Patchway	d				16 39											17 39									
Bristol Parkway 7	a								16 59											17 59					
	d			16 25											17 20										
Filton Abbey Wood	d			16 28	16 42					17 09					17 24	17 42					18 09				
Bristol Temple Meads 10	a			16 40	16 51					17 19					17 34	17 51					18 19				
	d	16 30		16 49		17 00				17 22				17 30	17 49		18 00				18 22				18 30
Keynsham	d			16 56											17 56										
Oldfield Park	d			17 03											18 03										
Bath Spa 7	a	16 41		17 06		17 11				17 34				17 41	18 06		18 11				18 34				18 41

A 🛒 from Bristol Temple Meads

B R from Bristol Temple Meads ◇ to Bristol Temple Meads

When events are being held at the Millenium Stadium, services are subject to alteration. Please check times before travelling.

Table 132R

Saturdays

14 December to 28 December

Cardiff - Gloucester, Bristol and Bath Spa

Network Diagram - see first Page of Table 132

		GW	GW	AW		GW ◇1 ⊏P	GW ◇	XC ◇1 🚲	AW ◇ 🚲	GW ◇1 ⊏P	GW	GW	GW ◇1 ⊏P	GW ◇		AW ◇	GW ◇1 ⊏P	GW	GW	XC ◇1	AW ◇	GW ◇1 ⊏P	GW ◇	XC ◇1
Cardiff Central 7	d		18 00	18 12		18 25	18 30	18 45	18 50			19 00	19 25	19 30		19 34		19 55		20 00	20 10	20 25	20 30	20 50
Newport (South Wales)	a		18 13	18 25		18 39	18 42	18 59	19 03			19 13	19 39	19 42		19 46		20 08		20 13	20 24	20 39	20 43	21 03
	d		18 15	18 27		18 39	18 44	19 00				19 15	19 39	19 44				20 10		20 15		20 39	20 44	21 05
Severn Tunnel Jn	d		18 26	18 38								19 26						20 21		20 25				
Caldicot	d			18 40																20 28				
Chepstow	d			18 49				19 18												20 36				
Lydney	d			18 58																20 45				
Gloucester 7	a			19 20				19 44												21 04				21 48
Pilning	d																							
Patchway	d		18 39									19 39						20 34						
Bristol Parkway 7	a					18 59							19 59									21 01		
	d	18 25									19 20													
Filton Abbey Wood	d	18 28	18 42				19 09				19 23	19 42		20 09				20 39					21 08	
Bristol Temple Meads 10	a	18 39	18 51				19 19				19 36	19 51		20 19				20 48					21 19	
	d	18 49					19 22			19 30	19 49			20 22			20 33		20 49				21 22	
Keynsham	d	18 56									19 56								20 56					
Oldfield Park	d	19 03									20 03								21 03					
Bath Spa 7	a	19 06					19 34			19 41	20 06			20 34			20 44		21 06				21 34	

		AW ◇	GW ◇1 ⊏P	GW	GW	AW	SW 1	XC	GW ◇1 ⊏P	AW ◇		GW	GW	AW
Cardiff Central 7	d	20 55		21 00		21 12		21 30		21 54		22 00		23 20
Newport (South Wales)	a	21 08		21 13		21 25		21 42		22 10		22 13		23 37
	d			21 15		21 27		21 44				22 16		23 39
Severn Tunnel Jn	d			21 26		21 38						22 35		23 56
Caldicot	d					21 40								23 59
Chepstow	d					21 49								00 08
Lydney	d					21 58								00 17
Gloucester 7	a					22 22								00 38
Pilning	d													
Patchway	d			21 38								22 48		
Bristol Parkway 7	a													
	d													
Filton Abbey Wood	d			21 42								22 52		
Bristol Temple Meads 10	a			21 50				22 24				23 00		
	d		21 47		22 00		22 23		22 30				23 11	
Keynsham	d				22 07								23 18	
Oldfield Park	d				22 14								23 25	
Bath Spa 7	a		22 01		22 17		22 34		22 41				23 27	

Saturdays

4 January to 8 February

		AW	GW	GW ◇1 ⊏P	AW	AW ◇	GW ◇	GW ◇1 ⊏P	AW ◇ 🚲	AW ◇ 🚲		GW ◇1 ⊏P	AW	GW ◇1 ⊏P	GW ◇1 ⊏P	GW	GW ◇1 ⊏P	GW ◇	XC ◇1	AW ◇ 🚲		GW ◇1 ⊏P	GW ◇1 ⊏P	GW	XC ◇1
Cardiff Central 7	d				00 30	04 35		04 55	05 20	05 40		05 55	06 12	06 25				06 30	06 40	06 50		06 55			07 00
Newport (South Wales)	a				00 43	04 50		05 09	05 33	05 55		06 09	06 25	06 38				06 43	06 53	07 02		07 08			07 13
	d							05 09				06 09	06 28	06 39				06 44	06 55			07 09			07 15
Severn Tunnel Jn	d		00 03										06 39					06 55	07 05						07 25
Caldicot	d	00 01											06 41						07 08						
Chepstow	d	00 10											06 50						07 16						
Lydney	d	00 19											06 59						07 25						
Gloucester 7	a	00 39											07 20						07 44						
Pilning	d																								
Patchway	d		00 16																						07 37
Bristol Parkway 7	a							05 36				06 29		06 59								07 29			
	d							05 42																	
Filton Abbey Wood	d		00 20															07 09							07 41
Bristol Temple Meads 10	a		00 33					05 54										07 19							07 51
	d			05 30			05 49	06 00							06 30	06 49	07 00	07 22					07 30	07 49	
Keynsham	d						05 56									06 56								07 56	
Oldfield Park	d						06 03									07 03								08 03	
Bath Spa 7	a			05 41			06 05	06 11							06 41	07 05	07 11	07 34					07 41	08 05	

When events are being held at the Millenium Stadium, services are subject to alteration. Please check times before travelling.

Table 132R

Saturdays

4 January to 8 February

Cardiff - Gloucester, Bristol and Bath Spa

Network Diagram - see first Page of Table 132

		GW		AW	AW	GW	GW	XC	AW	GW	GW	GW		SW	GW	GW	GW	GW	XC	AW	GW	GW		GW	GW
		◇1			◇	◇1	◇	◇1	◇	◇1	◇	◇1		◇1		◇1	◇1	◇	◇1	◇	◇1	◇		◇1	
		🍽			☕	🍽			☕	🍽		Ø				🍽	Ø			☕	🍽			🍽	
Cardiff Central 7	d			07 12	07 21	07 25	07 30	07 45	07 50			07 55			08 00		08 25	08 30	08 45	08 50				08 55	09 00
Newport (South Wales)	a			07 25	07 34	07 39	07 42	07 59	08 02			08 08			08 13		08 38	08 42	08 58	09 02				09 08	09 13
	d			07 27		07 39	07 44	08 00				08 09			08 15		08 39	08 44	09 00					09 09	09 15
Severn Tunnel Jn	d			07 38			07 55								08 26			08 55							09 26
Caldicot	d			07 40																					
Chepstow	d			07 49															09 19						
Lydney	d			07 58				08 25																	
Gloucester 7	a			08 21				08 44											09 46						
Pilning	d														08 32										
Patchway	d														08 39										09 39
Bristol Parkway 7	a					07 59						08 30					08 59							09 30	
	d										08 20											09 20			
Filton Abbey Wood	d						08 09				08 23				08 42			09 09				09 23			09 42
Bristol Temple Meads 10	a						08 19				08 34				08 53			09 19				09 36			09 51
	d	08 00					08 22			08 30	08 39			08 51		09 00		09 22			09 30	09 49			
Keynsham	d										08 46			08 58								09 56			
Oldfield Park	d										08 53											10 03			
Bath Spa 7	a	08 11					08 34			08 41	08 56			09 05		09 11		09 34			09 41	10 05			

		GW	AW	AW	GW	GW	XC	AW		GW	GW	GW	GW	AW	AW	GW	GW	XC		AW	GW	GW	GW	GW	AW
		◇1		◇	◇1	◇	◇1	◇		◇1			◇1			◇1	◇	◇1		◇	◇1	◇		◇1	◇
						A											A								
		🍽		☕	🍽	☕	☕	☕		🍽			🍽			🍽	☕			☕	🍽			🍽	☕
Cardiff Central 7	d		09 12	09 21	09 25	09 30	09 45	09 55				10 00		10 12	10 20	10 25	10 30	10 45		10 55			11 00		11 21
Newport (South Wales)	a		09 24	09 34	09 39	09 42	09 58	10 07				10 13		10 25	10 35	10 39	10 42	10 58		11 07			11 13		11 34
	d		09 26		09 39	09 44	10 00					10 15		10 27		10 39	10 44	11 00					11 15		
Severn Tunnel Jn	d		09 36			09 55						10 26		10 38									11 26		
Caldicot	d		09 38											10 40											
Chepstow	d		09 48				10 18							10 49											
Lydney	d		09 56											10 58				11 25							
Gloucester 7	a		10 19				10 44							11 21				11 44							
Pilning	d																								
Patchway	d											10 39											11 39		
Bristol Parkway 7	a				09 59											10 59									
	d										10 25											11 21			
Filton Abbey Wood	d					10 09					10 28	10 42					11 09					11 24	11 42		
Bristol Temple Meads 10	a					10 18					10 39	10 52					11 19					11 35	11 51		
	d	10 00				10 22				10 30	10 49		11 00				11 22				11 30	11 49		12 00	
Keynsham	d										10 56											11 56			
Oldfield Park	d										11 03											12 03			
Bath Spa 7	a	10 11				10 34				10 41	11 05		11 11				11 34				11 41	12 05		12 11	

		GW	GW	XC		AW	GW	GW	GW	SW	AW	GW	GW	GW		XC	AW	GW	GW	GW	GW	AW	AW	GW	
								■																	
		◇1	◇	◇1		◇	◇1	◇		◇1		◇1	◇1	◇		◇1	◇	◇1			◇1		◇	◇1	
			A					B																	
		🍽	☕	☕		☕	🍽			☕		🍽	🍽			☕	☕	🍽			🍽	☕	☕	🍽	
Cardiff Central 7	d	11 25	11 30	11 45		11 55			12 00		12 12	12 25		12 30		12 45	12 55			13 00		13 12	13 21	13 25	
Newport (South Wales)	a	11 39	11 42	11 58		12 07			12 13		12 25	12 39		12 42		12 59	13 07			13 13		13 26	13 34	13 38	
	d	11 39	11 44	12 00					12 15		12 27	12 39		12 44		13 00				13 15		13 27		13 39	
Severn Tunnel Jn	d								12 26		12 38									13 26		13 37			
Caldicot	d										12 40											13 39			
Chepstow	d			12 18							12 49					13 18						13 48			
Lydney	d										12 58											13 57			
Gloucester 7	a			12 44							13 21					13 44						14 19			
Pilning	d																								
Patchway	d								12 39											13 39					
Bristol Parkway 7	a	11 59										12 59												13 59	
	d							12 25											13 20						
Filton Abbey Wood	d		12 09					12 28	12 42					13 09					13 23	13 42					
Bristol Temple Meads 10	a		12 19					12 39	12 51					13 19					13 34	13 53					
	d		12 22				12 30	12 43		12 51			13 00	13 22				13 30	13 49		14 00				
Keynsham	d							12 50		12 58									13 56						
Oldfield Park	d							12 57											14 03						
Bath Spa 7	a		12 34				12 41	13 00		13 05			13 11	13 34				13 41	14 05		14 11				

A ☕ from Bristol Temple Meads

B ■ from Bristol Temple Meads ◇ to Bristol Temple Meads

When events are being held at the Millenium Stadium, services are subject to alteration. Please check times before travelling.

Table 132R

Saturdays

4 January to 8 February

Cardiff - Gloucester, Bristol and Bath Spa

Network Diagram - see first Page of Table 132

		GW	XC	AW	GW	GW		GW	GW	AW	GW	GW	XC	AW	GW	GW		GW	SW	AW	AW	GW	GW	GW	XC
		◇	◇1 🛒	◇ 🛒	◇1 ☕	◇			◇1 ☕	◇ 🛒	◇1 ☕	◇	◇1 🛒	◇ 🛒	◇1 ☕				◇1		R 🛒	◇1 ☕	◇1 ☕	◇	◇1 🛒
Cardiff Central [7]	d	13 30	13 45	13 55				14 00		14 18	14 25	14 30	14 45	14 55				15 00		15 12	15 21	15 25		15 30	15 45
Newport (South Wales)	a	13 42	13 58	14 07				14 13		14 34	14 39	14 42	14 58	15 07				15 13		15 25	15 34	15 39		15 42	15 58
	d	13 44	14 00					14 15			14 39	14 44	15 00					15 15		15 27		15 39		15 44	16 00
Severn Tunnel Jn	d							14 26										15 26		15 37					
Caldicot	d																			15 38					
Chepstow	d												15 18							15 47					16 18
Lydney	d		14 25																	15 56					
Gloucester [7]	a		14 44										15 44							16 19					16 44
Pilning	d																								
Patchway	d							14 39										15 39							
Bristol Parkway [7]	a										14 59											15 59			
	d					14 22										15 20									
Filton Abbey Wood	d	14 09				14 25		14 42				15 09				15 23		15 42						16 09	
Bristol Temple Meads [10]	a	14 19				14 38		14 51				15 19				15 35		15 51						16 19	
	d	14 22			14 30	14 49			15 00			15 22			15 30	15 39			15 51				16 00	16 22	
Keynsham	d					14 56										15 46			15 58						
Oldfield Park	d					15 03										15 53									
Bath Spa [7]	a	14 34			14 41	15 05			15 11			15 34			15 41	15 56			16 05				16 11	16 34	

		AW		GW	GW	GW	GW	AW	AW	GW	GW	XC		AW	GW	GW	GW	GW	AW	AW	GW	GW		XC	AW
		R 🛒		◇1 ☕	◇		◇1 ☕			◇1 ☕	R	◇1 🛒		R 🛒	◇1 ☕	◇		◇1 ☕		R	◇1 ☕	◇		◇1 🛒	R 🛒
Cardiff Central [7]	d	15 55				16 00		16 12	16 19	16 25	16 30	16 45		16 55			17 00		17 12	17 21	17 25	17 30		17 45	17 55
Newport (South Wales)	a	16 07				16 13		16 23	16 32	16 39	16 42	16 58		17 07			17 13		17 27	17 33	17 39	17 42		17 58	18 07
	d					16 15		16 26		16 39	16 44	17 00					17 15		17 27		17 39	17 44		18 00	
Severn Tunnel Jn	d					16 26		16 38			16 55						17 26		17 38			17 55			
Caldicot	d							16 40											17 40						
Chepstow	d							16 49											17 49					18 18	
Lydney	d							16 58				17 25							17 58						
Gloucester [7]	a							17 19				17 44							18 20					18 44	
Pilning	d																								
Patchway	d					16 39											17 39								
Bristol Parkway [7]	a									16 59											17 59				
	d				16 25											17 20									
Filton Abbey Wood	d				16 28	16 42					17 09					17 24	17 42					18 09			
Bristol Temple Meads [10]	a				16 40	16 51					17 19					17 34	17 51					18 19			
	d			16 30	16 49		17 00				17 22				17 30	17 49		18 00				18 22			
Keynsham	d				16 56											17 56									
Oldfield Park	d				17 03											18 03									
Bath Spa [7]	a			16 41	17 06		17 11				17 34				17 41	18 06		18 11				18 34			

		GW	GW	GW	AW	GW	GW	XC		AW	GW	GW	GW	GW	GW	AW	GW	GW		GW	XC	AW	GW	GW	XC
		◇1 ☕				◇1 ☕	◇	◇1 🛒		◇ 🛒	◇1 ☕			◇1 ☕	◇	◇	◇1 ☕				◇1	◇	◇1 ☕	◇	◇1
Cardiff Central [7]	d			18 00	18 12	18 25	18 30	18 45		18 50			19 00	19 25	19 30	19 34		19 55			20 00	20 10	20 25	20 30	20 50
Newport (South Wales)	a			18 13	18 25	18 39	18 42	18 59		19 03			19 13	19 39	19 42	19 46		20 08			20 13	20 24	20 39	20 43	21 03
	d			18 15	18 27	18 39	18 44	19 00					19 15	19 39	19 44			20 10			20 15		20 39	20 44	21 05
Severn Tunnel Jn	d			18 26	18 38								19 26					20 21			20 25				
Caldicot	d				18 40																20 28				
Chepstow	d				18 49			19 18													20 36				
Lydney	d				18 58																20 45				
Gloucester [7]	a				19 20			19 44													21 04				21 48
Pilning	d																								
Patchway	d			18 39									19 39					20 34							
Bristol Parkway [7]	a					18 59								19 59									21 01		
	d		18 25									19 20													
Filton Abbey Wood	d		18 28	18 42			19 09					19 23	19 42		20 09			20 39						21 08	
Bristol Temple Meads [10]	a		18 39	18 51			19 19					19 36	19 51		20 19			20 48						21 19	
	d	18 30	18 49				19 22				19 30	19 49			20 22		20 33			20 49				21 22	
Keynsham	d		18 56									19 56								20 56					
Oldfield Park	d		19 03									20 03								21 03					
Bath Spa [7]	a	18 41	19 06				19 34				19 41	20 06			20 34		20 44			21 06				21 34	

When events are being held at the Millenium Stadium, services are subject to alteration. Please check times before travelling.

Table 132R

Saturdays

4 January to 8 February

Cardiff - Gloucester, Bristol and Bath Spa

Network Diagram - see first Page of Table 132

		AW	GW	GW	GW	AW	SW	XC	GW	AW	GW	GW	AW
		◇	◇1				1		◇1	◇			
			🍴						🍴				
Cardiff Central 7	d	20 55		21 00		21 12		21 30		21 54	22 00		23 20
Newport (South Wales)	a	21 08		21 13		21 25		21 42		22 10	22 13		23 37
	d			21 15		21 27		21 44			22 16		23 39
Severn Tunnel Jn	d			21 26		21 38					22 35		23 56
Caldicot	d					21 40							23 59
Chepstow	d					21 49							00 08
Lydney	d					21 58							00 17
Gloucester 7	a					22 22							00 38
Pilning	d												
Patchway	d			21 38							22 48		
Bristol Parkway 7	a												
	d												
Filton Abbey Wood	d			21 42							22 52		
Bristol Temple Meads 10	a			21 50				22 24			23 00		
	d		21 47		22 00		22 23		22 30			23 11	
Keynsham	d				22 07							23 18	
Oldfield Park	d				22 14							23 25	
Bath Spa 7	a		22 01		22 17		22 34		22 41			23 27	

Saturdays

15 February to 22 March

		AW	GW	GW	AW	AW	GW	GW	AW	AW	GW	AW	GW	GW	GW	GW	GW	XC	AW	GW	GW	GW	XC
				◇1		◇	◇	◇1	◇	◇	◇1		◇1	◇1		◇1	◇	◇1	◇	◇1	◇1		◇1
				🍴				🍴	🛒	🛒	🍴		🍴	🍴		🍴			🛒	🍴	🍴		
Cardiff Central 7	d				00 30	04 35		04 55	05 20	05 40	05 55	06 12	06 25				06 30	06 40	06 50	06 55			07 00
Newport (South Wales)	a				00 43	04 50		05 09	05 33	05 55	06 09	06 25	06 38				06 43	06 53	07 02	07 08			07 13
	d							05 09			06 09	06 28	06 39				06 44	06 55		07 09			07 15
Severn Tunnel Jn	d		00 03									06 39					06 55	07 05					07 25
Caldicot	d	00 01										06 41						07 08					
Chepstow	d	00 10										06 50						07 16					
Lydney	d	00 19										06 59						07 25					
Gloucester 7	a	00 39										07 20						07 44					
Pilning	d																						
Patchway	d		00 16																				07 37
Bristol Parkway 7	a							05 36			06 29		06 59							07 29			
	d							05 42															
Filton Abbey Wood	d		00 20														07 09						07 41
Bristol Temple Meads 10	a		00 33					05 54									07 19						07 51
	d			05 30			05 49	06 00						06 30	06 49	07 00	07 22				07 30	07 49	
Keynsham	d						05 56								06 56							07 56	
Oldfield Park	d						06 03								07 03							08 03	
Bath Spa 7	a			05 41			06 05	06 11						06 41	07 05	07 11	07 34				07 41	08 05	

		GW	AW	AW	GW	GW	XC	AW	GW	GW	GW	SW	GW	GW	GW	GW	XC	AW	GW	GW	GW	GW	GW
		◇1		◇	◇1	◇	◇1	◇	◇1	◇	◇1	◇1		◇1	◇1	◇	◇1	◇	◇1	◇	◇1		◇1
		🍴		🛒	🍴			🛒	🍴		Ø			🍴	Ø			🛒	🍴		🍴		🍴
Cardiff Central 7	d		07 12	07 21	07 25	07 30	07 45	07 50			07 55		08 00		08 25	08 30	08 45	08 50			08 55	09 00	
Newport (South Wales)	a		07 25	07 34	07 39	07 42	07 59	08 02			08 08		08 13		08 38	08 42	08 58	09 02			09 08	09 13	
	d		07 27		07 39	07 44	08 00				08 09		08 15		08 39	08 44	09 00				09 09	09 15	
Severn Tunnel Jn	d		07 38			07 55							08 26			08 55						09 26	
Caldicot	d		07 40																				
Chepstow	d		07 49														09 19						
Lydney	d		07 58				08 25																
Gloucester 7	a		08 21				08 44										09 46						
Pilning	d												08 32										
Patchway	d												08 39									09 39	
Bristol Parkway 7	a				07 59						08 30				08 59						09 30		
	d									08 20										09 20			
Filton Abbey Wood	d					08 09				08 23			08 42			09 09				09 23		09 42	
Bristol Temple Meads 10	a					08 19				08 34			08 53			09 19				09 36		09 51	
	d	08 00				08 22			08 30	08 39		08 51		09 00		09 22			09 30	09 49			10 00
Keynsham	d									08 46		08 58								09 56			
Oldfield Park	d									08 53										10 03			
Bath Spa 7	a	08 11				08 34			08 41	08 56		09 05		09 11		09 34			09 41	10 05			10 11

When events are being held at the Millenium Stadium, services are subject to alteration. Please check times before travelling.

Table 132R

Saturdays

15 February to 22 March

Cardiff - Gloucester, Bristol and Bath Spa

Network Diagram - see first Page of Table 132

		AW	AW	GW	GW	XC	AW	GW		GW	GW	GW	AW	AW	GW	GW	XC	AW		GW	GW	GW	GW	AW	GW
			◇	◇1	◇	◇1	◇	◇1				◇1			◇1	◇	◇1	◇		◇1	◇		◇1	◇	◇1
					A											A									
			[trolley]	[refreshments]	[trolley]	[trolley]	[trolley]	[refreshments]				[refreshments]			[refreshments]	[trolley]		[trolley]		[refreshments]			[refreshments]	[trolley]	[refreshments]
Cardiff Central 7	d	09 12	09 21	09 25	09 30	09 45	09 55				10 00		10 12	10 20	10 25	10 30	10 45	10 55				11 00		11 21	11 25
Newport (South Wales)	a	09 24	09 34	09 39	09 42	09 58	10 07				10 13		10 25	10 35	10 39	10 42	10 58	11 07				11 13		11 34	11 39
	d	09 26		09 39	09 44	10 00					10 15		10 27		10 39	10 44	11 00					11 15			11 39
Severn Tunnel Jn	d	09 36			09 55						10 26		10 38									11 26			
Caldicot	d	09 38											10 40												
Chepstow	d	09 48				10 18							10 49												
Lydney	d	09 56											10 58				11 25								
Gloucester 7	a	10 19				10 44							11 21				11 44								
Pilning	d																								
Patchway	d										10 39											11 39			
Bristol Parkway 7	a			09 59											10 59										11 59
	d									10 25											11 21				
Filton Abbey Wood	d				10 09					10 28	10 42					11 09					11 24	11 42			
Bristol Temple Meads 10	a				10 18					10 39	10 52					11 19					11 35	11 51			
	d				10 22			10 30		10 49		11 00				11 22				11 30	11 49		12 00		
Keynsham	d									10 56											11 56				
Oldfield Park	d									11 03											12 03				
Bath Spa 7	a				10 34			10 41		11 05		11 11				11 34				11 41	12 05		12 11		

		GW	XC	AW		GW	GW	GW	SW	AW	GW	GW	GW	XC		AW	GW	GW	GW	GW	AW	AW	GW	GW	
							R																		
		◇	◇1	◇		◇1	◇		◇1		◇1	◇1	◇	◇1		◇	◇1			◇1		◇	◇1	◇	
		A					B																		
		[trolley]	[trolley]	[trolley]		[refreshments]			[trolley]		[refreshments]	[refreshments]		[trolley]		[trolley]	[refreshments]			[refreshments]	[trolley]	[trolley]	[refreshments]		
Cardiff Central 7	d	11 30	11 45	11 55				12 00		12 12	12 25		12 30	12 45		12 55			13 00		13 12	13 21	13 25	13 30	
Newport (South Wales)	a	11 42	11 58	12 07				12 13		12 25	12 39		12 42	12 59		13 07			13 13		13 26	13 34	13 38	13 42	
	d	11 44	12 00					12 15		12 27	12 39		12 44	13 00					13 15		13 27		13 39	13 44	
Severn Tunnel Jn	d							12 26		12 38									13 26		13 37				
Caldicot	d									12 40											13 39				
Chepstow	d		12 18							12 49				13 18							13 48				
Lydney	d									12 58											13 57				
Gloucester 7	a		12 44							13 21				13 44							14 19				
Pilning	d																								
Patchway	d							12 39											13 39						
Bristol Parkway 7	a										12 59												13 59		
	d						12 25											13 20							
Filton Abbey Wood	d	12 09					12 28	12 42					13 09					13 23	13 42					14 09	
Bristol Temple Meads 10	a	12 19					12 39	12 51					13 19					13 34	13 53					14 19	
	d	12 22				12 30	12 43		12 51			13 00	13 22				13 30	13 49		14 00				14 22	
Keynsham	d						12 50		12 58									13 56							
Oldfield Park	d						12 57											14 03							
Bath Spa 7	a	12 34				12 41	13 00		13 05			13 11	13 34				13 41	14 05		14 11				14 34	

		XC	AW	GW	GW	GW	GW	AW	GW	GW		XC	AW	GW	GW	GW	SW	AW	AW	GW		GW	GW	XC	AW
																			R						R
		◇1	◇	◇1	◇		◇1	◇	◇1	◇		◇1	◇	◇1			◇1			◇1		◇1	◇	◇1	
		[trolley]	[trolley]	[refreshments]			[refreshments]	[trolley]	[refreshments]			[trolley]	[trolley]	[refreshments]					[trolley]	[refreshments]		[refreshments]		[trolley]	[trolley]
Cardiff Central 7	d	13 45	13 55			14 00		14 18	14 25	14 30		14 45	14 55			15 00		15 12	15 21	15 25			15 30	15 45	15 55
Newport (South Wales)	a	13 58	14 07			14 13		14 34	14 39	14 42		14 58	15 07			15 13		15 25	15 34	15 39			15 42	15 58	16 07
	d	14 00				14 15			14 39	14 44		15 00				15 15		15 27		15 39			15 44	16 00	
Severn Tunnel Jn	d					14 26										15 26		15 37							
Caldicot	d																	15 38							
Chepstow	d											15 18						15 47						16 18	
Lydney	d	14 25																15 56							
Gloucester 7	a	14 44										15 44						16 19						16 44	
Pilning	d																								
Patchway	d					14 39										15 39									
Bristol Parkway 7	a								14 59											15 59					
	d				14 22										15 20										
Filton Abbey Wood	d				14 25	14 42				15 09					15 23	15 42							16 09		
Bristol Temple Meads 10	a				14 38	14 51				15 19					15 35	15 51							16 19		
	d			14 30	14 49		15 00			15 22				15 30	15 39		15 51					16 00	16 22		
Keynsham	d				14 56										15 46		15 58								
Oldfield Park	d				15 03										15 53										
Bath Spa 7	a			14 41	15 05		15 11			15 34				15 41	15 56		16 05					16 11	16 34		

A [trolley] from Bristol Temple Meads

B R from Bristol Temple Meads ◇ to Bristol Temple Meads

When events are being held at the Millenium Stadium, services are subject to alteration. Please check times before travelling.

Table 132R

Saturdays

15 February to 22 March

Cardiff - Gloucester, Bristol and Bath Spa

Network Diagram - see first Page of Table 132

		GW		GW	GW	GW	AW	AW	GW	GW	XC	AW		GW	GW	GW	GW	AW	AW	GW	GW	XC		AW	GW
		◇1 ☕		◇		◇1 ☕			◇1 ☕	R	◇1 🛒	R 🛒		◇1 ☕	◇		◇1 ☕		R	◇1 ☕	◇	◇1 🛒		R 🛒	◇1 ☕
Cardiff Central 7	d				16 00		16 12	16 19	16 25	16 30	16 45	16 55				17 00		17 12	17 21	17 25	17 30	17 45		17 55	
Newport (South Wales)	a				16 13		16 23	16 32	16 39	16 42	16 58	17 07				17 13		17 27	17 33	17 39	17 42	17 58		18 07	
	d				16 15		16 26		16 39	16 44	17 00					17 15		17 27		17 39	17 44	18 00			
Severn Tunnel Jn	d				16 26		16 38			16 55						17 26		17 38			17 55				
Caldicot	d						16 40											17 40							
Chepstow	d						16 49											17 49				18 18			
Lydney	d						16 58				17 25							17 58							
Gloucester 7	a						17 19				17 44							18 20				18 44			
Pilning	d																								
Patchway	d				16 39											17 39									
Bristol Parkway 7	a								16 59											17 59					
	d			16 25											17 20										
Filton Abbey Wood	d			16 28	16 42					17 09					17 24	17 42					18 09				
Bristol Temple Meads 10	a			16 40	16 51					17 19					17 34	17 51					18 19				
	d	16 30		16 49		17 00				17 22				17 30	17 49		18 00				18 22				18 30
Keynsham	d			16 56											17 56										
Oldfield Park	d			17 03											18 03										
Bath Spa 7	a	16 41		17 06		17 11				17 34				17 41	18 06		18 11				18 34				18 41

		GW	GW	AW	GW	GW	XC	AW		GW	GW	GW	GW	GW	AW	GW	GW	GW		XC	AW	GW	GW	XC	AW
					◇1 ☕	◇	◇1 🛒	◇ 🛒		◇1 ☕			◇1 ☕	◇	◇	◇1 ☕				◇1	◇	◇1 ☕	◇	◇1	◇
Cardiff Central 7	d		18 00	18 12	18 25	18 30	18 45	18 50				19 00	19 25	19 30	19 34		19 55			20 00	20 10	20 25	20 30	20 50	20 55
Newport (South Wales)	a		18 13	18 25	18 39	18 42	18 59	19 03				19 13	19 39	19 42	19 46		20 08			20 13	20 24	20 39	20 43	21 03	21 08
	d		18 15	18 27	18 39	18 44	19 00					19 15	19 39	19 44			20 10			20 15		20 39	20 44	21 05	
Severn Tunnel Jn	d		18 26	18 38								19 26					20 21			20 25					
Caldicot	d			18 40																20 28					
Chepstow	d			18 49			19 18													20 36					
Lydney	d			18 58																20 45					
Gloucester 7	a			19 20			19 44													21 04				21 48	
Pilning	d																								
Patchway	d		18 39									19 39					20 34								
Bristol Parkway 7	a				18 59								19 59									21 01			
	d	18 25									19 20														
Filton Abbey Wood	d	18 28	18 42			19 09					19 23	19 42		20 09			20 39						21 08		
Bristol Temple Meads 10	a	18 39	18 51			19 19					19 36	19 51		20 19			20 48						21 19		
	d	18 49				19 22				19 30	19 49			20 22		20 33		20 49					21 22		
Keynsham	d	18 56									19 56							20 56							
Oldfield Park	d	19 03									20 03							21 03							
Bath Spa 7	a	19 06				19 34				19 41	20 06			20 34		20 44		21 06					21 34		

		GW	GW	GW		AW	SW	XC	GW	AW	GW	GW	AW
		◇1 ☕					1		◇1 ☕	◇			
Cardiff Central 7	d		21 00			21 12		21 30		21 54	22 00		23 20
Newport (South Wales)	a		21 13			21 25		21 42		22 10	22 13		23 37
	d		21 15			21 27		21 44			22 16		23 39
Severn Tunnel Jn	d		21 26			21 38					22 35		23 56
Caldicot	d					21 40							23 59
Chepstow	d					21 49							00 08
Lydney	d					21 58							00 17
Gloucester 7	a					22 22							00 38
Pilning	d												
Patchway	d		21 38								22 48		
Bristol Parkway 7	a												
	d												
Filton Abbey Wood	d		21 42								22 52		
Bristol Temple Meads 10	a		21 50					22 24			23 00		
	d	21 47		22 00			22 23		22 30			23 11	
Keynsham	d			22 07								23 18	
Oldfield Park	d			22 14								23 25	
Bath Spa 7	a	22 01		22 17			22 34		22 41			23 27	

When events are being held at the Millenium Stadium, services are subject to alteration. Please check times before travelling.

Table 132R

Saturdays

29 March to 17 May

Cardiff - Gloucester, Bristol and Bath Spa

Network Diagram - see first Page of Table 132

		AW	GW	GW	AW	AW		GW	GW	AW	AW	GW	AW	GW	GW	GW		GW	GW	XC	AW	GW	GW	GW	XC
				◇1		◇		◇	◇1	◇	◇	◇1		◇1	◇1			◇1	◇	◇1	◇	◇1	◇1		◇1
				ꝑ					ꝑ	🚲	🚲	ꝑ		ꝑ	ꝑ			ꝑ			🚲	ꝑ	ꝑ		
Cardiff Central 7	d				00 30	04 35			04 55	05 20	05 40	05 55	06 12	06 25					06 30	06 40	06 50	06 55			07 00
Newport (South Wales)	a				00 43	04 50			05 09	05 33	05 55	06 09	06 25	06 38					06 43	06 53	07 02	07 08			07 13
	d								05 09			06 09	06 28	06 39					06 44	06 55		07 09			07 15
Severn Tunnel Jn	d		00 03										06 39						06 55	07 05					07 25
Caldicot	d	00 01											06 41							07 08					
Chepstow	d	00 10											06 50							07 16					
Lydney	d	00 19											06 59							07 25					
Gloucester 7	a	00 39											07 20							07 44					
Pilning	d																								
Patchway	d		00 16																						07 37
Bristol Parkway 7	a								05 36			06 29		06 59								07 29			
	d								05 42																
Filton Abbey Wood	d		00 20																07 09						07 41
Bristol Temple Meads 10	a		00 33						05 54										07 19						07 51
	d			05 30				05 49	06 00						06 30	06 49		07 00	07 22				07 30	07 49	
Keynsham	d							05 56								06 56								07 56	
Oldfield Park	d							06 03								07 03								08 03	
Bath Spa 7	a			05 41				06 05	06 11						06 41	07 05		07 11	07 34				07 41	08 05	

		GW		AW	AW	GW	GW	XC	AW	GW	GW	GW		SW	GW	GW	GW	GW	XC	AW	GW	GW		GW	GW
		◇1			◇	◇1	◇	◇1	◇	◇1	◇	◇1		◇1		◇1	◇1	◇	◇1	◇	◇1	◇		◇1	
		ꝑ			🚲	ꝑ			🚲	ꝑ		Ø				ꝑ	Ø			🚲	ꝑ			ꝑ	
Cardiff Central 7	d			07 12	07 21	07 25	07 30	07 45	07 50			07 55			08 00		08 25	08 30	08 45	08 50				08 55	09 00
Newport (South Wales)	a			07 25	07 34	07 39	07 42	07 59	08 02			08 08			08 13		08 38	08 42	08 58	09 02				09 08	09 13
	d			07 27		07 39	07 44	08 00				08 09			08 15		08 39	08 44	09 00					09 09	09 15
Severn Tunnel Jn	d			07 38			07 55								08 26			08 55							09 26
Caldicot	d			07 40																					
Chepstow	d			07 49															09 19						
Lydney	d			07 58				08 25																	
Gloucester 7	a			08 21				08 44											09 46						
Pilning	d														08 32										
Patchway	d														08 39										09 39
Bristol Parkway 7	a					07 59						08 30					08 59							09 30	
	d										08 20											09 20			
Filton Abbey Wood	d						08 09				08 23				08 42			09 09				09 23			09 42
Bristol Temple Meads 10	a						08 19				08 34				08 53			09 19				09 36			09 51
	d	08 00					08 22			08 30	08 39			08 51		09 00		09 22			09 30	09 49			
Keynsham	d										08 46			08 58								09 56			
Oldfield Park	d										08 53											10 03			
Bath Spa 7	a	08 11					08 34			08 41	08 56			09 05		09 11		09 34			09 41	10 05			

		GW	AW	AW	GW	GW	XC	AW		GW	GW	GW	GW	AW	AW	GW	GW	XC		AW	GW	GW	GW	GW	AW
		◇1		◇	◇1	◇	◇1	◇		◇1			◇1			◇1	◇	◇1		◇	◇1	◇		◇1	◇
						A											A								
		ꝑ		🚲	ꝑ	🚲	🚲	🚲		ꝑ			ꝑ			ꝑ	🚲			🚲	ꝑ			ꝑ	🚲
Cardiff Central 7	d		09 12	09 21	09 25	09 30	09 45	09 55				10 00		10 12	10 20	10 25	10 30	10 45		10 55			11 00		11 21
Newport (South Wales)	a		09 24	09 34	09 39	09 42	09 58	10 07				10 13		10 25	10 35	10 39	10 42	10 58		11 07			11 13		11 34
	d		09 26		09 39	09 44	10 00					10 15		10 27		10 39	10 44	11 00					11 15		
Severn Tunnel Jn	d		09 36			09 55						10 26		10 38									11 26		
Caldicot	d		09 38											10 40											
Chepstow	d		09 48				10 18							10 49											
Lydney	d		09 56											10 58				11 25							
Gloucester 7	a		10 19				10 44							11 21				11 44							
Pilning	d																								
Patchway	d											10 39											11 39		
Bristol Parkway 7	a				09 59											10 59									
	d										10 25											11 21			
Filton Abbey Wood	d					10 09					10 28	10 42					11 09					11 24	11 42		
Bristol Temple Meads 10	a					10 18					10 39	10 52					11 19					11 35	11 51		
	d	10 00				10 22				10 30	10 49		11 00				11 22				11 30	11 49		12 00	
Keynsham	d										10 56											11 56			
Oldfield Park	d										11 03											12 03			
Bath Spa 7	a	10 11				10 34				10 41	11 05		11 11				11 34				11 41	12 05		12 11	

A 🚲 from Bristol Temple Meads

When events are being held at the Millenium Stadium, services are subject to alteration. Please check times before travelling.

Table 132R

Saturdays

29 March to 17 May

Cardiff - Gloucester, Bristol and Bath Spa

Network Diagram - see first Page of Table 132

		GW	GW	XC	AW	GW	GW	GW	SW	AW		GW	GW	GW	XC	AW	GW	GW	GW	GW		AW	AW	GW	GW
							R																		
		◇1	◇	◇1	◇	◇1	◇		◇1			◇1	◇1	◇	◇1	◇	◇1			◇1			◇	◇1	◇
			A				B																		
		☕	🛒	🛒	🛒	☕			🛒			☕	☕		🛒	🛒	☕			☕		🛒	🛒	☕	
Cardiff Central 7	d	11 25	11 30	11 45	11 55			12 00		12 12		12 25		12 30	12 45	12 55			13 00			13 12	13 21	13 25	13 30
Newport (South Wales)	a	11 39	11 42	11 58	12 07			12 13		12 25		12 39		12 42	12 59	13 07			13 13			13 26	13 34	13 38	13 42
	d	11 39	11 44	12 00				12 15		12 27		12 39		12 44	13 00				13 15			13 27		13 39	13 44
Severn Tunnel Jn	d							12 26		12 38									13 26			13 37			
Caldicot	d									12 40												13 39			
Chepstow	d			12 18						12 49					13 18							13 48			
Lydney	d									12 58												13 57			
Gloucester 7	a			12 44						13 21					13 44							14 19			
Pilning	d																								
Patchway	d							12 39											13 39						
Bristol Parkway 7	a	11 59										12 59												13 59	
	d						12 25											13 20							
Filton Abbey Wood	d		12 09				12 28	12 42						13 09				13 23	13 42						14 09
Bristol Temple Meads 10	a		12 19				12 39	12 51						13 19				13 34	13 53						14 19
	d		12 22			12 30	12 43		12 51				13 00	13 22			13 30	13 49		14 00					14 22
Keynsham	d						12 50		12 58									13 56							
Oldfield Park	d						12 57											14 03							
Bath Spa 7	a		12 34			12 41	13 00		13 05				13 11	13 34			13 41	14 05		14 11					14 34

		XC	AW	GW	GW	GW		GW	AW	GW	GW	XC	AW	GW	GW	GW		SW	AW	AW	GW	GW	GW	XC	AW
																				R					R
		◇1	◇	◇1	◇			◇1	◇	◇1	◇	◇1	◇	◇1				◇1			◇1	◇1	◇	◇1	
		🛒	🛒	☕				☕	🛒	☕		🛒	🛒	☕						🛒	☕	☕		🛒	🛒
Cardiff Central 7	d	13 45	13 55			14 00			14 18	14 25	14 30	14 45	14 55			15 00			15 12	15 21	15 25		15 30	15 45	15 55
Newport (South Wales)	a	13 58	14 07			14 13			14 34	14 39	14 42	14 58	15 07			15 13			15 25	15 34	15 39		15 42	15 58	16 07
	d	14 00				14 15				14 39	14 44	15 00				15 15			15 27		15 39		15 44	16 00	
Severn Tunnel Jn	d					14 26										15 26			15 37						
Caldicot	d																		15 38						
Chepstow	d											15 18							15 47					16 18	
Lydney	d	14 25																	15 56						
Gloucester 7	a	14 44										15 44							16 19					16 44	
Pilning	d																								
Patchway	d					14 39										15 39									
Bristol Parkway 7	a									14 59											15 59				
	d				14 22										15 20										
Filton Abbey Wood	d				14 25	14 42					15 09				15 23	15 42							16 09		
Bristol Temple Meads 10	a				14 38	14 51					15 19				15 35	15 51							16 19		
	d			14 30	14 49			15 00			15 22			15 30	15 39			15 51				16 00	16 22		
Keynsham	d				14 56										15 46			15 58							
Oldfield Park	d				15 03										15 53										
Bath Spa 7	a			14 41	15 05			15 11			15 34			15 41	15 56			16 05				16 11	16 34		

		GW		GW	GW	GW	AW	AW	GW	GW	XC	AW		GW	GW	GW	GW	AW	AW	GW	GW	XC		AW	GW
										R		R							R					R	
		◇1		◇		◇1			◇1		◇1			◇1	◇		◇1			◇1	◇	◇1			◇1
		☕				☕			☕		🛒	🛒		☕			☕			☕		🛒		🛒	☕
Cardiff Central 7	d				16 00		16 12	16 19	16 25	16 30	16 45	16 55				17 00		17 12	17 21	17 25	17 30	17 45		17 55	
Newport (South Wales)	a				16 13		16 23	16 32	16 39	16 42	16 58	17 07				17 13		17 27	17 33	17 39	17 42	17 58		18 07	
	d				16 15		16 26		16 39	16 44	17 00					17 15		17 27		17 39	17 44	18 00			
Severn Tunnel Jn	d				16 26		16 38			16 55						17 26		17 38			17 55				
Caldicot	d						16 40											17 40							
Chepstow	d						16 49											17 49				18 18			
Lydney	d						16 58				17 25							17 58							
Gloucester 7	a						17 19				17 44							18 20				18 44			
Pilning	d																								
Patchway	d				16 39											17 39									
Bristol Parkway 7	a								16 59											17 59					
	d			16 25											17 20										
Filton Abbey Wood	d			16 28	16 42					17 09					17 24	17 42					18 09				
Bristol Temple Meads 10	a			16 40	16 51					17 19					17 34	17 51					18 19				
	d	16 30		16 49		17 00				17 22				17 30	17 49		18 00				18 22				18 30
Keynsham	d			16 56											17 56										
Oldfield Park	d			17 03											18 03										
Bath Spa 7	a	16 41		17 06		17 11				17 34				17 41	18 06		18 11				18 34				18 41

A 🛒 from Bristol Temple Meads

B R from Bristol Temple Meads ◇ to Bristol Temple Meads

When events are being held at the Millenium Stadium, services are subject to alteration. Please check times before travelling.

Table 132R

Saturdays

29 March to 17 May

Cardiff - Gloucester, Bristol and Bath Spa

Network Diagram - see first Page of Table 132

		GW	GW	AW		GW	GW	XC	AW	GW	GW	GW	GW	GW		AW	GW	GW	GW	XC	AW	GW	GW	XC	
						◇■	◇	◇■	◇	◇■			◇■	◇		◇	◇■			◇■	◇	◇■	◇	◇■	
						☕		🛒	🛒	☕			☕				☕					☕			
Cardiff Central [7]	d		18 00	18 12		18 25	18 30	18 45	18 50			19 00	19 25	19 30		19 34		19 55		20 00	20 10	20 25	20 30	20 50	
Newport (South Wales)	a		18 13	18 25		18 39	18 42	18 59	19 03			19 13	19 39	19 42		19 46		20 08		20 13	20 24	20 39	20 43	21 03	
	d		18 15	18 27		18 39	18 44	19 00				19 15	19 39	19 44				20 10		20 15		20 39	20 44	21 05	
Severn Tunnel Jn	d		18 26	18 38								19 26						20 21		20 25					
Caldicot	d			18 40																20 28					
Chepstow	d			18 49				19 18												20 36					
Lydney	d			18 58																20 45					
Gloucester [7]	a			19 20				19 44												21 04				21 48	
Pilning	d																								
Patchway	d		18 39									19 39						20 34							
Bristol Parkway [7]	a					18 59							19 59									21 01			
	d	18 25									19 20														
Filton Abbey Wood	d	18 28	18 42				19 09				19 23	19 42		20 09				20 39					21 08		
Bristol Temple Meads [10]	a	18 39	18 51				19 19				19 36	19 51		20 19				20 48					21 19		
	d	18 49					19 22			19 30	19 49			20 22			20 33		20 49				21 22		
Keynsham	d	18 56									19 56								20 56						
Oldfield Park	d	19 03									20 03								21 03						
Bath Spa [7]	a	19 06					19 34			19 41	20 06			20 34			20 44		21 06				21 34		

		AW	GW	GW	GW	AW	SW	XC	GW	AW		GW	GW	AW
		◇	◇■				■		◇■	◇				
			☕						☕					
Cardiff Central [7]	d	20 55		21 00		21 12		21 30		21 54		22 00		23 20
Newport (South Wales)	a	21 08		21 13		21 25		21 42		22 10		22 13		23 37
	d			21 15		21 27		21 44				22 16		23 39
Severn Tunnel Jn	d			21 26		21 38						22 35		23 56
Caldicot	d					21 40								23 59
Chepstow	d					21 49								00 08
Lydney	d					21 58								00 17
Gloucester [7]	a					22 22								00 38
Pilning	d													
Patchway	d			21 38								22 48		
Bristol Parkway [7]	a													
	d													
Filton Abbey Wood	d			21 42								22 52		
Bristol Temple Meads [10]	a			21 50				22 24				23 00		
	d		21 47		22 00		22 23		22 30				23 11	
Keynsham	d				22 07								23 18	
Oldfield Park	d				22 14								23 25	
Bath Spa [7]	a		22 01		22 17		22 34		22 41				23 27	

Sundays

8 December to 29 December

		AW	GW	GW	GW	GW	GW	AW	GW	GW		GW	AW	GW	GW	GW	AW	AW	XC	GW		GW	GW	GW	AW
																							■		
			◇■	◇■	■	◇■	◇	◇	◇■	◇■		◇	◇	◇■	◇	◇■		◇	◇■	◇■		◇■	◇	◇■	◇
		A																	B				C		
			☕	☕	☕	☕		🛒	☕	☕			🛒	☕		☕		🛒	🛒	☕		☕		☕	🛒
Cardiff Central [7]	d			07 45			08 05	08 30	09 05			09 15	09 20		10 08	10 15	10 23	10 35	10 45				11 08	11 15	11 35
Newport (South Wales)	a			08 01			08 21	08 47	09 18			09 27	09 38		10 20	10 31	10 36	10 48	10 57				11 20	11 31	11 49
	d			08 03			08 23		09 19			09 29			10 22	10 32	10 38		10 59				11 22	11 32	
Severn Tunnel Jn	d						08 41					09 47			10 39		10 56						11 39		
Caldicot	d																10 58								
Chepstow	d	00 08															11 07								
Lydney	d	00 17															11 16								
Gloucester [7]	a	00 38															11 37		11 49						
Pilning	d																								
Patchway	d											10 00													
Bristol Parkway [7]	a			08 31					09 46							10 59								11 59	
	d																								
Filton Abbey Wood	d						08 55					10 03			10 54								11 54		
Bristol Temple Meads [10]	a						09 04					10 15			11 02								12 03		
	d		07 45		08 15	08 45	09 10			09 48		10 15		10 30	11 09					11 30		12 00	12 15		
Keynsham	d						09 17								11 15										
Oldfield Park	d						09 24								11 22										
Bath Spa [7]	a		07 56		08 26	08 57	09 27			09 59		10 27		10 41	11 25					11 41		12 11	12 26		

A not 8 December

B 🛒 from Newport (South Wales)

C ■ from Bristol Temple Meads ◇ to Bristol Temple Meads

When events are being held at the Millenium Stadium, services are subject to alteration. Please check times before travelling.

Table 132R

Sundays

8 December to 29 December

Cardiff - Gloucester, Bristol and Bath Spa

Network Diagram - see first Page of Table 132

		XC		GW	GW	GW	AW	AW	XC	GW	GW	GW		GW	AW	AW	XC	GW	GW	GW	AW	XC		AW	GW
		◇1		R 1 ☕	◇	R 1 ☕		◇ 🛒	◇1 🛒	R 1 ☕		◇		R 1 ☕	R	R 🛒	◇1	◇1 ☕	◇	R 1 ☕		◇1 🛒		R 🛒	R 1 ☕
Cardiff Central 7	d	11 45			12 08	12 15	12 25	12 40	12 45			13 08		13 15	13 22	13 40	13 45		14 08	14 15	14 25	14 45		14 53	
Newport (South Wales)	a	11 57			12 20	12 31	12 39	12 52	12 57			13 20		13 31	13 35	13 52	13 57		14 20	14 31	14 38	14 57		15 05	
	d	11 59			12 21	12 32	12 40		12 59			13 22		13 32			13 59		14 22	14 32	14 40	14 59			
Severn Tunnel Jn	d				12 39		12 58					13 39							14 39		14 59				
Caldicot	d						12 59														15 01				
Chepstow	d						13 08														15 10				
Lydney	d						13 17														15 19				
Gloucester 7	a	12 46					13 36		13 47								14 46				15 40	15 46			
Pilning	d																								
Patchway	d				12 52																				
Bristol Parkway 7	a					12 59								13 59						14 59					
	d																								
Filton Abbey Wood	d				12 56							13 54							14 54						
Bristol Temple Meads 10	a				13 04							14 02							15 03						
	d			12 30	13 10					13 30	13 55	14 15						14 30	15 10						15 30
Keynsham	d				13 17						14 02								15 17						
Oldfield Park	d				13 24						14 10								15 25						
Bath Spa 7	a			12 41	13 27					13 41	14 12	14 27						14 41	15 27						15 41

		GW	SW	GW	GW	AW	XC	AW		GW	GW	GW	GW	AW	GW	GW	GW	AW		XC	GW	GW	GW	AW	GW
		◇1 ☕	◇1	◇	R 1 ☕	R 🛒	◇1 🛒	R 🛒		◇1 ☕	◇1 ☕	◇	R 1 ☕		R 1 ☕	◇	◇	R 🛒		◇1 🛒	◇1 ☕	◇	◇1 ☕	R	◇1 ☕
Cardiff Central 7	d			15 08	15 15	15 22	15 45	15 56				16 08	16 15	16 23		16 35		16 41		16 45		17 08	17 15	17 35	
Newport (South Wales)	a			15 20	15 31	15 35	15 57	16 08				16 20	16 31	16 36		16 47		16 53		16 57		17 20	17 31	17 48	
	d			15 22	15 32		15 59					16 22	16 32	16 38		16 49				16 59		17 22	17 32		
Severn Tunnel Jn	d			15 39								16 32		16 56								17 39			
Caldicot	d													16 58											
Chepstow	d													17 07											
Lydney	d													17 16											
Gloucester 7	a						16 46							17 37						17 46					
Pilning	d																								
Patchway	d			15 52																					
Bristol Parkway 7	a				15 59								16 59										17 59		
	d																								
Filton Abbey Wood	d			15 54								16 46				17 19						17 54			
Bristol Temple Meads 10	a			16 04								16 56				17 27						18 04			
	d	16 00	16 04	16 14						16 30	17 00	17 14			17 30	17 40	17 43				18 00	18 09			18 30
Keynsham	d		16 11									17 21					17 50					18 16			
Oldfield Park	d											17 28					17 58					18 23			
Bath Spa 7	a	16 11	16 18	16 26						16 41	17 11	17 30			17 41	17 52	18 00				18 11	18 26			18 41

		GW	XC	GW		GW	GW	AW	AW	XC	GW	GW	GW	GW		AW	XC	GW	GW	GW	AW	XC	GW	AW	
		◇	◇1 🛒	R 1 ☕		◇1 ☕	◇		R 🛒	◇1 🛒	◇1 ☕	◇1 ☕	◇			◇	◇1	◇1 ☕	◇1 ☕	◇		◇1	◇1 ☕	◇	
Cardiff Central 7	d	17 40	17 45	17 50			18 08	18 23	18 40	18 45	18 50		19 08			19 40	19 45	19 50		20 18	20 23	20 45	20 55	21 04	
Newport (South Wales)	a	17 52	17 57	18 03			18 20	18 36	18 52	18 57	19 03		19 20			19 53	19 58	20 03		20 30	20 36	20 57	21 08	21 17	
	d	17 54	17 59	18 04			18 22	18 38		18 59	19 04		19 22				20 00	20 04		20 31	20 38	20 59	21 09		
Severn Tunnel Jn	d						18 39	18 56					19 39							20 48	20 56				
Caldicot	d							18 58													20 58				
Chepstow	d							19 07													21 07				
Lydney	d							19 16													21 16				
Gloucester 7	a		18 46					19 38		19 47							20 48				21 41	21 47			
Pilning	d																								
Patchway	d						18 52																		
Bristol Parkway 7	a			18 31							19 31							20 31					21 36		
	d																								
Filton Abbey Wood	d	18 23					18 54						19 54							21 02					
Bristol Temple Meads 10	a	18 33					19 06						20 06							21 11					
	d	18 50				19 00	19 10					20 00	20 15	20 49					21 00	21 25					
Keynsham	d						19 17							20 56											
Oldfield Park	d						19 24							21 04											
Bath Spa 7	a	19 02				19 11	19 27					20 11	20 27	21 06					21 11	21 37					

When events are being held at the Millenium Stadium, services are subject to alteration. Please check times before travelling.

Table 132R

Sundays

8 December to 29 December

Cardiff - Gloucester, Bristol and Bath Spa

Network Diagram - see first Page of Table 132

		SW	GW	GW	GW	AW	AW
		[1]	◇[1]				◇
			☕				
Cardiff Central [7]	d				22 00	22 30	23 00
Newport (South Wales)	a				22 17	22 47	23 18
	d				22 19	22 49	
Severn Tunnel Jn	d				22 36	23 06	
Caldicot	d					23 09	
Chepstow	d					23 18	
Lydney	d					23 27	
Gloucester [7]	a					23 48	
Pilning	d						
Patchway	d				22 49		
Bristol Parkway [7]	a						
	d						
Filton Abbey Wood	d				22 52		
Bristol Temple Meads [10]	a				23 00		
	d	21 35	22 10	22 15	23 10		
Keynsham	d			22 22			
Oldfield Park	d			22 30			
Bath Spa [7]	a	21 47	22 22	22 32	23 22		

Sundays

5 January to 9 February

		AW	GW	GW	GW	GW	AW	GW	GW	GW	GW	GW	AW	GW	GW	GW	AW	AW	XC	GW	GW	GW	AW
																					[R]		
				◇[1]	◇[1]	[1]	◇	◇[1]	◇	◇[1]	◇[1]	◇	◇	◇[1]	◇	◇[1]		◇	◇[1]	◇[1]	◇	◇[1]	◇
																			A		B		
			🚌																				
				☕	☕	☕	🛒	☕		☕	☕		🛒	☕		☕		🛒	🛒	☕		☕	🛒
Cardiff Central [7]	d		07 35				08 30			09 00		09 15	09 20		10 08	10 15	10 23	10 35	10 45		11 08	11 15	11 35
Newport (South Wales)	a		07 58				08 47			09 13		09 27	09 38		10 20	10 31	10 36	10 48	10 57		11 20	11 31	11 49
	d			08 08						09 14		09 29			10 22	10 32	10 38		10 59		11 22	11 32	
Severn Tunnel Jn	d			08 29								09 47			10 33		10 56				11 33		
Caldicot	d																10 58						
Chepstow	d	00 08															11 07						
Lydney	d	00 17															11 16						
Gloucester [7]	a	00 38															11 37		11 49				
Pilning	d																						
Patchway	d											10 00											
Bristol Parkway [7]	a			08 41						09 34						10 53						11 53	
	d								08 52														
Filton Abbey Wood	d								08 55			10 03			10 48						11 48		
Bristol Temple Meads [10]	a								09 04			10 15			10 56						11 57		
	d				07 40	08 25		08 40	09 10		09 48	10 15		10 20	11 09					11 20	12 15		
Keynsham	d								09 17						11 15								
Oldfield Park	d								09 24						11 22								
Bath Spa [7]	a				07 51	08 36		08 55	09 27		09 59	10 27		10 32	11 25					11 31	12 26		

		XC	GW	GW	GW	AW	AW	XC	GW	GW	GW	GW	AW	AW	XC	GW	GW	GW	AW	XC	AW	GW	GW
			[R]		[R]				[R]			[R]	[R]	[R]				[R]			[R]	[R]	
		◇[1]	[1]	◇	[1]		◇	◇[1]	[1]		◇	[1]			◇[1]	◇[1]	◇	[1]		◇[1]		[1]	◇[1]
			☕		☕		🛒	🛒	☕			☕		🛒		☕		☕		🛒	🛒	☕	☕
Cardiff Central [7]	d	11 45		12 08	12 15	12 25	12 40	12 45			13 08	13 15	13 22	13 40	13 45		14 08	14 15	14 25	14 45	14 53		
Newport (South Wales)	a	11 57		12 20	12 31	12 39	12 52	12 57			13 20	13 31	13 35	13 52	13 57		14 20	14 31	14 38	14 57	15 05		
	d	11 59		12 21	12 32	12 40		12 59			13 22	13 32			13 59		14 22	14 32	14 40	14 59			
Severn Tunnel Jn	d			12 33		12 58					13 33						14 33		14 59				
Caldicot	d					12 59													15 01				
Chepstow	d					13 08													15 10				
Lydney	d					13 17													15 19				
Gloucester [7]	a	12 46				13 36		13 47							14 46				15 40	15 46			
Pilning	d																						
Patchway	d			12 46																			
Bristol Parkway [7]	a				12 53							13 53						14 53					
	d																						
Filton Abbey Wood	d			12 50							13 48						14 48						
Bristol Temple Meads [10]	a			12 58							13 56						14 59						
	d		12 25	13 10					13 25	13 55	14 15					14 30	15 10					15 20	15 55
Keynsham	d			13 17						14 02							15 17						
Oldfield Park	d			13 24						14 10							15 25						
Bath Spa [7]	a		12 37	13 27					13 37	14 12	14 27					14 41	15 27					15 32	16 06

A 🛒 from Newport (South Wales)

B [R] from Bristol Temple Meads ◇ to Bristol Temple Meads

When events are being held at the Millenium Stadium, services are subject to alteration. Please check times before travelling.

Table 132R

Sundays

5 January to 9 February

Cardiff - Gloucester, Bristol and Bath Spa

Network Diagram - see first Page of Table 132

		SW	GW	GW	AW	XC	AW	GW	GW	GW	GW	AW	GW	GW	GW	AW	XC	GW	GW	GW	AW	GW	GW
		◇1	◇	R 1 🍴	R 🛒	◇1 🛒	R 🛒	◇1 🍴	◇1 🍴	◇	R 1 🍴		R 1 🍴	◇	◇	R 🛒	◇1 🛒	◇1 🍴	◇	◇1 🍴	R	◇1 🍴	◇
Cardiff Central 7	d		15 08	15 15	15 22	15 45	15 56			16 08	16 15	16 23		16 35		16 41	16 45		17 08	17 15	17 35		17 40
Newport (South Wales)	a		15 20	15 31	15 35	15 57	16 08			16 20	16 31	16 36		16 47		16 53	16 57		17 20	17 31	17 48		17 52
	d		15 22	15 32		15 59				16 22	16 32	16 38		16 49			16 59		17 22	17 31			17 54
Severn Tunnel Jn	d		15 32							16 32		16 56							17 36				
Caldicot	d											16 58											
Chepstow	d											17 07											
Lydney	d											17 16											
Gloucester 7	a					16 46						17 37					17 46						
Pilning	d																						
Patchway	d		15 45																				
Bristol Parkway 7	a			15 53							16 53									17 53			
	d																						
Filton Abbey Wood	d		15 47							16 46				17 19					17 51				18 23
Bristol Temple Meads 10	a		15 57							16 56				17 27					18 02				18 33
	d	16 04	16 14					16 30	16 55	17 14			17 25	17 40	17 43			18 00	18 09			18 20	18 50
Keynsham	d	16 11								17 21					17 50				18 16				
Oldfield Park	d									17 28					17 58				18 23				
Bath Spa 7	a	16 18	16 26					16 41	17 06	17 30			17 36	17 52	18 00			18 11	18 26			18 31	19 02

		XC	GW	GW	GW	AW	AW	XC	GW	GW	GW	AW	XC	GW	GW	GW	GW	AW	XC	GW	AW	SW
		◇1 🛒	R 1 🍴	◇1 🍴	◇		R 🛒	◇1 🛒	◇1 🍴	◇1 🍴	◇	◇	◇1	◇1 🍴	◇1 🍴		◇		◇1	◇1 🍴	◇	1
Cardiff Central 7	d	17 45	17 50		18 08	18 23	18 40	18 45	18 50		19 08	19 40	19 45	19 50			20 18	20 23	20 45	20 55	21 04	
Newport (South Wales)	a	17 57	18 03		18 20	18 36	18 52	18 57	19 03		19 20	19 53	19 58	20 03			20 30	20 36	20 57	21 08	21 17	
	d	17 59	18 04		18 22	18 38		18 59	19 04		19 22		20 00	20 04			20 31	20 38	20 59	21 09		
Severn Tunnel Jn	d				18 39	18 56					19 39						20 48	20 56				
Caldicot	d					18 58												20 58				
Chepstow	d					19 07												21 07				
Lydney	d					19 16												21 16				
Gloucester 7	a	18 46				19 38		19 47					20 48					21 41	21 47			
Pilning	d																					
Patchway	d				18 52																	
Bristol Parkway 7	a		18 27						19 31					20 31						21 36		
	d																					
Filton Abbey Wood	d				18 54						19 54						21 02					
Bristol Temple Meads 10	a				19 06						20 06						21 11					
	d			19 00	19 10					19 55	20 15				20 55	21 00	21 25					21 35
Keynsham	d				19 17											21 07						
Oldfield Park	d				19 24											21 15						
Bath Spa 7	a			19 12	19 27					20 07	20 27				21 06	21 17	21 37					21 47

		GW	GW	GW	AW	AW
		◇1 🍴				◇
Cardiff Central 7	d			22 00	22 30	23 00
Newport (South Wales)	a			22 17	22 47	23 18
	d			22 19	22 49	
Severn Tunnel Jn	d			22 36	23 06	
Caldicot	d				23 09	
Chepstow	d				23 18	
Lydney	d				23 27	
Gloucester 7	a				23 48	
Pilning	d					
Patchway	d			22 49		
Bristol Parkway 7	a					
	d					
Filton Abbey Wood	d			22 52		
Bristol Temple Meads 10	a			23 00		
	d	22 10	22 15	23 10		
Keynsham	d		22 22			
Oldfield Park	d		22 30			
Bath Spa 7	a	22 22	22 32	23 22		

When events are being held at the Millenium Stadium, services are subject to alteration. Please check times before travelling.

Table 132R

Sundays

16 February to 23 March

Cardiff - Gloucester, Bristol and Bath Spa

Network Diagram - see first Page of Table 132

		AW	GW	GW	GW	GW		GW	AW	GW	GW	GW	AW	GW	GW	GW		AW	AW	XC	GW	GW	GW	GW	AW
																							R		
			◇1	◇1	1	◇1		◇	◇	◇1	◇1	◇	◇	◇1	◇	◇1			◇	◇1	◇1	◇1	◇	◇1	◇
																				A			B		
			☕	☕	☕	☕			🛒	☕	☕		🛒	☕		☕			🛒	🛒	☕	☕		☕	🛒
Cardiff Central 7	d			07 45				08 05	08 30	08 55		09 13	09 20		10 08	10 15		10 23	10 35	10 45			11 08	11 15	11 35
Newport (South Wales)	a			08 01				08 21	08 47	09 08		09 25	09 38		10 20	10 31		10 36	10 48	10 57			11 20	11 31	11 49
	d			08 03				08 23		09 10		09 27			10 22	10 32		10 38		10 59			11 22	11 32	
Severn Tunnel Jn	d							08 41				09 45			10 39			10 56					11 39		
Caldicot	d																	10 58							
Chepstow	d	00 08																11 07							
Lydney	d	00 17																11 16							
Gloucester 7	a	00 38																11 37		11 49					
Pilning	d																								
Patchway	d											09 58													
Bristol Parkway 7	a			08 31						09 37						10 59								11 59	
	d																								
Filton Abbey Wood	d							08 55				10 01			10 54								11 54		
Bristol Temple Meads 10	a							09 04				10 11			11 02								12 03		
	d		07 40		08 15	08 45		09 10			09 48	10 13		10 20	11 09						11 20	12 00	12 15		
Keynsham	d							09 17							11 15										
Oldfield Park	d							09 24							11 22										
Bath Spa 7	a		07 51		08 26	08 57		09 27			09 59	10 23		10 31	11 25						11 31	12 11	12 26		

		XC		GW	GW	GW	AW	AW	XC	GW	GW	GW		GW	AW	AW	XC	GW	GW	GW	AW	XC		AW	GW
						R				R				R	R	R				R				R	R
		◇1		◇1	◇	1		◇	◇1	1		◇		1			◇1	◇1	◇	1		◇1			1
				☕		☕		🛒	🛒	☕				☕		🛒		☕		☕		🛒		🛒	☕
Cardiff Central 7	d	11 45			12 08	12 15	12 25	12 40	12 45			13 08		13 15	13 22	13 40	13 45		14 08	14 15	14 25	14 45		14 53	
Newport (South Wales)	a	11 57			12 20	12 31	12 39	12 52	12 57			13 20		13 31	13 35	13 52	13 57		14 20	14 31	14 38	14 57		15 05	
	d	11 59			12 21	12 32	12 40		12 59			13 22		13 32			13 59		14 22	14 32	14 40	14 59			
Severn Tunnel Jn	d				12 39		12 58					13 39							14 39		14 59				
Caldicot	d						12 59														15 01				
Chepstow	d						13 08														15 10				
Lydney	d						13 17														15 19				
Gloucester 7	a	12 46					13 36		13 47								14 46				15 40	15 46			
Pilning	d																								
Patchway	d				12 52																				
Bristol Parkway 7	a					12 59								13 59						14 59					
	d																								
Filton Abbey Wood	d				12 56							13 54							14 54						
Bristol Temple Meads 10	a				13 04							14 02							15 03						
	d			12 25	13 10					13 25	13 55	14 15						14 25	15 10						15 24
Keynsham	d				13 17						14 02								15 17						
Oldfield Park	d				13 24						14 10								15 25						
Bath Spa 7	a			12 37	13 27					13 36	14 12	14 27						14 36	15 27						15 35

		GW	SW	GW	GW	AW	XC	AW		GW	GW	GW	GW	AW	GW	GW	GW	AW		XC	GW	GW	GW	AW	GW
					R	R		R					R					R						R	
		◇1	◇1	◇	1		◇1			◇1	◇1	◇	1		◇1	◇	◇			◇1	◇1	◇	◇1		◇1
		☕			☕	🛒	🛒	🛒		☕	☕		☕		☕			🛒		🛒	☕		☕		☕
Cardiff Central 7	d			15 08	15 15	15 22	15 45	15 56				16 08	16 15	16 23		16 35		16 41		16 45		17 08	17 15	17 35	
Newport (South Wales)	a			15 20	15 31	15 35	15 57	16 08				16 20	16 31	16 36		16 47		16 53		16 57		17 20	17 31	17 48	
	d			15 22	15 32		15 59					16 22	16 32	16 38		16 49				16 59		17 22	17 32		
Severn Tunnel Jn	d			15 39								16 38		16 56								17 39			
Caldicot	d													16 58											
Chepstow	d													17 07											
Lydney	d													17 16											
Gloucester 7	a						16 46							17 37						17 46					
Pilning	d																								
Patchway	d			15 52																					
Bristol Parkway 7	a				15 59								16 59										17 59		
	d																								
Filton Abbey Wood	d			15 54								16 53				17 19						17 54			
Bristol Temple Meads 10	a			16 04								17 03				17 27						18 04			
	d	16 00	16 04	16 14						16 20	16 55	17 14			17 25	17 40	17 43				18 00	18 09			18 20
Keynsham	d		16 11									17 21					17 50					18 16			
Oldfield Park	d											17 28					17 58					18 23			
Bath Spa 7	a	16 11	16 18	16 26						16 31	17 06	17 30			17 36	17 52	18 00				18 11	18 26			18 31

A 🛒 from Newport (South Wales)

B R from Bristol Temple Meads ◇ to Bristol Temple Meads

When events are being held at the Millenium Stadium, services are subject to alteration. Please check times before travelling.

Table 132R

Sundays

16 February to 23 March

Cardiff - Gloucester, Bristol and Bath Spa

Network Diagram - see first Page of Table 132

		GW	XC	GW	GW	GW	AW	AW	XC	GW	GW	GW	GW	AW	XC	GW	GW	GW	AW	XC	GW	AW	SW
						R		R															
		◇	◇1	◇1	◇	1			◇1	◇1	◇1	◇		◇	◇1	◇1	◇1	◇		◇1	◇1	◇	1
			🛒	☕		☕		🛒	🛒	☕	☕					☕	☕				☕		
Cardiff Central 7	d	17 40	17 45		18 08	18 15	18 23	18 40	18 45	18 50		19 08		19 40	19 45	19 50		20 18	20 23	20 45	20 55	21 04	
Newport (South Wales)	a	17 52	17 57		18 20	18 31	18 36	18 52	18 57	19 03		19 20		19 53	19 58	20 03		20 30	20 36	20 57	21 08	21 17	
	d	17 54	17 59		18 22	18 32	18 38		18 59	19 04		19 22			20 00	20 04		20 31	20 38	20 59	21 09		
Severn Tunnel Jn	d				18 39		18 56					19 39						20 48	20 56				
Caldicot	d						18 58												20 58				
Chepstow	d						19 07												21 07				
Lydney	d						19 16												21 16				
Gloucester 7	a		18 46				19 38		19 47						20 48				21 41	21 47			
Pilning	d																						
Patchway	d				18 52																		
Bristol Parkway 7	a					18 59				19 31						20 31					21 36		
	d																						
Filton Abbey Wood	d	18 23			18 54							19 54						21 02					
Bristol Temple Meads 10	a	18 33			19 06							20 06						21 11					
	d	18 50		19 00	19 10						20 00	20 15	20 49				21 00	21 21					21 35
Keynsham	d				19 17								20 56										
Oldfield Park	d				19 24								21 04										
Bath Spa 7	a	19 02		19 11	19 27						20 11	20 27	21 06				21 11	21 33					21 47

		GW	GW	GW	AW	AW
		◇1				◇
		☕				
Cardiff Central 7	d			22 00	22 30	23 00
Newport (South Wales)	a			22 17	22 47	23 18
	d			22 19	22 49	
Severn Tunnel Jn	d			22 36	23 06	
Caldicot	d				23 09	
Chepstow	d				23 18	
Lydney	d				23 27	
Gloucester 7	a				23 48	
Pilning	d					
Patchway	d			22 49		
Bristol Parkway 7	a					
	d					
Filton Abbey Wood	d			22 52		
Bristol Temple Meads 10	a			23 00		
	d	22 10	22 15	23 10		
Keynsham	d		22 22			
Oldfield Park	d		22 30			
Bath Spa 7	a	22 22	22 32	23 22		

Sundays

30 March to 11 May

		AW	GW	GW	GW	GW	GW	AW	GW	GW	GW	AW	GW	GW	GW	AW	AW	XC	GW	GW	GW	GW	AW
																					R		
			◇1	◇1	1	◇1	◇	◇	◇1	◇1	◇	◇	◇1	◇	◇1		◇	◇1	◇1	◇1	◇	◇1	◇
																		A			B		
			☕	☕	☕	☕		🛒	☕	☕		🛒	☕		☕		🛒	🛒	☕	☕		☕	🛒
Cardiff Central 7	d			07 45			08 05	08 30	08 55		09 13	09 20		10 08	10 15	10 23	10 35	10 45			11 08	11 15	11 35
Newport (South Wales)	a			08 01			08 21	08 47	09 08		09 25	09 38		10 20	10 31	10 36	10 48	10 57			11 20	11 31	11 49
	d			08 03			08 23		09 10		09 27			10 22	10 32	10 38		10 59			11 22	11 32	
Severn Tunnel Jn	d						08 41				09 45			10 39		10 56					11 39		
Caldicot	d															10 58							
Chepstow	d	00 08														11 07							
Lydney	d	00 17														11 16							
Gloucester 7	a	00 38														11 37		11 49					
Pilning	d																						
Patchway	d										09 58												
Bristol Parkway 7	a			08 32					09 37						10 56							11 56	
	d																						
Filton Abbey Wood	d						08 55				10 01			10 54							11 54		
Bristol Temple Meads 10	a						09 04				10 13			11 02							12 03		
	d		07 40		08 15	08 45	09 10			09 48	10 13		10 20	11 09					11 20	12 00	12 15		
Keynsham	d						09 17							11 15									
Oldfield Park	d						09 24							11 22									
Bath Spa 7	a		07 51		08 26	08 57	09 27			09 59	10 23		10 31	11 25					11 31	12 11	12 26		

A 🛒 from Newport (South Wales)

B R from Bristol Temple Meads ◇ to Bristol Temple Meads

When events are being held at the Millenium Stadium, services are subject to alteration. Please check times before travelling.

Table 132R

Sundays

30 March to 11 May

Cardiff - Gloucester, Bristol and Bath Spa

Network Diagram - see first Page of Table 132

		XC		GW	GW	GW	AW	AW	XC	GW	GW	GW		GW	AW	AW	XC	GW	GW	GW	AW	XC		AW	GW
		◇1		R 1 ☕	◇	R 1 ☕		◇ 🛒	◇1 🛒	R 1 ☕		◇		R 1 ☕	R	R 🛒	◇1	◇1 ☕	◇	R 1 ☕		◇1 🛒		R 🛒	R 1 ☕
Cardiff Central 7	d	11 45			12 08	12 15	12 25	12 40	12 45			13 08		13 15	13 22	13 40	13 45		14 08	14 15	14 25	14 45		14 53	
Newport (South Wales)	a	11 57			12 20	12 31	12 39	12 52	12 57			13 20		13 31	13 35	13 52	13 57		14 20	14 31	14 38	14 57		15 05	
	d	11 59			12 21	12 32	12 40		12 59			13 22		13 32			13 59		14 22	14 32	14 40	14 59			
Severn Tunnel Jn	d				12 33		12 58					13 33							14 33		14 59				
Caldicot	d						12 59														15 01				
Chepstow	d						13 08														15 10				
Lydney	d						13 17														15 19				
Gloucester 7	a	12 46					13 36		13 47								14 46				15 40	15 46			
Pilning	d																								
Patchway	d				12 46																				
Bristol Parkway 7	a					12 56								13 56						14 56					
	d																								
Filton Abbey Wood	d				12 50							13 48							14 50						
Bristol Temple Meads 10	a				12 58							13 56							14 59						
	d			12 25	13 10					13 25	13 55	14 15						14 25	15 10						15 23
Keynsham	d				13 17						14 02								15 17						
Oldfield Park	d				13 24						14 10								15 25						
Bath Spa 7	a			12 37	13 27					13 36	14 12	14 27						14 36	15 27						15 34

		GW	SW	GW	GW	AW	XC	AW		GW	GW	GW	GW	AW	GW	GW	GW	AW		XC	GW	GW	GW	AW	GW
		◇1 ☕	◇1	◇	R 1 ☕	R 🛒	◇1 🛒	R 🛒		◇1 ☕	◇1 ☕	◇	R 1 ☕		R 1 ☕	◇	◇	R 🛒		◇1 🛒	◇1 ☕	◇	◇1 ☕	R	◇1 ☕
Cardiff Central 7	d			15 08	15 15	15 22	15 45	15 56				16 08	16 15	16 23		16 35		16 41		16 45		17 08	17 15	17 35	
Newport (South Wales)	a			15 20	15 31	15 35	15 57	16 08				16 20	16 31	16 36		16 47		16 53		16 57		17 20	17 31	17 48	
	d			15 22	15 32		15 59					16 22	16 32	16 38		16 49				16 59		17 22	17 32		
Severn Tunnel Jn	d			15 32								16 38		16 56								17 36			
Caldicot	d													16 58											
Chepstow	d													17 07											
Lydney	d													17 16											
Gloucester 7	a						16 46							17 37						17 46					
Pilning	d																								
Patchway	d			15 45																					
Bristol Parkway 7	a				15 56								16 55										17 55		
	d																								
Filton Abbey Wood	d			15 47								16 53				17 19						17 51			
Bristol Temple Meads 10	a			15 57								17 02				17 27						18 02			
	d	16 00	16 04	16 14						16 20	17 00	17 14			17 25	17 40	17 43				18 00	18 09			18 20
Keynsham	d		16 11									17 21					17 50					18 16			
Oldfield Park	d											17 28					17 58					18 23			
Bath Spa 7	a	16 11	16 18	16 26						16 31	17 11	17 30			17 36	17 52	18 00				18 11	18 26			18 31

		GW	XC	GW		GW	GW	AW	AW	XC	GW	GW	GW	GW		AW	XC	GW	GW	GW	AW	XC	GW	AW	
		◇	◇1 🛒	◇1 ☕		◇	R 1 ☕		R 🛒	◇1 🛒	◇1 ☕	◇1 ☕	◇			◇	◇1	◇1 ☕	◇1 ☕	◇		◇1	◇1 ☕	◇	
Cardiff Central 7	d	17 40	17 45			18 08	18 15	18 23	18 40	18 45	18 50		19 08			19 40	19 45	19 50		20 18	20 23	20 45	20 55	21 04	
Newport (South Wales)	a	17 52	17 57			18 20	18 31	18 36	18 52	18 57	19 03		19 20			19 53	19 58	20 03		20 30	20 36	20 57	21 08	21 17	
	d	17 54	17 59			18 22	18 32	18 38		18 59	19 04		19 22				20 00	20 04		20 31	20 38	20 59	21 09		
Severn Tunnel Jn	d					18 39		18 56					19 39							20 48	20 56				
Caldicot	d							18 58													20 58				
Chepstow	d							19 07													21 07				
Lydney	d							19 16													21 16				
Gloucester 7	a		18 46					19 38		19 47							20 48				21 41	21 47			
Pilning	d																								
Patchway	d					18 52																			
Bristol Parkway 7	a						18 55				19 24							20 25					21 36		
	d																								
Filton Abbey Wood	d	18 23				18 54							19 54							21 02					
Bristol Temple Meads 10	a	18 33				19 06							20 06							21 11					
	d	18 50		19 00		19 10						20 00	20 15	20 49					21 00	21 25					
Keynsham	d					19 17								20 56											
Oldfield Park	d					19 24								21 04											
Bath Spa 7	a	19 02		19 11		19 27						20 11	20 27	21 06					21 11	21 37					

When events are being held at the Millenium Stadium, services are subject to alteration. Please check times before travelling.

Table 132R

Sundays

30 March to 11 May

Cardiff - Gloucester, Bristol and Bath Spa

Network Diagram - see first Page of Table 132

		SW	GW	GW		GW	AW	AW
		1	◇1					◇
Cardiff Central 7	d					22 00	22 30	23 00
Newport (South Wales)	a					22 17	22 47	23 18
	d					22 19	22 49	
Severn Tunnel Jn	d					22 36	23 06	
Caldicot	d						23 09	
Chepstow	d						23 18	
Lydney	d						23 27	
Gloucester 7	a						23 48	
Pilning	d							
Patchway	d					22 49		
Bristol Parkway 7	a							
	d							
Filton Abbey Wood	d					22 52		
Bristol Temple Meads 10	a					23 00		
	d	21 35	22 10	22 15		23 10		
Keynsham	d			22 22				
Oldfield Park	d			22 30				
Bath Spa 7	a	21 47	22 22	22 32		23 22		

When events are being held at the Millenium Stadium, services are subject to alteration. Please check times before travelling.

Table 133

Bristol - Avonmouth and Severn Beach

Mondays to Fridays

9 December to 16 May

Network Diagram - see first Page of Table 132

Miles			GW	GW	GW	GW	GW	GW	GW	GW	GW	GW ◇	GW	GW	GW ◇	GW	GW	GW	GW	GW	GW	GW	GW
0	**Bristol Temple Meads [10]**	d	05 24	05 48	06 19	06 30	06 50	07 04	07 19	07 47	08 03	08 10	08 36	08 44	09 10	09 16	09 48	10 03	10 34	10 45	11 16	11 44	12 03
1	Lawrence Hill	d	05 27		06 22	06 33	06 53	07 07	07 22	07 50	08 06	08 13	08 39	08 47	09 13	09 19	09 51		10 37	10 49	11 19	11 47	
1½	Stapleton Road	d	05 29	05 51	06a24	06 35	06a55	07 09	07a24	07a52	08 08	08a15	08 41	08a49	09a15	09 21	09a53	10 07	10 39	10a51	11 21	11a49	12 07
2¾	Montpelier	d	05 32	05 55		06 39		07 12			08 11		08 45			09 24		10 10	10 42		11 24		12 10
3¼	Redland	d	05 34	05 57		06 41		07 14			08 13		08 47			09 26		10 12	10 44		11 26		12 12
4	Clifton Down	d	05 37	06 00		06 44		07 17			08 17		08 52			09 29		10 17	10 48		11 29		12 17
6	Sea Mills	d	05 41	06 04		06 48		07 21			08 21		08 56			09 33		10 21	10 52		11 33		12 21
7¼	Shirehampton	d	05 45	06 07		06 52		07 24			08 25		08 59			09 37		10 25	10 56		11 37		12 25
9	Avonmouth [2]	d	05 49	06a14		06 56		07 30			08a31		09a06			09 40		10a31	11a02		11 40		12a31
10	St Andrews Road	d	05x52			06x59		07x33								09x44					11x44		
13½	**Severn Beach**	a	06 01			07 07		07 41								09 53					11 53		

		GW	GW	GW	GW	GW	GW	GW	GW	GW	GW	GW	GW	GW	GW	GW	GW	GW	GW	GW	GW	GW
Bristol Temple Meads [10]	d	12 34	12 45	13 16	13 46	14 03	14 34	14 45	15 16	15 45	16 03	16 15	16 35	16 44	17 10	17 16	17 46	18 03	18 21	18 48	19 21	19 33	19 45
Lawrence Hill	d	12 37	12 47	13 19	13 47		14 37	14 47	15 19	15 47	16 06	16 18	16 37	16 47	17 13	17 19	17 47	18 06	18 24	18 51	19 24	19 36	19 47
Stapleton Road	d	12 39	12a50	13 21	13a50	14 07	14 39	14a49	15 21	15a50	16 07	16a20	16 39	16a49	17a15	17 21	17a49	18 07	18a26	18 53	19a26	19 38	19a50
Montpelier	d	12 42		13 24		14 10	14 42		15 24		16 10		16 42			17 24		18 10		18 57		19 41	
Redland	d	12 44		13 26		14 12	14 44		15 26		16 12		16 44			17 26		18 12		18 59		19 43	
Clifton Down	d	12 48		13 29		14 17	14 48		15 29		16 17		16 48			17 29		18 17		19 08		19 46	
Sea Mills	d	12 52		13 33		14 21	14 52		15 33		16 21		16 52			17 33		18 21		19 12		19 50	
Shirehampton	d	12 56		13 37		14 25	14 56		15 37		16 25		16 56			17 37		18 25		19 16		19 54	
Avonmouth [2]	d	13a02		13 40		14a31	15a02		15 40		16a30		17a02			17 40		18 29		19a22		20a00	
St Andrews Road	d			13x44					15x44							17x44		18x32					
Severn Beach	a			13 53					15 53							17 53		18 40					

		GW	GW	GW	GW
Bristol Temple Meads [10]	d	20 34	21 19	21 37	22 16
Lawrence Hill	d	20 37	21 22	21 40	22 19
Stapleton Road	d	20 39	21a24	21 42	22 21
Montpelier	d	20 42		21 45	22 24
Redland	d	20 44		21 47	22 26
Clifton Down	d	20 48		21 52	22 29
Sea Mills	d	20 52		21 56	22 33
Shirehampton	d	20 56		21 59	22 37
Avonmouth [2]	d	20 59		22a05	22 40
St Andrews Road	d	21x02			22x44
Severn Beach	a	21 11			22 53

Saturdays

14 December to 17 May

		GW	GW	GW	GW	GW	GW	GW (bus)	GW	GW	GW	GW	GW	GW	GW	GW (bus)	GW	GW	GW	GW	GW	GW	GW
Bristol Temple Meads [10]	d	06 03	06 34	06 50	07 16	07 47	08 03		08 20	08 34	08 45	09 16	09 21	09 45	10 03		10 21	10 34	10 45	11 16	11 21	11 45	12 03
Lawrence Hill	d		06 37	06 53	07 19	07 50	08 06		08 23	08 37	08 48	09 19		09 48				10 37	10 48	11 19		11 48	
Stapleton Road	d	06 07	06 39	06a55	07 21	07a52	08 07		08a25	08 39	08a50	09 21	09a24	09a50	10 07		10a24	10 39	10a50	11 21	11a24	11a50	12 07
Montpelier	d	06 10	06 42		07 24		08 10			08 42		09 24			10 10			10 42		11 24			12 10
Redland	d	06 12	06 44		07 26		08 12			08 44		09 26			10 12			10 44		11 26			12 12
Clifton Down	d	06 17	06 48		07 29		08 17			08 48		09 29			10 17			10 48		11 29			12 17
Sea Mills	d	06 21	06 52		07 33		08 21			08 52		09 33			10 21			10 52		11 33			12 21
Shirehampton	d	06 25	06 56		07 37		08 25			08 56		09 37			10 25			10 56		11 37			12 25
Avonmouth [2]	d	06a31	07a02		07 40		08a31	08 33		09a02		09 40			10a31	10 33		11a02		11 40			12a31
St Andrews Road	d				07x44			08x36				09x44				10x36				11x44			
Severn Beach	a				07 53			08 48				09 53				10 48				11 53			

		GW (bus)	GW	GW	GW	GW	GW	GW	GW	GW (bus)	GW	GW	GW	GW	GW	GW	GW	GW (bus)	GW	GW	GW	GW	GW
Bristol Temple Meads [10]	d		12 21	12 34	12 45	13 16	13 21	13 45	14 03		14 21	14 34	14 45	15 16	15 21	15 45	16 03		16 21	16 34	16 45	17 16	17 21
Lawrence Hill	d			12 37	12 48	13 19		13 48				14 37	14 48	15 19		15 48	16 06			16 37	16 48	17 19	
Stapleton Road	d		12a25	12 39	12a50	13 21	13a24	13a50	14 07		14a25	14 39	14a50	15 21	15a24	15a50	16 07		16a25	16 39	16a50	17 21	17a24
Montpelier	d			12 42		13 24			14 10			14 42		15 24			16 10			16 42		17 24	
Redland	d			12 44		13 26			14 12			14 44		15 26			16 12			16 44		17 26	
Clifton Down	d			12 48		13 29			14 17			14 48		15 29			16 17			16 48		17 29	
Sea Mills	d			12 52		13 33			14 21			14 52		15 33			16 21			16 52		17 33	
Shirehampton	d			12 56		13 37			14 25			14 56		15 37			16 25			16 56		17 37	
Avonmouth [2]	d	12 33		13a02		13 40			14a31	14 33		15a02		15 40			16a30	16 33		17a02		17 40	
St Andrews Road	d	12x36				13x44				14x36				15x44				16x36				17x44	
Severn Beach	a	12 48				13 53				14 48				15 53				16 48				17 53	

		GW	GW	GW	GW	GW	GW	GW	GW	GW
Bristol Temple Meads [10]	d	17 45	18 03	18 21	18 45	19 03	19 45	20 34	21 40	22 16
Lawrence Hill	d	17 48	18 06		18 48	19 06	19 48	20 37	21 43	22 19
Stapleton Road	d	17a50	18 07	18a24	18a50	19 07	19a50	20 39	21 45	22 21
Montpelier	d		18 10			19 10		20 42	21 48	22 24
Redland	d		18 12			19 12		20 44	21 50	22 26
Clifton Down	d		18 17			19 17		20 48	21 54	22 29
Sea Mills	d		18 21			19 21		20 52	21 58	22 33
Shirehampton	d		18 25			19 25		20 56	22 01	22 37
Avonmouth [2]	d		18 29			19 29		20 59	22a08	22 40
St Andrews Road	d		18x32			19x32		21x02		22x44
Severn Beach	a		18 40			19 40		21 11		22 53

Table 133

Sundays

8 December to 11 May

Bristol - Avonmouth and Severn Beach

Network Diagram - see first Page of Table 132

		GW	GW	GW	GW		GW	GW	GW	GW
				◇						
Bristol Temple Meads 10	d	09 08	10 23	11 23	12 23		15 23	16 23	16 52	17 53
Lawrence Hill	d	09 11	10 26	11 26	12 26		15 26	16 26	16 55	17 56
Stapleton Road	d	09 13	10 28	11 28	12 28	and	15 28	16 28	16 58	17 58
Montpelier	d	09 16	10 31	11 31	12 31	hourly	15 31	16 31	17 01	18 01
Redland	d	09 18	10 33	11 33	12 33	until	15 33	16 33	17 03	18 03
Clifton Down	d	09 21	10 36	11 36	12 36		15 36	16 36	17 06	18 06
Sea Mills	d	09 25	10 40	11 40	12 40		15 40	16 40	17 10	18 10
Shirehampton	d	09 29	10 44	11 43	12 44		15 44	16 44	17 13	18 14
Avonmouth 2	d	09 33	10a49	11a47	12a49		15a49	16a47	17 17	18a17
St Andrews Road	d	09x36							17x21	
Severn Beach	a	09 43							17 28	

Table 133R

Mondays to Fridays

9 December to 16 May

Severn Beach and Avonmouth - Bristol

Network Diagram - see first Page of Table 132

Miles			GW	GW	GW	GW	GW	GW		GW	GW	GW	GW	GW	GW	GW	GW	GW		GW	GW	GW	GW	GW	GW
			MX										◇							◇					
0	**Severn Beach**	d		06 03				07 18		07 54						09 54						11 54			
3½	St Andrews Road	d		06x09				07x24		08x00						10x00						12x00			
4½	Avonmouth [2]	d		06 13	06 30			07 28		08 04		08 38		09 16		10 04		10 35			11 16	12 04	12 35		13 16
6	Shirehampton	d		06 17	06 33			07 32		08 07		08 41		09 19		10 07		10 38			11 19	12 07	12 38		13 19
7½	Sea Mills	d		06 21	06 37			07 36		08 11		08 45		09 23		10 11		10 42			11 23	12 11	12 42		13 23
9½	Clifton Down	d		06 26	06 43			07 40		08 16		08 51		09 30		10 16		10 48			11 31	12 16	12 48		13 31
10¼	Redland	d		06 28	06 45			07 44		08 19		08 53		09 32		10 19		10 51			11 34	12 19	12 51		13 34
10¾	Montpelier	d		06 30	06 47			07 46		08 21		08 55		09 34		10 21		10 53			11 36	12 21	12 53		13 36
12	Stapleton Road	d	00 25	06 36	06 53	07 07	07 33	07 52		08 26	08 54	09 01	09 29	09 39	09 44	10 25	10 33	10 59		11 29	11 40	12 25	12 59	13 29	13 40
12½	Lawrence Hill	d	00 27	06 38	06 55	07 09	07 35	07 55		08 28	08 56	09 03	09 31	09 41			10 35	11 01		11 31	11 42		13 01	13 31	13 42
13½	**Bristol Temple Meads [10]**	a	00 33	06 41	07 01	07 12	07 40	07 58		08 32	09 02	09 10	09 35	09 48	09 52	10 32	10 39	11 10		11 35	11 49	12 32	13 10	13 35	13 50

		GW	GW	GW		GW	GW	GW	GW	GW	GW	GW	GW	GW		GW	GW	GW	GW	GW	GW	GW	GW	GW	
			◇						◇			◇													
Severn Beach	d	13 54						15 54									17 54		18 44					21 29	
St Andrews Road	d	14x00						16x00									18x00		18x50					21x35	
Avonmouth [2]	d	14 04		14 35			15 16	16 04			16 35		17 16				18 04		18 54		19 33	20 01		21 39	
Shirehampton	d	14 07		14 38			15 19	16 07			16 38		17 19				18 07		18 58		19 36	20 04		21 43	
Sea Mills	d	14 11		14 42			15 23	16 11			16 42		17 23				18 11		19 02		19 40	20 08		21 47	
Clifton Down	d	14 16		14 48			15 31	16 16			16 48		17 31				18 15		19 13		19 46	20 13		21 52	
Redland	d	14 19		14 51			15 34	16 19			16 51		17 34				18 19		19 15		19 49	20 16		21 54	
Montpelier	d	14 21		14 53			15 36	16 21			16 53		17 36				18 21		19 17		19 51	20 18		21 56	
Stapleton Road	d	14 25	14 32	14 59		15 30	15 40	16 24	16 32	16 56	17 00	17 29	17 40	17 58		18 19	18 25	18 33	19 22	19 30	19 56	20 22	20 33	22 02	
Lawrence Hill	d		14 34	15 01		15 31	15 42		16 34	16 58	17 02	17 31	17 42	18 00			18 27	18 35	19 24	19 32	19 58	20 24	20 35	22 04	
Bristol Temple Meads [10]	a	14 32	14 39	15 10		15 36	15 50	16 32	16 38	17 01	17 10	17 36	17 50	18 04		18 25	18 34	18 38	19 28	19 35	20 04	20 32	20 39	22 07	

		GW	GW	GW
Severn Beach	d			22 54
St Andrews Road	d			23x00
Avonmouth [2]	d	22 16		23 04
Shirehampton	d	22 19		23 07
Sea Mills	d	22 23		23 11
Clifton Down	d	22 34		23 16
Redland	d	22 37		23 19
Montpelier	d	22 39		23 21
Stapleton Road	d	22 44	22 58	23 25
Lawrence Hill	d	22 46	23 01	23 27
Bristol Temple Meads [10]	a	22 53	23 05	23 32

Saturdays

14 December to 17 May

		GW	GW	GW	GW	GW	GW	GW	GW	GW		GW	GW	GW	GW	GW	GW	GW	GW	GW		GW	GW	GW	GW
							bus	◇						bus	◇			■		bus					◇
Severn Beach	d				07 54		08 55			09 54				10 55			11 54			12 55				13 54	
St Andrews Road	d				08x00		09x07			10x00				11x07			12x00			13x07				14x00	
Avonmouth [2]	d		06 35	07 15	08 04	08 35	09a10		09 16	10 04			10 35	11a10		11 16	12 04		12 35	13a10			13 16	14 04	
Shirehampton	d		06 38	07 18	08 07	08 38			09 19	10 07			10 38			11 19	12 07		12 38				13 19	14 07	
Sea Mills	d		06 42	07 22	08 11	08 42			09 23	10 11			10 42			11 23	12 11		12 42				13 23	14 11	
Clifton Down	d		06 47	07 31	08 16	08 47			09 30	10 16			10 48			11 31	12 16		12 48				13 31	14 16	
Redland	d		06 50	07 33	08 19	08 50			09 32	10 19			10 51			11 34	12 19		12 50				13 34	14 19	
Montpelier	d		06 52	07 35	08 21	08 52			09 34	10 21			10 53			11 36	12 21		12 52				13 36	14 21	
Stapleton Road	d	00 25	06 56	07 40	08 25	08 55		09 29	09 39	10 25		10 34	10 59		11 30	11 40	12 25	12 34	12 56			13 28	13 40	14 25	14 31
Lawrence Hill	d	00 27	06 58	07 42	08 27	08 57		09 31	09 41			10 36	11 01		11 31	11 42		12 36	12 58			13 30	13 42		14 33
Bristol Temple Meads [10]	a	00 33	07 06	07 49	08 32	09 06		09 36	09 48	10 32		10 39	11 10		11 35	11 50	12 32	12 39	13 06			13 34	13 50	14 32	14 38

		GW	GW	GW	GW	GW		GW	GW	GW	GW	GW	GW	GW	GW	GW		GW	GW	GW	GW	GW			
			bus					◇		bus	◇														
Severn Beach	d		14 55			15 54				16 55			17 54			18 54		19 47		21 31		22 54			
St Andrews Road	d		15x07			16x00				17x07			18x00			19x00		19x53		21x35		23x00			
Avonmouth [2]	d	14 35	15a10		15 16	16 04			16 35	17a10		17 16	18 04			19 04		19 57		21 39	22 16	23 04			
Shirehampton	d	14 38			15 19	16 07			16 38			17 19	18 07			19 07		20 00		21 43	22 19	23 07			
Sea Mills	d	14 42			15 23	16 11			16 42			17 23	18 11			19 11		20 04		21 47	22 23	23 11			
Clifton Down	d	14 48			15 31	16 16			16 47			17 31	18 16			19 29		20 09		21 52	22 31	23 16			
Redland	d	14 51			15 34	16 19			16 50			17 34	18 19			19 31		20 12		21 54	22 34	23 19			
Montpelier	d	14 53			15 36	16 21			16 52			17 36	18 21			19 33		20 14		21 56	22 36	23 21			
Stapleton Road	d	14 59		15 28	15 40	16 24		16 34	16 55		17 29	17 40	18 25	18 34	19 29	19 39		20 17	20 34	22 02	22 40	23 25			
Lawrence Hill	d	15 01		15 30	15 42			16 36	16 57		17 31	17 42	18 27	18 36	19 31	19 41		20 19	20 36	22 04	22 42	23 27			
Bristol Temple Meads [10]	a	15 10		15 35	15 50	16 32		16 40	17 07		17 34	17 50	18 32	18 39	19 36	19 44		20 26	20 39	22 09	22 50	23 32			

Table 133R

Sundays

8 December to 11 May

Severn Beach and Avonmouth - Bristol

Network Diagram - see first Page of Table 132

		GW	GW		GW	GW	GW	GW
Severn Beach	d	09 46					17 42	
St Andrews Road	d	09x52					17x48	
Avonmouth 2	d	09 56	10 52		15 52	16 52	17 52	18 22
Shirehampton	d	09 59	10 55	and	15 55	16 55	17 56	18 25
Sea Mills	d	10 03	10 59	hourly	15 59	16 59	18 00	18 29
Clifton Down	d	10 08	11 04	until	16 04	17 07	18 06	18 34
Redland	d	10 11	11 07		16 07	17 10	18 09	18 37
Montpelier	d	10 13	11 09		16 09	17 12	18 11	18 39
Stapleton Road	d	10 16	11 13		16 13	17 16	18 15	18 43
Lawrence Hill	d	10 18	11 15		16 15	17 18	18 17	18 45
Bristol Temple Meads 10	a	10 21	11 20		16 20	17 22	18 22	18 47

Table 134

Gloucester - Taunton

Mondays to Fridays

9 December to 16 May

Network Diagram - see first Page of Table 132

Miles			GW MX	GW MX	GW ◇	GW 1	XC ◇1	GW ◇	GW	GW	GW ◇ 🚲		GW	GW	XC ◇1	GW	XC ◇1 🚲	GW ■ 🚲	GW	GW ◇	XC ◇1 🚲		GW ◇	GW	GW ◇1 A Ø
0	**Gloucester 7**	d								06 16			06 42			07 10				07 39					
13	Cam & Dursley	d								06 32			06 57			07 25				07 53					
28	Yate	d								06 45			07 12			07 40				08 08					
34	**Bristol Parkway 7**	a								06 54			07 21			07 48				08 19					
—		d						06 23		06 57			07 23			07 49	07 55		08 12	08 19	08 26			08 45	
35¼	Filton Abbey Wood	d		00 20				06 27		07 01	07 09		07 28		07 41	07 53		08 09	08 16	08 23			08 42	08 49	
38¼	Stapleton Road	d		00 25						07 07			07 33											08 54	
38¾	Lawrence Hill	d		00 27						07 09			07 35											08 56	
39¾	**Bristol Temple Meads 10**	a		00 33				06 35		07 12	07 18		07 40		07 51	08 02	08 05	08 18	08 24	08 36	08 39		08 53	09 02	
—		d			05 20	06 03	06 34	06 42	06 48	07 18				07 49			08 10		08 26		08 44		08 55		09 13
40¾	Bedminster	d							06 50					07 51					08 28						
41½	Parson Street	d							06 53					07 53					08 30						
47¾	Nailsea & Backwell	d				06 14			07 02	07 28				08 02					08 39				09 03		
51¾	Yatton	d				06 21			07 07	07 33				08 07					08 45				09 08		
55¾	Worle	d				06 27			07 12	07 39				08 13					08 51				09 14		
58½	Weston Milton	d							07 18					08 18					08 56						
59¾	**Weston-super-Mare**	a			05 39	06 36		07 02	07 23	07 48				08 24					08 59				09 22		
—		d			05 41			07 06		07 49									09 01				09 29		
67¼	Highbridge & Burnham	d			05 51			07 17		08 00									09 11				09 40		
73½	Bridgwater	d	00 02		05 59			07 25		08 08									09 19				09 48		
85¼	**Taunton**	a	00s14		06 12		07 06	07 38		08 24							08 41		09 33		09 15		10 01		09 45

		XC ◇1 🚲	GW ◇ 🚲	GW	GW ◇	XC ◇1 🚲	GW		GW ◇	XC ◇1 🚲	GW ◇ 🚲	GW	GW	XC ◇1 🚲	GW	XC ◇1 🚲	GW ◇ 🚲		GW	GW ◇	XC ◇1 🚲	GW ◇1 B	GW	XC ◇1 🚲	GW ◇ 🚲
Gloucester 7	d				08 41								09 45							10 41					
Cam & Dursley	d				08 56								10 00							10 56					
Yate	d				09 10								10 14							11 10					
Bristol Parkway 7	a				09 19								10 23							11 19					
	d	08 54		09 12	09 20	09 26	09 35			09 54		10 12	10 23	10 30		10 54			11 12	11 20	11 31			11 54	
Filton Abbey Wood	d		09 09	09 16	09 23		09 39		09 42		10 09	10 16	10 26		10 42		11 09		11 16	11 23			11 42		12 09
Stapleton Road	d				09 29		09 44						10 33							11 29					
Lawrence Hill	d				09 31								10 35							11 31					
Bristol Temple Meads 10	a	09 14	09 18	09 24	09 35	09 38	09 52		09 53	10 08	10 19	10 24	10 39	10 42	10 51	11 10	11 18		11 24	11 35	11 40		11 51	12 05	12 19
	d			09 28		09 44			09 55			10 26		10 44	10 53	11 15			11 26		11 44	11 47	11 53		
Bedminster	d			09 30								10 28							11 28						
Parson Street	d			09 32								10 30							11 30						
Nailsea & Backwell	d			09 41					10 03			10 39			11 03				11 39				12 03		
Yatton	d			09 47					10 08			10 45			11 08				11 45				12 08		
Worle	d			09 53					10 14			10 51			11 14				11 51				12 14		
Weston Milton	d			09 58								10 56							11 56						
Weston-super-Mare	a			10 01					10 22			11 00			11 21	11 32			12 00			12 06	12 21		
	d								10 23						11 23	11 37						12 07	12 22		
Highbridge & Burnham	d								10 34						11 34								12 33		
Bridgwater	d								10 42						11 42								12 41		
Taunton	a					10 17			10 59					11 16	11 57	12 00					12 15	12 29	12 57		

		GW	GW ■		XC ◇1 🚲	GW	XC ◇1 🚲	GW ◇ 🚲	GW	GW	XC ◇1 🚲	GW ◇	XC ◇1 🚲		GW ◇ 🚲	GW	GW ◇	XC ◇1 🚲	GW	XC ◇1 🚲	GW ◇ 🚲	GW	GW		XC ◇1 🚲
Gloucester 7	d		11 47							12 41							13 46						14 41		
Cam & Dursley	d		12 00							12 56							14 00						14 56		
Yate	d		12 14							13 10							14 14						15 10		
Bristol Parkway 7	a		12 23							13 18							14 22						15 18		
	d	12 12	12 23		12 32		12 54		13 12	13 19	13 32		13 58			14 12	14 23	14 32		14 54		15 12	15 20		15 31
Filton Abbey Wood	d	12 16	12 26			12 42		13 09	13 16	13 23		13 42			14 09	14 16	14 26		14 42		15 09	15 16	15 23		
Stapleton Road	d									13 29							14 32						15 30		
Lawrence Hill	d									13 31							14 34						15 31		
Bristol Temple Meads 10	a	12 24	12 35		12 41	12 51	13 09	13 19	13 24	13 35	13 41	13 52	14 08		14 18	14 24	14 39	14 41	14 51	15 10	15 17	15 24	15 36		15 41
	d	12 26			12 44	12 53			13 26		13 44	13 57				14 26		14 44	14 53	15 13		15 26			15 44
Bedminster	d	12 29							13 29							14 28						15 28			
Parson Street	d	12 31							13 31							14 30						15 30			
Nailsea & Backwell	d	12 39				13 03			13 39			14 07				14 39			15 03			15 39			
Yatton	d	12 45				13 08			13 45			14 12				14 45			15 08			15 45			
Worle	d	12 51				13 14			13 51			14 18				14 51			15 14			15 51			
Weston Milton	d	12 56							13 56							14 56						15 56			
Weston-super-Mare	a	13 00				13 21			14 00			14 24				15 00			15 22			16 00			
	d					13 22						14 25							15 28						
Highbridge & Burnham	d					13 33						14 36							15 38						
Bridgwater	d					13 41						14 44							15 46						
Taunton	a				13 16	13 58					14 15	14 57						15 16	16 01	15 44					16 15

A The Merchant Venturer

B The Torbay Express

For connections from London Paddington please see Table 125

For full services to Brighton, Portsmouth Harbour, Westbury and Weymouth please see Table 123

Table 134

Mondays to Fridays

9 December to 16 May

Gloucester - Taunton

Network Diagram - see first Page of Table 132

		GW	GW	XC	GW		GW	GW	GW	XC	GW	GW	GW	XC	GW		GW	GW	GW	XC	GW	GW	XC	GW	GW
																	R							R	R
				◇1	◇1		◇		◇	◇1				◇1	◇1				◇	◇1			◇1		1
				🚲	🍴		🚲			🚲				🚲	🍴		🚲			🚲			🚲	🚲	🍴
Gloucester 7	d								15 46										16 40						
Cam & Dursley	d								16 00										16 56						
Yate	d								16 14										17 10						
Bristol Parkway 7	a								16 22										17 19						
	d		15 53	15 57				16 12	16 23	16 34		16 46		16 54				17 12	17 20	17 27		17 48	17 55		
Filton Abbey Wood	d	15 42	15a56				16 09	16 16	16 26		16 42	16 50	16 55				17 09	17 16	17 23		17 43	17 52		18 09	
Stapleton Road	d								16 32			16 56							17 29			17 58			
Lawrence Hill	d								16 34			16 58							17 31			18 00			
Bristol Temple Meads 10	a	15 52		16 10			16 18	16 24	16 38	16 44	16 51	17 01	17 04	17 10			17 18	17 24	17 36	17 39	17 53	18 04	18 07	18 18	
	d	15 53			16 18			16 26		16 46	16 53			17 13	17 17			17 26		17 44	17 55				18 20
Bedminster	d	15 56						16 28			16 56							17 28			17 58				
Parson Street	d	15 59						16 30			16 59							17 30			18 01				
Nailsea & Backwell	d	16 07			16 29			16 39			17 07				17 27			17 39			18 09				18 31
Yatton	d	16 12			16 36			16 45			17 13				17 33			17 45			18 15				18 38
Worle	d	16 18			16 43			16 51			17 19				17 40			17 51			18 21				18 45
Weston Milton	d	16 22						16 56			17 24							17 56			18 25				
Weston-super-Mare	a	16 25			16 52			17 00			17 27				17 52			18 00			18 29				18 51
	d	16 27									17 28										18 30				18 55
Highbridge & Burnham	d	16 37									17 38										18 41				19 09
Bridgwater	d	16 45									17 46										18 49				19 17
Taunton	a	17 00								17 17	18 01			17 44						18 15	19 03				19 28

			GW	GW	XC	GW	XC	GW	GW	GW	XC		GW	XC	GW	GW	GW	GW	XC	XC	GW		XC	GW	GW
																			FO	FX					
								R							R									R	
					◇1		◇1	1	◇		◇1			◇1	1	◇			◇1	◇1			◇1	1	◇
																			A	A					
					🚲		🚲	🍴	🚲		🚲			🚲	🍴				🚲	🚲			🚲	🍴	
Gloucester 7	d			17 46						18 41								19 45							
Cam & Dursley	d			18 00						18 56								20 00							
Yate	d			18 14						19 10								20 15							
Bristol Parkway 7	a			18 23						19 20								20 23							
	d		18 12	18 23	18 29		18 55			19 20	19 28			20 00			20 11	20 24	20 30	20 30			20 56		
Filton Abbey Wood	d		18 16	18 27		18 43			19 09	19 24			19 42			20 09	20 15	20 27			20 42				21 08
Stapleton Road	d		18 19	18 33						19 30								20 33							
Lawrence Hill	d			18 35						19 32								20 35							
Bristol Temple Meads 10	a		18 25	18 38	18 41	18 51	19 05		19 18	19 35	19 38		19 51	20 09		20 17	20 24	20 39	20 42	20 42	20 53		21 05		21 19
	d		18 26		18 44	18 56		19 15			19 44		19 55		20 17				20 44	20 45	20 55		21 13	21 18	
Bedminster	d		18 27			18 59							19 57								20 57				
Parson Street	d		18 30			19 01							19 59								20 59				
Nailsea & Backwell	d		18 39			19 09		19 25					20 08		20 28						21 08			21 28	
Yatton	d		18 44			19 15		19 32					20 13		20 35						21 13			21 35	
Worle	d		18 50			19 21		19 38					20 19		20 43						21 19			21 42	
Weston Milton	d		18 54			19 25		19 43					20 23		20 48						21 23				
Weston-super-Mare	a		19 00			19 28		19 48					20 27		20 53						21 27			21 50	
	d					19 30		19 57					20 29								21 33				
Highbridge & Burnham	d					19 40							20 39								21 44				
Bridgwater	d					19 48							20 47								21 52				
Taunton	a				19 15	20 04		20 23			20 16		21 02						21 16	21 16	22 07		21 44		

		XC	GW	GW	GW	XC	GW		XC	GW	GW	GW	GW	GW	XC
		◇1		◇	1	◇1			◇1				◇1		◇1
		A													
		🚲											🍴		
Gloucester 7	d				21 15				22 06			22 28			
Cam & Dursley	d				21 29										
Yate	d				21 41										
Bristol Parkway 7	a				21 50				22 32			23 04			
	d	21 26			21 51	22 02			22 33			23 05			23 21
Filton Abbey Wood	d		21 42		21 56		22 09			22 52				23 26	
Stapleton Road	d									22 58					
Lawrence Hill	d									23 01					
Bristol Temple Meads 10	a	21 36	21 52		22 11	22 13	22 22		22 43	23 05		23 19		23 37	23 40
	d	21 44		21 56							23 06		23 35		
Bedminster	d			21 58							23 10				
Parson Street	d			22 00							23 12				
Nailsea & Backwell	d			22 09							23 20		23s45		
Yatton	d			22 13							23 26		23s52		
Worle	d			22 19							23 32		23s58		
Weston Milton	d			22 23							23 37				
Weston-super-Mare	a			22 28							23 40		00s05		
	d			22 29							23 42				
Highbridge & Burnham	d			22 40							23 54		00s16		
Bridgwater	d			22 48							00 02		00s24		
Taunton	a	22 15		23 01							00s14		00s36		

A 🚲 to Bristol Temple Meads

For connections from London Paddington please see Table 125

For full services to Brighton, Portsmouth Harbour, Westbury and Weymouth please see Table 123

Table 134

Gloucester - Taunton

Saturdays

14 December to 28 December

Network Diagram - see first Page of Table 132

		GW	GW	GW	GW	XC		GW	GW	GW	GW	GW	XC	GW	XC	GW		GW	GW	XC	GW	XC	GW	GW	GW
				◇	◇1 ☕	◇1			◇			◇	◇1		◇1 🚲	◇			◇	◇1 🚲		◇1 🚲	R 1 ☕	◇	
Gloucester 7	d										06 20			07 02					07 40						
Cam & Dursley	d										06 37			07 15					07 55						
Yate	d										06 51			07 30					08 10						
Bristol Parkway 7	a										07 01			07 39					08 18						
	d				05 42						07 01			07 40	07 54			08 12	08 20	08 25		08 54			09 12
Filton Abbey Wood	d		00 20								07 05	07 09	07 41	07 45		08 09		08 16	08 23		08 42			09 09	09 16
Stapleton Road	d		00 25																						
Lawrence Hill	d		00 27																						
Bristol Temple Meads 10	a		00 33		05 54						07 13	07 19	07 51	07 55	08 05	08 19		08 24	08 34	08 38	08 53	09 06		09 19	09 24
	d			05 24		06 08		06 18	06 36	06 48	07 18			07 57	08 11			08 25		08 45	08 57		09 17		09 25
Bedminster	d									06 50	07 21							08 27							09 27
Parson Street	d									06 53	07 23							08 30							09 30
Nailsea & Backwell	d							06 28		07 01	07 31			08 07				08 39			09 07				09 39
Yatton	d							06 33		07 06	07 36			08 12				08 44			09 12				09 44
Worle	d							06 39		07 12	07 42			08 18				08 50			09 18				09 50
Weston Milton	d									07 17	07 46							08 55							09 55
Weston-super-Mare	a			05 43				06 44	06 55	07 22	07 50			08 24				09 01			09 24				10 01
	d			05 45				06 46	06 56		07 51										09 32				
Highbridge & Burnham	d			05 55				06 57			08 02										09 44				
Bridgwater	d	00 02		06 03				07 05			08 10										09 52				
Taunton	a	00s14		06 16		07 14		07 19	07 24		08 24				08 42					09 16	10 06		09 50		

		GW		XC	GW	XC	GW	GW	GW	XC	GW	XC		GW	GW	GW	XC	GW	XC	GW	GW	GW		XC	GW
		◇		◇1 🚲		◇1 🚲	◇			◇1 🚲		◇1 🚲		◇		◇	◇1 🚲		◇1 🚲	◇		R		◇1 🚲	
Gloucester 7	d	08 41							09 46							10 41						11 46			
Cam & Dursley	d	08 56							10 02							10 56						12 02			
Yate	d	09 11							10 16							11 11						12 16			
Bristol Parkway 7	a	09 19							10 24							11 20						12 24			
	d	09 20		09 26		09 54		10 12	10 25	10 30		10 55			11 12	11 21	11 25		11 54		12 12	12 25		12 31	
Filton Abbey Wood	d	09 23			09 42		10 09	10 16	10 28		10 42			11 09	11 16	11 24		11 42		12 09	12 16	12 28			12 42
Stapleton Road	d	09 29							10 34							11 30						12 34			
Lawrence Hill	d	09 31							10 36							11 31						12 36			
Bristol Temple Meads 10	a	09 36		09 38	09 51	10 04	10 18	10 24	10 39	10 42	10 52	11 09		11 19	11 24	11 35	11 38	11 51	12 04	12 19	12 24	12 39		12 42	12 51
	d			09 44	09 55			10 25		10 44	10 53	11 12			11 25		11 44	11 53			12 25			12 44	12 53
Bedminster	d							10 27							11 27						12 27				
Parson Street	d							10 30							11 30						12 30				
Nailsea & Backwell	d				10 03			10 39			11 03				11 39			12 03			12 39				13 03
Yatton	d				10 08			10 44			11 08				11 44			12 08			12 44				13 08
Worle	d				10 14			10 50			11 14				11 50			12 14			12 50				13 14
Weston Milton	d							10 55							11 55						12 56				
Weston-super-Mare	a				10 22			11 01			11 21	11 29			12 01			12 20			13 01				13 21
	d				10 23						11 23	11 39						12 22							13 23
Highbridge & Burnham	d				10 34						11 34							12 33							13 34
Bridgwater	d				10 42						11 42							12 41							13 42
Taunton	a			10 17	10 59					11 15	11 56	11 59					12 16	12 57						13 15	13 59

		XC	GW	GW	GW	XC	GW	XC		GW	GW	GW	XC	GW	XC	GW	GW	GW		XC	GW	XC	GW	GW	GW
		◇1 🚲	◇			◇1 🚲		◇1 🚲		◇		◇	◇1 🚲		◇1 🚲	◇				◇1 🚲		◇1 🚲	◇		◇
Gloucester 7	d				12 41							13 42						14 41							15 46
Cam & Dursley	d				12 56							13 58						14 56							16 02
Yate	d				13 11							14 13						15 11							16 16
Bristol Parkway 7	a				13 19							14 21						15 19							16 24
	d	12 54		13 12	13 20	13 25		13 56			14 12	14 22	14 28		14 59		15 12	15 20		15 25		15 55		16 12	16 25
Filton Abbey Wood	d		13 09	13 16	13 23		13 42			14 09	14 16	14 25		14 42		15 09	15 16	15 23			15 42		16 09	16 16	16 28
Stapleton Road	d				13 28							14 31						15 28							16 34
Lawrence Hill	d				13 30							14 33						15 30							16 36
Bristol Temple Meads 10	a	13 07	13 19	13 24	13 34	13 38	13 53	14 05		14 19	14 24	14 38	14 40	14 51	15 09	15 19	15 24	15 35		15 38	15 51	16 07	16 19	16 24	16 40
	d			13 25		13 44	13 55				14 25		14 44	14 53	15 12		15 26			15 44	15 53			16 26	
Bedminster	d			13 27							14 27						15 28							16 28	
Parson Street	d			13 30			13 59				14 30						15 30							16 30	
Nailsea & Backwell	d			13 39			14 07				14 39			15 03			15 39				16 03			16 39	
Yatton	d			13 44			14 12				14 44			15 08			15 45				16 08			16 45	
Worle	d			13 50			14 18				14 50			15 14			15 51				16 14			16 51	
Weston Milton	d			13 55							14 55						15 56							16 56	
Weston-super-Mare	a			14 01			14 23				15 01			15 21			16 01				16 22			17 01	
	d						14 23							15 23							16 23				
Highbridge & Burnham	d						14 34							15 35							16 34				
Bridgwater	d						14 42							15 43							16 42				
Taunton	a					14 15	15 01						15 17	16 00	15 43					16 15	16 57				

For connections from London Paddington please see Table 125

For full services to Brighton, Portsmouth Harbour, Westbury and Weymouth please see Table 123

Table 134

Saturdays

14 December to 28 December

Gloucester - Taunton

Network Diagram - see first Page of Table 132

		XC	GW	XC	GW	GW	GW	XC	GW	XC		GW	GW	GW	GW	XC	GW	XC	GW	GW		GW	GW	XC	GW
		◇1 🛒		◇1 🛒	[R]		◇	◇1 🛒		◇1 🛒		◇1 🍴	◇			◇1 🛒		◇1 🛒	◇1 🍴	◇				◇1 🛒	
Gloucester [7]	d						16 41								17 46								18 41		
Cam & Dursley	d						16 56								18 02								18 56		
Yate	d						17 11								18 16								19 11		
Bristol Parkway [7]	a						17 19								18 24								19 20		
	d	16 30		16 54		17 12	17 20	17 26		17 54				18 12	18 25	18 30		18 54				19 12	19 20	19 26	
Filton Abbey Wood	d		16 42		17 09	17 16	17 24		17 42				18 09	18 16	18 28		18 42			19 09		19 15	19 23		19 42
Stapleton Road	d						17 29								18 34								19 29		
Lawrence Hill	d						17 31								18 36								19 31		
Bristol Temple Meads [10]	a	16 42	16 51	17 07	17 19	17 24	17 34	17 38	17 51	18 07			18 19	18 24	18 39	18 42	18 51	19 04		19 19		19 25	19 36	19 38	19 51
	d	16 44	16 53	17 10		17 26		17 44	17 53			18 18		18 26		18 44	18 53		19 18					19 44	19 53
Bedminster	d					17 28								18 28											
Parson Street	d					17 30								18 30											
Nailsea & Backwell	d		17 03			17 39			18 03					18 39			19 03		19 30						20 03
Yatton	d		17 08			17 45			18 08					18 45			19 08		19 37						20 08
Worle	d		17 14			17 51			18 14					18 51			19 14		19 43						20 14
Weston Milton	d					17 56								18 56			19 20								20 20
Weston-super-Mare	a		17 22			18 01			18 22			18 36		19 01			19 23		19 50						20 23
	d		17 23						18 23			18 40					19 23								20 24
Highbridge & Burnham	d		17 34						18 34								19 34								20 34
Bridgwater	d		17 42						18 42								19 42								20 42
Taunton	a	17 17	17 59	17 41				18 15	18 56			19 06				19 15	19 59							20 15	20 59

		XC	GW	GW	GW	GW		XC	GW	GW	XC	GW	XC	GW	GW	GW		XC	GW	XC	GW				
		◇1 🛒	◇1 🍴	◇				◇1 A 🛒		◇1 🍴	◇1 A 🛒	◇	◇1 A 🛒		◇			◇1	◇1 🍴	◇1					
Gloucester [7]	d					19 46										21 14				22 05					
Cam & Dursley	d					20 02										21 30									
Yate	d					20 16										21 44									
Bristol Parkway [7]	a					20 24										21 53				22 30					
	d	19 56			20 17	20 25		20 30			20 54		21 21			21 53		21 59		22 30					
Filton Abbey Wood	d			20 09	20 21	20 28			20 39			21 08		21 42		21 57					22 52				
Stapleton Road	d					20 34																			
Lawrence Hill	d					20 36																			
Bristol Temple Meads [10]	a	20 05		20 19	20 30	20 39		20 42	20 48		21 04	21 19	21 35	21 50		22 05		22 12		22 41	23 00				
	d		20 15					20 44		20 55	21 11		21 44		21 59				22 17						
Bedminster	d														22 01										
Parson Street	d														22 03										
Nailsea & Backwell	d									21 04					22 12				22s27						
Yatton	d									21 11					22 18				22s34						
Worle	d									21 17					22 24				22s40						
Weston Milton	d									21 22					22 28										
Weston-super-Mare	a		20 36							21 26					22 31				22s47						
	d		20 38							21 26					22 33										
Highbridge & Burnham	d									21 40					22 44				22s58						
Bridgwater	d									21 47					22 52				23s05						
Taunton	a		21 03					21 15		22 00	21 42		22 15		23 05				23 17						

Saturdays

4 January to 8 February

		GW	GW	GW	GW	XC	GW	GW	GW	GW		GW	XC	GW	XC	GW	GW	GW	XC	GW		XC	GW	GW	GW
				◇	◇1 🍴	◇1		◇				◇	◇1		◇1 🛒	◇		◇	◇1 🛒			◇1 🛒	[R] 1 🍴	◇	
Gloucester [7]	d									06 20				07 02				07 40							
Cam & Dursley	d									06 37				07 15				07 55							
Yate	d									06 51				07 30				08 10							
Bristol Parkway [7]	a									07 01				07 39				08 18							
	d				05 42					07 01				07 40	07 54		08 12	08 20	08 25			08 54			09 12
Filton Abbey Wood	d		00 20							07 05		07 09	07 41	07 45		08 09	08 16	08 23		08 42				09 09	09 16
Stapleton Road	d		00 25																						
Lawrence Hill	d		00 27																						
Bristol Temple Meads [10]	a		00 33		05 54					07 13		07 19	07 51	07 55	08 05	08 19	08 24	08 34	08 38	08 53		09 06		09 19	09 24
	d			05 24		06 08	06 18	06 36	06 48	07 18				07 57	08 11		08 25		08 45	08 57			09 17		09 25
Bedminster	d								06 50	07 21							08 27								09 27
Parson Street	d								06 53	07 23							08 30								09 30
Nailsea & Backwell	d						06 28		07 01	07 31				08 07			08 39			09 07					09 39
Yatton	d						06 33		07 06	07 36				08 12			08 44			09 12					09 44
Worle	d						06 39		07 12	07 42				08 18			08 50			09 18					09 50
Weston Milton	d								07 17	07 46							08 55								09 55
Weston-super-Mare	a			05 43			06 44	06 55	07 22	07 50				08 24			09 01			09 24					10 01
	d			05 45			06 46	06 56		07 51										09 32					
Highbridge & Burnham	d			05 55			06 57			08 02										09 44					
Bridgwater	d	00 02		06 03			07 05			08 10										09 52					
Taunton	a	00s14		06 16		07 14	07 19	07 24		08 24					08 42				09 16	10 06			09 50		

A 🛒 to Bristol Temple Meads

For connections from London Paddington please see Table 125

For full services to Brighton, Portsmouth Harbour, Westbury and Weymouth please see Table 123

Table 134

Gloucester - Taunton

Saturdays

4 January to 8 February

Network Diagram - see first Page of Table 132

		GW		XC	GW	XC	GW	GW	GW	XC	GW	XC		GW	GW	GW	XC	GW	XC	GW	GW	GW		XC	GW
		◇		◇1 ⚲		◇1 ⚲	◇			◇1 ⚲		◇1 ⚲		◇		◇	◇1 ⚲		◇1 ⚲	◇		R		◇1 ⚲	
Gloucester 7	d	08 41							09 46							10 41						11 46			
Cam & Dursley	d	08 56							10 02							10 56						12 02			
Yate	d	09 11							10 16							11 11						12 16			
Bristol Parkway 7	a	09 19							10 24							11 20						12 24			
	d	09 20		09 26		09 54		10 12	10 25	10 30		10 55			11 12	11 21	11 25		11 54		12 12	12 25		12 31	
Filton Abbey Wood	d	09 23			09 42		10 09	10 16	10 28		10 42			11 09	11 16	11 24		11 42		12 09	12 16	12 28			12 42
Stapleton Road	d	09 29							10 34							11 30						12 34			
Lawrence Hill	d	09 31							10 36							11 31						12 36			
Bristol Temple Meads 10	a	09 36		09 38	09 51	10 04	10 18	10 24	10 39	10 42	10 52	11 09		11 19	11 24	11 35	11 38	11 51	12 04	12 19	12 24	12 39		12 42	12 51
	d			09 44	09 55			10 25		10 44	10 53	11 12			11 25		11 44	11 53			12 25			12 44	12 53
Bedminster	d							10 27							11 27						12 27				
Parson Street	d							10 30							11 30						12 30				
Nailsea & Backwell	d				10 03			10 39			11 03				11 39			12 03			12 39				13 03
Yatton	d				10 08			10 44			11 08				11 44			12 08			12 44				13 08
Worle	d				10 14			10 50			11 14				11 50			12 14			12 50				13 14
Weston Milton	d							10 55							11 55						12 56				
Weston-super-Mare	a				10 22			11 01			11 21	11 29			12 01			12 20			13 01				13 21
	d				10 23						11 23	11 39						12 22							13 23
Highbridge & Burnham	d				10 34						11 34							12 33							13 34
Bridgwater	d				10 42						11 42							12 41							13 42
Taunton	a			10 17	10 59					11 15	11 56	11 59					12 16	12 57						13 15	13 59

		XC	GW	GW	GW	XC	GW	XC		GW	GW	GW	XC	GW	XC	GW	GW	GW		XC	GW	XC	GW	GW	GW
		◇1 ⚲	◇			◇1 ⚲		◇1 ⚲		◇		◇	◇1 ⚲		◇1 ⚲	◇				◇1 ⚲		◇1 ⚲	◇		◇
Gloucester 7	d				12 41							13 42						14 41							15 46
Cam & Dursley	d				12 56							13 58						14 56							16 02
Yate	d				13 11							14 13						15 11							16 16
Bristol Parkway 7	a				13 19							14 21						15 19							16 24
	d	12 54		13 12	13 20	13 25		13 56			14 12	14 22	14 28		14 59		15 12	15 20		15 25		15 55		16 12	16 25
Filton Abbey Wood	d		13 09	13 16	13 23		13 42			14 09	14 16	14 25		14 42		15 09	15 16	15 23			15 42		16 09	16 16	16 28
Stapleton Road	d				13 28							14 31						15 28							16 34
Lawrence Hill	d				13 30							14 33						15 30							16 36
Bristol Temple Meads 10	a	13 07	13 19	13 24	13 34	13 38	13 53	14 05		14 19	14 24	14 38	14 40	14 51	15 09	15 19	15 24	15 35		15 38	15 51	16 07	16 19	16 24	16 40
	d			13 25		13 44	13 55				14 25		14 44	14 53	15 12		15 26			15 44	15 53			16 26	
Bedminster	d			13 27							14 27						15 28							16 28	
Parson Street	d			13 30			13 59				14 30						15 30							16 30	
Nailsea & Backwell	d			13 39			14 07				14 39			15 03			15 39				16 03			16 39	
Yatton	d			13 44			14 12				14 44			15 08			15 45				16 08			16 45	
Worle	d			13 50			14 18				14 50			15 14			15 51				16 14			16 51	
Weston Milton	d			13 55							14 55						15 56							16 56	
Weston-super-Mare	a			14 01			14 23				15 01			15 21			16 01				16 22			17 01	
	d						14 23							15 23							16 23				
Highbridge & Burnham	d						14 34							15 35							16 34				
Bridgwater	d						14 42							15 43							16 42				
Taunton	a					14 15	15 01						15 17	16 00	15 43					16 15	16 57				

		XC	GW	XC		GW	GW	GW	XC	GW	XC	GW	GW	GW		GW	XC	GW	XC	GW	GW	GW	GW	XC	
		◇1 ⚲		◇1 ⚲		R		◇	◇1 ⚲		◇1 ⚲	◇	◇1 ⊓				◇1 ⚲		◇1 ⚲	◇1 ⊓	◇			◇1 ⚲	
Gloucester 7	d							16 41								17 46							18 41		
Cam & Dursley	d							16 56								18 02							18 56		
Yate	d							17 11								18 16							19 11		
Bristol Parkway 7	a							17 19								18 24							19 20		
	d	16 30		16 54			17 12	17 20	17 26		17 54			18 12		18 25	18 30		18 54			19 12	19 20	19 26	
Filton Abbey Wood	d		16 42			17 09	17 16	17 24		17 42		18 09		18 16		18 28		18 42			19 09	19 15	19 23		
Stapleton Road	d							17 29								18 34							19 29		
Lawrence Hill	d							17 31								18 36							19 31		
Bristol Temple Meads 10	a	16 42	16 51	17 07		17 19	17 24	17 34	17 38	17 51	18 07	18 19		18 24		18 39	18 42	18 51	19 04		19 19	19 25	19 36	19 38	
	d	16 44	16 53	17 10			17 26		17 44	17 53			18 20	18 26			18 44	18 53		19 19				19 44	
Bedminster	d						17 28							18 28											
Parson Street	d						17 30							18 30											
Nailsea & Backwell	d		17 03				17 39			18 03				18 39				19 03		19 31					
Yatton	d		17 08				17 45			18 08				18 45				19 08		19 38					
Worle	d		17 14				17 51			18 14				18 51				19 14		19 44					
Weston Milton	d						17 56							18 56				19 20							
Weston-super-Mare	a		17 22				18 01			18 22			18 38	19 01				19 23		19 51					
	d		17 23							18 23			18 43					19 23							
Highbridge & Burnham	d		17 34							18 34								19 34							
Bridgwater	d		17 42							18 42								19 42							
Taunton	a	17 17	17 59	17 41					18 15	18 56			19 09				19 15	19 59						20 15	

For connections from London Paddington please see Table 125

For full services to Brighton, Portsmouth Harbour, Westbury and Weymouth please see Table 123

Table 134

Gloucester - Taunton

Saturdays

4 January to 8 February

Network Diagram - see first Page of Table 132

		GW	XC	GW	GW	GW	GW	XC	GW		GW	XC	GW	XC	GW	GW	GW	XC	GW		XC	GW			
			◇1	◇1	◇			◇1			◇1	◇1	◇	◇1		◇		◇1	◇1		◇1				
								A				A		A											
			🛒	☕				🛒			☕	🛒		🛒					☕						
Gloucester 7	d						19 46										21 14				22 05				
Cam & Dursley	d						20 02										21 30								
Yate	d						20 16										21 44								
Bristol Parkway 7	a						20 24										21 53				22 30				
	d		19 56			20 17	20 25	20 30				20 54		21 21			21 53	21 59			22 30				
Filton Abbey Wood	d	19 42			20 09	20 21	20 28		20 39				21 08		21 42		21 57					22 52			
Stapleton Road	d						20 34																		
Lawrence Hill	d						20 36																		
Bristol Temple Meads 10	a	19 51	20 05		20 19	20 30	20 39	20 42	20 48			21 04	21 19	21 35	21 50		22 05	22 12			22 41	23 00			
	d	19 53		20 18				20 44			20 55	21 11		21 44		21 59			22 21						
Bedminster	d															22 01									
Parson Street	d															22 03									
Nailsea & Backwell	d	20 03									21 04					22 12			22s32						
Yatton	d	20 08									21 11					22 18			22s38						
Worle	d	20 14									21 17					22 24			22s45						
Weston Milton	d	20 20									21 22					22 28									
Weston-super-Mare	a	20 23		20 39							21 26					22 31			22s51						
	d	20 24		20 41							21 26					22 33									
Highbridge & Burnham	d	20 34									21 40					22 44			23s02						
Bridgwater	d	20 42									21 47					22 52			23s10						
Taunton	a	20 59		21 06				21 15			22 00	21 42		22 15		23 05			23 22						

Saturdays

15 February to 22 March

		GW	GW	GW	GW	XC	GW	GW	GW	GW		GW	XC	GW	XC	GW	GW	GW	XC	GW		XC	GW	GW	GW
																							R		
				◇	◇1	◇1		◇				◇	◇1		◇1	◇		◇	◇1			◇1	1	◇	
					☕										🛒				🛒			🛒	☕		
Gloucester 7	d									06 20				07 02				07 40							
Cam & Dursley	d									06 37				07 15				07 55							
Yate	d									06 51				07 30				08 10							
Bristol Parkway 7	a									07 01				07 39				08 18							
	d				05 42					07 01				07 40	07 54		08 12	08 20	08 25			08 54			09 12
Filton Abbey Wood	d		00 20							07 05		07 09	07 41	07 45		08 09	08 16	08 23		08 42				09 09	09 16
Stapleton Road	d		00 25																						
Lawrence Hill	d		00 27																						
Bristol Temple Meads 10	a		00 33		05 54					07 13		07 19	07 51	07 55	08 05	08 19	08 24	08 34	08 38	08 53		09 06		09 19	09 24
	d			05 24		06 08	06 18	06 36	06 48	07 18				07 57	08 11		08 25		08 45	08 57			09 17		09 25
Bedminster	d								06 50	07 21							08 27								09 27
Parson Street	d								06 53	07 23							08 30								09 30
Nailsea & Backwell	d						06 28		07 01	07 31				08 07			08 39			09 07					09 39
Yatton	d						06 33		07 06	07 36				08 12			08 44			09 12					09 44
Worle	d						06 39		07 12	07 42				08 18			08 50			09 18					09 50
Weston Milton	d								07 17	07 46							08 55								09 55
Weston-super-Mare	a			05 43			06 44	06 55	07 22	07 50				08 24			09 01			09 24					10 01
	d			05 45			06 46	06 56		07 51										09 32					
Highbridge & Burnham	d			05 55			06 57			08 02										09 44					
Bridgwater	d	00 02		06 03			07 05			08 10										09 52					
Taunton	a	00s14		06 16		07 14	07 19	07 24		08 24					08 42				09 16	10 06			09 50		

		GW	XC	GW	XC	GW		GW	GW	XC	GW	XC	GW	GW	GW	XC		GW	XC	GW	GW	GW	XC	GW	XC
																						R			
		◇	◇1		◇1	◇				◇1		◇1	◇		◇	◇1			◇1	◇			◇1		◇1
			🛒		🛒					🛒		🛒				🛒			🛒				🛒		🛒
Gloucester 7	d	08 41							09 46						10 41							11 46			
Cam & Dursley	d	08 56							10 02						10 56							12 02			
Yate	d	09 11							10 16						11 11							12 16			
Bristol Parkway 7	a	09 19							10 24						11 20							12 24			
	d	09 20	09 26		09 54			10 12	10 25	10 30		10 55		11 12	11 21	11 25			11 54		12 12	12 25	12 31		12 54
Filton Abbey Wood	d	09 23		09 42		10 09		10 16	10 28		10 42		11 09	11 16	11 24			11 42		12 09	12 16	12 28		12 42	
Stapleton Road	d	09 29							10 34						11 30							12 34			
Lawrence Hill	d	09 31							10 36						11 31							12 36			
Bristol Temple Meads 10	a	09 36	09 38	09 51	10 04	10 18		10 24	10 39	10 42	10 52	11 09	11 19	11 24	11 35	11 38		11 51	12 04	12 19	12 24	12 39	12 42	12 51	13 07
	d		09 44	09 55				10 25		10 44	10 53	11 12		11 25		11 44		11 53			12 25		12 44	12 53	
Bedminster	d							10 27						11 27							12 27				
Parson Street	d							10 30						11 30							12 30				
Nailsea & Backwell	d			10 03				10 39			11 03			11 39				12 03			12 39			13 03	
Yatton	d			10 08				10 44			11 08			11 44				12 08			12 44			13 08	
Worle	d			10 14				10 50			11 14			11 50				12 14			12 50			13 14	
Weston Milton	d							10 55						11 55							12 56				
Weston-super-Mare	a			10 22				11 01			11 21	11 29		12 01				12 20			13 01			13 21	
	d			10 23							11 23	11 39						12 22						13 23	
Highbridge & Burnham	d			10 34							11 34							12 33						13 34	
Bridgwater	d			10 42							11 42							12 41						13 42	
Taunton	a		10 17	10 59						11 15	11 56	11 59				12 16		12 57					13 15	13 59	

A 🛒 to Bristol Temple Meads

For connections from London Paddington please see Table 125

For full services to Brighton, Portsmouth Harbour, Westbury and Weymouth please see Table 123

Table 134

Saturdays

15 February to 22 March

Gloucester - Taunton

Network Diagram - see first Page of Table 132

		GW	GW	GW	XC	GW	XC	GW		GW	GW	XC	GW	XC	GW	GW	GW	XC		GW	XC	GW	GW	GW	XC
		◇			◇1 🚲		◇1 🚲	◇			◇	◇1 🚲		◇1 🚲	◇			◇1 🚲			◇1 🚲	◇		◇	◇1 🚲
Gloucester 7	d			12 41							13 42						14 41							15 46	
Cam & Dursley	d			12 56							13 58						14 56							16 02	
Yate	d			13 11							14 13						15 11							16 16	
Bristol Parkway 7	a			13 19							14 21						15 19							16 24	
	d		13 12	13 20	13 25		13 56			14 12	14 22	14 28		14 59		15 12	15 20	15 25			15 55		16 12	16 25	16 30
Filton Abbey Wood	d	13 09	13 16	13 23		13 42		14 09		14 16	14 25		14 42		15 09	15 16	15 23			15 42		16 09	16 16	16 28	
Stapleton Road	d			13 28							14 31						15 28							16 34	
Lawrence Hill	d			13 30							14 33						15 30							16 36	
Bristol Temple Meads 10	a	13 19	13 24	13 34	13 38	13 53	14 05	14 19		14 24	14 38	14 40	14 51	15 09	15 19	15 24	15 35	15 38		15 51	16 07	16 19	16 24	16 40	16 42
	d		13 25		13 44	13 55				14 25		14 44	14 53	15 12		15 26		15 44		15 53			16 26		16 44
Bedminster	d		13 27							14 27						15 28							16 28		
Parson Street	d		13 30			13 59				14 30						15 30							16 30		
Nailsea & Backwell	d		13 39			14 07				14 39			15 03			15 39				16 03			16 39		
Yatton	d		13 44			14 12				14 44			15 08			15 45				16 08			16 45		
Worle	d		13 50			14 18				14 50			15 14			15 51				16 14			16 51		
Weston Milton	d		13 55							14 55						15 56							16 56		
Weston-super-Mare	a		14 01			14 23				15 01			15 21			16 01				16 22			17 01		
	d					14 23							15 23							16 23					
Highbridge & Burnham	d					14 34							15 35							16 34					
Bridgwater	d					14 42							15 43							16 42					
Taunton	a				14 15	15 01						15 17	16 00	15 43				16 15		16 57					17 17

		GW	XC	GW		GW	GW	XC	GW	XC	GW	GW	GW	GW		XC	GW	XC	GW	GW	GW	GW	XC	GW	
			◇1 🚲	R			◇	◇1 🚲		◇1 🚲	◇1 🛒	◇				◇1 🚲		◇1 🚲	◇1 🛒	◇			◇1 🚲		
Gloucester 7	d						16 41							17 46								18 41			
Cam & Dursley	d						16 56							18 02								18 56			
Yate	d						17 11							18 16								19 11			
Bristol Parkway 7	a						17 19							18 24								19 20			
	d		16 54			17 12	17 20	17 26		17 54			18 12	18 25		18 30		18 54			19 12	19 20	19 26		
Filton Abbey Wood	d	16 42		17 09		17 16	17 24		17 42			18 09	18 16	18 28			18 42			19 09	19 15	19 23		19 42	
Stapleton Road	d						17 29							18 34								19 29			
Lawrence Hill	d						17 31							18 36								19 31			
Bristol Temple Meads 10	a	16 51	17 07	17 19		17 24	17 34	17 38	17 51	18 07		18 19	18 24	18 39		18 42	18 51	19 04		19 19	19 25	19 36	19 38	19 51	
	d	16 53	17 10			17 26		17 44	17 53		18 18		18 26			18 44	18 53		19 18				19 44	19 53	
Bedminster	d					17 28							18 28												
Parson Street	d					17 30							18 30												
Nailsea & Backwell	d	17 03				17 39			18 03				18 39				19 03		19 30					20 03	
Yatton	d	17 08				17 45			18 08				18 45				19 08		19 37					20 08	
Worle	d	17 14				17 51			18 14				18 51				19 14		19 43					20 14	
Weston Milton	d					17 56							18 56				19 20							20 20	
Weston-super-Mare	a	17 22				18 01			18 22		18 36		19 01				19 23		19 50					20 23	
	d	17 23							18 23		18 40						19 23							20 24	
Highbridge & Burnham	d	17 34							18 34								19 34							20 34	
Bridgwater	d	17 42							18 42								19 42							20 42	
Taunton	a	17 59	17 41					18 15	18 56		19 06					19 15	19 59						20 15	20 59	

		XC	GW	GW	GW	GW	XC	GW	GW	XC		GW	XC	GW	GW	GW	XC	GW	XC	GW					
		◇1 🚲	◇1 🛒	◇			◇1 A 🚲		◇1 🛒	◇1 🚲		◇	◇1 A 🚲		◇		◇1	◇1 🛒	◇1						
Gloucester 7	d					19 46										21 14			22 05						
Cam & Dursley	d					20 02										21 30									
Yate	d					20 16										21 44									
Bristol Parkway 7	a					20 24										21 53			22 30						
	d	19 56			20 17	20 25	20 30			20 54			21 21			21 53	21 59		22 30						
Filton Abbey Wood	d			20 09	20 21	20 28		20 39				21 08		21 42		21 57				22 52					
Stapleton Road	d					20 34																			
Lawrence Hill	d					20 36																			
Bristol Temple Meads 10	a	20 05		20 19	20 30	20 39	20 42	20 48		21 04		21 19	21 35	21 50		22 05	22 12		22 41	23 00					
	d		20 15				20 44		20 55				21 44		21 59			22 17							
Bedminster	d														22 01										
Parson Street	d														22 03										
Nailsea & Backwell	d								21 04						22 12			22s27							
Yatton	d								21 11						22 18			22s34							
Worle	d								21 17						22 24			22s40							
Weston Milton	d								21 22						22 28										
Weston-super-Mare	a		20 36						21 26						22 31			22s47							
	d		20 38						21 26						22 33										
Highbridge & Burnham	d								21 40						22 44			22s58							
Bridgwater	d								21 47						22 52			23s05							
Taunton	a		21 03				21 15		22 00				22 15		23 05			23 17							

A 🚲 to Bristol Temple Meads

For connections from London Paddington please see Table 125

For full services to Brighton, Portsmouth Harbour, Westbury and Weymouth please see Table 123

Table 134

Saturdays

29 March to 17 May

Gloucester - Taunton

Network Diagram - see first Page of Table 132

		GW	GW	GW	GW	XC		GW	GW	GW	GW	GW	XC	GW	XC	GW		GW	GW	XC	GW	XC	GW	GW	GW
				◇	◇1 🍴	◇1			◇			◇	◇1		◇1 🛒	◇			◇	◇1 🛒		◇1 🛒	R 1 🍴	◇	
Gloucester 7	d										06 20			07 02					07 40						
Cam & Dursley	d										06 37			07 15					07 55						
Yate	d										06 51			07 30					08 10						
Bristol Parkway 7	a										07 01			07 39					08 18						
	d				05 42						07 01			07 40	07 54			08 12	08 20	08 25		08 54			09 12
Filton Abbey Wood	d		00 20								07 05	07 09	07 41	07 45		08 09		08 16	08 23		08 42			09 09	09 16
Stapleton Road	d		00 25																						
Lawrence Hill	d		00 27																						
Bristol Temple Meads 10	a		00 33		05 54						07 13	07 19	07 51	07 55	08 05	08 19		08 24	08 34	08 38	08 53	09 06		09 19	09 24
	d			05 24		06 08		06 18	06 36	06 48	07 18			07 57	08 11			08 25		08 45	08 57		09 17		09 25
Bedminster	d									06 50	07 21							08 27							09 27
Parson Street	d									06 53	07 23							08 30							09 30
Nailsea & Backwell	d							06 28		07 01	07 31			08 07				08 39			09 07				09 39
Yatton	d							06 33		07 06	07 36			08 12				08 44			09 12				09 44
Worle	d							06 39		07 12	07 42			08 18				08 50			09 18				09 50
Weston Milton	d									07 17	07 46							08 55							09 55
Weston-super-Mare	a			05 43				06 44	06 55	07 22	07 50			08 24				09 01			09 24				10 01
	d			05 45				06 46	06 56		07 51										09 32				
Highbridge & Burnham	d			05 55				06 57			08 02										09 44				
Bridgwater	d	00 02		06 03				07 05			08 10										09 52				
Taunton	a	00s14		06 16		07 14		07 19	07 24		08 24				08 42					09 16	10 06		09 50		

		GW		XC	GW	XC	GW	GW	GW	XC	GW	XC		GW	GW	GW	XC	GW	XC	GW	GW	GW		XC	GW
		◇		◇1 🛒		◇1 🛒	◇			◇1 🛒		◇1 🛒		◇		◇	◇1 🛒		◇1 🛒	◇		R		◇1 🛒	
Gloucester 7	d	08 41							09 46							10 41						11 46			
Cam & Dursley	d	08 56							10 02							10 56						12 02			
Yate	d	09 11							10 16							11 11						12 16			
Bristol Parkway 7	a	09 19							10 24							11 20						12 24			
	d	09 20		09 26		09 54		10 12	10 25	10 30		10 55			11 12	11 21	11 25		11 54		12 12	12 25		12 31	
Filton Abbey Wood	d	09 23			09 42		10 09	10 16	10 28		10 42			11 09	11 16	11 24		11 42		12 09	12 16	12 28			12 42
Stapleton Road	d	09 29							10 34							11 30						12 34			
Lawrence Hill	d	09 31							10 36							11 31						12 36			
Bristol Temple Meads 10	a	09 36		09 38	09 51	10 04	10 18	10 24	10 39	10 42	10 52	11 09		11 19	11 24	11 35	11 38	11 51	12 04	12 19	12 24	12 39		12 42	12 51
	d			09 44	09 55			10 25		10 44	10 53	11 12			11 25		11 44	11 53			12 25			12 44	12 53
Bedminster	d							10 27							11 27						12 27				
Parson Street	d							10 30							11 30						12 30				
Nailsea & Backwell	d				10 03			10 39			11 03				11 39			12 03			12 39				13 03
Yatton	d				10 08			10 44			11 08				11 44			12 08			12 44				13 08
Worle	d				10 14			10 50			11 14				11 50			12 14			12 50				13 14
Weston Milton	d							10 55							11 55						12 56				
Weston-super-Mare	a				10 22			11 01			11 21	11 29			12 01			12 20			13 01				13 21
	d				10 23						11 23	11 39						12 22							13 23
Highbridge & Burnham	d				10 34						11 34							12 33							13 34
Bridgwater	d				10 42						11 42							12 41							13 42
Taunton	a			10 17	10 59					11 15	11 56	11 59					12 16	12 57						13 15	13 59

		XC	GW	GW	GW	XC	GW	XC		GW	GW	GW	XC	GW	XC	GW	GW	GW		XC	GW	XC	GW	GW	GW
		◇1 🛒	◇			◇1 🛒		◇1 🛒		◇		◇	◇1 🛒		◇1 🛒	◇				◇1 🛒		◇1 🛒	◇		◇
Gloucester 7	d				12 41							13 42						14 41							15 46
Cam & Dursley	d				12 56							13 58						14 56							16 02
Yate	d				13 11							14 13						15 11							16 16
Bristol Parkway 7	a				13 19							14 21						15 19							16 24
	d	12 54		13 12	13 20	13 25		13 56			14 12	14 22	14 28		14 59		15 12	15 20		15 25		15 55		16 12	16 25
Filton Abbey Wood	d		13 09	13 16	13 23		13 42			14 09	14 16	14 25		14 42		15 09	15 16	15 23			15 42		16 09	16 16	16 28
Stapleton Road	d				13 28							14 31						15 28							16 34
Lawrence Hill	d				13 30							14 33						15 30							16 36
Bristol Temple Meads 10	a	13 07	13 19	13 24	13 34	13 38	13 53	14 05		14 19	14 24	14 38	14 40	14 51	15 09	15 19	15 24	15 35		15 38	15 51	16 07	16 19	16 24	16 40
	d			13 25		13 44	13 55				14 25		14 44	14 53	15 12		15 26			15 44	15 53			16 26	
Bedminster	d			13 27							14 27						15 28							16 28	
Parson Street	d			13 30			13 59				14 30						15 30							16 30	
Nailsea & Backwell	d			13 39			14 07				14 39			15 03			15 39				16 03			16 39	
Yatton	d			13 44			14 12				14 44			15 08			15 45				16 08			16 45	
Worle	d			13 50			14 18				14 50			15 14			15 51				16 14			16 51	
Weston Milton	d			13 55							14 55						15 56							16 56	
Weston-super-Mare	a			14 01			14 23				15 01			15 21			16 01				16 22			17 01	
	d						14 23							15 23							16 23				
Highbridge & Burnham	d						14 34							15 35							16 34				
Bridgwater	d						14 42							15 43							16 42				
Taunton	a					14 15	15 01						15 17	16 00	15 43					16 15	16 57				

For connections from London Paddington please see Table 125

For full services to Brighton, Portsmouth Harbour, Westbury and Weymouth please see Table 123

Table 134

Saturdays

29 March to 17 May

Gloucester - Taunton

Network Diagram - see first Page of Table 132

		XC	GW	XC	GW	GW	GW	XC	GW	XC		GW	GW	GW	GW	XC	GW	XC	GW	GW		GW	GW	XC	GW
		◇1 🛒		◇1 🛒	■		◇	◇1 🛒		◇1 🛒		◇1 ☕	◇			◇1 🛒		◇1 🛒	◇1 ☕	◇				◇1 🛒	
Gloucester 7	d						16 41								17 46								18 41		
Cam & Dursley	d						16 56								18 02								18 56		
Yate	d						17 11								18 16								19 11		
Bristol Parkway 7	a						17 19								18 24								19 20		
	d	16 30		16 54		17 12	17 20	17 26		17 54				18 12	18 25	18 30		18 54				19 12	19 20	19 26	
Filton Abbey Wood	d		16 42		17 09	17 16	17 24		17 42				18 09	18 16	18 28		18 42			19 09		19 15	19 23		19 42
Stapleton Road	d						17 29								18 34								19 29		
Lawrence Hill	d						17 31								18 36								19 31		
Bristol Temple Meads 10	a	16 42	16 51	17 07	17 19	17 24	17 34	17 38	17 51	18 07			18 19	18 24	18 39	18 42	18 51	19 04		19 19		19 25	19 36	19 38	19 51
	d	16 44	16 53	17 10		17 26		17 44	17 53			18 18		18 26		18 44	18 53		19 18					19 44	19 53
Bedminster	d					17 28								18 28											
Parson Street	d					17 30								18 30											
Nailsea & Backwell	d		17 03			17 39			18 03					18 39			19 03		19 30						20 03
Yatton	d		17 08			17 45			18 08					18 45			19 08		19 37						20 08
Worle	d		17 14			17 51			18 14					18 51			19 14		19 43						20 14
Weston Milton	d					17 56								18 56			19 20								20 20
Weston-super-Mare	a		17 22			18 01			18 22			18 36		19 01			19 23		19 50						20 23
	d		17 23						18 23			18 40					19 23								20 24
Highbridge & Burnham	d		17 34						18 34								19 34								20 34
Bridgwater	d		17 42						18 42								19 42								20 42
Taunton	a	17 17	17 59	17 41				18 15	18 56			19 06				19 15	19 59							20 15	20 59

		XC	GW	GW	GW	GW		XC	GW	GW	XC	GW	XC	GW	GW	GW		XC	GW	XC	GW				
		◇1 🛒	◇1 ☕	◇				◇1 A 🛒		◇1 ☕	◇1 A 🛒	◇	◇1 A 🛒		◇			◇1	◇1 ☕	◇1					
Gloucester 7	d					19 46										21 14				22 05					
Cam & Dursley	d					20 02										21 30									
Yate	d					20 16										21 44									
Bristol Parkway 7	a					20 24										21 53				22 30					
	d	19 56			20 17	20 25		20 30			20 54		21 21			21 53		21 59		22 30					
Filton Abbey Wood	d			20 09	20 21	20 28			20 39			21 08		21 42		21 57					22 52				
Stapleton Road	d					20 34																			
Lawrence Hill	d					20 36																			
Bristol Temple Meads 10	a	20 05		20 19	20 30	20 39		20 42	20 48		21 04	21 19	21 35	21 50		22 05		22 12		22 41	23 00				
	d		20 15					20 44		20 55	21 11		21 44		21 59				22 17						
Bedminster	d														22 01										
Parson Street	d														22 03										
Nailsea & Backwell	d									21 04					22 12				22s27						
Yatton	d									21 11					22 18				22s34						
Worle	d									21 17					22 24				22s40						
Weston Milton	d									21 22					22 28										
Weston-super-Mare	a		20 36							21 26					22 31				22s47						
	d		20 38							21 26					22 33										
Highbridge & Burnham	d									21 40					22 44				22s58						
Bridgwater	d									21 47					22 52				23s05						
Taunton	a		21 03					21 15		22 00	21 42		22 15		23 05				23 17						

Sundays

8 December to 29 December

		GW	GW	XC	GW	GW	XC	GW	GW	GW		XC	GW	GW	XC	GW	GW	XC	GW	GW		GW	XC	GW	GW
		◇	◇	◇1 🛒	◇		◇1 🛒	◇1 ☕	◇			◇1 🛒	◇		◇1 🛒	◇1 ☕	■	◇1 🛒	◇				◇1 🛒	◇1 ☕	◇
Gloucester 7	d													10 18								12 19			
Cam & Dursley	d													10 33								12 34			
Yate	d													10 47								12 48			
Bristol Parkway 7	a													10 53								12 58			
	d											10 21		10 56	11 41			12 42				12 58	13 21		
Filton Abbey Wood	d				08 55				10 03				10 54	10 59			11 54		12 56			13 04			13 54
Stapleton Road	d									10 16															
Lawrence Hill	d									10 18															
Bristol Temple Meads 10	a				09 04				10 15	10 21		10 31	11 02	11 07	11 51		12 03	12 51	13 04			13 12	13 31		14 02
	d	07 30	08 28	08 44		09 05	09 48	10 00		10 23		10 44		11 10	11 54	12 00		12 54		13 08			13 44	13 55	
Bedminster	d																								
Parson Street	d																								
Nailsea & Backwell	d		08 38			09 13				10 33				11 20		12 08				13 18				14 08	
Yatton	d	07 43	08 43			09 20				10 38				11 25		12 15				13 23				14 14	
Worle	d		08 49			09 26				10 44				11 31		12 21				13 29				14 21	
Weston Milton	d																								
Weston-super-Mare	a	07 52	08 55			09 35				10 50				11 37		12 31				13 34				14 28	
	d	07 53	08 59							10 58				11 38						13 36					
Highbridge & Burnham	d		09 10							11 09				11 48						13 47					
Bridgwater	d	08 09	09 18							11 17				11 56						13 55					
Taunton	a	08 22	09 31	09 15			10 19	10 33		11 31		11 15		12 10	12 26			13 26		14 09			14 15		

A 🛒 to Bristol Temple Meads

For connections from London Paddington please see Table 125

For full services to Brighton, Portsmouth Harbour, Westbury and Weymouth please see Table 123

Table 134

Sundays

8 December to 29 December

Gloucester - Taunton

Network Diagram - see first Page of Table 132

		XC		GW	GW	GW	XC	XC	GW	GW	GW	XC		GW	XC	GW	GW	XC	GW	GW	XC	GW		GW	GW
		◇1 🚲		◇1 ☕	◇		◇1 🚲	◇1 🚲		◇		◇1 🚲			◇1 🚲	R 1 ☕	◇	◇1 🚲		◇	◇1 🚲	◇		◇	
Gloucester 7	d										15 12														17 19
Cam & Dursley	d										15 27														17 34
Yate	d										15 41														17 48
Bristol Parkway 7	a										15 49														17 56
	d	14 21					14 54	15 24			15 54	16 00			16 21			16 55			17 21				17 57
Filton Abbey Wood	d				14 54					15 54	15 57						16 46			17 19		17 54			18 00
Stapleton Road	d																								
Lawrence Hill	d													←											
Bristol Temple Meads 10	a	14 31			15 03		15 08	15 34		16 04	16 08	16 11		16 08	16 35		16 56	17 08		17 27	17 33	18 04			18 09
	d	14 44		14 55		15 05		15 44	15 55		16 25	16 14		16 25	16 44	16 55			17 25		17 44			18 06	
Bedminster	d					15 08			15 58		→								17 28						
Parson Street	d								16 00																
Nailsea & Backwell	d					15 17			16 08					16 35		17 07			17 37					18 16	
Yatton	d					15 23			16 14					16 40		17 13			17 43					18 21	
Worle	d					15 29			16 20					16 46		17 20			17 49					18 27	
Weston Milton	d					15 34								16 51					17 54						
Weston-super-Mare	a					15 37			16 25					16 55		17 29			17 58					18 33	
	d								16 29							17 31								18 35	
Highbridge & Burnham	d								16 39															18 45	
Bridgwater	d								16 47															18 53	
Taunton	a	15 15		15 30				16 14	17 02			16 45			17 15	17 55					18 18			19 07	

		XC	GW	XC	GW	GW	XC	GW		XC	GW	GW	XC	GW	XC	GW	XC	GW		XC	GW	GW	XC	XC	GW
		◇1 🚲	◇	◇1 🚲		◇	◇1 🚲	R 1 ☕		◇1 🚲	◇		◇1 🚲		◇1 A 🚲	◇1 ☕	◇1 🚲	◇		◇1 A 🚲	◇1 ☕		◇1	◇1	
Gloucester 7	d											19 19										21 15		22 07	
Cam & Dursley	d											19 34										21 31			
Yate	d											19 48										21 45			
Bristol Parkway 7	a											19 56										21 53		22 33	
	d	18 02		18 21			18 55			19 22		19 57	20 04		20 21		20 57			21 21		21 55	21 59	22 33	
Filton Abbey Wood	d		18 23			18 54					19 54	20 00						21 02				21 58			22 52
Stapleton Road	d				18 43																				
Lawrence Hill	d				18 45																				
Bristol Temple Meads 10	a	18 13	18 33	18 36	18 47	19 06	19 08			19 32	20 06	20 09	20 14		20 31		21 06	21 11		21 29		22 07	22 10	22 44	23 00
	d			18 44	19 06			19 25		19 44			20 19	20 25	20 44	20 55				21 44	21 55				
Bedminster	d				19 09									20 28											
Parson Street	d				19 11																				
Nailsea & Backwell	d				19 19			19 33						20 36		21 07					22 06				
Yatton	d				19 25			19 40						20 42		21 13					22 12				
Worle	d				19 31			19 45						20 48		21 20					22 19				
Weston Milton	d				19 34																				
Weston-super-Mare	a				19 38			19 56					20 36	20 53		21 27					22 28				
	d				19 40								20 37	20 58		21 28									
Highbridge & Burnham	d				19 51									21 09											
Bridgwater	d				19 59									21 17											
Taunton	a			19 15	20 13					20 17			20 58	21 33	21 15	21 50				22 15					

		XC	GW	XC
		◇1		◇1
Gloucester 7	d			
Cam & Dursley	d			
Yate	d			
Bristol Parkway 7	a			
	d	22 53		23 22
Filton Abbey Wood	d			
Stapleton Road	d			
Lawrence Hill	d			
Bristol Temple Meads 10	a	23 06		23 33
	d		23 11	
Bedminster	d		23 14	
Parson Street	d		23 16	
Nailsea & Backwell	d		23 24	
Yatton	d		23 30	
Worle	d		23 36	
Weston Milton	d		23 41	
Weston-super-Mare	a		23 44	
	d			
Highbridge & Burnham	d			
Bridgwater	d			
Taunton	a			

A 🚲 to Bristol Temple Meads

For connections from London Paddington please see Table 125

For full services to Brighton, Portsmouth Harbour, Westbury and Weymouth please see Table 123

Table 134

Sundays

Gloucester - Taunton

5 January to 9 February

Network Diagram - see first Page of Table 132

		GW	GW	XC	GW	GW		XC	GW	GW	GW	XC	GW	GW	XC	GW		GW	XC	GW	GW	GW	XC	GW	GW
		◇	◇	◇1 🛒	◇			◇1 🛒	◇1 ☕	◇		◇1 🛒	◇		◇1 🛒	R		◇1 ☕	◇1 🛒	◇			◇1 🛒	◇1 ☕	◇
Gloucester 7	d													10 18								12 19			
Cam & Dursley	d													10 33								12 34			
Yate	d													10 47								12 48			
Bristol Parkway 7	a													10 53								12 58			
	d				08 52							10 21		10 56	11 41				12 42			12 58	13 40		
Filton Abbey Wood	d				08 55					10 03			10 48	10 59		11 48				12 50		13 04			13 48
Stapleton Road	d										10 16														
Lawrence Hill	d										10 18														
Bristol Temple Meads 10	a				09 04					10 15	10 21	10 31	10 56	11 07	11 51	11 57			12 51	12 58		13 12	13 50		13 56
	d	07 30	08 28	08 44		09 05		09 48	10 00		10 23	10 44		11 10	11 54			12 00	12 54		13 08		13 52	13 55	
Bedminster	d																								
Parson Street	d																								
Nailsea & Backwell	d		08 38			09 13					10 33			11 20				12 08			13 18			14 08	
Yatton	d	07 43	08 43			09 20					10 38			11 25				12 15			13 23			14 14	
Worle	d		08 49			09 26					10 44			11 31				12 21			13 29			14 21	
Weston Milton	d																								
Weston-super-Mare	a	07 52	08 55			09 35					10 50			11 37				12 31			13 34			14 28	
	d	07 53	08 59								10 58			11 38							13 36				
Highbridge & Burnham	d		09 10								11 09			11 48							13 47				
Bridgwater	d	08 09	09 18								11 17			11 56							13 55				
Taunton	a	08 22	09 31	09 15				10 19	10 33		11 31	11 15		12 10	12 26				13 26		14 09		14 24		

		XC		GW	GW	GW	XC	XC	GW	GW	GW	XC		GW	XC	GW	GW	XC	GW	GW	XC	GW		GW	GW
		◇1 🛒		◇1 ☕	◇		◇1 🛒	◇1 🛒		◇		◇1 🛒			◇1 🛒	R 1 ☕	◇	◇1 🛒		◇	◇1 🛒	◇		◇	
Gloucester 7	d										15 16														17 19
Cam & Dursley	d										15 30														17 34
Yate	d										15 44														17 48
Bristol Parkway 7	a										15 52														17 56
	d	14 21					14 54	15 40			15 54	16 00			16 21			16 55			17 21				17 57
Filton Abbey Wood	d				14 48					15 47	15 57						16 46			17 19		17 51			18 00
Stapleton Road	d																								
Lawrence Hill	d													←											
Bristol Temple Meads 10	a	14 31			14 59		15 08	15 50		15 57	16 08	16 11		16 08	16 35		16 56	17 08		17 27	17 33	18 02			18 09
	d	14 44		14 55		15 05		15 52	15 55		16 25	16 14		16 25	16 44	16 55			17 25		17 44			18 06	
Bedminster	d					15 08			15 58		→								17 28						
Parson Street	d								16 00																
Nailsea & Backwell	d					15 17			16 08					16 35		17 07			17 37					18 16	
Yatton	d					15 23			16 14					16 40		17 13			17 43					18 21	
Worle	d					15 29			16 20					16 46		17 20			17 49					18 27	
Weston Milton	d					15 34								16 51					17 54						
Weston-super-Mare	a					15 37			16 25					16 55		17 29			17 58					18 33	
	d								16 29							17 31								18 35	
Highbridge & Burnham	d								16 39															18 45	
Bridgwater	d								16 47															18 53	
Taunton	a	15 15		15 30				16 24	17 02			16 45			17 15	17 55					18 18			19 07	

		XC	GW	XC	GW	GW	XC	GW		XC	GW	GW	XC	GW	XC	GW	XC	GW		XC	GW	GW	XC	XC	GW
		◇1 🛒	◇	◇1 🛒		◇	◇1 🛒	R 1 ☕		◇1 🛒	◇		◇1 🛒		◇1 A 🛒	◇1 ☕	◇1 🛒	◇		◇1 A 🛒	◇1 ☕		◇1	◇1	
Gloucester 7	d											19 19										21 15		22 07	
Cam & Dursley	d											19 34										21 31			
Yate	d											19 48										21 45			
Bristol Parkway 7	a											19 56										21 53		22 33	
	d	18 02		18 21			18 55			19 22		19 57	20 04		20 21		20 57			21 21		21 55	21 59	22 33	
Filton Abbey Wood	d		18 23			18 54					19 54	20 00						21 02				21 58			22 52
Stapleton Road	d				18 43																				
Lawrence Hill	d				18 45																				
Bristol Temple Meads 10	a	18 13	18 33	18 36	18 47	19 06	19 08			19 32	20 06	20 09	20 14		20 31		21 06	21 11		21 29		22 07	22 10	22 44	23 00
	d			18 44	19 06			19 25		19 44			20 19	20 25	20 44	20 55				21 44	21 55				
Bedminster	d				19 09									20 28											
Parson Street	d				19 11																				
Nailsea & Backwell	d				19 19			19 33						20 36		21 07					22 06				
Yatton	d				19 25			19 40						20 42		21 14					22 12				
Worle	d				19 31			19 45						20 48		21 20					22 19				
Weston Milton	d				19 34																				
Weston-super-Mare	a				19 38			19 56					20 36	20 53		21 28					22 28				
	d				19 40								20 37	20 58		21 28									
Highbridge & Burnham	d				19 51									21 09											
Bridgwater	d				19 59									21 17											
Taunton	a			19 15	20 13					20 17			20 58	21 33	21 15	21 51				22 15					

A 🛒 to Bristol Temple Meads

For connections from London Paddington please see Table 125

For full services to Brighton, Portsmouth Harbour, Westbury and Weymouth please see Table 123

Table 134

Sundays

5 January to 9 February

Gloucester - Taunton

Network Diagram - see first Page of Table 132

		XC	GW	XC
		◇1		◇1
Gloucester 7	d			
Cam & Dursley	d			
Yate	d			
Bristol Parkway 7	a			
	d	22 53		23 22
Filton Abbey Wood	d			
Stapleton Road	d			
Lawrence Hill	d			
Bristol Temple Meads 10	a	23 06		23 33
	d		23 11	
Bedminster	d		23 14	
Parson Street	d		23 16	
Nailsea & Backwell	d		23 24	
Yatton	d		23 30	
Worle	d		23 36	
Weston Milton	d		23 41	
Weston-super-Mare	a		23 44	
	d			
Highbridge & Burnham	d			
Bridgwater	d			
Taunton	a			

Sundays

16 February to 23 March

		GW	GW	XC	GW	GW	XC	GW	GW	GW		XC	GW
		◇	◇	◇1 🛒	◇		◇1 🛒	◇1 🍴	◇			◇1 🛒	◇
Gloucester 7	d												
Cam & Dursley	d												
Yate	d												
Bristol Parkway 7	a												
	d											10 21	
Filton Abbey Wood	d				08 55				10 01				10 54
Stapleton Road	d									10 16			
Lawrence Hill	d									10 18			
Bristol Temple Meads 10	a				09 04				10 11	10 21		10 31	11 02
	d	07 45	08 28	08 44		09 05	09 48	10 00		10 23		10 44	
Bedminster	d												
Parson Street	d												
Nailsea & Backwell	d		08 38			09 13				10 33			
Yatton	d	07 57	08 45			09 20				10 38			
Worle	d		08 51			09 26				10 44			
Weston Milton	d												
Weston-super-Mare	a	08 06	08 57			09 35				10 50			
	d	08 07	08 58							10 58			
Highbridge & Burnham	d		09 08							11 09			
Bridgwater	d	08 21	09 15							11 17			
Taunton	a	08 32	09 26	09 15			10 19	10 33		11 31		11 15	

		GW	XC	GW	GW	XC	GW	GW		GW	XC	GW	GW
					R								
			◇1 🛒	◇1 🍴		◇1 🛒	◇				◇1 🛒	◇1 🍴	◇
Gloucester 7	d	10 18								12 19			
Cam & Dursley	d	10 33								12 34			
Yate	d	10 47								12 48			
Bristol Parkway 7	a	10 53								12 58			
	d	10 56	11 41			12 42				12 58	13 40		
Filton Abbey Wood	d	10 59			11 54		12 56			13 04			13 54
Stapleton Road	d												
Lawrence Hill	d												
Bristol Temple Meads 10	a	11 07	11 51		12 03	12 51	13 04			13 12	13 49		14 02
	d	11 10	11 54	12 00		12 54		13 08			13 52	14 00	
Bedminster	d												
Parson Street	d												
Nailsea & Backwell	d	11 20		12 08				13 18				14 10	
Yatton	d	11 25		12 15				13 23				14 16	
Worle	d	11 31		12 21				13 29				14 23	
Weston Milton	d												
Weston-super-Mare	a	11 37		12 31				13 34				14 31	
	d	11 38						13 36					
Highbridge & Burnham	d	11 48						13 47					
Bridgwater	d	11 56						13 55					
Taunton	a	12 10	12 26			13 26		14 09			14 24		

		XC	GW	GW	XC	GW		XC	GW	GW	GW	XC	XC
		◇1 🛒	◇1 🍴	◇	◇1 🛒			◇1 🛒		◇		◇1 🛒	◇1 🛒
Gloucester 7	d										15 16		
Cam & Dursley	d										15 30		
Yate	d										15 44		
Bristol Parkway 7	a										15 52		
	d	14 21			14 54			15 40			15 54	16 00	16 21
Filton Abbey Wood	d			14 54						15 54	15 57		
Stapleton Road	d												
Lawrence Hill	d												
Bristol Temple Meads 10	a	14 31		15 03	15 08			15 50		16 04	16 08	16 11	16 35
	d	14 44	15 00			15 20		15 52	15 55		16 25		16 44
Bedminster	d					15 23			15 58				
Parson Street	d								16 00				
Nailsea & Backwell	d					15 32			16 08		16 35		
Yatton	d					15 38			16 14		16 40		
Worle	d					15 44			16 20		16 46		
Weston Milton	d					15 49					16 51		
Weston-super-Mare	a					15 52			16 25		16 55		
	d								16 29				
Highbridge & Burnham	d								16 39				
Bridgwater	d								16 47				
Taunton	a	15 15	15 34					16 24	17 02				17 15

		GW	GW	XC		GW	GW	XC	GW	GW	GW	XC	GW
		R											
		1 🍴	◇	◇1 🛒			◇	◇1 🛒	◇		◇	◇1 🛒	◇
Gloucester 7	d									17 19			
Cam & Dursley	d									17 34			
Yate	d									17 48			
Bristol Parkway 7	a									17 56			
	d			16 55				17 21		17 57		18 02	
Filton Abbey Wood	d		16 53				17 19		17 54	18 00			18 23
Stapleton Road	d												
Lawrence Hill	d												
Bristol Temple Meads 10	a		17 03	17 08			17 27	17 33	18 04	18 09		18 13	18 33
	d	17 00				17 25		17 44			18 10		
Bedminster	d					17 28							
Parson Street	d												
Nailsea & Backwell	d	17 11				17 37					18 20		
Yatton	d	17 17				17 43					18 25		
Worle	d	17 24				17 49					18 31		
Weston Milton	d					17 54							
Weston-super-Mare	a	17 31				17 58					18 37		
	d	17 33									18 38		
Highbridge & Burnham	d										18 49		
Bridgwater	d										18 57		
Taunton	a	17 55						18 18			19 11		

For connections from London Paddington please see Table 125

For full services to Brighton, Portsmouth Harbour, Westbury and Weymouth please see Table 123

Table 134

Gloucester - Taunton

Sundays

16 February to 23 March

Network Diagram - see first Page of Table 132

		XC	GW	GW	XC	GW	XC	GW		GW	XC	GW	XC	GW	XC	GW	XC	GW		GW	XC	XC	GW	XC	GW
		◇1 ⊥o		◇	◇1 ⊥o	■ 1 ⊏P	◇1 ⊥o	◇			◇1 ⊥o		◇1 A ⊥o	◇1 ⊏P	◇1 ⊥o	◇	◇1 A ⊥o	◇1 ⊏P			◇1	◇1		◇1	
Gloucester 7	d									19 19										21 15		22 07			
Cam & Dursley	d									19 34										21 31					
Yate	d									19 48										21 45					
Bristol Parkway 7	a									19 56										21 53		22 33			
	d	18 21			18 55		19 22			19 57	20 04		20 21		20 57		21 21			21 55	21 59	22 33		22 53	
Filton Abbey Wood	d			18 54				19 54		20 00						21 02				21 58			22 52		
Stapleton Road	d		18 43																						
Lawrence Hill	d		18 45																						
Bristol Temple Meads 10	a	18 36	18 47	19 06	19 08		19 32	20 06		20 09	20 14		20 31		21 06	21 11	21 29			22 07	22 10	22 44	23 00	23 06	
	d	18 44	19 06			19 25	19 44					20 25	20 44	21 00			21 44	22 00							23 11
Bedminster	d		19 09									20 28													23 14
Parson Street	d		19 11																						23 16
Nailsea & Backwell	d		19 19			19 33						20 36		21 10				22 11							23 24
Yatton	d		19 25			19 40						20 42		21 17				22 16							23 30
Worle	d		19 31			19 45						20 48		21 23				22 24							23 36
Weston Milton	d		19 34																						23 41
Weston-super-Mare	a		19 38			19 56						20 53		21 31				22 34							23 44
	d		19 40									20 58		21 32											
Highbridge & Burnham	d		19 51									21 09													
Bridgwater	d		19 59									21 17													
Taunton	a	19 15	20 13				20 17					21 33	21 15	21 54			22 15								

		XC
		◇1
Gloucester 7	d	
Cam & Dursley	d	
Yate	d	
Bristol Parkway 7	a	
	d	23 22
Filton Abbey Wood	d	
Stapleton Road	d	
Lawrence Hill	d	
Bristol Temple Meads 10	a	23 33
	d	
Bedminster	d	
Parson Street	d	
Nailsea & Backwell	d	
Yatton	d	
Worle	d	
Weston Milton	d	
Weston-super-Mare	a	
	d	
Highbridge & Burnham	d	
Bridgwater	d	
Taunton	a	

Sundays

30 March to 11 May

		GW	GW	XC	GW	GW	XC	GW	GW	GW		XC	GW	GW	XC	GW	GW	XC	GW	GW		GW	XC	GW	GW
		◇	◇	◇1 ⊥o	◇		◇1 ⊥o	◇1 ⊏P	◇			◇1 ⊥o	◇		◇1 ⊥o	◇1 ⊏P	■	◇1 ⊥o	◇				◇1 ⊥o	◇	◇1 ⊏P
Gloucester 7	d													10 18								12 19			
Cam & Dursley	d													10 33								12 34			
Yate	d													10 47								12 48			
Bristol Parkway 7	a													10 53								12 58			
	d											10 21		10 56	11 41			12 42				12 58	13 21		
Filton Abbey Wood	d				08 55				10 01				10 54	10 59			11 54		12 50			13 04		13 48	
Stapleton Road	d									10 16															
Lawrence Hill	d									10 18															
Bristol Temple Meads 10	a				09 04				10 13	10 21		10 31	11 02	11 07	11 51		12 03	12 51	12 58			13 12	13 31	13 56	
	d	07 30	08 28	08 44		09 05	09 48	10 00		10 23		10 44		11 10	11 54	12 00		12 54		13 08			13 44		14 00
Bedminster	d																								
Parson Street	d																								
Nailsea & Backwell	d		08 38			09 13				10 33				11 20		12 09				13 18					14 10
Yatton	d	07 43	08 43			09 20				10 38				11 25		12 15				13 23					14 16
Worle	d		08 49			09 26				10 44				11 31		12 22				13 29					14 23
Weston Milton	d																								
Weston-super-Mare	a	07 52	08 55			09 35				10 50				11 37		12 31				13 34					14 30
	d	07 53	08 59							10 58				11 38						13 36					
Highbridge & Burnham	d		09 10							11 09				11 48						13 47					
Bridgwater	d	08 09	09 18							11 17				11 56						13 55					
Taunton	a	08 22	09 31	09 15			10 19	10 33		11 31		11 15		12 10	12 26			13 26		14 09			14 15		

A ⊥o to Bristol Temple Meads

For connections from London Paddington please see Table 125

For full services to Brighton, Portsmouth Harbour, Westbury and Weymouth please see Table 123

Table 134

Sundays

30 March to 11 May

Gloucester - Taunton

Network Diagram - see first Page of Table 132

		XC		GW	GW	GW	XC	XC	GW	GW	GW	XC		GW	XC	GW	GW	XC	GW	GW	XC	GW		GW	GW
																R									
		◇1		◇	◇1		◇1	◇1		◇		◇1			◇1	1	◇	◇1		◇	◇1	◇			◇
		🚲			🍴		🚲	🚲				🚲			🚲	🍴		🚲			🚲				
Gloucester 7	d										15 12													17 19	
Cam & Dursley	d										15 27													17 34	
Yate	d										15 41													17 48	
Bristol Parkway 7	a										15 49													17 56	
	d	14 21					14 54	15 24			15 54	16 00			16 21			16 55			17 21			17 57	
Filton Abbey Wood	d			14 50						15 47	15 57						16 53			17 19		17 51		18 00	
Stapleton Road	d																								
Lawrence Hill	d													←											
Bristol Temple Meads 10	a	14 31		14 59			15 08	15 34		15 57	16 08	16 11		16 08	16 35		17 02	17 08		17 27	17 33	18 02		18 09	
	d	14 44			15 00	15 05		15 44	15 55		16 25	16 14		16 25	16 44	16 55			17 25		17 44				18 10
Bedminster	d					15 08			15 58		→								17 28						
Parson Street	d								16 00																
Nailsea & Backwell	d					15 17			16 08					16 35		17 07			17 37						18 20
Yatton	d					15 23			16 14					16 40		17 14			17 43						18 25
Worle	d					15 29			16 20					16 46		17 20			17 49						18 31
Weston Milton	d					15 34								16 51					17 54						
Weston-super-Mare	a					15 37			16 25					16 55		17 28			17 58						18 37
	d								16 29							17 30									18 38
Highbridge & Burnham	d								16 39																18 49
Bridgwater	d								16 47																18 57
Taunton	a	15 15			15 30			16 14	17 02			16 45			17 15	17 53					18 18				19 11

		XC	GW	XC	GW	GW	XC	GW		XC	GW	GW	XC	GW	XC	GW	XC	GW		XC	GW	GW	XC	XC	GW
								R																	
		◇1	◇	◇1		◇	◇1	1		◇1	◇		◇1		◇1	◇1	◇1	◇		◇1	◇1		◇1	◇1	
															A					A					
		🚲		🚲			🚲	🍴		🚲			🚲		🚲	🍴	🚲			🚲	🍴				
Gloucester 7	d											19 19										21 15		22 07	
Cam & Dursley	d											19 34										21 31			
Yate	d											19 48										21 45			
Bristol Parkway 7	a											19 56										21 53		22 33	
	d	18 02		18 21			18 55			19 22		19 57	20 04		20 21		20 57			21 21		21 55	21 59	22 33	
Filton Abbey Wood	d		18 23			18 54					19 54	20 00						21 02				21 58			22 52
Stapleton Road	d				18 43																				
Lawrence Hill	d				18 45																				
Bristol Temple Meads 10	a	18 13	18 33	18 36	18 47	19 06	19 08			19 32	20 06	20 09	20 14		20 31		21 06	21 11		21 29		22 07	22 10	22 44	23 00
	d			18 44	19 06			19 25		19 44			20 19	20 25	20 44	20 55				21 44	21 55				
Bedminster	d				19 09									20 28											
Parson Street	d				19 11																				
Nailsea & Backwell	d				19 19			19 33						20 36		21 07					22 06				
Yatton	d				19 25			19 40						20 42		21 14					22 12				
Worle	d				19 31			19 45						20 48		21 20					22 19				
Weston Milton	d				19 34																				
Weston-super-Mare	a				19 38			19 56					20 36	20 53		21 28					22 28				
	d				19 40								20 37	20 58		21 28									
Highbridge & Burnham	d				19 51									21 09											
Bridgwater	d				19 59									21 17											
Taunton	a			19 15	20 13					20 17			20 58	21 33	21 15	21 50				22 15					

		XC	GW	XC
		◇1		◇1
Gloucester 7	d			
Cam & Dursley	d			
Yate	d			
Bristol Parkway 7	a			
	d	22 53		23 22
Filton Abbey Wood	d			
Stapleton Road	d			
Lawrence Hill	d			
Bristol Temple Meads 10	a	23 06		23 33
	d		23 11	
Bedminster	d		23 14	
Parson Street	d		23 16	
Nailsea & Backwell	d		23 24	
Yatton	d		23 30	
Worle	d		23 36	
Weston Milton	d		23 41	
Weston-super-Mare	a		23 44	
	d			
Highbridge & Burnham	d			
Bridgwater	d			
Taunton	a			

A 🚲 to Bristol Temple Meads

For connections from London Paddington please see Table 125

For full services to Brighton, Portsmouth Harbour, Westbury and Weymouth please see Table 123

Table 134R

Taunton - Gloucester

Mondays to Fridays

9 December to 16 May

Network Diagram - see first Page of Table 132

Miles			GW MO	XC	GW	GW	GW	XC	GW	GW	XC	GW	GW	GW	GW	XC	GW	GW	GW	GW	XC	GW	GW
				◇1				◇1 🛒		R 1 🍽	◇1 🛒	◇1 🍽		R 1 A 🍽		◇1 🛒			◇	◇1 🍽	◇1 🛒	◇	
0	**Taunton**	d				05 12							06 02		06 34	06 50				06 54			
11¾	Bridgwater	d				05 24							06 14		06 46					07 05			
18	Highbridge & Burnham	d				05 32							06 21		06 54					07 13			
25¾	**Weston-super-Mare**	a				05 43							06 32		07 04					07 24			
—		d				05 47				06 20			06 36	06 48	07 08					07 25			07 37
27	Weston Milton	d								06 25			06 39	06 53	07 11								07 40
29½	Worle	d				05 52				06 31			06 43	06 59	07 15					07 32			07 44
33½	Yatton	d				05 59				06 38			06 49	07 06	07 21					07 39			07 49
37½	Nailsea & Backwell	d	00 07			06 05				06 45			06 55	07 13	07 27					07 46			07 55
43¾	Parson Street	d											07 02		07 34								08 02
44½	Bedminster	d	00 16										07 05		07 36			←					08 04
45½	**Bristol Temple Meads 10**	a	00 20			06 17				06 55			07 09	07 23	07 41	07 25		07 41		07 57			08 09
—		d		05 20	05 54		06 19	06 27	06 50		07 00	07 16	07 19		07 47	07 30	07 34	07 47	07 54		08 00	08 10	08 24
46½	Lawrence Hill	d					06 22		06 53				07 22		→			07 50				08 13	
47	Stapleton Road	d					06 25		06 56				07 24					07 52				08 16	
50	Filton Abbey Wood	d			06a01		06a30		07a01			07a23	07 30				07 43	07 59	08a00			08 22	08a32
51¼	**Bristol Parkway 7**	a		05 29				06 37			07 08		07 33			07 38	07 47	08 05			08 08	08 29	
—		d															07 48						
57½	Yate	d															07 57						
72¼	Cam & Dursley	d															08 10						
85¼	**Gloucester 7**	a															08 29						

		GW	GW	XC	GW	GW	GW	XC	GW	GW	GW	XC	GW	GW	GW	GW	XC	GW	GW	XC	GW	GW
		◇1 🍽		◇1 🛒			R 🛒	◇1 🛒	◇			◇1 🛒			◇ 🛒	◇1 🍽	◇1 🛒			◇1 🛒	◇	
Taunton	d	07 12	07 36	07 51				08 12			08 36	08 51				09 05			09 38	09 51		
Bridgwater	d	07 23	07 48								08 48								09 50			
Highbridge & Burnham	d	07 31	07 56								08 56								09 57			
Weston-super-Mare	a	07 42	08 06					08 32			09 08					09 27			10 08			
	d	07 49	08 08					08 33		08 41	09 10					09 29		09 45	10 10			
Weston Milton	d	07 54	08 11							08 44	09 13								10 13			
Worle	d	07 59	08 16							08 48	09 18							09 50	10 17			
Yatton	d	08 06	08 22							08 54	09 24					09 40		09 56	10 23			
Nailsea & Backwell	d	08 13	08 28							09 01	09 30					09 47		10 02	10 29			
Parson Street	d		08 35							09 08	09 36								10 36			
Bedminster	d		08 37			←				09 11	09 39			←					10 39			←
Bristol Temple Meads 10	a	08 25	08 41	08 26		08 41		08 52		09 15	09 43	09 25		09 43		09 57		10 13	10 42	10 25		10 42
	d		08 44	08 30	08 41	08 44	08 54	09 00	09 10	09 21	09 48	09 30	09 41	09 48	09 56		10 00	10 21	10 45	10 30	10 41	10 45
Lawrence Hill	d		→			08 47			09 13		→			09 51					→			10 49
Stapleton Road	d					08 49			09 15					09 53								10 52
Filton Abbey Wood	d				08 48	08 55	09a01		09 23	09a30			09 48	09 59	10a03			10a30			10 48	10 57
Bristol Parkway 7	a			08 38	08 52	09 03		09 08	09 28			09 38	09 52	10 03			10 08			10 38	10 54	11 04
	d				08 52								09 52								10 55	
Yate	d				09 02								10 01								11 04	
Cam & Dursley	d				09 14								10 14								11 18	
Gloucester 7	a				09 32								10 32								11 34	

		GW	XC	GW	XC	GW	GW	GW	GW	XC	GW	GW	XC	GW	GW	GW	XC	GW	XC	GW	GW	GW	GW
		◇ 🛒	◇1 🛒	◇	◇1 🛒			◇ 🛒		◇1 🛒	◇1 🍽		◇1 🛒	◇		◇ 🛒	◇1 🛒		◇1 🛒			◇ 🛒	
Taunton	d			10 07	10 51				11 04	11 17	11 26		11 51					12 07	12 51				13 07
Bridgwater	d			10 19					11 16									12 19					13 19
Highbridge & Burnham	d			10 27					11 24									12 27					13 27
Weston-super-Mare	a			10 38					11 34									12 38					13 38
	d			10 39			11 10		11 45						12 10			12 39			13 10		13 39
Weston Milton	d						11 13								12 13						13 13		
Worle	d			10 45			11 17		11 50						12 17			12 45			13 17		13 45
Yatton	d			10 51			11 23		11 56						12 23			12 51			13 23		13 51
Nailsea & Backwell	d			10 57			11 29		12 02						12 29			12 57			13 29		13 57
Parson Street	d						11 36								12 36						13 36		
Bedminster	d						11 39					←			12 39						13 39		
Bristol Temple Meads 10	a			11 11	11 23		11 43		12 12	11 51	11 58	12 12	12 23		12 43			13 09	13 24		13 42		14 11
	d	10 54	11 00	11 21	11 30	11 41	11 44	11 54	12 21	12 00		12 21	12 30	12 41	12 45	12 54	13 00	13 21	13 30	13 41	13 46	13 54	14 21
Lawrence Hill	d						11 47		→						12 47						13 47		→
Stapleton Road	d						11 50								12 50						13 50		
Filton Abbey Wood	d	11a01		11a30		11 48	11 55	12a01				12a30		12 48	12 55	13a01		13a30		13 48	13 55	14a01	
Bristol Parkway 7	a		11 08		11 38	11 52	12 03			12 08			12 38	12 52	13 03		13 08		13 38	13 52	14 03		
	d					11 52								12 52						13 52			
Yate	d					12 01								13 01						14 01			
Cam & Dursley	d					12 14								13 14						14 14			
Gloucester 7	a					12 33								13 34						14 33			

A The Bristolian

For connections to London Paddington please see Table 125

For full services to Cardiff Central, Cheltenham Spa, Gloucester and Great Malvern please see Table 123

Table 134R

Mondays to Fridays

9 December to 16 May

Taunton - Gloucester

Network Diagram - see first Page of Table 132

		XC		GW	XC	GW	GW	GW	XC	GW	GW	XC		GW	GW	GW	GW	XC	GW	GW	XC	GW		GW	GW
																									R
		◇1			◇1	◇		◇	◇1	◇		◇1			◇		◇	◇1			◇1				
		🛒			🛒			🛒	🛒			🛒					🛒	🛒			🛒				🛒
Taunton	d	13 16			13 52					14 10		14 52						15 11		15 15	15 51				
Bridgwater	d									14 22										15 27					
Highbridge & Burnham	d									14 30										15 34					
Weston-super-Mare	a									14 41								15 36		15 45					
	d						14 10			14 42						15 10		15 38		15 45				16 10	
Weston Milton	d						14 13									15 13								16 13	
Worle	d						14 17			14 48						15 17				15 50				16 17	
Yatton	d						14 23			14 54						15 23				15 56				16 23	
Nailsea & Backwell	d						14 29			15 00						15 29				16 02				16 29	
Parson Street	d						14 36									15 36								16 36	
Bedminster	d			←			14 39									15 39								16 39	
Bristol Temple Meads 10	a	13 55		14 11	14 25		14 43			15 11		15 25				15 43		15 55		16 15	16 26			16 43	
	d	14 00		14 21	14 30	14 41	14 45	14 54	15 00		15 21	15 30		15 34	15 41	15 45	15 54	16 00	16 15	16 24	16 30	16 41		16 44	16 54
Lawrence Hill	d						14 47									15 47			16 18					16 47	
Stapleton Road	d						14 50									15 50			16 20					16 50	
Filton Abbey Wood	d			14a30		14 48	14 55	15a01			15a30				15 48	15 55	16a01		16 26	16a30		16 48		16 55	17a01
Bristol Parkway 7	a	14 08			14 39	14 51	15 03		15 08			15 39		15 46	15 52	16 03		16 08	16 34		16 38	16 52		17 03	
	d					14 52									15 52							16 52			
Yate	d					15 01									16 01							17 01			
Cam & Dursley	d					15 14									16 14							17 14			
Gloucester 7	a					15 34									16 33							17 34			

		XC	GW	GW	XC	GW	GW	GW		GW	GW	XC	GW	XC	GW	GW	GW	GW		XC	GW	XC	GW	GW	GW
										R								R							
		◇1			◇1	◇1	◇					◇1		◇1	◇1					◇1		◇1			◇
		🛒			🛒	☕				🛒		🛒		🛒	☕			🛒		🛒		🛒			🛒
Taunton	d			16 07	16 52						17 06	17 22		17 51							18 08	18 53			
Bridgwater	d			16 19							17 17										18 19				
Highbridge & Burnham	d			16 27							17 25										18 27				
Weston-super-Mare	a			16 37							17 37										18 38				
	d			16 39		17 10		17 15			17 38				18 08		18 15				18 39			19 10	
Weston Milton	d			16 42							17 41										18 43			19 13	
Worle	d			16 45				17 21			17 46						18 21				18 45			19 17	
Yatton	d			16 51				17 26			17 52						18 27				18 51			19 23	
Nailsea & Backwell	d			16 57				17 32			17 58						18 33				18 57			19 29	
Parson Street	d										18 05										19 07				
Bedminster	d			17 07							18 07		←								19 09				
Bristol Temple Meads 10	a			17 11	17 24	17 30		17 44			18 14	17 53	18 14	18 23	18 28		18 44				19 13	19 25		19 43	
	d	17 00	17 10	17 21	17 30		17 41	17 46		17 54	18 21	18 00	18 21	18 30		18 41	18 48	18 54		19 00	19 21	19 30	19 41	19 45	19 54
Lawrence Hill	d		17 13					17 47			→		18 24				18 51				19 24			19 47	
Stapleton Road	d		17 16					17 49					18 26				18a53				19 26			19 50	
Filton Abbey Wood	d		17 22	17a30			17 48	17 55		18a01			18a30			18 48		19a01			19a30		19 48	19 55	20a01
Bristol Parkway 7	a	17 08	17 27		17 39		17 53	18 03				18 08		18 38		18 52				19 08		19 39	19 52	20 03	
	d						17 53									18 52							19 52		
Yate	d						18 01									19 01							20 01		
Cam & Dursley	d						18 14									19 13							20 14		
Gloucester 7	a						18 33									19 30							20 32		

		XC	XC	GW		XC	GW	GW	GW	GW	GW	GW	XC ThFO	XC MTWO		GW	GW	GW	GW	GW	GW
		◇1	◇1			◇1		◇			◇1	◇	◇1	◇1		1		◇1	◇	◇	
						A															
						🛒		🛒			☕							☕			
Taunton	d			19 10		19 51				20 30	21 15		21 18	21 18				21 29		22 23	22 45
Bridgwater	d			19 22						20 42								21 40			22 57
Highbridge & Burnham	d			19 29						20 50								21 47			23 05
Weston-super-Mare	a			19 40						21 00								21 59		22 47	23 15
	d			19 49						21 02						21 34		22 01		22 49	23 17
Weston Milton	d									21 05						21 38					23 20
Worle	d			19 54						21 09						21 43		22 08			23 24
Yatton	d			20 01						21 14						21 50		22 15			23 30
Nailsea & Backwell	d			20 06						21 20						21 56		22 22			23 36
Parson Street	d									21 27											23 42
Bedminster	d									21 29											23 45
Bristol Temple Meads 10	a			20 19		20 24				21 35	21 47		21 51	21 52		22 06		22 32		23 12	23 51
	d	20 00	20 15			20 30	20 41	20 54	21 19			21 54	22 00	22 00			22 12		22 54		
Lawrence Hill	d								21 22												
Stapleton Road	d								21 24												
Filton Abbey Wood	d		20a21				20 48	21a01	21a30			22a01					22 19		23a01		
Bristol Parkway 7	a	20 08				20 38	20 52						22 08	22 08			22 23				
	d	20 09					20 52										22 23				
Yate	d						21 01										22 32				
Cam & Dursley	d						21 14										22 45				
Gloucester 7	a	20 35					21 32										23 03				

A 🛒 to Bristol Temple Meads

For connections to London Paddington please see Table 125

For full services to Cardiff Central, Cheltenham Spa, Gloucester and Great Malvern please see Table 123

Table 134R

Saturdays

Taunton - Gloucester

14 December to 28 December

Network Diagram - see first Page of Table 132

		XC	GW	GW	GW	GW		XC	GW	GW	XC	GW	GW	GW	GW	XC		GW	GW	XC	GW	GW	GW	GW	XC
		◇1 🛒		◇1		◇1 ☕		◇1 🛒			◇1 🛒				◇1 ☕	◇1 🛒				◇1 🛒			◇	◇1 ☕	◇1 🛒
Taunton	d		05 28							06 34	06 51				06 54				07 35	07 51				07 59	08 12
Bridgwater	d		05 40							06 46					07 05				07 47					08 10	
Highbridge & Burnham	d		05 48							06 54					07 12				07 55					08 17	
Weston-super-Mare	a		05 59							07 05					07 24				08 05					08 27	
	d		06 01			06 24				07 08					07 24			07 37	08 06					08 30	
Weston Milton	d		06 04							07 11								07 40	08 09						
Worle	d		06 07			06 32				07 16					07 32			07 44	08 14						
Yatton	d		06 12			06 39				07 21					07 39			07 49	08 20					08 41	
Nailsea & Backwell	d		06 18			06 45				07 27					07 46			07 55	08 26					08 47	
Parson Street	d		06 29							07 35								08 02	08 35						
Bedminster	d		06 31							07 37			←					08 04	08 37			←			
Bristol Temple Meads 10	a		06 34			06 56				07 41	07 23		07 41		07 58			08 10	08 40	08 23		08 40		08 57	08 48
	d	06 15		06 46	06 50			07 00	07 21	07 47	07 30	07 41	07 47	07 54		08 00		08 20	08 45	08 30	08 41	08 45	08 54		09 00
Lawrence Hill	d				06 53					→			07 50					08 23	→			08 48			
Stapleton Road	d				06 56								07 52					08 25				08 50			
Filton Abbey Wood	d			06 54	07a01				07a29			07 48	07 59	08a00				08a30			08 48	08 56	09a01		
Bristol Parkway 7	a	06 23		06 58				07 08			07 38	07 52	08 05			08 08				08 38	08 52	09 03			09 08
	d	06 24										07 52									08 52				
Yate	d											08 01									09 01				
Cam & Dursley	d											08 14									09 14				
Gloucester 7	a	06 52										08 33									09 33				

		GW		XC	GW	GW	GW	XC	GW	XC	GW	GW		GW	XC	GW	GW	XC	GW	GW	GW	GW		XC	GW
				◇1 🛒			◇	◇1 🛒		◇1 🛒	◇			◇	◇1 🛒		◇1 ☕	◇1 🛒	◇		◇			◇1 🛒	
Taunton	d			08 51					09 10	09 51						10 12	10 45	10 51				11 07		11 17	
Bridgwater	d								09 22							10 24						11 19			
Highbridge & Burnham	d								09 30							10 32						11 27			
Weston-super-Mare	a								09 42							10 42						11 37			
	d	08 39				09 10			09 44			10 10				10 43				11 10		11 39			
Weston Milton	d					09 13						10 13								11 13					
Worle	d	08 45				09 17			09 49			10 17				10 49				11 17		11 45			
Yatton	d	08 51				09 22			09 55			10 22				10 55				11 23		11 51			
Nailsea & Backwell	d	08 57				09 28			10 01			10 28				11 01				11 29		11 57			
Parson Street	d					09 35						10 35								11 35					
Bedminster	d					09 38						10 37								11 38					←
Bristol Temple Meads 10	a	09 08		09 24		09 43			10 13	10 24		10 42				11 13	11 24	11 25		11 43		12 10		11 54	12 10
	d	09 21		09 30	09 41	09 45	09 54	10 00	10 21	10 30	10 41	10 45		10 54	11 00	11 21		11 30	11 41	11 45	11 54	12 21		12 00	12 21
Lawrence Hill	d					09 48						10 48								11 48		→			
Stapleton Road	d	09 25				09 50			10 25			10 50				11 25				11 50					12 25
Filton Abbey Wood	d	09a30			09 48	09 56	10a01		10a30		10 48	10 56		11a01		11a30			11 48	11 56	12a01				12a29
Bristol Parkway 7	a			09 38	09 52	10 03		10 08		10 38	10 52	11 03			11 08			11 38	11 52	12 03				12 08	
	d				09 52						10 52								11 52						
Yate	d				10 01						11 01								12 01						
Cam & Dursley	d				10 14						11 14								12 14						
Gloucester 7	a				10 33						11 32								12 33						

		XC	GW	GW	GW	XC	GW	XC		GW	GW	GW	GW	XC	GW	XC	GW	GW		GW	XC	GW	XC	GW	GW
		◇1 🛒	◇		◇	◇1 🛒		◇1 🛒		◇		◇		◇1 🛒		◇1 🛒	◇			◇	◇1 🛒		◇1 🛒	◇	
Taunton	d	11 51					12 07	12 51					13 07	13 16		13 52						14 07	14 51		
Bridgwater	d						12 19						13 19									14 19			
Highbridge & Burnham	d						12 27						13 27									14 27			
Weston-super-Mare	a						12 37						13 37									14 37			
	d			12 10			12 39				13 10		13 39					14 10				14 39			15 10
Weston Milton	d			12 13							13 13							14 13							15 13
Worle	d			12 17			12 45				13 17		13 45					14 17				14 45			15 17
Yatton	d			12 22			12 51				13 22		13 51					14 22				14 51			15 22
Nailsea & Backwell	d			12 28			12 57				13 28		13 57					14 28				14 57			15 28
Parson Street	d			12 35							13 35							14 35							15 35
Bedminster	d			12 37							13 37				←			14 37							15 37
Bristol Temple Meads 10	a	12 24		12 42			13 09	13 23			13 42		14 11	13 54	14 11	14 25		14 42				15 10	15 24		15 42
	d	12 30	12 41	12 45	12 54	13 00	13 21	13 30		13 41	13 45	13 54	14 21	14 00	14 21	14 30	14 41	14 45		14 54	15 00	15 21	15 30	15 41	15 45
Lawrence Hill	d			12 48							13 48		→					14 48							15 48
Stapleton Road	d			12 50			13 25				13 51				14 25			14 50				15 25			15 50
Filton Abbey Wood	d		12 48	12 56	13a01		13a30			13 48	13 57	14a01			14a30		14 48	14 56		15a01		15a30		15 48	15 56
Bristol Parkway 7	a	12 38	12 52	13 00		13 08		13 38		13 52	14 03			14 08		14 39	14 52	15 03			15 08		15 38	15 52	16 03
	d		12 52							13 52							14 52							15 52	
Yate	d		13 01							14 01							15 01							16 01	
Cam & Dursley	d		13 14							14 14							15 14							16 14	
Gloucester 7	a		13 35							14 33							15 33							16 33	

For connections to London Paddington please see Table 125

For full services to Cardiff Central, Cheltenham Spa, Gloucester and Great Malvern please see Table 123

Table 134R

Saturdays

14 December to 28 December

Taunton - Gloucester

Network Diagram - see first Page of Table 132

		GW	XC	GW	XC	GW	GW	GW	XC	GW		XC	GW	GW	GW	GW	XC	GW	XC	GW		GW	GW	XC	GW
																							R		
		◇	◇1		◇1			◇	◇1			◇1	◇		◇		◇1		◇1					◇1	
			🚲		🚲				🚲			🚲					🚲		🚲					🚲	
Taunton	d		15 03	15 07	15 51					16 07		16 51				17 07	17 21		17 51						18 07
Bridgwater	d			15 19						16 19						17 19									18 19
Highbridge & Burnham	d			15 27						16 27						17 27									18 27
Weston-super-Mare	a		15 23	15 37						16 37						17 37									18 37
	d		15 29	15 39			16 10			16 39				17 10		17 39						18 10			18 41
Weston Milton	d						16 13							17 13								18 13			
Worle	d			15 45			16 17			16 45				17 17		17 45						18 17			18 47
Yatton	d			15 51			16 22			16 51				17 22		17 51						18 22			18 53
Nailsea & Backwell	d			15 57			16 28			16 57				17 28		17 57						18 28			18 59
Parson Street	d						16 35			17 04				17 35								18 35			
Bedminster	d						16 37							17 37				←				18 37			
Bristol Temple Meads 10	a		15 49	16 09	16 24		16 42			17 11		17 24		17 42		18 11	17 53	18 11	18 24			18 42			19 10
	d	15 54	16 00	16 21	16 30	16 41	16 45	16 54	17 00	17 21		17 30	17 41	17 45	17 54	18 21	18 00	18 21	18 30	18 41		18 45	18 54	19 00	19 21
Lawrence Hill	d						16 48							17 48		→						18 48			
Stapleton Road	d			16 25			16 50			17 25				17 50				18 25				18 50			
Filton Abbey Wood	d	16a01		16a30		16 48	16 56	17a01		17a30			17 48	17 56	18a01			18a30		18 48		18 56	19a01		19a28
Bristol Parkway 7	a		16 08		16 38	16 52	17 03		17 08			17 38	17 52	18 03			18 08		18 38	18 52		19 03		19 08	
	d					16 52							17 52							18 52					
Yate	d					17 01							18 01							19 01					
Cam & Dursley	d					17 14							18 14							19 14					
Gloucester 7	a					17 33							18 33							19 33					

		XC	GW	GW	GW	XC		GW	XC	XC	GW	GW	GW	GW	GW	GW	GW		GW	GW	GW	GW				
		◇1			◇	◇1			◇1	◇1	◇1			◇		◇1	◇			◇1		◇				
										A																
		🚲								🚲	☕					☕				☕						
Taunton	d	18 52						19 07		19 51				20 17	21 14				21 30	21 35						
Bridgwater	d							19 19						20 29						21 47						
Highbridge & Burnham	d							19 27						20 37						21 55						
Weston-super-Mare	a							19 37						20 48					21 51	22 05						
	d			19 10				19 39			20 10			20 50					21 53	22 07						
Weston Milton	d			19 13										20 53						22 10						
Worle	d			19 17				19 45						20 57						22 14						
Yatton	d			19 22				19 51						21 03						22 20						
Nailsea & Backwell	d			19 28				19 57						21 09						22 26						
Parson Street	d			19 35										21 17						22 33						
Bedminster	d			19 37										21 19						22 36						
Bristol Temple Meads 10	a	19 24		19 42				20 09		20 23	20 30			21 24	21 47				22 12	22 42						
	d	19 30	19 41	19 45	19 54	20 00			20 10	20 30		20 43	20 54	21 29		21 54		22 06			22 54					
Lawrence Hill	d			19 48																						
Stapleton Road	d			19 50																						
Filton Abbey Wood	d		19 48	19 56	20a01				20a16			20 48	21a01	21a36		22a01		22 14			23a01					
Bristol Parkway 7	a	19 39	19 52	20 03		20 08				20 38		20 52						22 17								
	d		19 52									20 52						22 18								
Yate	d		20 01									21 04						22 28								
Cam & Dursley	d		20 14									21 18						22 43								
Gloucester 7	a		20 33									21 34						23 01								

Saturdays

4 January to 8 February

		XC	GW	GW	GW	GW	XC	GW	GW	XC		GW	GW	GW	GW	XC	GW	GW	XC	GW		GW	GW	GW	XC
		◇1		◇1		◇1	◇1			◇1					◇1	◇1			◇1				◇	◇1	◇1
		🚲				☕	🚲			🚲					☕	🚲			🚲					☕	🚲
Taunton	d		05 28						06 34	06 51					06 54			07 35	07 51					07 59	08 12
Bridgwater	d		05 40						06 46						07 05			07 47						08 10	
Highbridge & Burnham	d		05 48						06 54						07 12			07 55						08 17	
Weston-super-Mare	a		05 59						07 05						07 24			08 05						08 27	
	d		06 01			06 24			07 08						07 24		07 37	08 06						08 30	
Weston Milton	d		06 04						07 11								07 40	08 09							
Worle	d		06 07			06 32			07 16						07 32		07 44	08 14							
Yatton	d		06 12			06 39			07 21						07 39		07 49	08 20						08 41	
Nailsea & Backwell	d		06 18			06 45			07 27						07 46		07 55	08 26						08 47	
Parson Street	d		06 29						07 35								08 02	08 35							
Bedminster	d		06 31						07 37				←				08 04	08 37				←			
Bristol Temple Meads 10	a		06 34			06 56			07 41	07 23			07 41		07 58		08 10	08 40	08 23			08 40		08 57	08 48
	d	06 15		06 46	06 50		07 00	07 21	07 47	07 30		07 41	07 47	07 54		08 00	08 20	08 45	08 30	08 41		08 45	08 54		09 00
Lawrence Hill	d				06 53				→				07 50				08 23	→				08 48			
Stapleton Road	d				06 56								07 52				08 25					08 50			
Filton Abbey Wood	d			06 54	07a01			07a29				07 48	07 59	08a00			08a30			08 48		08 56	09a01		
Bristol Parkway 7	a	06 23		06 58			07 08			07 38		07 52	08 05			08 08			08 38	08 52		09 03			09 08
	d	06 24										07 52								08 52					
Yate	d											08 01								09 01					
Cam & Dursley	d											08 14								09 14					
Gloucester 7	a	06 52										08 33								09 33					

A 🚲 to Bristol Temple Meads

For connections to London Paddington please see Table 125

For full services to Cardiff Central, Cheltenham Spa, Gloucester and Great Malvern please see Table 123

Table 134R

Saturdays

4 January to 8 February

Taunton - Gloucester

Network Diagram - see first Page of Table 132

		GW		XC ◇1 🛒	GW	GW	GW ◇	XC ◇1 🛒	GW	XC ◇1 🛒	GW ◇	GW		GW ◇	XC ◇1 🛒	GW	GW ◇1 ⊡	XC ◇1 🛒	GW ◇	GW	GW ◇	GW		XC ◇1 🛒	GW
Taunton	d			08 51					09 10	09 51						10 12	10 45	10 51				11 07		11 17	
Bridgwater	d								09 22							10 24						11 19			
Highbridge & Burnham	d								09 30							10 32						11 27			
Weston-super-Mare	a								09 42							10 42						11 37			
	d	08 39				09 10			09 44			10 10				10 43				11 10		11 39			
Weston Milton	d					09 13						10 13								11 13					
Worle	d	08 45				09 17			09 49			10 17				10 49				11 17		11 45			
Yatton	d	08 51				09 22			09 55			10 22				10 55				11 23		11 51			
Nailsea & Backwell	d	08 57				09 28			10 01			10 28				11 01				11 29		11 57			
Parson Street	d					09 35						10 35								11 35					
Bedminster	d					09 38						10 37								11 38					←
Bristol Temple Meads 10	a	09 08		09 24		09 43			10 13	10 24		10 42				11 13	11 24	11 25		11 43		12 10		11 54	12 10
	d	09 21		09 30	09 41	09 45	09 54	10 00	10 21	10 30	10 41	10 45		10 54	11 00	11 21		11 30	11 41	11 45	11 54	12 21		12 00	12 21
Lawrence Hill	d					09 48						10 48								11 48		→			
Stapleton Road	d	09 25				09 50			10 25			10 50				11 25				11 50					12 25
Filton Abbey Wood	d	09a30			09 48	09 56	10a01		10a30		10 48	10 56		11a01		11a30			11 48	11 56	12a01				12a29
Bristol Parkway 7	a			09 38	09 52	10 03		10 08		10 38	10 52	11 03			11 08			11 38	11 52	12 03				12 08	
	d				09 52						10 52								11 52						
Yate	d				10 01						11 01								12 01						
Cam & Dursley	d				10 14						11 14								12 14						
Gloucester 7	a				10 33						11 32								12 33						

		XC ◇1 🛒	GW ◇	GW	GW ◇	XC ◇1 🛒	GW	XC ◇1 🛒		GW ◇	GW	GW ◇	GW	XC ◇1 🛒	GW	XC ◇1 🛒	GW ◇	GW		GW ◇	XC ◇1 🛒	GW	XC ◇1 🛒	GW ◇	GW
Taunton	d	11 51					12 07	12 51					13 07	13 16		13 52						14 07	14 51		
Bridgwater	d						12 19						13 19									14 19			
Highbridge & Burnham	d						12 27						13 27									14 27			
Weston-super-Mare	a						12 37						13 37									14 37			
	d			12 10			12 39				13 10		13 39					14 10				14 39			15 10
Weston Milton	d			12 13							13 13							14 13							15 13
Worle	d			12 17			12 45				13 17		13 45					14 17				14 45			15 17
Yatton	d			12 22			12 51				13 22		13 51					14 22				14 51			15 22
Nailsea & Backwell	d			12 28			12 57				13 28		13 57					14 28				14 57			15 28
Parson Street	d			12 35							13 35							14 35							15 35
Bedminster	d			12 37							13 37				←			14 37							15 37
Bristol Temple Meads 10	a	12 24		12 42			13 09	13 23			13 42		14 11	13 54	14 11	14 25		14 42				15 10	15 24		15 42
	d	12 30	12 41	12 45	12 54	13 00	13 21	13 30		13 41	13 45	13 54	14 21	14 00	14 21	14 30	14 41	14 45		14 54	15 00	15 21	15 30	15 41	15 45
Lawrence Hill	d			12 48							13 48		→					14 48							15 48
Stapleton Road	d			12 50			13 25				13 51				14 25			14 50				15 25			15 50
Filton Abbey Wood	d		12 48	12 56	13a01		13a30			13 48	13 57	14a01			14a30		14 48	14 56		15a01		15a30		15 48	15 56
Bristol Parkway 7	a	12 38	12 52	13 00		13 08		13 38		13 52	14 03			14 08		14 39	14 52	15 03			15 08		15 38	15 52	16 03
	d		12 52							13 52							14 52							15 52	
Yate	d		13 01							14 01							15 01							16 01	
Cam & Dursley	d		13 14							14 14							15 14							16 14	
Gloucester 7	a		13 35							14 33							15 33							16 33	

		GW ◇	XC ◇1 🛒	GW		XC ◇1 🛒	GW	GW	GW ◇	XC ◇1 🛒	GW	XC ◇1 🛒	GW ◇	GW		GW ◇	GW	XC ◇1 🛒	GW	XC ◇1 🛒	GW	GW	GW R	XC ◇1 🛒	
Taunton	d		15 03	15 07		15 51					16 07	16 51					17 07	17 21		17 51					
Bridgwater	d			15 19							16 19						17 19								
Highbridge & Burnham	d			15 27							16 27						17 27								
Weston-super-Mare	a		15 23	15 37							16 37						17 37								
	d		15 29	15 39				16 10			16 39			17 10			17 39					18 10			
Weston Milton	d							16 13						17 13								18 13			
Worle	d			15 45				16 17			16 45			17 17			17 45					18 17			
Yatton	d			15 51				16 22			16 51			17 22			17 51					18 22			
Nailsea & Backwell	d			15 57				16 28			16 57			17 28			17 57					18 28			
Parson Street	d							16 35			17 04			17 35								18 35			
Bedminster	d							16 37						17 37					←			18 37			
Bristol Temple Meads 10	a		15 49	16 09		16 24		16 42			17 11	17 24		17 42			18 11	17 53	18 11	18 24		18 42			
	d	15 54	16 00	16 21		16 30	16 41	16 45	16 54	17 00	17 21	17 30	17 41	17 45		17 54	18 21	18 00	18 21	18 30	18 41	18 45	18 54	19 00	
Lawrence Hill	d							16 48						17 48			→					18 48			
Stapleton Road	d			16 25				16 50			17 25			17 50					18 25			18 50			
Filton Abbey Wood	d	16a01		16a30			16 48	16 56	17a01		17a30		17 48	17 56		18a01			18a30		18 48	18 56	19a01		
Bristol Parkway 7	a		16 08			16 38	16 52	17 03		17 08		17 38	17 52	18 03				18 08		18 38	18 52	19 03		19 08	
	d						16 52						17 52								18 52				
Yate	d						17 01						18 01								19 01				
Cam & Dursley	d						17 14						18 14								19 14				
Gloucester 7	a						17 33						18 33								19 33				

For connections to London Paddington please see Table 125

For full services to Cardiff Central, Cheltenham Spa, Gloucester and Great Malvern please see Table 123

Table 134R

Saturdays

4 January to 8 February

Taunton - Gloucester

Network Diagram - see first Page of Table 132

		GW	XC ◇1 🛒	GW	GW	GW ◇	XC ◇1	GW	XC ◇1		XC ◇1 A 🛒	GW ◇1 □P	GW	GW ◇	GW	GW ◇1 □P	GW ◇	GW	GW ◇1 □P		GW	GW ◇			
Taunton	d	18 07	18 52					19 07			19 51				20 17	21 14			21 30		21 35				
Bridgwater	d	18 19						19 19							20 29						21 47				
Highbridge & Burnham	d	18 27						19 27							20 37						21 55				
Weston-super-Mare	a	18 37						19 37							20 48				21 51		22 05				
	d	18 41			19 10			19 39				20 10			20 50				21 53		22 07				
Weston Milton	d				19 13										20 53						22 10				
Worle	d	18 47			19 17			19 45							20 57						22 14				
Yatton	d	18 53			19 22			19 51							21 03						22 20				
Nailsea & Backwell	d	18 59			19 28			19 57							21 09						22 26				
Parson Street	d				19 35										21 17						22 33				
Bedminster	d				19 37										21 19						22 36				
Bristol Temple Meads 10	a	19 10	19 24		19 42			20 09			20 23	20 30			21 24	21 47			22 12		22 42				
	d	19 21	19 30	19 41	19 45	19 54	20 00		20 10		20 30		20 43	20 54	21 29		21 54	22 06				22 54			
Lawrence Hill	d				19 48																				
Stapleton Road	d				19 50																				
Filton Abbey Wood	d	19a28		19 48	19 56	20a01			20a16				20 48	21a01	21a36		22a01	22 14				23 01			
Bristol Parkway 7	a		19 39	19 52	20 03		20 08				20 38		20 52					22 17				23 07			
	d			19 52									20 52					22 18							
Yate	d			20 01									21 04					22 28							
Cam & Dursley	d			20 14									21 18					22 43							
Gloucester 7	a			20 33									21 34					23 01							

Saturdays

15 February to 22 March

		XC ◇1 🛒	GW	GW ◇1	GW	GW ◇1 □P	XC ◇1 🛒	GW	GW	XC ◇1 🛒		GW	GW	GW	GW ◇1 □P	XC ◇1 🛒	GW	GW	XC ◇1 🛒	GW		GW	GW ◇	GW ◇1 □P	XC ◇1 🛒
Taunton	d		05 28						06 34	06 51					06 54			07 35	07 51					07 59	08 12
Bridgwater	d		05 40						06 46						07 05			07 47						08 10	
Highbridge & Burnham	d		05 48						06 54						07 12			07 55						08 17	
Weston-super-Mare	a		05 59						07 05						07 24			08 05						08 27	
	d		06 01			06 24			07 08						07 24		07 37	08 06						08 30	
Weston Milton	d		06 04						07 11								07 40	08 09							
Worle	d		06 07			06 32			07 16						07 32		07 44	08 14							
Yatton	d		06 12			06 39			07 21						07 39		07 49	08 20						08 41	
Nailsea & Backwell	d		06 18			06 45			07 27						07 46		07 55	08 26						08 47	
Parson Street	d		06 29						07 35								08 02	08 35							
Bedminster	d		06 31						07 37				←				08 04	08 37				←			
Bristol Temple Meads 10	a		06 34			06 56			07 41	07 23			07 41		07 58		08 10	08 40	08 23			08 40		08 57	08 48
	d	06 15		06 46	06 50		07 00	07 21	07 47	07 30		07 41	07 47	07 54		08 00	08 20	08 45	08 30	08 41		08 45	08 54		09 00
Lawrence Hill	d				06 53				↪				07 50				08 23	↪				08 48			
Stapleton Road	d				06 56								07 52				08 25					08 50			
Filton Abbey Wood	d			06 54	07a01			07a29				07 48	07 59	08a00			08a30			08 48		08 56	09a01		
Bristol Parkway 7	a	06 23		06 58			07 08			07 38		07 52	08 05			08 08			08 38	08 52		09 03			09 08
	d	06 24										07 52								08 52					
Yate	d											08 01								09 01					
Cam & Dursley	d											08 14								09 14					
Gloucester 7	a	06 52										08 33								09 33					

		GW	XC ◇1 🛒	GW	GW	GW ◇		XC ◇1 🛒	GW	XC ◇1 🛒	GW ◇	GW	GW ◇	XC ◇1 🛒	GW	GW ◇1 □P		XC ◇1 🛒	GW ◇	GW	GW ◇	GW	XC ◇1 🛒	GW	XC ◇1 🛒
Taunton	d		08 51						09 10	09 51					10 12	10 45		10 51				11 07	11 17		11 51
Bridgwater	d								09 22						10 24							11 19			
Highbridge & Burnham	d								09 30						10 32							11 27			
Weston-super-Mare	a								09 42						10 42							11 37			
	d	08 39			09 10				09 44			10 10			10 43					11 10		11 39			
Weston Milton	d				09 13							10 13								11 13					
Worle	d	08 45			09 17				09 49			10 17			10 49					11 17		11 45			
Yatton	d	08 51			09 22				09 55			10 22			10 55					11 23		11 51			
Nailsea & Backwell	d	08 57			09 28				10 01			10 28			11 01					11 29		11 57			
Parson Street	d				09 35							10 35								11 35					
Bedminster	d				09 38							10 37								11 38				←	
Bristol Temple Meads 10	a	09 08	09 24		09 43				10 13	10 24		10 42			11 13	11 24		11 25		11 43		12 10	11 54	12 10	12 24
	d	09 21	09 30	09 41	09 45	09 54		10 00	10 21	10 30	10 41	10 45	10 54	11 00	11 21			11 30	11 41	11 45	11 54	12 21	12 00	12 21	12 30
Lawrence Hill	d				09 48							10 48								11 48		↪			
Stapleton Road	d	09 25			09 50				10 25			10 50			11 25					11 50				12 25	
Filton Abbey Wood	d	09a30		09 48	09 56	10a01			10a30		10 48	10 56	11a01		11a30				11 48	11 56	12a01			12a29	
Bristol Parkway 7	a		09 38	09 52	10 03			10 08		10 38	10 52	11 03		11 08				11 38	11 52	12 03			12 08		12 38
	d			09 52							10 52								11 52						
Yate	d			10 01							11 01								12 01						
Cam & Dursley	d			10 14							11 14								12 14						
Gloucester 7	a			10 33							11 32								12 33						

A 🛒 to Bristol Temple Meads

For connections to London Paddington please see Table 125

For full services to Cardiff Central, Cheltenham Spa, Gloucester and Great Malvern please see Table 123

Table 134R

Saturdays

Taunton - Gloucester

15 February to 22 March

Network Diagram - see first Page of Table 132

		GW	GW	GW	XC	GW	XC	GW		GW	GW	GW	XC	GW	XC	GW	GW	GW		XC	GW	XC	GW	GW	GW
		◇		◇	◇1		◇1	◇			◇		◇1		◇1	◇		◇		◇1		◇1	◇		◇
					🚲		🚲						🚲		🚲					🚲		🚲			
Taunton	d					12 07	12 51					13 07	13 16		13 52						14 07	14 51			
Bridgwater	d					12 19						13 19									14 19				
Highbridge & Burnham	d					12 27						13 27									14 27				
Weston-super-Mare	a					12 37						13 37									14 37				
	d		12 10			12 39				13 10		13 39					14 10				14 39			15 10	
Weston Milton	d		12 13							13 13							14 13							15 13	
Worle	d		12 17			12 45				13 17		13 45					14 17				14 45			15 17	
Yatton	d		12 22			12 51				13 22		13 51					14 22				14 51			15 22	
Nailsea & Backwell	d		12 28			12 57				13 28		13 57					14 28				14 57			15 28	
Parson Street	d		12 35							13 35							14 35							15 35	
Bedminster	d		12 37							13 37				↩			14 37							15 37	
Bristol Temple Meads [10]	a		12 42			13 09	13 23			13 42		14 11	13 54	14 11	14 25		14 42				15 10	15 24		15 42	
	d	12 41	12 45	12 54	13 00	13 21	13 30	13 41		13 45	13 54	14 21	14 00	14 21	14 30	14 41	14 45	14 54		15 00	15 21	15 30	15 41	15 45	15 54
Lawrence Hill	d		12 48							13 48		↪					14 48							15 48	
Stapleton Road	d		12 50			13 25				13 51				14 25			14 50				15 25			15 50	
Filton Abbey Wood	d	12 48	12 56	13a01		13a30		13 48		13 57	14a01			14a30		14 48	14 56	15a01			15a30		15 48	15 56	16a01
Bristol Parkway [7]	a	12 52	13 00		13 08		13 38	13 52		14 03			14 08		14 39	14 52	15 03			15 08		15 38	15 52	16 03	
	d	12 52						13 52								14 52							15 52		
Yate	d	13 01						14 01								15 01							16 01		
Cam & Dursley	d	13 14						14 14								15 14							16 14		
Gloucester [7]	a	13 35						14 33								15 33							16 33		

		XC	GW	XC		GW	GW	GW	XC	GW	XC	GW	GW	GW		GW	XC	GW	XC	GW	GW	GW	XC	GW	
																						■			
		◇1		◇1				◇	◇1		◇1	◇		◇			◇1		◇1				◇1		
		🚲		🚲					🚲		🚲						🚲		🚲				🚲		
Taunton	d	15 03	15 07	15 51						16 07	16 51					17 07	17 21		17 51					18 07	
Bridgwater	d		15 19							16 19						17 19								18 19	
Highbridge & Burnham	d		15 27							16 27						17 27								18 27	
Weston-super-Mare	a	15 23	15 37							16 37						17 37								18 37	
	d	15 29	15 39				16 10			16 39			17 10			17 39					18 10			18 41	
Weston Milton	d						16 13						17 13								18 13				
Worle	d		15 45				16 17			16 45			17 17			17 45					18 17			18 47	
Yatton	d		15 51				16 22			16 51			17 22			17 51					18 22			18 53	
Nailsea & Backwell	d		15 57				16 28			16 57			17 28			17 57					18 28			18 59	
Parson Street	d						16 35			17 04			17 35								18 35				
Bedminster	d						16 37						17 37					↩			18 37				
Bristol Temple Meads [10]	a	15 49	16 09	16 24			16 42			17 11	17 24		17 42			18 11	17 53	18 11	18 24		18 42			19 10	
	d	16 00	16 21	16 30		16 41	16 45	16 54	17 00	17 21	17 30	17 41	17 45	17 54		18 21	18 00	18 21	18 30	18 41	18 45	18 54	19 00	19 21	
Lawrence Hill	d						16 48						17 48			↪					18 48				
Stapleton Road	d		16 25				16 50			17 25			17 50					18 25			18 50				
Filton Abbey Wood	d		16a30			16 48	16 56	17a01		17a30		17 48	17 56	18a01				18a30		18 48	18 56	19a01		19a28	
Bristol Parkway [7]	a	16 08		16 38		16 52	17 03		17 08		17 38	17 52	18 03				18 08		18 38	18 52	19 03		19 08		
	d					16 52						17 52								18 52					
Yate	d					17 01						18 01								19 01					
Cam & Dursley	d					17 14						18 14								19 14					
Gloucester [7]	a					17 33						18 33								19 33					

		XC	GW	GW	GW	XC	GW	XC	XC	GW		GW	GW	GW	GW	GW	GW	GW	GW	GW
		◇1			◇	◇1		◇1	◇1	◇1			◇		◇1	◇		◇1		◇
									A											
		🚲							🚲	☕					☕			☕		
Taunton	d	18 52					19 07		19 51					20 17	21 14			21 30	21 35	
Bridgwater	d						19 19							20 29					21 47	
Highbridge & Burnham	d						19 27							20 37					21 55	
Weston-super-Mare	a						19 37							20 48				21 51	22 05	
	d			19 10			19 39			20 10				20 50				21 53	22 07	
Weston Milton	d			19 13										20 53					22 10	
Worle	d			19 17			19 45							20 57					22 14	
Yatton	d			19 22			19 51							21 03					22 20	
Nailsea & Backwell	d			19 28			19 57							21 09					22 26	
Parson Street	d			19 35										21 17					22 33	
Bedminster	d			19 37										21 19					22 36	
Bristol Temple Meads [10]	a	19 24		19 42			20 09		20 23	20 30				21 24	21 47			22 12	22 42	
	d	19 30	19 41	19 45	19 54	20 00		20 10	20 30			20 43	20 54	21 29		21 54	22 06			22 54
Lawrence Hill	d			19 48																
Stapleton Road	d			19 50																
Filton Abbey Wood	d		19 48	19 56	20a01			20a16				20 48	21a01	21a36		22a01	22 14			23a01
Bristol Parkway [7]	a	19 39	19 52	20 03		20 08			20 38			20 52					22 17			
	d		19 52									20 52					22 18			
Yate	d		20 01									21 04					22 28			
Cam & Dursley	d		20 14									21 18					22 43			
Gloucester [7]	a		20 33									21 34					23 01			

A 🚲 to Bristol Temple Meads

For connections to London Paddington please see Table 125

For full services to Cardiff Central, Cheltenham Spa, Gloucester and Great Malvern please see Table 123

Table 134R

Saturdays

29 March to 17 May

Taunton - Gloucester

Network Diagram - see first Page of Table 132

		XC	GW	GW	GW	GW		XC	GW	GW	XC	GW	GW	GW	GW	XC		GW	GW	XC	GW	GW	GW	GW	XC
		◇1		◇1		◇1		◇1			◇1				◇1	◇1				◇1			◇	◇1	◇1
Taunton	d		05 28							06 34	06 51				06 54				07 35	07 51				07 59	08 12
Bridgwater	d		05 40							06 46					07 05				07 47					08 10	
Highbridge & Burnham	d		05 48							06 54					07 12				07 55					08 17	
Weston-super-Mare	a		05 59							07 05					07 24				08 05					08 27	
	d		06 01			06 24				07 08					07 24			07 37	08 06					08 30	
Weston Milton	d		06 04							07 11								07 40	08 09						
Worle	d		06 07			06 32				07 16					07 32			07 44	08 14						
Yatton	d		06 12			06 39				07 21					07 39			07 49	08 20					08 41	
Nailsea & Backwell	d		06 18			06 45				07 27					07 46			07 55	08 26					08 47	
Parson Street	d		06 29							07 35								08 02	08 35						
Bedminster	d		06 31							07 37			←					08 04	08 37			←			
Bristol Temple Meads 10	a		06 34			06 56				07 41	07 23		07 41		07 58			08 10	08 40	08 23		08 40		08 57	08 48
	d	06 15		06 46	06 50			07 00	07 21	07 47	07 30	07 41	07 47	07 54		08 00		08 20	08 45	08 30	08 41	08 45	08 54		09 00
Lawrence Hill	d				06 53					→			07 50					08 23	→			08 48			
Stapleton Road	d				06 56								07 52					08 25				08 50			
Filton Abbey Wood	d			06 54	07a01				07a29			07 48	07 59	08a00				08a30			08 48	08 56	09a01		
Bristol Parkway 7	a	06 23		06 58				07 08			07 38	07 52	08 05			08 08				08 38	08 52	09 03			09 08
	d	06 24										07 52									08 52				
Yate	d											08 01									09 01				
Cam & Dursley	d											08 14									09 14				
Gloucester 7	a	06 52										08 33									09 33				

		GW		XC	GW	GW	GW	XC	GW	XC	GW	GW		GW	XC	GW	GW	XC	GW	GW	GW	GW		XC	GW
				◇1			◇	◇1		◇1	◇			◇	◇1		◇1	◇1	◇		◇			◇1	
Taunton	d			08 51					09 10	09 51						10 12	10 45	10 51				11 07		11 17	
Bridgwater	d								09 22							10 24						11 19			
Highbridge & Burnham	d								09 30							10 32						11 27			
Weston-super-Mare	a								09 42							10 42						11 37			
	d	08 39				09 10			09 44			10 10				10 43				11 10		11 39			
Weston Milton	d					09 13						10 13								11 13					
Worle	d	08 45				09 17			09 49			10 17				10 49				11 17		11 45			
Yatton	d	08 51				09 22			09 55			10 22				10 55				11 23		11 51			
Nailsea & Backwell	d	08 57				09 28			10 01			10 28				11 01				11 29		11 57			
Parson Street	d					09 35						10 35								11 35					
Bedminster	d					09 38						10 37								11 38					←
Bristol Temple Meads 10	a	09 08		09 24		09 43			10 13	10 24		10 42				11 13	11 24	11 25		11 43		12 10		11 54	12 10
	d	09 21		09 30	09 41	09 45	09 54	10 00	10 21	10 30	10 41	10 45		10 54	11 00	11 21		11 30	11 41	11 45	11 54	12 21		12 00	12 21
Lawrence Hill	d					09 48						10 48								11 48		→			
Stapleton Road	d	09 25				09 50			10 25			10 50				11 25				11 50					12 25
Filton Abbey Wood	d	09a30			09 48	09 56	10a01		10a30		10 48	10 56		11a01		11a30			11 48	11 56	12a01				12a29
Bristol Parkway 7	a			09 38	09 52	10 03		10 08		10 38	10 52	11 03			11 08			11 38	11 52	12 03				12 08	
	d				09 52						10 52								11 52						
Yate	d				10 01						11 01								12 01						
Cam & Dursley	d				10 14						11 14								12 14						
Gloucester 7	a				10 33						11 32								12 33						

		XC	GW	GW	GW	XC	GW	XC		GW	GW	GW	GW	XC	GW	XC	GW	GW		GW	XC	GW	XC	GW	GW
		◇1	◇		◇	◇1		◇1		◇		◇		◇1		◇1	◇			◇	◇1		◇1	◇	
Taunton	d	11 51					12 07	12 51					13 07	13 16		13 52						14 07	14 51		
Bridgwater	d						12 19						13 19									14 19			
Highbridge & Burnham	d						12 27						13 27									14 27			
Weston-super-Mare	a						12 37						13 37									14 37			
	d			12 10			12 39				13 10		13 39					14 10				14 39			15 10
Weston Milton	d			12 13							13 13							14 13							15 13
Worle	d			12 17			12 45				13 17		13 45					14 17				14 45			15 17
Yatton	d			12 22			12 51				13 22		13 51					14 22				14 51			15 22
Nailsea & Backwell	d			12 28			12 57				13 28		13 57					14 28				14 57			15 28
Parson Street	d			12 35							13 35							14 35							15 35
Bedminster	d			12 37							13 37				←			14 37							15 37
Bristol Temple Meads 10	a	12 24		12 42			13 09	13 23			13 42		14 11	13 54	14 11	14 25		14 42				15 10	15 24		15 42
	d	12 30	12 41	12 45	12 54	13 00	13 21	13 30		13 41	13 45	13 54	14 21	14 00	14 21	14 30	14 41	14 45		14 54	15 00	15 21	15 30	15 41	15 45
Lawrence Hill	d			12 48							13 48		→					14 48							15 48
Stapleton Road	d			12 50			13 25				13 51				14 25			14 50				15 25			15 50
Filton Abbey Wood	d		12 48	12 56	13a01		13a30			13 48	13 57	14a01			14a30		14 48	14 56		15a01		15a30		15 48	15 56
Bristol Parkway 7	a	12 38	12 52	13 00		13 08		13 38		13 52	14 03			14 08		14 39	14 52	15 03			15 08		15 38	15 52	16 03
	d		12 52							13 52							14 52							15 52	
Yate	d		13 01							14 01							15 01							16 01	
Cam & Dursley	d		13 14							14 14							15 14							16 14	
Gloucester 7	a		13 35							14 33							15 33							16 33	

For connections to London Paddington please see Table 125

For full services to Cardiff Central, Cheltenham Spa, Gloucester and Great Malvern please see Table 123

Table 134R

Taunton - Gloucester

Saturdays

29 March to 17 May

Network Diagram - see first Page of Table 132

		GW	XC	GW	XC	GW	GW	GW	XC	GW		XC	GW	GW	GW	GW	XC	GW	XC	GW		GW	GW	XC	GW
		◇	◇1 🚲		◇1 🚲			◇	◇1 🚲			◇1 🚲	◇		◇		◇1 🚲		◇1 🚲				R	◇1 🚲	
Taunton	d		15 03	15 07	15 51					16 07		16 51				17 07	17 21		17 51						18 07
Bridgwater	d			15 19						16 19						17 19									18 19
Highbridge & Burnham	d			15 27						16 27						17 27									18 27
Weston-super-Mare	a		15 23	15 37						16 37						17 37									18 37
	d		15 29	15 39			16 10			16 39				17 10		17 39						18 10			18 41
Weston Milton	d						16 13							17 13								18 13			
Worle	d			15 45			16 17			16 45				17 17		17 45						18 17			18 47
Yatton	d			15 51			16 22			16 51				17 22		17 51						18 22			18 53
Nailsea & Backwell	d			15 57			16 28			16 57				17 28		17 57						18 28			18 59
Parson Street	d						16 35			17 04				17 35								18 35			
Bedminster	d						16 37							17 37				←				18 37			
Bristol Temple Meads 10	a		15 49	16 09	16 24		16 42			17 11		17 24		17 42		18 11	17 53	18 11	18 24			18 42			19 10
	d	15 54	16 00	16 21	16 30	16 41	16 45	16 54	17 00	17 21		17 30	17 41	17 45	17 54	18 21	18 00	18 21	18 30	18 41		18 45	18 54	19 00	19 21
Lawrence Hill	d						16 48							17 48		→						18 48			
Stapleton Road	d			16 25			16 50			17 25				17 50				18 25				18 50			
Filton Abbey Wood	d	16a01		16a30		16 48	16 56	17a01		17a30			17 48	17 56	18a01			18a30		18 48		18 56	19a01		19a28
Bristol Parkway 7	a		16 08		16 38	16 52	17 03		17 08			17 38	17 52	18 03			18 08		18 38	18 52		19 03		19 08	
	d					16 52							17 52							18 52					
Yate	d					17 01							18 01							19 01					
Cam & Dursley	d					17 14							18 14							19 14					
Gloucester 7	a					17 33							18 33							19 33					

		XC	GW	GW	GW	XC		GW	XC	XC	GW	GW	GW	GW	GW	GW		GW	GW	GW	GW				
		◇1 🚲			◇	◇1			◇1	◇1 A 🚲	◇1 🍽		◇		◇1 🍽	◇			◇1 🍽		◇				
Taunton	d	18 52						19 07		19 51				20 17	21 14				21 30	21 35					
Bridgwater	d							19 19						20 29						21 47					
Highbridge & Burnham	d							19 27						20 37						21 55					
Weston-super-Mare	a							19 37						20 48					21 51	22 05					
	d			19 10				19 39			20 10			20 50					21 53	22 07					
Weston Milton	d			19 13										20 53						22 10					
Worle	d			19 17				19 45						20 57						22 14					
Yatton	d			19 22				19 51						21 03						22 20					
Nailsea & Backwell	d			19 28				19 57						21 09						22 26					
Parson Street	d			19 35										21 17						22 33					
Bedminster	d			19 37										21 19						22 36					
Bristol Temple Meads 10	a	19 24		19 42				20 09		20 23	20 30			21 24	21 47				22 12	22 42					
	d	19 30	19 41	19 45	19 54	20 00			20 10	20 30		20 43	20 54	21 29		21 54		22 06			22 54				
Lawrence Hill	d			19 48																					
Stapleton Road	d			19 50																					
Filton Abbey Wood	d		19 48	19 56	20a01				20a16			20 48	21a01	21a36		22a01		22 14			23a01				
Bristol Parkway 7	a	19 39	19 52	20 03		20 08				20 38		20 52						22 17							
	d		19 52									20 52						22 18							
Yate	d		20 01									21 04						22 28							
Cam & Dursley	d		20 14									21 18						22 43							
Gloucester 7	a		20 33									21 34						23 01							

Sundays

8 December to 29 December

		GW	XC	GW	GW	GW	GW	XC	GW	XC		GW	GW	GW	GW	XC	XC	GW	XC	GW		GW	XC	XC	GW
		◇1 🍽	◇1 🚲	◇			◇1 🍽	◇1 🚲	◇	◇1 🚲		R			R 1 🍽	◇1 🚲	◇1 🚲	R 1 🍽	◇1 🚲	◇			◇1 🚲	◇1 🚲	
Taunton	d			08 35					10 19	10 51				11 36	11 48	11 52	12 01		12 51			13 04	13 25	13 51	
Bridgwater	d			08 47					10 31					11 48								13 16			
Highbridge & Burnham	d			08 55					10 39					11 55								13 23			
Weston-super-Mare	a			09 06					10 49					12 05			12 20					13 34			
	d	08 12		09 08			09 56		10 51					12 11			12 22	12 51				13 43			
Weston Milton	d			09 11										12 14								13 46			
Worle	d	08 19		09 15			10 03		10 57					12 18				12 58				13 50			
Yatton	d	08 26		09 21			10 10		11 03					12 24				13 05				13 56			
Nailsea & Backwell	d	08 32		09 27			10 16		11 09					12 30				13 12				14 02			
Parson Street	d																								
Bedminster	d													12 38											
Bristol Temple Meads 10	a	08 42		09 38			10 27		11 19	11 24				12 42	12 23	12 27	12 44	13 20	13 26			14 13	13 57	14 23	
	d		09 15		09 41	09 48		10 30	11 23	11 30		11 48	12 11			12 30	13 00		13 30	13 48			14 00	14 30	14 41
Lawrence Hill	d								11 26																
Stapleton Road	d								11a28																
Filton Abbey Wood	d				09 46	09a55						11a55	12 16							13a55					14 46
Bristol Parkway 7	a		09 23		09 51			10 38		11 38			12 20			12 38	13 08		13 38				14 08	14 38	14 50
	d		09 24		09 52								12 21												14 51
Yate	d				10 02								12 32												15 03
Cam & Dursley	d				10 16								12 46												15 17
Gloucester 7	a		09 52		10 32								13 03												15 33

A 🚲 to Bristol Temple Meads

For connections to London Paddington please see Table 125

For full services to Cardiff Central, Cheltenham Spa, Gloucester and Great Malvern please see Table 123

Table 134R

Sundays

8 December to 29 December

Taunton - Gloucester

Network Diagram - see first Page of Table 132

		GW		XC	GW	XC	GW	XC	GW	XC	GW	GW		GW	XC	GW	XC	GW	GW	GW	XC	GW		GW	XC
					R											R			R						
		◇		◇1	1	◇1	◇	◇1		◇1		◇			◇1	1	◇1	◇		◇1	◇1			◇1	◇1
				🛒	🍴	🛒		🛒		🛒					🛒	🍴	🛒			🍴	🛒			🍴	🛒
Taunton	d					14 52			15 08	15 52					16 00	16 40	16 52			16 59		17 09		17 42	17 52
Bridgwater	d								15 20											17 10		17 20			
Highbridge & Burnham	d								15 27											17 18		17 27			
Weston-super-Mare	a								15 37						16 20	17 00				17 28		17 38			
	d				14 51				15 39					16 10	16 30	17 02		17 09		17 29		17 42			
Weston Milton	d								15 42					16 13				17 12							
Worle	d				14 58				15 46					16 18				17 16				17 47			
Yatton	d				15 05				15 52					16 24				17 22		17 40		17 53			
Nailsea & Backwell	d				15 11				15 58					16 30				17 28		17 46		17 59			
Parson Street	d													16 37											
Bedminster	d													16 40				17 36							
Bristol Temple Meads 10	a				15 20	15 26			16 09	16 26				16 45	16 49	17 20	17 26	17 40		17 56		18 10		18 17	18 27
	d	14 48		15 00		15 30	15 48	16 00		16 30	16 41	16 48		16 52	17 00		17 30		17 48		18 00				18 30
Lawrence Hill	d													16 55											
Stapleton Road	d													16a57											
Filton Abbey Wood	d	14a55					15a55				16 46	16a55							17a55						
Bristol Parkway 7	a			15 08		15 39		16 08		16 39	16 50				17 08		17 39				18 08				18 38
	d										16 50														
Yate	d										17 02														
Cam & Dursley	d										17 16														
Gloucester 7	a										17 32														

		GW	GW	GW	XC	GW	XC	GW		GW	XC	XC	GW	GW	GW	GW	GW	GW		XC	GW	GW	GW		
			◇		◇1	◇	◇1	◇		◇1	◇1	◇1		◇	◇1		◇	◇1		◇1		◇			
											A														
					🛒		🛒			🍴	🛒	🛒			🍴			🍴							
Taunton	d					18 18	18 49			18 57	19 24	19 52				20 25		21 23			21 35				
Bridgwater	d					18 30				19 07						20 37					21 48				
Highbridge & Burnham	d					18 37				19 14						20 45					21 55				
Weston-super-Mare	a					18 48				19 25						20 56					22 05				
	d			18 16		18 49				19 27					20 26	20 58					22 07		23 48		
Weston Milton	d			18 19												21 01					22 10		23 51		
Worle	d			18 24		18 55									20 33	21 06							23 55		
Yatton	d			18 30		19 00				19 36					20 39	21 12					22 18		23 59		
Nailsea & Backwell	d			18 36		19 06				19 42					20 46	21 18					22 24		00 07		
Parson Street	d			18 43																					
Bedminster	d			18 46												21 27					22 32		00 16		
Bristol Temple Meads 10	a			18 50		19 17	19 24			19 53	19 57	20 25			20 56	21 31		21 55			22 37		00 20		
	d	18 41	18 48		19 00		19 30	19 48			20 00	20 30	20 41	20 48			21 48			22 10		22 48			
Lawrence Hill	d																								
Stapleton Road	d																								
Filton Abbey Wood	d	18 46	18a55					19a55					20 46	20a55			21a55					22a55			
Bristol Parkway 7	a	18 50			19 08		19 38				20 08	20 39	20 50							22 19					
	d	18 50											20 50												
Yate	d	19 02											21 02												
Cam & Dursley	d	19 16											21 16												
Gloucester 7	a	19 32											21 33												

Sundays

5 January to 9 February

		GW	XC	GW	GW	GW	GW	XC	GW	XC		GW	GW	GW	GW	XC	XC	GW	XC	GW		GW	XC	XC	GW
												R			R			R							
		◇1	◇1	◇			◇1	◇1	◇	◇1					1	◇1	◇1	1	◇1	◇			◇1	◇1	
		🍴	🛒				🍴	🛒		🛒					🍴	🛒	🛒	🍴	🛒				🛒	🛒	
Taunton	d			08 35					10 09	10 51				11 36	11 48	11 52	12 01		12 51			13 04	13 25	13 51	
Bridgwater	d			08 47					10 21					11 48								13 16			
Highbridge & Burnham	d			08 55					10 29					11 55								13 23			
Weston-super-Mare	a			09 06					10 39					12 05			12 20					13 34			
	d	08 10		09 08			09 47		10 41					12 11			12 22	12 51				13 43			
Weston Milton	d			09 11										12 14								13 46			
Worle	d	08 17		09 15			09 54		10 47					12 18				12 58				13 50			
Yatton	d	08 24		09 21			10 01		10 53					12 24				13 05				13 56			
Nailsea & Backwell	d	08 30		09 27			10 07		10 59					12 30				13 12				14 02			
Parson Street	d																								
Bedminster	d													12 38											
Bristol Temple Meads 10	a	08 40		09 38			10 17		11 09	11 24				12 42	12 23	12 27	12 44	13 20	13 26			14 13	13 57	14 23	
	d		09 15		09 41	09 48		10 30	11 23	11 30		11 48	12 11			12 30	13 00		13 30	13 48			14 00	14 30	14 38
Lawrence Hill	d								11 26																
Stapleton Road	d								11a28																
Filton Abbey Wood	d				09 46	09a55						11a55	12 16							13a55					14 43
Bristol Parkway 7	a		09 23		09 51			10 38		11 38			12 20			12 38	13 08		13 38				14 08	14 38	14 47
	d		09 24		09 52								12 21												14 48
Yate	d				10 02								12 32												14 59
Cam & Dursley	d				10 16								12 46												15 13
Gloucester 7	a		09 52		10 32								13 03												15 30

A 🛒 to Bristol Temple Meads

For connections to London Paddington please see Table 125

For full services to Cardiff Central, Cheltenham Spa, Gloucester and Great Malvern please see Table 123

Table 134R

Taunton - Gloucester

Sundays

5 January to 9 February

Network Diagram - see first Page of Table 132

	GW		XC	GW	XC	GW	XC	GW	XC	GW	GW		GW	XC	GW	XC	GW	GW	GW	XC	GW		GW	XC
				R											R			R						
	◇		◇1	1	◇1	◇	◇1		◇1		◇			◇1	1	◇1	◇		◇1	◇1			◇1	◇1
			🛒	☕	🛒		🛒		🛒					🛒	☕	🛒			☕	🛒			☕	🛒
Taunton d					14 52			15 08	15 52					16 00	16 40	16 52			16 59		17 09		17 42	17 52
Bridgwater d								15 20											17 10		17 20			
Highbridge & Burnham d								15 27											17 18		17 27			
Weston-super-Mare a								15 37						16 20	17 00				17 28		17 38			
d				14 48				15 39					16 10	16 30	17 02		17 09		17 29		17 42			
Weston Milton d								15 42					16 13				17 12							
Worle d				14 55				15 46					16 18				17 16				17 47			
Yatton d				15 02				15 52					16 24				17 22		17 40		17 53			
Nailsea & Backwell d				15 08				15 58					16 30				17 28		17 46		17 59			
Parson Street d													16 37											
Bedminster d													16 40				17 36							
Bristol Temple Meads 10 a				15 20	15 26			16 09	16 26				16 45	16 49	17 20	17 26	17 40		17 56		18 10		18 17	18 27
d	14 48		15 00		15 30	15 48	16 00		16 30	16 38	16 48		16 52	17 00		17 30		17 48		18 00				18 30
Lawrence Hill d													16 55											
Stapleton Road d													16a57											
Filton Abbey Wood d	14a55					15a55				16 43	16a55							17a55						
Bristol Parkway 7 a			15 08		15 39		16 08		16 39	16 47				17 08		17 39				18 08				18 39
d										16 48														
Yate d										16 59														
Cam & Dursley d										17 13														
Gloucester 7 a										17 32														

	GW	GW	GW	XC	GW	XC	GW		GW	XC	XC	GW	GW	GW	GW	GW	GW		XC	GW	GW	GW		
		◇		◇1	◇	◇1	◇		◇1	◇1	◇1		◇	◇1		◇	◇1		◇1		◇			
										A														
				🛒		🛒			☕	🛒	🛒			☕			☕							
Taunton d					18 18	18 49			18 57	19 24	19 52				20 25		21 23			21 35				
Bridgwater d					18 30				19 07						20 37					21 48				
Highbridge & Burnham d					18 37				19 14						20 45					21 55				
Weston-super-Mare a					18 48				19 25						20 56					22 05				
d			18 16		18 49				19 27					20 21	20 58					22 07		23 48		
Weston Milton d			18 19												21 01					22 10		23 51		
Worle d			18 24		18 55									20 28	21 06							23 55		
Yatton d			18 30		19 00				19 36					20 34	21 12					22 18		23 59		
Nailsea & Backwell d			18 36		19 06				19 42					20 41	21 18					22 24		00 07		
Parson Street d			18 43																					
Bedminster d			18 46												21 27					22 32		00 16		
Bristol Temple Meads 10 a			18 50		19 17	19 24			19 53	19 57	20 25			20 51	21 31		21 55			22 37		00 20		
d	18 41	18 48		19 00		19 30	19 48			20 00	20 30	20 41	20 48			21 48			22 10		22 48			
Lawrence Hill d																								
Stapleton Road d																								
Filton Abbey Wood d	18 46	18a55					19a55					20 46	20a55			21a55					22a55			
Bristol Parkway 7 a	18 50			19 08		19 38				20 08	20 39	20 50							22 19					
d	18 50											20 50												
Yate d	19 02											21 02												
Cam & Dursley d	19 16											21 16												
Gloucester 7 a	19 32											21 33												

Sundays

16 February to 23 March

	GW	XC	GW	GW	GW	GW	XC	GW	XC		GW	GW	GW	GW	XC	XC	GW	XC	GW		GW	XC	GW	GW
											R						R							
	◇1	◇1	◇			◇1	◇1	◇	◇1					◇1	◇1	◇1	1	◇1	◇			◇1		◇
	☕	🛒				☕	🛒		🛒					☕	🛒	🛒	☕	🛒				🛒		
Taunton d			08 35					10 09	10 51				11 36	11 48	11 52			12 51			13 04	13 51		
Bridgwater d			08 47					10 21					11 48								13 16			
Highbridge & Burnham d			08 55					10 29					11 55								13 23			
Weston-super-Mare a			09 06					10 39					12 05								13 34			
d	08 12		09 08			09 47		10 41					12 11				12 51				13 43			
Weston Milton d			09 11										12 14								13 46			
Worle d	08 19		09 15			09 54		10 47					12 18				12 58				13 50			
Yatton d	08 26		09 21			10 01		10 53					12 24				13 05				13 56			
Nailsea & Backwell d	08 32		09 27			10 07		10 59					12 30				13 11				14 02			
Parson Street d																								
Bedminster d													12 38											
Bristol Temple Meads 10 a	08 42		09 38			10 17		11 09	11 24				12 42	12 23	12 27		13 19	13 26			14 13	14 23		
d		09 15		09 41	09 48		10 30	11 23	11 30		11 48	12 11			12 30	13 00		13 30	13 48			14 30	14 38	14 48
Lawrence Hill d								11 26																
Stapleton Road d								11a28																
Filton Abbey Wood d				09 46	09a55						11a55	12 16							13a55				14 43	14a55
Bristol Parkway 7 a		09 23		09 51			10 38		11 38			12 20			12 38	13 08		13 38				14 38	14 47	
d		09 24		09 52								12 21											14 48	
Yate d				10 02								12 32											14 59	
Cam & Dursley d				10 16								12 46											15 13	
Gloucester 7 a		09 52		10 32								13 03											15 30	

A 🛒 to Bristol Temple Meads

For connections to London Paddington please see Table 125

For full services to Cardiff Central, Cheltenham Spa, Gloucester and Great Malvern please see Table 123

Table 134R

Sundays

16 February to 23 March

Taunton - Gloucester

Network Diagram - see first Page of Table 132

		XC		GW	XC	GW	XC	GW	XC	GW	GW	GW		XC	GW	XC	GW	GW	GW	XC	GW	GW		XC	GW
				R														R							
		◇1		1	◇1	◇	◇1		◇1		◇			◇1	◇1	◇1	◇		◇1	◇1		◇1		◇1	
		🛒		☕	🛒		🛒		🛒					🛒	☕	🛒			☕	🛒		☕		🛒	
Taunton	d				14 52			15 08	15 52						16 40	16 52			17 00		17 09	17 43		17 51	
Bridgwater	d							15 20											17 10		17 20				
Highbridge & Burnham	d							15 27											17 18		17 27				
Weston-super-Mare	a							15 37							17 00				17 28		17 40				
	d			14 51				15 39				16 10			17 02		17 09		17 29		17 43				
Weston Milton	d							15 42				16 13					17 12								
Worle	d			14 58				15 46				16 18					17 16				17 48				
Yatton	d			15 05				15 52				16 24					17 22		17 40		17 54				
Nailsea & Backwell	d			15 11				15 58				16 30					17 28		17 46		18 00				
Parson Street	d											16 37													
Bedminster	d											16 40					17 36								
Bristol Temple Meads 10	a			15 20	15 26			16 09	16 26			16 45			17 20	17 26	17 40		17 56		18 11	18 17		18 26	
	d	15 00			15 30	15 48	16 00		16 30	16 41	16 48	16 52		17 00		17 30		17 48		18 00				18 30	18 41
Lawrence Hill	d											16 55													
Stapleton Road	d											16a57													
Filton Abbey Wood	d					15a55				16 46	16a55							17a55							18 46
Bristol Parkway 7	a	15 08			15 39		16 08		16 39	16 50				17 08		17 39				18 08				18 39	18 50
	d									16 50															18 50
Yate	d									17 02															19 02
Cam & Dursley	d									17 16															19 16
Gloucester 7	a									17 32															19 32

		GW	GW	XC	GW	XC	GW	XC		XC	GW	GW	GW	GW	GW	XC	GW	GW		GW	GW
		◇		◇1	◇	◇1	◇	◇1		◇1		◇	◇1		◇	◇1	◇1			◇	
				🛒		🛒							☕				☕				
Taunton	d				18 28	18 49				19 50				20 25		21 11	21 32	21 35			
Bridgwater	d				18 40									20 37				21 48			
Highbridge & Burnham	d				18 47									20 45				21 55			
Weston-super-Mare	a				18 58									20 56				22 05			
	d		18 16		19 08								20 26	20 58				22 07			23 48
Weston Milton	d		18 19											21 01				22 10			23 51
Worle	d		18 24		19 14								20 33	21 06							23 55
Yatton	d		18 30		19 19								20 39	21 12				22 18			23 59
Nailsea & Backwell	d		18 36		19 25								20 46	21 18				22 24			00 07
Parson Street	d		18 43																		
Bedminster	d		18 46											21 27				22 32			00 16
Bristol Temple Meads 10	a		18 50		19 36	19 24				20 23			20 56	21 31		21 48	22 03	22 37			00 20
	d	18 48		19 00		19 30	19 48	20 00		20 30	20 41	20 48			21 48	22 10				22 48	
Lawrence Hill	d																				
Stapleton Road	d																				
Filton Abbey Wood	d	18a55					19a55				20 46	20a55			21a55					22a55	
Bristol Parkway 7	a			19 08		19 38		20 08		20 38	20 50					22 19					
	d										20 50										
Yate	d										21 02										
Cam & Dursley	d										21 16										
Gloucester 7	a										21 33										

Sundays

30 March to 11 May

		GW	XC	GW	GW	GW	GW	XC	GW	XC		GW	GW	GW	GW	XC	XC	GW	XC	GW		GW	XC	XC	GW
												R			R			R							
		◇1	◇1	◇			◇1	◇1	◇	◇1					1	◇1	◇1	1	◇1	◇			◇1	◇1	
		☕	🛒				☕	🛒		🛒					☕	🛒	🛒	☕	🛒				🛒	🛒	
Taunton	d			08 35					10 09	10 51				11 36	11 48	11 52	12 01		12 51			13 04	13 25	13 51	
Bridgwater	d			08 47					10 21					11 48								13 16			
Highbridge & Burnham	d			08 55					10 29					11 55								13 23			
Weston-super-Mare	a			09 06					10 39					12 05			12 20					13 34			
	d	08 12		09 08			09 47		10 41					12 11			12 22	12 51				13 43			
Weston Milton	d			09 11										12 14								13 46			
Worle	d	08 19		09 15			09 54		10 47					12 18				12 58				13 50			
Yatton	d	08 26		09 21			10 01		10 53					12 24				13 05				13 56			
Nailsea & Backwell	d	08 32		09 27			10 07		10 59					12 30				13 12				14 02			
Parson Street	d																								
Bedminster	d													12 38											
Bristol Temple Meads 10	a	08 42		09 38			10 17		11 09	11 24				12 42	12 23	12 27	12 44	13 20	13 26			14 13	13 57	14 23	
	d		09 15		09 41	09 48		10 30	11 23	11 30		11 48	12 11			12 30	13 00		13 30	13 48			14 00	14 30	14 38
Lawrence Hill	d								11 26																
Stapleton Road	d								11a28																
Filton Abbey Wood	d				09 46	09a55						11a55	12 16							13a55					14 43
Bristol Parkway 7	a		09 23		09 51			10 38		11 38			12 20			12 38	13 08		13 38				14 08	14 38	14 47
	d		09 24		09 52								12 21												14 48
Yate	d				10 02								12 32												14 59
Cam & Dursley	d				10 16								12 46												15 13
Gloucester 7	a		09 52		10 32								13 03												15 30

For connections to London Paddington please see Table 125

For full services to Cardiff Central, Cheltenham Spa, Gloucester and Great Malvern please see Table 123

Table 134R

Sundays

30 March to 11 May

Taunton - Gloucester

Network Diagram - see first Page of Table 132

		GW	XC	GW	XC	GW	XC	GW	XC	GW	GW	GW	XC	GW	XC	GW	GW	GW	XC	GW	GW	XC
		◇	◇ 1 🚲	R 1 ☕	◇ 1 🚲	◇	◇ 1 🚲		◇ 1 🚲		◇		◇ 1 🚲	R 1 ☕	◇ 1 🚲	◇	R	◇ 1 ☕	◇ 1 🚲		◇ 1 ☕	◇ 1 🚲
Taunton	d				14 52			15 08	15 52				16 00	16 40	16 52			16 59		17 09	17 42	17 52
Bridgwater	d							15 20										17 10		17 20		
Highbridge & Burnham	d							15 27										17 18		17 27		
Weston-super-Mare	a							15 37					16 20	17 00				17 28		17 38		
	d			14 51				15 39				16 10	16 30	17 02		17 09		17 29		17 42		
Weston Milton	d							15 42				16 13				17 12						
Worle	d			14 58				15 46				16 18				17 16				17 47		
Yatton	d			15 05				15 52				16 24				17 22		17 40		17 53		
Nailsea & Backwell	d			15 11				15 58				16 30				17 28		17 46		17 59		
Parson Street	d											16 37										
Bedminster	d											16 40				17 36						
Bristol Temple Meads 10	a			15 20	15 26			16 09	16 26			16 45	16 49	17 20	17 26	17 40		17 56		18 10	18 15	18 27
	d	14 48	15 00		15 30	15 48	16 00		16 30	16 38	16 48	16 52	17 00		17 30		17 48		18 00			18 30
Lawrence Hill	d											16 55										
Stapleton Road	d											16a57										
Filton Abbey Wood	d	14a55				15a55				16 43	16a55						17a55					
Bristol Parkway 7	a		15 08		15 39		16 08		16 39	16 47			17 08		17 39				18 08			18 38
	d									16 48												
Yate	d									16 59												
Cam & Dursley	d									17 13												
Gloucester 7	a									17 32												

		GW	GW	GW	XC	GW	XC	GW	GW	XC	XC	GW	GW	GW	GW	GW	GW	XC	GW	GW	GW
			◇		◇ 1 🚲	◇	◇ 1 🚲	◇	◇ 1 ☕	◇ 1 A 🚲	◇ 1 🚲		◇	◇ 1 ☕		◇	◇ 1 ☕	◇ 1		◇	
Taunton	d					18 18	18 49		18 57	19 24	19 52				20 25		21 23		21 35		
Bridgwater	d					18 30			19 07						20 37				21 48		
Highbridge & Burnham	d					18 37			19 14						20 45				21 55		
Weston-super-Mare	a					18 48			19 25						20 56				22 05		
	d			18 16		18 49			19 27					20 26	20 58				22 07		23 48
Weston Milton	d			18 19											21 01				22 10		23 51
Worle	d			18 24		18 55								20 33	21 06						23 55
Yatton	d			18 30		19 00			19 36					20 39	21 12				22 18		23 59
Nailsea & Backwell	d			18 36		19 06			19 42					20 46	21 18				22 24		00 07
Parson Street	d			18 43																	
Bedminster	d			18 46											21 27				22 32		00 16
Bristol Temple Meads 10	a			18 50		19 17	19 24		19 53	19 57	20 25			20 56	21 31		21 55		22 37		00 20
	d	18 41	18 48		19 00		19 30	19 48		20 00	20 30	20 41	20 48			21 48		22 10		22 48	
Lawrence Hill	d																				
Stapleton Road	d																				
Filton Abbey Wood	d	18 46	18a55					19a55				20 46	20a55			21a55				22a55	
Bristol Parkway 7	a	18 50			19 08		19 38			20 08	20 39	20 50						22 19			
	d	18 50										20 50									
Yate	d	19 02										21 02									
Cam & Dursley	d	19 16										21 16									
Gloucester 7	a	19 32										21 33									

A 🚲 to Bristol Temple Meads

For connections to London Paddington please see Table 125

For full services to Cardiff Central, Cheltenham Spa, Gloucester and Great Malvern please see Table 123

Route Diagram for Tables 135, 136, 139, 140, 142, 143, 144

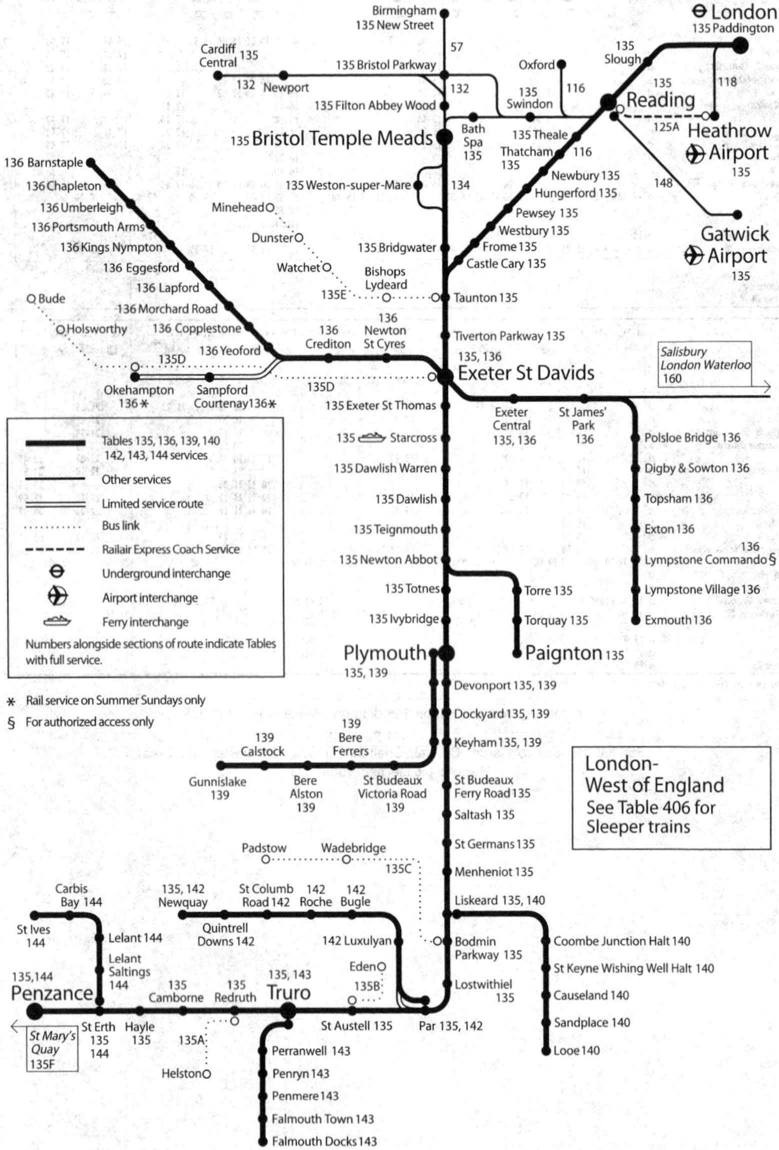

TOCs operating on this network - First Great Western (GW), Cross Country (XC), South West Trains (SW)

Table 135

Mondays to Fridays

9 December to 16 May

London and Birmingham - Devon and Cornwall

Route Diagram - see first Page of Table 135

Miles	Miles			GW MX	GW MX	XC MO ◇1	GW MO R A 🛏 ☕	GW MX R A 🛏 ☕	GW	GW	GW	XC MX ◇1	GW	GW MO R A 🛏 ☕	GW 1 ☕	GW	GW 1	GW ◇	GW	GW	XC ◇1
0	—	**London Paddington 15** ⊖	d																		
18½	—	Slough 3	d																		
36	—	**Reading 7**	d				00u37	00u37													
41¼	—	Theale	d																		
49½	—	Thatcham	d																		
53	—	Newbury	d																		
61½	—	Hungerford	d																		
75¼	—	Pewsey	d																		
95½	—	Westbury	d																		
101¼	—	Frome	d																		
115¼	—	Castle Cary	d																		
—	0	**Birmingham New Street 12**	d																		
—	—	Cardiff Central 7	d																		
—	—	Newport (South Wales)	d																		
—	—	Swindon	d																		
—	87	Bristol Parkway 7	d																		
—	88¼	Filton Abbey Wood	d																		
—	—	Bath Spa 7	d																		
—	92¾	**Bristol Temple Meads 10**	d															05 20			06 34
—	112¾	Weston-super-Mare	d															05 41			
—	126½	Bridgwater	d	00 02														05 59			
143	138¼	Taunton	d	00s14				02 35										06 14			07 07
157¼	—	Tiverton Parkway	d	00s31														06 29			07 19
173¾	—	**Exeter St Davids 6**	a	00 50			03 05	03 06										06 47			07 33
—	—	Exmouth	d																	06 45	
—	—	Exeter Central	d																	07 12	
—	—	**Exeter St Davids 6**	d				04 35	04 11		05 34	06 11					06 28		06 55		07 18	07 35
174¾	—	Exeter St Thomas	d							05 38	06 14							06 58		07 21	
182¼	—	Starcross	d							05 46	06 22							07 07		07 29	
184¼	—	Dawlish Warren	d							05 51	06 27							07 12		07 34	
185¾	—	Dawlish	d							05 55	06 31					06 42		07 16		07 38	
188¾	—	Teignmouth	d							06 00	06 36					06 47		07 21		07 43	
193¾	—	Newton Abbot	a				04 55	04 31		06 07	06 44					06 55		07 28		07 50	07 54
—	—		d				04 56	04 33	05 42	06 09	06 45					06 55	07 06	07 28		07 52	07 55
—	5¼	Torre	d						05 50	06 17	06 53						07 15			08 00	
—	6	Torquay	d						05 53	06 20	06 56						07 20			08 03	
—	8¼	Paignton	a						06 00	06 28	07 06						07 29			08 12	
202½	—	Totnes	d													07 09		07 42			08 07
214	—	Ivybridge	d											←		07 26		07 58			
225¾	—	**Plymouth**	a				05 35	05 14						05 35		07 40		08 11			08 34
—	—		d			05 43	06 28	05 43				06 28		06 28	07 02	07 53		08 14			
227	—	Devonport	d				↪								07 07			08 17			
227½	—	Dockyard	d																		
228	—	Keyham	d																		
228¾	—	St Budeaux Ferry Road	d																		
230	—	Saltash	d												07 15	08 02		08 24			
235	—	St Germans	d												07 23	08 09		08 31			
240¼	—	Menheniot	d																		
243½	—	Liskeard 6	d			06 08		06 08				06 51		07 09	07 36	08 20		08 43			
252½	—	Bodmin Parkway	d			06 22		06 22				07 03		07 23	07 49	08 33		08 55			
256	—	Lostwithiel	d			06 28		06 28				07 08		07 29	07 55	08 40		09 00			
260½	—	Par	d			06 37		06 37				07 15		07 38	08 04	08a54		09 08	09 17		
—	—	Newquay	a																10 09		
265	—	St Austell	d			06 46		06 46				07 21		07 46	08 11			09 16			
279½	—	Truro	d		00 04	07 06		07 06				07 39		08 06	08 30			09 34			
288½	—	Redruth	d		00 17	07 18		07 18				07 50		08 20	08 42			09 47			
292	—	Camborne	d		00 23	07 26		07 26				07 56		08 27	08 48			09 53			
298	—	Hayle	d		00 30	07 35		07 35				08 04		08 38	08 57			10 00			
299½	—	St Erth	d		00 34	07 41		07 42				08 10	08 28	08 45	09 02			10 08			
305¼	—	**Penzance**	a		00 45	07 53		07 53				08 19	08 40	08 59	09 12			10 16			

A The Night Riviera

For connections from Heathrow Airport, Gatwick Airport and Oxford please see Tables 125A, 148 and 116

For the complete service between Westbury and Castle Cary refer to table 123

Table 135 — Mondays to Fridays

9 December to 16 May

London and Birmingham - Devon and Cornwall

Route Diagram - see first Page of Table 135

Station		GW	GW	GW	GW	XC	GW	GW	XC	GW	GW	GW	GW	XC	GW	GW	GW	GW	XC	GW	GW	GW	GW
			◇			◇1	◇1	◇	◇1		◇1	◇	◇	◇1		◇1	◇	◇	◇1			◇1	◇
							A				B											C	
						trolley	restaurant		trolley		restaurant Ø			trolley		restaurant			trolley			restaurant Ø	
London Paddington 15 ⊖	d						07 06				07 30					09 06						10 06	
Slough 3	d																						
Reading 7	d						07 33				07 57					09u35						10u32	
Theale	d																						
Thatcham	d																						
Newbury	d						07 48																
Hungerford	d																						
Pewsey	d						08 07																
Westbury	d						08 25																
Frome	d																						
Castle Cary	d															10 31							
Birmingham New Street 12	d					06 42			07 12					08 12					09 20				
Cardiff Central 7	d												08 00					09 00					
Newport (South Wales)	d												08 15					09 15					
Swindon	d										08 27												
Bristol Parkway 7	d		06 23			07 55			08 26					09 26					10 30				
Filton Abbey Wood	d		06 27										08 42					09 42					
Bath Spa 7	d										08 57												
Bristol Temple Meads 10	d		06 42			08 10			08 44		09 13		08 55	09 44				09 55	10 44				
Weston-super-Mare	d		07 06										09 29					10 23					
Bridgwater	d		07 25										09 48					10 42					
Taunton	d		07 39			08 42	09 02		09 16		09 46		10 02	10 18		10 53		11 00	11 17				
Tiverton Parkway	d		07 54			08 54	09 15		09 28					10 30		11 06		11 16	11 30				
Exeter St Davids 6	a		08 12			09 07	09 30		09 42		10 11		10 33	10 45		11 22		11 33	11 44			12 08	
Exmouth	d	07 14			08 23					09 23					10 23						11 23		
Exeter Central	d	07 43			08 50			09 30		09 53					10 50						11 50		
Exeter St Davids 6	d	07 50	08 14	08 23	08 58	09 09	09 33	09 35	09 43	09 58	10 14		10 34	10 46	10 56	11 25		11 35	11 46		11 56	12 08	
Exeter St Thomas	d	07 53		08 27	09 01					10 01					10 59						11 59		
Starcross	d	08 01		08 36	09 09					10 10					11 07						12 07		
Dawlish Warren	d	08 06		08 41	09 21					10 15			10 46		11 12						12 22		
Dawlish	d	08 10		08 45	09 25					10 19			10 50		11 16						12 27		
Teignmouth	d	08 15		08 50	09 30					10 24			10 55		11 21						12 32		
Newton Abbot	a	08 22	08 35	08 57	09 37	09 28	09 53	09 57	10 01	10 30	10 34		11 02	11 06	11 29	11 44		11 55	12 04		12 39	12 29	
	d	08 24	08 35	08 59	09 39	09 29	09 56	09 58	10 03	10 40	10 36		11 03	11 07	11 30	11 45		11 57	12 06	12 11	12 40	12 29	
Torre	d	08 33		09 07	09 47		10 05			10 48			11 12		11 38					12 19	12 49		
Torquay	d	08 36		09 10	09 50	09 41	10 09			10 51			11 15		11 41					12 22	12 52		
Paignton	a	08 44		09 17	09 57	09 46	10 19			11 00			11 27		11 51					12 30	13 00		
Totnes	d		08 49					10 11	10 17		10 49			11 21		11 58		12 10	12 19				
Ivybridge	d		09 05					10 28										12 27					
Plymouth	a		09 19					10 42	10 46		11 17			11 47		12 27		12 42	12 47			13 06	
	d		09 21					10 43			11 20						12 39					13 11	
Devonport	d		09 24																				
Dockyard	d																						
Keyham	d																						
St Budeaux Ferry Road	d							10 49															
Saltash	d		09 31					10 54									12 48						
St Germans	d		09 38					11 01									12 55						
Menheniot	d																						
Liskeard 6	d		09 50					11 13			11 44						13 07					13 35	
Bodmin Parkway	d		10 02					11 25			11 57						13 19					13 48	
Lostwithiel	d		10 07					11 30									13 24						
Par	d		10 15					11 38			12 09	12 13					13 32					14 00	14 07
Newquay	a											13 01											14 59
St Austell	d		10 22					11 45			12 16						13 39					14 07	
Truro	d		10 40					12 03			12 34						13 57					14 25	
Redruth	d		10 53					12 16			12 46						14 10					14 37	
Camborne	d		10 59					12 22			12 53						14 16					14 45	
Hayle	d		11 06					12 29									14 23					14 54	
St Erth	d		11 10					12 33			13 05						14 28					14 59	
Penzance	a		11 23					12 43			13 17						14 39					15 11	

A The Devon Express

B The Merchant Venturer. Restaurant from Taunton Ø to Taunton

C The Cornish Riveira. Restaurant from Newton Abbot Ø to Newton Abbot

For connections from Heathrow Airport, Gatwick Airport and Oxford please see Tables 125A, 148 and 116

For the complete service between Westbury and Castle Cary refer to table 123

Table 135

Mondays to Fridays

9 December to 16 May

London and Birmingham - Devon and Cornwall

Route Diagram - see first Page of Table 135

		XC	XC	GW	GW	GW	GW	GW	XC	GW	GW	GW	GW	GW	XC	GW	GW	GW	GW	GW	GW	GW
		◇[1]	◇[1]			◇[1]		◇[1]	◇[1]			◇[1]	◇		◇[1]		◇[1]			◇[1]	◇	
						A		B				C								D		
		[trolley]	[trolley]			[buffet]		[buffet][Ø]	[trolley]			[restaurant][buffet]			[trolley]		[buffet]			[buffet][Ø]		
London Paddington [15] ⊖	d					10 00		11 06				12 06					12 18			13 03		
Slough [3]	d																					
Reading [7]	d					10 27		11u33				12u33					12 49			13u33		
Theale	d																12 57					
Thatcham	d																13 05					
Newbury	d																13 13					
Hungerford	d																13 22					
Pewsey	d							12 03									13 40					
Westbury	d							12 21									13 58					
Frome	d																					
Castle Cary	d							12 40									14 16					
Birmingham New Street [12]	d	09 42	10 20						11 20						12 20							
Cardiff Central [7]	d																				13 00	
Newport (South Wales)	d																				13 15	
Swindon	d					10 55																
Bristol Parkway [7]	d	10 54	11 31						12 32						13 32							
Filton Abbey Wood	d																				13 42	
Bath Spa [7]	d					11 24																
Bristol Temple Meads [10]	d	11 15	11 44			11 47			12 44						13 44						13 57	
Weston-super-Mare	d	11 37				12 07															14 25	
Bridgwater	d																				14 44	
Taunton	d	12 01	12 16			12 29		13 02	13 17						14 16		14a41			14 48	14 58	
Tiverton Parkway	d	12 13	12 28					13 15	13 30						14 28					15 01	15 13	
Exeter St Davids [6]	a	12 26	12 42			12 55		13 31	13 44			14 08			14 42					15 17	15 32	
Exmouth	d						12 23				13 23								14 23			
Exeter Central	d						12 50				13 50								14 50			
Exeter St Davids [6]	d	12 28	12 43		12 49	12 57	13 03	13 33	13 46		13 56	14 08			14 43				14 56	15 18		
Exeter St Thomas	d						13 06				13 59								14 59			
Starcross	d						13 15				14 07								15 07			
Dawlish Warren	d						13 20				14 23								15 12			
Dawlish	d	12 40				13 09	13 24				14 27								15 16			
Teignmouth	d	12 45				13 15	13 29				14 32								15 21			
Newton Abbot	a	12 51	13 01		13 12	13 23	13 36	13 52	14 04		14 40	14 28			15 01				15 29	15 39		
	d	12 52	13 03		13 13	13 23	13 38	13 53	14 06	14 10	14 41	14 29		14 50	15 03			15 07	15 30	15 39		15 58
Torre	d				13 22		13 46			14 18	14 49							15 15	15 38			
Torquay	d	13 04			13 25	13 35	13 49			14 21	14 52							15 18	15 41			
Paignton	a	13 10			13 34	13 43	13 58			14 29	15 00							15 26	15 51			
Totnes	d		13 15					14 06	14 19					15 02	15 15					15 53		16 11
Ivybridge	d													15 19								16 28
Plymouth	a		13 41					14 36	14 46			15 06		15 37	15 41					16 22		16 44
	d			13 53								15 12				15 57						
Devonport	d															16 00						
Dockyard	d															16x01						
Keyham	d															16 03						
St Budeaux Ferry Road	d															16 06						
Saltash	d			14 02												16 11						
St Germans	d			14 09												16 18						
Menheniot	d															16x25						
Liskeard [6]	d			14 21								15 36				16 32						
Bodmin Parkway	d			14 33								15 49				16 44						
Lostwithiel	d			14 38												16 49						
Par	d			14 46								16 01	16 10			16 57						
Newquay	a												17 02									
St Austell	d			14 53								16 08				17 06						
Truro	d			15 11								16 26				17 23						
Redruth	d			15 24								16 38				17 36						
Camborne	d			15 30								16 46				17 42						
Hayle	d			15 37								16 55				17 50						
St Erth	d			15 42								17 00				17 54						
Penzance	a			15 53								17 12				18 06						

A The Torbay Express

B The Mayflower. [buffet] from Taunton [Ø] to Taunton

C The Royal Duchy. Restaurant for customers joining at Paddington + Reading. [buffet] from Newton Abbot [restaurant] to Newton Abbot

D [buffet] from Newton Abbot [Ø] to Newton Abbot

For connections from Heathrow Airport, Gatwick Airport and Oxford please see Tables 125A, 148 and 116

For the complete service between Westbury and Castle Cary refer to table 123

Table 135

Mondays to Fridays

9 December to 16 May

London and Birmingham - Devon and Cornwall

Route Diagram - see first Page of Table 135

		GW	XC	GW	XC	GW	GW	GW	GW	GW		XC	GW	GW	GW	GW	GW	GW	XC	GW		XC	GW	GW	GW
														FO											
			◇[1]		◇[1]			◇[1]	◇			◇[1]		◇				◇[1]	◇[1]			◇[1]	◇[1]		
								A										B	C			D			
			🛒		🛒			🍽⊘				🛒						🍽⊘	🛒			🛒	🍽		
London Paddington [15] ⊖	d							14 06										15 06					16 06		
Slough [3]	d																								
Reading [7]	d							14u34										15u33					16u32		
Theale	d																								
Thatcham	d																								
Newbury	d																								
Hungerford	d																								
Pewsey	d																	16 03							
Westbury	d													15 20				16 23							
Frome	d													15 31											
Castle Cary	d													15 50				16 41							
Birmingham New Street [12]	d		13 20		13 42							14 20							15 20			15 42			
Cardiff Central [7]	d																								
Newport (South Wales)	d																								
Swindon	d																								
Bristol Parkway [7]	d		14 32		14 54							15 31							16 34			16 54			
Filton Abbey Wood	d																								
Bath Spa [7]	d																								
Bristol Temple Meads [10]	d		14 44		15 13							15 44							16 46			17 13			
Weston-super-Mare	d																								
Bridgwater	d																								
Taunton	d		15 17		15 45			15 49				16 16		16 26				17 05	17 18			17 45	17 50		
Tiverton Parkway	d		15 30		15 57			16 02				16 28		16 41				17 18	17 30			17 57	18 03		
Exeter St Davids [6]	a		15 45		16 12			16 18				16 41		17 02				17 34	17 44			18 11	18 19		
Exmouth	d					15 23				15 53						16 55									17 58
Exeter Central	d					15 50				16 20					16 46	17 22				17 45					18 25
Exeter St Davids [6]	d		15 47			15 56	16 05	16 20		16 26		16 43			16 56	17 28		17 35	17 45	17 50		18 12	18 22		18 30
Exeter St Thomas	d					15 59				16 29					16 59	17 31				17 54					18 33
Starcross	d					16 07				16 37					17 07	17 39				18 02					18 42
Dawlish Warren	d					16 12	16 18			16 42					17 12	17 50				18 07					18 47
Dawlish	d					16 16	16 22			16 46					17 16	17 54				18 11		18 24			18 51
Teignmouth	d					16 21	16 27			16 51					17 21	17 59				18 16		18 29			18 56
Newton Abbot	a		16 05			16 30	16 35	16 39		16 58		17 02			17 29	18 06		17 56	18 10	18 23		18 35	18 42		19 03
	d	15 59	16 07			16 30	16 48	16 40		17 00		17 04			17 30	18 10		17 57	18 12	18 25		18 37	18 43		19 11
Torre	d	16 07				16 38				17 08					17 38	18 18				18 33					19 19
Torquay	d	16 10				16 41				17 11					17 41	18 21				18 36		18 48			19 22
Paignton	a	16 18				16 51				17 20					17 51	18 30				18 45		18 55			19 30
Totnes	d		16 20				17 02	16 53				17 16						18 10	18 24				18 56		
Ivybridge	d						17 19																19 12		
Plymouth	a		16 48				17 34	17 21				17 42						18 38	18 50				19 26		
	d			17 04				17 23					17 55				18 17	18 42	19 01				19 31		
Devonport	d			17 07													18 20								
Dockyard	d			17x08													18x21								
Keyham	d			17 10													18 23								
St Budeaux Ferry Road	d			17 13													18 25								
Saltash	d			17 17				17 34					18 04				18 31						19 40		
St Germans	d			17 24				17 41									18 38								
Menheniot	d			17x32													18x45								
Liskeard [6]	d			17a40				17 54					18 20				18a53	19 07	19 24				19 57		
Bodmin Parkway	d							18 07					18 32					19 19	19 36				20 10		
Lostwithiel	d							18 13					18 37												
Par	d							18 22	18 29				18 45					19 31	19 47				20 22	20 28	
Newquay	a								19 21															21 20	
St Austell	d							18 29					18 53					19 39	19 53				20 29		
Truro	d							18 47					19 10					20 00	20 11				20 47		
Redruth	d							18 59					19 23					20 10	20 26				20 59		
Camborne	d							19 07					19 29					20 18	20 32				21 07		
Hayle	d							19 16					19 36												
St Erth	d							19 21					19 42					20 28	20 44				21 20		
Penzance	a							19 33					19 54					20 42	20 52				21 31		

A 🍽 from Newton Abbot ⊘ to Newton Abbot

B The Cornishman. 🍽 from Newton Abbot ⊘ to Newton Abbot

C 🛒 to Plymouth

D 🛒 to Newton Abbot

For connections from Heathrow Airport, Gatwick Airport and Oxford please see Tables 125A, 148 and 116

For the complete service between Westbury and Castle Cary refer to table 123

Table 135

Mondays to Fridays

9 December to 16 May

London and Birmingham - Devon and Cornwall

Route Diagram - see first Page of Table 135

		XC	GW	GW	GW	GW	XC	GW	GW		GW	GW	XC	GW	GW	GW		GW	GW	XC	XC	GW	XC	GW	GW
			FX	FO										FX	FO	FO		FX		FO	FX	FX			
																■		■							
		◇1	◇1	◇1	◇1		◇1	◇1	◇1		◇1	◇1	◇1	◇1	◇1	1		1		◇1	◇1		◇1	◇1	
		A					A				B					C		C		D	D				
		🛒	⊡	⊡	⊡		🛒	⊡	⊡		✕⊡	⊡	🛒	⊡	⊡	✕⊡		✕⊡		🛒	🛒		🛒	⊡	
London Paddington [15] ⊖	d		16 36	16 36	17 03			17 06	17 33		18 03	18 05		18 35	18 35	19 03		19 03						19 45	
Slough [3]	d																								
Reading [7]	d		17 04	17 04	17u30			17 39	18 01		18u31	18 37		19 03	19 03	19u33		19 33						20 12	
Theale	d							17 48				18 46													
Thatcham	d							17 58				18 56													
Newbury	d		17 19	17 19	17 48			18 05	18 19			19 03		19 19	19 19	19 50		19 50						20 28	
Hungerford	d		17 29	17 29				18 19				19 17		19 29	19 29										
Pewsey	d		17 44	17 44					18 41			19 36		19 47	19 47									20 48	
Westbury	d		18 03	18 03					19 01			19 55		20 06	20 06									21 06	
Frome	d											20a06													
Castle Cary	d		18 21	18 21					19 19					20 24	20 24									21 26	
Birmingham New Street [12]	d	16 12					17 12						18 12							19 12	19 12		19 42		
Cardiff Central [7]	d																								
Newport (South Wales)	d																								
Swindon	d																								
Bristol Parkway [7]	d	17 27					18 29						19 28							20 30	20 30		20 56		
Filton Abbey Wood	d																								
Bath Spa [7]	d							19 24																	
Bristol Temple Meads [10]	d	17 44					18 44	19a41					19 44							20 44	20 45		21 13		
Weston-super-Mare	d																								
Bridgwater	d																								
Taunton	d	18 16	18 44	18 44	18 52		19 16		19 42		19 48		20 17	20 46	20 46	20 54		20 54		21 17	21 17		21 45	21 48	
Tiverton Parkway	d	18 28	18 57	18 57	19 05		19 28		19 55				20 29	20 59	20 59	21 07		21 07		21 29	21 29		21 57	22 02	
Exeter St Davids [6]	a	18 42	19 14	19 14	19 21		19 42		20 09		20 13		20 42	21 16	21 16	21 23		21 23		21 43	21 43		22 11	22 18	
Exmouth	d					18 55																			22 05
Exeter Central	d					19 21													21 21						22 31
Exeter St Davids [6]	d	18 46		19 14	19 22	19 28	19 44		20 20		20 16		20 44		21 17	21 25		21 25	21 29	21 45	21 45		22 12	22 19	22 37
Exeter St Thomas	d					19 31			20 24										21 32						22 40
Starcross	d					19 39			20 33										21 40						22 48
Dawlish Warren	d					19 44			20 38										21 45						22 59
Dawlish	d					19 48			20 43										21 49						23 03
Teignmouth	d					19 53			20 50										21 54						23 08
Newton Abbot	a	19 06		19 34	19 42	20 00	20 04		20 57		20 36		21 01		21 36	21 44		21 44	22 01	22 04	22 04		22 30	22 39	23 15
	d	19 08		19 35	19 42	20 09	20 06		20 58		20 36		21 03		21 37	21 45		21 45	22 03	22 06	22 06		22 32	22 40	23 16
Torre	d					20 17			21 08										22 11						23 24
Torquay	d					20 20			21 12										22 14						23 27
Paignton	a					20 29			21 22										22 23						23 37
Totnes	d	19 21			19 56		20 18				20 50		21 16			21 58		21 58		22 17	22 17		22 44	22 53	
Ivybridge	d																							23 10	
Plymouth	a	19 46		20 15	20 24		20 44				21 18		21 46		22 15	22 26		22 26		22 43	22 43		23 13	23 25	
	d	19 49			20 26		20 50				21 20					22 29						22 45			
Devonport	d																								
Dockyard	d																								
Keyham	d																								
St Budeaux Ferry Road	d																								
Saltash	d				20 37											22 39						22 54			
St Germans	d				20 44											22 46						23 01			
Menheniot	d																								
Liskeard [6]	d	20 12			20 56		21 13				21 45					22 59						23 13			
Bodmin Parkway	d	20 24			21 09		21 25				21 59					23 13						23 25			
Lostwithiel	d						21 31									23 19						23 30			
Par	d	20 35			21 21		21 38				22 11					23 28						23 38			
Newquay	a																								
St Austell	d	20 42			21 28		21 45				22 18					23 35						23 45			
Truro	d	21 02			21 46		22 03				22 37					23 53						00 04			
Redruth	d	21 16			21 58		22 14				22 48					00 06						00 17			
Camborne	d	21 23					22 20									00 14						00 23			
Hayle	d				22 11		22 28									00 22						00 30			
St Erth	d	21 34			22 16		22 33			22 45						00 28						00 34			
Penzance	a	21 42			22 30		22 42			22 57	23 13					00 40						00 45			

A 🛒 to Plymouth

B Restaurant service available for customers joining at PAD + RDG. The Golden Hind. ⊡ from Taunton ✕ to Taunton

C Restaurant for customers joining at Pad, Reading + Newbury. The Armada. ⊡ from Taunton ✕ to Taunton

D 🛒 to Bristol Temple Meads

For connections from Heathrow Airport, Gatwick Airport and Oxford please see Tables 125A, 148 and 116

For the complete service between Westbury and Castle Cary refer to table 123

Table 135

Mondays to Fridays

9 December to 16 May

London and Birmingham - Devon and Cornwall

Route Diagram - see first Page of Table 135

		XC	GW	GW	GW	GW	GW
		◇1	◇1	◇		◇1	
		A					B
London Paddington 15 ⊖	d		20 35			21 45	23 45
Slough 3	d						
Reading 7	d		21 02			22 11	00u37
Theale	d						
Thatcham	d						
Newbury	d		21 19				
Hungerford	d						
Pewsey	d		21 38				
Westbury	d		21 56				
Frome	d						
Castle Cary	d		22 15				
Birmingham New Street 12	d	20 12					
Cardiff Central 7	d						
Newport (South Wales)	d						
Swindon	d					22 49	
Bristol Parkway 7	d	21 26					
Filton Abbey Wood	d						
Bath Spa 7	d					23 19	
Bristol Temple Meads 10	d	21 44		21 56	23 06	23 35	
Weston-super-Mare	d			22 29	23 42	00s05	
Bridgwater	d			22 48	00 02	00s24	
Taunton	d	22 16	22 37	23 03	00s14	00s36	02 35
Tiverton Parkway	d	22 28	22 50	23 18	00s31	00s49	
Exeter St Davids 6	a	22 42	23 06	23 37	00 50	01 07	03 06
Exmouth	d						
Exeter Central	d						
Exeter St Davids 6	d	22 43	23 08				04 11
Exeter St Thomas	d						
Starcross	d						
Dawlish Warren	d						
Dawlish	d						
Teignmouth	d						
Newton Abbot	a	23 06	23 28				04 31
	d	23 07	23 28				04 33
Torre	d						
Torquay	d						
Paignton	a						
Totnes	d	23 20	23 42				
Ivybridge	d						
Plymouth	a	23 45	00 11				05 14
	d						05 43
Devonport	d						
Dockyard	d						
Keyham	d						
St Budeaux Ferry Road	d						
Saltash	d						
St Germans	d						
Menheniot	d						
Liskeard 6	d						06 08
Bodmin Parkway	d						06 22
Lostwithiel	d						06 28
Par	d						06 37
Newquay	a						
St Austell	d						06 46
Truro	d						07 06
Redruth	d						07 18
Camborne	d						07 26
Hayle	d						07 35
St Erth	d						07 42
Penzance	a						07 53

A to Bristol Temple Meads

B The Night Riviera

For connections from Heathrow Airport, Gatwick Airport and Oxford please see Tables 125A, 148 and 116

For the complete service between Westbury and Castle Cary refer to table 123

Table 135

Saturdays

14 December to 28 December

London and Birmingham - Devon and Cornwall

Route Diagram - see first Page of Table 135

		GW	GW	GW	GW	GW	GW	GW	GW	XC		GW	GW	GW	GW	XC	GW	GW	GW	GW		GW	XC	GW	XC
			R 1		R					◇1			◇			◇1		◇					◇1		◇1
			A		B																				
			🍴		🛏 🍴																		🛒		🛒
London Paddington 15 ⊖	d																								
Slough 3	d																								
Reading 7	d				00u37																				
Theale	d																								
Thatcham	d																								
Newbury	d																								
Hungerford	d																								
Pewsey	d																								
Westbury	d																								
Frome	d																								
Castle Cary	d																								
Birmingham New Street 12	d																						06 42		07 12
Cardiff Central 7	d																								
Newport (South Wales)	d																								
Swindon	d																								
Bristol Parkway 7	d																						07 54		08 25
Filton Abbey Wood	d																								
Bath Spa 7	d																								
Bristol Temple Meads 10	d												05 24			06 08		06 36					08 11		08 45
Weston-super-Mare	d												05 45					06 56							
Bridgwater	d	00 02											06 03												
Taunton	d	00s14			02 35								06 18			07 15		07 25					08 43		09 17
Tiverton Parkway	d	00s31											06 33			07 27		07 41					08 55		09 29
Exeter St Davids 6	a	00 50			03 06								06 52			07 41		07 59					09 08		09 41
Exmouth	d																07 15					08 23			
Exeter Central	d																07 43					08 50			
Exeter St Davids 6	d				04 11		05 18	05 36	06 11				06 56			07 42	07 50	08 00		08 37		08 56	09 10	09 28	09 44
Exeter St Thomas	d						05 22	05 40	06 14				06 59				07 53	08 04				08 59			
Starcross	d						05 30	05 48	06 22				07 05				08 01					09 07			
Dawlish Warren	d						05 35	05 53	06 27				07 10				08 06					09 24			
Dawlish	d						05 39	05 57	06 31				07 14				08 10	08 17		08 51		09 28			
Teignmouth	d						05 44	06 02	06 36				07 19				08 15	08 22		08 56		09 33			
Newton Abbot	a				04 31		05 51	06 09	06 45				07 26			08 00	08 22	08 29		09 03		09 40	09 28	09 48	10 02
	d				04 33		05 52	06 11	06 45				07 26		07 40	08 02	08 24	08 31		09 06		09 41	09 29	09 49	10 03
Torre	d						06 00	06 19	06 53						07 48		08 32					09 50			
Torquay	d						06 03	06 22	06 56						07 51		08 35			09 16		09 53	09 41		
Paignton	a						06 11	06 30	07 06						07 59		08 44			09 25		10 01	09 47		
Totnes	d												07 40			08 14		08 45						10 02	10 16
Ivybridge	d												07 56					09 02						10 19	
Plymouth	a				05 14								08 13			08 41		09 16						10 32	10 41
	d				05 43					06 28			08 18					09 19	09 51					10 33	
Devonport	d												08 21						09 54						
Dockyard	d																								
Keyham	d																								
St Budeaux Ferry Road	d																							10 39	
Saltash	d												08 28					09 28	10 01					10 44	
St Germans	d												08 35					09 36	10 08					10 51	
Menheniot	d																		10x15						
Liskeard 6	d				06 08					06 51			08 47					09 49	10 22					11 03	
Bodmin Parkway	d				06 22					07 03			08 59					10 02	10 34					11 15	
Lostwithiel	d				06 28					07 08			09 04						10 39					11 20	
Par	d			06 09	06 37	06 52				07 14			09 12	09 18				10 14	10 46					11 28	
Newquay	a					07 44								10 10											
St Austell	d			06 16	06 46					07 21			09 20					10 22	10 54					11 37	
Truro	d			06 35	07 06					07 37			09 37					10 40	11 10					11 55	
Redruth	d		00 06	06 48	07 18					07 49			09 50					10 55	11 24					12 08	
Camborne	d		00 14	06 54	07 26					07 56			09 56					11 02	11 30					12 14	
Hayle	d		00 22	07 01	07 35					08 04			10 03					11 10	11 38					12 21	
St Erth	d		00 28	07 04	07 42					08 10		08 28	10 08					11 18	11 42					12 25	
Penzance	a		00 40	07 16	07 53					08 18		08 40	10 18					11 26	11 55					12 36	

A Restaurant for customers joining at Pad, Reading + Newbury. The Armada

B The Night Riviera

For connections from Heathrow Airport, Gatwick Airport and Oxford please see Tables 125A, 148 and 116

For the complete service between Westbury and Castle Cary refer to table 123

Table 135

Saturdays

14 December to 28 December

London and Birmingham - Devon and Cornwall

Route Diagram - see first Page of Table 135

		GW	GW	GW	GW	GW	XC	GW	GW	GW	XC	GW	GW	GW	GW	XC	XC	GW	GW	GW	GW	XC	GW
			■																				
			◇1	◇			◇1	◇1		◇1	◇1	◇		◇1	◇	◇1	◇1				◇1	◇1	
			A							B				B							B		
			⊡				⊼	⊡		⊡⊘	⊼			⊡⊘		⊼	⊼				⊡⊘	⊼	
London Paddington 15 ⊖	d		07 30					08 18		09 06				10 06							11 06		
Slough 3	d																						
Reading 7	d		07 57					08 48		09 32				10 33							11 32		
Theale	d							08 58															
Thatcham	d							09 07															
Newbury	d							09 14															
Hungerford	d							09 23															
Pewsey	d							09 41													12 02		
Westbury	d							09 57													12 21		
Frome	d																						
Castle Cary	d							10 17													12 39		
Birmingham New Street 12	d						08 12				09 12					09 42	10 12					11 12	
Cardiff Central 7	d																						
Newport (South Wales)	d																						
Swindon	d		08 30																				
Bristol Parkway 7	d						09 26				10 30					10 55	11 25					12 31	
Filton Abbey Wood	d																						
Bath Spa 7	d		09 00																				
Bristol Temple Meads 10	d		09 17				09 44				10 44					11 12	11 44					12 44	
Weston-super-Mare	d															11 39							
Bridgwater	d																						
Taunton	d		09 51				10 17	10 40		10 48	11 17					12 00	12 17				13 02	13 17	
Tiverton Parkway	d						10 30	10 53		11 01	11 29					12 12	12 29				13 15	13 29	
Exeter St Davids 6	a		10 16				10 45	11 09		11 17	11 41			12 09		12 26	12 41				13 31	13 42	
Exmouth	d	09 23							10 23				11 23							12 23			13 23
Exeter Central	d	09 52				10 30			10 50				11 50							12 50			13 50
Exeter St Davids 6	d	09 58	10 19		10 25	10 35	10 47		10 56	11 19	11 45		11 56	12 11		12 28	12 44	12 52		12 56	13 33	13 44	13 57
Exeter St Thomas	d	09 59							10 59				11 59							12 59			13 59
Starcross	d	10 07							11 07				12 07							13 07			14 07
Dawlish Warren	d	10 12				10 47			11 12				12 12					13 04		13 12			14 24
Dawlish	d	10 16				10 51			11 16				12 16			12 40		13 08		13 16			14 28
Teignmouth	d	10 21				10 56			11 21				12 21			12 45		13 13		13 21			14 33
Newton Abbot	a	10 30	10 38		10 46	11 03	11 09		11 29	11 38	12 03		12 29	12 31		12 51	13 02	13 20		13 29	13 51	14 02	14 41
	d	10 31	10 39		10 48	11 04	11 10		11 30	11 38	12 04		12 36	12 32		12 53	13 03	13 21		13 30	13 53	14 03	14 42
Torre	d	10 39			10 56				11 38				12 43							13 38			14 50
Torquay	d	10 42			10 59	11 14			11 41				12 46			13 04				13 41			14 53
Paignton	a	10 50			11 07	11 23			11 51				12 54			13 11				13 49			15 01
Totnes	d		10 52				11 24			11 52	12 17						13 16	13 34			14 05	14 16	
Ivybridge	d									12 07								13 50					
Plymouth	a		11 20				11 51			12 24	12 42			13 13			13 41	14 05			14 34	14 41	
	d		11 23									12 44		13 15					14 15				
Devonport	d																						
Dockyard	d																						
Keyham	d																						
St Budeaux Ferry Road	d																						
Saltash	d											12 53							14 24				
St Germans	d											13 00							14 32				
Menheniot	d																						
Liskeard 6	d		11 47									13 12		13 40					14 45				
Bodmin Parkway	d		12 00									13 24		13 54					14 58				
Lostwithiel	d											13 29							15 04				
Par	d		12 11	12 15								13 37		14 06	14 10				15 12				
Newquay	a			13 07											14 57								
St Austell	d		12 19									13 45		14 14					15 21				
Truro	d		12 37									14 02		14 30					15 39				
Redruth	d		12 49									14 15		14 44					15 53				
Camborne	d		12 56									14 21		14 50					16 00				
Hayle	d											14 28		15 00									
St Erth	d		13 08									14 33		15 05					16 12				
Penzance	a		13 20									14 42		15 17					16 21				

A ◇ from Exeter St Davids ■ to Exeter St Davids

B ⊡ from Newton Abbot ⊘ to Newton Abbot

For connections from Heathrow Airport, Gatwick Airport and Oxford please see Tables 125A, 148 and 116

For the complete service between Westbury and Castle Cary refer to table 123

Table 135

Saturdays

14 December to 28 December

London and Birmingham - Devon and Cornwall

Route Diagram - see first Page of Table 135

		GW		GW	GW	XC	GW	GW	GW	GW	XC	XC		GW	GW	GW	GW	GW	XC	GW	GW	GW		GW	XC
										■															
		◇1		◇		◇1		◇1		1	◇1	◇1					◇1	◇	◇1					◇1	◇1
		A																							B
		🍴⊘				🛒		🍴		🍴	🛒	🛒					🍴		🛒					🍴	🛒
London Paddington 15 ⊖	d	12 06						12 18		13 06							14 06							15 06	
Slough 3	d																								
Reading 7	d	12 33						12 48		13 32							14 34							15 32	
Theale	d							12 56																	
Thatcham	d							13 05																	
Newbury	d							13 13																	
Hungerford	d							13 21																	
Pewsey	d							13 39																16 03	
Westbury	d							13 58																16 22	
Frome	d																								
Castle Cary	d							14 15																16 40	
Birmingham New Street 12	d					12 12					13 12	13 42							14 12						15 12
Cardiff Central 7	d																								
Newport (South Wales)	d																								
Swindon	d																								
Bristol Parkway 7	d					13 25					14 28	14 59							15 25						16 30
Filton Abbey Wood	d																								
Bath Spa 7	d																								
Bristol Temple Meads 10	d					13 44					14 44	15 12							15 44						16 44
Weston-super-Mare	d																								
Bridgwater	d																								
Taunton	d					14 17		14a38		14 48	15 17	15 44					15 49		16 17					17 02	17 18
Tiverton Parkway	d					14 29				15 01	15 30	15 56					16 02		16 29					17 15	17 30
Exeter St Davids 6	a	14 10				14 42				15 17	15 44	16 10					16 18		16 41					17 30	17 45
Exmouth	d								14 23						15 23							16 55			
Exeter Central	d								14 50						15 50						16 48	17 21			
Exeter St Davids 6	d	14 11			14 30	14 44			14 56	15 18	15 46				15 57		16 19		16 44		16 56	17 27		17 34	17 47
Exeter St Thomas	d								14 59						15 59						16 59	17 30			
Starcross	d								15 07						16 07						17 07	17 35			
Dawlish Warren	d				14 42				15 12						16 12						17 12	17 49			
Dawlish	d				14 46				15 16						16 16						17 16	17 53			
Teignmouth	d				14 51				15 21						16 21						17 21	17 58			
Newton Abbot	a	14 30			14 58	15 02			15 29	15 39	16 04				16 29		16 39		17 02		17 29	18 05		17 53	18 10
	d	14 32			15 00	15 04			15 30	15 39	16 06			16 18	16 30		16 40		17 03		17 30	18 09		17 55	18 12
Torre	d				15 08				15 38						16 38						17 38	18 17			
Torquay	d				15 11				15 41						16 41						17 41	18 20			
Paignton	a				15 19				15 51						16 51						17 51	18 27			
Totnes	d					15 16				15 53	16 19			16 31			16 53		17 16					18 08	18 25
Ivybridge	d													16 47			17 09								
Plymouth	a	15 09				15 42				16 20	16 46			17 05			17 24		17 41					18 36	18 52
	d	15 11					16 03			16 26							17 26			17 52				18 41	18 55
Devonport	d																			17 55					
Dockyard	d																			17x57					
Keyham	d																			17 59					
St Budeaux Ferry Road	d																			18 01					
Saltash	d						16 12													18 06					
St Germans	d						16 19													18 12					
Menheniot	d						16x27													18x19					
Liskeard 6	d	15 36					16 33			16 50							17 51			18 26				19 06	19 19
Bodmin Parkway	d	15 49					16 45			17 03							18 03			18 38				19 19	19 34
Lostwithiel	d						16 50													18 44					
Par	d	16 01		16 15			16 57										18 16	18 21		18 52				19 31	19 45
Newquay	a			17 07														19 13							
St Austell	d	16 08					17 05			17 20							18 23			18 59				19 39	19 53
Truro	d	16 26					17 23			17 37							18 41			19 17				20 00	20 12
Redruth	d	16 38					17 36			17 50							18 53			19 30				20 10	20 27
Camborne	d	16 46					17 42			17 57							19 01			19 36				20 18	20 35
Hayle	d						17 49			18 06										19 43					
St Erth	d	16 57					17 54			18 12						18 32	19 12			19 48				20 29	20 46
Penzance	a	17 09					18 03			18 24						18 44	19 24			19 57				20 40	20 56

A 🍴 from Newton Abbot ⊘ to Newton Abbot   B 🛒 to Plymouth

For connections from Heathrow Airport, Gatwick Airport and Oxford please see Tables 125A, 148 and 116

For the complete service between Westbury and Castle Cary refer to table 123

Table 135

Saturdays

14 December to 28 December

London and Birmingham - Devon and Cornwall

Route Diagram - see first Page of Table 135

		GW	GW	XC	GW	GW	XC	GW		GW	GW	GW	GW	XC	GW	GW	XC	GW		GW	XC	XC	GW	XC	GW
		1		◇1	◇1		◇1					◇1	◇1	◇1		◇1	◇1			◇1	◇1	◇1	◇1	◇1	◇
		A					B							B							C	C		C	
				[trolley]	[catering]		[trolley]					[catering]	[catering]	[trolley]		[catering]	[trolley]			[catering]	[trolley]	[trolley]	[catering]	[trolley]	
London Paddington 15 ⊖	d				16 06							17 06	16 30			18 06				19 06			20 06		
Slough 3	d																								
Reading 7	d				16 33							17 32	16 57			18 33				19 32			20 35		
Theale	d																								
Thatcham	d																								
Newbury	d																			19 49			20 50		
Hungerford	d																								
Pewsey	d											18 03								20 08			21 10		
Westbury	d											18 23								20 27			21 29		
Frome	d																								
Castle Cary	d											18 41								20 44			21 47		
Birmingham New Street 12	d			15 42			16 12							17 12			18 12				19 12	19 42		20 12	
Cardiff Central 7	d																								
Newport (South Wales)	d																								
Swindon	d												17 30												
Bristol Parkway 7	d			16 54			17 26							18 30			19 26				20 30	20 54		21 21	
Filton Abbey Wood	d																								
Bath Spa 7	d												18 00												
Bristol Temple Meads 10	d			17 10			17 44						18 18	18 44			19 44				20 44	21 11		21 44	21 59
Weston-super-Mare	d												18 40												22 33
Bridgwater	d																								22 52
Taunton	d			17 42	17 49		18 17					19 02	19 06	19 17		19 47	20 17			21 07	21 17	21 43	22 09	22 17	23 05
Tiverton Parkway	d			17 54	18 02		18 29					19 15	19 21	19 29			20 29			21 20	21 29	21 55	22 22	22 29	23 20
Exeter St Davids 6	a			18 07	18 18		18 41					19 31	19 36	19 43		20 13	20 41			21 36	21 42	22 09	22 37	22 43	23 38
Exmouth	d					17 55									19 38			20 08							
Exeter Central	d					18 21									20 01			20 35							
Exeter St Davids 6	d	17 53		18 09	18 20	18 27	18 46	18 56		19 16		19 34	19 39	19 45	20 07	20 16	20 44	20 56		21 39	21 45	22 10	22 39	22 46	
Exeter St Thomas	d					18 29				19 19					20 10			20 59							
Starcross	d					18 37				19 27					20 18			21 07							
Dawlish Warren	d	18 05				18 42				19 32					20 32			21 12							
Dawlish	d	18 09		18 21		18 46		19 09		19 36					20 36			21 16					22 52		
Teignmouth	d	18 14		18 26		18 51		19 14		19 41					20 41			21 21					22 58		
Newton Abbot	a	18 21		18 32	18 40	18 59	19 04	19 21		19 49		19 53	19 58	20 03	20 48	20 37	21 02	21 28		21 58	22 04	22 28	23 04	23 10	
	d	18 22		18 33	18 41	19 01	19 05	19 22		19 50		19 54	19 59	20 05	20 49	20 37	21 03	21 30		21 59	22 08	22 30	23 06	23 12	
Torre	d					19 09				19 58			20 09		20 57			21 38							
Torquay	d			18 45		19 12		19 32		20 01			20 12		21 00			21 41							
Paignton	a			18 51		19 21		19 40		20 09			20 21		21 07			21 48							
Totnes	d	18 35			18 54		19 18					20 07		20 17		20 51	21 16			22 12	22 21	22 42	23 19	23 27	
Ivybridge	d	18 51			19 11																				
Plymouth	a	19 05			19 26		19 43					20 35		20 43		21 19	21 41			22 40	22 47	23 08	23 47	23 53	
	d	19 08					19 48					20 38		20 58		21 20									
Devonport	d																								
Dockyard	d																								
Keyham	d																								
St Budeaux Ferry Road	d																								
Saltash	d	19 17										20 49													
St Germans	d	19 24										20 56													
Menheniot	d																								
Liskeard 6	d	19 36					20 11					21 08		21 25		21 45									
Bodmin Parkway	d	19 48					20 23					21 21		21 37		21 59									
Lostwithiel	d	19 53					20 28																		
Par	d	20 01	20 15				20 36					21 33		21 48		22 11									
Newquay	a		21 07																						
St Austell	d	20 08					20 42					21 43		21 55		22 18									
Truro	d	20 26					21 02					22 03		22 13		22 36									
Redruth	d	20 43					21 13					22 13		22 28		22 48									
Camborne	d	20 49					21 19							22 35		22 56									
Hayle	d						21 27									23 03									
St Erth	d	20 58					21 32				22 20	22 30		22 46		23 09									
Penzance	a	21 08					21 43				22 32	22 42		22 54		23 22									

A 1 from Plymouth B [trolley] to Plymouth C [trolley] to Bristol Temple Meads

For connections from Heathrow Airport, Gatwick Airport and Oxford please see Tables 125A, 148 and 116

For the complete service between Westbury and Castle Cary refer to table 123

Table 135

Saturdays

14 December to 28 December

London and Birmingham - Devon and Cornwall

Route Diagram - see first Page of Table 135

		GW ◇1
London Paddington 15 ⊖	d	20 30
Slough 3	d	
Reading 7	d	20 57
Theale	d	
Thatcham	d	
Newbury	d	
Hungerford	d	
Pewsey	d	
Westbury	d	
Frome	d	
Castle Cary	d	
Birmingham New Street 12	d	
Cardiff Central 7	d	
Newport (South Wales)	d	
Swindon	d	21 30
Bristol Parkway 7	d	
Filton Abbey Wood	d	
Bath Spa 7	d	22 00
Bristol Temple Meads 10	d	22 17
Weston-super-Mare	d	22s47
Bridgwater	d	23s05
Taunton	d	23 19
Tiverton Parkway	d	23 32
Exeter St Davids 6	a	23 48
Exmouth	d	
Exeter Central	d	
Exeter St Davids 6	d	
Exeter St Thomas	d	
Starcross	d	
Dawlish Warren	d	
Dawlish	d	
Teignmouth	d	
Newton Abbot	a	
	d	
Torre	d	
Torquay	d	
Paignton	a	
Totnes	d	
Ivybridge	d	
Plymouth	a	
	d	
Devonport	d	
Dockyard	d	
Keyham	d	
St Budeaux Ferry Road	d	
Saltash	d	
St Germans	d	
Menheniot	d	
Liskeard 6	d	
Bodmin Parkway	d	
Lostwithiel	d	
Par	d	
Newquay	a	
St Austell	d	
Truro	d	
Redruth	d	
Camborne	d	
Hayle	d	
St Erth	d	
Penzance	a	

For connections from Heathrow Airport, Gatwick Airport and Oxford please see Tables 125A, 148 and 116

For the complete service between Westbury and Castle Cary refer to table 123

Table 135

Saturdays

4 January to 8 February

London and Birmingham - Devon and Cornwall

Route Diagram - see first Page of Table 135

		GW	GW	GW	GW	GW	GW	GW	GW	XC		GW	GW	GW	GW	XC	GW	GW	GW	GW		GW	XC	GW	XC
			■		■																				
			1							◇1			◇			◇1		◇					◇1		◇1
			A		B																				
					🛏																				
			🍴		🍴																		🛒		🛒
London Paddington 15 ⊖	d																								
Slough 3	d																								
Reading 7	d				00u37																				
Theale	d																								
Thatcham	d																								
Newbury	d																								
Hungerford	d																								
Pewsey	d																								
Westbury	d																								
Frome	d																								
Castle Cary	d																								
Birmingham New Street 12	d																						06 42		07 12
Cardiff Central 7	d																								
Newport (South Wales)	d																								
Swindon	d																								
Bristol Parkway 7	d																						07 54		08 25
Filton Abbey Wood	d																								
Bath Spa 7	d																								
Bristol Temple Meads 10	d												05 24			06 08		06 36					08 11		08 45
Weston-super-Mare	d												05 45					06 56							
Bridgwater	d	00 02											06 03												
Taunton	d	00s14			02 35								06 18			07 15		07 25					08 43		09 17
Tiverton Parkway	d	00s31											06 33			07 27		07 41					08 55		09 29
Exeter St Davids 6	a	00 50			03 06								06 52			07 41		07 59					09 08		09 41
Exmouth	d																07 15					08 23			
Exeter Central	d																07 43					08 50			
Exeter St Davids 6	d				04 11		05 18	05 36	06 11				06 56			07 42	07 50	08 00		08 37		08 56	09 10	09 28	09 44
Exeter St Thomas	d						05 22	05 40	06 14				06 59				07 53	08 04				08 59			
Starcross	d						05 30	05 48	06 22				07 05				08 01					09 07			
Dawlish Warren	d						05 35	05 53	06 27				07 10				08 06					09 24			
Dawlish	d						05 39	05 57	06 31				07 14				08 10	08 17		08 51		09 28			
Teignmouth	d						05 44	06 02	06 36				07 19				08 15	08 22		08 56		09 33			
Newton Abbot	a				04 31		05 51	06 09	06 45				07 26			08 00	08 22	08 29		09 03		09 40	09 28	09 48	10 02
	d				04 33		05 52	06 11	06 45				07 26		07 40	08 02	08 24	08 31		09 06		09 41	09 29	09 49	10 03
Torre	d						06 00	06 19	06 53						07 48		08 32					09 50			
Torquay	d						06 03	06 22	06 56						07 51		08 35			09 16		09 53	09 41		
Paignton	a						06 11	06 30	07 06						07 59		08 44			09 25		10 01	09 47		
Totnes	d												07 40			08 14		08 45						10 02	10 16
Ivybridge	d												07 56					09 02						10 19	
Plymouth	a				05 14								08 13			08 41		09 16						10 32	10 41
	d				05 43					06 28			08 18					09 19	09 51					10 33	
Devonport	d												08 21						09 54						
Dockyard	d																								
Keyham	d																								
St Budeaux Ferry Road	d																							10 39	
Saltash	d												08 28					09 28	10 01					10 44	
St Germans	d												08 35					09 36	10 08					10 51	
Menheniot	d																		10x15						
Liskeard 6	d				06 08					06 51			08 47					09 49	10 22					11 03	
Bodmin Parkway	d				06 22					07 03			08 59					10 02	10 34					11 15	
Lostwithiel	d				06 28					07 08			09 04						10 39					11 20	
Par	d			06 09	06 37	06 52				07 14			09 12	09 18				10 14	10 46					11 28	
Newquay	a					07 44								10 10											
St Austell	d			06 16	06 46					07 21			09 20					10 22	10 54					11 37	
Truro	d			06 35	07 06					07 37			09 37					10 40	11 10					11 55	
Redruth	d		00 06	06 48	07 18					07 49			09 50					10 55	11 24					12 08	
Camborne	d		00 14	06 54	07 26					07 56			09 56					11 02	11 30					12 14	
Hayle	d		00 22	07 01	07 35					08 04			10 03					11 10	11 38					12 21	
St Erth	d		00 28	07 04	07 42					08 10		08 28	10 08					11 18	11 42					12 25	
Penzance	a		00 40	07 16	07 53					08 18		08 40	10 18					11 26	11 55					12 36	

A Restaurant for customers joining at Pad, Reading + Newbury. The Armada

B The Night Riviera

For connections from Heathrow Airport, Gatwick Airport and Oxford please see Tables 125A, 148 and 116

For the complete service between Westbury and Castle Cary refer to table 123

Table 135

Saturdays

4 January to 8 February

London and Birmingham - Devon and Cornwall

Route Diagram - see first Page of Table 135

		GW	GW	GW	GW	GW		XC	GW	GW	GW	XC	GW	GW	GW	GW		XC	XC	GW	GW	GW	GW	XC	GW
			R																						
			◇1	◇				◇1	◇1		◇1	◇1	◇		◇1	◇		◇1	◇1				◇1	◇1	
			A								B				B								B		
			🍴					🛒	🍴		🍴⊘	🛒			🍴⊘			🛒	🛒				🍴⊘	🛒	
London Paddington 15 ⊖	d		07 22						08 13		09 00				10 00								11 00		
Slough 3	d																								
Reading 7	d		07 59						08 48		09 35				10 35								11 35		
Theale	d								08 58																
Thatcham	d								09 07																
Newbury	d								09 14																
Hungerford	d								09 23																
Pewsey	d								09 41														12 05		
Westbury	d								09 57														12 24		
Frome	d																								
Castle Cary	d								10 17														12 42		
Birmingham New Street 12	d							08 12				09 12						09 42	10 12					11 12	
Cardiff Central 7	d																								
Newport (South Wales)	d																								
Swindon	d		08 32																						
Bristol Parkway 7	d							09 26				10 30						10 55	11 25					12 31	
Filton Abbey Wood	d																								
Bath Spa 7	d		09 01																						
Bristol Temple Meads 10	d		09 17					09 44				10 44						11 12	11 44					12 44	
Weston-super-Mare	d																	11 39							
Bridgwater	d																								
Taunton	d		09 51					10 17	10 40		10 51	11 17						12 00	12 17				13 05	13 17	
Tiverton Parkway	d							10 30	10 53		11 04	11 29						12 12	12 29				13 18	13 29	
Exeter St Davids 6	a		10 18					10 45	11 09		11 20	11 41			12 10			12 26	12 41				13 34	13 42	
Exmouth	d	09 23								10 23				11 23								12 23			13 23
Exeter Central	d	09 52				10 30				10 50				11 50								12 50			13 50
Exeter St Davids 6	d	09 58	10 19		10 25	10 35		10 47		10 56	11 22	11 45		11 56	12 13			12 28	12 44	12 52		12 56	13 36	13 44	13 57
Exeter St Thomas	d	09 59								10 59				11 59								12 59			13 59
Starcross	d	10 07								11 07				12 07								13 07			14 07
Dawlish Warren	d	10 12				10 47				11 12				12 12						13 04		13 12			14 24
Dawlish	d	10 16				10 51				11 16				12 16				12 40		13 08		13 16			14 28
Teignmouth	d	10 21				10 56				11 21				12 21				12 45		13 13		13 21			14 33
Newton Abbot	a	10 30	10 39		10 46	11 03		11 09		11 29	11 41	12 03		12 29	12 33			12 51	13 02	13 20		13 29	13 54	14 02	14 41
	d	10 31	10 39		10 48	11 04		11 10		11 30	11 42	12 04		12 36	12 33			12 53	13 03	13 21		13 30	13 56	14 03	14 42
Torre	d	10 39			10 56					11 38				12 43								13 38			14 50
Torquay	d	10 42			10 59	11 14				11 41				12 46				13 04				13 41			14 53
Paignton	a	10 50			11 07	11 23				11 51				12 54				13 11				13 49			15 01
Totnes	d		10 53					11 24			11 55	12 17							13 16	13 34			14 08	14 18	
Ivybridge	d										12 10									13 50					
Plymouth	a		11 21					11 51			12 27	12 42			13 14				13 41	14 05			14 37	14 44	
	d		11 23										12 44		13 17						14 15				
Devonport	d																								
Dockyard	d																								
Keyham	d																								
St Budeaux Ferry Road	d																								
Saltash	d												12 53								14 24				
St Germans	d												13 00								14 32				
Menheniot	d																								
Liskeard 6	d		11 47										13 12		13 42						14 45				
Bodmin Parkway	d		12 00										13 24		13 56						14 58				
Lostwithiel	d												13 29								15 04				
Par	d		12 11	12 15									13 37		14 08	14 10					15 12				
Newquay	a			13 07												14 57									
St Austell	d		12 20										13 45		14 15						15 21				
Truro	d		12 37										14 02		14 32						15 39				
Redruth	d		12 49										14 15		14 45						15 53				
Camborne	d		12 57										14 21		14 52						16 00				
Hayle	d												14 28		15 02										
St Erth	d		13 08										14 33		15 07						16 12				
Penzance	a		13 20										14 42		15 19						16 21				

A ◇ from Exeter St Davids R to Exeter St Davids

B 🍴 from Newton Abbot ⊘ to Newton Abbot

For connections from Heathrow Airport, Gatwick Airport and Oxford please see Tables 125A, 148 and 116

For the complete service between Westbury and Castle Cary refer to table 123

Table 135

Saturdays

4 January to 8 February

London and Birmingham - Devon and Cornwall

Route Diagram - see first Page of Table 135

		GW	GW	GW	XC	GW	GW	GW	GW	XC	XC	GW	GW	GW	GW	GW	XC	GW	GW	GW	GW	XC
		◇1	◇		◇1		◇1		R 1	◇1	◇1				◇1	◇	◇1				◇1	◇1
		A																				B
		☕Ø			🛒		☕		☕	🛒	🛒				☕		🛒				☕	🛒
London Paddington 15 ⊖	d	12 00					12 13		13 00						14 00						15 00	
Slough 3	d																					
Reading 7	d	12 34					12 48		13 35						14 35						15 34	
Theale	d						12 56															
Thatcham	d						13 05															
Newbury	d						13 13															
Hungerford	d						13 21															
Pewsey	d						13 39														16 05	
Westbury	d						13 58														16 24	
Frome	d																					
Castle Cary	d						14 15														16 42	
Birmingham New Street 12	d				12 12					13 12	13 42						14 12					15 12
Cardiff Central 7	d																					
Newport (South Wales)	d																					
Swindon	d																					
Bristol Parkway 7	d				13 25					14 28	14 59						15 25					16 30
Filton Abbey Wood	d																					
Bath Spa 7	d																					
Bristol Temple Meads 10	d				13 44					14 44	15 12						15 44					16 44
Weston-super-Mare	d																					
Bridgwater	d																					
Taunton	d				14 17		14a38		14 51	15 17	15 44				15 50		16 17				17 04	17 18
Tiverton Parkway	d				14 29				15 04	15 30	15 56				16 03		16 29				17 17	17 30
Exeter St Davids 6	a	14 11			14 42				15 20	15 44	16 10				16 19		16 41				17 32	17 45
Exmouth	d							14 23					15 23							16 55		
Exeter Central	d							14 50					15 50						16 48	17 21		
Exeter St Davids 6	d	14 12		14 30	14 44			14 56	15 21	15 46			15 57		16 20		16 44		16 56	17 27	17 36	17 47
Exeter St Thomas	d							14 59					15 59						16 59	17 30		
Starcross	d							15 07					16 07						17 07	17 35		
Dawlish Warren	d			14 42				15 12					16 12						17 12	17 49		
Dawlish	d			14 46				15 16					16 16						17 16	17 53		
Teignmouth	d			14 51				15 21					16 21						17 21	17 58		
Newton Abbot	a	14 31		14 58	15 02			15 29	15 42	16 04			16 29		16 40		17 02		17 29	18 05	17 55	18 10
	d	14 33		15 00	15 04			15 30	15 42	16 06		16 18	16 30		16 41		17 03		17 30	18 09	17 57	18 12
Torre	d			15 08				15 38					16 38						17 38	18 17		
Torquay	d			15 11				15 41					16 41						17 41	18 20		
Paignton	a			15 19				15 51					16 51						17 51	18 27		
Totnes	d				15 16				15 56	16 19		16 31			16 54		17 16				18 10	18 25
Ivybridge	d											16 47			17 10							
Plymouth	a	15 10			15 42				16 23	16 46		17 05			17 25		17 41				18 38	18 52
	d	15 12				16 03			16 29						17 27			17 52			18 43	18 55
Devonport	d																	17 55				
Dockyard	d																	17x57				
Keyham	d																	17 59				
St Budeaux Ferry Road	d																	18 01				
Saltash	d					16 12												18 06				
St Germans	d					16 19												18 12				
Menheniot	d					16x27												18x19				
Liskeard 6	d	15 37				16 33			16 53						17 52			18 26			19 08	19 21
Bodmin Parkway	d	15 50				16 45			17 06						18 04			18 38			19 21	19 36
Lostwithiel	d					16 50												18 44				
Par	d	16 02	16 15			16 57									18 17	18 21		18 52			19 33	19 47
Newquay	a		17 07													19 13						
St Austell	d	16 09				17 05			17 23						18 24			18 59			19 40	19 55
Truro	d	16 28				17 23			17 40						18 42			19 17			20 01	20 14
Redruth	d	16 39				17 36			17 53						18 54			19 30			20 11	20 27
Camborne	d	16 47				17 42			18 00						19 02			19 36			20 19	20 35
Hayle	d					17 49			18 09									19 43				
St Erth	d	16 58				17 54			18 15					18 32	19 13			19 48			20 30	20 46
Penzance	a	17 10				18 03			18 27					18 44	19 25			19 57			20 41	20 56

A ☕ from Newton Abbot Ø to Newton Abbot

B 🛒 to Plymouth

For connections from Heathrow Airport, Gatwick Airport and Oxford please see Tables 125A, 148 and 116

For the complete service between Westbury and Castle Cary refer to table 123

Table 135

Saturdays

4 January to 8 February

London and Birmingham - Devon and Cornwall

Route Diagram - see first Page of Table 135

		GW	GW	XC	GW	GW	XC	GW	GW	GW	GW	GW	XC	GW	GW	XC	GW	GW	XC	XC	GW	XC	GW
		1		◇1	◇1		◇1				◇1	◇1	◇1		◇1	◇1		◇1	◇1	◇1	◇1	◇1	◇
		A					B						B						C	C		C	
				🛒	🍴		🛒				🍴	🍴	🛒		🍴	🛒		🍴	🛒	🛒	🍴	🛒	
London Paddington 15 ⊖	d				16 00						17 00	16 22			18 00			19 00			20 00		
Slough 3	d																						
Reading 7	d				16 35						17 35	16 59			18 35			19 35			20 36		
Theale	d																						
Thatcham	d																						
Newbury	d																	19 52			20 51		
Hungerford	d																						
Pewsey	d										18 06							20 11			21 11		
Westbury	d										18 25							20 30			21 30		
Frome	d																						
Castle Cary	d										18 44							20 47			21 48		
Birmingham New Street 12	d			15 42			16 12						17 12			18 12			19 12	19 42		20 12	
Cardiff Central 7	d																						
Newport (South Wales)	d																						
Swindon	d											17 33											
Bristol Parkway 7	d			16 54			17 26						18 30			19 26			20 30	20 54		21 21	
Filton Abbey Wood	d																						
Bath Spa 7	d											18 03											
Bristol Temple Meads 10	d			17 10			17 44					18 20	18 44			19 44			20 44	21 11		21 44	21 59
Weston-super-Mare	d											18 43											22 33
Bridgwater	d																						22 52
Taunton	d			17 42	17 50		18 17				19 05	19 10	19 17		19 49	20 17		21 10	21 17	21 43	22 10	22 17	23 05
Tiverton Parkway	d			17 54	18 03		18 29				19 18	19 23	19 29			20 29		21 23	21 29	21 55	22 23	22 29	23 20
Exeter St Davids 6	a			18 07	18 19		18 41				19 34	19 37	19 43		20 14	20 41		21 39	21 44	22 09	22 38	22 43	23 38
Exmouth	d					17 55								19 38			20 08						
Exeter Central	d					18 21								20 01			20 35						
Exeter St Davids 6	d	17 53		18 09	18 22	18 27	18 46	18 56	19 16		19 36	19 40	19 45	20 07	20 17	20 44	20 56	21 42	21 47	22 10	22 40	22 46	
Exeter St Thomas	d					18 29			19 19					20 10			20 59						
Starcross	d					18 37			19 27					20 18			21 07						
Dawlish Warren	d	18 05				18 42			19 32					20 32			21 12						
Dawlish	d	18 09		18 21		18 46		19 09	19 36					20 36			21 16				22 53		
Teignmouth	d	18 14		18 26		18 51		19 14	19 41					20 41			21 21				22 59		
Newton Abbot	a	18 21		18 32	18 42	18 59	19 04	19 21	19 49		19 55	19 59	20 04	20 48	20 37	21 02	21 28	22 01	22 08	22 28	23 06	23 11	
	d	18 22		18 33	18 42	19 01	19 05	19 22	19 50		19 56	20 00	20 05	20 49	20 37	21 03	21 30	22 02	22 12	22 30	23 07	23 14	
Torre	d					19 09			19 58			20 10		20 57			21 38						
Torquay	d			18 45		19 12		19 32	20 01			20 15		21 00			21 41						
Paignton	a			18 51		19 21		19 40	20 09			20 22		21 07			21 48						
Totnes	d	18 35			18 56		19 18				20 09		20 19		20 51	21 16		22 15	22 25	22 42	23 21	23 30	
Ivybridge	d	18 51			19 12																		
Plymouth	a	19 05			19 28		19 43				20 37		20 45		21 19	21 41		22 43	22 50	23 08	23 48	23 55	
	d	19 08					19 48				20 40		20 58		21 20								
Devonport	d																						
Dockyard	d																						
Keyham	d																						
St Budeaux Ferry Road	d																						
Saltash	d	19 17									20 51												
St Germans	d	19 24									20 58												
Menheniot	d																						
Liskeard 6	d	19 36					20 11				21 10		21 25		21 45								
Bodmin Parkway	d	19 48					20 23				21 23		21 37		21 59								
Lostwithiel	d	19 53					20 28																
Par	d	20 01	20 15				20 36				21 35		21 48		22 11								
Newquay	a		21 07																				
St Austell	d	20 08					20 42				21 45		21 55		22 18								
Truro	d	20 26					21 02				22 05		22 13		22 36								
Redruth	d	20 43					21 13				22 15		22 30		22 48								
Camborne	d	20 49					21 19						22 37		22 56								
Hayle	d						21 27								23 03								
St Erth	d	20 58					21 32			22 20	22 32		22 48		23 09								
Penzance	a	21 08					21 43			22 32	22 44		22 56		23 22								

A 1 from Plymouth
B 🛒 to Plymouth
C 🛒 to Bristol Temple Meads

For connections from Heathrow Airport, Gatwick Airport and Oxford please see Tables 125A, 148 and 116

For the complete service between Westbury and Castle Cary refer to table 123

Table 135

Saturdays

4 January to 8 February

London and Birmingham - Devon and Cornwall

Route Diagram - see first Page of Table 135

		GW ◇1
London Paddington 15 ⊖	d	20 21
Slough 3	d	
Reading 7	d	21 02
Theale	d	
Thatcham	d	
Newbury	d	
Hungerford	d	
Pewsey	d	
Westbury	d	
Frome	d	
Castle Cary	d	
Birmingham New Street 12	d	
Cardiff Central 7	d	
Newport (South Wales)	d	
Swindon	d	21 35
Bristol Parkway 7	d	
Filton Abbey Wood	d	
Bath Spa 7	d	22 05
Bristol Temple Meads 10	d	22 21
Weston-super-Mare	d	22s51
Bridgwater	d	23s10
Taunton	d	23 23
Tiverton Parkway	d	23 36
Exeter St Davids 6	a	23 52
Exmouth	d	
Exeter Central	d	
Exeter St Davids 6	d	
Exeter St Thomas	d	
Starcross	d	
Dawlish Warren	d	
Dawlish	d	
Teignmouth	d	
Newton Abbot	a	
	d	
Torre	d	
Torquay	d	
Paignton	a	
Totnes	d	
Ivybridge	d	
Plymouth	a	
	d	
Devonport	d	
Dockyard	d	
Keyham	d	
St Budeaux Ferry Road	d	
Saltash	d	
St Germans	d	
Menheniot	d	
Liskeard 6	d	
Bodmin Parkway	d	
Lostwithiel	d	
Par	d	
Newquay	a	
St Austell	d	
Truro	d	
Redruth	d	
Camborne	d	
Hayle	d	
St Erth	d	
Penzance	a	

For connections from Heathrow Airport, Gatwick Airport and Oxford please see Tables 125A, 148 and 116

For the complete service between Westbury and Castle Cary refer to table 123

Table 135

Saturdays

15 February to 22 March

London and Birmingham - Devon and Cornwall

Route Diagram - see first Page of Table 135

		GW	GW	GW	GW	GW	GW	GW	GW	XC	GW	GW	GW	GW	XC	GW	GW	GW	GW	GW	XC	GW	XC
			R 1 A		R B					◇1		◇			◇1		◇				◇1		◇1
London Paddington 15 ⊖	d																						
Slough 3	d																						
Reading 7	d				00u37																		
Theale	d																						
Thatcham	d																						
Newbury	d																						
Hungerford	d																						
Pewsey	d																						
Westbury	d																						
Frome	d																						
Castle Cary	d																						
Birmingham New Street 12	d																				06 42		07 12
Cardiff Central 7	d																						
Newport (South Wales)	d																						
Swindon	d																						
Bristol Parkway 7	d																				07 54		08 25
Filton Abbey Wood	d																						
Bath Spa 7	d																						
Bristol Temple Meads 10	d											05 24			06 08		06 36				08 11		08 45
Weston-super-Mare	d											05 45					06 56						
Bridgwater	d	00 02										06 03											
Taunton	d	00s14			02 35							06 18			07 15		07 25				08 43		09 17
Tiverton Parkway	d	00s31										06 33			07 27		07 41				08 55		09 29
Exeter St Davids 6	a	00 50			03 06							06 52			07 41		07 59				09 08		09 41
Exmouth	d															07 15				08 23			
Exeter Central	d															07 43				08 50			
Exeter St Davids 6	d				04 11		05 18	05 36	06 11			06 56			07 42	07 50	08 00		08 37	08 56	09 10	09 28	09 44
Exeter St Thomas	d						05 22	05 40	06 14			06 59				07 53	08 04			08 59			
Starcross	d						05 30	05 48	06 22			07 05				08 01				09 07			
Dawlish Warren	d						05 35	05 53	06 27			07 10				08 06				09 24			
Dawlish	d						05 39	05 57	06 31			07 14				08 10	08 17		08 51	09 28			
Teignmouth	d						05 44	06 02	06 36			07 19				08 15	08 22		08 56	09 33			
Newton Abbot	a				04 31		05 51	06 09	06 45			07 26			08 00	08 22	08 29		09 03	09 40	09 28	09 48	10 02
	d				04 33		05 52	06 11	06 45			07 26		07 40	08 02	08 24	08 31		09 06	09 41	09 29	09 49	10 03
Torre	d						06 00	06 19	06 53					07 48		08 32				09 50			
Torquay	d						06 03	06 22	06 56					07 51		08 35			09 16	09 53	09 41		
Paignton	a						06 11	06 30	07 06					07 59		08 44			09 25	10 01	09 47		
Totnes	d											07 40			08 14		08 45					10 02	10 16
Ivybridge	d											07 56					09 02					10 19	
Plymouth	a				05 14							08 13			08 41		09 16					10 32	10 41
	d				05 43					06 28		08 18					09 19	09 51				10 33	
Devonport	d											08 21						09 54					
Dockyard	d																						
Keyham	d																						
St Budeaux Ferry Road	d																					10 39	
Saltash	d											08 28					09 28	10 01				10 44	
St Germans	d											08 35					09 36	10 08				10 51	
Menheniot	d																	10x15					
Liskeard 6	d				06 08					06 51		08 47					09 49	10 22				11 03	
Bodmin Parkway	d				06 22					07 03		08 59					10 02	10 34				11 15	
Lostwithiel	d				06 28					07 08		09 04						10 39				11 20	
Par	d			06 09	06 37	06 52				07 14		09 12	09 18				10 14	10 46				11 28	
Newquay	a					07 44							10 10										
St Austell	d			06 16	06 46					07 21		09 20					10 22	10 54				11 37	
Truro	d			06 35	07 06					07 37		09 37					10 40	11 10				11 55	
Redruth	d		00 06	06 48	07 18					07 49		09 50					10 55	11 24				12 08	
Camborne	d		00 14	06 54	07 26					07 56		09 56					11 02	11 30				12 14	
Hayle	d		00 22	07 01	07 35					08 04		10 03					11 10	11 38				12 21	
St Erth	d		00 28	07 04	07 42					08 10	08 28	10 08					11 18	11 42				12 25	
Penzance	a		00 40	07 16	07 53					08 18	08 40	10 18					11 26	11 55				12 36	

A Restaurant for customers joining at Pad, Reading + Newbury. The Armada

B The Night Riviera

For connections from Heathrow Airport, Gatwick Airport and Oxford please see Tables 125A, 148 and 116

For the complete service between Westbury and Castle Cary refer to table 123

Table 135

Saturdays

15 February to 22 March

London and Birmingham - Devon and Cornwall

Route Diagram - see first Page of Table 135

		GW	GW	GW	GW	GW		XC	GW	GW	GW	XC	GW	GW	GW	GW		XC	XC	GW	GW	GW	GW	XC	GW
			R																						
			◇1	◇				◇1	◇1		◇1	◇1	◇		◇1	◇		◇1	◇1				◇1	◇1	
			A								B				B								B		
			🍴					🛒	🍴		🍴Ø	🛒			🍴Ø			🛒	🛒				🍴Ø	🛒	
London Paddington 15 ⊖	d		07 30						08 18		09 06				10 06								11 06		
Slough 3	d																								
Reading 7	d		07 57						08 48		09 32				10 33								11 32		
Theale	d								08 58																
Thatcham	d								09 07																
Newbury	d								09 14																
Hungerford	d								09 23																
Pewsey	d								09 41														12 02		
Westbury	d								09 57														12 21		
Frome	d																								
Castle Cary	d								10 17														12 39		
Birmingham New Street 12	d							08 12				09 12						09 42	10 12					11 12	
Cardiff Central 7	d																								
Newport (South Wales)	d																								
Swindon	d		08 30																						
Bristol Parkway 7	d							09 26				10 30						10 55	11 25					12 31	
Filton Abbey Wood	d																								
Bath Spa 7	d		09 00																						
Bristol Temple Meads 10	d		09 17					09 44				10 44						11 12	11 44					12 44	
Weston-super-Mare	d																	11 39							
Bridgwater	d																								
Taunton	d		09 51					10 17	10 40		10 48	11 17						12 00	12 17				13 02	13 17	
Tiverton Parkway	d							10 30	10 53		11 01	11 29						12 12	12 29				13 15	13 29	
Exeter St Davids 6	a		10 16					10 45	11 09		11 17	11 41			12 09			12 26	12 41				13 31	13 42	
Exmouth	d	09 23								10 23				11 23								12 23			13 23
Exeter Central	d	09 52				10 30				10 50				11 50								12 50			13 50
Exeter St Davids 6	d	09 58	10 19		10 25	10 35		10 47		10 56	11 19	11 45		11 56	12 11			12 28	12 44	12 52		12 56	13 33	13 44	13 57
Exeter St Thomas	d	09 59								10 59				11 59								12 59			13 59
Starcross	d	10 07								11 07				12 07								13 07			14 07
Dawlish Warren	d	10 12				10 47				11 12				12 12						13 04		13 12			14 24
Dawlish	d	10 16				10 51				11 16				12 16				12 40		13 08		13 16			14 28
Teignmouth	d	10 21				10 56				11 21				12 21				12 45		13 13		13 21			14 33
Newton Abbot	a	10 30	10 38		10 46	11 03		11 09		11 29	11 38	12 03		12 29	12 31			12 51	13 02	13 20		13 29	13 51	14 02	14 41
	d	10 31	10 39		10 48	11 04		11 10		11 30	11 38	12 04		12 36	12 32			12 53	13 03	13 21		13 30	13 53	14 03	14 42
Torre	d	10 39			10 56					11 38				12 43								13 38			14 50
Torquay	d	10 42			10 59	11 14				11 41				12 46				13 04				13 41			14 53
Paignton	a	10 50			11 07	11 23				11 51				12 54				13 11				13 49			15 01
Totnes	d		10 52					11 24			11 52	12 17							13 16	13 34			14 05	14 16	
Ivybridge	d										12 07									13 50					
Plymouth	a		11 20					11 51			12 24	12 42			13 13				13 41	14 05			14 34	14 41	
	d		11 23										12 44		13 15						14 15				
Devonport	d																								
Dockyard	d																								
Keyham	d																								
St Budeaux Ferry Road	d																								
Saltash	d												12 53								14 24				
St Germans	d												13 00								14 32				
Menheniot	d																								
Liskeard 6	d		11 47										13 12		13 40						14 45				
Bodmin Parkway	d		12 00										13 24		13 54						14 58				
Lostwithiel	d												13 29								15 04				
Par	d		12 11	12 15									13 37		14 06	14 10					15 12				
Newquay	a			13 07												14 57									
St Austell	d		12 19										13 45		14 14						15 21				
Truro	d		12 37										14 02		14 30						15 39				
Redruth	d		12 49										14 15		14 44						15 53				
Camborne	d		12 56										14 21		14 50						16 00				
Hayle	d												14 28		15 00										
St Erth	d		13 08										14 33		15 05						16 12				
Penzance	a		13 20										14 42		15 17						16 21				

A ◇ from Exeter St Davids ■ to Exeter St Davids

B 🍴 from Newton Abbot Ø to Newton Abbot

For connections from Heathrow Airport, Gatwick Airport and Oxford please see Tables 125A, 148 and 116

For the complete service between Westbury and Castle Cary refer to table 123

Table 135

Saturdays

15 February to 22 March

London and Birmingham - Devon and Cornwall

Route Diagram - see first Page of Table 135

		GW	GW	GW	XC	GW	GW	GW	GW	XC	XC	GW	GW	GW	GW	GW	XC	GW	GW	GW	GW	XC
									R													
		◇1	◇		◇1		◇1		1	◇1	◇1				◇1	◇	◇1				◇1	◇1
		A																				B
		🍽⊘			🛒		🍽		🍽	🛒	🛒				🍽		🛒				🍽	🛒
London Paddington 15 ⊖	d	12 06					12 18		13 06						14 06						15 06	
Slough 3	d																					
Reading 7	d	12 33					12 48		13 32						14 34						15 32	
Theale	d						12 56															
Thatcham	d						13 05															
Newbury	d						13 13															
Hungerford	d						13 21															
Pewsey	d						13 39														16 03	
Westbury	d						13 58														16 22	
Frome	d																					
Castle Cary	d						14 15														16 40	
Birmingham New Street 12	d				12 12					13 12	13 42						14 12					15 12
Cardiff Central 7	d																					
Newport (South Wales)	d																					
Swindon	d																					
Bristol Parkway 7	d				13 25					14 28	14 59						15 25					16 30
Filton Abbey Wood	d																					
Bath Spa 7	d																					
Bristol Temple Meads 10	d				13 44					14 44	15 12						15 44					16 44
Weston-super-Mare	d																					
Bridgwater	d																					
Taunton	d				14 17		14a38		14 48	15 17	15 44				15 49		16 17				17 02	17 18
Tiverton Parkway	d				14 29				15 01	15 30	15 56				16 02		16 29				17 15	17 30
Exeter St Davids 6	a	14 10			14 42				15 17	15 44	16 10				16 18		16 41				17 30	17 45
Exmouth	d							14 23					15 23							16 55		
Exeter Central	d							14 50					15 50						16 48	17 21		
Exeter St Davids 6	d	14 11		14 30	14 44			14 56	15 18	15 46			15 57		16 19		16 44		16 56	17 27	17 34	17 47
Exeter St Thomas	d							14 59					15 59						16 59	17 30		
Starcross	d							15 07					16 07						17 07	17 35		
Dawlish Warren	d			14 42				15 12					16 12						17 12	17 49		
Dawlish	d			14 46				15 16					16 16						17 16	17 53		
Teignmouth	d			14 51				15 21					16 21						17 21	17 58		
Newton Abbot	a	14 30		14 58	15 02			15 29	15 39	16 04			16 29		16 39		17 02		17 29	18 05	17 53	18 10
	d	14 32		15 00	15 04			15 30	15 39	16 06		16 18	16 30		16 40		17 03		17 30	18 09	17 55	18 12
Torre	d			15 08				15 38					16 38						17 38	18 17		
Torquay	d			15 11				15 41					16 41						17 41	18 20		
Paignton	a			15 19				15 51					16 51						17 51	18 27		
Totnes	d				15 16				15 53	16 19		16 31			16 53		17 16				18 08	18 25
Ivybridge	d											16 47			17 09							
Plymouth	a	15 09			15 42				16 20	16 46		17 05			17 24		17 41				18 36	18 52
	d	15 11				16 03			16 26						17 26			17 52			18 41	18 55
Devonport	d																	17 55				
Dockyard	d																	17x57				
Keyham	d																	17 59				
St Budeaux Ferry Road	d																	18 01				
Saltash	d					16 12												18 06				
St Germans	d					16 19												18 12				
Menheniot	d					16x27												18x19				
Liskeard 6	d	15 36				16 33			16 50						17 51			18 26			19 06	19 19
Bodmin Parkway	d	15 49				16 45			17 03						18 03			18 38			19 19	19 34
Lostwithiel	d					16 50												18 44				
Par	d	16 01	16 15			16 57									18 16	18 21		18 52			19 31	19 45
Newquay	a		17 07													19 13						
St Austell	d	16 08				17 05			17 20						18 23			18 59			19 39	19 53
Truro	d	16 26				17 23			17 37						18 41			19 17			20 00	20 12
Redruth	d	16 38				17 36			17 50						18 53			19 30			20 10	20 27
Camborne	d	16 46				17 42			17 57						19 01			19 36			20 18	20 35
Hayle	d					17 49			18 06									19 43				
St Erth	d	16 57				17 54			18 12					18 32	19 12			19 48			20 29	20 46
Penzance	a	17 09				18 03			18 24					18 44	19 24			19 57			20 40	20 56

A 🍽 from Newton Abbot ⊘ to Newton Abbot **B** 🛒 to Plymouth

For connections from Heathrow Airport, Gatwick Airport and Oxford please see Tables 125A, 148 and 116

For the complete service between Westbury and Castle Cary refer to table 123

Table 135

Saturdays

15 February to 22 March

London and Birmingham - Devon and Cornwall

Route Diagram - see first Page of Table 135

		GW	GW	XC	GW	GW	XC	GW		GW	GW	GW	GW	XC	GW	GW	XC	GW		GW	XC	GW	GW	XC	GW
		1		◇1	◇1		◇1					◇1	◇1	◇1		◇1	◇1			◇1	◇1	◇1		◇1	◇
		A					B							B							C			C	
				[trolley]	[buffet]		[trolley]					[buffet]	[buffet]	[trolley]		[buffet]	[trolley]			[buffet]	[trolley]	[buffet]	[bus]	[trolley]	
London Paddington 15 ⊖	d				16 06							17 06	16 30			18 06				19 06		20 06			
Slough 3	d																								
Reading 7	d				16 33							17 32	16 57			18 33				19 32		20 35			
Theale	d																								
Thatcham	d																								
Newbury	d																			19 49		20 50			
Hungerford	d																								
Pewsey	d											18 03								20 08		21 10			
Westbury	d											18 23								20 27		21 29			
Frome	d																								
Castle Cary	d											18 41								20 44		21 47			
Birmingham New Street 12	d			15 42			16 12							17 12			18 12				19 12			20 12	
Cardiff Central 7	d																								
Newport (South Wales)	d																								
Swindon	d												17 30												
Bristol Parkway 7	d			16 54			17 26							18 30			19 26				20 30			21 21	
Filton Abbey Wood	d																								
Bath Spa 7	d												18 00												
Bristol Temple Meads 10	d			17 10			17 44						18 18	18 44			19 44				20 44			21 44	21 59
Weston-super-Mare	d												18 40												22 33
Bridgwater	d																								22 52
Taunton	d			17 42	17 49		18 17					19 02	19 06	19 17		19 47	20 17			21 07	21 17	22 09		22 17	23 05
Tiverton Parkway	d			17 54	18 02		18 29					19 15	19 21	19 29			20 29			21 20	21 29	22 25	22 29	22 30	23 20
Exeter St Davids 6	a			18 07	18 18		18 41					19 31	19 36	19 43		20 13	20 41			21 36	21 42	22 40		22 44	23 38
Exmouth	d					17 55									19 38			20 08							
Exeter Central	d					18 21									20 01			20 35							
Exeter St Davids 6	d	17 53		18 09	18 20	18 27	18 46	18 56		19 16		19 34	19 39	19 45	20 07	20 16	20 44	20 56		21 39	21 45				
Exeter St Thomas	d					18 29				19 19					20 10			20 59							
Starcross	d					18 37				19 27					20 18			21 07							
Dawlish Warren	d	18 05				18 42				19 32					20 32			21 12							
Dawlish	d	18 09		18 21		18 46		19 09		19 36					20 36			21 16							
Teignmouth	d	18 14		18 26		18 51		19 14		19 41					20 41			21 21							
Newton Abbot	a	18 21		18 32	18 40	18 59	19 04	19 21		19 49		19 53	19 58	20 03	20 48	20 37	21 02	21 28		21 58	22 04				
	d	18 22		18 33	18 41	19 01	19 05	19 22		19 50		19 54	19 59	20 05	20 49	20 37	21 03	21 30		21 59	22 08				
Torre	d					19 09				19 58			20 09		20 57			21 38							
Torquay	d			18 45		19 12		19 32		20 01			20 12		21 00			21 41							
Paignton	a			18 51		19 21		19 40		20 09			20 21		21 07			21 48							
Totnes	d	18 35			18 54		19 18					20 07		20 17		20 51	21 16			22 12	22 21				
Ivybridge	d	18 51			19 11																				
Plymouth	a	19 05			19 26		19 43					20 35		20 43		21 19	21 41			22 40	22 47		23 49		
	d	19 08					19 48					20 38		20 58		21 20									
Devonport	d																								
Dockyard	d																								
Keyham	d																								
St Budeaux Ferry Road	d																								
Saltash	d	19 17										20 49													
St Germans	d	19 24										20 56													
Menheniot	d																								
Liskeard 6	d	19 36					20 11					21 08		21 25		21 45									
Bodmin Parkway	d	19 48					20 23					21 21		21 37		21 59									
Lostwithiel	d	19 53					20 28																		
Par	d	20 01	20 15				20 36					21 33		21 48		22 11									
Newquay	a		21 07																						
St Austell	d	20 08					20 42					21 43		21 55		22 18									
Truro	d	20 26					21 02					22 03		22 13		22 36									
Redruth	d	20 43					21 13					22 13		22 28		22 48									
Camborne	d	20 49					21 19							22 35		22 56									
Hayle	d						21 27									23 03									
St Erth	d	20 58					21 32				22 20	22 30		22 46		23 09									
Penzance	a	21 08					21 43				22 32	22 42		22 54		23 22									

A 1 from Plymouth
B [trolley] to Plymouth
C [trolley] to Bristol Temple Meads

For connections from Heathrow Airport, Gatwick Airport and Oxford please see Tables 125A, 148 and 116

For the complete service between Westbury and Castle Cary refer to table 123

Table 135

Saturdays

15 February to 22 March

London and Birmingham - Devon and Cornwall

Route Diagram - see first Page of Table 135

		GW	GW	XC
		◇1		
			🚌	🚌
		☕		
London Paddington 15 ⊖	d	20 30		
Slough 3	d			
Reading 7	d	20 57		
Theale	d			
Thatcham	d			
Newbury	d			
Hungerford	d			
Pewsey	d			
Westbury	d			
Frome	d			
Castle Cary	d			
Birmingham New Street 12	d			
Cardiff Central 7	d			
Newport (South Wales)	d			
Swindon	d	21 30		
Bristol Parkway 7	d			
Filton Abbey Wood	d			
Bath Spa 7	d	22 00		
Bristol Temple Meads 10	d	22 17		
Weston-super-Mare	d	22s47		
Bridgwater	d	23s05		
Taunton	d	23 19		
Tiverton Parkway	d	23 32		
Exeter St Davids 6	a	23 48		
Exmouth	d			
Exeter Central	d			
Exeter St Davids 6	d		22 48	22 50
Exeter St Thomas	d			
Starcross	d			
Dawlish Warren	d			
Dawlish	d		23 01	
Teignmouth	d		23 09	
Newton Abbot	a		23 29	23 20
	d		23 29	23 20
Torre	d			
Torquay	d			
Paignton	a			
Totnes	d		23 54	23 45
Ivybridge	d			
Plymouth	a		00 39	00 30
	d			
Devonport	d			
Dockyard	d			
Keyham	d			
St Budeaux Ferry Road	d			
Saltash	d			
St Germans	d			
Menheniot	d			
Liskeard 6	d			
Bodmin Parkway	d			
Lostwithiel	d			
Par	d			
Newquay	a			
St Austell	d			
Truro	d			
Redruth	d			
Camborne	d			
Hayle	d			
St Erth	d			
Penzance	a			

For connections from Heathrow Airport, Gatwick Airport and Oxford please see Tables 125A, 148 and 116

For the complete service between Westbury and Castle Cary refer to table 123

Table 135

Saturdays

29 March to 17 May

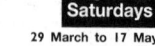

London and Birmingham - Devon and Cornwall

Route Diagram - see first Page of Table 135

		GW	GW	GW	GW	GW	GW	GW	GW	XC	GW	GW	GW	GW	XC	GW	GW	GW	GW	GW	XC	GW	XC
			R 1 A		R B					◇1		◇			◇1		◇				◇1		◇1
London Paddington 15 ⊖	d																						
Slough 3	d																						
Reading 7	d				00u37																		
Theale	d																						
Thatcham	d																						
Newbury	d																						
Hungerford	d																						
Pewsey	d																						
Westbury	d																						
Frome	d																						
Castle Cary	d																						
Birmingham New Street 12	d																				06 42		07 12
Cardiff Central 7	d																						
Newport (South Wales)	d																						
Swindon	d																						
Bristol Parkway 7	d																				07 54		08 25
Filton Abbey Wood	d																						
Bath Spa 7	d																						
Bristol Temple Meads 10	d											05 24			06 08		06 36				08 11		08 45
Weston-super-Mare	d											05 45					06 56						
Bridgwater	d	00 02										06 03											
Taunton	d	00s14			02 35							06 18			07 15		07 25				08 43		09 17
Tiverton Parkway	d	00s31										06 33			07 27		07 41				08 55		09 29
Exeter St Davids 6	a	00 50			03 06							06 52			07 41		07 59				09 08		09 41
Exmouth	d															07 15				08 23			
Exeter Central	d															07 43				08 50			
Exeter St Davids 6	d				04 11		05 18	05 36	06 11			06 56			07 42	07 50	08 00		08 37	08 56	09 10	09 28	09 44
Exeter St Thomas	d						05 22	05 40	06 14			06 59				07 53	08 04			08 59			
Starcross	d						05 30	05 48	06 22			07 05				08 01				09 07			
Dawlish Warren	d						05 35	05 53	06 27			07 10				08 06				09 24			
Dawlish	d						05 39	05 57	06 31			07 14				08 10	08 17		08 51	09 28			
Teignmouth	d						05 44	06 02	06 36			07 19				08 15	08 22		08 56	09 33			
Newton Abbot	a				04 31		05 51	06 09	06 45			07 26			08 00	08 22	08 29		09 03	09 40	09 28	09 48	10 02
	d				04 33		05 52	06 11	06 45			07 26		07 40	08 02	08 24	08 31		09 06	09 41	09 29	09 49	10 03
Torre	d						06 00	06 19	06 53					07 48		08 32				09 50			
Torquay	d						06 03	06 22	06 56					07 51		08 35			09 16	09 53	09 41		
Paignton	a						06 11	06 30	07 06					07 59		08 44			09 25	10 01	09 47		
Totnes	d											07 40			08 14		08 45					10 02	10 16
Ivybridge	d											07 56					09 02					10 19	
Plymouth	a				05 14							08 13			08 41		09 16					10 32	10 41
	d				05 43					06 28		08 18					09 19	09 51				10 33	
Devonport	d											08 21						09 54					
Dockyard	d																						
Keyham	d																						
St Budeaux Ferry Road	d																					10 39	
Saltash	d											08 28					09 28	10 01				10 44	
St Germans	d											08 35					09 36	10 08				10 51	
Menheniot	d																	10x15					
Liskeard 6	d				06 08					06 51		08 47					09 49	10 22				11 03	
Bodmin Parkway	d				06 22					07 03		08 59					10 02	10 34				11 15	
Lostwithiel	d				06 28					07 08		09 04						10 39				11 20	
Par	d			06 09	06 37	06 52				07 14		09 12	09 18				10 14	10 46				11 28	
Newquay	a					07 44							10 10										
St Austell	d			06 16	06 46					07 21		09 20					10 22	10 54				11 37	
Truro	d			06 35	07 06					07 37		09 37					10 40	11 10				11 55	
Redruth	d		00 06	06 48	07 18					07 49		09 50					10 55	11 24				12 08	
Camborne	d		00 14	06 54	07 26					07 56		09 56					11 02	11 30				12 14	
Hayle	d		00 22	07 01	07 35					08 04		10 03					11 10	11 38				12 21	
St Erth	d		00 28	07 04	07 42					08 10	08 28	10 08					11 18	11 42				12 25	
Penzance	a		00 40	07 16	07 53					08 18	08 40	10 18					11 26	11 55				12 36	

A Restaurant for customers joining at Pad, Reading + Newbury. The Armada

B The Night Riviera

For connections from Heathrow Airport, Gatwick Airport and Oxford please see Tables 125A, 148 and 116

For the complete service between Westbury and Castle Cary refer to table 123

Table 135

Saturdays

29 March to 17 May

London and Birmingham - Devon and Cornwall

Route Diagram - see first Page of Table 135

		GW	GW	GW	GW	GW		XC	GW	GW	GW	XC	GW	GW	GW	GW		XC	XC	GW	GW	GW	GW	XC	GW
			[B]																						
			◇1	◇				◇1	◇1		◇1	◇1	◇		◇1	◇		◇1	◇1				◇1	◇1	
			A								B				B								B		
			☕					🛒	☕		☕Ø	🛒			☕Ø			🛒	🛒				☕Ø	🛒	
London Paddington 15 ⊖	d		07 30						08 18		09 06				10 06								11 06		
Slough 3	d																								
Reading 7	d		07 57						08 48		09 32				10 33								11 32		
Theale	d								08 58																
Thatcham	d								09 07																
Newbury	d								09 14																
Hungerford	d								09 23																
Pewsey	d								09 41														12 02		
Westbury	d								09 57														12 21		
Frome	d																								
Castle Cary	d								10 17														12 39		
Birmingham New Street 12	d							08 12				09 12						09 42	10 12					11 12	
Cardiff Central 7	d																								
Newport (South Wales)	d																								
Swindon	d		08 30																						
Bristol Parkway 7	d							09 26				10 30						10 55	11 25					12 31	
Filton Abbey Wood	d																								
Bath Spa 7	d		09 00																						
Bristol Temple Meads 10	d		09 17					09 44				10 44						11 12	11 44					12 44	
Weston-super-Mare	d																	11 39							
Bridgwater	d																								
Taunton	d		09 51					10 17	10 40		10 48	11 17						12 00	12 17				13 02	13 17	
Tiverton Parkway	d							10 30	10 53		11 01	11 29						12 12	12 29				13 15	13 29	
Exeter St Davids 6	a		10 16					10 45	11 09		11 17	11 41			12 09			12 26	12 41				13 31	13 42	
Exmouth	d	09 23								10 23				11 23								12 23			13 23
Exeter Central	d	09 52				10 30				10 50				11 50								12 50			13 50
Exeter St Davids 6	d	09 58	10 19		10 25	10 35		10 47		10 56	11 19	11 45		11 56	12 11			12 28	12 44	12 52		12 56	13 33	13 44	13 57
Exeter St Thomas	d	09 59								10 59				11 59								12 59			13 59
Starcross	d	10 07								11 07				12 07								13 07			14 07
Dawlish Warren	d	10 12				10 47				11 12				12 12						13 04		13 12			14 24
Dawlish	d	10 16				10 51				11 16				12 16				12 40		13 08		13 16			14 28
Teignmouth	d	10 21				10 56				11 21				12 21				12 45		13 13		13 21			14 33
Newton Abbot	a	10 30	10 38		10 46	11 03		11 09		11 29	11 38	12 03		12 29	12 31			12 51	13 02	13 20		13 29	13 51	14 02	14 41
	d	10 31	10 39		10 48	11 04		11 10		11 30	11 38	12 04		12 36	12 32			12 53	13 03	13 21		13 30	13 53	14 03	14 42
Torre	d	10 39			10 56					11 38				12 43								13 38			14 50
Torquay	d	10 42			10 59	11 14				11 41				12 46				13 04				13 41			14 53
Paignton	a	10 50			11 07	11 23				11 51				12 54				13 11				13 49			15 01
Totnes	d		10 52					11 24			11 52	12 17							13 16	13 34			14 05	14 16	
Ivybridge	d										12 07									13 50					
Plymouth	a		11 20					11 51			12 24	12 42			13 13				13 41	14 05			14 34	14 41	
	d		11 23										12 44		13 15						14 15				
Devonport	d																								
Dockyard	d																								
Keyham	d																								
St Budeaux Ferry Road	d																								
Saltash	d												12 53								14 24				
St Germans	d												13 00								14 32				
Menheniot	d																								
Liskeard 6	d		11 47										13 12		13 40						14 45				
Bodmin Parkway	d		12 00										13 24		13 54						14 58				
Lostwithiel	d												13 29								15 04				
Par	d		12 11	12 15									13 37		14 06	14 10					15 12				
Newquay	a			13 07												14 57									
St Austell	d		12 19										13 45		14 14						15 21				
Truro	d		12 37										14 02		14 30						15 39				
Redruth	d		12 49										14 15		14 44						15 53				
Camborne	d		12 56										14 21		14 50						16 00				
Hayle	d												14 28		15 00										
St Erth	d		13 08										14 33		15 05						16 12				
Penzance	a		13 20										14 42		15 17						16 21				

A ◇ from Exeter St Davids [B] to Exeter St Davids

B ☕ from Newton Abbot Ø to Newton Abbot

For connections from Heathrow Airport, Gatwick Airport and Oxford please see Tables 125A, 148 and 116

For the complete service between Westbury and Castle Cary refer to table 123

Table 135

Saturdays

29 March to 17 May

London and Birmingham - Devon and Cornwall

Route Diagram - see first Page of Table 135

		GW		GW	GW	XC	GW	GW	GW	GW	XC	XC		GW	GW	GW	GW	GW	XC	GW	GW	GW		GW	XC
		◇1		◇		◇1		◇1		■ 1	◇1	◇1					◇1	◇	◇1					◇1	◇1
		A																							B
		☕⊘				🛒		☕		☕	🛒	🛒					☕		🛒					☕	🛒
London Paddington 15 ⊖	d	12 06						12 18		13 06							14 06							15 06	
Slough 3	d																								
Reading 7	d	12 33						12 48		13 32							14 34							15 32	
Theale	d							12 56																	
Thatcham	d							13 05																	
Newbury	d							13 13																	
Hungerford	d							13 21																	
Pewsey	d							13 39																16 03	
Westbury	d							13 58																16 22	
Frome	d																								
Castle Cary	d							14 15																16 40	
Birmingham New Street 12	d					12 12					13 12	13 42							14 12						15 12
Cardiff Central 7	d																								
Newport (South Wales)	d																								
Swindon	d																								
Bristol Parkway 7	d					13 25					14 28	14 59							15 25						16 30
Filton Abbey Wood	d																								
Bath Spa 7	d																								
Bristol Temple Meads 10	d					13 44					14 44	15 12							15 44						16 44
Weston-super-Mare	d																								
Bridgwater	d																								
Taunton	d					14 17		14a38		14 48	15 17	15 44					15 49		16 17					17 02	17 18
Tiverton Parkway	d					14 29				15 01	15 30	15 56					16 02		16 29					17 15	17 30
Exeter St Davids 6	a	14 10				14 42				15 17	15 44	16 10					16 18		16 41					17 30	17 45
Exmouth	d								14 23						15 23							16 55			
Exeter Central	d								14 50						15 50						16 48	17 21			
Exeter St Davids 6	d	14 11			14 30	14 44			14 56	15 18	15 46				15 57		16 19		16 44		16 56	17 27		17 34	17 47
Exeter St Thomas	d								14 59						15 59						16 59	17 30			
Starcross	d								15 07						16 07						17 07	17 35			
Dawlish Warren	d				14 42				15 12						16 12						17 12	17 49			
Dawlish	d				14 46				15 16						16 16						17 16	17 53			
Teignmouth	d				14 51				15 21						16 21						17 21	17 58			
Newton Abbot	a	14 30			14 58	15 02			15 29	15 39	16 04				16 29		16 39		17 02		17 29	18 05		17 53	18 10
	d	14 32			15 00	15 04			15 30	15 39	16 06			16 18	16 30		16 40		17 03		17 30	18 09		17 55	18 12
Torre	d				15 08				15 38						16 38						17 38	18 17			
Torquay	d				15 11				15 41						16 41						17 41	18 20			
Paignton	a				15 19				15 51						16 51						17 51	18 27			
Totnes	d					15 16				15 53	16 19			16 31			16 53		17 16					18 08	18 25
Ivybridge	d													16 47			17 09								
Plymouth	a	15 09				15 42				16 20	16 46			17 05			17 24		17 41					18 36	18 52
	d	15 11					16 03			16 26							17 26			17 52				18 41	18 55
Devonport	d																			17 55					
Dockyard	d																			17x57					
Keyham	d																			17 59					
St Budeaux Ferry Road	d																			18 01					
Saltash	d						16 12													18 06					
St Germans	d						16 19													18 12					
Menheniot	d						16x27													18x19					
Liskeard 6	d	15 36					16 33			16 50							17 51			18 26				19 06	19 19
Bodmin Parkway	d	15 49					16 45			17 03							18 03			18 38				19 19	19 34
Lostwithiel	d						16 50													18 44					
Par	d	16 01		16 15			16 57										18 16	18 21		18 52				19 31	19 45
Newquay	a			17 07														19 13							
St Austell	d	16 08					17 05			17 20							18 23			18 59				19 39	19 53
Truro	d	16 26					17 23			17 37							18 41			19 17				20 00	20 12
Redruth	d	16 38					17 36			17 50							18 53			19 30				20 10	20 27
Camborne	d	16 46					17 42			17 57							19 01			19 36				20 18	20 35
Hayle	d						17 49			18 06										19 43					
St Erth	d	16 57					17 54			18 12						18 32	19 12			19 48				20 29	20 46
Penzance	a	17 09					18 03			18 24						18 44	19 24			19 57				20 40	20 56

A ☕ from Newton Abbot ⊘ to Newton Abbot   B 🛒 to Plymouth

For connections from Heathrow Airport, Gatwick Airport and Oxford please see Tables 125A, 148 and 116

For the complete service between Westbury and Castle Cary refer to table 123

Table 135

Saturdays

29 March to 17 May

London and Birmingham - Devon and Cornwall

Route Diagram - see first Page of Table 135

		GW	GW	XC	GW	GW	XC	GW	GW	GW	GW	GW	XC	GW	GW	XC	GW	GW	XC	XC	GW	XC	GW
		■1		◇■1	◇■1		◇■1				◇■1	◇■1	◇■1		◇■1	◇■1		◇■1	◇■1	◇■1	◇■1	◇■1	◇
		A					B						B						C	C		C	
				⊼	ꝏ		⊼				ꝏ	ꝏ	⊼		ꝏ	⊼		ꝏ	⊼	⊼	ꝏ	⊼	
London Paddington 15 ⊖	d				16 06						17 06	16 30			18 06			19 06			20 06		
Slough 3	d																						
Reading 7	d				16 33						17 32	16 57			18 33			19 32			20 35		
Theale	d																						
Thatcham	d																						
Newbury	d																	19 49			20 50		
Hungerford	d																						
Pewsey	d										18 03							20 08			21 10		
Westbury	d										18 23							20 27			21 29		
Frome	d																						
Castle Cary	d										18 41							20 44			21 47		
Birmingham New Street 12	d			15 42			16 12						17 12			18 12			19 12	19 42		20 12	
Cardiff Central 7	d																						
Newport (South Wales)	d																						
Swindon	d											17 30											
Bristol Parkway 7	d			16 54			17 26						18 30			19 26			20 30	20 54		21 21	
Filton Abbey Wood	d																						
Bath Spa 7	d											18 00											
Bristol Temple Meads 10	d			17 10			17 44					18 18	18 44			19 44			20 44	21 11		21 44	21 59
Weston-super-Mare	d											18 40											22 33
Bridgwater	d																						22 52
Taunton	d			17 42	17 49		18 17				19 02	19 06	19 17		19 47	20 17		21 07	21 17	21 43	22 09	22 17	23 05
Tiverton Parkway	d			17 54	18 02		18 29				19 15	19 21	19 29			20 29		21 20	21 29	21 55	22 22	22 29	23 20
Exeter St Davids 6	a			18 07	18 18		18 41				19 31	19 36	19 43		20 13	20 41		21 36	21 42	22 09	22 37	22 43	23 38
Exmouth	d					17 55								19 38			20 08						
Exeter Central	d					18 21								20 01			20 35						
Exeter St Davids 6	d	17 53		18 09	18 20	18 27	18 46	18 56	19 16		19 34	19 39	19 45	20 07	20 16	20 44	20 56	21 39	21 45	22 10	22 39	22 46	
Exeter St Thomas	d					18 29			19 19					20 10			20 59						
Starcross	d					18 37			19 27					20 18			21 07						
Dawlish Warren	d	18 05				18 42			19 32					20 32			21 12						
Dawlish	d	18 09		18 21		18 46		19 09	19 36					20 36			21 16				22 52		
Teignmouth	d	18 14		18 26		18 51		19 14	19 41					20 41			21 21				22 58		
Newton Abbot	a	18 21		18 32	18 40	18 59	19 04	19 21	19 49		19 53	19 58	20 03	20 48	20 37	21 02	21 28	21 58	22 04	22 28	23 05	23 10	
	d	18 22		18 33	18 41	19 01	19 05	19 22	19 50		19 54	19 59	20 05	20 49	20 37	21 03	21 30	21 59	22 08	22 30	23 06	23 12	
Torre	d					19 09			19 58			20 09		20 57			21 38						
Torquay	d			18 45		19 12		19 32	20 01			20 12		21 00			21 41						
Paignton	a			18 51		19 21		19 40	20 09			20 21		21 07			21 48						
Totnes	d	18 35			18 54		19 18				20 07		20 17		20 51	21 16		22 12	22 21	22 42	23 20	23 27	
Ivybridge	d	18 51			19 11																		
Plymouth	a	19 05			19 26		19 43				20 35		20 43		21 19	21 41		22 40	22 47	23 08	23 47	23 53	
	d	19 08					19 48				20 38		20 58		21 20								
Devonport	d																						
Dockyard	d																						
Keyham	d																						
St Budeaux Ferry Road	d																						
Saltash	d	19 17									20 49												
St Germans	d	19 24									20 56												
Menheniot	d																						
Liskeard 6	d	19 36					20 11				21 08		21 25		21 45								
Bodmin Parkway	d	19 48					20 23				21 21		21 37		21 59								
Lostwithiel	d	19 53					20 28																
Par	d	20 01	20 15				20 36				21 33		21 48		22 11								
Newquay	a		21 07																				
St Austell	d	20 08					20 42				21 43		21 55		22 18								
Truro	d	20 26					21 02				22 03		22 13		22 36								
Redruth	d	20 43					21 13				22 13		22 28		22 48								
Camborne	d	20 49					21 19						22 35		22 56								
Hayle	d						21 27								23 03								
St Erth	d	20 58					21 32			22 20	22 30		22 46		23 09								
Penzance	a	21 08					21 43			22 32	22 42		22 54		23 22								

A ■1 from Plymouth
B ⊼ to Plymouth
C ⊼ to Bristol Temple Meads

For connections from Heathrow Airport, Gatwick Airport and Oxford please see Tables 125A, 148 and 116

For the complete service between Westbury and Castle Cary refer to table 123

Table 135

Saturdays

29 March to 17 May

London and Birmingham - Devon and Cornwall

Route Diagram - see first Page of Table 135

		GW ◇1
London Paddington 15 ⊖	d	20 30
Slough 3	d	
Reading 7	d	20 57
Theale	d	
Thatcham	d	
Newbury	d	
Hungerford	d	
Pewsey	d	
Westbury	d	
Frome	d	
Castle Cary	d	
Birmingham New Street 12	d	
Cardiff Central 7	d	
Newport (South Wales)	d	
Swindon	d	21 30
Bristol Parkway 7	d	
Filton Abbey Wood	d	
Bath Spa 7	d	22 00
Bristol Temple Meads 10	d	22 17
Weston-super-Mare	d	22s47
Bridgwater	d	23s05
Taunton	d	23 19
Tiverton Parkway	d	23 32
Exeter St Davids 6	a	23 48
Exmouth	d	
Exeter Central	d	
Exeter St Davids 6	d	
Exeter St Thomas	d	
Starcross	d	
Dawlish Warren	d	
Dawlish	d	
Teignmouth	d	
Newton Abbot	a	
	d	
Torre	d	
Torquay	d	
Paignton	a	
Totnes	d	
Ivybridge	d	
Plymouth	a	
	d	
Devonport	d	
Dockyard	d	
Keyham	d	
St Budeaux Ferry Road	d	
Saltash	d	
St Germans	d	
Menheniot	d	
Liskeard 6	d	
Bodmin Parkway	d	
Lostwithiel	d	
Par	d	
Newquay	a	
St Austell	d	
Truro	d	
Redruth	d	
Camborne	d	
Hayle	d	
St Erth	d	
Penzance	a	

For connections from Heathrow Airport, Gatwick Airport and Oxford please see Tables 125A, 148 and 116

For the complete service between Westbury and Castle Cary refer to table 123

Table 135

Sundays

8 December to 29 December

London and Birmingham - Devon and Cornwall

Route Diagram - see first Page of Table 135

		GW	GW	GW	GW	XC	GW	GW	XC	GW	GW	GW	GW	XC	GW	GW	GW	XC	GW	GW	GW	GW	XC
					◇	◇1		◇	◇1		◇1	◇1		◇1			◇1	◇1		◇1			◇1
														A									
						🚲			🚲		☕	☕		🚲			☕	🚲		☕			🚲
London Paddington 15 ⊖	d										08 00	08 57					09 57			10 57			
Slough 3	d																						
Reading 7	d										08 39	09 32					10 32			11 32			
Theale	d																						
Thatcham	d																						
Newbury	d											09 47											
Hungerford	d																						
Pewsey	d																11 05						
Westbury	d											10 21											
Frome	d																						
Castle Cary	d																11 34						
Birmingham New Street 12	d													09 12				10 30					11 30
Cardiff Central 7	d																						
Newport (South Wales)	d																						
Swindon	d										09 18												
Bristol Parkway 7	d													10 21				11 41					12 42
Filton Abbey Wood	d																						
Bath Spa 7	d										09 47												
Bristol Temple Meads 10	d				07 30	08 44		08 28	09 48		10 00			10 44				11 54					12 54
Weston-super-Mare	d				07 53			08 59															
Bridgwater	d				08 09			09 18															
Taunton	d				08 24	09 16		09 32	10 20		10 34	10 57		11 16			11 57	12 26		12 47			13 26
Tiverton Parkway	d				08 39	09 28		09 48	10 32		10 48	11 11		11 28				12 37					13 38
Exeter St Davids 6	a				08 56	09 41		10 05	10 46		11 03	11 26		11 41			12 21	12 54		13 14			13 54
Exmouth	d						09 10			10 21					11 24				12 28				
Exeter Central	d						09 36			10 48					11 52				12 54			13 20	
Exeter St Davids 6	d	08 52			09 05	09 43	09 54	10 06	10 47	10 53	11 05	11 26		11 43	11 57	12 15	12 23	12 56	13 00	13 15		13 25	13 55
Exeter St Thomas	d	08 55					09 57			10 56					12 00								
Starcross	d	09 03					10 05			11 04					12 08								
Dawlish Warren	d	09 08					10 10			11 09					12 13				13 11				
Dawlish	d	09 12			09 18		10 14	10 21		11 13	11 19				12 17				13 15			13 38	
Teignmouth	d	09 17			09 23		10 19	10 26		11 18	11 25				12 22				13 20			13 43	
Newton Abbot	a	09 24			09 30	10 01	10 26	10 31	11 05	11 25	11 32	11 47		12 01	12 29	12 35	12 43	13 14	13 27	13 35		13 50	14 14
	d	09 26			09 30	10 02	10 37	10 33	11 07	11 27	11 32	11 47		12 02	12 31	12 36	12 44	13 16	13 28	13 37		13 52	14 15
Torre	d	09 34					10 45			11 35					12 39				13 36			14 00	
Torquay	d	09 37					10 48			11 38					12 42				13 39			14 03	
Paignton	a	09 44					10 54			11 45					12 50				13 46			14 10	
Totnes	d				09 43	10 15		10 46	11 19		11 46	12 02		12 15		12 48	12 57	13 29					14 29
Ivybridge	d				10 00											13 04							
Plymouth	a				10 14	10 40		11 15	11 45		12 17	12 32		12 40		13 17	13 27	13 56		14 14			14 55
	d		09 15		10 15			11 15				12 35		12 55		13 32				14 20	14 50		
Devonport	d				10 19																		
Dockyard	d																						
Keyham	d																						
St Budeaux Ferry Road	d		09 21																				
Saltash	d		09 25		10 26			11 26								13 40					14 59		
St Germans	d		09 31		10 33			11 33								13 47					15 06		
Menheniot	d				10x41																		
Liskeard 6	d		09 43		10 47			11 45				12 59		13 18		13 59				14 44	15 18		
Bodmin Parkway	d		09 55		10 59			11 57				13 12		13 30		14 11				14 58	15 30		
Lostwithiel	d		10 01		11 04			12 02													15 36		
Par	d		10 09	10 18	11 12			12 10				13 24	13 31	13 41		14 22					15 44		
Newquay	a			11 10									14 23										
St Austell	d		10 16		11 21			12 18				13 31		13 50		14 30				15 14	15 51		
Truro	d		10 35		11 40			12 35				13 50		14 08		14 46				15 32	16 10		
Redruth	d		10 48		11 53			12 48				14 02		14 19		15 00				15 43	16 23		
Camborne	d		10 54		11 59			12 54				14 10		14 25		15 06				15 51	16 29		
Hayle	d		11 01		12 06			13 01													16 36		
St Erth	d		11 06		12 10			13 06				14 22		14 37		15 17				16 03	16 41		
Penzance	a		11 18		12 20			13 16				14 33		14 49		15 26				16 21	16 51		

A 🚲 to Plymouth

For connections from Heathrow Airport, Gatwick Airport and Oxford please see Tables 125A, 148 and 116

For the complete service between Westbury and Castle Cary refer to table 123

Table 135

Sundays

8 December to 29 December

London and Birmingham - Devon and Cornwall

Route Diagram - see first Page of Table 135

		GW	GW	GW	GW	XC	GW	GW	GW	XC	GW	GW	GW	GW	XC	GW	XC	GW	GW	XC	GW	GW	GW
			◇1	◇1	◇	◇1		◇1		◇1	◇1		◇	◇1	◇1		◇1		◇1	◇1		◇1	
																				A			
			℞	℞		🛒		℞		🛒	℞			℞	🛒		🛒		℞	🛒		℞	
London Paddington 15 ⊖	d		11 27	11 57				12 57			13 03			13 57					14 57			15 57	
Slough 3	d																						
Reading 7	d		12 06	12 32				13 32			13 38			14 32					15 32			16 32	
Theale	d																						
Thatcham	d																						
Newbury	d			12 48										14 48								16 48	
Hungerford	d																						
Pewsey	d		12 38																				
Westbury	d		13 05					14 20														17 24	
Frome	d																						
Castle Cary	d		13 24											15 35								17 43	
Birmingham New Street 12	d					12 12				13 12					14 12		14 42			15 12			
Cardiff Central 7	d																						
Newport (South Wales)	d																						
Swindon	d										14 11												
Bristol Parkway 7	d					13 21				14 21					15 24		16 00			16 21			
Filton Abbey Wood	d																						
Bath Spa 7	d										14 40												
Bristol Temple Meads 10	d					13 44				14 44	14 55				15 44		16 14			16 44			
Weston-super-Mare	d																						
Bridgwater	d																						
Taunton	d		13 46	13 54		14 16		14 56		15 16	15 31			15 56	16 14		16 46		16 51	17 16		18 05	
Tiverton Parkway	d		14 00			14 28		15 09		15 28					16 25		16 58		17 04	17 28		18 18	
Exeter St Davids 6	a		14 15	14 21		14 42		15 24		15 41	15 54			16 22	16 42		17 11		17 19	17 41		18 36	
Exmouth	d	13 24					14 31					15 24				16 24					17 24		
Exeter Central	d	13 50					14 59		15 20			15 50				16 50					17 50		
Exeter St Davids 6	d	14 00	14 15	14 23		14 43	15 05	15 25	15 31	15 43	15 55	16 00	16 10	16 24	16 43	16 57	17 13		17 21	17 43	17 56	18 37	
Exeter St Thomas	d	14 03										16 03	16 12								17 59		
Starcross	d	14 11										16 11									18 07		
Dawlish Warren	d	14 16										16 16									18 12		
Dawlish	d	14 20	14 29				15 17		15 43			16 20	16 25			17 10	17 25				18 16		
Teignmouth	d	14 25	14 35				15 22		15 48			16 25	16 30			17 15	17 30				18 21		
Newton Abbot	a	14 33	14 42	14 47		15 01	15 29	15 46	15 55	16 01	16 16	16 32	16 36	16 42	17 02	17 22	17 36		17 40	18 01	18 28	18 57	
	d	14 36	14 42	14 47		15 02	15 30	15 46	15 56	16 01	16 16	16 33	16 37	16 43	17 03	17 23	17 38		17 40	18 01	18 29	18 59	
Torre	d	14 44					15 39		16 04			16 41				17 32					18 37		
Torquay	d	14 47	14 54				15 42		16 07			16 44				17 35	17 49				18 40		
Paignton	a	14 53	15 03				15 50		16 15			16 51				17 42	17 56				18 47		
Totnes	d			15 01		15 15		16 00		16 15			16 52	17 01	17 17				17 56	18 15			
Ivybridge	d												17 08										
Plymouth	a			15 29		15 41		16 29		16 40	16 55		17 22	17 30	17 43				18 22	18 40		19 36	
	d			15 35				16 35					17 35						18 25	18 53			19 43
Devonport	d																						
Dockyard	d																						
Keyham	d																						
St Budeaux Ferry Road	d																						
Saltash	d												17 44										19 52
St Germans	d												17 51										19 59
Menheniot	d												17x59										
Liskeard 6	d			15 57				16 59					18 05						18 50	19 16			20 11
Bodmin Parkway	d			16 12				17 12					18 17						19 04	19 28			20 23
Lostwithiel	d												18 22										20 28
Par	d			16 24	16 30			17 23					18 30						19 16	19 39			20 36
Newquay	a				17 22																		
St Austell	d			16 32				17 31					18 37						19 23	19 46			20 43
Truro	d			16 50				17 49					18 55						19 41	20 03			21 00
Redruth	d			17 02				18 02					19 08						19 53	20 14			21 14
Camborne	d			17 10				18 10					19 14						20 04	20 22			21 20
Hayle	d												19 21										21 27
St Erth	d			17 22				18 22					19 25					20 05	20 16	20 33			21 32
Penzance	a			17 35				18 33					19 37					20 14	20 28	20 41			21 42

A 🛒 to Plymouth

For connections from Heathrow Airport, Gatwick Airport and Oxford please see Tables 125A, 148 and 116

For the complete service between Westbury and Castle Cary refer to table 123

Table 135

Sundays

8 December to 29 December

London and Birmingham - Devon and Cornwall

Route Diagram - see first Page of Table 135

		XC		GW	GW	GW	XC	GW	GW	XC	GW	GW		XC	XC	GW	GW	GW	XC	GW	GW
																					■
		◇1			◇1	◇	◇1		◇1	◇1		◇1		◇1	◇1	◇1		◇1	◇1	◇1	
							A								B				B		C
																					🛏
		🛒			🍽		🛒		🍽	🛒		🍽		🛒	🛒	🍽		🍽	🛒	🍽	🍽
London Paddington 15 ⊖	d				16 57				17 57			18 57				19 03		19 57		20 57	23 50
Slough 3	d																				
Reading 7	d				17 32				18 32			19 32				19 38		20 32		21 34	00u37
Theale	d																				
Thatcham	d																				
Newbury	d								18 48									20 48			
Hungerford	d																				
Pewsey	d								19 08									21 08			
Westbury	d								19 27									21 27			
Frome	d																				
Castle Cary	d											20 30						21 45			
Birmingham New Street 12	d	16 12					17 12			18 12				18 42	19 12				20 12		
Cardiff Central 7	d																				
Newport (South Wales)	d																				
Swindon	d															20 11					
Bristol Parkway 7	d	17 21					18 21			19 22				20 04	20 21				21 21		
Filton Abbey Wood	d																				
Bath Spa 7	d															20 40					
Bristol Temple Meads 10	d	17 44				18 06	18 44			19 44				20 19	20 44	20 55			21 44		
Weston-super-Mare	d					18 35								20 37		21 28					
Bridgwater	d					18 53															
Taunton	d	18 19			18 50	19 08	19 17		20 00	20 18		20 51		20 59	21 16	21 52		22 06	22 16	22s49	
Tiverton Parkway	d	18 31			19 03	19 23	19 29		20 15	20 30		21 05		21 12	21 28	22 05		22 19	22 28	23s03	
Exeter St Davids 6	a	18 45			19 19	19 41	19 47		20 30	20 44		21 21		21 27	21 41	22 20		22 36	22 45	23 19	03 05
Exmouth	d			18 24				19 24			20 24						21 24				
Exeter Central	d			18 49				19 50			20 50						21 50				
Exeter St Davids 6	d	18 46		18 56	19 20		19 49	19 56	20 31	20 44	21 00	21 22		21 30	21 43		21 56	22 37	22 46		04 35
Exeter St Thomas	d			18 59				19 59									21 59				
Starcross	d			19 07				20 07									22 07				
Dawlish Warren	d			19 12				20 12									22 12				
Dawlish	d			19 16				20 16			21 13	21 36		21 42			22 16				
Teignmouth	d			19 21				20 21			21 18	21 42		21 47			22 21				
Newton Abbot	a	19 04		19 28	19 39		20 07	20 28	20 53	21 02	21 25	21 48		21 54	22 01		22 29	22 57	23 04		04 55
	d	19 06		19 30	19 39		20 08	20 30	20 54	21 05	21 26	21 49		21 56	22 02		22 30	22 58	23 06		04 56
Torre	d			19 38				20 38			21 35						22 38				
Torquay	d			19 41				20 41			21 38						22 41				
Paignton	a			19 48				20 48			21 45						22 49				
Totnes	d	19 18			19 55		20 21		21 07	21 16		22 03			22 19			23 11	23 20		
Ivybridge	d																				
Plymouth	a	19 44			20 22		20 46		21 34	21 43		22 31		22 37	22 45			23 40	23 47		05 35
	d				20 25		20 50		21 40												06 28
Devonport	d																				
Dockyard	d																				
Keyham	d																				
St Budeaux Ferry Road	d																				
Saltash	d																				
St Germans	d																				
Menheniot	d																				
Liskeard 6	d				20 49		21 13		22 04												07 09
Bodmin Parkway	d				21 02		21 25		22 17												07 23
Lostwithiel	d																				07 29
Par	d				21 13		21 36		22 30												07 38
Newquay	a																				
St Austell	d				21 20		21 42		22 38												07 46
Truro	d				21 37		22 00		22 53												08 06
Redruth	d				21 51		22 11		23 08												08 20
Camborne	d				21 57		22 20		23 15												08 27
Hayle	d																				08 38
St Erth	d				22 10		22 31		23 27												08 45
Penzance	a				22 22		22 43		23 38												08 59

A 🛒 to Plymouth

B 🛒 to Bristol Temple Meads

C The Night Riviera

For connections from Heathrow Airport, Gatwick Airport and Oxford please see Tables 125A, 148 and 116

For the complete service between Westbury and Castle Cary refer to table 123

Table 135

Sundays

5 January to 9 February

London and Birmingham - Devon and Cornwall

Route Diagram - see first Page of Table 135

		GW	GW	GW	GW	XC	GW	GW	XC	GW		GW	GW	GW	XC	GW	GW	GW	XC	GW		GW	GW	GW	XC
					◇	◇1		◇	◇1			◇1	◇1		◇1			◇1	◇1			◇1			◇1
															A										
						[trolley]			[trolley]			[restaurant]	[restaurant]		[trolley]			[restaurant]	[trolley]			[restaurant]			[trolley]
London Paddington 15 ⊖	d											08 00	08 57					09 57				10 57			
Slough 3	d																								
Reading 7	d											08 39	09 32					10 33				11 32			
Theale	d																								
Thatcham	d																								
Newbury	d												09 47												
Hungerford	d																								
Pewsey	d																	11 05							
Westbury	d												10 21												
Frome	d																								
Castle Cary	d																	11 34							
Birmingham New Street 12	d														09 12				10 30						11 30
Cardiff Central 7	d																								
Newport (South Wales)	d																								
Swindon	d											09 13													
Bristol Parkway 7	d														10 21				11 41						12 42
Filton Abbey Wood	d																								
Bath Spa 7	d											09 42													
Bristol Temple Meads 10	d				07 30	08 44		08 28	09 48			10 00			10 44				11 54						12 54
Weston-super-Mare	d				07 53			08 59																	
Bridgwater	d				08 09			09 18																	
Taunton	d				08 24	09 16		09 32	10 20			10 34	10 57		11 16			11 57	12 26			12 47			13 26
Tiverton Parkway	d				08 39	09 28		09 48	10 32			10 48	11 11		11 28				12 37						13 38
Exeter St Davids 6	a				08 56	09 41		10 05	10 46			11 03	11 26		11 41			12 21	12 54			13 14			13 54
Exmouth	d						09 10			10 21						11 24				12 28					
Exeter Central	d						09 36			10 48						11 52				12 54				13 20	
Exeter St Davids 6	d	08 52			09 05	09 43	09 54	10 06	10 47	10 53		11 05	11 26		11 43	11 57	12 15	12 23		13 00		13 15		13 25	13 55
Exeter St Thomas	d	08 55					09 57			10 56						12 00									
Starcross	d	09 03					10 05			11 04						12 08									
Dawlish Warren	d	09 08					10 10			11 09						12 13				13 11					
Dawlish	d	09 12			09 18		10 14	10 21		11 13		11 19				12 17				13 15				13 38	
Teignmouth	d	09 17			09 23		10 19	10 26		11 18		11 25				12 22				13 20				13 43	
Newton Abbot	a	09 24			09 30	10 01	10 26	10 31	11 05	11 25		11 32	11 47		12 01	12 29	12 35	12 43		13 27		13 35		13 50	14 14
	d	09 26			09 30	10 02	10 37	10 33	11 07	11 27		11 32	11 47		12 02	12 31	12 36	12 44		13 28		13 37		13 52	14 15
Torre	d	09 34					10 45			11 35						12 39				13 36				14 00	
Torquay	d	09 37					10 48			11 38						12 42				13 39				14 03	
Paignton	a	09 44					10 54			11 45						12 50				13 46				14 10	
Totnes	d				09 43	10 15		10 46	11 19			11 46	12 02		12 15		12 48	12 57							14 29
Ivybridge	d				10 00												13 04								
Plymouth	a				10 14	10 40		11 15	11 45			12 14	12 32		12 40		13 17	13 27				14 14			14 55
	d		09 15		10 15			11 15					12 35		12 55		13 32					14 20	14 50		
Devonport	d				10 19																				
Dockyard	d																								
Keyham	d																								
St Budeaux Ferry Road	d		09 21																						
Saltash	d		09 25		10 26			11 26									13 40						14 59		
St Germans	d		09 31		10 33			11 33									13 47						15 06		
Menheniot	d				10x41																				
Liskeard 6	d		09 43		10 47			11 45					12 59		13 18		13 59					14 44	15 18		
Bodmin Parkway	d		09 55		10 59			11 57					13 12		13 30		14 11					14 58	15 30		
Lostwithiel	d		10 01		11 04			12 02															15 36		
Par	d		10 09	10 18	11 12			12 10					13 24	13 31	13 41		14 22						15 44		
Newquay	a			11 10										14 23											
St Austell	d		10 16		11 21			12 18					13 31		13 50		14 30					15 14	15 51		
Truro	d		10 35		11 40			12 35					13 50		14 08		14 46					15 32	16 10		
Redruth	d		10 48		11 53			12 48					14 02		14 19		15 00					15 43	16 23		
Camborne	d		10 54		11 59			12 54					14 10		14 25		15 06					15 51	16 29		
Hayle	d		11 01		12 06			13 01															16 36		
St Erth	d		11 06		12 10			13 06					14 22		14 37		15 17					16 03	16 41		
Penzance	a		11 18		12 20			13 16					14 32		14 49		15 26					16 21	16 51		

A [trolley] to Plymouth

For connections from Heathrow Airport, Gatwick Airport and Oxford please see Tables 125A, 148 and 116

For the complete service between Westbury and Castle Cary refer to table 123

Table 135

Sundays

5 January to 9 February

London and Birmingham - Devon and Cornwall

Route Diagram - see first Page of Table 135

		GW	GW	GW	GW	XC	GW	GW	GW	XC	GW	GW	GW	GW	XC	GW	XC	GW	GW	XC	GW	GW	GW
			◇1	◇1	◇	◇1		◇1		◇1		◇1	◇	◇1	◇1		◇1		◇1	◇1		◇1	
																				A			
			🍴	🍴		🛒		🍴		🛒		🍴		🍴	🛒		🛒		🍴	🛒		🍴	
London Paddington 15 ⊖	d		11 27	11 57				12 57				13 03		13 57					14 57			15 57	
Slough 3	d																						
Reading 7	d		12 04	12 32				13 32				13 38		14 32					15 32			16 32	
Theale	d																						
Thatcham	d																						
Newbury	d			12 48										14 48								16 48	
Hungerford	d																						
Pewsey	d		12 38																				
Westbury	d		13 05					14 20														17 24	
Frome	d																						
Castle Cary	d		13 24											15 35								17 43	
Birmingham New Street 12	d					12 30				13 12					14 30		14 42			15 12			
Cardiff Central 7	d																						
Newport (South Wales)	d																						
Swindon	d											14 11											
Bristol Parkway 7	d					13 40				14 21					15 40		16 00			16 21			
Filton Abbey Wood	d																						
Bath Spa 7	d											14 41											
Bristol Temple Meads 10	d					13 52				14 44		14 55			15 52		16 14			16 44			
Weston-super-Mare	d																						
Bridgwater	d																						
Taunton	d		13 46	13 54		14 25		14 56		15 16		15 31		15 56	16 25		16 46		16 51	17 16		18 06	
Tiverton Parkway	d		13 59			14 38		15 09		15 28					16 38		16 58		17 04	17 28		18 18	
Exeter St Davids 6	a		14 15	14 21		14 52		15 24		15 41		15 55		16 22	16 52		17 11		17 19	17 41		18 36	
Exmouth	d	13 24					14 31				15 24					16 24					17 24		
Exeter Central	d	13 50					14 59		15 20		15 50					16 50					17 50		
Exeter St Davids 6	d	14 00	14 15	14 23		14 54	15 05	15 25	15 31	15 43	15 56	15 59	16 10	16 24	16 54	16 57	17 13		17 21	17 43	17 56	18 37	
Exeter St Thomas	d	14 03											16 12								17 59		
Starcross	d	14 11																			18 07		
Dawlish Warren	d	14 16									16 13										18 12		
Dawlish	d	14 20	14 29				15 17		15 43		16 17		16 25			17 10	17 25				18 16		
Teignmouth	d	14 25	14 35				15 22		15 48		16 22		16 30			17 15	17 30				18 21		
Newton Abbot	a	14 33	14 42	14 47		15 12	15 29	15 46	15 55	16 01	16 29	16 20	16 36	16 42	17 12	17 22	17 36		17 40	18 01	18 28	18 57	
	d	14 36	14 42	14 47		15 13	15 30	15 46	15 56	16 01	16 30	16 21	16 37	16 43	17 14	17 23	17 38		17 40	18 01	18 29	18 59	
Torre	d	14 44					15 39		16 04		16 38					17 32					18 37		
Torquay	d	14 47	14 54				15 42		16 07		16 41					17 35	17 49				18 40		
Paignton	a	14 53	15 03				15 50		16 15		16 48					17 42	17 56				18 47		
Totnes	d			15 01		15 27		16 00		16 15			16 52	17 01	17 27				17 56	18 15			
Ivybridge	d												17 08										
Plymouth	a			15 29		15 54		16 29		16 40		16 59	17 22	17 30	17 54				18 22	18 40		19 36	
	d			15 35				16 35					17 35						18 25	18 53			19 43
Devonport	d																						
Dockyard	d																						
Keyham	d																						
St Budeaux Ferry Road	d																						
Saltash	d												17 44										19 52
St Germans	d												17 51										19 59
Menheniot	d												17x59										
Liskeard 6	d			15 57				16 59					18 05						18 50	19 16			20 11
Bodmin Parkway	d			16 12				17 12					18 17						19 04	19 28			20 23
Lostwithiel	d												18 22										20 28
Par	d			16 24	16 30			17 23					18 30						19 16	19 39			20 36
Newquay	a				17 22																		
St Austell	d			16 32				17 31					18 37						19 23	19 46			20 43
Truro	d			16 50				17 49					18 55						19 41	20 03			21 00
Redruth	d			17 02				18 02					19 08						19 53	20 14			21 14
Camborne	d			17 10				18 10					19 14						20 04	20 22			21 20
Hayle	d												19 21										21 27
St Erth	d			17 22				18 22					19 25					20 05	20 16	20 33			21 32
Penzance	a			17 35				18 34					19 37					20 14	20 28	20 41			21 42

A 🛒 to Plymouth

For connections from Heathrow Airport, Gatwick Airport and Oxford please see Tables 125A, 148 and 116

For the complete service between Westbury and Castle Cary refer to table 123

Table 135

Sundays

5 January to 9 February

London and Birmingham - Devon and Cornwall

Route Diagram - see first Page of Table 135

		XC		GW	GW	GW	XC	GW	GW	XC	GW	GW		XC	XC	GW	GW	GW	XC	GW	GW
																					■
		◇1			◇1	◇	◇1		◇1	◇1		◇1		◇1	◇1	◇1		◇1	◇1	◇1	
							A								B				B		C
																					🛏
		🛒			🍴		🛒		🍴	🛒		🍴		🛒	🛒	🍴		🍴	🛒	🍴	🍴
London Paddington 15 ⊖	d				16 57				17 57			18 57				19 03		19 57		20 57	23 50
Slough 3	d																				
Reading 7	d				17 32				18 32			19 32				19 38		20 32		21 32	00u37
Theale	d																				
Thatcham	d																				
Newbury	d								18 48									20 48			
Hungerford	d																				
Pewsey	d								19 08									21 08			
Westbury	d								19 27									21 27			
Frome	d																				
Castle Cary	d											20 30						21 45			
Birmingham New Street 12	d	16 12					17 12			18 12				18 42	19 12				20 12		
Cardiff Central 7	d																				
Newport (South Wales)	d																				
Swindon	d															20 11					
Bristol Parkway 7	d	17 21					18 21			19 22				20 04	20 21				21 21		
Filton Abbey Wood	d																				
Bath Spa 7	d															20 40					
Bristol Temple Meads 10	d	17 44				18 06	18 44			19 44				20 19	20 44	20 55			21 44		
Weston-super-Mare	d					18 35								20 37		21 28					
Bridgwater	d					18 53															
Taunton	d	18 19			18 50	19 08	19 17		20 00	20 18		20 51		20 59	21 16	21 52		22 06	22 16	22s49	
Tiverton Parkway	d	18 31			19 03	19 23	19 29		20 15	20 30		21 05		21 12	21 28	22 05		22 19	22 28	23s03	
Exeter St Davids 6	a	18 45			19 19	19 41	19 47		20 30	20 44		21 21		21 27	21 41	22 20		22 36	22 45	23 19	03 05
Exmouth	d			18 24				19 24			20 24						21 24				
Exeter Central	d			18 49				19 50			20 50						21 50				
Exeter St Davids 6	d	18 46		18 56	19 20		19 49	19 56	20 31	20 44	21 00	21 22		21 30	21 43		21 56	22 37	22 46		04 35
Exeter St Thomas	d			18 59				19 59									21 59				
Starcross	d			19 07				20 07									22 07				
Dawlish Warren	d			19 12				20 12									22 12				
Dawlish	d			19 16				20 16			21 13	21 36		21 42			22 16				
Teignmouth	d			19 21				20 21			21 18	21 42		21 47			22 21				
Newton Abbot	a	19 04		19 28	19 39		20 07	20 28	20 53	21 02	21 25	21 48		21 54	22 01		22 29	22 57	23 04		04 55
	d	19 06		19 30	19 39		20 08	20 30	20 54	21 05	21 26	21 49		21 56	22 02		22 30	22 58	23 06		04 56
Torre	d			19 38				20 38			21 35						22 38				
Torquay	d			19 41				20 41			21 38						22 41				
Paignton	a			19 48				20 48			21 45						22 49				
Totnes	d	19 18			19 55		20 21		21 07	21 16		22 03			22 19			23 11	23 20		
Ivybridge	d																				
Plymouth	a	19 44			20 22		20 46		21 34	21 43		22 31		22 37	22 45			23 40	23 47		05 35
	d				20 25		20 50		21 40												06 28
Devonport	d																				
Dockyard	d																				
Keyham	d																				
St Budeaux Ferry Road	d																				
Saltash	d																				
St Germans	d																				
Menheniot	d																				
Liskeard 6	d				20 49		21 13		22 04												07 09
Bodmin Parkway	d				21 02		21 25		22 17												07 23
Lostwithiel	d																				07 29
Par	d				21 13		21 36		22 30												07 38
Newquay	a																				
St Austell	d				21 20		21 42		22 38												07 46
Truro	d				21 37		22 00		22 53												08 06
Redruth	d				21 51		22 11		23 08												08 20
Camborne	d				21 57		22 20		23 15												08 27
Hayle	d																				08 38
St Erth	d				22 10		22 31		23 27												08 45
Penzance	a				22 22		22 43		23 38												08 59

A 🛒 to Plymouth   B 🛒 to Bristol Temple Meads   C The Night Riviera

For connections from Heathrow Airport, Gatwick Airport and Oxford please see Tables 125A, 148 and 116

For the complete service between Westbury and Castle Cary refer to table 123

Table 135

Sundays

16 February to 23 March

London and Birmingham - Devon and Cornwall

Route Diagram - see first Page of Table 135

		GW	GW	GW	GW	GW	GW	GW	GW	XC		XC	GW	GW	GW	GW	GW	GW	XC	XC		XC	GW	GW	GW
		◇							◇1	◇1			◇					◇1	◇1				◇1		
					bus	bus		bus				bus		bus	bus		bus			bus		bus		bus	bus
									cup	trolley								cup	trolley				cup		
London Paddington 15 ⊖	d																						08 00		
Slough 3	d																								
Reading 7	d																						08 39		
Theale	d																								
Thatcham	d																								
Newbury	d																								
Hungerford	d																								
Pewsey	d																								
Westbury	d																								
Frome	d																								
Castle Cary	d																								
Birmingham New Street 12	d																								
Cardiff Central 7	d																								
Newport (South Wales)	d																								
Swindon	d																						09 12		
Bristol Parkway 7	d																								
Filton Abbey Wood	d																								
Bath Spa 7	d																						09 42		
Bristol Temple Meads 10	d	07 45								08 44			08 28						09 48				10 00		
Weston-super-Mare	d	08 07											08 58												
Bridgwater	d	08 21											09 15												
Taunton	d	08 33								09 16			09 28						10 20				10 34		
Tiverton Parkway	d	08 48						09 00		09 28		09 35	09 43				10 00		10 32			10 40	10 48		
Exeter St Davids 6	a	09 04								09 41			09 58						10 46				11 06		
Exmouth	d																								
Exeter Central	d														08u45										09u45
Exeter St Davids 6	d				08 20	08 35								09 14						09 50				10 14	
Exeter St Thomas	d														08 53										09 53
Starcross	d														09 17										10 17
Dawlish Warren	d														09 29										10 29
Dawlish	d					08 48								09 27	09 36										10 36
Teignmouth	d					08 56								09 35	09 44										10 44
Newton Abbot	a				08 55	09 16								09 55	10 04					10 25				10 49	11 04
	d				08 55		09 26							09 55		10 10				10 25				10 51	
Torre	d						09 34									10 18									
Torquay	d						09 37									10 21									
Paignton	a						09 42									10 26									
Totnes	d				09 20									10 20						10 50				11 16	
Ivybridge	d				09 50									10 50											
Plymouth	a				10 20			10 20				10 55		11 20			11 20			11 35		12 00		12 01	
	d		09 15						10 30									11 30							
Devonport	d								10 35																
Dockyard	d																								
Keyham	d																								
St Budeaux Ferry Road	d		09 21																						
Saltash	d		09 25						10 43									11 40							
St Germans	d		09 31						10 51									11 48							
Menheniot	d								10x59									11x56							
Liskeard 6	d		09 43						11 06									12 03							
Bodmin Parkway	d		09 55						11 19									12 16							
Lostwithiel	d		10 01						11 25									12 22							
Par	d		10 09	10 18					11 34									12 30							
Newquay	a			11 10																					
St Austell	d		10 16						11 41									12 37							
Truro	d		10 35						12 00									12 56							
Redruth	d		10 48						12 12									13 08							
Camborne	d		10 54						12 19									13 14							
Hayle	d		11 01						12 28									13 23							
St Erth	d		11 06						12 34									13 29							
Penzance	a		11 18						12 45									13 40							

For connections from Heathrow Airport, Gatwick Airport and Oxford please see Tables 125A, 148 and 116

For the complete service between Westbury and Castle Cary refer to table 123

Table 135

Sundays

16 February to 23 March

London and Birmingham - Devon and Cornwall

Route Diagram - see first Page of Table 135

		GW	GW	GW	XC	GW		XC	XC	XC	GW	GW	GW	GW	GW	XC		GW	GW	XC	XC	GW	GW	GW	GW
				◇1				◇1		◇1		◇1								◇1		◇1			
			🚌		🚌	🚌			🚌				🚌	🚌	🚌	🚌			🚌		🚌		🚌	🚌	🚌
				☕				🛒				☕								🛒		☕			
London Paddington 15 ⊖	d			08 57								09 57										10 57			
Slough 3	d																								
Reading 7	d			09 32								10 32										11 32			
Theale	d																								
Thatcham	d																								
Newbury	d			09 47																					
Hungerford	d																								
Pewsey	d											11 05													
Westbury	d			10 21																					
Frome	d																								
Castle Cary	d											11 34													
Birmingham New Street 12	d							09 12												10 30					
Cardiff Central 7	d																								
Newport (South Wales)	d																								
Swindon	d																								
Bristol Parkway 7	d							10 21												11 41					
Filton Abbey Wood	d																								
Bath Spa 7	d																								
Bristol Temple Meads 10	d							10 44												11 54					
Weston-super-Mare	d																								
Bridgwater	d																								
Taunton	d			10 57				11 16				11 57								12 26		12 47			
Tiverton Parkway	d		10 57	11 11		11 22		11 28	11 35			12 13							12 20	12 37	12 45	13 05			
Exeter St Davids 6	a			11 31				11 41				12 28								12 54		13 21			
Exmouth	d																								
Exeter Central	d														11u00										12u01
Exeter St Davids 6	d				10 55								11 16	11 41		11 50							12 15	12 38	
Exeter St Thomas	d														11 08										12 09
Starcross	d														11 32										12 33
Dawlish Warren	d														11 44										12 45
Dawlish	d												11 29		11 51										12 52
Teignmouth	d												11 37		11 59										13 00
Newton Abbot	a				11 30								11 57	12 16	12 19	12 25							12 50	13 13	13 20
	d	11 15			11 30								11 57	12 16		12 25		12 30					12 50	13 13	
Torre	d	11 23																12 38							
Torquay	d	11 26																12 41							
Paignton	a	11 31																12 46							
Totnes	d				11 55								12 22	12 41		12 50							13 15	13 38	
Ivybridge	d																						13 45		
Plymouth	a		12 17		12 40	12 42			12 55				13 07	13 26		13 35			13 40		14 05		14 15	14 23	
	d									13 07															
Devonport	d																								
Dockyard	d																								
Keyham	d																								
St Budeaux Ferry Road	d																								
Saltash	d																								
St Germans	d																								
Menheniot	d																								
Liskeard 6	d									13 30															
Bodmin Parkway	d									13 42															
Lostwithiel	d																								
Par	d									13 53	14 00														
Newquay	a										14 52														
St Austell	d									13 59															
Truro	d									14 17															
Redruth	d									14 28															
Camborne	d									14 34															
Hayle	d																								
St Erth	d									14 46															
Penzance	a									14 54															

For connections from Heathrow Airport, Gatwick Airport and Oxford please see Tables 125A, 148 and 116

For the complete service between Westbury and Castle Cary refer to table 123

Table 135

Sundays

16 February to 23 March

London and Birmingham - Devon and Cornwall

Route Diagram - see first Page of Table 135

		GW		GW	GW	GW	XC	XC	XC	GW	GW	GW		GW	GW	GW	GW	XC	XC	XC	GW	GW		GW	GW
				🚌	◇1 ☕	◇	◇1 🛒	🚌	🚌	◇1 ☕	◇1 ☕	🚌		🚌		🚌	◇	◇1 🛒	🚌	🚌	◇1 ☕	🚌		🚌	
London Paddington 15 ⊖	d									11 27	11 57										12 57				
Slough 3	d																								
Reading 7	d									12 03	12 32										13 32				
Theale	d																								
Thatcham	d																								
Newbury	d										12 48														
Hungerford	d																								
Pewsey	d									12 38															
Westbury	d									13 05											14 20				
Frome	d																								
Castle Cary	d									13 24															
Birmingham New Street 12	d						11 30											12 30							
Cardiff Central 7	d																								
Newport (South Wales)	d																								
Swindon	d																								
Bristol Parkway 7	d						12 42											13 40							
Filton Abbey Wood	d																								
Bath Spa 7	d																								
Bristol Temple Meads 10	d						12 54											13 52							
Weston-super-Mare	d																								
Bridgwater	d																								
Taunton	d						13 26			13 46	13 54							14 25			14 56				
Tiverton Parkway	d			13 15			13 38		13 45	14 01	14 10					14 20		14 37		14 45	15 09				
Exeter St Davids 6	a						13 54			14 18	14 27							14 52			15 28				
Exmouth	d																								
Exeter Central	d													13u04										13u56	
Exeter St Davids 6	d							13 05				13 31							14 05			14 37			
Exeter St Thomas	d													13 12										14 04	
Starcross	d													13 36										14 28	
Dawlish Warren	d													13 48										14 40	
Dawlish	d											13 44		13 55										14 47	
Teignmouth	d											13 52		14 03										14 55	
Newton Abbot	a							13 40				14 12		14 23					14 40			15 12		15 15	
	d	13 30						13 40				14 12			14 30				14 40			15 12			15 25
Torre	d	13 38													14 38										15 33
Torquay	d	13 41													14 41										15 36
Paignton	a	13 46													14 46										15 41
Totnes	d							14 05				14 37							15 05			15 37			
Ivybridge	d																								
Plymouth	a			14 35				14 50	15 05			15 22				15 40			15 50	16 05		16 22			
	d				14 45												15 50								
Devonport	d																								
Dockyard	d																								
Keyham	d																								
St Budeaux Ferry Road	d																								
Saltash	d																16 00								
St Germans	d																16 07								
Menheniot	d																								
Liskeard 6	d				15 09												16 19								
Bodmin Parkway	d				15 24												16 31								
Lostwithiel	d																16 37								
Par	d				15 35	16 05											16 45								
Newquay	a					16 57																			
St Austell	d				15 43												16 52								
Truro	d				16 01												17 11								
Redruth	d				16 12												17 24								
Camborne	d				16 20												17 30								
Hayle	d																17 37								
St Erth	d				16 31												17 42								
Penzance	a				16 43												17 52								

For connections from Heathrow Airport, Gatwick Airport and Oxford please see Tables 125A, 148 and 116

For the complete service between Westbury and Castle Cary refer to table 123

Table 135

Sundays

16 February to 23 March

London and Birmingham - Devon and Cornwall

Route Diagram - see first Page of Table 135

		GW	XC	XC	GW	GW	GW	XC		GW	GW	GW	GW	XC	GW	GW	XC	XC		GW	GW	GW	GW	GW	GW
			◇1		◇1					◇1		◇1				◇1	◇1			◇1					
		🚌		🚌		🚌		🚌			🚌		🚌	🚌	🚌			🚌			🚌		🚌	🚌	🚌
			🛒		☕					☕		☕				☕	🛒			☕					
London Paddington 15 ⊖	d									13 03		13 57								14 57					
Slough 3	d																								
Reading 7	d									13 38		14 34								15 32					
Theale	d																								
Thatcham	d																								
Newbury	d											14 48													
Hungerford	d																								
Pewsey	d																								
Westbury	d																								
Frome	d																								
Castle Cary	d											15 35													
Birmingham New Street 12	d		13 12														14 30								
Cardiff Central 7	d																								
Newport (South Wales)	d																								
Swindon	d									14 15															
Bristol Parkway 7	d		14 21														15 40								
Filton Abbey Wood	d																								
Bath Spa 7	d									14 44															
Bristol Temple Meads 10	d		14 44							15 00							15 52								
Weston-super-Mare	d																								
Bridgwater	d																								
Taunton	d		15 16							15 34		15 56					16 25			16 51					
Tiverton Parkway	d	15 20	15 28					15 40		15 51	15 58	16 13			16 20		16 38	16 45		17 07					
Exeter St Davids 6	a		15 41							16 06		16 33					16 52			17 23					
Exmouth	d																								
Exeter Central	d					15u17																			16u08
Exeter St Davids 6	d			15 00									15 38	15 55							16 17		16 17	16 43	
Exeter St Thomas	d																								16 16
Starcross	d																								16 40
Dawlish Warren	d																								16 52
Dawlish	d					15 33							15 51										16 30		16 59
Teignmouth	d					15 41							15 59										16 38		17 07
Newton Abbot	a			15 35		16 01							16 19	16 30							16 52		16 58	17 18	17 27
	d			15 35			16 06						16 19	16 30							16 52	16 58	16 58	17 18	
Torre	d						16 14															17 06			
Torquay	d						16 17															17 09			
Paignton	a						16 22															17 14			
Totnes	d			16 00									16 44	16 55							17 17		17 23	17 43	
Ivybridge	d																				17 47		17 53		
Plymouth	a	16 40		16 45				17 00			17 18		17 29	17 40	17 40			18 05			18 17		18 23	18 28	
	d				16 50											17 50									
Devonport	d																								
Dockyard	d																								
Keyham	d																								
St Budeaux Ferry Road	d																								
Saltash	d															18 00									
St Germans	d															18 08									
Menheniot	d															18x16									
Liskeard 6	d				17 13											18 21									
Bodmin Parkway	d				17 26											18 34									
Lostwithiel	d															18 42									
Par	d				17 39											18 51									
Newquay	a																								
St Austell	d				17 45											18 56									
Truro	d				18 03											19 15									
Redruth	d				18 16											19 27									
Camborne	d				18 24											19 35									
Hayle	d															19 46									
St Erth	d				18 37											19 52									
Penzance	a				18 47											20 02									

For connections from Heathrow Airport, Gatwick Airport and Oxford please see Tables 125A, 148 and 116

For the complete service between Westbury and Castle Cary refer to table 123

Table 135

Sundays

16 February to 23 March

London and Birmingham - Devon and Cornwall

Route Diagram - see first Page of Table 135

		GW	XC	XC	GW	GW	XC	GW	GW	XC	GW	GW	XC	GW	GW	GW	XC	XC	GW	GW	XC	GW
			◇1					◇1		◇1						◇1	◇1		◇1		◇1	◇
		[bus]		[bus]		[bus]	[bus]				[bus]		[bus]	[bus]	[bus]			[bus]		[bus]		
			[trolley]					[restaurant]								[restaurant]	[trolley]		[restaurant]		[trolley]	
London Paddington 15 ⊖	d							15 57											16 57			
Slough 3	d																					
Reading 7	d							16 32											17 32			
Theale	d																					
Thatcham	d																					
Newbury	d							16 48														
Hungerford	d																					
Pewsey	d																					
Westbury	d							17 24														
Frome	d																					
Castle Cary	d							17 43														
Birmingham New Street 12	d		15 12														16 12				17 12	
Cardiff Central 7	d																					
Newport (South Wales)	d																					
Swindon	d																					
Bristol Parkway 7	d		16 21														17 21				18 21	
Filton Abbey Wood	d																					
Bath Spa 7	d																					
Bristol Temple Meads 10	d		16 44														17 44				18 44	18 10
Weston-super-Mare	d																					18 38
Bridgwater	d																					18 57
Taunton	d		17 16					18 06									18 19		18 50		19 17	19 20
Tiverton Parkway	d	17 13	17 28				17 35	18 18							18 25		18 31	18 40	19 03	19 12	19 29	19 36
Exeter St Davids 6	a		17 41					18 38									18 45		19 23		19 47	19 54
Exmouth	d																					
Exeter Central	d					17u05								18u01								
Exeter St Davids 6	d			17 00							17 33		17 55									
Exeter St Thomas	d													18 09								
Starcross	d													18 33								
Dawlish Warren	d													18 45								
Dawlish	d					17 21								18 52								
Teignmouth	d					17 29								19 00								
Newton Abbot	a			17 35		17 49					18 08		18 30	19 20								
	d			17 35	17 40						18 08	18 30	18 30									
Torre	d				17 48							18 38										
Torquay	d				17 51							18 41										
Paignton	a				17 56							18 46										
Totnes	d			18 00							18 33		18 55									
Ivybridge	d																					
Plymouth	a	18 33		18 45			18 55				19 18		19 40		19 45			20 00		20 32		
	d									19 05						19 55						
Devonport	d																					
Dockyard	d																					
Keyham	d																					
St Budeaux Ferry Road	d																					
Saltash	d															20 05						
St Germans	d															20 13						
Menheniot	d																					
Liskeard 6	d									19 28						20 23						
Bodmin Parkway	d									19 40						20 37						
Lostwithiel	d															20 44						
Par	d									19 51						20 52						
Newquay	a																					
St Austell	d									19 57						20 59						
Truro	d									20 15						21 17						
Redruth	d									20 26						21 29						
Camborne	d									20 33						21 38						
Hayle	d															21 47						
St Erth	d								20 05	20 44						21 51						
Penzance	a								20 14	20 53						22 03						

For connections from Heathrow Airport, Gatwick Airport and Oxford please see Tables 125A, 148 and 116

For the complete service between Westbury and Castle Cary refer to table 123

Table 135

Sundays

16 February to 23 March

London and Birmingham - Devon and Cornwall

Route Diagram - see first Page of Table 135

		GW	GW	XC	XC	XC	GW	GW	GW	GW		XC	GW	GW	GW	XC	XC	GW	GW	GW		GW	XC	XC	XC
					◇1		◇1								◇	◇1		◇1					◇1		
																							A		
		bus		bus		bus		bus	bus			bus	bus	bus			bus		bus			bus		bus	bus
							☕								trolley	trolley		☕					trolley		
London Paddington 15 ⊖	d						17 57											18 57							
Slough 8	d																								
Reading 7	d						18 32											19 32							
Theale	d																								
Thatcham	d																								
Newbury	d						18 48																		
Hungerford	d																								
Pewsey	d						19 08																		
Westbury	d						19 27																		
Frome	d																								
Castle Cary	d																	20 30							
Birmingham New Street 12	d															18 12							19 12		
Cardiff Central 7	d																								
Newport (South Wales)	d																								
Swindon	d																								
Bristol Parkway 7	d															19 22							20 21		
Filton Abbey Wood	d																								
Bath Spa 7	d																								
Bristol Temple Meads 10	d															19 44							20 44		
Weston-super-Mare	d																								
Bridgwater	d																								
Taunton	d						20 00									20 18		20 51					21 16		
Tiverton Parkway	d					19 40	20 15							20 25		20 30	20 40	21 05				21 16	21 28		21 40
Exeter St Davids 6	a						20 35									20 44		21 24					21 41		
Exmouth	d																								
Exeter Central	d								19u01				20u01												
Exeter St Davids 6	d	18 48		18 55				19 32				19 55							20 45					20 55	
Exeter St Thomas	d								19 09				20 09												
Starcross	d								19 33				20 33												
Dawlish Warren	d								19 45				20 45												
Dawlish	d								19 52				20 52												
Teignmouth	d								20 00				21 00												
Newton Abbot	a	19 23		19 30				20 07	20 20			20 30	21 20						21 20					21 30	
	d	19 23	19 30	19 30				20 07		20 30		20 30							21 20	21 30				21 30	
Torre	d		19 38							20 38										21 38					
Torquay	d		19 41							20 41										21 41					
Paignton	a		19 46							20 46										21 46					
Totnes	d	19 48		19 55				20 32				20 55							21 45					21 55	
Ivybridge	d																								
Plymouth	a	20 33		20 40		21 00		21 17				21 40		21 45			22 00		22 30			22 36		22 40	23 00
	d				20 50										21 55										
Devonport	d																								
Dockyard	d																								
Keyham	d																								
St Budeaux Ferry Road	d																								
Saltash	d																								
St Germans	d																								
Menheniot	d																								
Liskeard 6	d				21 13										22 19										
Bodmin Parkway	d				21 25										22 32										
Lostwithiel	d																								
Par	d				21 36										22 44										
Newquay	a																								
St Austell	d				21 42										22 51										
Truro	d				22 00										23 10										
Redruth	d				22 11										23 23										
Camborne	d				22 18										23 29										
Hayle	d																								
St Erth	d				22 29										23 39										
Penzance	a				22 37										23 50										

A trolley to Bristol Temple Meads

For connections from Heathrow Airport, Gatwick Airport and Oxford please see Tables 125A, 148 and 116

For the complete service between Westbury and Castle Cary refer to table 123

Table 135

Sundays

16 February to 23 March

London and Birmingham - Devon and Cornwall

Route Diagram - see first Page of Table 135

		GW	GW	XC	GW	GW		XC	GW	GW	GW	XC	GW	GW	XC	GW
																R
		◇1	◇1	◇1									◇1			
				A												B
					🚌	🚌		🚌		🚌	🚌	🚌		🚌	🚌	🛏
		🍴	🍴	🍴									🍴			🍴
London Paddington 15 ⊖	d	19 03	19 57										20 57			23 50
Slough 3	d															
Reading 7	d	19 38	20 32										21 32			00u38
Theale	d															
Thatcham	d															
Newbury	d		20 48													
Hungerford	d															
Pewsey	d		21 08													
Westbury	d		21 27													
Frome	d															
Castle Cary	d		21 45													
Birmingham New Street 12	d			20 12												
Cardiff Central 7	d															
Newport (South Wales)	d															
Swindon	d	20 16														
Bristol Parkway 7	d			21 21												
Filton Abbey Wood	d															
Bath Spa 7	d	20 45														
Bristol Temple Meads 10	d	21 00		21 44												
Weston-super-Mare	d	21 32														
Bridgwater	d															
Taunton	d	21 56	22 06	22 16									22s49			
Tiverton Parkway	d	22 09	22 19	22 28							22 31	22 40	23s03			
Exeter St Davids 6	a	22 25	22 38	22 46									23 19			03 05
Exmouth	d															
Exeter Central	d					21u01				22u01						
Exeter St Davids 6	d				21 34			21 50						22 48	22 55	04 35
Exeter St Thomas	d					21 09				22 09						
Starcross	d					21 33				22 33						
Dawlish Warren	d					21 45				22 45						
Dawlish	d				21 47	21 52				22 52						
Teignmouth	d				21 55	22 00				23 00						
Newton Abbot	a				22 15	22 20		22 25		23 20				23 23	23 30	04 55
	d				22 17			22 25	22 30					23 23	23 30	04 56
Torre	d								22 38							
Torquay	d								22 41							
Paignton	a								22 46							
Totnes	d				22 42			22 50						23 48	23 55	
Ivybridge	d															
Plymouth	a				23 27			23 35			23 51	23 59		00 33	00 40	05 35
	d															06 28
Devonport	d															
Dockyard	d															
Keyham	d															
St Budeaux Ferry Road	d															
Saltash	d															
St Germans	d															
Menheniot	d															
Liskeard 6	d															07 09
Bodmin Parkway	d															07 23
Lostwithiel	d															07 29
Par	d															07 38
Newquay	a															
St Austell	d															07 46
Truro	d															08 06
Redruth	d															08 20
Camborne	d															08 27
Hayle	d															08 38
St Erth	d															08 45
Penzance	a															08 59

A 🍴 to Bristol Temple Meads

B The Night Riviera

For connections from Heathrow Airport, Gatwick Airport and Oxford please see Tables 125A, 148 and 116

For the complete service between Westbury and Castle Cary refer to table 123

Table 135

Sundays

30 March to 11 May

London and Birmingham - Devon and Cornwall

Route Diagram - see first Page of Table 135

		GW	GW	GW	GW	XC	GW	GW	XC	GW	GW	GW	GW	XC	GW	GW	GW	XC	GW	GW	GW	GW	XC
					◇	◇1		◇	◇1		◇1	◇1		◇1			◇1	◇1		◇1			◇1
														A									
						🛒			🛒		🍴	🍴		🛒			🍴	🛒		🍴			🛒
London Paddington 15 ⊖	d										08 00	08 57					09 57			10 57			
Slough 3	d																						
Reading 7	d										08 34	09 32					10 32			11 32			
Theale	d																						
Thatcham	d																						
Newbury	d											09 48											
Hungerford	d																						
Pewsey	d																11 05						
Westbury	d											10 21											
Frome	d																						
Castle Cary	d																11 34						
Birmingham New Street 12	d													09 12				10 30					11 30
Cardiff Central 7	d																						
Newport (South Wales)	d																						
Swindon	d										09 11												
Bristol Parkway 7	d													10 21				11 41					12 42
Filton Abbey Wood	d																						
Bath Spa 7	d										09 40												
Bristol Temple Meads 10	d				07 30	08 44		08 28	09 48		10 00			10 44				11 54					12 54
Weston-super-Mare	d				07 53			08 59															
Bridgwater	d				08 09			09 18															
Taunton	d				08 24	09 16		09 32	10 20		10 34	10 57		11 16			11 57	12 26		12 47			13 26
Tiverton Parkway	d				08 39	09 28		09 48	10 32		10 48	11 11		11 28				12 37					13 38
Exeter St Davids 6	a				08 56	09 41		10 05	10 46		11 03	11 26		11 41			12 21	12 54		13 14			13 54
Exmouth	d						09 10			10 21					11 24				12 28				
Exeter Central	d						09 36			10 48					11 52				12 54			13 20	
Exeter St Davids 6	d	08 52			09 05	09 43	09 54	10 06	10 47	10 53	11 05	11 26		11 43	11 57	12 15	12 23	12 56	13 00	13 15		13 25	13 55
Exeter St Thomas	d	08 55					09 57			10 56					12 00								
Starcross	d	09 03					10 05			11 04					12 08								
Dawlish Warren	d	09 08					10 10			11 09					12 13				13 11				
Dawlish	d	09 12			09 18		10 14	10 21		11 13	11 19				12 17				13 15			13 38	
Teignmouth	d	09 17			09 23		10 19	10 26		11 18	11 25				12 22				13 20			13 43	
Newton Abbot	a	09 24			09 30	10 01	10 26	10 31	11 05	11 25	11 32	11 47		12 01	12 29	12 35	12 43	13 14	13 27	13 35		13 50	14 14
	d	09 26			09 30	10 02	10 37	10 33	11 07	11 27	11 32	11 47		12 02	12 31	12 36	12 44	13 16	13 28	13 37		13 52	14 15
Torre	d	09 34					10 45			11 35					12 39				13 36			14 00	
Torquay	d	09 37					10 48			11 38					12 42				13 39			14 03	
Paignton	a	09 44					10 54			11 45					12 50				13 46			14 10	
Totnes	d				09 43	10 15		10 46	11 19		11 46	12 02		12 15		12 48	12 57	13 29					14 29
Ivybridge	d				10 00											13 04							
Plymouth	a				10 14	10 40		11 15	11 45		12 17	12 31		12 40		13 17	13 27	13 56		14 14			14 55
	d		09 15		10 15			11 15				12 35		12 55		13 32				14 20	14 50		
Devonport	d				10 19																		
Dockyard	d																						
Keyham	d																						
St Budeaux Ferry Road	d		09 21																				
Saltash	d		09 25		10 26			11 26								13 40					14 59		
St Germans	d		09 31		10 33			11 33								13 47					15 06		
Menheniot	d				10x41																		
Liskeard 6	d		09 43		10 47			11 45				12 59		13 18		13 59				14 44	15 18		
Bodmin Parkway	d		09 55		10 59			11 57				13 12		13 30		14 11				14 58	15 30		
Lostwithiel	d		10 01		11 04			12 02													15 36		
Par	d		10 09	10 18	11 12			12 10				13 24	13 31	13 41		14 22					15 44		
Newquay	a			11 10									14 23										
St Austell	d		10 16		11 21			12 18				13 31		13 50		14 30				15 14	15 51		
Truro	d		10 35		11 40			12 35				13 50		14 08		14 46				15 32	16 10		
Redruth	d		10 48		11 53			12 48				14 02		14 19		15 00				15 43	16 23		
Camborne	d		10 54		11 59			12 54				14 10		14 25		15 06				15 51	16 29		
Hayle	d		11 01		12 06			13 01													16 36		
St Erth	d		11 06		12 10			13 06				14 22		14 37		15 17				16 03	16 41		
Penzance	a		11 18		12 20			13 16				14 32		14 49		15 26				16 21	16 51		

A 🛒 to Plymouth

For connections from Heathrow Airport, Gatwick Airport and Oxford please see Tables 125A, 148 and 116

For the complete service between Westbury and Castle Cary refer to table 123

Table 135

Sundays

30 March to 11 May

London and Birmingham - Devon and Cornwall

Route Diagram - see first Page of Table 135

		GW	GW	GW	GW	XC		GW	GW	GW	XC	GW	GW	GW	GW	XC		GW	XC	GW	GW	XC	GW	GW	GW
			◇1	◇1	◇	◇1			◇1		◇1		◇1	◇	◇1	◇1			◇1		◇1	◇1		◇1	
																						A			
			[buffet]	[buffet]		[trolley]			[buffet]		[trolley]		[buffet]		[buffet]	[trolley]			[trolley]		[buffet]	[trolley]		[buffet]	
London Paddington 15 ⊖	d		11 33	11 57					12 57				13 03		13 57						14 57			15 57	
Slough 3	d																								
Reading 7	d		12 06	12 32					13 32				13 34		14 32						15 32			16 32	
Theale	d																								
Thatcham	d																								
Newbury	d			12 48											14 48									16 48	
Hungerford	d																								
Pewsey	d		12 38																						
Westbury	d		13 05						14 20															17 24	
Frome	d																								
Castle Cary	d		13 24												15 36									17 43	
Birmingham New Street 12	d					12 12					13 12					14 12			14 42			15 12			
Cardiff Central 7	d																								
Newport (South Wales)	d																								
Swindon	d												14 13												
Bristol Parkway 7	d					13 21					14 21					15 24			16 00			16 21			
Filton Abbey Wood	d																								
Bath Spa 7	d												14 42												
Bristol Temple Meads 10	d					13 44					14 44		15 00			15 44			16 14			16 44			
Weston-super-Mare	d																								
Bridgwater	d																								
Taunton	d		13 46	13 54		14 16			14 56		15 16		15 31		15 56	16 14			16 46		16 51	17 16		18 05	
Tiverton Parkway	d		14 00			14 28			15 09		15 28					16 25			16 58		17 04	17 28		18 18	
Exeter St Davids 6	a		14 15	14 21		14 42			15 24		15 41		15 55		16 23	16 42			17 11		17 19	17 41		18 36	
Exmouth	d	13 24						14 31				15 24						16 24					17 24		
Exeter Central	d	13 50						14 59		15 20		15 50						16 50					17 50		
Exeter St Davids 6	d	14 00	14 15	14 23		14 43		15 05	15 25	15 31	15 43	15 56	15 59	16 10	16 24	16 43		16 56	17 13		17 21	17 43	17 56	18 37	
Exeter St Thomas	d	14 03												16 12									17 59		
Starcross	d	14 11																					18 07		
Dawlish Warren	d	14 16										16 13											18 12		
Dawlish	d	14 20	14 29					15 17		15 43		16 17		16 25				17 09	17 25				18 16		
Teignmouth	d	14 25	14 35					15 22		15 48		16 22		16 30				17 14	17 30				18 21		
Newton Abbot	a	14 33	14 42	14 47		15 01		15 29	15 46	15 55	16 01	16 29	16 20	16 36	16 43	17 02		17 21	17 36		17 40	18 01	18 28	18 57	
	d	14 36	14 42	14 47		15 02		15 30	15 46	15 56	16 01	16 30	16 21	16 37	16 43	17 03		17 22	17 38		17 40	18 01	18 29	18 59	
Torre	d	14 44						15 39		16 04		16 38						17 31					18 37		
Torquay	d	14 47	14 54					15 42		16 07		16 41						17 34	17 49				18 40		
Paignton	a	14 53	15 03					15 50		16 15		16 48						17 41	17 56				18 47		
Totnes	d			15 01		15 15			16 00		16 15			16 52	17 01	17 17					17 56	18 15			
Ivybridge	d													17 08											
Plymouth	a			15 29		15 41			16 29		16 40		16 59	17 22	17 30	17 43					18 22	18 40		19 36	
	d			15 35					16 35					17 35							18 25	18 53			19 43
Devonport	d																								
Dockyard	d																								
Keyham	d																								
St Budeaux Ferry Road	d																								
Saltash	d													17 44											19 52
St Germans	d													17 51											19 59
Menheniot	d													17x59											
Liskeard 6	d			15 57					16 59					18 05							18 50	19 16			20 11
Bodmin Parkway	d			16 12					17 12					18 17							19 04	19 28			20 23
Lostwithiel	d													18 22											20 28
Par	d			16 24	16 30				17 23					18 30							19 16	19 39			20 36
Newquay	a				17 22																				
St Austell	d			16 32					17 31					18 37							19 23	19 46			20 43
Truro	d			16 50					17 49					18 55							19 41	20 03			21 00
Redruth	d			17 02					18 02					19 08							19 53	20 14			21 14
Camborne	d			17 10					18 10					19 14							20 04	20 22			21 20
Hayle	d													19 21											21 27
St Erth	d			17 22					18 22					19 25						20 05	20 16	20 33			21 32
Penzance	a			17 35					18 33					19 37						20 14	20 28	20 41			21 42

A [trolley] to Plymouth

For connections from Heathrow Airport, Gatwick Airport and Oxford please see Tables 125A, 148 and 116

For the complete service between Westbury and Castle Cary refer to table 123

Table 135

Sundays

30 March to 11 May

London and Birmingham - Devon and Cornwall

Route Diagram - see first Page of Table 135

		XC	GW	GW	XC	GW	GW	GW	XC	GW	GW	XC	XC	GW	GW	GW	XC	GW	GW
		◇1		◇1	◇1	◇		◇1	◇1		◇1	◇1	◇1	◇1		◇1	◇1	◇1	R
					A								B				B		C
London Paddington 15 ⊖	d			16 57				17 57			18 57			19 03		19 57		20 57	23 50
Slough 3	d																		
Reading 7	d			17 32				18 32			19 32			19 34		20 32		21 32	00u37
Theale	d																		
Thatcham	d																		
Newbury	d							18 48								20 48			
Hungerford	d																		
Pewsey	d							19 08								21 08			
Westbury	d							19 27								21 27			
Frome	d																		
Castle Cary	d										20 30					21 45			
Birmingham New Street 12	d	16 12			17 12				18 12			18 42	19 12				20 12		
Cardiff Central 7	d																		
Newport (South Wales)	d																		
Swindon	d													20 11					
Bristol Parkway 7	d	17 21			18 21				19 22			20 04	20 21				21 21		
Filton Abbey Wood	d																		
Bath Spa 7	d													20 41					
Bristol Temple Meads 10	d	17 44			18 44	18 10			19 44			20 19	20 44	20 55			21 44		
Weston-super-Mare	d					18 38						20 37		21 28					
Bridgwater	d					18 57													
Taunton	d	18 19		18 50	19 17	19 20		20 00	20 18		20 51	20 59	21 16	21 52		22 06	22 16	22s49	
Tiverton Parkway	d	18 31		19 03	19 29	19 36		20 15	20 30		21 05	21 12	21 28	22 05		22 19	22 28	23s03	
Exeter St Davids 6	a	18 45		19 19	19 47	19 54		20 30	20 44		21 21	21 27	21 41	22 20		22 36	22 45	23 19	03 05
Exmouth	d		18 24				19 24			20 24					21 24				
Exeter Central	d		18 49				19 50			20 50					21 50				
Exeter St Davids 6	d	18 46	18 56	19 20	19 49		19 56	20 31	20 44	21 00	21 22	21 30	21 43		21 56	22 37	22 46		04 35
Exeter St Thomas	d		18 59				19 59								21 59				
Starcross	d		19 07				20 07								22 07				
Dawlish Warren	d		19 12				20 12								22 12				
Dawlish	d		19 16				20 16			21 13	21 36	21 42			22 16				
Teignmouth	d		19 21				20 21			21 18	21 42	21 47			22 21				
Newton Abbot	a	19 04	19 28	19 39	20 07		20 28	20 53	21 02	21 25	21 48	21 54	22 01		22 29	22 57	23 04		04 55
	d	19 06	19 30	19 39	20 08		20 30	20 54	21 05	21 26	21 49	21 56	22 02		22 30	22 58	23 06		04 56
Torre	d		19 38				20 38			21 35					22 38				
Torquay	d		19 41				20 41			21 38					22 41				
Paignton	a		19 48				20 48			21 45					22 49				
Totnes	d	19 18		19 55	20 21			21 07	21 16		22 03		22 19			23 11	23 20		
Ivybridge	d																		
Plymouth	a	19 44		20 22	20 46			21 34	21 43		22 31	22 37	22 45			23 40	23 47		05 35
	d			20 25	20 50			21 40											06 28
Devonport	d																		
Dockyard	d																		
Keyham	d																		
St Budeaux Ferry Road	d																		
Saltash	d																		
St Germans	d																		
Menheniot	d																		
Liskeard 6	d			20 49	21 13			22 04											07 09
Bodmin Parkway	d			21 02	21 25			22 17											07 23
Lostwithiel	d																		07 29
Par	d			21 13	21 36			22 30											07 38
Newquay	a																		
St Austell	d			21 20	21 42			22 38											07 46
Truro	d			21 37	22 00			22 53											08 06
Redruth	d			21 51	22 11			23 08											08 20
Camborne	d			21 57	22 20			23 15											08 27
Hayle	d																		08 38
St Erth	d			22 10	22 31			23 27											08 45
Penzance	a			22 22	22 43			23 38											08 59

A to Plymouth   B to Bristol Temple Meads   C The Night Riviera

For connections from Heathrow Airport, Gatwick Airport and Oxford please see Tables 125A, 148 and 116

For the complete service between Westbury and Castle Cary refer to table 123

Table 135R

Mondays to Fridays

9 December to 16 May

Cornwall and Devon - Birmingham and London

Route Diagram - see first Page of Table 135

Miles	Miles			GW	GW	GW	GW	GW	GW	GW	GW	GW	GW	GW	GW	GW	XC	GW	GW	GW	GW	GW	XC
				MO	MO	MO	MO	MX	MX	MO													
				■	■	■			■	■													
											◇1	◇1	◇1	◇1		◇1	◇1	◇1		◇1	◇1		◇1
				A	B	C	D		E	F	G	H		I						J	K		
				🛏	🛏	🛏	🚌		🛏	🛏													
				⊏P	⊏P	⊏P			⊏P	⊏P	⊏P	⊏P	⊏P	⊏P⊘		⊏P	🍴	⊏P		⊏P⊘	⊏P⊘		🍴
0	—	**Penzance**	d																				
5¾	—	St Erth	d																				
7¼	—	Hayle	d																				
13¼	—	Camborne	d																				
16¾	—	Redruth	d																				
25¾	—	Truro	d																				
40¼	—	St Austell	d																				
—	—	Newquay	d																				
44¾	—	Par	d																				
49¼	—	Lostwithiel	d																				
52¾	—	Bodmin Parkway	d																				
61¾	—	Liskeard 6	d																				
65	—	Menheniot	d																				
70¼	—	St Germans	d																				
75¼	—	Saltash	d																				
76½	—	St Budeaux Ferry Road	d																				
77¼	—	Keyham	d																				
77¾	—	Dockyard	d																				
78¼	—	Devonport	d																				
79½	—	**Plymouth**	a																				
—	—		d							01 50						05 09	05 20	05 30		05 53	05 53		06 25
90¼	—	Ivybridge	d																				
102¾	—	Totnes	d						00 20	02 18							05 45	05 58					06 50
—	0	Paignton	d																06 10			06 34	
—	2¼	Torquay	d																06 15			06 39	
—	3	Torre	d																06 18			06 42	
111½	8¼	Newton Abbot	a						00 32	02 29						05 45	05 56	06 09	06 26	06 29	06 29	06 50	07 01
—	—		d	00 01	00 01	00 01			00 33	02 31						05 47	06 02	06 11	06 34	06 31	06 31	06 52	07 03
116½	—	Teignmouth	d					00 06								05 54			06 41			06 59	
119¾	—	Dawlish	d					00 11										06 21	06 46			07 04	
121	—	Dawlish Warren	d					00 16											06 51			07 15	
123	—	Starcross	d				00 12	00 20											06 55			07 19	
130½	—	Exeter St Thomas	d				00 36	00 29											07 04			07 28	
131½	—	**Exeter St Davids 6**	a	00 23	00 23	00 23		00 34	00 55	02 53						06 10	06 19	06 33	07 09	06 51	06 51	07 33	07 21
—	—	Exeter Central	a				00s44												07 14			07 39	
—	—	Exmouth	a																07 43			08 18	
—	—	**Exeter St Davids 6**	d	01 06	01 06	01 06	00a49		01 06	03 02				05 46	06 00	06 12	06 22	06 35		06 52	06 52		07 23
148	—	Tiverton Parkway	d											06 02	06 17	06 27	06 36	06 51					07 37
162¼	—	Taunton	d						01 42					06 17	06 34	06 54	06 50	07 06		07 18	07 18		07 51
—	11¾	Bridgwater	a												06 46	07 04							
—	25¾	Weston-super-Mare	a												07 04	07 24							
—	45½	**Bristol Temple Meads 10**	a								05d18	05d18			07 41	07 57	07 25						08 26
—	—	Bath Spa 7	a													08 11							
—	—	Filton Abbey Wood	a												07 58								
—	51¼	Bristol Parkway 7	a												08 05		07 38						08 38
—	—	Swindon	a													08 40							
—	—	Newport (South Wales)	a																				
—	—	Cardiff Central 7	a																				
—	138¼	**Birmingham New Street 12**	a														08 55						09 56
190	—	Castle Cary	d											06 39				07 27					
204	—	Frome	d										06 05										
209¾	—	Westbury	d								06 03	06 03	06 16	07 01				07 51					
230	—	Pewsey	d								06 22	06 22	06 33	07 19				08 09					
243¾	—	Hungerford	a								06 35	06 35	06 51	07 32									
252¼	—	Newbury	a								06 48	06 49	07 06	07 46				08 29					
255¾	—	Thatcham	a								06 55	06 56	07 14										
264½	—	Theale	a								07 05	07 06	07 24										
269¾	—	**Reading 7**	a	04s03	04s04	04s09			04s00	05s11	07 15	07 20	07 37	08 06		09 14		08 50		08 32	08 32		
286¾	—	Slough 3	a																				
305¼	—	**London Paddington 15** ⊖	a	05 08	05 08	05 08			05 23	06 09	07 53	07 53	08 09	08 38		09 44		09 21		09 00	09 06		

A from 31 March. The Night Riviera
B until 30 December. The Night Riviera
C from 6 January until 10 February. The Night Riviera
D from 17 February until 24 March
E The Night Riviera
F from 17 February until 24 March. The Night Riviera
G from 24 March
H until 21 March
I ⊏P from Reading ⊘ to Reading
J until 7 March. The Armada. ⊏P from Reading ⊘ to Reading
K from 10 March. The Armada. ⊏P from Reading ⊘ to Reading

For connections to Oxford, Gatwick Airport and Heathrow Airport please see Tables 116, 148 and 125A

For connections from Swansea please see Table 128. For connections from Plymouth and Exeter St Davids please see Table 135. For connections to Bournemouth please see Table 158

Table 135R

Mondays to Fridays

9 December to 16 May

Cornwall and Devon - Birmingham and London

Route Diagram - see first Page of Table 135

		XC	GW	GW MO	GW MX	GW	GW	XC	GW	GW	GW	XC	GW	GW	GW	GW	XC	XC	GW	GW	XC	GW	GW
		◇1 A 🛒		◇1 B ✕☕	◇1 B ✕☕		◇1 ☕	◇1 🛒	◇1 C ☕⊘		◇	◇1 D 🛒		◇1 C ☕⊘			◇1 🛒	◇1 🛒	◇1 ☕		■ ◇1 E 🛒	■ 1 F ☕	
Penzance	d			05 05	05 05	05 21			05 41		06 00	06 28		06 45	06 55				07 41		08 28	08 44	08 57
St Erth	d										06 09	06 36		06 55	07a03				07 51		08 36	08 54	09a05
Hayle	d					05 31					06 12								07 55				
Camborne	d					05 40			05 58		06 21	06 46		07 06					08 05		08 46	09 06	
Redruth	d			05 25	05 25				06 05		06 27	06 52		07 13					08 12		08 52	09 13	
Truro	d			05 38	05 38	05a55			06 18		06 39	07 04		07 26					08 25		09 04	09 26	
St Austell	d			05 55	05 55				06 35		06 56	07 20		07 44					08 43		09 20	09 43	
Newquay	d																						
Par	d								06 43		07 03	07 28		07 52					08 51		09 28	09 51	
Lostwithiel	d								06 51		07 10			08 00									
Bodmin Parkway	d			06 11	06 13				06 57		07 16	07 38		08 06					09 03		09 38	10 03	
Liskeard 6	d			06 26	06 26				07 11		07 29	07 53		08 20					09 16		09 51	10 16	
Menheniot	d										07x33												
St Germans	d								07 22		07 41			08 31					09 27				
Saltash	d								07 30		07 48			08 39					09 35				
St Budeaux Ferry Road	d										07 52												
Keyham	d										07 54												
Dockyard	d										07x56												
Devonport	d										07 58												
Plymouth	a			06 51	06 51				07 41		08 04	08 20		08 49					09 46		10 18	10 41	
	d			06 55	06 55			07 25	07 48		08 09	08 25		08 53			09 25		09 48		10 25	10 44	
Ivybridge	d										08 25			09 08					10 03				
Totnes	d							07 50	08 16		08 40	08 50		09 23			09 50		10 19		10 50		
Paignton	d	07 02	07 11				07 40			08 23			09 13			09 34		10 07		10 15			
Torquay	d	07 08	07 16				07 46			08 28			09 18			09 39		10 13		10 23			
Torre	d		07 19				07 50			08 31			09 21			09 42				10 26			
Newton Abbot	a	07 18	07 27	07 30	07 30		07 58	08 01	08 27	08 39	08 52	09 01	09 29	09 34		09 50	10 01	10 23	10 31	10 35	11 01		
	d	07 19	07 37	07 32	07 32		08 06	08 03	08 29	08 41	08 52	09 03	09 39	09 36		09 52	10 03	10 24	10 32	10 36	11 03		
Teignmouth	d	07 26	07 45				08 13			08 48	08 59		09 46			09 59		10 31		10 44			
Dawlish	d	07 31	07 50				08 19			08 53	09 04		09 51			10 04		10 36		10 49			
Dawlish Warren	d		07 55							08 58			09 55			10 15				10 53			
Starcross	d		07 59				08 25			09 02			09 59			10 19				10 57			
Exeter St Thomas	d		08 09				08 34			09 11			10 09			10 29				11 07			
Exeter St Davids 6	a	07 43	08 14	07 52	07 52		08 39	08 21	08 49	09 15	09 18	09 22	10 14	09 56		10 34	10 21	10 48	10 54	11 10	11 21	11 38	
Exeter Central	a		08 19							09 21			10 21							11 21			
Exmouth	a		08 48							09 50			10 50							11 50			
Exeter St Davids 6	d	07 45		07 53	07 53		08 41	08 23	08 51		09 33	09 23		09 58			10 23	10 50	10 56		11 23	11 40	
Tiverton Parkway	d	07 58						08 37	09 06		09 50	09 37		10 13			10 37	11 03	11 11		11 37		
Taunton	d	08 12		08 19	08 19		09 05	08 51	09 21		10 07	09 51		10 28			10 51	11 17	11 26		11 51		
Bridgwater	a										10 19												
Weston-super-Mare	a	08 32					09 27				10 38												
Bristol Temple Meads 10	a	08 52					09 57	09 25			11 11	10 25					11 23	11 51	11 58		12 23		
Bath Spa 7	a						10 11												12 12				
Filton Abbey Wood	a										11 30												
Bristol Parkway 7	a	09 08						09 38				10 38					11 38	12 08			12 38		
Swindon	a						10 40												12 40				
Newport (South Wales)	a										11 58												
Cardiff Central 7	a										12 18												
Birmingham New Street 12	a	10 25						10 55				11 58					12 55	13 26			13 56		
Castle Cary	d								09 42														
Frome	d																						
Westbury	d								10 01					11 05									
Pewsey	d								10 18														
Hungerford	a																						
Newbury	a																						
Thatcham	a																						
Theale	a																						
Reading 7	a			09 32	09 32		11 08		10 50					11 50					13 09			13 16	
Slough 3	a																						
London Paddington 15 ⊖	a			10 02	10 02		11 38		11 24					12 23					13 38			13 44	

A 🛒 from Newton Abbot

B The Golden Hind. Restaurant available after Plymouth for customers until Taunton. ☕ to Plymouth ☕ from Reading ✕ from Plymouth to Reading

C ☕ to Plymouth ☕ from Reading ⊘ from Plymouth to Reading

D 🛒 from Plymouth

E 🛒 ◇ from Plymouth ■ to Plymouth

F The Cornish Riviera

For connections to Oxford, Gatwick Airport and Heathrow Airport please see Tables 116, 148 and 125A

For connections from Swansea please see Table 128. For connections from Plymouth and Exeter St Davids please see Table 135. For connections to Bournemouth please see Table 158

Table 135R

Mondays to Fridays

9 December to 16 May

Cornwall and Devon - Birmingham and London

Route Diagram - see first Page of Table 135

		GW	GW	XC		GW	XC	GW	GW	GW	XC	GW	GW	GW		GW	GW	GW	XC	XC	GW	GW	GW	GW
							R			R														
		◇1		◇1			◇1	◇		1	◇1	◇	◇			◇1	◇1		◇1	◇1	◇	◇	◇1	◇1
							A			B						C	D							E
		☕		⊼			⊼			✕☕	⊼					✕☕	✕☕		⊼	⊼			☕	☕
Penzance	d						09 40			10 00		10 46									11 41			
St Erth	d						09 48			10 10		10 55									11 50			
Hayle	d						09 52					10 58									11 53			
Camborne	d						10 01			10 21		11 07									12 02			
Redruth	d						10 08			10 28		11 13									12 08			
Truro	d						10 19			10 41		11 25									12 19			
St Austell	d						10 35			10 58		11 42									12 36			
Newquay	d							10 13														13 03		
Par	d						10 43	11a02		11 07		11 50									12 44	13a52		
Lostwithiel	d						10 50					11 56									12 50			
Bodmin Parkway	d						10 56			11 19		12 02									12 56			
Liskeard 6	d						11 09			11 33		12 17									13 09			
Menheniot	d																				13x13			
St Germans	d											12 28									13 22			
Saltash	d											12 35									13 29			
St Budeaux Ferry Road	d																							
Keyham	d																							
Dockyard	d																							
Devonport	d																							
Plymouth	a						11 39			11 58		12 45									13 39			
	d			11 25			11 50			12 01	12 24					12 56	12 56		13 24		13 43			
Ivybridge	d																				13 58			
Totnes	d			11 50			12 15			12 29	12 50					13 24	13 24		13 50		14 13			
Paignton	d	11 06	11 23			11 44			12 13				12 48	13 13				13 38		14 01				14 15
Torquay	d	11 12	11 28			11 49			12 18				12 54	13 18				13 43		14 07				14 21
Torre	d	11 16	11 31			11 52			12 21				12 57	13 21				13 46						
Newton Abbot	a	11 24	11 39	12 01		12 02	12 26		12 30	12 41	13 01		13 05	13 30		13 35	13 35	13 56	14 01	14 17	14 27			14 31
	d	11 26	11 41	12 03			12 28		12 31	12 42	13 03		13 07	13 41		13 37	13 37		14 03	14 18				14 33
Teignmouth	d	11 33	11 48						12 38				13 14	13 48						14 25				14 40
Dawlish	d	11 39	11 53						12 43				13 19	13 53						14 30				14 46
Dawlish Warren	d		11 58						12 54					13 58										
Starcross	d		12 02						12 58					14 02										
Exeter St Thomas	d		12 11						13 07					14 11										
Exeter St Davids 6	a	11 52	12 16	12 21			12 46		13 13	13 02	13 22		13 32	14 16		13 57	13 57		14 22	14 42				14 59
Exeter Central	a		12 21						13 21					14 21										
Exmouth	a		12 50						13 50					14 50										
Exeter St Davids 6	d	11 55		12 23			12 48			13 04	13 24		13 36			13 59	13 59		14 24	14 44				15 01
Tiverton Parkway	d	12 09		12 37			13 02			13 19	13 38		13 53						14 38	14 57				15 16
Taunton	d	12 24		12 51			13 16			13 34	13 52		14 10			14 24	14 24		14 52	15 11			15 23	15 31
Bridgwater	a												14 21											
Weston-super-Mare	a												14 41							15 36				
Bristol Temple Meads 10	a			13 24			13 55				14 25		15 11						15 25	15 55				
Bath Spa 7	a																							
Filton Abbey Wood	a																							
Bristol Parkway 7	a			13 38			14 08				14 39								15 39	16 08				
Swindon	a																							
Newport (South Wales)	a																							
Cardiff Central 7	a																							
Birmingham New Street 12	a			14 55			15 23				15 56								16 56	17 23				
Castle Cary	d	12 45														14 45	14 45							15 52
Frome	d																						15 55	
Westbury	d	13 06														15 04	15 04						16 08	
Pewsey	d	13 22																					16 25	
Hungerford	a	13 39																					16 39	
Newbury	a	13 50																					16 48	
Thatcham	a	13 57																					16 55	
Theale	a	14 07																					17 04	
Reading 7	a	14 20								14 50						15 49	15 50						17 16	16 49
Slough 3	a																						17 32	
London Paddington 15 ⊖	a	14 54								15 21						16 22	16 22						17 52	17 24

A ⊼ ◇ from Plymouth R to Plymouth

B Restaurant available after PLY for customers joining until TAU. The Cornishman. ☕ to Plymouth ☕ from Reading ✕ from Plymouth to Reading

C from 10 March. Restaurant available for customers joining until Castle Cary. ☕ from Westbury ✕ to Westbury

D until 7 March. Restaurant available for customers joining until Castle Cary. ☕ from Westbury ✕ to Westbury

E until 7 March. The Torbay Express

For connections to Oxford, Gatwick Airport and Heathrow Airport please see Tables 116, 148 and 125A

For connections from Swansea please see Table 128. For connections from Plymouth and Exeter St Davids please see Table 135. For connections to Bournemouth please see Table 158

Table 135R

Mondays to Fridays

9 December to 16 May

Cornwall and Devon - Birmingham and London

Route Diagram - see first Page of Table 135

		GW	GW	GW	XC	GW	GW	GW	GW	XC		GW	XC	GW	GW	GW	GW	XC	GW	GW		GW	GW	XC	GW
		◇1			◇1		◇1		◇	◇1			◇1	◇1	◇1	◇		◇1	◇			◇1		◇1	
		A					B							C	D										
		🍴			⊥		🍴			⊥			⊥	🍴	🍴			⊥				🍴		⊥	
Penzance	d								12 51					14 00	14 00				14 49						
St Erth	d								13 03					14 10	14 10				14 58						
Hayle	d								13 06										15 01						
Camborne	d								13 15					14 21	14 21				15 10						
Redruth	d								13 21					14 28	14 28				15 16						
Truro	d								13 32					14 41	14 41				15 27						
St Austell	d								13 49					14 58	14 58				15 44						
Newquay	d															15 01									
Par	d								13 57					15 06	15 06	15a47			15 52						
Lostwithiel	d								14 04										15 58						
Bodmin Parkway	d								14 10					15 18	15 18				16 04						
Liskeard 6	d								14 23					15 31	15 31				16 17						
Menheniot	d																		16 22						
St Germans	d								14 34										16 30						
Saltash	d								14 42										16 38						
St Budeaux Ferry Road	d																		16 42						
Keyham	d																		16 44						
Dockyard	d																		16x46						
Devonport	d																		16 48						
Plymouth	a								14 51					15 56	15 56				16 52						
	d				14 25		15 00		15 08	15 24				16 00	16 00			16 25				16 57		17 24	
Ivybridge	d								15 23													17 12			
Totnes	d				14 50		15 28		15 38	15 50				16 28	16 28			16 50				17 28		17 50	
Paignton	d	14 15	14 23	14 39		15 13		15 32				16 12					16 30			16 55			17 26		17 53
Torquay	d	14 21	14 28	14 44		15 18		15 37				16 17					16 35			17 00			17 31		17 58
Torre	d		14 31	14 47		15 21		15 40				16 21					16 38			17 03			17 34		18 01
Newton Abbot	a	14 31	14 39	14 57	15 01	15 29	15 39	15 50	15 52	16 01		16 29		16 39	16 39		16 46	17 01		17 11		17 38	17 42	18 01	18 09
	d	14 33	14 41		15 03	15 31	15 41			16 03		16 31		16 41	16 41		16 48	17 03		17 13		17 41	17 44	18 03	18 11
Teignmouth	d	14 40	14 48			15 38						16 38					16 55			17 20			17 51		18 18
Dawlish	d	14 46	14 53			15 43						16 43					17 00			17 25			17 56		18 23
Dawlish Warren	d		14 58			15 54						16 54					17 05			17 30			18 01		18 28
Starcross	d		15 02			15 58						16 58								17 34			18 05		18 32
Exeter St Thomas	d		15 11			16 07						17 07								17 43			18 14		18 41
Exeter St Davids 6	a	14 59	15 16		15 21	16 13	16 01			16 22		17 12		17 01	17 01		17 18	17 21		17 50		18 01	18 18	18 23	18 46
Exeter Central	a		15 21			16 21						17 21								17 55			18 23		18 53
Exmouth	a		15 50			16 50						17 51								18 25			18 52		19 23
Exeter St Davids 6	d	15 01			15 23		16 03			16 24			16 54	17 03	17 03			17 23				18 03		18 25	
Tiverton Parkway	d	15 16			15 37		16 17			16 38			17 08	17 18	17 18			17 37				18 17		18 39	
Taunton	d	15 31			15 51		16 31			16 52			17 22	17 32	17 32			17 51				18 31		18 53	
Bridgwater	a																								
Weston-super-Mare	a																								
Bristol Temple Meads 10	a				16 26					17 24			17 53					18 23						19 25	
Bath Spa 7	a																								
Filton Abbey Wood	a																								
Bristol Parkway 7	a				16 38					17 39			18 08					18 38						19 39	
Swindon	a																								
Newport (South Wales)	a																								
Cardiff Central 7	a																								
Birmingham New Street 12	a				17 55					18 55			19 23					19 56						20 52	
Castle Cary	d	15 52																				18 54			
Frome	d																								
Westbury	d																					19 13			
Pewsey	d																					19 29			
Hungerford	a																								
Newbury	a																					19 49			
Thatcham	a																								
Theale	a																								
Reading 7	a	16 50					17 49							18 51	18 53							20 06			
Slough 3	a																								
London Paddington 15 ⊖	a	17 24					18 21							19 24	19 24							20 39			

A from 10 March. The Torbay Express

B The Mayflower

C from 10 March. The Royal Duchy

D until 7 March. The Royal Duchy

For connections to Oxford, Gatwick Airport and Heathrow Airport please see Tables 116, 148 and 125A

For connections from Swansea please see Table 128. For connections from Plymouth and Exeter St Davids please see Table 135. For connections to Bournemouth please see Table 158

Table 135R

Mondays to Fridays

9 December to 16 May

Cornwall and Devon - Birmingham and London

Route Diagram - see first Page of Table 135

		GW	GW	GW	GW	XC	GW	GW	GW	GW	GW	GW	GW	GW	GW	GW	GW	XC	XC	GW	GW	GW	GW
								FX	FO			FX	FO	FX	FO			ThFO	MT WO				FX
			◇[1]			◇[1]		◇	◇	◇		◇[1]	◇[1]	◇[1]	◇[1]			◇[1]	◇[1]		[1]		
			A			B																	
			⊐P∅			🛒						⊐P	⊐P	⊐P	⊐P								
Penzance	d		16 00					16 44	16 44					17 39	17 39		19 16						20 18
St Erth	d		16 10					16 53	16 53					17 49	17 49		19 25						20 27
Hayle	d							16 56	16 56					17 53	17 53		19 28						20 32
Camborne	d		16 20					17 05	17 05					18 03	18 03		19 37						20 41
Redruth	d		16 28					17 11	17 11					18 11	18 11		19 43						20 49
Truro	d		16 41					17 24	17 24					18 23	18 23		19 55						21 02
St Austell	d		16 58					17 41	17 41					18 40	18 40		20 12						21 19
Newquay	d									17 22						19 25							
Par	d		17 07					17 48	17 48	18a13				18 49	18 49	20a13	20 19						21 27
Lostwithiel	d		17 14					17 55	17 55								20 26						21 34
Bodmin Parkway	d		17 21					18 01	18 01					19 01	19 01		20 32						21 40
Liskeard [6]	d		17 34	17 49				18 14	18 14					19 14	19 14		20 45						21 53
Menheniot	d																20 49						
St Germans	d			18 00				18 25	18 25								20 58						22 04
Saltash	d			18 07				18 32	18 32								21 05						22 12
St Budeaux Ferry Road	d			18 12													21 09						
Keyham	d																21 11						
Dockyard	d																21x13						
Devonport	d																21 15						
Plymouth	a		18 00	18 19				18 42	18 42					19 39	19 39		21 20						22 25
	d	17 45	18 03			18 25		18 44	18 44					19 42	19 42							21 25	
Ivybridge	d	18 02						18 59	18 59													21 40	
Totnes	d	18 17	18 31			18 50		19 14	19 14					20 10	20 10							21 55	
Paignton	d				18 35		18 52				19 33							20 14	20 14	20 34	21 31		
Torquay	d				18 40		18 57				19 38							20 20	20 20	20 39	21 37		
Torre	d				18 43						19 41									20 42	21 41		
Newton Abbot	a	18 29	18 43		18 50	19 01	19 07	19 26	19 26		19 49			20 21	20 21			20 30	20 30	20 50	21 57	22 06	
	d	18 30	18 44		18 53	19 03	19 09	19 27	19 27		19 50			20 23	20 23			20 31	20 31	20 52		22 07	
Teignmouth	d	18 37			19 00		19 16				19 58									20 59		22 14	
Dawlish	d	18 43			19 05		19 21				20 03									21 04		22 19	
Dawlish Warren	d	18 47			19 16		19 26				20 07									21 09		22 23	
Starcross	d				19 20						20 11									21 13		22 27	
Exeter St Thomas	d				19 29						20 21									21 22		22 36	
Exeter St Davids [6]	a	18 59	19 03		19 33	19 21	19 40	19 49	19 49		20 26			20 43	20 43			20 50	20 50	21 28		22 40	
Exeter Central	a										20 33									21 34			
Exmouth	a										21 01									22 02			
Exeter St Davids [6]	d		19 06			19 23			19 49			19 55		20 45	20 45			20 52	20 52				
Tiverton Parkway	d		19 21			19 37			20 06			20 10		21 00	21 00			21 04	21 04				
Taunton	d		19 36			19 51			20a22			20 25	20 27	21 15	21 15			21 18	21 18				
Bridgwater	a																						
Weston-super-Mare	a																						
Bristol Temple Meads [10]	a					20 24								21 47	21 47			21 51	21 52				
Bath Spa [7]	a													22 01	22 01								
Filton Abbey Wood	a																						
Bristol Parkway [7]	a					20 38												22 08	22 08				
Swindon	a													22 33	22 33								
Newport (South Wales)	a																						
Cardiff Central [7]	a																						
Birmingham New Street [12]	a					22 04												23 43	23 43				
Castle Cary	d											20 46	20 46										
Frome	d																						
Westbury	d											21 05	21 05										
Pewsey	d											21 22	21 22										
Hungerford	a																						
Newbury	a											21 42	21 42										
Thatcham	a																						
Theale	a																						
Reading [7]	a		20 50									21 59	21 59	23 06	23 08								
Slough [3]	a																						
London Paddington [15] ⊖	a		21 21									22 38	22 30	23 44	23 42								

A ⊐P to Plymouth ⊐P from Reading ∅ from Plymouth to Reading

B 🛒 to Bristol Temple Meads

For connections to Oxford, Gatwick Airport and Heathrow Airport please see Tables 116, 148 and 125A

For connections from Swansea please see Table 128. For connections from Plymouth and Exeter St Davids please see Table 135. For connections to Bournemouth please see Table 158

Table 135R

Mondays to Fridays

9 December to 16 May

Cornwall and Devon - Birmingham and London

Route Diagram - see first Page of Table 135

		GW	GW	GW	GW	GW	GW	GW	XC
		FO					FO	FX	
		■1		◇			■	■	◇■1
							A	A	
							bed	bed	
		cup					cup	cup	
Penzance	d	20 18					21 45	21 45	22 08
St Erth	d	20 27					21 55	21 55	22 16
Hayle	d	20 32							22 20
Camborne	d	20 41					22 07	22 07	22 30
Redruth	d	20 49					22 14	22 14	22 36
Truro	d	21 02					22 27	22 27	22 48
St Austell	d	21 19					22 45	22 45	23 04
Newquay	d		21 26						
Par	d	21 27	22a16				22 54	22 54	23 12
Lostwithiel	d	21 34							23 19
Bodmin Parkway	d	21 40					23 06	23 06	23 26
Liskeard ■	d	21 53					23 21	23 21	23 38
Menheniot	d								
St Germans	d	22 04							
Saltash	d	22 12							
St Budeaux Ferry Road	d								
Keyham	d								
Dockyard	d								
Devonport	d								
Plymouth	a	22 25					23 45	23 45	00 03
	d						23 51	23 51	
Ivybridge	d								
Totnes	d						00 20	00 20	
Paignton	d				22 30	23 41			
Torquay	d				22 35	23 46			
Torre	d				22 38	23 49			
Newton Abbot	a				22 46	23 57	00 32	00 32	
	d				22 48	23 59	00 33	00 33	
Teignmouth	d				22 55	00 06			
Dawlish	d				23 00	00 11			
Dawlish Warren	d				23 05	00 16			
Starcross	d				23 09	00 20			
Exeter St Thomas	d				23 18	00 29			
Exeter St Davids ■	a				23 22	00 34	00 55	00 55	
Exeter Central	a								
Exmouth	a								
Exeter St Davids ■	d			21 49			01 06	01 06	
Tiverton Parkway	d			22 06					
Taunton	d			22 23			01 42	01 42	
Bridgwater	a								
Weston-super-Mare	a			22 47					
Bristol Temple Meads ■	a			23 12					
Bath Spa ■	a								
Filton Abbey Wood	a								
Bristol Parkway ■	a								
Swindon	a								
Newport (South Wales)	a								
Cardiff Central ■	a								
Birmingham New Street ■	a								
Castle Cary	d								
Frome	d								
Westbury	d								
Pewsey	d								
Hungerford	a								
Newbury	a								
Thatcham	a								
Theale	a								
Reading ■	a						04s00	04s00	
Slough ■	a								
London Paddington ■ ⊖	a						05 13	05 23	

A The Night Riviera

For connections to Oxford, Gatwick Airport and Heathrow Airport please see Tables 116, 148 and 125A

For connections from Swansea please see Table 128. For connections from Plymouth and Exeter St Davids please see Table 135. For connections to Bournemouth please see Table 158

Table 135R

Saturdays

14 December to 28 December

Cornwall and Devon - Birmingham and London

Route Diagram - see first Page of Table 135

		GW	GW	GW	GW	XC	GW	GW	GW	XC		GW	XC	GW	GW	XC	GW	GW	GW	GW		XC	GW	GW	GW
			■																						■
						◇1	◇1			◇1		◇1	◇1		◇1	◇1			◇1			◇1			1
			A										B		C				D			E			
			[sleeper] [restaurant]			[trolley]	[restaurant]			[trolley]		[restaurant]	[trolley]		[restaurant]	[trolley]			[restaurant]			[trolley]			[restaurant]
Penzance	d				05 20												05 37					06 30	06 41		06 50
St Erth	d																05 45					06 38	06a49		07 00
Hayle	d																05 48					06 41			
Camborne	d				05 37												05 58					06 51			07 11
Redruth	d				05 43												06 04					06 57			07 18
Truro	d				05a55												06 15					07 09			07 31
St Austell	d																06 32					07 25			07 48
Newquay	d																								
Par	d																06 39					07 32			07 56
Lostwithiel	d																06 46					07 39			08 04
Bodmin Parkway	d																06 52					07 46			08 10
Liskeard 6	d																07 07					07 58			08 23
Menheniot	d																07x11								
St Germans	d																07 19								
Saltash	d																07 26								
St Budeaux Ferry Road	d																07 30								
Keyham	d																07 32								
Dockyard	d																07x34								
Devonport	d																07 36								
Plymouth	a																07 42					08 22			08 49
	d					05 25	05 40			06 25					06 55	07 25			07 47	08 06		08 25			08 52
Ivybridge	d																			08 21					
Totnes	d		00 20			05 50	06 07			06 50						07 50			08 14	08 35		08 50			09 19
Paignton	d							06 13	06 34				07 02	07 11				08 06						09 04	
Torquay	d							06 18	06 39				07 08	07 16				08 11						09 09	
Torre	d							06 21	06 42					07 19				08 14						09 12	
Newton Abbot	a		00 32			06 01	06 18	06 29	06 50	07 01			07 18	07 27	07 30	08 01		08 22	08 26	08 47		09 01		09 20	09 30
	d		00 33			06 03	06 20	06 31	06 52	07 03			07 19		07 32	08 03		08 34	08 27	08 48		09 03		09 35	09 32
Teignmouth	d	00 06						06 38	06 59				07 26					08 41		08 55				09 42	
Dawlish	d	00 11						06 43	07 04				07 31					08 46		09 00				09 47	
Dawlish Warren	d	00 16						06 48	07 15									08 51						09 52	
Starcross	d	00 20						06 52	07 19									08 55						09 56	
Exeter St Thomas	d	00 29						07 01	07 28									09 04						10 05	
Exeter St Davids 6	a	00 34	00 55			06 21	06 40	07 06	07 33	07 21			07 43		07 52	08 21		09 09	08 47	09 16		09 21		10 10	09 52
Exeter Central	a							07 14	07 39									09 21						10 21	
Exmouth	a							07 43	08 18									09 50						10 50	
Exeter St Davids 6	d		01 06	06 00		06 23	06 41			07 23		07 29	07 45		07 54	08 23			08 49			09 23			09 54
Tiverton Parkway	d			06 17		06 37	06 56			07 37		07 44	07 58		08 09	08 37			09 04			09 37			10 09
Taunton	d		01 42	06 34		06 51	07 11			07 51		07 59	08 12		08 24	08 51			09 19			09 51			10 24
Bridgwater	a			06 46								08 09													
Weston-super-Mare	a			07 05								08 27													
Bristol Temple Meads 10	a			07 41		07 23				08 23		08 57	08 48			09 24						10 24			
Bath Spa 7	a											09 11													
Filton Abbey Wood	a			07 58																					
Bristol Parkway 7	a			08 05		07 38				08 38			09 08			09 38						10 38			
Swindon	a											09 40													
Newport (South Wales)	a																								
Cardiff Central 7	a																								
Birmingham New Street 12	a					08 56				09 55			10 25			10 56						11 55			
Castle Cary	d						07 33												09 40						
Frome	d																								
Westbury	d						07 56												09 59						11 02
Pewsey	d						08 13												10 17						
Hungerford	a																								
Newbury	a						08 33																		
Thatcham	a																								
Theale	a																								
Reading 7	a		04s00				08 51					10 11			09 41				10 51						11 53
Slough 3	a																								
London Paddington 15 ⊖	a		05 13				09 21					10 39			10 11				11 24						12 23

A The Night Riviera
B [trolley] from Newton Abbot
C [restaurant] from Reading Ø to Reading
D [restaurant] from Castle Cary Ø to Castle Cary
E [trolley] from Plymouth

For connections to Oxford, Gatwick Airport and Heathrow Airport please see Tables 116, 148 and 125A

For connections from Swansea please see Table 128. For connections from Plymouth and Exeter St Davids please see Table 135. For connections to Bournemouth please see Table 158

Table 135R

Saturdays

14 December to 28 December

Cornwall and Devon - Birmingham and London

Route Diagram - see first Page of Table 135

		GW	GW	GW	XC	GW	XC	GW	GW	XC	GW	GW	GW	GW	GW	XC	XC	GW	GW	GW	GW	XC	GW
		◇	◇1		◇1		◇1		◇1	◇1	◇1	◇1				◇1	◇1	◇		◇1		◇1	
										A							A						
			café		trolley		trolley		café	trolley	café	café				trolley	trolley			café		trolley	
Penzance	d					07 35			07 59	08 28	08 45		08 54				09 43			10 00			10 37
St Erth	d					07 48			08 09	08 36	08 55		09a02				09 51			10 10			10 45
Hayle	d					07 52			08 13														10 48
Camborne	d					08 02			08 23	08 46	09 06						10 01			10 21			10 58
Redruth	d					08 09			08 30	08 52	09 13						10 07			10 28			11 04
Truro	d					08 20			08 43	09 04	09 26						10 19			10 41			11 15
St Austell	d					08 36			09 01	09 20	09 43						10 35			10 58			11 32
Newquay	d	07 48																10 12					
Par	d	08a39				08 44			09 09	09 28	09 51						10 42	11a01		11 07			11 39
Lostwithiel	d					08 51											10 49						11 46
Bodmin Parkway	d					08 57			09 20	09 38	10 03						10 56			11 18			11 52
Liskeard 6	d					09 10			09 33	09 51	10 16						11 08			11 31			12 07
Menheniot	d																						12x11
St Germans	d					09 22																	12 18
Saltash	d					09 29																	12 26
St Budeaux Ferry Road	d																						
Keyham	d																						
Dockyard	d																						
Devonport	d																						
Plymouth	a					09 40			09 59	10 18	10 40						11 32			11 59			12 37
	d				09 25				10 02	10 25	10 44					11 25	11 48			12 00		12 24	
Ivybridge	d								10 17											12 15			
Totnes	d				09 50				10 31	10 50						11 50	12 13			12 29		12 50	
Paignton	d		09 18	09 30			10 07	10 23						10 56	11 13				12 13		12 43		
Torquay	d		09 25	09 35			10 13	10 28						11 01	11 18				12 18		12 48		
Torre	d		09 29	09 38				10 31						11 04	11 21				12 21				
Newton Abbot	a		09 38	09 47	10 01		10 23	10 38	10 43	11 01				11 12	11 29	12 01	12 24		12 30	12 41	12 58	13 01	
	d		09 39	09 48	10 03		10 24	10 47	10 44	11 03				11 23	11 41	12 03	12 25		12 32	12 42	13 06	13 03	
Teignmouth	d		09 49	09 56			10 31	10 55						11 30	11 48				12 39		13 13		
Dawlish	d		09 57	10 02			10 36	11 00						11 35	11 53				12 44		13 18		
Dawlish Warren	d		10 02	10 07				11 04						11 40	11 58				12 55		13 23		
Starcross	d													11 44	12 02				12 59				
Exeter St Thomas	d													11 53	12 11				13 08				
Exeter St Davids 6	a		10 13	10 18	10 21		10 48	11 16	11 04	11 21	11 38			11 58	12 16	12 21	12 44		13 13	13 02	13 35	13 22	
Exeter Central	a							11 21							12 21				13 21				
Exmouth	a							11 50							12 50				13 50				
Exeter St Davids 6	d		10 15		10 23		10 50		11 06	11 23	11 40	11 54				12 23	12 48			13 04		13 24	
Tiverton Parkway	d		10 30		10 37		11 03		11 21	11 37		12 09				12 37	13 02			13 19		13 38	
Taunton	d		10 45		10 51		11 17		11 36	11 51		12 24				12 51	13 16			13 34		13 52	
Bridgwater	a																						
Weston-super-Mare	a																						
Bristol Temple Meads 10	a		11 24		11 25		11 54			12 24						13 23	13 54					14 25	
Bath Spa 7	a		11 41																				
Filton Abbey Wood	a																						
Bristol Parkway 7	a				11 38		12 08			12 38						13 38	14 08					14 39	
Swindon	a		12 09																				
Newport (South Wales)	a																						
Cardiff Central 7	a																						
Birmingham New Street 12	a				12 55		13 26			13 55						14 55	15 26					15 55	
Castle Cary	d											12 45											
Frome	d																						
Westbury	d											13 05											
Pewsey	d											13 22											
Hungerford	a											13 39											
Newbury	a											13 49											
Thatcham	a											13 56											
Theale	a											14 05											
Reading 7	a		12 45						12 53		13 19	14 22								14 53			
Slough 3	a																						
London Paddington 15 ⊖	a		13 15						13 22		13 47	14 50								15 21			

A trolley from Plymouth

For connections to Oxford, Gatwick Airport and Heathrow Airport please see Tables 116, 148 and 125A

For connections from Swansea please see Table 128. For connections from Plymouth and Exeter St Davids please see Table 135. For connections to Bournemouth please see Table 158

Table 135R

Saturdays

14 December to 28 December

Cornwall and Devon - Birmingham and London

Route Diagram - see first Page of Table 135

		GW		GW	XC	GW	GW	XC	GW	GW	GW	XC		GW	GW	GW	GW	XC	GW	GW	XC	GW		GW	XC
				◇1	◇1	◇	◇	◇1		◇1	◇1	◇1		◇		◇1		◇1			◇1	◇1		◇	◇1
				A							B														
				⊐P⌀	⊥o			⊥o		⊐P	⊐P⌀	⊥o				⊐P		⊥o			⊥o	⊐P			⊥o
Penzance	d			10 58		11 46								13 00								14 01			
St Erth	d			11 08		11 56								13 09								14 11			
Hayle	d					12 00								13 12											
Camborne	d			11 19		12 10								13 21								14 22			
Redruth	d			11 26		12 16								13 27								14 29			
Truro	d			11 39		12 29								13 38								14 42			
St Austell	d			11 56		12 47								13 55								14 59			
Newquay	d						13 09																	14 59	
Par	d					12 55	13a58							14 03								15 07		15a48	
Lostwithiel	d					13 02								14 09											
Bodmin Parkway	d			12 13		13 09								14 15								15 19			
Liskeard 6	d			12 26		13 23								14 28								15 33			
Menheniot	d					13x28																			
St Germans	d					13 36								14 39											
Saltash	d					13 45								14 47											
St Budeaux Ferry Road	d																								
Keyham	d																								
Dockyard	d																								
Devonport	d													14 52											
Plymouth	a			12 52		13 55								14 58								15 58			
	d			12 54	13 25						14 00	14 25				15 04		15 25	15 32			16 01			16 25
Ivybridge	d																		15 47						
Totnes	d			13 21	13 50							14 50				15 31		15 50	16 01			16 28			16 50
Paignton	d	13 13						13 53	14 13						15 13		15 43			16 13					
Torquay	d	13 18						13 59	14 18						15 18		15 48			16 18					
Torre	d	13 21							14 21						15 21					16 21					
Newton Abbot	a	13 29		13 34	14 01			14 09	14 29		14 35	15 01			15 29	15 42	15 58	16 01	16 13	16 29		16 41			17 01
	d	13 41		13 35	14 03			14 10	14 40		14 36	15 03			15 34	15 44	16 09	16 03		16 31		16 41			17 03
Teignmouth	d	13 48						14 17	14 48						15 42		16 16			16 38					
Dawlish	d	13 53						14 22	14 53						15 47		16 21			16 43					
Dawlish Warren	d	13 58							14 57						15 58					16 55					
Starcross	d	14 02							15 01						16 02					16 59					
Exeter St Thomas	d	14 11							15 11						16 12					17 08					
Exeter St Davids 6	a	14 16		13 55	14 21			14 34	15 15		14 56	15 21			16 15	16 04	16 34	16 21		17 15		17 01			17 21
Exeter Central	a	14 21							15 21						16 21		16 44			17 21					
Exmouth	a	14 50							15 50						16 50					17 50					
Exeter St Davids 6	d			13 57	14 23			14 36			14 59	15 23				16 06		16 23			16 53	17 03			17 23
Tiverton Parkway	d				14 37			14 49			15 14	15 37				16 21		16 37			17 07	17 17			17 37
Taunton	d			14 23	14 51			15 03		15 19	15 29	15 51				16 36		16 51			17 21	17 32			17 51
Bridgwater	a																								
Weston-super-Mare	a							15 23																	
Bristol Temple Meads 10	a				15 24			15 49				16 24						17 24			17 53				18 24
Bath Spa 7	a																								
Filton Abbey Wood	a																								
Bristol Parkway 7	a				15 38			16 08				16 38						17 38			18 08				18 38
Swindon	a																								
Newport (South Wales)	a																								
Cardiff Central 7	a																								
Birmingham New Street 12	a				16 55			17 26				17 55						18 55			19 26				19 58
Castle Cary	d			14 44							15 50														
Frome	d									15 55															
Westbury	d			15 03						16 07															
Pewsey	d									16 25															
Hungerford	a									16 41															
Newbury	a									16 52															
Thatcham	a									17 00															
Theale	a									17 08															
Reading 7	a			15 51						17 20	16 49					17 52						18 48			
Slough 3	a																								
London Paddington 15 ⊖	a			16 23						17 51	17 21					18 21						19 22			

A ⊐P to Plymouth ⊐P from Reading ⌀ from Plymouth to Reading

B ⊐P from Reading ⌀ to Reading

For connections to Oxford, Gatwick Airport and Heathrow Airport please see Tables 116, 148 and 125A

For connections from Swansea please see Table 128. For connections from Plymouth and Exeter St Davids please see Table 135. For connections to Bournemouth please see Table 158

Table 135R

Saturdays

14 December to 28 December

Cornwall and Devon - Birmingham and London

Route Diagram - see first Page of Table 135

		GW	GW	GW	XC	GW	GW	GW		XC	GW	GW	GW	GW	GW	GW	GW	GW		GW	GW	GW	GW	GW	XC
		◇		◇1	◇1			◇1		◇1			◇			◇1					1				◇1
										A															
				🍴	🛒			🍴		🛒						🍴									
Penzance	d	14 52						15 52				16 41				17 40	18 50						19 06		21 32
St Erth	d	15 01						16 02				16 51				17 50	18a58						19 15		21 42
Hayle	d	15 04										16 55				17 54							19 18		
Camborne	d	15 14						16 13				17 05				18 04							19 27		21 53
Redruth	d	15 20						16 20				17 12				18 11							19 33		22 00
Truro	d	15 31						16 33				17 25				18 24							19 44		22 13
St Austell	d	15 48						16 51				17 43				18 41							20 01		22 30
Newquay	d												17 21					19 17						21 18	
Par	d	15 55						16 59				17 51	18a10			18 49		20a03					20 09	22 09	22 38
Lostwithiel	d	16 02						17 06				17 58											20 15	22 18	
Bodmin Parkway	d	16 08						17 13				18 05				19 01							20 21	22 24	22 49
Liskeard 6	d	16 21						17 26				18 19				19 14							20 34	22 37	23 02
Menheniot	d	16x25																					20x39	22x41	
St Germans	d	16 33										18 31											20 47	22 49	
Saltash	d	16 39										18 38											20 54	22 55	
St Budeaux Ferry Road	d																						20 58	22 59	
Keyham	d																						21 00	23 01	
Dockyard	d																						21x02	23x03	
Devonport	d																						21 04	23 05	
Plymouth	a	16 51						17 51				18 49				19 39							21 10	23 12	23 27
	d			16 57	17 24		17 38	17 54		18 25		18 51				19 42							21 15		
Ivybridge	d			17 12			17 53					19 07											21 30		
Totnes	d			17 27	17 50		18 07	18 21		18 50		19 22				20 09							21 44		
Paignton	d		17 13			17 52					18 53			19 21	19 50					20 13	20 46	21 13			
Torquay	d		17 18			17 57					18 58			19 26	19 55					20 18	20 52	21 18			
Torre	d		17 21			18 00					19 01			19 29						20 21		21 21			
Newton Abbot	a		17 29	17 38	18 01	18 08	18 19	18 32		19 01	19 10	19 34		19 38	20 05	20 20				20 29	21 02	21 29	21 56		
	d		17 43	17 40	18 03	18 10	18 19	18 34		19 03	19 12	19 35		19 40	20 07	20 22				20 31	21 04	21 31	21 56		
Teignmouth	d		17 50			18 17	18 26				19 19	19 43		19 47	20 14					20 38		21 38	22 03		
Dawlish	d		17 55			18 22	18 31				19 24	19 48		19 52	20 19					20 43		21 43	22 08		
Dawlish Warren	d		18 00			18 27	18 36				19 29			20 04	20 24					20 48		21 48			
Starcross	d		18 04			18 31					19 33			20 08						20 52		21 52			
Exeter St Thomas	d		18 13			18 40					19 42			20 17						21 01		22 01			
Exeter St Davids 6	a		18 18	18 00	18 22	18 46	18 48	18 54		19 21	19 45	20 01		20 25	20 36	20 42				21 05	21 24	22 05	22 22		
Exeter Central	a		18 23			18 53								20 33											
Exmouth	a		18 52			19 22								21 01											
Exeter St Davids 6	d			18 02	18 24			18 56		19 23						20 44									
Tiverton Parkway	d			18 17	18 38			19 11		19 37						20 59									
Taunton	d			18 32	18 52			19 26		19 51						21 14									
Bridgwater	a																								
Weston-super-Mare	a																								
Bristol Temple Meads 10	a				19 24					20 23						21 47									
Bath Spa 7	a															22 01									
Filton Abbey Wood	a																								
Bristol Parkway 7	a				19 39					20 38															
Swindon	a															22 29									
Newport (South Wales)	a																								
Cardiff Central 7	a																								
Birmingham New Street 12	a				20 52					21 52															
Castle Cary	d			18 53				19 47																	
Frome	d																								
Westbury	d			19 12				20 06																	
Pewsey	d							20 23																	
Hungerford	a																								
Newbury	a			19 45																					
Thatcham	a																								
Theale	a																								
Reading 7	a			20 07				20 58								23 04									
Slough 3	a																								
London Paddington 15 ⊖	a			20 37				21 32								23 37									

A 🛒 to Bristol Temple Meads

For connections to Oxford, Gatwick Airport and Heathrow Airport please see Tables 116, 148 and 125A

For connections from Swansea please see Table 128. For connections from Plymouth and Exeter St Davids please see Table 135. For connections to Bournemouth please see Table 158

Table 135R

Saturdays

14 December to 28 December

Cornwall and Devon - Birmingham and London

Route Diagram - see first Page of Table 135

		GW
Penzance	d	
St Erth	d	
Hayle	d	
Camborne	d	
Redruth	d	
Truro	d	
St Austell	d	
Newquay	d	
Par	d	
Lostwithiel	d	
Bodmin Parkway	d	
Liskeard 6	d	
Menheniot	d	
St Germans	d	
Saltash	d	
St Budeaux Ferry Road	d	
Keyham	d	
Dockyard	d	
Devonport	d	
Plymouth	a	
	d	
Ivybridge	d	
Totnes	d	
Paignton	d	21 53
Torquay	d	21 58
Torre	d	22 01
Newton Abbot	a	22 09
	d	22 11
Teignmouth	d	22 18
Dawlish	d	22 23
Dawlish Warren	d	22 28
Starcross	d	22 32
Exeter St Thomas	d	22 41
Exeter St Davids 6	a	22 45
Exeter Central	a	
Exmouth	a	
Exeter St Davids 6	d	
Tiverton Parkway	d	
Taunton	d	
Bridgwater	a	
Weston-super-Mare	a	
Bristol Temple Meads 10	a	
Bath Spa 7	a	
Filton Abbey Wood	a	
Bristol Parkway 7	a	
Swindon	a	
Newport (South Wales)	a	
Cardiff Central 7	a	
Birmingham New Street 12	a	
Castle Cary	d	
Frome	d	
Westbury	d	
Pewsey	d	
Hungerford	a	
Newbury	a	
Thatcham	a	
Theale	a	
Reading 7	a	
Slough 3	a	
London Paddington 15 ⊖	a	

For connections to Oxford, Gatwick Airport and Heathrow Airport please see Tables 116, 148 and 125A

For connections from Swansea please see Table 128. For connections from Plymouth and Exeter St Davids please see Table 135. For connections to Bournemouth please see Table 158

Table 135R

Saturdays

4 January to 8 February

Cornwall and Devon - Birmingham and London

Route Diagram - see first Page of Table 135

		GW	GW	GW	GW	XC	GW	GW	GW	XC		GW	XC	GW	GW	XC	GW	GW	GW	GW		XC	GW	GW	GW
			R																						R
						◇1	◇1			◇1		◇1	◇1		◇1	◇1			◇1			◇1			1
			A										B		C				D			E			
			[sleeper] [restaurant]			[trolley]	[restaurant]			[trolley]		[restaurant]	[trolley]		[restaurant] ⊘	[trolley]			[restaurant] ⊘			[trolley]			[restaurant]
Penzance	d				05 20												05 37					06 30	06 41		06 50
St Erth	d																05 45					06 38	06a49		07 00
Hayle	d																05 48					06 41			
Camborne	d				05 37												05 58					06 51			07 11
Redruth	d				05 43												06 04					06 57			07 18
Truro	d				05a55												06 15					07 09			07 31
St Austell	d																06 32					07 25			07 48
Newquay	d																								
Par	d																06 39					07 32			07 56
Lostwithiel	d																06 46					07 39			08 04
Bodmin Parkway	d																06 52					07 46			08 10
Liskeard 6	d																07 07					07 58			08 23
Menheniot	d																07x11								
St Germans	d																07 19								
Saltash	d																07 26								
St Budeaux Ferry Road	d																07 30								
Keyham	d																07 32								
Dockyard	d																07x34								
Devonport	d																07 36								
Plymouth	a																07 42					08 22			08 49
	d					05 25	05 40			06 25					06 55	07 25			07 47	08 06		08 25			08 52
Ivybridge	d																			08 21					
Totnes	d		00 20			05 50	06 07			06 50						07 50			08 14	08 35		08 50			09 19
Paignton	d							06 13	06 34				07 02	07 11				08 06						09 04	
Torquay	d							06 18	06 39				07 08	07 16				08 11						09 09	
Torre	d							06 21	06 42					07 19				08 14						09 12	
Newton Abbot	a		00 32			06 01	06 18	06 29	06 50	07 01			07 18	07 27	07 30	08 01		08 22	08 26	08 47		09 01		09 20	09 30
	d		00 33			06 03	06 20	06 31	06 52	07 03			07 19		07 32	08 03		08 34	08 27	08 48		09 03		09 35	09 32
Teignmouth	d	00 06						06 38	06 59				07 26					08 41		08 55				09 42	
Dawlish	d	00 11						06 43	07 04				07 31					08 46		09 00				09 47	
Dawlish Warren	d	00 16						06 48	07 15									08 51						09 52	
Starcross	d	00 20						06 52	07 19									08 55						09 56	
Exeter St Thomas	d	00 29						07 01	07 28									09 04						10 05	
Exeter St Davids 6	a	00 34	00 55			06 21	06 40	07 06	07 33	07 21			07 43		07 52	08 21		09 09	08 47	09 16		09 21		10 10	09 52
Exeter Central	a							07 14	07 39									09 21						10 21	
Exmouth	a							07 43	08 18									09 50						10 50	
Exeter St Davids 6	d		01 06	06 00		06 23	06 41			07 23		07 29	07 45		07 54	08 23			08 49			09 23			09 54
Tiverton Parkway	d			06 17		06 37	06 56			07 37		07 44	07 58		08 09	08 37			09 04			09 37			10 09
Taunton	d		01 42	06 34		06 51	07 11			07 51		07 59	08 12		08 24	08 51			09 19			09 51			10 24
Bridgwater	a			06 46								08 09													
Weston-super-Mare	a			07 05								08 27													
Bristol Temple Meads 10	a			07 41		07 23				08 23		08 57	08 48			09 24						10 24			
Bath Spa 7	a											09 11													
Filton Abbey Wood	a			07 58																					
Bristol Parkway 7	a			08 05		07 38				08 38			09 08			09 38						10 38			
Swindon	a											09 40													
Newport (South Wales)	a																								
Cardiff Central 7	a																								
Birmingham New Street 12	a					08 56				09 55			10 25			10 56						11 55			
Castle Cary	d						07 33												09 40						
Frome	d																								
Westbury	d						07 56												09 59						11 02
Pewsey	d						08 13												10 17						
Hungerford	a																								
Newbury	a						08 33																		
Thatcham	a																								
Theale	a																								
Reading 7	a		04s00				08 53					10 11			09 41				10 51						11 53
Slough 3	a																								
London Paddington 15 ⊖	a		05 13				09 31					10 52			10 22				11 32						12 30

A The Night Riviera
B [trolley] from Newton Abbot
C [restaurant] from Reading ⊘ to Reading
D [restaurant] from Castle Cary ⊘ to Castle Cary
E [trolley] from Plymouth

For connections to Oxford, Gatwick Airport and Heathrow Airport please see Tables 116, 148 and 125A

For connections from Swansea please see Table 128. For connections from Plymouth and Exeter St Davids please see Table 135. For connections to Bournemouth please see Table 158

Table 135R

Saturdays

4 January to 8 February

Cornwall and Devon - Birmingham and London

Route Diagram - see first Page of Table 135

		GW	GW	GW	XC	GW	XC	GW	GW	XC	GW	GW	GW	GW	GW	XC	XC	GW	GW	GW	GW	XC	GW
		◇	◇1		◇1		◇1		◇1	◇1	◇1	◇1				◇1	◇1	◇		◇1		◇1	
										A							A						
			🍴		🛒		🛒		🍴	🛒	🍴	🍴				🛒	🛒			🍴		🛒	
Penzance	d					07 35			07 59	08 28	08 45		08 54				09 43			10 00			10 37
St Erth	d					07 48			08 09	08 36	08 55		09a02				09 51			10 10			10 45
Hayle	d					07 52			08 13														10 48
Camborne	d					08 02			08 23	08 46	09 06						10 01			10 21			10 58
Redruth	d					08 09			08 30	08 52	09 13						10 07			10 28			11 04
Truro	d					08 20			08 43	09 04	09 26						10 19			10 41			11 15
St Austell	d					08 36			09 01	09 20	09 43						10 35			10 58			11 32
Newquay	d	07 48																10 12					
Par	d	08a39				08 44			09 09	09 28	09 51						10 42	11a01		11 07			11 39
Lostwithiel	d					08 51											10 49						11 46
Bodmin Parkway	d					08 57			09 20	09 38	10 03						10 56			11 18			11 52
Liskeard 6	d					09 10			09 33	09 51	10 16						11 08			11 31			12 07
Menheniot	d																						12x11
St Germans	d					09 22																	12 18
Saltash	d					09 29																	12 26
St Budeaux Ferry Road	d																						
Keyham	d																						
Dockyard	d																						
Devonport	d																						
Plymouth	a					09 40			09 59	10 18	10 40						11 32			11 59			12 37
	d				09 25				10 02	10 25	10 44					11 25	11 48			12 00		12 24	
Ivybridge	d								10 17											12 15			
Totnes	d				09 50				10 31	10 50						11 50	12 13			12 29		12 50	
Paignton	d		09 18	09 30			10 07	10 23						10 56	11 13				12 13		12 43		
Torquay	d		09 25	09 35			10 13	10 28						11 01	11 18				12 18		12 48		
Torre	d		09 29	09 38				10 31						11 04	11 21				12 21				
Newton Abbot	a		09 38	09 47	10 01		10 23	10 38	10 43	11 01				11 12	11 29	12 01	12 24		12 30	12 41	12 58	13 01	
	d		09 39	09 48	10 03		10 24	10 47	10 44	11 03				11 23	11 41	12 03	12 25		12 32	12 42	13 06	13 03	
Teignmouth	d		09 49	09 56			10 31	10 55						11 30	11 48				12 39		13 13		
Dawlish	d		09 57	10 02			10 36	11 00						11 35	11 53				12 44		13 18		
Dawlish Warren	d		10 02	10 07				11 04						11 40	11 58				12 55		13 23		
Starcross	d													11 44	12 02				12 59				
Exeter St Thomas	d													11 53	12 11				13 08				
Exeter St Davids 6	a		10 13	10 18	10 21		10 48	11 16	11 04	11 21	11 38			11 58	12 16	12 21	12 44		13 13	13 02	13 35	13 22	
Exeter Central	a							11 21							12 21				13 21				
Exmouth	a							11 50							12 50				13 50				
Exeter St Davids 6	d		10 15		10 23		10 50		11 06	11 23	11 40	11 54				12 23	12 48			13 04		13 24	
Tiverton Parkway	d		10 30		10 37		11 03		11 21	11 37		12 09				12 37	13 02			13 19		13 38	
Taunton	d		10 45		10 51		11 17		11 36	11 51		12 24				12 51	13 16			13 34		13 52	
Bridgwater	a																						
Weston-super-Mare	a																						
Bristol Temple Meads 10	a		11 24		11 25		11 54			12 24						13 23	13 54					14 25	
Bath Spa 7	a		11 41																				
Filton Abbey Wood	a																						
Bristol Parkway 7	a				11 38		12 08			12 38						13 38	14 08					14 39	
Swindon	a		12 09																				
Newport (South Wales)	a																						
Cardiff Central 7	a																						
Birmingham New Street 12	a				12 55		13 26			13 55						14 55	15 26					15 55	
Castle Cary	d											12 45											
Frome	d																						
Westbury	d											13 05											
Pewsey	d											13 22											
Hungerford	a											13 39											
Newbury	a											13 49											
Thatcham	a											13 56											
Theale	a											14 05											
Reading 7	a		12 45						12 53		13 19	14 21								14 53			
Slough 3	a																						
London Paddington 15 ⊖	a		13 26						13 31		13 57	14 59								15 31			

A 🛒 from Plymouth

For connections to Oxford, Gatwick Airport and Heathrow Airport please see Tables 116, 148 and 125A

For connections from Swansea please see Table 128. For connections from Plymouth and Exeter St Davids please see Table 135. For connections to Bournemouth please see Table 158

Table 135R

Saturdays

4 January to 8 February

Cornwall and Devon - Birmingham and London

Route Diagram - see first Page of Table 135

		GW		GW	XC	GW	GW	XC	GW	GW	GW	XC		GW	GW	GW	GW	XC	GW	GW	XC	GW		GW	XC
				◇1	◇1	◇	◇	◇1		◇1	◇1	◇1		◇		◇1		◇1			◇1	◇1		◇	◇1
				A							B														
				⊏P⊘	⊼			⊼		⊏P	⊏P⊘	⊼				⊏P		⊼			⊼	⊏P			⊼
Penzance	d			10 58		11 46								13 00								14 01			
St Erth	d			11 08		11 56								13 09								14 11			
Hayle	d					12 00								13 12											
Camborne	d			11 19		12 10								13 21								14 22			
Redruth	d			11 26		12 16								13 27								14 29			
Truro	d			11 39		12 29								13 38								14 42			
St Austell	d			11 56		12 47								13 55								14 59			
Newquay	d						13 09																	14 59	
Par	d					12 55	13a58							14 03								15 07		15a48	
Lostwithiel	d					13 02								14 09											
Bodmin Parkway	d			12 13		13 09								14 15								15 19			
Liskeard 6	d			12 26		13 23								14 28								15 33			
Menheniot	d					13x28																			
St Germans	d					13 36								14 39											
Saltash	d					13 45								14 47											
St Budeaux Ferry Road	d																								
Keyham	d																								
Dockyard	d																								
Devonport	d													14 52											
Plymouth	a			12 52		13 55								14 58								15 58			
	d			12 54	13 25						14 00	14 25				15 04		15 25	15 32			16 01			16 25
Ivybridge	d																		15 47						
Totnes	d			13 21	13 50							14 50				15 31		15 50	16 01			16 28			16 50
Paignton	d	13 13						13 53	14 13						15 13		15 43			16 13					
Torquay	d	13 18						13 59	14 18						15 18		15 48			16 18					
Torre	d	13 21							14 21						15 21					16 21					
Newton Abbot	a	13 29		13 34	14 01			14 09	14 29		14 35	15 01			15 29	15 42	15 58	16 01	16 13	16 29		16 41			17 01
	d	13 41		13 35	14 03			14 10	14 40		14 36	15 03			15 34	15 44	16 09	16 03		16 31		16 41			17 03
Teignmouth	d	13 48						14 17	14 48						15 42		16 16			16 38					
Dawlish	d	13 53						14 22	14 53						15 47		16 21			16 43					
Dawlish Warren	d	13 58							14 57						15 58					16 55					
Starcross	d	14 02							15 01						16 02					16 59					
Exeter St Thomas	d	14 11							15 11						16 12					17 08					
Exeter St Davids 6	a	14 16		13 55	14 21			14 34	15 15		14 56	15 21			16 15	16 04	16 34	16 21		17 15		17 01			17 21
Exeter Central	a	14 21							15 21						16 21		16 44			17 21					
Exmouth	a	14 50							15 50						16 50					17 50					
Exeter St Davids 6	d			13 57	14 23			14 36			14 59	15 23				16 06		16 23			16 53	17 03			17 23
Tiverton Parkway	d				14 37			14 49			15 14	15 37				16 21		16 37			17 07	17 17			17 37
Taunton	d			14 23	14 51			15 03		15 19	15 29	15 51				16 36		16 51			17 21	17 32			17 51
Bridgwater	a																								
Weston-super-Mare	a							15 23																	
Bristol Temple Meads 10	a				15 24			15 49				16 24						17 24			17 53				18 24
Bath Spa 7	a																								
Filton Abbey Wood	a																								
Bristol Parkway 7	a				15 38			16 08				16 38						17 38			18 08				18 38
Swindon	a																								
Newport (South Wales)	a																								
Cardiff Central 7	a																								
Birmingham New Street 12	a				16 55			17 26				17 55						18 55			19 26				19 58
Castle Cary	d			14 44							15 50														
Frome	d									15 55															
Westbury	d			15 03						16 07															
Pewsey	d									16 25															
Hungerford	a									16 41															
Newbury	a									16 52															
Thatcham	a									17 00															
Theale	a									17 08															
Reading 7	a			15 49						17 20	16 49					17 52						18 48			
Slough 3	a																								
London Paddington 15 ⊖	a			16 30						17 57	17 30					18 30						19 34			

A ⊏P to Plymouth ⊏P from Reading ⊘ from Plymouth to Reading

B ⊏P from Reading ⊘ to Reading

For connections to Oxford, Gatwick Airport and Heathrow Airport please see Tables 116, 148 and 125A

For connections from Swansea please see Table 128. For connections from Plymouth and Exeter St Davids please see Table 135. For connections to Bournemouth please see Table 158

Table 135R

Saturdays

4 January to 8 February

Cornwall and Devon - Birmingham and London

Route Diagram - see first Page of Table 135

		GW	GW	GW	XC	GW	GW	GW		XC	GW	GW	GW	GW	GW	GW	GW	GW		GW	GW	GW	GW	GW	XC
		◇		◇[1]	◇[1]			◇[1]		◇[1]			◇			◇[1]					[1]				◇[1]
										A															
				🍽	🛒			🍽		🛒						🍽									
Penzance	d	14 52						15 52				16 41				17 40	18 50						19 06		21 32
St Erth	d	15 01						16 02				16 51				17 50	18a58						19 15		21 42
Hayle	d	15 04										16 55				17 54							19 18		
Camborne	d	15 14						16 13				17 05				18 04							19 27		21 53
Redruth	d	15 20						16 20				17 12				18 11							19 33		22 00
Truro	d	15 31						16 33				17 25				18 24							19 44		22 13
St Austell	d	15 48						16 51				17 43				18 41							20 01		22 30
Newquay	d												17 21					19 17						21 18	
Par	d	15 55						16 59				17 51	18a10			18 49		20a03					20 09	22 09	22 38
Lostwithiel	d	16 02						17 06				17 58											20 15	22 18	
Bodmin Parkway	d	16 08						17 13				18 05				19 01							20 21	22 24	22 49
Liskeard [6]	d	16 21						17 26				18 19				19 14							20 34	22 37	23 02
Menheniot	d	16x25																					20x39	22x41	
St Germans	d	16 33										18 31											20 47	22 49	
Saltash	d	16 39										18 38											20 54	22 55	
St Budeaux Ferry Road	d																						20 58	22 59	
Keyham	d																						21 00	23 01	
Dockyard	d																						21x02	23x03	
Devonport	d																						21 04	23 05	
Plymouth	a	16 51						17 51				18 49				19 39							21 10	23 12	23 27
	d			16 57	17 24		17 38	17 54		18 25		18 51				19 42							21 15		
Ivybridge	d			17 12			17 53					19 07											21 30		
Totnes	d			17 27	17 50		18 07	18 21		18 50		19 22				20 09							21 44		
Paignton	d		17 13			17 52					18 53			19 21	19 50					20 13	20 46	21 13			
Torquay	d		17 18			17 57					18 58			19 26	19 55					20 18	20 52	21 18			
Torre	d		17 21			18 00					19 01			19 29						20 21		21 21			
Newton Abbot	a		17 29	17 38	18 01	18 08	18 19	18 32		19 01	19 10	19 34		19 38	20 05	20 20				20 29	21 02	21 29	21 56		
	d		17 43	17 40	18 03	18 10	18 19	18 34		19 03	19 12	19 35		19 40	20 07	20 22				20 31	21 04	21 31	21 56		
Teignmouth	d		17 50			18 17	18 26				19 19	19 43		19 47	20 14					20 38		21 38	22 03		
Dawlish	d		17 55			18 22	18 31				19 24	19 48		19 52	20 19					20 43		21 43	22 08		
Dawlish Warren	d		18 00			18 27	18 36				19 29			20 04	20 24					20 48		21 48			
Starcross	d		18 04			18 31					19 33			20 08						20 52		21 52			
Exeter St Thomas	d		18 13			18 40					19 42			20 17						21 01		22 01			
Exeter St Davids [6]	a		18 18	18 00	18 22	18 46	18 48	18 54		19 21	19 45	20 01		20 25	20 36	20 42				21 05	21 24	22 05	22 22		
Exeter Central	a		18 23			18 53								20 33											
Exmouth	a		18 52			19 22								21 01											
Exeter St Davids [6]	d			18 02	18 24			18 56		19 23						20 44									
Tiverton Parkway	d			18 17	18 38			19 11		19 37						20 59									
Taunton	d			18 32	18 52			19 26		19 51						21 14									
Bridgwater	a																								
Weston-super-Mare	a																								
Bristol Temple Meads [10]	a				19 24					20 23						21 47									
Bath Spa [7]	a															22 01									
Filton Abbey Wood	a																								
Bristol Parkway [7]	a				19 39					20 38															
Swindon	a															22 29									
Newport (South Wales)	a																								
Cardiff Central [7]	a																								
Birmingham New Street [12]	a				20 52					21 52															
Castle Cary	d			18 53				19 47																	
Frome	d																								
Westbury	d			19 12				20 06																	
Pewsey	d							20 23																	
Hungerford	a																								
Newbury	a			19 45																					
Thatcham	a																								
Theale	a																								
Reading [7]	a			20 07				20 58								23 11									
Slough [3]	a																								
London Paddington [15] ⊖	a			20 51				21 41								23 53									

A 🛒 to Bristol Temple Meads

For connections to Oxford, Gatwick Airport and Heathrow Airport please see Tables 116, 148 and 125A

For connections from Swansea please see Table 128. For connections from Plymouth and Exeter St Davids please see Table 135. For connections to Bournemouth please see Table 158

Table 135R

Saturdays

4 January to 8 February

Cornwall and Devon - Birmingham and London

Route Diagram - see first Page of Table 135

		GW
Penzance	d	
St Erth	d	
Hayle	d	
Camborne	d	
Redruth	d	
Truro	d	
St Austell	d	
Newquay	d	
Par	d	
Lostwithiel	d	
Bodmin Parkway	d	
Liskeard 6	d	
Menheniot	d	
St Germans	d	
Saltash	d	
St Budeaux Ferry Road	d	
Keyham	d	
Dockyard	d	
Devonport	d	
Plymouth	a	
	d	
Ivybridge	d	
Totnes	d	
Paignton	d	21 53
Torquay	d	21 58
Torre	d	22 01
Newton Abbot	a	22 09
	d	22 11
Teignmouth	d	22 18
Dawlish	d	22 23
Dawlish Warren	d	22 28
Starcross	d	22 32
Exeter St Thomas	d	22 41
Exeter St Davids 6	a	22 45
Exeter Central	a	
Exmouth	a	
Exeter St Davids 6	d	
Tiverton Parkway	d	
Taunton	d	
Bridgwater	a	
Weston-super-Mare	a	
Bristol Temple Meads 10	a	
Bath Spa 7	a	
Filton Abbey Wood	a	
Bristol Parkway 7	a	
Swindon	a	
Newport (South Wales)	a	
Cardiff Central 7	a	
Birmingham New Street 12	a	
Castle Cary	d	
Frome	d	
Westbury	d	
Pewsey	d	
Hungerford	a	
Newbury	a	
Thatcham	a	
Theale	a	
Reading 7	a	
Slough 3	a	
London Paddington 15 ⊖	a	

For connections to Oxford, Gatwick Airport and Heathrow Airport please see Tables 116, 148 and 125A

For connections from Swansea please see Table 128. For connections from Plymouth and Exeter St Davids please see Table 135. For connections to Bournemouth please see Table 158

Table 135R

Saturdays

15 February to 22 March

Cornwall and Devon - Birmingham and London

Route Diagram - see first Page of Table 135

		GW	GW	GW	GW	XC	GW	GW	GW	XC	GW	XC	GW	GW	XC	GW	GW	GW	GW	XC	GW	GW	GW
			R			◇1	◇1			◇1	◇1	◇1		◇1	◇1			◇1		◇1			R 1
			A 🛏									B		C				D		E			
			🍴			☕	🍴			☕	🍴	☕		🍴Ø	☕			🍴Ø		☕			🍴
Penzance	d				05 20											05 37				06 30	06 41		06 50
St Erth	d															05 45				06 38	06a49		07 00
Hayle	d															05 48				06 41			
Camborne	d				05 37											05 58				06 51			07 11
Redruth	d				05 43											06 04				06 57			07 18
Truro	d				05a55											06 15				07 09			07 31
St Austell	d															06 32				07 25			07 48
Newquay	d																						
Par	d															06 39				07 32			07 56
Lostwithiel	d															06 46				07 39			08 04
Bodmin Parkway	d															06 52				07 46			08 10
Liskeard 6	d															07 07				07 58			08 23
Menheniot	d															07x11							
St Germans	d															07 19							
Saltash	d															07 26							
St Budeaux Ferry Road	d															07 30							
Keyham	d															07 32							
Dockyard	d															07x34							
Devonport	d															07 36							
Plymouth	a															07 42				08 22			08 49
	d					05 25	05 40			06 25				06 55	07 25			07 47	08 06	08 25			08 52
Ivybridge	d																		08 21				
Totnes	d		00 20			05 50	06 07			06 50					07 50			08 14	08 35	08 50			09 19
Paignton	d							06 13	06 34			07 02	07 11				08 06					09 04	
Torquay	d							06 18	06 39			07 08	07 16				08 11					09 09	
Torre	d							06 21	06 42				07 19				08 14					09 12	
Newton Abbot	a		00 32			06 01	06 18	06 29	06 50	07 01		07 18	07 27	07 30	08 01		08 22	08 26	08 47	09 01		09 20	09 30
	d		00 33			06 03	06 20	06 31	06 52	07 03		07 19		07 32	08 03		08 34	08 27	08 48	09 03		09 35	09 32
Teignmouth	d	00 06						06 38	06 59			07 26					08 41		08 55			09 42	
Dawlish	d	00 11						06 43	07 04			07 31					08 46		09 00			09 47	
Dawlish Warren	d	00 16						06 48	07 15								08 51					09 52	
Starcross	d	00 20						06 52	07 19								08 55					09 56	
Exeter St Thomas	d	00 29						07 01	07 28								09 04					10 05	
Exeter St Davids 6	a	00 34	00 55			06 21	06 40	07 06	07 33	07 21		07 43		07 52	08 21		09 09	08 47	09 16	09 21		10 10	09 52
Exeter Central	a							07 14	07 39								09 21					10 21	
Exmouth	a							07 43	08 18								09 50					10 50	
Exeter St Davids 6	d		01 06	06 00		06 23	06 41			07 23	07 29	07 45		07 54	08 23			08 49		09 23			09 54
Tiverton Parkway	d			06 17		06 37	06 56			07 37	07 44	07 58		08 09	08 37			09 04		09 37			10 09
Taunton	d		01 42	06 34		06 51	07 11			07 51	07 59	08 12		08 24	08 51			09 19		09 51			10 24
Bridgwater	a			06 46							08 09												
Weston-super-Mare	a			07 05							08 27												
Bristol Temple Meads 10	a			07 41		07 23				08 23	08 57	08 48			09 24					10 24			
Bath Spa 7	a										09 11												
Filton Abbey Wood	a			07 58																			
Bristol Parkway 7	a			08 05		07 38				08 38		09 08			09 38					10 38			
Swindon	a										09 40												
Newport (South Wales)	a																						
Cardiff Central 7	a																						
Birmingham New Street 12	a					08 56				09 55		10 25			10 56					11 55			
Castle Cary	d						07 33											09 40					
Frome	d																						
Westbury	d						07 56											09 59					11 02
Pewsey	d						08 13											10 17					
Hungerford	a																						
Newbury	a						08 33																
Thatcham	a																						
Theale	a																						
Reading 7	a		04s00				08 51				10 11			09 41				10 51					11 53
Slough 3	a																						
London Paddington 15 ⊖	a		05 13				09 21				10 39			10 11				11 24					12 23

A The Night Riviera

B ☕ from Newton Abbot

C 🍴 from Reading Ø to Reading

D 🍴 from Castle Cary Ø to Castle Cary

E ☕ from Plymouth

For connections to Oxford, Gatwick Airport and Heathrow Airport please see Tables 116, 148 and 125A

For connections from Swansea please see Table 128. For connections from Plymouth and Exeter St Davids please see Table 135. For connections to Bournemouth please see Table 158

Table 135R

Saturdays

15 February to 22 March

Cornwall and Devon - Birmingham and London

Route Diagram - see first Page of Table 135

		GW	GW	GW	XC	GW		XC	GW	GW	XC	GW	GW	GW	GW	GW		XC	XC	GW	GW	GW	GW	XC	GW
		◇	◇1		◇1			◇1		◇1	◇1	◇1	◇1					◇1	◇1	◇		◇1		◇1	
											A								A						
			☕		🛒			🛒		☕	🛒	☕	☕					🛒	🛒			☕		🛒	
Penzance	d					07 35				07 59	08 28	08 45		08 54					09 43			10 00			10 37
St Erth	d					07 48				08 09	08 36	08 55		09a02					09 51			10 10			10 45
Hayle	d					07 52				08 13															10 48
Camborne	d					08 02				08 23	08 46	09 06							10 01			10 21			10 58
Redruth	d					08 09				08 30	08 52	09 13							10 07			10 28			11 04
Truro	d					08 20				08 43	09 04	09 26							10 19			10 41			11 15
St Austell	d					08 36				09 01	09 20	09 43							10 35			10 58			11 32
Newquay	d	07 48																		10 12					
Par	d	08a39				08 44				09 09	09 28	09 51							10 42	11a01		11 07			11 39
Lostwithiel	d					08 51													10 49						11 46
Bodmin Parkway	d					08 57				09 20	09 38	10 03							10 56			11 18			11 52
Liskeard 6	d					09 10				09 33	09 51	10 16							11 08			11 31			12 07
Menheniot	d																								12x11
St Germans	d					09 22																			12 18
Saltash	d					09 29																			12 26
St Budeaux Ferry Road	d																								
Keyham	d																								
Dockyard	d																								
Devonport	d																								
Plymouth	a					09 40				09 59	10 18	10 40							11 32			11 59			12 37
	d				09 25					10 02	10 25	10 44						11 25	11 48			12 00		12 24	
Ivybridge	d									10 17												12 15			
Totnes	d				09 50					10 31	10 50							11 50	12 13			12 29		12 50	
Paignton	d		09 18	09 30				10 07	10 23						10 56	11 13					12 13		12 43		
Torquay	d		09 25	09 35				10 13	10 28						11 01	11 18					12 18		12 48		
Torre	d		09 29	09 38					10 31						11 04	11 21					12 21				
Newton Abbot	a		09 38	09 47	10 01			10 23	10 38	10 43	11 01				11 12	11 29		12 01	12 24		12 30	12 41	12 58	13 01	
	d		09 39	09 48	10 03			10 24	10 47	10 44	11 03				11 23	11 41		12 03	12 25		12 32	12 42	13 06	13 03	
Teignmouth	d		09 49	09 56				10 31	10 55						11 30	11 48					12 39		13 13		
Dawlish	d		09 57	10 02				10 36	11 00						11 35	11 53					12 44		13 18		
Dawlish Warren	d		10 02	10 07					11 04						11 40	11 58					12 55		13 23		
Starcross	d														11 44	12 02					12 59				
Exeter St Thomas	d														11 53	12 11					13 08				
Exeter St Davids 6	a		10 13	10 18	10 21			10 48	11 16	11 04	11 21	11 38			11 58	12 16		12 21	12 44		13 13	13 02	13 35	13 22	
Exeter Central	a								11 21							12 21					13 21				
Exmouth	a								11 50							12 50					13 50				
Exeter St Davids 6	d		10 15		10 23			10 50		11 06	11 23	11 40	11 54					12 23	12 48			13 04		13 24	
Tiverton Parkway	d		10 30		10 37			11 03		11 21	11 37		12 09					12 37	13 02			13 19		13 38	
Taunton	d		10 45		10 51			11 17		11 36	11 51		12 24					12 51	13 16			13 34		13 52	
Bridgwater	a																								
Weston-super-Mare	a																								
Bristol Temple Meads 10	a		11 24		11 25			11 54			12 24							13 23	13 54					14 25	
Bath Spa 7	a		11 41																						
Filton Abbey Wood	a																								
Bristol Parkway 7	a				11 38			12 08			12 38							13 38	14 08					14 39	
Swindon	a		12 09																						
Newport (South Wales)	a																								
Cardiff Central 7	a																								
Birmingham New Street 12	a				12 55			13 26			13 55							14 55	15 26					15 55	
Castle Cary	d												12 45												
Frome	d																								
Westbury	d												13 05												
Pewsey	d												13 22												
Hungerford	a												13 39												
Newbury	a												13 49												
Thatcham	a												13 56												
Theale	a												14 05												
Reading 7	a		12 45							12 53		13 19	14 22									14 53			
Slough 3	a																								
London Paddington 15 ⊖	a		13 15							13 22		13 47	14 50									15 21			

A 🛒 from Plymouth

For connections to Oxford, Gatwick Airport and Heathrow Airport please see Tables 116, 148 and 125A

For connections from Swansea please see Table 128. For connections from Plymouth and Exeter St Davids please see Table 135. For connections to Bournemouth please see Table 158

Table 135R

Saturdays

15 February to 22 March

Cornwall and Devon - Birmingham and London

Route Diagram - see first Page of Table 135

		GW		GW	XC	GW	GW	XC	GW	GW	GW	XC		GW	GW	GW	GW	XC	GW	GW	XC	GW		GW	XC
				◇1	◇1	◇	◇	◇1		◇1	◇1	◇1		◇		◇1		◇1			◇1	◇1		◇	◇1
				A							B														
				🍽∅	🛒			🛒		🍽	🍽∅	🛒				🍽		🛒			🛒	🍽			🛒
Penzance	d			10 58		11 46								13 00								14 01			
St Erth	d			11 08		11 56								13 09								14 11			
Hayle	d					12 00								13 12											
Camborne	d			11 19		12 10								13 21								14 22			
Redruth	d			11 26		12 16								13 27								14 29			
Truro	d			11 39		12 29								13 38								14 42			
St Austell	d			11 56		12 47								13 55								14 59			
Newquay	d						13 09																	14 59	
Par	d					12 55	13a58							14 03								15 07		15a48	
Lostwithiel	d					13 02								14 09											
Bodmin Parkway	d			12 13		13 09								14 15								15 19			
Liskeard 6	d			12 26		13 23								14 28								15 33			
Menheniot	d					13x28																			
St Germans	d					13 36								14 39											
Saltash	d					13 45								14 47											
St Budeaux Ferry Road	d																								
Keyham	d																								
Dockyard	d																								
Devonport	d													14 52											
Plymouth	a			12 52		13 55								14 58								15 58			
	d			12 54	13 25						14 00	14 25				15 04		15 25	15 32			16 01			16 25
Ivybridge	d																		15 47						
Totnes	d			13 21	13 50							14 50				15 31		15 50	16 01			16 28			16 50
Paignton	d	13 13						13 53	14 13						15 13		15 43			16 13					
Torquay	d	13 18						13 59	14 18						15 18		15 48			16 18					
Torre	d	13 21							14 21						15 21					16 21					
Newton Abbot	a	13 29		13 34	14 01			14 09	14 29		14 35	15 01			15 29	15 42	15 58	16 01	16 13	16 29		16 41			17 01
	d	13 41		13 35	14 03			14 10	14 40		14 36	15 03			15 34	15 44	16 09	16 03		16 31		16 41			17 03
Teignmouth	d	13 48						14 17	14 48						15 42		16 16			16 38					
Dawlish	d	13 53						14 22	14 53						15 47		16 21			16 43					
Dawlish Warren	d	13 58							14 57						15 58					16 55					
Starcross	d	14 02							15 01						16 02					16 59					
Exeter St Thomas	d	14 11							15 11						16 12					17 08					
Exeter St Davids 6	a	14 16		13 55	14 21			14 34	15 15		14 56	15 21			16 15	16 04	16 34	16 21		17 15		17 01			17 21
Exeter Central	a	14 21							15 21						16 21		16 44			17 21					
Exmouth	a	14 50							15 50						16 50					17 50					
Exeter St Davids 6	d			13 57	14 23			14 36			14 59	15 23				16 06		16 23			16 53	17 03			17 23
Tiverton Parkway	d				14 37			14 49			15 14	15 37				16 21		16 37			17 07	17 17			17 37
Taunton	d			14 23	14 51			15 03		15 19	15 29	15 51				16 36		16 51			17 21	17 32			17 51
Bridgwater	a																								
Weston-super-Mare	a							15 23																	
Bristol Temple Meads 10	a				15 24			15 49				16 24						17 24			17 53				18 24
Bath Spa 7	a																								
Filton Abbey Wood	a																								
Bristol Parkway 7	a				15 38			16 08				16 38						17 38			18 08				18 38
Swindon	a																								
Newport (South Wales)	a																								
Cardiff Central 7	a																								
Birmingham New Street 12	a				16 55			17 26				17 55						18 55			19 26				19 58
Castle Cary	d			14 44							15 50														
Frome	d									15 55															
Westbury	d			15 03						16 07															
Pewsey	d									16 25															
Hungerford	a									16 41															
Newbury	a									16 52															
Thatcham	a									17 00															
Theale	a									17 08															
Reading 7	a			15 51						17 20	16 49					17 52						18 48			
Slough 3	a																								
London Paddington 15 ⊖	a			16 23						17 51	17 21					18 21						19 22			

A 🍽 to Plymouth 🍽 from Reading ∅ from Plymouth to Reading

B 🍽 from Reading ∅ to Reading

For connections to Oxford, Gatwick Airport and Heathrow Airport please see Tables 116, 148 and 125A

For connections from Swansea please see Table 128. For connections from Plymouth and Exeter St Davids please see Table 135. For connections to Bournemouth please see Table 158

Table 135R

Saturdays

15 February to 22 March

Cornwall and Devon - Birmingham and London

Route Diagram - see first Page of Table 135

		GW	GW	GW	XC	GW	GW	GW	XC	GW	GW	GW	GW	GW	GW	GW	GW	GW	GW	GW	GW	GW	XC
		◇		◇1	◇1			◇1	◇1			◇			◇1				1				◇1
									A														
				[buffet]	[trolley]			[buffet]	[trolley]						[buffet]								
Penzance	d	14 52						15 52			16 41				17 40	18 50					19 06		21 32
St Erth	d	15 01						16 02			16 51				17 50	18a58					19 15		21 42
Hayle	d	15 04									16 55				17 54						19 18		
Camborne	d	15 14						16 13			17 05				18 04						19 27		21 53
Redruth	d	15 20						16 20			17 12				18 11						19 33		22 00
Truro	d	15 31						16 33			17 25				18 24						19 44		22 13
St Austell	d	15 48						16 51			17 43				18 41						20 01		22 30
Newquay	d											17 21					19 17					21 18	
Par	d	15 55						16 59			17 51	18a10			18 49		20a03				20 09	22 09	22 38
Lostwithiel	d	16 02						17 06			17 58										20 15	22 18	
Bodmin Parkway	d	16 08						17 13			18 05				19 01						20 21	22 24	22 49
Liskeard 6	d	16 21						17 26			18 19				19 14						20 34	22 37	23 02
Menheniot	d	16x25																			20x39	22x41	
St Germans	d	16 33									18 31										20 47	22 49	
Saltash	d	16 39									18 38										20 54	22 55	
St Budeaux Ferry Road	d																				20 58	22 59	
Keyham	d																				21 00	23 01	
Dockyard	d																				21x02	23x03	
Devonport	d																				21 04	23 05	
Plymouth	a	16 51						17 51			18 49				19 39						21 10	23 12	23 27
	d			16 57	17 24		17 38	17 54	18 25		18 51				19 42						21 15		
Ivybridge	d			17 12			17 53				19 07										21 30		
Totnes	d			17 27	17 50		18 07	18 21	18 50		19 22				20 09						21 44		
Paignton	d		17 13			17 52				18 53			19 21	19 50				20 13	20 46	21 13			
Torquay	d		17 18			17 57				18 58			19 26	19 55				20 18	20 52	21 18			
Torre	d		17 21			18 00				19 01			19 29					20 21		21 21			
Newton Abbot	a		17 29	17 38	18 01	18 08	18 19	18 32	19 01	19 10	19 34		19 38	20 05	20 20			20 29	21 02	21 29	21 56		
	d		17 43	17 40	18 03	18 10	18 19	18 34	19 03	19 12	19 35		19 40	20 07	20 22			20 31	21 04	21 31	21 56		
Teignmouth	d		17 50			18 17	18 26			19 19	19 43		19 47	20 14				20 38		21 38	22 03		
Dawlish	d		17 55			18 22	18 31			19 24	19 48		19 52	20 19				20 43		21 43	22 08		
Dawlish Warren	d		18 00			18 27	18 36			19 29			20 04	20 24				20 48		21 48			
Starcross	d		18 04			18 31				19 33			20 08					20 52		21 52			
Exeter St Thomas	d		18 13			18 40				19 42			20 17					21 01		22 01			
Exeter St Davids 6	a		18 18	18 00	18 22	18 46	18 48	18 54	19 21	19 45	20 01		20 25	20 36	20 42			21 05	21 24	22 05	22 22		
Exeter Central	a		18 23			18 53							20 33										
Exmouth	a		18 52			19 22							21 01										
Exeter St Davids 6	d			18 02	18 24			18 56	19 23						20 44								
Tiverton Parkway	d			18 17	18 38			19 11	19 37						20 59								
Taunton	d			18 32	18 52			19 26	19 51						21 14								
Bridgwater	a																						
Weston-super-Mare	a																						
Bristol Temple Meads 10	a				19 24				20 23						21 47								
Bath Spa 7	a														22 01								
Filton Abbey Wood	a																						
Bristol Parkway 7	a				19 39				20 38														
Swindon	a														22 29								
Newport (South Wales)	a																						
Cardiff Central 7	a																						
Birmingham New Street 12	a				20 52				21 52														
Castle Cary	d			18 53				19 47															
Frome	d																						
Westbury	d			19 12				20 06															
Pewsey	d							20 23															
Hungerford	a																						
Newbury	a			19 45																			
Thatcham	a																						
Theale	a																						
Reading 7	a			20 07				20 58							23 07								
Slough 3	a																						
London Paddington 15 ⊖	a			20 37				21 32							23 40								

A [trolley] to Bristol Temple Meads

For connections to Oxford, Gatwick Airport and Heathrow Airport please see Tables 116, 148 and 125A

For connections from Swansea please see Table 128. For connections from Plymouth and Exeter St Davids please see Table 135. For connections to Bournemouth please see Table 158

Table 135R

Saturdays

15 February to 22 March

Cornwall and Devon - Birmingham and London

Route Diagram - see first Page of Table 135

		GW	GW 🚌
Penzance	d		
St Erth	d		
Hayle	d		
Camborne	d		
Redruth	d		
Truro	d		
St Austell	d		
Newquay	d		
Par	d		
Lostwithiel	d		
Bodmin Parkway	d		
Liskeard 6	d		
Menheniot	d		
St Germans	d		
Saltash	d		
St Budeaux Ferry Road	d		
Keyham	d		
Dockyard	d		
Devonport	d		
Plymouth	a		
	d		
Ivybridge	d		
Totnes	d		
Paignton	d	21 53	
Torquay	d	21 58	
Torre	d	22 01	
Newton Abbot	a	22 10	
	d		22 18
Teignmouth	d		22 36
Dawlish	d		22 46
Dawlish Warren	d		22 53
Starcross	d		23 05
Exeter St Thomas	d		23 29
Exeter St Davids 6	a		23 42
Exeter Central	a		
Exmouth	a		
Exeter St Davids 6	d		
Tiverton Parkway	d		
Taunton	d		
Bridgwater	a		
Weston-super-Mare	a		
Bristol Temple Meads 10	a		
Bath Spa 7	a		
Filton Abbey Wood	a		
Bristol Parkway 7	a		
Swindon	a		
Newport (South Wales)	a		
Cardiff Central 7	a		
Birmingham New Street 12	a		
Castle Cary	d		
Frome	d		
Westbury	d		
Pewsey	d		
Hungerford	a		
Newbury	a		
Thatcham	a		
Theale	a		
Reading 7	a		
Slough 8	a		
London Paddington 15 ⊖	a		

For connections to Oxford, Gatwick Airport and Heathrow Airport please see Tables 116, 148 and 125A

For connections from Swansea please see Table 128. For connections from Plymouth and Exeter St Davids please see Table 135. For connections to Bournemouth please see Table 158

Table 135R

Saturdays

29 March to 17 May

Cornwall and Devon - Birmingham and London

Route Diagram - see first Page of Table 135

		GW	GW	GW	GW	XC	GW	GW	GW	XC	GW	XC	GW	GW	XC	GW	GW	GW	GW	XC	GW	GW	GW
			[R]																				[R]
						◇1	◇1			◇1	◇1	◇1		◇1	◇1			◇1		◇1			1
			A									B		C				D		E			
			[sleeper] [buffet]			[trolley]	[buffet]			[trolley]	[buffet]	[trolley]		[buffet]⊘	[trolley]			[buffet]⊘		[trolley]			[buffet]
Penzance	d				05 20											05 37				06 30	06 41		06 50
St Erth	d															05 45				06 38	06a49		07 00
Hayle	d															05 48				06 41			
Camborne	d				05 37											05 58				06 51			07 11
Redruth	d				05 43											06 04				06 57			07 18
Truro	d				05a55											06 15				07 09			07 31
St Austell	d															06 32				07 25			07 48
Newquay	d																						
Par	d															06 39				07 32			07 56
Lostwithiel	d															06 46				07 39			08 04
Bodmin Parkway	d															06 52				07 46			08 10
Liskeard 6	d															07 07				07 58			08 23
Menheniot	d															07x11							
St Germans	d															07 19							
Saltash	d															07 26							
St Budeaux Ferry Road	d															07 30							
Keyham	d															07 32							
Dockyard	d															07x34							
Devonport	d															07 36							
Plymouth	a															07 42				08 22			08 49
	d					05 25	05 40			06 25				06 55	07 25			07 47	08 06	08 25			08 52
Ivybridge	d																		08 21				
Totnes	d		00 20			05 50	06 07			06 50					07 50			08 14	08 35	08 50			09 19
Paignton	d							06 13	06 34			07 02	07 11				08 06					09 04	
Torquay	d							06 18	06 39			07 08	07 16				08 11					09 09	
Torre	d							06 21	06 42				07 19				08 14					09 12	
Newton Abbot	a		00 32			06 01	06 18	06 29	06 50	07 01		07 18	07 27	07 30	08 01		08 22	08 26	08 47	09 01		09 20	09 30
	d		00 33			06 03	06 20	06 31	06 52	07 03		07 19		07 32	08 03		08 34	08 27	08 48	09 03		09 35	09 32
Teignmouth	d	00 06						06 38	06 59			07 26					08 41		08 55			09 42	
Dawlish	d	00 11						06 43	07 04			07 31					08 46		09 00			09 47	
Dawlish Warren	d	00 16						06 48	07 15								08 51					09 52	
Starcross	d	00 20						06 52	07 19								08 55					09 56	
Exeter St Thomas	d	00 29						07 01	07 28								09 04					10 05	
Exeter St Davids 6	a	00 34	00 55			06 21	06 40	07 06	07 33	07 21		07 43		07 52	08 21		09 09	08 47	09 16	09 21		10 10	09 52
Exeter Central	a							07 14	07 39								09 21					10 21	
Exmouth	a							07 43	08 18								09 50					10 50	
Exeter St Davids 6	d		01 06	06 00		06 23	06 41			07 23	07 29	07 45		07 54	08 23			08 49		09 23			09 54
Tiverton Parkway	d			06 17		06 37	06 56			07 37	07 44	07 58		08 09	08 37			09 04		09 37			10 09
Taunton	d		01 42	06 34		06 51	07 11			07 51	07 59	08 12		08 24	08 51			09 19		09 51			10 24
Bridgwater	a			06 46							08 09												
Weston-super-Mare	a			07 05							08 27												
Bristol Temple Meads 10	a			07 41		07 23				08 23	08 57	08 48			09 24					10 24			
Bath Spa 7	a										09 11												
Filton Abbey Wood	a			07 58																			
Bristol Parkway 7	a			08 05		07 38				08 38		09 08			09 38					10 38			
Swindon	a										09 40												
Newport (South Wales)	a																						
Cardiff Central 7	a																						
Birmingham New Street 12	a					08 56				09 55		10 25			10 56					11 55			
Castle Cary	d						07 33											09 40					
Frome	d																						
Westbury	d						07 56											09 59					11 02
Pewsey	d						08 13											10 17					
Hungerford	a																						
Newbury	a						08 33																
Thatcham	a																						
Theale	a																						
Reading 7	a		04s00				08 51				10 11			09 41				10 51					11 53
Slough 3	a																						
London Paddington 15 ⊖	a		05 13				09 21				10 39			10 11				11 24					12 23

A The Night Riviera

B [trolley] from Newton Abbot

C [buffet] from Reading ⊘ to Reading

D [buffet] from Castle Cary ⊘ to Castle Cary

E [trolley] from Plymouth

For connections to Oxford, Gatwick Airport and Heathrow Airport please see Tables 116, 148 and 125A

For connections from Swansea please see Table 128. For connections from Plymouth and Exeter St Davids please see Table 135. For connections to Bournemouth please see Table 158

Table 135R

Saturdays

29 March to 17 May

Cornwall and Devon - Birmingham and London

Route Diagram - see first Page of Table 135

		GW	GW	GW	XC	GW		XC	GW	GW	XC	GW	GW	GW	GW	GW		XC	XC	GW	GW	GW	GW	XC	GW
		◇	◇1		◇1			◇1		◇1	◇1	◇1	◇1					◇1	◇1	◇		◇1		◇1	
											A								A						
			[buffet]		[trolley]			[trolley]		[buffet]	[trolley]	[buffet]	[buffet]					[trolley]	[trolley]			[buffet]		[trolley]	
Penzance	d					07 35				07 59	08 28	08 45		08 54					09 43			10 00			10 37
St Erth	d					07 48				08 09	08 36	08 55		09a02					09 51			10 10			10 45
Hayle	d					07 52				08 13															10 48
Camborne	d					08 02				08 23	08 46	09 06							10 01			10 21			10 58
Redruth	d					08 09				08 30	08 52	09 13							10 07			10 28			11 04
Truro	d					08 20				08 43	09 04	09 26							10 19			10 41			11 15
St Austell	d					08 36				09 01	09 20	09 43							10 35			10 58			11 32
Newquay	d	07 48																		10 12					
Par	d	08a39				08 44				09 09	09 28	09 51							10 42	11a01		11 07			11 39
Lostwithiel	d					08 51													10 49						11 46
Bodmin Parkway	d					08 57				09 20	09 38	10 03							10 56			11 18			11 52
Liskeard 6	d					09 10				09 33	09 51	10 16							11 08			11 31			12 07
Menheniot	d																								12x11
St Germans	d					09 22																			12 18
Saltash	d					09 29																			12 26
St Budeaux Ferry Road	d																								
Keyham	d																								
Dockyard	d																								
Devonport	d																								
Plymouth	a					09 40				09 59	10 18	10 40							11 32			11 59			12 37
	d				09 25					10 02	10 25	10 44						11 25	11 48			12 00		12 24	
Ivybridge	d									10 17												12 15			
Totnes	d				09 50					10 31	10 50							11 50	12 13			12 29		12 50	
Paignton	d		09 18	09 30				10 07	10 23						10 56	11 13					12 13		12 43		
Torquay	d		09 25	09 35				10 13	10 28						11 01	11 18					12 18		12 48		
Torre	d		09 29	09 38					10 31						11 04	11 21					12 21				
Newton Abbot	a		09 38	09 47	10 01			10 23	10 38	10 43	11 01				11 12	11 29		12 01	12 24		12 30	12 41	12 58	13 01	
	d		09 39	09 48	10 03			10 24	10 47	10 44	11 03				11 23	11 41		12 03	12 25		12 32	12 42	13 06	13 03	
Teignmouth	d		09 49	09 56				10 31	10 55						11 30	11 48					12 39		13 13		
Dawlish	d		09 57	10 02				10 36	11 00						11 35	11 53					12 44		13 18		
Dawlish Warren	d		10 02	10 07					11 04						11 40	11 58					12 55		13 23		
Starcross	d														11 44	12 02					12 59				
Exeter St Thomas	d														11 53	12 11					13 08				
Exeter St Davids 6	a		10 13	10 18	10 21			10 48	11 16	11 04	11 21	11 38			11 58	12 16		12 21	12 44		13 13	13 02	13 35	13 22	
Exeter Central	a								11 21							12 21					13 21				
Exmouth	a								11 50							12 50					13 50				
Exeter St Davids 6	d		10 15		10 23			10 50		11 06	11 23	11 40	11 54					12 23	12 48			13 04		13 24	
Tiverton Parkway	d		10 30		10 37			11 03		11 21	11 37		12 09					12 37	13 02			13 19		13 38	
Taunton	d		10 45		10 51			11 17		11 36	11 51		12 24					12 51	13 16			13 34		13 52	
Bridgwater	a																								
Weston-super-Mare	a																								
Bristol Temple Meads 10	a		11 24		11 25			11 54			12 24							13 23	13 54					14 25	
Bath Spa 7	a		11 41																						
Filton Abbey Wood	a																								
Bristol Parkway 7	a				11 38			12 08			12 38							13 38	14 08					14 39	
Swindon	a		12 09																						
Newport (South Wales)	a																								
Cardiff Central 7	a																								
Birmingham New Street 12	a				12 55			13 26			13 55							14 55	15 26					15 55	
Castle Cary	d												12 45												
Frome	d																								
Westbury	d												13 05												
Pewsey	d												13 22												
Hungerford	a												13 39												
Newbury	a												13 49												
Thatcham	a												13 56												
Theale	a												14 05												
Reading 7	a		12 45							12 53		13 19	14 22									14 53			
Slough 3	a																								
London Paddington 15 ⊖	a		13 15							13 22		13 47	14 50									15 21			

A [trolley] from Plymouth

For connections to Oxford, Gatwick Airport and Heathrow Airport please see Tables 116, 148 and 125A

For connections from Swansea please see Table 128. For connections from Plymouth and Exeter St Davids please see Table 135. For connections to Bournemouth please see Table 158

Table 135R

Saturdays

29 March to 17 May

Cornwall and Devon - Birmingham and London

Route Diagram - see first Page of Table 135

		GW	GW	XC	GW	GW	XC	GW	GW	GW	XC	GW	GW	GW	GW	XC	GW	GW	XC	GW	GW	XC
			◇1	◇1	◇	◇	◇1		◇1	◇1	◇1	◇		◇1		◇1			◇1	◇1	◇	◇1
			A							B												
			⊏P⊘	🛒			🛒		⊏P	⊏P⊘	🛒			⊏P		🛒			🛒	⊏P		🛒
Penzance	d		10 58		11 46							13 00								14 01		
St Erth	d		11 08		11 56							13 09								14 11		
Hayle	d				12 00							13 12										
Camborne	d		11 19		12 10							13 21								14 22		
Redruth	d		11 26		12 16							13 27								14 29		
Truro	d		11 39		12 29							13 38								14 42		
St Austell	d		11 56		12 47							13 55								14 59		
Newquay	d					13 09															14 59	
Par	d				12 55	13a58						14 03								15 07	15a48	
Lostwithiel	d				13 02							14 09										
Bodmin Parkway	d		12 13		13 09							14 15								15 19		
Liskeard 6	d		12 26		13 23							14 28								15 33		
Menheniot	d				13x28																	
St Germans	d				13 36							14 39										
Saltash	d				13 45							14 47										
St Budeaux Ferry Road	d																					
Keyham	d																					
Dockyard	d																					
Devonport	d											14 52										
Plymouth	a		12 52		13 55							14 58								15 58		
	d		12 54	13 25						14 00	14 25			15 04		15 25	15 32			16 01		16 25
Ivybridge	d																15 47					
Totnes	d		13 21	13 50							14 50			15 31		15 50	16 01			16 28		16 50
Paignton	d	13 13					13 53	14 13					15 13		15 43			16 13				
Torquay	d	13 18					13 59	14 18					15 18		15 48			16 18				
Torre	d	13 21						14 21					15 21					16 21				
Newton Abbot	a	13 29	13 34	14 01			14 09	14 29		14 35	15 01		15 29	15 42	15 58	16 01	16 13	16 29		16 41		17 01
	d	13 41	13 35	14 03			14 10	14 40		14 36	15 03		15 34	15 44	16 09	16 03		16 31		16 41		17 03
Teignmouth	d	13 48					14 17	14 48					15 42		16 16			16 38				
Dawlish	d	13 53					14 22	14 53					15 47		16 21			16 43				
Dawlish Warren	d	13 58						14 57					15 58					16 55				
Starcross	d	14 02						15 01					16 02					16 59				
Exeter St Thomas	d	14 11						15 11					16 12					17 08				
Exeter St Davids 6	a	14 16	13 55	14 21			14 34	15 15		14 56	15 21		16 15	16 04	16 34	16 21		17 15		17 01		17 21
Exeter Central	a	14 21						15 21					16 21		16 44			17 21				
Exmouth	a	14 50						15 50					16 50					17 50				
Exeter St Davids 6	d		13 57	14 23			14 36			14 59	15 23			16 06		16 23			16 53	17 03		17 23
Tiverton Parkway	d			14 37			14 49			15 14	15 37			16 21		16 37			17 07	17 17		17 37
Taunton	d		14 23	14 51			15 03		15 19	15 29	15 51			16 36		16 51			17 21	17 32		17 51
Bridgwater	a																					
Weston-super-Mare	a						15 23															
Bristol Temple Meads 10	a			15 24			15 49				16 24					17 24			17 53			18 24
Bath Spa 7	a																					
Filton Abbey Wood	a																					
Bristol Parkway 7	a			15 38			16 08				16 38					17 38			18 08			18 38
Swindon	a																					
Newport (South Wales)	a																					
Cardiff Central 7	a																					
Birmingham New Street 12	a			16 55			17 26				17 55					18 55			19 26			19 58
Castle Cary	d		14 44							15 50												
Frome	d								15 55													
Westbury	d		15 03						16 07													
Pewsey	d								16 25													
Hungerford	a								16 41													
Newbury	a								16 52													
Thatcham	a								17 00													
Theale	a								17 08													
Reading 7	a		15 51						17 20	16 49				17 52						18 48		
Slough 3	a																					
London Paddington 15	⊖ a		16 23						17 51	17 21				18 21						19 22		

A ⊏P to Plymouth ⊏P from Reading ⊘ from Plymouth to Reading

B ⊏P from Reading ⊘ to Reading

For connections to Oxford, Gatwick Airport and Heathrow Airport please see Tables 116, 148 and 125A

For connections from Swansea please see Table 128. For connections from Plymouth and Exeter St Davids please see Table 135. For connections to Bournemouth please see Table 158

Table 135R

Saturdays

29 March to 17 May

Cornwall and Devon - Birmingham and London

Route Diagram - see first Page of Table 135

		GW	GW	GW	XC	GW	GW	GW		XC	GW	GW	GW	GW	GW	GW	GW	GW		GW	GW	GW	GW	GW	XC
		◇		◇1	◇1			◇1		◇1			◇			◇1					1				◇1
										A															
				🍴	🍴			🍴		🍴						🍴									
Penzance	d	14 52						15 52				16 41				17 40	18 50						19 06		21 32
St Erth	d	15 01						16 02				16 51				17 50	18a58						19 15		21 42
Hayle	d	15 04										16 55				17 54							19 18		
Camborne	d	15 14						16 13				17 05				18 04							19 27		21 53
Redruth	d	15 20						16 20				17 12				18 11							19 33		22 00
Truro	d	15 31						16 33				17 25				18 24							19 44		22 13
St Austell	d	15 48						16 51				17 43				18 41							20 01		22 30
Newquay	d												17 21					19 17						21 18	
Par	d	15 55						16 59				17 51	18a10			18 49		20a03					20 09	22 09	22 38
Lostwithiel	d	16 02						17 06				17 58											20 15	22 18	
Bodmin Parkway	d	16 08						17 13				18 05				19 01							20 21	22 24	22 49
Liskeard 6	d	16 21						17 26				18 19				19 14							20 34	22 37	23 02
Menheniot	d	16x25																					20x39	22x41	
St Germans	d	16 33										18 31											20 47	22 49	
Saltash	d	16 39										18 38											20 54	22 55	
St Budeaux Ferry Road	d																						20 58	22 59	
Keyham	d																						21 00	23 01	
Dockyard	d																						21x02	23x03	
Devonport	d																						21 04	23 05	
Plymouth	a	16 51						17 51				18 49				19 39							21 10	23 12	23 27
	d			16 57	17 24		17 38	17 54		18 25		18 51				19 42							21 15		
Ivybridge	d			17 12			17 53					19 07											21 30		
Totnes	d			17 27	17 50		18 07	18 21		18 50		19 22				20 09							21 44		
Paignton	d		17 13			17 52					18 53			19 21	19 50					20 13	20 46	21 13			
Torquay	d		17 18			17 57					18 58			19 26	19 55					20 18	20 52	21 18			
Torre	d		17 21			18 00					19 01			19 29						20 21		21 21			
Newton Abbot	a		17 29	17 38	18 01	18 08	18 19	18 32		19 01	19 10	19 34		19 38	20 05	20 20				20 29	21 02	21 29	21 56		
	d		17 43	17 40	18 03	18 10	18 19	18 34		19 03	19 12	19 35		19 40	20 07	20 22				20 31	21 04	21 31	21 56		
Teignmouth	d		17 50			18 17	18 26				19 19	19 43		19 47	20 14					20 38		21 38	22 03		
Dawlish	d		17 55			18 22	18 31				19 24	19 48		19 52	20 19					20 43		21 43	22 08		
Dawlish Warren	d		18 00			18 27	18 36				19 29			20 04	20 24					20 48		21 48			
Starcross	d		18 04			18 31					19 33			20 08						20 52		21 52			
Exeter St Thomas	d		18 13			18 40					19 42			20 17						21 01		22 01			
Exeter St Davids 6	a		18 18	18 00	18 22	18 46	18 48	18 54		19 21	19 45	20 01		20 25	20 36	20 42				21 05	21 24	22 05	22 22		
Exeter Central	a		18 23			18 53								20 33											
Exmouth	a		18 52			19 22								21 01											
Exeter St Davids 6	d			18 02	18 24			18 56		19 23						20 44									
Tiverton Parkway	d			18 17	18 38			19 11		19 37						20 59									
Taunton	d			18 32	18 52			19 26		19 51						21 14									
Bridgwater	a																								
Weston-super-Mare	a																								
Bristol Temple Meads 10	a				19 24					20 23						21 47									
Bath Spa 7	a															22 01									
Filton Abbey Wood	a																								
Bristol Parkway 7	a				19 39					20 38															
Swindon	a															22 29									
Newport (South Wales)	a																								
Cardiff Central 7	a																								
Birmingham New Street 12	a				20 52					21 52															
Castle Cary	d			18 53				19 47																	
Frome	d																								
Westbury	d			19 12				20 06																	
Pewsey	d							20 23																	
Hungerford	a																								
Newbury	a			19 45																					
Thatcham	a																								
Theale	a																								
Reading 7	a			20 07				20 58								23 07									
Slough 3	a																								
London Paddington 15 ⊖	a			20 37				21 32								23 42									

A 🍴 to Bristol Temple Meads

For connections to Oxford, Gatwick Airport and Heathrow Airport please see Tables 116, 148 and 125A

For connections from Swansea please see Table 128. For connections from Plymouth and Exeter St Davids please see Table 135. For connections to Bournemouth please see Table 158

Table 135R

Saturdays

29 March to 17 May

Cornwall and Devon - Birmingham and London

Route Diagram - see first Page of Table 135

		GW
Penzance	d	
St Erth	d	
Hayle	d	
Camborne	d	
Redruth	d	
Truro	d	
St Austell	d	
Newquay	d	
Par	d	
Lostwithiel	d	
Bodmin Parkway	d	
Liskeard 6	d	
Menheniot	d	
St Germans	d	
Saltash	d	
St Budeaux Ferry Road	d	
Keyham	d	
Dockyard	d	
Devonport	d	
Plymouth	a	
	d	
Ivybridge	d	
Totnes	d	
Paignton	d	21 53
Torquay	d	21 58
Torre	d	22 01
Newton Abbot	a	22 09
	d	22 11
Teignmouth	d	22 18
Dawlish	d	22 23
Dawlish Warren	d	22 28
Starcross	d	22 32
Exeter St Thomas	d	22 41
Exeter St Davids 6	a	22 45
Exeter Central	a	
Exmouth	a	
Exeter St Davids 6	d	
Tiverton Parkway	d	
Taunton	d	
Bridgwater	a	
Weston-super-Mare	a	
Bristol Temple Meads 10	a	
Bath Spa 7	a	
Filton Abbey Wood	a	
Bristol Parkway 7	a	
Swindon	a	
Newport (South Wales)	a	
Cardiff Central 7	a	
Birmingham New Street 12	a	
Castle Cary	d	
Frome	d	
Westbury	d	
Pewsey	d	
Hungerford	a	
Newbury	a	
Thatcham	a	
Theale	a	
Reading 7	a	
Slough 3	a	
London Paddington 15 ⊖	a	

For connections to Oxford, Gatwick Airport and Heathrow Airport please see Tables 116, 148 and 125A

For connections from Swansea please see Table 128. For connections from Plymouth and Exeter St Davids please see Table 135. For connections to Bournemouth please see Table 158

Table 135R

Sundays

8 December to 29 December

Cornwall and Devon - Birmingham and London

Route Diagram - see first Page of Table 135

		GW	GW	GW	GW	XC	GW	GW	XC	XC		GW	GW	XC	GW	GW	GW	XC	XC	GW		XC	GW	GW	XC
								R								R							R		
		◇	◇[1]	◇	◇[1]	◇[1]		[1]	◇[1]	◇[1]			◇[1]	◇[1]		[1]	◇	◇[1]	◇[1]			◇[1]	[1]		◇[1]
														A											
			🍴		🍴	🛒		🍴	🛒	🛒			🍴	🛒		🍴		🛒	🛒			🛒	🍴		🛒
Penzance	d												08 35	09 30		09 47							11 00	11 45	
St Erth	d												08 44	09 38		09 57							11 10	11a53	
Hayle	d												08 49												
Camborne	d												09 00	09 48		10 08							11 23		
Redruth	d												09 06	09 54		10 14							11 29		
Truro	d												09 20	10 06		10 27							11 42		
St Austell	d												09 36	10 22		10 44							11 59		
Newquay	d																11 12								
Par	d												09 45	10 30		10 53	12a01						12 07		
Lostwithiel	d																								
Bodmin Parkway	d												09 57	10 40		11 06							12 19		
Liskeard [6]	d												10 10	10 53		11 19							12 33		
Menheniot	d																								
St Germans	d															11 30									
Saltash	d												10 28												
St Budeaux Ferry Road	d																								
Keyham	d																								
Dockyard	d																								
Devonport	d																								
Plymouth	a												10 35	11 17		11 44							12 58		
	d				08 40	09 25		10 10	10 25				10 40	11 25		11 45		12 00	12 25			12 52	13 00		13 24
Ivybridge	d																								
Totnes	d				09 07	09 50		10 40	10 50				11 07	11 50		12 15			12 50				13 28		13 50
Paignton	d						09 49			10 50		11 00			11 49					12 57					
Torquay	d						09 54			10 56		11 05			11 54					13 02					
Torre	d						09 57					11 08			11 57					13 05					
Newton Abbot	a				09 19	10 01	10 05	10 52	11 01	11 06		11 16	11 19	12 01	12 05	12 28		12 34	13 01	13 13		13 26	13 40		14 01
	d				09 21	10 03	10 07	10 54	11 03	11 08		11 25	11 21	12 03	12 07	12 29		12 36	13 03	13 15		13 27	13 41		14 03
Teignmouth	d				09 28		10 14			11 15		11 32			12 14					13 22					
Dawlish	d				09 34		10 19			11 20		11 37			12 19					13 27					
Dawlish Warren	d						10 24								12 24										
Starcross	d						10 28								12 28										
Exeter St Thomas	d						10 37								12 37										
Exeter St Davids [6]	a				09 47	10 21	10 41	11 14	11 21	11 31		11 51	11 41	12 21	12 42	12 49		12 55	13 21	13 41		13 46	14 01		14 22
Exeter Central	a						10 49					11 58			12 51					13 51					
Exmouth	a						11 18					12 25			13 20					14 18					
Exeter St Davids [6]	d	08 01	08 43	09 35	09 49	10 23		11 18	11 23	11 33			11 43	12 23		12 50		12 57	13 23			13 48	14 03		14 24
Tiverton Parkway	d	08 18	08 58	09 53		10 37		11 33	11 37	11 47			11 58	12 37				13 11	13 37				14 17		14 38
Taunton	d	08 35	09 12	10 19	10 14	10 51		11 48	11 52	12 01			12 12	12 51		13 16		13 25	13 51				14 32		14 52
Bridgwater	a	08 46		10 31																					
Weston-super-Mare	a	09 06		10 49						12 20															
Bristol Temple Meads [10]	a	09 38		11 19		11 24		12 23	12 27	12 44				13 26				13 57	14 23			14 40			15 26
Bath Spa [7]	a							12 41																	
Filton Abbey Wood	a																								
Bristol Parkway [7]	a					11 38			12 38	13 08				13 38				14 08	14 38			15 08			15 39
Swindon	a							13 10																	
Newport (South Wales)	a																								
Cardiff Central [7]	a																								
Birmingham New Street [12]	a					12 49			13 48	14 27				14 48				15 27	15 48			16 26			16 49
Castle Cary	d		09 34										12 33												
Frome	d																								
Westbury	d		09 54		10 52								12 53			13 59									
Pewsey	d		10 11										13 10												
Hungerford	a																								
Newbury	a		10 31		11 26								13 30												
Thatcham	a																								
Theale	a																								
Reading [7]	a		10 48		11 45			13 48					13 50			14 49							15 49		
Slough [3]	a																								
London Paddington [15] ⊖	a		11 29		12 29			14 23					14 30			15 30							16 27		

A 🛒 from Plymouth

For connections to Oxford, Gatwick Airport and Heathrow Airport please see Tables 116, 148 and 125A

For connections from Swansea please see Table 128. For connections from Plymouth and Exeter St Davids please see Table 135. For connections to Bournemouth please see Table 158

Table 135R

Sundays

8 December to 29 December

Cornwall and Devon - Birmingham and London

Route Diagram - see first Page of Table 135

		GW	GW	GW	GW	XC		XC	GW	GW	GW	XC	GW	GW	GW	GW		GW	GW	XC	GW	GW	GW	GW	XC
			◇1 ☕			◇1 🛒		◇1 A 🛒		R 1 ☕	R 1 ☕	◇1 🛒	◇1 ☕		◇1 ☕	◇			◇1 ☕	◇1 🛒		◇	◇	R 1 ☕	◇1 A 🛒
Penzance	d				12 05			12 30		12 56						13 41						14 40		15 00	15 30
St Erth	d				12 14			12 40		13 06						13 51						14 50		15 10	15 38
Hayle	d							12 44								13 54						14 53			
Camborne	d				12 25			12 56		13 19						14 04						15 02		15 22	15 49
Redruth	d				12 31			13 02		13 25						14 10						15 08		15 29	15 55
Truro	d				12 43			13 14		13 38						14 21						15 19		15 41	16 07
St Austell	d				12 59			13 30		13 56						14 38						15 36		15 59	16 23
Newquay	d																						15 10		
Par	d				13 06			13 38		14 03						14 45						15 43	15a59	16 07	16 31
Lostwithiel	d				13 13			13 45								14 52						15 50			
Bodmin Parkway	d				13 19			13 51		14 16						14 58						15 56		16 18	16 41
Liskeard 6	d				13 33			14 04		14 29						15 11						16 09		16 31	16 53
Menheniot	d				13x38																				
St Germans	d				13 46											15 21						16 19			
Saltash	d				13 54											15 29						16 27			
St Budeaux Ferry Road	d																								
Keyham	d																								
Dockyard	d																								
Devonport	d																								
Plymouth	a				14 03			14 28		14 54						15 38						16 37		16 57	17 17
	d		13 44		14 07	14 24		14 35		14 55	15 10	15 24			15 43	15 49			16 10	16 25		16 38		17 00	17 25
Ivybridge	d				14 22											16 07						16 53			
Totnes	d		14 11		14 36	14 50		15 00		15 25		15 50			16 10	16 21			16 37	16 48		17 07		17 28	17 50
Paignton	d	13 50		14 19					14 57				15 45	15 55				16 23			16 55				
Torquay	d	13 55		14 24					15 02				15 51	16 00				16 28			17 00				
Torre	d	13 58		14 27					15 05				15 56	16 03				16 31			17 03				
Newton Abbot	a	14 06	14 23	14 35	14 48	15 01		15 11	15 13	15 37	15 46	16 01	16 04	16 11	16 22	16 33		16 39	16 49	16 59	17 11	17 19		17 39	18 01
	d	14 07	14 25	14 37	14 49	15 03		15 12	15 15	15 38	15 48	16 03	16 05	16 12	16 23	16 34		16 40	16 50	17 01	17 12	17 20		17 40	18 02
Teignmouth	d	14 14		14 44	14 56				15 22				16 13	16 19				16 47			17 19	17 27			
Dawlish	d	14 19		14 49	15 01				15 27				16 18	16 24				16 52			17 24	17 32			
Dawlish Warren	d	14 24		14 54										16 28				17 03			17 29				
Starcross	d	14 28		14 58														17 07							
Exeter St Thomas	d	14 37		15 07														17 16							
Exeter St Davids 6	a	14 40	14 44	15 12	15 16	15 22		15 31	15 41	15 58	16 08	16 22	16 32	16 40	16 44	16 55		17 21	17 10	17 22	17 41	17 45		18 01	18 20
Exeter Central	a	14 53		15 17					15 53					16 51				17 26			17 51				
Exmouth	a	15 20							16 20					17 18							18 18				
Exeter St Davids 6	d		14 47			15 24		15 33		16 01	16 10	16 24	16 34		16 45				17 12	17 24		17 47		18 02	18 22
Tiverton Parkway	d					15 37		15 46		16 16	16 25	16 37			17 01				17 27	17 38				18 19	18 36
Taunton	d		15 12			15 52		16 00		16 31	16 40	16 52	16 59		17 15				17 42	17 52		18 18		18 34	18 49
Bridgwater	a												17 09									18 29			
Weston-super-Mare	a							16 20			17 00		17 28									18 48			
Bristol Temple Meads 10	a					16 26		16 49			17 20	17 26	17 56						18 17	18 27		19 17			19 24
Bath Spa 7	a										17 41		18 11						18 41						
Filton Abbey Wood	a																								
Bristol Parkway 7	a					16 39		17 08				17 39								18 38					19 38
Swindon	a										18 10		18 40						19 10						
Newport (South Wales)	a																								
Cardiff Central 7	a																								
Birmingham New Street 12	a					17 48		18 28				18 48								19 48					20 49
Castle Cary	d		15 34												17 37										
Frome	d																								
Westbury	d		15 52												17 56										
Pewsey	d		16 10												18 13										
Hungerford	a																								
Newbury	a		16 31												18 33										
Thatcham	a																								
Theale	a																								
Reading 7	a		16 49							17 49	18 46		19 14		18 49				19 42					19 49	
Slough 3	a																								
London Paddington 15 ⊖	a		17 30							18 30	19 22		19 58		19 29				20 23					20 29	

A 🛒 from Plymouth

For connections to Oxford, Gatwick Airport and Heathrow Airport please see Tables 116, 148 and 125A

For connections from Swansea please see Table 128. For connections from Plymouth and Exeter St Davids please see Table 135. For connections to Bournemouth please see Table 158

Table 135R

Sundays

8 December to 29 December

Cornwall and Devon - Birmingham and London

Route Diagram - see first Page of Table 135

		GW	GW	XC	GW	GW	XC	GW	GW	GW	GW	GW	GW	GW	GW	GW	GW
																	R
			◇1	◇1	◇1		◇1		◇1		◇1						
				A													B
																	🛏
			☕	🛒	☕		🛒		☕		☕						☕
Penzance	d				16 10				17 25				19 00	20 05			21 15
St Erth	d				16 21				17 34				19 09	20 14			21 25
Hayle	d													20 17			
Camborne	d				16 33				17 46				19 20	20 26			21 38
Redruth	d				16 40				17 53				19 26	20 32			21 45
Truro	d				16 53				18 05				19 38	20 44			22 00
St Austell	d				17 10				18 24				19 55	21 01			22 18
Newquay	d					17 30											
Par	d				17 17	18a19			18 32				20 03	21 09			
Lostwithiel	d												20 09				
Bodmin Parkway	d				17 29				18 43				20 15	21 21			22 35
Liskeard 6	d				17 42				18 56				20 28	21 35			22 50
Menheniot	d												20x33				
St Germans	d												20 41				
Saltash	d				18 00								20 47				
St Budeaux Ferry Road	d																
Keyham	d																
Dockyard	d																
Devonport	d												20 54				
Plymouth	a				18 10				19 21				21 00	22 00			23 15
	d		17 45		18 10		18 24		19 25		19 55		21 15				23 20
Ivybridge	d																
Totnes	d		18 13		18 40		18 50		19 52				21 42				23 48
Paignton	d	17 49		18 20				18 55		19 55		20 55			21 52	23 00	
Torquay	d	17 54		18 26				19 00		20 00		21 00			21 57	23 05	
Torre	d	17 57						19 03		20 03		21 03			22 00	23 08	
Newton Abbot	a	18 05	18 25	18 36	18 52		19 01	19 11	20 04	20 11	20 31	21 11	21 54		22 08	23 16	23 59
	d	18 07	18 26	18 37	18 52		19 03	19 13	20 05	20 13	20 32	21 13	21 55		22 09	23 18	00 01
Teignmouth	d	18 14						19 20		20 20		21 20	22 02		22 16	23 25	
Dawlish	d	18 19						19 25		20 25		21 25	22 07		22 21	23 30	
Dawlish Warren	d	18 24						19 30		20 30					22 26	23 35	
Starcross	d	18 28						19 34		20 34					22 30	23 39	
Exeter St Thomas	d	18 37						19 43		20 43					22 39	23 48	
Exeter St Davids 6	a	18 40	18 47	18 56	19 14		19 22	19 48	20 25	20 49	20 53	21 40	22 21		22 42	23 52	00 23
Exeter Central	a	18 53						19 54		20 55		21 51			22 51		
Exmouth	a	19 19						20 21		21 22		22 18			23 18		
Exeter St Davids 6	d		18 49	18 58	19 16		19 24		20 26		20 55						01 06
Tiverton Parkway	d			19 11	19 31		19 37		20 42		21 10						
Taunton	d		19 15	19 24	19 45		19 52		20 55		21 23						
Bridgwater	a																
Weston-super-Mare	a																
Bristol Temple Meads 10	a			19 57			20 25				21 55						
Bath Spa 7	a										22 22						
Filton Abbey Wood	a																
Bristol Parkway 7	a			20 08			20 39										
Swindon	a										22 50						
Newport (South Wales)	a																
Cardiff Central 7	a																
Birmingham New Street 12	a			21 18			21 48										
Castle Cary	d				20 07				21 19								
Frome	d																
Westbury	d		19 51		20 27				21 40								
Pewsey	d								21 58								
Hungerford	a																
Newbury	a		20 24						22 18								
Thatcham	a																
Theale	a																
Reading 7	a		20 49		21 19				22 39		23 29						04s04
Slough 3	a																
London Paddington 15 ⊖	a		21 29		22 00				23 18		00 13						05 08

A 🛒 to Bristol Temple Meads

B The Night Riviera

For connections to Oxford, Gatwick Airport and Heathrow Airport please see Tables 116, 148 and 125A

For connections from Swansea please see Table 128. For connections from Plymouth and Exeter St Davids please see Table 135. For connections to Bournemouth please see Table 158

Table 135R

Sundays

5 January to 9 February

Cornwall and Devon - Birmingham and London

Route Diagram - see first Page of Table 135

		GW ◇	GW ◇1 🍴	GW ◇	GW ◇1 🍴	XC ◇1 🛒	GW	GW ■ 1 🍴	XC ◇1 🛒	XC ◇1 🛒		GW	GW ◇1 🍴	XC ◇1 🛒	GW	GW ■ 1 🍴	GW ◇	XC ◇1 🛒	GW	XC ◇1 🛒		XC ◇1 🛒	GW ■ 1 🍴	GW	XC ◇1 🛒
Penzance	d												08 35	09 30		09 47							11 00	11 45	
St Erth	d												08 44	09 38		09 57							11 10	11a53	
Hayle	d												08 49												
Camborne	d												09 00	09 48		10 08							11 23		
Redruth	d												09 06	09 54		10 14							11 29		
Truro	d												09 20	10 06		10 27							11 42		
St Austell	d												09 36	10 22		10 44							11 59		
Newquay	d																11 12								
Par	d												09 45	10 30		10 53	12a01						12 07		
Lostwithiel	d																								
Bodmin Parkway	d												09 57	10 40		11 06							12 19		
Liskeard 6	d												10 10	10 53		11 19							12 33		
Menheniot	d																								
St Germans	d															11 30									
Saltash	d												10 28												
St Budeaux Ferry Road	d																								
Keyham	d																								
Dockyard	d																								
Devonport	d																								
Plymouth	a												10 35	11 17		11 44							12 58		
	d				08 40	09 25		10 10	10 25				10 40	11 25		11 45		12 00				12 52	13 00		13 24
Ivybridge	d																								
Totnes	d				09 07	09 50		10 40	10 50				11 07	11 50		12 15							13 28		13 50
Paignton	d						09 49			10 50		11 00			11 49				12 57						
Torquay	d						09 54			10 56		11 05			11 54				13 02						
Torre	d						09 57					11 08			11 57				13 05						
Newton Abbot	a				09 19	10 01	10 05	10 52	11 01	11 06		11 16	11 19	12 01	12 05	12 28		12 34	13 13			13 26	13 40		14 01
	d				09 21	10 03	10 07	10 54	11 03	11 08		11 25	11 21	12 03	12 07	12 29		12 36	13 15			13 27	13 41		14 03
Teignmouth	d				09 28		10 14			11 15		11 32			12 14				13 22						
Dawlish	d				09 34		10 19			11 20		11 37			12 19				13 27						
Dawlish Warren	d						10 24								12 24										
Starcross	d						10 28								12 28										
Exeter St Thomas	d						10 37								12 37										
Exeter St Davids 6	a				09 47	10 21	10 41	11 14	11 21	11 31		11 51	11 41	12 21	12 42	12 49		12 55	13 41			13 46	14 01		14 22
Exeter Central	a						10 49					11 58			12 51				13 51						
Exmouth	a						11 18					12 25			13 20				14 18						
Exeter St Davids 6	d	08 01	08 43	09 33	09 49	10 23		11 18	11 23	11 33			11 43	12 23		12 50		12 57		13 23		13 48	14 03		14 24
Tiverton Parkway	d	08 18	08 58	09 51		10 37		11 33	11 37	11 47			11 58	12 37				13 11		13 37			14 17		14 38
Taunton	d	08 35	09 12	10 09	10 14	10 51		11 48	11 52	12 01			12 12	12 51		13 16		13 25		13 51			14 32		14 52
Bridgwater	a	08 46		10 21																					
Weston-super-Mare	a	09 06		10 39						12 20															
Bristol Temple Meads 10	a	09 38		11 09		11 24		12 23	12 27	12 44				13 26				13 57		14 23		14 40			15 26
Bath Spa 7	a							12 37																	
Filton Abbey Wood	a																								
Bristol Parkway 7	a					11 38			12 38	13 08				13 38				14 08		14 38		15 08			15 39
Swindon	a							13 05																	
Newport (South Wales)	a																								
Cardiff Central 7	a																								
Birmingham New Street 12	a					12 49			13 48	14 27				14 48				15 27		15 48		16 26			16 49
Castle Cary	d		09 34										12 33												
Frome	d																								
Westbury	d		09 54		10 52								12 53			13 59									
Pewsey	d		10 11										13 10												
Hungerford	a																								
Newbury	a		10 31		11 26								13 30												
Thatcham	a																								
Theale	a																								
Reading 7	a		10 48		11 45			13 45					13 50			14 49							15 49		
Slough 3	a																								
London Paddington 15 ⊖	a		11 29		12 29			14 26					14 30			15 30							16 34		

For connections to Oxford, Gatwick Airport and Heathrow Airport please see Tables 116, 148 and 125A

For connections from Swansea please see Table 128. For connections from Plymouth and Exeter St Davids please see Table 135. For connections to Bournemouth please see Table 158

Table 135R

Sundays

5 January to 9 February

Cornwall and Devon - Birmingham and London

Route Diagram - see first Page of Table 135

		GW	GW	GW	GW	XC	XC	GW	GW	GW	XC	GW	GW	GW	GW	GW	GW	XC	GW	GW	GW	GW	XC
			◇1 (restaurant)			◇1 (trolley)	◇1 A (trolley)		R 1 (restaurant)	R 1 (restaurant)	◇1 (trolley)	◇1 (restaurant)		◇1 (restaurant)	◇		◇1 (restaurant)	◇1 (trolley)		◇	◇	R 1 (restaurant)	◇1 A (trolley)
Penzance	d				12 05		12 30		12 56						13 41					14 40		15 00	15 30
St Erth	d				12 14		12 40		13 06						13 51					14 50		15 10	15 38
Hayle	d						12 44								13 54					14 53			
Camborne	d				12 25		12 56		13 19						14 04					15 02		15 22	15 49
Redruth	d				12 31		13 02		13 25						14 10					15 08		15 29	15 55
Truro	d				12 43		13 14		13 38						14 21					15 19		15 41	16 07
St Austell	d				12 59		13 30		13 56						14 38					15 36		15 59	16 23
Newquay	d																				15 10		
Par	d				13 06		13 38		14 03						14 45					15 43	15a59	16 07	16 31
Lostwithiel	d				13 13		13 45								14 52					15 50			
Bodmin Parkway	d				13 19		13 51		14 16						14 58					15 56		16 18	16 41
Liskeard 6	d				13 33		14 04		14 29						15 11					16 09		16 31	16 53
Menheniot	d				13x38																		
St Germans	d				13 46										15 21					16 19			
Saltash	d				13 54										15 29					16 27			
St Budeaux Ferry Road	d																						
Keyham	d																						
Dockyard	d																						
Devonport	d																						
Plymouth	a				14 03		14 28		14 54						15 38					16 37		16 57	17 17
	d		13 44		14 07	14 24	14 35		14 55	15 10	15 24			15 43	15 49		16 10	16 25		16 38		17 00	17 25
Ivybridge	d				14 22										16 07					16 53			
Totnes	d		14 11		14 36	14 50	15 00		15 25		15 50			16 10	16 21		16 37	16 49		17 07		17 28	17 50
Paignton	d	13 50		14 19				14 57				15 45	15 55			16 23			16 55				
Torquay	d	13 55		14 24				15 02				15 51	16 00			16 28			17 00				
Torre	d	13 58		14 27				15 05				15 56	16 03			16 31			17 03				
Newton Abbot	a	14 06	14 23	14 35	14 48	15 01	15 11	15 13	15 37	15 46	16 01	16 04	16 11	16 22	16 33	16 39	16 49	17 00	17 11	17 19		17 39	18 01
	d	14 07	14 25	14 37	14 49	15 03	15 12	15 15	15 38	15 48	16 03	16 05	16 12	16 23	16 34	16 40	16 50	17 02	17 12	17 20		17 40	18 02
Teignmouth	d	14 14		14 44	14 56			15 22				16 13	16 19			16 47			17 19	17 27			
Dawlish	d	14 19		14 49	15 01			15 27				16 18	16 24			16 52			17 24	17 32			
Dawlish Warren	d	14 24		14 54									16 28			17 03			17 29				
Starcross	d	14 28		14 58												17 07							
Exeter St Thomas	d	14 37		15 07												17 16							
Exeter St Davids 6	a	14 40	14 44	15 12	15 16	15 22	15 31	15 41	15 58	16 08	16 22	16 32	16 40	16 44	16 55	17 21	17 10	17 22	17 41	17 45		18 01	18 20
Exeter Central	a	14 53		15 17				15 53					16 51			17 26			17 51				
Exmouth	a	15 20						16 20					17 18						18 18				
Exeter St Davids 6	d		14 47			15 24	15 33		16 01	16 10	16 24	16 34		16 45			17 12	17 24		17 47		18 02	18 22
Tiverton Parkway	d					15 37	15 46		16 16	16 25	16 37			17 01			17 27	17 38				18 19	18 36
Taunton	d		15 12			15 52	16 00		16 31	16 40	16 52	16 59		17 15			17 42	17 52		18 18		18 34	18 49
Bridgwater	a											17 09								18 29			
Weston-super-Mare	a						16 20			17 00		17 28								18 48			
Bristol Temple Meads 10	a					16 26	16 49			17 20	17 26	17 56					18 17	18 27		19 17			19 24
Bath Spa 7	a									17 36		18 11					18 31						
Filton Abbey Wood	a																						
Bristol Parkway 7	a					16 39	17 08				17 39							18 39					19 38
Swindon	a									18 05		18 40					18 59						
Newport (South Wales)	a																						
Cardiff Central 7	a																						
Birmingham New Street 12	a					17 48	18 28				18 48							19 49					20 49
Castle Cary	d		15 34											17 37									
Frome	d																						
Westbury	d		15 52											17 56									
Pewsey	d		16 10											18 13									
Hungerford	a																						
Newbury	a		16 31											18 33									
Thatcham	a																						
Theale	a																						
Reading 7	a		16 49						17 49	18 46		19 20		18 49			19 42					19 49	
Slough 3	a																						
London Paddington 15 ⊖	a		17 27						18 30	19 27		19 58		19 29			20 19					20 30	

A (trolley) from Plymouth

For connections to Oxford, Gatwick Airport and Heathrow Airport please see Tables 116, 148 and 125A

For connections from Swansea please see Table 128. For connections from Plymouth and Exeter St Davids please see Table 135. For connections to Bournemouth please see Table 158

Table 135R

Sundays

5 January to 9 February

Cornwall and Devon - Birmingham and London

Route Diagram - see first Page of Table 135

		GW	GW	XC	GW	GW	XC	GW	GW	GW	GW	GW	GW	GW	GW	GW	GW
			◇1	◇1 A	◇1		◇1		◇1		◇1						R B 🛏
			🍽	🛒	🍽		🛒		🍽		🍽						🍽
Penzance	d				16 10				17 25				19 00	20 05			21 15
St Erth	d				16 21				17 34				19 09	20 14			21 25
Hayle	d													20 17			
Camborne	d				16 33				17 46				19 20	20 26			21 38
Redruth	d				16 40				17 53				19 26	20 32			21 45
Truro	d				16 53				18 05				19 38	20 44			22 00
St Austell	d				17 10				18 24				19 55	21 01			22 18
Newquay	d					17 30											
Par	d				17 17	18a19			18 32				20 03	21 09			
Lostwithiel	d												20 09				
Bodmin Parkway	d				17 29				18 43				20 15	21 21			22 35
Liskeard 6	d				17 42				18 56				20 28	21 35			22 50
Menheniot	d												20x33				
St Germans	d												20 41				
Saltash	d				18 00								20 47				
St Budeaux Ferry Road	d																
Keyham	d																
Dockyard	d																
Devonport	d												20 54				
Plymouth	a				18 10				19 21				21 00	22 00			23 15
	d		17 45		18 10		18 24		19 25		19 55		21 15				23 20
Ivybridge	d																
Totnes	d		18 13		18 40		18 50		19 52				21 42				23 48
Paignton	d	17 49		18 20				18 55		19 55		20 55			21 52	23 00	
Torquay	d	17 54		18 26				19 00		20 00		21 00			21 57	23 05	
Torre	d	17 57						19 03		20 03		21 03			22 00	23 08	
Newton Abbot	a	18 05	18 25	18 36	18 52		19 01	19 11	20 04	20 11	20 31	21 11	21 54		22 08	23 16	23 59
	d	18 07	18 26	18 37	18 52		19 03	19 13	20 05	20 13	20 32	21 13	21 55		22 09	23 18	00 01
Teignmouth	d	18 14						19 20		20 20		21 20	22 02		22 16	23 25	
Dawlish	d	18 19						19 25		20 25		21 25	22 07		22 21	23 30	
Dawlish Warren	d	18 24						19 30		20 30					22 26	23 35	
Starcross	d	18 28						19 34		20 34					22 30	23 39	
Exeter St Thomas	d	18 37						19 43		20 43					22 39	23 48	
Exeter St Davids 6	a	18 40	18 47	18 56	19 14		19 22	19 48	20 25	20 49	20 53	21 40	22 21		22 42	23 52	00 23
Exeter Central	a	18 53						19 54		20 55		21 51			22 51		
Exmouth	a	19 19						20 21		21 22		22 18			23 18		
Exeter St Davids 6	d		18 49	18 58	19 16		19 24		20 26		20 55						01 06
Tiverton Parkway	d			19 11	19 31		19 37		20 42		21 10						
Taunton	d		19 15	19 24	19 45		19 52		20 55		21 23						
Bridgwater	a																
Weston-super-Mare	a																
Bristol Temple Meads 10	a			19 57			20 25				21 55						
Bath Spa 7	a										22 22						
Filton Abbey Wood	a																
Bristol Parkway 7	a			20 08			20 39										
Swindon	a										22 50						
Newport (South Wales)	a																
Cardiff Central 7	a																
Birmingham New Street 12	a			21 18			21 48										
Castle Cary	d				20 07				21 19								
Frome	d																
Westbury	d		19 51		20 27				21 40								
Pewsey	d								21 58								
Hungerford	a																
Newbury	a		20 24						22 18								
Thatcham	a																
Theale	a																
Reading 7	a		20 49		21 14				22 40		23 32						04s09
Slough 3	a																
London Paddington 15 ⊖	a		21 29		22 03				23 22		00 13						05 08

A 🛒 to Bristol Temple Meads

B The Night Riviera

For connections to Oxford, Gatwick Airport and Heathrow Airport please see Tables 116, 148 and 125A

For connections from Swansea please see Table 128. For connections from Plymouth and Exeter St Davids please see Table 135. For connections to Bournemouth please see Table 158

Table 135R

Sundays

16 February to 23 March

Cornwall and Devon - Birmingham and London

Route Diagram - see first Page of Table 135

		GW	GW	XC	GW	GW	GW	GW	GW	XC	GW	XC	GW	GW	GW	GW	GW	XC	XC	GW	GW	GW	GW
			◇		◇1	◇	◇1			◇1			◇1				◇1		◇1				◇1
		bus		bus					bus		bus	bus			bus	bus		bus			bus	bus	
					buffet		buffet			trolley			buffet				buffet		trolley				buffet
Penzance	d												08 05										
St Erth	d												08 13										
Hayle	d												08 19										
Camborne	d												08 29										
Redruth	d												08 35										
Truro	d												08 49										
St Austell	d												09 05										
Newquay	d																						
Par	d												09 14										
Lostwithiel	d																						
Bodmin Parkway	d												09 26										
Liskeard [6]	d												09 39										
Menheniot	d																						
St Germans	d																						
Saltash	d												09 56										
St Budeaux Ferry Road	d																						
Keyham	d																						
Dockyard	d																						
Devonport	d																						
Plymouth	a												10 05										
	d	07 48		08 25							09 20	09 25						10 25			10 50		
Ivybridge	d																						
Totnes	d	08 33		09 10							10 05	10 10			10 29			11 10			11 35		
Paignton	d							09 49						10 30						11 36			
Torquay	d							09 54						10 35						11 41			
Torre	d							09 56						10 37						11 43			
Newton Abbot	a	08 58		09 35				10 05			10 30	10 35		10 46	10 54			11 35		11 52	12 00		
	d	08 58		09 35					10 15		10 30	10 35			10 54	11 25		11 35			12 02	12 15	
Teignmouth	d								10 33							11 43						12 33	
Dawlish	d								10 43							11 53						12 43	
Dawlish Warren	d								10 50													12 50	
Starcross	d								11 02													13 02	
Exeter St Thomas	d								11 26													13 26	
Exeter St Davids [6]	a	09 33		10 10							11 05	11 10			11 29			12 10			12 37		
Exeter Central	a								11s34							12s09						13s34	
Exmouth	a																						
Exeter St Davids [6]	d		08 01		08 43	09 33	09 43		11a39	10 23						12a14	11 15		11 23			13a39	11 39
Tiverton Parkway	d		08 18		08 58	09 51	10 01			10 37							11 33		11 37				11 58
Taunton	d		08 35		09 12	10 09	10 14			10 51							11 48		11 52				12 12
Bridgwater	a		08 46			10 21																	
Weston-super-Mare	a		09 06			10 39																	
Bristol Temple Meads [10]	a		09 38			11 09				11 24							12 23		12 27				
Bath Spa [7]	a																12 37						
Filton Abbey Wood	a																						
Bristol Parkway [7]	a									11 38									12 38				
Swindon	a																13 05						
Newport (South Wales)	a																						
Cardiff Central [7]	a																						
Birmingham New Street [12]	a									12 49									13 48				
Castle Cary	d				09 34																		12 33
Frome	d																						
Westbury	d				09 54		10 52																12 53
Pewsey	d				10 11																		13 10
Hungerford	a																						
Newbury	a				10 31		11 26																13 30
Thatcham	a																						
Theale	a																						
Reading [7]	a				10 48		11 45										13 44						13 50
Slough [3]	a																						
London Paddington [15] ⊖	a				11 29		12 29										14 23						14 30

For connections to Oxford, Gatwick Airport and Heathrow Airport please see Tables 116, 148 and 125A

For connections from Swansea please see Table 128. For connections from Plymouth and Exeter St Davids please see Table 135. For connections to Bournemouth please see Table 158

Table 135R

Sundays

16 February to 23 March

Cornwall and Devon - Birmingham and London

Route Diagram - see first Page of Table 135

		GW	XC	XC	GW	GW	GW	XC	GW	XC	XC	GW	GW	GW	GW	GW	GW	GW	XC	GW	XC	GW	GW
		◇1	🚌	◇1	◇1		🚌	◇1	🚌	◇1	🚌	◇	🚌	◇1			🚌	R 1	🚌	🚌	◇1	◇1	
		🍴		🛒	🍴			🛒						🍴				🍴			🛒	🍴	
Penzance	d	09 15								10 35				11 17	11 45								
St Erth	d	09 25								10 43				11 26	11a53								
Hayle	d																						
Camborne	d	09 36								10 53				11 38									
Redruth	d	09 42								10 59				11 44									
Truro	d	09 55								11 11				11 58									
St Austell	d	10 13								11 27				12 15									
Newquay	d											11 25											
Par	d	10 21								11 35		12a14		12 23									
Lostwithiel	d																						
Bodmin Parkway	d	10 33								11 45				12 35									
Liskeard 6	d	10 46								11 58				12 48									
Menheniot	d																						
St Germans	d	10 58																					
Saltash	d																						
St Budeaux Ferry Road	d																						
Keyham	d																						
Dockyard	d																						
Devonport	d																						
Plymouth	a	11 14								12 22				13 14									
	d		11 25						12 09		12 30		12 45						13 25				
Ivybridge	d																						
Totnes	d		12 10						12 54		13 15		13 30						14 10				
Paignton	d					12 50										13 50							14 50
Torquay	d					12 55										13 55							14 55
Torre	d					12 57										13 57							14 57
Newton Abbot	a		12 35			13 06			13 19		13 40		13 55			14 06			14 35				15 06
	d		12 35				13 15		13 19		13 40		13 55				14 15		14 35	14 45			
Teignmouth	d						13 33										14 33			15 03			
Dawlish	d						13 43										14 43			15 13			
Dawlish Warren	d																			15 20			
Starcross	d																			15 32			
Exeter St Thomas	d																			15 56			
Exeter St Davids 6	a		13 10						13 54		14 15		14 30						15 10				
Exeter Central	a						13s59										14s59			16s04			
Exmouth	a																						
Exeter St Davids 6	d			12 23	12 45		14a04	13 23									15a04	14 04		16a09	14 24	14 40	
Tiverton Parkway	d			12 37	13 03			13 37										14 21			14 38	14 58	
Taunton	d			12 51	13 16			13 51										14 36			14 52	15 12	
Bridgwater	a																						
Weston-super-Mare	a																						
Bristol Temple Meads 10	a			13 26				14 23													15 26		
Bath Spa 7	a																						
Filton Abbey Wood	a																						
Bristol Parkway 7	a			13 38				14 38													15 39		
Swindon	a																						
Newport (South Wales)	a																						
Cardiff Central 7	a																						
Birmingham New Street 12	a			14 48				15 48													16 49		
Castle Cary	d																					15 34	
Frome	d																						
Westbury	d				13 59																	15 52	
Pewsey	d																					16 10	
Hungerford	a																						
Newbury	a																					16 31	
Thatcham	a																						
Theale	a																						
Reading 7	a				14 49													15 52				16 49	
Slough 3	a																						
London Paddington 15 ⊖	a				15 30													16 30				17 30	

For connections to Oxford, Gatwick Airport and Heathrow Airport please see Tables 116, 148 and 125A

For connections from Swansea please see Table 128. For connections from Plymouth and Exeter St Davids please see Table 135. For connections to Bournemouth please see Table 158

Table 135R

Sundays

16 February to 23 March

Cornwall and Devon - Birmingham and London

Route Diagram - see first Page of Table 135

		GW	GW	GW	GW	XC	XC	XC	GW	GW	GW
		🚌	◇	🚌	🚌	◇1 🛒	🚌	◇1	🚌	◇	
Penzance	d		12 00					12 30		13 15	
St Erth	d		12 08					12 40		13 24	
Hayle	d							12 44		13 27	
Camborne	d		12 20					12 56		13 37	
Redruth	d		12 26					13 02		13 43	
Truro	d		12 37					13 14		13 54	
St Austell	d		12 54					13 30		14 11	
Newquay	d										
Par	d		13 01					13 38		14 18	
Lostwithiel	d		13 08					13 45		14 25	
Bodmin Parkway	d		13 14					13 51		14 31	
Liskeard [6]	d		13 27					14 04		14 44	
Menheniot	d		13 32								
St Germans	d		13 39							14 54	
Saltash	d		13 46							15 02	
St Budeaux Ferry Road	d										
Keyham	d										
Dockyard	d										
Devonport	d										
Plymouth	a		13 57					14 28		15 12	
	d	13 47		14 05			14 25		14 35		
Ivybridge	d	14 12									
Totnes	d	14 47		14 50			15 10		15 20		
Paignton	d										15 45
Torquay	d										15 50
Torre	d										15 52
Newton Abbot	a	15 12		15 15			15 35		15 45		16 01
	d	15 12		15 15	15 20		15 35		15 45		
Teignmouth	d				15 38						
Dawlish	d				15 48						
Dawlish Warren	d										
Starcross	d										
Exeter St Thomas	d										
Exeter St Davids [6]	a	15 47		15 50			16 10		16 20		
Exeter Central	a				16s04						
Exmouth	a										
Exeter St Davids [6]	d				16a09	15 24					
Tiverton Parkway	d					15 37					
Taunton	d					15 52					
Bridgwater	a										
Weston-super-Mare	a										
Bristol Temple Meads [10]	a					16 26					
Bath Spa [7]	a										
Filton Abbey Wood	a										
Bristol Parkway [7]	a					16 39					
Swindon	a										
Newport (South Wales)	a										
Cardiff Central [7]	a										
Birmingham New Street [12]	a					17 48					
Castle Cary	d										
Frome	d										
Westbury	d										
Pewsey	d										
Hungerford	a										
Newbury	a										
Thatcham	a										
Theale	a										
Reading [7]	a										
Slough [3]	a										
London Paddington [15] ⊖	a										

		GW	GW	GW	XC	GW	GW	XC	GW	GW	GW	GW
		🚌	B 1 🍴	🚌	🚌	◇1 🍴	◇1 🍴	◇1 🛒		🚌	◇1 🍴	🚌
Penzance	d					13 50						
St Erth	d					13 58						
Hayle	d											
Camborne	d					14 11						
Redruth	d					14 17						
Truro	d					14 30						
St Austell	d					14 47						
Newquay	d											
Par	d					14 56						
Lostwithiel	d											
Bodmin Parkway	d					15 07						
Liskeard [6]	d					15 20						
Menheniot	d											
St Germans	d											
Saltash	d					15 38						
St Budeaux Ferry Road	d											
Keyham	d											
Dockyard	d											
Devonport	d											
Plymouth	a					15 47						
	d			15 19	15 25							15 54
Ivybridge	d											16 19
Totnes	d			16 04	16 10							16 54
Paignton	d								16 30			
Torquay	d								16 35			
Torre	d								16 37			
Newton Abbot	a			16 29	16 35				16 46			17 19
	d	16 11		16 29	16 35					16 55		17 19
Teignmouth	d	16 29								17 13		
Dawlish	d	16 39								17 23		
Dawlish Warren	d	16 46										
Starcross	d	16 58										
Exeter St Thomas	d	17 22										
Exeter St Davids [6]	a			17 04	17 10							17 54
Exeter Central	a	17s30								17s39		
Exmouth	a											
Exeter St Davids [6]	d	17a35	15 57				16 07	16 24		17a44	16 30	
Tiverton Parkway	d		16 15				16 25	16 37			16 45	
Taunton	d		16 31				16 40	16 52			17 00	
Bridgwater	a										17 09	
Weston-super-Mare	a						17 00				17 28	
Bristol Temple Meads [10]	a						17 20	17 26			17 56	
Bath Spa [7]	a						17 36				18 11	
Filton Abbey Wood	a											
Bristol Parkway [7]	a							17 39				
Swindon	a						18 05				18 40	
Newport (South Wales)	a											
Cardiff Central [7]	a											
Birmingham New Street [12]	a							18 48				
Castle Cary	d											
Frome	d											
Westbury	d											
Pewsey	d											
Hungerford	a											
Newbury	a											
Thatcham	a											
Theale	a											
Reading [7]	a		17 49				18 39				19 20	
Slough [3]	a											
London Paddington [15] ⊖	a		18 30				19 22				19 58	

For connections to Oxford, Gatwick Airport and Heathrow Airport please see Tables 116, 148 and 125A

For connections from Swansea please see Table 128. For connections from Plymouth and Exeter St Davids please see Table 135. For connections to Bournemouth please see Table 158

Table 135R

Sundays

16 February to 23 March

Cornwall and Devon - Birmingham and London

Route Diagram - see first Page of Table 135

		XC	GW	GW	GW	GW	GW	GW	XC	GW	GW	GW	GW	GW	GW	XC	XC	XC	GW	GW	GW	GW	GW
		🚌	◇1 ☕	◇	◇1 ☕	◇1 ☕		🚌	◇1 🛒	🚌	◇	R 1 ☕		🚌	🚌	◇1 🛒	◇1	🚌		🚌	◇1 ☕		🚌
Penzance	d		14 30														15 30						
St Erth	d		14 40														15 38						
Hayle	d		14 44																				
Camborne	d		14 55														15 49						
Redruth	d		15 02														15 55						
Truro	d		15 15														16 07						
St Austell	d		15 33														16 23						
Newquay	d			15 10															17 10				
Par	d		15 41	15a59													16 31		17a59				
Lostwithiel	d		15 48																				
Bodmin Parkway	d		15 55														16 41						
Liskeard 6	d		16 08														16 53						
Menheniot	d																						
St Germans	d		16 19																				
Saltash	d		16 28																				
St Budeaux Ferry Road	d																						
Keyham	d																						
Dockyard	d																						
Devonport	d																						
Plymouth	a		16 38														17 16						
	d	16 25								16 52				17 00				17 20		18 00			
Ivybridge	d													17 25									
Totnes	d	17 10								17 37				18 00				18 05		18 45			
Paignton	d						17 20						18 00									18 55	
Torquay	d						17 25						18 05									19 00	
Torre	d						17 27						18 07									19 02	
Newton Abbot	a	17 35					17 36			18 02			18 16	18 25				18 30		19 10		19 11	
	d	17 35						17 46		18 02				18 25	18 30			18 30		19 10			19 20
Teignmouth	d							18 04							18 48								19 38
Dawlish	d							18 14							18 58								19 48
Dawlish Warren	d							18 21							19 05								19 55
Starcross	d							18 33							19 17								20 07
Exeter St Thomas	d							18 57							19 41								20 31
Exeter St Davids 6	a	18 10								18 32				19 00				19 05		19 45			
Exeter Central	a							19s05							19s49								20s39
Exmouth	a																						
Exeter St Davids 6	d				16 42	17 11		19a10	17 23		17 54	17 59			19a54	18 23					18 46		20a44
Tiverton Parkway	d				17 01	17 29			17 37		18 11	18 19				18 36					19 03		
Taunton	d				17 15	17 43			17 51		18 28	18 34				18 49					19 17		
Bridgwater	a										18 39												
Weston-super-Mare	a										18 58												
Bristol Temple Meads 10	a					18 17			18 26		19 36					19 24							
Bath Spa 7	a					18 31																	
Filton Abbey Wood	a																						
Bristol Parkway 7	a								18 39							19 38							
Swindon	a					18 59																	
Newport (South Wales)	a																						
Cardiff Central 7	a																						
Birmingham New Street 12	a								19 49							20 49							
Castle Cary	d				17 37																		
Frome	d																						
Westbury	d				17 56																19 54		
Pewsey	d				18 13																		
Hungerford	a																						
Newbury	a				18 33																20 26		
Thatcham	a																						
Theale	a																						
Reading 7	a				18 49	19 32						19 49									20 49		
Slough 3	a																						
London Paddington 15 ⊖	a				19 30	20 13						20 30									21 29		

For connections to Oxford, Gatwick Airport and Heathrow Airport please see Tables 116, 148 and 125A

For connections from Swansea please see Table 128. For connections from Plymouth and Exeter St Davids please see Table 135. For connections to Bournemouth please see Table 158

Table 135R

Sundays

16 February to 23 March

Cornwall and Devon - Birmingham and London

Route Diagram - see first Page of Table 135

		GW	GW	XC	GW	XC	GW	GW	GW	GW	GW	XC	GW	GW	GW	GW	GW	GW	GW	GW	GW	GW
																						R
		◇1			◇1	◇1				◇1		◇1			◇1							
																						A
			bus	bus				bus	bus					bus			bus	bus			bus	sleeper
		refreshments			refreshments					refreshments					refreshments							refreshments
Penzance	d				16 59						19 00								20 05			21 15
St Erth	d				17 09						19 09								20 14			21 25
Hayle	d																		20 17			
Camborne	d				17 22						19 20								20 26			21 38
Redruth	d				17 29						19 26								20 32			21 45
Truro	d				17 41						19 38								20 44			22 00
St Austell	d				18 00						19 55								21 01			22 18
Newquay	d																					
Par	d				18 08						20 03								21 09			
Lostwithiel	d										20 09											
Bodmin Parkway	d				18 19						20 15								21 21			22 35
Liskeard 6	d				18 32						20 28								21 35			22 50
Menheniot	d										20x33											
St Germans	d										20 41											
Saltash	d				18 49						20 48											
St Budeaux Ferry Road	d																					
Keyham	d																					
Dockyard	d																					
Devonport	d										20 56											
Plymouth	a				19 00						20 59								22 00			23 15
	d		18 29	18 40				19 08										21 15				01 50
Ivybridge	d																					
Totnes	d		19 14	19 25				19 53										22 00				02 18
Paignton	d						19 55						20 55			21 52				23 00		
Torquay	d						20 00						21 00			21 57				23 05		
Torre	d						20 02						21 02			21 59				23 07		
Newton Abbot	a		19 39	19 50			20 11	20 18					21 11			22 08		22 25		23 16		02 29
	d		19 39	19 50				20 18	20 20					21 20			22 15	22 25			23 25	02 31
Teignmouth	d								20 38					21 38			22 33	22 43			23 43	
Dawlish	d								20 48					21 48			22 43	22 55			23 53	
Dawlish Warren	d								20 55								22 50				23 59	
Starcross	d								21 07								23 02				00 12	
Exeter St Thomas	d								21 31								23 26				00 36	
Exeter St Davids 6	a		20 14	20 25				20 50										23 36				02 53
Exeter Central	a								21s39					22s04			23s34				00s44	
Exmouth	a																					
Exeter St Davids 6	d	19 13				19 23			21a44	20 23		20 44		22a09	21 00		23a39				00a49	03 02
Tiverton Parkway	d	19 31				19 35				20 42		20 58			21 17							
Taunton	d	19 45				19 50				20 55		21 11			21 32							
Bridgwater	a																					
Weston-super-Mare	a																					
Bristol Temple Meads 10	a					20 23						21 48			22 03							
Bath Spa 7	a														22 22							
Filton Abbey Wood	a																					
Bristol Parkway 7	a					20 38						22 19										
Swindon	a														22 50							
Newport (South Wales)	a																					
Cardiff Central 7	a																					
Birmingham New Street 12	a					21 49						23 40										
Castle Cary	d	20 07								21 19												
Frome	d																					
Westbury	d	20 27								21 40												
Pewsey	d									21 58												
Hungerford	a																					
Newbury	a									22 18												
Thatcham	a																					
Theale	a																					
Reading 7	a	21 19								22 37					23 29							05s11
Slough 3	a																					
London Paddington 15 ⊖	a	21 59								23 17					00 13							06 09

A The Night Riviera

For connections to Oxford, Gatwick Airport and Heathrow Airport please see Tables 116, 148 and 125A

For connections from Swansea please see Table 128. For connections from Plymouth and Exeter St Davids please see Table 135. For connections to Bournemouth please see Table 158

Table 135R

Sundays

30 March to 11 May

Cornwall and Devon - Birmingham and London

Route Diagram - see first Page of Table 135

		GW	GW	GW	GW	XC	GW	GW	XC	XC	GW	GW	XC	GW	GW	GW	XC	XC	GW	XC	GW	GW	XC
								[R]							[R]						[R]		
		◇	◇[1]	◇	◇[1]	◇[1]		[1]	◇[1]	◇[1]		◇[1]	◇[1]		[1]	◇	◇[1]	◇[1]		◇[1]	[1]		◇[1]
													A										
			[restaurant]		[restaurant]	[trolley]		[restaurant]	[trolley]	[trolley]		[restaurant]	[trolley]		[restaurant]		[trolley]	[trolley]		[trolley]	[restaurant]		[trolley]
Penzance	d											08 35	09 30		09 47						11 00	11 45	
St Erth	d											08 44	09 38		09 57						11 10	11a53	
Hayle	d											08 49											
Camborne	d											09 00	09 48		10 08						11 23		
Redruth	d											09 06	09 54		10 14						11 29		
Truro	d											09 20	10 06		10 27						11 42		
St Austell	d											09 36	10 22		10 44						11 59		
Newquay	d															11 12							
Par	d											09 45	10 30		10 53	12a01					12 07		
Lostwithiel	d																						
Bodmin Parkway	d											09 57	10 40		11 06						12 19		
Liskeard [6]	d											10 10	10 53		11 19						12 33		
Menheniot	d																						
St Germans	d														11 30								
Saltash	d											10 28											
St Budeaux Ferry Road	d																						
Keyham	d																						
Dockyard	d																						
Devonport	d																						
Plymouth	a											10 35	11 17		11 44						12 58		
	d				08 40	09 25		10 10	10 25			10 40	11 25		11 45		12 00	12 25		12 52	13 00		13 24
Ivybridge	d																						
Totnes	d				09 07	09 50		10 40	10 50			11 07	11 50		12 15			12 50			13 28		13 50
Paignton	d						09 49			10 50	11 00			11 49					12 57				
Torquay	d						09 54			10 56	11 05			11 54					13 02				
Torre	d						09 57				11 08			11 57					13 05				
Newton Abbot	a				09 19	10 01	10 05	10 52	11 01	11 06	11 16	11 19	12 01	12 05	12 28		12 34	13 01	13 13	13 26	13 40		14 01
	d				09 21	10 03	10 07	10 54	11 03	11 08	11 25	11 21	12 03	12 07	12 29		12 36	13 03	13 15	13 27	13 41		14 03
Teignmouth	d				09 28		10 14			11 15	11 32			12 14					13 22				
Dawlish	d				09 34		10 19			11 20	11 37			12 19					13 27				
Dawlish Warren	d						10 24							12 24									
Starcross	d						10 28							12 28									
Exeter St Thomas	d						10 37							12 37									
Exeter St Davids [6]	a				09 47	10 21	10 41	11 14	11 21	11 31	11 51	11 41	12 21	12 42	12 49		12 55	13 21	13 41	13 46	14 01		14 22
Exeter Central	a						10 49				11 58			12 51					13 51				
Exmouth	a						11 18				12 25			13 20					14 18				
Exeter St Davids [6]	d	08 01	08 43	09 33	09 49	10 23		11 18	11 23	11 33		11 43	12 23		12 50		12 57	13 23		13 48	14 03		14 24
Tiverton Parkway	d	08 18	08 58	09 51		10 37		11 33	11 37	11 47		11 58	12 37				13 11	13 37			14 17		14 38
Taunton	d	08 35	09 12	10 09	10 14	10 51		11 48	11 52	12 01		12 12	12 51		13 16		13 25	13 51			14 32		14 52
Bridgwater	a	08 46		10 21																			
Weston-super-Mare	a	09 06		10 39						12 20													
Bristol Temple Meads [10]	a	09 38		11 09		11 24		12 23	12 27	12 44			13 26				13 57	14 23		14 40			15 26
Bath Spa [7]	a							12 37															
Filton Abbey Wood	a																						
Bristol Parkway [7]	a					11 38			12 38	13 08			13 38				14 08	14 38		15 08			15 39
Swindon	a							13 05															
Newport (South Wales)	a																						
Cardiff Central [7]	a																						
Birmingham New Street [12]	a					12 49			13 48	14 27			14 48				15 27	15 48		16 26			16 49
Castle Cary	d		09 34									12 33											
Frome	d																						
Westbury	d		09 54		10 52							12 53			13 59								
Pewsey	d		10 11									13 10											
Hungerford	a																						
Newbury	a		10 31		11 26							13 30											
Thatcham	a																						
Theale	a																						
Reading [7]	a		10 48		11 45			13 44				13 50			14 49						15 49		
Slough [3]	a																						
London Paddington [15] ⊖	a		11 27		12 29			14 25				14 30			15 29						16 27		

A [trolley] from Plymouth

For connections to Oxford, Gatwick Airport and Heathrow Airport please see Tables 116, 148 and 125A

For connections from Swansea please see Table 128. For connections from Plymouth and Exeter St Davids please see Table 135. For connections to Bournemouth please see Table 158

Table 135R

Sundays

30 March to 11 May

Cornwall and Devon - Birmingham and London

Route Diagram - see first Page of Table 135

		GW	GW	GW	GW	XC	XC	GW	GW	GW	XC	GW	GW	GW	GW	GW	GW	XC	GW	GW	GW	GW	XC
									R	R												R	
			◇1			◇1	◇1		1	1	◇1	◇1		◇1	◇		◇1	◇1		◇	◇	1	◇1
							A																A
			🍴			🛒	🛒		🍴	🍴	🛒	🍴		🍴			🍴	🛒				🍴	🛒
Penzance	d				12 05		12 30		12 56						13 41					14 40		15 00	15 30
St Erth	d				12 14		12 40		13 06						13 51					14 50		15 10	15 38
Hayle	d						12 44								13 54					14 53			
Camborne	d				12 25		12 56		13 19						14 04					15 02		15 22	15 49
Redruth	d				12 31		13 02		13 25						14 10					15 08		15 29	15 55
Truro	d				12 43		13 14		13 38						14 21					15 19		15 41	16 07
St Austell	d				12 59		13 30		13 56						14 38					15 36		15 59	16 23
Newquay	d																				15 10		
Par	d				13 06		13 38		14 03						14 45					15 43	15a59	16 07	16 31
Lostwithiel	d				13 13		13 45								14 52					15 50			
Bodmin Parkway	d				13 19		13 51		14 16						14 58					15 56		16 18	16 41
Liskeard 6	d				13 33		14 04		14 29						15 11					16 09		16 31	16 53
Menheniot	d				13x38																		
St Germans	d				13 46										15 21					16 19			
Saltash	d				13 54										15 29					16 27			
St Budeaux Ferry Road	d																						
Keyham	d																						
Dockyard	d																						
Devonport	d																						
Plymouth	a				14 03		14 28		14 54						15 38					16 37		16 57	17 17
	d		13 44		14 07	14 24	14 35		14 55	15 10	15 24			15 43	15 49		16 08	16 25		16 38		17 00	17 25
Ivybridge	d				14 22										16 07					16 53			
Totnes	d		14 11		14 36	14 50	15 00		15 25		15 50			16 10	16 21		16 37	16 48		17 07		17 28	17 50
Paignton	d	13 50		14 19				14 57				15 45	15 55			16 23			16 55				
Torquay	d	13 55		14 24				15 02				15 51	16 00			16 28			17 00				
Torre	d	13 58		14 27				15 05				15 56	16 03			16 31			17 03				
Newton Abbot	a	14 06	14 23	14 35	14 48	15 01	15 11	15 13	15 37	15 46	16 01	16 04	16 11	16 22	16 33	16 39	16 49	16 59	17 11	17 19		17 39	18 01
	d	14 07	14 25	14 37	14 49	15 03	15 12	15 15	15 38	15 48	16 03	16 05	16 12	16 23	16 34	16 40	16 50	17 01	17 12	17 20		17 40	18 02
Teignmouth	d	14 14		14 44	14 56			15 22				16 13	16 19			16 47			17 19	17 27			
Dawlish	d	14 19		14 49	15 01			15 27				16 18	16 24			16 52			17 24	17 32			
Dawlish Warren	d	14 24		14 54									16 28			17 03			17 29				
Starcross	d	14 28		14 58												17 07							
Exeter St Thomas	d	14 37		15 07												17 16							
Exeter St Davids 6	a	14 40	14 44	15 12	15 16	15 22	15 31	15 41	15 58	16 08	16 22	16 32	16 40	16 44	16 55	17 21	17 10	17 22	17 41	17 45		18 01	18 20
Exeter Central	a	14 53		15 17				15 53					16 51			17 26			17 51				
Exmouth	a	15 20						16 20					17 18						18 18				
Exeter St Davids 6	d		14 47			15 24	15 33		16 01	16 10	16 24	16 34		16 45			17 12	17 24		17 47		18 02	18 22
Tiverton Parkway	d					15 37	15 46		16 16	16 25	16 37			17 01			17 27	17 38				18 19	18 36
Taunton	d		15 12			15 52	16 00		16 31	16 40	16 52	16 59		17 15			17 42	17 52		18 18		18 34	18 49
Bridgwater	a											17 09								18 29			
Weston-super-Mare	a						16 20			17 00		17 28								18 48			
Bristol Temple Meads 10	a					16 26	16 49			17 20	17 26	17 56					18 15	18 27		19 17			19 24
Bath Spa 7	a									17 36		18 11					18 31						
Filton Abbey Wood	a																						
Bristol Parkway 7	a					16 39	17 08				17 39							18 38					19 38
Swindon	a									18 05		18 40					18 59						
Newport (South Wales)	a																						
Cardiff Central 7	a																						
Birmingham New Street 12	a					17 48	18 28				18 48							19 48					20 49
Castle Cary	d		15 34											17 37									
Frome	d																						
Westbury	d		15 52											17 56									
Pewsey	d		16 10											18 13									
Hungerford	a																						
Newbury	a		16 31											18 33									
Thatcham	a																						
Theale	a																						
Reading 7	a		16 49						17 49	18 39		19 20		18 49			19 33					19 49	
Slough 3	a																						
London Paddington 15 ⊖	a		17 30						18 30	19 25		19 57		19 29			20 22					20 29	

A 🛒 from Plymouth

For connections to Oxford, Gatwick Airport and Heathrow Airport please see Tables 116, 148 and 125A

For connections from Swansea please see Table 128. For connections from Plymouth and Exeter St Davids please see Table 135. For connections to Bournemouth please see Table 158

Table 135R

Sundays

30 March to 11 May

Cornwall and Devon - Birmingham and London

Route Diagram - see first Page of Table 135

		GW	GW	XC	GW	GW	XC	GW	GW	GW	GW	GW	GW	GW	GW	GW	GW
			◇1	◇1	◇1		◇1		◇1		◇1						
				A													B
Penzance	d				16 10				17 25				19 00	20 05			21 15
St Erth	d				16 21				17 34				19 09	20 14			21 25
Hayle	d													20 17			
Camborne	d				16 33				17 46				19 20	20 26			21 38
Redruth	d				16 40				17 53				19 26	20 32			21 45
Truro	d				16 53				18 05				19 38	20 44			22 00
St Austell	d				17 10				18 24				19 55	21 01			22 18
Newquay	d					17 30											
Par	d				17 17	18a19			18 32				20 03	21 09			
Lostwithiel	d												20 09				
Bodmin Parkway	d				17 29				18 43				20 15	21 21			22 35
Liskeard 6	d				17 42				18 56				20 28	21 35			22 50
Menheniot	d												20x33				
St Germans	d												20 41				
Saltash	d				18 00								20 47				
St Budeaux Ferry Road	d																
Keyham	d																
Dockyard	d																
Devonport	d												20 54				
Plymouth	a				18 10				19 21				21 00	22 00			23 15
	d		17 45		18 10		18 24		19 25		19 55		21 15				23 20
Ivybridge	d																
Totnes	d		18 13		18 40		18 50		19 52				21 42				23 48
Paignton	d	17 49		18 20				18 55		19 55		20 55			21 52	23 00	
Torquay	d	17 54		18 26				19 00		20 00		21 00			21 57	23 05	
Torre	d	17 57						19 03		20 03		21 03			22 00	23 08	
Newton Abbot	a	18 05	18 25	18 36	18 52		19 01	19 11	20 04	20 11	20 31	21 11	21 54		22 08	23 16	23 59
	d	18 07	18 26	18 37	18 52		19 03	19 13	20 05	20 13	20 32	21 13	21 55		22 09	23 18	00 01
Teignmouth	d	18 14						19 20		20 20		21 20	22 02		22 16	23 25	
Dawlish	d	18 19						19 25		20 25		21 25	22 07		22 21	23 30	
Dawlish Warren	d	18 24						19 30		20 30					22 26	23 35	
Starcross	d	18 28						19 34		20 34					22 30	23 39	
Exeter St Thomas	d	18 37						19 43		20 43					22 39	23 48	
Exeter St Davids 6	a	18 40	18 47	18 56	19 14		19 22	19 48	20 25	20 49	20 53	21 40	22 21		22 42	23 52	00 23
Exeter Central	a	18 53						19 54		20 55		21 51			22 51		
Exmouth	a	19 19						20 21		21 22		22 18			23 18		
Exeter St Davids 6	d		18 49	18 58	19 16		19 24		20 26		20 55						01 06
Tiverton Parkway	d			19 11	19 31		19 37		20 42		21 10						
Taunton	d		19 15	19 24	19 45		19 52		20 55		21 23						
Bridgwater	a																
Weston-super-Mare	a																
Bristol Temple Meads 10	a			19 57			20 25				21 55						
Bath Spa 7	a										22 22						
Filton Abbey Wood	a																
Bristol Parkway 7	a			20 08			20 39										
Swindon	a										22 50						
Newport (South Wales)	a																
Cardiff Central 7	a																
Birmingham New Street 12	a			21 18			21 48										
Castle Cary	d				20 07				21 19								
Frome	d																
Westbury	d		19 51		20 27				21 40								
Pewsey	d								21 58								
Hungerford	a																
Newbury	a		20 24						22 18								
Thatcham	a																
Theale	a																
Reading 7	a		20 49		21 14				22 40		23 29						04s03
Slough 3	a																
London Paddington 15 ⊖	a		21 29		21 52				23 23		00 06						05 08

A to Bristol Temple Meads

B The Night Riviera

For connections to Oxford, Gatwick Airport and Heathrow Airport please see Tables 116, 148 and 125A

For connections from Swansea please see Table 128. For connections from Plymouth and Exeter St Davids please see Table 135. For connections to Bournemouth please see Table 158

Table 135A

Redruth - Helston

Bus Service

Mondays to Fridays

9 December to 16 May

Route Diagram - see first Page of Table 135

		GW	GW	GW	GW	GW	GW	GW	GW	GW	GW	GW	GW	GW	GW	GW	GW
		BHX	BHX		BHX	BHX		BHX	BHX		BHX	BHX		BHX	BHX		BHX
		A	A	B	A	A	B	A	A	B	A	A	B	C	A	B	A
		🚌	🚌	🚌	🚌	🚌	🚌	🚌	🚌	🚌	🚌	🚌	🚌	🚌	🚌	🚌	🚌
Redruth	d	08 00	09 10	10 00	10 10	11 10	11 55	12 10	13 10	13 55	14 10	15 10	15 55	16 10	17 10	18 00	18 20
Helston Coinagehall St	a	08 34	09 42	10 32	10 42	11 42	12 27	12 42	13 42	14 27	14 42	15 42	16 27	16 42	17 42	18 32	18 52

Saturdays

14 December to 17 May

		GW	GW		GW	GW
		🚌	🚌	and hourly until	🚌	🚌
Redruth	d	08 00	09 10		17 10	18 20
Helston Coinagehall St	a	08 29	09 42		17 42	18 52

Sundays

8 December to 11 May

		GW	GW	GW	GW	GW
		🚌	🚌	🚌	🚌	🚌
Redruth	d	10 00	11 55	13 55	15 55	18 00
Helston Coinagehall St	a	10 32	12 27	14 27	16 27	18 32

A not 25 December, 26 December, 1 January, 18 April, 21 April, 5 May

B 1 January, 18 April, 21 April, 5 May

C not 25 December, 26 December, 1 January, 18 April, 21 April, 5 May. Runs during College Holidays only.

Table 135A-R

Mondays to Fridays

9 December to 16 May

Helston - Redruth

Bus Service

Route Diagram - see first Page of Table 135

		GW	GW	GW	GW	GW	GW	GW	GW	GW
		BHX	BHX	BHX		BHX	BHX		BHX	BHX
		A	A	A	B	A	A	B	A	A
Helston Coinagehall St	d	07 10	08 10	09 30	10 20	10 30	11 30	12 20	12 30	13 30
Redruth	a	07 44	08 55	10 04	10 57	11 04	12 04	12 57	13 04	14 04

		GW	GW	GW	GW	GW	GW	GW	GW
			BHX	BHX	BHX		BHX	BHX	
		B	A	C	D	B	A	A	B
Helston Coinagehall St	d	14 20	14 30	15 15	15 35	16 20	16 35	17 40	18 20
Redruth	a	14 57	15 04	15 59	16 09	16 57	17 09	18 14	18 57

Saturdays

14 December to 17 May

		GW	GW	GW	and hourly until	GW	GW	GW	GW
Helston Coinagehall St	d	07 10	08 10	09 30		14 30	15 35	16 35	17 40
Redruth	a	07 44	08 44	10 04		15 04	16 09	17 09	18 14

Sundays

8 December to 11 May

		GW	GW	GW	GW	GW
Helston Coinagehall St	d	10 20	12 20	14 20	16 20	18 20
Redruth	a	10 57	12 57	14 57	16 57	18 57

A not 25 December, 26 December, 1 January, 18 April, 21 April, 5 May

B 1 January, 18 April, 21 April, 5 May

C not 25 December, 26 December, 1 January, 18 April, 21 April, 5 May. Runs on Schooldays only.

D not 25 December, 26 December, 1 January, 18 April, 21 April, 5 May. Runs during School Holidays only.

Table 135B

Mondays to Fridays

9 December to 16 May

St. Austell - Eden Project

Bus Service

Route Diagram - see first Page of Table 135

		GW	GW	GW	GW	GW	GW	GW	GW	GW	GW	GW	GW	GW	GW	GW	GW	GW
		BHX		BHX		BHX		BHX	BHX		BHX		BHX		BHX		BHX	
		A	B	A	B	A	B	A	C	B	A	B	A	B	A	B	A	B
		🚌	🚌	🚌	🚌	🚌	🚌	🚌	🚌	🚌	🚌	🚌	🚌	🚌	🚌	🚌	🚌	🚌
St Austell	d	08 45	08 50	09 30	10 35	10 40	11 40	11 50	12 30	13 35	13 55	14 45	15 02	15 35	16 10	16 25	17 05	17 10
Eden Project	a	09 04	09 09	09 49	10 54	10 59	11 59	12 09	12 49	13 54	14 14	15 04	15 21	15 54	16 29	16 44	17 24	17 29

Saturdays

14 December to 17 May

		GW	GW	GW	GW	GW	GW	GW	GW
		🚌	🚌	🚌	🚌	🚌	🚌	🚌	🚌
St Austell	d	08 45	09 30	10 40	12 05	13 55	15 02	15 50	17 00
Eden Project	a	09 04	09 49	10 59	12 24	14 14	15 21	16 09	17 19

Sundays

8 December to 11 May

		GW	GW	GW	GW	GW	GW	GW	GW	GW
		🚌	🚌	🚌	🚌	🚌	🚌	🚌	🚌	🚌
St Austell	d	08 50	10 35	11 40	12 30	13 35	14 45	15 35	16 25	17 10
Eden Project	a	09 09	10 54	11 59	12 49	13 54	15 04	15 54	16 44	17 29

A not 25 December, 26 December, 1 January, 18 April, 21 April, 5 May

B 1 January, 18 April, 21 April, 5 May

C not 25 December, 26 December

Table 135B-R

Mondays to Fridays

9 December to 16 May

Eden Project - St. Austell

Bus Service

Route Diagram - see first Page of Table 135

		GW	GW		GW	GW	GW	GW	GW	GW	GW	GW	GW		GW	GW	GW	GW	GW
		BHX			BHX		BHX		BHX	BHX					BHX		BHX		
		A	B		A	B	A	B	A	A	B	C	B		A	B	A	B	C
Eden Project	d	09 10	09 50		09 55	11 00	11 15	12 00	12 10	13 00	13 05	14 25	15 15		15 22	16 05	16 30	16 50	18 00
St Austell	a	09 29	10 09		10 14	11 19	11 34	12 19	12 29	13 19	13 24	14 44	15 34		15 41	16 24	16 49	17 09	18 19

Saturdays

14 December to 17 May

		GW	GW	GW	GW	GW	GW	GW	GW
Eden Project	d	09 10	09 55	11 15	13 15	14 25	15 22	16 25	17 55
St Austell	a	09 29	10 14	11 34	13 34	14 44	15 41	16 44	18 14

Sundays

8 December to 11 May

		GW	GW	GW	GW	GW	GW	GW	GW	GW
Eden Project	d	09 50	11 00	12 00	13 05	14 25	15 15	16 05	16 50	18 00
St Austell	a	10 09	11 19	12 19	13 24	14 44	15 34	16 24	17 09	18 19

A not 25 December, 26 December, 1 January, 18 April, 21 April, 5 May

B 1 January, 18 April, 21 April, 5 May

C not 25 December, 26 December

Table 135C

Mondays to Saturdays

9 December to 17 May

Bodmin - Wadebridge and Padstow

Bus Service

Route Diagram - see first Page of Table 135

		GW	GW	GW	GW	GW	GW	GW	GW	GW	GW	GW	GW	GW	GW
		BHX	BHX		BHX	BHX	BHX		BHX		BHX		BHX		BHX
		A	A	B	A	B	A	B	A	B	A	B	A	B	A
		Bus	Bus	Bus	Bus	Bus	Bus	Bus	Bus	Bus	Bus	Bus	Bus	Bus	Bus
Bodmin Parkway	d	07 30	08 30	09 30	10 30	11 30	12 30	13 30	14 30	15 30	16 30	17 30	18 30	19 30	22 10
Bodmin Mount Folly	a	07 40	08 40	09 40	10 40	11 40	12 40	13 40	14 40	15 40	16 40	17 40	18 40	19 40	22 20
Wadebridge Bus Station	a	08 00	09 00	10 00	11 00	12 00	13 00	14 00	15 00	16 00	17 00	18 00	19 00	20 00	22 40
Padstow Old Rly Station	a	08 27	09 27	10 27	11 27	12 27	13 27	14 27	15 27	16 27	17 27	18 27	19 27	20 27	23 07

Sundays

8 December to 11 May

		GW	GW	GW	GW	GW	GW
		Bus	Bus	Bus	Bus	Bus	Bus
Bodmin Parkway	d	09 30	11 30	13 30	15 30	17 30	19 30
Bodmin Mount Folly	a	09 40	11 40	13 40	15 40	17 40	19 40
Wadebridge Bus Station	a	10 00	12 00	14 00	16 00	18 00	20 00
Padstow Old Rly Station	a	10 27	12 27	14 27	16 27	18 27	20 27

A not 25 December, 26 December, 1 January, 18 April, 21 April, 5 May

B not 25 December, 26 December, 1 January

Table 135C-R

Mondays to Saturdays

9 December to 17 May

Padstow and Wadebridge - Bodmin

Bus Service

Route Diagram - see first Page of Table 135

		GW	GW	GW	GW	GW	GW	GW	GW	GW	GW	GW	GW	GW	GW
		A	A	B	A	B	A	B	A	B	A	B	A	B	A
		🚌	🚌	🚌	🚌	🚌	🚌	🚌	🚌	🚌	🚌	🚌	🚌	🚌	🚌
Padstow Old Rly Station	d	06 30	07 30	08 30	09 30	10 30	11 30	12 30	13 30	14 30	15 30	16 30	17 30	18 30	20 30
Wadebridge Bus Station	d	06 55	07 55	08 55	09 55	10 55	11 55	12 55	13 55	14 55	15 55	16 55	17 55	18 55	20 55
Bodmin Mount Folly	d	07 15	08 15	09 15	10 15	11 15	12 15	13 15	14 15	15 15	16 15	17 15	18 15	19 15	21 15
Bodmin Parkway	a	07 25	08 25	09 25	10 25	11 25	12 25	13 25	14 25	15 25	16 25	17 25	18 25	19 25	21 25

Sundays

8 December to 11 May

		GW	GW	GW	GW	GW	GW
		🚌	🚌	🚌	🚌	🚌	🚌
Padstow Old Rly Station	d	08 30	10 30	12 30	14 30	16 30	18 30
Wadebridge Bus Station	d	08 55	10 55	12 55	14 55	16 55	18 55
Bodmin Mount Folly	d	09 15	11 15	13 15	15 15	17 15	19 15
Bodmin Parkway	a	09 25	11 25	13 25	15 25	17 25	19 25

A not 25 December, 26 December, 1 January, 18 April, 21 April, 5 May

B not 25 December, 26 December, 1 January

Table 135D

Mondays to Saturdays

9 December to 17 May

Exeter - Okehampton, Holsworthy and Bude

Bus Service

Route Diagram - see first Page of Table 135

		GW	GW	GW	GW	GW	GW	GW	GW	GW	GW	GW	GW	GW	GW	GW	GW
					SX	SO											
		BHX	BHX	BHX	BHX			BHX	BHX			BHX	BHX	BHX			
		A	A	A	A		B	A	A	B	B	A	A	A	A	B	A
Exeter St Davids	d	06 45	07 57	09 30	09 45	09 45	10 30	11 30	11 43	12 30	13 30	13 43	14 30	15 30	15 45	16 30	17 00
Okehampton West Street	a	07 23	08 42	10 10	10 23	10 25	11 22	12 10	12 23	13 22	14 10	14 23	15 22	16 10	16 23	17 22	17 52
Holsworthy Library	a	08 01			11 01	11 03			13 01	14 02		15 01			17 01		
Holsworthy Cattle Market	a																
Bude Strand	a	08 35			11 25	11 25			13 25	14 25		15 25			17 25		

		GW	GW	GW	GW
		BHX	BHX		BHX
		B	A	B	A
Exeter St Davids	d	17 30	17 55	18 00	19 00
Okehampton West Street	a	18 10	18 33	18 52	19 52
Holsworthy Library	a		19 11	19 32	
Holsworthy Cattle Market	a				
Bude Strand	a		19 35	19 55	

Sundays

8 December to 11 May

		GW	GW	GW	GW	GW	GW
Exeter St Davids	d	10 30	12 30	13 30	16 30	17 30	18 00
Okehampton West Street	a	11 22	13 22	14 10	17 22	18 10	18 52
Holsworthy Library	a		14 02				19 32
Holsworthy Cattle Market	a						
Bude Strand	a		14 25				19 55

A not 25 December, 26 December, 1 January, 18 April, 21 April, 5 May

B not 25 December, 26 December, 1 January

Table 135D-R

Mondays to Saturdays

9 December to 17 May

Bude, Holsworthy and Okehampton - Exeter

Bus Service

Route Diagram - see first Page of Table 135

		GW	GW	GW	GW	GW	GW	GW	GW	GW	GW	GW	GW	GW	GW	GW	GW
		BHX		BHX													BHX
		A	A	A	A	B	A	A	A	B	A	C	A	A	B	A	C
Bude Strand	d			06 25			08 30		09 00	09 30			11 30			13 30	
Holsworthy Church	d			06 50			08 55		09 22	09 55			11 52			13 52	
Holsworthy Cattle Market	d																
Okehampton West Street	d	06 55	07 25	07 35	08 45	09 03	09 33	09 45	10 05	10 33	10 33	11 45	12 35	13 45	14 33	14 35	15 45
Exeter St Davids	a	07 57	08 15	08 15	09 25	09 55	10 25	10 25	10 45	11 25	11 25	12 25	13 15	14 25	15 25	15 15	16 25

		GW	GW	GW
			BHX	BHX
		C	A	A
Bude Strand	d	15 30		17 40
Holsworthy Church	d	15 55		18 02
Holsworthy Cattle Market	d			
Okehampton West Street	d	16 38	17 45	18 45
Exeter St Davids	a	17x30	18 25	19 25

Sundays

8 December to 11 May

		GW	GW	GW	GW	GW	GW
Bude Strand	d		09 30				15 30
Holsworthy Church	d		09 55				15 55
Holsworthy Cattle Market	d						
Okehampton West Street	d	09 03	10 33	11 45	14 33	15 45	16 38
Exeter St Davids	a	09 55	11 25	12 25	15 25	16 25	17 30

A not 25 December, 26 December, 1 January, 18 April, 21 April, 5 May

B 18 April, 21 April, 5 May

C not 25 December, 26 December, 1 January

Table 135E

Mondays to Saturdays

9 December to 17 May

Taunton - Watchet, Dunster and Minehead

Bus Service

Route Diagram - see first Page of Table 135

		GW SX BHX A	GW SO	GW SX BHX A	GW SO	GW SX BHX A	GW SO	GW SX BHX A	GW B	GW SO	GW SX BHX A	GW SO C	GW SX BHX D	GW B	GW SO C	GW SX BHX D	GW BHX D	GW B	GW BHX D	GW BHX D	GW E
Taunton	d	05 41	06 41	06 41	07 11	07 13	07 44	07 47	08 07	08 14	08 17	08 44	08 47	09 07	09 14	09 17	09 47	10 08	10 17	10 47	11 08
Bishops Lydeard Hithermead	a																				
Watchet (West Somerset Ry)	a	06 25	07 25	07 25	07 55	07 58	08 28	08 32	08 52	08 58	09 02	09 31	09 35	09 53	10 03	10 06	10 36	10 54	11 06	11 36	11 54
Dunster Steep	a	06 39	07 40	07 41	08 11	08 15	08 44	08 49	09 08	09 14	09 19	09 48	09 52	10 09	10 20	10 23	10 53	11 10	11 23	11 53	12 10
Minehead Parade	a	06 47	07 48	07 49	08 19	08 23	08 52	08 57	09 16	09 22	09 27	09 56	10 00	10 17	10 28	10 31	11 01	11 18	11 31	12 01	12 18
Minehead Butlins	a	06 52	07 53	07 54	08 24	08 28	08 57	09 02	09 21	09 27	09 32	10 01	10 05	10 22	10 33	10 36	11 06	11 23	11 36	12 06	12 23

		GW BHX D	GW BHX D	GW E	GW BHX D	GW BHX D	GW E	GW BHX D	GW BHX D	GW E	GW BHX D	GW F	GW E	GW BHX D	GW F	GW E	GW BHX D	GW SO	GW SX BHX A	GW SX BHX A	GW SO
Taunton	d	11 17	11 47	12 08	12 17	12 47	13 08	13 17	13 47	14 08	14 17	14 47	15 08	15 17	15 47	16 08	16 17	16 47	16 47	17 12	17 17
Bishops Lydeard Hithermead	a																				
Watchet (West Somerset Ry)	a	12 06	12 36	12 54	13 06	13 36	13 54	14 06	14 36	14 54	15 06	15 36	15 54	16 06	16 36	16 54	17 06	17 33	17 36	18 01	18 03
Dunster Steep	a	12 23	12 53	13 10	13 23	13 53	14 10	14 23	14 53	15 10	15 23	15 53	16 10	16 23	16 53	17 10	17 23	17 50	17 53	18 18	18 20
Minehead Parade	a	12 31	13 01	13 18	13 31	14 01	14 18	14 31	15 01	15 18	15 31	16 01	16 18	16 31	17 01	17 18	17 31	17 58	18 01	18 26	18 28
Minehead Butlins	a	12 36	13 06	13 23	13 36	14 06	14 23	14 36	15 06	15 23	15 36	16 06	16 23	16 36	17 06	17 23	17 36	18 03	18 06	18 31	18 33

		GW E	GW SO	GW SX BHX A	GW SO	GW SX BHX A	GW BHX A
Taunton	d	17 18	17 47	17 47	18 22	18 22	20 06
Bishops Lydeard Hithermead	a						
Watchet (West Somerset Ry)	a	18 04	18 32	18 36	19 07	19 11	20 50
Dunster Steep	a	18 20	18 49	18 53	19 21	19 28	21 04
Minehead Parade	a	18 28	18 57	19 01	19 29	19 34	21 12
Minehead Butlins	a	18 33	19 02	19 06	19 34	19 39	21 17

Sundays

8 December to 11 May

		GW	GW G	GW G	GW G	GW G	GW G	GW G	GW G	GW G	GW G
Taunton	d	08 07	09 07	10 08	11 08	12 08	13 08	14 08	15 08	16 08	17 18
Bishops Lydeard Hithermead	a										
Watchet (West Somerset Ry)	a	08 52	09 53	10 54	11 54	12 54	13 54	14 54	15 54	16 54	18 04
Dunster Steep	a	09 08	10 09	11 10	12 10	13 10	14 10	15 10	16 10	17 10	18 20
Minehead Parade	a	09 16	10 17	11 18	12 18	13 18	14 18	15 18	16 18	17 18	18 28
Minehead Butlins	a	09 21	10 22	11 23	12 23	13 23	14 23	15 23	16 23	17 23	18 33

A not 25 December, 26 December, 1 January, 18 April, 21 April, 5 May
B 1 January, 18 April, 21 April, 5 May
C Also stops at WSR stn 3 min later on rly operating days
D not 25 December, 26 December, 1 January, 18 April, 21 April, 5 May. Also stops at WSR stn 3 min later on rly operating days.
E 1 January, 18 April, 21 April, 5 May. Also stops at WSR stn 3 min later on rly operating days.
F not 25 December, 26 December, 1 January, 18 April, 21 April, 5 May. Also stops at WSR stn 3 min later on rly operating days
G Also stops at WSR stn 2 min later on rly operating days

WSR is an abbreviation for West Somerset Railway

Table 135E-R

Mondays to Saturdays

9 December to 17 May

Minehead, Dunster and Watchet - Taunton

Bus Service

Route Diagram - see first Page of Table 135

		GW	GW	GW	GW	GW	GW	GW	GW	GW	GW	GW	GW	GW	GW	GW	GW	GW	GW	GW	GW
				SX	SO	SX	SO	SX		SO	SX	SO	SX		SO	SX	SO	SX			
				BHX		BHX		BHX	BHX		BHX		BHX			BHX		BHX			BHX
		A	A	A		A		A	A		A		A	B		A		A	B	C	C
Minehead Butlins	d	05 45	06 30	06 50	07 00	07 00	07 50	07 50	08 20	08 50	08 50	09 20	09 20	09 30	09 50	09 50	10 20	10 20	10 30	10 50	11 20
Minehead Bancks Street	d	05 50	06 35	06 58	07 05	07 08	08 00	08 00	08 30	09 00	09 00	09 30	09 30	09 38	10 00	10 00	10 30	10 30	10 38	11 00	11 30
Dunster Steep	d	05 58	06 43	07 06	07 13	07 16	08 08	08 08	08 38	09 08	09 08	09 38	09 38	09 46	10 08	10 08	10 38	10 38	10 46	11 08	11 38
Watchet (West Somerset Ry)	d	06 13	06 58	07 25	07 28	07 35	08 27	08 27	08 57	09 27	09 27	09 57	09 57	10 04	10 27	10 27	10 57	10 57	11 04	11 27	11 57
Bishops Lydeard Hithermead	d																				
Taunton	a	06 55	07 40	08 13	08 10	08 23	09 10	09 12	09 40	10 11	10 14	10 41	10 44	10 47	11 11	11 14	11 41	11 44	11 47	12 14	12 44

		GW	GW	GW	GW	GW	GW	GW	GW	GW	GW	GW	GW	GW	GW	GW	GW	GW	GW	GW	GW
															SO	SX	SO	SX		SO	SX
				BHX						BHX		BHX	BHX			BHX		BHX			BHX
		B	C	C	B	C	C	B	C	C	B	C	C	D	E	C	E	C	D	E	C
Minehead Butlins	d	11 30	11 50	12 20	12 30	12 50	13 20	13 30	13 50	14 20	14 30	14 50	15 20	15 30	15 50	15 50	16 20	16 20	16 30	16 50	16 50
Minehead Bancks Street	d	11 38	12 00	12 30	12 38	13 00	13 30	13 38	14 00	14 30	14 38	15 00	15 30	15 38	15 58	16 00	16 28	16 30	16 38	16 58	17 00
Dunster Steep	d	11 46	12 08	12 38	12 46	13 08	13 38	13 46	14 08	14 38	14 46	15 08	15 38	15 46	16 06	16 08	16 36	16 38	16 46	17 06	17 08
Watchet (West Somerset Ry)	d	12 04	12 27	12 57	13 04	13 27	13 57	14 04	14 27	14 57	15 04	15 27	15 57	16 04	16 25	16 27	16 55	16 57	17 04	17 25	17 27
Bishops Lydeard Hithermead	d																				
Taunton	a	12 47	13 14	13 44	13 47	14 14	14 44	14 47	15 14	15 44	15 47	16 14	16 44	16 47	17 12	17 14	17 42	17 44	17 47	18 12	18 14

		GW	GW	GW	GW	GW	GW
		SO	SX				
			BHX				
		E	C	D	C	D	A
Minehead Butlins	d	17 20	17 20	17 30	17 50	18 35	18 40
Minehead Bancks Street	d	17 28	17 30	17 38	18 00	18 45	18 45
Dunster Steep	d	17 36	17 38	17 46	18 08	18 51	18 53
Watchet (West Somerset Ry)	d	17 55	17 57	18 04	18 27	19 09	19 08
Bishops Lydeard Hithermead	d						
Taunton	a	18 42	18 44	18 47	19 14	19 49	19 50

Sundays

8 December to 11 May

		GW	GW	GW	GW	GW	GW	GW	GW	GW	GW
		E	E	E	E	E	E	E	E	E	
Minehead Butlins	d	09 30	10 30	11 30	12 30	13 30	14 30	15 30	16 30	17 30	18 35
Minehead Bancks Street	d	09 38	10 38	11 38	12 38	13 38	14 38	15 38	16 38	17 38	18 45
Dunster Steep	d	09 46	10 46	11 46	12 46	13 46	14 46	15 46	16 46	17 46	18 51
Watchet (West Somerset Ry)	d	10 04	11 04	12 04	13 04	14 04	15 04	16 04	17 04	18 04	19 09
Bishops Lydeard Hithermead	d										
Taunton	a	10 47	11 47	12 47	13 47	14 47	15 47	16 47	17 47	18 47	19 49

A not 25 December, 26 December, 1 January, 18 April, 21 April, 5 May

B 1 January, 18 April, 21 April, 5 May

C not 25 December, 26 December, 1 January, 18 April, 21 April, 5 May. Also stops at WSR stn 3 min earlier on rly operating days

D 1 January, 18 April, 21 April, 5 May. Also stops at WSR stn 3 min earlier on rly operating days

E Also stops at WSR stn 3 min earlier on rly operating days

WSR is an abbreviation for West Somerset Railway

Table 135F

Mondays to Saturdays

9 December to 17 May

Penzance - St Mary's (Isles of Scilly)

Route Diagram - see first Page of Table 135

		GW SX A
Penzance Quay	⛴ d	09 15
St. Marys Quay	⛴ a	12 00

A from 24 March

No Sunday Service

Table 135F-R

Mondays to Saturdays

9 December to 17 May

St Mary's (Isles of Scilly) - Penzance

Route Diagram - see first Page of Table 135

		GW TThX A
St. Marys Quay	⛴ d	15 00
Penzance Quay	⛴ a	17 45

A from 24 March

No Sunday Service

Table 136

Mondays to Fridays

9 December to 16 May

Exmouth - Exeter - Barnstaple

Route Diagram - see first Page of Table 135

Miles	Miles			GW MO	GW MX	GW	SW	GW	GW	SW	GW	SW		GW	GW	GW	GW	GW	SW	GW	GW	SW		GW	GW
							[1]			[1]		[1]						◇	◇[1]			◇[1]			
0	—	**Exmouth**	d		00 02			06 12	06 45		07 14			07 53		08 23	08 53			09 23	09 53			10 23	10 53
2	—	Lympstone Village	d	00 03	00 06			06 16	06 49		07 18			07 57		08 27	08 57			09 27	09 57			10 27	10 57
3	—	Lympstone Commando	d	00x04	00x07			06x17	06x52		07x20			07x58		08x29	08x58			09x28				10x28	
3½	—	Exton	d	00x06	00x09			06x19	06x53		07x21			08x00		08x30	09x00			09x30				10x30	
5	—	Topsham	d	00 11	00 14			06 24	06 58		07 29			08 06		08 35	09 05			09 35	10 05			10 35	11 05
7	—	Digby & Sowton	d	00 15	00 19			06 29	07 03		07 33			08 12		08 40	09 10			09 40	10 10			10 40	11 10
9	—	Polsloe Bridge	d	00 19	00 22			06 32	07 06		07 37			08 16		08 44	09 14			09 44				10 44	
10	—	St James' Park	d	00 21	00 25			06 35	07 09		07 40			08 18	08 34	08 47	09 17	09 27		09 47				10 47	
10½	—	**Exeter Central**	a	00 24	00s27			06 37	07 11		07 42			08 22	08 36	08 49	09 19	09 29		09 51	10 16			10 49	11 16
—	—		d	00 25			06 32	06 38	07 12	07 39	07 43	08 18		08 24	08 37	08 50	09 20	09 30	09 41	09 53	10 17	10 39		10 50	11 17
11¼	—	**Exeter St Davids [6]**	a	00 28	00 31		06 35	06 41	07 15	07 42	07 46	08 21		08 26	08 42	08 54	09 24	09 33	09 44	09 56	10 21	10 42		10 54	11 21
—	—		d			05 50		06 48						08 31			09 27				10 27				11 27
15½	—	Newton St Cyres	d																						
18¼	0	Crediton	d			06 01		06 59						08 42			09 38				10 38				11 38
21¾	3½	Yeoford	d			06x07		07x05						08x48			09x44				10x44				11x44
—	14¼	Sampford Courtenay	d																						
—	18	Okehampton	a																						
24½	—	Copplestone	d			06x12		07x10						08x53			09x49				10x49				11x49
26¼	—	Morchard Road	d					07x13						08x56			09x52				10x52				11x52
28¾	—	Lapford	d					07x17																	
32½	—	Eggesford	d			06 27		07 33						09 11			10 08				11 08				12 08
36½	—	Kings Nympton	d					07x38						09x17											
39¼	—	Portsmouth Arms	d					07x43																	
43½	—	Umberleigh	d			06x41		07x49						09x27			10x23				11x23				12x23
45¾	—	Chapelton	d					07x53																	
50¼	—	**Barnstaple**	a			06 55		08 01						09 39			10 35				11 35				12 35

		SW	GW	GW	SW	GW	GW	SW		GW	GW	SW	GW	GW	SW	GW	GW	SW		GW	GW	GW	SW	GW	GW
		◇[1]			◇[1]			◇[1]				◇[1]			◇[1]			◇[1]					◇[1]		
Exmouth	d		11 23	11 53		12 23	12 53			13 23	13 53		14 23	14 53		15 23	15 53				16 25	16 55			17 25
Lympstone Village	d		11 27	11 57		12 27	12 57			13 27	13 57		14 27	14 57		15 27	15 57				16 29	16 59			17 29
Lympstone Commando	d		11x28			12x28				13x28			14x28			15x28	15x58				16x30	17x00			17x30
Exton	d		11x30			12x30				13x30			14x30			15x30	16x00				16x32	17x02			17x32
Topsham	d		11 35	12 05		12 35	13 05			13 35	14 05		14 35	15 05		15 35	16 05				16 37	17 07			17 37
Digby & Sowton	d		11 40	12 10		12 40	13 10			13 40	14 10		14 40	15 10		15 40	16 10				16 42	17 12			17 42
Polsloe Bridge	d		11 44			12 44				13 44			14 44			15 44	16 14				16 46	17 15			17 45
St James' Park	d		11 47			12 47				13 47			14 47			15 47	16 17			16 43	16 48	17 18			17 48
Exeter Central	a		11 49	12 16		12 49	13 16			13 49	14 16		14 49	15 16		15 49	16 19			16 45	16 51	17 21			17 50
	d	11 39	11 50	12 17	12 39	12 50	13 17	13 39		13 50	14 17	14 39	14 50	15 17	15 41	15 50	16 20	16 37		16 46	16 53	17 22	17 36	17 45	17 51
Exeter St Davids [6]	a	11 42	11 54	12 21	12 42	12 54	13 21	13 42		13 54	14 21	14 42	14 54	15 21	15 44	15 54	16 25	16 42		16 49	16 56	17 25	17 39	17 48	17 55
	d			12 27			13 27				14 27			15 27							16 57				17 57
Newton St Cyres	d																								18x04
Crediton	d			12 38			13 38				14 38			15 38							17 08				18 11
Yeoford	d			12x44			13x44				14x44			15x44							17x15				18x17
Sampford Courtenay	d																								
Okehampton	a																								
Copplestone	d			12x49			13x49				14x49			15x49							17x19				18x22
Morchard Road	d			12x52			13x52				14x52			15x52							17x22				18x25
Lapford	d																				17x27				18x29
Eggesford	d			13 08			14 08				15 08			16 08							17 37				18 41
Kings Nympton	d						14x15														17x44				18x48
Portsmouth Arms	d																								18x52
Umberleigh	d			13x23			14x23				15x23			16x23							17x54				18x59
Chapelton	d																								19x03
Barnstaple	a			13 37			14 37				15 35			16 35							18 07				19 13

		GW	SW	GW		GW	GW	SW	GW	GW	SW	GW	GW	GW		SW	GW	GW	SW	GW FO	GW	SW			
			◇[1]					◇[1]			◇[1]					◇[1]			◇[1]			◇[1]			
Exmouth	d	17 58		18 27			18 55		19 35	20 08				21 04				22 05			23 10				
Lympstone Village	d	18 02		18 31			18 59		19 39	20 12				21 08				22 09			23 14				
Lympstone Commando	d	18x04					19x00			20x13				21x09				22x10			23x15				
Exton	d	18x06					19x02			20x15				21x11				22x12			23x17				
Topsham	d	18 11		18 37			19 07		19 49	20 20				21 16				22 17			23 22				
Digby & Sowton	d	18 15		18 42			19 12		19 54	20 25				21 21				22 22			23 27				
Polsloe Bridge	d	18 19					19 15			20 28				21 24				22 25			23 30				
St James' Park	d	18 21					19 18			20 31				21 27				22 28			23 33				
Exeter Central	a	18 24		18 49			19 20		20 00	20 34				21 29				22 30			23 36				
	d	18 25	18 39	18 49		19 02	19 21	19 42	20 01	20 35	20 40	20 55	21 21	21 30		21 44	21 55	22 31	22 44	22 49	23 37	23 57			
Exeter St Davids [6]	a	18 28	18 42	18 53		19 06	19 25	19 46	20 05	20 38	20 44	20 58	21 25	21 34		21 47	22 00	22 34	22 47	22 52	23 41	00 01			
	d			18 57								21 00								22 53					
Newton St Cyres	d			19x04								21x07													
Crediton	d			19 11								21 14								23 05					
Yeoford	d			19x17								21x20								23x11					
Sampford Courtenay	d																								
Okehampton	a																								
Copplestone	d			19x22								21x26								23x16					
Morchard Road	d			19x25								21x29								23x19					
Lapford	d											21x33								23x23					
Eggesford	d			19 42								21 43								23 33					
Kings Nympton	d											21x48								23x39					
Portsmouth Arms	d											21x53													
Umberleigh	d			19x56								21x59								23x49					
Chapelton	d											22x03													
Barnstaple	a			20 08								22 13								23 59					

For connections at Exeter St Davids please see Table 135

Table 136

Saturdays

14 December to 17 May

Exmouth - Exeter - Barnstaple

Route Diagram - see first Page of Table 135

		GW	GW	SW	GW	SW	GW	SW	GW	GW		GW	SW	GW	GW	GW	SW	GW	GW	SW		GW	GW	SW	GW
				1		1		1					◇1				◇1			◇1				◇1	
Exmouth	d	00 02			06 12		07 15		07 53	08 23		08 53		09 23	09 53			10 23	10 53			11 23	11 53		12 23
Lympstone Village	d	00 06			06 16		07 19		07 57	08 27		08 57		09 27	09 57			10 27	10 57			11 27	11 57		12 27
Lympstone Commando	d	00x07			06x17		07x21		07x58	08x29		08x58		09x28	09x58			10x28	10x58			11x28	11x58		12x28
Exton	d	00x09			06x19		07x22		08x00	08x30		09x00		09x30				10x30				11x30			12x30
Topsham	d	00 14			06 24		07 29		08 08	08 35		09 05		09 35	10 05			10 35	11 05			11 35	12 05		12 35
Digby & Sowton	d	00 19			06 29		07 33		08 13	08 40		09 10		09 40	10 10			10 40	11 10			11 40	12 10		12 40
Polsloe Bridge	d	00 22			06 32		07 37		08 17	08 44		09 14		09 44				10 44				11 44			12 44
St James' Park	d	00 25			06 35		07 40		08 20	08 47		09 17		09 47				10 47				11 47			12 47
Exeter Central	a	00s27			06 37		07 42		08 23	08 49		09 19		09 50	10 16			10 49	11 16			11 49	12 16		12 49
	d			06 32	06 38	07 39	07 43	08 19	08 26	08 50		09 20	09 41	09 52	10 17	10 30	10 39	10 50	11 17	11 39		11 50	12 17	12 39	12 50
Exeter St Davids [6]	a	00 31		06 35	06 41	07 42	07 46	08 22	08 28	08 54		09 24	09 44	09 54	10 21	10 33	10 42	10 54	11 21	11 42		11 54	12 21	12 42	12 54
	d		05 54		06 55				08 31			09 27			10 27				11 27				12 27		
Newton St Cyres	d																								
Crediton	d		06 05		07 06				08 42			09 38			10 38				11 38				12 38		
Yeoford	d		06x11		07x12				08x48			09x44			10x44				11x44				12x44		
Sampford Courtenay	d																								
Okehampton	a																								
Copplestone	d		06x16		07x18				08x53			09x49			10x49				11x49				12x49		
Morchard Road	d				07x21				08x56			09x52			10x52				11x52				12x52		
Lapford	d				07x25																				
Eggesford	d		06 31		07 38				09 11			10 08			11 08				12 08				13 08		
Kings Nympton	d				07x43				09x17																
Portsmouth Arms	d				07x48																				
Umberleigh	d		06x45		07x54				09x27			10x23			11x23				12x23				13x23		
Chapelton	d				07x58																				
Barnstaple	a		06 59		08 07				09 39			10 35			11 35				12 35				13 37		

		GW	SW	GW	GW	SW		GW	GW	SW	GW	GW	SW	GW	GW	GW		GW	SW	GW	GW	SW	GW	GW	SW
			◇1			◇1				◇1			◇1						◇1			◇1			◇1
Exmouth	d	12 53		13 23	13 53			14 23	14 53		15 23	15 53			16 25			16 55		17 25	17 55		18 27	18 55	
Lympstone Village	d	12 57		13 27	13 57			14 27	14 57		15 27	15 57			16 29			16 59		17 29	17 59		18 31	18 59	
Lympstone Commando	d	12x58		13x28	13x58			14x28	14x58		15x28	15x58			16x30			17x00		17x30	18x01			19x00	
Exton	d			13x30				14x30			15x30	16x00			16x32			17x02		17x32	18x03			19x02	
Topsham	d	13 05		13 35	14 05			14 35	15 05		15 35	16 05			16 37			17 07		17 37	18 07		18 37	19 07	
Digby & Sowton	d	13 10		13 40	14 10			14 40	15 10		15 40	16 10			16 42			17 12		17 42	18 12		18 42	19 12	
Polsloe Bridge	d			13 44				14 44			15 44	16 14			16 46			17 15		17 45	18 15			19 15	
St James' Park	d			13 47	14 17			14 47			15 47	16 17			16 48	17 05		17 18		17 48	18 18			19 18	
Exeter Central	a	13 16		13 49	14 20			14 49	15 16		15 49	16 19			16 51	17 07		17 20		17 50	18 20		18 49	19 20	
	d	13 17	13 39	13 50	14 21	14 39		14 50	15 17	15 39	15 50	16 20	16 39	16 48	16 53	17 08		17 21	17 39	17 51	18 21	18 38	18 49	19 21	19 39
Exeter St Davids [6]	a	13 21	13 42	13 54	14 24	14 42		14 54	15 21	15 42	15 54	16 25	16 42	16 51	16 56	17 11		17 24	17 42	17 55	18 26	18 42	18 53	19 25	19 42
	d	13 27			14 27				15 27						16 57					17 57			18 57		
Newton St Cyres	d																			18x04			19x04		
Crediton	d	13 38			14 38				15 38						17 08					18 11			19 11		
Yeoford	d	13x44			14x44				15x44						17x15					18x17			19x18		
Sampford Courtenay	d																								
Okehampton	a																								
Copplestone	d	13x49			14x49				15x49						17x19					18x22			19x22		
Morchard Road	d	13x52			14x52				15x52						17x22					18x25			19x25		
Lapford	d														17x27					18x29					
Eggesford	d	14 08			15 08				16 08						17 37					18 41			19 42		
Kings Nympton	d	14x15													17x44					18x48					
Portsmouth Arms	d																			18x52					
Umberleigh	d	14x23			15x23				16x23						17x54					18x59			19x56		
Chapelton	d																			19x03					
Barnstaple	a	14 37			15 35				16 35						18 07					19 13			20 08		

		GW		GW	SW	GW	GW	SW	GW	GW	GW
					◇1			◇1			
Exmouth	d	19 38		20 08			21 04		22 11	23 10	23 43
Lympstone Village	d	19 42		20 12			21 08		22 15	23 14	23 47
Lympstone Commando	d			20x13			21x09		22x16	23x15	23x48
Exton	d			20x15			21x11		22x18	23x17	23x50
Topsham	d	19 49		20 20			21 16		22 23	23 22	23 55
Digby & Sowton	d	19 54		20 25			21 21		22 28	23 27	23 59
Polsloe Bridge	d			20 28			21 24		22 31	23 30	00 03
St James' Park	d			20 31			21 27		22 34	23 33	00 06
Exeter Central	a	20 00		20 34			21 29		22 36	23 36	00 08
	d	20 01		20 35	20 40	20 52	21 30	21 39	22 37	23 37	00 09
Exeter St Davids [6]	a	20 05		20 38	20 43	20 55	21 34	21 42	22 40	23 41	00 14
	d					21 00					
Newton St Cyres	d					21x07					
Crediton	d					21 14					
Yeoford	d					21x20					
Sampford Courtenay	d										
Okehampton	a										
Copplestone	d					21x26					
Morchard Road	d					21x29					
Lapford	d					21x33					
Eggesford	d					21 43					
Kings Nympton	d					21x48					
Portsmouth Arms	d					21x53					
Umberleigh	d					21x59					
Chapelton	d					22x03					
Barnstaple	a					22 13					

For connections at Exeter St Davids please see Table 135

Table 136

Sundays

8 December to 11 May

Exmouth - Exeter - Barnstaple

Route Diagram - see first Page of Table 135

		GW	GW	SW	GW	GW	SW	GW	GW	SW		GW	GW	SW	GW	GW	SW	GW	GW	SW		GW	GW	SW	GW
				1			◇1			◇1				◇1			◇1			◇1				◇1	
		A						B	C							B							B		B
Exmouth	d				09 10			10 21	10 21			11 24			12 28			13 24				14 31			15 24
Lympstone Village	d				09 14			10 25	10 25			11 28			12 32			13 28				14 35			15 28
Lympstone Commando	d				09x15			10x26	10x26			11x29			12x33			13x29				14x36			15x29
Exton	d				09x17			10x28	10x28			11x31			12x35			13x31				14x38			15x31
Topsham	d				09 22			10 33	10 33			11 36			12 40			13 36				14 43			15 36
Digby & Sowton	d				09 27			10 38	10 38			11 41			12 45			13 41				14 48			15 41
Polsloe Bridge	d	00 03			09 30			10 41	10 41			11 44			12 48			13 44				14 51			15 44
St James' Park	d	00 06			09 33			10 44	10 44			11 47			12 51			13 47				14 54			15 47
Exeter Central	a	00 08			09 36			10 46	10 46			11 49			12 53			13 49				14 58			15 49
	d	00 09		08 56	09 36		10 42	10 48	10 51	11 42		11 52	11 59	12 42	12 54	13 20	13 42	13 50	14 04	14 42		14 59	15 20	15 42	15 50
Exeter St Davids 6	a	00 14		08 59	09 40		10 45	10 51	10 54	11 45		11 55	12 02	12 45	12 57	13 23	13 45	13 53	14 07	14 45		15 03	15 23	15 45	15 53
	d		08 39			09 53							12 03						14 08						
Newton St Cyres	d		08x47										12x11												
Crediton	d		08 53			10 04							12 17						14 20						
Yeoford	d		09x00			10x11							12x24						14x27						
Sampford Courtenay	d																								
Okehampton	a																								
Copplestone	d		09x05			10x16							12x30						14x33						
Morchard Road	d		09x08			10x19							12x33						14x36						
Lapford	d		09x12										12x37												
Eggesford	d		09 22			10 31							12 46						14 48						
Kings Nympton	d		09x29										12x52						14x54						
Portsmouth Arms	d		09x33										12x57						14x59						
Umberleigh	d		09x40			10x46							13x03						15x05						
Chapelton	d		09x44										13x07												
Barnstaple	a		09 52			10 57							13 14						15 15						

		GW	GW	SW	GW	SW		GW	GW	SW	GW	SW	GW	GW	SW	GW		SW	GW	GW	SW	GW	GW	GW	
				◇1		◇1				◇1		◇1			◇1			◇1			◇1				
		C																	B	C					
Exmouth	d	15 24			16 24			17 24			18 24		19 24			20 24			21 24	21 24		22 29	23 29	23 59	
Lympstone Village	d	15 28			16 28			17 28			18 28		19 28			20 28			21 28	21 28		22 33	23 33	00 03	
Lympstone Commando	d	15x29			16x29			17x29			18x29		19x29			20x29			21x29	21x29		22x34	23x34	00x04	
Exton	d	15x31			16x31			17x31			18x31		19x31			20x31			21x31	21x31		22x36	23x36	00x06	
Topsham	d	15 36			16 36			17 36			18 35		19 36			20 36			21 36	21 36		22 42	23 42	00 11	
Digby & Sowton	d	15 41			16 41			17 41			18 40		19 41			20 41			21 41	21 41		22 46	23 47	00 15	
Polsloe Bridge	d	15 44			16 44			17 44			18 43		19 44			20 44			21 44	21 44		22 50	23 50	00 19	
St James' Park	d	15 47			16 47			17 47			18 46		19 47			20 47			21 47	21 47		22 53	23 53	00 21	
Exeter Central	a	15 49			16 49			17 49			18 48		19 49			20 49			21 49	21 49		22 55	23 55	00 24	
	d	15 54	15 59	16 42	16 50	17 42		17 50	18 03	18 42	18 49	19 42	19 50	19 56	20 42	20 50		21 43	21 50	21 50	22 45	22 56	23 56	00 25	
Exeter St Davids 6	a	15 57	16 02	16 45	16 53	17 45		17 53	18 06	18 45	18 53	19 45	19 53	19 59	20 45	20 53		21 46	21 53	21 54	22 48	22 59	23 59	00 28	
	d		16 04						18 07					20 01											
Newton St Cyres	d		16x12											20x08											
Crediton	d		16 19						18 18					20 18											
Yeoford	d		16x26						18x25					20x24											
Sampford Courtenay	d																								
Okehampton	a																								
Copplestone	d		16x31						18x30					20x30											
Morchard Road	d		16x34						18x33					20x33											
Lapford	d		16x38											20x37											
Eggesford	d		16 45						18 46					20 47											
Kings Nympton	d		16x53											20x52											
Portsmouth Arms	d		16x56											20x57											
Umberleigh	d		17x04						19x00					21x03											
Chapelton	d		17x08											21x07											
Barnstaple	a		17 17						19 10					21 15											

A not 8 December **B** until 9 February, from 30 March **C** from 16 February until 23 March

For connections at Exeter St Davids please see Table 135

Table 136R

Mondays to Fridays

9 December to 16 May

Barnstaple - Exeter - Exmouth

Route Diagram - see first Page of Table 135

Miles	Miles			SW ◇1	GW	GW	GW	SW ◇1	GW	SW ◇1	GW	GW	GW	SW ◇1	GW	GW	GW	SW ◇1	GW	GW	SW ◇1	GW	GW
0	—	**Barnstaple**	d									07 00							08 43			09 43	
4¼	—	Chapelton	d									07x05											
6¾	—	Umberleigh	d									07x09							08x51			09x51	
10¾	—	Portsmouth Arms	d									07x16											
13¾	—	Kings Nympton	d									07x21							09x03				
17½	—	Eggesford	d									07 30							09 10			10 07	
21½	—	Lapford	d									07x35							09x16				
23¾	—	Morchard Road	d									07x40							09x20			10x16	
25½	—	Copplestone	d									07x43							09x24			10x20	
—	0	Okehampton	d																				
—	3¾	Sampford Courtenay	d																				
28½	14½	Yeoford	d									07x48							09x28			10x24	
32	18	Crediton	d									07 55							09 37			10 37	
34¾	—	Newton St Cyres	d									07x58											
39	—	**Exeter St Davids** 6	a									08 07							09 48			10 48	
—	—		d	05 10	05 44	06 06	06 29	06 41	07 11	07 25	07 36	08 09	08 16	08 23	08 48	08 59	09 18	09 25	09 50	10 18	10 25	10 50	11 18
39¾	—	**Exeter Central**	a	05 13	05 47	06 09	06 32	06 44	07 14	07 28	07 39	08 12	08 19	08 26	08 51	09 02	09 21	09 28	09 53	10 21	10 28	10 53	11 21
—	—		d		05 48	06 10	06 39		07 15		07 52	08 13	08 20		08 52	09 03	09 22		09 54	10 22		10 54	11 22
40¼	—	St James' Park	d			06 12	06 41		07 17		07 54	08a17	08 22		08 54	09a07	09 24			10 24			11 24
41¼	—	Polsloe Bridge	d			06 15	06 44		07 20		07 57		08 25		08 57		09 27			10 27			11 27
43¼	—	Digby & Sowton	d		05 54	06 19	06 48		07 24		08 01		08 29		09 01		09 31		10 01	10 31		11 01	11 31
45¼	—	Topsham	d		05 58	06 25	06 57		07 28		08 05		08 35		09 05		09 35		10 05	10 35		11 05	11 35
46¾	—	Exton	d			06x27	07x00		07x31		08x08		08x38		09x08		09x38			10x38			11x38
47¼	—	Lympstone Commando	d			06x29	07x02		07x33		08x10		08x40		09x10		09x40			10x40			11x40
48¼	—	Lympstone Village	d		06 03	06 31	07 05		07 36		08 13		08 43		09 13		09 43		10 11	10 43		11 11	11 43
50¼	—	**Exmouth**	a		06 10	06 38	07 10		07 43		08 18		08 48		09 20		09 50		10 19	10 50		11 19	11 50

		SW ◇1	GW	GW	SW ◇1	GW	GW	SW ◇1	GW	GW	SW ◇1	GW	GW	SW ◇1	GW	GW	GW	SW ◇1	GW	GW	SW ◇1	SW 1	GW
Barnstaple	d		10 43			11 43			12 43			13 43			14 43				15 43				
Chapelton	d																						
Umberleigh	d		10x51			11x51			12x51			13x51			14x51				15x51				
Portsmouth Arms	d																						
Kings Nympton	d								13x02														
Eggesford	d		11 07			12 07			13 07			14 07			15 07				16 07				
Lapford	d																						
Morchard Road	d		11x16			12x16			13x16			14x16			15x16				16x16				
Copplestone	d		11x20			12x20			13x20			14x20			15x20				16x20				
Okehampton	d																						
Sampford Courtenay	d																						
Yeoford	d		11x24			12x24			13x24			14x24			15x24				16x24				
Crediton	d		11 37			12 37			13 37			14 37			15 37				16 37				
Newton St Cyres	d																						
Exeter St Davids 6	a		11 48			12 48			13 48			14 48			15 48				16 48				
	d	11 25	11 50	12 18	12 25	12 50	13 18	13 25	13 50	14 18	14 25	14 51	15 18	15 25	15 50	16 08	16 18	16 24	16 50	17 18	17 25	17 46	17 52
Exeter Central	a	11 28	11 53	12 21	12 28	12 53	13 21	13 28	13 53	14 21	14 28	14 54	15 21	15 28	15 53	16 11	16 21	16 27	16 53	17 21	17 28	17 49	17 55
	d		11 54	12 22		12 54	13 22		13 54	14 22		14 55	15 22		15 54	16 12	16 22		16 54	17 22			17 56
St James' Park	d			12 24			13 24			14 24			15 24			16a16	16 24		16 56	17 24			17 58
Polsloe Bridge	d			12 27			13 27			14 27			15 27				16 27		16 59	17 27			18 01
Digby & Sowton	d		12 01	12 31		13 01	13 31		14 01	14 31		15 01	15 31		16 01		16 31		17 03	17 31			18 05
Topsham	d		12 05	12 35		13 05	13 35		14 05	14 35		15 05	15 35		16 05		16 37		17 07	17 37			18 09
Exton	d			12x38			13x38			14x38			15x38				16x38		17x10	17x38			18x12
Lympstone Commando	d			12x40			13x40			14x40			15x40				16x40		17x12	17x40			18x14
Lympstone Village	d		12 11	12 43		13 11	13 43		14 11	14 43		15 11	15 43		16 11		16 43		17 15	17 43			18 17
Exmouth	a		12 19	12 50		13 19	13 50		14 19	14 50		15 19	15 50		16 19		16 50		17 22	17 51			18 25

		GW	SW ◇1	GW	GW	SW ◇1	GW	GW	SW ◇1	GW	GW	SW 1	GW	GW	GW	SW 1	GW
Barnstaple	d			17 08			18 13	19 16						20 24			22 16
Chapelton	d			17x14													
Umberleigh	d			17x18			18x21	19x24						20x32			22x24
Portsmouth Arms	d						18x28										
Kings Nympton	d			17 29			18x33										
Eggesford	d			17 37			18 40	19 40						20 49			22 40
Lapford	d			17 43			18x47										
Morchard Road	d			17x46			18x51	19x49						20x58			22x48
Copplestone	d			17x50			18x55	19x53						21x01			22x52
Okehampton	d																
Sampford Courtenay	d																
Yeoford	d			17x54			18x59	19x57						21x05			22x56
Crediton	d			18 12			19 12	20 06						21 16			23 05
Newton St Cyres	d			18x15				20x09						21x19			23x08
Exeter St Davids 6	a			18 29			19 28	20 18						21 34			23 16
	d	18 20	18 25	18 33	18 50	19 25	19 32	20 19	20 25	20 30	21 14	21 25	21 31	21 38	22 31	22 57	23 28
Exeter Central	a	18 23	18 28	18 38	18 53	19 28	19 35	20 24	20 28	20 33	21 19	21 28	21 34	21 41	22 34	23 00	23 31
	d	18 24			18 54		19 37			20 34			21 34		22 35		23 32
St James' Park	d	18 26			18 56		19 39			20 36			21 36		22 37		23 34
Polsloe Bridge	d	18 29			18 59		19 42			20 39			21 39		22 40		23 37
Digby & Sowton	d	18 33			19 03		19 46			20 43			21 43		22 44		23 41
Topsham	d	18 37			19 07		19 50			20 47			21 49		22 48		23 45
Exton	d	18x38			19x10		19x53			20x49			21x51		22x50		23x47
Lympstone Commando	d	18x40			19x12		19x55			20x51			21x53		22x52		23x49
Lympstone Village	d	18 43			19 15		19 58			20 54			21 56		22 56		23 52
Exmouth	a	18 52			19 23		20 04			21 01			22 02		23 00		23 59

For connections at Exeter St Davids please see Table 135

Table 136R

Saturdays

14 December to 17 May

Barnstaple - Exeter - Exmouth

Route Diagram - see first Page of Table 135

		GW	SW	GW	GW	SW	GW	SW	GW	GW		SW	GW	GW	SW	GW	GW	SW	GW	GW		SW	GW	GW	SW
			◇1			◇1		◇1				◇1			◇1			◇1				◇1			◇1
Barnstaple	d	00 05								07 08						08 43			09 43				10 43		
Chapelton	d									07x13															
Umberleigh	d									07x17						08x51			09x51				10x51		
Portsmouth Arms	d									07x24															
Kings Nympton	d									07x29						09x02									
Eggesford	d	00s27								07 38						09 07			10 07				11 07		
Lapford	d									07x43						09x14									
Morchard Road	d									07x48						09x17			10x16				11x16		
Copplestone	d									07x51						09x22			10x20				11x20		
Okehampton	d																								
Sampford Courtenay	d																								
Yeoford	d									07x57						09x25			10x24				11x24		
Crediton	d	00s47								08 04						09 37			10 37				11 37		
Newton St Cyres	d									08x07															
Exeter St Davids 6	a	01 00								08 16						09 48			10 48				11 48		
	d		05 10	05 44	06 29	06 41	07 11	07 25	07 36	08 16		08 24	08 48	09 18	09 25	09 50	10 18	10 25	10 50	11 18		11 25	11 50	12 18	12 25
Exeter Central	a		05 13	05 47	06 32	06 44	07 14	07 28	07 39	08 19		08 27	08 51	09 21	09 28	09 51	10 21	10 28	10 51	11 21		11 28	11 51	12 21	12 28
	d			05 48	06 39		07 15		07 52	08 20			08 52	09 22		09 52	10 22		10 52	11 22			11 52	12 22	
St James' Park	d				06 41		07 17		07 54	08 23			08 54	09 24		09 54	10 24			11 24				12 24	
Polsloe Bridge	d				06 44		07 20		07 57	08 27			08 57	09 27		09 57	10 27			11 27				12 27	
Digby & Sowton	d			05 54	06 48		07 24		08 01	08 31			09 01	09 31		10 01	10 31		11 01	11 31			12 01	12 31	
Topsham	d			05 58	06 52		07 28		08 05	08 35			09 05	09 35		10 05	10 35		11 05	11 35			12 05	12 35	
Exton	d				06x54		07x31		08x08	08x38			09x08	09x38		10x08	10x38			11x38				12x38	
Lympstone Commando	d				06x56		07x33		08x10	08x40			09x10	09x40		10x10	10x40		11x09	11x40			12x09	12x40	
Lympstone Village	d			06 03	06 59		07 36		08 13	08 43			09 13	09 43		10 11	10 43		11 11	11 43			12 11	12 43	
Exmouth	a			06 10	07 04		07 43		08 18	08 48			09 20	09 50		10 19	10 50		11 19	11 50			12 19	12 50	

		GW	GW	SW	GW	GW		SW	GW	GW	SW	GW	GW	SW	GW	GW		GW	GW	SW	GW	GW	SW	GW	SW
				◇1				◇1			◇1			◇1						◇1			◇1		◇1
Barnstaple	d	11 43			12 43				13 43			14 43				15 43		17 08							
Chapelton	d																	17x14							
Umberleigh	d	11x51			12x51				13x51			14x51				15x51		17x18							
Portsmouth Arms	d																								
Kings Nympton	d				13x02													17x29							
Eggesford	d	12 07			13 07				14 07			15 07				16 07		17 37							
Lapford	d																	17x43							
Morchard Road	d	12x16			13x16				14x16			15x16				16x16		17x46							
Copplestone	d	12x20			13x20				14x20			15x20				16x20		17x50							
Okehampton	d																								
Sampford Courtenay	d																								
Yeoford	d	12x24			13x24				14x24			15x24				16x24		17x54							
Crediton	d	12 37			13 37				14 37			15 37				16 37		18 10							
Newton St Cyres	d																	18x13							
Exeter St Davids 6	a	12 48			13 48				14 48			15 48				16 48		18 22							
	d	12 50	13 18	13 25	13 50	14 18		14 25	14 50	15 18	15 25	15 50	16 18	16 25	16 41	16 50			17 18	17 25	17 50	18 20	18 25	18 50	19 25
Exeter Central	a	12 51	13 21	13 28	13 51	14 21		14 28	14 51	15 21	15 28	15 51	16 21	16 28	16 44	16 53			17 21	17 28	17 53	18 23	18 28	18 53	19 28
	d	12 52	13 22		13 52	14 22			14 52	15 22		15 52	16 22			16 54			17 22		17 54	18 24		18 54	
St James' Park	d		13 24		13 54	14 24				15 24		15 57	16 24			16 56			17 24		17 56	18 26		18 56	
Polsloe Bridge	d		13 27			14 27				15 27			16 27			16 59			17 27		17 59	18 29		18 59	
Digby & Sowton	d	13 01	13 31		14 01	14 31			15 01	15 31		16 01	16 31			17 03			17 31		18 03	18 33		19 03	
Topsham	d	13 05	13 35		14 05	14 35			15 05	15 35		16 05	16 37			17 07			17 37		18 07	18 37		19 07	
Exton	d		13x38			14x38				15x38			16x38			17x10			17x38		18x10	18x38		19x10	
Lympstone Commando	d	13x09	13x40		14x09	14x40			15x09	15x40		16x09	16x40			17x12			17x40		18x12	18x40		19x12	
Lympstone Village	d	13 11	13 43		14 11	14 43			15 11	15 43		16 11	16 43			17 15			17 43		18 15	18 43		19 15	
Exmouth	a	13 19	13 50		14 19	14 50			15 19	15 50		16 19	16 50			17 22			17 50		18 22	18 52		19 22	

		GW		GW	SW	GW	SW	GW	GW	GW	GW	SW		GW
					◇1		1					1		
Barnstaple	d	18 13		19 16				20 24		22 18				
Chapelton	d									22x23				
Umberleigh	d	18x21		19x24				20x32		22x27				
Portsmouth Arms	d	18x28								22x34				
Kings Nympton	d	18x33								22x39				
Eggesford	d	18 40		19 40				20 49		22 47				
Lapford	d	18x47								22x52				
Morchard Road	d	18x51		19x49				20x58		22x57				
Copplestone	d	18x55		19x53				21x01		23x00				
Okehampton	d													
Sampford Courtenay	d													
Yeoford	d	18x59		19x58				21x06		23x05				
Crediton	d	19 11		20 06				21 16		23 13				
Newton St Cyres	d			20x09				21x19		23x16				
Exeter St Davids 6	a	19 24		20 18				21 30		23 26				
	d	19 32		20 20	20 25	20 30	21 25	21 32	21 38		22 36	22 57		23 06
Exeter Central	a	19 35		20 24	20 28	20 33	21 28	21 37	21 41		22 39	23 00		23 09
	d	19 36				20 34			21 42		22 40			23 10
St James' Park	d	19 38				20 36			21 44		22 42			23 12
Polsloe Bridge	d	19 41				20 39			21 47		22 45			23 15
Digby & Sowton	d	19 45				20 43			21 51		22 49			23 19
Topsham	d	19 49				20 47			21 55		22 53			23 23
Exton	d	19x52				20x49			21x57		22x56			23x25
Lympstone Commando	d	19x54				20x51			21x59		22x58			23x27
Lympstone Village	d	19 57				20 54			22 03		23 01			23 31
Exmouth	a	20 03				21 01			22 09		23 08			23 36

For connections at Exeter St Davids please see Table 135

Table 136R

Sundays

Barnstaple - Exeter - Exmouth

8 December to 11 May

Route Diagram - see first Page of Table 135

		GW	SW	GW	SW	GW	GW	SW	GW	SW		GW	GW	SW	GW	SW	GW	GW	GW	SW		GW	SW	GW	GW
			◇1		◇1			◇1		◇1				◇1		◇1				◇1			◇1		
																			A						
Barnstaple	d						10 00					11 26					13 24							15 23	
Chapelton	d						10x06										13x30								
Umberleigh	d						10x10					11x34					13x33							15x31	
Portsmouth Arms	d						10x17										13x41							15x38	
Kings Nympton	d						10x22										13x46							15x43	
Eggesford	d						10 32					11 52					13 54							15 52	
Lapford	d						10x37										14x00								
Morchard Road	d						10x41					12x00					14x04							16x00	
Copplestone	d						10x45					12x04					14x07							16x03	
Okehampton	d																								
Sampford Courtenay	d																								
Yeoford	d						10x50					12x09					14x13							16x09	
Crediton	d						10 58					12 18					14 21							16 17	
Newton St Cyres	d						11x01					12x21					14x25							16x21	
Exeter St Davids 6	a						11 11					12 32					14 33							16 29	
	d	08 30	09 25	09 45	10 25	10 46	11 13	11 25	11 55	12 25		12 33	12 48	13 25	13 48	14 25	14 35	14 50	15 14	15 25		15 50	16 25	16 31	16 48
Exeter Central	a	08 33	09 28	09 48	10 28	10 49	11 16	11 28	11 58	12 28		12 36	12 51	13 28	13 51	14 28	14 38	14 53	15 17	15 28		15 53	16 28	16 34	16 51
	d	08 34		09 49		10 52			11 59				12 53		13 52			14 54				15 53			16 52
St James' Park	d	08 36		09 51		10 54			12 01				12 55		13 54			14 56				15 55			16 54
Polsloe Bridge	d	08 39		09 54		10 57			12 04				12 58		13 57			14 59				15 58			16 57
Digby & Sowton	d	08 43		09 58		11 01			12 08				13 02		14 01			15 03				16 02			17 01
Topsham	d	08 47		10 03		11 05			12 12				13 07		14 06			15 08				16 07			17 05
Exton	d	08x49		10x05		11x07			12x14				13x09		14x08			15x10				16x09			17x07
Lympstone Commando	d	08x51		10x07		11x09			12x16				13x11		14x10			15x12				16x11			17x09
Lympstone Village	d	08 55		10 10		11 13			12 20				13 14		14 13			15 15				16 15			17 13
Exmouth	a	09 00		10 15		11 18			12 25				13 20		14 18			15 20				16 20			17 18

		GW	SW	GW	SW	GW		GW	GW	GW	SW	GW	SW	GW	SW	GW		GW	GW	SW	GW				
			◇1		◇1						◇1		◇1		1					1					
		A							A	B															
Barnstaple	d					17 20			19 20	19 20						21 30									
Chapelton	d					17x25										21x36									
Umberleigh	d					17x29			19x28	19x28						21x39									
Portsmouth Arms	d					17x36										21x47									
Kings Nympton	d					17x41										21x52									
Eggesford	d					17 50			19 45	19 45						22 00									
Lapford	d					17x55										22x06									
Morchard Road	d					18x00			19x53	19x53						22x10									
Copplestone	d					18x03			19x57	19x57						22x13									
Okehampton	d																								
Sampford Courtenay	d																								
Yeoford	d					18x09			20x02	20x02						22x19									
Crediton	d					18 18			20 15	20 15						22 28									
Newton St Cyres	d					18x22			20x18	20x18						22x31									
Exeter St Davids 6	a					18 31			20 27	20 28						22 41									
	d	17 23	17 25	17 48	18 25	18 32		18 50			19 25	19 51	20 25	20 52	21 25			21 48	22 48	23 15	23 25				
Exeter Central	a	17 26	17 28	17 51	18 28	18 35		18 53			19 28	19 54	20 28	20 55	21 28			21 51	22 51	23 18	23 28				
	d			17 51				18 54				19 55		20 55				21 51	22 52		23 29				
St James' Park	d			17 53				18 56				19 57		20 57				21 53	22 54		23 31				
Polsloe Bridge	d			17 56				18 59				20 00		21 00				21 56	22 57		23 34				
Digby & Sowton	d			18 00				19 03				20 04		21 04				22 00	23 01		23 38				
Topsham	d			18 05				19 07				20 08		21 08				22 05	23 06		23 42				
Exton	d			18x07				19x09				20x10		21x10				22x07	23x08		23x44				
Lympstone Commando	d			18x09				19x12				20x12		21x12				22x09	23x11		23x46				
Lympstone Village	d			18 13				19 15				20 16		21 16				22 13	23 13		23 50				
Exmouth	a			18 18				19 19				20 21		21 22				22 18	23 18		23 54				

A until 9 February, from 30 March

B from 16 February until 23 March

For connections at Exeter St Davids please see Table 135

Table 139

Plymouth - Gunnislake

Mondays to Fridays

9 December to 16 May

Route Diagram - see first Page of Table 135

Miles			GW	GW	GW	GW	GW	GW	GW	GW	GW		GW	GW	GW	GW	GW	GW	GW
					1 ☕	◇		◇	◇										
0	**Plymouth**	d	05 06	06 41	07 02	08 14	08 40	09 21	10 43	10 54	12 54		14 54	15 57	16 38	17 04	18 17	18 23	21 31
1¼	Devonport	d		06 44	07a06	08a17	08 43	09a24		10 57	12 57		14 57	16 00	16 41	17 07	18 20	18 26	21 34
1½	Dockyard	d		06x45			08x44			10x58	12x58		14x58	16x01	16x42	17x08	18x21	18x27	21x35
2¼	Keyham	d		06 47			08 46			11 00	13 00		15 00	16 03	16 44	17 10	18 23	18 29	21 37
—	St Budeaux Ferry Road	a							10 49					16 06		17 13	18 25		
3	St Budeaux Victoria Road	d	05 12	06 51			08 50			11 04	13 04		15 04		16 48			18 33	21 41
7¼	Bere Ferrers	d		06 58			08 57			11 11	13 11		15 11		16 55			18 40	21 48
10	Bere Alston	a	05 25	07 05			09 04			11 18	13 19		15 18		17 02			18 47	21 55
—		d	05 27	07 07			09 06			11 20	13 20		15 20		17 04			18 49	21 57
11¾	Calstock	d	05 34	07 14			09 13			11 27	13 27		15 27		17 11			18 56	22 04
14½	**Gunnislake**	a	05 50	07 27			09 26			11 40	13 41		15 40		17 24			19 09	22 17

Saturdays

14 December to 17 May

		GW	GW	GW	GW	GW	GW	GW	GW	GW		GW	GW	GW
			◇											
Plymouth	d	06 40	08 18	08 54	09 51	10 33	10 54	12 54	14 47	16 38		17 52	18 23	21 31
Devonport	d	06 43	08a21	08 57	09a54		10 57	12 57	14 50	16 41		17 55	18 26	21 34
Dockyard	d	06x44		08x58			10x58	12x58	14x51	16x42		17x57	18x27	21x35
Keyham	d	06 46		09 00			11 00	13 00	14 53	16 44		17 59	18 29	21 37
St Budeaux Ferry Road	a					10 39						18 00		
St Budeaux Victoria Road	d	06 50		09 04			11 04	13 04	14 57	16 48			18 33	21 41
Bere Ferrers	d	06 57		09 11			11 11	13 11	15 04	16 55			18 40	21 48
Bere Alston	a	07 04		09 18			11 18	13 18	15 11	17 02			18 47	21 55
	d	07 06		09 20			11 20	13 20	15 13	17 04			18 49	21 57
Calstock	d	07 13		09 27			11 27	13 27	15 20	17 11			18 56	22 04
Gunnislake	a	07 26		09 40			11 40	13 40	15 33	17 25			19 09	22 17

Sundays

8 December to 11 May

		GW	GW	GW	GW	GW	GW	GW	GW	GW
				◇	◇ 1					
				A	B				A	B
					☕					
Plymouth	d	09 15	09 30	10 15	10 30	11 40	13 45	15 40	17 45	17 53
Devonport	d		09 33	10a19	10a34	11 43	13 48	15 43	17 48	17 56
Dockyard	d		09x34			11x44	13x49	15x44	17x49	17x57
Keyham	d		09 36			11 46	13 51	15 46	17 51	17 59
St Budeaux Ferry Road	a	09 21								
St Budeaux Victoria Road	d		09 40			11 50	13 55	15 50	17 55	18 03
Bere Ferrers	d		09 47			11 57	14 02	15 57	18 02	18 10
Bere Alston	a		09 54			12 04	14 09	16 04	18 09	18 17
	d		09 56			12 06	14 11	16 06	18 11	18 19
Calstock	d		10 03			12 13	14 18	16 13	18 18	18 26
Gunnislake	a		10 16			12 26	14 31	16 26	18 31	18 39

A until 9 February, from 30 March

B from 16 February until 23 March

Table 139R

Gunnislake - Plymouth

Mondays to Fridays

9 December to 16 May

Route Diagram - see first Page of Table 135

Miles			GW	GW ◇	GW	GW	GW		GW	GW	GW ◇	GW	GW	GW	GW	GW
0	**Gunnislake**	d	05 51		07 31	09 29	11 45		13 45	15 45		17 29		19 13		22 21
3	Calstock	d	06 02		07 42	09 40	11 56		13 56	15 56		17 40		19 24		22 32
4½	Bere Alston	a	06 08		07 49	09 47	12 03		14 03	16 03		17 47		19 31		22 39
—		d	06 11		07 51	09 49	12 05		14 05	16 05		17 49		19 33		22 41
7½	Bere Ferrers	d	06 16		07 56	09 54	12 10		14 10	16 10		17 54		19 38		22 46
11½	St Budeaux Victoria Road	d	06 25		08 05	10 03	12 19		14 19	16 19		18 03		19 47		22 55
—	St Budeaux Ferry Road	d		07 52							16 42		18 12		21 09	
12½	Keyham	d	06 27	07 54	08 07	10 05	12 21		14 21	16 21	16 44	18 05		19 49	21 11	22 57
13	Dockyard	d	06x29	07x56	08x09	10x07	12x23		14x23	16x23	16x46	18x07		19x51	21x13	22x59
13½	Devonport	d	06 31	07 58	08 11	10 09	12 25		14 25	16 25	16 48	18 09		19 53	21 15	23 01
14½	**Plymouth**	a	06 36	08 04	08 17	10 14	12 30		14 30	16 30	16 52	18 14	18 19	19 58	21 20	23 06

Saturdays

14 December to 17 May

		GW	GW	GW	GW	GW	GW ◇	GW	GW	GW		GW	GW	GW
Gunnislake	d		07 31	09 45	11 45	13 45		15 45	17 29	19 17			22 21	
Calstock	d		07 42	09 56	11 56	13 56		15 56	17 40	19 28			22 32	
Bere Alston	a		07 49	10 03	12 03	14 03		16 03	17 47	19 35			22 39	
	d		07 51	10 05	12 05	14 05		16 05	17 49	19 37			22 41	
Bere Ferrers	d		07 56	10 10	12 10	14 10		16 10	17 54	19 42			22 46	
St Budeaux Victoria Road	d		08 05	10 19	12 19	14 19		16 19	18 03	19 51			22 55	
St Budeaux Ferry Road	d	07 30										20 58		22 59
Keyham	d	07 32	08 07	10 21	12 21	14 21		16 21	18 05	19 53		21 00	22 57	23 01
Dockyard	d	07x34	08x09	10x23	12x23	14x23		16x23	18x07	19x55		21x02	22x59	23x03
Devonport	d	07 36	08 11	10 25	12 25	14 25	14 52	16 25	18 09	19 57		21 04	23 01	23 05
Plymouth	a	07 42	08 17	10 30	12 30	14 30	14 58	16 30	18 14	20 02		21 10	23 06	23 12

Sundays

8 December to 11 May

		GW	GW	GW	GW	GW	GW A	GW B
Gunnislake	d	10 25	12 45	14 45	16 54	18 44		
Calstock	d	10 36	12 56	14 56	17 05	18 55		
Bere Alston	a	10 43	13 03	15 03	17 12	19 02		
	d	10 45	13 05	15 05	17 14	19 04		
Bere Ferrers	d	10 50	13 10	15 10	17 19	19 09		
St Budeaux Victoria Road	d	10 59	13 19	15 19	17 28	19 18		
St Budeaux Ferry Road	d							
Keyham	d	11 01	13 21	15 21	17 30	19 20		
Dockyard	d	11x03	13x23	15x23	17x32	19x22		
Devonport	d	11 05	13 25	15 25	17 34	19 24	20§56	20§54
Plymouth	a	11 10	13 30	15 30	17 39	19 29	20§59	21§00

A from 16 February until 23 March

B until 9 February, from 30 March

Table 140

Liskeard - Looe

Mondays to Fridays

9 December to 16 May

Route Diagram - see first Page of Table 135

Miles			GW	GW	GW	GW	GW	GW	GW	GW	GW		GW	GW	GW
0	**Liskeard** 6	d	06 05	07 14	08 33	09 58	11 18	12 15	13 19	14 28	15 41		16 41	18 01	19 18
2	Coombe Junction Halt	a			08 39	10 04									
—		d			08 42	10 07									
3¾	St Keyne Wishing Well Halt	d	06x17	07x26	08x48	10x13		12x27	13x31		15x53		16x53	18x13	19x31
5	Causeland	d	06x21	07x30	08x52	10x17		12x31	13x35		15x57		16x57	18x17	19x33
6½	Sandplace	d	06x24	07x33	08x56	10x20		12x34	13x38		16x00		17x00	18x20	19x38
8¾	**Looe**	a	06 36	07 45	09 04	10 29	11 46	12 46	13 50	14 56	16 12		17 12	18 32	19 49

Saturdays

14 December to 17 May

		GW	GW	GW	GW	GW	GW	GW	GW	GW		GW	GW	GW
Liskeard 6	d	06 01	07 12	08 35	09 58	11 08	12 12	13 24	14 28	15 42		16 56	18 01	19 28
Coombe Junction Halt	a			08 41	10 04									
	d			08 44	10 06									
St Keyne Wishing Well Halt	d	06x13	07x24	08x50	10x13		12x24	13x37		15x54		17x09	18x13	19x41
Causeland	d	06x17	07x28	08x54	10x17		12x28	13x40		15x58		17x12	18x17	19x43
Sandplace	d	06x20	07x31	08x58	10x20		12x31	13x44		16x01		17x16	18x20	19x48
Looe	a	06 32	07 43	09 06	10 29	11 36	12 43	13 55	14 56	16 13		17 27	18 32	19 59

Sundays

8 December to 11 May

Liskeard 6	d
Coombe Junction Halt	a
	d
St Keyne Wishing Well Halt	d
Causeland	d
Sandplace	d
Looe	a

For connections at Liskeard please see Table 135

Table 140R

Mondays to Fridays

9 December to 16 May

Looe - Liskeard

Route Diagram - see first Page of Table 135

Miles			GW	GW	GW	GW	GW	GW		GW	GW	GW	GW	GW	GW
0	**Looe**	d	06 37	07 46	09 09	10 32	11 47	12 47		13 51	14 57	16 13	17 15	18 33	19 52
2¼	Sandplace	d	06x42	07x51	09x14	10x37		12x52			15x02		17x20	18x38	19x57
3¾	Causeland	d	06x46	07x55	09x18	10x41		12x56			15x06		17x24	18x42	20x01
5	St Keyne Wishing Well Halt	d	06x49	07x58	09x21	10x44		12x59			15x09		17x27	18x45	20x04
6¾	Coombe Junction Halt	a			09 27	10 50									
—		d			09 29	10 52									
8¾	**Liskeard** 6	a	07 05	08 14	09 40	11 03	12 11	13 17		14 15	15 25	16 39	17 43	19 01	20 22

Saturdays

14 December to 17 May

		GW	GW	GW	GW	GW	GW	GW	GW	GW		GW	GW	GW
Looe	d	06 33	07 47	09 09	10 32	11 37	12 44	13 56	14 56	16 14		17 28	18 33	20 00
Sandplace	d	06x38	07x52	09x14	10x37		12x49		15x01	16x19		17x33	18x38	20x05
Causeland	d	06x42	07x56	09x18	10x41		12x53		15x05	16x23		17x37	18x42	20x09
St Keyne Wishing Well Halt	d	06x45	07x59	09x21	10x45		12x56		15x08	16x27		17x41	18x45	20x13
Coombe Junction Halt	a			09 27	10 50									
	d			09 29	10 52									
Liskeard 6	a	07 01	08 15	09 40	11 03	12 01	13 12	14 20	15 25	16 44		17 58	19 01	20 28

Sundays

8 December to 11 May

Looe	d
Sandplace	d
Causeland	d
St Keyne Wishing Well Halt	d
Coombe Junction Halt	a
	d
Liskeard 6	a

For connections at Liskeard please see Table 135

No Sunday Service in Winter

Table 142

Par - Newquay

Mondays to Fridays

9 December to 16 May

Route Diagram - see first Page of Table 135

Miles			GW	GW	GW	GW	GW	GW
				◇	◇	◇	◇	
0	**Par**	d	09 17	12 13	14 07	16 10	18 29	20 28
4¼	Luxulyan	d	09x28	.	14x18	16x21	18x40	20x39
6¼	Bugle	d	09x34	12x30	14x24	16x26	18x46	20x45
8¾	Roche	d	09x38	.	14x29	16x32	18x50	20x49
14½	St Columb Road	d	09x50	.	14x40	16x43	19x02	21x01
18¼	Quintrell Downs	d	09 58	.	14 48	16 51	19 10	21 09
20¾	**Newquay**	a	10 09	13 01	14 59	17 02	19 21	21 20

Saturdays

14 December to 17 May

		GW	GW	GW	GW	GW	GW	GW
				◇	◇	◇	◇	
Par	d	06 52	09 18	12 15	14 10	16 15	18 21	20 15
Luxulyan	d	07x03	09x29	12x26	.	16x26	18x32	20x26
Bugle	d	07x09	09x35	12x32	14x27	16x32	18x38	20x32
Roche	d	07x14	09x39	12x37	.	16x37	18x43	20x37
St Columb Road	d	07x25	09x51	12x48	.	16x48	18x54	20x48
Quintrell Downs	d	07 33	09 59	12 56	.	16 56	19 02	20 56
Newquay	a	07 44	10 10	13 07	14 57	17 07	19 13	21 07

Sundays

8 December to 11 May

		GW	GW	GW	GW	GW
					◇	◇
			A	B	B	A
Par	d	10 18	13§31	14§00	16§05	16§30
Luxulyan	d	10x29	13x42	14x11	16x16	16x41
Bugle	d	10x35	13x48	14x17	16x22	16x47
Roche	d	10x40	13x53	14x22	16x27	16x52
St Columb Road	d	10x51	14x04	14x33	16x38	17x03
Quintrell Downs	d	10 59	14§12	14§41	16§46	17§11
Newquay	a	11 10	14§23	14§52	16§57	17§22

A until 9 February, from 30 March

B from 16 February until 23 March

For connections at Par please see Table 135

Table 142R

Mondays to Fridays

9 December to 16 May

Newquay - Par

Route Diagram - see first Page of Table 135

Miles			GW	GW	GW		GW	GW	GW
			◇	◇	◇		◇		
0	**Newquay**	d	10 13	13 03	15 01		17 22	19 25	21 26
2½	Quintrell Downs	d	10 19	13 09	15 07		17 28	19 31	21 32
6½	St Columb Road	d	10x26	13x16			17x35		21x39
12	Roche	d	10x38	13x28			17x47		21x51
14½	Bugle	d	10x42	13x32	15x28		17x51	19x54	21x55
16½	Luxulyan	d	10x48	13x38			17x57		22x01
20¾	**Par**	a	11 02	13 52	15 47		18 13	20 13	22 16

Saturdays

14 December to 17 May

		GW	GW	GW	GW	GW	GW	GW
		◇	◇	◇	◇	◇		
Newquay	d	07 48	10 12	13 09	14 59	17 21	19 17	21 18
Quintrell Downs	d	07 54	10 18	13 15	15 05	17 27	19 23	21 24
St Columb Road	d	08x02	10x26	13x23	15x13	17x35		21x32
Roche	d	08x13	10x37	13x34	15x24	17x46		21x43
Bugle	d	08x18	10x42	13x39	15x29	17x51	19x46	21x48
Luxulyan	d	08x23	10x47	13x44	15x34	17x56		21x53
Par	a	08 39	11 01	13 58	15 48	18 10	20 03	22 07

Sundays

8 December to 11 May

		GW	GW	GW	GW	GW
		◇	◇	◇		
		A	B		B	A
Newquay	d	11ʃ12	11ʃ25	15 10	17ʃ10	17ʃ30
Quintrell Downs	d	11ʃ18	11ʃ31	15 16	17ʃ16	17ʃ36
St Columb Road	d	11x26	11x39	15x24	17x24	17x44
Roche	d	11x37	11x50	15x35	17x35	17x55
Bugle	d	11x42	11x55	15x40	17x40	18x00
Luxulyan	d	11x47	12x00	15x45	17x45	18x05
Par	a	12ʃ01	12ʃ14	15 59	17ʃ59	18ʃ19

A until 9 February, from 30 March

B from 16 February until 23 March

For connections at Par please see Table 135

Table 143

Truro - Falmouth

Mondays to Fridays

9 December to 16 May

Route Diagram - see first Page of Table 135

Miles			GW	GW	GW	GW	GW	GW		GW	GW	GW	GW	GW	GW	GW	GW	GW	GW	GW
0	**Truro**	d	06 04	06 31	07 16	07 47	08 20	08 51	and at the same minutes past each hour until	15 20	15 51	16 20	16 51	17 27	17 59	18 31	19 02	20 04	21 05	22 08
4¼	Perranwell	d	06x10	06x37	07x22	07x53	08x26			15x26		16x26	16x57	17x33	18x05	18x37	19x08	20x10	21x11	22x14
8¼	Penryn	d	06 18	06 45	07 30	08 01	08 34	09 04		15 34	16 04	16 34	17 05	17 41	18 13	18 45	19 16	20 18	21 19	22 22
10¼	Penmere	d	06 23	06 50	07 35	08 06	08 39	09 09		15 39	16 09	16 39	17 10	17 46	18 18	18 50	19 21	20 23	21 24	22 27
11¾	Falmouth Town	d	06 26	06 53	07 38	08 09	08 42	09 12		15 42	16 12	16 42	17 13	17 49	18 21	18 53	19 24	20 26	21 27	22 30
12¼	**Falmouth Docks**	a	06 28	06 55	07 40	08 11	08 44	09 14		15 44	16 14	16 44	17 15	17 51	18 23	18 55	19 26	20 28	21 29	22 32

Saturdays

14 December to 17 May

		GW	GW	GW	GW	GW	GW		GW	GW	GW	GW	GW	GW	GW	GW	GW	GW	GW
Truro	d	06 04	06 31	07 14	07 47	08 20	08 51	and at the same minutes past each hour until	15 20	15 51	16 20	16 51	17 27	17 59	18 31	19 02	20 04	21 05	22 06
Perranwell	d	06x10	06x37	07x19	07x53	08x26			15x26		16x26	16x57	17x33	18x05	18x37	19x08	20x10	21x11	22x12
Penryn	d	06 18	06 45	07 27	08 01	08 34	09 04		15 34	16 04	16 34	17 05	17 41	18 13	18 45	19 16	20 18	21 19	22 20
Penmere	d	06 23	06 50	07 32	08 06	08 39	09 09		15 39	16 09	16 39	17 10	17 46	18 18	18 50	19 21	20 23	21 24	22 25
Falmouth Town	d	06 26	06 53	07 35	08 09	08 42	09 12		15 42	16 12	16 42	17 13	17 49	18 21	18 53	19 24	20 26	21 27	22 28
Falmouth Docks	a	06 28	06 55	07 38	08 11	08 44	09 14		15 44	16 14	16 44	17 15	17 51	18 23	18 55	19 26	20 28	21 29	22 30

Sundays

8 December to 9 February

		GW	GW	GW	GW	GW	GW	GW	GW	GW	GW	GW
Truro	d	09 01	10 42	12 09	13 08	14 12	15 35	17 00	18 13	19 46	21 03	22 04
Perranwell	d	09x08	10x49	12x16	13x15	14x19	15x42	17x07	18x20	19x53	21x10	22x11
Penryn	d	09 15	10 56	12 23	13 22	14 26	15 49	17 14	18 27	20 00	21 17	22 18
Penmere	d	09 20	11 01	12 28	13 27	14 31	15 53	17 19	18 32	20 05	21 22	22 23
Falmouth Town	d	09 23	11 04	12 31	13 30	14 34	15 56	17 22	18 35	20 08	21 25	22 26
Falmouth Docks	a	09 25	11 06	12 33	13 32	14 36	16 00	17 24	18 37	20 10	21 27	22 28

Sundays

16 February to 23 March

		GW	GW	GW	GW	GW	GW	GW	GW	GW	GW	GW
Truro	d	09 12	10 45	12 09	13 08	14 12	15 35	16 43	18 13	19 46	21 03	22 04
Perranwell	d	09x19	10x52	12x16	13x15	14x19	15x42	16x50	18x20	19x53	21x10	22x11
Penryn	d	09 26	10 59	12 23	13 22	14 26	15 49	16 57	18 27	20 00	21 17	22 18
Penmere	d	09 31	11 04	12 28	13 27	14 31	15 53	17 02	18 32	20 05	21 22	22 23
Falmouth Town	d	09 34	11 07	12 31	13 30	14 34	15 56	17 05	18 35	20 08	21 25	22 26
Falmouth Docks	a	09 36	11 09	12 33	13 32	14 36	16 00	17 07	18 37	20 10	21 27	22 28

Sundays

30 March to 11 May

		GW	GW	GW	GW	GW	GW	GW	GW	GW	GW	GW
Truro	d	09 01	10 42	12 09	13 08	14 12	15 35	17 00	18 13	19 46	21 03	22 04
Perranwell	d	09x08	10x49	12x16	13x15	14x19	15x42	17x07	18x20	19x53	21x10	22x11
Penryn	d	09 15	10 56	12 23	13 22	14 26	15 49	17 14	18 27	20 00	21 17	22 18
Penmere	d	09 20	11 01	12 28	13 27	14 31	15 53	17 19	18 32	20 05	21 22	22 23
Falmouth Town	d	09 23	11 04	12 31	13 30	14 34	15 56	17 22	18 35	20 08	21 25	22 26
Falmouth Docks	a	09 25	11 06	12 33	13 32	14 36	16 00	17 24	18 37	20 10	21 27	22 28

For connections at Truro please see Table 135

Table 143R

Falmouth - Truro

Mondays to Fridays

9 December to 16 May

Route Diagram - see first Page of Table 135

Miles			GW	GW	GW	GW	GW	GW	GW	GW	GW	GW	GW	GW	GW		GW	GW	GW	GW	GW	GW
0	**Falmouth Docks**	d	06 31	07 16	07 47	08 20	08 50	09 20	09 50	10 20	10 50	11 20	11 50	12 20	12 50	and at the same minutes past each hour until	15 20	15 50	16 20	16 50	17 27	17 59
0½	Falmouth Town	d	06 34	07 19	07 50	08 23	08 53	09 23	09 53	10 23	10 53	11 23	11 53	12 23	12 53		15 23	15 53	16 23	16 53	17 30	18 02
2	Penmere	d	06 37	07 22	07 53	08 26	08 56	09 26	09 56	10 26	10 56	11 26	11 56	12 26	12 56		15 26	15 56	16 26	16 56	17 33	18 05
4	Penryn	d	06 45	07 30	08 01	08 34	09 04	09 34	10 04	10 34	11 04	11 34	12 04	12 34	13 04		15 34	16 04	16 34	17 04	17 40	18 13
8	Perranwell	d	06x51	07x36	08x07	08x40	.....	09x40	.....	10x40	.....	11x40	.....	12x40	.....		15x40	.....	16x40	17x11	17x48	18x19
12¼	**Truro**	a	06 59	07 44	08 15	08 48	09 18	09 48	10 18	10 48	11 18	11 48	12 17	12 48	13 18		15 48	16 18	16 48	17 19	17 55	18 27

		GW	GW	GW	GW	GW	GW
Falmouth Docks	d	18 31	19 02	19 29	20 31	21 32	22 35
Falmouth Town	d	18 34	19 05	19 32	20 34	21 35	22 38
Penmere	d	18 37	19 08	19 35	20 37	21 38	22 41
Penryn	d	18 45	19 16	19 40	20 42	21 43	22 46
Perranwell	d	18x51	19x22	19x46	20x48	21x49	22x52
Truro	a	18 59	19 30	19 55	20 57	21 59	23 02

Saturdays

14 December to 17 May

		GW	GW	GW	GW	GW		GW	GW	GW	GW	GW	GW	GW	GW	GW	GW	GW	GW
Falmouth Docks	d	06 31	07 15	07 47	08 20	08 50	and at the same minutes past each hour until	15 20	15 50	16 20	16 51	17 27	17 59	18 31	19 02	19 29	20 31	21 32	22 33
Falmouth Town	d	06 34	07 18	07 50	08 23	08 53		15 23	15 53	16 23	16 53	17 30	18 02	18 34	19 05	19 32	20 34	21 35	22 36
Penmere	d	06 37	07 21	07 53	08 26	08 56		15 26	15 56	16 26	16 56	17 33	18 05	18 37	19 08	19 35	20 37	21 38	22 39
Penryn	d	06 45	07 29	08 01	08 34	09 04		15 34	16 04	16 34	17 04	17 40	18 13	18 45	19 16	19 40	20 42	21 43	22 44
Perranwell	d	06x51	07x35	08x07	08x40	.....		15x40	.....	16x40	17x11	17x48	18x19	18x51	19x22	19x46	20x48	21x49	22x50
Truro	a	06 59	07 43	08 15	08 48	09 18		15 48	16 18	16 48	17 19	17 55	18 27	18 59	19 30	19 55	20 57	21 58	23 00

Sundays

8 December to 9 February

		GW	GW	GW	GW	GW	GW	GW	GW	GW	GW	GW
Falmouth Docks	d	09 35	11 09	12 35	13 35	14 39	16 14	17 30	18 40	20 13	21 30	22 32
Falmouth Town	d	09 38	11 12	12 39	13 38	14 42	16 17	17 33	18 43	20 16	21 33	22 35
Penmere	d	09 41	11 15	12 42	13 41	14 45	16 20	17 36	18 46	20 19	21 36	22 38
Penryn	d	09 46	11 20	12 47	13 49	14 50	16 25	17 41	18 51	20 24	21 40	22 43
Perranwell	d	09x53	11x27	12x54	13x56	14x57	16x32	17x48	18x58	20x31	21x47	22x50
Truro	a	10 01	11 35	13 02	14 03	15 05	16 39	17 56	19 06	20 39	21 55	23 01

Sundays

16 February to 23 March

		GW	GW	GW	GW	GW	GW	GW	GW	GW	GW	GW
Falmouth Docks	d	09 39	11 18	12 35	13 35	14 39	16 14	17 10	18 40	20 13	21 30	22 32
Falmouth Town	d	09 42	11 21	12 39	13 38	14 42	16 17	17 13	18 43	20 16	21 33	22 35
Penmere	d	09 45	11 24	12 42	13 41	14 45	16 20	17 16	18 46	20 19	21 36	22 38
Penryn	d	09 50	11 29	12 47	13 49	14 50	16 25	17 21	18 51	20 24	21 40	22 43
Perranwell	d	09x57	11x36	12x54	13x56	14x57	16x32	17x28	18x58	20x31	21x47	22x50
Truro	a	10 05	11 44	13 02	14 03	15 05	16 39	17 36	19 06	20 39	21 55	23 01

Sundays

30 March to 11 May

		GW	GW	GW	GW	GW	GW	GW	GW	GW	GW	GW
Falmouth Docks	d	09 35	11 09	12 35	13 35	14 39	16 14	17 30	18 40	20 13	21 30	22 32
Falmouth Town	d	09 38	11 12	12 39	13 38	14 42	16 17	17 33	18 43	20 16	21 33	22 35
Penmere	d	09 41	11 15	12 42	13 41	14 45	16 20	17 36	18 46	20 19	21 36	22 38
Penryn	d	09 46	11 20	12 47	13 49	14 50	16 25	17 41	18 51	20 24	21 40	22 43
Perranwell	d	09x53	11x27	12x54	13x56	14x57	16x32	17x48	18x58	20x31	21x47	22x50
Truro	a	10 01	11 35	13 02	14 03	15 05	16 39	17 56	19 06	20 39	21 55	23 01

For connections at Truro please see Table 135

Table 144

St Erth - St Ives

Mondays to Fridays

9 December to 16 May

Route Diagram - see first Page of Table 135

Miles			GW	GW	GW	GW	GW	GW	GW	GW	GW		GW	GW	GW	GW	GW	GW	GW	GW	GW		GW	GW	GW
—	Penzance	d	06 55		08 57																				
0	**St Erth**	d	07 03	08 01	09 05	09 38	10 18	10 48	11 18	11 48	12 18		12 48	13 18	13 48	14 18	14 48	15 18	15 48	16 18	16 48		17 17	17 48	18 18
0¾	Lelant Saltings	d			09 09	09 41	10 21	10 51	11 21	11 51	12 21		12 51	13 21	13 51	14 21	14 51	15 21	15 51	16 21			17 20		18 21
1	Lelant	d	07x07	08x03	09x10																16x50			17x50	18x22
3	Carbis Bay	d	07 12	08 09	09 16	09 47		10 57		11 57			12 57		13 57		14 57		15 57		16 56			17 56	18 27
4¼	**St Ives**	a	07 15	08 14	09 19	09 52	10 31	11 02	11 31	12 02	12 31		13 02	13 31	14 02	14 31	15 02	15 31	16 02	16 31	17 01		17 30	18 01	18 33

		GW	GW	GW	GW	GW	GW		GW
Penzance	d								
St Erth	d	18 48	19 18	19 48	20 18	20 48	21 23		21 58
Lelant Saltings	d		19 21		20 21				22 01
Lelant	d	18x51		19x51		20x51	21x25		22x02
Carbis Bay	d	18 56		19 56		20 56	21 31		22 08
St Ives	a	19 03	19 31	20 01	20 31	21 02	21 36		22 13

Saturdays

14 December to 17 May

		GW	GW	GW	GW	GW	GW	GW	GW	GW		GW	GW	GW	GW	GW	GW	GW	GW	GW		GW	GW	GW	GW
Penzance	d	06 41		08 54																				18 50	
St Erth	d	06 50	08 00	09 03	09 35	10 13	10 48	11 18	11 48	12 18		12 48	13 18	13 48	14 18	14 48	15 18	15 48	16 18	16 48		17 17	17 59	18 59	19 53
Lelant Saltings	d			09 06	09 38	10 16	10 51	11 21	11 51	12 21		12 51	13 21	13 51	14 21	14 51	15 21	15 51	16 21			17 20	18 02	19 02	19 56
Lelant	d	06x53	08x03	09x08																16x51			18x04	19x04	19x58
Carbis Bay	d	06 58	08 08	09 13	09 44		10 57		11 57			12 57		13 57		14 57		15 57		16 56		17 26	18 09	19 09	20 03
St Ives	a	07 03	08 13	09 18	09 49	10 26	11 02	11 31	12 02	12 31		13 02	13 31	14 02	14 31	15 02	15 31	16 02	16 31	17 01		17 31	18 13	19 14	20 07

		GW	GW	GW
Penzance	d			
St Erth	d	20 33	21 06	21 47
Lelant Saltings	d	20 36	21 07	21 48
Lelant	d	20x38	21x09	21x50
Carbis Bay	d	20 43	21 14	21 55
St Ives	a	20 47	21 19	22 01

Sundays

8 December to 11 May

		GW	GW	GW	GW	GW	GW	GW	GW	GW		GW	GW	GW	GW	GW
Penzance	d	11 45														
St Erth	d	11 56	12 30	13 18	13 48	14 18	14 48	15 18	15 48	16 18		16 48	17 18	17 48	18 30	19 30
Lelant Saltings	d	11 59	12 33	13 21	13 51	14 21	14 51	15 21	15 51	16 21		16 51	17 21	17 51	18 33	19 33
Lelant	d	12x01												17x53	18x35	19x35
Carbis Bay	d	12 06	12 39		13 57		14 57		15 57			16 57		17 58	18 40	19 40
St Ives	a	12 12	12 44	13 31	14 02	14 31	15 02	15 31	16 02	16 31		17 02	17 31	18 02	18 45	19 45

For connections at St Erth please see Table 135

Table 144R

St Ives - St Erth

Mondays to Fridays

9 December to 16 May

Route Diagram - see first Page of Table 135

Miles			GW	GW	GW	GW	GW	GW		GW	GW	GW	GW	GW	GW	GW	GW	GW		GW	GW	GW	GW	GW	GW
0	**St Ives**	d	07 25	08 15	09 22	09 53	10 33	11 03		11 33	12 03	12 33	13 03	13 33	14 03	14 33	15 03	15 33		16 03	16 33	17 03	17 31	18 03	18 33
1¼	Carbis Bay	d	07 28	08 18	09 25		10 36			11 36		12 36		13 36		14 36		15 36			16 36		17 34		18 36
3¼	Lelant	d	07x33	08x23	09x30																			18x10	18x41
3½	Lelant Saltings	d			09 33		10 43			11 43		12 43		13 43	14 13	14 43	15 13	15 43		16 13	16 43	17 12	17 41	18 13	18 44
4¼	**St Erth**	a	07 37	08 28	09 37	10 05	10 47	11 16		11 47	12 16	12 47	13 16	13 47	14 17	14 47	15 17	15 47		16 17	16 47	17 16	17 44	18 17	18 48
—	Penzance	a		08 40																					

		GW	GW	GW		GW	GW	GW	GW
St Ives	d	19 05	19 32	20 03		20 33	21 03	21 37	22 31
Carbis Bay	d		19 35			20 36	21 06	21 40	22 34
Lelant	d		19x40			20x41	21x11	21x45	22x39
Lelant Saltings	d		19 43	20 12		20 44	21 14		22 41
St Erth	a	19 16	19 47	20 16		20 47	21 18	21 50	22 45
Penzance	a								22 57

Saturdays

14 December to 17 May

		GW	GW	GW	GW	GW	GW	GW	GW	GW		GW	GW	GW	GW	GW	GW	GW	GW	GW		GW	GW	GW	GW
St Ives	d	07 12	08 15	09 20	09 50	10 27	11 03	11 33	12 03	12 33		13 03	13 33	14 03	14 33	15 03	15 33	16 03	16 33	17 03		17 32	18 17	19 26	20 10
Carbis Bay	d	07 15	08 18	09 23		10 30		11 36		12 36			13 36		14 36		15 36		16 36			17 35	18 20	19 29	20 13
Lelant	d	07x20	08x23			10x35																17x40	18x25	19x34	20x18
Lelant Saltings	d			09 30		10 38		11 43		12 43			13 43	14 12	14 43	15 12	15 43	16 12	16 43	17 12		17 43	18 28	19 37	20 21
St Erth	a	07 24	08 27	09 33	10 00	10 40	11 13	11 47	12 15	12 47		13 15	13 47	14 14	14 47	15 16	15 47	16 16	16 46	17 16		17 45	18 31	19 41	20 23
Penzance	a		08 40																				18 44		

		GW	GW	GW
St Ives	d	20 49	21 24	22 05
Carbis Bay	d	20 52	21 27	22 08
Lelant	d	20x57	21x32	22x13
Lelant Saltings	d	21 00	21 35	22 16
St Erth	a	21 02	21 37	22 19
Penzance	a			22 32

Sundays

8 December to 11 May

		GW	GW	GW	GW	GW	GW	GW	GW	GW		GW	GW	GW	GW	GW
St Ives	d	12 13	12 48	13 33	14 03	14 33	15 03	15 33	16 03	16 33		17 03	17 33	18 03	18 50	19 50
Carbis Bay	d	12 16	12 51	13 36		14 36		15 36		16 36			17 36		18 51	19 53
Lelant	d	12x21												18x10	18x58	19x58
Lelant Saltings	d	12 24	12 58	13 43	14 12	14 43	15 12	15 43	16 12	16 43		17 12	17 43	18 13	19 01	20 01
St Erth	a	12 26	13 00	13 45	14 16	14 45	15 14	15 45	16 16	16 47		17 16	17 47	18 17	19 03	20 04
Penzance	a															20 14

For connections at St Erth please see Table 135

Network Diagram for Tables 148, 149

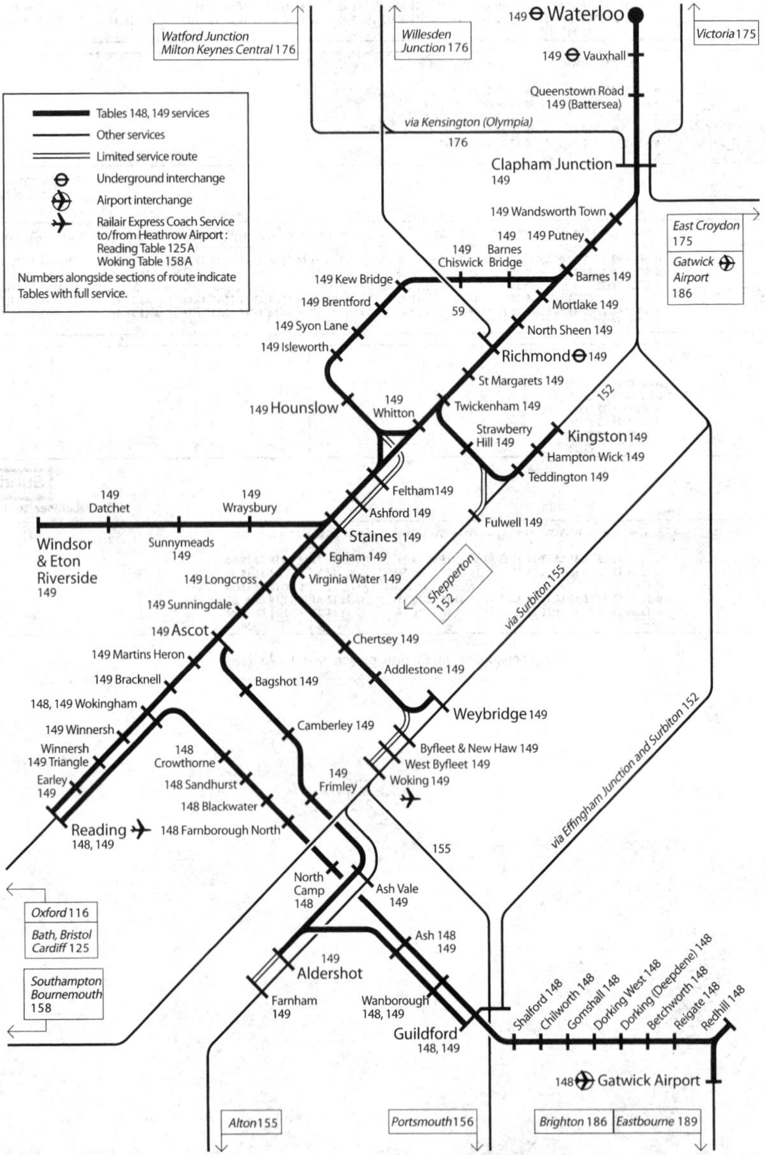
Tables 148, 149 services
Other services
Limited service route
Underground interchange
Airport interchange
Railair Express Coach Service to/from Heathrow Airport: Reading Table 125A Woking Table 158A
Numbers alongside sections of route indicate Tables with full service.
Watford Junction Milton Keynes Central 176
Willesden Junction 176
Victoria 175
149 Waterloo
149 Vauxhall
Queenstown Road 149 (Battersea)
via Kensington (Olympia)
176
Clapham Junction 149
149 Wandsworth Town
149 Putney
149 Barnes
149 Chiswick
Barnes Bridge
East Croydon 175
Gatwick Airport 186
Barnes 149
149 Kew Bridge
149 Brentford
149 Syon Lane
149 Isleworth
59
Mortlake 149
North Sheen 149
Richmond 149
St Margarets 149
152
149 Hounslow
149 Whitton
Twickenham 149
Strawberry Hill 149
Kingston 149
Hampton Wick 149
Teddington 149
Feltham 149
Ashford 149
Fulwell 149
149 Datchet
149 Wraysbury
Staines 149
Windsor & Eton Riverside 149
Sunnymeads 149
Egham 149
149 Longcross
Virginia Water 149
Shepperton 152
via Surbiton 155
149 Sunningdale
149 Ascot
Chertsey 149
149 Martins Heron
Addlestone 149
149 Bracknell
Bagshot 149
148, 149 Wokingham
Weybridge 149
149 Winnersh
Camberley 149
Byfleet & New Haw 149
West Byfleet 149
Winnersh 149 Triangle
148 Crowthorne
Woking 149
Earley 149
148 Sandhurst
149 Frimley
via Effingham Junction and Surbiton 152
148 Blackwater
Reading 148, 149
148 Farnborough North
155
North Camp 148
Ash Vale 149
Oxford 116
Bath, Bristol Cardiff 125
Ash 148 149
149 Aldershot
Southampton Bournemouth 158
Farnham 149
Wanborough 148, 149
Guildford 148, 149
Shalford 148
Chilworth 148
Gomshall 148
Dorking West 148
Dorking (Deepdene) 148
Betchworth 148
Reigate 148
Redhill 148
148 Gatwick Airport
Alton 155
Portsmouth 156
Brighton 186
Eastbourne 189

TOCs operating on this network - South West Trains (SW), First Great Western (GW), Cross Country (XC)

Table 148

Mondays to Fridays

9 December to 16 May

Reading - Guildford, Redhill and Gatwick Airport

Network Diagram - see first Page of Table 148

Miles				GW	GW	GW	GW	GW	GW	GW	GW	GW		GW	GW	GW	GW	GW	GW	GW	GW	GW		GW	GW	GW
				MO	MX																					
				1	1	1	1	1	1	1	1	1		1	1	1	1	1	1	1	1	1		1	1	1
0	**Reading [7]**	149	d			04 34	05 24	05 54	06 06	06 34	07 04	07 34		08 04	08 20	08 34	09 04	09 34	10 04	10 34	11 04	11 34		12 04	12 34	13 04
6¾	Wokingham	149	d			04 43	05 33	06 03	06 16	06 43	07 13	07 43		08 13	08 29	08 43	09 13	09 43	10 13	10 43	11 13	11 43		12 13	12 43	13 13
10	Crowthorne		d					06 09	06 21		07 18	07 48		08 18	08 34		09 18		10 18		11 18			12 18		13 18
11½	Sandhurst		d					06 12	06 25		07 22	07 52		08 22	08 38		09 22		10 22		11 22			12 22		13 22
13½	Blackwater		d			04 51	05 41	06 16	06 28	06 51	07 25	07 55		08 25	08 41	08 51	09 25	09 51	10 25	10 51	11 25	11 51		12 25	12 51	13 25
15½	Farnborough North		d					06 20	06 33		07 30	08 00		08 30	08 46		09 30		10 30		11 30			12 30		13 30
17½	North Camp		d		00 04	04 57	05 48	06 24	06 37	06 57	07 34	08 04		08 34	08 50	09 01	09 34	09 57	10 34	10 57	11 34	11 57		12 34	12 57	13 34
19½	Ash [5]	149	d		00 08			06 28	06 41		07 38	08 08		08 38	08 54		09 38		10 38		11 38			12 38		13 38
21½	Wanborough	149	d		00 13			06 33																		
25¾	**Guildford**	149	a		00 20	05 09	05 59	06 40	06 50	07 09	07 47	08 17		08 47	09 03	09 13	09 47	10 08	10 47	11 08	11 47	12 08		12 47	13 08	13 47
—			d		00 21	05 10	06 00	06 43	06 58	07 10	07 48	08 18		08 48	09 04	09 13	09 48	10 10	10 48	11 10	11 48	12 10		12 48	13 10	13 48
27¾	Shalford		d					06 48	07a04		07 53			08 53	09a11		09 53		10 53		11 53			12 53		13 53
29¾	Chilworth		d					06 52			07 57			08 57			09 57				11 57					13 57
33½	Gomshall		d					06 58			08 04			09 04			10 04				12 04					14 04
38¼	Dorking West		d					07 06			08 11			09 11					11 06					13 06		
39	Dorking Deepdene		d	00 19	00 38	05 26	06 17	07 08		07 26	08 14	08 35		09 14		09 30	10 11	10 26	11 08	11 26	12 11	12 26		13 08	13 26	14 11
41¾	Betchworth		d					07 13			08 19			09 19					11 13					13 13		
44½	Reigate	186	d	00 26	00 45	05 34	06 24	07 18		07 34	08 24	08 42		09 24		09 37	10 19	10 34	11 19	11 34	12 19	12 34		13 19	13 34	14 19
46½	**Redhill**	186	a	00 30	00 49	05 39	06 29	07 24		07 38	08 30	08 46		09 30		09 42	10 25	10 38	11 25	11 38	12 25	12 38		13 25	13 38	14 25
52¼	**Gatwick Airport [10]**	186	a	00 41	01 03	05 54	06 41			07 50		08 59				09 59		10 50		11 50		12 50			13 50	

			GW	GW	GW	GW	GW	GW		GW	GW	GW	GW	GW	XC	GW	GW	GW		GW	GW	GW	GW	GW	GW	
																								FX	FO	
			1	1	1	1	1	1		1	1	1	1	1	◇1	1	1	1		1	1	1	1	1	1	
Reading [7]	149	d	13 34	14 04	14 34	15 04	15 28	16 04		16 34	16 51	17 04	17 34	18 04	18 21	18 34	19 04	19 34		20 04	20 34	21 34	22 34	23 34	23 34	
Wokingham	149	d	13 43	14 13	14 43	15 13	15 39	16 13		16 43	17 00	17 13	17 43	18 13		18 43	19 13	19 43		20 13	20 43	21 43	22 43	23 43		
Crowthorne		d		14 18		15 18	15 44	16 18			17 06	17 18	17 48	18 18			19 18			20 18		21 48	22 48	23 49	23 49	
Sandhurst		d		14 22		15 22	15 48	16 22			17 10	17 22	17 52	18 22			19 22			20 22		21 52	22 52	23 52	23 52	
Blackwater		d	13 51	14 25	14 51	15 25	15 51	16 25		16 51	17 13	17 25	17 55	18 25		18 51	19 25	19 51		20 25	20 51	21 55	22 55	23 56	23 56	
Farnborough North		d		14 30		15 30		16 30			17 18	17 30	18 00	18 30			19 30			20 30		22 00	23 00	23 59	23 59	
North Camp		d	13 57	14 34	14 57	15 34	15 57	16 34		16 57	17 22	17 34	18 04	18 34		18 57	19 34	19 57		20 34	20 57	22 04	23 04	00 04	00 04	
Ash [5]	149	d		14 38		15 38		16 38			17 26	17 38	18 08	18 38			19 38			20 38		22 08	23 08	00 08	00 08	
Wanborough	149	d						16 42				17 42												00 13	00 13	
Guildford	149	a	14 08	14 47	15 08	15 47	16 08	16 49		17 08	17 35	17 49	18 17	18 50	18 59	19 08	19 47	20 08		20 47	21 08	22 17	23 17	00 20	00 20	
		d	14 10	14 48	15 10	15 48	16 10	16 50		17 10	17 40	17 50	18 18	18 54		19 10	19 48	20 10		20 48	21 10	22 18	23 18	00 21	00 21	
Shalford		d		14 53		15 53	16 15	16 55			17a48	17 55		18 59			19a55			20 53	21 15	22 23	23 23			
Chilworth		d				15 57		16 59				17 59		19 03						20 58	21 19		23 27			
Gomshall		d				16 04		17 06				18 06		19 10		19 21				21 04	21 25		23 34			
Dorking West		d		15 06			16 28	17 13				18 13		19 17						21 12	21 33		23 41			
Dorking Deepdene		d	14 26	15 08	15 26	16 11	16 30	17 16		17 26		18 16	18 35	19 20		19 29		20 26		21 14	21 35	22 37	23 44	00 38	00 38	
Betchworth		d		15 13		16 16		17 21				18 21		19 25						21 19	21 40		23 49			
Reigate	186	d	14 34	15 19	15 34	16 21	16 38	17 26		17 34		18 26	18 42	19 30		19 36		20 34		21 24	21 45	22 44	23 54	00 45	00 45	
Redhill	186	a	14 38	15 25	15 38	16 27	16 42	17 32		17 38		18 32	18 47	19 35		19 40		20 38		21 30	21 49	22 48	23 58	00 49	00 49	
Gatwick Airport [10]	186	a	14 50		15 50		16 59			17 54			19 00			19 56		20 50			22 06	23 06	00 11	01 03	01 03	

Saturdays

14 December to 17 May

			GW	GW	GW	GW	GW	GW	GW	GW	GW		GW	GW	GW	GW	GW	GW	GW	GW	GW		GW	GW	GW	GW
			1	1	1	1	1	1	1	1	1		1	1	1	1	1	1	1	1	1		1	1	1	1
Reading [7]	149	d		04 34	05 34	06 04	06 34	07 04	07 34	08 04	08 34		09 04	09 34	10 04	10 34	11 04	11 34	12 04	12 34	13 04		13 34	14 04	14 34	15 04
Wokingham	149	d		04 43	05 43	06 13	06 43	07 13	07 43	08 13	08 43		09 13	09 43	10 13	10 43	11 13	11 43	12 13	12 43	13 13		13 43	14 13	14 43	15 13
Crowthorne		d				06 18		07 18		08 18			09 18		10 18		11 18		12 18		13 18			14 18		15 18
Sandhurst		d				06 22		07 22		08 22			09 22		10 22		11 22		12 22		13 22			14 22		15 22
Blackwater		d		04 51	05 51	06 25	06 51	07 25	07 51	08 25	08 51		09 25	09 51	10 25	10 51	11 25	11 51	12 25	12 51	13 25		13 51	14 25	14 51	15 25
Farnborough North		d				06 30		07 30		08 30			09 30		10 30		11 30		12 30		13 30			14 30		15 30
North Camp		d	00 04	04 57	05 57	06 34	06 57	07 34	07 57	08 34	08 57		09 34	09 57	10 34	10 57	11 34	11 57	12 34	12 57	13 34		13 57	14 34	14 57	15 34
Ash [5]	149	d	00 08			06 38		07 38		08 38			09 38		10 38		11 38		12 38		13 38			14 38		15 38
Wanborough	149	d	00 13																							
Guildford	149	a	00 20	05 08	06 08	06 47	07 09	07 47	08 08	08 47	09 08		09 47	10 08	10 47	11 08	11 47	12 08	12 47	13 08	13 47		14 08	14 47	15 08	15 47
		d	00 21	05 10	06 10	06 48	07 10	07 48	08 10	08 48	09 10		09 48	10 10	10 48	11 10	11 48	12 10	12 48	13 10	13 48		14 10	14 48	15 10	15 48
Shalford		d				06 53		07 53		08 53			09 53		10 53		11 53		12 53		13 53			14 53		15 53
Chilworth		d						07 57					09 57				11 57				13 57					15 57
Gomshall		d						08 04					10 04				12 04				14 04					16 04
Dorking West		d				07 06				09 06					11 06				13 06					15 06		
Dorking Deepdene		d	00 38	05 26	06 26	07 08	07 26	08 11	08 26	09 08	09 26		10 11	10 26	11 08	11 26	12 11	12 26	13 08	13 26	14 11		14 26	15 08	15 26	16 11
Betchworth		d				07 13				09 13					11 13				13 13					15 13		
Reigate	186	d	00 45	05 34	06 34	07 19	07 34	08 19	08 34	09 19	09 34		10 19	10 34	11 19	11 34	12 19	12 34	13 19	13 34	14 19		14 34	15 19	15 34	16 19
Redhill	186	a	00 49	05 39	06 39	07 25	07 39	08 25	08 38	09 25	09 38		10 25	10 38	11 25	11 38	12 25	12 38	13 25	13 38	14 25		14 38	15 25	15 38	16 25
Gatwick Airport [10]	186	a	01 03	05 58	06 50		07 50		08 50		09 50			10 50		11 50		12 50		13 50			14 50		15 50	

Table 148

Saturdays

14 December to 17 May

Reading - Guildford, Redhill and Gatwick Airport

Network Diagram - see first Page of Table 148

			GW 1	GW 1	GW 1	GW 1	GW 1	GW 1	GW 1	GW 1	GW 1	GW 1	GW 1	GW 1	XC ◇1	GW 1	GW 1
Reading 7	149	d	15 34	16 04	16 34	17 04	17 34	18 04	18 34	19 04	19 34	20 04	20 34	21 34	22 15	22 34	23 34
Wokingham	149	d	15 43	16 13	16 43	17 13	17 43	18 13	18 43	19 13	19 43	20 13	20 43	21 43	-	22 43	-
Crowthorne		d	-	16 18	-	17 18	-	18 18	-	19 18	-	20 18	-	21 48	-	22 48	23 48
Sandhurst		d	-	16 22	-	17 22	-	18 22	-	19 22	-	20 22	-	21 52	-	22 52	23 52
Blackwater		d	15 51	16 25	16 51	17 25	17 51	18 25	18 51	19 25	19 51	20 25	20 51	21 55	-	22 55	23 55
Farnborough North		d	-	16 30	-	17 30	-	18 30	-	19 30	-	20 30	-	22 00	-	23 00	23 59
North Camp		d	15 57	16 34	16 57	17 34	17 57	18 34	18 57	19 34	19 57	20 34	20 57	22 04	-	23 04	00 04
Ash 5	149	d	-	16 38	-	17 38	-	18 38	-	19 38	-	20 38	-	22 08	-	23 08	00 08
Wanborough	149	d	-	-	-	-	-	-	-	-	-	-	-	-	-	-	00 12
Guildford	149	a	16 08	16 47	17 08	17 47	18 08	18 47	19 08	19 47	20 08	20 47	21 08	22 17	22 59	23 17	00 19
		d	16 10	16 48	17 10	17 48	18 10	18 48	19 10	19 48	20 10	20 48	21 10	22 18	-	23 18	00 21
Shalford		d	-	16 53	-	17 53	-	18 53	-	19 53	-	20 53	21 15	22 23	-	23 23	-
Chilworth		d	-	-	-	17 57	-	-	-	19 57	-	-	21 19	-	-	23 27	-
Gomshall		d	-	-	-	18 04	-	-	-	20 04	-	-	21 25	-	-	23 34	-
Dorking West		d	-	17 06	-	-	-	19 06	-	-	-	21 06	-	22 36	-	23 41	-
Dorking Deepdene		d	16 26	17 08	17 26	18 11	18 26	19 08	19 26	20 11	20 26	21 08	21 33	22 38	-	23 44	00 37
Betchworth		d	-	17 13	-	-	-	19 13	-	-	-	21 13	-	22 43	-	23 49	-
Reigate	186	d	16 34	17 19	17 34	18 19	18 34	19 19	19 34	20 19	20 34	21 19	21 40	22 48	-	23 54	00 45
Redhill	186	a	16 38	17 25	17 38	18 25	18 38	19 25	19 38	20 25	20 38	21 26	21 44	22 52	-	23 58	00 49
Gatwick Airport 10	186	a	16 50	-	17 50	-	18 50	-	19 50	-	20 50	-	21 59	23 05	-	00 10	01 00

Sundays

8 December to 11 May

			GW 1	GW 1	GW 1	GW 1	GW 1	GW 1	GW 1	GW 1	GW 1	GW 1	GW 1	GW 1	GW 1	GW 1	GW 1	GW 1	GW 1	XC ◇1	GW 1	GW 1
Reading 7	149	d	-	06 03	07 03	08 18	09 18	10 18	11 18	12 18	13 18	14 18	15 18	16 18	17 18	18 18	19 18	20 18	21 18	22 14	22 18	23 15
Wokingham	149	d	-	06 11	07 11	08 26	09 27	10 26	11 27	12 26	13 27	14 26	15 27	16 26	17 27	18 26	19 27	20 26	21 27	-	22 26	23 24
Crowthorne		d	-	-	07 17	-	09 32	-	11 32	-	13 32	-	15 32	-	17 32	-	19 32	-	21 32	-	-	23 29
Sandhurst		d	-	-	07 21	-	09 36	-	11 36	-	13 36	-	15 36	-	17 36	-	19 36	-	21 36	-	-	23 33
Blackwater		d	-	06 20	07 24	08 34	09 39	10 34	11 39	12 34	13 39	14 34	15 39	16 34	17 39	18 34	19 39	20 34	21 39	-	22 34	23 36
Farnborough North		d	-	-	07 29	-	09 44	-	11 44	-	13 44	-	15 44	-	17 44	-	19 44	-	21 44	-	-	23 41
North Camp		d	00 04	06 27	07 33	08 41	09 48	10 41	11 48	12 41	13 48	14 41	15 48	16 41	17 48	18 41	19 48	20 41	21 48	-	22 41	23 45
Ash 5	149	d	00 08	-	07 37	-	09 52	-	11 52	-	13 52	-	15 52	-	17 52	-	19 52	-	21 52	-	-	23 49
Wanborough	149	d	00 12	-	-	-	-	-	-	-	-	-	-	-	-	-	-	-	-	-	-	-
Guildford	149	a	00 19	06 38	07 46	08 52	10 01	10 52	12 01	12 52	14 01	14 52	16 01	16 52	18 01	18 52	20 01	20 52	22 01	22 42	22 52	23 58
		d	00 21	06 40	07 47	08 56	10 02	10 56	12 02	12 56	14 02	14 56	16 02	16 56	18 02	18 56	20 02	20 56	22 02	-	22 56	23 59
Shalford		d	-	-	-	09 01	-	11 01	-	13 01	-	15 01	-	17 01	-	19 01	-	21 01	-	-	23 01	-
Chilworth		d	-	-	-	09 05	-	11 05	-	13 05	-	15 05	-	17 05	-	19 05	-	21 05	-	-	23 05	-
Gomshall		d	-	-	-	09 11	-	11 11	-	13 11	-	15 11	-	17 11	-	19 11	-	21 11	-	-	23 11	-
Dorking West		d	-	-	-	09 19	-	11 19	-	13 19	-	15 19	-	17 19	-	19 19	-	21 19	-	-	23 19	-
Dorking Deepdene		d	00 37	06 57	08 04	09 20	10 21	11 20	12 21	13 20	14 21	15 20	16 21	17 20	18 21	19 20	20 21	21 20	22 21	-	23 20	00 19
Betchworth		d	-	-	-	09 26	-	11 26	-	13 26	-	15 26	-	17 26	-	19 26	-	21 26	-	-	23 26	-
Reigate	186	d	00 45	07 05	08 13	09 30	10 31	11 30	12 31	13 30	14 31	15 30	16 31	17 30	18 31	19 30	20 31	21 30	22 31	-	23 30	00 26
Redhill	186	a	00 49	07 09	08 18	09 36	10 36	11 36	12 36	13 36	14 36	15 36	16 36	17 36	18 36	19 36	20 36	21 36	22 36	-	23 36	00 30
Gatwick Airport 10	186	a	01 00	07 29	08 31	09 47	10 48	11 47	12 48	13 47	14 48	15 47	16 48	17 47	18 48	19 47	20 48	21 47	22 48	-	23 47	00 41

Table 148R

Mondays to Fridays

9 December to 16 May

Gatwick Airport, Redhill and Guildford - Reading

Network Diagram - see first Page of Table 148

Miles	Station			GW MO 1	GW MX 1	XC ◇1	GW 1	GW 1	GW 1	GW 1	GW 1	GW 1	GW 1	GW 1	GW 1 A	GW 1 B	GW 1	GW 1	GW 1	GW 1	GW 1	GW 1	GW 1	GW 1
0	**Gatwick Airport 10**	186	d				05 31	05 56			06 58		07 58				09 07		10 03		11 03		12 03	
5¾	**Redhill**	186	d				05 43	06 13	06 24		07 10	07 28	08 08	08 33			09 23	09 34	10 13	10 34	11 13	11 34	12 13	12 34
—	Reigate	186	d				05 49	06 18	06 28		07 15	07 32	08 13	08 37			09 28	09 38	10 18	10 38	11 18	11 38	12 18	12 38
10½	Betchworth		d						06 33			07 37		08 42				09 43		10 43				12 43
13¼	Dorking Deepdene		d				05 56	06 25	06 37		07 22	07 41	08 20	08 46			09 35	09 47	10 25	10 47	11 25	11 45	12 25	12 47
14	Dorking West		d						06 40			07 44		08 49				09 50		10 50				12 50
18¾	Gomshall		d						06 48		07 30	07 52		08 57				09 58				11 53		
22½	Chilworth		d						06 54			07 58		09 03				10 04				11 59		
24½	Shalford		d						06 58	07 21		08 02		09 07	09 19	09 19		10 08		11 03		12 03		13 03
26½	**Guildford**		a				06 12	06 41	07 03	07 25	07 41	08 06	08 36	09 11	09 23	09 23	09 53	10 12	10 42	11 08	11 42	12 08	12 42	13 08
—			d		00 02	06 02	06 13	06 43	07 04	07 27	07 43	08 13	08 38	09 13	09 25	09 25	09 54	10 14	10 44	11 09	11 44	12 09	12 44	13 09
30¾	Wanborough	149	d				06 20		07 12			08 20			09 32	09 32								
32¾	Ash 5	149	d	00 01			06 25	06 52	07 16	07 36	07 52	08 25		09 22	09 37	09 37		10 23		11 19		12 19		13 19
34¾	North Camp		d	00 05	00 14		06 29	06 56	07 20	07 41	07 56	08 29	08 50	09 26	09 41	09 41		10 27	10 56	11 23	11 56	12 23	12 56	13 23
36¾	Farnborough North		d	00 09			06 33	07 00	07 24	07 45	08 00	08 33			09 45	09 45		10 31		11 27		12 27		13 27
38¾	Blackwater		d	00 14	00 20		06 37	07 05	07 29	07 49	08 05	08 37	08 56	09 33	09 49	09 49		10 36	11 02	11 31	12 02	12 31	13 02	13 31
40¾	Sandhurst		d	00 16			06 41	07 08	07 32	07 53	08 08	08 41			09 53	09 53		10 39		11 35		12 35		13 35
42¼	Crowthorne		d	00 20			06 45	07 12	07 36	07 57	08 12	08 45			09 57	09 57		10 43		11 39		12 39		13 39
45½	Wokingham	149	d	00 25	00 29		06 50	07 17	07 41	08 02	08 17	08 50	09 04	09 41	10 03	10 03		10 48	11 10	11 44	12 10	12 44	13 10	13 44
52¼	**Reading 7**	149	a	00 37	00 39	06 31	06 58	07 29	07 52	08 17	08 28	09 00	09 17	09 51	10 17	10 21	10 23	10 59	11 19	11 54	12 19	12 54	13 19	13 54

Station			GW 1	GW 1	GW 1	GW 1	GW 1	GW 1	GW 1	GW 1	GW 1	GW 1	GW 1 B	GW 1 A	GW 1	GW 1	GW 1	GW 1	GW 1	GW 1	GW 1	GW 1	GW 1
Gatwick Airport 10	186	d	13 03		14 03		15 03		16 03		17 03				18 03		19 13		20 03		21 03		22 22
Redhill	186	d	13 13	13 34	14 13	14 34	15 13	15 29	16 13	16 32	17 13		17 43	17 43	18 13	18 43	19 26		20 13	20 34	21 13	21 35	22 33
Reigate	186	d	13 18	13 38	14 18	14 38	15 18	15 34	16 18	16 36	17 18		17 48	17 48	18 18	18 47	19 30		20 18	20 40	21 18	21 39	22 38
Betchworth		d				14 43		15 38		16 41			17 52	17 52		18 52				20 45		21 44	22 43
Dorking Deepdene		d	13 25	13 45	14 25	14 47	15 25	15 43	16 25	16 45	17 25		17 57	17 57	18 25	18 56	19 37		20 25	20 49	21 25	21 48	22 47
Dorking West		d				14 50		15 45					17 59	17 59		18 59				20 52		21 51	22 50
Gomshall		d		13 53				15 53		16 53			18 07	18 07		19 07				21 00		21 59	22 58
Chilworth		d		13 59				15 59		16 59			18 13	18 13		19 13				21 06		22 05	23 04
Shalford		d		14 03		15 03		16 03		17 03		17 58	18 17	18 17		19 17		20 02		21 10		22 09	23 08
Guildford		a	13 42	14 08	14 42	15 08	15 42	16 08	16 42	17 08	17 43	18 02	18 22	18 22	18 41	19 22	19 54	20 06	20 42	21 14	21 42	22 13	23 12
		d	13 44	14 09	14 44	15 09	15 44	16 14	16 44	17 09	17 44	18 04	18 26	18 26	18 47	19 36	19 55	20 10	20 44	21 16	21 44	22 15	23 14
Wanborough	149	d																					23 21
Ash 5	149	d		14 19		15 19		16 24		17 19	17 54	18 14	18 35	18 35		19 46		20 19		21 25		22 23	23 26
North Camp		d	13 56	14 23	14 56	15 23	15 56	16 28	16 56	17 23	17 58	18 18	18 39	18 39	19 01	19 50	20 07	20 23	20 56	21 29	21 56	22 27	23 30
Farnborough North		d		14 27		15 27		16 32		17 27	18 02	18 22	18 42	18 42		19 54		20 27		21 33		22 31	23 34
Blackwater		d	14 02	14 31	15 02	15 31	16 02	16 36	17 02	17 31	18 07	18 27	18 47	18 47	19 07	19 58	20 14	20 31	21 02	21 38	22 02	22 36	23 38
Sandhurst		d		14 35		15 35		16 40		17 35		18 30	18 51	18 51		20 02		20 35		21 41		22 39	23 42
Crowthorne		d		14 39		15 39		16 44		17 39		18 34	18 59	18 59		20 06		20 39		21 45		22 43	23 46
Wokingham	149	d	14 10	14 44	15 10	15 43	16 10	16 48	17 10	17 44	18 15	18 39	19 04	19 04	19 15	20 11	20 22	20 43	21 10	21 50	22 10	22 48	23 51
Reading 7	149	a	14 19	14 54	15 19	15 54	16 24	17 00	17 19	17 54	18 24	18 50	19 16	19 17	19 25	20 21	20 34	20 56	21 19	22 01	22 19	23 04	00 02

Station			GW FX 1	GW FO 1
Gatwick Airport 10	186	d	23 18	23 18
Redhill	186	d	23 34	23 34
Reigate	186	d	23 38	23 38
Betchworth		d		
Dorking Deepdene		d	23 45	23 45
Dorking West		d		
Gomshall		d		
Chilworth		d		
Shalford		d		
Guildford		a	00 01	00 01
		d	00 02	00 02
Wanborough	149	d		
Ash 5	149	d		
North Camp		d	00 14	00 14
Farnborough North		d		
Blackwater		d	00 20	00 20
Sandhurst		d		
Crowthorne		d		
Wokingham	149	d	00 29	00 29
Reading 7	149	a	00 39	00 43

A from 30 December

B until 27 December

Table 148R

Saturdays
14 December to 17 May

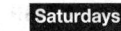

Gatwick Airport, Redhill and Guildford - Reading

Network Diagram - see first Page of Table 148

		GW	XC	GW	GW	GW	GW	GW	GW	GW	GW	GW	GW	GW	GW	GW	GW	GW	GW	GW	GW	GW	GW
		1	◇1	1	1	1	1	1	1	1	1	1	1	1	1	1	1	1	1	1	1	1	1
				A	B																		
Gatwick Airport 10	186 d			05 31	05 31	06 03		07 03		08 03		09 03		10 03		11 03		12 03		13 03		14 03	
Redhill	186 d			05 41	05 41	06 13	06 34	07 13	07 34	08 13	08 34	09 13	09 34	10 13	10 34	11 13	11 34	12 13	12 34	13 13	13 34	14 13	14 34
Reigate	186 d			05 47	05 47	06 18	06 38	07 18	07 38	08 18	08 38	09 18	09 38	10 18	10 38	11 18	11 38	12 18	12 38	13 18	13 38	14 18	14 38
Betchworth	d						06 43				08 43				10 43				12 43				14 43
Dorking Deepdene	d			05 54	05 54	06 25	06 47	07 25	07 45	08 25	08 47	09 25	09 45	10 25	10 47	11 25	11 45	12 25	12 47	13 25	13 45	14 25	14 47
Dorking West	d						06 50				08 50				10 50				12 50				14 50
Gomshall	d								07 53				09 53				11 53				13 53		
Chilworth	d								07 59				09 59				11 59				13 59		
Shalford	d						07 03		08 03		09 03		10 03		11 03		12 03		13 03		14 03		15 03
Guildford	a			06 12	06 12	06 43	07 08	07 41	08 08	08 42	09 08	09 42	10 08	10 42	11 08	11 42	12 08	12 42	13 08	13 42	14 08	14 42	15 08
	d	00 02	06 09	06 12	06 12	06 44	07 09	07 44	08 09	08 44	09 09	09 44	10 09	10 44	11 09	11 44	12 09	12 44	13 09	13 44	14 09	14 44	15 09
Wanborough	149 d			06 21	06 21																		
Ash 5	149 d			06 24	06 24		07 19		08 19		09 19		10 19		11 19		12 19		13 19		14 19		15 19
North Camp	d	00 14		06 28	06 28	06 56	07 23	07 56	08 23	08 56	09 23	09 56	10 23	10 56	11 23	11 56	12 23	12 56	13 23	13 56	14 23	14 56	15 23
Farnborough North	d			06 32	06 32		07 27		08 27		09 27		10 27		11 27		12 27		13 27		14 27		15 27
Blackwater	d	00 20		06 38	06 38	07 02	07 31	08 02	08 31	09 02	09 31	10 02	10 31	11 02	11 31	12 02	12 31	13 02	13 31	14 02	14 31	15 02	15 31
Sandhurst	d			06 40	06 40		07 35		08 35		09 35		10 35		11 35		12 35		13 35		14 35		15 35
Crowthorne	d			06 44	06 44		07 39		08 39		09 39		10 39		11 39		12 39		13 39		14 39		15 39
Wokingham	149 d	00 29		06 49	06 49	07 10	07 44	08 10	08 44	09 10	09 44	10 10	10 44	11 10	11 44	12 10	12 44	13 10	13 44	14 10	14 44	15 10	15 44
Reading 7	149 a	00 43	06 43	07 01	07 02	07 19	07 54	08 19	08 54	09 19	09 54	10 19	10 54	11 19	11 54	12 19	12 54	13 19	13 54	14 19	14 54	15 19	15 54

		GW	GW	GW	GW	GW	GW	GW	GW	GW	GW	GW	GW	GW	GW	GW	GW
		1	1	1	1	1	1	1	1	1	1	1	1	1	1	1	1
Gatwick Airport 10	186 d	15 03		16 03		17 03		18 03		19 03		20 03		21 03		22 22	23 18
Redhill	186 d	15 13	15 34	16 13	16 34	17 13	17 34	18 13	18 34	19 13	19 34	20 13	20 34	21 13	21 36	22 33	23 28
Reigate	186 d	15 18	15 38	16 18	16 38	17 18	17 38	18 18	18 38	19 18	19 38	20 18	20 38	21 18	21 40	22 38	23 33
Betchworth	d				16 43				18 43				20 43			22 43	
Dorking Deepdene	d	15 25	15 45	16 25	16 47	17 25	17 45	18 25	18 47	19 25	19 45	20 25	20 47	21 25	21 47	22 47	23 40
Dorking West	d				16 50				18 50				20 50			22 50	
Gomshall	d		15 53				17 53				19 53				21 55	22 58	
Chilworth	d		15 59				17 59				19 59				22 01	23 04	
Shalford	d		16 03		17 03		18 03		19 03		20 03		21 03		22 05	23 08	
Guildford	a	15 42	16 08	16 42	17 08	17 42	18 08	18 42	19 08	19 42	20 08	20 42	21 08	21 42	22 13	23 13	00 01
	d	15 44	16 09	16 44	17 09	17 44	18 09	18 44	19 09	19 44	20 09	20 44	21 09	21 44	22 14	23 14	00 02
Wanborough	149 d															23 22	
Ash 5	149 d		16 19		17 19		18 19		19 19		20 19		21 19		22 24	23 26	
North Camp	d	15 56	16 23	16 56	17 23	17 56	18 23	18 56	19 23	19 56	20 23	20 56	21 23	21 56	22 28	23 30	00 14
Farnborough North	d		16 27		17 27		18 27		19 27		20 27		21 27		22 32	23 34	
Blackwater	d	16 02	16 31	17 02	17 31	18 02	18 31	19 02	19 31	20 02	20 31	21 02	21 31	22 02	22 36	23 39	00 20
Sandhurst	d		16 35		17 35		18 35		19 35		20 35		21 35		22 40	23 42	
Crowthorne	d		16 39		17 39		18 39		19 39		20 39		21 39		22 44	23 46	
Wokingham	149 d	16 10	16 44	17 10	17 44	18 10	18 44	19 10	19 44	20 10	20 44	21 10	21 44	22 10	22 49	23 51	00 29
Reading 7	149 a	16 19	16 54	17 19	17 54	18 19	18 54	19 19	19 54	20 19	20 54	21 19	21 54	22 19	22 57	00 01	00 37

Sundays
8 December to 11 May

		GW	GW	GW	GW	GW	GW	GW	XC	XC	XC
		1	1	1	1	1	1	1	◇1	◇1	◇1
									C 🍴	D	E 🍴
Gatwick Airport 10	186 d		06 10	07 10	08 10	09 08	10 08	11 08			
Redhill	186 d		06 20	07 20	08 19	09 20	10 19	11 20			
Reigate	186 d		06 24	07 24	08 23	09 24	10 23	11 24			
Betchworth	d				08 28		10 28				
Dorking Deepdene	d		06 32	07 32	08 32	09 32	10 32	11 32			
Dorking West	d				08 35		10 35				
Gomshall	d				08 43		10 43				
Chilworth	d				08 49		10 49				
Shalford	d				08 53		10 53				
Guildford	a		06 49	07 50	08 57	09 50	10 57	11 50			
	d	00 02	06 51	07 52	08 59	09 52	10 59	11 52	12 14	12 14	12 14
Wanborough	149 d										
Ash 5	149 d			08 02		10 02		12 02			
North Camp	d	00 14	07 03	08 06	09 11	10 06	11 11	12 06			
Farnborough North	d			08 10		10 10		12 10			
Blackwater	d	00 20	07 09	08 14	09 17	10 14	11 17	12 14			
Sandhurst	d			08 18		10 18		12 18			
Crowthorne	d			08 22		10 22		12 22			
Wokingham	149 d	00 29	07 17	08 26	09 26	10 26	11 26	12 26			
Reading 7	149 a	00 37	07 26	08 35	09 37	10 35	11 35	12 35	12 45	12 45	12 49

		GW	GW	GW	GW	GW	GW	GW	GW	GW	GW	GW	GW
		1	1	1	1	1	1	1	1	1	1	1	1
Gatwick Airport 10	186 d	12 08	13 08	14 08	15 08	16 08	17 08	18 08	19 08	20 08	21 08	22 08	23 08
Redhill	186 d	12 19	13 20	14 19	15 20	16 19	17 20	18 19	19 20	20 19	21 20	22 19	23 20
Reigate	186 d	12 23	13 24	14 23	15 24	16 23	17 24	18 23	19 24	20 23	21 24	22 23	23 24
Betchworth	d	12 28		14 28		16 28		18 28		20 28		22 28	
Dorking Deepdene	d	12 32	13 32	14 32	15 32	16 32	17 32	18 32	19 32	20 32	21 32	22 32	23 32
Dorking West	d	12 35		14 35		16 35		18 35		20 35		22 35	
Gomshall	d	12 43		14 43		16 43		18 43		20 43		22 43	
Chilworth	d	12 49		14 49		16 49		18 49		20 49		22 49	
Shalford	d	12 53		14 53		16 53		18 53		20 53		22 53	
Guildford	a	12 57	13 50	14 57	15 50	16 57	17 50	18 57	19 50	20 57	21 50	22 57	23 50
	d	12 59	13 52	14 59	15 52	16 59	17 52	18 59	19 52	20 59	21 52	22 59	23 52
Wanborough	149 d												
Ash 5	149 d		14 02		16 02		18 02		20 02		22 02		00 01
North Camp	d	13 11	14 06	15 11	16 06	17 11	18 06	19 11	20 06	21 11	22 06	23 11	00 05
Farnborough North	d		14 10		16 10		18 10		20 10		22 10		00 09
Blackwater	d	13 17	14 14	15 17	16 14	17 17	18 14	19 17	20 14	21 17	22 14	23 17	00 14
Sandhurst	d		14 18		16 18		18 18		20 18		22 18		00 16
Crowthorne	d		14 22		16 22		18 22		20 22		22 22		00 20
Wokingham	149 d	13 26	14 26	15 26	16 26	17 26	18 26	19 26	20 26	21 26	22 26	23 26	00 25
Reading 7	149 a	13 35	14 35	15 35	16 35	17 35	18 35	19 35	20 35	21 35	22 36	23 36	00 37

A from 15 February
B from 4 January until 8 February
C from 30 March
D from 16 February until 23 March
E until 29 December

Table 149

Mondays to Fridays

9 December to 16 May

London - Hounslow, Richmond, Kingston, Windsor, Weybridge, Ascot, Guildford and Reading

Network Diagram - see first Page of Table 148

Miles	Miles	Miles	Station		SW MX 1 A	SW MX A	SW MO 1 A	SW MX 1 A	SW MX 1 B	SW 1	SW MX A	SW MO 1 A	SW MX A	SW MO C	SW MX A	SW MO A	SW MX A	SW MX A	SW 1	SW	SW D	SW	SW 1
0	—	0	**London Waterloo 15** ⊖	d																00 18			05 05
1¼	—	1¼	Vauxhall ⊖	d													00 02			00 22			05 09
2¾	—	2¾	Queenstown Rd.(Battersea)	d																00 25			05 12
4	—	4	**Clapham Junction 10**	d													00 08	00 02		00 29			05 15
4¾	—	4¾	Wandsworth Town	d														00 05		00 32			05 18
5¾	—	5¾	Putney	d													00 12	00 08		00 35			05 21
7	0	7	Barnes	d												00 03		00 12		00 38			05 24
—	0½	—	Barnes Bridge	d														00 14					
—	1½	—	Chiswick	d														00 17					
—	2½	—	Kew Bridge	d														00 20					
—	3½	—	Brentford	d														00 23					
—	4¼	—	Syon Lane	d														00 25					
—	5	—	Isleworth	d														00 27					
—	6½	—	**Hounslow**	d							00 01							00 31					
8¼	—	8¼	Mortlake	d												00 05				00 40			05 26
9	—	9	North Sheen	d												00 07				00 42			05 28
9¾	—	9¾	**Richmond** ⊖	d											00 06	00 10	00 18			00 45			05 31
10¾	—	10¾	St Margarets	d									00 01			00 12				00 47			05 33
11¼	—	11¼	Twickenham	a									00 03		00 10	00 14	00 21			00 49			05 35
—	—	—		d								00 03	00 04		00 10	00 15	00 22			00 50	04 52		05 36
12¼	—	—	Strawberry Hill	d									00 09							00s53	04 55		
12½	—	—	Fulwell	a																			
13½	—	—	Teddington	a									00 12							00s56	04 58		
14¾	—	—	Hampton Wick	a									00 14							00s59	05 01		
15¼	—	—	**Kingston**	a									00 16							01 01	05 03		
—	—	12½	Whitton	d												00 18	00 25						05 39
—	—	14¾	Feltham	d							00 06	00 09			00 16	00 22	00 29	00 36					05 43
—	—	17½	Ashford (Surrey)	d		00 03					00 10					00 26	00 33	00 40					05 47
0	—	19	**Staines**	d		00 07					00 14	00 15		00 21	00 23	00a30	00a37	00a46	05 23			05 44	05 53
2½	—	—	Wraysbury	d		00 11																	
3¾	—	—	Sunnymeads	d		00 14																	
4¾	—	—	Datchet	d		00 17																	
6¾	—	—	**Windsor & Eton Riverside**	a		00 21																	
—	—	21	Egham	d							00 19	00 20		00s25	00 27				05 27			05 49	05 57
0	—	23¾	Virginia Water	a							00 23	00 24		00s30	00 31				05 31			05 53	06 01
—	—	—		d				00 01			00 23	00 24			00 31				05 31			05 53	06 01
2½	—	—	Chertsey	d							00 29			00s35								05 59	
4	—	—	Addlestone	d							00 32			00s38								06 02	
5	—	—	**Weybridge**	a							00 36											06 07	
—	—	25¼	Longcross	d																			
—	—	27	Sunningdale	d				00 08				00 29			00 37				05 37				06 07
—	0	29	**Ascot 3**	d			00 04	00 13	00 23			00 34			00 42				05 43				06 13
—	3¼	—	Bagshot	d					00 29														
—	6½	—	Camberley	a					00 35														
—	8¾	—	Frimley	d					00 40														
—	12	—	Ash Vale	d					00 47														
—	14½	—	**Aldershot**	a					00s52														
—	—	—		d						06 08													
—	17¼	—	Ash 5	d						06 15													
—	19¼	—	Wanborough	d						06 18													
—	23½	—	**Guildford**	a						06 25													
—	—	31¼	Martins Heron	d			00 08	00 17				00 38			00 46				05 47				06 17
—	—	32¼	Bracknell	d			00 11	00 20				00 41			00 49				05 50				06 20
—	—	36¾	**Wokingham**	d			00 18	00 32				00 48			00 56				05 57				06 27
—	—	38¾	Winnersh	d			00 21	00 36				00 51							06 00				06 30
—	—	39¼	Winnersh Triangle	d	00 02		00 23	00 38				00 53							06 02				06 32
—	—	40½	Earley	d	00 05		00 26	00 40				00 56							06 05				06 35
—	—	43½	**Reading 7**	a	00 10		00 31	00 45				01 01			01 04				06 10				06 40

A From London Waterloo
B To Farnham
C To Woking
D To London Waterloo

The xx15 and xx45 services from London Waterloo to Whitton continues to London Waterloo via Brentford

The xx03 and xx33 London Waterloo to Kingston services continues to London Waterloo via Wimbledon

The xx07 and xx37 services from London Waterloo to Whitton continues to London Waterloo via Richmond

Table 149

Mondays to Fridays

9 December to 16 May

London - Hounslow, Richmond, Kingston, Windsor, Weybridge, Ascot, Guildford and Reading

Network Diagram - see first Page of Table 148

		SW	SW	SW	SW	SW	SW	SW	SW		SW	SW	SW	SW	SW	SW	SW	SW	SW		SW	SW	SW	SW	SW
					■1	■1	■1	■1							■1		■1								■1
			A						A			A		A		B		C			D	A	A	A	
London Waterloo [15] ⊖	d		05 33				05 50				05 58	06 03		06 15	06 20			06 22	06 28				06 33	06 45	06 50
Vauxhall ⊖	d		05 37								06 02	06 07		06 19				06 26	06 32				06 37	06 49	
Queenstown Rd.(Battersea)	d		05 40									06 10		06 22				06 29					06 40	06 52	
Clapham Junction [10]	d		05 43				05 58				06 08	06 13		06 25	06 28			06 32	06 38				06 43	06 55	06 58
Wandsworth Town	d		05 46									06 16		06 28				06 35					06 46	06 58	
Putney	d		05 49								06 12	06 19		06 31				06 38	06 42				06 49	07 01	
Barnes	d		05 52									06 22		06 35				06 42					06 52	07 05	
Barnes Bridge	d																	06 44							
Chiswick	d																	06 47							
Kew Bridge	d																	06 50							
Brentford	d																	06 53							
Syon Lane	d																	06 55							
Isleworth	d																	06 57							
Hounslow	d												06 31					07 01				06 48			
Mortlake	d		05 54									06 24		06 37									06 54	07 07	
North Sheen	d		05 56									06 26		06 39		←							06 56	07 09	
Richmond ⊖	d		05 59				06 06				06 18	06 29		06 42	06 36	06 42			06 48				06 59	07 12	07 06
St Margarets	d		06 01									06 31		→		06 44							07 01	→	
Twickenham	a		06 03				06 10				06 21	06 33			06 40	06 46			06 51			06 56	07 03		07 10
	d	05 53	06 04				06 10		06 17		06 22	06 34			06 40	06 47			06 52				07 04		07 10
Strawberry Hill	d		06 07									06 37											07 07		
Fulwell	a																								
Teddington	a		06 10									06 40											07 10		
Hampton Wick	a		06 14									06 44											07 14		
Kingston	a		06 16									06 46											07 16		
Whitton	d	05 56							06a20		06 25					06a50			06 55		←				
Feltham	d	06 00					06 16				06 29		06 36		06 46			07 06	06 59		07 06				07 16
Ashford (Surrey)	d	06 04									06 33		06 40					→	07 03		07 10				
Staines	d	06 08		06 14			06 23				06 37		06 44		06 53				07 07		07 14				07 23
Wraysbury	d	06 12									06 41								07 11						
Sunnymeads	d	06 15									06 44								07 14						
Datchet	d	06 18									06 47								07 17						
Windsor & Eton Riverside	a	06 22									06 51								07 21						
Egham	d			06 19			06 27						06 49		06 57						07 19				07 27
Virginia Water	a			06 23			06 31						06 53		07 01						07 23				07 31
	d			06 23			06 31						06 53		07 01						07 23				07 31
Chertsey	d			06 29									06 59								07 29				
Addlestone	d			06 32									07 02								07 32				
Weybridge	a			06 37									07 07								07 37				
Longcross	d						06 35								07 05										07 35
Sunningdale	d						06 37								07 07										07 37
Ascot [3]	d					06 23	06 43	06 53							07 13		07 23								07 43
Bagshot	d					06 29		06 59									07 29								
Camberley	a					06 35		07 05									07 35								
Frimley	d					06 43		07 13									07 43								
Ash Vale	d					06 49		07 19									07 49								
Aldershot	a					06 56		07 26									07 54								
	d				06 38	07 08		07 38									08 08								
Ash [5]	d				06 45	07 15		07 45									08 15								
Wanborough	d				06 48	07 18		07 48									08 18								
Guildford	a				06 55	07 25		07 55									08 25								
Martins Heron	d						06 47								07 17										07 47
Bracknell	d						06 50								07 20										07 50
Wokingham	d						06 57								07 27										07 57
Winnersh	d						07 00								07 30										08 00
Winnersh Triangle	d						07 02								07 32										08 02
Earley	d						07 05								07 35										08 05
Reading [7]	a						07 10								07 40										08 10

A To London Waterloo

B From London Waterloo to Whitton continues to London Waterloo

C To Weybridge

D From London Waterloo

The xx15 and xx45 services from London Waterloo to Whitton continues to London Waterloo via Brentford

The xx03 and xx33 London Waterloo to Kingston services continues to London Waterloo via Wimbledon

The xx07 and xx37 services from London Waterloo to Whitton continues to London Waterloo via Richmond

Table 149

Mondays to Fridays

9 December to 16 May

London - Hounslow, Richmond, Kingston, Windsor, Weybridge, Ascot, Guildford and Reading

Network Diagram - see first Page of Table 148

		SW	SW	SW	SW		SW	SW	SW	SW	SW	SW	SW	SW	SW		SW	SW	SW	SW	SW	SW	SW	SW	SW
			1								1				1							1		1	
		A		B			C	D	D	D		A	B				C	D		D	D		A		B
London Waterloo 15 ⊖	d			06 52	06 58			07 03		07 15	07 20		07 22	07 28				07 33	07 37		07 45	07 50			07 52
Vauxhall ⊖	d			06 56	07 02			07 07		07 19			07 26	07 32				07 37	07 41		07 49				07 56
Queenstown Rd.(Battersea)	d			06 59				07 10		07 22			07 29					07 40	07 44		07 52				07 59
Clapham Junction 10	d			07 02	07 08			07 13		07 25	07 28		07 32	07 38				07 43	07 47		07 55	07 58			08 02
Wandsworth Town	d			07 05				07 16		07 28			07 35					07 46	07 50		07 58				08 05
Putney	d			07 08	07 12			07 19		07 31			07 38	07 42				07 49	07 53		08 01				08 08
Barnes	d			07 12				07 22		07 35			07 42					07 52	07 57		08 05				08 12
Barnes Bridge	d			07 14									07 44						07 59						08 14
Chiswick	d			07 17									07 47						08 02						08 17
Kew Bridge	d			07 20									07 50						08 05						08 20
Brentford	d			07 23									07 53						08 08						08 23
Syon Lane	d			07 25									07 55						08 10						08 25
Isleworth	d			07 27									07 57						08 12						08 27
Hounslow	d			07 31									08 01						08a18						08 31
Mortlake	d							07 24		07 37								07 54			08 07				
North Sheen	d	←						07 26		07 39		←						07 56			08 09		←		
Richmond ⊖	d	07 12			07 18			07 29		07 42	07 36	07 42		07 48	07 54			07 59			08 12	08 06	08 12		
St Margarets	d	07 14						07 31		→		07 44						08 01			→		08 14		
Twickenham	a	07 16			07 21			07 33			07 40	07 46		07 51	07 57			08 03				08 10	08 16		
	d	07 17			07 22			07 34	07 37		07 40	07 47		07 52	07 58			08 04		08 07		08 10	08 17		
Strawberry Hill	d							07 37	07 46									08 07		08 16					
Fulwell	a																								
Teddington	a							07 40	07 49									08 10		08 19					
Hampton Wick	a							07 44	07 51									08 14		08 21					
Kingston	a							07 46	07 53									08 16		08 23					
Whitton	d	07a20			07 25		←					07a50		07 55			←						08a20		
Feltham	d			07 36	07 29		07 36				07 46		08 08	07 59	08 04		08 08					08 16			08 38
Ashford (Surrey)	d			→	07 33		07 40						→	08 03	08 08		08 12								→
Staines	d				07 37		07 44				07 53			08 07	08 12		08 16					08 23			
Wraysbury	d				07 41									08 11											
Sunnymeads	d				07 44									08 14											
Datchet	d				07 47									08 17											
Windsor & Eton Riverside	a				07 51									08 21											
Egham	d						07 49				07 57				08 16		08 21					08 27			
Virginia Water	a						07 53				08 01						08 25					08 31			
	d						07 53				08 01						08 25					08 31			
Chertsey	d						07 59										08 31								
Addlestone	d						08 02										08 34								
Weybridge	a						08 07										08 38								
Longcross	d										08 05											08 35			
Sunningdale	d										08 07											08 37			
Ascot 3	d		07 53								08 13				08 26							08 43		08 53	
Bagshot	d		07 59												08 32									08 59	
Camberley	a		08 05												08 38									09 05	
Frimley	d		08 13												08 43									09 13	
Ash Vale	d		08 19												08 49									09 19	
Aldershot	a		08 24												08 54									09 25	
	d		08 38												09 08									09 38	
Ash 5	d		08 45												09 15									09 45	
Wanborough	d		08 48												09 18									09 48	
Guildford	a		08 55												09 25									09 55	
Martins Heron	d										08 17											08 47			
Bracknell	d										08 20											08 50			
Wokingham	d										08 27											08 57			
Winnersh	d										08 30											09 00			
Winnersh Triangle	d										08 32											09 02			
Earley	d										08 35											09 05			
Reading 7	a										08 40											09 10			

A From London Waterloo to Whitton continues to London Waterloo
B To Weybridge
C From London Waterloo
D To London Waterloo

The xx15 and xx45 services from London Waterloo to Whitton continues to London Waterloo via Brentford

The xx03 and xx33 London Waterloo to Kingston services continues to London Waterloo via Wimbledon

The xx07 and xx37 services from London Waterloo to Whitton continues to London Waterloo via Richmond

Table 149

Mondays to Fridays

9 December to 16 May

London - Hounslow, Richmond, Kingston, Windsor, Weybridge, Ascot, Guildford and Reading

Network Diagram - see first Page of Table 148

		SW	SW	SW	SW	SW	SW	SW	SW	SW	SW	SW	SW	SW	SW	SW	SW	SW	SW	SW	SW	SW
				■1					■1		■1				■1					■1		■1
			A		B	C	A	A		D		E		A		B	C	A	A		D	
London Waterloo ■15 ⊖	d	07 58	08 03	08 07			08 10	08 15	08 20			08 22	08 28	08 33	08 37			08 40	08 43	08 50		
Vauxhall ⊖	d	08 02	08 07				08 14	08 19				08 26	08 32	08 37				08 44	08 47			
Queenstown Rd.(Battersea)	d		08 10				08 17	08 22				08 29		08 40				08 47	08 50			
Clapham Junction ■10	d	08 08	08 13	08 16			08 20	08 25	08 28			08 32	08 38	08 43	08 45			08 50	08 55	08 58		
Wandsworth Town	d		08 16				08 23	08 28				08 35		08 46				08 53	08 58			
Putney	d	08 12	08 19				08 26	08 31				08 38	08 42	08 49				08 56	09 01			
Barnes	d		08 23				08 29	08 35				08 42		08 52				08 59	09 05			
Barnes Bridge	d						08 31					08 44						09 01				
Chiswick	d						08 34					08 47						09 03				
Kew Bridge	d						08 36					08 50						09 06				
Brentford	d						08 39					08 53						09 09				
Syon Lane	d						08 41					08 55						09 11				
Isleworth	d						08 43					08 57						09 13				
Hounslow	d						08 48					09 01						09 18				
Mortlake	d		08 25					08 37						08 54					09 07			
North Sheen	d		08 27			←		08 39		←				08 56			←		09 09		←	
Richmond ⊖	d	08 18	08 30	08 24		08 30		08 42	08 36	08 42			08 48	08 59	08 54		08 59		09 12	09 06	09 12	
St Margarets	d		→			08 32		→		08 44				→			09 01		→		09 14	
Twickenham	a	08 21		08 28		08 34			08 40	08 46			08 51		08 57		09 03			09 10	09 16	
	d	08 22		08 28		08 35			08 40	08 47			08 52		08 58		09 04			09 10	09 17	
Strawberry Hill	d					08 38											09 07					
Fulwell	a																					
Teddington	a					08 41											09 10					
Hampton Wick	a					08 44											09 14					
Kingston	a					08 46											09 16					
Whitton	d	08 25			←		08a53			08a50			08 55			←		09a23			09a20	
Feltham	d	08 29		08 34	08 38				08 46			09 08	08 59		09 04	09 08				09 16		
Ashford (Surrey)	d	08 33		08 38	08 42							→	09 03		09 08	09 12						
Staines	d	08 37		08 42	08 46				08 53				09 07		09 12	09 16				09 23		
Wraysbury	d	08 41											09 11									
Sunnymeads	d	08 44											09 14									
Datchet	d	08 47											09 17									
Windsor & Eton Riverside	a	08 51											09 21									
Egham	d			08 47	08 51				08 57						09 16	09 21				09 27		
Virginia Water	a			08 51	08 55				09 01						09 20	09 25				09 31		
	d			08 51	08 55				09 01						09 20	09 25				09 31		
Chertsey	d				09 01											09 31						
Addlestone	d				09 04											09 34						
Weybridge	a				09 08											09 38						
Longcross	d			08 54																		
Sunningdale	d			08 58					09 07						09 26					09 37		
Ascot ■3	d			09 02					09 13		09 23				09 30					09 43		09 53
Bagshot	d										09 29											09 59
Camberley	a										09 35											10 05
Frimley	d										09 43											10 13
Ash Vale	d										09 49											10 19
Aldershot	a										09 54											10 24
	d										10 08											10 38
Ash ■5	d										10 15											10 45
Wanborough	d										10 18											10 48
Guildford	a										10 25											10 55
Martins Heron	d			09 06					09 17						09 34					09 47		
Bracknell	d			09 10					09 20						09 38					09 50		
Wokingham	d			09 17					09 27						09 47					09 57		
Winnersh	d			09 20					09 30											10 00		
Winnersh Triangle	d			09 22					09 32											10 02		
Earley	d			09 25					09 35											10 05		
Reading ■7	a			09 30					09 40						09 55					10 10		

A To London Waterloo
B From London Waterloo
C From London Waterloo to Kingston continues to London Waterloo
D From London Waterloo to Whitton continues to London Waterloo
E To Weybridge

The xx15 and xx45 services from London Waterloo to Whitton continues to London Waterloo via Brentford

The xx03 and xx33 London Waterloo to Kingston services continues to London Waterloo via Wimbledon

The xx07 and xx37 services from London Waterloo to Whitton continues to London Waterloo via Richmond

Table 149

Mondays to Fridays

9 December to 16 May

London - Hounslow, Richmond, Kingston, Windsor, Weybridge, Ascot, Guildford and Reading

Network Diagram - see first Page of Table 148

Station		SW A	SW	SW B	SW C	SW C	SW C	SW ■1	SW D	SW ■1	SW A	SW	SW B	SW C	SW C	SW C	SW ■1	SW D	SW ■1	SW A	SW	SW B	SW C
London Waterloo ■15 ⊖	d	08 52	08 58		09 03	09 07	09 15	09 20			09 22	09 28		09 33	09 37	09 45	09 50			09 52	09 58		10 03
Vauxhall ⊖	d	08 56	09 02		09 07	09 11	09 19				09 26	09 32		09 37	09 41	09 49				09 56	10 02		10 07
Queenstown Rd.(Battersea)	d	08 59			09 10	09 14	09 22				09 29			09 40	09 44	09 52				09 59			10 10
Clapham Junction ■10	d	09 02	09 08		09 13	09 17	09 25	09 28			09 32	09 38		09 43	09 47	09 55	09 58			10 02	10 08		10 13
Wandsworth Town	d	09 05			09 16	09 20	09 28				09 35			09 46	09 50	09 58				10 05			10 16
Putney	d	09 08	09 12		09 19	09 23	09 31				09 38	09 42		09 49	09 53	10 01				10 08	10 12		10 19
Barnes	d	09 12			09 22	09 27	09 35				09 42			09 52	09 57	10 05				10 12			10 22
Barnes Bridge	d	09 14				09 29					09 44				09 59					10 14			
Chiswick	d	09 17				09 32					09 47				10 02					10 17			
Kew Bridge	d	09 20				09 35					09 50				10 05					10 20			
Brentford	d	09 23				09 38					09 53				10 08					10 23			
Syon Lane	d	09 25				09 40					09 55				10 10					10 25			
Isleworth	d	09 27				09 42					09 57				10 12					10 27			
Hounslow	d	09 31				09 48					10 01				10 18					10 31			
Mortlake	d				09 24		09 37							09 54		10 07							10 24
North Sheen	d				09 26		09 39		←					09 56		10 09		←					10 26
Richmond ⊖	d		09 18		09 29		09 42	09 36	09 42			09 48		09 59		10 12	10 06	10 12			10 18		10 29
St Margarets	d				09 31		→		09 44					10 01		→		10 14					10 31
Twickenham	a		09 21		09 33			09 40	09 46			09 51		10 03			10 10	10 16			10 21		10 33
	d		09 22		09 34			09 40	09 47			09 52		10 04			10 10	10 17			10 22		10 34
Strawberry Hill	d				09 37									10 07									10 37
Fulwell	a																						
Teddington	a				09 40									10 10									10 40
Hampton Wick	a				09 44									10 14									10 44
Kingston	a				09 46									10 16									10 46
Whitton	d		09 25	←		09a53			09a50			09 55	←		10a26			10a20			10 25	←	
Feltham	d	09 36	09 29	09 36				09 46			10 06	09 59	10 06				10 16			10 36	10 29	10 36	
Ashford (Surrey)	d	→	09 33	09 40							→	10 03	10 10							→	10 33	10 40	
Staines	d		09 37	09 44				09 53				10 07	10 14				10 23				10 37	10 44	
Wraysbury	d		09 41									10 11									10 41		
Sunnymeads	d		09 44									10 14									10 44		
Datchet	d		09 47									10 17									10 47		
Windsor & Eton Riverside	a		09 51									10 21									10 51		
Egham	d			09 49				09 57					10 19				10 27					10 49	
Virginia Water	a			09 53				10 01					10 23				10 31					10 53	
	d			09 53				10 01					10 23				10 31					10 53	
Chertsey	d			09 59									10 29									10 59	
Addlestone	d			10 02									10 32									11 02	
Weybridge	a			10 07									10 37									11 07	
Longcross	d																						
Sunningdale	d							10 07									10 37						
Ascot ■3	d							10 13		10 23							10 43		10 53				
Bagshot	d									10 29									10 59				
Camberley	a									10 35									11 05				
Frimley	d									10 43									11 13				
Ash Vale	d									10 49									11 19				
Aldershot	a									10 54									11 24				
	d									11 08									11 38				
Ash ■5	d									11 15									11 45				
Wanborough	d									11 18									11 48				
Guildford	a									11 25									11 55				
Martins Heron	d							10 17									10 47						
Bracknell	d							10 20									10 50						
Wokingham	d							10 27									10 57						
Winnersh	d							10 30									11 00						
Winnersh Triangle	d							10 32									11 02						
Earley	d							10 35									11 05						
Reading ■7	a							10 40									11 10						

A To Weybridge
B From London Waterloo
C To London Waterloo
D From London Waterloo to Whitton continues to London Waterloo

The xx15 and xx45 services from London Waterloo to Whitton continues to London Waterloo via Brentford

The xx03 and xx33 London Waterloo to Kingston services continues to London Waterloo via Wimbledon

The xx07 and xx37 services from London Waterloo to Whitton continues to London Waterloo via Richmond

Table 149

Mondays to Fridays

9 December to 16 May

London - Hounslow, Richmond, Kingston, Windsor, Weybridge, Ascot, Guildford and Reading

Network Diagram - see first Page of Table 148

		SW	SW		SW	SW	SW	SW	SW	SW	SW	SW	SW		SW	SW	SW	SW	SW	SW	SW	SW	SW		SW
					■1		■1								■1		■1								■1
		A	A			B		C		D	A	A	A			B		C		D	A	A	A		
London Waterloo ■15 ⊖	d	10 07	10 15		10 20			10 22	10 28		10 33	10 37	10 45		10 50			10 52	10 58		11 03	11 07	11 15		11 20
Vauxhall ⊖	d	10 11	10 19					10 26	10 32		10 37	10 41	10 49					10 56	11 02		11 07	11 11	11 19		
Queenstown Rd.(Battersea)	d	10 14	10 22					10 29			10 40	10 44	10 52					10 59			11 10	11 14	11 22		
Clapham Junction ■10	d	10 17	10 25		10 28			10 32	10 38		10 43	10 47	10 55		10 58			11 02	11 08		11 13	11 17	11 25		11 28
Wandsworth Town	d	10 20	10 28					10 35			10 46	10 50	10 58					11 05			11 16	11 20	11 28		
Putney	d	10 23	10 31					10 38	10 42		10 49	10 53	11 01					11 08	11 12		11 19	11 23	11 31		
Barnes	d	10 27	10 35					10 42			10 52	10 57	11 05					11 12			11 22	11 27	11 35		
Barnes Bridge	d	10 29						10 44				10 59						11 14				11 29			
Chiswick	d	10 32						10 47				11 02						11 17				11 32			
Kew Bridge	d	10 35						10 50				11 05						11 20				11 35			
Brentford	d	10 38						10 53				11 08						11 23				11 38			
Syon Lane	d	10 40						10 55				11 10						11 25				11 40			
Isleworth	d	10 42						10 57				11 12						11 27				11 42			
Hounslow	d	10 48						11 01				11 18						11 31				11 48			
Mortlake	d		10 37								10 54		11 07								11 24		11 37		
North Sheen	d		10 39			←					10 56		11 09			←					11 26		11 39		
Richmond ⊖	d		10 42		10 36	10 42			10 48		10 59		11 12		11 06	11 12			11 18		11 29		11 42		11 36
St Margarets	d		↪			10 44					11 01		↪			11 14					11 31		↪		
Twickenham	a				10 40	10 46			10 51		11 03				11 10	11 16			11 21		11 33				11 40
	d				10 40	10 47			10 52		11 04				11 10	11 17			11 22		11 34				11 40
Strawberry Hill	d										11 07										11 37				
Fulwell	a																								
Teddington	a										11 10										11 40				
Hampton Wick	a										11 14										11 44				
Kingston	a										11 16										11 46				
Whitton	d	10a56				10a50			10 55	←		11a23				11a20			11 25	←		11a53			
Feltham	d				10 46			11 06	10 59	11 06					11 16			11 36	11 29	11 36					11 46
Ashford (Surrey)	d							↪	11 03	11 10								↪	11 33	11 40					
Staines	d				10 53				11 07	11 14					11 23				11 37	11 44					11 53
Wraysbury	d								11 11										11 41						
Sunnymeads	d								11 14										11 44						
Datchet	d								11 17										11 47						
Windsor & Eton Riverside	a								11 21										11 51						
Egham	d				10 57					11 19					11 27					11 49					11 57
Virginia Water	a				11 01					11 23					11 31					11 53					12 01
	d				11 01					11 23					11 31					11 53					12 01
Chertsey	d									11 29										11 59					
Addlestone	d									11 32										12 02					
Weybridge	a									11 37										12 07					
Longcross	d																								
Sunningdale	d				11 07										11 37										12 07
Ascot ■3	d				11 13		11 23								11 43		11 53								12 13
Bagshot	d						11 29										11 59								
Camberley	a						11 35										12 05								
Frimley	d						11 43										12 13								
Ash Vale	d						11 49										12 19								
Aldershot	a						11 54										12 24								
	d						12 08										12 38								
Ash ■5	d						12 15										12 45								
Wanborough	d						12 18										12 48								
Guildford	a						12 25										12 55								
Martins Heron	d				11 17										11 47										12 17
Bracknell	d				11 20										11 50										12 20
Wokingham	d				11 27										11 57										12 27
Winnersh	d				11 30										12 00										12 30
Winnersh Triangle	d				11 32										12 02										12 32
Earley	d				11 35										12 05										12 35
Reading ■7	a				11 40										12 10										12 40

A To London Waterloo

B From London Waterloo to Whitton continues to London Waterloo

C To Weybridge

D From London Waterloo

The xx15 and xx45 services from London Waterloo to Whitton continues to London Waterloo via Brentford

The xx03 and xx33 London Waterloo to Kingston services continues to London Waterloo via Wimbledon

The xx07 and xx37 services from London Waterloo to Whitton continues to London Waterloo via Richmond

Table 149

Mondays to Fridays

9 December to 16 May

London - Hounslow, Richmond, Kingston, Windsor, Weybridge, Ascot, Guildford and Reading

Network Diagram - see first Page of Table 148

		SW	SW	SW	SW	SW	SW	SW	SW	SW	SW	SW	SW	SW	SW	SW	SW	SW	SW	SW	SW	SW	SW
			■1							■1		■1							■1		■1		
		A		B		C	D	D	D		A		B		C	D	D	D		A		B	
London Waterloo ■15 ⊖	d			11 22	11 28		11 33	11 37	11 45	11 50			11 52	11 58		12 03	12 07	12 15	12 20			12 22	12 28
Vauxhall ⊖	d			11 26	11 32		11 37	11 41	11 49				11 56	12 02		12 07	12 11	12 19				12 26	12 32
Queenstown Rd.(Battersea)	d			11 29			11 40	11 44	11 52				11 59			12 10	12 14	12 22				12 29	
Clapham Junction ■10	d			11 32	11 38		11 43	11 47	11 55	11 58			12 02	12 08		12 13	12 17	12 25	12 28			12 32	12 38
Wandsworth Town	d			11 35			11 46	11 50	11 58				12 05			12 16	12 20	12 28				12 35	
Putney	d			11 38	11 42		11 49	11 53	12 01				12 08	12 12		12 19	12 23	12 31				12 38	12 42
Barnes	d			11 42			11 52	11 57	12 05				12 12			12 22	12 27	12 35				12 42	
Barnes Bridge	d			11 44				11 59					12 14				12 29					12 44	
Chiswick	d			11 47				12 02					12 17				12 32					12 47	
Kew Bridge	d			11 50				12 05					12 20				12 35					12 50	
Brentford	d			11 53				12 08					12 23				12 38					12 53	
Syon Lane	d			11 55				12 10					12 25				12 40					12 55	
Isleworth	d			11 57				12 12					12 27				12 42					12 57	
Hounslow	d			12 01				12 18					12 31				12 48					13 01	
Mortlake	d						11 54		12 07							12 24		12 37					
North Sheen	d	←					11 56		12 09		←					12 26		12 39		←			
Richmond ⊖	d	11 42			11 48		11 59		12 12	12 06	12 12			12 18		12 29		12 42	12 36	12 42			12 48
St Margarets	d	11 44					12 01		↪		12 14					12 31		↪		12 44			
Twickenham	a	11 46			11 51		12 03			12 10	12 16			12 21		12 33			12 40	12 46			12 51
	d	11 47			11 52		12 04			12 10	12 17			12 22		12 34			12 40	12 47			12 52
Strawberry Hill	d						12 07									12 37							
Fulwell	a																						
Teddington	a						12 10									12 40							
Hampton Wick	a						12 14									12 44							
Kingston	a						12 16									12 46							
Whitton	d	11a50			11 55	←		12a23			12a20			12 25	←		12a53			12a50			12 55
Feltham	d			12 06	11 59	12 06				12 16			12 36	12 29	12 36				12 46			13 06	12 59
Ashford (Surrey)	d			↪	12 03	12 10							↪	12 33	12 40							↪	13 03
Staines	d				12 07	12 14				12 23				12 37	12 44				12 53				13 07
Wraysbury	d				12 11									12 41									13 11
Sunnymeads	d				12 14									12 44									13 14
Datchet	d				12 17									12 47									13 17
Windsor & Eton Riverside	a				12 21									12 51									13 21
Egham	d					12 19				12 27					12 49				12 57				
Virginia Water	a					12 23				12 31					12 53				13 01				
	d					12 23				12 31					12 53				13 01				
Chertsey	d					12 29									12 59								
Addlestone	d					12 32									13 02								
Weybridge	a					12 37									13 07								
Longcross	d																						
Sunningdale	d									12 37									13 07				
Ascot ■3	d		12 23							12 43		12 53							13 13		13 23		
Bagshot	d		12 29									12 59									13 29		
Camberley	a		12 35									13 05									13 35		
Frimley	d		12 43									13 13									13 43		
Ash Vale	d		12 49									13 19									13 49		
Aldershot	a		12 54									13 24									13 54		
	d		13 08									13 38									14 08		
Ash ■5	d		13 15									13 45									14 15		
Wanborough	d		13 18									13 48									14 18		
Guildford	a		13 25									13 55									14 25		
Martins Heron	d									12 47									13 17				
Bracknell	d									12 50									13 20				
Wokingham	d									12 57									13 27				
Winnersh	d									13 00									13 30				
Winnersh Triangle	d									13 02									13 32				
Earley	d									13 05									13 35				
Reading ■7	a									13 10									13 40				

A From London Waterloo to Whitton continues to London Waterloo
B To Weybridge
C From London Waterloo
D To London Waterloo

The xx15 and xx45 services from London Waterloo to Whitton continues to London Waterloo via Brentford

The xx03 and xx33 London Waterloo to Kingston services continues to London Waterloo via Wimbledon

The xx07 and xx37 services from London Waterloo to Whitton continues to London Waterloo via Richmond

Table 149

Mondays to Fridays

9 December to 16 May

London - Hounslow, Richmond, Kingston, Windsor, Weybridge, Ascot, Guildford and Reading

Network Diagram - see first Page of Table 148

		SW	SW	SW	SW	SW 1	SW	SW 1	SW	SW	SW	SW	SW	SW	SW 1	SW	SW 1	SW	SW	SW	SW	SW	SW
		A	B	B	B		C		D		A	B	B	B		C		D		A	B	B	B
London Waterloo 15 ⊖	d		12 33	12 37	12 45	12 50			12 52	12 58		13 03	13 07	13 15	13 20			13 22	13 28		13 33	13 37	13 45
Vauxhall ⊖	d		12 37	12 41	12 49				12 56	13 02		13 07	13 11	13 19				13 26	13 32		13 37	13 41	13 49
Queenstown Rd.(Battersea)	d		12 40	12 44	12 52				12 59			13 10	13 14	13 22				13 29			13 40	13 44	13 52
Clapham Junction 10	d		12 43	12 47	12 55	12 58			13 02	13 08		13 13	13 17	13 25	13 28			13 32	13 38		13 43	13 47	13 55
Wandsworth Town	d		12 46	12 50	12 58				13 05			13 16	13 20	13 28				13 35			13 46	13 50	13 58
Putney	d		12 49	12 53	13 01				13 08	13 12		13 19	13 23	13 31				13 38	13 42		13 49	13 53	14 01
Barnes	d		12 52	12 57	13 05				13 12			13 22	13 27	13 35				13 42			13 52	13 57	14 05
Barnes Bridge	d			12 59					13 14				13 29					13 44				13 59	
Chiswick	d			13 02					13 17				13 32					13 47				14 02	
Kew Bridge	d			13 05					13 20				13 35					13 50				14 05	
Brentford	d			13 08					13 23				13 38					13 53				14 08	
Syon Lane	d			13 10					13 25				13 40					13 55				14 10	
Isleworth	d			13 12					13 27				13 42					13 57				14 12	
Hounslow	d			13 18					13 31				13 48					14 01				14 18	
Mortlake	d		12 54		13 07							13 24		13 37							13 54		14 07
North Sheen	d		12 56		13 09		←					13 26		13 39		←					13 56		14 09
Richmond ⊖	d		12 59		13 12	13 06	13 12			13 18		13 29		13 42	13 36	13 42			13 48		13 59		14 12
St Margarets	d		13 01		↪		13 14					13 31		↪		13 44					14 01		↪
Twickenham	a		13 03			13 10	13 16			13 21		13 33			13 40	13 46			13 51		14 03		
	d		13 04			13 10	13 17			13 22		13 34			13 40	13 47			13 52		14 04		
Strawberry Hill	d		13 07									13 37									14 07		
Fulwell	a																						
Teddington	a		13 10									13 40									14 10		
Hampton Wick	a		13 14									13 44									14 14		
Kingston	a		13 16									13 46									14 16		
Whitton	d	←		13a23			13a20			13 25	←		13a53			13a50			13 55	←		14a23	
Feltham	d	13 06				13 16			13 36	13 29	13 36				13 46			14 06	13 59	14 06			
Ashford (Surrey)	d	13 10							↪	13 33	13 40							↪	14 03	14 10			
Staines	d	13 14				13 23				13 37	13 44				13 53				14 07	14 14			
Wraysbury	d									13 41									14 11				
Sunnymeads	d									13 44									14 14				
Datchet	d									13 47									14 17				
Windsor & Eton Riverside	a									13 51									14 21				
Egham	d	13 19				13 27					13 49				13 57					14 19			
Virginia Water	a	13 23				13 31					13 53				14 01					14 23			
	d	13 23				13 31					13 53				14 01					14 23			
Chertsey	d	13 29									13 59									14 29			
Addlestone	d	13 32									14 02									14 32			
Weybridge	a	13 37									14 07									14 37			
Longcross	d					13 35																	
Sunningdale	d					13 37									14 07								
Ascot 3	d					13 43		13 53							14 13		14 23						
Bagshot	d							13 59									14 29						
Camberley	a							14 05									14 35						
Frimley	d							14 13									14 43						
Ash Vale	d							14 19									14 49						
Aldershot	a							14 24									14 54						
	d							14 38									15 08						
Ash 5	d							14 45									15 15						
Wanborough	d							14 48									15 18						
Guildford	a							14 55									15 25						
Martins Heron	d					13 47									14 17								
Bracknell	d					13 50									14 20								
Wokingham	d					13 57									14 27								
Winnersh	d					14 00									14 30								
Winnersh Triangle	d					14 02									14 32								
Earley	d					14 05									14 35								
Reading 7	a					14 10									14 40								

A From London Waterloo
B To London Waterloo
C From London Waterloo to Whitton continues to London Waterloo
D To Weybridge

The xx15 and xx45 services from London Waterloo to Whitton continues to London Waterloo via Brentford

The xx03 and xx33 London Waterloo to Kingston services continues to London Waterloo via Wimbledon

The xx07 and xx37 services from London Waterloo to Whitton continues to London Waterloo via Richmond

Table 149

Mondays to Fridays

9 December to 16 May

London - Hounslow, Richmond, Kingston, Windsor, Weybridge, Ascot, Guildford and Reading

Network Diagram - see first Page of Table 148

Station		SW 1	SW A	SW 1	SW B	SW	SW C	SW D	SW D	SW D	SW 1	SW A	SW 1	SW B	SW	SW C	SW D	SW D	SW D	SW 1	SW A	SW 1
London Waterloo 15 ⊖	d	13 50			13 52	13 58		14 03	14 07	14 15	14 20			14 22	14 28		14 33	14 37	14 45	14 50		
Vauxhall ⊖	d				13 56	14 02		14 07	14 11	14 19				14 26	14 32		14 37	14 41	14 49			
Queenstown Rd.(Battersea)	d				13 59			14 10	14 14	14 22				14 29			14 40	14 44	14 52			
Clapham Junction 10	d	13 58			14 02	14 08		14 13	14 17	14 25	14 28			14 32	14 38		14 43	14 47	14 55	14 58		
Wandsworth Town	d				14 05			14 16	14 20	14 28				14 35			14 46	14 50	14 58			
Putney	d				14 08	14 12		14 19	14 23	14 31				14 38	14 42		14 49	14 53	15 01			
Barnes	d				14 12			14 22	14 27	14 35				14 42			14 52	14 57	15 05			
Barnes Bridge	d				14 14				14 29					14 44				14 59				
Chiswick	d				14 17				14 32					14 47				15 02				
Kew Bridge	d				14 20				14 35					14 50				15 05				
Brentford	d				14 23				14 38					14 53				15 08				
Syon Lane	d				14 25				14 40					14 55				15 10				
Isleworth	d				14 27				14 42					14 57				15 12				
Hounslow	d				14 31				14 48					15 01				15 18				
Mortlake	d							14 24		14 37							14 54		15 07			
North Sheen	d		←					14 26		14 39		←					14 56		15 09		←	
Richmond ⊖	d	14 06	14 12			14 18		14 29		14 42	14 36	14 42			14 48		14 59		15 12	15 06	15 12	
St Margarets	d		14 14					14 31		→		14 44					15 01		→		15 14	
Twickenham	a	14 10	14 16			14 21		14 33			14 40	14 46			14 51		15 03			15 10	15 16	
	d	14 10	14 17			14 22		14 34			14 40	14 47			14 52		15 04			15 10	15 17	
Strawberry Hill	d							14 37									15 07					
Fulwell	a																					
Teddington	a							14 40									15 10					
Hampton Wick	a							14 44									15 14					
Kingston	a							14 46									15 16					
Whitton	d		14a20			14 25	←		14a53			14a50			14 55	←		15a23			15a20	
Feltham	d	14 16			14 36	14 29	14 36				14 46			15 06	14 59	15 06				15 16		
Ashford (Surrey)	d				→	14 33	14 40							→	15 03	15 10						
Staines	d	14 23				14 37	14 44				14 53				15 07	15 14				15 23		
Wraysbury	d					14 41									15 11							
Sunnymeads	d					14 44									15 14							
Datchet	d					14 47									15 17							
Windsor & Eton Riverside	a					14 51									15 21							
Egham	d	14 27					14 49				14 57					15 19				15 27		
Virginia Water	a	14 31					14 53				15 01					15 23				15 31		
	d	14 31					14 53				15 01					15 23				15 31		
Chertsey	d						14 59									15 29						
Addlestone	d						15 02									15 32						
Weybridge	a						15 07									15 37						
Longcross	d																					
Sunningdale	d	14 37									15 07									15 37		
Ascot 3	d	14 43		14 53							15 13		15 23							15 43		15 53
Bagshot	d			14 59									15 29									15 59
Camberley	a			15 05									15 35									16 05
Frimley	d			15 13									15 43									16 13
Ash Vale	d			15 19									15 49									16 19
Aldershot	a			15 24									15 54									16 24
	d			15 38									16 08									16 38
Ash 5	d			15 45									16 15									16 45
Wanborough	d			15 48									16 18									16 48
Guildford	a			15 55									16 25									16 55
Martins Heron	d	14 47									15 17									15 47		
Bracknell	d	14 50									15 20									15 50		
Wokingham	d	14 57									15 27									15 57		
Winnersh	d	15 00									15 30									16 00		
Winnersh Triangle	d	15 02									15 32									16 02		
Earley	d	15 05									15 35									16 05		
Reading 7	a	15 10									15 40									16 10		

A From London Waterloo to Whitton continues to London Waterloo
B To Weybridge
C From London Waterloo
D To London Waterloo

The xx15 and xx45 services from London Waterloo to Whitton continues to London Waterloo via Brentford

The xx03 and xx33 London Waterloo to Kingston services continues to London Waterloo via Wimbledon

The xx07 and xx37 services from London Waterloo to Whitton continues to London Waterloo via Richmond

Table 149

Mondays to Fridays

9 December to 16 May

London - Hounslow, Richmond, Kingston, Windsor, Weybridge, Ascot, Guildford and Reading

Network Diagram - see first Page of Table 148

		SW	SW	SW	SW	SW	SW		SW	SW	SW	SW	SW	SW	SW	SW	SW		SW	SW	SW	SW	SW	SW	SW
									■1		■1								■1		■1				◇■1
		A		B	C	C	C			D		A		B	C	C	C			D		A		C	
London Waterloo ■15 ⊖	d	14 52	14 58		15 03	15 07	15 15		15 20			15 22	15 28		15 33	15 37	15 45		15 50			15 52	15 58	16 01	16 05
Vauxhall ⊖	d	14 56	15 02		15 07	15 11	15 19					15 26	15 32		15 37	15 41	15 49					15 56	16 02	16 05	16 09
Queenstown Rd.(Battersea)	d	14 59			15 10	15 14	15 22					15 29			15 40	15 44	15 52					15 59		16 08	
Clapham Junction ■10	d	15 02	15 08		15 13	15 17	15 25		15 28			15 32	15 38		15 43	15 47	15 55		15 58			16 02	16 08	16 11	16 15
Wandsworth Town	d	15 05			15 16	15 20	15 28					15 35			15 46	15 50	15 58					16 05		16 14	
Putney	d	15 08	15 12		15 19	15 23	15 31					15 38	15 42		15 49	15 53	16 01					16 08	16 12	16 17	
Barnes	d	15 12			15 22	15 27	15 35					15 42			15 52	15 57	16 05					16 12		16 22	
Barnes Bridge	d	15 14				15 29						15 44				15 59						16 14			
Chiswick	d	15 17				15 32						15 47				16 02						16 17			
Kew Bridge	d	15 20				15 35						15 50				16 05						16 20			
Brentford	d	15 23				15 38						15 53				16 08						16 23			
Syon Lane	d	15 25				15 40						15 55				16 10						16 25			
Isleworth	d	15 27				15 42						15 57				16 12						16 27			
Hounslow	d	15 31				15 48						16 01				16 18						16 31			
Mortlake	d				15 24		15 37								15 54		16 07							16 24	
North Sheen	d				15 26		15 39			⟵					15 56		16 09			⟵				16 26	
Richmond ⊖	d		15 18		15 29		15 42		15 36	15 42			15 48		15 59		16 12		16 06	16 12			16 18	16 29	16 23
St Margarets	d				15 31		↪			15 44					16 01		↪			16 14				↪	
Twickenham	a		15 21		15 33				15 40	15 46			15 51		16 03				16 10	16 16			16 21		16 27
	d		15 22		15 34				15 40	15 47			15 52		16 04				16 10	16 17			16 22		16 27
Strawberry Hill	d				15 37										16 07										
Fulwell	a																								
Teddington	a				15 40										16 10										
Hampton Wick	a				15 44										16 14										
Kingston	a				15 46										16 16										
Whitton	d		15 25	⟵		15a53				15a50			15 55	⟵		16a23				16a20			16 25		
Feltham	d	15 36	15 29	15 36					15 46			16 06	15 59	16 06					16 16			16 38	16 29		16 33
Ashford (Surrey)	d	↪	15 33	15 40								↪	16 03	16 10								↪	16 33		16 37
Staines	d		15 37	15 44					15 53				16 07	16 14					16 23				16 37		16 41
Wraysbury	d		15 41										16 11										16 41		
Sunnymeads	d		15 44										16 14										16 44		
Datchet	d		15 47										16 17										16 47		
Windsor & Eton Riverside	a		15 51										16 21										16 51		
Egham	d			15 49					15 57					16 19					16 27						16 46
Virginia Water	a			15 53					16 01					16 23					16 31						16 50
	d			15 53					16 01					16 23					16 31						16 50
Chertsey	d			15 59										16 29											
Addlestone	d			16 02										16 32											
Weybridge	a			16 07										16 37											
Longcross	d																								
Sunningdale	d								16 07										16 37						16 55
Ascot ■3	d								16 13		16 23								16 43		16 53				17 00
Bagshot	d										16 29										16 59				
Camberley	a										16 35										17 05				
Frimley	d										16 43										17 13				
Ash Vale	d										16 49										17 19				
Aldershot	a										16 54										17 24				
	d										17 08										17 38				
Ash ■5	d										17 15										17 45				
Wanborough	d										17 18										17 48				
Guildford	a										17 25										17 55				
Martins Heron	d								16 17										16 47						17 04
Bracknell	d								16 20										16 50						17 07
Wokingham	d								16 27										16 57						17 17
Winnersh	d								16 30										17 00						
Winnersh Triangle	d								16 32										17 02						
Earley	d								16 35										17 05						
Reading ■7	a								16 40										17 10						17 27

A To Weybridge
B From London Waterloo
C To London Waterloo
D From London Waterloo to Whitton continues to London Waterloo

The xx15 and xx45 services from London Waterloo to Whitton continues to London Waterloo via Brentford

The xx03 and xx33 London Waterloo to Kingston services continues to London Waterloo via Wimbledon

The xx07 and xx37 services from London Waterloo to Whitton continues to London Waterloo via Richmond

Table 149

Mondays to Fridays

9 December to 16 May

London - Hounslow, Richmond, Kingston, Windsor, Weybridge, Ascot, Guildford and Reading

Network Diagram - see first Page of Table 148

		SW	SW		SW	SW	SW	SW	SW	SW	SW	SW	SW		SW	SW	SW	SW	SW	SW	SW	SW	SW		SW
							◇1		1	◇	◇		◇1		◇				◇1		◇	◇			◇1
		A	B		C	C		D		E		C			A	B	C	C		D	E		C		
London Waterloo 15 ⊖	d				16 07	16 15	16 20			16 22	16 28	16 31	16 35				16 37	16 45	16 50		16 52	16 58	17 01		17 05
Vauxhall ⊖	d				16 11	16 19				16 26	16 32	16 35	16 39				16 41	16 49			16 56	17 02	17 05		17 09
Queenstown Rd.(Battersea)	d				16 14	16 22				16 29		16 38					16 44	16 52			16 59		17 08		
Clapham Junction 10	d				16 17	16 25	16 28			16 32	16 38	16 41	16 45				16 47	16 55	16 58		17 02	17 08	17 11		17 15
Wandsworth Town	d				16 20	16 28				16 35		16 44					16 50	16 58			17 05		17 14		
Putney	d				16 23	16 31				16 38	16 42	16 47					16 53	17 01			17 08	17 12	17 17		
Barnes	d				16 27	16 35				16 42		16 52					16 57	17 05			17 12		17 22		
Barnes Bridge	d				16 29					16 44							16 59				17 14				
Chiswick	d				16 32					16 47							17 02				17 17				
Kew Bridge	d				16 35					16 50							17 05				17 20				
Brentford	d				16 38					16 53							17 08				17 23				
Syon Lane	d				16 40					16 55							17 10				17 25				
Isleworth	d				16 42					16 57							17 12				17 27				
Hounslow	d				16 48					17 01							17 18				17 31				
Mortlake	d					16 37						16 54						17 07					17 24		
North Sheen	d		←			16 39		←				16 56				←		17 09		←			17 26		
Richmond ⊖	d		16 29			16 42	16 36	16 42			16 48	16 59	16 53			16 59		17 12	17 06	17 12		17 18	17 29		17 23
St Margarets	d		16 31			→		16 44				→				17 01		→		17 14			→		
Twickenham	a		16 33				16 40	16 46			16 51		16 57			17 03			17 10	17 16		17 21			17 27
	d		16 34				16 40	16 47			16 52		16 57			17 04			17 10	17 17		17 22			17 27
Strawberry Hill	d		16 37													17 07									
Fulwell	a																								
Teddington	a		16 42													17 12									
Hampton Wick	a		16 46													17 16									
Kingston	a		16 48													17 18									
Whitton	d	←			16a53			16a50			16 55				←		17a23			17a20		17 25			
Feltham	d	16 38					16 46			17 08	16 59		17 03		17 08				17 16		17 38	17 29			17 33
Ashford (Surrey)	d	16 42								→	17 03		17 07		17 12						→	17 33			17 37
Staines	d	16 46					16 53				17 07		17 11		17 16				17 23			17 37			17 41
Wraysbury	d										17 11											17 41			
Sunnymeads	d										17 14											17 44			
Datchet	d										17 17											17 47			
Windsor & Eton Riverside	a										17 23											17 53			
Egham	d	16 51					16 57						17 16		17 21				17 27						17 46
Virginia Water	a	16 55					17 01						17 20		17 25				17 31						17 50
	d	16 55					17 01						17 20		17 25				17 31						17 50
Chertsey	d	17 01													17 31										
Addlestone	d	17 04													17 34										
Weybridge	a	17 08													17 40										
Longcross	d												17 23												
Sunningdale	d						17 07						17 27						17 37						17 55
Ascot 3	d						17 13		17 23				17 31						17 43						18 01
Bagshot	d								17 29																18 07
Camberley	a								17 35																18 13
Frimley	d								17 43																18 17
Ash Vale	d								17 49																18 24
Aldershot	a								17 54																18 31
	d								18 08																
Ash 5	d								18 15																
Wanborough	d								18 18																
Guildford	a								18 25																
Martins Heron	d						17 17						17 35						17 47						
Bracknell	d						17 20						17 39						17 50						
Wokingham	d						17 27						17 47						17 57						
Winnersh	d						17 30												18 00						
Winnersh Triangle	d						17 32												18 02						
Earley	d						17 35												18 05						
Reading 7	a						17 42						17 58						18 12						

A From London Waterloo

B From London Waterloo to Kingston continues to London Waterloo

C To London Waterloo

D From London Waterloo to Whitton continues to London Waterloo

E To Weybridge

The xx15 and xx45 services from London Waterloo to Whitton continues to London Waterloo via Brentford

The xx03 and xx33 London Waterloo to Kingston services continues to London Waterloo via Wimbledon

The xx07 and xx37 services from London Waterloo to Whitton continues to London Waterloo via Richmond

Table 149

Mondays to Fridays

9 December to 16 May

London - Hounslow, Richmond, Kingston, Windsor, Weybridge, Ascot, Guildford and Reading

Network Diagram - see first Page of Table 148

		SW	SW	SW	SW	SW	SW	SW	SW	SW	SW	SW	SW	SW	SW	SW	SW	SW	SW	SW	SW	SW	SW
		◇				1		◇1		1	◇	◇		◇1	◇					◇1		◇	◇
		A	B	C	C		C		D		E		C		A	B	C	F	C		D	E	
London Waterloo 15 ⊖	d			17 07	17 13		17 15	17 20			17 22	17 28	17 31	17 35			17 37	17 43	17 45	17 50		17 52	17 58
Vauxhall ⊖	d			17 11	17 17		17 19				17 26	17 32	17 35	17 39			17 41	17 47	17 49			17 56	18 02
Queenstown Rd.(Battersea)	d			17 14			17 22				17 29		17 38				17 44		17 52			17 59	
Clapham Junction 10	d			17 17	17 23		17 25	17 28			17 32	17 38	17 41	17 45			17 47	17 53	17 55	17 58		18 02	18 08
Wandsworth Town	d			17 20			17 28				17 35		17 44				17 50		17 58			18 05	
Putney	d			17 23	17 27		17 31				17 38	17 42	17 47				17 53	17 57	18 01			18 08	18 12
Barnes	d			17 27			17 35				17 42		17 52				17 57		18 05			18 12	
Barnes Bridge	d			17 29							17 44						17 59					18 14	
Chiswick	d			17 32							17 47						18 02					18 17	
Kew Bridge	d			17 35							17 50						18 05					18 20	
Brentford	d			17 38							17 53						18 08					18 23	
Syon Lane	d			17 40							17 55						18 10					18 25	
Isleworth	d			17 42							17 57						18 12					18 27	
Hounslow	d			17 48							18 01						18 18					18 31	
Mortlake	d						17 37						17 54						18 07				
North Sheen	d		←				17 39		←				17 56			←			18 09		←		
Richmond ⊖	d		17 29		17 33		17 42	17 36	17 42			17 48	17 59	17 53		17 59		18 03	18 12	18 06	18 12		18 18
St Margarets	d		17 31				→		17 44				→			18 01			→		18 14		
Twickenham	a		17 33		17 37			17 40	17 46			17 51		17 57		18 03		18 07		18 10	18 16		18 21
	d		17 34		17 37			17 40	17 47			17 52		17 57		18 04		18 07		18 10	18 17		18 22
Strawberry Hill	d		17 37		17 41											18 07		18 11					
Fulwell	a																	18 13					
Teddington	a		17 42		17 46											18 12							
Hampton Wick	a		17 46		17 54											18 16							
Kingston	a		17 48		17 56											18 18							
Whitton	d	←		17a53					17a50			17 55			←		18a23				18a20		18 25
Feltham	d	17 38						17 46			18 08	17 59		18 03	18 08					18 16		18 38	18 29
Ashford (Surrey)	d	17 42									→	18 03		18 07	18 12							→	18 33
Staines	d	17 46						17 53				18 07		18 11	18 16					18 23			18 37
Wraysbury	d											18 11											18 41
Sunnymeads	d											18 14											18 44
Datchet	d											18 17											18 47
Windsor & Eton Riverside	a											18 23											18 53
Egham	d	17 51						17 57						18 16	18 21					18 27			
Virginia Water	a	17 55						18 01						18 20	18 25					18 31			
	d	17 55						18 01						18 20	18 25					18 31			
Chertsey	d	18 01													18 31								
Addlestone	d	18 04													18 34								
Weybridge	a	18 10													18 40								
Longcross	d																			18 35			
Sunningdale	d							18 07						18 25						18 37			
Ascot 3	d							18 13		18 23				18 30						18 43			
Bagshot	d									18 29													
Camberley	a									18 35													
Frimley	d									18 43													
Ash Vale	d									18 49													
Aldershot	a									18 54													
	d					18 38				19 08													
Ash 5	d					18 45				19 15													
Wanborough	d					18 48				19 18													
Guildford	a					18 55				19 25													
Martins Heron	d							18 17						18 34						18 47			
Bracknell	d							18 20						18 37						18 50			
Wokingham	d							18 27						18 47						18 57			
Winnersh	d							18 30												19 00			
Winnersh Triangle	d							18 32												19 02			
Earley	d							18 35												19 05			
Reading 7	a							18 42						18 57						19 12			

A From London Waterloo
B From London Waterloo to Kingston continues to London Waterloo
C To London Waterloo
D From London Waterloo to Whitton continues to London Waterloo
E To Weybridge
F To Shepperton

The xx15 and xx45 services from London Waterloo to Whitton continues to London Waterloo via Brentford

The xx03 and xx33 London Waterloo to Kingston services continues to London Waterloo via Wimbledon

The xx07 and xx37 services from London Waterloo to Whitton continues to London Waterloo via Richmond

Table 149

Mondays to Fridays

9 December to 16 May

London - Hounslow, Richmond, Kingston, Windsor, Weybridge, Ascot, Guildford and Reading

Network Diagram - see first Page of Table 148

		SW	SW	SW	SW	SW	SW	SW	SW	SW	SW	SW	SW	SW	SW	SW	SW	SW	SW	SW	SW	SW	SW
			◇1	◇				1		◇1		1	◇	◇		◇1	◇					◇1	
		A		B	C	A	D		A		E		F		A		B	C	A	D	A		E
London Waterloo 15 ⊖	d	18 01	18 05			18 07	18 13		18 15	18 20			18 22	18 28	18 31	18 35			18 37	18 43	18 45	18 50	
Vauxhall ⊖	d	18 05	18 09			18 11	18 17		18 19				18 26	18 32	18 35	18 39			18 41	18 47	18 49		
Queenstown Rd.(Battersea)	d	18 08				18 14			18 22				18 29		18 38				18 44		18 52		
Clapham Junction 10	d	18 11	18 15			18 17	18 23		18 25	18 28			18 32	18 38	18 41	18 45			18 47	18 53	18 55	18 58	
Wandsworth Town	d	18 14				18 20			18 28				18 35		18 44				18 50		18 58		
Putney	d	18 17				18 23	18 27		18 31				18 38	18 42	18 47				18 53	18 57	19 01		
Barnes	d	18 22				18 27			18 35				18 42		18 52				18 57		19 05		
Barnes Bridge	d					18 29							18 44						18 59				
Chiswick	d					18 32							18 47						19 02				
Kew Bridge	d					18 35							18 50						19 05				
Brentford	d					18 38							18 53						19 08				
Syon Lane	d					18 40							18 55						19 10				
Isleworth	d					18 42							18 57						19 12				
Hounslow	d					18 48							19 01						19 18				
Mortlake	d	18 24							18 37						18 54						19 07		
North Sheen	d	18 26			←				18 39		←				18 56			←			19 09		←
Richmond ⊖	d	18 29	18 23		18 29		18 33		18 42	18 36	18 42			18 48	18 59	18 53		18 59		19 03	19 12	19 06	19 12
St Margarets	d	→			18 31				→		18 44				→			19 01			→		19 14
Twickenham	a		18 27		18 33		18 37			18 40	18 46			18 51		18 57		19 03		19 07		19 10	19 16
	d		18 27		18 34		18 37			18 40	18 47			18 52		18 57		19 04		19 07		19 10	19 17
Strawberry Hill	d				18 37		18 41											19 07		19 11			
Fulwell	a						18 43													19 13			
Teddington	a				18 42													19 12					
Hampton Wick	a				18 46													19 16					
Kingston	a				18 48													19 18					
Whitton	d			←		18a53					18a50			18 55			←		19a23				19a20
Feltham	d		18 33	18 38						18 46			19 08	18 59		19 03	19 08					19 16	
Ashford (Surrey)	d		18 37	18 42									→	19 03		19 07	19 12						
Staines	d		18 41	18 46						18 53				19 07		19 11	19 16					19 23	
Wraysbury	d													19 11									
Sunnymeads	d													19 14									
Datchet	d													19 17									
Windsor & Eton Riverside	a													19 23									
Egham	d		18 46	18 51						18 57						19 16	19 21					19 27	
Virginia Water	a		18 50	18 55						19 01						19 20	19 25					19 31	
	d		18 50	18 55						19 01						19 20	19 25					19 31	
Chertsey	d			19 01													19 31						
Addlestone	d			19 04													19 34						
Weybridge	a			19 10													19 40						
Longcross	d																						
Sunningdale	d		18 55							19 07						19 25						19 37	
Ascot 3	d		19 02							19 13		19 23				19 30						19 43	
Bagshot	d		19 08									19 29											
Camberley	a		19 14									19 35											
Frimley	d		19 19									19 43											
Ash Vale	d		19 26									19 49											
Aldershot	a		19 34									19 54											
	d							19 38				20 08											
Ash 5	d							19 45				20 15											
Wanborough	d							19 48				20 18											
Guildford	a							19 55				20 25											
Martins Heron	d									19 17						19 34						19 47	
Bracknell	d									19 20						19 37						19 50	
Wokingham	d									19 27						19 47						19 57	
Winnersh	d									19 30												20 00	
Winnersh Triangle	d									19 32												20 02	
Earley	d									19 35												20 05	
Reading 7	a									19 42						19 57						20 12	

A To London Waterloo
B From London Waterloo
C From London Waterloo to Kingston continues to London Waterloo
D To Shepperton
E From London Waterloo to Whitton continues to London Waterloo
F To Weybridge

The xx15 and xx45 services from London Waterloo to Whitton continues to London Waterloo via Brentford

The xx03 and xx33 London Waterloo to Kingston services continues to London Waterloo via Wimbledon

The xx07 and xx37 services from London Waterloo to Whitton continues to London Waterloo via Richmond

Table 149

Mondays to Fridays

9 December to 16 May

London - Hounslow, Richmond, Kingston, Windsor, Weybridge, Ascot, Guildford and Reading

Network Diagram - see first Page of Table 148

		SW	SW	SW	SW	SW	SW	SW	SW	SW	SW	SW	SW	SW	SW	SW	SW	SW	SW	SW	SW	SW
		1	◇	◇		1	◇				1		1							1		1
			A		B		C	D	B	B		E		A		C	B	B	B		E	
London Waterloo 15 ⊖	d		18 52	18 58	19 01	19 05			19 07	19 15	19 20			19 22	19 28		19 33	19 37	19 45	19 50		
Vauxhall ⊖	d		18 56	19 02	19 05	19 09			19 11	19 19				19 26	19 32		19 37	19 41	19 49			
Queenstown Rd.(Battersea)	d		18 59		19 08				19 14	19 22				19 29			19 40	19 44	19 52			
Clapham Junction 10	d		19 02	19 08	19 11	19 15			19 17	19 25	19 28			19 32	19 38		19 43	19 47	19 55	19 58		
Wandsworth Town	d		19 05		19 14				19 20	19 28				19 35			19 46	19 50	19 58			
Putney	d		19 08	19 12	19 17				19 23	19 31				19 38	19 42		19 49	19 53	20 01			
Barnes	d		19 12		19 22				19 27	19 35				19 42			19 52	19 57	20 05			
Barnes Bridge	d		19 14						19 29					19 44				19 59				
Chiswick	d		19 17						19 32					19 47				20 02				
Kew Bridge	d		19 20						19 35					19 50				20 05				
Brentford	d		19 23						19 38					19 53				20 08				
Syon Lane	d		19 25						19 40					19 55				20 10				
Isleworth	d		19 27						19 42					19 57				20 12				
Hounslow	d		19 31						19 48					20 01				20 18				
Mortlake	d				19 24					19 37							19 54		20 07			
North Sheen	d				19 26			←		19 39		←					19 56		20 09		←	
Richmond ⊖	d			19 18	19 29	19 23		19 29		19 42	19 36	19 42			19 48		19 59		20 12	20 06	20 12	
St Margarets	d				→			19 31		→		19 44					20 01		→		20 14	
Twickenham	a			19 21		19 27		19 33			19 40	19 46			19 51		20 03			20 10	20 16	
	d			19 22		19 27		19 34			19 40	19 47			19 52		20 04			20 10	20 17	
Strawberry Hill	d							19 37									20 07					
Fulwell	a																					
Teddington	a							19 42									20 10					
Hampton Wick	a							19 46									20 14					
Kingston	a							19 48									20 16					
Whitton	d			19 25			←		19a53			19a50			19 55	←		20a23			20a20	
Feltham	d		19 38	19 29		19 33	19 38				19 46			20 06	19 59	20 06				20 16		
Ashford (Surrey)	d		→	19 33		19 37	19 42							→	20 03	20 10						
Staines	d			19 37		19 41	19 46				19 53				20 07	20 14				20 23		
Wraysbury	d			19 41											20 11							
Sunnymeads	d			19 44											20 14							
Datchet	d			19 47											20 17							
Windsor & Eton Riverside	a			19 53											20 21							
Egham	d					19 46	19 51				19 57					20 19				20 27		
Virginia Water	a					19 50	19 55				20 01					20 23				20 31		
	d					19 50	19 55				20 01					20 23				20 31		
Chertsey	d						20 01									20 29						
Addlestone	d						20 04									20 32						
Weybridge	a						20 10									20 37						
Longcross	d																					
Sunningdale	d					19 55					20 07									20 37		
Ascot 3	d	19 53				20 00					20 13		20 23							20 43		20 53
Bagshot	d	19 59											20 29									20 59
Camberley	a	20 05											20 35									21 05
Frimley	d	20 13											20 43									21 13
Ash Vale	d	20 19											20 49									21 19
Aldershot	a	20 24											20 54									21 24
	d	20 38											21 08									21 38
Ash 5	d	20 45											21 15									21 45
Wanborough	d	20 48											21 18									21 48
Guildford	a	20 55											21 25									21 55
Martins Heron	d					20 04					20 17									20 47		
Bracknell	d					20 07					20 20									20 50		
Wokingham	d					20 17					20 27									20 57		
Winnersh	d										20 30									21 00		
Winnersh Triangle	d										20 32									21 02		
Earley	d										20 35									21 05		
Reading 7	a					20 25					20 40									21 10		

A To Weybridge
B To London Waterloo
C From London Waterloo
D From London Waterloo to Kingston continues to London Waterloo
E From London Waterloo to Whitton continues to London Waterloo

The xx15 and xx45 services from London Waterloo to Whitton continues to London Waterloo via Brentford

The xx03 and xx33 London Waterloo to Kingston services continues to London Waterloo via Wimbledon

The xx07 and xx37 services from London Waterloo to Whitton continues to London Waterloo via Richmond

Table 149

Mondays to Fridays

9 December to 16 May

London - Hounslow, Richmond, Kingston, Windsor, Weybridge, Ascot, Guildford and Reading

Network Diagram - see first Page of Table 148

		SW	SW	SW	SW	SW	SW	SW	SW	SW	SW	SW	SW	SW	SW	SW	SW	SW	SW	SW	SW	SW	SW
								1		1	1								1				
		A		B	C	C	C		D			A		B	C	C	C		D	A		B	C
London Waterloo 15 ⊖	d	19 52	19 58		20 03	20 07	20 15	20 20				20 22	20 28		20 33	20 37	20 45	20 50		20 52	20 58		21 03
Vauxhall ⊖	d	19 56	20 02		20 07	20 11	20 19					20 26	20 32		20 37	20 41	20 49			20 56	21 02		21 07
Queenstown Rd.(Battersea)	d	19 59			20 10	20 14	20 22					20 29			20 40	20 44	20 52			20 59			21 10
Clapham Junction 10	d	20 02	20 08		20 13	20 17	20 25	20 28				20 32	20 38		20 43	20 47	20 55	20 58		21 02	21 08		21 13
Wandsworth Town	d	20 05			20 16	20 20	20 28					20 35			20 46	20 50	20 58			21 05			21 16
Putney	d	20 08	20 12		20 19	20 23	20 31					20 38	20 42		20 49	20 53	21 01			21 08	21 12		21 19
Barnes	d	20 12			20 22	20 27	20 35					20 42			20 52	20 57	21 05			21 12			21 22
Barnes Bridge	d	20 14				20 29						20 44				20 59				21 14			
Chiswick	d	20 17				20 32						20 47				21 02				21 17			
Kew Bridge	d	20 20				20 35						20 50				21 05				21 20			
Brentford	d	20 23				20 38						20 53				21 08				21 23			
Syon Lane	d	20 25				20 40						20 55				21 10				21 25			
Isleworth	d	20 27				20 42						20 57				21 12				21 27			
Hounslow	d	20 31				20 48						21 01				21 18				21 31			
Mortlake	d				20 24		20 37								20 54		21 07						21 24
North Sheen	d				20 26		20 39		←						20 56		21 09		←				21 26
Richmond ⊖	d		20 18		20 29		20 42	20 36	20 42				20 48		20 59		21 12	21 06	21 12		21 18		21 29
St Margarets	d				20 31		↪		20 44						21 01		↪		21 14				21 31
Twickenham	a		20 21		20 33			20 40	20 46				20 51		21 03			21 10	21 16		21 21		21 33
	d		20 22		20 34			20 40	20 47				20 52		21 04			21 10	21 17		21 22		21 34
Strawberry Hill	d				20 37										21 07								21 37
Fulwell	a																						
Teddington	a				20 40										21 10								21 40
Hampton Wick	a				20 44										21 14								21 44
Kingston	a				20 46										21 16								21 46
Whitton	d		20 25	←		20a53			20a50				20 55	←		21a23			21a20		21 25	←	
Feltham	d	20 36	20 29	20 36				20 46				21 06	20 59	21 06				21 16		21 36	21 29	21 36	
Ashford (Surrey)	d	↪	20 33	20 40								↪	21 03	21 10						↪	21 33	21 40	
Staines	d		20 37	20 44				20 53					21 07	21 14				21 23			21 37	21 44	
Wraysbury	d		20 41										21 11								21 41		
Sunnymeads	d		20 44										21 14								21 44		
Datchet	d		20 47										21 17								21 47		
Windsor & Eton Riverside	a		20 51										21 21								21 51		
Egham	d			20 49				20 57						21 19				21 27				21 49	
Virginia Water	a			20 53				21 01						21 23				21 31				21 53	
	d			20 53				21 01						21 23				21 31				21 53	
Chertsey	d			20 59										21 29								21 59	
Addlestone	d			21 02										21 32								22 02	
Weybridge	a			21 07										21 37								22 07	
Longcross	d																						
Sunningdale	d							21 07										21 37					
Ascot 3	d							21 13		21 23								21 43					
Bagshot	d									21 29													
Camberley	a									21 35													
Frimley	d									21 43													
Ash Vale	d									21 49													
Aldershot	a									21 54													
	d									22 08	22 38												
Ash 5	d									22 15	22 45												
Wanborough	d									22 18	22 48												
Guildford	a									22 25	22 55												
Martins Heron	d							21 17										21 47					
Bracknell	d							21 20										21 50					
Wokingham	d							21 27										21 57					
Winnersh	d							21 30										22 00					
Winnersh Triangle	d							21 32										22 02					
Earley	d							21 35										22 05					
Reading 7	a							21 40										22 10					

A To Weybridge
B From London Waterloo
C To London Waterloo
D From London Waterloo to Whitton continues to London Waterloo

The xx15 and xx45 services from London Waterloo to Whitton continues to London Waterloo via Brentford

The xx03 and xx33 London Waterloo to Kingston services continues to London Waterloo via Wimbledon

The xx07 and xx37 services from London Waterloo to Whitton continues to London Waterloo via Richmond

Table 149

Mondays to Fridays

9 December to 16 May

London - Hounslow, Richmond, Kingston, Windsor, Weybridge, Ascot, Guildford and Reading

Network Diagram - see first Page of Table 148

		SW	SW		SW 1	SW	SW 1	SW	SW	SW	SW	SW	SW		SW 1	SW	SW	SW	SW	SW	SW 1	SW 1	SW		SW
		A	A			B		C		D	A	A	E			D	C		D	A		F	C		
London Waterloo 15 ⊖	d	21 07	21 15		21 20			21 22	21 28		21 33	21 37	21 45		21 50		21 52	21 58		22 03	22 20		22 22		22 28
Vauxhall ⊖	d	21 11	21 19					21 26	21 32		21 37	21 41	21 49				21 56	22 02		22 07			22 26		22 32
Queenstown Rd.(Battersea)	d	21 14	21 22					21 29			21 40	21 44	21 52				21 59			22 10			22 29		
Clapham Junction 10	d	21 17	21 25		21 28			21 32	21 38		21 43	21 47	21 55		21 58		22 02	22 08		22 13	22 28		22 32		22 38
Wandsworth Town	d	21 20	21 28					21 35			21 46	21 50	21 58				22 05			22 16			22 35		
Putney	d	21 23	21 31					21 38	21 42		21 49	21 53	22 01				22 08	22 12		22 19			22 38		22 42
Barnes	d	21 27	21 35					21 42			21 52	21 57	22 05				22 12			22 22			22 42		
Barnes Bridge	d	21 29						21 44				21 59					22 14						22 44		
Chiswick	d	21 32						21 47				22 02					22 17						22 47		
Kew Bridge	d	21 35						21 50				22 05					22 20						22 50		
Brentford	d	21 38						21 53				22 08					22 23						22 53		
Syon Lane	d	21 40						21 55				22 10					22 25						22 55		
Isleworth	d	21 42						21 57				22 12					22 27						22 57		
Hounslow	d	21 48						22 01				22 18					22 31						23 01		
Mortlake	d		21 37								21 54		22 07							22 24					
North Sheen	d		21 39			←					21 56		22 09			←				22 26					
Richmond ⊖	d		21 42		21 36	21 42			21 48		21 59		22 12		22 06	22 12		22 18		22 29	22 36				22 48
St Margarets	d		↪			21 44					22 01		↪			22 14				22 31					
Twickenham	a				21 40	21 46			21 51		22 03				22 10	22 16		22 21		22 33	22 40				22 51
	d				21 40	21 47			21 52		22 04				22 10			22 22		22 34	22 40				22 52
Strawberry Hill	d										22 07									22 37					
Fulwell	a																								
Teddington	a										22 10									22 40					
Hampton Wick	a										22 14									22 44					
Kingston	a										22 16									22 46					
Whitton	d	21a53				21a50			21 55	←		22a23						22 25	←						22 55
Feltham	d				21 46			22 06	21 59	22 06					22 16		22 36	22 29	22 36		22 46		23 06		22 59
Ashford (Surrey)	d							↪	22 03	22 10							↪	22 33	22 40				↪		23 03
Staines	d				21 53				22 07	22 14					22 23			22 37	22 44		22 53				23 07
Wraysbury	d								22 11									22 41							23 11
Sunnymeads	d								22 14									22 44							23 14
Datchet	d								22 17									22 47							23 17
Windsor & Eton Riverside	a								22 21									22 51							23 21
Egham	d				21 57					22 19					22 27				22 49		22 57				
Virginia Water	a				22 01					22 23					22 31				22 53		23 01				
	d				22 01					22 23					22 31				22 53		23 01				
Chertsey	d									22 29									22 59						
Addlestone	d									22 32									23 02						
Weybridge	a									22 37									23 07						
Longcross	d																								
Sunningdale	d				22 07										22 37						23 07				
Ascot 3	d				22 13		22 23								22 43						23 13	23 23			
Bagshot	d						22 29															23 29			
Camberley	a						22 35															23 35			
Frimley	d						22 43															23 43			
Ash Vale	d						22 49															23 49			
Aldershot	a						22 54															23 54			
	d						23 08																		
Ash 5	d						23 15																		
Wanborough	d						23 18																		
Guildford	a						23 25																		
Martins Heron	d				22 17										22 47						23 17				
Bracknell	d				22 20										22 50						23 20				
Wokingham	d				22 27										22 57						23 27				
Winnersh	d				22 30										23 00						23 30				
Winnersh Triangle	d				22 32										23 02						23 32				
Earley	d				22 35										23 05						23 35				
Reading 7	a				22 40										23 10						23 40				

A To London Waterloo
B From London Waterloo to Whitton continues to London Waterloo
C To Weybridge
D From London Waterloo
E To Twickenham
F To Farnham

The xx15 and xx45 services from London Waterloo to Whitton continues to London Waterloo via Brentford

The xx03 and xx33 London Waterloo to Kingston services continues to London Waterloo via Wimbledon

The xx07 and xx37 services from London Waterloo to Whitton continues to London Waterloo via Richmond

Table 149

Mondays to Fridays

9 December to 16 May

London - Hounslow, Richmond, Kingston, Windsor, Weybridge, Ascot, Guildford and Reading

Network Diagram - see first Page of Table 148

		SW	SW	SW	SW	SW	SW	SW	SW	SW	SW	SW	SW	SW	SW	SW	SW
				1					1								
		A	B		C		D	B		E		A			F		A
London Waterloo 15 ⊖	d		22 33	22 50	22 52	22 58		23 03	23 20	23 22	23 28		23 33	23 50	23 52	23 58	
Vauxhall ⊖	d		22 37		22 56	23 02		23 07		23 26	23 32		23 37		23 56	00 02	
Queenstown Rd.(Battersea)	d		22 40		22 59			23 10		23 29			23 40		23 59		
Clapham Junction 10	d		22 43	22 58	23 02	23 08		23 13	23 28	23 32	23 38		23 43	23 58	00 02	00 08	
Wandsworth Town	d		22 46		23 05			23 16		23 35			23 46		00 05		
Putney	d		22 49		23 08	23 12		23 19		23 38	23 42		23 49		00 08	00 12	
Barnes	d		22 52		23 12			23 22		23 42			23 52		00 12		
Barnes Bridge	d				23 14					23 44					00 14		
Chiswick	d				23 17					23 47					00 17		
Kew Bridge	d				23 20					23 50					00 20		
Brentford	d				23 23					23 53					00 23		
Syon Lane	d				23 25					23 55					00 25		
Isleworth	d				23 27					23 57					00 27		
Hounslow	d				23 31					00 01					00 31		
Mortlake	d		22 54					23 24					23 54				
North Sheen	d		22 56					23 26					23 56				
Richmond ⊖	d		22 59	23 06		23 18		23 29	23 36		23 48		23 59	00 06		00 18	
St Margarets	d		23 01					23 31					00 01				
Twickenham	a		23 03	23 10		23 21		23 33	23 40		23 51		00 03	00 10		00 21	
	d		23 04	23 10		23 22		23 34	23 40		23 52		00 04	00 10		00 22	
Strawberry Hill	d		23 07					23 37					00 09				
Fulwell	a																
Teddington	a		23 10					23 40					00 12				
Hampton Wick	a		23 14					23 44					00 14				
Kingston	a		23 16					23 46					00 16				
Whitton	d	←				23 25	←				23 55	←				00 25	←
Feltham	d	23 06		23 16	23 36	23 29	23 36		23 46	00 06	23 59	00 06		00 16	00 36	00 29	00 36
Ashford (Surrey)	d	23 10			→	23 33	23 40			→	00 03	00 10			→	00 33	00 40
Staines	d	23 14		23 23		23 37	23 44		23 53		00 07	00 14		00 23		00a37	00a46
Wraysbury	d					23 41					00 11						
Sunnymeads	d					23 44					00 14						
Datchet	d					23 47					00 17						
Windsor & Eton Riverside	a					23 51					00 21						
Egham	d	23 19		23 27			23 49		23 57			00 19		00 27			
Virginia Water	a	23 23		23 31			23 53		00 01			00 23		00 31			
	d	23 23		23 31			23 53		00 01			00 23		00 31			
Chertsey	d	23 29					23 59					00 29					
Addlestone	d	23 32					00a02					00 32					
Weybridge	a	23 37										00 36					
Longcross	d																
Sunningdale	d			23 37					00 08					00 37			
Ascot 3	d			23 43					00 13					00 42			
Bagshot	d																
Camberley	a																
Frimley	d																
Ash Vale	d																
Aldershot	a																
	d																
Ash 5	d																
Wanborough	d																
Guildford	a																
Martins Heron	d			23 47					00 17					00 46			
Bracknell	d			23 50					00 20					00 49			
Wokingham	d			23 57					00 32					00 56			
Winnersh	d			23 59					00 36								
Winnersh Triangle	d			00 02					00 38								
Earley	d			00 05					00 40								
Reading 7	a			00 10					00 45					01 04			

A From London Waterloo
B To London Waterloo
C To Woking
D From London Waterloo to Woking
E To Weybridge
F To Staines

The xx15 and xx45 services from London Waterloo to Whitton continues to London Waterloo via Brentford

The xx03 and xx33 London Waterloo to Kingston services continues to London Waterloo via Wimbledon

The xx07 and xx37 services from London Waterloo to Whitton continues to London Waterloo via Richmond

Table 149

Saturdays

14 December to 17 May

London - Hounslow, Richmond, Kingston, Windsor, Weybridge, Ascot, Guildford and Reading

Network Diagram - see first Page of Table 148

		SW	SW ■1	SW ■1	SW	SW	SW	SW ■1	SW ■1	SW	SW	SW ■1	SW	SW	SW	SW ■1	SW	SW	SW	SW	SW ■1	SW	SW
		A	A	A	A	A	A	B	C	A	A			D			D		D				D
London Waterloo ■15 ⊖	d												00 18			05 05			05 33		05 50	05 58	06 03
Vauxhall ⊖	d									00 02			00 22			05 09			05 37			06 02	06 07
Queenstown Rd.(Battersea)	d												00 25			05 12			05 40				06 10
Clapham Junction ■10	d									00 08	00 02		00 29			05 15			05 43		05 58	06 08	06 13
Wandsworth Town	d										00 05		00 32			05 18			05 46				06 16
Putney	d									00 12	00 08		00 35			05 21			05 49			06 12	06 19
Barnes	d										00 12		00 38			05 24			05 52				06 22
Barnes Bridge	d										00 14												
Chiswick	d										00 17												
Kew Bridge	d										00 20												
Brentford	d										00 23												
Syon Lane	d										00 25												
Isleworth	d										00 27												
Hounslow	d					00 01					00 31												
Mortlake	d												00 40			05 26			05 54				06 24
North Sheen	d												00 42			05 28			05 56				06 26
Richmond ⊖	d						00 06			00 18			00 45			05 31			05 59		06 06	06 18	06 29
St Margarets	d	00 01											00 47			05 33			06 01				06 31
Twickenham	a	00 03					00 10			00 21			00 49			05 35			06 03		06 10	06 21	06 33
	d	00 04					00 10			00 22			00 50	04 52		05 36	05 38	05 53	06 04		06 10	06 22	06 34
Strawberry Hill	d	00 09											00s53	04 55					06 07				06 37
Fulwell	a																						
Teddington	a	00 12											00s56	04 58					06 10				06 40
Hampton Wick	a	00 14											00s59	05 01					06 14				06 44
Kingston	a	00 16											01 01	05 03					06 16				06 46
Whitton	d									00 25						05 39	05a41	05 56				06 25	
Feltham	d					00 06	00 16			00 29	00 36					05 43		06 00			06 16	06 29	
Ashford (Surrey)	d				00 03	00 10				00 33	00 40					05 47		06 04				06 33	
Staines	d				00 07	00 14	00 23			00a37	00a46	05 23			05 44	05 53		06 08		06 16	06 23	06 37	
Wraysbury	d				00 11													06 12				06 41	
Sunnymeads	d				00 14													06 15				06 44	
Datchet	d				00 17													06 18				06 47	
Windsor & Eton Riverside	a				00 21													06 22				06 51	
Egham	d					00 19	00 27					05 27			05 49	05 57				06 20	06 27		
Virginia Water	a					00 23	00 31					05 31			05 53	06 01				06 25	06 31		
	d			00 01		00 23	00 31					05 31			05 53	06 01				06 25	06 31		
Chertsey	d					00 29									05 59					06 30			
Addlestone	d					00 32									06 02					06 33			
Weybridge	a					00 36									06 07					06 38			
Longcross	d																						
Sunningdale	d			00 08			00 37					05 37				06 07					06 37		
Ascot ■3	d			00 13			00 42	00 45				05 43				06 13					06 43		
Bagshot	d							00 51															
Camberley	a							00 57															
Frimley	d							01 01															
Ash Vale	d							01 08															
Aldershot	a							01s13															
	d								06 08														
Ash ■5	d								06 15														
Wanborough	d								06 18														
Guildford	a								06 25														
Martins Heron	d			00 17			00 46					05 47				06 17					06 47		
Bracknell	d			00 20			00 49					05 50				06 20					06 50		
Wokingham	d			00 32			00 56					05 57				06 27					06 57		
Winnersh	d			00 36								06 00				06 30					07 00		
Winnersh Triangle	d		00 02	00 38								06 02				06 32					07 02		
Earley	d		00 05	00 40								06 05				06 35					07 05		
Reading ■7	a		00 10	00 45			01 04					06 10				06 40					07 10		

A From London Waterloo
B To Farnham
C From Farnham
D To London Waterloo

The xx15 and xx45 services from London Waterloo to Whitton continues to London Waterloo via Brentford

The xx03 and xx33 London Waterloo to Kingston services continues to London Waterloo via Wimbledon

The xx07 and xx37 services from London Waterloo to Whitton continues to London Waterloo via Richmond

Table 149

Saturdays

14 December to 17 May

London - Hounslow, Richmond, Kingston, Windsor, Weybridge, Ascot, Guildford and Reading

Network Diagram - see first Page of Table 148

Station		SW 1	SW	SW 1	SW 1	SW 1		SW 1	SW A	SW	SW B	SW C	SW 1	SW 1	SW A	SW		SW B	SW C	SW C	SW 1	SW D	SW 1	SW A	SW
London Waterloo 15 ⊖	d					06 20			06 22	06 28		06 33	06 50		06 52	06 58			07 03	07 15	07 20			07 22	07 28
Vauxhall ⊖	d								06 26	06 32		06 37			06 56	07 02			07 07	07 19				07 26	07 32
Queenstown Rd.(Battersea)	d								06 29			06 40			06 59				07 10	07 22				07 29	
Clapham Junction 10	d					06 28			06 32	06 38		06 43	06 58		07 02	07 08			07 13	07 25	07 28			07 32	07 38
Wandsworth Town	d								06 35			06 46			07 05				07 16	07 28				07 35	
Putney	d								06 38	06 42		06 49			07 08	07 12			07 19	07 31				07 38	07 42
Barnes	d								06 42			06 52			07 12				07 22	07 35				07 42	
Barnes Bridge	d								06 44						07 14									07 44	
Chiswick	d								06 47						07 17									07 47	
Kew Bridge	d								06 50						07 20									07 50	
Brentford	d								06 53						07 23									07 53	
Syon Lane	d								06 55						07 25									07 55	
Isleworth	d								06 57						07 27									07 57	
Hounslow	d								07 01						07 31									08 01	
Mortlake	d											06 54							07 24	07 37					
North Sheen	d											06 56							07 26	07 39		←			
Richmond ⊖	d					06 36				06 48		06 59	07 06			07 18			07 29	07 42	07 36	07 42			07 48
St Margarets	d											07 01							07 31	↪		07 44			
Twickenham	a					06 40				06 51		07 03	07 10			07 21			07 33		07 40	07 46			07 51
	d					06 40				06 52		07 04	07 10			07 22			07 34		07 40	07 47			07 52
Strawberry Hill	d											07 07							07 37						
Fulwell	a																								
Teddington	a											07 10							07 40						
Hampton Wick	a											07 14							07 44						
Kingston	a											07 16							07 46						
Whitton	d									06 55	←					07 25		←				07a50			07 55
Feltham	d					06 46			07 06	06 59	07 06		07 16		07 36	07 29		07 36			07 46			08 06	07 59
Ashford (Surrey)	d								↪	07 03	07 10				↪	07 33		07 40						↪	08 03
Staines	d		06 44			06 53				07 07	07 14		07 23			07 37		07 44			07 53				08 07
Wraysbury	d									07 11						07 41									08 11
Sunnymeads	d									07 14						07 44									08 14
Datchet	d									07 17						07 47									08 17
Windsor & Eton Riverside	a									07 21						07 51									08 21
Egham	d		06 49			06 57					07 19		07 27					07 49			07 57				
Virginia Water	a		06 53			07 01					07 23		07 31					07 53			08 01				
	d		06 53			07 01					07 23		07 31					07 53			08 01				
Chertsey	d		06 59								07 29							07 59							
Addlestone	d		07 02								07 32							08 02							
Weybridge	a		07 07								07 37							08 07							
Longcross	d																								
Sunningdale	d					07 07							07 37								08 07				
Ascot 3	d				06 53	07 13							07 43	07 53							08 13		08 23		
Bagshot	d				06 59									07 59									08 29		
Camberley	a				07 05									08 05									08 35		
Frimley	d				07 13									08 13									08 43		
Ash Vale	d				07 19									08 19									08 49		
Aldershot	a				07 24									08 24									08 54		
	d	06 38		07 08	07 38			08 08						08 38									09 08		
Ash 5	d	06 45		07 15	07 45			08 15						08 45									09 15		
Wanborough	d	06 48		07 18	07 48			08 18						08 48									09 18		
Guildford	a	06 55		07 25	07 55			08 25						08 55									09 25		
Martins Heron	d					07 17							07 47								08 17				
Bracknell	d					07 20							07 50								08 20				
Wokingham	d					07 27							07 57								08 27				
Winnersh	d					07 30							08 00								08 30				
Winnersh Triangle	d					07 32							08 02								08 32				
Earley	d					07 35							08 05								08 35				
Reading 7	a					07 40							08 10								08 40				

A To Weybridge
B From London Waterloo
C To London Waterloo
D From London Waterloo to Whitton continues to London Waterloo

The xx15 and xx45 services from London Waterloo to Whitton continues to London Waterloo via Brentford

The xx03 and xx33 London Waterloo to Kingston services continues to London Waterloo via Wimbledon

The xx07 and xx37 services from London Waterloo to Whitton continues to London Waterloo via Richmond

Table 149

Saturdays

14 December to 17 May

London - Hounslow, Richmond, Kingston, Windsor, Weybridge, Ascot, Guildford and Reading

Network Diagram - see first Page of Table 148

		SW	SW	SW	SW	SW 1	SW	SW 1	SW	SW	SW	SW	SW	SW	SW 1	SW	SW 1	SW	SW	SW	SW	SW
		A	B	B	B		C		D		A	B	B	B		C		D		A	B	B
London Waterloo 15 ⊖	d		07 33	07 37	07 45	07 50			07 52	07 58		08 03	08 07	08 15	08 20			08 22	08 28		08 33	08 37
Vauxhall ⊖	d		07 37	07 41	07 49				07 56	08 02		08 07	08 11	08 19				08 26	08 32		08 37	08 41
Queenstown Rd.(Battersea)	d		07 40	07 44	07 52				07 59			08 10	08 14	08 22				08 29			08 40	08 44
Clapham Junction 10	d		07 43	07 47	07 55	07 58			08 02	08 08		08 13	08 17	08 25	08 28			08 32	08 38		08 43	08 47
Wandsworth Town	d		07 46	07 50	07 58				08 05			08 16	08 20	08 28				08 35			08 46	08 50
Putney	d		07 49	07 53	08 01				08 08	08 12		08 19	08 23	08 31				08 38	08 42		08 49	08 53
Barnes	d		07 52	07 57	08 05				08 12			08 22	08 27	08 35				08 42			08 52	08 57
Barnes Bridge	d			07 59					08 14				08 29					08 44				08 59
Chiswick	d			08 02					08 17				08 32					08 47				09 02
Kew Bridge	d			08 05					08 20				08 35					08 50				09 05
Brentford	d			08 08					08 23				08 38					08 53				09 08
Syon Lane	d			08 10					08 25				08 40					08 55				09 10
Isleworth	d			08 12					08 27				08 42					08 57				09 12
Hounslow	d			08 18					08 31				08 48					09 01				09 18
Mortlake	d		07 54		08 07							08 24		08 37							08 54	
North Sheen	d		07 56		08 09		←					08 26		08 39		←					08 56	
Richmond ⊖	d		07 59		08 12	08 06	08 12			08 18		08 29		08 42	08 36	08 42			08 48		08 59	
St Margarets	d		08 01		→		08 14					08 31		→		08 44					09 01	
Twickenham	a		08 03			08 10	08 16			08 21		08 33			08 40	08 46			08 51		09 03	
	d		08 04			08 10	08 17			08 22		08 34			08 40	08 47			08 52		09 04	
Strawberry Hill	d		08 07									08 37									09 07	
Fulwell	a																					
Teddington	a		08 10									08 40									09 10	
Hampton Wick	a		08 14									08 44									09 14	
Kingston	a		08 16									08 46									09 16	
Whitton	d	←		08a23			08a20			08 25	←		08a53			08a50			08 55	←		09a23
Feltham	d	08 06				08 16			08 36	08 29	08 36				08 46			09 06	08 59	09 06		
Ashford (Surrey)	d	08 10							→	08 33	08 40							→	09 03	09 10		
Staines	d	08 14				08 23				08 37	08 44				08 53				09 07	09 14		
Wraysbury	d									08 41									09 11			
Sunnymeads	d									08 44									09 14			
Datchet	d									08 47									09 17			
Windsor & Eton Riverside	a									08 51									09 21			
Egham	d	08 19				08 27					08 49				08 57					09 19		
Virginia Water	a	08 23				08 31					08 53				09 01					09 23		
	d	08 23				08 31					08 53				09 01					09 23		
Chertsey	d	08 29									08 59									09 29		
Addlestone	d	08 32									09 02									09 32		
Weybridge	a	08 37									09 07									09 37		
Longcross	d																					
Sunningdale	d					08 37									09 07							
Ascot 3	d					08 43		08 53							09 13		09 23					
Bagshot	d							08 59									09 29					
Camberley	a							09 05									09 35					
Frimley	d							09 13									09 43					
Ash Vale	d							09 19									09 49					
Aldershot	a							09 24									09 54					
	d							09 38									10 08					
Ash 5	d							09 45									10 15					
Wanborough	d							09 48									10 18					
Guildford	a							09 55									10 25					
Martins Heron	d					08 47									09 17							
Bracknell	d					08 50									09 20							
Wokingham	d					08 57									09 27							
Winnersh	d					09 00									09 30							
Winnersh Triangle	d					09 02									09 32							
Earley	d					09 05									09 35							
Reading 7	a					09 10									09 40							

A From London Waterloo
B To London Waterloo
C From London Waterloo to Whitton continues to London Waterloo
D To Weybridge

The xx15 and xx45 services from London Waterloo to Whitton continues to London Waterloo via Brentford

The xx03 and xx33 London Waterloo to Kingston services continues to London Waterloo via Wimbledon

The xx07 and xx37 services from London Waterloo to Whitton continues to London Waterloo via Richmond

Table 149

Saturdays

14 December to 17 May

London - Hounslow, Richmond, Kingston, Windsor, Weybridge, Ascot, Guildford and Reading

Network Diagram - see first Page of Table 148

		SW	SW	SW	SW	SW	SW	SW
			1		1			
		A		B		C		D
London Waterloo 15 ⊖	d	08 45	08 50			08 52	08 58	
Vauxhall ⊖	d	08 49				08 56	09 02	
Queenstown Rd.(Battersea)	d	08 52				08 59		
Clapham Junction 10	d	08 55	08 58			09 02	09 08	
Wandsworth Town	d	08 58				09 05		
Putney	d	09 01				09 08	09 12	
Barnes	d	09 05				09 12		
Barnes Bridge	d					09 14		
Chiswick	d					09 17		
Kew Bridge	d					09 20		
Brentford	d					09 23		
Syon Lane	d					09 25		
Isleworth	d					09 27		
Hounslow	d					09 31		
Mortlake	d	09 07						
North Sheen	d	09 09		←				
Richmond ⊖	d	09 12	09 06	09 12			09 18	
St Margarets	d	→		09 14				
Twickenham	a		09 10	09 16			09 21	
	d		09 10	09 17			09 22	
Strawberry Hill	d							
Fulwell	a							
Teddington	a							
Hampton Wick	a							
Kingston	a							
Whitton	d			09a20			09 25	←
Feltham	d		09 16			09 36	09 29	09 36
Ashford (Surrey)	d					→	09 33	09 40
Staines	d		09 23				09 37	09 44
Wraysbury	d						09 41	
Sunnymeads	d						09 44	
Datchet	d						09 47	
Windsor & Eton Riverside	a						09 51	
Egham	d		09 27					09 49
Virginia Water	a		09 31					09 53
	d		09 31					09 53
Chertsey	d							09 59
Addlestone	d							10 02
Weybridge	a							10 07
Longcross	d							
Sunningdale	d		09 37					
Ascot 3	d		09 43		09 53			
Bagshot	d				09 59			
Camberley	a				10 05			
Frimley	d				10 13			
Ash Vale	d				10 19			
Aldershot	a				10 24			
	d				10 38			
Ash 5	d				10 45			
Wanborough	d				10 48			
Guildford	a				10 55			
Martins Heron	d		09 47					
Bracknell	d		09 50					
Wokingham	d		09 57					
Winnersh	d		10 00					
Winnersh Triangle	d		10 02					
Earley	d		10 05					
Reading 7	a		10 10					

		SW	SW	SW	SW	SW	SW	SW	SW	SW
					1		1			
		A	A	A		B		C		D
London Waterloo 15 ⊖	d	09 03	09 07	09 15	09 20			09 22	09 28	
Vauxhall ⊖	d	09 07	09 11	09 19				09 26	09 32	
Queenstown Rd.(Battersea)	d	09 10	09 14	09 22				09 29		
Clapham Junction 10	d	09 13	09 17	09 25	09 28			09 32	09 38	
Wandsworth Town	d	09 16	09 20	09 28				09 35		
Putney	d	09 19	09 23	09 31				09 38	09 42	
Barnes	d	09 22	09 27	09 35				09 42		
Barnes Bridge	d		09 29					09 44		
Chiswick	d		09 32					09 47		
Kew Bridge	d		09 35					09 50		
Brentford	d		09 38					09 53		
Syon Lane	d		09 40					09 55		
Isleworth	d		09 42					09 57		
Hounslow	d		09 48					10 01		
Mortlake	d	09 24		09 37						
North Sheen	d	09 26		09 39		←				
Richmond ⊖	d	09 29		09 42	09 36	09 42			09 48	
St Margarets	d	09 31		→		09 44				
Twickenham	a	09 33			09 40	09 46			09 51	
	d	09 34			09 40	09 47			09 52	
Strawberry Hill	d	09 37								
Fulwell	a									
Teddington	a	09 40								
Hampton Wick	a	09 44								
Kingston	a	09 46								
Whitton	d		09a53			09a50			09 55	←
Feltham	d				09 46			10 06	09 59	10 06
Ashford (Surrey)	d							→	10 03	10 10
Staines	d				09 53				10 07	10 14
Wraysbury	d								10 11	
Sunnymeads	d								10 14	
Datchet	d								10 17	
Windsor & Eton Riverside	a								10 21	
Egham	d				09 57					10 19
Virginia Water	a				10 01					10 23
	d				10 01					10 23
Chertsey	d									10 29
Addlestone	d									10 32
Weybridge	a									10 37
Longcross	d									
Sunningdale	d				10 07					
Ascot 3	d				10 13		10 23			
Bagshot	d						10 29			
Camberley	a						10 35			
Frimley	d						10 43			
Ash Vale	d						10 49			
Aldershot	a						10 54			
	d						11 08			
Ash 5	d						11 15			
Wanborough	d						11 18			
Guildford	a						11 25			
Martins Heron	d				10 17					
Bracknell	d				10 20					
Wokingham	d				10 27					
Winnersh	d				10 30					
Winnersh Triangle	d				10 32					
Earley	d				10 35					
Reading 7	a				10 40					

		SW	SW	SW	SW	SW	SW
					1		1
		A	A	A		B	
London Waterloo 15 ⊖	d	09 33	09 37	09 45	09 50		
Vauxhall ⊖	d	09 37	09 41	09 49			
Queenstown Rd.(Battersea)	d	09 40	09 44	09 52			
Clapham Junction 10	d	09 43	09 47	09 55	09 58		
Wandsworth Town	d	09 46	09 50	09 58			
Putney	d	09 49	09 53	10 01			
Barnes	d	09 52	09 57	10 05			
Barnes Bridge	d		09 59				
Chiswick	d		10 02				
Kew Bridge	d		10 05				
Brentford	d		10 08				
Syon Lane	d		10 10				
Isleworth	d		10 12				
Hounslow	d		10 18				
Mortlake	d	09 54		10 07			
North Sheen	d	09 56		10 09		←	
Richmond ⊖	d	09 59		10 12	10 06	10 12	
St Margarets	d	10 01		→		10 14	
Twickenham	a	10 03			10 10	10 16	
	d	10 04			10 10	10 17	
Strawberry Hill	d	10 07					
Fulwell	a						
Teddington	a	10 10					
Hampton Wick	a	10 14					
Kingston	a	10 16					
Whitton	d		10a23			10a20	
Feltham	d				10 16		
Ashford (Surrey)	d						
Staines	d				10 23		
Wraysbury	d						
Sunnymeads	d						
Datchet	d						
Windsor & Eton Riverside	a						
Egham	d				10 27		
Virginia Water	a				10 31		
	d				10 31		
Chertsey	d						
Addlestone	d						
Weybridge	a						
Longcross	d						
Sunningdale	d				10 37		
Ascot 3	d				10 43		10 53
Bagshot	d						10 59
Camberley	a						11 05
Frimley	d						11 13
Ash Vale	d						11 19
Aldershot	a						11 24
	d						11 38
Ash 5	d						11 45
Wanborough	d						11 48
Guildford	a						11 55
Martins Heron	d				10 47		
Bracknell	d				10 50		
Wokingham	d				10 57		
Winnersh	d				11 00		
Winnersh Triangle	d				11 02		
Earley	d				11 05		
Reading 7	a				11 10		

A To London Waterloo

B From London Waterloo to Whitton continues to London Waterloo

C To Weybridge

D From London Waterloo

The xx15 and xx45 services from London Waterloo to Whitton continues to London Waterloo via Brentford

The xx03 and xx33 London Waterloo to Kingston services continues to London Waterloo via Wimbledon

The xx07 and xx37 services from London Waterloo to Whitton continues to London Waterloo via Richmond

Table 149

Saturdays

14 December to 17 May

London - Hounslow, Richmond, Kingston, Windsor, Weybridge, Ascot, Guildford and Reading

Network Diagram - see first Page of Table 148

		SW	SW	SW		SW	SW	SW	SW	SW	SW	SW	SW	SW		SW	SW	SW	SW	SW	SW	SW	SW	SW	
									1		1								1		1				
		A		B		C	C	C		D		A		B		C	C	C		D		A		B	
London Waterloo 15 ⊖	d	09 52	09 58			10 03	10 07	10 15	10 20			10 22	10 28			10 33	10 37	10 45	10 50			10 52	10 58		
Vauxhall ⊖	d	09 56	10 02			10 07	10 11	10 19				10 26	10 32			10 37	10 41	10 49				10 56	11 02		
Queenstown Rd.(Battersea)	d	09 59				10 10	10 14	10 22				10 29				10 40	10 44	10 52				10 59			
Clapham Junction 10	d	10 02	10 08			10 13	10 17	10 25	10 28			10 32	10 38			10 43	10 47	10 55	10 58			11 02	11 08		
Wandsworth Town	d	10 05				10 16	10 20	10 28				10 35				10 46	10 50	10 58				11 05			
Putney	d	10 08	10 12			10 19	10 23	10 31				10 38	10 42			10 49	10 53	11 01				11 08	11 12		
Barnes	d	10 12				10 22	10 27	10 35				10 42				10 52	10 57	11 05				11 12			
Barnes Bridge	d	10 14					10 29					10 44					10 59					11 14			
Chiswick	d	10 17					10 32					10 47					11 02					11 17			
Kew Bridge	d	10 20					10 35					10 50					11 05					11 20			
Brentford	d	10 23					10 38					10 53					11 08					11 23			
Syon Lane	d	10 25					10 40					10 55					11 10					11 25			
Isleworth	d	10 27					10 42					10 57					11 12					11 27			
Hounslow	d	10 31					10 48					11 01					11 18					11 31			
Mortlake	d					10 24		10 37								10 54		11 07							
North Sheen	d					10 26		10 39		←						10 56		11 09		←					
Richmond ⊖	d		10 18			10 29		10 42	10 36	10 42			10 48			10 59		11 12	11 06	11 12			11 18		
St Margarets	d					10 31		↪		10 44						11 01		↪		11 14					
Twickenham	a		10 21			10 33			10 40	10 46			10 51			11 03			11 10	11 16			11 21		
	d		10 22			10 34			10 40	10 47			10 52			11 04			11 10	11 17			11 22		
Strawberry Hill	d					10 37										11 07									
Fulwell	a																								
Teddington	a					10 40										11 10									
Hampton Wick	a					10 44										11 14									
Kingston	a					10 46										11 16									
Whitton	d		10 25	←			10a53			10a50			10 55	←			11a23			11a20			11 25	←	
Feltham	d	10 36	10 29	10 36					10 46			11 06	10 59	11 06					11 16			11 36	11 29	11 36	
Ashford (Surrey)	d	↪	10 33	10 40								↪	11 03	11 10								↪	11 33	11 40	
Staines	d		10 37	10 44					10 53				11 07	11 14					11 23				11 37	11 44	
Wraysbury	d		10 41										11 11										11 41		
Sunnymeads	d		10 44										11 14										11 44		
Datchet	d		10 47										11 17										11 47		
Windsor & Eton Riverside	a		10 51										11 21										11 51		
Egham	d			10 49					10 57					11 19					11 27					11 49	
Virginia Water	a			10 53					11 01					11 23					11 31					11 53	
	d			10 53					11 01					11 23					11 31					11 53	
Chertsey	d			10 59										11 29										11 59	
Addlestone	d			11 02										11 32										12 02	
Weybridge	a			11 07										11 37										12 07	
Longcross	d																								
Sunningdale	d								11 07										11 37						
Ascot 3	d								11 13		11 23								11 43		11 53				
Bagshot	d										11 29										11 59				
Camberley	a										11 35										12 05				
Frimley	d										11 43										12 13				
Ash Vale	d										11 49										12 19				
Aldershot	a										11 54										12 24				
	d										12 08										12 38				
Ash 5	d										12 15										12 45				
Wanborough	d										12 18										12 48				
Guildford	a										12 25										12 55				
Martins Heron	d								11 17										11 47						
Bracknell	d								11 20										11 50						
Wokingham	d								11 27										11 57						
Winnersh	d								11 30										12 00						
Winnersh Triangle	d								11 32										12 02						
Earley	d								11 35										12 05						
Reading 7	a								11 40										12 10						

A To Weybridge
B From London Waterloo
C To London Waterloo
D From London Waterloo to Whitton continues to London Waterloo

The xx15 and xx45 services from London Waterloo to Whitton continues to London Waterloo via Brentford

The xx03 and xx33 London Waterloo to Kingston services continues to London Waterloo via Wimbledon

The xx07 and xx37 services from London Waterloo to Whitton continues to London Waterloo via Richmond

Table 149

Saturdays

14 December to 17 May

London - Hounslow, Richmond, Kingston, Windsor, Weybridge, Ascot, Guildford and Reading

Network Diagram - see first Page of Table 148

		SW	SW	SW	SW	SW	SW	SW	SW	SW	SW	SW	SW	SW	SW	SW	SW	SW	SW	SW	SW	SW	SW
					■1		■1							■1		■1							■1
		A	A	A		B		C		D	A	A	A		B		C		D	A	A	A	
London Waterloo ■15 ⊖	d	11 03	11 07	11 15	11 20			11 22	11 28		11 33	11 37	11 45	11 50			11 52	11 58		12 03	12 07	12 15	12 20
Vauxhall ⊖	d	11 07	11 11	11 19				11 26	11 32		11 37	11 41	11 49				11 56	12 02		12 07	12 11	12 19	
Queenstown Rd.(Battersea)	d	11 10	11 14	11 22				11 29			11 40	11 44	11 52				11 59			12 10	12 14	12 22	
Clapham Junction ■10	d	11 13	11 17	11 25	11 28			11 32	11 38		11 43	11 47	11 55	11 58			12 02	12 08		12 13	12 17	12 25	12 28
Wandsworth Town	d	11 16	11 20	11 28				11 35			11 46	11 50	11 58				12 05			12 16	12 20	12 28	
Putney	d	11 19	11 23	11 31				11 38	11 42		11 49	11 53	12 01				12 08	12 12		12 19	12 23	12 31	
Barnes	d	11 22	11 27	11 35				11 42			11 52	11 57	12 05				12 12			12 22	12 27	12 35	
Barnes Bridge	d		11 29					11 44				11 59					12 14				12 29		
Chiswick	d		11 32					11 47				12 02					12 17				12 32		
Kew Bridge	d		11 35					11 50				12 05					12 20				12 35		
Brentford	d		11 38					11 53				12 08					12 23				12 38		
Syon Lane	d		11 40					11 55				12 10					12 25				12 40		
Isleworth	d		11 42					11 57				12 12					12 27				12 42		
Hounslow	d		11 48					12 01				12 18					12 31				12 48		
Mortlake	d	11 24		11 37							11 54		12 07							12 24		12 37	
North Sheen	d	11 26		11 39		←					11 56		12 09		←					12 26		12 39	
Richmond ⊖	d	11 29		11 42	11 36	11 42			11 48		11 59		12 12	12 06	12 12			12 18		12 29		12 42	12 36
St Margarets	d	11 31		→		11 44					12 01		→		12 14					12 31		→	
Twickenham	a	11 33			11 40	11 46			11 51		12 03			12 10	12 16			12 21		12 33			12 40
	d	11 34			11 40	11 47			11 52		12 04			12 10	12 17			12 22		12 34			12 40
Strawberry Hill	d	11 37									12 07									12 37			
Fulwell	a																						
Teddington	a	11 40									12 10									12 40			
Hampton Wick	a	11 44									12 14									12 44			
Kingston	a	11 46									12 16									12 46			
Whitton	d		11a53			11a50			11 55	←		12a23			12a20			12 25	←		12a53		
Feltham	d				11 46			12 06	11 59	12 06				12 16			12 36	12 29	12 36				12 46
Ashford (Surrey)	d							→	12 03	12 10							→	12 33	12 40				
Staines	d				11 53				12 07	12 14				12 23				12 37	12 44				12 53
Wraysbury	d								12 11									12 41					
Sunnymeads	d								12 14									12 44					
Datchet	d								12 17									12 47					
Windsor & Eton Riverside	a								12 21									12 51					
Egham	d				11 57					12 19				12 27					12 49				12 57
Virginia Water	a				12 01					12 23				12 31					12 53				13 01
	d				12 01					12 23				12 31					12 53				13 01
Chertsey	d									12 29									12 59				
Addlestone	d									12 32									13 02				
Weybridge	a									12 37									13 07				
Longcross	d																						
Sunningdale	d				12 07									12 37									13 07
Ascot ■3	d				12 13		12 23							12 43		12 53							13 13
Bagshot	d						12 29									12 59							
Camberley	a						12 35									13 05							
Frimley	d						12 43									13 13							
Ash Vale	d						12 49									13 19							
Aldershot	a						12 54									13 24							
	d						13 08									13 38							
Ash ■5	d						13 15									13 45							
Wanborough	d						13 18									13 48							
Guildford	a						13 25									13 55							
Martins Heron	d				12 17									12 47									13 17
Bracknell	d				12 20									12 50									13 20
Wokingham	d				12 27									12 57									13 27
Winnersh	d				12 30									13 00									13 30
Winnersh Triangle	d				12 32									13 02									13 32
Earley	d				12 35									13 05									13 35
Reading ■7	a				12 40									13 10									13 40

A To London Waterloo
B From London Waterloo to Whitton continues to London Waterloo
C To Weybridge
D From London Waterloo

The xx15 and xx45 services from London Waterloo to Whitton continues to London Waterloo via Brentford

The xx03 and xx33 London Waterloo to Kingston services continues to London Waterloo via Wimbledon

The xx07 and xx37 services from London Waterloo to Whitton continues to London Waterloo via Richmond

Table 149

Saturdays

14 December to 17 May

London - Hounslow, Richmond, Kingston, Windsor, Weybridge, Ascot, Guildford and Reading

Network Diagram - see first Page of Table 148

		SW	SW	SW	SW	SW	SW	SW	SW	SW	SW	SW	SW	SW	SW	SW	SW	SW	SW	SW	SW	SW	SW
			1							1		1							1		1		
		A		B		C	D	D	D		A		B		C	D	D	D		A		B	
London Waterloo 15	d			12 22	12 28		12 33	12 37	12 45	12 50			12 52	12 58		13 03	13 07	13 15	13 20			13 22	13 28
Vauxhall	d			12 26	12 32		12 37	12 41	12 49				12 56	13 02		13 07	13 11	13 19				13 26	13 32
Queenstown Rd.(Battersea)	d			12 29			12 40	12 44	12 52				12 59			13 10	13 14	13 22				13 29	
Clapham Junction 10	d			12 32	12 38		12 43	12 47	12 55	12 58			13 02	13 08		13 13	13 17	13 25	13 28			13 32	13 38
Wandsworth Town	d			12 35			12 46	12 50	12 58				13 05			13 16	13 20	13 28				13 35	
Putney	d			12 38	12 42		12 49	12 53	13 01				13 08	13 12		13 19	13 23	13 31				13 38	13 42
Barnes	d			12 42			12 52	12 57	13 05				13 12			13 22	13 27	13 35				13 42	
Barnes Bridge	d			12 44				12 59					13 14				13 29					13 44	
Chiswick	d			12 47				13 02					13 17				13 32					13 47	
Kew Bridge	d			12 50				13 05					13 20				13 35					13 50	
Brentford	d			12 53				13 08					13 23				13 38					13 53	
Syon Lane	d			12 55				13 10					13 25				13 40					13 55	
Isleworth	d			12 57				13 12					13 27				13 42					13 57	
Hounslow	d			13 01				13 18					13 31				13 48					14 01	
Mortlake	d						12 54		13 07							13 24		13 37					
North Sheen	d	←					12 56		13 09		←					13 26		13 39		←			
Richmond	d	12 42			12 48		12 59		13 12	13 06	13 12			13 18		13 29		13 42	13 36	13 42			13 48
St Margarets	d	12 44					13 01		→		13 14					13 31		→		13 44			
Twickenham	a	12 46			12 51		13 03			13 10	13 16			13 21		13 33			13 40	13 46			13 51
	d	12 47			12 52		13 04			13 10	13 17			13 22		13 34			13 40	13 47			13 52
Strawberry Hill	d						13 07									13 37							
Fulwell	a																						
Teddington	a						13 10									13 40							
Hampton Wick	a						13 14									13 44							
Kingston	a						13 16									13 46							
Whitton	d	12a50			12 55	←		13a23			13a20			13 25	←		13a53			13a50			13 55
Feltham	d			13 06	12 59	13 06				13 16			13 36	13 29	13 36				13 46			14 06	13 59
Ashford (Surrey)	d			→	13 03	13 10							→	13 33	13 40							→	14 03
Staines	d				13 07	13 14				13 23				13 37	13 44				13 53				14 07
Wraysbury	d				13 11									13 41									14 11
Sunnymeads	d				13 14									13 44									14 14
Datchet	d				13 17									13 47									14 17
Windsor & Eton Riverside	a				13 21									13 51									14 21
Egham	d					13 19				13 27					13 49				13 57				
Virginia Water	a					13 23				13 31					13 53				14 01				
	d					13 23				13 31					13 53				14 01				
Chertsey	d					13 29									13 59								
Addlestone	d					13 32									14 02								
Weybridge	a					13 37									14 07								
Longcross	d																						
Sunningdale	d									13 37									14 07				
Ascot 3	d		13 23							13 43		13 53							14 13		14 23		
Bagshot	d		13 29									13 59									14 29		
Camberley	a		13 35									14 05									14 35		
Frimley	d		13 43									14 13									14 43		
Ash Vale	d		13 49									14 19									14 49		
Aldershot	a		13 54									14 24									14 54		
	d		14 08									14 38									15 08		
Ash 5	d		14 15									14 45									15 15		
Wanborough	d		14 18									14 48									15 18		
Guildford	a		14 25									14 55									15 25		
Martins Heron	d									13 47									14 17				
Bracknell	d									13 50									14 20				
Wokingham	d									13 57									14 27				
Winnersh	d									14 00									14 30				
Winnersh Triangle	d									14 02									14 32				
Earley	d									14 05									14 35				
Reading 7	a									14 10									14 40				

A From London Waterloo to Whitton continues to London Waterloo

B To Weybridge

C From London Waterloo

D To London Waterloo

The xx15 and xx45 services from London Waterloo to Whitton continues to London Waterloo via Brentford

The xx03 and xx33 London Waterloo to Kingston services continues to London Waterloo via Wimbledon

The xx07 and xx37 services from London Waterloo to Whitton continues to London Waterloo via Richmond

Table 149

Saturdays

14 December to 17 May

London - Hounslow, Richmond, Kingston, Windsor, Weybridge, Ascot, Guildford and Reading

Network Diagram - see first Page of Table 148

		SW		SW	SW	SW	SW	SW	SW	SW	SW	SW		SW	SW	SW	SW	SW	SW	SW	SW	SW		SW	SW
							■1		■1								■1		■1						
		A		B	B	B		C		D		A		B	B	B		C		D		A		B	B
London Waterloo ■15 ⊖	d			13 33	13 37	13 45	13 50			13 52	13 58			14 03	14 07	14 15	14 20			14 22	14 28			14 33	14 37
Vauxhall ⊖	d			13 37	13 41	13 49				13 56	14 02			14 07	14 11	14 19				14 26	14 32			14 37	14 41
Queenstown Rd.(Battersea)	d			13 40	13 44	13 52				13 59				14 10	14 14	14 22				14 29				14 40	14 44
Clapham Junction ■10	d			13 43	13 47	13 55	13 58			14 02	14 08			14 13	14 17	14 25	14 28			14 32	14 38			14 43	14 47
Wandsworth Town	d			13 46	13 50	13 58				14 05				14 16	14 20	14 28				14 35				14 46	14 50
Putney	d			13 49	13 53	14 01				14 08	14 12			14 19	14 23	14 31				14 38	14 42			14 49	14 53
Barnes	d			13 52	13 57	14 05				14 12				14 22	14 27	14 35				14 42				14 52	14 57
Barnes Bridge	d				13 59					14 14					14 29					14 44					14 59
Chiswick	d				14 02					14 17					14 32					14 47					15 02
Kew Bridge	d				14 05					14 20					14 35					14 50					15 05
Brentford	d				14 08					14 23					14 38					14 53					15 08
Syon Lane	d				14 10					14 25					14 40					14 55					15 10
Isleworth	d				14 12					14 27					14 42					14 57					15 12
Hounslow	d				14 18					14 31					14 48					15 01					15 18
Mortlake	d			13 54		14 07								14 24		14 37								14 54	
North Sheen	d			13 56		14 09		←						14 26		14 39		←						14 56	
Richmond ⊖	d			13 59		14 12	14 06	14 12			14 18			14 29		14 42	14 36	14 42			14 48			14 59	
St Margarets	d			14 01		→		14 14						14 31		→		14 44						15 01	
Twickenham	a			14 03			14 10	14 16			14 21			14 33			14 40	14 46			14 51			15 03	
	d			14 04			14 10	14 17			14 22			14 34			14 40	14 47			14 52			15 04	
Strawberry Hill	d			14 07										14 37										15 07	
Fulwell	a																								
Teddington	a			14 10										14 40										15 10	
Hampton Wick	a			14 14										14 44										15 14	
Kingston	a			14 16										14 46										15 16	
Whitton	d	←			14a23			14a20			14 25	←			14a53			14a50			14 55	←			15a23
Feltham	d	14 06					14 16			14 36	14 29	14 36					14 46			15 06	14 59	15 06			
Ashford (Surrey)	d	14 10								→	14 33	14 40								→	15 03	15 10			
Staines	d	14 14					14 23				14 37	14 44					14 53				15 07	15 14			
Wraysbury	d										14 41										15 11				
Sunnymeads	d										14 44										15 14				
Datchet	d										14 47										15 17				
Windsor & Eton Riverside	a										14 51										15 21				
Egham	d	14 19					14 27					14 49					14 57					15 19			
Virginia Water	a	14 23					14 31					14 53					15 01					15 23			
	d	14 23					14 31					14 53					15 01					15 23			
Chertsey	d	14 29										14 59										15 29			
Addlestone	d	14 32										15 02										15 32			
Weybridge	a	14 37										15 07										15 37			
Longcross	d																								
Sunningdale	d						14 37										15 07								
Ascot ■3	d						14 43		14 53								15 13		15 23						
Bagshot	d								14 59										15 29						
Camberley	a								15 05										15 35						
Frimley	d								15 13										15 43						
Ash Vale	d								15 19										15 49						
Aldershot	a								15 24										15 54						
	d								15 38										16 08						
Ash ■5	d								15 45										16 15						
Wanborough	d								15 48										16 18						
Guildford	a								15 55										16 25						
Martins Heron	d						14 47										15 17								
Bracknell	d						14 50										15 20								
Wokingham	d						14 57										15 27								
Winnersh	d						15 00										15 30								
Winnersh Triangle	d						15 02										15 32								
Earley	d						15 05										15 35								
Reading ■7	a						15 10										15 40								

A From London Waterloo
B To London Waterloo
C From London Waterloo to Whitton continues to London Waterloo
D To Weybridge

The xx15 and xx45 services from London Waterloo to Whitton continues to London Waterloo via Brentford

The xx03 and xx33 London Waterloo to Kingston services continues to London Waterloo via Wimbledon

The xx07 and xx37 services from London Waterloo to Whitton continues to London Waterloo via Richmond

Table 149

Saturdays

14 December to 17 May

London - Hounslow, Richmond, Kingston, Windsor, Weybridge, Ascot, Guildford and Reading

Network Diagram - see first Page of Table 148

		SW	SW	SW	SW	SW	SW	SW	SW	SW	SW	SW	SW	SW	SW	SW	SW	SW	SW	SW	SW	SW	SW
			1		1							1		1							1		1
		A		B		C		D	A	A	A		B		C		D	A	A	A		B	
London Waterloo 15 ⊖	d	14 45	14 50			14 52	14 58		15 03	15 07	15 15	15 20			15 22	15 28		15 33	15 37	15 45	15 50		
Vauxhall ⊖	d	14 49				14 56	15 02		15 07	15 11	15 19				15 26	15 32		15 37	15 41	15 49			
Queenstown Rd.(Battersea)	d	14 52				14 59			15 10	15 14	15 22				15 29			15 40	15 44	15 52			
Clapham Junction 10	d	14 55	14 58			15 02	15 08		15 13	15 17	15 25	15 28			15 32	15 38		15 43	15 47	15 55	15 58		
Wandsworth Town	d	14 58				15 05			15 16	15 20	15 28				15 35			15 46	15 50	15 58			
Putney	d	15 01				15 08	15 12		15 19	15 23	15 31				15 38	15 42		15 49	15 53	16 01			
Barnes	d	15 05				15 12			15 22	15 27	15 35				15 42			15 52	15 57	16 05			
Barnes Bridge	d					15 14				15 29					15 44				15 59				
Chiswick	d					15 17				15 32					15 47				16 02				
Kew Bridge	d					15 20				15 35					15 50				16 05				
Brentford	d					15 23				15 38					15 53				16 08				
Syon Lane	d					15 25				15 40					15 55				16 10				
Isleworth	d					15 27				15 42					15 57				16 12				
Hounslow	d					15 31				15 48					16 01				16 18				
Mortlake	d	15 07							15 24		15 37							15 54		16 07			
North Sheen	d	15 09		←					15 26		15 39		←					15 56		16 09		←	
Richmond ⊖	d	15 12	15 06	15 12			15 18		15 29		15 42	15 36	15 42			15 48		15 59		16 12	16 06	16 12	
St Margarets	d	→		15 14					15 31		→		15 44					16 01		→		16 14	
Twickenham	a		15 10	15 16			15 21		15 33			15 40	15 46			15 51		16 03			16 10	16 16	
	d		15 10	15 17			15 22		15 34			15 40	15 47			15 52		16 04			16 10	16 17	
Strawberry Hill	d								15 37									16 07					
Fulwell	a																						
Teddington	a								15 40									16 10					
Hampton Wick	a								15 44									16 14					
Kingston	a								15 46									16 16					
Whitton	d			15a20			15 25	←		15a53			15a50			15 55	←		16a23			16a20	
Feltham	d		15 16			15 36	15 29	15 36				15 46			16 06	15 59	16 06				16 16		
Ashford (Surrey)	d					→	15 33	15 40							→	16 03	16 10						
Staines	d		15 23				15 37	15 44				15 53				16 07	16 14				16 23		
Wraysbury	d						15 41									16 11							
Sunnymeads	d						15 44									16 14							
Datchet	d						15 47									16 17							
Windsor & Eton Riverside	a						15 51									16 21							
Egham	d		15 27					15 49				15 57					16 19				16 27		
Virginia Water	a		15 31					15 53				16 01					16 23				16 31		
	d		15 31					15 53				16 01					16 23				16 31		
Chertsey	d							15 59									16 29						
Addlestone	d							16 02									16 32						
Weybridge	a							16 07									16 37						
Longcross	d																						
Sunningdale	d		15 37									16 07									16 37		
Ascot 3	d		15 43		15 53							16 13		16 23							16 43		16 53
Bagshot	d				15 59									16 29									16 59
Camberley	a				16 05									16 35									17 05
Frimley	d				16 13									16 43									17 13
Ash Vale	d				16 19									16 49									17 19
Aldershot	a				16 24									16 54									17 24
	d				16 38									17 08									17 38
Ash 5	d				16 45									17 15									17 45
Wanborough	d				16 48									17 18									17 48
Guildford	a				16 55									17 25									17 55
Martins Heron	d		15 47									16 17									16 47		
Bracknell	d		15 50									16 20									16 50		
Wokingham	d		15 57									16 27									16 57		
Winnersh	d		16 00									16 30									17 00		
Winnersh Triangle	d		16 02									16 32									17 02		
Earley	d		16 05									16 35									17 05		
Reading 7	a		16 10									16 40									17 10		

A To London Waterloo
B From London Waterloo to Whitton continues to London Waterloo
C To Weybridge
D From London Waterloo

The xx15 and xx45 services from London Waterloo to Whitton continues to London Waterloo via Brentford

The xx03 and xx33 London Waterloo to Kingston services continues to London Waterloo via Wimbledon

The xx07 and xx37 services from London Waterloo to Whitton continues to London Waterloo via Richmond

Table 149

Saturdays

14 December to 17 May

London - Hounslow, Richmond, Kingston, Windsor, Weybridge, Ascot, Guildford and Reading

Network Diagram - see first Page of Table 148

		SW	SW	SW		SW	SW	SW	SW	SW	SW	SW	SW	SW		SW	SW	SW	SW	SW	SW	SW	SW	SW	
									■1		■1								■1		■1				
		A		B		C	C	C		D		A		B		C	C	C		D		A		B	
London Waterloo ■15 ⊖	d	15 52	15 58			16 03	16 07	16 15	16 20			16 22	16 28			16 33	16 37	16 45	16 50			16 52	16 58		
Vauxhall ⊖	d	15 56	16 02			16 07	16 11	16 19				16 26	16 32			16 37	16 41	16 49				16 56	17 02		
Queenstown Rd.(Battersea)	d	15 59				16 10	16 14	16 22				16 29				16 40	16 44	16 52				16 59			
Clapham Junction ■10	d	16 02	16 08			16 13	16 17	16 25	16 28			16 32	16 38			16 43	16 47	16 55	16 58			17 02	17 08		
Wandsworth Town	d	16 05				16 16	16 20	16 28				16 35				16 46	16 50	16 58				17 05			
Putney	d	16 08	16 12			16 19	16 23	16 31				16 38	16 42			16 49	16 53	17 01				17 08	17 12		
Barnes	d	16 12				16 22	16 27	16 35				16 42				16 52	16 57	17 05				17 12			
Barnes Bridge	d	16 14					16 29					16 44					16 59					17 14			
Chiswick	d	16 17					16 32					16 47					17 02					17 17			
Kew Bridge	d	16 20					16 35					16 50					17 05					17 20			
Brentford	d	16 23					16 38					16 53					17 08					17 23			
Syon Lane	d	16 25					16 40					16 55					17 10					17 25			
Isleworth	d	16 27					16 42					16 57					17 12					17 27			
Hounslow	d	16 31					16 48					17 01					17 18					17 31			
Mortlake	d					16 24		16 37								16 54		17 07							
North Sheen	d					16 26		16 39		←						16 56		17 09		←					
Richmond ⊖	d		16 18			16 29		16 42	16 36	16 42			16 48			16 59		17 12	17 06	17 12			17 18		
St Margarets	d					16 31		→		16 44						17 01		→		17 14					
Twickenham	a		16 21			16 33			16 40	16 46			16 51			17 03			17 10	17 16			17 21		
	d		16 22			16 34			16 40	16 47			16 52			17 04			17 10	17 17			17 22		
Strawberry Hill	d					16 37										17 07									
Fulwell	a																								
Teddington	a					16 40										17 10									
Hampton Wick	a					16 44										17 14									
Kingston	a					16 46										17 16									
Whitton	d		16 25	←			16a53			16a50			16 55	←			17a23			17a20			17 25	←	
Feltham	d	16 36	16 29	16 36					16 46			17 06	16 59	17 06					17 16			17 36	17 29	17 36	
Ashford (Surrey)	d	→	16 33	16 40								→	17 03	17 10								→	17 33	17 40	
Staines	d		16 37	16 44					16 53				17 07	17 14					17 23				17 37	17 44	
Wraysbury	d		16 41										17 11										17 41		
Sunnymeads	d		16 44										17 14										17 44		
Datchet	d		16 47										17 17										17 47		
Windsor & Eton Riverside	a		16 51										17 21										17 51		
Egham	d			16 49					16 57					17 19					17 27					17 49	
Virginia Water	a			16 53					17 01					17 23					17 31					17 53	
	d			16 53					17 01					17 23					17 31					17 53	
Chertsey	d			16 59										17 29										17 59	
Addlestone	d			17 02										17 32										18 02	
Weybridge	a			17 07										17 37										18 07	
Longcross	d																								
Sunningdale	d								17 07										17 37						
Ascot ■8	d								17 13		17 23								17 43		17 53				
Bagshot	d										17 29										17 59				
Camberley	a										17 35										18 05				
Frimley	d										17 43										18 13				
Ash Vale	d										17 49										18 19				
Aldershot	a										17 54										18 24				
	d										18 08										18 38				
Ash ■5	d										18 15										18 45				
Wanborough	d										18 18										18 48				
Guildford	a										18 25										18 55				
Martins Heron	d								17 17										17 47						
Bracknell	d								17 20										17 50						
Wokingham	d								17 27										17 57						
Winnersh	d								17 30										18 00						
Winnersh Triangle	d								17 32										18 02						
Earley	d								17 35										18 05						
Reading ■7	a								17 40										18 10						

A To Weybridge
B From London Waterloo
C To London Waterloo
D From London Waterloo to Whitton continues to London Waterloo

The xx15 and xx45 services from London Waterloo to Whitton continues to London Waterloo via Brentford

The xx03 and xx33 London Waterloo to Kingston services continues to London Waterloo via Wimbledon

The xx07 and xx37 services from London Waterloo to Whitton continues to London Waterloo via Richmond

Table 149

Saturdays

14 December to 17 May

London - Hounslow, Richmond, Kingston, Windsor, Weybridge, Ascot, Guildford and Reading

Network Diagram - see first Page of Table 148

		SW	SW	SW	SW	SW	SW	SW	SW	SW	SW	SW	SW	SW	SW	SW	SW	SW	SW	SW	SW	SW	SW
					1		1							1		1							1
		A	A	A		B		C		D	A	A	A		B		C		D	A	A	A	
London Waterloo 15 ⊖	d	17 03	17 07	17 15	17 20			17 22	17 28		17 33	17 37	17 45	17 50			17 52	17 58		18 03	18 07	18 15	18 20
Vauxhall ⊖	d	17 07	17 11	17 19				17 26	17 32		17 37	17 41	17 49				17 56	18 02		18 07	18 11	18 19	
Queenstown Rd.(Battersea)	d	17 10	17 14	17 22				17 29			17 40	17 44	17 52				17 59			18 10	18 14	18 22	
Clapham Junction 10	d	17 13	17 17	17 25	17 28			17 32	17 38		17 43	17 47	17 55	17 58			18 02	18 08		18 13	18 17	18 25	18 28
Wandsworth Town	d	17 16	17 20	17 28				17 35			17 46	17 50	17 58				18 05			18 16	18 20	18 28	
Putney	d	17 19	17 23	17 31				17 38	17 42		17 49	17 53	18 01				18 08	18 12		18 19	18 23	18 31	
Barnes	d	17 22	17 27	17 35				17 42			17 52	17 57	18 05				18 12			18 22	18 27	18 35	
Barnes Bridge	d		17 29					17 44				17 59					18 14				18 29		
Chiswick	d		17 32					17 47				18 02					18 17				18 32		
Kew Bridge	d		17 35					17 50				18 05					18 20				18 35		
Brentford	d		17 38					17 53				18 08					18 23				18 38		
Syon Lane	d		17 40					17 55				18 10					18 25				18 40		
Isleworth	d		17 42					17 57				18 12					18 27				18 42		
Hounslow	d		17 48					18 01				18 18					18 31				18 48		
Mortlake	d	17 24		17 37							17 54		18 07							18 24		18 37	
North Sheen	d	17 26		17 39		←					17 56		18 09		←					18 26		18 39	
Richmond ⊖	d	17 29		17 42	17 36	17 42			17 48		17 59		18 12	18 06	18 12			18 18		18 29		18 42	18 36
St Margarets	d	17 31		→		17 44					18 01		→		18 14					18 31		→	
Twickenham	a	17 33			17 40	17 46			17 51		18 03			18 10	18 16			18 21		18 33			18 40
	d	17 34			17 40	17 47			17 52		18 04			18 10	18 17			18 22		18 34			18 40
Strawberry Hill	d	17 37									18 07									18 37			
Fulwell	a																						
Teddington	a	17 40									18 10									18 40			
Hampton Wick	a	17 44									18 14									18 44			
Kingston	a	17 46									18 16									18 46			
Whitton	d		17a53			17a50			17 55	←		18a23			18a20			18 25	←		18a53		
Feltham	d				17 46			18 06	17 59	18 06				18 16			18 36	18 29	18 36				18 46
Ashford (Surrey)	d							→	18 03	18 10							→	18 33	18 40				
Staines	d				17 53				18 07	18 14				18 23				18 37	18 44				18 53
Wraysbury	d								18 11									18 41					
Sunnymeads	d								18 14									18 44					
Datchet	d								18 17									18 47					
Windsor & Eton Riverside	a								18 21									18 51					
Egham	d				17 57					18 19				18 27					18 49				18 57
Virginia Water	a				18 01					18 23				18 31					18 53				19 01
	d				18 01					18 23				18 31					18 53				19 01
Chertsey	d									18 29									18 59				
Addlestone	d									18 32									19 02				
Weybridge	a									18 37									19 07				
Longcross	d																						
Sunningdale	d				18 07									18 37									19 07
Ascot 3	d				18 13		18 23							18 43		18 53							19 13
Bagshot	d						18 29									18 59							
Camberley	a						18 35									19 05							
Frimley	d						18 43									19 13							
Ash Vale	d						18 49									19 19							
Aldershot	a						18 54									19 24							
	d						19 08									19 38							
Ash 5	d						19 15									19 45							
Wanborough	d						19 18									19 48							
Guildford	a						19 25									19 55							
Martins Heron	d				18 17									18 47									19 17
Bracknell	d				18 20									18 50									19 20
Wokingham	d				18 27									18 57									19 27
Winnersh	d				18 30									19 00									19 30
Winnersh Triangle	d				18 32									19 02									19 32
Earley	d				18 35									19 05									19 35
Reading 7	a				18 40									19 10									19 40

A To London Waterloo
B From London Waterloo to Whitton continues to London Waterloo
C To Weybridge
D From London Waterloo

The xx15 and xx45 services from London Waterloo to Whitton continues to London Waterloo via Brentford

The xx03 and xx33 London Waterloo to Kingston services continues to London Waterloo via Wimbledon

The xx07 and xx37 services from London Waterloo to Whitton continues to London Waterloo via Richmond

Table 149

Saturdays

14 December to 17 May

London - Hounslow, Richmond, Kingston, Windsor, Weybridge, Ascot, Guildford and Reading

Network Diagram - see first Page of Table 148

Station		SW A	SW [1]	SW B	SW	SW C	SW D	SW D	SW D	SW [1]	SW A	SW [1]	SW B	SW	SW C	SW D	SW D	SW D	SW [1]	SW A	SW [1]	SW B	SW
London Waterloo [15] ⊖	d			18 22	18 28		18 33	18 37	18 45	18 50			18 52	18 58		19 03	19 07	19 15	19 20			19 22	19 28
Vauxhall ⊖	d			18 26	18 32		18 37	18 41	18 49				18 56	19 02		19 07	19 11	19 19				19 26	19 32
Queenstown Rd.(Battersea)	d			18 29			18 40	18 44	18 52				18 59			19 10	19 14	19 22				19 29	
Clapham Junction [10]	d			18 32	18 38		18 43	18 47	18 55	18 58			19 02	19 08		19 13	19 17	19 25	19 28			19 32	19 38
Wandsworth Town	d			18 35			18 46	18 50	18 58				19 05			19 16	19 20	19 28				19 35	
Putney	d			18 38	18 42		18 49	18 53	19 01				19 08	19 12		19 19	19 23	19 31				19 38	19 42
Barnes	d			18 42			18 52	18 57	19 05				19 12			19 22	19 27	19 35				19 42	
Barnes Bridge	d			18 44				18 59					19 14				19 29					19 44	
Chiswick	d			18 47				19 02					19 17				19 32					19 47	
Kew Bridge	d			18 50				19 05					19 20				19 35					19 50	
Brentford	d			18 53				19 08					19 23				19 38					19 53	
Syon Lane	d			18 55				19 10					19 25				19 40					19 55	
Isleworth	d			18 57				19 12					19 27				19 42					19 57	
Hounslow	d			19 01				19 18					19 31				19 48					20 01	
Mortlake	d						18 54		19 07							19 24		19 37					
North Sheen	d	←					18 56		19 09		←					19 26		19 39		←			
Richmond ⊖	d	18 42			18 48		18 59		19 12	19 06	19 12			19 18		19 29		19 42	19 36	19 42			19 48
St Margarets	d	18 44					19 01		→		19 14					19 31		→		19 44			
Twickenham	a	18 46			18 51		19 03			19 10	19 16			19 21		19 33			19 40	19 46			19 51
	d	18 47			18 52		19 04			19 10	19 17			19 22		19 34			19 40	19 47			19 52
Strawberry Hill	d						19 07									19 37							
Fulwell	a																						
Teddington	a						19 10									19 40							
Hampton Wick	a						19 14									19 44							
Kingston	a						19 16									19 46							
Whitton	d	18a50			18 55	←		19a23			19a20			19 25	←		19a53			19a50			19 55
Feltham	d			19 06	18 59	19 06				19 16			19 36	19 29	19 36				19 46			20 06	19 59
Ashford (Surrey)	d			→	19 03	19 10							→	19 33	19 40							→	20 03
Staines	d				19 07	19 14				19 23				19 37	19 44				19 53				20 07
Wraysbury	d				19 11									19 41									20 11
Sunnymeads	d				19 14									19 44									20 14
Datchet	d				19 17									19 47									20 17
Windsor & Eton Riverside	a				19 21									19 51									20 21
Egham	d					19 19				19 27					19 49				19 57				
Virginia Water	a					19 23				19 31					19 53				20 01				
	d					19 23				19 31					19 53				20 01				
Chertsey	d					19 29									19 59								
Addlestone	d					19 32									20 02								
Weybridge	a					19 37									20 07								
Longcross	d																						
Sunningdale	d									19 37									20 07				
Ascot [3]	d		19 23							19 43		19 53							20 13		20 23		
Bagshot	d		19 29									19 59									20 29		
Camberley	a		19 35									20 05									20 35		
Frimley	d		19 43									20 13									20 43		
Ash Vale	d		19 49									20 19									20 49		
Aldershot	a		19 54									20 24									20 54		
	d		20 08									20 38									21 08		
Ash [5]	d		20 15									20 45									21 15		
Wanborough	d		20 18									20 48									21 18		
Guildford	a		20 25									20 55									21 25		
Martins Heron	d									19 47									20 17				
Bracknell	d									19 50									20 20				
Wokingham	d									19 57									20 27				
Winnersh	d									20 00									20 30				
Winnersh Triangle	d									20 02									20 32				
Earley	d									20 05									20 35				
Reading [7]	a									20 10									20 40				

A From London Waterloo to Whitton continues to London Waterloo

B To Weybridge

C From London Waterloo

D To London Waterloo

The xx15 and xx45 services from London Waterloo to Whitton continues to London Waterloo via Brentford

The xx03 and xx33 London Waterloo to Kingston services continues to London Waterloo via Wimbledon

The xx07 and xx37 services from London Waterloo to Whitton continues to London Waterloo via Richmond

Table 149

Saturdays

14 December to 17 May

London - Hounslow, Richmond, Kingston, Windsor, Weybridge, Ascot, Guildford and Reading

Network Diagram - see first Page of Table 148

		SW		SW	SW	SW	SW	SW	SW	SW	SW	SW		SW	SW	SW	SW	SW	SW	SW	SW	SW		SW	SW
							1		1								1		1	1					
		A		B	B	B		C		D		A		B	B	B		C			D			A	B
London Waterloo 15 ⊖	d			19 33	19 37	19 45	19 50			19 52	19 58			20 03	20 07	20 15	20 20				20 22	20 28			20 33
Vauxhall ⊖	d			19 37	19 41	19 49				19 56	20 02			20 07	20 11	20 19					20 26	20 32			20 37
Queenstown Rd.(Battersea)	d			19 40	19 44	19 52				19 59				20 10	20 14	20 22					20 29				20 40
Clapham Junction 10	d			19 43	19 47	19 55	19 58			20 02	20 08			20 13	20 17	20 25	20 28				20 32	20 38			20 43
Wandsworth Town	d			19 46	19 50	19 58				20 05				20 16	20 20	20 28					20 35				20 46
Putney	d			19 49	19 53	20 01				20 08	20 12			20 19	20 23	20 31					20 38	20 42			20 49
Barnes	d			19 52	19 57	20 05				20 12				20 22	20 27	20 35					20 42				20 52
Barnes Bridge	d				19 59					20 14					20 29						20 44				
Chiswick	d				20 02					20 17					20 32						20 47				
Kew Bridge	d				20 05					20 20					20 35						20 50				
Brentford	d				20 08					20 23					20 38						20 53				
Syon Lane	d				20 10					20 25					20 40						20 55				
Isleworth	d				20 12					20 27					20 42						20 57				
Hounslow	d				20 18					20 31					20 48						21 01				
Mortlake	d			19 54		20 07								20 24		20 37									20 54
North Sheen	d			19 56		20 09		←						20 26		20 39		←							20 56
Richmond ⊖	d			19 59		20 12	20 06	20 12			20 18			20 29		20 42	20 36	20 42				20 48			20 59
St Margarets	d			20 01		→		20 14						20 31		→		20 44							21 01
Twickenham	a			20 03			20 10	20 16			20 21			20 33			20 40	20 46				20 51			21 03
	d			20 04			20 10	20 17			20 22			20 34			20 40	20 47				20 52			21 04
Strawberry Hill	d			20 07										20 37											21 07
Fulwell	a																								
Teddington	a			20 10										20 40											21 10
Hampton Wick	a			20 14										20 44											21 14
Kingston	a			20 16										20 46											21 16
Whitton	d	←			20a23			20a20			20 25	←			20a53			20a50				20 55		←	
Feltham	d	20 06					20 16			20 36	20 29	20 36					20 46				21 06	20 59		21 06	
Ashford (Surrey)	d	20 10								→	20 33	20 40									→	21 03		21 10	
Staines	d	20 14					20 23				20 37	20 44					20 53					21 07		21 14	
Wraysbury	d										20 41											21 11			
Sunnymeads	d										20 44											21 14			
Datchet	d										20 47											21 17			
Windsor & Eton Riverside	a										20 51											21 21			
Egham	d	20 19					20 27					20 49					20 57							21 19	
Virginia Water	a	20 23					20 31					20 53					21 01							21 23	
	d	20 23					20 31					20 53					21 01							21 23	
Chertsey	d	20 29										20 59												21 29	
Addlestone	d	20 32										21 02												21 32	
Weybridge	a	20 37										21 07												21 37	
Longcross	d																								
Sunningdale	d						20 37										21 07								
Ascot 3	d						20 43		20 53								21 13		21 23						
Bagshot	d								20 59										21 29						
Camberley	a								21 05										21 35						
Frimley	d								21 13										21 43						
Ash Vale	d								21 19										21 49						
Aldershot	a								21 24										21 54						
	d								21 38										22 08	22 38					
Ash 5	d								21 45										22 15	22 45					
Wanborough	d								21 48										22 18	22 48					
Guildford	a								21 55										22 25	22 55					
Martins Heron	d						20 47										21 17								
Bracknell	d						20 50										21 20								
Wokingham	d						20 57										21 27								
Winnersh	d						21 00										21 30								
Winnersh Triangle	d						21 02										21 32								
Earley	d						21 05										21 35								
Reading 7	a						21 10										21 40								

A From London Waterloo
B To London Waterloo
C From London Waterloo to Whitton continues to London Waterloo
D To Weybridge

The xx15 and xx45 services from London Waterloo to Whitton continues to London Waterloo via Brentford

The xx03 and xx33 London Waterloo to Kingston services continues to London Waterloo via Wimbledon

The xx07 and xx37 services from London Waterloo to Whitton continues to London Waterloo via Richmond

Table 149

Saturdays

14 December to 17 May

London - Hounslow, Richmond, Kingston, Windsor, Weybridge, Ascot, Guildford and Reading

Network Diagram - see first Page of Table 148

		SW	SW	SW	SW	SW	SW	SW	SW	SW	SW	SW	SW	SW	SW	SW	SW	SW	SW	SW	SW	SW	SW
				1								1		1							1		
		A	A		B	C		D	A	A	A		B		C		D	A	A	E		D	C
London Waterloo 15 ⊖	d	20 37	20 45	20 50		20 52	20 58		21 03	21 07	21 15	21 20			21 22	21 28		21 33	21 37	21 45	21 50		21 52
Vauxhall ⊖	d	20 41	20 49			20 56	21 02		21 07	21 11	21 19				21 26	21 32		21 37	21 41	21 49			21 56
Queenstown Rd.(Battersea)	d	20 44	20 52			20 59			21 10	21 14	21 22				21 29			21 40	21 44	21 52			21 59
Clapham Junction 10	d	20 47	20 55	20 58		21 02	21 08		21 13	21 17	21 25	21 28			21 32	21 38		21 43	21 47	21 55	21 58		22 02
Wandsworth Town	d	20 50	20 58			21 05			21 16	21 20	21 28				21 35			21 46	21 50	21 58			22 05
Putney	d	20 53	21 01			21 08	21 12		21 19	21 23	21 31				21 38	21 42		21 49	21 53	22 01			22 08
Barnes	d	20 57	21 05			21 12			21 22	21 27	21 35				21 42			21 52	21 57	22 05			22 12
Barnes Bridge	d	20 59				21 14				21 29					21 44				21 59				22 14
Chiswick	d	21 02				21 17				21 32					21 47				22 02				22 17
Kew Bridge	d	21 05				21 20				21 35					21 50				22 05				22 20
Brentford	d	21 08				21 23				21 38					21 53				22 08				22 23
Syon Lane	d	21 10				21 25				21 40					21 55				22 10				22 25
Isleworth	d	21 12				21 27				21 42					21 57				22 12				22 27
Hounslow	d	21 18				21 31				21 48					22 01				22 18				22 31
Mortlake	d		21 07						21 24		21 37							21 54		22 07			
North Sheen	d		21 09		←				21 26		21 39		←					21 56		22 09		←	
Richmond ⊖	d		21 12	21 06	21 12		21 18		21 29		21 42	21 36	21 42			21 48		21 59		22 12	22 06	22 12	
St Margarets	d		→		21 14				21 31		→		21 44					22 01		→		22 14	
Twickenham	a			21 10	21 16		21 21		21 33			21 40	21 46			21 51		22 03			22 10	22 16	
	d			21 10	21 17		21 22		21 34			21 40	21 47			21 52		22 04			22 10		
Strawberry Hill	d								21 37									22 07					
Fulwell	a																						
Teddington	a								21 40									22 10					
Hampton Wick	a								21 44									22 14					
Kingston	a								21 46									22 16					
Whitton	d	21a23			21a20		21 25	←		21a53			21a50			21 55	←		22a23				
Feltham	d			21 16		21 36	21 29	21 36				21 46			22 06	21 59	22 06				22 16		22 36
Ashford (Surrey)	d					→	21 33	21 40							→	22 03	22 10						→
Staines	d			21 23			21 37	21 44				21 53				22 07	22 14				22 23		
Wraysbury	d						21 41									22 11							
Sunnymeads	d						21 44									22 14							
Datchet	d						21 47									22 17							
Windsor & Eton Riverside	a						21 51									22 21							
Egham	d			21 27				21 49				21 57					22 19				22 27		
Virginia Water	a			21 31				21 53				22 01					22 23				22 31		
	d			21 31				21 53				22 01					22 23				22 31		
Chertsey	d							21 59									22 29						
Addlestone	d							22 02									22 32						
Weybridge	a							22 07									22 37						
Longcross	d																						
Sunningdale	d			21 37								22 07									22 37		
Ascot 8	d			21 43								22 13		22 23							22 43		
Bagshot	d													22 29									
Camberley	a													22 35									
Frimley	d													22 43									
Ash Vale	d													22 49									
Aldershot	a													22 54									
	d													23 08									
Ash 5	d													23 15									
Wanborough	d													23 18									
Guildford	a													23 25									
Martins Heron	d			21 47								22 17									22 47		
Bracknell	d			21 50								22 20									22 50		
Wokingham	d			21 57								22 27									22 57		
Winnersh	d			22 00								22 30									23 00		
Winnersh Triangle	d			22 02								22 32									23 02		
Earley	d			22 05								22 35									23 05		
Reading 7	a			22 10								22 40									23 10		

A To London Waterloo
B From London Waterloo to Whitton continues to London Waterloo
C To Weybridge
D From London Waterloo
E To Twickenham

The xx15 and xx45 services from London Waterloo to Whitton continues to London Waterloo via Brentford

The xx03 and xx33 London Waterloo to Kingston services continues to London Waterloo via Wimbledon

The xx07 and xx37 services from London Waterloo to Whitton continues to London Waterloo via Richmond

Table 149

Saturdays

14 December to 17 May

London - Hounslow, Richmond, Kingston, Windsor, Weybridge, Ascot, Guildford and Reading

Network Diagram - see first Page of Table 148

Station		SW	SW	SW	SW	SW	SW	SW	SW	SW	SW	SW	SW	SW	SW	SW	SW	SW	SW	SW	SW	SW
					1	1					1					1						
			A	B			C		A	B		D		E	B		C		A			F
London Waterloo 15 ⊖	d	21 58		22 03	22 20		22 22	22 28		22 33	22 50	22 52	22 58		23 03	23 20	23 22	23 28		23 33	23 50	23 52
Vauxhall ⊖	d	22 02		22 07			22 26	22 32		22 37		22 56	23 02		23 07		23 26	23 32		23 37		23 56
Queenstown Rd.(Battersea)	d			22 10			22 29			22 40		22 59			23 10		23 29			23 40		23 59
Clapham Junction 10	d	22 08		22 13	22 28		22 32	22 38		22 43	22 58	23 02	23 08		23 13	23 28	23 32	23 38		23 43	23 58	00 02
Wandsworth Town	d			22 16			22 35			22 46		23 05			23 16		23 35			23 46		00 05
Putney	d	22 12		22 19			22 38	22 42		22 49		23 08	23 12		23 19		23 38	23 42		23 49		00 08
Barnes	d			22 22			22 42			22 52		23 12			23 22		23 42			23 52		00 12
Barnes Bridge	d						22 44					23 14					23 44					00 14
Chiswick	d						22 47					23 17					23 47					00 17
Kew Bridge	d						22 50					23 20					23 50					00 20
Brentford	d						22 53					23 23					23 53					00 23
Syon Lane	d						22 55					23 25					23 55					00 25
Isleworth	d						22 57					23 27					23 57					00 27
Hounslow	d						23 01					23 31					00 01					00 31
Mortlake	d			22 24						22 54					23 24					23 54		
North Sheen	d			22 26						22 56					23 26					23 56		
Richmond ⊖	d	22 18		22 29	22 36			22 48		22 59	23 06		23 18		23 29	23 36		23 48		23 59	00 06	
St Margarets	d			22 31						23 01					23 31					00 01		
Twickenham	a	22 21		22 33	22 40			22 51		23 03	23 10		23 21		23 33	23 40		23 51		00 03	00 10	
	d	22 22		22 34	22 40			22 52		23 04	23 10		23 22		23 34	23 40		23 52		00 04	00 10	
Strawberry Hill	d			22 37						23 07					23 37					00 09		
Fulwell	a																					
Teddington	a			22 40						23 10					23 41					00 12		
Hampton Wick	a			22 44						23 14					23 44					00 14		
Kingston	a			22 46						23 16					23 46					00 16		
Whitton	d	22 25	←					22 55	←				23 25	←				23 55	←			
Feltham	d	22 29	22 36		22 46		23 06	22 59	23 06		23 16	23 36	23 29	23 36		23 46	00 06	23 59	00 06		00 16	00 36
Ashford (Surrey)	d	22 33	22 40				→	23 03	23 10			→	23 33	23 40			→	00 03	00 10			→
Staines	d	22 37	22 44		22 53			23 07	23 14		23 23		23 37	23 44		23 53		00 07	00 14		00 23	
Wraysbury	d	22 41						23 11					23 41					00 11				
Sunnymeads	d	22 44						23 14					23 44					00 14				
Datchet	d	22 47						23 17					23 47					00 17				
Windsor & Eton Riverside	a	22 51						23 21					23 51					00 21				
Egham	d		22 49		22 57				23 19		23 27			23 49		23 57			00 19		00 27	
Virginia Water	a		22 53		23 01				23 23		23 31			23 53		00 01			00 23		00 31	
	d		22 53		23 01				23 23		23 31			23 53		00 01			00 23		00 31	
Chertsey	d		22 59						23 29					23 59					00 29			
Addlestone	d		23 02						23 32					00a02					00 32			
Weybridge	a		23 07						23 37										00 36			
Longcross	d																					
Sunningdale	d				23 07						23 37					00 08					00 37	
Ascot 3	d				23 13	23 23					23 43					00 13					00 42	
Bagshot	d					23 29																
Camberley	a					23 35																
Frimley	d					23 43																
Ash Vale	d					23 49																
Aldershot	a					23 54																
	d																					
Ash 5	d																					
Wanborough	d																					
Guildford	a																					
Martins Heron	d				23 17						23 47					00 17					00 46	
Bracknell	d				23 20						23 50					00 20					00 49	
Wokingham	d				23 27						23 57					00 32					00 56	
Winnersh	d				23 30						23 59					00 36						
Winnersh Triangle	d				23 32						00 02					00 38						
Earley	d				23 35						00 05					00 40						
Reading 7	a				23 40						00 10					00 45					01 04	

A From London Waterloo
B To London Waterloo
C To Weybridge
D To Woking
E From London Waterloo to Woking
F To Staines

The xx15 and xx45 services from London Waterloo to Whitton continues to London Waterloo via Brentford

The xx03 and xx33 London Waterloo to Kingston services continues to London Waterloo via Wimbledon

The xx07 and xx37 services from London Waterloo to Whitton continues to London Waterloo via Richmond

Table 149

Saturdays

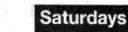

14 December to 17 May

London - Hounslow, Richmond, Kingston, Windsor, Weybridge, Ascot, Guildford and Reading

Network Diagram - see first Page of Table 148

		SW	SW A
London Waterloo 15 ⊖	d	23 58	
Vauxhall ⊖	d	00 02	
Queenstown Rd.(Battersea)	d		
Clapham Junction 10	d	00 08	
Wandsworth Town	d		
Putney	d	00 12	
Barnes	d		
Barnes Bridge	d		
Chiswick	d		
Kew Bridge	d		
Brentford	d		
Syon Lane	d		
Isleworth	d		
Hounslow	d		
Mortlake	d		
North Sheen	d		
Richmond ⊖	d	00 18	
St Margarets	d		
Twickenham	a	00 21	
	d	00 22	
Strawberry Hill	d		
Fulwell	a		
Teddington	a		
Hampton Wick	a		
Kingston	a		
Whitton	d	00 25	⟵
Feltham	d	00 29	00 36
Ashford (Surrey)	d	00 33	00 40
Staines	d	00a37	00a46
Wraysbury	d		
Sunnymeads	d		
Datchet	d		
Windsor & Eton Riverside	a		
Egham	d		
Virginia Water	a		
	d		
Chertsey	d		
Addlestone	d		
Weybridge	a		
Longcross	d		
Sunningdale	d		
Ascot 3	d		
Bagshot	d		
Camberley	a		
Frimley	d		
Ash Vale	d		
Aldershot	a		
	d		
Ash 5	d		
Wanborough	d		
Guildford	a		
Martins Heron	d		
Bracknell	d		
Wokingham	d		
Winnersh	d		
Winnersh Triangle	d		
Earley	d		
Reading 7	a		

A From London Waterloo

The xx15 and xx45 services from London Waterloo to Whitton continues to London Waterloo via Brentford

The xx03 and xx33 London Waterloo to Kingston services continues to London Waterloo via Wimbledon

The xx07 and xx37 services from London Waterloo to Whitton continues to London Waterloo via Richmond

Table 149

Sundays

8 December to 11 May

London - Hounslow, Richmond, Kingston, Windsor, Weybridge, Ascot, Guildford and Reading

Network Diagram - see first Page of Table 148

		SW	SW	SW	SW	SW	SW	SW	SW	SW		SW	SW	SW	SW	SW	SW	SW	SW	SW		SW	SW	SW	SW
			1	1				1	1									1	1			1			1
		A	A	A	A	A	A	B	A	A		A			C		D			C				D	
London Waterloo 15 ⊖	d													00 18	06 14	06 44		07 09		07 14			07 44	07 50	08 09
Vauxhall ⊖	d									00 02				00 22	06 18	06 48		07 13		07 18			07 48	07 54	08 13
Queenstown Rd.(Battersea)	d													00 26	06 21	06 51				07 21			07 51	07 57	
Clapham Junction 10	d									00 08		00 02		00 29	06 24	06 54		07 19		07 24			07 54	08 00	08 19
Wandsworth Town	d											00 05		00 32	06 27	06 57				07 27			07 57	08 03	
Putney	d									00 12		00 08		00 35	06 30	07 00		07 23		07 30			08 00	08 06	08 23
Barnes	d											00 12		00 38	06 33	07 03				07 33			08 03	08 09	
Barnes Bridge	d											00 14												08 11	
Chiswick	d											00 17												08 13	
Kew Bridge	d											00 20												08 16	
Brentford	d											00 23												08 19	
Syon Lane	d											00 25												08 21	
Isleworth	d											00 27												08 23	
Hounslow	d					00 01						00 31												08 26	
Mortlake	d													00 40	06 35	07 05				07 35			08 05		
North Sheen	d													00 42	06 37	07 07				07 37			08 07		
Richmond ⊖	d						00 06			00 18				00 45	06 40	07 10		07 29		07 40			08 10		08 29
St Margarets	d	00 01												00 47	06 42	07 12				07 42			08 12		
Twickenham	a	00 03					00 10			00 21				00 49	06 44	07 14		07 32		07 44			08 14		08 32
	d	00 04					00 10			00 22				00 50	06 45	07 15		07 33		07 45			08 15		08 33
Strawberry Hill	d	00 09												00s53	06 49					07 49					
Fulwell	a																								
Teddington	a	00 12												00s56	06 52					07 52					
Hampton Wick	a	00 14												00s59	06 57					07 57					
Kingston	a	00 16												01 01	06 59					07 59					
Whitton	d									00 25						07 18							08 18		
Feltham	d					00 06	00 16			00 29		00 36				07 22		07 39					08 22	08 32	08 39
Ashford (Surrey)	d				00 03	00 10				00 33		00 40				07 26							08 26	08 36	
Staines	d				00 07	00 14	00 23			00a37		00a46	06 32			07 30	07 40	07 45				08 15	08 30	08 40	08 45
Wraysbury	d				00 11											07 34							08 34		
Sunnymeads	d				00 14											07 37							08 37		
Datchet	d				00 17											07 40							08 40		
Windsor & Eton Riverside	a				00 21											07 44							08 44		
Egham	d					00 19	00 27						06 36				07 45	07 50				08 20		08 45	08 50
Virginia Water	a					00 23	00 31						06 41				07 49	07 54				08 24		08 49	08 54
	d			00 01		00 23	00 31						06 41				07 49	07 54				08 24		08 49	08 54
Chertsey	d					00 29							06 46				07 55							08 55	
Addlestone	d					00 32							06 49				07a58							08a58	
Weybridge	a					00 36							06 53												
Longcross	d																								
Sunningdale	d			00 08			00 37											07 59				08 29			08 59
Ascot 3	d			00 13			00 42	00 45										08 04	08 13			08 34			09 04
Bagshot	d							00 51											08 19						
Camberley	a							00 57											08 25						
Frimley	d							01 01											08 29						
Ash Vale	d							01 08											08 36						
Aldershot	a							01s13											08 41						
	d								07 48										08 48						
Ash 5	d								07 55										08 55						
Wanborough	d								07 58										08 58						
Guildford	a								08 05										09 05						
Martins Heron	d			00 17			00 46											08 08				08 38			09 08
Bracknell	d			00 20			00 49											08 11				08 41			09 11
Wokingham	d			00 32			00 56											08 18				08 48			09 18
Winnersh	d			00 36														08 21				08 51			09 21
Winnersh Triangle	d		00 02	00 38														08 23				08 53			09 23
Earley	d		00 05	00 40														08 26				08 56			09 26
Reading 7	a		00 10	00 45			01 04											08 31				09 01			09 31

A From London Waterloo
B To Farnham
C To London Waterloo
D To Woking

The xx14 London Waterloo to Kingston services continues to London Waterloo via Wimbledon

Table 149

Sundays

8 December to 11 May

London - Hounslow, Richmond, Kingston, Windsor, Weybridge, Ascot, Guildford and Reading

Network Diagram - see first Page of Table 148

		SW 1	SW A	SW 1	SW	SW B	SW 1	SW 1	SW A	SW	SW 1	SW	SW B	SW 1	SW 1	SW A	SW	SW 1	SW	SW B	SW 1	SW 1	SW A
London Waterloo 15 ⊖	d		08 14	08 39	08 44	08 50	09 09		09 14	09 25	09 39	09 44	09 50	10 09		10 14	10 25	10 39	10 44	10 50	11 09		11 14
Vauxhall ⊖	d		08 18	08 43	08 48	08 54	09 13		09 18	09 29	09 43	09 48	09 54	10 13		10 18	10 29	10 43	10 48	10 54	11 13		11 19
Queenstown Rd.(Battersea)	d		08 21		08 51	08 57			09 21			09 51	09 57			10 21			10 51	10 57			11 22
Clapham Junction 10	d		08 24	08 49	08 54	09 00	09 19		09 24	09 35	09 49	09 54	10 00	10 19		10 24	10 35	10 49	10 54	11 00	11 19		11 25
Wandsworth Town	d		08 27		08 57	09 03			09 27			09 57	10 03			10 27			10 57	11 03			11 28
Putney	d		08 30	08 53	09 00	09 06	09 23		09 30	09 39	09 53	10 00	10 06	10 23		10 30	10 39	10 53	11 00	11 06	11 23		11 31
Barnes	d		08 33		09 03	09 09			09 33			10 03	10 09			10 33			11 03	11 09			11 34
Barnes Bridge	d					09 11							10 11							11 11			
Chiswick	d					09 13							10 13							11 13			
Kew Bridge	d					09 16							10 16							11 16			
Brentford	d					09 19							10 19							11 19			
Syon Lane	d					09 21							10 21							11 21			
Isleworth	d					09 23							10 23							11 23			
Hounslow	d					09 26							10 26							11 26			
Mortlake	d		08 35		09 05				09 35			10 05				10 35			11 05				11 36
North Sheen	d		08 37		09 07				09 37			10 07				10 37			11 07				11 38
Richmond ⊖	d		08 40	08 59	09 10		09 29		09 40	09 45	09 59	10 10		10 29		10 40	10 45	10 59	11 10		11 29		11 41
St Margarets	d		08 42		09 12				09 42			10 12				10 42			11 12				11 43
Twickenham	a		08 44	09 02	09 14		09 32		09 44	09 48	10 02	10 14		10 32		10 44	10 48	11 02	11 14		11 32		11 45
	d		08 45	09 03	09 15		09 33		09 45	09 49	10 03	10 15		10 33		10 45	10 49	11 03	11 15		11 33		11 46
Strawberry Hill	d		08 49						09 49							10 49							11 50
Fulwell	a																						
Teddington	a		08 52						09 52							10 52							11 53
Hampton Wick	a		08 57						09 57							10 57							11 57
Kingston	a		08 59						09 59							10 59							11 59
Whitton	d				09 18					09 52		10 18					10 52		11 18				
Feltham	d			09 09	09 22	09 32	09 39			09 56	10 09	10 22	10 32	10 39			10 56	11 09	11 22	11 32	11 39		
Ashford (Surrey)	d				09 26	09 36				10 00		10 26	10 36				11 00		11 26	11 36			
Staines	d			09 15	09 30	09 40	09 45			10 04	10 15	10 30	10 40	10 45			11 04	11 15	11 30	11 40	11 45		
Wraysbury	d				09 34							10 34							11 34				
Sunnymeads	d				09 37							10 37							11 37				
Datchet	d				09 40					10 12		10 40					11 12		11 40				
Windsor & Eton Riverside	a				09 44					10 16		10 44					11 16		11 44				
Egham	d			09 20		09 45	09 50				10 20		10 45	10 50				11 20		11 45	11 50		
Virginia Water	a			09 24		09 49	09 54				10 24		10 49	10 54				11 24		11 49	11 54		
	d			09 24		09 49	09 54				10 24		10 49	10 54				11 24		11 49	11 54		
Chertsey	d					09 55							10 55							11 55			
Addlestone	d					09a58							10a58							11a58			
Weybridge	a																						
Longcross	d																						
Sunningdale	d			09 29			09 59				10 29			10 59				11 29			11 59		
Ascot 3	d	09 13		09 34			10 04	10 13			10 34			11 04	11 13			11 34			12 04	12 13	
Bagshot	d	09 19						10 19							11 19							12 19	
Camberley	a	09 25						10 25							11 25							12 25	
Frimley	d	09 29						10 29							11 29							12 29	
Ash Vale	d	09 36						10 36							11 36							12 36	
Aldershot	a	09 41						10 41							11 41							12 41	
	d	09 48						10 48							11 48							12 48	
Ash 5	d	09 55						10 55							11 55							12 55	
Wanborough	d	09 58						10 58							11 58							12 58	
Guildford	a	10 05						11 05							12 05							13 05	
Martins Heron	d			09 38			10 08				10 38			11 08				11 38			12 08		
Bracknell	d			09 41			10 11				10 41			11 11				11 41			12 11		
Wokingham	d			09 48			10 18				10 48			11 18				11 48			12 18		
Winnersh	d			09 51			10 21				10 51			11 21				11 51			12 21		
Winnersh Triangle	d			09 53			10 23				10 53			11 23				11 53			12 23		
Earley	d			09 56			10 26				10 56			11 26				11 56			12 26		
Reading 7	a			10 01			10 31				11 01			11 31				12 01			12 31		

A To London Waterloo

B To Woking

The xx14 London Waterloo to Kingston services continues to London Waterloo via Wimbledon

Table 149

Sundays

8 December to 11 May

London - Hounslow, Richmond, Kingston, Windsor, Weybridge, Ascot, Guildford and Reading

Network Diagram - see first Page of Table 148

		SW		SW	SW	SW	SW	SW	SW	SW	SW	SW		SW	SW	SW	SW	SW	SW	SW	SW	SW		
				■1			■1	■1			■1				■1	■1			■1					
						A			B					A			B				A			
London Waterloo ■15 ⊖	d	11 25		11 39	11 44	11 50	12 09		12 14	12 25	12 39	12 44		12 50	13 09		13 14	13 25	13 39	13 44	13 50	13 56		
Vauxhall ⊖	d	11 29		11 43	11 48	11 54	12 13		12 19	12 29	12 43	12 48		12 54	13 13		13 18	13 29	13 43	13 48	13 54	14 00		
Queenstown Rd.(Battersea)	d				11 51	11 57			12 22			12 51		12 57			13 21			13 51	13 57	14 03		
Clapham Junction ■10	d	11 35		11 49	11 54	12 00	12 19		12 25	12 35	12 49	12 54		13 00	13 19		13 24	13 35	13 49	13 54	14 00	14 06		
Wandsworth Town	d				11 57	12 03			12 28			12 57		13 03			13 27			13 57	14 03	14 09		
Putney	d	11 39		11 53	12 00	12 06	12 23		12 31	12 39	12 53	13 00		13 06	13 23		13 30	13 39	13 53	14 00	14 06	14 12		
Barnes	d				12 03	12 09			12 34			13 03		13 09			13 33			14 03	14 09	14 15		
Barnes Bridge	d					12 11								13 11							14 11			
Chiswick	d					12 13								13 13							14 13			
Kew Bridge	d					12 16								13 16							14 16			
Brentford	d					12 19								13 19							14 19			
Syon Lane	d					12 21								13 21							14 21			
Isleworth	d					12 23								13 23							14 23			
Hounslow	d					12 26								13 26							14 26			
Mortlake	d				12 05				12 36			13 05					13 35			14 05		14 17		
North Sheen	d				12 07				12 38			13 07					13 37			14 07		14 19		
Richmond ⊖	d	11 45		11 59	12 10		12 29		12 41	12 45	12 59	13 10			13 29		13 40	13 45	13 59	14 10		14 22		
St Margarets	d				12 12				12 43			13 12					13 42			14 12		14 24		
Twickenham	a	11 48		12 02	12 14		12 32		12 45	12 48	13 02	13 14			13 32		13 44	13 48	14 02	14 14		14 26		
	d	11 49		12 03	12 15		12 33		12 46	12 49	13 03	13 15			13 33		13 45	13 49	14 03	14 15		14 27		
Strawberry Hill	d								12 50								13 49					14 30		
Fulwell	a																							
Teddington	a								12 53								13 52					14 33		
Hampton Wick	a								12 57								13 57					14 36		
Kingston	a								12 59								13 59					14 38		
Whitton	d	11 52			12 18					12 52		13 18						13 52		14 18			**and at the same minutes past each hour until**	
Feltham	d	11 56		12 09	12 22	12 32	12 39			12 56	13 09	13 22		13 32	13 39			13 56	14 09	14 22	14 32			
Ashford (Surrey)	d	12 00			12 26	12 36				13 00		13 26		13 36				14 00		14 26	14 36			
Staines	d	12 04		12 15	12 30	12 40	12 45			13 04	13 15	13 30		13 40	13 45			14 04	14 15	14 30	14 40			
Wraysbury	d				12 34							13 34								14 34				
Sunnymeads	d				12 37							13 37								14 37				
Datchet	d	12 12			12 40					13 12		13 40						14 12		14 40				
Windsor & Eton Riverside	a	12 16			12 44					13 16		13 44						14 16		14 44				
Egham	d			12 20		12 45	12 50				13 20			13 45	13 50				14 20		14 45			
Virginia Water	a			12 24		12 49	12 54				13 24			13 49	13 54				14 24		14 49			
	d			12 24		12 49	12 54				13 24			13 49	13 54				14 24		14 49			
Chertsey	d					12 55								13 55							14 55			
Addlestone	d					12a58								13a58							14a58			
Weybridge	a																							
Longcross	d																							
Sunningdale	d			12 29			12 59				13 29				13 59				14 29					
Ascot ■3	d			12 34			13 04	13 13			13 34				14 04	14 13			14 34					
Bagshot	d							13 19								14 19								
Camberley	a							13 25								14 25								
Frimley	d							13 29								14 29								
Ash Vale	d							13 36								14 36								
Aldershot	a							13 41								14 41								
	d							13 48								14 48								
Ash ■5	d							13 55								14 55								
Wanborough	d							13 58								14 58								
Guildford	a							14 05								15 05								
Martins Heron	d			12 38			13 08				13 38				14 08				14 38					
Bracknell	d			12 41			13 11				13 41				14 11				14 41					
Wokingham	d			12 48			13 18				13 48				14 18				14 48					
Winnersh	d			12 51			13 21				13 51				14 21				14 51					
Winnersh Triangle	d			12 53			13 23				13 53				14 23				14 53					
Earley	d			12 56			13 26				13 56				14 26				14 56					
Reading ■7	a			13 01			13 31				14 01				14 31				15 01					

A To Woking

B To London Waterloo

The xx14 London Waterloo to Kingston services continues to London Waterloo via Wimbledon

Table 149

Sundays

8 December to 11 May

London - Hounslow, Richmond, Kingston, Windsor, Weybridge, Ascot, Guildford and Reading

Network Diagram - see first Page of Table 148

		SW 1	SW 1	SW A	SW	SW 1	SW	SW B	SW	SW 1	SW 1	SW A	SW	SW 1	SW	SW B	SW	SW 1	SW 1	SW A	SW 1	SW	SW B
London Waterloo 15 ⊖	d	19 09		19 14	19 25	19 39	19 44	19 50	19 56	20 09		20 14	20 25	20 39	20 44	20 50	20 56	21 09		21 14	21 39	21 44	21 50
Vauxhall ⊖	d	19 13		19 18	19 29	19 43	19 48	19 54	20 00	20 13		20 18	20 29	20 43	20 48	20 54	21 00	21 13		21 18	21 43	21 48	21 54
Queenstown Rd.(Battersea)	d			19 21			19 51	19 57	20 03			20 21			20 51	20 57	21 03			21 21		21 51	21 57
Clapham Junction 10	d	19 19		19 24	19 35	19 49	19 54	20 00	20 06	20 19		20 24	20 35	20 49	20 54	21 00	21 06	21 19		21 24	21 49	21 54	22 00
Wandsworth Town	d			19 27			19 57	20 03	20 09			20 27			20 57	21 03	21 09			21 27		21 57	22 03
Putney	d	19 23		19 30	19 39	19 53	20 00	20 06	20 12	20 23		20 30	20 39	20 53	21 00	21 06	21 12	21 23		21 30	21 53	22 00	22 06
Barnes	d			19 33			20 03	20 09	20 15			20 33			21 03	21 09	21 15			21 33		22 03	22 09
Barnes Bridge	d							20 11								21 11							22 11
Chiswick	d							20 13								21 13							22 13
Kew Bridge	d							20 16								21 16							22 16
Brentford	d							20 19								21 19							22 19
Syon Lane	d							20 21								21 21							22 21
Isleworth	d							20 23								21 23							22 23
Hounslow	d							20 26								21 26							22 26
Mortlake	d			19 35			20 05		20 17			20 35			21 05		21 17			21 35		22 05	
North Sheen	d			19 37			20 07		20 19			20 37			21 07		21 19			21 37		22 07	
Richmond ⊖	d	19 29		19 40	19 45	19 59	20 10		20 22	20 29		20 40	20 45	20 59	21 10		21 22	21 29		21 40	21 59	22 10	
St Margarets	d			19 42			20 12		20 24			20 42			21 12		21 24			21 42		22 12	
Twickenham	a	19 32		19 44	19 48	20 02	20 14		20 26	20 32		20 44	20 48	21 02	21 14		21 26	21 32		21 44	22 02	22 14	
	d	19 33		19 45	19 49	20 03	20 15		20 27	20 33		20 45	20 49	21 03	21 15		21 27	21 33		21 45	22 03	22 15	
Strawberry Hill	d			19 49					20 30			20 49					21 30			21 49			
Fulwell	a																						
Teddington	a			19 52					20 33			20 52					21 33			21 52			
Hampton Wick	a			19 57					20 36			20 57					21 36			21 57			
Kingston	a			19 59					20 38			20 59					21 38			21 59			
Whitton	d				19 52		20 18						20 52		21 18							22 18	
Feltham	d	19 39			19 56	20 09	20 22	20 32		20 39			20 56	21 09	21 22	21 32		21 39			22 09	22 22	22 32
Ashford (Surrey)	d				20 00		20 26	20 36					21 00		21 26	21 36						22 26	22 36
Staines	d	19 45			20 04	20 15	20 30	20 40		20 45			21a04	21 15	21 30	21 40		21 45			22 15	22 30	22 40
Wraysbury	d						20 34								21 34							22 34	
Sunnymeads	d						20 37								21 37							22 37	
Datchet	d				20 12		20 40								21 40							22 40	
Windsor & Eton Riverside	a				20 16		20 44								21 44							22 44	
Egham	d	19 50				20 20		20 45		20 50				21 20		21 45		21 50			22 20		22 45
Virginia Water	a	19 54				20 24		20 49		20 54				21 24		21 49		21 54			22 24		22 49
	d	19 54				20 24		20 49		20 54				21 24		21 49		21 54			22 24		22 49
Chertsey	d							20 55								21 55							22 55
Addlestone	d							20a58								21a58							22a58
Weybridge	a																						
Longcross	d																						
Sunningdale	d	19 59				20 29				20 59				21 29				21 59			22 29		
Ascot 3	d	20 04	20 13			20 34				21 04	21 13			21 34				22 04	22 13		22 34		
Bagshot	d		20 19								21 19								22 19				
Camberley	a		20 25								21 25								22 25				
Frimley	d		20 29								21 29								22 29				
Ash Vale	d		20 36								21 36								22 36				
Aldershot	a		20 41								21 41								22 41				
	d		20 48								21 48								22 48				
Ash 5	d		20 55								21 55								22 55				
Wanborough	d		20 58								21 58								22 58				
Guildford	a		21 05								22 05								23 05				
Martins Heron	d	20 08				20 38				21 08				21 38				22 08			22 38		
Bracknell	d	20 11				20 41				21 11				21 41				22 11			22 41		
Wokingham	d	20 18				20 48				21 18				21 48				22 18			22 48		
Winnersh	d	20 21				20 51				21 21				21 51				22 21			22 51		
Winnersh Triangle	d	20 23				20 53				21 23				21 53				22 23			22 53		
Earley	d	20 26				20 56				21 26				21 56				22 26			22 56		
Reading 7	a	20 31				21 01				21 31				22 01				22 31			23 01		

A To London Waterloo

B To Woking

The xx14 London Waterloo to Kingston services continues to London Waterloo via Wimbledon

Table 149

Sundays

8 December to 11 May

London - Hounslow, Richmond, Kingston, Windsor, Weybridge, Ascot, Guildford and Reading

Network Diagram - see first Page of Table 148

		SW	SW 1	SW 1	SW	SW 1	SW	SW	SW	SW 1	SW	SW 1	SW
				A	B			C					
London Waterloo 15 ⊖	d	21 56	22 09		22 14	22 39	22 44	22 50	22 56	23 09	23 14	23 39	23 44
Vauxhall ⊖	d	22 00	22 13		22 18	22 43	22 48	22 54	23 00	23 13	23 18	23 43	23 48
Queenstown Rd.(Battersea)	d	22 03			22 21		22 51	22 57	23 03		23 21		23 51
Clapham Junction 10	d	22 06	22 19		22 24	22 49	22 54	23 00	23 06	23 19	23 24	23 49	23 54
Wandsworth Town	d	22 09			22 27		22 57	23 03	23 09		23 27		23 57
Putney	d	22 12	22 23		22 30	22 53	23 00	23 06	23 12	23 23	23 30	23 53	23 59
Barnes	d	22 15			22 33		23 03	23 09	23 15		23 33		00 03
Barnes Bridge	d							23 11					
Chiswick	d							23 13					
Kew Bridge	d							23 16					
Brentford	d							23 19					
Syon Lane	d							23 21					
Isleworth	d							23 23					
Hounslow	d							23 26					
Mortlake	d	22 17			22 35		23 05		23 17		23 35		00 05
North Sheen	d	22 19			22 37		23 07		23 19		23 37		00 07
Richmond ⊖	d	22 22	22 29		22 40	22 59	23 10		23 22	23 29	23 40	23 59	00 10
St Margarets	d	22 24			22 42		23 12		23 24		23 42		00 12
Twickenham	a	22 26	22 32		22 44	23 02	23 14		23 26	23 32	23 44	00 02	00 14
	d	22 27	22 33		22 45	23 03	23 15		23 27	23 33	23 45	00 03	00 15
Strawberry Hill	d	22 30			22 49				23 30		23 48		
Fulwell	a												
Teddington	a	22 33			22 52				23 33		23 51		
Hampton Wick	a	22 36			22 57				23 36		23 54		
Kingston	a	22 38			22 59				23 38		23 56		
Whitton	d						23 18						00 18
Feltham	d		22 39			23 09	23 22	23 32		23 39		00 09	00 22
Ashford (Surrey)	d						23 26	23 36					00 26
Staines	d		22 45			23 15	23 30	23 40		23 45		00 15	00a30
Wraysbury	d						23 34						
Sunnymeads	d						23 37						
Datchet	d						23 40						
Windsor & Eton Riverside	a						23 44						
Egham	d		22 50			23 20		23 45		23 50		00 20	
Virginia Water	a		22 54			23 24		23 49		23 54		00 24	
	d		22 54			23 24		23 49		23 54		00 24	
Chertsey	d							23 55					
Addlestone	d							23a58					
Weybridge	a												
Longcross	d												
Sunningdale	d		22 59			23 29				23 59		00 29	
Ascot 3	d		23 04	23 13		23 34				00 04		00 34	
Bagshot	d			23 19									
Camberley	a			23 25									
Frimley	d			23 29									
Ash Vale	d			23 36									
Aldershot	a			23 41									
	d												
Ash 5	d												
Wanborough	d												
Guildford	a												
Martins Heron	d		23 08			23 38				00 08		00 38	
Bracknell	d		23 11			23 41				00 11		00 41	
Wokingham	d		23 18			23 48				00 18		00 48	
Winnersh	d		23 21			23 51				00 21		00 51	
Winnersh Triangle	d		23 23			23 53				00 23		00 53	
Earley	d		23 26			23 56				00 26		00 56	
Reading 7	a		23 31			00 01				00 31		01 01	

A To Farnham **B** To London Waterloo **C** To Woking

The xx14 London Waterloo to Kingston services continues to London Waterloo via Wimbledon

Table 149R

Mondays to Fridays

9 December to 16 May

Reading, Guildford, Ascot, Weybridge, Windsor, Kingston, Richmond and Hounslow - London

Network Diagram - see first Page of Table 148

Miles	Miles	Miles	Miles			SW MO	SW MX	SW MO	SW MX	SW MX	SW	SW	SW	SW	SW	SW	SW	SW	SW	SW	SW	SW	SW
								[1]		[1]								◇	◇	◇	◇[1]	[1]	
						A	B	C	B	C	B			D				E		A			F
—	—	0	—	**Reading [7]**	d																05 42		
—	—	3	—	Earley	d																05 47		
—	—	4¼	—	Winnersh Triangle	d																05 49		
—	—	4¾	—	Winnersh	d																05 51		
—	—	6¾	—	**Wokingham**	d																05 56		
—	—	11¼	—	Bracknell	d																06 02		
—	—	12¼	—	Martins Heron	d																06 05		
—	0	—	—	**Guildford**	d																		
—	4¼	—	—	Wanborough	d																		
—	6¼	—	—	Ash [5]	d																		
—	9	—	—	**Aldershot**	a																		
—	—	—	—		d																	05 58	
—	11½	—	—	Ash Vale	d																	06 02	
—	14¾	—	—	Frimley	d																	06 10	
—	17	—	—	Camberley	a																	06 14	
—	—	—	—		d																	06 18	
—	20¼	—	—	Bagshot	d																	06 23	
—	23½	14½	—	**Ascot [3]**	d																06 10	06a30	
—	—	16½	—	Sunningdale	d																06 13		
—	—	18¼	—	Longcross	d																		
5¼	—	—	—	**Weybridge**	d																		
7	—	—	—	Addlestone	d													05 39					
8½	—	—	—	Chertsey	d													05 42					
11	—	20¼	—	Virginia Water	a													05 47			06 19		
—	—	—	—		d													05 54			06 19		
—	—	22½	—	Egham	d													05 57			06 23		
—	—	—	0	**Windsor & Eton Riverside**	d														05 53				
—	—	—	2	Datchet	d														05 56				
—	—	—	3	Sunnymeads	d														05 59				
—	—	—	4¼	Wraysbury	d														06 02				
—	—	24½	6¾	**Staines**	d							04 58			05 37			06 03	06 08		06 29		
—	—	26	—	Ashford (Surrey)	d							05 01			05 40			06 06	06 11				
—	—	28¾	—	Feltham	d					00 05		05 06			05 45			06 11	06 16		06 35		
—	—	31	—	Whitton	d							05 10			05 49				06 20				06 20
0	—	—	—	**Kingston**	d						01 17						05 59						
0½	—	—	—	Hampton Wick	d						01s22						06 01						
1¾	—	—	—	Teddington	d						01s25						06 05						
2¾	—	—	—	Fulwell	d									05 36									
3	—	—	—	Strawberry Hill	d				00 03		01a28			05 38			06 08						
4	—	32¼	—	Twickenham	a				00 06	00 10		05 13		05 42	05 52		06 12		06 23		06 40		
—	—	—	—		d					00 11		05 13		05 43	05 53		06 13		06 23		06 41		
4½	—	32¾	—	St Margarets	d							05 15		05 45			06 15						
5½	—	33¾	—	**Richmond** ⊖	d					00 15		05 19		05 49	05 58		06 19		06 28		06 45		
6¼	—	34½	—	North Sheen	d							05 21		05 51			06 21						
7	—	35¼	—	Mortlake	d							05 23		05 53			06 23						
—	0	—	—	**Hounslow**	d								05 31			06 01		06 16					06 31
—	—	—	—	Isleworth	d								05 34			06 04		06 19					06 34
—	2¼	—	—	Syon Lane	d								05 36			06 06		06 21					06 36
—	3	—	—	Brentford	d								05 39			06 09		06 24					06 39
—	4	—	—	Kew Bridge	d								05 41			06 11		06 26					06 41
—	5	—	—	Chiswick	d								05 44			06 14		06 29					06 44
—	6	—	—	Barnes Bridge	d								05 46			06 16		06 31					06 46
8¼	6½	36½	—	Barnes	d							05 26	05 49	05 56		06 19	06 26	06 34		←			06 49
9½	—	37¾	—	Putney	d			00 02				05 29	05 52	05 59	06 04	06 22	06 29	06 37	06 34	06 37	06 52		06 52
10½	—	38¾	—	Wandsworth Town	d		00 02					05 32	05 55	06 02		06 25	06 32	→		06 40			06 55
11¼	—	39½	—	Clapham Junction [10]	d	00 02	00 05	00 07		00 24		05 35	05 58	06 05	06 09	06 28	06 35		06 39	06 43	06 56		06 58
12½	—	41¾	—	Queenstown Rd.(Battersea)	d	00 05	00 08					05 38	06 01	06 08		06 31	06 38			06 46			07 01
14	—	42¼	—	Vauxhall ⊖	d	00 08	00 12	00 12				05 42	06 05	06 12	06 15	06 35	06 42		06 45	06 50			07 05
15¼	—	43½	—	**London Waterloo [15]** ⊖	a	00 13	00 16	00 17		00 38		05 46	06 09	06 16	06 19	06 39	06 46		06 49	06 56	07 07		07 11

A From Woking
B From London Waterloo
C From Reading
D From Shepperton
E From Woking to London Waterloo
F From Twickenham

The xx23 and xx53 services from Whitton originates at London Waterloo via Brentford

The xx20 and xx50 from Whitton originates at London Waterloo via Richmond

The xx29 and xx59 from Kingston originates at London Waterloo via Wimbledon

Table 149R

Mondays to Fridays

9 December to 16 May

Reading, Guildford, Ascot, Weybridge, Windsor, Kingston, Richmond and Hounslow - London

Network Diagram - see first Page of Table 148

		SW	SW	SW	SW	SW	SW	SW	SW	SW	SW	SW	SW	SW	SW	SW	SW	SW	SW	SW	SW	SW	SW
				◇				◇	◇1			◇		◇	◇			◇1	1	◇	◇1		◇
		A	B		C	D	E	B		F	F	G	H		I	J	F			B		F	G
Reading 7	d								06 12												06 42		
Earley	d								06 17												06 47		
Winnersh Triangle	d								06 19												06 49		
Winnersh	d								06 21												06 51		
Wokingham	d								06 26												06 56		
Bracknell	d								06 32												07 02		
Martins Heron	d								06 35												07 05		
Guildford	d																		06 30				
Wanborough	d																		06 36				
Ash 5	d																		06 40				
Aldershot	a																		06 47				
	d																	06 28					
Ash Vale	d																	06 32					
Frimley	d																	06 40					
Camberley	a																	06 44					
	d																	06 47					
Bagshot	d																	06 52					
Ascot 3	d								06 40									06 59			07 10		
Sunningdale	d								06 43									07 02			07 13		
Longcross	d																						
Weybridge	d							06 32												07 02			
Addlestone	d							06 36												07 06			
Chertsey	d							06 39												07 09			
Virginia Water	a							06 44	06 49									07 08		07 14	07 19		
	d							06 45	06 49									07 08		07 15	07 19		
Egham	d							06 48	06 53									07 12		07 18	07 23		
Windsor & Eton Riverside	d			06 23										06 53									
Datchet	d			06 26										06 56									
Sunnymeads	d			06 29										06 59									
Wraysbury	d			06 32										07 02									
Staines	d		06 33	06 38				06 54	06 59					07 08				07 18		07 24	07 29		
Ashford (Surrey)	d		06 36	06 41				06 57						07 11				07 21		07 27			
Feltham	d		06 41	06 46				07 02	07 05					07 16				07 26		07 32	07 35		
Whitton	d			06 50		06 50	06 53							07 20			07 20	07 30					
Kingston	d	06 29									06 59											07 29	
Hampton Wick	d	06 31									07 01											07 31	
Teddington	d	06 35									07 05											07 35	
Fulwell	d												07 12										
Strawberry Hill	d	06 38									07 08		07 14									07 38	
Twickenham	a	06 42		06 53			06 56		07 10		07 12		07 18	07 23				07 33			07 40	07 42	
	d	06 43		06 53			06 58		07 11		07 13		07 27	07 23				07 33			07 41	07 43	
St Margarets	d	06 45					07 00				07 15		07 29									07 45	
Richmond ⊖	d	06 49		06 58			07 04		07 15		07 19		07 32	07 28				07 38			07 45	07 49	
North Sheen	d	06 51					07 06				07 21		07 34									07 51	
Mortlake	d	06 53					07 08				07 23		07 37									07 53	
Hounslow	d		06 46			06 59		07 14									07 29			07 44			
Isleworth	d		06 49			07 02		07 17									07 32			07 47			
Syon Lane	d		06 51			07 05		07 20									07 35			07 50			
Brentford	d		06 54			07 08		07 23									07 38			07 53			
Kew Bridge	d		06 56			07 10		07 25									07 40			07 55			
Chiswick	d		06 59			07 13		07 28									07 43			07 58			
Barnes Bridge	d		07 01			07 16		07 31		←		←					07 46			08 01			←
Barnes	d	06 56	07 04		←	07 19	07 11	07 34		07 19	07 26	07 34	07 40		←	←	07 49			08 04		07 56	08 04
Putney	d	06 59	07 07	07 04	07 07	→	07 14	→	07 22	07 22	07 29	07 37	07 43	07 34	07 37	07 43	07 52			→		07 59	08 07
Wandsworth Town	d	07 02	→		07 10		07 17			07 25	07 32	→	→		07 40	07 46	07 55					08 02	→
Clapham Junction 10	d	07 05		07 09	07 13		07 20		07 26	07 28	07 35			07 39	07 43	07 49	07 58	07 47			07 54	08 05	
Queenstown Rd.(Battersea)	d	07 08			07 16		07 23			07 31	07 38				07 46	07 52	08 01					08 08	
Vauxhall ⊖	d	07 12		07 15	07 20		07 27			07 35	07 42			07 45	07 50	07 56	08 05	07 53				08 12	
London Waterloo 15 ⊖	a	07 18		07 21	07 28		07 34		07 37	07 42	07 48			07 51	07 58	08 04	08 10	07 59			08 06	08 18	

A From Wimbledon
B To London Waterloo
C From Staines
D From London Waterloo to Barnes continues to London Waterloo
E From Hounslow
F From London Waterloo
G From Weybridge to London Waterloo
H From Shepperton to London Waterloo
I From Weybridge
J From Shepperton

The xx23 and xx53 services from Whitton originates at London Waterloo via Brentford

The xx20 and xx50 from Whitton originates at London Waterloo via Richmond

The xx29 and xx59 from Kingston originates at London Waterloo via Wimbledon

Table 149R

Mondays to Fridays

9 December to 16 May

Reading, Guildford, Ascot, Weybridge, Windsor, Kingston, Richmond and Hounslow - London

Network Diagram - see first Page of Table 148

		SW	SW	SW	SW	SW	SW	SW	SW	SW	SW	SW	SW	SW	SW	SW	SW	SW	SW	SW	SW	SW	SW
			◇	◇			◇1	1	◇1		◇	◇1		◇	◇			◇1	◇	◇1	1		◇
		A		B	C	D				D	E		A		B	C	D		E			D	F
Reading 7	d								07 12			07 24								07 42			
Earley	d								07 17											07 47			
Winnersh Triangle	d								07 19											07 49			
Winnersh	d								07 21											07 51			
Wokingham	d								07 26			07 33								07 56			
Bracknell	d								07 32			07 39								08 02			
Martins Heron	d								07 35			07 42								08 05			
Guildford	d							07 00													07 30		
Wanborough	d							07 06													07 36		
Ash 5	d							07 10													07 40		
Aldershot	a							07 17													07 47		
	d						07 00											07 30			08 00		
Ash Vale	d						07 04											07 34			08 04		
Frimley	d						07 10											07 40			08 10		
Camberley	a						07 14											07 44			08 14		
	d						07 17											07 47			08 18		
Bagshot	d						07 22											07 52			08 23		
Ascot 3	d						07 29		07 40			07 47						07 59		08 10	08a30		
Sunningdale	d						07 32		07 43			07 50						08 02		08 13			
Longcross	d																			08 16			
Weybridge	d										07 32								08 03				
Addlestone	d										07 36								08 07				
Chertsey	d										07 39								08 10				↩
Virginia Water	a						07 38				07 44	07 55						08 08	08 15	08 19			08 15
	d						07 38				07 50	07 55						08 08	08 24	08 19			08 24
Egham	d						07 42		07 50		07 54	07 58						08 12	↪	08 23			08 27
Windsor & Eton Riverside	d		07 23											07 53									
Datchet	d		07 26											07 56									
Sunnymeads	d		07 29											07 59									
Wraysbury	d		07 32											08 02									
Staines	d		07 38				07 48		07 56		07 59	08 04		08 08				08 18		08 29			08 33
Ashford (Surrey)	d		07 41				07 51				08 02			08 11				08 21					08 36
Feltham	d		07 46				07 56		08 02		08 07	08 12		08 16				08 26		08 35			08 41
Whitton	d		07 50			07 50	08 00							08 20			08 20	08 30					
Kingston	d									07 59												08 29	
Hampton Wick	d									08 01												08 31	
Teddington	d									08 05												08 35	
Fulwell	d	07 42											08 12										
Strawberry Hill	d	07 44								08 08			08 14									08 38	
Twickenham	a	07 48	07 53				08 03		08 09	08 12		08 17	08 18	08 23				08 33		08 40		08 42	
	d	07 57	07 53				08 03		08 09	08 13		08 18	08 27	08 23				08 33		08 41		08 43	
St Margarets	d	07 59								08 15			08 29									08 45	
Richmond ⊖	d	08 02	07 58				08 08		08 14	08 19		08 24	08 32	08 28				08 38		08 45		08 49	
North Sheen	d	08 04								08 21			08 34									08 51	
Mortlake	d	08 07								08 23			08 37									08 53	
Hounslow	d					07 59					08 14						08 31						08 46
Isleworth	d					08 02					08 17						08 34						08 49
Syon Lane	d					08 05					08 20						08 36						08 51
Brentford	d					08 08					08 23						08 39						08 54
Kew Bridge	d					08 10					08 25						08 41						08 56
Chiswick	d					08 13					08 28						08 44						08 59
Barnes Bridge	d					08 16					08 31						08 46						09 01
Barnes	d	08 10		↩	↩	08 19				08 26	08 34		08 40		↩	↩	08 49					08 56	09 04
Putney	d	08 13	08 04	08 07	08 13	08 22				08 29	08 37		08 43	08 34	08 37	08 43	08 52					08 59	09 07
Wandsworth Town	d	↪		08 10	08 16	08 25				08 32	↪		↪		08 40	08 46	08 55					09 02	↪
Clapham Junction 10	d		08 09	08 13	08 19	08 28	08 17		08 22	08 35		08 33		08 39	08 43	08 49	08 58	08 47		08 54		09 05	
Queenstown Rd.(Battersea)	d			08 16	08 22	08 31				08 38					08 46	08 52	09 01					09 08	
Vauxhall ⊖	d		08 15	08 20	08 26	08 35	08 23			08 42		08 38		08 45	08 50	08 56	09 05	08 53				09 12	
London Waterloo 15 ⊖	a		08 21	08 28	08 34	08 42	08 29		08 38	08 49		08 46		08 51	08 58	09 04	09 13	09 00		09 06		09 18	

A From Shepperton to London Waterloo
B From Weybridge
C From Shepperton
D From London Waterloo
E To London Waterloo
F From Weybridge to London Waterloo

The xx23 and xx53 services from Whitton originates at London Waterloo via Brentford

The xx20 and xx50 from Whitton originates at London Waterloo via Richmond

The xx29 and xx59 from Kingston originates at London Waterloo via Wimbledon

Table 149R

Mondays to Fridays

9 December to 16 May

Reading, Guildford, Ascot, Weybridge, Windsor, Kingston, Richmond and Hounslow - London

Network Diagram - see first Page of Table 148

Station		SW ◇		SW ◇ A	SW ◇ B	SW C	SW D	SW ◇ 1	SW D	SW 1	SW D	SW ◇ E	
Reading 7	d							08 12					
Earley	d							08 17					
Winnersh Triangle	d							08 19					
Winnersh	d							08 21					
Wokingham	d							08 26					
Bracknell	d							08 32					
Martins Heron	d							08 35					
Guildford	d									08 00			
Wanborough	d									08 06			
Ash 5	d									08 10			
Aldershot	a									08 17			
	d									08 30			
Ash Vale	d									08 34			
Frimley	d									08 40			
Camberley	a									08 44			
	d									08 48			
Bagshot	d									08 53			
Ascot 3	d							08 40		09a00			
Sunningdale	d							08 43					
Longcross	d							08 46					
Weybridge	d				08 33								
Addlestone	d				08 37								
Chertsey	d				08 40							←	
Virginia Water	a				08 45			08 49				08 45	
	d				08 54			08 49				08 54	
Egham	d				→			08 53				08 57	
Windsor & Eton Riverside	d	08 23											
Datchet	d	08 26											
Sunnymeads	d	08 29											
Wraysbury	d	08 32											
Staines	d	08 38						08 59				09 03	
Ashford (Surrey)	d	08 41										09 06	
Feltham	d	08 46						09 05				09 11	
Whitton	d	08 50				08 50	08 53						
Kingston	d										08 59		
Hampton Wick	d										09 01		
Teddington	d										09 05		
Fulwell	d												
Strawberry Hill	d										09 08		
Twickenham	a	08 53					08 56	09 10			09 12		
	d	08 53					08 58	09 11			09 13		
St Margarets	d						09 00				09 15		
Richmond ⊖	d	08 58					09 04	09 15			09 19		
North Sheen	d						09 06				09 21		
Mortlake	d						09 08				09 23		
Hounslow	d					09 01						09 16	
Isleworth	d					09 04						09 19	
Syon Lane	d					09 06						09 21	
Brentford	d					09 09						09 24	
Kew Bridge	d					09 11						09 26	
Chiswick	d					09 14						09 29	
Barnes Bridge	d					09 16			←			09 31	
Barnes	d			←		09 19	09 11		09 19		09 26	09 34	
Putney	d	09 04		09 07		→	09 14		09 22		09 29	09 37	
Wandsworth Town	d			09 10			09 17		09 25		09 32	→	
Clapham Junction 10	d	09 09		09 13			09 20	09 24	09 28		09 35		
Queenstown Rd.(Battersea)	d			09 16			09 23		09 31		09 38		
Vauxhall ⊖	d	09 15		09 20			09 27		09 35		09 42		
London Waterloo 15 ⊖	a	09 21		09 28			09 34	09 34	09 43		09 48		

Station		SW ◇	SW ◇ A	SW B	SW C	SW D	SW 1	SW D	SW 1	SW D		SW E	SW
Reading 7	d						08 42						
Earley	d						08 47						
Winnersh Triangle	d						08 49						
Winnersh	d						08 51						
Wokingham	d						08 56						
Bracknell	d						09 02						
Martins Heron	d						09 05						
Guildford	d								08 30				
Wanborough	d								08 36				
Ash 5	d								08 40				
Aldershot	a								08 47				
	d								09 00				
Ash Vale	d								09 04				
Frimley	d								09 10				
Camberley	a								09 14				
	d								09 18				
Bagshot	d								09 23				
Ascot 3	d						09 10		09a30				
Sunningdale	d						09 13						
Longcross	d						09 16						
Weybridge	d			09 03									
Addlestone	d			09 07									
Chertsey	d			09 10								←	
Virginia Water	a			09 15			09 19					09 15	
	d			09 24			09 19					09 24	
Egham	d			→			09 23					09 27	
Windsor & Eton Riverside	d	08 53											09 23
Datchet	d	08 56											09 26
Sunnymeads	d	08 59											09 29
Wraysbury	d	09 02											09 32
Staines	d	09 08					09 29					09 33	09 38
Ashford (Surrey)	d	09 11										09 36	09 41
Feltham	d	09 16					09 35					09 41	09 46
Whitton	d	09 20			09 20	09 23							09 50
Kingston	d									09 29			
Hampton Wick	d									09 31			
Teddington	d									09 35			
Fulwell	d												
Strawberry Hill	d									09 38			
Twickenham	a	09 23				09 26	09 40			09 42			09 53
	d	09 23				09 28	09 41			09 43			09 53
St Margarets	d					09 30				09 45			
Richmond ⊖	d	09 28				09 34	09 45			09 49			09 58
North Sheen	d					09 36				09 51			
Mortlake	d					09 38				09 53			
Hounslow	d				09 31							09 46	
Isleworth	d				09 34							09 49	
Syon Lane	d				09 36							09 51	
Brentford	d				09 39							09 54	
Kew Bridge	d				09 41							09 56	
Chiswick	d				09 44							09 59	
Barnes Bridge	d				09 46			←				10 01	
Barnes	d		←		09 49	09 41		09 49		09 56		10 04	
Putney	d	09 34	09 37		→	09 44		09 52		09 59		10 07	10 04
Wandsworth Town	d		09 40			09 47		09 55		10 02		→	
Clapham Junction 10	d	09 39	09 43			09 50	09 54	09 58		10 05			10 09
Queenstown Rd.(Battersea)	d		09 46			09 53		10 01		10 08			
Vauxhall ⊖	d	09 45	09 50			09 57		10 05		10 12			10 15
London Waterloo 15 ⊖	a	09 51	09 58			10 02	10 04	10 11		10 16			10 19

A From Weybridge
B To London Waterloo
C From London Waterloo to Barnes continues to London Waterloo
D From London Waterloo
E From Weybridge to London Waterloo

The xx23 and xx53 services from Whitton originates at London Waterloo via Brentford

The xx20 and xx50 from Whitton originates at London Waterloo via Richmond

The xx29 and xx59 from Kingston originates at London Waterloo via Wimbledon

Table 149R

Mondays to Fridays

9 December to 16 May

Reading, Guildford, Ascot, Weybridge, Windsor, Kingston, Richmond and Hounslow - London

Network Diagram - see first Page of Table 148

Station		SW A	SW B	SW C	SW D	SW [1]	SW D	SW D		SW E	SW	SW [1]	SW A	SW [1]	SW B	SW C	SW D	SW [1]		SW D	SW D	SW E	SW	SW [1]	SW A
Reading [7]	d					09 12						09 25						09 42						09 56	
Earley	d					09 17						09 30						09 47						10 01	
Winnersh Triangle	d					09 19						09 32						09 49						10 03	
Winnersh	d					09 21						09 34						09 51						10 05	
Wokingham	d					09 26						09 39						09 56						10 10	
Bracknell	d					09 32						09 46						10 02						10 16	
Martins Heron	d					09 35						09 49						10 05						10 19	
Guildford	d													09 00											
Wanborough	d													09 06											
Ash [5]	d													09 10											
Aldershot	a													09 17											
	d													09 30											
Ash Vale	d													09 34											
Frimley	d													09 40											
Camberley	a													09 44											
	d													09 48											
Bagshot	d													09 53											
Ascot [3]	d					09 40						09 55		10a00				10 10						10 25	
Sunningdale	d					09 43						09 58						10 13						10 28	
Longcross	d																								
Weybridge	d		09 33												10 03										
Addlestone	d		09 37												10 07										
Chertsey	d		09 40							←					10 10							←			
Virginia Water	a		09 45			09 49				09 45		10 03			10 15			10 19				10 15		10 33	
	d		09 54			09 49				09 54		10 03			10 24			10 19				10 24		10 33	
Egham	d		→			09 53				09 57		10 06			→			10 23				10 27		10 36	
Windsor & Eton Riverside	d										09 53												10 23		
Datchet	d										09 56												10 26		
Sunnymeads	d										09 59												10 29		
Wraysbury	d										10 02												10 32		
Staines	d					09 59				10 03	10 08	10 14						10 29				10 33	10 38	10 44	
Ashford (Surrey)	d									10 06	10 11											10 36	10 41		
Feltham	d					10 05				10 11	10 16	10 20						10 35				10 41	10 46	10 50	
Whitton	d			09 50	09 53						10 20					10 20	10 26						10 50		
Kingston	d							09 59													10 29				
Hampton Wick	d							10 01													10 31				
Teddington	d							10 05													10 35				
Fulwell	d																								
Strawberry Hill	d							10 08													10 38				
Twickenham	a				09 56	10 10		10 12			10 23	10 26					10 28	10 40			10 42		10 53	10 57	
	d				09 58	10 11		10 13			10 23	10 27					10 28	10 41			10 43		10 53	10 57	
St Margarets	d				10 00			10 15									10 30				10 45				
Richmond ⊖	d				10 04	10 15		10 19			10 28	10 32					10 34	10 45			10 49		10 58	11 02	
North Sheen	d				10 06			10 21									10 36				10 51				
Mortlake	d				10 08			10 23									10 38				10 53				
Hounslow	d			10 01						10 16						10 31						10 46			
Isleworth	d			10 04						10 19						10 34						10 49			
Syon Lane	d			10 06						10 21						10 36						10 51			
Brentford	d			10 09						10 24						10 39						10 54			
Kew Bridge	d			10 11						10 26						10 41						10 56			
Chiswick	d			10 14						10 29						10 44						10 59			
Barnes Bridge	d			10 16			←			10 31						10 46				←		11 01			
Barnes	d	←		10 19	10 11		10 19	10 26		10 34			←			10 49	10 41			10 49	10 56	11 04			←
Putney	d	10 07		→	10 14		10 22	10 29		10 37	10 34		10 37			→	10 44			10 52	10 59	11 07	11 04		11 07
Wandsworth Town	d	10 10			10 17		10 25	10 32		→			10 40				10 47			10 55	11 02	→			11 10
Clapham Junction [10]	d	10 13			10 20	10 24	10 28	10 35			10 39	10 42	10 43				10 50	10 54		10 58	11 05		11 09	11 12	11 13
Queenstown Rd.(Battersea)	d	10 16			10 23		10 31	10 38					10 47				10 53			11 01	11 08				11 17
Vauxhall ⊖	d	10 20			10 27		10 35	10 42			10 45		10 50				10 57			11 05	11 12		11 15		11 20
London Waterloo [15] ⊖	a	10 26			10 32	10 34	10 41	10 46			10 49	10 53	10 56				11 02	11 04		11 11	11 16		11 19	11 25	11 27

A From Weybridge
B To London Waterloo
C From London Waterloo to Barnes continues to London Waterloo
D From London Waterloo
E From Weybridge to London Waterloo

The xx23 and xx53 services from Whitton originates at London Waterloo via Brentford

The xx20 and xx50 from Whitton originates at London Waterloo via Richmond

The xx29 and xx59 from Kingston originates at London Waterloo via Wimbledon

Table 149R

Mondays to Fridays

9 December to 16 May

Reading, Guildford, Ascot, Weybridge, Windsor, Kingston, Richmond and Hounslow - London

Network Diagram - see first Page of Table 148

		SW	SW	SW	SW	SW	SW	SW	SW	SW	SW	SW	SW	SW	SW	SW	SW	SW	SW	SW	SW	SW
		1				1		1								1		1				
			A	B	C		C		C	D		E	A	B	C		C		C	D		E
Reading 7	d					10 12										10 42						
Earley	d					10 17										10 47						
Winnersh Triangle	d					10 19										10 49						
Winnersh	d					10 21										10 51						
Wokingham	d					10 26										10 56						
Bracknell	d					10 32										11 02						
Martins Heron	d					10 35										11 05						
Guildford	d	09 30						10 00										10 30				
Wanborough	d	09 36						10 06										10 36				
Ash 5	d	09 40						10 10										10 40				
Aldershot	a	09 47						10 17										10 47				
	d	10 00						10 30										11 00				
Ash Vale	d	10 04						10 34										11 04				
Frimley	d	10 10						10 40										11 10				
Camberley	a	10 14						10 44										11 14				
	d	10 18						10 48										11 18				
Bagshot	d	10 23						10 53										11 23				
Ascot 3	d	10a30				10 40		11a00								11 10		11a30				
Sunningdale	d					10 43										11 13						
Longcross	d																					
Weybridge	d		10 33										11 03									
Addlestone	d		10 37										11 07									
Chertsey	d		10 40							←			11 10							←		
Virginia Water	a		10 45			10 49				10 45			11 15			11 19				11 15		
	d		10 54			10 49				10 54			11 24			11 19				11 24		
Egham	d		→			10 53				10 57			→			11 23				11 27		
Windsor & Eton Riverside	d										10 53										11 23	
Datchet	d										10 56										11 26	
Sunnymeads	d										10 59										11 29	
Wraysbury	d										11 02										11 32	
Staines	d					10 59				11 03	11 08					11 29				11 33	11 38	
Ashford (Surrey)	d									11 06	11 11									11 36	11 41	
Feltham	d					11 05				11 11	11 16					11 35				11 41	11 46	
Whitton	d			10 50	10 56						11 20			11 20	11 23						11 50	
Kingston	d								10 59										11 29			
Hampton Wick	d								11 01										11 31			
Teddington	d								11 05										11 35			
Fulwell	d																					
Strawberry Hill	d								11 08										11 38			
Twickenham	a				10 58	11 10			11 12		11 23				11 26	11 40			11 42		11 53	
	d				10 58	11 11			11 13		11 23				11 28	11 41			11 43		11 53	
St Margarets	d				11 00				11 15						11 30				11 45			
Richmond ⊖	d				11 04	11 15			11 19		11 28				11 34	11 45			11 49		11 58	
North Sheen	d				11 06				11 21						11 36				11 51			
Mortlake	d				11 08				11 23						11 38				11 53			
Hounslow	d			11 01						11 16				11 31						11 46		
Isleworth	d			11 04						11 19				11 34						11 49		
Syon Lane	d			11 06						11 21				11 36						11 51		
Brentford	d			11 09						11 24				11 39						11 54		
Kew Bridge	d			11 11						11 26				11 41						11 56		
Chiswick	d			11 14						11 29				11 44						11 59		
Barnes Bridge	d			11 16			←			11 31				11 46			←			12 01		
Barnes	d			11 19	11 11		11 19		11 26	11 34		←		11 49	11 41		11 49		11 56	12 04		←
Putney	d			→	11 14		11 22		11 29	11 37	11 34	11 37		→	11 44		11 52		11 59	12 07	12 04	12 07
Wandsworth Town	d				11 17		11 25		11 32	→		11 40			11 47		11 55		12 02	→		12 10
Clapham Junction 10	d				11 20	11 24	11 28		11 35		11 39	11 43			11 50	11 54	11 58		12 05		12 09	12 13
Queenstown Rd.(Battersea)	d				11 23		11 31		11 38			11 46			11 53		12 01		12 08			12 16
Vauxhall ⊖	d				11 27		11 35		11 42		11 45	11 50			11 57		12 05		12 12		12 15	12 20
London Waterloo 15 ⊖	a				11 32	11 34	11 41		11 46		11 49	11 56			12 02	12 04	12 11		12 16		12 19	12 26

A To London Waterloo
B From London Waterloo to Barnes continues to London Waterloo
C From London Waterloo
D From Weybridge to London Waterloo
E From Weybridge

The xx23 and xx53 services from Whitton originates at London Waterloo via Brentford

The xx20 and xx50 from Whitton originates at London Waterloo via Richmond

The xx29 and xx59 from Kingston originates at London Waterloo via Wimbledon

Table 149R

Mondays to Fridays

9 December to 16 May

Reading, Guildford, Ascot, Weybridge, Windsor, Kingston, Richmond and Hounslow - London

Network Diagram - see first Page of Table 148

		SW	SW	SW	SW	SW	SW	SW	SW	SW		SW	SW	SW	SW	SW	SW	SW	SW	SW		SW	SW	SW	SW
					1		1									1		1							
		A	B	C		C		C	D			E	A	B	C		C		C	D			E	A	B
Reading 7	d				11 12											11 42									
Earley	d				11 17											11 47									
Winnersh Triangle	d				11 19											11 49									
Winnersh	d				11 21											11 51									
Wokingham	d				11 26											11 56									
Bracknell	d				11 32											12 02									
Martins Heron	d				11 35											12 05									
Guildford	d						11 00											11 30							
Wanborough	d						11 06											11 36							
Ash 5	d						11 10											11 40							
Aldershot	a						11 17											11 47							
	d						11 30											12 00							
Ash Vale	d						11 34											12 04							
Frimley	d						11 40											12 10							
Camberley	a						11 44											12 14							
	d						11 48											12 18							
Bagshot	d						11 53											12 23							
Ascot 3	d				11 40		12a00									12 10		12a30							
Sunningdale	d				11 43											12 13									
Longcross	d																								
Weybridge	d	11 33											12 03											12 33	
Addlestone	d	11 37											12 07											12 37	
Chertsey	d	11 40							←				12 10							←				12 40	
Virginia Water	a	11 45			11 49				11 45				12 15			12 19				12 15				12 45	
	d	11 54			11 49				11 54				12 24			12 19				12 24				12 54	
Egham	d	→			11 53				11 57				→			12 23				12 27				→	
Windsor & Eton Riverside	d									11 53												12 23			
Datchet	d									11 56												12 26			
Sunnymeads	d									11 59												12 29			
Wraysbury	d									12 02												12 32			
Staines	d				11 59				12 03	12 08						12 29				12 33		12 38			
Ashford (Surrey)	d								12 06	12 11										12 36		12 41			
Feltham	d				12 05				12 11	12 16						12 35				12 41		12 46			
Whitton	d		11 50	11 53						12 20				12 20	12 23							12 50			12 50
Kingston	d							11 59											12 29						
Hampton Wick	d							12 01											12 31						
Teddington	d							12 05											12 35						
Fulwell	d																								
Strawberry Hill	d							12 08											12 38						
Twickenham	a			11 56	12 10			12 12		12 23					12 26	12 40			12 42			12 53			
	d			11 58	12 11			12 13		12 23					12 28	12 41			12 43			12 53			
St Margarets	d			12 00				12 15							12 30				12 45						
Richmond ⊖	d			12 04	12 15			12 19		12 28					12 34	12 45			12 49			12 58			
North Sheen	d			12 06				12 21							12 36				12 51						
Mortlake	d			12 08				12 23							12 38				12 53						
Hounslow	d		12 01						12 16					12 31						12 46					13 01
Isleworth	d		12 04						12 19					12 34						12 49					13 04
Syon Lane	d		12 06						12 21					12 36						12 51					13 06
Brentford	d		12 09						12 24					12 39						12 54					13 09
Kew Bridge	d		12 11						12 26					12 41						12 56					13 11
Chiswick	d		12 14						12 29					12 44						12 59					13 14
Barnes Bridge	d		12 16			←			12 31					12 46			←			13 01					13 16
Barnes	d		12 19	12 11		12 19		12 26	12 34			←		12 49	12 41		12 49		12 56	13 04			←		13 19
Putney	d		→	12 14		12 22		12 29	12 37	12 34		12 37		→	12 44		12 52		12 59	13 07		13 04	13 07		→
Wandsworth Town	d			12 17		12 25		12 32	→			12 40			12 47		12 55		13 02	→			13 10		
Clapham Junction 10	d			12 20	12 25	12 28		12 35		12 39		12 43			12 50	12 54	12 58		13 05			13 09	13 13		
Queenstown Rd.(Battersea)	d			12 23		12 31		12 38				12 46			12 53		13 01		13 08				13 16		
Vauxhall ⊖	d			12 27		12 35		12 42		12 45		12 50			12 57		13 05		13 12			13 15	13 20		
London Waterloo 15 ⊖	a			12 32	12 34	12 41		12 46		12 49		12 56			13 02	13 04	13 11		13 16			13 19	13 26		

A To London Waterloo
B From London Waterloo to Barnes continues to London Waterloo
C From London Waterloo
D From Weybridge to London Waterloo
E From Weybridge

The xx23 and xx53 services from Whitton originates at London Waterloo via Brentford

The xx20 and xx50 from Whitton originates at London Waterloo via Richmond

The xx29 and xx59 from Kingston originates at London Waterloo via Wimbledon

Table 149R

Mondays to Fridays

9 December to 16 May

Reading, Guildford, Ascot, Weybridge, Windsor, Kingston, Richmond and Hounslow - London

Network Diagram - see first Page of Table 148

		SW	SW ■1	SW	SW ■1	SW		SW	SW	SW	SW	SW	SW	SW ■1	SW	SW ■1		SW	SW	SW	SW	SW	SW	SW	SW ■1
		A		A		A		B		C	D	E	A		A			A	B		C	D	E	A	
Reading ■7	d		12 12											12 42											13 12
Earley	d		12 17											12 47											13 17
Winnersh Triangle	d		12 19											12 49											13 19
Winnersh	d		12 21											12 51											13 21
Wokingham	d		12 26											12 56											13 26
Bracknell	d		12 32											13 02											13 32
Martins Heron	d		12 35											13 05											13 35
Guildford	d				12 00											12 30									
Wanborough	d				12 06											12 36									
Ash ■5	d				12 10											12 40									
Aldershot	a				12 17											12 47									
	d				12 30											13 00									
Ash Vale	d				12 34											13 04									
Frimley	d				12 40											13 10									
Camberley	a				12 44											13 14									
	d				12 48											13 18									
Bagshot	d				12 53											13 23									
Ascot ■3	d		12 40		13a00									13 10		13a30									13 40
Sunningdale	d		12 43											13 13											13 43
Longcross	d													13 16											
Weybridge	d										13 03											13 33			
Addlestone	d										13 07											13 37			
Chertsey	d							←			13 10								←			13 40			
Virginia Water	a		12 49					12 45			13 15			13 19					13 15			13 45			13 49
	d		12 49					12 54			13 24			13 19					13 24			13 54			13 49
Egham	d		12 53					12 57			→			13 23					13 27			→			13 53
Windsor & Eton Riverside	d								12 53											13 23					
Datchet	d								12 56											13 26					
Sunnymeads	d								12 59											13 29					
Wraysbury	d								13 02											13 32					
Staines	d		12 59					13 03	13 08					13 29					13 33	13 38					13 59
Ashford (Surrey)	d							13 06	13 11										13 36	13 41					
Feltham	d		13 05					13 11	13 16					13 35					13 41	13 46					14 05
Whitton	d	12 53							13 20			13 20	13 23							13 50			13 50	13 53	
Kingston	d					12 59												13 29							
Hampton Wick	d					13 01												13 31							
Teddington	d					13 05												13 35							
Fulwell	d																								
Strawberry Hill	d					13 08												13 38							
Twickenham	a	12 56	13 10			13 12			13 23				13 26	13 40				13 42		13 53				13 56	14 10
	d	12 58	13 11			13 13			13 23				13 28	13 41				13 43		13 53				13 58	14 11
St Margarets	d	13 00				13 15							13 30					13 45						14 00	
Richmond ⊖	d	13 04	13 15			13 19			13 28				13 34	13 45				13 49		13 58				14 04	14 15
North Sheen	d	13 06				13 21							13 36					13 51						14 06	
Mortlake	d	13 08				13 23							13 38					13 53						14 08	
Hounslow	d							13 16				13 31							13 46				14 01		
Isleworth	d							13 19				13 34							13 49				14 04		
Syon Lane	d							13 21				13 36							13 51				14 06		
Brentford	d							13 24				13 39							13 54				14 09		
Kew Bridge	d							13 26				13 41							13 56				14 11		
Chiswick	d							13 29				13 44							13 59				14 14		
Barnes Bridge	d			←				13 31				13 46			←				14 01				14 16		
Barnes	d	13 11		13 19		13 26		13 34		←		13 49	13 41		13 49			13 56	14 04		←		14 19	14 11	
Putney	d	13 14		13 22		13 29		13 37	13 34	13 37		→	13 44		13 52			13 59	14 07	14 04	14 07		→	14 14	
Wandsworth Town	d	13 17		13 25		13 32		→		13 40			13 47		13 55			14 02	→		14 10			14 17	
Clapham Junction ■10	d	13 20	13 24	13 28		13 35			13 39	13 43			13 50	13 54	13 58			14 05		14 09	14 13			14 20	14 24
Queenstown Rd.(Battersea)	d	13 23		13 31		13 38				13 46			13 53		14 01			14 08			14 16			14 23	
Vauxhall ⊖	d	13 27		13 35		13 42			13 45	13 50			13 57		14 05			14 12		14 15	14 20			14 27	
London Waterloo ■15 ⊖	a	13 32	13 34	13 41		13 46			13 49	13 56			14 02	14 04	14 11			14 16		14 19	14 26			14 32	14 34

A From London Waterloo
B From Weybridge to London Waterloo
C From Weybridge
D To London Waterloo
E From London Waterloo to Barnes continues to London Waterloo

The xx23 and xx53 services from Whitton originates at London Waterloo via Brentford

The xx20 and xx50 from Whitton originates at London Waterloo via Richmond

The xx29 and xx59 from Kingston originates at London Waterloo via Wimbledon

Table 149R

Mondays to Fridays

9 December to 16 May

Reading, Guildford, Ascot, Weybridge, Windsor, Kingston, Richmond and Hounslow - London

Network Diagram - see first Page of Table 148

		SW		SW	SW	SW	SW	SW	SW	SW	SW	SW		SW	SW	SW	SW	SW	SW	SW	SW	SW		SW	SW
				1								1			1									1	
		A			A	B		C	D	E	A			A		A	B		C	D	E	A			A
Reading 7	d											13 42												14 12	
Earley	d											13 47												14 17	
Winnersh Triangle	d											13 49												14 19	
Winnersh	d											13 51												14 21	
Wokingham	d											13 56												14 26	
Bracknell	d											14 02												14 32	
Martins Heron	d											14 05												14 35	
Guildford	d			13 00											13 30										
Wanborough	d			13 06											13 36										
Ash 5	d			13 10											13 40										
Aldershot	a			13 17											13 47										
	d			13 30											14 00										
Ash Vale	d			13 34											14 04										
Frimley	d			13 40											14 10										
Camberley	a			13 44											14 14										
	d			13 48											14 18										
Bagshot	d			13 53											14 23										
Ascot 3	d			14a00								14 10			14a30									14 40	
Sunningdale	d											14 13												14 43	
Longcross	d																								
Weybridge	d								14 03											14 33					
Addlestone	d								14 07											14 37					
Chertsey	d					←			14 10								←			14 40					
Virginia Water	a					13 45			14 15			14 19					14 15			14 45				14 49	
	d					13 54			14 24			14 19					14 24			14 54				14 49	
Egham	d					13 57			→			14 23					14 27			→				14 53	
Windsor & Eton Riverside	d						13 53											14 23							
Datchet	d						13 56											14 26							
Sunnymeads	d						13 59											14 29							
Wraysbury	d						14 02											14 32							
Staines	d					14 03	14 08					14 29					14 33	14 38						14 59	
Ashford (Surrey)	d					14 06	14 11										14 36	14 41							
Feltham	d					14 11	14 16					14 35					14 41	14 46						15 05	
Whitton	d						14 20			14 20	14 23							14 50			14 50	14 53			
Kingston	d				13 59											14 29									
Hampton Wick	d				14 01											14 31									
Teddington	d				14 05											14 35									
Fulwell	d																								
Strawberry Hill	d				14 08											14 38									
Twickenham	a				14 12		14 23				14 26	14 40				14 42		14 53				14 56		15 10	
	d				14 13		14 23				14 28	14 41				14 43		14 53				14 58		15 11	
St Margarets	d				14 15						14 30					14 45						15 00			
Richmond ⊖	d				14 19		14 28				14 34	14 45				14 49		14 58				15 04		15 15	
North Sheen	d				14 21						14 36					14 51						15 06			
Mortlake	d				14 23						14 38					14 53						15 08			
Hounslow	d					14 16				14 31							14 46				15 01				
Isleworth	d					14 19				14 34							14 49				15 04				
Syon Lane	d					14 21				14 36							14 51				15 06				
Brentford	d					14 24				14 39							14 54				15 09				
Kew Bridge	d					14 26				14 41							14 56				15 11				
Chiswick	d					14 29				14 44							14 59				15 14				
Barnes Bridge	d	←				14 31				14 46				←			15 01				15 16				←
Barnes	d	14 19			14 26	14 34		←		14 49	14 41			14 49		14 56	15 04		←		15 19	15 11			15 19
Putney	d	14 22			14 29	14 37	14 34	14 37		→	14 44			14 52		14 59	15 07	15 04	15 07		→	15 14			15 22
Wandsworth Town	d	14 25			14 32	→		14 40			14 47			14 55		15 02	→		15 10			15 17			15 25
Clapham Junction 10	d	14 28			14 35		14 39	14 43			14 50	14 54		14 58		15 05		15 09	15 13			15 20		15 24	15 28
Queenstown Rd.(Battersea)	d	14 31			14 38			14 46			14 53			15 01		15 08			15 16			15 23			15 31
Vauxhall ⊖	d	14 35			14 42		14 45	14 50			14 57			15 05		15 12		15 15	15 20			15 27			15 35
London Waterloo 15 ⊖	a	14 41			14 46		14 49	14 56			15 02	15 04		15 11		15 16		15 19	15 26			15 32		15 34	15 41

A From London Waterloo
B From Weybridge to London Waterloo
C From Weybridge
D To London Waterloo
E From London Waterloo to Barnes continues to London Waterloo

The xx23 and xx53 services from Whitton originates at London Waterloo via Brentford

The xx20 and xx50 from Whitton originates at London Waterloo via Richmond

The xx29 and xx59 from Kingston originates at London Waterloo via Wimbledon

Table 149R

Mondays to Fridays

9 December to 16 May

Reading, Guildford, Ascot, Weybridge, Windsor, Kingston, Richmond and Hounslow - London

Network Diagram - see first Page of Table 148

		SW [1]	SW	SW	SW	SW	SW	SW	SW	SW [1]	SW	SW [1]	SW	SW	SW	SW	SW	SW	SW	SW [1]	SW	SW [1]	SW
			A	B		C	D	E	A		A		A	B		C	D	E	A		A		A
Reading [7]	d									14 42										15 12			
Earley	d									14 47										15 17			
Winnersh Triangle	d									14 49										15 19			
Winnersh	d									14 51										15 21			
Wokingham	d									14 56										15 26			
Bracknell	d									15 02										15 32			
Martins Heron	d									15 05										15 35			
Guildford	d	14 00										14 30										15 00	
Wanborough	d	14 06										14 36										15 06	
Ash [5]	d	14 10										14 40										15 10	
Aldershot	a	14 17										14 47										15 17	
	d	14 30										15 00										15 30	
Ash Vale	d	14 34										15 04										15 34	
Frimley	d	14 40										15 10										15 40	
Camberley	a	14 44										15 14										15 44	
	d	14 48										15 18										15 48	
Bagshot	d	14 53										15 23										15 53	
Ascot [3]	d	15a00								15 10		15a30								15 40		16a00	
Sunningdale	d									15 13										15 43			
Longcross	d																						
Weybridge	d						15 03										15 33						
Addlestone	d						15 07										15 37						
Chertsey	d			←			15 10							←			15 40						
Virginia Water	a			14 45			15 15			15 19				15 15			15 45			15 49			
	d			14 54			15 24			15 19				15 24			15 54			15 49			
Egham	d			14 57			↪			15 23				15 27			↪			15 53			
Windsor & Eton Riverside	d				14 53										15 23								
Datchet	d				14 56										15 26								
Sunnymeads	d				14 59										15 29								
Wraysbury	d				15 02										15 32								
Staines	d			15 03	15 08					15 29				15 33	15 38					15 59			
Ashford (Surrey)	d			15 06	15 11									15 36	15 41								
Feltham	d			15 11	15 16					15 35				15 41	15 46					16 05			
Whitton	d				15 20			15 20	15 23						15 50			15 50	15 53				
Kingston	d		14 59										15 29										15 59
Hampton Wick	d		15 01										15 31										16 01
Teddington	d		15 05										15 35										16 05
Fulwell	d																						
Strawberry Hill	d		15 08										15 38										16 08
Twickenham	a		15 12		15 23				15 26	15 40			15 42		15 53				15 56	16 10			16 12
	d		15 13		15 23				15 28	15 41			15 43		15 53				15 58	16 11			16 13
St Margarets	d		15 15						15 30				15 45						16 00				16 15
Richmond ⊖	d		15 19		15 28				15 34	15 45			15 49		15 58				16 04	16 15			16 19
North Sheen	d		15 21						15 36				15 51						16 06				16 21
Mortlake	d		15 23						15 38				15 53						16 08				16 23
Hounslow	d			15 16				15 31						15 46				16 01					
Isleworth	d			15 19				15 34						15 49				16 04					
Syon Lane	d			15 21				15 36						15 51				16 06					
Brentford	d			15 24				15 39						15 54				16 09					
Kew Bridge	d			15 26				15 41						15 56				16 11					
Chiswick	d			15 29				15 44						15 59				16 14					
Barnes Bridge	d			15 31				15 46			←			16 01				16 16			←		
Barnes	d		15 26	15 34		←		15 49	15 41		15 49		15 56	16 04		←		16 19	16 11		16 19		16 26
Putney	d		15 29	15 37	15 34	15 37		↪	15 44		15 52		15 59	16 07	16 04	16 07		↪	16 14		16 22		16 29
Wandsworth Town	d		15 32	↪		15 40			15 47		15 55		16 02	↪		16 10			16 17		16 25		16 32
Clapham Junction [10]	d		15 35		15 39	15 43			15 50	15 54	15 58		16 05		16 09	16 13			16 20	16 24	16 28		16 35
Queenstown Rd.(Battersea)	d		15 38			15 46			15 53		16 01		16 08			16 16			16 23		16 31		16 38
Vauxhall ⊖	d		15 42		15 45	15 50			15 57		16 05		16 12		16 15	16 20			16 27		16 35		16 42
London Waterloo [15] ⊖	a		15 46		15 49	15 56			16 02	16 05	16 11		16 19		16 19	16 26			16 32	16 34	16 41		16 49

A From London Waterloo
B From Weybridge to London Waterloo
C From Weybridge
D To London Waterloo
E From London Waterloo to Barnes continues to London Waterloo

The xx23 and xx53 services from Whitton originates at London Waterloo via Brentford

The xx20 and xx50 from Whitton originates at London Waterloo via Richmond

The xx29 and xx59 from Kingston originates at London Waterloo via Wimbledon

Table 149R

Mondays to Fridays

9 December to 16 May

Reading, Guildford, Ascot, Weybridge, Windsor, Kingston, Richmond and Hounslow - London

Network Diagram - see first Page of Table 148

Station		SW A	SW	SW B		SW C	SW D	SW E	SW 1	SW E	SW 1	SW E	SW A	SW		SW B	SW C	SW D	SW E	SW 1	SW E	SW 1	SW E	SW A	
Reading 7	d								15 42											16 12					
Earley	d								15 47											16 17					
Winnersh Triangle	d								15 49											16 19					
Winnersh	d								15 51											16 21					
Wokingham	d								15 56											16 26					
Bracknell	d								16 02											16 32					
Martins Heron	d								16 05											16 35					
Guildford	d										15 30											16 00			
Wanborough	d										15 36											16 06			
Ash 5	d										15 40											16 10			
Aldershot	a										15 47											16 17			
	d										16 00											16 30			
Ash Vale	d										16 04											16 34			
Frimley	d										16 10											16 40			
Camberley	a										16 14											16 44			
	d										16 18											16 48			
Bagshot	d										16 23											16 53			
Ascot 3	d								16 10		16a30									16 40		17a00			
Sunningdale	d								16 13											16 43					
Longcross	d																								
Weybridge	d					16 03											16 33								
Addlestone	d					16 07											16 37								
Chertsey	d	←				16 10							←				16 40							←	
Virginia Water	a	15 45				16 15			16 19				16 15				16 45			16 49				16 45	
	d	15 54				16 24			16 19				16 24				16 54			16 49				16 54	
Egham	d	15 57				→			16 23				16 27				→			16 53				16 57	
Windsor & Eton Riverside	d		15 53											16 23											
Datchet	d		15 56											16 26											
Sunnymeads	d		15 59											16 29											
Wraysbury	d		16 02											16 32											
Staines	d	16 03	16 08						16 29				16 33	16 38						16 59				17 03	
Ashford (Surrey)	d	16 06	16 11										16 36	16 41										17 06	
Feltham	d	16 11	16 16						16 35				16 41	16 46						17 05				17 11	
Whitton	d		16 20				16 20	16 23						16 50				16 50	16 53						
Kingston	d											16 29											16 59		
Hampton Wick	d											16 31											17 01		
Teddington	d											16 35											17 05		
Fulwell	d																								
Strawberry Hill	d											16 38											17 08		
Twickenham	a		16 23					16 26	16 40			16 42		16 53					16 56	17 10			17 12		
	d		16 23					16 28	16 41			16 43		16 53					16 58	17 11			17 13		
St Margarets	d							16 30				16 45							17 00				17 15		
Richmond ⊖	d		16 28					16 34	16 45			16 49		16 58					17 04	17 15			17 19		
North Sheen	d							16 36				16 51							17 06				17 21		
Mortlake	d							16 38				16 53							17 08				17 23		
Hounslow	d	16 16					16 31						16 46					17 01						17 16	
Isleworth	d	16 19					16 34						16 49					17 04						17 19	
Syon Lane	d	16 21					16 36						16 51					17 06						17 21	
Brentford	d	16 24					16 39						16 54					17 09						17 24	
Kew Bridge	d	16 26					16 41						16 56					17 11						17 26	
Chiswick	d	16 29					16 44						16 59					17 14						17 29	
Barnes Bridge	d	16 31					16 46			←			17 01					17 16			←			17 31	
Barnes	d	16 34		←			16 49	16 41		16 49		16 56	17 04			←		17 19	17 11		17 19		17 26	17 34	
Putney	d	16 37	16 34	16 37			→	16 44		16 52		16 59	17 07	17 05		17 07		→	17 14		17 22		17 29	17 37	
Wandsworth Town	d	→		16 40				16 47		16 55		17 02	→			17 10			17 17		17 25		17 32	→	
Clapham Junction 10	d		16 39	16 43				16 50	16 54	16 58		17 05		17 09		17 13			17 20	17 24	17 28		17 35		
Queenstown Rd.(Battersea)	d			16 46				16 53		17 01		17 08				17 16			17 23		17 31		17 38		
Vauxhall ⊖	d		16 45	16 50				16 57		17 05		17 12		17 15		17 20			17 27		17 35		17 42		
London Waterloo 15 ⊖	a		16 49	16 56				17 02	17 04	17 11		17 19		17 19		17 26			17 32	17 33	17 41		17 49		

A From Weybridge to London Waterloo
B From Weybridge
C To London Waterloo
D From London Waterloo to Barnes continues to London Waterloo
E From London Waterloo

The xx23 and xx53 services from Whitton originates at London Waterloo via Brentford

The xx20 and xx50 from Whitton originates at London Waterloo via Richmond

The xx29 and xx59 from Kingston originates at London Waterloo via Wimbledon

Table 149R

Mondays to Fridays

9 December to 16 May

Reading, Guildford, Ascot, Weybridge, Windsor, Kingston, Richmond and Hounslow - London

Network Diagram - see first Page of Table 148

		SW	SW	SW	SW	SW	SW	SW	SW	SW	SW	SW	SW	SW	SW	SW	SW	SW	SW	SW	SW	SW	SW
							1		1							1						1	1
			A	B	C	D		D		D	E		A	C	D		D	D	B		A		
Reading 7	d						16 42									17 12						17 22	
Earley	d						16 47									17 17						17 27	
Winnersh Triangle	d						16 49									17 19						17 29	
Winnersh	d						16 51									17 21						17 31	
Wokingham	d						16 56									17 26						17 36	
Bracknell	d						17 02									17 32						17 42	
Martins Heron	d						17 05									17 35						17 45	
Guildford	d								16 30														17 00
Wanborough	d								16 36														17 06
Ash 5	d								16 40														17 10
Aldershot	a								16 47														17 17
	d								17 00														17 30
Ash Vale	d								17 04														17 34
Frimley	d								17 10														17 40
Camberley	a								17 14														17 44
	d								17 18														17 48
Bagshot	d								17 23														17 53
Ascot 3	d						17 10		17a30							17 40						17 55	18a00
Sunningdale	d						17 13									17 43						17 58	
Longcross	d						17 16																
Weybridge	d			17 03															17 37				
Addlestone	d			17 07															17 41				
Chertsey	d			17 10							←								17 44				
Virginia Water	a			17 15			17 19				17 15					17 49			17 49			18 03	
	d			17 24			17 19				17 24					17 49			17 54			18 03	
Egham	d			→			17 23				17 27					17 53			17 57			18 06	
Windsor & Eton Riverside	d	16 53										17 23								17 53			
Datchet	d	16 56										17 26								17 56			
Sunnymeads	d	16 59										17 29								17 59			
Wraysbury	d	17 02										17 32								18 02			
Staines	d	17 08					17 29				17 33	17 38				17 59			18 03	18 08		18 14	
Ashford (Surrey)	d	17 11									17 36	17 41							18 06	18 11			
Feltham	d	17 16					17 35				17 41	17 46				18 05			18 11	18 16		18 20	
Whitton	d	17 20			17 20	17 23						17 50		17 50	17 53					18 20			
Kingston	d									17 29								17 59					
Hampton Wick	d									17 31								18 01					
Teddington	d									17 35								18 05					
Fulwell	d																						
Strawberry Hill	d									17 38								18 08					
Twickenham	a	17 23				17 26	17 40			17 42		17 53			17 56	18 10		18 12		18 23			
	d	17 23				17 28	17 41			17 43		17 53			17 58	18 11		18 13		18 23			
St Margarets	d					17 30				17 45					18 00			18 15					
Richmond ⊖	d	17 28				17 34	17 45			17 49		17 58			18 04	18 15		18 19		18 28			
North Sheen	d					17 36				17 51					18 06			18 21					
Mortlake	d					17 38				17 53					18 08			18 23					
Hounslow	d				17 31						17 46			18 01					18 16			18 26	
Isleworth	d				17 34						17 49			18 04					18 19				
Syon Lane	d				17 36						17 51			18 06					18 21				
Brentford	d				17 39						17 54			18 09					18 24			18 31	
Kew Bridge	d				17 41						17 56			18 11					18 26				
Chiswick	d				17 44						17 59			18 14					18 29				
Barnes Bridge	d				17 46			←			18 01			18 16			←		18 31				
Barnes	d		←		17 49	17 41		17 49		17 56	18 04		←	18 19	18 11		18 19	18 26	18 34		←		
Putney	d	17 34	17 37		→	17 44		17 52		17 59	18 07	18 04	18 07	→	18 14		18 22	18 29	18 37	18 34	18 37	18 39	
Wandsworth Town	d		17 40			17 47		17 55		18 02	→		18 10		18 17		18 25	18 32	→		18 40		
Clapham Junction 10	d	17 39	17 43			17 50	17 54	17 58		18 05		18 09	18 13		18 20	18 24	18 28	18 35		18 39	18 43	18 44	
Queenstown Rd.(Battersea)	d		17 46			17 53		18 01		18 08			18 16		18 23		18 31	18 38			18 46		
Vauxhall ⊖	d	17 45	17 50			17 57		18 05		18 12		18 15	18 20		18 27		18 35	18 42		18 45	18 50		
London Waterloo 15 ⊖	a	17 49	17 56			18 02	18 04	18 11		18 19		18 19	18 26		18 32	18 34	18 41	18 49		18 49	18 56	18 56	

A From Weybridge
B To London Waterloo
C From London Waterloo to Barnes continues to London Waterloo
D From London Waterloo
E From Weybridge to London Waterloo

The xx23 and xx53 services from Whitton originates at London Waterloo via Brentford

The xx20 and xx50 from Whitton originates at London Waterloo via Richmond

The xx29 and xx59 from Kingston originates at London Waterloo via Wimbledon

Table 149R

Mondays to Fridays

9 December to 16 May

Reading, Guildford, Ascot, Weybridge, Windsor, Kingston, Richmond and Hounslow - London

Network Diagram - see first Page of Table 148

		SW A	SW B	SW 1	SW B	SW B	SW C	SW	SW D	SW 1	SW 1	SW A	SW B	SW 1	SW B	SW 1	SW B	SW C	SW	SW D	SW A	SW B	SW 1
Reading 7	d			17 42						17 53				18 12									18 42
Earley	d			17 47						17 58				18 17									18 47
Winnersh Triangle	d			17 49						18 00				18 19									18 49
Winnersh	d			17 51						18 02				18 21									18 51
Wokingham	d			17 56						18 07				18 26									18 56
Bracknell	d			18 02						18 13				18 32									19 02
Martins Heron	d			18 05						18 16				18 35									19 05
Guildford	d										17 30					18 00							
Wanborough	d										17 36					18 06							
Ash 5	d										17 40					18 10							
Aldershot	a										17 47					18 17							
	d										18 00					18 30							
Ash Vale	d										18 04					18 34							
Frimley	d										18 10					18 40							
Camberley	a										18 14					18 44							
	d										18 18					18 48							
Bagshot	d										18 23					18 53							
Ascot 3	d			18 10						18 25	18a30			18 40		19a00							19 10
Sunningdale	d			18 13						18 28				18 43									19 13
Longcross	d			18 16										18 46									19 16
Weybridge	d						18 07											18 37					
Addlestone	d						18 11											18 41					
Chertsey	d						18 14											18 44					
Virginia Water	a			18 19			18 19			18 33				18 49				18 49					19 19
	d			18 19			18 24			18 33				18 49				18 54					19 19
Egham	d			18 23			18 27			18 37				18 53				18 57					19 23
Windsor & Eton Riverside	d							18 23											18 53				
Datchet	d							18 26											18 56				
Sunnymeads	d							18 29											18 59				
Wraysbury	d							18 32											19 02				
Staines	d			18 29			18 33	18 38		18 44				18 59				19 03	19 08				19 29
Ashford (Surrey)	d						18 36	18 41										19 06	19 11				
Feltham	d			18 35			18 41	18 46		18 50				19 05				19 11	19 16				19 35
Whitton	d	18 20	18 23					18 50				18 50	18 53						19 20		19 20	19 23	
Kingston	d					18 29											18 59						
Hampton Wick	d					18 31											19 01						
Teddington	d					18 35											19 05						
Fulwell	d																						
Strawberry Hill	d					18 38											19 08						
Twickenham	a		18 26	18 40		18 42		18 53					18 56	19 10			19 12		19 23			19 26	19 40
	d		18 28	18 41		18 43		18 53					18 58	19 11			19 13		19 23			19 28	19 41
St Margarets	d		18 30			18 45							19 00				19 15					19 30	
Richmond ⊖	d		18 34	18 45		18 49		18 58					19 04	19 15			19 19		19 28			19 34	19 45
North Sheen	d		18 36			18 51							19 06				19 21					19 36	
Mortlake	d		18 38			18 53							19 08				19 23					19 38	
Hounslow	d	18 31					18 46			18 56		19 01						19 16			19 31		
Isleworth	d	18 34					18 49					19 04						19 19			19 34		
Syon Lane	d	18 36					18 51					19 06						19 21			19 36		
Brentford	d	18 39					18 54			19 01		19 09						19 24			19 39		
Kew Bridge	d	18 41					18 56					19 11						19 26			19 41		
Chiswick	d	18 44					18 59					19 14						19 29			19 44		
Barnes Bridge	d	18 46			←		19 01					19 16			←			19 31			19 46		
Barnes	d	18 49	18 41		18 49	18 56	19 04		←			19 19	19 11		19 19		19 26	19 34		←	19 49	19 41	
Putney	d	→	18 44		18 52	18 59	19 07	19 04	19 07	19 09		→	19 14		19 22		19 29	19 37	19 34	19 37	→	19 44	
Wandsworth Town	d		18 47		18 55	19 02	→		19 10				19 17		19 25		19 32	→		19 40		19 47	
Clapham Junction 10	d		18 50	18 54	18 58	19 05		19 09	19 13	19 14			19 20	19 24	19 28		19 35		19 39	19 43		19 50	19 54
Queenstown Rd.(Battersea)	d		18 53		19 01	19 08			19 16				19 23		19 31		19 38			19 46		19 53	
Vauxhall ⊖	d		18 57		19 05	19 12		19 15	19 20				19 27		19 35		19 42		19 45	19 50		19 57	
London Waterloo 15 ⊖	a		19 02	19 04	19 11	19 16		19 19	19 26	19 28			19 32	19 34	19 41		19 46		19 49	19 56		20 02	20 04

A From London Waterloo to Barnes continues to London Waterloo
B From London Waterloo
C To London Waterloo
D From Weybridge

The xx23 and xx53 services from Whitton originates at London Waterloo via Brentford

The xx20 and xx50 from Whitton originates at London Waterloo via Richmond

The xx29 and xx59 from Kingston originates at London Waterloo via Wimbledon

Table 149R

Mondays to Fridays

9 December to 16 May

Reading, Guildford, Ascot, Weybridge, Windsor, Kingston, Richmond and Hounslow - London

Network Diagram - see first Page of Table 148

		SW		SW	SW	SW	SW	SW	SW	SW	SW	SW		SW	SW	SW	SW	SW	SW	SW	SW	SW		SW	SW
								■1	■1			■1			■1									■1	
		A		A	B		C			D	A			A		A	B		C	B	D	A			A
Reading ■7	d							18 52				19 12												19 42	
Earley	d							18 57				19 17												19 47	
Winnersh Triangle	d							18 59				19 19												19 49	
Winnersh	d							19 01				19 21												19 51	
Wokingham	d							19 06				19 26												19 56	
Bracknell	d							19 12				19 32												20 02	
Martins Heron	d							19 15				19 35												20 05	
Guildford	d								18 30						19 00										
Wanborough	d								18 36						19 06										
Ash ■5	d								18 40						19 10										
Aldershot	a								18 47						19 17										
	d								19 00						19 30										
Ash Vale	d								19 04						19 34										
Frimley	d								19 10						19 40										
Camberley	a								19 14						19 44										
	d								19 18						19 48										
Bagshot	d								19 23						19 53										
Ascot ■3	d							19 20	19a30			19 40			20a00									20 10	
Sunningdale	d							19 23				19 43												20 13	
Longcross	d											19 46												20 16	
Weybridge	d				19 07												19 37			20 03					
Addlestone	d				19 11												19 41			20 07					
Chertsey	d				19 14												19 44			20 10					
Virginia Water	a				19 19			19 28				19 49					19 49			20 15				20 19	
	d				19 24			19 28				19 49					19 54			20 24				20 19	
Egham	d				19 27			19 31				19 53					19 57			↪				20 23	
Windsor & Eton Riverside	d					19 23												19 53							
Datchet	d					19 26												19 56							
Sunnymeads	d					19 29												19 59							
Wraysbury	d					19 32												20 02							
Staines	d				19 33	19 38		19a40				19 59					20 03	20 08						20 29	
Ashford (Surrey)	d				19 36	19 41											20 06	20 11							
Feltham	d				19 41	19 46						20 05					20 11	20 16						20 35	
Whitton	d					19 50				19 50	19 53							20 20			20 20	20 23			
Kingston	d			19 29												19 59									
Hampton Wick	d			19 31												20 01									
Teddington	d			19 35												20 05									
Fulwell	d																								
Strawberry Hill	d			19 38												20 08									
Twickenham	a			19 42		19 53					19 56	20 10				20 12		20 23				20 26		20 40	
	d			19 43		19 53					19 58	20 11				20 13		20 23				20 28		20 41	
St Margarets	d			19 45							20 00					20 15						20 30			
Richmond ⊖	d			19 49		19 58					20 04	20 15				20 19		20 28				20 34		20 45	
North Sheen	d			19 51							20 06					20 21						20 36			
Mortlake	d			19 53							20 08					20 23						20 38			
Hounslow	d				19 46					20 01							20 16				20 31				
Isleworth	d				19 49					20 04							20 19				20 34				
Syon Lane	d				19 51					20 06							20 21				20 36				
Brentford	d				19 54					20 09							20 24				20 39				
Kew Bridge	d				19 56					20 11							20 26				20 41				
Chiswick	d				19 59					20 14							20 29				20 44				
Barnes Bridge	d	←			20 01					20 16				←			20 31				20 46				←
Barnes	d	19 49		19 56	20 04		←			20 19	20 11			20 19		20 26	20 34		←		20 49	20 41			20 49
Putney	d	19 52		19 59	20 07	20 04	20 07			↪	20 14			20 22		20 29	20 37	20 34	20 37		↪	20 44			20 52
Wandsworth Town	d	19 55		20 02	→		20 10				20 17			20 25		20 32	→		20 40			20 47			20 55
Clapham Junction ■10	d	19 58		20 05		20 09	20 13				20 20	20 24		20 28		20 35		20 39	20 43			20 50		20 54	20 58
Queenstown Rd.(Battersea)	d	20 01		20 08			20 16				20 23			20 31		20 38			20 46			20 53			21 01
Vauxhall ⊖	d	20 05		20 12		20 15	20 20				20 27			20 35		20 42		20 45	20 50			20 57			21 05
London Waterloo ■15 ⊖	a	20 09		20 16		20 19	20 26				20 32	20 34		20 41		20 46		20 49	20 56			21 02		21 04	21 11

A From London Waterloo
B To London Waterloo
C From Weybridge
D From London Waterloo to Barnes continues to London Waterloo

The xx23 and xx53 services from Whitton originates at London Waterloo via Brentford

The xx20 and xx50 from Whitton originates at London Waterloo via Richmond

The xx29 and xx59 from Kingston originates at London Waterloo via Wimbledon

Table 149R

Mondays to Fridays

9 December to 16 May

Reading, Guildford, Ascot, Weybridge, Windsor, Kingston, Richmond and Hounslow - London

Network Diagram - see first Page of Table 148

		SW 1	SW A	SW B	SW	SW C	SW D	SW E	SW A	SW 1	SW A	SW 1	SW 1	SW A	SW B	SW	SW C	SW D	SW E	SW A	SW 1	SW A	SW A
Reading 7	d									20 12											20 42		
Earley	d									20 17											20 47		
Winnersh Triangle	d									20 19											20 49		
Winnersh	d									20 21											20 51		
Wokingham	d									20 26											20 56		
Bracknell	d									20 32											21 02		
Martins Heron	d									20 35											21 05		
Guildford	d	19 30										20 00	20 30										
Wanborough	d	19 36										20 06	20 36										
Ash 5	d	19 40										20 10	20 40										
Aldershot	a	19 47										20 17	20 47										
	d	20 00										20 30											
Ash Vale	d	20 04										20 34											
Frimley	d	20 10										20 40											
Camberley	a	20 14										20 44											
	d	20 18										20 48											
Bagshot	d	20 23										20 53											
Ascot 3	d	20a30								20 40		21a00									21 10		
Sunningdale	d									20 43											21 13		
Longcross	d									20 46													
Weybridge	d						20 33											21 03					
Addlestone	d						20 37											21 07					
Chertsey	d			←			20 40								←			21 10					
Virginia Water	a			20 15			20 45			20 49					20 45			21 15			21 19		
	d			20 24			20 54			20 49					20 54			21 24			21 19		
Egham	d			20 27			→			20 53					20 57			→			21 23		
Windsor & Eton Riverside	d				20 23											20 53							
Datchet	d				20 26											20 56							
Sunnymeads	d				20 29											20 59							
Wraysbury	d				20 32											21 02							
Staines	d			20 33	20 38					20 59					21 03	21 08					21 29		
Ashford (Surrey)	d			20 36	20 41										21 06	21 11							
Feltham	d			20 41	20 46					21 05					21 11	21 16					21 35		
Whitton	d				20 50			20 50	20 53							21 20			21 20	21 23			
Kingston	d		20 29											20 59									21 29
Hampton Wick	d		20 31											21 01									21 31
Teddington	d		20 35											21 05									21 35
Fulwell	d																						
Strawberry Hill	d		20 38											21 08									21 38
Twickenham	a		20 42		20 53				20 56	21 10				21 12		21 23				21 26	21 40		21 42
	d		20 43		20 53				20 58	21 11				21 13		21 23				21 28	21 41		21 43
St Margarets	d		20 45						21 00					21 15						21 30			21 45
Richmond ⊖	d		20 49		20 58				21 04	21 15				21 19		21 28				21 34	21 45		21 49
North Sheen	d		20 51						21 06					21 21						21 36			21 51
Mortlake	d		20 53						21 08					21 23						21 38			21 53
Hounslow	d			20 46				21 01							21 16				21 31				
Isleworth	d			20 49				21 04							21 19				21 34				
Syon Lane	d			20 51				21 06							21 21				21 36				
Brentford	d			20 54				21 09							21 24				21 39				
Kew Bridge	d			20 56				21 11							21 26				21 41				
Chiswick	d			20 59				21 14							21 29				21 44				
Barnes Bridge	d			21 01				21 16			←				21 31				21 46			←	
Barnes	d		20 56	21 04		←		21 19	21 11		21 19			21 26	21 34		←		21 49	21 41		21 49	21 56
Putney	d		20 59	21 07	21 04	21 07		→	21 14		21 22			21 29	21 37	21 34	21 37		→	21 44		21 52	21 59
Wandsworth Town	d		21 02	→		21 10			21 17		21 25			21 32	→		21 40			21 47		21 55	22 02
Clapham Junction 10	d		21 05		21 09	21 13			21 20	21 24	21 28			21 35		21 39	21 43			21 50	21 54	21 58	22 05
Queenstown Rd.(Battersea)	d		21 08			21 16			21 23		21 31			21 38			21 46			21 53		22 01	22 08
Vauxhall ⊖	d		21 12		21 15	21 20			21 27		21 35			21 42		21 45	21 50			21 57		22 05	22 12
London Waterloo 15 ⊖	a		21 16		21 19	21 26			21 32	21 34	21 41			21 46		21 49	21 56			22 02	22 04	22 11	22 16

A From London Waterloo
B From Weybridge to London Waterloo
C From Weybridge
D To London Waterloo
E From London Waterloo to Barnes continues to London Waterloo

The xx23 and xx53 services from Whitton originates at London Waterloo via Brentford

The xx20 and xx50 from Whitton originates at London Waterloo via Richmond

The xx29 and xx59 from Kingston originates at London Waterloo via Wimbledon

Table 149R

Mondays to Fridays

9 December to 16 May

Reading, Guildford, Ascot, Weybridge, Windsor, Kingston, Richmond and Hounslow - London

Network Diagram - see first Page of Table 148

		SW	SW	SW		SW	SW	SW	SW	SW	SW	SW	SW	SW		SW	SW	SW	SW	SW	SW	SW	SW	SW	
									■1		■1	■1								■1					
		A		B		C	D	E		E			E	A			B	E	C		E	A		B	
Reading 7	d								21 12											21 42					
Earley	d								21 17											21 47					
Winnersh Triangle	d								21 19											21 49					
Winnersh	d								21 21											21 51					
Wokingham	d								21 26											21 56					
Bracknell	d								21 32											22 02					
Martins Heron	d								21 35											22 05					
Guildford	d										21 00	21 30													
Wanborough	d										21 06	21 36													
Ash 5	d										21 10	21 40													
Aldershot	a										21 17	21 47													
	d										21 30														
Ash Vale	d										21 34														
Frimley	d										21 40														
Camberley	a										21 44														
	d										21 48														
Bagshot	d										21 53														
Ascot 3	d								21 40		22a00									22 10					
Sunningdale	d								21 43											22 13					
Longcross	d																								
Weybridge	d					21 33													22 03						
Addlestone	d					21 37													22 07						
Chertsey	d	←				21 40								←					22 10			←			
Virginia Water	a	21 15				21 45			21 49					21 45					22 15	22 19		22 15			
	d	21 24				21 54			21 49					21 54					22 24	22 19		22 24			
Egham	d	21 27				→			21 53					21 57					→	22 23		22 27			
Windsor & Eton Riverside	d		21 23													21 53							22 23		
Datchet	d		21 26													21 56							22 26		
Sunnymeads	d		21 29													21 59							22 29		
Wraysbury	d		21 32													22 02							22 32		
Staines	d	21 33	21 38						21 59					22 03		22 08				22 29		22 33	22 38		
Ashford (Surrey)	d	21 36	21 41											22 06		22 11						22 36	22 41		
Feltham	d	21 41	21 46						22 05					22 11		22 16				22 35		22 41	22 46		
Whitton	d		21 50				21 50	21 53								22 20		22 23					22 50		
Kingston	d												21 59								22 29				
Hampton Wick	d												22 01								22 31				
Teddington	d												22 05								22 35				
Fulwell	d																								
Strawberry Hill	d												22 08								22 38				
Twickenham	a		21 53					21 56	22 10				22 12			22 23		22 26		22 40	22 42		22 53		
	d		21 53					21 58	22 11				22 13			22 23		22 28		22 41	22 43		22 53		
St Margarets	d							22 00					22 15					22 30			22 45				
Richmond ⊖	d		21 58					22 04	22 15				22 19			22 28		22 34		22 45	22 49		22 58		
North Sheen	d							22 06					22 21					22 36			22 51				
Mortlake	d							22 08					22 23					22 38			22 53				
Hounslow	d	21 46					22 01							22 16								22 46			
Isleworth	d	21 49					22 04							22 19								22 49			
Syon Lane	d	21 51					22 06							22 21								22 51			
Brentford	d	21 54					22 09							22 24								22 54			
Kew Bridge	d	21 56					22 11							22 26								22 56			
Chiswick	d	21 59					22 14							22 29								22 59			
Barnes Bridge	d	22 01					22 16			←				22 31								23 01			
Barnes	d	22 04		←			22 19	22 11		22 19			22 26	22 34			←	22 41			22 56	23 04		←	
Putney	d	22 07	22 04	22 07			→	22 14		22 22			22 29	22 37		22 34	22 37	22 44			22 59	23 07	23 04	23 07	
Wandsworth Town	d	→		22 10				22 17		22 25			22 32	→			22 40	22 47			23 02	→		23 10	
Clapham Junction 10	d		22 09	22 13				22 20	22 24	22 28			22 35			22 39	22 43	22 50		22 54	23 05		23 09	23 13	
Queenstown Rd.(Battersea)	d			22 16				22 23		22 31			22 38				22 46	22 53			23 08			23 16	
Vauxhall ⊖	d		22 15	22 20				22 27		22 35			22 42			22 45	22 50	22 57			23 12		23 15	23 20	
London Waterloo 15 ⊖	a		22 19	22 26				22 32	22 34	22 41			22 46			22 49	22 57	23 02		23 04	23 16		23 19	23 26	

A From Weybridge to London Waterloo
B From Weybridge
C To London Waterloo
D From London Waterloo to Barnes continues to London Waterloo
E From London Waterloo

The xx23 and xx53 services from Whitton originates at London Waterloo via Brentford

The xx20 and xx50 from Whitton originates at London Waterloo via Richmond

The xx29 and xx59 from Kingston originates at London Waterloo via Wimbledon

Table 149R

Mondays to Fridays

9 December to 16 May

Reading, Guildford, Ascot, Weybridge, Windsor, Kingston, Richmond and Hounslow - London

Network Diagram - see first Page of Table 148

		SW	SW	SW	SW	SW	SW	SW	SW	SW		SW	SW	SW	SW	SW	SW	SW	SW	SW		SW			
			■1	■1	■1							■1						■1		■1		■1			
		A				B	C		D	E			D		B	B	E		D						
Reading ■7	d		22 12									22 42						23 12							
Earley	d		22 17									22 47						23 17							
Winnersh Triangle	d		22 19									22 49						23 19							
Winnersh	d		22 21									22 51						23 21							
Wokingham	d		22 26									22 56						23 26							
Bracknell	d		22 32									23 02						23 32							
Martins Heron	d		22 35									23 05						23 35							
Guildford	d			22 00	22 30															23 00		23 30			
Wanborough	d			22 06	22 36															23 06		23 36			
Ash ■5	d			22 10	22 40															23 10		23 40			
Aldershot	a			22 17	22 47															23 17		23 47			
	d			22 30																23 30					
Ash Vale	d			22 34																23 34					
Frimley	d			22 40																23 40					
Camberley	a			22 44																23 44					
	d			22 48																23 48					
Bagshot	d			22 53																23 53					
Ascot ■3	d		22 40	23a00								23 10						23 40		00a01					
Sunningdale	d		22 43									23 13						23 43							
Longcross	d																								
Weybridge	d	22 33								23 03							23 33								
Addlestone	d	22 37								23 07							23 37								
Chertsey	d	22 40					←			23 10			←				23 40		←						
Virginia Water	a	22 45	22 49				22 45			23 15		23 19	23 15				23 45	23 49	23 45						
	d	22 54	22 49				22 54			23 24		23 19	23 24				23 54	23 49	23 54						
Egham	d	→	22 53				22 57			→		23 23	23 27				→	23 53	23 57						
Windsor & Eton Riverside	d							22 53						23 28											
Datchet	d							22 56						23 31											
Sunnymeads	d							22 59						23 34											
Wraysbury	d							23 02						23 37											
Staines	d		22 59				23 03	23 08				23 29	23a32	23a42				23 59	00a02						
Ashford (Surrey)	d						23 06	23 11																	
Feltham	d		23 05				23 11	23 16				23 35						00 05							
Whitton	d							23 20																	
Kingston	d					22 59									23 29	23 55									
Hampton Wick	d					23 01									23 31	23 57									
Teddington	d					23 05									23 35	23 59									
Fulwell	d																								
Strawberry Hill	d					23 08									23 38	00 03									
Twickenham	a		23 10			23 12		23 23				23 40			23 42	00 06		00 10							
	d		23 11			23 13		23 23				23 41			23 43			00 11							
St Margarets	d					23 15									23 45										
Richmond ⊖	d		23 15			23 19		23 28				23 45			23 49			00 15							
North Sheen	d					23 21									23 51										
Mortlake	d					23 23									23 53										
Hounslow	d						23 16																		
Isleworth	d						23 19																		
Syon Lane	d						23 21																		
Brentford	d						23 24																		
Kew Bridge	d						23 26																		
Chiswick	d						23 29																		
Barnes Bridge	d						23 31																		
Barnes	d					23 26	23 34		←						23 56										
Putney	d					23 29	23 37	23 34	23 37						23 59										
Wandsworth Town	d					23 32	→		23 40						00 02										
Clapham Junction ■10	d		23 24			23 35		23 39	23 43			23 54			00 05			00 24							
Queenstown Rd.(Battersea)	d					23 38			23 46						00 08										
Vauxhall ⊖	d					23 42		23 45	23 50						00 12										
London Waterloo ■15 ⊖	a		23 34			23 47		23 49	23 56			00 04			00 16			00 38							

A To London Waterloo
B From London Waterloo
C From Weybridge to London Waterloo
D From Weybridge
E To Staines

The xx23 and xx53 services from Whitton originates at London Waterloo via Brentford

The xx20 and xx50 from Whitton originates at London Waterloo via Richmond

The xx29 and xx59 from Kingston originates at London Waterloo via Wimbledon

Table 149R

Saturdays

14 December to 17 May

Reading, Guildford, Ascot, Weybridge, Windsor, Kingston, Richmond and Hounslow - London

Network Diagram - see first Page of Table 148

		SW	SW	SW	SW	SW	SW	SW	SW	SW		SW	SW	SW	SW	SW	SW	SW	SW	SW		SW	SW	SW	SW
				1												1	1							1	
		A	A	B	A			C		D			E		F			G	H			I	H		A
Reading 7	d															05 42								06 12	
Earley	d															05 47								06 17	
Winnersh Triangle	d															05 49								06 19	
Winnersh	d															05 51								06 21	
Wokingham	d															05 56								06 26	
Bracknell	d															06 02								06 32	
Martins Heron	d															06 05								06 35	
Guildford	d																								
Wanborough	d																								
Ash 5	d																								
Aldershot	a																								
	d																06 00								
Ash Vale	d																06 04								
Frimley	d																06 10								
Camberley	a																06 14								
	d																06 18								
Bagshot	d																06 23								
Ascot 3	d															06 10	06a30							06 40	
Sunningdale	d															06 13								06 43	
Longcross	d																								
Weybridge	d																						06 33		
Addlestone	d												05 39										06 37		
Chertsey	d												05 42										06 40		
Virginia Water	a												05 47			06 19							06 45	06 49	
	d												05 54			06 19							06 54	06 49	
Egham	d												05 57			06 23							↪	06 53	
Windsor & Eton Riverside	d													05 53						06 23					
Datchet	d													05 56						06 26					
Sunnymeads	d													05 59						06 29					
Wraysbury	d													06 02						06 32					
Staines	d					04 58			05 37				06 03	06 08		06 29			06 33	06 38				06 59	
Ashford (Surrey)	d					05 01			05 40				06 06	06 11					06 36	06 41					
Feltham	d			00 05		05 06			05 45				06 11	06 16		06 35			06 41	06 46				07 05	
Whitton	d					05 10		05 41	05 49					06 20						06 50					
Kingston	d				01 17							05 59						06 29							06 59
Hampton Wick	d				01s19							06 01						06 31							07 01
Teddington	d				01s22							06 05						06 35							07 05
Fulwell	d																								
Strawberry Hill	d		00 03		01a28		05 38					06 08						06 38							07 08
Twickenham	a		00 06	00 10		05 13	05 41		05 52			06 12		06 23		06 40		06 42		06 53				07 10	07 12
	d			00 11		05 13	05 43		05 53			06 13		06 23		06 41		06 43		06 53				07 11	07 13
St Margarets	d					05 15	05 45					06 15						06 45							07 15
Richmond ⊖	d			00 15		05 19	05 49		05 58			06 19		06 28		06 45		06 49		06 58				07 15	07 19
North Sheen	d					05 21	05 51					06 21						06 51							07 21
Mortlake	d					05 23	05 53					06 23						06 53							07 23
Hounslow	d							05 46					06 16						06 46						
Isleworth	d							05 49					06 19						06 49						
Syon Lane	d							05 51					06 21						06 51						
Brentford	d							05 54					06 24						06 54						
Kew Bridge	d							05 56					06 26						06 56						
Chiswick	d							05 59					06 29						06 59						
Barnes Bridge	d							06 01					06 31						07 01						
Barnes	d					05 26	05 56	06 04		←		06 26	06 34		←			06 56	07 04			←			07 26
Putney	d					05 29	05 59	06 07	06 04	06 07		06 29	06 37	06 34	06 37			06 59	07 07	07 04		07 07			07 29
Wandsworth Town	d	00 02				05 32	06 02	→		06 10		06 32	→		06 40			07 02	→			07 10			07 32
Clapham Junction 10	d	00 05		00 24		05 35	06 05		06 09	06 13		06 35		06 39	06 43	06 54		07 05		07 09		07 13		07 24	07 35
Queenstown Rd.(Battersea)	d	00 08				05 38	06 08			06 16		06 38			06 46			07 08				07 16			07 38
Vauxhall ⊖	d	00 12				05 42	06 12		06 15	06 20		06 42		06 45	06 50			07 12		07 15		07 20			07 42
London Waterloo 15 ⊖	a	00 16		00 38		05 46	06 16		06 19	06 26		06 46		06 49	06 56	07 04		07 16		07 19		07 26		07 34	07 46

A From London Waterloo
B From Reading
C From Twickenham to London Waterloo
D From Twickenham
E From Woking to London Waterloo
F From Woking
G From Wimbledon
H To London Waterloo
I From Staines

The xx23 and xx53 services from Whitton originates at London Waterloo via Brentford

The xx20 and xx50 from Whitton originates at London Waterloo via Richmond

The xx29 and xx59 from Kingston originates at London Waterloo via Wimbledon

Table 149R

Saturdays

14 December to 17 May

Reading, Guildford, Ascot, Weybridge, Windsor, Kingston, Richmond and Hounslow - London

Network Diagram - see first Page of Table 148

Station		SW	SW	SW	SW	SW		SW	SW	SW	SW	SW	SW	SW	SW	SW		SW	SW	SW	SW	SW	SW	SW	SW
						1		1								1		1							
		A		B	C					D	A		B		C				D	D	A		B	C	E
Reading 7	d					06 42										07 12									
Earley	d					06 47										07 17									
Winnersh Triangle	d					06 49										07 19									
Winnersh	d					06 51										07 21									
Wokingham	d					06 56										07 26									
Bracknell	d					07 02										07 32									
Martins Heron	d					07 05										07 35									
Guildford	d							06 30										07 00							
Wanborough	d							06 36										07 06							
Ash 5	d							06 40										07 10							
Aldershot	a							06 47										07 17							
	d							07 00										07 30							
Ash Vale	d							07 04										07 34							
Frimley	d							07 10										07 40							
Camberley	a							07 14										07 44							
	d							07 18										07 48							
Bagshot	d							07 23										07 53							
Ascot 3	d					07 10		07a30								07 40		08a00							
Sunningdale	d					07 13										07 43									
Longcross	d																								
Weybridge	d				07 03										07 33									08 03	
Addlestone	d				07 07										07 37									08 07	
Chertsey	d	←			07 10						←				07 40						←			08 10	
Virginia Water	a	06 45			07 15	07 19					07 15				07 45	07 49					07 45			08 15	
	d	06 54			07 24	07 19					07 24				07 54	07 49					07 54			08 24	
Egham	d	06 57			→	07 23					07 27				→	07 53					07 57			→	
Windsor & Eton Riverside	d		06 53									07 23										07 53			
Datchet	d		06 56									07 26										07 56			
Sunnymeads	d		06 59									07 29										07 59			
Wraysbury	d		07 02									07 32										08 02			
Staines	d	07 03	07 08			07 29					07 33	07 38				07 59					08 03	08 08			
Ashford (Surrey)	d	07 06	07 11								07 36	07 41									08 06	08 11			
Feltham	d	07 11	07 16			07 35					07 41	07 46				08 05					08 11	08 16			
Whitton	d		07 20									07 50							07 50			08 20			08 20
Kingston	d									07 29										07 59					
Hampton Wick	d									07 31										08 01					
Teddington	d									07 35										08 05					
Fulwell	d																								
Strawberry Hill	d									07 38										08 08					
Twickenham	a		07 23			07 40				07 42		07 53				08 10				08 12		08 23			
	d		07 23			07 41				07 43		07 53		07 58		08 11				08 13		08 23			
St Margarets	d									07 45				08 00						08 15					
Richmond ⊖	d		07 28			07 45				07 49		07 58		08 04		08 15				08 19		08 28			
North Sheen	d									07 51				08 06						08 21					
Mortlake	d									07 53				08 08						08 23					
Hounslow	d	07 16							07 31		07 46								08 01		08 16				08 31
Isleworth	d	07 19							07 34		07 49								08 04		08 19				08 34
Syon Lane	d	07 21							07 36		07 51								08 06		08 21				08 36
Brentford	d	07 24							07 39		07 54								08 09		08 24				08 39
Kew Bridge	d	07 26							07 41		07 56								08 11		08 26				08 41
Chiswick	d	07 29							07 44		07 59								08 14		08 29				08 44
Barnes Bridge	d	07 31							07 46		08 01								08 16		08 31				08 46
Barnes	d	07 34		←					07 49	07 56	08 04		←	08 11					08 19	08 26	08 34		←		08 49
Putney	d	07 37	07 34	07 37					07 52	07 59	08 07	08 04	08 07	08 14					08 22	08 29	08 37	08 34	08 37		→
Wandsworth Town	d	→		07 40					07 55	08 02	→		08 10	08 17					08 25	08 32	→		08 40		
Clapham Junction 10	d		07 39	07 43		07 54			07 58	08 05		08 09	08 13	08 20		08 24			08 28	08 35		08 39	08 43		
Queenstown Rd.(Battersea)	d			07 46					08 01	08 08			08 16	08 23					08 31	08 38			08 46		
Vauxhall ⊖	d		07 45	07 50					08 05	08 12		08 15	08 20	08 27					08 35	08 42		08 45	08 50		
London Waterloo 15 ⊖	a		07 49	07 56		08 04			08 11	08 16		08 19	08 26	08 32		08 34			08 41	08 46		08 49	08 56		

A From Weybridge to London Waterloo
B From Weybridge
C To London Waterloo
D From London Waterloo
E From London Waterloo to Barnes continues to London Waterloo

The xx23 and xx53 services from Whitton originates at London Waterloo via Brentford

The xx20 and xx50 from Whitton originates at London Waterloo via Richmond

The xx29 and xx59 from Kingston originates at London Waterloo via Wimbledon

Table 149R

Saturdays

14 December to 17 May

Reading, Guildford, Ascot, Weybridge, Windsor, Kingston, Richmond and Hounslow - London

Network Diagram - see first Page of Table 148

		SW A		SW [1]	SW A	SW [1]	SW A	SW B	SW	SW C	SW D	SW E		SW A	SW [1]	SW A	SW [1]	SW A	SW B	SW	SW C	SW D		SW E	SW A
Reading [7]	d			07 42											08 12										
Earley	d			07 47											08 17										
Winnersh Triangle	d			07 49											08 19										
Winnersh	d			07 51											08 21										
Wokingham	d			07 56											08 26										
Bracknell	d			08 02											08 32										
Martins Heron	d			08 05											08 35										
Guildford	d					07 30											08 00								
Wanborough	d					07 36											08 06								
Ash [5]	d					07 40											08 10								
Aldershot	a					07 47											08 17								
	d					08 00											08 30								
Ash Vale	d					08 04											08 34								
Frimley	d					08 10											08 40								
Camberley	a					08 14											08 44								
	d					08 18											08 48								
Bagshot	d					08 23											08 53								
Ascot [3]	d			08 10		08a30									08 40		09a00								
Sunningdale	d			08 13											08 43										
Longcross	d																								
Weybridge	d										08 33											09 03			
Addlestone	d										08 37											09 07			
Chertsey	d							←			08 40								←			09 10			
Virginia Water	a			08 19				08 15			08 45				08 49				08 45			09 15			
	d			08 19				08 24			08 54				08 49				08 54			09 24			
Egham	d			08 23				08 27			↪				08 53				08 57			↪			
Windsor & Eton Riverside	d								08 23											08 53					
Datchet	d								08 26											08 56					
Sunnymeads	d								08 29											08 59					
Wraysbury	d								08 32											09 02					
Staines	d			08 29				08 33	08 38						08 59				09 03	09 08					
Ashford (Surrey)	d							08 36	08 41										09 06	09 11					
Feltham	d			08 35				08 41	08 46						09 05				09 11	09 16					
Whitton	d	08 23							08 50			08 50		08 53						09 20				09 20	09 23
Kingston	d						08 29											08 59							
Hampton Wick	d						08 31											09 01							
Teddington	d						08 35											09 05							
Fulwell	d																								
Strawberry Hill	d						08 38											09 08							
Twickenham	a	08 26		08 40			08 42		08 53					08 56	09 10			09 12		09 23					09 26
	d	08 28		08 41			08 43		08 53					08 58	09 11			09 13		09 23					09 28
St Margarets	d	08 30					08 45							09 00				09 15							09 30
Richmond ⊖	d	08 34		08 45			08 49		08 58					09 04	09 15			09 19		09 28					09 34
North Sheen	d	08 36					08 51							09 06				09 21							09 36
Mortlake	d	08 38					08 53							09 08				09 23							09 38
Hounslow	d							08 46				09 01							09 16					09 31	
Isleworth	d							08 49				09 04							09 19					09 34	
Syon Lane	d							08 51				09 06							09 21					09 36	
Brentford	d							08 54				09 09							09 24					09 39	
Kew Bridge	d							08 56				09 11							09 26					09 41	
Chiswick	d							08 59				09 14							09 29					09 44	
Barnes Bridge	d				←			09 01				09 16				←			09 31					09 46	
Barnes	d	08 41			08 49		08 56	09 04		←		09 19		09 11		09 19		09 26	09 34		←			09 49	09 41
Putney	d	08 44			08 52		08 59	09 07	09 04	09 07		↪		09 14		09 22		09 29	09 37	09 34	09 37			↪	09 44
Wandsworth Town	d	08 47			08 55		09 02	↪		09 10				09 17		09 25		09 32	↪		09 40				09 47
Clapham Junction [10]	d	08 50		08 54	08 58		09 05		09 09	09 13				09 20	09 24	09 28		09 35		09 39	09 43				09 50
Queenstown Rd.(Battersea)	d	08 53			09 01		09 08			09 16				09 23		09 31		09 38			09 46				09 53
Vauxhall ⊖	d	08 57			09 05		09 12		09 15	09 20				09 27		09 35		09 42		09 45	09 50				09 57
London Waterloo [15] ⊖	a	09 02		09 04	09 11		09 16		09 19	09 26				09 32	09 34	09 41		09 46		09 49	09 56				10 02

A From London Waterloo
B From Weybridge to London Waterloo
C From Weybridge
D To London Waterloo
E From London Waterloo to Barnes continues to London Waterloo

The xx23 and xx53 services from Whitton originates at London Waterloo via Brentford

The xx20 and xx50 from Whitton originates at London Waterloo via Richmond

The xx29 and xx59 from Kingston originates at London Waterloo via Wimbledon

Table 149R

Saturdays

14 December to 17 May

Reading, Guildford, Ascot, Weybridge, Windsor, Kingston, Richmond and Hounslow - London

Network Diagram - see first Page of Table 148

		SW 1	SW	SW 1	SW	SW	SW	SW	SW	SW	SW	SW 1	SW	SW 1	SW	SW	SW	SW	SW	SW	SW	SW 1	SW
			A		A	B		C	D	E	A		A		A	B		C	D	E	A		A
Reading 7	d	08 42										09 12										09 42	
Earley	d	08 47										09 17										09 47	
Winnersh Triangle	d	08 49										09 19										09 49	
Winnersh	d	08 51										09 21										09 51	
Wokingham	d	08 56										09 26										09 56	
Bracknell	d	09 02										09 32										10 02	
Martins Heron	d	09 05										09 35										10 05	
Guildford	d			08 30										09 00									
Wanborough	d			08 36										09 06									
Ash 5	d			08 40										09 10									
Aldershot	a			08 47										09 17									
	d			09 00										09 30									
Ash Vale	d			09 04										09 34									
Frimley	d			09 10										09 40									
Camberley	a			09 14										09 44									
	d			09 18										09 48									
Bagshot	d			09 23										09 53									
Ascot 3	d	09 10		09a30								09 40		10a00								10 10	
Sunningdale	d	09 13										09 43										10 13	
Longcross	d																						
Weybridge	d								09 33										10 03				
Addlestone	d								09 37										10 07				
Chertsey	d					←			09 40							←			10 10				
Virginia Water	a	09 19				09 15			09 45			09 49				09 45			10 15			10 19	
	d	09 19				09 24			09 54			09 49				09 54			10 24			10 19	
Egham	d	09 23				09 27			↪			09 53				09 57			↪			10 23	
Windsor & Eton Riverside	d						09 23										09 53						
Datchet	d						09 26										09 56						
Sunnymeads	d						09 29										09 59						
Wraysbury	d						09 32										10 02						
Staines	d	09 29				09 33	09 38					09 59				10 03	10 08					10 29	
Ashford (Surrey)	d					09 36	09 41									10 06	10 11						
Feltham	d	09 35				09 41	09 46					10 05				10 11	10 16					10 35	
Whitton	d						09 50			09 50	09 53						10 20			10 20	10 23		
Kingston	d				09 29										09 59								
Hampton Wick	d				09 31										10 01								
Teddington	d				09 35										10 05								
Fulwell	d																						
Strawberry Hill	d				09 38										10 08								
Twickenham	a	09 40			09 42		09 53				09 56	10 10			10 12		10 23				10 26	10 40	
	d	09 41			09 43		09 53				09 58	10 11			10 13		10 23				10 28	10 41	
St Margarets	d				09 45						10 00				10 15						10 30		
Richmond ⊖	d	09 45			09 49		09 58				10 04	10 15			10 19		10 28				10 34	10 45	
North Sheen	d				09 51						10 06				10 21						10 36		
Mortlake	d				09 53						10 08				10 23						10 38		
Hounslow	d					09 46				10 01						10 16				10 31			
Isleworth	d					09 49				10 04						10 19				10 34			
Syon Lane	d					09 51				10 06						10 21				10 36			
Brentford	d					09 54				10 09						10 24				10 39			
Kew Bridge	d					09 56				10 11						10 26				10 41			
Chiswick	d					09 59				10 14						10 29				10 44			
Barnes Bridge	d		←			10 01				10 16			←			10 31				10 46			←
Barnes	d		09 49		09 56	10 04		←		10 19	10 11		10 19		10 26	10 34		←		10 49	10 41		10 49
Putney	d		09 52		09 59	10 07	10 04	10 07		↪	10 14		10 22		10 29	10 37	10 34	10 37		↪	10 44		10 52
Wandsworth Town	d		09 55		10 02	↪		10 10			10 17		10 25		10 32	↪		10 40			10 47		10 55
Clapham Junction 10	d	09 54	09 58		10 05		10 09	10 13			10 20	10 24	10 28		10 35		10 39	10 43			10 50	10 54	10 58
Queenstown Rd.(Battersea)	d		10 01		10 08			10 16			10 23		10 31		10 38			10 46			10 53		11 01
Vauxhall ⊖	d		10 05		10 12		10 15	10 20			10 27		10 35		10 42		10 45	10 50			10 57		11 05
London Waterloo 15 ⊖	a	10 04	10 11		10 16		10 19	10 26			10 32	10 34	10 41		10 46		10 49	10 56			11 02	11 04	11 11

A From London Waterloo
B From Weybridge to London Waterloo
C From Weybridge
D To London Waterloo
E From London Waterloo to Barnes continues to London Waterloo

The xx23 and xx53 services from Whitton originates at London Waterloo via Brentford

The xx20 and xx50 from Whitton originates at London Waterloo via Richmond

The xx29 and xx59 from Kingston originates at London Waterloo via Wimbledon

Table 149R

Saturdays

14 December to 17 May

Reading, Guildford, Ascot, Weybridge, Windsor, Kingston, Richmond and Hounslow - London

Network Diagram - see first Page of Table 148

		SW 1	SW	SW		SW	SW	SW	SW	SW	SW 1	SW	SW 1	SW		SW	SW	SW	SW	SW	SW	SW 1	SW	SW 1
			A	B			C	D	E	A		A		A		B		C	D	E	A		A	
Reading 7	d										10 12											10 42		
Earley	d										10 17											10 47		
Winnersh Triangle	d										10 19											10 49		
Winnersh	d										10 21											10 51		
Wokingham	d										10 26											10 56		
Bracknell	d										10 32											11 02		
Martins Heron	d										10 35											11 05		
Guildford	d	09 30											10 00											10 30
Wanborough	d	09 36											10 06											10 36
Ash 5	d	09 40											10 10											10 40
Aldershot	a	09 47											10 17											10 47
	d	10 00											10 30											11 00
Ash Vale	d	10 04											10 34											11 04
Frimley	d	10 10											10 40											11 10
Camberley	a	10 14											10 44											11 14
	d	10 18											10 48											11 18
Bagshot	d	10 23											10 53											11 23
Ascot 3	d	10a30									10 40		11a00									11 10		11a30
Sunningdale	d										10 43											11 13		
Longcross	d																							
Weybridge	d							10 33											11 03					
Addlestone	d							10 37											11 07					
Chertsey	d			←				10 40								←			11 10					
Virginia Water	a			10 15				10 45			10 49					10 45			11 15			11 19		
	d			10 24				10 54			10 49					10 54			11 24			11 19		
Egham	d			10 27				→			10 53					10 57			→			11 23		
Windsor & Eton Riverside	d					10 23											10 53							
Datchet	d					10 26											10 56							
Sunnymeads	d					10 29											10 59							
Wraysbury	d					10 32											11 02							
Staines	d			10 33		10 38					10 59					11 03	11 08					11 29		
Ashford (Surrey)	d			10 36		10 41										11 06	11 11							
Feltham	d			10 41		10 46					11 05					11 11	11 16					11 35		
Whitton	d					10 50			10 50	10 53							11 20			11 20	11 23			
Kingston	d		10 29											10 59										
Hampton Wick	d		10 31											11 01										
Teddington	d		10 35											11 05										
Fulwell	d																							
Strawberry Hill	d		10 38											11 08										
Twickenham	a		10 42			10 53				10 56	11 10			11 12			11 23				11 26	11 40		
	d		10 43			10 53				10 58	11 11			11 13			11 23				11 28	11 41		
St Margarets	d		10 45							11 00				11 15							11 30			
Richmond ⊖	d		10 49			10 58				11 04	11 15			11 19			11 28				11 34	11 45		
North Sheen	d		10 51							11 06				11 21							11 36			
Mortlake	d		10 53							11 08				11 23							11 38			
Hounslow	d			10 46					11 01							11 16				11 31				
Isleworth	d			10 49					11 04							11 19				11 34				
Syon Lane	d			10 51					11 06							11 21				11 36				
Brentford	d			10 54					11 09							11 24				11 39				
Kew Bridge	d			10 56					11 11							11 26				11 41				
Chiswick	d			10 59					11 14							11 29				11 44				
Barnes Bridge	d			11 01					11 16			←				11 31				11 46			←	
Barnes	d		10 56	11 04			←		11 19	11 11		11 19		11 26		11 34		←		11 49	11 41		11 49	
Putney	d		10 59	11 07		11 04	11 07		→	11 14		11 22		11 29		11 37	11 34	11 37		→	11 44		11 52	
Wandsworth Town	d		11 02	→			11 10			11 17		11 25		11 32		→		11 40			11 47		11 55	
Clapham Junction 10	d		11 05			11 09	11 13			11 20	11 24	11 28		11 35			11 39	11 43			11 50	11 54	11 58	
Queenstown Rd.(Battersea)	d		11 08				11 16			11 23		11 31		11 38				11 46			11 53		12 01	
Vauxhall ⊖	d		11 12			11 15	11 20			11 27		11 35		11 42			11 45	11 50			11 57		12 05	
London Waterloo 15 ⊖	a		11 16			11 19	11 26			11 32	11 34	11 41		11 46			11 49	11 56			12 02	12 04	12 11	

A From London Waterloo
B From Weybridge to London Waterloo
C From Weybridge
D To London Waterloo
E From London Waterloo to Barnes continues to London Waterloo

The xx23 and xx53 services from Whitton originates at London Waterloo via Brentford

The xx20 and xx50 from Whitton originates at London Waterloo via Richmond

The xx29 and xx59 from Kingston originates at London Waterloo via Wimbledon

Table 149R

Saturdays

14 December to 17 May

Reading, Guildford, Ascot, Weybridge, Windsor, Kingston, Richmond and Hounslow - London

Network Diagram - see first Page of Table 148

		SW	SW	SW	SW	SW	SW	SW	SW	SW		SW	SW	SW	SW	SW	SW	SW	SW	SW		SW	SW	SW	SW
									1			1								1			1		
		A	B		C	D	E	A		A			A	B		C	D	E	A			A		A	B
Reading 7	d								11 12											11 42					
Earley	d								11 17											11 47					
Winnersh Triangle	d								11 19											11 49					
Winnersh	d								11 21											11 51					
Wokingham	d								11 26											11 56					
Bracknell	d								11 32											12 02					
Martins Heron	d								11 35											12 05					
Guildford	d											11 00											11 30		
Wanborough	d											11 06											11 36		
Ash 5	d											11 10											11 40		
Aldershot	a											11 17											11 47		
	d											11 30											12 00		
Ash Vale	d											11 34											12 04		
Frimley	d											11 40											12 10		
Camberley	a											11 44											12 14		
	d											11 48											12 18		
Bagshot	d											11 53											12 23		
Ascot 3	d								11 40			12a00								12 10			12a30		
Sunningdale	d								11 43											12 13					
Longcross	d																								
Weybridge	d					11 33											12 03								
Addlestone	d					11 37											12 07								
Chertsey	d		↤			11 40								↤			12 10								↤
Virginia Water	a		11 15			11 45			11 49					11 45			12 15			12 19					12 15
	d		11 24			11 54			11 49					11 54			12 24			12 19					12 24
Egham	d		11 27			↦			11 53					11 57			↦			12 23					12 27
Windsor & Eton Riverside	d			11 23											11 53										
Datchet	d			11 26											11 56										
Sunnymeads	d			11 29											11 59										
Wraysbury	d			11 32											12 02										
Staines	d		11 33	11 38					11 59					12 03	12 08					12 29					12 33
Ashford (Surrey)	d		11 36	11 41										12 06	12 11										12 36
Feltham	d		11 41	11 46					12 05					12 11	12 16					12 35					12 41
Whitton	d			11 50			11 50	11 53							12 20			12 20	12 23						
Kingston	d	11 29											11 59											12 29	
Hampton Wick	d	11 31											12 01											12 31	
Teddington	d	11 35											12 05											12 35	
Fulwell	d																								
Strawberry Hill	d	11 38											12 08											12 38	
Twickenham	a	11 42		11 53				11 56	12 10				12 12		12 23				12 26	12 40				12 42	
	d	11 43		11 53				11 58	12 11				12 13		12 23				12 28	12 41				12 43	
St Margarets	d	11 45						12 00					12 15						12 30					12 45	
Richmond ⊖	d	11 49		11 58				12 04	12 15				12 19		12 28				12 34	12 45				12 49	
North Sheen	d	11 51						12 06					12 21						12 36					12 51	
Mortlake	d	11 53						12 08					12 23						12 38					12 53	
Hounslow	d		11 46				12 01							12 16				12 31							12 46
Isleworth	d		11 49				12 04							12 19				12 34							12 49
Syon Lane	d		11 51				12 06							12 21				12 36							12 51
Brentford	d		11 54				12 09							12 24				12 39							12 54
Kew Bridge	d		11 56				12 11							12 26				12 41							12 56
Chiswick	d		11 59				12 14							12 29				12 44							12 59
Barnes Bridge	d		12 01				12 16			↤				12 31				12 46				↤			13 01
Barnes	d	11 56	12 04		↤		12 19	12 11		12 19			12 26	12 34		↤		12 49	12 41			12 49		12 56	13 04
Putney	d	11 59	12 07	12 04	12 07		↦	12 14		12 22			12 29	12 37	12 34	12 37		↦	12 44			12 52		12 59	13 07
Wandsworth Town	d	12 02	↦		12 10			12 17		12 25			12 32	↦		12 40			12 47			12 55		13 02	↦
Clapham Junction 10	d	12 05		12 09	12 13			12 20	12 24	12 28			12 35		12 39	12 43			12 50	12 54		12 58		13 05	
Queenstown Rd.(Battersea)	d	12 08			12 16			12 23		12 31			12 38			12 46			12 53			13 01		13 08	
Vauxhall ⊖	d	12 12		12 15	12 20			12 27		12 35			12 42		12 45	12 50			12 57			13 05		13 12	
London Waterloo 15 ⊖	a	12 16		12 19	12 26			12 32	12 34	12 41			12 46		12 49	12 56			13 02	13 04		13 11		13 16	

A From London Waterloo
B From Weybridge to London Waterloo
C From Weybridge
D To London Waterloo
E From London Waterloo to Barnes continues to London Waterloo

The xx23 and xx53 services from Whitton originates at London Waterloo via Brentford

The xx20 and xx50 from Whitton originates at London Waterloo via Richmond

The xx29 and xx59 from Kingston originates at London Waterloo via Wimbledon

Table 149R

Saturdays

14 December to 17 May

Reading, Guildford, Ascot, Weybridge, Windsor, Kingston, Richmond and Hounslow - London

Network Diagram - see first Page of Table 148

		SW	SW	SW	SW	SW		SW	SW	SW	SW	SW	SW	SW	SW	SW		SW	SW	SW	SW	SW	SW	SW	SW
								1		1									1		1				
			A	B	C	D			D		D	E		A	B	C		D		D		D	E		A
Reading 7	d							12 12											12 42						
Earley	d							12 17											12 47						
Winnersh Triangle	d							12 19											12 49						
Winnersh	d							12 21											12 51						
Wokingham	d							12 26											12 56						
Bracknell	d							12 32											13 02						
Martins Heron	d							12 35											13 05						
Guildford	d									12 00											12 30				
Wanborough	d									12 06											12 36				
Ash 5	d									12 10											12 40				
Aldershot	a									12 17											12 47				
	d									12 30											13 00				
Ash Vale	d									12 34											13 04				
Frimley	d									12 40											13 10				
Camberley	a									12 44											13 14				
	d									12 48											13 18				
Bagshot	d									12 53											13 23				
Ascot 3	d							12 40		13a00									13 10		13a30				
Sunningdale	d							12 43											13 13						
Longcross	d																								
Weybridge	d			12 33											13 03										
Addlestone	d			12 37											13 07										
Chertsey	d			12 40								←			13 10								←		
Virginia Water	a			12 45				12 49				12 45			13 15				13 19				13 15		
	d			12 54				12 49				12 54			13 24				13 19				13 24		
Egham	d			↪				12 53				12 57			↪				13 23				13 27		
Windsor & Eton Riverside	d	12 23											12 53											13 23	
Datchet	d	12 26											12 56											13 26	
Sunnymeads	d	12 29											12 59											13 29	
Wraysbury	d	12 32											13 02											13 32	
Staines	d	12 38						12 59				13 03	13 08						13 29				13 33	13 38	
Ashford (Surrey)	d	12 41										13 06	13 11										13 36	13 41	
Feltham	d	12 46						13 05				13 11	13 16						13 35				13 41	13 46	
Whitton	d	12 50			12 50	12 53							13 20			13 20		13 23						13 50	
Kingston	d										12 59											13 29			
Hampton Wick	d										13 01											13 31			
Teddington	d										13 05											13 35			
Fulwell	d																								
Strawberry Hill	d										13 08											13 38			
Twickenham	a	12 53				12 56		13 10			13 12		13 23					13 26	13 40			13 42		13 53	
	d	12 53				12 58		13 11			13 13		13 23					13 28	13 41			13 43		13 53	
St Margarets	d					13 00					13 15							13 30				13 45			
Richmond ⊖	d	12 58				13 04		13 15			13 19		13 28					13 34	13 45			13 49		13 58	
North Sheen	d					13 06					13 21							13 36				13 51			
Mortlake	d					13 08					13 23							13 38				13 53			
Hounslow	d				13 01							13 16				13 31							13 46		
Isleworth	d				13 04							13 19				13 34							13 49		
Syon Lane	d				13 06							13 21				13 36							13 51		
Brentford	d				13 09							13 24				13 39							13 54		
Kew Bridge	d				13 11							13 26				13 41							13 56		
Chiswick	d				13 14							13 29				13 44							13 59		
Barnes Bridge	d				13 16				←			13 31				13 46				←			14 01		
Barnes	d		←		13 19	13 11			13 19		13 26	13 34		←		13 49		13 41		13 49		13 56	14 04		←
Putney	d	13 04	13 07		↪	13 14			13 22		13 29	13 37	13 34	13 37		↪		13 44		13 52		13 59	14 07	14 04	14 07
Wandsworth Town	d		13 10			13 17			13 25		13 32	↪		13 40				13 47		13 55		14 02	↪		14 10
Clapham Junction 10	d	13 09	13 13			13 20		13 24	13 28		13 35		13 39	13 43				13 50	13 54	13 58		14 05		14 09	14 13
Queenstown Rd.(Battersea)	d		13 16			13 23			13 31		13 38			13 46				13 53		14 01		14 08			14 16
Vauxhall ⊖	d	13 15	13 20			13 27			13 35		13 42		13 45	13 50				13 57		14 05		14 12		14 15	14 20
London Waterloo 15 ⊖	a	13 19	13 26			13 32		13 34	13 41		13 46		13 49	13 56				14 02	14 04	14 11		14 16		14 19	14 26

A From Weybridge
B To London Waterloo
C From London Waterloo to Barnes continues to London Waterloo
D From London Waterloo
E From Weybridge to London Waterloo

The xx23 and xx53 services from Whitton originates at London Waterloo via Brentford

The xx20 and xx50 from Whitton originates at London Waterloo via Richmond

The xx29 and xx59 from Kingston originates at London Waterloo via Wimbledon

Table 149R

Saturdays

14 December to 17 May

Reading, Guildford, Ascot, Weybridge, Windsor, Kingston, Richmond and Hounslow - London

Network Diagram - see first Page of Table 148

Station		SW A	SW B	SW C	SW 1	SW C	SW 1	SW C	SW D	SW	SW E	SW A	SW B	SW C	SW 1	SW C	SW 1	SW C	SW D	SW	SW E	SW A
Reading 7	d				13 12										13 42							
Earley	d				13 17										13 47							
Winnersh Triangle	d				13 19										13 49							
Winnersh	d				13 21										13 51							
Wokingham	d				13 26										13 56							
Bracknell	d				13 32										14 02							
Martins Heron	d				13 35										14 05							
Guildford	d						13 00										13 30					
Wanborough	d						13 06										13 36					
Ash 5	d						13 10										13 40					
Aldershot	a						13 17										13 47					
	d						13 30										14 00					
Ash Vale	d						13 34										14 04					
Frimley	d						13 40										14 10					
Camberley	a						13 44										14 14					
	d						13 48										14 18					
Bagshot	d						13 53										14 23					
Ascot 3	d				13 40		14a00								14 10		14a30					
Sunningdale	d				13 43										14 13							
Longcross	d																					
Weybridge	d	13 33										14 03										14 33
Addlestone	d	13 37										14 07										14 37
Chertsey	d	13 40							←			14 10							←			14 40
Virginia Water	a	13 45			13 49				13 45			14 15			14 19				14 15			14 45
	d	13 54			13 49				13 54			14 24			14 19				14 24			14 54
Egham	d	→			13 53				13 57			→			14 23				14 27			→
Windsor & Eton Riverside	d									13 53										14 23		
Datchet	d									13 56										14 26		
Sunnymeads	d									13 59										14 29		
Wraysbury	d									14 02										14 32		
Staines	d				13 59				14 03	14 08					14 29				14 33	14 38		
Ashford (Surrey)	d								14 06	14 11									14 36	14 41		
Feltham	d				14 05				14 11	14 16					14 35				14 41	14 46		
Whitton	d		13 50	13 53						14 20			14 20	14 23						14 50		
Kingston	d							13 59										14 29				
Hampton Wick	d							14 01										14 31				
Teddington	d							14 05										14 35				
Fulwell	d																					
Strawberry Hill	d							14 08										14 38				
Twickenham	a			13 56	14 10			14 12		14 23				14 26	14 40			14 42		14 53		
	d			13 58	14 11			14 13		14 23				14 28	14 41			14 43		14 53		
St Margarets	d			14 00				14 15						14 30				14 45				
Richmond ⊖	d			14 04	14 15			14 19		14 28				14 34	14 45			14 49		14 58		
North Sheen	d			14 06				14 21						14 36				14 51				
Mortlake	d			14 08				14 23						14 38				14 53				
Hounslow	d		14 01						14 16				14 31						14 46			
Isleworth	d		14 04						14 19				14 34						14 49			
Syon Lane	d		14 06						14 21				14 36						14 51			
Brentford	d		14 09						14 24				14 39						14 54			
Kew Bridge	d		14 11						14 26				14 41						14 56			
Chiswick	d		14 14						14 29				14 44						14 59			
Barnes Bridge	d		14 16			←			14 31				14 46			←			15 01			
Barnes	d		14 19	14 11		14 19		14 26	14 34		←		14 49	14 41		14 49		14 56	15 04		←	
Putney	d		→	14 14		14 22		14 29	14 37	14 34	14 37		→	14 44		14 52		14 59	15 07	15 04	15 07	
Wandsworth Town	d			14 17		14 25		14 32	→		14 40			14 47		14 55		15 02	→		15 10	
Clapham Junction 10	d			14 20	14 24	14 28		14 35		14 39	14 43			14 50	14 54	14 58		15 05		15 09	15 13	
Queenstown Rd.(Battersea)	d			14 23		14 31		14 38			14 46			14 53		15 01		15 08			15 16	
Vauxhall ⊖	d			14 27		14 35		14 42		14 45	14 50			14 57		15 05		15 12		15 15	15 20	
London Waterloo 15 ⊖	a			14 32	14 34	14 41		14 46		14 49	14 56			15 02	15 04	15 11		15 16		15 19	15 26	

A To London Waterloo
B From London Waterloo to Barnes continues to London Waterloo
C From London Waterloo
D From Weybridge to London Waterloo
E From Weybridge

The xx23 and xx53 services from Whitton originates at London Waterloo via Brentford

The xx20 and xx50 from Whitton originates at London Waterloo via Richmond

The xx29 and xx59 from Kingston originates at London Waterloo via Wimbledon

Table 149R

Saturdays

14 December to 17 May

Reading, Guildford, Ascot, Weybridge, Windsor, Kingston, Richmond and Hounslow - London

Network Diagram - see first Page of Table 148

		SW	SW	SW	SW	SW	SW	SW		SW	SW	SW	SW	SW	SW	SW	SW	SW		SW	SW	SW	SW	SW	SW
				1		1									1		1								
		A	B		B		B	C			D	E	A	B		B		B		C		D	E	A	B
Reading 7	d			14 12											14 42										
Earley	d			14 17											14 47										
Winnersh Triangle	d			14 19											14 49										
Winnersh	d			14 21											14 51										
Wokingham	d			14 26											14 56										
Bracknell	d			14 32											15 02										
Martins Heron	d			14 35											15 05										
Guildford	d					14 00											14 30								
Wanborough	d					14 06											14 36								
Ash 5	d					14 10											14 40								
Aldershot	a					14 17											14 47								
	d					14 30											15 00								
Ash Vale	d					14 34											15 04								
Frimley	d					14 40											15 10								
Camberley	a					14 44											15 14								
	d					14 48											15 18								
Bagshot	d					14 53											15 23								
Ascot 8	d			14 40		15a00									15 10		15a30								
Sunningdale	d			14 43											15 13										
Longcross	d																								
Weybridge	d											15 03											15 33		
Addlestone	d											15 07											15 37		
Chertsey	d							←				15 10								←			15 40		
Virginia Water	a			14 49				14 45				15 15			15 19					15 15			15 45		
	d			14 49				14 54				15 24			15 19					15 24			15 54		
Egham	d			14 53				14 57				→			15 23					15 27			→		
Windsor & Eton Riverside	d									14 53											15 23				
Datchet	d									14 56											15 26				
Sunnymeads	d									14 59											15 29				
Wraysbury	d									15 02											15 32				
Staines	d			14 59				15 03		15 08					15 29					15 33	15 38				
Ashford (Surrey)	d							15 06		15 11										15 36	15 41				
Feltham	d			15 05				15 11		15 16					15 35					15 41	15 46				
Whitton	d	14 50	14 53							15 20			15 20	15 23							15 50			15 50	15 53
Kingston	d						14 59											15 29							
Hampton Wick	d						15 01											15 31							
Teddington	d						15 05											15 35							
Fulwell	d																								
Strawberry Hill	d						15 08											15 38							
Twickenham	a		14 56	15 10			15 12			15 23				15 26	15 40			15 42			15 53				15 56
	d		14 58	15 11			15 13			15 23				15 28	15 41			15 43			15 53				15 58
St Margarets	d		15 00				15 15							15 30				15 45							16 00
Richmond ⊖	d		15 04	15 15			15 19			15 28				15 34	15 45			15 49			15 58				16 04
North Sheen	d		15 06				15 21							15 36				15 51							16 06
Mortlake	d		15 08				15 23							15 38				15 53							16 08
Hounslow	d	15 01						15 16					15 31							15 46				16 01	
Isleworth	d	15 04						15 19					15 34							15 49				16 04	
Syon Lane	d	15 06						15 21					15 36							15 51				16 06	
Brentford	d	15 09						15 24					15 39							15 54				16 09	
Kew Bridge	d	15 11						15 26					15 41							15 56				16 11	
Chiswick	d	15 14						15 29					15 44							15 59				16 14	
Barnes Bridge	d	15 16			←			15 31					15 46			←				16 01				16 16	
Barnes	d	15 19	15 11		15 19		15 26	15 34			←		15 49	15 41		15 49		15 56		16 04		←		16 19	16 11
Putney	d	→	15 14		15 22		15 29	15 37		15 34	15 37		→	15 44		15 52		15 59		16 07	16 04	16 07		→	16 14
Wandsworth Town	d		15 17		15 25		15 32	→			15 40			15 47		15 55		16 02		→		16 10			16 17
Clapham Junction 10	d		15 20	15 24	15 28		15 35			15 39	15 43			15 50	15 54	15 58		16 05			16 09	16 13			16 20
Queenstown Rd.(Battersea)	d		15 23		15 31		15 38				15 46			15 53		16 01		16 08				16 16			16 23
Vauxhall ⊖	d		15 27		15 35		15 42			15 45	15 50			15 57		16 05		16 12			16 15	16 20			16 27
London Waterloo 15 ⊖	a		15 32	15 34	15 41		15 46			15 49	15 56			16 02	16 04	16 11		16 16			16 19	16 26			16 32

A From London Waterloo to Barnes continues to London Waterloo
B From London Waterloo
C From Weybridge to London Waterloo
D From Weybridge
E To London Waterloo

The xx23 and xx53 services from Whitton originates at London Waterloo via Brentford

The xx20 and xx50 from Whitton originates at London Waterloo via Richmond

The xx29 and xx59 from Kingston originates at London Waterloo via Wimbledon

Table 149R

Saturdays

14 December to 17 May

Reading, Guildford, Ascot, Weybridge, Windsor, Kingston, Richmond and Hounslow - London

Network Diagram - see first Page of Table 148

		SW 1	SW A	SW 1	SW A	SW B	SW	SW C	SW D	SW E	SW A	SW 1	SW A	SW 1	SW A	SW B	SW	SW C	SW D	SW E	SW A	SW 1
Reading 7	d	15 12										15 42										16 12
Earley	d	15 17										15 47										16 17
Winnersh Triangle	d	15 19										15 49										16 19
Winnersh	d	15 21										15 51										16 21
Wokingham	d	15 26										15 56										16 26
Bracknell	d	15 32										16 02										16 32
Martins Heron	d	15 35										16 05										16 35
Guildford	d			15 00										15 30								
Wanborough	d			15 06										15 36								
Ash 5	d			15 10										15 40								
Aldershot	a			15 17										15 47								
	d			15 30										16 00								
Ash Vale	d			15 34										16 04								
Frimley	d			15 40										16 10								
Camberley	a			15 44										16 14								
	d			15 48										16 18								
Bagshot	d			15 53										16 23								
Ascot 3	d	15 40		16a00								16 10		16a30								16 40
Sunningdale	d	15 43										16 13										16 43
Longcross	d																					
Weybridge	d								16 03										16 33			
Addlestone	d								16 07										16 37			
Chertsey	d					←			16 10							←			16 40			
Virginia Water	a	15 49				15 45			16 15			16 19				16 15			16 45			16 49
	d	15 49				15 54			16 24			16 19				16 24			16 54			16 49
Egham	d	15 53				15 57			↪			16 23				16 27			↪			16 53
Windsor & Eton Riverside	d						15 53										16 23					
Datchet	d						15 56										16 26					
Sunnymeads	d						15 59										16 29					
Wraysbury	d						16 02										16 32					
Staines	d	15 59				16 03	16 08					16 29				16 33	16 38					16 59
Ashford (Surrey)	d					16 06	16 11									16 36	16 41					
Feltham	d	16 05				16 11	16 16					16 35				16 41	16 46					17 05
Whitton	d						16 20			16 20	16 23						16 50			16 50	16 53	
Kingston	d				15 59										16 29							
Hampton Wick	d				16 01										16 31							
Teddington	d				16 05										16 35							
Fulwell	d																					
Strawberry Hill	d				16 08										16 38							
Twickenham	a	16 10			16 12		16 23				16 26	16 40			16 42		16 53				16 56	17 10
	d	16 11			16 13		16 23				16 28	16 41			16 43		16 53				16 58	17 11
St Margarets	d				16 15						16 30				16 45						17 00	
Richmond ⊖	d	16 15			16 19		16 28				16 34	16 45			16 49		16 58				17 04	17 15
North Sheen	d				16 21						16 36				16 51						17 06	
Mortlake	d				16 23						16 38				16 53						17 08	
Hounslow	d					16 16				16 31						16 46				17 01		
Isleworth	d					16 19				16 34						16 49				17 04		
Syon Lane	d					16 21				16 36						16 51				17 06		
Brentford	d					16 24				16 39						16 54				17 09		
Kew Bridge	d					16 26				16 41						16 56				17 11		
Chiswick	d					16 29				16 44						16 59				17 14		
Barnes Bridge	d		←			16 31				16 46			←			17 01				17 16		
Barnes	d		16 19		16 26	16 34		←		16 49	16 41		16 49		16 56	17 04		←		17 19	17 11	
Putney	d		16 22		16 29	16 37	16 34	16 37		↪	16 44		16 52		16 59	17 07	17 04	17 07		↪	17 14	
Wandsworth Town	d		16 25		16 32	↪		16 40			16 47		16 55		17 02	↪		17 10			17 17	
Clapham Junction 10	d	16 24	16 28		16 35		16 39	16 43			16 50	16 54	16 58		17 05		17 09	17 13			17 20	17 24
Queenstown Rd.(Battersea)	d		16 31		16 38			16 46			16 53		17 01		17 08			17 16			17 23	
Vauxhall ⊖	d		16 35		16 42		16 45	16 50			16 57		17 05		17 12		17 15	17 20			17 27	
London Waterloo 15 ⊖	a	16 34	16 41		16 46		16 49	16 56			17 02	17 04	17 11		17 16		17 19	17 26			17 32	17 34

A From London Waterloo
B From Weybridge to London Waterloo
C From Weybridge
D To London Waterloo
E From London Waterloo to Barnes continues to London Waterloo

The xx23 and xx53 services from Whitton originates at London Waterloo via Brentford

The xx20 and xx50 from Whitton originates at London Waterloo via Richmond

The xx29 and xx59 from Kingston originates at London Waterloo via Wimbledon

Table 149R

Saturdays

14 December to 17 May

Reading, Guildford, Ascot, Weybridge, Windsor, Kingston, Richmond and Hounslow - London

Network Diagram - see first Page of Table 148

		SW	SW	SW	SW	SW	SW	SW	SW	SW		SW	SW	SW	SW	SW	SW	SW	SW	SW		SW	SW	SW	SW
			1									1		1									1		1
		A		A	B		C	D	E	A			A		A	B		C	D	E		A		A	
Reading 7	d											16 42											17 12		
Earley	d											16 47											17 17		
Winnersh Triangle	d											16 49											17 19		
Winnersh	d											16 51											17 21		
Wokingham	d											16 56											17 26		
Bracknell	d											17 02											17 32		
Martins Heron	d											17 05											17 35		
Guildford	d		16 00											16 30											17 00
Wanborough	d		16 06											16 36											17 06
Ash 5	d		16 10											16 40											17 10
Aldershot	a		16 17											16 47											17 17
	d		16 30											17 00											17 30
Ash Vale	d		16 34											17 04											17 34
Frimley	d		16 40											17 10											17 40
Camberley	a		16 44											17 14											17 44
	d		16 48											17 18											17 48
Bagshot	d		16 53											17 23											17 53
Ascot 3	d		17a00									17 10		17a30									17 40		18a00
Sunningdale	d											17 13											17 43		
Longcross	d																								
Weybridge	d							17 03											17 33						
Addlestone	d							17 07											17 37						
Chertsey	d				←			17 10								←			17 40						
Virginia Water	a				16 45			17 15				17 19				17 15			17 45				17 49		
	d				16 54			17 24				17 19				17 24			17 54				17 49		
Egham	d				16 57			→				17 23				17 27			→				17 53		
Windsor & Eton Riverside	d					16 53											17 23								
Datchet	d					16 56											17 26								
Sunnymeads	d					16 59											17 29								
Wraysbury	d					17 02											17 32								
Staines	d				17 03	17 08						17 29				17 33	17 38						17 59		
Ashford (Surrey)	d				17 06	17 11										17 36	17 41								
Feltham	d				17 11	17 16						17 35				17 41	17 46						18 05		
Whitton	d					17 20			17 20	17 23							17 50			17 50		17 53			
Kingston	d			16 59											17 29										
Hampton Wick	d			17 01											17 31										
Teddington	d			17 05											17 35										
Fulwell	d																								
Strawberry Hill	d			17 08											17 38										
Twickenham	a			17 12		17 23				17 26		17 40			17 42		17 53					17 56	18 10		
	d			17 13		17 23				17 28		17 41			17 43		17 53					17 58	18 11		
St Margarets	d			17 15						17 30					17 45							18 00			
Richmond ⊖	d			17 19		17 28				17 34		17 45			17 49		17 58					18 04	18 15		
North Sheen	d			17 21						17 36					17 51							18 06			
Mortlake	d			17 23						17 38					17 53							18 08			
Hounslow	d				17 16				17 31							17 46				18 01					
Isleworth	d				17 19				17 34							17 49				18 04					
Syon Lane	d				17 21				17 36							17 51				18 06					
Brentford	d				17 24				17 39							17 54				18 09					
Kew Bridge	d				17 26				17 41							17 56				18 11					
Chiswick	d				17 29				17 44							17 59				18 14					
Barnes Bridge	d	←			17 31				17 46				←			18 01				18 16				←	
Barnes	d	17 19		17 26	17 34		←		17 49	17 41			17 49		17 56	18 04		←		18 19		18 11		18 19	
Putney	d	17 22		17 29	17 37	17 34	17 37		→	17 44			17 52		17 59	18 07	18 04	18 07		→		18 14		18 22	
Wandsworth Town	d	17 25		17 32	→		17 40			17 47			17 55		18 02	→		18 10				18 17		18 25	
Clapham Junction 10	d	17 28		17 35		17 39	17 43			17 50		17 54	17 58		18 05		18 09	18 13				18 20	18 24	18 28	
Queenstown Rd.(Battersea)	d	17 31		17 38			17 46			17 53			18 01		18 08			18 16				18 23		18 31	
Vauxhall ⊖	d	17 35		17 42		17 45	17 50			17 57			18 05		18 12		18 15	18 20				18 27		18 35	
London Waterloo 15 ⊖	a	17 41		17 46		17 49	17 56			18 02		18 04	18 11		18 16		18 19	18 26				18 32	18 34	18 41	

A From London Waterloo
B From Weybridge to London Waterloo
C From Weybridge
D To London Waterloo
E From London Waterloo to Barnes continues to London Waterloo

The xx23 and xx53 services from Whitton originates at London Waterloo via Brentford

The xx20 and xx50 from Whitton originates at London Waterloo via Richmond

The xx29 and xx59 from Kingston originates at London Waterloo via Wimbledon

Table 149R

Saturdays

14 December to 17 May

Reading, Guildford, Ascot, Weybridge, Windsor, Kingston, Richmond and Hounslow - London

Network Diagram - see first Page of Table 148

		SW A	SW B	SW	SW C	SW D	SW E	SW A	SW 1	SW A	SW 1	SW A	SW B	SW	SW C	SW D	SW E	SW A	SW 1	SW A	SW 1	SW A	SW B
Reading 7	d								17 42										18 12				
Earley	d								17 47										18 17				
Winnersh Triangle	d								17 49										18 19				
Winnersh	d								17 51										18 21				
Wokingham	d								17 56										18 26				
Bracknell	d								18 02										18 32				
Martins Heron	d								18 05										18 35				
Guildford	d										17 30										18 00		
Wanborough	d										17 36										18 06		
Ash 5	d										17 40										18 10		
Aldershot	a										17 47										18 17		
	d										18 00										18 30		
Ash Vale	d										18 04										18 34		
Frimley	d										18 10										18 40		
Camberley	a										18 14										18 44		
	d										18 18										18 48		
Bagshot	d										18 23										18 53		
Ascot 3	d								18 10		18a30								18 40		19a00		
Sunningdale	d								18 13										18 43				
Longcross	d																						
Weybridge	d					18 03										18 33							
Addlestone	d					18 07										18 37							
Chertsey	d		←			18 10							←			18 40							←
Virginia Water	a		17 45			18 15			18 19				18 15			18 45			18 49				18 45
	d		17 54			18 24			18 19				18 24			18 54			18 49				18 54
Egham	d		17 57			→			18 23				18 27			→			18 53				18 57
Windsor & Eton Riverside	d			17 53										18 23									
Datchet	d			17 56										18 26									
Sunnymeads	d			17 59										18 29									
Wraysbury	d			18 02										18 32									
Staines	d		18 03	18 08					18 29				18 33	18 38					18 59				19 03
Ashford (Surrey)	d		18 06	18 11									18 36	18 41									19 06
Feltham	d		18 11	18 16					18 35				18 41	18 46					19 05				19 11
Whitton	d			18 20			18 20	18 23						18 50			18 50	18 53					
Kingston	d	17 59										18 29										18 59	
Hampton Wick	d	18 01										18 31										19 01	
Teddington	d	18 05										18 35										19 05	
Fulwell	d																						
Strawberry Hill	d	18 08										18 38										19 08	
Twickenham	a	18 12		18 23				18 26	18 40			18 42		18 53				18 56	19 10			19 12	
	d	18 13		18 23				18 28	18 41			18 43		18 53				18 58	19 11			19 13	
St Margarets	d	18 15						18 30				18 45						19 00				19 15	
Richmond ⊖	d	18 19		18 28				18 34	18 45			18 49		18 58				19 04	19 15			19 19	
North Sheen	d	18 21						18 36				18 51						19 06				19 21	
Mortlake	d	18 23						18 38				18 53						19 08				19 23	
Hounslow	d		18 16				18 31						18 46				19 01						19 16
Isleworth	d		18 19				18 34						18 49				19 04						19 19
Syon Lane	d		18 21				18 36						18 51				19 06						19 21
Brentford	d		18 24				18 39						18 54				19 09						19 24
Kew Bridge	d		18 26				18 41						18 56				19 11						19 26
Chiswick	d		18 29				18 44						18 59				19 14						19 29
Barnes Bridge	d		18 31				18 46			←			19 01				19 16			←			19 31
Barnes	d	18 26	18 34		←		18 49	18 41		18 49		18 56	19 04		←		19 19	19 11		19 19		19 26	19 34
Putney	d	18 29	18 37	18 34	18 37		→	18 44		18 52		18 59	19 07	19 04	19 07		→	19 14		19 22		19 29	19 37
Wandsworth Town	d	18 32	→		18 40			18 47		18 55		19 02	→		19 10			19 17		19 25		19 32	→
Clapham Junction 10	d	18 35		18 39	18 43			18 50	18 54	18 58		19 05		19 09	19 13			19 20	19 24	19 28		19 35	
Queenstown Rd.(Battersea)	d	18 38			18 46			18 53		19 01		19 08			19 16			19 23		19 31		19 38	
Vauxhall ⊖	d	18 42		18 45	18 50			18 57		19 05		19 12		19 15	19 20			19 27		19 35		19 42	
London Waterloo 15 ⊖	a	18 46		18 49	18 56			19 02	19 04	19 11		19 16		19 19	19 26			19 32	19 34	19 41		19 46	

A From London Waterloo
B From Weybridge to London Waterloo
C From Weybridge
D To London Waterloo
E From London Waterloo to Barnes continues to London Waterloo

The xx23 and xx53 services from Whitton originates at London Waterloo via Brentford

The xx20 and xx50 from Whitton originates at London Waterloo via Richmond

The xx29 and xx59 from Kingston originates at London Waterloo via Wimbledon

Table 149R

Saturdays

14 December to 17 May

Reading, Guildford, Ascot, Weybridge, Windsor, Kingston, Richmond and Hounslow - London

Network Diagram - see first Page of Table 148

		SW		SW	SW	SW	SW	SW	SW	SW	SW	SW		SW	SW	SW	SW	SW	SW	SW	SW	SW		SW	SW
								1		1									1		1				
				A	B	C	D		D		D	E			A	B	C	D		D		D		E	
Reading 7	d							18 42											19 12						
Earley	d							18 47											19 17						
Winnersh Triangle	d							18 49											19 19						
Winnersh	d							18 51											19 21						
Wokingham	d							18 56											19 26						
Bracknell	d							19 02											19 32						
Martins Heron	d							19 05											19 35						
Guildford	d									18 30											19 00				
Wanborough	d									18 36											19 06				
Ash 5	d									18 40											19 10				
Aldershot	a									18 47											19 17				
	d									19 00											19 30				
Ash Vale	d									19 04											19 34				
Frimley	d									19 10											19 40				
Camberley	a									19 14											19 44				
	d									19 18											19 48				
Bagshot	d									19 23											19 53				
Ascot 3	d							19 10		19a30									19 40		20a00				
Sunningdale	d							19 13											19 43						
Longcross	d																								
Weybridge	d				19 03											19 33									
Addlestone	d				19 07											19 37									
Chertsey	d				19 10							←				19 40								←	
Virginia Water	a				19 15			19 19				19 15				19 45			19 49					19 45	
	d				19 24			19 19				19 24				19 54			19 49					19 54	
Egham	d				→			19 23				19 27				→			19 53					19 57	
Windsor & Eton Riverside	d	18 53												19 23											19 53
Datchet	d	18 56												19 26											19 56
Sunnymeads	d	18 59												19 29											19 59
Wraysbury	d	19 02												19 32											20 02
Staines	d	19 08						19 29				19 33		19 38					19 59					20 03	20 08
Ashford (Surrey)	d	19 11										19 36		19 41										20 06	20 11
Feltham	d	19 16						19 35				19 41		19 46					20 05					20 11	20 16
Whitton	d	19 20				19 20	19 23							19 50			19 50	19 53							20 20
Kingston	d										19 29											19 59			
Hampton Wick	d										19 31											20 01			
Teddington	d										19 35											20 05			
Fulwell	d																								
Strawberry Hill	d										19 38											20 08			
Twickenham	a	19 23					19 26	19 40			19 42			19 53				19 56	20 10			20 12			20 23
	d	19 23					19 28	19 41			19 43			19 53				19 58	20 11			20 13			20 23
St Margarets	d						19 30				19 45							20 00				20 15			
Richmond ⊖	d	19 28					19 34	19 45			19 49			19 58				20 04	20 15			20 19			20 28
North Sheen	d						19 36				19 51							20 06				20 21			
Mortlake	d						19 38				19 53							20 08				20 23			
Hounslow	d					19 31						19 46					20 01							20 16	
Isleworth	d					19 34						19 49					20 04							20 19	
Syon Lane	d					19 36						19 51					20 06							20 21	
Brentford	d					19 39						19 54					20 09							20 24	
Kew Bridge	d					19 41						19 56					20 11							20 26	
Chiswick	d					19 44						19 59					20 14							20 29	
Barnes Bridge	d					19 46			←			20 01					20 16			←				20 31	
Barnes	d			←		19 49	19 41		19 49		19 56	20 04			←		20 19	20 11		20 19		20 26		20 34	
Putney	d	19 34		19 37		→	19 44		19 52		19 59	20 07		20 04	20 07		→	20 14		20 22		20 29		20 37	20 34
Wandsworth Town	d			19 40			19 47		19 55		20 02	→			20 10			20 17		20 25		20 32		→	
Clapham Junction 10	d	19 39		19 43			19 50	19 54	19 58		20 05			20 09	20 13			20 20	20 24	20 28		20 35			20 39
Queenstown Rd.(Battersea)	d			19 46			19 53		20 01		20 08				20 16			20 23		20 31		20 38			
Vauxhall ⊖	d	19 45		19 50			19 57		20 05		20 12			20 15	20 20			20 27		20 35		20 42			20 45
London Waterloo 15 ⊖	a	19 49		19 56			20 02	20 04	20 11		20 16			20 19	20 26			20 32	20 34	20 41		20 46			20 49

A From Weybridge
B To London Waterloo
C From London Waterloo to Barnes continues to London Waterloo
D From London Waterloo
E From Weybridge to London Waterloo

The xx23 and xx53 services from Whitton originates at London Waterloo via Brentford

The xx20 and xx50 from Whitton originates at London Waterloo via Richmond

The xx29 and xx59 from Kingston originates at London Waterloo via Wimbledon

Table 149R

Saturdays

14 December to 17 May

Reading, Guildford, Ascot, Weybridge, Windsor, Kingston, Richmond and Hounslow - London

Network Diagram - see first Page of Table 148

		SW	SW	SW	SW	SW	SW	SW	SW	SW	SW	SW	SW	SW	SW	SW	SW	SW	SW	SW	SW	SW	SW
						1		1								1		1	1				
		A	B	C	D		D		D	E		A	B	C	D		D			D	E		A
Reading 7	d					19 42										20 12							
Earley	d					19 47										20 17							
Winnersh Triangle	d					19 49										20 19							
Winnersh	d					19 51										20 21							
Wokingham	d					19 56										20 26							
Bracknell	d					20 02										20 32							
Martins Heron	d					20 05										20 35							
Guildford	d							19 30										20 00	20 30				
Wanborough	d							19 36										20 06	20 36				
Ash 5	d							19 40										20 10	20 40				
Aldershot	a							19 47										20 17	20 47				
	d							20 00										20 30					
Ash Vale	d							20 04										20 34					
Frimley	d							20 10										20 40					
Camberley	a							20 14										20 44					
	d							20 18										20 48					
Bagshot	d							20 23										20 53					
Ascot 3	d					20 10		20a30								20 40		21a00					
Sunningdale	d					20 13										20 43							
Longcross	d																						
Weybridge	d		20 03										20 33										
Addlestone	d		20 07										20 37										
Chertsey	d		20 10							←			20 40								←		
Virginia Water	a		20 15			20 19				20 15			20 45			20 49					20 45		
	d		20 24			20 19				20 24			20 54			20 49					20 54		
Egham	d		↪			20 23				20 27			↪			20 53					20 57		
Windsor & Eton Riverside	d										20 23											20 53	
Datchet	d										20 26											20 56	
Sunnymeads	d										20 29											20 59	
Wraysbury	d										20 32											21 02	
Staines	d					20 29				20 33	20 38					20 59					21 03	21 08	
Ashford (Surrey)	d									20 36	20 41										21 06	21 11	
Feltham	d					20 35				20 41	20 46					21 05					21 11	21 16	
Whitton	d			20 20	20 23						20 50			20 50	20 53							21 20	
Kingston	d								20 29											20 59			
Hampton Wick	d								20 31											21 01			
Teddington	d								20 35											21 05			
Fulwell	d																						
Strawberry Hill	d								20 38											21 08			
Twickenham	a				20 26	20 40			20 42		20 53				20 56	21 10				21 12		21 23	
	d				20 28	20 41			20 43		20 53				20 58	21 11				21 13		21 23	
St Margarets	d				20 30				20 45						21 00					21 15			
Richmond ⊖	d				20 34	20 45			20 49		20 58				21 04	21 15				21 19		21 28	
North Sheen	d				20 36				20 51						21 06					21 21			
Mortlake	d				20 38				20 53						21 08					21 23			
Hounslow	d			20 31						20 46				21 01							21 16		
Isleworth	d			20 34						20 49				21 04							21 19		
Syon Lane	d			20 36						20 51				21 06							21 21		
Brentford	d			20 39						20 54				21 09							21 24		
Kew Bridge	d			20 41						20 56				21 11							21 26		
Chiswick	d			20 44						20 59				21 14							21 29		
Barnes Bridge	d			20 46			←			21 01				21 16			←				21 31		
Barnes	d	←		20 49	20 41		20 49		20 56	21 04		←		21 19	21 11		21 19			21 26	21 34		←
Putney	d	20 37		↪	20 44		20 52		20 59	21 07	21 04	21 07		↪	21 14		21 22			21 29	21 37	21 34	21 37
Wandsworth Town	d	20 40			20 47		20 55		21 02	↪		21 10			21 17		21 25			21 32	↪		21 40
Clapham Junction 10	d	20 43			20 50	20 54	20 58		21 05		21 09	21 13			21 20	21 24	21 28			21 35		21 39	21 43
Queenstown Rd.(Battersea)	d	20 46			20 53		21 01		21 08			21 16			21 23		21 31			21 38			21 46
Vauxhall ⊖	d	20 50			20 57		21 05		21 12		21 15	21 20			21 27		21 35			21 42		21 45	21 50
London Waterloo 15 ⊖	a	20 56			21 02	21 04	21 11		21 16		21 19	21 26			21 32	21 34	21 41			21 46		21 49	21 56

A From Weybridge
B To London Waterloo
C From London Waterloo to Barnes continues to London Waterloo
D From London Waterloo
E From Weybridge to London Waterloo

The xx23 and xx53 services from Whitton originates at London Waterloo via Brentford

The xx20 and xx50 from Whitton originates at London Waterloo via Richmond

The xx29 and xx59 from Kingston originates at London Waterloo via Wimbledon

Table 149R

Saturdays

14 December to 17 May

Reading, Guildford, Ascot, Weybridge, Windsor, Kingston, Richmond and Hounslow - London

Network Diagram - see first Page of Table 148

		SW	SW	SW	SW ■1	SW	SW	SW	SW	SW	SW	SW	SW	SW ■1	SW	SW ■1	SW ■1	SW	SW	SW	SW	SW
		A	B	C		C	C	D		E	A	B	C		C			C	D		E	C
Reading ■7	d				20 42									21 12								
Earley	d				20 47									21 17								
Winnersh Triangle	d				20 49									21 19								
Winnersh	d				20 51									21 21								
Wokingham	d				20 56									21 26								
Bracknell	d				21 02									21 32								
Martins Heron	d				21 05									21 35								
Guildford	d															21 00	21 30					
Wanborough	d															21 06	21 36					
Ash ■5	d															21 10	21 40					
Aldershot	a															21 17	21 47					
	d															21 30						
Ash Vale	d															21 34						
Frimley	d															21 40						
Camberley	a															21 44						
	d															21 48						
Bagshot	d															21 53						
Ascot ■3	d				21 10									21 40		22a00						
Sunningdale	d				21 13									21 43								
Longcross	d																					
Weybridge	d	21 03									21 33											
Addlestone	d	21 07									21 37											
Chertsey	d	21 10						←			21 40								←			
Virginia Water	a	21 15			21 19			21 15			21 45			21 49					21 45			
	d	21 24			21 19			21 24			21 54			21 49					21 54			
Egham	d	→			21 23			21 27			→			21 53					21 57			
Windsor & Eton Riverside	d								21 23											21 53		
Datchet	d								21 26											21 56		
Sunnymeads	d								21 29											21 59		
Wraysbury	d								21 32											22 02		
Staines	d				21 29			21 33	21 38					21 59					22 03	22 08		
Ashford (Surrey)	d							21 36	21 41										22 06	22 11		
Feltham	d				21 35			21 41	21 46					22 05					22 11	22 16		
Whitton	d		21 20	21 23					21 50			21 50	21 53							22 20		22 23
Kingston	d						21 29											21 59				
Hampton Wick	d						21 31											22 01				
Teddington	d						21 35											22 05				
Fulwell	d																					
Strawberry Hill	d						21 38											22 08				
Twickenham	a			21 26	21 40		21 42		21 53				21 56	22 10				22 12		22 23		22 26
	d			21 28	21 41		21 43		21 53				21 58	22 11				22 13		22 23		22 28
St Margarets	d			21 30			21 45						22 00					22 15				22 30
Richmond ⊖	d			21 34	21 45		21 49		21 58				22 04	22 15				22 19		22 28		22 34
North Sheen	d			21 36			21 51						22 06					22 21				22 36
Mortlake	d			21 38			21 53						22 08					22 23				22 38
Hounslow	d		21 31					21 46				22 01							22 16			
Isleworth	d		21 34					21 49				22 04							22 19			
Syon Lane	d		21 36					21 51				22 06							22 21			
Brentford	d		21 39					21 54				22 09							22 24			
Kew Bridge	d		21 41					21 56				22 11							22 26			
Chiswick	d		21 44					21 59				22 14							22 29			
Barnes Bridge	d		21 46			←		22 01				22 16			←				22 31			
Barnes	d		21 49	21 41		21 49	21 56	22 04		←		22 19	22 11		22 19			22 26	22 34		←	22 41
Putney	d		→	21 44		21 52	21 59	22 07	22 04	22 07		→	22 14		22 22			22 29	22 37	22 34	22 37	22 44
Wandsworth Town	d			21 47		21 55	22 02	→		22 10			22 17		22 25			22 32	→		22 40	22 47
Clapham Junction ■10	d			21 50	21 54	21 58	22 05		22 09	22 13			22 20	22 24	22 28			22 35		22 39	22 43	22 50
Queenstown Rd.(Battersea)	d			21 53		22 01	22 08			22 16			22 23		22 31			22 38			22 46	22 53
Vauxhall ⊖	d			21 57		22 05	22 12		22 15	22 20			22 27		22 35			22 42		22 45	22 50	22 57
London Waterloo ■15 ⊖	a			22 02	22 04	22 11	22 16		22 19	22 26			22 32	22 34	22 41			22 46		22 49	22 56	23 02

A To London Waterloo
B From London Waterloo to Barnes continues to London Waterloo
C From London Waterloo
D From Weybridge to London Waterloo
E From Weybridge

The xx23 and xx53 services from Whitton originates at London Waterloo via Brentford

The xx20 and xx50 from Whitton originates at London Waterloo via Richmond

The xx29 and xx59 from Kingston originates at London Waterloo via Wimbledon

Table 149R

Saturdays

14 December to 17 May

Reading, Guildford, Ascot, Weybridge, Windsor, Kingston, Richmond and Hounslow - London

Network Diagram - see first Page of Table 148

		SW	SW	SW	SW	SW	SW	SW	SW	SW		SW	SW	SW	SW	SW	SW	SW	SW	SW		SW	SW	SW	SW
			1						1	1		1						1							1
		A		B	C		D	A					B	C		D	E		D			B	B	E	
Reading 7	d		21 42						22 12									22 42							23 12
Earley	d		21 47						22 17									22 47							23 17
Winnersh Triangle	d		21 49						22 19									22 49							23 19
Winnersh	d		21 51						22 21									22 51							23 21
Wokingham	d		21 56						22 26									22 56							23 26
Bracknell	d		22 02						22 32									23 02							23 32
Martins Heron	d		22 05						22 35									23 05							23 35
Guildford	d									22 00		22 30													
Wanborough	d									22 06		22 36													
Ash 5	d									22 10		22 40													
Aldershot	a									22 17		22 47													
	d									22 30															
Ash Vale	d									22 34															
Frimley	d									22 40															
Camberley	a									22 44															
	d									22 48															
Bagshot	d									22 53															
Ascot 3	d		22 10						22 40	23a00								23 10							23 40
Sunningdale	d		22 13						22 43									23 13							23 43
Longcross	d																								
Weybridge	d	22 03						22 33									23 03							23 33	
Addlestone	d	22 07						22 37									23 07							23 37	
Chertsey	d	22 10			←			22 40						←			23 10		←					23 40	
Virginia Water	a	22 15	22 19		22 15			22 45	22 49					22 45			23 15	23 19	23 15					23 45	23 49
	d	22 24	22 19		22 24			22 54	22 49					22 54			23 24	23 19	23 24					23 54	23 49
Egham	d	→	22 23		22 27			→	22 53					22 57			→	23 23	23 27					→	23 53
Windsor & Eton Riverside	d					22 23									22 53					23 28					
Datchet	d					22 26									22 56					23 31					
Sunnymeads	d					22 29									22 59					23 34					
Wraysbury	d					22 32									23 02					23 37					
Staines	d		22 29		22 33	22 38			22 59					23 03	23 08			23 29	23a32	23a42					23 59
Ashford (Surrey)	d				22 36	22 41								23 06	23 11										
Feltham	d		22 35		22 41	22 46			23 05					23 11	23 16			23 35							00 05
Whitton	d					22 50									23 20										
Kingston	d			22 29									22 59									23 29	23 55		
Hampton Wick	d			22 31									23 01									23 31	23 57		
Teddington	d			22 35									23 05									23 35	23 59		
Fulwell	d																								
Strawberry Hill	d			22 38									23 08									23 38	00 03		
Twickenham	a		22 40	22 42		22 53			23 10				23 12		23 23			23 40				23 42	00 06		00 10
	d		22 41	22 43		22 53			23 11				23 13		23 23			23 41				23 43			00 11
St Margarets	d			22 45									23 15									23 45			
Richmond ⊖	d		22 45	22 49		22 58			23 15				23 19		23 28			23 45				23 49			00 15
North Sheen	d			22 51									23 21									23 51			
Mortlake	d			22 53									23 23									23 53			
Hounslow	d				22 46									23 16											
Isleworth	d				22 49									23 19											
Syon Lane	d				22 51									23 21											
Brentford	d				22 54									23 24											
Kew Bridge	d				22 56									23 26											
Chiswick	d				22 59									23 29											
Barnes Bridge	d				23 01									23 31											
Barnes	d			22 56	23 04		←						23 26	23 34		←						23 56			
Putney	d			22 59	23 07	23 04	23 07						23 29	23 37	23 34	23 37						23 59			
Wandsworth Town	d			23 02	→		23 10						23 32	→		23 40						00 02			
Clapham Junction 10	d		22 54	23 05		23 09	23 13		23 24				23 35		23 39	23 43		23 54				00 05			00 25
Queenstown Rd.(Battersea)	d			23 08			23 16						23 38			23 46						00 08			
Vauxhall ⊖	d			23 12		23 15	23 20						23 42		23 45	23 50						00 12			
London Waterloo 15 ⊖	a		23 04	23 17		23 19	23 26		23 34				23 46		23 49	23 56		00 02				00 16			00 37

A To London Waterloo
B From London Waterloo
C From Weybridge to London Waterloo
D From Weybridge
E To Staines

The xx23 and xx53 services from Whitton originates at London Waterloo via Brentford

The xx20 and xx50 from Whitton originates at London Waterloo via Richmond

The xx29 and xx59 from Kingston originates at London Waterloo via Wimbledon

Table 149R

Saturdays

14 December to 17 May

Reading, Guildford, Ascot, Weybridge, Windsor, Kingston, Richmond and Hounslow - London

Network Diagram - see first Page of Table 148

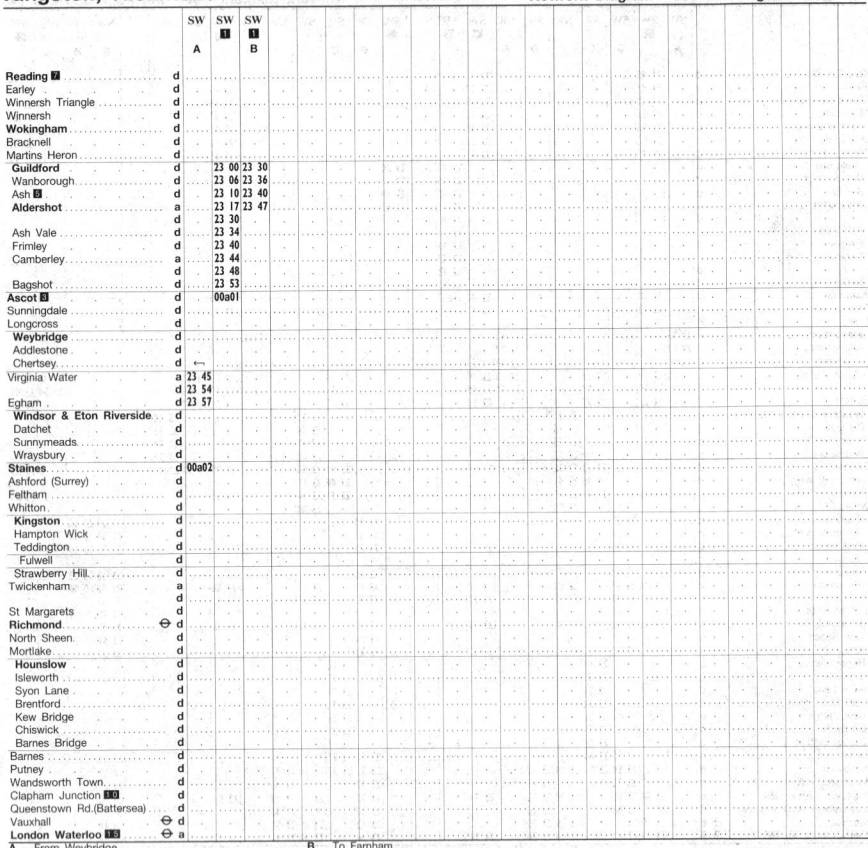

		SW	SW 1	SW 1
		A		B
Reading 7	d			
Earley	d			
Winnersh Triangle	d			
Winnersh	d			
Wokingham	d			
Bracknell	d			
Martins Heron	d			
Guildford	d		23 00	23 30
Wanborough	d		23 06	23 36
Ash 5	d		23 10	23 40
Aldershot	a		23 17	23 47
	d		23 30	
Ash Vale	d		23 34	
Frimley	d		23 40	
Camberley	a		23 44	
	d		23 48	
Bagshot	d		23 53	
Ascot 3	d		00a01	
Sunningdale	d			
Longcross	d			
Weybridge	d			
Addlestone	d			
Chertsey	d	←		
Virginia Water	a	23 45		
	d	23 54		
Egham	d	23 57		
Windsor & Eton Riverside	d			
Datchet	d			
Sunnymeads	d			
Wraysbury	d			
Staines	d	00a02		
Ashford (Surrey)	d			
Feltham	d			
Whitton	d			
Kingston	d			
Hampton Wick	d			
Teddington	d			
Fulwell	d			
Strawberry Hill	d			
Twickenham	a			
	d			
St Margarets	d			
Richmond ⊖	d			
North Sheen	d			
Mortlake	d			
Hounslow	d			
Isleworth	d			
Syon Lane	d			
Brentford	d			
Kew Bridge	d			
Chiswick	d			
Barnes Bridge	d			
Barnes	d			
Putney	d			
Wandsworth Town	d			
Clapham Junction 10	d			
Queenstown Rd.(Battersea)	d			
Vauxhall ⊖	d			
London Waterloo 15 ⊖	a			

A From Weybridge

B To Farnham

The xx23 and xx53 services from Whitton originates at London Waterloo via Brentford

The xx20 and xx50 from Whitton originates at London Waterloo via Richmond

The xx29 and xx59 from Kingston originates at London Waterloo via Wimbledon

Table 149R

Sundays

8 December to 11 May

Reading, Guildford, Ascot, Weybridge, Windsor, Kingston, Richmond and Hounslow - London

Network Diagram - see first Page of Table 148

		SW A	SW A	SW ■1 B	SW C	SW C	SW C	SW	SW	SW ■1	SW C	SW	SW D	SW ■1	SW C	SW ■1	SW ■1	SW	SW D	SW ■1	SW C	SW ■1	SW ■1
Reading ■7	d													07 54		08 24				08 54		09 24	
Earley	d													07 59		08 29				08 59		09 29	
Winnersh Triangle	d													08 01		08 31				09 01		09 31	
Winnersh	d													08 03		08 33				09 03		09 33	
Wokingham	d													08 08		08 38				09 08		09 38	
Bracknell	d													08 14		08 44				09 14		09 44	
Martins Heron	d													08 17		08 47				09 17		09 47	
Guildford	d									07 17							08 17						09 17
Wanborough	d									07 23							08 23						09 23
Ash ■5	d									07 27							08 27						09 27
Aldershot	a									07 34							08 34						09 34
	d									07 40							08 40						09 40
Ash Vale	d									07 45							08 45						09 45
Frimley	d									07 51							08 51						09 51
Camberley	a									07 55							08 55						09 55
	d									07 55							08 55						09 55
Bagshot	d									08 01							09 01						10 01
Ascot ■3	d									08a07				08 22		08 52	09a07			09 22		09 52	10a07
Sunningdale	d													08 25		08 55				09 25		09 55	
Longcross	d																						
Weybridge	d								07 00														
Addlestone	d								07 04				08 04						09 04				
Chertsey	d								07 07				08 07						09 07				
Virginia Water	a								07 12				08 12	08 30		09 00			09 12	09 30		10 00	
	d								07 12				08 12	08 30		09 00			09 12	09 30		10 00	
Egham	d								07 16				08 16	08 34		09 04			09 16	09 34		10 04	
Windsor & Eton Riverside	d							07 01				08 01						09 01					
Datchet	d							07 04				08 04						09 04					
Sunnymeads	d							07 07				08 07						09 07					
Wraysbury	d							07 10				08 10						09 10					
Staines	d							07 16	07 21			08 16	08 21	08 39		09 09		09 16	09 21	09 39		10 09	
Ashford (Surrey)	d							07 19	07 24			08 19	08 24					09 19	09 24				
Feltham	d			00 05				07 24	07 29			08 24	08 29	08 46		09 16		09 24	09 29	09 46		10 16	
Whitton	d							07 28				08 28						09 28					
Kingston	d				01 17	02 11	06 49				07 49				08 49						09 49		
Hampton Wick	d				01s22	02s13	06 51				07 51				08 51						09 51		
Teddington	d				01s25	02s15	06 56				07 56				08 56						09 56		
Fulwell	d																						
Strawberry Hill	d		00 03		01a28	02s18	06 59				07 59				08 59						09 59		
Twickenham	a		00 06	00 10		02 22	07 02	07 31			08 02	08 31		08 51	09 02	09 21		09 31		09 51	10 02	10 21	
	d			00 11			07 03	07 32			08 03	08 32		08 51	09 03	09 21		09 32		09 51	10 03	10 21	
St Margarets	d						07 05	07 34			08 05	08 34			09 05			09 34			10 05		
Richmond ⊖	d			00 15			07 09	07 37			08 09	08 37		08 56	09 09	09 26		09 37		09 56	10 09	10 26	
North Sheen	d						07 11	07 39			08 11	08 39			09 11			09 39			10 11		
Mortlake	d						07 13	07 42			08 13	08 42			09 13			09 42			10 13		
Hounslow	d								07 35				08 35						09 35				
Isleworth	d								07 38				08 38						09 38				
Syon Lane	d								07 40				08 40						09 40				
Brentford	d								07 42				08 42						09 42				
Kew Bridge	d								07 45				08 45						09 45				
Chiswick	d								07 47				08 47						09 47				
Barnes Bridge	d								07 50				08 50						09 50				
Barnes	d						07 16	07 45	07 53		08 16	08 45	08 53		09 16			09 45	09 53		10 16		
Putney	d						07 19	07 48	07 56		08 19	08 48	08 56	09 02	09 19	09 32		09 48	09 56	10 02	10 19	10 32	
Wandsworth Town	d	00 02					07 22	07 51	07 59		08 22	08 51	08 59		09 22			09 51	09 59		10 22		
Clapham Junction ■10	d	00 05		00 25			07 25	07 54	08 02		08 25	08 54	09 02	09 07	09 25	09 37		09 54	10 02	10 07	10 25	10 37	
Queenstown Rd.(Battersea)	d	00 08					07 28	07 57	08 05		08 28	08 57	09 05		09 28			09 57	10 05		10 28		
Vauxhall ⊖	d	00 12					07 32	08 00	08 08		08 32	09 00	09 08	09 12	09 32	09 42		10 00	10 08	10 12	10 32	10 42	
London Waterloo ■15 ⊖	a	00 16		00 37			07 41	08 06	08 13		08 41	09 06	09 13	09 23	09 41	09 53		10 05	10 13	10 23	10 41	10 53	

A From London Waterloo
B From Reading
C From London Waterloo
D From Woking

The xx49 Kingston to London Waterloo services originate at London Waterloo via Wimbledon

Table 149R

Sundays

8 December to 11 May

Reading, Guildford, Ascot, Weybridge, Windsor, Kingston, Richmond and Hounslow - London

Network Diagram - see first Page of Table 148

		SW	SW	SW	SW	SW		SW	SW	SW	SW	SW	SW	SW	SW	SW		SW	SW	SW	SW	SW	SW	SW	SW
				1				1	1			1			1	1				1			1	1	
			A			B					A			B					A			B			
Reading 7	d			09 54				10 24				10 54			11 24					11 54			12 24		
Earley	d			09 59				10 29				10 59			11 29					11 59			12 29		
Winnersh Triangle	d			10 01				10 31				11 01			11 31					12 01			12 31		
Winnersh	d			10 03				10 33				11 03			11 33					12 03			12 33		
Wokingham	d			10 08				10 38				11 08			11 38					12 08			12 38		
Bracknell	d			10 14				10 44				11 14			11 44					12 14			12 44		
Martins Heron	d			10 17				10 47				11 17			11 47					12 17			12 47		
Guildford	d								10 17							11 17								12 17	
Wanborough	d								10 23							11 23								12 23	
Ash 5	d								10 27							11 27								12 27	
Aldershot	a								10 34							11 34								12 34	
	d								10 40							11 40								12 40	
Ash Vale	d								10 45							11 45								12 45	
Frimley	d								10 51							11 51								12 51	
Camberley	a								10 55							11 55								12 55	
	d								10 55							11 55								12 55	
Bagshot	d								11 01							12 01								13 01	
Ascot 3	d			10 22				10 52	11a07			11 22			11 52	12a07				12 22			12 52	13a07	
Sunningdale	d			10 25				10 55				11 25			11 55					12 25			12 55		
Longcross	d																								
Weybridge	d																								
Addlestone	d		10 04								11 04								12 04						
Chertsey	d		10 07								11 07								12 07						
Virginia Water	a		10 12	10 30				11 00			11 12	11 30			12 00				12 12	12 30			13 00		
	d		10 12	10 30				11 00			11 12	11 30			12 00				12 12	12 30			13 00		
Egham	d		10 16	10 34				11 04			11 16	11 34			12 04				12 16	12 34			13 04		
Windsor & Eton Riverside	d	10 01			10 34					11 01			11 34					12 01			12 34				
Datchet	d	10 04			10 37					11 04			11 37					12 04			12 37				
Sunnymeads	d	10 07								11 07								12 07							
Wraysbury	d	10 10								11 10								12 10							
Staines	d	10 16	10 21	10 39	10 45			11 09		11 16	11 21	11 39	11 45		12 09			12 16	12 21	12 39	12 45		13 09		
Ashford (Surrey)	d	10 19	10 24		10 48					11 19	11 24		11 48					12 19	12 24		12 48				
Feltham	d	10 24	10 29	10 46	10 53			11 16		11 24	11 29	11 46	11 53		12 16			12 24	12 29	12 46	12 53		13 16		
Whitton	d	10 28			10 57					11 28			11 57					12 28			12 57				
Kingston	d					10 49								11 49								12 49			13 11
Hampton Wick	d					10 51								11 51								12 51			13 13
Teddington	d					10 56								11 56								12 56			13 16
Fulwell	d																								
Strawberry Hill	d					10 59								11 59								12 59			13 19
Twickenham	a	10 31		10 51	11 00	11 02		11 21		11 31		11 51	12 00	12 02	12 21			12 31		12 51	13 00	13 02	13 21		13 22
	d	10 32		10 51	11 01	11 03		11 21		11 32		11 51	12 01	12 03	12 21			12 32		12 51	13 01	13 03	13 21		13 23
St Margarets	d	10 34				11 05				11 34				12 05				12 34				13 05			13 25
Richmond ⊖	d	10 37		10 56	11 05	11 09		11 26		11 37		11 56	12 05	12 09	12 26			12 37		12 56	13 05	13 09	13 26		13 29
North Sheen	d	10 39				11 11				11 39				12 11				12 39				13 11			13 31
Mortlake	d	10 42				11 13				11 42				12 13				12 42				13 13			13 33
Hounslow	d		10 35								11 35								12 35						
Isleworth	d		10 38								11 38								12 38						
Syon Lane	d		10 40								11 40								12 40						
Brentford	d		10 42								11 42								12 42						
Kew Bridge	d		10 45								11 45								12 45						
Chiswick	d		10 47								11 47								12 47						
Barnes Bridge	d		10 50								11 50								12 50						
Barnes	d	10 45	10 53			11 16				11 45	11 53			12 16				12 45	12 53			13 16			13 36
Putney	d	10 48	10 56	11 02	11 14	11 19		11 32		11 48	11 56	12 02	12 14	12 19	12 32			12 48	12 56	13 02	13 14	13 19	13 32		13 39
Wandsworth Town	d	10 51	10 59			11 22				11 51	11 59			12 22				12 51	12 59			13 22			13 42
Clapham Junction 10	d	10 53	11 02	11 07	11 18	11 25		11 37		11 53	12 02	12 07	12 18	12 25	12 37			12 53	13 02	13 07	13 18	13 25	13 37		13 45
Queenstown Rd.(Battersea)	d	10 57	11 05			11 28				11 57	12 05			12 28				12 57	13 05			13 28			13 48
Vauxhall ⊖	d	11 00	11 08	11 12	11 24	11 32		11 42		12 00	12 08	12 12	12 24	12 32	12 42			13 00	13 08	13 12	13 24	13 32	13 42		13 52
London Waterloo 15 ⊖	a	11 05	11 13	11 23	11 29	11 41		11 53		12 05	12 13	12 23	12 29	12 41	12 53			13 05	13 13	13 23	13 29	13 41	13 53		14 00

A From Woking

B From London Waterloo

The xx49 Kingston to London Waterloo services originate at London Waterloo via Wimbledon

Table 149R

Sundays

8 December to 11 May

Reading, Guildford, Ascot, Weybridge, Windsor, Kingston, Richmond and Hounslow - London

Network Diagram - see first Page of Table 148

Station		SW		SW A	SW 1	SW	SW B	SW 1	SW 1	SW	SW	SW A	SW 1	SW	SW B	SW 1		SW 1	SW	SW	SW A	SW 1	SW	SW B
Reading 7	d				12 54			13 24					13 54			14 24						19 54		
Earley	d				12 59			13 29					13 59			14 29						19 59		
Winnersh Triangle	d				13 01			13 31					14 01			14 31						20 01		
Winnersh	d				13 03			13 33					14 03			14 33						20 03		
Wokingham	d				13 08			13 38					14 08			14 38						20 08		
Bracknell	d				13 14			13 44					14 14			14 44						20 14		
Martins Heron	d				13 17			13 47					14 17			14 47						20 17		
Guildford	d								13 17									19 17						
Wanborough	d								13 23									19 23						
Ash 5	d								13 27									19 27						
Aldershot	a								13 34									19 34						
	d								13 40									19 40						
Ash Vale	d								13 45									19 45						
Frimley	d								13 51									19 51						
Camberley	a								13 55									19 55						
	d								13 55									19 55						
Bagshot	d								14 01									20 01						
Ascot 3	d				13 22			13 52	14a07				14 22			14 52		20a07				20 22		
Sunningdale	d				13 25			13 55					14 25			14 55						20 25		
Longcross	d																							
Weybridge	d																							
Addlestone	d			13 04								14 04									20 04			
Chertsey	d			13 07								14 07									20 07			
Virginia Water	a			13 12	13 30			14 00				14 12	14 30			15 00					20 12	20 30		
	d			13 12	13 30			14 00				14 12	14 30			15 00					20 12	20 30		
Egham	d			13 16	13 34			14 04				14 16	14 34			15 04	and at the same minutes past each hour until				20 16	20 34		
Windsor & Eton Riverside	d	13 01				13 34					14 01			14 34						20 01			20 34	
Datchet	d	13 04				13 37					14 04			14 37						20 04			20 37	
Sunnymeads	d	13 07									14 07									20 07				
Wraysbury	d	13 10									14 10									20 10				
Staines	d	13 16		13 21	13 39	13 45		14 09			14 16	14 21	14 39	14 45		15 09				20 16	20 21	20 39	20 45	
Ashford (Surrey)	d	13 19		13 24		13 48					14 19	14 24		14 48						20 19	20 24		20 48	
Feltham	d	13 24		13 29	13 46	13 53		14 16			14 24	14 29	14 46	14 53		15 16				20 24	20 29	20 46	20 53	
Whitton	d	13 28				13 57					14 28			14 57						20 28			20 57	
Kingston	d						13 49			14 11					14 49				20 11					20 49
Hampton Wick	d						13 51			14 13					14 51				20 13					20 51
Teddington	d						13 56			14 16					14 56				20 16					20 56
Fulwell	d																							
Strawberry Hill	d						13 59			14 19					14 59				20 19					20 59
Twickenham	a	13 31			13 51	14 00	14 02	14 21		14 22	14 31		14 51	15 00	15 02	15 21			20 22	20 31		20 51	21 00	21 02
	d	13 32			13 51	14 01	14 03	14 21		14 23	14 32		14 51	15 01	15 03	15 21			20 23	20 32		20 51	21 01	21 03
St Margarets	d	13 34					14 05			14 25	14 34				15 05				20 25	20 34				21 05
Richmond ⊖	d	13 37			13 56	14 05	14 09	14 26		14 29	14 37		14 56	15 05	15 09	15 26			20 29	20 37		20 56	21 05	21 09
North Sheen	d	13 39					14 11			14 31	14 39				15 11				20 31	20 39				21 11
Mortlake	d	13 42					14 13			14 33	14 42				15 13				20 33	20 42				21 13
Hounslow	d			13 35								14 35									20 35			
Isleworth	d			13 38								14 38									20 38			
Syon Lane	d			13 40								14 40									20 40			
Brentford	d			13 42								14 42									20 42			
Kew Bridge	d			13 45								14 45									20 45			
Chiswick	d			13 47								14 47									20 47			
Barnes Bridge	d			13 50								14 50									20 50			
Barnes	d	13 45		13 53			14 16			14 36	14 45	14 53			15 16				20 36	20 45	20 53			21 16
Putney	d	13 48		13 56	14 02	14 14	14 19	14 32		14 39	14 48	14 56	15 02	15 14	15 19	15 32			20 39	20 48	20 56	21 02	21 14	21 19
Wandsworth Town	d	13 51		13 59			14 22			14 42	14 51	14 59			15 22				20 42	20 51	20 59			21 22
Clapham Junction 10	d	13 54		14 02	14 07	14 18	14 25	14 37		14 45	14 54	15 02	15 07	15 18	15 25	15 37			20 45	20 54	21 02	21 07	21 18	21 25
Queenstown Rd.(Battersea)	d	13 57		14 05			14 28			14 48	14 57	15 05			15 28				20 48	20 57	21 05			21 28
Vauxhall ⊖	d	14 00		14 08	14 12	14 24	14 32	14 42		14 52	15 00	15 08	15 12	15 24	15 32	15 42			20 52	21 00	21 08	21 12	21 24	21 32
London Waterloo 15 ⊖	a	14 05		14 13	14 23	14 29	14 41	14 53		15 00	15 05	15 13	15 18	15 29	15 36	15 48			21 00	21 05	21 13	21 18	21 29	21 36

A From Woking

B From London Waterloo

The xx49 Kingston to London Waterloo services originate at London Waterloo via Wimbledon

Table 149R

Sundays

8 December to 11 May

Reading, Guildford, Ascot, Weybridge, Windsor, Kingston, Richmond and Hounslow - London

Network Diagram - see first Page of Table 148

		SW [1]	SW [1]	SW	SW	SW	SW [1]	SW	SW [1]	SW [1]	SW	SW	SW	SW [1]	SW	SW [1]	SW [1]	SW	SW	SW	SW [1]	SW [1]
						A		B					A		B					A		
Reading [7]	d	20 24					20 54		21 24					21 54		22 24					22 54	
Earley	d	20 29					20 59		21 29					21 59		22 29					22 59	
Winnersh Triangle	d	20 31					21 01		21 31					22 01		22 31					23 01	
Winnersh	d	20 33					21 03		21 33					22 03		22 33					23 03	
Wokingham	d	20 38					21 08		21 38					22 08		22 38					23 08	
Bracknell	d	20 44					21 14		21 44					22 14		22 44					23 14	
Martins Heron	d	20 47					21 17		21 47					22 17		22 47					23 17	
Guildford	d		20 17							21 17							22 17					23 17
Wanborough	d		20 23							21 23							22 23					23 23
Ash [5]	d		20 27							21 27							22 27					23 27
Aldershot	a		20 34							21 34							22 34					23 34
	d		20 40							21 40							22 40					
Ash Vale	d		20 45							21 45							22 45					
Frimley	d		20 51							21 51							22 51					
Camberley	a		20 55							21 55							22 55					
	d		20 55							21 55							22 55					
Bagshot	d		21 01							22 01							23 01					
Ascot [3]	d	20 52	21a07				21 22		21 52	22a07				22 22		22 52	23a07				23 22	
Sunningdale	d	20 55					21 25		21 55					22 25		22 55					23 25	
Longcross	d																					
Weybridge	d																					
Addlestone	d					21 04							22 04							23 04		
Chertsey	d					21 07							22 07							23 07		
Virginia Water	a	21 00				21 12	21 30		22 00				22 12	22 30		23 00				23 12	23 30	
	d	21 00				21 12	21 30		22 00				22 12	22 30		23 00				23 12	23 30	
Egham	d	21 04				21 16	21 34		22 04				22 16	22 34		23 04				23 16	23 34	
Windsor & Eton Riverside	d				21 01							22 01							23 01			
Datchet	d				21 04							22 04							23 04			
Sunnymeads	d				21 07							22 07							23 07			
Wraysbury	d				21 10							22 10							23 10			
Staines	d	21 09			21 16	21 21	21 39		22 09			22 16	22 21	22 39		23 09			23 16	23 21	23 39	
Ashford (Surrey)	d				21 19	21 24						22 19	22 24						23 19	23 24		
Feltham	d	21 16			21 24	21 29	21 46		22 16			22 24	22 29	22 46		23 16			23 24	23 29	23 46	
Whitton	d				21 28							22 28							23 28			
Kingston	d			21 11				21 49			22 11				22 49			23 11				
Hampton Wick	d			21 13				21 51			22 13				22 51			23 13				
Teddington	d			21 16				21 56			22 16				22 56			23 16				
Fulwell	d																					
Strawberry Hill	d			21 19				21 59			22 19				22 59			23 19				
Twickenham	a	21 21		21 22	21 31		21 51	22 02	22 21		22 22	22 31		22 51	23 02	23 21		23 22	23 31		23 51	
	d	21 21		21 23	21 32		21 51	22 03	22 21		22 23	22 32		22 51	23 03	23 21		23 23	23 32		23 51	
St Margarets	d			21 25	21 34			22 05			22 25	22 34			23 05			23 25	23 34			
Richmond ⊖	d	21 26		21 29	21 37		21 56	22 09	22 26		22 29	22 37		22 56	23 09	23 26		23 29	23 37		23 56	
North Sheen	d			21 31	21 39			22 11			22 31	22 39			23 11			23 31	23 39			
Mortlake	d			21 33	21 42			22 13			22 33	22 42			23 13			23 33	23 42			
Hounslow	d					21 35							22 35							23 35		
Isleworth	d					21 38							22 38							23 38		
Syon Lane	d					21 40							22 40							23 40		
Brentford	d					21 42							22 42							23 42		
Kew Bridge	d					21 45							22 45							23 45		
Chiswick	d					21 47							22 47							23 47		
Barnes Bridge	d					21 50							22 50							23 50		
Barnes	d			21 36	21 45	21 53		22 16			22 36	22 45	22 53		23 16			23 36	23 45	23 53		
Putney	d	21 32		21 39	21 48	21 56	22 02	22 19	22 32		22 39	22 48	22 56	23 02	23 19	23 32		23 39	23 48	23 56	00 02	
Wandsworth Town	d			21 42	21 51	21 59		22 22			22 42	22 51	22 59		23 22			23 42	23 51	23 59		
Clapham Junction [10]	d	21 37		21 45	21 54	22 02	22 07	22 25	22 37		22 45	22 54	23 02	23 07	23 25	23 37		23 45	23 54	00 02	00 07	
Queenstown Rd.(Battersea)	d			21 48	21 57	22 05		22 28			22 48	22 57	23 05		23 28			23 48	23 57	00 05		
Vauxhall ⊖	d	21 42		21 52	22 00	22 08	22 12	22 32	22 42		22 52	23 00	23 08	23 12	23 32	23 42		23 52	23 59	00 08	00 12	
London Waterloo [15] ⊖	a	21 48		22 00	22 05	22 13	22 18	22 36	22 48		23 00	23 05	23 13	23 18	23 36	23 48		23 59	00 05	00 13	00 17	

A From Woking

B From London Waterloo

The xx49 Kingston to London Waterloo services originate at London Waterloo via Wimbledon

Table 149R

Sundays

8 December to 11 May

Reading, Guildford, Ascot, Weybridge, Windsor, Kingston, Richmond and Hounslow - London

Network Diagram - see first Page of Table 148

Station		SW A
Reading 7	d	
Earley	d	
Winnersh Triangle	d	
Winnersh	d	
Wokingham	d	
Bracknell	d	
Martins Heron	d	
Guildford	d	
Wanborough	d	
Ash 5	d	
Aldershot	a	
	d	
Ash Vale	d	
Frimley	d	
Camberley	a	
	d	
Bagshot	d	
Ascot 3	d	
Sunningdale	d	
Longcross	d	
Weybridge	d	
Addlestone	d	
Chertsey	d	
Virginia Water	a	
	d	
Egham	d	
Windsor & Eton Riverside	d	
Datchet	d	
Sunnymeads	d	
Wraysbury	d	
Staines	d	
Ashford (Surrey)	d	
Feltham	d	
Whitton	d	
Kingston	d	23 47
Hampton Wick	d	23 49
Teddington	d	23 51
Fulwell	d	
Strawberry Hill	d	23a54
Twickenham	a	
	d	
St Margarets	d	
Richmond ⊖	d	
North Sheen	d	
Mortlake	d	
Hounslow	d	
Isleworth	d	
Syon Lane	d	
Brentford	d	
Kew Bridge	d	
Chiswick	d	
Barnes Bridge	d	
Barnes	d	
Putney	d	
Wandsworth Town	d	
Clapham Junction 10	d	
Queenstown Rd.(Battersea)	d	
Vauxhall ⊖	d	
London Waterloo 15 ⊖	a	

A From London Waterloo

The xx49 Kingston to London Waterloo services originate at London Waterloo via Wimbledon

Network Diagram for Table 152

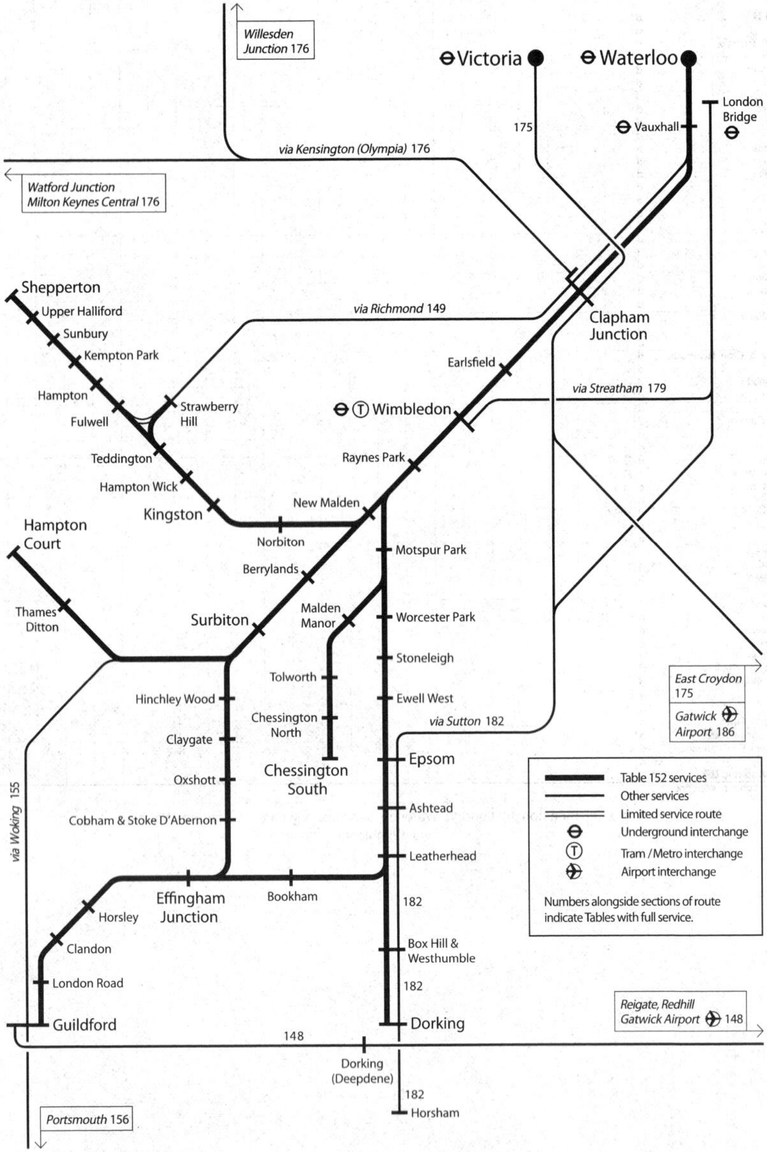

TOCs operating on this network - South West Trains (SW), Southern (SN)

Table 152

Mondays to Fridays

9 December to 16 May

London - Chessington South, Dorking, Guildford, Shepperton and Hampton Court

Network Diagram - see first Page of Table 152

Miles	Miles	Miles	Miles	Miles	Station		SN MO A	SW MO B	SW MO B	SW MX B	SW MX B	SW MX B	SW MX B	SW MO	SW MX	SW MX	SW MX	SW	SW 1 C	SW	SW 1 D	SW
0	—	—	—	0	**London Waterloo** 15 ⊖	d								00 01	00 09	00 15	00 27	00 42	05 00	05 12	05 20	
1¼	—	—	—	1¼	Vauxhall ⊖	d							00 01	00 04	00 13	00 19	00 31	00 46	05 04	05 16	05 24	
4	—	—	—	4	**Clapham Junction** 10	d							00 06	00 09	00 20	00 25	00 37	00 51	05 11	05 21	05 29	
5½	—	—	—	5½	Earlsfield	d					00 02		00 09	00 12	00 23	00 29	00s41		05 14	05 24	05 32	
7¼	—	—	—	7¼	**Wimbledon** 6 ⊖	d					00 06		00 13	00 16	00 27	00 33	00 45	01 05	05 18	05 28	05 36	05 49
8¾	—	0	0	8¾	Raynes Park 6	d						00 01	00 16	00 19		00 36	00 48	01 08		05 31		
—	—	1	1	—	Motspur Park	d						00 04				00 38						
—	—	—	2½	—	Malden Manor	d																
—	—	—	3½	—	Tolworth	d																
—	—	—	4½	—	Chessington North	d																
—	—	—	5¼	—	**Chessington South**	a																
—	—	2	—	—	Worcester Park	d						00 06				00 41						
—	—	3¼	—	—	Stoneleigh	d						00 09				00 44						
—	—	4¼	—	—	Ewell West	d			00 03			00 12				00 46						
—	—	5½	—	—	**Epsom** 3	a			00 06			00 15				00 50						
—	—	—	—	—		d						00 19										
—	—	7½	—	—	Ashtead	d						00 23										
—	0	9¼	—	—	Leatherhead	d	00 01					00 26										
—	—	12½	—	—	Box Hill & Westhumble	d	00 05															
—	—	13¼	—	—	**Dorking** 4	a	00 08															
9¾	—	—	—	9¾	New Malden 6	d							00 19	00 22			00 50	01 11		05 34		
—	—	—	—	11¼	Norbiton	d							00 22					01 14		05 37		
—	—	—	—	12	Kingston	a							00 25					01 17		05 40		
—	—	—	—	—		d							00 25					01 17		05 40		
—	—	—	—	12½	Hampton Wick	d							00 27					01s22		05 42		
—	—	—	—	13¾	Teddington	d							00 30					01s25		05 45		
—	—	—	—	—	Strawberry Hill	a												01 28				
—	—	—	—	14¾	Fulwell	d							00 34							05 49		
—	—	—	—	16½	Hampton	d							00 38							05 53		
—	—	—	—	18¼	Kempton Park	d							00 41							05 56		
—	—	—	—	18¾	Sunbury	d							00 43							05 58		
—	—	—	—	19¼	Upper Halliford	d							00 45							06 00		
—	—	—	—	20¾	**Shepperton**	a							00 48							06 03		
11	—	—	—	—	Berrylands	d								00 25			00s53					
12	—	—	0	—	**Surbiton** 6	d				00 05	00 14			00 31	00 35		00a56		05 26		05 44	05 57
—	—	—	2	—	Thames Ditton	d				00 09												
—	—	—	3	—	**Hampton Court**	a				00 12												
14	—	—	—	—	Hinchley Wood	d					00 18			00 35								06 01
15¼	—	—	—	—	Claygate	d					00 20			00 38								06 04
17	—	—	—	—	Oxshott	d					00 24			00 41								06 07
19	—	—	—	—	Cobham & Stoke D'abernon	d					00 27			00 45								06 11
—	2½	—	—	—	Bookham	d						00 31										
21¼	4¼	—	—	—	Effingham Junction 6	d					00 32	00 36		00 49								06 15
22¼	—	—	—	—	Horsley	d					00 34	00 39		00 52								06 18
25½	—	—	—	—	Clandon	d					00 39	00 44		00 57								06 23
28¾	—	—	—	—	London Road (Guildford)	d		00 03			00 44	00 49		01 02								06 28
30	—	—	—	—	**Guildford**	a		00 07			00 48	00 53		01 06	01 07				06 00		06 21	06 32

Station		SW	SW E	SW F	SW F	SW	SW	SW	SW	SW	SN G	SW	SW	SW F	SW	SW	SW
London Waterloo 15 ⊖	d	05 47	05 50				06 03	06 06	06 12	06 16		06 20	06 24	06 27	06 33	06 36	06 39
Vauxhall ⊖	d	05 51	05 54				06 07	06 10	06 16	06 20		06 24	06 28	06 31	06 37	06 40	06 43
Clapham Junction 10	d	05 56	05 59				06 12	06 15	06 21	06 25		06 29	06 33	06 36	06 42	06 45	06 48
Earlsfield	d	05 59	06 02				06 15	06 18	06 24	06 28		06 32	06 36	06 39	06 45	06 48	06 51
Wimbledon 6 ⊖	d	06 03	06 06		06 13	06 16	06 19	06 22	06 28	06 33		06 36	06 40	06 43	06 49	06 52	06 55
Raynes Park 6	d	06 06			06 16	06 19		06 25	06 31	06 35			06 43	06 46		06 55	06 58
Motspur Park	d	06 09				06 21				06 39			06 46				
Malden Manor	d					06 25				06 41							
Tolworth	d					06 27				06 45							
Chessington North	d					06 30				06 48							
Chessington South	a					06 32				06 51							
Worcester Park	d	06 11											06 48				07 02
Stoneleigh	d	06 14											06 51				07 05
Ewell West	d	06 17											06 54				07 08
Epsom 3	a	06 20											06 57				07 11
	d	06 21									06 50		06 58				07 12
Ashtead	d	06 25											07 02				07 16
Leatherhead	d	06 28									06 56		07 05				07 19
Box Hill & Westhumble	d																
Dorking 4	a												07 11				
New Malden 6	d				06 19			06 28	06 34					06 49		06 58	
Norbiton	d				06 22				06 37					06 52			
Kingston	a				06 25				06 40					06 55			
	d			05 59	06 29				06 40					06 59			
Hampton Wick	d			06 01	06 31				06 42					07 01			
Teddington	d			06 05	06 35				06 45					07 05			
Strawberry Hill	a			06 08	06 38									07 08			
Fulwell	d								06 49								
Hampton	d								06 53								
Kempton Park	d								06 56								
Sunbury	d								06 58								
Upper Halliford	d								07 00								
Shepperton	a								07 03								
Berrylands	d							06 30								07 00	
Surbiton 6	d		06a13				06 27	06 35				06 44			06 57	07 05	
Thames Ditton	d							06 39								07 09	
Hampton Court	a							06 42								07 12	
Hinchley Wood	d						06 31								07 01		
Claygate	d						06 34								07 04		
Oxshott	d						06 37								07 07		
Cobham & Stoke D'abernon	d						06 41								07 11		
Bookham	d	06 33									07 01						07 24
Effingham Junction 6	d	06 37					06 45				07 05				07 15		07a28
Horsley	d						06 48								07 18		
Clandon	d						06 53								07 23		
London Road (Guildford)	d	06 46					06 58								07 28		
Guildford	a	06 50					07 02				07 17	07 19			07 32		

A From London Victoria
B From London Waterloo
C To Portsmouth Harbour
D To Portsmouth & Southsea
E To Woking
F To London Waterloo
G From Sutton (Surrey)

The xx27 and xx57 London Waterloo to Strawberry Hill services continues to London Waterloo via Richmond

Table 152

Mondays to Fridays

9 December to 16 May

London - Chessington South, Dorking, Guildford, Shepperton and Hampton Court

Network Diagram - see first Page of Table 152

		SW	SW	SW	SW	SW	SW	SW	SN	SW	SW	SW	SW	SW	SW	SW	SW	SW	SW
						A			B				C		A				
London Waterloo 15 ⊖	d	06 42	06 46	06 50	06 54	06 57	07 03	07 06		07 09	07 12	07 16	07 20	07 24	07 27	07 33	07 36	07 39	07 42
Vauxhall ⊖	d	06 46	06 50	06 54	06 58	07 01	07 07	07 10		07 13	07 16	07 20	07 24	07 28	07 31	07 37	07 40	07 43	07 46
Clapham Junction 10	d	06 51	06 55	06 59	07 03	07 06	07 12	07 15		07 18	07 21	07 25	07 29	07 33	07 36	07 42	07 45	07 48	07 51
Earlsfield	d	06 54	06 58	07 02	07 06	07 09	07 15	07 18		07 21	07 24	07 28	07 32	07 36	07 39	07 45	07 48	07 51	07 54
Wimbledon 6 ⊖	d	06 58	07 02	07 06	07 10	07 13	07 19	07 22		07 25	07 28	07 32	07 36	07 40	07 43	07 49	07 52	07 55	07 58
Raynes Park 6	d	07 01	07 05		07 13	07 16		07 25		07 28	07 31	07 35		07 43	07 46		07 55	07 58	08 01
Motspur Park	d		07 08		07 16					07 31		07 38		07 46				08 01	
Malden Manor	d		07 11									07 41							
Tolworth	d		07 14									07 44							
Chessington North	d		07 17									07 47							
Chessington South	a		07 20									07 50							
Worcester Park	d				07 18					07 33				07 48				08 03	
Stoneleigh	d				07 21					07 36				07 51				08 06	
Ewell West	d				07 24					07 39				07 54				08 09	
Epsom 3	a				07 27					07 42				07 58				08 13	
	d				07 28				07 37					07 58				08 17	
Ashtead	d				07 32				07 41					08 02				08 21	
Leatherhead	d				07 35				07 44					08 05				08 24	
Box Hill & Westhumble	d																		
Dorking 4	a				07 41									08 12					
New Malden 6	d	07 04				07 19		07 28			07 34				07 49		07 58		08 04
Norbiton	d	07 07				07 22					07 37				07 52				08 07
Kingston	a	07 10				07 25					07 40				07 55				08 10
	d	07 10				07 29					07 40				07 59				08 10
Hampton Wick	d	07 12				07 31					07 42				08 01				08 12
Teddington	d	07 15				07 35					07 45				08 05				08 15
Strawberry Hill	a					07 38									08 08				
Fulwell	d	07 19									07 49								08 19
Hampton	d	07 23									07 53								08 23
Kempton Park	d	07 26									07 56								08 26
Sunbury	d	07 28									07 58								08 28
Upper Halliford	d	07 30									08 00								08 30
Shepperton	a	07 33									08 03								08 33
Berrylands	d							07 30									08 00		
Surbiton 6	d			07 14			07 27	07 35					07a43			07 57	08 05		
Thames Ditton	d							07 39									08 09		
Hampton Court	a							07 42									08 12		
Hinchley Wood	d						07 31									08 01			
Claygate	d						07 34									08 04			
Oxshott	d						07 37									08 07			
Cobham & Stoke D'abernon	d						07 41									08 11			
Bookham	d								07 50									08 29	
Effingham Junction 6	d						07 45		07 53							08 15		08 33	
Horsley	d						07 48									08 18		08 36	
Clandon	d						07 53									08 23		08 41	
London Road (Guildford)	d						07 58		08 02							08 28		08 46	
Guildford	a			07 47			08 02		08 06							08 32		08 50	

		SW	SW	SW	SW	SW	SW	SW	SW	SW	SW	SW	SW	SW	SW	SW	SW	SW	SW
					A						C		A						C
London Waterloo 15 ⊖	d	07 46	07 50	07 54	07 57	08 03	08 06	08 09	08 12	08 16	08 20	08 24	08 27	08 33	08 36	08 39	08 42	08 46	08 50
Vauxhall ⊖	d	07 50	07 54	07 58	08 01	08 07	08 10	08 13	08 16	08 20	08 24	08 28	08 31	08 37	08 40	08 43	08 46	08 50	08 54
Clapham Junction 10	d	07 55	07 59	08 03	08 06	08 12	08 15	08 18	08 21	08 25	08 29	08 33	08 36	08 42	08 45	08 48	08 51	08 55	08 59
Earlsfield	d	07 58	08 02	08 06	08 09	08 15	08 18	08 21	08 24	08 28	08 32	08 36	08 39	08 45	08 48	08 51	08 54	08 58	09 02
Wimbledon 6 ⊖	d	08 02	08 06	08 10	08 13	08 19	08 22	08 25	08 28	08 32	08 36	08 40	08 43	08 49	08 52	08 55	08 58	09 02	09 06
Raynes Park 6	d	08 05		08 13	08 16		08 25	08 28	08 31	08 35		08 43	08 46		08 55	08 58	09 01	09 05	
Motspur Park	d	08 08		08 16				08 31		08 38		08 46				09 01		09 08	
Malden Manor	d	08 11								08 41								09 11	
Tolworth	d	08 14								08 44								09 14	
Chessington North	d	08 17								08 47								09 17	
Chessington South	a	08 20								08 50								09 20	
Worcester Park	d			08 18				08 33				08 48				09 03			
Stoneleigh	d			08 21				08 36				08 51				09 06			
Ewell West	d			08 24				08 39				08 54				09 09			
Epsom 3	a			08 27				08 42				08 57				09 16			
	d			08 28				08 47				08 58				09 17			
Ashtead	d			08 32				08 51				09 02				09 21			
Leatherhead	d			08 35				08 54				09 05				09 24			
Box Hill & Westhumble	d																		
Dorking 4	a			08 41								09 11							
New Malden 6	d				08 19		08 28		08 34				08 49		08 58		09 04		
Norbiton	d				08 22				08 37				08 52				09 07		
Kingston	a				08 25				08 40				08 55				09 10		
	d				08 29				08 40				08 59				09 10		
Hampton Wick	d				08 31				08 42				09 01				09 12		
Teddington	d				08 35				08 45				09 05				09 15		
Strawberry Hill	a				08 38								09 08						
Fulwell	d								08 49								09 19		
Hampton	d								08 53								09 23		
Kempton Park	d								08 56								09 26		
Sunbury	d								08 58								09 28		
Upper Halliford	d								09 00								09 30		
Shepperton	a								09 03								09 33		
Berrylands	d						08 30								09 00				
Surbiton 6	d		08 14			08 27	08 35				08a43			08 57	09 05				09a13
Thames Ditton	d						08 39								09 09				
Hampton Court	a						08 42								09 12				
Hinchley Wood	d					08 31								09 01					
Claygate	d					08 34								09 04					
Oxshott	d					08 37								09 07					
Cobham & Stoke D'abernon	d					08 41								09 11					
Bookham	d							08 59								09 29			
Effingham Junction 6	d					08 45		09 03						09 15		09 33			
Horsley	d					08 48		09 06						09 18		09 36			
Clandon	d					08 53		09 11						09 23		09 41			
London Road (Guildford)	d					08 58		09 16						09 28		09 46			
Guildford	a		08 50			09 04		09 20						09 32		09 50			

A To London Waterloo
B From London Victoria
C To Woking

The xx27 and xx57 London Waterloo to Strawberry Hill services continues to London Waterloo via Richmond

Table 152

Mondays to Fridays

9 December to 16 May

London - Chessington South, Dorking, Guildford, Shepperton and Hampton Court

Network Diagram - see first Page of Table 152

		SW	SW A	SW	SW	SW	SW	SW	SW B	SW	SW A	SW	SW	SW	SW	SW	SW B	SW	SW A
London Waterloo 15 ⊖	d	08 54	08 57	09 03	09 06	09 09	09 12	09 16	09 20	09 24	09 27	09 33	09 36	09 39	09 42	09 46	09 50	09 54	09 57
Vauxhall ⊖	d	08 58	09 01	09 07	09 10	09 13	09 16	09 20	09 24	09 28	09 31	09 37	09 40	09 43	09 46	09 50	09 54	09 58	10 01
Clapham Junction 10	d	09 03	09 06	09 12	09 15	09 18	09 21	09 25	09 29	09 33	09 36	09 42	09 45	09 48	09 51	09 55	09 59	10 03	10 06
Earlsfield	d	09 06	09 09	09 15	09 18	09 21	09 24	09 28	09 32	09 36	09 39	09 45	09 48	09 51	09 54	09 58	10 02	10 06	10 09
Wimbledon 6 ⊖	d	09 10	09 13	09 19	09 22	09 25	09 28	09 32	09 36	09 40	09 43	09 49	09 52	09 55	09 58	10 02	10 06	10 10	10 13
Raynes Park 6	d	09 13	09 16		09 25	09 28	09 31	09 35		09 43	09 46		09 55	09 58	10 01	10 05		10 13	10 16
Motspur Park	d	09 16				09 31		09 38		09 46				10 01		10 08		10 16	
Malden Manor	d							09 41								10 11			
Tolworth	d							09 44								10 14			
Chessington North	d							09 47								10 17			
Chessington South	a							09 50								10 20			
Worcester Park	d	09 18				09 33				09 48				10 03				10 18	
Stoneleigh	d	09 21				09 36				09 51				10 06				10 21	
Ewell West	d	09 24				09 39				09 54				10 09				10 24	
Epsom 3	a	09 27				09 42				09 57				10 16				10 27	
	d	09 28				09 47				09 58				10 17				10 28	
Ashtead	d	09 32				09 51				10 02				10 21				10 32	
Leatherhead	d	09 35				09 54				10 05				10 24				10 35	
Box Hill & Westhumble	d																		
Dorking 4	a	09 41								10 11								10 41	
New Malden 6	d		09 19		09 28		09 34				09 49		09 58		10 04				10 19
Norbiton	d		09 22				09 37				09 52				10 07				10 22
Kingston	a		09 25				09 40				09 55				10 10				10 25
	d		09 29				09 40				09 59				10 10				10 29
Hampton Wick	d		09 31				09 42				10 01				10 12				10 31
Teddington	d		09 35				09 45				10 05				10 15				10 35
Strawberry Hill	a		09 38								10 08								10 38
Fulwell	d						09 49								10 19				
Hampton	d						09 53								10 23				
Kempton Park	d						09 56								10 26				
Sunbury	d						09 58								10 28				
Upper Halliford	d						10 00								10 30				
Shepperton	a						10 03								10 33				
Berrylands	d				09 30								10 00						
Surbiton 6	d			09 27	09 35				09a43			09 57	10 05				10a13		
Thames Ditton	d				09 39								10 09						
Hampton Court	a				09 42								10 12						
Hinchley Wood	d			09 31								10 01							
Claygate	d			09 34								10 04							
Oxshott	d			09 37								10 07							
Cobham & Stoke D'abernon	d			09 41								10 11							
Bookham	d					09 59								10 29					
Effingham Junction 6	d			09 45		10 03						10 15		10 33					
Horsley	d			09 48		10 06						10 18		10 36					
Clandon	d			09 53		10 11						10 23		10 41					
London Road (Guildford)	d			09 58		10 16						10 28		10 46					
Guildford	a			10 02		10 20						10 32		10 50					

		SW	SW	SW	SW	SW	SW B	SW	SW A	SW	SW	SW	SW	SW	SW B	SW	SW A	SW	SW
London Waterloo 15 ⊖	d	10 03	10 06	10 09	10 12	10 16	10 20	10 24	10 27	10 33	10 36	10 39	10 42	10 46	10 50	10 54	10 57	11 03	11 06
Vauxhall ⊖	d	10 07	10 10	10 13	10 16	10 20	10 24	10 28	10 31	10 37	10 40	10 43	10 46	10 50	10 54	10 58	11 01	11 07	11 10
Clapham Junction 10	d	10 12	10 15	10 18	10 21	10 25	10 29	10 33	10 36	10 42	10 45	10 48	10 51	10 55	10 59	11 03	11 06	11 12	11 15
Earlsfield	d	10 15	10 18	10 21	10 24	10 28	10 32	10 36	10 39	10 45	10 48	10 51	10 54	10 58	11 02	11 06	11 09	11 15	11 18
Wimbledon 6 ⊖	d	10 19	10 22	10 25	10 28	10 32	10 36	10 40	10 43	10 49	10 52	10 55	10 58	11 02	11 06	11 10	11 13	11 19	11 22
Raynes Park 6	d		10 25	10 28	10 31	10 35		10 43	10 46		10 55	10 58	11 01	11 05		11 13	11 16		11 25
Motspur Park	d			10 31		10 38		10 46				11 01		11 08		11 16			
Malden Manor	d					10 41								11 11					
Tolworth	d					10 44								11 14					
Chessington North	d					10 47								11 17					
Chessington South	a					10 50								11 20					
Worcester Park	d			10 33				10 48				11 03				11 18			
Stoneleigh	d			10 36				10 51				11 06				11 21			
Ewell West	d			10 39				10 54				11 09				11 24			
Epsom 3	a			10 46				10 57				11 16				11 27			
	d			10 47				10 58				11 17				11 28			
Ashtead	d			10 51				11 02				11 21				11 32			
Leatherhead	d			10 54				11 05				11 24				11 35			
Box Hill & Westhumble	d																		
Dorking 4	a							11 11								11 41			
New Malden 6	d		10 28		10 34				10 49		10 58		11 04				11 19		11 28
Norbiton	d				10 37				10 52				11 07				11 22		
Kingston	a				10 40				10 55				11 10				11 25		
	d				10 40				10 59				11 10				11 29		
Hampton Wick	d				10 42				11 01				11 12				11 31		
Teddington	d				10 45				11 05				11 15				11 35		
Strawberry Hill	a								11 08								11 38		
Fulwell	d				10 49								11 19						
Hampton	d				10 53								11 23						
Kempton Park	d				10 56								11 26						
Sunbury	d				10 58								11 28						
Upper Halliford	d				11 00								11 30						
Shepperton	a				11 03								11 33						
Berrylands	d		10 30								11 00								11 30
Surbiton 6	d	10 27	10 35				10a43			10 57	11 05				11a13			11 27	11 35
Thames Ditton	d		10 39								11 09								11 39
Hampton Court	a		10 42								11 12								11 42
Hinchley Wood	d	10 31								11 01								11 31	
Claygate	d	10 34								11 04								11 34	
Oxshott	d	10 37								11 07								11 37	
Cobham & Stoke D'abernon	d	10 41								11 11								11 41	
Bookham	d			10 59								11 29							
Effingham Junction 6	d	10 45		11 03						11 15		11 33						11 45	
Horsley	d	10 48		11 06						11 18		11 36						11 48	
Clandon	d	10 53		11 11						11 23		11 41						11 53	
London Road (Guildford)	d	10 58		11 16						11 28		11 46						11 58	
Guildford	a	11 02		11 20						11 32		11 50						12 02	

A To London Waterloo

B To Woking

The xx27 and xx57 London Waterloo to Strawberry Hill services continues to London Waterloo via Richmond

Table 152

Mondays to Fridays

9 December to 16 May

London - Chessington South, Dorking, Guildford, Shepperton and Hampton Court

Network Diagram - see first Page of Table 152

		SW	SW	SW	SW A	SW	SW B	SW	SW	SW	SW	SW	SW A	SW
London Waterloo 15 ⊖	d	11 09	11 12	11 16	11 20	11 24	11 27	11 33	11 36	11 39	11 42	11 46	11 50	11 54
Vauxhall ⊖	d	11 13	11 16	11 20	11 24	11 28	11 31	11 37	11 40	11 43	11 46	11 50	11 54	11 58
Clapham Junction 10	d	11 18	11 21	11 25	11 29	11 33	11 36	11 42	11 45	11 48	11 51	11 55	11 59	12 03
Earlsfield	d	11 21	11 24	11 28	11 32	11 36	11 39	11 45	11 48	11 51	11 54	11 58	12 02	12 06
Wimbledon 6 ⊖	d	11 25	11 28	11 32	11 36	11 40	11 43	11 49	11 52	11 55	11 58	12 02	12 06	12 10
Raynes Park 6	d	11 28	11 31	11 35		11 43	11 46		11 55	11 58	12 01	12 05		12 13
Motspur Park	d	11 31		11 38		11 46				12 01		12 08		12 16
Malden Manor	d			11 41								12 11		
Tolworth	d			11 44								12 14		
Chessington North	d			11 47								12 17		
Chessington South	a			11 50								12 20		
Worcester Park	d	11 33				11 48				12 03				12 18
Stoneleigh	d	11 36				11 51				12 06				12 21
Ewell West	d	11 39				11 54				12 09				12 24
Epsom 3	a	11 46				11 57				12 16				12 27
	d	11 47				11 58				12 17				12 28
Ashtead	d	11 51				12 02				12 21				12 32
Leatherhead	d	11 54				12 05				12 24				12 35
Box Hill & Westhumble	d													
Dorking 4	a					12 11								12 41
New Malden 6	d		11 34				11 49		11 58		12 04			
Norbiton	d		11 37				11 52				12 07			
Kingston	a		11 40				11 55				12 10			
	d		11 40				11 59				12 10			
Hampton Wick	d		11 42				12 01				12 12			
Teddington	d		11 45				12 05				12 15			
Strawberry Hill	a						12 08							
Fulwell	d		11 49								12 19			
Hampton	d		11 53								12 23			
Kempton Park	d		11 56								12 26			
Sunbury	d		11 58								12 28			
Upper Halliford	d		12 00								12 30			
Shepperton	a		12 03								12 33			
Berrylands	d								12 00					
Surbiton 6	d				11a43			11 57	12 05				12a13	
Thames Ditton	d								12 09					
Hampton Court	a								12 12					
Hinchley Wood	d							12 01						
Claygate	d							12 04						
Oxshott	d							12 07						
Cobham & Stoke D'abernon	d							12 11						
Bookham	d	11 59								12 29				
Effingham Junction 6	d	12 03						12 15		12 33				
Horsley	d	12 06						12 18		12 36				
Clandon	d	12 11						12 23		12 41				
London Road (Guildford)	d	12 16						12 28		12 46				
Guildford	a	12 20						12 32		12 50				

		SW B	SW	SW	SW	SW	SW	SW A	SW	SW B
London Waterloo 15 ⊖	d	11 57	12 03	12 06	12 09	12 12	12 16	12 20	12 24	12 27
Vauxhall ⊖	d	12 01	12 07	12 10	12 13	12 16	12 20	12 24	12 28	12 31
Clapham Junction 10	d	12 06	12 12	12 15	12 18	12 21	12 25	12 29	12 33	12 36
Earlsfield	d	12 09	12 15	12 18	12 21	12 24	12 28	12 32	12 36	12 39
Wimbledon 6 ⊖	d	12 13	12 19	12 22	12 25	12 28	12 32	12 36	12 40	12 43
Raynes Park 6	d	12 16		12 25	12 28	12 31	12 35		12 43	12 46
Motspur Park	d				12 31		12 38		12 46	
Malden Manor	d						12 41			
Tolworth	d						12 44			
Chessington North	d						12 47			
Chessington South	a						12 50			
Worcester Park	d				12 33				12 48	
Stoneleigh	d				12 36				12 51	
Ewell West	d				12 39				12 54	
Epsom 3	a				12 46				12 57	
	d				12 47				12 58	
Ashtead	d				12 51				13 02	
Leatherhead	d				12 54				13 05	
Box Hill & Westhumble	d									
Dorking 4	a								13 11	
New Malden 6	d	12 19		12 28		12 34				12 49
Norbiton	d	12 22				12 37				12 52
Kingston	a	12 25				12 40				12 55
	d	12 29				12 40				12 59
Hampton Wick	d	12 31				12 42				13 01
Teddington	d	12 35				12 45				13 05
Strawberry Hill	a	12 38								13 08
Fulwell	d					12 49				
Hampton	d					12 53				
Kempton Park	d					12 56				
Sunbury	d					12 58				
Upper Halliford	d					13 00				
Shepperton	a					13 03				
Berrylands	d			12 30						
Surbiton 6	d		12 27	12 35				12a43		
Thames Ditton	d			12 39						
Hampton Court	a			12 42						
Hinchley Wood	d		12 31							
Claygate	d		12 34							
Oxshott	d		12 37							
Cobham & Stoke D'abernon	d		12 41							
Bookham	d				12 59					
Effingham Junction 6	d		12 45		13 03					
Horsley	d		12 48		13 06					
Clandon	d		12 53		13 11					
London Road (Guildford)	d		12 58		13 16					
Guildford	a		13 02		13 20					

		SW	SW	SW	SW	SW	SW A	SW	SW B	SW	SW	SW	SW	SW	SW A
London Waterloo 15 ⊖	d	12 33	12 36	12 39	12 42	12 46	12 50	12 54	12 57	13 03	13 06	13 09	13 12	13 16	13 20
Vauxhall ⊖	d	12 37	12 40	12 43	12 46	12 50	12 54	12 58	13 01	13 07	13 10	13 13	13 16	13 20	13 24
Clapham Junction 10	d	12 42	12 45	12 48	12 51	12 55	12 59	13 03	13 06	13 12	13 15	13 18	13 21	13 25	13 29
Earlsfield	d	12 45	12 48	12 51	12 54	12 58	13 02	13 06	13 09	13 15	13 18	13 21	13 24	13 28	13 32
Wimbledon 6 ⊖	d	12 49	12 52	12 55	12 58	13 02	13 06	13 10	13 13	13 19	13 22	13 25	13 28	13 32	13 36
Raynes Park 6	d		12 55	12 58	13 01	13 05		13 13	13 16		13 25	13 28	13 31	13 35	
Motspur Park	d			13 01		13 08		13 16				13 31		13 38	
Malden Manor	d					13 11								13 41	
Tolworth	d					13 14								13 44	
Chessington North	d					13 17								13 47	
Chessington South	a					13 20								13 50	
Worcester Park	d			13 03				13 18				13 33			
Stoneleigh	d			13 06				13 21				13 36			
Ewell West	d			13 09				13 24				13 39			
Epsom 3	a			13 16				13 27				13 46			
	d			13 17				13 28				13 47			
Ashtead	d			13 21				13 32				13 51			
Leatherhead	d			13 24				13 35				13 54			
Box Hill & Westhumble	d														
Dorking 4	a							13 41							
New Malden 6	d		12 58		13 04				13 19		13 28		13 34		
Norbiton	d				13 07				13 22				13 37		
Kingston	a				13 10				13 25				13 40		
	d				13 10				13 29				13 40		
Hampton Wick	d				13 12				13 31				13 42		
Teddington	d				13 15				13 35				13 45		
Strawberry Hill	a								13 38						
Fulwell	d				13 19								13 49		
Hampton	d				13 23								13 53		
Kempton Park	d				13 26								13 56		
Sunbury	d				13 28								13 58		
Upper Halliford	d				13 30								14 00		
Shepperton	a				13 33								14 03		
Berrylands	d		13 00								13 30				
Surbiton 6	d	12 57	13 05				13a13			13 27	13 35				13a43
Thames Ditton	d		13 09								13 39				
Hampton Court	a		13 12								13 42				
Hinchley Wood	d	13 01								13 31					
Claygate	d	13 04								13 34					
Oxshott	d	13 07								13 37					
Cobham & Stoke D'abernon	d	13 11								13 41					
Bookham	d			13 29								13 59			
Effingham Junction 6	d	13 15		13 33						13 45		14 03			
Horsley	d	13 18		13 36						13 48		14 06			
Clandon	d	13 23		13 41						13 53		14 11			
London Road (Guildford)	d	13 28		13 46						13 58		14 16			
Guildford	a	13 32		13 50						14 02		14 20			

A To Woking

B To London Waterloo

The xx27 and xx57 London Waterloo to Strawberry Hill services continues to London Waterloo via Richmond

Table 152

Mondays to Fridays

9 December to 16 May

London - Chessington South, Dorking, Guildford, Shepperton and Hampton Court

Network Diagram - see first Page of Table 152

Station		SW	SW A	SW	SW	SW	SW	SW	SW B	SW	SW A	SW	SW	SW	SW	SW	SW B	SW	SW A	SW	SW	SW	SW	SW	SW B	SW	SW A	SW	SW	SW	SW	SW	SW B	SW	SW A	SW	SW
London Waterloo 15 ⊖	d	13 24	13 27	13 33	13 36	13 39	13 42	13 46	13 50	13 54	13 57	14 03	14 06	14 09	14 12	14 16	14 20	14 24	14 27	14 33	14 36	14 39	14 42	14 46	14 50	14 54	14 57	15 03	15 06	15 09	15 12	15 16	15 20	15 24	15 27	15 33	15 36
Vauxhall ⊖	d	13 28	13 31	13 37	13 40	13 43	13 46	13 50	13 54	13 58	14 01	14 07	14 10	14 13	14 16	14 20	14 24	14 28	14 31	14 37	14 40	14 43	14 46	14 50	14 54	14 58	15 01	15 07	15 10	15 13	15 16	15 20	15 24	15 28	15 31	15 37	15 40
Clapham Junction 10	d	13 33	13 36	13 42	13 45	13 48	13 51	13 55	13 59	14 03	14 06	14 12	14 15	14 18	14 21	14 25	14 29	14 33	14 36	14 42	14 45	14 48	14 51	14 55	14 59	15 03	15 06	15 12	15 15	15 18	15 21	15 25	15 29	15 33	15 36	15 42	15 45
Earlsfield	d	13 36	13 39	13 45	13 48	13 51	13 54	13 58	14 02	14 06	14 09	14 15	14 18	14 21	14 24	14 28	14 32	14 36	14 39	14 45	14 48	14 51	14 54	14 58	15 02	15 06	15 09	15 15	15 18	15 21	15 24	15 28	15 32	15 36	15 39	15 45	15 48
Wimbledon 6 ⊖	d	13 40	13 43	13 49	13 52	13 55	13 58	14 02	14 06	14 10	14 13	14 19	14 22	14 25	14 28	14 32	14 36	14 40	14 43	14 49	14 52	14 55	14 58	15 02	15 06	15 10	15 13	15 19	15 22	15 25	15 28	15 32	15 36	15 40	15 43	15 49	15 52
Raynes Park 6	d	13 43	13 46		13 55	13 58	14 01	14 05		14 13	14 16		14 25	14 28	14 31	14 35		14 43	14 46		14 55	14 58	15 01	15 05		15 13	15 16		15 25	15 28	15 31	15 35		15 43	15 46		15 55
Motspur Park	d	13 46				14 01		14 08		14 16				14 31		14 38		14 46				15 01		15 08		15 16				15 31		15 38		15 46			
Malden Manor	d							14 11								14 41								15 11								15 41					
Tolworth	d							14 14								14 44								15 14								15 44					
Chessington North	d							14 17								14 47								15 17								15 47					
Chessington South	a							14 20								14 50								15 20								15 50					
Worcester Park	d	13 48				14 03				14 18				14 33				14 48				15 03				15 18				15 33				15 48			
Stoneleigh	d	13 51				14 06				14 21				14 36				14 51				15 06				15 21				15 36				15 51			
Ewell West	d	13 54				14 09				14 24				14 39				14 54				15 09				15 24				15 39				15 54			
Epsom 3	a	13 57				14 16				14 27				14 46				14 57				15 16				15 27				15 46				15 57			
	d	13 58				14 17				14 28				14 47				14 58				15 17				15 28				15 47				15 58			
Ashtead	d	14 02				14 21				14 32				14 51				15 02				15 21				15 32				15 51				16 02			
Leatherhead	d	14 05				14 24				14 35				14 54				15 05				15 24				15 35				15 54				16 05			
Box Hill & Westhumble	d																																				
Dorking 4	a	14 11								14 41								15 11								15 41								16 11			
New Malden 6	d		13 49		13 58		14 04				14 19		14 28		14 34				14 49		14 58		15 04				15 19		15 28		15 34				15 49		15 58
Norbiton	d		13 52				14 07				14 22				14 37				14 52				15 07				15 22				15 37				15 52		
Kingston	a		13 55				14 10				14 25				14 40				14 55				15 10				15 25				15 40				15 55		
	d		13 59				14 10				14 29				14 40				14 59				15 10				15 29				15 40				15 59		
Hampton Wick	d		14 01				14 12				14 31				14 42				15 01				15 12				15 31				15 42				16 01		
Teddington	d		14 05				14 15				14 35				14 45				15 05				15 15				15 35				15 45				16 05		
Strawberry Hill	a		14 08								14 38								15 08								15 38								16 08		
Fulwell	d						14 19								14 49								15 19								15 49						
Hampton	d						14 23								14 53								15 23								15 53						
Kempton Park	d						14 26								14 56								15 26								15 56						
Sunbury	d						14 28								14 58								15 28								15 58						
Upper Halliford	d						14 30								15 00								15 30								16 00						
Shepperton	a						14 33								15 03								15 33								16 03						
Berrylands	d				14 00								14 30								15 00								15 30								16 00
Surbiton 6	d			13 57	14 05				14a13			14 27	14 35				14a43			14 57	15 05				15a13			15 27	15 35				15a43			15 57	16 05
Thames Ditton	d				14 09								14 39								15 09								15 39								16 09
Hampton Court	a				14 12								14 42								15 12								15 42								16 12
Hinchley Wood	d			14 01								14 31								15 01								15 31								16 01	
Claygate	d			14 04								14 34								15 04								15 34								16 04	
Oxshott	d			14 07								14 37								15 07								15 37								16 07	
Cobham & Stoke D'abernon	d			14 11								14 41								15 11								15 41								16 11	
Bookham	d					14 29								14 59								15 29								15 59							
Effingham Junction 6	d			14 15		14 33						14 45		15 03						15 15		15 33						15 45		16 03						16 15	
Horsley	d			14 18		14 36						14 48		15 06						15 18		15 36						15 48		16 06						16 18	
Clandon	d			14 23		14 41						14 53		15 11						15 23		15 41						15 53		16 11						16 23	
London Road (Guildford)	d			14 28		14 46						14 58		15 16						15 28		15 46						15 58		16 16						16 28	
Guildford	a			14 32		14 50						15 02		15 20						15 32		15 50						16 02		16 20						16 32	

A To London Waterloo

B To Woking

The xx27 and xx57 London Waterloo to Strawberry Hill services continues to London Waterloo via Richmond

Table 152

Mondays to Fridays

9 December to 16 May

London - Chessington South, Dorking, Guildford, Shepperton and Hampton Court

Network Diagram - see first Page of Table 152

		SW	SW	SW	SW	SW	SW	SW	SW	SW	SW	SW	SW	SW
					A		B						A	
London Waterloo 15 ⊖	d	15 39	15 42	15 46	15 50	15 54	15 57	16 03	16 06	16 09	16 12	16 16	16 20	16 24
Vauxhall ⊖	d	15 43	15 46	15 50	15 54	15 58	16 01	16 07	16 10	16 13	16 16	16 20	16 24	16 28
Clapham Junction 10	d	15 48	15 51	15 55	15 59	16 03	16 06	16 12	16 15	16 18	16 21	16 25	16 29	16 33
Earlsfield	d	15 51	15 54	15 58	16 02	16 06	16 09	16 15	16 18	16 21	16 24	16 28	16 32	16 36
Wimbledon 6 ⊖	d	15 55	15 58	16 02	16 06	16 10	16 13	16 19	16 22	16 25	16 28	16 32	16 36	16 40
Raynes Park 6	d	15 58	16 01	16 05		16 13	16 16		16 25	16 28	16 31	16 35		16 43
Motspur Park	d	16 01		16 08		16 16				16 31		16 38		16 46
Malden Manor	d			16 11								16 41		
Tolworth	d			16 14								16 44		
Chessington North	d			16 17								16 47		
Chessington South	a			16 20								16 52		
Worcester Park	d	16 03				16 18				16 33				16 48
Stoneleigh	d	16 06				16 21				16 36				16 51
Ewell West	d	16 09				16 24				16 39				16 54
Epsom 3	a	16 15				16 27				16 46				16 57
	d	16 17				16 28				16 47				16 58
Ashtead	d	16 21				16 32				16 51				17 02
Leatherhead	d	16 24				16 35				16 54				17 05
Box Hill & Westhumble	d													17 10
Dorking 4	a					16 41								17 14
New Malden 6	d		16 04				16 19		16 28		16 34			
Norbiton	d		16 07				16 22				16 37			
Kingston	a		16 10				16 25				16 40			
	d		16 10				16 29				16 40			
Hampton Wick	d		16 12				16 31				16 42			
Teddington	d		16 15				16 35				16 45			
Strawberry Hill	a						16 38							
Fulwell	d		16 19								16 49			
Hampton	d		16 23								16 53			
Kempton Park	d		16 26								16 56			
Sunbury	d		16 28								16 58			
Upper Halliford	d		16 30								17 00			
Shepperton	a		16 33								17 05			
Berrylands	d								16 30					
Surbiton 6	d				16a13			16 27	16 35				16a43	
Thames Ditton	d								16 39					
Hampton Court	a								16 44					
Hinchley Wood	d							16 31						
Claygate	d							16 34						
Oxshott	d							16 37						
Cobham & Stoke D'abernon	d							16 41						
Bookham	d	16 29								16 59				
Effingham Junction 6	d	16 33						16 45		17 03				
Horsley	d	16 36						16 48		17 06				
Clandon	d	16 41						16 53		17 11				
London Road (Guildford)	d	16 46						16 58		17 16				
Guildford	a	16 50						17 04		17 22				

		SW	SW	SW	SW	SW	SW	SW	SW	SW
		B						A		B
London Waterloo 15 ⊖	d	16 27	16 33	16 36	16 39	16 42	16 46	16 50	16 54	16 57
Vauxhall ⊖	d	16 31	16 37	16 40	16 43	16 46	16 50	16 54	16 58	17 01
Clapham Junction 10	d	16 36	16 42	16 45	16 48	16 51	16 55	16 59	17 03	17 06
Earlsfield	d	16 39	16 45	16 48	16 51	16 54	16 58	17 02	17 06	17 09
Wimbledon 6 ⊖	d	16 43	16 49	16 52	16 55	16 58	17 02	17 06	17 10	17 13
Raynes Park 6	d	16 46		16 55	16 58	17 01	17 05		17 13	17 16
Motspur Park	d				17 01		17 08		17 16	
Malden Manor	d						17 11			
Tolworth	d						17 14			
Chessington North	d						17 17			
Chessington South	a						17 22			
Worcester Park	d				17 03				17 18	
Stoneleigh	d				17 06				17 21	
Ewell West	d				17 09				17 24	
Epsom 3	a				17 12				17 27	
	d				17 17				17 28	
Ashtead	d				17 21				17 32	
Leatherhead	d				17 24				17 35	
Box Hill & Westhumble	d								17 40	
Dorking 4	a								17 44	
New Malden 6	d	16 49		16 58		17 04				17 19
Norbiton	d	16 52				17 07				17 22
Kingston	a	16 55				17 10				17 25
	d	16 59				17 10				17 29
Hampton Wick	d	17 01				17 12				17 31
Teddington	d	17 05				17 15				17 35
Strawberry Hill	a	17 08								17 38
Fulwell	d					17 19				
Hampton	d					17 23				
Kempton Park	d					17 26				
Sunbury	d					17 28				
Upper Halliford	d					17 30				
Shepperton	a					17 35				
Berrylands	d			17 00						
Surbiton 6	d		16 57	17 05				17a13		
Thames Ditton	d			17 09						
Hampton Court	a			17 14						
Hinchley Wood	d		17 01							
Claygate	d		17 04							
Oxshott	d		17 07							
Cobham & Stoke D'abernon	d		17 11							
Bookham	d				17 29					
Effingham Junction 6	d		17 15		17 33					
Horsley	d		17 18		17 36					
Clandon	d		17 23		17 41					
London Road (Guildford)	d		17 28		17 46					
Guildford	a		17 34		17 52					

		SW	SW	SN	SW	SW	SW	SW	SW	SW	SW	SW	SW
				C				A		B			
London Waterloo 15 ⊖	d	17 02	17 06		17 09	17 12	17 16	17 20	17 24	17 27	17 30	17 32	17 36
Vauxhall ⊖	d	17 07	17 10		17 13	17 16	17 20	17 24	17 28	17 31	17 34	17 37	17 40
Clapham Junction 10	d	17 12	17 15		17 18	17 21	17 25	17 29	17 33	17 36	17 39	17 42	17 45
Earlsfield	d	17 15	17 18		17 21	17 24	17 28	17 32	17 36	17 39	17 42	17 45	17 48
Wimbledon 6 ⊖	d	17 19	17 22		17 25	17 28	17 32	17 36	17 40	17 43	17 46	17 49	17 52
Raynes Park 6	d		17 25		17 28	17 31	17 35		17 43	17 46	17 49		17 55
Motspur Park	d				17 31		17 38				17 52		
Malden Manor	d						17 41						
Tolworth	d						17 44						
Chessington North	d						17 47						
Chessington South	a						17 52						
Worcester Park	d				17 33				17 47		17 54		
Stoneleigh	d				17 36						17 57		
Ewell West	d				17 39						18 00		
Epsom 3	a				17 42				17 54		18 07		
	d			17 37	17 47				17 54				
Ashtead	d			17 41	17 51				17 58				
Leatherhead	d			17 44	17 54				18 01				
Box Hill & Westhumble	d								18 06				
Dorking 4	a								18 11				
New Malden 6	d		17 28			17 34				17 49			17 58
Norbiton	d					17 37				17 52			
Kingston	a					17 40				17 55			
	d					17 40				17 59			
Hampton Wick	d					17 42				18 01			
Teddington	d					17 45				18 05			
Strawberry Hill	a									18 08			
Fulwell	d					17 49							
Hampton	d					17 53							
Kempton Park	d					17 56							
Sunbury	d					17 58							
Upper Halliford	d					18 00							
Shepperton	a					18 06							
Berrylands	d		17 30										18 00
Surbiton 6	d	17 27	17 35					17a43				17 57	18 05
Thames Ditton	d		17 39										18 09
Hampton Court	a		17 44										18 14
Hinchley Wood	d	17 31										18 05	
Claygate	d	17 34										18 08	
Oxshott	d	17 37										18 11	
Cobham & Stoke D'abernon	d	17 41										18 15	
Bookham	d			17 50	17 59								
Effingham Junction 6	d	17 45		17 53	18a05							18 20	
Horsley	d	17 48		17 56								18 22	
Clandon	d	17 53		18 01								18 27	
London Road (Guildford)	d	17 58		18 06								18 32	
Guildford	a	18 04		18 13								18 38	

A To Woking

B To London Waterloo

C From London Victoria

The xx27 and xx57 London Waterloo to Strawberry Hill services continues to London Waterloo via Richmond

Table 152

Mondays to Fridays

9 December to 16 May

London - Chessington South, Dorking, Guildford, Shepperton and Hampton Court

Network Diagram - see first Page of Table 152

Station		SN	SW	SW	SW	SW	SW	SW	SW	SW	SW	SW	SW
		A					B		C				
London Waterloo 15 ⊖	d		17 39	17 43	17 42	17 46	17 50	17 54	17 57	18 00	18 02	18 06	18 09
Vauxhall ⊖	d		17 43	17 47	17 46	17 50	17 54	17 58	18 01	18 04	18 07	18 10	18 13
Clapham Junction 10	d		17 48	17 53	17 51	17 55	17 59	18 03	18 06	18 09	18 12	18 15	18 18
Earlsfield	d		17 51		17 54	17 58	18 02	18 06	18 09	18 12	18 15	18 18	18 21
Wimbledon 6 ⊖ ⛴	d		17 55		17 58	18 02	18 06	18 10	18 13	18 16	18 19	18 22	18 25
Raynes Park 6	d		17 58		18 01	18 05		18 13	18 16	18 19		18 25	18 28
Motspur Park	d		18 01			18 08				18 22			18 31
Malden Manor	d					18 11							
Tolworth	d					18 14							
Chessington North	d					18 17							
Chessington South	a					18 22							
Worcester Park	d		18 03					18 17		18 24			18 33
Stoneleigh	d		18 06							18 27			18 36
Ewell West	d		18 09							18 30			18 39
Epsom 3	a		18 15					18 24		18 35			18 46
	d	18 10	18 17					18 24					18 47
Ashtead	d	18 14	18 21					18 28					18 51
Leatherhead	d	18 18	18 24					18 31					18 54
Box Hill & Westhumble	d							18 36					
Dorking 4	a							18 41					
New Malden 6	d				18 04				18 19			18 28	
Norbiton	d				18 07				18 22				
Kingston	a				18 10				18 25				
	d				18 10				18 29				
Hampton Wick	d				18 12				18 31				
Teddington	d				18 15				18 35				
Strawberry Hill	a			18 11					18 38				
Fulwell	d			18 13	18 19								
Hampton	d			18 17	18 23								
Kempton Park	d				18 26								
Sunbury	d			18 21	18 28								
Upper Halliford	d			18 23	18 30								
Shepperton	a			18 28	18 40								
Berrylands	d											18 30	
Surbiton 6	d						18a13				18 27	18 35	
Thames Ditton	d											18 39	
Hampton Court	a											18 44	
Hinchley Wood	d										18 35		
Claygate	d										18 38		
Oxshott	d										18 41		
Cobham & Stoke D'abernon	d										18 45		
Bookham	d	18 23	18 29										18 59
Effingham Junction 6	d	18 27	18a42								18 50		19 03
Horsley	d	18 30									18 52		19 06
Clandon	d	18 35									18 57		19 11
London Road (Guildford)	d	18 40									19 02		19 16
Guildford	a	18 46									19 09		19 22

Station		SW	SW	SW	SW	SW	SW	SW	SW	SW
					B		C			
London Waterloo 15 ⊖	d	18 13	18 12	18 16	18 20	18 24	18 27	18 30	18 32	18 36
Vauxhall ⊖	d	18 17	18 16	18 20	18 24	18 28	18 31	18 34	18 37	18 40
Clapham Junction 10	d	18 23	18 21	18 25	18 29	18 33	18 36	18 39	18 42	18 45
Earlsfield	d		18 24	18 28	18 32	18 36	18 39	18 42	18 45	18 48
Wimbledon 6 ⊖ ⛴	d		18 28	18 32	18 36	18 40	18 43	18 46	18 49	18 52
Raynes Park 6	d		18 31	18 35		18 43	18 46	18 49		18 55
Motspur Park	d			18 38				18 52		
Malden Manor	d			18 41						
Tolworth	d			18 44						
Chessington North	d			18 47						
Chessington South	a			18 52						
Worcester Park	d					18 47		18 54		
Stoneleigh	d							18 57		
Ewell West	d							19 00		
Epsom 3	a					18 54		19 07		
	d					18 54				
Ashtead	d					18 58				
Leatherhead	d					19 01				
Box Hill & Westhumble	d					19 06				
Dorking 4	a					19 11				
New Malden 6	d		18 34				18 49			18 58
Norbiton	d		18 37				18 52			
Kingston	a		18 40				18 55			
	d		18 40				18 59			
Hampton Wick	d		18 42				19 01			
Teddington	d		18 45				19 05			
Strawberry Hill	a	18 41					19 08			
Fulwell	d	18 43	18 49							
Hampton	d	18 47	18 53							
Kempton Park	d		18 56							
Sunbury	d	18 51	18 58							
Upper Halliford	d	18 53	19 00							
Shepperton	a	18 58	19 10							
Berrylands	d									19 00
Surbiton 6	d				18a43				18 57	19 05
Thames Ditton	d									19 09
Hampton Court	a									19 14
Hinchley Wood	d								19 01	
Claygate	d								19 04	
Oxshott	d								19 07	
Cobham & Stoke D'abernon	d								19 11	
Bookham	d									
Effingham Junction 6	d								19 15	
Horsley	d								19 18	
Clandon	d								19 23	
London Road (Guildford)	d								19 28	
Guildford	a								19 34	

Station		SW	SW	SW	SW	SW	SW	SW	SW	SW	SW	SW	SW	SW	SW
							B		C						
London Waterloo 15 ⊖	d	18 39	18 43	18 42	18 46	18 48	18 50	18 54	18 57	19 00	19 02	19 06	19 09	19 12	19 16
Vauxhall ⊖	d	18 43	18 47	18 46	18 50		18 54	18 58	19 01	19 04	19 07	19 10	19 13	19 16	19 20
Clapham Junction 10	d	18 48	18 53	18 51	18 55		18 59	19 03	19 06	19 09	19 12	19 15	19 18	19 21	19 25
Earlsfield	d	18 51		18 54	18 58		19 02	19 06	19 09	19 12	19 15	19 18	19 21	19 24	19 28
Wimbledon 6 ⊖ ⛴	d	18 55		18 58	19 02		19 06	19 10	19 13	19 16	19 19	19 22	19 25	19 28	19 32
Raynes Park 6	d	18 58		19 01	19 05			19 13	19 16	19 19		19 25	19 28	19 31	19 35
Motspur Park	d	19 01			19 08					19 22			19 31		19 38
Malden Manor	d				19 11										19 41
Tolworth	d				19 14										19 44
Chessington North	d				19 17										19 47
Chessington South	a				19 22										19 50
Worcester Park	d	19 03						19 17		19 24			19 33		
Stoneleigh	d	19 06								19 27			19 36		
Ewell West	d	19 09								19 30			19 39		
Epsom 3	a	19 16						19 24		19 35			19 45		
	d	19 17						19 24					19 47		
Ashtead	d	19 21						19 28					19 51		
Leatherhead	d	19 24						19 31					19 54		
Box Hill & Westhumble	d							19 36							
Dorking 4	a							19 41							
New Malden 6	d			19 04					19 19			19 28		19 34	
Norbiton	d			19 07					19 22					19 37	
Kingston	a			19 10					19 25					19 40	
	d			19 10					19 29					19 40	
Hampton Wick	d			19 12					19 31					19 42	
Teddington	d			19 15					19 35					19 45	
Strawberry Hill	a		19 11						19 38						
Fulwell	d		19 13	19 19										19 49	
Hampton	d		19 17	19 23										19 53	
Kempton Park	d			19 26										19 56	
Sunbury	d		19 21	19 28										19 58	
Upper Halliford	d		19 23	19 30										20 00	
Shepperton	a		19 28	19 36										20 03	
Berrylands	d											19 30			
Surbiton 6	d					19 06	19a13				19 27	19 35			
Thames Ditton	d											19 39			
Hampton Court	a											19 42			
Hinchley Wood	d					19 10					19 31				
Claygate	d					19 13					19 34				
Oxshott	d					19 16					19 37				
Cobham & Stoke D'abernon	d					19 20					19 41				
Bookham	d	19 29											19 59		
Effingham Junction 6	d	19 33				19 24					19 45		20 03		
Horsley	d	19 36				19 27					19 48		20 06		
Clandon	d	19 41				19 32					19 53		20 11		
London Road (Guildford)	d	19 46				19 37					19 58		20 16		
Guildford	a	19 52				19 43					20 02		20 20		

A From London Bridge **B** To Woking **C** To London Waterloo

The xx27 and xx57 London Waterloo to Strawberry Hill services continues to London Waterloo via Richmond

Table 152

Mondays to Fridays

9 December to 16 May

London - Chessington South, Dorking, Guildford, Shepperton and Hampton Court

Network Diagram - see first Page of Table 152

		SW	SW A	SW	SW	SW	SW	SW	SW B	SW	SW A	SW	SW	SW
London Waterloo 15 ⊖	d	19 24	19 27	19 33	19 36	19 39	19 42	19 46	19 50	19 54	19 57	20 03	20 06	20 09
Vauxhall ⊖	d	19 28	19 31	19 37	19 40	19 43	19 46	19 50	19 54	19 58	20 01	20 07	20 10	20 13
Clapham Junction 10	d	19 33	19 36	19 42	19 45	19 48	19 51	19 55	19 59	20 03	20 06	20 12	20 15	20 18
Earlsfield	d	19 36	19 39	19 45	19 48	19 51	19 54	19 58	20 02	20 06	20 09	20 15	20 18	20 21
Wimbledon 6 ⊖	d	19 40	19 43	19 49	19 52	19 55	19 58	20 02	20 06	20 10	20 13	20 19	20 22	20 25
Raynes Park 6	d	19 43	19 46		19 55	19 58	20 01	20 05		20 13	20 16		20 25	20 28
Motspur Park	d	19 46				20 01		20 08		20 16				20 31
Malden Manor	d							20 11						
Tolworth	d							20 14						
Chessington North	d							20 17						
Chessington South	a							20 20						
Worcester Park	d	19 48				20 03				20 18				20 33
Stoneleigh	d	19 51				20 06				20 21				20 36
Ewell West	d	19 54				20 09				20 24				20 39
Epsom 3	a	19 57				20 16				20 27				20 42
	d	19 58				20 17								20 43
Ashtead	d	20 02				20 21								20 47
Leatherhead	d	20 05				20 24								20 50
Box Hill & Westhumble	d	20 10												20 55
Dorking 4	a	20 14												20 57
New Malden 6	d		19 49		19 58		20 04				20 19		20 28	
Norbiton	d		19 52				20 07				20 22			
Kingston	a		19 55				20 10				20 25			
	d		19 59				20 10				20 29			
Hampton Wick	d		20 01				20 12				20 31			
Teddington	d		20 05				20 15				20 35			
Strawberry Hill	a		20 08								20 38			
Fulwell	d						20 19							
Hampton	d						20 23							
Kempton Park	d						20 26							
Sunbury	d						20 28							
Upper Halliford	d						20 30							
Shepperton	a						20 33							
Berrylands	d				20 00								20 30	
Surbiton 6	d			19 57	20 05				20a13			20 27	20 35	
Thames Ditton	d				20 09								20 39	
Hampton Court	a				20 12								20 42	
Hinchley Wood	d			20 01								20 31		
Claygate	d			20 04								20 34		
Oxshott	d			20 07								20 37		
Cobham & Stoke D'abernon	d			20 11								20 41		
Bookham	d					20 29								
Effingham Junction 6	d			20 15		20 33						20 45		
Horsley	d			20 18		20 36						20 48		
Clandon	d			20 23		20 41						20 53		
London Road (Guildford)	d			20 28		20 46						20 58		
Guildford	a			20 32		20 50						21 02		

		SW	SW	SW B	SW	SW A	SW	SW	SW	SW
London Waterloo 15 ⊖	d	20 12	20 16	20 20	20 24	20 27	20 33	20 36	20 39	20 42
Vauxhall ⊖	d	20 16	20 20	20 24	20 28	20 31	20 37	20 40	20 43	20 46
Clapham Junction 10	d	20 21	20 25	20 29	20 33	20 36	20 42	20 45	20 48	20 51
Earlsfield	d	20 24	20 28	20 32	20 36	20 39	20 45	20 48	20 51	20 54
Wimbledon 6 ⊖	d	20 28	20 32	20 36	20 40	20 43	20 49	20 52	20 55	20 58
Raynes Park 6	d	20 31	20 35		20 43	20 46		20 55	20 58	21 01
Motspur Park	d		20 38		20 46				21 01	
Malden Manor	d		20 41							
Tolworth	d		20 44							
Chessington North	d		20 47							
Chessington South	a		20 50							
Worcester Park	d				20 48				21 03	
Stoneleigh	d				20 51				21 06	
Ewell West	d				20 54				21 09	
Epsom 3	a				20 57				21 12	
	d								21 13	
Ashtead	d								21 17	
Leatherhead	d								21 20	
Box Hill & Westhumble	d									
Dorking 4	a									
New Malden 6	d	20 34				20 49		20 58		21 04
Norbiton	d	20 37				20 52				21 07
Kingston	a	20 40				20 55				21 10
	d	20 40				20 59				21 10
Hampton Wick	d	20 42				21 01				21 12
Teddington	d	20 45				21 05				21 15
Strawberry Hill	a					21 08				
Fulwell	d	20 49								21 19
Hampton	d	20 53								21 23
Kempton Park	d	20 56								21 26
Sunbury	d	20 58								21 28
Upper Halliford	d	21 00								21 30
Shepperton	a	21 03								21 33
Berrylands	d							21 00		
Surbiton 6	d			20a43			20 57	21 05		
Thames Ditton	d							21 09		
Hampton Court	a							21 12		
Hinchley Wood	d						21 01			
Claygate	d						21 04			
Oxshott	d						21 07			
Cobham & Stoke D'abernon	d						21 11			
Bookham	d								21 25	
Effingham Junction 6	d						21 15		21 29	
Horsley	d						21 18		21 32	
Clandon	d						21 23		21 37	
London Road (Guildford)	d						21 28		21 42	
Guildford	a						21 32		21 46	

		SW	SW B	SW	SW A	SW	SW	SW	SW B	SW	SW A	SW	SW	SW	SW
London Waterloo 15 ⊖	d	20 46	20 50	20 54	20 57	21 03	21 09	21 12	21 20	21 24	21 27	21 33	21 36	21 39	21 42
Vauxhall ⊖	d	20 50	20 54	20 58	21 01	21 07	21 13	21 16	21 24	21 28	21 31	21 37	21 40	21 43	21 46
Clapham Junction 10	d	20 55	20 59	21 03	21 06	21 12	21 18	21 21	21 29	21 33	21 36	21 42	21 45	21 48	21 51
Earlsfield	d	20 58	21 02	21 06	21 09	21 15	21 21	21 24	21 32	21 36	21 39	21 45	21 48	21 51	21 54
Wimbledon 6 ⊖	d	21 02	21 06	21 10	21 13	21 19	21 25	21 28	21 36	21 40	21 43	21 49	21 52	21 55	21 58
Raynes Park 6	d	21 05		21 13	21 16		21 28	21 31		21 43	21 46		21 55	21 58	22 01
Motspur Park	d	21 08		21 16			21 31			21 46				22 01	
Malden Manor	d	21 11													
Tolworth	d	21 14													
Chessington North	d	21 17													
Chessington South	a	21 20													
Worcester Park	d			21 18			21 33			21 48				22 03	
Stoneleigh	d			21 21			21 36			21 51				22 06	
Ewell West	d			21 24			21 39			21 54				22 09	
Epsom 3	a			21 27			21 42			21 57				22 12	
	d						21 43							22 13	
Ashtead	d						21 47							22 17	
Leatherhead	d						21 50							22 20	
Box Hill & Westhumble	d						21 55								
Dorking 4	a						21 57								
New Malden 6	d				21 19			21 34			21 49		21 58		22 04
Norbiton	d				21 22			21 37			21 52				22 07
Kingston	a				21 25			21 40			21 55				22 10
	d				21 29			21 40			21 59				22 10
Hampton Wick	d				21 31			21 42			22 01				22 12
Teddington	d				21 35			21 45			22 05				22 15
Strawberry Hill	a				21 38						22 08				
Fulwell	d							21 49							22 19
Hampton	d							21 53							22 23
Kempton Park	d							21 56							22 26
Sunbury	d							21 58							22 28
Upper Halliford	d							22 00							22 30
Shepperton	a							22 03							22 33
Berrylands	d												22 00		
Surbiton 6	d		21a13			21 27			21a43			21 57	22 05		
Thames Ditton	d												22 09		
Hampton Court	a												22 12		
Hinchley Wood	d					21 31						22 01			
Claygate	d					21 34						22 04			
Oxshott	d					21 37						22 07			
Cobham & Stoke D'abernon	d					21 41						22 11			
Bookham	d													22 25	
Effingham Junction 6	d					21 45						22 15		22 29	
Horsley	d					21 48						22 18		22 32	
Clandon	d					21 53						22 23		22 37	
London Road (Guildford)	d					21 58						22 28		22 42	
Guildford	a					22 02						22 32		22 46	

A To London Waterloo

B To Woking

The xx27 and xx57 London Waterloo to Strawberry Hill services continues to London Waterloo via Richmond

Table 152

London - Chessington South, Dorking, Guildford, Shepperton and Hampton Court

Mondays to Fridays

9 December to 16 May

Network Diagram - see first Page of Table 152

		SW	SW	SW	SW	SW	SW	SW	SW	SW	SW	SW	SW	SW	SW	SW	SW	SW	SW	SW	SW	SW	SW	SW	SW	SW
					A				B	A					B	A					B	C				
London Waterloo 15 ⊖	d	21 46	21 50	21 54	21 57	22 03	22 09	22 12	22 20	22 27	22 33	22 36	22 39	22 42	22 50	22 57	23 00	23 03	23 09	23 12	23 20	23 27	23 36	23 42	23 50	23 57
Vauxhall ⊖	d	21 50	21 54	21 58	22 01	22 07	22 13	22 16	22 24	22 31	22 37	22 40	22 43	22 46	22 54	23 01	23 04	23 07	23 13	23 16	23 24	23 31	23 40	23 46	23 54	00 01
Clapham Junction 10	d	21 55	21 59	22 03	22 06	22 12	22 18	22 21	22 29	22 36	22 42	22 45	22 48	22 51	22 59	23 06	23 09	23 12	23 18	23 21	23 29	23 36	23 45	23 51	23 59	00 06
Earlsfield	d	21 58	22 02	22 06	22 09	22 15	22 21	22 24	22 32	22 39	22 45	22 48	22 51	22 54	23 02	23 09	23 12	23 15	23 21	23 24	23 32	23 39	23 48	23 54	00 02	00 09
Wimbledon 6 ⊖	d	22 02	22 06	22 10	22 13	22 19	22 25	22 28	22 36	22 43	22 49	22 52	22 55	22 58	23 06	23 13	23 16	23 19	23 25	23 28	23 36	23 43	23 52	23 58	00 06	00 13
Raynes Park 6	d	22 05		22 13	22 16		22 28	22 31		22 46		22 55	22 58	23 01		23 16	23 19		23 28	23 31		23 46	23 55	00 01		00 16
Motspur Park	d	22 08		22 16			22 31						23 01				23 22		23 31					00 04		
Malden Manor	d	22 11															23 25									
Tolworth	d	22 14															23 28									
Chessington North	d	22 17															23 31									
Chessington South	a	22 20															23 33									
Worcester Park	d			22 18			22 33						23 03						23 33					00 06		
Stoneleigh	d			22 21			22 36						23 06						23 36					00 09		
Ewell West	d			22 24			22 39						23 09						23 39					00 12		
Epsom 3	a			22 27			22 42						23 12						23 42					00 15		
	d						22 43						23 13						23 43					00 19		
Ashtead	d						22 47						23 17						23 47					00 23		
Leatherhead	d						22 50						23 20						23 50					00 26		
Box Hill & Westhumble	d						22 55												23 55							
Dorking 4	a						22 57												23 57							
New Malden 6	d				22 19			22 34		22 49		22 58		23 04		23 19				23 34		23 49	23 58			00 19
Norbiton	d				22 22			22 37		22 52				23 07		23 22				23 37		23 52				00 22
Kingston	a				22 25			22 40		22 55				23 10		23 25				23 40		23 55				00 25
	d				22 29			22 40		22 59				23 10		23 29				23 40		23 55				00 25
Hampton Wick	d				22 31			22 42		23 01				23 12		23 31				23 42		23 57				00 27
Teddington	d				22 35			22 45		23 05				23 15		23 35				23 45		23 59				00 30
Strawberry Hill	a				22 38					23 08						23 38						00 03				
Fulwell	d							22 49						23 19						23 49						00 34
Hampton	d							22 53						23 23						23 53						00 38
Kempton Park	d							22 56						23 26						23 56						00 41
Sunbury	d							22 58						23 28						23 58						00 43
Upper Halliford	d							23 00						23 30						23 59						00 45
Shepperton	a							23 03						23 33						00 03						00 48
Berrylands	d											23 00											23 59			
Surbiton 6	d		22 14			22 27			22a43		22 57	23 05			23a13			23 27			23a43		00 05		00 14	
Thames Ditton	d											23 09											00 09			
Hampton Court	a											23 12											00 12			
Hinchley Wood	d					22 31					23 01							23 31							00 18	
Claygate	d					22 34					23 04							23 34							00 20	
Oxshott	d					22 37					23 07							23 37							00 24	
Cobham & Stoke D'abernon	d					22 41					23 11							23 41							00 27	
Bookham	d												23 25											00 31		
Effingham Junction 6	d					22 45					23 15		23 29					23 45						00 36	00 32	
Horsley	d					22 48					23 18		23 32					23 48						00 39	00 34	
Clandon	d					22 53					23 23		23 37					23 53						00 44	00 39	
London Road (Guildford)	d					22 58					23 28		23 42					23 58						00 49	00 44	
Guildford	a		22 47			23 02					23 32		23 46					00 02						00 53	00 48	

A To London Waterloo

B To Woking

C To Twickenham

The xx27 and xx57 London Waterloo to Strawberry Hill services continues to London Waterloo via Richmond

Table 152

Saturdays

14 December to 17 May

London - Chessington South, Dorking, Guildford, Shepperton and Hampton Court

Network Diagram - see first Page of Table 152

Station		SW	SW	SW	SW	SW	SW	SW	SW	SW 1
		A	A	A	A			B		C
London Waterloo 15 ⊖	d					00 09	00 15	00 27	00 42	05 00
Vauxhall ⊖	d				00 01	00 13	00 19	00 31	00 46	05 04
Clapham Junction 10	d				00 06	00 20	00 25	00 37	00 51	05 11
Earlsfield	d		00 02		00 09	00 23	00 29	00s41		05 14
Wimbledon 6 ⊖ ⇌	d		00 06		00 13	00 27	00 33	00 45	01 05	05 18
Raynes Park 6	d			00 01	00 16		00 36	00 48	01 08	
Motspur Park	d			00 04			00 38			
Malden Manor	d									
Tolworth	d									
Chessington North	d									
Chessington South	a									
Worcester Park	d			00 06			00 41			
Stoneleigh	d			00 09			00 44			
Ewell West	d			00 12			00 46			
Epsom 3	a			00 15			00 50			
	d			00 19						
Ashtead	d			00 23						
Leatherhead	d			00 26						
Box Hill & Westhumble	d									
Dorking 4	a									
New Malden 6	d				00 19			00 50	01 11	
Norbiton	d				00 22				01 14	
Kingston	a				00 25				01 17	
	d				00 25				01 17	
Hampton Wick	d				00 27				01s19	
Teddington	d				00 30				01s22	
Strawberry Hill	a								01 28	
Fulwell	d				00 34					
Hampton	d				00 38					
Kempton Park	d				00 41					
Sunbury	d				00 43					
Upper Halliford	d				00 45					
Shepperton	a				00 48					
Berrylands	d							00s53		
Surbiton 6	d	00 05	00 14			00 35		00s56		05 26
Thames Ditton	d	00 09								
Hampton Court	a	00 12								
Hinchley Wood	d		00 18							
Claygate	d		00 20							
Oxshott	d		00 24							
Cobham & Stoke D'abernon	d		00 27							
Bookham	d			00 31						
Effingham Junction 6	d		00 32	00 36						
Horsley	d		00 34	00 39						
Clandon	d		00 39	00 44						
London Road (Guildford)	d		00 44	00 49						
Guildford	a		00 48	00 53		01 07				06 00

Station		SW	SW 1	SW	SW	SW	SW	SW	SW	SW
			D	B	E	E				B
London Waterloo 15 ⊖	d	05 12	05 20	05 50			06 06	06 12	06 16	06 20
Vauxhall ⊖	d	05 16	05 24	05 54			06 10	06 16	06 20	06 24
Clapham Junction 10	d	05 21	05 29	05 59			06 15	06 21	06 25	06 29
Earlsfield	d	05 24	05 32	06 02			06 18	06 24	06 28	06 32
Wimbledon 6 ⊖ ⇌	d	05 28	05 36	06 06		06 13	06 22	06 28	06 32	06 36
Raynes Park 6	d	05 31				06 16	06 25	06 31	06 35	
Motspur Park	d								06 38	
Malden Manor	d								06 41	
Tolworth	d								06 44	
Chessington North	d								06 47	
Chessington South	a								06 50	
Worcester Park	d									
Stoneleigh	d									
Ewell West	d									
Epsom 3	a									
	d									
Ashtead	d									
Leatherhead	d									
Box Hill & Westhumble	d									
Dorking 4	a									
New Malden 6	d	05 34				06 19	06 28	06 34		
Norbiton	d	05 37				06 22		06 37		
Kingston	a	05 40				06 25		06 40		
	d	05 40			05 59	06 29		06 40		
Hampton Wick	d	05 42			06 01	06 31		06 42		
Teddington	d	05 45			06 05	06 35		06 45		
Strawberry Hill	a				06 08	06 38				
Fulwell	d	05 49						06 49		
Hampton	d	05 53						06 53		
Kempton Park	d	05 56						06 56		
Sunbury	d	05 58						06 58		
Upper Halliford	d	06 00						07 00		
Shepperton	a	06 03						07 03		
Berrylands	d						06 30			
Surbiton 6	d		05 44	06a13			06 35			06a43
Thames Ditton	d						06 39			
Hampton Court	a						06 42			
Hinchley Wood	d									
Claygate	d									
Oxshott	d									
Cobham & Stoke D'abernon	d									
Bookham	d									
Effingham Junction 6	d									
Horsley	d									
Clandon	d									
London Road (Guildford)	d									
Guildford	a		06 23							

Station		SW	SW	SW	SW	SW	SW	SW	SW	SW
		E						B	E	
London Waterloo 15 ⊖	d	06 27	06 33	06 36	06 39	06 42	06 46	06 50	06 57	07 03
Vauxhall ⊖	d	06 31	06 37	06 40	06 43	06 46	06 50	06 54	07 01	07 07
Clapham Junction 10	d	06 36	06 42	06 45	06 48	06 51	06 55	06 59	07 06	07 12
Earlsfield	d	06 39	06 45	06 48	06 51	06 54	06 58	07 02	07 09	07 15
Wimbledon 6 ⊖ ⇌	d	06 43	06 49	06 52	06 55	06 58	07 02	07 06	07 13	07 19
Raynes Park 6	d	06 46		06 55	06 58	07 01	07 05		07 16	
Motspur Park	d				07 01		07 08			
Malden Manor	d						07 11			
Tolworth	d						07 14			
Chessington North	d						07 17			
Chessington South	a						07 20			
Worcester Park	d				07 03					
Stoneleigh	d				07 06					
Ewell West	d				07 09					
Epsom 3	a				07 16					
	d				07 17					
Ashtead	d				07 21					
Leatherhead	d				07 24					
Box Hill & Westhumble	d									
Dorking 4	a									
New Malden 6	d	06 49		06 58		07 04			07 19	
Norbiton	d	06 52				07 07			07 22	
Kingston	a	06 55				07 10			07 25	
	d	06 59				07 10			07 29	
Hampton Wick	d	07 01				07 12			07 31	
Teddington	d	07 05				07 15			07 35	
Strawberry Hill	a	07 08							07 38	
Fulwell	d					07 19				
Hampton	d					07 23				
Kempton Park	d					07 26				
Sunbury	d					07 28				
Upper Halliford	d					07 30				
Shepperton	a					07 33				
Berrylands	d			07 00						
Surbiton 6	d		06 57	07 05				07a13		07 27
Thames Ditton	d			07 09						
Hampton Court	a			07 12						
Hinchley Wood	d		07 01							07 31
Claygate	d		07 04							07 34
Oxshott	d		07 07							07 37
Cobham & Stoke D'abernon	d		07 11							07 41
Bookham	d				07 29					
Effingham Junction 6	d		07 15		07 33					07 45
Horsley	d		07 18		07 36					07 48
Clandon	d		07 23		07 41					07 53
London Road (Guildford)	d		07 28		07 46					07 58
Guildford	a		07 32		07 50					08 02

Station		SW	SW	SW	SW	SW	SW	SW	SW	SW
						B		E		
London Waterloo 15 ⊖	d	07 06	07 09	07 12	07 16	07 20	07 24	07 27	07 33	07 36
Vauxhall ⊖	d	07 10	07 13	07 16	07 20	07 24	07 28	07 31	07 37	07 40
Clapham Junction 10	d	07 15	07 18	07 21	07 25	07 29	07 33	07 36	07 42	07 45
Earlsfield	d	07 18	07 21	07 24	07 28	07 32	07 36	07 39	07 45	07 48
Wimbledon 6 ⊖ ⇌	d	07 22	07 25	07 28	07 32	07 36	07 40	07 43	07 49	07 52
Raynes Park 6	d	07 25	07 28	07 31	07 35		07 43	07 46		07 55
Motspur Park	d		07 31		07 38		07 46			
Malden Manor	d				07 41					
Tolworth	d				07 44					
Chessington North	d				07 47					
Chessington South	a				07 50					
Worcester Park	d		07 33				07 48			
Stoneleigh	d		07 36				07 51			
Ewell West	d		07 39				07 54			
Epsom 3	a		07 46				07 57			
	d		07 47				07 58			
Ashtead	d		07 51				08 02			
Leatherhead	d		07 54				08 05			
Box Hill & Westhumble	d									
Dorking 4	a						08 11			
New Malden 6	d	07 28		07 34				07 49		07 58
Norbiton	d			07 37				07 52		
Kingston	a			07 40				07 55		
	d			07 40				07 59		
Hampton Wick	d			07 42				08 01		
Teddington	d			07 45				08 05		
Strawberry Hill	a							08 08		
Fulwell	d			07 49						
Hampton	d			07 53						
Kempton Park	d			07 56						
Sunbury	d			07 58						
Upper Halliford	d			08 00						
Shepperton	a			08 03						
Berrylands	d	07 30								08 00
Surbiton 6	d	07 35				07a43			07 57	08 05
Thames Ditton	d	07 39								08 09
Hampton Court	a	07 42								08 12
Hinchley Wood	d								08 01	
Claygate	d								08 04	
Oxshott	d								08 07	
Cobham & Stoke D'abernon	d								08 11	
Bookham	d		07 59							
Effingham Junction 6	d		08 03						08 15	
Horsley	d		08 06						08 18	
Clandon	d		08 11						08 23	
London Road (Guildford)	d		08 16						08 28	
Guildford	a		08 20						08 32	

A From London Waterloo
B To Woking
C To Haslemere
D To Portsmouth Harbour
E To London Waterloo

The xx27 and xx57 London Waterloo to Strawberry Hill services continues to London Waterloo via Richmond

Table 152

Saturdays

14 December to 17 May

London - Chessington South, Dorking, Guildford, Shepperton and Hampton Court

Network Diagram - see first Page of Table 152

		SW	SW	SW	SW A	SW	SW B	SW	SW	SW	SW	SW	SW A	SW	SW B	SW	SW	SW	SW
London Waterloo 15 ⊖	d	07 39	07 42	07 46	07 50	07 54	07 57	08 03	08 06	08 09	08 12	08 16	08 20	08 24	08 27	08 33	08 36	08 39	08 42
Vauxhall ⊖	d	07 43	07 46	07 50	07 54	07 58	08 01	08 07	08 10	08 13	08 16	08 20	08 24	08 28	08 31	08 37	08 40	08 43	08 46
Clapham Junction 10	d	07 48	07 51	07 55	07 59	08 03	08 06	08 12	08 15	08 18	08 21	08 25	08 29	08 33	08 36	08 42	08 45	08 48	08 51
Earlsfield	d	07 51	07 54	07 58	08 02	08 06	08 09	08 15	08 18	08 21	08 24	08 28	08 32	08 36	08 39	08 45	08 48	08 51	08 54
Wimbledon 6 ⊖	d	07 55	07 58	08 02	08 06	08 10	08 13	08 19	08 22	08 25	08 28	08 32	08 36	08 40	08 43	08 49	08 52	08 55	08 58
Raynes Park 6	d	07 58	08 01	08 05		08 13	08 16		08 25	08 28	08 31	08 35		08 43	08 46		08 55	08 58	09 01
Motspur Park	d	08 01		08 08		08 16				08 31		08 38		08 46				09 01	
Malden Manor	d			08 11								08 41							
Tolworth	d			08 14								08 44							
Chessington North	d			08 17								08 47							
Chessington South	a			08 20								08 50							
Worcester Park	d	08 03				08 18				08 33				08 48				09 03	
Stoneleigh	d	08 06				08 21				08 36				08 51				09 06	
Ewell West	d	08 09				08 24				08 39				08 54				09 09	
Epsom 3	a	08 16				08 27				08 46				08 57				09 16	
	d	08 17				08 28				08 47				08 58				09 17	
Ashtead	d	08 21				08 32				08 51				09 02				09 21	
Leatherhead	d	08 24				08 35				08 54				09 05				09 24	
Box Hill & Westhumble	d																		
Dorking 4	a					08 41								09 11					
New Malden 6	d		08 04				08 19		08 28		08 34				08 49		08 58		09 04
Norbiton	d		08 07				08 22				08 37				08 52				09 07
Kingston	a		08 10				08 25				08 40				08 55				09 10
	d		08 10				08 29				08 40				08 59				09 10
Hampton Wick	d		08 12				08 31				08 42				09 01				09 12
Teddington	d		08 15				08 35				08 45				09 05				09 15
Strawberry Hill	a						08 38								09 08				
Fulwell	d		08 19								08 49								09 19
Hampton	d		08 23								08 53								09 23
Kempton Park	d		08 26								08 56								09 26
Sunbury	d		08 28								08 58								09 28
Upper Halliford	d		08 30								09 00								09 30
Shepperton	a		08 33								09 03								09 33
Berrylands	d								08 30								09 00		
Surbiton 6	d				08a13			08 27	08 35				08a43			08 57	09 05		
Thames Ditton	d								08 39								09 09		
Hampton Court	a								08 42								09 12		
Hinchley Wood	d							08 31								09 01			
Claygate	d							08 34								09 04			
Oxshott	d							08 37								09 07			
Cobham & Stoke D'abernon	d							08 41								09 11			
Bookham	d	08 29								08 59								09 29	
Effingham Junction 6	d	08 33						08 45		09 03						09 15		09 33	
Horsley	d	08 36						08 48		09 06						09 18		09 36	
Clandon	d	08 41						08 53		09 11						09 23		09 41	
London Road (Guildford)	d	08 46						08 58		09 16						09 28		09 46	
Guildford	a	08 50						09 02		09 20						09 32		09 50	

		SW	SW A	SW	SW B	SW	SW	SW	SW	SW	SW A	SW	SW B	SW	SW	SW	SW	SW	SW A
London Waterloo 15 ⊖	d	08 46	08 50	08 54	08 57	09 03	09 06	09 09	09 12	09 16	09 20	09 24	09 27	09 33	09 36	09 39	09 42	09 46	09 50
Vauxhall ⊖	d	08 50	08 54	08 58	09 01	09 07	09 10	09 13	09 16	09 20	09 24	09 28	09 31	09 37	09 40	09 43	09 46	09 50	09 54
Clapham Junction 10	d	08 55	08 59	09 03	09 06	09 12	09 15	09 18	09 21	09 25	09 29	09 33	09 36	09 42	09 45	09 48	09 51	09 55	09 59
Earlsfield	d	08 58	09 02	09 06	09 09	09 15	09 18	09 21	09 24	09 28	09 32	09 36	09 39	09 45	09 48	09 51	09 54	09 58	10 02
Wimbledon 6 ⊖	d	09 02	09 06	09 10	09 13	09 19	09 22	09 25	09 28	09 32	09 36	09 40	09 43	09 49	09 52	09 55	09 58	10 02	10 06
Raynes Park 6	d	09 05		09 13	09 16		09 25	09 28	09 31	09 35		09 43	09 46		09 55	09 58	10 01	10 05	
Motspur Park	d	09 08		09 16				09 31		09 38		09 46				10 01		10 08	
Malden Manor	d	09 11								09 41								10 11	
Tolworth	d	09 14								09 44								10 14	
Chessington North	d	09 17								09 47								10 17	
Chessington South	a	09 20								09 50								10 20	
Worcester Park	d			09 18				09 33				09 48				10 03			
Stoneleigh	d			09 21				09 36				09 51				10 06			
Ewell West	d			09 24				09 39				09 54				10 09			
Epsom 3	a			09 27				09 46				09 57				10 16			
	d			09 28				09 47				09 58				10 17			
Ashtead	d			09 32				09 51				10 02				10 21			
Leatherhead	d			09 35				09 54				10 05				10 24			
Box Hill & Westhumble	d																		
Dorking 4	a			09 41								10 11							
New Malden 6	d				09 19		09 28		09 34				09 49		09 58		10 04		
Norbiton	d				09 22				09 37				09 52				10 07		
Kingston	a				09 25				09 40				09 55				10 10		
	d				09 29				09 40				09 59				10 10		
Hampton Wick	d				09 31				09 42				10 01				10 12		
Teddington	d				09 35				09 45				10 05				10 15		
Strawberry Hill	a				09 38								10 08						
Fulwell	d								09 49								10 19		
Hampton	d								09 53								10 23		
Kempton Park	d								09 56								10 26		
Sunbury	d								09 58								10 28		
Upper Halliford	d								10 00								10 30		
Shepperton	a								10 03								10 33		
Berrylands	d						09 30								10 00				
Surbiton 6	d		09a13			09 27	09 35				09a43			09 57	10 05				10a13
Thames Ditton	d						09 39								10 09				
Hampton Court	a						09 42								10 12				
Hinchley Wood	d					09 31								10 01					
Claygate	d					09 34								10 04					
Oxshott	d					09 37								10 07					
Cobham & Stoke D'abernon	d					09 41								10 11					
Bookham	d							09 59								10 29			
Effingham Junction 6	d					09 45		10 03						10 15		10 33			
Horsley	d					09 48		10 06						10 18		10 36			
Clandon	d					09 53		10 11						10 23		10 41			
London Road (Guildford)	d					09 58		10 16						10 28		10 46			
Guildford	a					10 02		10 20						10 32		10 50			

A To Woking

B To London Waterloo

The xx27 and xx57 London Waterloo to Strawberry Hill services continues to London Waterloo via Richmond

Table 152

Saturdays

14 December to 17 May

London - Chessington South, Dorking, Guildford, Shepperton and Hampton Court

Network Diagram - see first Page of Table 152

Station		SW	SW A	SW	SW	SW	SW	SW	SW B	SW
London Waterloo 15 ⊖	d	09 54	09 57	10 03	10 06	10 09	10 12	10 16	10 20	10 24
Vauxhall ⊖	d	09 58	10 01	10 07	10 10	10 13	10 16	10 20	10 24	10 28
Clapham Junction 10	d	10 03	10 06	10 12	10 15	10 18	10 21	10 25	10 29	10 33
Earlsfield	d	10 06	10 09	10 15	10 18	10 21	10 24	10 28	10 32	10 36
Wimbledon 6 ⊖	d	10 10	10 13	10 19	10 22	10 25	10 28	10 32	10 36	10 40
Raynes Park 6	d	10 13	10 16		10 25	10 28	10 31	10 35		10 43
Motspur Park	d	10 16				10 31		10 38		10 46
Malden Manor	d							10 41		
Tolworth	d							10 44		
Chessington North	d							10 47		
Chessington South	a							10 50		
Worcester Park	d	10 18				10 33				10 48
Stoneleigh	d	10 21				10 36				10 51
Ewell West	d	10 24				10 39				10 54
Epsom 3	a	10 27				10 46				10 57
	d	10 28				10 47				10 58
Ashtead	d	10 32				10 51				11 02
Leatherhead	d	10 35				10 54				11 05
Box Hill & Westhumble	d									
Dorking 4	a	10 41								11 11
New Malden 6	d		10 19		10 28		10 34			
Norbiton	d		10 22				10 37			
Kingston	a		10 25				10 40			
	d		10 29				10 40			
Hampton Wick	d		10 31				10 42			
Teddington	d		10 35				10 45			
Strawberry Hill	a		10 38							
Fulwell	d						10 49			
Hampton	d						10 53			
Kempton Park	d						10 56			
Sunbury	d						10 58			
Upper Halliford	d						11 00			
Shepperton	a						11 03			
Berrylands	d				10 30					
Surbiton 6	d			10 27	10 35				10a43	
Thames Ditton	d				10 39					
Hampton Court	a				10 42					
Hinchley Wood	d			10 31						
Claygate	d			10 34						
Oxshott	d			10 37						
Cobham & Stoke D'abernon	d			10 41						
Bookham	d					10 59				
Effingham Junction 6	d			10 45		11 03				
Horsley	d			10 48		11 06				
Clandon	d			10 53		11 11				
London Road (Guildford)	d			10 58		11 16				
Guildford	a			11 02		11 20				

Station		SW A	SW	SW	SW	SW	SW	SW B	SW	SW A
London Waterloo 15 ⊖	d	10 27	10 33	10 36	10 39	10 42	10 46	10 50	10 54	10 57
Vauxhall ⊖	d	10 31	10 37	10 40	10 43	10 46	10 50	10 54	10 58	11 01
Clapham Junction 10	d	10 36	10 42	10 45	10 48	10 51	10 55	10 59	11 03	11 06
Earlsfield	d	10 39	10 45	10 48	10 51	10 54	10 58	11 02	11 06	11 09
Wimbledon 6 ⊖	d	10 43	10 49	10 52	10 55	10 58	11 02	11 06	11 10	11 13
Raynes Park 6	d	10 46		10 55	10 58	11 01	11 05		11 13	11 16
Motspur Park	d				11 01		11 08		11 16	
Malden Manor	d						11 11			
Tolworth	d						11 14			
Chessington North	d						11 17			
Chessington South	a						11 20			
Worcester Park	d				11 03				11 18	
Stoneleigh	d				11 06				11 21	
Ewell West	d				11 09				11 24	
Epsom 3	a				11 16				11 27	
	d				11 17				11 28	
Ashtead	d				11 21				11 32	
Leatherhead	d				11 24				11 35	
Box Hill & Westhumble	d									
Dorking 4	a								11 41	
New Malden 6	d	10 49		10 58		11 04				11 19
Norbiton	d	10 52				11 07				11 22
Kingston	a	10 55				11 10				11 25
	d	10 59				11 10				11 29
Hampton Wick	d	11 01				11 12				11 31
Teddington	d	11 05				11 15				11 35
Strawberry Hill	a	11 08								11 38
Fulwell	d					11 19				
Hampton	d					11 23				
Kempton Park	d					11 26				
Sunbury	d					11 28				
Upper Halliford	d					11 30				
Shepperton	a					11 33				
Berrylands	d			11 00						
Surbiton 6	d		10 57	11 05				11a13		
Thames Ditton	d			11 09						
Hampton Court	a			11 12						
Hinchley Wood	d		11 01							
Claygate	d		11 04							
Oxshott	d		11 07							
Cobham & Stoke D'abernon	d		11 11							
Bookham	d				11 29					
Effingham Junction 6	d		11 15		11 33					
Horsley	d		11 18		11 36					
Clandon	d		11 23		11 41					
London Road (Guildford)	d		11 28		11 46					
Guildford	a		11 32		11 50					

Station		SW	SW	SW	SW	SW	SW B	SW	SW A	SW
London Waterloo 15 ⊖	d	11 03	11 06	11 09	11 12	11 16	11 20	11 24	11 27	11 33
Vauxhall ⊖	d	11 07	11 10	11 13	11 16	11 20	11 24	11 28	11 31	11 37
Clapham Junction 10	d	11 12	11 15	11 18	11 21	11 25	11 29	11 33	11 36	11 42
Earlsfield	d	11 15	11 18	11 21	11 24	11 28	11 32	11 36	11 39	11 45
Wimbledon 6 ⊖	d	11 19	11 22	11 25	11 28	11 32	11 36	11 40	11 43	11 49
Raynes Park 6	d		11 25	11 28	11 31	11 35		11 43	11 46	
Motspur Park	d			11 31		11 38		11 46		
Malden Manor	d					11 41				
Tolworth	d					11 44				
Chessington North	d					11 47				
Chessington South	a					11 50				
Worcester Park	d			11 33				11 48		
Stoneleigh	d			11 36				11 51		
Ewell West	d			11 39				11 54		
Epsom 3	a			11 46				11 57		
	d			11 47				11 58		
Ashtead	d			11 51				12 02		
Leatherhead	d			11 54				12 05		
Box Hill & Westhumble	d									
Dorking 4	a							12 11		
New Malden 6	d		11 28		11 34				11 49	
Norbiton	d				11 37				11 52	
Kingston	a				11 40				11 55	
	d				11 40				11 59	
Hampton Wick	d				11 42				12 01	
Teddington	d				11 45				12 05	
Strawberry Hill	a								12 08	
Fulwell	d				11 49					
Hampton	d				11 53					
Kempton Park	d				11 56					
Sunbury	d				11 58					
Upper Halliford	d				12 00					
Shepperton	a				12 03					
Berrylands	d		11 30							
Surbiton 6	d	11 27	11 35				11a43			11 57
Thames Ditton	d		11 39							
Hampton Court	a		11 42							
Hinchley Wood	d	11 31								12 01
Claygate	d	11 34								12 04
Oxshott	d	11 37								12 07
Cobham & Stoke D'abernon	d	11 41								12 11
Bookham	d			11 59						
Effingham Junction 6	d	11 45		12 03						12 15
Horsley	d	11 48		12 06						12 18
Clandon	d	11 53		12 11						12 23
London Road (Guildford)	d	11 58		12 16						12 28
Guildford	a	12 02		12 20						12 32

Station		SW	SW	SW	SW	SW B	SW	SW A	SW	SW
London Waterloo 15 ⊖	d	11 36	11 39	11 42	11 46	11 50	11 54	11 57	12 03	12 06
Vauxhall ⊖	d	11 40	11 43	11 46	11 50	11 54	11 58	12 01	12 07	12 10
Clapham Junction 10	d	11 45	11 48	11 51	11 55	11 59	12 03	12 06	12 12	12 15
Earlsfield	d	11 48	11 51	11 54	11 58	12 02	12 06	12 09	12 15	12 18
Wimbledon 6 ⊖	d	11 52	11 55	11 58	12 02	12 06	12 10	12 13	12 19	12 22
Raynes Park 6	d	11 55	11 58	12 01	12 05		12 13	12 16		12 25
Motspur Park	d		12 01		12 08		12 16			
Malden Manor	d				12 11					
Tolworth	d				12 14					
Chessington North	d				12 17					
Chessington South	a				12 20					
Worcester Park	d		12 03				12 18			
Stoneleigh	d		12 06				12 21			
Ewell West	d		12 09				12 24			
Epsom 3	a		12 16				12 27			
	d		12 17				12 28			
Ashtead	d		12 21				12 32			
Leatherhead	d		12 24				12 35			
Box Hill & Westhumble	d									
Dorking 4	a						12 41			
New Malden 6	d	11 58		12 04				12 19		12 28
Norbiton	d			12 07				12 22		
Kingston	a			12 10				12 25		
	d			12 10				12 29		
Hampton Wick	d			12 12				12 31		
Teddington	d			12 15				12 35		
Strawberry Hill	a							12 38		
Fulwell	d			12 19						
Hampton	d			12 23						
Kempton Park	d			12 26						
Sunbury	d			12 28						
Upper Halliford	d			12 30						
Shepperton	a			12 33						
Berrylands	d	12 00								12 30
Surbiton 6	d	12 05				12a13			12 27	12 35
Thames Ditton	d	12 09								12 39
Hampton Court	a	12 12								12 42
Hinchley Wood	d								12 31	
Claygate	d								12 34	
Oxshott	d								12 37	
Cobham & Stoke D'abernon	d								12 41	
Bookham	d		12 29							
Effingham Junction 6	d		12 33						12 45	
Horsley	d		12 36						12 48	
Clandon	d		12 41						12 53	
London Road (Guildford)	d		12 46						12 58	
Guildford	a		12 50						13 02	

A To London Waterloo

B To Woking

The xx27 and xx57 London Waterloo to Strawberry Hill services continues to London Waterloo via Richmond

Table 152

Saturdays

14 December to 17 May

London - Chessington South, Dorking, Guildford, Shepperton and Hampton Court

Network Diagram - see first Page of Table 152

Station		SW	SW	SW	SW A	SW	SW B	SW	SW	SW
London Waterloo 15 ⊖	d	12 09	12 12	12 16	12 20	12 24	12 27	12 33	12 36	12 39
Vauxhall ⊖	d	12 13	12 16	12 20	12 24	12 28	12 31	12 37	12 40	12 43
Clapham Junction 10	d	12 18	12 21	12 25	12 29	12 33	12 36	12 42	12 45	12 48
Earlsfield	d	12 21	12 24	12 28	12 32	12 36	12 39	12 45	12 48	12 51
Wimbledon 6 ⊖	d	12 25	12 28	12 32	12 36	12 40	12 43	12 49	12 52	12 55
Raynes Park 6	d	12 28	12 31	12 35		12 43	12 46		12 55	12 58
Motspur Park	d	12 31		12 38		12 46				13 01
Malden Manor	d			12 41						
Tolworth	d			12 44						
Chessington North	d			12 47						
Chessington South	a			12 50						
Worcester Park	d	12 33				12 48				13 03
Stoneleigh	d	12 36				12 51				13 06
Ewell West	d	12 39				12 54				13 09
Epsom 3	a	12 46				12 57				13 16
	d	12 47				12 58				13 17
Ashtead	d	12 51				13 02				13 21
Leatherhead	d	12 54				13 05				13 24
Box Hill & Westhumble	d									
Dorking 4	a					13 11				
New Malden 6	d		12 34				12 49		12 58	
Norbiton	d		12 37				12 52			
Kingston	a		12 40				12 55			
	d		12 40				12 59			
Hampton Wick	d		12 42				13 01			
Teddington	d		12 45				13 05			
Strawberry Hill	a						13 08			
Fulwell	d		12 49							
Hampton	d		12 53							
Kempton Park	d		12 56							
Sunbury	d		12 58							
Upper Halliford	d		13 00							
Shepperton	a		13 03							
Berrylands	d								13 00	
Surbiton 6	d				12a43			12 57	13 05	
Thames Ditton	d								13 09	
Hampton Court	a								13 12	
Hinchley Wood	d							13 01		
Claygate	d							13 04		
Oxshott	d							13 07		
Cobham & Stoke D'abernon	d							13 11		
Bookham	d	12 59								13 29
Effingham Junction 6	d	13 03						13 15		13 33
Horsley	d	13 06						13 18		13 36
Clandon	d	13 11						13 23		13 41
London Road (Guildford)	d	13 16						13 28		13 46
Guildford	a	13 20						13 32		13 50

Station		SW	SW	SW A	SW	SW B	SW	SW	SW	SW
London Waterloo 15 ⊖	d	12 42	12 46	12 50	12 54	12 57	13 03	13 06	13 09	13 12
Vauxhall ⊖	d	12 46	12 50	12 54	12 58	13 01	13 07	13 10	13 13	13 16
Clapham Junction 10	d	12 51	12 55	12 59	13 03	13 06	13 12	13 15	13 18	13 21
Earlsfield	d	12 54	12 58	13 02	13 06	13 09	13 15	13 18	13 21	13 24
Wimbledon 6 ⊖	d	12 58	13 02	13 06	13 10	13 13	13 19	13 22	13 25	13 28
Raynes Park 6	d	13 01	13 05		13 13	13 16		13 25	13 28	13 31
Motspur Park	d		13 08		13 16				13 31	
Malden Manor	d		13 11							
Tolworth	d		13 14							
Chessington North	d		13 17							
Chessington South	a		13 20							
Worcester Park	d				13 18				13 33	
Stoneleigh	d				13 21				13 36	
Ewell West	d				13 24				13 39	
Epsom 3	a				13 27				13 46	
	d				13 28				13 47	
Ashtead	d				13 32				13 51	
Leatherhead	d				13 35				13 54	
Box Hill & Westhumble	d									
Dorking 4	a				13 41					
New Malden 6	d	13 04				13 19		13 28		13 34
Norbiton	d	13 07				13 22				13 37
Kingston	a	13 10				13 25				13 40
	d	13 10				13 29				13 40
Hampton Wick	d	13 12				13 31				13 42
Teddington	d	13 15				13 35				13 45
Strawberry Hill	a					13 38				
Fulwell	d	13 19								13 49
Hampton	d	13 23								13 53
Kempton Park	d	13 26								13 56
Sunbury	d	13 28								13 58
Upper Halliford	d	13 30								14 00
Shepperton	a	13 33								14 03
Berrylands	d							13 30		
Surbiton 6	d			13a13			13 27	13 35		
Thames Ditton	d							13 39		
Hampton Court	a							13 42		
Hinchley Wood	d						13 31			
Claygate	d						13 34			
Oxshott	d						13 37			
Cobham & Stoke D'abernon	d						13 41			
Bookham	d								13 59	
Effingham Junction 6	d						13 45		14 03	
Horsley	d						13 48		14 06	
Clandon	d						13 53		14 11	
London Road (Guildford)	d						13 58		14 16	
Guildford	a						14 02		14 20	

Station		SW	SW A	SW	SW B	SW	SW	SW	SW	SW
London Waterloo 15 ⊖	d	13 16	13 20	13 24	13 27	13 33	13 36	13 39	13 42	13 46
Vauxhall ⊖	d	13 20	13 24	13 28	13 31	13 37	13 40	13 43	13 46	13 50
Clapham Junction 10	d	13 25	13 29	13 33	13 36	13 42	13 45	13 48	13 51	13 55
Earlsfield	d	13 28	13 32	13 36	13 39	13 45	13 48	13 51	13 54	13 58
Wimbledon 6 ⊖	d	13 32	13 36	13 40	13 43	13 49	13 52	13 55	13 58	14 02
Raynes Park 6	d	13 35		13 43	13 46		13 55	13 58	14 01	14 05
Motspur Park	d	13 38		13 46				14 01		14 08
Malden Manor	d	13 41								14 11
Tolworth	d	13 44								14 14
Chessington North	d	13 47								14 17
Chessington South	a	13 50								14 20
Worcester Park	d			13 48				14 03		
Stoneleigh	d			13 51				14 06		
Ewell West	d			13 54				14 09		
Epsom 3	a			13 57				14 16		
	d			13 58				14 17		
Ashtead	d			14 02				14 21		
Leatherhead	d			14 05				14 24		
Box Hill & Westhumble	d									
Dorking 4	a			14 11						
New Malden 6	d				13 49		13 58		14 04	
Norbiton	d				13 52				14 07	
Kingston	a				13 55				14 10	
	d				13 59				14 10	
Hampton Wick	d				14 01				14 12	
Teddington	d				14 05				14 15	
Strawberry Hill	a				14 08					
Fulwell	d								14 19	
Hampton	d								14 23	
Kempton Park	d								14 26	
Sunbury	d								14 28	
Upper Halliford	d								14 30	
Shepperton	a								14 33	
Berrylands	d						14 00			
Surbiton 6	d		13a43			13 57	14 05			
Thames Ditton	d						14 09			
Hampton Court	a						14 12			
Hinchley Wood	d					14 01				
Claygate	d					14 04				
Oxshott	d					14 07				
Cobham & Stoke D'abernon	d					14 11				
Bookham	d							14 29		
Effingham Junction 6	d					14 15		14 33		
Horsley	d					14 18		14 36		
Clandon	d					14 23		14 41		
London Road (Guildford)	d					14 28		14 46		
Guildford	a					14 32		14 50		

Station		SW A	SW	SW B	SW	SW	SW	SW	SW	SW A
London Waterloo 15 ⊖	d	13 50	13 54	13 57	14 03	14 06	14 09	14 12	14 16	14 20
Vauxhall ⊖	d	13 54	13 58	14 01	14 07	14 10	14 13	14 16	14 20	14 24
Clapham Junction 10	d	13 59	14 03	14 06	14 12	14 15	14 18	14 21	14 25	14 29
Earlsfield	d	14 02	14 06	14 09	14 15	14 18	14 21	14 24	14 28	14 32
Wimbledon 6 ⊖	d	14 06	14 10	14 13	14 19	14 22	14 25	14 28	14 32	14 36
Raynes Park 6	d		14 13	14 16		14 25	14 28	14 31	14 35	
Motspur Park	d		14 16				14 31		14 38	
Malden Manor	d								14 41	
Tolworth	d								14 44	
Chessington North	d								14 47	
Chessington South	a								14 50	
Worcester Park	d		14 18				14 33			
Stoneleigh	d		14 21				14 36			
Ewell West	d		14 24				14 39			
Epsom 3	a		14 27				14 46			
	d		14 28				14 47			
Ashtead	d		14 32				14 51			
Leatherhead	d		14 35				14 54			
Box Hill & Westhumble	d									
Dorking 4	a		14 41							
New Malden 6	d			14 19		14 28		14 34		
Norbiton	d			14 22				14 37		
Kingston	a			14 25				14 40		
	d			14 29				14 40		
Hampton Wick	d			14 31				14 42		
Teddington	d			14 35				14 45		
Strawberry Hill	a			14 38						
Fulwell	d							14 49		
Hampton	d							14 53		
Kempton Park	d							14 56		
Sunbury	d							14 58		
Upper Halliford	d							15 00		
Shepperton	a							15 03		
Berrylands	d					14 30				
Surbiton 6	d	14a13			14 27	14 35				14a43
Thames Ditton	d					14 39				
Hampton Court	a					14 42				
Hinchley Wood	d				14 31					
Claygate	d				14 34					
Oxshott	d				14 37					
Cobham & Stoke D'abernon	d				14 41					
Bookham	d						14 59			
Effingham Junction 6	d				14 45		15 03			
Horsley	d				14 48		15 06			
Clandon	d				14 53		15 11			
London Road (Guildford)	d				14 58		15 16			
Guildford	a				15 02		15 20			

A To Woking

B To London Waterloo

The xx27 and xx57 London Waterloo to Strawberry Hill services continues to London Waterloo via Richmond

Table 152

Saturdays

14 December to 17 May

London - Chessington South, Dorking, Guildford, Shepperton and Hampton Court

Network Diagram - see first Page of Table 152

Station		SW	SW A	SW	SW	SW	SW	SW	SW B	SW
London Waterloo 15 ⊖	d	14 24	14 27	14 33	14 36	14 39	14 42	14 46	14 50	14 54
Vauxhall ⊖	d	14 28	14 31	14 37	14 40	14 43	14 46	14 50	14 54	14 58
Clapham Junction 10	d	14 33	14 36	14 42	14 45	14 48	14 51	14 55	14 59	15 03
Earlsfield	d	14 36	14 39	14 45	14 48	14 51	14 54	14 58	15 02	15 06
Wimbledon 6 ⊖	d	14 40	14 43	14 49	14 52	14 55	14 58	15 02	15 06	15 10
Raynes Park 6	d	14 43	14 46		14 55	14 58	15 01	15 05		15 13
Motspur Park	d	14 46				15 01		15 08		15 16
Malden Manor	d							15 11		
Tolworth	d							15 14		
Chessington North	d							15 17		
Chessington South	a							15 20		
Worcester Park	d	14 48				15 03				15 18
Stoneleigh	d	14 51				15 06				15 21
Ewell West	d	14 54				15 09				15 24
Epsom 3	a	14 57				15 16				15 27
	d	14 58				15 17				15 28
Ashtead	d	15 02				15 21				15 32
Leatherhead	d	15 05				15 24				15 35
Box Hill & Westhumble	d									
Dorking 4	a	15 11								15 41
New Malden 6	d		14 49		14 58		15 04			
Norbiton	d		14 52				15 07			
Kingston	a		14 55				15 10			
	d		14 59				15 10			
Hampton Wick	d		15 01				15 12			
Teddington	d		15 05				15 15			
Strawberry Hill	a		15 08							
Fulwell	d						15 19			
Hampton	d						15 23			
Kempton Park	d						15 26			
Sunbury	d						15 28			
Upper Halliford	d						15 30			
Shepperton	a						15 33			
Berrylands	d				15 00					
Surbiton 6	d			14 57	15 05				15a13	
Thames Ditton	d				15 09					
Hampton Court	a				15 12					
Hinchley Wood	d			15 01						
Claygate	d			15 04						
Oxshott	d			15 07						
Cobham & Stoke D'abernon	d			15 11						
Bookham	d					15 29				
Effingham Junction 6	d			15 15		15 33				
Horsley	d			15 18		15 36				
Clandon	d			15 23		15 41				
London Road (Guildford)	d			15 28		15 46				
Guildford	a			15 32		15 50				

Station		SW A	SW	SW	SW	SW	SW	SW B	SW	SW A
London Waterloo 15 ⊖	d	14 57	15 03	15 06	15 09	15 12	15 16	15 20	15 24	15 27
Vauxhall ⊖	d	15 01	15 07	15 10	15 13	15 16	15 20	15 24	15 28	15 31
Clapham Junction 10	d	15 06	15 12	15 15	15 18	15 21	15 25	15 29	15 33	15 36
Earlsfield	d	15 09	15 15	15 18	15 21	15 24	15 28	15 32	15 36	15 39
Wimbledon 6 ⊖	d	15 13	15 19	15 22	15 25	15 28	15 32	15 36	15 40	15 43
Raynes Park 6	d	15 16		15 25	15 28	15 31	15 35		15 43	15 46
Motspur Park	d				15 31		15 38		15 46	
Malden Manor	d						15 41			
Tolworth	d						15 44			
Chessington North	d						15 47			
Chessington South	a						15 50			
Worcester Park	d				15 33				15 48	
Stoneleigh	d				15 36				15 51	
Ewell West	d				15 39				15 54	
Epsom 3	a				15 46				15 57	
	d				15 47				15 58	
Ashtead	d				15 51				16 02	
Leatherhead	d				15 54				16 05	
Box Hill & Westhumble	d									
Dorking 4	a								16 11	
New Malden 6	d	15 19		15 28		15 34				15 49
Norbiton	d	15 22				15 37				15 52
Kingston	a	15 25				15 40				15 55
	d	15 29				15 40				15 59
Hampton Wick	d	15 31				15 42				16 01
Teddington	d	15 35				15 45				16 05
Strawberry Hill	a	15 38								16 08
Fulwell	d					15 49				
Hampton	d					15 53				
Kempton Park	d					15 56				
Sunbury	d					15 58				
Upper Halliford	d					16 00				
Shepperton	a					16 03				
Berrylands	d			15 30						
Surbiton 6	d		15 27	15 35				15a43		
Thames Ditton	d			15 39						
Hampton Court	a			15 42						
Hinchley Wood	d		15 31							
Claygate	d		15 34							
Oxshott	d		15 37							
Cobham & Stoke D'abernon	d		15 41							
Bookham	d				15 59					
Effingham Junction 6	d		15 45		16 03					
Horsley	d		15 48		16 06					
Clandon	d		15 53		16 11					
London Road (Guildford)	d		15 58		16 16					
Guildford	a		16 02		16 20					

Station		SW	SW	SW	SW	SW	SW B	SW	SW A	SW
London Waterloo 15 ⊖	d	15 33	15 36	15 39	15 42	15 46	15 50	15 54	15 57	16 03
Vauxhall ⊖	d	15 37	15 40	15 43	15 46	15 50	15 54	15 58	16 01	16 07
Clapham Junction 10	d	15 42	15 45	15 48	15 51	15 55	15 59	16 03	16 06	16 12
Earlsfield	d	15 45	15 48	15 51	15 54	15 58	16 02	16 06	16 09	16 15
Wimbledon 6 ⊖	d	15 49	15 52	15 55	15 58	16 02	16 06	16 10	16 13	16 19
Raynes Park 6	d		15 55	15 58	16 01	16 05		16 13	16 16	
Motspur Park	d			16 01		16 08		16 16		
Malden Manor	d					16 11				
Tolworth	d					16 14				
Chessington North	d					16 17				
Chessington South	a					16 20				
Worcester Park	d			16 03				16 18		
Stoneleigh	d			16 06				16 21		
Ewell West	d			16 09				16 24		
Epsom 3	a			16 16				16 27		
	d			16 17				16 28		
Ashtead	d			16 21				16 32		
Leatherhead	d			16 24				16 35		
Box Hill & Westhumble	d									
Dorking 4	a							16 41		
New Malden 6	d		15 58		16 04				16 19	
Norbiton	d				16 07				16 22	
Kingston	a				16 10				16 25	
	d				16 10				16 29	
Hampton Wick	d				16 12				16 31	
Teddington	d				16 15				16 35	
Strawberry Hill	a								16 38	
Fulwell	d				16 19					
Hampton	d				16 23					
Kempton Park	d				16 26					
Sunbury	d				16 28					
Upper Halliford	d				16 30					
Shepperton	a				16 33					
Berrylands	d		16 00							
Surbiton 6	d	15 57	16 05				16a13			16 27
Thames Ditton	d		16 09							
Hampton Court	a		16 12							
Hinchley Wood	d	16 01								16 31
Claygate	d	16 04								16 34
Oxshott	d	16 07								16 37
Cobham & Stoke D'abernon	d	16 11								16 41
Bookham	d			16 29						
Effingham Junction 6	d	16 15		16 33						16 45
Horsley	d	16 18		16 36						16 48
Clandon	d	16 23		16 41						16 53
London Road (Guildford)	d	16 28		16 46						16 58
Guildford	a	16 32		16 50						17 02

Station		SW	SW	SW	SW	SW B	SW	SW A	SW	SW
London Waterloo 15 ⊖	d	16 06	16 09	16 12	16 16	16 20	16 24	16 27	16 33	16 36
Vauxhall ⊖	d	16 10	16 13	16 16	16 20	16 24	16 28	16 31	16 37	16 40
Clapham Junction 10	d	16 15	16 18	16 21	16 25	16 29	16 33	16 36	16 42	16 45
Earlsfield	d	16 18	16 21	16 24	16 28	16 32	16 36	16 39	16 45	16 48
Wimbledon 6 ⊖	d	16 22	16 25	16 28	16 32	16 36	16 40	16 43	16 49	16 52
Raynes Park 6	d	16 25	16 28	16 31	16 35		16 43	16 46		16 55
Motspur Park	d		16 31		16 38		16 46			
Malden Manor	d				16 41					
Tolworth	d				16 44					
Chessington North	d				16 47					
Chessington South	a				16 50					
Worcester Park	d		16 33				16 48			
Stoneleigh	d		16 36				16 51			
Ewell West	d		16 39				16 54			
Epsom 3	a		16 46				16 57			
	d		16 47				16 58			
Ashtead	d		16 51				17 02			
Leatherhead	d		16 54				17 05			
Box Hill & Westhumble	d									
Dorking 4	a						17 11			
New Malden 6	d	16 28		16 34				16 49		16 58
Norbiton	d			16 37				16 52		
Kingston	a			16 40				16 55		
	d			16 40				16 59		
Hampton Wick	d			16 42				17 01		
Teddington	d			16 45				17 05		
Strawberry Hill	a							17 08		
Fulwell	d			16 49						
Hampton	d			16 53						
Kempton Park	d			16 56						
Sunbury	d			16 58						
Upper Halliford	d			17 00						
Shepperton	a			17 03						
Berrylands	d	16 30								17 00
Surbiton 6	d	16 35				16a43			16 57	17 05
Thames Ditton	d	16 39								17 09
Hampton Court	a	16 42								17 12
Hinchley Wood	d								17 01	
Claygate	d								17 04	
Oxshott	d								17 07	
Cobham & Stoke D'abernon	d								17 11	
Bookham	d		16 59							
Effingham Junction 6	d		17 03						17 15	
Horsley	d		17 06						17 18	
Clandon	d		17 11						17 23	
London Road (Guildford)	d		17 16						17 28	
Guildford	a		17 20						17 32	

A To London Waterloo

B To Woking

The xx27 and xx57 London Waterloo to Strawberry Hill services continues to London Waterloo via Richmond

Table 152

Saturdays

14 December to 17 May

London - Chessington South, Dorking, Guildford, Shepperton and Hampton Court

Network Diagram - see first Page of Table 152

Station		SW	SW	SW	SW A	SW	SW B	SW	SW	SW
London Waterloo 15 ⊖	d	16 39	16 42	16 46	16 50	16 54	16 57	17 03	17 06	17 09
Vauxhall ⊖	d	16 43	16 46	16 50	16 54	16 58	17 01	17 07	17 10	17 13
Clapham Junction 10	d	16 48	16 51	16 55	16 59	17 03	17 06	17 12	17 15	17 18
Earlsfield	d	16 51	16 54	16 58	17 02	17 06	17 09	17 15	17 18	17 21
Wimbledon 6 ⊖	d	16 55	16 58	17 02	17 06	17 10	17 13	17 19	17 22	17 25
Raynes Park 6	d	16 58	17 01	17 05		17 13	17 16		17 25	17 28
Motspur Park	d	17 01		17 08		17 16				17 31
Malden Manor	d			17 11						
Tolworth	d			17 14						
Chessington North	d			17 17						
Chessington South	a			17 20						
Worcester Park	d	17 03				17 18				17 33
Stoneleigh	d	17 06				17 21				17 36
Ewell West	d	17 09				17 24				17 39
Epsom 3	a	17 16				17 27				17 46
	d	17 17				17 28				17 47
Ashtead	d	17 21				17 32				17 51
Leatherhead	d	17 24				17 35				17 54
Box Hill & Westhumble	d									
Dorking 4	a					17 41				
New Malden 6	d		17 04				17 19		17 28	
Norbiton	d		17 07				17 22			
Kingston	a		17 10				17 25			
	d		17 10				17 29			
Hampton Wick	d		17 12				17 31			
Teddington	d		17 15				17 35			
Strawberry Hill	a						17 38			
Fulwell	d		17 19							
Hampton	d		17 23							
Kempton Park	d		17 26							
Sunbury	d		17 28							
Upper Halliford	d		17 30							
Shepperton	a		17 33							
Berrylands	d								17 30	
Surbiton 6	d				17a13			17 27	17 35	
Thames Ditton	d								17 39	
Hampton Court	a								17 42	
Hinchley Wood	d							17 31		
Claygate	d							17 34		
Oxshott	d							17 37		
Cobham & Stoke D'abernon	d							17 41		
Bookham	d	17 29								17 59
Effingham Junction 6	d	17 33						17 45		18 03
Horsley	d	17 36						17 48		18 06
Clandon	d	17 41						17 53		18 11
London Road (Guildford)	d	17 46						17 58		18 16
Guildford	a	17 50						18 02		18 20

Station		SW	SW	SW A	SW	SW B	SW	SW	SW	SW
London Waterloo 15 ⊖	d	17 12	17 16	17 20	17 24	17 27	17 33	17 36	17 39	17 42
Vauxhall ⊖	d	17 16	17 20	17 24	17 28	17 31	17 37	17 40	17 43	17 46
Clapham Junction 10	d	17 21	17 25	17 29	17 33	17 36	17 42	17 45	17 48	17 51
Earlsfield	d	17 24	17 28	17 32	17 36	17 39	17 45	17 48	17 51	17 54
Wimbledon 6 ⊖	d	17 28	17 32	17 36	17 40	17 43	17 49	17 52	17 55	17 58
Raynes Park 6	d	17 31	17 35		17 43	17 46		17 55	17 58	18 01
Motspur Park	d		17 38		17 46				18 01	
Malden Manor	d		17 41							
Tolworth	d		17 44							
Chessington North	d		17 47							
Chessington South	a		17 50							
Worcester Park	d				17 48				18 03	
Stoneleigh	d				17 51				18 06	
Ewell West	d				17 54				18 09	
Epsom 3	a				17 57				18 16	
	d				17 58				18 17	
Ashtead	d				18 02				18 21	
Leatherhead	d				18 05				18 24	
Box Hill & Westhumble	d									
Dorking 4	a				18 11					
New Malden 6	d	17 34				17 49		17 58		18 04
Norbiton	d	17 37				17 52				18 07
Kingston	a	17 40				17 55				18 10
	d	17 40				17 59				18 10
Hampton Wick	d	17 42				18 01				18 12
Teddington	d	17 45				18 05				18 15
Strawberry Hill	a					18 08				
Fulwell	d	17 49								18 19
Hampton	d	17 53								18 23
Kempton Park	d	17 56								18 26
Sunbury	d	17 58								18 28
Upper Halliford	d	18 00								18 30
Shepperton	a	18 03								18 33
Berrylands	d							18 00		
Surbiton 6	d			17a43			17 57	18 05		
Thames Ditton	d							18 09		
Hampton Court	a							18 12		
Hinchley Wood	d						18 01			
Claygate	d						18 04			
Oxshott	d						18 07			
Cobham & Stoke D'abernon	d						18 11			
Bookham	d								18 29	
Effingham Junction 6	d						18 15		18 33	
Horsley	d						18 18		18 36	
Clandon	d						18 23		18 41	
London Road (Guildford)	d						18 28		18 46	
Guildford	a						18 32		18 50	

Station		SW	SW A	SW	SW B	SW	SW	SW	SW	SW
London Waterloo 15 ⊖	d	17 46	17 50	17 54	17 57	18 03	18 06	18 09	18 12	18 16
Vauxhall ⊖	d	17 50	17 54	17 58	18 01	18 07	18 10	18 13	18 16	18 20
Clapham Junction 10	d	17 55	17 59	18 03	18 06	18 12	18 15	18 18	18 21	18 25
Earlsfield	d	17 58	18 02	18 06	18 09	18 15	18 18	18 21	18 24	18 28
Wimbledon 6 ⊖	d	18 02	18 06	18 10	18 13	18 19	18 22	18 25	18 28	18 32
Raynes Park 6	d	18 05		18 13	18 16		18 25	18 28	18 31	18 35
Motspur Park	d	18 08		18 16				18 31		18 38
Malden Manor	d	18 11								18 41
Tolworth	d	18 14								18 44
Chessington North	d	18 17								18 47
Chessington South	a	18 20								18 50
Worcester Park	d			18 18				18 33		
Stoneleigh	d			18 21				18 36		
Ewell West	d			18 24				18 39		
Epsom 3	a			18 27				18 46		
	d			18 28				18 47		
Ashtead	d			18 32				18 51		
Leatherhead	d			18 35				18 54		
Box Hill & Westhumble	d									
Dorking 4	a			18 41						
New Malden 6	d				18 19		18 28		18 34	
Norbiton	d				18 22				18 37	
Kingston	a				18 25				18 40	
	d				18 29				18 40	
Hampton Wick	d				18 31				18 42	
Teddington	d				18 35				18 45	
Strawberry Hill	a				18 38					
Fulwell	d								18 49	
Hampton	d								18 53	
Kempton Park	d								18 56	
Sunbury	d								18 58	
Upper Halliford	d								19 00	
Shepperton	a								19 03	
Berrylands	d						18 30			
Surbiton 6	d		18a13			18 27	18 35			
Thames Ditton	d						18 39			
Hampton Court	a						18 42			
Hinchley Wood	d					18 31				
Claygate	d					18 34				
Oxshott	d					18 37				
Cobham & Stoke D'abernon	d					18 41				
Bookham	d							18 59		
Effingham Junction 6	d					18 45		19 03		
Horsley	d					18 48		19 06		
Clandon	d					18 53		19 11		
London Road (Guildford)	d					18 58		19 16		
Guildford	a					19 02		19 20		

Station		SW A	SW	SW B	SW	SW	SW	SW	SW	SW A
London Waterloo 15 ⊖	d	18 20	18 24	18 27	18 33	18 36	18 39	18 42	18 46	18 50
Vauxhall ⊖	d	18 24	18 28	18 31	18 37	18 40	18 43	18 46	18 50	18 54
Clapham Junction 10	d	18 29	18 33	18 36	18 42	18 45	18 48	18 51	18 55	18 59
Earlsfield	d	18 32	18 36	18 39	18 45	18 48	18 51	18 54	18 58	19 02
Wimbledon 6 ⊖	d	18 36	18 40	18 43	18 49	18 52	18 55	18 58	19 02	19 06
Raynes Park 6	d		18 43	18 46		18 55	18 58	19 01	19 05	
Motspur Park	d		18 46				19 01		19 08	
Malden Manor	d								19 11	
Tolworth	d								19 14	
Chessington North	d								19 17	
Chessington South	a								19 20	
Worcester Park	d		18 48				19 03			
Stoneleigh	d		18 51				19 06			
Ewell West	d		18 54				19 09			
Epsom 3	a		18 57				19 16			
	d		18 58				19 17			
Ashtead	d		19 02				19 21			
Leatherhead	d		19 05				19 24			
Box Hill & Westhumble	d									
Dorking 4	a		19 11							
New Malden 6	d			18 49		18 58		19 04		
Norbiton	d			18 52				19 07		
Kingston	a			18 55				19 10		
	d			18 59				19 10		
Hampton Wick	d			19 01				19 12		
Teddington	d			19 05				19 15		
Strawberry Hill	a			19 08						
Fulwell	d							19 19		
Hampton	d							19 23		
Kempton Park	d							19 26		
Sunbury	d							19 28		
Upper Halliford	d							19 30		
Shepperton	a							19 33		
Berrylands	d					19 00				
Surbiton 6	d	18a43			18 57	19 05				19a13
Thames Ditton	d					19 09				
Hampton Court	a					19 12				
Hinchley Wood	d				19 01					
Claygate	d				19 04					
Oxshott	d				19 07					
Cobham & Stoke D'abernon	d				19 11					
Bookham	d						19 29			
Effingham Junction 6	d				19 15		19 33			
Horsley	d				19 18		19 36			
Clandon	d				19 23		19 41			
London Road (Guildford)	d				19 28		19 46			
Guildford	a				19 32		19 50			

A To Woking

B To London Waterloo

The xx27 and xx57 London Waterloo to Strawberry Hill services continues to London Waterloo via Richmond

Table 152

Saturdays

14 December to 17 May

London - Chessington South, Dorking, Guildford, Shepperton and Hampton Court

Network Diagram - see first Page of Table 152

Station		SW	SW A	SW	SW	SW	SW	SW	SW B	SW
London Waterloo 15 ⊖	d	18 54	18 57	19 03	19 06	19 09	19 12	19 16	19 20	19 24
Vauxhall ⊖	d	18 58	19 01	19 07	19 10	19 13	19 16	19 20	19 24	19 28
Clapham Junction 10	d	19 03	19 06	19 12	19 15	19 18	19 21	19 25	19 29	19 33
Earlsfield	d	19 06	19 09	19 15	19 18	19 21	19 24	19 28	19 32	19 36
Wimbledon 6 ⊖	d	19 10	19 13	19 19	19 22	19 25	19 28	19 32	19 36	19 40
Raynes Park 6	d	19 13	19 16		19 25	19 28	19 31	19 35		19 43
Motspur Park	d	19 16				19 31		19 38		19 46
Malden Manor	d							19 41		
Tolworth	d							19 44		
Chessington North	d							19 47		
Chessington South	a							19 50		
Worcester Park	d	19 18				19 33				19 48
Stoneleigh	d	19 21				19 36				19 51
Ewell West	d	19 24				19 39				19 54
Epsom 3	a	19 27				19 46				19 57
	d	19 28				19 47				19 58
Ashtead	d	19 32				19 51				20 02
Leatherhead	d	19 35				19 54				20 05
Box Hill & Westhumble	d									
Dorking 4	a	19 41								20 11
New Malden 6	d		19 19		19 28		19 34			
Norbiton	d		19 22				19 37			
Kingston	a		19 25				19 40			
	d		19 29				19 40			
Hampton Wick	d		19 31				19 42			
Teddington	d		19 35				19 45			
Strawberry Hill	a		19 38							
Fulwell	d						19 49			
Hampton	d						19 53			
Kempton Park	d						19 56			
Sunbury	d						19 58			
Upper Halliford	d						20 00			
Shepperton	a						20 03			
Berrylands	d				19 30					
Surbiton 6	d			19 27	19 35				19a43	
Thames Ditton	d				19 39					
Hampton Court	a				19 42					
Hinchley Wood	d			19 31						
Claygate	d			19 34						
Oxshott	d			19 37						
Cobham & Stoke D'abernon	d			19 41						
Bookham	d					19 59				
Effingham Junction 6	d			19 45		20 03				
Horsley	d			19 48		20 06				
Clandon	d			19 53		20 11				
London Road (Guildford)	d			19 58		20 16				
Guildford	a			20 02		20 20				

Station		SW A	SW	SW	SW	SW	SW	SW B	SW	SW A
London Waterloo 15 ⊖	d	19 27	19 33	19 36	19 39	19 42	19 46	19 50	19 54	19 57
Vauxhall ⊖	d	19 31	19 37	19 40	19 43	19 46	19 50	19 54	19 58	20 01
Clapham Junction 10	d	19 36	19 42	19 45	19 48	19 51	19 55	19 59	20 03	20 06
Earlsfield	d	19 39	19 45	19 48	19 51	19 54	19 58	20 02	20 06	20 09
Wimbledon 6 ⊖	d	19 43	19 49	19 52	19 55	19 58	20 02	20 06	20 10	20 13
Raynes Park 6	d	19 46		19 55	19 58	20 01	20 05		20 13	20 16
Motspur Park	d				20 01		20 08		20 16	
Malden Manor	d						20 11			
Tolworth	d						20 14			
Chessington North	d						20 17			
Chessington South	a						20 20			
Worcester Park	d				20 03				20 18	
Stoneleigh	d				20 06				20 21	
Ewell West	d				20 09				20 24	
Epsom 3	a				20 16				20 27	
	d				20 17					
Ashtead	d				20 21					
Leatherhead	d				20 24					
Box Hill & Westhumble	d									
Dorking 4	a									
New Malden 6	d	19 49		19 58		20 04				20 19
Norbiton	d	19 52				20 07				20 22
Kingston	a	19 55				20 10				20 25
	d	19 59				20 10				20 29
Hampton Wick	d	20 01				20 12				20 31
Teddington	d	20 05				20 15				20 35
Strawberry Hill	a	20 08								20 38
Fulwell	d					20 19				
Hampton	d					20 23				
Kempton Park	d					20 26				
Sunbury	d					20 28				
Upper Halliford	d					20 30				
Shepperton	a					20 33				
Berrylands	d			20 00						
Surbiton 6	d		19 57	20 05				20a13		
Thames Ditton	d			20 09						
Hampton Court	a			20 12						
Hinchley Wood	d		20 01							
Claygate	d		20 04							
Oxshott	d		20 07							
Cobham & Stoke D'abernon	d		20 11							
Bookham	d				20 29					
Effingham Junction 6	d		20 15		20 33					
Horsley	d		20 18		20 36					
Clandon	d		20 23		20 41					
London Road (Guildford)	d		20 28		20 46					
Guildford	a		20 32		20 50					

Station		SW	SW	SW	SW	SW	SW B	SW	SW A	SW
London Waterloo 15 ⊖	d	20 03	20 06	20 09	20 12	20 16	20 20	20 24	20 27	20 33
Vauxhall ⊖	d	20 07	20 10	20 13	20 16	20 20	20 24	20 28	20 31	20 37
Clapham Junction 10	d	20 12	20 15	20 18	20 21	20 25	20 29	20 33	20 36	20 42
Earlsfield	d	20 15	20 18	20 21	20 24	20 28	20 32	20 36	20 39	20 45
Wimbledon 6 ⊖	d	20 19	20 22	20 25	20 28	20 32	20 36	20 40	20 43	20 49
Raynes Park 6	d		20 25	20 28	20 31	20 35		20 43	20 46	
Motspur Park	d			20 31		20 38		20 46		
Malden Manor	d					20 41				
Tolworth	d					20 44				
Chessington North	d					20 47				
Chessington South	a					20 50				
Worcester Park	d			20 33				20 48		
Stoneleigh	d			20 36				20 51		
Ewell West	d			20 39				20 54		
Epsom 3	a			20 46				20 57		
	d			20 47						
Ashtead	d			20 51						
Leatherhead	d			20 54						
Box Hill & Westhumble	d									
Dorking 4	a			21 00						
New Malden 6	d		20 28		20 34				20 49	
Norbiton	d				20 37				20 52	
Kingston	a				20 40				20 55	
	d				20 40				20 59	
Hampton Wick	d				20 42				21 01	
Teddington	d				20 45				21 05	
Strawberry Hill	a								21 08	
Fulwell	d				20 49					
Hampton	d				20 53					
Kempton Park	d				20 56					
Sunbury	d				20 58					
Upper Halliford	d				21 00					
Shepperton	a				21 03					
Berrylands	d		20 30							
Surbiton 6	d	20 27	20 35				20a43			20 57
Thames Ditton	d		20 39							
Hampton Court	a		20 42							
Hinchley Wood	d	20 31								21 01
Claygate	d	20 34								21 04
Oxshott	d	20 37								21 07
Cobham & Stoke D'abernon	d	20 41								21 11
Bookham	d									
Effingham Junction 6	d	20 45								21 15
Horsley	d	20 48								21 18
Clandon	d	20 53								21 23
London Road (Guildford)	d	20 58								21 28
Guildford	a	21 02								21 32

Station		SW	SW	SW	SW	SW B	SW	SW A	SW	SW
London Waterloo 15 ⊖	d	20 36	20 39	20 42	20 46	20 50	20 54	20 57	21 03	21 09
Vauxhall ⊖	d	20 40	20 43	20 46	20 50	20 54	20 58	21 01	21 07	21 13
Clapham Junction 10	d	20 45	20 48	20 51	20 55	20 59	21 03	21 06	21 12	21 18
Earlsfield	d	20 48	20 51	20 54	20 58	21 02	21 06	21 09	21 15	21 21
Wimbledon 6 ⊖	d	20 52	20 55	20 58	21 02	21 06	21 10	21 13	21 19	21 25
Raynes Park 6	d	20 55	20 58	21 01	21 05		21 13	21 16		21 28
Motspur Park	d		21 01		21 08		21 16			21 31
Malden Manor	d				21 11					
Tolworth	d				21 14					
Chessington North	d				21 17					
Chessington South	a				21 20					
Worcester Park	d		21 03				21 18			21 33
Stoneleigh	d		21 06				21 21			21 36
Ewell West	d		21 09				21 24			21 39
Epsom 3	a		21 16				21 27			21 46
	d		21 17							21 47
Ashtead	d		21 21							21 51
Leatherhead	d		21 24							21 54
Box Hill & Westhumble	d									
Dorking 4	a									22 00
New Malden 6	d	20 58		21 04				21 19		
Norbiton	d			21 07				21 22		
Kingston	a			21 10				21 25		
	d			21 10				21 29		
Hampton Wick	d			21 12				21 31		
Teddington	d			21 15				21 35		
Strawberry Hill	a							21 38		
Fulwell	d			21 19						
Hampton	d			21 23						
Kempton Park	d			21 26						
Sunbury	d			21 28						
Upper Halliford	d			21 30						
Shepperton	a			21 33						
Berrylands	d	21 00								
Surbiton 6	d	21 05				21a13			21 27	
Thames Ditton	d	21 09								
Hampton Court	a	21 12								
Hinchley Wood	d								21 31	
Claygate	d								21 34	
Oxshott	d								21 37	
Cobham & Stoke D'abernon	d								21 41	
Bookham	d		21 29							
Effingham Junction 6	d		21 33						21 45	
Horsley	d		21 36						21 48	
Clandon	d		21 41						21 53	
London Road (Guildford)	d		21 46						21 58	
Guildford	a		21 50						22 02	

A To London Waterloo

B To Woking

The xx27 and xx57 London Waterloo to Strawberry Hill services continues to London Waterloo via Richmond

Table 152

Saturdays

14 December to 17 May

London - Chessington South, Dorking, Guildford, Shepperton and Hampton Court

Network Diagram - see first Page of Table 152

Station		SW	SW A	SW	SW B	SW	SW	SW	SW	SW	SW	SW	SW B	SW	SW	SW	SW A	SW B	SW	SW	SW	SW	SW A	SW B	SW	SW	SW	SW	SW A	SW C	SW	SW	SW	SW
London Waterloo 15 ⊖	d	21 12	21 20	21 24	21 27	21 33	21 36	21 39	21 42	21 46	21 50	21 54	21 57	22 03	22 09	22 12	22 20	22 27	22 33	22 36	22 39	22 42	22 50	22 57	23 00	23 03	23 09	23 12	23 20	23 27	23 36	23 42	23 50	23 57
Vauxhall ⊖	d	21 16	21 24	21 28	21 31	21 37	21 40	21 43	21 46	21 50	21 54	21 58	22 01	22 07	22 13	22 16	22 24	22 31	22 37	22 40	22 43	22 46	22 54	23 01	23 04	23 07	23 13	23 16	23 24	23 31	23 40	23 46	23 54	00 01
Clapham Junction 10	d	21 21	21 29	21 33	21 36	21 42	21 45	21 48	21 51	21 55	21 59	22 03	22 06	22 12	22 18	22 21	22 29	22 36	22 42	22 45	22 48	22 51	22 59	23 06	23 09	23 12	23 18	23 21	23 29	23 36	23 45	23 51	23 59	00 06
Earlsfield	d	21 24	21 32	21 36	21 39	21 45	21 48	21 51	21 54	21 58	22 02	22 06	22 09	22 15	22 21	22 24	22 32	22 39	22 45	22 48	22 51	22 54	23 02	23 09	23 12	23 15	23 21	23 24	23 32	23 39	23 48	23 54	00 02	00 09
Wimbledon 6 ⊖	d	21 28	21 36	21 40	21 43	21 49	21 52	21 55	21 58	22 02	22 06	22 10	22 13	22 19	22 25	22 28	22 36	22 43	22 49	22 52	22 55	22 58	23 06	23 13	23 16	23 19	23 25	23 28	23 36	23 43	23 52	23 58	00 06	00 13
Raynes Park 6	d	21 31		21 43	21 46		21 55	21 58	22 01	22 05		22 13	22 16		22 28	22 31		22 46		22 55	22 58	23 01		23 16	23 19		23 28	23 31		23 46	23 55	00 01		00 16
Motspur Park	d			21 46				22 01		22 08		22 16			22 31						23 01				23 22		23 31					00 04		
Malden Manor	d									22 11															23 25									
Tolworth	d									22 14															23 28									
Chessington North	d									22 17															23 31									
Chessington South	a									22 20															23 33									
Worcester Park	d			21 48				22 03				22 18			22 33						23 03						23 33					00 06		
Stoneleigh	d			21 51				22 06				22 21			22 36						23 06						23 36					00 09		
Ewell West	d			21 54				22 09				22 24			22 39						23 09						23 39					00 12		
Epsom 3	a			21 57				22 16				22 27			22 46						23 12						23 42					00 15		
	d							22 17							22 47						23 17						23 47					00 19		
Ashtead	d							22 21							22 51						23 21						23 51					00 23		
Leatherhead	d							22 24							22 54						23 24						23 54					00 26		
Box Hill & Westhumble	d																																	
Dorking 4	a														23 00												00 01							
New Malden 6	d	21 34			21 49		21 58		22 04				22 19			22 34		22 49		22 58		23 04		23 19				23 34		23 49	23 58			00 19
Norbiton	d	21 37			21 52				22 07				22 22			22 37		22 52				23 07		23 22				23 37		23 52				00 22
Kingston	a	21 40			21 55				22 10				22 25			22 40		22 55				23 10		23 25				23 40		23 55				00 25
	d	21 40			21 59				22 10				22 29			22 40		22 59				23 10		23 29				23 40		23 55				00 25
Hampton Wick	d	21 42			22 01				22 12				22 31			22 42		23 01				23 12		23 31				23 42		23 57				00 27
Teddington	d	21 45			22 05				22 15				22 35			22 45		23 05				23 15		23 35				23 45		23 59				00 30
Strawberry Hill	a				22 08								22 38					23 08						23 38						00 03				
Fulwell	d	21 49							22 19							22 49						23 19						23 49						00 34
Hampton	d	21 53							22 23							22 53						23 23						23 53						00 38
Kempton Park	d	21 56							22 26							22 56						23 26						23 56						00 41
Sunbury	d	21 58							22 28							22 58						23 28						23 58						00 43
Upper Halliford	d	22 00							22 30							23 00						23 30						23 59						00 45
Shepperton	a	22 03							22 33							23 03						23 33						00 03						00 48
Berrylands	d						22 00													23 00											23 59			
Surbiton 6	d		21a43			21 57	22 05				22 14			22 27			22a43		22 57	23 05			23a13			23 27			23a43		00 05		00 14	
Thames Ditton	d						22 09													23 09											00 09			
Hampton Court	a						22 12													23 12											00 12			
Hinchley Wood	d					22 01								22 31					23 01							23 31							00 18	
Claygate	d					22 04								22 34					23 04							23 34							00 20	
Oxshott	d					22 07								22 37					23 07							23 37							00 24	
Cobham & Stoke D'abernon	d					22 11								22 41					23 11							23 41							00 27	
Bookham	d							22 29													23 29											00 31		
Effingham Junction 6	d					22 15		22 33						22 45					23 15		23 33					23 45						00 36	00 32	
Horsley	d					22 18		22 36						22 48					23 18		23 36					23 48						00 39	00 34	
Clandon	d					22 23		22 41						22 53					23 23		23 41					23 53						00 44	00 39	
London Road (Guildford)	d					22 28		22 46						22 58					23 28		23 46					23 58						00 49	00 44	
Guildford	a					22 32		22 50			22 47			23 02					23 32		23 50					00 02						00 53	00 48	

A To Woking
B To London Waterloo
C To Twickenham

The xx27 and xx57 London Waterloo to Strawberry Hill services continues to London Waterloo via Richmond

Table 152

Sundays

8 December to 11 May

London - Chessington South, Dorking, Guildford, Shepperton and Hampton Court

Network Diagram - see first Page of Table 152

Station		SW A	SW A	SW A	SW A	SW	SW	SW B	SW	SW C
London Waterloo 15 ⊖	d					00 09	00 15	00 27	00 42	01 42
Vauxhall ⊖	d				00 01	00 13	00 19	00 31	00 46	01 46
Clapham Junction 10	d				00 06	00 20	00 25	00 37	00 51	01 53
Earlsfield	d		00 02		00 09	00 23	00 29	00s41		
Wimbledon 6 ⊖	d		00 06		00 13	00 27	00 33	00 45	01 05	01 59
Raynes Park 6	d			00 01	00 16		00 36	00 48	01 08	02 02
Motspur Park	d			00 04			00 38			
Malden Manor	d									
Tolworth	d									
Chessington North	d									
Chessington South	a									
Worcester Park	d			00 06			00 41			
Stoneleigh	d			00 09			00 44			
Ewell West	d			00 12			00 46			
Epsom 3	a			00 15			00 50			
	d			00 19						
Ashtead	d			00 23						
Leatherhead	d			00 26						
Box Hill & Westhumble	d									
Dorking 4	a									
New Malden 6	d				00 19			00 50	01 11	02 04
Norbiton	d				00 22				01 14	02 08
Kingston	a				00 25				01 17	02 10
	d				00 25				01 17	02 11
Hampton Wick	d				00 27				01s22	02s13
Teddington	d				00 30				01s25	02s15
Strawberry Hill	a								01 28	02s18
Fulwell	d				00 34					
Hampton	d				00 38					
Kempton Park	d				00 41					
Sunbury	d				00 43					
Upper Halliford	d				00 45					
Shepperton	a				00 48					
Berrylands	d							00s53		
Surbiton 6	d	00 05	00 14			00 35		00s56		
Thames Ditton	d	00 09								
Hampton Court	a	00 12								
Hinchley Wood	d		00 18							
Claygate	d		00 20							
Oxshott	d		00 24							
Cobham & Stoke D'abernon	d		00 27							
Bookham	d			00 31						
Effingham Junction 6	d		00 32	00 36						
Horsley	d		00 34	00 39						
Clandon	d		00 39	00 44						
London Road (Guildford)	d		00 44	00 49						
Guildford	a		00 48	00 53		01 07				

Station		SW D	SW	SW	SW	SW	SW	SW D	SW	SW
London Waterloo 15 ⊖	d	06 18		06 57			07 10	07 18		07 27
Vauxhall ⊖	d	06 22		07 01			07 14	07 22		07 31
Clapham Junction 10	d	06 27		07 06			07 19	07 27		07 36
Earlsfield	d			07 09			07 22	07 30		07 39
Wimbledon 6 ⊖	d	06 34	06 48	07 13	07 16	07 20	07 26	07 34	07 38	07 43
Raynes Park 6	d	06 37	06 52	07 17		07 23		07 38	07 40	07 47
Motspur Park	d		06 55			07 26			07 43	
Malden Manor	d								07 46	
Tolworth	d								07 49	
Chessington North	d								07 52	
Chessington South	a								07 56	
Worcester Park	d		06 57			07 28				
Stoneleigh	d		07 00			07 31				
Ewell West	d		07 03			07 34				
Epsom 3	a		07 06			07 37				
	d									
Ashtead	d									
Leatherhead	d									
Box Hill & Westhumble	d									
Dorking 4	a									
New Malden 6	d	06 40		07 19				07 40		07 49
Norbiton	d	06 43						07 44		
Kingston	a	06 46						07 46		
	d	06 49						07 49		
Hampton Wick	d	06 51						07 51		
Teddington	d	06 56						07 56		
Strawberry Hill	a	06 59						07 59		
Fulwell	d									
Hampton	d									
Kempton Park	d									
Sunbury	d									
Upper Halliford	d									
Shepperton	a									
Berrylands	d			07 22						07 52
Surbiton 6	d			07 26	07 32		07 35			07 56
Thames Ditton	d			07 30						08 00
Hampton Court	a			07 33						08 03
Hinchley Wood	d				07 36					
Claygate	d				07 39					
Oxshott	d				07 42					
Cobham & Stoke D'abernon	d				07 46					
Bookham	d									
Effingham Junction 6	d				07 50					
Horsley	d				07 53					
Clandon	d				07 58					
London Road (Guildford)	d				08 03					
Guildford	a				08 07		08 14			

Station		SW	SW	SW	SW	SW	SW	SW	SW	SW D
London Waterloo 15 ⊖	d		07 40	07 48	07 57			08 02	08 10	08 18
Vauxhall ⊖	d		07 44	07 52	08 01			08 06	08 14	08 22
Clapham Junction 10	d		07 49	07 57	08 06			08 11	08 19	08 27
Earlsfield	d		07 52	08 00	08 09			08 14	08 22	08 30
Wimbledon 6 ⊖	d	07 48	07 56	08 04	08 13	08 02	08 08	08 18	08 26	08 34
Raynes Park 6	d	07 52		08 07	08 17	08 05	08 10	08 23		08 38
Motspur Park	d	07 55					08 13	08 25		
Malden Manor	d						08 16			
Tolworth	d						08 19			
Chessington North	d						08 22			
Chessington South	a						08 26			
Worcester Park	d	07 57						08 28		
Stoneleigh	d	08 00						08 31		
Ewell West	d	08 03						08 33		
Epsom 3	a	08 06						08 37		
	d	08 08						08 38		
Ashtead	d	08 12						08 42		
Leatherhead	d	08 15						08 45		
Box Hill & Westhumble	d									
Dorking 4	a							08 51		
New Malden 6	d			08 11	08 19	08 08				08 40
Norbiton	d			08 13						08 44
Kingston	a			08 16						08 46
	d			08 16						08 49
Hampton Wick	d			08 18						08 51
Teddington	d			08 22						08 56
Strawberry Hill	a									08 59
Fulwell	d			08 25						
Hampton	d			08 30						
Kempton Park	d			08 32						
Sunbury	d			08 35						
Upper Halliford	d			08 37						
Shepperton	a			08 40						
Berrylands	d				08 22	08 10				
Surbiton 6	d		08 05		08 26	08 32			08 35	
Thames Ditton	d				08 30					
Hampton Court	a				08 33					
Hinchley Wood	d					08 36				
Claygate	d					08 39				
Oxshott	d					08 42				
Cobham & Stoke D'abernon	d					08 46				
Bookham	d	08 21								
Effingham Junction 6	d	08 25				08 50				
Horsley	d	08 27				08 53				
Clandon	d	08 32				08 58				
London Road (Guildford)	d	08 37				09 03				
Guildford	a	08 41	08 40			09 07			09 10	

Station		SW	SW	SW	SW	SW	SW	SW	SW	SW
London Waterloo 15 ⊖	d	08 21	08 27	08 33	08 40	08 48	08 51	08 57		09 02
Vauxhall ⊖	d	08 25	08 31	08 37	08 44	08 52	08 55	09 01		09 06
Clapham Junction 10	d	08 30	08 36	08 41	08 49	08 57	09 00	09 06		09 11
Earlsfield	d	08 33	08 39	08 44	08 52	09 00	09 03	09 09		09 14
Wimbledon 6 ⊖	d	08 37	08 43	08 48	08 56	09 04	09 07	09 13	09 17	09 18
Raynes Park 6	d	08 41	08 47	08 53		09 07	09 11	09 16		09 22
Motspur Park	d	08 43		08 55			09 13			09 25
Malden Manor	d	08 47					09 17			
Tolworth	d	08 49					09 19			
Chessington North	d	08 52					09 22			
Chessington South	a	08 56					09 25			
Worcester Park	d			08 58						09 27
Stoneleigh	d			09 01						09 30
Ewell West	d			09 03						09 33
Epsom 3	a			09 07						09 36
	d			09 08						09 38
Ashtead	d			09 12						09 42
Leatherhead	d			09 15						09 45
Box Hill & Westhumble	d									
Dorking 4	a									09 51
New Malden 6	d		08 49			09 10		09 19		
Norbiton	d					09 13				
Kingston	a					09 15				
	d					09 16				
Hampton Wick	d					09 18				
Teddington	d					09 21				
Strawberry Hill	a									
Fulwell	d					09 25				
Hampton	d					09 29				
Kempton Park	d					09 32				
Sunbury	d					09 34				
Upper Halliford	d					09 36				
Shepperton	a					09 40				
Berrylands	d		08 52					09 21		
Surbiton 6	d		08 56		09 05			09 25	09 32	
Thames Ditton	d		09 00					09 30		
Hampton Court	a		09 03					09 33		
Hinchley Wood	d								09 36	
Claygate	d								09 39	
Oxshott	d								09 42	
Cobham & Stoke D'abernon	d								09 46	
Bookham	d			09 21						
Effingham Junction 6	d			09 25					09 50	
Horsley	d			09 27					09 53	
Clandon	d			09 32					09 58	
London Road (Guildford)	d			09 37					10 03	
Guildford	a			09 41	09 40				10 07	

A from London Waterloo

B To Woking

C To Twickenham

D To London Waterloo

The xx18 London Waterloo to Strawberry Hill services continues to London Waterloo via Richmond

Table 152

Sundays

8 December to 11 May

London - Chessington South, Dorking, Guildford, Shepperton and Hampton Court

Network Diagram - see first Page of Table 152

Station		SW	SW A	SW	SW	SW	SW	SW	SW	SW
London Waterloo 15 ⊖	d	09 10	09 18	09 21	09 27	09 32	09 40	09 48	09 51	09 57
Vauxhall ⊖	d	09 14	09 22	09 25	09 31	09 36	09 44	09 52	09 55	10 01
Clapham Junction 10	d	09 19	09 27	09 30	09 36	09 41	09 49	09 57	10 00	10 06
Earlsfield	d	09 22	09 30	09 33	09 39	09 44	09 52	10 00	10 03	10 09
Wimbledon 6 ⊖	d	09 26	09 34	09 37	09 43	09 48	09 56	10 04	10 07	10 13
Raynes Park 6	d		09 37	09 40	09 46	09 52		10 07	10 10	10 16
Motspur Park	d			09 43		09 55			10 13	
Malden Manor	d			09 46					10 16	
Tolworth	d			09 49					10 19	
Chessington North	d			09 52					10 22	
Chessington South	a			09 55					10 25	
Worcester Park	d					09 57				
Stoneleigh	d					10 00				
Ewell West	d					10 03				
Epsom 3	a					10 06				
	d					10 08				
Ashtead	d					10 12				
Leatherhead	d					10 15				
Box Hill & Westhumble	d									
Dorking 4	a									
New Malden 6	d		09 40		09 49			10 10		10 19
Norbiton	d		09 43					10 13		
Kingston	a		09 46					10 16		
	d		09 49					10 16		
Hampton Wick	d		09 51					10 18		
Teddington	d		09 56					10 21		
Strawberry Hill	a		09 59							
Fulwell	d							10 25		
Hampton	d							10 29		
Kempton Park	d							10 32		
Sunbury	d							10 34		
Upper Halliford	d							10 36		
Shepperton	a							10 39		
Berrylands	d				09 51					10 21
Surbiton 6	d	09 35			09 55		10 05			10 25
Thames Ditton	d				10 00					10 30
Hampton Court	a				10 03					10 33
Hinchley Wood	d									
Claygate	d									
Oxshott	d									
Cobham & Stoke D'abernon	d									
Bookham	d					10 21				
Effingham Junction 6	d					10 25				
Horsley	d					10 27				
Clandon	d					10 32				
London Road (Guildford)	d					10 37				
Guildford	a	10 10				10 41	10 44			

Station		SW	SW	SW	SW A	SW	SW	SW	SW	SW
London Waterloo 15 ⊖	d		10 02	10 10	10 18	10 21	10 27	10 32	10 40	10 48
Vauxhall ⊖	d		10 06	10 14	10 22	10 25	10 31	10 36	10 44	10 52
Clapham Junction 10	d		10 11	10 19	10 27	10 30	10 36	10 41	10 49	10 57
Earlsfield	d		10 14	10 22	10 30	10 33	10 39	10 44	10 52	11 00
Wimbledon 6 ⊖	d	10 17	10 18	10 26	10 34	10 37	10 43	10 48	10 56	11 04
Raynes Park 6	d		10 22		10 37	10 40	10 46	10 52		11 07
Motspur Park	d		10 25			10 43		10 55		
Malden Manor	d					10 46				
Tolworth	d					10 49				
Chessington North	d					10 52				
Chessington South	a					10 55				
Worcester Park	d		10 27					10 57		
Stoneleigh	d		10 30					11 00		
Ewell West	d		10 33					11 03		
Epsom 3	a		10 36					11 06		
	d		10 38					11 08		
Ashtead	d		10 42					11 12		
Leatherhead	d		10 45					11 15		
Box Hill & Westhumble	d									
Dorking 4	a		10 51							
New Malden 6	d				10 40		10 49			11 10
Norbiton	d				10 43					11 13
Kingston	a				10 46					11 16
	d				10 49					11 16
Hampton Wick	d				10 51					11 18
Teddington	d				10 56					11 21
Strawberry Hill	a				10 59					
Fulwell	d									11 25
Hampton	d									11 29
Kempton Park	d									11 32
Sunbury	d									11 34
Upper Halliford	d									11 36
Shepperton	a									11 39
Berrylands	d						10 51			
Surbiton 6	d	10 32		10 35			10 55		11 05	
Thames Ditton	d						11 00			
Hampton Court	a						11 03			
Hinchley Wood	d	10 36								
Claygate	d	10 39								
Oxshott	d	10 42								
Cobham & Stoke D'abernon	d	10 46								
Bookham	d							11 21		
Effingham Junction 6	d	10 50						11 25		
Horsley	d	10 53						11 27		
Clandon	d	10 58						11 32		
London Road (Guildford)	d	11 03						11 37		
Guildford	a	11 07		11 14				11 41	11 44	

Station		SW	SW	SW	SW	SW	SW A	SW	SW	SW
London Waterloo 15 ⊖	d	10 51	10 57		11 02	11 10	11 18	11 21	11 27	11 32
Vauxhall ⊖	d	10 55	11 01		11 06	11 14	11 22	11 25	11 31	11 36
Clapham Junction 10	d	11 00	11 06		11 11	11 19	11 27	11 30	11 36	11 42
Earlsfield	d	11 03	11 09		11 14	11 22	11 30	11 33	11 39	11 45
Wimbledon 6 ⊖	d	11 07	11 13	11 17	11 18	11 26	11 34	11 37	11 43	11 49
Raynes Park 6	d	11 10	11 16		11 22		11 37	11 40	11 46	11 52
Motspur Park	d	11 13			11 25			11 43		11 55
Malden Manor	d	11 16						11 46		
Tolworth	d	11 19						11 49		
Chessington North	d	11 22						11 52		
Chessington South	a	11 25						11 55		
Worcester Park	d				11 27					11 57
Stoneleigh	d				11 30					12 00
Ewell West	d				11 33					12 03
Epsom 3	a				11 36					12 06
	d				11 38					12 08
Ashtead	d				11 42					12 12
Leatherhead	d				11 45					12 15
Box Hill & Westhumble	d									
Dorking 4	a				11 51					
New Malden 6	d		11 19				11 40		11 49	
Norbiton	d						11 43			
Kingston	a						11 46			
	d						11 49			
Hampton Wick	d						11 51			
Teddington	d						11 56			
Strawberry Hill	a						11 59			
Fulwell	d									
Hampton	d									
Kempton Park	d									
Sunbury	d									
Upper Halliford	d									
Shepperton	a									
Berrylands	d		11 21						11 51	
Surbiton 6	d		11 25	11 32		11 35			11 55	
Thames Ditton	d		11 30						12 00	
Hampton Court	a		11 33						12 03	
Hinchley Wood	d			11 36						
Claygate	d			11 39						
Oxshott	d			11 42						
Cobham & Stoke D'abernon	d			11 46						
Bookham	d									12 21
Effingham Junction 6	d			11 50						12 25
Horsley	d			11 53						12 27
Clandon	d			11 58						12 32
London Road (Guildford)	d			12 03						12 37
Guildford	a			12 07		12 14				12 41

Station		SW	SW	SW	SW	SW	SW	SW	SW A	SW
London Waterloo 15 ⊖	d	11 40	11 48	11 51	11 57		12 02	12 10	12 18	12 21
Vauxhall ⊖	d	11 44	11 52	11 55	12 01		12 06	12 14	12 22	12 25
Clapham Junction 10	d	11 49	11 57	12 00	12 06		12 11	12 19	12 27	12 30
Earlsfield	d	11 52	12 00	12 03	12 09		12 14	12 22	12 30	12 33
Wimbledon 6 ⊖	d	11 56	12 04	12 07	12 13	12 17	12 18	12 26	12 34	12 37
Raynes Park 6	d		12 07	12 10	12 16		12 22		12 37	12 40
Motspur Park	d			12 13			12 25			12 43
Malden Manor	d			12 16						12 46
Tolworth	d			12 19						12 49
Chessington North	d			12 22						12 52
Chessington South	a			12 25						12 55
Worcester Park	d						12 27			
Stoneleigh	d						12 30			
Ewell West	d						12 33			
Epsom 3	a						12 36			
	d						12 38			
Ashtead	d						12 42			
Leatherhead	d						12 45			
Box Hill & Westhumble	d									
Dorking 4	a						12 51			
New Malden 6	d		12 10		12 19				12 40	
Norbiton	d		12 13						12 43	
Kingston	a		12 16						12 46	
	d		12 16						12 49	
Hampton Wick	d		12 18						12 51	
Teddington	d		12 21						12 56	
Strawberry Hill	a								12 59	
Fulwell	d		12 25							
Hampton	d		12 29							
Kempton Park	d		12 32							
Sunbury	d		12 34							
Upper Halliford	d		12 36							
Shepperton	a		12 39							
Berrylands	d				12 21					
Surbiton 6	d	12 05			12 25	12 32		12 35		
Thames Ditton	d				12 30					
Hampton Court	a				12 33					
Hinchley Wood	d					12 36				
Claygate	d					12 39				
Oxshott	d					12 42				
Cobham & Stoke D'abernon	d					12 46				
Bookham	d									
Effingham Junction 6	d					12 50				
Horsley	d					12 53				
Clandon	d					12 58				
London Road (Guildford)	d					13 03				
Guildford	a	12 44				13 07		13 14		

A To London Waterloo

The xx18 London Waterloo to Strawberry Hill services continues to London Waterloo via Richmond

Table 152

Sundays

8 December to 11 May

London - Chessington South, Dorking, Guildford, Shepperton and Hampton Court

Network Diagram - see first Page of Table 152

Station		SW	SW	SW	SW A	SW	SW	SW	SW	SW
London Waterloo 15 ⊖	d	12 27	12 32	12 40		12 48	12 51	12 57	13 00	13 02
Vauxhall ⊖	d	12 31	12 36	12 44		12 52	12 55	13 01	13 04	13 06
Clapham Junction 10	d	12 36	12 42	12 49		12 57	13 00	13 06	13 09	13 11
Earlsfield	d	12 39	12 45	12 52		13 00	13 03	13 09	13 12	13 14
Wimbledon 5 ⊖ 🚋	d	12 43	12 49	12 56		13 04	13 07	13 13	13 16	13 18
Raynes Park 5	d	12 46	12 52			13 07	13 10	13 16		13 22
Motspur Park	d		12 55				13 13			13 25
Malden Manor	d						13 16			
Tolworth	d						13 19			
Chessington North	d						13 22			
Chessington South	a						13 25			
Worcester Park	d		12 57							13 27
Stoneleigh	d		13 00							13 30
Ewell West	d		13 03							13 33
Epsom 3	a		13 06							13 36
	d		13 08							13 38
Ashtead	d		13 12							13 42
Leatherhead	d		13 15							13 45
Box Hill & Westhumble	d									
Dorking 4	a									13 51
New Malden 5	d	12 49				13 10		13 19		
Norbiton	d					13 13				
Kingston	a					13 16				
	d				13 11	13 16				
Hampton Wick	d				13 13	13 18				
Teddington	d				13 16	13 21				
Strawberry Hill	a				13 19					
Fulwell	d					13 25				
Hampton	d					13 29				
Kempton Park	d					13 32				
Sunbury	d					13 34				
Upper Halliford	d					13 36				
Shepperton	a					13 39				
Berrylands	d	12 51						13 21		
Surbiton 5	d	12 55		13 05				13 25	13 32	
Thames Ditton	d	13 00						13 30		
Hampton Court	a	13 03						13 33		
Hinchley Wood	d								13 36	
Claygate	d								13 39	
Oxshott	d								13 42	
Cobham & Stoke D'abernon	d								13 46	
Bookham	d		13 21							
Effingham Junction 5	d		13 25						13 50	
Horsley	d		13 27						13 53	
Clandon	d		13 32						13 58	
London Road (Guildford)	d		13 37						14 03	
Guildford	a		13 41	13 44					14 07	

Station		SW	SW A	SW	SW	SW	SW	SW A	SW	SW
London Waterloo 15 ⊖	d	13 10	13 18	13 21	13 27	13 32	13 40		13 48	13 51
Vauxhall ⊖	d	13 14	13 22	13 25	13 31	13 36	13 44		13 52	13 55
Clapham Junction 10	d	13 19	13 27	13 30	13 36	13 41	13 49		13 57	14 00
Earlsfield	d	13 22	13 30	13 33	13 39	13 44	13 52		14 00	14 03
Wimbledon 5 ⊖ 🚋	d	13 26	13 34	13 37	13 43	13 48	13 56		14 04	14 07
Raynes Park 5	d		13 37	13 40	13 46	13 52			14 07	14 10
Motspur Park	d			13 43		13 55				14 13
Malden Manor	d			13 46						14 16
Tolworth	d			13 49						14 19
Chessington North	d			13 52						14 22
Chessington South	a			13 55						14 25
Worcester Park	d					13 57				
Stoneleigh	d					14 00				
Ewell West	d					14 03				
Epsom 3	a					14 06				
	d					14 08				
Ashtead	d					14 12				
Leatherhead	d					14 15				
Box Hill & Westhumble	d									
Dorking 4	a									
New Malden 5	d		13 40		13 49				14 10	
Norbiton	d		13 43						14 13	
Kingston	a		13 46						14 16	
	d		13 49					14 11	14 16	
Hampton Wick	d		13 51					14 13	14 18	
Teddington	d		13 56					14 16	14 21	
Strawberry Hill	a		13 59					14 19		
Fulwell	d								14 25	
Hampton	d								14 29	
Kempton Park	d								14 32	
Sunbury	d								14 34	
Upper Halliford	d								14 36	
Shepperton	a								14 39	
Berrylands	d				13 51					
Surbiton 5	d	13 35			13 55		14 05			
Thames Ditton	d				14 00					
Hampton Court	a				14 03					
Hinchley Wood	d									
Claygate	d									
Oxshott	d									
Cobham & Stoke D'abernon	d									
Bookham	d					14 21				
Effingham Junction 5	d					14 25				
Horsley	d					14 27				
Clandon	d					14 32				
London Road (Guildford)	d					14 37				
Guildford	a	14 14				14 41	14 44			

Station		SW	SW	SW	SW	SW A	SW	SW	SW	SW
London Waterloo 15 ⊖	d	13 57	14 00	14 02	14 10	14 18	14 21	14 27	14 32	14 40
Vauxhall ⊖	d	14 01	14 04	14 06	14 14	14 22	14 25	14 31	14 36	14 44
Clapham Junction 10	d	14 06	14 09	14 11	14 19	14 27	14 30	14 36	14 41	14 49
Earlsfield	d	14 09	14 12	14 14	14 22	14 30	14 33	14 39	14 44	14 52
Wimbledon 5 ⊖ 🚋	d	14 13	14 16	14 18	14 26	14 34	14 37	14 43	14 48	14 56
Raynes Park 5	d	14 16		14 22		14 37	14 40	14 46	14 52	
Motspur Park	d			14 25			14 43		14 55	
Malden Manor	d						14 46			
Tolworth	d						14 49			
Chessington North	d						14 52			
Chessington South	a						14 55			
Worcester Park	d			14 27					14 57	
Stoneleigh	d			14 30					15 00	
Ewell West	d			14 33					15 03	
Epsom 3	a			14 36					15 06	
	d			14 38					15 08	
Ashtead	d			14 42					15 12	
Leatherhead	d			14 45					15 15	
Box Hill & Westhumble	d									
Dorking 4	a			14 51						
New Malden 5	d	14 19				14 40		14 49		
Norbiton	d					14 43				
Kingston	a					14 46				
	d					14 49				
Hampton Wick	d					14 51				
Teddington	d					14 56				
Strawberry Hill	a					14 59				
Fulwell	d									
Hampton	d									
Kempton Park	d									
Sunbury	d									
Upper Halliford	d									
Shepperton	a									
Berrylands	d	14 21						14 51		
Surbiton 5	d	14 25	14 32		14 35			14 55		15 05
Thames Ditton	d	14 30						15 00		
Hampton Court	a	14 33						15 03		
Hinchley Wood	d		14 36							
Claygate	d		14 39							
Oxshott	d		14 42							
Cobham & Stoke D'abernon	d		14 46							
Bookham	d								15 21	
Effingham Junction 5	d		14 50						15 25	
Horsley	d		14 53						15 27	
Clandon	d		14 58						15 32	
London Road (Guildford)	d		15 03						15 37	
Guildford	a		15 07		15 14				15 41	15 44

Station		SW A	SW	SW	SW	SW	SW	SW	SW A	SW
London Waterloo 15 ⊖	d		14 48	14 51	14 57	15 00	15 02	15 10	15 18	15 21
Vauxhall ⊖	d		14 52	14 55	15 01	15 04	15 06	15 14	15 22	15 25
Clapham Junction 10	d		14 57	15 00	15 06	15 09	15 11	15 19	15 27	15 30
Earlsfield	d		15 00	15 03	15 09	15 12	15 14	15 22	15 30	15 33
Wimbledon 5 ⊖ 🚋	d		15 04	15 07	15 13	15 16	15 18	15 26	15 34	15 37
Raynes Park 5	d		15 07	15 10	15 16		15 22		15 37	15 40
Motspur Park	d			15 13			15 25			15 43
Malden Manor	d			15 16						15 46
Tolworth	d			15 19						15 49
Chessington North	d			15 22						15 52
Chessington South	a			15 25						15 55
Worcester Park	d						15 27			
Stoneleigh	d						15 30			
Ewell West	d						15 33			
Epsom 3	a						15 36			
	d						15 38			
Ashtead	d						15 42			
Leatherhead	d						15 45			
Box Hill & Westhumble	d									
Dorking 4	a						15 51			
New Malden 5	d		15 10		15 19				15 40	
Norbiton	d		15 13						15 43	
Kingston	a		15 16						15 46	
	d	15 11	15 16						15 49	
Hampton Wick	d	15 13	15 18						15 51	
Teddington	d	15 16	15 21						15 56	
Strawberry Hill	a	15 19							15 59	
Fulwell	d		15 25							
Hampton	d		15 29							
Kempton Park	d		15 32							
Sunbury	d		15 34							
Upper Halliford	d		15 36							
Shepperton	a		15 39							
Berrylands	d				15 21					
Surbiton 5	d				15 25	15 32		15 35		
Thames Ditton	d				15 30					
Hampton Court	a				15 33					
Hinchley Wood	d					15 36				
Claygate	d					15 39				
Oxshott	d					15 42				
Cobham & Stoke D'abernon	d					15 46				
Bookham	d									
Effingham Junction 5	d					15 50				
Horsley	d					15 53				
Clandon	d					15 58				
London Road (Guildford)	d					16 03				
Guildford	a					16 07		16 14		

A To London Waterloo

The xx18 London Waterloo to Strawberry Hill services continues to London Waterloo via Richmond

Table 152

Sundays

8 December to 11 May

London - Chessington South, Dorking, Guildford, Shepperton and Hampton Court

Network Diagram - see first Page of Table 152

Station		SW	SW	SW	SW A	SW	SW	SW	SW	SW
London Waterloo 15 ⊖	d	15 27	15 32	15 40		15 48	15 51	15 57	16 00	16 02
Vauxhall ⊖	d	15 31	15 36	15 44		15 52	15 55	16 01	16 04	16 06
Clapham Junction 10	d	15 36	15 41	15 49		15 57	16 00	16 06	16 09	16 11
Earlsfield	d	15 39	15 44	15 52		16 00	16 03	16 09	16 12	16 14
Wimbledon 6 ⊖	d	15 43	15 48	15 56		16 04	16 07	16 13	16 16	16 18
Raynes Park 6	d	15 46	15 52			16 07	16 10	16 16		16 22
Motspur Park	d		15 55				16 13			16 25
Malden Manor	d						16 16			
Tolworth	d						16 19			
Chessington North	d						16 22			
Chessington South	a						16 25			
Worcester Park	d		15 57							16 27
Stoneleigh	d		16 00							16 30
Ewell West	d		16 03							16 33
Epsom 3	a		16 06							16 36
	d		16 08							16 38
Ashtead	d		16 12							16 42
Leatherhead	d		16 15							16 45
Box Hill & Westhumble	d									
Dorking 4	a									16 51
New Malden 6	d	15 49				16 10		16 19		
Norbiton	d					16 13				
Kingston	a					16 16				
	d				16 11	16 16				
Hampton Wick	d				16 13	16 18				
Teddington	d				16 16	16 21				
Strawberry Hill	a				16 19					
Fulwell	d					16 25				
Hampton	d					16 29				
Kempton Park	d					16 32				
Sunbury	d					16 34				
Upper Halliford	d					16 36				
Shepperton	a					16 39				
Berrylands	d	15 51						16 21		
Surbiton 6	d	15 55		16 05				16 25	16 32	
Thames Ditton	d	16 00						16 30		
Hampton Court	a	16 03						16 33		
Hinchley Wood	d								16 36	
Claygate	d								16 39	
Oxshott	d								16 42	
Cobham & Stoke D'abernon	d								16 46	
Bookham	d		16 21							
Effingham Junction 6	d		16 25						16 50	
Horsley	d		16 27						16 53	
Clandon	d		16 32						16 58	
London Road (Guildford)	d		16 37						17 03	
Guildford	a		16 41	16 44					17 07	

Station		SW	SW A	SW	SW	SW	SW	SW A	SW	SW
London Waterloo 15 ⊖	d	16 10	16 18	16 21	16 27	16 32	16 40		16 48	16 51
Vauxhall ⊖	d	16 14	16 22	16 25	16 31	16 36	16 44		16 52	16 55
Clapham Junction 10	d	16 19	16 27	16 30	16 36	16 41	16 49		16 57	17 00
Earlsfield	d	16 22	16 30	16 33	16 39	16 44	16 52		17 00	17 03
Wimbledon 6 ⊖	d	16 26	16 34	16 37	16 43	16 48	16 56		17 04	17 07
Raynes Park 6	d		16 37	16 40	16 46	16 52			17 07	17 10
Motspur Park	d			16 43		16 55				17 13
Malden Manor	d			16 46						17 16
Tolworth	d			16 49						17 19
Chessington North	d			16 52						17 22
Chessington South	a			16 55						17 25
Worcester Park	d					16 57				
Stoneleigh	d					17 00				
Ewell West	d					17 03				
Epsom 3	a					17 06				
	d					17 08				
Ashtead	d					17 12				
Leatherhead	d					17 15				
Box Hill & Westhumble	d									
Dorking 4	a									
New Malden 6	d		16 40		16 49				17 10	
Norbiton	d		16 43						17 13	
Kingston	a		16 46						17 16	
	d		16 49					17 11	17 16	
Hampton Wick	d		16 51					17 13	17 18	
Teddington	d		16 56					17 16	17 21	
Strawberry Hill	a		16 59					17 19		
Fulwell	d								17 25	
Hampton	d								17 29	
Kempton Park	d								17 32	
Sunbury	d								17 34	
Upper Halliford	d								17 36	
Shepperton	a								17 39	
Berrylands	d				16 51					
Surbiton 6	d	16 35			16 55		17 05			
Thames Ditton	d				17 00					
Hampton Court	a				17 03					
Hinchley Wood	d									
Claygate	d									
Oxshott	d									
Cobham & Stoke D'abernon	d									
Bookham	d					17 21				
Effingham Junction 6	d					17 25				
Horsley	d					17 27				
Clandon	d					17 32				
London Road (Guildford)	d					17 37				
Guildford	a	17 14				17 41	17 44			

Station		SW	SW	SW	SW	SW A	SW	SW	SW	SW
London Waterloo 15 ⊖	d	16 57	17 00	17 02	17 10	17 18	17 21	17 27	17 32	17 40
Vauxhall ⊖	d	17 01	17 04	17 06	17 14	17 22	17 25	17 31	17 36	17 44
Clapham Junction 10	d	17 06	17 09	17 11	17 19	17 27	17 30	17 36	17 41	17 49
Earlsfield	d	17 09	17 12	17 14	17 22	17 30	17 33	17 39	17 44	17 52
Wimbledon 6 ⊖	d	17 13	17 16	17 18	17 26	17 34	17 37	17 43	17 48	17 56
Raynes Park 6	d	17 16		17 22		17 37	17 40	17 46	17 52	
Motspur Park	d			17 25			17 43		17 55	
Malden Manor	d						17 46			
Tolworth	d						17 49			
Chessington North	d						17 52			
Chessington South	a						17 55			
Worcester Park	d			17 27					17 57	
Stoneleigh	d			17 30					18 00	
Ewell West	d			17 33					18 03	
Epsom 3	a			17 36					18 06	
	d			17 38					18 08	
Ashtead	d			17 42					18 12	
Leatherhead	d			17 45					18 15	
Box Hill & Westhumble	d									
Dorking 4	a			17 51						
New Malden 6	d	17 19				17 40		17 49		
Norbiton	d					17 43				
Kingston	a					17 46				
	d					17 49				
Hampton Wick	d					17 51				
Teddington	d					17 56				
Strawberry Hill	a					17 59				
Fulwell	d									
Hampton	d									
Kempton Park	d									
Sunbury	d									
Upper Halliford	d									
Shepperton	a									
Berrylands	d	17 21						17 51		
Surbiton 6	d	17 25	17 32		17 35			17 55		18 05
Thames Ditton	d	17 30						18 00		
Hampton Court	a	17 33						18 03		
Hinchley Wood	d		17 36							
Claygate	d		17 39							
Oxshott	d		17 42							
Cobham & Stoke D'abernon	d		17 46							
Bookham	d								18 21	
Effingham Junction 6	d		17 50						18 25	
Horsley	d		17 53						18 27	
Clandon	d		17 58						18 32	
London Road (Guildford)	d		18 03						18 37	
Guildford	a		18 07		18 14				18 41	18 44

Station		SW A	SW	SW	SW	SW	SW	SW	SW A	SW
London Waterloo 15 ⊖	d		17 48	17 51	17 57	18 00	18 02	18 10	18 18	18 21
Vauxhall ⊖	d		17 52	17 55	18 01	18 04	18 06	18 14	18 22	18 25
Clapham Junction 10	d		17 57	18 00	18 06	18 09	18 11	18 19	18 27	18 30
Earlsfield	d		18 00	18 03	18 09	18 12	18 14	18 22	18 30	18 33
Wimbledon 6 ⊖	d		18 04	18 07	18 13	18 16	18 18	18 26	18 34	18 37
Raynes Park 6	d		18 07	18 10	18 16		18 22		18 37	18 40
Motspur Park	d			18 13			18 25			18 43
Malden Manor	d			18 16						18 46
Tolworth	d			18 19						18 49
Chessington North	d			18 22						18 52
Chessington South	a			18 25						18 55
Worcester Park	d						18 27			
Stoneleigh	d						18 30			
Ewell West	d						18 33			
Epsom 3	a						18 36			
	d						18 38			
Ashtead	d						18 42			
Leatherhead	d						18 45			
Box Hill & Westhumble	d									
Dorking 4	a						18 51			
New Malden 6	d		18 10		18 19				18 40	
Norbiton	d		18 13						18 43	
Kingston	a		18 16						18 46	
	d	18 11	18 16						18 49	
Hampton Wick	d	18 13	18 18						18 51	
Teddington	d	18 16	18 21						18 56	
Strawberry Hill	a	18 19							18 59	
Fulwell	d		18 25							
Hampton	d		18 29							
Kempton Park	d		18 32							
Sunbury	d		18 34							
Upper Halliford	d		18 36							
Shepperton	a		18 39							
Berrylands	d				18 21					
Surbiton 6	d				18 25	18 32		18 35		
Thames Ditton	d				18 30					
Hampton Court	a				18 33					
Hinchley Wood	d					18 36				
Claygate	d					18 39				
Oxshott	d					18 42				
Cobham & Stoke D'abernon	d					18 46				
Bookham	d									
Effingham Junction 6	d					18 50				
Horsley	d					18 53				
Clandon	d					18 58				
London Road (Guildford)	d					19 03				
Guildford	a					19 07		19 14		

A To London Waterloo

The xx18 London Waterloo to Strawberry Hill services continues to London Waterloo via Richmond

Table 152

Sundays

8 December to 11 May

London - Chessington South, Dorking, Guildford, Shepperton and Hampton Court

Network Diagram - see first Page of Table 152

		SW	SW	SW	SW A	SW	SW	SW	SW	SW
London Waterloo 15 ⊖	d	18 27	18 32	18 40		18 48	18 51	18 57	19 00	19 02
Vauxhall ⊖	d	18 31	18 36	18 44		18 52	18 55	19 01	19 04	19 06
Clapham Junction 10	d	18 36	18 41	18 49		18 57	19 00	19 06	19 09	19 11
Earlsfield	d	18 39	18 44	18 52		19 00	19 03	19 09	19 12	19 14
Wimbledon 6 ⊖	d	18 43	18 48	18 56		19 04	19 07	19 13	19 16	19 18
Raynes Park 6	d	18 46	18 52			19 07	19 10	19 16		19 22
Motspur Park	d		18 55				19 13			19 25
Malden Manor	d						19 16			
Tolworth	d						19 19			
Chessington North	d						19 22			
Chessington South	a						19 25			
Worcester Park	d		18 57							19 27
Stoneleigh	d		19 00							19 30
Ewell West	d		19 03							19 33
Epsom 3	a		19 06							19 36
	d		19 08							19 38
Ashtead	d		19 12							19 42
Leatherhead	d		19 15							19 45
Box Hill & Westhumble	d									
Dorking 4	a									19 51
New Malden 6	d	18 49				19 10		19 19		
Norbiton	d					19 13				
Kingston	a					19 16				
	d				19 11	19 16				
Hampton Wick	d				19 13	19 18				
Teddington	d				19 16	19 21				
Strawberry Hill	a				19 19					
Fulwell	d					19 25				
Hampton	d					19 29				
Kempton Park	d					19 32				
Sunbury	d					19 34				
Upper Halliford	d					19 36				
Shepperton	a					19 39				
Berrylands	d	18 51						19 21		
Surbiton 6	d	18 55		19 05				19 25	19 32	
Thames Ditton	d	19 00						19 30		
Hampton Court	a	19 03						19 33		
Hinchley Wood	d								19 36	
Claygate	d								19 39	
Oxshott	d								19 42	
Cobham & Stoke D'abernon	d								19 46	
Bookham	d		19 21							
Effingham Junction 6	d		19 25						19 50	
Horsley	d		19 27						19 53	
Clandon	d		19 32						19 58	
London Road (Guildford)	d		19 37						20 03	
Guildford	a		19 41	19 44					20 07	

		SW	SW A	SW	SW	SW	SW	SW A	SW	SW
London Waterloo 15 ⊖	d	19 10	19 18	19 21	19 27	19 32	19 40		19 48	19 57
Vauxhall ⊖	d	19 14	19 22	19 25	19 31	19 36	19 44		19 52	20 01
Clapham Junction 10	d	19 19	19 27	19 30	19 36	19 41	19 49		19 57	20 06
Earlsfield	d	19 22	19 30	19 33	19 39	19 44	19 52		20 00	20 09
Wimbledon 6 ⊖	d	19 26	19 34	19 37	19 43	19 48	19 56		20 04	20 13
Raynes Park 6	d		19 37	19 40	19 46	19 52			20 07	20 16
Motspur Park	d			19 43		19 55				
Malden Manor	d			19 46						
Tolworth	d			19 49						
Chessington North	d			19 52						
Chessington South	a			19 55						
Worcester Park	d					19 57				
Stoneleigh	d					20 00				
Ewell West	d					20 03				
Epsom 3	a					20 06				
	d					20 08				
Ashtead	d					20 12				
Leatherhead	d					20 15				
Box Hill & Westhumble	d									
Dorking 4	a									
New Malden 6	d		19 40		19 49				20 10	20 19
Norbiton	d		19 43						20 13	
Kingston	a		19 46						20 16	
	d		19 49					20 11	20 16	
Hampton Wick	d		19 51					20 13	20 18	
Teddington	d		19 56					20 16	20 21	
Strawberry Hill	a		19 59					20 19		
Fulwell	d								20 25	
Hampton	d								20 29	
Kempton Park	d								20 32	
Sunbury	d								20 34	
Upper Halliford	d								20 36	
Shepperton	a								20 39	
Berrylands	d				19 51					20 21
Surbiton 6	d	19 35			19 55		20 05			20 25
Thames Ditton	d				20 00					20 30
Hampton Court	a				20 03					20 33
Hinchley Wood	d									
Claygate	d									
Oxshott	d									
Cobham & Stoke D'abernon	d									
Bookham	d					20 21				
Effingham Junction 6	d					20 25				
Horsley	d					20 27				
Clandon	d					20 32				
London Road (Guildford)	d					20 37				
Guildford	a	20 14				20 41	20 44			

		SW	SW	SW	SW A	SW	SW	SW	SW	SW A
London Waterloo 15 ⊖	d	20 00	20 02	20 10	20 18	20 21	20 27	20 32	20 40	
Vauxhall ⊖	d	20 04	20 06	20 14	20 22	20 25	20 31	20 36	20 44	
Clapham Junction 10	d	20 09	20 11	20 19	20 27	20 30	20 36	20 41	20 49	
Earlsfield	d	20 12	20 14	20 22	20 30	20 33	20 39	20 44	20 52	
Wimbledon 6 ⊖	d	20 16	20 18	20 26	20 34	20 37	20 43	20 48	20 56	
Raynes Park 6	d		20 22		20 37	20 40	20 46	20 52		
Motspur Park	d		20 25			20 43		20 55		
Malden Manor	d					20 46				
Tolworth	d					20 49				
Chessington North	d					20 52				
Chessington South	a					20 55				
Worcester Park	d		20 27					20 57		
Stoneleigh	d		20 30					21 00		
Ewell West	d		20 33					21 03		
Epsom 3	a		20 36					21 06		
	d		20 38					21 08		
Ashtead	d		20 42					21 12		
Leatherhead	d		20 45					21 15		
Box Hill & Westhumble	d									
Dorking 4	a		20 51							
New Malden 6	d				20 40		20 49			
Norbiton	d				20 43					
Kingston	a				20 46					
	d				20 49					21 11
Hampton Wick	d				20 51					21 13
Teddington	d				20 56					21 16
Strawberry Hill	a				20 59					21 19
Fulwell	d									
Hampton	d									
Kempton Park	d									
Sunbury	d									
Upper Halliford	d									
Shepperton	a									
Berrylands	d						20 51			
Surbiton 6	d	20 32		20 35			20 55		21 05	
Thames Ditton	d						21 00			
Hampton Court	a						21 03			
Hinchley Wood	d	20 36								
Claygate	d	20 39								
Oxshott	d	20 42								
Cobham & Stoke D'abernon	d	20 46								
Bookham	d							21 21		
Effingham Junction 6	d	20 50						21 25		
Horsley	d	20 53						21 27		
Clandon	d	20 58						21 32		
London Road (Guildford)	d	21 03						21 37		
Guildford	a	21 07		21 14				21 41	21 44	

		SW	SW	SW	SW	SW	SW A	SW	SW	SW
London Waterloo 15 ⊖	d	20 48	20 57	21 00	21 02	21 10	21 18	21 21	21 32	21 40
Vauxhall ⊖	d	20 52	21 01	21 04	21 06	21 14	21 22	21 25	21 36	21 44
Clapham Junction 10	d	20 57	21 06	21 09	21 11	21 19	21 27	21 30	21 41	21 49
Earlsfield	d	21 00	21 09	21 12	21 14	21 22	21 30	21 33	21 44	21 52
Wimbledon 6 ⊖	d	21 04	21 13	21 16	21 18	21 26	21 34	21 37	21 48	21 56
Raynes Park 6	d	21 07	21 16		21 22		21 37	21 40	21 52	
Motspur Park	d				21 25			21 43	21 55	
Malden Manor	d							21 46		
Tolworth	d							21 49		
Chessington North	d							21 52		
Chessington South	a							21 55		
Worcester Park	d				21 27				21 57	
Stoneleigh	d				21 30				22 00	
Ewell West	d				21 33				22 03	
Epsom 3	a				21 36				22 06	
	d				21 38				22 08	
Ashtead	d				21 42				22 12	
Leatherhead	d				21 45				22 15	
Box Hill & Westhumble	d									
Dorking 4	a				21 51					
New Malden 6	d	21 10	21 19				21 40			
Norbiton	d	21 13					21 43			
Kingston	a	21 16					21 46			
	d	21 16					21 49			
Hampton Wick	d	21 18					21 51			
Teddington	d	21 21					21 56			
Strawberry Hill	a						21 59			
Fulwell	d	21 25								
Hampton	d	21 29								
Kempton Park	d	21 32								
Sunbury	d	21 34								
Upper Halliford	d	21 36								
Shepperton	a	21 39								
Berrylands	d		21 21							
Surbiton 6	d		21 25	21 32		21 35				22 05
Thames Ditton	d		21 30							
Hampton Court	a		21 33							
Hinchley Wood	d			21 36						
Claygate	d			21 39						
Oxshott	d			21 42						
Cobham & Stoke D'abernon	d			21 46						
Bookham	d								22 21	
Effingham Junction 6	d			21 50					22 25	
Horsley	d			21 53					22 27	
Clandon	d			21 58					22 32	
London Road (Guildford)	d			22 03					22 37	
Guildford	a			22 07		22 14			22 41	22 44

A To London Waterloo

The xx18 London Waterloo to Strawberry Hill services continues to London Waterloo via Richmond

Table 152

Sundays

8 December to 11 May

London - Chessington South, Dorking, Guildford, Shepperton and Hampton Court

Network Diagram - see first Page of Table 152

		SW	SW	SW	SW	SW	SW	SW	SW	SW	SW	SW	SW	SW	SW	SW	SW	SW	SW	SW
		A						A				A								
London Waterloo 15 ⊖	d		21 48	21 57	22 00	22 02	22 10	22 18	22 21	22 32	22 40		22 48	22 51	22 57	23 00	23 02	23 10	23 18	23 32
Vauxhall ⊖	d		21 52	22 01	22 04	22 06	22 14	22 22	22 25	22 36	22 44		22 52	22 55	23 01	23 04	23 06	23 14	23 22	23 36
Clapham Junction 10	d		21 57	22 06	22 09	22 11	22 19	22 27	22 30	22 41	22 49		22 57	23 00	23 06	23 09	23 11	23 19	23 27	23 41
Earlsfield	d		22 00	22 09	22 12	22 14	22 22	22 30	22 33	22 44	22 52		23 00	23 03	23 09	23 12	23 14	23 22	23 30	23 44
Wimbledon 6 ⊖	d		22 04	22 13	22 16	22 18	22 26	22 34	22 37	22 48	22 56		23 04	23 07	23 13	23 16	23 18	23 26	23 34	23 48
Raynes Park 6	d		22 07	22 16		22 22		22 37	22 40	22 52			23 07	23 10	23 16		23 22		23 37	23 52
Motspur Park	d					22 25			22 43	22 55				23 13			23 25			23 55
Malden Manor	d								22 46					23 16						
Tolworth	d								22 49					23 19						
Chessington North	d								22 52					23 22						
Chessington South	a								22 55					23 25						
Worcester Park	d					22 27				22 57							23 27			23 57
Stoneleigh	d					22 30				23 00							23 30			23 59
Ewell West	d					22 33				23 03							23 33			00 03
Epsom 3	a					22 36				23 06							23 36			00 06
	d					22 38				23 08										
Ashtead	d					22 42				23 12										
Leatherhead	d					22 45				23 15										
Box Hill & Westhumble	d																			
Dorking 4	a					22 51														
New Malden 6	d		22 10	22 19				22 40					23 10		23 19				23 40	
Norbiton	d		22 13					22 43					23 13						23 43	
Kingston	a		22 16					22 46					23 16						23 46	
	d	22 11	22 16					22 49				23 11	23 16						23 47	
Hampton Wick	d	22 13	22 18					22 51				23 13	23 18						23 49	
Teddington	d	22 16	22 21					22 56				23 16	23 21						23 51	
Strawberry Hill	a	22 19						22 59				23 19							23 54	
Fulwell	d		22 25										23 25							
Hampton	d		22 29										23 29							
Kempton Park	d		22 32										23 32							
Sunbury	d		22 34										23 34							
Upper Halliford	d		22 36										23 36							
Shepperton	a		22 39										23 39							
Berrylands	d			22 21											23 21					
Surbiton 6	d			22 25	22 32		22 35				23 05				23 25	23 32		23 35		
Thames Ditton	d			22 30											23 30					
Hampton Court	a			22 33											23 33					
Hinchley Wood	d				22 36											23 36				
Claygate	d				22 39											23 39				
Oxshott	d				22 42											23 42				
Cobham & Stoke D'abernon	d				22 46											23 46				
Bookham	d									23 21										
Effingham Junction 6	d				22 50					23 25						23 50				
Horsley	d				22 53					23 27						23 53				
Clandon	d				22 58					23 32						23 58				
London Road (Guildford)	d				23 03					23 37						00 03				
Guildford	a				23 07		23 13			23 41	23 45					00 07		00 13		

A To London Waterloo

The xx18 London Waterloo to Strawberry Hill services continues to London Waterloo via Richmond

Table 152R

Mondays to Fridays

9 December to 16 May

Hampton Court, Shepperton, Guildford, Dorking and Chessington South - London

Network Diagram - see first Page of Table 152

Miles	Miles	Miles	Miles	Miles	Station		SW MO	SW MX	SW MX	SW MX	SW MX	SW MX 1	SW	SW	SW	SW	SW	SW	SW	SW	SW	SW
							A	B	C	D	D	E		F								D
0	—	—	—	—	**Guildford**	d							04 25		04 58			05 14		05 37		
1¼	—	—	—	—	London Road (Guildford)	d									05 02					05 41		
4½	—	—	—	—	Clandon	d									05 07					05 46		
7¾	—	—	—	—	Horsley	d									05 11					05 50		
8¾	0	—	—	—	Effingham Junction 6	d									05 15					05 53		
—	1¾	—	—	—	Bookham	d									05 18							
11	—	—	—	—	Cobham & Stoke d'Abernon	d														05 57		
13	—	—	—	—	Oxshott	d														06 00		
14¾	—	—	—	—	Claygate	d														06 03		
16	—	—	—	—	Hinchley Wood	d														06 06		
—	—	—	0	—	**Hampton Court**	d													05 54			
—	—	—	1	—	Thames Ditton	d													05 56			
18	—	—	3	—	**Surbiton** 6	d						00 08	04 54					05 56	06 02	06 11		
19	—	—	—	—	Berrylands	d													06 04			
—	—	—	—	0	**Shepperton**	d										05 23						
—	—	—	—	1½	Upper Halliford	d										05 26						
—	—	—	—	2	Sunbury	d										05 28						
—	—	—	—	2½	Kempton Park	d																
—	—	—	—	4¼	Hampton	d										05 33						
—	—	—	—	6	Fulwell	d										05 36						
—	—	—	0	—	Strawberry Hill	d				00 09				04 55		05 38						06 07
—	—	—	1¼	7	Teddington	d				00 12				04 59			05 44					06 11
—	—	—	—	8¼	Hampton Wick	d				00 14				05 01			05 46					06 14
—	—	—	—	8¾	Kingston	a				00 16				05 03			05 48					06 16
—	—	—	—	—		d								05 04			05 49					06 19
—	—	—	—	9½	Norbiton	d								05 06			05 51					06 21
20	—	—	—	11	New Malden 6	d								05 10			05 55		06 07			06 25
—	—	0	—	—	**Dorking** 4	d															05 48	
—	—	0¾	—	—	Box Hill & Westhumble	d															05 50	
—	4½	4	—	—	Leatherhead	d									05 23						05 56	
—	—	5¾	—	—	Ashtead	d									05 27						05 59	
—	—	7¾	—	—	**Epsom** 3	a									05 31						06 04	
—	—	—	—	—		d									05 33						06 04	
—	—	9	—	—	Ewell West	d									05 36						06 07	
—	—	10	—	—	Stoneleigh	d									05 39						06 10	
—	—	11¼	—	—	Worcester Park	d									05 41						06 12	
—	0	—	—	—	**Chessington South**	d																
—	0¾	—	—	—	Chessington North	d																
—	1¾	—	—	—	Tolworth	d																
—	2¾	—	—	—	Malden Manor	d																
—	3¾	12¾	—	—	Motspur Park	d									05 45						06 16	
21¼	5¼	13¾	—	12	Raynes Park 6	d	00 01							05 13	05 49		05 58		06 10		06 19	06 28
22¾	6¾	14¾	—	13½	**Wimbledon** 6 ⊖	d	00a04					00 16	05 02	05 17	05 53		06 02	06 05	06 14	06 20	06 23	06 32
24½	8½	16½	—	15¼	Earlsfield	d								05 21	05 58		06 05	06 08	06 17	06 24	06 27	06 35
26	10	18	—	16¾	**Clapham Junction** 10	d					00 05	00 23	05 09	05 25	06 02	06 05	06 09	06 12	06 21	06 28	06 31	06 39
28¾	12¾	20¾	—	19½	Vauxhall ⊖	d		00 02	00 05		00 12			05 30	06 07	06 12	06 14	06 17	06 26	06 33	06 36	06 44
30	14	22	—	20¾	**London Waterloo** 15 ⊖	a		00 10	00 14		00 16	00 33	05 18	05 35	06 11	06 16	06 19	06 22	06 31	06 37	06 40	06 49

Station		SW	SW	SW	SW	SW	SW	SW	SW	SW	SW	SW	SW	SW	SW	SW	SW
		G							D	G							D
Guildford	d					05 58	06 06							06 28	06 36		
London Road (Guildford)	d					06 02	06 10							06 32	06 40		
Clandon	d					06 07	06 15							06 37	06 45		
Horsley	d					06 11	06 19							06 41	06 49		
Effingham Junction 6	d					06 15	06 23							06 47	06 53		
Bookham	d					06 18								06 50			
Cobham & Stoke d'Abernon	d						06 26								06 56		
Oxshott	d						06 30								07 00		
Claygate	d						06 33								07 03		
Hinchley Wood	d						06 36								07 06		
Hampton Court	d			06 23								06 53					
Thames Ditton	d			06 25								06 55					
Surbiton 6	d	06 28		06 31			06 41			06 57		07 01			07 11		
Berrylands	d			06 34								07 03					
Shepperton	d				06 10								06 40				
Upper Halliford	d				06 13								06 43				
Sunbury	d				06 15								06 45				
Kempton Park	d																
Hampton	d				06 20								06 50				
Fulwell	d				06 23								06 53				
Strawberry Hill	d								06 37								07 07
Teddington	d				06 28				06 41				06 58				07 11
Hampton Wick	d				06 30				06 44				07 00				07 14
Kingston	a				06 32				06 46				07 02				07 16
	d				06 33				06 48				07 03				07 18
Norbiton	d				06 35				06 50				07 05				07 20
New Malden 6	d			06 37	06 40				06 55			07 06	07 10				07 25
Dorking 4	d										06 31						
Box Hill & Westhumble	d										06 33						
Leatherhead	d					06 23					06 38			06 55			
Ashtead	d					06 27					06 42			06 58			
Epsom 3	a					06 31					06 46			07 03			
	d		06 18			06 33					06 47			07 03			
Ewell West	d		06 21			06 36					06 50			07 06			
Stoneleigh	d		06 24			06 39					06 52			07 09			
Worcester Park	d		06 27			06 41					06 55			07 11			
Chessington South	d							06 39								07 09	
Chessington North	d							06 41								07 11	
Tolworth	d							06 43								07 13	
Malden Manor	d							06 46								07 16	
Motspur Park	d		06 30			06 45		06 50			06 59			07 15		07 20	
Raynes Park 6	d		06 34	06 40	06 43	06 49		06 54	06 58		07 04	07 10	07 13	07 19		07 24	07 28
Wimbledon 6 ⊖	d	06 35	06 38	06 44	06 47	06 53	06 50	06 58	07 02	07 05	07 08	07 14	07 17	07 23	07 20	07 28	07 32
Earlsfield	d	06 39	06 42	06 48	06 51	06 57	06 54	07 02	07 06	07 09	07 12	07 18	07 21	07 27	07 24	07 32	07 36
Clapham Junction 10	d	06 43	06 46	06 52	06 55	07 01	06 58	07 06	07 10	07 13	07 16	07 22	07 25	07 31	07 28	07 36	07 40
Vauxhall ⊖	d	06 48	06 51	06 57	07 00	07 06	07 03	07 11	07 15	07 18	07 21	07 27	07 30	07 36	07 33	07 41	07 45
London Waterloo 15 ⊖	a	06 52	06 55	07 03	07 06	07 12	07 09	07 17	07 21	07 24	07 27	07 33	07 36	07 42	07 39	07 47	07 51

A From Hampton Court
B From Shepperton
C From Guildford
D From London Waterloo
E From Portsmouth Harbour
F From Twickenham
G From Woking

The xx07 and xx37 Strawberry Hill to London Waterloo services originates from London Waterloo via Richmond

Table 152R

Mondays to Fridays

9 December to 16 May

Hampton Court, Shepperton, Guildford, Dorking and Chessington South - London

Network Diagram - see first Page of Table 152

Station		SW	SW	SW	SW	SW	SW	SW	SW	SW	SW	SW A	SW	SW
Guildford	d							06 58	07 06	07 16				
London Road (Guildford)	d							07 02	07 10	07 20				
Clandon	d							07 07	07 15	07 25				
Horsley	d							07 11	07 19	07 29				
Effingham Junction 6	d							07 16	07 23	07 33				
Bookham	d							07 19						
Cobham & Stoke d'Abernon	d								07 26	07 37				
Oxshott	d								07 30	07 41				
Claygate	d								07 33	07 44				
Hinchley Wood	d								07 36	07 47				
Hampton Court	d					07 24								
Thames Ditton	d					07 26								
Surbiton 6	d					07 32			07 41	07 53				
Berrylands	d					07 34								
Shepperton	d				07 00		07 10							07 30
Upper Halliford	d				07 03		07 13							07 33
Sunbury	d				07 05		07 15							07 35
Kempton Park	d													
Hampton	d				07 09		07 20							07 39
Fulwell	d				07 12		07 23							07 42
Strawberry Hill	d				07 14							07 37		07 44
Teddington	d		07 19				07 28					07 41		
Hampton Wick	d		07 21				07 30					07 44		
Kingston	a		07 23				07 32					07 46		
	d		07 25				07 33					07 48		
Norbiton	d		07 27				07 35					07 50		
New Malden 6	d		07 31			07 37	07 40		07 45			07 55		
Dorking 4	d	07 01											07 31	
Box Hill & Westhumble	d	07 03											07 33	
Leatherhead	d	07 08						07 26					07 38	
Ashtead	d	07 12						07 29					07 42	
Epsom 3	a	07 16						07 34					07 46	
	d	07 17		07 22				07 34					07 47	
Ewell West	d			07 25				07 37						
Stoneleigh	d			07 27				07 40						
Worcester Park	d	07 24		07 30				07 43					07 54	
Chessington South	d										07 39			
Chessington North	d										07 41			
Tolworth	d										07 43			
Malden Manor	d										07 46			
Motspur Park	d			07 33				07 46			07 50			
Raynes Park 6	d	07 31	07 34	07 37		07 40	07 43	07 50			07 54	07 58	08 01	
Wimbledon 6 ⊖	d	07 35	07 38	07 41		07 44	07 47	07 54	07 50		07 58	08 02	08 05	
Earlsfield	d	07 39	07 42	07 45		07 48	07 51	07 58	07 54		08 02	08 06	08 09	
Clapham Junction 10	d	07 43	07 46	07 49	07 49	07 52	07 55	08 02	07 58		08 06	08 10	08 13	08 19
Vauxhall ⊖	d	07 48	07 51	07 54	07 56	07 57	08 00	08 07	08 03		08 11	08 15	08 18	08 26
London Waterloo 15 ⊖	a	07 54	07 57	08 00	08 04	08 04	08 06	08 13	08 11	08 13	08 17	08 21	08 24	08 34

Station		SW B	SW	SN C	SW	SW	SW	SW	SW	SW A
Guildford	d			07 23				07 36		
London Road (Guildford)	d			07 27				07 40		
Clandon	d							07 45		
Horsley	d							07 49		
Effingham Junction 6	d			07 36			07 46	07 53		
Bookham	d			07 39			07 49			
Cobham & Stoke d'Abernon	d							07 56		
Oxshott	d							08 00		
Claygate	d							08 03		
Hinchley Wood	d							08 06		
Hampton Court	d				07 53					
Thames Ditton	d				07 55					
Surbiton 6	d				08 01			08 11		
Berrylands	d				08 03					
Shepperton	d					07 40				
Upper Halliford	d					07 43				
Sunbury	d					07 45				
Kempton Park	d									
Hampton	d					07 50				
Fulwell	d					07 53				
Strawberry Hill	d	07 46								08 07
Teddington	d	07 49				07 58				08 11
Hampton Wick	d	07 51				08 00				08 14
Kingston	a	07 53				08 02				08 16
	d	07 55				08 03				08 18
Norbiton	d	07 57				08 05				08 20
New Malden 6	d	08 01			08 06	08 10		08 15		08 25
Dorking 4	d									
Box Hill & Westhumble	d									
Leatherhead	d			07 45			07 55			
Ashtead	d			07 48			07 59			
Epsom 3	a			07 53			08 03			
	d		07 52				08 04			
Ewell West	d		07 55				08 07			
Stoneleigh	d		07 57				08 09			
Worcester Park	d		08 00				08 12			
Chessington South	d								08 09	
Chessington North	d								08 11	
Tolworth	d								08 13	
Malden Manor	d								08 16	
Motspur Park	d		08 03				08 16		08 20	
Raynes Park 6	d	08 04	08 07		08 10	08 13	08 20		08 24	08 28
Wimbledon 6 ⊖	d	08 08	08 11		08 14	08 17	08 24	08 20	08 28	08 32
Earlsfield	d	08 12	08 15		08 18	08 21	08 28	08 24	08 32	08 36
Clapham Junction 10	d	08 16	08 19		08 22	08 25	08 32	08 28	08 36	08 40
Vauxhall ⊖	d	08 21	08 24		08 27	08 30	08 37	08 33	08 41	08 45
London Waterloo 15 ⊖	a	08 27	08 30		08 33	08 36	08 43	08 40	08 47	08 51

Station		SW	SW	SW B	SW	SW	SW	SW	SW	SW	SW A	SW	SN D	SW	SW
Guildford	d							07 58	08 07				08 16	08 20	
London Road (Guildford)	d							08 02	08 11				08 19		
Clandon	d							08 07	08 16				08 24		
Horsley	d							08 11	08 20				08 29		
Effingham Junction 6	d							08 16	08 24				08 32		
Bookham	d							08 19					08 35		
Cobham & Stoke d'Abernon	d								08 27						
Oxshott	d								08 31						
Claygate	d								08 34						
Hinchley Wood	d								08 37						
Hampton Court	d					08 23									08 53
Thames Ditton	d					08 25									08 55
Surbiton 6	d					08 31			08 42					08 57	09 01
Berrylands	d					08 33									09 03
Shepperton	d		08 00				08 10								
Upper Halliford	d		08 03				08 13								
Sunbury	d		08 05				08 15								
Kempton Park	d														
Hampton	d		08 09				08 20								
Fulwell	d		08 12				08 23								
Strawberry Hill	d		08 14	08 16							08 38				
Teddington	d			08 19			08 28				08 41				
Hampton Wick	d			08 21			08 30				08 44				
Kingston	a			08 23			08 32				08 46				
	d			08 25			08 33				08 48				
Norbiton	d			08 27			08 35				08 50				
New Malden 6	d			08 31		08 36	08 40				08 55				09 06
Dorking 4	d	08 01										08 31			
Box Hill & Westhumble	d	08 03										08 33			
Leatherhead	d	08 08						08 24				08 38	08 41		
Ashtead	d	08 12						08 27				08 42	08 45		
Epsom 3	a	08 16						08 32				08 46	08 49		
	d	08 17			08 22			08 33				08 47			
Ewell West	d				08 25			08 36				08 50			
Stoneleigh	d				08 27			08 39				08 53			
Worcester Park	d	08 24			08 30			08 41				08 56			
Chessington South	d									08 39					
Chessington North	d									08 41					
Tolworth	d									08 43					
Malden Manor	d									08 46					
Motspur Park	d				08 33			08 45		08 50		08 59			
Raynes Park 6	d	08 31		08 34	08 37	08 40	08 43	08 49		08 54	08 58	09 04			09 10
Wimbledon 6 ⊖	d	08 35		08 38	08 41	08 44	08 47	08 53		08 58	09 02	09 08		09 05	09 14
Earlsfield	d	08 39		08 42	08 45	08 48	08 51	08 57		09 02	09 06	09 12		09 09	09 18
Clapham Junction 10	d	08 43	08 49	08 46	08 49	08 52	08 55	09 01		09 06	09 10	09 16		09 13	09 22
Vauxhall ⊖	d	08 48	08 56	08 51	08 54	08 57	09 00	09 06		09 11	09 15	09 21		09 18	09 27
London Waterloo 15 ⊖	a	08 54	09 04	08 57	09 00	09 03	09 06	09 12	09 01	09 17	09 21	09 27		09 24	09 33

A From London Waterloo
B From Twickenham
C To London Bridge
D To London Victoria

The xx07 and xx37 Strawberry Hill to London Waterloo services originates from London Waterloo via Richmond

Table 152R

Mondays to Fridays

9 December to 16 May

Hampton Court, Shepperton, Guildford, Dorking and Chessington South - London

Network Diagram - see first Page of Table 152

Station		SW	SW	SW	SW	SW A	SW	SW	SW	SW	SW	SW	SW	SW A
Guildford	d			08 36			08 46				08 58	09 07		
London Road (Guildford)	d			08 40							09 02	09 11		
Clandon	d			08 45							09 07	09 16		
Horsley	d			08 49							09 11	09 20		
Effingham Junction 6	d		08 48	08 53							09 15	09 23		
Bookham	d		08 51								09 18			
Cobham & Stoke d'Abernon	d			08 56								09 27		
Oxshott	d			09 00								09 30		
Claygate	d			09 03								09 33		
Hinchley Wood	d			09 06								09 36		
Hampton Court	d								09 23					
Thames Ditton	d								09 25					
Surbiton 6	d			09 11			09 27		09 31			09 41		
Berrylands	d								09 33					
Shepperton	d	08 40								09 10				
Upper Halliford	d	08 43								09 13				
Sunbury	d	08 45								09 15				
Kempton Park	d									09 17				
Hampton	d	08 50								09 20				
Fulwell	d	08 53								09 23				
Strawberry Hill	d					09 07								09 37
Teddington	d	08 58				09 11				09 28				09 41
Hampton Wick	d	09 00				09 14				09 30				09 44
Kingston	a	09 02				09 16				09 32				09 46
	d	09 03				09 18				09 33				09 48
Norbiton	d	09 05				09 20				09 35				09 50
New Malden 6	d	09 10				09 25			09 36	09 40				09 55
Dorking 4	d							09 01						
Box Hill & Westhumble	d							09 03						
Leatherhead	d		08 56					09 08			09 23			
Ashtead	d		08 59					09 12			09 27			
Epsom 3	a		09 04					09 16			09 31			
	d		09 04					09 17			09 34			
Ewell West	d		09 07					09 20			09 37			
Stoneleigh	d		09 10					09 23			09 39			
Worcester Park	d		09 12					09 26			09 42			
Chessington South	d				09 09								09 39	
Chessington North	d				09 11								09 41	
Tolworth	d				09 13								09 43	
Malden Manor	d				09 16								09 46	
Motspur Park	d		09 16		09 20			09 29			09 45		09 49	
Raynes Park 6	d	09 13	09 19		09 24	09 28		09 34	09 40	09 43	09 49		09 53	09 58
Wimbledon 6 ⊖	d	09 17	09 23	09 20	09 28	09 32	09 35	09 38	09 44	09 47	09 53	09 50	09 57	10 02
Earlsfield	d	09 21	09 27	09 24	09 31	09 36	09 39	09 42	09 47	09 50	09 57	09 54	10 01	10 05
Clapham Junction 10	d	09 25	09 31	09 28	09 35	09 40	09 43	09 46	09 51	09 54	10 01	09 58	10 05	10 09
Vauxhall ⊖	d	09 30	09 36	09 33	09 40	09 45	09 48	09 51	09 56	09 59	10 06	10 03	10 10	10 14
London Waterloo 15 ⊖	a	09 36	09 42	09 39	09 47	09 51	09 54	09 57	10 01	10 04	10 10	10 07	10 15	10 19

Station		SW B	SW	SW	SW	SW	SW	SW	SW A	SW B
Guildford	d					09 28	09 37			
London Road (Guildford)	d					09 32	09 41			
Clandon	d					09 37	09 46			
Horsley	d					09 41	09 50			
Effingham Junction 6	d					09 45	09 53			
Bookham	d					09 48				
Cobham & Stoke d'Abernon	d						09 57			
Oxshott	d						10 00			
Claygate	d						10 03			
Hinchley Wood	d						10 06			
Hampton Court	d			09 54						
Thames Ditton	d			09 56						
Surbiton 6	d	09 56		10 02			10 11			10 26
Berrylands	d			10 04						
Shepperton	d				09 40					
Upper Halliford	d				09 43					
Sunbury	d				09 45					
Kempton Park	d				09 47					
Hampton	d				09 50					
Fulwell	d				09 53					
Strawberry Hill	d								10 07	
Teddington	d				09 58				10 11	
Hampton Wick	d				10 00				10 14	
Kingston	a				10 02				10 16	
	d				10 03				10 18	
Norbiton	d				10 05				10 20	
New Malden 6	d			10 07	10 10				10 25	
Dorking 4	d		09 35							
Box Hill & Westhumble	d									
Leatherhead	d		09 41			09 53				
Ashtead	d		09 44			09 57				
Epsom 3	a		09 49			10 01				
	d		09 49			10 04				
Ewell West	d		09 52			10 07				
Stoneleigh	d		09 54			10 09				
Worcester Park	d		09 57			10 12				
Chessington South	d							10 09		
Chessington North	d							10 11		
Tolworth	d							10 13		
Malden Manor	d							10 16		
Motspur Park	d		10 00			10 15		10 19		
Raynes Park 6	d		10 04	10 10	10 13	10 19		10 23	10 28	
Wimbledon 6 ⊖	d	10 05	10 08	10 14	10 17	10 23	10 20	10 27	10 32	10 35
Earlsfield	d	10 08	10 12	10 17	10 20	10 27	10 24	10 31	10 35	10 38
Clapham Junction 10	d	10 12	10 16	10 21	10 24	10 31	10 28	10 35	10 39	10 42
Vauxhall ⊖	d	10 17	10 21	10 26	10 29	10 36	10 33	10 40	10 44	10 47
London Waterloo 15 ⊖	a	10 22	10 25	10 31	10 34	10 40	10 37	10 45	10 49	10 52

Station		SW	SW	SW	SW	SW	SW	SW A	SW B	SW	SW	SW	SW	SW	SW
Guildford	d				09 58	10 07							10 28	10 37	
London Road (Guildford)	d				10 02	10 11							10 32	10 41	
Clandon	d				10 07	10 16							10 37	10 46	
Horsley	d				10 11	10 20							10 41	10 50	
Effingham Junction 6	d				10 15	10 23							10 45	10 53	
Bookham	d				10 18								10 48		
Cobham & Stoke d'Abernon	d					10 27								10 57	
Oxshott	d					10 30								11 00	
Claygate	d					10 33								11 03	
Hinchley Wood	d					10 36								11 06	
Hampton Court	d		10 24								10 54				
Thames Ditton	d		10 26								10 56				
Surbiton 6	d		10 32			10 41			10 56		11 02			11 11	
Berrylands	d		10 34								11 04				
Shepperton	d			10 10								10 40			
Upper Halliford	d			10 13								10 43			
Sunbury	d			10 15								10 45			
Kempton Park	d			10 17								10 47			
Hampton	d			10 20								10 50			
Fulwell	d			10 23								10 53			
Strawberry Hill	d							10 37							
Teddington	d			10 28				10 41				10 58			
Hampton Wick	d			10 30				10 44				11 00			
Kingston	a			10 32				10 46				11 02			
	d			10 33				10 48				11 03			
Norbiton	d			10 35				10 50				11 05			
New Malden 6	d		10 37	10 40				10 55			11 07	11 10			
Dorking 4	d	10 05								10 35					
Box Hill & Westhumble	d														
Leatherhead	d	10 11			10 23					10 41			10 53		
Ashtead	d	10 14			10 27					10 44			10 57		
Epsom 3	a	10 19			10 31					10 49			11 01		
	d	10 19			10 34					10 49			11 04		
Ewell West	d	10 22			10 37					10 52			11 07		
Stoneleigh	d	10 24			10 39					10 54			11 09		
Worcester Park	d	10 27			10 42					10 57			11 12		
Chessington South	d						10 39								11 09
Chessington North	d						10 41								11 11
Tolworth	d						10 43								11 13
Malden Manor	d						10 46								11 16
Motspur Park	d	10 30			10 45		10 49			11 00			11 15		11 19
Raynes Park 6	d	10 34	10 40	10 43	10 49		10 53	10 58		11 04	11 10	11 13	11 19		11 23
Wimbledon 6 ⊖	d	10 38	10 44	10 47	10 53	10 50	10 57	11 02	11 05	11 08	11 14	11 17	11 23	11 20	11 27
Earlsfield	d	10 42	10 47	10 50	10 57	10 54	11 01	11 05	11 08	11 12	11 17	11 20	11 27	11 24	11 31
Clapham Junction 10	d	10 46	10 51	10 54	11 01	10 58	11 05	11 09	11 12	11 16	11 21	11 24	11 31	11 28	11 35
Vauxhall ⊖	d	10 51	10 56	10 59	11 06	11 03	11 10	11 14	11 17	11 21	11 26	11 29	11 36	11 33	11 40
London Waterloo 15 ⊖	a	10 55	11 01	11 04	11 10	11 07	11 15	11 19	11 22	11 25	11 31	11 34	11 40	11 37	11 45

A From London Waterloo

B From Woking

The xx07 and xx37 Strawberry Hill to London Waterloo services originates from London Waterloo via Richmond

Table 152R

Mondays to Fridays

9 December to 16 May

Hampton Court, Shepperton, Guildford, Dorking and Chessington South - London

Network Diagram - see first Page of Table 152

Station		SW A	SW B	SW	SW	SW	SW	SW	SW	SW A	SW B	SW	SW	SW
Guildford	d						10 58	11 07						
London Road (Guildford)	d						11 02	11 11						
Clandon	d						11 07	11 16						
Horsley	d						11 11	11 20						
Effingham Junction 6	d						11 15	11 23						
Bookham	d						11 18							
Cobham & Stoke d'Abernon	d							11 27						
Oxshott	d							11 30						
Claygate	d							11 33						
Hinchley Wood	d							11 36						
Hampton Court	d				11 24								11 54	
Thames Ditton	d				11 26								11 56	
Surbiton 6	d		11 26		11 32			11 41			11 56		12 02	
Berrylands	d				11 34								12 04	
Shepperton	d					11 10								11 40
Upper Halliford	d					11 13								11 43
Sunbury	d					11 15								11 45
Kempton Park	d					11 17								11 47
Hampton	d					11 20								11 50
Fulwell	d					11 23								11 53
Strawberry Hill	d	11 07								11 37				
Teddington	d	11 11				11 28				11 41				11 58
Hampton Wick	d	11 14				11 30				11 44				12 00
Kingston	a	11 16				11 32				11 46				12 02
	d	11 18				11 33				11 48				12 03
Norbiton	d	11 20				11 35				11 50				12 05
New Malden 6	d	11 25			11 37	11 40				11 55			12 07	12 10
Dorking 4	d			11 05								11 35		
Box Hill & Westhumble	d													
Leatherhead	d			11 11			11 23					11 41		
Ashtead	d			11 14			11 27					11 44		
Epsom 3	a			11 19			11 31					11 49		
	d			11 19			11 34					11 49		
Ewell West	d			11 22			11 37					11 52		
Stoneleigh	d			11 24			11 39					11 54		
Worcester Park	d			11 27			11 42					11 57		
Chessington South	d								11 39					
Chessington North	d								11 41					
Tolworth	d								11 43					
Malden Manor	d								11 46					
Motspur Park	d			11 30			11 45		11 49			12 00		
Raynes Park 6	d	11 28		11 34	11 40	11 43	11 49		11 53	11 58		12 04	12 10	12 13
Wimbledon 6 ⊖	d	11 32	11 35	11 38	11 44	11 47	11 53	11 50	11 57	12 02	12 05	12 08	12 14	12 17
Earlsfield	d	11 35	11 38	11 42	11 47	11 50	11 57	11 54	12 01	12 05	12 08	12 12	12 17	12 20
Clapham Junction 10	d	11 39	11 42	11 46	11 51	11 54	12 01	11 58	12 05	12 09	12 12	12 16	12 21	12 24
Vauxhall ⊖	d	11 44	11 47	11 51	11 56	11 59	12 06	12 03	12 10	12 14	12 17	12 21	12 26	12 29
London Waterloo 15 ⊖	a	11 49	11 52	11 55	12 01	12 04	12 10	12 07	12 15	12 19	12 22	12 25	12 31	12 34

Station		SW	SW	SW	SW A	SW B	SW	SW	SW	SW
Guildford	d	11 28	11 37							11 58
London Road (Guildford)	d	11 32	11 41							12 02
Clandon	d	11 37	11 46							12 07
Horsley	d	11 41	11 50							12 11
Effingham Junction 6	d	11 45	11 53							12 15
Bookham	d	11 48								12 18
Cobham & Stoke d'Abernon	d		11 57							
Oxshott	d		12 00							
Claygate	d		12 03							
Hinchley Wood	d		12 06							
Hampton Court	d							12 24		
Thames Ditton	d							12 26		
Surbiton 6	d		12 11			12 26		12 32		
Berrylands	d							12 34		
Shepperton	d								12 10	
Upper Halliford	d								12 13	
Sunbury	d								12 15	
Kempton Park	d								12 17	
Hampton	d								12 20	
Fulwell	d								12 23	
Strawberry Hill	d				12 07					
Teddington	d				12 11				12 28	
Hampton Wick	d				12 14				12 30	
Kingston	a				12 16				12 32	
	d				12 18				12 33	
Norbiton	d				12 20				12 35	
New Malden 6	d				12 25			12 37	12 40	
Dorking 4	d						12 05			
Box Hill & Westhumble	d									
Leatherhead	d	11 53					12 11			12 23
Ashtead	d	11 57					12 14			12 27
Epsom 3	a	12 01					12 19			12 31
	d	12 04					12 19			12 34
Ewell West	d	12 07					12 22			12 37
Stoneleigh	d	12 09					12 24			12 39
Worcester Park	d	12 12					12 27			12 42
Chessington South	d			12 09						
Chessington North	d			12 11						
Tolworth	d			12 13						
Malden Manor	d			12 16						
Motspur Park	d	12 15		12 19			12 30			12 45
Raynes Park 6	d	12 19		12 23	12 28		12 34	12 40	12 43	12 49
Wimbledon 6 ⊖	d	12 23	12 20	12 27	12 32	12 35	12 38	12 44	12 47	12 53
Earlsfield	d	12 27	12 24	12 31	12 35	12 38	12 42	12 47	12 50	12 57
Clapham Junction 10	d	12 31	12 28	12 35	12 39	12 42	12 46	12 51	12 54	13 01
Vauxhall ⊖	d	12 36	12 33	12 40	12 44	12 47	12 51	12 56	12 59	13 06
London Waterloo 15 ⊖	a	12 40	12 37	12 45	12 49	12 52	12 55	13 01	13 04	13 10

Station		SW	SW	SW A	SW B	SW	SW	SW	SW	SW	SW	SW A	SW B	SW	SW
Guildford	d	12 07							12 28	12 37					
London Road (Guildford)	d	12 11							12 32	12 41					
Clandon	d	12 16							12 37	12 46					
Horsley	d	12 20							12 41	12 50					
Effingham Junction 6	d	12 23							12 45	12 53					
Bookham	d								12 48						
Cobham & Stoke d'Abernon	d	12 27								12 57					
Oxshott	d	12 30								13 00					
Claygate	d	12 33								13 03					
Hinchley Wood	d	12 36								13 06					
Hampton Court	d						12 54								13 24
Thames Ditton	d						12 56								13 26
Surbiton 6	d	12 41			12 56		13 02			13 11			13 26		13 32
Berrylands	d						13 04								13 34
Shepperton	d							12 40							
Upper Halliford	d							12 43							
Sunbury	d							12 45							
Kempton Park	d							12 47							
Hampton	d							12 50							
Fulwell	d							12 53							
Strawberry Hill	d			12 37								13 07			
Teddington	d			12 41				12 58				13 11			
Hampton Wick	d			12 44				13 00				13 14			
Kingston	a			12 46				13 02				13 16			
	d			12 48				13 03				13 18			
Norbiton	d			12 50				13 05				13 20			
New Malden 6	d			12 55			13 07	13 10				13 25			13 37
Dorking 4	d					12 35								13 05	
Box Hill & Westhumble	d														
Leatherhead	d					12 41			12 53					13 11	
Ashtead	d					12 44			12 57					13 14	
Epsom 3	a					12 49			13 01					13 19	
	d					12 49			13 04					13 19	
Ewell West	d					12 52			13 07					13 22	
Stoneleigh	d					12 54			13 09					13 24	
Worcester Park	d					12 57			13 12					13 27	
Chessington South	d		12 39								13 09				
Chessington North	d		12 41								13 11				
Tolworth	d		12 43								13 13				
Malden Manor	d		12 46								13 16				
Motspur Park	d		12 49			13 00			13 15		13 19			13 30	
Raynes Park 6	d		12 53	12 58		13 04	13 10	13 13	13 19		13 23	13 28		13 34	13 40
Wimbledon 6 ⊖	d	12 50	12 57	13 02	13 05	13 08	13 14	13 17	13 23	13 20	13 27	13 32	13 35	13 38	13 44
Earlsfield	d	12 54	13 01	13 05	13 08	13 12	13 17	13 20	13 27	13 24	13 31	13 35	13 38	13 42	13 47
Clapham Junction 10	d	12 58	13 05	13 09	13 12	13 16	13 21	13 24	13 31	13 28	13 35	13 39	13 42	13 46	13 51
Vauxhall ⊖	d	13 03	13 10	13 14	13 17	13 21	13 26	13 29	13 36	13 33	13 40	13 44	13 47	13 51	13 56
London Waterloo 15 ⊖	a	13 07	13 15	13 19	13 22	13 25	13 31	13 34	13 40	13 37	13 45	13 49	13 52	13 55	14 01

A From London Waterloo

B From Woking

The xx07 and xx37 Strawberry Hill to London Waterloo services originates from London Waterloo via Richmond

Table 152R

Mondays to Fridays

9 December to 16 May

Hampton Court, Shepperton, Guildford, Dorking and Chessington South - London

Network Diagram - see first Page of Table 152

		SW	SW	SW	SW	SW A	SW B	SW	SW	SW	SW	SW	SW	SW A	SW B	SW	SW	SW	SW
Guildford	d		12 58	13 07							13 28	13 37							13 58
London Road (Guildford)	d		13 02	13 11							13 32	13 41							14 02
Clandon	d		13 07	13 16							13 37	13 46							14 07
Horsley	d		13 11	13 20							13 41	13 50							14 11
Effingham Junction	d		13 15	13 23							13 45	13 53							14 15
Bookham	d		13 18								13 48								14 18
Cobham & Stoke d'Abernon	d			13 27								13 57							
Oxshott	d			13 30								14 00							
Claygate	d			13 33								14 03							
Hinchley Wood	d			13 36								14 06							
Hampton Court	d								13 54								14 24		
Thames Ditton	d								13 56								14 26		
Surbiton	d			13 41			13 56		14 02			14 11			14 26		14 32		
Berrylands	d								14 04								14 34		
Shepperton	d	13 10								13 40								14 10	
Upper Halliford	d	13 13								13 43								14 13	
Sunbury	d	13 15								13 45								14 15	
Kempton Park	d	13 17								13 47								14 17	
Hampton	d	13 20								13 50								14 20	
Fulwell	d	13 23								13 53								14 23	
Strawberry Hill	d					13 37								14 07					
Teddington	d	13 28				13 41				13 58				14 11				14 28	
Hampton Wick	d	13 30				13 44				14 00				14 14				14 30	
Kingston	a	13 32				13 46				14 02				14 16				14 32	
	d	13 33				13 48				14 03				14 18				14 33	
Norbiton	d	13 35				13 50				14 05				14 20				14 35	
New Malden	d	13 40				13 55			14 07	14 10				14 25			14 37	14 40	
Dorking	d							13 35								14 05			
Box Hill & Westhumble	d																		
Leatherhead	d		13 23					13 41			13 53					14 11			14 23
Ashtead	d		13 27					13 44			13 57					14 14			14 27
Epsom	a		13 31					13 49			14 01					14 19			14 31
	d		13 34					13 49			14 04					14 19			14 34
Ewell West	d		13 37					13 52			14 07					14 22			14 37
Stoneleigh	d		13 39					13 54			14 09					14 24			14 39
Worcester Park	d		13 42					13 57			14 12					14 27			14 42
Chessington South	d				13 39								14 09						
Chessington North	d				13 41								14 11						
Tolworth	d				13 43								14 13						
Malden Manor	d				13 46								14 16						
Motspur Park	d		13 45		13 49			14 00			14 15		14 19			14 30			14 45
Raynes Park	d	13 43	13 49		13 53	13 58		14 04	14 10	14 13	14 19		14 23	14 28		14 34	14 40	14 43	14 49
Wimbledon	d	13 47	13 53	13 50	13 57	14 02	14 05	14 08	14 14	14 17	14 23	14 20	14 27	14 32	14 35	14 38	14 44	14 47	14 53
Earlsfield	d	13 50	13 57	13 54	14 01	14 05	14 08	14 12	14 17	14 20	14 27	14 24	14 31	14 35	14 38	14 42	14 47	14 50	14 57
Clapham Junction	d	13 54	14 01	13 58	14 05	14 09	14 12	14 16	14 21	14 24	14 31	14 28	14 35	14 39	14 42	14 46	14 51	14 54	15 01
Vauxhall	d	13 59	14 06	14 03	14 10	14 14	14 17	14 21	14 26	14 29	14 36	14 33	14 40	14 44	14 47	14 51	14 56	14 59	15 06
London Waterloo	a	14 04	14 10	14 07	14 15	14 19	14 22	14 25	14 31	14 34	14 40	14 37	14 45	14 49	14 52	14 55	15 01	15 04	15 10

		SW	SW	SW A	SW B	SW	SW	SW	SW	SW	SW	SW A	SW B	SW	SW	SW	SW	SW	SW
Guildford	d	14 07							14 28	14 37							14 58	15 07	
London Road (Guildford)	d	14 11							14 32	14 41							15 02	15 11	
Clandon	d	14 16							14 37	14 46							15 07	15 16	
Horsley	d	14 20							14 41	14 50							15 11	15 20	
Effingham Junction	d	14 23							14 45	14 53							15 15	15 23	
Bookham	d								14 48								15 18		
Cobham & Stoke d'Abernon	d	14 27								14 57								15 27	
Oxshott	d	14 30								15 00								15 30	
Claygate	d	14 33								15 03								15 33	
Hinchley Wood	d	14 36								15 06								15 36	
Hampton Court	d						14 54								15 24				
Thames Ditton	d						14 56								15 26				
Surbiton	d	14 41			14 56		15 02			15 11			15 26		15 32			15 41	
Berrylands	d						15 04								15 34				
Shepperton	d							14 40								15 10			
Upper Halliford	d							14 43								15 13			
Sunbury	d							14 45								15 15			
Kempton Park	d							14 47								15 17			
Hampton	d							14 50								15 20			
Fulwell	d							14 53								15 23			
Strawberry Hill	d			14 37								15 07							
Teddington	d			14 41				14 58				15 11				15 28			
Hampton Wick	d			14 44				15 00				15 14				15 30			
Kingston	a			14 46				15 02				15 16				15 32			
	d			14 48				15 03				15 18				15 33			
Norbiton	d			14 50				15 05				15 20				15 35			
New Malden	d			14 55			15 07	15 10				15 25			15 37	15 40			
Dorking	d					14 35								15 05					
Box Hill & Westhumble	d																		
Leatherhead	d					14 41			14 53					15 11			15 23		
Ashtead	d					14 44			14 57					15 14			15 27		
Epsom	a					14 49			15 01					15 19			15 31		
	d					14 49			15 04					15 19			15 34		
Ewell West	d					14 52			15 07					15 22			15 37		
Stoneleigh	d					14 54			15 09					15 24			15 39		
Worcester Park	d					14 57			15 12					15 27			15 42		
Chessington South	d		14 39								15 09								15 39
Chessington North	d		14 41								15 11								15 41
Tolworth	d		14 43								15 13								15 43
Malden Manor	d		14 46								15 16								15 46
Motspur Park	d		14 49			15 00			15 15		15 19			15 30			15 45		15 49
Raynes Park	d		14 53	14 58		15 04	15 10	15 13	15 19		15 23	15 28		15 34	15 40	15 43	15 49		15 53
Wimbledon	d	14 50	14 57	15 02	15 05	15 08	15 14	15 17	15 23	15 20	15 27	15 32	15 35	15 38	15 44	15 47	15 53	15 50	15 57
Earlsfield	d	14 54	15 01	15 05	15 08	15 12	15 17	15 20	15 27	15 24	15 31	15 35	15 38	15 42	15 47	15 50	15 57	15 54	16 01
Clapham Junction	d	14 58	15 05	15 09	15 12	15 16	15 21	15 24	15 31	15 28	15 35	15 39	15 42	15 46	15 51	15 54	16 01	15 58	16 05
Vauxhall	d	15 03	15 10	15 14	15 17	15 21	15 26	15 29	15 36	15 33	15 40	15 44	15 47	15 51	15 56	15 59	16 06	16 03	16 10
London Waterloo	a	15 07	15 15	15 19	15 22	15 25	15 31	15 34	15 40	15 37	15 45	15 49	15 52	15 55	16 01	16 04	16 10	16 07	16 15

A From London Waterloo

B From Woking

The xx07 and xx37 Strawberry Hill to London Waterloo services originates from London Waterloo via Richmond

Table 152R

Mondays to Fridays

9 December to 16 May

Hampton Court, Shepperton, Guildford, Dorking and Chessington South - London

Network Diagram - see first Page of Table 152

Station		SW A	SW B	SW	SW	SW	SW	SW	SW	SW A	SW B	SW	SW	SW	SW	SW	SW	SW A	SW B
Guildford	d						15 28	15 37							15 58	16 07			
London Road (Guildford)	d						15 32	15 41							16 02	16 11			
Clandon	d						15 37	15 46							16 07	16 16			
Horsley	d						15 41	15 50							16 11	16 20			
Effingham Junction 6	d						15 45	15 53							16 15	16 23			
Bookham	d						15 48								16 18				
Cobham & Stoke d'Abernon	d							15 57								16 27			
Oxshott	d							16 00								16 30			
Claygate	d							16 03								16 33			
Hinchley Wood	d							16 06								16 36			
Hampton Court	d				15 54								16 24						
Thames Ditton	d				15 56								16 26						
Surbiton 6	d		15 56		16 02			16 11			16 26		16 32			16 41			16 56
Berrylands	d				16 04								16 34						
Shepperton	d					15 40								16 10					
Upper Halliford	d					15 43								16 13					
Sunbury	d					15 45								16 15					
Kempton Park	d					15 47								16 17					
Hampton	d					15 50								16 20					
Fulwell	d					15 53								16 23					
Strawberry Hill	d	15 37								16 07								16 37	
Teddington	d	15 41				15 58				16 11				16 28				16 43	
Hampton Wick	d	15 44				16 00				16 14				16 30				16 46	
Kingston	a	15 46				16 02				16 16				16 32				16 48	
	d	15 48				16 03				16 18				16 33				16 48	
Norbiton	d	15 50				16 05				16 20				16 35				16 50	
New Malden 6	d	15 55			16 07	16 10				16 25			16 37	16 40				16 55	
Dorking 4	d			15 35								16 05							
Box Hill & Westhumble	d																		
Leatherhead	d			15 41			15 53					16 11			16 23				
Ashtead	d			15 44			15 57					16 14			16 27				
Epsom 3	a			15 49			16 01					16 19			16 31				
	d			15 49			16 04					16 19			16 34				
Ewell West	d			15 52			16 07					16 22			16 37				
Stoneleigh	d			15 54			16 09					16 24			16 39				
Worcester Park	d			15 57			16 12					16 27			16 42				
Chessington South	d								16 09								16 39		
Chessington North	d								16 11								16 41		
Tolworth	d								16 13								16 43		
Malden Manor	d								16 16								16 46		
Motspur Park	d			16 00			16 15		16 19			16 30			16 45		16 49		
Raynes Park 6	d	15 58		16 04	16 10	16 13	16 19		16 23	16 28		16 34	16 40	16 43	16 49		16 53	16 58	
Wimbledon 6 ⊖ ⛴	d	16 02	16 05	16 08	16 14	16 17	16 23	16 20	16 27	16 32	16 35	16 38	16 44	16 47	16 53	16 50	16 57	17 02	17 05
Earlsfield	d	16 05	16 08	16 12	16 17	16 20	16 27	16 24	16 31	16 35	16 38	16 42	16 47	16 50	16 57	16 54	17 01	17 05	17 08
Clapham Junction 10	d	16 09	16 12	16 16	16 21	16 24	16 31	16 28	16 35	16 39	16 42	16 46	16 51	16 54	17 01	16 58	17 05	17 09	17 12
Vauxhall ⊖	d	16 14	16 17	16 21	16 26	16 29	16 36	16 33	16 40	16 44	16 47	16 51	16 56	16 59	17 06	17 03	17 10	17 14	17 17
London Waterloo 15 ⊖	a	16 19	16 22	16 25	16 31	16 34	16 40	16 37	16 45	16 49	16 52	16 55	17 01	17 05	17 10	17 07	17 16	17 19	17 22

Station		SW	SW	SW	SW	SW	SW	SW A	SW B	SW	SW	SW	SW	SW	SW	SW A	SW B	SW	SW A
Guildford	d				16 28	16 37							16 58	17 07					
London Road (Guildford)	d				16 32	16 41							17 02	17 11					
Clandon	d				16 37	16 46							17 07	17 16					
Horsley	d				16 41	16 50							17 11	17 20					
Effingham Junction 6	d				16 45	16 53							17 15	17 23					
Bookham	d				16 48								17 18						
Cobham & Stoke d'Abernon	d					16 57								17 27					
Oxshott	d					17 00								17 30					
Claygate	d					17 03								17 33					
Hinchley Wood	d					17 06								17 36					
Hampton Court	d		16 54								17 24								
Thames Ditton	d		16 56								17 26								
Surbiton 6	d		17 02			17 11			17 26		17 32			17 41			17 56		
Berrylands	d		17 04								17 34								
Shepperton	d			16 40								17 10							
Upper Halliford	d			16 43								17 13							
Sunbury	d			16 45								17 15							
Kempton Park	d			16 47								17 17							
Hampton	d			16 50								17 20							
Fulwell	d			16 53								17 23							
Strawberry Hill	d							17 07								17 37			17 41
Teddington	d			16 58				17 13				17 28				17 43			17 52
Hampton Wick	d			17 00				17 16				17 30				17 46			17 54
Kingston	a			17 02				17 18				17 32				17 48			17 56
	d			17 03				17 18				17 33				17 48			17 58
Norbiton	d			17 05				17 20				17 35				17 50			18 00
New Malden 6	d		17 07	17 10				17 25			17 37	17 40				17 55			18 04
Dorking 4	d	16 35								17 05								17 35	
Box Hill & Westhumble	d																		
Leatherhead	d	16 41			16 53					17 11			17 23					17 41	
Ashtead	d	16 44			16 57					17 14			17 27					17 44	
Epsom 3	a	16 49			17 01					17 19			17 31					17 49	
	d	16 49			17 04					17 19			17 34					17 49	
Ewell West	d	16 52			17 07					17 22			17 37					17 52	
Stoneleigh	d	16 54			17 09					17 24			17 39					17 54	
Worcester Park	d	16 57			17 12					17 27			17 42					17 57	
Chessington South	d						17 09								17 39				
Chessington North	d						17 11								17 41				
Tolworth	d						17 13								17 43				
Malden Manor	d						17 16								17 46				
Motspur Park	d	17 00			17 15		17 19			17 30			17 45		17 49			18 00	
Raynes Park 6	d	17 04	17 10	17 13	17 19		17 23	17 28		17 34	17 40	17 43	17 49		17 53	17 58		18 04	18 07
Wimbledon 6 ⊖ ⛴	d	17 08	17 14	17 17	17 23	17 20	17 27	17 32	17 35	17 38	17 44	17 47	17 53	17 50	17 57	18 02	18 05	18 08	18 11
Earlsfield	d	17 12	17 17	17 20	17 27	17 24	17 31	17 35	17 38	17 42	17 47	17 50	17 57	17 54	18 01	18 05	18 08	18 12	18 15
Clapham Junction 10	d	17 16	17 21	17 24	17 31	17 28	17 35	17 39	17 42	17 46	17 51	17 54	18 01	17 58	18 05	18 09	18 12	18 16	18 19
Vauxhall ⊖	d	17 21	17 26	17 29	17 36	17 33	17 40	17 44	17 47	17 51	17 56	17 59	18 06	18 03	18 10	18 14	18 17	18 21	18 24
London Waterloo 15 ⊖	a	17 25	17 31	17 35	17 40	17 37	17 45	17 49	17 52	17 55	18 01	18 05	18 10	18 07	18 15	18 19	18 23	18 25	18 29

A From London Waterloo

B From Woking

The xx07 and xx37 Strawberry Hill to London Waterloo services originates from London Waterloo via Richmond

Table 152R

Mondays to Fridays
9 December to 16 May

Hampton Court, Shepperton, Guildford, Dorking and Chessington South - London

Network Diagram - see first Page of Table 152

Station		SW	SW	SW	SW	SW	SW A	SW B	SW	SW	SW	SW	SW	SW
Guildford	d			17 28	17 37							17 58	18 07	
London Road (Guildford)	d			17 32	17 41							18 02	18 11	
Clandon	d			17 37	17 46							18 07	18 16	
Horsley	d			17 41	17 50							18 11	18 20	
Effingham Junction 6	d			17 45	17 53							18 15	18 23	
Bookham	d			17 48								18 18		
Cobham & Stoke d'Abernon	d				17 57								18 27	
Oxshott	d				18 00								18 30	
Claygate	d				18 03								18 33	
Hinchley Wood	d				18 06								18 36	
Hampton Court	d	17 54								18 24				
Thames Ditton	d	17 56								18 26				
Surbiton 6	d	18 02			18 11			18 26		18 32			18 41	
Berrylands	d	18 04								18 34				
Shepperton	d		17 40								18 10			
Upper Halliford	d		17 43								18 13			
Sunbury	d		17 45								18 15			
Kempton Park	d		17 47								18 17			
Hampton	d		17 50								18 20			
Fulwell	d		17 53								18 23			
Strawberry Hill	d						18 07							
Teddington	d		17 58				18 13				18 28			
Hampton Wick	d		18 00				18 16				18 30			
Kingston	a		18 02				18 18				18 32			
	d		18 03				18 18				18 33			
Norbiton	d		18 05				18 20				18 35			
New Malden 6	d	18 07	18 10				18 25			18 37	18 40			
Dorking 4	d								18 05					
Box Hill & Westhumble	d													
Leatherhead	d			17 53					18 11			18 23		
Ashtead	d			17 57					18 14			18 27		
Epsom 3	a			18 01					18 19			18 31		
	d			18 04					18 19			18 34		
Ewell West	d			18 07					18 22			18 37		
Stoneleigh	d			18 09					18 24			18 39		
Worcester Park	d			18 12					18 27			18 42		
Chessington South	d					18 09								18 39
Chessington North	d					18 11								18 41
Tolworth	d					18 13								18 43
Malden Manor	d					18 16								18 46
Motspur Park	d			18 15		18 19			18 30			18 45		18 49
Raynes Park 6	d	18 10	18 13	18 19		18 23	18 28		18 34	18 40	18 43	18 49		18 53
Wimbledon 6 ⊖	d	18 14	18 17	18 23	18 20	18 27	18 32	18 35	18 38	18 44	18 47	18 53	18 50	18 57
Earlsfield	d	18 17	18 20	18 27	18 24	18 31	18 35	18 38	18 42	18 47	18 50	18 57	18 54	19 01
Clapham Junction 10	d	18 21	18 24	18 31	18 28	18 35	18 39	18 42	18 46	18 51	18 54	19 01	18 58	19 05
Vauxhall ⊖	d	18 26	18 29	18 36	18 33	18 40	18 44	18 47	18 51	18 56	18 59	19 06	19 03	19 10
London Waterloo 15 ⊖	a	18 31	18 35	18 40	18 37	18 47	18 49	18 52	18 55	19 01	19 05	19 10	19 07	19 14

Station		SW A	SW B	SW	SN C	SW	SW	SW	SW	SW
Guildford	d				18 22			18 37		
London Road (Guildford)	d				18 25			18 41		
Clandon	d				18 30			18 46		
Horsley	d				18 35			18 50		
Effingham Junction 6	d				18 39			18 53		
Bookham	d				18 42					
Cobham & Stoke d'Abernon	d							18 57		
Oxshott	d							19 00		
Claygate	d							19 03		
Hinchley Wood	d							19 06		
Hampton Court	d					18 54				
Thames Ditton	d					18 56				
Surbiton 6	d		18 56			19 02		19 11		
Berrylands	d					19 04				
Shepperton	d						18 36			
Upper Halliford	d						18 39			
Sunbury	d						18 41			
Kempton Park	d						18 43			
Hampton	d						18 50			
Fulwell	d						18 53			
Strawberry Hill	d	18 37								
Teddington	d	18 43					18 58			
Hampton Wick	d	18 46					19 00			
Kingston	a	18 48					19 02			
	d	18 48					19 03			
Norbiton	d	18 50					19 05			
New Malden 6	d	18 55				19 07	19 10			
Dorking 4	d			18 35					18 50	
Box Hill & Westhumble	d									
Leatherhead	d			18 41	18 47				18 56	
Ashtead	d			18 44	18 51				18 59	
Epsom 3	a			18 48	18 57				19 03	
	d			18 49					19 04	
Ewell West	d			18 52					19 07	
Stoneleigh	d			18 54					19 09	
Worcester Park	d			18 57					19 12	
Chessington South	d									19 09
Chessington North	d									19 11
Tolworth	d									19 13
Malden Manor	d									19 16
Motspur Park	d			19 00					19 15	19 20
Raynes Park 6	d	18 58		19 04		19 10	19 13		19 19	19 23
Wimbledon 6 ⊖	d	19 02	19 05	19 08		19 14	19 17	19 20	19 23	19 27
Earlsfield	d	19 05	19 09	19 12		19 17	19 20	19 24	19 27	19 31
Clapham Junction 10	d	19 09	19 12	19 16		19 21	19 24	19 28	19 31	19 35
Vauxhall ⊖	d	19 14	19 17	19 21		19 26	19 29	19 33	19 36	19 40
London Waterloo 15 ⊖	a	19 19	19 23	19 27		19 31	19 34	19 37	19 41	19 45

Station		SW A	SW B	SW	SW	SW	SW	SN D	SW	SW	SW A	SW B	SW	SW	SW
Guildford	d							19 04	19 07						
London Road (Guildford)	d							19 07	19 11						
Clandon	d							19 12	19 16						
Horsley	d							19 17	19 20						
Effingham Junction 6	d			18 59				19 20	19 23						
Bookham	d			19 02				19 23							
Cobham & Stoke d'Abernon	d								19 27						
Oxshott	d								19 30						
Claygate	d								19 33						
Hinchley Wood	d								19 36						
Hampton Court	d				19 24									19 54	
Thames Ditton	d				19 26									19 56	
Surbiton 6	d		19 26		19 32				19 41			19 56		20 02	
Berrylands	d				19 34									20 04	
Shepperton	d					19 06									19 40
Upper Halliford	d					19 09									19 43
Sunbury	d					19 11									19 45
Kempton Park	d					19 13									19 47
Hampton	d					19 20									19 50
Fulwell	d					19 23									19 53
Strawberry Hill	d	19 07									19 37				
Teddington	d	19 13				19 28					19 43				19 58
Hampton Wick	d	19 16				19 30					19 46				20 00
Kingston	a	19 18				19 32					19 48				20 03
	d	19 18				19 33					19 48				20 03
Norbiton	d	19 20				19 35					19 50				20 05
New Malden 6	d	19 25			19 37	19 40					19 55			20 07	20 10
Dorking 4	d												19 33		
Box Hill & Westhumble	d														
Leatherhead	d			19 08				19 28					19 39		
Ashtead	d			19 12				19 32					19 42		
Epsom 3	a			19 16				19 36					19 47		
	d			19 19			19 34						19 49		
Ewell West	d			19 22			19 37						19 52		
Stoneleigh	d			19 24			19 39						19 54		
Worcester Park	d			19 27			19 42						19 57		
Chessington South	d									19 39					
Chessington North	d									19 41					
Tolworth	d									19 43					
Malden Manor	d									19 46					
Motspur Park	d			19 30			19 45			19 49			20 00		
Raynes Park 6	d	19 28		19 34	19 40	19 43	19 49			19 53	19 58		20 04	20 10	20 13
Wimbledon 6 ⊖	d	19 32	19 35	19 38	19 44	19 47	19 53		19 50	19 57	20 02	20 05	20 08	20 14	20 17
Earlsfield	d	19 35	19 39	19 42	19 47	19 50	19 57		19 54	20 01	20 05	20 09	20 12	20 17	20 20
Clapham Junction 10	d	19 39	19 42	19 46	19 51	19 54	20 01		19 58	20 05	20 09	20 12	20 16	20 21	20 24
Vauxhall ⊖	d	19 44	19 47	19 51	19 56	19 59	20 06		20 03	20 10	20 14	20 17	20 21	20 26	20 29
London Waterloo 15 ⊖	a	19 49	19 52	19 55	20 01	20 04	20 10		20 07	20 15	20 19	20 22	20 25	20 31	20 35

A From London Waterloo
B From Woking
C To London Victoria
D To Sutton (Surrey)

The xx07 and xx37 Strawberry Hill to London Waterloo services originates from London Waterloo via Richmond

Table 152R

Mondays to Fridays

9 December to 16 May

Hampton Court, Shepperton, Guildford, Dorking and Chessington South - London

Network Diagram - see first Page of Table 152

		SW	SW	SW	SW A	SW B	SW	SW	SW	SW	SW	SW	SW A	SW B	SW	SW	SW	SW	SW	SW	SW A	SW B	SW	SW	SW	SW	SW	SW	SW A	SW B	SW	SW	SW	SW A	SW B	SW	SW
Guildford	d	19 28	19 37							19 58	20 07							20 37					20 46			21 07							21 37			21 46	
London Road (Guildford)	d	19 32	19 41							20 02	20 11							20 41					20 50			21 11							21 41			21 50	
Clandon	d	19 37	19 46							20 07	20 16							20 46					20 55			21 16							21 46			21 55	
Horsley	d	19 41	19 50							20 11	20 20							20 50					20 59			21 20							21 50			21 59	
Effingham Junction 6	d	19 45	19 53							20 15	20 23							20 53					21 03			21 23							21 53			22 03	
Bookham	d	19 48								20 18													21 06													22 06	
Cobham & Stoke d'Abernon	d		19 57								20 27							20 57								21 27							21 57				
Oxshott	d		20 00								20 30							21 00								21 30							22 00				
Claygate	d		20 03								20 33							21 03								21 33							22 03				
Hinchley Wood	d		20 06								20 36							21 06								21 36							22 06				
Hampton Court	d							20 24								20 54								21 24													22 24
Thames Ditton	d							20 26								20 56								21 26													22 26
Surbiton 6	d		20 11			20 26		20 32			20 41			20 56		21 02		21 11				21 26		21 32		21 41				21 56			22 11		22 26		22 32
Berrylands	d							20 34								21 04								21 34													22 34
Shepperton	d								20 10								20 40								21 10							21 40					
Upper Halliford	d								20 13								20 43								21 13							21 43					
Sunbury	d								20 15								20 45								21 15							21 45					
Kempton Park	d								20 17								20 47								21 17							21 47					
Hampton	d								20 20								20 50								21 20							21 50					
Fulwell	d								20 23								20 53								21 23							21 53					
Strawberry Hill	d				20 07								20 37								21 07								21 37					22 07			
Teddington	d				20 11				20 28				20 41				20 58				21 11				21 28				21 41			21 58		22 11			
Hampton Wick	d				20 14				20 30				20 44				21 00				21 14				21 30				21 44			22 00		22 14			
Kingston	a				20 16				20 32				20 46				21 02				21 16				21 32				21 46			22 02		22 16			
	d				20 18				20 33				20 48				21 03				21 18				21 33				21 48			22 03		22 18			
Norbiton	d				20 20				20 35				20 50				21 05				21 20				21 35				21 50			22 05		22 20			
New Malden 6	d				20 25			20 37	20 40				20 55			21 07	21 10				21 25			21 37	21 40				21 55			22 10		22 25			22 37
Dorking 4	d						20 05								20 35																21 35						
Box Hill & Westhumble	d																																				
Leatherhead	d	19 53					20 11			20 23					20 41								21 11								21 41					22 11	
Ashtead	d	19 57					20 14			20 27					20 44								21 14								21 44					22 14	
Epsom 3	a	20 01					20 19			20 31					20 49								21 19								21 49					22 19	
	d	20 04					20 19			20 34					20 49				21 04				21 19				21 34				21 49					22 19	
Ewell West	d	20 07					20 22			20 37					20 52				21 07				21 22				21 37				21 52					22 22	
Stoneleigh	d	20 09					20 24			20 39					20 54				21 09				21 24				21 39				21 54					22 24	
Worcester Park	d	20 12					20 27			20 42					20 57				21 12				21 27				21 42				21 57					22 27	
Chessington South	d			20 09								20 39								21 09								21 39									
Chessington North	d			20 11								20 41								21 11								21 41									
Tolworth	d			20 13								20 43								21 13								21 43									
Malden Manor	d			20 16								20 46								21 16								21 46									
Motspur Park	d	20 15		20 19			20 30			20 45		20 49			21 00				21 15	21 19			21 30				21 45	21 49			22 00					22 30	
Raynes Park 6	d	20 19		20 23	20 28		20 34	20 40	20 43	20 49		20 53	20 58		21 04	21 10	21 13		21 19	21 23	21 28		21 34	21 40	21 43		21 49	21 53	21 58		22 04	22 13		22 28		22 34	22 40
Wimbledon 6 ⊖	d	20 23	20 20	20 27	20 32	20 35	20 38	20 44	20 47	20 53	20 50	20 57	21 02	21 05	21 08	21 14	21 17	21 20	21 23	21 27	21 32	21 35	21 38	21 44	21 47	21 50	21 53	21 57	22 02	22 05	22 08	22 17	22 20	22 32	22 35	22 38	22 44
Earlsfield	d	20 27	20 24	20 31	20 35	20 39	20 42	20 47	20 50	20 57	20 54	21 01	21 05	21 09	21 12	21 17	21 20	21 24	21 27	21 31	21 35	21 38	21 42	21 47	21 50	21 54	21 57	22 01	22 05	22 08	22 12	22 20	22 24	22 35	22 38	22 42	22 47
Clapham Junction 10	d	20 31	20 28	20 35	20 39	20 42	20 46	20 51	20 54	21 01	20 58	21 05	21 09	21 12	21 16	21 21	21 24	21 28	21 31	21 35	21 39	21 42	21 46	21 51	21 54	21 58	22 01	22 05	22 09	22 12	22 16	22 24	22 28	22 39	22 42	22 46	22 51
Vauxhall ⊖	d	20 36	20 33	20 40	20 44	20 47	20 51	20 56	20 59	21 06	21 03	21 10	21 14	21 17	21 21	21 26	21 29	21 33	21 36	21 40	21 44	21 47	21 51	21 56	21 59	22 03	22 06	22 10	22 14	22 17	22 21	22 29	22 33	22 44	22 47	22 51	22 56
London Waterloo 15 ⊖	a	20 41	20 38	20 46	20 49	20 52	20 55	21 01	21 04	21 10	21 07	21 15	21 19	21 22	21 25	21 31	21 34	21 37	21 40	21 45	21 49	21 52	21 55	22 01	22 04	22 07	22 10	22 16	22 19	22 22	22 25	22 34	22 39	22 49	22 52	22 55	23 01

A From London Waterloo

B From Woking

The xx07 and xx37 Strawberry Hill to London Waterloo services originates from London Waterloo via Richmond

Table 152R

Mondays to Fridays

9 December to 16 May

Hampton Court, Shepperton, Guildford, Dorking and Chessington South - London

Network Diagram - see first Page of Table 152

		SW	SW	SW	SW	SW	SW	SW	SW	SW	SW	SW	SW	SW	SW	SW	SW	SW	SW
																		FO 1	FX 1
					A					A							A	B	B
Guildford	d		22 07			22 20			22 37		22 46	22 55			23 07			23 39	23 39
London Road (Guildford)	d		22 11						22 41		22 50				23 11				
Clandon	d		22 16						22 46		22 55				23 16				
Horsley	d		22 20						22 50		22 59				23 20				
Effingham Junction 6	d		22 23						22 53		23 03				23 23				
Bookham	d										23 06								
Cobham & Stoke d'Abernon	d		22 27						22 57						23 27				
Oxshott	d		22 30						23 00						23 30				
Claygate	d		22 33						23 03						23 33				
Hinchley Wood	d		22 36						23 06						23 36				
Hampton Court	d												23 24						
Thames Ditton	d												23 26						
Surbiton 6	d		22 41			22 56			23 11			23 30	23 33		23 41			00 08	00 08
Berrylands	d												23 35						
Shepperton	d	22 10						22 40						23 10					
Upper Halliford	d	22 13						22 43						23 13					
Sunbury	d	22 15						22 45						23 15					
Kempton Park	d	22 17						22 47						23 17					
Hampton	d	22 20						22 50						23 20					
Fulwell	d	22 23						22 53						23 23					
Strawberry Hill	d				22 37					23 07							23 37		
Teddington	d	22 28			22 41			22 58		23 11				23 28			23 41		
Hampton Wick	d	22 30			22 44			23 00		23 14				23 30			23 44		
Kingston	a	22 32			22 46			23 02		23 16				23 32			23 46		
	d	22 33			22 48			23 03		23 18				23 33			23 49		
Norbiton	d	22 35			22 50			23 05		23 20				23 35			23 51		
New Malden 6	d	22 40			22 55			23 10		23 25			23 38	23 41			23 55		
Dorking 4	d						22 35												
Box Hill & Westhumble	d																		
Leatherhead	d						22 41				23 11								
Ashtead	d						22 44				23 14								
Epsom 3	a						22 49				23 19								
	d						22 49				23 19								
Ewell West	d						22 52				23 22								
Stoneleigh	d						22 54				23 24								
Worcester Park	d						22 57				23 27								
Chessington South	d			22 39												23 39			
Chessington North	d			22 41												23 41			
Tolworth	d			22 43												23 43			
Malden Manor	d			22 46												23 46			
Motspur Park	d			22 49			23 00				23 30					23 49			
Raynes Park 6	d	22 43		22 53	22 58		23 04	23 13		23 28	23 37		23 41	23 43		23 54	23 58		
Wimbledon 6 ⊖ ⇌	d	22 47	22 50	22 57	23 02	23 05	23 08	23 17	23 20	23 32	23 41	23 37	23a45	23 50	23 53	23a57	00 02	00 16	00 16
Earlsfield	d	22 50	22 54	23 01	23 05	23 08	23 12	23 20	23 24	23 36	23 44	23 41		23 53	23 56		00 05		
Clapham Junction 10	d	22 54	22 58	23 05	23 09	23 12	23 16	23 24	23 28	23 40	23 48	23 45		23 57	23 59		00 09	00 23	00 23
Vauxhall ⊖	d	22 59	23 03	23 10	23 14	23 17	23 21	23 29	23 33	23 45	23 53	23 50		00 02	00 05		00 14		
London Waterloo 15 ⊖	a	23 04	23 07	23 15	23 19	23 23	23 27	23 34	23 37	23 49	23 58	23 54		00 10	00 14		00 22	00 32	00 33

A From London Waterloo

B From Portsmouth Harbour

The xx07 and xx37 Strawberry Hill to London Waterloo services originates from London Waterloo via Richmond

Table 152R

Saturdays

14 December to 17 May

Hampton Court, Shepperton, Guildford, Dorking and Chessington South - London

Network Diagram - see first Page of Table 152

		SW A	SW B	SW C	SW C	SW ■1 D	SW	SW E	SW	SW
Guildford	d						04 25			
London Road (Guildford)	d									
Clandon	d									
Horsley	d									
Effingham Junction ■6	d									
Bookham	d									
Cobham & Stoke d'Abernon	d									
Oxshott	d									
Claygate	d									
Hinchley Wood	d									
Hampton Court	d									
Thames Ditton	d									
Surbiton ■6	d					00 08	04 54			
Berrylands	d									
Shepperton	d									
Upper Halliford	d									
Sunbury	d									
Kempton Park	d									
Hampton	d									
Fulwell	d									
Strawberry Hill	d			00 09				04 55		
Teddington	d			00 12				04 59		05 44
Hampton Wick	d			00 14				05 01		05 46
Kingston	a			00 16				05 03		05 48
	d							05 04		05 49
Norbiton	d							05 06		05 51
New Malden ■6	d							05 10		05 55
Dorking ■4	d									
Box Hill & Westhumble	d									
Leatherhead	d									
Ashtead	d									
Epsom ■3	a									
	d								05 34	
Ewell West	d								05 37	
Stoneleigh	d								05 39	
Worcester Park	d								05 42	
Chessington South	d									
Chessington North	d									
Tolworth	d									
Malden Manor	d									
Motspur Park	d								05 45	
Raynes Park ■6	d							05 13	05 49	05 58
Wimbledon ■6 ⊖ ⛴	d					00 16	05 02	05 17	05 53	06 02
Earlsfield	d							05 21	05 58	06 05
Clapham Junction ■10	d				00 05	00 23	05 09	05 25	06 02	06 09
Vauxhall ⊖	d	00 02	00 05		00 12			05 30	06 07	06 14
London Waterloo ■15 ⊖	a	00 10	00 14		00 16	00 32	05 18	05 35	06 11	06 19

		SW	SW	SW	SW C	SW F	SW	SW	SW	SW
Guildford	d	05 14								
London Road (Guildford)	d									
Clandon	d									
Horsley	d									
Effingham Junction ■6	d									
Bookham	d									
Cobham & Stoke d'Abernon	d									
Oxshott	d									
Claygate	d									
Hinchley Wood	d									
Hampton Court	d		05 54				06 24			
Thames Ditton	d		05 56				06 26			
Surbiton ■6	d	05 57	06 02			06 27	06 32			
Berrylands	d		06 04				06 34			
Shepperton	d							06 10		
Upper Halliford	d							06 13		
Sunbury	d							06 15		
Kempton Park	d							06 17		
Hampton	d							06 20		
Fulwell	d							06 23		
Strawberry Hill	d				06 07					
Teddington	d				06 11			06 28		
Hampton Wick	d				06 14			06 30		
Kingston	a				06 16			06 32		
	d				06 18			06 33		
Norbiton	d				06 20			06 35		
New Malden ■6	d		06 07		06 25		06 37	06 40		
Dorking ■4	d									
Box Hill & Westhumble	d									
Leatherhead	d									
Ashtead	d									
Epsom ■3	a									
	d			06 04					06 34	
Ewell West	d			06 07					06 37	
Stoneleigh	d			06 09					06 39	
Worcester Park	d			06 12					06 42	
Chessington South	d									06 39
Chessington North	d									06 41
Tolworth	d									06 43
Malden Manor	d									06 46
Motspur Park	d			06 15					06 45	06 49
Raynes Park ■6	d		06 10	06 19	06 28		06 40	06 43	06 49	06 53
Wimbledon ■6 ⊖ ⛴	d	06 05	06 14	06 23	06 32	06 35	06 44	06 47	06 53	06 57
Earlsfield	d	06 08	06 17	06 27	06 35	06 38	06 47	06 50	06 57	07 01
Clapham Junction ■10	d	06 12	06 21	06 31	06 39	06 42	06 51	06 54	07 01	07 05
Vauxhall ⊖	d	06 17	06 26	06 36	06 44	06 47	06 56	06 59	07 06	07 10
London Waterloo ■15 ⊖	a	06 22	06 31	06 40	06 49	06 52	07 01	07 04	07 10	07 15

		SW C	SW F	SW	SW	SW	SW	SW	SW C	SW F
Guildford	d					06 28	06 38			
London Road (Guildford)	d					06 32	06 42			
Clandon	d					06 37	06 47			
Horsley	d					06 41	06 51			
Effingham Junction ■6	d					06 45	06 54			
Bookham	d					06 48				
Cobham & Stoke d'Abernon	d						06 58			
Oxshott	d						07 01			
Claygate	d						07 04			
Hinchley Wood	d						07 07			
Hampton Court	d			06 54						
Thames Ditton	d			06 56						
Surbiton ■6	d		06 57	07 02			07 12			07 27
Berrylands	d			07 04						
Shepperton	d				06 40					
Upper Halliford	d				06 43					
Sunbury	d				06 45					
Kempton Park	d				06 47					
Hampton	d				06 50					
Fulwell	d				06 53					
Strawberry Hill	d	06 37							07 07	
Teddington	d	06 41			06 58				07 11	
Hampton Wick	d	06 44			07 00				07 14	
Kingston	a	06 46			07 02				07 16	
	d	06 48			07 03				07 18	
Norbiton	d	06 50			07 05				07 20	
New Malden ■6	d	06 55		07 07	07 10				07 25	
Dorking ■4	d									
Box Hill & Westhumble	d									
Leatherhead	d					06 53				
Ashtead	d					06 57				
Epsom ■3	a					07 01				
	d					07 04				
Ewell West	d					07 07				
Stoneleigh	d					07 09				
Worcester Park	d					07 12				
Chessington South	d							07 09		
Chessington North	d							07 11		
Tolworth	d							07 13		
Malden Manor	d							07 16		
Motspur Park	d					07 15		07 19		
Raynes Park ■6	d	06 58		07 10	07 13	07 19		07 23	07 28	
Wimbledon ■6 ⊖ ⛴	d	07 02	07 05	07 14	07 17	07 23	07 20	07 27	07 32	07 35
Earlsfield	d	07 05	07 08	07 17	07 20	07 27	07 24	07 31	07 35	07 38
Clapham Junction ■10	d	07 09	07 12	07 21	07 24	07 31	07 28	07 35	07 39	07 42
Vauxhall ⊖	d	07 14	07 17	07 26	07 29	07 36	07 33	07 40	07 44	07 47
London Waterloo ■15 ⊖	a	07 19	07 22	07 31	07 34	07 40	07 37	07 45	07 49	07 52

		SW	SW	SW	SW	SW	SW C	SW F	SW	SW
Guildford	d			06 58	07 08					
London Road (Guildford)	d			07 02	07 12					
Clandon	d			07 07	07 17					
Horsley	d			07 11	07 21					
Effingham Junction ■6	d			07 15	07 24					
Bookham	d			07 18						
Cobham & Stoke d'Abernon	d				07 28					
Oxshott	d				07 31					
Claygate	d				07 34					
Hinchley Wood	d				07 37					
Hampton Court	d	07 24							07 54	
Thames Ditton	d	07 26							07 56	
Surbiton ■6	d	07 32			07 42			07 57	08 02	
Berrylands	d	07 34							08 04	
Shepperton	d		07 10							07 40
Upper Halliford	d		07 13							07 43
Sunbury	d		07 15							07 45
Kempton Park	d		07 17							07 47
Hampton	d		07 20							07 50
Fulwell	d		07 23							07 53
Strawberry Hill	d						07 37			
Teddington	d		07 28				07 41			07 58
Hampton Wick	d		07 30				07 44			08 00
Kingston	a		07 32				07 46			08 02
	d		07 33				07 48			08 03
Norbiton	d		07 35				07 50			08 05
New Malden ■6	d	07 37	07 40				07 55		08 07	08 10
Dorking ■4	d									
Box Hill & Westhumble	d									
Leatherhead	d			07 23						
Ashtead	d			07 27						
Epsom ■3	a			07 31						
	d			07 34						
Ewell West	d			07 37						
Stoneleigh	d			07 39						
Worcester Park	d			07 42						
Chessington South	d					07 39				
Chessington North	d					07 41				
Tolworth	d					07 43				
Malden Manor	d					07 46				
Motspur Park	d			07 45		07 49				
Raynes Park ■6	d	07 40	07 43	07 49		07 53	07 58		08 10	08 13
Wimbledon ■6 ⊖ ⛴	d	07 44	07 47	07 53	07 50	07 57	08 02	08 05	08 14	08 17
Earlsfield	d	07 47	07 50	07 57	07 54	08 01	08 05	08 08	08 17	08 20
Clapham Junction ■10	d	07 51	07 54	08 01	07 58	08 05	08 09	08 12	08 21	08 24
Vauxhall ⊖	d	07 56	07 59	08 06	08 03	08 10	08 14	08 17	08 26	08 29
London Waterloo ■15 ⊖	a	08 01	08 04	08 10	08 07	08 15	08 19	08 22	08 31	08 34

A From Shepperton
B From Guildford
C From London Waterloo
D From Portsmouth Harbour
E From Twickenham
F From Woking

The xx07 and xx37 Strawberry Hill to London Waterloo services originates from London Waterloo via Richmond

Table 152R

Saturdays

14 December to 17 May

Hampton Court, Shepperton, Guildford, Dorking and Chessington South - London

Network Diagram - see first Page of Table 152

		SW	SW	SW	SW A	SW B	SW	SW	SW	SW
Guildford	d	07 28	07 38							07 58
London Road (Guildford)	d	07 32	07 42							08 02
Clandon	d	07 37	07 47							08 07
Horsley	d	07 41	07 51							08 11
Effingham Junction 6	d	07 45	07 54							08 15
Bookham	d	07 48								08 18
Cobham & Stoke d'Abernon	d		07 58							
Oxshott	d		08 01							
Claygate	d		08 04							
Hinchley Wood	d		08 07							
Hampton Court	d							08 24		
Thames Ditton	d							08 26		
Surbiton 6	d		08 12			08 27		08 32		
Berrylands	d							08 34		
Shepperton	d								08 10	
Upper Halliford	d								08 13	
Sunbury	d								08 15	
Kempton Park	d								08 17	
Hampton	d								08 20	
Fulwell	d								08 23	
Strawberry Hill	d				08 07					
Teddington	d				08 11				08 28	
Hampton Wick	d				08 14				08 30	
Kingston	a				08 16				08 32	
	d				08 18				08 33	
Norbiton	d				08 20				08 35	
New Malden 6	d				08 25			08 37	08 40	
Dorking 4	d						08 05			
Box Hill & Westhumble	d									
Leatherhead	d	07 53					08 11			08 23
Ashtead	d	07 57					08 14			08 27
Epsom 3	a	08 01					08 19			08 31
	d	08 04					08 19			08 34
Ewell West	d	08 07					08 22			08 37
Stoneleigh	d	08 09					08 24			08 39
Worcester Park	d	08 12					08 27			08 42
Chessington South	d			08 09						
Chessington North	d			08 11						
Tolworth	d			08 13						
Malden Manor	d			08 16						
Motspur Park	d	08 15		08 19			08 30			08 45
Raynes Park 6	d	08 19		08 23	08 28		08 34	08 40	08 43	08 49
Wimbledon 6 ⊖ ⛴	d	08 23	08 20	08 27	08 32	08 35	08 38	08 44	08 47	08 53
Earlsfield	d	08 27	08 24	08 31	08 35	08 38	08 42	08 47	08 50	08 57
Clapham Junction 10	d	08 31	08 28	08 35	08 39	08 42	08 46	08 51	08 54	09 01
Vauxhall ⊖	d	08 36	08 33	08 40	08 44	08 47	08 51	08 56	08 59	09 06
London Waterloo 15 ⊖	a	08 40	08 37	08 45	08 49	08 52	08 55	09 01	09 04	09 10

		SW	SW	SW A	SW B	SW	SW	SW	SW	SW
Guildford	d	08 08							08 28	08 38
London Road (Guildford)	d	08 12							08 32	08 42
Clandon	d	08 17							08 37	08 47
Horsley	d	08 21							08 41	08 51
Effingham Junction 6	d	08 24							08 45	08 54
Bookham	d								08 48	
Cobham & Stoke d'Abernon	d	08 28								08 58
Oxshott	d	08 31								09 01
Claygate	d	08 34								09 04
Hinchley Wood	d	08 37								09 07
Hampton Court	d						08 54			
Thames Ditton	d						08 56			
Surbiton 6	d	08 42			08 57		09 02			09 12
Berrylands	d						09 04			
Shepperton	d							08 40		
Upper Halliford	d							08 43		
Sunbury	d							08 45		
Kempton Park	d							08 47		
Hampton	d							08 50		
Fulwell	d							08 53		
Strawberry Hill	d			08 37						
Teddington	d			08 41				08 58		
Hampton Wick	d			08 44				09 00		
Kingston	a			08 46				09 02		
	d			08 48				09 03		
Norbiton	d			08 50				09 05		
New Malden 6	d			08 55			09 07	09 10		
Dorking 4	d					08 35				
Box Hill & Westhumble	d									
Leatherhead	d					08 41			08 53	
Ashtead	d					08 44			08 57	
Epsom 3	a					08 49			09 01	
	d					08 49			09 04	
Ewell West	d					08 52			09 07	
Stoneleigh	d					08 54			09 09	
Worcester Park	d					08 57			09 12	
Chessington South	d		08 39							
Chessington North	d		08 41							
Tolworth	d		08 43							
Malden Manor	d		08 46							
Motspur Park	d		08 49			09 00			09 15	
Raynes Park 6	d		08 53	08 58		09 04	09 10	09 13	09 19	
Wimbledon 6 ⊖ ⛴	d	08 50	08 57	09 02	09 05	09 08	09 14	09 17	09 23	09 20
Earlsfield	d	08 54	09 01	09 05	09 08	09 12	09 17	09 20	09 27	09 24
Clapham Junction 10	d	08 58	09 05	09 09	09 12	09 16	09 21	09 24	09 31	09 28
Vauxhall ⊖	d	09 03	09 10	09 14	09 17	09 21	09 26	09 29	09 36	09 33
London Waterloo 15 ⊖	a	09 07	09 15	09 19	09 22	09 25	09 31	09 34	09 40	09 37

		SW	SW A	SW B	SW	SW	SW	SW	SW	SW
Guildford	d							08 58	09 08	
London Road (Guildford)	d							09 02	09 12	
Clandon	d							09 07	09 17	
Horsley	d							09 11	09 21	
Effingham Junction 6	d							09 15	09 24	
Bookham	d							09 18		
Cobham & Stoke d'Abernon	d								09 28	
Oxshott	d								09 31	
Claygate	d								09 34	
Hinchley Wood	d								09 37	
Hampton Court	d					09 24				
Thames Ditton	d					09 26				
Surbiton 6	d			09 27		09 32			09 42	
Berrylands	d					09 34				
Shepperton	d						09 10			
Upper Halliford	d						09 13			
Sunbury	d						09 15			
Kempton Park	d						09 17			
Hampton	d						09 20			
Fulwell	d						09 23			
Strawberry Hill	d		09 07							
Teddington	d		09 11				09 28			
Hampton Wick	d		09 14				09 30			
Kingston	a		09 16				09 32			
	d		09 18				09 33			
Norbiton	d		09 20				09 35			
New Malden 6	d		09 25			09 37	09 40			
Dorking 4	d				09 05					
Box Hill & Westhumble	d									
Leatherhead	d				09 11			09 23		
Ashtead	d				09 14			09 27		
Epsom 3	a				09 19			09 31		
	d				09 19			09 34		
Ewell West	d				09 22			09 37		
Stoneleigh	d				09 24			09 39		
Worcester Park	d				09 27			09 42		
Chessington South	d	09 09								09 39
Chessington North	d	09 11								09 41
Tolworth	d	09 13								09 43
Malden Manor	d	09 16								09 46
Motspur Park	d	09 19			09 30			09 45		09 49
Raynes Park 6	d	09 23	09 28		09 34	09 40	09 43	09 49		09 53
Wimbledon 6 ⊖ ⛴	d	09 27	09 32	09 35	09 38	09 44	09 47	09 53	09 50	09 57
Earlsfield	d	09 31	09 35	09 38	09 42	09 47	09 50	09 57	09 54	10 01
Clapham Junction 10	d	09 35	09 39	09 42	09 46	09 51	09 54	10 01	09 58	10 05
Vauxhall ⊖	d	09 40	09 44	09 47	09 51	09 56	09 59	10 06	10 03	10 10
London Waterloo 15 ⊖	a	09 45	09 49	09 52	09 55	10 01	10 04	10 10	10 07	10 15

		SW A	SW B	SW	SW	SW	SW	SW	SW	SW A
Guildford	d						09 28	09 38		
London Road (Guildford)	d						09 32	09 42		
Clandon	d						09 37	09 47		
Horsley	d						09 41	09 51		
Effingham Junction 6	d						09 45	09 54		
Bookham	d						09 48			
Cobham & Stoke d'Abernon	d							09 58		
Oxshott	d							10 01		
Claygate	d							10 04		
Hinchley Wood	d							10 07		
Hampton Court	d				09 54					
Thames Ditton	d				09 56					
Surbiton 6	d		09 57		10 02			10 12		
Berrylands	d				10 04					
Shepperton	d					09 40				
Upper Halliford	d					09 43				
Sunbury	d					09 45				
Kempton Park	d					09 47				
Hampton	d					09 50				
Fulwell	d					09 53				
Strawberry Hill	d	09 37								10 07
Teddington	d	09 41				09 58				10 11
Hampton Wick	d	09 44				10 00				10 14
Kingston	a	09 46				10 02				10 16
	d	09 48				10 03				10 18
Norbiton	d	09 50				10 05				10 20
New Malden 6	d	09 55			10 07	10 10				10 25
Dorking 4	d			09 35						
Box Hill & Westhumble	d									
Leatherhead	d			09 41			09 53			
Ashtead	d			09 44			09 57			
Epsom 3	a			09 49			10 01			
	d			09 49			10 04			
Ewell West	d			09 52			10 07			
Stoneleigh	d			09 54			10 09			
Worcester Park	d			09 57			10 12			
Chessington South	d								10 09	
Chessington North	d								10 11	
Tolworth	d								10 13	
Malden Manor	d								10 16	
Motspur Park	d			10 00			10 15		10 19	
Raynes Park 6	d	09 58		10 04	10 10	10 13	10 19		10 23	10 28
Wimbledon 6 ⊖ ⛴	d	10 02	10 05	10 08	10 14	10 17	10 23	10 20	10 27	10 32
Earlsfield	d	10 05	10 08	10 12	10 17	10 20	10 27	10 24	10 31	10 35
Clapham Junction 10	d	10 09	10 12	10 16	10 21	10 24	10 31	10 28	10 35	10 39
Vauxhall ⊖	d	10 14	10 17	10 21	10 26	10 29	10 36	10 33	10 40	10 44
London Waterloo 15 ⊖	a	10 19	10 22	10 25	10 31	10 34	10 40	10 37	10 45	10 49

A From London Waterloo

B From Woking

The xx07 and xx37 Strawberry Hill to London Waterloo services originates from London Waterloo via Richmond

Table 152R

Saturdays

14 December to 17 May

Hampton Court, Shepperton, Guildford, Dorking and Chessington South - London

Network Diagram - see first Page of Table 152

Station		SW A	SW	SW	SW	SW	SW	SW	SW B	SW A
Guildford	d					09 58	10 08			
London Road (Guildford)	d					10 02	10 12			
Clandon	d					10 07	10 17			
Horsley	d					10 11	10 21			
Effingham Junction 6	d					10 15	10 24			
Bookham	d					10 18				
Cobham & Stoke d'Abernon	d						10 28			
Oxshott	d						10 31			
Claygate	d						10 34			
Hinchley Wood	d						10 37			
Hampton Court	d			10 24						
Thames Ditton	d			10 26						
Surbiton 6	d	10 27		10 32			10 42			10 57
Berrylands	d			10 34						
Shepperton	d				10 10					
Upper Halliford	d				10 13					
Sunbury	d				10 15					
Kempton Park	d				10 17					
Hampton	d				10 20					
Fulwell	d				10 23					
Strawberry Hill	d								10 37	
Teddington	d				10 28				10 41	
Hampton Wick	d				10 30				10 44	
Kingston	a				10 32				10 46	
	d				10 33				10 48	
Norbiton	d				10 35				10 50	
New Malden 6	d			10 37	10 40				10 55	
Dorking 4	d		10 05							
Box Hill & Westhumble	d									
Leatherhead	d		10 11			10 23				
Ashtead	d		10 14			10 27				
Epsom 3	a		10 19			10 31				
	d		10 19			10 34				
Ewell West	d		10 22			10 37				
Stoneleigh	d		10 24			10 39				
Worcester Park	d		10 27			10 42				
Chessington South	d							10 39		
Chessington North	d							10 41		
Tolworth	d							10 43		
Malden Manor	d							10 46		
Motspur Park	d		10 30			10 45		10 49		
Raynes Park 6	d		10 34	10 40	10 43	10 49		10 53	10 58	
Wimbledon 6 ⊖ ⛴	d	10 35	10 38	10 44	10 47	10 53	10 50	10 57	11 02	11 05
Earlsfield	d	10 38	10 42	10 47	10 50	10 57	10 54	11 01	11 05	11 08
Clapham Junction 10	d	10 42	10 46	10 51	10 54	11 01	10 58	11 05	11 09	11 12
Vauxhall ⊖	d	10 47	10 51	10 56	10 59	11 06	11 03	11 10	11 14	11 17
London Waterloo 15 ⊖	a	10 52	10 55	11 01	11 04	11 10	11 07	11 15	11 19	11 22

Station		SW	SW	SW	SW	SW	SW	SW B	SW A	SW
Guildford	d				10 28	10 38				
London Road (Guildford)	d				10 32	10 42				
Clandon	d				10 37	10 47				
Horsley	d				10 41	10 51				
Effingham Junction 6	d				10 45	10 54				
Bookham	d				10 48					
Cobham & Stoke d'Abernon	d					10 58				
Oxshott	d					11 01				
Claygate	d					11 04				
Hinchley Wood	d					11 07				
Hampton Court	d		10 54							
Thames Ditton	d		10 56							
Surbiton 6	d		11 02			11 12			11 27	
Berrylands	d		11 04							
Shepperton	d			10 40						
Upper Halliford	d			10 43						
Sunbury	d			10 45						
Kempton Park	d			10 47						
Hampton	d			10 50						
Fulwell	d			10 53						
Strawberry Hill	d							11 07		
Teddington	d			10 58				11 11		
Hampton Wick	d			11 00				11 14		
Kingston	a			11 02				11 16		
	d			11 03				11 18		
Norbiton	d			11 05				11 20		
New Malden 6	d		11 07	11 10				11 25		
Dorking 4	d	10 35								11 05
Box Hill & Westhumble	d									
Leatherhead	d	10 41			10 53					11 11
Ashtead	d	10 44			10 57					11 14
Epsom 3	a	10 49			11 01					11 19
	d	10 49			11 04					11 19
Ewell West	d	10 52			11 07					11 22
Stoneleigh	d	10 54			11 09					11 24
Worcester Park	d	10 57			11 12					11 27
Chessington South	d						11 09			
Chessington North	d						11 11			
Tolworth	d						11 13			
Malden Manor	d						11 16			
Motspur Park	d	11 00			11 15		11 19			11 30
Raynes Park 6	d	11 04	11 10	11 13	11 19		11 23	11 28		11 34
Wimbledon 6 ⊖ ⛴	d	11 08	11 14	11 17	11 23	11 20	11 27	11 32	11 35	11 38
Earlsfield	d	11 12	11 17	11 20	11 27	11 24	11 31	11 35	11 38	11 42
Clapham Junction 10	d	11 16	11 21	11 24	11 31	11 28	11 35	11 39	11 42	11 46
Vauxhall ⊖	d	11 21	11 26	11 29	11 36	11 33	11 40	11 44	11 47	11 51
London Waterloo 15 ⊖	a	11 25	11 31	11 34	11 40	11 37	11 45	11 49	11 52	11 55

Station		SW	SW	SW	SW	SW	SW B	SW A	SW	SW
Guildford	d			10 58	11 08					
London Road (Guildford)	d			11 02	11 12					
Clandon	d			11 07	11 17					
Horsley	d			11 11	11 21					
Effingham Junction 6	d			11 15	11 24					
Bookham	d			11 18						
Cobham & Stoke d'Abernon	d				11 28					
Oxshott	d				11 31					
Claygate	d				11 34					
Hinchley Wood	d				11 37					
Hampton Court	d	11 24								11 54
Thames Ditton	d	11 26								11 56
Surbiton 6	d	11 32			11 42			11 57		12 02
Berrylands	d	11 34								12 04
Shepperton	d		11 10							
Upper Halliford	d		11 13							
Sunbury	d		11 15							
Kempton Park	d		11 17							
Hampton	d		11 20							
Fulwell	d		11 23							
Strawberry Hill	d						11 37			
Teddington	d		11 28				11 41			
Hampton Wick	d		11 30				11 44			
Kingston	a		11 32				11 46			
	d		11 33				11 48			
Norbiton	d		11 35				11 50			
New Malden 6	d	11 37	11 40				11 55			12 07
Dorking 4	d								11 35	
Box Hill & Westhumble	d									
Leatherhead	d			11 23					11 41	
Ashtead	d			11 27					11 44	
Epsom 3	a			11 31					11 49	
	d			11 34					11 49	
Ewell West	d			11 37					11 52	
Stoneleigh	d			11 39					11 54	
Worcester Park	d			11 42					11 57	
Chessington South	d					11 39				
Chessington North	d					11 41				
Tolworth	d					11 43				
Malden Manor	d					11 46				
Motspur Park	d			11 45		11 49			12 00	
Raynes Park 6	d	11 40	11 43	11 49		11 53	11 58		12 04	12 10
Wimbledon 6 ⊖ ⛴	d	11 44	11 47	11 53	11 50	11 57	12 02	12 05	12 08	12 14
Earlsfield	d	11 47	11 50	11 57	11 54	12 01	12 05	12 08	12 12	12 17
Clapham Junction 10	d	11 51	11 54	12 01	11 58	12 05	12 09	12 12	12 16	12 21
Vauxhall ⊖	d	11 56	11 59	12 06	12 03	12 10	12 14	12 17	12 21	12 26
London Waterloo 15 ⊖	a	12 01	12 04	12 10	12 07	12 15	12 19	12 22	12 25	12 31

Station		SW	SW	SW	SW	SW B	SW A	SW	SW	SW
Guildford	d		11 28	11 38						
London Road (Guildford)	d		11 32	11 42						
Clandon	d		11 37	11 47						
Horsley	d		11 41	11 51						
Effingham Junction 6	d		11 45	11 54						
Bookham	d		11 48							
Cobham & Stoke d'Abernon	d			11 58						
Oxshott	d			12 01						
Claygate	d			12 04						
Hinchley Wood	d			12 07						
Hampton Court	d								12 24	
Thames Ditton	d								12 26	
Surbiton 6	d			12 12			12 27		12 32	
Berrylands	d								12 34	
Shepperton	d	11 40								12 10
Upper Halliford	d	11 43								12 13
Sunbury	d	11 45								12 15
Kempton Park	d	11 47								12 17
Hampton	d	11 50								12 20
Fulwell	d	11 53								12 23
Strawberry Hill	d					12 07				
Teddington	d	11 58				12 11				12 28
Hampton Wick	d	12 00				12 14				12 30
Kingston	a	12 02				12 16				12 32
	d	12 03				12 18				12 33
Norbiton	d	12 05				12 20				12 35
New Malden 6	d	12 10				12 25			12 37	12 40
Dorking 4	d							12 05		
Box Hill & Westhumble	d									
Leatherhead	d		11 53					12 11		
Ashtead	d		11 57					12 14		
Epsom 3	a		12 01					12 19		
	d		12 04					12 19		
Ewell West	d		12 07					12 22		
Stoneleigh	d		12 09					12 24		
Worcester Park	d		12 12					12 27		
Chessington South	d				12 09					
Chessington North	d				12 11					
Tolworth	d				12 13					
Malden Manor	d				12 16					
Motspur Park	d		12 15		12 19			12 30		
Raynes Park 6	d	12 13	12 19		12 23	12 28		12 34	12 40	12 43
Wimbledon 6 ⊖ ⛴	d	12 17	12 23	12 20	12 27	12 32	12 35	12 38	12 44	12 47
Earlsfield	d	12 20	12 27	12 24	12 31	12 35	12 38	12 42	12 47	12 50
Clapham Junction 10	d	12 24	12 31	12 28	12 35	12 39	12 42	12 46	12 51	12 54
Vauxhall ⊖	d	12 29	12 36	12 33	12 40	12 44	12 47	12 51	12 56	12 59
London Waterloo 15 ⊖	a	12 34	12 40	12 37	12 45	12 49	12 52	12 55	13 01	13 04

A From Woking

B From London Waterloo

The xx07 and xx37 Strawberry Hill to London Waterloo services originates from London Waterloo via Richmond

Table 152R

Saturdays

14 December to 17 May

Hampton Court, Shepperton, Guildford, Dorking and Chessington South - London

Network Diagram - see first Page of Table 152

Station		SW	SW	SW	SW A	SW B	SW	SW	SW	SW
Guildford	d	11 58	12 08							12 28
London Road (Guildford)	d	12 02	12 12							12 32
Clandon	d	12 07	12 17							12 37
Horsley	d	12 11	12 21							12 41
Effingham Junction 6	d	12 15	12 24							12 45
Bookham	d	12 18								12 48
Cobham & Stoke d'Abernon	d		12 28							
Oxshott	d		12 31							
Claygate	d		12 34							
Hinchley Wood	d		12 37							
Hampton Court	d							12 54		
Thames Ditton	d							12 56		
Surbiton 6	d		12 42			12 57		13 02		
Berrylands	d							13 04		
Shepperton	d								12 40	
Upper Halliford	d								12 43	
Sunbury	d								12 45	
Kempton Park	d								12 47	
Hampton	d								12 50	
Fulwell	d								12 53	
Strawberry Hill	d				12 37					
Teddington	d				12 41				12 58	
Hampton Wick	d				12 44				13 00	
Kingston	a				12 46				13 02	
	d				12 48				13 03	
Norbiton	d				12 50				13 05	
New Malden 6	d				12 55			13 07	13 10	
Dorking 4	d						12 35			
Box Hill & Westhumble	d									
Leatherhead	d	12 23					12 41			12 53
Ashtead	d	12 27					12 44			12 57
Epsom 3	a	12 31					12 49			13 01
	d	12 34					12 49			13 04
Ewell West	d	12 37					12 52			13 07
Stoneleigh	d	12 39					12 54			13 09
Worcester Park	d	12 42					12 57			13 12
Chessington South	d			12 39						
Chessington North	d			12 41						
Tolworth	d			12 43						
Malden Manor	d			12 46						
Motspur Park	d	12 45		12 49			13 00			13 15
Raynes Park 6	d	12 49		12 53	12 58		13 04	13 10	13 13	13 19
Wimbledon 6 ⊖ ⇌	d	12 53	12 50	12 57	13 02	13 05	13 08	13 14	13 17	13 23
Earlsfield	d	12 57	12 54	13 01	13 05	13 08	13 12	13 17	13 20	13 27
Clapham Junction 10	d	13 01	12 58	13 05	13 09	13 12	13 16	13 21	13 24	13 31
Vauxhall ⊖	d	13 06	13 03	13 10	13 14	13 17	13 21	13 26	13 29	13 36
London Waterloo 15 ⊖	a	13 10	13 07	13 15	13 19	13 22	13 25	13 31	13 34	13 40

Station		SW	SW	SW A	SW B	SW	SW	SW	SW	SW
Guildford	d	12 38							12 58	13 08
London Road (Guildford)	d	12 42							13 02	13 12
Clandon	d	12 47							13 07	13 17
Horsley	d	12 51							13 11	13 21
Effingham Junction 6	d	12 54							13 15	13 24
Bookham	d								13 18	
Cobham & Stoke d'Abernon	d	12 58								13 28
Oxshott	d	13 01								13 31
Claygate	d	13 04								13 34
Hinchley Wood	d	13 07								13 37
Hampton Court	d						13 24			
Thames Ditton	d						13 26			
Surbiton 6	d	13 12			13 27		13 32			13 42
Berrylands	d						13 34			
Shepperton	d							13 10		
Upper Halliford	d							13 13		
Sunbury	d							13 15		
Kempton Park	d							13 17		
Hampton	d							13 20		
Fulwell	d							13 23		
Strawberry Hill	d			13 07						
Teddington	d			13 11				13 28		
Hampton Wick	d			13 14				13 30		
Kingston	a			13 16				13 32		
	d			13 18				13 33		
Norbiton	d			13 20				13 35		
New Malden 6	d			13 25			13 37	13 40		
Dorking 4	d					13 05				
Box Hill & Westhumble	d									
Leatherhead	d					13 11			13 23	
Ashtead	d					13 14			13 27	
Epsom 3	a					13 19			13 31	
	d					13 19			13 34	
Ewell West	d					13 22			13 37	
Stoneleigh	d					13 24			13 39	
Worcester Park	d					13 27			13 42	
Chessington South	d		13 09							
Chessington North	d		13 11							
Tolworth	d		13 13							
Malden Manor	d		13 16							
Motspur Park	d		13 19			13 30			13 45	
Raynes Park 6	d		13 23	13 28		13 34	13 40	13 43	13 49	
Wimbledon 6 ⊖ ⇌	d	13 20	13 27	13 32	13 35	13 38	13 44	13 47	13 53	13 50
Earlsfield	d	13 24	13 31	13 35	13 38	13 42	13 47	13 50	13 57	13 54
Clapham Junction 10	d	13 28	13 35	13 39	13 42	13 46	13 51	13 54	14 01	13 58
Vauxhall ⊖	d	13 33	13 40	13 44	13 47	13 51	13 56	13 59	14 06	14 03
London Waterloo 15 ⊖	a	13 37	13 45	13 49	13 52	13 55	14 01	14 04	14 10	14 07

Station		SW	SW A	SW B	SW	SW	SW	SW	SW	SW
Guildford	d							13 28	13 38	
London Road (Guildford)	d							13 32	13 42	
Clandon	d							13 37	13 47	
Horsley	d							13 41	13 51	
Effingham Junction 6	d							13 45	13 54	
Bookham	d							13 48		
Cobham & Stoke d'Abernon	d								13 58	
Oxshott	d								14 01	
Claygate	d								14 04	
Hinchley Wood	d								14 07	
Hampton Court	d					13 54				
Thames Ditton	d					13 56				
Surbiton 6	d			13 57		14 02			14 12	
Berrylands	d					14 04				
Shepperton	d						13 40			
Upper Halliford	d						13 43			
Sunbury	d						13 45			
Kempton Park	d						13 47			
Hampton	d						13 50			
Fulwell	d						13 53			
Strawberry Hill	d		13 37							
Teddington	d		13 41				13 58			
Hampton Wick	d		13 44				14 00			
Kingston	a		13 46				14 02			
	d		13 48				14 03			
Norbiton	d		13 50				14 05			
New Malden 6	d		13 55			14 07	14 10			
Dorking 4	d				13 35					
Box Hill & Westhumble	d									
Leatherhead	d				13 41			13 53		
Ashtead	d				13 44			13 57		
Epsom 3	a				13 49			14 01		
	d				13 49			14 04		
Ewell West	d				13 52			14 07		
Stoneleigh	d				13 54			14 09		
Worcester Park	d				13 57			14 12		
Chessington South	d	13 39								14 09
Chessington North	d	13 41								14 11
Tolworth	d	13 43								14 13
Malden Manor	d	13 46								14 16
Motspur Park	d	13 49			14 00			14 15		14 19
Raynes Park 6	d	13 53	13 58		14 04	14 10	14 13	14 19		14 23
Wimbledon 6 ⊖ ⇌	d	13 57	14 02	14 05	14 08	14 14	14 17	14 23	14 20	14 27
Earlsfield	d	14 01	14 05	14 08	14 12	14 17	14 20	14 27	14 24	14 31
Clapham Junction 10	d	14 05	14 09	14 12	14 16	14 21	14 24	14 31	14 28	14 35
Vauxhall ⊖	d	14 10	14 14	14 17	14 21	14 26	14 29	14 36	14 33	14 40
London Waterloo 15 ⊖	a	14 15	14 19	14 22	14 25	14 31	14 34	14 40	14 37	14 45

Station		SW A	SW B	SW	SW	SW	SW	SW	SW	SW A
Guildford	d						13 58	14 08		
London Road (Guildford)	d						14 02	14 12		
Clandon	d						14 07	14 17		
Horsley	d						14 11	14 21		
Effingham Junction 6	d						14 15	14 24		
Bookham	d						14 18			
Cobham & Stoke d'Abernon	d							14 28		
Oxshott	d							14 31		
Claygate	d							14 34		
Hinchley Wood	d							14 37		
Hampton Court	d				14 24					
Thames Ditton	d				14 26					
Surbiton 6	d		14 27		14 32			14 42		
Berrylands	d				14 34					
Shepperton	d					14 10				
Upper Halliford	d					14 13				
Sunbury	d					14 15				
Kempton Park	d					14 17				
Hampton	d					14 20				
Fulwell	d					14 23				
Strawberry Hill	d	14 07								14 37
Teddington	d	14 11				14 28				14 41
Hampton Wick	d	14 14				14 30				14 44
Kingston	a	14 16				14 32				14 46
	d	14 18				14 33				14 48
Norbiton	d	14 20				14 35				14 50
New Malden 6	d	14 25			14 37	14 40				14 55
Dorking 4	d			14 05						
Box Hill & Westhumble	d									
Leatherhead	d			14 11			14 23			
Ashtead	d			14 14			14 27			
Epsom 3	a			14 19			14 31			
	d			14 19			14 34			
Ewell West	d			14 22			14 37			
Stoneleigh	d			14 24			14 39			
Worcester Park	d			14 27			14 42			
Chessington South	d								14 39	
Chessington North	d								14 41	
Tolworth	d								14 43	
Malden Manor	d								14 46	
Motspur Park	d			14 30			14 45		14 49	
Raynes Park 6	d	14 28		14 34	14 40	14 43	14 49		14 53	14 58
Wimbledon 6 ⊖ ⇌	d	14 32	14 35	14 38	14 44	14 47	14 53	14 50	14 57	15 02
Earlsfield	d	14 35	14 38	14 42	14 47	14 50	14 57	14 54	15 01	15 05
Clapham Junction 10	d	14 39	14 42	14 46	14 51	14 54	15 01	14 58	15 05	15 09
Vauxhall ⊖	d	14 44	14 47	14 51	14 56	14 59	15 06	15 03	15 10	15 14
London Waterloo 15 ⊖	a	14 49	14 52	14 55	15 01	15 04	15 10	15 07	15 15	15 19

A From London Waterloo

B From Woking

The xx07 and xx37 Strawberry Hill to London Waterloo services originates from London Waterloo via Richmond

Table 152R

Saturdays

14 December to 17 May

Hampton Court, Shepperton, Guildford, Dorking and Chessington South - London

Network Diagram - see first Page of Table 152

		SW A	SW	SW	SW	SW	SW	SW	SW B	SW A	SW	SW	SW	SW	SW	SW	SW B	SW A	SW
Guildford	d					14 28	14 38							14 58	15 08				
London Road (Guildford)	d					14 32	14 42							15 02	15 12				
Clandon	d					14 37	14 47							15 07	15 17				
Horsley	d					14 41	14 51							15 11	15 21				
Effingham Junction 6	d					14 45	14 54							15 15	15 24				
Bookham	d					14 48								15 18					
Cobham & Stoke d'Abernon	d						14 58								15 28				
Oxshott	d						15 01								15 31				
Claygate	d						15 04								15 34				
Hinchley Wood	d						15 07								15 37				
Hampton Court	d			14 54								15 24							
Thames Ditton	d			14 56								15 26							
Surbiton 6	d	14 57		15 02			15 12			15 27		15 32			15 42			15 57	
Berrylands	d			15 04								15 34							
Shepperton	d				14 40								15 10						
Upper Halliford	d				14 43								15 13						
Sunbury	d				14 45								15 15						
Kempton Park	d				14 47								15 17						
Hampton	d				14 50								15 20						
Fulwell	d				14 53								15 23						
Strawberry Hill	d								15 07								15 37		
Teddington	d				14 58				15 11				15 28				15 41		
Hampton Wick	d				15 00				15 14				15 30				15 44		
Kingston	a				15 02				15 16				15 32				15 46		
	d				15 03				15 18				15 33				15 48		
Norbiton	d				15 05				15 20				15 35				15 50		
New Malden 6	d			15 07	15 10				15 25			15 37	15 40				15 55		
Dorking 4	d		14 35								15 05								15 35
Box Hill & Westhumble	d																		
Leatherhead	d		14 41			14 53					15 11			15 23					15 41
Ashtead	d		14 44			14 57					15 14			15 27					15 44
Epsom 3	a		14 49			15 01					15 19			15 31					15 49
	d		14 49			15 04					15 19			15 34					15 49
Ewell West	d		14 52			15 07					15 22			15 37					15 52
Stoneleigh	d		14 54			15 09					15 24			15 39					15 54
Worcester Park	d		14 57			15 12					15 27			15 42					15 57
Chessington South	d							15 09								15 39			
Chessington North	d							15 11								15 41			
Tolworth	d							15 13								15 43			
Malden Manor	d							15 16								15 46			
Motspur Park	d		15 00			15 15		15 19			15 30			15 45		15 49			16 00
Raynes Park 6	d		15 04	15 10	15 13	15 19		15 23	15 28		15 34	15 40	15 43	15 49		15 53	15 58		16 04
Wimbledon 6 ⊖	d	15 05	15 08	15 14	15 17	15 23	15 20	15 27	15 32	15 35	15 38	15 44	15 47	15 53	15 50	15 57	16 02	16 05	16 08
Earlsfield	d	15 08	15 12	15 17	15 20	15 27	15 24	15 31	15 35	15 38	15 42	15 47	15 50	15 57	15 54	16 01	16 05	16 08	16 12
Clapham Junction 10	d	15 12	15 16	15 21	15 24	15 31	15 28	15 35	15 39	15 42	15 46	15 51	15 54	16 01	15 58	16 05	16 09	16 12	16 16
Vauxhall ⊖	d	15 17	15 21	15 26	15 29	15 36	15 33	15 40	15 44	15 47	15 51	15 56	15 59	16 06	16 03	16 10	16 14	16 17	16 21
London Waterloo 15 ⊖	a	15 22	15 25	15 31	15 34	15 40	15 37	15 45	15 49	15 52	15 55	16 01	16 04	16 10	16 07	16 15	16 19	16 22	16 25

		SW	SW	SW	SW	SW	SW B	SW A	SW	SW	SW	SW	SW	SW	SW B	SW A	SW	SW	SW
Guildford	d			15 28	15 38							15 58	16 08						
London Road (Guildford)	d			15 32	15 42							16 02	16 12						
Clandon	d			15 37	15 47							16 07	16 17						
Horsley	d			15 41	15 51							16 11	16 21						
Effingham Junction 6	d			15 45	15 54							16 15	16 24						
Bookham	d			15 48								16 18							
Cobham & Stoke d'Abernon	d				15 58								16 28						
Oxshott	d				16 01								16 31						
Claygate	d				16 04								16 34						
Hinchley Wood	d				16 07								16 37						
Hampton Court	d	15 54								16 24								16 54	
Thames Ditton	d	15 56								16 26								16 56	
Surbiton 6	d	16 02			16 12			16 27		16 32			16 42			16 57		17 02	
Berrylands	d	16 04								16 34								17 04	
Shepperton	d		15 40								16 10								16 40
Upper Halliford	d		15 43								16 13								16 43
Sunbury	d		15 45								16 15								16 45
Kempton Park	d		15 47								16 17								16 47
Hampton	d		15 50								16 20								16 50
Fulwell	d		15 53								16 23								16 53
Strawberry Hill	d						16 07								16 37				
Teddington	d		15 58				16 11				16 28				16 41				16 58
Hampton Wick	d		16 00				16 14				16 30				16 44				17 00
Kingston	a		16 02				16 16				16 32				16 46				17 02
	d		16 03				16 18				16 33				16 48				17 03
Norbiton	d		16 05				16 20				16 35				16 50				17 05
New Malden 6	d	16 07	16 10				16 25			16 37	16 40				16 55			17 07	17 10
Dorking 4	d								16 05								16 35		
Box Hill & Westhumble	d																		
Leatherhead	d			15 53					16 11			16 23					16 41		
Ashtead	d			15 57					16 14			16 27					16 44		
Epsom 3	a			16 01					16 19			16 31					16 49		
	d			16 04					16 19			16 34					16 49		
Ewell West	d			16 07					16 22			16 37					16 52		
Stoneleigh	d			16 09					16 24			16 39					16 54		
Worcester Park	d			16 12					16 27			16 42					16 57		
Chessington South	d					16 09								16 39					
Chessington North	d					16 11								16 41					
Tolworth	d					16 13								16 43					
Malden Manor	d					16 16								16 46					
Motspur Park	d			16 15		16 19			16 30			16 45		16 49			17 00		
Raynes Park 6	d	16 10	16 13	16 19		16 23	16 28		16 34	16 40	16 43	16 49		16 53	16 58		17 04	17 10	17 13
Wimbledon 6 ⊖	d	16 14	16 17	16 23	16 20	16 27	16 32	16 35	16 38	16 44	16 47	16 53	16 50	16 57	17 02	17 05	17 08	17 14	17 17
Earlsfield	d	16 17	16 20	16 27	16 24	16 31	16 35	16 38	16 42	16 47	16 50	16 57	16 54	17 01	17 05	17 08	17 12	17 17	17 20
Clapham Junction 10	d	16 21	16 24	16 31	16 28	16 35	16 39	16 42	16 46	16 51	16 54	17 01	16 58	17 05	17 09	17 12	17 16	17 21	17 24
Vauxhall ⊖	d	16 26	16 29	16 36	16 33	16 40	16 44	16 47	16 51	16 56	16 59	17 06	17 03	17 10	17 14	17 17	17 21	17 26	17 29
London Waterloo 15 ⊖	a	16 31	16 34	16 40	16 37	16 45	16 49	16 52	16 55	17 01	17 04	17 10	17 07	17 15	17 19	17 22	17 25	17 31	17 34

A From Woking
B From London Waterloo

The xx07 and xx37 Strawberry Hill to London Waterloo services originates from London Waterloo via Richmond

Table 152R

Saturdays

14 December to 17 May

Hampton Court, Shepperton, Guildford, Dorking and Chessington South - London

Network Diagram - see first Page of Table 152

		SW	SW	SW	SW A	SW B	SW	SW	SW	SW	SW	SW	SW A	SW B	SW	SW	SW	SW	SW
Guildford	d	16 28	16 38							16 58	17 08							17 28	17 38
London Road (Guildford)	d	16 32	16 42							17 02	17 12							17 32	17 42
Clandon	d	16 37	16 47							17 07	17 17							17 37	17 47
Horsley	d	16 41	16 51							17 11	17 21							17 41	17 51
Effingham Junction 6	d	16 45	16 54							17 15	17 24							17 45	17 54
Bookham	d	16 48								17 18								17 48	
Cobham & Stoke d'Abernon	d		16 58								17 28								17 58
Oxshott	d		17 01								17 31								18 01
Claygate	d		17 04								17 34								18 04
Hinchley Wood	d		17 07								17 37								18 07
Hampton Court	d							17 24								17 54			
Thames Ditton	d							17 26								17 56			
Surbiton 6	d		17 12			17 27		17 32			17 42			17 57		18 02			18 12
Berrylands	d							17 34								18 04			
Shepperton	d								17 10								17 40		
Upper Halliford	d								17 13								17 43		
Sunbury	d								17 15								17 45		
Kempton Park	d								17 17								17 47		
Hampton	d								17 20								17 50		
Fulwell	d								17 23								17 53		
Strawberry Hill	d				17 07								17 37						
Teddington	d				17 11				17 28				17 41				17 58		
Hampton Wick	d				17 14				17 30				17 44				18 00		
Kingston	a				17 16				17 32				17 46				18 02		
	d				17 18				17 33				17 48				18 03		
Norbiton	d				17 20				17 35				17 50				18 05		
New Malden 6	d				17 25			17 37	17 40				17 55			18 07	18 10		
Dorking 4	d						17 05								17 35				
Box Hill & Westhumble	d																		
Leatherhead	d	16 53					17 11			17 23					17 41			17 53	
Ashtead	d	16 57					17 14			17 27					17 44			17 57	
Epsom 3	a	17 01					17 19			17 31					17 49			18 01	
	d	17 04					17 19			17 34					17 49			18 04	
Ewell West	d	17 07					17 22			17 37					17 52			18 07	
Stoneleigh	d	17 09					17 24			17 39					17 54			18 09	
Worcester Park	d	17 12					17 27			17 42					17 57			18 12	
Chessington South	d			17 09								17 39							
Chessington North	d			17 11								17 41							
Tolworth	d			17 13								17 43							
Malden Manor	d			17 16								17 46							
Motspur Park	d	17 15		17 19			17 30			17 45		17 49			18 00			18 15	
Raynes Park 6	d	17 19		17 23	17 28		17 34	17 40	17 43	17 49		17 53	17 58		18 04	18 10	18 13	18 19	
Wimbledon 6 ⊖ ⛴	d	17 23	17 20	17 27	17 32	17 35	17 38	17 44	17 47	17 53	17 50	17 57	18 02	18 05	18 08	18 14	18 17	18 23	18 20
Earlsfield	d	17 27	17 24	17 31	17 35	17 38	17 42	17 47	17 50	17 57	17 54	18 01	18 05	18 08	18 12	18 17	18 20	18 27	18 24
Clapham Junction 10	d	17 31	17 28	17 35	17 39	17 42	17 46	17 51	17 54	18 01	17 58	18 05	18 09	18 12	18 16	18 21	18 24	18 31	18 28
Vauxhall ⊖	d	17 36	17 33	17 40	17 44	17 47	17 51	17 56	17 59	18 06	18 03	18 10	18 14	18 17	18 21	18 26	18 29	18 36	18 33
London Waterloo 15 ⊖	a	17 40	17 37	17 45	17 49	17 52	17 55	18 01	18 04	18 10	18 07	18 15	18 19	18 22	18 25	18 31	18 34	18 40	18 37

		SW	SW A	SW B	SW	SW	SW	SW	SW	SW	SW A	SW B	SW	SW	SW	SW	SW	SW	SW A
Guildford	d							17 58	18 08							18 28	18 38		
London Road (Guildford)	d							18 02	18 12							18 32	18 42		
Clandon	d							18 07	18 17							18 37	18 47		
Horsley	d							18 11	18 21							18 41	18 51		
Effingham Junction 6	d							18 15	18 24							18 45	18 54		
Bookham	d							18 18								18 48			
Cobham & Stoke d'Abernon	d								18 28								18 58		
Oxshott	d								18 31								19 01		
Claygate	d								18 34								19 04		
Hinchley Wood	d								18 37								19 07		
Hampton Court	d					18 24								18 54					
Thames Ditton	d					18 26								18 56					
Surbiton 6	d			18 27		18 32			18 42			18 57		19 02			19 12		
Berrylands	d					18 34								19 04					
Shepperton	d						18 10								18 40				
Upper Halliford	d						18 13								18 43				
Sunbury	d						18 15								18 45				
Kempton Park	d						18 17								18 47				
Hampton	d						18 20								18 50				
Fulwell	d						18 23								18 53				
Strawberry Hill	d		18 07								18 37								19 07
Teddington	d		18 11				18 28				18 41				18 58				19 11
Hampton Wick	d		18 14				18 30				18 44				19 00				19 14
Kingston	a		18 16				18 32				18 46				19 02				19 16
	d		18 18				18 33				18 48				19 03				19 18
Norbiton	d		18 20				18 35				18 50				19 05				19 20
New Malden 6	d		18 25			18 37	18 40				18 55			19 07	19 10				19 25
Dorking 4	d				18 05								18 35						
Box Hill & Westhumble	d																		
Leatherhead	d				18 11			18 23					18 41			18 53			
Ashtead	d				18 14			18 27					18 44			18 57			
Epsom 3	a				18 19			18 31					18 49			19 01			
	d				18 19			18 34					18 49			19 04			
Ewell West	d				18 22			18 37					18 52			19 07			
Stoneleigh	d				18 24			18 39					18 54			19 09			
Worcester Park	d				18 27			18 42					18 57			19 12			
Chessington South	d	18 09								18 39								19 09	
Chessington North	d	18 11								18 41								19 11	
Tolworth	d	18 13								18 43								19 13	
Malden Manor	d	18 16								18 46								19 16	
Motspur Park	d	18 19			18 30			18 45		18 49			19 00			19 15		19 19	
Raynes Park 6	d	18 23	18 28		18 34	18 40	18 43	18 49		18 53	18 58		19 04	19 10	19 13	19 19		19 23	19 28
Wimbledon 6 ⊖ ⛴	d	18 27	18 32	18 35	18 38	18 44	18 47	18 53	18 50	18 57	19 02	19 05	19 08	19 14	19 17	19 23	19 20	19 27	19 32
Earlsfield	d	18 31	18 35	18 38	18 42	18 47	18 50	18 57	18 54	19 01	19 05	19 08	19 12	19 17	19 20	19 27	19 24	19 31	19 35
Clapham Junction 10	d	18 35	18 39	18 42	18 46	18 51	18 54	19 01	18 58	19 05	19 09	19 12	19 16	19 21	19 24	19 31	19 28	19 35	19 39
Vauxhall ⊖	d	18 40	18 44	18 47	18 51	18 56	18 59	19 06	19 03	19 10	19 14	19 17	19 21	19 26	19 29	19 36	19 33	19 40	19 44
London Waterloo 15 ⊖	a	18 45	18 49	18 52	18 55	19 01	19 04	19 10	19 07	19 15	19 19	19 22	19 25	19 31	19 34	19 40	19 37	19 45	19 49

A From London Waterloo

B From Woking

The xx07 and xx37 Strawberry Hill to London Waterloo services originates from London Waterloo via Richmond

Table 152R

Saturdays

14 December to 17 May

Hampton Court, Shepperton, Guildford, Dorking and Chessington South - London

Network Diagram - see first Page of Table 152

		SW A	SW	SW	SW	SW	SW	SW	SW B	SW A
Guildford	d					18 58	19 08			
London Road (Guildford)	d					19 02	19 12			
Clandon	d					19 07	19 17			
Horsley	d					19 11	19 21			
Effingham Junction 6	d					19 15	19 24			
Bookham	d					19 18				
Cobham & Stoke d'Abernon	d						19 28			
Oxshott	d						19 31			
Claygate	d						19 34			
Hinchley Wood	d						19 37			
Hampton Court	d			19 24						
Thames Ditton	d			19 26						
Surbiton 6	d	19 27		19 32			19 42			19 57
Berrylands	d			19 34						
Shepperton	d				19 10					
Upper Halliford	d				19 13					
Sunbury	d				19 15					
Kempton Park	d				19 17					
Hampton	d				19 20					
Fulwell	d				19 23					
Strawberry Hill	d								19 37	
Teddington	d				19 28				19 41	
Hampton Wick	d				19 30				19 44	
Kingston	a				19 32				19 46	
	d				19 33				19 48	
Norbiton	d				19 35				19 50	
New Malden 6	d			19 37	19 40				19 55	
Dorking 4	d		19 05							
Box Hill & Westhumble	d									
Leatherhead	d		19 11			19 23				
Ashtead	d		19 14			19 27				
Epsom 3	a		19 19			19 31				
	d		19 19			19 34				
Ewell West	d		19 22			19 37				
Stoneleigh	d		19 24			19 39				
Worcester Park	d		19 27			19 42				
Chessington South	d							19 39		
Chessington North	d							19 41		
Tolworth	d							19 43		
Malden Manor	d							19 46		
Motspur Park	d		19 30			19 45		19 49		
Raynes Park 6	d		19 34	19 40	19 43	19 49		19 53	19 58	
Wimbledon 6 ⊖ 🚋	d	19 35	19 38	19 44	19 47	19 53	19 50	19 57	20 02	20 05
Earlsfield	d	19 38	19 42	19 47	19 50	19 57	19 54	20 01	20 05	20 08
Clapham Junction 10	d	19 42	19 46	19 51	19 54	20 01	19 58	20 05	20 09	20 12
Vauxhall ⊖	d	19 47	19 51	19 56	19 59	20 06	20 03	20 10	20 14	20 17
London Waterloo 15 ⊖	a	19 52	19 55	20 01	20 04	20 10	20 07	20 15	20 19	20 22

		SW	SW	SW	SW	SW	SW	SW B	SW A	SW
Guildford	d				19 28	19 38				
London Road (Guildford)	d				19 32	19 42				
Clandon	d				19 37	19 47				
Horsley	d				19 41	19 51				
Effingham Junction 6	d				19 45	19 54				
Bookham	d				19 48					
Cobham & Stoke d'Abernon	d					19 58				
Oxshott	d					20 01				
Claygate	d					20 04				
Hinchley Wood	d					20 07				
Hampton Court	d		19 54							
Thames Ditton	d		19 56							
Surbiton 6	d		20 02			20 12			20 27	
Berrylands	d		20 04							
Shepperton	d			19 40						
Upper Halliford	d			19 43						
Sunbury	d			19 45						
Kempton Park	d			19 47						
Hampton	d			19 50						
Fulwell	d			19 53						
Strawberry Hill	d							20 07		
Teddington	d			19 58				20 11		
Hampton Wick	d			20 00				20 14		
Kingston	a			20 02				20 16		
	d			20 03				20 18		
Norbiton	d			20 05				20 20		
New Malden 6	d		20 07	20 10				20 25		
Dorking 4	d	19 35								20 05
Box Hill & Westhumble	d									
Leatherhead	d	19 41			19 53					20 11
Ashtead	d	19 44			19 57					20 14
Epsom 3	a	19 49			20 01					20 19
	d	19 49			20 04					20 19
Ewell West	d	19 52			20 07					20 22
Stoneleigh	d	19 54			20 09					20 24
Worcester Park	d	19 57			20 12					20 27
Chessington South	d						20 09			
Chessington North	d						20 11			
Tolworth	d						20 13			
Malden Manor	d						20 16			
Motspur Park	d	20 00			20 15		20 19			20 30
Raynes Park 6	d	20 04	20 10	20 13	20 19		20 23	20 28		20 34
Wimbledon 6 ⊖ 🚋	d	20 08	20 14	20 17	20 23	20 20	20 27	20 32	20 35	20 38
Earlsfield	d	20 12	20 17	20 20	20 27	20 24	20 31	20 35	20 38	20 42
Clapham Junction 10	d	20 16	20 21	20 24	20 31	20 28	20 35	20 39	20 42	20 46
Vauxhall ⊖	d	20 21	20 26	20 29	20 36	20 33	20 40	20 44	20 47	20 51
London Waterloo 15 ⊖	a	20 25	20 31	20 34	20 40	20 37	20 45	20 49	20 52	20 55

		SW	SW	SW	SW	SW	SW B	SW A	SW	SW
Guildford	d			19 58	20 08					
London Road (Guildford)	d			20 02	20 12					
Clandon	d			20 07	20 17					
Horsley	d			20 11	20 21					
Effingham Junction 6	d			20 15	20 24					
Bookham	d			20 18						
Cobham & Stoke d'Abernon	d				20 28					
Oxshott	d				20 31					
Claygate	d				20 34					
Hinchley Wood	d				20 37					
Hampton Court	d	20 24								20 54
Thames Ditton	d	20 26								20 56
Surbiton 6	d	20 32			20 42			20 57		21 02
Berrylands	d	20 34								21 04
Shepperton	d		20 10							
Upper Halliford	d		20 13							
Sunbury	d		20 15							
Kempton Park	d		20 17							
Hampton	d		20 20							
Fulwell	d		20 23							
Strawberry Hill	d						20 37			
Teddington	d		20 28				20 41			
Hampton Wick	d		20 30				20 44			
Kingston	a		20 32				20 46			
	d		20 33				20 48			
Norbiton	d		20 35				20 50			
New Malden 6	d	20 37	20 40				20 55			21 07
Dorking 4	d								20 35	
Box Hill & Westhumble	d									
Leatherhead	d			20 23					20 41	
Ashtead	d			20 27					20 44	
Epsom 3	a			20 31					20 49	
	d			20 34					20 49	
Ewell West	d			20 37					20 52	
Stoneleigh	d			20 39					20 54	
Worcester Park	d			20 42					20 57	
Chessington South	d					20 39				
Chessington North	d					20 41				
Tolworth	d					20 43				
Malden Manor	d					20 46				
Motspur Park	d			20 45		20 49			21 00	
Raynes Park 6	d	20 40	20 43	20 49		20 53	20 58		21 04	21 10
Wimbledon 6 ⊖ 🚋	d	20 44	20 47	20 53	20 50	20 57	21 02	21 05	21 08	21 14
Earlsfield	d	20 47	20 50	20 57	20 54	21 01	21 06	21 09	21 12	21 17
Clapham Junction 10	d	20 51	20 54	21 01	20 58	21 05	21 09	21 13	21 16	21 21
Vauxhall ⊖	d	20 56	20 59	21 06	21 03	21 10	21 14	21 18	21 21	21 26
London Waterloo 15 ⊖	a	21 01	21 04	21 10	21 07	21 15	21 19	21 23	21 25	21 31

		SW	SW	SW	SW	SW B	SW A	SW	SW	SW
Guildford	d		20 38					20 46		
London Road (Guildford)	d		20 42					20 50		
Clandon	d		20 47					20 55		
Horsley	d		20 51					20 59		
Effingham Junction 6	d		20 54					21 03		
Bookham	d							21 06		
Cobham & Stoke d'Abernon	d		20 58							
Oxshott	d		21 01							
Claygate	d		21 04							
Hinchley Wood	d		21 07							
Hampton Court	d								21 24	
Thames Ditton	d								21 26	
Surbiton 6	d		21 12				21 27		21 32	
Berrylands	d								21 34	
Shepperton	d	20 40								21 10
Upper Halliford	d	20 43								21 13
Sunbury	d	20 45								21 15
Kempton Park	d	20 47								21 17
Hampton	d	20 50								21 20
Fulwell	d	20 53								21 23
Strawberry Hill	d					21 07				
Teddington	d	20 58				21 11				21 28
Hampton Wick	d	21 00				21 14				21 30
Kingston	a	21 02				21 16				21 32
	d	21 03				21 18				21 33
Norbiton	d	21 05				21 20				21 35
New Malden 6	d	21 10				21 25			21 37	21 40
Dorking 4	d									
Box Hill & Westhumble	d									
Leatherhead	d							21 11		
Ashtead	d							21 14		
Epsom 3	a							21 19		
	d			21 04				21 19		
Ewell West	d			21 07				21 22		
Stoneleigh	d			21 09				21 24		
Worcester Park	d			21 12				21 27		
Chessington South	d				21 09					
Chessington North	d				21 11					
Tolworth	d				21 13					
Malden Manor	d				21 16					
Motspur Park	d			21 15	21 19			21 30		
Raynes Park 6	d	21 13		21 19	21 23	21 28		21 34	21 40	21 43
Wimbledon 6 ⊖ 🚋	d	21 17	21 20	21 23	21 27	21 32	21 35	21 38	21 44	21 47
Earlsfield	d	21 20	21 24	21 27	21 31	21 35	21 38	21 42	21 47	21 50
Clapham Junction 10	d	21 24	21 28	21 31	21 35	21 39	21 42	21 46	21 51	21 54
Vauxhall ⊖	d	21 29	21 33	21 36	21 40	21 44	21 47	21 51	21 56	21 59
London Waterloo 15 ⊖	a	21 34	21 37	21 40	21 45	21 49	21 52	21 55	22 01	22 04

A From Woking

B From London Waterloo

The xx07 and xx37 Strawberry Hill to London Waterloo services originates from London Waterloo via Richmond

Table 152R

Saturdays

14 December to 17 May

Hampton Court, Shepperton, Guildford, Dorking and Chessington South - London

Network Diagram - see first Page of Table 152

		SW	SW	SW	SW	SW	SW	SW	SW	SW
					A	B				A
Guildford	d	21 08							21 38	
London Road (Guildford)	d	21 12							21 42	
Clandon	d	21 17							21 47	
Horsley	d	21 21							21 51	
Effingham Junction 6	d	21 24							21 54	
Bookham	d									
Cobham & Stoke d'Abernon	d	21 28							21 58	
Oxshott	d	21 31							22 01	
Claygate	d	21 34							22 04	
Hinchley Wood	d	21 37							22 07	
Hampton Court	d									
Thames Ditton	d									
Surbiton 6	d	21 42				21 57			22 12	
Berrylands	d									
Shepperton	d							21 40		
Upper Halliford	d							21 43		
Sunbury	d							21 45		
Kempton Park	d							21 47		
Hampton	d							21 50		
Fulwell	d							21 53		
Strawberry Hill	d				21 37					22 07
Teddington	d				21 41			21 58		22 11
Hampton Wick	d				21 44			22 00		22 14
Kingston	a				21 46			22 02		22 16
	d				21 48			22 03		22 18
Norbiton	d				21 50			22 05		22 20
New Malden 6	d				21 55			22 10		22 25
Dorking 4	d						21 35			
Box Hill & Westhumble	d									
Leatherhead	d						21 41			
Ashtead	d						21 44			
Epsom 3	a						21 49			
	d		21 34				21 49			
Ewell West	d		21 37				21 52			
Stoneleigh	d		21 39				21 54			
Worcester Park	d		21 42				21 57			
Chessington South	d			21 39						
Chessington North	d			21 41						
Tolworth	d			21 43						
Malden Manor	d			21 46						
Motspur Park	d		21 45	21 49			22 00			
Raynes Park 6	d		21 49	21 53	21 58		22 04	22 13		22 28
Wimbledon 6 ⊖ ⛴	d	21 50	21 53	21 57	22 02	22 05	22 08	22 17	22 20	22 32
Earlsfield	d	21 54	21 57	22 01	22 05	22 08	22 12	22 20	22 24	22 35
Clapham Junction 10	d	21 58	22 01	22 05	22 09	22 12	22 16	22 24	22 28	22 39
Vauxhall ⊖	d	22 03	22 06	22 10	22 14	22 17	22 21	22 29	22 33	22 44
London Waterloo 15 ⊖	a	22 07	22 10	22 15	22 19	22 22	22 25	22 34	22 39	22 49

		SW	SW	SW	SW	SW	SW	SW	SW	SW
		B						A		
Guildford	d		21 46			22 08			22 20	
London Road (Guildford)	d		21 50			22 12				
Clandon	d		21 55			22 17				
Horsley	d		21 59			22 21				
Effingham Junction 6	d		22 03			22 24				
Bookham	d		22 06							
Cobham & Stoke d'Abernon	d					22 28				
Oxshott	d					22 31				
Claygate	d					22 34				
Hinchley Wood	d					22 37				
Hampton Court	d			22 24						
Thames Ditton	d			22 26						
Surbiton 6	d	22 27		22 32		22 42			22 57	
Berrylands	d			22 34						
Shepperton	d				22 10					
Upper Halliford	d				22 13					
Sunbury	d				22 15					
Kempton Park	d				22 17					
Hampton	d				22 20					
Fulwell	d				22 23					
Strawberry Hill	d							22 37		
Teddington	d				22 28			22 41		
Hampton Wick	d				22 30			22 44		
Kingston	a				22 32			22 46		
	d				22 33			22 48		
Norbiton	d				22 35			22 50		
New Malden 6	d			22 37	22 40			22 55		
Dorking 4	d									22 35
Box Hill & Westhumble	d									
Leatherhead	d		22 11							22 41
Ashtead	d		22 14							22 44
Epsom 3	a		22 19							22 49
	d		22 19							22 49
Ewell West	d		22 22							22 52
Stoneleigh	d		22 24							22 54
Worcester Park	d		22 27							22 57
Chessington South	d						22 39			
Chessington North	d						22 41			
Tolworth	d						22 43			
Malden Manor	d						22 46			
Motspur Park	d		22 30				22 49			23 00
Raynes Park 6	d		22 34	22 40	22 43		22 53	22 58		23 04
Wimbledon 6 ⊖ ⛴	d	22 35	22 38	22 44	22 47	22 50	22 57	23 02	23 05	23 08
Earlsfield	d	22 38	22 42	22 47	22 50	22 54	23 01	23 05	23 08	23 12
Clapham Junction 10	d	22 42	22 46	22 51	22 54	22 58	23 05	23 09	23 12	23 16
Vauxhall ⊖	d	22 47	22 51	22 56	22 59	23 03	23 10	23 14	23 17	23 21
London Waterloo 15 ⊖	a	22 52	22 55	23 01	23 04	23 07	23 15	23 19	23 22	23 25

		SW	SW	SW	SW	SW	SW	SW	SW	SW	SW	SW
												1
				A							A	C
Guildford	d		22 38		22 46	22 55			23 08			23 39
London Road (Guildford)	d		22 42		22 50				23 12			
Clandon	d		22 47		22 55				23 17			
Horsley	d		22 51		22 59				23 21			
Effingham Junction 6	d		22 54		23 03				23 24			
Bookham	d				23 06							
Cobham & Stoke d'Abernon	d		22 58						23 28			
Oxshott	d		23 01						23 31			
Claygate	d		23 04						23 34			
Hinchley Wood	d		23 07						23 37			
Hampton Court	d						23 24					
Thames Ditton	d						23 26					
Surbiton 6	d		23 12			23 30	23 33		23 42			00 08
Berrylands	d						23 35					
Shepperton	d	22 40						23 10				
Upper Halliford	d	22 43						23 13				
Sunbury	d	22 45						23 15				
Kempton Park	d	22 47						23 17				
Hampton	d	22 50						23 20				
Fulwell	d	22 53						23 23				
Strawberry Hill	d			23 07							23 37	
Teddington	d	22 58		23 11				23 28			23 41	
Hampton Wick	d	23 00		23 14				23 30			23 44	
Kingston	a	23 02		23 16				23 32			23 46	
	d	23 03		23 18				23 33			23 48	
Norbiton	d	23 05		23 20				23 35			23 50	
New Malden 6	d	23 10		23 25			23 38	23 40			23 55	
Dorking 4	d											
Box Hill & Westhumble	d											
Leatherhead	d				23 11							
Ashtead	d				23 14							
Epsom 3	a				23 19							
	d				23 19							
Ewell West	d				23 22							
Stoneleigh	d				23 24							
Worcester Park	d				23 27							
Chessington South	d									23 39		
Chessington North	d									23 41		
Tolworth	d									23 43		
Malden Manor	d									23 46		
Motspur Park	d				23 30					23 49		
Raynes Park 6	d	23 13		23 28	23 37		23 41	23 43		23 54	23 58	
Wimbledon 6 ⊖ ⛴	d	23 17	23 20	23 32	23 41	23 37	23 46	23 49	23 52	23a57	00 02	00 16
Earlsfield	d	23 20	23 24	23 35	23 44	23 41	23 50	23 53	23 56		00 05	
Clapham Junction 10	d	23 24	23 28	23 39	23 48	23 45	23 53	23 56	23 59		00 09	00 23
Vauxhall ⊖	d	23 29	23 33	23 44	23 53	23 50	23 58	00 01	00 05		00 15	
London Waterloo 15 ⊖	a	23 34	23 37	23 49	23 58	23 54	00 03	00 06	00 14		00 22	00 32

A From London Waterloo
B From Woking
C From Portsmouth Harbour

The xx07 and xx37 Strawberry Hill to London Waterloo services originates from London Waterloo via Richmond

Table 152R

Sundays

8 December to 11 May

Hampton Court, Shepperton, Guildford, Dorking and Chessington South - London

Network Diagram - see first Page of Table 152

		SW A	SW B	SW C	SW C	SW 1 D	SW E	SW F	SW	SW
Guildford	d								06 57	
London Road (Guildford)	d									
Clandon	d									
Horsley	d									
Effingham Junction 6	d									
Bookham	d									
Cobham & Stoke d'Abernon	d									
Oxshott	d									
Claygate	d									
Hinchley Wood	d									
Hampton Court	d									
Thames Ditton	d									
Surbiton 6	d					00 08	07 00		07 30	
Berrylands	d									
Shepperton	d									
Upper Halliford	d									
Sunbury	d									
Kempton Park	d									
Hampton	d									
Fulwell	d									
Strawberry Hill	d			00 09				06 49		
Teddington	d			00 12				06 55		
Hampton Wick	d			00 14				06 57		
Kingston	a			00 16				06 59		
	d							07 04		
Norbiton	d							07 06		
New Malden 6	d							07 10		
Dorking 4	d									
Box Hill & Westhumble	d									
Leatherhead	d									
Ashtead	d									
Epsom 3	a									
	d									07 24
Ewell West	d									07 27
Stoneleigh	d									07 29
Worcester Park	d									07 32
Chessington South	d									
Chessington North	d									
Tolworth	d									
Malden Manor	d									
Motspur Park	d									07 35
Raynes Park 6	d							07 13		07 38
Wimbledon 6 ⊖	d					00 16	07 08	07 20	07 38	07 42
Earlsfield	d						07 12	07 24	07 42	07 46
Clapham Junction 10	d				00 05	00 23	07 16	07 28	07 46	07 50
Vauxhall ⊖	d	00 01	00 05		00 12		07 21	07 33	07 51	07 55
London Waterloo 15 ⊖	a	00 06	00 14		00 16	00 32	07 25	07 37	07 55	08 04

		SW	SW	SW	SW	SW F	SW 1 G	SW	SW	SW
Guildford	d			07 27						07 50
London Road (Guildford)	d									07 54
Clandon	d									07 59
Horsley	d									08 03
Effingham Junction 6	d									08 06
Bookham	d									
Cobham & Stoke d'Abernon	d									08 10
Oxshott	d									08 13
Claygate	d									08 16
Hinchley Wood	d									08 19
Hampton Court	d		07 35					08 05		
Thames Ditton	d		07 37					08 07		
Surbiton 6	d		07 43	08 00			08 10	08 13		08 24
Berrylands	d		07 45					08 15		
Shepperton	d	07 11								
Upper Halliford	d	07 14								
Sunbury	d	07 16								
Kempton Park	d	07 18								
Hampton	d	07 21								
Fulwell	d	07 24								
Strawberry Hill	d					07 49				
Teddington	d	07 29				07 55				
Hampton Wick	d	07 31				07 57				
Kingston	a	07 33				07 59				
	d	07 34				08 04				
Norbiton	d	07 36				08 06				
New Malden 6	d	07 40	07 48			08 10		08 18		
Dorking 4	d									
Box Hill & Westhumble	d									
Leatherhead	d									
Ashtead	d									
Epsom 3	a									
	d				07 54					
Ewell West	d				07 57					
Stoneleigh	d				07 59					
Worcester Park	d				08 02					
Chessington South	d								08 10	
Chessington North	d								08 12	
Tolworth	d								08 14	
Malden Manor	d								08 17	
Motspur Park	d				08 05				08 20	
Raynes Park 6	d	07 43	07 51		08 08	08 13		08 21	08 24	
Wimbledon 6 ⊖	d	07 47	07 55	08 08	08 12	08 17	08 17	08 25	08 28	08a33
Earlsfield	d	07 51	07 59	08 12	08 17	08 20		08 28	08 31	
Clapham Junction 10	d	07 55	08 03	08 16	08 22	08 27	08 29	08 36	08 39	
Vauxhall ⊖	d	08 00	08 08	08 21	08 27	08 32		08 41	08 44	
London Waterloo 15 ⊖	a	08 09	08 17	08 25	08 34	08 36	08 39	08 49	08 52	

		SW	SW	SW	SW	SW	SW	SW	SW F	SW
Guildford	d	07 57					08 20	08 27		
London Road (Guildford)	d						08 24			
Clandon	d						08 29			
Horsley	d						08 33			
Effingham Junction 6	d						08 36			
Bookham	d						08 39			
Cobham & Stoke d'Abernon	d									
Oxshott	d									
Claygate	d									
Hinchley Wood	d									
Hampton Court	d				08 35					09 05
Thames Ditton	d				08 37					09 07
Surbiton 6	d	08 30			08 43			09 00		09 13
Berrylands	d				08 45					09 15
Shepperton	d			08 11						
Upper Halliford	d			08 14						
Sunbury	d			08 16						
Kempton Park	d			08 18						
Hampton	d			08 21						
Fulwell	d			08 24						
Strawberry Hill	d								08 49	
Teddington	d			08 29					08 55	
Hampton Wick	d			08 31					08 57	
Kingston	a			08 33					08 59	
	d			08 34					09 04	
Norbiton	d			08 36					09 06	
New Malden 6	d			08 40	08 48				09 10	09 18
Dorking 4	d									
Box Hill & Westhumble	d									
Leatherhead	d						08 45			
Ashtead	d						08 48			
Epsom 3	a						08 53			
	d		08 24				08 54			
Ewell West	d		08 27				08 57			
Stoneleigh	d		08 29				08 59			
Worcester Park	d		08 32				09 02			
Chessington South	d					08 40				
Chessington North	d					08 42				
Tolworth	d					08 44				
Malden Manor	d					08 47				
Motspur Park	d		08 35			08 50	09 05			
Raynes Park 6	d		08 38	08 43	08 51	08 54	09 08		09 13	09 21
Wimbledon 6 ⊖	d	08 38	08 42	08 47	08 55	08 58	09 12	09 08	09 17	09 25
Earlsfield	d	08 41	08 46	08 50	08 58	09 01	09 16	09 11	09 20	09 28
Clapham Junction 10	d	08 45	08 50	08 57	09 02	09 09	09 20	09 15	09 24	09 33
Vauxhall ⊖	d	08 50	08 55	09 02	09 07	09 14	09 25	09 20	09 29	09 38
London Waterloo 15 ⊖	a	08 55	09 04	09 09	09 17	09 24	09 30	09 25	09 34	09 47

		SW	SW	SW	SW	SW	SW	SW	SW	SW
Guildford	d		08 50	08 57					09 20	09 27
London Road (Guildford)	d		08 54						09 24	
Clandon	d		08 59						09 29	
Horsley	d		09 03						09 33	
Effingham Junction 6	d		09 06						09 36	
Bookham	d								09 39	
Cobham & Stoke d'Abernon	d		09 10							
Oxshott	d		09 13							
Claygate	d		09 16							
Hinchley Wood	d		09 19							
Hampton Court	d						09 35			
Thames Ditton	d						09 37			
Surbiton 6	d		09 24	09 30			09 43			10 00
Berrylands	d						09 45			
Shepperton	d					09 11				
Upper Halliford	d					09 14				
Sunbury	d					09 16				
Kempton Park	d					09 18				
Hampton	d					09 21				
Fulwell	d					09 24				
Strawberry Hill	d									
Teddington	d					09 29				
Hampton Wick	d					09 31				
Kingston	a					09 33				
	d					09 34				
Norbiton	d					09 36				
New Malden 6	d					09 40	09 48			
Dorking 4	d				09 08					
Box Hill & Westhumble	d									
Leatherhead	d				09 15				09 45	
Ashtead	d				09 18				09 48	
Epsom 3	a				09 23				09 53	
	d				09 24				09 54	
Ewell West	d				09 27				09 57	
Stoneleigh	d				09 29				09 59	
Worcester Park	d				09 32				10 02	
Chessington South	d	09 10						09 40		
Chessington North	d	09 12						09 42		
Tolworth	d	09 14						09 44		
Malden Manor	d	09 17						09 47		
Motspur Park	d	09 20			09 35			09 50	10 05	
Raynes Park 6	d	09 24			09 38	09 43	09 51	09 54	10 08	
Wimbledon 6 ⊖	d	09 28	09a33	09 38	09 42	09 47	09 55	09 58	10 12	10 08
Earlsfield	d	09 31		09 41	09 46	09 50	09 58	10 01	10 16	10 11
Clapham Junction 10	d	09 36		09 45	09 50	09 54	10 06	10 09	10 20	10 15
Vauxhall ⊖	d	09 41		09 50	09 55	09 59	10 11	10 14	10 25	10 20
London Waterloo 15 ⊖	a	09 50		09 55	10 04	10 09	10 20	10 23	10 29	10 25

A from Shepperton
B from Guildford
C from London Waterloo
D from Portsmouth Harbour
E From Woking
F From London Waterloo
G From Farnham

The xx49 Strawberry Hill to London Waterloo services originates from London Waterloo via Richmond

Table 152R

Sundays

8 December to 11 May

Hampton Court, Shepperton, Guildford, Dorking and Chessington South - London

Network Diagram - see first Page of Table 152

		SW	SW	SW	SW	SW	SW	SW	SW	SW
		A								
Guildford	d				09 50	09 57				
London Road (Guildford)	d				09 54					
Clandon	d				09 59					
Horsley	d				10 03					
Effingham Junction 6	d				10 06					
Bookham	d									
Cobham & Stoke d'Abernon	d				10 10					
Oxshott	d				10 13					
Claygate	d				10 16					
Hinchley Wood	d				10 19					
Hampton Court	d		10 05						10 35	
Thames Ditton	d		10 07						10 37	
Surbiton 6	d		10 13		10 24	10 30			10 43	
Berrylands	d		10 15						10 45	
Shepperton	d							10 11		
Upper Halliford	d							10 14		
Sunbury	d							10 16		
Kempton Park	d							10 18		
Hampton	d							10 21		
Fulwell	d							10 24		
Strawberry Hill	d	09 49								
Teddington	d	09 55						10 29		
Hampton Wick	d	09 57						10 31		
Kingston	a	09 59						10 33		
	d	10 04						10 34		
Norbiton	d	10 06						10 36		
New Malden 6	d	10 10	10 18					10 40	10 48	
Dorking 4	d						10 08			
Box Hill & Westhumble	d									
Leatherhead	d						10 15			
Ashtead	d						10 18			
Epsom 3	a						10 23			
	d						10 24			
Ewell West	d						10 27			
Stoneleigh	d						10 29			
Worcester Park	d						10 32			
Chessington South	d			10 10						10 40
Chessington North	d			10 12						10 42
Tolworth	d			10 14						10 44
Malden Manor	d			10 17						10 47
Motspur Park	d			10 20			10 35			10 50
Raynes Park 6	d	10 13	10 21	10 24			10 38	10 43	10 51	10 54
Wimbledon 6 ⊖	d	10 17	10 25	10 28	10a33	10 38	10 42	10 47	10 55	10 58
Earlsfield	d	10 20	10 28	10 31		10 41	10 46	10 50	10 58	11 01
Clapham Junction 10	d	10 24	10 32	10 36		10 45	10 50	10 54	11 02	11 05
Vauxhall ⊖	d	10 32	10 37	10 41		10 50	10 55	10 59	11 07	11 13
London Waterloo 15 ⊖	a	10 36	10 47	10 50		10 55	11 04	11 09	11 17	11 22

		SW	SW	SW	SW	SW	SW	SW	SW	SW
				A						
Guildford	d	10 20	10 27				10 50	10 57		
London Road (Guildford)	d	10 24					10 54			
Clandon	d	10 29					10 59			
Horsley	d	10 33					11 03			
Effingham Junction 6	d	10 36					11 06			
Bookham	d	10 39								
Cobham & Stoke d'Abernon	d						11 10			
Oxshott	d						11 13			
Claygate	d						11 16			
Hinchley Wood	d						11 19			
Hampton Court	d				11 05					
Thames Ditton	d				11 07					
Surbiton 6	d		11 00		11 13		11 24	11 30		
Berrylands	d				11 15					
Shepperton	d									11 11
Upper Halliford	d									11 14
Sunbury	d									11 16
Kempton Park	d									11 18
Hampton	d									11 21
Fulwell	d									11 24
Strawberry Hill	d			10 49						
Teddington	d			10 55						11 29
Hampton Wick	d			10 57						11 31
Kingston	a			10 59						11 33
	d			11 04						11 34
Norbiton	d			11 06						11 36
New Malden 6	d			11 10	11 18					11 40
Dorking 4	d								11 08	
Box Hill & Westhumble	d									
Leatherhead	d	10 45							11 15	
Ashtead	d	10 48							11 18	
Epsom 3	a	10 53							11 23	
	d	10 54							11 24	
Ewell West	d	10 57							11 27	
Stoneleigh	d	10 59							11 29	
Worcester Park	d	11 02							11 32	
Chessington South	d					11 10				
Chessington North	d					11 12				
Tolworth	d					11 14				
Malden Manor	d					11 17				
Motspur Park	d	11 05				11 20			11 35	
Raynes Park 6	d	11 08		11 13	11 21	11 24			11 38	11 43
Wimbledon 6 ⊖	d	11 12	11 08	11 17	11 25	11 28	11a33	11 38	11 42	11 47
Earlsfield	d	11 16	11 11	11 20	11 28	11 31		11 41	11 46	11 50
Clapham Junction 10	d	11 20	11 15	11 24	11 32	11 35		11 45	11 50	11 54
Vauxhall ⊖	d	11 25	11 20	11 32	11 37	11 40		11 50	11 55	11 59
London Waterloo 15 ⊖	a	11 29	11 25	11 36	11 47	11 50		11 55	12 04	12 09

		SW	SW	SW	SW	SW	SW	SW	SW	SW
						A				
Guildford	d			11 20	11 27				11 50	11 57
London Road (Guildford)	d			11 24					11 54	
Clandon	d			11 29					11 59	
Horsley	d			11 33					12 03	
Effingham Junction 6	d			11 36					12 06	
Bookham	d			11 39						
Cobham & Stoke d'Abernon	d								12 10	
Oxshott	d								12 13	
Claygate	d								12 16	
Hinchley Wood	d								12 19	
Hampton Court	d	11 35					12 05			
Thames Ditton	d	11 37					12 07			
Surbiton 6	d	11 43			12 00		12 13		12 24	12 30
Berrylands	d	11 45					12 15			
Shepperton	d									
Upper Halliford	d									
Sunbury	d									
Kempton Park	d									
Hampton	d									
Fulwell	d									
Strawberry Hill	d					11 50				
Teddington	d					11 55				
Hampton Wick	d					11 57				
Kingston	a					11 59				
	d					12 04				
Norbiton	d					12 06				
New Malden 6	d	11 48				12 10	12 18			
Dorking 4	d									
Box Hill & Westhumble	d									
Leatherhead	d			11 45						
Ashtead	d			11 48						
Epsom 3	a			11 53						
	d			11 54						
Ewell West	d			11 57						
Stoneleigh	d			11 59						
Worcester Park	d			12 02						
Chessington South	d		11 40					12 10		
Chessington North	d		11 42					12 12		
Tolworth	d		11 44					12 14		
Malden Manor	d		11 47					12 17		
Motspur Park	d		11 50	12 05				12 20		
Raynes Park 6	d	11 51	11 54	12 08		12 13	12 21	12 24		
Wimbledon 6 ⊖	d	11 55	11 58	12 12	12 08	12 17	12 25	12 28	12 31	12 38
Earlsfield	d	11 58	12 01	12 16	12 11	12 20	12 28	12 31	12 35	12 41
Clapham Junction 10	d	12 02	12 05	12 20	12 15	12 24	12 32	12 35	12 39	12 45
Vauxhall ⊖	d	12 07	12 13	12 25	12 20	12 29	12 37	12 40	12 44	12 50
London Waterloo 15 ⊖	a	12 17	12 22	12 29	12 25	12 34	12 47	12 50	12 48	12 55

		SW	SW	SW	SW	SW	SW	SW	SW	SW
								A		
Guildford	d					12 20	12 27			
London Road (Guildford)	d					12 24				
Clandon	d					12 29				
Horsley	d					12 33				
Effingham Junction 6	d					12 36				
Bookham	d					12 39				
Cobham & Stoke d'Abernon	d									
Oxshott	d									
Claygate	d									
Hinchley Wood	d									
Hampton Court	d			12 35					13 05	
Thames Ditton	d			12 37					13 07	
Surbiton 6	d			12 43			13 00		13 13	
Berrylands	d			12 45					13 15	
Shepperton	d		12 11							
Upper Halliford	d		12 14							
Sunbury	d		12 16							
Kempton Park	d		12 18							
Hampton	d		12 21							
Fulwell	d		12 24							
Strawberry Hill	d							12 50		
Teddington	d		12 29					12 55		
Hampton Wick	d		12 31					12 57		
Kingston	a		12 33					12 59		
	d		12 34					13 04		
Norbiton	d		12 36					13 06		
New Malden 6	d		12 40	12 48				13 10	13 18	
Dorking 4	d	12 08								
Box Hill & Westhumble	d									
Leatherhead	d	12 15				12 45				
Ashtead	d	12 18				12 48				
Epsom 3	a	12 23				12 53				
	d	12 24				12 54				
Ewell West	d	12 27				12 57				
Stoneleigh	d	12 29				12 59				
Worcester Park	d	12 32				13 02				
Chessington South	d				12 40					13 10
Chessington North	d				12 42					13 12
Tolworth	d				12 44					13 14
Malden Manor	d				12 47					13 17
Motspur Park	d	12 35			12 50	13 05				13 20
Raynes Park 6	d	12 38	12 43	12 51	12 54	13 08		13 13	13 21	13 24
Wimbledon 6 ⊖	d	12 42	12 47	12 55	12 58	13 12	13 08	13 17	13 25	13 28
Earlsfield	d	12 46	12 50	12 58	13 01	13 16	13 11	13 20	13 28	13 31
Clapham Junction 10	d	12 50	12 54	13 02	13 05	13 20	13 15	13 24	13 32	13 35
Vauxhall ⊖	d	12 55	12 59	13 07	13 10	13 25	13 20	13 29	13 37	13 40
London Waterloo 15 ⊖	a	13 04	13 06	13 12	13 15	13 29	13 25	13 34	13 42	13 45

A From London Waterloo

The xx49 Strawberry Hill to London Waterloo services originates from London Waterloo via Richmond

Table 152R

Sundays

8 December to 11 May

Hampton Court, Shepperton, Guildford, Dorking and Chessington South - London

Network Diagram - see first Page of Table 152

		SW	SW	SW	SW	SW	SW	SW	SW	SW A
Guildford	d	12 50	12 57					13 20	13 27	
London Road (Guildford)	d	12 54						13 24		
Clandon	d	12 59						13 29		
Horsley	d	13 03						13 33		
Effingham Junction 6	d	13 06						13 36		
Bookham	d							13 39		
Cobham & Stoke d'Abernon	d	13 10								
Oxshott	d	13 13								
Claygate	d	13 16								
Hinchley Wood	d	13 19								
Hampton Court	d					13 35				
Thames Ditton	d					13 37				
Surbiton 6	d	13 24	13 30			13 43			14 00	
Berrylands	d					13 45				
Shepperton	d				13 11					
Upper Halliford	d				13 14					
Sunbury	d				13 16					
Kempton Park	d				13 18					
Hampton	d				13 21					
Fulwell	d				13 24					
Strawberry Hill	d									13 49
Teddington	d				13 29					13 55
Hampton Wick	d				13 31					13 57
Kingston	a				13 33					13 59
	d				13 34					14 04
Norbiton	d				13 36					14 06
New Malden 6	d				13 40	13 48				14 10
Dorking 4	d			13 08						
Box Hill & Westhumble	d									
Leatherhead	d			13 15				13 45		
Ashtead	d			13 18				13 48		
Epsom 8	a			13 23				13 53		
	d			13 24				13 54		
Ewell West	d			13 27				13 57		
Stoneleigh	d			13 29				13 59		
Worcester Park	d			13 32				14 02		
Chessington South	d						13 40			
Chessington North	d						13 42			
Tolworth	d						13 44			
Malden Manor	d						13 47			
Motspur Park	d			13 35			13 50	14 05		
Raynes Park 6	d			13 38	13 43	13 51	13 54	14 08		14 13
Wimbledon 6 ⊖ ⛴	d	13 31	13 38	13 42	13 47	13 55	13 58	14 12	14 08	14 17
Earlsfield	d	13 35	13 41	13 46	13 50	13 58	14 01	14 16	14 11	14 20
Clapham Junction 10	d	13 39	13 45	13 50	13 54	14 02	14 05	14 20	14 15	14 24
Vauxhall ⊖	d	13 44	13 50	13 55	13 59	14 07	14 10	14 25	14 20	14 29
London Waterloo 15 ⊖	a	13 48	13 55	13 59	14 04	14 12	14 15	14 29	14 25	14 34

		SW	SW	SW	SW	SW	SW	SW A	SW	SW
Guildford	d			13 50	13 57					
London Road (Guildford)	d			13 54						
Clandon	d			13 59						
Horsley	d			14 03						
Effingham Junction 6	d			14 06						
Bookham	d									
Cobham & Stoke d'Abernon	d			14 10						
Oxshott	d			14 13						
Claygate	d			14 16						
Hinchley Wood	d			14 19						
Hampton Court	d	14 05							14 35	
Thames Ditton	d	14 07							14 37	
Surbiton 6	d	14 13		14 24	14 30				14 43	
Berrylands	d	14 15							14 45	
Shepperton	d						14 11			
Upper Halliford	d						14 14			
Sunbury	d						14 16			
Kempton Park	d						14 18			
Hampton	d						14 21			
Fulwell	d						14 24			
Strawberry Hill	d							14 30		
Teddington	d						14 29	14 33		
Hampton Wick	d						14 31	14 36		
Kingston	a						14 33	14 38		
	d						14 34			
Norbiton	d						14 36			
New Malden 6	d	14 18					14 40		14 48	
Dorking 4	d					14 08				
Box Hill & Westhumble	d									
Leatherhead	d					14 15				
Ashtead	d					14 18				
Epsom 8	a					14 23				
	d					14 24				
Ewell West	d					14 27				
Stoneleigh	d					14 29				
Worcester Park	d					14 32				
Chessington South	d		14 10							14 40
Chessington North	d		14 12							14 42
Tolworth	d		14 14							14 44
Malden Manor	d		14 17							14 47
Motspur Park	d		14 20			14 35				14 50
Raynes Park 6	d	14 21	14 24			14 38	14 43		14 51	14 54
Wimbledon 6 ⊖ ⛴	d	14 25	14 28	14 31	14 38	14 42	14 47		14 55	14 58
Earlsfield	d	14 28	14 31	14 35	14 41	14 46	14 50		14 58	15 01
Clapham Junction 10	d	14 32	14 35	14 39	14 45	14 50	14 54		15 02	15 05
Vauxhall ⊖	d	14 37	14 40	14 44	14 50	14 55	14 59		15 07	15 10
London Waterloo 15 ⊖	a	14 42	14 45	14 48	14 55	14 59	15 04		15 12	15 15

		SW	SW	SW A	SW	SW	SW	SW	SW	SW
Guildford	d	14 20	14 27				14 50	14 57		
London Road (Guildford)	d	14 24					14 54			
Clandon	d	14 29					14 59			
Horsley	d	14 33					15 03			
Effingham Junction 6	d	14 36					15 06			
Bookham	d	14 39								
Cobham & Stoke d'Abernon	d						15 10			
Oxshott	d						15 13			
Claygate	d						15 16			
Hinchley Wood	d						15 19			
Hampton Court	d				15 05					
Thames Ditton	d				15 07					
Surbiton 6	d		15 00		15 13		15 24	15 30		
Berrylands	d				15 15					
Shepperton	d									15 11
Upper Halliford	d									15 14
Sunbury	d									15 16
Kempton Park	d									15 18
Hampton	d									15 21
Fulwell	d									15 24
Strawberry Hill	d			14 49						
Teddington	d			14 55						15 29
Hampton Wick	d			14 57						15 31
Kingston	a			14 59						15 33
	d			15 04						15 34
Norbiton	d			15 06						15 36
New Malden 6	d			15 10	15 18					15 40
Dorking 4	d								15 08	
Box Hill & Westhumble	d									
Leatherhead	d	14 45							15 15	
Ashtead	d	14 48							15 18	
Epsom 8	a	14 53							15 23	
	d	14 54							15 24	
Ewell West	d	14 57							15 27	
Stoneleigh	d	14 59							15 29	
Worcester Park	d	15 02							15 32	
Chessington South	d					15 10				
Chessington North	d					15 12				
Tolworth	d					15 14				
Malden Manor	d					15 17				
Motspur Park	d	15 05				15 20			15 35	
Raynes Park 6	d	15 08		15 13	15 21	15 24			15 38	15 43
Wimbledon 6 ⊖ ⛴	d	15 12	15 08	15 17	15 25	15 28	15 31	15 38	15 42	15 47
Earlsfield	d	15 16	15 11	15 20	15 28	15 31	15 35	15 41	15 46	15 50
Clapham Junction 10	d	15 20	15 15	15 24	15 32	15 35	15 39	15 45	15 50	15 54
Vauxhall ⊖	d	15 25	15 20	15 29	15 37	15 40	15 44	15 50	15 55	15 59
London Waterloo 15 ⊖	a	15 29	15 25	15 34	15 42	15 45	15 48	15 55	15 59	16 04

		SW A	SW	SW	SW	SW	SW A	SW	SW	SW
Guildford	d				15 20	15 27				15 50
London Road (Guildford)	d				15 24					15 54
Clandon	d				15 29					15 59
Horsley	d				15 33					16 03
Effingham Junction 6	d				15 36					16 06
Bookham	d				15 39					
Cobham & Stoke d'Abernon	d									16 10
Oxshott	d									16 13
Claygate	d									16 16
Hinchley Wood	d									16 19
Hampton Court	d		15 35					16 05		
Thames Ditton	d		15 37					16 07		
Surbiton 6	d		15 43			16 00		16 13		16 24
Berrylands	d		15 45					16 15		
Shepperton	d									
Upper Halliford	d									
Sunbury	d									
Kempton Park	d									
Hampton	d									
Fulwell	d									
Strawberry Hill	d	15 30					15 49			
Teddington	d	15 33					15 55			
Hampton Wick	d	15 36					15 57			
Kingston	a	15 38					15 59			
	d						16 04			
Norbiton	d						16 06			
New Malden 6	d		15 48				16 10	16 18		
Dorking 4	d									
Box Hill & Westhumble	d									
Leatherhead	d				15 45					
Ashtead	d				15 48					
Epsom 8	a				15 53					
	d				15 54					
Ewell West	d				15 57					
Stoneleigh	d				15 59					
Worcester Park	d				16 02					
Chessington South	d			15 40					16 10	
Chessington North	d			15 42					16 12	
Tolworth	d			15 44					16 14	
Malden Manor	d			15 47					16 17	
Motspur Park	d			15 50	16 05				16 20	
Raynes Park 6	d		15 51	15 54	16 08		16 13	16 21	16 24	
Wimbledon 6 ⊖ ⛴	d		15 55	15 58	16 12	16 08	16 17	16 25	16 28	16 31
Earlsfield	d		15 58	16 01	16 16	16 11	16 20	16 28	16 31	16 35
Clapham Junction 10	d		16 02	16 05	16 20	16 15	16 24	16 32	16 35	16 39
Vauxhall ⊖	d		16 07	16 10	16 25	16 20	16 29	16 37	16 40	16 44
London Waterloo 15 ⊖	a		16 12	16 15	16 29	16 25	16 34	16 42	16 45	16 48

A From London Waterloo

The xx49 Strawberry Hill to London Waterloo services originates from London Waterloo via Richmond

Table 152R

Sundays

8 December to 11 May

Hampton Court, Shepperton, Guildford, Dorking and Chessington South - London

Network Diagram - see first Page of Table 152

		SW	SW	SW	SW A	SW	SW	SW	SW	SW A	SW	SW	SW	SW	SW	SW	SW A	SW	SW
Guildford	d	15 57						16 20	16 27				16 50	16 57					
London Road (Guildford)	d							16 24					16 54						
Clandon	d							16 29					16 59						
Horsley	d							16 33					17 03						
Effingham Junction 6	d							16 36					17 06						
Bookham	d							16 39											
Cobham & Stoke d'Abernon	d												17 10						
Oxshott	d												17 13						
Claygate	d												17 16						
Hinchley Wood	d												17 19						
Hampton Court	d					16 35					17 05							17 35	
Thames Ditton	d					16 37					17 07							17 37	
Surbiton 6	d	16 30				16 43			17 00		17 13		17 24	17 30				17 43	
Berrylands	d					16 45					17 15							17 45	
Shepperton	d			16 11												17 11			
Upper Halliford	d			16 14												17 14			
Sunbury	d			16 16												17 16			
Kempton Park	d			16 18												17 18			
Hampton	d			16 21												17 21			
Fulwell	d			16 24												17 24			
Strawberry Hill	d				16 30					16 49							17 30		
Teddington	d			16 29	16 33					16 55						17 29	17 33		
Hampton Wick	d			16 31	16 36					16 57						17 31	17 36		
Kingston	a			16 33	16 38					16 59						17 33	17 38		
	d			16 34						17 04						17 34			
Norbiton	d			16 36						17 06						17 36			
New Malden 6	d			16 40		16 48				17 10	17 18					17 40		17 48	
Dorking 4	d		16 08												17 08				
Box Hill & Westhumble	d																		
Leatherhead	d		16 15					16 45							17 15				
Ashtead	d		16 18					16 48							17 18				
Epsom 3	a		16 23					16 53							17 23				
	d		16 24					16 54							17 24				
Ewell West	d		16 27					16 57							17 27				
Stoneleigh	d		16 29					16 59							17 29				
Worcester Park	d		16 32					17 02							17 32				
Chessington South	d						16 40					17 10							17 40
Chessington North	d						16 42					17 12							17 42
Tolworth	d						16 44					17 14							17 44
Malden Manor	d						16 47					17 17							17 47
Motspur Park	d		16 35				16 50	17 05				17 20			17 35				17 50
Raynes Park 6	d		16 38	16 43		16 51	16 54	17 08		17 13	17 21	17 24			17 38	17 43		17 51	17 54
Wimbledon 6 ⊖	d	16 38	16 42	16 47		16 55	16 58	17 12	17 08	17 17	17 25	17 28	17 31	17 38	17 42	17 47		17 55	17 58
Earlsfield	d	16 41	16 46	16 50		16 58	17 01	17 16	17 11	17 20	17 28	17 31	17 35	17 41	17 46	17 50		17 58	18 01
Clapham Junction 10	d	16 45	16 50	16 54		17 02	17 05	17 20	17 15	17 24	17 32	17 35	17 39	17 45	17 50	17 54		18 02	18 05
Vauxhall ⊖	d	16 50	16 55	16 59		17 07	17 10	17 25	17 20	17 29	17 37	17 40	17 44	17 50	17 55	17 59		18 07	18 10
London Waterloo 15 ⊖	a	16 55	16 59	17 04		17 12	17 15	17 29	17 25	17 34	17 42	17 45	17 48	17 55	17 59	18 04		18 12	18 15

		SW	SW	SW A	SW	SW	SW	SW	SW	SW	SW A	SW	SW	SW	SW	SW A	SW	SW	SW
Guildford	d	17 20	17 27				17 50	17 57						18 20	18 27				18 50
London Road (Guildford)	d	17 24					17 54							18 24					18 54
Clandon	d	17 29					17 59							18 29					18 59
Horsley	d	17 33					18 03							18 33					19 03
Effingham Junction 6	d	17 36					18 06							18 36					19 06
Bookham	d	17 39												18 39					
Cobham & Stoke d'Abernon	d						18 10												19 10
Oxshott	d						18 13												19 13
Claygate	d						18 16												19 16
Hinchley Wood	d						18 19												19 19
Hampton Court	d				18 05							18 35					19 05		
Thames Ditton	d				18 07							18 37					19 07		
Surbiton 6	d		18 00		18 13		18 24	18 30				18 43			19 00		19 13		19 24
Berrylands	d				18 15							18 45					19 15		
Shepperton	d									18 11									
Upper Halliford	d									18 14									
Sunbury	d									18 16									
Kempton Park	d									18 18									
Hampton	d									18 21									
Fulwell	d									18 24									
Strawberry Hill	d			17 49							18 30					18 49			
Teddington	d			17 55						18 29	18 33					18 55			
Hampton Wick	d			17 57						18 31	18 36					18 57			
Kingston	a			17 59						18 33	18 38					18 59			
	d			18 04						18 34						19 04			
Norbiton	d			18 06						18 36						19 06			
New Malden 6	d			18 10	18 18					18 40		18 48				19 10	19 18		
Dorking 4	d								18 08										
Box Hill & Westhumble	d																		
Leatherhead	d	17 45							18 15					18 45					
Ashtead	d	17 48							18 18					18 48					
Epsom 3	a	17 53							18 23					18 53					
	d	17 54							18 24					18 54					
Ewell West	d	17 57							18 27					18 57					
Stoneleigh	d	17 59							18 29					18 59					
Worcester Park	d	18 02							18 32					19 02					
Chessington South	d					18 10							18 40					19 10	
Chessington North	d					18 12							18 42					19 12	
Tolworth	d					18 14							18 44					19 14	
Malden Manor	d					18 17							18 47					19 17	
Motspur Park	d	18 05				18 20			18 35				18 50	19 05				19 20	
Raynes Park 6	d	18 08		18 13	18 21	18 24			18 38	18 43		18 51	18 54	19 08		19 13	19 21	19 24	
Wimbledon 6 ⊖	d	18 12	18 08	18 17	18 25	18 28	18 31	18 38	18 42	18 47		18 55	18 58	19 12	19 08	19 17	19 25	19 28	19 31
Earlsfield	d	18 16	18 11	18 20	18 28	18 31	18 35	18 41	18 46	18 50		18 58	19 01	19 16	19 11	19 20	19 28	19 31	19 35
Clapham Junction 10	d	18 20	18 15	18 24	18 32	18 35	18 39	18 45	18 50	18 54		19 02	19 05	19 20	19 15	19 24	19 32	19 35	19 39
Vauxhall ⊖	d	18 25	18 20	18 29	18 37	18 40	18 44	18 50	18 55	18 59		19 07	19 10	19 25	19 20	19 29	19 37	19 40	19 44
London Waterloo 15 ⊖	a	18 29	18 25	18 34	18 42	18 45	18 48	18 55	18 59	19 04		19 12	19 15	19 29	19 25	19 34	19 42	19 45	19 48

A From London Waterloo

The xx49 Strawberry Hill to London Waterloo services originates from London Waterloo via Richmond

Table 152R

Sundays

8 December to 11 May

Hampton Court, Shepperton, Guildford, Dorking and Chessington South - London

Network Diagram - see first Page of Table 152

		SW	SW	SW	SW A	SW	SW	SW	SW	SW A
Guildford	d	18 57						19 20	19 27	
London Road (Guildford)	d							19 24		
Clandon	d							19 29		
Horsley	d							19 33		
Effingham Junction 6	d							19 36		
Bookham	d							19 39		
Cobham & Stoke d'Abernon	d									
Oxshott	d									
Claygate	d									
Hinchley Wood	d									
Hampton Court	d					19 35				
Thames Ditton	d					19 37				
Surbiton 6	d	19 30				19 43			20 00	
Berrylands	d					19 45				
Shepperton	d			19 11						
Upper Halliford	d			19 14						
Sunbury	d			19 16						
Kempton Park	d			19 18						
Hampton	d			19 21						
Fulwell	d			19 24						
Strawberry Hill	d				19 30					19 49
Teddington	d			19 29	19 33					19 55
Hampton Wick	d			19 31	19 36					19 57
Kingston	a			19 33	19 38					19 59
	d			19 34						20 04
Norbiton	d			19 36						20 06
New Malden 6	d			19 40		19 48				20 10
Dorking 4	d		19 08							
Box Hill & Westhumble	d									
Leatherhead	d		19 15					19 45		
Ashtead	d		19 18					19 48		
Epsom 3	a		19 23					19 53		
	d		19 24					19 54		
Ewell West	d		19 27					19 57		
Stoneleigh	d		19 29					19 59		
Worcester Park	d		19 32					20 02		
Chessington South	d						19 40			
Chessington North	d						19 42			
Tolworth	d						19 44			
Malden Manor	d						19 47			
Motspur Park	d		19 35				19 50	20 05		
Raynes Park 6	d		19 38	19 43		19 51	19 54	20 08		20 13
Wimbledon 6 ⊖ ⛴	d	19 38	19 42	19 47		19 55	19 58	20 12	20 08	20 17
Earlsfield	d	19 41	19 46	19 50		19 58	20 01	20 16	20 11	20 20
Clapham Junction 10	d	19 45	19 50	19 54		20 02	20 05	20 20	20 15	20 24
Vauxhall ⊖	d	19 50	19 55	19 59		20 07	20 10	20 25	20 20	20 29
London Waterloo 15 ⊖	a	19 55	19 59	20 04		20 12	20 15	20 29	20 25	20 34

		SW	SW	SW	SW	SW	SW	SW A	SW	SW
Guildford	d			19 50	19 57					20 20
London Road (Guildford)	d			19 54						20 24
Clandon	d			19 59						20 29
Horsley	d			20 03						20 33
Effingham Junction 6	d			20 06						20 36
Bookham	d									20 39
Cobham & Stoke d'Abernon	d			20 10						
Oxshott	d			20 13						
Claygate	d			20 16						
Hinchley Wood	d			20 19						
Hampton Court	d	20 05							20 35	
Thames Ditton	d	20 07							20 37	
Surbiton 6	d	20 13		20 24	20 30				20 43	
Berrylands	d	20 15							20 45	
Shepperton	d						20 11			
Upper Halliford	d						20 14			
Sunbury	d						20 16			
Kempton Park	d						20 18			
Hampton	d						20 21			
Fulwell	d						20 24			
Strawberry Hill	d							20 30		
Teddington	d						20 29	20 33		
Hampton Wick	d						20 31	20 36		
Kingston	a						20 33	20 38		
	d						20 34			
Norbiton	d						20 36			
New Malden 6	d	20 18					20 40		20 48	
Dorking 4	d					20 08				
Box Hill & Westhumble	d									
Leatherhead	d					20 15				20 45
Ashtead	d					20 18				20 48
Epsom 3	a					20 23				20 53
	d					20 24				20 54
Ewell West	d					20 27				20 57
Stoneleigh	d					20 29				20 59
Worcester Park	d					20 32				21 02
Chessington South	d		20 10							
Chessington North	d		20 12							
Tolworth	d		20 14							
Malden Manor	d		20 17							
Motspur Park	d		20 20			20 35				21 05
Raynes Park 6	d	20 21	20 24			20 38	20 43		20 51	21 08
Wimbledon 6 ⊖ ⛴	d	20 25	20 28	20 31	20 38	20 42	20 47		20 55	21 12
Earlsfield	d	20 28	20 31	20 35	20 41	20 46	20 50		20 58	21 16
Clapham Junction 10	d	20 32	20 35	20 39	20 45	20 50	20 54		21 02	21 20
Vauxhall ⊖	d	20 37	20 40	20 44	20 50	20 55	20 59		21 07	21 25
London Waterloo 15 ⊖	a	20 42	20 45	20 48	20 55	21 00	21 04		21 13	21 29

		SW	SW A	SW	SW	SW	SW	SW	SW	SW A
Guildford	d	20 27				20 50	20 57			
London Road (Guildford)	d					20 54				
Clandon	d					20 59				
Horsley	d					21 03				
Effingham Junction 6	d					21 06				
Bookham	d									
Cobham & Stoke d'Abernon	d					21 10				
Oxshott	d					21 13				
Claygate	d					21 16				
Hinchley Wood	d					21 19				
Hampton Court	d			21 05						
Thames Ditton	d			21 07						
Surbiton 6	d	21 00		21 13		21 24	21 30			
Berrylands	d			21 15						
Shepperton	d								21 11	
Upper Halliford	d								21 14	
Sunbury	d								21 16	
Kempton Park	d								21 18	
Hampton	d								21 21	
Fulwell	d								21 24	
Strawberry Hill	d		20 49							21 30
Teddington	d		20 55						21 29	21 33
Hampton Wick	d		20 57						21 31	21 36
Kingston	a		20 59						21 33	21 38
	d		21 04						21 34	
Norbiton	d		21 06						21 36	
New Malden 6	d		21 10	21 18					21 40	
Dorking 4	d							21 08		
Box Hill & Westhumble	d									
Leatherhead	d							21 15		
Ashtead	d							21 18		
Epsom 3	a							21 23		
	d							21 24		
Ewell West	d							21 27		
Stoneleigh	d							21 29		
Worcester Park	d							21 32		
Chessington South	d				21 10					
Chessington North	d				21 12					
Tolworth	d				21 14					
Malden Manor	d				21 17					
Motspur Park	d				21 20			21 35		
Raynes Park 6	d		21 13	21 21	21 24			21 38	21 43	
Wimbledon 6 ⊖ ⛴	d	21 08	21 17	21 25	21 28	21 31	21 38	21 42	21 47	
Earlsfield	d	21 11	21 20	21 28	21 31	21 35	21 41	21 46	21 50	
Clapham Junction 10	d	21 15	21 24	21 32	21 35	21 39	21 45	21 50	21 54	
Vauxhall ⊖	d	21 20	21 29	21 37	21 40	21 44	21 50	21 55	21 59	
London Waterloo 15 ⊖	a	21 25	21 35	21 42	21 45	21 48	21 55	22 00	22 04	

		SW	SW	SW	SW A	SW	SW	SW	SW	SW
Guildford	d		21 20	21 27				21 50	21 57	
London Road (Guildford)	d		21 24					21 54		
Clandon	d		21 29					21 59		
Horsley	d		21 33					22 03		
Effingham Junction 6	d		21 36					22 06		
Bookham	d		21 39							
Cobham & Stoke d'Abernon	d							22 10		
Oxshott	d							22 13		
Claygate	d							22 16		
Hinchley Wood	d							22 19		
Hampton Court	d	21 35				22 05				
Thames Ditton	d	21 37				22 07				
Surbiton 6	d	21 43		22 00		22 13		22 24	22 30	
Berrylands	d	21 45				22 15				
Shepperton	d									
Upper Halliford	d									
Sunbury	d									
Kempton Park	d									
Hampton	d									
Fulwell	d									
Strawberry Hill	d				21 49					
Teddington	d				21 55					
Hampton Wick	d				21 57					
Kingston	a				21 59					
	d				22 04					
Norbiton	d				22 06					
New Malden 6	d	21 48			22 10	22 18				
Dorking 4	d									22 08
Box Hill & Westhumble	d									
Leatherhead	d		21 45							22 15
Ashtead	d		21 48							22 18
Epsom 3	a		21 53							22 23
	d		21 54							22 24
Ewell West	d		21 57							22 27
Stoneleigh	d		21 59							22 29
Worcester Park	d		22 02							22 32
Chessington South	d						22 10			
Chessington North	d						22 12			
Tolworth	d						22 14			
Malden Manor	d						22 17			
Motspur Park	d		22 05				22 20			22 35
Raynes Park 6	d	21 51	22 08		22 13	22 21	22 24			22 38
Wimbledon 6 ⊖ ⛴	d	21 55	22 12	22 08	22 17	22 25	22 28	22 31	22 38	22 42
Earlsfield	d	21 58	22 16	22 11	22 20	22 28	22 31	22 35	22 41	22 46
Clapham Junction 10	d	22 02	22 20	22 15	22 24	22 32	22 35	22 39	22 45	22 50
Vauxhall ⊖	d	22 07	22 25	22 20	22 29	22 37	22 40	22 44	22 50	22 55
London Waterloo 15 ⊖	a	22 12	22 29	22 25	22 35	22 42	22 45	22 48	22 55	23 00

A From London Waterloo

The xx49 Strawberry Hill to London Waterloo services originates from London Waterloo via Richmond

Table 152R

Sundays
8 December to 11 May

Hampton Court, Shepperton, Guildford, Dorking and Chessington South - London

Network Diagram - see first Page of Table 152

		SW	SW	SW	SW A	SW A	SW	SW	SW	SW	SW	SW	SW A	SW	SW	SW A
Guildford	d		22 20	22 27					22 50	22 57						
London Road (Guildford)	d		22 24						22 54							
Clandon	d		22 29						22 59							
Horsley	d		22 33						23 03							
Effingham Junction 6	d		22 36						23 06							
Bookham	d		22 39													
Cobham & Stoke d'Abernon	d								23 10							
Oxshott	d								23 13							
Claygate	d								23 16							
Hinchley Wood	d								23 19							
Hampton Court	d						23 05								23 45	
Thames Ditton	d						23 07								23 47	
Surbiton 6	d			23 00			23 13		23 24	23 30					23 53	
Berrylands	d						23 15								23 55	
Shepperton	d	22 11										23 11				
Upper Halliford	d	22 14										23 14				
Sunbury	d	22 16										23 16				
Kempton Park	d	22 18										23 18				
Hampton	d	22 21										23 21				
Fulwell	d	22 24										23 24				
Strawberry Hill	d				22 30	22 49							23 30			23 48
Teddington	d	22 29			22 33	22 55						23 29	23 33			23 51
Hampton Wick	d	22 31			22 36	22 57						23 31	23 36			23 54
Kingston	a	22 33			22 38	22 59						23 33	23 38			23 56
	d	22 34				23 04						23 34				
Norbiton	d	22 36				23 06						23 36				
New Malden 6	d	22 40				23 10	23 18					23 40			23 58	
Dorking 4	d										23 08					
Box Hill & Westhumble	d															
Leatherhead	d		22 45								23 15					
Ashtead	d		22 48								23 18					
Epsom 3	a		22 53								23 23					
	d		22 54								23 24					
Ewell West	d		22 57								23 27					
Stoneleigh	d		22 59								23 29					
Worcester Park	d		23 02								23 32					
Chessington South	d							23 10						23 40		
Chessington North	d							23 12						23 42		
Tolworth	d							23 14						23 44		
Malden Manor	d							23 17						23 47		
Motspur Park	d		23 05					23 20			23 35			23 50		
Raynes Park 6	d	22 43	23 08			23 13	23 21	23 24			23 38	23 43		23 54	00 01	
Wimbledon 6 ⊖ ⇌	d	22 47	23 12	23 08		23 17	23 25	23 28	23 31	23 38	23 42	23 47		23a59	00a04	
Earlsfield	d	22 50	23 16	23 11		23 20	23 28	23 31	23 35	23 41	23 46	23 50				
Clapham Junction 10	d	22 54	23 20	23 15		23 24	23 32	23 35	23 39	23 45	23 50	23 54				
Vauxhall ⊖	d	22 59	23 25	23 20		23 29	23 37	23 40	23 44	23 50	23 55	23 59				
London Waterloo 15 ⊖	a	23 04	23 29	23 25		23 35	23 42	23 45	23 48	23 55	23 59	00 04				

A From London Waterloo

The xx49 Strawberry Hill to London Waterloo services originates from London Waterloo via Richmond

Network Diagram for Tables 155, 156, 157

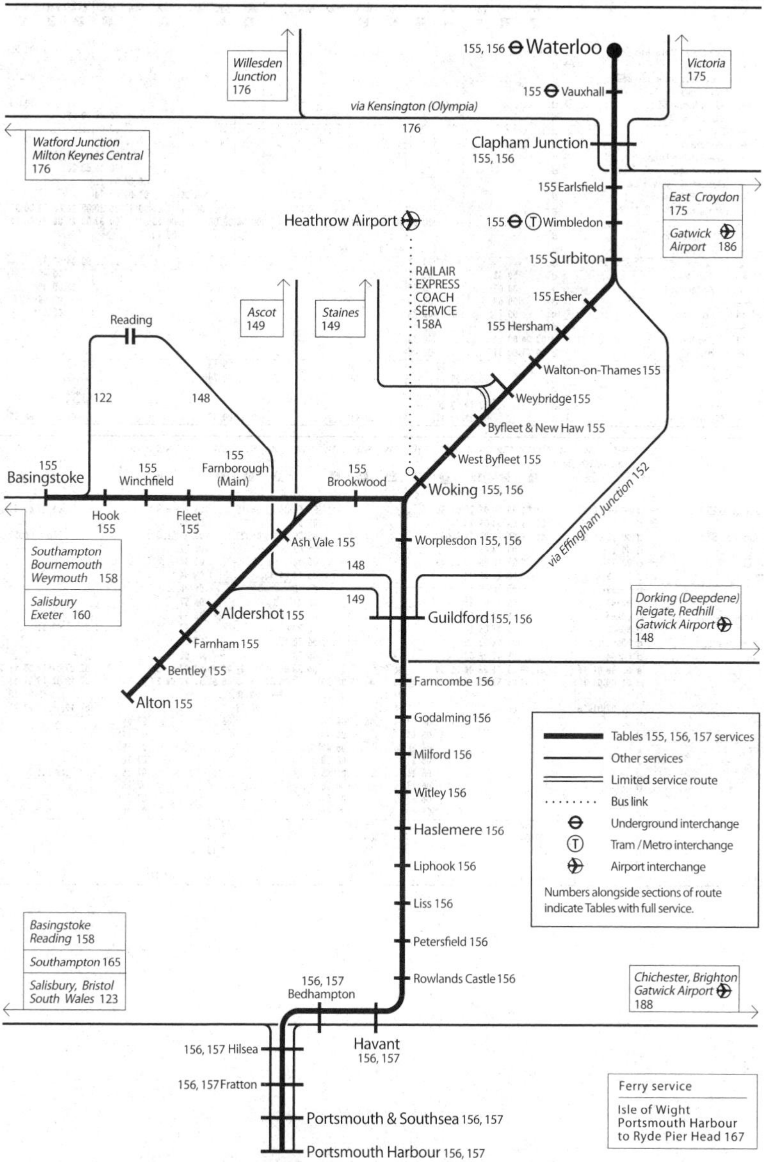

155, 156 Waterloo
155 Vauxhall
Willesden Junction 176
Victoria 175
via Kensington (Olympia)
176
Watford Junction
Milton Keynes Central
176
Clapham Junction
155, 156
155 Earlsfield
East Croydon 175
Gatwick Airport 186
Heathrow Airport
155 Wimbledon
155 Surbiton
RAILAIR EXPRESS COACH SERVICE 158A
155 Esher
155 Hersham
Ascot 149
Staines 149
Reading
Walton-on-Thames 155
122
148
Weybridge 155
Byfleet & New Haw 155
West Byfleet 155
155 Basingstoke
155 Winchfield
155 Farnborough (Main)
155 Brookwood
Woking 155, 156
via Effingham Junction 152
Hook 155
Fleet 155
Southampton Bournemouth Weymouth 158
Salisbury Exeter 160
Ash Vale 155
Worplesdon 155, 156
148
149
Aldershot 155
Guildford 155, 156
Dorking (Deepdene) Reigate, Redhill Gatwick Airport 148
Farnham 155
Bentley 155
Alton 155
Farncombe 156
Godalming 156
Milford 156
Witley 156
Haslemere 156
Liphook 156
Liss 156
Petersfield 156
Rowlands Castle 156
Tables 155, 156, 157 services
Other services
Limited service route
Bus link
Underground interchange
Tram / Metro interchange
Airport interchange
Numbers alongside sections of route indicate Tables with full service.
Basingstoke Reading 158
Southampton 165
Salisbury, Bristol South Wales 123
156, 157 Bedhampton
Chichester, Brighton Gatwick Airport 188
156, 157 Hilsea
Havant 156, 157
156, 157 Fratton
Ferry service
Isle of Wight Portsmouth Harbour to Ryde Pier Head 167
Portsmouth & Southsea 156, 157
Portsmouth Harbour 156, 157

TOCs operating on this network - South West Trains (SW), Southern (SN), First Great Western (GW)

Table 155

Mondays to Fridays

9 December to 16 May

London - Woking, Guildford, Alton and Basingstoke

Network Diagram - see first Page of Table 155

Miles	Miles	Miles			SW MX 1	SW MO 1	SW MO 1	SW MX 1	SW MX 1	SW MO 1	SW MX 1	SW MO	SW MX		SW MX 1	SW MO 1	SW MO	SW MX 1	SW MX	SW MO 1	SW MX 1	SW MO 1	SW MX 1		SW MX 1
0	—	—	**London Waterloo** 15 ⊖	d																			00 05		
1¼	—	—	Vauxhall ⊖	d																					
4	—	—	Clapham Junction 10	d																			00u12		
5½	—	—	Earlsfield	d																					
7¼	—	—	Wimbledon 6 ⊖	d																			00u18		
12	—	—	**Surbiton** 6	d																00 05	00 09				
14½	—	—	Esher	d																00 09					
16	—	—	Hersham	d																00 12					
17	—	—	Walton-on-Thames	d																00 15	00 16				
19	—	—	Weybridge	d																00 18	00 20				
20½	—	—	Byfleet & New Haw	d													00 02		00 06	00 21					
21¾	—	—	West Byfleet	d									00 03				00 05		00 09	00 24		←			
24½	0	—	**Woking**	a									00 08				00 11		00 15	00 30	00 26	00 30	00 35		
—	—	—		d					00 01	00 03	00 03	00 05			00 08	00 08		00 13		00 32	00 28	00 32	00 37		00 40
—	2½	—	Worplesdon	d														00 18		↦					
—	6	—	**Guildford**	a						00 10		00 13						00 24							
28	—	0	Brookwood	d				00 03	00 07												00 34	00 37			00 45
—	—	4½	Ash Vale	d		00 03			00 15													00 45			00 53
—	—	7	**Aldershot**	a		00 07			00 19													00 49			00 58
—	—	—		d		00 08			00 20													00 50			00 58
—	—	10	Farnham	a		00 13			00 25													00 55			01 04
—	—	—		d		00 14			00 26																01 04
—	—	14	Bentley	d	00 04	00 24			00 33																01s10
—	—	18¾	**Alton**	a	00 11	00 31			00 40																01 18
33¼	—	—	Farnborough (Main)	d				00 10			00 14					00 18					00 41				
36½	—	—	Fleet	d			00 04	00 16			00 20					00 24					00 47				
40	—	—	Winchfield	d			00 10	00 21													00s52				
42¼	—	—	Hook	d			00 14	00 26													00s57				
47¾	—	—	**Basingstoke**	a			00 21	00 33			00 33				00 27	00 39					01 06		00 55		

		SW MX	SW MO 1	SW MO	SW 1	SW 1	SW 1	SW ◇1	SW 1	SW 1	SW 1	SW 1	SW	SW 1	SW 1	SW 1	SW	SW ◇1	SW 1		SW	SW 1	SW 1	SW 1	SW
London Waterloo 15 ⊖	d	00 09	00 50		01 05	05 00	05 20	05 30					05 50	06 12	06 15		06 20	06 30				06 42	06 45		06 50
Vauxhall ⊖	d	00 13			01 09	05 04	05 24						05 54				06 24								06 54
Clapham Junction 10	d	00 20	00 57		01 15	05 11	05 29	05u37					05 59	06u19	06u22		06 29	06u37				06u49	06u52		06 59
Earlsfield	d	00 23				05 14	05 32						06 02				06 32								07 02
Wimbledon 6 ⊖	d	00 27			01s27	05 18	05 36	05 43					06 06				06 36								07 06
Surbiton 6	d	00 35			01s35	05 26	05 44						06 14	06 30			06 44					07 00			07 14
Esher	d	00s39				05 30	05 48						06 18				06 48								↦
Hersham	d	00s42				05 33	05 51						06 21				06 51								
Walton-on-Thames	d	00s44				05 37	05 54						06 24	06 37			06 54					07 07			
Weybridge	d	00s48				05 41	05 57						06 27	06 41			06 57					07 11			
Byfleet & New Haw	d	00s51				05 44	06 00						06 30				07 00								
West Byfleet	d	00s54		01 11		05 47	06 03			←			06 33			←	07 03				←			←	
Woking	a	00 58	01 16	01 20	01 48	05 51	06 08	05 59		06 08			06 38	06 48	06 41	06 48	07 07	06 56			07 07	07 18	07 11	07 18	
	d	01 00	01 18		01 49	05 53	06 11	06 01	06 02	06 11	06 19	06 30		06 50	06 43	06 50	07 10	06 57	06 58		07 10	07 19	07 13	07 19	
Worplesdon	d						↦			06 16				↦	06 48		↦					↦	07 18		
Guildford	a	01 07	01s26			06 00				06 21					06 53						07 19		07 23		
Brookwood	d								06 08		06 25	06 36				06 56			07 06					07 25	
Ash Vale	d								06 16			06 44							07 14						
Aldershot	a								06 20			06 49							07 19						
	d								06 21			06 50							07 20						
Farnham	a								06 26			06 55							07 25						
	d								06 27			06 56							07 26						
Bentley	d								06 33			07 02							07 32						
Alton	a								06 40			07 10							07 40						
Farnborough (Main)	d				01s58						06 33					07 04								07 33	
Fleet	d				02s04						06 38					07 09								07 38	
Winchfield	d										06 44					07 15								07 44	
Hook	d										06 48					07 19								07 48	
Basingstoke	a				02 16			06 20			06 58					07 28		07 16						07 56	

Table 155

Mondays to Fridays

9 December to 16 May

London - Woking, Guildford, Alton and Basingstoke

Network Diagram - see first Page of Table 155

			SW 1	SW ◇1 🚲	SW	SW 1	SW 1	SW 1	SW	SW 1	SW 1 🚲		SW ◇1 🚲	SW 1	SW	SW 1 🚲	SW 1	SW 1	SW ◇1 🚲	SW 1	SW		SW 1	SW 1 🚲	SW 1
London Waterloo 15 ⊖	d		06 53	07 10		07 12	07 15		07 20	07 23	07 30		07 35			07 39	07 42	07 45	07 50		07 50		07 53	08 00	
Vauxhall ⊖	d								07 24												07 54				
Clapham Junction 10	d		07u00	07u17		07u20	07u23		07 29	07u30						07u46		07u52	07u57		07 59		08u00		
Earlsfield	d								07 32												08 02				
Wimbledon 6 ⊖	d				←				07 36						←						08 06				
Surbiton 6	d		07 11		07 14	07 31			07 44	07 41					07 44		08 00				08 14		08 11		
Esher	d				07 18				↪						07 48						↪				
Hersham	d				07 21										07 51										
Walton-on-Thames	d				07 24	07 38									07 54		08 07								
Weybridge	d				07 27	07 42									07 57		08 11								
Byfleet & New Haw	d				07 30										08 00										
West Byfleet	d		07 21		07 33			←		07 51				←	08 03					←			08 21		←
Woking	a		07 26	07 35	07 37	07 48	07 42	07 48		07 59	07 55		07 58	07 59	08 08		08 18	08 12	08 15	08 18			08 29	08 24	08 29
	d		07 30	07 36	07 39	07 50	07 44	07 50		08 00	07 55		08 00	08 00			08 19	08 14	08 16	08 19			08 30	08 25	08 30
Worplesdon	d					↪	07 49			↪							↪	08 19					↪		
Guildford	a				07 47		07 54				08 04							08 24						08 35	
Brookwood	d		07 36					07 56						08 06						08 25					08 36
Ash Vale	d		07 44											08 14											08 44
Aldershot	a		07 49											08 19											08 49
	d		07 50											08 20											08 50
Farnham	a		07 55											08 25											08 55
	d		07 56											08 26											08 56
Bentley	d		08 02											08 32											09 02
Alton	a		08 10											08 39											09 10
Farnborough (Main)	d							08 03								08 13				08 33					
Fleet	d							08 09								08 19				08 38					
Winchfield	d							08 14												08 44					
Hook	d							08 19												08 48					
Basingstoke	a			07 55				08 26					08 19			08 31			08 35	08 58					

		SW ◇1 🚲	SW 1	SW	SW 1	SW 1	SW ◇1 🚲		SW 1	SW	SW 1	SW 1 🚲	SW ◇1 🚲	SW 1	SW	SW 1	SW 1		SW 1	SW ◇1 🚲	SW 1	SW	SW 1	SW 1 🚲	SW 1
London Waterloo 15 ⊖	d	08 05	08 09		08 12	08 15	08 20			08 20	08 23	08 30	08 35			08 39	08 42		08 45	08 50		08 50	08 53	09 00	
Vauxhall ⊖	d									08 24												08 54			
Clapham Junction 10	d	08u12			08u19	08u22	08u27			08 29						08u46			08u52			08 59	09u00		
Earlsfield	d									08 32												09 02			
Wimbledon 6 ⊖	d			←						08 36					←							09 06			
Surbiton 6	d			08 14	08 30					08 44	08 41				08 44		09 00					09 14	09 11		
Esher	d			08 18						↪					08 48							↪			
Hersham	d			08 21											08 51										
Walton-on-Thames	d			08 24	08 37										08 54		09 07								
Weybridge	d			08 27	08 41										08 57		09 11								
Byfleet & New Haw	d			08 30											09 00										
West Byfleet	d			08 33					←		08 51			←	09 03						←		09 21		←
Woking	a		08 33	08 37	08 49	08 42	08 46		08 49		09 00	08 55	08 58	09 00	09 08		09 18		09 11	09 15	09 18		09 29	09 24	09 29
	d		08 35	08 39	08 49	08 44	08 46		08 49		09 00	08 55		09 00			09 19		09 13	09 16	09 19		09 30	09 25	09 30
Worplesdon	d				↪	08 49					↪						↪		09 18				↪		
Guildford	a			08 50		08 54						09 05							09 23					09 33	
Brookwood	d								08 55					09 06							09 25				09 36
Ash Vale	d													09 14											09 44
Aldershot	a													09 19											09 49
	d													09 20											09 50
Farnham	a													09 25											09 55
	d													09 26											09 56
Bentley	d																								10 02
Alton	a													09 38											10 10
Farnborough (Main)	d		08 45						09 03							09 13					09 33				
Fleet	d								09 08							09 19					09 38				
Winchfield	d								09 14												09 44				
Hook	d								09 18												09 48				
Basingstoke	a	08 47	08 58				09 05		09 28							09 31				09 36	09 58				

Table 155

Mondays to Fridays

9 December to 16 May

London - Woking, Guildford, Alton and Basingstoke

Network Diagram - see first Page of Table 155

		SW ◇1	SW 1	SW	SW 1	SW 1	SW ◇1	SW 1	SW		SW 1	SW 1	SW ◇1	SW 1	SW	SW 1	SW 1	SW 1	SW ◇1		SW 1	SW	SW 1	SW 1	SW 1
London Waterloo 15 ⊖	d	09 05	09 09		09 12	09 15	09 20		09 20		09 23	09 30	09 35			09 39	09 42	09 45	09 50			09 50	09 53	10 00	
Vauxhall ⊖	d								09 24													09 54			
Clapham Junction 10	d	09u12			09u19	09u22	09u27		09 29							09u46		09u52				09 59	10u00		
Earlsfield	d								09 32													10 02			
Wimbledon 6 ⊖	d			←					09 36						←							10 06			
Surbiton 6	d			09 14	09 30				09 44		09 41				09 44		10 00					10 14	10 11		
Esher	d			09 18					→						09 48							→			
Hersham	d			09 21											09 51										
Walton-on-Thames	d			09 24	09 37										09 54		10 07								
Weybridge	d			09 27	09 41										09 57		10 11								
Byfleet & New Haw	d			09 30											10 00										
West Byfleet	d			09 33				←			09 51			←	10 03						←		10 21		←
Woking	a		09 33	09 38	09 48	09 42	09 45	09 48			09 59	09 54	09 58	09 59	10 08		10 18	10 11	10 14		10 18		10 29	10 24	10 29
	d		09 35		09 49	09 43	09 46	09 49			10 00	09 55		10 00			10 19	10 13	10 16		10 19		10 30	10 25	10 30
Worplesdon	d				→						→						→	10 18					→		
Guildford	a					09 51						10 03						10 23						10 33	
Brookwood	d							09 55						10 06							10 25				10 36
Ash Vale	d													10 14											10 44
Aldershot	a													10 19											10 49
	d													10 20											10 50
Farnham	a													10 25											10 55
	d													10 26											10 56
Bentley	d																								11 02
Alton	a													10 37											11 10
Farnborough (Main)	d		09 45					10 03								10 13					10 33				
Fleet	d							10 08								10 19					10 38				
Winchfield	d							10 14													10 44				
Hook	d							10 18													10 48				
Basingstoke	a	09 47	09 58				10 05	10 28								10 31			10 36		10 58				

		SW ◇1	SW 1	SW	SW 1		SW 1	SW ◇1	SW 1	SW	SW 1	SW 1	SW ◇1	SW 1	SW		SW 1	SW 1	SW 1	SW ◇1	SW 1	SW	SW 1	SW 1	SW 1
London Waterloo 15 ⊖	d	10 05	10 09		10 12		10 15	10 20		10 20	10 23	10 30	10 35				10 39	10 42	10 45	10 50		10 50	10 53	11 00	
Vauxhall ⊖	d									10 24												10 54			
Clapham Junction 10	d	10u12			10u19		10u22	10u27		10 29							10u46		10u52			10 59	11u00		
Earlsfield	d									10 32												11 02			
Wimbledon 6 ⊖	d			←						10 36					←							11 06			
Surbiton 6	d			10 14	10 30					10 44	10 41				10 44			11 00				11 14	11 11		
Esher	d			10 18						→					10 48							→			
Hersham	d			10 21											10 51										
Walton-on-Thames	d			10 24	10 37										10 54			11 07							
Weybridge	d			10 27	10 41										10 57			11 11							
Byfleet & New Haw	d			10 30											11 00										
West Byfleet	d			10 33					←		10 51			←	11 03						←		11 21		←
Woking	a		10 33	10 38	10 48		10 41	10 45	10 48		10 59	10 54	10 58	10 59	11 08			11 18	11 11	11 14	11 18		11 29	11 24	11 29
	d		10 35		10 49		10 43	10 46	10 49		11 00	10 55		11 00				11 19	11 13	11 16	11 19		11 30	11 25	11 30
Worplesdon	d				→						→							→	11 18				→		
Guildford	a						10 50					11 03							11 23					11 33	
Brookwood	d								10 55					11 06							11 25				11 36
Ash Vale	d													11 14											11 44
Aldershot	a													11 19											11 49
	d													11 20											11 50
Farnham	a													11 25											11 55
	d																								11 56
Bentley	d																								12 02
Alton	a																								12 10
Farnborough (Main)	d		10 45						11 03								11 13				11 33				
Fleet	d								11 08								11 19				11 38				
Winchfield	d								11 14												11 44				
Hook	d								11 18												11 48				
Basingstoke	a	10 47	10 58					11 05	11 28								11 31			11 36	11 58				

Table 155

Mondays to Fridays

9 December to 16 May

London - Woking, Guildford, Alton and Basingstoke

Network Diagram - see first Page of Table 155

		SW ◇1 🚲	SW 1	SW	SW 1	SW 1	SW ◇1 🚲		SW 1	SW	SW 1	SW 1 🚲	SW ◇1 🚲	SW 1	SW	SW 1	SW 1		SW 1	SW ◇1 🚲	SW 1	SW	SW 1	SW 1 🚲	SW 1
London Waterloo 15 ⊖	d	11 05	11 09		11 12	11 15	11 20			11 20	11 23	11 30	11 35			11 39	11 42		11 45	11 50		11 50	11 53	12 00	
Vauxhall ⊖	d									11 24												11 54			
Clapham Junction 10	d	11u12			11u19	11u22	11u27			11 29						11u46			11u52			11 59	12u00		
Earlsfield	d									11 32												12 02			
Wimbledon 6 ⊖	d			←						11 36					←							12 06			
Surbiton 6	d			11 14	11 30					11 44	11 41				11 44		12 00					12 14	12 11		
Esher	d			11 18						↳					11 48							↳			
Hersham	d			11 21											11 51										
Walton-on-Thames	d			11 24	11 37										11 54		12 07								
Weybridge	d			11 27	11 41										11 57		12 11								
Byfleet & New Haw	d			11 30											12 00										
West Byfleet	d			11 33					←		11 51			←	12 03						←		12 21		←
Woking	a		11 33	11 38	11 48	11 41	11 45		11 48		11 59	11 54	11 58	11 59	12 08		12 18		12 11	12 14	12 18		12 29	12 24	12 29
	d		11 35		11 49	11 43	11 46		11 49		12 00	11 55		12 00			12 19		12 13	12 16	12 19		12 30	12 25	12 30
Worplesdon	d				↳						↳						↳		12 18				↳		
Guildford	a					11 50						12 03							12 23					12 33	
Brookwood	d								11 55					12 06							12 25				12 36
Ash Vale	d													12 14											12 44
Aldershot	a													12 19											12 49
	d													12 20											12 50
Farnham	a													12 25											12 55
	d													12 26											12 56
Bentley	d																								13 02
Alton	a													12 37											13 10
Farnborough (Main)	d		11 45						12 03							12 13					12 33				
Fleet	d								12 08							12 19					12 38				
Winchfield	d								12 14												12 44				
Hook	d								12 18												12 48				
Basingstoke	a	11 47	11 58				12 05		12 28							12 31				12 36	12 58				

		SW ◇1 🚲	SW 1		SW	SW 1	SW 1	SW ◇1 🚲	SW 1	SW	SW 1	SW 1 🚲	SW ◇1 🚲		SW 1	SW	SW 1	SW 1	SW 1	SW ◇1 🚲	SW 1	SW	SW 1		SW 1 🚲
London Waterloo 15 ⊖	d	12 05	12 09			12 12	12 15	12 20		12 20	12 23	12 30	12 35				12 39	12 42	12 45	12 50		12 50	12 53		13 00
Vauxhall ⊖	d									12 24												12 54			
Clapham Junction 10	d	12u12				12u19	12u22	12u27		12 29							12u46		12u52			12 59	13u00		
Earlsfield	d									12 32												13 02			
Wimbledon 6 ⊖	d				←					12 36						←						13 06			
Surbiton 6	d				12 14	12 30				12 44	12 41					12 44		13 00				13 14	13 11		
Esher	d				12 18					↳						12 48						↳			
Hersham	d				12 21											12 51									
Walton-on-Thames	d				12 24	12 37										12 54		13 07							
Weybridge	d				12 27	12 41										12 57		13 11							
Byfleet & New Haw	d				12 30											13 00									
West Byfleet	d				12 33				←		12 51				←	13 03					←		13 21		
Woking	a		12 33		12 38	12 48	12 41	12 45	12 48		12 59	12 54	12 58		12 59	13 08		13 18	13 11	13 14	13 18		13 29		13 24
	d		12 35			12 49	12 43	12 46	12 49		13 00	12 55			13 00			13 19	13 13	13 16	13 19		13 30		13 25
Worplesdon	d					↳					↳							↳	13 18				↳		
Guildford	a						12 50					13 03							13 23						13 33
Brookwood	d								12 55						13 06						13 25				
Ash Vale	d														13 14										
Aldershot	a														13 19										
	d														13 20										
Farnham	a														13 25										
	d														13 26										
Bentley	d																								
Alton	a														13 37										
Farnborough (Main)	d		12 45						13 03								13 13				13 33				
Fleet	d								13 08								13 19				13 38				
Winchfield	d								13 14												13 44				
Hook	d								13 18												13 48				
Basingstoke	a	12 47	12 58					13 05	13 28								13 31			13 36	13 58				

Table 155

Mondays to Fridays

9 December to 16 May

London - Woking, Guildford, Alton and Basingstoke

Network Diagram - see first Page of Table 155

		SW 1	SW ◇1 🚲	SW 1	SW		SW 1	SW 1	SW ◇1 🚲	SW 1	SW	SW 1	SW 1 🚲	SW ◇1 🚲	SW 1		SW	SW 1	SW 1	SW 1	SW ◇1 🚲	SW 1	SW	SW 1	SW 1 🚲
London Waterloo 15 ⊖	d		13 05	13 09			13 12	13 15	13 20		13 20	13 23	13 30	13 35				13 39	13 42	13 45	13 50		13 50	13 53	14 00
Vauxhall ⊖	d										13 24												13 54		
Clapham Junction 10	d		13u12				13u19	13u22	13u27		13 29							13u46		13u52			13 59	14u00	
Earlsfield	d										13 32												14 02		
Wimbledon 6 ⊖	d				←						13 36						←						14 06		
Surbiton 6	d				13 14		13 30				13 44	13 41					13 44		14 00				14 14	14 11	
Esher	d				13 18						↪						13 48						↪		
Hersham	d				13 21												13 51								
Walton-on-Thames	d				13 24		13 37										13 54		14 07						
Weybridge	d				13 27		13 41										13 57		14 11						
Byfleet & New Haw	d				13 30												14 00								
West Byfleet	d	←			13 33					←		13 51			←		14 03					←		14 21	
Woking	a	13 29		13 33	13 38		13 48	13 41	13 45	13 48		13 59	13 54	13 58	13 59		14 08		14 18	14 11	14 14	14 18		14 29	14 24
	d	13 30		13 35			13 49	13 43	13 46	13 49		14 00	13 55		14 00				14 19	14 13	14 16	14 19		14 30	14 25
Worplesdon	d						↪					↪							↪	14 18				↪	
Guildford	a							13 50					14 03							14 23					14 33
Brookwood	d	13 36								13 55					14 06							14 25			
Ash Vale	d	13 44													14 14										
Aldershot	a	13 49													14 19										
	d	13 50													14 20										
Farnham	a	13 55													14 25										
	d	13 56													14 26										
Bentley	d	14 02																							
Alton	a	14 11													14 37										
Farnborough (Main)	d			13 45						14 03								14 13				14 33			
Fleet	d									14 08								14 19				14 38			
Winchfield	d									14 14												14 44			
Hook	d									14 18												14 48			
Basingstoke	a		13 47	13 58					14 05	14 28								14 31			14 36	14 58			

			SW 1	SW ◇1 🚲	SW 1	SW	SW 1	SW 1	SW ◇1 🚲	SW 1	SW		SW 1	SW 1 🚲	SW ◇1 🚲	SW 1	SW	SW 1	SW 1	SW 1	SW ◇1 🚲		SW 1	SW	SW 1
London Waterloo 15 ⊖	d			14 05	14 09		14 12	14 15	14 20		14 20		14 23	14 30	14 35			14 39	14 42	14 45	14 50			14 50	14 53
Vauxhall ⊖	d										14 24													14 54	
Clapham Junction 10	d			14u12			14u19	14u22	14u27		14 29							14u46		14u52				14 59	15u00
Earlsfield	d										14 32													15 02	
Wimbledon 6 ⊖	d					←					14 36						←							15 06	
Surbiton 6	d					14 14	14 30				14 44		14 41				14 44		15 00					15 14	15 11
Esher	d					14 18					↪						14 48							↪	
Hersham	d					14 21											14 51								
Walton-on-Thames	d					14 24	14 37										14 54		15 07						
Weybridge	d					14 27	14 41										14 57		15 11						
Byfleet & New Haw	d					14 30											15 00								
West Byfleet	d		←			14 33				←			14 51			←	15 03						←		15 21
Woking	a		14 29		14 33	14 38	14 48	14 41	14 45	14 48			14 59	14 54	14 58	14 59	15 08		15 18	15 11	15 14		15 18		15 29
	d		14 30		14 35		14 49	14 43	14 46	14 49			15 00	14 55		15 00			15 19	15 13	15 16		15 19		15 30
Worplesdon	d						↪						↪						↪	15 18					↪
Guildford	a							14 50						15 03						15 23					
Brookwood	d		14 36							14 55						15 06							15 25		
Ash Vale	d		14 44													15 14									
Aldershot	a		14 49													15 19									
	d		14 50													15 20									
Farnham	a		14 55													15 25									
	d		14 56													15 26									
Bentley	d		15 02																						
Alton	a		15 10													15 37									
Farnborough (Main)	d				14 45					15 03								15 13					15 33		
Fleet	d									15 08								15 19					15 38		
Winchfield	d									15 14													15 44		
Hook	d									15 18													15 48		
Basingstoke	a			14 47	14 58				15 05	15 28								15 31			15 36		15 58		

Table 155

Mondays to Fridays

9 December to 16 May

London - Woking, Guildford, Alton and Basingstoke

Network Diagram - see first Page of Table 155

		SW 1 🚲	SW 1		SW ◇1 🚲	SW 1	SW	SW 1	SW 1	SW ◇1 🚲	SW 1	SW	SW 1		SW 1 🚲	SW ◇1 🚲	SW 1	SW	SW 1	SW 1	SW 1	SW ◇1 🚲	SW 1		SW
London Waterloo 15 ⊖	d	15 00			15 05	15 09		15 12	15 15	15 20		15 20	15 23		15 30	15 35			15 39	15 42	15 45	15 50			15 50
Vauxhall ⊖	d											15 24													15 54
Clapham Junction 10	d				15u12			15u19	15u22	15u27		15 29							15u46		15u52	15u57			15 59
Earlsfield	d											15 32													16 02
Wimbledon 6 ⊖	d						←					15 36						←							16 06
Surbiton 6	d						15 14	15 30				15 44	15 41					15 44		16 00					16 14
Esher	d						15 18					→						15 48							→
Hersham	d						15 21											15 51							
Walton-on-Thames	d						15 24	15 37										15 54		16 07					
Weybridge	d						15 27	15 41										15 57		16 11					
Byfleet & New Haw	d						15 30											16 00							
West Byfleet	d		←				15 33				←		15 51				←	16 03					←		
Woking	a	15 24	15 29			15 33	15 38	15 48	15 41	15 45	15 48		15 59		15 54	15 58	15 59	16 08		16 18	16 11	16 15	16 18		
	d	15 25	15 30			15 35		15 49	15 43	15 46	15 49		16 00		15 55		16 00			16 19	16 13	16 16	16 19		
Worplesdon	d							→	15 48				→							→					
Guildford	a	15 33							15 53						16 03						16 20				
Brookwood	d		15 36								15 55						16 06						16 25		
Ash Vale	d		15 44														16 14								
Aldershot	a		15 49														16 19								
	d		15 50														16 20								
Farnham	a		15 55														16 25								
	d		15 56														16 26								
Bentley	d		16 02																						
Alton	a		16 10														16 37								
Farnborough (Main)	d					15 45					16 03								16 13				16 33		
Fleet	d										16 08								16 19				16 38		
Winchfield	d										16 14												16 44		
Hook	d										16 18												16 48		
Basingstoke	a				15 47	15 58				16 05	16 28								16 31			16 36	16 58		

		SW 1	SW 1 🚲	SW 1	SW ◇1 🚲	SW 1	SW	SW 1	SW 1		SW ◇1 🚲	SW 1	SW	SW 1	SW 1 🚲	SW 1	SW	SW 1	SW 1		SW 1	SW ◇1 🚲	SW 1	SW	SW 1
London Waterloo 15 ⊖	d	15 53	16 00		16 05	16 09		16 12	16 15		16 20		16 20	16 25	16 30			16 39	16 42		16 45	16 50		16 50	16 55
Vauxhall ⊖	d												16 24											16 54	
Clapham Junction 10	d	16u00			16u12			16u19	16u22		16u27		16 29					16u46			16u52	16u57		16 59	17u02
Earlsfield	d												16 32											17 02	
Wimbledon 6 ⊖	d						←						16 36				←							17 06	
Surbiton 6	d	16 11					16 14	16 30					16 44	16 41			16 44		17 00					17 14	
Esher	d						16 18						→				16 48							17 18	
Hersham	d						16 21										16 51							17 21	
Walton-on-Thames	d						16 24	16 37									16 54		17 07					17 24	
Weybridge	d						16 27	16 41									16 57		17 11					17 27	
Byfleet & New Haw	d						16 30										17 00							17 30	
West Byfleet	d	16 21		←			16 33					←		16 51		←	17 03						←	17 33	17 21
Woking	a	16 29	16 24	16 29		16 33	16 38	16 48	16 41		16 45	16 48		16 59	16 54	16 59	17 10		17 18		17 11		17 18	17 43	17 29
	d	16 30	16 25	16 30		16 35		16 49	16 43		16 46	16 49		17 00	16 55	17 00			17 19		17 13	17u16	17 19		17 30
Worplesdon	d	→						→	16 48					→					→						→
Guildford	a		16 33						16 53						17 03						17 20				
Brookwood	d			16 36								16 55				17 06							17 25		
Ash Vale	d			16 44												17 14									
Aldershot	a			16 49												17 19									
	d			16 50												17 20									
Farnham	a			16 55												17 25									
	d			16 56												17 26									
Bentley	d			17 02												17 32									
Alton	a			17 10												17 41									
Farnborough (Main)	d					16 45						17 03						17 13					17 33		
Fleet	d											17 08						17 19					17 38		
Winchfield	d											17 14											17 44		
Hook	d											17 18											17 48		
Basingstoke	a				16 47	16 58					17 05	17 30						17 31				17 36	18 00		

Table 155

Mondays to Fridays

9 December to 16 May

London - Woking, Guildford, Alton and Basingstoke

Network Diagram - see first Page of Table 155

		SW	SW	SW	SW	SW	SW	SW	SW	SW		SW	SW	SW	SW	SW	SW	SW	SW	SW		SW	SW	SW
		1	1	1	1	1	1	1	◇1			1	1	1	1		1	1	1	1		1	1	◇1
		🚲							🚲						🚲									🚲
London Waterloo 15 ⊖	d	17 00		17 02	17 09	17 12	17 15		17 20	17 20		17 23	17 25		17 30		17 32	17 39	17 41	17 45		17 48		17 50
Vauxhall ⊖	d									17 24														
Clapham Junction 10	d									17 29														
Earlsfield	d									17 32														
Wimbledon 6 ⊖	d									17 36						←								
Surbiton 6	d			17 18						17 44		17 39				17 44	17 48							
Esher	d			17 22						↪						17 48	17 52							
Hersham	d			17 25												17 51	17 55							
Walton-on-Thames	d			17 29												17 54	17 59							
Weybridge	d			17 33												17 57	18 03							
Byfleet & New Haw	d			17 36												18 00	18 06							
West Byfleet	d		←	17 39				←						←		18 03	18 09						←	
Woking	a	17 24	17 29	17 44	17 32	17 36	17 38	17 44				17 51	17 50	17 51	17 54	18 10	18 14	18 02				18 11	18 14	
	d	17 25	17 30	17 46	17 34	17 37	17 40	17 46	17u46			17 52	17 51	17 52	17 56		18 16	18 04				18 13	18 16	
Worplesdon	d	17 30		↪			17 45					↪			18 00		↪						18 21	
Guildford	a	17 36					17 51	17 56							18 06					18 21			18 29	
Brookwood	d		17 36			17 43								18 00					18 11					
Ash Vale	d		17 44										18 03											
Aldershot	a		17 49										18 08											
	d		17 50										18 09											
Farnham	a		17 55										18 14											
	d		17 56										18 15											
Bentley	d		18 02										18 24											
Alton	a		18 11										18 32											
Farnborough (Main)	d					17 51								18 08					18 19					
Fleet	d					17 56								18 13					18 24					
Winchfield	d					18 02								18 19					18 30					
Hook	d					18 06								18 23					18 34					
Basingstoke	a				17 52	18 16			18 05					18 32				18 22	18 45			18 31		18 37

		SW	SW	SW	SW	SW	SW		SW	SW	SW	SW	SW	SW	SW	SW	SW		SW	SW	SW	SW	SW	SW	SW
			1	1	1		1		1	1	1	1	1	◇1		1	1		1	1		1	1	1	1
							🚲							🚲						🚲					
London Waterloo 15 ⊖	d	17 50	17 53	17 55			18 00		18 02	18 09	18 12	18 15	18 18	18 20	18 20	18 23	18 25			18 30		18 32	18 39	18 41	18 45
Vauxhall ⊖	d	17 54													18 24										
Clapham Junction 10	d	17 59												18u27	18 29		18u33						18u46		
Earlsfield	d	18 02													18 32										
Wimbledon 6 ⊖	d	18 06				←									18 36						←				
Surbiton 6	d	18 14	18 09			18 14			18 18						18 44	18 40					18 44	18 48			
Esher	d	↪				18 18			18 22						↪						18 48	18 52			
Hersham	d					18 21			18 25												18 51	18 55			
Walton-on-Thames	d					18 24			18 29												18 54	18 59			
Weybridge	d					18 27			18 33												18 57	19 03			
Byfleet & New Haw	d					18 30			18 36												19 00	19 06			
West Byfleet	d		18 19		←	18 33			18 39										←		19 03	19 09			19 08
Woking	a		18 23	18 20	18 23	18 41			18 48	18 33			18 42	18 45		18 52	18 52		18 52	18 57	19 12	19 18	19 05		19 13
	d		18 25	18 21	18 25					18 35			18 43	18 46		18 54	18 53		18 54	18 58		19 20	19 06		19 14
Worplesdon	d		↪										18 48			↪						↪			
Guildford	a						18 32					18 50	18 54							19 06					19 22
Brookwood	d			18 27							18 41								19 02					19 13	
Ash Vale	d			18 35													19 05								
Aldershot	a			18 40													19 10								
	d			18 41													19 11								
Farnham	a			18 46													19 16								
	d			18 48													19 18								
Bentley	d			18 54													19 24								
Alton	a			19 03													19 33								
Farnborough (Main)	d				18 39						18 48								19 10					19 20	
Fleet	d				18 44						18 54								19 15					19 26	
Winchfield	d				18 50						18 59								19 21					19 31	
Hook	d				18 54						19 04								19 25					19 36	
Basingstoke	a				19 03					18 53	19 16			19 05					19 34				19 28	19 45	

Table 155

Mondays to Fridays

9 December to 16 May

London - Woking, Guildford, Alton and Basingstoke

Network Diagram - see first Page of Table 155

		SW ◇1 🚲	SW 1	SW	SW 1	SW 1 🚲	SW 1	SW ◇1 🚲	SW 1		SW 1	SW 1	SW ◇1 🚲	SW	SW 1	SW 1 🚲	SW ◇1 🚲	SW 1	SW 1		SW 1	SW 1	SW ◇1 🚲	SW 1	SW
London Waterloo 15 ⊖	d	18 50		18 50	18 55	19 00	19 02	19 05	19 09		19 12	19 15	19 20	19 20	19 25	19 30	19 35		19 39		19 42	19 45	19 50		19 50
Vauxhall ⊖	d			18 54										19 24											19 54
Clapham Junction 10	d			18 59	19u02			19u12			19u19	19u22	19u27	19 29	19u32				19u46			19u52			19 59
Earlsfield	d			19 02										19 32											20 02
Wimbledon 6 ⊖	d			19 06										19 36											20 06
Surbiton 6	d			19 14			19 18							19 44							20 00				20 14
Esher	d			19 18			19 22							19 48											↪
Hersham	d			19 21			19 25							19 51											
Walton-on-Thames	d			19 24			19 29							19 54							20 07				
Weybridge	d			19 27			19 33							19 57							20 11				
Byfleet & New Haw	d			19 30			19 36							20 00											
West Byfleet	d		←	19 33			19 39							20 03	19 51			←						←	
Woking	a	19 17	19 18	19 42	19 21	19 24	19 48		19 33		19 38	19 43	19 45	20 08	19 59	19 54	19 58	19 59			20 18	20 11	20 14	20 18	
	d	19 18	19 20		19 23	19 25			19 35		19 39	19 45	19 46		20 00	19 55		20 00			20 19	20 13	20 16	20 19	
Worplesdon	d					19 30									↪						↪	20 18			
Guildford	a					19 36						19 52				20 03						20 23			
Brookwood	d				19 30						19 45							20 06						20 25	
Ash Vale	d				19 37													20 14							
Aldershot	a				19 42													20 19							
	d				19 43													20 20							
Farnham	a				19 48													20 25							
	d				19 49													20 26							
Bentley	d				19 55													20 32							
Alton	a				20 04													20 39							
Farnborough (Main)	d		19 31						19 45		19 53								20 13					20 33	
Fleet	d		19 37								19 58								20 19					20 38	
Winchfield	d		19 42								20 04													20 44	
Hook	d		19 47								20 09													20 48	
Basingstoke	a	19 37	19 59					19 47	19 58		20 16		20 06						20 31				20 36	20 58	

		SW 1	SW 1 🚲	SW 1	SW ◇1 🚲		SW 1	SW	SW 1	SW 1	SW ◇1 🚲	SW 1	SW	SW 1	SW 1 🚲		SW ◇1 🚲	SW 1	SW	SW 1	SW 1	SW 1	SW 1	SW	SW 1
London Waterloo 15 ⊖	d	19 53	20 00		20 05		20 09		20 12	20 15	20 20		20 20	20 23	20 30		20 35			20 39	20 42	20 45		20 50	20 53
Vauxhall ⊖	d												20 24											20 54	
Clapham Junction 10	d	20u00			20u12				20u19	20u22	20u27		20 29							20u46		20u52		20 59	21u00
Earlsfield	d												20 32											21 02	
Wimbledon 6 ⊖	d							←					20 36						←					21 06	
Surbiton 6	d	20 11						20 14	20 30				20 44	20 41					20 44		21 00			21 14	21 11
Esher	d							20 18					↪						20 48					↪	
Hersham	d							20 21											20 51						
Walton-on-Thames	d							20 24	20 37										20 54		21 07				
Weybridge	d							20 27	20 41										20 57		21 11				
Byfleet & New Haw	d							20 30											21 00						
West Byfleet	d	20 21		←				20 33				←		20 51				←	21 03				←		21 21
Woking	a	20 29	20 24	20 29			20 33	20 38	20 48	20 41	20 45	20 48		20 59	20 54		20 58	20 59	21 08		21 18	21 11	21 18		21 29
	d	20 30	20 25	20 30			20 35		20 49	20 43	20 46	20 49		21 00	20 55			21 00			21 19	21 13	21 19		21 30
Worplesdon	d	↪							↪					↪							↪	21 18			↪
Guildford	a		20 33							20 50					21 03							21 23			
Brookwood	d			20 36								20 55						21 06					21 25		
Ash Vale	d			20 44														21 14							
Aldershot	a			20 49														21 19							
	d			20 50														21 20							
Farnham	a			20 55														21 25							
	d			20 56														21 26							
Bentley	d			21 02														21 32							
Alton	a			21 10														21 39							
Farnborough (Main)	d						20 45					21 03								21 13			21 33		
Fleet	d											21 08								21 19			21 38		
Winchfield	d											21 14											21 44		
Hook	d											21 18											21 48		
Basingstoke	a				20 47		20 58				21 05	21 28								21 31			21 58		

Table 155

Mondays to Fridays

9 December to 16 May

London - Woking, Guildford, Alton and Basingstoke

Network Diagram - see first Page of Table 155

		SW 1 🚲	SW 1	SW ◇1 🚲	SW	SW 1	SW ◇1 🚲		SW 1	SW	SW 1	SW 1	SW ◇1 🚲	SW 1	SW	SW 1	SW 1		SW 1	SW 1	SW	SW	SW 1	SW	SW ◇1 🚲
London Waterloo 15 ⊖	d	21 00		21 05		21 12	21 20			21 20	21 23	21 30	21 35			21 39	21 42		21 45		21 50	21 53	22 00		22 05
Vauxhall ⊖	d									21 24											21 54				
Clapham Junction 10	d			21u12		21u19	21u27			21 29						21u46			21u52		21 59	22u00			22u12
Earlsfield	d									21 32											22 02				
Wimbledon 6 ⊖	d				←					21 36					←						22 06				
Surbiton 6	d				21 14	21 30				21 44	21 41				21 44		22 00				22 14	22 11			
Esher	d				21 18					→					21 48						→				
Hersham	d				21 21										21 51										
Walton-on-Thames	d				21 24	21 37									21 54		22 07								
Weybridge	d				21 27	21 41									21 57		22 11								
Byfleet & New Haw	d				21 30										22 00										
West Byfleet	d		←		21 33				←		21 51			←	22 03					←		22 21		←	
Woking	a	21 24	21 29	21 31	21 38	21 48	21 45		21 48		21 59	21 54	21 58	21 59	22 08		22 18		22 11	22 18		22 29	22 24	22 29	22 31
	d	21 25	21 30	21 32		21 49	21 49		21 49		22 00	21 55		22 00			22 19		22 13	22 19		22 30	22 25	22 30	22 32
Worplesdon	d					→					→						→		22 18			→			
Guildford	a	21 33										22 03							22 23				22 33		
Brookwood	d		21 36						21 55					22 06						22 25				22 36	
Ash Vale	d		21 44											22 14										22 44	
Aldershot	a		21 49											22 19										22 49	
	d		21 50											22 20										22 50	
Farnham	a		21 55											22 25										22 55	
	d		21 56											22 26										22 56	
Bentley	d		22 02											22 32										23 02	
Alton	a		22 10											22 39										23 10	
Farnborough (Main)	d								22 03							22 13				22 33					
Fleet	d								22 08							22 19				22 38					
Winchfield	d								22 14											22 44					
Hook	d								22 18											22 48					
Basingstoke	a			21 50			22 12		22 28							22 31				22 58					22 50

		SW	SW 1		SW 1 🚲	SW 1	SW	SW 1	SW 1	SW ◇1 🚲	SW 1	SW	SW 1		SW 1	SW 1	SW 1	SW	SW	SW 1	SW ◇1	SW	SW 1		SW 1
London Waterloo 15 ⊖	d		22 12		22 20		22 20	22 23	22 30	22 35			22 39		22 42	22 45		22 50	22 52	22 53	23 05		23 12		23 15
Vauxhall ⊖	d						22 24											22 54	22 56						
Clapham Junction 10	d		22u19		22u27		22 29	22u30					22u46		22u49	22u52		22 59	23 02	23u00	23u12		23u19		23u22
Earlsfield	d						22 32											23 02							
Wimbledon 6 ⊖	d	←					22 36					←						23 06				←			
Surbiton 6	d	22 14	22 30				22 44	22 41				22 44			23 00			23 14		23 11		23 14	23 38		
Esher	d	22 18					→					22 48						→				23 18			
Hersham	d	22 21										22 51										23 21			
Walton-on-Thames	d	22 24	22 37									22 54			23 07							23 24	23 45		
Weybridge	d	22 27	22 41									22 57			23 11							23 27	23 49		
Byfleet & New Haw	d	22 30										23 00							00 06			23 30			
West Byfleet	d	22 33				←		22 51			←	23 03					←		00 09	23 21		23 33			
Woking	a	22 37	22 48		22 45	22 48		22 59	22 54	22 58	22 59	23 08			23 18	23 11	23 18		00 15	23 29	23 31	23 38	23 55		23 41
	d	22 39	22 49		22 49	22 49		23 00	22 55		23 00				23 19	23 13	23 19			23 30	23 32		23 57		23 43
Worplesdon	d		→					→							→	23 18							→		
Guildford	a	22 47							23 03							23 24									23 51
Brookwood	d					22 55					23 06						23 25			23 36					
Ash Vale	d										23 14									23 44					
Aldershot	a										23 19									23 49					
	d										23 20									23 50					
Farnham	a										23 25									23 55					
	d										23 26									23 58					
Bentley	d										23 33									00 04					
Alton	a										23 40									00 11					
Farnborough (Main)	d					23 03							23 16				23 33								
Fleet	d					23 08							23 21				23 38								
Winchfield	d					23 14											23 44								
Hook	d					23 18											23 48								
Basingstoke	a				23 09	23 27							23 33				23 57				23 51				

Table 155

Mondays to Fridays

9 December to 16 May

London - Woking, Guildford, Alton and Basingstoke

Network Diagram - see first Page of Table 155

		SW 1	SW	SW 1	SW 1	SW 1	SW	SW 1	SW 1
London Waterloo 15 ⊖	d		23 20	23 23	23 35	23 40		23 45	23 48
Vauxhall ⊖	d		23 24						
Clapham Junction 10	d		23 29	23u30	23u42	23u47		23u52	23u55
Earlsfield	d		23 32						
Wimbledon 6 ⊖	d		23 36				←		
Surbiton 6	d		23 44	23 41			23 44		00 09
Esher	d		↪				23 48		
Hersham	d						23 51		
Walton-on-Thames	d						23 54		00 16
Weybridge	d						23 57		00 20
Byfleet & New Haw	d						23 59		
West Byfleet	d	←		23 55			00 03		
Woking	a	23 55		23 59	00 01	00 06	00 08	00 11	00 26
	d	23 57		00 01	00 03	00 08		00 13	00 28
Worplesdon	d							00 18	
Guildford	a							00 24	
Brookwood	d	00 03		00 07					00 34
Ash Vale	d			00 15					
Aldershot	a			00 19					
	d			00 20					
Farnham	a			00 25					
	d			00 26					
Bentley	d			00 33					
Alton	a			00 40					
Farnborough (Main)	d	00 10			00 14				00 41
Fleet	d	00 16			00 20				00 47
Winchfield	d	00 21							00s52
Hook	d	00 26							00s57
Basingstoke	a	00 33			00 33	00 27			01 06

Saturdays

14 December to 17 May

		SW 1	SW 1	SW 1	SW 1	SW	SW 1	SW 1	SW	SW 1
London Waterloo 15 ⊖	d									
Vauxhall ⊖	d									
Clapham Junction 10	d									
Earlsfield	d									
Wimbledon 6 ⊖	d									
Surbiton 6	d									00 09
Esher	d									
Hersham	d									
Walton-on-Thames	d									00 16
Weybridge	d									00 20
Byfleet & New Haw	d								00 06	
West Byfleet	d					00 03			00 09	
Woking	a					00 08			00 15	00 26
	d			00 01	00 03		00 08	00 13		00 28
Worplesdon	d							00 18		
Guildford	a							00 24		
Brookwood	d	00 03		00 07						00 34
Ash Vale	d			00 15						
Aldershot	a			00 19						
	d			00 20						
Farnham	a			00 25						
	d			00 26						
Bentley	d		00 04	00 33						
Alton	a		00 11	00 40						
Farnborough (Main)	d	00 10			00 14					00 41
Fleet	d	00 16			00 20					00 47
Winchfield	d	00 21								00s52
Hook	d	00 26								00s57
Basingstoke	a	00 33			00 33		00 27			01 06

		SW 1	SW 1	SW	SW	SW 1	SW 1	SW 1	SW ◇1	SW 1	SW 1	SW 1	SW 1	SW
London Waterloo 15 ⊖	d	00 05		00 09	00 27	01 05	05 00	05 20	05 30					05 50
Vauxhall ⊖	d			00 13	00 31	01 09	05 04	05 24						05 54
Clapham Junction 10	d	00u12		00 20	00 37	01 15	05 11	05 29	05u37					05 59
Earlsfield	d			00 23	00s41		05 14	05 32						06 02
Wimbledon 6 ⊖	d	00u18		00 27	00 45	01s20	05 18	05 36	05 43					06 06
Surbiton 6	d			00 35	00s56	01s28	05 26	05 44						06 14
Esher	d			00s39			05 30	05 48						06 18
Hersham	d			00s42			05 33	05 51						06 21
Walton-on-Thames	d			00s44			05 37	05 54						06 24
Weybridge	d			00s48			05 41	05 57						06 27
Byfleet & New Haw	d			00s51			05 44	06 00						06 30
West Byfleet	d			00s54	01s07		05 47	06 03			←			06 33
Woking	a	00 35		00 58	01 12	01 41	05 51	06 08	05 59		06 08			06 38
	d	00 37	00 40	01 00		01 42	05 53	06 13	06 01	06 02	06 13	06 19	06 30	
Worplesdon	d							↪			06 18			
Guildford	a			01 07			06 00				06 23			
Brookwood	d		00 45							06 08		06 25	06 36	
Ash Vale	d		00 53							06 16			06 44	
Aldershot	a		00 58							06 20			06 49	
	d		00 58							06 21			06 50	
Farnham	a		01 04							06 26			06 55	
	d		01 04							06 27			06 56	
Bentley	d		01s10							06 33			07 02	
Alton	a		01 18							06 41			07 10	
Farnborough (Main)	d					01s51						06 33		
Fleet	d					01s57						06 38		
Winchfield	d											06 43		
Hook	d											06 48		
Basingstoke	a	00 55				02s09			06 20			06 58		

Table 155

Saturdays

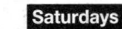

14 December to 17 May

London - Woking, Guildford, Alton and Basingstoke

Network Diagram - see first Page of Table 155

		SW 1		SW 1	SW 1	SW 1	SW	SW ◇1	SW 1	SW 1	SW 1	SW 1		SW	SW 1	SW ◇1 🚲	SW	SW 1	SW 1	SW 1	SW	SW 1		SW 1	SW ◇1
London Waterloo 15 ⊖	d	06 12		06 15			06 20	06 30		06 42	06 45			06 50	06 53	07 10		07 12	07 15		07 20	07 23		07 30	07 35
Vauxhall ⊖	d						06 24							06 54							07 24				
Clapham Junction 10	d	06u19		06u22			06 29	06u37		06u49	06u52			06 59	07u00	07u17		07u20	07u23		07 29	07u30			
Earlsfield	d						06 32							07 02							07 32				
Wimbledon 6 ⊖	d						06 36							07 06			←				07 36				
Surbiton 6	d	06 30					06 44			07 00				07 14	07 11		07 14	07 31			07 44	07 41			
Esher	d						06 48							↪			07 18				↪				
Hersham	d						06 51										07 21								
Walton-on-Thames	d	06 37					06 54			07 07							07 24	07 38							
Weybridge	d	06 41					06 57			07 11							07 27	07 42							
Byfleet & New Haw	d						07 00										07 30								
West Byfleet	d				←		07 03		←			←			07 21		07 33			←		07 51			
Woking	a	06 48		06 41	06 48		07 08	06 56		07 18	07 11	07 18			07 26	07 35	07 38	07 48	07 42	07 48		07 59		07 54	07 58
	d	06 49		06 43	06 49	07 00		06 57	07 00	07 19	07 13	07 19			07 30	07 36		07 50	07 44	07 50		08 00		07 55	08 00
Worplesdon	d	↪				↪				↪	07 18							↪				↪			
Guildford	a			06 51							07 23								07 51					08 03	
Brookwood	d				06 55				07 06			07 25			07 36					07 56					
Ash Vale	d								07 14						07 44										
Aldershot	a								07 19						07 49										
	d								07 20						07 50										
Farnham	a								07 25						07 55										
	d								07 26						07 56										
Bentley	d								07 32						08 02										
Alton	a								07 40						08 10										
Farnborough (Main)	d				07 03							07 33								08 03					
Fleet	d				07 08							07 38								08 09					
Winchfield	d				07 14							07 44								08 14					
Hook	d				07 18							07 48								08 19					
Basingstoke	a				07 28			07 16				07 58				07 57				08 28					08 20

		SW 1	SW	SW 1	SW 1	SW 1	SW ◇1 🚲	SW 1		SW	SW 1	SW 1	SW 1	SW ◇1	SW 1	SW	SW 1	SW 1		SW ◇1 🚲	SW 1	SW	SW 1	SW 1	SW ◇1 🚲
London Waterloo 15 ⊖	d			07 39	07 42	07 45	07 50			07 50	07 53	08 00		08 05	08 09		08 12	08 15		08 20		08 20	08 23	08 30	08 35
Vauxhall ⊖	d									07 54												08 24			
Clapham Junction 10	d			07u46		07u52	07u57			07 59	08u00			08u12			08u19	08u22		08u27		08 29			
Earlsfield	d									08 02												08 32			
Wimbledon 6 ⊖	d		←							08 06						←						08 36			
Surbiton 6	d		07 44		08 00					08 14	08 11					08 14	08 30					08 44	08 41		
Esher	d		07 48							↪						08 18						↪			
Hersham	d		07 51													08 21									
Walton-on-Thames	d		07 54		08 07											08 24	08 37								
Weybridge	d		07 57		08 11											08 27	08 41								
Byfleet & New Haw	d		08 00													08 30									
West Byfleet	d	←	08 03					←			08 21		←			08 33					←		08 51		
Woking	a	07 59	08 08		08 18	08 11	08 15	08 18			08 29	08 24	08 29		08 33	08 38	08 48	08 41		08 45	08 48		08 59	08 54	08 58
	d	08 00			08 19	08 13	08 16	08 19			08 30	08 25	08 30		08 35		08 49	08 43		08 46	08 49		09 00	08 55	
Worplesdon	d				↪	08 18					↪						↪						↪		
Guildford	a					08 23						08 33						08 50						09 03	
Brookwood	d	08 06						08 25					08 36								08 55				
Ash Vale	d	08 14											08 44												
Aldershot	a	08 19											08 49												
	d	08 20											08 50												
Farnham	a	08 25											08 55												
	d	08 26											08 56												
Bentley	d	08 32											09 02												
Alton	a	08 39											09 10												
Farnborough (Main)	d			08 13				08 33							08 45						09 03				
Fleet	d			08 19				08 38													09 08				
Winchfield	d							08 44													09 14				
Hook	d							08 48													09 18				
Basingstoke	a			08 31			08 36	08 58						08 47	08 58					09 05	09 28				

Table 155

Saturdays

14 December to 17 May

London - Woking, Guildford, Alton and Basingstoke

Network Diagram - see first Page of Table 155

		SW	SW	SW	SW	SW	SW	SW	SW	SW		SW	SW	SW	SW	SW	SW	SW	SW	SW		SW	SW	SW	SW
		1		1	1	1	◇1	1		1		1	1	◇1	1		1	1	◇1	1			1	1	◇1
							🚲					🚲		🚲					🚲					🚲	🚲
London Waterloo 15 ⊖	d			08 39	08 42	08 45	08 50		08 50	08 53		09 00		09 05	09 09		09 12	09 15	09 20			09 20	09 23	09 30	09 35
Vauxhall ⊖	d								08 54													09 24			
Clapham Junction 10	d			08u46		08u52			08 59	09u00				09u12			09u19	09u22	09u27			09 29			
Earlsfield	d								09 02													09 32			
Wimbledon 6 ⊖	d		←						09 06							←						09 36			
Surbiton 6	d		08 44		09 00				09 14	09 11						09 14	09 30					09 44	09 41		
Esher	d		08 48						↪							09 18						↪			
Hersham	d		08 51													09 21									
Walton-on-Thames	d		08 54		09 07											09 24	09 37								
Weybridge	d		08 57		09 11											09 27	09 41								
Byfleet & New Haw	d		09 00													09 30									
West Byfleet	d	←	09 03					←		09 21			←			09 33				←			09 51		
Woking	a	08 59	09 08		09 18	09 11	09 14	09 18		09 29		09 24	09 29		09 33	09 38	09 48	09 41	09 45	09 48			09 59	09 54	09 58
	d	09 00			09 19	09 13	09 16	09 19		09 30		09 25	09 30		09 35		09 49	09 43	09 46	09 49			10 00	09 55	
Worplesdon	d				↪	09 18				↪							↪						↪		
Guildford	a					09 23						09 33						09 50						10 03	
Brookwood	d	09 06						09 25					09 36							09 55					
Ash Vale	d	09 14											09 44												
Aldershot	a	09 19											09 49												
	d	09 20											09 50												
Farnham	a	09 25											09 55												
	d	09 26											09 56												
Bentley	d												10 02												
Alton	a	09 37											10 10												
Farnborough (Main)	d			09 13				09 33							09 45					10 03					
Fleet	d			09 19				09 38												10 08					
Winchfield	d							09 44												10 14					
Hook	d							09 48												10 18					
Basingstoke	a			09 31			09 36	09 58						09 47	09 58				10 05	10 28					

		SW	SW	SW	SW	SW		SW	SW	SW	SW	SW	SW	SW	SW	SW		SW	SW	SW	SW	SW	SW	SW	SW
		1		1	1	1		◇1	1		1	1	1	◇1	1			1	1	◇1	1		1	1	◇1
								🚲				🚲		🚲						🚲				🚲	🚲
London Waterloo 15 ⊖	d			09 39	09 42	09 45		09 50		09 50	09 53	10 00		10 05	10 09			10 12	10 15	10 20		10 20	10 23	10 30	10 35
Vauxhall ⊖	d									09 54												10 24			
Clapham Junction 10	d			09u46		09u52				09 59	10u00			10u12				10u19	10u22	10u27		10 29			
Earlsfield	d									10 02												10 32			
Wimbledon 6 ⊖	d		←							10 06						←						10 36			
Surbiton 6	d		09 44		10 00					10 14	10 11					10 14		10 30				10 44	10 41		
Esher	d		09 48							↪						10 18						↪			
Hersham	d		09 51													10 21									
Walton-on-Thames	d		09 54		10 07											10 24		10 37							
Weybridge	d		09 57		10 11											10 27		10 41							
Byfleet & New Haw	d		10 00													10 30									
West Byfleet	d	←	10 03						←		10 21		←			10 33					←		10 51		
Woking	a	09 59	10 08		10 18	10 11		10 14	10 18		10 29	10 24	10 29		10 33	10 38		10 48	10 41	10 45	10 48		10 59	10 54	10 58
	d	10 00			10 19	10 13		10 16	10 19		10 30	10 25	10 30		10 35			10 49	10 43	10 46	10 49		11 00	10 55	
Worplesdon	d				↪	10 18					↪							↪					↪		
Guildford	a					10 23						10 33							10 50					11 03	
Brookwood	d	10 06							10 25				10 36								10 55				
Ash Vale	d	10 14											10 44												
Aldershot	a	10 19											10 49												
	d	10 20											10 50												
Farnham	a	10 25											10 55												
	d	10 26											10 56												
Bentley	d												11 02												
Alton	a	10 37											11 10												
Farnborough (Main)	d			10 13					10 33						10 45						11 03				
Fleet	d			10 19					10 38												11 08				
Winchfield	d								10 44												11 14				
Hook	d								10 48												11 18				
Basingstoke	a			10 31				10 36	10 58					10 47	10 58					11 05	11 28				

Table 155

Saturdays

14 December to 17 May

London - Woking, Guildford, Alton and Basingstoke

Network Diagram - see first Page of Table 155

		SW 1	SW	SW 1	SW 1	SW 1	SW ◇1 🚲	SW 1		SW	SW 1	SW 1 🚲	SW 1	SW ◇1 🚲	SW 1	SW	SW 1	SW 1		SW ◇1 🚲	SW 1	SW	SW 1	SW 1 🚲	SW ◇1 🚲
London Waterloo 15 ⊖	d			10 39	10 42	10 45	10 50			10 50	10 53	11 00		11 05	11 09		11 12	11 15		11 20		11 20	11 23	11 30	11 35
Vauxhall ⊖	d									10 54												11 24			
Clapham Junction 10	d			10u46		10u52				10 59	11u00			11u12			11u19	11u22		11u27		11 29			
Earlsfield	d									11 02												11 32			
Wimbledon 6 ⊖	d		←							11 06						←						11 36			
Surbiton 6	d		10 44		11 00					11 14	11 11					11 14	11 30					11 44	11 41		
Esher	d		10 48							→						11 18						→			
Hersham	d		10 51													11 21									
Walton-on-Thames	d		10 54		11 07											11 24	11 37								
Weybridge	d		10 57		11 11											11 27	11 41								
Byfleet & New Haw	d		11 00													11 30									
West Byfleet	d	←	11 03					←			11 21		←			11 33					←		11 51		
Woking	a	10 59	11 08		11 18	11 11	11 14	11 18			11 29	11 24	11 29		11 33	11 38	11 48	11 41		11 45	11 48		11 59	11 54	11 58
	d	11 00			11 19	11 13	11 16	11 19			11 30	11 25	11 30		11 35		11 49	11 43		11 46	11 49		12 00	11 55	
Worplesdon	d				→	11 18					→						→						→		
Guildford	a					11 23						11 33						11 50						12 03	
Brookwood	d	11 06						11 25					11 36								11 55				
Ash Vale	d	11 14											11 44												
Aldershot	a	11 19											11 49												
	d	11 20											11 50												
Farnham	a	11 25											11 55												
	d	11 26											11 56												
Bentley	d												12 02												
Alton	a	11 37											12 10												
Farnborough (Main)	d			11 13				11 33							11 45						12 03				
Fleet	d			11 19				11 38													12 08				
Winchfield	d							11 44													12 14				
Hook	d							11 48													12 18				
Basingstoke	a			11 31			11 36	11 58						11 47	11 58					12 05	12 28				

		SW 1	SW	SW 1		SW 1	SW 1	SW ◇1 🚲	SW 1	SW	SW 1	SW 1 🚲	SW 1	SW ◇1 🚲		SW 1	SW	SW 1	SW 1	SW ◇1 🚲	SW 1	SW	SW 1	SW 1 🚲	
London Waterloo 15 ⊖	d			11 39		11 42	11 45	11 50		11 50	11 53	12 00		12 05		12 09		12 12	12 15	12 20		12 20	12 23	12 30	
Vauxhall ⊖	d									11 54												12 24			
Clapham Junction 10	d			11u46			11u52			11 59	12u00			12u12				12u19	12u22	12u27		12 29			
Earlsfield	d									12 02												12 32			
Wimbledon 6 ⊖	d		←							12 06							←					12 36			
Surbiton 6	d		11 44			12 00				12 14	12 11						12 14	12 30				12 44	12 41		
Esher	d		11 48							→							12 18					→			
Hersham	d		11 51														12 21								
Walton-on-Thames	d		11 54			12 07											12 24	12 37							
Weybridge	d		11 57			12 11											12 27	12 41							
Byfleet & New Haw	d		12 00														12 30								
West Byfleet	d	←	12 03						←		12 21		←				12 33				←		12 51		
Woking	a	11 59	12 08			12 18	12 11	12 14	12 18		12 29	12 24	12 29			12 33	12 38	12 48	12 41	12 45	12 48		12 59	12 54	
	d	12 00				12 19	12 13	12 16	12 19		12 30	12 25	12 30			12 35		12 49	12 43	12 46	12 49		13 00	12 55	
Worplesdon	d					→	12 18				→							→					→		
Guildford	a						12 23					12 33							12 50					13 03	
Brookwood	d	12 06							12 25				12 36								12 55				
Ash Vale	d	12 14											12 44												
Aldershot	a	12 19											12 49												
	d	12 20											12 50												
Farnham	a	12 25											12 55												
	d	12 26											12 56												
Bentley	d												13 02												
Alton	a	12 37											13 10												
Farnborough (Main)	d			12 13					12 33							12 45					13 03				
Fleet	d			12 19					12 38												13 08				
Winchfield	d								12 44												13 14				
Hook	d								12 48												13 18				
Basingstoke	a			12 31				12 36	12 58					12 47		12 58				13 05	13 28				

Table 155

Saturdays

14 December to 17 May

London - Woking, Guildford, Alton and Basingstoke

Network Diagram - see first Page of Table 155

		SW	SW	SW	SW	SW		SW	SW	SW	SW	SW	SW	SW	SW	SW		SW	SW	SW	SW	SW	SW	SW	SW
		◇**1** 🛒	**1**		**1**	**1**		**1**	◇**1** 🛒	**1**		**1**	**1** 🛒	**1**	◇**1** 🛒	**1**			**1**	**1**	◇**1** 🛒	**1**		**1**	**1** 🛒
London Waterloo 15 ⊖	d	12 35			12 39	12 42		12 45	12 50		12 50	12 53	13 00		13 05	13 09			13 12	13 15	13 20		13 20	13 23	13 30
Vauxhall ⊖	d										12 54												13 24		
Clapham Junction 10	d				12u46			12u52			12 59	13u00			13u12				13u19	13u22	13u27		13 29		
Earlsfield	d										13 02												13 32		
Wimbledon 5 ⊖	d			←							13 06							←					13 36		
Surbiton 5	d			12 44		13 00					13 14	13 11						13 14	13 30				13 44	13 41	
Esher	d			12 48							→							13 18					→		
Hersham	d			12 51														13 21							
Walton-on-Thames	d			12 54		13 07												13 24	13 37						
Weybridge	d			12 57		13 11												13 27	13 41						
Byfleet & New Haw	d			13 00														13 30							
West Byfleet	d		←	13 03						←		13 21		←				13 33				←		13 51	
Woking	a	12 58	12 59	13 08		13 18		13 11	13 14	13 18		13 29	13 24	13 29		13 33		13 38	13 48	13 41	13 45	13 48		13 59	13 54
	d		13 00			13 19		13 13	13 16	13 19		13 30	13 25	13 30		13 35			13 49	13 43	13 46	13 49		14 00	13 55
Worplesdon	d					→		13 18				→							→					→	
Guildford	a							13 23					13 33							13 50					14 03
Brookwood	d		13 06							13 25				13 36								13 55			
Ash Vale	d		13 14											13 44											
Aldershot	a		13 19											13 49											
	d		13 20											13 50											
Farnham	a		13 25											13 55											
	d		13 26											13 56											
Bentley	d													14 02											
Alton	a		13 37											14 10											
Farnborough (Main)	d				13 13					13 33						13 45						14 03			
Fleet	d				13 19					13 38												14 08			
Winchfield	d									13 44												14 14			
Hook	d									13 48												14 18			
Basingstoke	a				13 31				13 36	13 58					13 47	13 58					14 05	14 28			

		SW		SW	SW	SW	SW	SW	SW	SW	SW	SW		SW	SW	SW	SW	SW	SW	SW	SW	SW		SW	SW
		◇**1** 🛒		**1**		**1**	**1**	**1**	◇**1** 🛒	**1**		**1**		**1** 🛒	**1**	◇**1** 🛒	**1**		**1**	**1**	◇**1** 🛒	**1**			**1**
London Waterloo 15 ⊖	d	13 35				13 39	13 42	13 45	13 50		13 50	13 53		14 00		14 05	14 09		14 12	14 15	14 20			14 20	14 23
Vauxhall ⊖	d										13 54													14 24	
Clapham Junction 10	d					13u46		13u52			13 59	14u00				14u12			14u19	14u22	14u27			14 29	
Earlsfield	d										14 02													14 32	
Wimbledon 5 ⊖	d				←						14 06							←						14 36	
Surbiton 5	d				13 44		14 00				14 14	14 11						14 14	14 30					14 44	14 41
Esher	d				13 48						→							14 18						→	
Hersham	d				13 51													14 21							
Walton-on-Thames	d				13 54		14 07											14 24	14 37						
Weybridge	d				13 57		14 11											14 27	14 41						
Byfleet & New Haw	d				14 00													14 30							
West Byfleet	d			←	14 03					←		14 21			←			14 33				←			14 51
Woking	a	13 58		13 59	14 08		14 18	14 11	14 14	14 18		14 29		14 24	14 29		14 33	14 38	14 48	14 41	14 45	14 48			14 59
	d			14 00			14 19	14 13	14 16	14 19		14 30		14 25	14 30		14 35		14 49	14 43	14 46	14 49			15 00
Worplesdon	d						→	14 18				→							→						→
Guildford	a							14 23						14 33						14 50					
Brookwood	d			14 06						14 25					14 36							14 55			
Ash Vale	d			14 14											14 44										
Aldershot	a			14 19											14 49										
	d			14 20											14 50										
Farnham	a			14 25											14 55										
	d			14 26											14 56										
Bentley	d														15 02										
Alton	a			14 37											15 10										
Farnborough (Main)	d					14 13				14 33							14 45					15 03			
Fleet	d					14 19				14 38												15 08			
Winchfield	d									14 44												15 14			
Hook	d									14 48												15 18			
Basingstoke	a					14 31			14 36	14 58						14 47	14 58				15 05	15 28			

Table 155

Saturdays

14 December to 17 May

London - Woking, Guildford, Alton and Basingstoke

Network Diagram - see first Page of Table 155

		SW ■1 🚲	SW ◇■1 🚲	SW ■1		SW	SW ■1	SW ■1	SW ■1	SW ◇■1 🚲	SW ■1	SW	SW ■1	SW ■1 🚲		SW ■1	SW ◇■1 🚲	SW ■1	SW	SW ■1	SW ■1	SW ◇■1 🚲	SW ■1	SW	
London Waterloo 15 ⊖	d	14 30	14 35				14 39	14 42	14 45	14 50		14 50	14 53	15 00			15 05	15 09		15 12	15 15	15 20		15 20	
Vauxhall ⊖	d											14 54												15 24	
Clapham Junction 10	d						14u46		14u52			14 59	15u00				15u12			15u19	15u22	15u27		15 29	
Earlsfield	d											15 02												15 32	
Wimbledon 6 ⊖	d					←						15 06							←					15 36	
Surbiton 6	d					14 44		15 00				15 14	15 11						15 14	15 30				15 44	
Esher	d					14 48						→							15 18					→	
Hersham	d					14 51													15 21						
Walton-on-Thames	d					14 54		15 07											15 24	15 37					
Weybridge	d					14 57		15 11											15 27	15 41					
Byfleet & New Haw	d					15 00													15 30						
West Byfleet	d			←		15 03					←		15 21			←			15 33				←		
Woking	a	14 54	14 58	14 59		15 08		15 18	15 11	15 14	15 18		15 29	15 24		15 29		15 33	15 38	15 48	15 41	15 45	15 48		
	d	14 55		15 00				15 19	15 13	15 16	15 19		15 30	15 25		15 30		15 35		15 49	15 43	15 46	15 49		
Worplesdon	d							→	15 18				→							→					
Guildford	a	15 03							15 23					15 33							15 50				
Brookwood	d			15 06							15 25					15 36							15 55		
Ash Vale	d			15 14												15 44									
Aldershot	a			15 19												15 49									
	d			15 20												15 50									
Farnham	a			15 25												15 55									
	d			15 26												15 56									
Bentley	d															16 02									
Alton	a			15 37												16 10									
Farnborough (Main)	d						15 13				15 33							15 45					16 03		
Fleet	d						15 19				15 38												16 08		
Winchfield	d										15 44												16 14		
Hook	d										15 48												16 18		
Basingstoke	a						15 31			15 36	15 58						15 47	15 58				16 05	16 28		

		SW ■1	SW ■1 🚲	SW ◇■1 🚲	SW ■1	SW	SW ■1	SW ■1	SW ■1	SW ◇■1 🚲		SW ■1	SW	SW ■1	SW ■1 🚲	SW ■1	SW ◇■1 🚲	SW ■1	SW	SW ■1		SW ■1	SW ◇■1 🚲	SW ■1	SW
London Waterloo 15 ⊖	d	15 23	15 30	15 35			15 39	15 42	15 45	15 50			15 50	15 53	16 00		16 05	16 09		16 12		16 15	16 20		16 20
Vauxhall ⊖	d												15 54												16 24
Clapham Junction 10	d						15u46		15u52				15 59	16u00			16u12			16u19		16u22	16u27		16 29
Earlsfield	d												16 02												16 32
Wimbledon 6 ⊖	d					←							16 06						←						16 36
Surbiton 6	d	15 41				15 44		16 00					16 14	16 11					16 14	16 30					16 44
Esher	d					15 48							→						16 18						→
Hersham	d					15 51													16 21						
Walton-on-Thames	d					15 54		16 07											16 24	16 37					
Weybridge	d					15 57		16 11											16 27	16 41					
Byfleet & New Haw	d					16 00													16 30						
West Byfleet	d	15 51			←	16 03						←		16 21		←			16 33					←	
Woking	a	15 59	15 54	15 58	15 59	16 08		16 18	16 11	16 14		16 18		16 29	16 24	16 29		16 33	16 38	16 48		16 41	16 45	16 48	
	d	16 00	15 55		16 00			16 19	16 13	16 16		16 19		16 30	16 25	16 30		16 35		16 49		16 43	16 46	16 49	
Worplesdon	d	→						→	16 18					→						→					
Guildford	a		16 03						16 23						16 33							16 50			
Brookwood	d				16 06							16 25				16 36								16 55	
Ash Vale	d				16 14											16 44									
Aldershot	a				16 19											16 49									
	d				16 20											16 50									
Farnham	a				16 25											16 55									
	d				16 26											16 56									
Bentley	d															17 02									
Alton	a				16 37											17 10									
Farnborough (Main)	d						16 13					16 33						16 45						17 03	
Fleet	d						16 19					16 38												17 08	
Winchfield	d											16 44												17 14	
Hook	d											16 48												17 18	
Basingstoke	a						16 31			16 36		16 58					16 47	16 58					17 05	17 28	

Table 155

Saturdays

14 December to 17 May

London - Woking, Guildford, Alton and Basingstoke

Network Diagram - see first Page of Table 155

		SW 1		SW 1	SW ◇1	SW 1	SW	SW 1	SW 1	SW 1	SW ◇1	SW 1		SW	SW 1	SW 1	SW 1	SW ◇1	SW 1	SW	SW 1	SW 1		SW ◇1	SW 1
London Waterloo 15 ⊖	d	16 23		16 30	16 35			16 39	16 42	16 45	16 50			16 50	16 53	17 00		17 05	17 09		17 12	17 15		17 20	
Vauxhall ⊖	d													16 54											
Clapham Junction 10	d							16u46		16u52				16 59	17u00			17u12			17u19	17u22		17u27	
Earlsfield	d													17 02											
Wimbledon 6 ⊖	d						←							17 06						←					
Surbiton 6	d	16 41					16 44		17 00					17 14	17 11					17 14	17 30				
Esher	d						16 48							→						17 18					
Hersham	d						16 51													17 21					
Walton-on-Thames	d						16 54		17 07											17 24	17 37				
Weybridge	d						16 57		17 11											17 27	17 41				
Byfleet & New Haw	d						17 00													17 30					
West Byfleet	d	16 51				←	17 03					←			17 21		←			17 33					←
Woking	a	16 59		16 54	16 58	16 59	17 08		17 18	17 11	17 14	17 18			17 29	17 24	17 29		17 33	17 38	17 48	17 41		17 45	17 48
	d	17 00		16 55		17 00			17 19	17 13	17 16	17 19			17 30	17 25	17 30		17 35		17 49	17 43		17 46	17 49
Worplesdon	d	→							→	17 18					→						→				
Guildford	a			17 03						17 23						17 33						17 50			
Brookwood	d					17 06						17 25					17 36								17 55
Ash Vale	d					17 14											17 44								
Aldershot	a					17 19											17 49								
	d					17 20											17 50								
Farnham	a					17 25											17 55								
	d					17 26											17 56								
Bentley	d					17 32											18 02								
Alton	a					17 39											18 10								
Farnborough (Main)	d							17 13				17 33							17 45						18 03
Fleet	d							17 19				17 38													18 08
Winchfield	d											17 44													18 14
Hook	d											17 48													18 18
Basingstoke	a							17 31			17 36	17 58						17 47	17 58					18 05	18 28

		SW	SW 1	SW 1	SW ◇1	SW 1	SW	SW 1		SW 1	SW 1	SW ◇1	SW 1	SW	SW 1	SW 1	SW 1	SW ◇1		SW 1	SW	SW 1	SW 1	SW ◇1	SW 1
London Waterloo 15 ⊖	d	17 20	17 23	17 30	17 35			17 39		17 42	17 45	17 50		17 50	17 53	18 00		18 05		18 09		18 12	18 15	18 20	
Vauxhall ⊖	d	17 24												17 54											
Clapham Junction 10	d	17 29						17u46			17u52			17 59	18u00			18u12				18u19	18u22	18u27	
Earlsfield	d	17 32												18 02											
Wimbledon 6 ⊖	d	17 36					←							18 06							←				
Surbiton 6	d	17 44	17 41				17 44			18 00				18 14	18 11						18 14	18 30			
Esher	d	→					17 48							→							18 18				
Hersham	d						17 51														18 21				
Walton-on-Thames	d						17 54			18 07											18 24	18 37			
Weybridge	d						17 57			18 11											18 27	18 41			
Byfleet & New Haw	d						18 00														18 30				
West Byfleet	d		17 51			←	18 03						←		18 21		←				18 33				←
Woking	a		17 59	17 54	17 58	17 59	18 08			18 18	18 11	18 14	18 18		18 29	18 24	18 29			18 33	18 38	18 48	18 41	18 45	18 48
	d		18 00	17 55		18 00				18 19	18 13	18 16	18 19		18 30	18 25	18 30			18 35		18 49	18 43	18 46	18 49
Worplesdon	d		→							→	18 18				→							→			
Guildford	a			18 03							18 23					18 33							18 50		
Brookwood	d					18 06							18 25				18 36								18 55
Ash Vale	d					18 14											18 44								
Aldershot	a					18 19											18 49								
	d					18 20											18 50								
Farnham	a					18 25											18 55								
	d					18 26											18 56								
Bentley	d					18 32											19 02								
Alton	a					18 39											19 10								
Farnborough (Main)	d							18 13					18 33							18 45					19 03
Fleet	d							18 19					18 38												19 08
Winchfield	d												18 44												19 14
Hook	d												18 48												19 18
Basingstoke	a							18 31				18 36	18 58					18 47		18 58				19 05	19 28

Table 155

Saturdays

14 December to 17 May

London - Woking, Guildford, Alton and Basingstoke

Network Diagram - see first Page of Table 155

		SW	SW 1	SW 1 🚲	SW ◇1 🚲	SW 1	SW	SW 1	SW 1	SW 1		SW ◇1 🚲	SW 1	SW	SW 1	SW 1 🚲	SW 1	SW ◇1 🚲	SW 1	SW		SW 1	SW 1	SW 1	SW
London Waterloo 15 ⊖	d	18 20	18 23	18 30	18 35			18 39	18 42	18 45		18 50		18 50	18 53	19 00		19 05	19 09			19 12	19 15		19 20
Vauxhall ⊖	d	18 24												18 54											19 24
Clapham Junction 10	d	18 29						18u46		18u52				18 59	19u00			19u12				19u19	19u22		19 29
Earlsfield	d	18 32												19 02											19 32
Wimbledon 6 ⊖	d	18 36					↩							19 06						↩					19 36
Surbiton 6	d	18 44	18 41				18 44		19 00					19 14	19 11					19 14		19 30			19 44
Esher	d	↪					18 48							↪						19 18					↪
Hersham	d						18 51													19 21					
Walton-on-Thames	d						18 54		19 07											19 24		19 37			
Weybridge	d						18 57		19 11											19 27		19 41			
Byfleet & New Haw	d						19 00													19 30					
West Byfleet	d		18 51			↩	19 03						↩		19 21		↩			19 33				↩	
Woking	a		18 59	18 54	18 58	18 59	19 08		19 18	19 11		19 15	19 18		19 29	19 24	19 29		19 33	19 38		19 48	19 41	19 48	
	d		19 00	18 55		19 00			19 19	19 13		19 16	19 19		19 30	19 25	19 30		19 35			19 49	19 43	19 49	
Worplesdon	d		↪						↪	19 18					↪							↪			
Guildford	a			19 03						19 23						19 33							19 50		
Brookwood	d					19 06							19 25				19 36							19 55	
Ash Vale	d					19 14											19 44								
Aldershot	a					19 19											19 49								
	d					19 20											19 50								
Farnham	a					19 25											19 55								
	d					19 26											19 56								
Bentley	d					19 32											20 02								
Alton	a					19 39											20 10								
Farnborough (Main)	d							19 13					19 33						19 45					20 03	
Fleet	d							19 19					19 38											20 08	
Winchfield	d												19 44											20 14	
Hook	d												19 48											20 18	
Basingstoke	a							19 31				19 36	19 58					19 47	19 58					20 28	

		SW 1	SW 1 🚲	SW ◇1 🚲	SW 1	SW		SW 1	SW 1	SW 1	SW ◇1 🚲	SW 1	SW	SW 1	SW 1	SW 1		SW ◇1 🚲	SW 1	SW	SW 1	SW 1	SW ◇1 🚲	SW 1	SW
London Waterloo 15 ⊖	d	19 23	19 30	19 35				19 39	19 42	19 45	19 50		19 50	19 53	20 00			20 05	20 09		20 12	20 15	20 20		20 20
Vauxhall ⊖	d												19 54												20 24
Clapham Junction 10	d							19u46		19u52			19 59	20u00				20u12			20u19	20u22	20u27		20 29
Earlsfield	d												20 02												20 32
Wimbledon 6 ⊖	d					↩							20 06							↩					20 36
Surbiton 6	d	19 41				19 44			20 00				20 14	20 11						20 14	20 30				20 44
Esher	d					19 48							↪							20 18					↪
Hersham	d					19 51														20 21					
Walton-on-Thames	d					19 54			20 07											20 24	20 37				
Weybridge	d					19 57			20 11											20 27	20 41				
Byfleet & New Haw	d					20 00														20 30					
West Byfleet	d	19 51			↩	20 03						↩		20 21		↩				20 33				↩	
Woking	a	19 59	19 54	19 58	19 59	20 08			20 18	20 11	20 14	20 18		20 29	20 24	20 29			20 33	20 38	20 48	20 41	20 45	20 48	
	d	20 00	19 55		20 00				20 19	20 13	20 16	20 19		20 30	20 25	20 30			20 35		20 49	20 43	20 46	20 49	
Worplesdon	d	↪							↪	20 18				↪							↪				
Guildford	a		20 03							20 23					20 33							20 50			
Brookwood	d				20 06							20 25				20 36								20 55	
Ash Vale	d				20 14											20 44									
Aldershot	a				20 19											20 49									
	d				20 20											20 50									
Farnham	a				20 25											20 55									
	d				20 26											20 56									
Bentley	d				20 32											21 02									
Alton	a				20 39											21 10									
Farnborough (Main)	d							20 13				20 33							20 45					21 03	
Fleet	d							20 19				20 38												21 08	
Winchfield	d											20 44												21 14	
Hook	d											20 48												21 18	
Basingstoke	a							20 31			20 36	20 58						20 47	20 58				21 05	21 28	

Table 155

Saturdays

14 December to 17 May

London - Woking, Guildford, Alton and Basingstoke

Network Diagram - see first Page of Table 155

		SW 1	SW 1	SW ◇1 🚲	SW 1	SW	SW 1	SW 1		SW 1	SW 1	SW	SW 1	SW 1	SW 1	SW ◇1 🚲	SW	SW 1		SW ◇1 🚲	SW 1	SW	SW 1	SW 1	SW ◇1 🚲
London Waterloo 15 ⊖	d	20 23	20 30	20 35			20 39	20 42		20 45		20 50	20 53	21 00		21 05		21 12		21 20		21 20	21 23	21 30	21 35
Vauxhall ⊖	d											20 54										21 24			
Clapham Junction 10	d						20u46			20u52		20 59	21u00			21u12		21u19		21u27		21 29			
Earlsfield	d											21 02										21 32			
Wimbledon 6 ⊖	d					←						21 06					←					21 36			
Surbiton 6	d	20 41				20 44		21 00				21 14	21 11				21 14	21 30				21 44	21 41		
Esher	d					20 48						↪					21 18					↪			
Hersham	d					20 51											21 21								
Walton-on-Thames	d					20 54		21 07									21 24	21 37							
Weybridge	d					20 57		21 11									21 27	21 41							
Byfleet & New Haw	d					21 00											21 30								
West Byfleet	d	20 51			←	21 03					←		21 21		←		21 33				←		21 51		
Woking	a	20 59	20 54	20 58	20 59	21 08		21 18		21 11	21 18		21 29	21 24	21 29	21 31	21 38	21 48		21 45	21 48		21 59	21 54	21 58
	d	21 00	20 55		21 00			21 19		21 13	21 19		21 30	21 25	21 30	21 32		21 49		21 49	21 49		22 00	21 55	
Worplesdon	d	↪						↪		21 18			↪					↪					↪		
Guildford	a		21 03							21 23				21 33										22 03	
Brookwood	d				21 06						21 25				21 36						21 55				
Ash Vale	d				21 14										21 44										
Aldershot	a				21 19										21 49										
	d				21 20										21 50										
Farnham	a				21 25										21 55										
	d				21 26										21 56										
Bentley	d				21 32										22 02										
Alton	a				21 39										22 10										
Farnborough (Main)	d						21 13				21 33										22 03				
Fleet	d						21 19				21 38										22 08				
Winchfield	d										21 44										22 14				
Hook	d										21 48										22 18				
Basingstoke	a						21 31				21 58					21 50				22 12	22 25				

		SW 1	SW	SW 1		SW 1	SW 1	SW 1	SW	SW 1	SW 1	SW 1	SW ◇1 🚲	SW		SW 1	SW 1 🚲	SW 1	SW	SW 1	SW 1	SW ◇1 🚲	SW 1	SW	
London Waterloo 15 ⊖	d			21 39		21 42	21 45		21 50	21 53	22 00		22 05			22 12	22 20		22 20	22 23	22 30	22 35			
Vauxhall ⊖	d								21 54										22 24						
Clapham Junction 10	d			21u46			21u52		21 59	22u00			22u12			22u19	22u27		22 29	22u30					
Earlsfield	d								22 02										22 32						
Wimbledon 6 ⊖	d		←						22 06					←					22 36					←	
Surbiton 6	d		21 44			22 00			22 14	22 11				22 14		22 30			22 44	22 41				22 44	
Esher	d		21 48						↪					22 18					↪					22 48	
Hersham	d		21 51											22 21										22 51	
Walton-on-Thames	d		21 54			22 07								22 24		22 37								22 54	
Weybridge	d		21 57			22 11								22 27		22 41								22 57	
Byfleet & New Haw	d		22 00											22 30										23 00	
West Byfleet	d	←	22 03					←		22 21		←		22 33				←		22 51			←	23 03	
Woking	a	21 59	22 08			22 18	22 11	22 18		22 29	22 24	22 29	22 31	22 37		22 48	22 45	22 48		22 59	22 54	22 58	22 59	23 08	
	d	22 00				22 19	22 13	22 19		22 30	22 25	22 30	22 32	22 39		22 49	22 49	22 49		23 00	22 55		23 00		
Worplesdon	d					↪	22 18			↪						↪				↪					
Guildford	a						22 23				22 33			22 47							23 03				
Brookwood	d	22 06						22 25				22 36						22 55					23 06		
Ash Vale	d	22 14										22 44											23 14		
Aldershot	a	22 19										22 49											23 19		
	d	22 20										22 50											23 20		
Farnham	a	22 25										22 55											23 25		
	d	22 26										22 56											23 26		
Bentley	d	22 32										23 02											23 33		
Alton	a	22 39										23 10											23 40		
Farnborough (Main)	d			22 13				22 33										23 03							
Fleet	d			22 19				22 38										23 08							
Winchfield	d							22 44										23 14							
Hook	d							22 48										23 18							
Basingstoke	a			22 31				22 58					22 50				23 10	23 25							

Table 155

Saturdays

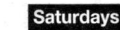

14 December to 17 May

London - Woking, Guildford, Alton and Basingstoke

Network Diagram - see first Page of Table 155

Station		SW 1	SW 1	SW 1	SW 1	SW	SW	SW 1	SW ◇1	SW	SW 1	SW 1	SW 1	SW	SW 1	SW 1	SW 1	SW	SW 1	SW 1
London Waterloo 15 ⊖	d	22 39	22 42	22 45		22 50	22 52	22 53	23 05		23 12	23 15		23 20	23 23	23 35	23 40		23 45	23 48
Vauxhall ⊖	d					22 54	22 56							23 24						
Clapham Junction 10	d	22u46	22u49	22u52		22 59	23 02	23u00	23u12		23u19	23u22		23 29	23u30	23u42	23u47		23u52	23u54
Earlsfield	d					23 02								23 32						
Wimbledon 6 ⊖	d					23 06				←				23 36				←		
Surbiton 6	d		23 00			23 14		23 11		23 14	23 38			23 44	23 41			23 44		00 09
Esher	d					↪				23 18				↪				23 48		
Hersham	d									23 21								23 51		
Walton-on-Thames	d		23 07							23 24	23 45							23 54		00 16
Weybridge	d		23 11							23 27	23 49							23 57		00 20
Byfleet & New Haw	d						00 06			23 30								23 59		
West Byfleet	d				←		00 09	23 21		23 33			←		23 55			00 03		
Woking	a		23 18	23 11	23 18		00 15	23 29	23 31	23 38	23 55	23 41	23 55		23 59	00 01	00 06	00 08	00 11	00 26
	d		23 19	23 13	23 19			23 30	23 32		23 57	23 43	23 57		00 01	00 03	00 08		00 13	00 28
Worplesdon	d		↪	23 18							↪								00 18	
Guildford	a			23 23								23 51							00 24	
Brookwood	d				23 25			23 36					00 03		00 07					00 34
Ash Vale	d							23 44							00 15					
Aldershot	a							23 49							00 19					
	d							23 50							00 20					
Farnham	a							23 55							00 25					
	d							23 58							00 26					
Bentley	d							00 04							00 33					
Alton	a							00 11							00 40					
Farnborough (Main)	d	23 16			23 33								00 10			00 14				00 41
Fleet	d	23 21			23 38								00 16			00 20				00 47
Winchfield	d				23 44								00 21							00s52
Hook	d				23 48								00 26							00s57
Basingstoke	a	23 34			23 55				23 50				00 33			00 33	00 27			01 06

Sundays

8 December to 11 May

Station		SW 1	SW 1	SW 1	SW 1	SW	SW 1	SW 1	SW	SW 1	SW 1	SW 1	SW	SW	SW 1	SW 1	SW 1	SW 1	SW	SW	SW	SW	SW ◇1
London Waterloo 15 ⊖	d										00 05		00 09	00 27	01 05				07 10		07 40	07 50	07 54
Vauxhall ⊖	d												00 13	00 31	01 09				07 14		07 44	07 54	
Clapham Junction 10	d										00u12		00 20	00 37	01 15				07 19		07 49	08 00	08u03
Earlsfield	d												00 23	00s41					07 22		07 52		
Wimbledon 6 ⊖	d										00u18		00 27	00 45	01s27				07 26		07 56		
Surbiton 6	d									00 09			00 35	00s56	01s35				07 35		08 05		
Esher	d												00s39						07 39		08 09		
Hersham	d												00s42						07 42		08 12		
Walton-on-Thames	d									00 16			00s44						07 45		08 15		
Weybridge	d									00 20			00s48						07 49		08 19		
Byfleet & New Haw	d								00 06				00s51						07 51	08 02	08 21	09 02	
West Byfleet	d					00 03			00 09				00s54	01s07					07 54	08 05	08 24	09 05	
Woking	a					00 08			00 15	00 26	00 35		00 58	01 12	01 48				07 59	08 11	08 29	09 11	08 27
	d			00 01	00 03		00 08	00 13		00 28	00 37	00 40	01 00		01 49	07 32	07 46	07 49	08 05		08 32		08 28
Worplesdon	d							00 18													↪		
Guildford	a							00 24					01 07			07 39			08 14				
Brookwood	d	00 03		00 07						00 34		00 45					07 51	07 55					
Ash Vale	d			00 15								00 53						08 03					
Aldershot	a			00 19								00 58						08 07					
	d			00 20								00 58						08 08					
Farnham	a			00 25								01 04						08 13					
	d			00 26								01 04						08 14					
Bentley	d		00 04	00 33								01s10						08 24					
Alton	a		00 11	00 40								01 18						08 31					
Farnborough (Main)	d	00 10			00 14					00 41					01s58		07 59						
Fleet	d	00 16			00 20					00 47					02s04		08 04						
Winchfield	d	00 21								00s52							08 10						
Hook	d	0 26								00s57							08 14						
Basingstoke	a	00 33			00 33		00 27			01 06	00 55				02s16		08 21						08 46

Table 155

Sundays

8 December to 11 May

London - Woking, Guildford, Alton and Basingstoke

Network Diagram - see first Page of Table 155

		SW		SW 1	SW 1		SW	SW ◇1 A ⚲		SW 1	SW	SW 1		SW ◇1	SW	SW	SW ◇1	SW	SW 1	SW 1		SW		SW ◇1 ⚲	
London Waterloo 15 ⊖	d			08 00	08 07		08 10	08 15				08 30		08 35	08 40	08 50	08 54		09 00	09 07		09 10		09 15	
Vauxhall ⊖	d						08 14								08 44	08 54						09 14			
Clapham Junction 10	d			08u09	08 15		08 19	08u23				08u39		08u45	08 49	09 00	09u03		09u09	09 15		09 19		09u22	
Earlsfield	d						08 22								08 52							09 22			
Wimbledon 6 ⊖	d				08 22		08 26								08 56					09 22		09 26			
Surbiton 6	d				08 30		08 35								09 05					09 30		09 35			
Esher	d						08 39								09 09							09 39			
Hersham	d						08 42								09 12							09 42			
Walton-on-Thames	d						08 45								09 15							09 45			
Weybridge	d						08 49								09 19							09 49			
Byfleet & New Haw	d						08 51								09 21	10 02						09 51			
West Byfleet	d	←					08 54			←	←				09 24	10 05		←				09 54			
Woking	a	08 29		08 34	08 42		08 59	08 46		08 42	08 59	09 03		09 08	09 29	10 11	09 27	09 29	09 34	09 42		09 59		09 46	
	d	08 32		08 35	08 46	08 49	09 02	08 47		08 49	09 02	09 04		09 09	09 32		09 28	09 32	09 35	09 46	09 49	10 02		09 47	
Worplesdon	d					→	→								→						→	→			
Guildford	a	08 40		08 43							09 10	09 12						09 40	09 43						
Brookwood	d				08 51					08 55										09 51					
Ash Vale	d									09 03															
Aldershot	a									09 07															
	d									09 08															
Farnham	a									09 13															
	d									09 14															
Bentley	d									09 24															
Alton	a									09 31															
Farnborough (Main)	d				08 59															09 59					
Fleet	d				09 04															10 04					
Winchfield	d				09 10															10 10					
Hook	d				09 14															10 14					
Basingstoke	a				09 21			09 06						09 28			09 46			10 21				10 06	

		SW 1	SW	SW 1	SW ◇1	SW	SW	SW ◇1		SW	SW 1	SW	SW 1		SW	SW ◇1 ⚲		SW 1		SW	SW 1	SW	SW ◇1 ⚲	SW	SW
London Waterloo 15 ⊖	d			09 30	09 35	09 40	09 50	09 54			10 00		10 07		10 10	10 15					10 30		10 35	10 40	10 50
Vauxhall ⊖	d					09 44	09 54								10 14									10 44	10 54
Clapham Junction 10	d			09u39	09u45	09 49	10 00	10u03			10u09		10 15		10 19	10u22					10u39		10u45	10 49	11 00
Earlsfield	d					09 52									10 22									10 52	
Wimbledon 6 ⊖	d					09 56							10 22		10 26									10 56	
Surbiton 6	d					10 05							10 30		10 35									11 05	
Esher	d					10 09									10 39									11 09	
Hersham	d					10 12									10 42									11 12	
Walton-on-Thames	d					10 15									10 45									11 15	
Weybridge	d					10 19									10 49									11 19	
Byfleet & New Haw	d					10 21	11 02								10 51									11 21	12 02
West Byfleet	d	←	←			10 24	11 05			←		←			10 54			←		←		←		11 24	12 05
Woking	a	09 42	09 59	10 03	10 08	10 29	11 11	10 26		10 29	10 31	10 29	10 42		10 59	10 45		10 42		10 59	11 01	10 59	11 07	11 29	12 11
	d	09 49	10 02	10 04	10 09	10 35		10 28		10 35	10 32	10 35	10 46	10 49	11 05	10 46		10 49		11 05	11 02	11 05	11 08	11 35	
Worplesdon	d					→				→				→	→					→				→	
Guildford	a		10 10	10 12							10 40	10 44									11 10	11 14			
Brookwood	d	09 55											10 51					10 55							
Ash Vale	d	10 03																11 03							
Aldershot	a	10 07																11 07							
	d	10 08																11 08							
Farnham	a	10 13																11 13							
	d	10 14																11 14							
Bentley	d	10 24																11 24							
Alton	a	10 31																11 31							
Farnborough (Main)	d												10 59												
Fleet	d												11 04												
Winchfield	d												11 10												
Hook	d												11 14												
Basingstoke	a				10 28			10 46					11 21			11 05							11 26		

A ⚲ from Woking

Table 155

Sundays

8 December to 11 May

London - Woking, Guildford, Alton and Basingstoke

Network Diagram - see first Page of Table 155

Station			SW	SW	SW	SW	SW		SW	SW		SW		SW	SW	SW	SW	SW	SW	SW	SW		SW	SW	
			◇1		1		1			◇1 🚲		1			1 🚲		◇1 🚲			◇1 🚲			1		
London Waterloo 15 ⊖	d		10 54		11 00		11 07		11 10	11 15					11 30		11 35	11 40	11 50	11 54			12 00		
Vauxhall ⊖	d								11 14									11 44	11 54						
Clapham Junction 10	d		11u03		11u09		11 16		11 19	11u22					11u39		11u45	11 49	12 00	12u03			12u09		
Earlsfield	d								11 22									11 52							
Wimbledon 6 ⊖	d						11 22		11 26									11 56							
Surbiton 6	d						11 30		11 35									12 05							
Esher	d								11 39									12 09							
Hersham	d								11 42									12 12							
Walton-on-Thames	d								11 45									12 15							
Weybridge	d								11 49									12 19							
Byfleet & New Haw	d								11 51									12 21	13 02						
West Byfleet	d			←		←			11 54			←		←		←		12 24	13 05		←			←	
Woking	a		11 26	11 29	11 31	11 29	11 42		11 59	11 45		11 42		11 59	12 01	11 59	12 07	12 29	13 11	12 26	12 29		12 31	12 29	
	d		11 28	11 35	11 32	11 35	11 46	11 49	12 05	11 46		11 49		12 05	12 02	12 05	12 08	12 35		12 28	12 35		12 32	12 35	
Worplesdon	d			↪				↪	↪					↪				↪			↪				
Guildford	a				11 40	11 44									12 10	12 14							12 40	12 44	
Brookwood	d						11 51					11 55													
Ash Vale	d											12 03													
Aldershot	a											12 07													
	d											12 08													
Farnham	a											12 13													
	d											12 14													
Bentley	d											12 24													
Alton	a											12 31													
Farnborough (Main)	d						11 59																		
Fleet	d						12 04																		
Winchfield	d						12 10																		
Hook	d						12 14																		
Basingstoke	a		11 46				12 21			12 05							12 26			12 46					

Station		SW		SW	SW		SW	SW		SW	SW	SW	SW	SW	SW	SW	SW	SW		SW		SW	SW		SW
		1			◇1 🚲		1			1 🚲		◇1 🚲			◇1 🚲		1			1			◇1 🚲		1
London Waterloo 15 ⊖	d	12 07		12 10	12 15					12 30		12 35	12 40	12 50	12 54		13 00			13 07		13 10	13 15		
Vauxhall ⊖	d			12 14									12 44	12 54								13 14			
Clapham Junction 10	d	12 16		12 19	12u22					12u39		12u45	12 49	13 00	13u03		13u09			13 15		13 19	13u22		
Earlsfield	d			12 22									12 52									13 22			
Wimbledon 6 ⊖	d	12 22		12 26									12 56							13 22		13 26			
Surbiton 6	d	12 30		12 35									13 05							13 30		13 35			
Esher	d			12 39									13 09									13 39			
Hersham	d			12 42									13 12									13 42			
Walton-on-Thames	d			12 45									13 15									13 45			
Weybridge	d			12 49									13 19									13 49			
Byfleet & New Haw	d			12 51									13 21	14 02								13 51			
West Byfleet	d			12 54			←	←			←		13 24	14 05		←		←				13 54			←
Woking	a	12 42		12 59	12 45		12 42	12 59		13 01	12 59	13 07	13 29	14 11	13 26	13 29	13 31	13 29		13 42		13 59	13 45		13 42
	d	12 46	12 49	13 05	12 46		12 49	13 05		13 02	13 05	13 08	13 35		13 28	13 35	13 32	13 35		13 46	13 49	14 05	13 46		13 49
Worplesdon	d		↪	↪				↪					↪			↪					↪	↪			
Guildford	a									13 10	13 14						13 40	13 44							
Brookwood	d	12 51					12 55													13 51					13 55
Ash Vale	d						13 03																		14 03
Aldershot	a						13 07																		14 07
	d						13 08																		14 08
Farnham	a						13 13																		14 13
	d						13 14																		14 14
Bentley	d						13 24																		14 24
Alton	a						13 31																		14 31
Farnborough (Main)	d	12 59																		13 59					
Fleet	d	13 04																		14 04					
Winchfield	d	13 10																		14 10					
Hook	d	13 14																		14 14					
Basingstoke	a	13 21			13 05							13 26			13 46					14 21			14 05		

Table 155

Sundays

8 December to 11 May

London - Woking, Guildford, Alton and Basingstoke

Network Diagram - see first Page of Table 155

		SW	SW 1 🛒	SW	SW ◇1 🛒	SW	SW	SW ◇1 🛒	SW	SW 1		SW	SW 1		SW	SW ◇1 🛒		SW 1	SW	SW 1 🛒		SW	SW ◇1 🛒	SW	SW
London Waterloo 15 ⊖	d		13 30		13 35	13 40	13 50	13 54		14 00			14 07		14 10	14 15				14 30			14 35	14 40	14 50
Vauxhall ⊖	d					13 44	13 54								14 14									14 44	14 54
Clapham Junction 10	d		13u39		13u42	13 49	14 00	14u03		14u09			14 15		14 19	14u22				14u39			14u42	14 49	15 00
Earlsfield	d					13 52									14 22									14 52	
Wimbledon 6 ⊖	d					13 56							14 22		14 26									14 56	
Surbiton 6	d					14 05							14 30		14 35									15 05	
Esher	d					14 09									14 39									15 09	
Hersham	d					14 12									14 42									15 12	
Walton-on-Thames	d					14 15									14 45									15 15	
Weybridge	d					14 19									14 49									15 19	
Byfleet & New Haw	d					14 21	15 02								14 51									15 21	16 02
West Byfleet	d	←		←		14 24	15 05		←			←			14 54			←	←			←		15 24	16 05
Woking	a	13 59	14 01	13 59	14 06	14 29	15 11	14 26	14 29	14 31		14 29	14 42		14 59	14 45		14 42	14 59	15 01		14 59	15 06	15 29	16 11
	d	14 05	14 02	14 05	14 07	14 35		14 28	14 35	14 32		14 35	14 46	14 49	15 05	14 46		14 49	15 05	15 02		15 05	15 07	15 35	
Worplesdon	d	↪				↪			↪					↪	↪				↪					↪	
Guildford	a		14 10	14 14						14 40		14 44								15 10		15 14			
Brookwood	d												14 51					14 55							
Ash Vale	d																	15 03							
Aldershot	a																	15 07							
	d																	15 08							
Farnham	a																	15 13							
	d																	15 14							
Bentley	d																	15 24							
Alton	a																	15 31							
Farnborough (Main)	d												14 59												
Fleet	d												15 04												
Winchfield	d												15 10												
Hook	d												15 14												
Basingstoke	a				14 26			14 46					15 21			15 05							15 26		

		SW ◇1 🛒	SW	SW 1	SW	SW 1			SW	SW ◇1 🛒		SW 1	SW	SW 1 🛒	SW	SW ◇1 🛒	SW 1			SW	SW	SW ◇1 🛒	SW	SW 1	SW
London Waterloo 15 ⊖	d	14 54		15 00		15 07			15 10	15 15				15 30		15 35	15 37			15 40	15 50	15 54		16 00	
Vauxhall ⊖	d								15 14											15 44	15 54				
Clapham Junction 10	d	15u03		15u09		15 15			15 19	15u22				15u39		15u42	15 46			15 49	16 00	16u03		16u09	
Earlsfield	d								15 22											15 52					
Wimbledon 6 ⊖	d					15 22			15 26								15 53			15 56					
Surbiton 6	d					15 30			15 35								16 02			16 05					
Esher	d								15 39											16 09					
Hersham	d								15 42											16 12					
Walton-on-Thames	d								15 45								16 09			16 15					
Weybridge	d								15 49								16 13			16 19					
Byfleet & New Haw	d								15 51											16 21	17 02				
West Byfleet	d		←		←				15 54			←	←		←					16 24	17 05		←		←
Woking	a	15 26	15 29	15 31	15 29	15 42			15 59	15 45		15 42	15 59	16 01	15 59	16 06	16 19			16 29	17 11	16 26	16 29	16 31	16 29
	d	15 28	15 35	15 32	15 35	15 46	15 49		16 05	15 46		15 49	16 05	16 02	16 05	16 07	16 23	16 26		16 35		16 28	16 35	16 32	16 35
Worplesdon	d		↪				↪		↪				↪							↪			↪		
Guildford	a			15 40	15 44									16 10	16 14									16 40	16 44
Brookwood	d					15 51						15 55					16 28	16 32							
Ash Vale	d											16 03						16 41							
Aldershot	a											16 07						16 45							
	d											16 08						16 46							
Farnham	a											16 13						16 51							
	d											16 14						16 55							
Bentley	d											16 24													
Alton	a											16 31						17 06							
Farnborough (Main)	d					15 59											16 36								
Fleet	d					16 04											16 41								
Winchfield	d					16 10																			
Hook	d					16 14																			
Basingstoke	a	15 46				16 21				16 05						16 26	16 54					16 46			

Table 155

Sundays

8 December to 11 May

London - Woking, Guildford, Alton and Basingstoke

Network Diagram - see first Page of Table 155

		SW 1		SW	SW ◇1 🚲		SW 1	SW	SW 1 🚲	SW		SW ◇1 🚲	SW 1		SW	SW	SW ◇1 🚲	SW	SW 1	SW		SW 1		SW	SW ◇1 🚲
London Waterloo 15 ⊖	d	16 07		16 10	16 15				16 30			16 35	16 37		16 40	16 50	16 54		17 00			17 07		17 10	17 15
Vauxhall ⊖	d			16 14											16 44	16 54								17 14	
Clapham Junction 10	d	16 15		16 19	16u22				16u39			16u42	16 46		16 49	17 00	17u03		17u09			17 15		17 19	17u22
Earlsfield	d			16 22											16 52									17 22	
Wimbledon 6 ⊖	d	16 22		16 26									16 53		16 56							17 22		17 26	
Surbiton 6	d	16 30		16 35									17 02		17 05							17 30		17 35	
Esher	d			16 39											17 09									17 39	
Hersham	d			16 42											17 12									17 42	
Walton-on-Thames	d			16 45									17 09		17 15									17 45	
Weybridge	d			16 49									17 13		17 19									17 49	
Byfleet & New Haw	d			16 51											17 21	18 02								17 51	
West Byfleet	d			16 54			←	←		←					17 24	18 05		←		←				17 54	
Woking	a	16 42		16 59	16 45		16 42	16 59	17 01	16 59		17 06	17 19		17 29	18 11	17 26	17 29	17 31	17 29		17 42		17 59	17 45
	d	16 46	16 49	17 05	16 46		16 49	17 05	17 02	17 05		17 07	17 23	17 26	17 35		17 28	17 35	17 32	17 35		17 46	17 49	18 05	17 46
Worplesdon	d		↪	↪				↪							↪			↪					↪	↪	
Guildford	a								17 10	17 14									17 40	17 44					
Brookwood	d	16 51					16 55						17 28	17 32								17 51			
Ash Vale	d						17 03							17 41											
Aldershot	a						17 07							17 45											
	d						17 08							17 46											
Farnham	a						17 13							17 51											
	d						17 14							17 55											
Bentley	d						17 24																		
Alton	a						17 31							18 06											
Farnborough (Main)	d	16 59											17 36									17 59			
Fleet	d	17 04											17 41									18 04			
Winchfield	d	17 10																				18 10			
Hook	d	17 14																				18 14			
Basingstoke	a	17 21			17 05							17 26	17 54				17 46					18 21			18 05

			SW 1	SW	SW 1 🚲	SW		SW ◇1 🚲	SW 1		SW	SW	SW ◇1 🚲	SW	SW 1	SW		SW 1		SW	SW ◇1 🚲		SW 1	SW	SW 1 🚲
London Waterloo 15 ⊖	d				17 30			17 35	17 37		17 40	17 50	17 54		18 00			18 07		18 10	18 15				18 30
Vauxhall ⊖	d										17 44	17 54								18 14					
Clapham Junction 10	d				17u39			17u42	17 46		17 49	18 00	18u03		18u09			18 15		18 19	18u22				18u39
Earlsfield	d										17 52									18 22					
Wimbledon 6 ⊖	d								17 53		17 56							18 22		18 26					
Surbiton 6	d								18 02		18 05							18 30		18 35					
Esher	d										18 09									18 39					
Hersham	d										18 12									18 42					
Walton-on-Thames	d								18 09		18 15									18 45					
Weybridge	d								18 13		18 19									18 49					
Byfleet & New Haw	d										18 21	19 02								18 51					
West Byfleet	d		←	←		←					18 24	19 05		←		←				18 54			←	←	
Woking	a		17 42	17 59	18 01	17 59		18 06	18 19		18 29	19 11	18 26	18 29	18 31	18 29		18 42		18 59	18 45		18 42	18 59	19 01
	d		17 49	18 05	18 02	18 05		18 07	18 23	18 26	18 35		18 28	18 35	18 32	18 35		18 46	18 49	19 05	18 46		18 49	19 05	19 02
Worplesdon	d			↪							↪			↪					↪	↪				↪	
Guildford	a				18 10	18 14									18 40	18 44									19 10
Brookwood	d		17 55						18 28	18 32								18 51					18 55		
Ash Vale	d		18 03							18 41													19 03		
Aldershot	a		18 07							18 45													19 07		
	d		18 08							18 46													19 08		
Farnham	a		18 13							18 51													19 13		
	d		18 14							18 55													19 14		
Bentley	d		18 24																				19 24		
Alton	a		18 31							19 06													19 31		
Farnborough (Main)	d								18 36									18 59							
Fleet	d								18 41									19 04							
Winchfield	d																	19 10							
Hook	d																	19 14							
Basingstoke	a							18 26	18 54				18 46					19 21			19 05				

Table 155

Sundays

8 December to 11 May

London - Woking, Guildford, Alton and Basingstoke

Network Diagram - see first Page of Table 155

		SW	SW	SW		SW	SW	SW	SW		SW	SW	SW		SW	SW		SW	SW		SW	SW	SW	SW	
			◇1	1				◇1			1		1			◇1		1			1		◇1	1	
			bike					bike								bike					bike		bike		
London Waterloo 15 ⊖	d		18 35	18 37		18 40	18 50	18 54			19 00		19 07		19 10	19 15					19 30		19 35	19 37	
Vauxhall ⊖	d					18 44	18 54								19 14										
Clapham Junction 10	d		18u42	18 46		18 49	19 00	19u03			19u09		19 15		19 19	19u22					19u39		19u42	19 46	
Earlsfield	d					18 52									19 22										
Wimbledon 6 ⊖	d			18 53		18 56							19 22		19 26									19 53	
Surbiton 6	d			19 02		19 05							19 30		19 35									20 02	
Esher	d					19 09									19 39										
Hersham	d					19 12									19 42										
Walton-on-Thames	d			19 09		19 15									19 45									20 09	
Weybridge	d			19 13		19 19									19 49									20 13	
Byfleet & New Haw	d					19 21	20 02								19 51										
West Byfleet	d	←				19 24	20 05		←			←			19 54			←	←			←			
Woking	a	18 59	19 06	19 19		19 29	20 11	19 26	19 29		19 31	19 29	19 42		19 59	19 45		19 42	19 59		20 01	19 59	20 06	20 19	
	d	19 05	19 07	19 23	19 26	19 35		19 28	19 35		19 32	19 35	19 46	19 49	20 05	19 46		19 49	20 05		20 02	20 05	20 07	20 23	20 26
Worplesdon	d					→			→					→	→				→						
Guildford	a	19 14									19 40	19 44									20 10	20 14			
Brookwood	d			19 28	19 32								19 51					19 55						20 28	20 32
Ash Vale	d				19 41													20 03							20 41
Aldershot	a				19 45													20 07							20 45
	d				19 46													20 08							20 46
Farnham	a				19 51													20 13							20 51
	d				19 55													20 14							20 55
Bentley	d																	20 24							
Alton	a				20 06													20 31							21 06
Farnborough (Main)	d			19 36									19 59											20 36	
Fleet	d			19 41									20 04											20 41	
Winchfield	d												20 10												
Hook	d												20 14												
Basingstoke	a		19 26	19 54				19 46					20 21			20 05							20 26	20 54	

		SW	SW	SW	SW		SW	SW	SW		SW	SW		SW	SW		SW	SW	SW	SW		SW	SW	SW	SW
				◇1			1		1			◇1		1			1		◇1	1				◇1	
												bike					bike		bike						
London Waterloo 15 ⊖	d	19 40	19 50	19 54			20 00		20 07		20 10	20 15					20 30		20 35	20 37		20 40	20 50	20 54	
Vauxhall ⊖	d	19 44	19 54								20 14											20 44	20 54		
Clapham Junction 10	d	19 49	20 00	20u03			20u09		20 15		20 19	20u22					20u39		20u42	20 46		20 49	21 00	21u03	
Earlsfield	d	19 52									20 22											20 52			
Wimbledon 6 ⊖	d	19 56							20 22		20 26									20 53		20 56			
Surbiton 6	d	20 05							20 30		20 35									21 02		21 05			
Esher	d	20 09									20 39											21 09			
Hersham	d	20 12									20 42											21 12			
Walton-on-Thames	d	20 15									20 45									21 09		21 15			
Weybridge	d	20 19									20 49									21 13		21 19			
Byfleet & New Haw	d	20 21	21 02								20 51											21 21	22 02		
West Byfleet	d	20 24	21 05		←			←			20 54			←	←			←				21 24	22 05		←
Woking	a	20 29	21 11	20 26	20 29		20 31	20 29	20 42		20 59	20 45		20 42	20 59		21 01	20 59	21 06	21 19		21 29	22 11	21 26	21 29
	d	20 35		20 28	20 35		20 32	20 35	20 46	20 49	21 05	20 46		20 49	21 05		21 02	21 05	21 07	21 23	21 26	21 35		21 28	21 35
Worplesdon	d	→			→					→	→				→							→			→
Guildford	a						20 40	20 44									21 10	21 14							
Brookwood	d								20 51					20 55						21 28	21 32				
Ash Vale	d													21 03							21 41				
Aldershot	a													21 07							21 45				
	d													21 08							21 46				
Farnham	a													21 13							21 51				
	d													21 14							21 55				
Bentley	d													21 24											
Alton	a													21 31							22 06				
Farnborough (Main)	d								20 59											21 36					
Fleet	d								21 04											21 41					
Winchfield	d								21 10																
Hook	d								21 14																
Basingstoke	a			20 46					21 21			21 05							21 26	21 54				21 46	

Table 155

Sundays

8 December to 11 May

London - Woking, Guildford, Alton and Basingstoke

Network Diagram - see first Page of Table 155

		SW	SW	SW		SW	SW	SW		SW	SW	SW	SW	SW	SW		SW	SW		SW	SW	SW	SW	SW	
		[1]		[1]			◇[1] 🚲	[1]		[1]		[1]		◇[1] 🚲	[1]					◇[1]		[1]		[1]	
London Waterloo [15] ⊖	d	21 00		21 07		21 10	21 15					21 30		21 35	21 37		21 40	21 50		21 54		22 00		22 07	
Vauxhall ⊖	d					21 14											21 44	21 54							
Clapham Junction [10]	d	21u09		21 15		21 19	21u22					21u39		21u42	21 46		21 49	22 00		22u03		22u09		22 15	
Earlsfield	d					21 22											21 52								
Wimbledon [6] ⊖	d			21 22		21 26									21 53		21 56							22 22	
Surbiton [6]	d			21 30		21 35									22 02		22 05							22 30	
Esher	d					21 39											22 09								
Hersham	d					21 42											22 12								
Walton-on-Thames	d					21 45									22 09		22 15								
Weybridge	d					21 49									22 13		22 19								
Byfleet & New Haw	d					21 51											22 21	23 02							
West Byfleet	d		←			21 54		←		←	←		←				22 24	23 05			←		←		
Woking	a	21 31	21 29	21 42		21 59	21 45			21 42	21 59	22 01	21 59	22 06	22 19		22 29	23 11		22 26	22 29	22 31	22 29	22 42	
	d	21 32	21 35	21 46	21 49	22 05	21 46	21 49		21 49	22 05	22 02	22 05	22 07	22 23	22 26	22 35			22 28	22 35	22 32	22 35	22 46	22 49
Worplesdon	d				→	→					→						→				→				→
Guildford	a	21 40	21 44									22 10	22 14									22 40	22 44		
Brookwood	d			21 51				21 55		21 55					22 28	22 32								22 51	
Ash Vale	d							22 03		22 03						22 41									
Aldershot	a							22 07		22 07						22 45									
	d							22 08		22 08						22 46									
Farnham	a							22 13		22 13						22 51									
	d							22 14		22 14						22 55									
Bentley	d							22 24		22 24															
Alton	a							22 31		22 31						23 06									
Farnborough (Main)	d			21 59											22 36									22 59	
Fleet	d			22 04											22 41									23 04	
Winchfield	d			22 10																				23 10	
Hook	d			22 14																				23 14	
Basingstoke	a			22 21			22 05							22 26	22 54					22 46				23 21	

		SW	SW	SW		SW	SW	SW	SW	SW		SW	SW	SW		SW	SW	SW	SW		SW	SW	SW	SW	
			[1] 🚲	[1]		[1]		[1]		[1]				◇[1] 🚲			[1]		[1]			[1]		[1]	
London Waterloo [15] ⊖	d	22 10	22 15					22 30		22 37		22 40	22 50	22 54			23 00		23 07		23 10	23 30		23 35	23 40
Vauxhall ⊖	d	22 14										22 44	22 54								23 14				23 44
Clapham Junction [10]	d	22 19	22u22					22u39		22 46		22 49	23 00	23u03			23u09		23 15		23 19	23u39		23u44	23 49
Earlsfield	d	22 22										22 52									23 22				23 52
Wimbledon [6] ⊖	d	22 26								22 53		22 56							23 22		23 26				23 56
Surbiton [6]	d	22 35								23 02		23 05							23 30		23 35				00 05
Esher	d	22 39										23 09									23 39				00 09
Hersham	d	22 42										23 12									23 42				00 12
Walton-on-Thames	d	22 45								23 09		23 15									23 45				00 15
Weybridge	d	22 49								23 13		23 19									23 49				00 18
Byfleet & New Haw	d	22 51										23 21	00 02								23 51				00 21
West Byfleet	d	22 54		←		←	←		←			23 24	00 05			←		←			23 54		←		00 24
Woking	a	22 59	22 45			22 42	22 59	23 01	22 59	23 19		23 29	00 11	23 26		23 29	23 31	23 29	23 42		23 59	00 01	23 59	00 07	00 30
	d	23 05	22 46	22 49		22 49	23 05	23 02	23 05	23 23	23 26	23 35		23 28		23 35	23 32	23 35	23 46	23 49	00 05	00 03	00 05	00 08	00 32
Worplesdon	d	→					→					→				→					→				
Guildford	a							23 10	23 13								23 40	23 45				00 10	00 13		
Brookwood	d			22 55		22 55				23 28	23 32								23 51	23 55					00 37
Ash Vale	d			23 03		23 03					23 41									00 03					00 45
Aldershot	a			23 07		23 07					23 45									00 07					00 49
	d			23 08		23 08					23 49									00 08					00 50
Farnham	a			23 13		23 13					23 54									00 13					00 55
	d			23 14		23 14					23 55									00 14					
Bentley	d			23 24		23 24														00 24					
Alton	a			23 31		23 31					00 06									00 31					
Farnborough (Main)	d									23 36									23 59					00 18	
Fleet	d									23 41									00 04					00 24	
Winchfield	d																		00 10						
Hook	d																		00 14						
Basingstoke	a		23 05							23 54				23 46					00 21					00 39	

Table 155R

Mondays to Fridays

9 December to 16 May

Basingstoke, Alton, Guildford and Woking - Waterloo

Network Diagram - see first Page of Table 155

Miles	Miles	Miles			SW MO ◇[1]	SW MO [1]	SW MX [1]	SW	SW ◇	SW	SW [1]	SW		SW	SW [1]	SW	SW [1]	SW [1]	SW ◇[1] 🚲	SW	SW ◇	SW [1]		SW [1]	SW
0	—	—	**Basingstoke**	d							04 54						05 39	05 54	05 59						
5½	—	—	Hook	d							05 01							06 01							
7¾	—	—	Winchfield	d							05 05							06 05							
11¼	—	—	Fleet	d			00 01				05 10						05 50	06 10							
14½	—	—	Farnborough (Main)	d			00 06				05 16						05 56	06 16							
—	0	—	**Alton**	d																		05 42			
—	4¾	—	Bentley	d																		05 49			
—	8¾	—	Farnham	a																		05 54			
—	—	—		d																		05 56			
—	11¾	—	**Aldershot**	d																		06 02			
—	14¾	—	Ash Vale	d																		06 07			
19¾	18¾	—	Brookwood	d			00 13				05 23							06 23				06 14			
—	—	0	**Guildford**	d		00 05		04 25		05 14					05 50										
—	—	3½	Worplesdon	d						05 19		←			05 55									←	
23½	—	6	**Woking**	a		00 13	00 18	04 33		05 24	05 28	05 24			06 00		06 05	06 28	06 18			06 19		06 28	
—	—	—		d	00 04		00 20	04 35	05 27	05 32	05 29	05 32		05 43	06 01	06 04	06 06	06 29	06 19			06 20		06 29	06 32
26	—	—	West Byfleet	d			00 25		05 32	→		05 36		05 47		06 08		→				06 25			06 36
27¼	—	—	Byfleet & New Haw	d					05 35			05 39				06 11									06 39
28¾	—	—	Weybridge	d			00 29					05 42		05 51		06 14									06 43
30¾	—	—	Walton-on-Thames	d			00 33					05 46		05 55		06 18									06 47
31¾	—	—	Hersham	d								05 48				06 20									06 49
33¼	—	—	Esher	d								05 51				06 23									06 52
35¾	—	—	**Surbiton** [6]	a			00 39	04 54			05 40	05 55		06 01		06 27						06 35		06 40	06 56
40½	—	—	Wimbledon [6] ⊖	a			00 47	05 01			05 48	06 04				06 35								06 47	07 04
42¼	—	—	Earlsfield	a								06 08				06 39				←	←				07 08
43¾	—	—	Clapham Junction [10]	a	00 23		00 53	05 08	06 43		06 00	06 12			06 20	06 42	06 25		06 38	06 42	06 43	06 46		06 54	07 12
46½	—	—	Vauxhall ⊖	a					→		06 07	06 17				→				06 47	06 49				→
47¾	—	—	**London Waterloo** [15] ⊖	a	00 33		01 04	05 18			06 12	06 22		06 20	06 29		06 34		06 49	06 52	06 56	06 54		07 04	

		SW [1]	SW [1] 🚲	SW	SW [1]	SW ◇[1] 🚲	SW [1]	SW		SW ◇[1] 🚲	SW [1]	SW [1]	SW [1]	SW [1]	SW [1]	SW ◇[1] 🚲	SW [1]	SW [1]		SW [1] 🚲	SW [1]	SW [1]	SW [1]	SW [1]	SW ◇[1]
Basingstoke	d				06 23	06 27				06 35					06 42	06 51					06 54	07 06	07 17		
Hook	d				06 31																07 01	07 13			
Winchfield	d				06 35																07 05	07 17			
Fleet	d				06 40										06 54						07 10	07 22			
Farnborough (Main)	d				06 46										07 00						07 16	07 28			
Alton	d						06 12											06 44							
Bentley	d						06 19											06 51							
Farnham	a						06 24											06 56							
	d						06 26											06 58							
Aldershot	d						06 32											07 04							
Ash Vale	d						06 37											07 09							
Brookwood	d				06 53		06 44											07 16			07 23				
Guildford	d	06 24	06 31										06 53				07 07			07 17					
Worplesdon	d	06 30									←		06 59												
Woking	a	06 35	06 40		06 58	06 46	06 49			06 53	06 58		07 03		07 10		07 15	07 21		07 25	07 28				
	d	06 37	06 41	06 41	06 59	06 47	06 50			06 55	06 59	07 02	07 05	07 07	07 11		07 17	07 22		07 26	07 29			07 32	07 40
West Byfleet	d			06 46	→							07 07		07 16										07 37	
Byfleet & New Haw	d			06 49										07 19											
Weybridge	d			06 52								07 11		07 22										07 41	
Walton-on-Thames	d			06 57								07 16		07 27										07 46	
Hersham	d			07 00								07 19		07 30										07 49	
Esher	d			07 03								07 22		07 33										07 52	
Surbiton [6]	a			07 07								07 26		07 37										07 56	
Wimbledon [6] ⊖	a																								
Earlsfield	a							←																	
Clapham Junction [10]	a	06 58	07 02				07 10	07 12		07 14	07 20		07 24			07 28									
Vauxhall ⊖	a							07 17																	
London Waterloo [15] ⊖	a	07 08	07 12	07 26		07 14	07 20	07 24		07 24	07 31	07 49	07 36	07 56	07 41	07 39	07 45	07 51		07 54	07 59	08 06	08 01	08 19	08 08

Table 155R

Mondays to Fridays

9 December to 16 May

Basingstoke, Alton, Guildford and Woking - Waterloo

Network Diagram - see first Page of Table 155

		SW	SW	SW	SW	SW	SW	SW	SW	SW		SW	SW	SW	SW	SW	SW	SW	SW	SW		SW	SW	SW	SW
		1	1	1	1	1	1	◇1	1	1		1	1	1	1	1		1	◇1	1		1	1		1
								🚲	🚲										🚲			🚲			
Basingstoke	d						07 24	07 29					07 36	07 47				07 52	07 59						08 05
Hook	d						07 31						07 43					07 59							08 12
Winchfield	d						07 35						07 47					08 04							08 16
Fleet	d						07 40						07 52					08 09							08 22
Farnborough (Main)	d						07 46						07 58					08 16							08 28
Alton	d				07 14															07 44					
Bentley	d				07 21															07 51					
Farnham	a				07 26															07 56					
	d				07 28							07 39								07 58					
Aldershot	d				07 34							07 46								08 04					
Ash Vale	d				07 39							07 50								08 09					
Brookwood	d				07 46		07 53					07 57						08 23		08 16					
Guildford	d	07 34				07 45			07 54							08 03						08 15		08 20	
Worplesdon	d	07 40				07 50									←							08 20	←		
Woking	a				07 51	07 55	07 58					08 03	08 08	08 05	08 08	08 11		08 28	08 18	08 21		08 26	08 28	08 30	08 38
	d			07 47	07 52	07 57	07 59			08 02		08 05	08 09	08 06	08 09	08 12	08 17	08 29	08 19	08 23		08 27	08 29	08 32	08 39
West Byfleet	d		07 46	07 54						08 06		08 16	→				08 26	→						08 36	→
Byfleet & New Haw	d		07 49	07 57								08 19					08 29							08 39	
Weybridge	d		07 52	08 01						08 11		08 22					08 32							08 43	
Walton-on-Thames	d		07 57	08 06						08 15		08 27					08 36							08 47	
Hersham	d		08 00	08 09						08 17		08 30					08 39							08 49	
Esher	d		08 03	08 13						08 20		08 33					08 43							08 52	
Surbiton 6	a		08 07	08 18						08 24		08 37					08 47							08 56	
Wimbledon 6 ⊖	a																							09 04	
Earlsfield	a																							09 08	
Clapham Junction 10	a																							09 12	
Vauxhall ⊖	a																							→	
London Waterloo 15 ⊖	a	08 11	08 26	08 36	08 22	08 24	08 29	08 14	08 32	08 46		08 59		08 34	08 39	08 41	09 06		08 46	08 52		08 55	09 00		

		SW	SW	SW	SW	SW		SW	SW	SW	SW	SW	SW	SW	SW	SW		SW	SW	SW	SW	SW	SW	SW	SW
		1	1	1	1	1		◇1	1		◇1	1	1	1	1			1	1	◇1		1	◇1	1	1
								🚲			🚲		🚲							🚲			🚲	🚲	
Basingstoke	d	08 16				08 24		08 29			08 35			08 43					08 54	08 59					
Hook	d					08 31													09 01						
Winchfield	d					08 35													09 05						
Fleet	d					08 40								08 54					09 10						
Farnborough (Main)	d					08 46								09 00					09 16						
Alton	d								08 14													08 44			
Bentley	d								08 21													08 51			
Farnham	a								08 26													08 56			
	d								08 28													08 58			
Aldershot	d								08 34													09 04			
Ash Vale	d								08 39													09 09			
Brookwood	d					08 53			08 46										09 23			09 16			
Guildford	d			08 31									08 54			08 46		09 03						09 17	
Worplesdon	d		←	08 37								←				08 51									
Woking	a	08 34	08 38	08 41		08 58		08 48	08 51		08 53	08 58				08 59		09 11	09 28	09 18		09 21		09 27	
	d	08 36	08 39	08 43	08 47	08 59		08 49	08 52		08 55	08 59				09 02		09 13	09 29	09 19		09 22	09 24	09 28	
West Byfleet	d				08 54	→										09 06			→			09 27			
Byfleet & New Haw	d				08 57											09 09									
Weybridge	d				09 02											09 13									
Walton-on-Thames	d				09 07											09 17									
Hersham	d				09 10											09 19									
Esher	d				09 13										←	09 22									
Surbiton 6	a				09 17							09 10			09 17	09 26						09 37			
Wimbledon 6 ⊖	a				→											09 34									
Earlsfield	a									←						09 38					←				←
Clapham Junction 10	a			09 03						09 12	09 14			09 26		09 42		09 32		09 38	09 42	09 50	09 43		09 50
Vauxhall ⊖	a									09 17						→					09 47	→			
London Waterloo 15 ⊖	a	09 03	09 10	09 13				09 17	09 21	09 24	09 25	09 29	09 31	09 38	09 40			09 43		09 51	09 54		09 53	09 55	09 59

Table 155R

Mondays to Fridays

9 December to 16 May

Basingstoke, Alton, Guildford and Woking - Waterloo

Network Diagram - see first Page of Table 155

		SW	SW	SW	SW	SW	SW	SW		SW	SW	SW	SW	SW	SW	SW	SW	SW		SW	SW	SW	SW	SW	SW
		1		1	1	1	◇1 🚲			1	◇1 🚲	1	1 🚲		1 🚲	1	1	◇1 🚲		◇1 🚲		1	1 🚲	1	
Basingstoke	d			09 17		09 24	09 30				09 36				09 43		09 54	09 57							
Hook	d					09 31											10 01								
Winchfield	d					09 35											10 05								
Fleet	d					09 40									09 54		10 10								
Farnborough (Main)	d			09 30		09 46									10 00		10 16								
Alton	d									09 14												09 44			
Bentley	d									09 21												09 51			
Farnham	a									09 26												09 56			
	d									09 28												09 58			
Aldershot	d									09 34												10 04			
Ash Vale	d									09 39												10 09			
Brookwood	d					09 53				09 46							10 23					10 16			
Guildford	d				09 34								09 47			10 02							10 17		
Worplesdon	d	←			09 40							←												←	
Woking	a	09 28		09 39	09 44	09 58	09 49			09 51	09 54	09 58	09 59			10 11	10 28	10 15				10 21	10 25	10 28	
	d	09 29	09 32	09 41	09 46	09 59	09 50			09 52	09 56	09 59	10 00	10 02		10 12	10 29	10 17		10 21		10 22	10 26	10 29	10 32
West Byfleet	d		09 36			→				09 57				10 06			→					10 27			10 36
Byfleet & New Haw	d		09 39											10 09											10 39
Weybridge	d	09 36	09 42									10 06		10 12										10 36	10 42
Walton-on-Thames	d	09 40	09 46									10 10		10 16										10 40	10 46
Hersham	d		09 48											10 18											10 48
Esher	d		09 51											10 21											10 51
Surbiton 6	a	09 46	09 55							10 07		10 16		10 25								10 37		10 46	10 55
Wimbledon 6 ⊖	a		10 04											10 34											11 04
Earlsfield	a		10 08					←						10 38							←				11 08
Clapham Junction 10	a	09 57	10 12		10 05		10 09	10 12			10 15			10 42	10 25	10 31		10 36			10 42	10 48		10 57	11 12
Vauxhall ⊖	a		→					10 17						→							10 47				→
London Waterloo 15 ⊖	a	10 05		10 08	10 13		10 19	10 22		10 25	10 23	10 36	10 27		10 34	10 40		10 49		10 49	10 52	10 57	10 51	11 05	

		SW	SW	SW		SW	SW	SW	SW	SW	SW	SW	SW	SW		SW	SW	SW	SW	SW	SW	SW	SW	SW	
		1	1	1		◇1 🚲	◇1 🚲		1	1 🚲	1	1		1		1	◇1 🚲	◇1 🚲		1	1 🚲	1		1	
Basingstoke	d	10 17		10 24		10 30	10 35				10 43					10 54	10 57							11 17	
Hook	d			10 31												11 01									
Winchfield	d			10 35												11 05									
Fleet	d			10 40							10 54					11 10									
Farnborough (Main)	d	10 30		10 46							11 00					11 16								11 30	
Alton	d								10 14											10 44					
Bentley	d								10 21											10 51					
Farnham	a								10 26											10 56					
	d								10 28											10 58					
Aldershot	d								10 34											11 04					
Ash Vale	d								10 39											11 09					
Brookwood	d			10 53					10 46							11 23				11 16					
Guildford	d		10 34							10 47				11 02							11 17				
Worplesdon	d		10 40									←										←			
Woking	a	10 39	10 44	10 58		10 49			10 51	10 57		10 58		11 11		11 28	11 15			11 21	11 25	11 28		11 39	
	d	10 41	10 46	10 59		10 50			10 52	10 59		10 59	11 02	11 12		11 29	11 17	11 21		11 22	11 26	11 29	11 32	11 41	
West Byfleet	d			→					10 57				11 06			→				11 27			11 36		
Byfleet & New Haw	d												11 09										11 39		
Weybridge	d											11 06	11 12									11 36	11 42		
Walton-on-Thames	d											11 10	11 16									11 40	11 46		
Hersham	d												11 18										11 48		
Esher	d												11 21										11 51		
Surbiton 6	a								11 07			11 16	11 25							11 37		11 46	11 55		
Wimbledon 6 ⊖	a												11 34										12 04		
Earlsfield	a							←					11 38						←				12 08		
Clapham Junction 10	a		11 05				11 12	11 12			11 25		11 42	11 31			11 36		11 42	11 48		11 57	12 12		
Vauxhall ⊖	a							11 17					→						11 47				→		
London Waterloo 15 ⊖	a	11 08	11 13			11 19	11 20	11 22	11 27	11 24	11 34	11 36		11 40			11 49	11 49	11 52	11 57	11 51	12 06		12 08	

Table 155R

Mondays to Fridays

9 December to 16 May

Basingstoke, Alton, Guildford and Woking - Waterloo

Network Diagram - see first Page of Table 155

		SW	SW	SW	SW	SW		SW	SW	SW	SW	SW	SW	SW	SW	SW		SW	SW	SW	SW	SW	SW	SW	SW
		1	1	◇1 🚲	◇1 🚲			1	1 🚲	1	1		1	1	◇1 🚲	◇1 🚲			1	1 🚲	1		1	1	1
Basingstoke	d		11 24	11 30	11 35					11 43				11 54	11 57								12 17		12 24
Hook	d		11 31											12 01											12 31
Winchfield	d		11 35											12 05											12 35
Fleet	d		11 40							11 54				12 10											12 40
Farnborough (Main)	d		11 46							12 00				12 16									12 30		12 46
Alton	d							11 15											11 44						
Bentley	d																		11 51						
Farnham	a							11 25											11 56						
	d							11 28											11 58						
Aldershot	d							11 34											12 04						
Ash Vale	d							11 39											12 09						
Brookwood	d		11 53					11 46						12 23					12 16						12 53
Guildford	d	11 34							11 47				12 02							12 17				12 34	
Worplesdon	d	11 40									←										←			12 40	
Woking	a	11 44	11 58	11 49				11 51	11 57		11 58		12 11	12 28	12 15				12 21	12 25	12 28		12 39	12 44	12 58
	d	11 46	11 59	11 50				11 52	11 59		11 59	12 02	12 12	12 29	12 17	12 21			12 22	12 26	12 29	12 32	12 41	12 46	12 59
West Byfleet	d		↪					11 57				12 06		↪					12 27			12 36			↪
Byfleet & New Haw	d											12 09										12 39			
Weybridge	d										12 06	12 12									12 36	12 42			
Walton-on-Thames	d										12 10	12 16									12 40	12 46			
Hersham	d											12 18										12 48			
Esher	d											12 21										12 51			
Surbiton 6	a							12 07			12 16	12 25							12 37		12 46	12 55			
Wimbledon 6 ⊖	a											12 34										13 04			
Earlsfield	a					←						12 38						←				13 08			
Clapham Junction 10	a	12 05			12 12	12 12				12 25		12 42	12 31		12 36			12 42	12 48		12 57	13 12		13 05	
Vauxhall ⊖	a					12 17						↪						12 47				↪			
London Waterloo 15 ⊖	a	12 13		12 19	12 20	12 22		12 27	12 23	12 34	12 36		12 40		12 49	12 49		12 52	12 57	12 51	13 05		13 07	13 13	

		SW		SW	SW	SW	SW	SW	SW	SW	SW	SW		SW	SW	SW	SW	SW	SW	SW	SW	SW		SW	SW
		◇1 🚲		◇1 🚲		1	1 🚲	1	1		1	1		◇1 🚲	◇1 🚲		1	1 🚲	1		1	1		1	◇1 🚲
Basingstoke	d	12 30		12 35				12 43				12 54		12 57							13 17			13 24	13 30
Hook	d											13 01												13 31	
Winchfield	d											13 05												13 35	
Fleet	d							12 54				13 10												13 40	
Farnborough (Main)	d							13 00				13 16									13 30			13 46	
Alton	d																12 44								
Bentley	d																12 51								
Farnham	a																12 56								
	d					12 28											12 58								
Aldershot	d					12 34											13 04								
Ash Vale	d					12 39											13 09								
Brookwood	d					12 46						13 23					13 16							13 53	
Guildford	d						12 47				13 02							13 17				13 34			
Worplesdon	d								←										←			13 40			
Woking	a	12 49				12 51	12 57		12 58		13 11	13 28		13 15			13 21	13 25	13 28		13 39	13 44		13 58	13 49
	d	12 50				12 52	12 59		12 59	13 02	13 12	13 29		13 17	13 21		13 22	13 26	13 29	13 32	13 41	13 46		13 59	13 50
West Byfleet	d					12 57				13 06		↪					13 27			13 36				↪	
Byfleet & New Haw	d									13 09										13 39					
Weybridge	d								13 06	13 12									13 36	13 42					
Walton-on-Thames	d								13 10	13 16									13 40	13 46					
Hersham	d									13 18										13 48					
Esher	d									13 21										13 51					
Surbiton 6	a					13 07			13 16	13 25							13 37		13 46	13 55					
Wimbledon 6 ⊖	a									13 34										14 04					
Earlsfield	a				←					13 38						←				14 08					
Clapham Junction 10	a			13 12	13 12			13 25		13 42	13 31			13 36		13 42	13 48		13 57	14 12		14 05			
Vauxhall ⊖	a				13 17					↪						13 47				↪					
London Waterloo 15 ⊖	a	13 19		13 20	13 22	13 25	13 23	13 34	13 36		13 40			13 49	13 49	13 52	13 57	13 51	14 05		14 07	14 13			14 19

Table 155R

Mondays to Fridays

9 December to 16 May

Basingstoke, Alton, Guildford and Woking - Waterloo

Network Diagram - see first Page of Table 155

		SW ◇1 🚲	SW	SW 1		SW 1 🚲	SW 1	SW 1	SW	SW 1	SW 1	SW ◇1 🚲	SW ◇1 🚲	SW		SW 1	SW 1 🚲	SW 1	SW	SW 1	SW 1	SW 1	SW ◇1 🚲	SW ◇1 🚲	
Basingstoke	d	13 35					13 43				13 54	13 57								14 17		14 24	14 30	14 35	
Hook	d										14 01											14 31			
Winchfield	d										14 05											14 35			
Fleet	d						13 54				14 10											14 40			
Farnborough (Main)	d						14 00				14 16									14 30		14 46			
Alton	d			13 15												13 44									
Bentley	d															13 51									
Farnham	a			13 25												13 56									
	d			13 28												13 58									
Aldershot	d			13 34												14 04									
Ash Vale	d			13 39												14 09									
Brookwood	d			13 46							14 23					14 16						14 53			
Guildford	d					13 47				14 02							14 17				14 34				
Worplesdon	d							←										←			14 40				
Woking	a			13 51		13 57		13 58		14 11	14 28	14 15				14 21	14 25	14 28		14 39	14 44	14 58	14 49		
	d			13 52		13 59		13 59	14 02	14 12	14 29	14 17	14 21			14 22	14 26	14 29	14 32	14 41	14 46	14 59	14 50		
West Byfleet	d			13 57					14 06		↪					14 27			14 36			↪			
Byfleet & New Haw	d								14 09										14 39						
Weybridge	d							14 06	14 12									14 36	14 42						
Walton-on-Thames	d							14 10	14 16									14 40	14 46						
Hersham	d								14 18										14 48						
Esher	d								14 21										14 51						
Surbiton 6	a			14 07				14 16	14 25							14 37		14 46	14 55						
Wimbledon 6 ⊖	a								14 34										15 04						
Earlsfield	a		←						14 38					←					15 08						
Clapham Junction 10	a	14 12	14 12				14 25		14 42	14 31		14 36		14 42		14 48		14 57	15 12		15 05			15 12	
Vauxhall ⊖	a		14 17						↪					14 47					↪						
London Waterloo 15 ⊖	a	14 20	14 22	14 25		14 23	14 34	14 36		14 40		14 49	14 49	14 52		14 57	14 51	15 05		15 08	15 13		15 19	15 20	

		SW	SW 1	SW 1 🚲	SW 1	SW 1	SW	SW 1	SW 1	SW ◇1 🚲		SW ◇1 🚲	SW	SW 1	SW 1 🚲	SW 1	SW	SW 1	SW 1	SW 1		SW ◇1 🚲	SW ◇1 🚲	SW	SW 1
Basingstoke	d				14 43				14 54	14 57								15 17		15 24		15 30	15 35		
Hook	d								15 01											15 31					
Winchfield	d								15 05											15 35					
Fleet	d				14 54				15 10											15 40					
Farnborough (Main)	d				15 00				15 16									15 30		15 46					
Alton	d		14 15											14 44											15 15
Bentley	d													14 51											
Farnham	a		14 25											14 56											15 25
	d		14 28											14 58											15 28
Aldershot	d		14 34											15 04											15 34
Ash Vale	d		14 39											15 09											15 39
Brookwood	d		14 46						15 23					15 16						15 53					15 46
Guildford	d			14 47				15 02							15 17				15 34						
Worplesdon	d					←										←			15 40						
Woking	a		14 51	14 57		14 58		15 11	15 28	15 15				15 21	15 25	15 28		15 39	15 44	15 58		15 49			15 51
	d		14 52	14 59		14 59	15 02	15 12	15 29	15 17		15 21		15 22	15 26	15 29	15 32	15 41	15 46	15 59		15 50			15 52
West Byfleet	d		14 57				15 06		↪					15 27			15 36			↪					15 57
Byfleet & New Haw	d						15 09										15 39								
Weybridge	d					15 06	15 12									15 36	15 42								
Walton-on-Thames	d					15 10	15 16									15 40	15 46								
Hersham	d						15 18										15 48								
Esher	d						15 21										15 51								
Surbiton 6	a		15 07			15 16	15 25							15 37		15 46	15 55								16 07
Wimbledon 6 ⊖	a						15 34										16 04								
Earlsfield	a	←					15 38						←				16 08							←	
Clapham Junction 10	a	15 12			15 25		15 42	15 31		15 36			15 42	15 50		15 57	16 12		16 05				16 12	16 12	
Vauxhall ⊖	a	15 17					↪						15 47				↪							16 17	
London Waterloo 15 ⊖	a	15 22	15 25	15 23	15 34	15 37		15 43		15 49		15 49	15 52	15 58	15 51	16 05		16 07	16 13			16 19	16 20	16 22	16 29

Table 155R

Mondays to Fridays

9 December to 16 May

Basingstoke, Alton, Guildford and Woking - Waterloo

Network Diagram - see first Page of Table 155

		SW 1 🛒		SW 1	SW 1	SW	SW 1	SW 1	SW ◇1 🛒	SW ◇1 🛒	SW	SW 1		SW 1 🛒	SW 1	SW	SW 1	SW 1	SW 1	SW ◇1 🛒	SW ◇1 🛒	SW		SW 1	SW 1
Basingstoke	d			15 43				15 54	15 57								16 17		16 24	16 30	16 35				
Hook	d							16 01											16 31						
Winchfield	d							16 05											16 35						
Fleet	d			15 54				16 10											16 40						
Farnborough (Main)	d			16 00				16 16									16 30		16 46						
Alton	d											15 44												16 15	
Bentley	d											15 51													
Farnham	a											15 56												16 25	
	d											15 58												16 28	
Aldershot	d											16 04												16 34	
Ash Vale	d											16 09												16 39	
Brookwood	d							16 23				16 16							16 53					16 46	
Guildford	d	15 47					16 00							16 17				16 34							16 47
Worplesdon	d				←		16 06								←			16 40							
Woking	a	15 57			15 58		16 11	16 28	16 15			16 21		16 25	16 28		16 39	16 44	16 58	16 49				16 51	16 57
	d	15 59			15 59	16 02	16 12	16 29	16 17	16 21		16 22		16 26	16 29	16 32	16 41	16 46	16 59	16 50				16 52	16 59
West Byfleet	d					16 06		→				16 27				16 36			→					16 57	
Byfleet & New Haw	d					16 09										16 39									
Weybridge	d				16 06	16 12									16 36	16 42									
Walton-on-Thames	d				16 10	16 16									16 40	16 46									
Hersham	d					16 18										16 48									
Esher	d					16 21										16 51									
Surbiton 6	a				16 16	16 25						16 37			16 46	16 55								17 07	
Wimbledon 6 ⊖	a					16 34										17 04									
Earlsfield	a					16 38					←					17 08						←			
Clapham Junction 10	a			16 25		16 42	16 31		16 36		16 42	16 48			16 57	17 12		17 05			17 12	17 12			
Vauxhall ⊖	a					→					16 47					→						17 17			
London Waterloo 15 ⊖	a	16 24		16 34	16 36		16 40		16 49	16 49	16 52	16 59		16 51	17 08		17 08	17 14		17 19	17 20	17 22		17 29	17 27

		SW 1	SW 1	SW	SW 1 🛒	SW 1	SW ◇1 🛒	SW ◇1 🛒		SW	SW 1	SW 1 🛒	SW 1	SW	SW 1	SW 1	SW 1	SW ◇1 🛒		SW	SW ◇1 🛒	SW 1	SW 1	SW 1	SW 1
Basingstoke	d		16 43			16 54	16 57								17 17		17 24	17 30			17 36			17 43	
Hook	d					17 01											17 31								
Winchfield	d					17 05											17 35								
Fleet	d		16 54			17 10											17 40							17 54	
Farnborough (Main)	d		17 00			17 16									17 30		17 46							18 00	
Alton	d										16 44											17 14			
Bentley	d										16 51											17 21			
Farnham	a										16 56											17 26			
	d										16 58											17 28			
Aldershot	d										17 04											17 34			
Ash Vale	d										17 09											17 39			
Brookwood	d					17 23					17 16						17 53					17 46			
Guildford	d				17 00							17 17				17 34							17 47		
Worplesdon	d	←			17 06								←			17 40									←
Woking	a	16 58			17 11	17 28	17 15				17 21	17 25	17 28		17 39	17 44	17 58	17 49				17 51	17 58		17 58
	d	16 59		17 02	17 12	17 29	17 17	17 21			17 22	17 26	17 29	17 32	17 41	17 46	17 59	17 51				17 52	17 59		17 59
West Byfleet	d			17 06		→					17 27			17 36			→					17 57			
Byfleet & New Haw	d			17 09										17 39											
Weybridge	d	17 06		17 12									17 36	17 42											18 06
Walton-on-Thames	d	17 10		17 16									17 40	17 46											18 10
Hersham	d			17 18										17 48											
Esher	d			17 21										17 51											
Surbiton 6	a	17 16		17 25							17 37		17 46	17 55								18 07			18 16
Wimbledon 6 ⊖	a			17 34										18 04											
Earlsfield	a			17 38						←				18 08						←					
Clapham Junction 10	a		17 25	17 42	17 31		17 36			17 42	17 48		17 57	18 12		18 05				18 12	18 12			18 25	
Vauxhall ⊖	a			→						17 47				→						18 17					
London Waterloo 15 ⊖	a	17 35	17 36		17 43		17 49	17 50		17 52	17 59	17 54	18 09		18 08	18 14		18 21		18 23	18 23	18 29	18 27	18 34	18 38

Table 155R

Mondays to Fridays

9 December to 16 May

Basingstoke, Alton, Guildford and Woking - Waterloo

Network Diagram - see first Page of Table 155

		SW	SW 1 🛒	SW 1	SW ◇1 🛒	SW ◇1 🛒	SW	SW 1	SW 1 🛒	SW 1		SW	SW 1	SW 1	SW 1	SW ◇1 🛒	SW	SW ◇1 🛒	SW 1	SW 1		SW 1	SW	SW 1 🛒	SW 1
Basingstoke	d			17 54	17 57								18 17		18 24	18 30		18 35		18 43					
Hook	d			18 01											18 31										
Winchfield	d			18 05											18 35										
Fleet	d			18 10											18 40					18 54					
Farnborough (Main)	d			18 16									18 30		18 46					19 00					
Alton	d							17 44											18 14						18 35
Bentley	d							17 51											18 23						18 42
Farnham	a							17 56											18 27						18 47
	d							17 58											18 28						18 58
Aldershot	d							18 04											18 34						19 04
Ash Vale	d							18 09											18 39						19 09
Brookwood	d			18 23				18 16							18 53				18 46						19 16
Guildford	d		18 00						18 17					18 34										18 55	
Worplesdon	d		18 06							←				18 40								←			
Woking	a		18 11	18 28	18 15			18 21		18 28			18 39	18 44	18 58	18 49			18 52			18 58		19 03	19 21
	d	18 02	18 12	18 29	18 17	18 21		18 22		18 29		18 32	18 41	18 46	18 59	18 50			18 52			18 59	19 02	19 05	19 22
West Byfleet	d	18 06		↪				18 27				18 36			↪				18 57				19 06		19 27
Byfleet & New Haw	d	18 09										18 39											19 09		
Weybridge	d	18 12								18 36		18 42										19 06	19 12		
Walton-on-Thames	d	18 16								18 40		18 46										19 10	19 16		
Hersham	d	18 18										18 48											19 18		
Esher	d	18 21										18 51											19 21		
Surbiton 6	a	18 25						18 37		18 47		18 55							19 07			19 16	19 25		19 37
Wimbledon 6 Θ	a	18 34										19 05											19 35		
Earlsfield	a	18 38					←					19 09					←						19 39		
Clapham Junction 10	a	18 42	18 31		18 36		18 42	18 48		18 58		19 11		19 05			19 11	19 12		19 26			19 41		19 48
Vauxhall Θ	a	↪					18 47					↪					19 16						19 46		↪
London Waterloo 15 Θ	a		18 43		18 49	18 47	18 52	18 57	18 59	19 06			19 08	19 13		19 19	19 23	19 20	19 25	19 34		19 39	19 52	19 29	

		SW 1	SW ◇1 🛒	SW ◇1 🛒	SW 1	SW 1		SW 1 🛒	SW	SW 1	SW 1	SW 1	SW ◇1 🛒	SW	SW ◇1 🛒	SW 1		SW 1 🛒	SW 1	SW 1	SW	SW 1	SW ◇1 🛒	SW	SW 1
Basingstoke	d	18 54	19 02							19 17		19 24	19 30		19 35				19 43						
Hook	d	19 01										19 31													
Winchfield	d	19 05										19 35													
Fleet	d	19 10										19 40							19 54						
Farnborough (Main)	d	19 16								19 30		19 46							20 00						
Alton	d															19 07									19 35
Bentley	d																								19 42
Farnham	a															19 17									19 47
	d															19 28									19 58
Aldershot	d															19 34									20 04
Ash Vale	d															19 39									20 09
Brookwood	d	19 23										19 53				19 46									20 16
Guildford	d							19 21			19 34							19 47				20 02			
Worplesdon	d					←					19 40									←					
Woking	a	19 28	19 21			19 28		19 28		19 39	19 45	19 58	19 49			19 51		19 57		19 58		20 11			20 21
	d	19 29	19 22	19 26		19 29		19 30	19 32	19 41	19 46	19 59	19 50			19 52		19 59		19 59	20 02	20 12	20 21		20 22
West Byfleet	d	↪							19 36			↪				19 57					20 06				20 27
Byfleet & New Haw	d								19 39												20 09				
Weybridge	d					19 36			19 42											20 06	20 12				
Walton-on-Thames	d					19 40			19 46											20 10	20 16				
Hersham	d								19 48												20 18				
Esher	d								19 51												20 21				
Surbiton 6	a					19 46			19 55							20 07				20 16	20 25				20 37
Wimbledon 6 Θ	a								20 05												20 35				
Earlsfield	a				←				20 09					←							20 39			←	
Clapham Junction 10	a		19 41		19 48	19 57			20 11		20 05			20 11	20 12				20 25		20 41	20 31		20 41	20 48
Vauxhall Θ	a								↪					20 16							↪			20 46	
London Waterloo 15 Θ	a		19 50	19 52	19 57	20 05		19 59		20 08	20 14		20 19	20 22	20 20	20 26		20 24	20 34	20 36		20 40	20 49	20 52	20 57

Table 155R

Mondays to Fridays

9 December to 16 May

Basingstoke, Alton, Guildford and Woking - Waterloo

Network Diagram - see first Page of Table 155

		SW 1	SW 1	SW ◇1	SW 1	SW	SW 1	SW 1		SW 1	SW 1	SW ◇1	SW 1	SW	SW 1	SW ◇1	SW	SW 1		SW 1	SW 1	SW ◇1	SW 1	SW	SW 1
Basingstoke	d		19 54	20 09			20 17				20 24	20 36			20 43						20 54	21 09			
Hook	d		20 01								20 31										21 01				
Winchfield	d		20 05								20 35										21 05				
Fleet	d		20 10								20 40				20 54						21 10				
Farnborough (Main)	d		20 16				20 30				20 46				21 00						21 16				
Alton	d							20 15										20 44							
Bentley	d																	20 51							
Farnham	a							20 25										20 56							
	d							20 28										20 58							
Aldershot	d							20 34										21 04							
Ash Vale	d							20 39										21 09							
Brookwood	d		20 23					20 46			20 53							21 16			21 23				
Guildford	d	20 17								20 39			20 47							21 17					21 39
Worplesdon	d									20 44															21 44
Woking	a	20 25	20 28	20 29			20 39	20 51		20 52	20 58		20 58		21 09			21 21		21 25	21 28	21 29			21 49
	d	20 26	20 29	20 30		20 32	20 41	20 52		20 53	20 59		21 00	21 02	21 10	21 21		21 22		21 26	21 29	21 30		21 32	21 50
West Byfleet	d					20 36		20 57						21 06				21 27						21 36	
Byfleet & New Haw	d					20 39								21 09										21 39	
Weybridge	d		20 36			20 42					21 06			21 12							21 36			21 42	
Walton-on-Thames	d		20 40			20 46					21 10			21 16							21 40			21 46	
Hersham	d					20 48								21 18										21 48	
Esher	d					20 51								21 21										21 51	
Surbiton 6	a		20 46			20 55		21 07			21 16			21 25				21 37			21 46			21 55	
Wimbledon 6 ⊖	a					21 05								21 34										22 04	
Earlsfield	a				←	21 09								21 38			←						←	22 08	
Clapham Junction 10	a		20 57	20 52	20 57	21 11				21 12		21 16		21 42	21 29		21 42	21 48			21 57	21 52	21 57	22 12	22 09
Vauxhall ⊖	a		↪			21 16								↪			21 47				↪			↪	
London Waterloo 15 ⊖	a	20 50		21 00	21 05	21 22	21 07	21 29		21 21	21 34	21 24	21 27		21 38	21 49	21 52	21 57		21 50		22 04	22 06		22 18

		SW	SW 1	SW 1		SW 1	SW	SW ◇1	SW 1	SW 1	SW	SW 1	SW 1	SW ◇1		SW 1	SW 1	SW	SW 1	SW	SW 1	SW 1	SW ◇1	SW 1	
Basingstoke	d					21 24		21 35	21 43				21 54	22 09								22 24	22 36		
Hook	d					21 31							22 01									22 31			
Winchfield	d					21 35							22 05									22 35			
Fleet	d					21 40			21 54				22 10									22 40			
Farnborough (Main)	d					21 46			22 00				22 16									22 46			
Alton	d		21 15									21 44									22 15				
Bentley	d											21 51													
Farnham	a		21 25									21 56									22 25				
	d		21 28									21 58									22 28				
Aldershot	d		21 34									22 04									22 34				
Ash Vale	d		21 39									22 09									22 39				
Brookwood	d		21 46			21 53						22 16	22 23								22 46	22 53			
Guildford	d			21 47														22 20	22 39						
Worplesdon	d																		22 44					←	
Woking	a		21 51	21 57		21 58			22 09			22 21	22 28	22 28				22 32	22 49		22 51	22 58	22 54	22 58	
	d		21 52	21 59		21 59	22 02		22 10	22 21		22 22	22 29	22 29				22 32	22 50		22 52	22 59	22 55	22 59	
West Byfleet	d		21 57				22 06					22 27						22 36			22 57	↪			
Byfleet & New Haw	d						22 09											22 39							
Weybridge	d					22 06	22 12						22 36					22 42						23 06	
Walton-on-Thames	d					22 10	22 16						22 40					22 46						23 10	
Hersham	d						22 18											22 48							
Esher	d						22 21											22 51							
Surbiton 6	a		22 07			22 16	22 25					22 37	22 46					22 55			23 07			23 16	
Wimbledon 6 ⊖	a						22 34											23 04							
Earlsfield	a	←					22 38				←					←	←	23 08		←					
Clapham Junction 10	a	22 12					22 42	22 14	22 29		22 42	22 52	22 57	22 48		22 52	22 57	23 12	23 09	23 12			23 14		
Vauxhall ⊖	a	22 17					↪				22 47	↪	↪					↪		23 17					
London Waterloo 15 ⊖	a	22 22	22 27	22 27		22 34		22 22	22 38	22 49	22 52			22 58		23 01	23 08		23 19	23 23	23 27		23 23	23 32	

Table 155R

Mondays to Fridays

9 December to 16 May

Basingstoke, Alton, Guildford and Woking - Waterloo

Network Diagram - see first Page of Table 155

		SW	SW 1	SW	SW 1		SW FX 1	SW FO 1	SW 1	SW FX 1	SW FO 1	SW FO 1	SW FX 1	SW 1	SW 1		SW 1
Basingstoke	d		22 43				22 54	22 54	23 13						23 44		
Hook	d						23 01	23 01							23 51		
Winchfield	d						23 05	23 05							23 55		
Fleet	d		22 54				23 10	23 10							00 01		
Farnborough (Main)	d		23 00				23 16	23 16							00 06		
Alton	d				22 44									23 15			23 46
Bentley	d				22 51												23 53
Farnham	a				22 56									23 25			23 58
	d				22 58									23 28			
Aldershot	d				23 04									23 34			
Ash Vale	d				23 09									23 39			
Brookwood	d				23 16		23 23	23 23						23 46	00 13		
Guildford	d	22 55										23 39	23 39				
Worplesdon	d									←	←	23 44	23 44				
Woking	a	23 05	23 09		23 21		23 28	23 28	23 31	23 28	23 28	23 49	23 49	23 51	00 18		
	d	23 06	23 10		23 22		23 33	23 33	23 32	23 33	23 33	23 56	23 56		00 20		
West Byfleet	d	23 10			23 27		→	→		23 37	23 37				00 25		
Byfleet & New Haw	d	23 13								23 40	23 40						
Weybridge	d	23 16								23 43	23 43				00 29		
Walton-on-Thames	d	23 20								23 47	23 47				00 33		
Hersham	d	23 22								23 49	23 49						
Esher	d	23 25								23 52	23 52						
Surbiton 6	a	23 29			23 37					23 57	23 57	00 08	00 08		00 39		
Wimbledon 6 ⊖	a	23 37								00 06	00 06	00 16	00 16		00 47		
Earlsfield	a	23 41		←													
Clapham Junction 10	a	23 44	23 29	23 44	23 51				23 55	00 21	00 21	00 22	00 22		00 53		
Vauxhall ⊖	a	→		23 49						00 30	00 31						
London Waterloo 15 ⊖	a		23 42	23 54	00 02				00 09	00 36	00 36	00 32	00 33		01 04		

Saturdays

14 December to 17 May

		SW 1	SW	SW	SW	SW 1	SW	SW	SW 1	SW 1		SW ◇1 🚲	SW	SW	SW 1	SW	SW 1	SW 1	SW ◇1 🚲	SW		SW 1	SW 1	SW 1	SW
Basingstoke	d					04 54				05 54		05 59						06 24	06 30					06 40	
Hook	d					05 01				06 01								06 31							
Winchfield	d					05 05				06 05								06 35							
Fleet	d	00 01				05 10				06 10								06 40							
Farnborough (Main)	d	00 06				05 16				06 16								06 46							
Alton	d																					06 14			
Bentley	d																					06 21			
Farnham	a																					06 26			
	d																					06 28			
Aldershot	d																					06 34			
Ash Vale	d																					06 39			
Brookwood	d	00 13				05 23				06 23								06 53				06 46			
Guildford	d		04 25		05 14				06 02								06 34								
Worplesdon	d				05 19		←								←		06 40						←		
Woking	a	00 18	04 33		05 24	05 28	05 24		06 11	06 28		06 18			06 28		06 44	06 58	06 49			06 51	06 58	06 58	
	d	00 20	04 35	05 27	05 33	05 29	05 33	06 03	06 13	06 29		06 19			06 29	06 33	06 46	06 59	06 50			06 52	06 59	07 00	07 03
West Byfleet	d	00 25		05 32	→		05 37	06 07		→						06 37		→				06 57			07 07
Byfleet & New Haw	d			05 35			05 40	06 10								06 40									07 10
Weybridge	d	00 29					05 43	06 13							06 36	06 43							07 06		07 13
Walton-on-Thames	d	00 33					05 47	06 17							06 40	06 47							07 10		07 17
Hersham	d						05 49	06 19								06 49									07 19
Esher	d						05 52	06 22								06 52									07 22
Surbiton 6	a	00 39	04 54			05 40	05 56	06 26							06 46	06 56						07 07	07 16		07 26
Wimbledon 6 ⊖	a	00 47	05 01			05 48	06 04	06 34								07 04									07 34
Earlsfield	a						06 08	06 38					←	←		07 08				←					07 38
Clapham Junction 10	a	00 53	05 08	06 43		06 00	06 12	06 42	06 32			06 38	06 42	06 43	06 57	07 12	07 05			07 12		07 18		07 23	07 42
Vauxhall ⊖	a			→		06 07	06 17	→					06 47	06 49		→				07 17					→
London Waterloo 15 ⊖	a	01 04	05 18			06 12	06 22		06 40			06 49	06 52	06 56	07 05		07 13		07 19	07 22		07 27	07 33	07 31	

Table 155R

Saturdays

14 December to 17 May

Basingstoke, Alton, Guildford and Woking - Waterloo

Network Diagram - see first Page of Table 155

		SW 1		SW 1	SW ◇1 ⊼	SW	SW 1	SW ◇1 ⊼	SW 1	SW	SW 1	SW 1		SW ◇1 ⊼	SW	SW 1	SW 1 ⊼	SW 1	SW	SW 1	SW 1	SW 1		SW ◇1 ⊼	SW
Basingstoke	d			06 54	06 57			07 09				07 24		07 30						07 43		07 54		07 57	
Hook	d			07 01								07 31										08 01			
Winchfield	d			07 05								07 35										08 05			
Fleet	d			07 10								07 40								07 54		08 10			
Farnborough (Main)	d			07 16								07 46								08 00		08 16			
Alton	d						06 44									07 14									
Bentley	d						06 51									07 21									
Farnham	a						06 56									07 26									
	d						06 58									07 28									
Aldershot	d						07 04									07 34									
Ash Vale	d						07 09									07 39									
Brookwood	d			07 23			07 16					07 53				07 46						08 23			
Guildford	d	07 02									07 34						07 47				08 02				
Worplesdon	d								←		07 40							←							
Woking	a	07 11		07 28	07 15		07 21	07 27	07 28		07 44	07 58		07 49		07 51	07 57	07 58		08 09	08 10	08 28		08 17	
	d	07 12		07 29	07 17		07 22	07 29	07 29	07 33	07 46	07 59		07 50		07 52	07 59	07 59	08 03	08 11	08 13	08 29		08 18	
West Byfleet	d			→			07 27			07 37		→				07 57			08 07			→			
Byfleet & New Haw	d									07 40									08 10						
Weybridge	d								07 36	07 43								08 06	08 13						
Walton-on-Thames	d								07 40	07 47								08 10	08 17						
Hersham	d									07 49									08 19						
Esher	d									07 52									08 22						
Surbiton 6	a						07 37		07 46	07 56						08 07		08 16	08 26						
Wimbledon 6 ⊖	a									08 04									08 34						
Earlsfield	a					←				08 08					←				08 38						←
Clapham Junction 10	a	07 31			07 36	07 42	07 50		07 57	08 12	08 05				08 12				08 42	08 30	08 33			08 37	08 42
Vauxhall ⊖	a					07 47				→					08 17				→						08 47
London Waterloo 15 ⊖	a	07 40			07 49	07 52	07 58	07 53	08 05		08 13			08 19	08 22	08 25	08 23	08 34		08 39	08 42			08 49	08 52

		SW 1	SW ◇1 ⊼	SW 1 ⊼	SW 1	SW	SW 1	SW 1		SW 1	SW ◇1 ⊼	SW ◇1 ⊼	SW	SW 1	SW 1 ⊼	SW 1	SW 1	SW		SW 1	SW 1	SW ◇1 ⊼	SW ◇1 ⊼	SW	SW 1
Basingstoke	d						08 17			08 24	08 30	08 35				08 43					08 54	08 57			
Hook	d									08 31											09 01				
Winchfield	d									08 35											09 05				
Fleet	d									08 40						08 54					09 10				
Farnborough (Main)	d						08 30			08 46						09 00					09 16				
Alton	d	07 44												08 14											08 44
Bentley	d	07 51												08 21											08 51
Farnham	a	07 56												08 26											08 56
	d	07 58												08 28											08 58
Aldershot	d	08 04												08 34											09 04
Ash Vale	d	08 09												08 39											09 09
Brookwood	d	08 16								08 53				08 46							09 23				09 16
Guildford	d			08 17				08 34							08 47					09 02					
Worplesdon	d				←			08 40									←								
Woking	a	08 21		08 26	08 28		08 39	08 44		08 58	08 49			08 51	08 57		08 58			09 11	09 28	09 15			09 21
	d	08 22	08 23	08 27	08 29	08 33	08 41	08 46		08 59	08 50			08 52	08 59		08 59	09 03		09 12	09 29	09 17	09 21		09 22
West Byfleet	d	08 27				08 37				→				08 57				09 07			→				09 27
Byfleet & New Haw	d					08 40												09 10							
Weybridge	d				08 36	08 43											09 06	09 13							
Walton-on-Thames	d				08 40	08 47											09 10	09 17							
Hersham	d					08 49												09 19							
Esher	d					08 52												09 22							
Surbiton 6	a	08 37			08 46	08 56								09 07			09 16	09 26							09 37
Wimbledon 6 ⊖	a					09 04												09 34							
Earlsfield	a					09 08							←					09 38						←	
Clapham Junction 10	a	08 49			08 57	09 12		09 05				09 12	09 12			09 25		09 42		09 31		09 36		09 42	09 48
Vauxhall ⊖	a					→							09 17					→						09 47	
London Waterloo 15 ⊖	a	08 58	08 49	08 51	09 05		09 08	09 13			09 19	09 20	09 22	09 25	09 23	09 34	09 36			09 40		09 49	09 49	09 52	09 57

Table 155R

Saturdays

14 December to 17 May

Basingstoke, Alton, Guildford and Woking - Waterloo

Network Diagram - see first Page of Table 155

		SW	SW	SW	SW	SW	SW	SW	SW	SW		SW	SW	SW	SW	SW	SW	SW	SW	SW		SW	SW	SW	SW
		1	1		1	1	1	◇1	◇1			1	1	1	1		1	1	◇1	◇1			1	1	1
		🚲						🚲	🚲				🚲						🚲	🚲				🚲	
Basingstoke	d				09 17		09 24	09 30	09 35					09 43				09 54	09 57						
Hook	d						09 31											10 01							
Winchfield	d						09 35											10 05							
Fleet	d						09 40							09 54				10 10							
Farnborough (Main)	d				09 30		09 46							10 00				10 16							
Alton	d											09 14											09 44		
Bentley	d											09 21											09 51		
Farnham	a											09 26											09 56		
	d											09 28											09 58		
Aldershot	d											09 34											10 04		
Ash Vale	d											09 39											10 09		
Brookwood	d						09 53					09 46						10 23					10 16		
Guildford	d	09 17				09 34							09 47				10 02							10 17	
Worplesdon	d		←			09 40									←										←
Woking	a	09 25	09 28		09 39	09 44	09 58	09 49				09 51	09 57		09 58		10 11	10 28	10 15				10 21	10 25	10 28
	d	09 26	09 29	09 33	09 41	09 46	09 59	09 50				09 52	09 59		09 59	10 03	10 12	10 29	10 17	10 21			10 22	10 26	10 29
West Byfleet	d			09 37			→					09 57				10 07		→					10 27		
Byfleet & New Haw	d			09 40												10 10									
Weybridge	d		09 36	09 43											10 06	10 13									10 36
Walton-on-Thames	d		09 40	09 47											10 10	10 17									10 40
Hersham	d			09 49												10 19									
Esher	d			09 52												10 22									
Surbiton 6	a		09 46	09 56								10 07			10 16	10 26							10 37		10 46
Wimbledon 6 ⊖	a			10 04												10 34									
Earlsfield	a			10 08						←						10 38						←			
Clapham Junction 10	a		09 57	10 12		10 05			10 12	10 12				10 25		10 42	10 31		10 36			10 42	10 48		10 57
Vauxhall ⊖	a			→						10 17						→						10 47			
London Waterloo 15 ⊖	a	09 51	10 05		10 07	10 13		10 19	10 20	10 22		10 25	10 23	10 34	10 36		10 40		10 49	10 49		10 52	10 57	10 51	11 05

		SW	SW	SW	SW	SW		SW	SW	SW	SW	SW	SW	SW	SW	SW		SW	SW	SW	SW	SW	SW	SW	SW
			1	1	1	◇1		◇1		1	1	1	1		1	1		◇1	◇1		1	1	1		1
						🚲		🚲			🚲							🚲	🚲			🚲			
Basingstoke	d		10 17		10 24	10 30		10 35				10 43				10 54		10 57							11 17
Hook	d				10 31											11 01									
Winchfield	d				10 35											11 05									
Fleet	d				10 40							10 54				11 10									
Farnborough (Main)	d		10 30		10 46							11 00				11 16									11 30
Alton	d									10 14											10 44				
Bentley	d									10 21											10 51				
Farnham	a									10 26											10 56				
	d									10 28											10 58				
Aldershot	d									10 34											11 04				
Ash Vale	d									10 39											11 09				
Brookwood	d				10 53					10 46						11 23					11 16				
Guildford	d			10 34							10 47				11 02							11 17			
Worplesdon	d			10 40									←										←		
Woking	a		10 39	10 44	10 58	10 49				10 51	10 57		10 58		11 11	11 28		11 15			11 21	11 25	11 28		11 39
	d	10 33	10 41	10 46	10 59	10 50				10 52	10 59		10 59	11 03	11 12	11 29		11 17	11 21		11 22	11 26	11 29	11 33	11 41
West Byfleet	d	10 37			→					10 57				11 07		→					11 27			11 37	
Byfleet & New Haw	d	10 40												11 10										11 40	
Weybridge	d	10 43											11 06	11 13									11 36	11 43	
Walton-on-Thames	d	10 47											11 10	11 17									11 40	11 47	
Hersham	d	10 49												11 19										11 49	
Esher	d	10 52												11 22										11 52	
Surbiton 6	a	10 56								11 07			11 16	11 26							11 37		11 46	11 56	
Wimbledon 6 ⊖	a	11 04												11 34										12 04	
Earlsfield	a	11 08							←					11 38						←				12 08	
Clapham Junction 10	a	11 12		11 05				11 12	11 12			11 25		11 42	11 31			11 36		11 42	11 48		11 57	12 12	
Vauxhall ⊖	a	→							11 17					→						11 47				→	
London Waterloo 15 ⊖	a		11 07	11 13		11 19		11 20	11 22	11 25	11 23	11 34	11 36		11 40			11 49	11 49	11 52	11 57	11 51	12 05		12 07

Table 155R

Saturdays

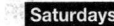

14 December to 17 May

Basingstoke, Alton, Guildford and Woking - Waterloo

Network Diagram - see first Page of Table 155

		SW 1	SW 1	SW ◇1 🚲	SW ◇1 🚲	SW	SW 1	SW 1 🚲		SW 1	SW 1	SW	SW 1	SW 1	SW ◇1 🚲	SW ◇1 🚲	SW	SW 1		SW 1 🚲	SW 1	SW	SW 1	SW 1	SW 1
Basingstoke	d		11 24	11 30	11 35					11 43				11 54	11 57								12 17		12 24
Hook	d		11 31											12 01											12 31
Winchfield	d		11 35											12 05											12 35
Fleet	d		11 40							11 54				12 10											12 40
Farnborough (Main)	d		11 46							12 00				12 16									12 30		12 46
Alton	d						11 15											11 44							
Bentley	d																	11 51							
Farnham	a						11 25											11 56							
	d						11 28											11 58							
Aldershot	d						11 34											12 04							
Ash Vale	d						11 39											12 09							
Brookwood	d		11 53				11 46							12 23				12 16							12 53
Guildford	d	11 34						11 47					12 02							12 17				12 34	
Worplesdon	d	11 40									←										←			12 40	
Woking	a	11 44	11 58	11 49			11 51	11 57			11 58		12 11	12 28	12 15			12 21		12 25	12 28		12 39	12 44	12 58
	d	11 46	11 59	11 50			11 52	11 59			11 59	12 03	12 12	12 29	12 17	12 21		12 22		12 26	12 29	12 33	12 41	12 46	12 59
West Byfleet	d		→				11 57					12 07		→				12 27				12 37			→
Byfleet & New Haw	d											12 10										12 40			
Weybridge	d										12 06	12 13									12 36	12 43			
Walton-on-Thames	d										12 10	12 17									12 40	12 47			
Hersham	d											12 19										12 49			
Esher	d											12 22										12 52			
Surbiton 6	a						12 07				12 16	12 26						12 37			12 46	12 56			
Wimbledon 6 ⊖	a											12 34										13 04			
Earlsfield	a					←						12 38					←					13 08			
Clapham Junction 10	a	12 05			12 12	12 12				12 25		12 42	12 31		12 36		12 42	12 48			12 57	13 12		13 05	
Vauxhall ⊖	a					12 17						→					12 47					→			
London Waterloo 15 ⊖	a	12 13		12 19	12 21	12 22	12 29	12 27		12 34	12 36		12 43		12 49	12 51	12 52	12 59		12 57	13 05		13 07	13 13	

		SW ◇1 🚲	SW ◇1 🚲	SW		SW 1	SW 1 🚲	SW 1	SW 1	SW	SW 1	SW 1	SW ◇1 🚲	SW ◇1 🚲		SW	SW 1	SW 1 🚲	SW 1	SW	SW 1	SW 1	SW 1	SW ◇1 🚲	
Basingstoke	d	12 30	12 35					12 43				12 54	12 57								13 17		13 24	13 30	
Hook	d											13 01											13 31		
Winchfield	d											13 05											13 35		
Fleet	d							12 54				13 10											13 40		
Farnborough (Main)	d							13 00				13 16									13 30		13 46		
Alton	d					12 15											12 44								
Bentley	d																12 51								
Farnham	a					12 25											12 56								
	d					12 28											12 58								
Aldershot	d					12 34											13 04								
Ash Vale	d					12 39											13 09								
Brookwood	d					12 46						13 23					13 16						13 53		
Guildford	d						12 47				13 02							13 17				13 34			
Worplesdon	d								←										←			13 40			
Woking	a	12 49				12 51	12 57		12 58		13 11	13 28	13 15				13 21	13 25	13 28		13 39	13 44	13 58	13 49	
	d	12 50				12 52	12 59		12 59	13 03	13 12	13 29	13 17	13 21			13 22	13 26	13 29	13 33	13 41	13 46	13 59	13 50	
West Byfleet	d					12 57				13 07		→					13 27			13 37			→		
Byfleet & New Haw	d									13 10										13 40					
Weybridge	d								13 06	13 13									13 36	13 43					
Walton-on-Thames	d								13 10	13 17									13 40	13 47					
Hersham	d									13 19										13 49					
Esher	d									13 22										13 52					
Surbiton 6	a					13 07			13 16	13 26							13 37		13 46	13 56					
Wimbledon 6 ⊖	a									13 34										14 04					
Earlsfield	a			←						13 38						←				14 08					
Clapham Junction 10	a		13 12	13 12				13 25		13 42	13 31		13 36			13 42	13 48		13 57	14 12		14 05			
Vauxhall ⊖	a			13 17						→						13 47				→					
London Waterloo 15 ⊖	a	13 19	13 21	13 22		13 29	13 27	13 34	13 36		13 43		13 49	13 51		13 52	13 59	13 57	14 05		14 07	14 14		14 19	

Table 155R

Saturdays

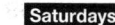

14 December to 17 May

Basingstoke, Alton, Guildford and Woking - Waterloo

Network Diagram - see first Page of Table 155

		SW ◇1 🚲	SW	SW 1	SW 1 🚲	SW 1		SW 1	SW	SW 1	SW 1	SW ◇1 🚲	SW ◇1 🚲	SW	SW 1	SW 1 🚲		SW 1	SW	SW 1	SW 1	SW 1	SW ◇1 🚲	SW ◇1 🚲	SW
Basingstoke	d	13 35				13 43					13 54	13 57								14 17		14 24	14 30	14 35	
Hook	d										14 01											14 31			
Winchfield	d										14 05											14 35			
Fleet	d					13 54					14 10											14 40			
Farnborough (Main)	d					14 00					14 16									14 30		14 46			
Alton	d			13 15											13 44										
Bentley	d														13 51										
Farnham	a			13 25											13 56										
	d			13 28											13 58										
Aldershot	d			13 34											14 04										
Ash Vale	d			13 39											14 09										
Brookwood	d			13 46							14 23				14 16							14 53			
Guildford	d				13 47					14 02						14 17					14 34				
Worplesdon	d							←										←			14 40				
Woking	a			13 51	13 57			13 58		14 11	14 28	14 15			14 21	14 25		14 28		14 39	14 44	14 58	14 49		
	d			13 52	13 59			13 59	14 03	14 12	14 29	14 17	14 21		14 22	14 26		14 29	14 33	14 41	14 46	14 59	14 50		
West Byfleet	d			13 57					14 07		→				14 27				14 37			→			
Byfleet & New Haw	d								14 10										14 40						
Weybridge	d							14 06	14 13									14 36	14 43						
Walton-on-Thames	d							14 10	14 17									14 40	14 47						
Hersham	d								14 19										14 49						
Esher	d								14 22										14 52						
Surbiton 6	a			14 07				14 16	14 26						14 37			14 46	14 56						
Wimbledon 6 ⊖	a								14 34										15 04						
Earlsfield	a		←						14 38					←					15 08						←
Clapham Junction 10	a	14 12	14 12			14 25			14 42	14 31		14 36		14 42	14 48			14 57	15 12		15 05			15 12	15 12
Vauxhall ⊖	a		14 17						→					14 47					→						15 17
London Waterloo 15 ⊖	a	14 21	14 22	14 29	14 27	14 34		14 36		14 41		14 49	14 51	14 52	14 59	14 57		15 05		15 07	15 14		15 19	15 21	15 22

		SW 1		SW 1 🚲	SW 1	SW 1	SW	SW 1	SW 1	SW ◇1 🚲	SW ◇1 🚲	SW		SW 1	SW 1 🚲	SW 1	SW	SW 1	SW 1	SW 1	SW ◇1 🚲	SW ◇1 🚲		SW	SW 1
Basingstoke	d				14 43				14 54	14 57								15 17		15 24	15 30	15 35			
Hook	d								15 01											15 31					
Winchfield	d								15 05											15 35					
Fleet	d				14 54				15 10											15 40					
Farnborough (Main)	d				15 00				15 16									15 30		15 46					
Alton	d	14 15												14 44											15 15
Bentley	d													14 51											
Farnham	a	14 25												14 56											15 25
	d	14 28												14 58											15 28
Aldershot	d	14 34												15 04											15 34
Ash Vale	d	14 39												15 09											15 39
Brookwood	d	14 46							15 23					15 16						15 53					15 46
Guildford	d			14 47				15 02							15 17				15 34						
Worplesdon	d					←										←			15 40						
Woking	a	14 51		14 57		14 58		15 11	15 28	15 15				15 21	15 25	15 28		15 39	15 44	15 58	15 49				15 51
	d	14 52		14 59		14 59	15 03	15 12	15 29	15 17	15 21			15 22	15 26	15 29	15 33	15 41	15 46	15 59	15 50				15 52
West Byfleet	d	14 57					15 07		→					15 27			15 37			→					15 57
Byfleet & New Haw	d						15 10										15 40								
Weybridge	d					15 06	15 13									15 36	15 43								
Walton-on-Thames	d					15 10	15 17									15 40	15 47								
Hersham	d						15 19										15 49								
Esher	d						15 22										15 52								
Surbiton 6	a	15 07				15 16	15 26							15 37		15 46	15 56								16 07
Wimbledon 6 ⊖	a						15 34										16 04								
Earlsfield	a						15 38					←					16 08							←	
Clapham Junction 10	a				15 25		15 42	15 31		15 36		15 42		15 48		15 57	16 12		16 05			16 12		16 12	
Vauxhall ⊖	a						→					15 47					→							16 17	
London Waterloo 15 ⊖	a	15 29		15 27	15 34	15 36		15 41		15 49	15 51	15 52		15 59	15 57	16 05		16 07	16 13		16 19	16 20		16 22	16 25

Table 155R

Saturdays

14 December to 17 May

Basingstoke, Alton, Guildford and Woking - Waterloo

Network Diagram - see first Page of Table 155

		SW 1 🚲	SW 1	SW 1		SW	SW 1	SW 1	SW ◇1 🚲	SW ◇1 🚲	SW	SW 1	SW 1 🚲	SW 1		SW	SW 1	SW 1	SW 1	SW ◇1 🚲	SW ◇1 🚲	SW	SW 1	SW 1 🚲	
Basingstoke	d		15 43					15 54	15 57								16 17		16 24	16 30	16 35				
Hook	d							16 01											16 31						
Winchfield	d							16 05											16 35						
Fleet	d		15 54					16 10											16 40						
Farnborough (Main)	d		16 00					16 16									16 30		16 46						
Alton	d											15 44											16 15		
Bentley	d											15 51													
Farnham	a											15 56											16 25		
	d											15 58											16 28		
Aldershot	d											16 04											16 34		
Ash Vale	d											16 09											16 39		
Brookwood	d							16 23				16 16							16 53				16 46		
Guildford	d	15 47					16 02						16 17					16 34						16 47	
Worplesdon	d			←										←				16 40							
Woking	a	15 57		15 58			16 11	16 28	16 15			16 21	16 25	16 28			16 39	16 44	16 58	16 49			16 51	16 57	
	d	15 59		15 59		16 03	16 12	16 29	16 17	16 21		16 22	16 26	16 29		16 33	16 41	16 46	16 59	16 50			16 52	16 59	
West Byfleet	d					16 07		↪				16 27				16 37			↪				16 57		
Byfleet & New Haw	d					16 10										16 40									
Weybridge	d			16 06		16 13								16 36		16 43									
Walton-on-Thames	d			16 10		16 17								16 40		16 47									
Hersham	d					16 19										16 49									
Esher	d					16 22										16 52									
Surbiton 6	a			16 16		16 26						16 37		16 46		16 56							17 07		
Wimbledon 6	⊖ a					16 34										17 04									
Earlsfield	a					16 38					←					17 08						←			
Clapham Junction 10	a		16 25			16 42	16 31		16 36		16 42	16 48		16 57		17 12		17 05			17 12	17 12			
Vauxhall	⊖ a					↪					16 47					↪						17 17			
London Waterloo 15	⊖ a	16 23	16 34	16 36			16 40		16 49	16 49	16 52	16 57	16 51	17 05			17 07	17 13		17 19	17 20	17 22	17 25	17 23	

		SW 1	SW 1	SW	SW 1	SW 1	SW ◇1 🚲	SW ◇1 🚲	SW	SW 1		SW 1 🚲	SW 1	SW	SW 1	SW 1	SW 1	SW ◇1 🚲	SW ◇1 🚲	SW		SW 1	SW 1 🚲	SW 1	SW 1
Basingstoke	d	16 43				16 54	16 57								17 17		17 24	17 30	17 35					17 43	
Hook	d					17 01											17 31								
Winchfield	d					17 05											17 35								
Fleet	d	16 54				17 10											17 40							17 54	
Farnborough (Main)	d	17 00				17 16									17 30		17 46							18 00	
Alton	d									16 44												17 15			
Bentley	d									16 51															
Farnham	a									16 56												17 25			
	d									16 58												17 28			
Aldershot	d									17 04												17 34			
Ash Vale	d									17 09												17 39			
Brookwood	d					17 23				17 16							17 53					17 46			
Guildford	d				17 02							17 17				17 34							17 47		
Worplesdon	d		←										←			17 40									←
Woking	a		16 58		17 11	17 28	17 15			17 21		17 25	17 28		17 39	17 44	17 58	17 49				17 51	17 57		17 58
	d		16 59	17 03	17 12	17 29	17 17	17 21		17 22		17 26	17 29	17 33	17 41	17 46	17 59	17 50				17 52	17 59		17 59
West Byfleet	d			17 07		↪				17 27				17 37			↪					17 57			
Byfleet & New Haw	d			17 10										17 40											
Weybridge	d		17 06	17 13									17 36	17 43											18 06
Walton-on-Thames	d		17 10	17 17									17 40	17 47											18 10
Hersham	d			17 19										17 49											
Esher	d			17 22										17 52											
Surbiton 6	a		17 16	17 26						17 37			17 46	17 56								18 07			18 16
Wimbledon 6	⊖ a			17 34										18 04											
Earlsfield	a			17 38					←					18 08						←					
Clapham Junction 10	a	17 25		17 42	17 31		17 36		17 42	17 48			17 57	18 12		18 05			18 12	18 12				18 25	
Vauxhall	⊖ a			↪					17 47					↪						18 17					
London Waterloo 15	⊖ a	17 34	17 36		17 40		17 49	17 49	17 52	17 57		17 51	18 05		18 07	18 13		18 19	18 20	18 22		18 25	18 23	18 34	18 36

Table 155R

Saturdays

14 December to 17 May

Basingstoke, Alton, Guildford and Woking - Waterloo

Network Diagram - see first Page of Table 155

		SW		SW ■1	SW ■1	SW ◇■1 🚲	SW ◇■1 🚲	SW	SW ■1	SW ■1	SW ■1	SW		SW ■1	SW ■1	SW ■1	SW ◇■1 🚲	SW ◇■1 🚲	SW	SW ■1	SW ■1 🚲	SW ■1		SW ■1	SW
Basingstoke	d				17 54	17 57								18 17		18 24	18 30	18 35				18 43			
Hook	d				18 01											18 31									
Winchfield	d				18 05											18 35									
Fleet	d				18 10											18 40						18 54			
Farnborough (Main)	d				18 16									18 30		18 46						19 00			
Alton	d								17 44											18 15					
Bentley	d								17 51																
Farnham	a								17 56											18 25					
	d								17 58											18 28					
Aldershot	d								18 04											18 34					
Ash Vale	d								18 09											18 39					
Brookwood	d				18 23				18 16							18 53				18 46					
Guildford	d			18 02						18 17					18 34						18 47				
Worplesdon	d										↩				18 40									↩	
Woking	a			18 11	18 28	18 15			18 21	18 25	18 28			18 39	18 44	18 58	18 49			18 51	18 57			18 58	
	d	18 03		18 12	18 29	18 17	18 21		18 22	18 26	18 29	18 33		18 41	18 46	18 59	18 50			18 52	18 59			18 59	19 03
West Byfleet	d	18 07			↪				18 27			18 37				↪				18 57					19 07
Byfleet & New Haw	d	18 10										18 40													19 10
Weybridge	d	18 13									18 36	18 43												19 06	19 13
Walton-on-Thames	d	18 17									18 40	18 47												19 10	19 17
Hersham	d	18 19										18 49													19 19
Esher	d	18 22										18 52													19 22
Surbiton ■6	a	18 26							18 37		18 46	18 56								19 07				19 16	19 26
Wimbledon ■6 ⊖	a	18 34										19 04													19 34
Earlsfield	a	18 38						↩				19 08							↩						19 38
Clapham Junction ■10	a	18 42		18 31		18 36		18 42	18 48		18 57	19 12			19 05			19 12	19 12			19 25			19 42
Vauxhall ⊖	a	↪						18 47				↪							19 17						↪
London Waterloo ■15 ⊖	a			18 40		18 49	18 49	18 52	18 57	18 51	19 05			19 07	19 13		19 19	19 20	19 22	19 25	19 23	19 34		19 36	

		SW ■1	SW ■1	SW ◇■1 🚲	SW ◇■1 🚲	SW	SW ■1	SW ■1		SW ■1	SW	SW ■1	SW ■1	SW ■1	SW ◇■1	SW ◇■1 🚲	SW	SW ■1		SW ■1	SW ■1	SW ■1	SW	SW ■1	SW ◇■1 🚲
Basingstoke	d		18 54	18 57								19 17		19 24	19 30	19 35					19 43				
Hook	d		19 01											19 31											
Winchfield	d		19 05											19 35											
Fleet	d		19 10											19 40							19 54				
Farnborough (Main)	d		19 16									19 30		19 46							20 00				
Alton	d						18 44											19 15							
Bentley	d						18 51																		
Farnham	a						18 56											19 25							
	d						18 58											19 28							
Aldershot	d						19 04											19 34							
Ash Vale	d						19 09											19 39							
Brookwood	d		19 23				19 16							19 53				19 46							
Guildford	d	19 02						19 17					19 34							19 47				20 02	
Worplesdon	d									↩			19 40									↩			
Woking	a	19 11	19 28	19 15			19 21	19 25		19 28		19 39	19 44	19 58	19 49			19 51		19 57		19 58		20 11	
	d	19 12	19 29	19 17	19 21		19 22	19 26		19 29	19 33	19 41	19 46	19 59	19 50			19 52		19 59		19 59	20 03	20 12	20 21
West Byfleet	d		↪				19 27				19 37			↪				19 57					20 07		
Byfleet & New Haw	d										19 40												20 10		
Weybridge	d									19 36	19 43											20 06	20 13		
Walton-on-Thames	d									19 40	19 47											20 10	20 17		
Hersham	d										19 49												20 19		
Esher	d										19 52												20 22		
Surbiton ■6	a						19 37			19 46	19 56							20 07				20 16	20 26		
Wimbledon ■6 ⊖	a										20 04												20 34		
Earlsfield	a					↩					20 08						↩						20 38		
Clapham Junction ■10	a	19 31		19 36		19 42	19 48			19 57	20 12		20 05			20 12	20 12				20 25		20 42	20 31	
Vauxhall ⊖	a					19 47					↪						20 17						↪		
London Waterloo ■15 ⊖	a	19 40		19 49	19 49	19 52	19 57	19 51		20 05		20 07	20 13		20 19	20 20	20 22	20 25		20 23	20 34	20 36		20 40	20 49

Table 155R

Saturdays

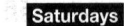

14 December to 17 May

Basingstoke, Alton, Guildford and Woking - Waterloo

Network Diagram - see first Page of Table 155

		SW	SW 1	SW 1	SW 1	SW ◇1 🛒	SW 1	SW	SW 1	SW 1		SW 1	SW 1	SW ◇1 🛒	SW 1	SW	SW 1	SW ◇1 🛒	SW	SW 1		SW 1	SW 1	SW ◇1 🛒	SW 1
Basingstoke	d				19 54	20 09			20 17				20 24	20 35			20 43						20 54	21 09	
Hook	d				20 01								20 31										21 01		
Winchfield	d				20 05								20 35										21 05		
Fleet	d				20 10								20 40				20 54						21 10		
Farnborough (Main)	d				20 16				20 30				20 46				21 00						21 16		
Alton	d		19 44							20 15										20 44					
Bentley	d		19 51																	20 51					
Farnham	a		19 56							20 25										20 56					
	d		19 58							20 28										20 58					
Aldershot	d		20 04							20 34										21 04					
Ash Vale	d		20 09							20 39										21 09					
Brookwood	d		20 16		20 23					20 46			20 53							21 16			21 23		
Guildford	d			20 17								20 39			20 47							21 17			
Worplesdon	d											20 44													
Woking	a		20 21	20 25	20 28	20 29			20 39	20 51		20 52	20 58		20 59		21 09			21 21		21 25	21 28	21 29	
	d		20 22	20 26	20 29	20 30		20 33	20 41	20 52		20 53	20 59		21 00	21 03	21 10	21 21		21 22		21 26	21 29	21 30	
West Byfleet	d		20 27					20 37		20 57						21 07				21 27					
Byfleet & New Haw	d							20 40								21 10									
Weybridge	d				20 36			20 43					21 06			21 13							21 36		
Walton-on-Thames	d				20 40			20 47					21 10			21 17							21 40		
Hersham	d							20 49								21 19									
Esher	d							20 52								21 22									
Surbiton 6	a		20 37		20 46			20 56		21 07			21 16			21 26				21 37			21 46		
Wimbledon 6 ⊖	a							21 05								21 34									
Earlsfield	a	←					←	21 09								21 38			←						←
Clapham Junction 10	a	20 42	20 48		20 57	20 52	20 57	21 12				21 12		21 16		21 42	21 29		21 42	21 48			21 57	21 52	21 57
Vauxhall ⊖	a	20 47			↪			21 17								↪			21 47				↪		
London Waterloo 15 ⊖	a	20 52	20 57	20 50		21 04	21 05	21 23	21 07	21 29		21 21	21 34	21 24	21 27		21 38	21 49	21 52	21 57		21 50		22 04	22 07

		SW	SW 1	SW	SW 1	SW 1		SW 1	SW	SW ◇1	SW 1	SW 1	SW	SW 1	SW 1	SW ◇1		SW 1	SW 1	SW	SW 1	SW	SW 1	SW 1	SW ◇1
Basingstoke	d							21 24		21 35	21 43				21 54	22 09								22 24	22 35
Hook	d							21 31							22 01									22 31	
Winchfield	d							21 35							22 05									22 35	
Fleet	d							21 40			21 54				22 10									22 40	
Farnborough (Main)	d							21 46			22 00				22 16									22 46	
Alton	d				21 15									21 44									22 15		
Bentley	d													21 51											
Farnham	a				21 25									21 56									22 25		
	d				21 28									21 58									22 28		
Aldershot	d				21 34									22 04									22 34		
Ash Vale	d				21 39									22 09									22 39		
Brookwood	d				21 46			21 53						22 16	22 23								22 46	22 53	
Guildford	d		21 39			21 49														22 20	22 39				
Worplesdon	d		21 44																		22 44				
Woking	a		21 49		21 51	21 57		21 58			22 09			22 21	22 28	22 28				22 32	22 49		22 51	22 58	22 53
	d	21 33	21 50		21 52	21 59		21 59	22 03		22 10	22 21		22 22	22 29	22 29				22 33	22 50		22 52	22 59	22 55
West Byfleet	d	21 37			21 57				22 07					22 27						22 37			22 57	↪	
Byfleet & New Haw	d	21 40							22 10											22 40					
Weybridge	d	21 43						22 06	22 13						22 36					22 43					
Walton-on-Thames	d	21 47						22 10	22 17						22 40					22 47					
Hersham	d	21 49							22 19											22 49					
Esher	d	21 52							22 22											22 52					
Surbiton 6	a	21 56			22 07			22 16	22 26					22 37	22 46					22 56			23 07		
Wimbledon 6 ⊖	a	22 04							22 34											23 04					
Earlsfield	a	22 08		←					22 38				←					←	←	23 08		←			
Clapham Junction 10	a	22 12	22 09	22 12					22 42	22 14	22 29		22 42	22 52	22 57	22 48		22 52	22 57	23 12	23 09	23 12			23 14
Vauxhall ⊖	a	↪		22 17					↪				22 47	↪	↪					↪		23 17			
London Waterloo 15 ⊖	a		22 18	22 22	22 27	22 24		22 34		22 22	22 38	22 49	22 52			22 57		23 01	23 05		23 18	23 22	23 28		23 22

		SW 1		SW	SW 1	SW	SW 1	SW 1	SW 1	SW 1	SW 1	SW 1		SW 1	SW 1
Basingstoke	d				22 43			22 54	23 14					23 44	
Hook	d							23 01						23 51	
Winchfield	d							23 05						23 55	
Fleet	d				22 54			23 10						00 01	
Farnborough (Main)	d				23 00			23 16						00 06	
Alton	d						22 44					23 15			23 46
Bentley	d						22 51								23 53
Farnham	a						22 56					23 25			23 58
	d						22 58					23 28			
Aldershot	d						23 04					23 34			
Ash Vale	d						23 09					23 39			
Brookwood	d						23 16	23 23				23 46		00 13	
Guildford	d			22 55							23 39				
Worplesdon	d	←									23 44				
Woking	a	22 58		23 05	23 09		23 21	23 28	23 32		23 49	23 51		00 18	
	d	22 59		23 06	23 10		23 22	23 33	23 33		23 56			00 20	
West Byfleet	d			23 10			23 27	23 37						00 25	
Byfleet & New Haw	d			23 13				23 40							
Weybridge	d	23 06		23 16				23 43						00 29	
Walton-on-Thames	d	23 10		23 20				23 47						00 33	
Hersham	d			23 22				23 49							
Esher	d			23 25				23 52							
Surbiton 6	a	23 16		23 29			23 37	23 57			00 07			00 39	
Wimbledon 6 ⊖	a			23 37				00 06			00 15			00 47	
Earlsfield	a			23 41		←				←					
Clapham Junction 10	a			23 44	23 29	23 44	23 48	00 21	23 52	00 21	00 22			00 53	
Vauxhall ⊖	a			↪		23 49		↪		00 30					
London Waterloo 15 ⊖	a	23 32			23 39	23 54	00 01		00 03	00 35	00 32			01 04	

Table 155R

Sundays

8 December to 11 May

Basingstoke, Alton, Guildford and Woking - Waterloo

Network Diagram - see first Page of Table 155

		SW	SW	SW	SW	SW	SW	SW	SW	SW		SW	SW	SW	SW	SW	SW	SW	SW	SW		SW	SW	SW	SW
		■1				■1	■1	◇■1 🛒				■1	■1		■1		◇■1 🛒			■1				■1	■1
Basingstoke	d					07 16		07 20					07 44				08 10							08 16	
Hook	d					07 23																		08 23	
Winchfield	d					07 27																		08 27	
Fleet	d	00 01				07 32																		08 32	
Farnborough (Main)	d	00 06				07 38																		08 38	
Alton	d																								08 15
Bentley	d																								08 23
Farnham	a																								08 28
	d						07 30																		08 30
Aldershot	d						07 36																		08 36
Ash Vale	d						07 41																		08 41
Brookwood	d	00 13				07 45	07 48																	08 45	08 48
Guildford	d			06 57	07 27									07 57	08 05				08 27	08 35					
Worplesdon	d											←													
Woking	a	00 18		07 05	07 35	07 50	07 54	07 39				07 50	08 02	08 05	08 13		08 28		08 35	08 42				08 50	08 54
	d	00 20	06 36	07 06	07 36	07 58		07 40		07 52		07 58	08 04	08 06	08 15		08 30		08 36	08 45			08 52	08 58	
West Byfleet	d	00 25	06 40	07 10	07 40	→				07 56				08 10					08 40				08 56		
Byfleet & New Haw	d		06 43	07 13	07 43					08 00				08 13					08 43				09 00		
Weybridge	d	00 29	06 46	07 16	07 46									08 16					08 46						
Walton-on-Thames	d	00 33	06 50	07 20	07 50									08 20					08 50						
Hersham	d		06 52	07 22	07 52									08 22					08 52						
Esher	d		06 55	07 25	07 55									08 25					08 55						
Surbiton ■6	a	00 39	06 59	07 29	07 59							08 09		08 29					08 59					09 09	
Wimbledon ■6 ⊖	a	00 47	07 07	07 37	08 07							08 17		08 37					09 07					09 19	
Earlsfield	a		07 12	07 42	08 12				←					08 41		←		←	09 11			←			
Clapham Junction ■10	a	00 53	07 15	07 45	08 15			08 03	08 15	09 01		08 24	08 31	08 45	08 37	08 45	08 51	09 01	09 15	09 06		09 15	10 01	09 26	
Vauxhall ⊖	a		07 20	07 50	→				08 20	→				→		08 50		09 08	→			09 20	→		
London Waterloo ■15 ⊖	a	01 04	07 25	07 55				08 20	08 25			08 39	08 46		08 49	08 55	09 12	09 13		09 16		09 25		09 39	

		SW	SW	SW	SW	SW		SW	SW	SW	SW	SW	SW	SW	SW	SW		SW	SW	SW	SW	SW	SW	SW	SW
		■1		■1		◇■1 🛒				■1			■1	■1	■1			■1	◇■1 🛒		◇■1 🛒			■1 🛒	
Basingstoke	d	08 44				09 10							09 16		09 44				10 00		10 10				
Hook	d												09 23												
Winchfield	d												09 27												
Fleet	d												09 32												
Farnborough (Main)	d												09 38												
Alton	d													09 15											
Bentley	d													09 23											
Farnham	a													09 28											
	d													09 30											
Aldershot	d													09 36											
Ash Vale	d													09 41											
Brookwood	d												09 45	09 48											
Guildford	d		08 57	09 05					09 27	09 35						09 57		10 05					10 27	10 35	
Worplesdon	d																								
Woking	a	09 02	09 05	09 15		09 28			09 35	09 42			09 50	09 54	10 02	10 05		10 15	10 19		10 28		10 35	10 42	
	d	09 04	09 06	09 15		09 30			09 36	09 45		09 52	09 58		10 04	10 06		10 15	10 20		10 30		10 36	10 45	
West Byfleet	d		09 10						09 40			09 56				10 10							10 40		
Byfleet & New Haw	d		09 13						09 43			10 00				10 13							10 43		
Weybridge	d		09 16						09 46							10 16							10 46		
Walton-on-Thames	d		09 20						09 50							10 20							10 50		
Hersham	d		09 22						09 52							10 22							10 52		
Esher	d		09 25						09 55							10 25							10 55		
Surbiton ■6	a		09 29						09 59				10 09			10 29							10 59		
Wimbledon ■6 ⊖	a		09 37						10 07				10 17			10 37							11 07		
Earlsfield	a		09 41		←			←	10 11		←					10 41				←		←	11 11		←
Clapham Junction ■10	a	09 30	09 45	09 38	09 45	09 57		10 01	10 15	10 04	10 15	11 01	10 23		10 27	10 45		10 35	10 39	10 45	10 49	11 01	11 15	11 04	11 15
Vauxhall ⊖	a		→		09 50			10 08	→		10 20	→				→				10 50		11 08	→		11 20
London Waterloo ■15 ⊖	a	09 41		09 48	09 55	10 11		10 13		10 14	10 25		10 34		10 39			10 46	10 50	10 55	11 04	11 13		11 14	11 25

Table 155R

Sundays

8 December to 11 May

Basingstoke, Alton, Guildford and Woking - Waterloo

Network Diagram - see first Page of Table 155

		SW	SW 1	SW 1	SW 1 🛒	SW	SW 1	SW ◇1 🛒		SW	SW ◇1 🛒	SW	SW	SW 1 🛒	SW	SW	SW 1	SW 1		SW 1 🛒	SW	SW 1	SW ◇1 🛒	SW	SW ◇1 🛒
Basingstoke	d		10 16		10 44			11 00			11 10						11 16			11 44			12 00		12 10
Hook	d		10 23														11 23								
Winchfield	d		10 27														11 27								
Fleet	d		10 32														11 32								
Farnborough (Main)	d		10 38														11 38								
Alton	d			10 15														11 15							
Bentley	d			10 23														11 23							
Farnham	a			10 28														11 28							
	d			10 30														11 30							
Aldershot	d			10 36														11 36							
Ash Vale	d			10 41														11 41							
Brookwood	d		10 45	10 48													11 45	11 48							
Guildford	d					10 57	11 06						11 27	11 35							11 57	12 06			
Worplesdon	d																								
Woking	a		10 50	10 54	11 02	11 05	11 13	11 18			11 28		11 35	11 42			11 50	11 54		12 02	12 05	12 13	12 18		12 28
	d	10 52	10 58		11 04	11 06	11 15	11 20			11 30		11 36	11 45		11 52	11 58			12 04	12 06	12 15	12 20		12 30
West Byfleet	d	10 56				11 10							11 40			11 56					12 10				
Byfleet & New Haw	d	11 00				11 13							11 43			12 00					12 13				
Weybridge	d					11 16							11 46								12 16				
Walton-on-Thames	d					11 20							11 50								12 20				
Hersham	d					11 22							11 52								12 22				
Esher	d					11 25							11 55								12 25				
Surbiton 6	a		11 09			11 29							11 59				12 09				12 29				
Wimbledon 6 ⊖	a		11 17			11 37							12 07				12 17				12 37				
Earlsfield	a					11 41				←		←	12 11		←						12 41			←	
Clapham Junction 10	a	12 01	11 23		11 27	11 45	11 34	11 39		11 45	11 49	12 01	12 15	12 04	12 15	13 01	12 23			12 27	12 45	12 34	12 39	12 45	12 49
Vauxhall ⊖	a	→				→				11 50		12 08	→		12 20	→					→			12 50	
London Waterloo 15 ⊖	a		11 34		11 39		11 49	11 50		11 55	12 04	12 13		12 14	12 25		12 34			12 37		12 44	12 49	12 55	13 04

		SW	SW	SW 1 🛒		SW	SW	SW 1	SW 1	SW 1 🛒	SW	SW 1	SW ◇1 🛒	SW		SW ◇1 🛒	SW	SW	SW 1 🛒	SW	SW	SW 1	SW 1	SW 1 🛒	
Basingstoke	d							12 16		12 44			13 00			13 10						13 16		13 44	
Hook	d							12 23														13 23			
Winchfield	d							12 27														13 27			
Fleet	d							12 32														13 32			
Farnborough (Main)	d							12 38														13 38			
Alton	d								12 15														13 15		
Bentley	d								12 23														13 23		
Farnham	a								12 28														13 28		
	d								12 30														13 30		
Aldershot	d								12 36														13 36		
Ash Vale	d								12 41														13 41		
Brookwood	d							12 45	12 48													13 45	13 48		
Guildford	d		12 27	12 35							12 57	13 05						13 27	13 35						
Worplesdon	d																								
Woking	a		12 35	12 42				12 50	12 54	13 02	13 05	13 13	13 18			13 28		13 35	13 42			13 50	13 54	14 02	
	d		12 36	12 45			12 52	12 58		13 04	13 06	13 15	13 20			13 30		13 36	13 45		13 52	13 58		14 04	
West Byfleet	d		12 40				12 56				13 10							13 40			13 56				
Byfleet & New Haw	d		12 43				13 00				13 13							13 43			14 00				
Weybridge	d		12 46								13 16							13 46							
Walton-on-Thames	d		12 50								13 20							13 50							
Hersham	d		12 52								13 22							13 52							
Esher	d		12 55								13 25							13 55							
Surbiton 6	a		12 59					13 09			13 29							13 59				14 09			
Wimbledon 6 ⊖	a		13 07					13 17			13 37							14 07				14 17			
Earlsfield	a	←	13 11			←					13 41			←			←	14 11		←					
Clapham Junction 10	a	13 01	13 15	13 04		13 15	14 01	13 23		13 27	13 45	13 34	13 39	13 45		13 49	14 01	14 15	14 04	14 15	15 01	14 23		14 27	
Vauxhall ⊖	a	13 08	→			13 20	→				→			13 50			14 08	→		14 20	→				
London Waterloo 15 ⊖	a	13 13		13 14		13 25		13 34		13 37		13 44	13 49	13 55		13 59	14 13		14 14	14 25		14 34		14 37	

Table 155R

Sundays

8 December to 11 May

Basingstoke, Alton, Guildford and Woking - Waterloo

Network Diagram - see first Page of Table 155

		SW	SW	SW	SW	SW		SW	SW	SW	SW	SW	SW	SW	SW	SW		SW	SW	SW	SW	SW	SW	SW	SW
			1	1	1	◇1 🛒			1	◇1 🛒	1	1			1 🛒				1	1	1 🛒		1	1	1
Basingstoke	d			13 50		14 00				14 10									14 16		14 44			14 50	
Hook	d																		14 23						
Winchfield	d																		14 27						
Fleet	d			14 02															14 32					15 02	
Farnborough (Main)	d			14 08															14 38					15 08	
Alton	d				13 45															14 15					14 45
Bentley	d																			14 23					
Farnham	a				13 55															14 28					14 55
	d				14 00															14 30					15 00
Aldershot	d				14 06															14 36					15 06
Ash Vale	d				14 11															14 41					15 11
Brookwood	d			14 15	14 18														14 45	14 48				15 15	15 18
Guildford	d	13 57	14 05											14 27	14 35							14 57	15 05		
Worplesdon	d								↩																
Woking	a	14 05	14 13	14 20	14 24	14 18			14 20	14 28				14 35	14 42				14 50	14 54	15 02	15 05	15 13	15 20	15 24
	d	14 06	14 15	14 28		14 20			14 28	14 30				14 36	14 45			14 52	14 58		15 04	15 06	15 15	15 28	
West Byfleet	d	14 10		↪										14 40				14 56				15 10		↪	
Byfleet & New Haw	d	14 13												14 43				15 00				15 13			
Weybridge	d	14 16							14 34					14 46								15 16			
Walton-on-Thames	d	14 20							14 38					14 50								15 20			
Hersham	d	14 22												14 52								15 22			
Esher	d	14 25												14 55								15 25			
Surbiton 6	a	14 29							14 45					14 59					15 09			15 29			
Wimbledon 6 ⊖	a	14 37							14 53					15 07					15 17			15 37			
Earlsfield	a	14 41						↩			↩	↩	↩	15 11		↩						15 41			
Clapham Junction 10	a	14 45	14 34			14 39		14 45	14 59	14 49	14 59	14 59	15 01	15 15	15 04	15 15		16 01	15 23		15 27	15 45	15 34		
Vauxhall ⊖	a	↪						14 50	↪				15 08	↪		15 20		↪				↪			
London Waterloo 15 ⊖	a		14 44			14 49		14 55		14 59	15 10	15 10	15 13		15 14	15 25			15 34		15 37		15 44		

		SW		SW	SW	SW	SW	SW	SW	SW	SW	SW		SW	SW	SW	SW	SW	SW	SW	SW	SW		SW	SW
		◇1 🛒			1	◇1 🛒	1	1			1 🛒				1	1	1 🛒		1	1	1	◇1 🛒			1
Basingstoke	d	15 00				15 10									15 16		15 44			15 50		16 00			
Hook	d														15 23										
Winchfield	d														15 27										
Fleet	d														15 32					16 02					
Farnborough (Main)	d														15 38					16 08					
Alton	d															15 15					15 45				
Bentley	d															15 23									
Farnham	a															15 28					15 55				
	d															15 30					16 00				
Aldershot	d															15 36					16 06				
Ash Vale	d															15 41					16 11				
Brookwood	d														15 45	15 48				16 15	16 18				
Guildford	d									15 27	15 35							15 57	16 05						
Worplesdon	d				↩																				↩
Woking	a	15 18			15 20	15 28				15 35	15 42				15 50	15 54	16 02	16 05	16 13	16 20	16 24	16 18			16 20
	d	15 20			15 28	15 30				15 36	15 45			15 52	15 58		16 04	16 06	16 15	16 28		16 20			16 28
West Byfleet	d									15 40				15 56				16 10		↪					
Byfleet & New Haw	d									15 43				16 00				16 13							
Weybridge	d				15 34					15 46								16 16							16 34
Walton-on-Thames	d				15 38					15 50								16 20							16 38
Hersham	d									15 52								16 22							
Esher	d									15 55								16 25							
Surbiton 6	a				15 45					15 59					16 09			16 29							16 45
Wimbledon 6 ⊖	a				15 53					16 07					16 17			16 37							16 53
Earlsfield	a			↩			↩	↩	↩	16 11		↩						16 41						↩	
Clapham Junction 10	a	15 39		15 45	15 59	15 49	15 59	15 59	16 01	16 15	16 04	16 15		17 01	16 23		16 27	16 45	16 34			16 39		16 45	16 59
Vauxhall ⊖	a			15 50	↪				16 08	↪		16 20		↪				↪						16 50	↪
London Waterloo 15 ⊖	a	15 49		15 55		15 59	16 10	16 10	16 13		16 14	16 25			16 34		16 37		16 44			16 49		16 55	

Table 155R

Sundays

8 December to 11 May

Basingstoke, Alton, Guildford and Woking - Waterloo

Network Diagram - see first Page of Table 155

		SW ◇1 🛒	SW 1	SW 1		SW	SW	SW 1 🛒	SW	SW	SW 1	SW 1	SW 1 🛒	SW		SW 1	SW 1	SW 1	SW ◇1 🛒	SW	SW 1	SW ◇1 🛒	SW 1	SW 1	
Basingstoke	d	16 10									16 16		16 44				16 50		17 00			17 10			
Hook	d										16 23														
Winchfield	d										16 27														
Fleet	d										16 32						17 02								
Farnborough (Main)	d										16 38						17 08								
Alton	d											16 15						16 45							
Bentley	d											16 23													
Farnham	a											16 28						16 55							
	d											16 30						17 00							
Aldershot	d											16 36						17 06							
Ash Vale	d											16 41						17 11							
Brookwood	d										16 45	16 48					17 15	17 18							
Guildford	d					16 27	16 35							16 57		17 05									
Worplesdon	d																				←				
Woking	a	16 28				16 35	16 42				16 50	16 54	17 02	17 05		17 13	17 20	17 24	17 18		17 20	17 28			
	d	16 30				16 36	16 45		16 52		16 58		17 04	17 06		17 15	17 28		17 20		17 28	17 30			
West Byfleet	d					16 40			16 56					17 10			→								
Byfleet & New Haw	d					16 43			17 00					17 13											
Weybridge	d					16 46								17 16							17 34				
Walton-on-Thames	d					16 50								17 20							17 38				
Hersham	d					16 52								17 22											
Esher	d					16 55								17 25											
Surbiton [6]	a					16 59					17 09			17 29							17 45				
Wimbledon [6] ⊖	a					17 07					17 17			17 37							17 53				
Earlsfield	a		←	←		←	17 11		←					17 41						←			←	←	
Clapham Junction [10]	a	16 49	16 59	16 59		17 01	17 15	17 04	17 15	18 01	17 23		17 27	17 45		17 34			17 39	17 45	17 59	17 49	17 59	17 59	
Vauxhall ⊖	a					17 08	→		17 20	→				→						17 50	→				
London Waterloo [15] ⊖	a	16 59	17 10	17 10		17 13		17 14	17 25		17 34		17 37			17 44			17 49	17 55		17 59	18 10	18 10	

		SW	SW	SW 1 🛒	SW	SW	SW 1	SW 1	SW 1 🛒	SW		SW 1	SW 1	SW 1	SW ◇1 🛒	SW	SW 1	SW ◇1 🛒	SW 1	SW 1		SW	SW	SW 1 🛒	SW
Basingstoke	d						17 16		17 44				17 50		18 00			18 10							
Hook	d						17 23																		
Winchfield	d						17 27																		
Fleet	d						17 32						18 02												
Farnborough (Main)	d						17 38						18 08												
Alton	d							17 15						17 45											
Bentley	d							17 23																	
Farnham	a							17 28						17 55											
	d							17 30						18 00											
Aldershot	d							17 36						18 06											
Ash Vale	d							17 41						18 11											
Brookwood	d						17 45	17 48					18 15	18 18											
Guildford	d		17 27	17 35						17 57		18 05											18 27	18 35	
Worplesdon	d																←								
Woking	a		17 35	17 42			17 50	17 54	18 02	18 05		18 13	18 20	18 24	18 18		18 20	18 28					18 35	18 42	
	d		17 36	17 45		17 52	17 58		18 04	18 06		18 15	18 28		18 20		18 28	18 30					18 36	18 45	
West Byfleet	d		17 40			17 56				18 10			→										18 40		
Byfleet & New Haw	d		17 43			18 00				18 13													18 43		
Weybridge	d		17 46							18 16							18 34						18 46		
Walton-on-Thames	d		17 50							18 20							18 38						18 50		
Hersham	d		17 52							18 22													18 52		
Esher	d		17 55							18 25													18 55		
Surbiton [6]	a		17 59				18 09			18 29							18 45						18 59		
Wimbledon [6] ⊖	a		18 07				18 17			18 37							18 53						19 07		
Earlsfield	a	←	18 11		←					18 41						←			←	←		←	19 11		←
Clapham Junction [10]	a	18 01	18 15	18 04	18 15	19 01	18 23		18 27	18 45		18 34			18 39	18 45	18 59	18 49	18 59	18 59		19 01	19 15	19 04	19 15
Vauxhall ⊖	a	18 08	→		18 20	→				→						18 50	→					19 08	→		19 20
London Waterloo [15] ⊖	a	18 13		18 14	18 25		18 34		18 37			18 44			18 49	18 55		18 59	19 10	19 10		19 13		19 14	19 25

Table 155R

Sundays

8 December to 11 May

Basingstoke, Alton, Guildford and Woking - Waterloo

Network Diagram - see first Page of Table 155

		SW		SW	SW	SW	SW	SW	SW	SW	SW	SW		SW	SW	SW	SW	SW	SW	SW	SW	SW		SW	SW
				■1	■1	■1		■1	■1	■1	◇■1 🛒			■1	◇■1 🛒	■1	■1			■1 🛒				■1	■1
Basingstoke	d			18 16		18 44			18 50		19 00				19 10									19 16	
Hook	d			18 23																				19 23	
Winchfield	d			18 27																				19 27	
Fleet	d			18 32					19 02															19 32	
Farnborough (Main)	d			18 38					19 08															19 38	
Alton	d				18 15					18 45															19 15
Bentley	d				18 23																				19 23
Farnham	a				18 28					18 55															19 28
	d				18 30					19 00															19 30
Aldershot	d				18 36					19 06															19 36
Ash Vale	d				18 41					19 11															19 41
Brookwood	d			18 45	18 48				19 15	19 18														19 45	19 48
Guildford	d						18 57	19 05											19 27	19 35					
Worplesdon	d													←											
Woking	a			18 50	18 54	19 02	19 05	19 13	19 20	19 24	19 18			19 20	19 28				19 35	19 42				19 50	19 54
	d	18 52		18 58		19 04	19 06	19 15	19 28		19 20			19 28	19 30				19 36	19 45		19 52		19 58	
West Byfleet	d	18 56					19 10		↪										19 40			19 56			
Byfleet & New Haw	d	19 00					19 13												19 43			20 00			
Weybridge	d						19 16							19 34					19 46						
Walton-on-Thames	d						19 20							19 38					19 50						
Hersham	d						19 22												19 52						
Esher	d						19 25												19 55						
Surbiton ■6	a			19 09			19 29							19 45					19 59					20 09	
Wimbledon ■6 ⊖	a			19 17			19 37							19 53					20 07					20 17	
Earlsfield	a						19 41					←				←	←	←	20 11		←				
Clapham Junction ■10	a	20 01		19 23		19 27	19 45	19 34			19 39	19 45		19 59	19 49	19 59	19 59	20 01	20 15	20 04	20 15	21 01		20 23	
Vauxhall ⊖	a	↪					↪					19 50		↪				20 08	↪		20 20	↪			
London Waterloo ■15 ⊖	a			19 34		19 37		19 44			19 49	19 55			19 59	20 10	20 10	20 13		20 14	20 25			20 34	

		SW	SW	SW	SW	SW	SW	SW		SW	SW	SW	SW	SW	SW	SW	SW	SW		SW	SW	SW	SW	SW	
		■1		■1	■1	■1	◇■1 🛒			■1	◇■1 A 🛒	■1	■1			■1				■1	■1	■1		■1	
Basingstoke	d	19 44			19 50		20 00				20 10									20 16		20 44			
Hook	d																			20 23					
Winchfield	d																			20 27					
Fleet	d				20 02															20 32					
Farnborough (Main)	d				20 08															20 38					
Alton	d					19 45															20 15				
Bentley	d																				20 23				
Farnham	a					19 55															20 28				
	d					20 00															20 30				
Aldershot	d					20 06															20 36				
Ash Vale	d					20 11															20 41				
Brookwood	d				20 15	20 18														20 45	20 48				
Guildford	d		19 57	20 05											20 27	20 35							20 57	21 05	
Worplesdon	d									←															
Woking	a	20 02	20 05	20 13	20 20	20 24	20 18			20 20	20 28				20 35	20 42				20 50	20 54	21 02	21 05	21 13	
	d	20 04	20 06	20 15	20 28		20 20			20 28	20 30				20 36	20 45		20 52		20 58		21 04	21 06	21 15	
West Byfleet	d		20 10		↪										20 40			20 56					21 10		
Byfleet & New Haw	d		20 13												20 43			21 00					21 13		
Weybridge	d		20 16							20 34					20 46								21 16		
Walton-on-Thames	d		20 20							20 38					20 50								21 20		
Hersham	d		20 22												20 52								21 22		
Esher	d		20 25												20 55								21 25		
Surbiton ■6	a		20 29							20 45					20 59					21 09			21 29		
Wimbledon ■6 ⊖	a		20 37							20 53					21 07					21 17			21 37		
Earlsfield	a		20 41					←				←	←	←	21 11		←						21 41		
Clapham Junction ■10	a	20 27	20 45	20 34			20 39	20 45		20 59	20 49	20 59	20 59	21 01	21 15	21 04	21 15	22 01		21 23		21 27	21 45	21 34	
Vauxhall ⊖	a		↪					20 50		↪				21 08	↪		21 20	↪					↪		
London Waterloo ■15 ⊖	a	20 37		20 44			20 49	20 55			20 59	21 10	21 10	21 13		21 14	21 25			21 34		21 37		21 44	

A 🛒 to Woking

Table 155R

Sundays

8 December to 11 May

Basingstoke, Alton, Guildford and Woking - Waterloo

Network Diagram - see first Page of Table 155

		SW	SW	SW	SW	SW	SW	SW	SW	SW	SW	SW	SW	SW	SW	SW	SW	SW	SW	SW	SW	SW
		1	1	◇1 🛒		1	◇1 🛒	1	1			1			1	1	1		1		1	1
Basingstoke	d	20 50		21 00			21 10								21 16		21 44				21 50	
Hook	d														21 23							
Winchfield	d														21 27							
Fleet	d	21 02													21 32						22 02	
Farnborough (Main)	d	21 08													21 38						22 08	
Alton	d		20 45													21 15						21 45
Bentley	d															21 23						
Farnham	a		20 55													21 28						21 55
	d		21 00													21 30						22 00
Aldershot	d		21 06													21 36						22 06
Ash Vale	d		21 11													21 41						22 11
Brookwood	d	21 15	21 18												21 45	21 48					22 15	22 18
Guildford	d										21 27	21 35						21 57	22 05			
Worplesdon	d					←																
Woking	a	21 20	21 24	21 18		21 20	21 28				21 35	21 42			21 50	21 54	22 02	22 05	22 13		22 21	22 24
	d	21 28		21 20		21 28	21 30				21 36	21 45		21 52	21 58		22 04	22 06	22 15		22 28	
West Byfleet	d	→									21 40			21 56				22 10				
Byfleet & New Haw	d										21 43			22 00				22 13				
Weybridge	d					21 34					21 46							22 16			22 34	
Walton-on-Thames	d					21 38					21 50							22 20			22 38	
Hersham	d										21 52							22 22				
Esher	d										21 55							22 25				
Surbiton 6	a					21 45					21 59				22 09			22 29			22 45	
Wimbledon 6 ⊖	a					21 53					22 07				22 17			22 37			22 53	
Earlsfield	a				←			←	←	←	22 11		←					22 41		←		
Clapham Junction 10	a			21 39	21 45	21 59	21 49	21 59	21 59	22 01	22 15	22 04	22 15	23 01	22 23		22 27	22 45	22 34	22 45	22 59	
Vauxhall ⊖	a				21 50	→				22 08	→		22 20	→				→		22 50	→	
London Waterloo 15 ⊖	a			21 49	21 55		21 59	22 10	22 10	22 13		22 14	22 25		22 34		22 37		22 44	22 55		

		SW	SW	SW	SW	SW	SW	SW	SW	SW	SW	SW	SW	SW	SW	SW	SW	SW	SW	SW	SW	SW	SW
		◇1	1	1			1			1	1	1		1		1		1	1	1	◇1		🚌
																						A	B
Basingstoke	d	22 10								22 16		22 44							23 16		23 44		
Hook	d									22 23									23 23				
Winchfield	d									22 27									23 27				
Fleet	d									22 32									23 32				
Farnborough (Main)	d									22 38									23 38				
Alton	d										22 15					22 45				23 15			
Bentley	d										22 23									23 23			
Farnham	a										22 28					22 55				23 28			
	d										22 30					23 00				23 30			
Aldershot	d										22 36					23 06				23 36			
Ash Vale	d										22 41					23 11				23 41			
Brookwood	d									22 45	22 48					23 18			23 45	23 48			
Guildford	d					22 27	22 35						22 57	23 05				23 35				00 05	00 10
Worplesdon	d																						
Woking	a	22 28				22 35	22 42			22 50	22 54	23 02	23 05	23 13		23 24		23 42	23 50	23 54	00 02	00 13	00 30
	d	22 30				22 36	22 45		22 52	22 58		23 04	23 06	23 15		23 28		23 45			00 04		
West Byfleet	d					22 40			22 56				23 10										
Byfleet & New Haw	d					22 43			23 00				23 13										
Weybridge	d					22 46							23 16			23 34							
Walton-on-Thames	d					22 50							23 20			23 38							
Hersham	d					22 52							23 22										
Esher	d					22 55							23 25										
Surbiton 6	a					22 59				23 09			23 29			23 45							
Wimbledon 6 ⊖	a					23 07				23 17			23 37			23 53							
Earlsfield	a		←	←	←	23 11		←					23 41		←		←						
Clapham Junction 10	a	22 49	22 59	22 59	23 01	23 15	23 04	23 15	00 01	23 23		23 27	23 45	23 34	23 45	23 59	00 01	00 04			00 23		
Vauxhall ⊖	a				23 08	→		23 20	→				→		23 50		00 08						
London Waterloo 15 ⊖	a	22 59	23 10	23 10	23 13		23 14	23 25		23 34		23 37		23 44	23 55	00 10	00 13	00 14			00 33		

A from Farncombe

B December 9 only

Table 156

Mondays to Fridays

9 December to 16 May

London - Guildford, Haslemere and Portsmouth

Network Diagram - see first Page of Table 155

Miles			SW	SW	SW	SW	SW	SW	SW	SW	SW	SW	SW	SW	SW	SW	SW	SW	SW	SW	SW	SW	SW
			MX	MO	MX	MO	MX	MO															
			1	1	1	1	1	1	1	1	1	1	1	1	1	1	1	1	1	1	1	1	1
															🚲			🚲			🚲		🚲
0	**London Waterloo** [15] ⊖	d						00 50		05 00	05 20	06 15	06 45	07 15	07 30		07 45	08 00		08 15	08 30	08 45	09 00
4	Clapham Junction [10]	d																					
24½	**Woking**	a						01 16		05 51	06 08	06 41	07 11	07 42	07 55		08 12	08 24		08 42	08 55	09 11	09 24
—		d				00 03	00 13	01 18		05 53	06 11	06 43	07 13	07 44	07 55		08 14	08 25		08 44	08 55	09 13	09 25
26¾	Worplesdon	d					00 18				06 16	06 48	07 18	07 49			08 19			08 49		09 18	
30¼	**Guildford**	a				00 10	00 24	01s26		06 00	06 21	06 53	07 23	07 54	08 04		08 24	08 35		08 54	09 05	09 23	09 33
—		d				00 12	00 25		05 15	06 04	06 30	06 55	07 25	07 56	08 04		08 26	08 39		08 56	09 07	09 25	09 34
33½	Farncombe	d					00 31			06 10	06 36	07 01	07 31	08 02			08 32			09 02		09 31	
34½	Godalming	d			00 01		00 34			06 13	06 39	07 04	07 34	08 05	08 12		08 35			09 05		09 34	
36¼	Milford (Surrey)	d					00s38			06 17	06 43	07 08	07 38	08 09			08 39			09 09			
38½	Witley	d					00s43			06 21	06 47	07 12	07 42	08 13		←	08 43		←	09 13			
43	**Haslemere** [4]	a			00 12	00 26	00 49		05 29	06 28	06 54	07 19	07 49	08 20	08 24	08 20	08 50	08 54	08 50	09 20	09 24	09 45	09 48
—		d		00 07	00 12	00 27	00 50		05 30	06 28	06 55	07 20	07 53	08 30	08 25	08 30	08 58	08 55	08 58		09 25	09 55	09 49
46¾	Liphook	d		00 12			00s55		05 35	06 33	07 00	07 25	07 59	↪		08 35	↪		09 03			↪	
51½	Liss	d	00 01	00 18			01s01		05 41	06 39	07 06	07 31	08 05			08 41			09 09				
55	Petersfield	d	00 06	00 23	00 23	00 38	01 06		05 46	06 45	07 11	07 36	08 11		08 36	08 46		09 06	09 15		09 36		10 00
63¼	Rowlands Castle	d	00 15	00 33			01s16		05 56	06 54	07 21	07 46	08 21			08 56			09 24				
66½	**Havant**	a	00 20	00 38	00 36	00 50	01 21	02s00	06 01	06 59	07 27	07 51	08 26		08 49	09 04		09 19	09 29		09 49		10 15
—		d	00 21	00 39	00 36	00 51	01 21		06 02	07 00	07 28	07 52	08 27		08 50	09 05		09 20	09 30		09 50		10 16
67¼	Bedhampton	a	00 24	00 41			01s24		06 04	07 02	07 30	07 54	08 29			09 07			09 32				
70½	Hilsea	a	00 29				01s29		06 10	07 08	07 37	08 00	08 35			09 13			09 38				
72¾	Fratton	a	00 33	00 49	00 45	01 00	01s33	02s10	06 14	07 12	07 41	08 04	08 39		08 58	09 17		09 28	09 42		09 59		10 24
73¾	**Portsmouth & Southsea**	a	00 37	00 53	00 50	01 04	01 37	02s14	06 18	07 16	07 46	08 07	08 43		09 02	09 20		09 32	09 46		10 02		10 28
74½	**Portsmouth Harbour** ⛴	a		00 58	00 54	01 09		02 19	06 22	07 20		08 12	08 48		09 07	09 26		09 37			10 07		10 33

		SW	SW	SW	SW	SW	SW	SW	SW		SW	SW	SW	SW	SW	SW	SW	SW	SW	SW	SW	SW	SW
		1	1	1	1	1	1	1	1		1	1	1	1	1	1	1	1	1	1	1	1	1
				🚲		🚲			🚲			🚲			🚲		🚲			🚲			🚲
London Waterloo [15] ⊖	d		09 15	09 30	09 45	10 00		10 15	10 30	and at the same minutes past each hour until	13 45	14 00		14 15	14 30	14 45	15 00		15 15	15 30		15 45	16 00
Clapham Junction [10]	d																						
Woking	a		09 42	09 54	10 11	10 24		10 41	10 54		14 11	14 24		14 41	14 54	15 11	15 24		15 41	15 54		16 11	16 24
	d		09 43	09 55	10 13	10 25		10 43	10 55		14 13	14 25		14 43	14 55	15 13	15 25		15 43	15 55		16 13	16 25
Worplesdon	d				10 18						14 18					15 18			15 48				
Guildford	a		09 51	10 03	10 23	10 33		10 50	11 03		14 23	14 33		14 50	15 03	15 23	15 33		15 53	16 03		16 20	16 33
	d		09 54	10 04	10 25	10 34		10 52	11 04		14 25	14 34		14 52	15 04	15 25	15 34		15 55	16 04		16 22	16 34
Farncombe	d		10 00		10 31			10 58			14 31			14 58		15 31			16 01			16 28	
Godalming	d		10 03		10 34			11 01			14 34			15 01		15 34			16 04			16 31	
Milford (Surrey)	d		10 07					11 05						15 05					16 08			16 35	
Witley	d	←	10 11				←	11 09					←	15 09				←	16 12		←	16 39	
Haslemere [4]	a	09 45	10 18	10 22	10 45	10 48	10 45	11 16	11 20		14 45	14 48	14 45	15 16	15 20	15 45	15 48	15 45	16 19	16 23	16 19	16 46	16 50
	d	09 55		10 23	10 55	10 49	10 55		11 21		14 55	14 49	14 55		15 21	15 55	15 49	15 55	16 29	16 24	16 29	16 55	16 51
Liphook	d	10 00			↪		11 00				↪		15 00			↪		16 00	↪		16 34	↪	
Liss	d	10 06					11 06						15 06					16 06			16 40		
Petersfield	d	10 11		10 34		11 00	11 11		11 32			15 00	15 11		15 32		16 00	16 11		16 35	16 45		17 02
Rowlands Castle	d	10 21					11 21						15 21					16 21			16 55		
Havant	a	10 26		10 49		11 15	11 26		11 49			15 15	15 26		15 49		16 15	16 26		16 49	17 03		17 15
	d	10 27		10 50		11 16	11 27		11 50			15 16	15 27		15 50		16 16	16 27		16 50	17 04		17 16
Bedhampton	a	10 29					11 29						15 29					16 29			17 07		
Hilsea	a	10 36					11 36						15 36					16 36			17 12		
Fratton	a	10 40		10 59		11 24	11 40		11 59			15 24	15 40		15 59		16 24	16 40		16 59	17 16		17 24
Portsmouth & Southsea	a	10 44		11 02		11 28	11 44		12 02			15 28	15 44		16 02		16 28	16 44		17 02	17 20		17 28
Portsmouth Harbour ⛴	a			11 07		11 33			12 07			15 33			16 07		16 33	16 49		17 07	17 26		17 35

		SW	SW	SW	SW	SW	SW	SW	SW	SW	SW	SW	SW	SW	SW	SW	SW	SW	SW	SW	SW	SW
		1	1	1	1	1	1	1	1	1	1	1	1	1	1	1	1	1	1	1	1	1
				🚲			🚲			🚲			🚲				🚲		🚲			🚲
																					A	
London Waterloo [15] ⊖	d		16 15	16 30		16 45	17 00		17 15	17 30		17 45	18 00		18 15	18 18	18 30	18 45	19 00		19 15	19 30
Clapham Junction [10]	d																					
Woking	a		16 41	16 54		17 11	17 24		17 38	17 54						18 42	18 57	19 13	19 24		19 43	19 54
	d		16 43	16 55		17 13	17 25		17 40	17 56						18 43	18 58	19 14	19 25		19 45	19 55
Worplesdon	d		16 48				17 30		17 45	18 00						18 48			19 30			
Guildford	a		16 53	17 03		17 20	17 36		17 51	18 06		18 21	18 32		18 50	18 54	19 06	19 22	19 36		19 52	20 03
	d		16 55	17 04		17 22	17 37		17 54	18 08		18 23	18 33		18 51	18 57	19 08	19 24	19 37		19 54	20 04
Farncombe	d		17 01			17 28			18 00			18 29				19 03		19 30			20 00	
Godalming	d		17 04			17 31			18 03	18 15		18 32	18 40			19 06	19 15	19 33			20 03	20 11
Milford (Surrey)	d		17 08			17 35			18 07			18 36				19 10		19 37			20 07	
Witley	d	←	17 12		←	17 39		←	18 11		←	18 40		←		19 14		19 41		←	20 11	
Haslemere [4]	a	16 46	17 19	17 23	17 19	17 46	17 53	17 46	18 18	18 25	18 18	18 49	18 51	18 49	19 05	19 23	19 25	19 48	19 52	19 48	20 18	20 22
	d	16 55	17 29	17 24	17 29	17 58	17 54	17 58	18 30	18 26	18 30	18 55	18 52	18 55	19 06		19 26	19 56	19 53	19 56	20 26	20 23
Liphook	d	17 00	↪		17 34	↪		18 03	↪		18 35	↪		19 00	19 11			↪		20 01	↪	
Liss	d	17 06			17 40			18 09			18 41			19 06	19 17					20 07		
Petersfield	d	17 11		17 35	17 45		18 05	18 14		18 37	18 46		19 03	19 12	19 23		19 37		20 04	20 13		20 34
Rowlands Castle	d	17 21			17 55			18 24			18 56			19 21	19 32					20 22		
Havant	a	17 26		17 49	18 03		18 19	18 29		18 50	19 01		19 15	19 28	19 40		19 50		20 16	20 27		20 48
	d	17 27		17 50	18 04		18 20	18 30		18 51	19 02		19 16		19 41		19 51		20 17	20 28		20 49
Bedhampton	a	17 29			18 07			18 32			19 04				19 44					20 31		
Hilsea	a	17 36			18 12			18 39			19 10				19 49					20 36		
Fratton	a	17 40		17 59	18 16		18 28	18 43		18 59	19 14		19 25		19 53		19 59		20 25	20 40		20 57
Portsmouth & Southsea	a	17 44		18 02	18 20		18 32	18 47		19 03			19 29		19 59		20 04		20 29	20 44		21 01
Portsmouth Harbour ⛴	a			18 09	18 28		18 39	18 52		19 10			19 36				20 10		20 34	20 51		21 06

A continues to Southampton Central on table 165

Table 156

Mondays to Fridays

9 December to 16 May

London - Guildford, Haslemere and Portsmouth

Network Diagram - see first Page of Table 155

Station		SW 1	SW 1	SW 1 🛒	SW 1	SW 1	SW 1 🛒	SW 1	SW 1 🛒	SW 1	SW 1	SW 1	SW 1	SW 1	SW 1	SW 1	SW 1	SW 1
London Waterloo 15 ⊖	d		19 45	20 00		20 15	20 30	20 45	21 00		21 30	21 45	22 00		22 30	22 45	23 15	23 45
Clapham Junction 10	d																	
Woking	a		20 11	20 24		20 41	20 54	21 11	21 24		21 54	22 11	22 24		22 54	23 11	23 41	00 11
	d		20 13	20 25		20 43	20 55	21 13	21 25		21 55	22 13	22 25		22 55	23 13	23 43	00 13
Worplesdon	d		20 18					21 18				22 18				23 18		00 18
Guildford	a		20 23	20 33		20 50	21 03	21 23	21 33		22 03	22 23	22 33		23 03	23 24	23 51	00 24
	d		20 25	20 34		20 52	21 04	21 25	21 34		22 04	22 25	22 34		23 04	23 25	23 52	00 25
Farncombe	d		20 31	20 40		20 58		21 31	21 40		22 10	22 31	22 40		23 10	23 31	23 58	00 31
Godalming	d		20 34	20 43		21 01	21 11	21 34	21 43		22 13	22 34	22 43		23 13	23 34	00 01	00 34
Milford (Surrey)	d		20 38			21 05		21 38				22 38				23 38		00s38
Witley	d	←	20 42		←	21 09		21 42		←		22 42		←		23 43		00s43
Haslemere 4	a	20 18	20 49	20 54	20 49	21 16	21 21	21 49	21 54	21 49	22 24	22 49	22 54	22 49	23 24	23 49	00 12	00 49
	d	20 26	20 58	20 55	20 58		21 22	21 58	21 55	21 58	22 25	22 58	22 55	22 58	23 25	23 50	00 12	00 50
Liphook	d	20 31	→		21 03			→		22 03		→		23 03		23 55		00s55
Liss	d	20 37			21 09					22 09				23 09		00 01		01s01
Petersfield	d	20 43		21 06	21 15		21 33		22 06	22 15	22 36		23 06	23 15	23 36	00 06	00 23	01 06
Rowlands Castle	d	20 52			21 24					22 24				23 24		00 15		01s16
Havant	a	21 00		21 18	21 29		21 45		22 18	22 29	22 48		23 18	23 29	23 48	00 20	00 36	01 21
	d			21 19	21 30		21 46		22 19	22 30	22 49		23 19	23 30	23 49	00 21	00 36	01 21
Bedhampton	a				21 33					22 33				23 33		00 24		01s24
Hilsea	a				21 41					22 38				23 38		00 29		01s29
Fratton	a			21 28	21 45		21 54		22 28	22 42	22 58		23 28	23 42	23 58	00 33	00 45	01s33
Portsmouth & Southsea	a			21 32	21 48		21 58		22 32	22 46	23 03		23 31	23 46	00 02	00 37	00 50	01 37
Portsmouth Harbour ⛴	a			21 37			22 02		22 37		23 08		23 36		00 07		00 54	

Saturdays

14 December to 17 May

Station		SW 1	SW 1	SW 1	SW 1	SW 1	SW 1	SW 1	SW 1	SW 1	SW 1	SW 1	SW 1	SW 1	SW 1	SW 1		SW 1	SW 1 🛒	SW 1	SW 1	SW 1 🛒
London Waterloo 15 ⊖	d					05 00	05 20	06 15	06 45	07 15	07 30	07 45	08 00		08 15	08 30	and at the same minutes past each hour until	12 45	13 00		13 15	13 30
Clapham Junction 10	d																					
Woking	a					05 51	06 08	06 41	07 11	07 42	07 54	08 11	08 24		08 41	08 54		13 11	13 24		13 41	13 54
	d			00 13		05 53	06 13	06 43	07 13	07 44	07 55	08 13	08 25		08 43	08 55		13 13	13 25		13 43	13 55
Worplesdon	d			00 18			06 18		07 18			08 18						13 18				
Guildford	a			00 24		06 00	06 23	06 51	07 23	07 51	08 03	08 23	08 33		08 50	09 03		13 23	13 33		13 50	14 03
	d			00 25	05 15	06 02	06 25	06 53	07 25	07 53	08 04	08 25	08 34		08 52	09 04		13 25	13 34		13 52	14 04
Farncombe	d			00 31		06 08	06 31	06 59	07 31	07 59		08 31			08 58			13 31			13 58	
Godalming	d		00 01	00 34		06 11	06 34	07 02	07 34	08 02		08 34			09 01			13 34			14 01	
Milford (Surrey)	d			00s38		06 15		07 06		08 06					09 05						14 05	
Witley	d			00s43		06 19		07 10		08 10				←	09 09					←	14 09	
Haslemere 4	a		00 12	00 49	05 29	06 26	06 44	07 17	07 44	08 17	08 21	08 45	08 48	08 45	09 16	09 20		13 45	13 48	13 45	14 16	14 20
	d		00 12	00 50	05 30		06 45		07 45		08 21	08 55	08 49	08 55		09 21		13 55	13 49	13 55		14 21
Liphook	d			00s55	05 35		06 50		07 50			→		09 00				→		14 00		
Liss	d	00 01		01s01	05 41		06 56		07 56					09 06						14 06		
Petersfield	d	00 06	00 23	01 06	05 46		07 01		08 01		08 32		09 00	09 11		09 32			14 00	14 11		14 32
Rowlands Castle	d	00 15		01s16	05 56		07 11		08 11					09 21						14 21		
Havant	a	00 20	00 36	01 21	06 01		07 19		08 16		08 49		09 15	09 26		09 49			14 15	14 26		14 49
	d	00 21	00 36	01 21	06 02		07 20		08 17		08 50		09 16	09 27		09 50			14 16	14 27		14 50
Bedhampton	a	00 24		01s24	06 04		07 22		08 19					09 29						14 29		
Hilsea	a	00 29		01s29	06 10		07 27		08 25					09 36						14 36		
Fratton	a	00 33	00 45	01s33	06 14		07 31		08 29		08 59		09 24	09 40		09 59			14 24	14 40		14 59
Portsmouth & Southsea	a	00 37	00 50	01 37	06 18		07 35		08 32		09 02		09 28	09 44		10 02			14 28	14 44		15 02
Portsmouth Harbour ⛴	a		00 54		06 22		07 40		08 37		09 07		09 33			10 07			14 33			15 07

Station		SW 1	SW 1 🛒	SW 1	SW 1	SW 1 🛒	SW 1	SW 1 🛒		SW 1	SW 1	SW 1 🛒	SW 1	SW 1 🛒	SW 1	SW 1	SW 1 🛒	SW 1	SW 1	SW 1	SW 1	SW 1	SW 1
London Waterloo 15 ⊖	d	13 45	14 00		14 15	14 30	14 45	15 00	and at the same minutes past each hour until		18 15	18 30	18 45	19 00		19 15	19 30	19 45	20 00		20 15	20 30	20 45
Clapham Junction 10	d																						
Woking	a	14 11	14 24		14 41	14 54	15 11	15 24			18 41	18 54	19 11	19 24		19 41	19 54	20 11	20 24		20 41	20 54	21 11
	d	14 13	14 25		14 43	14 55	15 13	15 25			18 43	18 55	19 13	19 25		19 43	19 55	20 13	20 25		20 43	20 55	21 13
Worplesdon	d	14 18					15 18						19 18					20 18					21 18
Guildford	a	14 23	14 33		14 50	15 03	15 23	15 33			18 50	19 03	19 23	19 33		19 50	20 03	20 23	20 33		20 50	21 03	21 23
	d	14 25	14 34		14 52	15 04	15 25	15 34			18 52	19 04	19 25	19 34		19 52	20 04	20 25	20 34		20 52	21 04	21 25
Farncombe	d	14 31			14 58		15 31				18 58		19 31			19 58		20 31			20 58		21 31
Godalming	d	14 34			15 01		15 34				19 01		19 34			20 01		20 34			21 01		21 34
Milford (Surrey)	d				15 05						19 05					20 05					21 05		21 38
Witley	d			←	15 09					←	19 09				←	20 09				←	21 09		21 42
Haslemere 4	a	14 45	14 48	14 45	15 16	15 20	15 45	15 48		18 45	19 16	19 20	19 45	19 48	19 45	20 16	20 20	20 45	20 48	20 45	21 16	21 20	21 49
	d	14 55	14 49	14 55		15 21	15 55	15 49		18 55		19 21	19 55	19 49	19 55		20 21	20 55	20 49	20 55		21 21	21 58
Liphook	d	→		15 00			→			19 00			→		20 00			→		21 00			→
Liss	d			15 06						19 06					20 06					21 06			
Petersfield	d		15 00	15 11		15 32		16 00		19 11		19 32		20 00	20 11		20 32		21 00	21 11		21 32	
Rowlands Castle	d			15 21						19 21					20 21					21 21			
Havant	a		15 14	15 26		15 49		16 15		19 26		19 49		20 15	20 29		20 49		21 15	21 26		21 44	
	d		15 16	15 27		15 50		16 16		19 27		19 50		20 16	20 30		20 50		21 16	21 27		21 45	
Bedhampton	a			15 29						19 29					20 32					21 29			
Hilsea	a			15 36						19 36					20 41					21 36			
Fratton	a		15 24	15 40		15 59		16 24		19 40		19 59		20 24	20 45		20 59		21 24	21 40		21 54	
Portsmouth & Southsea	a		15 28	15 44		16 02		16 28		19 44		20 02		20 28	20 48		21 02		21 28	21 43		21 58	
Portsmouth Harbour ⛴	a		15 33			16 07		16 33				20 07		20 33			21 07		21 33			22 03	

Table 156

Saturdays

14 December to 17 May

London - Guildford, Haslemere and Portsmouth

Network Diagram - see first Page of Table 155

		SW	SW	SW	SW	SW	SW	SW	SW	SW	SW
		1	1	1	1	1	1	1	1	1	1
London Waterloo 15 ⊖	d	21 00		21 30	21 45	22 00		22 30	22 45	23 15	23 45
Clapham Junction 10	d										
Woking	a	21 24		21 54	22 11	22 24		22 54	23 11	23 41	00 11
	d	21 25		21 55	22 13	22 25		22 55	23 13	23 43	00 13
Worplesdon	d				22 18				23 18		00 18
Guildford	a	21 33		22 03	22 23	22 33		23 03	23 23	23 51	00 24
	d	21 34		22 04	22 25	22 34		23 04	23 25	23 52	00 25
Farncombe	d	21 40		22 10	22 31	22 40		23 10	23 31	23 58	00 31
Godalming	d	21 43		22 13	22 34	22 43		23 13	23 34	00 01	00 34
Milford (Surrey)	d				22 38				23 38		00s38
Witley	d		←		22 42		←		23 42		00s43
Haslemere 4	a	21 54	21 49	22 24	22 49	22 54	22 49	23 24	23 49	00 12	00 49
	d	21 55	21 58	22 25	22 58	22 55	22 58	23 25	23 50	00 12	00 50
Liphook	d		22 03		→		23 03		23 55		00s55
Liss	d		22 09				23 09		00 01		01s01
Petersfield	d	22 06	22 15	22 36		23 06	23 15	23 36	00 06	00 23	01 06
Rowlands Castle	d		22 24				23 24		00 15		01s16
Havant	a	22 18	22 29	22 48		23 18	23 29	23 48	00 20	00 36	01 21
	d	22 19	22 30	22 49		23 19	23 30	23 49	00 21	00 36	01 21
Bedhampton	a		22 33				23 33		00 24		01s24
Hilsea	a		22 41				23 40		00 29		01s29
Fratton	a	22 28	22 45	22 58		23 28	23 44	23 58	00 33	00 45	01s33
Portsmouth & Southsea	a	22 32	22 49	23 02		23 31	23 48	00 02	00 37	00 49	01 37
Portsmouth Harbour ⛴	a	22 36	22 53	23 08		23 36	23 53	00 07		00 54	

Sundays

8 December to 11 May

		SW	SW	SW	SW	SW	SW	SW	SW	SW	SW		SW	SW
		1	1	1	1	1	1	1	1	1	1		1	1
														🛒
London Waterloo 15 ⊖	d					08 00	08 30	09 00	09 30	10 00	10 30		13 00	13 30
Clapham Junction 10	d													
Woking	a					08 34	09 03	09 34	10 03	10 31	11 01		13 31	14 01
	d			00 13	07 32	08 35	09 04	09 35	10 04	10 32	11 02		13 32	14 02
Worplesdon	d			00 18										
Guildford	a			00 24	07 39	08 43	09 12	09 43	10 12	10 40	11 10		13 40	14 10
	d			00 25	07 41	08 45	09 14	09 45	10 14	10 42	11 12	and at	13 42	14 12
Farncombe	d			00 31	07 48	08 53		09 53		10 48		the same	13 48	
Godalming	d		00 01	00 34	07 51	08 56		09 56		10 51		minutes	13 51	
Milford (Surrey)	d			00s38	07 55	09 00		10 00		10 55		past	13 55	
Witley	d			00s43	07 59	09 04		10 04		10 59		each	13 59	
Haslemere 4	a		00 12	00 49	08 06	09 11	09 28	10 11	10 28	11 06	11 26	hour until	14 06	14 26
	d		00 12	00 50	08 07	09 12	09 29	10 12	10 29	11 07	11 27		14 07	14 27
Liphook	d			00s55	08 12	09 17		10 17		11 12			14 12	
Liss	d	00 01		01s01	08 18	09 23		10 23		11 18			14 18	
Petersfield	d	00 06	00 23	01 06	08 23	09 28	09 40	10 28	10 40	11 23	11 38		14 23	14 38
Rowlands Castle	d	00 15		01s16	08 33	09 38		10 38		11 33			14 33	
Havant	a	00 20	00 36	01 21	08 38	09 43	09 52	10 43	10 52	11 38	11 50		14 38	14 50
	d	00 21	00 36	01 21	08 39	09 44	09 53	10 44	10 53	11 39	11 51		14 39	14 51
Bedhampton	a	00 24		01s24	08 41	09 46		10 46		11 41			14 41	
Hilsea	a	00 29		01s29										
Fratton	a	00 33	00 45	01s33	08 49	09 54	10 02	10 54	11 01	11 49	12 00		14 49	15 00
Portsmouth & Southsea	a	00 37	00 49	01 37	08 53	09 58	10 06	10 58	11 05	11 53	12 04		14 53	15 04
Portsmouth Harbour ⛴	a		00 54		08 57	10 03	10 11	11 03	11 11	11 58	12 11		14 58	15 11

		SW	SW	SW	SW	SW	SW	SW	SW	SW
		1	1	1	1	1	1	1	1	1
			🛒		🛒		🛒		🛒	
London Waterloo 15 ⊖	d	14 00	14 30	15 00	15 30	16 00	16 30	17 00	17 30	18 00
Clapham Junction 10	d									
Woking	a	14 31	15 01	15 31	16 01	16 31	17 01	17 31	18 01	18 31
	d	14 32	15 02	15 32	16 02	16 32	17 02	17 32	18 02	18 32
Worplesdon	d									
Guildford	a	14 40	15 10	15 40	16 10	16 40	17 10	17 40	18 10	18 40
	d	14 42	15 12	15 42	16 12	16 42	17 12	17 42	18 12	18 42
Farncombe	d	14 48		15 48		16 48		17 48		18 48
Godalming	d	14 51		15 51		16 51		17 51		18 51
Milford (Surrey)	d	14 55		15 55		16 55		17 55		18 55
Witley	d	14 59		15 59		16 59		17 59		18 59
Haslemere 4	a	15 06	15 26	16 06	16 26	17 06	17 26	18 06	18 26	19 06
	d	15 07	15 27	16 07	16 27	17 07	17 27	18 07	18 27	19 07
Liphook	d	15 12		16 12		17 12		18 12		19 12
Liss	d	15 18		16 18		17 18		18 18		19 18
Petersfield	d	15 23	15 38	16 23	16 38	17 23	17 38	18 23	18 38	19 23
Rowlands Castle	d	15 33		16 33		17 33		18 33		19 33
Havant	a	15 38	15 50	16 38	16 53	17 38	17 50	18 38	18 53	19 38
	d	15 39	15 51	16 39	16 54	17 39	17 51	18 39	18 54	19 39
Bedhampton	a	15 41		16 41		17 41		18 41		19 41
Hilsea	a									
Fratton	a	15 49	16 00	16 49	17 02	17 49	18 00	18 49	19 02	19 49
Portsmouth & Southsea	a	15 54	16 04	16 53	17 06	17 53	18 04	18 53	19 06	19 53
Portsmouth Harbour ⛴	a	15 58	16 11	16 58	17 11	17 58	18 11	18 58	19 11	19 58

		SW	SW	SW	SW	SW	SW	SW	SW	SW	SW	SW
		1	1	1	1	1	1	1	1	1	1	1
		🛒		🛒		🛒						
London Waterloo 15 ⊖	d	18 30	19 00	19 30	20 00	20 30	21 00	21 30	22 00	22 30	23 00	23 30
Clapham Junction 10	d											
Woking	a	19 01	19 31	20 01	20 31	21 01	21 31	22 01	22 31	23 01	23 31	00 01
	d	19 02	19 32	20 02	20 32	21 02	21 32	22 02	22 32	23 02	23 32	00 03
Worplesdon	d											
Guildford	a	19 10	19 40	20 10	20 40	21 10	21 40	22 10	22 40	23 10	23 40	00 10
	d	19 12	19 42	20 12	20 42	21 12	21 42	22 12	22 42	23 12	23 42	00 12
Farncombe	d		19 48		20 48		21 48		22 48		23 48	
Godalming	d		19 51		20 51		21 51		22 51		23 51	
Milford (Surrey)	d		19 55		20 55		21 55		22 55		23 55	
Witley	d		19 59		20 59		21 59		22 59		23 59	
Haslemere 4	a	19 26	20 06	20 26	21 06	21 26	22 06	22 26	23 06	23 26	00 06	00 26
	d	19 27	20 07	20 27	21 07	21 27	22 07	22 27	23 07	23 27	00 07	00 27
Liphook	d		20 12		21 12		22 12		23 12		00 12	
Liss	d		20 18		21 18		22 18		23 18		00 18	
Petersfield	d	19 38	20 23	20 38	21 23	21 38	22 23	22 38	23 23	23 38	00 23	00 38
Rowlands Castle	d		20 33		21 33		22 33		23 33		00 33	
Havant	a	19 50	20 38	20 50	21 38	21 50	22 38	22 50	23 38	23 50	00 38	00 50
	d	19 51	20 39	20 51	21 39	21 51	22 39	22 51	23 39	23 51	00 39	00 51
Bedhampton	a		20 41		21 41		22 41		23 41		00 41	
Hilsea	a											
Fratton	a	20 00	20 49	21 00	21 49	22 00	22 49	23 00	23 49	23 59	00 49	01 00
Portsmouth & Southsea	a	20 04	20 53	21 04	21 53	22 04	22 53	23 04	23 53	00 04	00 53	01 04
Portsmouth Harbour ⛴	a	20 11	20 58	21 09	21 58	22 08	22 58	23 09	23 58	00 09	00 58	01 09

Table 156R

Mondays to Fridays

9 December to 16 May

Portsmouth, Haslemere and Guildford - London

Network Diagram - see first Page of Table 155

Miles	Station		SW MO	SW MX	SW	SW	SW	SW	SW	SW	SW	SW	SW	SW	SW	SW	SW	SW	SW	SW	SW	SW	SW
			1	1	1	1	1	1	1	1	1	1	1	1	1	1	1	1	1	1	1	1	1
							trolley			trolley			trolley			trolley			trolley		trolley		trolley
0	**Portsmouth Harbour** ⛴	d			04 30		05 19		05 50	06 15			06 42		06 55	07 13		07 29	07 45		08 15		08 45
0¾	**Portsmouth & Southsea**	d			04 35		05 24		05 55	06 20			06 47		07 00	07 18		07 34	07 50		08 20	08 24	08 50
1¾	Fratton	d			04 39		05 28		05 59	06 24			06 51		07 04	07 22		07 38	07 54		08 24	08 28	08 54
4	Hilsea	d			04 43		05 32		06 03			06 42			07 08			07 42				08 32	
7¼	Bedhampton	d			04 48		05 37		06 08			06 47			07 13			07 48				08 37	
8	**Havant**	a			04 50		05 39		06 10	06 33		06 49	06 59		07 15	07 30		07 50	08 03		08 32	08 39	09 02
—		d			04 51		05 40		06 11	06 34		06 50	07 00	07 11	07 16	07 32		07 52	08 04		08 34	08 40	09 04
11¼	Rowlands Castle	d			04 57		05 46		06 16			06 56			07 22			07 57				08 46	
19½	Petersfield	d			05 08		05 57		06 29	06 48		07 07	07 14	07 25	07 33	07 46		08 09	08 18		08 48	08 57	09 18
23	Liss	d		00 02	05 13		06 02		06 34			07 12	07 20		07 38			08 14				09 02	
27¾	Liphook	d		00 09	05 20		06 09		06 41			07 19	07 27		07 45		←	08 21		←		09 09	
31½	**Haslemere** 4	a		00 15	05 25		06 14		06 46	07 01		07 25	07 33	07 38	07 51	07 59	07 51	08 27	08 30	08 27	09 01	09 15	09 31
—		d		00 15	05 26	06 00	06 16	06 30	06 47	07 02	07 10	07 26	07 35	07 40	08 07	08 00	08 07	08 39	08 32	08 39	09 02	09 15	09 32
36	Witley	d		00 21	05 32	06 06		06 36			07 16			07 46	→		08 13	→		08 45			
38¼	Milford (Surrey)	d		00 25	05 36	06 11		06 40			07 21			07 50			08 17			08 49			
40	Godalming	d		00 29	05 40	06 15		06 44	06 57		07 25	07 35	07 45	07 54			08 21			08 53		09 25	
41	Farncombe	d		00 32	05 43	06 18		06 47	07 00		07 28	07 38		07 57			08 25			08 57		09 28	
44¼	**Guildford**	a		00 37	05 48	06 23	06 29	06 52	07 06	07 15	07 33	07 43	07 52	08 02		08 13	08 30		08 46	09 02	09 15	09 33	09 45
—		d	00 05		05 50	06 24	06 31	06 53	07 07	07 17	07 34	07 45	07 54	08 03		08 15	08 31		08 54	09 03	09 17	09 34	09 47
47¾	Worplesdon	d			05 55	06 30		06 59			07 40	07 50				08 20	08 37					09 40	
50½	**Woking**	a	00 13		06 00	06 35	06 40	07 03	07 15	07 25		07 55		08 11		08 26	08 41			09 11	09 27	09 44	09 59
—		d			06 01	06 37	06 41	07 05	07 17	07 26		07 57		08 12		08 27	08 43			09 13	09 28	09 46	10 00
70½	Clapham Junction 10	a																					
74½	**London Waterloo** 15 ⊖	a			06 29	07 08	07 12	07 36	07 45	07 54	08 11	08 24	08 32	08 41		08 55	09 13		09 31	09 43	09 55	10 13	10 27

Station		SW	SW	SW	SW	SW	SW	SW	SW		SW	SW	SW	SW	SW	SW	SW	SW	SW	SW	SW	SW	SW
		1	1	1	1	1	1	1	1		1	1	1	1	1	1	1	1	1	1	1	1	1
			trolley		trolley		trolley		trolley			trolley		trolley		trolley		trolley		trolley			trolley
Portsmouth Harbour ⛴	d		09 15	09 19	09 45		10 15		10 45	and at the same minutes past each hour until		13 15		13 45		14 15		14 45		15 15			15 45
Portsmouth & Southsea	d		09 20	09 24	09 50		10 20	10 24	10 50			13 20	13 24	13 50		14 20	14 24	14 50		15 20	15 24		15 50
Fratton	d		09 24	09 28	09 54		10 24	10 28	10 54			13 24	13 28	13 54		14 24	14 28	14 54		15 24	15 28		15 54
Hilsea	d			09 32				10 32					13 32				14 32				15 32		
Bedhampton	d			09 37				10 37					13 37				14 37				15 37		
Havant	a		09 33	09 39	10 03		10 33	10 39	11 03			13 33	13 39	14 03		14 33	14 39	15 03		15 33	15 39		16 03
	d		09 34	09 40	10 04		10 34	10 40	11 04			13 34	13 40	14 04		14 34	14 40	15 04		15 34	15 40	15 54	16 04
Rowlands Castle	d			09 46				10 46					13 46				14 46				15 46		
Petersfield	d		09 48	09 57	10 18		10 48	10 57	11 18			13 48	13 57	14 18		14 48	14 57	15 18		15 48	15 57	16 10	16 18
Liss	d			10 02				11 02					14 02				15 02				16 02		16 23
Liphook	d			10 09				11 09					14 09				15 09				16 09		16 30
Haslemere 4	a		10 00	10 15	10 31		11 00	11 15	11 31			14 00	14 15	14 31		15 00	15 15	15 31		16 00	16 15	16 23	16 35
	d	09 39	10 02	10 15	10 32	10 39	11 02	11 15	11 32		13 39	14 02	14 15	14 32	14 39	15 02	15 15	15 32	15 37	16 02	16 15	16 24	16 37
Witley	d	09 45				10 45					13 45				14 45				15 43			16 30	16 43
Milford (Surrey)	d	09 49				10 49					13 49				14 49				15 47			16 34	16 47
Godalming	d	09 53		10 25		10 53		11 25			13 53		14 25		14 53		15 25		15 51		16 25	16 38	16 51
Farncombe	d	09 56		10 28		10 56		11 28			13 56		14 28		14 56		15 28		15 54		16 28	16 41	16 54
Guildford	a	10 01	10 15	10 33	10 46	11 01	11 15	11 33	11 45		14 01	14 15	14 33	14 45	15 01	15 15	15 33	15 45	15 59	16 15	16 33	16 46	16 59
	d	10 02	10 17	10 34	10 47	11 02	11 17	11 34	11 47		14 02	14 17	14 34	14 47	15 02	15 17	15 34	15 47	16 00	16 17	16 34	16 47	17 00
Worplesdon	d			10 40				11 40					14 40				15 40		16 06		16 40		17 06
Woking	a	10 11	10 25	10 44	10 57	11 11	11 25	11 44	11 57		14 11	14 25	14 44	14 57	15 11	15 25	15 44	15 57	16 11	16 25	16 44	16 57	17 11
	d	10 12	10 26	10 46	10 59	11 12	11 26	11 46	11 59		14 12	14 26	14 46	14 59	15 12	15 26	15 46	15 59	16 12	16 26	16 46	16 59	17 12
Clapham Junction 10	a																						
London Waterloo 15 ⊖	a	10 40	10 51	11 13	11 24	11 40	11 51	12 13	12 23		14 40	14 51	15 13	15 23	15 43	15 51	16 13	16 24	16 40	16 51	17 14	17 27	17 43

Station		SW	SW	SW	SW	SW	SW	SW	SW	SW	SW	SW	SW	SW	SW	SW	SW	SW	SW	SW FO	SW FX	SW
		1	1	1	1	1	1	1	1	1	1	1	1	1	1	1	1	1	1	1	1	1
		trolley			trolley	trolley		trolley	trolley		trolley											
Portsmouth Harbour ⛴	d	16 15			16 45	17 15	17 19	17 45	18 15		18 45		19 15	19 19	19 45	20 15	20 19	20 45	21 19	22 19	22 19	23 19
Portsmouth & Southsea	d	16 20	16 24		16 50	17 20	17 24	17 50	18 20	18 24	18 50		19 20	19 24	19 50	20 20	20 24	20 50	21 24	22 24	22 24	23 24
Fratton	d	16 24	16 28		16 54	17 24	17 28	17 54	18 24	18 28	18 54		19 24	19 28	19 54	20 24	20 28	20 54	21 28	22 28	22 28	23 28
Hilsea	d		16 32				17 32			18 32				19 32			20 32		21 32	22 32	22 32	23 32
Bedhampton	d		16 37				17 37			18 37				19 37			20 37		21 37	22 37	22 37	23 37
Havant	a	16 33	16 39		17 03	17 33	17 39	18 03	18 33	18 39	19 03		19 33	19 39	20 03	20 32	20 39	21 02	21 39	22 39	22 39	23 39
	d	16 34	16 40	16 56	17 04	17 34	17 40	18 04	18 34	18 40	19 04		19 34	19 40	20 04	20 34	20 40	21 04	21 40	22 40	22 40	23 40
Rowlands Castle	d		16 46				17 46			18 46				19 46			20 46		21 46	22 46	22 46	23 46
Petersfield	d	16 48	16 57	17 10	17 18	17 48	17 57	18 18	18 48	18 57	19 18		19 48	19 57	20 18	20 48	20 57	21 18	21 57	22 57	22 57	23 57
Liss	d		17 02		17 23		18 02			19 02				20 02			21 02		22 02	23 02	23 02	00 02
Liphook	d		17 09		17 30		18 09			19 09				20 09			21 09		22 09	23 09	23 09	00 09
Haslemere 4	a	17 00	17 15	17 23	17 35	18 01	18 15	18 31	19 00	19 14	19 31		20 01	20 15	20 31	21 01	21 15	21 31	22 14	23 14	23 14	00 15
	d	17 02	17 15	17 32	17 37	18 02	18 15	18 32	19 02	19 15	19 32	19 39	20 02	20 15	20 32	21 02	21 15	21 32	22 15	23 15	23 15	00 15
Witley	d				17 43			18 38				19 45		20 21			21 21		22 21	23 21	23 21	00 21
Milford (Surrey)	d				17 47			18 42				19 49		20 25			21 25		22 25	23 25	23 25	00 25
Godalming	d		17 25		17 51		18 25	18 46	19 11	19 25		19 53		20 29			21 29		22 29	23 29	23 29	00 29
Farncombe	d		17 28		17 54		18 28	18 49	19 14	19 28		19 56		20 32			21 32		22 32	23 32	23 32	00 32
Guildford	a	17 15	17 33	17 45	17 59	18 15	18 33	18 54	19 19	19 33	19 45	20 01	20 15	20 37	20 45	21 16	21 37	21 45	22 37	23 37	23 37	00 37
	d	17 17	17 34	17 47	18 00	18 17	18 34	18 55	19 21	19 34	19 47	20 02	20 17	20 39	20 47	21 17	21 39	21 47	22 39	23 39	23 39	
Worplesdon	d		17 40		18 06		18 40			19 40				20 44			21 44		22 44	23 44	23 44	
Woking	a	17 25	17 44	17 58	18 11		18 44	19 03	19 28	19 45	19 57	20 11	20 25	20 52	20 58	21 25	21 49	21 57	22 49	23 49	23 49	
	d	17 26	17 46	17 59	18 12		18 46	19 05	19 30	19 46	19 59	20 12	20 26	20 53	21 00	21 26	21 50	21 59	22 50	23 56	23 56	
Clapham Junction 10	a																					
London Waterloo 15 ⊖	a	17 54	18 14	18 27	18 43	18 59	19 13	19 29	19 59	20 14	20 24	20 40	20 50	21 21	21 27	21 50	22 18	22 27	23 19	00 32	00 33	

Table 156R

Saturdays

14 December to 17 May

Portsmouth, Haslemere and Guildford - London

Network Diagram - see first Page of Table 155

		SW	SW	SW	SW	SW	SW	SW	SW	SW		SW	SW	SW	SW	SW	SW	SW	SW	SW		SW	SW	SW	SW
		1	1	1	1	1	1	1	1	1		1	1	1	1	1	1	1	1	1		1	1	1	1
							🛒		🛒			🛒		🛒		🛒		🛒		🛒			🛒		🛒
Portsmouth Harbour ⛴	d		04 43	05 19		06 19	06 45		07 15			07 45		08 15		08 45		09 15		09 45			10 15		10 45
Portsmouth & Southsea	d		04 48	05 24		06 24	06 50		07 20	07 24		07 50		08 20	08 24	08 50		09 20	09 24	09 50			10 20	10 24	10 50
Fratton	d		04 52	05 28		06 28	06 54		07 24	07 28		07 54		08 24	08 28	08 54		09 24	09 28	09 54			10 24	10 28	10 54
Hilsea	d		04 56	05 32		06 32				07 32					08 32				09 32					10 32	
Bedhampton	d		05 01	05 37		06 37				07 37					08 37				09 37					10 37	
Havant	a		05 03	05 39		06 40	07 03		07 33	07 39		08 03		08 33	08 39	09 03		09 33	09 39	10 03			10 33	10 39	11 03
	d		05 04	05 40		06 40	07 04		07 34	07 40		08 04		08 34	08 40	09 04		09 34	09 40	10 04			10 34	10 40	11 04
Rowlands Castle	d		05 09	05 46		06 46				07 46					08 46				09 46					10 46	
Petersfield	d		05 20	05 57		06 57	07 18		07 48	07 57		08 18		08 48	08 57	09 18		09 48	09 57	10 18			10 48	10 57	11 18
Liss	d	00 02	05 25	06 02		07 02				08 02					09 02				10 02					11 02	
Liphook	d	00 09	05 32	06 09		07 09				08 09					09 09				10 09					11 09	
Haslemere 4	a	00 15	05 38	06 14		07 15	07 31		08 01	08 15		08 31		09 00	09 15	09 31		10 00	10 15	10 31			11 00	11 15	11 31
	d	00 15	05 39	06 15	06 39	07 15	07 32	07 39	08 02	08 15		08 32	08 39	09 02	09 15	09 32	09 39	10 02	10 15	10 32		10 39	11 02	11 15	11 32
Witley	d	00 21	05 45		06 45			07 45					08 45				09 45					10 45			
Milford (Surrey)	d	00 25	05 49		06 49			07 49					08 49				09 49					10 49			
Godalming	d	00 29	05 53	06 25	06 53	07 25		07 53		08 25			08 53		09 25		09 53		10 25			10 53		11 25	
Farncombe	d	00 32	05 56	06 28	06 56	07 28		07 56		08 28			08 56		09 28		09 56		10 28			10 56		11 28	
Guildford	a	00 37	06 01	06 33	07 01	07 33	07 45	08 01	08 15	08 33		08 45	09 01	09 15	09 33	09 45	10 01	10 15	10 33	10 45		11 01	11 15	11 33	11 45
	d		06 02	06 34	07 02	07 34	07 47	08 02	08 17	08 34		08 47	09 02	09 17	09 34	09 47	10 02	10 17	10 34	10 47		11 02	11 17	11 34	11 47
Worplesdon	d			06 40		07 40				08 40					09 40				10 40					11 40	
Woking	a		06 11	06 44	07 11	07 44	07 57	08 10	08 26	08 44		08 57	09 11	09 25	09 44	09 57	10 11	10 25	10 44	10 57		11 11	11 25	11 44	11 57
	d		06 13	06 46	07 12	07 46	07 59	08 13	08 27	08 46		08 59	09 12	09 26	09 46	09 59	10 12	10 26	10 46	10 59		11 12	11 26	11 46	11 59
Clapham Junction 10	a																								
London Waterloo 15 ⊖	a		06 40	07 13	07 40	08 13	08 23	08 42	08 51	09 13		09 23	09 40	09 51	10 13	10 23	10 40	10 51	11 13	11 23		11 40	11 51	12 13	12 27

		SW	SW	SW	SW	SW		SW	SW	SW	SW	SW	SW	SW	SW	SW		SW	SW	SW	SW	SW	SW	SW	SW
		1	1	1	1	1		1	1	1	1	1	1	1	1	1		1	1	1	1	1	1	1	1
			🛒		🛒			🛒		🛒		🛒		🛒		🛒			🛒		🛒		🛒		🛒
Portsmouth Harbour ⛴	d		11 15		11 45			12 15		12 45		13 15		13 45		14 15			14 45		15 15		15 45		16 15
Portsmouth & Southsea	d		11 20	11 24	11 50			12 20	12 24	12 50		13 20	13 24	13 50		14 20		14 24	14 50		15 20	15 24	15 50		16 20
Fratton	d		11 24	11 28	11 54			12 24	12 28	12 54		13 24	13 28	13 54		14 24		14 28	14 54		15 24	15 28	15 54		16 24
Hilsea	d			11 32					12 32				13 32					14 32				15 32			
Bedhampton	d			11 37					12 37				13 37					14 37				15 37			
Havant	a		11 33	11 39	12 03			12 33	12 39	13 03		13 33	13 39	14 03		14 33		14 39	15 03		15 33	15 39	16 03		16 33
	d		11 34	11 40	12 04			12 34	12 40	13 04		13 34	13 40	14 04		14 34		14 40	15 04		15 34	15 40	16 04		16 34
Rowlands Castle	d			11 46					12 46				13 46					14 46				15 46			
Petersfield	d		11 48	11 57	12 18			12 48	12 57	13 18		13 48	13 57	14 18		14 48		14 57	15 18		15 48	15 57	16 18		16 48
Liss	d			12 02					13 02				14 02					15 02				16 02			
Liphook	d			12 09					13 09				14 09					15 09				16 09			
Haslemere 4	a		12 00	12 15	12 31			13 00	13 15	13 31		14 00	14 15	14 31		15 00		15 15	15 31		16 00	16 15	16 31		17 00
	d	11 39	12 02	12 15	12 32	12 39		13 02	13 15	13 32	13 39	14 02	14 15	14 32	14 39	15 02		15 15	15 32	15 39	16 02	16 15	16 32	16 39	17 02
Witley	d	11 45				12 45					13 45				14 45					15 45				16 45	
Milford (Surrey)	d	11 49				12 49					13 49				14 49					15 49				16 49	
Godalming	d	11 53		12 25		12 53			13 25		13 53		14 25		14 53			15 25		15 53		16 25		16 53	
Farncombe	d	11 56		12 28		12 56			13 28		13 56		14 28		14 56			15 28		15 56		16 28		16 56	
Guildford	a	12 01	12 15	12 33	12 45	13 01		13 15	13 33	13 45	14 01	14 15	14 33	14 45	15 01	15 15		15 33	15 45	16 01	16 15	16 33	16 45	17 01	17 15
	d	12 02	12 17	12 34	12 47	13 02		13 17	13 34	13 47	14 02	14 17	14 34	14 47	15 02	15 17		15 34	15 47	16 02	16 17	16 34	16 47	17 02	17 17
Worplesdon	d			12 40					13 40				14 40					15 40				16 40			
Woking	a	12 11	12 25	12 44	12 57	13 11		13 25	13 44	13 57	14 11	14 25	14 44	14 57	15 11	15 25		15 44	15 57	16 11	16 25	16 44	16 57	17 11	17 25
	d	12 12	12 26	12 46	12 59	13 12		13 26	13 46	13 59	14 12	14 26	14 46	14 59	15 12	15 26		15 46	15 59	16 12	16 26	16 46	16 59	17 12	17 26
Clapham Junction 10	a																								
London Waterloo 15 ⊖	a	12 43	12 57	13 13	13 27	13 43		13 57	14 14	14 27	14 41	14 57	15 14	15 27	15 41	15 57		16 13	16 23	16 40	16 51	17 13	17 23	17 40	17 51

		SW		SW	SW	SW	SW	SW	SW	SW	SW	SW		SW	SW	SW	SW	SW	SW	SW	SW	SW		SW	
		1		1	1	1	1	1	1	1	1	1		1	1	1	1	1	1	1	1	1		1	
				🛒				🛒																	
Portsmouth Harbour ⛴	d			16 45			17 19	17 45		18 15		18 45			19 15		19 45	20 15		20 45	21 19	22 19		23 19	
Portsmouth & Southsea	d	16 24		16 50		17 10	17 24	17 50		18 20	18 24	18 50			19 20	19 24	19 50	20 20	20 24	20 50	21 24	22 24		23 24	
Fratton	d	16 28		16 54		17 14	17 28	17 54		18 24	18 28	18 54			19 24	19 28	19 54	20 24	20 28	20 54	21 28	22 28		23 28	
Hilsea	d	16 32				17 18	17 32				18 32					19 32			20 32		21 32	22 32		23 32	
Bedhampton	d	16 37				17 23	17 37				18 37					19 37			20 37		21 37	22 37		23 37	
Havant	a	16 39		17 03		17 25	17 39	18 03		18 33	18 39	19 03			19 33	19 39	20 03	20 32	20 39	21 02	21 39	22 39		23 39	
	d	16 40		17 04		17 26	17 40	18 04		18 34	18 40	19 04			19 34	19 40	20 04	20 34	20 40	21 04	21 40	22 40		23 40	
Rowlands Castle	d	16 46				17 32	17 46				18 46					19 46			20 46		21 46	22 46		23 46	
Petersfield	d	16 57		17 18		17 43	17 57	18 18		18 48	18 57	19 18			19 48	19 57	20 18	20 48	20 57	21 18	21 57	22 57		23 57	
Liss	d	17 02				17 48	18 02				19 02					20 02			21 02		22 02	23 02		00 02	
Liphook	d	17 09				17 55	18 09				19 09					20 09			21 09		22 09	23 09		00 09	
Haslemere 4	a	17 15		17 31		18 00	18 15	18 31		19 00	19 15	19 31			20 00	20 15	20 31	21 00	21 15	21 31	22 14	23 14		00 14	
	d	17 15		17 32	17 39	18 02	18 15	18 32	18 39	19 02	19 15	19 32		19 39	20 02	20 15	20 32	21 02	21 15	21 32	22 15	23 15		00 15	
Witley	d				17 45				18 45					19 45		20 21			21 21		22 21	23 21		00 21	
Milford (Surrey)	d				17 49				18 49					19 49		20 25			21 25		22 25	23 25		00 25	
Godalming	d	17 25			17 53		18 25		18 53		19 25			19 53		20 29			21 29		22 29	23 29		00 29	
Farncombe	d	17 28			17 56		18 28		18 56		19 28			19 56		20 32			21 32		22 32	23 32		00 32	
Guildford	a	17 33		17 45	18 01	18 15	18 33	18 45	19 01	19 15	19 33	19 45		20 01	20 15	20 37	20 45	21 15	21 37	21 47	22 37	23 37		00 37	
	d	17 34		17 47	18 02	18 17	18 34	18 47	19 02	19 17	19 34	19 47		20 02	20 17	20 39	20 47	21 17	21 39	21 49	22 39	23 39			
Worplesdon	d	17 40					18 40				19 40					20 44			21 44		22 44	23 44			
Woking	a	17 44		17 57	18 11	18 25	18 44	18 57	19 11	19 25	19 44	19 57		20 11	20 25	20 52	20 59	21 25	21 49	21 57	22 49	23 49			
	d	17 46		17 59	18 12	18 26	18 46	18 59	19 12	19 26	19 46	19 59		20 12	20 26	20 53	21 00	21 26	21 50	21 59	22 50	23 56			
Clapham Junction 10	a																								
London Waterloo 15 ⊖	a	18 13		18 23	18 40	18 51	19 13	19 23	19 40	19 51	20 13	20 23		20 40	20 50	21 21	21 27	21 50	22 18	22 24	23 18	00 32			

Table 156R

Sundays

8 December to 11 May

Portsmouth, Haslemere and Guildford - London

Network Diagram - see first Page of Table 155

		SW	SW	SW	SW	SW	SW	SW	SW	SW	SW	SW	SW		SW	SW	SW	SW
		1	1	1	1	1	1	1	1	1	1	1	1		1	1	1	1
								🛒		🛒		🛒						
Portsmouth Harbour ⛴	d		06 48	07 32	07 48	08 32	08 48	09 32	09 48	10 32	10 48	11 32	11 48		21 32	21 48	22 32	22 48
Portsmouth & Southsea	d		06 53	07 37	07 53	08 37	08 53	09 37	09 53	10 37	10 53	11 37	11 53		21 37	21 53	22 37	22 53
Fratton	d		06 57	07 41	07 57	08 41	08 57	09 41	09 57	10 41	10 57	11 41	11 57		21 41	21 57	22 41	22 57
Hilsea	d																	
Bedhampton	d		07 04		08 04		09 04		10 04		11 04		12 04			22 04		23 04
Havant	a		07 07	07 49	08 07	08 49	09 07	09 49	10 07	10 49	11 07	11 49	12 07		21 49	22 07	22 49	23 07
	d		07 07	07 50	08 07	08 50	09 07	09 50	10 07	10 50	11 07	11 50	12 07	and at	21 50	22 07	22 50	23 07
Rowlands Castle	d		07 13		08 13		09 13		10 13		11 13		12 13	the same		22 13		23 13
Petersfield	d		07 24	08 04	08 24	09 04	09 24	10 04	10 24	11 04	11 24	12 04	12 24	minutes	22 04	22 24	23 04	23 24
Liss	d	00 02	07 29		08 29		09 29		10 29		11 29		12 29	past		22 29		23 29
Liphook	d	00 09	07 36		08 36		09 36		10 36		11 36		12 36	each		22 36		23 36
Haslemere 4	a	00 14	07 41	08 16	08 41	09 16	09 41	10 16	10 41	11 16	11 41	12 16	12 41	hour until	22 16	22 41	23 16	23 41
	d	00 15	07 42	08 17	08 42	09 17	09 42	10 17	10 42	11 17	11 42	12 17	12 42		22 17	22 42	23 17	23 42
Witley	d	00 21	07 48		08 48		09 48		10 48		11 48		12 48			22 48		23 48
Milford (Surrey)	d	00 25	07 52		08 52		09 52		10 52		11 52		12 52			22 52		23 52
Godalming	d	00 29	07 56		08 56		09 56		10 56		11 56		12 56			22 56		23 56
Farncombe	d	00 32	07 59		08 59		09 59		10 59		11 59		12 59			22 59		23 59
Guildford	a	00 37	08 04	08 31	09 04	09 31	10 04	10 31	11 04	11 31	12 04	12 31	13 04		22 31	23 04	23 31	00 04
	d		08 05	08 35	09 05	09 35	10 05	10 35	11 06	11 35	12 06	12 35	13 05		22 35	23 05	23 35	00 05
Worplesdon	d																	
Woking	a		08 13	08 42	09 15	09 42	10 15	10 42	11 13	11 42	12 13	12 42	13 13		22 42	23 13	23 42	00 13
	d		08 15	08 45	09 15	09 45	10 15	10 45	11 15	11 45	12 15	12 45	13 15		22 45	23 15	23 45	
Clapham Junction 10	a																	
London Waterloo 15 ⊖	a		08 49	09 16	09 48	10 14	10 46	11 14	11 49	12 14	12 44	13 14	13 44		23 14	23 44	00 14	

Table 157

Mondays to Fridays

9 December to 16 May

Havant - Portsmouth Harbour

(Complete service)

Network Diagram - see first Page of Table 155

		SW	SW	SW	SW	SW	SW	SW	SW	SW		SW	SN	SN	SW	SN	SW	SN	SW	SW		SW	GW	SW	SW
		MX	MO	MO	MX	MX	MX	MO	MO	MX															
		1	1	1	1	1	1	1	1	1		1			1	1	1		1	1		1		1	1
Havant	d					00 21	00 36	00 39	00 51	01 21		04 40	05 21	05 40	06 02	06 13		06 53		07 00					07 28
Bedhampton	d					00 24		00 41		01s24		04 43			06 05	06 15		06 56		07 03					07 31
Hilsea	d				00 03	00 29				01s29		04 48			06 10	06 20	06 34	07 01	07 05	07 08		07 13		07 35	07 37
Fratton	d		00 01	00 04	00 08	00 34	00 46	00 50	01 01	01s33		04 52	05 30	05 49	06 15	06 25	06 41	07 05	07 09	07 12		07 17	07 35	07 39	07 42
Portsmouth & Southsea	a		00 04	00 08	00 11	00 37	00 50	00 53	01 04	01 37		04 55	05 33	05 52	06 18	06 28	06 44	07 08	07 12	07 16		07 22	07 38	07 42	07 46
	d	00 03	00 05	00 09	00 13		00 51	00 54	01 05			04 56	05 33	05 52	06 19	06 28	06 45	07 09	07 13	07 17			07 39	07 43	
Portsmouth Harbour ⛴	a	00 07	00 09	00 13	00 16		00 54	00 58	01 09			04 59	05 37	05 56	06 22	06 32	06 49	07 12	07 17	07 20			07 45	07 48	

		SN	SN	SW	SW	SN		SW	GW	SN	SW	SW	SN	SW	SW	SN		SW	SW	SW	GW	SW	SN	SN	SW
			1	1	1			1	◇		1	1	1	1 ⊥	1			1	1 ⊥	1	◇ ⊥	1		1	1 ⊥
Havant	d	07 35	07 41	07 52		07 58				08 22	08 27		08 44	08 50		09 01		09 05	09 20			09 30	09 33	09 46	09 50
Bedhampton	d	07 37		07 55		08 00				08 25	08 30							09 08				09 33	09 36		
Hilsea	d	07 42		08 00	08 02	08 05		08 08		08 30	08 35	08 44			09 05			09 13		09 33		09 38	09 42		
Fratton	d	07 47	07 50	08 04	08 07	08 10		08 13	08 21	08 34	08 40	08 49	08 53	08 59	09 10	09 13		09 17	09 29	09 37	09 42	09 43	09 47	09 55	09 59
Portsmouth & Southsea	a	07 50	07 53	08 07	08 10	08 15		08 19	08 24	08 37	08 43	08 52	08 56	09 02	09 13	09 17		09 20	09 32	09 42	09 46	09 46	09 50	09 58	10 02
	d		07 53	08 09	08 12	08 17		08 21	08 24	08 38	08 44	08 54	08 57	09 04	09 14	09 18		09 22	09 34		09 46			09 58	10 04
Portsmouth Harbour ⛴	a		07 58	08 12	08 15	08 20		08 24	08 30	08 41	08 48	08 57	09 02	09 07	09 18	09 21		09 26	09 37		09 52			10 02	10 07

		SW		SN	SW	SW	SW	GW	SN	SN	SW	SW		SN	SW	SW	SW	GW	SN	SN	SW	SW		SN	SW
		1			1 ⊥	1	1	▪ ⊥		1	1 ⊥	1			1 ⊥	1	1	◇ ⊥		1	1 ⊥	1			1 ⊥
Havant	d			10 07	10 16		10 27		10 32	10 46	10 50			11 05	11 16		11 27		11 32	11 46	11 50			12 05	12 16
Bedhampton	d						10 30		10 34								11 30		11 34						
Hilsea	d	10 03				10 33	10 36		10 42			11 03				11 33	11 36		11 42			12 03			
Fratton	d	10 08		10 16	10 25	10 37	10 40	10 44	10 47	10 55	10 59	11 08		11 14	11 25	11 37	11 40	11 42	11 47	11 55	11 59	12 08		12 14	12 25
Portsmouth & Southsea	a	10 11		10 19	10 28	10 42	10 44	10 47	10 50	10 58	11 02	11 11		11 17	11 28	11 42	11 44	11 46	11 50	11 58	12 02	12 11		12 17	12 28
	d	10 12		10 20	10 29			10 48		10 58	11 04	11 12		11 17	11 29			11 46		11 58	12 04	12 12		12 17	12 29
Portsmouth Harbour ⛴	a	10 18		10 23	10 33			10 54		11 02	11 07	11 18		11 21	11 33			11 54		12 02	12 07	12 18		12 21	12 33

		SW	SW	GW	SN	SN	SW	SW		SN	SW	SW	SW	GW	SN	SN	SW	SW		SN	SW	SW	SW	GW	SN
		1	1	◇ ⊥		1	1 ⊥	1			1 ⊥	1	1	◇ ⊥		1	1 ⊥	1			1 ⊥	1	1	◇ ⊥	
Havant	d		12 27		12 32	12 46	12 50			13 05	13 16		13 27		13 32	13 46	13 50			14 05	14 16		14 27		14 32
Bedhampton	d		12 30		12 34								13 30		13 34								14 30		14 34
Hilsea	d	12 33	12 36		12 42			13 03				13 33	13 36		13 42			14 03				14 33	14 36		14 42
Fratton	d	12 37	12 40	12 42	12 47	12 55	12 59	13 08		13 14	13 25	13 37	13 40	13 42	13 47	13 55	13 59	14 08		14 14	14 25	14 37	14 40	14 42	14 47
Portsmouth & Southsea	a	12 42	12 44	12 46	12 50	12 58	13 02	13 11		13 17	13 28	13 42	13 44	13 46	13 50	13 58	14 02	14 11		14 17	14 28	14 42	14 44	14 46	14 50
	d			12 46		12 58	13 04	13 12		13 17	13 29			13 46		13 58	14 04	14 12		14 17	14 29			14 46	
Portsmouth Harbour ⛴	a			12 54		13 02	13 07	13 18		13 21	13 33			13 54		14 02	14 07	14 18		14 21	14 33			14 54	

		SN	SW	SW		SN	SW	SW	SW	GW	SN	SN	SW	SW		SN	SN	SW	SW	SW	GW	SN	SN	SW	
		1	1 ⊥	1			1 ⊥	1	1	◇ ⊥		1	1 ⊥	1				1 ⊥	1	1	◇ ⊥		1	1 ⊥	
Havant	d	14 46	14 50			15 05	15 16		15 27		15 32	15 46	15 50			16 02	16 09	16 16		16 27		16 32	16 46	16 50	
Bedhampton	d								15 30		15 34					16 04				16 30		16 34			
Hilsea	d			15 03				15 33	15 36		15 42			16 03					16 33	16 36		16 42			
Fratton	d	14 55	14 59	15 08		15 14	15 25	15 37	15 40	15 42	15 47	15 55	15 59	16 08		16 12	16 18	16 25	16 37	16 40	16 42	16 47	16 55	16 59	
Portsmouth & Southsea	a	14 58	15 02	15 11		15 17	15 28	15 42	15 44	15 46	15 50	15 58	16 02	16 11		16 15	16 21	16 28	16 40	16 44	16 46	16 50	16 58	17 02	
	d	14 58	15 04	15 12		15 17	15 29			15 46		15 58	16 04	16 12		16 16	16 22	16 29	16 41	16 45	16 46		16 58	17 04	
Portsmouth Harbour ⛴	a	15 02	15 07	15 18		15 21	15 33			15 54		16 02	16 07	16 18		16 21	16 26	16 33	16 44	16 49	16 54		17 02	17 07	

		SW	SN	SW	SN	SW	SW	SW	SW	GW		SN	SW	SN	SW	SW	SN	SW	SW	SW		SW	SN	GW	SW
		1		1		1 ⊥		1	1	◇ ⊥		1	1 ⊥	1	1	1		1 ⊥	1	1		1		◇ ⊥	1 ⊥
Havant	d		17 00	17 04	17 09	17 16			17 27			17 32	17 50	17 54		18 04	18 13	18 20				18 30	18 34		18 51
Bedhampton	d		17 02	17 07					17 30			17 34		17 56		18 07						18 33	18 36		
Hilsea	d	17 03	17 07	17 12				17 33	17 36			17 42		18 01	18 04	18 12			18 33			18 39	18 42		
Fratton	d	17 08	17 12	17 17	17 19	17 25	17 32	17 37	17 40	17 42		17 47	17 59	18 06	18 09	18 17	18 22	18 29	18 37	18 40		18 43	18 46	18 48	19 00
Portsmouth & Southsea	a	17 11	17 16	17 20	17 22	17 28	17 35	17 42	17 44	17 46		17 50	18 02	18 09	18 12	18 20	18 25	18 32	18 41	18 43		18 47	18 49	18 52	19 03
	d	17 12	17 16	17 21		17 30	17 36			17 46			18 04	18 09	18 14	18 22	18 26	18 33		18 45		18 49		18 52	19 05
Portsmouth Harbour ⛴	a	17 18	17 20	17 26		17 35	17 40			17 54			18 09	18 15	18 20	18 28	18 31	18 39		18 50		18 52		19 00	19 10

		SN	SW	SN	SW	SW		SW	GW	SN	SW	SN	SW	SW	SN	SW		SW	SW	GW	SW	SN	SW	SN	SW
		1	1		1 ⊥	1		1	▪ ⊥		1	1	1 ⊥	1		1 ⊥		1	1	▪ ⊥	1 ⊥	1	1	1	1 ⊥
Havant	d	18 54		19 08	19 16					19 33	19 41	19 47	19 51		20 07	20 17			20 28		20 49	20 52		21 10	21 19
Bedhampton	d	18 57								19 35	19 44								20 31						
Hilsea	d	19 02	19 05			19 28		19 33		19 43	19 49			20 02				20 33	20 36				21 03		
Fratton	d	19 06	19 09	19 18	19 26	19 33		19 37	19 42	19 47	19 54	19 57	20 00	20 08	20 16	20 26		20 37	20 41	20 42	20 58	21 02	21 08	21 19	21 29
Portsmouth & Southsea	a	19 09	19 12	19 21	19 29	19 36		19 42	19 46	19 50	19 59	20 01	20 04	20 11	20 19	20 29		20 42	20 44	20 46	21 01	21 06	21 11	21 23	21 32
	d		19 14	19 21	19 30	19 38			19 46			20 01	20 05	20 12		20 31			20 45	20 46	21 03		21 13	21 23	21 33
Portsmouth Harbour ⛴	a		19 20	19 26	19 36	19 43			19 54			20 07	20 10	20 20		20 34			20 51	20 54	21 06		21 16	21 27	21 37

Table 157

Havant - Portsmouth Harbour

(Complete service)

Mondays to Fridays

9 December to 16 May

Network Diagram - see first Page of Table 155

		SW	GW	SW	SW	SN	SW	SN		SW	SW	SW	SN	GW	SW	SN	SW	SW		SW	SW	GW	SN	SW
		[1]	◇ 🛒	[1]	[1] 🛒	[1]	[1]			[1] 🛒	[1]	[1]		◇	[1]		[1]	[1]		[1]	[1]	◇	[1]	[1]
Havant	d			21 30	21 46	21 49		22 10		22 19		22 30	22 43		22 49	23 11	23 19				23 30		23 34	23 49
Bedhampton	d			21 33								22 33									23 33			
Hilsea	d	21 33		21 41			22 04				22 33	22 38						23 24		23 33	23 38			
Fratton	d	21 37	21 42	21 45	21 55	21 58	22 08	22 19		22 29	22 37	22 43	22 52	22 56	22 59	23 20	23 28	23 33		23 37	23 43	23 44	23 47	23 59
Portsmouth & Southsea	a	21 40	21 45	21 48	21 58	22 01	22 11	22 22		22 32	22 42	22 46	22 55	22 59	23 03	23 23	23 31	23 36		23 40	23 46	23 48	23 54	00 02
	d	21 41	21 46		21 58	22 02	22 13	22 22		22 33			22 56	22 59	23 05	23 24	23 33	23 37				23 48		00 03
Portsmouth Harbour ⛴	a	21 45	21 52		22 02	22 05	22 16	22 26		22 37			22 59	23 04	23 08	23 27	23 36	23 40				23 54		00 07

Saturdays

14 December to 17 May

		SW	SW	SW	SW	SW	SW	SN	SN	SN		SW	SW	SN	SN	SW	SN	SW	SW	GW		SN	SN	SW	SN
		[1]	[1]	[1]	[1]	[1]	[1]		[1]	[1]		[1]	[1]			[1]	[1]	[1]	[1]				[1]	[1]	
Havant	d			00 21	00 36	01 21	04 40	05 34	05 49	05 57		06 02		06 32	06 46		07 04	07 20				07 33	07 46		08 04
Bedhampton	d			00 24		01s24	04 43					06 05		06 34				07 22				07 35			
Hilsea	d		00 03	00 29		01s29	04 48					06 10	06 37	06 42		07 03		07 27	07 33			07 42		08 03	
Fratton	d		00 08	00 34	00 46	01s33	04 52	05 43	05 58	06 06		06 15	06 41	06 47	06 55	07 08	07 13	07 32	07 37	07 42		07 47	07 55	08 08	08 13
Portsmouth & Southsea	a		00 11	00 37	00 50	01 37	04 55	05 46	06 01	06 09		06 18	06 44	06 50	06 58	07 11	07 16	07 35	07 42	07 46		07 50	07 58	08 11	08 16
	d	00 03	00 13		00 51		04 57		06 01	06 09		06 19			06 58	07 12	07 16	07 36		07 46			07 59	08 13	08 16
Portsmouth Harbour ⛴	a	00 07	00 16		00 54		05 00		06 05	06 16		06 22			07 02	07 16	07 20	07 40		07 52			08 02	08 18	08 20

		SW	SW	GW	SN	SN		SW	SW	SN	SW	SW	SW	GW	SN	SN		SW	SW	SN	SW	SW	SW	GW	SN
		[1]	[1]	◇		[1]		[1]	[1]		[1]	[1]	[1]	◇		[1]		[1]	[1]		[1] 🛒	[1]	[1]	◇	
Havant	d	08 17			08 32	08 46		08 50		09 04	09 16		09 27		09 32	09 46		09 50		10 07	10 16		10 27		10 32
Bedhampton	d	08 20			08 34								09 30		09 34								10 30		10 34
Hilsea	d	08 25	08 33		08 42				09 04			09 33	09 36		09 42				10 03			10 33	10 36		10 43
Fratton	d	08 29	08 37	08 42	08 47	08 55		08 59	09 09	09 13	09 25	09 37	09 40	09 42	09 47	09 55		09 59	10 08	10 16	10 25	10 37	10 40	10 42	10 47
Portsmouth & Southsea	a	08 32	08 42	08 46	08 50	08 58		09 02	09 12	09 16	09 28	09 42	09 44	09 46	09 50	09 58		10 02	10 11	10 19	10 28	10 42	10 44	10 46	10 50
	d	08 34		08 46		08 59		09 04	09 13	09 16	09 29			09 46		09 58		10 04	10 12	10 20	10 29			10 46	
Portsmouth Harbour ⛴	a	08 37		08 52		09 02		09 07	09 18	09 20	09 33			09 52		10 02		10 07	10 18	10 23	10 33			10 52	

		SN		SW	SW	SN	SW	SW	SW	GW	SN	SN		SW	SW	SN	SW	SW	SW	GW	SN	SN		SW	SW
		[1]		[1] 🛒	[1]		[1] 🛒	[1]	[1]	◇		[1]		[1] 🛒	[1]		[1] 🛒	[1]	[1]	◇ 🛒		[1]		[1] 🛒	[1]
Havant	d	10 46		10 50		11 05	11 16		11 27		11 32	11 46		11 50		12 05	12 16		12 27		12 32	12 46		12 50	
Bedhampton	d								11 30		11 34								12 30		12 34				
Hilsea	d				11 03			11 33	11 36		11 42				12 03			12 33	12 36		12 42				13 03
Fratton	d	10 55		10 59	11 08	11 14	11 25	11 37	11 40	11 42	11 47	11 55		11 59	12 08	12 14	12 25	12 37	12 40	12 42	12 47	12 55		12 59	13 08
Portsmouth & Southsea	a	10 58		11 02	11 11	11 17	11 28	11 42	11 44	11 46	11 50	11 58		12 02	12 11	12 17	12 28	12 42	12 44	12 46	12 50	12 58		13 02	13 11
	d	10 58		11 04	11 12	11 17	11 29			11 46		11 58		12 04	12 12	12 17	12 29			12 46		12 58		13 04	13 12
Portsmouth Harbour ⛴	a	11 02		11 07	11 18	11 21	11 33			11 52		12 02		12 07	12 18	12 21	12 33			12 52		13 02		13 07	13 18

		SN	SW	SW	SW	GW	SN	SN		SW	SW	SN	SW	SW	SW	GW	SN	SN		SW	SW	SN	SW	SW	SW
			[1] 🛒	[1]	[1]	◇ 🛒		[1]		[1] 🛒	[1]		[1] 🛒	[1]	[1]	◇ 🛒		[1]		[1] 🛒	[1]		[1] 🛒	[1]	[1]
Havant	d	13 05	13 16		13 27		13 32	13 46		13 50		14 05	14 16		14 27		14 32	14 46		14 50		15 05	15 16		15 27
Bedhampton	d				13 30		13 34								14 30		14 34								15 30
Hilsea	d			13 33	13 36		13 42				14 03			14 33	14 36		14 42				15 03			15 33	15 36
Fratton	d	13 14	13 25	13 37	13 40	13 42	13 47	13 55		13 59	14 08	14 14	14 25	14 37	14 40	14 42	14 47	14 55		14 59	15 08	15 14	15 25	15 37	15 40
Portsmouth & Southsea	a	13 17	13 28	13 42	13 44	13 46	13 50	13 58		14 02	14 11	14 17	14 28	14 42	14 44	14 46	14 50	14 58		15 02	15 11	15 17	15 28	15 42	15 44
	d	13 17	13 29			13 46		13 58		14 04	14 12	14 17	14 29			14 46		14 58		15 04	15 12	15 17	15 29		
Portsmouth Harbour ⛴	a	13 21	13 33			13 52		14 02		14 07	14 18	14 21	14 33			14 52		15 02		15 07	15 18	15 21	15 33		

		GW	SN	SN		SW	SW	SN	SW	SW	SW	GW	SN	SN		SW	SW	SN	SW	SW	SW	GW	SN	SN	
		◇		[1]		[1] 🛒	[1]		[1] 🛒	[1]	[1]	◇		[1]		[1] 🛒	[1]		[1] 🛒	[1]	[1]	◇		[1]	
Havant	d		15 32	15 46		15 50		16 05	16 16		16 27		16 32	16 46		16 50		17 05	17 16		17 27		17 32	17 46	
Bedhampton	d		15 34								16 30		16 34								17 30		17 34		
Hilsea	d		15 42				16 03			16 33	16 36		16 42				17 03			17 33	17 36		17 42		
Fratton	d	15 42	15 47	15 55		15 59	16 08	16 14	16 25	16 37	16 40	16 42	16 47	16 55		16 59	17 08	17 14	17 25	17 37	17 40	17 42	17 47	17 55	
Portsmouth & Southsea	a	15 46	15 50	15 58		16 02	16 11	16 17	16 28	16 40	16 44	16 46	16 50	16 58		17 02	17 11	17 17	17 28	17 42	17 44	17 46	17 50	17 58	
	d	15 46		15 58		16 04	16 12	16 17	16 29	16 41		16 46		16 58		17 04	17 12	17 17	17 29			17 46		17 58	
Portsmouth Harbour ⛴	a	15 52		16 02		16 07	16 18	16 21	16 33	16 44		16 52		17 02		17 07	17 16	17 22	17 33			17 52		18 02	

		SW	SW	SN	SW	SW	SW	GW	SN	SN		SW	SW	SN	SW	SW	SW	GW	SN	SN		SW	SW	SN	SW
		[1] 🛒	[1]		[1] 🛒	[1]	[1]	◇		[1]		[1] 🛒	[1]		[1] 🛒	[1]	[1]	R		[1]		[1] 🛒	[1]	[1]	[1] 🛒
Havant	d	17 50		18 06	18 16		18 27		18 32	18 46		18 50		19 05	19 16		19 27		19 32	19 46		19 50		20 10	20 16
Bedhampton	d						18 30		18 34								19 30		19 34						
Hilsea	d		18 03			18 33	18 36		18 42				19 03			19 33	19 36		19 42				20 03		
Fratton	d	17 59	18 08	18 15	18 25	18 37	18 40	18 42	18 47	18 55		18 59	19 08	19 14	19 25	19 37	19 40	19 42	19 47	19 55		19 59	20 08	20 19	20 25
Portsmouth & Southsea	a	18 02	18 11	18 18	18 28	18 42	18 44	18 45	18 50	18 58		19 02	19 11	19 17	19 28	19 42	19 44	19 46	19 50	19 58		20 02	20 11	20 22	20 28
	d	18 04	18 12	18 19	18 29			18 45		18 58		19 04	19 12	19 17	19 29			19 46		19 58		20 04	20 12	20 22	20 29
Portsmouth Harbour ⛴	a	18 07	18 18	18 22	18 33			18 53		19 02		19 07	19 18	19 21	19 33			19 52		20 02		20 07	20 18	20 26	20 33

Table 157

Saturdays

14 December to 17 May

Havant - Portsmouth Harbour

(Complete service)

Network Diagram - see first Page of Table 155

		SW		GW	SW	SN	SW	SW	SN	SW	SW	SW		GW	SW	SN	SW	SN	SW	SW	GW	SW		SN	SW
		1		◇	1	1	1 🚲	1	1	1	1	1		◇	1	1	1		1	1	◇	1			1
Havant	d				20 30	20 46	20 50		21 10	21 16		21 27			21 45	21 49		22 10	22 19			22 30		22 43	22 49
Bedhampton	d				20 33							21 30										22 33			
Hilsea	d	20 37			20 41			21 03			21 33	21 36					22 03			22 33		22 41			
Fratton	d	20 41		20 42	20 45	20 55	20 59	21 08	21 19	21 25	21 37	21 40		21 42	21 55	21 59	22 08	22 19	22 29	22 37	22 42	22 45		22 52	22 59
Portsmouth & Southsea	a	20 44		20 46	20 48	20 58	21 02	21 11	21 22	21 28	21 40	21 43		21 46	21 58	22 02	22 11	22 22	22 32	22 40	22 46	22 49		22 55	23 02
	d			20 46		20 58	21 04	21 12	21 22	21 29	21 41			21 46	21 59	22 03	22 12	22 22	22 33	22 41	22 46	22 50		22 56	23 03
Portsmouth Harbour ⛴	a			20 52		21 02	21 07	21 16	21 26	21 33	21 45			21 52	22 03	22 06	22 18	22 26	22 36	22 47	22 52	22 53		22 59	23 08

		SW	SN	SW	SW	GW	SW	SN		SW
		1		1	1	◇	1	1		1
Havant	d		23 10	23 19			23 30	23 36		23 49
Bedhampton	d						23 33			
Hilsea	d	23 03			23 33		23 40			
Fratton	d	23 08	23 19	23 28	23 37	23 41	23 45	23 48		23 59
Portsmouth & Southsea	a	23 11	23 22	23 31	23 40	23 44	23 48	23 51		00 02
	d	23 12	23 22	23 33		23 45	23 50			00 03
Portsmouth Harbour ⛴	a	23 18	23 26	23 36		23 52	23 53			00 07

Sundays

8 December to 11 May

		SW	SW	SW	SW	SW	SN	SW	SW	SN		SW	SN	SW	SW	SN	SW	SW	SN	SW		SW	SW	SN	SW
		1 A	1 A	1 A	1 A	1 A	1	1	1	1		1	1	1	1	1	1	1	1	1		1	1	1	1
Havant	d			00⌇21	00⌇36	01⌇21	07 10			08 12			08 35	08 39		09 16		09 44	09 48	09 53				10 21	10 44
Bedhampton	d			00⌇24	⌇	01s24							08 37	08 41				09 46	09 50						10 46
Hilsea	d		00⌇03	00⌇29	⌇	01s29		07 26	08 00			08 26			09 00		09 26					10 00	10 26		
Fratton	d		00⌇07	00⌇34	00⌇46	01s33	07 19	07 30	08 04	08 21		08 30	08 45	08 50	09 04	09 25	09 30	09 55	09 59	10 03		10 08	10 30	10 32	10 55
Portsmouth & Southsea	a		00⌇11	00⌇37	00⌇49	01⌇37	07 22	07 33	08 08	08 24		08 33	08 48	08 53	09 08	09 28	09 33	09 58	10 03	10 06		10 11	10 33	10 35	10 58
	d	00⌇03	00⌇12		00⌇50		07 22		08 09	08 24			08 49	08 54	09 09	09 29		09 59	10 04	10 08		10 12		10 36	10 59
Portsmouth Harbour ⛴	a	00⌇07	00⌇16		00⌇54		07 26		08 13	08 28			08 52	08 57	09 13	09 35		10 03	10 07	10 11		10 15		10 39	11 03

		SN	SW	SW	SN	SW		GW	SW	SN	SW	SW	SN	SW	GW	SW		SN	SW	SW	SN	SW	SW	SN	SW
		1	1	1	1	1		◇	1	1	1	1	1	1	◇	1		1	1 🚲	1	1	1	1	1	1 🚲
Havant	d	10 48	10 53		11 14				11 39	11 47	11 51		12 20			12 39		12 47	12 51		13 14		13 39	13 47	13 51
Bedhampton	d	10 50							11 41	11 49						12 41		12 49					13 41	13 49	
Hilsea	d			11 00		11 26						12 00		12 28						13 00		13 26			
Fratton	d	10 58	11 02	11 08	11 23	11 30		11 41	11 50	11 57	12 01	12 04	12 29	12 33	12 41	12 50		12 57	13 01	13 04	13 23	13 30	13 50	13 57	14 01
Portsmouth & Southsea	a	11 03	11 05	11 11	11 26	11 33		11 45	11 53	12 00	12 04	12 08	12 32	12 36	12 45	12 53		13 00	13 04	13 08	13 26	13 33	13 53	14 00	14 04
	d	11 03	11 07	11 12	11 27			11 45	11 54	12 01	12 05	12 09	12 32		12 45	12 54		13 01	13 05	13 09	13 27		13 54	14 01	14 05
Portsmouth Harbour ⛴	a	11 07	11 11	11 15	11 30			11 52	11 58	12 05	12 11	12 13	12 36		12 52	12 58		13 05	13 11	13 13	13 30		13 58	14 05	14 11

		SW		SN	SW	GW	SW	SN	SW	SW	SN	SW		SW	SN	SW	SW	SN	SW	GW	SW	SN		SW	SW
		1		1	1	◇	1	1	1 🚲	1	1	1		1	1	1 🚲	1	1	1	◇	1	1		1 🚲	1
Havant	d			14 14			14 39	14 47	14 51		15 14			15 39	15 47	15 51		16 14			16 39	16 47		16 54	
Bedhampton	d						14 41	14 49						15 41	15 49						16 41	16 49			
Hilsea	d	14 00			14 26					15 00		15 26					16 00		16 26						17 00
Fratton	d	14 04		14 23	14 30	14 41	14 50	14 57	15 01	15 04	15 23	15 30		15 50	15 57	16 01	16 04	16 23	16 30	16 41	16 50	16 57		17 03	17 09
Portsmouth & Southsea	a	14 08		14 26	14 33	14 45	14 53	15 00	15 04	15 08	15 26	15 33		15 54	16 00	16 04	16 08	16 26	16 33	16 45	16 53	17 00		17 06	17 12
	d	14 09		14 27		14 45	14 54	15 01	15 05	15 09	15 27			15 54	16 01	16 05	16 09	16 27		16 45	16 54	17 01		17 08	17 13
Portsmouth Harbour ⛴	a	14 13		14 30		14 52	14 58	15 05	15 11	15 13	15 30			15 58	16 05	16 11	16 13	16 30		16 52	16 58	17 05		17 11	17 16

		SN	SW	GW	GW	SW	SN	SW		SW	SN	SW	GW	SW	SN	SW	SW	SN		SW	GW	SW	SN	SW	SW
		1	1	◇ B	◇ C	1	1	1 🚲		1	1	1	◇	1	1	1 🚲	1	1		1	◇	1	1	1 🚲	1
Havant	d	17 14				17 39	17 47	17 51			18 14			18 39	18 47	18 54		19 14				19 39	19 47	19 51	
Bedhampton	d					17 41	17 49							18 41	18 49							19 41	19 49		
Hilsea	d		17 26							18 00		18 26					19 00			19 26					20 00
Fratton	d	17 23	17 30	17⌇41	17⌇41	17 50	17 57	18 01		18 04	18 23	18 30	18 41	18 50	18 57	19 03	19 09	19 23		19 30	19 41	19 50	19 57	20 01	20 04
Portsmouth & Southsea	a	17 26	17 33	17⌇44	17⌇45	17 53	18 00	18 04		18 08	18 26	18 33	18 45	18 53	19 01	19 06	19 12	19 26		19 33	19 45	19 53	20 00	20 04	20 08
	d	17 27		17⌇45	17⌇45	17 54	18 01	18 05		18 09	18 27		18 45	18 54	19 02	19 08	19 13	19 27			19 45	19 54		20 05	20 09
Portsmouth Harbour ⛴	a	17 30		17⌇52	17⌇52	17 58	18 05	18 11		18 13	18 30		18 53	18 58	19 05	19 11	19 17	19 30			19 52	19 58		20 11	20 13

		SN	SW	GW		SW	SN	SW	SW	GW	SN	SW	GW	SW		SN	SW	SW	SN	SW	GW	SW	SN	GW	
		1	1	◇		1	1	1 🚲	1	◇	1	1	◇	1		1	1 🚲	1	1	1	◇	1	1		
Havant	d	20 14				20 39	20 47	20 51			21 14			21 39		21 47	21 51		22 14			22 39	22 44	22 47	
Bedhampton	d					20 41	20 49							21 41		21 49						22 41	22 46		
Hilsea	d		20 26						21 00			21 26						22 00		22 26					
Fratton	d	20 23	20 30	20 41		20 50	20 57	21 01	21 04	21 10	21 23	21 30	21 41	21 50		21 57	22 01	22 04	22 23	22 30	22 41	22 50	22 54	22 57	
Portsmouth & Southsea	a	20 26	20 33	20 47		20 53	21 00	21 04	21 08	21 15	21 26	21 33	21 43	21 53		22 00	22 04	22 10	22 26	22 33	22 43	22 53	22 57	23 00	
	d	20 27		20 47		20 54	21 01	21 05	21 09	21 15	21 27		21 44	21 54		22 01	22 05	22 11	22 27		22 44	22 54	22 58	23 00	
Portsmouth Harbour ⛴	a	20 30		20 52		20 58	21 05	21 09	21 13	21 26	21 30		21 49	21 58		22 04	22 08	22 14	22 30		22 52	22 58	23 02	23 05	

A not 8 December

B from 5 January

C until 29 December

Table 157

Sundays

8 December to 11 May

Havant - Portsmouth Harbour

(Complete service)

Network Diagram - see first Page of Table 155

		SW		SW	SW	SN	GW	SW	SW	SW
		1		1	1	1	◇	1	1	1
Havant	d	22 51				23 22		23 39	23 51	
Bedhampton	d							23 41		
Hilsea	d			23 00	23 24					23 59
Fratton	d	23 01		23 04	23 29	23 31	23 43	23 50	00 01	00 04
Portsmouth & Southsea	a	23 04		23 08	23 32	23 34	23 46	23 53	00 04	00 08
	d	23 05		23 09		23 35	23 47	23 54	00 05	00 09
Portsmouth Harbour ⛴	a	23 09		23 13		23 38	23 54	23 58	00 09	00 13

Table 157R

Mondays to Fridays

9 December to 16 May

Portsmouth Harbour - Havant

(Complete service)

Network Diagram - see first Page of Table 155

		SW	SW	SW	SW	SN		SW	SN	SW	GW	SN	SW	SW	SW	SW		SN	SW	SW	GW	GW	SW	SN	SW
											R														
		1	1	1	1	1		1	1	1			1	1	1	1		1	1	1		◇	1		1
					T						T		T			T					T	T	T		
Portsmouth Harbour ⛴	d	04 30	05 00		05 19	05 33		05 43	05 47	05 50	06 00	06 04	06 15		06 23	06 42		06 46	06 50	06 55	07 01	07 05	07 13	07 20	07 24
Portsmouth & Southsea	a	04 33	05 03		05 22	05 36		05 46	05 50	05 53	06 03	06 07	06 18		06 26	06 45		06 49	06 53	06 58	07 04	07 08	07 16	07 23	07 27
	d	04 35	05 05	05 16	05 24	05 37		05 48	05 51	05 55	06 04	06 08	06 20	06 23	06 28	06 47		06 50	06 55	07 00	07 05	07 09	07 18	07 24	07 29
Fratton	d	04 39	05 09	05 20	05 28	05 41		05 52	05 55	05 59	06a07	06 12	06 24	06 27	06 32	06 51		06 54	06 59	07 04	07 11	07a13	07 22	07 28	07 33
Hilsea	d	04 43	05a13	05a24	05 32	05 45		05a56	05 59	06 03				06a31	06a36			06 58	07a03	07 08					07a37
Bedhampton	d	04 48			05 37	05 50			06 04	06 08								07 03		07 13					
Havant	a	04 50			05 39	05 52			06 06	06 10		06 20	06 33			06 59		07 05		07 15	07 19		07 30	07 36	

		SW		SW	SW	SW	SN	SW	SN	SW	SW	GW		SN	SW	SW	SN	SW	SN	SW	SW	GW		SN	SW
		1		1	1	1			1	1	1				1	1		1	1	1	1				1
												◇										◇			
					T					T		T				T				T		T			
Portsmouth Harbour ⛴	d	07 29			07 45	07 55		08 05	08 10	08 15		08 23		08 29	08 33	08 45	08 51	08 59	09 12	09 15	09 19	09 23		09 29	09 33
Portsmouth & Southsea	a	07 32			07 48	07 58		08 08	08 13	08 18		08 26		08 32	08 36	08 48	08 54	09 02	09 15	09 18	09 22	09 26		09 32	09 36
	d	07 34		07 38	07 50	08 00	08 03	08 10	08 14	08 20	08 24	08 27		08 33	08 38	08 50	08 55	09 04	09 16	09 20	09 24	09 27		09 33	09 38
Fratton	d	07 38		07 42	07 54	08 04	08 07	08 13	08 18	08 24	08 28	08a31		08 37	08 42	08 54	08 59	09 08	09 20	09 24	09 28	09a31		09 37	09 42
Hilsea	d	07 42		07a46		08a08	08 11	08a17			08 32				08a46		09 04	09a12			09 32				09a46
Bedhampton	d	07 48					08 16				08 37						09 13				09 37				
Havant	a	07 50			08 03		08 18		08 26	08 32	08 39			08 45		09 02	09 15		09 29	09 33	09 39			09 45	

		SW	SN	SW	SN	SW	SW	GW		SN	SW	SW	SN	SW	SN	SW	SW	GW		SN	SW	SW	SN	SW	SN
		1		1	1	1	1				1	1		1	1	1	1				1	1		1	1
								◇										◇							
		T				T		T				T				T		T				T			
Portsmouth Harbour ⛴	d	09 45		09 59	10 12	10 15		10 23		10 29	10 33	10 45		10 59	11 12	11 15		11 23		11 29		11 45		11 59	12 12
Portsmouth & Southsea	a	09 48		10 02	10 15	10 18		10 26		10 32	10 36	10 48		11 02	11 15	11 18		11 26		11 32		11 48		12 02	12 15
	d	09 50	09 59	10 04	10 16	10 20	10 24	10 27		10 33	10 38	10 50	10 59	11 04	11 16	11 20	11 24	11 27		11 33	11 38	11 50	11 59	12 04	12 16
Fratton	d	09 54	10 04	10 08	10 20	10 24	10 28	10a31		10 37	10 42	10 54	11 04	11 08	11 20	11 24	11 28	11a31		11 37	11 42	11 54	12 04	12 08	12 20
Hilsea	d		10 08	10a12			10 32				10a46		11 08	11a12			11 32				11a46		12 08	12a12	
Bedhampton	d		10 13				10 37						11 13				11 37						12 13		
Havant	a	10 03	10 15		10 29	10 33	10 39			10 45		11 03	11 15		11 29	11 33	11 39			11 45		12 03	12 15		12 29

		SW	SW	GW		SN	SW	SW	SN	SW	SN	SW	SW	GW		SN	SW	SW	SN	SW	SN	SW	SW	GW	
																								R	
		1	1	◇			1	1		1	1	1	1	◇			1	1		1	1	1	1		
		T		T				T				T		T				T				T		T	
Portsmouth Harbour ⛴	d	12 15		12 23		12 29		12 45		12 59	13 12	13 15		13 23		13 29		13 45		13 59	14 12	14 15		14 23	
Portsmouth & Southsea	a	12 18		12 26		12 32		12 48		13 02	13 15	13 18		13 26		13 32		13 48		14 02	14 15	14 18		14 26	
	d	12 20	12 24	12 27		12 33	12 38	12 50	12 59	13 04	13 16	13 20	13 24	13 27		13 33	13 38	13 50	13 59	14 04	14 16	14 20	14 24	14 27	
Fratton	d	12 24	12 28	12a31		12 37	12 42	12 54	13 04	13 08	13 20	13 24	13 28	13a31		13 37	13 42	13 54	14 04	14 08	14 20	14 24	14 28	14a31	
Hilsea	d		12 32				12a46		13 08	13a12			13 32				13a46		14 08	14a12			14 32		
Bedhampton	d		12 37						13 13				13 37						14 13				14 37		
Havant	a	12 33	12 39			12 45		13 03	13 15		13 29	13 33	13 39			13 45		14 03	14 15		14 29	14 33	14 39		

		SN	SW	SW	SN	SW	SN	SW	SW	GW		SN	SW	SW	SN	SW	SN	SW	SW	GW		SN	SW	SN	SW
										R										R					
			1	1		1	1	1	1				1	1		1	1	1	1				1		1
				T				T		T				T				T		T					T
Portsmouth Harbour ⛴	d	14 29		14 45		14 59	15 12	15 15		15 23		15 29		15 45		15 59	16 12	16 15		16 23		16 29		16 40	16 45
Portsmouth & Southsea	a	14 32		14 48		15 02	15 15	15 18		15 26		15 32		15 48		16 02	16 15	16 18		16 26		16 32		16 44	16 48
	d	14 33	14 38	14 50	14 59	15 04	15 16	15 20	15 24	15 27		15 33	15 38	15 50	15 59	16 04	16 16	16 20	16 24	16 27		16 33	16 38	16 46	16 50
Fratton	d	14 37	14 42	14 54	15 04	15 08	15 20	15 24	15 28	15a31		15 37	15 42	15 54	16 04	16 08	16 20	16 24	16 28	16a31		16 37	16 42	16 50	16 54
Hilsea	d		14a46		15 08	15a12			15 32				15a46		16 08	16a12			16 32				16a46	16 54	
Bedhampton	d				15 14				15 37						16 13				16 37						
Havant	a	14 45		15 03	15 17		15 29	15 33	15 39			15 45		16 03	16 15		16 29	16 33	16 39			16 45		16 59	17 03

		SW	SN	SW	SN	SW		SW	GW	SN	SW	SN	SW	SN	SW	SW		SW	GW	SN	SW	SN	SW	SN	SW
				1	1	1		1			1		1	1	1	1		1		1	1		1		1
									◇										◇						
						T			T				T			T			T				T		
Portsmouth Harbour ⛴	d	16 49		16 59	17 12	17 15		17 19	17 23	17 29	17 33		17 45		17 59	18 15			18 23	18 27		18 37	18 45		18 59
Portsmouth & Southsea	a	16 53		17 02	17 15	17 18		17 22	17 26	17 32	17 36		17 48		18 02	18 18			18 26	18 30		18 40	18 48		19 02
	d	16 55	17 00	17 04	17 16	17 20		17 24	17 27	17 33	17 38	17 46	17 50	17 59	18 04	18 20		18 24	18 27	18 31	18 38	18 42	18 50	18 59	19 04
Fratton	d	16 58	17 04	17 08	17 20	17 24		17 28	17a31	17 37	17 42	17 50	17 54	18 04	18 08	18 24		18 28	18a31	18 35	18 42	18 46	18 54	19 04	19 08
Hilsea	d	17a02	17 08	17a12				17 32			17a46	17 54		18 08	18a12			18 32			18a46	18 50		19 08	19a12
Bedhampton	d		17 14					17 37						18 13				18 37						19 13	
Havant	a		17 17		17 29	17 33		17 39		17 45		17 59	18 03	18 15		18 33		18 39		18 43		18 56	19 03	19 15	

		SW		SW	GW	SN	SW	SN	SW	SN	SW	SW		SW	GW	SN	SW	SN	SW	SW	SN	SW		GW	SW
		1		1		1	1	1	1		1	1		1			1	1	1	1	1	1			1
					◇										◇										
Portsmouth Harbour ⛴	d	19 15		19 19	19 23			19 40	19 45		19 59	20 15		20 19	20 23			20 40	20 45	20 59		21 19		21 23	21 28
Portsmouth & Southsea	a	19 18		19 22	19 26			19 43	19 48		20 02	20 18		20 22	20 26			20 43	20 48	21 02		21 22		21 26	21 31
	d	19 20		19 24	19 27	19 32	19 38	19 44	19 50	19 59	20 04	20 20		20 24	20 27	20 32	20 38	20 44	20 50	21 04	21 15	21 24		21 27	21 33
Fratton	d	19 24		19 28	19a31	19 36	19 42	19 48	19 54	20 04	20 08	20 24		20 28	20a31	20 36	20 42	20 48	20 54	21 08	21 19	21 28		21a31	21 37
Hilsea	d			19 32			19a46			20 08	20a12			20 32			20a46			21a12	21 23	21 32			21 41
Bedhampton	d			19 37						20 14				20 37							21 28	21 37			21 47
Havant	a	19 33		19 39		19 46		19 56	20 03	20 16		20 32		20 39		20 44		20 56	21 02		21 30	21 39			21 52

Table 157R

Mondays to Fridays

9 December to 16 May

Portsmouth Harbour - Havant

(Complete service)

Network Diagram - see first Page of Table 155

		SW	SN	SW	SN	SW		SW	SW	SN	SN	SW	SW
		[1]	[1]	[1]		[1]		[1]	[1]			[1]	[1]
Portsmouth Harbour ⛴	d		21 40	21 54	22 15	22 19		22 28	22 33	22 44	23 15	23 19	23 24
Portsmouth & Southsea	a		21 43	21 57	22 18	22 22		22 31	22 37	22 47	23 18	23 22	23 27
	d	21 38	21 44	21 59	22 19	22 24		22 33	22 38	22 48	23 19	23 24	23 29
Fratton	d	21 42	21 48	22 03	22 23	22 28		22 37	22 42	22 52	23 23	23 28	23 33
Hilsea	d	21a46	21 52	22a07	22 27	22 32		22 41	22a46	22 56	23 27	23 32	23a37
Bedhampton	d		21 57		22 32	22 37		22 46		23 01	23 33	23 37	
Havant	a		21 59		22 34	22 39		22 53		23 05	23 36	23 39	

Saturdays

14 December to 17 May

		SW	SN	SW	SW	SW	SN	GW	SN	SW		SN	SW	SW	GW	SN	SW	SN	SW	SW		GW	SN	SW	SW
		[1]	[1]	[1]	[1]	[1]		◇	[1]	[1]		[1]	[1]	[1] 🚲			[1]	[1]	[1] 🚲	[1]		◇ 🚲		[1]	[1] 🚲
Portsmouth Harbour ⛴	d	04 43			05 19	05 48		06 00	06 12	06 19		06 29		06 45	06 48		06 59	07 12	07 15			07 23	07 29		07 45
Portsmouth & Southsea	a	04 46			05 22	05 51		06 03	06 15	06 22		06 32		06 48	06 53		07 02	07 15	07 18			07 26	07 32		07 48
	d	04 48	04 56	05 16	05 24	05 53	05 59	06 04	06 16	06 24		06 33	06 38	06 50	06 54	06 56	07 04	07 16	07 20	07 24		07 27	07 33	07 38	07 50
Fratton	d	04 52	05 00	05 20	05 28	05 57	06 04	06a07	06 20	06 28		06 37	06 42	06 54	06 58	07 01	07 08	07 20	07 24	07 28		07a30	07 37	07 42	07 54
Hilsea	d	04 56		05a24	05 32	06a01	06 08			06 32			06a46			07 05	07a12			07 32				07a46	
Bedhampton	d	05 01			05 37		06 13			06 37						07 13				07 37					
Havant	a	05 03	05 08		05 39		06 15		06 29	06 40		06 45		07 03	07 08	07 15		07 29	07 33	07 39			07 45		08 03

		SN	SW	SN	SW	SW		GW	SN	SW	SW	SN	SW	SN	SW	SW		GW	SN	SW	SW	SN	SW	SN	SW
			[1]	[1]	[1] 🚲	[1]		◇ 🚲		[1]	[1] 🚲		[1]	[1]	[1] 🚲	[1]		◇ 🚲		[1]	[1] 🚲		[1]	[1]	[1] 🚲
Portsmouth Harbour ⛴	d		07 59	08 12	08 15			08 23	08 29		08 45		08 59	09 12	09 15			09 23	09 29		09 45		09 59	10 12	10 15
Portsmouth & Southsea	a		08 02	08 15	08 18			08 26	08 32		08 48		09 02	09 15	09 18			09 26	09 32		09 48		10 02	10 15	10 18
	d	07 59	08 04	08 16	08 20	08 24		08 27	08 33	08 38	08 50	08 59	09 04	09 16	09 20	09 24		09 27	09 33	09 38	09 50	09 59	10 04	10 16	10 20
Fratton	d	08 04	08 08	08 20	08 24	08 28		08a30	08 37	08 42	08 54	09 04	09 08	09 20	09 24	09 28		09a30	09 37	09 42	09 54	10 04	10 08	10 20	10 24
Hilsea	d	08 08	08a12			08 32				08a46		09 08	09a12			09 32				09a46		10 08	10a12		
Bedhampton	d	08 13				08 37						09 13				09 37						10 13			
Havant	a	08 15		08 29	08 33	08 39			08 45		09 03	09 15		09 29	09 33	09 39			09 45		10 03	10 15		10 29	10 33

		SW		GW	SN	SW	SW	SN	SW	SN	SW	SW		GW	SN	SW	SW	SN	SW	SN	SW	SW		GW	SN
		[1]		◇		[1]	[1] 🚲		[1]	[1]	[1] 🚲	[1]		◇		[1]	[1] 🚲		[1]	[1]	[1] 🚲	[1]		◇	
Portsmouth Harbour ⛴	d			10 23	10 29		10 45		10 59	11 12	11 15			11 23	11 29		11 45		11 59	12 12	12 15			12 23	12 29
Portsmouth & Southsea	a			10 26	10 32		10 48		11 02	11 15	11 18			11 26	11 32		11 48		12 02	12 15	12 18			12 26	12 32
	d	10 24		10 27	10 33	10 38	10 50	10 59	11 04	11 16	11 20	11 24		11 27	11 33	11 38	11 50	11 59	12 04	12 16	12 20	12 24		12 27	12 33
Fratton	d	10 28		10a30	10 37	10 42	10 54	11 04	11 08	11 20	11 24	11 28		11a30	11 37	11 42	11 54	12 04	12 08	12 20	12 24	12 28		12a30	12 37
Hilsea	d	10 32				10a46		11 08	11a12			11 32				11a46		12 08	12a12			12 32			
Bedhampton	d	10 37						11 13				11 37						12 13				12 37			
Havant	a	10 39			10 45		11 03	11 15		11 29	11 33	11 39			11 45		12 03	12 15		12 29	12 33	12 39			12 45

		SW	SW	SN	SW	SN	SW	SW		GW	SN	SW	SW	SN	SW	SN	SW	SW		GW	SN	SW	SW	SN	SW
		[1]	[1] 🚲		[1]	[1]	[1] 🚲	[1]		◇		[1]	[1] 🚲		[1]	[1]	[1] 🚲	[1]		◇		[1]	[1] 🚲		[1]
Portsmouth Harbour ⛴	d		12 45		12 59	13 12	13 15			13 23	13 29		13 45		13 59	14 12	14 15			14 23	14 29		14 45		14 59
Portsmouth & Southsea	a		12 48		13 02	13 15	13 18			13 26	13 32		13 48		14 02	14 15	14 18			14 26	14 32		14 48		15 02
	d	12 38	12 50	12 59	13 04	13 16	13 20	13 24		13 27	13 33	13 38	13 50	13 59	14 04	14 16	14 20	14 24		14 27	14 33	14 38	14 50	14 59	15 04
Fratton	d	12 42	12 54	13 04	13 08	13 20	13 24	13 28		13a30	13 37	13 42	13 54	14 04	14 08	14 20	14 24	14 28		14a30	14 37	14 42	14 54	15 04	15 08
Hilsea	d	12a46		13 08	13a12			13 32				13a46		14 08	14a12			14 32				14a46		15 08	15a12
Bedhampton	d			13 13				13 37						14 13				14 37						15 14	
Havant	a		13 03	13 15		13 29	13 33	13 39			13 45		14 03	14 15		14 29	14 33	14 39			14 45		15 03	15 17	

		SN	SW	SW		GW	SN	SW	SW	SN	SW	SN	SW	SW		GW	SN	SW	SW	SN	SW	SW	SN	SW	
		[1]	[1] 🚲	[1]		◇		[1]	[1] 🚲		[1]	[1]	[1] 🚲	[1]		R		[1]	[1] 🚲		[1]	[1]	[1]	[1]	
Portsmouth Harbour ⛴	d	15 12	15 15			15 23	15 29		15 45		15 59	16 12	16 15			16 23	16 29		16 45		16 59		17 12	17 19	
Portsmouth & Southsea	a	15 15	15 18			15 26	15 32		15 48		16 02	16 15	16 18			16 26	16 32		16 48		17 02		17 15	17 22	
	d	15 16	15 20	15 24		15 27	15 33	15 38	15 50	15 59	16 04	16 16	16 20	16 24		16 27	16 33	16 38	16 50	16 59	17 04	17 10	17 16	17 24	
Fratton	d	15 20	15 24	15 28		15a30	15 37	15 42	15 54	16 04	16 08	16 20	16 24	16 28		16a31	16 37	16 42	16 54	17 04	17 08	17 14	17 20	17 28	
Hilsea	d			15 32				15a46		16 08	16a12			16 32				16a46		17 08	17a12	17 18		17 32	
Bedhampton	d			15 37						16 13				16 37						17 13		17 23		17 37	
Havant	a	15 29	15 33	15 39			15 45		16 03	16 15		16 29	16 33	16 39			16 45		17 03	17 15		17 25	17 29	17 39	

		GW	SN	SW	SW	SN	SW	SN	SW	SW		GW	SN	SW	SW	SN	SW	SN	SW	SW		GW	SN	SW	SW
		◇		[1]	[1] 🚲	[1]	[1]		[1]	[1]		◇		[1]	[1]		[1]	[1]	[1]	[1]		◇		[1]	[1]
Portsmouth Harbour ⛴	d	17 23	17 29	17 33	17 45		17 59	18 12	18 15			18 23	18 29		18 45		18 59	19 12	19 15			19 23	19 29		19 45
Portsmouth & Southsea	a	17 26	17 32	17 36	17 48		18 02	18 15	18 18			18 27	18 32		18 48		19 02	19 15	19 18			19 26	19 32		19 48
	d	17 27	17 33	17 38	17 50	17 59	18 04	18 16	18 20	18 24		18 27	18 33	18 38	18 50	18 59	19 04	19 16	19 20	19 24		19 27	19 33	19 38	19 50
Fratton	d	17a31	17 37	17 42	17 54	18 04	18 08	18 20	18 24	18 28		18a31	18 37	18 42	18 54	19 04	19 08	19 20	19 24	19 28		19a30	19 37	19 42	19 54
Hilsea	d			17a46		18 08	18a12			18 32				18a46		19 08	19a12			19 32				19a46	
Bedhampton	d					18 13				18 37						19 13				19 37					
Havant	a		17 45		18 03	18 15		18 29	18 33	18 39			18 45		19 03	19 15		19 29	19 33	19 39			19 45		20 03

Table 157R

Saturdays

14 December to 17 May

Portsmouth Harbour - Havant

(Complete service)

Network Diagram - see first Page of Table 155

		SN		SW	SW	SW	GW	SN	SW	SN	SW	SW		SN	SW	SW	SN	SW	SN	SW	SW	SN		SN	SW
				1	1	1	◇	1	1		1	1		1	1	1	1	1	1	1	1				1
Portsmouth Harbour ⛴	d			19 59	20 15		20 23	20 28		20 40	20 45	20 59		21 11	21 19		21 40	21 54	22 15	22 19	22 33	22 44		23 15	23 19
Portsmouth & Southsea	a			20 02	20 18		20 26	20 31		20 43	20 48	21 02		21 14	21 22		21 43	21 57	22 18	22 22	22 37	22 47		23 18	23 22
	d	19 59		20 04	20 20	20 24	20 27	20 32	20 38	20 45	20 50	21 04		21 15	21 24	21 38	21 44	21 59	22 19	22 24	22 38	22 48		23 19	23 24
Fratton	d	20 04		20 08	20 24	20 28	20a30	20 36	20 42	20 49	20 54	21 08		21 19	21 28	21 42	21 48	22 03	22 23	22 28	22 42	22 52		23 23	23 28
Hilsea	d	20 08		20a12		20 32			20a46	20 53		21a12		21 23	21 32	21a46	21 52	22a07	22 27	22 32	22a46	22 56		23 27	23 32
Bedhampton	d	20 13				20 37								21 28	21 37		21 57		22 32	22 37		23 01		23 33	23 37
Havant	a	20 15			20 32	20 39		20 44		20 58	21 02			21 30	21 39		21 59		22 34	22 39		23 05		23 36	23 39

		SW
		1
Portsmouth Harbour ⛴	d	23 24
Portsmouth & Southsea	a	23 28
	d	23 29
Fratton	d	23 33
Hilsea	d	23a37
Bedhampton	d	
Havant	a	

Sundays

8 December to 11 May

		SW	SW	SN	SW	SW	SW	SN	SW	SN		SW	SW	SW	SN	SW	GW	SN	SW	SW		SW	SN	SW	SN
		1	1	1	1	1	1	1	1	1		1	1	1	1	1	R	1	1 🛒	1 🛒		1	1	1	1
Portsmouth Harbour ⛴	d	06 37	06 48	07 14	07 17	07 32		07 44	07 48	08 14		08 17	08 32		08 44	08 48	09 08	09 14	09 17	09 32			09 44	09 48	10 14
Portsmouth & Southsea	a	06 40	06 51	07 17	07 20	07 35		07 47	07 51	08 17		08 20	08 35		08 47	08 51	09 11	09 17	09 20	09 35			09 47	09 51	10 17
	d	06 42	06 53	07 18	07 22	07 37	07 42	07 48	07 53	08 18		08 22	08 37	08 42	08 48	08 53	09 12	09 18	09 22	09 37		09 42	09 48	09 53	10 18
Fratton	d	06 46	06 57	07 22	07 26	07 41	07 46	07 52	07 57	08 22		08 26	08 41	08 46	08 52	08 57	09a15	09 22	09 26	09 41		09 46	09 52	09 57	10 22
Hilsea	d	06a50			07a30		07a50					08a30		08a50					09a30			09a50			
Bedhampton	d		07 04	07 30					08 04	08 30						09 04		09 30						10 04	10 30
Havant	a		07 07	07 32		07 49		08 00	08 07	08 32			08 49		09 00	09 07		09 32		09 49			10 00	10 07	10 32

		SW	SW	SW	SN	SW		GW	SN	SW	SW	SW	SN	SW	SN	SW		SW	SW	SN	SW	GW	SN	SW	SW
		1 🛒	1 🛒	1	1	1		◇	1	1 🛒	1 🛒	1	1	1	1	1 🛒		1 🛒	1	1	1	◇	1	1 🛒	1 🛒
Portsmouth Harbour ⛴	d	10 17	10 32		10 44	10 48		11 08	11 14	11 17	11 32		11 44	11 48	12 14	12 17		12 32		12 44	12 48	13 08	13 14	13 17	13 32
Portsmouth & Southsea	a	10 20	10 35		10 47	10 51		11 11	11 17	11 20	11 35		11 47	11 51	12 17	12 20		12 35		12 47	12 51	13 11	13 17	13 20	13 35
	d	10 22	10 37	10 42	10 48	10 53		11 12	11 18	11 22	11 37	11 42	11 48	11 53	12 18	12 22		12 37	12 42	12 48	12 53	13 12	13 18	13 22	13 37
Fratton	d	10 26	10 41	10 46	10 52	10 57		11a15	11 22	11 26	11 41	11 46	11 52	11 57	12 22	12 26		12 41	12 46	12 52	12 57	13a15	13 22	13 26	13 41
Hilsea	d	10a30		10a50						11a30		11a50				12a30			12a50					13a30	
Bedhampton	d					11 04			11 30					12 04	12 32						13 04		13 30		
Havant	a		10 49		11 00	11 07			11 32		11 49		12 00	12 07	12 34			12 49		13 00	13 07		13 32		13 49

		SW		SN	SW	GW	SN	SW	SW	SW	SN	SW		GW	SN	SW	SW	SW	SN	SW	GW	SN		SW	SW
		1		1	1	◇	1	1 🛒	1 🛒	1	1	1		R	1	1 🛒	1 🛒	1	1	1	◇	1		1 🛒	1 🛒
Portsmouth Harbour ⛴	d			13 44	13 48	14 08	14 14	14 17	14 32		14 44	14 48		15 08	15 14	15 17	15 32		15 44	15 48	16 08	16 14		16 17	16 32
Portsmouth & Southsea	a			13 47	13 51	14 11	14 17	14 20	14 35		14 47	14 51		15 11	15 17	15 20	15 35		15 47	15 51	16 11	16 17		16 20	16 35
	d	13 42		13 48	13 53	14 12	14 18	14 22	14 37	14 42	14 48	14 53		15 12	15 18	15 22	15 37	15 42	15 48	15 53	16 12	16 18		16 22	16 37
Fratton	d	13 46		13 52	13 57	14a15	14 22	14 26	14 41	14 46	14 52	14 57		15a15	15 22	15 26	15 41	15 46	15 52	15 57	16a15	16 22		16 26	16 41
Hilsea	d	13a50						14a30		14a50						15a30		15a50						16a30	
Bedhampton	d				14 04		14 30					15 04			15 30					16 04		16 30			
Havant	a			14 00	14 07		14 32		14 49		15 00	15 07			15 32		15 49		16 00	16 07		16 32			16 49

		SW	SN	SW	GW	SN	SW	SW		SW	SN	SW	GW	SN	SW	SW	SW	SN		SW	GW	SN	SW	SW	SW
		1	1	1	◇	1	1	1 🛒		1	1	1	◇	1	1	1 🛒	1	1		1	◇	1	1	1	1
Portsmouth Harbour ⛴	d		16 44	16 48	17 08	17 14	17 17	17 32			17 44	17 48	18 08	18 14	18 17	18 32		18 44		18 48	19 08	19 14	19 17	19 32	
Portsmouth & Southsea	a		16 47	16 51	17 11	17 17	17 20	17 35			17 47	17 51	18 11	18 17	18 20	18 35		18 47		18 51	19 11	19 17	19 20	19 35	
	d	16 42	16 48	16 53	17 12	17 18	17 22	17 37		17 42	17 48	17 53	18 12	18 18	18 22	18 37	18 42	18 48		18 53	19 12	19 18	19 22	19 37	19 42
Fratton	d	16 46	16 52	16 57	17a15	17 22	17 26	17 41		17 46	17 52	17 57	18a15	18 22	18 26	18 41	18 46	18 52		18 57	19a15	19 22	19 26	19 41	19 46
Hilsea	d	16a50					17a30			17a50					18a30		18a50						19a30		19a50
Bedhampton	d			17 04		17 30						18 04		18 30						19 04		19 30			
Havant	a		17 00	17 07		17 32		17 49			18 00	18 07		18 32		18 49		19 00		19 07		19 32		19 49	

		SN	SW	GW		SN	SW	SW	SW	SN	SW	SN	SW	SW		SW	SN	SW	GW	SN	SW	SW	SW	SN	
		1	1	◇		1	1	1	1	1	1	1	1	1		1	1	1		1	1	1	1	1	
Portsmouth Harbour ⛴	d	19 44	19 48	20 08			20 17	20 32		20 43	20 48	21 14	21 17	21 32			21 44	21 48	22 05	22 14	22 17	22 32		22 44	
Portsmouth & Southsea	a	19 47	19 51	20 11			20 20	20 35		20 46	20 51	21 17	21 20	21 35			21 47	21 51	22 11	22 17	22 20	22 35		22 47	
	d	19 48	19 53	20 12		20 15	20 22	20 37	20 42	20 47	20 53	21 18	21 22	21 37		21 42	21 48	21 53	22 12	22 18	22 22	22 37	22 42	22 48	
Fratton	d	19 52	19 57	20a15		20 19	20 26	20 41	20 46	20 51	20 57	21 22	21 26	21 41		21 46	21 52	21 57	22a15	22 22	22 26	22 41	22 46	22 52	
Hilsea	d						20a30		20a50				21a30			21a50					22a30		22a50		
Bedhampton	d		20 04			20 26					21 04	21 30						22 04		22 30					
Havant	a	20 00	20 07			20 29		20 49		20 59	21 07	21 32		21 49			22 00	22 07		22 32		22 49		23 00	

Table 157R

Sundays

8 December to 11 May

Portsmouth Harbour - Havant

(Complete service)

Network Diagram - see first Page of Table 155

		SW 1	SW 1
Portsmouth Harbour ⛴	d	22 48	23 17
Portsmouth & Southsea	a	22 51	23 20
	d	22 53	23 22
Fratton	d	22 57	23 26
Hilsea	d		23a30
Bedhampton	d	23 04	
Havant	a	23 07	

Network Diagram for Table 158

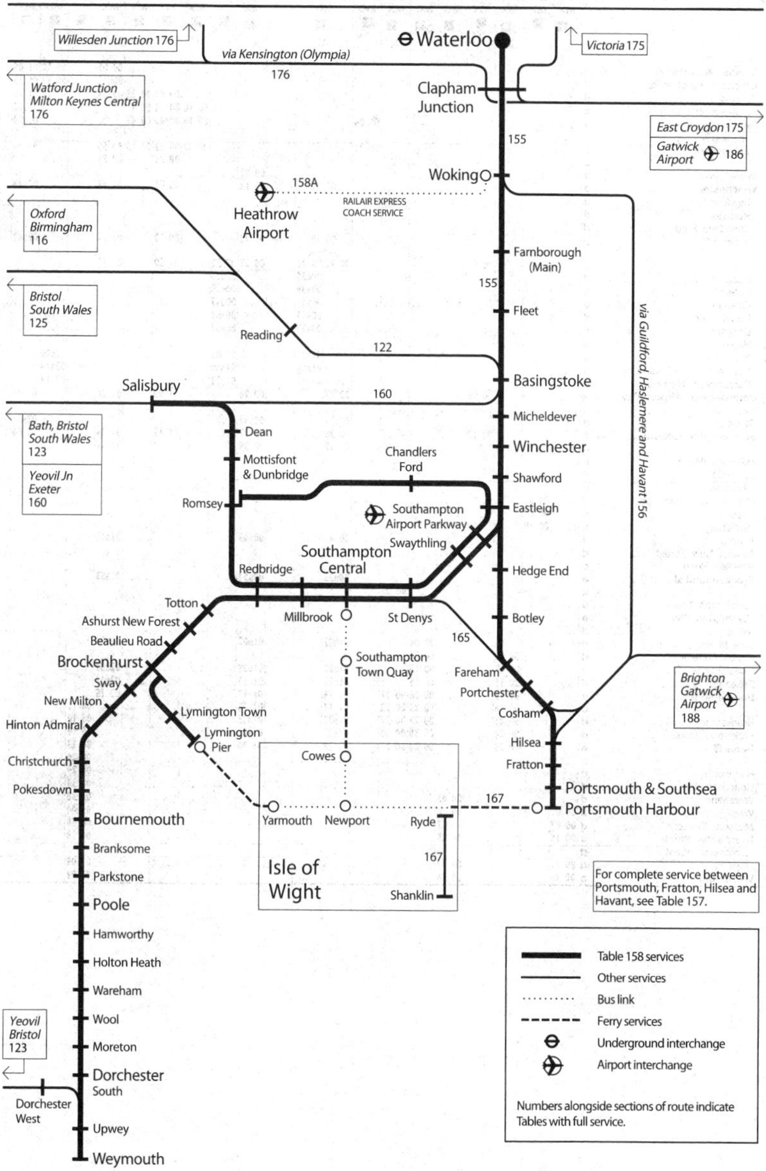

Willesden Junction 176
via Kensington (Olympia)
176
Waterloo
Victoria 175
Watford Junction
Milton Keynes Central
176
Clapham
Junction
155
East Croydon 175
Gatwick Airport 186
Woking
158A
Heathrow
Airport
RAILAIR EXPRESS
COACH SERVICE
Oxford
Birmingham
116
Farnborough
(Main)
155
Bristol
South Wales
125
Fleet
Reading
122
via Guildford, Haslemere and Havant 156
Basingstoke
Salisbury
160
Micheldever
Bath, Bristol
South Wales
123
Dean
Winchester
Yeovil Jn
Exeter
160
Mottisfont
& Dunbridge
Chandlers
Ford
Shawford
Romsey
Southampton
Airport Parkway
Eastleigh
Swaythling
Southampton
Central
Redbridge
Hedge End
Totton
Millbrook
St Denys
Botley
Ashurst New Forest
165
Beaulieu Road
Southampton
Town Quay
Brockenhurst
Fareham
Sway
Portchester
Brighton
Gatwick
Airport
188
New Milton
Lymington Town
Cosham
Hinton Admiral
Lymington
Pier
Hilsea
Christchurch
Cowes
Fratton
Pokesdown
Portsmouth & Southsea
167
Portsmouth Harbour
Yarmouth
Newport
Ryde
Bournemouth
Branksome
167
For complete service between Portsmouth, Fratton, Hilsea and Havant, see Table 157.
Parkstone
Isle of
Wight
Shanklin
Poole
Hamworthy
Table 158 services
Other services
Holton Heath
Bus link
Wareham
Ferry services
Wool
Underground interchange
Yeovil
Bristol
123
Moreton
Airport interchange
Dorchester
South
Dorchester
West
Numbers alongside sections of route indicate Tables with full service.
Upwey
Weymouth

TOCs operating on this network - South West Trains (SW), Southern (SN), First Great Western (GW), Cross Country (XC)

Table 158

Mondays to Fridays

9 December to 16 May

London - Basingstoke, Southampton, Romsey Lymington, Bournemouth and Weymouth

Network Diagram - see first Page of Table 158

Miles	Miles			SW	SW	SW	SW	SW	SW	SW	SW	SW		SW	SW	SW	SW	SW	SW	SW	SW	SW	SW
				MX	MX	MX	MX	MO	MO	MX	MO	MO		MX		MX	MX	MX	MX		MO	MX	
				◇1	1	◇1 trolley	1	◇1	◇1	◇1 trolley	1	◇1 trolley		◇1	1	1	1	1	1	1	1	1	1
0	—	**London Waterloo** 15 ⊖	d																00 05		00 50	01 05	
4	—	**Clapham Junction** 10	d																00u12		00 57	01 15	
24¼	—	**Woking**	d														00 03	00 28	00 37		01 18	01 49	
33¼	—	Farnborough (Main)	d													00 10	00 14	00 41				01s58	
36½	—	Fleet	d								00 04					00 16	00 20	00 47				02s04	
—	—	Reading 7	d																				
47¾	—	**Basingstoke**	a								00 21					00 33	00 33	01 06	00 55			02s16	
—	—		d														00 35		00 56				
58	—	Micheldever	d											00 03									
66½	—	**Winchester**	d									00 08		00 12			00 51		01 13			02s33	
69¾	—	Shawford	d																				
—	0	**Romsey**	d																				
—	5¼	Chandlers Ford	d																				
73½	0	Eastleigh 3	a									00 18		00 22			00 59		01 21			02s42	
—	—																						
—	—		d				00 02					00 22	00 30	00 23	00 30		01 00		01 22				06 00
—	4½	Hedge End	d										00s36		00s36								06 06
—	5½	Botley	d										00s39		00s39								06 10
—	11	Fareham	d										00s47		00s47								06 19
—	14¼	Portchester	d										00s53		00s53								06 24
—	16¾	Cosham	d										00s57		00s57								06 29
—	18¼	Hilsea	a																				06 33
—	20½	Fratton	a										01s05		01s05						02s10		06 40
—	21½	**Portsmouth & Southsea**	a										01s08		01s08						02s14		06 44
—	22¼	**Portsmouth Harbour** ⛴	a										01 12		01 12						02 19		06 49
75	—	**Southampton Airport Pkwy** ✈	d				00 06					00 27		00 28			01 05		01 26			02s46	
75¾	—	Swaythling	d																				
77¼	—	St Denys	d									00s31		00s32								02s51	
79¼	—	**Southampton Central** ⛴	a				00 13					00 36		00 37			01 12		01 35			02 56	
—	—		d									00 37		00 38					01 37				
80¼	—	Millbrook (Hants)	d																				
82	0	Redbridge	d																				
—	6	**Romsey**	d																				
—	9¾	Mottisfont & Dunbridge	d		00 01																		
—	13½	Dean	d		00 07																		
—	22½	**Salisbury**	a		00 19																		
82½	—	Totton	d									00s42		00s43					01s42				
85½	—	Ashurst New Forest	d																				
88	—	Beaulieu Road	d																				
92¾	0	**Brockenhurst** 3	a									00s53		00s54					01s53				
—	—		d							00 05													
—	4¾	Lymington Town	d																				
—	5¼	**Lymington Pier**	a																				
95½	—	Sway	d																				
98½	—	New Milton	d						00 04			01s01		01s02					02s00				
101	—	Hinton Admiral	d			00 02			00 08														
104¼	—	Christchurch	d			00 07			00 13			01s08		01s09					02s07				
106¼	—	Pokesdown	d			00 11			00 16			01s12		01s13					02s11				
108	—	**Bournemouth**	a			00 15			00 20	00 21		01 16		01 17					02 15				
—	—		d			00 16			00 22	00 22		01 17		01 18						06 11			
110¾	—	Branksome	d			00 21			00 27	00 27		01s22		01s23						06 16			
112	—	Parkstone (Dorset)	d			00 24			00 30	00 30		01s25		01s26						06 19			
113¾	—	**Poole** 4	a			00 28			00 34	00 35		01 29		01 30						06 23			
—	—		d																	06 24			
116	—	Hamworthy	d																	06 29			
118¾	—	Holton Heath	d																	06 33			
120¾	—	Wareham	d					00 03												06 38			
125¾	—	Wool	d	00 01				00 10												06 44			
130¼	—	Moreton (Dorset)	d	00 07				00 17												06 50			
135¾	—	**Dorchester South**	d	00 15				00 25												06 58			
—	—	Dorchester West	d																				
140½	—	Upwey	d	00 21				00 32												07 05			
142¾	—	**Weymouth**	a	00 26				00 36												07 09			

Table 158

Mondays to Fridays

9 December to 16 May

London - Basingstoke, Southampton, Romsey Lymington, Bournemouth and Weymouth

Network Diagram - see first Page of Table 158

		SW	SW	SW	SW	SW	SW	SW	SW	GW	SW	SW	SW	SW	SW	SW	SW	SW	SW	SW	SW	SW	SW
		MO	ThX																				
		🚌	1	1	1	1	1	1	1		◇1	1	1	1	1	1	1	1	1	◇1	1	1	1
London Waterloo 15 ⊖	d										05 30								06 12	06 30			
Clapham Junction 10	d										05u37								06u19	06u37			
Woking	d										06 01							06 19	06 50	06 57			
Farnborough (Main)	d																	06 33	07 04				
Fleet	d																	06 38	07 09				
Reading 7	d																						↩
Basingstoke	a										06 20							06 58	07 28	07 16			07 28
	d	02 23				05 40					06 21						06 55	07 00	07 30	07 18			07 30
Micheldever	d					05 50												07 10	↪				07 41
Winchester	d	02s58				05 59			06 18		06 38						07 11	07 19		07 34			07 50
Shawford	d								06 23								07 16						07 55
Romsey	d							05 58								07 07						07 13	
Chandlers Ford	d							06 06								07 14							
Eastleigh 3	a	03s13				06 07		06 11	06 28		06 47					07 20	07 22	07 29		07 43		07 49	08 00
	d					06 08		06 13	06 29		06 48		07 02			07 21	07 24	07 30		07 44		07 50	08 02
Hedge End	d								06 35				07 08					07 36					
Botley	d								06 39				07 12					07 40					
Fareham	d								06 50				07 21					07 48					
Portchester	d								06 55				07 26					07 53					
Cosham	d								07 00				07 30					07 58					
Hilsea	a								07 05				07 35					08 03					
Fratton	a								07 09				07 39					08 07					
Portsmouth & Southsea	a								07 12				07 42					08 11					
Portsmouth Harbour ⛴	a								07 17				07 48					08 16					
Southampton Airport Pkwy ✈	d	03s17				06 13		06 17			06 53					07 25	07 29			07 49			08 06
Swaythling	d					06 15		06 20								07 27	07 31						08 09
St Denys	d	03s25				06 18		06 24								07 30	07 34						08 12
Southampton Central ⛴	a	03 32				06 23		06 29			07 00					07 35	07 41			07 57			08 17
	d					06 25		06 30			07 01			07 19		07 37				08 00			08 19
Millbrook (Hants)	d							06 33						07 21		07 40							08 21
Redbridge	d							06 36						07 25		07 43							08 25
Romsey	d							06 44								07 51						08a03	
Mottisfont & Dunbridge	d							06 49								07 56							
Dean	d							06 55								08 02							
Salisbury	a							07 07								08 15							
Totton	d					06 30					07 07			07 28						08 05			08 28
Ashurst New Forest	d					06 35								07 32									08 32
Beaulieu Road	d													07 37									08 37
Brockenhurst 3	a					06 43					07 17			07 43						08 16			08 43
	d		05 59	06 16	06 29	06 44	06 59				07 18	07 29		07 44	07 59					08 17	08 29		08 44
Lymington Town	d		06 07		06 37		07 07					07 37			08 07						08 37		
Lymington Pier	a		06 10		06 40		07 10					07 40			08 10						08 40		
Sway	d			06 20		06 48					07 23			07 48						08 21			08 48
New Milton	d			06 25		06 53					07 28			07 53						08 26			08 53
Hinton Admiral	d			06 29		06 57					07 32			07 57						08 30			08 57
Christchurch	d			06 34		07 02					07 37			08 02						08 35			09 02
Pokesdown	d			06 38		07 06					07 40			08 06						08 39			09 06
Bournemouth	a			06 42		07 10					07 44			08 10						08 43			09 10
	d			06 44		07 11					07 46			08 11						08 44			09 11
Branksome	d			06 49		07 16					07 51			08 16						08 49			09 16
Parkstone (Dorset)	d			06 52		07 19					07 54			08 19						08 52			09 19
Poole 4	a			06 55		07 23					07 57			08 23						08 56			09 23
	d			06 57		07 24					07 58			08 24						08 57			09 24
Hamworthy	d			07 02		07 29					08 03			08 29						09 02			09 29
Holton Heath	d			07 06		07 33					08 07			08 33									09 33
Wareham	d			07 11		07 38					08 12			08 38						09 09			09 38
Wool	d			07 17		07 44					08 19			08 44						09 15			09 44
Moreton (Dorset)	d			07 23		07 50					08 25			08 50						09 21			09 50
Dorchester South	d			07 31		07 58					08 33			08 58						09 29			09 58
Dorchester West	d									08 09													
Upwey	d			07 38		08 05				08 17	08 40			09 05						09 36			10 05
Weymouth	a			07 42		08 09				08 24	08 44			09 09						09 40			10 09

Table 158

Mondays to Fridays

9 December to 16 May

London - Basingstoke, Southampton, Romsey Lymington, Bournemouth and Weymouth

Network Diagram - see first Page of Table 158

		SW	SW	SW	XC		SW	SW	SW	GW	SW	XC	SW	SW	SW		SW	XC	SW	SW	SW	SW	SW	SW	SW
		1	1	1	◇1		◇1	1	1	◇	1	◇1	◇1	1	1		1	◇1	◇1	1	1	1	1	◇1	1
							A						A						A					A	
					⚲		⚲				⚲		⚲	⚲				⚲	⚲		⚲			⚲	
London Waterloo 15 ⊖	d			06 42			07 35				07 39		08 05				08 09		08 35				08 39	09 05	
Clapham Junction 10	d			06u49							07u46		08u12										08u46	09u12	
Woking	d			07 19			08 00										08 35		09 00						
Farnborough (Main)	d			07 33							08 13						08 45						09 13		
Fleet	d			07 38							08 19												09 19		
Reading 7	d				07 46							08 18						08 46							
Basingstoke	a			07 56	08 08		08 19				08 31	08 40	08 47				08 58	09 09					09 31	09 47	
	d			08 00	08 10		08 20				08 33	08 42	08 49				09 00	09 10					09 33	09 49	
Micheldever	d			08 10													09 10								
Winchester	d			08 19	08 25		08 37				08 50	08 57	09 05				09 19	09 25	09 33				09 49	10 05	
Shawford	d			08 24							08 54												09 54		
Romsey	d		08 07						08 13						09 07							09 14			
Chandlers Ford	d		08 14												09 14										
Eastleigh 3	a		08 20	08 30			08 47		08 49		09 00				09 20		09 27					09 49	09 59		
	d		08 21	08 31			08 48		08 50		09 01				09 21		09 28					09 50	10 03		
Hedge End	d			08 37													09 34								
Botley	d			08 42													09 38								
Fareham	d			08 51													09 48								
Portchester	d			08 56													09 53								
Cosham	d			09 01													09 58								
Hilsea	a			09 05													10 03								
Fratton	a			09 09													10 07								
Portsmouth & Southsea	a			09 13													10 11								
Portsmouth Harbour ⛴	a			09 18													10 18								
Southampton Airport Pkwy ✈	d		08 25		08 33		08 52				09 05	09 09	09 14		09 25			09 33	09 42				10 08	10 14	
Swaythling	d		08 27												09 27										
St Denys	d		08 30											←	09 30										←
Southampton Central ⛴	a		08 35		08 44		08 59				09 15	09 17	09 22	09 15	09 35			09 41	09 49				10 18	10 22	10 18
	d		08 37		08 46		09 01				09 30		09 24	09 30	09 37			09 43	09 51				10 30	10 24	10 30
Millbrook (Hants)	d		08 40								↦				09 40								↦		
Redbridge	d		08 43												09 43										
Romsey	d		08 51						09a03						09 51							10a03			
Mottisfont & Dunbridge	d		08 56												09 56										
Dean	d		09 02												10 02										
Salisbury	a		09 15												10 15										
Totton	d						09 06							09 35											10 35
Ashurst New Forest	d													09 40											10 40
Beaulieu Road	d																				←				10 44
Brockenhurst 3	a				08 59		09 17						09 37	09 49				09 56	10 04		09 49			10 37	10 51
	d	08 59			09 00		09 18	09 29					09 38	10 16				09 57	10 05	10 12	10 16			10 38	11 16
Lymington Town	d	09 07						09 37						↦						10 20					↦
Lymington Pier	a	09 10						09 40												10 23					
Sway	d						09 22														10 20				
New Milton	d						09 27						09 45								10 25			10 45	
Hinton Admiral	d						09 31														10 29				
Christchurch	d						09 36						09 52								10 34			10 52	
Pokesdown	d						09 40						09 56								10 38			10 56	
Bournemouth	a				09 14		09 44						10 00					10 12	10 20		10 42			11 00	
	d						09 45						10 04						10 24		10 43			11 04	
Branksome	d						09 50												10 29		10 48				
Parkstone (Dorset)	d						09 53												10 32		10 51				
Poole 4	a						09 57						10 13						10 36		10 55			11 13	
	d						09 58						10 14						10 37					11 14	
Hamworthy	d						10 03						10 19						10 42					11 19	
Holton Heath	d												10 23											11 23	
Wareham	d						10 10						10 28						10 50					11 28	
Wool	d												10 35											11 35	
Moreton (Dorset)	d												10 41											11 41	
Dorchester South	d						10 26						10 54						11 06					11 49	
Dorchester West	d									10 48															
Upwey	d									10 55			11 01											11 55	
Weymouth	a						10 34			11 03			11 06						11 14					12 00	

A ⚲ to Bournemouth

Table 158

Mondays to Fridays

9 December to 16 May

London - Basingstoke, Southampton, Romsey Lymington, Bournemouth and Weymouth

Network Diagram - see first Page of Table 158

		SW	SW	SW	XC	SW	GW	SW	SW	SW	SW	XC	SW	SW	SW	SW	SW	XC	SW	SW	SW	SW
		1	1	1	◇1	1	◇	◇1	1	1	1	◇1	◇1	1	1	1	1	◇1	◇1	1	1	1
								A					A						A			
					⌶			⌶				⌶	⌶					⌶	⌶			
London Waterloo 15 ⊖	d			09 09				09 35			09 39		10 05				10 09		10 35			
Clapham Junction 10	d										09u46		10u12									
Woking	d			09 35				10 00									10 35		11 00			
Farnborough (Main)	d			09 45							10 13						10 45					
Fleet	d										10 19											
Reading 7	d				09 46							10 16						10 46				
Basingstoke	a			09 58	10 08						10 31	10 38	10 47				10 58	11 08				
	d			10 00	10 10						10 33	10 40	10 49				11 00	11 10				
Micheldever	d			10 10													11 10					
Winchester	d			10 19	10 25			10 33			10 49	10 55	11 05				11 19	11 25	11 33			
Shawford	d										10 54											
Romsey	d		10 07			10 20										11 07						11 20
Chandlers Ford	d		10 14													11 14						
Eastleigh 3	a		10 20	10 27		10 49					10 59					11 20	11 27					11 49
	d		10 21	10 28		10 50					11 00					11 21	11 28					11 50
Hedge End	d			10 34													11 34					
Botley	d			10 38													11 38					
Fareham	d			10 48													11 48					
Portchester	d			10 53													11 53					
Cosham	d			10 58													11 58					
Hilsea	a			11 03													12 03					
Fratton	a			11 07													12 07					
Portsmouth & Southsea	a			11 11													12 11					
Portsmouth Harbour ⛴	a			11 18													12 18					
Southampton Airport Pkwy ✈	d		10 25		10 33			10 42			11 05	11 09	11 14			11 25		11 33	11 42			
Swaythling	d		10 27													11 27						
St Denys	d		10 30											←		11 30						
Southampton Central ⛴	a		10 35		10 43			10 49			11 12	11 17	11 22	11 12		11 36		11 43	11 49			
	d		10 44		10 45			10 51			11 30		11 24	11 30		11 37		11 45	11 51			
Millbrook (Hants)	d		10 48								→					11 40						
Redbridge	d		10 51													11 43						
Romsey	d		10 59			11a03										11 51						12a03
Mottisfont & Dunbridge	d		11 04													11 56						
Dean	d		11 10													12 02						
Salisbury	a		11 22													12 15						
Totton	d													11 35								
Ashurst New Forest	d													11 40								
Beaulieu Road	d									←				11 44							←	
Brockenhurst 3	a				10 58			11 04		10 51			11 37	11 51				11 58	12 04		11 51	
	d	10 42			10 59			11 05	11 12	11 16			11 38	12 16	11 42			11 59	12 05	12 12	12 16	
Lymington Town	d	10 50							11 20					→	11 50					12 20		
Lymington Pier	a	10 53							11 23						11 53					12 23		
Sway	d									11 20											12 20	
New Milton	d									11 25			11 45								12 25	
Hinton Admiral	d									11 29											12 29	
Christchurch	d									11 34			11 52								12 34	
Pokesdown	d									11 38			11 56								12 38	
Bournemouth	a				11 12			11 20		11 42			12 00					12 12	12 20		12 42	
	d							11 24		11 43			12 04						12 24		12 43	
Branksome	d							11 29		11 48									12 29		12 48	
Parkstone (Dorset)	d							11 32		11 51									12 32		12 51	
Poole 4	a							11 36		11 55			12 13						12 36		12 55	
	d							11 37					12 14						12 37			
Hamworthy	d							11 42					12 19						12 42			
Holton Heath	d												12 23									
Wareham	d							11 49					12 28						12 49			
Wool	d												12 35									
Moreton (Dorset)	d												12 41									
Dorchester South	d							12 05					12 49						13 05			
Dorchester West	d						11 54															
Upwey	d						12 02						12 55									
Weymouth	a						12 09	12 13					13 00						13 13			

A ⌶ to Bournemouth

Table 158

Mondays to Fridays

9 December to 16 May

London - Basingstoke, Southampton, Romsey Lymington, Bournemouth and Weymouth

Network Diagram - see first Page of Table 158

		SW	SW	SW	SW	SW	SW	XC	SW	GW	SW	SW	SW	SW	XC	SW	SW	SW	SW	SW	XC	SW	SW
		1	◇1	1	1	1	1	◇1	1	◇	◇1	1	1	1	◇1	◇1	1	1	1	1	◇1	◇1	1
			A								A					A						A	
			✠					✠			✠				✠	✠					✠	✠	
London Waterloo 15 ⊖	d	10 39	11 05				11 09				11 35			11 39		12 05				12 09		12 35	
Clapham Junction 10	d	10u46	11u12											11u46		12u12							
Woking	d						11 35				12 00									12 35		13 00	
Farnborough (Main)	d	11 13					11 45							12 13						12 45			
Fleet	d	11 19												12 19									
Reading 7	d							11 46							12 16						12 45		
Basingstoke	a	11 31	11 47				11 58	12 08						12 31	12 39	12 47				12 58	13 08		
	d	11 33	11 49				12 00	12 10						12 33	12 40	12 49				13 00	13 10		
Micheldever	d						12 10													13 10			
Winchester	d	11 49	12 05				12 19	12 25			12 33			12 49	12 55	13 05				13 19	13 25	13 33	
Shawford	d	11 54												12 54									
Romsey	d					12 07			12 20										13 07				
Chandlers Ford	d					12 14													13 14				
Eastleigh 3	a	11 59				12 20	12 27		12 49					12 59					13 20	13 27			
	d	12 00				12 21	12 28		12 50					13 00					13 21	13 28			
Hedge End	d						12 34													13 34			
Botley	d						12 38													13 38			
Fareham	d						12 48													13 48			
Portchester	d						12 53													13 53			
Cosham	d						12 58													13 58			
Hilsea	a						13 03													14 03			
Fratton	a						13 07													14 07			
Portsmouth & Southsea	a						13 11													14 11			
Portsmouth Harbour ⛴	a						13 18													14 18			
Southampton Airport Pkwy ✈	d	12 05	12 14			12 25		12 33			12 42			13 05	13 09	13 14			13 25		13 33	13 42	
Swaythling	d					12 27													13 27				
St Denys	d			←		12 30											←		13 30				
Southampton Central ⛴	a	12 12	12 22	12 12		12 36		12 41			12 49			13 12	13 17	13 22	13 12		13 36		13 41	13 49	
	d	12 30	12 24	12 30		12 37		12 43			12 51			13 30		13 24	13 30		13 37		13 43	13 51	
Millbrook (Hants)	d	→				12 40								→					13 40				
Redbridge	d					12 43													13 43				
Romsey	d					12 51			13a03										13 51				
Mottisfont & Dunbridge	d					12 56													13 56				
Dean	d					13 02													14 02				
Salisbury	a					13 15													14 15				
Totton	d			12 35													13 35						
Ashurst New Forest	d			12 40													13 40						
Beaulieu Road	d												←				13 44						
Brockenhurst 3	a		12 37	12 51				12 56			13 04		12 51			13 37	13 51				13 56	14 04	
	d		12 38	13 16	12 42			12 57			13 05	13 12	13 16			13 38	14 16	13 42			13 57	14 05	14 12
Lymington Town	d			→	12 50							13 20					→	13 50					14 20
Lymington Pier	a				12 53							13 23						13 53					14 23
Sway	d												13 20										
New Milton	d		12 45										13 25			13 45							
Hinton Admiral	d												13 29										
Christchurch	d		12 52										13 34			13 52							
Pokesdown	d		12 56										13 38			13 56							
Bournemouth	a		13 00					13 10			13 20		13 42			14 00					14 10	14 20	
	d		13 04								13 24		13 43			14 04						14 24	
Branksome	d										13 29		13 48									14 29	
Parkstone (Dorset)	d										13 32		13 51									14 32	
Poole 4	a		13 13								13 36		13 55			14 13						14 36	
	d		13 14								13 37					14 14						14 37	
Hamworthy	d		13 19								13 42					14 19						14 42	
Holton Heath	d		13 23													14 23							
Wareham	d		13 28								13 49					14 28						14 49	
Wool	d		13 35													14 35							
Moreton (Dorset)	d		13 41													14 41							
Dorchester South	d		13 49								14 05					14 49						15 05	
Dorchester West	d									13 54													
Upwey	d		13 55							14 02						14 55							
Weymouth	a		14 00							14 09	14 13					15 00						15 13	

A ✠ to Bournemouth

Table 158

Mondays to Fridays

9 December to 16 May

London - Basingstoke, Southampton, Romsey Lymington, Bournemouth and Weymouth

Network Diagram - see first Page of Table 158

		SW	SW		SW	SW	SW	SW	SW	SW	XC	SW	SW		SW	SN	SW	SW	XC	SW	SW	SW	SW		SW
		1	1		1	◇1	1	1	1	1	◇1	◇1	1		1	1	1	1	◇1	◇1	1	1	1		1
						A 🛒					🛒	A 🛒							🛒	A 🛒					
London Waterloo 15 ⊖	d				12 39	13 05				13 09		13 35						13 39		14 05					14 09
Clapham Junction 10	d				12u46	13u12												13u46		14u12					
Woking	d									13 35		14 00													14 35
Farnborough (Main)	d				13 13					13 45								14 13							14 45
Fleet	d				13 19													14 19							
Reading 7	d										13 46								14 16						
Basingstoke	a				13 31	13 47				13 58	14 08							14 31	14 39	14 47					14 58
	d				13 33	13 49				14 00	14 10							14 33	14 40	14 49					15 00
Micheldever	d									14 10															15 10
Winchester	d				13 49	14 05				14 19	14 25	14 33						14 49	14 55	15 05					15 19
Shawford	d				13 54													14 54							
Romsey	d		13 20						14 07								14 13						15 07		
Chandlers Ford	d								14 14														15 14		
Eastleigh 3	a		13 49		13 59				14 20	14 27							14 49	14 59					15 20		15 27
	d		13 50		14 00				14 21	14 28						14 41	14 50	15 00					15 21		15 28
Hedge End	d									14 34															15 34
Botley	d									14 38															15 38
Fareham	d									14 48						14a55									15 48
Portchester	d									14 53															15 53
Cosham	d									14 58															15 58
Hilsea	a									15 03															16 03
Fratton	a									15 07															16 07
Portsmouth & Southsea	a									15 11															16 11
Portsmouth Harbour ⛴	a									15 18															16 18
Southampton Airport Pkwy ✈	d				14 05	14 14			14 25		14 35	14 42						15 05	15 09	15 14			15 25		
Swaythling	d								14 27														15 27		
St Denys	d						←		14 30												←		15 30		
Southampton Central ⛴	a				14 12	14 22	14 12		14 35		14 42	14 49						15 12	15 17	15 22	15 12		15 36		
	d				14 30	14 24	14 30		14 37		14 43	14 51						15 30		15 24	15 30		15 37		
Millbrook (Hants)	d				↪				14 40									↪					15 40		
Redbridge	d								14 43														15 43		
Romsey	d		14a03						14 51								15a03						15 51		
Mottisfont & Dunbridge	d								14 56														15 56		
Dean	d								15 02														16 02		
Salisbury	a								15 15														16 15		
Totton	d						14 35														15 35				
Ashurst New Forest	d						14 40														15 40				
Beaulieu Road	d	←													←										
Brockenhurst 3	a	13 51				14 37	14 51				14 56	15 04			14 51					15 37	15 51				
	d	14 16				14 38	15 16	14 42			14 57	15 05	15 12		15 16					15 38	16 28	15 42			
Lymington Town	d						↪	14 50					15 20								↪	15 50			
Lymington Pier	a							14 53					15 23									15 53			
Sway	d	14 20													15 20										
New Milton	d	14 25				14 45									15 25					15 45					
Hinton Admiral	d	14 29													15 29										
Christchurch	d	14 34				14 52									15 34					15 52					
Pokesdown	d	14 38				14 56									15 38					15 56					
Bournemouth	a	14 42				15 00					15 11	15 20			15 42					16 00					
	d	14 43				15 04						15 24			15 43					16 04					
Branksome	d	14 48										15 29			15 48										
Parkstone (Dorset)	d	14 51										15 32			15 51										
Poole 4	a	14 55				15 13						15 36			15 55					16 13					
	d					15 14						15 37								16 14					
Hamworthy	d					15 19						15 42								16 19					
Holton Heath	d					15 23														16 23					
Wareham	d					15 28						15 49								16 28					
Wool	d					15 35														16 35					
Moreton (Dorset)	d					15 41														16 41					
Dorchester South	d					15 49						16 05								16 49					
Dorchester West	d																								
Upwey	d					15 55														16 55					
Weymouth	a					16 00						16 13								17 00					

A 🛒 to Bournemouth

Table 158

Mondays to Fridays

9 December to 16 May

London - Basingstoke, Southampton, Romsey Lymington, Bournemouth and Weymouth

Network Diagram - see first Page of Table 158

		XC ◇1 🛒	SW 1	GW ◇	SW ◇1 A 🛒	SW 1	SW 1	SW 1	SW ◇1 A 🛒		SW 1	SW 1	SW 1	SW 1	XC ◇1 🛒	SW 1	SW ◇1 A 🛒		SW		SW 1	SW	SW 1	XC ◇1 🛒	SW ◇1 A 🛒
London Waterloo 15 ⊖	d				14 35			14 39	15 05					15 09			15 35						15 39		16 05
Clapham Junction 10	d							14u46	15u12														15u46		16u12
Woking	d				15 00									15 35			16 00								
Farnborough (Main)	d							15 13						15 45									16 13		
Fleet	d							15 19															16 19		
Reading 7	d	14 46													15 46									16 16	
Basingstoke	a	15 08						15 31	15 47					15 58	16 08								16 31	16 39	16 47
	d	15 10						15 33	15 49					16 00	16 10							16 24	16 33	16 40	16 49
Micheldever	d													16 10											
Winchester	d	15 25			15 33			15 49	16 05					16 19	16 25		16 33		16 38			16 45	16 50	17 00	17 05
Shawford	d							15 54											16 43				16 54		
Romsey	d		15 20										16 07								16 20				
Chandlers Ford	d												16 14												
Eastleigh 8	a		15 49					15 59					16 20	16 27					16 48		16 49	16 53	17 00		
	d		15 50					16 00					16 21	16 28					16 49		16 50	16 54	17 01		
Hedge End	d													16 34								17 00			
Botley	d													16 38								17 04			
Fareham	d													16 48								17 12			
Portchester	d													16 53								17 17			
Cosham	d													16 58								17 22			
Hilsea	a													17 03											
Fratton	a													17 07								17 31			
Portsmouth & Southsea	a													17 11								17 35			
Portsmouth Harbour ⛴	a													17 18								17 40			
Southampton Airport Pkwy ✈	d	15 33			15 42			16 05	16 14				16 25		16 33		16 42		16 54				17 05	17 08	17 14
Swaythling	d												16 27						16 56						
St Denys	d											←	16 30						16 59						
Southampton Central ⛴	a	15 41			15 49			16 15	16 22			16 15	16 36		16 41		16 49		17 04				17 12	17 17	17 22
	d	15 43			15 51			16 30	16 24			16 30	16 37		16 43		16 54	16 56	17 06				17 30		17 24
Millbrook (Hants)	d							→					16 40										→		
Redbridge	d												16 43												
Romsey	d		16a03										16 51								17a03				
Mottisfont & Dunbridge	d												16 56												
Dean	d												17 02												
Salisbury	a												17 15												
Totton	d											16 35						17 01	17a11						
Ashurst New Forest	d											16 40						17 06							
Beaulieu Road	d						←					16 44													
Brockenhurst 8	a	15 56			16 04		15 51		16 38			16 51			16 56		17 07	17 14							17 37
	d	15 57			16 05	16 12	16 28		16 39		16 42				16 57	17 12	17 08	17 16							17 38
Lymington Town	d					16 20					16 50					17 20									
Lymington Pier	a					16 23					16 53					17 23									
Sway	d						16 32		16 44									17 20							17 43
New Milton	d						16 37		16 49									17 25							17 48
Hinton Admiral	d						16 41		16 53									17 29							17 52
Christchurch	d						16 46		16 58									17 34							17 57
Pokesdown	d						16 50		17 01									17 38							18 00
Bournemouth	a	16 10			16 20		16 54		17 05						17 10		17 23	17 42							18 04
	d				16 24		16 55		17 07								17 24	17 43							18 09
Branksome	d				16 29		17 00										17 29	17 48							
Parkstone (Dorset)	d				16 32		17 03										17 32	17 51							
Poole 4	a				16 36		17 07		17 16								17 36	17 55							18 18
	d				16 37				17 17								17 37								18 19
Hamworthy	d				16 42				17 22								17 42								18 24
Holton Heath	d								17 26																18 28
Wareham	d				16 49				17 31								17 49								18 33
Wool	d				16 55				17 37								17 55								18 39
Moreton (Dorset)	d								17 43																18 45
Dorchester South	d				17 06				17 51								18 06								18 53
Dorchester West	d			16 58																					
Upwey	d			17 05					17 58																19 00
Weymouth	a			17 10	17 15				18 02								18 15								19 06

A 🛒 to Bournemouth

Table 158

Mondays to Fridays

9 December to 16 May

London - Basingstoke, Southampton, Romsey Lymington, Bournemouth and Weymouth

Network Diagram - see first Page of Table 158

		SW	SW	SN	SW	SW	XC	SW	GW	SW	SW		SW	SW	SW		SW	SW	SW	XC	SW	GW
		1	1	1	1	1	◇1	1	◇	1	◇1		1	1	◇1		1	1	1	◇1	1	◇
											A				A							
							[trolley]				[trolley]				[trolley]					[trolley]		
London Waterloo 15 ⊖	d					16 09					16 35			16 39	17 05				17 09			
Clapham Junction 10	d													16u46								
Woking	d					16 35					17u00								17 34			
Farnborough (Main)	d					16 45								17 13								
Fleet	d													17 19								
Reading 7	d						16 45													17 46		
Basingstoke	a					16 58	17 08							17 31					17 52	18 08		
	d					17 00	17 10						17 24	17 33					17 54	18 10		
Micheldever	d					17 10							17 34						18 04			
Winchester	d					17 19	17 25				17 33		17 44	17 49	18 00				18 14	18 25		
Shawford	d												17 49	17 54					18 18			
Romsey	d				17 07			17 20										18 07			18 20	
Chandlers Ford	d				17 14													18 14				
Eastleigh 3	a				17 20	17 27		17 49					17 54	17 59				18 20	18 24		18 49	
	d			17 16	17 21	17 28		17 50					17 55	18 01				18 21	18 25		18 50	
Hedge End	d					17 34								18 07					18 31			
Botley	d					17 39								18 11					18 36			
Fareham	d					17 48								18 23					18 45			
Portchester	d					17 53								18 28					18 50			
Cosham	d					17 58								18 33					18 55			
Hilsea	a					18 04													19 05			
Fratton	a					18 08								18 40					19 09			
Portsmouth & Southsea	a					18 12								18 43					19 12			
Portsmouth Harbour ⛴	a					18 20								18 50					19 20			
Southampton Airport Pkwy ✈	d			17 20	17 25		17 33				17 42		18 00		18 09			18 25		18 33		
Swaythling	d				17 27								18 02					18 27				
St Denys	d		←		17 30								18 05					18 30				
Southampton Central ⛴	a		17 12	17 28	17 36		17 41				17 49		18 10		18 16			18 36		18 44		
	d		17 30		17 37		17 43				17 53	17 56			18 21	18 24		18 40		18 45		
Millbrook (Hants)	d				17 40													18 48				
Redbridge	d				17 43													18 52				
Romsey	d				17 51			18a03										19 01			19a04	
Mottisfont & Dunbridge	d				17 56													19 06				
Dean	d				18 02													19 11				
Salisbury	a				18 15													19 24				
Totton	d		17 35									18 01				18 29						
Ashurst New Forest	d		17 40									18 06				18 34						
Beaulieu Road	d		17 44																			
Brockenhurst 3	a		17 51				17 56				18 07	18 14				18 42				18 58		
	d	17 42					17 57			18 12	18 08	18 16				18 43	18 48			18 59		
Lymington Town	d	17 50								18 20							18 56					
Lymington Pier	a	17 53								18 23							18 59					
Sway	d											18 20				18 47						
New Milton	d											18 25				18 52						
Hinton Admiral	d											18 29				18 57						
Christchurch	d											18 34				19 01						
Pokesdown	d											18 38				19 05						
Bournemouth	a						18 15				18 23	18 42			18 48	19 09				19 13		
	d										18 24				18 50	19 10						
Branksome	d										18 29				18 55	19 15						
Parkstone (Dorset)	d										18 32				18 58	19 18						
Poole 4	a										18 36				19 02	19 24						
	d										18 37				19 03							
Hamworthy	d										18 42				19 08							
Holton Heath	d														19 12							
Wareham	d										18 49				19 17							
Wool	d										18 55				19 23							
Moreton (Dorset)	d														19 29							
Dorchester South	d										19 08				19 37							
Dorchester West	d								18 58													19 54
Upwey	d								19 06						19 44							20 02
Weymouth	a								19 12		19 19				19 50							20 10

A [trolley] to Bournemouth

Table 158

Mondays to Fridays

9 December to 16 May

London - Basingstoke, Southampton, Romsey Lymington, Bournemouth and Weymouth

Network Diagram - see first Page of Table 158

		SW		SW	SW	SW	SW	SW	SW	SW	SW	XC	SW		SW	SW	SW	SW	SW	SW	SW	SW
		◇1		1	1	1	◇1	1		1	1	◇1	◇1		1	1	1	1	◇1	1	1	1
		A					A						A						A			
		🛒					🛒					🛒	🛒						🛒			
London Waterloo 15 ⊖	d	17 35			17 39	17 48	18 05				18 09		18 35					18 39	19 05			
Clapham Junction 10	d																	18u46	19u12			
Woking	d				18 04	18 13					18 35							19 06				
Farnborough (Main)	d																					
Fleet	d																					
Reading 7	d											18 46										
Basingstoke	a				18 22	18 31					18 53	19 08						19 28	19 47			
	d				18 24	18 33					18 55	19 10					19 24	19 30	19 49			
Micheldever	d				18 34						19 05							19 40				
Winchester	d	18 30			18 44	18 50	19 00		19 05		19 14	19 25	19 30				19 40	19 49	20 05			
Shawford	d				18 49				19 09		19 19						19 45	19 54				
Romsey	d									19 07						19 20						20 07
Chandlers Ford	d									19 14												20 14
Eastleigh 8	a				18 54	18 58			19 15	19 20	19 25					19 49	19 50	19 59				20 20
	d				18 55	18 59			19 16	19 21	19 29					19 50	19 51	20 00				20 21
Hedge End	d				19 01						19 35						19 57					
Botley	d				19 05						19 38						20 01					
Fareham	d				19 14						19 48						20a09					
Portchester	d				19 19						19 53											
Cosham	d				19 24						19 58											
Hilsea	a				19 28						20 02											
Fratton	a				19 32						20 06											
Portsmouth & Southsea	a				19 36						20 11											
Portsmouth Harbour ⛴	a				19 43						20 20											
Southampton Airport Pkwy ✈	d	18 39				19 03	19 09		19 20	19 25		19 33	19 39					20 05	20 14			20 25
Swaythling	d					19 06			19 23	19 27												20 27
St Denys	d					19 09			19 26	19 30										←		20 30
Southampton Central ⛴	a	18 46				19 18	19 18		19 33	19 35		19 41	19 46					20 16	20 22	20 16		20 36
	d	18 51	18 54				19 19			19 37		19 43	19 51	19 54				20 30	20 24	20 30		20 37
Millbrook (Hants)	d									19 40								↪				20 40
Redbridge	d									19 43												20 43
Romsey	d									19 51						20a03						20 51
Mottisfont & Dunbridge	d									19 56												20 56
Dean	d									20 02												21 02
Salisbury	a									20 15												21 15
Totton	d		18 59				19 25							19 59						20 35		
Ashurst New Forest	d		19 04											20 04						20 40		
Beaulieu Road	d																			20 44		
Brockenhurst 3	a		19 12				19 35					19 56		20 12					20 37	20 51		
	d		19 13	19 18			19 36	19 48				19 57		20 13	20 18				20 38	21 16	20 48	
Lymington Town	d			19 26				19 56							20 26					↪	20 56	
Lymington Pier	a			19 29				19 59							20 29						20 59	
Sway	d		19 17				19 41							20 17								
New Milton	d		19 22				19 46							20 22					20 45			
Hinton Admiral	d		19 26				19 50							20 26								
Christchurch	d		19 31				19 55							20 31					20 52			
Pokesdown	d		19 35				19 58							20 35					20 56			
Bournemouth	a	19 20	19 39				20 02					20 12	20 20	20 39					21 00			
	d	19 21	19 40				20 07						20 21	20 40					21 04			
Branksome	d	19 26	19 45				20 12						20 26	20 45								
Parkstone (Dorset)	d	19 29	19 48				20 15						20 29	20 48								
Poole 4	a	19 33	19 54				20 18						20 33	20 54					21 13			
	d	19 34					20 19						20 34						21 15			
Hamworthy	d	19 39					20 24						20 39						21 20			
Holton Heath	d						20 28															
Wareham	d	19 46					20 33						20 46						21 27			
Wool	d	19 52					20 40												21 33			
Moreton (Dorset)	d						20 46												21 39			
Dorchester South	d	20 03					20 54						21 02						21 47			
Dorchester West	d																					
Upwey	d						21 00												21 54			
Weymouth	a	20 15					21 07						21 13						21 58			

A 🛒 to Bournemouth

Table 158

Mondays to Fridays

9 December to 16 May

London - Basingstoke, Southampton, Romsey Lymington, Bournemouth and Weymouth

Network Diagram - see first Page of Table 158

		SW	XC	SW	SW	SW	SW	SW	SW	SW	SW	SW	SW	XC	SW	GW	SW	SW	SW	SW	SW	XC	SW
		1	◇1	1	◇1	1	1	1	1	◇1	1	1	1	◇1	1		◇1	1	1	◇1	1	◇1	◇1
					A												A						A
			🛒		🛒					🛒							🛒			🛒			🛒
London Waterloo 15 ⊖	d	19 09		19 15	19 35			19 39		20 05			20 09				20 35		20 39	21 05			21 35
Clapham Junction 10	d			19u22				19u46		20u12									20u46	21u12			
Woking	d	19 35		19 45	20 00								20 35				21 00			21 32			22 00
Farnborough (Main)	d	19 45						20 13					20 45						21 13				
Fleet	d							20 19											21 19				
Reading 7	d		19 47											20 46								21 46	
Basingstoke	a	19 58	20 09					20 31		20 47			20 58	21 09					21 31	21 50		22 09	
	d	20 00	20 10					20 33		20 49			21 00	21 10					21 33	21 52		22 10	
Micheldever	d	20 10						20 43					21 10						21 43				
Winchester	d	20 19	20 25		20 33			20 52		21 05			21 19	21 25			21 33		21 52	22 08		22 25	22 33
Shawford	d	20 24						20 57					21 24						21 57				
Romsey	d						20 20					21 07			21 20						22 07		
Chandlers Ford	d											21 14									22 14		
Eastleigh 3	a	20 29					20 49	21 02				21 20	21 30		21 49				22 02	22 17	22 21		
	d	20 30					20 50	21 03				21 21	21 31		21 50				22 03	22 18	22 22		
Hedge End	d	20 36											21 37										
Botley	d	20 40											21 41										
Fareham	d	20 49		21 19									21 49										
Portchester	d	20 54											21 54										
Cosham	d	20 59											21 59										
Hilsea	a	21 03											22 04										
Fratton	a	21 07											22 08										
Portsmouth & Southsea	a	21 11											22 11										
Portsmouth Harbour ⛴	a	21 16											22 16										
Southampton Airport Pkwy ✈	d		20 33		20 42			21 08		21 15		21 25		21 33			21 42		22 08	22 22	22 26	22 33	22 42
Swaythling	d											21 27									22 28		
St Denys	d											21 30									22 31		
Southampton Central ⛴	a		20 41	21 43	20 49			21 17		21 24		21 35		21 40			21 49		22 18	22 29	22 36	22 42	22 49
	d		20 43		20 51					21 25		21 37		21 42			21 51			22 31	22 38	22 43	22 51
Millbrook (Hants)	d											21 40									22 40		
Redbridge	d											21 43									22 44		
Romsey	d						21a03					21 51			22a03						22a51		
Mottisfont & Dunbridge	d											21 56											
Dean	d											22 02											
Salisbury	a											22 15											
Totton	d				20 56					21 31										22 36			
Ashurst New Forest	d									21 35										22 41			
Beaulieu Road	d					←																	
Brockenhurst 3	a		20 58		21 07	20 51				21 43				21 55			22 04			22 49		22 56	23 04
	d		20 59		21 08	21 16			21 18	21 44	21 48			21 56			22 05	22 18		22 50		22 59	23 05
Lymington Town	d								21 26		21 56							22 26					
Lymington Pier	a								21 29		21 59							22 29					
Sway	d					21 20				21 49										22 54			
New Milton	d					21 25				21 54										22 59			
Hinton Admiral	d					21 29				21 58										23 03			
Christchurch	d					21 34				22 03										23 08			
Pokesdown	d					21 38				22 06										23 12			
Bournemouth	a		21 15		21 22	21 42				22 10				22 15			22 20			23 16		23 21	23 25
	d				21 27	21 43				22 12							22 24			23 17			23 29
Branksome	d				21 32	21 48				22 17							22 29			23 22			23 35
Parkstone (Dorset)	d				21 35	21 51				22 20							22 32			23 25			23 38
Poole 4	a				21 38	21 57				22 23							22 36			23 29			23 41
	d				21 39												22 37						23 42
Hamworthy	d				21 44												22 42						23 47
Holton Heath	d																						
Wareham	d				21 51												22 49						23 54
Wool	d				21 58												22 55						00 01
Moreton (Dorset)	d				22 04												23 01						00 07
Dorchester South	d				22 12												23 09						00 15
Dorchester West	d															22 58							
Upwey	d				22 18											23 06	23 16						00 21
Weymouth	a				22 23											23 13	23 20						00 26

A 🛒 to Bournemouth

Table 158

Mondays to Fridays

9 December to 16 May

London - Basingstoke, Southampton, Romsey Lymington, Bournemouth and Weymouth

Network Diagram - see first Page of Table 158

		SW	SW	SW	XC	SW	SW	SW	SW	XC	SW	SW WX	SW	SW	SW
		1	1	1	◇1	1	◇1 🛒	1	1	◇1	◇1 🛒	1	1	◇1	1
London Waterloo 15 ⊖	d			21 39		21 42	22 05				22 35		22 39	23 05	23 35
Clapham Junction 10	d			21u46			22u12						22u46	23u12	23u42
Woking	d					22 19	22 32				23 00			23 32	00 03
Farnborough (Main)	d			22 13		22 33							23 16		00 14
Fleet	d			22 19		22 38							23 21		00 20
Reading 7	d				22 22				←	22 48					
Basingstoke	a			22 31	22 39	22 58	22 50		22 58	23 05			23 33	23 51	00 33
	d		22 21	22 33	22 40	23 00	22 52		23 00	23 09			23 34	23 53	00 35
Micheldever	d		22 31	22 43		→			23 10					00 03	
Winchester	d		22 40	22 52	22 57		23 08		23 19	23 25	23 33		23 51	00 12	00 51
Shawford	d		22 45	22 57					23 24				23 55		
Romsey	d	22 20						23 07				22 58			
Chandlers Ford	d							23 14							
Eastleigh 3	a	22 49	22 50	23 02			23 16	23 21	23 29			23 34	00 01	00 22	00 59
	d	22 50	22 51	23 03			23 17	23 22	23 30			23 36	00 02	00 23	01 00
Hedge End	d		22 57						23 36						
Botley	d		23 01						23 40						
Fareham	d		23 10						23 49						
Portchester	d		23 15						23 54						
Cosham	d		23 20						23 59						
Hilsea	a		23 24						00 03						
Fratton	a		23 32						00 07						
Portsmouth & Southsea	a		23 36						00 11						
Portsmouth Harbour ⛴	a		23 40						00 16						
Southampton Airport Pkwy ✈	d			23 08	23 13		23 22	23 26		23 37	23 42		00 06	00 28	01 05
Swaythling	d							23 28							
St Denys	d							23 31						00s32	
Southampton Central ⛴	a			23 17	23 20		23 29	23 37		23 43	23 49		00 13	00 37	01 12
	d						23 30	23 38			23 51			00 38	
Millbrook (Hants)	d							23 40							
Redbridge	d							23 44							
Romsey	d	23a03						23 56				23a48			
Mottisfont & Dunbridge	d							00 01							
Dean	d							00 07							
Salisbury	a							00 19							
Totton	d						23 36							00s43	
Ashurst New Forest	d						23 40								
Beaulieu Road	d														
Brockenhurst 3	a						23 48				00 04			00s54	
	d						23 49				00 05				
Lymington Town	d														
Lymington Pier	a														
Sway	d						23 54								
New Milton	d						23 58							01s02	
Hinton Admiral	d						00 02								
Christchurch	d						00 07							01s09	
Pokesdown	d						00 11							01s13	
Bournemouth	a						00 15				00 21			01 17	
	d						00 16				00 22			01 18	
Branksome	d						00 21				00 27			01s23	
Parkstone (Dorset)	d						00 24				00 30			01s26	
Poole 4	a						00 28				00 35			01 30	
	d														
Hamworthy	d														
Holton Heath	d														
Wareham	d														
Wool	d														
Moreton (Dorset)	d														
Dorchester South	d														
Dorchester West	d														
Upwey	d														
Weymouth	a														

Table 158

Saturdays

14 December to 17 May

London - Basingstoke, Southampton, Romsey Lymington, Bournemouth and Weymouth

Network Diagram - see first Page of Table 158

		SW	SW	SW	SW	SW	SW	SW	SW	SW		SW	SW	SW	SW	SW	SW	SW	SW	SW		SW	SW	GW	SW
		◇1	1	◇1 🚲	1	◇1 🚲	◇1	1	1	1		1	1	1	1	1	1	1	1	1		1	1		◇1
London Waterloo 15 ⊖	d												00 05		01 05										05 30
Clapham Junction 10	d												00u12		01 15										05u37
Woking	d									00 03		00 28	00 37		01 42										06 01
Farnborough (Main)	d								00 10	00 14		00 41			01s51										
Fleet	d								00 16	00 20		00 47			01s57										
Reading 7	d																								
Basingstoke	a								00 33	00 33		01 06	00 55		02s09										06 20
	d									00 35			00 56												06 21
Micheldever	d						00 03																		06 31
Winchester	d						00 12			00 51			01 13		02s26										06 41
Shawford	d																								
Romsey	d																			05 58					
Chandlers Ford	d																			06 06					
Eastleigh 3	a						00 22			00 59			01 21		02s35					06 11					06 50
	d				00 02		00 23	00 30		01 00			01 22							06 13		06 28			06 51
Hedge End	d							00s36														06 34			
Botley	d							00s39														06 38			
Fareham	d							00s47														06 48			
Portchester	d							00s53														06 53			
Cosham	d							00s57														06 58			
Hilsea	a																					07 03			
Fratton	a							01s05														07 07			
Portsmouth & Southsea	a							01s08														07 11			
Portsmouth Harbour ⛴	a							01 12														07 16			
Southampton Airport Pkwy ✈	d				00 06		00 28			01 05			01 26		02s39					06 17					06 56
Swaythling	d																			06 20					
St Denys	d						00s32								02s44					06 23					
Southampton Central ⛴	a				00 13		00 37			01 12			01 35		02 49					06 28					07 03
	d						00 38						01 37					06 21		06 30					07 05
Millbrook (Hants)	d																			06 32					
Redbridge	d																			06 36					
Romsey	d																			06 44					
Mottisfont & Dunbridge	d		00 01																	06 49					
Dean	d		00 07																	06 54					
Salisbury	a		00 19																	07 07					
Totton	d						00s43						01s42					06 26							07 10
Ashurst New Forest	d																	06 31							
Beaulieu Road	d																								
Brockenhurst 3	a						00s54						01s53					06 39							07 21
	d					00 05										06 12	06 16	06 40	06 42				07 12		07 22
Lymington Town	d															06 20			06 50				07 20		
Lymington Pier	a															06 22			06 52				07 22		
Sway	d																06 20	06 44							07 26
New Milton	d						01s02						02s00				06 25	06 49							07 31
Hinton Admiral	d			00 02													06 29	06 53							07 35
Christchurch	d			00 07			01s09						02s07				06 34	06 58							07 40
Pokesdown	d			00 11			01s13						02s11				06 38	07 02							07 44
Bournemouth	a			00 15		00 21	01 17						02 15				06 42	07 06							07 48
	d			00 16		00 22	01 18							06 11			06 44	07 11							07 49
Branksome	d			00 21		00 27	01s23							06 16			06 49	07 16							07 54
Parkstone (Dorset)	d			00 24		00 30	01s26							06 19			06 52	07 19							07 57
Poole 4	a			00 28		00 35	01 30							06 23			06 55	07 23							08 01
	d													06 24			06 57	07 24							08 02
Hamworthy	d													06 29			07 02	07 29							08 07
Holton Heath	d													06 33			07 06	07 33							
Wareham	d													06 38			07 11	07 38							08 14
Wool	d	00 01												06 44			07 17	07 44							08 20
Moreton (Dorset)	d	00 07												06 50			07 23	07 50							08 26
Dorchester South	d	00 15												06 58			07 31	07 58							08 34
Dorchester West	d																							08 03	
Upwey	d	00 21												07 05			07 38	08 05						08 11	08 41
Weymouth	a	00 26												07 09			07 42	08 09						08 17	08 45

Table 158

Saturdays

14 December to 17 May

London - Basingstoke, Southampton, Romsey Lymington, Bournemouth and Weymouth

Network Diagram - see first Page of Table 158

		SW 1	SW 1	SN 1	SW 1	SW 1	SW 1	SW ◇1	SW 1	SW 1	SW 1	SN 1	SW 1	SW 1	XC ◇1 🛒	SW 1	SW ◇1	SW 1	GW ◇	SW 1	XC ◇1	SW ◇1	SW 1
London Waterloo 15 ⊖	d							06 30						06 42			07 35			07 39		08 05	
Clapham Junction 10	d							06u37						06u49						07u46		08u12	
Woking	d					06 19		06 57						07 19			08 00						
Farnborough (Main)	d					06 33								07 33						08 13			
Fleet	d					06 38								07 38						08 19			
Reading 7	d														07 46						08 16		
Basingstoke	a					06 58		07 16						07 58	08 08		08 20			08 31	08 40	08 47	
	d					07 00		07 18						08 00	08 10		08 21			08 33	08 41	08 49	
Micheldever	d					07 10								08 10									
Winchester	d					07 19		07 34						08 19	08 25		08 38			08 49	08 56	09 05	
Shawford	d					07 24								08 24						08 54			
Romsey	d				07 07				07 13				08 07					08 13					
Chandlers Ford	d				07 14								08 14										
Eastleigh 3	a				07 20	07 29		07 42	07 49				08 20	08 30			08 46	08 49		08 59			
	d			07 14	07 21	07 30		07 43	07 50			08 14	08 21	08 31			08 47	08 50		09 00			
Hedge End	d					07 36								08 37									
Botley	d					07 40								08 41									
Fareham	d					07 49								08 49									
Portchester	d					07 54								08 54									
Cosham	d					07 59								08 59									
Hilsea	a					08 03								09 04									
Fratton	a					08 07								09 08									
Portsmouth & Southsea	a					08 11								09 12									
Portsmouth Harbour ⛴	a					08 18								09 18									
Southampton Airport Pkwy ✈	d			07 18	07 25			07 48				08 18	08 25		08 33		08 51			09 05	09 09	09 14	
Swaythling	d				07 27								08 27										
St Denys	d				07 30								08 30										←
Southampton Central ⛴	a			07 27	07 35			07 56				08 26	08 36		08 41		08 58			09 12	09 17	09 22	09 12
	d	07 21			07 37			08 00		08 19			08 37		08 43		09 00			09 30		09 24	09 30
Millbrook (Hants)	d				07 40								08 40							→			
Redbridge	d				07 43								08 43										
Romsey	d				07 51				08a03				08 51					09a03					
Mottisfont & Dunbridge	d				07 56								08 56										
Dean	d				08 02								09 02										
Salisbury	a				08 15								09 15										
Totton	d	07 26						08 05		08 24							09 05						09 35
Ashurst New Forest	d	07 31								08 29													09 40
Beaulieu Road	d									08 33													09 44
Brockenhurst 3	a	07 39						08 16		08 39					08 56		09 16					09 37	09 51
	d	07 40	07 42				08 12	08 17		08 40	08 42				08 58	09 12	09 17					09 38	10 16
Lymington Town	d		07 50				08 20				08 50					09 20							→
Lymington Pier	a		07 52				08 22				08 52					09 22							
Sway	d	07 44						08 21		08 45							09 21						
New Milton	d	07 49						08 26		08 50							09 26					09 45	
Hinton Admiral	d	07 53						08 30		08 54							09 30						
Christchurch	d	07 58						08 35		08 59							09 35					09 52	
Pokesdown	d	08 02						08 39		09 02							09 39					09 56	
Bournemouth	a	08 06						08 43		09 06					09 14		09 43					10 00	
	d	08 11						08 44		09 11							09 44					10 04	
Branksome	d	08 16						08 49		09 16							09 49						
Parkstone (Dorset)	d	08 19						08 52		09 19							09 52						
Poole 4	a	08 23						08 56		09 23							09 56					10 13	
	d	08 24						08 57		09 24							09 57					10 14	
Hamworthy	d	08 29						09 02		09 29							10 02					10 19	
Holton Heath	d	08 33								09 33												10 23	
Wareham	d	08 38						09 09		09 38							10 09					10 28	
Wool	d	08 44						09 15		09 44												10 35	
Moreton (Dorset)	d	08 50						09 21		09 50												10 41	
Dorchester South	d	08 58						09 29		09 58							10 27					10 49	
Dorchester West	d																		10 38				
Upwey	d	09 05						09 36		10 05									10 49			10 55	
Weymouth	a	09 09						09 40		10 09							10 35		10 57			11 00	

Table 158

Saturdays

14 December to 17 May

London - Basingstoke, Southampton, Romsey Lymington, Bournemouth and Weymouth

Network Diagram - see first Page of Table 158

		SW		SW	SW	XC	SW	SW	SW	SW	SW	SW		SW	SW	SN	SW	SW	XC	SW	GW	SW		SW	SW
		1		1	1	◇1	◇1	1	1	1	1	◇1		1	1	1	1	1	◇1	1	◇	◇1		1	1
							A					A										A			
						⊥	⊥					⊥							⊥			⊥			
London Waterloo 15 ⊖	d				08 09		08 35				08 39	09 05						09 09				09 35			
Clapham Junction 10	d										08u46	09u12													
Woking	d				08 35		09 00											09 35				10 00			
Farnborough (Main)	d				08 45						09 13							09 45							
Fleet	d										09 19														
Reading 7	d					08 46													09 46						
Basingstoke	a				08 58	09 08					09 31	09 47						09 58	10 08						
	d				09 00	09 10					09 33	09 49						10 00	10 10						
Micheldever	d				09 10													10 10							
Winchester	d				09 19	09 25	09 33				09 49	10 05						10 19	10 25			10 33			
Shawford	d										09 54														
Romsey	d			09 07						09 20							10 07			10 20					
Chandlers Ford	d			09 14													10 14								
Eastleigh 3	a			09 20	09 27					09 49	09 59						10 20	10 27		10 49					
	d			09 21	09 28					09 50	10 00					10 14	10 21	10 28		10 50					
Hedge End	d				09 34													10 34							
Botley	d				09 38													10 38							
Fareham	d				09 48													10 48							
Portchester	d				09 53													10 53							
Cosham	d				09 58													10 58							
Hilsea	a				10 03													11 03							
Fratton	a				10 07													11 07							
Portsmouth & Southsea	a				10 11													11 11							
Portsmouth Harbour ⛴	a				10 18													11 18							
Southampton Airport Pkwy ✈	d			09 25		09 33	09 42				10 05	10 14				10 18	10 25		10 33			10 42			
Swaythling	d			09 27													10 27								
St Denys	d			09 30										←			10 30								
Southampton Central ⛴	a			09 36		09 40	09 49				10 12	10 22		10 12		10 27	10 36		10 41			10 49			
	d			09 37		09 42	09 51				10 30	10 24		10 30			10 37		10 43			10 51			
Millbrook (Hants)	d			09 40							→						10 40								
Redbridge	d			09 43													10 44								
Romsey	d			09 51						10a03							10 59			11a03					
Mottisfont & Dunbridge	d			09 56													11 04								
Dean	d			10 02													11 10								
Salisbury	a			10 15													11 22								
Totton	d													10 35											
Ashurst New Forest	d													10 40											
Beaulieu Road	d								←																←
Brockenhurst 3	a					09 57	10 04		09 51			10 37		10 51					10 57			11 04			10 51
	d	09 42				09 58	10 05	10 12	10 16			10 38		11 16	10 42				10 58			11 05		11 12	11 16
Lymington Town	d	09 50						10 20						→	10 50									11 20	
Lymington Pier	a	09 52						10 22							10 52									11 22	
Sway	d								10 20																11 20
New Milton	d								10 25			10 45													11 25
Hinton Admiral	d								10 29																11 29
Christchurch	d								10 34			10 52													11 34
Pokesdown	d								10 38			10 56													11 38
Bournemouth	a					10 11	10 20		10 42			11 00							11 12			11 20			11 42
	d						10 24		10 43			11 04										11 24			11 43
Branksome	d						10 29		10 48													11 29			11 48
Parkstone (Dorset)	d						10 32		10 51													11 32			11 51
Poole 4	a						10 36		10 55			11 13										11 36			11 55
	d						10 37					11 14										11 37			
Hamworthy	d						10 42					11 19										11 42			
Holton Heath	d											11 23													
Wareham	d						10 49					11 28										11 49			
Wool	d											11 35													
Moreton (Dorset)	d											11 41													
Dorchester South	d						11 05					11 49										12 05			
Dorchester West	d																				11 54				
Upwey	d											11 55									12 02				
Weymouth	a						11 13					12 00									12 09	12 13			

A ⊥ to Bournemouth

Table 158

Saturdays

14 December to 17 May

London - Basingstoke, Southampton, Romsey Lymington, Bournemouth and Weymouth

Network Diagram - see first Page of Table 158

		SW	XC	SW	SW	SW	SW	SW		XC	SW	SW	SW	SW	SW	SW	SW	SW		SN	SW	SW	XC	SW	GW
		1	◇1 ⚒	◇1 A ⚒	1	1	1	1		◇1 ⚒	◇1 A ⚒	1	1	1	1	◇1 A ⚒	1	1		1	1	1	◇1 ⚒	1	◇
London Waterloo 15 ⊖	d	09 39		10 05				10 09			10 35				10 39	11 05						11 09			
Clapham Junction 10	d	09u46		10u12											10u46	11u12									
Woking	d							10 35			11 00											11 35			
Farnborough (Main)	d	10 13						10 45							11 13							11 45			
Fleet	d	10 19													11 19										
Reading 7	d		10 18							10 46													11 46		
Basingstoke	a	10 31	10 39	10 47				10 58		11 08					11 31	11 47						11 58	12 08		
	d	10 33	10 40	10 49				11 00		11 10					11 33	11 49						12 00	12 10		
Micheldever	d							11 10														12 10			
Winchester	d	10 49	10 55	11 05				11 19		11 25	11 33				11 49	12 05						12 19	12 25		
Shawford	d	10 54													11 54										
Romsey	d						11 07							11 20							12 07			12 20	
Chandlers Ford	d						11 14														12 14				
Eastleigh 3	a	10 59					11 20	11 27						11 49	11 59						12 20	12 27		12 49	
	d	11 00					11 21	11 28						11 50	12 00					12 14	12 21	12 28		12 50	
Hedge End	d							11 34														12 34			
Botley	d							11 38														12 38			
Fareham	d							11 48														12 48			
Portchester	d							11 53														12 53			
Cosham	d							11 58														12 58			
Hilsea	a							12 03														13 03			
Fratton	a							12 07														13 07			
Portsmouth & Southsea	a							12 11														13 11			
Portsmouth Harbour ⛴	a							12 18														13 18			
Southampton Airport Pkwy ✈	d	11 05	11 09	11 14			11 25			11 33	11 42				12 05	12 14				12 19	12 25		12 33		
Swaythling	d						11 27														12 27				
St Denys	d				←		11 30										←				12 30				
Southampton Central ⛴	a	11 12	11 17	11 22	11 12		11 36			11 41	11 49				12 12	12 22	12 12			12 27	12 36		12 41		
	d	11 30		11 24	11 30		11 37			11 43	11 51				12 30	12 24	12 30				12 37		12 43		
Millbrook (Hants)	d	↪					11 40								↪						12 40				
Redbridge	d						11 43														12 43				
Romsey	d						11 51							12a03							12 51			13a03	
Mottisfont & Dunbridge	d						11 56														12 56				
Dean	d						12 02														13 02				
Salisbury	a						12 15														13 15				
Totton	d				11 35												12 35								
Ashurst New Forest	d				11 40												12 40								
Beaulieu Road	d				11 44								←												
Brockenhurst 3	a			11 37	11 51					11 57	12 04		11 51			12 37	12 51						12 57		
	d			11 38	12 16	11 42				11 58	12 05	12 12	12 16			12 38	13 16	12 42					12 58		
Lymington Town	d				→	11 50						12 20					→	12 50							
Lymington Pier	a					11 52						12 22						12 52							
Sway	d												12 20												
New Milton	d			11 45									12 25			12 45									
Hinton Admiral	d												12 29												
Christchurch	d			11 52									12 34			12 52									
Pokesdown	d			11 56									12 38			12 56									
Bournemouth	a			12 00						12 11	12 20		12 42			13 00							13 11		
	d			12 04							12 24		12 43			13 04									
Branksome	d										12 29		12 48												
Parkstone (Dorset)	d										12 32		12 51												
Poole 3	a			12 13							12 36		12 55			13 13									
	d			12 14							12 37					13 14									
Hamworthy	d			12 19							12 42					13 19									
Holton Heath	d			12 23												13 23									
Wareham	d			12 28							12 49					13 28									
Wool	d			12 35												13 35									
Moreton (Dorset)	d			12 41												13 41									
Dorchester South	d			12 49							13 05					13 49									
Dorchester West	d																								13 54
Upwey	d			12 55												13 55									14 02
Weymouth	a			13 00							13 13					14 00									14 08

A ⚒ to Bournemouth

Table 158

Saturdays

14 December to 17 May

London - Basingstoke, Southampton, Romsey Lymington, Bournemouth and Weymouth

Network Diagram - see first Page of Table 158

		SW	SW	SW	SW	XC	SW	SW	SW	SW	SW	XC	SW	SW	SW	SW	SW	SW	SW	SW	SW	SW
		◇1	1	1	1	◇1	◇1	1	1	1	1	◇1	◇1	1	1	1	1	◇1	1	1	1	1
		A [trolley]				[trolley]	A [trolley]					[trolley]	A [trolley]					A [trolley]				
London Waterloo 15 ⊖	d	11 35			11 39		12 05				12 09		12 35				12 39	13 05				13 09
Clapham Junction 10	d				11u46		12u12										12u46	13u12				
Woking	d	12 00									12 35		13 00									13 35
Farnborough (Main)	d				12 13						12 45						13 13					13 45
Fleet	d				12 19												13 19					
Reading 7	d					12 16						12 46										
Basingstoke	a				12 31	12 40	12 47				12 58	13 08					13 31	13 47				13 58
	d				12 33	12 41	12 49				13 00	13 10					13 33	13 49				14 00
Micheldever	d										13 10											14 10
Winchester	d	12 33			12 49	12 56	13 05				13 19	13 25	13 33				13 49	14 05				14 19
Shawford	d				12 54												13 54					
Romsey	d									13 07						13 20					14 07	
Chandlers Ford	d									13 14											14 14	
Eastleigh 3	a				12 59					13 20	13 27					13 49	13 59				14 20	14 27
	d				13 00					13 21	13 28					13 50	14 00				14 21	14 28
Hedge End	d										13 34											14 34
Botley	d										13 38											14 38
Fareham	d										13 48											14 48
Portchester	d										13 53											14 53
Cosham	d										13 58											14 58
Hilsea	a										14 03											15 03
Fratton	a										14 07											15 07
Portsmouth & Southsea	a										14 11											15 11
Portsmouth Harbour ⛴	a										14 18											15 18
Southampton Airport Pkwy ✈	d	12 42			13 05	13 09	13 14			13 25		13 33	13 42				14 05	14 14			14 25	
Swaythling	d									13 27											14 27	
St Denys	d							←		13 30									←		14 30	
Southampton Central ⛴	a	12 49			13 12	13 17	13 22	13 12		13 36		13 41	13 49				14 12	14 22	14 12		14 35	
	d	12 51			13 30		13 24	13 30		13 37		13 43	13 51				14 30	14 24	14 30		14 37	
Millbrook (Hants)	d				↪					13 40							↪				14 40	
Redbridge	d									13 43											14 43	
Romsey	d									13 51						14a03					14 51	
Mottisfont & Dunbridge	d									13 56											14 56	
Dean	d									14 02											15 02	
Salisbury	a									14 15											15 15	
Totton	d							13 35											14 35			
Ashurst New Forest	d							13 40											14 40			
Beaulieu Road	d			←				13 44							←							
Brockenhurst 3	a	13 04		12 51			13 37	13 51				13 57	14 04		13 51			14 37	14 51			
	d	13 05	13 12	13 16			13 38	14 16	13 42			13 58	14 05	14 12	14 16			14 38	15 16	14 42		
Lymington Town	d		13 20					↪	13 50					14 20					↪	14 50		
Lymington Pier	a		13 22						13 52					14 22						14 52		
Sway	d			13 20											14 20							
New Milton	d			13 25			13 45								14 25			14 45				
Hinton Admiral	d			13 29											14 29							
Christchurch	d			13 34			13 52								14 34			14 52				
Pokesdown	d			13 38			13 56								14 38			14 56				
Bournemouth	a	13 20		13 42			14 00					14 11	14 20		14 42			15 00				
	d	13 24		13 43			14 04						14 24		14 43			15 04				
Branksome	d	13 29		13 48									14 29		14 48							
Parkstone (Dorset)	d	13 32		13 51									14 32		14 51							
Poole 4	a	13 36		13 55			14 13						14 36		14 55			15 13				
	d	13 37					14 14						14 37					15 14				
Hamworthy	d	13 42					14 19						14 42					15 19				
Holton Heath	d						14 23											15 23				
Wareham	d	13 49					14 28						14 49					15 28				
Wool	d						14 35											15 35				
Moreton (Dorset)	d						14 41											15 41				
Dorchester South	d	14 05					14 49						15 05					15 49				
Dorchester West	d																					
Upwey	d						14 55											15 55				
Weymouth	a	14 13					15 00						15 13					16 00				

A [trolley] to Bournemouth

Table 158

Saturdays

14 December to 17 May

London - Basingstoke, Southampton, Romsey Lymington, Bournemouth and Weymouth

Network Diagram - see first Page of Table 158

		XC	SW	SW	SW	SN	SW	SW	XC	SW		SW	SW	SW	SW	XC	SW	GW	SW	SW		SW	SW	SW	SW
		◇[1]	◇[1]	[1]	[1]	[1]	[1]	[1]	◇[1]	◇[1]		[1]	[1]	[1]	[1]	◇[1]	[1]	◇	◇[1]	[1]		[1]	[1]	◇[1]	[1]
			A																A					A	
		🛒	🛒						🛒	🛒						🛒			🛒					🛒	
London Waterloo [15] ⊖	d		13 35					13 39		14 05					14 09				14 35				14 39	15 05	
Clapham Junction [10]	d							13u46		14u12													14u46	15u12	
Woking	d		14 00												14 35				15 00						
Farnborough (Main)	d							14 13							14 45								15 13		
Fleet	d							14 19															15 19		
Reading [7]	d	13 46							14 16							14 46									
Basingstoke	a	14 08						14 31	14 40	14 47					14 58	15 08							15 31	15 47	
	d	14 10						14 33	14 41	14 49					15 00	15 10							15 33	15 49	
Micheldever	d														15 10										
Winchester	d	14 25	14 33					14 49	14 56	15 05					15 19	15 25			15 33				15 49	16 05	
Shawford	d							14 54															15 54		
Romsey	d						14 13							15 07			15 20								
Chandlers Ford	d													15 14											
Eastleigh [3]	a						14 49	14 59						15 20	15 27		15 49						15 59		
	d					14 41	14 50	15 00						15 21	15 28		15 50						16 00		
Hedge End	d														15 34										
Botley	d														15 38										
Fareham	d					14a59									15 48										
Portchester	d														15 53										
Cosham	d														15 58										
Hilsea	a														16 03										
Fratton	a														16 07										
Portsmouth & Southsea	a														16 11										
Portsmouth Harbour ⛴	a														16 18										
Southampton Airport Pkwy ✈	d	14 33	14 42					15 05	15 09	15 14				15 25		15 33			15 42				16 05	16 14	
Swaythling	d													15 27											
St Denys	d											←		15 30											←
Southampton Central ⛴	a	14 41	14 49					15 12	15 17	15 22		15 12		15 36		15 41			15 49				16 12	16 22	16 12
	d	14 43	14 51					15 30		15 24		15 30		15 37		15 43			15 51				16 30	16 24	16 30
Millbrook (Hants)	d							→						15 40									→		
Redbridge	d													15 43											
Romsey	d						15a03							15 51			16a03								
Mottisfont & Dunbridge	d													15 56											
Dean	d													16 02											
Salisbury	a													16 15											
Totton	d											15 35													16 35
Ashurst New Forest	d											15 40													16 40
Beaulieu Road	d				←							15 44										←			
Brockenhurst [3]	a	14 57	15 04		14 51					15 37		15 51				15 57			16 04			15 51		16 37	16 51
	d	14 58	15 05	15 12	15 16					15 38		16 16	15 42			15 58			16 05	16 12		16 16		16 38	17 16
Lymington Town	d			15 20								→	15 50							16 20					→
Lymington Pier	a			15 22									15 52							16 22					
Sway	d				15 20																	16 20			
New Milton	d				15 25					15 45												16 25		16 45	
Hinton Admiral	d				15 29																	16 29			
Christchurch	d				15 34					15 52												16 34		16 52	
Pokesdown	d				15 38					15 56												16 38		16 56	
Bournemouth	a	15 11	15 20		15 42					16 00						16 11			16 20			16 42		17 00	
	d		15 24		15 43					16 04									16 24			16 43		17 04	
Branksome	d		15 29		15 48														16 29			16 48			
Parkstone (Dorset)	d		15 32		15 51														16 32			16 51			
Poole [4]	a		15 36		15 55					16 13									16 36			16 55		17 13	
	d		15 37							16 14									16 37					17 14	
Hamworthy	d		15 42							16 19									16 42					17 19	
Holton Heath	d									16 23														17 23	
Wareham	d		15 49							16 28									16 49					17 28	
Wool	d									16 35														17 35	
Moreton (Dorset)	d									16 41														17 41	
Dorchester South	d		16 05							16 49									17 06					17 49	
Dorchester West	d																	16 58							
Upwey	d									16 55								17 05						17 55	
Weymouth	a		16 13							17 00								17 10	17 15					18 00	

A 🛒 to Bournemouth

Table 158

Saturdays

14 December to 17 May

London - Basingstoke, Southampton, Romsey Lymington, Bournemouth and Weymouth

Network Diagram - see first Page of Table 158

		SW	SN	SW	SW	XC	SW	SW	SW	SW	SW	XC	XC	SW	SW	SW	SW	SW	XC	SW	GW	SW	SW
		1	1	1	1	◇1	◇1	1	1	1	1	◇1	◇1	◇1	1	1	1	1	◇1	1	◇	◇1	1
							A					B	C	A								A	
						🍴	🍴					🍴	🍴	🍴					🍴			🍴	
London Waterloo 15 ⊖	d				15 09		15 35				15 39			16 05				16 09				16 35	
Clapham Junction 10	d										15u46			16u12									
Woking	d				15 35		16 00											16 35				17 00	
Farnborough (Main)	d				15 45						16 13							16 45					
Fleet	d										16 19												
Reading 7	d					15 46						16 15	16 16						16 46				
Basingstoke	a				15 58	16 08					16 31	16 40	16 40	16 47				16 58	17 08				
	d				16 00	16 10					16 33	16 41	16 41	16 49				17 00	17 10				
Micheldever	d				16 10													17 10					
Winchester	d				16 19	16 25	16 33				16 49	16 56	16 56	17 05				17 19	17 25			17 33	
Shawford	d										16 54												
Romsey	d			16 07						16 20							17 07			17 20			
Chandlers Ford	d			16 14													17 14						
Eastleigh 3	a			16 20	16 27					16 49	16 59						17 20	17 27		17 49			
	d		16 14	16 21	16 28					16 50	17 00						17 21	17 28		17 50			
Hedge End	d				16 34													17 34					
Botley	d				16 38													17 38					
Fareham	d				16 48													17 48					
Portchester	d				16 53													17 53					
Cosham	d				16 58													17 58					
Hilsea	a				17 03													18 03					
Fratton	a				17 07													18 07					
Portsmouth & Southsea	a				17 11													18 11					
Portsmouth Harbour ⛴	a				17 16													18 18					
Southampton Airport Pkwy ✈	d		16 18	16 25		16 33	16 42				17 05	17 09	17 09	17 14			17 25		17 33			17 42	
Swaythling	d			16 27													17 27						
St Denys	d			16 30											←		17 30						
Southampton Central ⛴	a		16 27	16 36		16 41	16 49				17 12	17 17	17 17	17 22	17 12		17 36		17 41			17 49	
	d			16 37		16 43	16 51				17 30			17 24	17 30		17 37		17 43			17 51	
Millbrook (Hants)	d			16 40							→						17 40						
Redbridge	d			16 43													17 43						
Romsey	d			16 51						17a03							17 51			18a03			
Mottisfont & Dunbridge	d			16 56													17 56						
Dean	d			17 02													18 02						
Salisbury	a			17 15													18 15						
Totton	d														17 35								
Ashurst New Forest	d														17 40								
Beaulieu Road	d								←						17 44								
Brockenhurst 3	a					16 57	17 04		16 51					17 37	17 51				17 57			18 04	
	d	16 42				16 58	17 05	17 12	17 16					17 38	18 16	17 42			17 58			18 05	18 12
Lymington Town	d	16 50						17 20							→	17 50							18 20
Lymington Pier	a	16 52						17 22								17 52							18 22
Sway	d								17 20														
New Milton	d								17 25					17 45									
Hinton Admiral	d								17 29														
Christchurch	d								17 34					17 52									
Pokesdown	d								17 38					17 56									
Bournemouth	a					17 11	17 20		17 42					18 00					18 11			18 20	
	d						17 24		17 43					18 04								18 24	
Branksome	d						17 29		17 48													18 29	
Parkstone (Dorset)	d						17 32		17 51													18 32	
Poole 4	a						17 36		17 55					18 13								18 36	
	d						17 37							18 14								18 37	
Hamworthy	d						17 42							18 19								18 42	
Holton Heath	d													18 23									
Wareham	d						17 49							18 28								18 49	
Wool	d													18 35									
Moreton (Dorset)	d													18 41									
Dorchester South	d						18 05							18 49								19 05	
Dorchester West	d																				18 54		
Upwey	d													18 55							19 02		
Weymouth	a						18 13							19 00							19 10	19 13	

A 🍴 to Bournemouth

B from 15 February

C from 4 January until 8 February

Table 158

Saturdays

14 December to 17 May

London - Basingstoke, Southampton, Romsey Lymington, Bournemouth and Weymouth

Network Diagram - see first Page of Table 158

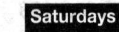

		SW		SW	SW	SW	SW	SW	SN	SW	SW	XC		SW	GW	SW	SW	SW	SW	XC	SW	SW		SW	SW
		1		1	1	◇1	1	1	1	1	1	◇1		1	◇	◇1	1	1	1	◇1	◇1	1		1	1
						A										B					B				
						☕						🛒				🛒				🛒	🛒				
London Waterloo 15 ⊖	d				16 39	17 05					17 09					17 35			17 39		18 05				
Clapham Junction 10	d				16u46	17u12													17u46		18u12				
Woking	d										17 35					18 00									
Farnborough (Main)	d				17 13						17 45								18 13						
Fleet	d				17 19														18 19						
Reading 7	d											17 45								18 15					
Basingstoke	a				17 31	17 47					17 58	18 08							18 31	18 40	18 47				
	d			17 24	17 33	17 49					18 00	18 10							18 33	18 41	18 49				
Micheldever	d			17 34							18 10														
Winchester	d			17 43	17 49	18 05					18 19	18 25				18 33			18 49	18 56	19 05				
Shawford	d			17 48	17 54														18 54						
Romsey	d									18 07				18 20											19 07
Chandlers Ford	d									18 14															19 14
Eastleigh 3	a			17 53	17 59					18 20	18 27			18 49					18 59						19 20
	d			17 54	18 00				18 14	18 21	18 28			18 50					19 00						19 21
Hedge End	d										18 34														
Botley	d										18 38														
Fareham	d										18 48														
Portchester	d										18 53														
Cosham	d										18 58														
Hilsea	a										19 03														
Fratton	a										19 07														
Portsmouth & Southsea	a										19 11														
Portsmouth Harbour ⛴	a										19 18														
Southampton Airport Pkwy ✈	d			17 59	18 05	18 14			18 18	18 25		18 33				18 42			19 05	19 09	19 14				19 25
Swaythling	d			18 01						18 27															19 27
St Denys	d			18 04			←			18 30												←			19 30
Southampton Central ⛴	a			18 10	18 14	18 22	18 14		18 27	18 36		18 40				18 49			19 12	19 17	19 22	19 12			19 36
	d				18 30	18 24	18 30			18 40		18 43				18 51			19 30		19 24	19 30			19 37
Millbrook (Hants)	d				→					18 48									→						19 40
Redbridge	d									18 52															19 43
Romsey	d									19 01				19a04											19 51
Mottisfont & Dunbridge	d									19 06															19 56
Dean	d									19 11															20 02
Salisbury	a									19 24															20 15
Totton	d						18 35															19 35			
Ashurst New Forest	d						18 40															19 40			
Beaulieu Road	d	←																←				19 44			
Brockenhurst 3	a	17 51				18 37	18 51					18 57				19 04		18 51			19 37	19 51			
	d	18 16				18 38	19 16	18 42				18 58				19 05	19 12	19 16			19 38	20 16		19 42	
Lymington Town	d						→	18 50									19 20					→		19 50	
Lymington Pier	a							18 52									19 22							19 52	
Sway	d	18 20																19 20							
New Milton	d	18 25				18 45												19 25			19 45				
Hinton Admiral	d	18 29																19 29							
Christchurch	d	18 34				18 52												19 34			19 52				
Pokesdown	d	18 38				18 56												19 38			19 56				
Bournemouth	a	18 42				19 00						19 11				19 20		19 42			20 00				
	d	18 43				19 04										19 24		19 43			20 04				
Branksome	d	18 48														19 29		19 48							
Parkstone (Dorset)	d	18 51														19 32		19 51							
Poole 4	a	18 55				19 13										19 36		19 55			20 13				
	d					19 14										19 37					20 14				
Hamworthy	d					19 19										19 42					20 19				
Holton Heath	d					19 23															20 23				
Wareham	d					19 28										19 49					20 28				
Wool	d					19 35															20 35				
Moreton (Dorset)	d					19 41															20 41				
Dorchester South	d					19 49										20 05					20 49				
Dorchester West	d														19 54										
Upwey	d					19 55									20 01						20 55				
Weymouth	a					20 00									20 09	20 13					21 00				

A ☕ to Bournemouth

B 🛒 to Bournemouth

Table 158

Saturdays

14 December to 17 May

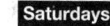

London - Basingstoke, Southampton, Romsey Lymington, Bournemouth and Weymouth

Network Diagram - see first Page of Table 158

		SW	XC	SW	SW	SW	SW	SW	SW	SW	SW	SN	SW	SW	XC	SW	SW	SW	SW	SW	SW	SW	SW
		1	◇1	◇1	1	1	1	1	◇1	1	1	1	1	1	◇1	◇1	1	1	1	1	◇1	1	1
				A					A							A							
			[trolley]	[trolley]					[trolley]						[trolley]	[trolley]					[trolley]		
London Waterloo 15 ⊖	d	18 09		18 35				18 39	19 05					19 09		19 35				19 39	20 05		
Clapham Junction 10	d							18u46	19u12											19u46	20u12		
Woking	d	18 35		19 00										19 35		20 00							
Farnborough (Main)	d	18 45						19 13						19 45						20 13			
Fleet	d							19 19												20 19			
Reading 7	d		18 45												19 46								
Basingstoke	a	18 58	19 08					19 31	19 47					19 58	20 08					20 31	20 47		
	d	19 00	19 10					19 33	19 49					20 00	20 10					20 33	20 49		
Micheldever	d	19 10												20 10									
Winchester	d	19 19	19 25	19 33				19 49	20 05					20 19	20 25	20 33				20 49	21 05		
Shawford	d							19 54												20 54			
Romsey	d						19 20						20 07						20 20				21 07
Chandlers Ford	d												20 14										21 14
Eastleigh 3	a	19 27					19 49	19 59					20 20	20 27					20 49	20 59			21 20
	d	19 28					19 50	20 00				20 14	20 21	20 28					20 50	21 00			21 21
Hedge End	d	19 34												20 34									
Botley	d	19 38												20 38									
Fareham	d	19 48												20 48									
Portchester	d	19 53												20 53									
Cosham	d	19 58												20 58									
Hilsea	a	20 03												21 03									
Fratton	a	20 07												21 07									
Portsmouth & Southsea	a	20 11												21 11									
Portsmouth Harbour ⛴	a	20 18												21 16									
Southampton Airport Pkwy ✈	d		19 33	19 42				20 05	20 14			20 18	20 25		20 33	20 42				21 05	21 14		21 25
Swaythling	d												20 27										21 27
St Denys	d									←			20 30										21 30
Southampton Central ⛴	a		19 41	19 49				20 14	20 22	20 14		20 27	20 36		20 41	20 49				21 12	21 22		21 35
	d		19 43	19 51				20 30	20 24	20 30			20 37		20 43	20 51					21 24		21 37
Millbrook (Hants)	d							↪					20 40										21 40
Redbridge	d												20 43										21 43
Romsey	d						20a03						20 51						21a03				21 51
Mottisfont & Dunbridge	d												20 56										21 56
Dean	d												21 02										22 02
Salisbury	a												21 15										22 15
Totton	d									20 35											21 29		
Ashurst New Forest	d									20 40											21 34		
Beaulieu Road	d					←												←					
Brockenhurst 3	a		19 57	20 04		19 51			20 37	20 51					20 57	21 04		20 51			21 42		
	d		19 58	20 05	20 12	20 16			20 38	21 16	20 42				20 58	21 05	21 12	21 16			21 43	21 48	
Lymington Town	d				20 20					↪	20 50						21 20					21 56	
Lymington Pier	a				20 22						20 52						21 22					21 58	
Sway	d					20 20												21 20			21 47		
New Milton	d					20 25			20 45									21 25			21 52		
Hinton Admiral	d					20 29												21 29			21 56		
Christchurch	d					20 34			20 52									21 34			22 01		
Pokesdown	d					20 38			20 56									21 38			22 05		
Bournemouth	a		20 11	20 20		20 42			21 00						21 11	21 20		21 42			22 09		
	d			20 24		20 43			21 04							21 24		21 43			22 10		
Branksome	d			20 29		20 48										21 29		21 48			22 15		
Parkstone (Dorset)	d			20 32		20 51										21 32		21 51			22 18		
Poole 4	a			20 36		20 55			21 13							21 36		21 55			22 23		
	d			20 37					21 14							21 37							
Hamworthy	d			20 42					21 19							21 42							
Holton Heath	d																						
Wareham	d			20 49					21 28							21 49							
Wool	d								21 35							21 55							
Moreton (Dorset)	d								21 41							22 01							
Dorchester South	d			21 05					21 49							22 09							
Dorchester West	d																						
Upwey	d								21 55							22 16							
Weymouth	a			21 13					22 00							22 20							

A [trolley] to Bournemouth

Table 158

Saturdays
14 December to 17 May

London - Basingstoke, Southampton, Romsey Lymington, Bournemouth and Weymouth

Network Diagram - see first Page of Table 158

		SW 1	XC ◇1	SW 1	GW	SW ◇1 A 🚲	SW 1	SW 1	SW 1	SW ◇1 🚲	SW 1	SW 1	XC ◇1	SW ◇1 A 🚲	SW 1	SW 1	SW 1	SW ◇1 🚲	SW 1	SW 1	XC ◇1 B	XC ◇1 C
London Waterloo 15 ⊖	d	20 09				20 35		20 39	20 42	21 05				21 35		21 39	21 42	22 05				
Clapham Junction 10	d							20u46		21u12						21u46		22u12				
Woking	d	20 35				21 00			21 19	21 32				22 00			22 19	22 32				
Farnborough (Main)	d	20 45						21 13	21 33							22 13	22 33					
Fleet	d							21 19	21 38							22 19	22 38					
Reading 7	d		20 46									←	21 45							←	22 49	22 53
Basingstoke	a	20 58	21 08					21 31	21 58	21 50		21 58	22 09			22 31	22 58	22 50		22 58	23 07	23 12
	d	21 00	21 10					21 33	22 00	21 52		22 00	22 10			22 33	23 00	22 52		23 00	23 10	23 13
Micheldever	d	21 10						21 43	→			22 10				22 43	→			23 10		
Winchester	d	21 19	21 25			21 33		21 52		22 08		22 19	22 25	22 33		22 53		23 08		23 19	23 25	23 28
Shawford	d							21 57								22 57						
Romsey	d			21 20							22 07				22 20				23 09			
Chandlers Ford	d										22 14								23 16			
Eastleigh 3	a	21 27		21 49				22 02		22 16	22 20	22 27			22 49	23 03		23 16	23 22	23 27		
	d	21 28		21 50				22 03		22 17	22 22	22 28			22 50	23 04		23 17	23 23	23 28		
Hedge End	d	21 34										22 34								23 34		
Botley	d	21 38										22 38								23 38		
Fareham	d	21 48										22 48								23 48		
Portchester	d	21 53										22 53								23 53		
Cosham	d	21 58										22 58								23 58		
Hilsea	a	22 03										23 03								00 03		
Fratton	a	22 07										23 07								00 07		
Portsmouth & Southsea	a	22 11										23 11								00 11		
Portsmouth Harbour ⛴	a	22 18										23 18								00 16		
Southampton Airport Pkwy ✈	d		21 33			21 42		22 08		22 22	22 26		22 33	22 42		23 08		23 22	23 27		23 33	23 36
Swaythling	d										22 28								23 29			
St Denys	d										22 31								23 32			
Southampton Central ⛴	a		21 41			21 49		22 17		22 29	22 36		22 40	22 49		23 17		23 29	23 38		23 41	23 43
	d		21 43			21 51				22 30	22 38		22 42	22 51				23 30	23 40			
Millbrook (Hants)	d										22 40								23 42			
Redbridge	d										22 44								23 46			
Romsey	d			22a03							22a51				23a03				23 57			
Mottisfont & Dunbridge	d																		00 02			
Dean	d																		00 08			
Salisbury	a																		00 20			
Totton	d									22 36								23 36				
Ashurst New Forest	d									22 40								23 40				
Beaulieu Road	d																					
Brockenhurst 3	a		21 57			22 04				22 48			22 56	23 04				23 48				
	d		21 58			22 05	22 18			22 49			22 58	23 05				23 49				
Lymington Town	d						22 26															
Lymington Pier	a						22 28															
Sway	d									22 54								23 54				
New Milton	d									22 59								23 58				
Hinton Admiral	d									23 03								00 02				
Christchurch	d									23 08								00 07				
Pokesdown	d									23 11								00 11				
Bournemouth	a		22 15			22 20				23 15			23 20	23 25				00 15				
	d					22 24				23 17				23 29				00 16				
Branksome	d					22 29				23 22				23 35				00 21				
Parkstone (Dorset)	d					22 32				23 25				23 38				00 24				
Poole 4	a					22 36				23 29				23 41				00 30				
	d					22 37								23 42								
Hamworthy	d					22 42								23 47								
Holton Heath	d																					
Wareham	d					22 49								23 54								
Wool	d					22 55								00 01								
Moreton (Dorset)	d					23 01								00 07								
Dorchester South	d					23 09								00 15								
Dorchester West	d				22 58																	
Upwey	d				23 06	23 16								00 21								
Weymouth	a				23 13	23 20								00 26								

A 🚲 to Bournemouth

B 14 December, 21 December, 28 December

C from 4 January until 8 February, from 29 March

Table 158

Saturdays

14 December to 17 May

London - Basingstoke, Southampton, Romsey Lymington, Bournemouth and Weymouth

Network Diagram - see first Page of Table 158

		XC	SW	SW	SW	SW	SW
		◇1	◇1	1	1	◇1	1
		A					
			⚲				
London Waterloo 15 ⊖	d		22 35		22 39	23 05	23 35
Clapham Junction 10	d				22u46	23u12	23u42
Woking	d		23 00			23 32	00 03
Farnborough (Main)	d				23 16		00 14
Fleet	d				23 21		00 20
Reading 7	d	22 46					
Basingstoke	a	23 13			23 34	23 50	00 33
	d	23 14			23 36	23 52	00 35
Micheldever	d					00 02	
Winchester	d	23 29	23 33		23 52	00 11	00 51
Shawford	d				23 57		
Romsey	d			23 00			
Chandlers Ford	d						
Eastleigh 3	a			23 35	00 02	00 19	00 59
	d			23 37	00 03	00 20	01 00
Hedge End	d						
Botley	d						
Fareham	d						
Portchester	d						
Cosham	d						
Hilsea	a						
Fratton	a						
Portsmouth & Southsea	a						
Portsmouth Harbour ⛴	a						
Southampton Airport Pkwy ✈	d	23 38	23 42		00 08	00 25	01 05
Swaythling	d						
St Denys	d					00s29	
Southampton Central ⛴	a	23 44	23 49		00 15	00 34	01 12
	d		23 51			00 35	
Millbrook (Hants)	d						
Redbridge	d						
Romsey	d			23a49			
Mottisfont & Dunbridge	d						
Dean	d						
Salisbury	a						
Totton	d					00s40	
Ashurst New Forest	d						
Beaulieu Road	d						
Brockenhurst 3	a		00 04			00s51	
	d		00 05				
Lymington Town	d						
Lymington Pier	a						
Sway	d						
New Milton	d					00s59	
Hinton Admiral	d						
Christchurch	d					01s06	
Pokesdown	d					01s10	
Bournemouth	a		00 21			01 14	
	d		00 22			01 15	
Branksome	d		00 27			01s20	
Parkstone (Dorset)	d		00 30			01s23	
Poole 4	a		00 35			01 27	
	d						
Hamworthy	d						
Holton Heath	d						
Wareham	d						
Wool	d						
Moreton (Dorset)	d						
Dorchester South	d						
Dorchester West	d						
Upwey	d						
Weymouth	a						

A from 15 February until 22 March

Table 158

Sundays

8 December to 9 February

London - Basingstoke, Southampton, Romsey Lymington, Bournemouth and Weymouth

Network Diagram - see first Page of Table 158

		SW ◇1	SW ◇1	SW 1	SW 1	SW ◇1	SW ◇1	SW 1	SW 1	SW 1	SW 1	SW 1	SW 1	SW 1	SW 1	SW 1	SW 1		SN 1	SW 1	SW 1	SW 1	SW 1
London Waterloo 15 ⊖	d											00 05		01 05									
Clapham Junction 10	d											00u12		01 15									
Woking	d									00 03	00 28	00 37		01 49									
Farnborough (Main)	d								00 10	00 14	00 41			01s58									
Fleet	d								00 16	00 20	00 47			02s04									
Reading 7	d																						
Basingstoke	a								00 33	00 33	01 06	00 55		02s16									
	d									00 35		00 56					07 48						
Micheldever	d						00 02										07 58						
Winchester	d						00 11			00 51		01 13		02s33			08 08						
Shawford	d																08 12						
Romsey	d																					08 35	08 39
Chandlers Ford	d																					08 42	
Eastleigh 3	a						00 19			00 59		01 21		02s42			08 18					08 47	09 13
	d				00 03		00 20	00 30		01 00		01 22					08 22	08 26	08 48			08 54	09 15
Hedge End	d							00s36										08 32					
Botley	d							00s39										08 36					
Fareham	d							00s47								07 44		08 44	09 02				
Portchester	d							00s53								07 49		08 49					
Cosham	d							00s57								07 54		08 54	09a10				
Hilsea	a															08 00		09 00					
Fratton	a							01s05								08 04		09 04					
Portsmouth & Southsea	a							01s08								08 08		09 08					
Portsmouth Harbour ⛴	a							01 12								08 13		09 13					
Southampton Airport Pkwy ✈	d				00 08		00 25			01 05		01 26		02s46			08 27					08 58	
Swaythling	d																					09 01	
St Denys	d						00s29							02s51								09 04	
Southampton Central ⛴	a				00 15		00 34			01 12		01 35		02 56			08 34					09 09	
	d						00 35					01 37					08 35			09 03		09 10	
Millbrook (Hants)	d																					09 13	
Redbridge	d																					09 16	
Romsey	d																					09 24	09a28
Mottisfont & Dunbridge	d			00 02																		09 29	
Dean	d			00 08																		09 35	
Salisbury	a			00 20																		09 49	
Totton	d						00s40					01s42					08 41						
Ashurst New Forest	d																08 45						
Beaulieu Road	d																08 50						
Brockenhurst 3	a						00s51					01s53					08 56			09 16			
	d					00 05									08 59		08 57			09 17	09 29		
Lymington Town	d														09 07						09 37		
Lymington Pier	a														09 09						09 39		
Sway	d																09 01						
New Milton	d						00s59					02s00					09 06			09 24			
Hinton Admiral	d		00 02														09 10						
Christchurch	d		00 07				01s06					02s07					09 15						
Pokesdown	d		00 11				01s10					02s11					09 19						
Bournemouth	a		00 15			00 21	01 14					02 15					09 23			09 34			
	d		00 16			00 22	01 15						08 39				09 24			09 39			
Branksome	d		00 21			00 27	01s20						08 44							09 44			
Parkstone (Dorset)	d		00 24			00 30	01s23						08 47							09 47			
Poole 4	a		00 30			00 35	01 27						08 50				09 33			09 50			
	d												08 51							09 51			
Hamworthy	d												08 56							09 56			
Holton Heath	d																						
Wareham	d												09 03							10 03			
Wool	d	00 01											09 10							10 10			
Moreton (Dorset)	d	00 07											09 16							10 16			
Dorchester South	d	00 15											09 24							10 24			
Dorchester West	d																						
Upwey	d	00 21											09 31							10 31			
Weymouth	a	00 26											09 35							10 35			

Table 158

Sundays

8 December to 9 February

London - Basingstoke, Southampton, Romsey Lymington, Bournemouth and Weymouth

Network Diagram - see first Page of Table 158

		SW	SW	SW	SW	SW	SW	SW	SW	SW	SW	XC	SW	SW	SW	SW	SW	SW	SW	XC	SW	SW	SW
		1	◇1		◇1	1	1	1	1	◇1		◇1	◇1	1	1	1	1	◇1		◇1	◇1	1	1
																					A		
												🛒								🛒	🛒		
London Waterloo 15 ⊖	d		07 54		08 35					08 54			09 35					09 54			10 35		
Clapham Junction 10	d		08u03		08u45					09u03			09u45					10u03			10u45		
Woking	d		08 28		09 09					09 28			10 09					10 28			11 08		
Farnborough (Main)	d																						
Fleet	d																						
Reading 7	d											09 53								10 53			
Basingstoke	a		08 46		09 28					09 46		10 09	10 28					10 46		11 09	11 26		
	d		08 48		09 29					09 48		10 10	10 29					10 48		11 10	11 28		
Micheldever	d		08 58							09 58								10 58					
Winchester	d		09 08		09 46					10 08		10 25	10 46					11 08		11 25	11 44		
Shawford	d									10 12													
Romsey	d						09 35	09 32							10 35	10 32							11 35
Chandlers Ford	d						09 42								10 42								11 42
Eastleigh 3	a		09 18				09 48	10 13		10 18					10 48	11 13		11 18					11 48
	d		09 22	09 26			09 54	10 15		10 22	10 26				10 54	11 15		11 22	11 26				11 54
Hedge End	d			09 32							10 32								11 32				
Botley	d			09 36							10 36								11 36				
Fareham	d			09 44							10 44								11 44				
Portchester	d			09 49							10 49								11 49				
Cosham	d			09 54							10 54								11 54				
Hilsea	a			10 00							11 00								12 00				
Fratton	a			10 08							11 08								12 04				
Portsmouth & Southsea	a			10 11							11 11								12 08				
Portsmouth Harbour ⛴	a			10 15							11 15								12 13				
Southampton Airport Pkwy ✈	d		09 27		09 55		09 58			10 27		10 34	10 55		10 58			11 27		11 34	11 53		11 58
Swaythling	d						10 01								11 01								12 01
St Denys	d						10 04								11 04								12 04
Southampton Central ⛴	a		09 34		10 02		10 09			10 34		10 42	11 02		11 09			11 34		11 42	11 59		12 09
	d		09 35		10 03		10 10			10 35		10 45	11 03		11 10			11 35		11 45	12 03		12 10
Millbrook (Hants)	d						10 13								11 13								12 13
Redbridge	d						10 16								11 16								12 16
Romsey	d						10 24	10a28							11 24	11a28							12 24
Mottisfont & Dunbridge	d														11 29								
Dean	d														11 35								
Salisbury	a						10 42								11 48								12 42
Totton	d		09 41							10 41								11 41					
Ashurst New Forest	d		09 45							10 45								11 45					
Beaulieu Road	d		09 50							10 50								11 50					
Brockenhurst 3	a		09 56		10 17					10 56		11 02	11 17					11 56		12 02	12 16		
	d	09 59	09 57		10 18	10 29			10 59	10 57		11 03	11 18	11 29			11 59	11 57		12 03	12 17	12 29	
Lymington Town	d	10 07				10 37			11 07					11 37			12 07					12 37	
Lymington Pier	a	10 09				10 39			11 09					11 39			12 09					12 39	
Sway	d		10 01							11 01								12 01					
New Milton	d		10 06		10 25					11 06			11 25					12 06			12 24		
Hinton Admiral	d		10 10							11 10								12 10					
Christchurch	d		10 15							11 15								12 15					
Pokesdown	d		10 19							11 19								12 19					
Bournemouth	a		10 23		10 35					11 23		11 26	11 35					12 23		12 26	12 34		
	d		10 24		10 39					11 24			11 39					12 24			12 39		
Branksome	d				10 44								11 44								12 44		
Parkstone (Dorset)	d				10 47								11 47								12 47		
Poole 4	a		10 33		10 50					11 33			11 50					12 33			12 50		
	d				10 51								11 51								12 51		
Hamworthy	d				10 56								11 56								12 56		
Holton Heath	d																						
Wareham	d				11 03								12 03								13 03		
Wool	d				11 10								12 10								13 10		
Moreton (Dorset)	d				11 16								12 16								13 16		
Dorchester South	d				11 24								12 24								13 24		
Dorchester West	d																						
Upwey	d				11 31								12 31								13 31		
Weymouth	a				11 35								12 35								13 35		

A 🛒 to Bournemouth

Table 158

Sundays

8 December to 9 February

London - Basingstoke, Southampton, Romsey Lymington, Bournemouth and Weymouth

Network Diagram - see first Page of Table 158

		SW		SW	SW		XC	SW	SW	SW	SW	SW		SW		XC	SW	SW	SW	SW	SW	SW			XC
		1		1	◇1		◇1	◇1	1	1	1	1		◇1		◇1	◇1	1	1	1	1	◇1			◇1
								A									A								
							🍽	🛒						🛒		🍽	🛒					🛒			🛒
London Waterloo 15 ⊖	d				10 54			11 35						11 54			12 35					12 54			
Clapham Junction 10	d				11u03			11u45						12u03			12u45					13u03			
Woking	d				11 28			12 08						12 28			13 08					13 28			
Farnborough (Main)	d																								
Fleet	d																								
Reading 7	d						11 53									12 53									13 53
Basingstoke	a				11 46		12 09	12 26						12 46		13 09	13 26					13 46			14 09
	d				11 48		12 10	12 28						12 48		13 10	13 28					13 48			14 10
Micheldever	d				11 58									12 58								13 58			
Winchester	d				12 08		12 25	12 44						13 08		13 25	13 44					14 08			14 25
Shawford	d				12 12																	14 12			
Romsey	d	11 32								12 35	12 32								13 35	13 32					
Chandlers Ford	d									12 42									13 42						
Eastleigh 3	a	12 13			12 18					12 48	13 13			13 18					13 48	14 13		14 18			
	d	12 15			12 22	12 26				12 54	13 15			13 22	13 26				13 54	14 15		14 22	14 26		
Hedge End	d					12 32									13 32								14 32		
Botley	d					12 36									13 36								14 36		
Fareham	d					12 44									13 44								14 44		
Portchester	d					12 49									13 49								14 49		
Cosham	d					12 54									13 54								14 54		
Hilsea	a					13 00									14 00								15 00		
Fratton	a					13 04									14 04								15 04		
Portsmouth & Southsea	a					13 08									14 08								15 08		
Portsmouth Harbour ⛴	a					13 13									14 13								15 13		
Southampton Airport Pkwy ✈	d				12 27		12 34	12 53		12 58				13 27		13 34	13 53		13 58			14 27			14 34
Swaythling	d									13 01									14 01						
St Denys	d									13 04									14 04						
Southampton Central ⛴	a				12 34		12 42	13 00		13 09				13 34		13 42	14 00		14 09			14 34			14 42
	d				12 35		12 45	13 03		13 10				13 35		13 45	14 03		14 10			14 35			14 45
Millbrook (Hants)	d									13 13									14 13						
Redbridge	d									13 16									14 16						
Romsey	d	12a28								13 24	13a28								14 24	14a28					
Mottisfont & Dunbridge	d									13 29															
Dean	d									13 35															
Salisbury	a									13 48									14 42						
Totton	d				12 41									13 41								14 41			
Ashurst New Forest	d				12 45									13 45								14 45			
Beaulieu Road	d				12 50									13 50								14 50			
Brockenhurst 3	a				12 56		13 02	13 16						13 56		14 01	14 16					14 56			15 02
	d			12 59	12 57		13 03	13 17	13 29			13 59		13 57		14 02	14 17	14 29			14 59	14 57			15 03
Lymington Town	d			13 07					13 37			14 07						14 37			15 07				
Lymington Pier	a			13 09					13 39			14 09						14 39			15 09				
Sway	d				13 01									14 01								15 01			
New Milton	d				13 06			13 24						14 06			14 24					15 06			
Hinton Admiral	d				13 10									14 10								15 10			
Christchurch	d				13 15									14 15								15 15			
Pokesdown	d				13 19									14 19								15 19			
Bournemouth	a				13 23		13 26	13 34						14 23		14 26	14 34					15 23			15 26
	d				13 24			13 39						14 24			14 39					15 24			
Branksome	d							13 44									14 44								
Parkstone (Dorset)	d							13 47									14 47								
Poole 4	a				13 33			13 50						14 33			14 50					15 33			
	d							13 51									14 51								
Hamworthy	d							13 56									14 56								
Holton Heath	d																								
Wareham	d							14 03									15 03								
Wool	d							14 10									15 10								
Moreton (Dorset)	d							14 16									15 16								
Dorchester South	d							14 24									15 24								
Dorchester West	d																								
Upwey	d							14 31									15 31								
Weymouth	a							14 35									15 35								

A 🛒 to Bournemouth

Table 158

Sundays

8 December to 9 February

London - Basingstoke, Southampton, Romsey Lymington, Bournemouth and Weymouth

Network Diagram - see first Page of Table 158

		GW	SW ◇1 A 🛒	SW 1	SW 1	SW 1	SW 1	SW ◇1 🛒		XC ◇1 ☕	SW ◇1 A 🛒	SW 1	SW 1	SW 1	SW 1	SW ◇1 🛒		XC ◇1 ☕	SW ◇1 A 🛒	SW 1	SW 1	SW 1	SW 1
London Waterloo 15 ⊖	d		13 35					13 54			14 35					14 54			15 35				
Clapham Junction 10	d		13u42					14u03			14u42					15u03			15u42				
Woking	d		14 07					14 28			15 07					15 28			16 07				
Farnborough (Main)	d																						
Fleet	d																						
Reading 7	d									14 53								15 53					
Basingstoke	a		14 26					14 46		15 09	15 26					15 46		16 09	16 26				
	d		14 28					14 48		15 10	15 28					15 48		16 10	16 28				
Micheldever	d							14 58								15 58							
Winchester	d		14 44					15 08		15 25	15 44					16 08		16 25	16 44				
Shawford	d															16 12							
Romsey	d				14 35	14 32							15 35	15 32							16 35	16 32	
Chandlers Ford	d				14 42								15 42								16 42		
Eastleigh 3	a				14 48	15 13		15 18					15 48	16 13		16 18					16 48	17 13	
	d				14 54	15 15		15 22	15 26				15 54	16 15		16 22	16 26				16 54	17 15	
Hedge End	d								15 32								16 32						
Botley	d								15 36								16 36						
Fareham	d								15 44								16 44						
Portchester	d								15 49								16 49						
Cosham	d								15 54								16 54						
Hilsea	a								16 00								17 00						
Fratton	a								16 04								17 08						
Portsmouth & Southsea	a								16 08								17 12						
Portsmouth Harbour ⛴	a								16 13								17 16						
Southampton Airport Pkwy ✈	d		14 53		14 58			15 27		15 34	15 53		15 58			16 27		16 34	16 53		16 58		
Swaythling	d				15 01								16 01								17 01		
St Denys	d				15 04								16 04								17 04		
Southampton Central ⛴	a		15 00		15 09			15 34		15 42	16 00		16 09			16 34		16 42	17 00		17 09		
	d		15 03		15 10			15 35		15 45	16 03		16 10			16 35		16 45	17 03		17 10		
Millbrook (Hants)	d				15 13								16 13								17 13		
Redbridge	d				15 16								16 16								17 16		
Romsey	d				15 24	15a28							16 24	16a28							17 24	17a28	
Mottisfont & Dunbridge	d				15 29																17 29		
Dean	d				15 35																17 35		
Salisbury	a				15 48								16 42								17 48		
Totton	d							15 41								16 41							
Ashurst New Forest	d							15 45								16 45							
Beaulieu Road	d							15 50								16 50							
Brockenhurst 3	a		15 16					15 56		16 02	16 16					16 56		17 02	17 16				
	d		15 17	15 29			15 59	15 57		16 03	16 17	16 29			16 59	16 57		17 03	17 17	17 29			17 59
Lymington Town	d			15 37			16 07					16 37			17 07					17 37			18 07
Lymington Pier	a			15 39			16 09					16 39			17 09					17 39			18 09
Sway	d							16 01								17 01							
New Milton	d		15 24					16 06			16 24					17 06			17 24				
Hinton Admiral	d							16 10								17 10							
Christchurch	d							16 15								17 15							
Pokesdown	d							16 19								17 19							
Bournemouth	a		15 34					16 23		16 26	16 34					17 23		17 26	17 34				
	d		15 39					16 24			16 39					17 24			17 39				
Branksome	d		15 44								16 44								17 44				
Parkstone (Dorset)	d		15 47								16 47								17 47				
Poole 4	a		15 50					16 33			16 50					17 33			17 50				
	d		15 51								16 51								17 51				
Hamworthy	d		15 56								16 56								17 56				
Holton Heath	d																						
Wareham	d		16 03								17 03								18 03				
Wool	d		16 10								17 10								18 10				
Moreton (Dorset)	d		16 16								17 16								18 16				
Dorchester South	d		16 24								17 24								18 24				
Dorchester West	d	16 01																					
Upwey	d	16 10	16 31								17 31								18 31				
Weymouth	a	16 15	16 35								17 35								18 35				

A 🛒 to Bournemouth

Table 158

Sundays

8 December to 9 February

London - Basingstoke, Southampton, Romsey Lymington, Bournemouth and Weymouth

Network Diagram - see first Page of Table 158

		SW		XC	SW	SW	SW	SW	SW	SW		XC	GW	SW	SW	SW	SW	SW	SW		XC	SW	SW
		◇1		◇1	◇1	1	1	1	1	◇1		◇1	◇	◇1	1	1	1	1	◇1		◇1	◇1	1
					A									A								A	
		🛒		⊓	🛒					🛒		⊓		🛒					🛒		⊓	🛒	
London Waterloo 15 ⊖	d	15 54			16 35					16 54				17 35					17 54			18 35	
Clapham Junction 10	d	16u03			16u42					17u03				17u42					18u03			18u42	
Woking	d	16 28			17 07					17 28				18 07					18 28			19 07	
Farnborough (Main)	d																						
Fleet	d																						
Reading 7	d			16 53								17 53									18 53		
Basingstoke	a	16 46		17 09	17 26					17 46		18 09		18 26					18 46		19 09	19 26	
	d	16 48		17 10	17 28					17 48		18 10		18 28					18 48		19 10	19 28	
Micheldever	d	16 58								17 58									18 58				
Winchester	d	17 08		17 25	17 44					18 08		18 25		18 44					19 08		19 25	19 44	
Shawford	d									18 12													
Romsey	d						17 35	17 32								18 35	18 32						
Chandlers Ford	d						17 42									18 42							
Eastleigh 8	a	17 18					17 48	18 13		18 18						18 48	19 13		19 18				
	d	17 22	17 26				17 54	18 15		18 22	18 26					18 54	19 15		19 22	19 26			
Hedge End	d		17 32								18 32									19 32			
Botley	d		17 36								18 36									19 36			
Fareham	d		17 44								18 44									19 44			
Portchester	d		17 49								18 49									19 49			
Cosham	d		17 54								18 54									19 54			
Hilsea	a		18 00								19 00									20 00			
Fratton	a		18 04								19 08									20 04			
Portsmouth & Southsea	a		18 08								19 12									20 08			
Portsmouth Harbour ⛴	a		18 13								19 17									20 13			
Southampton Airport Pkwy ✈	d	17 27		17 34	17 53		17 58			18 27		18 34		18 53		18 58			19 27		19 34	19 53	
Swaythling	d						18 01									19 01							
St Denys	d						18 04									19 04							
Southampton Central ⛴	a	17 34		17 40	18 00		18 09			18 34		18 42		19 00		19 09			19 34		19 40	20 00	
	d	17 35		17 45	18 03		18 10			18 35		18 45		19 03		19 10			19 35		19 45	20 03	
Millbrook (Hants)	d						18 13									19 13							
Redbridge	d						18 16									19 16							
Romsey	d						18 24	18a28								19 24	19a28						
Mottisfont & Dunbridge	d															19 29							
Dean	d															19 35							
Salisbury	a						18 42									19 48							
Totton	d	17 41								18 41									19 41				
Ashurst New Forest	d	17 45								18 45									19 45				
Beaulieu Road	d	17 50								18 50									19 50				
Brockenhurst 3	a	17 56		18 02	18 16					18 56		19 01		19 16					19 56		20 02	20 16	
	d	17 57		18 03	18 17	18 29			18 59	18 57		19 02		19 17	19 29			19 59	19 57		20 03	20 17	20 29
Lymington Town	d					18 37			19 07						19 37			20 07					20 37
Lymington Pier	a					18 39			19 09						19 39			20 09					20 39
Sway	d	18 01								19 01									20 01				
New Milton	d	18 06			18 24					19 06				19 24					20 06			20 24	
Hinton Admiral	d	18 10								19 10									20 10				
Christchurch	d	18 15								19 15									20 15				
Pokesdown	d	18 19								19 19									20 19				
Bournemouth	a	18 23		18 26	18 34					19 23		19 26		19 34					20 23		20 26	20 34	
	d	18 24			18 39					19 24				19 39					20 24			20 39	
Branksome	d				18 44									19 44								20 44	
Parkstone (Dorset)	d				18 47									19 47								20 47	
Poole 4	a	18 33			18 50					19 33				19 50					20 33			20 50	
	d				18 51									19 51								20 51	
Hamworthy	d				18 56									19 56								20 56	
Holton Heath	d																						
Wareham	d				19 03									20 03								21 03	
Wool	d				19 10									20 10								21 10	
Moreton (Dorset)	d				19 16									20 17								21 17	
Dorchester South	d				19 24									20 25								21 25	
Dorchester West	d												19 47										
Upwey	d				19 31								19 55	20 32								21 32	
Weymouth	a				19 35								20 01	20 36								21 36	

A 🛒 to Bournemouth

Table 158

Sundays

8 December to 9 February

London - Basingstoke, Southampton, Romsey Lymington, Bournemouth and Weymouth

Network Diagram - see first Page of Table 158

		SN	SW	SW	SW	SW		XC	SW	SW	SN	SW	SW	SW	SW		XC	GW	GW	SW	SW	SW
		1	1	1	1	◇1		◇1	◇1	1	1	1	1	1	◇1		◇1			◇1	1	1
									A									B	C	A		
London Waterloo 15 ⊖	d					18 54			19 35						19 54					20 35		
Clapham Junction 10	d					19u03			19u42						20u03					20u42		
Woking	d					19 28			20 07						20 28					21 07		
Farnborough (Main)	d																					
Fleet	d																					
Reading 7	d							19 53									20 53					
Basingstoke	a					19 46		20 09	20 26						20 46		21 09			21 26		
	d					19 48		20 10	20 28						20 48		21 10			21 28		
Micheldever	d					19 58									20 58							
Winchester	d					20 08		20 25	20 44						21 08		21 25			21 44		
Shawford	d					20 12																
Romsey	d		19 35	19 32								20 35	20 32								21 35	21 32
Chandlers Ford	d		19 42									20 42									21 42	
Eastleigh 3	a		19 48	20 13		20 18						20 48	21 13		21 18						21 48	22 13
	d	19 46	19 54	20 15		20 22	20 26				20 46	20 54	21 15		21 22	21 26					21 54	22 15
Hedge End	d						20 32									21 32						
Botley	d						20 36									21 36						
Fareham	d	20 03					20 44				21 02					21 44						
Portchester	d						20 49									21 49						
Cosham	d	20a11					20 54				21a10					21 54						
Hilsea	a						21 00									22 00						
Fratton	a						21 04									22 04						
Portsmouth & Southsea	a						21 08									22 10						
Portsmouth Harbour ⛴	a						21 13									22 14						
Southampton Airport Pkwy ✈	d		19 58			20 27		20 34	20 53			20 58			21 27		21 34			21 53	21 58	
Swaythling	d		20 01									21 01									22 01	
St Denys	d		20 04									21 04									22 04	
Southampton Central ⛴	a		20 09			20 34		20 42	21 00			21 09			21 34		21 43			22 00	22 09	
	d		20 10			20 35		20 45	21 03			21 10			21 35		21 45			22 03	22 10	
Millbrook (Hants)	d		20 13									21 13									22 13	
Redbridge	d		20 16									21 16									22 16	
Romsey	d		20 24	20a28								21 24	21a28								22a24	22a31
Mottisfont & Dunbridge	d											21 29										
Dean	d											21 35										
Salisbury	a		20 42									21 48										
Totton	d					20 41									21 41							
Ashurst New Forest	d					20 45									21 45							
Beaulieu Road	d					20 50									21 50							
Brockenhurst 3	a					20 56		21 02	21 16						21 56		22 02			22 16		
	d				20 59	20 57		21 03	21 17	21 29				21 59	21 57		22 03			22 17		
Lymington Town	d				21 07					21 37				22 07								
Lymington Pier	a				21 09					21 39				22 09								
Sway	d					21 01									22 01							
New Milton	d					21 06			21 24						22 06					22 24		
Hinton Admiral	d					21 10									22 10							
Christchurch	d					21 15									22 15							
Pokesdown	d					21 19									22 19							
Bournemouth	a					21 23		21 26	21 34						22 23		22 26			22 34		
	d					21 24			21 39						22 24					22 39		
Branksome	d								21 44											22 44		
Parkstone (Dorset)	d								21 47											22 47		
Poole 4	a					21 33			21 50						22 33					22 50		
	d								21 51											22 51		
Hamworthy	d								21 56											22 56		
Holton Heath	d																					
Wareham	d								22 03											23 03		
Wool	d								22 10											23 10		
Moreton (Dorset)	d								22 17											23 17		
Dorchester South	d								22 25											23 25		
Dorchester West	d																	22 53	23 04			
Upwey	d								22 32									23 01	23 19	23 32		
Weymouth	a								22 36									23 06	23 24	23 36		

A to Bournemouth

B until 29 December

C from 5 January

Table 158

Sundays

8 December to 9 February

London - Basingstoke, Southampton, Romsey Lymington, Bournemouth and Weymouth

Network Diagram - see first Page of Table 158

		SW		XC	SW	SW	SW	SW		SW	
		◇1		◇1	◇1	1	1	◇1		◇1	
					A						
					🛒					🛒	
London Waterloo 15 ⊖	d	20 54			21 35			21 54		22 54	
Clapham Junction 10	d	21u03			21u42			22u03		23u03	
Woking	d	21 28			22 07			22 28		23 28	
Farnborough (Main)	d										
Fleet	d										
Reading 7	d			21 53							
Basingstoke	a	21 46		22 09	22 26			22 46		23 46	
	d	21 48		22 10	22 28			22 48		23 48	
Micheldever	d	21 58						22 58		23 58	
Winchester	d	22 08		22 25	22 44			23 08		00 08	
Shawford	d	22 12									
Romsey	d					22 35	22 28				
Chandlers Ford	d					22 42					
Eastleigh 3	a	22 18				22 48	23 19	23 17		00 18	
	d	22 22	22 26			22 54	23 21	23 22	23 26	00 22	00 30
Hedge End	d		22 32						23 32		00s36
Botley	d		22 36						23 36		00s39
Fareham	d		22 44						23 44		00s47
Portchester	d		22 49						23 49		00s53
Cosham	d		22 54						23 54		00s57
Hilsea	a		23 00						23 59		
Fratton	a		23 04						00 04		01s05
Portsmouth & Southsea	a		23 08						00 08		01s08
Portsmouth Harbour ⛴	a		23 13						00 13		01 12
Southampton Airport Pkwy ✈	d	22 27		22 34	22 53	22 58		23 27		00 27	
Swaythling	d					23 01					
St Denys	d					23 04				00s31	
Southampton Central ⛴	a	22 34		22 42	23 00	23 09		23 34		00 36	
	d	22 35			23 03	23 10		23 35		00 37	
Millbrook (Hants)	d					23 13					
Redbridge	d					23 16					
Romsey	d					23 24	23a33				
Mottisfont & Dunbridge	d					23 29					
Dean	d					23 35					
Salisbury	a					23 51					
Totton	d	22 41						23 41		00s42	
Ashurst New Forest	d	22 45						23 45			
Beaulieu Road	d	22 50									
Brockenhurst 3	a	22 56			23 16			23 53		00s53	
	d	22 57			23 17			23 54			
Lymington Town	d										
Lymington Pier	a										
Sway	d	23 01						23 59			
New Milton	d	23 06			23 24			00 04		01s01	
Hinton Admiral	d	23 10						00 08			
Christchurch	d	23 15						00 13		01s08	
Pokesdown	d	23 19						00 16		01s12	
Bournemouth	a	23 23			23 34			00 20		01 16	
	d	23 24			23 39			00 22		01 17	
Branksome	d				23 44			00 27		01s22	
Parkstone (Dorset)	d				23 47			00 30		01s25	
Poole 4	a	23 33			23 50			00 34		01 29	
	d				23 51						
Hamworthy	d				23 56						
Holton Heath	d										
Wareham	d				00 03						
Wool	d				00 10						
Moreton (Dorset)	d				00 17						
Dorchester South	d				00 25						
Dorchester West	d										
Upwey	d				00 32						
Weymouth	a				00 36						

A 🛒 to Bournemouth

Table 158

Sundays

16 February to 23 March

London - Basingstoke, Southampton, Romsey Lymington, Bournemouth and Weymouth

Network Diagram - see first Page of Table 158

		SW	SW	SW	SW	SW	SW	SW	SW	SW		SW	SW	SW	SW	SW	SW	SW		SN		SW	SW	SW	SW
		◇1	◇1 bus	1	1	◇1 bus	◇1	1	1	1		1	1	1	1	1	1	1		1		1	1	1	1
London Waterloo 15 ⊖	d												00 05		01 05										
Clapham Junction 10	d												00u12		01 15										
Woking	d									00 03		00 28	00 37		01 49										
Farnborough (Main)	d								00 10	00 14		00 41			01s58										
Fleet	d								00 16	00 20		00 47			02s04										
Reading 7	d																								
Basingstoke	a								00 33	00 33		01 06	00 55		02s16										
	d									00 35			00 56					07 48							
Micheldever	d						00 02											07 58							
Winchester	d						00 11			00 51			01 13		02s33			08 08							
Shawford	d																	08 12							
Romsey	d																							08 35	08 39
Chandlers Ford	d																							08 42	
Eastleigh 3	a						00 19			00 59			01 21		02s42			08 18						08 47	09 13
	d				00 03		00 20	00 30		01 00			01 22					08 22	08 26	08 48				08 54	09 15
Hedge End	d							00s36											08 32						
Botley	d							00s39											08 36						
Fareham	d							00s47									07 44		08 44	09 02					
Portchester	d							00s53									07 49		08 49						
Cosham	d							00s57									07 54		08 54	09a10					
Hilsea	a																08 00		09 00						
Fratton	a							01s05									08 04		09 04						
Portsmouth & Southsea	a							01s08									08 08		09 08						
Portsmouth Harbour ⛴	a							01 12									08 13		09 13						
Southampton Airport Pkwy ✈	d				00 08		00 25			01 05			01 26		02s46			08 27						08 58	
Swaythling	d																							09 01	
St Denys	d						00s29								02s51									09 04	
Southampton Central ⛴	a				00 15		00 34			01 12			01 35		02 56			08 34						09 09	
	d						00 35						01 37					08 35				09 03		09 10	
Millbrook (Hants)	d																							09 13	
Redbridge	d																							09 16	
Romsey	d																							09 24	09a28
Mottisfont & Dunbridge	d			00 02																				09 29	
Dean	d			00 08																				09 35	
Salisbury	a			00 20																				09 49	
Totton	d						00s40						01s42					08 41							
Ashurst New Forest	d																	08 45							
Beaulieu Road	d																	08 50							
Brockenhurst 3	a						00s51						01s53					08 56				09 16			
	d					00 05										08 59		08 57				09 17	09 29		
Lymington Town	d															09 07							09 37		
Lymington Pier	a															09 09							09 39		
Sway	d																	09 01							
New Milton	d						00s59						02s00					09 06				09 24			
Hinton Admiral	d		00 02															09 10							
Christchurch	d		00 07				01s06						02s07					09 15							
Pokesdown	d		00 11				01s10						02s11					09 19							
Bournemouth	a		00 15			00 21	01 14						02 15					09 23				09 34			
	d		00 16			00 22	01 15							08 39				09 24				09 39			
Branksome	d		00 21			00 27	01s20							08 44								09 44			
Parkstone (Dorset)	d		00 24			00 30	01s23							08 47								09 47			
Poole 4	a		00 30			00 35	01 27							08 50				09 33				09 50			
	d													08 51								09 51			
Hamworthy	d													08 56								09 56			
Holton Heath	d																								
Wareham	d													09 03								10 03			
Wool	d	00 01												09 10								10 10			
Moreton (Dorset)	d	00 07												09 16								10 16			
Dorchester South	d	00 15												09 24								10 24			
Dorchester West	d																								
Upwey	d	00 21												09 31								10 31			
Weymouth	a	00 26												09 35								10 35			

Table 158

Sundays

16 February to 23 March

London - Basingstoke, Southampton, Romsey Lymington, Bournemouth and Weymouth

Network Diagram - see first Page of Table 158

		SW	SW		SW	SW		SW	SW	SW	SW		XC	SW	SW	SW		SW	SW	SW		XC	SW	SW	SW
		1	◇1		◇1	1		1	1	1	◇1		◇1	◇1	1	1		1	1	◇1		◇1	◇1	1	1
																							A		
													⚲									⚲	⚲		
London Waterloo 15 ⊖	d		07 54		08 35						08 54			09 35						09 54			10 35		
Clapham Junction 10	d		08u03		08u45						09u03			09u45						10u03			10u45		
Woking	d		08 28		09 09						09 28			10 09						10 28			11 08		
Farnborough (Main)	d																								
Fleet	d																								
Reading 7	d												09 53									10 41			
Basingstoke	a		08 46		09 28						09 46		10 09	10 28						10 46		11 09	11 26		
	d		08 48		09 29						09 48		10 10	10 29						10 48		11 10	11 28		
Micheldever	d		08 58								09 58									10 58					
Winchester	d		09 08		09 46						10 08		10 25	10 46						11 08		11 25	11 44		
Shawford	d										10 12														
Romsey	d							09 35	09 32							10 35		10 32							11 35
Chandlers Ford	d							09 42								10 42									11 42
Eastleigh 3	a		09 18					09 48	10 13		10 18					10 48		11 13		11 18					11 48
	d		09 22	09 26				09 54	10 15		10 22	10 26				10 54		11 15		11 22	11 26				11 54
Hedge End	d			09 32								10 32									11 32				
Botley	d			09 36								10 36									11 36				
Fareham	d			09 44								10 44									11 44				
Portchester	d			09 49								10 49									11 49				
Cosham	d			09 54								10 54									11 54				
Hilsea	a			10 00								11 00									12 00				
Fratton	a			10 08								11 08									12 04				
Portsmouth & Southsea	a			10 11								11 11									12 08				
Portsmouth Harbour ⛴	a			10 15								11 15									12 13				
Southampton Airport Pkwy ✈	d		09 27		09 55			09 58			10 27		10 34	10 55		10 58				11 27		11 34	11 53		11 58
Swaythling	d							10 01								11 01									12 01
St Denys	d							10 04								11 04									12 04
Southampton Central ⛴	a		09 34		10 02			10 09			10 34		10 42	11 02		11 09				11 34		11 42	11 59		12 09
	d		09 35		10 03			10 10			10 35		10 45	11 03		11 10				11 35		11 45	12 03		12 10
Millbrook (Hants)	d							10 13								11 13									12 13
Redbridge	d							10 16								11 16									12 16
Romsey	d							10 24	10a28							11 24		11a28							12 24
Mottisfont & Dunbridge	d															11 29									
Dean	d															11 35									
Salisbury	a							10 42								11 48									12 42
Totton	d		09 41								10 41									11 41					
Ashurst New Forest	d		09 45								10 45									11 45					
Beaulieu Road	d		09 50								10 50									11 50					
Brockenhurst 3	a		09 56		10 17						10 56		11 02	11 17						11 56		12 02	12 16		
	d	09 59	09 57		10 18	10 29				10 59	10 57		11 03	11 18	11 29				11 59	11 57		12 03	12 17	12 29	
Lymington Town	d	10 07				10 37				11 07					11 37				12 07					12 37	
Lymington Pier	a	10 09				10 39				11 09					11 39				12 09					12 39	
Sway	d		10 01								11 01									12 01					
New Milton	d		10 06		10 25						11 06			11 25						12 06			12 24		
Hinton Admiral	d		10 10								11 10									12 10					
Christchurch	d		10 15								11 15									12 15					
Pokesdown	d		10 19								11 19									12 19					
Bournemouth	a		10 23		10 35						11 23		11 26	11 35						12 23		12 26	12 34		
	d		10 24		10 39						11 24			11 39						12 24			12 39		
Branksome	d				10 44									11 44									12 44		
Parkstone (Dorset)	d				10 47									11 47									12 47		
Poole 4	a		10 33		10 50						11 33			11 50						12 33			12 50		
	d				10 51									11 51									12 51		
Hamworthy	d				10 56									11 56									12 56		
Holton Heath	d																								
Wareham	d				11 03									12 03									13 03		
Wool	d				11 10									12 10									13 10		
Moreton (Dorset)	d				11 16									12 16									13 16		
Dorchester South	d				11 24									12 24									13 24		
Dorchester West	d																								
Upwey	d				11 31									12 31									13 31		
Weymouth	a				11 35									12 35									13 35		

A ⚲ to Bournemouth

Table 158

Sundays

16 February to 23 March

London - Basingstoke, Southampton, Romsey Lymington, Bournemouth and Weymouth

Network Diagram - see first Page of Table 158

		SW		SW	SW		XC	SW	SW	SW	SW	SW		SW		XC	SW	SW	SW	SW	SW	SW			XC
		1		1	◇1		◇1	◇1	1	1	1	1		◇1		◇1	◇1	1	1	1	1	◇1			◇1
								A									A								
							⊡	⚲						⚲		⊡	⚲					⚲			⚲
London Waterloo 15 ⊖	d				10 54			11 35						11 54			12 35					12 54			
Clapham Junction 10	d				11u03			11u45						12u03			12u45					13u03			
Woking	d				11 28			12 08						12 28			13 08					13 28			
Farnborough (Main)	d																								
Fleet	d																								
Reading 7	d						11 42									12 41									13 41
Basingstoke	a				11 46		12 10	12 26						12 46		13 09	13 26					13 46			14 09
	d				11 48		12 10	12 28						12 48		13 10	13 28					13 48			14 10
Micheldever	d				11 58									12 58								13 58			
Winchester	d				12 08		12 25	12 44						13 08		13 25	13 44					14 08			14 25
Shawford	d				12 12																	14 12			
Romsey	d	11 32								12 35	12 32								13 35	13 32					
Chandlers Ford	d									12 42									13 42						
Eastleigh 8	a	12 13			12 18					12 48	13 13			13 18					13 48	14 13		14 18			
	d	12 15			12 22	12 26				12 54	13 15			13 22	13 26				13 54	14 15		14 22	14 26		
Hedge End	d					12 32									13 32								14 32		
Botley	d					12 36									13 36								14 36		
Fareham	d					12 44									13 44								14 44		
Portchester	d					12 49									13 49								14 49		
Cosham	d					12 54									13 54								14 54		
Hilsea	a					13 00									14 00								15 00		
Fratton	a					13 04									14 04								15 04		
Portsmouth & Southsea	a					13 08									14 08								15 08		
Portsmouth Harbour ⛴	a					13 13									14 13								15 13		
Southampton Airport Pkwy ✈	d				12 27		12 33	12 53		12 58				13 27		13 34	13 53		13 58			14 27			14 34
Swaythling	d									13 01									14 01						
St Denys	d									13 04									14 04						
Southampton Central ⛴	a				12 34		12 42	13 00		13 09				13 34		13 42	14 00		14 09			14 34			14 42
	d				12 35		12 45	13 03		13 10				13 35		13 45	14 03		14 10			14 35			14 45
Millbrook (Hants)	d									13 13									14 13						
Redbridge	d									13 16									14 16						
Romsey	d	12a28								13 24	13a28								14 24	14a28					
Mottisfont & Dunbridge	d									13 29															
Dean	d									13 35															
Salisbury	a									13 48									14 42						
Totton	d				12 41									13 41								14 41			
Ashurst New Forest	d				12 45									13 45								14 45			
Beaulieu Road	d				12 50									13 50								14 50			
Brockenhurst 3	a				12 56		13 02	13 16						13 56		14 01	14 16					14 56			15 02
	d			12 59	12 57		13 03	13 17	13 29			13 59		13 57		14 02	14 17	14 29			14 59	14 57			15 03
Lymington Town	d			13 07					13 37			14 07						14 37			15 07				
Lymington Pier	a			13 09					13 39			14 09						14 39			15 09				
Sway	d				13 01									14 01								15 01			
New Milton	d				13 06			13 24						14 06			14 24					15 06			
Hinton Admiral	d				13 10									14 10								15 10			
Christchurch	d				13 15									14 15								15 15			
Pokesdown	d				13 19									14 19								15 19			
Bournemouth	a				13 23		13 26	13 34						14 23		14 26	14 34					15 23			15 26
	d				13 24			13 39						14 24			14 39					15 24			
Branksome	d							13 44									14 44								
Parkstone (Dorset)	d							13 47									14 47								
Poole 4	a				13 33			13 50						14 33			14 50					15 33			
	d							13 51									14 51								
Hamworthy	d							13 56									14 56								
Holton Heath	d																								
Wareham	d							14 03									15 03								
Wool	d							14 10									15 10								
Moreton (Dorset)	d							14 16									15 16								
Dorchester South	d							14 24									15 24								
Dorchester West	d																								
Upwey	d							14 31									15 31								
Weymouth	a							14 35									15 35								

A ⚲ to Bournemouth

Table 158

Sundays

16 February to 23 March

London - Basingstoke, Southampton, Romsey Lymington, Bournemouth and Weymouth

Network Diagram - see first Page of Table 158

		GW	SW	SW	SW	SW	SW	SW			XC	SW	SW	SW	SW	SW	SW		XC		SW	SW	SW	SW	SW
			◇1	1	1	1	1	◇1			◇1	◇1	1	1	1	1	◇1		◇1		◇1	1	1	1	1
			A									A									A				
			trolley					trolley			buffet	trolley					trolley		buffet		trolley				
London Waterloo 15 ⊖	d		13 35					13 54				14 35					14 54				15 35				
Clapham Junction 10	d		13u42					14u03				14u42					15u03				15u42				
Woking	d		14 07					14 28				15 07					15 28				16 07				
Farnborough (Main)	d																								
Fleet	d																								
Reading 7	d										14 41								15 41						
Basingstoke	a		14 26					14 46			15 09	15 26					15 46		16 09		16 26				
	d		14 28					14 48			15 10	15 28					15 48		16 10		16 28				
Micheldever	d							14 58									15 58								
Winchester	d		14 44					15 08			15 25	15 44					16 08		16 25		16 44				
Shawford	d																16 12								
Romsey	d				14 35	14 32								15 35	15 32								16 35	16 32	
Chandlers Ford	d				14 42									15 42									16 42		
Eastleigh 3	a				14 48	15 13		15 18						15 48	16 13		16 18						16 48	17 13	
	d				14 54	15 15		15 22	15 26					15 54	16 15		16 22	16 26					16 54	17 15	
Hedge End	d								15 32									16 32							
Botley	d								15 36									16 36							
Fareham	d								15 44									16 44							
Portchester	d								15 49									16 49							
Cosham	d								15 54									16 54							
Hilsea	a								16 00									17 00							
Fratton	a								16 04									17 08							
Portsmouth & Southsea	a								16 08									17 12							
Portsmouth Harbour ⛴	a								16 13									17 16							
Southampton Airport Pkwy ✈	d		14 53		14 58			15 27			15 34	15 53		15 58			16 27		16 34		16 53		16 58		
Swaythling	d				15 01									16 01									17 01		
St Denys	d				15 04									16 04									17 04		
Southampton Central ⛴	a		15 00		15 09			15 34			15 42	16 00		16 09			16 34		16 42		17 00		17 09		
	d		15 03		15 10			15 35			15 45	16 03		16 10			16 35		16 45		17 03		17 10		
Millbrook (Hants)	d				15 13									16 13									17 13		
Redbridge	d				15 16									16 16									17 16		
Romsey	d				15 24	15a28								16 24	16a28								17 24	17a28	
Mottisfont & Dunbridge	d				15 29																		17 29		
Dean	d				15 35																		17 35		
Salisbury	a				15 48									16 42									17 48		
Totton	d							15 41									16 41								
Ashurst New Forest	d							15 45									16 45								
Beaulieu Road	d							15 50									16 50								
Brockenhurst 3	a		15 16					15 56			16 02	16 16					16 56		17 02		17 16				
	d		15 17	15 29			15 59	15 57			16 03	16 17	16 29			16 59	16 57		17 03		17 17	17 29			17 59
Lymington Town	d			15 37			16 07						16 37			17 07						17 37			18 07
Lymington Pier	a			15 39			16 09						16 39			17 09						17 39			18 09
Sway	d							16 01									17 01								
New Milton	d		15 24					16 06				16 24					17 06				17 24				
Hinton Admiral	d							16 10									17 10								
Christchurch	d							16 15									17 15								
Pokesdown	d							16 19									17 19								
Bournemouth	a		15 34					16 23			16 26	16 34					17 23		17 26		17 34				
	d		15 39					16 24				16 39					17 24				17 39				
Branksome	d		15 44									16 44									17 44				
Parkstone (Dorset)	d		15 47									16 47									17 47				
Poole 4	a		15 50					16 33				16 50					17 33				17 50				
	d		15 51									16 51									17 51				
Hamworthy	d		15 56									16 56									17 56				
Holton Heath	d																								
Wareham	d		16 03									17 03									18 03				
Wool	d		16 10									17 10									18 10				
Moreton (Dorset)	d		16 16									17 16									18 16				
Dorchester South	d		16 24									17 24									18 24				
Dorchester West	d	16 01																							
Upwey	d	16 10	16 31									17 31									18 31				
Weymouth	a	16 15	16 35									17 35									18 35				

A trolley to Bournemouth

Table 158

Sundays

16 February to 23 March

London - Basingstoke, Southampton, Romsey Lymington, Bournemouth and Weymouth

Network Diagram - see first Page of Table 158

		SW		XC	SW	SW	SW	SW	SW	SW		XC	GW	SW	SW	SW	SW	SW	SW		XC	SW	SW
		◇1		◇1	◇1	1	1	1	1	◇1		◇1	◇	◇1	1	1	1	1	◇1		◇1	◇1	1
					A									A								A	
London Waterloo 15 ⊖	d	15 54			16 35					16 54				17 35					17 54			18 35	
Clapham Junction 10	d	16u03			16u42					17u03				17u42					18u03			18u42	
Woking	d	16 28			17 07					17 28				18 07					18 28			19 07	
Farnborough (Main)	d																						
Fleet	d																						
Reading 7	d			16 44								17 41									18 41		
Basingstoke	a	16 46		17 09	17 26					17 46		18 09		18 26					18 46		19 09	19 26	
	d	16 48		17 10	17 28					17 48		18 10		18 28					18 48		19 10	19 28	
Micheldever	d	16 58								17 58									18 58				
Winchester	d	17 08		17 25	17 44					18 08		18 25		18 44					19 08		19 25	19 44	
Shawford	d									18 12													
Romsey	d						17 35	17 32								18 35	18 32						
Chandlers Ford	d						17 42									18 42							
Eastleigh 3	a	17 18					17 48	18 13		18 18						18 48	19 13		19 18				
	d	17 22	17 26				17 54	18 15		18 22	18 26					18 54	19 15		19 22	19 26			
Hedge End	d		17 32								18 32									19 32			
Botley	d		17 36								18 36									19 36			
Fareham	d		17 44								18 44									19 44			
Portchester	d		17 49								18 49									19 49			
Cosham	d		17 54								18 54									19 54			
Hilsea	a		18 00								19 00									20 00			
Fratton	a		18 04								19 08									20 04			
Portsmouth & Southsea	a		18 08								19 12									20 08			
Portsmouth Harbour ⛴	a		18 13								19 17									20 13			
Southampton Airport Pkwy ✈	d	17 27		17 34	17 53		17 58			18 27		18 34		18 53		18 58			19 27		19 34	19 53	
Swaythling	d						18 01									19 01							
St Denys	d						18 04									19 04							
Southampton Central ⛴	a	17 34		17 40	18 00		18 09			18 34		18 42		19 00		19 09			19 34		19 40	20 00	
	d	17 35		17 45	18 03		18 10			18 35		18 45		19 03		19 10			19 35		19 45	20 03	
Millbrook (Hants)	d						18 13									19 13							
Redbridge	d						18 16									19 16							
Romsey	d						18 24	18a28								19 24	19a28						
Mottisfont & Dunbridge	d															19 29							
Dean	d															19 35							
Salisbury	a						18 42									19 48							
Totton	d	17 41								18 41									19 41				
Ashurst New Forest	d	17 45								18 45									19 45				
Beaulieu Road	d	17 50								18 50									19 50				
Brockenhurst 3	a	17 56		18 02	18 16					18 56		19 01		19 16					19 56		20 02	20 16	
	d	17 57		18 03	18 17	18 29			18 59	18 57		19 02		19 17	19 29			19 59	19 57		20 03	20 17	20 29
Lymington Town	d					18 37			19 07						19 37			20 07					20 37
Lymington Pier	a					18 39			19 09						19 39			20 09					20 39
Sway	d	18 01								19 01									20 01				
New Milton	d	18 06			18 24					19 06				19 24					20 06			20 24	
Hinton Admiral	d	18 10								19 10									20 10				
Christchurch	d	18 15								19 15									20 15				
Pokesdown	d	18 19								19 19									20 19				
Bournemouth	a	18 23		18 26	18 34					19 23		19 26		19 34					20 23		20 26	20 34	
	d	18 24			18 39					19 24				19 39					20 24			20 39	
Branksome	d				18 44									19 44								20 44	
Parkstone (Dorset)	d				18 47									19 47								20 47	
Poole 4	a	18 33			18 50					19 33				19 50					20 33			20 50	
	d				18 51									19 51								20 51	
Hamworthy	d				18 56									19 56								20 56	
Holton Heath	d																						
Wareham	d				19 03									20 03								21 03	
Wool	d				19 10									20 10								21 10	
Moreton (Dorset)	d				19 16									20 17								21 17	
Dorchester South	d				19 24									20 25								21 25	
Dorchester West	d												19 47										
Upwey	d				19 31								19 55	20 32								21 32	
Weymouth	a				19 35								20 01	20 36								21 36	

A to Bournemouth

Table 158

Sundays

16 February to 23 March

London - Basingstoke, Southampton, Romsey Lymington, Bournemouth and Weymouth

Network Diagram - see first Page of Table 158

		SN	SW	SW	SW	SW	(SW)	XC	SW	SW	SN	SW	SW	SW	SW	(SW)	XC	GW	SW	SW	SW
		1	1	1	1	◇1		◇1	◇1	1	1	1	1	1	◇1		◇1		◇1	1	1
									A										A		
London Waterloo [15]	d					18 54			19 35						19 54				20 35		
Clapham Junction [10]	d					19u03			19u42						20u03				20u42		
Woking	d					19 28			20 07						20 28				21 07		
Farnborough (Main)	d																				
Fleet	d																				
Reading [7]	d							19 43									20 41				
Basingstoke	a					19 46		20 09	20 26						20 46		21 09		21 26		
	d					19 48		20 10	20 28						20 48		21 10		21 28		
Micheldever	d					19 58									20 58						
Winchester	d					20 08		20 25	20 44						21 08		21 25		21 44		
Shawford	d					20 12															
Romsey	d		19 35	19 32								20 35	20 32							21 35	21 32
Chandlers Ford	d		19 42									20 42								21 42	
Eastleigh [3]	a		19 48	20 13		20 18						20 48	21 13		21 18					21 48	22 13
	d	19 46	19 54	20 15		20 22	20 26				20 46	20 54	21 15		21 22	21 26				21 54	22 15
Hedge End	d						20 32									21 32					
Botley	d						20 36									21 36					
Fareham	d	20 03					20 44				21 02					21 44					
Portchester	d						20 49									21 49					
Cosham	d	20a11					20 54				21a10					21 54					
Hilsea	a						21 00									22 00					
Fratton	a						21 04									22 04					
Portsmouth & Southsea	a						21 08									22 10					
Portsmouth Harbour	a						21 13									22 14					
Southampton Airport Pkwy	d		19 58			20 27		20 34	20 53			20 58			21 27		21 34		21 53	21 58	
Swaythling	d		20 01									21 01								22 01	
St Denys	d		20 04									21 04								22 04	
Southampton Central	a		20 09			20 34		20 42	21 00			21 09			21 34		21 43		22 00	22 09	
	d		20 10			20 35		20 45	21 03			21 10			21 35		21 45		22 03	22 10	
Millbrook (Hants)	d		20 13									21 13								22 13	
Redbridge	d		20 16									21 16								22 16	
Romsey	d		20 24	20a28								21 24	21a28							22a24	22a31
Mottisfont & Dunbridge	d											21 29									
Dean	d											21 35									
Salisbury	a		20 42									21 48									
Totton	d					20 41									21 41						
Ashurst New Forest	d					20 45									21 45						
Beaulieu Road	d					20 50									21 50						
Brockenhurst [3]	a					20 56		21 02	21 16						21 56		22 02		22 16		
	d				20 59	20 57		21 03	21 17	21 29				21 59	21 57		22 03		22 17		
Lymington Town	d				21 07					21 37				22 07							
Lymington Pier	a				21 09					21 39				22 09							
Sway	d					21 01									22 01						
New Milton	d					21 06			21 24						22 06				22 24		
Hinton Admiral	d					21 10									22 10						
Christchurch	d					21 15									22 15						
Pokesdown	d					21 19									22 19						
Bournemouth	a					21 23		21 26	21 34						22 23		22 26		22 34		
	d					21 24			21 39						22 24				22 39		
Branksome	d								21 44										22 44		
Parkstone (Dorset)	d								21 47										22 47		
Poole [4]	a					21 33			21 50						22 33				22 50		
	d								21 51										22 51		
Hamworthy	d								21 56										22 56		
Holton Heath	d																				
Wareham	d								22 03										23 03		
Wool	d								22 10										23 10		
Moreton (Dorset)	d								22 17										23 17		
Dorchester South	d								22 25										23 25		
Dorchester West	d																	22 53			
Upwey	d								22 32									23 01	23 32		
Weymouth	a								22 36									23 06	23 36		

A to Bournemouth

Table 158

Sundays

16 February to 23 March

London - Basingstoke, Southampton, Romsey Lymington, Bournemouth and Weymouth

Network Diagram - see first Page of Table 158

Station		SW		XC	SW	SW	SW	SW		SW	
		◇1		◇1	◇1	1	1	◇1		◇1	
					A						
				☕	🛒					🛒	
London Waterloo 15 ⊖	d	20 54			21 35			21 54		22 54	
Clapham Junction 10	d	21u03			21u42			22u03		23u03	
Woking	d	21 28			22 07			22 28		23 28	
Farnborough (Main)	d										
Fleet	d										
Reading 7	d										
Basingstoke	a	21 46			22 26			22 46		23 46	
	d	21 48		22 11	22 28			22 48		23 48	
Micheldever	d	21 58						22 58		23 58	
Winchester	d	22 08		22 25	22 44			23 08		00 08	
Shawford	d	22 12									
Romsey	d					22 35	22 28				
Chandlers Ford	d					22 42					
Eastleigh 3	a	22 18				22 48	23 19	23 17		00 18	
	d	22 22	22 26			22 54	23 21	23 22	23 26	00 22	00 30
Hedge End	d		22 32						23 32		00s36
Botley	d		22 36						23 36		00s39
Fareham	d		22 44						23 44		00s47
Portchester	d		22 49						23 49		00s53
Cosham	d		22 54						23 54		00s57
Hilsea	a		23 00						23 59		
Fratton	a		23 04						00 04		01s05
Portsmouth & Southsea	a		23 08						00 08		01s08
Portsmouth Harbour ⛴	a		23 13						00 13		01 12
Southampton Airport Pkwy ✈	d	22 27		22 34	22 53	22 58		23 27		00 27	
Swaythling	d					23 01					
St Denys	d					23 04				00s31	
Southampton Central ⛴	a	22 34		22 42	23 00	23 09		23 34		00 36	
	d	22 35			23 03	23 10		23 35		00 37	
Millbrook (Hants)	d					23 13					
Redbridge	d					23 16					
Romsey	d					23 24	23a33				
Mottisfont & Dunbridge	d					23 29					
Dean	d					23 35					
Salisbury	a					23 51					
Totton	d	22 41						23 41		00s42	
Ashurst New Forest	d	22 45						23 45			
Beaulieu Road	d	22 50									
Brockenhurst 3	a	22 56			23 16			23 53		00s53	
	d	22 57			23 17			23 54			
Lymington Town	d										
Lymington Pier	a										
Sway	d	23 01						23 59			
New Milton	d	23 06			23 24			00 04		01s01	
Hinton Admiral	d	23 10						00 08			
Christchurch	d	23 15						00 13		01s08	
Pokesdown	d	23 19						00 16		01s12	
Bournemouth	a	23 23			23 34			00 20		01 16	
	d	23 24			23 39			00 22		01 17	
Branksome	d				23 44			00 27		01s22	
Parkstone (Dorset)	d				23 47			00 30		01s25	
Poole 4	a	23 33			23 50			00 34		01 29	
	d				23 51						
Hamworthy	d				23 56						
Holton Heath	d										
Wareham	d				00 03						
Wool	d				00 10						
Moreton (Dorset)	d				00 17						
Dorchester South	d				00 25						
Dorchester West	d										
Upwey	d				00 32						
Weymouth	a				00 36						

A 🛒 to Bournemouth

Table 158

Sundays

30 March to 11 May

London - Basingstoke, Southampton, Romsey Lymington, Bournemouth and Weymouth

Network Diagram - see first Page of Table 158

		SW	SW	SW	SW	SW	SW	SW	SW	SW		SW	SW	SW	SW	SW	SW	SW		SN		SW	SW	SW	SW
		◇1	◇1 (trolley)	1	1	◇1 (trolley)	◇1	1	1	1		1	1	1	1	1	1	1		1		1	1	1	1
London Waterloo 15 ⊖	d												00 05		01 05										
Clapham Junction 10	d												00u12		01 15										
Woking	d									00 03		00 28	00 37		01 49										
Farnborough (Main)	d								00 10	00 14		00 41			01s58										
Fleet	d								00 16	00 20		00 47			02s04										
Reading 7	d																								
Basingstoke	a								00 33	00 33		01 06	00 55		02s16										
	d									00 35			00 56					07 48							
Micheldever	d						00 02											07 58							
Winchester	d						00 11			00 51			01 13		02s33			08 08							
Shawford	d																	08 12							
Romsey	d																							08 35	08 39
Chandlers Ford	d																							08 42	
Eastleigh 3	a						00 19			00 59			01 21		02s42			08 18						08 47	09 13
	d				00 03		00 20	00 30		01 00			01 22					08 22	08 26	08 48				08 54	09 15
Hedge End	d							00s36											08 32						
Botley	d							00s39											08 36						
Fareham	d							00s47									07 44		08 44	09 02					
Portchester	d							00s53									07 49		08 49						
Cosham	d							00s57									07 54		08 54	09a10					
Hilsea	a																08 00		09 00						
Fratton	a							01s05									08 04		09 04						
Portsmouth & Southsea	a							01s08									08 08		09 08						
Portsmouth Harbour ⛴	a							01 12									08 13		09 13						
Southampton Airport Pkwy ✈	d				00 08		00 25			01 05			01 26		02s46			08 27						08 58	
Swaythling	d																							09 01	
St Denys	d						00s29								02s51									09 04	
Southampton Central ⛴	a				00 15		00 34			01 12			01 35		02 56			08 34						09 09	
	d						00 35						01 37					08 35				09 03		09 10	
Millbrook (Hants)	d																							09 13	
Redbridge	d																							09 16	
Romsey	d																							09 24	09a28
Mottisfont & Dunbridge	d			00 02																				09 29	
Dean	d			00 08																				09 35	
Salisbury	a			00 20																				09 49	
Totton	d						00s40						01s42					08 41							
Ashurst New Forest	d																	08 45							
Beaulieu Road	d																	08 50							
Brockenhurst 3	a						00s51						01s53					08 56				09 16			
	d					00 05										08 59		08 57				09 17	09 29		
Lymington Town	d															09 07							09 37		
Lymington Pier	a															09 09							09 39		
Sway	d																	09 01							
New Milton	d						00s59						02s00					09 06				09 24			
Hinton Admiral	d		00 02															09 10							
Christchurch	d		00 07				01s06						02s07					09 15							
Pokesdown	d		00 11				01s10						02s11					09 19							
Bournemouth	a		00 15			00 21	01 14						02 15					09 23				09 34			
	d		00 16			00 22	01 15							08 39				09 24				09 39			
Branksome	d		00 21			00 27	01s20							08 44								09 44			
Parkstone (Dorset)	d		00 24			00 30	01s23							08 47								09 47			
Poole 4	a		00 30			00 35	01 27							08 50				09 33				09 50			
	d													08 51								09 51			
Hamworthy	d													08 56								09 56			
Holton Heath	d																								
Wareham	d													09 03								10 03			
Wool	d	00 01												09 10								10 10			
Moreton (Dorset)	d	00 07												09 16								10 16			
Dorchester South	d	00 15												09 24								10 24			
Dorchester West	d																								
Upwey	d	00 21												09 31								10 31			
Weymouth	a	00 26												09 35								10 35			

Table 158

Sundays

30 March to 11 May

London - Basingstoke, Southampton, Romsey Lymington, Bournemouth and Weymouth

Network Diagram - see first Page of Table 158

		SW	SW		SW	SW	SW	SW	SW	SW		XC	SW	SW	SW	SW	SW	SW		XC	SW	SW	SW
		1	◇1		◇1	1	1	1	1	◇1		◇1	◇1	1	1	1	1	◇1		◇1	◇1	1	1
																					A		
												🛒								🛒	🛒		
London Waterloo 15 ⊖	d		07 54		08 35					08 54			09 35					09 54			10 35		
Clapham Junction 10	d		08u03		08u45					09u03			09u45					10u03			10u45		
Woking	d		08 28		09 09					09 28			10 09					10 28			11 08		
Farnborough (Main)	d																						
Fleet	d																						
Reading 7	d											09 53								10 53			
Basingstoke	a		08 46		09 28					09 46		10 09	10 28					10 46		11 09	11 26		
	d		08 48		09 29					09 48		10 10	10 29					10 48		11 10	11 28		
Micheldever	d		08 58							09 58								10 58					
Winchester	d		09 08		09 46					10 08		10 25	10 46					11 08		11 25	11 44		
Shawford	d									10 12													
Romsey	d						09 35	09 32							10 35	10 32							11 35
Chandlers Ford	d						09 42								10 42								11 42
Eastleigh 3	a		09 18				09 48	10 13		10 18					10 48	11 13		11 18					11 48
	d		09 22	09 26			09 54	10 15		10 22	10 26				10 54	11 15		11 22	11 26				11 54
Hedge End	d			09 32							10 32								11 32				
Botley	d			09 36							10 36								11 36				
Fareham	d			09 44							10 44								11 44				
Portchester	d			09 49							10 49								11 49				
Cosham	d			09 54							10 54								11 54				
Hilsea	a			10 00							11 00								12 00				
Fratton	a			10 08							11 08								12 04				
Portsmouth & Southsea	a			10 11							11 11								12 08				
Portsmouth Harbour ⛴	a			10 15							11 15								12 13				
Southampton Airport Pkwy ✈	d		09 27		09 55		09 58			10 27		10 34	10 55		10 58			11 27		11 34	11 53		11 58
Swaythling	d						10 01								11 01								12 01
St Denys	d						10 04								11 04								12 04
Southampton Central ⛴	a		09 34		10 02		10 09			10 34		10 42	11 02		11 09			11 34		11 42	11 59		12 09
	d		09 35		10 03		10 10			10 35		10 45	11 03		11 10			11 35		11 45	12 03		12 10
Millbrook (Hants)	d						10 13								11 13								12 13
Redbridge	d						10 16								11 16								12 16
Romsey	d						10 24	10a28							11 24	11a28							12 24
Mottisfont & Dunbridge	d														11 29								
Dean	d														11 35								
Salisbury	a						10 42								11 48								12 42
Totton	d		09 41							10 41								11 41					
Ashurst New Forest	d		09 45							10 45								11 45					
Beaulieu Road	d		09 50							10 50								11 50					
Brockenhurst 3	a		09 56		10 17					10 56		11 02	11 17					11 56		12 02	12 16		
	d	09 59	09 57		10 18	10 29			10 59	10 57		11 03	11 18	11 29			11 59	11 57		12 03	12 17	12 29	
Lymington Town	d	10 07				10 37			11 07					11 37			12 07					12 37	
Lymington Pier	a	10 09				10 39			11 09					11 39			12 09					12 39	
Sway	d		10 01							11 01								12 01					
New Milton	d		10 06		10 25					11 06			11 25					12 06			12 24		
Hinton Admiral	d		10 10							11 10								12 10					
Christchurch	d		10 15							11 15								12 15					
Pokesdown	d		10 19							11 19								12 19					
Bournemouth	a		10 23		10 35					11 23		11 26	11 35					12 23		12 26	12 34		
	d		10 24		10 39					11 24			11 39					12 24			12 39		
Branksome	d				10 44								11 44								12 44		
Parkstone (Dorset)	d				10 47								11 47								12 47		
Poole 4	a		10 33		10 50					11 33			11 50					12 33			12 50		
	d				10 51								11 51								12 51		
Hamworthy	d				10 56								11 56								12 56		
Holton Heath	d																						
Wareham	d				11 03								12 03								13 03		
Wool	d				11 10								12 10								13 10		
Moreton (Dorset)	d				11 16								12 16								13 16		
Dorchester South	d				11 24								12 24								13 24		
Dorchester West	d																						
Upwey	d				11 31								12 31								13 31		
Weymouth	a				11 35								12 35								13 35		

A 🛒 to Bournemouth

Table 158

Sundays

30 March to 11 May

London - Basingstoke, Southampton, Romsey Lymington, Bournemouth and Weymouth

Network Diagram - see first Page of Table 158

		SW		SW	SW		XC	SW	SW	SW	SW	SW		SW		XC	SW	SW	SW	SW	SW	SW			XC
		1		1	◇1		◇1	◇1	1	1	1	1		◇1		◇1	◇1	1	1	1	1	◇1			◇1
								A									A								
							🍴	🛒						🛒		🍴	🛒					🛒			🛒
London Waterloo 15 ⊖	d				10 54			11 35						11 54			12 35					12 54			
Clapham Junction 10	d				11u03			11u45						12u03			12u45					13u03			
Woking	d				11 28			12 08						12 28			13 08					13 28			
Farnborough (Main)	d																								
Fleet	d																								
Reading 7	d						11 53									12 53									13 53
Basingstoke	a				11 46		12 09	12 26						12 46		13 09	13 26					13 46			14 09
	d				11 48		12 10	12 28						12 48		13 10	13 28					13 48			14 10
Micheldever	d				11 58									12 58								13 58			
Winchester	d				12 08		12 25	12 44						13 08		13 25	13 44					14 08			14 25
Shawford	d				12 12																	14 12			
Romsey	d	11 32								12 35	12 32								13 35	13 32					
Chandlers Ford	d									12 42									13 42						
Eastleigh 3	a	12 13			12 18					12 48	13 13			13 18					13 48	14 13		14 18			
	d	12 15			12 22	12 26				12 54	13 15			13 22	13 26				13 54	14 15		14 22	14 26		
Hedge End	d					12 32									13 32								14 32		
Botley	d					12 36									13 36								14 36		
Fareham	d					12 44									13 44								14 44		
Portchester	d					12 49									13 49								14 49		
Cosham	d					12 54									13 54								14 54		
Hilsea	a					13 00									14 00								15 00		
Fratton	a					13 04									14 04								15 04		
Portsmouth & Southsea	a					13 08									14 08								15 08		
Portsmouth Harbour ⛴	a					13 13									14 13								15 13		
Southampton Airport Pkwy ✈	d				12 27		12 34	12 53		12 58				13 27		13 34	13 53		13 58			14 27			14 34
Swaythling	d									13 01									14 01						
St Denys	d									13 04									14 04						
Southampton Central ⛴	a				12 34		12 42	13 00		13 09				13 34		13 42	14 00		14 09			14 34			14 42
	d				12 35		12 45	13 03		13 10				13 35		13 45	14 03		14 10			14 35			14 45
Millbrook (Hants)	d									13 13									14 13						
Redbridge	d									13 16									14 16						
Romsey	d	12a28								13 24	13a28								14 24	14a28					
Mottisfont & Dunbridge	d									13 29															
Dean	d									13 35															
Salisbury	a									13 48									14 42						
Totton	d				12 41									13 41								14 41			
Ashurst New Forest	d				12 45									13 45								14 45			
Beaulieu Road	d				12 50									13 50								14 50			
Brockenhurst 3	a				12 56		13 02	13 16						13 56		14 01	14 16					14 56			15 02
	d			12 59	12 57		13 03	13 17	13 29			13 59		13 57		14 02	14 17	14 29			14 59	14 57			15 03
Lymington Town	d			13 07					13 37			14 07						14 37			15 07				
Lymington Pier	a			13 09					13 39			14 09						14 39			15 09				
Sway	d				13 01									14 01								15 01			
New Milton	d				13 06			13 24						14 06			14 24					15 06			
Hinton Admiral	d				13 10									14 10								15 10			
Christchurch	d				13 15									14 15								15 15			
Pokesdown	d				13 19									14 19								15 19			
Bournemouth	a				13 23		13 26	13 34						14 23		14 26	14 34					15 23			15 26
	d				13 24			13 39						14 24			14 39					15 24			
Branksome	d							13 44									14 44								
Parkstone (Dorset)	d							13 47									14 47								
Poole 4	a				13 33			13 50						14 33			14 50					15 33			
	d							13 51									14 51								
Hamworthy	d							13 56									14 56								
Holton Heath	d																								
Wareham	d							14 03									15 03								
Wool	d							14 10									15 10								
Moreton (Dorset)	d							14 16									15 16								
Dorchester South	d							14 24									15 24								
Dorchester West	d																								
Upwey	d							14 31									15 31								
Weymouth	a							14 35									15 35								

A 🛒 to Bournemouth

Table 158

Sundays

30 March to 11 May

London - Basingstoke, Southampton, Romsey Lymington, Bournemouth and Weymouth

Network Diagram - see first Page of Table 158

		GW	SW	SW	SW	SW	SW	SW			XC	SW	SW	SW	SW	SW	SW		XC		SW	SW	SW	SW	SW
			◇1	1	1	1	1	◇1			◇1	◇1	1	1	1	1	◇1		◇1		◇1	1	1	1	1
			A									A									A				
			🛒					🛒			☕	🛒					🛒		☕		🛒				
London Waterloo 15 ⊖	d		13 35					13 54				14 35					14 54				15 35				
Clapham Junction 10	d		13u42					14u03				14u42					15u03				15u42				
Woking	d		14 07					14 28				15 07					15 28				16 07				
Farnborough (Main)	d																								
Fleet	d																								
Reading 7	d										14 53								15 53						
Basingstoke	a		14 26					14 46			15 09	15 26					15 46		16 09		16 26				
	d		14 28					14 48			15 10	15 28					15 48		16 10		16 28				
Micheldever	d							14 58									15 58								
Winchester	d		14 44					15 08			15 25	15 44					16 08		16 25		16 44				
Shawford	d																16 12								
Romsey	d				14 35	14 32								15 35	15 32								16 35	16 32	
Chandlers Ford	d				14 42									15 42									16 42		
Eastleigh 8	a				14 48	15 13		15 18						15 48	16 13		16 18						16 48	17 13	
	d				14 54	15 15		15 22	15 26					15 54	16 15		16 22	16 26					16 54	17 15	
Hedge End	d								15 32									16 32							
Botley	d								15 36									16 36							
Fareham	d								15 44									16 44							
Portchester	d								15 49									16 49							
Cosham	d								15 54									16 54							
Hilsea	a								16 00									17 00							
Fratton	a								16 04									17 08							
Portsmouth & Southsea	a								16 08									17 12							
Portsmouth Harbour ⛴	a								16 13									17 16							
Southampton Airport Pkwy ✈	d		14 53		14 58			15 27			15 34	15 53		15 58			16 27		16 34		16 53		16 58		
Swaythling	d				15 01									16 01									17 01		
St Denys	d				15 04									16 04									17 04		
Southampton Central ⛴	a		15 00		15 09			15 34			15 42	16 00		16 09			16 34		16 42		17 00		17 09		
	d		15 03		15 10			15 35			15 45	16 03		16 10			16 35		16 45		17 03		17 10		
Millbrook (Hants)	d				15 13									16 13									17 13		
Redbridge	d				15 16									16 16									17 16		
Romsey	d				15 24	15a28								16 24	16a28								17 24	17a28	
Mottisfont & Dunbridge	d				15 29																		17 29		
Dean	d				15 35																		17 35		
Salisbury	a				15 48									16 42									17 48		
Totton	d							15 41									16 41								
Ashurst New Forest	d							15 45									16 45								
Beaulieu Road	d							15 50									16 50								
Brockenhurst 3	a		15 16					15 56			16 02	16 16					16 56		17 02		17 16				
	d		15 17	15 29			15 59	15 57			16 03	16 17	16 29			16 59	16 57		17 03		17 17	17 29			17 59
Lymington Town	d			15 37			16 07						16 37			17 07						17 37			18 07
Lymington Pier	a			15 39			16 09						16 39			17 09						17 39			18 09
Sway	d							16 01									17 01								
New Milton	d		15 24					16 06				16 24					17 06				17 24				
Hinton Admiral	d							16 10									17 10								
Christchurch	d							16 15									17 15								
Pokesdown	d							16 19									17 19								
Bournemouth	a		15 34					16 23			16 26	16 34					17 23		17 26		17 34				
	d		15 39					16 24				16 39					17 24				17 39				
Branksome	d		15 44									16 44									17 44				
Parkstone (Dorset)	d		15 47									16 47									17 47				
Poole 4	a		15 50					16 33				16 50					17 33				17 50				
	d		15 51									16 51									17 51				
Hamworthy	d		15 56									16 56									17 56				
Holton Heath	d																								
Wareham	d		16 03									17 03									18 03				
Wool	d		16 10									17 10									18 10				
Moreton (Dorset)	d		16 16									17 16									18 16				
Dorchester South	d		16 24									17 24									18 24				
Dorchester West	d	16 01																							
Upwey	d	16 10	16 31									17 31									18 31				
Weymouth	a	16 15	16 35									17 35									18 35				

A 🛒 to Bournemouth

Table 158

Sundays

30 March to 11 May

London - Basingstoke, Southampton, Romsey Lymington, Bournemouth and Weymouth

Network Diagram - see first Page of Table 158

		SW		XC	SW		SW	SW	SW	SW	SW		XC	GW	SW		SW	SW	SW	SW	SW		XC	SW	SW
		◇1		◇1	◇1		1	1	1	1	◇1		◇1	◇	◇1		1	1	1	1	◇1		◇1	◇1	1
					A										A									A	
		⊥		⊔	⊥						⊥		⊔		⊥						⊥		⊔	⊥	
London Waterloo 15 ⊖	d	15 54			16 35						16 54				17 35						17 54			18 35	
Clapham Junction 10	d	16u03			16u42						17u03				17u42						18u03			18u42	
Woking	d	16 28			17 07						17 28				18 07						18 28			19 07	
Farnborough (Main)	d																								
Fleet	d																								
Reading 7	d			16 53									17 53										18 53		
Basingstoke	a	16 46		17 09	17 26						17 46		18 09		18 26						18 46		19 09	19 26	
	d	16 48		17 10	17 28						17 48		18 10		18 28						18 48		19 10	19 28	
Micheldever	d	16 58									17 58										18 58				
Winchester	d	17 08		17 25	17 44						18 08		18 25		18 44						19 08		19 25	19 44	
Shawford	d										18 12														
Romsey	d							17 35	17 32									18 35	18 32						
Chandlers Ford	d							17 42										18 42							
Eastleigh 3	a	17 18						17 48	18 13		18 18							18 48	19 13		19 18				
	d	17 22	17 26					17 54	18 15		18 22	18 26						18 54	19 15		19 22	19 26			
Hedge End	d		17 32									18 32										19 32			
Botley	d		17 36									18 36										19 36			
Fareham	d		17 44									18 44										19 44			
Portchester	d		17 49									18 49										19 49			
Cosham	d		17 54									18 54										19 54			
Hilsea	a		18 00									19 00										20 00			
Fratton	a		18 04									19 08										20 04			
Portsmouth & Southsea	a		18 08									19 12										20 08			
Portsmouth Harbour ⛴	a		18 13									19 17										20 13			
Southampton Airport Pkwy ✈	d	17 27		17 34	17 53			17 58			18 27		18 34		18 53			18 58			19 27		19 34	19 53	
Swaythling	d							18 01										19 01							
St Denys	d							18 04										19 04							
Southampton Central ⛴	a	17 34		17 40	18 00			18 09			18 34		18 42		19 00			19 09			19 34		19 40	20 00	
	d	17 35		17 45	18 03			18 10			18 35		18 45		19 03			19 10			19 35		19 45	20 03	
Millbrook (Hants)	d							18 13										19 13							
Redbridge	d							18 16										19 16							
Romsey	d							18 24	18a28									19 24	19a28						
Mottisfont & Dunbridge	d																	19 29							
Dean	d																	19 35							
Salisbury	a							18 42										19 48							
Totton	d	17 41									18 41										19 41				
Ashurst New Forest	d	17 45									18 45										19 45				
Beaulieu Road	d	17 50									18 50										19 50				
Brockenhurst 3	a	17 56		18 02	18 16						18 56		19 01		19 16						19 56		20 02	20 16	
	d	17 57		18 03	18 17		18 29			18 59	18 57		19 02		19 17		19 29			19 59	19 57		20 03	20 17	20 29
Lymington Town	d						18 37			19 07							19 37			20 07					20 37
Lymington Pier	a						18 39			19 09							19 39			20 09					20 39
Sway	d	18 01									19 01										20 01				
New Milton	d	18 06			18 24						19 06				19 24						20 06			20 24	
Hinton Admiral	d	18 10									19 10										20 10				
Christchurch	d	18 15									19 15										20 15				
Pokesdown	d	18 19									19 19										20 19				
Bournemouth	a	18 23		18 26	18 34						19 23		19 26		19 34						20 23		20 26	20 34	
	d	18 24			18 39						19 24				19 39						20 24			20 39	
Branksome	d				18 44										19 44									20 44	
Parkstone (Dorset)	d				18 47										19 47									20 47	
Poole 4	a	18 33			18 50						19 33				19 50						20 33			20 50	
	d				18 51										19 51									20 51	
Hamworthy	d				18 56										19 56									20 56	
Holton Heath	d																								
Wareham	d				19 03										20 03									21 03	
Wool	d				19 10										20 10									21 10	
Moreton (Dorset)	d				19 16										20 17									21 17	
Dorchester South	d				19 24										20 25									21 25	
Dorchester West	d													19 47											
Upwey	d				19 31									19 55	20 32									21 32	
Weymouth	a				19 35									20 01	20 36									21 36	

A ⊥ to Bournemouth

Table 158

Sundays

30 March to 11 May

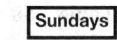

London - Basingstoke, Southampton, Romsey Lymington, Bournemouth and Weymouth

Network Diagram - see first Page of Table 158

		SN	SW	SW	SW	SW	SW	XC	SW	SW	SN	SW	SW	SW	SW	SW	XC	GW	SW	SW	SW
		1	1	1	1	◇1		◇1	◇1	1	1	1	1	1	◇1		◇1		◇1	1	1
									A										A		
						🛒		☕	🛒						🛒				🛒		
London Waterloo [15] ⊖	d					18 54			19 35						19 54				20 35		
Clapham Junction [10]	d					19u03			19u42						20u03				20u42		
Woking	d					19 28			20 07						20 28				21 07		
Farnborough (Main)	d																				
Fleet	d																				
Reading [7]	d							19 53									20 53				
Basingstoke	a					19 46		20 09	20 26						20 46		21 09		21 26		
	d					19 48		20 10	20 28						20 48		21 10		21 28		
Micheldever	d					19 58									20 58						
Winchester	d					20 08		20 25	20 44						21 08		21 25		21 44		
Shawford	d					20 12															
Romsey	d		19 35	19 32								20 35	20 32							21 35	21 32
Chandlers Ford	d		19 42									20 42								21 42	
Eastleigh [8]	a		19 48	20 13		20 18						20 48	21 13		21 18					21 48	22 13
	d	19 46	19 54	20 15		20 22	20 26				20 46	20 54	21 15		21 22	21 26				21 54	22 15
Hedge End	d						20 32									21 32					
Botley	d						20 36									21 36					
Fareham	d	20 03					20 44				21 02					21 44					
Portchester	d						20 49									21 49					
Cosham	d	20a11					20 54				21a10					21 54					
Hilsea	a						21 00									22 00					
Fratton	a						21 04									22 04					
Portsmouth & Southsea	a						21 08									22 10					
Portsmouth Harbour ⛴	a						21 13									22 14					
Southampton Airport Pkwy ✈	d		19 58			20 27		20 34	20 53			20 58			21 27		21 34		21 53	21 58	
Swaythling	d		20 01									21 01								22 01	
St Denys	d		20 04									21 04								22 04	
Southampton Central ⛴	a		20 09			20 34		20 42	21 00			21 09			21 34		21 43		22 00	22 09	
	d		20 10			20 35		20 45	21 03			21 10			21 35		21 45		22 03	22 10	
Millbrook (Hants)	d		20 13									21 13								22 13	
Redbridge	d		20 16									21 16								22 16	
Romsey	d		20 24	20a28								21 24	21a28							22a24	22a31
Mottisfont & Dunbridge	d											21 29									
Dean	d											21 35									
Salisbury	a		20 42									21 48									
Totton	d					20 41									21 41						
Ashurst New Forest	d					20 45									21 45						
Beaulieu Road	d					20 50									21 50						
Brockenhurst [3]	a					20 56		21 02	21 16						21 56		22 02		22 16		
	d				20 59	20 57		21 03	21 17	21 29				21 59	21 57		22 03		22 17		
Lymington Town	d				21 07					21 37				22 07							
Lymington Pier	a				21 09					21 39				22 09							
Sway	d					21 01									22 01						
New Milton	d					21 06			21 24						22 06				22 24		
Hinton Admiral	d					21 10									22 10						
Christchurch	d					21 15									22 15						
Pokesdown	d					21 19									22 19						
Bournemouth	a					21 23		21 26	21 34						22 23		22 26		22 34		
	d					21 24			21 39						22 24				22 39		
Branksome	d								21 44										22 44		
Parkstone (Dorset)	d								21 47										22 47		
Poole [4]	a					21 33			21 50						22 33				22 50		
	d								21 51										22 51		
Hamworthy	d								21 56										22 56		
Holton Heath	d																				
Wareham	d								22 03										23 03		
Wool	d								22 10										23 10		
Moreton (Dorset)	d								22 17										23 17		
Dorchester South	d								22 25										23 25		
Dorchester West	d																	22 53			
Upwey	d								22 32									23 01	23 32		
Weymouth	a								22 36									23 06	23 36		

A 🛒 to Bournemouth

Table 158

Sundays

30 March to 11 May

London - Basingstoke, Southampton, Romsey Lymington, Bournemouth and Weymouth

Network Diagram - see first Page of Table 158

		SW		XC	SW	SW	SW	SW		SW	
		◇1		◇1	◇1	1	1	◇1		◇1	
					A						
					🛒					🛒	
London Waterloo 15 ⊖	d	20 54			21 35			21 54		22 54	
Clapham Junction 10	d	21u03			21u42			22u03		23u03	
Woking	d	21 28			22 07			22 28		23 28	
Farnborough (Main)	d										
Fleet	d										
Reading 7	d			21 53							
Basingstoke	a	21 46		22 09	22 26			22 46		23 46	
	d	21 48		22 10	22 28			22 48		23 48	
Micheldever	d	21 58						22 58		23 58	
Winchester	d	22 08		22 25	22 44			23 08		00 08	
Shawford	d	22 12									
Romsey	d					22 35	22 28				
Chandlers Ford	d					22 42					
Eastleigh 3	a	22 18				22 48	23 19	23 17		00 18	
	d	22 22	22 26			22 54	23 21	23 22	23 26	00 22	00 30
Hedge End	d		22 32						23 32		00s36
Botley	d		22 36						23 36		00s39
Fareham	d		22 44						23 44		00s47
Portchester	d		22 49						23 49		00s53
Cosham	d		22 54						23 54		00s57
Hilsea	a		23 00						23 59		
Fratton	a		23 04						00 04		01s05
Portsmouth & Southsea	a		23 08						00 08		01s08
Portsmouth Harbour ⛴	a		23 13						00 13		01 12
Southampton Airport Pkwy ✈	d	22 27		22 34	22 53	22 58		23 27		00 27	
Swaythling	d					23 01					
St Denys	d					23 04				00s31	
Southampton Central ⛴	a	22 34		22 42	23 00	23 09		23 34		00 36	
	d	22 35			23 03	23 10		23 35		00 37	
Millbrook (Hants)	d					23 13					
Redbridge	d					23 16					
Romsey	d					23 24	23a33				
Mottisfont & Dunbridge	d					23 29					
Dean	d					23 35					
Salisbury	a					23 51					
Totton	d	22 41						23 41		00s42	
Ashurst New Forest	d	22 45						23 45			
Beaulieu Road	d	22 50									
Brockenhurst 3	a	22 56			23 16			23 53		00s53	
	d	22 57			23 17			23 54			
Lymington Town	d										
Lymington Pier	a										
Sway	d	23 01						23 59			
New Milton	d	23 06			23 24			00 04		01s01	
Hinton Admiral	d	23 10						00 08			
Christchurch	d	23 15						00 13		01s08	
Pokesdown	d	23 19						00 16		01s12	
Bournemouth	a	23 23			23 34			00 20		01 16	
	d	23 24			23 39			00 22		01 17	
Branksome	d				23 44			00 27		01s22	
Parkstone (Dorset)	d				23 47			00 30		01s25	
Poole 4	a	23 33			23 50			00 34		01 29	
	d				23 51						
Hamworthy	d				23 56						
Holton Heath	d										
Wareham	d				00 03						
Wool	d				00 10						
Moreton (Dorset)	d				00 17						
Dorchester South	d				00 25						
Dorchester West	d										
Upwey	d				00 32						
Weymouth	a				00 36						

A 🛒 to Bournemouth

Table 158R

Mondays to Fridays

9 December to 16 May

Weymouth, Bournemouth, Lymington, Romsey, Southampton and Basingstoke - London

Network Diagram - see first Page of Table 158

Miles	Miles			SW MX 1	SW MX 1	SW MX ◇1	SW 1	XC ◇1	SW 1	GW ◇	SW 1	SW 1	SW ◇1 🛒	SW 1	XC ◇1	SW 1	SW ◇1 🛒	SW 1	SW 1	SW 1	SW ◇1	SW 1
0	—	**Weymouth**	d							05 33												
2¼	—	Upwey	d							05 37												
—	—	Dorchester West	a							05 44												
7	—	**Dorchester South**	d																			
12½	—	Moreton (Dorset)	d																			
17	—	Wool	d																			
22	—	Wareham	d																			
24	—	Holton Heath	d																			
26¾	—	Hamworthy	d																			
29	—	**Poole 4**	a																			
—	—		d										05 00			05 26	05 45					
30¾	—	Parkstone (Dorset)	d										05 04			05 30						
32	—	Branksome	d										05 07			05 33						
34¾	—	**Bournemouth**	a										05 12			05 38	05 54					
—	—		d										05 15			05 40	05 57					
36½	—	Pokesdown	d										05 19			05 44						
38½	—	Christchurch	d										05 23			05 48						
41¾	—	Hinton Admiral	d													05 53						
44¼	—	New Milton	d										05 30			05 57						
47¼	—	Sway	d													06 02						
—	0	**Lymington Pier**	d																	06 14		
—	0½	Lymington Town	d																	06 16		
50	5¼	**Brockenhurst 3**	a										05 37			06 07	06 12			06 25		
—	—		d										05 38				06 14					
54¾	—	Beaulieu Road	d																			
57¼	—	Ashurst New Forest	d																			
60¼	—	Totton	d										05 49	06 14								
—	0	**Salisbury**	d								05 35											
—	9	Dean	d								05 47											
—	12¾	Mottisfont & Dunbridge	d								05 53											
—	16½	**Romsey**	d								05 58											
60¾	22½	Redbridge	d											06 16								
62½	—	Millbrook (Hants)	d											06 20					⟵			
63½	—	**Southampton Central** ⛴	a										05 54	06 24			06 27		06 24			
—	—		d				04 52	05 15				05 42	05 55	06 35	06 15		06 30		06 35			06 43
65½	—	St Denys	d			00 04	04 57					05 47		⟶					06 40			06 48
67	—	Swaythling	d			00 07	05 00					05 50							06 43			06 51
67¾	—	**Southampton Airport Pkwy** ✈	d			00 10	05 03	05 22				05 53	06 03		06 22		06 38		06 46		06 50	06 54
—	0	**Portsmouth Harbour** ⛴	d						05 00									05 43				
—	0¾	**Portsmouth & Southsea**	d						05 05									05 48				
—	1¾	Fratton	d						05 09									05 52				
—	4	Hilsea	d						05 13									05 56				
—	5½	Cosham	d						05 19									06 03				
—	8	Portchester	d						05 23									06 08				
—	11¼	Fareham	d						05 29									06 19				
—	16¾	Botley	d						05 37									06 27				
—	17¾	Hedge End	d		00 05				05 41									06 31				
69¼	22¼	Eastleigh 3	a		00 11	00 14	05 06		05 49			05 56	06 07					06 37	06 49		06 53	06 58
—	—		d		00 19		05 07		05 50				06 08					06 43	06 50		06 54	06 59
—	24¼	Chandlers Ford	d								06 06								06 55			
—	29½	**Romsey**	a								06 44								07 03			
73	—	Shawford	d				05 13		05 56									06 49				07 05
76¼	—	**Winchester**	d		00a28		05 19	05 31	06 02				06 18		06 31		06 48	06 55			07 05	07 11
84¾	—	Micheldever	d				05 27		06 10									07 04				
95	—	**Basingstoke**	a				05 38	05 46	06 20				06 34		06 46			07 14				07 27
—	—		d				05 39	05 47					06 35		06 47			07 17				07 36
—	—	Reading 7	a					06 04							07 04							
106¼	—	Fleet	d	00 01			05 50															07 52
109½	—	Farnborough (Main)	d	00 06			05 56															07 58
118½	—	**Woking**	a	00 18			06 05						06 53								07 38	08 08
138¾	—	**Clapham Junction 10**	a	00 53			06 25						07 14									
142¾	—	**London Waterloo 15** ⊖	a	01 04			06 34						07 24				07 47	08 01			08 08	08 39

Table 158R

Mondays to Fridays

9 December to 16 May

Weymouth, Bournemouth, Lymington, Romsey, Southampton and Basingstoke - London

Network Diagram - see first Page of Table 158

		SW	SW	SW	SW	SW	XC	SW	SW	SW	SW	SW	SW	SW	XC	SW	SW	SW	GW	SW	XC	SW	SW
		◇1	◇1	1	1	1	◇1	1	1	◇1	◇1	1	1	1	◇1	1	◇1	◇1	◇	1	◇1	1	1
											A							A					
		🛒	🛒				🛒			🛒	🛒						🛒	🛒			🛒		
Weymouth	d										05 55							06 25	06 40				
Upwey	d										05 59							06 29	06 45				
Dorchester West	a																		06 52				
Dorchester South	d										06 07							06 37					
Moreton (Dorset)	d										06 14							06 44					
Wool	d										06 20							06 50					
Wareham	d										06 27							06 57					
Holton Heath	d										06 31												
Hamworthy	d										06 36							07 04					
Poole 4	a										06 40							07 08					
	d		06 11								06 41							07 11					
Parkstone (Dorset)	d		06 15								06 45							07 15					
Branksome	d		06 18								06 49							07 19					
Bournemouth	a		06 23								06 54							07 24					
	d	06 04	06 25				06 30			06 34	06 56						07 04	07 26			07 30		
Pokesdown	d	06 08								06 38							07 08						
Christchurch	d	06 12								06 42							07 12						
Hinton Admiral	d	06 17								06 47							07 17						
New Milton	d	06 21								06 51							07 21						
Sway	d	06 26								06 56							07 26						
Lymington Pier	d								06 44						07 14							07 44	
Lymington Town	d								06 46						07 16							07 46	
Brockenhurst 3	a	06 31					06 46		06 55	07 01					07 25		07 31				07 46	07 55	
	d	06 33					06 49			07 03							07 33				07 49		
Beaulieu Road	d																						
Ashurst New Forest	d	06 41								07 11							07 41						
Totton	d	06 46								07 16							07 46						
Salisbury	d												06 50										
Dean	d												07 02										
Mottisfont & Dunbridge	d												07 08										
Romsey	d				07 07								07 13										08 07
Redbridge	d												07 23										
Millbrook (Hants)	d												07 26										
Southampton Central	a	06 51	06 55				07 01			07 21	07 25		07 30				07 51	07 55			08 03		
	d	07 00				07 10	07 15			07 30			07 35			07 38	08 00				08 15		
St Denys	d												07 40			07 43							
Swaythling	d												07 43			07 46							
Southampton Airport Pkwy	d	07 08				07 18	07 22			07 38			07 46			07 49	08 08				08 22		
Portsmouth Harbour	d			06 23								06 50								07 24			
Portsmouth & Southsea	d			06 28								06 55								07 29			
Fratton	d			06 32								06 59								07 33			
Hilsea	d			06 36								07 03								07 37			
Cosham	d			06 42								07 08								07 43			
Portchester	d			06 46								07 13								07 48			
Fareham	d			06 53								07 20								07 54			
Botley	d			07 01								07 28								08 01			
Hedge End	d			07 05								07 32								08 06			
Eastleigh 3	a			07 11	07 20	07 21						07 38	07 49			07 53				08 12			08 20
	d			07 13	07 21	07 30						07 43	07 50			07 54				08 13			08 21
Chandlers Ford	d												07 55										
Romsey	a				07 51								08 03										08 51
Shawford	d					07 36		←				07 49				08 00				08 20			
Winchester	d	07 18		07 22		07 42	07 31	07 42		07 48		07 55			08 01	08 06	08 18			08 26	08 31		
Micheldever	d			07 31		→						08 03											
Basingstoke	a			07 41			07 46	07 58				08 14			08 16	08 22	08 34			08 42	08 46		
	d			07 47			07 47	08 05				08 16			08 18	08 24	08 35			08 43	08 47		
Reading 7	a						08 03								08 36						09 03		
Fleet	d							08 22								08 40				08 54			
Farnborough (Main)	d							08 28								08 46				09 00			
Woking	a			08 05				08 38				08 34				08 58	08 53						
Clapham Junction 10	a																09 14			09 26			
London Waterloo 15 ⊖	a	08 16		08 34				09 10		08 50		09 03				09 29	09 25			09 38			

A 🛒 from Bournemouth

Table 158R

Mondays to Fridays

9 December to 16 May

Weymouth, Bournemouth, Lymington, Romsey, Southampton and Basingstoke - London

Network Diagram - see first Page of Table 158

		SW	SW	SW	SW	SW	SW	SW	SW	SW	SW	SW	SW	XC	SW	SW	SW	SW	SW	XC	SW	SW	SW
														R									
		1	1	◇1	1	1		1	1	◇1	1	1	1	1	◇1	1	1	1	1	◇1	1	◇1	1
				A											A							A	
		🛒		🛒				🛒		🛒	🛒			🛒	🛒					🛒		🛒	
Weymouth	d			06 55								07 25			07 55							08 20	
Upwey	d			06 59								07 29			07 59							08 24	
Dorchester West	a																						
Dorchester South	d			07 07								07 37			08 07							08 33	
Moreton (Dorset)	d			07 14								07 44			08 14							08 39	
Wool	d			07 20								07 50			08 20							08 45	
Wareham	d			07 27								07 57			08 27							08 53	
Holton Heath	d			07 31								08 01			08 31							08 56	
Hamworthy	d			07 36								08 06			08 36							09 01	
Poole 4	a			07 40								08 10			08 40							09 06	
	d	07 20		07 41						07 55		08 11			08 41						08 50	09 07	
Parkstone (Dorset)	d	07 24		07 45						07 59		08 15			08 45						08 54		
Branksome	d	07 27		07 49						08 02		08 19			08 49						08 57		
Bournemouth	a	07 32		07 54						08 07		08 24			08 54						09 02	09 16	
	d	07 34		07 59						08 10		08 25		08 45	08 59						09 05	09 18	
Pokesdown	d	07 38								08 14		08 29									09 09	09 22	
Christchurch	d	07 42								08 18		08 33									09 13	09 26	
Hinton Admiral	d	07 47								08 24		08 38									09 18		
New Milton	d	07 51								08 29		08 42									09 22	09 33	
Sway	d	07 56								08 34		08 47									09 27		
Lymington Pier	d								08 14				08 44						09 14				
Lymington Town	d								08 16				08 46						09 16				
Brockenhurst 3	a	08 01		08 14					08 25	08 39		08 52	08 55	08 58	09 14				09 25		09 32	09 40	
	d	08 03		08 15						08 41				09 00	09 15						09 33	09 41	
Beaulieu Road	d	08 08																					
Ashurst New Forest	d	08 12								08 48											09 40		
Totton	d	08 17								08 53											09 45		
Salisbury	d		07 50															08 50					
Dean	d		08 02															09 02					
Mottisfont & Dunbridge	d		08 08															09 08					
Romsey	d		08 13													09 07		09 14					
Redbridge	d		08 21															09 21					
Millbrook (Hants)	d		08 25			←		←										09 25					
Southampton Central ⛴	a	08 23	08 27	08 28		08 27		08 23		08 58				09 12	09 28			09 28			09 52	09 55	
	d	08 48	08 35	08 30		08 35		08 48		09 00				09 15	09 30			09 35		09 46	09 55	10 00	
St Denys	d	↪	↪			08 40		08 53										09 40					
Swaythling	d					08 43		08 56										09 43					
Southampton Airport Pkwy ✈	d			08 38		08 46		08 59		09 08				09 22	09 38			09 46		09 55	10 03	10 08	
Portsmouth Harbour ⛴	d				07 55		08 05										08 59						
Portsmouth & Southsea	d				08 00		08 10										09 04						
Fratton	d				08 04		08 13										09 08						
Hilsea	d				08 08		08 17										09 12						
Cosham	d				08 13		08 22										09 17						
Portchester	d				08 18		08 27										09 22						
Fareham	d				08 24		08 33										09 28						
Botley	d				08 31		08 41										09 35						
Hedge End	d				08 36		08 45										09 40						
Eastleigh 3	a				08 42	08 49	08 51	09 03								09 20	09 46	09 49			10 06		
	d				08 43	08 50	08 54	09 14								09 21	09 47	09 50			10 14		
Chandlers Ford	d					08 55												09 55					
Romsey	a					09 03										09 51		10 03					
Shawford	d				08 49			09 19			←										10 19		←
Winchester	d			08 48	08 56		09 03	09 25		09 18	09 25			09 31	09 48		09 56			10 03	10 25	10 18	10 25
Micheldever	d				09 04			↪									10 05				↪		
Basingstoke	a				09 15		09 19			09 35	09 41			09 46			10 15			10 18		10 34	10 41
	d				09 17					09 36	09 43			09 47			10 17			10 19		10 35	10 43
Reading 7	a													10 03						10 34			
Fleet	d										09 54												10 54
Farnborough (Main)	d				09 30						10 00						10 30						11 00
Woking	a			09 22	09 39					09 54					10 20		10 39						
Clapham Junction 10	a			09 43						10 15	10 25											11 12	11 25
London Waterloo 15 ⊖	a			09 53	10 08					10 23	10 34				10 49		11 08					11 20	11 34

A 🛒 from Bournemouth

Table 158R

Mondays to Fridays

9 December to 16 May

Weymouth, Bournemouth, Lymington, Romsey, Southampton and Basingstoke - London

Network Diagram - see first Page of Table 158

		GW	SW	SW	XC	SW	SW	SW	SW	SW		SW	SW	SW	XC	SW	SW	SW	SW	SW		XC	SW	SW
		◇	1	1	◇1	◇1	1	1	1	1		1	◇1	1	◇1	1	◇1	1	1	1		■ 1	1	1
						A							A				A							
					⌶	⌶							⌶		⌶		⌶					⌶		
Weymouth	d	08 53				09 03							09 20				10 03							
Upwey	d	08 58											09 24											
Dorchester West	a	09 05																						
Dorchester South	d					09 13							09 33				10 13							
Moreton (Dorset)	d												09 39											
Wool	d												09 45											
Wareham	d					09 28							09 53				10 28							
Holton Heath	d												09 56											
Hamworthy	d					09 35							10 01				10 35							
Poole 4	a					09 39							10 06				10 39							
	d		09 13			09 40				09 50			10 07				10 40						10 50	
Parkstone (Dorset)	d		09 17			09 44				09 54							10 44						10 54	
Branksome	d		09 20			09 48				09 57							10 48						10 57	
Bournemouth	a		09 25			09 53				10 02			10 17				10 54						11 02	
	d		09 27		09 45	09 55				10 05			10 22		10 45		10 59						11 05	
Pokesdown	d		09 30							10 09			10 26										11 09	
Christchurch	d		09 34							10 13			10 30										11 13	
Hinton Admiral	d		09 39							10 18													11 18	
New Milton	d		09 44							10 22			10 37										11 22	
Sway	d		09 48							10 27													11 27	
Lymington Pier	d			09 44								10 27				10 57								11 27
Lymington Town	d			09 46								10 29				10 59								11 29
Brockenhurst 3	a		09 53	09 55	09 59	10 10				10 32		10 38	10 44		10 58	11 08	11 14						11 32	11 38
	d		09 54		10 00	10 11				10 33			10 45		11 00		11 15						11 33	
Beaulieu Road	d																						11 38	
Ashurst New Forest	d									10 40													11 42	
Totton	d									10 45													11 47	
Salisbury	d								09 56											10 56				
Dean	d								10 08											11 08				
Mottisfont & Dunbridge	d								10 14											11 14				
Romsey	d						10 07		10 20									11 07		11 20				
Redbridge	d								10 27											11 27				
Millbrook (Hants)	d								10 31											11 31				
Southampton Central ⛴	a		10 09		10 12	10 26			10 34	10 53			10 58		11 12		11 28			11 34			11 53	
	d				10 15	10 30			10 35	10 55			11 00		11 15		11 30			11 35		11 46	11 55	
St Denys	d								10 40											11 40				
Swaythling	d								10 43											11 43				
Southampton Airport Pkwy ✈	d				10 22	10 38			10 46	11 03			11 08		11 22		11 38			11 46		11 53	12 03	
Portsmouth Harbour ⛴	d							09 59											10 59					
Portsmouth & Southsea	d							10 04											11 04					
Fratton	d							10 08											11 08					
Hilsea	d							10 12											11 12					
Cosham	d							10 17											11 17					
Portchester	d							10 22											11 22					
Fareham	d							10 28											11 28					
Botley	d							10 35											11 35					
Hedge End	d							10 40											11 40					
Eastleigh 3	a						10 20	10 46	10 49	11 06								11 20	11 46	11 49			12 06	
	d						10 21	10 47	10 50	11 14								11 21	11 47	11 50			12 14	
Chandlers Ford	d								10 55											11 55				
Romsey	a						10 59		11 03									11 51		12 03				
Shawford	d									11 19				←									12 19	
Winchester	d				10 31	10 48		10 56		11 25			11 18	11 25	11 31		11 48		11 56			12 02	12 25	
Micheldever	d							11 05		↦									12 05				↦	
Basingstoke	a				10 46			11 15					11 34	11 41	11 46				12 15			12 17		
	d				10 47			11 17					11 35	11 43	11 47				12 17			12 18		
Reading 7	a				11 03										12 03							12 33		
Fleet	d													11 54										
Farnborough (Main)	d							11 30						12 00					12 30					
Woking	a					11 19		11 39									12 19		12 39					
Clapham Junction 10	a												12 12	12 25										
London Waterloo 15 ⊖	a					11 49		12 08					12 20	12 34			12 49		13 07					

A ⌶ from Bournemouth

Table 158R

Mondays to Fridays

9 December to 16 May

Weymouth, Bournemouth, Lymington, Romsey, Southampton and Basingstoke - London

Network Diagram - see first Page of Table 158

		SW	SW	XC	SW	SW	GW	SW	SW	SW	SW	SW	SW	SW	XC	SW	SW	SW	SW	SW	XC	SW	SW
		◇1	1	◇1	1	◇1	◇	1	1	1	1	1	◇1	1	◇1	1	◇1	1	1	1	◇1	1	1
		A				A							A				A						
		🛒		🛒		🛒							🛒		🛒		🛒				🛒		
Weymouth	d	10 20				11 03	11 10						11 20				12 03						
Upwey	d	10 24					11 15						11 24										
Dorchester West	a						11 22																
Dorchester South	d	10 33				11 13							11 33				12 13						
Moreton (Dorset)	d	10 39											11 39										
Wool	d	10 45											11 45										
Wareham	d	10 53				11 28							11 53				12 28						
Holton Heath	d	10 56											11 56										
Hamworthy	d	11 01				11 35							12 01				12 35						
Poole 4	a	11 06				11 39							12 06				12 39						
	d	11 07				11 40					11 50		12 07				12 40					12 50	
Parkstone (Dorset)	d					11 44					11 54						12 44					12 54	
Branksome	d					11 48					11 57						12 48					12 57	
Bournemouth	a	11 17				11 54					12 02		12 17				12 54					13 02	
	d	11 22		11 45		11 59					12 05		12 22		12 45		12 59					13 05	
Pokesdown	d	11 26									12 09		12 26									13 09	
Christchurch	d	11 30									12 13		12 30									13 13	
Hinton Admiral	d										12 18											13 18	
New Milton	d	11 37									12 22		12 37									13 22	
Sway	d										12 27											13 27	
Lymington Pier	d				11 57							12 27				12 57							13 27
Lymington Town	d				11 59							12 29				12 59							13 29
Brockenhurst 3	a	11 44		11 58	12 08	12 14					12 32	12 38	12 44		12 58	13 08	13 14					13 32	13 38
	d	11 45		12 00		12 15					12 33		12 45		13 00		13 15					13 33	
Beaulieu Road	d																						
Ashurst New Forest	d										12 40											13 40	
Totton	d										12 45											13 45	
Salisbury	d									11 56										12 56			
Dean	d									12 08										13 08			
Mottisfont & Dunbridge	d									12 14										13 14			
Romsey	d							12 07		12 20								13 07		13 20			
Redbridge	d									12 27										13 27			
Millbrook (Hants)	d									12 31										13 31			
Southampton Central ⛴	a	11 58		12 12		12 28				12 34	12 52		12 58		13 12		13 28			13 34		13 53	
	d	12 00		12 15		12 30				12 35	12 55		13 00		13 15		13 30			13 35	13 46	13 55	
St Denys	d									12 40										13 40			
Swaythling	d									12 43										13 43			
Southampton Airport Pkwy ✈	d	12 08		12 22		12 38				12 46	13 03		13 08		13 22		13 38			13 46	13 53	14 03	
Portsmouth Harbour ⛴	d								11 59										12 59				
Portsmouth & Southsea	d								12 04										13 04				
Fratton	d								12 08										13 08				
Hilsea	d								12 12										13 12				
Cosham	d								12 17										13 17				
Portchester	d								12 22										13 22				
Fareham	d								12 28										13 28				
Botley	d								12 35										13 35				
Hedge End	d								12 40										13 40				
Eastleigh 3	a							12 20	12 46	12 49	13 06							13 20	13 46	13 49		14 06	
	d							12 21	12 47	12 50	13 14							13 21	13 47	13 50		14 14	
Chandlers Ford	d									12 55										13 55			
Romsey	a							12 51		13 03								13 51		14 03			
Shawford	d		←								13 19			←								14 19	
Winchester	d	12 18	12 25	12 31		12 48			12 56		13 25		13 18	13 25	13 31		13 48		13 56		14 03	14 25	
Micheldever	d								13 05		→								14 05			→	
Basingstoke	a	12 34	12 41	12 46					13 15				13 34	13 41	13 46				14 15		14 18		
	d	12 35	12 43	12 47					13 17				13 35	13 43	13 47				14 17		14 19		
Reading 7	a			13 03											14 03						14 34		
Fleet	d		12 54											13 54									
Farnborough (Main)	d		13 00						13 30					14 00					14 30				
Woking	a					13 19			13 39								14 19		14 39				
Clapham Junction 10	a	13 12	13 25										14 12	14 25									
London Waterloo 15 ⊖	a	13 20	13 34			13 49			14 07				14 20	14 34			14 49		15 08				

A 🛒 from Bournemouth

Table 158R

Mondays to Fridays

9 December to 16 May

Weymouth, Bournemouth, Lymington, Romsey, Southampton and Basingstoke - London

Network Diagram - see first Page of Table 158

		SW	SW		XC	SW	SW	SN	SW	GW	SW	SW	SW		SW	SW	SW	XC	SW	SW	SW	SW	SW		XC
		◇1	1		◇1	1	1	1	◇1	◇	1	1	1		1	◇1	1	◇1	1	◇1	1	1	1		◇1
		A							A							A				A					
		⊥			⊥				⊥							⊥		⊥		⊥					⊥
Weymouth	d	12 20							13 03	13 10						13 20				14 03					
Upwey	d	12 24								13 15						13 24									
Dorchester West	a									13 22															
Dorchester South	d	12 33							13 13							13 33				14 13					
Moreton (Dorset)	d	12 39														13 39									
Wool	d	12 45														13 45									
Wareham	d	12 53							13 28							13 53				14 28					
Holton Heath	d	12 56														13 56									
Hamworthy	d	13 01							13 35							14 01				14 35					
Poole 4	a	13 06							13 39							14 06				14 39					
	d	13 07							13 40				13 50			14 07				14 40					
Parkstone (Dorset)	d								13 44				13 54							14 44					
Branksome	d								13 48				13 57							14 48					
Bournemouth	a	13 17							13 54				14 02			14 17				14 54					
	d	13 22			13 45				13 59				14 05			14 22		14 45		14 59					
Pokesdown	d	13 26											14 09			14 26									
Christchurch	d	13 30											14 13			14 30									
Hinton Admiral	d												14 18												
New Milton	d	13 37											14 22			14 37									
Sway	d												14 27												
Lymington Pier	d					13 57									14 27				14 57						
Lymington Town	d					13 59									14 29				14 59						
Brockenhurst 3	a	13 44			13 58	14 08			14 14				14 32		14 38	14 44		14 58	15 08	15 14					
	d	13 45			14 00				14 15				14 33			14 45		15 00		15 15					
Beaulieu Road	d																								
Ashurst New Forest	d												14 40												
Totton	d												14 45												
Salisbury	d											13 50											14 56		
Dean	d											14 02											15 08		
Mottisfont & Dunbridge	d											14 08											15 14		
Romsey	d						14 07					14 13									15 07		15 20		
Redbridge	d											14 21											15 27		
Millbrook (Hants)	d											14 24											15 31		
Southampton Central ⛴	a	13 58			14 12				14 28			14 28	14 53			14 58		15 12		15 28			15 34		
	d	14 00			14 15			14 26	14 30			14 35	14 55			15 00		15 15		15 30			15 35		15 46
St Denys	d											14 40											15 40		
Swaythling	d											14 43											15 43		
Southampton Airport Pkwy ✈	d	14 08			14 22			14 34	14 38			14 46	15 03			15 08		15 22		15 38			15 46		15 53
Portsmouth Harbour ⛴	d										13 59											14 59			
Portsmouth & Southsea	d										14 04											15 04			
Fratton	d										14 08											15 08			
Hilsea	d										14 12											15 12			
Cosham	d										14 17											15 17			
Portchester	d										14 22											15 22			
Fareham	d										14 28											15 28			
Botley	d										14 35											15 35			
Hedge End	d										14 40											15 40			
Eastleigh 3	a						14 20	14 37			14 46	14 49	15 06								15 20	15 46	15 49		
	d						14 21				14 47	14 50	15 14								15 21	15 47	15 50		
Chandlers Ford	d											14 55											15 55		
Romsey	a						14 51					15 03									15 51		16 03		
Shawford	d		←										15 19				←								
Winchester	d	14 18	14 25		14 31				14 48		14 56		15 25			15 18	15 25	15 31		15 48		15 56			16 02
Micheldever	d										15 05		→									16 05			
Basingstoke	a	14 34	14 41		14 46						15 15					15 34	15 41	15 46				16 15			16 17
	d	14 35	14 43		14 47						15 17					15 35	15 43	15 47				16 17			16 18
Reading 7	a				15 03													16 03							16 33
Fleet	d		14 54														15 54								
Farnborough (Main)	d		15 00								15 30						16 00					16 30			
Woking	a								15 19		15 39									16 19		16 39			
Clapham Junction 10	a	15 12	15 25													16 12	16 25								
London Waterloo 15 ⊖	a	15 20	15 34						15 49		16 07					16 20	16 34			16 49		17 08			

A ⊥ from Bournemouth

Table 158R

Mondays to Fridays

9 December to 16 May

Weymouth, Bournemouth, Lymington, Romsey, Southampton and Basingstoke - London

Network Diagram - see first Page of Table 158

		SW 1	SW 1	SW ◇1 A ⚯	SW 1	XC ◇1 ⚯	SW 1	SW ◇1 A ⚯	GW ◇	SW 1	SW 1	SW 1	SW 1	SW 1	SW ◇1 A ⚯	SW 1	XC ◇1 ⚯	SW 1	SW ◇1 A ⚯	SW 1	SW	SW 1	SW 1
Weymouth	d			14 20				15 03	15 08						15 20				16 03				
Upwey	d			14 24					15 13						15 24								
Dorchester West	a								15 20														
Dorchester South	d			14 33				15 13							15 33				16 13				
Moreton (Dorset)	d			14 39											15 39								
Wool	d			14 45											15 45								
Wareham	d			14 53				15 28							15 53				16 28				
Holton Heath	d			14 56											15 56								
Hamworthy	d			15 01				15 35							16 01				16 35				
Poole 4	a			15 06				15 39							16 06				16 39				
	d	14 50		15 07				15 40					15 50		16 07				16 40				
Parkstone (Dorset)	d	14 54						15 44					15 54						16 44				
Branksome	d	14 57						15 48					15 57						16 48				
Bournemouth	a	15 02		15 17				15 54					16 02		16 17				16 54				
	d	15 05		15 22		15 45		15 59					16 05		16 22		16 45		16 59				
Pokesdown	d	15 09		15 26									16 09		16 26								
Christchurch	d	15 13		15 30									16 13		16 30								
Hinton Admiral	d	15 18											16 18										
New Milton	d	15 22		15 37									16 22		16 37								
Sway	d	15 27											16 27										
Lymington Pier	d		15 27				15 57							16 27				16 57					
Lymington Town	d		15 29				15 59							16 29				16 59					
Brockenhurst 3	a	15 32	15 38	15 44		15 58	16 08	16 14					16 32	16 38	16 44		16 58	17 08	17 14				
	d	15 33		15 45		16 00		16 15					16 33		16 45		17 00		17 15				
Beaulieu Road	d																						
Ashurst New Forest	d	15 40											16 40										
Totton	d	15 45											16 45										
Salisbury	d											15 56											16 56
Dean	d											16 08											17 08
Mottisfont & Dunbridge	d											16 14											17 14
Romsey	d									16 07		16 20								17 07			17 20
Redbridge	d											16 27											17 27
Millbrook (Hants)	d											16 31											17 31
Southampton Central ⛴	a	15 51		15 58		16 12		16 28				16 34	16 51		16 58		17 12		17 28				17 34
	d	15 55		16 00		16 15		16 30				16 35	16 52		17 00		17 15		17 30				17 35
St Denys	d											16 40	16 57										17 40
Swaythling	d											16 43	17 00										17 43
Southampton Airport Pkwy ✈	d	16 03		16 08		16 22		16 38				16 46	17 04		17 08		17 22		17 38				17 46
Portsmouth Harbour ⛴	d										15 59										16 49	16 59	
Portsmouth & Southsea	d										16 04										16 55	17 04	
Fratton	d										16 08										16 58	17 08	
Hilsea	d										16 12										17 02	17 12	
Cosham	d										16 17										17 07	17 17	
Portchester	d										16 22										17 11	17 22	
Fareham	d										16 28										17 18	17 28	
Botley	d										16 35										17 25	17 35	
Hedge End	d										16 40										17 29	17 40	
Eastleigh 3	a	16 07								16 20	16 46	16 49	17 07							17 20	17 35	17 46	17 49
	d	16 14								16 21	16 47	16 50	17 14							17 21		17 47	17 50
Chandlers Ford	d											16 55											17 55
Romsey	a									16 51		17 03								17 51			18 03
Shawford	d	16 19			←								17 19			←							
Winchester	d	16 25		16 18	16 25	16 31		16 48			16 56		17 25		17 18	17 25	17 31		17 48			17 56	
Micheldever	d	↪									17 05		↪									18 05	
Basingstoke	a			16 34	16 41	16 46					17 15				17 34	17 42	17 46					18 15	
	d			16 35	16 43	16 47					17 17				17 36	17 43	17 47					18 17	
Reading 7	a					17 03											18 03						
Fleet	d				16 54											17 54							
Farnborough (Main)	d				17 00						17 30					18 00						18 30	
Woking	a							17 20			17 39								18 19			18 39	
Clapham Junction 10	a			17 12	17 25										18 12	18 25							
London Waterloo 15 ⊖	a			17 20	17 36			17 50			18 08				18 23	18 34			18 47			19 08	

A ⚯ from Bournemouth

Table 158R

Mondays to Fridays

9 December to 16 May

Weymouth, Bournemouth, Lymington, Romsey, Southampton and Basingstoke - London

Network Diagram - see first Page of Table 158

		SW	XC	SW	SW	SW	SW	XC	SW	SW	SW	SW	SW	SW	SW	SW	SW	SW	GW	XC	SW	SW	SW
		■1	◇■1	■1	■1	◇■1	■1	◇■1	■1	■1		◇■1	■1	■1	■1	■1	◇■1	■1	◇	◇■1	◇■1	■1	■1
						A						A					A				A		
			⚲			⚲		⚲				⚲					⚲			⚲	⚲		
Weymouth	d					16 20						17 03					17 20		17 30		18 03		
Upwey	d					16 24											17 24		17 35				
Dorchester West	a																		17 42				
Dorchester South	d					16 33						17 13					17 33				18 13		
Moreton (Dorset)	d					16 39											17 39						
Wool	d					16 45											17 45						
Wareham	d					16 53						17 28					17 53				18 28		
Holton Heath	d					16 56											17 56						
Hamworthy	d					17 01						17 35					18 01				18 35		
Poole ■4	a					17 06						17 39					18 06				18 39		
	d			16 50		17 07						17 40			17 50		18 07				18 40		
Parkstone (Dorset)	d			16 54								17 44			17 54						18 44		
Branksome	d			16 57								17 48			17 57						18 48		
Bournemouth	a			17 02		17 17						17 54			18 02		18 17				18 54		
	d			17 05		17 22		17 45				17 59			18 05		18 22			18 45	18 59		
Pokesdown	d			17 09		17 26									18 09		18 26						
Christchurch	d			17 13		17 30									18 13		18 30						
Hinton Admiral	d			17 18											18 18								
New Milton	d			17 22		17 37									18 22		18 37						
Sway	d			17 27											18 27								
Lymington Pier	d				17 27				17 57							18 27						19 03	
Lymington Town	d				17 29				17 59							18 29						19 05	
Brockenhurst ■3	a			17 32	17 38	17 44		17 58	18 08			18 14			18 32	18 38	18 44			18 58	19 14	19 14	
	d	17 20		17 33		17 45		18 00				18 15			18 33		18 45			19 00	19 15		
Beaulieu Road	d														18 38								
Ashurst New Forest	d	17 27		17 40											18 42								
Totton	d	17 32		17 45											18 47								
Salisbury	d													17 56									
Dean	d													18 08									
Mottisfont & Dunbridge	d													18 14									
Romsey	d									18 07				18 20									19 07
Redbridge	d													18 27									
Millbrook (Hants)	d													18 31									
Southampton Central ⛴	a	17 41		17 53		17 58		18 12				18 28		18 34	18 53		18 58			19 12	19 28		
	d		17 46	17 55		18 00		18 15			18 17	18 30		18 35	18 55		19 00			19 15	19 30		
St Denys	d										18 22			18 40									
Swaythling	d										18 25			18 43									
Southampton Airport Pkwy ✈	d		17 53	18 03		18 08		18 22			18 28	18 38		18 46	19 03		19 08			19 22	19 38		
Portsmouth Harbour ⛴	d												17 59										
Portsmouth & Southsea	d												18 04										
Fratton	d												18 08										
Hilsea	d												18 12										
Cosham	d												18 17										
Portchester	d												18 22										
Fareham	d												18 28										
Botley	d												18 35										
Hedge End	d												18 40										
Eastleigh ■3	a			18 06						18 20	18 32		18 46	18 49	19 06								19 20
	d			18 14						18 21	18 33		18 47	18 50	19 14								19 21
Chandlers Ford	d													18 55									
Romsey	a									19 00				19 04									19 51
Shawford	d			18 19			←								19 19			←					
Winchester	d		18 02	18 25		18 18	18 25	18 31			18a41	18 48	18 56		19 25		19 18	19 25		19 31	19 48		
Micheldever	d			→									19 05		→								
Basingstoke	a		18 17			18 34	18 41	18 46					19 15				19 34	19 41		19 46			
	d		18 18			18 35	18 43	18 47					19 17				19 35	19 43		19 47			
Reading ■7	a		18 33					19 03												20 03			
Fleet	d						18 54											19 54					
Farnborough (Main)	d						19 00						19 30					20 00					
Woking	a											19 25	19 39								20 19		
Clapham Junction ■10	a					19 12	19 26										20 12	20 25					
London Waterloo ■15 ⊖	a					19 20	19 34					19 52	20 08				20 20	20 34			20 49		

A ⚲ from Bournemouth

Table 158R

Mondays to Fridays

9 December to 16 May

Weymouth, Bournemouth, Lymington, Romsey, Southampton and Basingstoke - London

Network Diagram - see first Page of Table 158

		SW 1	SW 1	SW 1	SW ◇1 A ✠	SW 1	SW 1	XC ◇1	SW ◇1 A ✠	SW 1	SW 1	SW 1	SW 1	SW 1	SW ◇1	SW 1	SW 1	SW 1	SW 1	SW 1	SW 1	SW 1
Weymouth	d				18 20				19 03						19 20							
Upwey	d				18 24										19 24							
Dorchester West	a																					
Dorchester South	d				18 33				19 13						19 37							
Moreton (Dorset)	d				18 39										19 43							
Wool	d				18 45										19 49							
Wareham	d				18 53				19 28						19 57							
Holton Heath	d				18 56																	
Hamworthy	d				19 01				19 35						20 03							
Poole 4	a				19 06				19 39						20 08							
	d			18 50	19 07				19 40					19 50	20 09							
Parkstone (Dorset)	d			18 54					19 44					19 54								
Branksome	d			18 57					19 48					19 57								
Bournemouth	a			19 02	19 17				19 54					20 02	20 18							
	d			19 05	19 22			19 45	19 59					20 05	20 22							
Pokesdown	d			19 09	19 26									20 09	20 26							
Christchurch	d			19 13	19 30									20 13	20 30							
Hinton Admiral	d			19 18										20 18								
New Milton	d			19 22	19 37									20 22	20 37							
Sway	d			19 27										20 27								
Lymington Pier	d						19 33			20 03							20 33	21 03				
Lymington Town	d						19 35			20 05							20 35	21 05				
Brockenhurst 3	a			19 32	19 44		19 44	19 58	20 14	20 14				20 32	20 44		20 44	21 14				
	d			19 33	19 45			20 00	20 15					20 33	20 45							
Beaulieu Road	d																					
Ashurst New Forest	d			19 41										20 40								
Totton	d			19 46										20 45								
Salisbury	d		18 56										19 56									20 56
Dean	d		19 08										20 08									21 08
Mottisfont & Dunbridge	d		19 14										20 14									21 14
Romsey	d		19 20								20 07		20 20						21 07			21 20
Redbridge	d		19 27										20 27									21 27
Millbrook (Hants)	d		19 31										20 31									21 31
Southampton Central ⛴	a		19 34	19 52	19 58			20 12	20 28				20 34	20 51	20 58							21 34
	d		19 35	19 55	20 00			20 15	20 30				20 35	20 55	21 00					21 30		21 35
St Denys	d		19 40										20 40									21 40
Swaythling	d		19 43										20 43									21 43
Southampton Airport Pkwy ✈	d		19 46	20 03	20 08			20 22	20 38				20 46	21 03	21 08					21 38		21 46
Portsmouth Harbour ⛴	d	18 59										19 59									20 59	
Portsmouth & Southsea	d	19 04										20 04									21 04	
Fratton	d	19 08										20 08									21 08	
Hilsea	d	19 12										20 12									21 12	
Cosham	d	19 17										20 17									21 17	
Portchester	d	19 22										20 22									21 22	
Fareham	d	19 28										20 28									21 28	
Botley	d	19 35										20 35									21 35	
Hedge End	d	19 40										20 40									21 40	
Eastleigh 3	a	19 46	19 49	20 06							20 20	20 46	20 49	21 06					21 20		21 46	21 49
	d	19 47	19 50	20 14							20 21	20 47	20 50	21 14					21 21		21 47	21 50
Chandlers Ford	d		19 55										20 55									21 55
Romsey	a		20 03								20 51		21 03						21 51			22 03
Shawford	d			20 19		←						20 53		21 19		←						
Winchester	d	19 56		20 25	20 18	20 25		20 31	20 48			20 59		21 25	21 18	21 25				21 48	21 56	
Micheldever	d	20 05		↪								21 07		↪							22 05	
Basingstoke	a	20 15			20 34	20 41		20 46				21 21			21 34	21 42					22 15	
	d	20 17			20 36	20 43		20 47				21 24			21 35	21 43					22 24	
Reading 7	a							21 04														
Fleet	d					20 54						21 40				21 54					22 40	
Farnborough (Main)	d	20 30				21 00						21 46				22 00					22 46	
Woking	a	20 39				21 09			21 19			21 58				22 09				22 19	22 58	
Clapham Junction 10	a				21 16	21 29									22 14	22 29						
London Waterloo 15 ⊖	a	21 07			21 24	21 38			21 49			22 34			22 22	22 38				22 49	23 32	

A ✠ from Bournemouth

Table 158R

Mondays to Fridays

9 December to 16 May

Weymouth, Bournemouth, Lymington, Romsey, Southampton and Basingstoke - London

Network Diagram - see first Page of Table 158

		SW	SW	SW	GW	SW	SW	SW	SW	SW	SW	SW	SW	SW	SW WX	SW	SW	SW
		1	◇1	1		1	1	1	1	1	1	1	1	1	1	1	◇1	1
Weymouth	d		20 10		20 21							21 10					22 10	23 10
Upwey	d		20 14		20 26							21 14					22 14	23 14
Dorchester West	a				20 33													
Dorchester South	d		20 22									21 22					22 22	23 22
Moreton (Dorset)	d		20 28									21 28					22 28	23 28
Wool	d		20 34									21 34					22 34	23 34
Wareham	d		20 42									21 42					22 42	23 42
Holton Heath	d																	
Hamworthy	d		20 48									21 48					22 48	23 48
Poole 4	a		20 53									21 53					22 53	23 53
	d		20 54									21 54					22 54	23 54
Parkstone (Dorset)	d		20 58									21 58					22 58	
Branksome	d		21 01									22 01					23 01	
Bournemouth	a		21 07									22 07					23 07	00 03
	d		21 12									22 12					23 12	
Pokesdown	d		21 16									22 16					23 16	
Christchurch	d		21 20									22 20					23 20	
Hinton Admiral	d		21 25									22 25					23 25	
New Milton	d		21 29									22 29					23 29	
Sway	d		21 34									22 34					23 34	
Lymington Pier	d					21 33	22 03						22 33					
Lymington Town	d					21 35	22 05						22 35					
Brockenhurst 3	a		21 39			21 44	22 14					22 39	22 44				23 39	
	d		21 40									22 40					23 40	
Beaulieu Road	d																	
Ashurst New Forest	d		21 47									22 47					23 47	
Totton	d		21 52									22 52					23 52	
Salisbury	d										21 56							
Dean	d										22 08							
Mottisfont & Dunbridge	d										22 14							
Romsey	d							22 07			22 20			23 07	22 58			
Redbridge	d										22 27				23 05			
Millbrook (Hants)	d										22 31				23 09			
Southampton Central ⛴	a		21 57								22 34	22 57			23 11		23 57	
	d	21 55	22 00						22 30		22 35	23 00			23 20		23 59	
St Denys	d										22 40				23 25		00 04	
Swaythling	d										22 43				23 28		00 07	
Southampton Airport Pkwy ✈	d	22 03	22 08						22 38		22 46	23 08			23 31		00 10	
Portsmouth Harbour ⛴	d									21 54						23 24		
Portsmouth & Southsea	d									21 59						23 29		
Fratton	d									22 03						23 33		
Hilsea	d									22 07						23 37		
Cosham	d									22 12						23 42		
Portchester	d									22 17						23 47		
Fareham	d									22 23						23 53		
Botley	d									22 30						23 59		
Hedge End	d									22 35						00 05		
Eastleigh 3	a	22 06						22 21	22 41	22 43	22 49	23 11		23 21	23 34	00 11	00 14	
	d	22 14						22 22	22 46		22 50	23 12		23 22	23 36	00 19		
Chandlers Ford	d										22 55				23 41			
Romsey	a							22 51			23 03			23 55	23 48			
Shawford	d	22 20		←								23 18						
Winchester	d	22 26	22 18	22 26					22 55			23 24				00a28		
Micheldever	d	↪										23 33						
Basingstoke	a		22 34	22 42					23 11			23 43						
	d		22 36	22 43					23 13			23 44						
Reading 7	a																	
Fleet	d			22 54								00 01						
Farnborough (Main)	d			23 00								00 06						
Woking	a		22 54	23 09					23 31			00 18						
Clapham Junction 10	a		23 14	23 29					23 55			00 53						
London Waterloo 15 ⊖	a		23 23	23 42					00 09			01 04						

Table 158R

Saturdays

14 December to 17 May

Weymouth, Bournemouth, Lymington, Romsey, Southampton and Basingstoke - London

Network Diagram - see first Page of Table 158

		SW	SW	SW	XC	SW	SW	SW	SW	SW	XC	SW	SW	SW	SW	SW	SW	XC	SW	XC	SW	SW	GW
		1	1	◇1	◇1	1	1	1	1	1	◇1	1	1	◇1	1	1	1	◇1	1	◇1	1	◇1	◇
																						A	
											[trolley]			[trolley]						[trolley]		[trolley]	
Weymouth	d																					05 42	06 38
Upwey	d																						06 43
Dorchester West	a																						06 50
Dorchester South	d																					05 52	
Moreton (Dorset)	d																						
Wool	d																					06 02	
Wareham	d																					06 10	
Holton Heath	d																					06 13	
Hamworthy	d																					06 18	
Poole 4	a																					06 23	
	d													05 28								06 24	
Parkstone (Dorset)	d													05 32								06 28	
Branksome	d													05 35								06 31	
Bournemouth	a													05 40								06 37	
	d													05 42				06 25		06 37		06 42	
Pokesdown	d													05 46								06 46	
Christchurch	d													05 50								06 50	
Hinton Admiral	d													05 55								06 55	
New Milton	d													05 59								06 59	
Sway	d													06 04								07 04	
Lymington Pier	d																06 27				06 57		
Lymington Town	d																06 29				06 59		
Brockenhurst 3	a													06 09			06 37	06 38		06 52	07 07	07 09	
	d													06 10				06 39		06 55		07 10	
Beaulieu Road	d																						
Ashurst New Forest	d													06 17								07 17	
Totton	d												06 14	06 22								07 22	
Salisbury	d								05 35														
Dean	d								05 47														
Mottisfont & Dunbridge	d								05 53														
Romsey	d								05 58														
Redbridge	d												06 16										
Millbrook (Hants)	d												06 20			←							
Southampton Central ⛴	a												06 22	06 27		06 22		06 52		07 07		07 27	
	d				05 09	05 12		05 30		06 00	06 15		06 35	06 30		06 35		06 53	07 00	07 15		07 30	
St Denys	d			00 04				05 35					→			06 40							
Swaythling	d			00 07				05 38								06 43							
Southampton Airport Pkwy ✈	d			00 10	05 16	05 20		05 41		06 08	06 22			06 38		06 46		07 01	07 08	07 22		07 38	
Portsmouth Harbour ⛴	d											05 48											
Portsmouth & Southsea	d											05 53											
Fratton	d											05 57											
Hilsea	d											06 01											
Cosham	d						05 09					06 06											
Portchester	d						05 14					06 11											
Fareham	d						05 20					06 17											
Botley	d						05 27					06 24											
Hedge End	d		00 05				05 32					06 29											
Eastleigh 3	a		00 11	00 14		05 23	05 38	05 45		06 11		06 37		06 41		06 49			07 11				
	d		00 19			05 24		05 46		06 13		06 47		06 42		06 50			07 14				
Chandlers Ford	d								06 06							06 55							
Romsey	a								06 43							07 03							
Shawford	d							05 52				06 53			←				07 19				
Winchester	d		00a28		05 25	05 34		06 00		06 23	06 31	07 00		06 52	07 00			07 09	07 25	07 31		07 48	
Micheldever	d							06 08				→			07 08								
Basingstoke	a				05 40	05 50		06 19		06 39	06 46			07 08	07 19			07 24	07 41	07 46			
	d				05 41	05 54		06 24		06 40	06 47			07 09	07 24			07 25	07 43	07 47			
Reading 7	a				05 58						07 04							07 42		08 03			
Fleet	d	00 01				06 10		06 40							07 40				07 54				
Farnborough (Main)	d	00 06				06 16		06 46							07 46				08 00				
Woking	a	00 18				06 28		06 58		06 58				07 27	07 58				08 09			08 21	
Clapham Junction 10	a	00 53				06 57				07 23									08 30				
London Waterloo 15 ⊖	a	01 04				07 05		07 33		07 31				07 53	08 34				08 39			08 49	

A [trolley] from Bournemouth

Table 158R

Saturdays

14 December to 17 May

Weymouth, Bournemouth, Lymington, Romsey, Southampton and Basingstoke - London

Network Diagram - see first Page of Table 158

		SW	SW	SW	XC	SW		SW	SW	SW	XC	SW	SW	SW	SW	SW		SW	SW	SW	SW	SW	XC	XC	SW
		1	1	1	◇1	1		1	◇1	1	◇1	1	1	1	◇1	1		1	1	1	◇1	1	◇1	◇1	1
															A						A		B	C	
Weymouth	d														06 55						07 20				
Upwey	d														06 59						07 24				
Dorchester West	a																								
Dorchester South	d														07 07						07 33				
Moreton (Dorset)	d														07 14						07 39				
Wool	d														07 20						07 45				
Wareham	d														07 27						07 53				
Holton Heath	d														07 31						07 56				
Hamworthy	d														07 36						08 01				
Poole 4	a														07 40						08 06				
	d					06 50			07 07						07 41				07 50		08 07				
Parkstone (Dorset)	d					06 54									07 45				07 54						
Branksome	d					06 57									07 49				07 57						
Bournemouth	a					07 02			07 17						07 54				08 02		08 17				
	d					07 05			07 22		07 45				07 59				08 05		08 22		08 45	08 45	
Pokesdown	d					07 09			07 26										08 09		08 26				
Christchurch	d					07 13			07 30										08 13		08 30				
Hinton Admiral	d					07 18													08 18						
New Milton	d					07 22			07 37										08 22		08 37				
Sway	d					07 27													08 27						
Lymington Pier	d							07 27				07 57								08 27					08 57
Lymington Town	d							07 29				07 59								08 29					08 59
Brockenhurst 3	a					07 32		07 37	07 44		07 58	08 07			08 14				08 32	08 37	08 44		08 58	08 58	09 07
	d					07 33			07 45		08 00				08 15				08 33		08 45		09 00	09 00	
Beaulieu Road	d																								
Ashurst New Forest	d					07 40													08 40						
Totton	d					07 45													08 45						
Salisbury	d			06 50										07 50											
Dean	d			07 02										08 02											
Mottisfont & Dunbridge	d			07 08										08 08											
Romsey	d	07 07		07 13									08 07	08 13											
Redbridge	d			07 21										08 21											
Millbrook (Hants)	d			07 24										08 24				←							
Southampton Central	a			07 27		07 52			07 58		08 12			08 27	08 28			08 27	08 52		08 58		09 12	09 12	
	d			07 35	07 47	07 55			08 00		08 15			08 35	08 30			08 35	08 55		09 00		09 15	09 15	
St Denys	d			07 40										→				08 40							
Swaythling	d			07 43														08 43							
Southampton Airport Pkwy	d			07 46	07 54	08 03			08 08		08 21				08 38			08 46	09 03		09 08		09 22	09 22	
Portsmouth Harbour	d		06 59													07 59									
Portsmouth & Southsea	d		07 04													08 04									
Fratton	d		07 08													08 08									
Hilsea	d		07 12													08 12									
Cosham	d		07 17													08 17									
Portchester	d		07 22													08 22									
Fareham	d		07 28													08 28									
Botley	d		07 35													08 35									
Hedge End	d		07 40													08 40									
Eastleigh 3	a	07 20	07 46	07 49		08 06							08 20			08 46		08 49	09 06						
	d	07 21	07 47	07 50		08 14							08 21			08 47		08 50	09 14						
Chandlers Ford	d			07 55														08 55							
Romsey	a	07 51		08 03									08 51					09 03							
Shawford	d					08 19				←									09 19			←			
Winchester	d		07 56		08 03	08 25			08 18	08 25	08 31				08 48	08 56			09 25		09 18	09 25	09 31	09 31	
Micheldever	d		08 05			→										09 05			→						
Basingstoke	a		08 15		08 17				08 34	08 41	08 46					09 15					09 34	09 41	09 46	09 46	
	d		08 17		08 19				08 35	08 43	08 47					09 17					09 35	09 43	09 47	09 47	
Reading 7	a				08 35						09 04												10 03	10 04	
Fleet	d									08 54												09 54			
Farnborough (Main)	d		08 30							09 00						09 30						10 00			
Woking	a		08 39												09 19	09 39									
Clapham Junction 10	a								09 12	09 25											10 12	10 25			
London Waterloo 15 ⊖	a		09 08						09 20	09 34					09 49	10 07					10 20	10 34			

A from Bournemouth B from 15 February C from 4 January until 8 February

Table 158R

Saturdays

14 December to 17 May

Weymouth, Bournemouth, Lymington, Romsey, Southampton and Basingstoke - London

Network Diagram - see first Page of Table 158

		SW	SW	SW	SW	XC	SW	SW	SW	SW	GW	XC	SW	SW	SW	SW	SW	SW	SW	SW	SW	XC
		◇1	1	1	1	◇1	1	1	◇1	1	◇	◇1	1	◇1	1	1	1	1	1	◇1	1	◇1
		A							A					A						A		B
		ꔃ				ꔃ			ꔃ			ꔃ		ꔃ						ꔃ		ꔃ
Weymouth	d	08 03							08 20		08 46			09 03						09 20		
Upwey	d								08 24		08 51									09 24		
Dorchester West	a										08 58											
Dorchester South	d	08 13							08 33					09 13						09 33		
Moreton (Dorset)	d								08 39											09 39		
Wool	d								08 45											09 45		
Wareham	d	08 28							08 53					09 28						09 53		
Holton Heath	d								08 56											09 56		
Hamworthy	d	08 35							09 01					09 35						10 01		
Poole 4	a	08 39							09 07					09 39						10 06		
	d	08 40					08 50		09 07					09 40				09 50		10 07		
Parkstone (Dorset)	d	08 44					08 54							09 44				09 54				
Branksome	d	08 48					08 57							09 48				09 57				
Bournemouth	a	08 54					09 02		09 17					09 54				10 02		10 17		
	d	08 59					09 05		09 22			09 45		09 59				10 05		10 22		10 45
Pokesdown	d						09 09		09 26									10 09		10 26		
Christchurch	d						09 13		09 30									10 13		10 30		
Hinton Admiral	d						09 18											10 18				
New Milton	d						09 22		09 37									10 22		10 37		
Sway	d						09 27											10 27				
Lymington Pier	d							09 27					09 57						10 27			
Lymington Town	d							09 29					09 59						10 29			
Brockenhurst 3	a	09 14					09 32	09 37	09 44			09 58	10 07	10 14				10 32	10 37	10 44		10 58
	d	09 15					09 33		09 45			10 00		10 15				10 33		10 45		11 00
Beaulieu Road	d						09 38															
Ashurst New Forest	d						09 42											10 40				
Totton	d						09 47											10 45				
Salisbury	d				08 56												09 56					
Dean	d				09 08												10 08					
Mottisfont & Dunbridge	d				09 14												10 14					
Romsey	d		09 07		09 20										10 07		10 20					
Redbridge	d				09 27												10 27					
Millbrook (Hants)	d				09 31												10 31					
Southampton Central ⛴	a	09 28			09 34		09 53		09 58			10 12		10 28			10 34	10 53		10 58		11 12
	d	09 30			09 35	09 47	09 55		10 00			10 15		10 30			10 35	10 55		11 00		11 15
St Denys	d				09 40												10 40					
Swaythling	d				09 43												10 43					
Southampton Airport Pkwy ✈	d	09 38			09 46	09 54	10 03		10 08			10 22		10 38			10 46	11 03		11 08		11 22
Portsmouth Harbour ⛴	d			08 59												09 59						
Portsmouth & Southsea	d			09 04												10 04						
Fratton	d			09 08												10 08						
Hilsea	d			09 12												10 12						
Cosham	d			09 17												10 17						
Portchester	d			09 22												10 22						
Fareham	d			09 28												10 28						
Botley	d			09 35												10 35						
Hedge End	d			09 40												10 40						
Eastleigh 3	a		09 20	09 46	09 49		10 06								10 20	10 46	10 49	11 06				
	d		09 21	09 47	09 50		10 14								10 21	10 47	10 50	11 14				
Chandlers Ford	d				09 55												10 55					
Romsey	a		09 51		10 03										10 59		11 03					
Shawford	d						10 19			←								11 19			←	
Winchester	d	09 48		09 56		10 03	10 25		10 18	10 25		10 31		10 48		10 56		11 25		11 18	11 25	11 31
Micheldever	d			10 05			→									11 05		→				
Basingstoke	a			10 15		10 17			10 34	10 41		10 46				11 15				11 34	11 41	11 46
	d			10 17		10 19			10 35	10 43		10 47				11 17				11 35	11 43	11 47
Reading 7	a					10 34						11 03										12 03
Fleet	d									10 54											11 54	
Farnborough (Main)	d			10 30						11 00						11 30					12 00	
Woking	a	10 19		10 39										11 19		11 39						
Clapham Junction 10	a								11 12	11 25										12 12	12 25	
London Waterloo 15 ⊖	a	10 49		11 07					11 20	11 34				11 49		12 07				12 21	12 34	

A ꔃ from Bournemouth

B from 15 February

Table 158R

Saturdays

14 December to 17 May

Weymouth, Bournemouth, Lymington, Romsey, Southampton and Basingstoke - London

Network Diagram - see first Page of Table 158

		XC	SW	SW	SW	SW	SW	XC		SW	SW	SW	SW	XC	SW	SW	GW	SW		SW	SW	SW	SW	SW	SW
		◇1	1	◇1	1	1	1	◇1		1	1	◇1	1	◇1	1	◇1	◇	1		1	1	1	1	◇1	1
		A		B								B				B								B	
		ꝏ		ꝏ				ꝏ				ꝏ		ꝏ		ꝏ								ꝏ	
Weymouth	d			10 03								10 20				11 03	11 10							11 20	
Upwey	d											10 24					11 15							11 24	
Dorchester West	a																11 23								
Dorchester South	d			10 13								10 33				11 13								11 33	
Moreton (Dorset)	d											10 39												11 39	
Wool	d											10 45												11 45	
Wareham	d			10 28								10 53				11 28								11 53	
Holton Heath	d											10 56												11 56	
Hamworthy	d			10 35								11 01				11 35								12 01	
Poole 4	a			10 39								11 06				11 39								12 06	
	d			10 40						10 50		11 07				11 40						11 50		12 07	
Parkstone (Dorset)	d			10 44						10 54						11 44						11 54			
Branksome	d			10 48						10 57						11 48						11 57			
Bournemouth	a			10 54						11 02		11 17				11 54						12 02		12 17	
	d	10 45		10 59						11 05		11 22		11 45		11 59						12 05		12 22	
Pokesdown	d									11 09		11 26										12 09		12 26	
Christchurch	d									11 13		11 30										12 13		12 30	
Hinton Admiral	d									11 18												12 18			
New Milton	d									11 22		11 37										12 22		12 37	
Sway	d									11 27												12 27			
Lymington Pier	d		10 57								11 27				11 57								12 27		
Lymington Town	d		10 59								11 29				11 59								12 29		
Brockenhurst 3	a	10 58	11 07	11 14						11 32	11 37	11 44		11 58	12 07	12 14						12 32	12 37	12 44	
	d	11 00		11 15						11 33		11 45		12 00		12 15						12 33		12 45	
Beaulieu Road	d									11 38															
Ashurst New Forest	d									11 42												12 40			
Totton	d									11 47												12 45			
Salisbury	d						10 56														11 56				
Dean	d						11 08														12 08				
Mottisfont & Dunbridge	d						11 14														12 14				
Romsey	d				11 07		11 20											12 07			12 20				
Redbridge	d						11 27														12 27				
Millbrook (Hants)	d						11 31														12 31				
Southampton Central ⛴	a	11 12		11 28			11 34			11 53		11 58		12 12		12 28					12 34	12 51		12 58	
	d	11 15		11 30			11 35	11 47		11 55		12 00		12 15		12 30					12 35	12 55		13 00	
St Denys	d						11 40														12 40				
Swaythling	d						11 43														12 43				
Southampton Airport Pkwy ✈	d	11 22		11 38			11 46	11 54		12 03		12 08		12 22		12 38					12 46	13 03		13 08	
Portsmouth Harbour ⛴	d					10 59														11 59					
Portsmouth & Southsea	d					11 04														12 04					
Fratton	d					11 08														12 08					
Hilsea	d					11 12														12 12					
Cosham	d					11 17														12 17					
Portchester	d					11 22														12 22					
Fareham	d					11 28														12 28					
Botley	d					11 35														12 35					
Hedge End	d					11 40														12 40					
Eastleigh 3	a				11 20	11 46	11 49			12 06								12 20		12 46	12 49	13 06			
	d				11 21	11 47	11 50			12 14								12 21		12 47	12 50	13 14			
Chandlers Ford	d						11 55														12 55				
Romsey	a				11 51		12 03											12 51			13 03				
Shawford	d									12 19			←									13 19			←
Winchester	d	11 31		11 48		11 56		12 03		12 25		12 18	12 25	12 31		12 48				12 56		13 25		13 18	13 25
Micheldever	d					12 05				→										13 05		→			
Basingstoke	a	11 46				12 15		12 17				12 34	12 41	12 46						13 15				13 34	13 41
	d	11 47				12 17		12 19				12 35	12 43	12 47						13 17				13 35	13 43
Reading 7	a	12 04						12 34						13 04											
Fleet	d												12 54												13 54
Farnborough (Main)	d					12 30							13 00							13 30					14 00
Woking	a			12 19		12 39										13 19				13 39					
Clapham Junction 10	a											13 12	13 25											14 12	14 25
London Waterloo 15 ⊖	a			12 51		13 07						13 21	13 34			13 51				14 07				14 21	14 34

A from 4 January until 8 February

B ꝏ from Bournemouth

Table 158R

Saturdays

14 December to 17 May

Weymouth, Bournemouth, Lymington, Romsey, Southampton and Basingstoke - London

Network Diagram - see first Page of Table 158

		XC	XC	SW	SW	SW	SW	SW	XC	SW	SW	SW	SW	XC	XC	SW	SW	SN	SW	GW	SW	SW
		◇1	◇1	1	◇1	1	1	1	◇1	1	1	◇1	1	◇1	◇1	1	1	1	◇1	◇	1	1
		A	B		C							C		B	A				C			
		(trolley)	(trolley)		(trolley)				(trolley)			(trolley)		(trolley)	(trolley)				(trolley)			
Weymouth	d				12 03							12 20							13 03	13 10		
Upwey	d											12 24								13 15		
Dorchester West	a																			13 22		
Dorchester South	d				12 13							12 33							13 13			
Moreton (Dorset)	d											12 39										
Wool	d											12 45										
Wareham	d				12 28							12 53							13 28			
Holton Heath	d											12 56										
Hamworthy	d				12 35							13 01							13 35			
Poole 4	a				12 39							13 06							13 39			
	d				12 40					12 50		13 07							13 40			
Parkstone (Dorset)	d				12 44					12 54									13 44			
Branksome	d				12 48					12 57									13 48			
Bournemouth	a				12 54					13 02		13 17							13 54			
	d	12 45	12 45		12 59					13 05		13 22		13 45	13 45				13 59			
Pokesdown	d									13 09		13 26										
Christchurch	d									13 13		13 30										
Hinton Admiral	d									13 18												
New Milton	d									13 22		13 37										
Sway	d									13 27												
Lymington Pier	d			12 57							13 27					13 57						
Lymington Town	d			12 59							13 29					13 59						
Brockenhurst 3	a	12 58	12 58	13 07	13 14					13 32	13 37	13 44		13 58	13 58	14 07			14 14			
	d	13 00	13 00		13 15					13 33		13 45		14 00	14 00				14 15			
Beaulieu Road	d									13 38												
Ashurst New Forest	d									13 42												
Totton	d									13 47												
Salisbury	d							12 56														13 50
Dean	d							13 08														14 02
Mottisfont & Dunbridge	d							13 14														14 08
Romsey	d					13 07		13 20									14 07					14 13
Redbridge	d							13 27														14 21
Millbrook (Hants)	d							13 31														14 24
Southampton Central ⛴	a	13 12	13 12		13 28			13 34		13 53		13 58		14 12	14 12				14 28			14 28
	d	13 15	13 15		13 30			13 35	13 47	13 55		14 00		14 15	14 15			14 26	14 30			14 35
St Denys	d							13 40														14 40
Swaythling	d							13 43														14 43
Southampton Airport Pkwy ✈	d	13 22	13 22		13 38			13 46	13 54	14 03		14 08		14 22	14 22			14 34	14 38			14 46
Portsmouth Harbour ⛴	d						12 59														13 59	
Portsmouth & Southsea	d						13 04														14 04	
Fratton	d						13 08														14 08	
Hilsea	d						13 12														14 12	
Cosham	d						13 17														14 17	
Portchester	d						13 22														14 22	
Fareham	d						13 28														14 28	
Botley	d						13 35														14 35	
Hedge End	d						13 40														14 40	
Eastleigh 3	a					13 20	13 46	13 49		14 06							14 20	14 37			14 46	14 49
	d					13 21	13 47	13 50		14 14							14 21				14 47	14 50
Chandlers Ford	d							13 55														14 55
Romsey	a					13 51		14 03									14 51					15 03
Shawford	d									14 19			←									
Winchester	d	13 31	13 31		13 48		13 56		14 03	14 25		14 18	14 25	14 31	14 31				14 48		14 56	
Micheldever	d						14 05			→											15 05	
Basingstoke	a	13 46	13 46				14 15		14 17			14 34	14 41	14 46	14 46						15 15	
	d	13 47	13 47				14 17		14 19			14 35	14 43	14 47	14 47						15 17	
Reading 7	a	14 03	14 04						14 34					15 03	15 04							
Fleet	d												14 54									
Farnborough (Main)	d						14 30						15 00								15 30	
Woking	a				14 19		14 39												15 19		15 39	
Clapham Junction 10	a											15 12	15 25									
London Waterloo 15 ⊖	a				14 51		15 07					15 21	15 34						15 51		16 07	

A from 4 January until 8 February

B from 15 February

C (trolley) from Bournemouth

Table 158R

Saturdays

14 December to 17 May

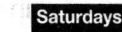

Weymouth, Bournemouth, Lymington, Romsey, Southampton and Basingstoke - London

Network Diagram - see first Page of Table 158

		SW	SW	SW	SW	XC	SW	SW	SW	SW	SW	XC	SW	SW	SW	SW	XC	SW	SW	GW	SW	SW	SW
		1	1	◇1	1	◇1	1	◇1	1	1	1	◇1	1	1	◇1	1	◇1	1	◇1	◇	1	1	1
				A				A							A				A				
				⚲		⚲		⚲				⚲			⚲		⚲		⚲				
Weymouth	d			13 20				14 03							14 20				15 03	15 08			
Upwey	d			13 24											14 24					15 13			
Dorchester West	a																			15 20			
Dorchester South	d			13 33				14 13							14 33				15 13				
Moreton (Dorset)	d			13 39											14 39								
Wool	d			13 45											14 45								
Wareham	d			13 53				14 28							14 53				15 28				
Holton Heath	d			13 56											14 56								
Hamworthy	d			14 01				14 35							15 01				15 35				
Poole 4	a			14 06				14 39							15 06				15 39				
	d	13 50		14 07				14 40					14 50		15 07				15 40				
Parkstone (Dorset)	d	13 54						14 44					14 54						15 44				
Branksome	d	13 57						14 48					14 57						15 48				
Bournemouth	a	14 02		14 17				14 54					15 02		15 17				15 54				
	d	14 05		14 22		14 45		14 59					15 05		15 22		15 45		15 59				
Pokesdown	d	14 09		14 26									15 09		15 26								
Christchurch	d	14 13		14 30									15 13		15 30								
Hinton Admiral	d	14 18											15 18										
New Milton	d	14 22		14 37									15 22		15 37								
Sway	d	14 27											15 27										
Lymington Pier	d		14 27				14 57							15 27				15 57					
Lymington Town	d		14 29				14 59							15 29				15 59					
Brockenhurst 3	a	14 32	14 37	14 44		14 58	15 07	15 14					15 32	15 37	15 44		15 58	16 07	16 14				
	d	14 33		14 45		15 00		15 15					15 33		15 45		16 00		16 15				
Beaulieu Road	d												15 38										
Ashurst New Forest	d	14 40											15 42										
Totton	d	14 45											15 47										
Salisbury	d										14 56												15 56
Dean	d										15 08												16 08
Mottisfont & Dunbridge	d										15 14												16 14
Romsey	d								15 07		15 20										16 07		16 20
Redbridge	d										15 27												16 27
Millbrook (Hants)	d										15 31												16 31
Southampton Central ⛴	a	14 51		14 58		15 12		15 28			15 34		15 53		15 58		16 12		16 28				16 34
	d	14 55		15 00		15 15		15 30			15 35	15 47	15 55		16 00		16 15		16 30				16 35
St Denys	d										15 40												16 40
Swaythling	d										15 43												16 43
Southampton Airport Pkwy ✈	d	15 03		15 08		15 22		15 38			15 46	15 54	16 03		16 08		16 22		16 38				16 46
Portsmouth Harbour ⛴	d									14 59												15 59	
Portsmouth & Southsea	d									15 04												16 04	
Fratton	d									15 08												16 08	
Hilsea	d									15 12												16 12	
Cosham	d									15 17												16 17	
Portchester	d									15 22												16 22	
Fareham	d									15 28												16 28	
Botley	d									15 35												16 35	
Hedge End	d									15 40												16 40	
Eastleigh 3	a	15 06							15 20	15 46	15 49		16 06								16 20	16 46	16 49
	d	15 14							15 21	15 47	15 50		16 14								16 21	16 47	16 50
Chandlers Ford	d										15 55												16 55
Romsey	a								15 51		16 03										16 51		17 03
Shawford	d	15 19			←								16 19			←							
Winchester	d	15 25		15 18	15 25	15 31		15 48		15 56		16 03	16 25		16 18	16 25	16 31		16 48			16 56	
Micheldever	d	→								16 05			→									17 05	
Basingstoke	a			15 34	15 41	15 46				16 15		16 17			16 34	16 41	16 46					17 15	
	d			15 35	15 43	15 47				16 17		16 18			16 35	16 43	16 47					17 17	
Reading 7	a					16 03						16 34					17 03						
Fleet	d				15 54											16 54							
Farnborough (Main)	d				16 00					16 30						17 00						17 30	
Woking	a							16 19		16 39									17 19			17 39	
Clapham Junction 10	a			16 12	16 25										17 12	17 25							
London Waterloo 15 ⊖	a			16 20	16 34			16 49		17 07					17 20	17 34			17 49			18 07	

A ⚲ from Bournemouth

Table 158R

Saturdays

14 December to 17 May

Weymouth, Bournemouth, Lymington, Romsey, Southampton and Basingstoke - London

Network Diagram - see first Page of Table 158

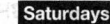

		SW	SW	SW	SW	XC	SW	SW	SW	SW	SW	XC	SW	SW	SW	SW	XC	SW	SW	SW	SW	SW	SW
		1	1	◇1	1	◇1	1	◇1	1	1	1	◇1	1	1	◇1	1	◇1	1	◇1	1	1	1	1
				A				A							A				A				
				trolley		trolley		trolley				trolley			trolley		trolley		trolley				
Weymouth	d			15 20				16 03							16 20				17 03				
Upwey	d			15 24											16 24								
Dorchester West	a																						
Dorchester South	d			15 33				16 13							16 33				17 13				
Moreton (Dorset)	d			15 39											16 39								
Wool	d			15 45											16 45								
Wareham	d			15 53				16 28							16 53				17 28				
Holton Heath	d			15 56											16 56								
Hamworthy	d			16 01				16 35							17 01				17 35				
Poole 4	a			16 06				16 39							17 06				17 39				
	d	15 50		16 07				16 40					16 50		17 07				17 40				17 50
Parkstone (Dorset)	d	15 54						16 44					16 54						17 44				17 54
Branksome	d	15 57						16 48					16 57						17 48				17 57
Bournemouth	a	16 02		16 17				16 54					17 02		17 17				17 54				18 02
	d	16 05		16 22		16 45		16 59					17 05		17 22		17 45		17 59				18 05
Pokesdown	d	16 09		16 26									17 09		17 26								18 09
Christchurch	d	16 13		16 30									17 13		17 30								18 13
Hinton Admiral	d	16 18											17 18										18 18
New Milton	d	16 22		16 37									17 22		17 37								18 22
Sway	d	16 27											17 27										18 27
Lymington Pier	d		16 27				16 57							17 27				17 57					
Lymington Town	d		16 29				16 59							17 29				17 59					
Brockenhurst 3	a	16 32	16 37	16 44		16 58	17 07	17 14					17 32	17 37	17 44		17 58	18 07	18 14				18 32
	d	16 33		16 45		17 00		17 15					17 33		17 45		18 00		18 15				18 33
Beaulieu Road	d												17 38										
Ashurst New Forest	d	16 40											17 42										18 40
Totton	d	16 45											17 47										18 45
Salisbury	d										16 56											17 56	
Dean	d										17 08											18 08	
Mottisfont & Dunbridge	d										17 14											18 14	
Romsey	d								17 07		17 20									18 07		18 20	
Redbridge	d										17 27											18 27	
Millbrook (Hants)	d										17 31											18 31	
Southampton Central ⛴	a	16 51		16 58		17 12		17 28			17 34		17 53		17 58		18 12		18 28			18 34	18 51
	d	16 55		17 00		17 15		17 30			17 35	17 47	17 55		18 00		18 15		18 30			18 35	18 55
St Denys	d										17 40											18 40	
Swaythling	d										17 43											18 43	
Southampton Airport Pkwy ✈	d	17 03		17 08		17 22		17 38			17 46	17 54	18 03		18 08		18 22		18 38			18 46	19 03
Portsmouth Harbour ⛴	d									16 59											17 59		
Portsmouth & Southsea	d									17 04											18 04		
Fratton	d									17 08											18 08		
Hilsea	d									17 12											18 12		
Cosham	d									17 17											18 17		
Portchester	d									17 22											18 22		
Fareham	d									17 28											18 28		
Botley	d									17 35											18 35		
Hedge End	d									17 40											18 40		
Eastleigh 3	a	17 06							17 20	17 46	17 49		18 06							18 20	18 46	18 49	19 06
	d	17 14							17 21	17 47	17 50		18 14							18 21	18 47	18 50	19 14
Chandlers Ford	d										17 55											18 55	
Romsey	a								17 51		18 03									19 00		19 04	
Shawford	d	17 19			←								18 19			←							19 19
Winchester	d	17 25		17 18	17 25	17 31		17 48		17 56		18 03	18 25		18 18	18 25	18 31		18 48		18 56		19 25
Micheldever	d	→								18 05			→								19 05		→
Basingstoke	a			17 34	17 41	17 46				18 15		18 17			18 34	18 41	18 46				19 15		
	d			17 35	17 43	17 47				18 17		18 18			18 35	18 43	18 47				19 17		
Reading 7	a					18 03						18 34					19 03						
Fleet	d				17 54											18 54							
Farnborough (Main)	d				18 00					18 30						19 00					19 30		
Woking	a							18 19		18 39									19 19		19 39		
Clapham Junction 10	a			18 12	18 25										19 12	19 25							
London Waterloo 15 ⊖	a			18 20	18 34			18 49		19 07					19 20	19 34			19 49		20 07		

A trolley from Bournemouth

Table 158R

Saturdays

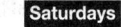

14 December to 17 May

Weymouth, Bournemouth, Lymington, Romsey, Southampton and Basingstoke - London

Network Diagram - see first Page of Table 158

		SW	SW	SW	GW	XC	SW	SW	SW	SW	SW	SW	SW	SW	SW	XC	SW	SW	SW	SW	SW	SW
		1	◇1	1	◇	◇1	1	◇1	1	1	1	1	1	◇1	1	◇1	1	◇1	1	1	1	1
			A					A						A				A				
			[trolley]			[trolley]		[trolley]						[trolley]				[trolley]				
Weymouth	d		17 20		17 28			18 03						18 20				19 03				
Upwey	d		17 24		17 33									18 24								
Dorchester West	a				17 40																	
Dorchester South	d		17 33					18 13						18 33				19 13				
Moreton (Dorset)	d		17 39											18 39								
Wool	d		17 45											18 45								
Wareham	d		17 53					18 28						18 53				19 28				
Holton Heath	d		17 56											18 56								
Hamworthy	d		18 01					18 35						19 01				19 35				
Poole 4	a		18 06					18 39						19 06				19 39				
	d		18 07					18 40				18 50		19 07				19 40				19 50
Parkstone (Dorset)	d							18 44				18 54						19 44				19 54
Branksome	d							18 48				18 57						19 48				19 57
Bournemouth	a		18 17					18 54				19 02		19 17				19 54				20 02
	d		18 22			18 45		18 59				19 05		19 22		19 45		19 59				20 05
Pokesdown	d		18 26									19 09		19 26								20 09
Christchurch	d		18 30									19 13		19 30								20 13
Hinton Admiral	d											19 18										20 18
New Milton	d		18 37									19 22		19 37								20 22
Sway	d											19 27										20 27
Lymington Pier	d	18 27					18 57						19 27				19 57					
Lymington Town	d	18 29					18 59						19 29				19 59					
Brockenhurst 3	a	18 37	18 44			18 58	19 07	19 14				19 32	19 37	19 44		19 58	20 07	20 14				20 32
	d		18 45			19 00		19 15				19 33		19 45		20 00		20 15				20 33
Beaulieu Road	d																					
Ashurst New Forest	d											19 40										20 40
Totton	d											19 45										20 45
Salisbury	d										18 56										19 56	
Dean	d										19 08										20 08	
Mottisfont & Dunbridge	d										19 14										20 14	
Romsey	d								19 07		19 20								20 07		20 20	
Redbridge	d										19 27										20 27	
Millbrook (Hants)	d										19 31										20 31	
Southampton Central ⛴	a		18 58			19 12		19 28			19 34	19 51		19 58		20 12		20 28			20 34	20 51
	d		19 00			19 15		19 30			19 35	19 55		20 00		20 15		20 30			20 35	20 55
St Denys	d										19 40										20 40	
Swaythling	d										19 43										20 43	
Southampton Airport Pkwy ✈	d		19 08			19 22		19 38			19 46	20 03		20 08		20 22		20 38			20 46	21 03
Portsmouth Harbour ⛴	d									18 59										19 59		
Portsmouth & Southsea	d									19 04										20 04		
Fratton	d									19 08										20 08		
Hilsea	d									19 12										20 12		
Cosham	d									19 17										20 17		
Portchester	d									19 22										20 22		
Fareham	d									19 28										20 28		
Botley	d									19 35										20 35		
Hedge End	d									19 40										20 40		
Eastleigh 3	a								19 20	19 46	19 49	20 06							20 20	20 46	20 49	21 06
	d								19 21	19 47	19 50	20 14							20 21	20 47	20 50	21 14
Chandlers Ford	d										19 55										20 55	
Romsey	a								19 51		20 03								20 51		21 03	
Shawford	d			←								20 19			←							21 19
Winchester	d		19 18	19 25		19 31		19 48		19 56		20 25		20 18	20 25	20 31		20 48		20 56		21 25
Micheldever	d									20 05		→								21 05		→
Basingstoke	a		19 34	19 41		19 46				20 15				20 34	20 41	20 46				21 17		
	d		19 35	19 43		19 47				20 17				20 35	20 43	20 47				21 24		
Reading 7	a					20 03										21 03						
Fleet	d			19 54											20 54					21 40		
Farnborough (Main)	d			20 00						20 30					21 00					21 46		
Woking	a							20 19		20 39					21 09			21 19		21 58		
Clapham Junction 10	a		20 12	20 25										21 16	21 29							
London Waterloo 15 ⊖	a		20 20	20 34				20 49		21 07				21 24	21 38			21 49		22 34		

A [trolley] from Bournemouth

Table 158R

Saturdays

14 December to 17 May

Weymouth, Bournemouth, Lymington, Romsey, Southampton and Basingstoke - London

Network Diagram - see first Page of Table 158

		SW 1	SW ◇1	SW 1	SW 1	SW 1	SW 1	SW 1	SW 1	SW 1	SW 1	SW ◇1	SW 1	GW	SW 1	SW 1	SW 1	SW 1	SW 1	SW 1	SW 1	SW 1	SW 1
Weymouth	d		19 20									20 10		20 21						21 10			
Upwey	d		19 24									20 14		20 26						21 14			
Dorchester West	a													20 33									
Dorchester South	d		19 33									20 22								21 22			
Moreton (Dorset)	d		19 39									20 28								21 28			
Wool	d		19 45									20 34								21 34			
Wareham	d		19 53									20 42								21 42			
Holton Heath	d																						
Hamworthy	d		20 01									20 48								21 48			
Poole 4	a		20 06									20 53								21 53			
	d		20 07									20 54								21 54			
Parkstone (Dorset)	d											20 58								21 58			
Branksome	d											21 01								22 01			
Bournemouth	a		20 17									21 07								22 07			
	d		20 22									21 12								22 12			
Pokesdown	d		20 26									21 16								22 16			
Christchurch	d		20 30									21 20								22 20			
Hinton Admiral	d											21 25								22 25			
New Milton	d		20 37									21 29								22 29			
Sway	d											21 34								22 34			
Lymington Pier	d	20 27			20 57		21 27								22 03						22 33		
Lymington Town	d	20 29			20 59		21 29								22 05						22 35		
Brockenhurst 3	a	20 37	20 44		21 07		21 37					21 39			22 13					22 39	22 43		
	d		20 45									21 40								22 40			
Beaulieu Road	d																						
Ashurst New Forest	d											21 47								22 47			
Totton	d											21 52								22 52			
Salisbury	d									20 56									21 56				
Dean	d									21 08									22 08				
Mottisfont & Dunbridge	d									21 14									22 14				
Romsey	d					21 07				21 20						22 07			22 20			23 09	23 00
Redbridge	d									21 27									22 27				23 08
Millbrook (Hants)	d									21 31									22 31				23 12
Southampton Central ⛴	a		20 58							21 34		21 57							22 34	22 57			23 15
	d		21 00					21 30		21 35	21 55	22 00						22 30	22 35	23 00			23 21
St Denys	d									21 40									22 40				23 26
Swaythling	d									21 43									22 43				23 29
Southampton Airport Pkwy ✈	d		21 08					21 38		21 46	22 03	22 08						22 38	22 46	23 08			23 32
Portsmouth Harbour ⛴	d								20 59								21 54						
Portsmouth & Southsea	d								21 04								21 59						
Fratton	d								21 08								22 03						
Hilsea	d								21 12								22 07						
Cosham	d								21 17								22 12						
Portchester	d								21 22								22 17						
Fareham	d								21 28								22 23						
Botley	d								21 35								22 30						
Hedge End	d								21 40								22 35						
Eastleigh 3	a					21 20			21 46	21 49	22 06					22 20	22 41	22 41	22 49	23 11		23 22	23 35
	d					21 21			21 47	21 50	22 14					22 22		22 46	22 50	23 12		23 23	23 37
Chandlers Ford	d									21 55									22 55				23 42
Romsey	a					21 51				22 03						22 51			23 03			23 57	23 49
Shawford	d			←							22 20		←							23 18			
Winchester	d		21 18	21 25				21 48	21 56		22 26	22 18	22 26					22 55		23 24			
Micheldever	d								22 05		→									23 33			
Basingstoke	a		21 34	21 41					22 15			22 34	22 42					23 11		23 43			
	d		21 35	21 43					22 24			22 35	22 43					23 14		23 44			
Reading 7	a																						
Fleet	d			21 54					22 40				22 54							00 01			
Farnborough (Main)	d			22 00					22 46				23 00							00 06			
Woking	a			22 09				22 19	22 58			22 53	23 09					23 32		00 18			
Clapham Junction 10	a		22 14	22 29								23 14	23 29					23 52		00 53			
London Waterloo 15 ⊖	a		22 22	22 38				22 49	23 32			23 22	23 39					00 03		01 04			

Table 158R

Saturdays

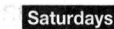

14 December to 17 May

Weymouth, Bournemouth, Lymington, Romsey, Southampton and Basingstoke - London

Network Diagram - see first Page of Table 158

		SW [1]	SW [1]	SW [1]
Weymouth	d		22 10	23 10
Upwey	d		22 14	23 14
Dorchester West	a			
Dorchester South	d		22 22	23 22
Moreton (Dorset)	d		22 28	23 28
Wool	d		22 34	23 34
Wareham	d		22 42	23 42
Holton Heath	d			
Hamworthy	d		22 48	23 48
Poole [4]	a		22 53	23 53
	d		22 54	23 54
Parkstone (Dorset)	d		22 58	
Branksome	d		23 01	
Bournemouth	a		23 07	00 03
	d		23 12	
Pokesdown	d		23 16	
Christchurch	d		23 20	
Hinton Admiral	d		23 25	
New Milton	d		23 29	
Sway	d		23 34	
Lymington Pier	d			
Lymington Town	d			
Brockenhurst [3]	a		23 39	
	d		23 40	
Beaulieu Road	d			
Ashurst New Forest	d		23 47	
Totton	d		23 52	
Salisbury	d			
Dean	d			
Mottisfont & Dunbridge	d			
Romsey	d			
Redbridge	d			
Millbrook (Hants)	d			
Southampton Central ⛴	a		23 57	
	d		23 59	
St Denys	d		00 04	
Swaythling	d		00 07	
Southampton Airport Pkwy ✈	d		00 10	
Portsmouth Harbour ⛴	d	23 24		
Portsmouth & Southsea	d	23 29		
Fratton	d	23 33		
Hilsea	d	23 37		
Cosham	d	23 42		
Portchester	d	23 47		
Fareham	d	23 53		
Botley	d	23 59		
Hedge End	d	00 05		
Eastleigh [8]	a	00 11	00 14	
	d	00 21		
Chandlers Ford	d			
Romsey	a			
Shawford	d			
Winchester	d	00a30		
Micheldever	d			
Basingstoke	a			
	d			
Reading [7]	a			
Fleet	d			
Farnborough (Main)	d			
Woking	a			
Clapham Junction [10]	a			
London Waterloo [15] ⊖	a			

Table 158R

Sundays

8 December to 9 February

Weymouth, Bournemouth, Lymington, Romsey, Southampton and Basingstoke - London

Network Diagram - see first Page of Table 158

		SW	SW	SW	SW	SW	SW	SW	SN	SW	SW	SW	SW	XC	SW	SW	SW	SW	SW	SW	SW	XC	SW
		[1]	[1]	[1]	[1]	[1]	◇[1]	[1]	[1]	[1]	[1]	◇[1]	[1]	◇[1]	◇[1]	[1]	[1]	[1]	[1]	◇[1]	[1]	◇[1]	[1]
							A					B			C					D			
							[trolley]							[trolley]	[trolley]				[trolley]	[trolley]		[trolley]	
Weymouth	d														07 48								
Upwey	d														07 52								
Dorchester West	a																						
Dorchester South	d														08 00								
Moreton (Dorset)	d														08 07								
Wool	d														08 13								
Wareham	d														08 20								
Holton Heath	d																						
Hamworthy	d														08 27								
Poole [4]	a														08 31								
	d						06 50					07 50			08 32					08 55			
Parkstone (Dorset)	d						06 54					07 54			08 36								
Branksome	d						06 57					07 57			08 40								
Bournemouth	a						07 02					08 02			08 46					09 04			
	d						07 06					08 06			08 50					09 06		09 40	
Pokesdown	d						07 10					08 10								09 10			
Christchurch	d						07 14					08 14								09 14			
Hinton Admiral	d						07 19					08 19								09 19			
New Milton	d						07 23					08 23			09 01					09 23			
Sway	d						07 28					08 28								09 28			
Lymington Pier	d															09 14							09 44
Lymington Town	d															09 16							09 46
Brockenhurst [3]	a						07 33					08 33			09 08	09 24				09 33		09 53	09 54
	d						07 34					08 34			09 09					09 34		09 57	
Beaulieu Road	d											08 39								09 39			
Ashurst New Forest	d						07 43					08 43								09 43			
Totton	d						07 48					08 48								09 48			
Salisbury	d							08 08		08 20							09 08						
Dean	d							08 20									09 20						
Mottisfont & Dunbridge	d							08 26									09 26						
Romsey	d							08 35		08 39							09 32	09 35					
Redbridge	d									08 46							09 39						
Millbrook (Hants)	d									08 50			←				09 43				←		
Southampton Central ⛴	a						07 53			08 52		08 53	08 52		09 23		09 45			09 53	09 45	10 10	
	d				06 55		07 55		08 27	08 59		08 55	08 59	09 15	09 25		09 59			09 55	09 59	10 15	
St Denys	d			00 04						↪			09 04				↪				10 04		
Swaythling	d			00 07									09 07								10 07		
Southampton Airport Pkwy ✈	d			00 10	07 03		08 03		08 36			09 03	09 10	09 22	09 33					10 03	10 10	10 22	
Portsmouth Harbour ⛴	d					07 17					08 17								09 17				
Portsmouth & Southsea	d					07 22					08 22								09 22				
Fratton	d					07 26					08 26								09 26				
Hilsea	d					07 30					08 30								09 30				
Cosham	d					07 35					08 35								09 35				
Portchester	d					07 40					08 40								09 40				
Fareham	d					07 46					08 46								09 46				
Botley	d					07 54					08 54								09 54				
Hedge End	d		00 05			07 58					08 58								09 58				
Eastleigh [3]	a		00 11	00 14	07 07	08 04	08 07		08 41		09 04	09 07	09 13					09 48	10 04	10 07	10 13		
	d		00 21		07 11	08 11					09 11		09 15					09 54	10 11		10 15		
Chandlers Ford	d							08 42					09 20								10 20		
Romsey	a							09 24					09 28					10 24			10 28		
Shawford	d										09 17												
Winchester	d		00a30		07 23	08 23					09 23			09 31	09 42				10 23			10 31	
Micheldever	d				07 32	08 32					09 32								10 32				
Basingstoke	a				07 42	08 42					09 42			09 46	09 58				10 42			10 46	
	d				07 44	08 44					09 44			09 47	10 00				10 44			10 47	
Reading [7]	a													10 04								11 03	
Fleet	d	00 01																					
Farnborough (Main)	d	00 06																					
Woking	a	00 18			08 02	09 02					10 02				10 19				11 02				
Clapham Junction [10]	a	00 53			08 31	09 30					10 27				10 39				11 27				
London Waterloo [15] ⊖	a	01 04			08 46	09 41					10 39				10 50				11 39				

A [trolley] ◇ to Eastleigh

B ◇ to Eastleigh

C [trolley] from Bournemouth

D [trolley] from Eastleigh ◇ to Eastleigh

Table 158R

Sundays

8 December to 9 February

Weymouth, Bournemouth, Lymington, Romsey, Southampton and Basingstoke - London

Network Diagram - see first Page of Table 158

		SW	SW	SW	SW	SW	SW		SW	XC	SW	SW	SW	SW	SW	SW	SW		SW	XC	SW	SW	SW	SW	SW
		◇1	1	1	1	1	◇1		1	◇1	1	◇1	1	1	1	1	◇1		1	◇1	1	◇1	1	1	1
		A					B					A					C					A			
		🛒				🛒	🛒			🛒		🛒				🛒	🛒			🛒		🛒			
Weymouth	d	08 48										09 48										10 48			
Upwey	d	08 52										09 52										10 52			
Dorchester West	a																								
Dorchester South	d	09 00										10 00										11 00			
Moreton (Dorset)	d	09 07										10 07										11 07			
Wool	d	09 13										10 13										11 13			
Wareham	d	09 20										10 20										11 20			
Holton Heath	d																								
Hamworthy	d	09 27										10 27										11 27			
Poole 4	a	09 31										10 31										11 31			
	d	09 32					09 55					10 32					10 55					11 32			
Parkstone (Dorset)	d	09 36										10 36										11 36			
Branksome	d	09 40										10 40										11 40			
Bournemouth	a	09 46					10 04					10 46					11 04					11 46			
	d	09 50					10 06			10 40		10 50					11 06			11 40		11 50			
Pokesdown	d						10 10										11 10								
Christchurch	d						10 14										11 14								
Hinton Admiral	d						10 19										11 19								
New Milton	d	10 01					10 23					11 01					11 23					12 01			
Sway	d						10 28										11 28								
Lymington Pier	d		10 14								10 44		11 14								11 44		12 14		
Lymington Town	d		10 16								10 46		11 16								11 46		12 16		
Brockenhurst 3	a	10 08	10 24				10 33			10 53	10 54	11 08	11 24				11 33			11 53	11 54	12 08	12 24		
	d	10 09					10 34			10 57		11 09					11 34			11 57		12 09			
Beaulieu Road	d						10 39										11 39								
Ashurst New Forest	d						10 43										11 43								
Totton	d						10 48										11 48								
Salisbury	d			10 13										11 08										12 13	
Dean	d													11 20											
Mottisfont & Dunbridge	d													11 26											
Romsey	d			10 32	10 35									11 32	11 35									12 32	12 35
Redbridge	d			10 39										11 39										12 39	
Millbrook (Hants)	d			10 43					←					11 43					←					12 43	
Southampton Central ⛴	a	10 23		10 45			10 53		10 45	11 10		11 23		11 45			11 53		11 45	12 10		12 23		12 45	
	d	10 25		10 59			10 55		10 59	11 15		11 25		11 59			11 55		11 59	12 15		12 25		12 59	
St Denys	d			→					11 04					→					12 04					→	
Swaythling	d								11 07										12 07						
Southampton Airport Pkwy ✈	d	10 33					11 03		11 10	11 22		11 33					12 03		12 10	12 22		12 33			
Portsmouth Harbour ⛴	d					10 17										11 17									
Portsmouth & Southsea	d					10 22										11 22									
Fratton	d					10 26										11 26									
Hilsea	d					10 30										11 30									
Cosham	d					10 35										11 35									
Portchester	d					10 40										11 40									
Fareham	d					10 46										11 46									
Botley	d					10 54										11 54									
Hedge End	d					10 58										11 58									
Eastleigh 3	a				10 48	11 04	11 07		11 13						11 48	12 04	12 07		12 13						12 48
	d				10 54		11 11		11 15						11 54		12 11		12 15						12 54
Chandlers Ford	d								11 20										12 20						
Romsey	a				11 24				11 28						12 24				12 28						13 24
Shawford	d						11 17																		
Winchester	d	10 42					11 23			11 31		11 42					12 23			12 31		12 42			
Micheldever	d						11 32										12 32								
Basingstoke	a	10 58					11 42			11 46		11 58					12 42			12 46		12 58			
	d	11 00					11 44			11 47		12 00					12 44			12 47		13 00			
Reading 7	a									12 02										13 03					
Fleet	d																								
Farnborough (Main)	d																								
Woking	a	11 18					12 02					12 18					13 02					13 18			
Clapham Junction 10	a	11 39					12 27					12 39					13 27					13 39			
London Waterloo 15 ⊖	a	11 50					12 37					12 49					13 37					13 49			

A 🛒 from Bournemouth

B 🛒 from Bournemouth ◇ to Eastleigh

C 🛒 from Eastleigh ◇ to Eastleigh

Table 158R

Sundays

8 December to 9 February

Weymouth, Bournemouth, Lymington, Romsey, Southampton and Basingstoke - London

Network Diagram - see first Page of Table 158

		SW	SW		SW	XC	SW	SW	SW	SW	SW	SW	SW		SW	XC	SW	SW	SW	SW	SW	SW	SW		SW
		1	◇1		1	◇1	1	◇1	1	1	1	1	◇1		1	◇1	1	◇1	1	1	1	1	◇1		1
			A					B					C					B					C		
		🚲	🚲			🚲		🚲				🚲	🚲			🚲		🚲				🚲	🚲		
Weymouth	d							11 48										12 48							
Upwey	d							11 52										12 52							
Dorchester West	a																								
Dorchester South	d							12 00										13 00							
Moreton (Dorset)	d							12 07										13 07							
Wool	d							12 13										13 13							
Wareham	d							12 20										13 20							
Holton Heath	d																								
Hamworthy	d							12 27										13 27							
Poole 4	a							12 31										13 31							
	d		11 55					12 32					12 55					13 32					13 55		
Parkstone (Dorset)	d							12 36										13 36							
Branksome	d							12 40										13 40							
Bournemouth	a		12 04					12 46					13 04					13 46					14 04		
	d		12 06			12 40		12 50					13 06			13 40		13 50					14 06		
Pokesdown	d		12 10										13 10										14 10		
Christchurch	d		12 14										13 14										14 14		
Hinton Admiral	d		12 19										13 19										14 19		
New Milton	d		12 23					13 01					13 23					14 01					14 23		
Sway	d		12 28										13 28										14 28		
Lymington Pier	d						12 44		13 14								13 44		14 14						
Lymington Town	d						12 46		13 16								13 46		14 16						
Brockenhurst 3	a		12 33			12 53	12 54	13 08	13 24				13 33			13 53	13 54	14 08	14 24				14 33		
	d		12 34			12 57		13 09					13 34			13 57		14 09					14 34		
Beaulieu Road	d		12 39										13 39										14 39		
Ashurst New Forest	d		12 43										13 43										14 43		
Totton	d		12 48										13 48										14 48		
Salisbury	d									13 08										14 13					
Dean	d									13 20															
Mottisfont & Dunbridge	d									13 26															
Romsey	d									13 32	13 35									14 32	14 35				
Redbridge	d									13 39										14 39					
Millbrook (Hants)	d				←					13 43					←					14 43					←
Southampton Central ⛴	a		12 53		12 45	13 10		13 23		13 45			13 53		13 45	14 10		14 23		14 45			14 53		14 45
	d		12 55		12 59	13 15		13 25		13 59			13 55		13 59	14 15		14 25		14 59			14 55		14 59
St Denys	d				13 04					↪					14 04					↪					15 04
Swaythling	d				13 07										14 07										15 07
Southampton Airport Pkwy ✈	d		13 03		13 10	13 22		13 33					14 03		14 10	14 22		14 33					15 03		15 10
Portsmouth Harbour ⛴	d	12 17										13 17										14 17			
Portsmouth & Southsea	d	12 22										13 22										14 22			
Fratton	d	12 26										13 26										14 26			
Hilsea	d	12 30										13 30										14 30			
Cosham	d	12 35										13 35										14 35			
Portchester	d	12 40										13 40										14 40			
Fareham	d	12 46										13 46										14 46			
Botley	d	12 54										13 54										14 54			
Hedge End	d	12 58										13 58										14 58			
Eastleigh 3	a	13 04	13 07		13 13						13 48	14 04	14 07		14 13						14 48	15 04	15 07		15 13
	d		13 11		13 15						13 54		14 11		14 15						14 54		15 11		15 15
Chandlers Ford	d				13 20										14 20										15 20
Romsey	a				13 28						14 24				14 28						15 24				15 28
Shawford	d		13 17																				15 17		
Winchester	d		13 23			13 31		13 42					14 23			14 31		14 42					15 23		
Micheldever	d		13 32										14 32										15 32		
Basingstoke	a		13 42			13 46		13 58					14 42			14 46		14 58					15 42		
	d		13 44			13 47		14 00					14 44			14 47		15 00					15 44		
Reading 7	a					14 02										15 03									
Fleet	d																								
Farnborough (Main)	d																								
Woking	a		14 02					14 18					15 02					15 18					16 02		
Clapham Junction 10	a		14 27					14 39					15 27					15 39					16 27		
London Waterloo 15 ⊖	a		14 37					14 49					15 37					15 49					16 37		

A 🚲 from Bournemouth ◇ to Eastleigh

B 🚲 from Bournemouth

C 🚲 from Eastleigh ◇ to Eastleigh

Table 158R

Sundays

8 December to 9 February

Weymouth, Bournemouth, Lymington, Romsey, Southampton and Basingstoke - London

Network Diagram - see first Page of Table 158

		XC	SW	SW	GW	SW	SW	SW	SW	SW	SW	XC	SW	SW	SW	SW	SW	SW	SW	SW	XC	SW	SW
		◇1	1	◇1	◇	1	1	1	1	◇1	1	◇1	1	◇1	1	1	1	1	◇1	1	◇1	1	◇1
				A						B				A					B				A
		🍴		🍴					🍴	🍴		🍴		🍴				🍴	🍴		🍴		🍴
Weymouth	d			13 48	14 00									14 48									15 48
Upwey	d			13 52	14 05									14 52									15 52
Dorchester West	a				14 12																		
Dorchester South	d			14 00										15 00									16 00
Moreton (Dorset)	d			14 07										15 07									16 07
Wool	d			14 13										15 13									16 13
Wareham	d			14 20										15 20									16 20
Holton Heath	d																						
Hamworthy	d			14 27										15 27									16 27
Poole 4	a			14 31										15 31									16 31
	d			14 32						14 55				15 32					15 55				16 32
Parkstone (Dorset)	d			14 36										15 36									16 36
Branksome	d			14 40										15 40									16 40
Bournemouth	a			14 46						15 04				15 46					16 04				16 46
	d	14 40		14 50						15 06		15 40		15 50					16 06		16 40		16 50
Pokesdown	d									15 10									16 10				
Christchurch	d									15 14									16 14				
Hinton Admiral	d									15 19									16 19				
New Milton	d			15 01						15 23				16 01					16 23				17 01
Sway	d									15 28									16 28				
Lymington Pier	d		14 44			15 14							15 44		16 14							16 44	
Lymington Town	d		14 46			15 16							15 46		16 16							16 46	
Brockenhurst 3	a	14 53	14 54	15 08		15 24				15 33		15 53	15 54	16 08	16 24				16 33		16 53	16 54	17 08
	d	14 57		15 09						15 34		15 57		16 09					16 34		16 57		17 09
Beaulieu Road	d									15 39									16 39				
Ashurst New Forest	d									15 43									16 43				
Totton	d									15 48									16 48				
Salisbury	d						15 08									16 13							
Dean	d						15 20																
Mottisfont & Dunbridge	d						15 26																
Romsey	d						15 32	15 35								16 32	16 35						
Redbridge	d						15 39									16 39							
Millbrook (Hants)	d						15 43				←					16 43				←			
Southampton Central ⛴	a	15 10		15 23			15 45			15 53	15 45	16 10		16 23		16 45			16 53	16 45	17 10		17 23
	d	15 15		15 25			15 59			15 55	15 59	16 15		16 25		16 59			16 55	16 59	17 15		17 25
St Denys	d						→				16 04					→				17 04			
Swaythling	d										16 07									17 07			
Southampton Airport Pkwy ✈	d	15 22		15 33						16 03	16 10	16 22		16 33					17 03	17 10	17 22		17 33
Portsmouth Harbour ⛴	d								15 17									16 17					
Portsmouth & Southsea	d								15 22									16 22					
Fratton	d								15 26									16 26					
Hilsea	d								15 30									16 30					
Cosham	d								15 35									16 35					
Portchester	d								15 40									16 40					
Fareham	d								15 46									16 46					
Botley	d								15 54									16 54					
Hedge End	d								15 58									16 58					
Eastleigh 3	a							15 48	16 04	16 07	16 13						16 48	17 04	17 07	17 13			
	d							15 54		16 11	16 15						16 54		17 11	17 15			
Chandlers Ford	d										16 20									17 20			
Romsey	a							16 24			16 28						17 24			17 28			
Shawford	d																		17 17				
Winchester	d	15 31		15 42						16 23		16 31		16 42					17 23		17 31		17 42
Micheldever	d									16 32									17 32				
Basingstoke	a	15 46		15 58						16 42		16 46		16 58					17 42		17 46		17 58
	d	15 47		16 00						16 44		16 47		17 00					17 44		17 47		18 00
Reading 7	a	16 02										17 02									18 04		
Fleet	d																						
Farnborough (Main)	d																						
Woking	a			16 18						17 02				17 18					18 02				18 18
Clapham Junction 10	a			16 39						17 27				17 39					18 27				18 39
London Waterloo 15 ⊖	a			16 49						17 37				17 49					18 37				18 49

A 🍴 from Bournemouth

B 🍴 from Eastleigh ◇ to Eastleigh

Table 158R

Sundays

8 December to 9 February

Weymouth, Bournemouth, Lymington, Romsey, Southampton and Basingstoke - London

Network Diagram - see first Page of Table 158

		SW	SW	SW	SW	SW	SW	XC	SW	SW	SW	SW	SW	SW	SW	SW	XC	SW	SW	GW	SW	SN	SW
		1	1	1	1	◇1	1	◇1	1	◇1	1	1	1	1	◇1	1	◇1	1	◇1	◇	1	1	1
						A				B					A				B				
								⚻		⚻							⚻		⚻				
Weymouth	d									16 48									17 48	17 56			
Upwey	d									16 52									17 52	18 01			
Dorchester West	a																			18 08			
Dorchester South	d									17 00									18 00				
Moreton (Dorset)	d									17 07									18 07				
Wool	d									17 13									18 13				
Wareham	d									17 20									18 20				
Holton Heath	d																						
Hamworthy	d									17 27									18 27				
Poole 4	a									17 31									18 31				
	d					16 55				17 32					17 55				18 32				
Parkstone (Dorset)	d									17 36									18 36				
Branksome	d									17 40									18 40				
Bournemouth	a					17 04				17 46					18 04				18 46				
	d					17 06		17 40		17 50					18 06		18 40		18 50				
Pokesdown	d					17 10									18 10								
Christchurch	d					17 14									18 14								
Hinton Admiral	d					17 19									18 19								
New Milton	d					17 23				18 01					18 23				19 01				
Sway	d					17 28									18 28								
Lymington Pier	d	17 14							17 44		18 14							18 44			19 14		
Lymington Town	d	17 16							17 46		18 16							18 46			19 16		
Brockenhurst 3	a	17 24				17 33		17 53	17 54	18 08	18 24				18 33		18 53	18 54	19 08		19 24		
	d					17 34		17 57		18 09					18 34		18 57		19 09				
Beaulieu Road	d					17 39									18 39								
Ashurst New Forest	d					17 43									18 43								
Totton	d					17 48									18 48								
Salisbury	d		17 08									18 13											19 08
Dean	d		17 20																				19 20
Mottisfont & Dunbridge	d		17 26																				19 26
Romsey	d		17 32	17 35								18 32	18 35										19 32
Redbridge	d		17 39									18 39											19 39
Millbrook (Hants)	d		17 43				←					18 43				←							19 43
Southampton Central ⛴	a		17 45			17 53	17 45	18 10		18 23		18 45			18 53	18 45	19 10		19 23				19 45
	d		17 59			17 55	17 59	18 15		18 25		18 59			18 55	18 59	19 15		19 25			19 30	19 59
St Denys	d		→				18 04					→				19 04							→
Swaythling	d						18 07									19 07							
Southampton Airport Pkwy ✈	d					18 03	18 10	18 22		18 33					19 03	19 10	19 22		19 33			19 38	
Portsmouth Harbour ⛴	d				17 17									18 17									
Portsmouth & Southsea	d				17 22									18 22									
Fratton	d				17 26									18 26									
Hilsea	d				17 30									18 30									
Cosham	d				17 35									18 35									
Portchester	d				17 40									18 40									
Fareham	d				17 46									18 46									
Botley	d				17 54									18 54									
Hedge End	d				17 58									18 58									
Eastleigh 3	a			17 48	18 04	18 07	18 13						18 48	19 04	19 07	19 13						19 42	
	d			17 54		18 11	18 15						18 54		19 11	19 15							
Chandlers Ford	d						18 20									19 20							
Romsey	a			18 24			18 28						19 24			19 28							
Shawford	d														19 17								
Winchester	d					18 23		18 31		18 42					19 23		19 31		19 42				
Micheldever	d					18 32									19 32								
Basingstoke	a					18 42		18 46		18 58					19 42		19 46		19 58				
	d					18 44		18 47		19 00					19 44		19 47		20 00				
Reading 7	a							19 02									20 03						
Fleet	d																						
Farnborough (Main)	d																						
Woking	a					19 02				19 18					20 02				20 18				
Clapham Junction 10	a					19 27				19 39					20 27				20 39				
London Waterloo 15 ⊖	a					19 37				19 49					20 37				20 49				

A ◇ to Eastleigh

B ⚻ from Bournemouth

Table 158R

Sundays

8 December to 9 February

Weymouth, Bournemouth, Lymington, Romsey, Southampton and Basingstoke - London

Network Diagram - see first Page of Table 158

		SW		SW	SW	SW	XC	SW	SW	SW	SN	SW		SW	SW	SW	SW	SW	SW	SW	SW	SW	SW		SW
		1		1	◇1	1	◇1	1	◇1	1	1	1		1	1	◇1	1	1	1	1	1	1	◇1		1
					A				B 🍴							A							A		
Weymouth	d								18 48														19 58		
Upwey	d								18 52														20 02		
Dorchester West	a																								
Dorchester South	d								19 00														20 10		
Moreton (Dorset)	d								19 07														20 17		
Wool	d								19 13														20 23		
Wareham	d								19 20														20 30		
Holton Heath	d																								
Hamworthy	d								19 27														20 37		
Poole 4	a								19 31														20 41		
	d				18 55				19 32							19 55							20 50		
Parkstone (Dorset)	d								19 36														20 54		
Branksome	d								19 40														20 57		
Bournemouth	a				19 04				19 46							20 04							21 03		
	d				19 06		19 40		19 50							20 06							21 06		
Pokesdown	d				19 10											20 10							21 10		
Christchurch	d				19 14											20 14							21 14		
Hinton Admiral	d				19 19											20 19							21 19		
New Milton	d				19 23				20 01							20 23							21 23		
Sway	d				19 28											20 28							21 28		
Lymington Pier	d							19 44		20 14								20 44	21 14						
Lymington Town	d							19 46		20 16								20 46	21 16						
Brockenhurst 3	a				19 33		19 53	19 54	20 08	20 24						20 33		20 54	21 24				21 33		
	d				19 34		19 57		20 09							20 34							21 34		
Beaulieu Road	d				19 39											20 39							21 39		
Ashurst New Forest	d				19 43											20 43							21 43		
Totton	d				19 48											20 48							21 48		
Salisbury	d											20 13								21 08					
Dean	d																			21 20					
Mottisfont & Dunbridge	d																			21 26					
Romsey	d	19 35										20 32		20 35						21 32	21 35				
Redbridge	d											20 39								21 39					
Millbrook (Hants)	d					←						20 43					←			21 43					←
Southampton Central	a				19 53	19 45	20 10		20 23			20 45				20 53	20 45			21 45			21 53		21 45
	d				19 55	19 59	20 15		20 25		20 29	20 59				20 55	20 59			21 59			21 55		21 59
St Denys	d					20 04						→					21 04			→					22 04
Swaythling	d					20 07											21 07								22 07
Southampton Airport Pkwy	d				20 03	20 10	20 22		20 33		20 38					21 03	21 10						22 03		22 10
Portsmouth Harbour	d			19 17											20 17							21 17			
Portsmouth & Southsea	d			19 22											20 22							21 22			
Fratton	d			19 26											20 26							21 26			
Hilsea	d			19 30											20 30							21 30			
Cosham	d			19 35											20 35							21 35			
Portchester	d			19 40											20 40							21 40			
Fareham	d			19 46											20 46							21 46			
Botley	d			19 54											20 54							21 54			
Hedge End	d			19 58											20 58							21 58			
Eastleigh 3	a	19 48		20 04	20 07	20 13					20 41			20 48	21 04	21 07	21 13				21 48	22 04	22 07		22 13
	d	19 54			20 11	20 15								20 54		21 11	21 15				21 54		22 11		22 15
Chandlers Ford	d					20 20											21 20								22 20
Romsey	a	20 24				20 28								21 24			21 28				22 24				22 31
Shawford	d															21 17									
Winchester	d				20 23		20 31		20 42							21 23							22 23		
Micheldever	d				20 32											21 32							22 32		
Basingstoke	a				20 42		20 46		20 58							21 42							22 42		
	d				20 44		20 47		21 00							21 44							22 44		
Reading 7	a						21 02																		
Fleet	d																								
Farnborough (Main)	d																								
Woking	a				21 02				21 18							22 02							23 02		
Clapham Junction 10	a				21 27				21 39							22 27							23 27		
London Waterloo 15 ⊖	a				21 37				21 49							22 37							23 37		

A ◇ to Eastleigh

B 🍴 from Bournemouth

Table 158R

Sundays

8 December to 9 February

Weymouth, Bournemouth, Lymington, Romsey, Southampton and Basingstoke - London

Network Diagram - see first Page of Table 158

		GW	SW 1	SW 1	SW 1	SW 1	SW 1	SW ◇1	SW 1		SW 1	SW 1	SW 1
Weymouth	d	20 09						20 58			21 58	22 58	
Upwey	d	20 14						21 02			22 02	23 02	
Dorchester West	a	20 21											
Dorchester South	d							21 10			22 10	23 10	
Moreton (Dorset)	d							21 17			22 17	23 17	
Wool	d							21 23			22 23	23 23	
Wareham	d							21 30			22 30	23 30	
Holton Heath	d												
Hamworthy	d							21 37			22 37	23 37	
Poole 4	a							21 41			22 41	23 41	
	d							21 50			22 50	23 50	
Parkstone (Dorset)	d							21 54			22 54	23 54	
Branksome	d							21 57			22 57	23 57	
Bournemouth	a							22 03			23 03	00 03	
	d							22 06			23 06		
Pokesdown	d							22 10			23 10		
Christchurch	d							22 14			23 14		
Hinton Admiral	d							22 19			23 19		
New Milton	d							22 23			23 23		
Sway	d							22 28			23 28		
Lymington Pier	d		21 44	22 14									
Lymington Town	d		21 46	22 16									
Brockenhurst 3	a		21 54	22 24				22 33			23 33		
	d							22 34			23 34		
Beaulieu Road	d							22 39					
Ashurst New Forest	d							22 43			23 43		
Totton	d							22 48			23 48		
Salisbury	d												
Dean	d												
Mottisfont & Dunbridge	d												
Romsey	d				22 28	22 35							
Redbridge	d				22 35								
Millbrook (Hants)	d				22 39				←				
Southampton Central ⛴	a				22 41			22 53	22 41		23 53		
	d				23 05			22 55	23 05				
St Denys	d				↪				23 10				
Swaythling	d								23 13				
Southampton Airport Pkwy ✈	d							23 03	23 16				
Portsmouth Harbour ⛴	d						22 17						23 17
Portsmouth & Southsea	d						22 22						23 22
Fratton	d						22 26						23 26
Hilsea	d						22 30						23 30
Cosham	d						22 35						23 35
Portchester	d						22 40						23 40
Fareham	d						22 46						23 46
Botley	d						22 54						23 54
Hedge End	d						22 58						23 58
Eastleigh 3	a					22 48	23 04	23 09	23 19				00 04
	d					22 54		23 11	23 21				
Chandlers Ford	d								23 26				
Romsey	a					23 24			23 33				
Shawford	d												
Winchester	d							23 23					
Micheldever	d							23 32					
Basingstoke	a							23 42					
	d							23 44					
Reading 7	a												
Fleet	d												
Farnborough (Main)	d												
Woking	a							00 02					
Clapham Junction 10	a							00 23					
London Waterloo 15 ⊖	a							00 33					

Table 158R

Sundays

16 February to 23 March

Weymouth, Bournemouth, Lymington, Romsey, Southampton and Basingstoke - London

Network Diagram - see first Page of Table 158

		SW	SW	SW	SW	SW	SW	SW	SN	SW	SW	SW	SW	XC	SW	SW	SW	SW	SW	SW	SW	XC	SW
		1	1	1	1	1	◇1	1	1	1	1	◇1	1	◇1	◇1	1	1	1	1	◇1	1	◇1	1
							A					B			C					D			
							✠							✠	✠				✠	✠		✠	
Weymouth	d														07 48								
Upwey	d														07 52								
Dorchester West	a																						
Dorchester South	d														08 00								
Moreton (Dorset)	d														08 07								
Wool	d														08 13								
Wareham	d														08 20								
Holton Heath	d																						
Hamworthy	d														08 27								
Poole 4	a														08 31								
	d						06 50					07 50			08 32					08 55			
Parkstone (Dorset)	d						06 54					07 54			08 36								
Branksome	d						06 57					07 57			08 40								
Bournemouth	a						07 02					08 02			08 46					09 04			
	d						07 06					08 06			08 50					09 06		09 40	
Pokesdown	d						07 10					08 10								09 10			
Christchurch	d						07 14					08 14								09 14			
Hinton Admiral	d						07 19					08 19								09 19			
New Milton	d						07 23					08 23			09 01					09 23			
Sway	d						07 28					08 28								09 28			
Lymington Pier	d															09 14							09 44
Lymington Town	d															09 16							09 46
Brockenhurst 3	a						07 33					08 33			09 08	09 24				09 33		09 53	09 54
	d						07 34					08 34			09 09					09 34		09 57	
Beaulieu Road	d											08 39								09 39			
Ashurst New Forest	d						07 43					08 43								09 43			
Totton	d						07 48					08 48								09 48			
Salisbury	d							08 08		08 20							09 08						
Dean	d							08 20									09 20						
Mottisfont & Dunbridge	d							08 26									09 26						
Romsey	d							08 35		08 39							09 32	09 35					
Redbridge	d									08 46							09 39						
Millbrook (Hants)	d									08 50			←				09 43				←		
Southampton Central	a						07 53			08 52		08 53	08 52		09 23		09 45			09 53	09 45	10 10	
	d				06 55		07 55		08 27	08 59		08 55	08 59	09 15	09 25		09 59			09 55	09 59	10 15	
St Denys	d			00 04						→			09 04				→				10 04		
Swaythling	d			00 07									09 07								10 07		
Southampton Airport Pkwy	d			00 10	07 03		08 03		08 36			09 03	09 10	09 22	09 33					10 03	10 10	10 22	
Portsmouth Harbour	d					07 17					08 17								09 17				
Portsmouth & Southsea	d					07 22					08 22								09 22				
Fratton	d					07 26					08 26								09 26				
Hilsea	d					07 30					08 30								09 30				
Cosham	d					07 35					08 35								09 35				
Portchester	d					07 40					08 40								09 40				
Fareham	d					07 46					08 46								09 46				
Botley	d					07 54					08 54								09 54				
Hedge End	d		00 05			07 58					08 58								09 58				
Eastleigh 3	a		00 11	00 14	07 07	08 04	08 07		08 41		09 04	09 07	09 13					09 48	10 04	10 07	10 13		
	d		00 21		07 11		08 11					09 11	09 15					09 54		10 11	10 15		
Chandlers Ford	d							08 42					09 20								10 20		
Romsey	a							09 24					09 28					10 24			10 28		
Shawford	d											09 17											
Winchester	d		00a30		07 23		08 23					09 23		09 31	09 42					10 23		10 31	
Micheldever	d				07 32		08 32					09 32								10 32			
Basingstoke	a				07 42		08 42					09 42		09 46	09 58					10 42		10 46	
	d				07 44		08 44					09 44		09 47	10 00					10 44		10 47	
Reading 7	a													10 15								11 15	
Fleet	d	00 01																					
Farnborough (Main)	d	00 06																					
Woking	a	00 18			08 02		09 02					10 02			10 19					11 02			
Clapham Junction 10	a	00 53			08 31		09 30					10 27			10 39					11 27			
London Waterloo 15 ⊖	a	01 04			08 46		09 41					10 39			10 50					11 39			

A ✠ ◇ to Eastleigh

B ◇ to Eastleigh

C ✠ from Bournemouth

D ✠ from Eastleigh ◇ to Eastleigh

Table 158R

Sundays

16 February to 23 March

Weymouth, Bournemouth, Lymington, Romsey, Southampton and Basingstoke - London

Network Diagram - see first Page of Table 158

		SW	SW	SW	SW	SW	SW	SW	XC	SW	SW	SW	SW	SW	SW	SW	SW	XC	SW	SW	SW	SW	SW
		◇1	1	1	1	1	◇1	1	◇1	1	◇1	1	1	1	1	◇1	1	◇1	1	◇1	1	1	1
		A					B				A					C				A			
		⚒				⚒	⚒		⚒		⚒				⚒	⚒		⚒		⚒			
Weymouth	d	08 48									09 48									10 48			
Upwey	d	08 52									09 52									10 52			
Dorchester West	a																						
Dorchester South	d	09 00									10 00									11 00			
Moreton (Dorset)	d	09 07									10 07									11 07			
Wool	d	09 13									10 13									11 13			
Wareham	d	09 20									10 20									11 20			
Holton Heath	d																						
Hamworthy	d	09 27									10 27									11 27			
Poole 4	a	09 31									10 31									11 31			
	d	09 32					09 55				10 32					10 55				11 32			
Parkstone (Dorset)	d	09 36									10 36									11 36			
Branksome	d	09 40									10 40									11 40			
Bournemouth	a	09 46					10 04				10 46					11 04				11 46			
	d	09 50					10 06		10 40		10 50					11 06		11 40		11 50			
Pokesdown	d						10 10									11 10							
Christchurch	d						10 14									11 14							
Hinton Admiral	d						10 19									11 19							
New Milton	d	10 01					10 23				11 01					11 23				12 01			
Sway	d						10 28									11 28							
Lymington Pier	d		10 14							10 44		11 14							11 44		12 14		
Lymington Town	d		10 16							10 46		11 16							11 46		12 16		
Brockenhurst 3	a	10 08	10 24				10 33		10 53	10 54	11 08	11 24				11 33		11 53	11 54	12 08	12 24		
	d	10 09					10 34		10 57		11 09					11 34		11 57		12 09			
Beaulieu Road	d						10 39									11 39							
Ashurst New Forest	d						10 43									11 43							
Totton	d						10 48									11 48							
Salisbury	d			10 13									11 08									12 13	
Dean	d												11 20										
Mottisfont & Dunbridge	d												11 26										
Romsey	d			10 32	10 35								11 32	11 35								12 32	12 35
Redbridge	d			10 39									11 39									12 39	
Millbrook (Hants)	d			10 43				←					11 43				←					12 43	
Southampton Central ⛴	a	10 23		10 45			10 53	10 45	11 10		11 23		11 45			11 53	11 45	12 10		12 23		12 45	
	d	10 25		10 59			10 55	10 59	11 15		11 25		11 59			11 55	11 59	12 15		12 25		12 59	
St Denys	d			↪				11 04					↪				12 04					↪	
Swaythling	d							11 07									12 07						
Southampton Airport Pkwy ✈	d	10 33					11 03	11 10	11 22		11 33					12 03	12 10	12 22		12 33			
Portsmouth Harbour ⛴	d					10 17									11 17								
Portsmouth & Southsea	d					10 22									11 22								
Fratton	d					10 26									11 26								
Hilsea	d					10 30									11 30								
Cosham	d					10 35									11 35								
Portchester	d					10 40									11 40								
Fareham	d					10 46									11 46								
Botley	d					10 54									11 54								
Hedge End	d					10 58									11 58								
Eastleigh 8	a				10 48	11 04	11 07	11 13						11 48	12 04	12 07	12 13						12 48
	d				10 54		11 11	11 15						11 54		12 11	12 15						12 54
Chandlers Ford	d							11 20									12 20						
Romsey	a				11 24			11 28						12 24			12 28						13 24
Shawford	d						11 17																
Winchester	d	10 42					11 23		11 31		11 42					12 23		12 31		12 42			
Micheldever	d						11 32									12 32							
Basingstoke	a	10 58					11 42		11 46		11 58					12 42		12 46		12 58			
	d	11 00					11 44		11 47		12 00					12 44		12 47		13 00			
Reading 7	a								12 15									13 15					
Fleet	d																						
Farnborough (Main)	d																						
Woking	a	11 18					12 02				12 18					13 02				13 18			
Clapham Junction 10	a	11 39					12 27				12 39					13 27				13 39			
London Waterloo 15 ⊖	a	11 50					12 37				12 49					13 37				13 49			

A ⚒ from Bournemouth

B ⚒ from Bournemouth ◇ to Eastleigh

C ⚒ from Eastleigh ◇ to Eastleigh

Table 158R

Sundays

16 February to 23 March

Weymouth, Bournemouth, Lymington, Romsey, Southampton and Basingstoke - London

Network Diagram - see first Page of Table 158

		SW	SW	SW	XC	SW	SW	SW	SW	SW	SW	SW	SW	XC	SW	SW	SW	SW	SW	SW	SW	SW
		1	◇1	1	◇1	1	◇1	1	1	1	1	◇1	1	◇1	1	◇1	1	1	1	1	◇1	1
			A				B					C				B					C	
		🛒	🛒		🛒		🛒				🛒	🛒		🛒		🛒				🛒	🛒	
Weymouth	d						11 48									12 48						
Upwey	d						11 52									12 52						
Dorchester West	a																					
Dorchester South	d						12 00									13 00						
Moreton (Dorset)	d						12 07									13 07						
Wool	d						12 13									13 13						
Wareham	d						12 20									13 20						
Holton Heath	d																					
Hamworthy	d						12 27									13 27						
Poole 4	a						12 31									13 31						
	d		11 55				12 32					12 55				13 32					13 55	
Parkstone (Dorset)	d						12 36									13 36						
Branksome	d						12 40									13 40						
Bournemouth	a		12 04				12 46					13 04				13 46					14 04	
	d		12 06		12 40		12 50					13 06		13 40		13 50					14 06	
Pokesdown	d		12 10									13 10									14 10	
Christchurch	d		12 14									13 14									14 14	
Hinton Admiral	d		12 19									13 19									14 19	
New Milton	d		12 23				13 01					13 23				14 01					14 23	
Sway	d		12 28									13 28									14 28	
Lymington Pier	d					12 44		13 14							13 44		14 14					
Lymington Town	d					12 46		13 16							13 46		14 16					
Brockenhurst 3	a		12 33		12 53	12 54	13 08	13 24				13 33		13 53	13 54	14 08	14 24				14 33	
	d		12 34		12 57		13 09					13 34		13 57		14 09					14 34	
Beaulieu Road	d		12 39									13 39									14 39	
Ashurst New Forest	d		12 43									13 43									14 43	
Totton	d		12 48									13 48									14 48	
Salisbury	d								13 08									14 13				
Dean	d								13 20													
Mottisfont & Dunbridge	d								13 26													
Romsey	d								13 32	13 35								14 32	14 35			
Redbridge	d								13 39									14 39				
Millbrook (Hants)	d			←					13 43				←					14 43				←
Southampton Central ⛴	a		12 53	12 45	13 10		13 23		13 45			13 53	13 45	14 10		14 23		14 45			14 53	14 45
	d		12 55	12 59	13 15		13 25		13 59			13 55	13 59	14 15		14 25		14 59			14 55	14 59
St Denys	d			13 04					↦				14 04					↦				15 04
Swaythling	d			13 07									14 07									15 07
Southampton Airport Pkwy ✈	d		13 03	13 10	13 22		13 33					14 03	14 10	14 22		14 33					15 03	15 10
Portsmouth Harbour ⛴	d	12 17									13 17									14 17		
Portsmouth & Southsea	d	12 22									13 22									14 22		
Fratton	d	12 26									13 26									14 26		
Hilsea	d	12 30									13 30									14 30		
Cosham	d	12 35									13 35									14 35		
Portchester	d	12 40									13 40									14 40		
Fareham	d	12 46									13 46									14 46		
Botley	d	12 54									13 54									14 54		
Hedge End	d	12 58									13 58									14 58		
Eastleigh 3	a	13 04	13 07	13 13						13 48	14 04	14 07	14 13						14 48	15 04	15 07	15 13
	d		13 11	13 15						13 54		14 11	14 15						14 54		15 11	15 15
Chandlers Ford	d			13 20									14 20									15 20
Romsey	a			13 28						14 24			14 28						15 24			15 28
Shawford	d		13 17																		15 17	
Winchester	d		13 23		13 31		13 42					14 23		14 31		14 42					15 23	
Micheldever	d		13 32									14 32									15 32	
Basingstoke	a		13 42		13 46		13 58					14 42		14 46		14 58					15 42	
	d		13 44		13 47		14 00					14 44		14 47		15 00					15 44	
Reading 7	a				14 15									15 15								
Fleet	d																					
Farnborough (Main)	d																					
Woking	a		14 02				14 18					15 02				15 18					16 02	
Clapham Junction 10	a		14 27				14 39					15 27				15 39					16 27	
London Waterloo 15 ⊖	a		14 37				14 49					15 37				15 49					16 37	

A 🛒 from Bournemouth ◇ to Eastleigh

B 🛒 from Bournemouth

C 🛒 from Eastleigh ◇ to Eastleigh

Table 158R

Sundays

16 February to 23 March

Weymouth, Bournemouth, Lymington, Romsey, Southampton and Basingstoke - London

Network Diagram - see first Page of Table 158

		XC	SW	SW	GW	SW	SW	SW	SW	SW	SW	XC	SW	SW	SW	SW	SW	SW	SW	SW	XC	SW	SW
		◇1	1	◇1	◇	1	1	1	1	◇1	1	◇1	1	◇1	1	1	1	1	◇1	1	◇1	1	◇1
				A						B				A					B				A
		✠		✠					✠	✠		✠		✠				✠	✠		✠		✠
Weymouth	d			13 48	14 00									14 48									15 48
Upwey	d			13 52	14 05									14 52									15 52
Dorchester West	a				14 12																		
Dorchester South	d			14 00										15 00									16 00
Moreton (Dorset)	d			14 07										15 07									16 07
Wool	d			14 13										15 13									16 13
Wareham	d			14 20										15 20									16 20
Holton Heath	d																						
Hamworthy	d			14 27										15 27									16 27
Poole 4	a			14 31										15 31									16 31
	d			14 32						14 55				15 32					15 55				16 32
Parkstone (Dorset)	d			14 36										15 36									16 36
Branksome	d			14 40										15 40									16 40
Bournemouth	a			14 46						15 04				15 46					16 04				16 46
	d	14 40		14 50						15 06		15 40		15 50					16 06		16 40		16 50
Pokesdown	d									15 10									16 10				
Christchurch	d									15 14									16 14				
Hinton Admiral	d									15 19									16 19				
New Milton	d			15 01						15 23				16 01					16 23				17 01
Sway	d									15 28									16 28				
Lymington Pier	d		14 44			15 14							15 44		16 14							16 44	
Lymington Town	d		14 46			15 16							15 46		16 16							16 46	
Brockenhurst 3	a	14 53	14 54	15 08		15 24				15 33		15 53	15 54	16 08	16 24				16 33		16 53	16 54	17 08
	d	14 57		15 09						15 34		15 57		16 09					16 34		16 57		17 09
Beaulieu Road	d									15 39									16 39				
Ashurst New Forest	d									15 43									16 43				
Totton	d									15 48									16 48				
Salisbury	d						15 08									16 13							
Dean	d						15 20																
Mottisfont & Dunbridge	d						15 26																
Romsey	d						15 32	15 35								16 32	16 35						
Redbridge	d						15 39									16 39							
Millbrook (Hants)	d						15 43				←					16 43				←			
Southampton Central ⛴	a	15 10		15 23			15 45			15 53	15 45	16 10		16 23		16 45			16 53	16 45	17 10		17 23
	d	15 15		15 25			15 59			15 55	15 59	16 15		16 25		16 59			16 55	16 59	17 15		17 25
St Denys	d						→				16 04					→				17 04			
Swaythling	d										16 07									17 07			
Southampton Airport Pkwy ✈	d	15 22		15 33						16 03	16 10	16 22		16 33					17 03	17 10	17 22		17 33
Portsmouth Harbour ⛴	d								15 17									16 17					
Portsmouth & Southsea	d								15 22									16 22					
Fratton	d								15 26									16 26					
Hilsea	d								15 30									16 30					
Cosham	d								15 35									16 35					
Portchester	d								15 40									16 40					
Fareham	d								15 46									16 46					
Botley	d								15 54									16 54					
Hedge End	d								15 58									16 58					
Eastleigh 3	a							15 48	16 04	16 07	16 13						16 48	17 04	17 07	17 13			
	d							15 54		16 11	16 15						16 54		17 11	17 15			
Chandlers Ford	d										16 20									17 20			
Romsey	a							16 24			16 28						17 24			17 28			
Shawford	d																		17 17				
Winchester	d	15 31		15 42						16 23		16 31		16 42					17 23		17 31		17 42
Micheldever	d									16 32									17 32				
Basingstoke	a	15 46		15 58						16 42		16 46		16 58					17 42		17 46		17 58
	d	15 47		16 00						16 44		16 47		17 00					17 44		17 47		18 00
Reading 7	a	16 15										17 15									18 15		
Fleet	d																						
Farnborough (Main)	d																						
Woking	a			16 18						17 02				17 18					18 02				18 18
Clapham Junction 10	a			16 39						17 27				17 39					18 27				18 39
London Waterloo 15 ⊖	a			16 49						17 37				17 49					18 37				18 49

A ✠ from Bournemouth

B ✠ from Eastleigh ◇ to Eastleigh

Table 158R

Sundays

16 February to 23 March

Weymouth, Bournemouth, Lymington, Romsey, Southampton and Basingstoke - London

Network Diagram - see first Page of Table 158

		SW 1	SW 1	SW 1	SW 1	SW ◇1 A	SW 1	XC ◇1 🛒	SW 1	SW ◇1 B 🛒	SW 1	SW 1	SW 1	SW 1	SW ◇1 A	SW 1	XC ◇1 🛒	SW 1	SW ◇1 B 🛒	GW ◇	SW 1	SN 1	SW 1
Weymouth	d									16 48									17 48	17 56			
Upwey	d									16 52									17 52	18 01			
Dorchester West	a																			18 08			
Dorchester South	d									17 00									18 00				
Moreton (Dorset)	d									17 07									18 07				
Wool	d									17 13									18 13				
Wareham	d									17 20									18 20				
Holton Heath	d																						
Hamworthy	d									17 27									18 27				
Poole 4	a									17 31									18 31				
	d					16 55				17 32					17 55				18 32				
Parkstone (Dorset)	d									17 36									18 36				
Branksome	d									17 40									18 40				
Bournemouth	a					17 04				17 46					18 04				18 46				
	d					17 06		17 40		17 50					18 06		18 40		18 50				
Pokesdown	d					17 10									18 10								
Christchurch	d					17 14									18 14								
Hinton Admiral	d					17 19									18 19								
New Milton	d					17 23				18 01					18 23				19 01				
Sway	d					17 28									18 28								
Lymington Pier	d	17 14							17 44		18 14							18 44			19 14		
Lymington Town	d	17 16							17 46		18 16							18 46			19 16		
Brockenhurst 3	a	17 24				17 33		17 53	17 54	18 08	18 24				18 33		18 53	18 54	19 08		19 24		
	d					17 34		17 57		18 09					18 34		18 57		19 09				
Beaulieu Road	d					17 39									18 39								
Ashurst New Forest	d					17 43									18 43								
Totton	d					17 48									18 48								
Salisbury	d		17 08									18 13											19 08
Dean	d		17 20																				19 20
Mottisfont & Dunbridge	d		17 26																				19 26
Romsey	d		17 32	17 35								18 32	18 35										19 32
Redbridge	d		17 39									18 39											19 39
Millbrook (Hants)	d		17 43				←					18 43				←							19 43
Southampton Central	a		17 45			17 53	17 45	18 10		18 23		18 45			18 53	18 45	19 10		19 23				19 45
	d		17 59			17 55	17 59	18 15		18 25		18 59			18 55	18 59	19 15		19 25			19 30	19 59
St Denys	d		→				18 04					→				19 04							→
Swaythling	d						18 07									19 07							
Southampton Airport Pkwy ✈	d					18 03	18 10	18 22		18 33					19 03	19 10	19 22		19 33			19 38	
Portsmouth Harbour ⛴	d				17 17									18 17									
Portsmouth & Southsea	d				17 22									18 22									
Fratton	d				17 26									18 26									
Hilsea	d				17 30									18 30									
Cosham	d				17 35									18 35									
Portchester	d				17 40									18 40									
Fareham	d				17 46									18 46									
Botley	d				17 54									18 54									
Hedge End	d				17 58									18 58									
Eastleigh 3	a			17 48	18 04	18 07	18 13						18 48	19 04	19 07	19 13						19 42	
	d			17 54		18 11	18 15						18 54		19 11	19 15							
Chandlers Ford	d						18 20									19 20							
Romsey	a			18 24			18 28						19 24			19 28							
Shawford	d														19 17								
Winchester	d					18 23		18 31		18 42					19 23		19 31		19 42				
Micheldever	d					18 32									19 32								
Basingstoke	a					18 42		18 46		18 58					19 42		19 46		19 58				
	d					18 44		18 47		19 00					19 44		19 47		20 00				
Reading 7	a							19 15									20 15						
Fleet	d																						
Farnborough (Main)	d																						
Woking	a					19 02				19 18					20 02				20 18				
Clapham Junction 10	a					19 27				19 39					20 27				20 39				
London Waterloo 15 ⊖	a					19 37				19 49					20 37				20 49				

A ◇ to Eastleigh

B 🛒 from Bournemouth

Table 158R

Sundays

16 February to 23 March

Weymouth, Bournemouth, Lymington, Romsey, Southampton and Basingstoke - London

Network Diagram - see first Page of Table 158

		SW 1	SW 1	SW ◇1 A	SW 1	XC ◇1	SW 1	SW ◇1 B	SW 1	SN 1	SW 1	SW 1	SW 1	SW ◇1 A	SW 1	SW 1	SW 1	SW 1	SW 1	SW 1	SW ◇1 A	SW 1
Weymouth	d							18 48													19 58	
Upwey	d							18 52													20 02	
Dorchester West	a																					
Dorchester South	d							19 00													20 10	
Moreton (Dorset)	d							19 07													20 17	
Wool	d							19 13													20 23	
Wareham	d							19 20													20 30	
Holton Heath	d																					
Hamworthy	d							19 27													20 37	
Poole 4	a							19 31													20 41	
	d			18 55				19 32						19 55							20 50	
Parkstone (Dorset)	d							19 36													20 54	
Branksome	d							19 40													20 57	
Bournemouth	a			19 04				19 46						20 04							21 03	
	d			19 06		19 40		19 50						20 06							21 06	
Pokesdown	d			19 10										20 10							21 10	
Christchurch	d			19 14										20 14							21 14	
Hinton Admiral	d			19 19										20 19							21 19	
New Milton	d			19 23				20 01						20 23							21 23	
Sway	d			19 28										20 28							21 28	
Lymington Pier	d						19 44		20 14							20 44	21 14					
Lymington Town	d						19 46		20 16							20 46	21 16					
Brockenhurst 3	a			19 33		19 53	19 54	20 08	20 24					20 33		20 54	21 24				21 33	
	d			19 34		19 57		20 09						20 34							21 34	
Beaulieu Road	d			19 39										20 39							21 39	
Ashurst New Forest	d			19 43										20 43							21 43	
Totton	d			19 48										20 48							21 48	
Salisbury	d										20 13							21 08				
Dean	d																	21 20				
Mottisfont & Dunbridge	d																	21 26				
Romsey	d	19 35									20 32	20 35						21 32	21 35			
Redbridge	d										20 39							21 39				
Millbrook (Hants)	d				←						20 43				←			21 43				←
Southampton Central ⛴	a			19 53	19 45	20 10		20 23			20 45			20 53	20 45			21 45			21 53	21 45
	d			19 55	19 59	20 15		20 25		20 29	20 59			20 55	20 59			21 59			21 55	21 59
St Denys	d				20 04						↪				21 04			↪				22 04
Swaythling	d				20 07										21 07							22 07
Southampton Airport Pkwy ✈	d			20 03	20 10	20 22		20 33		20 38				21 03	21 10						22 03	22 10
Portsmouth Harbour ⛴	d		19 17										20 17							21 17		
Portsmouth & Southsea	d		19 22										20 22							21 22		
Fratton	d		19 26										20 26							21 26		
Hilsea	d		19 30										20 30							21 30		
Cosham	d		19 35										20 35							21 35		
Portchester	d		19 40										20 40							21 40		
Fareham	d		19 46										20 46							21 46		
Botley	d		19 54										20 54							21 54		
Hedge End	d		19 58										20 58							21 58		
Eastleigh 3	a	19 48	20 04	20 07	20 13					20 41		20 48	21 04	21 07	21 13				21 48	22 04	22 07	22 13
	d	19 54	20 11		20 15							20 54	21 11		21 15				21 54	22 11		22 15
Chandlers Ford	d				20 20										21 20							22 20
Romsey	a	20 24			20 28							21 24			21 28				22 24			22 31
Shawford	d												21 17									
Winchester	d		20 23			20 31		20 42					21 23							22 23		
Micheldever	d		20 32										21 32							22 32		
Basingstoke	a		20 42			20 46		20 58					21 42							22 42		
	d		20 44			20 47		21 00					21 44							22 44		
Reading 7	a					21 15																
Fleet	d																					
Farnborough (Main)	d																					
Woking	a		21 02					21 18					22 02							23 02		
Clapham Junction 10	a		21 27					21 39					22 27							23 27		
London Waterloo 15 ⊖	a		21 37					21 49					22 37							23 37		

A ◇ to Eastleigh

B from Bournemouth

Table 158R

Sundays

16 February to 23 March

Weymouth, Bournemouth, Lymington, Romsey, Southampton and Basingstoke - London

Network Diagram - see first Page of Table 158

Station		GW	SW 1	SW 1	SW 1	SW 1	SW 1	SW ◇1	SW 1	SW 1	SW 1	SW 1
Weymouth	d	20 09						20 58		21 58	22 58	
Upwey	d	20 14						21 02		22 02	23 02	
Dorchester West	a	20 21										
Dorchester South	d							21 10		22 10	23 10	
Moreton (Dorset)	d							21 17		22 17	23 17	
Wool	d							21 23		22 23	23 23	
Wareham	d							21 30		22 30	23 30	
Holton Heath	d											
Hamworthy	d							21 37		22 37	23 37	
Poole 4	a							21 41		22 41	23 41	
	d							21 50		22 50	23 50	
Parkstone (Dorset)	d							21 54		22 54	23 54	
Branksome	d							21 57		22 57	23 57	
Bournemouth	a							22 03		23 03	00 03	
	d							22 06		23 06		
Pokesdown	d							22 10		23 10		
Christchurch	d							22 14		23 14		
Hinton Admiral	d							22 19		23 19		
New Milton	d							22 23		23 23		
Sway	d							22 28		23 28		
Lymington Pier	d		21 44	22 14								
Lymington Town	d		21 46	22 16								
Brockenhurst 3	a		21 54	22 24				22 33		23 33		
	d							22 34		23 34		
Beaulieu Road	d							22 39				
Ashurst New Forest	d							22 43		23 43		
Totton	d							22 48		23 48		
Salisbury	d											
Dean	d											
Mottisfont & Dunbridge	d											
Romsey	d				22 28	22 35						
Redbridge	d				22 35							
Millbrook (Hants)	d				22 39				←			
Southampton Central ⛴	a				22 41			22 53	22 41	23 53		
	d				23 05			22 55	23 05			
St Denys	d				→				23 10			
Swaythling	d								23 13			
Southampton Airport Pkwy ✈	d							23 03	23 16			
Portsmouth Harbour ⛴	d						22 17					23 17
Portsmouth & Southsea	d						22 22					23 22
Fratton	d						22 26					23 26
Hilsea	d						22 30					23 30
Cosham	d						22 35					23 35
Portchester	d						22 40					23 40
Fareham	d						22 46					23 46
Botley	d						22 54					23 54
Hedge End	d						22 58					23 58
Eastleigh 3	a					22 48	23 04	23 09	23 19			00 04
	d					22 54		23 11	23 21			
Chandlers Ford	d								23 26			
Romsey	a					23 24			23 33			
Shawford	d											
Winchester	d							23 23				
Micheldever	d							23 32				
Basingstoke	a							23 42				
	d							23 44				
Reading 7	a											
Fleet	d											
Farnborough (Main)	d											
Woking	a							00 02				
Clapham Junction 10	a							00 23				
London Waterloo 15 ⊖	a							00 33				

Table 158R

Sundays

30 March to 11 May

Weymouth, Bournemouth, Lymington, Romsey, Southampton and Basingstoke - London

Network Diagram - see first Page of Table 158

		SW	SW	SW	SW	SW	SW	SW	SN	SW	SW	SW	SW	XC	SW	SW	SW	SW	SW	SW	SW	XC	SW
		[1]	[1]	[1]	[1]	[1]	◇[1]	[1]	[1]	[1]	[1]	◇[1]	[1]	◇[1]	◇[1]	[1]	[1]	[1]	[1]	◇[1]	[1]	◇[1]	[1]
							A					B			C					D			
							🛒							🛒	🛒				🛒	🛒		🛒	
Weymouth	d														07 48								
Upwey	d														07 52								
Dorchester West	a																						
Dorchester South	d														08 00								
Moreton (Dorset)	d														08 07								
Wool	d														08 13								
Wareham	d														08 20								
Holton Heath	d																						
Hamworthy	d														08 27								
Poole [4]	a														08 31								
	d						06 50					07 50			08 32					08 55			
Parkstone (Dorset)	d						06 54					07 54			08 36								
Branksome	d						06 57					07 57			08 40								
Bournemouth	a						07 02					08 02			08 46					09 04			
	d						07 06					08 06			08 50					09 06		09 40	
Pokesdown	d						07 10					08 10								09 10			
Christchurch	d						07 14					08 14								09 14			
Hinton Admiral	d						07 19					08 19								09 19			
New Milton	d						07 23					08 23			09 01					09 23			
Sway	d						07 28					08 28								09 28			
Lymington Pier	d															09 14							09 44
Lymington Town	d															09 16							09 46
Brockenhurst [3]	a						07 33					08 33			09 08	09 24				09 33		09 53	09 54
	d						07 34					08 34			09 09					09 34		09 57	
Beaulieu Road	d											08 39								09 39			
Ashurst New Forest	d						07 43					08 43								09 43			
Totton	d						07 48					08 48								09 48			
Salisbury	d							08 08		08 20							09 08						
Dean	d							08 20									09 20						
Mottisfont & Dunbridge	d							08 26									09 26						
Romsey	d							08 35		08 39							09 32	09 35					
Redbridge	d									08 46							09 39						
Millbrook (Hants)	d									08 50			←				09 43				←		
Southampton Central ⛴	a						07 53			08 52		08 53	08 52		09 23		09 45			09 53	09 45	10 10	
	d				06 55		07 55		08 27	08 59		08 55	08 59	09 15	09 25		09 59			09 55	09 59	10 15	
St Denys	d			00 04						↪			09 04				↪				10 04		
Swaythling	d			00 07									09 07								10 07		
Southampton Airport Pkwy ✈	d			00 10	07 03		08 03		08 36			09 03	09 10	09 22	09 33					10 03	10 10	10 22	
Portsmouth Harbour ⛴	d					07 17					08 17								09 17				
Portsmouth & Southsea	d					07 22					08 22								09 22				
Fratton	d					07 26					08 26								09 26				
Hilsea	d					07 30					08 30								09 30				
Cosham	d					07 35					08 35								09 35				
Portchester	d					07 40					08 40								09 40				
Fareham	d					07 46					08 46								09 46				
Botley	d					07 54					08 54								09 54				
Hedge End	d		00 05			07 58					08 58								09 58				
Eastleigh [3]	a		00 11	00 14	07 07	08 04	08 07		08 41		09 04	09 07	09 13					09 48	10 04	10 07	10 13		
	d		00 21		07 11	08 11					09 11		09 15					09 54	10 11		10 15		
Chandlers Ford	d							08 42					09 20								10 20		
Romsey	a							09 24					09 28					10 24			10 28		
Shawford	d										09 17												
Winchester	d		00a30		07 23	08 23					09 23			09 31	09 42				10 23			10 31	
Micheldever	d				07 32	08 32					09 32								10 32				
Basingstoke	a				07 42	08 42					09 42			09 46	09 58				10 42			10 46	
	d				07 44	08 44					09 44			09 47	10 00				10 44			10 47	
Reading [7]	a													10 04								11 03	
Fleet	d	00 01																					
Farnborough (Main)	d	00 06																					
Woking	a	00 18			08 02	09 02					10 02				10 19				11 02				
Clapham Junction [10]	a	00 53			08 31	09 30					10 27				10 39				11 27				
London Waterloo [15] ⊖	a	01 04			08 46	09 41					10 39				10 50				11 39				

A 🛒 ◇ to Eastleigh

B ◇ to Eastleigh

C 🛒 from Bournemouth

D 🛒 from Eastleigh ◇ to Eastleigh

Table 158R

Sundays

30 March to 11 May

Weymouth, Bournemouth, Lymington, Romsey, Southampton and Basingstoke - London

Network Diagram - see first Page of Table 158

		SW	SW	SW	SW	SW	SW		SW	XC	SW	SW	SW	SW	SW	SW	SW		SW	XC	SW	SW	SW	SW	SW
		◇1	1	1	1	1	◇1		1	◇1	1	◇1	1	1	1	1	◇1		1	◇1	1	◇1	1	1	1
		A					B					A					C					A			
		🚌				🚌	🚌			🚌		🚌				🚌	🚌			🚌		🚌			
Weymouth	d	08 48										09 48										10 48			
Upwey	d	08 52										09 52										10 52			
Dorchester West	a																								
Dorchester South	d	09 00										10 00										11 00			
Moreton (Dorset)	d	09 07										10 07										11 07			
Wool	d	09 13										10 13										11 13			
Wareham	d	09 20										10 20										11 20			
Holton Heath	d																								
Hamworthy	d	09 27										10 27										11 27			
Poole 4	a	09 31										10 31										11 31			
	d	09 32					09 55					10 32					10 55					11 32			
Parkstone (Dorset)	d	09 36										10 36										11 36			
Branksome	d	09 40										10 40										11 40			
Bournemouth	a	09 46					10 04					10 46					11 04					11 46			
	d	09 50					10 06			10 40		10 50					11 06			11 40		11 50			
Pokesdown	d						10 10										11 10								
Christchurch	d						10 14										11 14								
Hinton Admiral	d						10 19										11 19								
New Milton	d	10 01					10 23					11 01					11 23					12 01			
Sway	d						10 28										11 28								
Lymington Pier	d		10 14								10 44		11 14								11 44		12 14		
Lymington Town	d		10 16								10 46		11 16								11 46		12 16		
Brockenhurst 3	a	10 08	10 24				10 33			10 53	10 54	11 08	11 24				11 33			11 53	11 54	12 08	12 24		
	d	10 09					10 34			10 57		11 09					11 34			11 57		12 09			
Beaulieu Road	d						10 39										11 39								
Ashurst New Forest	d						10 43										11 43								
Totton	d						10 48										11 48								
Salisbury	d			10 13										11 08										12 13	
Dean	d													11 20											
Mottisfont & Dunbridge	d													11 26											
Romsey	d			10 32	10 35									11 32	11 35									12 32	12 35
Redbridge	d			10 39										11 39										12 39	
Millbrook (Hants)	d			10 43					←					11 43					←					12 43	
Southampton Central ⛴	a	10 23		10 45			10 53		10 45	11 10		11 23		11 45			11 53		11 45	12 10		12 23		12 45	
	d	10 25		10 59			10 55		10 59	11 15		11 25		11 59			11 55		11 59	12 15		12 25		12 59	
St Denys	d			→					11 04					→					12 04					→	
Swaythling	d								11 07										12 07						
Southampton Airport Pkwy ✈	d	10 33					11 03		11 10	11 22		11 33					12 03		12 10	12 22		12 33			
Portsmouth Harbour ⛴	d					10 17										11 17									
Portsmouth & Southsea	d					10 22										11 22									
Fratton	d					10 26										11 26									
Hilsea	d					10 30										11 30									
Cosham	d					10 35										11 35									
Portchester	d					10 40										11 40									
Fareham	d					10 46										11 46									
Botley	d					10 54										11 54									
Hedge End	d					10 58										11 58									
Eastleigh 3	a				10 48	11 04	11 07		11 13						11 48	12 04	12 07		12 13						12 48
	d				10 54	11 11			11 15						11 54	12 11			12 15						12 54
Chandlers Ford	d								11 20										12 20						
Romsey	a				11 24				11 28						12 24				12 28						13 24
Shawford	d					11 17																			
Winchester	d	10 42				11 23				11 31		11 42				12 23				12 31		12 42			
Micheldever	d					11 32										12 32									
Basingstoke	a	10 58				11 42				11 46		11 58				12 42				12 46		12 58			
	d	11 00				11 44				11 47		12 00				12 44				12 47		13 00			
Reading 7	a									12 02										13 03					
Fleet	d																								
Farnborough (Main)	d																								
Woking	a	11 18				12 02						12 18				13 02						13 18			
Clapham Junction 10	a	11 39				12 27						12 39				13 27						13 39			
London Waterloo 15 ⊖	a	11 50				12 37						12 49				13 37						13 49			

A 🚌 from Bournemouth

B 🚌 from Bournemouth ◇ to Eastleigh

C 🚌 from Eastleigh ◇ to Eastleigh

Table 158R

Sundays

30 March to 11 May

Weymouth, Bournemouth, Lymington, Romsey, Southampton and Basingstoke - London

Network Diagram - see first Page of Table 158

		SW	SW		SW	XC	SW	SW	SW	SW	SW	SW	SW		SW	XC	SW	SW	SW	SW	SW	SW	SW		SW
		1	◇1		1	◇1	1	◇1	1	1	1	1	◇1		1	◇1	1	◇1	1	1	1	1	◇1		1
			A					B					C					B					C		
		🍴	🍴			🍴		🍴				🍴	🍴			🍴		🍴				🍴	🍴		
Weymouth	d							11 48										12 48							
Upwey	d							11 52										12 52							
Dorchester West	a																								
Dorchester South	d							12 00										13 00							
Moreton (Dorset)	d							12 07										13 07							
Wool	d							12 13										13 13							
Wareham	d							12 20										13 20							
Holton Heath	d																								
Hamworthy	d							12 27										13 27							
Poole 4	a							12 31										13 31							
	d		11 55					12 32					12 55					13 32					13 55		
Parkstone (Dorset)	d							12 36										13 36							
Branksome	d							12 40										13 40							
Bournemouth	a		12 04					12 46					13 04					13 46					14 04		
	d		12 06			12 40		12 50					13 06			13 40		13 50					14 06		
Pokesdown	d		12 10										13 10										14 10		
Christchurch	d		12 14										13 14										14 14		
Hinton Admiral	d		12 19										13 19										14 19		
New Milton	d		12 23					13 01					13 23					14 01					14 23		
Sway	d		12 28										13 28										14 28		
Lymington Pier	d						12 44		13 14								13 44		14 14						
Lymington Town	d						12 46		13 16								13 46		14 16						
Brockenhurst 3	a		12 33			12 53	12 54	13 08	13 24				13 33			13 53	13 54	14 08	14 24				14 33		
	d		12 34			12 57		13 09					13 34			13 57		14 09					14 34		
Beaulieu Road	d		12 39										13 39										14 39		
Ashurst New Forest	d		12 43										13 43										14 43		
Totton	d		12 48										13 48										14 48		
Salisbury	d									13 08										14 13					
Dean	d									13 20															
Mottisfont & Dunbridge	d									13 26															
Romsey	d									13 32	13 35									14 32	14 35				
Redbridge	d									13 39										14 39					
Millbrook (Hants)	d				←					13 43					←					14 43					←
Southampton Central ⛴	a		12 53		12 45	13 10		13 23		13 45			13 53		13 45	14 10		14 23		14 45			14 53		14 45
	d		12 55		12 59	13 15		13 25		13 59			13 55		13 59	14 15		14 25		14 59			14 55		14 59
St Denys	d				13 04					→					14 04					→					15 04
Swaythling	d				13 07										14 07										15 07
Southampton Airport Pkwy ✈	d		13 03		13 10	13 22		13 33					14 03		14 10	14 22		14 33					15 03		15 10
Portsmouth Harbour ⛴	d	12 17										13 17										14 17			
Portsmouth & Southsea	d	12 22										13 22										14 22			
Fratton	d	12 26										13 26										14 26			
Hilsea	d	12 30										13 30										14 30			
Cosham	d	12 35										13 35										14 35			
Portchester	d	12 40										13 40										14 40			
Fareham	d	12 46										13 46										14 46			
Botley	d	12 54										13 54										14 54			
Hedge End	d	12 58										13 58										14 58			
Eastleigh 3	a	13 04	13 07		13 13						13 48	14 04	14 07		14 13						14 48	15 04	15 07		15 13
	d	13 11			13 15						13 54	14 11			14 15						14 54	15 11			15 15
Chandlers Ford	d				13 20										14 20										15 20
Romsey	a				13 28						14 24				14 28						15 24				15 28
Shawford	d	13 17																				15 17			
Winchester	d	13 23				13 31		13 42				14 23				14 31		14 42				15 23			
Micheldever	d	13 32										14 32										15 32			
Basingstoke	a	13 42				13 46		13 58				14 42				14 46		14 58				15 42			
	d	13 44				13 47		14 00				14 44				14 47		15 00				15 44			
Reading 7	a					14 02										15 03									
Fleet	d																								
Farnborough (Main)	d																								
Woking	a	14 02						14 18				15 02						15 18				16 02			
Clapham Junction 10	a	14 27						14 39				15 27						15 39				16 27			
London Waterloo 15 ⊖	a	14 37						14 49				15 37						15 49				16 37			

A 🍴 from Bournemouth ◇ to Eastleigh

B 🍴 from Bournemouth

C 🍴 from Eastleigh ◇ to Eastleigh

Table 158R

Sundays

30 March to 11 May

Weymouth, Bournemouth, Lymington, Romsey, Southampton and Basingstoke - London

Network Diagram - see first Page of Table 158

		XC	SW	SW	GW	SW	SW	SW	SW	SW	SW	XC	SW	SW	SW	SW	SW	SW	SW	SW	XC	SW	SW
		◇1	1	◇1	◇	1	1	1	1	◇1	1	◇1	1	◇1	1	1	1	1	◇1	1	◇1	1	◇1
				A						B				A					B				A
		🚲		🚲					🚲	🚲		🚲		🚲				🚲	🚲		🚲		🚲
Weymouth	d			13 48	14 00									14 48									15 48
Upwey	d			13 52	14 05									14 52									15 52
Dorchester West	a				14 12																		
Dorchester South	d			14 00										15 00									16 00
Moreton (Dorset)	d			14 07										15 07									16 07
Wool	d			14 13										15 13									16 13
Wareham	d			14 20										15 20									16 20
Holton Heath	d																						
Hamworthy	d			14 27										15 27									16 27
Poole 4	a			14 31										15 31									16 31
	d			14 32						14 55				15 32					15 55				16 32
Parkstone (Dorset)	d			14 36										15 36									16 36
Branksome	d			14 40										15 40									16 40
Bournemouth	a			14 46						15 04				15 46					16 04				16 46
	d	14 40		14 50						15 06		15 40		15 50					16 06		16 40		16 50
Pokesdown	d									15 10									16 10				
Christchurch	d									15 14									16 14				
Hinton Admiral	d									15 19									16 19				
New Milton	d			15 01						15 23				16 01					16 23				17 01
Sway	d									15 28									16 28				
Lymington Pier	d		14 44			15 14							15 44		16 14							16 44	
Lymington Town	d		14 46			15 16							15 46		16 16							16 46	
Brockenhurst 3	a	14 53	14 54	15 08		15 24				15 33		15 53	15 54	16 08	16 24				16 33		16 53	16 54	17 08
	d	14 57		15 09						15 34		15 57		16 09					16 34		16 57		17 09
Beaulieu Road	d									15 39									16 39				
Ashurst New Forest	d									15 43									16 43				
Totton	d									15 48									16 48				
Salisbury	d						15 08									16 13							
Dean	d						15 20																
Mottisfont & Dunbridge	d						15 26																
Romsey	d						15 32	15 35								16 32	16 35						
Redbridge	d						15 39									16 39							
Millbrook (Hants)	d						15 43				←					16 43				←			
Southampton Central ⛴	a	15 10		15 23			15 45			15 53	15 45	16 10		16 23		16 45			16 53	16 45	17 10		17 23
	d	15 15		15 25			15 59			15 55	15 59	16 15		16 25		16 59			16 55	16 59	17 15		17 25
St Denys	d						→				16 04					→				17 04			
Swaythling	d										16 07									17 07			
Southampton Airport Pkwy ✈	d	15 22		15 33						16 03	16 10	16 22		16 33					17 03	17 10	17 22		17 33
Portsmouth Harbour ⛴	d								15 17									16 17					
Portsmouth & Southsea	d								15 22									16 22					
Fratton	d								15 26									16 26					
Hilsea	d								15 30									16 30					
Cosham	d								15 35									16 35					
Portchester	d								15 40									16 40					
Fareham	d								15 46									16 46					
Botley	d								15 54									16 54					
Hedge End	d								15 58									16 58					
Eastleigh 3	a							15 48	16 04	16 07	16 13						16 48	17 04	17 07	17 13			
	d							15 54	16 11		16 15						16 54	17 11		17 15			
Chandlers Ford	d										16 20									17 20			
Romsey	a							16 24			16 28						17 24			17 28			
Shawford	d																		17 17				
Winchester	d	15 31		15 42						16 23		16 31		16 42					17 23		17 31		17 42
Micheldever	d									16 32									17 32				
Basingstoke	a	15 46		15 58						16 42		16 46		16 58					17 42		17 46		17 58
	d	15 47		16 00						16 44		16 47		17 00					17 44		17 47		18 00
Reading 7	a	16 02										17 03									18 04		
Fleet	d																						
Farnborough (Main)	d																						
Woking	a			16 18						17 02				17 18					18 02				18 18
Clapham Junction 10	a			16 39						17 27				17 39					18 27				18 39
London Waterloo 15 ⊖	a			16 49						17 37				17 49					18 37				18 49

A 🚲 from Bournemouth

B 🚲 from Eastleigh ◇ to Eastleigh

Table 158R

Sundays
30 March to 11 May

Weymouth, Bournemouth, Lymington, Romsey, Southampton and Basingstoke - London

Network Diagram - see first Page of Table 158

		SW	SW	SW	SW	SW	SW	XC	SW	SW	SW	SW	SW	SW	SW	SW	XC	SW	SW	GW	SW	SN	SW
		1	1	1	1	◇1	1	◇1	1	◇1	1	1	1	1	◇1	1	◇1	1	◇1	◇	1	1	1
						A				B					A				B				
								🍴		🍴							🍴		🍴				
Weymouth	d									16 48									17 48	17 56			
Upwey	d									16 52									17 52	18 01			
Dorchester West	a																			18 08			
Dorchester South	d									17 00									18 00				
Moreton (Dorset)	d									17 07									18 07				
Wool	d									17 13									18 13				
Wareham	d									17 20									18 20				
Holton Heath	d																						
Hamworthy	d									17 27									18 27				
Poole 4	a									17 31									18 31				
	d					16 55				17 32					17 55				18 32				
Parkstone (Dorset)	d									17 36									18 36				
Branksome	d									17 40									18 40				
Bournemouth	a					17 04				17 46					18 04				18 46				
	d					17 06		17 40		17 50					18 06		18 40		18 50				
Pokesdown	d					17 10									18 10								
Christchurch	d					17 14									18 14								
Hinton Admiral	d					17 19									18 19								
New Milton	d					17 23				18 01					18 23				19 01				
Sway	d					17 28									18 28								
Lymington Pier	d	17 14							17 44		18 14							18 44			19 14		
Lymington Town	d	17 16							17 46		18 16							18 46			19 16		
Brockenhurst 3	a	17 24				17 33		17 53	17 54	18 08	18 24				18 33		18 53	18 54	19 08		19 24		
	d					17 34		17 57		18 09					18 34		18 57		19 09				
Beaulieu Road	d					17 39									18 39								
Ashurst New Forest	d					17 43									18 43								
Totton	d					17 48									18 48								
Salisbury	d		17 08									18 13											19 08
Dean	d		17 20																				19 20
Mottisfont & Dunbridge	d		17 26																				19 26
Romsey	d		17 32	17 35								18 32	18 35										19 32
Redbridge	d		17 39									18 39											19 39
Millbrook (Hants)	d		17 43				←					18 43				←							19 43
Southampton Central	a		17 45			17 53	17 45	18 10		18 23		18 45			18 53	18 45	19 10		19 23				19 45
	d		17 59			17 55	17 59	18 15		18 25		18 59			18 55	18 59	19 15		19 25			19 30	19 59
St Denys	d		↪				18 04					↪				19 04							↪
Swaythling	d						18 07									19 07							
Southampton Airport Pkwy	d					18 03	18 10	18 22		18 33					19 03	19 10	19 22		19 33			19 38	
Portsmouth Harbour	d				17 17									18 17									
Portsmouth & Southsea	d				17 22									18 22									
Fratton	d				17 26									18 26									
Hilsea	d				17 30									18 30									
Cosham	d				17 35									18 35									
Portchester	d				17 40									18 40									
Fareham	d				17 46									18 46									
Botley	d				17 54									18 54									
Hedge End	d				17 58									18 58									
Eastleigh 3	a			17 48	18 04	18 07	18 13						18 48	19 04	19 07	19 13						19 42	
	d			17 54	18 11		18 15						18 54	19 11		19 15							
Chandlers Ford	d						18 20									19 20							
Romsey	a			18 24			18 28						19 24			19 28							
Shawford	d													19 17									
Winchester	d				18 23			18 31		18 42				19 23			19 31		19 42				
Micheldever	d				18 32									19 32									
Basingstoke	a				18 42			18 46		18 58				19 42			19 46		19 58				
	d				18 44			18 47		19 00				19 44			19 47		20 00				
Reading 7	a							19 02									20 03						
Fleet	d																						
Farnborough (Main)	d																						
Woking	a				19 02					19 18				20 02					20 18				
Clapham Junction 10	a				19 27					19 39				20 27					20 39				
London Waterloo 15	a				19 37					19 49				20 37					20 49				

A ◇ to Eastleigh

B 🍴 from Bournemouth

Table 158R

Sundays

30 March to 11 May

Weymouth, Bournemouth, Lymington, Romsey, Southampton and Basingstoke - London

Network Diagram - see first Page of Table 158

		SW		SW	SW	SW	XC	SW	SW	SW	SN	SW		SW	SW	SW	SW	SW	SW	SW	SW	SW	SW		SW
		1		1	◇1	1	◇1	1	◇1	1	1	1		1	1	◇1	1	1	1	1	1	1	◇1		1
					A				B							A							A		
									⚲																
Weymouth	d								18 48														19 58		
Upwey	d								18 52														20 02		
Dorchester West	a																								
Dorchester South	d								19 00														20 10		
Moreton (Dorset)	d								19 07														20 17		
Wool	d								19 13														20 23		
Wareham	d								19 20														20 30		
Holton Heath	d																								
Hamworthy	d								19 27														20 37		
Poole 4	a								19 31														20 41		
	d				18 55				19 32							19 55							20 50		
Parkstone (Dorset)	d								19 36														20 54		
Branksome	d								19 40														20 57		
Bournemouth	a				19 04				19 46							20 04							21 03		
	d				19 06		19 40		19 50							20 06							21 06		
Pokesdown	d				19 10											20 10							21 10		
Christchurch	d				19 14											20 14							21 14		
Hinton Admiral	d				19 19											20 19							21 19		
New Milton	d				19 23				20 01							20 23							21 23		
Sway	d				19 28											20 28							21 28		
Lymington Pier	d							19 44		20 14								20 44	21 14						
Lymington Town	d							19 46		20 16								20 46	21 16						
Brockenhurst 3	a				19 33		19 53	19 54	20 08	20 24						20 33		20 54	21 24				21 33		
	d				19 34		19 57		20 09							20 34							21 34		
Beaulieu Road	d				19 39											20 39							21 39		
Ashurst New Forest	d				19 43											20 43							21 43		
Totton	d				19 48											20 48							21 48		
Salisbury	d											20 13								21 08					
Dean	d																			21 20					
Mottisfont & Dunbridge	d																			21 26					
Romsey	d	19 35										20 32		20 35						21 32	21 35				
Redbridge	d											20 39								21 39					
Millbrook (Hants)	d					←						20 43					←			21 43					←
Southampton Central	a				19 53	19 45	20 10		20 23			20 45				20 53	20 45			21 45			21 53		21 45
	d				19 55	19 59	20 15		20 25		20 29	20 59				20 55	20 59			21 59			21 55		21 59
St Denys	d					20 04						→					21 04			→					22 04
Swaythling	d					20 07											21 07								22 07
Southampton Airport Pkwy	d				20 03	20 10	20 22		20 33		20 38					21 03	21 10						22 03		22 10
Portsmouth Harbour	d			19 17											20 17							21 17			
Portsmouth & Southsea	d			19 22											20 22							21 22			
Fratton	d			19 26											20 26							21 26			
Hilsea	d			19 30											20 30							21 30			
Cosham	d			19 35											20 35							21 35			
Portchester	d			19 40											20 40							21 40			
Fareham	d			19 46											20 46							21 46			
Botley	d			19 54											20 54							21 54			
Hedge End	d			19 58											20 58							21 58			
Eastleigh 3	a	19 48		20 04	20 07	20 13					20 41			20 48	21 04	21 07	21 13				21 48	22 04	22 07		22 13
	d	19 54		20 11		20 15								20 54	21 11		21 15				21 54	22 11			22 15
Chandlers Ford	d					20 20											21 20								22 20
Romsey	a	20 24				20 28								21 24			21 28				22 24				22 31
Shawford	d														21 17										
Winchester	d			20 23			20 31		20 42						21 23							22 23			
Micheldever	d			20 32											21 32							22 32			
Basingstoke	a			20 42			20 46		20 58						21 42							22 42			
	d			20 44			20 47		21 00						21 44							22 44			
Reading 7	a						21 02																		
Fleet	d																								
Farnborough (Main)	d																								
Woking	a			21 02					21 18						22 02							23 02			
Clapham Junction 10	a			21 27					21 39						22 27							23 27			
London Waterloo 15 ⊖	a			21 37					21 49						22 37							23 37			

A ◇ to Eastleigh

B ⚲ from Bournemouth

Table 158R

Sundays
30 March to 11 May

Weymouth, Bournemouth, Lymington, Romsey, Southampton and Basingstoke - London

Network Diagram - see first Page of Table 158

		GW	SW ■	SW ■	SW ■	SW ■	SW ■	SW ◇■	SW ■	SW ■	SW ■	SW ■
Weymouth	d	20 09						20 58		21 58	22 58	
Upwey	d	20 14						21 02		22 02	23 02	
Dorchester West	a	20 21										
Dorchester South	d							21 10		22 10	23 10	
Moreton (Dorset)	d							21 17		22 17	23 17	
Wool	d							21 23		22 23	23 23	
Wareham	d							21 30		22 30	23 30	
Holton Heath	d											
Hamworthy	d							21 37		22 37	23 37	
Poole ■	a							21 41		22 41	23 41	
	d							21 50		22 50	23 50	
Parkstone (Dorset)	d							21 54		22 54	23 54	
Branksome	d							21 57		22 57	23 57	
Bournemouth	a							22 03		23 03	00 03	
	d							22 06		23 06		
Pokesdown	d							22 10		23 10		
Christchurch	d							22 14		23 14		
Hinton Admiral	d							22 19		23 19		
New Milton	d							22 23		23 23		
Sway	d							22 28		23 28		
Lymington Pier	d		21 44	22 14								
Lymington Town	d		21 46	22 16								
Brockenhurst ■	a		21 54	22 24				22 33		23 33		
	d							22 34		23 34		
Beaulieu Road	d							22 39				
Ashurst New Forest	d							22 43		23 43		
Totton	d							22 48		23 48		
Salisbury	d											
Dean	d											
Mottisfont & Dunbridge	d											
Romsey	d				22 28	22 35						
Redbridge	d				22 35							
Millbrook (Hants)	d				22 39				←			
Southampton Central ⛴	a				22 41			22 53	22 41	23 53		
	d				23 05			22 55	23 05			
St Denys	d				→				23 10			
Swaythling	d								23 13			
Southampton Airport Pkwy ✈	d							23 03	23 16			
Portsmouth Harbour ⛴	d						22 17					23 17
Portsmouth & Southsea	d						22 22					23 22
Fratton	d						22 26					23 26
Hilsea	d						22 30					23 30
Cosham	d						22 35					23 35
Portchester	d						22 40					23 40
Fareham	d						22 46					23 46
Botley	d						22 54					23 54
Hedge End	d						22 58					23 58
Eastleigh ■	a					22 48	23 04	23 09	23 19			00 04
	d					22 54		23 11	23 21			
Chandlers Ford	d								23 26			
Romsey	a					23 24			23 33			
Shawford	d											
Winchester	d							23 23				
Micheldever	d							23 32				
Basingstoke	a							23 42				
	d							23 44				
Reading ■	a											
Fleet	d											
Farnborough (Main)	d											
Woking	a							00 02				
Clapham Junction ■	a							00 23				
London Waterloo ■ ⊖	a							00 33				

Table 158A

Mondays to Saturdays

9 December to 17 May

Woking - Heathrow Railair

Express Coach Service

Network Diagram - see first Page of Table 158

		SW	SW	SW	SW	SW	SW	SW	SW	SW		SW	SW	SW	SW	SW	SW	SW	SW	SW		SW	SW	SW	SW
		SX	SX	SX	SX			SO	SX	SO		SX	SO	SX	SO	SX	SO	SO	SX	SX		SO	SO	SX	SX
Woking	d		05 20		05 50		06 20			06 50		06 50			07 20	07 20		07 50		07 50			08 20		08 20
Heathrow Terminal 5 Bus	d		05 45		06 15		06 45			07 15		07 25			07 45	08 00		08 15		08 30			08 45		09 00
Heathrow Central Bus Stn.	a		06 00		06 30		07 00			07 30		07 40			08 00	08 15		08 30		08 45			09 00		09 15
	d	05 45		06 15		06 45		07 15	07 15				07 45	07 45			08 30		08 30			09 00		09 00	
Heathrow Terminal 5 Bus	a	06 00		06 30		07 00		07 30	07 30				08 00	08 00			08 45		08 45			09 15		09 15	
Woking	a	06 30		07 00		07 30		08 00	08 05				08 30	08 40			09 15		09 25			09 45		09 55	

		SW	SW	SW	SW	SW		SW	SW	SW	SW	SW	SW	SW	SW	SW		SW	SW	SW	SW	SW	SW	SW	SW
		SO	SO	SX	SX	SO		SX	SO	SX															
Woking	d		08 50		08 50				09 35	09 35		10 05		10 35		11 05			11 35		12 05		12 35		13 05
Heathrow Terminal 5 Bus	d		09 15		09 30				10 00	10 10		10 30		11 00		11 30			12 00		12 30		13 00		13 30
Heathrow Central Bus Stn.	a		09 30		09 45				10 15	10 25		10 45		11 15		11 45			12 15		12 45		13 15		13 45
	d	09 30		09 30		10 00		10 00			10 30		11 00		11 30			12 00		12 30		13 00		13 30	
Heathrow Terminal 5 Bus	a	09 45		09 45		10 15		10 15			10 45		11 15		11 45			12 15		12 45		13 15		13 45	
Woking	a	10 15		10 25		10 45		10 50			11 15		11 45		12 15			12 45		13 15		13 45		14 15	

		SW		SW	SW	SW	SW	SW	SW	SW	SW	SW		SW	SW	SW	SW	SW	SW	SW	SW	SW		SW	SW
														SO	SX	SO	SX	SO	SX	SO	SX	SO		SX	SO
Woking	d			13 35		14 05		14 35		15 05		15 35				16 05	16 05			16 35	16 35				17 05
Heathrow Terminal 5 Bus	d			14 00		14 30		15 00		15 30		16 00				16 30	16 35			17 00	17 10				17 30
Heathrow Central Bus Stn.	a			14 15		14 45		15 15		15 45		16 15				16 45	16 50			17 15	17 25				17 45
	d	14 00			14 30		15 00		15 30		16 00			16 30	16 30			17 00	17 00			17 30		17 30	
Heathrow Terminal 5 Bus	a	14 15			14 45		15 15		15 45		16 15			16 45	16 45			17 15	17 15			17 45		17 45	
Woking	a	14 45			15 15		15 45		16 15		16 45			17 15	17 25			17 45	18 05			18 15		18 35	

		SW	SW	SW	SW	SW	SW	SW		SW	SW	SW	SW	SW	SW	SW	SW	SW		SW	SW	SW	SW	SW	SW
		SX	SO	SX	SO	SX	SO	SX		SO	SX	SO	SX	SO	SX		SO	SX			SO	SX		SO	SX
Woking	d	17 05			17 35	17 35				18 05	18 05			18 35	18 35		19 05	19 05			19 35	19 35		20 05	20 05
Heathrow Terminal 5 Bus	d	17 40			18 00	18 10				18 30	18 40			19 00	19 05		19 30	19 35			20 00	20 05		20 30	20 35
Heathrow Central Bus Stn.	a	17 55			18 15	18 25				18 45	18 55			19 15	19 20		19 45	19 45			20 15	20 15		20 45	20 45
	d		18 00	18 00			18 30	18 30				19 00	19 00			19 30				20 00			20 30		
Heathrow Terminal 5 Bus	a		18 15	18 15			18 45	18 45				19 15	19 15			19 45				20 15			20 45		
Woking	a		18 45	19 05			19 15	19 35				19 45	19 55			20 15				20 45			21 15		

		SW	SW	SW		SW	SW	SW	SW	SW
			SO	SX		SO	SX			
Woking	d		20 35	20 35		21 05	21 05		22 05	
Heathrow Terminal 5 Bus	d		21 00	21 05		21 30	21 35		22 30	
Heathrow Central Bus Stn.	a		21 15	21 15		21 45	21 45		22 45	
	d	21 15						22 15		23 15
Heathrow Terminal 5 Bus	a	21 30						22 30		23 30
Woking	a	22 00						23 00		23 59

Sundays

8 December to 11 May

		SW	SW	SW	SW	SW	SW	SW	SW	SW		SW	SW	SW	SW	SW	SW	SW	SW	SW		SW	SW	SW	SW
Woking	d		06 20		06 50		07 20		07 50			08 20		08 50		09 35		10 05		10 35			11 05		11 35
Heathrow Terminal 5 Bus	d		06 45		07 15		07 45		08 15			08 45		09 15		10 00		10 30		11 00			11 30		12 00
Heathrow Central Bus Stn.	a		07 00		07 30		08 00		08 30			09 00		09 30		10 15		10 45		11 15			11 45		12 15
	d	06 45		07 15		07 45		08 30		09 00			09 30		10 00		10 30		11 00			11 30		12 00	
Heathrow Terminal 5 Bus	a	07 00		07 30		08 00		08 45		09 15			09 45		10 15		10 45		11 15			11 45		12 15	
Woking	a	07 30		08 00		08 30		09 15		09 45			10 15		10 45		11 15		11 45			12 15		12 45	

		SW	SW	SW	SW	SW		SW	SW	SW	SW	SW	SW	SW	SW	SW		SW	SW	SW	SW	SW	SW	SW	SW
Woking	d		12 05		12 35			13 05		13 35		14 05		14 35		15 05			15 35		16 05		16 35		17 05
Heathrow Terminal 5 Bus	d		12 30		13 00			13 30		14 00		14 30		15 00		15 30			16 00		16 30		17 00		17 30
Heathrow Central Bus Stn.	a		12 45		13 15			13 45		14 15		14 45		15 15		15 45			16 15		16 45		17 15		17 45
	d	12 30		13 00		13 30			14 00		14 30		15 00		15 30			16 00		16 30		17 00		17 30	
Heathrow Terminal 5 Bus	a	12 45		13 15		13 45			14 15		14 45		15 15		15 45			16 15		16 45		17 15		17 45	
Woking	a	13 15		13 45		14 15			14 45		15 15		15 45		16 15			16 45		17 15		17 45		18 15	

		SW		SW	SW	SW	SW	SW	SW	SW	SW	SW		SW	SW	SW	SW	SW	SW	SW	SW
Woking	d			17 35		18 05		18 35		19 05		19 35			20 05		20 35	21 05		22 05	
Heathrow Terminal 5 Bus	d			18 00		18 30		19 00		19 30		20 00			20 30		21 00	21 30		22 30	
Heathrow Central Bus Stn.	a			18 15		18 45		19 15		19 45		20 15			20 45		21 15	21 45		22 45	
	d	18 00			18 30		19 00		19 30		20 00			20 30		21 15			22 15		23 15
Heathrow Terminal 5 Bus	a	18 15			18 45		19 15		19 45		20 15			20 45		21 30			22 30		23 30
Woking	a	18 45			19 15		19 45		20 15		20 45			21 15		22 00			23 00		23 59

Network Diagram for Table 160

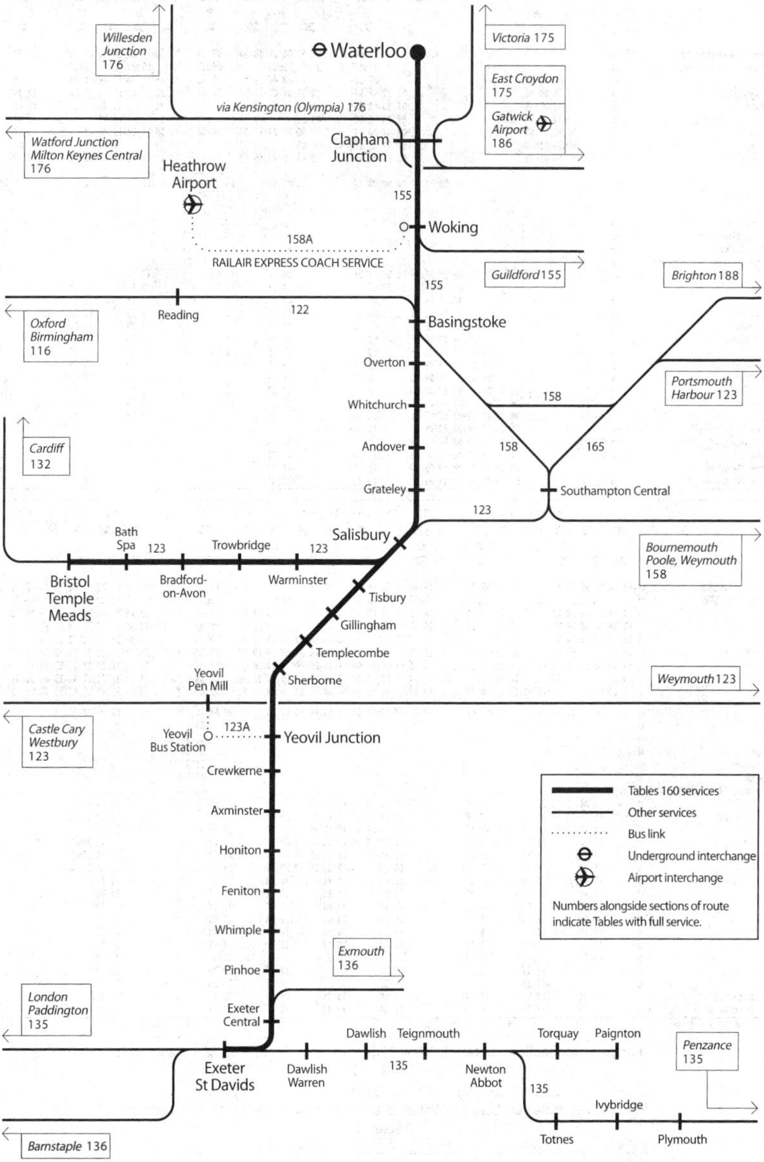

Willesden Junction 176
Waterloo
Victoria 175
East Croydon 175
Gatwick Airport 186
via Kensington (Olympia) 176
Clapham Junction
Watford Junction Milton Keynes Central 176
Heathrow Airport
155
Woking
158A
RAILAIR EXPRESS COACH SERVICE
Guildford 155
155
Brighton 188
Reading
122
Oxford Birmingham 116
Basingstoke
Overton
Whitchurch
158
Portsmouth Harbour 123
Andover
158
165
Cardiff 132
Grateley
Southampton Central
123
Bath Spa
123
Trowbridge
123
Salisbury
Bournemouth Poole, Weymouth 158
Bristol Temple Meads
Bradford-on-Avon
Warminster
Tisbury
Gillingham
Templecombe
Yeovil Pen Mill
Sherborne
Weymouth 123
Castle Cary Westbury 123
123A
Yeovil Bus Station
Yeovil Junction
Crewkerne
Axminster
Honiton
Feniton
Whimple
Pinhoe
Exmouth 136
London Paddington 135
Exeter Central
Dawlish
Teignmouth
Torquay
Paignton
Penzance 135
Exeter St Davids
Dawlish Warren
135
Newton Abbot
135
Ivybridge
Barnstaple 136
Totnes
Plymouth
Tables 160 services
Other services
Bus link
Underground interchange
Airport interchange
Numbers alongside sections of route indicate Tables with full service.

TOCs operating on this network - South West Trains (SW)

Table 160

Mondays to Fridays

9 December to 16 May

London - Salisbury and Exeter

Network Diagram - see first Page of Table 160

Miles			SW	SW	SW	SW	SW	SW	SW	SW	SW		SW	SW	SW	SW		SW	SW	SW	SW		SW	SW	
			MO	MX	MO																				
			◇1	1	1	1	1	1	◇1	◇1	◇1		◇1	◇1	◇1	◇1		◇1	◇1	◇1	◇1		◇1	◇1	
			A	A	A						B			B		B			B		B			B	
											🛒		🛒	🛒	🛒	🛒		🛒	🛒	🛒	🛒		🛒	🛒	
0	**London Waterloo 15** ⊖	d									07 10		07 50	08 20	08 50	09 20		09 50	10 20	10 50	11 20		11 50	12 20	
4	Clapham Junction 10	d									07u17		07u57	08u27		09u27			10u27		11u27			12u27	
24½	Woking	d		00 08	00 08						07 36		08 16	08 46	09 16	09 46		10 16	10 46	11 16	11 46		12 16	12 46	
47¾	**Basingstoke**	d		00 28	00 40					07 22	07 57		08 38	09 07	09 38	10 07		10 38	11 07	11 38	12 07		12 38	13 07	
55½	Overton	d		00s37	00s49					07 30	08 05		08 46		09 46			10 46		11 46			12 46		
59¼	Whitchurch (Hants)	d		00s42	00s54					07 35	08 10		08 51		09 51			10 51		11 51			12 51		
66½	Andover	d		00 50	01 02					07 44	08 19		09 00	09 24	10 00	10 24		11 00	11 24	12 00	12 24		13 00	13 24	
72¾	Grateley	d		00s58	01s10					07 51	08 26		09 07		10 07			11 07		12 07			13 07		
83¾	**Salisbury**	a		01 10	01 22					08 03	08 39		09 19	09 43	10 19	10 42		11 19	11 42	12 19	12 42		13 19	13 43	
—																									
—		d						06 08	07 40	08 08	08 47			09 47		10 47	10 52		11 47		12 47			13 47	13 52
—	Warminster	d															11 12								14 12
—	Westbury	d															11 21								14 21
—	Trowbridge	d															11 27								14 27
—	Bradford-on-Avon	d															11 33								14 33
—	Bath Spa 7	a															11 46								14 46
—	Bristol Temple Meads 10	a															12 05								15 05
96¼	Tisbury	d						06 29	07 59	08 27	09 06			10 06		11 06			12 06		13 06			14 06	
105¼	Gillingham (Dorset)	a						06 39	08 09	08 37	09 16			10 16		11 16			12 16		13 16			14 16	
—		d						06 42	08 11		09 17			10 17		11 17			12 17		13 17			14 17	
112¼	Templecombe	d						06 50	08 19		09 25			10 25		11 25			12 25		13 25			14 25	
118¼	Sherborne	d						06 57	08 26		09 32			10 32		11 32			12 32		13 32			14 32	
122¾	Yeovil Junction	a						07 03	08 32		09 38			10 38		11 38			12 38		13 38			14 38	
—		d					06 15	07 07	08 39		09 39			10 39		11 39			12 39		13 39			14 39	
131¾	Crewkerne	d					06 24	07 16	08 49		09 49			10 49		11 49			12 49		13 49			14 49	
144¾	Axminster	a					06 43	07 36	09 02		10 02			11 02		12 02			13 02		14 02			15 02	
—		d	00 08			05 52	06 56	07 37	09 03		10 03			11 03		12 03			13 03		14 03			15 03	
155	Honiton	a	00 19			06 03	07 07	07 48	09 15		10 15			11 15		12 15			13 15		14 15			15 15	
—		d	00 20			06 07	07 12	07 53	09 16		10 16			11 16		12 16			13 16		14 16			15 16	
159½	Feniton	d	00 25			06 12	07 18	07 59	09 21		10 21					12 21					14 21			15 21	
163¼	Whimple	d	00 30			06 17	07 23	08 04	09 26					11 24					13 24					15 26	
169	Pinhoe	d	00 39			06 26	07 32	08 12	09 35		10 33			11 32		12 33			13 32					15 35	
171¾	**Exeter Central**	a				06 30	07 37	08 17	09 39		10 37			11 37		12 37			13 37		14 37			15 39	
172¾	**Exeter St Davids 6**	a	00 46			06 35	07 42	08 21	09 44		10 42			11 42		12 42			13 42		14 42			15 44	

		SW	SW	SW	SW	SW	SW		SW	SW	SW	SW	SW	SW	SW	SW			SW	SW	SW	SW	SW		
		◇1	◇1	◇1	◇1	◇1	◇1		◇1	◇1	◇1	◇1	◇1	◇1	◇1	◇1			◇1	◇1	◇1	1	1		
			B	C	B		B		C	B	C	B	C	C		C				C	C				
		🛒	🛒	🛒	🛒	🛒	🛒		🛒	🛒	🛒	🛒	🛒	🛒	🛒	🛒			🛒	🛒	🛒	🛒			
London Waterloo 15 ⊖	d	12 50	13 20	13 50	14 20	14 50	15 20		15 50	16 20	16 50	17 20	17 50	18 20	18 50	19 20			19 50	20 20	21 20	22 20	23 40		
Clapham Junction 10	d		13u27		14u27		15u27		15u57	16u27	16u57			18u27		19u27				20u27	21u27	22u27	23u47		
Woking	d	13 16	13 46	14 16	14 46	15 16	15 46		16 16	16 46	17u16	17u46		18 46	19 18	19 46			20 16	20 46	21 49	22 49	00 08		
Basingstoke	d	13 38	14 07	14 38	15 07	15 38	16 07		16 38	17 07	17 38	18 07	18 38	19 07	19 39	20 07			20 38	21 07	22 14	23 11	00 28		
Overton	d	13 46		14 46		15 46			16 46	17 15	17 46	18 15	18 47	19 15	19 47	20 15			20 46	21 15	22 22	23 19	00s37		
Whitchurch (Hants)	d	13 51		14 51		15 51			16 51	17 20	17 51	18 20	18 52	19 20	19 52	20 20			20 51	21 20	22 27	23 24	00s42		
Andover	d	14 00	14 24	15 00	15 24	16 00	16 24		17 00	17 29	18 00	18 29	19 00	19 29	20 01	20 29			21 00	21 29	22 36	23 33	00 50		
Grateley	d	14 07		15 07		16 07			17 07	17 36	18 07	18 36	19 08	19 36	20 08	20 36			21 07	21 36	22 43	23 40	00s58		
Salisbury	a	14 19	14 42	15 19	15 42	16 19	16 42		17 19	17 48	18 19	18 48	19 20	19 48	20 22	20 49			21 19	21 48	22 55	23 52	01 10		
	d		14 47	15 23	15 47		16 47		17 23	17 53	18 23	18 53	19 23	19 53		20 53	20 57			22 06	23 03				
Warminster	d																21 17								
Westbury	d																21 25								
Trowbridge	d																21 31								
Bradford-on-Avon	d																21 37								
Bath Spa 7	a																21 50								
Bristol Temple Meads 10	a																22 06								
Tisbury	d		15 06	15 37	16 06		17 06		17 37	18 09	18 37	19 08	19 37	20 11		21 08				22 24	23s16				
Gillingham (Dorset)	a		15 16	15 47	16 16		17 16		17 47	18 19	18 47	19 18	19 48	20 21		21 18				22 34	23s27				
	d		15 17		16 17		17 17			18 20	18 51	19 19	19 54	20 22		21 19				22 35					
Templecombe	d		15 25		16 25		17 25			18 27	18 58	19 26	20 02	20 30		21 27				22 42	23s35				
Sherborne	d		15 32		16 32		17 32			18 35	19 06	19 34	20 09	20 37		21 34				22 50	23s42				
Yeovil Junction	a		15 38		16 38		17 38			18 40	19 14	19 39	20 17	20 43		21 40				22 55	23 48				
	d		15 39		16 39		17 39			18 42		19 41		20 44		21 41				22 57					
Crewkerne	d		15 49		16 49		17 49			18 51		19 50		20 54		21 51				23 06					
Axminster	a		16 02		17 02		18 02			19 04		20 03		21 07		22 04				23 19					
	d		16 03		17 03		18 03			19 05		20 04		21 08		22 05				23 20					
Honiton	a		16 15		17 15		18 14			19 18		20 16		21 19		22 18				23 31					
	d		16 16		17 16		18 18			19 19		20 17		21 20		22 19				23 32					
Feniton	d		16 21				18 23					20 22				22 25				23 38					
Whimple	d				17 24					19 27				21 28		22 30				23 43					
Pinhoe	d				17 31					19 36				21 37		22 38				23 51					
Exeter Central	a		16 35		17 35		18 37			19 40		20 39		21 42		22 43				23 56					
Exeter St Davids 6	a		16 42		17 39		18 42			19 46		20 44		21 47		22 47				00 01					

A From London Waterloo **B** 🛒 to Axminster **C** 🛒 to Salisbury

For Bus Connections between Yeovil Junction and Yeovil Pen Mill please see Table 123A

For services between London Waterloo to Woking and Basingstoke, please see Table 155

For services between Warminster to Bristol Temple Meads and Salisbury, please see Table 123

Table 160

Saturdays

14 December to 17 May

London - Salisbury and Exeter

Network Diagram - see first Page of Table 160

		SW	SW	SW	SW	SW	SW	SW	SW	SW		SW	SW		SW	SW	SW	SW	SW	SW			SW	SW	SW
		1	1	1	1	◇1	◇1	◇1	◇1	◇1		◇1	◇1		◇1	◇1	◇1	◇1	◇1	◇1			◇1	◇1	◇1
		A						B		B			B			B		B		B				B	
								🛒	🛒	🛒		🛒	🛒		🛒	🛒	🛒	🛒	🛒	🛒			🛒	🛒	🛒
London Waterloo [15] ⊖	d							07 10	07 50	08 20		08 50	09 20		09 50	10 20	10 50	11 20	11 50	12 20			12 50	13 20	13 50
Clapham Junction [10]	d							07u17	07u57	08u27			09u27			10u27		11u27		12u27				13u27	
Woking	d	00 08						07 36	08 16	08 46		09 16	09 46		10 16	10 46	11 16	11 46	12 16	12 46			13 16	13 46	14 16
Basingstoke	d	00 28				07 22		07 59	08 38	09 07		09 38	10 07		10 38	11 07	11 38	12 07	12 38	13 07			13 38	14 07	14 38
Overton	d	00s37				07 30		08 07	08 46			09 46			10 46		11 46		12 46				13 46		14 46
Whitchurch (Hants)	d	00s42				07 35		08 12	08 51			09 51			10 51		11 51		12 51				13 51		14 51
Andover	d	00 50				07 44		08 21	09 00	09 24		10 00	10 24		11 00	11 24	12 00	12 24	13 00	13 24			14 00	14 24	15 00
Grateley	d	00s58				07 51		08 28	09 07			10 07			11 07		12 07		13 07				14 07		15 07
Salisbury	a	01 10				08 05		08 42	09 19	09 42		10 19	10 42		11 19	11 42	12 19	12 42	13 19	13 42			14 19	14 42	15 19
	d				06 15		07 45	08 47		09 47			10 47	10 52		11 47		12 47		13 47	13 52			14 47	
Warminster	d													11 12							14 12				
Westbury	d													11 21							14 21				
Trowbridge	d													11 27							14 27				
Bradford-on-Avon	d													11 33							14 33				
Bath Spa [7]	a													11 46							14 46				
Bristol Temple Meads [10]	a													12 05							15 05				
Tisbury	d				06 29		07 59	09 06		10 06			11 06			12 06		13 06		14 06				15 06	
Gillingham (Dorset)	a				06 39		08 09	09 16		10 16			11 16			12 16		13 16		14 16				15 16	
	d				06 42		08 11	09 17		10 17			11 17			12 17		13 17		14 17				15 17	
Templecombe	d				06 50		08 19	09 25		10 25			11 25			12 25		13 25		14 25				15 25	
Sherborne	d				06 57		08 26	09 32		10 32			11 32			12 32		13 32		14 32				15 32	
Yeovil Junction	a				07 03		08 32	09 38		10 38			11 38			12 38		13 38		14 38				15 38	
	d			06 15	07 07		08 39	09 39		10 39			11 39			12 39		13 39		14 39				15 39	
Crewkerne	d			06 24	07 16		08 49	09 49		10 49			11 49			12 49		13 49		14 49				15 49	
Axminster	a			06 43	07 36		09 02	10 02		11 02			12 02			13 02		14 02		15 02				16 02	
	d		05 52	06 56	07 38		09 03	10 03		11 03			12 03			13 03		14 03		15 03				16 03	
Honiton	a		06 03	07 07	07 49		09 15	10 15		11 15			12 15			13 15		14 15		15 15				16 15	
	d		06 07	07 12	07 54		09 16	10 16		11 16			12 16			13 16		14 16		15 16				16 16	
Feniton	d		06 12	07 18	08 00		09 21	10 21					12 21					14 21						16 21	
Whimple	d		06 17	07 23	08 05		09 26			11 24						13 24				15 24					
Pinhoe	d		06 26	07 32	08 13		09 35	10 33		11 32			12 33			13 32				15 32				16 33	
Exeter Central	a		06 30	07 37	08 18		09 39	10 37		11 37			12 37			13 37		14 37		15 37				16 37	
Exeter St Davids [6]	a		06 35	07 42	08 22		09 44	10 42		11 42			12 42			13 42		14 42		15 42				16 42	

		SW	SW	SW	SW	SW	SW		SW	SW	SW	SW	SW		SW	SW	SW		SW	SW					
		◇1	◇1	◇1	◇1	◇1	◇1		◇1	◇1	◇1	◇1	◇1		◇1	◇1	◇1		1	1					
		B		B		B			B		C		C				C								
		🛒	🛒	🛒	🛒	🛒	🛒		🛒	🛒	🛒	🛒	🛒		🛒	🛒	🛒		🛒						
London Waterloo [15] ⊖	d	14 20	14 50	15 20	15 50	16 20	16 50		17 20	17 50	18 20	18 50	19 20		19 50	20 20	21 20		22 20	23 40					
Clapham Junction [10]	d	14u27		15u27		16u27			17u27		18u27		19u27			20u27	21u27		22u27	23u47					
Woking	d	14 46	15 16	15 46	16 16	16 46	17 16		17 46	18 16	18 46	19 16	19 46		20 16	20 46	21 49		22 49	00 08					
Basingstoke	d	15 07	15 38	16 07	16 38	17 07	17 38		18 07	18 38	19 07	19 38	20 07		20 38	21 07	22 14		23 11	00 28					
Overton	d		15 46		16 46		17 46			18 46		19 46	20 15		20 46	21 15	22 22		23 20	00s37					
Whitchurch (Hants)	d		15 51		16 51		17 51			18 51		19 51	20 20		20 51	21 20	22 27		23 25	00s42					
Andover	d	15 24	16 00	16 24	17 00	17 24	18 00		18 24	19 00	19 24	20 00	20 24		21 00	21 29	22 36		23 33	00 50					
Grateley	d		16 07		17 07		18 07			19 07		20 07	20 36		21 07	21 36	22 43		23 41	00s58					
Salisbury	a	15 42	16 19	16 42	17 19	17 42	18 19		18 43	19 19	19 43	20 19	20 42		21 19	21 48	22 55		23 53	01 10					
	d	15 47		16 47		17 47			18 47		19 47		20 47	20 57		21 53	23 03								
Warminster	d													21 17											
Westbury	d													21 25											
Trowbridge	d													21 31											
Bradford-on-Avon	d													21 37											
Bath Spa [7]	a													21 50											
Bristol Temple Meads [10]	a													22 06											
Tisbury	d	16 06		17 06		18 06			19 08		20 06		21 08			22 07	23s16								
Gillingham (Dorset)	a	16 16		17 16		18 16			19 18		20 16		21 18			22 17	23s27								
	d	16 17		17 17		18 17			19 19		20 17		21 19			22 18									
Templecombe	d	16 25		17 25		18 25			19 26		20 25		21 27			22 26	23s35								
Sherborne	d	16 32		17 32		18 32			19 34		20 32		21 34			22 33	23s42								
Yeovil Junction	a	16 38		17 38		18 38			19 39		20 38		21 40			22 41	23 48								
	d	16 39		17 39		18 39			19 41		20 39		21 41												
Crewkerne	d	16 49		17 49		18 49			19 50		20 49		21 51												
Axminster	a	17 02		18 02		19 02			20 03		21 02		22 04												
	d	17 03		18 03		19 03			20 05		21 03		22 05												
Honiton	a	17 15		18 16		19 15			20 16		21 16		22 18												
	d	17 16		18 17		19 16			20 17		21 17		22 19												
Feniton	d			18 23					20 23				22 25												
Whimple	d	17 24				19 24					21 25		22 30												
Pinhoe	d	17 32				19 32					21 33		22 38												
Exeter Central	a	17 37		18 37		19 37			20 39		21 38		22 43												
Exeter St Davids [6]	a	17 42		18 42		19 42			20 43		21 42		22 47												

A From London Waterloo

B 🛒 to Axminster

C 🛒 to Salisbury

For Bus Connections between Yeovil Junction and Yeovil Pen Mill please see Table 123A

For services between London Waterloo to Woking and Basingstoke, please see Table 155

For services between Warminster to Bristol Temple Meads and Salisbury, please see Table 123

Table 160

Sundays

8 December to 11 May

London - Salisbury and Exeter

Network Diagram - see first Page of Table 160

		SW	SW	SW	SW	SW	SW	SW	SW		SW	SW	SW	SW	SW	SW		SW	SW	SW	SW	SW
		1	1	◇1	◇1	◇1	◇1	◇1	◇1		◇1	◇1	◇1	◇1	◇1	◇1		◇1	◇1	◇1	1	1
		A			B	C	C	C	C		C	C	C	C	C	C		D	D	D		
					🛒	🛒	🛒	🛒	🛒		🛒	🛒	🛒	🛒	🛒	🛒		🛒	🛒	🛒	🛒	
London Waterloo 15 ⊖	d				08 15	09 15	10 15	11 15	12 15		13 15	14 15	15 15	16 15	17 15	18 15		19 15	20 15	21 15	22 15	23 35
Clapham Junction 10	d				08u23	09u22	10u22	11u22	12u22		13u22	14u22	15u22	16u22	17u22	18u22		19u22	20u22	21u22	22u22	23u44
Woking	d	00∫08			08 47	09 47	10 46	11 46	12 46		13 46	14 46	15 46	16 46	17 46	18 46		19 46	20 46	21 46	22 46	00 08
Basingstoke	d	00∫28		08 05	09 08	10 08	11 07	12 07	13 07		14 07	15 07	16 07	17 07	18 07	19 07		20 07	21 07	22 07	23 07	00 40
Overton	d	00s37		08 13	09 16		11 15		13 15			15 15		17 15		19 15			21 15		23 15	00s49
Whitchurch (Hants)	d	00s42		08 18	09 21		11 20		13 20			15 20		17 20		19 20			21 20		23 20	00s54
Andover	d	00∫50		08 27	09 30	10 25	11 29	12 24	13 29		14 24	15 29	16 24	17 29	18 24	19 29		20 24	21 29	22 26	23 29	01 02
Grateley	d	00s58		08 34		10 32		12 31			14 31		16 31		18 31			20 31		22 33	23 36	01s10
Salisbury	a	01∫10		08 46	09 46	10 45	11 45	12 45	13 45		14 45	15 45	16 45	17 45	18 45	19 45		20 45	21 45	22 45	23 48	01 22
	d		07 06	08 51	09 51	10 51	11 51	12 51	13 51	13 55	14 51	15 51	16 51	17 51	18 51	19 51	19 55	20 51	21 51	22 51		
Warminster	d									14 15							20 15					
Westbury	d									14 24							20 23					
Trowbridge	d									14 30							20 29					
Bradford-on-Avon	d									14 36							20 35					
Bath Spa 7	a									14 50							20 49					
Bristol Temple Meads 10	a									15 06							21 06					
Tisbury	d		07 20	09 10	10 10	11 10	12 10	13 10	14 10		15 10	16 10	17 10	18 10	19 10	20 10		21 10	22 10	23 11		
Gillingham (Dorset)	a		07 30	09 20	10 20	11 20	12 20	13 20	14 20		15 20	16 20	17 20	18 20	19 20	20 20		21 20	22 20	23 21		
	d		07 31	09 21	10 21	11 21	12 21	13 21	14 21		15 21	16 21	17 21	18 21	19 21	20 21		21 21	22 21	23 22		
Templecombe	d		07 38	09 28	10 28	11 28	12 28	13 28	14 28		15 28	16 28	17 28	18 28	19 28	20 28		21 28	22 28	23 30		
Sherborne	d		07 46	09 36	10 36	11 36	12 36	13 36	14 36		15 36	16 36	17 36	18 36	19 36	20 36		21 36	22 36	23 37		
Yeovil Junction	a		07 51	09 41	10 41	11 41	12 41	13 41	14 41		15 41	16 41	17 41	18 41	19 41	20 41		21 41	22 42	23 43		
	d		07 53	09 43	10 43	11 43	12 43	13 43	14 43		15 43	16 43	17 43	18 43	19 43	20 43		21 43		23 44		
Crewkerne	d		08 02	09 52	10 52	11 52	12 52	13 52	14 52		15 52	16 52	17 52	18 52	19 52	20 52		21 52		23 54		
Axminster	a		08 15	10 05	11 05	12 05	13 05	14 05	15 05		16 05	17 05	18 05	19 05	20 05	21 05		22 05		00 07		
	d		08 16	10 06	11 06	12 06	13 06	14 06	15 06		16 06	17 06	18 06	19 06	20 06	21 06		22 06		00 08		
Honiton	a		08 27	10 18	11 17	12 18	13 17	14 17	15 17		16 17	17 17	18 17	19 17	20 17	21 17		22 19		00 19		
	d		08 31	10 19	11 18	12 19	13 18	14 18	15 18		16 18	17 18	18 18	19 18	20 18	21 18		22 20		00 20		
Feniton	d		08 36	10 24		12 24		14 24			16 24		18 24		20 24	21 24		22 25		00 25		
Whimple	d		08 41		11 26		13 26		15 26			17 26		19 26		21 29		22 30		00 30		
Pinhoe	d		08 50	10 36	11 35	12 36	13 35		15 35			17 35		19 35		21 37		22 39		00 39		
Exeter Central	a		08 54	10 40	11 40	12 40	13 40	14 40	15 40		16 40	17 40	18 40	19 40	20 40	21 42		22 43				
Exeter St Davids 6	a		08 59	10 45	11 45	12 45	13 45	14 45	15 45		16 45	17 45	18 45	19 45	20 45	21 46		22 48		00 46		

A not 8 December. From London Waterloo
B 🛒 from Woking to Axminster
C 🛒 to Axminster
D 🛒 to Salisbury

For Bus Connections between Yeovil Junction and Yeovil Pen Mill please see Table 123A

For services between London Waterloo to Woking and Basingstoke, please see Table 155

For services between Warminster to Bristol Temple Meads and Salisbury, please see Table 123

Table 160R

Mondays to Fridays

9 December to 16 May

Exeter and Salisbury - London

Network Diagram - see first Page of Table 160

Miles			SW	SW	SW	SW	SW	SW	SW	SW	SW	SW	SW	SW	SW	SW	SW	SW	SW	SW	SW	SW
			MX																			
			1	◇1	◇1	◇1	◇1	◇1	◇1	◇1	◇1	◇1	◇1	◇1	◇1	◇1	◇1	◇1	◇1	◇1	◇1	◇1
			A			B	B	B	C	B	C	C	B	B	C		C		C		C	
				T	T	T	T	T	T	T	T	T	T	T	T	T	T	T	T	T	T	T
0	**Exeter St Davids 6**	d						05 10			06 41	07 25			08 23		09 25		10 25		11 25	
0¾	**Exeter Central**	d						05 14			06 45	07 30			08 27		09 30		10 30		11 30	
3½	Pinhoe	d						05 19			06 50	07 34			08 32		09 34		10 34		11 34	
9¼	Whimple	d						05 26			06 57				08 39		09 42				11 42	
13	Feniton	d						05 31			07 02				08 44				10 44			
17½	Honiton	a						05 38			07 10	07 47			08 51		09 51		10 50		11 51	
—		d						05 41	06 19		07 12	07 52			08 55		09 55		10 55		11 55	
27¾	Axminster	a						05 51	06 29		07 22	08 02			09 05		10 05		11 05		12 05	
—		d						05 52	06 30		07 23	08 03			09 06		10 06		11 06		12 06	
40¾	Crewkerne	d						06 05	06 43		07 36	08 16			09 19		10 19		11 19		12 19	
49¾	Yeovil Junction	a						06 14	06 52		07 45	08 25			09 27		10 27		11 27		12 27	
—		d	00 06			05 15	05 50	06 20	06 53	07 22	07 50	08 29			09 29		10 29		11 29		12 29	
54¼	Sherborne	d				05 21	05 56	06 26	07 00	07 28	07 56	08 35			09 35		10 35		11 35		12 35	
60¼	Templecombe	d				05 29	06 04	06 34	07 07	07 36	08 04	08 43			09 43		10 43		11 43		12 43	
67¾	Gillingham (Dorset)	a				05 36	06 11	06 41	07 14	07 43	08 11	08 50			09 50		10 50		11 50		12 50	
—		d				05 37	06 12	06 42	07 15	07 44	08 12	08 51	09 18		09 51		10 51		11 51		12 51	
76¼	Tisbury	d				05 47	06 24	06 52	07 26	07 54	08 22	09 01	09 28		10 01		11 01		12 01		13 01	
—	Bristol Temple Meads 10	d												08 51								
—	Bath Spa 7	d												09 07								
—	Bradford-on-Avon	d												09 20								
—	Trowbridge	d												09 27								
—	Westbury	d												09 39								
—	Warminster	d												09 46								
88¾	**Salisbury**	a	00 43			06 02	06 39	07 07	07 40	08 09	08 37	09 16	09 42	10 09	10 16		11 16		12 16		13 16	
—		d		05 15	05 43	06 06	06 45	07 15	07 45	08 15	08 47	09 21	09 47	10 21		10 47	11 21	11 47	12 21	12 47	13 21	13 47
99¾	Grateley	d		05 27	05 55	06 19	06 57	07 27	07 57	08 27	08 59		09 59			10 59		11 59		12 59		13 59
106	Andover	d		05 35	06 03	06 26	07 05	07 35	08 05	08 35	09 06	09 38	10 06	10 38		11 06	11 38	12 06	12 38	13 06	13 38	14 06
113¼	Whitchurch (Hants)	d		05 43	06 11	06 35	07 13	07 43	08 13	08 43	09 14		10 14			11 14		12 14		13 14		14 14
117	Overton	d		05 49	06 17	06 41	07 19	07 49	08 19	08 49	09 20		10 20			11 20		12 20		13 20		14 20
124¾	**Basingstoke**	a		05 58	06 26	06 49	07 28	07 58	08 28	08 58	09 28	09 55	10 28	10 55		11 28	11 55	12 28	12 55	13 28	13 55	14 28
148¼	Woking	a		06 18	06 46			08 18	08 48	09 18	09 49	10 15	10 49	11 15		11 49	12 15	12 49	13 15	13 49	14 15	14 49
168¼	Clapham Junction 10	a		06 38		07 28				09 38	10 09	10 36		11 36			12 36		13 36		14 36	
172½	**London Waterloo 15**	⊖ a		06 49	07 14	07 39	08 14	08 46	09 17	09 51	10 19	10 49	11 19	11 49		12 19	12 49	13 19	13 49	14 19	14 49	15 19

		SW	SW	SW	SW	SW	SW	SW	SW	SW	SW	SW	SW	SW	SW	SW	SW	SW	SW	SW
		◇1	◇1	◇1	◇1	◇1	◇1	◇1	◇1	◇1	◇1	◇1	◇1	◇1	1	◇1	◇1	◇1	1	1
			C		C		C	B	B	C		C		C		C				
		T	T	T	T	T	T	T	T	T	T	T	T	T		T				
Exeter St Davids 6	d		12 25		13 25		14 25			15 25		16 24		17 25	17 46	18 25	19 25	20 25	21 25	22 57
Exeter Central	d		12 30		13 30		14 30			15 30		16 29		17 30	17 50	18 30	19 30	20 30	21 30	23 01
Pinhoe	d		12 34		13 34					15 34		16 34		17 34	17 56	18 37	19 36		21 37	23 06
Whimple	d				13 42					15 42		16 40			18 02	18 44	19 43	20 41	21 44	23 13
Feniton	d		12 44				14 43					16 46		17 44	18 08	18 49		20 47	21 49	23 18
Honiton	a		12 50		13 51		14 50			15 51		16 52		17 50	18 17	18 55	19 52	20 53	21 55	23 25
	d		12 55		13 55		14 55			15 55		16 56		17 55	18 19	18 59	19 55	20 57	21 59	23 32
Axminster	a		13 05		14 05		15 05			16 05		17 06		18 05	18 29	19 09	20 05	21 07	22 09	23 42
	d		13 06		14 06		15 06			16 06		17 07		18 06		19 10	20 06	21 08	22 10	23 43
Crewkerne	d		13 19		14 19		15 19			16 19		17 20		18 19		19 23	20 19	21 21	22 23	23 56
Yeovil Junction	a		13 27		14 27		15 27			16 27		17 28		18 27		19 31	20 28	21 29	22 31	00 04
	d		13 29		14 29		15 29			16 29		17 30		18 29		19 33	20 29	21 31	22 33	00 06
Sherborne	d		13 35		14 35		15 35			16 35		17 36		18 35		19 39	20 36	21 37	22 39	
Templecombe	d		13 43		14 43		15 43			16 43		17 44		18 43		19 47	20 43	21 45	22 47	
Gillingham (Dorset)	a		13 50		14 50		15 50			16 50		17 51		18 50		19 54	20 50	21 52	22 54	
	d		13 51		14 51		15 51	16 18		16 51		17 52		18 51		19 55	20 51	21 53	22 55	
Tisbury	d		14 01		15 01		16 01	16 28		17 01		18 02		19 01		20 07	21 02	22 03	23 05	
Bristol Temple Meads 10	d	12 51							15 51											
Bath Spa 7	d	13 07							16 07											
Bradford-on-Avon	d	13 20							16 24											
Trowbridge	d	13 27							16 30											
Westbury	d	13 39							16 39											
Warminster	d	13 46							16 47											
Salisbury	a	14 10	14 16		15 16		16 16	16 43	17 09	17 16		18 22		19 23		20 22	21 22	22 18	23 29	00 43
	d	14 21		14 47	15 21	15 47	16 21	16 47	17 21		17 47	18 27	18 47	19 26		20 26	21 26	22 26		
Grateley	d			14 59		15 59		16 59			17 59		18 59	19 38		20 38	21 38	22 38		
Andover	d	14 38		15 06	15 38	16 06	16 38	17 06	17 38		18 06	18 44	19 06	19 45		20 45	21 45	22 45		
Whitchurch (Hants)	d			15 14		16 14		17 14			18 14		19 14	19 53		20 53	21 53	22 53		
Overton	d			15 20		16 20		17 20			18 20		19 20	19 59		20 59	21 59	22 59		
Basingstoke	a	14 55		15 28	15 55	16 28	16 55	17 29	17 55		18 28	19 01	19 28	20 08		21 08	22 07	23 07		
Woking	a	15 15		15 49	16 15	16 49	17 15	17 49	18 15		18 49	19 21	19 49	20 29		21 29	22 28			
Clapham Junction 10	a	15 36			16 36		17 36		18 36			19 41		20 52		21 52	22 48			
London Waterloo 15	⊖ a	15 49		16 19	16 49	17 19	17 49	18 21	18 49		19 19	19 50	20 19	21 00		22 04	22 58			

A From Exeter St Davids

B T from Salisbury

C T from Axminster

For Bus Connections between Yeovil Junction and Yeovil Pen Mill please see Table 123A

For services between London Waterloo and Woking, please see Table 155

For services between London Waterloo to Woking and Basingstoke, please see Table 155

For services between Warminster to Bristol Temple Meads and Salisbury, please see Table 1231

Table 160R

Saturdays

14 December to 17 May

Exeter and Salisbury - London

Network Diagram - see first Page of Table 160

		SW	SW	SW	SW	SW	SW	SW	SW	SW		SW	SW	SW	SW	SW	SW	SW	SW	SW		SW	SW	SW	SW
		1	◇1	◇1	◇1	◇1	◇1	◇1	◇1	◇1		◇1	◇1	◇1	◇1	◇1	◇1	◇1	◇1	◇1		◇1	◇1	◇1	◇1
		A					B	C		C		C		B	C		C		C			C			C
			trolley	trolley	trolley	trolley	trolley	trolley	trolley	trolley		trolley	trolley	trolley	trolley	trolley	trolley	trolley	trolley	trolley		trolley	trolley	trolley	trolley
Exeter St Davids 6	d						05 10			06 41		07 25			08 24		09 25		10 25			11 25			12 25
Exeter Central	d						05 14			06 45		07 30			08 28		09 30		10 30			11 30			12 30
Pinhoe	d						05 19			06 50		07 34			08 33		09 34		10 34			11 34			12 34
Whimple	d						05 26			06 57		07 41			08 39		09 42					11 42			
Feniton	d						05 31			07 02					08 45				10 44						12 44
Honiton	a						05 38			07 10		07 51			08 51		09 51		10 50			11 51			12 51
	d						05 41	06 19		07 13		07 55			08 55		09 55		10 55			11 55			12 55
Axminster	a						05 51	06 29		07 23		08 05			09 05		10 05		11 05			12 05			13 05
	d						05 52	06 30		07 24		08 06			09 06		10 06		11 06			12 06			13 06
Crewkerne	d						06 05	06 43		07 37		08 19			09 19		10 19		11 19			12 19			13 19
Yeovil Junction	a						06 14	06 52		07 45		08 27			09 27		10 27		11 27			12 27			13 27
	d	00 06					06 20	06 53		07 50		08 29			09 29		10 29		11 29			12 29			13 29
Sherborne	d						06 26	07 00		07 56		08 35			09 35		10 35		11 35			12 35			13 35
Templecombe	d						06 34	07 07		08 04		08 43			09 43		10 43		11 43			12 43			13 43
Gillingham (Dorset)	a						06 41	07 14		08 11		08 50			09 50		10 50		11 50			12 50			13 50
	d						06 42	07 15		08 12		08 51			09 51		10 51		11 51			12 51			13 51
Tisbury	d						06 52	07 26		08 22		09 01			10 01		11 01		12 01			13 01			14 01
Bristol Temple Meads 10	d													08 51										12 51	
Bath Spa 7	d													09 07										13 07	
Bradford-on-Avon	d													09 20										13 20	
Trowbridge	d													09 27										13 27	
Westbury	d													09 39										13 39	
Warminster	d													09 46										13 46	
Salisbury	a	00 43					07 07	07 40		08 37		09 16		10 09	10 16		11 16		12 16			13 16		14 10	14 16
	d		05 15	05 47	06 21	06 47	07 21	07 47	08 21	08 47		09 21	09 47		10 21	10 47	11 21	11 47	12 21	12 47		13 21	13 47		14 21
Grateley	d		05 27	05 59		06 59		07 59		08 59			09 59			10 59		11 59		12 59			13 59		
Andover	d		05 35	06 06	06 38	07 06	07 38	08 06	08 38	09 06		09 38	10 06		10 38	11 06	11 38	12 06	12 38	13 06		13 38	14 06		14 38
Whitchurch (Hants)	d		05 43	06 14		07 14		08 14		09 14			10 14			11 14		12 14		13 14			14 14		
Overton	d		05 49	06 20		07 20		08 20		09 20			10 20			11 20		12 20		13 20			14 20		
Basingstoke	a		05 58	06 28	06 55	07 28	07 55	08 28	08 55	09 28		09 55	10 28		10 55	11 28	11 55	12 28	12 55	13 28		13 55	14 28		14 55
Woking	a		06 18	06 49	07 15	07 49	08 17	08 49	09 15	09 49		10 15	10 49		11 15	11 49	12 15	12 49	13 15	13 49		14 15	14 49		15 15
Clapham Junction 10	a		06 38		07 36		08 37		09 36			10 36			11 36		12 36		13 36			14 36			15 36
London Waterloo 15 ⊖	a		06 49	07 19	07 49	08 19	08 49	09 19	09 49	10 19		10 49	11 19		11 49	12 19	12 49	13 19	13 49	14 19		14 49	15 19		15 49

		SW	SW	SW	SW	SW		SW	SW	SW	SW	SW	SW	SW	SW	SW		SW	SW
		◇1	◇1	◇1	◇1	◇1		◇1	◇1	◇1	◇1	◇1	◇1	◇1	◇1	◇1		1	1
			C		C			B	C		C	D	C	C					
		trolley	trolley	trolley	trolley	trolley		trolley	trolley	trolley	trolley	trolley	trolley	trolley					
Exeter St Davids 6	d		13 25		14 25				15 25		16 25		17 25	18 25	19 25	20 25		21 25	22 57
Exeter Central	d		13 30		14 30				15 30		16 30		17 30	18 30	19 30	20 30		21 30	23 01
Pinhoe	d		13 34						15 34				17 34	18 34	19 34	20 34		21 34	23 06
Whimple	d		13 42						15 42				17 42		19 42	20 41		21 42	23 13
Feniton	d				14 44						16 44		17 47	18 45		20 47		21 47	23 18
Honiton	a		13 51		14 50				15 51		16 50		17 53	18 51	19 51	20 53		21 53	23 25
	d		13 55		14 55				15 55		16 55		17 57	18 55	19 55	20 56		21 57	23 32
Axminster	a		14 05		15 05				16 05		17 05		18 07	19 05	20 05	21 06		22 07	23 42
	d		14 06		15 06				16 06		17 06		18 08	19 06	20 06	21 07		22 08	23 43
Crewkerne	d		14 19		15 19				16 19		17 19		18 21	19 19	20 19	21 20		22 21	23 56
Yeovil Junction	a		14 27		15 27				16 27		17 27		18 29	19 27	20 27	21 29		22 29	00 04
	d		14 29		15 29				16 29		17 29		18 31	19 29	20 29	21 30		22 31	00 06
Sherborne	d		14 35		15 35				16 35		17 35		18 37	19 35	20 35	21 37		22 37	
Templecombe	d		14 43		15 43				16 43		17 43		18 45	19 43	20 43	21 44		22 45	
Gillingham (Dorset)	a		14 50		15 50				16 50		17 50		18 52	19 50	20 50	21 51		22 52	
	d		14 51		15 51				16 51		17 51		18 53	19 51	20 51	21 52		22 53	
Tisbury	d		15 01		16 01				17 01		18 01		19 03	20 01	21 01	22 03		23 03	
Bristol Temple Meads 10	d							15 51											
Bath Spa 7	d							16 07											
Bradford-on-Avon	d							16 24											
Trowbridge	d							16 30											
Westbury	d							16 39											
Warminster	d							16 47											
Salisbury	a		15 16		16 16			17 09	17 16		18 16		19 18	20 16	21 16	22 23		23 29	00 41
	d	14 47	15 21	15 47	16 21	16 47			17 21	17 47	18 21	18 47	19 26	20 26	21 26	22 27			
Grateley	d	14 59		15 59		16 59				17 59		18 59	19 38	20 38	21 38	22 39			
Andover	d	15 06	15 38	16 06	16 38	17 06			17 38	18 06	18 38	19 06	19 45	20 45	21 45	22 47			
Whitchurch (Hants)	d	15 14		16 14		17 14				18 14		19 14	19 53	20 53	21 53	22 55			
Overton	d	15 20		16 20		17 20				18 20		19 20	19 59	20 59	21 59	23 00			
Basingstoke	a	15 28	15 55	16 28	16 55	17 28			17 55	18 28	18 55	19 28	20 08	21 08	22 07	23 09			
Woking	a	15 49	16 15	16 49	17 15	17 49			18 15	18 49	19 15	19 49	20 29	21 29	22 28				
Clapham Junction 10	a		16 36		17 36				18 36		19 36		20 52	21 52	22 48				
London Waterloo 15 ⊖	a	16 19	16 49	17 19	17 49	18 19			18 49	19 19	19 49	20 19	21 04	22 04	22 57				

A From Exeter St Davids
B trolley from Salisbury
C trolley from Axminster
D trolley to Basingstoke

For Bus Connections between Yeovil Junction and Yeovil Pen Mill please see Table 123A

For services between London Waterloo and Woking, please see Table 155

For services between London Waterloo to Woking and Basingstoke, please see Table 155

For services between Warminster to Bristol Temple Meads and Salisbury, please see Table 123

Table 160R

Sundays

8 December to 11 May

Exeter and Salisbury - London

Network Diagram - see first Page of Table 160

		SW	SW	SW	SW	SW	SW	SW	SW	SW	SW	SW	SW	SW	SW	SW	SW	SW	SW	SW	SW	SW
		[1]	◇[1]	◇[1]	◇[1]	◇[1]	◇[1]	◇[1]	◇[1]	◇[1]	◇[1]	◇[1]	◇[1]	◇[1]	◇[1]	◇[1]	◇[1]	◇[1]	◇[1]	◇[1]	[1]	[1]
		A			B	B	B	C	D	D	D	D	D	B	D	D	E	D				
			trolley	trolley	trolley	trolley	trolley	trolley	trolley	trolley	trolley	trolley	trolley	trolley	trolley	trolley	trolley	trolley				
Exeter St Davids [6]	d							09 25	10 25	11 25	12 25	13 25	14 25		15 25	16 25	17 25	18 25	19 25	20 25	21 25	23 15
Exeter Central	d							09 30	10 30	11 30	12 30	13 30	14 30		15 30	16 30	17 30	18 30	19 30	20 30	21 30	23 19
Pinhoe	d							09 35	10 37	11 37		13 37			15 37	16 37	17 37	18 37	19 37		21 37	23 24
Whimple	d							09 41		11 44		13 44			15 44		17 44		19 44	20 44	21 44	
Feniton	d							09 47	10 47		12 46		14 46			16 47		18 47		20 49	21 50	
Honiton	a							09 53	10 53	11 54	12 53	13 54	14 52		15 54	16 53	17 54	18 53	19 53	20 54	21 56	23s36
	d						08 58	09 57	10 57	11 57	12 57	13 57	14 57		15 57	16 57	17 57	18 57	19 57	20 57	21 59	
Axminster	a						09 08	10 07	11 07	12 07	13 07	14 07	15 07		16 07	17 07	18 07	19 07	20 07	21 08	22 09	23s51
	d						09 09	10 09	11 09	12 09	13 09	14 09	15 09		16 09	17 09	18 09	19 09	20 09	21 09	22 10	
Crewkerne	d						09 22	10 22	11 22	12 22	13 22	14 22	15 22		16 22	17 22	18 22	19 22	20 22	21 22	22 23	00s12
Yeovil Junction	a						09 30	10 30	11 30	12 30	13 30	14 30	15 30		16 30	17 30	18 30	19 30	20 30	21 31	22 32	00s21
	d	00 06			07 32		09 32	10 32	11 32	12 32	13 32	14 32	15 32		16 32	17 32	18 32	19 32	20 32	21 32	22 33	
Sherborne	d				07 38		09 38	10 38	11 38	12 38	13 38	14 38	15 38		16 38	17 38	18 38	19 38	20 38	21 38	22 40	
Templecombe	d				07 46		09 46	10 46	11 46	12 46	13 46	14 46	15 46		16 46	17 46	18 46	19 46	20 46	21 46	22 47	
Gillingham (Dorset)	a				07 53		09 53	10 53	11 53	12 53	13 53	14 53	15 53		16 53	17 53	18 53	19 53	20 53	21 53	22 54	
	d				07 54	08 54	09 54	10 54	11 54	12 54	13 54	14 54	15 54		16 54	17 54	18 54	19 54	20 54	21 54	22 56	
Tisbury	d				08 05	09 05	10 05	11 05	12 05	13 05	14 05	15 05	16 05		17 05	18 05	19 05	20 05	21 05	22 05	23 07	
Bristol Temple Meads [10]	d													16 04								
Bath Spa [7]	d													16 20								
Bradford-on-Avon	d													16 31								
Trowbridge	d													16 37								
Westbury	d													16 46								
Warminster	d													16 53								
Salisbury	a	00 41			08 20	09 20	10 20	11 20	12 20	13 20	14 20	15 20	16 20	17 16	17 20	18 20	19 20	20 20	21 20	22 20	23 21	00 57
	d		06 45	07 27	08 27	09 27	10 27	11 27	12 27	13 27	14 27	15 27	16 27		17 27	18 27	19 27	20 27	21 27	22 27		
Grateley	d			07 39	08 39	09 39		11 39		13 39		15 39			17 39		19 39		21 39	22 39		
Andover	d		07 02	07 46	08 46	09 46	10 44	11 46	12 44	13 46	14 44	15 46	16 44		17 46	18 44	19 46	20 44	21 46	22 46		
Whitchurch (Hants)	d			07 54	08 54		10 52		12 52		14 52		16 52			18 52		20 52		22 54		
Overton	d			08 00	09 00		10 58		12 58		14 58		16 58			18 58		20 58		23 00		
Basingstoke	a		07 19	08 08	09 08	10 02	11 06	12 04	13 06	14 02	15 06	16 02	17 06		18 02	19 06	20 02	21 06	22 03	23 08		
Woking	a		07 39	08 28	09 28	10 28	11 28	12 28	13 28	14 28	15 28	16 28	17 28		18 28	19 28	20 28	21 28	22 28			
Clapham Junction [10]	a		08 03	08 51	09 57	10 49	11 49	12 49	13 49	14 49	15 49	16 49	17 49		18 49	19 49	20 49	21 49	22 49			
London Waterloo [15] ⊖	a		08 20	09 12	10 11	11 04	12 04	13 04	13 59	14 59	15 59	16 59	17 59		18 59	19 59	20 59	21 59	22 59			

A not 8 December. From Exeter St Davids
B trolley from Salisbury
C trolley from Yeovil Junction
D trolley from Axminster
E trolley from Axminster to Woking

For Bus Connections between Yeovil Junction and Yeovil Pen Mill please see Table 123A

For services between London Waterloo and Woking, please see Table 155

For services between London Waterloo to Woking and Basingstoke, please see Table 155

For services between Warminster to Bristol Temple Meads and Salisbury, please see Table 123

Network Diagram for Tables 165, 167

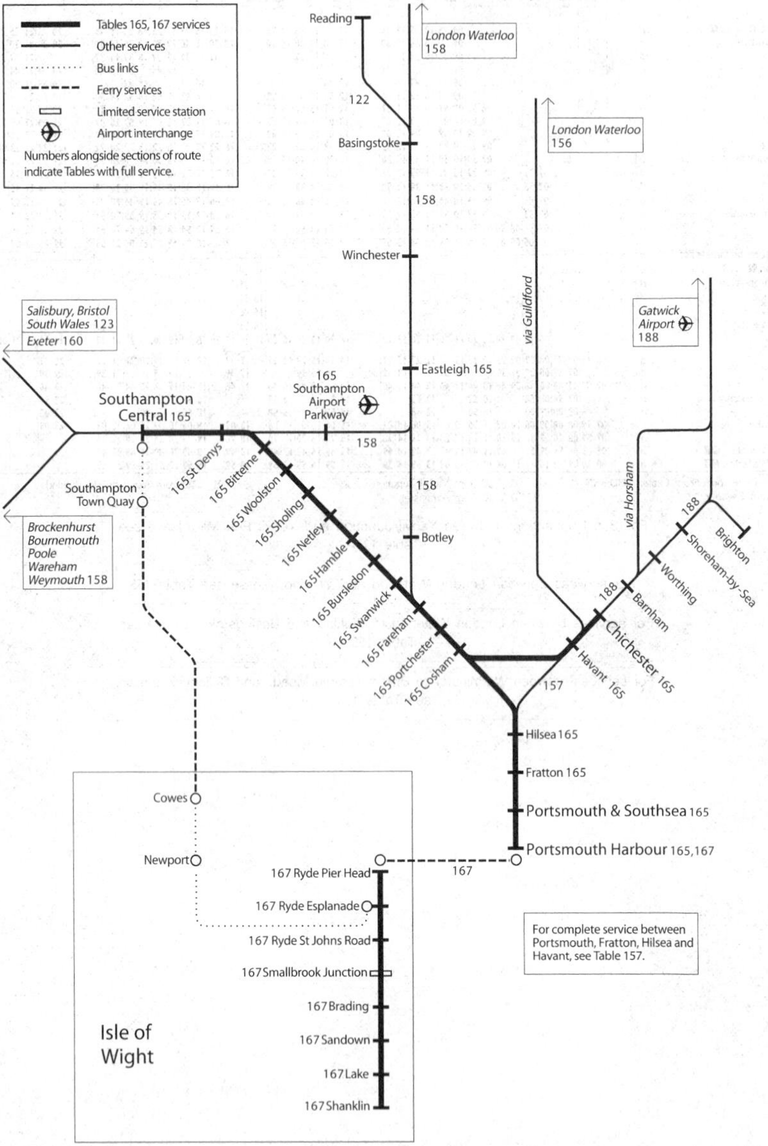

TOCs operating on this network - South West Trains (SW), Southern (SN), First Great Western (GW), Island Line (IL)

Table 165

Mondays to Fridays

9 December to 16 May

Portsmouth and Fareham - Southampton

Network Diagram - see first Page of Table 165

Miles	Miles			SW	SN	SW	SW	GW	SN	SW	SW	SN	SW	GW	SN	SN	SW	SW	SN	SW	SW	GW	SN
								R															
				1	1	1	1		1	1	1	1	1	◇	1	1	1	1	1	1		◇	1
								🛒						🛒								🛒	
0	—	**Portsmouth Harbour** ⛴	d	05 00			05 43	06 00			06 23		06 50	07 05			07 24			07 55	08 05	08 23	
0¾	—	**Portsmouth & Southsea**	d	05 05		05 16	05 48	06 04		06 23	06 28		06 55	07 09			07 29	07 38		08 00	08 10	08 27	
1¾	—	Fratton	d	05 09		05 20	05 52	06 08		06 27	06 32		06 59	07 13			07 33	07 42		08 04	08 13	08 31	
4	—	Hilsea	d	05 13		05 24	05 56			06 31	06 36		07 03				07 37	07 46		08 08	08 17		
—	0	**Chichester** 4	d		05 06				06 09			06 26			07 08	07 13			07 52				08 22
—	8¾	Havant	d		05 17				06 20			06 40			07 19	07 31			08 03				08 37
5½	12¾	Cosham	d	05 19	05 24	05 29	06 03	06 15	06 27	06 36	06 42	06 50	07 08	07 21	07 26	07 38	07 43	07 51	08 09	08 13	08 22	08 39	08 45
8	—	Portchester	d	05 23	05 28	05 34	06 08			06 41	06 46	06 54	07 13		07 30		07 48	07 56	08 13	08 18	08 27		08 49
11¼	—	**Fareham**	a	05 28	05 33	05 39	06 13	06 23	06 36	06 46	06 51	06 59	07 18	07 28	07 35	07 46	07 53	08 01	08 18	08 23	08 32	08 46	08 54
—	—		d	05 29	05 34	05 40	06 19	06 24	06 37	06 47	06 53	07 00	07 20	07 29	07 36	07 47	07 54	08 03	08 19	08 24	08 33	08 47	08 55
15	—	Swanwick	d		05 40	05 46			06 43	06 53		07 06			07 42	07 53		08 09	08 26				09 01
17	—	Bursledon	d			05 50				06 57								08 13	08 29				
18¼	—	Hamble	d			05 53				07 00								08 16	08 32				
19	—	Netley	d		05 46	05 55				07 02					07 48	07 59		08 18	08 34				
20¾	—	Sholing	d			05 59				07 06								08 22	08 38				
21½	—	Woolston	d		05 50	06 01				07 08					07 52	08 04		08 24	08 40				
23¼	—	Bitterne	d			06 05				07 12								08 28	08 43				
—	—	Eastleigh	a	05 49			06 37				07 11		07 38				08 12			08 42	08 51		
23¾	—	St Denys	d			06 08				07 15						08 08		08 31	08 46				
—	—	Southampton Airport Parkway	a																				
25¾	—	**Southampton Central** ⛴	a		05 59	06 13		06 45	07 02	07 21		07 25		07 50	08 01	08 13		08 38	08 52			09 08	09 19

		SW	SW	SN	GW	SN	SW	GW	SW	SN	GW	SN	SW	SW	SN	GW	SN	SW	SW	SN	GW	SN	SW
		1	1	1	◇	1	1	◇	1	1	◇	1	1	1	1	◇	1	1	1	1	◇	1	1
					🛒			🛒			🛒					🛒					🛒		
Portsmouth Harbour ⛴	d	08 33	08 59		09 23		09 33		09 59		10 23		10 33	10 59		11 23			11 59		12 23		
Portsmouth & Southsea	d	08 38	09 04		09 27		09 38		10 04		10 27		10 38	11 04		11 27		11 38	12 04		12 27		12 38
Fratton	d	08 42	09 08		09 31		09 42		10 08		10 31		10 42	11 08		11 31		11 42	12 08		12 31		12 42
Hilsea	d	08 46	09 12				09 46		10 12				10 46	11 12				11 46	12 12				12 46
Chichester 4	d			09 08		09 25		09 46		10 06		10 25			11 05		11 25			12 05		12 25	
Havant	d			09 23		09 39		09 58		10 20		10 37			11 19		11 37			12 19		12 37	
Cosham	d	08 51	09 17	09 30	09 39	09 46	09 51	10 05	10 17	10 28	10 39	10 46	10 51	11 17	11 26	11 39	11 46	11 51	12 17	12 26	12 39	12 46	12 51
Portchester	d	08 56	09 22				09 56		10 22	10 32			10 56	11 22	11 30			11 56	12 22	12 30			12 56
Fareham	a	09 01	09 27	09 37	09 46	09 53	10 01	10 12	10 27	10 37	10 46	10 53	11 01	11 27	11 35	11 46	11 53	12 01	12 27	12 35	12 46	12 53	13 01
	d	09 03	09 28	09 38	09 47	09 54	10 03	10 13	10 28	10 38	10 47	10 54	11 03	11 28	11 36	11 47	11 54	12 03	12 28	12 36	12 47	12 54	13 03
Swanwick	d	09 09		09 44		10 00	10 09			10 44		11 00	11 09		11 42		12 00	12 09		12 42		13 00	13 09
Bursledon	d	09 13					10 13						11 13					12 13					13 13
Hamble	d	09 16					10 16						11 16					12 16					13 16
Netley	d	09 18					10 18						11 18					12 18					13 18
Sholing	d	09 22					10 22						11 22					12 22					13 22
Woolston	d	09 24					10 24						11 24					12 24					13 24
Bitterne	d	09 28					10 28						11 28					12 28					13 28
Eastleigh	a		09 46						10 46					11 46					12 46				
St Denys	d	09 31					10 31						11 31					12 31					13 31
Southampton Airport Parkway	a																						
Southampton Central ⛴	a	09 38		10 01	10 08	10 20	10 38	10 40		11 01	11 08	11 19	11 38		12 01	12 08	12 19	12 38		12 59	13 08	13 19	13 38

		SW	SN	GW	SN	SW	SW	SN	GW	SN	SW	SW	SN	GW	SN	SW	SW	SN	GW	SN	SW	SW
									R					R					R			
		1	1	◇	1	1	1	1		1	1	1	1		1	1	1	1		1	1	
				🛒					🛒					🛒					🛒			
Portsmouth Harbour ⛴	d	12 59		13 23			13 59		14 23			14 59		15 23			15 59		16 23			16 49
Portsmouth & Southsea	d	13 04		13 27		13 38	14 04		14 27		14 38	15 04		15 27		15 38	16 04		16 27		16 38	16 55
Fratton	d	13 08		13 31		13 42	14 08		14 31		14 42	15 08		15 31		15 42	16 08		16 31		16 42	16 58
Hilsea	d	13 12				13 46	14 12				14 46	15 12				15 46	16 12				16 46	17 02
Chichester 4	d		13 05		13 25			14 05		14 25			15 05		15 25			16 05		16 26		
Havant	d		13 19		13 37			14 19		14 37			15 19		15 37			16 19		16 38		
Cosham	d	13 17	13 26	13 39	13 46	13 51	14 17	14 26	14 39	14 46	14 51	15 17	15 26	15 39	15 46	15 51	16 17	16 26	16 39	16 46	16 51	17 07
Portchester	d	13 22	13 30			13 56	14 22	14 30			14 56	15 22	15 30			15 56	16 22	16 30			16 56	17 11
Fareham	a	13 27	13 35	13 46	13 53	14 01	14 27	14 35	14 46	14 53	15 01	15 27	15 35	15 46	15 53	16 01	16 27	16 35	16 46	16 53	17 01	17 16
	d	13 28	13 36	13 47	13 54	14 03	14 28	14 36	14 47	14 54	15 03	15 28	15 36	15 47	15 54	16 03	16 28	16 36	16 47	16 56	17 03	17 18
Swanwick	d		13 42		14 00	14 09		14 42		15 00	15 09		15 42		16 00	16 09		16 42			17 09	
Bursledon	d					14 13					15 13					16 13					17 13	
Hamble	d					14 16					15 16					16 16					17 16	
Netley	d					14 18					15 18					16 18					17 18	
Sholing	d					14 22					15 22					16 22					17 22	
Woolston	d					14 24					15 24					16 24					17 24	
Bitterne	d					14 28					15 28					16 28					17 28	
Eastleigh	a	13 46			14n37		14 46					15 46					16 46			17 11		17 35
St Denys	d					14 31					15 31					16 31					17 31	
Southampton Airport Parkway	a				14n33															17 20		
Southampton Central ⛴	a		13 59	14 08	14 19	14 39		14 59	15 08	15 19	15 38		15 59	16 08	16 20	16 38		17 01	17 08	17 28	17 38	

Table 165

Mondays to Fridays

9 December to 16 May

Portsmouth and Fareham - Southampton

Network Diagram - see first Page of Table 165

		SW	SN	GW	SN	SW		GW	SW	SN	GW	SN	SW	SW	SN	GW		SN	SW	SW	SN	GW	SN	SW	SW
		1	1	◇	1	1		◇	1	1	◇	1	1	1	1	◇		1	1	1	1	◇	1	1	1
				🛒				🛒			🛒														
Portsmouth Harbour ⛴	d	16 59		17 23		17 33			17 59		18 23			18 59		19 23				19 59		20 23			
Portsmouth & Southsea	d	17 04		17 27		17 38			18 04		18 27		18 38	19 04		19 27			19 38	20 04		20 27		20 38	
Fratton	d	17 08		17 31		17 42			18 08		18 31		18 42	19 08		19 31			19 42	20 08		20 31		20 42	
Hilsea	d	17 12				17 46			18 12				18 46	19 12					19 46	20 12				20 46	
Chichester 4	d		17 05		17 25			17 47		18 05		18 25			19 03			19 20			20 04		20 27		
Havant	d		17 19		17 37			17 58		18 23		18 37			19 21			19 37			20 25		20 38		21 01
Cosham	d	17 17	17 27	17 39	17 46	17 51		18 05	18 17	18 30	18 39	18 44	18 51	19 17	19 29	19 38		19 46	19 51	20 17	20 33		20 45	20 51	21 08
Portchester	d	17 22	17 31			17 56			18 22	18 34			18 56	19 22	19 33				19 56	20 22			20 49	20 56	21 13
Fareham	a	17 27	17 36	17 46	17 53	18 01		18 12	18 27	18 39	18 46	18 52	19 01	19 27	19 38	19 46		19 54	20 01	20 27	20 40	20 46	20 54	21 01	21 18
	d	17 28	17 37	17 47	17 54	18 03		18 13	18 28	18 40	18 47	18 53	19 03	19 28	19 39	19 47		19 55	20 03	20 28	20 41	20 47	20 55	21 03	21 19
Swanwick	d		17 43		18 00	18 09				18 46		18 59	19 09		19 45			20 01	20 09		20 47		21 01	21 09	
Bursledon	d					18 13							19 13						20 13					21 13	
Hamble	d					18 16							19 16						20 16					21 16	
Netley	d		17 49			18 18							19 18						20 18					21 18	
Sholing	d					18 22							19 22						20 22					21 22	
Woolston	d		17 53			18 24							19 24						20 24					21 24	
Bitterne	d					18 28							19 28						20 28					21 28	
Eastleigh	a	17 46							18 46					19 46						20 46					
St Denys	d		17 58			18 31							19 31						20 31					21 31	
Southampton Airport Parkway	a																								
Southampton Central ⛴	a		18 03	18 08	18 20	18 38		18 40		19 04	19 08	19 20	19 38		20 03	20 08		20 18	20 38		21 05	21 08	21 19	21 38	21 43

		SW		SN	GW	SN	SW	SW	SW	SN	SW	SW		SW
		1		1		1	1	1	1	1	1	1		1
Portsmouth Harbour ⛴	d	20 59			21 23				21 54		22 33			23 24
Portsmouth & Southsea	d	21 04			21 27		21 38		21 59		22 38			23 29
Fratton	d	21 08			21 31		21 42		22 03		22 42			23 33
Hilsea	d	21 12					21 46		22 07		22 46			23 37
Chichester 4	d			21 05		21 26				22 05				
Havant	d			21 26		21 37		21 58		22 26		22 59		
Cosham	d	21 17		21 34		21 44	21 51	22 05	22 12	22 34	22 51	23 08		23 42
Portchester	d	21 22		21 38			21 56		22 17		22 56	23 13		23 47
Fareham	a	21 27		21 43	21 47	21 51	22 01	22 12	22 22	22 42	23 01	23 18		23 52
	d	21 28		21 43	21 48	21 52	22 03		22 23	22 43	23 03			23 53
Swanwick	d			21 49		21 58	22 09			22 49	23 09			
Bursledon	d						22 13				23 13			
Hamble	d						22 16				23 16			
Netley	d						22 18				23 18			
Sholing	d						22 22				23 22			
Woolston	d			21 58			22 24				23 24			
Bitterne	d						22 28				23 28			
Eastleigh	a	21 46							22 43					00 11
St Denys	d			22 02			22 31				23 31			
Southampton Airport Parkway	a													
Southampton Central ⛴	a			22 07	22 21	22 16	22 38			23 07	23 39			

Saturdays

14 December to 17 May

		SW	SN	SW	SN	SW	GW	SN	SN	SW		SW	SN	GW	SN	SW	SW	SN	GW	SN		SW	SW	SN	GW
		1	1	1	1	1	◇	1	1	1		1	1	◇	1	1	1	1	◇	1		1	1	1	◇
														🛒					🛒						🛒
Portsmouth Harbour ⛴	d					05 48	06 00					06 59		07 23			07 59		08 23				08 59		09 23
Portsmouth & Southsea	d			05 16		05 53	06 04			06 38		07 04		07 27		07 38	08 04		08 27			08 38	09 04		09 27
Fratton	d			05 20		05 57	06 08			06 42		07 08		07 31		07 42	08 08		08 31			08 42	09 08		09 31
Hilsea	d			05 24		06 01				06 46		07 12				07 46	08 12					08 46	09 12		
Chichester 4	d		05 05		05 28			06 06	06 23				07 08		07 25			08 06		08 25				09 05	
Havant	d		05 16		05 39			06 24	06 37				07 23		07 37			08 20		08 37				09 19	
Cosham	d	05 09	05 23	05 29	05 49	06 06	06 19	06 30	06 46	06 51		07 17	07 30	07 39	07 46	07 51	08 17	08 28	08 39	08 46		08 51	09 17	09 26	09 39
Portchester	d	05 14	05 27	05 34		06 11		06 34		06 56		07 22	07 34			07 56	08 22	08 32				08 56	09 22	09 30	
Fareham	a	05 19	05 32	05 39	05 57	06 16	06 27	06 39	06 53	07 01		07 27	07 39	07 46	07 53	08 01	08 27	08 37	08 46	08 53		09 01	09 27	09 35	09 46
	d	05 20	05 33	05 40	05 58	06 17	06 28	06 40	06 57	07 03		07 28	07 39	07 47	07 57	08 03	08 28	08 38	08 47	08 54		09 03	09 28	09 36	09 47
Swanwick	d		05 39	05 46	06 04			06 46		07 09			07 45			08 09		08 44		09 00		09 09		09 42	
Bursledon	d			05 50						07 13						08 13						09 13			
Hamble	d			05 53						07 16						08 16						09 16			
Netley	d		05 45	05 55						07 18						08 18						09 18			
Sholing	d			05 59						07 22						08 22						09 22			
Woolston	d		05 49	06 01						07 24						08 24						09 24			
Bitterne	d			06 05						07 28						08 28						09 28			
Eastleigh	a	05 38				06 37			07 10			07 46			08 10		08 46						09 46		
St Denys	d			06 08						07 31						08 31						09 31			
Southampton Airport Parkway	a								07 17						08 17										
Southampton Central ⛴	a		05 58	06 13	06 24		06 49	07 05	07 27	07 38			08 03	08 07	08 26	08 38		09 01	09 08	09 19		09 38		09 59	10 08

Table 165

Saturdays

14 December to 17 May

Portsmouth and Fareham - Southampton

Network Diagram - see first Page of Table 165

		SN		SW	GW	SW	SN	GW	SN	SW	SW	SN		GW	SN	SW	SW	SN	GW	SN	SW	SW		SN	GW
		1		1	◇	1	1	◇	1	1	1	1		◇	1	1	1	1	◇	1	1	1		1	◇
Portsmouth Harbour	d					09 59		10 23			10 59			11 23			11 59		12 23			12 59			13 23
Portsmouth & Southsea	d			09 38		10 04		10 27		10 38	11 04			11 27		11 38	12 04		12 27		12 38	13 04			13 27
Fratton	d			09 42		10 08		10 31		10 42	11 08			11 31		11 42	12 08		12 31		12 42	13 08			13 31
Hilsea	d			09 46		10 12				10 46	11 12					11 46	12 12				12 46	13 12			
Chichester 4	d	09 25			09 49		10 05		10 25			11 05			11 25			12 05		12 25				13 05	
Havant	d	09 37			10 00		10 19		10 37			11 19			11 37			12 19		12 37				13 19	
Cosham	d	09 46		09 51	10 06	10 17	10 26	10 39	10 46	10 51	11 17	11 26		11 39	11 46	11 51	12 17	12 26	12 39	12 46	12 51	13 17		13 26	13 39
Portchester	d			09 56		10 22	10 30			10 56	11 22	11 30				11 56	12 22	12 30			12 56	13 22		13 30	
Fareham	a	09 53		10 01	10 15	10 27	10 35	10 46	10 53	11 01	11 27	11 35		11 46	11 53	12 01	12 27	12 35	12 46	12 53	13 01	13 27		13 35	13 46
	d	09 57		10 03	10 16	10 28	10 36	10 47	10 54	11 03	11 28	11 36		11 47	11 57	12 03	12 28	12 36	12 47	12 54	13 03	13 28		13 36	13 47
Swanwick	d			10 09			10 42		11 00	11 09		11 42				12 09		12 42		13 00	13 09			13 42	
Bursledon	d			10 13						11 13						12 13					13 13				
Hamble	d			10 16						11 16						12 16					13 16				
Netley	d			10 18						11 18						12 18					13 18				
Sholing	d			10 22						11 22						12 22					13 22				
Woolston	d			10 24						11 24						12 24					13 24				
Bitterne	d			10 28						11 28						12 28					13 28				
Eastleigh	a	10 10				10 46					11 46				12 10		12 46					13 46			
St Denys	d			10 31						11 31						12 31					13 31				
Southampton Airport Parkway	a	10 17													12 18										
Southampton Central	a	10 27		10 38	10 40		10 59	11 08	11 19	11 38		11 59		12 08	12 27	12 38		12 59	13 08	13 19	13 38			13 59	14 08

		SN	SW	SW	SN	GW	SN	SW		SW	SN	GW	SN	SW	SW	SN	GW	SN		SW	SW	SN	GW	SN	SW
																	R								
		1	1	1	1	◇	1	1		1	1	◇	1	1	1	1		1		1	1	1	◇	1	1
Portsmouth Harbour	d			13 59		14 23				14 59		15 23			15 59		16 23				16 59		17 23		17 33
Portsmouth & Southsea	d		13 38	14 04		14 27		14 38		15 04		15 27		15 38	16 04		16 27			16 38	17 04		17 27		17 38
Fratton	d		13 42	14 08		14 31		14 42		15 08		15 31		15 42	16 08		16 31			16 42	17 08		17 31		17 42
Hilsea	d		13 46	14 12				14 46		15 12				15 46	16 12					16 46	17 12				17 46
Chichester 4	d	13 25			14 05		14 25				15 05		15 25			16 05		16 25				17 05		17 25	
Havant	d	13 37			14 19		14 37				15 19		15 37			16 19		16 37				17 19		17 37	
Cosham	d	13 46	13 51	14 17	14 26	14 39	14 46	14 51		15 17	15 26	15 39	15 46	15 51	16 17	16 26	16 39	16 46		16 51	17 17	17 26	17 39	17 46	17 51
Portchester	d		13 56	14 22	14 30			14 56		15 22	15 30			15 56	16 22	16 30				16 56	17 22	17 30			17 56
Fareham	a	13 53	14 01	14 27	14 35	14 46	14 53	15 01		15 27	15 35	15 46	15 53	16 01	16 27	16 35	16 46	16 53		17 01	17 27	17 35	17 46	17 53	18 01
	d	13 54	14 03	14 28	14 36	14 47	14 54	15 03		15 28	15 36	15 47	15 57	16 03	16 28	16 36	16 47	16 54		17 03	17 28	17 36	17 47	17 57	18 03
Swanwick	d	14 00	14 09		14 42		15 00	15 09			15 42			16 09		16 42		17 00		17 09		17 42			18 09
Bursledon	d		14 13					15 13						16 13						17 13					18 13
Hamble	d		14 16					15 16						16 16						17 16					18 16
Netley	d		14 18					15 18						16 18						17 18					18 18
Sholing	d		14 22					15 22						16 22						17 22					18 22
Woolston	d		14 24					15 24						16 24						17 24					18 24
Bitterne	d		14 28					15 28						16 28						17 28					18 28
Eastleigh	a			14 46						15 46			16 10		16 46						17 46			18 10	
St Denys	d		14 31					15 31						16 31						17 31					18 31
Southampton Airport Parkway	a												16 17											18 17	
Southampton Central	a	14 19	14 39		14 59	15 08	15 19	15 38			15 59	16 08	16 27	16 38		16 59	17 08	17 19		17 38		17 59	18 08	18 27	18 38

		GW	SW	SN		GW	SN	SW	SW	SN	GW	SN	SW	SW		SN	GW	SN	SW	SW	SN	SN	SW	SW	
		◇	1	1		◇	1	1	1	1	◇	1	1	1		1	◇	1	1	1	1	1	1	1	
Portsmouth Harbour	d		17 59			18 23			18 59		19 23			19 59			20 23			20 59				21 54	
Portsmouth & Southsea	d		18 04			18 27		18 38	19 04		19 27		19 38	20 04			20 27		20 38	21 04			21 38	21 59	
Fratton	d		18 08			18 31		18 42	19 08		19 31		19 42	20 08			20 31		20 42	21 08			21 42	22 03	
Hilsea	d		18 12					18 46	19 12				19 46	20 12					20 46	21 12			21 46	22 07	
Chichester 4	d	17 46		18 05			18 25			19 05		19 25				20 05		20 25			21 05	21 28			
Havant	d	18 00		18 19			18 37			19 19		19 37				20 26		20 37			21 23	21 40			
Cosham	d	18 06	18 17	18 26		18 39	18 46	18 51	19 17	19 26	19 39	19 46	19 51	20 17		20 32		20 46	20 51	21 17	21 29	21 47	21 51	22 12	
Portchester	d		18 22	18 30				18 56	19 22	19 30			19 56	20 22		20 36			20 56	21 22	21 33		21 56	22 17	
Fareham	a	18 14	18 27	18 35		18 46	18 53	19 01	19 27	19 35	19 46	19 53	20 01	20 27		20 41	20 45	20 53	21 01	21 27	21 38	21 54	22 01	22 22	
	d	18 15	18 28	18 36		18 47	18 54	19 03	19 28	19 36	19 47	19 57	20 03	20 28		20 42	20 47	20 55	21 03	21 28	21 39	21 55	22 03	22 23	
Swanwick	d			18 42			19 00	19 09		19 42			20 09			20 48		21 01	21 09		21 45	22 01	22 09		
Bursledon	d							19 13					20 13						21 13				22 13		
Hamble	d							19 16					20 16						21 16				22 16		
Netley	d							19 18					20 18						21 18				22 18		
Sholing	d							19 22					20 22						21 22				22 22		
Woolston	d							19 24					20 24						21 24				22 24		
Bitterne	d							19 28					20 28						21 28				22 28		
Eastleigh	a		18 46						19 46			20 10		20 46						21 46				22 41	
St Denys	d							19 31					20 31						21 31				22 31		
Southampton Airport Parkway	a											20 17													
Southampton Central	a	18 43		18 59		19 08	19 19	19 38		19 59	20 09	20 27	20 38			21 05	21 10	21 19	21 38		22 02	22 20	22 38		

Table 165

Saturdays

14 December to 17 May

Portsmouth and Fareham - Southampton

Network Diagram - see first Page of Table 165

		SN	SW	SW
		1	1	1
Portsmouth Harbour ⛴	d		22 33	23 24
Portsmouth & Southsea	d		22 38	23 29
Fratton	d		22 42	23 33
Hilsea	d		22 46	23 37
Chichester 4	d	22 05		
Havant	d	22 26		
Cosham	d	22 34	22 51	23 42
Portchester	d		22 56	23 47
Fareham	a	22 41	23 01	23 52
	d	22 42	23 03	23 53
Swanwick	d	22 48	23 09	
Bursledon	d		23 13	
Hamble	d		23 16	
Netley	d		23 18	
Sholing	d		23 22	
Woolston	d		23 24	
Bitterne	d		23 28	
Eastleigh	a			00 11
St Denys	d		23 31	
Southampton Airport Parkway	a			
Southampton Central ⛴	a	23 05	23 36	

Sundays

8 December to 11 May

		SW	SW	SW	SN	SW	SW	SN	GW	SW		SW	SN
									R				
		1	1	1	1	1	1	1		1		1	1
										🚲			
Portsmouth Harbour ⛴	d	06 37	07 17			08 17			09 08	09 17			
Portsmouth & Southsea	d	06 42	07 22	07 42		08 22	08 42		09 12	09 22		09 42	
Fratton	d	06 46	07 26	07 46		08 26	08 46		09 16	09 26		09 46	
Hilsea	d	06 50	07 30	07 50		08 30	08 50			09 30		09 50	
Chichester 4	d				07 52			08 56					09 56
Havant	d				08 04			09 08					10 08
Cosham	d	06 55	07 35	07 55	08 11	08 35	08 55	09 15	09 23	09 35		09 55	10 15
Portchester	d	07 00	07 40	08 00		08 40	09 00			09 40		10 00	
Fareham	a	07 05	07 45	08 05	08 18	08 45	09 05	09 23	09 31	09 45		10 05	10 22
	d	07 06	07 46	08 06	08 19	08 46	09 06	09 23	09 32	09 46		10 06	10 23
Swanwick	d	07 12		08 12	08 26		09 12	09 29				10 12	10 29
Bursledon	d	07 16		08 16			09 16					10 16	
Hamble	d	07 19		08 19			09 19					10 19	
Netley	d	07 21		08 21			09 21					10 21	
Sholing	d	07 25		08 25			09 25					10 25	
Woolston	d	07 27		08 27			09 27					10 27	
Bitterne	d	07 31		08 31			09 31					10 31	
Eastleigh	a		08 04			09 04				10 04			
St Denys	d	07 34		08 34			09 34					10 34	
Southampton Airport Parkway	a												
Southampton Central ⛴	a	07 40		08 40	08 43		09 40	09 48	09 53			10 40	10 46

		SW	SW	SN	GW	SW	SW	SN		GW	SW	SW	SN
		1	1	1	◇	1	1	1		◇	1	1	1
		🚲				🚲					🚲		
Portsmouth Harbour ⛴	d	10 17			11 08	11 17					12 17		
Portsmouth & Southsea	d	10 22	10 42		11 12	11 22	11 42				12 22	12 42	
Fratton	d	10 26	10 46		11 16	11 26	11 46				12 26	12 46	
Hilsea	d	10 30	10 50			11 30	11 50				12 30	12 50	
Chichester 4	d			10 56				11 56		12 01			12 56
Havant	d			11 08				12 08		12 12			13 08
Cosham	d	10 35	10 55	11 15	11 23	11 35	11 55	12 15		12 23	12 35	12 55	13 15
Portchester	d	10 40	11 00			11 40	12 00				12 40	13 00	
Fareham	a	10 45	11 05	11 22	11 31	11 45	12 05	12 22		12 31	12 45	13 05	13 22
	d	10 46	11 06	11 23	11 32	11 46	12 06	12 23		12 32	12 46	13 06	13 23
Swanwick	d		11 12	11 29			12 12	12 29				13 12	13 29
Bursledon	d		11 16				12 16					13 16	
Hamble	d		11 19				12 19					13 19	
Netley	d		11 21				12 21					13 21	
Sholing	d		11 25				12 25					13 25	
Woolston	d		11 27				12 27					13 27	
Bitterne	d		11 31				12 31					13 31	
Eastleigh	a	11 04				12 04					13 04		
St Denys	d		11 34				12 34					13 34	
Southampton Airport Parkway	a												
Southampton Central ⛴	a		11 40	11 46	11 53		12 40	12 46		12 53		13 40	13 46

		GW	SW	SW	SN	GW		SW	SW	SN	GW	SW	SW
											R		
		◇	1	1	1	◇		1	1	1		1	1
			🚲					🚲				🚲	
Portsmouth Harbour ⛴	d	13 08	13 17			14 08		14 17			15 08	15 17	
Portsmouth & Southsea	d	13 12	13 22	13 42		14 12		14 22	14 42		15 12	15 22	15 42
Fratton	d	13 16	13 26	13 46		14 16		14 26	14 46		15 16	15 26	15 46
Hilsea	d		13 30	13 50				14 30	14 50			15 30	15 50
Chichester 4	d				13 56					14 56			
Havant	d				14 08					15 08			
Cosham	d	13 23	13 35	13 55	14 15	14 23		14 35	14 55	15 15	15 23	15 35	15 55
Portchester	d		13 40	14 00				14 40	15 00			15 40	16 00
Fareham	a	13 31	13 45	14 05	14 22	14 31		14 45	15 05	15 22	15 31	15 45	16 05
	d	13 32	13 46	14 06	14 23	14 32		14 46	15 06	15 23	15 32	15 46	16 06
Swanwick	d			14 12	14 29				15 12	15 29			16 12
Bursledon	d			14 16					15 16				16 16
Hamble	d			14 19					15 19				16 19
Netley	d			14 21					15 21				16 21
Sholing	d			14 25					15 25				16 25
Woolston	d			14 27					15 27				16 27
Bitterne	d			14 31					15 31				16 31
Eastleigh	a		14 04					15 04				16 04	
St Denys	d			14 34					15 34				16 34
Southampton Airport Parkway	a												
Southampton Central ⛴	a	13 53		14 40	14 46	14 53			15 40	15 46	15 53		16 40

		SN	GW	SW		GW	SW	SN	GW	SW	SW	SN	GW
		1	◇	1		◇	1	1	◇	1	1	1	◇
				🚲									
Portsmouth Harbour ⛴	d		16 08	16 17					17 08	17 17			18 08
Portsmouth & Southsea	d		16 12	16 22			16 42		17 12	17 22	17 42		18 12
Fratton	d		16 16	16 26			16 46		17 16	17 26	17 46		18 16
Hilsea	d			16 30			16 50			17 30	17 50		
Chichester 4	d	15 56				16 37		16 56				17 56	
Havant	d	16 08				16 48		17 08				18 08	
Cosham	d	16 15	16 23	16 35		16 55	17 00	17 15	17 23	17 35	17 55	18 15	18 23
Portchester	d			16 40			17 04			17 40	18 00		
Fareham	a	16 22	16 31	16 45		17 03	17 09	17 22	17 31	17 45	18 05	18 22	18 31
	d	16 23	16 32	16 46		17 03	17 10	17 23	17 32	17 46	18 06	18 23	18 32
Swanwick	d	16 29					17 17	17 29			18 12	18 29	
Bursledon	d						17 20				18 16		
Hamble	d						17 24				18 19		
Netley	d						17 26				18 21		
Sholing	d						17 30				18 25		
Woolston	d						17 32				18 27		
Bitterne	d						17 35				18 31		
Eastleigh	a			17 04						18 04			
St Denys	d						17 38				18 34		
Southampton Airport Parkway	a												
Southampton Central ⛴	a	16 46	16 53			17 24	17 43	17 47	17 53		18 40	18 46	18 53

Table 165

Sundays

8 December to 11 May

Portsmouth and Fareham - Southampton

Network Diagram - see first Page of Table 165

		SW ■1	GW ◇	SW ■1	SN ■1	GW ◇	SW ■1	SW ■1	SN ■1	GW ◇	SW ■1	SW ■1	SN ■1	SW ■1	SW ■1	SN ■1	GW	SW ■1	SW ■1	SW ■1
Portsmouth Harbour ⛴	d	18 17				19 08	19 17			20 08	20 17			21 17			22 05	22 17		23 17
Portsmouth & Southsea	d	18 22		18 42		19 12	19 22	19 42		20 12	20 22	20 42		21 22	21 42		22 12	22 22	22 42	23 22
Fratton	d	18 26		18 46		19 16	19 26	19 46		20 16	20 26	20 46		21 26	21 46		22 16	22 26	22 46	23 26
Hilsea	d	18 30		18 50			19 30	19 50			20 30	20 50		21 30	21 50			22 30	22 50	23 30
Chichester ■4	d		18 32		18 56				19 56				20 56			21 56				
Havant	d		18 50		19 08				20 08				21 08			22 08				
Cosham	d	18 35	18 57	19 00	19 15	19 23	19 35	19 55	20 15		20 35	20 55	21 15	21 35	21 55	22 15		22 35	22 55	23 35
Portchester	d	18 40		19 04			19 40	20 00			20 40	21 00		21 40	22 00			22 40	23 00	23 40
Fareham	a	18 45	19 04	19 09	19 22	19 31	19 45	20 05	20 22	20 31	20 45	21 05	21 22	21 45	22 05	22 22	22 31	22 45	23 05	23 45
	d	18 46	19 05	19 10	19 23	19 32	19 46	20 06	20 23	20 32	20 46	21 06	21 23	21 46	22 06	22 23	22 32	22 46	23 06	23 46
Swanwick	d			19 17	19 29			20 12	20 29			21 12	21 29		22 12	22 29			23 12	
Bursledon	d			19 20				20 16				21 16			22 16				23 16	
Hamble	d			19 24				20 19				21 19			22 19				23 19	
Netley	d			19 26				20 21				21 21			22 21				23 21	
Sholing	d			19 30				20 25				21 25			22 25				23 25	
Woolston	d			19 32				20 27				21 27			22 27				23 27	
Bitterne	d			19 35				20 31				21 31			22 31				23 31	
Eastleigh	a	19 04					20 04				21 04			22 04				23 04		00 04
St Denys	d			19 38				20 34				21 34			22 34				23 34	
Southampton Airport Parkway	a																			
Southampton Central ⛴	a		19 26	19 43	19 47	19 53		20 40	20 46	20 53		21 40	21 46		22 40	22 46	22 53		23 40	

Table 165R

Mondays to Fridays

9 December to 16 May

Southampton - Fareham and Portsmouth

Network Diagram - see first Page of Table 165

Miles	Miles			SW	SN	SW	SN	SW	SW	GW		SW	SN	SW	SW	SN	GW	SW	SN	SW		SN	SW	GW	SN
				[1]	[1]	[1]	[1]	[1]	[1]			[1]	[1]	[1]	[1]	[1]	◇	[1]	[1]	[1]		[1]	[1]	◇ 🛒	[1]
—	—	**Southampton Central** ⛴	d		05 48		06 10		06 21	06 53			07 06		07 17	07 33	07 42	07 51	08 10			08 33	08 44	09 05	09 10
1¼	—	**Southampton Airport Parkway**	d																						
0	—	Eastleigh	d	00 30		06 00		06 29				07 02		07 30						08 31					
3¾	—	St Denys	d						06 28						07 23			07 57	08 15				08 49		
4¼	—	Bitterne	d						06 30						07 25			08 00					08 52		
6	—	Woolston	d		05 57		06 19		06 34				07 15		07 29			08 03					08 55		
6¾	—	Sholing	d						06 36						07 31			08 06					08 58		
8½	—	Netley	d						06 40						07 35			08 10					09 02		
9¼	—	Hamble	d						06 42						07 37			08 12					09 04		
10½	—	Bursledon	d						06 45						07 40			08 15					09 07		
12½	—	Swanwick	d		06 06		06 27		06 49				07 24		07 44	07 51		08 20	08 28			08 50	09 11		09 28
16¼	—	**Fareham**	a	00s47	06 12	06 17	06 33	06 49	06 57	07 15		07 20	07 30	07 47	07 52	07 58	08 05	08 27	08 34	08 50		08 56	09 17	09 27	09 36
—	—		d		06 13	06 19	06 34	06 50	06 58	07 16		07 21	07 31	07 48	07 53	07 58	08 06	08 28	08 35	08 51		08 57	09 18	09 27	09 37
19½	—	Portchester	d	00s53	06 18	06 24	06 40	06 55	07 03			07 26	07 36	07 53	07 58			08 33	08 40	08 56			09 23		09 42
22	0	Cosham	d	00s57	06 23	06 29	06 44	07 00	07 08	07 25		07 30	07 40	07 58	08 03	08 07	08 14	08 38	08 44	09 01		09 05	09 28	09 35	09 46
—	4	Havant	a		06 37		06 53						07 46			08 13			08 50			09 11			09 53
—	12¾	**Chichester** [4]	a		06 58		07 07						08 08			08 27			09 11			09 24			10 10
23½	—	Hilsea	a			06 33		07 05	07 13			07 35		08 03	08 08			08 44		09 05			09 33		
25¾	—	Fratton	a	01s05		06 40		07 09	07 17	07 34		07 39		08 07	08 12		08 20	08 48		09 09			09 37	09 42	
26¾	—	**Portsmouth & Southsea**	a	01s08		06 44		07 12	07 22	07 38		07 42		08 11	08 19		08 24	08 52		09 13			09 42	09 46	
27½	—	**Portsmouth Harbour** ⛴	a	01 12		06 49		07 17		07 45		07 48		08 16	08 24		08 30	08 57		09 18				09 52	

		SW	SN	SW	GW	SN		SW	SN	SW	GW	SN	SW	SN	SW	GW		SN	SW	SN	SW	GW	SN	SW	SN
		[1]	[1]	[1]	[R] 🛒	[1]		[1]	[1]	[1]	◇ 🛒	[1]	[1]	[1]	[1]	◇ 🛒		[1]	[1]	[1]	[1]	◇ 🛒	[1]	[1]	[1]
Southampton Central ⛴	d		09 33	09 44	10 05	10 13			10 33	10 44	11 05	11 13		11 33	11 44	12 05		12 13		12 33	12 44	13 05	13 13		13 33
Southampton Airport Parkway	d																								
Eastleigh	d	09 28						10 28					11 28						12 28					13 28	
St Denys	d			09 49						10 49					11 49						12 49				
Bitterne	d			09 52						10 52					11 52						12 52				
Woolston	d			09 55						10 55					11 55						12 55				
Sholing	d			09 58						10 58					11 58						12 58				
Netley	d			10 02						11 02					12 02						13 02				
Hamble	d			10 04						11 04					12 04						13 04				
Bursledon	d			10 07						11 07					12 07						13 07				
Swanwick	d		09 50	10 11		10 32			10 50	11 11		11 33		11 50	12 11			12 33		12 50	13 11		13 33		13 50
Fareham	a	09 46	09 56	10 17	10 27	10 38		10 46	10 56	11 17	11 27	11 39	11 46	11 56	12 17	12 27		12 39	12 46	12 56	13 17	13 27	13 39	13 46	13 56
	d	09 48	09 56	10 18	10 28	10 39		10 48	10 57	11 18	11 27	11 40	11 48	11 57	12 18	12 27		12 40	12 48	12 56	13 18	13 27	13 40	13 48	13 56
Portchester	d	09 53		10 23		10 44		10 53		11 23		11 45	11 53		12 23			12 45	12 53		13 23		13 45	13 53	
Cosham	d	09 58	10 05	10 28	10 36	10 48		10 58	11 05	11 28	11 35	11 49	11 58	12 05	12 28	12 35		12 49	12 58	13 05	13 28	13 35	13 49	13 58	14 05
Havant	a		10 11			10 55			11 11			11 55		12 11				12 55		13 11			13 55		14 11
Chichester [4]	a		10 23			11 10			11 24			12 10		12 24				13 10		13 23			14 10		14 23
Hilsea	a	10 03		10 33				11 03		11 33			12 03		12 33				13 03		13 33			14 03	
Fratton	a	10 07		10 37	10 43			11 07		11 37	11 42		12 07		12 37	12 42			13 07		13 37	13 42		14 07	
Portsmouth & Southsea	a	10 11		10 42	10 47			11 11		11 42	11 46		12 11		12 42	12 46			13 11		13 42	13 46		14 11	
Portsmouth Harbour ⛴	a	10 18			10 54			11 18			11 54		12 18			12 54			13 18			13 54		14 18	

		SW		GW	SN	SW	SN	GW	SW	GW	SN	SW		SN	SW	GW	SN	SW	SW	SN	SW	SW		GW	SN
		[1]		◇ 🛒	[1]	[1]	[1]	[R] 🛒	[1]	◇ 🛒	[1]	[1]		[1]	[1]	◇ 🛒	[1]	[1]	[1]	[1]		[1]		◇ 🛒	[1]
Southampton Central ⛴	d	13 44		14 05	14 13		14 26	14 34	14 44	15 05	15 13			15 33	15 44	16 05	16 12			16 33		16 44		17 05	17 13
Southampton Airport Parkway	d						14 34																		
Eastleigh	d					14 28	14 41					15 28							16 28		16 54				
St Denys	d	13 49							14 49						15 49							16 49			
Bitterne	d	13 52							14 52						15 52							16 52			
Woolston	d	13 55							14 55						15 55							16 55			
Sholing	d	13 58							14 58						15 58							16 58			
Netley	d	14 02							15 02						16 02							17 02			
Hamble	d	14 04							15 04						16 04							17 04			
Bursledon	d	14 07							15 07						16 07							17 07			
Swanwick	d	14 11			14 33				15 11		15 33			15 50	16 11		16 29			16 50		17 11			17 33
Fareham	a	14 17		14 27	14 39	14 46	14 55	14 58	15 17	15 27	15 39	15 46		15 56	16 17	16 27	16 35		16 47	16 56	17 11	17 17		17 27	17 39
	d	14 18		14 27	14 40	14 48	14 56	14 59	15 18	15 27	15 40	15 48		15 57	16 18	16 27	16 36	16 44	16 48	16 57	17 12	17 18		17 27	17 40
Portchester	d	14 23			14 45	14 53			15 23		15 45	15 53			16 23		16 41		16 53		17 17	17 23			17 45
Cosham	d	14 28		14 35	14 49	14 58		15 07	15 28	15 35	15 49	15 58		16 05	16 28	16 35	16 45		16 58	17 05	17 22	17 28		17 35	17 49
Havant	a				14 55		15 08	15 14			15 57			16 11			16 51	16 56		17 11					17 55
Chichester [4]	a				15 10		15 19	15 25			16 12			16 24			17 08			17 25					18 10
Hilsea	a	14 33				15 03			15 33			16 03			16 33				17 03			17 33			
Fratton	a	14 37		14 42		15 07			15 37	15 42		16 07			16 37	16 42			17 07		17 31	17 37		17 42	
Portsmouth & Southsea	a	14 42		14 46		15 11			15 42	15 46		16 11			16 40	16 46			17 11		17 35	17 42		17 46	
Portsmouth Harbour ⛴	a			14 54		15 18				15 54		16 18			16 44	16 54			17 18		17 40			17 54	

Table 165R

Mondays to Fridays

9 December to 16 May

Southampton - Fareham and Portsmouth

Network Diagram - see first Page of Table 165

		SW	SN	SW	SW	GW	SN	SW	SN	SW	SW	GW	SN	SW	SN	SW	SW	GW	SN	SW	SN	SW
		1	1	1	1	◇ 🛒	1	1	1	1	1	R 🛒	1	1	1	1	1	R 🛒	1	1	1	1
Southampton Central ⛴	d		17 33	17 44		18 05	18 11		18 33		18 44	19 05	19 12		19 33		19 44	20 05	20 11		20 33	20 44
Southampton Airport Parkway	d																					
Eastleigh	d	17 28			18 01			18 25		18 55				19 29		19 51				20 30		
St Denys	d			17 49							18 49						19 49					20 49
Bitterne	d			17 52							18 52						19 52					20 52
Woolston	d			17 55							18 55						19 55					20 55
Sholing	d			17 58							18 58						19 58					20 58
Netley	d			18 02							19 02						20 02					21 02
Hamble	d			18 04							19 04						20 04					21 04
Bursledon	d			18 07							19 07						20 07					21 07
Swanwick	d		17 50	18 11			18 28		18 50		19 11		19 29		19 51		20 11		20 28		20 50	21 11
Fareham	a	17 46	17 56	18 17	18 22	18 27	18 34	18 44	18 56	19 13	19 17	19 27	19 35	19 46	19 57	20 09	20 17	20 27	20 34	20 48	20 56	21 17
	d	17 48	17 56	18 18	18 23	18 27	18 35	18 45	18 56	19 14	19 18	19 27	19 36	19 48	19 57	20 09	20 18	20 27	20 35	20 49	20 57	21 18
Portchester	d	17 53		18 23	18 28		18 40	18 50		19 19	19 23		19 41	19 53			20 23		20 40	20 54		21 23
Cosham	d	17 58	18 05	18 28	18 33	18 35	18 44	18 55	19 05	19 24	19 28	19 35	19 46	19 58	20 06		20 28		20 44	20 59	21 06	21 28
Havant	a		18 11				18 50		19 11				19 52		20 12	20 21			20 50		21 12	
Chichester 4	a		18 24				19 05		19 22				20 06		20 24				21 05		21 24	
Hilsea	a	18 04		18 33				19 05		19 28	19 33			20 02			20 33			21 03		21 33
Fratton	a	18 08		18 37	18 40	18 48		19 09		19 32	19 37	19 42		20 06			20 37	20 42		21 07		21 37
Portsmouth & Southsea	a	18 12		18 41	18 43	18 52		19 12		19 36	19 42	19 46		20 11			20 42	20 46		21 11		21 40
Portsmouth Harbour ⛴	a	18 20			18 50	19 00		19 20		19 43		19 54		20 20				20 54		21 16		21 45

		GW	SN	SW	SN	SW	SN	GW	SN	SW	SW	GW	SN	SW
		◇ 🛒	1	1	1	1	1	◇	1	1	1	◇		1
Southampton Central ⛴	d	21 05	21 13		21 33	21 44	22 13	22 04	22 33		22 44	23 05	23 12	
Southampton Airport Parkway	d													
Eastleigh	d			21 31						22 51				23 30
St Denys	d					21 49					22 49		23 22	
Bitterne	d					21 52					22 52			
Woolston	d					21 55					22 55			
Sholing	d					21 58					22 58			
Netley	d					22 02					23 02			
Hamble	d					22 04					23 04			
Bursledon	d					22 07					23 07			
Swanwick	d		21 33		21 51	22 11	22 30		22 50		23 11			
Fareham	a	21 27	21 39	21 48	21 57	22 17	22 36	22 42	22 56	23 09	23 17	23 27	23 38	23 48
	d	21 27	21 40	21 49	21 58	22 18	22 37	22 42	22 57	23 10	23 18	23 27	23 38	23 49
Portchester	d		21 45	21 54	22 03	22 23	22 42			23 15	23 23			23 54
Cosham	d		21 49	21 59	22 07	22 28	22 47		23 05	23 20	23 28		23 46	23 59
Havant	a		21 55		22 13		22 56		23 11				23 53	
Chichester 4	a		22 06		22 34		23 11		23 22				00 04	
Hilsea	a			22 04		22 33				23 24	23 33			00 03
Fratton	a	21 41		22 08		22 37		22 56		23 32	23 37	23 44		00 07
Portsmouth & Southsea	a	21 45		22 11		22 42		22 59		23 36	23 40	23 48		00 11
Portsmouth Harbour ⛴	a	21 52		22 16				23 04		23 40		23 54		00 16

Saturdays

14 December to 17 May

		SW	SW	SN	SW	SN	SW	GW	SN	SW	SN	SW	GW	SN	SW	SN	SW	GW	SN	SW	SN	SW	GW
		1	1	1	1	1	1		1	1	1	1	◇	1	1	1	1	◇	1	1	1	1	◇
Southampton Central ⛴	d		05 44	06 13		06 33	06 44	07 05	07 13		07 33	07 44	08 05	08 13		08 33	08 44	09 05	09 13		09 33	09 44	10 05
Southampton Airport Parkway	d																						
Eastleigh	d	00 30			06 28					07 30					08 31					09 28			
St Denys	d		05 49				06 49					07 49					08 49					09 49	
Bitterne	d		05 52				06 52					07 52					08 52					09 52	
Woolston	d		05 55				06 55					07 55					08 55					09 55	
Sholing	d		05 58				06 58					07 58					08 58					09 58	
Netley	d		06 02				07 02					08 02					09 02					10 02	
Hamble	d		06 04				07 04					08 04					09 04					10 04	
Bursledon	d		06 07				07 07					08 07					09 07					10 07	
Swanwick	d		06 11	06 33		06 50	07 11		07 33		07 50	08 11		08 33		08 50	09 11		09 33		09 50	10 11	
Fareham	a	00s47	06 20	06 39	06 46	06 56	07 17	07 27	07 39	07 48	07 56	08 17	08 27	08 39	08 48	08 56	09 17	09 27	09 39	09 46	09 56	10 17	10 27
	d		06 21	06 40	06 48	06 56	07 18	07 27	07 40	07 49	07 56	08 18	08 27	08 40	08 49	08 56	09 18	09 27	09 40	09 48	09 56	10 18	10 27
Portchester	d	00s53	06 26	06 45	06 53		07 23		07 45	07 54		08 23		08 45	08 54		09 23		09 45	09 53		10 23	
Cosham	d	00s57	06 31	06 49	06 58	07 05	07 28	07 35	07 49	07 59	08 05	08 28	08 35	08 49	08 59	09 05	09 28	09 35	09 49	09 58	10 05	10 28	10 35
Havant	a			06 55		07 11			07 55		08 11			08 55		09 11			09 55		10 11		
Chichester 4	a			07 10		07 23			08 10		08 23			09 10		09 23			10 10		10 23		
Hilsea	a		06 37		07 03		07 33			08 03		08 33			09 04		09 33			10 03		10 33	
Fratton	a	01s05	06 41		07 07		07 37	07 42		08 07		08 37	08 42		09 08		09 37	09 42		10 07		10 37	10 42
Portsmouth & Southsea	a	01s08	06 44		07 11		07 42	07 46		08 11		08 42	08 46		09 12		09 42	09 46		10 11		10 42	10 46
Portsmouth Harbour ⛴	a	01 12			07 16			07 52		08 18			08 52		09 18			09 52		10 18			10 52

Table 165R

Saturdays

14 December to 17 May

Southampton - Fareham and Portsmouth

Network Diagram - see first Page of Table 165

		SN		SW	SN	SW	GW	SN	SW	SN	SW	GW		SN	SW	SN	SW	GW	SN	SW	SN	SW		GW	SN
		1		1	1	1	◇	1	1	1	1	◇		1	1	1	1	◇	1	1	1	1		◇	1
Southampton Central	d	10 13			10 33	10 44	11 05	11 13		11 33	11 44	12 05		12 13		12 33	12 44	13 05	13 13		13 33	13 44		14 05	14 13
Southampton Airport Parkway	d																								
Eastleigh	d			10 28					11 28						12 28					13 28					
St Denys	d					10 49					11 49						12 49					13 49			
Bitterne	d					10 52					11 52						12 52					13 52			
Woolston	d					10 55					11 55						12 55					13 55			
Sholing	d					10 58					11 58						12 58					13 58			
Netley	d					11 02					12 02						13 02					14 02			
Hamble	d					11 04					12 04						13 04					14 04			
Bursledon	d					11 07					12 07						13 07					14 07			
Swanwick	d	10 33			10 50	11 11		11 33		11 50	12 11			12 33		12 50	13 11		13 33		13 50	14 11			14 33
Fareham	a	10 39		10 46	10 56	11 17	11 27	11 39	11 46	11 56	12 17	12 27		12 39	12 46	12 56	13 17	13 27	13 39	13 46	13 56	14 17		14 27	14 39
	d	10 40		10 48	10 56	11 18	11 27	11 40	11 48	11 56	12 18	12 27		12 40	12 48	12 56	13 18	13 27	13 40	13 48	13 56	14 18		14 27	14 40
Portchester	d	10 45		10 53		11 23		11 45	11 53		12 23			12 45	12 53		13 23		13 45	13 53		14 23			14 45
Cosham	d	10 49		10 58	11 05	11 28	11 35	11 49	11 58	12 05	12 28	12 35		12 49	12 58	13 05	13 28	13 35	13 49	13 58	14 05	14 28		14 35	14 49
Havant	a	10 55			11 11			11 55		12 11				12 55		13 11			13 55		14 11				14 55
Chichester 4	a	11 10			11 23			12 10		12 23				13 10		13 23			14 10		14 23				15 10
Hilsea	a			11 03		11 33			12 03		12 33				13 03		13 33			14 03		14 33			
Fratton	a			11 07		11 37	11 42		12 07		12 37	12 42			13 07		13 37	13 42		14 07		14 37		14 42	
Portsmouth & Southsea	a			11 11		11 42	11 46		12 11		12 42	12 46			13 11		13 42	13 46		14 11		14 42		14 46	
Portsmouth Harbour	a			11 18			11 52		12 18			12 52			13 18			13 52		14 18				14 52	

		SW	GW	SN	SW	GW	SN	SW		SN	SW	GW	SN	SW	SN	SW	GW	SN		SW	SN	SW	GW	SN	SW
		1	◇	1	1	◇	1	1		1	1	◇	1	1	1	1	◇	1		1	1	1	◇	1	1
Southampton Central	d		14 34	14 26	14 44	15 05	15 13			15 33	15 44	16 05	16 13		16 33	16 44	17 05	17 13			17 33	17 44	18 04	18 11	
Southampton Airport Parkway	d			14 34																					
Eastleigh	d	14 28		14 41				15 28						16 28						17 28					18 28
St Denys	d				14 49						15 49					16 49						17 49			
Bitterne	d				14 52						15 52					16 52						17 52			
Woolston	d				14 55						15 55					16 55						17 55			
Sholing	d				14 58						15 58					16 58						17 58			
Netley	d				15 02						16 02					17 02						18 02			
Hamble	d				15 04						16 04					17 04						18 04			
Bursledon	d				15 07						16 07					17 07						18 07			
Swanwick	d				15 11		15 33			15 50	16 11		16 33		16 50	17 11		17 33			17 50	18 11		18 28	
Fareham	a	14 46	14 54	14 59	15 17	15 27	15 39	15 46		15 56	16 17	16 27	16 39	16 46	16 56	17 17	17 27	17 39		17 46	17 56	18 17	18 27	18 34	18 46
	d	14 48	14 55	15 00	15 18	15 27	15 40	15 48		15 56	16 18	16 27	16 40	16 48	16 56	17 18	17 27	17 40		17 48	17 56	18 18	18 27	18 35	18 48
Portchester	d	14 53			15 23		15 45	15 53			16 23		16 45	16 53		17 23		17 45		17 53		18 23		18 40	18 53
Cosham	d	14 58	15 03		15 28	15 35	15 49	15 58		16 05	16 28	16 35	16 49	16 58	17 05	17 28	17 35	17 49		17 58	18 05	18 28	18 35	18 44	18 58
Havant	a		15 10	15 14			15 55			16 11			16 55		17 11			17 55			18 11			18 50	
Chichester 4	a		15 21	15 25			16 10			16 23			17 10		17 23			18 10			18 23			19 05	
Hilsea	a	15 03			15 33			16 03			16 33			17 03		17 33				18 03		18 33			19 03
Fratton	a	15 07			15 37	15 42		16 07			16 37	16 42		17 07		17 37	17 42			18 07		18 37	18 42		19 07
Portsmouth & Southsea	a	15 11			15 42	15 46		16 11			16 40	16 46		17 11		17 42	17 46			18 11		18 42	18 45		19 11
Portsmouth Harbour	a	15 18				15 52		16 18			16 44	16 52		17 16			17 52			18 18			18 53		19 18

		SN	SW	GW		SN	SW	SN	SW	GW	SN	SW	SN	SW		GW	SN	SW	SN	SW	GW	SN	SW	SN	
				R																					
		1	1			1	1	1	1	◇	1	1	1	1		◇	1	1	1	1	◇	1	1	1	
Southampton Central	d	18 33	18 44	19 05		19 09		19 33	19 44	20 05	20 11		20 33	20 44		21 05	21 13		21 33	21 44	22 05	22 13		22 33	
Southampton Airport Parkway	d																								
Eastleigh	d						19 28					20 28						21 28					22 28		
St Denys	d		18 49						19 49					20 49						21 49					
Bitterne	d		18 52						19 52					20 52						21 52					
Woolston	d		18 55						19 55					20 55						21 55					
Sholing	d		18 58						19 58					20 58						21 58					
Netley	d		19 02						20 02					21 02						22 02					
Hamble	d		19 04						20 04					21 04						22 04					
Bursledon	d		19 07						20 07					21 07						22 07					
Swanwick	d	18 50	19 11			19 28		19 50	20 11		20 28		20 50	21 11			21 33		21 50	22 11		22 31		22 50	
Fareham	a	18 56	19 17	19 27		19 34	19 46	19 56	20 17	20 27	20 34	20 46	20 56	21 17		21 27	21 39	21 46	21 56	22 17	22 26	22 38	22 46	22 56	
	d	18 56	19 18	19 27		19 35	19 48	19 56	20 18	20 27	20 35	20 48	20 56	21 18		21 27	21 40	21 48	21 57	22 18	22 27	22 39	22 48	23 00	
Portchester	d		19 23			19 40	19 53		20 23		20 40	20 53		21 23			21 45	21 53	22 02	22 23		22 44	22 53		
Cosham	d	19 05	19 28	19 35		19 44	19 58	20 05	20 28		20 44	20 58	21 05	21 28			21 49	21 58	22 06	22 28		22 48	22 58	23 08	
Havant	a	19 11				19 51		20 11			20 50		21 11				21 55		22 12			22 54		23 14	
Chichester 4	a	19 23				20 06		20 23			21 05		21 24				22 06		22 33			23 09		23 25	
Hilsea	a		19 33				20 03		20 37			21 03		21 33				22 03		22 33			23 03		
Fratton	a		19 37	19 42			20 07		20 41	20 42		21 07		21 37		21 42		22 07		22 37	22 42		23 07		
Portsmouth & Southsea	a		19 42	19 46			20 11		20 44	20 46		21 11		21 40		21 46		22 11		22 40	22 46		23 11		
Portsmouth Harbour	a			19 52			20 18			20 52		21 16		21 45		21 52		22 18		22 47	22 52		23 18		

Table 165R

Saturdays

14 December to 17 May

Southampton - Fareham and Portsmouth

Network Diagram - see first Page of Table 165

		SW	GW	SW
		1	◇	1
Southampton Central	d	22 44	23 05	
Southampton Airport Parkway	d			
Eastleigh	d			23 28
St Denys	d	22 49		
Bitterne	d	22 52		
Woolston	d	22 55		
Sholing	d	22 58		
Netley	d	23 02		
Hamble	d	23 04		
Bursledon	d	23 07		
Swanwick	d	23 11		
Fareham	a	23 17	23 26	23 46
	d	23 18	23 27	23 48
Portchester	d	23 23		23 53
Cosham	d	23 28		23 58
Havant	a			
Chichester 4	a			
Hilsea	a	23 33		00 03
Fratton	a	23 37	23 40	00 07
Portsmouth & Southsea	a	23 40	23 44	00 11
Portsmouth Harbour	a		23 52	00 16

Sundays

8 December to 11 May

		SW	SW	SW	SN	SW	SW	GW	SN	SW		SW	SN	SW	SW	SN	SW	GW	SW	SN		SW	GW	GW	SW
		1	1	1	1	1	1		1	1		1	1	1	1	1	1	◇	1	1		1	◇ A	◇ B	1
Southampton Central	d		06 35		07 30	07 35		08 31	08 27	08 35			09 30	09 35		10 30	10 35	11 04		11 30		11 35	12 04	12 04	
Southampton Airport Parkway	d								08 36																
Eastleigh	d	00 30					08 26		08 48			09 26			10 26				11 26						12 26
St Denys	d		06 41			07 41				08 41				09 41			10 41					11 41			
Bitterne	d		06 43			07 43				08 43				09 43			10 43					11 43			
Woolston	d		06 47			07 47				08 47				09 47			10 47					11 47			
Sholing	d		06 49			07 49				08 49				09 49			10 49					11 49			
Netley	d		06 53			07 53				08 53				09 53			10 53					11 53			
Hamble	d		06 55			07 55				08 55				09 55			10 55					11 55			
Bursledon	d		06 58			07 58				08 58				09 58			10 58					11 58			
Swanwick	d		07 02		07 47	08 02				09 02			09 47	10 02		10 47	11 02			11 47		12 02			
Fareham	a	00s47	07 09		07 53	08 09	08 43	08 51	09 02	09 09		09 43	09 53	10 09	10 43	10 53	11 09	11 26	11 43	11 53		12 09	12 26	12 26	12 43
	d		07 10	07 44	07 54	08 10	08 44	08 52	09 02	09 10		09 44	09 54	10 10	10 44	10 54	11 10	11 26	11 44	11 54		12 10	12 26	12 26	12 44
Portchester	d	00s53	07 15	07 49		08 15	08 49			09 15		09 49		10 15	10 49		11 15		11 49			12 15			12 49
Cosham	d	00s57	07 20	07 54	08 03	08 20	08 54	09 00	09 11	09 20		09 54	10 03	10 20	10 54	11 03	11 20	11 34	11 54	12 03		12 20	12 34	12 34	12 54
Havant	a				08 10			09 11	09 17				10 10			11 10				12 10					
Chichester 4	a				08 23			09 22	09 29				10 23			11 23				12 23					
Hilsea	a		07 26	08 00		08 26	09 00			09 26		10 00		10 26	11 00		11 26		12 00			12 28			13 00
Fratton	a	01s05	07 30	08 04		08 30	09 04			09 30		10 08		10 30	11 08		11 30	11 40	12 04			12 32	12 40	12 41	13 04
Portsmouth & Southsea	a	01s08	07 33	08 08		08 33	09 08			09 33		10 11		10 33	11 11		11 33	11 45	12 08			12 36	12 45	12 45	13 08
Portsmouth Harbour	a	01 12		08 13			09 13					10 15			11 15			11 52	12 13				12 52	12 52	13 13

		SN	SW	GW	SW	SN		SW	GW	SW	SN	SW	SW	GW	SN	SW		GW	SW	SN	SW	GW	GW	SW	SN
		1	1	◇	1	1		1	◇	1	1	1	1	◇	1	1		◇	1	1	1	◇ A	◇ B	1	1
Southampton Central	d	12 30	12 35	13 06		13 30		13 35	14 04		14 30	14 35		15 22	15 30	15 35		16 04		16 30	16 35	17 04	17 04		17 30
Southampton Airport Parkway	d																								
Eastleigh	d				13 26					14 26			15 26						16 26					17 26	
St Denys	d		12 41					13 41				14 41				15 41					16 41				
Bitterne	d		12 43					13 43				14 43				15 43					16 43				
Woolston	d		12 47					13 47				14 47				15 47					16 47				
Sholing	d		12 49					13 49				14 49				15 49					16 49				
Netley	d		12 53					13 53				14 53				15 53					16 53				
Hamble	d		12 55					13 55				14 55				15 55					16 55				
Bursledon	d		12 58					13 58				14 58				15 58					16 58				
Swanwick	d	12 47	13 02			13 47		14 02			14 47	15 02			15 47	16 02				16 47	17 02				17 47
Fareham	a	12 53	13 09	13 29	13 43	13 53		14 09	14 26	14 43	14 53	15 09	15 43	15 50	15 58	16 09		16 26	16 43	16 53	17 09	17 26	17 26	17 43	17 53
	d	12 54	13 10	13 30	13 44	13 54		14 10	14 26	14 44	14 54	15 10	15 44	15 51	15 59	16 10		16 26	16 44	16 54	17 10	17 26	17 26	17 44	17 54
Portchester	d		13 15		13 49			14 15		14 49		15 15	15 49			16 15			16 49		17 15			17 49	
Cosham	d	13 03	13 20	13 38	13 54	14 03		14 20	14 34	14 54	15 03	15 20	15 54	16 01	16 08	16 20		16 34	16 54	17 03	17 20	17 34	17 34	17 54	18 03
Havant	a	13 10		13 46		14 10					15 10			16 11	16 14					17 10					18 10
Chichester 4	a	13 23		13 57		14 23					15 23			16 22	16 27					17 23					18 23
Hilsea	a		13 26		14 00			14 26		15 00		15 26	16 00			16 26			17 00		17 26			18 00	
Fratton	a		13 30		14 04			14 30	14 40	15 04		15 30	16 04			16 30		16 40	17 08		17 30	17 40	17 40	18 04	
Portsmouth & Southsea	a		13 33		14 08			14 33	14 45	15 08		15 33	16 08			16 33		16 45	17 12		17 33	17 44	17 45	18 08	
Portsmouth Harbour	a				14 13				14 52	15 13			16 13					16 52	17 16			17 52	17 52	18 13	

A from 5 January

B until 29 December

Table 165R

Sundays

8 December to 11 May

Southampton - Fareham and Portsmouth

Network Diagram - see first Page of Table 165

		SW	GW	SW	SN	SW	GW	SW		GW	SN	SW	GW	SW	GW	SN	SW	GW		SW	SN	SW	GW	SN	SW
		1	◇	1	1	1	◇	1		◇	1	1	◇	1	◇	1	1	◇		1	1	1	◇	1	1
Southampton Central	d	17 35	18 04		18 30	18 35	19 04			19 26	19 30	19 35	20 04		20 31	20 29	20 35	21 04			21 30	21 35	22 04	22 15	
Southampton Airport Parkway	d										19 38					20 38									
Eastleigh	d			18 26				19 26			19 46			20 26		20 46				21 26					22 26
St Denys	d	17 41				18 41						19 41					20 41					21 41			
Bitterne	d	17 43				18 43						19 43					20 43					21 43			
Woolston	d	17 47				18 47						19 47					20 47					21 47			
Sholing	d	17 49				18 49						19 49					20 49					21 49			
Netley	d	17 53				18 53						19 53					20 53					21 53			
Hamble	d	17 55				18 55						19 55					20 55					21 55			
Bursledon	d	17 58				18 58						19 58					20 58					21 58			
Swanwick	d	18 02			18 47	19 02						20 02					21 02				21 47	22 02		22 32	
Fareham	a	18 09	18 26	18 43	18 53	19 09	19 26	19 43		19 48	20 02	20 09	20 26	20 43	20 54	21 02	21 10	21 26		21 43	21 53	22 09	22 26	22 38	22 43
	d	18 10	18 26	18 44	18 54	19 10	19 26	19 44		19 49	20 03	20 10	20 26	20 44	20 55	21 02	21 10	21 26		21 44	21 54	22 10	22 26	22 39	22 44
Portchester	d	18 15		18 49		19 15		19 49				20 15		20 49			21 15			21 49		22 15			22 49
Cosham	d	18 20	18 34	18 54	19 03	19 20	19 34	19 54		19 58	20 12	20 20		20 54		21 11	21 20			21 54	22 03	22 20		22 48	22 54
Havant	a				19 10					20 09	20 18					21 17					22 10			22 54	
Chichester [4]	a				19 23					20 20	20 30					21 29					22 23			23 06	
Hilsea	a	18 26		19 00		19 26		20 00				20 26		21 00			21 26			22 00		22 26			23 00
Fratton	a	18 30	18 40	19 08		19 30	19 40	20 04				20 30	20 40	21 04	21 09		21 30	21 40		22 04		22 30	22 40		23 04
Portsmouth & Southsea	a	18 33	18 45	19 12		19 33	19 45	20 08				20 33	20 47	21 08	21 15		21 33	21 43		22 10		22 33	22 43		23 08
Portsmouth Harbour	a		18 53	19 17			19 52	20 13					20 52	21 13	21 26			21 49		22 14			22 52		23 13

		SW	SN	GW		SW
		1	1	◇		1
Southampton Central	d	22 35	22 52	23 08		
Southampton Airport Parkway	d					
Eastleigh	d					23 26
St Denys	d	22 41				
Bitterne	d	22 43				
Woolston	d	22 47				
Sholing	d	22 49				
Netley	d	22 53				
Hamble	d	22 55				
Bursledon	d	22 58				
Swanwick	d	23 02	23 11			
Fareham	a	23 09	23 17	23 29		23 43
	d	23 10	23 17	23 30		23 44
Portchester	d	23 15				23 49
Cosham	d	23 20	23 26			23 54
Havant	a		23 32			
Chichester [4]	a		23 44			
Hilsea	a	23 24				23 59
Fratton	a	23 28		23 43		00 04
Portsmouth & Southsea	a	23 32		23 46		00 08
Portsmouth Harbour	a			23 54		00 13

Table 167

To and from the Isle of Wight via Portsmouth and Ryde

Mondays to Fridays

9 December to 16 May

Network Diagram - see first Page of Table 165

Miles			IL	IL	IL	IL	IL	IL	IL	IL	IL		IL	IL	IL	IL	IL	IL	IL	IL	IL		IL	IL	IL
—	**Portsmouth Harbour** ⛴	d	05b15		06b15	06c40	07 15	07e40	08 15	08e40	09 15		09f40	10 15	10f40	11 15	11f40	12 15	12f40	13 15	13f40		14 15	14f40	15 15
0	**Ryde Pier Head**	d	05 49	06 07	06 49	07 07	07 49	08 07	08 49	09 07	09 49		10 07	10 49	11 07	11 49	12 07	12 49	13 07	13 49	14 07		14 49	15 07	15 49
—	**Ryde Esplanade**	d	05 51	06 09	06 52	07 09	07 52	08 09	08 52	09 09	09 52		10 09	10 52	11 09	11 52	12 09	12 52	13 09	13 52	14 09		14 52	15 09	15 52
1¼	Ryde St Johns Road	d	05 55	06 13	06 55	07 13	07 55	08 13	08 55	09 13	09 55		10 13	10 55	11 13	11 55	12 13	12 55	13 13	13 55	14 13		14 55	15 13	15 55
2¼	Smallbrook Junction §	d												10 58		11 58	12 15	12 58	13 15				14 58	15 15	15 58
4¾	Brading	d	06 02	06 20	07 03	07 20	08 03	08 20	09 03	09 20	10 03		10 20	11 03	11 20	12 03	12 20	13 03	13 20	14 03	14 20		15 03	15 20	16 03
6½	Sandown	d	06 07	06 25	07 07	07 25	08 07	08 25	09 07	09 25	10 07		10 25	11 07	11 25	12 07	12 25	13 07	13 25	14 07	14 25		15 07	15 25	16 07
7¼	Lake	d	06 09	06 27	07 10	07 27	08 10	08 27	09 10	09 27	10 10		10 27	11 10	11 27	12 10	12 27	13 10	13 27	14 10	14 27		15 10	15 27	16 10
8½	**Shanklin**	a	06 12	06 30	07 13	07 30	08 13	08 30	09 13	09 30	10 13		10 30	11 13	11 30	12 13	12 30	13 13	13 30	14 13	14 30		15 13	15 30	16 13

		IL	IL	IL	IL	IL	IL		IL	IL	IL	IL	IL	IL
Portsmouth Harbour ⛴	d	15f40	16 15	16e40	17 15	17e40	18 15		18e45	19 15		20g15	21g15	22g15
Ryde Pier Head	d	16 07	16 49	17 07	17 49	18 07	18 49		19 07	19 49	20 07	20 45	21 45	22 45
Ryde Esplanade	d	16 09	16 52	17 09	17 52	18 09	18 52		19 09	19 52	20 09	20 47	21 47	22 47
Ryde St Johns Road	d	16 13	16 55	17 13	17 55	18 13	18 55		19 13	19 55	20 13	20 51	21 51	22a51
Smallbrook Junction §	d	16 15												
Brading	d	16 20	17 03	17 20	18 03	18 20	19 03		19 20	20 03	20 20	20 57	21 57	
Sandown	d	16 25	17 07	17 25	18 07	18 25	19 07		19 25	20 07	20 25	21 01	22 01	
Lake	d	16 27	17 10	17 27	18 10	18 27	19 10		19 27	20 10	20 27	21 04	22 04	
Shanklin	a	16 30	17 13	17 30	18 13	18 30	19 13		19 30	20 13	20 30	21 07	22 07	

Saturdays

14 December to 17 May

		IL	IL	IL	IL	IL	IL	IL	IL	IL		IL	IL	IL	IL	IL	IL	IL	IL	IL		IL	IL	IL	IL
Portsmouth Harbour ⛴	d			06 15		07 15		08 15		09 15		09h40	10 15	10h40	11 15	11h40	12 15	12h40	13 15	13h40		14 15	14h40	15 15	15h40
Ryde Pier Head	d	05 49	06 07	06 49	07 07	07 49	08 07	08 49	09 07	09 49		10 07	10 49	11 07	11 49	12 07	12 49	13 07	13 49	14 07		14 49	15 07	15 49	16 07
Ryde Esplanade	d	05 51	06 09	06 52	07 09	07 52	08 09	08 52	09 09	09 52		10 09	10 52	11 09	11 52	12 09	12 52	13 09	13 52	14 09		14 52	15 09	15 52	16 09
Ryde St Johns Road	d	05 55	06 13	06 55	07 13	07 55	08 13	08 55	09 13	09 55		10 13	10 55	11 13	11 55	12 13	12 55	13 13	13 55	14 13		14 55	15 13	15 55	16 13
Smallbrook Junction §	d												10 58		11 58	12 15	12 58	13 15				14 58	15 15	15 58	16 15
Brading	d	06 02	06 20	07 03	07 20	08 03	08 20	09 03	09 20	10 03		10 20	11 03	11 20	12 03	12 20	13 03	13 20	14 03	14 20		15 03	15 20	16 03	16 20
Sandown	d	06 07	06 25	07 07	07 25	08 07	08 25	09 07	09 25	10 07		10 25	11 07	11 25	12 07	12 25	13 07	13 25	14 07	14 25		15 07	15 25	16 07	16 25
Lake	d	06 09	06 27	07 10	07 27	08 10	08 27	09 10	09 27	10 10		10 27	11 10	11 27	12 10	12 27	13 10	13 27	14 10	14 27		15 10	15 27	16 10	16 27
Shanklin	a	06 12	06 30	07 13	07 30	08 13	08 30	09 13	09 30	10 13		10 30	11 13	11 30	12 13	12 30	13 13	13 30	14 13	14 30		15 13	15 30	16 13	16 30

		IL	IL	IL	IL	IL		IL	IL	IL	IL	IL	IL
Portsmouth Harbour ⛴	d	16 15	16h40	17 15	17h40	18 15			19 15		20 15	21 15	22 15
Ryde Pier Head	d	16 49	17 07	17 49	18 07	18 49		19 07	19 49	20 07	20 45	21 45	22 45
Ryde Esplanade	d	16 52	17 09	17 52	18 09	18 52		19 09	19 52	20 09	20 47	21 47	22 47
Ryde St Johns Road	d	16 55	17 13	17 55	18 13	18 55		19 13	19 55	20 13	20 51	21 51	22a51
Smallbrook Junction §	d												
Brading	d	17 03	17 20	18 03	18 20	19 03		19 20	20 03	20 20	20 57	21 57	
Sandown	d	17 07	17 25	18 07	18 25	19 07		19 25	20 07	20 25	21 01	22 01	
Lake	d	17 10	17 27	18 10	18 27	19 10		19 27	20 10	20 27	21 04	22 04	
Shanklin	a	17 13	17 30	18 13	18 30	19 13		19 30	20 13	20 30	21 07	22 07	

Sundays

8 December to 11 May

		IL	IL	IL A	IL	IL A	IL	IL A	IL	IL A		IL	IL A	IL	IL	IL	IL	IL	IL	IL		IL	IL	IL	IL
Portsmouth Harbour ⛴	d		07 15		08 15		09 15		10 15			11 15		12 15		13 15		14 15		15 15			16 15		17 15
Ryde Pier Head	d	06 49	07 49		08 49	09 07	09 49	10 07	10 49	11 07		11 49	12 07	12 49	13 07	13 49	14 07	14 49	15 07	15 49		16 07	16 49	17 07	17 49
Ryde Esplanade	d	06 52	07 52		08 52	09 09	09 52	10 09	10 52	11 09		11 52	12 09	12 52	13 09	13 52	14 09	14 52	15 09	15 52		16 09	16 52	17 09	17 52
Ryde St Johns Road	d	06 55	07 55	08 13	08 55	09 13	09 55	10 13	10 55	11 13		11 55	12 13	12 55	13 13	13 55	14 13	14 55	15 13	15 55		16 13	16 55	17 13	17 55
Smallbrook Junction §	d								10 58			11 58	12 15	12 58	13 15			14 58	15 15	15 58		16 15			
Brading	d	07 03	08 03	08 20	09 03	09 20	10 03	10 20	11 03	11 20		12 03	12 20	13 03	13 20	14 03	14 20	15 03	15 20	16 03		16 20	17 03	17 20	18 03
Sandown	d	07 07	08 07	08 25	09 07	09 25	10 07	10 25	11 07	11 25		12 07	12 25	13 07	13 25	14 07	14 25	15 07	15 25	16 07		16 25	17 07	17 25	18 07
Lake	d	07 10	08 10	08 27	09 10	09 27	10 10	10 27	11 10	11 27		12 10	12 27	13 10	13 27	14 10	14 27	15 10	15 27	16 10		16 27	17 10	17 27	18 10
Shanklin	a	07 13	08 13	08 30	09 13	09 30	10 13	10 30	11 13	11 30		12 13	12 30	13 13	13 30	14 13	14 30	15 13	15 30	16 13		16 30	17 13	17 30	18 13

		IL	IL	IL A	IL	IL A		IL	IL	IL
Portsmouth Harbour ⛴	d		18 15		19 15			20 15	21 15	22 15
Ryde Pier Head	d	18 07	18 49	19 07	19 49	20 07		20 45	21 45	22 45
Ryde Esplanade	d	18 09	18 52	19 09	19 52	20 09		20 47	21 47	22 47
Ryde St Johns Road	d	18 13	18 55	19 13	19 55	20a13		20 51	21 51	22a51
Smallbrook Junction §	d									
Brading	d	18 20	19 03	19 20	20 03			20 57	21 57	
Sandown	d	18 25	19 07	19 25	20 07			21 01	22 01	
Lake	d	18 27	19 10	19 27	20 10			21 04	22 04	
Shanklin	a	18 30	19 13	19 30	20 13			21 07	22 07	

§ Smallbrook Jn. is only open for access to the I.O.W Steam Railway. For days of operation please enquire locally.

b not 26 December, 1 January

c not from 24 December until 26 December, 31 December until 1 January or 3 March until 28 March

e not from 24 December until 26 December or 31 December until 1 January

f 24 December, 31 December

g not 24 December, 31 December

h from 12 April

A from 20 April

Table 167R

To and from the Isle of Wight via Portsmouth and Ryde

Mondays to Fridays

9 December to 16 May

Network Diagram - see first Page of Table 165

		IL	IL	IL	IL	IL		IL	IL	IL	IL	IL	IL	IL	IL	IL		IL	IL	IL	IL	IL	IL	IL	IL
Shanklin	d			06 18	06 38	07 18		07 38	08 18	08 38	09 18	09 38	10 18	10 38	11 18	11 38		12 18	12 38	13 18	13 38	14 18	14 38	15 18	15 38
Lake	d			06 21	06 41	07 21		07 41	08 21	08 41	09 21	09 41	10 21	10 41	11 21	11 41		12 21	12 41	13 21	13 41	14 21	14 41	15 21	15 41
Sandown	d			06 24	06 44	07 24		07 44	08 24	08 44	09 24	09 44	10 24	10 44	11 24	11 44		12 24	12 44	13 24	13 44	14 24	14 44	15 24	15 44
Brading	d			06 28	06 48	07 28		07 48	08 28	08 48	09 28	09 48	10 28	10 48	11 28	11 48		12 28	12 48	13 28	13 48	14 28	14 48	15 28	15 48
Smallbrook Junction §	d													10 53		11 53		12 33	12 53	13 33			14 53	15 33	15 53
Ryde St Johns Road	d	05 35	05 56	06 35	06 55	07 35		07 55	08 35	08 55	09 35	09 55	10 35	10 55	11 35	11 55		12 35	12 55	13 35	13 55	14 35	14 55	15 35	15 55
Ryde Esplanade	d	05 40	06 00	06 40	07 00	07 40		08 00	08 40	09 00	09 40	10 00	10 40	11 00	11 40	12 00		12 40	13 00	13 40	14 00	14 40	15 00	15 40	16 00
Ryde Pier Head	a	05 42	06 02	06 42	07 02	07 42		08 02	08 42	09 02	09 42	10 02	10 42	11 02	11 42	12 02		12 42	13 02	13 42	14 02	14 42	15 02	15 42	16 02
Portsmouth Harbour ⛴	a	*06b09*		*07b09*	*07c32*	*08 09*		*08c32*	*09 09*	*09c32*	*10 09*	*10e32*	*11 09*	*11e32*	*12 09*	*12e32*		*13 09*	*13e32*	*14 09*	*14e32*	*15 09*	*15e32*	*16 09*	*16e32*

		IL		IL	IL	IL	IL	IL	IL	IL	IL	IL		IL	IL										
Shanklin	d	16 18		16 38	17 18	17 38	18 18	18 38	19 18	19 38	20 18	20 38		21 18	22 18										
Lake	d	16 21		16 41	17 21	17 41	18 21	18 41	19 21	19 41	20 21	20 41		21 21	22 21										
Sandown	d	16 24		16 44	17 24	17 44	18 24	18 44	19 24	19 44	20 24	20 44		21 24	22 24										
Brading	d	16 28		16 48	17 28	17 48	18 28	18 48	19 28	19 48	20 28	20 48		21 28	22 28										
Smallbrook Junction §	d	16 33																							
Ryde St Johns Road	d	16 35		16 55	17 35	17 55	18 35	18 55	19 35	19 55	20 34	20a54		21 34	22 34										
Ryde Esplanade	d	16 40		17 00	17 40	18 00	18 40	19 00	19 40	20 00	20 38			21 38	22 38										
Ryde Pier Head	a	16 42		17 02	17 42	18 02	18 42	19 02	19 42	20 02	20 41			21 41	22 41										
Portsmouth Harbour ⛴	a	*17 09*		*17c32*	*18 09*	*18c32*	*19 09*	*19f37*	*20 09*		*21g09*			*22g09*	*23g09*										

Saturdays

14 December to 17 May

		IL	IL	IL	IL	IL	IL	IL	IL	IL		IL	IL	IL	IL	IL	IL	IL	IL	IL		IL	IL	IL	IL
Shanklin	d			06 18	06 38	07 18	07 38	08 18	08 38	09 18		09 38	10 18	10 38	11 18	11 38	12 18	12 38	13 18	13 38		14 18	14 38	15 18	15 38
Lake	d			06 21	06 41	07 21	07 41	08 21	08 41	09 21		09 41	10 21	10 41	11 21	11 41	12 21	12 41	13 21	13 41		14 21	14 41	15 21	15 41
Sandown	d			06 24	06 44	07 24	07 44	08 24	08 44	09 24		09 44	10 24	10 44	11 24	11 44	12 24	12 44	13 24	13 44		14 24	14 44	15 24	15 44
Brading	d			06 28	06 48	07 28	07 48	08 28	08 48	09 28		09 48	10 28	10 48	11 28	11 48	12 28	12 48	13 28	13 48		14 28	14 48	15 28	15 48
Smallbrook Junction §	d													10 53		11 53	12 33	12 53	13 33				14 53	15 33	15 53
Ryde St Johns Road	d	05 35	05 56	06 35	06 55	07 35	07 55	08 35	08 55	09 35		09 55	10 35	10 55	11 35	11 55	12 35	12 55	13 35	13 55		14 35	14 55	15 35	15 55
Ryde Esplanade	d	05 40	06 00	06 40	07 00	07 40	08 00	08 40	09 00	09 40		10 00	10 40	11 00	11 40	12 00	12 40	13 00	13 40	14 00		14 40	15 00	15 40	16 00
Ryde Pier Head	a	05 42	06 02	06 42	07 02	07 42	08 02	08 42	09 02	09 42		10 02	10 42	11 02	11 42	12 02	12 42	13 02	13 42	14 02		14 42	15 02	15 42	16 02
Portsmouth Harbour ⛴	a			*07 09*		*08 09*		*09 09*		*10 09*		*10h32*	*11 09*	*11h32*	*12 09*	*12h32*	*13 09*	*13h32*	*14 09*	*14h32*		*15 09*	*15h32*	*16 09*	*16h32*

		IL	IL	IL	IL	IL		IL	IL	IL	IL	IL	IL	IL											
Shanklin	d	16 18	16 38	17 18	17 38	18 18		18 38	19 18	19 38	20 18	20 38	21 18	22 18											
Lake	d	16 21	16 41	17 21	17 41	18 21		18 41	19 21	19 41	20 21	20 41	21 21	22 21											
Sandown	d	16 24	16 44	17 24	17 44	18 24		18 44	19 24	19 44	20 24	20 44	21 24	22 24											
Brading	d	16 28	16 48	17 28	17 48	18 28		18 48	19 28	19 48	20 28	20 48	21 28	22 28											
Smallbrook Junction §	d	16 33																							
Ryde St Johns Road	d	16 35	16 55	17 35	17 55	18 35		18 55	19 35	19 55	20 34	20a54	21 34	22 34											
Ryde Esplanade	d	16 40	17 00	17 40	18 00	18 40		19 00	19 40	20 00	20 38		21 38	22 38											
Ryde Pier Head	a	16 42	17 02	17 42	18 02	18 42		19 02	19 42	20 02	20 41		21 41	22 41											
Portsmouth Harbour ⛴	a	*17 09*	*17h32*	*18 09*	*18h32*	*19 09*			*20 09*		*21 09*		*22 09*	*23 09*											

Sundays

8 December to 11 May

		IL	IL	IL	IL A	IL	IL A	IL	IL A	IL		IL A	IL	IL A	IL B	IL	IL	IL	IL	IL		IL	IL	IL	IL
Shanklin	d		07 18	08 18	08 38	09 18	09 38	10 18	10 38	11 18		11 38	12 18	12 38		13 18	13 38	14 18	14 38	15 18		15 38	16 18	16 38	17 18
Lake	d		07 21	08 21	08 41	09 21	09 41	10 21	10 41	11 21		11 41	12 21	12 41		13 21	13 41	14 21	14 41	15 21		15 41	16 21	16 41	17 21
Sandown	d		07 24	08 24	08 44	09 24	09 44	10 24	10 44	11 24		11 44	12 24	12 44		13 24	13 44	14 24	14 44	15 24		15 44	16 24	16 44	17 24
Brading	d		07 28	08 28	08 48	09 28	09 48	10 28	10 48	11 28		11 48	12 28	12 48		13 28	13 48	14 28	14 48	15 28		15 48	16 28	16 48	17 28
Smallbrook Junction §	d								10 53			11 53	12 33	12 53		13 33			14 53	15 33		15 53	16 33		
Ryde St Johns Road	d	06 35	07 35	08 35	08 55	09 35	09 55	10 35	10 55	11 35		11 55	12 35	12 55	12 55	13 35	13 55	14 35	14 55	15 35		15 55	16 35	16 55	17 35
Ryde Esplanade	d	06 40	07 40	08 40	09 00	09 40	10 00	10 40	11 00	11 40		12 00	12 40	13 00	13 00	13 40	14 00	14 40	15 00	15 40		16 00	16 40	17 00	17 40
Ryde Pier Head	a	06 42	07 42	08 42	09 02	09 42	10 02	10 42	11 02	11 42		12 02	12 42	13 02	13 02	13 42	14 02	14 42	15 02	15 42		16 02	16 42	17 02	17 42
Portsmouth Harbour ⛴	a		*08 09*	*09 09*		*10 09*		*11 09*		*12 09*			*13 09*			*14 09*		*15 09*		*16 09*			*17 09*		*18 09*

		IL	IL	IL B	IL A	IL		IL A	IL	IL	IL														
Shanklin	d	17 38	18 18	18 38	18 38	19 18		19 38	20 18	21 18	22 18														
Lake	d	17 41	18 21	18 41	18 41	19 21		19 41	20 21	21 21	22 21														
Sandown	d	17 44	18 24	18 44	18 44	19 24		19 44	20 24	21 24	22 24														
Brading	d	17 48	18 28	18 48	18 48	19 28		19 48	20 28	21 28	22 28														
Smallbrook Junction §	d																								
Ryde St Johns Road	d	17 55	18 35	18a54	18 55	19 35		19 55	20 34	21 34	22 34														
Ryde Esplanade	d	18 00	18 40		19 00	19 40		20 00	20 38	21 38	22 38														
Ryde Pier Head	a	18 02	18 42		19 02	19 42		20 02	20 41	21 41	22 41														
Portsmouth Harbour ⛴	a		*19 09*			*20 09*		*21 09*	*21 09*	*22 09*	*23 09*														

§ Smallbrook Jn. is only open for access to the I.O.W Steam Railway. For days of operation please enquire locally
b not 26 December, 1 January
c not from 24 December until 26 December, or from 31 December until 1 January
e 24 December, 31 December
f not from 24 December until 26 December, 31 December until 1 January or 3 March until 28 March
g not 24 December, 31 December
h from 12 April
A from 20 April
B until 13 April

Network Diagram for Tables 170, 171, 172

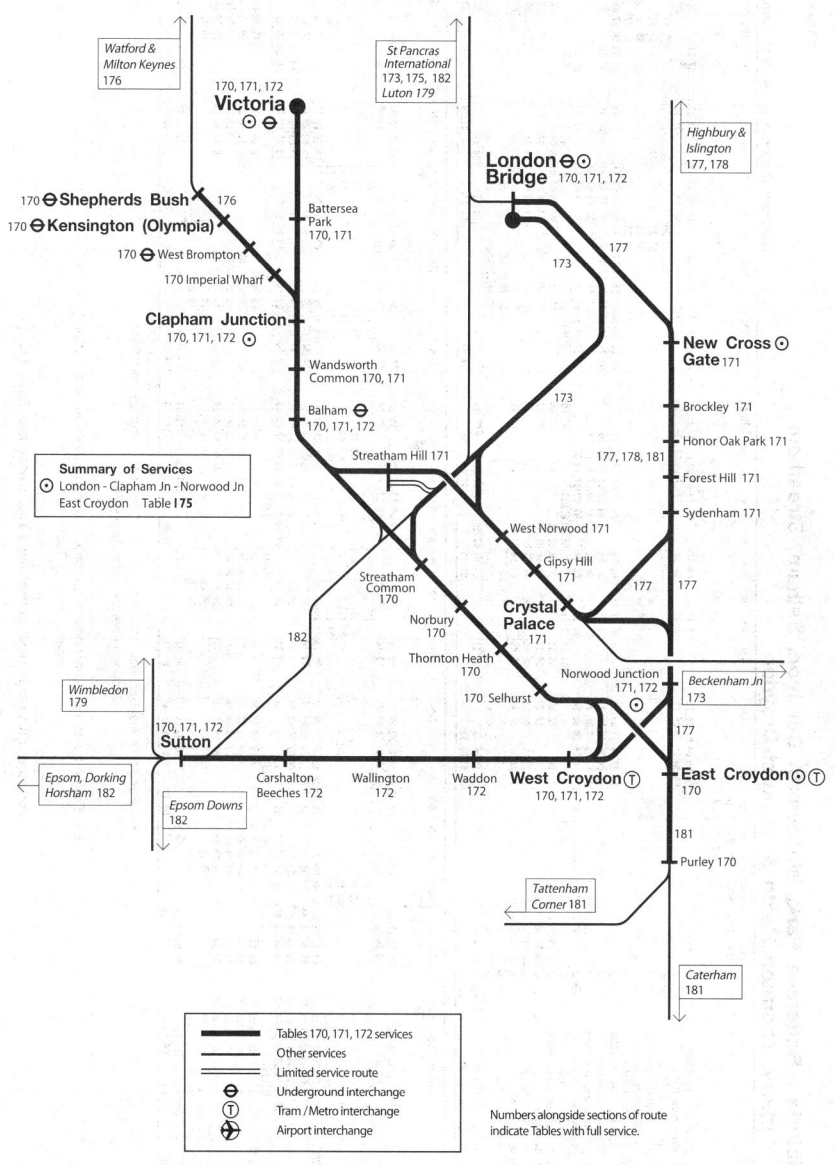

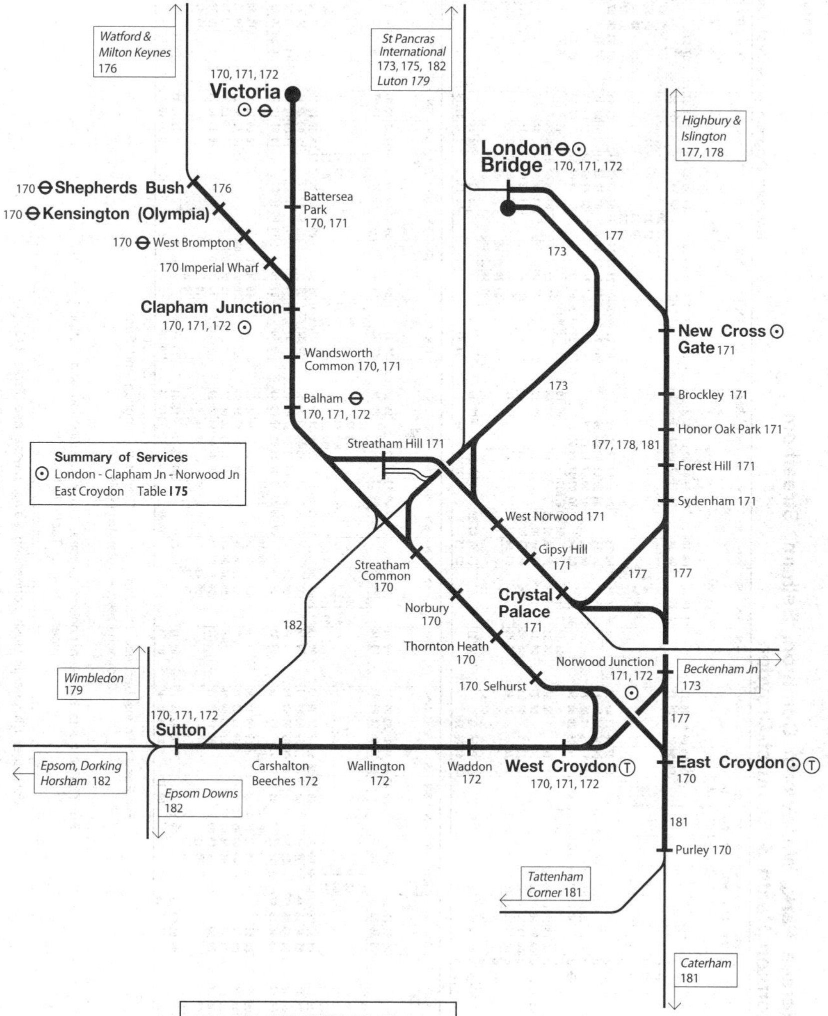

(thick line)	Tables 170, 171, 172 services
(thin line)	Other services
(double line)	Limited service route
⊖	Underground interchange
Ⓣ	Tram / Metro interchange
✈	Airport interchange

Numbers alongside sections of route indicate Tables with full service.

TOCs operating on this network - Southern (SN), First Capital Connect (FC),

Table 170

Mondays to Fridays

9 December to 16 May

London Victoria - Battersea Park, Wandsworth Common, Balham, Streatham Common, Norbury, Thornton Heath & Selhurst-Croydon

Network Diagram - see first Page of Table 170

Miles	Miles	Miles	Miles	Station		SN MX	SN MO	SN MX	SN MO	SN MX	SN MX [1]	SN	SN	SN	SN	SN	SN [1]	SN	SN	SN	SN	SN	SN
0	0	—	—	London Victoria [15] ⊖	d							06 00	06 06	06 13		06 19		06 30		06 49	07 00	07 08	
1¼	1¼	—	—	**Battersea Park**	d							06 04	06 10	06 17		06 23		06 34		06 53	07 04	07 12	
—	—	—	0	Shepherd's Bush ⊖	d												06 21						
—	—	—	0½	Kensington (Olympia) ⊖	d												06 24						
—	—	—	1½	West Brompton ⊖	d						00 02						06 27						
—	—	—	2½	Imperial Wharf	d						00 03						06 29						
2¾	2¾	—	4	Clapham Junction [10]	a						00 07	06 07	06 13	06 20		06 26	06 34	06 38		06 56	07 07	07 15	
—	—	—	—	Clapham Junction	d				00 02	00 02		06 08	06 14	06 21		06 27		06 38		06 57	07 08	07 16	
4	4	—	5¼	**Wandsworth Common**	d		00 01	00 02	00 05	00 05		06 11	06 17	06 24		06 30		06 41		07 00	07 11	07 19	
4½	4½	—	6	**Balham** [4] ⊖	d		00 03	00 04	00a07	00 08		06 14	06 20	06 26		06 32		06 44		07 02	07 13	07 21	
—	—	0	—	London Bridge	d					00a41					06 10	07a06			06 40	07a37			07 10
6¾	6¾	8¼	7¾	**Streatham Common** [4]	d	00 05	00 07	00 08				06 18		06 30	06 35			06 48	07 05		07 18		07 34
7½	7½	9	8¾	**Norbury**	d	00 08	00 09	00 11				06 20		06 33	06 37			06 50	07 08		07 21		07 37
8¾	8¾	10¼	10	**Thornton Heath**	d	00 11	00 12	00 14				06 23		06 36	06 40			06 53	07 11		07 24		07 40
9½	9½	11	10¾	**Selhurst** [4]	d	00 14	00 15	00 17				06 26		06 40	06 43			06 56	07 14		07 27		07 43
—	10½	—	11¾	East Croydon	a		00 18							06 45									
—	13½	—	—	Purley	a		00 31							06 52									
10½	—	12¼	—	West Croydon [4]	a	00 19		00 21				06 32	06 43		06 51			07 02	07 20		07 32	07 44	07 49
15	—	—	—	Sutton (Surrey) [4]	a			00 34				06 44	06 56					07 15			07 44	07 58	

Station		SN	SN	SN	SN	SN [1]	SN	SN	SN	SN	SN	SN [1]	SN	SN	SN	SN
London Victoria [15] ⊖	d	07 15	07 17	07 20	07 23		07 30	07 45		07 47	07 52		08 05	08 08	08 15	
Battersea Park	d		07 21	07 24			07 34			07 51			08 09	08 12	08 19	
Shepherd's Bush ⊖	d					07 20						07 54				
Kensington (Olympia) ⊖	d					07 23						07 57				
West Brompton ⊖	d					07 26						08 00				
Imperial Wharf	d					07 28						08 03				
Clapham Junction [10]	a	07 21	07 24	07 27	07 29	07 33	07 38	07 51		07 54	07 58	08 07	08 12	08 16	08 22	
Clapham Junction	d	07 21	07 25	07 28	07 30		07 38	07 51		07 55	07 58		08 14	08 17	08 23	
Wandsworth Common	d			07 31			07 41	07 54		07 58			08 17	08 20	08 26	
Balham [4] ⊖	d	07 26	07 29	07 33			07 44	07 57		08 00	08 03		08 19	08 22	08 28	
London Bridge	d		08a07						07 40		08a37					08 10
Streatham Common [4]	d			07 37			07 48	08 01	08 05				08 23		08 32	08 36
Norbury	d			07 40			07 50	08 04	08 08				08 26		08 35	08 38
Thornton Heath	d			07 43			07 53	08 07	08 11				08 29		08 38	08 41
Selhurst [4]	d			07 46			07 56	08 09	08 14				08 32		08 41	08 44
East Croydon	a			07 49	07 46			08 12							08 44	
Purley	a			07 58	07 54			08 22							08 54	
West Croydon [4]	a						08 02		08 24				08 36	08 44		08 50
Sutton (Surrey) [4]	a	07 43					08 16			08 19			08 48	08 57		

Station		SN	SN	SN [1]	SN	SN	SN	SN	SN	SN	SN	SN	SN	SN	SN [1]	SN	SN	SN	SN
London Victoria [15] ⊖	d	08 22	08 26		08 31	08 36		08 43		08 47	08 49	08 52	09 03	09 05		09 13		09 17	09 19
Battersea Park	d	08 26			08 36	08 40		08 47			08 53	08 56	09 07	09 10		09 17			09 23
Shepherd's Bush ⊖	d			08 05			08 34								09 07				
Kensington (Olympia) ⊖	d			08 08			08 36								09 09				
West Brompton ⊖	d			08 11			08 39								09 12				
Imperial Wharf	d			08 14			08 42								09 15				
Clapham Junction [10]	a	08 29	08 32	08 18	08 39	08 43	08 46	08 50		08 53	08 56	08 59	09 10	09 13	09 20	09 20		09 23	09 26
Clapham Junction	d	08 30	08 33	08 36	08 40	08 44		08 51		08 54	08 57	09 00	09 11	09 14		09 21		09 24	09 27
Wandsworth Common	d	08 33	08 36	08 39	08 43	08 47		08 54			09 00	09 03	09 14	09 17		09 24			09 30
Balham [4] ⊖	d	08 35	08 38	08 42	08 46	08 49		08 56		09 00	09 02	09 05	09 16	09 20		09 26		09 30	09 32
London Bridge	d	09a14							08 40		09a37						09 10		10a11
Streatham Common [4]	d		08 42	08 48	08 51			09 00	09 05			09 09	09 20			09 30	09 35		
Norbury	d		08 45	08 50	08 54			09 03	09 08			09 12	09 23			09 33	09 38		
Thornton Heath	d		08 48	08 53	08 57			09 06	09 11			09 15	09 26			09 36	09 41		
Selhurst [4]	d		08 52	08 57	09 00			09 09	09 14			09 18	09 29			09 39	09 44		
East Croydon	a			09 04				09 12								09 42			
Purley	a							09 22								09 52			
West Croydon [4]	a		08 56		09 05	09 13			09 19			09 22	09 33	09 43			09 48		
Sutton (Surrey) [4]	a		09 08		09 18	09 26				09 19		09 39	09 46	09 56				09 49	

Station		SN	SN [1]	SN	SN	SN	SN	SN	SN	SN	SN [1]	SN	SN	SN	SN	SN	SN	SN	SN
London Victoria [15] ⊖	d	09 22		09 33	09 36		09 43		09 47	09 49		09 53	10 03	10 06	10 13		10 17	10 19	10 23
Battersea Park	d			09 37	09 40		09 47			09 53			10 07	10 10	10 17			10 23	
Shepherd's Bush ⊖	d		09 19			09 33					09 44								
Kensington (Olympia) ⊖	d		09 22			09 35					09 47								
West Brompton ⊖	d		09 24			09 37					09 50								
Imperial Wharf	d		09 27			09 40					09 52								
Clapham Junction [10]	a	09 29	09 31	09 40	09 43	09 45	09 50		09 53	09 56	09 57	09 59	10 10	10 13	10 20		10 23	10 26	10 29
Clapham Junction	d	09 30	09 34	09 41	09 44		09 51		09 54	09 57		10 00	10 11	10 14	10 21		10 24	10 27	10 30
Wandsworth Common	d	09 33	09 37	09 44	09 47		09 54			10 00		10 03	10 14	10 17	10 24			10 30	10 33
Balham [4] ⊖	d	09 35	09 40	09 46	09 50		09 56		10 00	10 02		10 05	10 16	10 20	10 26		10 30	10 32	10 35
London Bridge	d							09 40		10a41						10 10		11a11	
Streatham Common [4]	d	09 39	09 44	09 50			10 00	10 05				10 09	10 20		10 30	10 35			10 39
Norbury	d	09 42	09 47	09 53			10 03	10 08				10 12	10 23		10 33	10 38			10 42
Thornton Heath	d	09 45	09 50	09 56			10 06	10 11				10 15	10 26		10 36	10 41			10 45
Selhurst [4]	d	09 48	09 53	09 59			10 09	10 14				10 18	10 29		10 39	10 44			10 48
East Croydon	a		09 56				10 14								10 42				
Purley	a						10 23								10 52				
West Croydon [4]	a	09 52		10 03	10 13			10 18				10 22	10 33	10 43		10 48			10 52
Sutton (Surrey) [4]	a	10 06		10 16	10 26				10 19			10 39	10 46	10 56			10 49		11 06

For Faster Trains between London Victoria, Clapham Junction and East Croydon, please refer to Table 175

For Faster trains between London Victoria, Clapham Junction and Sutton, please refer to Table 182

For other Shepherds Bush connecting trains, please see Table 176

Table 170

Mondays to Fridays

9 December to 16 May

London Victoria - Battersea Park, Wandsworth Common, Balham, Streatham Common, Norbury, Thornton Heath & Selhurst-Croydon

Network Diagram - see first Page of Table 170

	SN 1	SN	SN	SN	SN	SN	SN	SN	SN	SN	SN	SN	SN	SN	SN	SN 1	SN	SN
London Victoria 15 ⊖ d		10 33	10 36	10 43		10 47	10 49	10 53	11 03	11 06	11 13		11 17	11 19	11 23		11 33	11 36
Battersea Park d		10 37	10 40	10 47			10 53		11 07	11 10	11 17			11 23			11 37	11 40
Shepherd's Bush ⊖ d	10 21															11 19		
Kensington (Olympia) ⊖ d	10 24															11 21		
West Brompton ⊖ d	10 27															11 24		
Imperial Wharf d	10 29															11 26		
Clapham Junction 10 a	10 34	10 40	10 43	10 50		10 53	10 56	10 59	11 10	11 13	11 20		11 23	11 26	11 29	11 31	11 40	11 43
Clapham Junction d	10 34	10 41	10 44	10 51		10 54	10 57	11 00	11 11	11 14	11 21		11 24	11 27	11 30	11 34	11 41	11 44
Wandsworth Common d	10 37	10 44	10 47	10 54			11 00	11 03	11 14	11 17	11 24			11 30	11 33	11 37	11 44	11 47
Balham 4 ⊖ d	10 40	10 46	10 50	10 56		11 00	11 02	11 05	11 16	11 20	11 26		11 30	11 32	11 35	11 40	11 46	11 50
London Bridge d					10 40		11a41					11 10		12a11				
Streatham Common 4 d	10 44	10 50		11 00	11 05			11 09	11 20		11 30	11 35			11 39	11 44	11 50	
Norbury d	10 47	10 53		11 03	11 08			11 12	11 23		11 33	11 38			11 42	11 46	11 53	
Thornton Heath d	10 50	10 56		11 06	11 11			11 15	11 26		11 36	11 41			11 45	11 49	11 56	
Selhurst 4 d	10 53	10 59		11 09	11 15			11 18	11 29		11 39	11 45			11 48	11 52	11 59	
East Croydon a	10 56			11 12							11 42					11 56		
Purley a				11 22							11 52							
West Croydon 4 a		11 03	11 13		11 19			11 23	11 33	11 43		11 49			11 53		12 03	12 13
Sutton (Surrey) 4 a		11 16	11 26			11 19		11 39	11 46	11 56			11 49		12 06		12 16	12 26

	SN	SN	SN	SN	SN	SN	SN	SN	SN	SN	SN	SN	SN 1	SN	SN	SN	SN	SN
London Victoria 15 ⊖ d	11 43		11 47	11 49	11 53	12 03	12 06	12 13		12 17	12 19	12 23		12 33	12 36	12 43		12 47
Battersea Park d	11 47			11 53		12 07	12 10	12 17			12 23			12 37	12 40	12 47		
Shepherd's Bush ⊖ d													12 20					
Kensington (Olympia) ⊖ d													12 23					
West Brompton ⊖ d													12 26					
Imperial Wharf d													12 28					
Clapham Junction 10 a	11 50		11 53	11 56	11 59	12 10	12 13	12 20		12 23	12 26	12 29	12 33	12 40	12 43	12 50		12 53
Clapham Junction d	11 51		11 54	11 57	12 00	12 11	12 14	12 21		12 24	12 27	12 30	12 35	12 41	12 44	12 51		12 54
Wandsworth Common d	11 54			12 00	12 03	12 14	12 17	12 24			12 30	12 33	12 38	12 44	12 47	12 54		
Balham 4 ⊖ d	11 57		12 00	12 02	12 05	12 16	12 20	12 26		12 30	12 32	12 35	12 41	12 46	12 50	12 56		13 00
London Bridge d		11 40		12a41					12 10		13a11						12 40	
Streatham Common 4 d	12 01	12 05			12 09	12 20		12 30	12 35			12 39	12 45	12 50		13 00	13 05	
Norbury d	12 03	12 08			12 12	12 23		12 33	12 38			12 42	12 47	12 53		13 03	13 08	
Thornton Heath d	12 06	12 11			12 15	12 26		12 36	12 41			12 45	12 50	12 56		13 06	13 11	
Selhurst 4 d	12 09	12 14			12 18	12 29		12 39	12 44			12 48	12 53	12 59		13 09	13 14	
East Croydon a	12 12							12 42					12 57			13 12		
Purley a	12 22							12 52								13 22		
West Croydon 4 a		12 18			12 22	12 33	12 43		12 48			12 52		13 03	13 13		13 18	
Sutton (Surrey) 4 a			12 19		12 39	12 46	12 56			12 49		13 06		13 16	13 26			13 19

	SN	SN	SN	SN	SN	SN	SN	SN	SN	SN 1	SN	SN	SN	SN	SN	SN	SN	SN
London Victoria 15 ⊖ d	12 49	12 53	13 03	13 06	13 13		13 17	13 19	13 23		13 33	13 36	13 43		13 47	13 49	13 53	14 03
Battersea Park d	12 53		13 07	13 10	13 17			13 23			13 37	13 40	13 47			13 53		14 07
Shepherd's Bush ⊖ d										13 20								
Kensington (Olympia) ⊖ d										13 22								
West Brompton ⊖ d										13 25								
Imperial Wharf d										13 28								
Clapham Junction 10 a	12 56	12 59	13 10	13 13	13 20		13 23	13 26	13 29	13 33	13 40	13 43	13 50		13 53	13 56	13 59	14 10
Clapham Junction d	12 57	13 00	13 11	13 14	13 21		13 24	13 27	13 30	13 35	13 41	13 44	13 51		13 54	13 57	14 00	14 11
Wandsworth Common d	13 00	13 03	13 14	13 17	13 24			13 30	13 33	13 38	13 44	13 47	13 54			14 00	14 03	14 14
Balham 4 ⊖ d	13 02	13 05	13 16	13 20	13 26		13 30	13 32	13 35	13 40	13 46	13 50	13 56		14 00	14 02	14 05	14 16
London Bridge d	13a41					13 10		14a11						13 40		14a41		
Streatham Common 4 d		13 09	13 20		13 30	13 35			13 39	13 44	13 50		14 00	14 05			14 09	14 20
Norbury d		13 12	13 23		13 33	13 38			13 42	13 47	13 53		14 03	14 08			14 12	14 23
Thornton Heath d		13 15	13 26		13 36	13 41			13 45	13 50	13 56		14 06	14 11			14 15	14 26
Selhurst 4 d		13 18	13 29		13 39	13 44			13 48	13 52	13 59		14 09	14 14			14 18	14 29
East Croydon a					13 42					13 56			14 12					
Purley a					13 52								14 22					
West Croydon 4 a		13 22	13 33	13 43		13 48			13 53		14 03	14 13		14 18			14 22	14 33
Sutton (Surrey) 4 a		13 39	13 46	13 56			13 49		14 06		14 16	14 26			14 19		14 39	14 46

	SN	SN	SN	SN	SN	SN	SN 1	SN	SN	SN	SN	SN	SN	SN	SN	SN	SN	SN
London Victoria 15 ⊖ d	14 06	14 13		14 17	14 19	14 23		14 33	14 36	14 43		14 47	14 49	14 53	15 03	15 06	15 13	
Battersea Park d	14 10	14 17			14 23			14 37	14 40	14 47			14 53		15 07	15 10	15 17	
Shepherd's Bush ⊖ d							14 20											
Kensington (Olympia) ⊖ d							14 23											
West Brompton ⊖ d							14 26											
Imperial Wharf d							14 29											
Clapham Junction 10 a	14 13	14 20		14 23	14 26	14 29	14 33	14 40	14 43	14 50		14 53	14 56	14 59	15 10	15 13	15 20	
Clapham Junction d	14 14	14 21		14 24	14 27	14 30	14 34	14 41	14 44	14 51		14 54	14 57	15 00	15 11	15 14	15 21	
Wandsworth Common d	14 17	14 24			14 30	14 33	14 37	14 44	14 47	14 54			15 00	15 03	15 14	15 17	15 24	
Balham 4 ⊖ d	14 20	14 26		14 30	14 32	14 35	14 39	14 46	14 50	14 56		15 00	15 02	15 05	15 16	15 20	15 26	
London Bridge d			14 10		15a11						14 40		15a41					15 10
Streatham Common 4 d		14 30	14 35			14 39	14 43	14 50		15 00	15 05			15 09	15 20		15 30	15 35
Norbury d		14 33	14 38			14 42	14 46	14 53		15 03	15 08			15 12	15 23		15 33	15 38
Thornton Heath d		14 36	14 41			14 45	14 49	14 56		15 06	15 11			15 15	15 26		15 36	15 41
Selhurst 4 d		14 39	14 44			14 48	14 52	14 59		15 09	15 14			15 18	15 29		15 39	15 44
East Croydon a		14 42					14 55			15 12							15 42	
Purley a		14 52								15 22							15 52	
West Croydon 4 a	14 43		14 48			14 52		15 03	15 13		15 18			15 22	15 33	15 43		15 48
Sutton (Surrey) 4 a	14 56			14 49		15 06		15 16	15 26			15 19		15 39	15 46	15 56		

For Faster Trains between London Victoria, Clapham Junction and East Croydon, please refer to Table 175

For Faster trains between London Victoria, Clapham Junction and Sutton, please refer to Table 182

For other Shepherds Bush connecting trains, please see Table 176

Table 170

Mondays to Fridays

9 December to 16 May

London Victoria - Battersea Park, Wandsworth Common, Balham, Streatham Common, Norbury, Thornton Heath & Selhurst-Croydon

Network Diagram - see first Page of Table 170

		SN	SN	SN	SN 1	SN	SN	SN	SN	SN	SN	SN	SN
London Victoria 15 ⊖	d	15 17	15 19	15 23		15 33	15 36	15 43		15 47	15 49	15 53	16 03
Battersea Park	d		15 23			15 37	15 40	15 47			15 53		16 07
Shepherd's Bush ⊖	d				15 22								
Kensington (Olympia) ⊖	d				15 24								
West Brompton ⊖	d				15 26								
Imperial Wharf	d				15 29								
Clapham Junction 10	a	15 23	15 26	15 29	15 33	15 40	15 43	15 50		15 53	15 56	15 59	16 10
Clapham Junction	d	15 24	15 27	15 30	15 34	15 41	15 44	15 51		15 54	15 57	16 00	16 11
Wandsworth Common	d		15 30	15 33	15 37	15 44	15 47	15 54			16 00	16 03	16 14
Balham 4 ⊖	d	15 30	15 32	15 35	15 40	15 46	15 50	15 56		16 00	16 02	16 05	16 16
London Bridge	d		16a11						15 40		16a41		
Streatham Common 4	d			15 39	15 44	15 50		16 00	16 05			16 09	16 20
Norbury	d			15 42	15 46	15 53		16 03	16 08			16 12	16 23
Thornton Heath	d			15 45	15 49	15 56		16 06	16 11			16 15	16 26
Selhurst 4	d			15 48	15 52	15 59		16 09	16 14			16 18	16 29
East Croydon	a				15 56			16 12					
Purley	a							16 22					
West Croydon 4	a			15 52		16 03	16 13		16 18			16 22	16 33
Sutton (Surrey) 4	a	15 49		16 06		16 16	16 26			16 19		16 36	16 47

		SN	SN	SN	SN	SN	SN 1	SN	SN	SN	SN	SN	SN
London Victoria 15 ⊖	d	16 07	16 13		16 19	16 23		16 31	16 33		16 39	16 43	
Battersea Park	d	16 11	16 17		16 23				16 37			16 47	
Shepherd's Bush ⊖	d						16 20						
Kensington (Olympia) ⊖	d						16 23						
West Brompton ⊖	d						16 26						
Imperial Wharf	d						16 28						
Clapham Junction 10	a	16 14	16 20		16 26	16 29	16 33	16 37	16 40		16 44	16 50	
Clapham Junction	d	16 15	16 21		16 27	16 30	16 34	16 38	16 41		16 45	16 51	
Wandsworth Common	d	16 18	16 24		16 30	16 33	16 37		16 44			16 54	
Balham 4 ⊖	d	16 20	16 26		16 32	16 35	16 40		16 46			16 56	
London Bridge	d			16 10	17a12					16 20			16 40
Streatham Common 4	d		16 30	16 35		16 39	16 44		16 50	16 54		17 00	17 06
Norbury	d		16 33	16 38		16 42	16 47		16 53	16 56		17 03	17 08
Thornton Heath	d		16 36	16 41		16 45	16 50		16 56	16 59		17 06	17 11
Selhurst 4	d		16 39	16 44		16a47	16 54		16 59	17a02		17 09	17 14
East Croydon	a		16 42				16 58				16 55	17 12	
Purley	a		16 52								17 05	17 25	
West Croydon 4	a	16 45		16 49					17 03				17 19
Sutton (Surrey) 4	a	16 57						17 03	17 16				

		SN	SN	SN	SN	SN	SN	SN	SN	SN 1	SN	SN	SN
London Victoria 15 ⊖	d	16 49	17 01		17 07	17 09	17 13		17 22		17 31	17 33	17 37
Battersea Park	d	16 53	17 05		17 11		17 17		17 26			17 37	17 41
Shepherd's Bush ⊖	d									17 20			
Kensington (Olympia) ⊖	d									17 23			
West Brompton ⊖	d									17 26			
Imperial Wharf	d									17 29			
Clapham Junction 10	a	16 56	17 08		17 14	17 15	17 20		17 29	17 33	17 37	17 40	17 44
Clapham Junction	d	16 57	17 09		17 15	17 15	17 21		17 30	17 34	17 37	17 41	17 45
Wandsworth Common	d	17 00	17 12		17 18		17 24		17 33	17 37		17 44	17 48
Balham 4 ⊖	d	17 03	17 14		17 20		17 26		17 35	17 40	17 43	17 46	17 51
London Bridge	d	17a43		16 50				17 10	18a13				
Streatham Common 4	d		17 18	17 22			17 30	17 36		17 45		17 50	
Norbury	d		17 21	17 24			17 33	17 39		17 48		17 53	
Thornton Heath	d		17 24	17 27			17 36	17 42		17 51		17 56	
Selhurst 4	d		17 27	17a30			17a40	17 45		17 55		17 59	
East Croydon	a					17 27				18 00			
Purley	a					17 36							
West Croydon 4	a		17 32		17 43			17 50				18 03	18 16
Sutton (Surrey) 4	a		17 45		17 55						18 05	18 16	18 28

		SN	SN	SN	SN	SN	SN	SN	SN	SN	SN	SN	SN
London Victoria 15 ⊖	d	17 38	17 44		17 52		18 01	18 03	18 07	18 08	18 13		18 22
Battersea Park	d		17 48		17 56			18 07	18 11		18 17		18 26
Shepherd's Bush ⊖	d					17 47							
Kensington (Olympia) ⊖	d					17 49							
West Brompton ⊖	d					17 52							
Imperial Wharf	d					17 55							
Clapham Junction 10	a	17 43	17 51		17 59	17 59	18 07	18 10	18 14	18 14	18 20		18 29
Clapham Junction	d	17 44	17 52		18 00	18 02	18 08	18 11	18 15	18 14	18 21		18 30
Wandsworth Common	d		17 55		18 03	18 05		18 14	18 18		18 24		18 33
Balham 4 ⊖	d		17 57		18 05	18 08	18 12	18 16	18 20		18 26		18 35
London Bridge	d			17 40	18a45							18 10	19a13
Streatham Common 4	d		18 01	18 06		18 15		18 20			18 30	18 36	
Norbury	d		18 04	18 09		18 18		18 23			18 33	18 39	
Thornton Heath	d		18 07	18 12		18 21		18 26			18 36	18 42	
Selhurst 4	d		18a11	18 17		18 26		18 29			18a40	18 47	
East Croydon	a	17 55				18 32				18 27			
Purley	a	18 05				18 40				18 37			
West Croydon 4	a			18 22				18 34	18 44			18 52	
Sutton (Surrey) 4	a						18 36	18 47	18 58				

		SN 1	SN	SN	SN	SN	SN	SN	SN	SN	SN	SN	SN
London Victoria 15 ⊖	d		18 32	18 36	18 38	18 45		18 52	18 59	19 06	19 15		19 22
Battersea Park	d		18 36	18 40		18 49		18 56	19 04	19 10	19 19		19 26
Shepherd's Bush ⊖	d	18 20											
Kensington (Olympia) ⊖	d	18 22											
West Brompton ⊖	d	18 25											
Imperial Wharf	d	18 28											
Clapham Junction 10	a	18 33	18 39	18 43	18 44	18 52		18 59	19 08	19 13	19 22		19 29
Clapham Junction	d	18 34	18 40	18 44	18 44	18 53		19 00	19 08	19 14	19 23		19 30
Wandsworth Common	d	18 37	18 43	18 47		18 56		19 03	19 11	19 17	19 26		19 33
Balham 4 ⊖	d	18 40	18 45	18 49		18 58		19 05	19 14	19 20	19 28		19 35
London Bridge	d						18 40	19a41				19 10	20a11
Streatham Common 4	d	18 46	18 50			19 02	19 06		19 18		19 32	19 36	
Norbury	d	18 49	18 52			19 05	19 09		19 20		19 35	19 39	
Thornton Heath	d	18 52	18 55			19 08	19 12		19 23		19 38	19 42	
Selhurst 4	d	18 56	19 00			19 10	19 15		19 27		19 42	19 45	
East Croydon	a	19 02			18 57	19 13					19 45		
Purley	a				19 06	19 23					19 54		
West Croydon 4	a		19 04	19 14			19 22		19 32	19 44		19 51	
Sutton (Surrey) 4	a		19 16	19 28					19 44	19 57			

		SN 1	SN	SN	SN	SN	SN	SN	SN	SN	SN	SN	SN
London Victoria 15 ⊖	d		19 30	19 34	19 36	19 45		19 52	20 00	20 03	20 06	20 15	
Battersea Park	d		19 34		19 40	19 49		19 56	20 04		20 10	20 19	
Shepherd's Bush ⊖	d	19 20											
Kensington (Olympia) ⊖	d	19 22											
West Brompton ⊖	d	19 25											
Imperial Wharf	d	19 27											
Clapham Junction 10	a	19 32	19 38	19 41	19 44	19 52		19 59	20 08	20 11	20 14	20 22	
Clapham Junction	d	19 34	19 38	19 41	19 44	19 53		20 00	20 08	20 11	20 14	20 23	
Wandsworth Common	d	19 37	19 41		19 47	19 56		20 03	20 11		20 17	20 26	
Balham 4 ⊖	d	19 40	19 44	19 47	19 50	19 59		20 05	20 14	20 17	20 20	20 28	
London Bridge	d						19 40	20a43					20 10
Streatham Common 4	d	19 44	19 48			20 03	20 05		20 18			20 32	20 35
Norbury	d	19 47	19 51			20 06	20 08		20 20			20 35	20 38
Thornton Heath	d	19 50	19 54			20 09	20 12		20 23			20 38	20 41
Selhurst 4	d	19a54	19 57			20 12	20 15		20 27			20 41	20 44
East Croydon	a					20 15						20 45	
Purley	a					20 24						20 54	
West Croydon 4	a		20 02		20 13		20 19		20 32		20 43		20 49
Sutton (Surrey) 4	a		20 14	20 09	20 26				20 44	20 40	20 56		

For Faster Trains between London Victoria, Clapham Junction and East Croydon, please refer to Table 175

For Faster trains between London Victoria, Clapham Junction and Sutton, please refer to Table 182

For other Shepherds Bush connecting trains, please see Table 176

Table 170

Mondays to Fridays

9 December to 16 May

London Victoria - Battersea Park, Wandworth Common, Balham, Streatham Common, Norbury, Thornton Heath & Selhurst-Croydon

Network Diagram - see first Page of Table 170

		SN	SN 1	SN	SN	SN	SN	SN	SN	SN	SN	SN	SN	SN	SN	SN 1	SN	SN	SN
London Victoria 15	⊖ d	20 22		20 30	20 33	20 36	20 45		20 52	21 00	21 03	21 06	21 15		21 23		21 30	21 33	21 36
Battersea Park	d	20 26		20 34		20 40	20 49		20 56	21 04		21 10	21 19		21 27		21 34		21 40
Shepherd's Bush	⊖ d		20 22													21 20			
Kensington (Olympia)	⊖ d		20 24													21 22			
West Brompton	⊖ d		20 27													21 24			
Imperial Wharf	d		20 29													21 27			
Clapham Junction 10	a	20 29	20 34	20 38	20 41	20 44	20 52		20 59	21 08	21 11	21 14	21 22		21 30	21 32	21 38	21 41	21 44
Clapham Junction	d	20 30		20 38	20 41	20 44	20 53		21 00	21 08	21 11	21 14	21 23		21 31		21 38	21 41	21 44
Wandsworth Common	d	20 33		20 41		20 47	20 56		21 03	21 11		21 17	21 26		21 34		21 41		21 47
Balham 4	⊖ d	20 35		20 44	20 47	20 50	20 58		21 05	21 14	21 17	21 20	21 28		21 36		21 44	21 47	21 50
London Bridge	d	21a11						20 40	21a43					21 10	22a11				
Streatham Common 4	d			20 48			21 02	21 05		21 18			21 32	21 35			21 48		
Norbury	d			20 50			21 05	21 08		21 20			21 35	21 38			21 50		
Thornton Heath	d			20 53			21 08	21 11		21 23			21 38	21 41			21 53		
Selhurst 4	d			20 57			21 11	21 14		21 27			21 41	21 44			21 57		
East Croydon	a						21 15						21 45						
Purley	a						21 24						21 54						
West Croydon 4	a			21 02		21 13		21 19		21 32		21 43		21 49			22 02		22 13
Sutton (Surrey) 4	a			21 14	21 06	21 26				21 44	21 36	21 56					22 14	22 06	22 26

		SN	SN	SN	SN	SN	SN	SN	SN	SN	SN 1	SN	SN	SN	SN	SN	SN 1	SN	SN
London Victoria 15	⊖ d	21 45		21 52	22 00	22 03	22 06	22 15		22 22		22 30	22 33	22 36	22 45			22 52	23 00
Battersea Park	d	21 49		21 56	22 04		22 10	22 19		22 26		22 34		22 40	22 49			22 56	23 04
Shepherd's Bush	⊖ d										22 19						22 52		
Kensington (Olympia)	⊖ d										22 21						22 54		
West Brompton	⊖ d										22 24						22 57		
Imperial Wharf	d										22 27						22a59		
Clapham Junction 10	a	21 52		21 59	22 08	22 11	22 14	22 22		22 29	22 31	22 38	22 41	22 44	22 52			22 59	23 08
Clapham Junction	d	21 53		22 00	22 08	22 11	22 14	22 23		22 30		22 38	22 41	22 46	22 53			23 00	23 08
Wandsworth Common	d	21 56		22 03	22 11		22 17	22 26		22 33		22 41		22 49	22 56			23 03	23 11
Balham 4	⊖ d	21 58		22 05	22 14	22 17	22 20	22 28		22 35		22 44	22 46	22 52	22 58			23 05	23 14
London Bridge	d		21 40	22a41					22 10	23a11						22 40		23a44	
Streatham Common 4	d	22 02	22 05		22 18			22 32	22 36			22 48			23 02	23 05			23 18
Norbury	d	22 05	22 08		22 20			22 35	22 38			22 50			23 05	23 08			23 20
Thornton Heath	d	22 08	22 11		22 23			22 38	22 41			22 53			23 08	23 11			23 23
Selhurst 4	d	22 11	22 14		22 27			22 41	22 44			22 57			23 11	23 14			23 26
East Croydon	a	22 15						22 44							23 14				
Purley	a	22 24						22 54							23 24				
West Croydon 4	a		22 19		22 32		22 43		22 49			23 02		23 13		23 19			23 32
Sutton (Surrey) 4	a				22 44	22 36	22 56					23 14	23 05	23 26					23 44

		SN	SN	SN	SN	SN	SN 1	SN	SN	SN FO	SN	SN	SN	SN 1
London Victoria 15	⊖ d	23 03	23 06	23 15		23 22		23 33	23 38	23 45		23 51	23 54	
Battersea Park	d		23 10	23 19		23 26		23 37	23 42	23 49		23 55	23 58	
Shepherd's Bush	⊖ d						23 21							23 55
Kensington (Olympia)	⊖ d						23 23							23 57
West Brompton	⊖ d						23 27							00 02
Imperial Wharf	d						23 30							00 03
Clapham Junction 10	a	23 11	23 14	23 22		23 29	23 35	23 40	23 45	23 52		23 58	00 01	00 07
Clapham Junction	d	23 11	23 14	23 23		23 30	23 38	23 41	23 46	23 53		23 59	00 02	
Wandsworth Common	d		23 17	23 26		23 33		23 44	23 49	23 56		00 02	00 05	
Balham 4	⊖ d	23 17	23 20	23 28		23 35	23 42	23 46	23 51	23 58		00 04	00 08	
London Bridge	d				23 10	00a11					23 40		00a41	
Streatham Common 4	d			23 32	23 35		23 46	23 50		00 02	00 05	00 08		
Norbury	d			23 35	23 38		23 49	23 53		00 05	00 08	00 11		
Thornton Heath	d			23 38	23 41		23 52	23 56		00 08	00 11	00 14		
Selhurst 4	d			23 41	23 44		23 55	23 59		00 11	00 14	00 17		
East Croydon	a			23 44			23 59			00 14				
Purley	a			23 53						00 23				
West Croydon 4	a		23 41		23 49			00 03	00 14		00 19	00 21		
Sutton (Surrey) 4	a	23 36	23 54					00 16				00 34		

For Faster Trains between London Victoria, Clapham Junction and East Croydon, please refer to Table 175

For Faster trains between London Victoria, Clapham Junction and Sutton, please refer to Table 182

For other Shepherds Bush connecting trains, please see Table 176

Table 170

Saturdays

14 December to 17 May

London Victoria - Battersea Park, Wandsworth Common, Balham, Streatham Common, Norbury, Thornton Heath & Selhurst-Croydon

Network Diagram - see first Page of Table 170

		SN	SN	SN	SN	SN	SN	SN	SN	SN	SN	SN	SN	SN	SN	SN	SN	SN	SN
						1								1		1			
London Victoria 15 ⊖	d						00 07	00 17		00 21	00 23	00 34	00 37	06 02	06 23		06 43		06 53
Battersea Park	d						00 11	00 21			00 27	00 38	00 41				06 47		
Shepherd's Bush ⊖	d															06 20			
Kensington (Olympia) ⊖	d															06 23			
West Brompton ⊖	d					00 02										06 26			
Imperial Wharf	d					00 03										06 28			
Clapham Junction 10	a					00 07	00 15	00 24		00 27	00 30	00 41	00 44	06 07	06 29	06 33	06 50		06 59
Clapham Junction	d				00 02		00 16	00 25		00 28	00 31	00 42	00 45	06 08	06 30	06 34	06 51		07 00
Wandsworth Common	d			00 02	00 05		00 19	00 28			00 34	00 45	00 48		06 33	06 37	06 54		07 03
Balham 4 ⊖	d			00 04	00 08		00 21	00 30		00 33	00 36	00 47	00 50		06 35	06 40	06 56		07 05
London Bridge	d				00a41				00 18									06 40	
Streatham Common 4	d	00 02	00 05	00 08				00 34	00 45			00 51			06 39	06 44	07 00	07 05	07 09
Norbury	d	00 05	00 08	00 11				00 37	00 48			00 54			06 42	06 46	07 03	07 08	07 12
Thornton Heath	d	00 08	00 11	00 14				00 40	00 51			00 57			06 45	06 49	07 06	07 11	07 15
Selhurst 4	d	00 11	00 14	00 17				00 42	00 53			01 00			06 48	06 52	07 09	07 13	07 18
East Croydon	a	00 14						00 45						06 17		06 56	07 12		
Purley	a	00 23						00 59						06 23			07 21		
West Croydon 4	a		00 19	00 21			00 43		00 57		01 00	01 04	01 13		06 52			07 19	07 22
Sutton (Surrey) 4	a			00 34						00 52		01 16			07 06				07 39

		SN	SN	SN	SN	SN	SN	SN	SN	SN	SN	SN	SN	SN	SN	SN	SN	SN	SN
							1												
London Victoria 15 ⊖	d	07 06	07 13		07 17	07 23		07 33	07 36	07 43		07 47	07 49	07 53	08 03	08 06	08 13		08 17
Battersea Park	d	07 11	07 17					07 37	07 40	07 47			07 53		08 07	08 10	08 17		
Shepherd's Bush ⊖	d						07 22												
Kensington (Olympia) ⊖	d						07 25												
West Brompton ⊖	d						07 28												
Imperial Wharf	d						07 30												
Clapham Junction 10	a	07 14	07 20		07 23	07 29	07 35	07 40	07 43	07 50		07 53	07 56	07 59	08 10	08 13	08 20		08 23
Clapham Junction	d	07 14	07 21		07 24	07 30	07 35	07 41	07 44	07 51		07 54	07 57	08 00	08 11	08 14	08 21		08 24
Wandsworth Common	d	07 18	07 24			07 33	07 38	07 44	07 47	07 54			08 00	08 03	08 14	08 17	08 24		
Balham 4 ⊖	d	07 20	07 26		07 30	07 35	07 41	07 46	07 50	07 56		08 00	08 02	08 05	08 16	08 20	08 26		08 30
London Bridge	d			07 10							07 40		08a41					08 10	
Streatham Common 4	d		07 30	07 35		07 39	07 45	07 50		08 00	08 05			08 09	08 20		08 30	08 35	
Norbury	d		07 33	07 38		07 42	07 47	07 53		08 03	08 08			08 12	08 23		08 33	08 38	
Thornton Heath	d		07 36	07 41		07 45	07 50	07 56		08 06	08 11			08 15	08 26		08 36	08 41	
Selhurst 4	d		07 39	07 43		07 48	07 53	07 59		08 09	08 14			08 18	08 29		08 39	08 44	
East Croydon	a		07 42				07 57			08 12							08 42		
Purley	a		07 51							08 21							08 52		
West Croydon 4	a	07 43		07 49		07 52		08 03	08 13		08 18			08 22	08 33	08 43		08 48	
Sutton (Surrey) 4	a	07 56			07 49	08 06		08 16	08 26			08 19		08 39	08 46	08 56			08 49

		SN	SN	SN	SN	SN	SN	SN	SN	SN	SN	SN	SN	SN	SN	SN	SN	SN	SN
				1															1
London Victoria 15 ⊖	d	08 19	08 23		08 33	08 36	08 43		08 47	08 49	08 53	09 03	09 06	09 13		09 17	09 19	09 23	
Battersea Park	d	08 23			08 37	08 40	08 47			08 53		09 07	09 10	09 17			09 23		
Shepherd's Bush ⊖	d			08 19															09 20
Kensington (Olympia) ⊖	d			08 22															09 23
West Brompton ⊖	d			08 25															09 26
Imperial Wharf	d			08 27															09 28
Clapham Junction 10	a	08 26	08 29	08 33	08 40	08 43	08 50		08 53	08 56	08 59	09 10	09 13	09 20		09 23	09 26	09 29	09 33
Clapham Junction	d	08 27	08 30	08 34	08 41	08 44	08 51		08 54	08 57	09 00	09 11	09 14	09 21		09 24	09 27	09 30	09 34
Wandsworth Common	d	08 30	08 33	08 37	08 44	08 47	08 54			09 00	09 03	09 14	09 17	09 24			09 30	09 33	09 37
Balham 4 ⊖	d	08 32	08 35	08 40	08 46	08 50	08 56		09 00	09 02	09 05	09 16	09 20	09 26		09 30	09 32	09 35	09 40
London Bridge	d	09a11						08 40		09a41					09 10		10a11		
Streatham Common 4	d		08 39	08 44	08 50		09 00	09 05			09 09	09 20		09 30	09 35			09 39	09 44
Norbury	d		08 42	08 46	08 53		09 03	09 08			09 12	09 23		09 33	09 38			09 42	09 46
Thornton Heath	d		08 45	08 49	08 56		09 06	09 11			09 15	09 26		09 36	09 41			09 45	09 49
Selhurst 4	d		08 48	08 52	08 59		09 09	09 14			09 18	09 29		09 39	09 44			09 48	09 52
East Croydon	a			08 56			09 12							09 42					09 56
Purley	a						09 21							09 51					
West Croydon 4	a		08 52		09 03	09 13		09 18			09 22	09 33	09 43		09 48			09 52	
Sutton (Surrey) 4	a		09 06		09 16	09 26			09 19		09 39	09 46	09 56			09 49		10 06	

		SN	SN	SN	SN	SN	SN	SN	SN	SN	SN	SN	SN	SN	SN	SN	SN	SN	SN
																1			
London Victoria 15 ⊖	d	09 33	09 36	09 43		09 47	09 49	09 53	10 03	10 06	10 13		10 17	10 19	10 23		10 33	10 36	10 43
Battersea Park	d	09 37	09 40	09 47			09 53		10 07	10 10	10 17			10 23			10 37	10 40	10 47
Shepherd's Bush ⊖	d															10 20			
Kensington (Olympia) ⊖	d															10 23			
West Brompton ⊖	d															10 26			
Imperial Wharf	d															10 28			
Clapham Junction 10	a	09 40	09 43	09 50		09 53	09 56	09 59	10 10	10 13	10 20		10 23	10 26	10 29	10 33	10 40	10 43	10 50
Clapham Junction	d	09 41	09 44	09 51		09 54	09 57	10 00	10 11	10 14	10 21		10 24	10 27	10 30	10 34	10 41	10 44	10 51
Wandsworth Common	d	09 44	09 47	09 54			10 00	10 03	10 14	10 17	10 24			10 30	10 33	10 37	10 44	10 47	10 54
Balham 4 ⊖	d	09 46	09 50	09 56		10 00	10 02	10 05	10 16	10 20	10 26		10 30	10 32	10 35	10 40	10 46	10 50	10 56
London Bridge	d				09 40		10a41					10 10		11a11					
Streatham Common 4	d	09 50		10 00	10 05			10 09	10 20		10 30	10 35			10 39	10 44	10 50		11 00
Norbury	d	09 53		10 03	10 08			10 12	10 23		10 33	10 38			10 42	10 46	10 53		11 03
Thornton Heath	d	09 56		10 06	10 11			10 15	10 26		10 36	10 41			10 45	10 49	10 56		11 06
Selhurst 4	d	09 59		10 09	10 14			10 18	10 29		10 39	10 44			10 48	10 52	10 59		11 09
East Croydon	a			10 12							10 42					10 56			11 12
Purley	a			10 21							10 51								11 21
West Croydon 4	a	10 03	10 13		10 18			10 22	10 33	10 43		10 48			10 52		11 03	11 13	
Sutton (Surrey) 4	a	10 16	10 26			10 19		10 39	10 46	10 56			10 49		11 06		11 16	11 26	

For Faster Trains between London Victoria, Clapham Junction and East Croydon, please refer to Table 175

For Faster trains between London Victoria, Clapham Junction and Sutton, please refer to Table 182

For other Shepherds Bush connecting trains, please see Table 176

Table 170

Saturdays

14 December to 17 May

London Victoria - Battersea Park, Wandworth Common, Balham, Streatham Common, Norbury, Thornton Heath & Selhurst-Croydon

Network Diagram - see first Page of Table 170

		SN	SN	SN	SN	SN	SN	SN	SN	SN	SN	SN	SN [1]	SN	SN	SN	SN	SN	SN
London Victoria [15] ⊖	d		10 47	10 49	10 53	11 03	11 06	11 13		11 17	11 19	11 23		11 33	11 36	11 43		11 47	11 49
Battersea Park	d			10 53		11 07	11 10	11 17			11 23			11 37	11 40	11 47			11 53
Shepherd's Bush ⊖	d												11 20						
Kensington (Olympia) ⊖	d												11 23						
West Brompton ⊖	d												11 26						
Imperial Wharf	d												11 28						
Clapham Junction [10]	a		10 53	10 56	10 59	11 10	11 13	11 20		11 23	11 26	11 29	11 33	11 40	11 43	11 50		11 53	11 56
Clapham Junction	d		10 54	10 57	11 00	11 11	11 14	11 21		11 24	11 27	11 30	11 34	11 41	11 44	11 51		11 54	11 57
Wandsworth Common	d			11 00	11 03	11 14	11 17	11 24			11 30	11 33	11 37	11 44	11 47	11 54			12 00
Balham [4] ⊖	d		11 00	11 02	11 05	11 16	11 20	11 26		11 30	11 32	11 35	11 40	11 46	11 50	11 56		12 00	12 02
London Bridge	d	10 40		11a41					11 10		12a11						11 40		12a41
Streatham Common [4]	d	11 05			11 09	11 20		11 30	11 35			11 39	11 44	11 50		12 00	12 05		
Norbury	d	11 08			11 12	11 23		11 33	11 38			11 42	11 46	11 53		12 03	12 08		
Thornton Heath	d	11 11			11 15	11 26		11 36	11 41			11 45	11 49	11 56		12 06	12 11		
Selhurst [4]	d	11 14			11 18	11 29		11 39	11 44			11 48	11 52	11 59		12 09	12 14		
East Croydon 🚋	a							11 42					11 56			12 12			
Purley	a							11 51								12 21			
West Croydon [4] 🚋	a	11 18			11 22	11 33	11 43		11 48			11 52		12 03	12 13		12 18		
Sutton (Surrey) [4]	a		11 19		11 39	11 46	11 56			11 49		12 06		12 16	12 26			12 19	

		SN	SN	SN	SN	SN	SN	SN	SN	SN [1]	SN	SN	SN	SN	SN	SN	SN	SN	SN
London Victoria [15] ⊖	d	11 53	12 03	12 06	12 13		12 17	12 19	12 23		12 33	12 36	12 43		12 47	12 49	12 53	13 03	13 06
Battersea Park	d		12 07	12 10	12 17			12 23			12 37	12 40	12 47			12 53		13 07	13 10
Shepherd's Bush ⊖	d									12 19									
Kensington (Olympia) ⊖	d									12 22									
West Brompton ⊖	d									12 25									
Imperial Wharf	d									12 27									
Clapham Junction [10]	a	11 59	12 10	12 13	12 20		12 23	12 26	12 29	12 32	12 40	12 43	12 50		12 53	12 56	12 59	13 10	13 13
Clapham Junction	d	12 00	12 11	12 14	12 21		12 24	12 27	12 30	12 33	12 41	12 44	12 51		12 54	12 57	13 00	13 11	13 14
Wandsworth Common	d	12 03	12 14	12 17	12 24			12 30	12 33	12 36	12 44	12 47	12 54			13 00	13 03	13 14	13 17
Balham [4] ⊖	d	12 05	12 16	12 20	12 26		12 30	12 32	12 35	12 40	12 46	12 50	12 56		13 00	13 02	13 05	13 16	13 20
London Bridge	d					12 10		13a11						12 40		13a41			
Streatham Common [4]	d	12 09	12 20		12 30	12 35			12 39	12 44	12 50		13 00	13 05			13 09	13 20	
Norbury	d	12 12	12 23		12 33	12 38			12 42	12 46	12 53		13 03	13 08			13 12	13 23	
Thornton Heath	d	12 15	12 26		12 36	12 41			12 45	12 49	12 56		13 06	13 11			13 15	13 26	
Selhurst [4]	d	12 18	12 29		12 39	12 44			12 48	12 52	12 59		13 09	13 14			13 18	13 29	
East Croydon 🚋	a				12 42					12 56			13 12						
Purley	a				12 51								13 21						
West Croydon [4] 🚋	a	12 22	12 33	12 43		12 48			12 52		13 03	13 13		13 18			13 22	13 33	13 43
Sutton (Surrey) [4]	a	12 39	12 46	12 56			12 49		13 06		13 16	13 26			13 19		13 39	13 46	13 56

		SN	SN	SN	SN	SN	SN [1]	SN	SN	SN	SN	SN	SN	SN	SN	SN	SN	SN	SN
London Victoria [15] ⊖	d	13 13		13 17	13 19	13 23		13 33	13 36	13 43		13 47	13 49	13 53	14 03	14 06	14 13		14 17
Battersea Park	d	13 17			13 23			13 37	13 40	13 47			13 53		14 07	14 10	14 17		
Shepherd's Bush ⊖	d						13 19												
Kensington (Olympia) ⊖	d						13 22												
West Brompton ⊖	d						13 25												
Imperial Wharf	d						13 27												
Clapham Junction [10]	a	13 20		13 23	13 26	13 29	13 33	13 40	13 43	13 50		13 53	13 56	13 59	14 10	14 13	14 20		14 23
Clapham Junction	d	13 21		13 24	13 27	13 30	13 34	13 41	13 44	13 51		13 54	13 57	14 00	14 11	14 14	14 21		14 24
Wandsworth Common	d	13 24			13 30	13 33	13 37	13 44	13 47	13 54			14 00	14 03	14 14	14 17	14 24		
Balham [4] ⊖	d	13 26		13 30	13 32	13 35	13 40	13 46	13 50	13 56		14 00	14 02	14 05	14 16	14 20	14 26		14 30
London Bridge	d		13 10		14a11						13 40		14a41					14 10	
Streatham Common [4]	d	13 30	13 35			13 39	13 44	13 50		14 00	14 05			14 09	14 20		14 30	14 35	
Norbury	d	13 33	13 38			13 42	13 46	13 53		14 03	14 08			14 12	14 23		14 33	14 38	
Thornton Heath	d	13 36	13 41			13 45	13 49	13 56		14 06	14 11			14 15	14 26		14 36	14 41	
Selhurst [4]	d	13 39	13 44			13 48	13 52	13 59		14 09	14 14			14 18	14 29		14 39	14 44	
East Croydon 🚋	a	13 42					13 56			14 12							14 42		
Purley	a	13 51								14 22							14 52		
West Croydon [4] 🚋	a		13 48			13 52		14 03	14 13		14 18			14 22	14 33	14 43		14 48	
Sutton (Surrey) [4]	a			13 49		14 06		14 16	14 26			14 19		14 39	14 46	14 56			14 49

		SN	SN	SN [1]	SN	SN	SN	SN	SN	SN	SN	SN	SN	SN	SN	SN	SN	SN	SN [1]
London Victoria [15] ⊖	d	14 19	14 23		14 33	14 36	14 43		14 47	14 49	14 53	15 03	15 06	15 13		15 17	15 19	15 23	
Battersea Park	d	14 23			14 37	14 40	14 47			14 53		15 07	15 10	15 17			15 23		
Shepherd's Bush ⊖	d			14 20															15 20
Kensington (Olympia) ⊖	d			14 23															15 22
West Brompton ⊖	d			14 26															15 25
Imperial Wharf	d			14 28															15 28
Clapham Junction [10]	a	14 26	14 29	14 33	14 40	14 43	14 50		14 53	14 56	14 59	15 10	15 13	15 20		15 23	15 26	15 29	15 33
Clapham Junction	d	14 27	14 30	14 34	14 41	14 44	14 51		14 54	14 57	15 00	15 11	15 14	15 21		15 24	15 27	15 30	15 34
Wandsworth Common	d	14 30	14 33	14 37	14 44	14 47	14 54			15 00	15 03	15 14	15 17	15 24			15 30	15 33	15 37
Balham [4] ⊖	d	14 32	14 35	14 40	14 46	14 50	14 56		15 00	15 02	15 05	15 16	15 20	15 26		15 30	15 32	15 35	15 40
London Bridge	d	15a11						14 40		15a41					15 10		16a11		
Streatham Common [4]	d		14 39	14 44	14 50		15 00	15 05			15 09	15 20		15 30	15 35			15 39	15 44
Norbury	d		14 42	14 46	14 53		15 03	15 08			15 12	15 23		15 33	15 38			15 42	15 46
Thornton Heath	d		14 45	14 49	14 56		15 06	15 11			15 15	15 26		15 36	15 41			15 45	15 49
Selhurst [4]	d		14 48	14 52	14 59		15 09	15 14			15 18	15 29		15 39	15 44			15 48	15 52
East Croydon 🚋	a			14 56			15 12							15 42					15 56
Purley	a						15 21							15 51					
West Croydon [4] 🚋	a		14 52		15 03	15 13		15 18			15 22	15 33	15 43		15 48			15 52	
Sutton (Surrey) [4]	a		15 06		15 16	15 26			15 19		15 39	15 46	15 56			15 49		16 06	

For Faster Trains between London Victoria, Clapham Junction and East Croydon, please refer to Table 175

For Faster trains between London Victoria, Clapham Junction and Sutton, please refer to Table 182

For other Shepherds Bush connecting trains, please see Table 176

Table 170

Saturdays

14 December to 17 May

London Victoria - Battersea Park, Wandworth Common, Balham, Streatham Common, Norbury, Thornton Heath & Selhurst-Croydon

Network Diagram - see first Page of Table 170

Station		SN	SN	SN	SN	SN	SN	SN	SN	SN
London Victoria 15 ⊖	d	15 33	15 36	15 43		15 47	15 49	15 53	16 03	16 06
Battersea Park	d	15 37	15 40	15 47			15 53		16 07	16 10
Shepherd's Bush ⊖	d									
Kensington (Olympia) ⊖	d									
West Brompton ⊖	d									
Imperial Wharf	d									
Clapham Junction 10	a	15 40	15 43	15 50		15 53	15 56	15 59	16 10	16 13
Clapham Junction	d	15 41	15 44	15 51		15 54	15 57	16 00	16 11	16 14
Wandsworth Common	d	15 44	15 47	15 54			16 00	16 03	16 14	16 17
Balham 4 ⊖	d	15 46	15 50	15 56		16 00	16 02	16 05	16 16	16 20
London Bridge	d				15 40		16a41			
Streatham Common 4	d	15 50		16 00	16 05			16 09	16 20	
Norbury	d	15 53		16 03	16 08			16 12	16 23	
Thornton Heath	d	15 56		16 06	16 11			16 15	16 26	
Selhurst 4	d	15 59		16 09	16 14			16 18	16 29	
East Croydon 🚋	a			16 12						
Purley	a			16 21						
West Croydon 4 🚋	a	16 03	16 13		16 18			16 22	16 33	16 43
Sutton (Surrey) 4	a	16 16	16 26			16 19		16 39	16 46	16 56

Station		SN	SN	SN	SN	SN	SN [1]	SN	SN	SN
London Victoria 15 ⊖	d	16 13		16 17	16 19	16 23		16 33	16 36	16 43
Battersea Park	d	16 17			16 23			16 37	16 40	16 47
Shepherd's Bush ⊖	d						16 20			
Kensington (Olympia) ⊖	d						16 22			
West Brompton ⊖	d						16 25			
Imperial Wharf	d						16 28			
Clapham Junction 10	a	16 20		16 23	16 26	16 29	16 33	16 40	16 43	16 50
Clapham Junction	d	16 21		16 24	16 27	16 30	16 34	16 41	16 44	16 51
Wandsworth Common	d	16 24			16 30	16 33	16 37	16 44	16 47	16 54
Balham 4 ⊖	d	16 26		16 30	16 32	16 35	16 40	16 46	16 50	16 56
London Bridge	d		16 10		17a11					
Streatham Common 4	d	16 30	16 35			16 39	16 44	16 50		17 00
Norbury	d	16 33	16 38			16 42	16 46	16 53		17 03
Thornton Heath	d	16 36	16 41			16 45	16 49	16 56		17 06
Selhurst 4	d	16 39	16 44			16 48	16 52	16 59		17 09
East Croydon 🚋	a	16 42					16 56			17 12
Purley	a	16 51								17 21
West Croydon 4 🚋	a		16 48			16 52		17 03	17 13	
Sutton (Surrey) 4	a			16 49		17 06		17 16	17 26	

Station		SN	SN	SN	SN	SN	SN	SN	SN	SN
London Victoria 15 ⊖	d		16 47	16 49	16 53	17 03	17 06	17 13		17 17
Battersea Park	d			16 53		17 07	17 10	17 17		
Shepherd's Bush ⊖	d									
Kensington (Olympia) ⊖	d									
West Brompton ⊖	d									
Imperial Wharf	d									
Clapham Junction 10	a		16 53	16 56	16 59	17 10	17 13	17 20		17 23
Clapham Junction	d		16 54	16 57	17 00	17 11	17 14	17 21		17 24
Wandsworth Common	d			17 00	17 03	17 14	17 17	17 24		
Balham 4 ⊖	d		17 00	17 02	17 05	17 16	17 20	17 26		17 30
London Bridge	d	16 40		17a41					17 10	
Streatham Common 4	d	17 05			17 09	17 20		17 30	17 35	
Norbury	d	17 08			17 12	17 23		17 33	17 38	
Thornton Heath	d	17 11			17 15	17 26		17 36	17 41	
Selhurst 4	d	17 14			17 18	17 29		17 39	17 44	
East Croydon 🚋	a							17 42		
Purley	a							17 51		
West Croydon 4 🚋	a	17 18			17 22	17 33	17 43		17 48	
Sutton (Surrey) 4	a		17 19		17 39	17 46	17 56			17 49

Station		SN	SN	SN [1]	SN	SN	SN	SN	SN	SN
London Victoria 15 ⊖	d	17 19	17 23		17 33	17 36	17 43		17 47	17 49
Battersea Park	d	17 23			17 37	17 40	17 47			17 53
Shepherd's Bush ⊖	d			17 20						
Kensington (Olympia) ⊖	d			17 22						
West Brompton ⊖	d			17 25						
Imperial Wharf	d			17 28						
Clapham Junction 10	a	17 26	17 29	17 32	17 40	17 43	17 50		17 53	17 56
Clapham Junction	d	17 27	17 30	17 34	17 41	17 44	17 51		17 54	17 57
Wandsworth Common	d	17 30	17 33	17 37	17 44	17 47	17 54			18 00
Balham 4 ⊖	d	17 32	17 35	17 40	17 46	17 50	17 56		18 00	18 02
London Bridge	d	18a11						17 40		18a41
Streatham Common 4	d		17 39	17 44	17 50		18 00	18 05		
Norbury	d		17 42	17 46	17 53		18 03	18 08		
Thornton Heath	d		17 45	17 49	17 56		18 06	18 11		
Selhurst 4	d		17 48	17 52	17 59		18 09	18 14		
East Croydon 🚋	a			17 56			18 12			
Purley	a						18 21			
West Croydon 4 🚋	a		17 52		18 03	18 13		18 18		
Sutton (Surrey) 4	a		18 06		18 16	18 26			18 19	

Station		SN	SN	SN	SN	SN	SN	SN	SN	SN [1]
London Victoria 15 ⊖	d	17 53	18 03	18 06	18 13		18 17	18 19	18 23	
Battersea Park	d		18 07	18 10	18 17			18 23		
Shepherd's Bush ⊖	d									18 20
Kensington (Olympia) ⊖	d									18 22
West Brompton ⊖	d									18 25
Imperial Wharf	d									18 27
Clapham Junction 10	a	17 59	18 10	18 13	18 20		18 23	18 26	18 29	18 32
Clapham Junction	d	18 00	18 11	18 14	18 21		18 24	18 27	18 30	18 34
Wandsworth Common	d	18 03	18 14	18 17	18 24			18 30	18 33	18 37
Balham 4 ⊖	d	18 05	18 16	18 20	18 26		18 30	18 32	18 35	18 40
London Bridge	d					18 10		19a11		
Streatham Common 4	d	18 09	18 20		18 30	18 35			18 39	18 44
Norbury	d	18 12	18 23		18 33	18 38			18 42	18 47
Thornton Heath	d	18 15	18 26		18 36	18 41			18 45	18 50
Selhurst 4	d	18 18	18 29		18 39	18 44			18 48	18 53
East Croydon 🚋	a				18 42					18 56
Purley	a				18 51					
West Croydon 4 🚋	a	18 22	18 33	18 43		18 48			18 52	
Sutton (Surrey) 4	a	18 39	18 46	18 56			18 49		19 06	

Station		SN	SN	SN	SN	SN	SN	SN	SN	SN
London Victoria 15 ⊖	d	18 33	18 36	18 43		18 47	18 49	18 53	19 03	19 06
Battersea Park	d	18 37	18 40	18 47			18 53		19 07	19 10
Shepherd's Bush ⊖	d									
Kensington (Olympia) ⊖	d									
West Brompton ⊖	d									
Imperial Wharf	d									
Clapham Junction 10	a	18 40	18 43	18 50		18 53	18 56	18 59	19 10	19 13
Clapham Junction	d	18 41	18 44	18 51		18 54	18 57	19 00	19 11	19 14
Wandsworth Common	d	18 44	18 47	18 54			19 00	19 03	19 14	19 17
Balham 4 ⊖	d	18 46	18 50	18 56		19 00	19 02	19 05	19 16	19 20
London Bridge	d				18 40		19a41			
Streatham Common 4	d	18 50		19 00	19 05			19 09	19 20	
Norbury	d	18 53		19 03	19 08			19 12	19 23	
Thornton Heath	d	18 56		19 06	19 11			19 15	19 26	
Selhurst 4	d	18 59		19 09	19 14			19 18	19 29	
East Croydon 🚋	a			19 12						
Purley	a			19 21						
West Croydon 4 🚋	a	19 03	19 13		19 18			19 22	19 33	19 43
Sutton (Surrey) 4	a	19 16	19 26			19 19		19 39	19 46	19 56

Station		SN	SN	SN	SN	SN	SN [1]	SN	SN	SN
London Victoria 15 ⊖	d	19 13		19 17	19 19	19 23		19 33	19 36	19 43
Battersea Park	d	19 17			19 23			19 37	19 40	19 47
Shepherd's Bush ⊖	d						19 20			
Kensington (Olympia) ⊖	d						19 22			
West Brompton ⊖	d						19 25			
Imperial Wharf	d						19 27			
Clapham Junction 10	a	19 20		19 23	19 26	19 29	19 32	19 40	19 43	19 50
Clapham Junction	d	19 21		19 24	19 27	19 30	19 34	19 41	19 44	19 51
Wandsworth Common	d	19 24			19 30	19 33	19 37	19 44	19 47	19 54
Balham 4 ⊖	d	19 26		19 30	19 32	19 35	19 40	19 46	19 50	19 56
London Bridge	d		19 10		20a11					
Streatham Common 4	d	19 30	19 35			19 39	19 45	19 50		20 00
Norbury	d	19 33	19 38			19 42	19 48	19 53		20 03
Thornton Heath	d	19 36	19 41			19 45	19 51	19 56		20 06
Selhurst 4	d	19 39	19 44			19 48	19 54	19 59		20 09
East Croydon 🚋	a	19 42					19 57			20 12
Purley	a	19 51								20 21
West Croydon 4 🚋	a		19 48			19 52		20 03	20 14	
Sutton (Surrey) 4	a			19 49		20 06		20 16	20 27	

Station		SN	SN	SN	SN	SN [1]	SN	SN	SN	SN
London Victoria 15 ⊖	d		19 47	19 49	19 53		20 03	20 06	20 13	
Battersea Park	d			19 53			20 07	20 10	20 17	
Shepherd's Bush ⊖	d					19 58				
Kensington (Olympia) ⊖	d					20 01				
West Brompton ⊖	d					20 03				
Imperial Wharf	d					20 06				
Clapham Junction 10	a		19 53	19 56	19 59	20 10	20 10	20 13	20 20	
Clapham Junction	d		19 54	19 57	20 00		20 11	20 14	20 21	
Wandsworth Common	d			20 00	20 03		20 14	20 17	20 24	
Balham 4 ⊖	d		20 00	20 02	20 05		20 16	20 20	20 26	
London Bridge	d	19 40		20a41						20 10
Streatham Common 4	d	20 05			20 09		20 20		20 30	20 35
Norbury	d	20 08			20 12		20 23		20 33	20 38
Thornton Heath	d	20 11			20 15		20 26		20 36	20 41
Selhurst 4	d	20 14			20 18		20 29		20 39	20 44
East Croydon 🚋	a								20 42	
Purley	a								20 51	
West Croydon 4 🚋	a	20 18			20 24		20 33	20 44		20 48
Sutton (Surrey) 4	a		20 19		20 39		20 46	20 57		

For Faster Trains between London Victoria, Clapham Junction and East Croydon, please refer to Table 175

For Faster trains between London Victoria, Clapham Junction and Sutton, please refer to Table 182

For other Shepherds Bush connecting trains, please see Table 176

Table 170

Saturdays

14 December to 17 May

London Victoria - Battersea Park, Wandworth Common, Balham, Streatham Common, Norbury, Thornton Heath & Selhurst-Croydon

Network Diagram - see first Page of Table 170

		SN	SN	SN	SN 1	SN	SN	SN	SN	SN
London Victoria 15 ⊖	d	20 17	20 19	20 23		20 33	20 36	20 43		20 47
Battersea Park	d		20 23			20 37	20 40	20 47		
Shepherd's Bush ⊖	d				20 20					
Kensington (Olympia) ⊖	d				20 23					
West Brompton ⊖	d				20 26					
Imperial Wharf	d				20 28					
Clapham Junction 10	a	20 23	20 26	20 29	20 33	20 40	20 43	20 50		20 53
Clapham Junction	d	20 24	20 27	20 30	20 34	20 41	20 44	20 51		20 54
Wandsworth Common	d		20 30	20 33	20 37	20 44	20 47	20 54		
Balham 4 ⊖	d	20 30	20 32	20 35	20 40	20 46	20 50	20 56		21 00
London Bridge	d		21a11						20 40	
Streatham Common 4	d			20 39	20 44	20 50		21 00	21 05	
Norbury	d			20 42	20 47	20 53		21 03	21 08	
Thornton Heath	d			20 45	20 50	20 56		21 06	21 11	
Selhurst 4	d			20 48	20 55	20 59		21 09	21 14	
East Croydon 🚊	a				20 59			21 12		
Purley	a							21 21		
West Croydon 4 🚊	a			20 54		21 03	21 14		21 18	
Sutton (Surrey) 4	a	20 49		21 07		21 16	21 27			21 19

		SN	SN	SN	SN	SN	SN 1	SN	SN	SN
London Victoria 15 ⊖	d	20 49	20 53	21 03	21 06	21 13			21 17	21 19
Battersea Park	d	20 53		21 07	21 10	21 17				21 23
Shepherd's Bush ⊖	d						21 09			
Kensington (Olympia) ⊖	d						21 11			
West Brompton ⊖	d						21 14			
Imperial Wharf	d						21 16			
Clapham Junction 10	a	20 56	20 59	21 10	21 13	21 20	21 21		21 23	21 26
Clapham Junction	d	20 57	21 00	21 11	21 14	21 21			21 24	21 27
Wandsworth Common	d	21 00	21 03	21 14	21 17	21 24				21 30
Balham 4 ⊖	d	21 02	21 05	21 16	21 20	21 26			21 30	21 32
London Bridge	d	21a41						21 10		22a11
Streatham Common 4	d		21 09	21 20		21 30		21 35		
Norbury	d		21 12	21 23		21 33		21 38		
Thornton Heath	d		21 15	21 26		21 36		21 41		
Selhurst 4	d		21 18	21 29		21 39		21 44		
East Croydon 🚊	a					21 42				
Purley	a					21 51				
West Croydon 4 🚊	a		21 24	21 33	21 44			21 48		
Sutton (Surrey) 4	a		21 39	21 46	21 57				21 49	

		SN	SN	SN	SN	SN	SN	SN	SN	SN
London Victoria 15 ⊖	d	21 23	21 33	21 36	21 43		21 47	21 49	21 53	22 03
Battersea Park	d		21 37	21 40	21 47			21 53		22 07
Shepherd's Bush ⊖	d									
Kensington (Olympia) ⊖	d									
West Brompton ⊖	d									
Imperial Wharf	d									
Clapham Junction 10	a	21 29	21 40	21 43	21 50		21 53	21 56	21 59	22 10
Clapham Junction	d	21 30	21 41	21 44	21 51		21 54	21 57	22 00	22 11
Wandsworth Common	d	21 33	21 44	21 47	21 54			22 00	22 03	22 14
Balham 4 ⊖	d	21 35	21 46	21 50	21 56		22 00	22 02	22 05	22 16
London Bridge	d					21 40		22a41		
Streatham Common 4	d	21 39	21 50		22 00	22 05			22 09	22 20
Norbury	d	21 42	21 53		22 03	22 08			22 12	22 23
Thornton Heath	d	21 45	21 56		22 06	22 11			22 15	22 26
Selhurst 4	d	21 48	21 59		22 09	22 14			22 18	22 29
East Croydon 🚊	a				22 12					
Purley	a				22 21					
West Croydon 4 🚊	a	21 54	22 03	22 13		22 18			22 22	22 33
Sutton (Surrey) 4	a	22 07	22 16	22 26			22 19		22 39	22 46

		SN	SN	SN 1	SN	SN	SN	SN	SN	SN
London Victoria 15 ⊖	d	22 06	22 13			22 17	22 19	22 23	22 33	22 36
Battersea Park	d	22 10	22 17				22 23		22 37	22 40
Shepherd's Bush ⊖	d			22 10						
Kensington (Olympia) ⊖	d			22 12						
West Brompton ⊖	d			22 14						
Imperial Wharf	d			22 17						
Clapham Junction 10	a	22 13	22 20	22 21		22 23	22 26	22 29	22 40	22 43
Clapham Junction	d	22 14	22 21			22 24	22 27	22 30	22 41	22 44
Wandsworth Common	d	22 17	22 24				22 30	22 33	22 44	22 47
Balham 4 ⊖	d	22 20	22 26			22 30	22 32	22 35	22 46	22 50
London Bridge	d				22 10		23a11			
Streatham Common 4	d		22 30		22 35			22 39	22 50	
Norbury	d		22 33		22 38			22 42	22 53	
Thornton Heath	d		22 36		22 41			22 45	22 56	
Selhurst 4	d		22 39		22 44			22 48	22 59	
East Croydon 🚊	a		22 43							
Purley	a		22 53							
West Croydon 4 🚊	a	22 43			22 48			22 52	23 03	23 13
Sutton (Surrey) 4	a	22 56				22 49		23 06	23 16	23 26

		SN	SN	SN	SN	SN	SN	SN	SN	SN
London Victoria 15 ⊖	d	22 43		22 47	22 49	22 53	23 03	23 06	23 15	
Battersea Park	d	22 47			22 53		23 07	23 10	23 19	
Shepherd's Bush ⊖	d									
Kensington (Olympia) ⊖	d									
West Brompton ⊖	d									
Imperial Wharf	d									
Clapham Junction 10	a	22 50		22 53	22 56	22 59	23 10	23 13	23 22	
Clapham Junction	d	22 51		22 54	22 57	23 00	23 11	23 14	23 23	
Wandsworth Common	d	22 54			23 00	23 03	23 14	23 17	23 26	
Balham 4 ⊖	d	22 56		23 00	23 02	23 06	23 16	23 20	23 28	
London Bridge	d		22 40		23a44					23 10
Streatham Common 4	d	23 00	23 05			23 10	23 20		23 32	23 35
Norbury	d	23 03	23 08			23 12	23 23		23 35	23 38
Thornton Heath	d	23 06	23 11			23 15	23 26		23 38	23 41
Selhurst 4	d	23 09	23 14			23 18	23 29		23 41	23 44
East Croydon 🚊	a	23 13							23 44	
Purley	a	23 22							23 53	
West Croydon 4 🚊	a		23 18			23 22	23 33	23 43		23 49
Sutton (Surrey) 4	a			23 19		23 39	23 46	23 56		

		SN	SN 1	SN	SN	SN	SN	SN	SN	SN 1
London Victoria 15 ⊖	d	23 19		23 34	23 38	23 45		23 51	23 54	
Battersea Park	d	23 23		23 38	23 42	23 49		23 55	23 58	
Shepherd's Bush ⊖	d		23 14							23 51
Kensington (Olympia) ⊖	d		23 16							23 53
West Brompton ⊖	d		23 19							23 55
Imperial Wharf	d		23 21							23 58
Clapham Junction 10	a	23 26	23 26	23 41	23 45	23 52		23 58	00 01	00 02
Clapham Junction	d	23 27	23 35	23 42	23 46	23 53		23 59	00 02	
Wandsworth Common	d	23 30		23 45	23 49	23 56		00 02	00 05	
Balham 4 ⊖	d	23 32	23 40	23 47	23 51	23 58		00 04	00 07	
London Bridge	d	00a11					23 40		00a41	
Streatham Common 4	d		23 44	23 51		00 02	00 05	00 08		
Norbury	d		23 46	23 54		00 05	00 08	00 11		
Thornton Heath	d		23 49	23 57		00 08	00 11	00 14		
Selhurst 4	d		23a52	23 59		00 11	00 14	00 17		
East Croydon 🚊	a					00 14				
Purley	a					00 23				
West Croydon 4 🚊	a			00 03	00 14		00 18	00 21		
Sutton (Surrey) 4	a			00 16				00 35		

For Faster Trains between London Victoria, Clapham Junction and East Croydon, please refer to Table 175

For Faster trains between London Victoria, Clapham Junction and Sutton, please refer to Table 182

For other Shepherds Bush connecting trains, please see Table 176

Table 170

Sundays

8 December to 11 May

London Victoria - Battersea Park, Wandworth Common, Balham, Streatham Common, Norbury, Thornton Heath & Selhurst-Croydon

Network Diagram - see first Page of Table 170

	SN	SN	SN	SN	SN	SN	SN	SN	SN	SN	SN	SN
London Victoria [15] ⊖ d					00 07	00 16		00 22	00 34	00 37	06 36	07 06
Battersea Park d					00 11	00 20		00 26	00 38	00 41		
Shepherd's Bush ⊖ d												
Kensington (Olympia) ⊖ d												
West Brompton ⊖ d												
Imperial Wharf d												
Clapham Junction [10] a					00 15	00 23		00 29	00 41	00 44	06 42	07 12
Clapham Junction d				00 02	00 15	00 24		00 30	00 42	00 45	06 42	07 12
Wandsworth Common d			00 02	00 05	00 18	00 27		00 33	00 45	00 48		
Balham [4] ⊖ d			00 04	00 07	00 21	00 29		00 35	00 47	00 50	06 47	07 17
London Bridge d				00a41			00 18					
Streatham Common [4] d	00 02	00 05	00 08			00 33	00 43		00 51		06 51	07 21
Norbury d	00 05	00 08	00 11			00 36	00 46		00 54		06 53	07 23
Thornton Heath d	00 08	00 11	00 14			00 39	00 49		00 57		06 56	07 26
Selhurst [4] d	00 11	00 14	00 17			00 41	00 53		01 00		06 59	07 29
East Croydon a	00 14					00 44					07 02	07 32
Purley a	00 23					00 59					07 13	07 43
West Croydon [4] a		00 18	00 21		00 43		00 57	01 00	01 04	01 13		
Sutton (Surrey) [4] a			00 35						01 16			

	SN	SN	SN	SN	SN [1]	SN	SN	SN	SN	SN	SN	SN
London Victoria [15] ⊖ d	07 17	07 20	07 35	07 49		07 52	08 05	08 19	08 23	08 35	08 49	08 52
Battersea Park d		07 24				07 56			08 27			08 56
Shepherd's Bush ⊖ d					07 47							
Kensington (Olympia) ⊖ d					07 49							
West Brompton ⊖ d					07 51							
Imperial Wharf d					07 54							
Clapham Junction [10] a	07 23	07 27	07 41	07 56	07 58	07 59	08 11	08 26	08 30	08 41	08 56	08 59
Clapham Junction d	07 23	07 28	07 41	07 57		08 00	08 12	08 27	08 31	08 42	08 57	09 00
Wandsworth Common d		07 31				08 03			08 34			09 03
Balham [4] ⊖ d	07 28	07 34	07 46	08 01		08 06	08 16	08 31	08 36	08 46	09 01	09 06
London Bridge d												
Streatham Common [4] d	07 32			08 05				08 35		08 50	09 05	
Norbury d	07 34			08 08				08 38		08 53	09 08	
Thornton Heath d	07 37			08 11				08 41		08 56	09 11	
Selhurst [4] d	07 40			08 13				08 43		08 58	09 13	
East Croydon a			08 07				08 40			09 02		
Purley a			08 14				08 48			09 10		
West Croydon [4] a	07 48	08 00		08 18		08 30		08 48	09 00		09 18	09 30
Sutton (Surrey) [4] a	08 01	08 13		08 31		08 43		09 01	09 13		09 31	09 44

	SN [1]	SN	SN	SN	SN	SN	SN	SN [1]	SN	SN	SN	SN
London Victoria [15] ⊖ d		09 08	09 19	09 22	09 24	09 38	09 49		09 52	09 54	10 08	10 19
Battersea Park d					09 28					09 58		
Shepherd's Bush ⊖ d	08 51							09 45				
Kensington (Olympia) ⊖ d	08 53							09 47				
West Brompton ⊖ d	08 56							09 50				
Imperial Wharf d	08 59							09 53				
Clapham Junction [10] a	09 03	09 14	09 25	09 28	09 31	09 44	09 55	09 58	09 58	10 01	10 14	10 25
Clapham Junction d		09 14	09 26	09 29	09 32	09 44	09 56		09 59	10 02	10 14	10 26
Wandsworth Common d					09 35					10 05		
Balham [4] ⊖ d		09 19	09 30	09 33	09 38	09 49	10 00		10 03	10 07	10 19	10 30
London Bridge d												
Streatham Common [4] d		09 23	09 34			09 53	10 04				10 23	10 34
Norbury d		09 26	09 37			09 56	10 07				10 26	10 37
Thornton Heath d		09 29	09 40			09 59	10 10				10 29	10 40
Selhurst [4] d		09 32	09 43			10 02	10 13				10 32	10 43
East Croydon a		09 35				10 05					10 35	
Purley a		09 42				10 12					10 42	
West Croydon [4] a			09 48		10 02		10 18			10 31		10 48
Sutton (Surrey) [4] a			10 01	09 52	10 16		10 31		10 22	10 46		11 01

	SN	SN	SN	SN	SN [1]	SN	SN	SN	SN	SN	SN	SN	SN	SN	SN [1]	
London Victoria [15] ⊖ d	10 22	10 24	10 38	10 49		10 52	10 54	11 08	11 19	11 22	11 24	11 38	11 49	11 52		and at the same minutes past each hour until
Battersea Park d		10 28					10 58				11 28					
Shepherd's Bush ⊖ d					10 44										11 48	
Kensington (Olympia) ⊖ d					10 47										11 51	
West Brompton ⊖ d					10 49										11 53	
Imperial Wharf d					10 52										11 56	
Clapham Junction [10] a	10 28	10 31	10 44	10 55	10 56	10 58	11 01	11 14	11 25	11 28	11 31	11 44	11 55	11 58	12 00	
Clapham Junction d	10 29	10 32	10 44	10 56		10 59	11 02	11 14	11 26	11 29	11 32	11 44	11 56	11 59		
Wandsworth Common d		10 35					11 05				11 35					
Balham [4] ⊖ d	10 33	10 37	10 49	11 00		11 03	11 07	11 19	11 30	11 33	11 37	11 49	12 00	12 03		
London Bridge d																
Streatham Common [4] d			10 53	11 04				11 23	11 34			11 53	12 04			
Norbury d			10 56	11 07				11 26	11 37			11 56	12 07			
Thornton Heath d			10 59	11 10				11 29	11 40			11 59	12 10			
Selhurst [4] d			11 02	11 13				11 32	11 43			12 02	12 13			
East Croydon a			11 05					11 35				12 05				
Purley a			11 12					11 42				12 12				
West Croydon [4] a		11 01		11 18			11 31		11 48		12 01		12 18			
Sutton (Surrey) [4] a	10 52	11 16		11 31		11 22	11 46		12 01	11 52	12 16		12 31	12 22		

	SN	SN	SN	SN	SN	SN	SN	SN	SN [1]
London Victoria [15] ⊖ d	13 54	14 08	14 19	14 22	14 24	14 38	14 49	14 52	
Battersea Park d	13 58				14 28				
Shepherd's Bush ⊖ d									14 48
Kensington (Olympia) ⊖ d									14 51
West Brompton ⊖ d									14 53
Imperial Wharf d									14 56
Clapham Junction [10] a	14 01	14 14	14 25	14 28	14 31	14 44	14 55	14 58	15 00
Clapham Junction d	14 02	14 14	14 26	14 29	14 32	14 44	14 56	14 59	
Wandsworth Common d	14 05				14 35				
Balham [4] ⊖ d	14 07	14 19	14 30	14 33	14 37	14 49	15 00	15 03	
London Bridge d									
Streatham Common [4] d		14 23	14 34			14 53	15 04		
Norbury d		14 26	14 37			14 56	15 07		
Thornton Heath d		14 29	14 40			14 59	15 10		
Selhurst [4] d		14 32	14 43			15 02	15 13		
East Croydon a		14 35				15 05			
Purley a		14 42				15 12			
West Croydon [4] a	14 31		14 48		15 01		15 18		
Sutton (Surrey) [4] a	14 46		15 01	14 52	15 16		15 31	15 22	

	SN	SN	SN	SN	SN	SN	SN	SN	SN [1]	SN	SN	SN
London Victoria [15] ⊖ d	14 54	15 07	15 19	15 22	15 24	15 38	15 49	15 52		15 54	16 08	16 19
Battersea Park d	14 58				15 28					15 58		
Shepherd's Bush ⊖ d									15 48			
Kensington (Olympia) ⊖ d									15 51			
West Brompton ⊖ d									15 53			
Imperial Wharf d									15 56			
Clapham Junction [10] a	15 01	15 13	15 25	15 28	15 31	15 44	15 55	15 58	16 00	16 01	16 14	16 25
Clapham Junction d	15 02	15 13	15 26	15 29	15 32	15 44	15 56	15 59		16 02	16 14	16 26
Wandsworth Common d	15 05				15 35					16 05		
Balham [4] ⊖ d	15 07	15 18	15 30	15 33	15 37	15 49	16 00	16 03		16 07	16 19	16 30
London Bridge d												
Streatham Common [4] d		15 22	15 34			15 53	16 04				16 23	16 34
Norbury d		15 25	15 37			15 56	16 07				16 26	16 37
Thornton Heath d		15 28	15 40			15 59	16 10				16 29	16 40
Selhurst [4] d		15 31	15 43			16 02	16 13				16 32	16 43
East Croydon a		15 35				16 05					16 35	
Purley a		15 42				16 12					16 42	
West Croydon [4] a	15 31		15 48		16 01		16 18			16 31		16 48
Sutton (Surrey) [4] a	15 46		16 01	15 52	16 16		16 31	16 22		16 46		17 01

For Faster Trains between London Victoria, Clapham Junction and East Croydon, please refer to Table 175

For Faster trains between London Victoria, Clapham Junction and Sutton, please refer to Table 182

For other Shepherds Bush connecting trains, please see Table 176

Table 170

Sundays
8 December to 11 May

London Victoria - Battersea Park, Wandworth Common, Balham, Streatham Common, Norbury, Thornton Heath & Selhurst-Croydon

Network Diagram - see first Page of Table 170

		SN	SN	SN	SN	SN	SN 1	SN	SN	SN	SN	SN	SN	SN	SN	SN 1
London Victoria 15 ⊖	d	16 22	16 24	16 38	16 49	16 52		16 54	17 08	17 19	17 22	17 24	17 38	17 49	17 52	
Battersea Park	d		16 28					16 58				17 28				
Shepherd's Bush ⊖	d						16 48									17 48
Kensington (Olympia) ⊖	d						16 50									17 50
West Brompton ⊖	d						16 53									17 53
Imperial Wharf	d						16 56									17 56
Clapham Junction 10	a	16 28	16 31	16 44	16 55	16 58	17 00	17 01	17 14	17 25	17 28	17 31	17 44	17 55	17 58	18 00
Clapham Junction	d	16 29	16 32	16 44	16 56	16 59		17 02	17 14	17 26	17 29	17 32	17 44	17 56	17 59	
Wandsworth Common	d		16 35					17 05				17 35				
Balham 4 ⊖	d	16 33	16 37	16 49	17 00	17 03		17 07	17 19	17 30	17 33	17 37	17 49	18 00	18 03	
London Bridge	d															
Streatham Common 4	d			16 53	17 04				17 23	17 34			17 53	18 04		
Norbury	d			16 56	17 07				17 26	17 37			17 56	18 07		
Thornton Heath	d			16 59	17 10				17 29	17 40			17 59	18 10		
Selhurst 4	d			17 02	17 13				17 32	17 43			18 02	18 13		
East Croydon 🚋	a			17 05					17 35				18 05			
Purley	a			17 12					17 42				18 12			
West Croydon 4 🚋	a		17 01		17 18			17 31		17 48		18 01		18 18		
Sutton (Surrey) 4	a	16 52	17 16		17 31	17 22		17 46		18 01	17 52	18 16		18 31	18 22	

		SN	SN	SN	SN	SN	SN	SN	SN	SN 1	SN	SN	SN	SN	SN	SN	SN	SN	SN 1	SN	SN	SN
London Victoria 15 ⊖	d	17 54	18 08	18 19	18 22	18 24	18 38	18 49	18 52		18 54	19 08	19 19	19 22	19 24	19 38	19 49	19 52		19 54	20 08	20 19
Battersea Park	d	17 58				18 28					18 58				19 28					19 58		
Shepherd's Bush ⊖	d									18 48									19 48			
Kensington (Olympia) ⊖	d									18 50									19 51			
West Brompton ⊖	d									18 53									19 53			
Imperial Wharf	d									18 55									19 56			
Clapham Junction 10	a	18 01	18 14	18 25	18 28	18 31	18 44	18 55	18 58	19 00	19 01	19 14	19 25	19 28	19 31	19 44	19 55	19 58	20 00	20 01	20 14	20 25
Clapham Junction	d	18 02	18 14	18 26	18 29	18 32	18 44	18 56	18 59		19 02	19 14	19 26	19 29	19 32	19 44	19 56	19 59		20 02	20 14	20 26
Wandsworth Common	d	18 05				18 35					19 05				19 35					20 05		
Balham 4 ⊖	d	18 07	18 19	18 30	18 33	18 37	18 49	19 00	19 03		19 07	19 19	19 30	19 33	19 37	19 49	20 00	20 03		20 07	20 19	20 30
London Bridge	d																					
Streatham Common 4	d		18 23	18 34			18 53	19 04				19 23	19 34			19 53	20 04				20 23	20 34
Norbury	d		18 26	18 37			18 56	19 07				19 26	19 37			19 56	20 07				20 26	20 37
Thornton Heath	d		18 29	18 40			18 59	19 10				19 29	19 40			19 59	20 10				20 29	20 40
Selhurst 4	d		18 32	18 43			19 02	19 13				19 32	19 43			20 02	20 13				20 32	20 43
East Croydon 🚋	a		18 35				19 05					19 35				20 05					20 35	
Purley	a		18 42				19 12					19 42				20 12					20 42	
West Croydon 4 🚋	a	18 31		18 48		19 01		19 18			19 31		19 48		20 01		20 18			20 31		20 48
Sutton (Surrey) 4	a	18 46		19 01	18 52	19 16		19 31	19 22		19 46		20 01	19 52	20 16		20 31	20 22		20 46		21 01

		SN	SN	SN	SN 1	SN	SN	SN	SN	SN	SN	SN 1	SN	SN	SN	SN
London Victoria 15 ⊖	d	20 24	20 38	20 49		20 54	21 08	21 19	21 24	21 38	21 49		21 54	22 08	22 19	22 24
Battersea Park	d	20 28				20 58			21 28				21 58			22 28
Shepherd's Bush ⊖	d				20 48							21 45				
Kensington (Olympia) ⊖	d				20 50							21 48				
West Brompton ⊖	d				20 53							21 50				
Imperial Wharf	d				20 56							21 53				
Clapham Junction 10	a	20 31	20 44	20 55	21 00	21 01	21 14	21 25	21 31	21 44	21 55	21 58	22 01	22 14	22 25	22 31
Clapham Junction	d	20 32	20 44	20 56		21 02	21 14	21 26	21 32	21 44	21 56		22 02	22 14	22 26	22 32
Wandsworth Common	d	20 35				21 05			21 35				22 05			22 35
Balham 4 ⊖	d	20 37	20 49	21 00		21 07	21 19	21 30	21 38	21 49	22 00		22 07	22 19	22 30	22 38
London Bridge	d															
Streatham Common 4	d		20 53	21 04			21 23	21 34		21 53	22 04			22 23	22 34	
Norbury	d		20 56	21 07			21 26	21 37		21 56	22 07			22 26	22 37	
Thornton Heath	d		20 59	21 10			21 29	21 40		21 59	22 10			22 29	22 40	
Selhurst 4	d		21 02	21 13			21 32	21 43		22 02	22 13			22 32	22 43	
East Croydon 🚋	a		21 05				21 35			22 05				22 35		
Purley	a		21 12				21 42			22 12				22 42		
West Croydon 4 🚋	a	21 01		21 18		21 31		21 48	22 01		22 18		22 31		22 48	23 01
Sutton (Surrey) 4	a	21 16		21 31		21 46		22 01	22 16		22 31		22 46		23 01	23 16

		SN	SN	SN 1	SN	SN	SN	SN	SN	SN 1	SN	SN
London Victoria 15 ⊖	d	22 38	22 49		22 54	23 08	23 19	23 24	23 36		23 50	23 54
Battersea Park	d				22 58		23 23	23 28	23 40			23 58
Shepherd's Bush ⊖	d			22 46						23 42		
Kensington (Olympia) ⊖	d			22 48						23 44		
West Brompton ⊖	d			22 51						23 47		
Imperial Wharf	d			22 53						23 49		
Clapham Junction 10	a	22 44	22 55	22 58	23 01	23 14	23 26	23 31	23 43	23 54	23 56	00 01
Clapham Junction	d	22 44	22 56		23 02	23 14	23 27	23 32	23 44	23 54	23 57	00 02
Wandsworth Common	d				23 05		23 30	23 35	23 47		00 01	00 05
Balham 4 ⊖	d	22 49	23 00		23 07	23 19	23 32	23 37	23 49		00 03	00a07
London Bridge	d											
Streatham Common 4	d	22 53	23 04			23 23	23 36		23 53		00 07	
Norbury	d	22 56	23 07			23 26	23 39		23 56		00 09	
Thornton Heath	d	22 59	23 10			23 29	23 42		23 59		00 12	
Selhurst 4	d	23 02	23 13			23 32	23 45		00a01		00 15	
East Croydon 🚋	a	23 05				23 35				00 15	00 18	
Purley	a	23 12				23 45					00 31	
West Croydon 4 🚋	a		23 18		23 31		23 49	00 01				
Sutton (Surrey) 4	a		23 31		23 46		00 02					

For Faster Trains between London Victoria, Clapham Junction and East Croydon, please refer to Table 175

For Faster trains between London Victoria, Clapham Junction and Sutton, please refer to Table 182

For other Shepherds Bush connecting trains, please see Table 176

Table 170R

Mondays to Fridays

9 December to 16 May

Croydon-Selhurst, Thornton Heath, Norbury, Streatham Common, Balham, Wandsworth Common & Battersea Park - London Victoria

Network Diagram - see first Page of Table 170

Miles	Miles	Miles	Miles	Station		SN MO 1	SN MX	SN MO	SN MO 1	SN MX	SN	SN 1	SN	SN 1	SN	SN	SN	SN 1	SN	SN	SN
0	—	—	—	Sutton (Surrey) 4	d												05 49		06 08		
4½	—	—	0	West Croydon 4	d												06 01				
—	0	—	—	Purley	d									05 22		05 41		06 01			
3	—	0	—	East Croydon	d				00 01					05 28	05 34	05 50		06 06		06 18	
5½	4¼	1	1¼	Selhurst 4	d				00 04				05 26	05 31		05 53	06 06	06 10		06 21	
—	5	1	2	Thornton Heath	d								05 28			05 55	06 08			06 23	
2¾	6	3	3¼	Norbury	d			00 01					05 31			05 58	06 11			06 26	
8½	7	4	4	Streatham Common 4	d			00 04					05 34			06 01	06 13			06 29	
—	—	—	10½	London Bridge	a																
10½	9	6	—	Balham 4	d		00 01	00 08		00 22	04 57	05 25	05 38	05 39	05 54	06 05	06 18		06 27	06 33	06 39
11	9½	6½	—	Wandsworth Common	d		00 03	00 10		00 24						06 07	06 20			06 35	06 41
12½	10¾	8	—	Clapham Junction	a		00 06	00 13	00 16	00 28	05 01	05 29	05 42	05 42	05 58	06 11	06 23	06 18	06 31	06 39	06 44
—	—	—	—	Clapham Junction 10	d	00 01	00 07	00 14	00 17	00 28	05 01	05 30	05 42	05 43	05 58	06 11	06 24	06 18	06 31	06 39	06 45
—	—	9¼	—	Imperial Wharf	d							05 39									
—	—	10¼	—	West Brompton	d							05 41									
—	—	11¼	—	Kensington (Olympia)	d							05 44									
—	—	11¾	—	Shepherd's Bush	d							05a47									
13¾	12¼	—	—	Battersea Park	d		00 10	00 17		00 32			05 46		06 02	06 15	06 27			06 43	06 48
15	13½	—	—	London Victoria 15	a	00 07	00 15	00 22	00 24	00 36	05 09		05 51	05 49	06 07	06 19	06 33	06 25	06 38	06 48	06 53

Station		SN	SN	SN	SN	SN	SN	SN	SN	SN	SN	SN	SN	SN	SN	SN	SN
Sutton (Surrey) 4	d	06 15						06 44					07 14		07 22		
West Croydon 4	d	06 27	06 31					06 58	07 01			07 17	07 27	07 31	07 34		
Purley	d																
East Croydon	d					06 45					07 18						07 47
Selhurst 4	d	06 31	06 35		06 43	06 48		07 02	07 05		07 21		07 32	07 35	07 38		07 51
Thornton Heath	d	06 33	06 37		06 45	06 50		07 04	07 07		07 23		07 34	07 37	07 40		07 53
Norbury	d	06 36	06 40		06 48	06 53		07 07	07 10		07 26		07 37	07 40	07 43		07 56
Streatham Common 4	d	06 39	06 43		06 51	06 56		07 10	07 13		07 28		07 39	07 43	07 46		07 59
London Bridge	a		07 10						07 45					08 13			
Balham 4	d	06 43		06 52	06 55	07 00	07 09	07 15		07 25	07 32	07 40	07 44		07 51	07 55	08 03
Wandsworth Common	d	06 45				07 02	07 11	07 17		07 27	07 34	07 43	07 46		07 53	07 57	08 06
Clapham Junction	a	06 48		06 56	06 59	07 06	07 14	07 21		07 31	07 38	07 46	07 50		07 57	08 01	08 09
Clapham Junction 10	d	06 49		06 57	07 00	07 06	07 15	07 21		07 31	07 38	07 47	07 50		07 57	08 01	08 10
Imperial Wharf	d																
West Brompton	d																
Kensington (Olympia)	d																
Shepherd's Bush	d																
Battersea Park	d	06 52				07 10	07 18	07 25		07 35	07 42	07 50	07 54		08 01	08 05	08 13
London Victoria 15	a	07 00		07 06	07 08	07 16	07 25	07 29		07 39	07 48	07 57	07 59		08 07	08 11	08 20

Station		SN	SN	SN	SN	SN	SN	SN	SN 1	SN	SN	SN	SN	SN	SN	SN	SN	SN	SN
Sutton (Surrey) 4	d			07 45	07 59		07 53					08 14	08 29						08 45
West Croydon 4	d	07 47		07 58		08 01	08 05				08 19	08 26		08 31				08 47	08 58
Purley	d		07 40																
East Croydon	d		07 50						08 07	08 17						08 39	08 48		
Selhurst 4	d		07 54	08 02		08 05	08 09		08 13	08 21		08 31		08 35		08 43	08 51		09 02
Thornton Heath	d		07 56	08 04		08 07	08 11		08 16	08 23		08 33		08 37		08 46	08 53		09 04
Norbury	d		07 59	08 07		08 10	08 14		08 20	08 26		08 36		08 40		08 49	08 56		09 07
Streatham Common 4	d		08 02	08 10		08 13	08 17		08 23	08 28		08 39		08 43		08 52	08 59		09 10
London Bridge	a					08 43								09 14					
Balham 4	d	08 10	08 06	08 15	08 19		08 22	08 25	08 28	08 33	08 41	08 44	08 48		08 55	08 58	09 04	09 11	09 15
Wandsworth Common	d	08 12	08 09	08 17				08 27	08 30	08 35	08 43	08 46	08 51		08 57	09 00	09 06	09 13	09 17
Clapham Junction	a	08 16	08 13	08 21	08 24		08 27	08 31	08 36	08 39	08 47	08 50	08 54		09 01	09 04	09 10	09 17	09 21
Clapham Junction 10	d	08 16	08 19	08 21	08 24		08 27	08 31	08 39	08 39	08 47	08 50	08 55		09 01	09 05	09 10	09 17	09 21
Imperial Wharf	d		08 24						08 44							09 09			
West Brompton	d		08 27						08 47							09 12			
Kensington (Olympia)	d		08 31						08 50							09 16			
Shepherd's Bush	d		08a33						08a53							09a18			
Battersea Park	d	08 20		08 25				08 35		08 44	08 51	08 54			09 05		09 14	09 21	09 25
London Victoria 15	a	08 27		08 29	08 32		08 36	08 41		08 52	08 57	08 59	09 04		09 11		09 20	09 27	09 29

Station		SN	SN	SN 1	SN	SN	SN	SN	SN	SN	SN	SN	SN	SN	SN	SN	SN	SN 1	SN
Sutton (Surrey) 4	d					09 03		09 15	09 30	09 23			09 33		09 46	09 52			
West Croydon 4	d	09 01				09 15	09 25	09 28		09 35			09 45	09 55	09 58	10 04			
Purley	d				09 08							09 38							10 08
East Croydon	d			09 08	09 17							09 47						10 10	10 17
Selhurst 4	d	09 05		09 13	09 21		09 30	09 33		09 39		09 51		09 59	10 02	10 09		10 14	10 21
Thornton Heath	d	09 07		09 16	09 23		09 32	09 35		09 41		09 53		10 01	10 04	10 11		10 16	10 23
Norbury	d	09 10		09 19	09 26		09 35	09 38		09 44		09 56		10 04	10 07	10 14		10 19	10 26
Streatham Common 4	d	09 13		09 21	09 29		09 37	09 40		09 47		09 58		10 07	10 10	10 17		10 22	10 28
London Bridge	a	09 43					10 03							10 33					
Balham 4	d		09 25	09 28	09 33	09 41		09 45	09 49	09 52	09 56	10 03	10 09		10 14	10 21	10 25	10 29	10 32
Wandsworth Common	d		09 27	09 30	09 35	09 43		09 47		09 54	09 58	10 05	10 11		10 16	10 23	10 27	10 31	10 34
Clapham Junction	a		09 31	09 34	09 39	09 46		09 50	09 53	09 58	10 02	10 08	10 15		10 20	10 27	10 31	10 35	10 38
Clapham Junction 10	d		09 31	09 39	09 39	09 47		09 51	09 54	09 58	10 02	10 09	10 15		10 20	10 27	10 31	10 39	10 38
Imperial Wharf	d			09 44														10 44	
West Brompton	d			09 47														10 47	
Kensington (Olympia)	d			09 50														10 50	
Shepherd's Bush	d			09a53														10a53	
Battersea Park	d		09 35		09 43	09 50		09 54			10 06	10 12	10 19		10 24		10 35		10 42
London Victoria 15	a		09 42		09 47	09 57		09 59	10 01	10 05	10 11	10 17	10 26		10 28	10 34	10 39		10 46

For Faster Trains between London Victoria, Clapham Junction and East Croydon, please refer to Table 175

For Faster trains between London Victoria, Clapham Junction and Sutton, please refer to Table 182

For other Shepherds Bush connecting trains, please see Table 176

Table 170R

Mondays to Fridays

9 December to 16 May

Croydon-Selhurst, Thornton Heath, Norbury, Streatham Common, Balham, Wandworth Common & Battersea Park - London Victoria

Network Diagram - see first Page of Table 170

Station		SN	SN	SN	SN	SN	SN	SN	SN	SN	SN	SN	SN	SN	SN [1]	SN	SN
Sutton (Surrey) 4	d	10 03		10 15	10 29	10 22			10 33		10 45	10 59	10 52				11 03
West Croydon 4	d	10 15	10 25	10 28		10 34			10 45	10 55	10 58		11 04				11 15
Purley	d							10 38								11 08	
East Croydon	d							10 47							11 11	11 17	
Selhurst 4	d		10 29	10 32		10 39		10 51		10 59	11 02		11 09		11 15	11 21	
Thornton Heath	d		10 31	10 34		10 41		10 53		11 01	11 04		11 11		11 17	11 23	
Norbury	d		10 34	10 37		10 44		10 56		11 04	11 07		11 14		11 20	11 26	
Streatham Common 4	d		10 37	10 40		10 47		10 58		11 07	11 10		11 17		11 23	11 28	
London Bridge	a		11 04							11 34							
Balham 4 ⊖	d	10 39		10 44	10 48	10 51	10 55	11 02	11 09		11 14	11 18	11 21	11 25	11 28	11 32	11 40
Wandsworth Common	d	10 41		10 46		10 53	10 57	11 04	11 11		11 16		11 23	11 27	11 30	11 34	11 42
Clapham Junction	a	10 45		10 49	10 52	10 57	11 01	11 08	11 14		11 20	11 22	11 26	11 32	11 34	11 38	11 45
Clapham Junction 10	d	10 45		10 50	10 53	10 57	11 01	11 08	11 15		11 20	11 23	11 27	11 32	11 39	11 38	11 46
Imperial Wharf	d														11 44		
West Brompton ⊖	d														11 47		
Kensington (Olympia) ⊖	d														11 50		
Shepherd's Bush ⊖	d														11a53		
Battersea Park	d	10 49		10 53			11 05	11 12	11 18		11 24			11 36		11 42	11 49
London Victoria 15 ⊖	a	10 56		10 58	11 00	11 06	11 09	11 16	11 23		11 28	11 30	11 34	11 40		11 46	11 54

Station		SN	SN	SN	SN	SN	SN	SN	SN	SN	SN	SN	SN	SN [1]	SN	SN	SN	SN	SN	SN	SN
Sutton (Surrey) 4	d		11 15	11 29	11 22			11 33		11 45	11 59	11 52				12 03		12 15	12 29	12 22	
West Croydon 4	d	11 25	11 28		11 34			11 45	11 55	11 58		12 04				12 15	12 25	12 28		12 34	
Purley	d						11 38								12 08						
East Croydon	d						11 47							12 10	12 17						
Selhurst 4	d	11 29	11 32		11 39		11 51		11 59	12 02		12 09		12 14	12 21		12 29	12 32		12 39	
Thornton Heath	d	11 31	11 34		11 41		11 53		12 01	12 04		12 11		12 16	12 23		12 31	12 34		12 41	
Norbury	d	11 34	11 37		11 44		11 56		12 04	12 07		12 14		12 19	12 26		12 34	12 37		12 44	
Streatham Common 4	d	11 37	11 40		11 47		11 58		12 07	12 10		12 17		12 22	12 28		12 37	12 40		12 47	
London Bridge	a	12 04							12 34								13 04				
Balham 4 ⊖	d		11 44	11 48	11 51	11 55	12 02	12 09		12 14	12 18	12 21	12 25	12 28	12 32	12 39		12 44	12 48	12 51	12 55
Wandsworth Common	d		11 46		11 53	11 57	12 04	12 11		12 16		12 23	12 27	12 30	12 34	12 41		12 46		12 53	12 57
Clapham Junction	a		11 49	11 52	11 56	12 01	12 08	12 14		12 19	12 22	12 26	12 31	12 34	12 38	12 44		12 49	12 52	12 56	13 01
Clapham Junction 10	d		11 50	11 53	11 57	12 01	12 08	12 15		12 20	12 23	12 27	12 31	12 39	12 38	12 45		12 50	12 53	12 57	13 01
Imperial Wharf	d													12 44							
West Brompton ⊖	d													12 47							
Kensington (Olympia) ⊖	d													12 50							
Shepherd's Bush ⊖	d													12a53							
Battersea Park	d		11 53			12 05	12 12	12 18		12 23			12 35		12 42	12 48		12 53			13 05
London Victoria 15 ⊖	a		11 58	12 00	12 04	12 09	12 16	12 23		12 28	12 30	12 34	12 39		12 46	12 53		12 58	13 00	13 04	13 09

Station		SN	SN	SN	SN	SN	SN	SN	SN [1]	SN	SN	SN	SN	SN	SN	SN	SN
Sutton (Surrey) 4	d		12 33		12 45	12 59	12 52				13 03		13 15	13 29	13 22		
West Croydon 4	d		12 45	12 55	12 58		13 04				13 15	13 25	13 28		13 34		
Purley	d	12 38								13 08							13 38
East Croydon	d	12 47							13 10	13 17							13 47
Selhurst 4	d	12 51		12 59	13 02		13 09		13 13	13 21		13 29	13 32		13 39		13 51
Thornton Heath	d	12 53		13 01	13 04		13 11		13 16	13 23		13 31	13 34		13 41		13 53
Norbury	d	12 56		13 04	13 07		13 14		13 19	13 26		13 34	13 37		13 44		13 56
Streatham Common 4	d	12 58		13 07	13 10		13 17		13 21	13 28		13 37	13 40		13 47		13 58
London Bridge	a			13 34								14 04					
Balham 4 ⊖	d	13 02	13 09		13 14	13 18	13 21	13 25	13 28	13 32	13 39		13 44	13 48	13 51	13 55	14 02
Wandsworth Common	d	13 04	13 11		13 16		13 23	13 27	13 30	13 34	13 41		13 46		13 53	13 57	14 04
Clapham Junction	a	13 08	13 15		13 19	13 22	13 26	13 31	13 34	13 38	13 44		13 49	13 52	13 56	14 01	14 08
Clapham Junction 10	d	13 08	13 15		13 20	13 23	13 27	13 31	13 39	13 38	13 45		13 50	13 53	13 57	14 01	14 08
Imperial Wharf	d								13 44								
West Brompton ⊖	d								13 47								
Kensington (Olympia) ⊖	d								13 50								
Shepherd's Bush ⊖	d								13a53								
Battersea Park	d	13 12	13 19		13 23			13 35		13 42	13 48		13 53			14 05	14 12
London Victoria 15 ⊖	a	13 16	13 24		13 28	13 30	13 36	13 39		13 46	13 53		13 58	14 00	14 04	14 09	14 16

Station		SN	SN	SN	SN	SN	SN	SN [1]	SN	SN	SN	SN	SN	SN	SN	SN	SN	SN	SN	SN	SN
Sutton (Surrey) 4	d	13 33		13 45	13 59	13 52				14 03		14 15	14 29	14 22			14 33		14 45	14 59	14 52
West Croydon 4	d	13 45	13 55	13 58		14 04				14 15	14 25	14 28		14 34			14 45	14 55	14 58		15 04
Purley	d								14 08							14 38					
East Croydon	d							14 10	14 17							14 47					
Selhurst 4	d		13 59	14 02		14 09		14 13	14 21		14 29	14 32		14 39		14 51		14 59	15 02		15 09
Thornton Heath	d		14 01	14 04		14 11		14 16	14 23		14 31	14 34		14 41		14 53		15 01	15 04		15 11
Norbury	d		14 04	14 07		14 14		14 19	14 26		14 34	14 37		14 44		14 56		15 04	15 07		15 14
Streatham Common 4	d		14 07	14 10		14 17		14 21	14 28		14 37	14 40		14 47		14 58		15 07	15 10		15 17
London Bridge	a		14 34								15 04							15 33			
Balham 4 ⊖	d	14 09		14 14	14 18	14 21	14 25	14 28	14 32	14 39		14 44	14 48	14 51	14 55	15 02	15 09		15 14	15 18	15 22
Wandsworth Common	d	14 11		14 16		14 23	14 27	14 30	14 34	14 41		14 46		14 53	14 57	15 04	15 11		15 16		15 24
Clapham Junction	a	14 14		14 19	14 22	14 26	14 31	14 34	14 38	14 44		14 49	14 52	14 56	15 01	15 08	15 14		15 19	15 22	15 28
Clapham Junction 10	d	14 15		14 20	14 23	14 27	14 31	14 39	14 38	14 45		14 50	14 53	14 57	15 01	15 08	15 15		15 20	15 23	15 28
Imperial Wharf	d							14 44													
West Brompton ⊖	d							14 47													
Kensington (Olympia) ⊖	d							14 50													
Shepherd's Bush ⊖	d							14a53													
Battersea Park	d	14 18		14 23			14 35		14 42	14 48		14 53			15 05	15 12	15 18		15 23		
London Victoria 15 ⊖	a	14 23		14 28	14 30	14 34	14 39		14 46	14 53		14 58	15 00	15 04	15 09	15 16	15 24		15 28	15 30	15 36

For Faster Trains between London Victoria, Clapham Junction and East Croydon, please refer to Table 175

For Faster trains between London Victoria, Clapham Junction and Sutton, please refer to Table 182

For other Shepherds Bush connecting trains, please see Table 176

Table 170R

Mondays to Fridays
9 December to 16 May

Croydon-Selhurst, Thornton Heath, Norbury, Streatham Common, Balham, Wandworth Common & Battersea Park - London Victoria

Network Diagram - see first Page of Table 170

		SN	SN 1	SN	SN	SN	SN	SN	SN	SN	SN	SN	SN	SN	SN	SN	SN
Sutton (Surrey) 4	d				15 03		15 15	15 29	15 22			15 33		15 45	15 59	15 52	
West Croydon 4	d				15 15	15 25	15 28		15 34			15 45	15 55	15 58		16 04	
Purley	d			15 08							15 38						
East Croydon	d		15 10	15 17							15 47						
Selhurst 4	d		15 13	15 21		15 29	15 32		15 39		15 51		15 59	16 02		16 09	
Thornton Heath	d		15 16	15 23		15 31	15 34		15 41		15 53		16 01	16 04		16 11	
Norbury	d		15 19	15 26		15 34	15 37		15 44		15 56		16 04	16 07		16 14	
Streatham Common 4	d		15 21	15 28		15 37	15 40		15 47		15 58		16 07	16 10		16 17	
London Bridge	a					16 03							16 33				
Balham 4	d	15 25	15 29	15 32	15 39		15 44	15 48	15 51	15 55	16 02	16 09		16 14	16 18	16 21	16 25
Wandsworth Common	d	15 27	15 31	15 34	15 41		15 46		15 53	15 57	16 04	16 11		16 16		16 23	16 27
Clapham Junction	a	15 31	15 35	15 38	15 44		15 49	15 52	15 56	16 01	16 08	16 14		16 19	16 23	16 26	16 31
Clapham Junction 10	d	15 31	15 39	15 38	15 45		15 50	15 53	15 57	16 01	16 08	16 15		16 20	16 23	16 27	16 31
Imperial Wharf	d		15 44														
West Brompton	d		15 47														
Kensington (Olympia)	d		15 50														
Shepherd's Bush	d		15a53														
Battersea Park	d	15 35		15 42	15 49		15 53			16 05	16 12	16 18		16 23			16 35
London Victoria 15	a	15 39		15 46	15 54		15 58	16 00	16 04	16 10	16 16	16 23		16 28	16 30	16 34	16 40

		SN 1	SN	SN	SN	SN	SN	SN	SN	SN	SN	SN	SN	SN	SN	SN	SN 1	SN	SN	SN	SN
Sutton (Surrey) 4	d			16 03	16 13		16 29	16 22			16 33	16 42		16 59	16 52				17 03	17 13	
West Croydon 4	d			16 15	16 25	16 28		16 34			16 45	16 55	16 58		17 04				17 17	17 25	17 28
Purley	d		16 08							16 38								17 08			
East Croydon	d	16 10	16 17							16 47							17 10	17 17			
Selhurst 4	d	16 13	16 21		16 30	16 33		16 39		16 50		16 59	17 02		17 09		17 13	17 20		17 29	17 32
Thornton Heath	d	16 16	16 23		16 32	16 35		16 41		16 52		17 01	17 04		17 11		17 16	17 22		17 31	17 34
Norbury	d	16 19	16 26		16 35	16 38		16 44		16 55		17 04	17 07		17 14		17 19	17 25		17 34	17 37
Streatham Common 4	d	16 21	16 28		16 37	16 40		16 47		16 58		17 07	17 10		17 17		17 21	17 28		17 37	17 40
London Bridge	a					17 04							17 34								18 04
Balham 4	d	16 28	16 32	16 39	16 42		16 48	16 51	16 55	17 02	17 09	17 14		17 19	17 22	17 25	17 28	17 32	17 39	17 44	
Wandsworth Common	d	16 30	16 34	16 41	16 44			16 53	16 57	17 04	17 11	17 16			17 24	17 27	17 30	17 34	17 41	17 46	
Clapham Junction	a	16 34	16 38	16 45	16 48		16 53	16 56	17 01	17 07	17 14	17 19		17 23	17 27	17 31	17 34	17 37	17 44	17 49	
Clapham Junction 10	d	16 39	16 38	16 45	16 48		16 53	16 57	17 01	17 08	17 15	17 20		17 24	17 28	17 31	17 39	17 38	17 45	17 50	
Imperial Wharf	d	16 44															17 44				
West Brompton	d	16 47															17 47				
Kensington (Olympia)	d	16 50															17 50				
Shepherd's Bush	d	16a53															17a53				
Battersea Park	d		16 42	16 49	16 52				17 05	17 11	17 18	17 23				17 35		17 41	17 48	17 53	
London Victoria 15	a		16 46	16 53	16 58		17 00	17 04	17 10	17 16	17 23	17 28		17 31	17 35	17 42		17 48	17 55	17 58	

		SN	SN	SN	SN	SN	SN	SN 1	SN	SN	SN	SN	SN	SN	SN	SN	SN
Sutton (Surrey) 4	d			17 33	17 43					18 03	18 12				18 33	18 43	
West Croydon 4	d			17 48	17 55	17 58				18 15	18 26	18 29			18 45	18 56	18 59
Purley	d		17 38						18 08					18 37			
East Croydon	d		17 47					18 10	18 17					18 47			
Selhurst 4	d		17 50		17 59	18 02		18 13	18 20		18 30	18 33		18 51		19 00	19 03
Thornton Heath	d		17 52		18 01	18 04		18 16	18 22		18 32	18 35		18 53		19 02	19 05
Norbury	d		17 55		18 04	18 07		18 19	18 25		18 35	18 38		18 56		19 05	19 08
Streatham Common 4	d		17 58		18 07	18 10		18 21	18 28		18 38	18 41		18 58		19 08	19 11
London Bridge	a					18 34						19 04					19 34
Balham 4	d	17 56	18 02	18 11	18 14		18 25	18 29	18 33	18 40	18 44		18 55	19 02	19 09	19 14	
Wandsworth Common	d	17 58	18 04	18 13	18 16		18 27	18 31	18 35	18 42	18 46		18 57	19 04	19 11	19 16	
Clapham Junction	a	18 02	18 08	18 16	18 19		18 31	18 35	18 39	18 45	18 49		19 01	19 08	19 14	19 19	
Clapham Junction 10	d	18 02	18 08	18 17	18 20		18 32	18 39	18 39	18 46	18 50		19 01	19 08	19 15	19 20	
Imperial Wharf	d							18 44									
West Brompton	d							18 47									
Kensington (Olympia)	d							18 50									
Shepherd's Bush	d							18a53									
Battersea Park	d	18 06	18 12	18 20	18 23		18 35			18 49			19 05		19 18	19 23	
London Victoria 15	a	18 12	18 16	18 25	18 28		18 41		18 46	18 54	18 57		19 12	19 15	19 25	19 28	

		SN	SN 1	SN	SN	SN	SN	SN	SN	SN	SN	SN	SN	SN	SN	SN	SN	SN	SN	SN	SN
Sutton (Surrey) 4	d					19 16				19 46				20 23	20 36			20 33		20 52	21 06
West Croydon 4	d				19 26	19 29			19 57	19 59			20 26	20 35				20 45	20 55	21 04	
Purley	d			19 08				19 38				20 08					20 38				
East Croydon	d		19 10	19 17				19 47				20 17					20 47				
Selhurst 4	d		19 13	19 20	19 30	19 33		19 50	20 01	20 03		20 20	20 30	20 39			20 50		20 59	21 09	
Thornton Heath	d		19 16	19 22	19 32	19 35		19 52	20 03	20 05		20 22	20 32	20 41			20 52		21 01	21 11	
Norbury	d		19 19	19 25	19 35	19 38		19 55	20 06	20 08		20 25	20 35	20 44			20 55		21 04	21 14	
Streatham Common 4	d		19 21	19 28	19 38	19 41		19 58	20 08	20 11		20 28	20 38	20 47			20 58		21 07	21 17	
London Bridge	a				20 04				20 33				21 03						21 33		
Balham 4	d	19 25	19 28	19 32		19 46	19 55	20 02		20 15	20 25	20 32		20 51	20 54	20 56	21 02	21 08		21 21	21 24
Wandsworth Common	d	19 27	19 30	19 34		19 48	19 57	20 04		20 17	20 27	20 34		20 53		20 58	21 04	21 10		21 23	
Clapham Junction	a	19 31	19 34	19 37		19 51	20 01	20 07		20 20	20 31	20 37		20 56	20 59	21 02	21 07	21 14		21 26	21 29
Clapham Junction 10	d	19 31	19 39	19 38		19 52	20 01	20 08		20 21	20 31	20 38		20 57	21 00	21 03	21 08	21 14		21 27	21 30
Imperial Wharf	d		19 44																		
West Brompton	d		19 47																		
Kensington (Olympia)	d		19 50																		
Shepherd's Bush	d		19a53																		
Battersea Park	d	19 35		19 41		19 55	20 05	20 11		20 24	20 35	20 41				21 06	21 11	21 18			
London Victoria 15	a	19 41		19 48		20 00	20 09	20 18		20 29	20 39	20 46		21 04	21 09	21 11	21 18	21 22		21 34	21 37

For Faster Trains between London Victoria, Clapham Junction and East Croydon, please refer to Table 175

For Faster trains between London Victoria, Clapham Junction and Sutton, please refer to Table 182

For other Shepherds Bush connecting trains, please see Table 176

Table 170R

Mondays to Fridays

9 December to 16 May

Croydon-Selhurst, Thornton Heath, Norbury, Streatham Common, Balham, Wandworth Common & Battersea Park - London Victoria

Network Diagram - see first Page of Table 170

		SN	SN	SN	SN	SN	SN	SN	SN	SN	SN	SN	SN	SN	SN
Sutton (Surrey) 4	d			21 06		21 22	21 36			21 32		21 52	22 06		
West Croydon 4	d			21 18	21 25	21 34				21 47	21 55	22 04			
Purley	d		21 08						21 38						22 08
East Croydon	d		21 17						21 47						22 17
Selhurst 4	d		21 20		21 29	21 39			21 50		21 59	22 09			22 20
Thornton Heath	d		21 22		21 31	21 41			21 52		22 01	22 11			22 22
Norbury	d		21 25		21 34	21 44			21 55		22 04	22 14			22 25
Streatham Common 4	d		21 28		21 37	21 47			21 58		22 07	22 17			22 28
London Bridge	a				22 03						22 33				
Balham 4 ⊖	d	21 26	21 32	21 39		21 51	21 54	21 56	22 02	22 09		22 21	22 24	22 26	22 32
Wandsworth Common	d	21 28	21 34	21 41		21 53		21 58	22 04	22 11		22 23		22 28	22 34
Clapham Junction	a	21 32	21 37	21 44		21 56	21 59	22 02	22 07	22 14		22 26	22 29	22 32	22 37
Clapham Junction 10	d	21 33	21 38	21 45		21 57	22 00	22 03	22 08	22 15		22 27	22 30	22 33	22 38
Imperial Wharf	d														
West Brompton ⊖	d														
Kensington (Olympia) ⊖	d														
Shepherd's Bush ⊖	d														
Battersea Park	d	21 36	21 41	21 48				22 06	22 11	22 18				22 36	22 41
London Victoria 15 ⊖	a	21 41	21 48	21 53		22 04	22 07	22 11	22 18	22 23		22 34	22 38	22 41	22 48

		SN	SN	SN	SN	SN	SN	SN	SN	SN	SN	SN FX	SN FO	SN	SN
Sutton (Surrey) 4	d	22 05		22 22	22 36			22 32		22 52	23 06				23 06
West Croydon 4	d	22 17	22 25	22 34				22 47	22 55	23 04					23 18
Purley	d						22 38							23 08	
East Croydon	d						22 47							23 17	
Selhurst 4	d		22 29	22 39			22 50		22 59	23 09				23 20	
Thornton Heath	d		22 31	22 41			22 52		23 01	23 11				23 22	
Norbury	d		22 34	22 44			22 55		23 04	23 14				23 25	
Streatham Common 4	d		22 37	22 47			22 58		23 07	23 17				23 28	
London Bridge	a		23 03						23 33						
Balham 4 ⊖	d	22 39		22 51	22 54	22 56	23 02	23 09		23 21	23 24	23 26	23 26	23 32	23 40
Wandsworth Common	d	22 41		22 53		22 58	23 04	23 11		23 23		23 28	23 28	23 34	23 42
Clapham Junction	a	22 44		22 56	22 59	23 02	23 07	23 15		23 26	23 29	23 32	23 32	23 37	23 45
Clapham Junction 10	d	22 45		22 57	23 00	23 03	23 08	23 15		23 27	23 30	23 33	23 33	23 38	23 46
Imperial Wharf	d														
West Brompton ⊖	d														
Kensington (Olympia) ⊖	d														
Shepherd's Bush ⊖	d														
Battersea Park	d	22 48				23 07	23 11	23 19				23 37	23 37	23 41	23 49
London Victoria 15 ⊖	a	22 53		23 06	23 09	23 11	23 18	23 25		23 34	23 37	23 41	23 44	23 48	23 54

Saturdays

14 December to 17 May

		SN	SN	SN 1	SN	SN	SN 1	SN	SN	SN	SN	SN	SN
Sutton (Surrey) 4	d											06 45	06 59
West Croydon 4	d							06 18		06 45	06 55	06 58	
Purley	d								06 38				
East Croydon	d						06 10		06 47				
Selhurst 4	d					06 01	06 13		06 51		07 00	07 02	
Thornton Heath	d					06 03	06 16		06 53		07 02	07 04	
Norbury	d					06 06	06 19		06 56		07 05	07 07	
Streatham Common 4	d					06 08	06 21		06 58		07 07	07 10	
London Bridge	a										07 33		
Balham 4 ⊖	d	00 01	00 22	05 33	06 09	06 12	06 28	06 39	07 02	07 09		07 14	07 18
Wandsworth Common	d	00 03	00 24		06 11	06 14	06 30	06 41	07 04	07 11		07 16	
Clapham Junction	a	00 06	00 28	05 37	06 14	06 18	06 34	06 44	07 08	07 14		07 19	07 22
Clapham Junction 10	d	00 07	00 28	05 38	06 15	06 18	06 36	06 45	07 08	07 15		07 20	07 23
Imperial Wharf	d			05 42			06 41						
West Brompton ⊖	d			05 45			06 44						
Kensington (Olympia) ⊖	d			05 49			06 47						
Shepherd's Bush ⊖	d			05a51			06a50						
Battersea Park	d	00 10	00 32		06 18	06 22		06 48	07 12	07 19		07 23	
London Victoria 15 ⊖	a	00 15	00 36		06 23	06 26		06 53	07 16	07 24		07 28	07 30

		SN 1	SN	SN	SN	SN	SN	SN	SN	SN	SN	SN	SN
Sutton (Surrey) 4	d					07 15	07 29						07 45
West Croydon 4	d			07 25		07 28					07 55		07 58
Purley	d		07 08							07 38			
East Croydon	d	07 10	07 17							07 47			
Selhurst 4	d	07 13	07 20	07 30		07 32		07 39		07 50	08 00		08 02
Thornton Heath	d	07 16	07 22	07 32		07 34		07 41		07 52	08 02		08 04
Norbury	d	07 19	07 25	07 35		07 37		07 44		07 55	08 05		08 07
Streatham Common 4	d	07 21	07 28	07 37		07 40		07 47		07 58	08 07		08 10
London Bridge	a			08 03							08 33		
Balham 4 ⊖	d	07 28	07 32		07 39	07 44	07 48	07 51	07 55	08 02		08 09	08 14
Wandsworth Common	d	07 30	07 34		07 41	07 46		07 53	07 57	08 04		08 11	08 16
Clapham Junction	a	07 34	07 37		07 44	07 49	07 52	07 56	08 01	08 07		08 14	08 19
Clapham Junction 10	d	07 39	07 38		07 45	07 50	07 53	07 57	08 01	08 08		08 15	08 20
Imperial Wharf	d	07 44											
West Brompton ⊖	d	07 47											
Kensington (Olympia) ⊖	d	07 50											
Shepherd's Bush ⊖	d	07a53											
Battersea Park	d		07 41		07 48	07 53			08 05	08 11		08 18	08 23
London Victoria 15 ⊖	a		07 46		07 53	07 58	08 00	08 04	08 09	08 16		08 23	08 28

		SN	SN	SN	SN 1	SN	SN	SN	SN	SN	SN	SN	SN
Sutton (Surrey) 4	d	07 59					08 03		08 15	08 29	08 22		
West Croydon 4	d						08 15	08 25	08 28		08 34		
Purley	d					08 08							08 38
East Croydon	d				08 10	08 17							08 47
Selhurst 4	d		08 09		08 13	08 20		08 30	08 32		08 39		08 50
Thornton Heath	d		08 11		08 16	08 22		08 32	08 34		08 41		08 52
Norbury	d		08 14		08 19	08 25		08 35	08 37		08 44		08 55
Streatham Common 4	d		08 17		08 21	08 28		08 37	08 40		08 47		08 58
London Bridge	a							09 03					
Balham 4 ⊖	d	08 18	08 21	08 25	08 28	08 32	08 39		08 44	08 48	08 51	08 55	09 02
Wandsworth Common	d		08 23	08 27	08 30	08 34	08 41		08 46		08 53	08 57	09 04
Clapham Junction	a	08 22	08 26	08 31	08 34	08 37	08 44		08 49	08 52	08 56	09 01	09 07
Clapham Junction 10	d	08 23	08 27	08 31	08 39	08 38	08 45		08 50	08 53	08 57	09 01	09 08
Imperial Wharf	d				08 44								
West Brompton ⊖	d				08 47								
Kensington (Olympia) ⊖	d				08 50								
Shepherd's Bush ⊖	d				08a53								
Battersea Park	d			08 35		08 41	08 48		08 53			09 05	09 11
London Victoria 15 ⊖	a	08 30	08 34	08 39		08 46	08 53		08 58	09 00	09 04	09 09	09 16

For Faster Trains between London Victoria, Clapham Junction and East Croydon, please refer to Table 175

For Faster trains between London Victoria, Clapham Junction and Sutton, please refer to Table 182

For other Shepherds Bush connecting trains, please see Table 176

Table 170R

Saturdays

14 December to 17 May

Croydon-Selhurst, Thornton Heath, Norbury, Streatham Common, Balham, Wandworth Common & Battersea Park - London Victoria

Network Diagram - see first Page of Table 170

		SN	SN	SN	SN	SN	SN	SN 1	SN	SN	SN	SN	SN	SN	SN	SN	SN	SN	SN	SN	SN	SN
Sutton (Surrey) 4	d	08 33		08 45	08 59	08 52				09 03		09 15	09 29	09 22			09 33		09 45	09 59	09 52	
West Croydon 4	d	08 45	08 55	08 58		09 04				09 15	09 25	09 28		09 34			09 45	09 55	09 58		10 04	
Purley	d								09 08							09 38						
East Croydon	d							09 10	09 17							09 47						
Selhurst 4	d		09 00	09 02		09 09		09 13	09 20		09 30	09 32		09 39		09 50		10 00	10 02		10 09	
Thornton Heath	d		09 02	09 04		09 11		09 16	09 22		09 32	09 34		09 41		09 52		10 02	10 04		10 11	
Norbury	d		09 05	09 07		09 14		09 19	09 25		09 35	09 37		09 44		09 55		10 05	10 07		10 14	
Streatham Common 4	d		09 07	09 10		09 17		09 21	09 28		09 37	09 40		09 47		09 58		10 07	10 10		10 17	
London Bridge	a		09 33								10 03							10 33				
Balham 4 ⊖	d	09 09		09 14	09 18	09 21	09 25	09 28	09 32	09 39		09 44	09 48	09 51	09 55	10 02	10 09		10 14	10 18	10 21	10 25
Wandsworth Common	d	09 11		09 16		09 23	09 27	09 30	09 34	09 41		09 46		09 53	09 57	10 04	10 11		10 16		10 23	10 27
Clapham Junction	a	09 14		09 19	09 22	09 26	09 32	09 34	09 37	09 44		09 49	09 52	09 56	10 01	10 07	10 14		10 19	10 22	10 26	10 31
Clapham Junction 10	d	09 15		09 20	09 23	09 27	09 33	09 39	09 38	09 45		09 50	09 53	09 57	10 01	10 08	10 15		10 20	10 23	10 27	10 31
Imperial Wharf	d							09 44														
West Brompton ⊖	d							09 47														
Kensington (Olympia) ⊖	d							09 50														
Shepherd's Bush ⊖	d							09a53														
Battersea Park	d	09 18		09 23			09 36		09 41	09 48		09 53			10 05	10 11	10 18		10 23			10 35
London Victoria 15 ⊖	a	09 23		09 28	09 30	09 34	09 41		09 46	09 53		09 58	10 00	10 04	10 09	10 16	10 23		10 28	10 30	10 34	10 39

			SN 1	SN	SN	SN	SN	SN	SN	SN	SN	SN	SN	SN	SN	SN	SN	SN 1
Sutton (Surrey) 4	d	and at the same minutes past each hour until			16 03		16 15	16 29	16 22			16 33		16 45	16 59	16 52		
West Croydon 4	d				16 15	16 25	16 28		16 34			16 45	16 55	16 58		17 04		
Purley	d			16 08							16 38							
East Croydon	d		16 10	16 17							16 47							17 10
Selhurst 4	d		16 13	16 20		16 30	16 32		16 39		16 50		17 00	17 02		17 09		17 13
Thornton Heath	d		16 16	16 22		16 32	16 34		16 41		16 52		17 02	17 04		17 11		17 16
Norbury	d		16 19	16 25		16 35	16 37		16 44		16 55		17 05	17 07		17 14		17 19
Streatham Common 4	d		16 21	16 28		16 37	16 40		16 47		16 58		17 07	17 10		17 17		17 21
London Bridge	a					17 03							17 33					
Balham 4 ⊖	d		16 28	16 32	16 39		16 44	16 48	16 51	16 55	17 02	17 09		17 14	17 18	17 21	17 25	17 28
Wandsworth Common	d		16 30	16 34	16 41		16 46		16 53	16 57	17 04	17 11		17 16		17 23	17 27	17 30
Clapham Junction	a		16 34	16 37	16 44		16 49	16 52	16 56	17 01	17 07	17 14		17 19	17 22	17 26	17 31	17 34
Clapham Junction 10	d		16 39	16 38	16 45		16 50	16 53	16 57	17 01	17 08	17 15		17 20	17 23	17 27	17 31	17 39
Imperial Wharf	d		16 44															17 44
West Brompton ⊖	d		16 47															17 47
Kensington (Olympia) ⊖	d		16 50															17 50
Shepherd's Bush ⊖	d		16a53															17a53
Battersea Park	d			16 41	16 48		16 53			17 05	17 11	17 18		17 23			17 35	
London Victoria 15 ⊖	a			16 46	16 53		16 58	17 00	17 04	17 09	17 16	17 23		17 28	17 30	17 34	17 39	

		SN	SN	SN	SN	SN	SN	SN	SN	SN	SN	SN	SN	SN	SN	SN 1	SN	SN	SN
Sutton (Surrey) 4	d		17 03		17 15	17 29	17 22			17 33		17 45	17 59	17 52				18 03	
West Croydon 4	d		17 15	17 25	17 28		17 34			17 45	17 55	17 58		18 04				18 15	18 25
Purley	d	17 08							17 38								18 08		
East Croydon	d	17 17							17 47							18 10	18 17		
Selhurst 4	d	17 20		17 30	17 32		17 39		17 50		18 00	18 02		18 09		18 13	18 20		18 30
Thornton Heath	d	17 22		17 32	17 34		17 41		17 52		18 02	18 04		18 11		18 16	18 22		18 32
Norbury	d	17 25		17 35	17 37		17 44		17 55		18 05	18 07		18 14		18 19	18 25		18 35
Streatham Common 4	d	17 28		17 37	17 40		17 47		17 58		18 07	18 10		18 17		18 21	18 28		18 37
London Bridge	a			18 03							18 33								19 03
Balham 4 ⊖	d	17 33	17 39		17 44	17 48	17 51	17 55	18 02	18 09		18 14	18 18	18 21	18 25	18 28	18 32	18 39	
Wandsworth Common	d	17 35	17 41		17 46		17 53	17 57	18 04	18 11		18 16		18 23	18 27	18 30	18 34	18 41	
Clapham Junction	a	17 38	17 44		17 49	17 52	17 56	18 01	18 07	18 14		18 19	18 22	18 26	18 31	18 34	18 37	18 44	
Clapham Junction 10	d	17 39	17 45		17 50	17 53	17 57	18 01	18 08	18 15		18 20	18 23	18 27	18 31	18 39	18 38	18 45	
Imperial Wharf	d															18 44			
West Brompton ⊖	d															18 47			
Kensington (Olympia) ⊖	d															18 50			
Shepherd's Bush ⊖	d															18a53			
Battersea Park	d	17 42	17 48		17 53			18 05	18 11	18 18		18 23			18 35		18 41	18 48	
London Victoria 15 ⊖	a	17 47	17 53		17 58	18 00	18 04	18 09	18 16	18 23		18 28	18 30	18 34	18 39		18 46	18 53	

		SN	SN	SN	SN	SN	SN	SN	SN	SN	SN	SN	SN 1	SN	SN	SN	SN	SN	SN
Sutton (Surrey) 4	d	18 15	18 29	18 22			18 33		18 45	18 59	18 52				19 03		19 15	19 29	19 22
West Croydon 4	d	18 28		18 34			18 45	18 55	18 58		19 04				19 15	19 25	19 28		19 34
Purley	d					18 38								19 08					
East Croydon	d					18 47							19 10	19 17					
Selhurst 4	d	18 32		18 39		18 50		19 00	19 02		19 09		19 13	19 20		19 30	19 32		19 39
Thornton Heath	d	18 34		18 41		18 52		19 02	19 04		19 11		19 16	19 22		19 32	19 34		19 41
Norbury	d	18 37		18 44		18 55		19 05	19 07		19 14		19 19	19 25		19 35	19 37		19 44
Streatham Common 4	d	18 40		18 47		18 58		19 07	19 10		19 17		19 21	19 28		19 37	19 40		19 47
London Bridge	a							19 33								20 03			
Balham 4 ⊖	d	18 44	18 48	18 51	18 55	19 02	19 09		19 14	19 18	19 21	19 25	19 28	19 32	19 39		19 44	19 48	19 51
Wandsworth Common	d	18 46		18 53	18 57	19 04	19 11		19 16		19 23	19 27	19 30	19 34	19 41		19 46		19 53
Clapham Junction	a	18 49	18 52	18 56	19 01	19 07	19 14		19 19	19 22	19 26	19 31	19 34	19 37	19 44		19 49	19 52	19 56
Clapham Junction 10	d	18 50	18 53	18 57	19 01	19 08	19 15		19 20	19 23	19 27	19 31	19 38	19 38	19 45		19 50	19 53	19 57
Imperial Wharf	d												19 42						
West Brompton ⊖	d												19 45						
Kensington (Olympia) ⊖	d												19 48						
Shepherd's Bush ⊖	d												19a50						
Battersea Park	d	18 53			19 05	19 11	19 18		19 23			19 35		19 41	19 48		19 53		
London Victoria 15 ⊖	a	18 58	19 00	19 04	19 09	19 16	19 23		19 28	19 30	19 34	19 39		19 46	19 53		19 58	20 00	20 04

For Faster Trains between London Victoria, Clapham Junction and East Croydon, please refer to Table 175

For Faster trains between London Victoria, Clapham Junction and Sutton, please refer to Table 182

For other Shepherds Bush connecting trains, please see Table 176

Table 170R

Saturdays

14 December to 17 May

Croydon-Selhurst, Thornton Heath, Norbury, Streatham Common, Balham, Wandworth Common & Battersea Park - London Victoria

Network Diagram - see first Page of Table 170

		SN	SN	SN	SN	SN	SN	SN	SN	SN	SN	SN	SN	SN	SN	SN	SN	SN
Sutton (Surrey) 4	d			19 33		19 45	19 59	19 52			20 03		20 15	20 29	20 22			20 33
West Croydon 4	d			19 45	19 55	19 58		20 04			20 15	20 25	20 28		20 34			20 45
Purley	d		19 38							20 08							20 38	
East Croydon	d		19 47							20 17							20 47	
Selhurst 4	d		19 50		20 00	20 02		20 09		20 20		20 30	20 32		20 39		20 50	
Thornton Heath	d		19 52		20 02	20 04		20 11		20 22		20 32	20 34		20 41		20 52	
Norbury	d		19 55		20 05	20 07		20 14		20 25		20 35	20 37		20 44		20 55	
Streatham Common 4	d		19 58		20 07	20 10		20 17		20 28		20 37	20 40		20 47		20 58	
London Bridge	a				20 33							21 03						
Balham 4 ⊖	d	19 55	20 02	20 09		20 14	20 18	20 21	20 25	20 32	20 39		20 44	20 48	20 51	20 55	21 02	21 09
Wandsworth Common	d	19 57	20 04	20 11		20 16		20 23	20 27	20 34	20 41		20 46		20 53	20 57	21 04	21 11
Clapham Junction	a	20 01	20 07	20 14		20 19	20 22	20 26	20 31	20 37	20 44		20 49	20 52	20 56	21 01	21 07	21 14
Clapham Junction 10	d	20 01	20 08	20 15		20 20	20 23	20 27	20 31	20 38	20 45		20 50	20 53	20 57	21 01	21 08	21 15
Imperial Wharf	d																	
West Brompton ⊖	d																	
Kensington (Olympia) ⊖	d																	
Shepherd's Bush ⊖	d																	
Battersea Park	d	20 05	20 11	20 18		20 23			20 35	20 41	20 48		20 53			21 05	21 11	21 18
London Victoria 15 ⊖	a	20 09	20 16	20 23		20 28	20 30	20 34	20 39	20 46	20 53		20 58	21 00	21 04	21 09	21 16	21 23

		SN	SN	SN	SN	SN	SN	SN	SN	SN	SN	SN	SN	SN	SN	SN	SN	SN	SN	SN
Sutton (Surrey) 4	d		20 45	20 59	20 52			21 03		21 15	21 29	21 22			21 33		21 45	21 59	21 52	
West Croydon 4	d	20 55	20 58		21 04			21 15	21 25	21 28		21 34			21 45	21 55	21 58		22 04	
Purley	d						21 08							21 38						
East Croydon	d						21 17							21 47						
Selhurst 4	d	21 00	21 02		21 09		21 20		21 30	21 32		21 39		21 50		22 00	22 02		22 10	
Thornton Heath	d	21 02	21 04		21 11		21 22		21 32	21 34		21 41		21 52		22 02	22 04		22 12	
Norbury	d	21 05	21 07		21 14		21 25		21 35	21 37		21 44		21 55		22 05	22 07		22 15	
Streatham Common 4	d	21 07	21 10		21 17		21 28		21 37	21 40		21 47		21 58		22 07	22 10		22 17	
London Bridge	a	21 33							22 03							22 33				
Balham 4 ⊖	d		21 14	21 18	21 21	21 25	21 32	21 39		21 44	21 48	21 51	21 55	22 02	22 09		22 14	22 18	22 22	22 25
Wandsworth Common	d		21 16		21 23	21 27	21 34	21 41		21 46		21 53	21 57	22 04	22 11		22 16		22 24	22 27
Clapham Junction	a		21 19	21 22	21 26	21 31	21 37	21 44		21 49	21 52	21 56	22 01	22 07	22 14		22 19	22 22	22 27	22 31
Clapham Junction 10	d		21 20	21 23	21 27	21 31	21 38	21 45		21 50	21 53	21 57	22 01	22 08	22 15		22 20	22 23	22 27	22 31
Imperial Wharf	d																			
West Brompton ⊖	d																			
Kensington (Olympia) ⊖	d																			
Shepherd's Bush ⊖	d																			
Battersea Park	d		21 23			21 35	21 41	21 48		21 53			22 05	22 11	22 18		22 23			22 35
London Victoria 15 ⊖	a		21 28	21 30	21 34	21 39	21 46	21 53		21 58	22 00	22 04	22 09	22 16	22 23		22 28	22 30	22 34	22 39

		SN	SN	SN	SN	SN	SN	SN	SN	SN	SN	SN	SN	SN	SN	SN	SN	SN	SN	SN
Sutton (Surrey) 4	d		22 03		22 15	22 29	22 22			22 33		22 45	22 59	22 52			23 03	23 15	23 22	
West Croydon 4	d		22 15	22 25	22 28		22 34			22 45	22 55	22 58		23 04			23 15	23 28	23 34	
Purley	d	22 08							22 38							23 08				
East Croydon	d	22 17							22 47							23 17				
Selhurst 4	d	22 20		22 30	22 32		22 39		22 50		23 00	23 02		23 09		23 20		23 32	23 39	
Thornton Heath	d	22 22		22 32	22 34		22 41		22 52		23 02	23 04		23 11		23 22		23 34	23 41	
Norbury	d	22 25		22 35	22 37		22 44		22 55		23 05	23 07		23 14		23 25		23 37	23 44	
Streatham Common 4	d	22 28		22 37	22 40		22 47		22 58		23 07	23 10		23 17		23 28		23 40	23 46	
London Bridge	a			23 03							23 33									
Balham 4 ⊖	d	22 32	22 39		22 44	22 48	22 51	22 55	23 02	23 09		23 14	23 18	23 21	23 25	23 32	23 39	23 44	23 50	23 55
Wandsworth Common	d	22 34	22 41		22 46		22 53	22 57	23 04	23 11		23 16		23 23	23 27	23 34	23 41	23 46	23 52	23 57
Clapham Junction	a	22 37	22 44		22 49	22 52	22 56	23 01	23 07	23 16		23 20	23 23	23 26	23 31	23 37	23 45	23 49	23 56	00 01
Clapham Junction 10	d	22 38	22 45		22 50	22 53	22 57	23 01	23 08	23 16		23 20	23 23	23 27	23 31	23 38	23 45	23 50	23 56	00 02
Imperial Wharf	d																			
West Brompton ⊖	d																			
Kensington (Olympia) ⊖	d																			
Shepherd's Bush ⊖	d																			
Battersea Park	d	22 41	22 48		22 53			23 05	23 11	23 20		23 24			23 35	23 41	23 49	23 53		00 05
London Victoria 15 ⊖	a	22 46	22 53		22 58	23 00	23 04	23 09	23 18	23 24		23 29	23 31	23 34	23 41	23 48	23 54	23 58	00 04	00 10

For Faster Trains between London Victoria, Clapham Junction and East Croydon, please refer to Table 175

For Faster trains between London Victoria, Clapham Junction and Sutton, please refer to Table 182

For other Shepherds Bush connecting trains, please see Table 176

Table 170R

Sundays

8 December to 11 May

Croydon-Selhurst, Thornton Heath, Norbury, Streatham Common, Balham, Wandworth Common & Battersea Park - London Victoria

Network Diagram - see first Page of Table 170

		SN	SN	SN 1	SN	SN	SN	SN	SN	SN 1	SN	SN	SN	SN	SN	SN	SN	SN	SN
Sutton (Surrey) 4	d							06 55			07 13		07 25				07 55		
West Croydon 4	d							07 07				07 22	07 37			07 52	08 07		
Purley	d			05 21						07 15					07 48				08 23
East Croydon	d			05 26	06 41				07 13	07 24				07 43	07 54			08 14	08 30
Selhurst 4	d				06 44	06 48		07 11	07 17	07 27			07 41	07 47	07 57		08 14	08 18	08 33
Thornton Heath	d				06 46	06 50		07 13	07 19				07 43	07 49	07 59		08 16	08 20	08 35
Norbury	d				06 49	06 53		07 16	07 22				07 46	07 52	08 02		08 19	08 23	08 38
Streatham Common 4	d				06 51	06 55		07 19	07 25				07 49	07 54	08 04		08 22	08 27	08 40
London Bridge	a					07 19			07 50					08 19				08 50	
Balham 4	d		00 24	05 42	06 55		07 17	07 23			07 37	07 44	07 53		08 09	08 19	08 26		08 44
Wandsworth Common	d		00 26		06 57		07 19					07 46				08 21			
Clapham Junction	a		00 30	05 46	07 01		07 22	07 27		07 38	07 41	07 49	07 57		08 14	08 24	08 31		08 48
Clapham Junction 10	d	00 02	00 30	05 46	07 01		07 23	07 27		07 38	07 41	07 50	07 57		08 14	08 25	08 31		08 49
Imperial Wharf	d																		
West Brompton	⊖ d																		
Kensington (Olympia)	⊖ d																		
Shepherd's Bush	⊖ d																		
Battersea Park	d	00 05	00 34		07 05		07 26					07 53				08 28			
London Victoria 15	⊖ a	00 10	00 38	05 54	07 09		07 31	07 34		07 46	07 48	07 58	08 05		08 22	08 33	08 38		08 56

		SN	SN	SN	SN	SN	SN	SN	SN	SN	SN	SN	SN	SN	SN 1	SN	SN	SN	SN	SN
Sutton (Surrey) 4	d	08 10	08 25			08 40	08 58	08 55			09 10	09 28	09 25				09 40	09 58	09 55	
West Croydon 4	d	08 22	08 37			08 52		09 07			09 22		09 37				09 52		10 07	
Purley	d				08 49					09 19						09 47				
East Croydon	d			08 44	08 55				09 12	09 25				09 42	09 50	09 53				10 12
Selhurst 4	d		08 45	08 48	08 58			09 11	09 16	09 28			09 41	09 46	09 54	09 56			10 11	10 16
Thornton Heath	d		08 47	08 50	09 00			09 13	09 18	09 30			09 43	09 48		09 58			10 13	10 18
Norbury	d		08 50	08 53	09 03			09 16	09 21	09 33			09 46	09 51		10 01			10 16	10 21
Streatham Common 4	d		08 53	08 55	09 06			09 19	09 25	09 36			09 49	09 55		10 04			10 19	10 25
London Bridge	a			09 19					09 49					10 19						10 49
Balham 4	d	08 49	08 57		09 10	09 13	09 18	09 23		09 40	09 43	09 47	09 53			10 08	10 13	10 17	10 23	
Wandsworth Common	d	08 51				09 15					09 45						10 15			
Clapham Junction	a	08 54	09 01		09 14	09 19	09 22	09 27		09 44	09 48	09 51	09 57		10 02	10 12	10 18	10 21	10 27	
Clapham Junction 10	d	08 55	09 01		09 14	09 19	09 22	09 27		09 44	09 49	09 52	09 57		10 02	10 13	10 19	10 22	10 27	
Imperial Wharf	d																			
West Brompton	⊖ d																			
Kensington (Olympia)	⊖ d																			
Shepherd's Bush	⊖ d																			
Battersea Park	d	08 58				09 23					09 52						10 22			
London Victoria 15	⊖ a	09 03	09 08		09 21	09 27	09 29	09 34		09 51	09 57	09 59	10 04		10 09	10 20	10 27	10 29	10 34	

		SN 1	SN		SN	SN	SN	SN	SN 1	SN	SN	SN	SN	SN	SN 1	SN
Sutton (Surrey) 4	d			and at the same minutes past each hour until	18 10	18 28	18 25				18 40	18 58	18 55			
West Croydon 4	d				18 22		18 37				18 52		19 07			
Purley	d		10 17							18 47						19 17
East Croydon	d	10 20	10 23					18 42	18 50	18 53				19 12	19 20	19 23
Selhurst 4	d	10 24	10 26				18 41	18 46	18 54	18 56			19 11	19 16	19 24	19 26
Thornton Heath	d		10 28				18 43	18 48		18 58			19 13	19 18		19 28
Norbury	d		10 31				18 46	18 51		19 01			19 16	19 21		19 31
Streatham Common 4	d		10 34				18 49	18 55		19 04			19 19	19 25		19 34
London Bridge	a							19 19						19 49		
Balham 4	⊖ d		10 38		18 43	18 47	18 53			19 08	19 13	19 17	19 23			19 38
Wandsworth Common	d				18 45						19 15					
Clapham Junction	a	10 32	10 42		18 48	18 51	18 57		19 02	19 12	19 18	19 21	19 27		19 32	19 42
Clapham Junction 10	d	10 32	10 43		18 49	18 52	18 57		19 02	19 13	19 19	19 22	19 27		19 32	19 43
Imperial Wharf	d															
West Brompton	⊖ d															
Kensington (Olympia)	⊖ d															
Shepherd's Bush	⊖ d															
Battersea Park	d				18 52						19 22					
London Victoria 15	⊖ a	10 39	10 50		18 57	18 59	19 04		19 09	19 20	19 27	19 29	19 34		19 39	19 50

		SN	SN	SN	SN	SN 1	SN	SN	SN	SN	SN	SN 1	SN	SN	SN	SN	SN	SN 1	SN	SN	SN	SN
Sutton (Surrey) 4	d	19 10	19 28	19 25				19 40	19 58	19 55				20 10	20 28	20 25				20 40	20 55	
West Croydon 4	d	19 22		19 37				19 52		20 07				20 22		20 37				20 52	21 07	
Purley	d						19 47						20 17						20 47			
East Croydon	d				19 42	19 50	19 53				20 12	20 20	20 23				20 42	20 50	20 53			21 12
Selhurst 4	d			19 41	19 46	19 54	19 56			20 11	20 16	20 24	20 26			20 41	20 46	20 54	20 56		21 11	21 16
Thornton Heath	d			19 43	19 48		19 58			20 13	20 18		20 28			20 43	20 48		20 58		21 13	21 18
Norbury	d			19 46	19 51		20 01			20 16	20 21		20 31			20 46	20 51		21 01		21 16	21 21
Streatham Common 4	d			19 49	19 55		20 04			20 19	20 25		20 34			20 49	20 55		21 04		21 19	21 25
London Bridge	a				20 19						20 49						21 19					21 49
Balham 4	⊖ d	19 43	19 47	19 53			20 08	20 13	20 18	20 23			20 38	20 43	20 48	20 53			21 08	21 13	21 23	
Wandsworth Common	d	19 45						20 15						20 45						21 15		
Clapham Junction	a	19 48	19 51	19 57		20 02	20 12	20 18	20 22	20 27		20 32	20 42	20 48	20 52	20 57		21 02	21 12	21 19	21 27	
Clapham Junction 10	d	19 49	19 52	19 57		20 02	20 13	20 19	20 22	20 27		20 32	20 43	20 49	20 52	20 57		21 02	21 13	21 19	21 27	
Imperial Wharf	d																					
West Brompton	⊖ d																					
Kensington (Olympia)	⊖ d																					
Shepherd's Bush	⊖ d																					
Battersea Park	d	19 52						20 22						20 52						21 23		
London Victoria 15	⊖ a	19 57	19 59	20 04		20 09	20 20	20 27	20 29	20 34		20 39	20 50	20 57	20 59	21 04		21 09	21 20	21 27	21 34	

For Faster Trains between London Victoria, Clapham Junction and East Croydon, please refer to Table 175

For Faster trains between London Victoria, Clapham Junction and Sutton, please refer to Table 182

For other Shepherds Bush connecting trains, please see Table 176

Table 170R

Sundays

8 December to 11 May

Croydon-Selhurst, Thornton Heath, Norbury, Streatham Common, Balham, Wandworth Common & Battersea Park - London Victoria

Network Diagram - see first Page of Table 170

		SN	SN	SN	SN	SN 1	SN	SN	SN	SN	SN
Sutton (Surrey) 4	d		21 10	21 25				21 40	21 55		
West Croydon 4	d		21 22	21 37				21 52	22 07		
Purley	d	21 17					21 47				22 17
East Croydon	d	21 23			21 42	21 50	21 53			22 12	22 23
Selhurst 4	d	21 26		21 41	21 46	21 54	21 56		22 11	22 16	22 26
Thornton Heath	d	21 28		21 43	21 48		21 58		22 13	22 18	22 28
Norbury	d	21 31		21 46	21 51		22 01		22 16	22 21	22 31
Streatham Common 4	d	21 34		21 49	21 55		22 04		22 19	22 25	22 34
London Bridge	a				22 19					22 49	
Balham 4 ⊖	d	21 38	21 43	21 53			22 08	22 13	22 23		22 38
Wandsworth Common	d		21 45					22 15			
Clapham Junction	a	21 42	21 49	21 57		22 02	22 12	22 19	22 27		22 42
Clapham Junction 10	d	21 43	21 49	21 57		22 02	22 13	22 19	22 27		22 43
Imperial Wharf	d										
West Brompton ⊖	d										
Kensington (Olympia) ⊖	d										
Shepherd's Bush ⊖	d										
Battersea Park	d		21 53					22 23			
London Victoria 15 ⊖	a	21 50	21 57	22 04		22 09	22 20	22 27	22 34		22 52

		SN	SN	SN	SN 1	SN	SN 1	SN	SN	SN	SN	SN 1	SN	SN 1
Sutton (Surrey) 4	d	22 10	22 25					22 40	22 55	23 10	23 25		23 40	
West Croydon 4	d	22 22	22 37					22 52	23 07	23 22	23 37		23 52	
Purley	d					22 47	22 50							23 55
East Croydon	d			22 42	22 50	22 53	22 56					23 47		00 01
Selhurst 4	d		22 41	22 46	22 54	22 57	22 59		23 11		23 41	23 50	23 56	00 04
Thornton Heath	d		22 43	22 48		22 59			23 13		23 43		23 58	
Norbury	d		22 46	22 51		23 02			23 16		23 46		00 01	
Streatham Common 4	d		22 49	22 55		23 04			23 19		23 49		00 04	
London Bridge	a			23 19										
Balham 4 ⊖	d	22 43	22 53			23 08		23 13	23 23	23 43	23 53		00 08	
Wandsworth Common	d	22 45						23 15		23 45			00 10	
Clapham Junction	a	22 49	22 57		23 02	23 12	23 07	23 19	23 27	23 49	23 57	23 59	00 13	00 16
Clapham Junction 10	d	22 49	22 57		23 02	23 13	23 07	23 19	23 27	23 49	23 57	00 01	00 14	00 17
Imperial Wharf	d													
West Brompton ⊖	d													
Kensington (Olympia) ⊖	d													
Shepherd's Bush ⊖	d													
Battersea Park	d	22 53						23 23		23 53			00 17	
London Victoria 15 ⊖	a	22 57	23 04		23 09	23 22	23 14	23 27	23 34	23 57	00 05	00 07	00 22	00 24

For Faster Trains between London Victoria, Clapham Junction and East Croydon, please refer to Table 175

For Faster trains between London Victoria, Clapham Junction and Sutton, please refer to Table 182

For other Shepherds Bush connecting trains, please see Table 176

Table 171

Mondays to Fridays

9 December to 16 May

London Victoria - Streatham Hill, West Norwood, Gipsy Hill and Crystal Palace - Norwood Junction & Croydon

Network Diagram - see first Page of Table 170

Miles	Miles			SN MX	SN MO	SN MX	SN MX	SN	SN	SN	SN	SN	SN	SN	SN	SN	SN	SN	SN	SN	SN	SN	SN
0	—	London Victoria [15] ⊖	d					06 06	06 19			06 36	06 49			07 08	07 17		07 36	07 52			08 08
1¼	—	Battersea Park [4]	d					06 10	06 23			06 40	06 53			07 12	07 21		07 40				08 12
—	—	Clapham Junction [10]	d		00 02	00 02		06 14	06 27			06 44	06 57			07 16	07 25		07 44	07 58			08 17
4	—	Wandsworth Common	d		00 05	00 05		06 17	06 30			06 47	07 00			07 19			07 47				08 20
5	—	Balham [4] ⊖	d		00 07	00 08		06 20	06 32			06 50	07 02			07 21	07 29		07 50	08 03			08 22
6	—	**Streatham Hill**	d		00 11	00 11		06 23	06 35		06 43	06 53	07 05		07 12	07 24	07 32		07 53	08 06		08 15	08 25
—	0	London Bridge	d				00 03			06 20				06 50				07 20			07 50		
7¼	6¾	**West Norwood [4]**	d		00 14	00 14	00 24	06 26	06 39	06 42	06 46	06 56	07 09	07 12	07 15	07 28	07 38	07 42	07 58	08 09	08 16	08 19	08 29
8¼	7¾	**Gipsy Hill**	d	00 01	00 17	00 17	00 27	06 29	06 42	06 45	06 49	06 59	07 12	07 15	07 18	07 31	07 41	07 45	08 01	08 12	08 19	08 22	08 32
9	8½	**Crystal Palace [4]**	a	00 04	00 20	00 20	00 29	06 32	06 44	06 48	06 52	07 02	07 14	07 17	07 21	07 33	07 43	07 47	08 04	08 15	08 22	08 25	08 35
—	—	Crystal Palace	d	00 04	00 20	00 21	00 29	06 32	06 44		06 53	07 02	07 15		07 21	07 33	07 44		08 04	08 15		08 25	08 35
—	—	Sydenham	a			00 24			06 48		06 56		07 18		07 24		07 48			08 18		08 28	
—	—	Forest Hill	a			00 27			06 50		06 59		07 21		07 27		07 50			08 21		08 31	
—	—	Honor Oak Park	a			00 29			06 53		07 01		07 23		07 29		07 53			08 23		08 33	
—	—	Brockley	a			00 32			06 55		07 04		07 26		07 32		07 55			08 26		08 36	
—	—	New Cross Gate	a			00 34			06 58		07 06		07 28		07 34		07 58			08 28		08 38	
—	—	London Bridge	a			00 41			07 06		07 17		07 37		07 43		08 07			08 37		08 47	
—	—	Norwood Junction [2]	a	00 09	00 25		00 34	06 37				07 07				07 38			08 08				08 39
—	—		d	00 09				06 39				07 09				07 39			08 09				08 40
12¼	—	West Croydon	a	00 14				06 43				07 13				07 44			08 14				08 44
16¾	—	Sutton (Surrey)	a					06 56				07 26				07 58			08 27				08 57

		SN	SN	SN	SN	SN	SN	SN	SN	SN	SN	SN	SN	SN	SN	SN	SN	SN	SN	
London Victoria [15] ⊖	d			08 22	08 36	08 49		09 05	09 19		09 36	09 49		10 06	10 19		10 36	10 49		
Battersea Park [4]	d			08 26	08 40	08 53		09 10	09 23		09 40	09 53		10 10	10 23		10 40	10 53		
Clapham Junction [10]	d			08 30	08 44	08 57		09 14	09 27		09 44	09 57		10 14	10 27		10 44	10 57		
Wandsworth Common	d			08 33	08 47	09 00		09 17	09 30		09 47	10 00		10 17	10 30		10 47	11 00		
Balham [4] ⊖	d			08 35	08 49	09 02		09 20	09 32		09 50	10 02		10 20	10 32		10 50	11 02		
Streatham Hill	d	08 35		08 45	08 52	09 05		09 23	09 35		09 53	10 05		10 23	10 35		10 53	11 05		
London Bridge	d		08 19				08 50			09 20			09 49			10 25			10 55	and at
West Norwood [4]	d	08 38	08 42	08 48	08 56	09 09	09 12	09 28	09 40	09 43	09 57	10 09	10 12	10 27	10 40	10 47	10 57	11 10	11 17	the same
Gipsy Hill	d	08 41	08 45	08 51	08 59	09 12	09 15	09 31	09 43	09 46	10 00	10 12	10 15	10 30	10 43	10 50	11 00	11 13	11 20	minutes
Crystal Palace [4]	a	08 44	08 47	08 54	09 01	09 14	09 17	09 33	09 46	09 48	10 02	10 15	10 18	10 32	10 46	10 52	11 02	11 16	11 22	past
Crystal Palace	d	08 44		08 54	09 01	09 14		09 33	09 51		10 02	10 21		10 32	10 51		11 02	11 21		each
Sydenham	a	08 47		08 58		09 18			09 54			10 24			10 54			11 24		hour until
Forest Hill	a	08 50		09 00		09 20			09 57			10 27			10 57			11 27		
Honor Oak Park	a	08 52		09 03		09 23			09 59			10 29			10 59			11 29		
Brockley	a	08 55		09 05		09 25			10 02			10 32			11 02			11 32		
New Cross Gate	a	08 57		09 08		09 28			10 04			10 34			11 04			11 34		
London Bridge	a	09 08		09 14		09 37			10 11			10 41			11 11			11 41		
Norwood Junction [2]	a				09 06			09 38			10 07			10 37			11 07			
	d				09 09			09 39			10 09			10 39			11 09			
West Croydon	a				09 13			09 43			10 13			10 43			11 13			
Sutton (Surrey)	a				09 26			09 56			10 26			10 56			11 26			

		SN	SN	SN	SN	SN	SN	SN	SN	SN	SN	SN	SN	SN	SN	SN	SN	SN	SN	SN	SN	SN	SN
London Victoria [15] ⊖	d	13 06	13 19		13 36	13 49		14 06	14 19		14 36	14 49		15 06	15 19		15 36		15 49		16 07	16 19	
Battersea Park [4]	d	13 10	13 23		13 40	13 53		14 10	14 23		14 40	14 53		15 10	15 23		15 40		15 53		16 11	16 23	
Clapham Junction [10]	d	13 14	13 27		13 44	13 57		14 14	14 27		14 44	14 57		15 14	15 27		15 44		15 57		16 15	16 27	
Wandsworth Common	d	13 17	13 30		13 47	14 00		14 17	14 30		14 47	15 00		15 17	15 30		15 47		16 00		16 18	16 30	
Balham [4] ⊖	d	13 20	13 32		13 50	14 02		14 20	14 32		14 50	15 02		15 20	15 32		15 50		16 02		16 20	16 32	
Streatham Hill	d	13 23	13 35		13 53	14 05		14 23	14 35		14 53	15 05		15 23	15 35		15 53	16 01	16 05		16 23	16 35	
London Bridge	d			13 25			13 55			14 25			14 55			15 25		16a23		16 00			16 30
West Norwood [4]	d	13 27	13 40	13 47	13 57	14 10	14 17	14 27	14 40	14 47	14 57	15 10	15 18	15 27	15 40	15 48	15 57		16 10	16 21	16 27	16 39	16 51
Gipsy Hill	d	13 30	13 43	13 50	14 00	14 13	14 20	14 30	14 43	14 50	15 00	15 13	15 21	15 30	15 43	15 51	16 00		16 13	16 24	16 30	16 44	16 54
Crystal Palace [4]	a	13 32	13 46	13 52	14 02	14 16	14 22	14 32	14 46	14 52	15 02	15 16	15 23	15 32	15 46	15 53	16 02		16 16	16 27	16 32	16 46	16 57
Crystal Palace	d	13 32	13 51		14 02	14 21		14 32	14 51		15 02	15 21		15 32	15 51		16 02		16 21		16 32	16 50	
Sydenham	a		13 54			14 24			14 54			15 24			15 54				16 24			16 54	
Forest Hill	a		13 57			14 27			14 57			15 27			15 57				16 27			16 56	
Honor Oak Park	a		13 59			14 29			14 59			15 29			15 59				16 29			16 59	
Brockley	a		14 02			14 32			15 02			15 32			16 02				16 32			17 01	
New Cross Gate	a		14 04			14 34			15 04			15 34			16 04				16 34			17 04	
London Bridge	a		14 11			14 41			15 11			15 41			16 11				16 41			17 12	
Norwood Junction [2]	a	13 37			14 07			14 37			15 07			15 37			16 07				16 37		
	d	13 39			14 09			14 39			15 09			15 39			16 09				16 39		
West Croydon	a	13 43			14 13			14 43			15 13			15 43			16 13				16 45		
Sutton (Surrey)	a	13 56			14 26			14 56			15 26			15 56			16 26				16 57		

For complete service between London Victoria and Balham, please see Table 170

For Faster Trains between London Victoria, Clapham Junction and East Croydon, please refer to Table 175

For Faster trains between London Victoria, Clapham Junction and Sutton, please refer to Table 182

For Shepherds Bush connecting trains, please see table 176

For East Croydon & Purley connecting trains, please see Table 181

Table 171

Mondays to Fridays

9 December to 16 May

London Victoria - Streatham Hill, West Norwood, Gipsy Hill and Crystal Palace - Norwood Junction & Croydon

Network Diagram - see first Page of Table 170

Station		SN	SN	SN	SN	SN	SN	SN	SN		SN	SN	SN	SN	SN	SN	SN	SN	SN		SN	SN	SN	SN	SN
London Victoria 15 ⊖	d	16 37	16 49		17 07	17 22		17 37	17 52			18 07	18 22		18 36	18 52		19 06	19 22				19 36		19 52
Battersea Park 4	d	16 41	16 53		17 11	17 26		17 41	17 56			18 11	18 26		18 40	18 56		19 10	19 26				19 40		19 56
Clapham Junction 10	d	16 45	16 57		17 15	17 30		17 45	18 00			18 15	18 30		18 44	19 00		19 14	19 30				19 44		20 00
Wandsworth Common	d	16 48	17 00		17 18	17 33		17 48	18 03			18 18	18 33		18 47	19 03		19 17	19 33				19 47		20 03
Balham 4 ⊖	d	16 50	17 03		17 20	17 35		17 51	18 05			18 20	18 35		18 49	19 05		19 20	19 35				19 50		20 05
Streatham Hill	d	16 53	17 06		17 23	17 38		17 54	18 08			18 23	18 38		18 52	19 08		19 23	19 38				19 53		20 08
London Bridge	d			17 00			17 30				18 00			18 30			18 59				19 20	19 30		19 50	
West Norwood 4	d	16 57	17 09	17 22	17 27	17 42	17 51	17 57	18 14		18 22	18 27	18 42	18 51	18 57	19 12	19 22	19 27	19 42		19 45	19 51	19 57	20 12	20 15
Gipsy Hill	d	17 00	17 12	17 25	17 30	17 45	17 54	18 00	18 17		18 25	18 30	18 45	18 54	19 00	19 15	19 25	19 30	19 45		19 48	19 54	20 00	20 15	20 18
Crystal Palace 4	a	17 03	17 15	17 28	17 33	17 47	17 57	18 03	18 19		18 28	18 33	18 47	18 57	19 03	19 19	19 28	19 32	19 47		19 50	19 57	20 02	20 17	20 20
Crystal Palace	d	17 03	17 21		17 33	17 48		18 04	18 20			18 33	18 51		19 03	19 21		19 32	19 51		19 51		20 02	20 17	20 21
Sydenham	a		17 24			17 54			18 24				18 54			19 24			19 54						20 24
Forest Hill	a		17 27			17 57			18 27				18 57			19 27			19 57						20 27
Honor Oak Park	a		17 29			17 59			18 29				18 59			19 29			19 59						20 29
Brockley	a		17 32			18 02			18 32				19 02			19 32			20 02						20 32
New Cross Gate	a		17 34			18 04			18 34				19 04			19 34			20 04						20 34
London Bridge	a		17 43			18 13			18 45				19 13			19 41			20 11						20 43
Norwood Junction 2	a	17 07			17 37			18 08				18 37			19 07			19 37			19 55		20 07	20 23	
	d	17 09			17 38			18 10				18 39			19 09			19 39			19 58		20 09	20 24	
West Croydon	a	17 13			17 43			18 16				18 44			19 14			19 44			20 06		20 13	20 29	
Sutton (Surrey)	a	17 26			17 55			18 28				18 58			19 28			19 57					20 26		

Station		SN	SN	SN	SN		SN	SN	SN	SN	SN	SN	SN	SN	SN		SN	SN	SN	SN	SN	SN	SN	SN	SN
London Victoria 15 ⊖	d		20 06	20 22			20 36	20 52		21 06	21 23		21 36	21 52			22 06	22 22		22 36	22 52		23 06	23 22	
Battersea Park 4	d		20 10	20 26			20 40	20 56		21 10	21 27		21 40	21 56			22 10	22 26		22 40	22 56		23 10	23 26	
Clapham Junction 10	d		20 14	20 30			20 44	21 00		21 14	21 31		21 44	22 00			22 14	22 30		22 46	23 00		23 14	23 30	
Wandsworth Common	d		20 17	20 33			20 47	21 03		21 17	21 34		21 47	22 03			22 17	22 33		22 49	23 03		23 17	23 33	
Balham 4 ⊖	d		20 20	20 35			20 50	21 05		21 20	21 36		21 50	22 05			22 20	22 35		22 52	23 05		23 20	23 35	
Streatham Hill	d		20 23	20 38			20 53	21 08		21 23	21 39		21 53	22 08			22 23	22 38		22 55	23 08		23 23	23 38	
London Bridge	d	20 00			20 25				20 55			21 25			21 55				22 25			23 00			23 30
West Norwood 4	d	20 22	20 27	20 42	20 48		20 57	21 12	21 18	21 27	21 43	21 47	21 57	22 12	22 17		22 27	22 42	22 47	22 58	23 12	23 21	23 26	23 42	23 51
Gipsy Hill	d	20 25	20 30	20 45	20 51		21 00	21 15	21 21	21 30	21 46	21 50	22 00	22 15	22 20		22 30	22 45	22 50	23 01	23 15	23 24	23 29	23 45	23 54
Crystal Palace 4	a	20 27	20 33	20 47	20 53		21 03	21 17	21 23	21 33	21 48	21 52	22 03	22 17	22 22		22 33	22 47	22 52	23 04	23 17	23 26	23 32	23 47	23 56
Crystal Palace	d		20 33	20 51			21 03	21 21		21 33	21 51		22 03	22 21			22 33	22 51		23 04	23 21	23 26	23 32	23 51	23 56
Sydenham	a			20 54				21 27			21 54			22 24				22 54			23 24			23 54	
Forest Hill	a			20 57				21 29			21 57			22 27				22 57			23 27			23 57	
Honor Oak Park	a			20 59				21 32			21 59			22 29				22 59			23 29			23 59	
Brockley	a			21 02				21 34			22 02			22 32				23 02			23 32			00 02	
New Cross Gate	a			21 04				21 37			22 04			22 34				23 04			23 34			00 04	
London Bridge	a			21 11				21 43			22 11			22 41				23 11			23 44			00 11	
Norwood Junction 2	a		20 37				21 07			21 37			22 07				22 37			23 08		23 32	23 36		00 01
	d		20 39				21 09			21 39			22 09				22 39			23 09			23 37		
West Croydon	a		20 43				21 13			21 43			22 13				22 43			23 13			23 41		
Sutton (Surrey)	a		20 56				21 26			21 56			22 26				22 56			23 26			23 54		

Station			SN	SN
London Victoria 15 ⊖	d		23 38	23 54
Battersea Park 4	d		23 42	23 58
Clapham Junction 10	d		23 46	00 02
Wandsworth Common	d		23 49	00 05
Balham 4 ⊖	d		23 51	00 08
Streatham Hill	d		23 54	00 11
London Bridge	d			
West Norwood 4	d		23 58	00 14
Gipsy Hill	d		00 01	00 17
Crystal Palace 4	a		00 04	00 20
Crystal Palace	d		00 04	00 21
Sydenham	a			00 24
Forest Hill	a			00 27
Honor Oak Park	a			00 29
Brockley	a			00 32
New Cross Gate	a			00 34
London Bridge	a			00 41
Norwood Junction 2	a		00 09	
	d		00 09	
West Croydon	a		00 14	
Sutton (Surrey)	a			

For complete service between London Victoria and Balham, please see Table 170

For Faster Trains between London Victoria, Clapham Junction and East Croydon, please refer to Table 175

For Faster trains between London Victoria, Clapham Junction and Sutton, please refer to Table 182

For Shepherds Bush connecting trains, please see table 176

For East Croydon & Purley connecting trains, please see Table 181

Table 171

Saturdays

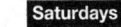

14 December to 17 May

London Victoria - Streatham Hill, West Norwood, Gipsy Hill and Crystal Palace - Norwood Junction & Croydon

Network Diagram - see first Page of Table 170

		SN	SN	SN	SN	SN	SN	SN	SN	SN	SN	SN	SN	SN	SN	SN		SN	SN	SN	SN	SN	SN
London Victoria 15 ⊖	d				00 07	00 23		00 37		07 06		07 36	07 49		08 06	08 19	and at the same minutes past each hour until		18 36	18 49		19 06	19 19
Battersea Park 4	d				00 11	00 27		00 41		07 11		07 40	07 53		08 10	08 23			18 40	18 53		19 10	19 23
Clapham Junction 10	d		00 02		00 16	00 31		00 45		07 14		07 44	07 57		08 14	08 27			18 44	18 57		19 14	19 27
Wandsworth Common	d		00 05		00 19	00 34		00 48		07 18		07 47	08 00		08 17	08 30			18 47	19 00		19 17	19 30
Balham 4 ⊖	d		00 08		00 21	00 36		00 50		07 20		07 50	08 02		08 20	08 32			18 50	19 02		19 20	19 32
Streatham Hill	d		00 11		00 24	00 39		00 53	06 53	07 23		07 53	08 05		08 23	08 35			18 53	19 05		19 23	19 35
London Bridge	d			00 03			00 33				07 25			07 55				18 25			18 55		
West Norwood 4	d		00 14	00 24	00 28	00 43	00 54	00 58	06 57	07 27	07 47	07 57	08 10	08 17	08 27	08 40		18 47	18 57	19 10	19 17	19 27	19 40
Gipsy Hill	d	00 01	00 17	00 27	00 31	00 46	00 57	01 01	07 00	07 30	07 50	08 00	08 13	08 20	08 30	08 43		18 50	19 00	19 13	19 20	19 30	19 43
Crystal Palace 4	a	00 04	00 20	00 29	00 33	00 48	00 59	01 04	07 02	07 32	07 52	08 02	08 16	08 22	08 32	08 46		18 52	19 02	19 16	19 22	19 32	19 46
Crystal Palace	d	00 04	00 21	00 29	00 33	00 48	00 59	01 04	07 02	07 32		08 02	08 21		08 32	08 51			19 02	19 21		19 32	19 51
Sydenham	a		00 24										08 24			08 54				19 24			19 54
Forest Hill	a		00 27										08 27			08 57				19 27			19 57
Honor Oak Park	a		00 29										08 29			08 59				19 29			19 59
Brockley	a		00 32										08 32			09 02				19 32			20 02
New Cross Gate	a		00 34										08 34			09 04				19 34			20 04
London Bridge	a		00 41										08 41			09 11				19 41			20 11
Norwood Junction 2	a	00 09		00 34	00 38	00 53	01 04	01 08	07 07	07 37		08 07			08 37				19 07			19 37	
	d	00 09			00 38	00 53		01 09	07 09	07 39		08 09			08 39				19 09			19 39	
West Croydon	a	00 14			00 43	01 00		01 13	07 14	07 43		08 13			08 43				19 13			19 43	
Sutton (Surrey)	a								07 27	07 56		08 26			08 56				19 26			19 56	

		SN	SN	SN	SN	SN	SN	SN	SN	SN		SN	SN	SN	SN	SN	SN	SN	SN	SN		SN	SN	SN	SN
London Victoria 15 ⊖	d		19 36	19 49		20 06	20 19		20 36	20 49			21 06	21 19		21 36	21 49		22 06	22 19			22 36	22 49	
Battersea Park 4	d		19 40	19 53		20 10	20 23		20 40	20 53			21 10	21 23		21 40	21 53		22 10	22 23			22 40	22 53	
Clapham Junction 10	d		19 44	19 57		20 14	20 27		20 44	20 57			21 14	21 27		21 44	21 57		22 14	22 27			22 44	22 57	
Wandsworth Common	d		19 47	20 00		20 17	20 30		20 47	21 00			21 17	21 30		21 47	22 00		22 17	22 30			22 47	23 00	
Balham 4 ⊖	d		19 50	20 02		20 20	20 32		20 50	21 02			21 20	21 32		21 50	22 02		22 20	22 32			22 50	23 02	
Streatham Hill	d		19 53	20 05		20 23	20 35		20 53	21 05			21 23	21 35		21 53	22 05		22 23	22 35			22 53	23 05	
London Bridge	d	19 25			19 55			20 25				20 55			21 25			21 55				22 25			23 00
West Norwood 4	d	19 47	19 57	20 10	20 17	20 27	20 40	20 47	20 57	21 10		21 17	21 27	21 40	21 47	21 57	22 10	22 17	22 27	22 40		22 47	22 57	23 10	23 21
Gipsy Hill	d	19 50	20 00	20 13	20 20	20 30	20 43	20 50	21 00	21 13		21 20	21 30	21 43	21 50	22 00	22 13	22 20	22 30	22 43		22 50	23 00	23 13	23 24
Crystal Palace 4	a	19 52	20 02	20 16	20 22	20 32	20 46	20 52	21 02	21 16		21 22	21 32	21 46	21 52	22 02	22 16	22 22	22 32	22 46		22 52	23 03	23 16	23 26
Crystal Palace	d		20 02	20 21		20 32	20 51		21 02	21 21			21 32	21 51		22 02	22 21		22 32	22 51			23 03	23 21	23 26
Sydenham	a			20 24			20 54			21 24				21 54			22 24			22 54				23 24	
Forest Hill	a			20 27			20 57			21 27				21 57			22 27			22 57				23 27	
Honor Oak Park	a			20 29			20 59			21 29				21 59			22 29			22 59				23 29	
Brockley	a			20 32			21 02			21 32				22 02			22 32			23 02				23 32	
New Cross Gate	a			20 34			21 04			21 34				22 04			22 34			23 04				23 34	
London Bridge	a			20 41			21 11			21 41				22 11			22 41			23 11				23 44	
Norwood Junction 2	a		20 07			20 37			21 07				21 37			22 07			22 37				23 07		23 32
	d		20 09			20 39			21 09				21 39			22 09			22 39				23 09		
West Croydon	a		20 14			20 44			21 14				21 44			22 13			22 43				23 13		
Sutton (Surrey)	a		20 27			20 57			21 27				21 57			22 26			22 56				23 26		

		SN	SN	SN	SN	SN
London Victoria 15 ⊖	d	23 06	23 19		23 38	23 54
Battersea Park 4	d	23 10	23 23		23 42	23 58
Clapham Junction 10	d	23 14	23 27		23 46	00 02
Wandsworth Common	d	23 17	23 30		23 49	00 05
Balham 4 ⊖	d	23 20	23 32		23 51	00 07
Streatham Hill	d	23 23	23 35		23 54	00 10
London Bridge	d			23 30		
West Norwood 4	d	23 27	23 40	23 51	23 58	00 14
Gipsy Hill	d	23 30	23 43	23 54	00 01	00 17
Crystal Palace 4	a	23 32	23 46	23 56	00 03	00 19
Crystal Palace	d	23 32	23 51	23 56	00 03	00 21
Sydenham	a		23 54			00 24
Forest Hill	a		23 57			00 27
Honor Oak Park	a		23 59			00 29
Brockley	a		00 02			00 32
New Cross Gate	a		00 04			00 35
London Bridge	a		00 11			00 41
Norwood Junction 2	a	23 37		00 01	00 08	
	d	23 39			00 09	
West Croydon	a	23 43			00 14	
Sutton (Surrey)	a	23 56				

For complete service between London Victoria and Balham, please see Table 170

For Faster Trains between London Victoria, Clapham Junction and East Croydon, please refer to Table 175

For Faster trains between London Victoria, Clapham Junction and Sutton, please refer to Table 182

For Shepherds Bush connecting trains, please see table 176

For East Croydon & Purley connecting trains, please see Table 181

Table 171

Sundays

8 December to 11 May

London Victoria - Streatham Hill, West Norwood, Gipsy Hill and Crystal Palace - Norwood Junction & Croydon

Network Diagram - see first Page of Table 170

Station		SN	SN	SN	SN	SN		SN	SN	SN	SN	SN	SN	SN	SN	SN		SN	SN	SN	SN	SN	SN	SN	SN
London Victoria 15 ⊖	d				00 07	00 22			00 37	07 20		07 52		08 23		08 52			09 24		09 54		10 24		10 54
Battersea Park 4	d				00 11	00 26			00 41	07 24		07 56		08 27		08 56			09 28		09 58		10 28		10 58
Clapham Junction 10	d		00 02		00 15	00 30			00 45	07 28		08 00		08 31		09 00			09 32		10 02		10 32		11 02
Wandsworth Common	d		00 05		00 18	00 33			00 48	07 31		08 03		08 34		09 03			09 35		10 05		10 35		11 05
Balham 4 ⊖	d		00 07		00 21	00 35			00 50	07 34		08 06		08 36		09 06			09 38		10 07		10 37		11 07
Streatham Hill	d		00 10		00 24	00 38			00 53	07 37		08 09		08 39		09 09			09 41		10 11		10 41		11 11
London Bridge	d			00 03				00 33			07 36		08 06		08 36			09 06		09 36		10 06		10 36	
West Norwood 4	d		00 14	00 24	00 28	00 42		00 54	00 58	07 44	07 57	08 13	08 27	08 43	08 57	09 13		09 27	09 46	09 57	10 16	10 27	10 46	10 57	11 16
Gipsy Hill	d	00 01	00 17	00 27	00 31	00 45		00 57	01 01	07 47	08 00	08 16	08 30	08 46	09 00	09 16		09 30	09 49	10 00	10 19	10 30	10 49	11 00	11 19
Crystal Palace 4	a	00 03	00 19	00 29	00 33	00 47		00 59	01 03	07 50	08 02	08 19	08 32	08 49	09 02	09 19		09 32	09 52	10 02	10 22	10 32	10 52	11 02	11 22
Crystal Palace	d	00 03	00 21	00 29	00 33	00 47		00 59	01 03	07 50		08 19		08 49		09 19			09 52		10 22		10 52		11 22
Sydenham	a		00 24																						
Forest Hill	a		00 27																						
Honor Oak Park	a		00 29																						
Brockley	a		00 32																						
New Cross Gate	a		00 35																						
London Bridge	a		00 41																						
Norwood Junction 2	a	00 08		00 34	00 38	00 52		01 04	01 08	07 55		08 24		08 54		09 25			09 56		10 26		10 56		11 26
	d	00 09			00 38	00 52			01 08	07 56		08 25		08 56		09 26			09 57		10 27		10 57		11 27
West Croydon	a	00 14			00 43	01 00			01 13	08 00		08 30		09 00		09 30			10 02		10 31		11 01		11 31
Sutton (Surrey)	a									08 13		08 43		09 13		09 44			10 16		10 46		11 16		11 46

Station		SN		SN	SN	SN	SN	SN	SN	SN	SN	SN		SN	SN	SN	SN	SN	SN	SN	SN	SN	SN	
London Victoria 15 ⊖	d			11 24		11 54		12 24		12 54		13 24			13 54		14 24		14 54		15 24		15 54	and at the same minutes past each hour until
Battersea Park 4	d			11 28		11 58		12 28		12 58		13 28			13 58		14 28		14 58		15 28		15 58	
Clapham Junction 10	d			11 32		12 02		12 32		13 02		13 32			14 02		14 32		15 02		15 32		16 02	
Wandsworth Common	d			11 35		12 05		12 35		13 05		13 35			14 05		14 35		15 05		15 35		16 05	
Balham 4 ⊖	d			11 37		12 07		12 37		13 07		13 37			14 07		14 37		15 07		15 37		16 07	
Streatham Hill	d			11 41		12 11		12 41		13 11		13 41			14 11		14 41		15 11		15 41		16 11	
London Bridge	d	11 06			11 36		12 06		12 36		13 06			13 36		14 06		14 36		15 06		15 36		
West Norwood 4	d	11 27		11 46	11 57	12 16	12 29	12 46	12 57	13 16	13 27	13 46		13 57	14 16	14 27	14 46	14 57	15 16	15 27	15 46	15 57	16 16	
Gipsy Hill	d	11 30		11 49	12 00	12 19	12 32	12 49	13 00	13 19	13 30	13 49		14 00	14 19	14 30	14 49	15 00	15 19	15 30	15 49	16 00	16 19	
Crystal Palace 4	a	11 32		11 52	12 02	12 22	12 34	12 51	13 02	13 22	13 32	13 52		14 02	14 22	14 32	14 52	15 02	15 22	15 32	15 51	16 02	16 21	
Crystal Palace	d			11 52		12 22		12 51		13 22		13 52			14 22		14 52		15 22		15 51		16 21	
Sydenham	a																							
Forest Hill	a																							
Honor Oak Park	a																							
Brockley	a																							
New Cross Gate	a																							
London Bridge	a																							
Norwood Junction 2	a			11 56		12 26		12 56		13 26		13 56			14 26		14 56		15 26		15 56		16 26	
	d			11 57		12 27		12 57		13 27		13 57			14 27		14 57		15 27		15 57		16 27	
West Croydon	a			12 01		12 31		13 01		13 31		14 01			14 31		15 01		15 31		16 01		16 31	
Sutton (Surrey)	a			12 16		12 46		13 16		13 46		14 16			14 46		15 16		15 46		16 16		16 46	

Station		SN	SN	SN	SN		SN	SN	SN	SN	SN	SN	SN	SN	SN		SN	SN
London Victoria 15 ⊖	d		20 24		20 54			21 24		21 54		22 24		22 54			23 24	23 54
Battersea Park 4	d		20 28		20 58			21 28		21 58		22 28		22 58			23 28	23 58
Clapham Junction 10	d		20 32		21 02			21 32		22 02		22 32		23 02			23 32	00 02
Wandsworth Common	d		20 35		21 05			21 35		22 05		22 35		23 05			23 35	00 05
Balham 4 ⊖	d		20 37		21 07			21 38		22 07		22 38		23 07			23 37	00 07
Streatham Hill	d		20 41		21 11			21 41		22 11		22 41		23 11			23 41	00 11
London Bridge	d	20 06		20 36			21 06		21 36		22 06		22 36		23 06			
West Norwood 4	d	20 27	20 46	20 57	21 16		21 27	21 46	21 57	22 16	22 27	22 46	22 57	23 16	23 27		23 46	00 14
Gipsy Hill	d	20 30	20 49	21 00	21 19		21 30	21 49	22 00	22 19	22 30	22 49	23 00	23 19	23 30		23 49	00 17
Crystal Palace 4	a	20 32	20 51	21 02	21 21		21 32	21 51	22 02	22 21	22 32	22 51	23 02	23 21	23 32		23 51	00 20
Crystal Palace	d		20 51		21 21			21 51		22 21		22 51		23 21			23 51	00 20
Sydenham	a																	
Forest Hill	a																	
Honor Oak Park	a																	
Brockley	a																	
New Cross Gate	a																	
London Bridge	a																	
Norwood Junction 2	a		20 56		21 26			21 56		22 26		22 56		23 26			23 56	00 25
	d		20 57		21 27			21 57		22 27		22 57		23 27			23 56	
West Croydon	a		21 01		21 31			22 01		22 31		23 01		23 31			00 01	
Sutton (Surrey)	a		21 16		21 46			22 16		22 46		23 16		23 46				

For complete service between London Victoria and Balham, please see Table 170

For Faster Trains between London Victoria, Clapham Junction and East Croydon, please refer to Table 175

For Faster trains between London Victoria, Clapham Junction and Sutton, please refer to Table 182

For Shepherds Bush connecting trains, please see table 176

For East Croydon & Purley connecting trains, please see Table 181

Table 171R

Mondays to Fridays

9 December to 16 May

Croydon & Norwood Junction- Crystal Palace, Gipsy Hill, West Norwood and Streatham Hill - London Victoria

Network Diagram - see first Page of Table 170

Miles	Miles			SN MX	SN	SN	SN	SN	SN	SN		SN	SN	SN	SN	SN	SN	SN	SN	SN		SN	SN	SN	SN
0	—	Sutton (Surrey) 4	d																						
4½	—	West Croydon 4	d											07 17			07 47			08 19				08 47	
—	—	Norwood Junction 2	a											07 22			07 52			08 23				08 52	
—	—		d		05 38	05 53	06 21		06 47	06 51				07 22			07 52			08 24				08 53	
—	—	London Bridge	d					06 18				06 49			07 21			07 53				08 20			08 51
—	—	New Cross Gate	d					06 25				06 56			07 26			07 58				08 26			08 57
—	—	Brockley	d					06 27				06 59			07 29			08 01				08 29			09 00
—	—	Honor Oak Park	d	00 01				06 30				07 02			07 32			08 04				08 32			09 03
—	—	Forest Hill	d	00 04				06 33				07 04			07 34			08 06				08 34			09 05
—	—	Sydenham	d	00 06				06 35				07 07			07 37			08 09				08 37			09 08
7¾	0	Crystal Palace	a	00 10	05 42	05 57	06 25	06 39	06 51	06 55		07 10		07 26	07 40		07 56	08 12		08 28		08 40		08 57	09 11
—	—	**Crystal Palace 4**	d	00 10	05 42	05 57	06 25	06 40	06 51	06 55		07 11	07 22	07 27	07 41	07 52	07 56	08 13	08 24	08 28		08 41	08 52	08 57	09 12
8½	0¾	**Gipsy Hill**	a	00 13	05 44	06 00	06 28	06 42	06 53	06 58		07 14	07 25	07 29	07 44	07 55	07 59	08 15	08 27	08 31		08 44	08 55	09 00	09 15
9½	1¾	**West Norwood 4**	a	00 16	05 47	06 03	06 31	06 45	06 56	07 01		07 17	07 28	07 32	07 47	07 58	08 02	08 18	08 30	08 34		08 47	08 58	09 03	09 18
—	8½	London Bridge	a			06 23			07 25				07 55			08 25			08 55				09 25		
10¾	—	**Streatham Hill**	a	00 19	05 51		06 34	06 49		07 04		07 20		07 36	07 50		08 05	08 22		08 37		08 50		09 06	09 21
11¾	—	Balham 4 ⊖	a	00 22	05 54		06 38	06 52		07 08		07 24		07 40	07 54		08 09	08 25		08 41		08 54		09 10	09 25
12¾	—	Wandsworth Common	a	00 24			06 41			07 11		07 27		07 42	07 57		08 12	08 27		08 43		08 57		09 13	09 27
14	—	Clapham Junction	a	00 28	05 58		06 44	06 56		07 14		07 31		07 46	08 01		08 16	08 31		08 47		09 01		09 17	09 31
15½	—	Battersea Park 4	a	00 32	06 02		06 48			07 18		07 35		07 50	08 05		08 20	08 35		08 51		09 05		09 21	09 35
16¾	—	London Victoria 15 ⊖	a	00 36	06 07		06 53	07 06		07 25		07 39		07 57	08 11		08 27	08 41		08 57		09 11		09 27	09 42

		SN	SN	SN	SN	SN		SN	SN	SN	SN	SN	SN	SN	SN	SN		SN	SN	SN	SN	SN	SN	SN	SN
Sutton (Surrey) 4	d		09 03			09 33				10 03			10 33			11 03				11 33			12 03		
West Croydon 4	d		09 15			09 45				10 15			10 45			11 15				11 45			12 15		
Norwood Junction 2	a		09 20			09 50				10 20			10 50			11 21				11 51			12 20		
	d		09 22			09 51				10 22			10 52			11 22				11 52			12 22		
London Bridge	d			09 22				09 52			10 22			10 52				11 22			11 52			12 22	
New Cross Gate	d			09 28				09 57			10 27			10 57				11 27			11 57			12 27	
Brockley	d			09 30				10 00			10 30			11 00				11 30			12 00			12 30	
Honor Oak Park	d			09 33				10 03			10 33			11 03				11 33			12 03			12 33	
Forest Hill	d			09 36				10 05			10 35			11 05				11 35			12 05			12 35	
Sydenham	d			09 38				10 08			10 38			11 08				11 38			12 08			12 38	
Crystal Palace	a		09 26	09 42		09 55		10 11		10 26	10 41		10 56	11 11		11 26		11 41		11 56	12 11		12 26	12 41	
Crystal Palace 4	d	09 22	09 26	09 43	09 51	09 55		10 13	10 20	10 26	10 43	10 51	10 56	11 13	11 20	11 26		11 43	11 52	11 56	12 13	12 20	12 26	12 43	12 50
Gipsy Hill	a	09 25	09 29	09 46	09 54	09 58		10 15	10 23	10 29	10 45	10 54	10 59	11 15	11 23	11 29		11 45	11 55	11 59	12 15	12 23	12 29	12 45	12 53
West Norwood 4	a	09 28	09 32	09 49	09 57	10 01		10 18	10 26	10 32	10 48	10 57	11 02	11 18	11 26	11 32		11 48	11 58	12 02	12 18	12 26	12 32	12 48	12 56
London Bridge	a	09 55			10 19				10 48			11 18			11 48				12 18			12 48			13 18
Streatham Hill	a		09 35	09 52		10 05		10 22		10 35	10 52		11 05	11 22		11 35		11 52		12 05	12 22		12 35	12 52	
Balham 4 ⊖	a		09 40	09 56		10 09		10 25		10 39	10 55		11 09	11 25		11 40		11 55		12 09	12 25		12 39	12 55	
Wandsworth Common	a		09 43	09 58		10 11		10 27		10 41	10 57		11 11	11 27		11 42		11 57		12 11	12 27		12 41	12 57	
Clapham Junction	a		09 46	10 02		10 15		10 31		10 45	11 01		11 14	11 32		11 45		12 01		12 14	12 31		12 44	13 01	
Battersea Park 4	a		09 50	10 06		10 19		10 35		10 49	11 05		11 18	11 36		11 49		12 05		12 18	12 35		12 48	13 05	
London Victoria 15 ⊖	a		09 57	10 11		10 26		10 39		10 56	11 09		11 23	11 40		11 54		12 09		12 23	12 39		12 53	13 09	

		SN		SN	SN	SN	SN	SN	SN	SN	SN	SN		SN	SN	SN	SN	SN	SN	SN	SN	SN		SN	SN
Sutton (Surrey) 4	d	12 33				13 03			13 33			14 03				14 33			15 03			15 33			
West Croydon 4	d	12 45				13 15			13 45			14 15				14 45			15 15			15 45			
Norwood Junction 2	a	12 50				13 20			13 50			14 20				14 50			15 20			15 50			
	d	12 51				13 22			13 52			14 22				14 52			15 22			15 52			
London Bridge	d			12 52			13 22			13 52				14 22			14 52			15 22				15 52	
New Cross Gate	d			12 57			13 27			13 57				14 27			14 57			15 27				15 57	
Brockley	d			13 00			13 30			14 00				14 30			15 00			15 30				16 00	
Honor Oak Park	d			13 03			13 33			14 03				14 33			15 03			15 33				16 03	
Forest Hill	d			13 05			13 35			14 05				14 35			15 05			15 35				16 05	
Sydenham	d			13 08			13 38			14 08				14 38			15 08			15 38				16 08	
Crystal Palace	a	12 55		13 11		13 26	13 41		13 56	14 11		14 26		14 41		14 56	15 11		15 26	15 41		15 56		16 11	
Crystal Palace 4	d	12 55		13 13	13 20	13 26	13 43	13 50	13 56	14 13	14 20	14 26		14 43	14 50	14 56	15 13	15 20	15 26	15 43	15 47	15 56		16 13	16 17
Gipsy Hill	a	12 58		13 15	13 23	13 29	13 45	13 53	13 59	14 15	14 23	14 29		14 45	14 53	14 59	15 15	15 23	15 29	15 45	15 49	15 59		16 15	16 19
West Norwood 4	a	13 01		13 18	13 26	13 32	13 48	13 56	14 02	14 18	14 26	14 32		14 48	14 56	15 02	15 18	15 26	15 32	15 48	15 52	16 02		16 18	16 22
London Bridge	a				13 48			14 18			14 48				15 18			15 48			16 13				16 43
Streatham Hill	a	13 05		13 22		13 35	13 52		14 05	14 22		14 35		14 52		15 05	15 22		15 35	15 52		16 05		16 22	
Balham 4 ⊖	a	13 09		13 25		13 39	13 55		14 09	14 25		14 38		14 55		15 09	15 25		15 39	15 55		16 09		16 25	
Wandsworth Common	a	13 11		13 27		13 41	13 57		14 11	14 27		14 41		14 57		15 11	15 27		15 41	15 57		16 11		16 27	
Clapham Junction	a	13 15		13 31		13 44	14 01		14 14	14 31		14 44		15 01		15 14	15 31		15 44	16 01		16 14		16 31	
Battersea Park 4	a	13 19		13 35		13 48	14 05		14 18	14 35		14 48		15 05		15 18	15 35		15 49	16 05		16 18		16 35	
London Victoria 15 ⊖	a	13 24		13 39		13 53	14 09		14 23	14 39		14 53		15 09		15 24	15 39		15 54	16 10		16 23		16 40	

For complete service between London Victoria and Balham, please see Table 170

For Faster Trains between London Victoria, Clapham Junction and East Croydon, please refer to Table 175

For Faster trains between London Victoria, Clapham Junction and Sutton, please refer to Table 182

For East Croydon & Purley connecting trains, please see Table 181

For Shepherds Bush connecting trains, please see table 176

Table 171R

Mondays to Fridays

9 December to 16 May

Croydon & Norwood Junction- Crystal Palace, Gipsy Hill, West Norwood and Streatham Hill - London Victoria

Network Diagram - see first Page of Table 170

		SN	SN	SN		SN	SN	SN	SN	SN	SN	SN	SN	SN		SN	SN	SN	SN	SN	SN	SN	SN	SN	
Sutton (Surrey) 4	d	16 03				16 33				17 03				17 33				18 03			18 33			19 05	
West Croydon 4	d	16 15				16 45				17 17				17 48				18 15			18 45			19 18	
Norwood Junction 2	a	16 21				16 50				17 22				17 54				18 21			18 51			19 22	
	d	16 22				16 52			17 20	17 23			17 50	17 55				18 24			18 52			19 23	
London Bridge	d		16 22				16 52				17 19					17 52			18 21			18 52			
New Cross Gate	d		16 27				16 57				17 26					17 58			18 26			18 57			
Brockley	d		16 30				17 00				17 29					18 01			18 29			19 00			
Honor Oak Park	d		16 33				17 03				17 32					18 04			18 32			19 03			
Forest Hill	d		16 35				17 05				17 34					18 06			18 34			19 05			
Sydenham	d		16 38				17 08				17 37					18 09			18 37			19 08			
Crystal Palace	a	16 26	16 41			16 56	17 11		17 24	17 27	17 40		17 54	17 59		18 12		18 28	18 42		18 56	19 11		19 27	
Crystal Palace 4	d	16 26	16 43	16 47		16 56	17 13	17 17	17 24	17 27	17 44	17 48	17 54	17 59		18 13	18 17	18 28	18 43	18 48	18 56	19 13	19 17	19 27	
Gipsy Hill	a	16 29	16 45	16 49		16 59	17 15	17 19	17 26	17 29	17 46	17 50	17 56	18 01		18 15	18 19	18 30	18 45	18 50	18 59	19 15	19 19	19 30	
West Norwood 4	a	16 32	16 48	16 52		17 02	17 18	17 22	17 29	17 32	17 49	17 53	17 59	18 04		18 18	18 22	18 33	18 48	18 53	19 02	19 18	19 22	19 33	
London Bridge	a			17 13				17 43	17 53			18 14	18 23				18 43			19 14			19 43		
Streatham Hill	a	16 35	16 52			17 05	17 22			17 36	17 53			18 08		18 22		18 37	18 52		19 05	19 22		19 36	
Balham 4 ⊖	a	16 39	16 55			17 09	17 25			17 39	17 56			18 11		18 25		18 40	18 55		19 09	19 25		19 39	
Wandsworth Common	a	16 41	16 57			17 11	17 27			17 41	17 58			18 13		18 27		18 42	18 57		19 11	19 27		19 42	
Clapham Junction	a	16 45	17 01			17 14	17 31			17 44	18 02			18 16		18 31		18 45	19 01		19 14	19 31		19 45	
Battersea Park 4	a	16 49	17 05			17 18	17 35			17 48	18 06			18 20		18 35		18 49	19 05		19 18	19 35		19 49	
London Victoria 15 ⊖	a	16 53	17 10			17 23	17 42			17 55	18 12			18 25		18 41		18 54	19 12		19 25	19 41		19 54	

		SN	SN	SN	SN	SN	SN	SN	SN	SN		SN	SN	SN	SN	SN	SN	SN	SN	SN		SN	SN	SN	SN FX
Sutton (Surrey) 4	d			19 32			20 03			20 33				21 06			21 32			22 05				22 32	
West Croydon 4	d			19 44			20 16			20 45				21 18			21 47			22 17				22 47	
Norwood Junction 2	a			19 51			20 21			20 50				21 22			21 52			22 22				22 51	
	d			19 52			20 21			20 52				21 23			21 53			22 23				22 52	
London Bridge	d	19 22			19 54			20 22				20 52			21 22			21 52				22 23			22 52
New Cross Gate	d	19 27			19 59			20 27				20 57			21 27			21 57				22 28			22 57
Brockley	d	19 30			20 02			20 30				21 00			21 30			22 00				22 31			23 00
Honor Oak Park	d	19 33			20 05			20 33				21 03			21 33			22 03				22 34			23 03
Forest Hill	d	19 35			20 07			20 35				21 05			21 35			22 05				22 36			23 05
Sydenham	d	19 38			20 10			20 38				21 08			21 38			22 08				22 39			23 08
Crystal Palace	a	19 41		19 56	20 13		20 25	20 41		20 56		21 11		21 27	21 41		21 57	22 11		22 27		22 42		22 57	23 11
Crystal Palace 4	d	19 43	19 50	19 56	20 13	20 20	20 25	20 43	20 50	20 56		21 13	21 20	21 27	21 43	21 50	21 57	22 13	22 20	22 27		22 43	22 52	22 57	23 13
Gipsy Hill	a	19 45	19 53	19 58	20 16	20 23	20 28	20 45	20 53	20 59		21 15	21 23	21 29	21 45	21 53	21 59	22 15	22 23	22 29		22 45	22 55	22 59	23 15
West Norwood 4	a	19 48	19 56	20 01	20 19	20 26	20 31	20 48	20 56	21 02		21 18	21 26	21 32	21 48	21 56	22 02	22 18	22 26	22 32		22 48	22 58	23 02	23 18
London Bridge	a		20 18			20 48			21 18				21 48			22 18			22 48				23 19		
Streatham Hill	a	19 52		20 05	20 22		20 36	20 52		21 05		21 22		21 36	21 52		22 06	22 22		22 36		22 52		23 06	23 22
Balham 4 ⊖	a	19 55		20 08	20 25		20 39	20 56		21 08		21 26		21 39	21 56		22 09	22 26		22 39		22 56		23 09	23 26
Wandsworth Common	a	19 57		20 10	20 27		20 41	20 58		21 10		21 28		21 41	21 58		22 11	22 28		22 41		22 58		23 11	23 28
Clapham Junction	a	20 01		20 14	20 31		20 44	21 02		21 14		21 32		21 44	22 02		22 14	22 32		22 44		23 02		23 15	23 32
Battersea Park 4	a	20 05		20 18	20 35		20 48	21 06		21 18		21 36		21 48	22 06		22 18	22 36		22 48		23 07		23 19	23 37
London Victoria 15 ⊖	a	20 09		20 22	20 39		20 53	21 11		21 22		21 41		21 53	22 11		22 23	22 41		22 53		23 11		23 25	23 41

		SN FO	SN	SN	SN	SN
Sutton (Surrey) 4	d			23 06		
West Croydon 4	d			23 18		
Norwood Junction 2	a			23 22		
	d			23 23		
London Bridge	d	22 52			23 24	23 50
New Cross Gate	d	22 57			23 29	23 56
Brockley	d	23 00			23 32	23 58
Honor Oak Park	d	23 03			23 35	00 01
Forest Hill	d	23 05			23 37	00 04
Sydenham	d	23 08			23 40	00 06
Crystal Palace	a	23 11		23 27	23 43	00 10
Crystal Palace 4	d	23 13	23 20	23 27	23 45	00 10
Gipsy Hill	a	23 15	23 23	23 29	23 47	00 13
West Norwood 4	a	23 18	23 26	23 32	23 50	00 16
London Bridge	a		23 48			
Streatham Hill	a	23 22		23 36	23 54	00 19
Balham 4 ⊖	a	23 26		23 39	23 58	00 22
Wandsworth Common	a	23 28		23 42	00 03	00 24
Clapham Junction	a	23 32		23 45	00 06	00 28
Battersea Park 4	a	23 37		23 49	00 10	00 32
London Victoria 15 ⊖	a	23 44		23 54	00 15	00 36

For complete service between London Victoria and Balham, please see Table 170

For Faster Trains between London Victoria, Clapham Junction and East Croydon, please refer to Table 175

For Faster trains between London Victoria, Clapham Junction and Sutton, please refer to Table 182

For East Croydon & Purley connecting trains, please see Table 181

For Shepherds Bush connecting trains, please see table 176

Table 171R

Saturdays

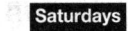

14 December to 17 May

Croydon & Norwood Junction- Crystal Palace, Gipsy Hill, West Norwood and Streatham Hill - London Victoria

Network Diagram - see first Page of Table 170

		SN	SN	SN	SN	SN	SN	SN	SN	SN	SN	SN	SN	SN	SN	SN	SN	SN	SN	SN	SN
Sutton (Surrey) 4	d											08 03			08 33			09 03			09 33
West Croydon 4	d			06 18		06 45						08 15			08 45			09 15			09 45
Norwood Junction 2	a			06 22		06 52						08 20			08 50			09 20			09 50
	d		05 52	06 23	06 41	06 53	07 23		07 53			08 22			08 52			09 22			09 52
London Bridge	d												08 22			08 52			09 22		
New Cross Gate	d												08 27			08 57			09 27		
Brockley	d												08 30			09 00			09 30		
Honor Oak Park	d	00 01											08 33			09 03			09 33		
Forest Hill	d	00 04											08 35			09 05			09 35		
Sydenham	d	00 06											08 38			09 08			09 38		
Crystal Palace	a	00 10	05 56	06 27	06 45	06 57	07 27		07 57			08 26	08 41		08 56	09 11		09 26	09 41		09 56
Crystal Palace 4	d	00 10	05 56	06 27	06 45	06 57	07 27	07 43	07 57	08 13	08 20	08 26	08 43	08 50	08 56	09 13	09 20	09 26	09 43	09 50	09 56
Gipsy Hill	a	00 13	05 59	06 29	06 47	06 59	07 29	07 45	07 59	08 15	08 23	08 29	08 45	08 53	08 58	09 15	09 23	09 29	09 45	09 53	09 59
West Norwood 4	a	00 16	06 02	06 32	06 50	07 02	07 32	07 48	08 02	08 18	08 26	08 32	08 48	08 56	09 01	09 18	09 26	09 32	09 48	09 56	10 02
London Bridge	a				07 14						08 48			09 18			09 48			10 18	
Streatham Hill	a	00 19	06 05	06 36		07 06	07 36	07 52	08 06	08 22		08 35	08 52		09 06	09 22		09 35	09 52		10 05
Balham 4 ⊖	a	00 22	06 09	06 39		07 09	07 39	07 55	08 09	08 25		08 39	08 55		09 09	09 25		09 39	09 55		10 09
Wandsworth Common	a	00 24	06 11	06 41		07 11	07 41	07 57	08 11	08 27		08 41	08 57		09 11	09 27		09 41	09 57		10 11
Clapham Junction	a	00 28	06 14	06 44		07 14	07 44	08 01	08 14	08 31		08 44	09 01		09 14	09 32		09 44	10 01		10 14
Battersea Park 4	a	00 32	06 18	06 48		07 19	07 48	08 05	08 18	08 35		08 48	09 05		09 18	09 36		09 48	10 05		10 18
London Victoria 15 ⊖	a	00 36	06 23	06 53		07 24	07 53	08 09	08 23	08 39		08 53	09 09		09 23	09 41		09 53	10 09		10 23

		SN		SN	SN	SN	SN	SN	SN	SN	SN	SN	SN	SN	SN	SN	SN	SN	SN
Sutton (Surrey) 4	d				21 03			21 33			22 03			22 33			23 03		
West Croydon 4	d				21 15			21 45			22 15			22 45			23 15		
Norwood Junction 2	a				21 20			21 50			22 20			22 50			23 20		
	d				21 22			21 52			22 22			22 52			23 22		
London Bridge	d	09 52				21 22			21 52			22 22			22 52			23 22	23 52
New Cross Gate	d	09 57				21 27			21 57			22 27			22 57			23 27	23 57
Brockley	d	10 00	and at			21 30			22 00			22 30			23 00			23 30	00 01
Honor Oak Park	d	10 03	the same			21 33			22 03			22 33			23 03			23 33	00 03
Forest Hill	d	10 05	minutes			21 35			22 05			22 35			23 05			23 35	00 05
Sydenham	d	10 08	past			21 38			22 08			22 38			23 08			23 38	00 08
Crystal Palace	a	10 11	each		21 26	21 41		21 56	22 11		22 26	22 41		22 56	23 11		23 26	23 41	00 11
Crystal Palace 4	d	10 13	hour until	21 20	21 26	21 43	21 50	21 56	22 13	22 20	22 26	22 43	22 50	22 56	23 13	23 20	23 26	23 43	00 11
Gipsy Hill	a	10 15		21 23	21 29	21 45	21 53	21 59	22 15	22 23	22 29	22 45	22 53	22 59	23 15	23 23	23 29	23 45	00 14
West Norwood 4	a	10 18		21 26	21 32	21 48	21 56	22 02	22 18	22 26	22 32	22 48	22 56	23 02	23 18	23 26	23 32	23 48	00 17
London Bridge	a			21 48			22 18			22 48			23 18			23 48			
Streatham Hill	a	10 22			21 35	21 52		22 05	22 22		22 35	22 52		23 05	23 22		23 35	23 52	00 20
Balham 4 ⊖	a	10 25			21 39	21 55		22 09	22 25		22 39	22 55		23 09	23 25		23 39	23 55	00 24
Wandsworth Common	a	10 27			21 41	21 57		22 11	22 27		22 41	22 57		23 11	23 27		23 41	23 57	00 26
Clapham Junction	a	10 31			21 44	22 01		22 14	22 31		22 44	23 01		23 16	23 31		23 45	00 01	00 30
Battersea Park 4	a	10 35			21 48	22 05		22 18	22 35		22 48	23 05		23 20	23 35		23 49	00 05	00 34
London Victoria 15 ⊖	a	10 39			21 53	22 09		22 23	22 39		22 53	23 09		23 24	23 41		23 54	00 10	00 38

For complete service between London Victoria and Balham, please see Table 170

For Faster Trains between London Victoria, Clapham Junction and East Croydon, please refer to Table 175

For Faster trains between London Victoria, Clapham Junction and Sutton, please refer to Table 182

For East Croydon & Purley connecting trains, please see Table 181

For Shepherds Bush connecting trains, please see table 176

Table 171R

Sundays

8 December to 11 May

Croydon & Norwood Junction- Crystal Palace, Gipsy Hill, West Norwood and Streatham Hill - London Victoria

Network Diagram - see first Page of Table 170

Station		SN	SN	SN	SN	SN		SN	SN	SN	SN	SN	SN	SN	SN	SN		SN	SN	SN	SN	SN	SN	SN	SN
Sutton (Surrey) 4	d									08 10		08 40		09 10		09 40			10 10		10 40		11 10		11 40
West Croydon 4	d				07 22			07 52		08 22		08 52		09 22		09 52			10 22		10 52		11 22		11 52
Norwood Junction 2	a				07 26			07 56		08 26		08 56		09 26		09 56			10 26		10 56		11 26		11 56
	d		06 57		07 27			07 57		08 27		08 57		09 27		09 57			10 27		10 57		11 27		11 57
London Bridge	d																								
New Cross Gate	d																								
Brockley	d	00 01																							
Honor Oak Park	d	00 03																							
Forest Hill	d	00 05																							
Sydenham	d	00 08																							
Crystal Palace	a	00 11	07 01		07 31			08 01		08 31		09 01		09 31		10 01			10 31		11 01		11 31		12 01
Crystal Palace 4	d	00 11	07 01	07 07	07 31	07 38		08 01	08 08	08 31	08 38	09 01	09 08	09 31	09 37	10 01		10 07	10 31	10 37	11 01	11 07	11 31	11 37	12 01
Gipsy Hill	a	00 14	07 03	07 09	07 33	07 40		08 03	08 10	08 33	08 40	09 03	09 10	09 33	09 39	10 03		10 09	10 33	10 39	11 03	11 09	11 33	11 39	12 03
West Norwood 4	a	00 17	07 06	07 12	07 36	07 43		08 06	08 13	08 36	08 43	09 06	09 13	09 36	09 42	10 06		10 12	10 36	10 42	11 06	11 12	11 36	11 42	12 06
London Bridge	a			07 33		08 04			08 34		09 04		09 34		10 03			10 33		11 03		11 33		12 03	
Streatham Hill	a	00 20	07 11		07 40			08 10		08 40		09 10		09 40		10 10			10 40		11 10		11 40		12 10
Balham 4 ⊖	a	00 24	07 17		07 44			08 19		08 49		09 13		09 43		10 13			10 43		11 13		11 43		12 13
Wandsworth Common	a	00 26	07 19		07 46			08 21		08 51		09 15		09 45		10 15			10 45		11 15		11 45		12 15
Clapham Junction	a	00 30	07 22		07 49			08 24		08 54		09 19		09 48		10 18			10 48		11 18		11 48		12 18
Battersea Park 4	a	00 34	07 26		07 53			08 28		08 58		09 23		09 52		10 22			10 52		11 22		11 52		12 22
London Victoria 15 ⊖	a	00 38	07 31		07 58			08 33		09 03		09 27		09 57		10 27			10 57		11 27		11 57		12 27

Station		SN		SN	SN	SN	SN	SN	SN			SN	SN	SN	SN		SN	SN	SN	SN	SN	SN	SN	SN	SN
Sutton (Surrey) 4	d			12 10		12 40		13 10				19 40		20 10			20 40		21 10		21 40		22 10		22 40
West Croydon 4	d			12 22		12 52		13 22				19 52		20 22			20 52		21 22		21 52		22 22		22 52
Norwood Junction 2	a			12 26		12 56		13 26				19 56		20 26			20 56		21 26		21 56		22 26		22 56
	d			12 27		12 57		13 27				19 57		20 27			20 57		21 27		21 57		22 27		22 57
London Bridge	d																								
New Cross Gate	d																								
Brockley	d									and at the same minutes past each hour until															
Honor Oak Park	d																								
Forest Hill	d																								
Sydenham	d																								
Crystal Palace	a			12 31		13 01		13 31				20 01		20 31			21 01		21 31		22 01		22 31		23 01
Crystal Palace 4	d	12 07		12 31	12 39	13 01	13 07	13 31	13 37			20 01	20 07	20 31	20 37		21 01	21 07	21 31	21 37	22 01	22 07	22 31	22 37	23 01
Gipsy Hill	a	12 09		12 33	12 41	13 03	13 09	13 33	13 39			20 03	20 09	20 33	20 39		21 03	21 09	21 33	21 39	22 03	22 09	22 33	22 39	23 03
West Norwood 4	a	12 12		12 36	12 44	13 06	13 12	13 36	13 42			20 06	20 12	20 36	20 42		21 06	21 12	21 36	21 42	22 06	22 12	22 36	22 42	23 06
London Bridge	a	12 33			13 05		13 33		14 03				20 33		21 03			21 33		22 03		22 33		23 03	
Streatham Hill	a			12 40		13 10		13 40				20 10		20 40			21 10		21 40		22 10		22 40		23 10
Balham 4 ⊖	a			12 43		13 13		13 43				20 13		20 43			21 13		21 43		22 13		22 43		23 13
Wandsworth Common	a			12 45		13 15		13 45				20 15		20 45			21 15		21 45		22 15		22 45		23 15
Clapham Junction	a			12 48		13 18		13 48				20 18		20 48			21 19		21 49		22 19		22 49		23 19
Battersea Park 4	a			12 52		13 22		13 52				20 22		20 52			21 23		21 53		22 23		22 53		23 23
London Victoria 15 ⊖	a			12 57		13 27		13 57				20 27		20 57			21 27		21 57		22 27		22 57		23 27

Station			SN	SN	SN
Sutton (Surrey) 4	d			23 10	
West Croydon 4	d			23 22	
Norwood Junction 2	a			23 26	
	d			23 27	
London Bridge	d				
New Cross Gate	d				
Brockley	d				
Honor Oak Park	d				
Forest Hill	d				
Sydenham	d				
Crystal Palace	a			23 31	
Crystal Palace 4	d		23 07	23 31	23 37
Gipsy Hill	a		23 09	23 33	23 39
West Norwood 4	a		23 12	23 36	23 42
London Bridge	a		23 33		00 03
Streatham Hill	a			23 40	
Balham 4 ⊖	a			23 43	
Wandsworth Common	a			23 45	
Clapham Junction	a			23 49	
Battersea Park 4	a			23 53	
London Victoria 15 ⊖	a			23 57	

For complete service between London Victoria and Balham, please see Table 170

For Faster Trains between London Victoria, Clapham Junction and East Croydon, please refer to Table 175

For Faster trains between London Victoria, Clapham Junction and Sutton, please refer to Table 182

For East Croydon & Purley connecting trains, please see Table 181

For Shepherds Bush connecting trains, please see table 176

Table 172

Mondays to Fridays

9 December to 16 May

London and West Croydon-Waddon, Wallington & Carshalton Beeches-Sutton

Network Diagram - see first Page of Table 170

Miles	Miles			SN MX	SN MX	SN	SN	SN	SN	SN	SN	SN	SN	SN	SN	SN	SN	SN	SN	SN	SN	SN	SN
0	0	London Victoria 15 ⊖	d						06 00	06 06	06 30	06 36	07 00	07 08	07 30	07 36	08 05	08 08	08 26	08 31	08 36	08 52	09 03
—	—	Clapham Junction 10	d						06 08	06 14	06 38	06 44	07 08	07 16	07 38	07 44	08 14	08 17	08 33	08 40	08 44	09 00	09 11
4¾	4¾	Balham 4 ⊖	d		00 04				06 14	06 20	06 44	06 50	07 13	07 21	07 44	07 50	08 19	08 22	08 38	08 46	08 49	09 05	09 16
—	—	London Bridge	d					05 36															
—	7	Norwood Junction	a					06 00		06 37		07 07		07 38		08 08		08 39			09 06		
—	—	Norwood Junction 2	d				05 53	06 00		06 39		07 09		07 39		08 09		08 40			09 09		
10¾	12	West Croydon 4	a		00 21		05 57	06 05	06 32	06 43	07 02	07 13	07 32	07 44	08 02	08 14	08 36	08 44	08 56	09 05	09 13	09 22	09 33
—	—	**West Croydon**	d	00 04	00 22	05 45	05 58	06 05	06 32	06 44	07 03	07 14	07 32	07 46	08 04	08 15	08 36	08 45	08 56	09 06	09 14	09 24	09 34
11¾	13	**Waddon**	d	00 06	00 24	05 47	06 00	06 08	06 35	06 46	07 05	07 16	07 35	07 48	08 06	08 17	08 39	08 47	08 59	09 08	09 16	09 26	09 36
13¼	14½	**Wallington**	d	00 10	00 28	05 51	06 04	06 11	06 38	06 50	07 09	07 20	07 38	07 52	08 10	08 21	08 42	08 51	09 02	09 12	09 20	09 30	09 40
14	15½	**Carshalton Beeches**	d	00 12	00 30	05 53	06 06	06 14	06 41	06 52	07 11	07 22	07 41	07 54	08 12	08 23	08 45	08 53	09 05	09 14	09 22	09 32	09 42
15	16½	Sutton (Surrey) 4	a	00 16	00 34	05 57	06 10	06 17	06 44	06 56	07 15	07 26	07 44	07 58	08 16	08 27	08 48	08 57	09 08	09 18	09 26	09 39	09 46

		SN	SN	SN	SN	SN	SN	SN	SN	SN	SN	SN	SN	SN	SN	SN	SN	SN	SN	SN	SN	SN	SN
London Victoria 15 ⊖	d	09 05	09 22	09 33	09 36	09 53	10 03	10 06	10 23	10 33	10 36	10 53	11 03	11 06	11 23	11 33	11 36	11 53	12 03	12 06	12 23	12 33	12 36
Clapham Junction 10	d	09 14	09 30	09 41	09 44	10 00	10 11	10 14	10 30	10 41	10 44	11 00	11 11	11 14	11 30	11 41	11 44	12 00	12 11	12 14	12 30	12 41	12 44
Balham 4 ⊖	d	09 20	09 35	09 46	09 50	10 05	10 16	10 20	10 35	10 46	10 50	11 05	11 16	11 20	11 35	11 46	11 50	12 05	12 16	12 20	12 35	12 46	12 50
London Bridge	d																						
Norwood Junction	a	09 38			10 07			10 37			11 07			11 37			12 07			12 37			13 07
Norwood Junction 2	d	09 39			10 09			10 39			11 09			11 39			12 09			12 39			13 09
West Croydon 4	a	09 43	09 52	10 03	10 13	10 22	10 33	10 43	10 52	11 03	11 13	11 23	11 33	11 43	11 53	12 03	12 13	12 22	12 33	12 43	12 52	13 03	13 13
West Croydon	d	09 44	09 54	10 04	10 14	10 24	10 34	10 44	10 54	11 04	11 14	11 24	11 34	11 44	11 54	12 04	12 14	12 24	12 34	12 44	12 54	13 04	13 14
Waddon	d	09 46	09 56	10 06	10 16	10 26	10 36	10 46	10 56	11 06	11 16	11 26	11 36	11 46	11 56	12 06	12 16	12 26	12 36	12 46	12 56	13 06	13 16
Wallington	d	09 50	10 00	10 10	10 20	10 30	10 40	10 50	11 00	11 10	11 20	11 30	11 40	11 50	12 00	12 10	12 20	12 30	12 40	12 50	13 00	13 10	13 20
Carshalton Beeches	d	09 52	10 02	10 12	10 22	10 32	10 42	10 52	11 02	11 12	11 22	11 32	11 42	11 52	12 02	12 12	12 22	12 32	12 42	12 52	13 02	13 12	13 22
Sutton (Surrey) 4	a	09 56	10 06	10 16	10 26	10 39	10 46	10 56	11 06	11 16	11 26	11 39	11 46	11 56	12 06	12 16	12 26	12 39	12 46	12 56	13 06	13 16	13 26

		SN	SN	SN	SN	SN	SN	SN	SN	SN	SN	SN	SN	SN	SN	SN	SN	SN	SN	SN	SN	SN
London Victoria 15 ⊖	d	12 53	13 03	13 06	13 23	13 33	13 36	13 53	14 03	14 06	14 23	14 33	14 36	14 53	15 03	15 06	15 23	15 33	15 36	15 53	16 03	16 07
Clapham Junction 10	d	13 00	13 11	13 14	13 30	13 41	13 44	14 00	14 11	14 14	14 30	14 41	14 44	15 00	15 11	15 14	15 30	15 41	15 44	16 00	16 11	16 15
Balham 4 ⊖	d	13 05	13 16	13 20	13 35	13 46	13 50	14 05	14 16	14 20	14 35	14 46	14 50	15 05	15 16	15 20	15 35	15 46	15 50	16 05	16 16	16 20
London Bridge	d																					
Norwood Junction	a			13 37			14 07			14 37			15 07			15 37			16 07			16 37
Norwood Junction 2	d			13 39			14 09			14 39			15 09			15 39			16 09			16 39
West Croydon 4	a	13 22	13 33	13 43	13 53	14 03	14 13	14 22	14 33	14 43	14 52	15 03	15 13	15 22	15 33	15 43	15 52	16 03	16 13	16 22	16 33	16 45
West Croydon	d	13 24	13 34	13 44	13 54	14 04	14 14	14 24	14 34	14 44	14 54	15 04	15 14	15 24	15 34	15 44	15 54	16 04	16 14	16 24	16 34	16 45
Waddon	d	13 26	13 36	13 46	13 56	14 06	14 16	14 26	14 36	14 46	14 56	15 06	15 16	15 26	15 36	15 46	15 56	16 06	16 16	16 26	16 36	16 47
Wallington	d	13 30	13 40	13 50	14 00	14 10	14 20	14 30	14 40	14 50	15 00	15 10	15 20	15 30	15 40	15 50	16 00	16 10	16 20	16 30	16 40	16 51
Carshalton Beeches	d	13 32	13 42	13 52	14 02	14 12	14 22	14 32	14 42	14 52	15 02	15 12	15 22	15 32	15 42	15 52	16 02	16 12	16 22	16 32	16 42	16 53
Sutton (Surrey) 4	a	13 39	13 46	13 56	14 06	14 16	14 26	14 39	14 46	14 56	15 06	15 16	15 26	15 39	15 46	15 56	16 06	16 16	16 26	16 36	16 47	16 57

		SN	SN	SN	SN	SN	SN	SN	SN	SN	SN	SN	SN	SN	SN	SN	SN	SN	SN	SN	SN	SN	SN
London Victoria 15 ⊖	d	16 33	16 37		17 01	17 07		17 33	17 37		18 03	18 07		18 32	18 36	18 59	19 06		19 30	19 36	20 00	20 06	20 30
Clapham Junction 10	d	16 41	16 45		17 09	17 15		17 41	17 45		18 11	18 15		18 40	18 44	19 08	19 14		19 38	19 44	20 08	20 14	20 38
Balham 4 ⊖	d	16 46	16 50		17 14	17 20		17 46	17 51		18 16	18 20		18 45	18 49	19 14	19 20		19 44	19 50	20 14	20 20	20 44
London Bridge	d			17 04			17 29			18 02			18 32					19 30					
Norwood Junction	a		17 07	17 16		17 37	17 41		18 08	18 14		18 37	18 45		19 07		19 37	19 43		20 07		20 37	
Norwood Junction 2	d		17 09	17 17		17 38	17 42		18 10	18 15		18 39	18 45		19 09		19 39	19 43		20 09		20 39	
West Croydon 4	a	17 03	17 13	17 21	17 32	17 43	17 47	18 03	18 16	18 19	18 34	18 44	18 50	19 04	19 14	19 32	19 44	19 48	20 02	20 13	20 32	20 43	21 02
West Croydon	d	17 04	17 14	17 22	17 33	17 43	17 47	18 04	18 16	18 21	18 35	18 45	18 51	19 04	19 15	19 32	19 45	19 49	20 02	20 14	20 32	20 44	21 02
Waddon	d	17 06	17 16	17 24	17 35	17 46	17 50	18 06	18 18	18 23	18 37	18 47	18 53	19 07	19 17	19 35	19 47	19 52	20 05	20 16	20 35	20 46	21 05
Wallington	d	17 10	17 20	17 28	17 39	17 49	17 53	18 10	18 22	18 27	18 41	18 51	18 57	19 10	19 21	19 38	19 51	19 55	20 08	20 20	20 38	20 50	21 08
Carshalton Beeches	d	17 12	17 22	17 30	17 41	17 52	17 56	18 12	18 24	18 29	18 43	18 53	18 59	19 13	19 23	19 41	19 53	19 58	20 11	20 22	20 41	20 52	21 11
Sutton (Surrey) 4	a	17 16	17 26	17 34	17 45	17 55	17 59	18 16	18 28	18 33	18 47	18 58	19 03	19 16	19 28	19 44	19 57	20 01	20 14	20 26	20 44	20 56	21 14

		SN	SN	SN	SN	SN	SN	SN	SN	SN	SN	SN	SN	SN
London Victoria 15 ⊖	d	20 36	21 00	21 06	21 30	21 36	22 00	22 06	22 30	22 36	23 00	23 06	23 33	23 51
Clapham Junction 10	d	20 44	21 08	21 14	21 38	21 44	22 08	22 14	22 38	22 46	23 08	23 14	23 41	23 59
Balham 4 ⊖	d	20 50	21 14	21 20	21 44	21 50	22 14	22 20	22 44	22 52	23 14	23 20	23 46	00 04
London Bridge	d													
Norwood Junction	a	21 07		21 37		22 07		22 37		23 08		23 36		
Norwood Junction 2	d	21 09		21 39		22 09		22 39		23 09		23 37		
West Croydon 4	a	21 13	21 32	21 43	22 02	22 13	22 32	22 43	23 02	23 13	23 32	23 41	00 03	00 21
West Croydon	d	21 14	21 32	21 44	22 02	22 14	22 32	22 44	23 02	23 14	23 32	23 42	00 04	00 22
Waddon	d	21 16	21 35	21 46	22 05	22 16	22 35	22 46	23 05	23 16	23 35	23 44	00 06	00 24
Wallington	d	21 20	21 38	21 50	22 08	22 20	22 38	22 50	23 08	23 20	23 38	23 48	00 10	00 28
Carshalton Beeches	d	21 22	21 41	21 52	22 11	22 22	22 41	22 52	23 11	23 22	23 41	23 50	00 12	00 30
Sutton (Surrey) 4	a	21 26	21 44	21 56	22 14	22 26	22 44	22 56	23 14	23 26	23 44	23 54	00 16	00 34

For Faster trains between London Victoria, Clapham Junction and Sutton, please refer to Table 182

For London Bridge connections at Norwood Junction, please see table 175

For Shepherds Bush connections at Clapham Junction, please see table 176

Table 172

Saturdays

14 December to 17 May

London and West Croydon-Waddon, Wallington & Carshalton Beeches-Sutton

Network Diagram - see first Page of Table 170

		SN	SN	SN	SN	SN	SN	SN	SN	SN	SN	SN	SN	SN	and at the same minutes past each hour until	SN	SN	SN	SN	SN	SN		SN	SN
London Victoria 15 ⊖	d			00 34		06 23		06 53	07 06	07 23	07 33	07 36	07 53	08 03		18 06	18 23	18 33	18 36	18 53	19 03		19 06	19 23
Clapham Junction 10	d			00 42		06 30		07 00	07 14	07 30	07 41	07 44	08 00	08 11		18 14	18 30	18 41	18 44	19 00	19 11		19 14	19 30
Balham 4 ⊖	d		00 04	00 47		06 35		07 05	07 20	07 35	07 46	07 50	08 05	08 16		18 20	18 35	18 46	18 50	19 05	19 16		19 20	19 35
London Bridge	d																							
Norwood Junction	a								07 37			08 07				18 37			19 07				19 37	
Norwood Junction 2	d						07 09		07 39			08 09				18 39			19 09				19 39	
West Croydon 4	a		00 21	01 04		06 52	07 14	07 22	07 43	07 52	08 03	08 13	08 22	08 33		18 43	18 52	19 03	19 13	19 22	19 33		19 43	19 52
West Croydon	d	00 04	00 22	01 04	06 45	06 54	07 15	07 24	07 44	07 54	08 04	08 14	08 24	08 34		18 44	18 54	19 04	19 14	19 24	19 34		19 44	19 54
Waddon	d	00 06	00 24	01 07	06 47	06 56	07 17	07 26	07 46	07 56	08 06	08 16	08 26	08 36		18 46	18 56	19 06	19 16	19 26	19 36		19 46	19 56
Wallington	d	00 10	00 28	01 10	06 51	07 00	07 21	07 30	07 50	08 00	08 10	08 20	08 30	08 40		18 50	19 00	19 10	19 20	19 30	19 40		19 50	20 00
Carshalton Beeches	d	00 12	00 30	01 13	06 53	07 02	07 23	07 32	07 52	08 02	08 12	08 22	08 32	08 42		18 52	19 02	19 12	19 22	19 32	19 42		19 52	20 02
Sutton (Surrey) 4	a	00 16	00 34	01 16	06 57	07 06	07 27	07 39	07 56	08 06	08 16	08 26	08 39	08 46		18 56	19 06	19 16	19 26	19 39	19 46		19 56	20 06

		SN	SN	SN	SN	SN	SN	SN		SN	SN	SN	SN	SN	SN	SN	SN	SN		SN	SN	SN	SN	SN	SN
London Victoria 15 ⊖	d	19 33	19 36	19 53	20 03	20 06	20 23	20 33		20 36	20 53	21 03	21 06	21 23	21 33	21 36	21 53	22 03		22 06	22 23	22 33	22 36	22 53	23 03
Clapham Junction 10	d	19 41	19 44	20 00	20 11	20 14	20 30	20 41		20 44	21 00	21 11	21 14	21 30	21 41	21 44	22 00	22 11		22 14	22 30	22 41	22 44	23 00	23 11
Balham 4 ⊖	d	19 46	19 50	20 05	20 16	20 20	20 35	20 46		20 50	21 05	21 16	21 20	21 35	21 46	21 50	22 05	22 16		22 20	22 35	22 46	22 50	23 06	23 16
London Bridge	d																								
Norwood Junction	a		20 07			20 37				21 07			21 37			22 07				22 37			23 07		
Norwood Junction 2	d		20 09			20 39				21 09			21 39			22 09				22 39			23 09		
West Croydon 4	a	20 03	20 14	20 24	20 33	20 44	20 54	21 03		21 14	21 24	21 33	21 44	21 54	22 03	22 13	22 22	22 33		22 43	22 52	23 03	23 13	23 22	23 33
West Croydon	d	20 04	20 15	20 25	20 34	20 45	20 55	21 04		21 15	21 25	21 34	21 45	21 55	22 04	22 14	22 24	22 34		22 44	22 54	23 04	23 14	23 24	23 34
Waddon	d	20 06	20 17	20 27	20 36	20 47	20 57	21 06		21 17	21 27	21 36	21 47	21 57	22 06	22 16	22 26	22 36		22 46	22 56	23 06	23 16	23 26	23 36
Wallington	d	20 10	20 21	20 31	20 40	20 51	21 01	21 10		21 21	21 31	21 40	21 51	22 01	22 10	22 20	22 30	22 40		22 50	23 00	23 10	23 20	23 30	23 40
Carshalton Beeches	d	20 12	20 23	20 33	20 42	20 53	21 03	21 12		21 23	21 33	21 42	21 53	22 03	22 12	22 22	22 32	22 42		22 52	23 02	23 12	23 22	23 32	23 42
Sutton (Surrey) 4	a	20 16	20 27	20 39	20 46	20 57	21 07	21 16		21 27	21 39	21 46	21 57	22 07	22 16	22 26	22 39	22 46		22 56	23 06	23 16	23 26	23 39	23 46

		SN	SN	SN
London Victoria 15 ⊖	d	23 06	23 34	23 51
Clapham Junction 10	d	23 14	23 42	23 59
Balham 4 ⊖	d	23 20	23 47	00 04
London Bridge	d			
Norwood Junction	a	23 37		
Norwood Junction 2	d	23 39		
West Croydon 4	a	23 43	00 03	00 21
West Croydon	d	23 44	00 04	00 22
Waddon	d	23 46	00 06	00 24
Wallington	d	23 50	00 10	00 28
Carshalton Beeches	d	23 52	00 12	00 30
Sutton (Surrey) 4	a	23 56	00 16	00 35

Sundays

8 December to 11 May

		SN A	SN A	SN	SN	SN	SN	SN	SN	SN		SN	SN	SN	SN	SN	SN	SN	SN	SN	and at the same minutes past each hour until
London Victoria 15 ⊖	d			00 34	06 49	07 17	07 20	07 49	07 52	08 19		08 23	08 49	08 52	09 19	09 24	09 49	09 54	10 19	10 24	
Clapham Junction 10	d			00 42	06 57	07 23	07 28	07 57	08 00	08 27		08 31	08 57	09 00	09 26	09 32	09 56	10 02	10 26	10 32	
Balham 4 ⊖	d		00 04	00 47	07 02	07 28	07 34	08 01	08 06	08 31		08 36	09 01	09 06	09 30	09 38	10 00	10 07	10 30	10 37	
London Bridge	d																				
Norwood Junction	a						07 55		08 24			08 54		09 25		09 56		10 26		10 56	
Norwood Junction 2	d						07 56		08 25			08 56		09 26		09 57		10 27		10 57	
West Croydon 4	a		00 21	01 04	07 19	07 48	08 00	08 18	08 30	08 48		09 00	09 18	09 30	09 48	10 02	10 18	10 31	10 48	11 01	
West Croydon	d	00 04	00 22	01 04	07 20	07 49	08 01	08 19	08 31	08 49		09 01	09 19	09 31	09 49	10 04	10 19	10 34	10 49	11 04	
Waddon	d	00 06	00 24	01 07	07 22	07 51	08 03	08 21	08 33	08 51		09 03	09 21	09 33	09 51	10 07	10 21	10 36	10 51	11 06	
Wallington	d	00 10	00 28	01 10	07 26	07 55	08 07	08 25	08 37	08 55		09 07	09 25	09 37	09 55	10 10	10 25	10 40	10 55	11 10	
Carshalton Beeches	d	00 12	00 30	01 13	07 28	07 57	08 09	08 27	08 39	08 57		09 09	09 27	09 39	09 57	10 13	10 27	10 42	10 57	11 12	
Sutton (Surrey) 4	a	00 16	00 35	01 16	07 32	08 01	08 13	08 31	08 43	09 01		09 13	09 31	09 44	10 01	10 16	10 31	10 46	11 01	11 16	

		SN	SN	SN	SN		SN	SN	SN	SN	SN	SN	SN	SN	SN		SN	SN
London Victoria 15 ⊖	d	19 49	19 54	20 19	20 24		20 49	20 54	21 19	21 24	21 49	21 54	22 19	22 24	22 49		22 54	23 19
Clapham Junction 10	d	19 56	20 02	20 26	20 32		20 56	21 02	21 26	21 32	21 56	22 02	22 26	22 32	22 56		23 02	23 27
Balham 4 ⊖	d	20 00	20 07	20 30	20 37		21 00	21 07	21 30	21 38	22 00	22 07	22 30	22 38	23 00		23 07	23 32
London Bridge	d																	
Norwood Junction	a		20 26		20 56			21 26		21 56		22 26		22 56			23 26	
Norwood Junction 2	d		20 27		20 57			21 27		21 57		22 27		22 57			23 27	
West Croydon 4	a	20 18	20 31	20 48	21 01		21 18	21 31	21 48	22 01	22 18	22 31	22 48	23 01	23 18		23 31	23 49
West Croydon	d	20 19	20 34	20 49	21 04		21 19	21 34	21 49	22 04	22 19	22 34	22 49	23 04	23 19		23 34	23 50
Waddon	d	20 21	20 36	20 51	21 06		21 21	21 36	21 51	22 06	22 21	22 36	22 51	23 06	23 21		23 36	23 52
Wallington	d	20 25	20 40	20 55	21 10		21 25	21 40	21 55	22 10	22 25	22 40	22 55	23 10	23 25		23 40	23 56
Carshalton Beeches	d	20 27	20 42	20 57	21 12		21 27	21 42	21 57	22 12	22 27	22 42	22 57	23 12	23 27		23 42	23 58
Sutton (Surrey) 4	a	20 31	20 46	21 01	21 16		21 31	21 46	22 01	22 16	22 31	22 46	23 01	23 16	23 31		23 46	00 02

A not 8 December

For Faster trains between London Victoria, Clapham Junction and Sutton, please refer to Table 182

For London Bridge connections at Norwood Junction, please see table 175

For Shepherds Bush connections at Clapham Junction, please see table 176

Table 172R

Mondays to Fridays

9 December to 16 May

Carshalton Beeches & Wallington, Waddon - West Croydon and London Victoria

Network Diagram - see first Page of Table 170

Miles	Miles			SN MX	SN	SN	SN	SN	SN	SN	SN	SN	SN	SN	SN	SN	SN	SN	SN	SN	SN	SN	SN
0	0	Sutton (Surrey) 4	d		05 33	05 49	06 03	06 15	06 32	06 44	07 00	07 14	07 22	07 32	07 45	07 53	08 05	08 14	08 32	08 45	09 03	09 15	09 23
1	1	**Carshalton Beeches**	d		05 36	05 52	06 06	06 18	06 35	06 48	07 03	07 18	07 25	07 35	07 48	07 56	08 08	08 17	08 35	08 48	09 06	09 18	09 26
1¾	2	**Wallington**	d		05 39	05 55	06 08	06 20	06 37	06 50	07 06	07 20	07 27	07 37	07 50	07 58	08 10	08 19	08 38	08 50	09 08	09 20	09 28
3¼	3½	**Waddon**	d	00 01	05 42	05 58	06 11	06 23	06 40	06 53	07 10	07 23	07 30	07 40	07 53	08 01		08 22	08 41	08 53	09 11	09 23	09 31
4¼	4½	**West Croydon**	a	00 04	05 45	06 01	06 14	06 26	06 43	06 57	07 13	07 27	07 33	07 43	07 57	08 04	08 15	08 25	08 44	08 57	09 14	09 27	09 34
—	—	West Croydon 4	d		05 45	06 01	06 15	06 27	06 44	06 58	07 14	07 27	07 34	07 44	07 58	08 05	08 15	08 26	08 44	08 58	09 15	09 28	09 35
—	9½	Norwood Junction 2	a		05 50		06 19		06 49		07 19			07 49			08 20		08 50		09 20		
—	—	Norwood Junction	d		05 50		06 20		06 50		07 19			07 49			08 21		08 51		09 22		
—	—	London Bridge	a		06 14		06 33		07 04		07 33			08 05			08 33		09 05				
10¼	11¾	Balham	a			06 17		06 43		07 14		07 43	07 50		08 14	08 21		08 44		09 14	09 40	09 44	09 52
12¼	13¾	Clapham Junction	a			06 23		06 48		07 21		07 50	07 57		08 21	08 27		08 50		09 21	09 46	09 50	09 58
15	16½	London Victoria 15 ⊖	a			06 33		07 00		07 29		07 59	08 07		08 29	08 36		08 59		09 29	09 57	09 59	10 05

		SN	SN	SN	SN	SN	SN	SN	SN	SN	SN	SN	SN	SN	SN	SN	SN	SN	SN	SN	SN	SN	SN
Sutton (Surrey) 4	d	09 33	09 46	09 52	10 03	10 15	10 22	10 33	10 45	10 52	11 03	11 15	11 22	11 33	11 45	11 52	12 03	12 15	12 22	12 33	12 45	12 52	13 03
Carshalton Beeches	d	09 36	09 49	09 55	10 06	10 18	10 25	10 36	10 48	10 55	11 06	11 18	11 25	11 36	11 48	11 55	12 06	12 18	12 25	12 36	12 48	12 55	13 06
Wallington	d	09 38	09 51	09 57	10 08	10 20	10 27	10 38	10 51	10 57	11 08	11 20	11 27	11 38	11 50	11 57	12 08	12 20	12 27	12 38	12 50	12 57	13 08
Waddon	d	09 41	09 54	10 00	10 11	10 23	10 30	10 41	10 54	11 00	11 11	11 23	11 30	11 41	11 53	12 00	12 11	12 23	12 30	12 41	12 53	13 00	13 11
West Croydon	a	09 44	09 57	10 03	10 14	10 27	10 33	10 44	10 57	11 03	11 14	11 27	11 33	11 44	11 57	12 03	12 14	12 27	12 33	12 44	12 57	13 03	13 14
West Croydon 4	d	09 45	09 58	10 04	10 15	10 28	10 34	10 45	10 58	11 04	11 15	11 28	11 34	11 45	11 58	12 04	12 15	12 28	12 34	12 45	12 58	13 04	13 15
Norwood Junction 2	a	09 50			10 20			10 50			11 21			11 51			12 20			12 50			13 20
Norwood Junction	d	09 51			10 22			10 52			11 22			11 52			12 22			12 51			13 22
London Bridge	a																						
Balham	a	10 09	10 14	10 21	10 39	10 44	10 51	11 09	11 14	11 21	11 40	11 44	11 51	12 09	12 14	12 21	12 39	12 44	12 51	13 09	13 14	13 21	13 39
Clapham Junction	a	10 15	10 20	10 27	10 45	10 49	10 57	11 14	11 20	11 26	11 45	11 49	11 56	12 14	12 19	12 26	12 44	12 49	12 56	13 15	13 19	13 26	13 44
London Victoria 15 ⊖	a	10 26	10 28	10 34	10 56	10 58	11 06	11 23	11 28	11 34	11 54	11 58	12 04	12 23	12 28	12 34	12 53	12 58	13 04	13 24	13 28	13 36	13 53

		SN	SN	SN	SN	SN	SN	SN	SN	SN	SN	SN	SN	SN	SN	SN	SN	SN	SN	SN	SN	SN
Sutton (Surrey) 4	d	13 15	13 22	13 33	13 45	13 52	14 03	14 15	14 22	14 33	14 45	14 52	15 03	15 15	15 22	15 33	15 45	15 52	16 03	16 13	16 22	16 33
Carshalton Beeches	d	13 18	13 25	13 36	13 48	13 55	14 06	14 18	14 25	14 36	14 48	14 55	15 06	15 18	15 25	15 36	15 48	15 55	16 06	16 16	16 25	16 36
Wallington	d	13 20	13 27	13 38	13 50	13 57	14 08	14 20	14 27	14 38	14 50	14 57	15 08	15 20	15 27	15 38	15 50	15 57	16 08	16 19	16 27	16 38
Waddon	d	13 23	13 30	13 41	13 53	14 00	14 11	14 23	14 30	14 41	14 53	15 00	15 11	15 23	15 30	15 41	15 53	16 00	16 11	16 22	16 30	16 41
West Croydon	a	13 27	13 33	13 44	13 57	14 03	14 14	14 27	14 33	14 44	14 57	15 03	15 14	15 27	15 33	15 44	15 57	16 03	16 14	16 25	16 33	16 44
West Croydon 4	d	13 28	13 34	13 45	13 58	14 04	14 15	14 28	14 34	14 45	14 58	15 04	15 15	15 28	15 34	15 45	15 58	16 04	16 15	16 25	16 34	16 45
Norwood Junction 2	a			13 50			14 20			14 50			15 20			15 50			16 21			16 50
Norwood Junction	d			13 52			14 22			14 52			15 22			15 52			16 22			16 52
London Bridge	a																					
Balham	a	13 44	13 51	14 09	14 14	14 21	14 38	14 44	14 51	15 09	15 14	15 22	15 39	15 44	15 51	16 09	16 14	16 21	16 39	16 42	16 51	17 09
Clapham Junction	a	13 49	13 56	14 14	14 19	14 26	14 44	14 49	14 56	15 14	15 19	15 28	15 44	15 49	15 56	16 14	16 19	16 26	16 45	16 48	16 56	17 14
London Victoria 15 ⊖	a	13 58	14 04	14 23	14 28	14 34	14 53	14 58	15 04	15 24	15 28	15 36	15 54	15 58	16 04	16 23	16 28	16 34	16 53	16 58	17 04	17 23

		SN	SN	SN	SN	SN	SN	SN	SN	SN	SN	SN	SN	SN	SN	SN	SN	SN	SN	SN	SN	SN	SN
Sutton (Surrey) 4	d	16 42	16 52	17 03	17 13	17 33	17 43	18 03	18 12	18 33	18 43	19 05	19 16	19 32	19 46	20 03	20 23	20 33	20 52	21 06	21 22	21 32	21 52
Carshalton Beeches	d	16 45	16 55	17 06	17 16	17 36	17 46	18 06	18 15	18 36	18 46	19 08	19 19	19 35	19 49	20 06	20 26	20 36	20 55	21 09	21 25	21 35	21 55
Wallington	d	16 47	16 57	17 08	17 18	17 39	17 48	18 08	18 18	18 39	18 48	19 10	19 21	19 38	19 51	20 08	20 28	20 38	20 57	21 11	21 27	21 37	21 57
Waddon	d	16 50	17 00	17 11	17 21	17 42	17 51	18 11	18 21	18 42	18 51	19 13	19 24	19 41	19 54	20 11	20 31	20 41	21 00	21 14	21 30	21 40	22 00
West Croydon	a	16 54	17 03	17 14	17 24	17 45	17 54	18 14	18 25	18 45	18 55	19 16	19 28	19 44	19 58	20 15	20 34	20 44	21 03	21 17	21 33	21 43	22 03
West Croydon 4	d	16 55	17 04	17 17	17 25	17 48	17 55	18 15	18 26	18 45	18 56	19 18	19 29	19 44	19 59	20 16	20 35	20 45	21 04	21 18	21 34	21 47	22 04
Norwood Junction 2	a			17 22		17 54		18 21		18 51		19 22		19 51		20 21		20 50		21 22		21 52	
Norwood Junction	d			17 23		17 55		18 24		18 52		19 23		19 52		20 21		20 52		21 23		21 53	
London Bridge	a																						
Balham	a	17 13	17 22	17 39	17 41	18 11	18 13	18 40	18 43	19 09	19 13	19 39	19 45	20 08	20 15	20 39	20 51	21 08	21 21	21 39	21 51	22 09	22 21
Clapham Junction	a	17 19	17 27	17 44	17 49	18 16	18 19	18 45	18 49	19 14	19 19	19 45	19 51	20 14	20 20	20 44	20 56	21 14	21 26	21 44	21 56	22 14	22 26
London Victoria 15 ⊖	a	17 28	17 35	17 55	17 58	18 25	18 28	18 54	18 57	19 25	19 28	19 54	20 00	20 22	20 29	20 53	21 04	21 22	21 34	21 53	22 04	22 23	22 34

		SN	SN	SN	SN	SN	SN	SN	SN	SN
Sutton (Surrey) 4	d	22 05	22 22	22 32	22 52	23 06	23 20	23 30	23 41	23 53
Carshalton Beeches	d	22 08	22 25	22 35	22 55	23 09	23 23	23 33	23 44	23 56
Wallington	d	22 10	22 27	22 37	22 57	23 11	23 25	23 35	23 46	23 58
Waddon	d	22 13	22 30	22 40	23 00	23 14	23 28	23 38	23 49	00 01
West Croydon	a	22 16	22 33	22 43	23 03	23 17	23 31	23 41	23 52	00 04
West Croydon 4	d	22 17	22 34	22 47	23 04	23 18				
Norwood Junction 2	a	22 22		22 51		23 22				
Norwood Junction	d	22 23		22 52		23 23				
London Bridge	a									
Balham	a	22 39	22 51	23 09	23 21	23 39				
Clapham Junction	a	22 44	22 56	23 15	23 26	23 45				
London Victoria 15 ⊖	a	22 53	23 06	23 25	23 34	23 54				

For Faster trains between London Victoria, Clapham Junction and Sutton, please refer to Table 182

For London Bridge connections at Norwood Junction, please see table 175

For Shepherds Bush connections at Clapham Junction, please see table 176

Table 172R

Saturdays

14 December to 17 May

Carshalton Beeches & Wallington, Waddon - West Croydon and London Victoria

Network Diagram - see first Page of Table 170

		SN	SN	SN	SN	SN	SN	SN	SN	SN	SN	SN	SN		SN	SN	SN	SN	SN	SN	SN	SN	SN
Sutton (Surrey) [4]	d		06 45	07 03	07 15	07 33	07 45	08 03	08 15	08 22	08 33	08 45	08 52	and at the same minutes past each hour until	14 03	14 15	14 22	14 33	14 45	14 52	15 03	15 15	15 22
Carshalton Beeches	d		06 48	07 06	07 18	07 36	07 48	08 06	08 18	08 25	08 36	08 48	08 55		14 06	14 18	14 25	14 36	14 48	14 55	15 06	15 18	15 25
Wallington	d		06 50	07 08	07 20	07 38	07 50	08 08	08 20	08 27	08 38	08 50	08 57		14 08	14 20	14 27	14 38	14 50	14 57	15 08	15 20	15 27
Waddon	d	00 01	06 53	07 11	07 23	07 41	07 53	08 11	08 23	08 30	08 41	08 53	09 00		14 11	14 23	14 30	14 41	14 53	15 00	15 11	15 23	15 30
West Croydon	a	00 04	06 57	07 14	07 27	07 44	07 57	08 14	08 27	08 33	08 44	08 57	09 03		14 14	14 27	14 33	14 44	14 57	15 03	15 14	15 27	15 33
West Croydon [4] [tram]	d		06 58	07 15	07 28	07 45	07 58	08 15	08 28	08 34	08 45	08 58	09 04		14 15	14 28	14 34	14 45	14 58	15 04	15 15	15 28	15 34
Norwood Junction [2]	a			07 19		07 49		08 20			08 50				14 20			14 50			15 20		
Norwood Junction	d			07 20		07 50		08 22			08 52				14 22			14 52			15 22		
London Bridge	a			07 43		08 11																	
Balham	a		07 14		07 44		08 14	08 39	08 44	08 51	09 09	09 14	09 21		14 39	14 44	14 51	15 09	15 14	15 21	15 39	15 44	15 51
Clapham Junction	a		07 19		07 49		08 19	08 44	08 49	08 56	09 14	09 19	09 26		14 44	14 49	14 56	15 14	15 19	15 26	15 44	15 49	15 56
London Victoria [15] [underground]	a		07 28		07 58		08 28	08 53	08 58	09 04	09 23	09 28	09 34		14 53	14 58	15 04	15 23	15 28	15 34	15 53	15 58	16 04

		SN	SN	SN	SN	SN	SN	SN		SN	SN	SN	SN	SN	SN	SN	SN	SN	SN	SN	SN	SN	SN
Sutton (Surrey) [4]	d	15 33	15 45	15 52	16 03	16 15	16 22	16 33	and at the same minutes past each hour until	20 45	20 52	21 03	21 15	21 22	21 33	21 45	21 52	22 03	22 15	22 22	22 33	22 45	22 52
Carshalton Beeches	d	15 36	15 48	15 55	16 06	16 18	16 25	16 36		20 48	20 55	21 06	21 18	21 25	21 36	21 48	21 55	22 06	22 18	22 25	22 36	22 48	22 55
Wallington	d	15 38	15 50	15 57	16 08	16 20	16 27	16 38		20 50	20 57	21 08	21 20	21 27	21 38	21 50	21 57	22 08	22 20	22 27	22 38	22 51	22 57
Waddon	d	15 41	15 53	16 00	16 11	16 23	16 30	16 41		20 53	21 00	21 11	21 23	21 30	21 41	21 53	22 00	22 11	22 23	22 30	22 41	22 54	23 00
West Croydon	a	15 45	15 57	16 03	16 14	16 27	16 33	16 44		20 57	21 03	21 14	21 27	21 33	21 44	21 57	22 03	22 14	22 27	22 33	22 44	22 57	23 03
West Croydon [4] [tram]	d	15 45	15 58	16 04	16 15	16 28	16 34	16 45		20 58	21 04	21 15	21 28	21 34	21 45	21 58	22 04	22 15	22 28	22 34	22 45	22 58	23 04
Norwood Junction [2]	a	15 50			16 20			16 50				21 20			21 50			22 20			22 50		
Norwood Junction	d	15 52			16 22			16 52				21 22			21 52			22 22			22 52		
London Bridge	a																						
Balham	a	16 09	16 14	16 21	16 39	16 44	16 51	17 09		21 14	21 21	21 39	21 44	21 51	22 09	22 14	22 21	22 39	22 44	22 51	23 09	23 14	23 21
Clapham Junction	a	16 14	16 19	16 26	16 44	16 49	16 56	17 14		21 19	21 26	21 44	21 49	21 56	22 14	22 19	22 27	22 44	22 49	22 56	23 16	23 20	23 26
London Victoria [15] [underground]	a	16 23	16 28	16 34	16 53	16 58	17 04	17 23		21 28	21 34	21 53	21 58	22 04	22 23	22 28	22 34	22 53	22 58	23 04	23 24	23 29	23 34

		SN	SN	SN	SN	SN	SN	SN
Sutton (Surrey) [4]	d	23 03	23 15	23 22	23 30	23 34	23 46	23 59
Carshalton Beeches	d	23 06	23 18	23 25	23 33	23 37	23 49	00 02
Wallington	d	23 08	23 20	23 27	23 35	23 39	23 51	00 04
Waddon	d	23 11	23 23	23 30	23 38	23 42	23 54	00 07
West Croydon	a	23 14	23 27	23 33	23 41	23 45	23 57	00 10
West Croydon [4] [tram]	d	23 15	23 28	23 34				
Norwood Junction [2]	a	23 20						
Norwood Junction	d	23 22						
London Bridge	a							
Balham	a	23 39	23 44	23 50				
Clapham Junction	a	23 45	23 49	23 56				
London Victoria [15] [underground]	a	23 54	23 58	00 04				

Sundays

8 December to 11 May

		SN A	SN	SN	SN	SN	SN	SN	SN	SN	SN	SN		SN	SN	SN	SN	SN	SN	SN	SN	SN	SN
Sutton (Surrey) [4]	d		06 55	07 25	07 55	08 10	08 25	08 40	08 55	09 10	09 25	09 40	and at the same minutes past each hour until	18 55	19 10	19 25	19 40	19 55	20 10	20 25	20 40	20 55	21 10
Carshalton Beeches	d	00s02	06 58	07 28	07 58	08 13	08 28	08 43	08 58	09 13	09 28	09 43		18 58	19 13	19 28	19 43	19 58	20 13	20 28	20 43	20 58	21 13
Wallington	d	00s04	07 00	07 30	08 00	08 15	08 30	08 45	09 00	09 15	09 30	09 45		19 00	19 15	19 30	19 45	20 00	20 15	20 30	20 45	21 00	21 15
Waddon	d	00s07	07 03	07 33	08 03	08 18	08 33	08 48	09 03	09 18	09 33	09 48		19 03	19 18	19 33	19 48	20 03	20 18	20 33	20 48	21 03	21 18
West Croydon	a	00s10	07 06	07 36	08 06	08 21	08 36	08 51	09 06	09 21	09 36	09 51		19 06	19 21	19 36	19 51	20 06	20 21	20 36	20 51	21 06	21 21
West Croydon [4] [tram]	d		07 07	07 37	08 07	08 22	08 37	08 52	09 07	09 22	09 37	09 52		19 07	19 22	19 37	19 52	20 07	20 22	20 37	20 52	21 07	21 22
Norwood Junction [2]	a					08 26		08 56		09 26		09 56			19 26		19 56		20 26		20 56		21 26
Norwood Junction	d					08 27		08 57		09 27		09 57			19 27		19 57		20 27		20 57		21 27
London Bridge	a																						
Balham	a		07 23	07 53	08 26	08 49	08 57	09 13	09 23	09 43	09 53	10 13		19 23	19 43	19 53	20 13	20 23	20 43	20 53	21 13	21 23	21 43
Clapham Junction	a		07 27	07 57	08 31	08 54	09 01	09 19	09 27	09 48	09 57	10 18		19 27	19 48	19 57	20 18	20 27	20 48	20 57	21 19	21 27	21 49
London Victoria [15] [underground]	a		07 34	08 05	08 38	09 03	09 08	09 27	09 34	09 57	10 04	10 27		19 34	19 57	20 04	20 27	20 34	20 57	21 04	21 27	21 34	21 57

		SN	SN	SN	SN	SN	SN	SN	SN	SN	SN
Sutton (Surrey) [4]	d	21 25	21 40	21 55	22 10	22 25	22 40	22 55	23 10	23 25	23 40
Carshalton Beeches	d	21 28	21 43	21 58	22 13	22 28	22 43	22 58	23 13	23 28	23 43
Wallington	d	21 30	21 45	22 00	22 15	22 30	22 45	23 00	23 15	23 30	23 45
Waddon	d	21 33	21 48	22 03	22 18	22 33	22 48	23 03	23 18	23 33	23 48
West Croydon	a	21 36	21 51	22 06	22 21	22 36	22 51	23 06	23 21	23 36	23 51
West Croydon [4] [tram]	d	21 37	21 52	22 07	22 22	22 37	22 52	23 07	23 22	23 37	23 52
Norwood Junction [2]	a		21 56		22 26		22 56		23 26		
Norwood Junction	d		21 57		22 27		22 57		23 27		
London Bridge	a										
Balham	a	21 53	22 13	22 23	22 43	22 53	23 13	23 23	23 43	23 53	00 08
Clapham Junction	a	21 57	22 19	22 27	22 49	22 57	23 19	23 27	23 49	23 57	00 13
London Victoria [15] [underground]	a	22 04	22 27	22 34	22 57	23 04	23 27	23 34	23 57	00 05	00 22

A not 8 December

For Faster trains between London Victoria, Clapham Junction and Sutton, please refer to Table 182

For London Bridge connections at Norwood Junction, please see table 175

For Shepherds Bush connections at Clapham Junction, please see table 176

Network Diagram for Tables 173, 177, 178, 179

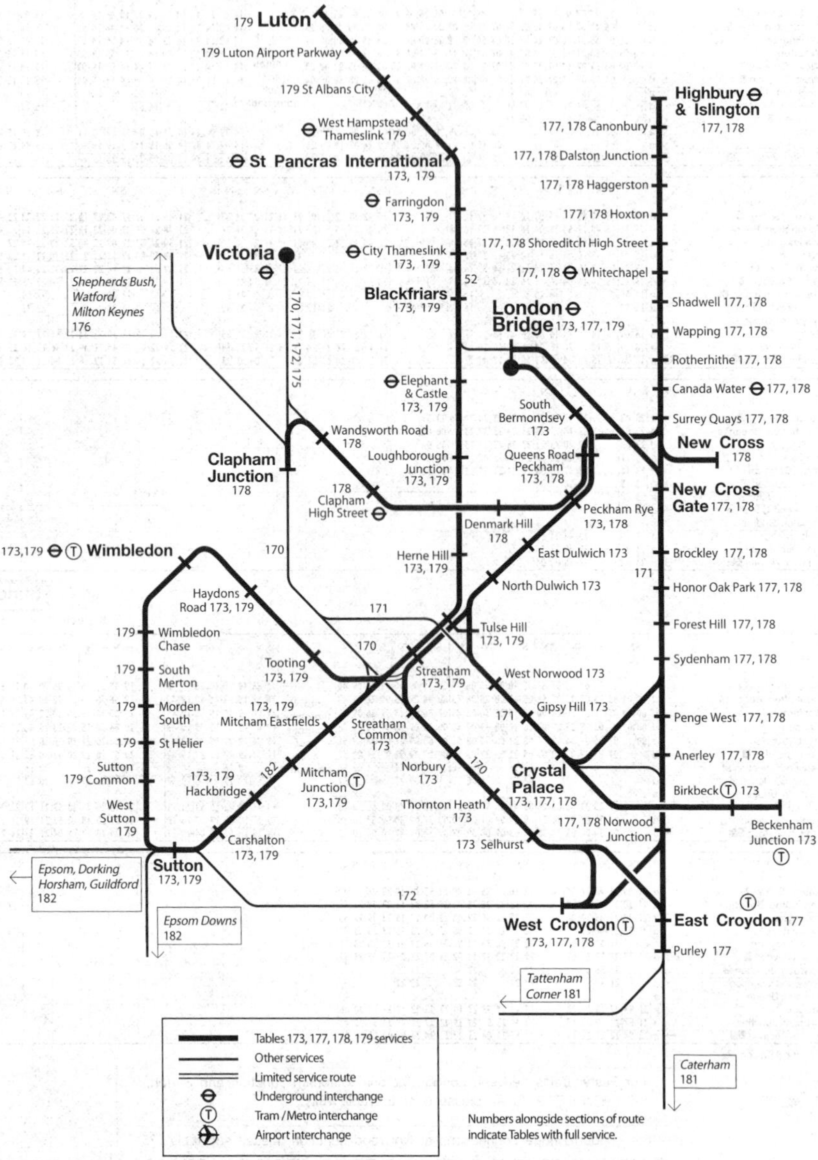
179 Luton
179 Luton Airport Parkway
179 St Albans City
West Hampstead Thameslink 179
St Pancras International 173, 179
Farringdon 173, 179
City Thameslink 173, 179
Blackfriars 173, 179
52
Victoria
170, 171, 172, 175
Shepherds Bush, Watford, Milton Keynes 176
Elephant & Castle 173, 179
London Bridge 173, 177, 179
South Bermondsey 173
Wandsworth Road 178
Loughborough Junction 173, 179
Queens Road Peckham 173, 178
Clapham Junction 178
178 Clapham High Street
Denmark Hill 178
Peckham Rye 173, 178
Highbury & Islington 177, 178
177, 178 Canonbury
177, 178 Dalston Junction
177, 178 Haggerston
177, 178 Hoxton
177, 178 Shoreditch High Street
177, 178 Whitechapel
Shadwell 177, 178
Wapping 177, 178
Rotherhithe 177, 178
Canada Water 177, 178
Surrey Quays 177, 178
New Cross 178
New Cross Gate 177, 178
Brockley 177, 178
171
Honor Oak Park 177, 178
Forest Hill 177, 178
Sydenham 177, 178
Penge West 177, 178
Anerley 177, 178
Birkbeck 173
Beckenham Junction 173
173,179 Wimbledon
170
Herne Hill 173, 179
East Dulwich 173
North Dulwich 173
Haydons Road 173, 179
171
Tulse Hill 173, 179
170
179 Wimbledon Chase
179 South Merton
179 Morden South
179 St Helier
179 Sutton Common
West Sutton 179
Tooting 173, 179
Streatham 173, 179
West Norwood 173
171
Gipsy Hill 173
173, 179 Mitcham Eastfields
Streatham Common 173
Norbury 173
170
Crystal Palace 173, 177, 178
182
173, 179 Hackbridge
Mitcham Junction 173,179
Thornton Heath 173
177, 178 Norwood Junction
Carshalton 173, 179
173 Selhurst
Sutton 173, 179
Epsom, Dorking Horsham, Guildford 182
172
Epsom Downs 182
West Croydon 173, 177, 178
East Croydon 177
Purley 177
Tattenham Corner 181
Caterham 181
Tables 173, 177, 178, 179 services
Other services
Limited service route
Underground interchange
Tram / Metro interchange
Airport interchange
Numbers alongside sections of route indicate Tables with full service.

TOCs operating on this network - Southern (SN), First Capital Connect (FC), London Overground (LO)

Table 173

Mondays to Fridays

9 December to 16 May

London Bridge - South Bermondsey, Queens Road Peckham, Peckham Rye, East Dulwich, North Dulwich, Tulse Hill and Streatham

Network Diagram - see first Page of Table 173

Miles	Miles	Miles	Miles			SN MX A	FC MX B	SN MX C	FC	SN	FC B	SN	SN	FC D		SN	SN	FC B	SN	SN	FC B	SN	FC 1 E	SN
0	0	—	—	London Bridge 4 ⊖	d			00 03		06 00		06 10	06 20			06 30	06 40		06 50	06 58		07 10		07 20
1¾	1¾	—	—	**South Bermondsey**	d			00 07		06 04		06 14	06 24			06 34	06 44		06 54	07 02		07 14		07 24
2¾	2¾	—	—	Queens Rd Peckham	d			00 09		06 07		06 17	06 27			06 37	06 47		06 57	07 05		07 16		07 27
3½	3½	—	—	Peckham Rye 4	d			00 12		06 10		06 20	06 30			06 39	06 50		07 00	07 08		07 19		07 30
4¼	4¼	—	—	**East Dulwich**	d			00 15		06 13		06 23	06 33			06 42	06 53		07 03	07 11		07 22		07 33
4¾	4¾	—	—	**North Dulwich**	d			00 17		06 15		06 25	06 35			06 44	06 55		07 05	07 13		07 24		07 35
—	—	0	0	St Pancras International	d				05 36		05 54			06 12				06 34			06 52		07 04	
—	—	1¼	1¼	Farringdon	d				05 42		06 00			06 18				06 40			06 58		07 10	
—	—	1½	1½	City Thameslink	d				05 44		06 03			06 21				06 43			07 01		07 13	
—	—	2	2	London Blackfriars	d				05 47		06 06			06 24				06 46			07 04		07 16	
—	—	3¼	3¼	Elephant & Castle	d				05 50		06 09			06 27				06 49			07 07		07 19	
—	—	5	5	Loughborough Jn	d						06 13			06 31				06 53			07 11		07 23	
—	—	6	6	Herne Hill	d				05 57		06 17			06 35				06 57			07 15		07 27	
6	6	7	7	**Tulse Hill**	d		00 02	00 21	06 02	06 19	06 22	06 28	06 39	06 42		06 48	06 59	07 02	07 09	07 17	07 20	07 28	07 31	07 39
—	6¾	—	—	West Norwood	a			00 24					06 42						07 12					07 42
—	7¾	—	—	Gipsy Hill	a			00 27					06 45						07 15					07 45
—	8½	—	—	Crystal Palace	a			00 29					06 48						07 17					07 47
—	10	—	—	**Birkbeck**	a								06 52						07 22					07 52
—	11½	—	—	Beckenham Junction	a								06 56						07 26					07 56
7½	—	8½	8½	**Streatham**	d	00 02	00 06		06 05	06 22	06 25	06 32		06 45		06 51	07 02	07 05		07 20	07 23	07 31	07 34	
8	—	—	—	Streatham Common	a	00 05						06 35					07 05					07 34		
9	—	—	—	Norbury	a	00 08						06 37					07 08					07 37		
10¼	—	—	—	Thornton Heath	a	00 11						06 40					07 11					07 40		
11	—	—	—	Selhurst	a	00 13						06 43					07 13					07 42		
12¼	—	—	—	West Croydon	a	00 19						06 51					07 20					07 49		
—	—	10	—	Tooting	a		00 10		06 10	06 27						06 56		07 11		07 25			07 38	
—	—	11½	—	Haydons Road	a		00 13		06 13	06 30						06 59		07 14		07 28			07 41	
—	—	12¼	—	Wimbledon	a		00 18		06 15	06 33						07 01		07 17		07 31			07 44	
—	—	—	10¼	Mitcham Eastfields	a						06 29			06 49							07 27			
—	—	—	11¼	Mitcham Junction	a						06 32			06 52							07 30			
—	—	—	12½	Hackbridge	a						06 35			06 55							07 33			
—	—	—	13¼	Carshalton	a						06 38			06 58							07 36			
—	—	—	14½	Sutton (Surrey)	a		00 39		06 33		06 43			07 03				07 35			07 39		08 07	

		FC 1 F	SN	SN	FC G	SN	SN	FC B	SN	SN		FC B	SN H	FC I	SN	FC 1 E	SN	FC B	SN	SN		FC I	SN	FC I	SN
London Bridge 4 ⊖	d		07 30	07 40		07 50	08 00		08 10	08 19			08 29		08 40		08 50		09 00	09 10			09 20		09 30
South Bermondsey	d		07 34	07 44		07 54	08 04		08 14	08 23			08 33		08 44		08 54		09 04	09 14			09 24		09 34
Queens Rd Peckham	d		07 36	07 47		07 57	08 07		08 17	08 26			08 35		08 47		08 57		09 07	09 17			09 26		09 37
Peckham Rye 4	d		07 39	07 50		08 00	08 09		08 20	08 30			08 38		08 50		09 00		09 10	09 20			09 29		09 40
East Dulwich	d		07 42	07 53		08 03	08 12		08 23	08 33			08 41		08 53		09 03		09 13	09 23			09 32		09 43
North Dulwich	d		07 44	07 55		08 05	08 14		08 25	08 35			08 43		08 55		09 05		09 15	09 25			09 34		09 45
St Pancras International	d	07 16			07 32			07 52				08 12		08 24		08 36		08 44				08 56		09 16	
Farringdon	d	07 22			07 38			07 58				08 18		08 30		08 42		08 50				09 02		09 22	
City Thameslink	d	07 25			07 41			08 01				08 21		08 33		08 45		08 53				09 05		09 25	
London Blackfriars	d	07 28			07 44			08 04				08 24		08 36		08 48		08 56				09 08		09 28	
Elephant & Castle	d	07 33			07 47			08 07				08 27		08 39				09 00				09 12		09 31	
Loughborough Jn	d	07 37			07 51			08 11				08 31						09 04				09 16		09 35	
Herne Hill	d	07 41			07 57			08 17				08 36		08 46		08 57		09 11				09 25		09 41	
Tulse Hill	d	07 45	07 48	07 59	08 05	08 13	08 18	08 21	08 29	08 39		08 40	08 47	08 51	08 59	09 01	09 09	09 16	09a18	09 29		09 31	09 38	09 46	09a48
West Norwood	a					08 16				08 42							09 12						09 43		
Gipsy Hill	a					08 19				08 45							09 15						09 46		
Crystal Palace	a					08 22				08 47							09 17						09 48		
Birkbeck	a					08 26				08 52							09 22						09 53		
Beckenham Junction	a					08 29				08 56							09 26						09 56		
Streatham	d	07 48	07 51	08 02	08 08		08 21	08 24	08 33			08 44	08 50	08 54	09 02	09 05		09 20		09 32		09 35		09 50	
Streatham Common	a			08 05					08 36						09 05					09 35					
Norbury	a			08 08					08 38						09 08					09 38					
Thornton Heath	a			08 11					08 41						09 11					09 41					
Selhurst	a			08 13					08 44						09 13					09 43					
West Croydon	a			08 24					08 50						09 19					09 48					
Tooting	a		07 56		08 13		08 26					08 48				09 10						09 40			
Haydons Road	a		07 59		08 16		08 30					08 51				09 13						09 43			
Wimbledon	a		08 03		08 18		08 33					08 54				09 16						09 46			
Mitcham Eastfields	a	07 52						08 28						08 58				09 24						09 54	
Mitcham Junction	a	07 55						08 31						09 01				09 27						09 57	
Hackbridge	a	07 58						08 34						09 04				09 30						10 00	
Carshalton	a	08 01						08 37						09 07				09 33						10 03	
Sutton (Surrey)	a	08 04			08 37			08 40				09 12	09 02	09 10		09 37		09 36				10 05		10 06	

A From London Bridge
B From Luton
C To Norwood Junction
D From West Hampstead Thameslink
E From Bedford
F From Bedford. 1 to London Blackfriars
G From Flitwick
H To Epsom
I From St Albans City

Other trains operate between Peckham Rye, Denmark Hill and London Victoria and London Thameslink see table 195

For Denmark Hill, Clapham High Street, Wandsworth Road, Clapham Junction and East London Line connecting trains, please see Table 178

Table 173

Mondays to Fridays

9 December to 16 May

London Bridge - South Bermondsey, Queens Road Peckham, Peckham Rye, East Dulwich, North Dulwich, Tulse Hill and Streatham

Network Diagram - see first Page of Table 173

		SN	FC A	SN	FC B	SN		SN	FC A	SN	FC B	SN	FC A	SN	FC B	SN		FC A	SN	FC B	SN	FC A	SN	FC B	SN
London Bridge 4 ⊖	d	09 40		09 49		10 00		10 10		10 25		10 40		10 55		11 10			11 25		11 40		11 55		12 10
South Bermondsey	d	09 44		09 53		10 04		10 14		10 29		10 44		10 59		11 14			11 29		11 44		11 59		12 14
Queens Rd Peckham	d	09 47		09 56		10 07		10 17		10 32		10 47		11 02		11 17			11 32		11 47		12 02		12 17
Peckham Rye 4	d	09 50		09 59		10 10		10 20		10 35		10 50		11 05		11 20			11 35		11 50		12 05		12 20
East Dulwich	d	09 53		10 02		10 13		10 23		10 38		10 53		11 08		11 23			11 38		11 53		12 08		12 23
North Dulwich	d	09 55		10 04		10 15		10 25		10 40		10 55		11 10		11 25			11 40		11 55		12 10		12 25
St Pancras International	d		09 34		09 48				10 04		10 19		10 34		10 49			11 04		11 19		11 34		11 48	
Farringdon	d		09 40		09 53				10 09		10 25		10 39		10 55			11 09		11 25		11 39		11 53	
City Thameslink	d		09 43		09 57				10 13		10 27		10 43		10 57			11 13		11 27		11 43		11 57	
London Blackfriars	d		09 46		10 00				10 16		10 30		10 46		11 00			11 16		11 30		11 46		12 00	
Elephant & Castle	d		09 49		10 03				10 19		10 33		10 49		11 03			11 19		11 33		11 49		12 03	
Loughborough Jn	d		09 53		10 07				10 23		10 37		10 53		11 07			11 23		11 37		11 53		12 07	
Herne Hill	d		09 57		10 11				10 27		10 41		10 57		11 11			11 27		11 41		11 57		12 11	
Tulse Hill	d	09 59	10 01	10 08	10 16	10a18		10 29	10 31	10 44	10 46	10 59	11 01	11 14	11 16	11 29		11 31	11 44	11 46	11 59	12 01	12 14	12 16	12 29
West Norwood	a			10 12						10 47				11 17					11 47				12 17		
Gipsy Hill	a			10 15						10 50				11 20					11 50				12 20		
Crystal Palace	a			10 18						10 52				11 22					11 52				12 22		
Birkbeck	a			10 22						10 57				11 27					11 57				12 27		
Beckenham Junction	a			10 25						11 01				11 31					12 01				12 31		
Streatham	d	10 02	10 05		10 20			10 32	10 35		10 50	11 02	11 05		11 20	11 32		11 35		11 50	12 02	12 05		12 20	12 32
Streatham Common	a	10 05						10 35				11 05				11 35					12 05				12 35
Norbury	a	10 08						10 38				11 08				11 38					12 08				12 38
Thornton Heath	a	10 11						10 41				11 11				11 41					12 11				12 41
Selhurst	a	10 13						10 43				11 13				11 44					12 13				12 43
West Croydon	a	10 18						10 48				11 19				11 49					12 18				12 48
Tooting	a		10 10						10 40				11 10					11 40				12 10			
Haydons Road	a		10 13						10 43				11 13					11 43				12 13			
Wimbledon	a		10 16						10 46				11 16					11 46				12 16			
Mitcham Eastfields	a				10 24						10 54				11 24					11 54				12 24	
Mitcham Junction	a				10 27						10 57				11 27					11 57				12 27	
Hackbridge	a				10 30						11 00				11 30					12 00				12 30	
Carshalton	a				10 33						11 03				11 33					12 03				12 33	
Sutton (Surrey)	a		10 35		10 36				11 05		11 06		11 35		11 36			12 05		12 06		12 35		12 36	

		FC A		SN	FC B	SN	FC A	SN	FC B	SN	FC A	SN		FC B	SN	FC A	SN	FC B	SN	FC A	SN	FC B		SN	FC A
London Bridge 4 ⊖	d			12 25		12 40		12 55		13 10		13 25			13 40		13 55		14 10		14 25			14 40	
South Bermondsey	d			12 29		12 44		12 59		13 14		13 29			13 44		13 59		14 14		14 29			14 44	
Queens Rd Peckham	d			12 32		12 47		13 02		13 17		13 32			13 47		14 02		14 17		14 32			14 47	
Peckham Rye 4	d			12 35		12 50		13 05		13 20		13 35			13 50		14 05		14 20		14 35			14 50	
East Dulwich	d			12 38		12 53		13 08		13 23		13 38			13 53		14 08		14 23		14 38			14 53	
North Dulwich	d			12 40		12 55		13 10		13 25		13 40			13 55		14 10		14 25		14 40			14 55	
St Pancras International	d	12 04			12 18		12 34		12 48		13 04			13 18		13 34		13 48		14 04		14 18			14 34
Farringdon	d	12 09			12 23		12 39		12 53		13 09			13 23		13 39		13 53		14 09		14 23			14 39
City Thameslink	d	12 13			12 27		12 43		12 57		13 13			13 27		13 43		13 57		14 13		14 27			14 43
London Blackfriars	d	12 16			12 30		12 46		13 00		13 16			13 30		13 46		14 00		14 16		14 30			14 46
Elephant & Castle	d	12 19			12 33		12 49		13 03		13 19			13 33		13 49		14 03		14 19		14 33			14 49
Loughborough Jn	d	12 23			12 37		12 53		13 07		13 23			13 37		13 53		14 07		14 23		14 37			14 53
Herne Hill	d	12 27			12 41		12 57		13 11		13 27			13 41		13 57		14 11		14 27		14 41			14 57
Tulse Hill	d	12 31		12 44	12 46	12 59	13 01	13 14	13 16	13 29	13 31	13 44		13 46	13 59	14 01	14 14	14 16	14 29	14 31	14 44	14 46		14 59	15 01
West Norwood	a			12 47				13 17				13 47					14 17				14 47				
Gipsy Hill	a			12 50				13 20				13 50					14 20				14 50				
Crystal Palace	a			12 52				13 22				13 52					14 22				14 52				
Birkbeck	a			12 57				13 27				13 57					14 27				14 57				
Beckenham Junction	a			13 01				13 31				14 01					14 31				15 01				
Streatham	d	12 35			12 50	13 02	13 05		13 20	13 32	13 35			13 50	14 02	14 05		14 20	14 32	14 35		14 50		15 02	15 05
Streatham Common	a					13 05				13 35					14 05				14 35					15 05	
Norbury	a					13 08				13 38					14 08				14 38					15 08	
Thornton Heath	a					13 11				13 41					14 11				14 41					15 11	
Selhurst	a					13 13				13 43					14 13				14 43					15 13	
West Croydon	a					13 18				13 48					14 18				14 48					15 18	
Tooting	a	12 40					13 10				13 40					14 10				14 40					15 10
Haydons Road	a	12 43					13 13				13 43					14 13				14 43					15 13
Wimbledon	a	12 46					13 16				13 46					14 16				14 46					15 16
Mitcham Eastfields	a				12 54				13 24					13 54				14 24				14 54			
Mitcham Junction	a				12 57				13 27					13 57				14 27				14 57			
Hackbridge	a				13 00				13 30					14 00				14 30				15 00			
Carshalton	a				13 03				13 33					14 03				14 33				15 03			
Sutton (Surrey)	a	13 05			13 06		13 35		13 36		14 05			14 06		14 35		14 36		15 05		15 06			15 35

A From Luton

B From St Albans City

Other trains operate between Peckham Rye, Denmark Hill and London Victoria and London Thameslink see table 195

For Denmark Hill, Clapham High Street, Wandsworth Road, Clapham Junction and East London Line connecting trains, please see Table 178

Table 173

Mondays to Fridays

9 December to 16 May

London Bridge - South Bermondsey, Queens Road Peckham, Peckham Rye, East Dulwich, North Dulwich, Tulse Hill and Streatham

Network Diagram - see first Page of Table 173

		SN	FC	SN	FC	SN	FC	SN		FC	FC	SN	SN	FC	SN	FC	SN	SN		FC	SN	SN	FC	SN	FC
			A		B		A			B	A			B		A				B			A		B
London Bridge 4 ⊖	d	14 55		15 10		15 25		15 40				16 00	16 10		16 20		16 30	16 40			16 50	17 00		17 10	
South Bermondsey	d	14 59		15 14		15 29		15 44				16 04	16 14		16 24		16 34	16 44			16 54	17 04		17 14	
Queens Rd Peckham	d	15 02		15 17		15 32		15 47				16 06	16 17		16 26		16 37	16 47			16 56	17 07		17 17	
Peckham Rye 4	d	15 06		15 20		15 36		15 50				16 09	16 20		16 29		16 40	16 50			16 59	17 10		17 20	
East Dulwich	d	15 09		15 23		15 39		15 53				16 12	16 23		16 32		16 43	16 53			17 02	17 13		17 23	
North Dulwich	d	15 11		15 25		15 41		15 55				16 14	16 25		16 34		16 45	16 55			17 04	17 15		17 25	
St Pancras International	d		14 48		15 04		15 18			15 34	15 48			16 04		16 18				16 34			16 50		17 02
Farringdon	d		14 53		15 09		15 23			15 39	15 53			16 09		16 23				16 39			16 55		17 07
City Thameslink	d		14 57		15 13		15 27			15 43	15 57			16 13		16 27				16 43			16 59		17 11
London Blackfriars	d		15 00		15 16		15 30			15 46	16 00			16 16		16 30				16 46			17 02		17 14
Elephant & Castle	d		15 03		15 19		15 33			15 49	16 03			16 19		16 33				16 49			17 06		17 18
Loughborough Jn	d		15 07		15 23		15 37			15 53	16 07			16 23		16 37				16 53			17 10		17 22
Herne Hill	d		15 11		15 27		15 41			15 57	16 11			16 27		16 41				16 57			17 16		17 26
Tulse Hill	d	15 15	15 16	15 29	15 31	15 45	15 46	15 59		16 01	16 16	16 18	16 29	16 32	16 38	16 47	16 48	16 59		17 02	17 08	17 19	17 20	17 29	17 32
West Norwood	a	15 18				15 48						16 21					16 51					17 22			
Gipsy Hill	a	15 21				15 51						16 24					16 54					17 25			
Crystal Palace	a	15 23				15 53						16 27					16 57					17 28			
Birkbeck	a	15 28				15 58						16 31					17 01					17 32			
Beckenham Junction	a	15 31				16 01						16 34					17 04					17 35			
Streatham	d		15 20	15 32	15 35		15 50	16 02		16 05	16 20		16 32	16 36	16 42	16 51		17 02		17 06	17 12		17 24	17 32	17 36
Streatham Common	a			15 35				16 05					16 35		16 54			17 06			17 21			17 35	
Norbury	a			15 38				16 08					16 38		16 56			17 08			17 24			17 38	
Thornton Heath	a			15 41				16 11					16 41		16 59			17 11			17 27			17 42	
Selhurst	a			15 43				16 13					16 43		17 02			17 14			17 30			17 45	
West Croydon	a			15 48				16 18					16 49					17 19						17 50	
Tooting	a				15 40					16 10				16 40						17 10					17 40
Haydons Road	a				15 43					16 13				16 43						17 13					17 43
Wimbledon	a				15 46					16 16				16 46						17 16					17 46
Mitcham Eastfields	a		15 24				15 54				16 24					16 55							17 28		
Mitcham Junction	a		15 27				15 57				16 27					16 58							17 31		
Hackbridge	a		15 30				16 00				16 30					17 01							17 34		
Carshalton	a		15 33				16 03				16 33					17 04							17 37		
Sutton (Surrey)	a		15 36		16 05		16 06			16 35	16 36			17 05		17 08				17 37			17 40		18 07

		SN	SN	FC		SN	FC	SN	SN	FC	SN	FC	SN	SN		FC	SN	FC	SN	FC	SN	SN	FC	SN
																1								
		C		A			B	C		A		B	C			D		A	E	B			D	
London Bridge 4 ⊖	d	17 20	17 30			17 40		17 50	18 00		18 10		18 20	18 30			18 40		18 50		18 59	19 10		19 20
South Bermondsey	d	17 24	17 34			17 44		17 54	18 04		18 14		18 24	18 34			18 44		18 54		19 04	19 14		19 24
Queens Rd Peckham	d	17 27	17 36			17 47		17 57	18 07		18 17		18 26	18 36			18 47		18 57		19 07	19 17		19 27
Peckham Rye 4	d	17 30	17 39			17 50		18 00	18 10		18 20		18 29	18 39			18 50		19 00		19 10	19 20		19 30
East Dulwich	d	17 33	17 42			17 53		18 03	18 13		18 23		18 32	18 42			18 53		19 03		19 13	19 23		19 33
North Dulwich	d	17 35	17 44			17 55		18 05	18 15		18 25		18 34	18 44			18 55		19 05		19 15	19 25		19 35
St Pancras International	d			17 18			17 32			17 52		18 04				18 22		18 38		18 48			19 04	
Farringdon	d			17 23			17 37			17 57		18 09				18 27		18 43		18 53			19 09	
City Thameslink	d			17 27			17 41			18 01		18 13				18 31		18 47		18 57			19 13	
London Blackfriars	d			17 30			17 44			18 04		18 16				18 34		18 50		19 00			19 16	
Elephant & Castle	d			17 34			17 48			18 08		18 20				18 38		18 54		19 04			19 19	
Loughborough Jn	d			17 38			17 52			18 12		18 24				18 42		18 58		19 08			19 23	
Herne Hill	d			17 43			17 57			18 17		18 28				18 48		19 02		19 12			19 27	
Tulse Hill	d	17 39	17 48	17 48		17 59	18 02	18 09	18 19	18 22	18 29	18 32	18 38	18 48		18 52	18 59	19 06	19 09	19 16	19 19	19 29	19 31	19 42
West Norwood	a		17 51						18 22					18 51							19 22			19 45
Gipsy Hill	a		17 54						18 25					18 54							19 25			19 48
Crystal Palace	a		17 57						18 28					18 57							19 28			19 50
Birkbeck	a		18 01						18 32					19 01							19 32			
Beckenham Junction	a		18 04						18 35					19 04							19 35			
Streatham	d	17 44		17 52		18 02	18 06	18 13		18 26	18 32	18 36	18 42			18 56	19 02	19 10	19 15	19 20		19 32	19 35	
Streatham Common	a					18 05					18 35						19 05					19 35		
Norbury	a					18 08					18 38						19 08					19 38		
Thornton Heath	a					18 12					18 42						19 12					19 42		
Selhurst	a					18 17					18 47						19 15					19 45		
West Croydon	a					18 22					18 52						19 22					19 51		20 06
Tooting	a						18 10					18 40						19 15					19 40	
Haydons Road	a						18 13					18 43						19 21					19 43	
Wimbledon	a						18 16					18 46						19 23					19 46	
Mitcham Eastfields	a	17 48		17 55				18 17		18 29			18 47			18 59			19 19	19 24				
Mitcham Junction	a	17 51		17 58				18 20		18 32			18 50			19 02			19 22	19 27				
Hackbridge	a	17 55		18 02				18 24		18 36			18 54			19 06			19 26	19 30				
Carshalton	a	17 57		18 04				18 26		18 38			18 56			19 08			19 28	19 33				
Sutton (Surrey)	a	18 02		18 08			18 37	18 30		18 42		19 07	19 00			19 12		19 41	19 32	19 36			20 07	

A From St Albans City
B From Luton
C To Wimbledon
D From Bedford
E To Epsom

Other trains operate between Peckham Rye, Denmark Hill and London Victoria and London Thameslink see table 195

For Denmark Hill, Clapham High Street, Wandsworth Road, Clapham Junction and East London Line connecting trains, please see Table 178

Table 173

Mondays to Fridays

9 December to 16 May

London Bridge - South Bermondsey, Queens Road Peckham, Peckham Rye, East Dulwich, North Dulwich, Tulse Hill and Streatham

Network Diagram - see first Page of Table 173

		FC A	SN	SN	FC B	SN	FC A	SN	SN	FC C		SN	FC B
London Bridge 4 ⊖	d		19 30	19 40		19 50		20 00	20 10			20 25	
South Bermondsey	d		19 34	19 44		19 54		20 04	20 14			20 29	
Queens Rd Peckham	d		19 36	19 47		19 57		20 07	20 17			20 32	
Peckham Rye 4	d		19 39	19 50		20 00		20 10	20 20			20 36	
East Dulwich	d		19 42	19 53		20 03		20 13	20 23			20 39	
North Dulwich	d		19 44	19 55		20 05		20 15	20 25			20 41	
St Pancras International	d	19 18			19 34		19 48			20 04			20 18
Farringdon	d	19 23			19 39		19 53			20 09			20 23
City Thameslink	d	19 27			19 43		19 57			20 13			20 27
London Blackfriars	d	19 30			19 46		20 00			20 16			20 30
Elephant & Castle	d	19 33			19 49		20 03			20 19			20 33
Loughborough Jn	d	19 37			19 53		20 07			20 23			20 37
Herne Hill	d	19 41			19 57		20 11			20 27			20 41
Tulse Hill	d	19 46	19 48	19 59	20 01	20 09	20 16	20 19	20 29	20 31		20 45	20 50
West Norwood	a		19 51			20 12		20 22				20 48	
Gipsy Hill	a		19 54			20 15		20 25				20 51	
Crystal Palace	a		19 57			20 17		20 27				20 53	
Birkbeck	a		20 01					20 32				20 58	
Beckenham Junction	a		20 04					20 36				21 01	
Streatham	d	19 50		20 02	20 05		20 20		20 32	20 35			20 53
Streatham Common	a			20 05					20 35				
Norbury	a			20 08					20 38				
Thornton Heath	a			20 11					20 41				
Selhurst	a			20 14					20 43				
West Croydon	a			20 19		20 29			20 49				
Tooting	a				20 10					20 40			
Haydons Road	a				20 13					20 43			
Wimbledon	a				20 16					20 46			
Mitcham Eastfields	a	19 54					20 24						20 57
Mitcham Junction	a	19 57					20 27						21 00
Hackbridge	a	20 00					20 30						21 03
Carshalton	a	20 03					20 33						21 06
Sutton (Surrey)	a	20 06			20 39		20 36			21 09			21 10

		SN	FC C	SN	FC A	SN	FC C	SN		SN	FC C	SN	SN
London Bridge 4 ⊖	d	20 40		20 55		21 10		21 25		21 40		21 55	22 10
South Bermondsey	d	20 44		20 59		21 14		21 29		21 44		21 59	22 14
Queens Rd Peckham	d	20 47		21 02		21 17		21 32		21 47		22 02	22 17
Peckham Rye 4	d	20 50		21 06		21 20		21 35		21 50		22 05	22 20
East Dulwich	d	20 53		21 09		21 23		21 38		21 53		22 08	22 23
North Dulwich	d	20 55		21 11		21 25		21 40		21 55		22 10	22 25
St Pancras International	d		20 34		20 48		21 06				21 36		
Farringdon	d		20 39		20 53		21 10				21 40		
City Thameslink	d		20 43		20 57		21 13				21 43		
London Blackfriars	d		20 46		21 00		21 16				21 46		
Elephant & Castle	d		20 49		21 03		21 19				21 49		
Loughborough Jn	d		20 53		21 07		21 23				21 53		
Herne Hill	d		20 57		21 11		21 27				21 57		
Tulse Hill	d	20 59	21 01	21 15	21 20	21 29	21 31	21 44		21 59	22 01	22 14	22 29
West Norwood	a			21 18				21 47				22 17	
Gipsy Hill	a			21 21				21 50				22 20	
Crystal Palace	a			21 23				21 52				22 22	
Birkbeck	a			21 28				21 57				22 27	
Beckenham Junction	a			21 31				22 01				22 31	
Streatham	d	21 02	21 05		21 23	21 32	21 35			22 02	22 05		22 32
Streatham Common	a	21 05				21 35				22 05			22 36
Norbury	a	21 08				21 38				22 08			22 38
Thornton Heath	a	21 11				21 41				22 11			22 41
Selhurst	a	21 13				21 43				22 13			22 44
West Croydon	a	21 19				21 49				22 19			22 49
Tooting	a		21 10				21 40				22 10		
Haydons Road	a		21 13				21 43				22 13		
Wimbledon	a		21 16				21 46				22 16		
Mitcham Eastfields	a				21 27								
Mitcham Junction	a				21 30								
Hackbridge	a				21 33								
Carshalton	a				21 36								
Sutton (Surrey)	a		21 39		21 40		22 09				22 39		

		FC C	SN	SN	FC C	SN D		SN	FC C	SN D	SN	FC C
London Bridge 4 ⊖	d		22 25	22 40		23 00		23 10		23 30	23 40	
South Bermondsey	d		22 29	22 44		23 04		23 14		23 34	23 44	
Queens Rd Peckham	d		22 32	22 47		23 06		23 17		23 36	23 47	
Peckham Rye 4	d		22 35	22 50		23 09		23 20		23 39	23 50	
East Dulwich	d		22 38	22 53		23 12		23 23		23 42	23 53	
North Dulwich	d		22 40	22 55		23 14		23 25		23 44	23 55	
St Pancras International	d	22 06			22 36				23 06			23 38
Farringdon	d	22 10			22 40				23 10			23 43
City Thameslink	d	22 13			22 43							
London Blackfriars	d	22 16			22 46				23 16			23 48
Elephant & Castle	d	22 19			22 49				23 19			23 51
Loughborough Jn	d	22 23			22 53				23s23			
Herne Hill	d	22 27			22 57				23 27			23 58
Tulse Hill	d	22 31	22 44	22 59	23 01	23 18		23 29	23 31	23 48	23 59	00 02
West Norwood	a		22 47			23 21				23 51		
Gipsy Hill	a		22 50			23 24				23 54		
Crystal Palace	a		22 52			23 26				23 56		
Birkbeck	a		22 57									
Beckenham Junction	a		23 01									
Streatham	d	22 35		23 02	23 05			23 32	23 35		00 02	00 06
Streatham Common	a			23 05				23 35			00 05	
Norbury	a			23 08				23 38			00 08	
Thornton Heath	a			23 11				23 41			00 11	
Selhurst	a			23 13				23 43			00 13	
West Croydon	a			23 19				23 49			00 19	
Tooting	a	22 40			23 10				23 40			00 10
Haydons Road	a	22 43			23 13				23 43			00 13
Wimbledon	a	22 46			23 16				23 46			00 18
Mitcham Eastfields	a											
Mitcham Junction	a											
Hackbridge	a											
Carshalton	a											
Sutton (Surrey)	a	23 09			23 35				00 09			00 39

A From St Albans City
B From Bedford
C From Luton
D To Norwood Junction

Other trains operate between Peckham Rye, Denmark Hill and London Victoria and London Thameslink see table 195

For Denmark Hill, Clapham High Street, Wandsworth Road, Clapham Junction and East London Line connecting trains, please see Table 178

Table 173

Saturdays

14 December to 17 May

London Bridge - South Bermondsey, Queens Road Peckham, Peckham Rye, East Dulwich, North Dulwich, Tulse Hill and Streatham

Network Diagram - see first Page of Table 173

		SN A	FC B	SN C	SN	SN C	FC D	FC	FC B	SN	FC D	FC B	SN	FC D	SN	FC B	SN	FC D	SN	FC B	SN	FC B	SN
London Bridge 4 ⊖	d			00 03	00 18	00 33				06 40			07 10		07 25		07 40		07 55		08 10		08 25
South Bermondsey	d			00 07	00 22	00 37				06 44			07 14		07 29		07 44		07 59		08 14		08 29
Queens Rd Peckham	d			00 09	00 25	00 39				06 47			07 17		07 32		07 47		08 02		08 17		08 32
Peckham Rye 4	d			00 12	00 28	00 42				06 50			07 20		07 35		07 50		08 05		08 20		08 35
East Dulwich	d			00 15	00 31	00 45				06 53			07 23		07 38		07 53		08 08		08 23		08 38
North Dulwich	d			00 17	00 33	00 47				06 55			07 25		07 40		07 55		08 10		08 25		08 40
St Pancras International	d						05 48		06 18		06 34	06 48		07 04		07 18		07 34		07 48		08 04	
Farringdon	d						05 53		06 23		06 39	06 53		07 09		07 23		07 39		07 53		08 09	
City Thameslink	d																						
London Blackfriars	d						06 00	06 16	06 30		06 46	07 00		07 16		07 30		07 46		08 00		08 16	
Elephant & Castle	d						06 03	06 19	06 33		06 49	07 03		07 19		07 33		07 49		08 03		08 19	
Loughborough Jn	d										06 53	07 07		07 23		07 37		07 53		08 07		08 23	
Herne Hill	d						06 11	06 27	06 41		06 57	07 11		07 27		07 41		07 57		08 11		08 27	
Tulse Hill	d		00 02	00 21	00 37	00 51	06 16	06 31	06 46	06 59	07 01	07 16	07 29	07 31	07 44	07 46	07 59	08 01	08 14	08 16	08 29	08 31	08 44
West Norwood	a			00 24		00 54									07 47				08 17				08 47
Gipsy Hill	a			00 27		00 57									07 50				08 20				08 50
Crystal Palace	a			00 29		00 59									07 52				08 22				08 52
Birkbeck	a														07 57				08 27				08 57
Beckenham Junction	a														08 01				08 31				09 01
Streatham	d	00 02	00 06		00 42		06 20	06 35	06 50	07 02	07 05	07 20	07 32	07 35		07 50	08 02	08 05		08 20	08 32	08 35	
Streatham Common	a	00 05			00 45					07 05			07 35				08 05				08 35		
Norbury	a	00 08			00 48					07 08			07 38				08 08				08 38		
Thornton Heath	a	00 11			00 51					07 11			07 41				08 11				08 41		
Selhurst	a	00 13			00 53					07 13			07 43				08 13				08 43		
West Croydon	a	00 19			00 57					07 19			07 49				08 18				08 48		
Tooting	a		00 10					06 40			07 10			07 40				08 10				08 40	
Haydons Road	a		00 13					06 43			07 13			07 43				08 13				08 43	
Wimbledon	a		00 18					06 46			07 16			07 46				08 16				08 46	
Mitcham Eastfields	a						06 24		06 54			07 24				07 54				08 24			
Mitcham Junction	a						06 27		06 57			07 27				07 57				08 27			
Hackbridge	a						06 30		07 00			07 30				08 00				08 30			
Carshalton	a						06 33		07 03			07 33				08 03				08 33			
Sutton (Surrey)	a		00 39				06 36	07 05	07 06		07 35	07 36		08 05		08 06		08 35		08 36		09 05	

		FC B	SN	FC B	SN	FC B	SN	FC B	SN	FC E	SN	FC B	SN	FC E		SN	FC B	SN	FC E	SN	FC B	SN	FC E
London Bridge 4 ⊖	d		08 40		08 55		09 10		09 25		09 40		09 55			19 10		19 25		19 40		19 55	
South Bermondsey	d		08 44		08 59		09 14		09 29		09 44		09 59			19 14		19 29		19 44		19 59	
Queens Rd Peckham	d		08 47		09 02		09 17		09 32		09 47		10 02			19 17		19 32		19 47		20 02	
Peckham Rye 4	d		08 50		09 05		09 20		09 35		09 50		10 05			19 20		19 35		19 50		20 05	
East Dulwich	d		08 53		09 08		09 23		09 38		09 53		10 08			19 23		19 38		19 53		20 08	
North Dulwich	d		08 55		09 10		09 25		09 40		09 55		10 10			19 25		19 40		19 55		20 10	
St Pancras International	d	08 18		08 34		08 48		09 04		09 18		09 34		09 48			19 04		19 18		19 34		19 48
Farringdon	d	08 23		08 39		08 53		09 09		09 23		09 39		09 53			19 09		19 23		19 39		19 53
City Thameslink	d							09 13		09 27		09 43		09 57			19 13		19 27		19 43		19 57
London Blackfriars	d	08 30		08 46		09 00		09 16		09 30		09 46		10 00			19 16		19 30		19 46		20 00
Elephant & Castle	d	08 33		08 49		09 03		09 19		09 33		09 49		10 03			19 19		19 33		19 49		20 03
Loughborough Jn	d	08 37		08 53		09 07		09 23		09 37		09 53		10 07			19 23		19 37		19 53		20 07
Herne Hill	d	08 41		08 57		09 11		09 27		09 41		09 57		10 11			19 27		19 41		19 57		20 11
Tulse Hill	d	08 46	08 59	09 01	09 14	09 16	09 29	09 31	09 44	09 46	09 59	10 01	10 14	10 16	and at the same minutes past each hour until	19 29	19 31	19 44	19 46	19 59	20 01	20 14	20 16
West Norwood	a				09 17				09 47				10 17					19 47				20 17	
Gipsy Hill	a				09 20				09 50				10 20					19 50				20 20	
Crystal Palace	a				09 22				09 52				10 22					19 52				20 22	
Birkbeck	a				09 27				09 57				10 27					19 57				20 27	
Beckenham Junction	a				09 31				10 01				10 31					20 01				20 31	
Streatham	d	08 50	09 02	09 05		09 20	09 32	09 35		09 50	10 02	10 05		10 20		19 32	19 35		19 50	20 02	20 05		20 20
Streatham Common	a		09 05				09 35				10 05					19 35				20 05			
Norbury	a		09 08				09 38				10 08					19 38				20 08			
Thornton Heath	a		09 11				09 41				10 11					19 41				20 11			
Selhurst	a		09 13				09 43				10 13					19 43				20 13			
West Croydon	a		09 18				09 48				10 18					19 48				20 18			
Tooting	a			09 10				09 40				10 10					19 40				20 10		
Haydons Road	a			09 13				09 43				10 13					19 43				20 13		
Wimbledon	a			09 16				09 46				10 16					19 46				20 16		
Mitcham Eastfields	a	08 54				09 24				09 54				10 24					19 54				20 24
Mitcham Junction	a	08 57				09 27				09 57				10 27					19 57				20 27
Hackbridge	a	09 00				09 30				10 00				10 30					20 00				20 30
Carshalton	a	09 03				09 33				10 03				10 33					20 03				20 33
Sutton (Surrey)	a	09 06		09 35		09 36		10 05		10 06		10 35		10 36			20 05		20 06		20 35		20 36

A From London Bridge
B From Luton
C To Norwood Junction
D From West Hampstead Thameslink
E From St Albans City

Other trains operate between Peckham Rye, Denmark Hill and London Victoria and London Thameslink see table 195

For Denmark Hill, Clapham High Street, Wandsworth Road, Clapham Junction and East London Line connecting trains, please see Table 178

Table 173

Saturdays

14 December to 17 May

London Bridge - South Bermondsey, Queens Road Peckham, Peckham Rye, East Dulwich, North Dulwich, Tulse Hill and Streatham

Network Diagram - see first Page of Table 173

		SN	FC A	SN	FC B	SN	FC A	SN	FC B	SN
London Bridge 4 ⊖	d	20 10		20 25		20 40		20 55		21 10
South Bermondsey	d	20 14		20 29		20 44		20 59		21 14
Queens Rd Peckham	d	20 17		20 32		20 47		21 02		21 17
Peckham Rye 4	d	20 20		20 35		20 50		21 05		21 20
East Dulwich	d	20 23		20 38		20 53		21 08		21 23
North Dulwich	d	20 25		20 40		20 55		21 10		21 25
St Pancras International	d		20 04		20 18		20 36		20 48	
Farringdon	d		20 09		20 23		20 40		20 53	
City Thameslink	d		20 13		20 27		20 43		20 57	
London Blackfriars	d		20 16		20 30		20 46		21 00	
Elephant & Castle	d		20 19		20 33		20 49		21 03	
Loughborough Jn	d		20 23		20 37		20 53		21 07	
Herne Hill	d		20 27		20 41		20 57		21 11	
Tulse Hill	d	20 29	20 31	20 44	20 46	20 59	21 01	21 14	21 16	21 29
West Norwood	a			20 47				21 17		
Gipsy Hill	a			20 50				21 20		
Crystal Palace	a			20 52				21 22		
Birkbeck	a			20 57				21 27		
Beckenham Junction	a			21 01				21 31		
Streatham	d	20 32	20 35		20 50	21 02	21 05		21 20	21 32
Streatham Common	a	20 35				21 05				21 35
Norbury	a	20 38				21 08				21 38
Thornton Heath	a	20 41				21 11				21 41
Selhurst	a	20 43				21 13				21 43
West Croydon	a	20 48				21 18				21 48
Tooting	a		20 40				21 10			
Haydons Road	a		20 43				21 13			
Wimbledon	a		20 46				21 16			
Mitcham Eastfields	a				20 54				21 24	
Mitcham Junction	a				20 57				21 27	
Hackbridge	a				21 00				21 30	
Carshalton	a				21 03				21 33	
Sutton (Surrey)	a		21 05		21 06		21 35		21 42	

		FC A	SN	SN	FC A	SN	SN	FC A	SN	SN	FC A	SN C	SN	FC A
London Bridge 4 ⊖	d		21 25	21 40		21 55	22 10		22 25	22 40		23 00	23 10	
South Bermondsey	d		21 29	21 44		21 59	22 14		22 29	22 44		23 04	23 14	
Queens Rd Peckham	d		21 32	21 47		22 02	22 17		22 32	22 47		23 06	23 17	
Peckham Rye 4	d		21 35	21 50		22 05	22 20		22 35	22 50		23 09	23 20	
East Dulwich	d		21 38	21 53		22 08	22 23		22 38	22 53		23 12	23 23	
North Dulwich	d		21 40	21 55		22 10	22 25		22 40	22 55		23 14	23 25	
St Pancras International	d	21 06			21 36			22 06			22 36			23 06
Farringdon	d	21 10			21 40			22 10			22 40			23 10
City Thameslink	d													
London Blackfriars	d	21 16			21 46			22 16			22 46			23 16
Elephant & Castle	d	21 19			21 49			22 19			22 49			23 19
Loughborough Jn	d	21 23			21 53			22 23			22 53			23 23
Herne Hill	d	21 27			21 57			22 27			22 57			23 27
Tulse Hill	d	21 31	21 44	21 59	22 01	22 14	22 29	22 31	22 44	22 59	23 01	23 18	23 29	23 31
West Norwood	a		21 47			22 17			22 47			23 21		
Gipsy Hill	a		21 50			22 20			22 50			23 24		
Crystal Palace	a		21 52			22 22			22 52			23 26		
Birkbeck	a		21 57			22 27			22 57					
Beckenham Junction	a		22 01			22 31			23 01					
Streatham	d	21 35		22 02	22 05		22 32	22 35		23 02	23 05		23 32	23 35
Streatham Common	a			22 05			22 35			23 05			23 35	
Norbury	a			22 08			22 38			23 08			23 38	
Thornton Heath	a			22 11			22 41			23 11			23 41	
Selhurst	a			22 13			22 43			23 13			23 43	
West Croydon	a			22 18			22 48			23 18			23 49	
Tooting	a	21 40			22 10			22 40			23 10			23 40
Haydons Road	a	21 43			22 13			22 43			23 13			23 43
Wimbledon	a	21 46			22 16			22 46			23 16			23 46
Mitcham Eastfields	a													
Mitcham Junction	a													
Hackbridge	a													
Carshalton	a													
Sutton (Surrey)	a	22 05			22 35			23 05			23 35			00 05

		SN C	SN	FC A
London Bridge 4 ⊖	d	23 30	23 40	
South Bermondsey	d	23 34	23 44	
Queens Rd Peckham	d	23 36	23 47	
Peckham Rye 4	d	23 39	23 50	
East Dulwich	d	23 42	23 53	
North Dulwich	d	23 44	23 55	
St Pancras International	d			23 38
Farringdon	d			23 43
City Thameslink	d			
London Blackfriars	d			23 48
Elephant & Castle	d			23 50
Loughborough Jn	d			
Herne Hill	d			23 58
Tulse Hill	d	23 48	23 59	00 02
West Norwood	a	23 51		
Gipsy Hill	a	23 54		
Crystal Palace	a	23 56		
Birkbeck	a			
Beckenham Junction	a			
Streatham	d		00 02	00 06
Streatham Common	a		00 05	
Norbury	a		00 08	
Thornton Heath	a		00 11	
Selhurst	a		00 13	
West Croydon	a		00 18	
Tooting	a			00 10
Haydons Road	a			00 13
Wimbledon	a			00 16
Mitcham Eastfields	a			
Mitcham Junction	a			
Hackbridge	a			
Carshalton	a			
Sutton (Surrey)	a			00 35

A From Luton **B** From St Albans City **C** To Norwood Junction

Other trains operate between Peckham Rye, Denmark Hill and London Victoria and London Thameslink see table 195

For Denmark Hill, Clapham High Street, Wandsworth Road, Clapham Junction and East London Line connecting trains, please see Table 178

Table 173

Sundays

8 December to 11 May

London Bridge - South Bermondsey, Queens Road Peckham, Peckham Rye, East Dulwich, North Dulwich, Tulse Hill and Streatham

Network Diagram - see first Page of Table 173

		SN A	FC B	SN C	SN	SN C	SN D	SN	SN D	SN		SN D	SN	SN D	FC	SN	FC E	SN D	FC	SN		FC E	SN D	FC	SN
London Bridge 4 ⊖	d			00 03	00 18	00 33	07 21	07 36	07 51	08 06		08 21	08 36	08 51		09 06		09 21		09 36			09 51		10 06
South Bermondsey	d			00 07	00 22	00 37	07 25	07 40	07 55	08 10		08 25	08 40	08 55		09 10		09 25		09 40			09 55		10 10
Queens Rd Peckham	d			00 09	00 24	00 39	07 27	07 42	07 57	08 12		08 27	08 42	08 57		09 12		09 27		09 42			09 57		10 12
Peckham Rye 4	d			00 12	00 27	00 42	07 30	07 45	08 00	08 15		08 30	08 45	09 00		09 15		09 30		09 45			10 00		10 15
East Dulwich	d			00 15	00 30	00 45	07 33	07 48	08 03	08 18		08 33	08 48	09 03		09 18		09 33		09 48			10 03		10 18
North Dulwich	d			00 17	00 32	00 47	07 35	07 50	08 05	08 20		08 35	08 50	09 05		09 20		09 35		09 50			10 05		10 20
St Pancras International	d																09 06					09 36			
Farringdon	d																09 11					09 41			
City Thameslink	d																								
London Blackfriars	d														08 58		09 16		09 28			09 46		09 58	
Elephant & Castle	d														09 01		09 19		09 31			09 49		10 01	
Loughborough Jn	d														09 05		09 23		09 35			09 53		10 05	
Herne Hill	d														09 09		09 27		09 39			09 57		10 09	
Tulse Hill	d		00 02	00 21	00 35	00 51	07 39	07 54	08 09	08 24		08 39	08 54	09 09	09 14	09 24	09 32	09 39	09 44	09 54		10 02	10 09	10 14	10 24
West Norwood	a			00 24		00 54		07 57		08 27			08 57			09 27				09 57					10 27
Gipsy Hill	a			00 27		00 57		08 00		08 30			09 00			09 30				10 00					10 30
Crystal Palace	a			00 29		00 59		08 02		08 32			09 02			09 32				10 02					10 32
Birkbeck	a																								
Beckenham Junction	a																								
Streatham	d	00 02	00 06		00 39		07 42		08 12			08 42		09 12	09 18		09 36	09 42	09 48			10 06	10 12	10 18	
Streatham Common	a	00 05			00 43		07 45		08 18			08 47		09 15				09 45					10 15		
Norbury	a	00 08			00 46		07 48		08 20			08 50		09 18				09 48					10 18		
Thornton Heath	a	00 11			00 49		07 51		08 23			08 53		09 21				09 51					10 21		
Selhurst	a	00 13			00 51		07 54		08 26			08 55		09 23				09 53					10 23		
West Croydon	a	00 18			00 57																				
Tooting	a		00 10														09 42					10 12			
Haydons Road	a		00 13														09 45					10 15			
Wimbledon	a		00 16														09 47					10 17			
Mitcham Eastfields	a														09 22				09 52					10 22	
Mitcham Junction	a														09 25				09 55					10 25	
Hackbridge	a														09 29				09 59					10 29	
Carshalton	a														09 31				10 01					10 31	
Sutton (Surrey)	a		00 35												09 35		10 05		10 05			10 35		10 35	

		FC E	SN D	FC	SN	FC E		SN D	FC	SN	FC E	SN D	FC	SN	FC E	SN D		FC	SN	FC E	SN D	FC	SN	FC E	SN D
London Bridge 4 ⊖	d		10 21		10 36			10 51		11 06		11 21		11 36		11 51			12 06		12 21		12 36		12 51
South Bermondsey	d		10 25		10 40			10 55		11 10		11 25		11 40		11 55			12 10		12 25		12 40		12 55
Queens Rd Peckham	d		10 27		10 42			10 57		11 12		11 27		11 42		11 57			12 14		12 27		12 42		12 57
Peckham Rye 4	d		10 30		10 45			11 00		11 15		11 30		11 45		12 00			12 17		12 30		12 45		13 00
East Dulwich	d		10 33		10 48			11 03		11 18		11 33		11 48		12 03			12 20		12 33		12 48		13 03
North Dulwich	d		10 35		10 50			11 05		11 20		11 35		11 50		12 05			12 22		12 35		12 50		13 05
St Pancras International	d	10 06				10 36					11 06				11 36					12 06				12 36	
Farringdon	d	10 11				10 41					11 11				11 41					12 11				12 41	
City Thameslink	d																								
London Blackfriars	d	10 16		10 28		10 46			10 58		11 16		11 28		11 46			11 58		12 16		12 28		12 46	
Elephant & Castle	d	10 19		10 31		10 49			11 01		11 19		11 31		11 49			12 01		12 19		12 31		12 49	
Loughborough Jn	d	10 23		10 35		10 53			11 05		11 23		11 35		11 53			12 05		12 23		12 35		12 53	
Herne Hill	d	10 27		10 39		10 57			11 09		11 27		11 39		11 57			12 09		12 27		12 39		12 57	
Tulse Hill	d	10 32	10 39	10 44	10 54	11 02		11 09	11 14	11 24	11 32	11 39	11 44	11 54	12 02	12 09		12 14	12 26	12 32	12 39	12 44	12 54	13 02	13 09
West Norwood	a				10 57					11 27				11 57					12 29				12 57		
Gipsy Hill	a				11 00					11 30				12 00					12 32				13 00		
Crystal Palace	a				11 02					11 32				12 02					12 34				13 02		
Birkbeck	a																								
Beckenham Junction	a																								
Streatham	d	10 36	10 42	10 48		11 06		11 12	11 18		11 36	11 42	11 48		12 06	12 12		12 18		12 36	12 42	12 48		13 06	13 12
Streatham Common	a		10 45					11 15				11 45				12 15					12 45				13 15
Norbury	a		10 48					11 18				11 48				12 18					12 48				13 18
Thornton Heath	a		10 51					11 21				11 51				12 21					12 51				13 21
Selhurst	a		10 53					11 23				11 53				12 23					12 53				13 23
West Croydon	a																								
Tooting	a	10 42				11 12					11 42				12 12					12 42				13 12	
Haydons Road	a	10 45				11 15					11 45				12 15					12 45				13 15	
Wimbledon	a	10 47				11 17					11 47				12 17					12 47				13 17	
Mitcham Eastfields	a			10 52					11 22				11 52					12 22				12 52			
Mitcham Junction	a			10 55					11 25				11 55					12 25				12 55			
Hackbridge	a			10 59					11 29				11 59					12 29				12 59			
Carshalton	a			11 01					11 31				12 01					12 31				13 01			
Sutton (Surrey)	a	11 05		11 05		11 35			11 35		12 05		12 05		12 35			12 35		13 05		13 05		13 35	

A from London Bridge
B from Luton
C To Norwood Junction
D To East Croydon
E From Luton

Other trains operate between Peckham Rye, Denmark Hill and London Victoria and London Thameslink see table 195

For Denmark Hill, Clapham High Street, Wandsworth Road, Clapham Junction and East London Line connecting trains, please see Table 178

Table 173

Sundays

8 December to 11 May

London Bridge - South Bermondsey, Queens Road Peckham, Peckham Rye, East Dulwich, North Dulwich, Tulse Hill and Streatham

Network Diagram - see first Page of Table 173

Station		FC	SN		FC A	SN B	FC	SN	FC A	SN B	FC	SN
London Bridge 4 ⊖	d		13 06			19 21		19 36		19 51		20 06
South Bermondsey	d		13 10			19 25		19 40		19 55		20 10
Queens Rd Peckham	d		13 12			19 27		19 42		19 57		20 12
Peckham Rye 4	d		13 15			19 30		19 45		20 00		20 15
East Dulwich	d		13 18			19 33		19 48		20 03		20 18
North Dulwich	d		13 20			19 35		19 50		20 05		20 20
St Pancras International	d				19 06				19 36			
Farringdon	d				19 11				19 41			
City Thameslink	d											
London Blackfriars	d	12 58			19 16		19 28		19 46		19 58	
Elephant & Castle	d	13 01			19 19		19 31		19 49		20 01	
Loughborough Jn	d	13 05			19 23		19 35		19 53		20 05	
Herne Hill	d	13 09		and at the same minutes past each hour until	19 27		19 39		19 57		20 09	
Tulse Hill	d	13 14	13 24		19 32	19 39	19 44	19 54	20 02	20 09	20 14	20 24
West Norwood	a		13 27					19 57				20 27
Gipsy Hill	a		13 30					20 00				20 30
Crystal Palace	a		13 32					20 02				20 32
Birkbeck	a											
Beckenham Junction	a											
Streatham	d	13 18			19 36	19 42	19 48		20 06	20 12	20 18	
Streatham Common	a					19 45				20 15		
Norbury	a					19 48				20 18		
Thornton Heath	a					19 51				20 21		
Selhurst	a					19 53				20 23		
West Croydon	a											
Tooting	a				19 42				20 12			
Haydons Road	a				19 45				20 15			
Wimbledon	a				19 47				20 17			
Mitcham Eastfields	a	13 22					19 52				20 22	
Mitcham Junction	a	13 25					19 55				20 25	
Hackbridge	a	13 29					19 59				20 29	
Carshalton	a	13 31					20 01				20 31	
Sutton (Surrey)	a	13 35			20 05		20 05		20 35		20 35	

Station			FC A	SN B	FC	SN	FC A	SN B	SN	FC A	SN B		SN
London Bridge 4 ⊖	d			20 21		20 36		20 51	21 06		21 21		21 36
South Bermondsey	d			20 25		20 40		20 55	21 10		21 25		21 40
Queens Rd Peckham	d			20 27		20 42		20 57	21 12		21 27		21 42
Peckham Rye 4	d			20 30		20 45		21 00	21 15		21 30		21 45
East Dulwich	d			20 33		20 48		21 03	21 18		21 33		21 48
North Dulwich	d			20 35		20 50		21 05	21 20		21 35		21 50
St Pancras International	d		20 06				20 36			21 06			
Farringdon	d		20 11				20 41			21 11			
City Thameslink	d												
London Blackfriars	d		20 16		20 28		20 46			21 16			
Elephant & Castle	d		20 19		20 31		20 49			21 19			
Loughborough Jn	d		20 23		20 35		20 53			21 23			
Herne Hill	d		20 27		20 39		20 57			21 27			
Tulse Hill	d		20 32	20 39	20 44	20 54	21 02	21 09	21 24	21 32	21 39		21 54
West Norwood	a					20 57			21 27				21 57
Gipsy Hill	a					21 00			21 30				22 00
Crystal Palace	a					21 02			21 32				22 02
Birkbeck	a												
Beckenham Junction	a												
Streatham	d		20 36	20 42	20 48		21 06	21 12		21 36	21 42		
Streatham Common	a			20 45				21 15			21 45		
Norbury	a			20 48				21 18			21 48		
Thornton Heath	a			20 51				21 21			21 51		
Selhurst	a			20 53				21 23			21 53		
West Croydon	a												
Tooting	a		20 42				21 12			21 42			
Haydons Road	a		20 45				21 15			21 45			
Wimbledon	a		20 47				21 17			21 47			
Mitcham Eastfields	a				20 52								
Mitcham Junction	a				20 55								
Hackbridge	a				20 59								
Carshalton	a				21 01								
Sutton (Surrey)	a		21 05		21 05		21 35			22 05			

Station		SN B	SN	SN B	SN	SN B	SN	SN B
London Bridge 4 ⊖	d	21 51	22 06	22 21	22 36	22 51	23 06	23 21
South Bermondsey	d	21 55	22 10	22 25	22 40	22 55	23 10	23 25
Queens Rd Peckham	d	21 57	22 12	22 27	22 42	22 57	23 12	23 27
Peckham Rye 4	d	22 00	22 15	22 30	22 45	23 00	23 15	23 30
East Dulwich	d	22 03	22 18	22 33	22 48	23 03	23 18	23 33
North Dulwich	d	22 05	22 20	22 35	22 50	23 05	23 20	23 35
St Pancras International	d							
Farringdon	d							
City Thameslink	d							
London Blackfriars	d							
Elephant & Castle	d							
Loughborough Jn	d							
Herne Hill	d							
Tulse Hill	d	22 09	22 24	22 39	22 54	23 09	23 24	23 39
West Norwood	a		22 27		22 57		23 27	
Gipsy Hill	a		22 30		23 00		23 30	
Crystal Palace	a		22 32		23 02		23 32	
Birkbeck	a							
Beckenham Junction	a							
Streatham	d	22 12		22 42		23 12		23 42
Streatham Common	a	22 15		22 45		23 15		23 45
Norbury	a	22 18		22 48		23 18		23 48
Thornton Heath	a	22 21		22 51		23 21		23 51
Selhurst	a	22 23		22 53		23 23		23 53
West Croydon	a							
Tooting	a							
Haydons Road	a							
Wimbledon	a							
Mitcham Eastfields	a							
Mitcham Junction	a							
Hackbridge	a							
Carshalton	a							
Sutton (Surrey)	a							

A From Luton

B To East Croydon

Other trains operate between Peckham Rye, Denmark Hill and London Victoria and London Thameslink see table 195

For Denmark Hill, Clapham High Street, Wandsworth Road, Clapham Junction and East London Line connecting trains, please see Table 178

Table 173R

Mondays to Fridays

9 December to 16 May

Tulse Hill, Streatham, North Dulwich, East Dulwich, Peckham Rye, Queens Road Peckham and South Bermondsey - London Bridge

Network Diagram - see first Page of Table 173

Miles	Miles	Miles	Miles	Miles			SN	SN A	SN B	FC C	SN	FC D	SN E	SN B	FC F	SN	SN	SN B	FC D	SN	FC D	SN	SN B	FC C
—	—	—	—	0	Sutton (Surrey)	d	05 37		06 14	06 05		06 34		06 53	06 45			07 20	07 05		07 36		07 50	07 40
—	—	—	—	1¼	Carshalton	d	05 40		06 17			06 37		06 56				07 23			07 39		07 53	
—	—	—	—	2¼	Hackbridge	d	05 42		06 19			06 39		06 58				07 25			07 41		07 55	
—	—	—	—	3¼	Mitcham Junction	d	05 46		06 23			06 42		07 02				07 29			07 44		07 59	
—	—	—	—	4½	Mitcham Eastfields	d	05 49		06 26			06 45		07 05				07 32			07 47		08 02	
—	—	—	0	—	Wimbledon	d				06 28					07 06				07 26					08 00
—	—	—	0¾	—	Haydons Road	d				06 30					07 08				07 28					08 02
—	—	—	2	—	Tooting	d				06 33					07 11				07 31					08 06
0	—	—	—	—	West Croydon	d					06 31					07 01				07 31				
1¼	—	—	—	—	Selhurst	d					06 35					07 05				07 35				
2	—	—	—	—	Thornton Heath	d					06 37					07 07				07 37				
3	—	—	—	—	Norbury	d					06 40					07 10				07 40				
4	—	—	—	—	Streatham Common	d					06 43					07 13				07 43				
4½	—	—	3½	6¼	**Streatham**	d	05 53		06 30	06 38	06 46	06 49		07 10	07 16	07 19		07 35	07 38	07 47	07 52		08 09	08 12
—	0	—	—	—	Beckenham Junction	d											07 15					07 45		
—	1½	—	—	—	**Birkbeck**	d											07 18					07 48		
—	3	—	—	—	Crystal Palace	d		05 57					06 51				07 22					07 52		
—	3¾	—	—	—	Gipsy Hill	d		06 00					06 53				07 25					07 55		
—	4¾	—	—	—	West Norwood	d		06 03					06 56				07 28					07 58		
6	5½	—	5	7¾	**Tulse Hill**	d	05 56	06 06	06 34	06 42	06 50	06 53	07 04	07 14	07 20	07 24	07 34	07 44	07 43	07 54	07 57	08 04	08 14	08 16
—	—	—	6	8¾	Herne Hill	a				06 46		06 56			07 23				07 46		08 01			08 20
—	—	—	7	9¾	Loughborough Jn	a				06 49		07 00			07 27				07 50		08 04			08 24
—	—	—	9	11¾	Elephant & Castle	a				06 53		07 05			07 31				07 54		08 08			08 28
—	—	—	10¼	13	London Blackfriars 3	⊖ a				06 57		07 09			07 35				07 58		08 12			08 32
—	—	—	10¾	13½	City Thameslink	a				07 00		07 14			07 38				08 00		08 15			08 35
—	—	—	11¼	14	Farringdon	a				07 04		07 18			07 42				08 03		08 19			08 39
—	—	—	12½	15¼	St Pancras International	a				07 08		07 22			07 46				08 08		08 23			08 43
7½	6¾	—	—	—	**North Dulwich**	d	05 59	06 09	06 37		06 53		07 07	07 17		07 27	07 37	07 47		07 57		08 07	08 17	
8	7¼	—	—	—	**East Dulwich**	d	06 01	06 11	06 39		06 55		07 09	07 20		07 30	07 40	07 50		08 00		08 10	08 20	
—	—	—	—	—	Peckham Rye 4	d	06 04	06 14	06 42		06 58		07 12	07 23		07 33	07 43	07 53		08 03		08 13	08 23	
9½	8¾	5½	—	—	Queens Rd Peckham	d	06 06	06 16	06 44		07 00		07 15	07 25		07 35	07 45	07 55		08 06		08 15	08 26	
10½	9¾	—	—	—	**South Bermondsey**	d	06 09	06 19	06 47		07 03		07 17	07 28		07 38	07 48	07 58		08 08		08 18	08 28	
—	—	—	—	—	London Bridge 4	⊖ a	06 13	06 23	06 51		07 10		07 25	07 33		07 45	07 55	08 03		08 13		08 25	08 33	

		SN	FC D	SN	FC C	SN B	SN	FC D	SN	FC C	SN B	SN	FC G	SN	FC C	SN	FC D	SN	FC C	SN	FC D	SN
Sutton (Surrey)	d		08 08		08 08	08 23		08 39		08 41	08 53		09 13		09 11		09 38		09 37		10 08	
Carshalton	d		08 11			08 26		08 42			08 56		09 16				09 41				10 11	
Hackbridge	d		08 13			08 28		08 44			08 58		09 18				09 43				10 13	
Mitcham Junction	d		08 16			08 32		08 47			09 02		09 21				09 46				10 16	
Mitcham Eastfields	d		08 19			08 35		08 50			09 05		09 24				09 49				10 19	
Wimbledon	d				08 28					08 58					09 28				09 58			
Haydons Road	d				08 30					09 00					09 30				10 00			
Tooting	d				08 33					09 03					09 33				10 03			
West Croydon	d	08 01					08 31					09 01				09 25				09 55		
Selhurst	d	08 05					08 35					09 05				09 30				09 59		
Thornton Heath	d	08 07					08 37					09 07				09 32				10 01		
Norbury	d	08 10					08 40					09 10				09 35				10 04		
Streatham Common	d	08 13					08 43					09 13				09 37				10 07		
Streatham	d	08 17	08 23		08 39	08 42	08 47	08 54		09 08	09 11	09 17	09 28		09 38	09 41	09 53		10 08	10 11	10 23	
Beckenham Junction	d			08 15					08 45					09 15				09 44				10 13
Birkbeck	d			08 18					08 48					09 18				09 47				10 16
Crystal Palace	d			08 24					08 52					09 22				09 51				10 20
Gipsy Hill	d			08 27					08 55					09 25				09 54				10 23
West Norwood	d			08 30					08 58					09 28				09 57				10 26
Tulse Hill	d	08 24	08 28	08 34	08 43	08 46	08 55	08 58	09 04	09 16	09 15	09 26	09 32	09 34	09 42	09 45	09 57	10 01	10 12	10 15	10 27	10 31
Herne Hill	a		08 31		08 47			09 01		09 19			09 35		09 46		10 01		10 16		10 31	
Loughborough Jn	a		08 36		08 50			09 05		09 23			09 40		09 50		10 04		10 19		10 34	
Elephant & Castle	a		08 40		08 57			09 09		09 29			09 44		09 54		10 08		10 23		10 38	
London Blackfriars 3	⊖ a		08 45		09 01			09 13		09 33			09 49		09 59		10 12		10 27		10 42	
City Thameslink	a		08 48		09 04			09 16		09 36			09 52		10 02		10 16		10 32		10 46	
Farringdon	a		08 52		09 08			09 20		09 40			09 56		10 06		10 19		10 35		10 49	
St Pancras International	a		08 56		09 12			09 24		09 44			10 00		10 10		10 23		10 40		10 53	
North Dulwich	d	08 27		08 37		08 49	08 58		09 07		09 18	09 29		09 37		09 48		10 04		10 18		10 34
East Dulwich	d	08 30		08 40		08 51	09 01		09 10		09 20	09 31		09 40		09 50		10 06		10 20		10 36
Peckham Rye 4	d	08 33		08 43		08 54	09 04		09 13		09 23	09 34		09 43		09 53		10 09		10 23		10 39
Queens Rd Peckham	d	08 35		08 45		08 56	09 06		09 15		09 26	09 36		09 45		09 56		10 12		10 26		10 41
South Bermondsey	d	08 38		08 48		08 59	09 09		09 18		09 28	09 39		09 48		09 58		10 14		10 28		10 44
London Bridge 4	⊖ a	08 43		08 55		09 03	09 14		09 25		09 33	09 43		09 55		10 03		10 19		10 33		10 48

A From East Croydon
B From Wimbledon
C To Luton
D To St Albans City
E From Norwood Junction
F To Bedford
G To Kentish Town

Other trains operate between Peckham Rye, Denmark Hill and London Victoria and London Thameslink see table 195

For Denmark Hill, Clapham High Street, Wandsworth Road, Clapham Junction and East London Line connecting trains, please see Table 178

Table 173R

Mondays to Fridays

9 December to 16 May

Tulse Hill, Streatham, North Dulwich, East Dulwich, Peckham Rye, Queens Road Peckham and South Bermondsey - London Bridge

Network Diagram - see first Page of Table 173

		FC A	SN	FC B	SN	FC A	SN		FC B	SN	FC C	SN	FC B	SN	FC A	SN	FC B		SN	FC A	SN	FC B	SN	FC A	SN
Sutton (Surrey)	d	10 07		10 38		10 37			11 08		11 07		11 38		11 37		12 08			12 07		12 38		12 37	
Carshalton	d			10 41					11 11				11 41				12 11					12 41			
Hackbridge	d			10 43					11 13				11 43				12 13					12 43			
Mitcham Junction	d			10 46					11 16				11 46				12 16					12 46			
Mitcham Eastfields	d			10 49					11 19				11 49				12 19					12 49			
Wimbledon	d	10 28				10 58					11 28				11 58					12 28				12 58	
Haydons Road	d	10 30				11 00					11 30				12 00					12 30				13 00	
Tooting	d	10 33				11 03					11 33				12 03					12 33				13 03	
West Croydon	d		10 25				10 55					11 25				11 55					12 25				12 55
Selhurst	d		10 29				10 59					11 29				11 59					12 29				12 59
Thornton Heath	d		10 31				11 01					11 31				12 01					12 31				13 01
Norbury	d		10 34				11 04					11 34				12 04					12 34				13 04
Streatham Common	d		10 37				11 07					11 37				12 07					12 37				13 07
Streatham	d	10 38	10 41	10 53		11 08	11 11		11 23		11 38	11 41	11 53		12 08	12 11	12 23			12 38	12 41	12 53		13 08	13 11
Beckenham Junction	d				10 43					11 13				11 43					12 13				12 43		
Birkbeck	d				10 46					11 16				11 46					12 16				12 46		
Crystal Palace	d				10 51					11 20				11 52					12 20				12 50		
Gipsy Hill	d				10 54					11 23				11 55					12 23				12 53		
West Norwood	d				10 57					11 26				11 58					12 26				12 56		
Tulse Hill	d	10 42	10 46	10 57	11 01	11 12	11 16		11 27	11 31	11 42	11 46	11 57	12 01	12 12	12 16	12 27		12 31	12 42	12 46	12 57	13 01	13 12	13 16
Herne Hill	a	10 46		11 01		11 16			11 31		11 46		12 01		12 16		12 31			12 46		13 01		13 16	
Loughborough Jn	a	10 49		11 04		11 19			11 34		11 49		12 04		12 19		12 34			12 49		13 04		13 19	
Elephant & Castle	a	10 53		11 08		11 23			11 38		11 53		12 08		12 23		12 38			12 53		13 08		13 23	
London Blackfriars 3 ⊖	a	10 57		11 12		11 27			11 42		11 57		12 12		12 27		12 42			12 57		13 12		13 27	
City Thameslink	a	11 02		11 16		11 32			11 46		12 02		12 16		12 32		12 46			13 02		13 16		13 32	
Farringdon	a	11 06		11 19		11 36			11 49		12 06		12 19		12 36		12 49			13 06		13 19		13 36	
St Pancras International	a	11 10		11 23		11 40			11 53		12 10		12 23		12 40		12 53			13 10		13 23		13 40	
North Dulwich	d		10 49		11 04		11 19			11 34		11 49		12 04		12 19			12 34		12 49		13 04		13 19
East Dulwich	d		10 51		11 06		11 21			11 36		11 51		12 06		12 21			12 36		12 51		13 06		13 21
Peckham Rye 4	d		10 54		11 09		11 24			11 39		11 54		12 09		12 24			12 39		12 54		13 09		13 24
Queens Rd Peckham	d		10 57		11 11		11 27			11 41		11 57		12 11		12 27			12 41		12 56		13 11		13 27
South Bermondsey	d		10 59		11 14		11 29			11 44		11 59		12 14		12 29			12 44		12 59		13 14		13 29
London Bridge 4 ⊖	a		11 04		11 18		11 34			11 48		12 04		12 18		12 34			12 48		13 04		13 18		13 34

		FC B	SN		FC A	SN	FC B	SN	FC A	SN	FC B	SN	FC A		SN	FC B	SN	FC A	SN	FC B	SN	FC A	SN		SN
Sutton (Surrey)	d	13 08			13 07		13 38		13 37		14 08		14 07			14 38		14 37		15 08		15 07			
Carshalton	d	13 11					13 41				14 11					14 41				15 11					
Hackbridge	d	13 13					13 43				14 13					14 43				15 13					
Mitcham Junction	d	13 16					13 46				14 16					14 46				15 16					
Mitcham Eastfields	d	13 19					13 49				14 19					14 49				15 19					
Wimbledon	d				13 28				13 58				14 28					14 58				15 28			
Haydons Road	d				13 30				14 00				14 30					15 00				15 30			
Tooting	d				13 33				14 03				14 33					15 03				15 33			
West Croydon	d					13 25				13 55					14 25				14 55				15 25		
Selhurst	d					13 29				13 59					14 29				14 59				15 29		
Thornton Heath	d					13 31				14 01					14 31				15 01				15 31		
Norbury	d					13 34				14 04					14 34				15 04				15 34		
Streatham Common	d					13 37				14 07					14 37				15 07				15 37		
Streatham	d	13 23			13 38	13 41	13 53		14 08	14 11	14 23		14 38		14 41	14 53		15 08	15 11	15 23		15 38	15 41		
Beckenham Junction	d		13 13					13 43				14 13					14 43				15 13				15 40
Birkbeck	d		13 16					13 46				14 16					14 46				15 16				15 43
Crystal Palace	d		13 20					13 50				14 20					14 50				15 20				15 47
Gipsy Hill	d		13 23					13 53				14 23					14 53				15 23				15 49
West Norwood	d		13 26					13 56				14 26					14 56				15 26				15 52
Tulse Hill	d	13 27	13 31		13 42	13 46	13 57	14 01	14 12	14 16	14 27	14 31	14 42		14 46	14 57	15 01	15 12	15 15	15 27	15 31	15 42	15 46		15 56
Herne Hill	a	13 31			13 46		14 01		14 16		14 31		14 46			15 01		15 16		15 31		15 46			
Loughborough Jn	a	13 34			13 49		14 04		14 19		14 34		14 49			15 04		15 19		15 34		15 49			
Elephant & Castle	a	13 38			13 53		14 08		14 23		14 38		14 53			15 08		15 23		15 38		15 53			
London Blackfriars 3 ⊖	a	13 42			13 57		14 12		14 27		14 42		14 57			15 12		15 27		15 42		15 57			
City Thameslink	a	13 46			14 02		14 16		14 32		14 46		15 02			15 16		15 32		15 46		16 02			
Farringdon	a	13 49			14 06		14 19		14 36		14 49		15 06			15 19		15 36		15 49		16 06			
St Pancras International	a	13 53			14 10		14 23		14 40		14 53		15 10			15 23		15 40		15 53		16 10			
North Dulwich	d		13 34			13 49		14 04		14 19		14 34			14 49		15 04		15 18		15 34		15 49		15 59
East Dulwich	d		13 36			13 51		14 06		14 21		14 36			14 51		15 06		15 20		15 36		15 51		16 01
Peckham Rye 4	d		13 39			13 54		14 09		14 24		14 39			14 54		15 09		15 23		15 39		15 53		16 04
Queens Rd Peckham	d		13 41			13 57		14 11		14 27		14 41			14 57		15 11		15 26		15 41		15 56		16 06
South Bermondsey	d		13 44			13 59		14 14		14 29		14 44			14 59		15 14		15 28		15 44		15 58		16 09
London Bridge 4 ⊖	a		13 48			14 04		14 18		14 34		14 48			15 04		15 18		15 33		15 48		16 03		16 13

A To Luton B To St Albans City C To Bedford

Other trains operate between Peckham Rye, Denmark Hill and London Victoria and London Thameslink see table 195

For Denmark Hill, Clapham High Street, Wandsworth Road, Clapham Junction and East London Line connecting trains, please see Table 178

Table 173R

Mondays to Fridays

9 December to 16 May

Tulse Hill, Streatham, North Dulwich, East Dulwich, Peckham Rye, Queens Road Peckham and South Bermondsey - London Bridge

Network Diagram - see first Page of Table 173

		FC	SN	FC	SN	SN	FC	SN	FC		SN	SN	FC	SN	FC	SN	SN	FC	SN		FC	SN	SN	FC	SN
													1												
		A	B	C			A		A				D		C			A	E		C			A	E
Sutton (Surrey)	d	15 38		15 37			16 08		16 07				16 38		16 37			17 08			17 11			17 42	
Carshalton	d	15 41					16 11						16 41					17 11						17 45	
Hackbridge	d	15 43					16 13						16 43					17 13						17 47	
Mitcham Junction	d	15 46					16 16						16 46					17 16						17 50	
Mitcham Eastfields	d	15 49					16 19						16 49					17 19						17 53	
Wimbledon	d			15 58					16 30						17 00						17 30				
Haydons Road	d			16 00					16 32						17 02						17 32				
Tooting	d			16 03					16 35						17 05						17 35				
West Croydon	d				15 55						16 28					16 58						17 28			
Selhurst	d				15 59						16 33					17 02						17 32			
Thornton Heath	d				16 01						16 35					17 04						17 34			
Norbury	d				16 04						16 38					17 07						17 37			
Streatham Common	d				16 07						16 40					17 10						17 40			
Streatham	d	15 53		16 08	16 11		16 23		16 40		16 43		16 53		17 10	17 13		17 23			17 40	17 43		17 57	
Beckenham Junction	d					16 10						16 40					17 10						17 41		
Birkbeck	d					16 13						16 43					17 13						17 44		
Crystal Palace	d					16 17						16 47					17 17		17 24				17 48		17 54
Gipsy Hill	d					16 19						16 49					17 19		17 26				17 50		17 56
West Norwood	d					16 22						16 52					17 22		17 29				17 53		17 59
Tulse Hill	d	15 57	16 05	16 12	16 15	16 26	16 27	16 37	16 46		16 47	16 56	16 57	17 07	17 16	17 17	17 26	17 27	17 35		17 44	17 47	17 57	18 01	18 04
Herne Hill	a	16 01		16 16			16 31		16 50				17 01		17 20			17 31			17 47			18 05	
Loughborough Jn	a	16 04		16 19			16 34		16 53						17 24			17 34			17 51			18 09	
Elephant & Castle	a	16 08		16 23			16 38		16 59				17 07		17 28			17 38			17 55			18 13	
London Blackfriars **3** ⊖	a	16 12		16 29			16 42		17 03				17 11		17 31			17 43			17 59			18 17	
City Thameslink	a	16 16		16 32			16 46		17 06				17 14		17 34			17 48			18 02			18 20	
Farringdon	a	16 19		16 35			16 49		17 09				17 17		17 37			17 51			18 05			18 23	
St Pancras International	a	16 23		16 39			16 53		17 13				17 21		17 41			17 55			18 09			18 27	
North Dulwich	d		16 08		16 18	16 29		16 40			16 50	16 59		17 10		17 20	17 29		17 38			17 50	18 00		18 07
East Dulwich	d		16 10		16 20	16 31		16 42			16 52	17 01		17 12		17 22	17 31		17 40			17 52	18 02		18 09
Peckham Rye **4**	d		16 13		16 23	16 34		16 44			16 55	17 04		17 14		17 25	17 34		17 42			17 55	18 05		18 12
Queens Rd Peckham	d		16 16		16 26	16 36		16 47			16 57	17 06		17 17		17 27	17 36		17 45			17 57	18 07		18 14
South Bermondsey	d		16 19		16 28	16 39		16 49			17 00	17 09		17 19		17 30	17 39		17 49			18 00	18 10		18 17
London Bridge **4** ⊖	a		16 23		16 33	16 43		16 54			17 04	17 13		17 24		17 34	17 43		17 53			18 04	18 14		18 23

		FC	SN	SN	SN		FC	SN	FC	SN	SN	FC	SN	SN	FC		SN	SN	SN	FC	SN	FC	SN	FC	SN
		C		F			G		C		F	A			C			F		A		C		A	
Sutton (Surrey)	d	17 41		18 03			18 08		18 11		18 30	18 38			18 43			19 00		19 08		19 13		19 42	
Carshalton	d						18 11					18 41								19 11				19 45	
Hackbridge	d						18 13					18 43								19 13				19 47	
Mitcham Junction	d						18 16					18 46								19 16				19 50	
Mitcham Eastfields	d						18 19					18 49								19 19				19 53	
Wimbledon	d	18 00		18a20				18 21	18 30		18a50			18 51	19 00			19a18			19 20	19 30			
Haydons Road	d	18 02						18 23	18 32					18 53	19 02						19 22	19 32			
Tooting	d	18 05						18 26	18 35					18 56	19 05						19 26	19 35			
West Croydon	d		17 58							18 29							18 59						19 26		
Selhurst	d		18 02							18 33							19 03						19 30		
Thornton Heath	d		18 04							18 35							19 05						19 32		
Norbury	d		18 07							18 38							19 08						19 35		
Streatham Common	d		18 10							18 41							19 11						19 38		
Streatham	d	18 10	18 13				18 23	18 31	18 40	18 44		18 53		19 01	19 10		19 14			19 23	19 30	19 40	19 43	19 57	
Beckenham Junction	d				18 10								18 41						19 10						19 43
Birkbeck	d				18 13								18 44						19 13						19 46
Crystal Palace	d				18 17								18 48						19 17						19 50
Gipsy Hill	d				18 19								18 50						19 19						19 53
West Norwood	d				18 22								18 53						19 22						19 56
Tulse Hill	d	18 16	18 17		18 26		18 28	18 36	18 44	18 47		18 57	18 57	19 05	19 14		19 17		19 26	19 27	19 35	19 44	19 47	20 01	20 01
Herne Hill	a	18 19					18 31		18 47			19 01			19 17					19 31		19 47		20 05	
Loughborough Jn	a	18 23					18 35		18 51			19 05			19 20					19 34		19 50		20 08	
Elephant & Castle	a	18 27					18 39		18 55			19 09			19 24					19 38		19 54		20 12	
London Blackfriars **3** ⊖	a	18 31					18 43		18 59			19 13			19 28					19 42		19 58		20 16	
City Thameslink	a	18 34					18 46		19 02			19 20			19 32					19 48		20 02		20 20	
Farringdon	a	18 37					18 49		19 05			19 23			19 36					19 51		20 06		20 23	
St Pancras International	a	18 41					18 53		19 09			19 27			19 40					19 55		20 10		20 27	
North Dulwich	d		18 20		18 29			18 39		18 50			19 00	19 08			19 20		19 29		19 38		19 50		20 04
East Dulwich	d		18 22		18 31			18 41		18 52			19 02	19 10			19 22		19 31		19 40		19 52		20 06
Peckham Rye **4**	d		18 25		18 34			18 43		18 55			19 05	19 13			19 25		19 34		19 43		19 54		20 09
Queens Rd Peckham	d		18 27		18 36			18 46		18 57			19 07	19 16			19 27		19 36		19 45		19 57		20 11
South Bermondsey	d		18 30		18 39			18 48		19 00			19 10	19 18			19 30		19 39		19 48		19 59		20 14
London Bridge **4** ⊖	a		18 34		18 43			18 53		19 04			19 14	19 23			19 34		19 43		19 53		20 04		20 18

A To St Albans City
B From Streatham Hill
C To Luton
D To Bedford. **1** to Farringdon
E From Norwood Junction
F From London Bridge
G To Bedford

Other trains operate between Peckham Rye, Denmark Hill and London Victoria and London Thameslink see table 195

For Denmark Hill, Clapham High Street, Wandsworth Road, Clapham Junction and East London Line connecting trains, please see Table 178

Table 173R

Mondays to Fridays

9 December to 16 May

Tulse Hill, Streatham, North Dulwich, East Dulwich, Peckham Rye, Queens Road Peckham and South Bermondsey - London Bridge

Network Diagram - see first Page of Table 173

		FC A	SN	FC B	SN	FC A	SN	FC B	SN	FC A		SN	FC B	SN	SN	FC C	SN	SN	FC C	SN		SN	FC C	SN
Sutton (Surrey)	d	19 37		20 12		20 07		20 42		20 37			21 12			21 17			21 47				22 17	
Carshalton	d			20 15				20 45					21 15											
Hackbridge	d			20 17				20 47					21 17											
Mitcham Junction	d			20 20				20 50					21 20											
Mitcham Eastfields	d			20 23				20 53					21 23											
Wimbledon	d	19 56				20 26				20 56						21 38			22 08				22 38	
Haydons Road	d	19 58				20 28				20 58						21 40			22 10				22 40	
Tooting	d	20 01				20 31				21 01						21 43			22 13				22 43	
West Croydon	d		19 57				20 26					20 55			21 25			21 55				22 25		
Selhurst	d		20 01				20 30					20 59			21 29			21 59				22 29		
Thornton Heath	d		20 03				20 32					21 01			21 31			22 01				22 31		
Norbury	d		20 06				20 35					21 04			21 34			22 04				22 34		
Streatham Common	d		20 08				20 38					21 07			21 37			22 07				22 37		
Streatham	d	20 06	20 11	20 27		20 36	20 41	20 57		21 06		21 10	21 27		21 40	21 49		22 10	22 19			22 40	22 49	
Beckenham Junction	d				20 13				20 43					21 13			21 43			22 13				22 45
Birkbeck	d				20 16				20 46					21 16			21 46			22 16				22 48
Crystal Palace	d				20 20				20 50					21 20			21 50			22 20				22 52
Gipsy Hill	d				20 23				20 53					21 23			21 53			22 23				22 55
West Norwood	d				20 26				20 56					21 26			21 56			22 26				22 58
Tulse Hill	d	20 12	20 15	20 31	20 31	20 42	20 45	21 01	21 01	21 12		21 15	21 31	21 31	21 45	21 53	22 01	22 15	22 23	22 31		22 45	22 53	23 02
Herne Hill	a	20 16		20 35		20 46		21 05		21 16			21 35			21 56			22 26				22 56	
Loughborough Jn	a	20 19		20 38		20 49		21 08		21 19			21 38			22 00			22 30				23 00	
Elephant & Castle	a	20 23		20 42		20 53		21 12		21 23			21 42			22 04			22 34				23 04	
London Blackfriars ■3 ⊖	a	20 27		20 46		20 57		21 16		21 27			21 46			22 07			22 37				23 07	
City Thameslink	a	20 32		20 50		21 02		21 20		21 32			21 50			22 10			22 40					
Farringdon	a	20 36		20 53		21 06		21 23		21 36			21 53			22 13			22 43				23 13	
St Pancras International	a	20 40		20 57		21 10		21 27		21 40			21 57			22 17			22 47				23 17	
North Dulwich	d		20 18		20 34		20 48		21 04			21 18		21 34	21 48		22 04	22 18		22 34		22 48		23 05
East Dulwich	d		20 20		20 36		20 50		21 06			21 20		21 36	21 50		22 06	22 20		22 36		22 50		23 07
Peckham Rye ■4	d		20 23		20 39		20 52		21 09			21 23		21 39	21 53		22 09	22 23		22 39		22 53		23 09
Queens Rd Peckham	d		20 25		20 41		20 55		21 11			21 26		21 41	21 56		22 11	22 26		22 41		22 56		23 12
South Bermondsey	d		20 28		20 44		20 57		21 14			21 28		21 44	21 58		22 14	22 28		22 44		22 58		23 14
London Bridge ■4 ⊖	a		20 33		20 48		21 03		21 18			21 33		21 48	22 03		22 18	22 33		22 48		23 03		23 19

		SN	FC C	SN
Sutton (Surrey)	d		22 47	
Carshalton	d			
Hackbridge	d			
Mitcham Junction	d			
Mitcham Eastfields	d			
Wimbledon	d		23 08	
Haydons Road	d		23 10	
Tooting	d		23 13	
West Croydon	d	22 55		
Selhurst	d	22 59		
Thornton Heath	d	23 01		
Norbury	d	23 04		
Streatham Common	d	23 07		
Streatham	d	23 10	23 19	
Beckenham Junction	d			23 13
Birkbeck	d			23 16
Crystal Palace	d			23 20
Gipsy Hill	d			23 23
West Norwood	d			23 26
Tulse Hill	d	23 15	23 23	23 31
Herne Hill	a		23 26	
Loughborough Jn	a			
Elephant & Castle	a		23 33	
London Blackfriars ■3 ⊖	a		23 37	
City Thameslink	a			
Farringdon	a		23 43	
St Pancras International	a		23 47	
North Dulwich	d	23 18		23 34
East Dulwich	d	23 20		23 36
Peckham Rye ■4	d	23 24		23 39
Queens Rd Peckham	d	23 26		23 41
South Bermondsey	d	23 29		23 44
London Bridge ■4 ⊖	a	23 33		23 48

A To Luton
B To St Albans City
C To Bedford

Other trains operate between Peckham Rye, Denmark Hill and London Victoria and London Thameslink see table 195

For Denmark Hill, Clapham High Street, Wandsworth Road, Clapham Junction and East London Line connecting trains, please see Table 178

Table 173R

Saturdays

14 December to 17 May

Tulse Hill, Streatham, North Dulwich, East Dulwich, Peckham Rye, Queens Road Peckham and South Bermondsey - London Bridge

Network Diagram - see first Page of Table 173

		SN A	FC B	SN	FC C	FC B	SN	FC C	FC B	SN		FC C	SN	FC B	SN	FC C	SN	FC B	SN	FC C	
Sutton (Surrey)	d		06 37		07 08	07 07		07 38	07 37			08 08		08 07		08 38		08 37		09 08	
Carshalton	d				07 11			07 41				08 11				08 41				09 11	
Hackbridge	d				07 13			07 43				08 13				08 43				09 13	
Mitcham Junction	d				07 16			07 46				08 16				08 46				09 16	
Mitcham Eastfields	d				07 19			07 49				08 19				08 49				09 19	
Wimbledon	d		06 58			07 28			07 58					08 28				08 58			
Haydons Road	d		07 00			07 30			08 00					08 30				09 00			
Tooting	d		07 03			07 33			08 03					08 33				09 03			
West Croydon	d			06 55			07 25			07 55					08 25				08 55		
Selhurst	d			07 00			07 30			08 00					08 30				09 00		
Thornton Heath	d			07 02			07 32			08 02					08 32				09 02		
Norbury	d			07 05			07 35			08 05					08 35				09 05		
Streatham Common	d			07 07			07 37			08 07					08 37				09 07		
Streatham	d		07 08	07 11	07 23	07 38	07 41	07 53	08 08	08 11		08 23		08 38	08 41	08 53		09 08	09 11	09 23	and at the same minutes past each hour until
Beckenham Junction	d												08 13				08 43				
Birkbeck	d												08 16				08 46				
Crystal Palace	d	06 45											08 20				08 50				
Gipsy Hill	d	06 47											08 23				08 53				
West Norwood	d	06 50											08 26				08 56				
Tulse Hill	d	06 54	07 12	07 15	07 27	07 42	07 45	07 57	08 12	08 15		08 27	08 31	08 42	08 45	08 57	09 01	09 12	09 15	09 27	
Herne Hill	a		07 16		07 31	07 46		08 01	08 16			08 31		08 46		09 01		09 16		09 31	
Loughborough Jn	a		07 19		07 34	07 49		08 04	08 19			08 34		08 49		09 04		09 19		09 34	
Elephant & Castle	a		07 23		07 38	07 53		08 08	08 23			08 38		08 53		09 08		09 23		09 38	
London Blackfriars 3 ⊖	a		07 27		07 42	07 57		08 12	08 27			08 42		08 57		09 12		09 27		09 42	
City Thameslink	a													09 02		09 16		09 32		09 46	
Farringdon	a		07 36		07 49	08 06		08 19	08 36			08 49		09 06		09 19		09 36		09 49	
St Pancras International	a		07 40		07 53	08 10		08 23	08 40			08 53		09 10		09 23		09 40		09 53	
North Dulwich	d	06 57		07 18			07 48			08 18			08 34		08 48		09 04		09 18		
East Dulwich	d	06 59		07 20			07 50			08 20			08 36		08 50		09 06		09 20		
Peckham Rye 4	d	07 05		07 23			07 53			08 23			08 39		08 53		09 09		09 23		
Queens Rd Peckham	d	07 07		07 26			07 56			08 26			08 41		08 56		09 11		09 26		
South Bermondsey	d	07 10		07 28			07 58			08 28			08 44		08 58		09 14		09 28		
London Bridge 4 ⊖	a	07 14		07 33			08 03			08 33			08 48		09 03		09 18		09 33		

		SN	FC B	SN	FC D	SN	FC B	SN	FC C		SN	FC B	SN	FC C	SN	FC B	SN	FC C	SN		SN	FC D	SN	SN	FC D
Sutton (Surrey)	d		19 07		19 38		19 37		20 08			20 07		20 38		20 37		21 08				21 15			21 45
Carshalton	d				19 41				20 11					20 41				21 11							
Hackbridge	d				19 43				20 13					20 43				21 13							
Mitcham Junction	d				19 46				20 16					20 46				21 16							
Mitcham Eastfields	d				19 49				20 19					20 49				21 19							
Wimbledon	d		19 28				19 58					20 28				20 58						21 38			22 08
Haydons Road	d		19 30				20 00					20 30				21 00						21 40			22 10
Tooting	d		19 33				20 03					20 33				21 03						21 43			22 13
West Croydon	d			19 25				19 55					20 25				20 55				21 25			21 55	
Selhurst	d			19 30				20 00					20 30				21 00				21 30			22 00	
Thornton Heath	d			19 32				20 02					20 32				21 02				21 32			22 02	
Norbury	d			19 35				20 05					20 35				21 05				21 35			22 05	
Streatham Common	d			19 37				20 07					20 37				21 07				21 37			22 07	
Streatham	d		19 38	19 41	19 53		20 08	20 11	20 23			20 38	20 41	20 53		21 08	21 11	21 23			21 41	21 49		22 11	22 19
Beckenham Junction	d	19 13				19 43					20 13				20 43				21 13				21 43		
Birkbeck	d	19 16				19 46					20 16				20 46				21 16				21 46		
Crystal Palace	d	19 20				19 50					20 20				20 50				21 20				21 50		
Gipsy Hill	d	19 23				19 53					20 23				20 53				21 23				21 53		
West Norwood	d	19 26				19 56					20 26				20 56				21 26				21 56		
Tulse Hill	d	19 31	19 42	19 45	19 57	20 01	20 12	20 15	20 27		20 31	20 42	20 45	20 57	21 01	21 12	21 15	21 27	21 31		21 45	21 53	22 01	22 15	22 23
Herne Hill	a		19 46		20 01		20 16		20 31			20 46		21 01		21 16		21 31				21 56			22 26
Loughborough Jn	a		19 49		20 04		20 19		20 34			20 49		21 04		21 19		21 34				22 00			22 30
Elephant & Castle	a		19 53		20 08		20 23		20 38			20 53		21 08		21 23		21 38				22 04			22 34
London Blackfriars 3 ⊖	a		19 57		20 12		20 27		20 42			20 57		21 12		21 27		21 42				22 07			22 37
City Thameslink	a		20 02		20 16		20 32		20 46																
Farringdon	a		20 06		20 19		20 36		20 49			21 06		21 19		21 36		21 49				22 13			22 43
St Pancras International	a		20 10		20 23		20 40		20 53			21 10		21 23		21 40		21 53				22 17			22 47
North Dulwich	d	19 34		19 48		20 04		20 18			20 34		20 48		21 04		21 18		21 34		21 48		22 04	22 18	
East Dulwich	d	19 36		19 50		20 06		20 20			20 36		20 50		21 06		21 20		21 36		21 50		22 06	22 20	
Peckham Rye 4	d	19 39		19 53		20 09		20 23			20 39		20 53		21 09		21 23		21 39		21 53		22 09	22 23	
Queens Rd Peckham	d	19 41		19 56		20 11		20 26			20 41		20 56		21 11		21 26		21 41		21 56		22 11	22 26	
South Bermondsey	d	19 44		19 58		20 14		20 28			20 44		20 58		21 14		21 28		21 44		21 58		22 14	22 28	
London Bridge 4 ⊖	a	19 48		20 03		20 18		20 33			20 48		21 03		21 18		21 33		21 48		22 03		22 18	22 33	

A From Norwood Junction
B To Luton
C To St Albans City
D To Bedford

Other trains operate between Peckham Rye, Denmark Hill and London Victoria and London Thameslink see table 195

For Denmark Hill, Clapham High Street, Wandsworth Road, Clapham Junction and East London Line connecting trains, please see Table 178

Table 173R

Saturdays

14 December to 17 May

Tulse Hill, Streatham, North Dulwich, East Dulwich, Peckham Rye, Queens Road Peckham and South Bermondsey - London Bridge

Network Diagram - see first Page of Table 173

Station		SN	SN	FC A	SN	SN	FC A	SN
Sutton (Surrey)	d			22 15			22 45	
Carshalton	d							
Hackbridge	d							
Mitcham Junction	d							
Mitcham Eastfields	d							
Wimbledon	d			22 38			23 08	
Haydons Road	d			22 40			23 10	
Tooting	d			22 43			23 13	
West Croydon	d		22 25			22 55		
Selhurst	d		22 30			23 00		
Thornton Heath	d		22 32			23 02		
Norbury	d		22 35			23 05		
Streatham Common	d		22 37			23 07		
Streatham	d		22 41	22 49		23 11	23 19	
Beckenham Junction	d	22 13			22 43			23 13
Birkbeck	d	22 16			22 46			23 16
Crystal Palace	d	22 20			22 50			23 20
Gipsy Hill	d	22 23			22 53			23 23
West Norwood	d	22 26			22 56			23 26
Tulse Hill	d	22 31	22 45	22 53	23 01	23 15	23 23	23 31
Herne Hill	a			22 56			23 26	
Loughborough Jn	a			23 00				
Elephant & Castle	a			23 04			23 33	
London Blackfriars 3 ⊖	a			23 07			23 37	
City Thameslink	a							
Farringdon	a			23 13			23 43	
St Pancras International	a			23 17			23 47	
North Dulwich	d	22 34	22 48		23 04	23 18		23 34
East Dulwich	d	22 36	22 50		23 06	23 20		23 36
Peckham Rye 4	d	22 39	22 53		23 09	23 23		23 39
Queens Rd Peckham	d	22 41	22 56		23 11	23 26		23 41
South Bermondsey	d	22 44	22 58		23 14	23 28		23 44
London Bridge 4 ⊖	a	22 48	23 03		23 18	23 33		23 48

Sundays

8 December to 11 May

Station		SN	SN	SN B	SN	SN B	SN	SN B	SN	SN B	SN	SN B	SN	SN B	FC C	SN	FC	SN B	FC C	SN	FC	SN B	FC C
Sutton (Surrey)	d														09 37		10 08		10 07		10 38		10 37
Carshalton	d																10 11				10 41		
Hackbridge	d																10 13				10 43		
Mitcham Junction	d																10 16				10 46		
Mitcham Eastfields	d																10 19				10 49		
Wimbledon	d														09 56				10 26				10 56
Haydons Road	d														09 58				10 28				10 58
Tooting	d														10 01				10 31				11 01
West Croydon	d																						
Selhurst	d	06 48		07 17		07 47		08 18		08 48		09 16		09 46				10 16				10 46	
Thornton Heath	d	06 50		07 19		07 49		08 20		08 50		09 18		09 48				10 18				10 48	
Norbury	d	06 53		07 22		07 52		08 23		08 53		09 21		09 51				10 21				10 51	
Streatham Common	d	06 55		07 25		07 54		08 27		08 55		09 25		09 55				10 25				10 55	
Streatham	d	06 58		07 28		07 58		08 30		08 58		09 28		09 58	10 06		10 23	10 28	10 36		10 53	10 58	11 06
Beckenham Junction	d																						
Birkbeck	d																						
Crystal Palace	d		07 07		07 38		08 08		08 38		09 08		09 37			10 07				10 37			
Gipsy Hill	d		07 09		07 40		08 10		08 40		09 10		09 39			10 09				10 39			
West Norwood	d		07 12		07 43		08 13		08 43		09 13		09 42			10 12				10 42			
Tulse Hill	d	07 02	07 16	07 32	07 47	08 02	08 17	08 33	08 47	09 02	09 17	09 32	09 46	10 02	10 10	10 16	10 27	10 32	10 40	10 46	10 57	11 02	11 10
Herne Hill	a														10 14		10 31		10 44		11 01		11 14
Loughborough Jn	a														10 17		10 34		10 47		11 04		11 17
Elephant & Castle	a														10 21		10 39		10 51		11 09		11 21
London Blackfriars 3 ⊖	a														10 25		10 43		10 55		11 13		11 25
City Thameslink	a																						
Farringdon	a														10 32				11 02				11 32
St Pancras International	a														10 36				11 06				11 36
North Dulwich	d	07 05	07 19	07 35	07 50	08 05	08 20	08 36	08 50	09 05	09 20	09 35	09 49	10 05		10 19		10 35		10 49		11 05	
East Dulwich	d	07 07	07 21	07 37	07 52	08 07	08 22	08 38	08 52	09 07	09 22	09 37	09 51	10 07		10 21		10 37		10 51		11 07	
Peckham Rye 4	d	07 10	07 23	07 39	07 54	08 10	08 24	08 41	08 55	09 10	09 24	09 40	09 53	10 10		10 23		10 40		10 53		11 10	
Queens Rd Peckham	d	07 12	07 26	07 42	07 57	08 12	08 27	08 43	08 57	09 12	09 27	09 42	09 56	10 12		10 26		10 42		10 56		11 12	
South Bermondsey	d	07 15	07 28	07 44	08 00	08 15	08 29	08 46	09 00	09 15	09 29	09 45	09 58	10 15		10 28		10 45		10 58		11 15	
London Bridge 4 ⊖	a	07 19	07 33	07 50	08 04	08 19	08 34	08 50	09 04	09 19	09 34	09 49	10 03	10 19		10 33		10 49		11 03		11 19	

A To Bedford

B From East Croydon

C To Luton

Other trains operate between Peckham Rye, Denmark Hill and London Victoria and London Thameslink see table 195

For Denmark Hill, Clapham High Street, Wandsworth Road, Clapham Junction and East London Line connecting trains, please see Table 178

Table 173R

Sundays

8 December to 11 May

Tulse Hill, Streatham, North Dulwich, East Dulwich, Peckham Rye, Queens Road Peckham and South Bermondsey - London Bridge

Network Diagram - see first Page of Table 173

		SN	FC	SN A	FC B	SN	FC	SN A	FC B	SN	FC	SN A	FC B	SN	FC	SN A	FC B	SN	FC	SN A	FC B	SN	
Sutton (Surrey)	d		11 08		11 07		11 38		11 37		12 08		12 07		12 38		12 37		13 08		13 07		
Carshalton	d		11 11				11 41				12 11				12 41				13 11				
Hackbridge	d		11 13				11 43				12 13				12 43				13 13				
Mitcham Junction	d		11 16				11 46				12 16				12 46				13 16				
Mitcham Eastfields	d		11 19				11 49				12 19				12 49				13 19				
Wimbledon	d				11 26				11 56				12 26				12 56				13 26		
Haydons Road	d				11 28				11 58				12 28				12 58				13 28		
Tooting	d				11 31				12 01				12 31				13 01				13 31		
West Croydon	d																						
Selhurst	d			11 16				11 46				12 16				12 46				13 16			
Thornton Heath	d			11 18				11 48				12 18				12 48				13 18			
Norbury	d			11 21				11 51				12 21				12 51				13 21			
Streatham Common	d			11 25				11 55				12 25				12 55				13 25			and at
Streatham	d		11 23	11 28	11 36		11 53	11 58	12 06		12 23	12 28	12 36		12 53	12 58	13 06		13 23	13 28	13 36		the same
Beckenham Junction	d																						minutes
Birkbeck	d																						past
Crystal Palace	d	11 07				11 37				12 07				12 39				13 07				13 37	each
Gipsy Hill	d	11 09				11 39				12 09				12 41				13 09				13 39	hour until
West Norwood	d	11 12				11 42				12 12				12 44				13 12				13 42	
Tulse Hill	d	11 16	11 27	11 32	11 40	11 46	11 57	12 02	12 10	12 16	12 27	12 32	12 40	12 48	12 57	13 02	13 10	13 16	13 27	13 32	13 40	13 46	
Herne Hill	a		11 31		11 44		12 01		12 14		12 31		12 44		13 01		13 14		13 31		13 44		
Loughborough Jn	a		11 34		11 47		12 04		12 17		12 34		12 47		13 04		13 17		13 34		13 47		
Elephant & Castle	a		11 39		11 51		12 09		12 21		12 39		12 51		13 09		13 21		13 39		13 51		
London Blackfriars [3] ⊖	a		11 43		11 55		12 13		12 25		12 43		12 55		13 13		13 25		13 43		13 55		
City Thameslink	a																						
Farringdon	a				12 02				12 32				13 02				13 32				14 02		
St Pancras International	a				12 06				12 36				13 06				13 36				14 06		
North Dulwich	d	11 19		11 35		11 49		12 05		12 19		12 35		12 51		13 05		13 19		13 35		13 49	
East Dulwich	d	11 21		11 37		11 51		12 07		12 21		12 37		12 53		13 07		13 21		13 37		13 51	
Peckham Rye [4]	d	11 23		11 40		11 53		12 10		12 23		12 40		12 55		13 10		13 23		13 40		13 53	
Queens Rd Peckham	d	11 26		11 42		11 56		12 12		12 26		12 42		12 58		13 12		13 26		13 42		13 56	
South Bermondsey	d	11 28		11 45		11 58		12 15		12 28		12 45		13 00		13 15		13 28		13 45		13 58	
London Bridge [4] ⊖	a	11 33		11 49		12 03		12 19		12 33		12 49		13 05		13 19		13 33		13 49		14 03	

		FC	SN A	FC C	SN	FC	SN A	FC C	SN	FC D	FC E	SN A	SN	FC	SN A	SN	SN A	SN	SN
Sutton (Surrey)	d	20 38		20 37		21 08		21 07		21 38	21 38			22 08					
Carshalton	d	20 41				21 11				21 41	21 41			22 11					
Hackbridge	d	20 43				21 13				21 43	21 43			22 13					
Mitcham Junction	d	20 46				21 16				21 46	21 46			22 16					
Mitcham Eastfields	d	20 49				21 19				21 49	21 49			22 19					
Wimbledon	d			20 56				21 26											
Haydons Road	d			20 58				21 28											
Tooting	d			21 01				21 31											
West Croydon	d																		
Selhurst	d		20 46				21 16					21 46			22 16		22 46		
Thornton Heath	d		20 48				21 18					21 48			22 18		22 48		
Norbury	d		20 51				21 21					21 51			22 21		22 51		
Streatham Common	d		20 55				21 25					21 55			22 25		22 55		
Streatham	d	20 53	20 58	21 06		21 23	21 28	21 36		21 53	21 53	21 58		22 23	22 28		22 58		
Beckenham Junction	d																		
Birkbeck	d																		
Crystal Palace	d				21 07				21 37				22 07			22 37		23 07	23 37
Gipsy Hill	d				21 09				21 39				22 09			22 39		23 09	23 39
West Norwood	d				21 12				21 42				22 12			22 42		23 12	23 42
Tulse Hill	d	20 57	21 02	21 10	21 16	21 27	21 32	21 40	21 46	21 57	21 57	22 02	22 16	22 27	22 32	22 46	23 02	23 16	23 46
Herne Hill	a	21 01		21 14		21 31		21 44		22 01	22 01			22 31					
Loughborough Jn	a	21 04		21 17		21 34		21 47		22 04	22 04			22 34					
Elephant & Castle	a	21 09		21 21		21 39		21 51		22 09	22 09			22 39					
London Blackfriars [3] ⊖	a	21 13		21 25		21 43		21 55		22 13	22 13			22 43					
City Thameslink	a																		
Farringdon	a			21 32				22 02			22 19								
St Pancras International	a			21 36				22 06			22 24								
North Dulwich	d		21 05		21 19		21 35		21 49			22 05	22 19		22 35	22 49	23 05	23 19	23 49
East Dulwich	d		21 07		21 21		21 37		21 51			22 07	22 21		22 37	22 51	23 07	23 21	23 51
Peckham Rye [4]	d		21 10		21 23		21 40		21 53			22 10	22 23		22 40	22 53	23 10	23 23	23 53
Queens Rd Peckham	d		21 12		21 26		21 42		21 56			22 12	22 26		22 42	22 56	23 12	23 26	23 56
South Bermondsey	d		21 15		21 28		21 45		21 58			22 15	22 28		22 45	22 58	23 15	23 28	23 58
London Bridge [4] ⊖	a		21 19		21 33		21 49		22 03			22 19	22 33		22 49	23 03	23 19	23 33	00 03

A From East Croydon
B To Luton
C To Bedford
D until 29 December
E from 5 January. To Bedford

Other trains operate between Peckham Rye, Denmark Hill and London Victoria and London Thameslink see table 195

For Denmark Hill, Clapham High Street, Wandsworth Road, Clapham Junction and East London Line connecting trains, please see Table 178

Network Diagram for Tables 175, 186, 188

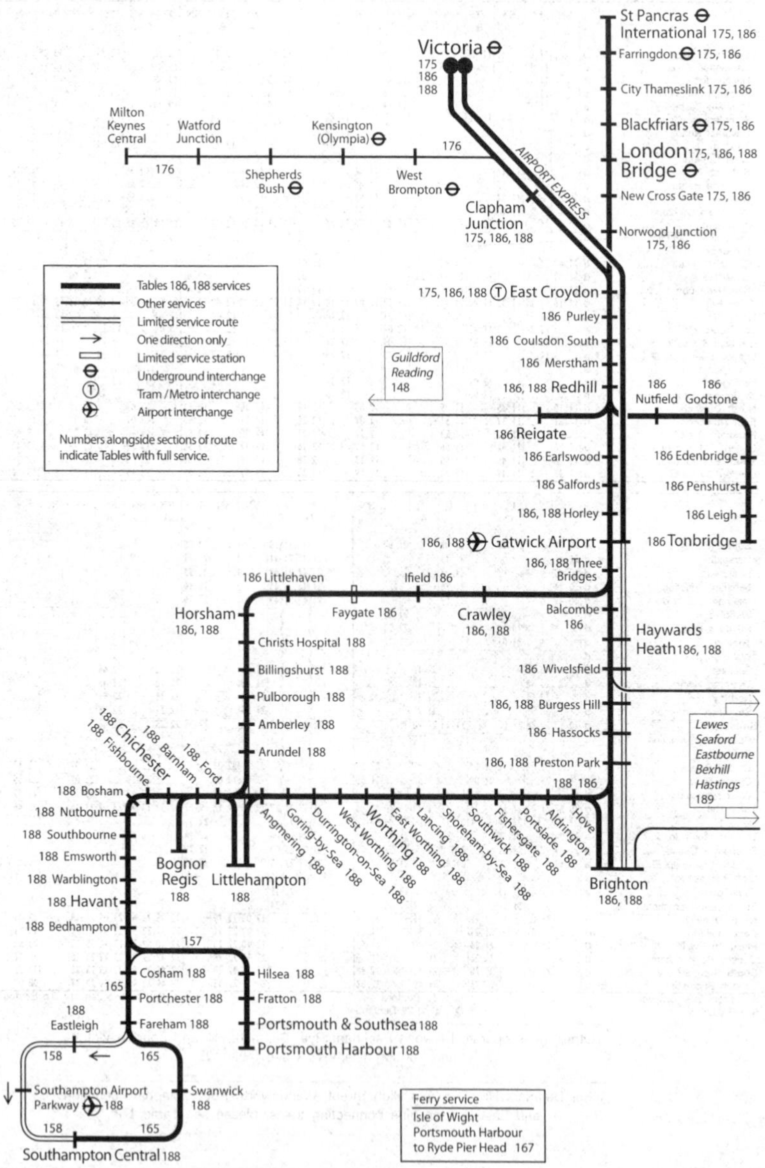
St Pancras International 175, 186
Farringdon 175, 186
City Thameslink 175, 186
Blackfriars 175, 186
London Bridge 175, 186, 188
New Cross Gate 175, 186
Norwood Junction 175, 186
Victoria 175 186 188
Milton Keynes Central
Watford Junction
Kensington (Olympia)
176
Shepherds Bush
West Brompton
AIRPORT EXPRESS
Clapham Junction 175, 186, 188
Tables 186, 188 services
Other services
Limited service route
One direction only
Limited service station
Underground interchange
Tram / Metro interchange
Airport interchange
Numbers alongside sections of route indicate Tables with full service.
175, 186, 188 East Croydon
186 Purley
186 Coulsdon South
186 Merstham
186, 188 Redhill
Guildford Reading 148
186 Nutfield
186 Godstone
186 Reigate
186 Earlswood
186 Salfords
186, 188 Horley
186, 188 Gatwick Airport
186 Edenbridge
186 Penshurst
186 Leigh
186 Tonbridge
186, 188 Three Bridges
186 Littlehaven
Ifield 186
Horsham 186, 188
Faygate 186
Crawley 186, 188
Balcombe 186
Haywards Heath 186, 188
Christs Hospital 188
Billingshurst 188
Pulborough 188
Amberley 188
Arundel 188
186 Wivelsfield
186, 188 Burgess Hill
186 Hassocks
186, 188 Preston Park
188 186
Lewes Seaford Eastbourne Bexhill Hastings 189
188 Chichester
188 Fishbourne
188 Barnham
188 Ford
188 Bosham
188 Nutbourne
188 Southbourne
188 Emsworth
188 Warblington
188 Havant
188 Bedhampton
Bognor Regis 188
Littlehampton 188
Angmering 188
Goring-by-Sea 188
Durrington-on-Sea 188
West Worthing 188
Worthing 188
East Worthing 188
Lancing 188
Shoreham-by-Sea 188
Southwick 188
Fishersgate 188
Portslade 188
Aldrington 188
Hove
Brighton 186, 188
157
Cosham 188
165
Portchester 188
Fareham 188
Hilsea 188
Fratton 188
Portsmouth & Southsea 188
Portsmouth Harbour 188
188 Eastleigh
158
165
Southampton Airport Parkway 188
Swanwick 188
158
165
Southampton Central 188
Ferry service
Isle of Wight Portsmouth Harbour to Ryde Pier Head 167

TOCs operating on this network - Southern (SN), First Great Western (GW), First Capital Connect (FC)

Table 175

Mondays to Fridays

9 December to 16 May

London - Norwood Junction and East Croydon - Summary of Fast Trains

Summary of Fast Trains

Network Diagram - see first Page of Table 175

	SN	FC	SN	FC	FC	SN	FC	SN	FC		SN	FC	FC	SN	FC	FC	SN	FC	FC		SN	SN	FC	SN
	MX			MO																				
	1	1	1	1	1	1	1	1	1		1	1	1	1	1	1	1	1	1		1	1	1	1
		A		B	A								C											
London Victoria 15 ⊖ d	00 05		00 14			01 00		02 00			03 00			04 00			05 01				05 25	05 32		05 52
Clapham Junction 10 d	00 12		00 21			01 09		02 09			03 09			04 09			05 08				05 32	05 38		05 59
St Pancras International 15 ⊖ d				00 14	00 24		00 54		01 54			02 54	03 25		03 54	04 24		04 54	05 12				05 32	
Farringdon 3 ⊖ d				00 19	00 29													04 59	05 18				05 38	
City Thameslink 3 d																			05 21				05 41	
London Blackfriars 3 ⊖ d		00 05		00 25	00 35		01 05		02 05			03 05	03 36		04 05	04 35		05 05	05 24				05 44	
London Bridge 4 ⊖ d		00 12			00 42														05 30				05 50	
New Cross Gate d																								
Norwood Junction 2 a																					05 50			
East Croydon a	00 26	00 28	00 35	00 56	00 56	01 23	01 34	02 24	02 34		03 24	03 34	04 04	04 26	04 34	05 04	05 22	05 31	05 47		05 54	05 48	06 05	06 09

	SN	SN	SN	FC	SN		SN	SN	SN	FC	SN	SN	SN	FC	SN		SN	SN	FC	SN	SN	SN	SN	SN
	1	1	1	1	1		1	1	1	1	1	1	1	1	1		1	1	1	1	1	1	1	
London Victoria 15 ⊖ d	06 02	06 06			06 21		06 24	06 32			06 47	06 51	06 54				07 02	07 10		07 17				07 23
Clapham Junction 10 d	06 08	06 12			06 27		06 30	06 38			06 53	06 57	07 00				07 08	07 16		07 23				07 30
St Pancras International 15 ⊖ d				06 02						06 22				06 38					06 58					
Farringdon 3 ⊖ d				06 08						06 28				06 44					07 04					
City Thameslink 3 d				06 11						06 31				06 47					07 07					
London Blackfriars 3 ⊖ d				06 14						06 34				06 50					07 09					
London Bridge 4 ⊖ d			06 08	06 20					06 38	06 42				07 00	07 03				07 16		07 19	07 23	07 25	
New Cross Gate d																								
Norwood Junction 2 a																					07 29	07 34	07 37	
East Croydon a	06 17	06 22	06 22	06 33	06 38		06 40	06 48	06 52	06 54	07 03	07 06	07 10	07 14	07 16		07 17	07 26	07 30	07 33	07 33	07 38	07 42	07 46

	SN		SN	SN	FC	SN	SN	SN	SN	SN	SN		SN	SN	SN	FC	SN	SN	SN	FC	SN		SN	SN
	1		1	1	1		1	1	1	1	1		1	1	1	1	1		1	1	1		1	1
London Victoria 15 ⊖ d			07 32	07 36			07 47			07 52			08 02		08 07		08 10		08 17				08 21	
Clapham Junction 10 d			07 38	07 42			07 53			07 58			08 08		08 13		08 16		08 23				08 27	
St Pancras International 15 ⊖ d					07 20											07 44				07 56				
Farringdon 3 ⊖ d					07 26											07 50				08 02				
City Thameslink 3 d					07 29											07 53				08 05				
London Blackfriars 3 ⊖ d					07 32											07 56				08 08				
London Bridge 4 ⊖ d	07 30				07 42	07 44		07 51	07 55		07 58			08 00				08 14		08 18	08 23			08 25
New Cross Gate d	07 36					07 50								08 08										
Norwood Junction 2 a	07 43							08 01			08 10			08 15				08 27						08 36
East Croydon a	07 47		07 52	07 52	07 54	08 01	08 03	08 06	08 08	08 10	08 15		08 18	08 19	08 22	08 26	08 27	08 30	08 34	08 37	08 37		08 40	08 40

	SN	SN	SN	SN	SN	SN	FC		SN	SN	SN	SN	FC	SN	SN	SN	SN		FC	SN	SN	SN	FC	SN
	1	1	1	1	1		1		1	1	1	1	1	1	1		1		1	1	1		1	1
					trolley					trolley						trolley					trolley			
London Victoria 15 ⊖ d	08 23		08 32		08 37					08 47	08 49	08 53		09 02		09 06					09 17			09 23
Clapham Junction 10 d	08 30		08 38		08 43					08 53	08 56	08 59		09 08		09 12					09 23			09 29
St Pancras International 15 ⊖ d							08 20						08 32						08 48				09 04	
Farringdon 3 ⊖ d							08 26						08 38						08 54				09 10	
City Thameslink 3 d							08 29						08 41						08 57				09 13	
London Blackfriars 3 ⊖ d							08 32						08 44						09 00				09 16	
London Bridge 4 ⊖ d		08 30		08 28		08 40			08 42						09 01		09 03		09 12	09 15		09 20	09 27	
New Cross Gate d				08 37					08 48						09 09									
Norwood Junction 2 a				08 45					08 55						09 16					09 25		09 32		
East Croydon a	08 42	08 47	08 48	08 50	08 52	08 55	08 57		08 59	09 03	09 07	09 10	09 12	09 18	09 20	09 21	09 22		09 24	09 29	09 32	09 36	09 39	09 39

	SN	SN	SN		FC	SN	SN	SN	SN	FC	SN	SN	SN		SN	SN	FC	SN	SN	SN	FC	SN	SN	
	1	1	1		1	1	1		1	1	1	1	1		1	1	1	1	1		1	1	1	
							trolley								trolley				trolley					
London Victoria 15 ⊖ d	09 32		09 36				09 47		09 51		09 53	10 02			10 06				10 17			10 23	10 32	
Clapham Junction 10 d	09 38		09 42				09 53				09 59	10 08			10 12				10 23			10 29	10 38	
St Pancras International 15 ⊖ d					09 22					09 40							09 54				10 10			
Farringdon 3 ⊖ d					09 28					09 45							09 59				10 15			
City Thameslink 3 d					09 31					09 48							10 03				10 18			
London Blackfriars 3 ⊖ d					09 34					09 50							10 05				10 20			
London Bridge 4 ⊖ d		09 32			09 42	09 45		09 50		09 57			10 03			10 08	10 12	10 15		10 20	10 27			
New Cross Gate d		09 38											10 08											
Norwood Junction 2 a		09 46				09 55		10 02					10 16					10 25		10 32				
East Croydon a	09 48	09 50	09 51		09 54	09 59	10 02	10 06	10 07	10 09	10 09	10 17	10 20		10 21	10 22	10 24	10 29	10 32	10 36	10 39	10 39	10 48	

	SN	SN	FC	SN	SN	SN	SN	FC	SN		SN	SN	SN	SN	FC	SN	SN	SN	FC		SN	SN	SN	SN
	1	1	1	1	1		1	1	1		1	1	1	1	1	1	1		1		1	1	1	1
					trolley																			trolley
London Victoria 15 ⊖ d		10 36			10 47		10 51		10 53		11 02		11 06				11 17				11 23	11 32		11 36
Clapham Junction 10 d		10 42			10 53				10 59		11 08		11 12				11 23				11 29	11 38		11 42
St Pancras International 15 ⊖ d			10 24					10 40							10 54				11 10					
Farringdon 3 ⊖ d			10 29					10 45							10 59				11 15					
City Thameslink 3 d			10 33					10 48							11 03				11 18					
London Blackfriars 3 ⊖ d			10 35					10 50							11 05				11 20					
London Bridge 4 ⊖ d	10 33		10 42	10 45		10 50		10 57				11 03		11 08	11 12	11 15		11 20	11 27				11 33	
New Cross Gate d	10 38											11 08											11 38	
Norwood Junction 2 a	10 46			10 55		11 02						11 16				11 25		11 32					11 46	
East Croydon a	10 50	10 51	10 54	10 59	11 02	11 06	11 07	11 09	11 09		11 17	11 20	11 21	11 23	11 24	11 29	11 32	11 36	11 39		11 39	11 48	11 50	11 51

A MX from 3 January

B from 6 January

C 1 from London Blackfriars

Table 175

Mondays to Fridays

9 December to 16 May

London - Norwood Junction and East Croydon - Summary of Fast Trains

Summary of Fast Trains

Network Diagram - see first Page of Table 175

		FC		SN	SN	SN	SN	FC	SN	SN	SN	SN		SN	FC	SN	SN	SN	FC	SN	SN	SN		SN	FC
		1		1	1		1	1	1	1	1	1		1	1	1	1		1	1	1	1		1	1
												🚲												🚲	
London Victoria 15	⊖ d				11 47		11 51		11 53	12 02		12 06					12 17			12 23	12 32			12 36	
Clapham Junction 10	d				11 53				11 59	12 08		12 12					12 23			12 29	12 38			12 42	
St Pancras International 15	⊖ d	11 24						11 40							11 54				12 10						12 24
Farringdon 3	⊖ d	11 29						11 45							11 59				12 15						12 29
City Thameslink 3	d	11 33						11 48							12 03				12 18						12 33
London Blackfriars 3	⊖ d	11 35						11 50							12 05				12 20						12 35
London Bridge 4	⊖ d	11 42		11 45		11 50		11 57			12 03			12 08	12 12	12 15		12 20	12 27			12 33			12 42
New Cross Gate	d										12 08											12 38			
Norwood Junction 2	a			11 55		12 02					12 16					12 25		12 32				12 46			
East Croydon	a	11 54		11 59	12 02	12 06	12 07	12 09	12 09	12 17	12 20	12 21		12 22	12 24	12 29	12 32	12 36	12 39	12 39	12 48	12 50		12 51	12 54

		SN	SN	SN	SN	FC	SN	SN		SN	SN	SN	FC	SN	SN	SN	FC	SN		SN	SN	SN	FC	SN	SN
		1	1		1	1	1	1		1	1	1	1	1	1		1	1		1	1	1	1	1	1
											🚲											🚲			
London Victoria 15	⊖ d		12 47		12 51		12 53	13 02			13 06				13 17			13 23		13 32		13 36			13 47
Clapham Junction 10	d		12 53				12 59	13 08			13 12				13 23			13 29		13 38		13 42			13 53
St Pancras International 15	⊖ d					12 40							12 54				13 10						13 24		
Farringdon 3	⊖ d					12 45							12 59				13 15						13 29		
City Thameslink 3	d					12 48							13 03				13 18						13 33		
London Blackfriars 3	⊖ d					12 50							13 05				13 20						13 35		
London Bridge 4	⊖ d	12 45		12 50		12 57				13 03		13 08	13 12	13 15		13 20	13 27				13 33		13 42	13 45	
New Cross Gate	d									13 08											13 38				
Norwood Junction 2	a	12 55		13 02						13 16				13 25		13 32					13 46			13 55	
East Croydon	a	12 59	13 02	13 06	13 07	13 09	13 09	13 17		13 20	13 21	13 23	13 24	13 29	13 32	13 36	13 39	13 39		13 48	13 50	13 51	13 54	13 59	14 02

		SN	SN	FC		SN	SN	SN	SN	SN	FC	SN	SN	SN		FC	SN	SN	SN	SN	FC	SN	SN	SN	
			1	1		1	1	1	1	1	1	1	1			1	1	1	1	1	1	1	1		
									🚲											🚲					
London Victoria 15	⊖ d		13 51			13 53	14 02		14 06				14 17				14 23	14 32		14 36			14 47		
Clapham Junction 10	d					13 59	14 08		14 12				14 23				14 29	14 38		14 42			14 53		
St Pancras International 15	⊖ d			13 40							13 54					14 09					14 24				
Farringdon 3	⊖ d			13 45							13 59					14 14					14 29				
City Thameslink 3	d			13 48							14 03					14 18					14 33				
London Blackfriars 3	⊖ d			13 50							14 05					14 20					14 35				
London Bridge 4	⊖ d	13 50		13 57				14 03		14 08	14 12	14 15		14 20		14 27			14 33		14 42	14 45		14 50	
New Cross Gate	d							14 08											14 38						
Norwood Junction 2	a	14 02						14 16				14 25		14 32					14 46			14 55		15 02	
East Croydon	a	14 06	14 07	14 09		14 09	14 17	14 20	14 21	14 23	14 25	14 29	14 32	14 36		14 39	14 40	14 48	14 50	14 51	14 54	14 59	15 02	15 06	

		SN	FC	SN	SN	SN	SN	SN	FC	SN		SN	SN	FC	SN	SN	SN	SN	SN	FC		SN	SN	SN	SN
		1	1	1	1	1	1	1	1	1		1		1	1	1	1	1	1	1		1	1		1
							🚲											🚲							
London Victoria 15	⊖ d	14 51		14 53	15 02		15 06					15 17			15 23	15 32		15 36					15 47		15 51
Clapham Junction 10	d			14 59	15 08		15 12					15 23			15 29	15 38		15 42					15 53		
St Pancras International 15	⊖ d		14 40						14 54					15 10						15 24					
Farringdon 3	⊖ d		14 45						14 59					15 15						15 29					
City Thameslink 3	d		14 48						15 03					15 18						15 33					
London Blackfriars 3	⊖ d		14 50						15 05					15 20						15 35					
London Bridge 4	⊖ d		14 57			15 03		15 08	15 12	15 15			15 20	15 27			15 33		15 38	15 42		15 45		15 50	
New Cross Gate	d					15 08											15 38								
Norwood Junction 2	a					15 16				15 25			15 32				15 46					15 55		16 02	
East Croydon	a	15 07	15 09	15 09	15 17	15 20	15 21	15 23	15 24	15 29		15 32	15 36	15 39	15 40	15 47	15 50	15 51	15 52	15 54		15 59	16 02	16 06	16 07

		FC	SN	SN	SN	SN		SN	FC	SN	SN	SN	SN	FC	SN	SN		SN	SN	SN	SN	FC	SN	SN	SN
		1	1	1	1	1		1	1	1	1	1		1	1	1		1	1	1		1	1		1
						🚲					🚲								🚲				🚲		
London Victoria 15	⊖ d		15 53	16 02		16 06					16 17	16 19			16 23	16 32			16 36		16 39		16 47		16 49
Clapham Junction 10	d		15 59	16 08		16 12					16 23	16 26			16 29	16 38			16 42		16 45		16 53		16 56
St Pancras International 15	⊖ d	15 40							15 54					16 10								16 22			
Farringdon 3	⊖ d	15 45							15 59					16 15								16 27			
City Thameslink 3	d	15 48							16 03					16 18								16 31			
London Blackfriars 3	⊖ d	15 50							16 05					16 20								16 36			
London Bridge 4	⊖ d	15 57			16 03			16 08	16 12	16 15			16 20	16 27				16 30		16 38		16 43		16 48	
New Cross Gate	d				16 09													16 36							
Norwood Junction 2	a				16 16					16 25			16 32					16 43						17 01	
East Croydon	a	16 09	16 09	16 17	16 20	16 21		16 23	16 24	16 29	16 33	16 36	16 36	16 39	16 39	16 47		16 47	16 52	16 52	16 55	16 59	17 03	17 05	17 06

		SN		SN	SN	SN	SN	SN	FC	SN	SN	SN		SN	SN	SN	SN	SN	FC	SN	SN	SN		SN	SN
		1		1	1	1	1	1	1		1	1			1	1	1	1	1	1	1	1			1
																		🚲							
London Victoria 15	⊖ d	16 53				17 02	17 06			17 09		17 17				17 21	17 23	17 27			17 34			17 38	
Clapham Junction 10	d	16 59				17 08	17 12			17 15		17 23				17 27	17 30	17 33			17 40			17 44	
St Pancras International 15	⊖ d								16 46										17 08						
Farringdon 3	⊖ d								16 51										17 13						
City Thameslink 3	d								16 55										17 17						
London Blackfriars 3	⊖ d								16 58										17 20						
London Bridge 4	⊖ d			16 57	16 59			17 08			17 15			17 17	17 23					17 32		17 42			17 44
New Cross Gate	d																								
Norwood Junction 2	a				17 10									17 30						17 43					
East Croydon	a	17 09		17 09	17 14	17 17	17 21	17 22	17 26	17 27	17 29	17 32		17 34	17 35	17 36	17 40	17 42	17 47	17 49	17 50	17 54		17 55	17 57

Table 175

Mondays to Fridays

9 December to 16 May

London - Norwood Junction and East Croydon - Summary of Fast Trains

Summary of Fast Trains

Network Diagram - see first Page of Table 175

	SN 1	SN	SN 1		SN 1	FC 1	SN 1	SN 1	SN 1 🚲	SN 1	SN 1	SN 1	FC 1		SN 1	SN	SN 1	SN 1	SN	SN 1	SN 1	SN 1	FC 1	
London Victoria 15 ⊖ d	17 46				17 49		17 53		17 57		18 04					18 08		18 17			18 19	18 23		
Clapham Junction 10 d	17 52				17 56		18 00		18 04		18 11					18 14		18 23			18 26	18 29		
St Pancras International 15 ⊖ d						17 28							17 40										18 08	
Farringdon 3 ⊖ d						17 33							17 45										18 13	
City Thameslink 3 d						17 37							17 49										18 17	
London Blackfriars 3 ⊖ d						17 40							17 52										18 20	
London Bridge 4 ⊖ d		17 46	17 50					17 56		17 59		18 08			18 12		18 16		18 18	18 23			18 28	
New Cross Gate d																								
Norwood Junction 2 a		17 58								18 09									18 30					
East Croydon a	18 01	18 02	18 05		18 06	18 08	18 10	18 10	18 13	18 13	18 20	18 21	18 24		18 24	18 27	18 30	18 32	18 34	18 36	18 37	18 40	18 41	

	SN 1	SN 1	SN 1	SN	FC 1	SN 1	SN 1 🚲	SN	SN 1		FC 1	SN 1	SN 1	SN 1	SN 1 🚲	SN 1	FC 1	SN 1	SN 1 🚲		FC 1	SN 1	SN 1	SN 1
London Victoria 15 ⊖ d	18 26		18 34	18 38			18 47		18 51			18 53	19 02		19 06			19 10	19 17			19 23	19 32	
Clapham Junction 10 d	18 32		18 41	18 44			18 53		18 57			19 00	19 08		19 12			19 16	19 23			19 29	19 38	
St Pancras International 15 ⊖ d					18 18						18 34						18 54				19 09			
Farringdon 3 ⊖ d					18 23						18 39						18 59				19 14			
City Thameslink 3 d					18 27						18 43						19 03				19 18			
London Blackfriars 3 ⊖ d					18 30						18 46						19 05				19 20			
London Bridge 4 ⊖ d		18 30				18 47		18 49			18 57			18 59		19 08	19 12				19 27			19 33
New Cross Gate d														19 07										19 39
Norwood Junction 2 a		18 41						19 01						19 14										19 46
East Croydon a	18 41	18 45	18 51	18 57	19 00	19 00	19 03	19 05	19 07		19 10	19 10	19 18	19 19	19 22	19 22	19 24	19 26	19 33		19 39	19 39	19 48	19 50

	SN 1	FC 1	SN 1	SN 1 🚲	SN 1		FC 1	SN 1	SN 1	SN 1	SN 1	FC 1	SN 1	SN 1	SN 1		SN 1	SN 1	SN 1	SN 1	FC 1	SN 1	SN 1	SN 1
London Victoria 15 ⊖ d	19 36		19 40	19 47				19 53	20 02		20 06		20 10	20 17	20 23			20 32		20 36		20 40	20 47	
Clapham Junction 10 d	19 42		19 46	19 53				19 59	20 08		20 12		20 16	20 23	20 29			20 38		20 42		20 46	20 53	
St Pancras International 15 ⊖ d		19 24					19 39					19 54									20 24			
Farringdon 3 ⊖ d		19 29					19 44					19 59									20 29			
City Thameslink 3 d		19 33					19 48					20 03									20 33			
London Blackfriars 3 ⊖ d		19 35					19 50					20 05									20 35			
London Bridge 4 ⊖ d		19 42			19 52		19 57			20 04		20 12					20 28		20 34		20 42			20 58
New Cross Gate d																								
Norwood Junction 2 a					20 03					20 16									20 45					
East Croydon a	19 52	19 54	19 56	20 03	20 06		20 09	20 09	20 19	20 19	20 22	20 24	20 26	20 33	20 39		20 40	20 48	20 49	20 52	20 54	20 56	21 03	21 10

	SN 1		SN 1	SN 1	SN 1	FC 1	SN 1	SN 1	SN 1	SN 1	SN 1		SN 1	FC 1	SN 1	SN 1	SN 1	SN 1	SN 1	SN 1	FC 1		SN 1	SN 1
London Victoria 15 ⊖ d	20 53		21 02		21 06		21 10	21 17	21 23		21 32		21 36		21 40	21 47	21 53	22 02		22 06			22 10	22 17
Clapham Junction 10 d	21 00		21 08		21 12		21 16	21 23	21 29		21 38		21 42		21 46	21 53	21 59	22 08		22 12			22 16	22 23
St Pancras International 15 ⊖ d						20 54								21 24							21 54			
Farringdon 3 ⊖ d						20 59								21 29							21 59			
City Thameslink 3 d						21 03								21 33							22 03			
London Blackfriars 3 ⊖ d						21 05								21 35							22 05			
London Bridge 4 ⊖ d				21 04		21 12				21 26				21 42					22 04		22 12			
New Cross Gate d																								
Norwood Junction 2 a				21 15						21 37									22 15					
East Croydon a	21 11		21 18	21 19	21 22	21 24	21 26	21 33	21 39	21 41	21 48		21 51	21 54	21 56	22 03	22 09	22 18	22 19	22 22	22 24		22 26	22 33

	SN 1	SN	SN 1	SN 1	FC 1	SN 1	SN 1		SN 1	SN	SN 1	SN 1	SN 1	FC 1	SN 1	SN 1	SN 1		SN 1	SN 1	FC 1	SN 1	FC 1	
London Victoria 15 ⊖ d	22 23		22 32	22 36		22 40	22 47		22 53		23 02		23 06		23 10	23 17	23 24		23 32	23 40		23 47		
Clapham Junction 10 d	22 29		22 38	22 42		22 46	22 53		22 59		23 08		23 12		23 16	23 23	23 30		23 38	23 46		23 53		
St Pancras International 15 ⊖ d					22 24									22 54							23 24		23 54	
Farringdon 3 ⊖ d					22 29									22 59							23 29		23 59	
City Thameslink 3 d					22 33									23 03										
London Blackfriars 3 ⊖ d					22 35									23 05							23 35		00 05	
London Bridge 4 ⊖ d		22 26			22 42					22 56		23 04		23 12							23 42		00 12	
New Cross Gate d																								
Norwood Junction 2 a		22 38								23 07		23 15												
East Croydon a	22 39	22 42	22 48	22 51	22 54	22 56	23 03		23 09	23 11	23 19	23 19	23 22	23 24	23 26	23 33	23 40		23 48	23 55	23 56	00 04	00 28	

Saturdays

14 December to 17 May

	SN 1	FC 1	SN 1	FC 1	SN 1	FC 1	SN 1	FC 1	SN 1		FC 1	FC 1	SN 1	FC 1	FC 1	SN 1	FC 1	SN 1	SN 1		FC 1	SN 1	SN 1	FC 1
London Victoria 15 ⊖ d	00 05		00 14		01 00		02 00		03 00				04 00			05 02		05 23	05 32			06 02		
Clapham Junction 10 d	00 12		00 21		01 09		02 09		03 09				04 09			05 09		05 29	05 38			06 08		
St Pancras International 15 ⊖ d				00 24		00 54		01 54			02 54	03 25		03 54	04 24		04 54				05 34			05 53
Farringdon 3 ⊖ d				00 29													04 59				05 39			05 59
City Thameslink 3 d																								
London Blackfriars 3 ⊖ d		00 05		00 35		01 05		02 05			03 05	03 36		04 05	04 35		05 05				05 45			06 05
London Bridge 4 ⊖ d		00 12		00 42																	05 52		06 08	06 12
New Cross Gate d																								
Norwood Junction 2 a																		05 46						
East Croydon a	00 26	00 28	00 36	00 56	01 23	01 34	02 23	02 34	03 23		03 34	04 04	04 23	04 34	05 04	05 23	05 31	05 50	05 47		06 04	06 17	06 22	06 24

Table 175

Saturdays

14 December to 17 May

London - Norwood Junction and East Croydon - Summary of Fast Trains

Summary of Fast Trains

Network Diagram - see first Page of Table 175

		SN		SN	FC	SN	FC	SN	SN	SN	SN	FC		SN	FC	SN	SN	SN	SN	FC	SN	SN		SN	SN
		1		1	1		1	1	1	1	1	1			1	1	1	1	1	1	1	1			1
London Victoria 15 ⊖	d	06 23		06 32				06 53		07 06						07 23	07 32		07 36			07 47			07 51
Clapham Junction 10	d	06 29		06 38				06 59		07 12						07 29	07 38		07 42			07 53			
St Pancras International 15 ⊖	d				06 24		06 40					06 54			07 10					07 24					
Farringdon 3 ⊖	d				06 29		06 45					06 59			07 15					07 29					
City Thameslink 3	d																								
London Blackfriars 3 ⊖	d				06 35		06 50					07 05			07 20					07 35					
London Bridge 4 ⊖	d				06 42	06 50	06 57		07 03		07 08	07 12		07 20	07 27			07 33		07 42	07 45			07 50	
New Cross Gate	d								07 08									07 38							
Norwood Junction 2	a					07 02			07 16					07 32				07 46			07 55			08 02	
East Croydon	a	06 39		06 47	06 54	07 06	07 09	07 09	07 20	07 22	07 22	07 24		07 36	07 39	07 39	07 47	07 50	07 52	07 54	07 59	08 02		08 06	08 07

		FC	SN	SN	SN	SN	SN	FC		SN	SN	SN	FC	SN	SN	SN	SN	FC		SN	SN	SN	SN	FC	
		1	1	1	1	1	1	1		1	1		1	1	1	1	1	1		1	1		1	1	
London Victoria 15 ⊖	d		07 53	08 02		08 06					08 17			08 23	08 32		08 36				08 47		08 51		
Clapham Junction 10	d		07 59	08 08		08 12					08 23			08 29	08 38		08 42				08 53				
St Pancras International 15 ⊖	d	07 40						07 54					08 10					08 24						08 40	
Farringdon 3 ⊖	d	07 45						07 59					08 15					08 29						08 45	
City Thameslink 3	d																								
London Blackfriars 3 ⊖	d	07 50						08 05					08 20					08 35						08 50	
London Bridge 4 ⊖	d	07 57			08 03		08 08	08 12		08 15		08 20	08 27			08 33		08 42		08 45		08 50		08 57	
New Cross Gate	d				08 08											08 38									
Norwood Junction 2	a				08 16					08 25		08 32				08 46				08 55		09 02			
East Croydon	a	08 09	08 09	08 17	08 20	08 22	08 22	08 24		08 29	08 32	08 36	08 39	08 39	08 47	08 50	08 52	08 54		08 59	09 02	09 06	09 07	09 09	

		SN	SN	SN	SN	SN	FC	SN	SN	SN	FC	SN	SN	SN	SN	FC	SN	SN	SN	SN	FC				
		1	1	1	1 trolley	1	1	1	1		1	1	1	1	1 trolley	1	1	1		1	1				
London Victoria 15 ⊖	d	08 53	09 02		09 06				09 17			09 23	09 32		09 36			09 47		09 51		and at the same minutes past each hour until			
Clapham Junction 10	d	08 59	09 08		09 12				09 23			09 29	09 38		09 42			09 53							
St Pancras International 15 ⊖	d						08 54				09 10					09 24					09 40				
Farringdon 3 ⊖	d						08 59				09 15					09 29					09 45				
City Thameslink 3	d						09 03				09 18					09 33					09 48				
London Blackfriars 3 ⊖	d						09 05				09 20					09 35					09 50				
London Bridge 4 ⊖	d			09 03		09 08	09 12	09 15		09 20	09 27			09 33		09 42	09 45		09 50		09 57				
New Cross Gate	d			09 08										09 38											
Norwood Junction 2	a			09 16				09 25		09 32				09 46			09 55		10 02						
East Croydon	a	09 09	09 17	09 20	09 22	09 22	09 24	09 29	09 32	09 36	09 39	09 39	09 47	09 50	09 52	09 54	09 59	10 02	10 06	10 07	10 09				

		SN	SN	SN	SN	SN	FC	SN	SN	SN	FC	SN	SN	SN	SN	FC	SN	SN	SN	SN	FC		SN	SN	SN
		1	1	1	1 trolley	1	1	1	1		1	1	1	1	1 trolley	1	1	1		1	1		1	1	1
London Victoria 15 ⊖	d	17 53	18 02		18 06				18 17			18 23	18 32		18 36			18 47		18 51			18 53	19 02	
Clapham Junction 10	d	17 59	18 08		18 12				18 23			18 29	18 38		18 42			18 53					18 59	19 08	
St Pancras International 15 ⊖	d						17 54				18 10					18 24					18 40				
Farringdon 3 ⊖	d						17 59				18 15					18 29					18 45				
City Thameslink 3	d						18 03				18 18					18 33					18 48				
London Blackfriars 3 ⊖	d						18 05				18 20					18 35					18 50				
London Bridge 4 ⊖	d			18 03		18 08	18 12	18 15		18 20	18 27			18 33		18 42	18 45		18 50		18 57				19 03
New Cross Gate	d			18 08										18 38											19 08
Norwood Junction 2	a			18 16				18 25		18 32				18 46			18 55		19 02						19 16
East Croydon	a	18 09	18 17	18 20	18 22	18 22	18 24	18 29	18 32	18 36	18 39	18 39	18 47	18 50	18 52	18 54	18 59	19 02	19 06	19 07	19 09		19 09	19 17	19 20

		SN	SN	FC	SN	SN	FC		SN	SN	SN	SN	FC	SN	SN	SN	FC		SN	SN	SN	SN	FC	SN	SN
		1 trolley	1	1	1		1		1	1	1	1	1	1		1	1		1	1	1	1	1	1	1
London Victoria 15 ⊖	d	19 06			19 17				19 23	19 32		19 36		19 47		19 51			19 53	20 02	20 06			20 10	20 17
Clapham Junction 10	d	19 12			19 23				19 29	19 38		19 42		19 53					19 59	20 08	20 12			20 16	20 23
St Pancras International 15 ⊖	d			18 54			19 10						19 24				19 40						19 54		
Farringdon 3 ⊖	d			18 59			19 15						19 29				19 45						19 59		
City Thameslink 3	d			19 03			19 18						19 33				19 48						20 03		
London Blackfriars 3 ⊖	d			19 05			19 20						19 35				19 50						20 05		
London Bridge 4 ⊖	d		19 08	19 12		19 20	19 27				19 33		19 42		19 50		19 57					20 08	20 12		
New Cross Gate	d										19 38														
Norwood Junction 2	a					19 32					19 46				20 02							20 19			
East Croydon	a	19 22	19 22	19 24	19 33	19 36	19 39		19 39	19 47	19 50	19 52	19 54	20 02	20 06	20 07	20 09		20 09	20 17	20 22	20 22	20 24	20 29	20 32

		SN	SN		SN	SN	SN	FC	SN	SN	SN	SN	SN		SN	SN	FC	SN	SN	SN	SN	SN	SN		FC
			1		1	1	1	1	1	1		1	1		1	1	1	1	1		1	1	1		1
London Victoria 15 ⊖	d		20 21		20 23	20 32	20 36		20 40	20 47		20 53	21 02		21 06			21 10	21 17		21 23	21 32	21 36		
Clapham Junction 10	d				20 29	20 38	20 42		20 46	20 53		20 59	21 08		21 12			21 16	21 23		21 29	21 38	21 42		
St Pancras International 15 ⊖	d							20 24									20 54								21 24
Farringdon 3 ⊖	d							20 29									20 59								21 29
City Thameslink 3	d							20 33									21 03								
London Blackfriars 3 ⊖	d							20 35									21 05								21 35
London Bridge 4 ⊖	d	20 20						20 42			20 50					21 08	21 12			21 20					21 42
New Cross Gate	d																								
Norwood Junction 2	a	20 32									21 02					21 19				21 32					
East Croydon	a	20 36	20 37		20 39	20 47	20 52	20 54	20 57	21 02	21 06	21 09	21 17		21 22	21 22	21 24	21 27	21 33	21 36	21 39	21 47	21 52		21 54

Table 175

Saturdays

14 December to 17 May

London - Norwood Junction and East Croydon - Summary of Fast Trains

Summary of Fast Trains

Network Diagram - see first Page of Table 175

	SN 1	SN 1	SN	SN 1		SN 1	SN 1	SN 1	FC 1	SN 1	SN 1	SN	SN 1	SN 1		SN 1	FC 1	SN 1	SN 1	SN	SN 1	SN 1	SN 1	SN 1
London Victoria 15 ⊖ d	21 40	21 47		21 53		22 02	22 06			22 10	22 17		22 23	22 32		22 36		22 40	22 47		22 53	23 02		23 06
Clapham Junction 10 d	21 46	21 53		21 59		22 08	22 12			22 16	22 23		22 29	22 38		22 42		22 46	22 53		22 59	23 08		23 12
St Pancras International 15 ⊖ d									21 54								22 24							
Farringdon 3 ⊖ d									21 59								22 29							
City Thameslink 3 d																								
London Blackfriars 3 ⊖ d									22 05								22 35							
London Bridge 4 ⊖ d			21 50					22 08	22 12			22 20					22 42			22 50			23 04	
New Cross Gate d																								
Norwood Junction 2 a			22 02					22 19				22 32								23 02			23 15	
East Croydon a	21 57	22 03	22 07	22 09		22 17	22 22	22 22	22 24	22 27	22 33	22 36	22 39	22 47		22 52	22 54	22 57	23 03	23 06	23 09	23 17	23 19	23 22

		FC 1	SN 1	SN 1	SN 1	SN 1	SN 1	FC 1	SN 1	FC 1
London Victoria 15 ⊖ d			23 10	23 17	23 24	23 32	23 40		23 47	
Clapham Junction 10 d			23 16	23 23	23 30	23 38	23 46		23 53	
St Pancras International 15 ⊖ d		22 54						23 24		23 54
Farringdon 3 ⊖ d		22 59						23 29		23 59
City Thameslink 3 d										
London Blackfriars 3 ⊖ d		23 05						23 35		00 05
London Bridge 4 ⊖ d		23 12						23 42		00 12
New Cross Gate d										
Norwood Junction 2 a										
East Croydon a		23 24	23 27	23 32	23 40	23 52	23 55	23 56	00 04	00 28

Sundays

8 December to 29 December

	SN 1	FC 1	SN 1	FC 1	SN 1	FC 1	SN 1	SN 1	SN 1		SN 1	SN 1	SN 1	FC 1	SN 1	SN 1	FC 1	SN 1	SN 1		FC 1	SN 1	SN 1	SN 1
London Victoria 15 ⊖ d	00 05		00 14		01 00		02 00	03 00	04 00		05 02	05 47	06 32		07 02	07 26			07 47			08 02	08 17	08 32
Clapham Junction 10 d	00 12		00 21		01 09		02 09	03 09	04 09		05 09	05 54	06 39		07 09	07 33			07 54			08 09	08 24	08 39
St Pancras International 15 ⊖ d				00 24		00 54											07 24				07 50			
Farringdon 3 ⊖ d				00 29													07 29				07 55			
City Thameslink 3 d																								
London Blackfriars 3 ⊖ d		00 05		00 35		01 05								06 51			07 34				08 00			
London Bridge 4 ⊖ d		00 12		00 42													07 41	07 43			08 09			
New Cross Gate d																								
Norwood Junction 2 a																								
East Croydon a	00 27	00 28	00 35	00 56	01 25	01 34	02 25	03 25	04 25		05 24	06 09	06 54	07 23	07 25	07 47	07 54	07 56	08 10		08 21	08 23	08 37	08 52

	SN 1	FC 1	SN 1 🚲	SN 1	SN 1	SN 1	FC 1	SN 1	FC 1	SN 1	SN 1	SN 1	SN 1	FC 1	SN 1 🚲	FC 1	and at the same minutes past each hour until	SN 1	SN 1	SN 1 🚲	FC 1	SN 1	FC 1
London Victoria 15 ⊖ d			08 47	08 53	09 02	09 06		09 17		09 23	09 27	09 32			09 47			11 53	12 02	12 06		12 17	
Clapham Junction 10 d			08 54	08 59	09 08	09 12		09 23		09 29	09 33	09 38			09 53			11 59	12 08	12 12		12 23	
St Pancras International 15 ⊖ d		08 24					08 54		09 10					09 24		09 40					11 54		12 10
Farringdon 3 ⊖ d		08 29					08 59		09 15					09 29		09 45					11 59		12 15
City Thameslink 3 d																							
London Blackfriars 3 ⊖ d		08 34					09 04		09 19					09 34		09 49					12 04		12 19
London Bridge 4 ⊖ d	08 35	08 41					09 11		09 26				09 35	09 41		09 56					12 11		12 26
New Cross Gate d																							
Norwood Junction 2 a	08 46												09 46										
East Croydon a	08 54	08 55	09 05	09 09	09 17	09 22	09 25	09 32	09 39	09 39	09 42	09 48	09 50	09 55	10 02	10 09		12 09	12 17	12 22	12 25	12 32	12 39

	SN 1	SN 1	SN 1 🚲	SN 1	FC 1	SN 1 🚲	FC 1		SN 1	SN 1	SN 1 🚲	FC 1	SN 1	FC 1	SN 1	SN 1	SN 1 🚲	SN 1	FC 1	SN 1 🚲	FC 1	SN 1	SN 1	
London Victoria 15 ⊖ d	12 23	12 27	12 32			12 47			12 53	13 02	13 06		13 17		13 23	13 27	13 32			13 47		13 53	14 02	
Clapham Junction 10 d	12 29	12 33	12 38			12 53			12 59	13 08	13 12		13 23		13 29	13 33	13 38			13 53		13 59	14 08	
St Pancras International 15 ⊖ d					12 24		12 40					12 54		13 10					13 24		13 40			
Farringdon 3 ⊖ d					12 29		12 45					12 59		13 15					13 29		13 45			
City Thameslink 3 d																								
London Blackfriars 3 ⊖ d					12 34		12 49					13 04		13 19					13 34		13 49			
London Bridge 4 ⊖ d				12 35	12 41		12 56					13 11		13 26				13 35	13 41		13 56			
New Cross Gate d																								
Norwood Junction 2 a				12 46														13 46						
East Croydon a	12 39	12 42	12 48	12 50	12 55	13 02	13 09		13 09	13 17	13 21	13 25	13 32	13 39	13 39	13 42	13 48	13 50	13 55	14 02	14 09	14 09	14 17	

	SN 1 🚲	and at the same minutes past each hour until	FC 1	SN 1	FC 1	SN 1	SN 1	SN 1 🚲	SN 1	FC 1	SN 1 🚲	FC 1	SN 1	SN 1	SN 1 🚲		FC 1	SN 1	SN 1	SN 1	SN 1	SN 1	FC 1
London Victoria 15 ⊖ d	14 06			18 17		18 23	18 27	18 32			18 47		18 53	19 02	19 06			19 17	19 23	19 27	19 32		
Clapham Junction 10 d	14 12			18 23		18 29	18 33	18 38			18 53		18 59	19 08	19 12			19 23	19 29	19 33	19 38		
St Pancras International 15 ⊖ d			17 54		18 10					18 24		18 40					18 54						19 24
Farringdon 3 ⊖ d			17 59		18 15					18 29		18 45					18 59						19 29
City Thameslink 3 d																							
London Blackfriars 3 ⊖ d			18 04		18 19					18 34		18 49					19 04						19 34
London Bridge 4 ⊖ d			18 11		18 26				18 35	18 41		18 56					19 11					19 35	19 41
New Cross Gate d																							
Norwood Junction 2 a									18 46													19 46	
East Croydon a	14 22		18 25	18 32	18 39	18 39	18 42	18 48	18 50	18 55	19 02	19 09	19 09	19 17	19 22		19 25	19 32	19 39	19 42	19 48	19 50	19 55

Table 175

Sundays

8 December to 29 December

London - Norwood Junction and East Croydon - Summary of Fast Trains

Summary of Fast Trains

Network Diagram - see first Page of Table 175

	SN	SN	SN	SN	FC	SN	SN	SN		SN	FC	SN	SN	SN	SN	FC	SN	SN		SN	FC	SN	SN	SN
	1	1	1	1	1	1	1	1		1	1	1	1	1	1	1	1	1		1	1	1	1	1
	🛒																							
London Victoria 15 ⊖ d	19 47	19 53	20 02	20 06		20 17	20 27	20 32				20 47	20 53	21 02	21 06		21 17	21 27				21 47	21 53	22 02
Clapham Junction 10 d	19 53	19 59	20 08	20 12		20 23	20 33	20 38				20 53	20 59	21 08	21 12		21 23	21 33				21 53	21 59	22 08
St Pancras International 15 ⊖ d					19 54						20 24					20 54					21 24			
Farringdon 3 ⊖ d					19 59						20 29					20 59					21 29			
City Thameslink 3 d																								
London Blackfriars 3 ⊖ d					20 04						20 34					21 04					21 34			
London Bridge 4 ⊖ d					20 11					20 35	20 41					21 11				21 35	21 41			
New Cross Gate d																								
Norwood Junction 2 a										20 46										21 46				
East Croydon a	20 02	20 09	20 17	20 22	20 25	20 32	20 42	20 48		20 50	20 55	21 02	21 09	21 17	21 22	21 25	21 32	21 42		21 50	21 55	22 02	22 09	22 17

	FC	SN	SN	SN		FC	SN	SN	SN	FC	SN	SN	FC	SN		SN	FC
	1	1	1	1		1	1	1	1	1	1	1	1			1	1
London Victoria 15 ⊖ d		22 17	22 27				22 36	22 47	23 04		23 17	23 32		23 47			
Clapham Junction 10 d		22 23	22 33				22 42	22 53	23 10		23 23	23 38		23 53		23 54	
St Pancras International 15 ⊖ d	21 54					22 24				22 54			23 24				23 54
Farringdon 3 ⊖ d	21 59					22 29				22 59			23 29				23 59
City Thameslink 3 d																	
London Blackfriars 3 ⊖ d	22 04					22 34				23 04			23 34				00 05
London Bridge 4 ⊖ d	22 11			22 35		22 41				23 11			23 41				00 12
New Cross Gate d																	
Norwood Junction 2 a				22 46													
East Croydon a	22 25	22 32	22 42	22 50		22 55	22 56	23 03	23 21	23 25	23 37	23 52	23 56	00 05		00 15	00 28

Sundays

5 January to 11 May

	SN	FC	SN	FC	SN	FC	SN	SN	SN		SN	SN	SN	FC	SN	SN	FC	SN	SN		FC	SN	SN	SN
	1	1	1	1	1	1	1	1	1		1	1	1	1	1	1	1	1	1		1	1	1	1
London Victoria 15 ⊖ d	00 05		00 14		01 00		02 00	03 00	04 00		05 02	05 47	06 32		07 02	07 26			07 47			08 02	08 17	08 32
Clapham Junction 10 d	00 12		00 21		01 09		02 09	03 09	04 09		05 09	05 54	06 39		07 09	07 33			07 54			08 09	08 24	08 39
St Pancras International 15 ⊖ d				00 24		00 54											07 10				07 40			
Farringdon 3 ⊖ d				00 29													07 15				07 45			
City Thameslink 3 d																								
London Blackfriars 3 ⊖ d		00 05		00 35		01 05								06 51			07 21				07 51			
London Bridge 4 ⊖ d		00 12		00 42														07 43						
New Cross Gate d																								
Norwood Junction 2 a																								
East Croydon a	00 27	00 28	00 35	00 56	01 25	01 34	02 25	03 25	04 25		05 24	06 09	06 54	07 23	07 25	07 47	07 52	07 56	08 10		08 21	08 23	08 37	08 52

	SN	FC	SN	SN	SN	SN	FC	SN	FC	SN	SN	SN	SN	FC	SN	FC		SN	SN	SN	FC	SN	FC
	1	1	1	1	1	1	1	1	1	1	1	1	1	1	1	1		1	1	1	1	1	1
			🛒												🛒					🛒			
London Victoria 15 ⊖ d			08 47	08 53	09 02	09 06		09 17		09 23	09 27	09 32			09 47		and at the same minutes past each hour until	11 53	12 02	12 06		12 17	
Clapham Junction 10 d			08 54	08 59	09 08	09 12		09 23		09 29	09 33	09 38			09 53			11 59	12 08	12 12		12 23	
St Pancras International 15 ⊖ d		08 10					08 40		08 54					09 10		09 24					11 40		11 54
Farringdon 3 ⊖ d		08 15					08 45		08 59					09 15		09 29					11 45		11 59
City Thameslink 3 d																							
London Blackfriars 3 ⊖ d		08 21					08 51		09 04					09 21		09 34					11 51		12 04
London Bridge 4 ⊖ d	08 35												09 35										
New Cross Gate d																							
Norwood Junction 2 a	08 46												09 46										
East Croydon a	08 54	08 55	09 05	09 09	09 17	09 22	09 25	09 32	09 39	09 39	09 42	09 48	09 50	09 55	10 02	10 09		12 09	12 17	12 22	12 25	12 32	12 39

	SN	SN	SN	SN	FC	SN	FC		SN	SN	SN	FC	SN	FC	SN	SN	SN	SN	FC	SN	FC	SN	SN
	1	1	1	1	1	1	1		1	1	1	1	1	1	1	1	1	1	1	1	1	1	1
			🛒			🛒					🛒						🛒			🛒			
London Victoria 15 ⊖ d	12 23	12 27	12 32			12 47			12 53	13 02	13 06		13 17		13 23	13 27	13 32			13 47		13 53	14 02
Clapham Junction 10 d	12 29	12 33	12 38			12 53			12 59	13 08	13 12		13 23		13 29	13 33	13 38			13 53		13 59	14 08
St Pancras International 15 ⊖ d					12 10		12 24					12 40		12 54					13 10		13 24		
Farringdon 3 ⊖ d					12 15		12 29					12 45		12 59					13 15		13 29		
City Thameslink 3 d																							
London Blackfriars 3 ⊖ d					12 21		12 34					12 51		13 04					13 21		13 34		
London Bridge 4 ⊖ d				12 35														13 35					
New Cross Gate d																							
Norwood Junction 2 a				12 46														13 46					
East Croydon a	12 39	12 42	12 48	12 50	12 55	13 02	13 09		13 09	13 17	13 21	13 25	13 32	13 39	13 39	13 42	13 48	13 50	13 55	14 02	14 09	14 09	14 17

	SN		FC	SN	FC	SN	SN	SN	SN	FC	SN	FC	SN	SN	SN		FC	SN	SN	SN	SN	SN	FC
	1		1	1	1	1	1	1	1	1	1	1	1	1	1		1	1	1	1	1	1	1
	🛒							🛒			🛒				🛒								
London Victoria 15 ⊖ d	14 06	and at the same minutes past each hour until		18 17		18 23	18 27	18 32			18 47		18 53	19 02	19 06			19 17	19 23	19 27	19 32		
Clapham Junction 10 d	14 12			18 23		18 29	18 33	18 38			18 53		18 59	19 08	19 12			19 23	19 29	19 33	19 38		
St Pancras International 15 ⊖ d			17 40		17 54					18 10		18 24					18 40						19 10
Farringdon 3 ⊖ d			17 45		17 59					18 15		18 29					18 45						19 15
City Thameslink 3 d																							
London Blackfriars 3 ⊖ d			17 51		18 04					18 21		18 34					18 51						19 21
London Bridge 4 ⊖ d									18 35													19 35	
New Cross Gate d																							
Norwood Junction 2 a									18 46													19 46	
East Croydon a	14 22		18 25	18 32	18 39	18 39	18 42	18 48	18 50	18 55	19 02	19 09	19 09	19 17	19 22		19 25	19 32	19 39	19 42	19 48	19 50	19 55

Table 175

Sundays

5 January to 11 May

London - Norwood Junction and East Croydon - Summary of Fast Trains

Summary of Fast Trains | **Network Diagram - see first Page of Table 175**

		SN	SN	SN	SN	FC	SN	SN	SN		SN	FC	SN	SN	SN	SN	FC	SN	SN		SN	FC	SN	SN	SN
		1 ⚲	1	1	1	1	1	1	1		1	1	1	1	1	1	1	1	1		1	1	1	1	1
London Victoria 15 ⊖	d	19 47	19 53	20 02	20 06		20 17	20 27	20 32				20 47	20 53	21 02	21 06		21 17	21 27				21 47	21 53	22 02
Clapham Junction 10	d	19 53	19 59	20 08	20 12		20 23	20 33	20 38				20 53	20 59	21 08	21 12		21 23	21 33				21 53	21 59	22 08
St Pancras International 15 ⊖	d					19 40						20 10					20 40					21 10			
Farringdon 3 ⊖	d					19 45						20 15					20 45					21 15			
City Thameslink 3	d																								
London Blackfriars 3 ⊖	d					19 51						20 21					20 51					21 21			
London Bridge 4 ⊖	d										20 35										21 35				
New Cross Gate	d																								
Norwood Junction 2	a										20 46										21 46				
East Croydon	a	20 02	20 09	20 17	20 22	20 25	20 32	20 42	20 48		20 50	20 55	21 02	21 09	21 17	21 22	21 25	21 32	21 42		21 50	21 55	22 02	22 09	22 17

		FC	SN	SN	SN		FC	SN	SN	SN	FC	SN	SN	FC	SN		SN	FC
		1	1	1	1		1	1	1	1	1	1	1	1			1	1
London Victoria 15 ⊖	d		22 17	22 27				22 36	22 47	23 04		23 17	23 32		23 47			
Clapham Junction 10	d		22 23	22 33				22 42	22 53	23 10		23 23	23 38		23 53		23 54	
St Pancras International 15 ⊖	d	21 40					22 10				22 40			23 10				23 40
Farringdon 3 ⊖	d	21 45					22 15				22 45			23 15				23 45
City Thameslink 3	d																	
London Blackfriars 3 ⊖	d	21 51					22 21				22 51			23 21				23 51
London Bridge 4 ⊖	d				22 35													
New Cross Gate	d																	
Norwood Junction 2	a				22 46													
East Croydon	a	22 25	22 32	22 42	22 50		22 55	22 56	23 03	23 21	23 25	23 37	23 52	23 56	00 05		00 15	00 28

Table 175R

Mondays to Fridays

9 December to 16 May

East Croydon & Norwood Junction - London - Summary of Fast Trains

Summary of Fast Trains — **Network Diagram - see first Page of Table 175**

		SN MO 1	FC 1 A	FC MO 1 B	SN 1	FC MO 1 C		FC MX 1	FC MO 1 B	SN	SN 1	FC 1 D	SN 1	FC 1 D	SN 1	FC 1 D		SN 1	FC 1 E	FC 1 F	FC 1	FC 1	SN 1	SN 1	SN 1
East Croydon	d	00 01	00 02	00 02	00 18	00 36		00 36	00 36	00 49	01 31	01 40	02 27	02 40	03 28	03 40		04 32	04 40	05 16	05 48	06 02	06 06	06 09	06 11
Norwood Junction 2	d																								
New Cross Gate	a																								
London Bridge 4 ⊖	a		00 21			00 51		00 52												05 34	06 02	06 15		06 23	
London Blackfriars 3 ⊖	a		00 28	00 30		00 58		00 58	01 03			02 08		03 08		04 08			05 08	05 41	06 10	06 23			
City Thameslink 3	a																		05 11	05 44	06 14	06 26			
Farringdon 3 ⊖	a		00 34	00 36																05 47	06 18	06 30			
St Pancras International 15 ⊖	a		00 38	00 40		01 09		01 08	01 13			02 20		03 20		04 20			05 18	05 52	06 22	06 34			
Clapham Junction 10	a	00 16			00 31					01 02	01 45		02 41		03 41			04 51					06 18		06 21
London Victoria 15 ⊖	a	00 24			00 39					01 09	01 53		02 49		03 49			04 59					06 25		06 29

		SN 1		SN 1	SN 1	SN 1	SN	FC 1	SN	SN 1	SN 1	FC 1		SN 1	SN	SN 1	SN 1	SN 1	FC 1	SN	SN 1	SN 1		FC 1	SN
East Croydon	d	06 16		06 24	06 28	06 31	06 31	06 32	06 36	06 39	06 42	06 45		06 54	06 57	06 59	07 00	07 05	07 09	07 12	07 15	07 15		07 23	07 26
Norwood Junction 2	d						06 37		06 40											07 16					
New Cross Gate	a																								
London Bridge 4 ⊖	a			06 39			06 49	06 46	06 52	06 55		06 58		07 09		07 13	07 17		07 23	07 28					
London Blackfriars 3 ⊖	a							06 52				07 04							07 30					07 51	
City Thameslink 3	a							06 54				07 08							07 32					07 56	
Farringdon 3 ⊖	a							06 58				07 12							07 36					08 00	
St Pancras International 15 ⊖	a							07 02				07 16							07 40					08 04	
Clapham Junction 10	a	06 25			06 37	06 40					06 51				07 06			07 16			07 24	07 27			07 36
London Victoria 15 ⊖	a	06 32			06 45	06 48					07 00				07 15			07 28			07 32	07 35			07 45

		SN 1	SN 1	SN 1	SN 1	SN 1	SN 1 (trolley)	SN		SN 1	SN 1	SN 1	FC 1	SN	SN 1	SN 1	SN 1	SN 1		SN 1	SN 1	SN 1	SN 1	SN	SN 1 (trolley)
East Croydon	d	07 28	07 29	07 31	07 31	07 35	07 39	07 41		07 42	07 44	07 46	07 54	07 56	07 57	07 59	08 01	08 02		08 04	08 05	08 08	08 11	08 11	08 14
Norwood Junction 2	d							07 45																08 16	
New Cross Gate	a																								
London Bridge 4 ⊖	a	07 45	07 45		07 47	07 52		07 58				08 00			08 11	08 15		08 17		08 19	08 23			08 28	
London Blackfriars 3 ⊖	a												08 20												
City Thameslink 3	a												08 23												
Farringdon 3 ⊖	a												08 27												
St Pancras International 15 ⊖	a												08 31												
Clapham Junction 10	a			07 40			07 48			07 51	07 54			08 06			08 10					08 17	08 20		08 23
London Victoria 15 ⊖	a			07 49			07 57			08 00	08 03			08 15			08 19					08 25	08 29		08 32

		SN 1	SN 1	FC 1		SN 1	SN	SN 1	SN 1	SN 1	SN 1	SN 1	SN 1	FC 1		SN 1	SN	SN 1	SN 1 (trolley)	SN 1	FC 1	SN	SN 1	SN 1	
East Croydon	d	08 15	08 21	08 23		08 25	08 26	08 28	08 29	08 30	08 33	08 33	08 37	08 39		08 43	08 43	08 46	08 50	08 51	08 54	08 54	08 56	08 58	
Norwood Junction 2	d																08 48								
New Cross Gate	a																								
London Bridge 4 ⊖	a					08 41		08 43	08 47		08 49	08 52					09 00			09 06	09 08		09 11		
London Blackfriars 3 ⊖	a			08 53										09 09							09 21				
City Thameslink 3	a			08 56										09 12							09 24				
Farringdon 3 ⊖	a			09 00										09 16							09 27				
St Pancras International 15 ⊖	a			09 04										09 20							09 32				
Clapham Junction 10	a	08 26	08 32				08 38			08 41			08 48			08 52		08 56	09 01			09 04		09 07	
London Victoria 15 ⊖	a	08 35	08 42				08 47			08 50			08 56			09 01		09 05	09 09			09 13		09 16	

		SN 1	SN 1	SN	FC 1	SN 1	SN 1 (trolley)	SN 1	SN	SN 1		SN 1	SN 1	FC 1	SN 1	SN 1 (trolley)	SN 1	SN 1	SN 1	FC 1		SN	SN 1 (trolley)	SN 1	SN 1
East Croydon	d	08 59	09 02	09 05	09 09	09 11	09 14	09 14	09 22	09 23		09 26	09 31	09 32	09 34	09 39	09 39	09 42	09 44	09 47		09 51	09 53	09 55	10 00
Norwood Junction 2	d			09 09					09 26								09 43					09 55		09 59	
New Cross Gate	a								09 34															10 07	
London Bridge 4 ⊖	a	09 16	09 18	09 25					09 41					09 46	09 49		09 55			10 00		10 09		10 13	
London Blackfriars 3 ⊖	a				09 37									09 53						10 08					
City Thameslink 3	a				09 40									09 56						10 10					
Farringdon 3 ⊖	a				09 44									10 00						10 14					
St Pancras International 15 ⊖	a				09 48									10 04						10 18					
Clapham Junction 10	a					09 20	09 23	09 26		09 32		09 35	09 41			09 48		09 51	09 55				10 02		10 09
London Victoria 15 ⊖	a					09 27	09 32	09 35		09 42		09 43	09 50			09 58		09 58	10 05				10 11		10 16

		FC 1	SN 1	SN 1	SN 1 (trolley)	SN 1		FC 1	SN	SN 1 (trolley)	SN 1	SN 1	FC 1	SN 1	SN 1	SN 1 (trolley)		SN 1	FC 1	SN	SN 1 (trolley)	SN 1	SN 1	FC 1	SN 1
East Croydon	d	10 02	10 08	10 08	10 11	10 14		10 17	10 21	10 23	10 25	10 28	10 32	10 33	10 38	10 41		10 44	10 47	10 51	10 53	10 55	11 00	11 02	11 07
Norwood Junction 2	d		10 13						10 25		10 30				10 43					10 55		11 00			11 13
New Cross Gate	a										10 38											11 08			
London Bridge 4 ⊖	a	10 15	10 25					10 30	10 39		10 44		10 45	10 49	10 55				11 00	11 09		11 14		11 15	11 25
London Blackfriars 3 ⊖	a	10 23						10 37					10 52						11 07					11 22	
City Thameslink 3	a	10 26						10 40					10 56						11 10					11 26	
Farringdon 3 ⊖	a	10 29						10 44					10 59						11 14					11 29	
St Pancras International 15 ⊖	a	10 33						10 48					11 03						11 18					11 33	
Clapham Junction 10	a			10 17	10 20	10 25				10 32		10 37				10 50		10 55			11 02		11 09		
London Victoria 15 ⊖	a			10 25	10 28	10 35				10 40		10 44				10 58		11 02			11 10		11 16		

A MX from 3 January
B from 6 January
C until 30 December
D 1 to London Blackfriars
E 1 to City Thameslink
F 1 from Farringdon

Table 175R

Mondays to Fridays

9 December to 16 May

East Croydon & Norwood Junction - London - Summary of Fast Trains

Summary of Fast Trains

Network Diagram - see first Page of Table 175

	SN	SN	SN	FC	SN	SN	SN		SN	FC	SN	SN	SN	SN	FC	SN	SN		SN	SN	FC	SN	SN	SN
	1	1	1	1		1 🚲	1		1	1	1	1	1	1	1		1 🚲		1	1	1	1	1	1
East Croydon d	11 08	11 11	11 14	11 17	11 21	11 23	11 25		11 28	11 32	11 33	11 38	11 41	11 44	11 47	11 51	11 53		11 55	12 00	12 02	12 08	12 08	12 12
Norwood Junction 2 d					11 25		11 29					11 43				11 55			11 59			12 13		
New Cross Gate a							11 37												12 07					
London Bridge 4 ⊖ a				11 30	11 39		11 43			11 45	11 49	11 55			12 00	12 09			12 13		12 15	12 25		
London Blackfriars 3 ⊖ a				11 37						11 52					12 07						12 22			
City Thameslink 3 a				11 40						11 56					12 10						12 26			
Farringdon 3 ⊖ a				11 44						11 59					12 14						12 29			
St Pancras International 15 ⊖ a				11 48						12 03					12 18						12 33			
Clapham Junction 10 a	11 17	11 20	11 25			11 32			11 37				11 50	11 55			12 02			12 09			12 17	12 21
London Victoria 15 ⊖ a	11 24	11 27	11 32			11 41			11 44				11 57	12 02			12 10			12 18			12 24	12 28

	SN	FC	SN		SN	SN	SN	FC	SN	SN	SN	SN	FC		SN	SN	SN	SN	FC	SN	SN	SN	SN	
	1	1			1 🚲	1	1	1	1	1	1	1	1		1	1 🚲	1	1	1	1	1	1	1	
East Croydon d	12 14	12 17	12 21		12 23	12 25	12 28	12 32	12 33	12 38	12 40	12 44	12 47		12 51	12 53	12 55	13 00	13 02	13 08	13 08	13 11	13 14	
Norwood Junction 2 d			12 25			12 29				12 43					12 55		13 00			13 13				
New Cross Gate a						12 37											13 07							
London Bridge 4 ⊖ a		12 30	12 39			12 43		12 45	12 49	12 55			13 00		13 09		13 14		13 15	13 25				
London Blackfriars 3 ⊖ a		12 37						12 52					13 07						13 22					
City Thameslink 3 a		12 40						12 56					13 10						13 26					
Farringdon 3 ⊖ a		12 44						12 59					13 14						13 29					
St Pancras International 15 ⊖ a		12 48						13 03					13 18						13 33					
Clapham Junction 10 a	12 25				12 32		12 37				12 49	12 55				13 02		13 09			13 17	13 20	13 25	
London Victoria 15 ⊖ a	12 32				12 40		12 44				12 56	13 02				13 10		13 16			13 24	13 27	13 32	

	FC	SN	SN	SN	SN	FC	SN	SN	SN		SN	FC	SN	SN	SN	SN	FC	SN	SN		SN	SN	FC	SN
	1		1 🚲	1	1	1	1	1	1		1	1		1 🚲	1	1	1	1	1		1	1	1	
East Croydon d	13 17	13 21	13 23	13 25	13 28	13 32	13 33	13 38	13 40		13 44	13 47	13 51	13 53	13 55	14 00	14 02	14 08	14 08		14 11	14 14	14 17	14 21
Norwood Junction 2 d		13 25		13 29				13 43					13 55		13 59			14 13						14 25
New Cross Gate a				13 37											14 07									
London Bridge 4 ⊖ a	13 30	13 39		13 43		13 45	13 49	13 55				14 00	14 09		14 13		14 15	14 25					14 30	14 39
London Blackfriars 3 ⊖ a	13 37					13 52						14 07					14 22						14 37	
City Thameslink 3 a	13 40					13 56						14 10					14 26						14 40	
Farringdon 3 ⊖ a	13 44					13 59						14 14					14 29						14 44	
St Pancras International 15 ⊖ a	13 48					14 03						14 18					14 33						14 48	
Clapham Junction 10 a			13 32		13 37				13 50		13 55			14 02		14 09			14 17		14 20	14 25		
London Victoria 15 ⊖ a			13 40		13 44				13 57		14 02			14 10		14 16			14 24		14 28	14 32		

	SN	SN	SN	FC	SN		SN	SN	SN	FC	SN	SN	SN	SN	FC		SN	SN	SN	SN	FC	SN	SN	SN
	1 🚲	1	1	1	1		1	1	1	1		1 🚲	1	1	1		1	1	1	1	1		1 🚲	1
East Croydon d	14 23	14 25	14 28	14 32	14 33		14 38	14 40	14 44	14 47	14 51	14 53	14 55	15 00	15 02		15 08	15 08	15 11	15 14	15 17	15 21	15 23	15 25
Norwood Junction 2 d		14 29					14 43				14 55		14 59				15 13					15 25		15 29
New Cross Gate a		14 37											15 07											15 37
London Bridge 4 ⊖ a		14 43		14 45	14 49		14 55			15 00	15 09		15 13		15 15		15 25				15 30	15 39		15 43
London Blackfriars 3 ⊖ a				14 52						15 07					15 22						15 37			
City Thameslink 3 a				14 56						15 10					15 26						15 40			
Farringdon 3 ⊖ a				14 59						15 14					15 29						15 44			
St Pancras International 15 ⊖ a				15 03						15 18					15 33						15 48			
Clapham Junction 10 a	14 32		14 37					14 49	14 55			15 02		15 09				15 17	15 20	15 25			15 32	
London Victoria 15 ⊖ a	14 40		14 44					14 57	15 02			15 10		15 20				15 24	15 27	15 35			15 40	

	SN		FC	SN	SN	SN	SN	FC	SN	SN	SN		SN	FC	SN	SN	SN	SN	FC	SN	SN		SN	FC
	1		1	1	1	1 🚲	1	1		1 🚲	1		1	1	1	1	1 🚲	1	1		1		1 🚲	1
East Croydon d	15 28		15 32	15 33	15 38	15 40	15 44	15 47	15 51	15 53	15 55		16 00	16 02	16 08	16 08	16 11	16 14	16 17	16 21	16 24		16 24	16 28
Norwood Junction 2 d					15 43				15 55		15 59				16 13					16 25	16 28			
New Cross Gate a											16 07										16 36			
London Bridge 4 ⊖ a			15 45	15 49	15 55			16 00	16 09		16 13			16 15	16 25					16 39	16 43			
London Blackfriars 3 ⊖ a			15 52					16 07						16 25					16 48					16 55
City Thameslink 3 a			15 56					16 10						16 28					16 54					16 58
Farringdon 3 ⊖ a			15 59					16 13						16 31					16 57					17 01
St Pancras International 15 ⊖ a			16 03					16 17						16 35					17 01					17 05
Clapham Junction 10 a	15 37					15 49	15 54			16 02			16 09			16 17	16 20	16 25					16 33	
London Victoria 15 ⊖ a	15 46					15 57	16 05			16 10			16 16			16 24	16 28	16 35					16 42	

	SN	SN	SN	SN	SN	SN	FC		SN	SN	SN	FC	SN	SN	FC	SN	SN		SN	FC	SN	SN	SN	SN
	1	1	1	1	1 🚲	1	1			1 🚲	1	1	1	1	1	1 🚲	1			1	1	1 🚲	1	1
East Croydon d	16 30	16 33	16 38	16 40	16 41	16 44	16 47		16 51	16 54	16 55	16 58	17 01	17 07	17 09	17 13	17 14		17 21	17 23	17 25	17 25	17 30	17 36
Norwood Junction 2 d				16 46					16 55		17 01								17 25		17 31			
New Cross Gate a											17 08										17 38			
London Bridge 4 ⊖ a		16 47		17 00					17 08		17 14				17 27				17 37		17 49			17 53
London Blackfriars 3 ⊖ a							17 19					17 25			17 35					17 49				
City Thameslink 3 a							17 24					17 28			17 38					17 54				
Farringdon 3 ⊖ a							17 27					17 31			17 41					17 57				
St Pancras International 15 ⊖ a							17 31					17 35			17 45					18 01				
Clapham Junction 10 a	16 39		16 47		16 50	16 55				17 03			17 10	17 18		17 23	17 26					17 34	17 39	
London Victoria 15 ⊖ a	16 46		16 56		16 58	17 05				17 12			17 17	17 26		17 30	17 33					17 42	17 46	

Table 175R

Mondays to Fridays

9 December to 16 May

East Croydon & Norwood Junction - London - Summary of Fast Trains

Summary of Fast Trains

Network Diagram - see first Page of Table 175

	SN	SN	SN	FC	SN	SN	SN	SN	FC		SN	SN	SN	SN	SN	FC	SN	SN	SN		SN	FC	SN	SN
	1	1	1	1		1	1	1	1		1		1	1	1	1		1	1		1	1	1	1
		🛒						🛒						🛒				🛒						
East Croydon d	17 39	17 42	17 44	17 47	17 51	17 53	17 55	17 57	17 58		18 02	18 08	18 09	18 12	18 14	18 16	18 22	18 25	18 27		18 31	18 32	18 36	18 40
Norwood Junction 2 d					17 55		17 59					18 12					18 29							
New Cross Gate a							18 07																	
London Bridge 4 ⊖ a				18 13	18 09		18 15					18 24					18 41					18 46	18 50	
London Blackfriars 3 ⊖ a				18 21					18 25							18 51						18 55		
City Thameslink 3 a				18 24					18 28							18 54						18 58		
Farringdon 3 ⊖ a				18 27					18 31							18 57						19 01		
St Pancras International 15 ⊖ a				18 31					18 35							19 01						19 05		
Clapham Junction 10 a	17 48	17 51	17 57			18 02		18 06			18 12		18 18	18 21	18 25			18 34	18 37		18 40			18 49
London Victoria 15 ⊖ a	17 56	17 58	18 05			18 09		18 14			18 20		18 26	18 29	18 35			18 42	18 44		18 47			18 56

	SN	SN	FC	SN	SN		SN	SN	SN	FC	SN	SN	SN	FC	SN		SN	SN	FC	SN	SN	SN	SN	FC
	1	1	1	1	1		1	1	1	1	1	1	1	1	1		1	1	1	1	1	1	1	1
	🛒											🛒												
East Croydon d	18 43	18 44	18 47	18 53	18 55		18 57	18 57	19 00	19 02	19 10	19 12	19 14	19 17	19 24		19 26	19 29	19 32	19 34	19 39	19 42	19 44	19 47
Norwood Junction 2 d							19 02				19 13													
New Cross Gate a																								
London Bridge 4 ⊖ a			19 00				19 15			19 15	19 25			19 30					19 45	19 49				20 00
London Blackfriars 3 ⊖ a			19 09							19 22				19 37					19 52					20 07
City Thameslink 3 a			19 12							19 26				19 40					19 56					20 10
Farringdon 3 ⊖ a			19 15							19 29				19 44					19 59					20 14
St Pancras International 15 ⊖ a			19 19							19 33				19 48					20 03					20 18
Clapham Junction 10 a	18 52	18 55		19 02	19 05			19 08	19 11			19 21	19 25		19 33		19 36	19 39			19 48	19 51	19 55	
London Victoria 15 ⊖ a	18 59	19 05		19 09	19 13			19 15	19 18			19 28	19 35		19 41		19 44	19 47			19 56	19 59	20 05	

	SN		SN	SN	FC	SN	SN	SN	SN	FC	SN		SN	SN	FC	SN	SN	SN	FC	SN	SN		SN	SN
	1		1	1	1	1	1	1	1	1	1		1	1	1	1	1	1	1	1	1		1	1
							🛒																	
East Croydon d	19 54		19 59	20 01	20 02	20 07	20 09	20 12	20 14	20 17	20 24		20 26	20 30	20 32	20 34	20 40	20 44	20 47	20 54	20 55		20 57	21 00
Norwood Junction 2 d																								
New Cross Gate a																								
London Bridge 4 ⊖ a					20 15	20 21				20 30					20 45	20 48			21 00		21 09			
London Blackfriars 3 ⊖ a					20 22					20 37					20 52				21 07					
City Thameslink 3 a					20 26					20 40					20 56				21 10					
Farringdon 3 ⊖ a					20 29					20 44					20 59				21 14					
St Pancras International 15 ⊖ a					20 33					20 48					21 03				21 18					
Clapham Junction 10 a	20 03		20 08	20 11			20 18	20 21	20 25		20 33		20 36	20 40			20 49	20 55		21 03			21 07	21 11
London Victoria 15 ⊖ a	20 10		20 15	20 20			20 26	20 29	20 35		20 40		20 44	20 50			20 58	21 03		21 10			21 15	21 18

	FC	SN	SN	FC	SN	SN	SN		FC	SN	SN	SN	SN	SN	SN	FC	SN		SN	SN	SN	SN	SN	FC
	1	1	1	1	1	1	1		1	1	1	1	1	1	1	1	1		1	1	1	1	1	1
East Croydon d	21 02	21 09	21 14	21 17	21 24	21 26	21 30		21 32	21 34	21 41	21 44	21 54	21 57	22 00	22 02	22 09		22 14	22 17	22 24	22 25	22 30	22 32
Norwood Junction 2 d																								
New Cross Gate a																								
London Bridge 4 ⊖ a	21 15			21 30					21 45	21 49						22 15				22 33				22 45
London Blackfriars 3 ⊖ a	21 22			21 37					21 52							22 22								22 52
City Thameslink 3 a	21 26			21 40					21 56							22 24								22 53
Farringdon 3 ⊖ a	21 29			21 44					21 59							22 28								22 58
St Pancras International 15 ⊖ a	21 33			21 48					22 03							22 31								23 02
Clapham Junction 10 a		21 18	21 25		21 33	21 37	21 40				21 50	21 55	22 03	22 06	22 10		22 18		22 25		22 33	22 36	22 40	
London Victoria 15 ⊖ a		21 28	21 32		21 40	21 44	21 47				21 58	22 02	22 11	22 14	22 17		22 26		22 32		22 41	22 44	22 47	

	SN	SN	SN		SN	SN	SN	FC	SN	SN	SN	FC	SN		SN									
	1	1	1		1	1	1	1	1	1	1	1			1									
		🛒																						
East Croydon d	22 34	22 41	22 44		22 54	22 56	23 00	23 02	23 14	23 20	23 30	23 32	23 43		23 55									
Norwood Junction 2 d													23a47											
New Cross Gate a																								
London Bridge 4 ⊖ a	22 49							23 15				23 45												
London Blackfriars 3 ⊖ a								23 22				23 51												
City Thameslink 3 a																								
Farringdon 3 ⊖ a								23 28				23 58												
St Pancras International 15 ⊖ a								23 32				00 02												
Clapham Junction 10 a		22 50	22 55		23 03	23 06	23 10		23 25	23 32	23 42				00 10									
London Victoria 15 ⊖ a		22 57	23 05		23 13	23 15	23 18		23 35	23 39	23 52				00 18									

Saturdays

14 December to 17 May

	FC	SN	FC	SN	SN	FC	SN	FC	SN		FC	SN	FC	FC	SN	FC	SN	SN	FC		SN	SN	FC	SN
	1	1	1		1	1	1	1	1		1	1	1	1	1	1	1	1	1		1	1	1	1
						A		A			A		B	B		B								
East Croydon d	00 02	00 18	00 36	00 49	01 31	01 40	02 28	02 40	03 28		03 40	04 30	04 40	05 16	05 28	05 48	06 07	06 11	06 17		06 25	06 41	06 47	06 53
Norwood Junction 2 d																					06 29			
New Cross Gate a																					06 37			
London Bridge 4 ⊖ a	00 21		00 52													06 02			06 30		06 43		07 00	
London Blackfriars 3 ⊖ a	00 28		00 58			02 08		03 08			04 08		05 08	05 43		06 08			06 37				07 07	
City Thameslink 3 a																								
Farringdon 3 ⊖ a	00 34												05 15	05 50		06 13			06 43				07 13	
St Pancras International 15 ⊖ a	00 38		01 08			02 20		03 20			04 20		05 20	05 54		06 18			06 47				07 17	
Clapham Junction 10 a		00 31		01 02	01 45		02 41		03 41			04 43			05 47		06 18	06 21				06 50		07 02
London Victoria 15 ⊖ a		00 39		01 10	01 53		02 49		03 49			04 51			05 56		06 26	06 30				06 57		07 09

A 1 to London Blackfriars

B 1 to Farringdon

Table 175R

Saturdays

14 December to 17 May

East Croydon & Norwood Junction - London - Summary of Fast Trains

Summary of Fast Trains **Network Diagram - see first Page of Table 175**

		SN		SN	SN	SN	FC	SN	SN	SN	FC	SN		SN	SN	SN	FC	SN	SN	SN	SN	FC		SN	SN
		1		1	1	1	1	1	1	1	1	1		1	1	1	1		1	1	1	1		1	1
East Croydon	d	06 55		07 07	07 10	07 14	07 17	07 23	07 25	07 30	07 32	07 34		07 39	07 41	07 44	07 47	07 51	07 53	07 55	07 59	08 02		08 07	08 08
Norwood Junction 2	d	07 00		07 13					07 29					07 45				07 55		08 00				08 13	
New Cross Gate	a	07 07							07 37											08 07					
London Bridge 4 ⊖	a	07 13		07 25			07 30		07 43		07 45	07 49		07 57			08 00	08 09		08 13		08 15		08 25	
London Blackfriars 3 ⊖	a						07 37				07 52						08 07					08 22			
City Thameslink 3	a																								
Farringdon 3 ⊖	a						07 44				07 59						08 14					08 29			
St Pancras International 15 ⊖	a						07 48				08 03						08 18					08 33			
Clapham Junction 10	a				07 19	07 25		07 32		07 39					07 50	07 55			08 02		08 08				08 17
London Victoria 15 ⊖	a				07 27	07 32		07 40		07 46					07 58	08 02			08 10		08 16				08 24

		SN	SN	FC	SN	SN	SN	SN		FC	SN	SN	SN	SN	FC	SN	SN	SN		SN	FC	SN	SN	SN	SN
		1	1	1		1	1	1		1	1	1	1	1	1		1	1		1	1	1	1	1	1
						🛒											🛒								
East Croydon	d	08 11	08 14	08 17	08 21	08 23	08 25	08 27		08 32	08 33	08 37	08 40	08 44	08 47	08 51	08 53	08 55		08 59	09 02	09 07	09 08	09 11	09 14
Norwood Junction 2	d				08 25		08 29					08 43				08 55		08 59				09 13			
New Cross Gate	a						08 37											09 07							
London Bridge 4 ⊖	a			08 30	08 39		08 43			08 45	08 49	08 55			09 00	09 09		09 13			09 15	09 25			
London Blackfriars 3 ⊖	a			08 37						08 52					09 07						09 22				
City Thameslink 3	a														09 10						09 26				
Farringdon 3 ⊖	a			08 44						08 59					09 14						09 29				
St Pancras International 15 ⊖	a			08 48						09 03					09 18						09 33				
Clapham Junction 10	a	08 20	08 25			08 32		08 36					08 49	08 55			09 02			09 08			09 17	09 20	09 25
London Victoria 15 ⊖	a	08 28	08 32			08 40		08 44					08 57	09 02			09 10			09 16			09 24	09 28	09 32

		FC	SN	SN		SN	SN	FC	SN	SN	SN	SN	FC	SN		SN	SN	SN	FC	SN	SN	SN	SN	FC	
		1		1		1	1	1	1	1	1	1	1			1	1	1	1	1	1	1	1	1	
				🛒												🛒									
East Croydon	d	09 17	09 21	09 23		09 25	09 27	09 32	09 33	09 37	09 41	09 44	09 47	09 51		09 53	09 55	09 59	10 02	10 07	10 08	10 11	10 14	10 17	
Norwood Junction 2	d		09 25			09 29				09 43				09 55			09 59			10 13					
New Cross Gate	a					09 37											10 07								
London Bridge 4 ⊖	a	09 30	09 39			09 43		09 45	09 49	09 55			10 00	10 09			10 13		10 15	10 25				10 30	
London Blackfriars 3 ⊖	a	09 37						09 52					10 07						10 22					10 37	
City Thameslink 3	a	09 40						09 56					10 10						10 26					10 40	
Farringdon 3 ⊖	a	09 44						09 59					10 14						10 29					10 44	
St Pancras International 15 ⊖	a	09 48						10 03					10 18						10 33					10 48	
Clapham Junction 10	a			09 32			09 36				09 50	09 55				10 02		10 08			10 17	10 20	10 25		
London Victoria 15 ⊖	a			09 40			09 44				09 58	10 02				10 10		10 16			10 24	10 28	10 32		

		SN	SN	SN	SN	FC	SN	SN	SN	SN		FC	SN	SN	SN	SN	FC	SN	SN	SN		SN	FC	SN	SN
			1	1	1	1	1	1	1	1		1		1	1	1	1	1	1	1		1	1		1
			🛒											🛒											🛒
East Croydon	d	10 21	10 23	10 25	10 27	10 32	10 33	10 37	10 40	10 44		10 47	10 51	10 53	10 55	10 59	11 02	11 07	11 08	11 11		11 14	11 17	11 21	11 23
Norwood Junction 2	d	10 25		10 29				10 43					10 55		10 59			11 13						11 25	
New Cross Gate	a			10 37											11 07										
London Bridge 4 ⊖	a	10 39		10 43		10 45	10 49	10 55				11 00	11 09		11 13		11 15	11 25					11 30	11 39	
London Blackfriars 3 ⊖	a					10 52						11 07					11 22						11 37		
City Thameslink 3	a					10 56						11 10					11 26						11 40		
Farringdon 3 ⊖	a					10 59						11 14					11 29						11 44		
St Pancras International 15 ⊖	a					11 03						11 18					11 33						11 48		
Clapham Junction 10	a		10 32		10 36				10 49	10 55				11 02		11 08			11 17	11 20		11 25			11 32
London Victoria 15 ⊖	a		10 40		10 44				10 57	11 02				11 10		11 16			11 24	11 28		11 32			11 40

		SN	SN	FC	SN	SN		SN	SN	FC	SN	SN	SN	SN	FC	SN		SN	SN	SN	FC	SN	SN	SN	SN
		1	1	1	1	1		1	1	1		1	1	1	1	1		1	1	1	1		1	1	1
												🛒											🛒		
East Croydon	d	11 25	11 27	11 32	11 33	11 37		11 40	11 44	11 47	11 51	11 53	11 55	11 59	12 02	12 07		12 08	12 11	12 14	12 17	12 21	12 23	12 25	12 27
Norwood Junction 2	d	11 29				11 43					11 55		11 59			12 13						12 25		12 29	
New Cross Gate	a	11 37											12 07											12 37	
London Bridge 4 ⊖	a	11 43		11 45	11 49	11 55				12 00	12 09		12 13		12 15	12 25					12 30	12 39		12 43	
London Blackfriars 3 ⊖	a			11 52						12 07					12 22						12 37				
City Thameslink 3	a			11 56						12 10					12 26						12 40				
Farringdon 3 ⊖	a			11 59						12 14					12 29						12 44				
St Pancras International 15 ⊖	a			12 03						12 18					12 33						12 48				
Clapham Junction 10	a		11 36					11 49	11 55			12 02		12 08				12 17	12 20	12 25			12 32		12 36
London Victoria 15 ⊖	a		11 44					11 57	12 02			12 10		12 16				12 24	12 28	12 32			12 40		12 44

		FC		SN	SN	SN	SN	FC	SN	SN	SN	SN		FC	SN	SN	SN	SN	FC	SN	SN	SN		SN	FC
		1		1	1	1	1	1		1	1	1		1	1	1	1	1	1		1	1		1	1
										🛒											🛒				
East Croydon	d	12 32		12 33	12 38	12 40	12 44	12 47	12 51	12 53	12 55	12 59		13 02	13 07	13 08	13 11	13 14	13 17	13 21	13 23	13 25		13 27	13 32
Norwood Junction 2	d				12 43				12 55		12 59				13 13					13 25		13 29			
New Cross Gate	a										13 07											13 37			
London Bridge 4 ⊖	a	12 45		12 49	12 55			13 00	13 09		13 13			13 15	13 25				13 30	13 39		13 43			13 45
London Blackfriars 3 ⊖	a	12 52						13 07						13 22					13 37						13 52
City Thameslink 3	a	12 56						13 10						13 26					13 40						13 56
Farringdon 3 ⊖	a	12 59						13 14						13 29					13 44						13 59
St Pancras International 15 ⊖	a	13 03						13 18						13 33					13 48						14 03
Clapham Junction 10	a					12 49	12 55			13 02		13 08				13 17	13 20	13 25			13 32			13 36	
London Victoria 15 ⊖	a					12 57	13 02			13 10		13 16				13 24	13 28	13 32			13 40			13 44	

Table 175R

Saturdays

14 December to 17 May

East Croydon & Norwood Junction - London - Summary of Fast Trains

Summary of Fast Trains | **Network Diagram - see first Page of Table 175**

	SN	SN	SN		SN	FC	SN	SN	SN	SN	FC	SN	SN		SN	SN	FC	SN	SN	SN	SN	FC	SN	
	1	1	1		1	1		1	1	1	1	1	1		1	1	1		1	1	1	1	1	
								(trolley)											(trolley)					
East Croydon d	13 34	13 37	13 40		13 44	13 47	13 51	13 53	13 55	13 59	14 02	14 07	14 08		14 12	14 14	14 17	14 21	14 23	14 25	14 28	14 32	14 33	
Norwood Junction [2] d		13 43					13 55		13 59			14 13						14 25		14 29				
New Cross Gate a									14 07											14 37				
London Bridge [4] ⊖ a	13 49	13 55				14 00	14 09		14 13		14 15	14 25					14 30	14 39		14 43		14 45	14 49	
London Blackfriars [3] ⊖ a						14 07					14 22						14 37					14 52		
City Thameslink [3] a						14 10					14 26						14 40					14 56		
Farringdon [3] ⊖ a						14 14					14 29						14 44					14 59		
St Pancras International [15] ⊖ a						14 18					14 33						14 48					15 03		
Clapham Junction [10] a			13 49		13 55			14 02		14 08			14 17		14 21	14 25			14 32		14 37			
London Victoria [15] ⊖ a			13 57		14 02			14 10		14 16			14 24		14 28	14 32			14 40		14 44			

	SN	SN	SN	FC	SN	SN	SN	SN	FC		SN	SN	SN	SN	FC	SN	SN	SN	SN		FC	SN	SN	SN
	1	1	1	1		1	1	1	1		1	1	1	1	1		1	1	1		1	1	1	1
						(trolley)											(trolley)							
East Croydon d	14 37	14 40	14 44	14 47	14 51	14 53	14 55	14 59	15 02		15 07	15 08	15 11	15 14	15 17	15 21	15 23	15 25	15 28		15 32	15 33	15 37	15 40
Norwood Junction [2] d	14 43				14 55		14 59				15 13					15 25		15 29					15 43	
New Cross Gate a							15 07											15 37						
London Bridge [4] ⊖ a	14 55			15 00	15 09		15 13		15 15		15 25				15 30	15 39		15 43			15 45	15 49	15 55	
London Blackfriars [3] ⊖ a				15 07					15 22						15 37						15 52			
City Thameslink [3] a				15 10					15 26						15 40						15 56			
Farringdon [3] ⊖ a				15 14					15 29						15 44						15 59			
St Pancras International [15] ⊖ a				15 18					15 33						15 48						16 03			
Clapham Junction [10] a		14 49	14 55			15 02		15 08				15 17	15 20	15 25			15 32		15 37					15 49
London Victoria [15] ⊖ a		14 57	15 02			15 10		15 16				15 24	15 28	15 32			15 40		15 45					15 57

	SN	FC	SN	SN	SN		SN	FC	SN	SN	SN	SN	FC	SN	SN		SN	SN	FC	SN	SN	SN	SN	FC
	1	1		1	1		1	1	1	1	1	1	1		1		1	1	1	1	1	1	1	1
				(trolley)											(trolley)									
East Croydon d	15 44	15 47	15 51	15 53	15 55		15 59	16 02	16 07	16 08	16 11	16 14	16 17	16 21	16 23		16 25	16 27	16 32	16 33	16 37	16 40	16 44	16 47
Norwood Junction [2] d			15 55		15 59				16 13					16 25			16 29				16 43			
New Cross Gate a					16 07												16 37							
London Bridge [4] ⊖ a		16 00	16 09		16 13			16 15	16 25				16 30	16 39			16 43		16 45	16 49	16 55			17 00
London Blackfriars [3] ⊖ a		16 07						16 22					16 37						16 52					17 07
City Thameslink [3] a		16 10						16 26					16 40						16 56					17 10
Farringdon [3] ⊖ a		16 14						16 29					16 44						16 59					17 14
St Pancras International [15] ⊖ a		16 18						16 33					16 48						17 03					17 18
Clapham Junction [10] a	15 55			16 02			16 08			16 17	16 20	16 25			16 32			16 36				16 49	16 55	
London Victoria [15] ⊖ a	16 02			16 10			16 16			16 24	16 28	16 32			16 40			16 44				16 57	17 02	

	SN		SN	SN	SN	FC	SN	SN	SN	SN	FC		SN	SN	SN	SN	FC	SN	SN	SN	SN		FC	SN
			1	1	1	1	1	1	1	1	1			1	1	1	1	1	1	1	1		1	
			(trolley)											(trolley)										
East Croydon d	16 51		16 53	16 55	16 59	17 02	17 07	17 08	17 11	17 14	17 17		17 21	17 23	17 25	17 27	17 32	17 33	17 37	17 40	17 44		17 47	17 51
Norwood Junction [2] d	16 55			16 59			17 13						17 25		17 29				17 43					17 55
New Cross Gate a				17 07											17 37									
London Bridge [4] ⊖ a	17 09			17 13		17 15	17 25				17 30		17 39		17 43		17 45	17 49	17 55				18 00	18 09
London Blackfriars [3] ⊖ a						17 22					17 37						17 52						18 07	
City Thameslink [3] a						17 26					17 40						17 56						18 10	
Farringdon [3] ⊖ a						17 29					17 44						17 59						18 14	
St Pancras International [15] ⊖ a						17 33					17 48						18 03						18 18	
Clapham Junction [10] a			17 02		17 08			17 17	17 20	17 25				17 32		17 36				17 49	17 55			
London Victoria [15] ⊖ a			17 10		17 16			17 24	17 28	17 32				17 40		17 44				17 57	18 02			

	SN	SN	SN	FC	SN	SN	SN		SN	FC	SN	SN	SN	SN	FC	SN	SN		SN	SN	FC	SN	SN	SN
	1	1	1	1	1	1	1		1	1		1	1	1	1	1	1		1	1	1		1	1
	(trolley)											(trolley)												
East Croydon d	17 53	17 55	17 59	18 02	18 07	18 08	18 11		18 14	18 17	18 22	18 23	18 25	18 27	18 32	18 33	18 37		18 40	18 44	18 47	18 51	18 53	18 55
Norwood Junction [2] d		17 59			18 13						18 26		18 29				18 43					18 55		18 59
New Cross Gate a		18 07											18 37											19 07
London Bridge [4] ⊖ a		18 13		18 15	18 25					18 30	18 39		18 43		18 45	18 49	18 55				19 00	19 09		19 13
London Blackfriars [3] ⊖ a				18 22						18 37					18 52						19 07			
City Thameslink [3] a				18 26						18 40					18 56						19 10			
Farringdon [3] ⊖ a				18 29						18 44					18 59						19 14			
St Pancras International [15] ⊖ a				18 33						18 48					19 03						19 18			
Clapham Junction [10] a	18 02		18 08			18 17	18 20		18 25			18 32		18 36					18 49	18 55			19 02	
London Victoria [15] ⊖ a	18 10		18 16			18 24	18 28		18 32			18 40		18 44					18 57	19 02			19 10	

	SN	FC	SN		SN	SN	SN	FC	SN	SN	SN	SN	FC		SN	SN	SN	SN	FC	SN	SN	SN	SN	
	1	1	1		1	1	1	1		1	1	1	1		1	1	1	1	1		1	1	1	
East Croydon d	18 59	19 02	19 07		19 08	19 11	19 14	19 17	19 21	19 23	19 26	19 29	19 32		19 33	19 38	19 42	19 44	19 47	19 51	19 53	19 57	20 00	
Norwood Junction [2] d			19 13						19 25											19 55				
New Cross Gate a																								
London Bridge [4] ⊖ a		19 15	19 25					19 30	19 39				19 45		19 49				20 00	20 09				
London Blackfriars [3] ⊖ a		19 22						19 37					19 52						20 07					
City Thameslink [3] a		19 26						19 40					19 56						20 10					
Farringdon [3] ⊖ a		19 29						19 44					19 59						20 14					
St Pancras International [15] ⊖ a		19 33						19 48					20 03						20 18					
Clapham Junction [10] a	19 08				19 17	19 20	19 25			19 32	19 36	19 40				19 47	19 51	19 55			20 02	20 07	20 11	
London Victoria [15] ⊖ a	19 16				19 24	19 28	19 35			19 40	19 43	19 50				19 54	19 58	20 05			20 10	20 14	20 20	

Table 175R

Saturdays

14 December to 17 May

East Croydon & Norwood Junction - London - Summary of Fast Trains

Summary of Fast Trains

Network Diagram - see first Page of Table 175

	FC 1	SN 1	SN 1	FC 1	SN		SN 1	SN 1	SN 1	FC 1	SN 1	SN 1	SN 1	FC 1	SN		SN 1	SN 1	SN 1	FC 1	SN 1	SN 1	FC 1	SN
East Croydon d	20 02	20 11	20 14	20 17	20 21		20 23	20 26	20 30	20 32	20 34	20 41	20 44	20 47	20 51		20 53	20 56	21 00	21 02	21 09	21 14	21 17	21 21
Norwood Junction 2 d					20 25										20 55									21 25
New Cross Gate a																								
London Bridge 4 ⊖ a	20 15			20 30	20 39					20 45	20 49			21 00	21 09					21 15			21 30	21 39
London Blackfriars 3 ⊖ a	20 22			20 37						20 52				21 07						21 22			21 37	
City Thameslink 3 a	20 26			20 40						20 56														
Farringdon 3 ⊖ a	20 29			20 44						20 59				21 14						21 29			21 44	
St Pancras International 15 ⊖ a	20 33			20 48						21 03				21 18						21 33			21 48	
Clapham Junction 10 a		20 20	20 25				20 32	20 36	20 40			20 50	20 55				21 02	21 07	21 10		21 18	21 25		
London Victoria 15 ⊖ a		20 27	20 32				20 40	20 43	20 50			20 58	21 02				21 10	21 14	21 17		21 26	21 32		

	SN 1		SN 1	SN 1	FC 1	SN 1	SN 1	SN 1	SN	SN 1	SN 1		SN 1	FC 1	SN 1	SN 1	SN	SN 1	SN 1	SN 1	FC 1		SN 1	SN 1 🚲
East Croydon d	21 23		21 26	21 30	21 32	21 35	21 42	21 44	21 51	21 53	21 56		22 00	22 02	22 09	22 14	22 21	22 23	22 26	22 31	22 32		22 35	22 40
Norwood Junction 2 d									21 55								22 25							
New Cross Gate a																								
London Bridge 4 ⊖ a					21 45	21 49			22 09					22 15			22 39				22 45		22 49	
London Blackfriars 3 ⊖ a					21 52									22 22							22 52			
City Thameslink 3 a																								
Farringdon 3 ⊖ a					21 59									22 28							22 58			
St Pancras International 15 ⊖ a					22 03									22 32							23 02			
Clapham Junction 10 a	21 32		21 36	21 41			21 51	21 55		22 02	22 06		22 10		22 18	22 25		22 32	22 36	22 40				22 49
London Victoria 15 ⊖ a	21 40		21 43	21 48			21 58	22 02		22 10	22 13		22 17		22 26	22 32		22 40	22 43	22 50				22 57

	SN 1	SN	SN 1	SN 1	FC 1	SN 1	SN		SN 1	FC 1	SN	SN 1
East Croydon d	22 44	22 51	22 56	23 00	23 02	23 14	23 21		23 30	23 32	23 43	23 55
Norwood Junction 2 d		22 55					23 25				23a47	
New Cross Gate a												
London Bridge 4 ⊖ a		23 09			23 15		23 39			23 44		
London Blackfriars 3 ⊖ a					23 22					23 52		
City Thameslink 3 a												
Farringdon 3 ⊖ a					23 28					23 58		
St Pancras International 15 ⊖ a					23 32					00 02		
Clapham Junction 10 a	22 55		23 06	23 10		23 25			23 41			00 10
London Victoria 15 ⊖ a	23 02		23 13	23 20		23 32			23 52			00 17

Sundays

8 December to 29 December

	FC 1	SN 1	FC 1	SN	SN 1	SN 1	SN 1	SN 1	FC		SN 1	FC	FC 1	SN 1	SN 1	FC 1	SN 1	FC 1	SN 1		SN 1 🚲	SN 1	FC 1	SN 1
East Croydon d	00 02	00 17	00 36	00 49	01 43	02 40	03 40	04 40	05 37		05 58	06 27	06 57	07 06	07 24	07 27	07 48	07 57	08 04		08 10	08 22	08 27	08 41
Norwood Junction 2 d																	07 54							
New Cross Gate a																								
London Bridge 4 ⊖ a	00 21		00 51										07 15			07 45	08 05	08 15					08 45	
London Blackfriars 3 ⊖ a	00 28		00 58						06 04			06 54	07 23			07 53		08 23					08 53	
City Thameslink 3 a																								
Farringdon 3 ⊖ a	00 34												07 30			08 00		08 30					09 00	
St Pancras International 15 ⊖ a	00 38		01 08										07 34			08 04		08 34					09 04	
Clapham Junction 10 a		00 33		01 02	01 57	02 53	03 53	04 55			06 12			07 18	07 38				08 17		08 27	08 35		08 57
London Victoria 15 ⊖ a		00 41		01 09	02 05	03 05	04 05	05 05			06 21			07 29	07 46				08 25		08 35	08 43		09 05

	SN 1	FC 1	SN 1	SN 1	SN 1 🚲		SN 1 🚲	SN 1	FC 1	SN 1	SN 1 🚲	FC 1	SN 1	SN 1	SN 1	FC 1	SN 1 🚲	SN 1 🚲	FC 1	SN 1	SN 1	FC 1	
East Croydon d	08 52	08 56	08 59	09 03	09 10		09 16	09 30	09 33	09 39	09 46	09 47	09 50	09 56	10 00	10 03	10 09	10 14	10 17	10 20	10 30	10 33	and at the same minutes past each hour until
Norwood Junction 2 d	08 56													10 02									
New Cross Gate a																							
London Bridge 4 ⊖ a	09 08	09 15							09 45			10 00		10 14		10 15			10 30			10 45	
London Blackfriars 3 ⊖ a		09 23							09 53			10 07				10 22			10 37			10 52	
City Thameslink 3 a																							
Farringdon 3 ⊖ a		09 29							09 59			10 14				10 28			10 44			10 58	
St Pancras International 15 ⊖ a		09 34							10 04			10 18				10 32			10 48			11 02	
Clapham Junction 10 a			09 08	09 12	09 19		09 25	09 39		09 48	09 55		10 02		10 09		10 18	10 23		10 32	10 39		
London Victoria 15 ⊖ a			09 15	09 19	09 26		09 32	09 46		09 56	10 03		10 09		10 17		10 26	10 30		10 39	10 46		

	SN 1	SN 1	FC 1	SN 1	SN 1	SN 1	FC 1	SN 1 🚲	SN 1	FC 1	SN 1	SN 1	FC 1		SN 1	SN 1	SN 1	SN 1	SN 1	FC 1	SN 1	SN 1	SN 1	
East Croydon d	18 39	18 46	18 47	18 50	18 56	19 00	19 03	19 09	19 14	19 17	19 20	19 30	19 33		19 39	19 46	19 50	19 56	20 00	20 03	20 09	20 14	20 20	
Norwood Junction 2 d					19 02													20 02						
New Cross Gate a																								
London Bridge 4 ⊖ a			19 00		19 14		19 15			19 30			19 45					20 14		20 15				
London Blackfriars 3 ⊖ a			19 07				19 22			19 37			19 52							20 22				
City Thameslink 3 a																								
Farringdon 3 ⊖ a			19 14				19 28			19 44			19 58							20 28				
St Pancras International 15 ⊖ a			19 18				19 32			19 48			20 02							20 32				
Clapham Junction 10 a	18 48	18 55		19 02		19 09		19 18	19 23		19 32	19 39			19 48	19 55	20 02		20 09		20 18	20 23	20 32	
London Victoria 15 ⊖ a	18 56	19 03		19 09		19 17		19 26	19 30		19 39	19 46			19 56	20 03	20 09		20 17		20 26	20 30	20 39	

Table 175R

Sundays

8 December to 29 December

East Croydon & Norwood Junction - London - Summary of Fast Trains

Summary of Fast Trains — Network Diagram - see first Page of Table 175

	SN 1	FC 1	SN 1	SN 1	SN 1		SN 1	SN 1	FC 1	SN 1	SN 1	SN 1	FC 1	SN 1	SN 1		SN 1	SN 1	FC 1	SN 1	SN 1	FC 1	SN 1	SN 1
East Croydon d	20 30	20 33	20 39	20 46	20 50		20 56	21 00	21 03	21 09	21 14	21 30	21 33	21 39	21 50		21 56	22 00	22 03	22 09	22 30	22 33	22 50	22 56
Norwood Junction 2 d							21 02										22 02							
New Cross Gate a																								
London Bridge 4 ⊖ a		20 45					21 14		21 15				21 45				22 14		22 15			22 45		
London Blackfriars 3 ⊖ a		20 52							21 22				21 52						22 23			22 53		
City Thameslink 3 a																								
Farringdon 3 ⊖ a		20 58							21 28				21 58						22 29			22 59		
St Pancras International 15 ⊖ a		21 02							21 32				22 02						22 34			23 04		
Clapham Junction 10 a	20 39		20 48	20 55	21 02			21 09		21 18	21 23	21 39		21 48	22 02			22 09		22 18	22 39		23 02	23 07
London Victoria 15 ⊖ a	20 46		20 56	21 05	21 09			21 17		21 26	21 30	21 46		21 56	22 09			22 17		22 26	22 46		23 09	23 14

	SN 1		FC 1	SN	SN 1	FC 1	SN 1																	
East Croydon d	23 00		23 03	23 17	23 30	23 33	23 47																	
Norwood Junction 2 d				23a21																				
New Cross Gate a																								
London Bridge 4 ⊖ a			23 15			23 45																		
London Blackfriars 3 ⊖ a			23 23			23 53																		
City Thameslink 3 a																								
Farringdon 3 ⊖ a			23 29			23 59																		
St Pancras International 15 ⊖ a			23 34			00 03																		
Clapham Junction 10 a	23 10				23 39		23 59																	
London Victoria 15 ⊖ a	23 20				23 46		00 07																	

Sundays

5 January to 11 May

	FC 1	SN 1	FC 1	SN	SN 1	SN 1	SN 1	SN 1	FC		SN 1	FC	FC 1	SN 1	SN 1	FC 1	SN 1	FC 1	SN 1		SN 1 🛒	SN 1	FC 1	SN 1
East Croydon d	00 02	00 17	00 36	00 49	01 43	02 40	03 40	04 40	05 37		05 58	06 27	06 57	07 06	07 24	07 27	07 48	07 57	08 04		08 10	08 22	08 27	08 41
Norwood Junction 2 d																	07 54							
New Cross Gate a																								
London Bridge 4 ⊖ a	00 21		00 51														08 05							
London Blackfriars 3 ⊖ a	00 28		00 58						06 04			06 54	07 23			07 54		08 24					08 54	
City Thameslink 3 a																								
Farringdon 3 ⊖ a	00 34												07 30			08 00		08 30					09 00	
St Pancras International 15 ⊖ a	00 38		01 08										07 34			08 04		08 34					09 04	
Clapham Junction 10 a		00 33		01 02	01 57	02 53	03 53	04 55			06 12			07 18	07 38				08 17		08 27	08 35		08 57
London Victoria 15 ⊖ a		00 41		01 09	02 05	03 05	04 05	05 05			06 21			07 29	07 46				08 25		08 35	08 43		09 05

	SN 1	FC 1	SN 1	SN 1	SN 1 🛒		SN 1 🛒	FC 1	SN 1	FC 1	SN 1	SN 1 🛒	FC 1	SN 1	SN 1	SN 1	FC 1	SN 1 🛒	SN 1 🛒	FC 1	SN 1			
East Croydon d	08 52	08 56	08 59	09 03	09 10		09 16	09 17	09 30	09 33	09 39	09 46	09 47	09 50	09 56	10 00	10 03	10 09	10 14	10 17	10 20	and at the same minutes past each hour until		
Norwood Junction 2 d	08 56														10 02									
New Cross Gate a																								
London Bridge 4 ⊖ a	09 08														10 14									
London Blackfriars 3 ⊖ a		09 24						09 49		10 07			10 19				10 37			10 49				
City Thameslink 3 a																								
Farringdon 3 ⊖ a		09 30						10 00		10 14			10 28				10 44			10 58				
St Pancras International 15 ⊖ a		09 34						10 04		10 18			10 32				10 48			11 02				
Clapham Junction 10 a			09 08	09 12	09 19		09 25		09 39		09 48	09 55		10 02		10 09		10 18	10 23		10 32			
London Victoria 15 ⊖ a			09 15	09 19	09 26		09 32		09 46		09 56	10 03		10 09		10 17		10 26	10 30		10 39			

	SN 1	FC 1	SN 1	SN 1	FC 1	SN 1	SN 1	SN 1	FC 1	SN 1	SN 1	FC 1	SN 1		SN 1	FC 1	SN 1	SN 1	SN 1	SN 1	SN 1	FC 1	SN 1	
East Croydon d	19 30	19 33	19 39	19 46	19 47	19 50	19 56	20 00	20 03	20 09	20 14	20 17	20 20		20 30	20 33	20 39	20 46	20 50	20 56	21 00	21 03	21 09	
Norwood Junction 2 d							20 02													21 02				
New Cross Gate a																								
London Bridge 4 ⊖ a							20 14													21 14				
London Blackfriars 3 ⊖ a		20 07			20 19				20 37			20 49				21 07						21 37		
City Thameslink 3 a																								
Farringdon 3 ⊖ a		20 14			20 28				20 44			20 58				21 14						21 44		
St Pancras International 15 ⊖ a		20 18			20 32				20 48			21 02				21 18						21 48		
Clapham Junction 10 a	19 39		19 48	19 55		20 02		20 09		20 18	20 23		20 32		20 39		20 48	20 55	21 02		21 09		21 18	
London Victoria 15 ⊖ a	19 46		19 56	20 03		20 09		20 17		20 26	20 30		20 39		20 46		20 56	21 05	21 09		21 17		21 26	

	SN 1	SN 1	FC 1	SN 1	SN 1	SN 1	SN 1	FC 1	SN 1		SN 1	FC 1	SN 1	SN 1	SN 1	FC 1	SN	SN 1	FC 1		SN 1			
East Croydon d	21 14	21 30	21 33	21 39	21 50	21 56	22 00	22 03	22 09		22 30	22 33	22 50	22 56	23 00	23 03	23 17	23 30	23 33		23 47			
Norwood Junction 2 d						22 02											23a21							
New Cross Gate a																								
London Bridge 4 ⊖ a						22 14																		
London Blackfriars 3 ⊖ a			22 07					22 37				23 07				23 37			00 05					
City Thameslink 3 a																								
Farringdon 3 ⊖ a			22 14					22 44				23 14				23 44			00 14					
St Pancras International 15 ⊖ a			22 18					22 48				23 18				23 48			00 18					
Clapham Junction 10 a	21 23	21 39		21 48	22 02		22 09		22 18		22 39		23 02	23 07	23 10			23 39			23 59			
London Victoria 15 ⊖ a	21 30	21 46		21 56	22 09		22 17		22 26		22 46		23 09	23 14	23 20			23 46			00 07			

Network Diagram for Table 176

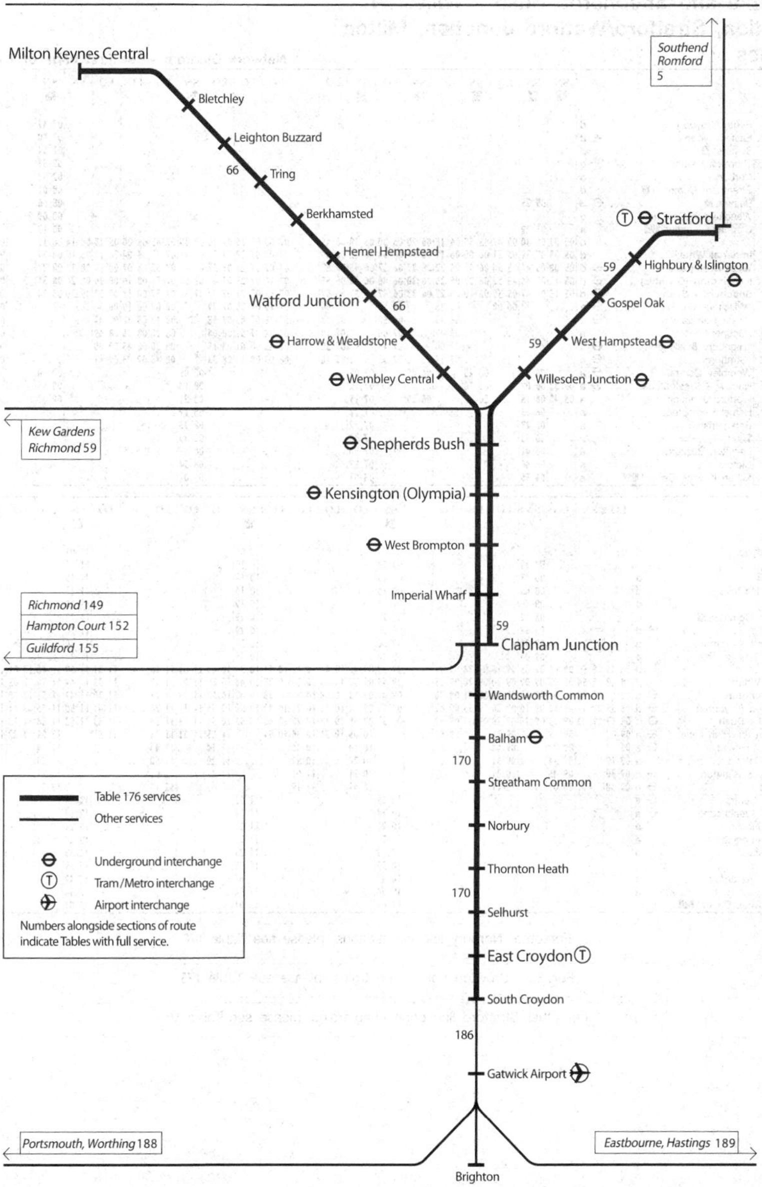

TOCs operating on this network - Southern (SN), London Overground (LO)

Table 176

Mondays to Fridays

9 December to 16 May

East Croydon, Balham and Clapham Junction-Imperial Wharf, West Brompton, Kensington Olympia and Shepherds Bush - Willesden Junction, Stratford/Watford Junction, Milton Keynes

Network Diagram - see first Page of Table 176

Miles	Miles	Station		SN [1]	SN [1]	LO	SN [1]	LO	SN [1]	LO	SN [1]	LO		LO	LO	LO	SN [1]	LO	LO	LO	SN	SN [1]		LO	SN [1]
—	—	South Croydon	d																			07 47			
0	—	East Croydon 🚊	d																			07 50			08 07
1	—	Selhurst [4]	d																			07 54			08 13
1¾	—	Thornton Heath	d																			07 56			08 16
3	—	Norbury	d																			07 59			08 20
4	—	Streatham Common [4]	d																			08 02			08 23
5¾	—	Balham [4] ⊖	d		05 25																	08 06			08 28
6½	—	Wandsworth Common	d																			08 09			08 30
7¾	—	Clapham Junction [10]	a		05 29																	08 13			08 36
—	—		d	05 01	05 30	05 47	05 55	06 15	06 20	06 30	06 38	06 45		07 00	07 15	07 30	07 39	07 45	08 00	08 10	08 14	08 19		08 30	08 39
8¾	—	**Imperial Wharf**	d	05 05	05 39	05 51	06 00	06 19	06 24	06 34	06 42	06 49		07 04	07 19	07 34	07 44	07 49	08 04	08 14	08 19	08 24		08 34	08 44
9½	—	**West Brompton** ⊖	d	05 08	05 41	05 54	06 03	06 22	06 27	06 37	06 45	06 52		07 07	07 22	07 37	07 47	07 52	08 07	08 17	08 22	08 27		08 37	08 47
11½	—	**Kensington (Olympia)** ⊖	d	05 12	05 44	05 57	06 07	06 25	06 30	06 40	06 49	06 55		07 10	07 25	07 40	07 50	07 55	08 10	08 20	08 26	08 31		08 40	08 50
12¾	0	**Shepherd's Bush** ⊖	d	05 15	05 47	05 59	06 10	06 27	06 33	06 42	06 52	06 57		07 12	07 27	07 42	07 53	07 57	08 12	08 22	08a30	08 34		08 42	08 53
—	1½	Willesden Jn. High Level ⊖	a			06 08		06 35		06 50		07 04		07 19	07 35	07 49		08 04	08 19	08 30				08 49	
—	4	West Hampstead ⊖	a					06 43		06 58		07 13		07 28	07 43	07 58		08 13	08 28	08 43				08 58	
—	6	Gospel Oak	a					06 49		07 04		07 19		07 34	07 51	08 04		08 20	08 35	08 49				09 04	
—	8¾	Highbury & Islington ⊖	a					07 00		07 15		07 30		07 45	08 01	08 15		08 30	08 45	09 00				09 15	
—	13½	Stratford ⊖	a					07 18		07 33		07 48		08 03	08 19	08 33		08 48	09 03	09 17				09 33	
17	—	Wembley Central ⊖	a		06 02		06 25		06 49		07 07						08 09					08 50			09 09
20½	—	Harrow & Wealdstone ⊖	a	05 33	06 08		06 30				07 12						08 14					08 55			09 14
25	—	Watford Junction	a	05 40	06 15		06 37		06 59		07 19						08 21					09 03			09 21
32	—	Hemel Hempstead	a		06 23						07 27						08 29								09 29
35½	—	Berkhamsted	a		06 27						07 32						08 33								09 33
39¼	—	Tring	a		06 33						07 38						08 39								09 39
47¾	—	Leighton Buzzard	a		06 41						07 50						08 47								09 47
54¼	—	Bletchley	a		06 48						07 57						08 54								09 54
57¼	—	Milton Keynes Central [10]	a		06 56						08 03						09 01								10 01

Station		LO	SN	LO	SN	LO	SN	LO		SN [1]	LO	LO	LO	LO	SN [1]	LO	LO	LO		LO	SN [1]	LO	LO	LO	LO
South Croydon	d														10 07						11 07				
East Croydon 🚊	d				08 39					09 08					10 10						11 11				
Selhurst [4]	d				08 43					09 13					10 14						11 15				
Thornton Heath	d				08 46					09 16					10 16						11 17				
Norbury	d				08 49					09 19					10 19						11 20				
Streatham Common [4]	d				08 52					09 21					10 22						11 23				
Balham [4] ⊖	d				08 58					09 28					10 29						11 28				
Wandsworth Common	d				09 00					09 30					10 31						11 30				
Clapham Junction [10]	a				09 04					09 34					10 35						11 34				
	d	08 45	08 50	09 01	09 05	09 16	09 24	09 31		09 39	09 46	10 01	10 16	10 31	10 39	10 46	11 01	11 16		11 31	11 39	11 46	12 01	12 16	12 31
Imperial Wharf	d	08 49	08 54	09 05	09 09	09 20	09 28	09 35		09 44	09 50	10 05	10 20	10 35	10 44	10 50	11 05	11 20		11 35	11 44	11 50	12 05	12 20	12 35
West Brompton ⊖	d	08 52	08 57	09 08	09 12	09 23	09 31	09 38		09 47	09 53	10 08	10 23	10 38	10 47	10 53	11 08	11 23		11 38	11 47	11 53	12 08	12 23	12 38
Kensington (Olympia) ⊖	d	08 55	09 01	09 11	09 16	09 26	09 35	09 41		09 50	09 56	10 11	10 26	10 41	10 50	10 56	11 11	11 26		11 41	11 50	11 56	12 11	12 26	12 41
Shepherd's Bush ⊖	d	08 57	09a03	09 13	09a18	09 28	09a37	09 43		09 53	09 58	10 13	10 28	10 43	10 53	10 58	11 13	11 28		11 43	11 53	11 58	12 13	12 28	12 43
Willesden Jn. High Level ⊖	a	09 04		09 19		09 35		09 51			10 05	10 21	10 36	10 51		11 05	11 21	11 35		11 51		12 05	12 22	12 35	12 51
West Hampstead ⊖	a	09 13		09 28		09 44					10 14		10 45			11 14		11 44				12 14		12 44	
Gospel Oak	a	09 19		09 34		09 51					10 20		10 51			11 20		11 50				12 20		12 50	
Highbury & Islington ⊖	a	09 30		09 45		10 01					10 31		11 01			11 31		12 01				12 32		13 01	
Stratford ⊖	a	09 48		10 05		10 19					10 49		11 19			11 49		12 19				12 51		13 19	
Wembley Central ⊖	a									10 09					11 09						12 09				
Harrow & Wealdstone ⊖	a									10 14					11 14						12 14				
Watford Junction	a									10 21					11 21						12 21				
Hemel Hempstead	a									10 29					11 29						12 29				
Berkhamsted	a									10 33					11 33						12 33				
Tring	a									10 39					11 39						12 39				
Leighton Buzzard	a									10 47					11 47						12 47				
Bletchley	a									10 54					11 54						12 54				
Milton Keynes Central [10]	a									11 01					12 01						13 01				

For other Norbury line connections, please see Table 170

For East Croydon connecting trains, please see Table 175

For other Stratford line connecting trains, please see Table 59

Table 176

Mondays to Fridays

9 December to 16 May

East Croydon, Balham and Clapham Junction-Imperial Wharf, West Brompton, Kensington Olympia and Shepherds Bush - Willesden Junction, Stratford/Watford Junction, Milton Keynes

Network Diagram - see first Page of Table 176

		SN 1	LO	LO	LO	LO	SN 1	LO	LO	LO		LO	SN 1	LO	LO	LO	LO	SN 1	LO	LO		LO	LO	SN 1	LO
South Croydon	d	12 07					13 07						14 07					15 07						16 07	
East Croydon	d	12 10					13 10						14 10					15 10						16 10	
Selhurst 4	d	12 14					13 13						14 13					15 13						16 13	
Thornton Heath	d	12 16					13 16						14 16					15 16						16 16	
Norbury	d	12 19					13 19						14 19					15 19						16 19	
Streatham Common 4	d	12 22					13 21						14 21					15 21						16 21	
Balham 4 ⊖	d	12 28					13 28						14 28					15 29						16 28	
Wandsworth Common	d	12 30					13 30						14 30					15 31						16 30	
Clapham Junction 10	a	12 34					13 34						14 34					15 35						16 34	
	d	12 39	12 46	13 01	13 16	13 31	13 39	13 46	14 01	14 16		14 31	14 39	14 46	15 01	15 16	15 30	15 39	15 46	16 00		16 15	16 30	16 39	16 45
Imperial Wharf	d	12 44	12 50	13 05	13 20	13 35	13 44	13 50	14 05	14 20		14 35	14 44	14 55	15 05	15 20	15 34	15 44	15 50	16 04		16 19	16 34	16 44	16 49
West Brompton ⊖	d	12 47	12 53	13 08	13 23	13 38	13 47	13 53	14 08	14 23		14 38	14 47	14 58	15 08	15 23	15 37	15 47	15 53	16 07		16 22	16 37	16 47	16 52
Kensington (Olympia) ⊖	d	12 50	12 56	13 11	13 26	13 41	13 50	13 56	14 11	14 26		14 41	14 50	15 01	15 11	15 26	15 40	15 50	15 56	16 10		16 25	16 40	16 50	16 55
Shepherd's Bush ⊖	d	12 53	12 58	13 13	13 28	13 43	13 53	13 58	14 13	14 28		14 43	14 53	15 03	15 13	15 28	15 42	15 53	15 58	16 12		16 27	16 42	16 53	16 57
Willesden Jn. High Level ⊖	a		13 05	13 21	13 35	13 52		14 05	14 20	14 35		14 51		15 09	15 20	15 35	15 50		16 04	16 20		16 35	16 49		17 04
West Hampstead ⊖	a		13 14		13 44			14 14		14 44				15 18		15 44	15 59		16 14	16 28		16 43	16 58		17 13
Gospel Oak	a		13 20		13 50			14 21		14 50				15 25		15 50	16 05		16 21	16 34		16 49	17 04		17 19
Highbury & Islington ⊖	a		13 31		14 01			14 31		15 01				15 37		16 01	16 16		16 30	16 45		17 00	17 15		17 30
Stratford ⊖	a		13 49		14 19			14 49		15 19				15 54		16 18	16 32		16 49	17 03		17 18	17 33		17 50
Wembley Central ⊖	a	13 09					14 09						15 09					16 09						17 09	
Harrow & Wealdstone ⊖	a	13 14					14 14						15 14					16 14						17 14	
Watford Junction	a	13 21					14 21						15 21					16 21						17 21	
Hemel Hempstead	a	13 29					14 29						15 29					16 29						17 29	
Berkhamsted	a	13 33					14 33						15 33					16 33						17 33	
Tring	a	13 39					14 39						15 39					16 39						17 39	
Leighton Buzzard	a	13 47					14 47						15 47					16 47						17 47	
Bletchley	a	13 54					14 54						15 54					16 54						17 54	
Milton Keynes Central 10	a	14 01					15 01						16 01					17 01						18 01	

		SN	LO	LO	SN	LO		SN 1	LO	LO	LO	LO	SN 1	LO	LO	LO		LO	SN 1	LO	LO	LO	LO	SN 1	LO
South Croydon	d							17 07																	
East Croydon	d							17 10					18 10						19 10						
Selhurst 4	d							17 13					18 13						19 13						
Thornton Heath	d							17 16					18 16						19 16						
Norbury	d							17 19					18 19						19 19						
Streatham Common 4	d							17 21					18 21						19 21						
Balham 4 ⊖	d							17 28					18 29						19 28						
Wandsworth Common	d							17 30					18 31						19 30						
Clapham Junction 10	a							17 34					18 35						19 34						
	d	16 49	17 00	17 15	17 20	17 30		17 39	17 45	18 00	18 15	18 30	18 39	18 45	19 00	19 16		19 31	19 39	19 46	20 01	20 16	20 31	20 39	20 46
Imperial Wharf	d	16 53	17 04	17 19	17 24	17 34		17 44	17 49	18 04	18 19	18 34	18 44	18 49	19 04	19 20		19 35	19 44	19 50	20 05	20 20	20 35	20 44	20 50
West Brompton ⊖	d	16 56	17 07	17 22	17 27	17 37		17 47	17 52	18 07	18 22	18 37	18 47	18 52	19 07	19 23		19 38	19 47	19 53	20 08	20 23	20 38	20 47	20 53
Kensington (Olympia) ⊖	d	16a59	17 10	17 25	17 30	17 40		17 50	17 55	18 10	18 25	18 40	18 50	18 55	19 10	19 26		19 41	19 50	19 56	20 11	20 26	20 41	20 50	20 56
Shepherd's Bush ⊖	d		17 12	17 27	17a32	17 42		17 53	17 57	18 12	18 27	18 42	18 53	18 57	19 12	19 28		19 43	19 53	19 58	20 13	20 28	20 43	20 53	20 58
Willesden Jn. High Level ⊖	a		17 19	17 34		17 49			18 04	18 19	18 34	18 49		19 03	19 19	19 35		19 51		20 06	20 21	20 36	20 51		21 06
West Hampstead ⊖	a		17 28	17 43		17 58			18 13	18 28	18 43	18 58		19 13	19 28	19 43				20 13					
Gospel Oak	a		17 34	17 49		18 04			18 19	18 34	18 49	19 04		19 19	19 34	19 49				20 19					
Highbury & Islington ⊖	a		17 45	18 00		18 15			18 30	18 45	19 00	19 15		19 30	19 45	20 00				20 30					
Stratford ⊖	a		18 05	18 20		18 35			18 50	19 05	19 18	19 33		19 47	20 03	20 19				20 49					
Wembley Central ⊖	a							18 09					19 09						20 09					21 09	
Harrow & Wealdstone ⊖	a							18 14					19 14						20 14					21 14	
Watford Junction	a							18 21					19 21						20 21					21 21	
Hemel Hempstead	a							18 29					19 29						20 29					21 29	
Berkhamsted	a							18 33					19 33						20 33					21 33	
Tring	a							18 39					19 39						20 39					21 39	
Leighton Buzzard	a							18 48					19 47						20 47					21 49	
Bletchley	a							18 54					19 54						20 55					21 57	
Milton Keynes Central 10	a							19 00					20 01						21 01					22 05	

For other Norbury line connections, please see Table 170

For East Croydon connecting trains, please see Table 175

For other Stratford line connecting trains, please see Table 59

Table 176

Mondays to Fridays

9 December to 16 May

East Croydon, Balham and Clapham Junction-Imperial Wharf, West Brompton, Kensington Olympia and Shepherds Bush - Willesden Junction, Stratford/Watford Junction, Milton Keynes

Network Diagram - see first Page of Table 176

		LO	LO	LO	SN 1	LO	LO	LO		LO	SN 1	LO	LO	LO
South Croydon	d													
East Croydon	d													
Selhurst 4	d													
Thornton Heath	d													
Norbury	d													
Streatham Common 4	d													
Balham 4 ⊖	d													
Wandsworth Common	d													
Clapham Junction 10	a													
	d	21 01	21 16	21 31	21 39	21 46	22 01	22 16		22 31	22 39	22 46	23 01	23 31
Imperial Wharf	d	21 05	21 20	21 35	21 44	21 50	22 05	22 20		22 35	22 44	22 50	23 05	23 35
West Brompton ⊖	d	21 08	21 23	21 38	21 47	21 53	22 08	22 23		22 38	22 47	22 53	23 08	23 38
Kensington (Olympia) ⊖	d	21 11	21 26	21 41	21 50	21 56	22 11	22 26		22 41	22 50	22 56	23 11	23 41
Shepherd's Bush ⊖	d	21 13	21 28	21 43	21 53	21 58	22 13	22 28		22 43	22 53	22 58	23 13	23 43
Willesden Jn. High Level ⊖	a	21 21	21 36	21 51		22 06	22 21	22 36		22 51		23 06	23 21	23 56
West Hampstead ⊖	a													
Gospel Oak	a													
Highbury & Islington ⊖	a													
Stratford ⊖	a													
Wembley Central ⊖	a													
Harrow & Wealdstone ⊖	a				22 15						23 16			
Watford Junction	a				22 22						23 23			
Hemel Hempstead	a													
Berkhamsted	a													
Tring	a													
Leighton Buzzard	a													
Bletchley	a													
Milton Keynes Central 10	a													

Saturdays

14 December to 17 May

		SN 1	SN 1	LO	SN 1	LO	LO	SN 1	LO	LO		LO	LO	SN 1	LO	LO	LO	LO	SN 1	LO		LO	LO	LO	SN 1
South Croydon	d													07 07					08 07						09 07
East Croydon	d							06 10						07 10					08 10						09 10
Selhurst 4	d							06 13						07 13					08 13						09 13
Thornton Heath	d							06 16						07 16					08 16						09 16
Norbury	d							06 19						07 19					08 19						09 19
Streatham Common 4	d							06 21						07 21					08 21						09 21
Balham 4 ⊖	d		05 33					06 28						07 28					08 28						09 28
Wandsworth Common	d							06 30						07 30					08 30						09 30
Clapham Junction 10	a		05 37					06 34						07 34					08 34						09 34
	d	05 08	05 38	05 48	06 09	06 16	06 31	06 36	06 46	07 01		07 16	07 31	07 39	07 46	08 01	08 16	08 31	08 39	08 46		09 01	09 16	09 31	09 39
Imperial Wharf	d	05 12	05 42	05 52	06 13	06 20	06 35	06 41	06 50	07 05		07 20	07 35	07 44	07 50	08 05	08 20	08 35	08 44	08 50		09 05	09 20	09 35	09 44
West Brompton ⊖	d	05 15	05 45	05 55	06 16	06 23	06 38	06 44	06 53	07 08		07 23	07 38	07 47	07 53	08 08	08 23	08 38	08 47	08 53		09 08	09 23	09 38	09 47
Kensington (Olympia) ⊖	d	05 19	05 49	05 58	06 20	06 26	06 41	06 47	06 56	07 11		07 26	07 41	07 50	07 56	08 11	08 26	08 41	08 50	08 56		09 11	09 26	09 41	09 50
Shepherd's Bush ⊖	d	05 22	05 52	06 00	06 23	06 28	06 43	06 50	06 58	07 13		07 28	07 43	07 53	07 58	08 13	08 28	08 43	08 53	08 58		09 13	09 28	09 43	09 53
Willesden Jn. High Level ⊖	a			06 08		06 35	06 50		07 05	07 20		07 35	07 51		08 05	08 21	08 35	08 51		09 05		09 21	09 35	09 51	
West Hampstead ⊖	a					06 44			07 14			07 44			08 14		08 44			09 14			09 44		
Gospel Oak	a					06 50			07 20			07 50			08 20		08 50			09 20			09 50		
Highbury & Islington ⊖	a					07 01			07 31			08 01			08 31		09 01			09 31			10 01		
Stratford ⊖	a					07 19			07 49			08 19			08 49		09 19			09 49			10 19		
Wembley Central ⊖	a		06 07		06 38			07 09						08 09					09 09						10 09
Harrow & Wealdstone ⊖	a	05 40	06 12		06 43			07 14						08 14					09 14						10 14
Watford Junction	a	05 47	06 19		06 50			07 21						08 21					09 21						10 21
Hemel Hempstead	a		06 27					07 29						08 29					09 29						10 29
Berkhamsted	a		06 32					07 33						08 33					09 33						10 33
Tring	a		06 38					07 39						08 39					09 39						10 39
Leighton Buzzard	a		06 46					07 47						08 47					09 47						10 47
Bletchley	a		06 54					07 54						08 54					09 54						10 54
Milton Keynes Central 10	a		07 00					08 00						09 00					10 00						11 00

For other Norbury line connections, please see Table 170

For East Croydon connecting trains, please see Table 175

For other Stratford line connecting trains, please see Table 59

Table 176

Saturdays

14 December to 17 May

East Croydon, Balham and Clapham Junction-Imperial Wharf, West Brompton, Kensington Olympia and Shepherds Bush - Willesden Junction, Stratford/Watford Junction, Milton Keynes

Network Diagram - see first Page of Table 176

		LO		LO	LO	LO	SN 1	LO	LO	LO	LO	SN 1		LO	LO	LO	LO	SN 1	LO	LO	LO	LO		SN 1	LO
South Croydon	d						10 07					11 07						12 07						13 07	
East Croydon	d						10 10					11 10						12 10						13 10	
Selhurst 4	d						10 13					11 13						12 13						13 13	
Thornton Heath	d						10 16					11 16						12 16						13 16	
Norbury	d						10 19					11 19						12 19						13 19	
Streatham Common 4	d						10 21					11 21						12 21						13 21	
Balham 4 ⊖	d						10 28					11 28						12 28						13 28	
Wandsworth Common	d						10 30					11 30						12 30						13 30	
Clapham Junction 10	a						10 34					11 34						12 34						13 34	
	d	09 46		10 01	10 16	10 31	10 39	10 46	11 01	11 16	11 31	11 39		11 46	12 01	12 16	12 31	12 39	12 46	13 01	13 16	13 31		13 39	13 46
Imperial Wharf	d	09 50		10 05	10 20	10 35	10 44	10 50	11 05	11 20	11 35	11 44		11 50	12 05	12 20	12 35	12 44	12 50	13 05	13 20	13 35		13 44	13 50
West Brompton ⊖	d	09 53		10 08	10 23	10 38	10 47	10 53	11 08	11 23	11 38	11 47		11 53	12 08	12 23	12 38	12 47	12 53	13 08	13 23	13 38		13 47	13 53
Kensington (Olympia) ⊖	d	09 56		10 11	10 26	10 41	10 50	10 56	11 11	11 26	11 41	11 50		11 56	12 11	12 26	12 41	12 50	12 56	13 11	13 26	13 41		13 50	13 56
Shepherd's Bush ⊖	d	09 58		10 13	10 28	10 43	10 53	10 58	11 13	11 28	11 43	11 53		11 58	12 13	12 28	12 43	12 53	12 58	13 13	13 28	13 43		13 53	13 58
Willesden Jn. High Level ⊖	a	10 05		10 21	10 35	10 51		11 05	11 20	11 35	11 51			12 05	12 21	12 35	12 51		13 05	13 21	13 35	13 51			14 05
West Hampstead ⊖	a	10 14			10 44			11 14		11 44				12 14		12 44			13 14		13 44				14 15
Gospel Oak	a	10 20			10 50			11 20		11 50				12 20		12 50			13 20		13 50				14 21
Highbury & Islington ⊖	a	10 31			11 01			11 31		12 01				12 31		13 01			13 31		14 01				14 31
Stratford ⊖	a	10 49			11 19			11 49		12 19				12 49		13 19			13 49		14 19				14 49
Wembley Central ⊖	a						11 09					12 09						13 09						14 09	
Harrow & Wealdstone ⊖	a						11 14					12 14						13 14						14 14	
Watford Junction	a						11 21					12 21						13 21						14 21	
Hemel Hempstead	a						11 29					12 29						13 29						14 29	
Berkhamsted	a						11 33					12 33						13 33						14 33	
Tring	a						11 39					12 39						13 39						14 39	
Leighton Buzzard	a						11 47					12 47						13 47						14 47	
Bletchley	a						11 54					12 54						13 54						14 54	
Milton Keynes Central 10	a						12 00					13 00						14 00						15 00	

		LO	LO	LO	SN 1	LO	LO	LO		LO	SN 1	LO	LO	LO	LO	SN 1	LO	LO		LO	LO	SN 1	LO	LO	LO
South Croydon	d				14 07						15 07					16 07						17 07			
East Croydon	d				14 10						15 10					16 10						17 10			
Selhurst 4	d				14 13						15 13					16 13						17 13			
Thornton Heath	d				14 16						15 16					16 16						17 16			
Norbury	d				14 19						15 19					16 19						17 19			
Streatham Common 4	d				14 21						15 21					16 21						17 21			
Balham 4 ⊖	d				14 28						15 28					16 28						17 28			
Wandsworth Common	d				14 30						15 30					16 30						17 30			
Clapham Junction 10	a				14 34						15 34					16 34						17 34			
	d	14 01	14 16	14 31	14 39	14 46	15 01	15 16		15 31	15 39	15 46	16 01	16 16	16 31	16 39	16 46	17 01		17 16	17 31	17 39	17 46	18 01	18 16
Imperial Wharf	d	14 05	14 20	14 35	14 44	14 50	15 05	15 20		15 35	15 44	15 50	16 05	16 20	16 35	16 44	16 50	17 05		17 20	17 35	17 44	17 50	18 05	18 20
West Brompton ⊖	d	14 08	14 23	14 38	14 47	14 53	15 08	15 23		15 38	15 47	15 53	16 08	16 23	16 38	16 47	16 53	17 08		17 23	17 38	17 47	17 53	18 08	18 23
Kensington (Olympia) ⊖	d	14 11	14 26	14 41	14 50	14 56	15 11	15 26		15 41	15 50	15 56	16 11	16 26	16 41	16 50	16 56	17 11		17 26	17 41	17 50	17 56	18 11	18 26
Shepherd's Bush ⊖	d	14 13	14 28	14 43	14 53	14 58	15 13	15 28		15 43	15 53	15 58	16 13	16 28	16 43	16 53	16 58	17 13		17 28	17 43	17 53	17 58	18 13	18 28
Willesden Jn. High Level ⊖	a	14 21	14 35	14 51		15 05	15 21	15 35		15 51		16 05	16 21	16 35	16 50		17 05	17 21		17 35	17 51		18 05	18 21	18 35
West Hampstead ⊖	a		14 44			15 14		15 44				16 14		16 44			17 14			17 44			18 14		18 44
Gospel Oak	a		14 50			15 20		15 50				16 20		16 50			17 20			17 50			18 20		18 50
Highbury & Islington ⊖	a		15 01			15 31		16 01				16 31		17 01			17 31			18 01			18 31		19 01
Stratford ⊖	a		15 19			15 49		16 21				16 51		17 21			17 51			18 21			18 51		19 21
Wembley Central ⊖	a				15 09						16 09					17 09						18 09			
Harrow & Wealdstone ⊖	a				15 14						16 14					17 14						18 14			
Watford Junction	a				15 21						16 21					17 21						18 21			
Hemel Hempstead	a				15 29						16 29					17 29						18 29			
Berkhamsted	a				15 33						16 33					17 33						18 33			
Tring	a				15 39						16 39					17 39						18 39			
Leighton Buzzard	a				15 47						16 47					17 47						18 47			
Bletchley	a				15 54						16 54					17 54						18 54			
Milton Keynes Central 10	a				16 00						17 00					18 00						19 00			

For other Norbury line connections, please see Table 170

For East Croydon connecting trains, please see Table 175

For other Stratford line connecting trains, please see Table 59

Table 176

Saturdays

14 December to 17 May

East Croydon, Balham and Clapham Junction-Imperial Wharf, West Brompton, Kensington Olympia and Shepherds Bush - Willesden Junction, Stratford/Watford Junction, Milton Keynes

Network Diagram - see first Page of Table 176

		LO	SN 1	LO	LO	LO	LO	SN 1	LO	LO	LO	SN 1	LO	LO	LO	LO	LO	SN 1	LO	LO	LO	LO	SN 1
South Croydon	d		18 07					19 07															
East Croydon	d		18 10					19 10															
Selhurst 4	d		18 13					19 13															
Thornton Heath	d		18 16					19 16															
Norbury	d		18 19					19 19															
Streatham Common 4	d		18 21					19 21															
Balham 4 ⊖	d		18 28					19 28															
Wandsworth Common	d		18 30					19 30															
Clapham Junction 10	a		18 34					19 34															
	d	18 31	18 39	18 46	19 01	19 16	19 31	19 38	19 46	20 01	20 16	20 25	20 31	20 46	21 01	21 16	21 31	21 39	21 46	22 01	22 16	22 31	22 39
Imperial Wharf	d	18 35	18 44	18 50	19 05	19 20	19 35	19 42	19 50	20 05	20 20	20 29	20 35	20 50	21 05	21 20	21 35	21 44	21 50	22 05	22 20	22 35	22 44
West Brompton ⊖	d	18 38	18 47	18 53	19 08	19 23	19 38	19 45	19 53	20 08	20 23	20 32	20 38	20 53	21 08	21 23	21 38	21 47	21 53	22 08	22 23	22 38	22 47
Kensington (Olympia) ⊖	d	18 41	18 50	18 56	19 11	19 26	19 41	19 48	19 56	20 11	20 26	20 36	20 41	20 56	21 11	21 26	21 41	21 50	21 56	22 11	22 26	22 41	22 50
Shepherd's Bush ⊖	d	18 43	18 53	18 58	19 13	19 28	19 43	19 50	19 58	20 13	20 28	20 39	20 43	20 58	21 13	21 28	21 43	21 53	21 58	22 13	22 28	22 43	22 53
Willesden Jn. High Level ⊖	a	18 51		19 05	19 21	19 35	19 51		20 05	20 21	20 36		20 51	21 06	21 21	21 36	21 51		22 06	22 21	22 36	22 51	
West Hampstead ⊖	a			19 14		19 44			20 14														
Gospel Oak	a			19 20		19 50			20 20														
Highbury & Islington ⊖	a			19 31		20 01			20 31														
Stratford ⊖	a			19 51		20 21			20 49														
Wembley Central ⊖	a		19 09																				
Harrow & Wealdstone ⊖	a		19 14					20 08				21 02						22 13					23 12
Watford Junction	a		19 21					20 15				21 09						22 20					23 19
Hemel Hempstead	a																						
Berkhamsted	a																						
Tring	a																						
Leighton Buzzard	a																						
Bletchley	a																						
Milton Keynes Central 10	a																						

		LO	LO	LO
South Croydon	d			
East Croydon	d			
Selhurst 4	d			
Thornton Heath	d			
Norbury	d			
Streatham Common 4	d			
Balham 4 ⊖	d			
Wandsworth Common	d			
Clapham Junction 10	a			
	d	22 46	23 01	23 31
Imperial Wharf	d	22 50	23 05	23 35
West Brompton ⊖	d	22 53	23 08	23 38
Kensington (Olympia) ⊖	d	22 56	23 11	23 41
Shepherd's Bush ⊖	d	22 58	23 13	23 43
Willesden Jn. High Level ⊖	a	23 06	23 24	23 51
West Hampstead ⊖	a			
Gospel Oak	a			
Highbury & Islington ⊖	a			
Stratford ⊖	a			
Wembley Central ⊖	a			
Harrow & Wealdstone ⊖	a			
Watford Junction	a			
Hemel Hempstead	a			
Berkhamsted	a			
Tring	a			
Leighton Buzzard	a			
Bletchley	a			
Milton Keynes Central 10	a			

For other Norbury line connections, please see Table 170

For East Croydon connecting trains, please see Table 175

For other Stratford line connecting trains, please see Table 59

Table 176

Sundays

8 December to 11 May

East Croydon, Balham and Clapham Junction-Imperial Wharf, West Brompton, Kensington Olympia and Shepherds Bush - Willesden Junction, Stratford/Watford Junction, Milton Keynes

Network Diagram - see first Page of Table 176

		SN 1	SN 1	LO	LO	SN 1		LO	LO	SN 1	LO	LO	LO	LO	SN 1	LO		LO	LO	LO	SN 1	LO	LO	LO	LO
South Croydon	d																								
East Croydon	d																								
Selhurst 4	d																								
Thornton Heath	d																								
Norbury	d																								
Streatham Common 4	d																								
Balham 4 ⊖	d																								
Wandsworth Common	d																								
Clapham Junction 10	a																								
	d	07 24	08 15	08 31	09 01	09 15		09 31	10 01	10 15	10 21	10 31	10 46	11 01	11 15	11 21		11 31	11 46	12 01	12 05	12 16	12 31	12 46	13 01
Imperial Wharf	d	07 28	08 19	08 35	09 05	09 19		09 35	10 05	10 19	10 25	10 35	10 50	11 05	11 19	11 25		11 35	11 50	12 05	12 09	12 20	12 35	12 50	13 05
West Brompton ⊖	d	07 31	08 22	08 38	09 08	09 22		09 38	10 08	10 22	10 28	10 38	10 53	11 08	11 22	11 28		11 38	11 53	12 08	12 12	12 23	12 38	12 53	13 08
Kensington (Olympia) ⊖	d	07 34	08 26	08 41	09 11	09 26		09 41	10 11	10 26	10 31	10 41	10 56	11 11	11 26	11 31		11 41	11 56	12 11	12 16	12 26	12 41	12 56	13 11
Shepherd's Bush ⊖	d	07a36	08 29	08 43	09 13	09 29		09 43	10 13	10 29	10 33	10 43	10 58	11 13	11 29	11 33		11 43	11 58	12 13	12 19	12 28	12 43	12 58	13 13
Willesden Jn. High Level ⊖	a			08 51	09 21			09 51	10 21		10 40	10 51	11 05	11 21		11 40		11 51	12 05	12 21		12 35	12 51	13 05	13 21
West Hampstead ⊖	a										10 49		11 14			11 49			12 14			12 44		13 14	
Gospel Oak	a										10 55		11 20			11 55			12 20			12 50		13 20	
Highbury & Islington ⊖	a										11 06		11 31			12 06			12 31			13 01		13 31	
Stratford ⊖	a										11 24		11 49			12 24			12 49			13 19		13 49	
Wembley Central ⊖	a																								
Harrow & Wealdstone ⊖	a		08 49			09 48				10 48					11 48						12 37				
Watford Junction	a		08 56			09 58				10 56					11 56						12 44				
Hemel Hempstead	a																								
Berkhamsted	a																								
Tring	a																								
Leighton Buzzard	a																								
Bletchley	a																								
Milton Keynes Central 10	a																								

		SN 1		LO	LO	LO	LO	SN 1	LO	LO	LO	LO		SN 1	LO	LO	LO	LO	SN 1	LO	LO	LO		LO	SN 1
South Croydon	d																								
East Croydon	d																								
Selhurst 4	d																								
Thornton Heath	d																								
Norbury	d																								
Streatham Common 4	d																								
Balham 4 ⊖	d																								
Wandsworth Common	d																								
Clapham Junction 10	a																								
	d	13 05		13 16	13 31	13 46	14 01	14 05	14 16	14 31	14 46	15 01		15 05	15 16	15 31	15 46	16 01	16 05	16 16	16 31	16 46		17 01	17 05
Imperial Wharf	d	13 09		13 20	13 35	13 50	14 05	14 09	14 20	14 35	14 50	15 05		15 09	15 20	15 35	15 50	16 05	16 09	16 20	16 35	16 50		17 05	17 09
West Brompton ⊖	d	13 12		13 23	13 38	13 53	14 08	14 12	14 23	14 38	14 53	15 08		15 12	15 23	15 38	15 53	16 08	16 12	16 23	16 38	16 53		17 08	17 12
Kensington (Olympia) ⊖	d	13 16		13 26	13 41	13 56	14 11	14 16	14 26	14 41	14 56	15 11		15 16	15 26	15 41	15 56	16 11	16 16	16 26	16 41	16 56		17 11	17 16
Shepherd's Bush ⊖	d	13 19		13 28	13 43	13 58	14 13	14 19	14 28	14 43	14 58	15 13		15 19	15 28	15 43	15 58	16 13	16 19	16 28	16 43	16 58		17 13	17 19
Willesden Jn. High Level ⊖	a			13 35	13 51	14 05	14 22		14 35	14 51	15 05	15 21			15 35	15 51	16 05	16 21		16 35	16 51	17 05		17 21	
West Hampstead ⊖	a			13 44		14 14			14 44		15 14				15 44		16 14			16 44		17 14			
Gospel Oak	a			13 50		14 20			14 50		15 20				15 50		16 20			16 50		17 20			
Highbury & Islington ⊖	a			14 01		14 31			15 01		15 31				16 01		16 31			17 01		17 31			
Stratford ⊖	a			14 19		14 49			15 19		15 49				16 19		16 49			17 19		17 49			
Wembley Central ⊖	a																								
Harrow & Wealdstone ⊖	a	13 37						14 37						15 37					16 37						17 37
Watford Junction	a	13 44						14 44						15 44					16 44						17 44
Hemel Hempstead	a																								
Berkhamsted	a																								
Tring	a																								
Leighton Buzzard	a																								
Bletchley	a																								
Milton Keynes Central 10	a																								

For other Norbury line connections, please see Table 170

For East Croydon connecting trains, please see Table 175

For other Stratford line connecting trains, please see Table 59

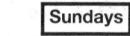

Table 176

Sundays

8 December to 11 May

East Croydon, Balham and Clapham Junction-Imperial Wharf, West Brompton, Kensington Olympia and Shepherds Bush - Willesden Junction, Stratford/Watford Junction, Milton Keynes

Network Diagram - see first Page of Table 176

		LO	LO	LO	LO	SN [1]	LO	LO	LO	LO	SN [1]	LO	LO	LO	LO	SN [1]	LO	LO	LO	LO	SN [1]	LO
South Croydon	d																					
East Croydon 🚌	d																					
Selhurst [4]	d																					
Thornton Heath	d																					
Norbury	d																					
Streatham Common [4]	d																					
Balham [4] ⊖	d																					
Wandsworth Common	d																					
Clapham Junction [10]	a																					
	d	17 16	17 31	17 46	18 01	18 05	18 16	18 31	18 46	19 01	19 05	19 16	19 31	19 46	20 01	20 05	20 16	20 31	20 46	21 01	21 15	21 16
Imperial Wharf	d	17 20	17 35	17 50	18 05	18 09	18 20	18 35	18 50	19 05	19 09	19 20	19 35	19 50	20 05	20 09	20 20	20 35	20 50	21 05	21 19	21 20
West Brompton ⊖	d	17 23	17 38	17 53	18 08	18 12	18 23	18 38	18 53	19 08	19 12	19 23	19 38	19 53	20 08	20 12	20 23	20 38	20 53	21 08	21 22	21 23
Kensington (Olympia) ⊖	d	17 26	17 41	17 56	18 11	18 16	18 26	18 41	18 56	19 11	19 16	19 26	19 41	19 56	20 11	20 16	20 26	20 41	20 56	21 11	21 25	21 26
Shepherd's Bush ⊖	d	17 28	17 43	17 58	18 13	18 19	18 28	18 43	18 58	19 13	19 19	19 28	19 43	19 58	20 13	20 19	20 28	20 43	20 58	21 13	21 28	21 32
Willesden Jn. High Level ⊖	a	17 35	17 51	18 05	18 21		18 35	18 51	19 05	19 21		19 35	19 51	20 05	20 21		20 36	20 51	21 08	21 21		21 42
West Hampstead ⊖	a	17 44		18 14			18 44		19 14			19 44		20 14								
Gospel Oak	a	17 50		18 20			18 50		19 20			19 50		20 20								
Highbury & Islington ⊖	a	18 01		18 31			19 01		19 31			20 01		20 31								
Stratford ⊖	a	18 19		18 49			19 19		19 49			20 19		20 49								
Wembley Central ⊖	a																					
Harrow & Wealdstone ⊖	a					18 37					19 36					20 37					21 46	
Watford Junction	a					18 44					19 43					20 44					21 53	
Hemel Hempstead	a																					
Berkhamsted	a																					
Tring	a																					
Leighton Buzzard	a																					
Bletchley	a																					
Milton Keynes Central [10]	a																					

		LO	LO	LO	SN [1]	LO	LO	LO
South Croydon	d							
East Croydon 🚌	d							
Selhurst [4]	d							
Thornton Heath	d							
Norbury	d							
Streatham Common [4]	d							
Balham [4] ⊖	d							
Wandsworth Common	d							
Clapham Junction [10]	a							
	d	21 31	21 46	22 01	22 15	22 21	22 46	23 16
Imperial Wharf	d	21 35	21 50	22 05	22 19	22 25	22 50	23 20
West Brompton ⊖	d	21 38	21 53	22 08	22 22	22 28	22 53	23 23
Kensington (Olympia) ⊖	d	21 41	21 56	22 11	22 26	22 31	22 56	23 26
Shepherd's Bush ⊖	d	21 43	21 58	22 13	22 29	22 33	22 58	23 28
Willesden Jn. High Level ⊖	a	21 51	22 08	22 23		22 41	23 08	23 36
West Hampstead ⊖	a							
Gospel Oak	a							
Highbury & Islington ⊖	a							
Stratford ⊖	a							
Wembley Central ⊖	a							
Harrow & Wealdstone ⊖	a				22 49			
Watford Junction	a				22 56			
Hemel Hempstead	a							
Berkhamsted	a							
Tring	a							
Leighton Buzzard	a							
Bletchley	a							
Milton Keynes Central [10]	a							

For other Norbury line connections, please see Table 170

For East Croydon connecting trains, please see Table 175

For other Stratford line connecting trains, please see Table 59

Table 176R

Mondays to Fridays

9 December to 16 May

Milton Keynes, Watford Junction/Stratford, Willesden Junction-Shepherds Bush, Kensington Olympia, West Brompton and Imperial Wharf-Clapham Junction, Balham and East Croydon

Network Diagram - see first Page of Table 176

Miles	Miles			SN MX 1	LO	SN 1	LO	LO	LO	SN 1		LO	LO	LO	SN 1	SN 1	LO	LO	SN	LO		LO	SN	LO	SN 1
0	—	Milton Keynes Central 10	d													07 01									08 13
3	—	Bletchley	d													07 05									08 17
9½	—	Leighton Buzzard	d													07 12									08 24
18	—	Tring	d													07 21									08 35
21¾	—	Berkhamsted	d													07 26									08 40
25¼	—	Hemel Hempstead	d													07 30									08 44
32¼	—	Watford Junction	d			05 54				06 53					07 23	07 38									08 52
36¾	—	Harrow & Wealdstone ⊖	d			06 00				06 59					07 30	07 44									08 58
40¼	—	Wembley Central ⊖	d			06 05				07 04					07 35	07 49									09 03
—	0	Stratford 7 ⊖	d					06 05	06 20			06 35	06 50	07 02			07 17	07 35		07 50		08 03		08 20	
—	4¾	Highbury & Islington ⊖	d					06 19	06 34			06 49	07 04	07 17			07 32	07 49		08 04		08 18		08 34	
—	7½	Gospel Oak	d					06 30	06 45			07 00	07 15	07 27			07 43	08 00		08 15		08 28		08 45	
—	9½	West Hampstead ⊖	d					06 36	06 51			07 06	07 21	07 33			07 49	08 06		08 21		08 34		08 51	
—	12	Willesden Jn. High Level ⊖	d		06 01		06 33	06 46	07 01			07 16	07 31	07 43			08 01	08 16		08 31		08 45		09 01	
44½	13½	**Shepherd's Bush** ⊖	d		06 07	06 21	06 39	06 53	07 08	07 20		07 24	07 39	07 50	07 54	08 05	08 09	08 23	08 34	08 38		08 53	09 07	09 09	09 19
45¾	—	**Kensington (Olympia)** ⊖	d		06 09	06 24	06 41	06 55	07 10	07 23		07 26	07 41	07 52	07 57	08 08	08 11	08 25	08 36	08 40		08 55	09 09	09 11	09 22
47¾	—	**West Brompton** ⊖	d	00 02	06 12	06 27	06 44	06 58	07 13	07 26		07 29	07 43	07 55	08 00	08 11	08 12	08 28	08 39	08 43		08 58	09 12	09 14	09 24
48½	—	**Imperial Wharf**	d	00 03	06 15	06 29	06 47	07 01	07 16	07 28		07 32	07 46	07 58	08 03	08 14	08 15	08 31	08 42	08 46		09 01	09 15	09 17	09 27
49½	—	Clapham Junction 10	a	00 07	06 22	06 34	06 53	07 08	07 23	07 33		07 40	07 54	08 05	08 07	08 18	08 23	08 38	08 46	08 54		09 08	09 20	09 24	09 31
—	—		d													08 36									09 34
50¾	—	Wandsworth Common	a													08 39									09 37
51½	—	Balham 4 ⊖	a													08 41									09 40
53¼	—	Streatham Common 4	a													08 48									09 44
54¼	—	Norbury	a													08 50									09 47
55½	—	Thornton Heath	a													08 53									09 50
56¼	—	Selhurst 4	a													08 56									09 52
57¼	—	East Croydon	a													09 04									09 56
—	—	South Croydon	a																						10 00

		LO	SN	LO	SN 1	LO		LO	SN 1	LO	LO	LO	LO	SN 1	LO	LO		LO	LO	SN 1	LO	LO	LO	LO	SN 1
Milton Keynes Central 10	d								09 13					10 13						11 13					12 13
Bletchley	d								09 17					10 17						11 17					12 17
Leighton Buzzard	d								09 24					10 24						11 24					12 24
Tring	d								09 34					10 34						11 34					12 33
Berkhamsted	d								09 39					10 39						11 39					12 38
Hemel Hempstead	d								09 43					10 43						11 43					12 42
Watford Junction	d				09 15				09 53					10 51						11 53					12 51
Harrow & Wealdstone ⊖	d				09 22				09 59					10 59						11 59					12 59
Wembley Central ⊖	d				09 27				10 05					11 03						12 04					13 03
Stratford 7 ⊖	d	08 35		08 50		09 05		09 20		09 35	09 50	10 05			10 35			11 05			11 35		12 05		
Highbury & Islington ⊖	d	08 49		09 04		09 19		09 34		09 49	10 04	10 20			10 49			11 19			11 49		12 19		
Gospel Oak	d	09 00		09 15		09 30		09 45		10 00	10 15	10 30			11 00			11 30			12 00		12 30		
West Hampstead ⊖	d	09 07		09 21		09 36		09 51		10 06	10 21	10 36			11 06			11 36			12 06		12 36		
Willesden Jn. High Level ⊖	d	09 16		09 31		09 46		10 01		10 17	10 32	10 46	11 01		11 16	11 31		11 46	12 01		12 16	12 31	12 46	13 01	
Shepherd's Bush ⊖	d	09 24	09 33	09 38	09 44	09 54		10 09	10 21	10 26	10 39	10 53	11 09	11 19	11 23	11 38		11 53	12 08	12 20	12 24	12 38	12 53	13 08	13 20
Kensington (Olympia) ⊖	d	09 26	09 35	09 40	09 47	09 56		10 12	10 24	10 29	10 41	10 55	11 11	11 21	11 25	11 40		11 55	12 10	12 23	12 27	12 40	12 55	13 10	13 22
West Brompton ⊖	d	09 28	09 37	09 43	09 50	09 58		10 14	10 27	10 30	10 43	10 57	11 13	11 24	11 27	11 42		11 57	12 12	12 26	12 29	12 42	12 57	13 12	13 25
Imperial Wharf	d	09 31	09 40	09 46	09 52	10 01		10 17	10 29	10 33	10 46	11 00	11 16	11 26	11 30	11 45		12 00	12 15	12 28	12 32	12 45	13 00	13 15	13 28
Clapham Junction 10	a	09 38	09 45	09 53	09 57	10 08		10 24	10 34	10 40	10 54	11 08	11 23	11 31	11 38	11 52		12 08	12 22	12 33	12 39	12 52	13 08	13 22	13 33
	d								10 34					11 34						12 35					13 35
Wandsworth Common	a								10 37					11 37						12 38					13 38
Balham 4 ⊖	a								10 40					11 40						12 41					13 40
Streatham Common 4	a								10 44					11 44						12 45					13 44
Norbury	a								10 47					11 46						12 47					13 47
Thornton Heath	a								10 50					11 49						12 50					13 50
Selhurst 4	a								10 52					11 52						12 53					13 52
East Croydon	a								10 56					11 56						12 57					13 56
South Croydon	a								11 00					12 01						13 01					14 01

For other Norbury line connections, please see Table 170

For East Croydon connecting trains, please see Table 175

For other Stratford line connecting trains, please see Table 59

Table 176R

Mondays to Fridays

9 December to 16 May

Milton Keynes, Watford Junction/Stratford, Willesden Junction-Shepherds Bush, Kensington Olympia, West Brompton and Imperial Wharf-Clapham Junction, Balham and East Croydon

Network Diagram - see first Page of Table 176

		LO	LO	LO	LO	SN	LO	LO	LO	LO	SN	LO	LO	LO	LO	SN	LO	SN	LO	LO	SN	LO	SN
						1					1					1							1
Milton Keynes Central 10	d					13 13					14 13					15 13							16 13
Bletchley	d					13 17					14 17					15 17							16 17
Leighton Buzzard	d					13 24					14 24					15 24							16 24
Tring	d					13 34					14 34					15 34							16 34
Berkhamsted	d					13 39					14 39					15 39							16 39
Hemel Hempstead	d					13 43					14 43					15 43							16 43
Watford Junction	d					13 52					14 52					15 52							16 52
Harrow & Wealdstone ⊖	d					13 59					14 59					15 59							16 59
Wembley Central ⊖	d					14 04					15 03					16 04							17 04
Stratford 7 ⊖	d	12 35		13 05			13 35		14 05			14 35		15 05			15 35		15 50			16 20	
Highbury & Islington ⊖	d	12 49		13 19			13 49		14 19			14 49		15 19			15 49		16 04			16 34	
Gospel Oak	d	13 00		13 30			14 00		14 30			15 00		15 30			16 00		16 15			16 45	
West Hampstead ⊖	d	13 06		13 36			14 06		14 36			15 06		15 36			16 06		16 21			16 51	
Willesden Jn. High Level ⊖	d	13 16	13 31	13 46	14 01		14 16	14 31	14 46	15 00		15 16	15 31	15 46	16 02		16 16		16 31	16 46		17 01	
Shepherd's Bush ⊖	d	13 24	13 38	13 53	14 08	14 20	14 24	14 38	14 53	15 07	15 22	15 25	15 38	15 53	16 07	16 20	16 24		16 38	16 53		17 08	17 20
Kensington (Olympia) ⊖	d	13 26	13 40	13 55	14 10	14 23	14 27	14 40	14 55	15 09	15 24	15 27	15 40	15 55	16 09	16 23	16 27	16 35	16 40	16 55	17 04	17 11	17 23
West Brompton ⊖	d	13 28	13 42	13 58	14 12	14 26	14 29	14 42	14 58	15 12	15 26	15 30	15 42	15 58	16 12	16 26	16 29	16 37	16 43	16 57	17 06	17 13	17 26
Imperial Wharf	d	13 31	13 45	14 01	14 15	14 29	14 32	14 45	15 01	15 15	15 29	15 33	15 45	16 01	16 15	16 28	16 32	16 40	16 46	17 00	17 09	17 16	17 29
Clapham Junction 10	a	13 39	13 52	14 08	14 22	14 33	14 39	14 52	15 08	15 22	15 33	15 39	15 52	16 08	16 21	16 33	16 38	16 44	16 53	17 07	17 13	17 23	17 33
	d					14 34					15 34					16 34							17 34
Wandsworth Common	a					14 37					15 37					16 37							17 37
Balham 4 ⊖	a					14 39					15 40					16 40							17 40
Streatham Common 4	a					14 43					15 44					16 44							17 44
Norbury	a					14 46					15 46					16 47							17 47
Thornton Heath	a					14 49					15 49					16 50							17 51
Selhurst 4	a					14 51					15 52					16 54							17 54
East Croydon	a					14 55					15 56					16 58							18 00
South Croydon	a					15 01					16 01					17 02							

		LO	LO	SN	LO	LO	SN	LO	LO	LO	LO	SN	LO	LO	LO	LO	SN	LO	LO	LO	LO	SN
							1					1					1					1
Milton Keynes Central 10	d						17 13					18 13					19 15					20 13
Bletchley	d						17 17					18 17					19 20					20 17
Leighton Buzzard	d						17 24					18 24					19 27					20 24
Tring	d						17 34					18 34					19 36					20 34
Berkhamsted	d						17 39					18 39					19 41					20 39
Hemel Hempstead	d						17 43					18 43					19 45					20 43
Watford Junction	d						17 51					18 52					19 54					20 51
Harrow & Wealdstone ⊖	d						17 59					18 59					20 02					20 59
Wembley Central ⊖	d						18 03					19 04					20 06					21 04
Stratford 7 ⊖	d	16 35	16 50		17 05	17 20		17 35	17 50	18 05	18 20		18 35	18 48	19 05			19 35		20 05		
Highbury & Islington ⊖	d	16 49	17 04		17 19	17 35		17 49	18 04	18 19	18 34		18 50	19 02	19 19			19 49		20 19		
Gospel Oak	d	17 03	17 17		17 30	17 45		18 02	18 16	18 30	18 45		19 01	19 13	19 30			20 00		20 30		
West Hampstead ⊖	d	17 09	17 23		17 36	17 51		18 08	18 22	18 36	18 51		19 06	19 19	19 36			20 06		20 36		
Willesden Jn. High Level ⊖	d	17 19	17 32		17 46	18 01		18 18	18 31	18 46	19 01		19 16	19 31	19 46	20 00		20 17	20 31	20 46	21 01	
Shepherd's Bush ⊖	d	17 26	17 39	17 47	17 54	18 09	18 20	18 24	18 39	18 53	19 08	19 20	19 24	19 38	19 53	20 06	20 22	20 26	20 38	20 53	21 07	21 20
Kensington (Olympia) ⊖	d	17 28	17 41	17 49	17 56	18 11	18 22	18 26	18 41	18 55	19 10	19 22	19 26	19 40	19 56	20 08	20 24	20 28	20 40	20 55	21 09	21 22
West Brompton ⊖	d	17 30	17 44	17 52	17 59	18 13	18 25	18 29	18 44	18 58	19 13	19 25	19 28	19 43	19 58	20 11	20 27	20 31	20 42	20 58	21 12	21 24
Imperial Wharf	d	17 33	17 47	17 55	18 02	18 16	18 28	18 32	18 47	19 01	19 16	19 27	19 31	19 46	20 01	20 14	20 29	20 34	20 45	21 01	21 15	21 27
Clapham Junction 10	a	17 40	17 53	17 59	18 08	18 24	18 33	18 39	18 53	19 08	19 23	19 32	19 37	19 53	20 09	20 21	20 34	20 40	20 52	21 08	21 22	21 32
	d			18 02			18 34					19 34										
Wandsworth Common	a			18 05			18 37					19 37										
Balham 4 ⊖	a			18 08			18 40					19 40										
Streatham Common 4	a			18 15			18 46					19 44										
Norbury	a			18 18			18 49					19 47										
Thornton Heath	a			18 21			18 52					19 50										
Selhurst 4	a			18 24			18 54					19 54										
East Croydon	a			18 32			19 02															
South Croydon	a			18 35																		

For other Norbury line connections, please see Table 170

For East Croydon connecting trains, please see Table 175

For other Stratford line connecting trains, please see Table 59

Table 176R

Mondays to Fridays

9 December to 16 May

Milton Keynes, Watford Junction/Stratford, Willesden Junction-Shepherds Bush, Kensington Olympia, West Brompton and Imperial Wharf-Clapham Junction, Balham and East Croydon

Network Diagram - see first Page of Table 176

		LO	LO	LO	LO	SN 1	LO		LO	SN 1	LO	SN 1	LO	SN 1
Milton Keynes Central 10	d					21 13						22 11		
Bletchley	d					21 17						22 15		
Leighton Buzzard	d					21 24						22 22		
Tring	d					21 34						22 34		
Berkhamsted	d					21 39						22 39		
Hemel Hempstead	d					21 43						22 44		
Watford Junction	d					21 52				22 27		22 54		23 29
Harrow & Wealdstone ⊖	d					21 59				22 33		23 01		23 35
Wembley Central ⊖	d													
Stratford 7 ⊖	d	20 35												
Highbury & Islington ⊖	d	20 49												
Gospel Oak	d	21 00												
West Hampstead ⊖	d	21 06												
Willesden Jn. High Level ⊖	d	21 16	21 31	21 46	22 01		22 16		22 31		23 01		23 31	
Shepherd's Bush ⊖	d	21 24	21 38	21 53	22 07	22 19	22 25		22 37	22 52	23 07	23 21	23 37	23 55
Kensington (Olympia) ⊖	d	21 26	21 40	21 55	22 09	22 21	22 27		22 39	22 54	23 09	23 23	23 39	23 57
West Brompton ⊖	d	21 28	21 42	21 58	22 12	22 24	22 29		22 42	22 57	23 12	23 27	23 42	00 02
Imperial Wharf	d	21 31	21 45	22 01	22 15	22 27	22 32		22 45	22 59	23 15	23 30	23 45	00 03
Clapham Junction 10	a	21 37	21 52	22 08	22 22	22 31	22 38		22 52	23 05	23 22	23 35	23 52	00 07
	d											23 38		
Wandsworth Common	a													
Balham 4 ⊖	a											23 42		
Streatham Common 4	a											23 46		
Norbury	a											23 49		
Thornton Heath	a											23 52		
Selhurst 4	a											23 54		
East Croydon	a											23 59		
South Croydon	a													

Saturdays

14 December to 17 May

		SN 1	LO	SN 1	LO	LO	LO	SN 1	LO	LO		LO	LO	SN 1	LO	LO	LO	LO	SN 1	LO		LO	LO	LO	SN 1
Milton Keynes Central 10	d													07 13					08 13						09 13
Bletchley	d													07 17					08 17						09 17
Leighton Buzzard	d													07 24					08 24						09 24
Tring	d													07 33					08 34						09 34
Berkhamsted	d													07 38					08 39						09 39
Hemel Hempstead	d													07 42					08 43						09 43
Watford Junction	d			05 52				06 55						07 51					08 52						09 52
Harrow & Wealdstone ⊖	d			05 58				07 01						07 58					08 59						09 59
Wembley Central ⊖	d							07 06						08 03					09 04						10 04
Stratford 7 ⊖	d					06 05			06 35			07 05			07 35		08 05			08 35			09 05		
Highbury & Islington ⊖	d					06 19			06 49			07 19			07 49		08 19			08 49			09 19		
Gospel Oak	d					06 30			07 00			07 30			08 00		08 30			09 01			09 30		
West Hampstead ⊖	d					06 36			07 06			07 36			08 06		08 36			09 07			09 36		
Willesden Jn. High Level ⊖	d		06 02		06 31	06 46	07 01		07 16	07 31		07 46	08 01		08 16	08 31	08 46	09 01		09 16		09 31	09 46	10 01	
Shepherd's Bush ⊖	d		06 08	06 20	06 37	06 53	07 08	07 22	07 26	07 38		07 53	08 08	08 19	08 24	08 38	08 53	09 07	09 20	09 24		09 37	09 53	10 08	10 20
Kensington (Olympia) ⊖	d		06 10	06 23	06 39	06 56	07 10	07 25	07 29	07 40		07 56	08 10	08 22	08 26	08 40	08 56	09 09	09 23	09 27		09 39	09 55	10 10	10 23
West Brompton ⊖	d	00 02	06 13	06 26	06 42	06 58	07 12	07 28	07 32	07 42		07 58	08 12	08 25	08 29	08 42	08 58	09 12	09 26	09 30		09 42	09 58	10 12	10 26
Imperial Wharf	d	00 03	06 16	06 28	06 45	07 01	07 15	07 30	07 35	07 45		08 01	08 15	08 27	08 32	08 45	09 01	09 15	09 28	09 33		09 45	10 01	10 15	10 28
Clapham Junction 10	a	00 07	06 22	06 33	06 52	07 08	07 22	07 35	07 41	07 52		08 08	08 22	08 33	08 38	08 52	09 08	09 22	09 33	09 39		09 52	10 08	10 22	10 33
	d			06 34				07 35						08 34					09 34						10 34
Wandsworth Common	a			06 37				07 38						08 37					09 37						10 37
Balham 4 ⊖	a			06 40				07 41						08 40					09 40						10 40
Streatham Common 4	a			06 44				07 45						08 44					09 44						10 44
Norbury	a			06 46				07 47						08 46					09 46						10 46
Thornton Heath	a			06 49				07 50						08 49					09 49						10 49
Selhurst 4	a			06 52				07 53						08 52					09 52						10 52
East Croydon	a			06 56				07 57						08 56					09 56						10 56
South Croydon	a			07 00				08 00						09 00					10 00						11 00

For other Norbury line connections, please see Table 170

For East Croydon connecting trains, please see Table 175

For other Stratford line connecting trains, please see Table 59

Table 176R

Saturdays

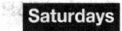

14 December to 17 May

Milton Keynes, Watford Junction/Stratford, Willesden Junction-Shepherds Bush, Kensington Olympia, West Brompton and Imperial Wharf-Clapham Junction, Balham and East Croydon

Network Diagram - see first Page of Table 176

		LO	LO	LO	LO	SN 1	LO	LO	LO	LO	SN 1	LO	LO	LO	LO	SN 1	LO	LO	LO	LO	SN 1	LO
Milton Keynes Central 10	d					10 13					11 13					12 13					13 13	
Bletchley	d					10 17					11 17					12 17					13 17	
Leighton Buzzard	d					10 24					11 24					12 24					13 24	
Tring	d					10 34					11 34					12 34					13 34	
Berkhamsted	d					10 39					11 39					12 39					13 39	
Hemel Hempstead	d					10 43					11 43					12 43					13 43	
Watford Junction	d					10 52					11 52					12 52					13 53	
Harrow & Wealdstone ⊖	d					10 59					11 58					12 58					13 59	
Wembley Central ⊖	d					11 04					12 03					13 03					14 04	
Stratford 7 ⊖	d	09 35		10 05			10 35		11 05			11 35		12 05			12 35		13 05			13 35
Highbury & Islington ⊖	d	09 49		10 19			10 49		11 19			11 49		12 19			12 49		13 19			13 49
Gospel Oak	d	10 00		10 30			11 00		11 30			12 00		12 30			13 00		13 30			14 00
West Hampstead ⊖	d	10 06		10 36			11 06		11 36			12 06		12 36			13 06		13 36			14 06
Willesden Jn. High Level ⊖	d	10 16	10 31	10 46	11 01		11 16	11 31	11 46	12 01		12 16	12 31	12 46	13 01		13 16	13 31	13 46	14 01		14 16
Shepherd's Bush ⊖	d	10 24	10 38	10 53	11 08	11 20	11 24	11 37	11 53	12 08	12 19	12 23	12 38	12 53	13 08	13 19	13 24	13 38	13 53	14 08	14 20	14 24
Kensington (Olympia) ⊖	d	10 27	10 40	10 56	11 10	11 23	11 27	11 39	11 56	12 10	12 22	12 26	12 40	12 56	13 10	13 22	13 26	13 40	13 56	14 10	14 23	14 27
West Brompton ⊖	d	10 30	10 42	10 58	11 12	11 26	11 30	11 42	11 58	12 12	12 25	12 29	12 42	12 58	13 12	13 25	13 29	13 42	13 58	14 12	14 26	14 30
Imperial Wharf	d	10 33	10 45	11 01	11 15	11 28	11 33	11 45	12 01	12 15	12 27	12 32	12 45	13 01	13 15	13 27	13 32	13 45	14 01	14 15	14 28	14 33
Clapham Junction 10	a	10 39	10 52	11 08	11 22	11 33	11 39	11 52	12 08	12 22	12 32	12 38	12 52	13 08	13 22	13 33	13 38	13 52	14 08	14 22	14 33	14 39
	d					11 34					12 33					13 34					14 34	
Wandsworth Common	a					11 37					12 36					13 37					14 37	
Balham 4 ⊖	a					11 40					12 40					13 40					14 40	
Streatham Common 4	a					11 44					12 44					13 44					14 44	
Norbury	a					11 46					12 46					13 46					14 46	
Thornton Heath	a					11 49					12 49					13 49					14 49	
Selhurst 4	a					11 52					12 52					13 52					14 52	
East Croydon	a					11 56					12 56					13 56					14 56	
South Croydon	a					12 00					13 00					14 00					15 00	

		LO	LO	LO	SN 1	LO	LO	LO	LO	SN 1	LO	LO	LO	LO	SN 1	LO	LO	LO	LO	SN 1	LO	LO	LO
Milton Keynes Central 10	d				14 13					15 13					16 13					17 13			
Bletchley	d				14 17					15 17					16 17					17 17			
Leighton Buzzard	d				14 24					15 24					16 24					17 24			
Tring	d				14 34					15 34					16 34					17 34			
Berkhamsted	d				14 39					15 39					16 39					17 39			
Hemel Hempstead	d				14 43					15 43					16 43					17 43			
Watford Junction	d				14 51					15 51					16 52					17 51			
Harrow & Wealdstone ⊖	d				14 59					15 59					16 59					17 59			
Wembley Central ⊖	d				15 03					16 03					17 03					18 03			
Stratford 7 ⊖	d		14 05			14 35		15 05			15 35		16 05			16 35		17 05			17 35		18 05
Highbury & Islington ⊖	d		14 19			14 49		15 19			15 49		16 19			16 49		17 19			17 49		18 19
Gospel Oak	d		14 30			15 00		15 30			16 00		16 30			17 00		17 30			18 00		18 30
West Hampstead ⊖	d		14 36			15 06		15 36			16 06		16 36			17 06		17 36			18 06		18 36
Willesden Jn. High Level ⊖	d	14 31	14 46	15 01		15 16	15 31	15 46	16 01		16 16	16 31	16 46	17 01		17 16	17 31	17 46	18 01		18 16	18 31	18 46
Shepherd's Bush ⊖	d	14 38	14 53	15 08	15 20	15 24	15 38	15 53	16 07	16 20	16 24	16 38	16 53	17 08	17 20	17 24	17 38	17 53	18 08	18 20	18 24	18 38	18 53
Kensington (Olympia) ⊖	d	14 40	14 56	15 10	15 22	15 26	15 40	15 56	16 09	16 22	16 26	16 40	16 56	17 10	17 22	17 26	17 40	17 56	18 10	18 22	18 26	18 40	18 56
West Brompton ⊖	d	14 42	14 58	15 12	15 25	15 29	15 42	15 58	16 12	16 25	16 29	16 42	16 58	17 12	17 25	17 29	17 42	17 58	18 13	18 25	18 29	18 42	18 58
Imperial Wharf	d	14 45	15 01	15 15	15 28	15 32	15 45	16 01	16 15	16 28	16 32	16 45	17 01	17 15	17 28	17 32	17 45	18 01	18 16	18 27	18 32	18 45	19 01
Clapham Junction 10	a	14 52	15 08	15 22	15 33	15 38	15 52	16 08	16 22	16 33	16 38	16 52	17 08	17 22	17 32	17 38	17 52	18 08	18 22	18 32	18 38	18 52	19 08
	d				15 34					16 34					17 34					18 34			
Wandsworth Common	a				15 37					16 37					17 37					18 37			
Balham 4 ⊖	a				15 40					16 40					17 40					18 40			
Streatham Common 4	a				15 44					16 44					17 44					18 44			
Norbury	a				15 46					16 46					17 46					18 47			
Thornton Heath	a				15 49					16 49					17 49					18 50			
Selhurst 4	a				15 52					16 52					17 52					18 52			
East Croydon	a				15 56					16 56					17 56					18 56			
South Croydon	a				16 00					17 00					18 00					19 00			

For other Norbury line connections, please see Table 170

For East Croydon connecting trains, please see Table 175

For other Stratford line connecting trains, please see Table 59

Table 176R

Saturdays

14 December to 17 May

Milton Keynes, Watford Junction/Stratford, Willesden Junction-Shepherds Bush, Kensington Olympia, West Brompton and Imperial Wharf-Clapham Junction, Balham and East Croydon

Network Diagram - see first Page of Table 176

		LO	SN 1	LO	LO	LO	SN 1	LO	SN 1	LO		LO	LO	SN 1	LO	LO	LO	LO	SN 1	LO		LO	LO	LO	SN 1
Milton Keynes Central 10	d		18 13						19 14																
Bletchley	d		18 17						19 18																
Leighton Buzzard	d		18 24						19 25																
Tring	d		18 34						19 34																
Berkhamsted	d		18 39						19 39																
Hemel Hempstead	d		18 43						19 43																
Watford Junction	d		18 51				19 31		19 51					20 43					21 44						22 48
Harrow & Wealdstone ⊖	d		18 59				19 37		20 01					20 49					21 50						22 55
Wembley Central ⊖	d		19 03				19 42																		
Stratford 7 ⊖	d			18 35		19 05				19 35			20 05			20 35									
Highbury & Islington ⊖	d			18 49		19 19				19 49			20 19			20 49									
Gospel Oak	d			19 00		19 30				20 00			20 30			21 00									
West Hampstead ⊖	d			19 06		19 36				20 06			20 36			21 06									
Willesden Jn. High Level ⊖	d	19 01		19 16	19 31	19 46		20 01		20 16		20 31	20 46		21 01	21 16	21 31	21 46		22 01		22 16	22 31	23 01	
Shepherd's Bush ⊖	d	19 08	19 20	19 24	19 37	19 53	19 58	20 08	20 20	20 24		20 38	20 53	21 09	21 12	21 23	21 38	21 53	22 10	22 12		22 23	22 38	23 08	23 14
Kensington (Olympia) ⊖	d	19 10	19 22	19 26	19 39	19 56	20 01	20 10	20 23	20 27		20 40	20 56	21 11	21 14	21 25	21 40	21 55	22 12	22 14		22 25	22 40	23 10	23 16
West Brompton ⊖	d	19 12	19 25	19 29	19 42	19 58	20 03	20 12	20 26	20 29		20 42	20 58	21 14	21 17	21 27	21 42	21 57	22 14	22 17		22 27	22 42	23 12	23 19
Imperial Wharf	d	19 15	19 27	19 32	19 45	20 01	20 06	20 15	20 28	20 32		20 45	21 01	21 16	21 20	21 30	21 45	22 00	22 17	22 20		22 30	22 45	23 15	23 21
Clapham Junction 10	a	19 22	19 32	19 38	19 52	20 08	20 10	20 22	20 33	20 39		20 52	21 08	21 21	21 26	21 38	21 52	22 07	22 21	22 26		22 37	22 52	23 22	23 26
	d		19 34						20 34																23 35
Wandsworth Common	a		19 37						20 37																
Balham 4 ⊖	a		19 39						20 40																23 39
Streatham Common 4	a		19 45						20 44																23 44
Norbury	a		19 48						20 47																23 46
Thornton Heath	a		19 51						20 50																23 49
Selhurst 4	a		19 53						20 52																23 52
East Croydon	a		19 57						20 59																
South Croydon	a																								

		LO	SN 1
Milton Keynes Central 10	d		
Bletchley	d		
Leighton Buzzard	d		
Tring	d		
Berkhamsted	d		
Hemel Hempstead	d		
Watford Junction	d		23 25
Harrow & Wealdstone ⊖	d		23 31
Wembley Central ⊖	d		
Stratford 7 ⊖	d		
Highbury & Islington ⊖	d		
Gospel Oak	d		
West Hampstead ⊖	d		
Willesden Jn. High Level ⊖	d	23 31	
Shepherd's Bush ⊖	d	23 37	23 51
Kensington (Olympia) ⊖	d	23 39	23 53
West Brompton ⊖	d	23 42	23 55
Imperial Wharf	d	23 45	23 58
Clapham Junction 10	a	23 51	00 02
	d		
Wandsworth Common	a		
Balham 4 ⊖	a		
Streatham Common 4	a		
Norbury	a		
Thornton Heath	a		
Selhurst 4	a		
East Croydon	a		
South Croydon	a		

For other Norbury line connections, please see Table 170

For East Croydon connecting trains, please see Table 175

For other Stratford line connecting trains, please see Table 59

Table 176R

Sundays

8 December to 11 May

Milton Keynes, Watford Junction/Stratford, Willesden Junction-Shepherds Bush, Kensington Olympia, West Brompton and Imperial Wharf-Clapham Junction, Balham and East Croydon

Network Diagram - see first Page of Table 176

		SN 1	LO	SN 1	LO	LO		SN 1	LO	LO	LO	LO	SN 1	LO	LO	LO		LO	SN 1	LO	LO	LO	LO	SN 1	LO
Milton Keynes Central 10	d																								
Bletchley	d																								
Leighton Buzzard	d																								
Tring	d																								
Berkhamsted	d																								
Hemel Hempstead	d																								
Watford Junction	d							09 17					10 17						11 22					12 22	
Harrow & Wealdstone ⊖	d							09 23					10 23						11 28					12 29	
Wembley Central ⊖	d																								
Stratford 7 ⊖	d															10 35				11 05		11 35			12 05
Highbury & Islington ⊖	d															10 49				11 19		11 49			12 19
Gospel Oak	d															11 00				11 30		12 00			12 30
West Hampstead ⊖	d															11 06				11 36		12 06			12 36
Willesden Jn. High Level ⊖	d		08 32		09 02	09 32			09 48	10 02	10 16	10 32		10 46	11 02	11 16		11 32		11 46	12 02	12 16	12 32		12 46
Shepherd's Bush ⊖	d	07 47	08 39	08 51	09 08	09 39		09 45	09 54	10 08	10 24	10 38	10 44	10 54	11 10	11 23		11 39	11 48	11 53	12 09	12 23	12 39	12 48	12 53
Kensington (Olympia) ⊖	d	07 49	08 41	08 53	09 10	09 41		09 47	09 56	10 10	10 26	10 40	10 47	10 56	11 12	11 26		11 41	11 51	11 56	12 11	12 26	12 41	12 51	12 56
West Brompton ⊖	d	07 51	08 43	08 56	09 12	09 43		09 50	09 57	10 13	10 27	10 43	10 49	10 57	11 14	11 28		11 43	11 53	11 57	12 13	12 28	12 43	12 53	12 57
Imperial Wharf	d	07 54	08 46	08 59	09 15	09 46		09 53	10 00	10 16	10 30	10 46	10 52	11 00	11 17	11 31		11 46	11 56	12 00	12 16	12 31	12 46	12 56	13 00
Clapham Junction 10	a	07 58	08 53	09 03	09 23	09 54		09 58	10 08	10 26	10 37	10 54	10 56	11 07	11 26	11 40		11 54	12 00	12 08	12 23	12 38	12 53	13 00	13 08
	d																								
Wandsworth Common	a																								
Balham 4 ⊖	a																								
Streatham Common 4	a																								
Norbury	a																								
Thornton Heath	a																								
Selhurst 4	a																								
East Croydon	a																								
South Croydon	a																								

		LO		LO	LO	SN 1	LO	LO	LO	LO	SN 1	LO		LO	LO	LO	SN 1	LO	LO	LO	LO	SN 1		LO	LO
Milton Keynes Central 10	d																								
Bletchley	d																								
Leighton Buzzard	d																								
Tring	d																								
Berkhamsted	d																								
Hemel Hempstead	d																								
Watford Junction	d					13 22					14 22						15 22					16 22			
Harrow & Wealdstone ⊖	d					13 28					14 28						15 28					16 28			
Wembley Central ⊖	d																								
Stratford 7 ⊖	d			12 35			13 05		13 35			14 05			14 35			15 05		15 35				16 05	
Highbury & Islington ⊖	d			12 49			13 19		13 49			14 19			14 49			15 19		15 49				16 19	
Gospel Oak	d			13 00			13 30		14 00			14 30			15 00			15 30		16 00				16 30	
West Hampstead ⊖	d			13 06			13 36		14 06			14 36			15 06			15 36		16 06				16 36	
Willesden Jn. High Level ⊖	d	13 02		13 16	13 32		13 46	14 02	14 16	14 32		14 46		15 02	15 16	15 32		15 46	16 02	16 16	16 32			16 46	17 02
Shepherd's Bush ⊖	d	13 09		13 23	13 39	13 48	13 53	14 09	14 23	14 39	14 48	14 53		15 09	15 23	15 39	15 48	15 53	16 09	16 23	16 39	16 48		16 53	17 09
Kensington (Olympia) ⊖	d	13 11		13 26	13 41	13 51	13 56	14 11	14 26	14 41	14 51	14 56		15 11	15 26	15 41	15 51	15 56	16 11	16 26	16 41	16 50		16 56	17 11
West Brompton ⊖	d	13 13		13 28	13 43	13 53	13 57	14 13	14 28	14 43	14 53	14 57		15 13	15 28	15 43	15 53	15 57	16 13	16 28	16 43	16 53		16 57	17 13
Imperial Wharf	d	13 16		13 31	13 46	13 56	14 00	14 16	14 31	14 46	14 56	15 00		15 16	15 31	15 46	15 56	16 00	16 16	16 31	16 46	16 56		17 00	17 16
Clapham Junction 10	a	13 23		13 38	13 53	14 00	14 08	14 23	14 38	14 53	15 00	15 08		15 22	15 38	15 53	16 00	16 08	16 23	16 38	16 53	17 00		17 08	17 23
	d																								
Wandsworth Common	a																								
Balham 4 ⊖	a																								
Streatham Common 4	a																								
Norbury	a																								
Thornton Heath	a																								
Selhurst 4	a																								
East Croydon	a																								
South Croydon	a																								

For other Norbury line connections, please see Table 170

For East Croydon connecting trains, please see Table 175

For other Stratford line connecting trains, please see Table 59

Table 176R

Sundays

8 December to 11 May

Milton Keynes, Watford Junction/Stratford, Willesden Junction-Shepherds Bush, Kensington Olympia, West Brompton and Imperial Wharf-Clapham Junction, Balham and East Croydon

Network Diagram - see first Page of Table 176

		LO	LO	SN		LO	LO	LO	LO	SN	LO	LO	LO	LO		SN	LO	LO	LO	LO	SN	LO	LO	LO
				1						1						1					1			
Milton Keynes Central 10	d																							
Bletchley	d																							
Leighton Buzzard	d																							
Tring	d																							
Berkhamsted	d																							
Hemel Hempstead	d																							
Watford Junction	d			17 22						18 22						19 22					20 22			
Harrow & Wealdstone ⊖	d			17 28						18 28						19 28					20 28			
Wembley Central ⊖	d																							
Stratford 7 ⊖	d	16 35				17 05		17 35			18 05		18 35				19 05		19 35			20 05		20 35
Highbury & Islington ⊖	d	16 49				17 19		17 49			18 19		18 49				19 19		19 49			20 19		20 49
Gospel Oak	d	17 00				17 30		18 00			18 30		19 00				19 30		20 00			20 30		21 00
West Hampstead ⊖	d	17 06				17 36		18 06			18 36		19 06				19 36		20 06			20 36		21 06
Willesden Jn. High Level ⊖	d	17 16	17 32			17 46	18 02	18 16	18 32		18 46	19 02	19 16	19 32			19 46	20 02	20 16	20 32		20 46	21 02	21 16
Shepherd's Bush ⊖	d	17 23	17 39	17 48		17 53	18 09	18 23	18 39	18 48	18 53	19 09	19 23	19 39		19 48	19 53	20 09	20 23	20 39	20 48	20 53	21 08	21 23
Kensington (Olympia) ⊖	d	17 26	17 41	17 50		17 56	18 11	18 26	18 41	18 50	18 56	19 11	19 26	19 41		19 51	19 56	20 11	20 26	20 41	20 50	20 56	21 10	21 26
West Brompton ⊖	d	17 28	17 43	17 53		17 57	18 13	18 28	18 43	18 53	18 57	19 13	19 28	19 43		19 53	19 57	20 13	20 28	20 43	20 53	20 58	21 12	21 28
Imperial Wharf	d	17 31	17 46	17 56		18 00	18 16	18 31	18 46	18 55	19 00	19 16	19 31	19 46		19 56	20 00	20 16	20 31	20 46	20 56	21 01	21 15	21 31
Clapham Junction 10	a	17 38	17 53	18 00		18 08	18 23	18 38	18 53	19 00	19 08	19 23	19 38	19 53		20 00	20 08	20 23	20 38	20 53	21 00	21 08	21 23	21 38
	d																							
Wandsworth Common	a																							
Balham 4 ⊖	a																							
Streatham Common 4	a																							
Norbury	a																							
Thornton Heath	a																							
Selhurst 4	a																							
East Croydon	a																							
South Croydon	a																							

		LO	SN	LO	LO	LO	SN	LO	LO	SN
			1				1			1
Milton Keynes Central 10	d									
Bletchley	d									
Leighton Buzzard	d									
Tring	d									
Berkhamsted	d									
Hemel Hempstead	d									
Watford Junction	d		21 17				22 17			23 17
Harrow & Wealdstone ⊖	d		21 23				22 23			23 23
Wembley Central ⊖	d									
Stratford 7 ⊖	d			21 05						
Highbury & Islington ⊖	d			21 19						
Gospel Oak	d			21 30						
West Hampstead ⊖	d			21 36						
Willesden Jn. High Level ⊖	d	21 32		21 46	22 02	22 32		22 46	23 18	
Shepherd's Bush ⊖	d	21 39	21 45	21 53	22 08	22 38	22 46	22 53	23 23	23 42
Kensington (Olympia) ⊖	d	21 41	21 48	21 56	22 10	22 40	22 48	22 55	23 25	23 44
West Brompton ⊖	d	21 44	21 50	21 58	22 12	22 43	22 51	22 57	23 27	23 47
Imperial Wharf	d	21 47	21 53	22 01	22 15	22 46	22 53	23 00	23 30	23 49
Clapham Junction 10	a	21 53	21 58	22 08	22 26	22 53	22 58	23 09	23 39	23 54
	d									23 54
Wandsworth Common	a									
Balham 4 ⊖	a									
Streatham Common 4	a									
Norbury	a									
Thornton Heath	a									
Selhurst 4	a									
East Croydon	a									00 15
South Croydon	a									

For other Norbury line connections, please see Table 170

For East Croydon connecting trains, please see Table 175

For other Stratford line connecting trains, please see Table 59

Table 177

Mondays to Fridays

9 December to 16 May

London Bridge-New Cross Gate,Brockley, Honor Oak Park, Forest Hill, Sydenham, Crystal Palace, Penge West, Anerley-Norwood Junction and Croydon

Network Diagram - see first Page of Table 173

Miles	Miles	Miles	Miles			SN MO A	SN MX A	LO MO B	LO MX B	SN MX C	LO MX D	SN MX E	SN MX		SN F	LO	LO	LO	SN E	LO	LO	SN G	LO	LO	
0	—	—	0	London Bridge 4 ⊖	d							00 06	00 36		05 36				06 06			06 18			
—	—	0	—	Highbury & Islington	d													05 35			05 55				
—	—	0½	—	Canonbury	d													05 37			05 57				
—	0	1½	—	Dalston Junction	d													05 40			06 00		06 10		
—	0½	2	—	Haggerston	d													05 41			06 01		06 11		
—	1	2½	—	Hoxton	d													05 43			06 03		06 13		
—	1¾	3¼	—	Shoreditch High Street	d													05 46			06 06		06 16		
—	2¼	3¾	—	Whitechapel	d													05 48			06 08		06 18		
—	3	4½	—	Shadwell	d													05 50			06 10		06 20		
—	3½	5	—	Wapping	d													05 52			06 12		06 22		
—	4	5½	—	Rotherhithe	d													05 54			06 14		06 24		
—	4¼	5¾	—	Canada Water	d													05 56			06 16		06 26		
—	4½	6	—	Surrey Quays	d													05 57			06 17		06 27		
2¾	5¾	7¼	2¾	New Cross Gate 4	d						00 02	00 11	00 41		05 41	05 47	05 52	06 02	06 11	06 17	06 22	06 25	06 32	06 37	
3¾	6½	8	3¾	**Brockley**	d						00 04	00 14	00 44		05 44	05 49	05 54	06 04	06 14	06 19	06 24	06 27	06 34	06 39	
4¾	7½	9	4¾	**Honor Oak Park**	d					00 01	00 07	00 17	00 47		05 47	05 52	05 57	06 07	06 17	06 22	06 27	06 30	06 37	06 42	
5½	8½	10	5½	**Forest Hill 4**	d					00 04	00 10	00 19	00 49		05 49	05 55	06 00	06 10	06 19	06 25	06 30	06 33	06 40	06 45	
6¼	9¼	10¾	6¼	**Sydenham**	d			00 01	00 02	00 06	00 12	00 22	00 52		05 52	05 57	06 02	06 12	06 22	06 27	06 32	06 35	06 42	06 47	
—	—	12	7½	**Crystal Palace 4**	a				00 07	00 10							06 07				06 37	06 39		06 52	
7	10	—	—	**Penge West**	d			00 03			00 15	00 24	00 54		05 54	06 00		06 15	06 24	06 30			06 45		
7½	10½	—	—	**Anerley**	d		00 01	00 05			00 17	00 26	00 56		05 56	06 02		06 17	06 26	06 32			06 47		
8¾	11½	—	—	Norwood Junction 2	a		00 04	00 08			00 20	00 29	00 59		06 00	06 05		06 18	06 29	06 35			06 50		
—	—	—	—	Norwood Junction	d			00 08			00 20				06 00	06 05		06 20		06 35			06 50		
—	13¼	—	—	West Croydon 4	a			00 14			00 27				06 05	06 14		06 30		06 41			07 00		
—	—	—	—	Norwood Junction	d	00 03	00 05					00 30	01 00						06 30						
10¼	—	—	—	East Croydon	a	00 07	00 08					00 37	01 03						06 33						
13¼	—	—	—	Purley	a	00 17	00 18					00 47							06 44						

		SN E	LO	LO	SN G	SN E	LO	LO	SN E	LO		LO	SN G	LO	LO	SN E	LO	LO	SN G	LO		LO	SN E	LO	LO
London Bridge 4 ⊖	d	06 36			06 49	06 54			07 06				07 21			07 36			07 53				08 06		
Highbury & Islington	d			06 25				06 40				06 55			07 10			07 25				07 40			07 55
Canonbury	d			06 27				06 42				06 57			07 12			07 27				07 42			07 57
Dalston Junction	d			06 30			06 40	06 45		06 55		07 00		07 10	07 15		07 25	07 30		07 40		07 45		07 55	08 00
Haggerston	d			06 31			06 41	06 46		06 56		07 01		07 11	07 16		07 26	07 31		07 41		07 46		07 56	08 01
Hoxton	d			06 33			06 43	06 48		06 58		07 03		07 13	07 18		07 28	07 33		07 43		07 48		07 58	08 03
Shoreditch High Street	d			06 36			06 46	06 51		07 01		07 06		07 16	07 21		07 31	07 36		07 46		07 51		08 01	08 06
Whitechapel	d			06 38			06 48	06 53		07 03		07 08		07 18	07 23		07 33	07 38		07 48		07 53		08 03	08 08
Shadwell	d			06 40			06 50	06 55		07 05		07 10		07 20	07 25		07 35	07 40		07 50		07 55		08 05	08 10
Wapping	d			06 42			06 52	06 57		07 07		07 12		07 22	07 27		07 37	07 42		07 52		07 57		08 07	08 12
Rotherhithe	d			06 44			06 54	06 59		07 09		07 14		07 24	07 29		07 39	07 44		07 54		07 59		08 09	08 14
Canada Water	d			06 46			06 56	07 01		07 11		07 16		07 26	07 31		07 41	07 46		07 56		08 01		08 11	08 16
Surrey Quays	d			06 47			06 57	07 02		07 12		07 17		07 27	07 32		07 42	07 47		07 57		08 02		08 12	08 17
New Cross Gate 4	d	06 41	06 47	06 52	06 56	06 59	07 02	07 07	07 11	07 17		07 22	07 26	07 32	07 37	07 41	07 47	07 52	07 58	08 02		08 07	08 11	08 17	08 22
Brockley	d	06 44	06 49	06 54	06 59	07 02	07 04	07 09	07 14	07 19		07 24	07 29	07 34	07 39	07 44	07 49	07 54	08 01	08 04		08 09	08 14	08 19	08 24
Honor Oak Park	d	06 47	06 52	06 57	07 02	07 05	07 07	07 12	07 17	07 22		07 27	07 32	07 37	07 42	07 47	07 52	07 57	08 04	08 07		08 12	08 17	08 22	08 27
Forest Hill 4	d	06 49	06 55	07 00	07 04	07 07	07 10	07 15	07 19	07 25		07 30	07 34	07 40	07 45	07 49	07 55	08 00	08 06	08 10		08 15	08 19	08 25	08 30
Sydenham	d	06 52	06 57	07 02	07 07	07 10	07 12	07 17	07 22	07 27		07 32	07 37	07 42	07 47	07 52	07 57	08 02	08 09	08 12		08 17	08 22	08 27	08 32
Crystal Palace 4	a			07 07	07 10			07 22				07 37	07 40		07 52			08 07	08 12			08 22			08 37
Penge West	d	06 54	07 00			07 12	07 15		07 24	07 30				07 45		07 54	08 00			08 15			08 24	08 30	
Anerley	d	06 56	07 02			07 14	07 17		07 26	07 32				07 47		07 56	08 02			08 17			08 26	08 32	
Norwood Junction 2	a	06 59	07 05			07 17	07 20		07 30	07 35				07 50		07 59	08 05			08 20			08 29	08 35	
Norwood Junction	d		07 05				07 20			07 35				07 50			08 05			08 20				08 35	
West Croydon 4	a		07 10				07 30			07 41				08 00			08 11			08 30				08 41	
Norwood Junction	d	07 00				07 18			07 31							08 00							08 30		
East Croydon	a	07 03				07 21			07 37							08 03							08 33		
Purley	a	07 13				07 32			07 47							08 13							08 43		

A From London Bridge to Caterham
B From Highbury and Islington Ell
C From London Bridge to London Victoria
D From Dalston Junction Stn Ell
E To Caterham
F To Sutton (Surrey)
G To London Victoria

For Fast trains between London Bridge & New Cross Gate to Norwood Jn & East Croydon, see Table 175

For full service between Highbury & Islington and Surrey Quays, please see Table 178

For Sutton connections at West Croydon, please see table 172

Table 177

Mondays to Fridays

9 December to 16 May

London Bridge-New Cross Gate,Brockley, Honor Oak Park, Forest Hill, Sydenham, Crystal Palace, Penge West, Anerley-Norwood Junction and Croydon

Network Diagram - see first Page of Table 173

		SN A		LO	LO	SN B	LO	LO	SN A	LO	LO	SN B		LO	LO	SN A	LO	LO	SN B	LO	LO	SN A		LO	LO
London Bridge ④ ⊖	d	08 20				08 34			08 51			09 06				09 22			09 36			09 52			
Highbury & Islington	d				08 10			08 25			08 40				08 55			09 10			09 25				09 40
Canonbury	d				08 12			08 27			08 42				08 57			09 12			09 27				09 42
Dalston Junction	d			08 10	08 15		08 25	08 30		08 40	08 45			08 55	09 00		09 10	09 15		09 25	09 30			09 40	09 45
Haggerston	d			08 11	08 16		08 26	08 31		08 41	08 46			08 56	09 01		09 11	09 16		09 26	09 31			09 41	09 46
Hoxton	d			08 13	08 18		08 28	08 33		08 43	08 48			08 58	09 03		09 13	09 18		09 28	09 33			09 43	09 48
Shoreditch High Street	d			08 16	08 21		08 31	08 36		08 46	08 51			09 01	09 06		09 16	09 21		09 31	09 36			09 46	09 51
Whitechapel	d			08 18	08 23		08 33	08 38		08 48	08 53			09 03	09 08		09 18	09 23		09 33	09 38			09 48	09 53
Shadwell	d			08 20	08 25		08 35	08 40		08 50	08 55			09 05	09 10		09 20	09 25		09 35	09 40			09 50	09 55
Wapping	d			08 22	08 27		08 37	08 42		08 52	08 57			09 07	09 12		09 22	09 27		09 37	09 42			09 52	09 57
Rotherhithe	d			08 24	08 29		08 39	08 44		08 54	08 59			09 09	09 14		09 24	09 29		09 39	09 44			09 54	09 59
Canada Water	d			08 26	08 31		08 41	08 46		08 56	09 01			09 11	09 16		09 26	09 31		09 41	09 46			09 56	10 01
Surrey Quays	d			08 27	08 32		08 42	08 47		08 57	09 02			09 12	09 17		09 27	09 32		09 42	09 47			09 57	10 02
New Cross Gate ④	d	08 26		08 32	08 37	08 41	08 47	08 52	08 57	09 02	09 07	09 12		09 17	09 22	09 28	09 32	09 37	09 41	09 47	09 52	09 57		10 02	10 07
Brockley	d	08 29		08 34	08 39	08 44	08 49	08 54	09 00	09 04	09 09	09 14		09 19	09 24	09 30	09 34	09 39	09 44	09 49	09 54	10 00		10 04	10 09
Honor Oak Park	d	08 32		08 37	08 42	08 47	08 52	08 57	09 03	09 07	09 12	09 17		09 22	09 27	09 33	09 37	09 42	09 47	09 52	09 57	10 03		10 07	10 12
Forest Hill ④	d	08 34		08 40	08 45	08 49	08 55	09 00	09 05	09 10	09 15	09 20		09 25	09 30	09 36	09 40	09 45	09 49	09 55	10 00	10 05		10 10	10 15
Sydenham	d	08 37		08 42	08 47	08 52	08 57	09 02	09 08	09 12	09 17	09 22		09 27	09 32	09 38	09 42	09 47	09 52	09 57	10 02	10 08		10 12	10 17
Crystal Palace ④	a	08 40			08 52			09 07	09 11		09 22				09 37	09 42		09 52			10 07	10 11			10 22
Penge West	d			08 45		08 54	09 00			09 15		09 25		09 30			09 45		09 54	10 00				10 15	
Anerley	d			08 47		08 56	09 02			09 17		09 27		09 32			09 47		09 56	10 02				10 17	
Norwood Junction ②	a			08 50		08 59	09 05			09 20		09 30		09 35			09 50		09 59	10 05				10 20	
Norwood Junction	d			08 50			09 05			09 20				09 35			09 50			10 05				10 20	
West Croydon ④ 🚋	a			09 00			09 11			09 30				09 41			10 00			10 11				10 30	
Norwood Junction	d					09 00						09 30							10 00						
East Croydon 🚋	a					09 06						09 33							10 03						
Purley	a					09 16						09 43							10 13						

		SN B	LO	LO	SN A	LO	LO	SN B		LO	LO	SN A	LO	LO	SN B	LO	LO	SN A		LO	LO	SN B	LO	LO	SN A
London Bridge ④ ⊖	d	10 06			10 22			10 36				10 52			11 06			11 22				11 36			11 52
Highbury & Islington	d			09 55			10 10				10 25			10 40			10 55				11 10			11 25	
Canonbury	d			09 57			10 12				10 27			10 42			10 57				11 12			11 27	
Dalston Junction	d		09 55	10 00		10 10	10 15			10 25	10 30		10 40	10 45		10 55	11 00			11 10	11 15		11 25	11 30	
Haggerston	d		09 56	10 01		10 11	10 16			10 26	10 31		10 41	10 46		10 56	11 01			11 11	11 16		11 26	11 31	
Hoxton	d		09 58	10 03		10 13	10 18			10 28	10 33		10 43	10 48		10 58	11 03			11 13	11 18		11 28	11 33	
Shoreditch High Street	d		10 01	10 06		10 16	10 21			10 31	10 36		10 46	10 51		11 01	11 06			11 16	11 21		11 31	11 36	
Whitechapel	d		10 03	10 08		10 18	10 23			10 33	10 38		10 48	10 53		11 03	11 08			11 18	11 23		11 33	11 38	
Shadwell	d		10 05	10 10		10 20	10 25			10 35	10 40		10 50	10 55		11 05	11 10			11 20	11 25		11 35	11 40	
Wapping	d		10 07	10 12		10 22	10 27			10 37	10 42		10 52	10 57		11 07	11 12			11 22	11 27		11 37	11 42	
Rotherhithe	d		10 09	10 14		10 24	10 29			10 39	10 44		10 54	10 59		11 09	11 14			11 24	11 29		11 39	11 44	
Canada Water	d		10 11	10 16		10 26	10 31			10 41	10 46		10 56	11 01		11 11	11 16			11 26	11 31		11 41	11 46	
Surrey Quays	d		10 12	10 17		10 27	10 32			10 42	10 47		10 57	11 02		11 12	11 17			11 27	11 32		11 42	11 47	
New Cross Gate ④	d	10 11	10 17	10 22	10 27	10 32	10 37	10 41		10 47	10 52	10 57	11 02	11 07	11 11	11 17	11 22	11 27		11 32	11 37	11 41	11 47	11 52	11 57
Brockley	d	10 14	10 19	10 24	10 30	10 34	10 39	10 44		10 49	10 54	11 00	11 04	11 09	11 14	11 19	11 24	11 30		11 34	11 39	11 44	11 49	11 54	12 00
Honor Oak Park	d	10 17	10 22	10 27	10 33	10 37	10 42	10 47		10 52	10 57	11 03	11 07	11 12	11 17	11 22	11 27	11 33		11 37	11 42	11 47	11 52	11 57	12 03
Forest Hill ④	d	10 19	10 25	10 30	10 35	10 40	10 45	10 49		10 55	11 00	11 05	11 10	11 15	11 19	11 25	11 30	11 35		11 40	11 45	11 49	11 55	12 00	12 05
Sydenham	d	10 22	10 27	10 32	10 38	10 42	10 47	10 52		10 57	11 02	11 08	11 12	11 17	11 22	11 27	11 32	11 38		11 42	11 47	11 52	11 57	12 02	12 08
Crystal Palace ④	a			10 37	10 41		10 52				11 07	11 11		11 22			11 37	11 41			11 52			12 07	12 11
Penge West	d	10 24	10 30			10 45		10 54		11 00			11 15		11 24	11 30				11 45		11 54	12 00		
Anerley	d	10 26	10 32			10 47		10 56		11 02			11 17		11 26	11 32				11 47		11 56	12 02		
Norwood Junction ②	a	10 29	10 35			10 50		10 59		11 05			11 20		11 29	11 35				11 50		11 59	12 05		
Norwood Junction	d		10 35			10 50				11 05			11 20			11 35				11 50			12 05		
West Croydon ④ 🚋	a		10 41			11 00				11 11			11 30			11 41				12 00			12 11		
Norwood Junction	d	10 30						11 00							11 30							12 00			
East Croydon 🚋	a	10 33						11 03							11 33							12 03			
Purley	a	10 43						11 13							11 43							12 13			

A To London Victoria

B To Caterham

For Fast trains between London Bridge & New Cross Gate to Norwood Jn & East Croydon, see Table 175

For full service between Highbury & Islington and Surrey Quays, please see Table 178

For Sutton connections at West Croydon, please see table 172

Table 177

Mondays to Fridays

9 December to 16 May

London Bridge-New Cross Gate,Brockley, Honor Oak Park, Forest Hill, Sydenham, Crystal Palace, Penge West, Anerley-Norwood Junction and Croydon

Network Diagram - see first Page of Table 173

Station		LO	LO	SN A	LO	LO	SN B	LO	LO	SN A	LO	LO	SN B	LO		LO	SN A	LO	LO	SN B	LO	LO	SN A
London Bridge 4 ⊖	d			12 06			12 22			12 36			12 52				15 06			15 22			15 36
Highbury & Islington	d		11 40			11 55			12 10			12 25				14 40			14 55			15 10	
Canonbury	d		11 42			11 57			12 12			12 27				14 42			14 57			15 12	
Dalston Junction	d	11 40	11 45		11 55	12 00		12 10	12 15		12 25	12 30		12 40		14 45		14 55	15 00		15 10	15 15	
Haggerston	d	11 41	11 46		11 56	12 01		12 11	12 16		12 26	12 31		12 41		14 46		14 56	15 01		15 11	15 16	
Hoxton	d	11 43	11 48		11 58	12 03		12 13	12 18		12 28	12 33		12 43		14 48		14 58	15 03		15 13	15 18	
Shoreditch High Street	d	11 46	11 51		12 01	12 06		12 16	12 21		12 31	12 36		12 46		14 51		15 01	15 06		15 16	15 21	
Whitechapel	d	11 48	11 53		12 03	12 08		12 18	12 23		12 33	12 38		12 48		14 53		15 03	15 08		15 18	15 23	
Shadwell	d	11 50	11 55		12 05	12 10		12 20	12 25		12 35	12 40		12 50		14 55		15 05	15 10		15 20	15 25	
Wapping	d	11 52	11 57		12 07	12 12		12 22	12 27		12 37	12 42		12 52	and at	14 57		15 07	15 12		15 22	15 27	
Rotherhithe	d	11 54	11 59		12 09	12 14		12 24	12 29		12 39	12 44		12 54	the same	14 59		15 09	15 14		15 24	15 29	
Canada Water	d	11 56	12 01		12 11	12 16		12 26	12 31		12 41	12 46		12 56	minutes	15 01		15 11	15 16		15 26	15 31	
Surrey Quays	d	11 57	12 02		12 12	12 17		12 27	12 32		12 42	12 47		12 57	past	15 02		15 12	15 17		15 27	15 32	
New Cross Gate 4	d	12 02	12 07	12 11	12 17	12 22	12 27	12 32	12 37	12 41	12 47	12 52	12 57	13 02	each	15 07	15 11	15 17	15 22	15 27	15 32	15 37	15 41
Brockley	d	12 04	12 09	12 14	12 19	12 24	12 30	12 34	12 39	12 44	12 49	12 54	13 00	13 04	hour until	15 09	15 14	15 19	15 24	15 30	15 34	15 39	15 44
Honor Oak Park	d	12 07	12 12	12 17	12 22	12 27	12 33	12 37	12 42	12 47	12 52	12 57	13 03	13 07		15 12	15 17	15 22	15 27	15 33	15 37	15 42	15 47
Forest Hill 4	d	12 10	12 15	12 19	12 25	12 30	12 35	12 40	12 45	12 49	12 55	13 00	13 05	13 10		15 15	15 19	15 25	15 30	15 35	15 40	15 45	15 49
Sydenham	d	12 12	12 17	12 22	12 27	12 32	12 38	12 42	12 47	12 52	12 57	13 02	13 08	13 12		15 17	15 22	15 27	15 32	15 38	15 42	15 47	15 52
Crystal Palace 4	a		12 22			12 37	12 41		12 52			13 07	13 11			15 22			15 37	15 41		15 52	
Penge West	d	12 15		12 24	12 30			12 45		12 54	13 00			13 15			15 24	15 30			15 45		15 54
Anerley	d	12 17		12 26	12 32			12 47		12 56	13 02			13 17			15 26	15 32			15 47		15 56
Norwood Junction 2	a	12 20		12 29	12 35			12 50		12 59	13 05			13 20			15 29	15 35			15 50		15 59
Norwood Junction	d	12 20			12 35			12 50			13 05			13 20				15 35			15 50		
West Croydon 4	a	12 29			12 41			13 00			13 11			13 30				15 41			16 00		
Norwood Junction	d			12 30						13 00							15 30						16 00
East Croydon	a			12 33						13 03							15 33						16 03
Purley	a			12 43						13 13							15 43						16 13

Station		LO	LO	SN B	LO	LO	SN A	LO	LO	SN B	LO	LO	SN	LO	LO	SN B	LO	LO	SN	LO	LO	SN B	LO
London Bridge 4 ⊖	d			15 52			16 06			16 22			16 36			16 52			17 06			17 19	
Highbury & Islington	d		15 25			15 40			15 55			16 10			16 25			16 40			16 55		
Canonbury	d		15 27			15 42			15 57			16 12			16 27			16 42			16 57		
Dalston Junction	d	15 25	15 30		15 40	15 45		15 55	16 00		16 10	16 15		16 25	16 30		16 40	16 45		16 55	17 00		17 10
Haggerston	d	15 26	15 31		15 41	15 46		15 56	16 01		16 11	16 16		16 26	16 31		16 41	16 46		16 56	17 01		17 11
Hoxton	d	15 28	15 33		15 43	15 48		15 58	16 03		16 13	16 18		16 28	16 33		16 43	16 48		16 58	17 03		17 13
Shoreditch High Street	d	15 31	15 36		15 46	15 51		16 01	16 06		16 16	16 21		16 31	16 36		16 46	16 51		17 01	17 06		17 16
Whitechapel	d	15 33	15 38		15 48	15 53		16 03	16 08		16 18	16 23		16 33	16 38		16 48	16 53		17 03	17 08		17 18
Shadwell	d	15 35	15 40		15 50	15 55		16 05	16 10		16 20	16 25		16 35	16 40		16 50	16 55		17 05	17 10		17 20
Wapping	d	15 37	15 42		15 52	15 57		16 07	16 12		16 22	16 27		16 37	16 42		16 52	16 57		17 07	17 12		17 22
Rotherhithe	d	15 39	15 44		15 54	15 59		16 09	16 14		16 24	16 29		16 39	16 44		16 54	16 59		17 09	17 14		17 24
Canada Water	d	15 41	15 46		15 56	16 01		16 11	16 16		16 26	16 31		16 41	16 46		16 56	17 01		17 11	17 16		17 26
Surrey Quays	d	15 42	15 47		15 57	16 02		16 12	16 17		16 27	16 32		16 42	16 47		16 57	17 02		17 12	17 17		17 27
New Cross Gate 4	d	15 47	15 52	15 57	16 02	16 07	16 11	16 17	16 22	16 27	16 32	16 37	16 41	16 47	16 52	16 57	17 02	17 07	17 11	17 17	17 22	17 26	17 32
Brockley	d	15 49	15 54	16 00	16 04	16 09	16 14	16 19	16 24	16 30	16 34	16 39	16 44	16 49	16 54	17 00	17 04	17 09	17 14	17 19	17 24	17 29	17 34
Honor Oak Park	d	15 52	15 57	16 03	16 07	16 12	16 17	16 22	16 27	16 33	16 37	16 42	16 47	16 52	16 57	17 03	17 07	17 12	17 17	17 22	17 27	17 32	17 37
Forest Hill 4	d	15 55	16 00	16 05	16 10	16 15	16 19	16 25	16 30	16 35	16 40	16 45	16 49	16 55	17 00	17 05	17 10	17 15	17 19	17 25	17 30	17 34	17 40
Sydenham	d	15 57	16 02	16 08	16 12	16 17	16 22	16 27	16 32	16 38	16 42	16 47	16 52	16 57	17 02	17 08	17 12	17 17	17 22	17 27	17 32	17 37	17 42
Crystal Palace 4	a		16 07	16 11		16 22			16 37	16 41		16 52			17 07	17 11		17 22			17 37	17 40	
Penge West	d	16 00			16 15		16 24	16 30			16 45		16 54	17 00			17 15		17 24	17 30			17 45
Anerley	d	16 02			16 17		16 26	16 32			16 47		16 56	17 02			17 17		17 26	17 32			17 47
Norwood Junction 2	a	16 05			16 20		16 29	16 35			16 50		16 59	17 05			17 20		17 29	17 35			17 50
Norwood Junction	d	16 05			16 20			16 35			16 50		17 00	17 05			17 20		17 30	17 35			17 50
West Croydon 4	a	16 11			16 30			16 41			17 00		17 07	17 11			17 30		17 37	17 41			17 59
Norwood Junction	d						16 30																
East Croydon	a						16 33																
Purley	a						16 43																

A To Caterham

B To London Victoria

For Fast trains between London Bridge & New Cross Gate to Norwood Jn & East Croydon, see Table 175

For full service between Highbury & Islington and Surrey Quays, please see Table 178

For Sutton connections at West Croydon, please see table 172

Table 177

Mondays to Fridays

9 December to 16 May

London Bridge-New Cross Gate,Brockley, Honor Oak Park, Forest Hill, Sydenham, Crystal Palace, Penge West, Anerley-Norwood Junction and Croydon

Network Diagram - see first Page of Table 173

		LO	SN	LO	LO	SN A	LO		LO	SN	LO	LO	SN A	LO	LO	SN	LO		LO	SN A	LO	LO	SN B	LO	LO
London Bridge 4 ⊖	d		17 36			17 52				18 06			18 21			18 36				18 52			19 06		
Highbury & Islington	d	17 10			17 25				17 40			17 55			18 10				18 25			18 40			18 55
Canonbury	d	17 12			17 27				17 42			17 57			18 12				18 27			18 42			18 57
Dalston Junction	d	17 15		17 25	17 30		17 40		17 45		17 55	18 00		18 10	18 15		18 25		18 30		18 40	18 45		18 55	19 00
Haggerston	d	17 16		17 26	17 31		17 41		17 46		17 56	18 01		18 11	18 16		18 26		18 31		18 41	18 46		18 56	19 01
Hoxton	d	17 18		17 28	17 33		17 43		17 48		17 58	18 03		18 13	18 18		18 28		18 33		18 43	18 48		18 58	19 03
Shoreditch High Street	d	17 21		17 31	17 36		17 46		17 51		18 01	18 06		18 16	18 21		18 31		18 36		18 46	18 51		19 01	19 06
Whitechapel	d	17 23		17 33	17 38		17 48		17 53		18 03	18 08		18 18	18 23		18 33		18 38		18 48	18 53		19 03	19 08
Shadwell	d	17 25		17 35	17 40		17 50		17 55		18 05	18 10		18 20	18 25		18 35		18 40		18 50	18 55		19 05	19 10
Wapping	d	17 27		17 37	17 42		17 52		17 57		18 07	18 12		18 22	18 27		18 37		18 42		18 52	18 57		19 07	19 12
Rotherhithe	d	17 29		17 39	17 44		17 54		17 59		18 09	18 14		18 24	18 29		18 39		18 44		18 54	18 59		19 09	19 14
Canada Water	d	17 31		17 41	17 46		17 56		18 01		18 11	18 16		18 26	18 31		18 41		18 46		18 56	19 01		19 11	19 16
Surrey Quays	d	17 32		17 42	17 47		17 57		18 02		18 12	18 17		18 27	18 32		18 42		18 47		18 57	19 02		19 12	19 17
New Cross Gate 4	d	17 37	17 41	17 47	17 52	17 58	18 02		18 07	18 11	18 17	18 22	18 26	18 32	18 37	18 41	18 47		18 52	18 57	19 02	19 07	19 11	19 17	19 22
Brockley	d	17 39	17 44	17 49	17 54	18 01	18 04		18 09	18 14	18 19	18 24	18 29	18 34	18 39	18 44	18 49		18 54	19 00	19 04	19 09	19 14	19 19	19 24
Honor Oak Park	d	17 42	17 47	17 52	17 57	18 04	18 07		18 12	18 17	18 22	18 27	18 32	18 37	18 42	18 47	18 52		18 57	19 03	19 07	19 12	19 17	19 22	19 27
Forest Hill 4	d	17 45	17 49	17 55	18 00	18 06	18 10		18 15	18 19	18 25	18 30	18 34	18 40	18 45	18 49	18 55		19 00	19 05	19 10	19 15	19 19	19 25	19 30
Sydenham	d	17 47	17 52	17 57	18 02	18 09	18 12		18 17	18 22	18 27	18 32	18 37	18 42	18 47	18 52	18 57		19 02	19 08	19 12	19 17	19 22	19 27	19 32
Crystal Palace 4	a	17 52			18 07	18 12			18 22			18 37	18 42		18 52				19 07	19 11		19 22			19 37
Penge West	d		17 54	18 00			18 15			18 24	18 30			18 45		18 54	19 00				19 15		19 24	19 30	
Anerley	d		17 56	18 02			18 17			18 26	18 32			18 47		18 56	19 02				19 17		19 26	19 32	
Norwood Junction 2	a		17 59	18 05			18 20			18 29	18 35			18 50		18 59	19 05				19 20		19 29	19 35	
Norwood Junction	d		18 00	18 05			18 20			18 32	18 35			18 50		19 02	19 05				19 20			19 35	
West Croydon 4	a		18 08	18 11			18 26			18 39	18 42			19 01		19 09	19 11				19 30			19 41	
Norwood Junction	d																						19 30		
East Croydon	a																						19 33		
Purley	a																						19 43		

		SN A	LO		LO	SN B	LO	LO	SN A	LO	LO	SN B	LO		LO	SN A	LO	LO	SN B	LO	LO	SN A	LO		LO
London Bridge 4 ⊖	d	19 22				19 36			19 54			20 06				20 22			20 36			20 52			
Highbury & Islington	d				19 10			19 25			19 40				19 55			20 10			20 25				20 40
Canonbury	d				19 12			19 27			19 42				19 57			20 12			20 27				20 42
Dalston Junction	d		19 10		19 15		19 25	19 30		19 40	19 45		19 55		20 00		20 10	20 15		20 25	20 30		20 40		20 45
Haggerston	d		19 11		19 16		19 26	19 31		19 41	19 46		19 56		20 01		20 11	20 16		20 26	20 31		20 41		20 46
Hoxton	d		19 13		19 18		19 28	19 33		19 43	19 48		19 58		20 03		20 13	20 18		20 28	20 33		20 43		20 48
Shoreditch High Street	d		19 16		19 21		19 31	19 36		19 46	19 51		20 01		20 06		20 16	20 21		20 31	20 36		20 46		20 51
Whitechapel	d		19 18		19 23		19 33	19 38		19 48	19 53		20 03		20 08		20 18	20 23		20 33	20 38		20 48		20 53
Shadwell	d		19 20		19 25		19 35	19 40		19 50	19 55		20 05		20 10		20 20	20 25		20 35	20 40		20 50		20 55
Wapping	d		19 22		19 27		19 37	19 42		19 52	19 57		20 07		20 12		20 22	20 27		20 37	20 42		20 52		20 57
Rotherhithe	d		19 24		19 29		19 39	19 44		19 54	19 59		20 09		20 14		20 24	20 29		20 39	20 44		20 54		20 59
Canada Water	d		19 26		19 31		19 41	19 46		19 56	20 01		20 11		20 16		20 26	20 31		20 41	20 46		20 56		21 01
Surrey Quays	d		19 27		19 32		19 42	19 47		19 57	20 02		20 12		20 17		20 27	20 32		20 42	20 47		20 57		21 02
New Cross Gate 4	d	19 27	19 32		19 37	19 41	19 47	19 52	19 59	20 02	20 07	20 11	20 17		20 22	20 27	20 32	20 37	20 41	20 47	20 52	20 57	21 02		21 07
Brockley	d	19 30	19 34		19 39	19 44	19 49	19 54	20 02	20 04	20 09	20 14	20 19		20 24	20 30	20 34	20 39	20 44	20 49	20 54	21 00	21 04		21 09
Honor Oak Park	d	19 33	19 37		19 42	19 47	19 52	19 57	20 05	20 07	20 12	20 17	20 22		20 27	20 33	20 37	20 42	20 47	20 52	20 57	21 03	21 07		21 12
Forest Hill 4	d	19 35	19 40		19 45	19 49	19 55	20 00	20 07	20 10	20 15	20 19	20 25		20 30	20 35	20 40	20 45	20 49	20 55	21 00	21 05	21 10		21 15
Sydenham	d	19 38	19 42		19 47	19 52	19 57	20 02	20 10	20 12	20 17	20 22	20 27		20 32	20 38	20 42	20 47	20 52	20 57	21 02	21 08	21 12		21 17
Crystal Palace 4	a	19 41			19 52			20 07	20 13		20 22				20 37	20 41		20 52			21 07	21 11			21 22
Penge West	d		19 45			19 54	20 00			20 15		20 24	20 30				20 45		20 54	21 00			21 15		
Anerley	d		19 47			19 56	20 02			20 17		20 26	20 32				20 47		20 56	21 02			21 17		
Norwood Junction 2	a		19 50			19 59	20 05			20 20		20 29	20 35				20 50		20 59	21 05			21 20		
Norwood Junction	d		19 50				20 05			20 20			20 35				20 50			21 05			21 20		
West Croydon 4	a		19 56				20 11			20 26			20 41				21 00			21 11			21 26		
Norwood Junction	d					20 00						20 30							21 00						
East Croydon	a					20 03						20 33							21 03						
Purley	a					20 13						20 43							21 13						

A To London Victoria

B To Caterham

For Fast trains between London Bridge & New Cross Gate to Norwood Jn & East Croydon, see Table 175

For full service between Highbury & Islington and Surrey Quays, please see Table 178

For Sutton connections at West Croydon, please see table 172

Table 177

Mondays to Fridays

9 December to 16 May

London Bridge-New Cross Gate,Brockley, Honor Oak Park, Forest Hill, Sydenham, Crystal Palace, Penge West, Anerley-Norwood Junction and Croydon

Network Diagram - see first Page of Table 173

		SN A	LO	LO	SN B		LO	LO	SN A	LO	LO	SN B	LO	LO	SN A		LO	LO	SN B	LO	LO	SN A	LO	SN B	LO
London Bridge 4 ⊖	d	21 06			21 22				21 36			21 52			22 08				22 23			22 38		22 52	
Highbury & Islington	d			20 55				21 10			21 25			21 40				21 55			22 10		22 25		
Canonbury	d			20 57				21 12			21 27			21 42				21 57			22 12		22 27		
Dalston Junction	d		20 55	21 00			21 10	21 15		21 25	21 30		21 40	21 45			21 55	22 00		22 10	22 15		22 30		22 40
Haggerston	d		20 56	21 01			21 11	21 16		21 26	21 31		21 41	21 46			21 56	22 01		22 11	22 16		22 31		22 41
Hoxton	d		20 58	21 03			21 13	21 18		21 28	21 33		21 43	21 48			21 58	22 03		22 13	22 18		22 33		22 43
Shoreditch High Street	d		21 01	21 06			21 16	21 21		21 31	21 36		21 46	21 51			22 01	22 06		22 16	22 21		22 36		22 46
Whitechapel	d		21 03	21 08			21 18	21 23		21 33	21 38		21 48	21 53			22 03	22 08		22 18	22 23		22 38		22 48
Shadwell	d		21 05	21 10			21 20	21 25		21 35	21 40		21 50	21 55			22 05	22 10		22 20	22 25		22 40		22 50
Wapping	d		21 07	21 12			21 22	21 27		21 37	21 42		21 52	21 57			22 07	22 12		22 22	22 27		22 42		22 52
Rotherhithe	d		21 09	21 14			21 24	21 29		21 39	21 44		21 54	21 59			22 09	22 14		22 24	22 29		22 44		22 54
Canada Water	d		21 11	21 16			21 26	21 31		21 41	21 46		21 56	22 01			22 11	22 16		22 26	22 31		22 46		22 56
Surrey Quays	d		21 12	21 17			21 27	21 32		21 42	21 47		21 57	22 02			22 12	22 17		22 27	22 32		22 47		22 57
New Cross Gate 4	d	21 11	21 17	21 22	21 27		21 32	21 37	21 41	21 47	21 52	21 57	22 02	22 07	22 13		22 17	22 22	22 28	22 32	22 37	22 43	22 52	22 57	23 02
Brockley	d	21 14	21 19	21 24	21 30		21 34	21 39	21 44	21 49	21 54	22 00	22 04	22 09	22 16		22 19	22 24	22 31	22 34	22 39	22 46	22 54	23 00	23 04
Honor Oak Park	d	21 17	21 22	21 27	21 33		21 37	21 42	21 47	21 52	21 57	22 03	22 07	22 12	22 19		22 22	22 27	22 34	22 37	22 42	22 49	22 57	23 03	23 07
Forest Hill 4	d	21 19	21 25	21 30	21 35		21 40	21 45	21 49	21 55	22 00	22 05	22 10	22 15	22 21		22 25	22 30	22 36	22 40	22 45	22 51	23 00	23 05	23 10
Sydenham	d	21 22	21 27	21 32	21 38		21 42	21 47	21 52	21 57	22 02	22 08	22 12	22 17	22 24		22 27	22 32	22 39	22 42	22 47	22 54	23 02	23 08	23 12
Crystal Palace 4	a			21 37	21 41			21 52			22 07	22 11		22 22				22 37	22 42		22 52		23 07	23 11	
Penge West	d	21 24	21 30				21 45		21 54	22 00			22 15		22 26		22 30			22 45		22 56			23 15
Anerley	d	21 26	21 32				21 47		21 56	22 02			22 17		22 28		22 32			22 47		22 58			23 17
Norwood Junction 2	a	21 29	21 35				21 50		21 59	22 05			22 20		22 31		22 35			22 50		23 01			23 20
Norwood Junction	d		21 35				21 50			22 05			22 20				22 35			22 50					23 20
West Croydon 4 🚋	a		21 41				22 00			22 11			22 30				22 41			23 00					23 30
Norwood Junction	d	21 30							22 00						22 32							23 02			
East Croydon 🚋	a	21 33							22 03						22 35							23 06			
Purley	a	21 43							22 13						22 45							23 16			

			LO	SN A	LO	SN B	LO	LO	SN A	LO	SN B		LO
London Bridge 4 ⊖	d			23 06		23 24			23 41		23 50		
Highbury & Islington	d		22 40		22 55			23 10		23 25			
Canonbury	d		22 42		22 57			23 12		23 27			
Dalston Junction	d		22 45		23 00		23 10	23 15		23 30			23 40
Haggerston	d		22 46		23 01		23 11	23 16		23 31			23 41
Hoxton	d		22 48		23 03		23 13	23 18		23 33			23 43
Shoreditch High Street	d		22 51		23 06		23 16	23 21		23 36			23 46
Whitechapel	d		22 53		23 08		23 18	23 23		23 38			23 48
Shadwell	d		22 55		23 10		23 20	23 25		23 40			23 50
Wapping	d		22 57		23 12		23 22	23 27		23 42			23 52
Rotherhithe	d		22 59		23 14		23 24	23 29		23 44			23 54
Canada Water	d		23 01		23 16		23 26	23 31		23 46			23 56
Surrey Quays	d		23 02		23 17		23 27	23 32		23 47			23 57
New Cross Gate 4	d		23 07	23 11	23 22	23 29	23 32	23 37	23 46	23 52	23 56		00 02
Brockley	d		23 09	23 14	23 24	23 32	23 34	23 39	23 49	23 54	23 58		00 04
Honor Oak Park	d		23 12	23 17	23 27	23 35	23 37	23 42	23 52	23 57	00 01		00 07
Forest Hill 4	d		23 15	23 19	23 30	23 37	23 40	23 45	23 54	23 58	00 04		00 10
Sydenham	d		23 17	23 22	23 32	23 40	23 42	23 47	23 57	00 02	00 06		00 12
Crystal Palace 4	a		23 22		23 37	23 43		23 52		00 07	00 10		
Penge West	d			23 24			23 45		23 59				00 15
Anerley	d			23 26			23 47		00 01				00 17
Norwood Junction 2	a			23 29			23 50		00 04				00 20
Norwood Junction	d						23 50						00 20
West Croydon 4 🚋	a						23 59						00 27
Norwood Junction	d			23 30					00 05				
East Croydon 🚋	a			23 33					00 08				
Purley	a			23 43					00 18				

A To Caterham

B To London Victoria

For Fast trains between London Bridge & New Cross Gate to Norwood Jn & East Croydon, see Table 175

For full service between Highbury & Islington and Surrey Quays, please see Table 178

For Sutton connections at West Croydon, please see table 172

Table 177

Saturdays

14 December to 17 May

London Bridge-New Cross Gate,Brockley, Honor Oak Park, Forest Hill, Sydenham, Crystal Palace, Penge West, Anerley-Norwood Junction and Croydon

Network Diagram - see first Page of Table 173

Station		SN	LO	SN	LO	SN		SN		LO	LO	LO	LO	LO	LO	LO	SN	LO	LO	LO	LO	SN	LO	LO	LO
		A	B	C	D	E											E					E			
London Bridge 4 ⊖	d					00 06		00 36									06 36					07 06			
Highbury & Islington	d											05 35		05 55					06 25		06 40			06 55	
Canonbury	d											05 37		05 57					06 27		06 42			06 57	
Dalston Junction	d											05 40		06 00	06 10				06 30	06 40	06 45		06 55	07 00	07 10
Haggerston	d											05 41		06 01	06 11				06 31	06 41	06 46		06 56	07 01	07 11
Hoxton	d											05 43		06 03	06 13				06 33	06 43	06 48		06 58	07 03	07 13
Shoreditch High Street	d											05 46		06 06	06 16				06 36	06 46	06 51		07 01	07 06	07 16
Whitechapel	d											05 48		06 08	06 18				06 38	06 48	06 53		07 03	07 08	07 18
Shadwell	d											05 50		06 10	06 20				06 40	06 50	06 55		07 05	07 10	07 20
Wapping	d											05 52		06 12	06 22				06 42	06 52	06 57		07 07	07 12	07 22
Rotherhithe	d											05 54		06 14	06 24				06 44	06 54	06 59		07 09	07 14	07 24
Canada Water	d											05 56		06 16	06 26				06 46	06 56	07 01		07 11	07 16	07 26
Surrey Quays	d											05 57		06 17	06 27				06 47	06 57	07 02		07 12	07 17	07 27
New Cross Gate 4	d				00 02	00 11		00 41		05 47	05 52	06 02	06 17	06 22	06 32	06 37	06 41	06 47	06 52	07 02	07 07	07 11	07 17	07 22	07 32
Brockley	d				00 04	00 14		00 44		05 49	05 54	06 04	06 19	06 24	06 34	06 39	06 44	06 49	06 54	07 04	07 09	07 14	07 19	07 24	07 34
Honor Oak Park	d			00 01	00 07	00 17		00 47		05 52	05 57	06 07	06 22	06 27	06 37	06 42	06 47	06 52	06 57	07 07	07 12	07 17	07 22	07 27	07 37
Forest Hill 4	d			00 04	00 10	00 19		00 49		05 55	06 00	06 10	06 25	06 30	06 40	06 45	06 49	06 55	07 00	07 10	07 15	07 19	07 25	07 30	07 40
Sydenham	d		00 02	00 06	00 12	00 22		00 52		05 57	06 02	06 12	06 27	06 32	06 42	06 47	06 52	06 57	07 02	07 12	07 17	07 22	07 27	07 32	07 42
Crystal Palace 4	a		00 07	00 10							06 07			06 37		06 52			07 07		07 22			07 37	
Penge West	d				00 15	00 24		00 54		06 00		06 15	06 30		06 45		06 54	07 00		07 15		07 24	07 30		07 45
Anerley	d	00 01			00 17	00 26		00 56		06 02		06 17	06 32		06 47		06 56	07 02		07 17		07 26	07 32		07 47
Norwood Junction 2	a	00 04			00 20	00 29		00 59		06 05		06 18	06 35		06 50		06 59	07 05		07 20		07 29	07 35		07 50
Norwood Junction	d				00 20					06 05		06 20	06 35		06 50			07 05		07 20			07 35		07 50
West Croydon 4	a				00 27					06 14		06 30	06 41		07 00			07 11		07 30			07 41		08 00
Norwood Junction	d	00 05				00 30		01 00									07 00					07 30			
East Croydon	a	00 08				00 33		01 03									07 03					07 33			
Purley	a	00 18				00 47											07 12					07 42			

Station		LO		SN	LO	LO	LO	LO	SN	LO	LO	SN	LO	LO	SN	LO	LO	SN		LO	LO	SN	LO	LO
				E					E			F			E			F	and at the same minutes past each hour until			E		
London Bridge 4 ⊖	d			07 36					08 06			08 22			08 36			08 52				19 06		
Highbury & Islington	d	07 10				07 25		07 40			07 55			08 10			08 25				18 40			18 55
Canonbury	d	07 12				07 27		07 42			07 57			08 12			08 27				18 42			18 57
Dalston Junction	d	07 15			07 25	07 30	07 40	07 45		07 55	08 00		08 10	08 15		08 25	08 30			18 40	18 45		18 55	19 00
Haggerston	d	07 16			07 26	07 31	07 41	07 46		07 56	08 01		08 11	08 16		08 26	08 31			18 41	18 46		18 56	19 01
Hoxton	d	07 18			07 28	07 33	07 43	07 48		07 58	08 03		08 13	08 18		08 28	08 33			18 43	18 48		18 58	19 03
Shoreditch High Street	d	07 21			07 31	07 36	07 46	07 51		08 01	08 06		08 16	08 21		08 31	08 36			18 46	18 51		19 01	19 06
Whitechapel	d	07 23			07 33	07 38	07 48	07 53		08 03	08 08		08 18	08 23		08 33	08 38			18 48	18 53		19 03	19 08
Shadwell	d	07 25			07 35	07 40	07 50	07 55		08 05	08 10		08 20	08 25		08 35	08 40			18 50	18 55		19 05	19 10
Wapping	d	07 27			07 37	07 42	07 52	07 57		08 07	08 12		08 22	08 27		08 37	08 42			18 52	18 57		19 07	19 12
Rotherhithe	d	07 29			07 39	07 44	07 54	07 59		08 09	08 14		08 24	08 29		08 39	08 44			18 54	18 59		19 09	19 14
Canada Water	d	07 31			07 41	07 46	07 56	08 01		08 11	08 16		08 26	08 31		08 41	08 46			18 56	19 01		19 11	19 16
Surrey Quays	d	07 32			07 42	07 47	07 57	08 02		08 12	08 17		08 27	08 32		08 42	08 47			18 57	19 02		19 12	19 17
New Cross Gate 4	d	07 37		07 41	07 47	07 52	08 02	08 07	08 11	08 17	08 22	08 27	08 32	08 37	08 41	08 47	08 52	08 57		19 02	19 07	19 11	19 17	19 22
Brockley	d	07 39		07 44	07 49	07 54	08 04	08 09	08 14	08 19	08 24	08 30	08 34	08 39	08 44	08 49	08 54	09 00		19 04	19 09	19 14	19 19	19 24
Honor Oak Park	d	07 42		07 47	07 52	07 57	08 07	08 12	08 17	08 22	08 27	08 33	08 37	08 42	08 47	08 52	08 57	09 03		19 07	19 12	19 17	19 22	19 27
Forest Hill 4	d	07 45		07 49	07 55	08 00	08 10	08 15	08 19	08 25	08 30	08 35	08 40	08 45	08 49	08 55	09 00	09 05		19 10	19 15	19 19	19 25	19 30
Sydenham	d	07 47		07 52	07 57	08 02	08 12	08 17	08 22	08 27	08 32	08 38	08 42	08 47	08 52	08 57	09 02	09 08		19 12	19 17	19 22	19 27	19 32
Crystal Palace 4	a	07 52				08 07		08 22			08 37	08 41		08 52			09 07	09 11			19 22			19 37
Penge West	d			07 54	08 00		08 15		08 24	08 30			08 45		08 54	09 00				19 15		19 24	19 30	
Anerley	d			07 56	08 02		08 17		08 26	08 32			08 47		08 56	09 02				19 17		19 26	19 32	
Norwood Junction 2	a			07 59	08 05		08 20		08 29	08 35			08 50		08 59	09 05				19 20		19 29	19 35	
Norwood Junction	d				08 05		08 20			08 35			08 50			09 05				19 20			19 35	
West Croydon 4	a				08 11		08 30			08 41			09 00			09 11				19 30			19 41	
Norwood Junction	d			08 00					08 30						09 00							19 30		
East Croydon	a			08 03					08 33						09 03							19 33		
Purley	a			08 12					08 42						09 12							19 42		

A From London Bridge to Caterham
B From Highbury and Islington Ell
C From London Bridge to London Victoria
D From Dalston Junction Stn Ell
E To Caterham
F To London Victoria

For Fast trains between London Bridge & New Cross Gate to Norwood Jn & East Croydon, see Table 175

For full service between Highbury & Islington and Surrey Quays, please see Table 178

For Sutton connections at West Croydon, please see table 172

Table 177

Saturdays

14 December to 17 May

London Bridge-New Cross Gate,Brockley, Honor Oak Park, Forest Hill, Sydenham, Crystal Palace, Penge West, Anerley-Norwood Junction and Croydon

Network Diagram - see first Page of Table 173

Station		SN A	LO	LO	SN B	LO	LO	SN A	LO	LO	SN B	LO	LO	SN A	LO	LO	SN B	LO	LO	SN A	LO	LO	SN B
London Bridge 4 ⊖	d	19 22			19 36			19 52			20 06			20 22			20 36			20 52			21 06
Highbury & Islington	d			19 10			19 25			19 40			19 55			20 10			20 25			20 40	
Canonbury	d			19 12			19 27			19 42			19 57			20 12			20 27			20 42	
Dalston Junction	d		19 10	19 15		19 25	19 30		19 40	19 45		19 55	20 00		20 10	20 15		20 25	20 30		20 40	20 45	
Haggerston	d		19 11	19 16		19 26	19 31		19 41	19 46		19 56	20 01		20 11	20 16		20 26	20 31		20 41	20 46	
Hoxton	d		19 13	19 18		19 28	19 33		19 43	19 48		19 58	20 03		20 13	20 18		20 28	20 33		20 43	20 48	
Shoreditch High Street	d		19 16	19 21		19 31	19 36		19 46	19 51		20 01	20 06		20 16	20 21		20 31	20 36		20 46	20 51	
Whitechapel	d		19 18	19 23		19 33	19 38		19 48	19 53		20 03	20 08		20 18	20 23		20 33	20 38		20 48	20 53	
Shadwell	d		19 20	19 25		19 35	19 40		19 50	19 55		20 05	20 10		20 20	20 25		20 35	20 40		20 50	20 55	
Wapping	d		19 22	19 27		19 37	19 42		19 52	19 57		20 07	20 12		20 22	20 27		20 37	20 42		20 52	20 57	
Rotherhithe	d		19 24	19 29		19 39	19 44		19 54	19 59		20 09	20 14		20 24	20 29		20 39	20 44		20 54	20 59	
Canada Water	d		19 26	19 31		19 41	19 46		19 56	20 01		20 11	20 16		20 26	20 31		20 41	20 46		20 56	21 01	
Surrey Quays	d		19 27	19 32		19 42	19 47		19 57	20 02		20 12	20 17		20 27	20 32		20 42	20 47		20 57	21 02	
New Cross Gate 4	d	19 27	19 32	19 37	19 41	19 47	19 52	19 57	20 02	20 07	20 11	20 17	20 22	20 27	20 32	20 37	20 41	20 47	20 52	20 57	21 02	21 07	21 11
Brockley	d	19 30	19 34	19 39	19 44	19 49	19 54	20 00	20 04	20 09	20 14	20 19	20 24	20 30	20 34	20 39	20 44	20 49	20 54	21 00	21 04	21 09	21 14
Honor Oak Park	d	19 33	19 37	19 42	19 47	19 52	19 57	20 03	20 07	20 12	20 17	20 22	20 27	20 33	20 37	20 42	20 47	20 52	20 57	21 03	21 07	21 12	21 17
Forest Hill 4	d	19 35	19 40	19 45	19 49	19 55	20 00	20 05	20 10	20 15	20 19	20 25	20 30	20 35	20 40	20 45	20 49	20 55	21 00	21 05	21 10	21 15	21 19
Sydenham	d	19 38	19 42	19 47	19 52	19 57	20 02	20 08	20 12	20 17	20 22	20 27	20 32	20 38	20 42	20 47	20 52	20 57	21 02	21 08	21 12	21 17	21 22
Crystal Palace 4	a	19 41		19 52			20 07	20 11		20 22			20 37	20 41		20 52			21 07	21 11		21 22	
Penge West	d		19 45		19 54	20 00			20 15		20 24	20 30			20 45		20 54	21 00			21 15		21 24
Anerley	d		19 47		19 56	20 02			20 17		20 26	20 32			20 47		20 56	21 02			21 17		21 26
Norwood Junction 2	a		19 50		19 59	20 05			20 20		20 29	20 35			20 50		20 59	21 05			21 20		21 29
Norwood Junction	d		19 50			20 05			20 20			20 35			20 50			21 05			21 20		
West Croydon 4	a		20 00			20 11			20 28			20 41			21 00			21 11			21 30		
Norwood Junction	d				20 00						20 30						21 00						21 30
East Croydon	a				20 03						20 33						21 03						21 33
Purley	a				20 12						20 42						21 12						21 42

Station		LO	LO	SN A	LO	LO	SN B	LO	LO	SN A	LO	LO	SN B	LO	LO	SN A	LO	LO	SN B	LO	SN A	LO
London Bridge 4 ⊖	d			21 22			21 36			21 52			22 06			22 22			22 36		22 52	
Highbury & Islington	d		20 55			21 10			21 25			21 40			21 55			22 10		22 25		
Canonbury	d		20 57			21 12			21 27			21 42			21 57			22 12		22 27		
Dalston Junction	d	20 55	21 00		21 10	21 15		21 25	21 30		21 40	21 45		21 55	22 00		22 10	22 15		22 30		22 40
Haggerston	d	20 56	21 01		21 11	21 16		21 26	21 31		21 41	21 46		21 56	22 01		22 11	22 16		22 31		22 41
Hoxton	d	20 58	21 03		21 13	21 18		21 28	21 33		21 43	21 48		21 58	22 03		22 13	22 18		22 33		22 43
Shoreditch High Street	d	21 01	21 06		21 16	21 21		21 31	21 36		21 46	21 51		22 01	22 06		22 16	22 21		22 36		22 46
Whitechapel	d	21 03	21 08		21 18	21 23		21 33	21 38		21 48	21 53		22 03	22 08		22 18	22 23		22 38		22 48
Shadwell	d	21 05	21 10		21 20	21 25		21 35	21 40		21 50	21 55		22 05	22 10		22 20	22 25		22 40		22 50
Wapping	d	21 07	21 12		21 22	21 27		21 37	21 42		21 52	21 57		22 07	22 12		22 22	22 27		22 42		22 52
Rotherhithe	d	21 09	21 14		21 24	21 29		21 39	21 44		21 54	21 59		22 09	22 14		22 24	22 29		22 44		22 54
Canada Water	d	21 11	21 16		21 26	21 31		21 41	21 46		21 56	22 01		22 11	22 16		22 26	22 31		22 46		22 56
Surrey Quays	d	21 12	21 17		21 27	21 32		21 42	21 47		21 57	22 02		22 12	22 17		22 27	22 32		22 47		22 57
New Cross Gate 4	d	21 17	21 22	21 27	21 32	21 37	21 41	21 47	21 52	21 57	22 02	22 07	22 11	22 17	22 22	22 27	22 32	22 37	22 41	22 52	22 57	23 02
Brockley	d	21 19	21 24	21 30	21 34	21 39	21 44	21 49	21 54	22 00	22 04	22 09	22 14	22 19	22 24	22 30	22 34	22 39	22 44	22 54	23 00	23 04
Honor Oak Park	d	21 22	21 27	21 33	21 37	21 42	21 47	21 52	21 57	22 03	22 07	22 12	22 17	22 22	22 27	22 33	22 37	22 42	22 47	22 57	23 03	23 07
Forest Hill 4	d	21 25	21 30	21 35	21 40	21 45	21 49	21 55	22 00	22 05	22 10	22 15	22 19	22 25	22 30	22 35	22 40	22 45	22 49	23 00	23 05	23 10
Sydenham	d	21 27	21 32	21 38	21 42	21 47	21 52	21 57	22 02	22 08	22 12	22 17	22 22	22 27	22 32	22 38	22 42	22 47	22 52	23 02	23 08	23 12
Crystal Palace 4	a		21 37	21 41		21 52			22 07	22 11		22 23			22 37	22 41		22 52		23 07	23 11	
Penge West	d	21 30			21 45		21 54	22 00			22 15		22 24	22 30			22 45		22 54			23 15
Anerley	d	21 32			21 47		21 56	22 02			22 17		22 26	22 32			22 47		22 56			23 17
Norwood Junction 2	a	21 35			21 50		21 59	22 05			22 20		22 29	22 35			22 50		22 59			23 20
Norwood Junction	d	21 35			21 50			22 05			22 20			22 35			22 50					23 20
West Croydon 4	a	21 41			22 00			22 11			22 30			22 41			23 00					23 30
Norwood Junction	d						22 00						22 30						23 00			
East Croydon	a						22 03						22 33						23 03			
Purley	a						22 12						22 42						23 12			

A To London Victoria

B To Caterham

For Fast trains between London Bridge & New Cross Gate to Norwood Jn & East Croydon, see Table 175

For full service between Highbury & Islington and Surrey Quays, please see Table 178

For Sutton connections at West Croydon, please see table 172

Table 177

Saturdays

14 December to 17 May

London Bridge-New Cross Gate,Brockley, Honor Oak Park, Forest Hill, Sydenham, Crystal Palace, Penge West, Anerley-Norwood Junction and Croydon

Network Diagram - see first Page of Table 173

		LO	SN A	LO	SN B	LO	LO	SN A	LO		SN B	LO
London Bridge 4 ⊖	d		23 06		23 22			23 41			23 52	
Highbury & Islington	d	22 40		22 55			23 10		23 25			
Canonbury	d	22 42		22 57			23 12		23 27			
Dalston Junction	d	22 45		23 00		23 10	23 15		23 30			23 40
Haggerston	d	22 46		23 01		23 11	23 16		23 31			23 41
Hoxton	d	22 48		23 03		23 13	23 18		23 33			23 43
Shoreditch High Street	d	22 51		23 06		23 16	23 21		23 36			23 46
Whitechapel	d	22 53		23 08		23 18	23 23		23 38			23 48
Shadwell	d	22 55		23 10		23 20	23 25		23 40			23 50
Wapping	d	22 57		23 12		23 22	23 27		23 42			23 52
Rotherhithe	d	22 59		23 14		23 24	23 29		23 44			23 54
Canada Water	d	23 01		23 16		23 26	23 31		23 46			23 56
Surrey Quays	d	23 02		23 17		23 27	23 32		23 47			23 57
New Cross Gate 4	d	23 07	23 11	23 22	23 27	23 32	23 37	23 46	23 52		23 57	00 02
Brockley	d	23 09	23 14	23 24	23 30	23 34	23 39	23 49	23 54		00 01	00 04
Honor Oak Park	d	23 12	23 17	23 27	23 33	23 37	23 42	23 52	23 57		00 03	00 07
Forest Hill 4	d	23 15	23 19	23 30	23 35	23 40	23 45	23 54	23 58		00 05	00 10
Sydenham	d	23 17	23 22	23 32	23 38	23 42	23 47	23 57	00 02		00 08	00 12
Crystal Palace 4	a	23 22		23 37	23 41		23 53		00 07		00 11	
Penge West	d		23 24			23 45		23 59				00 15
Anerley	d		23 26			23 47		00 01				00 17
Norwood Junction 2	a		23 29			23 50		00 04				00 20
Norwood Junction	d					23 50						00 20
West Croydon 4	a					23 59						00 26
Norwood Junction	d		23 30					00 05				
East Croydon	a		23 33					00 08				
Purley	a		23 42					00 18				

Sundays

8 December to 11 May

		SN C	LO D	SN E	LO F	SN A	SN		LO	LO	SN G	LO	SN
London Bridge 4 ⊖	d					00 06	00 36				07 24		07 39
Highbury & Islington	d									06 51			
Canonbury	d									06 53			
Dalston Junction	d									06 56		07 12	
Haggerston	d									06 57		07 13	
Hoxton	d									06 59		07 15	
Shoreditch High Street	d									07 02		07 18	
Whitechapel	d									07 04		07 20	
Shadwell	d									07 06		07 22	
Wapping	d									07 08		07 24	
Rotherhithe	d									07 10		07 26	
Canada Water	d									07 12		07 28	
Surrey Quays	d									07 13		07 29	
New Cross Gate 4	d				00 02	00 11	00 41		07 04	07 18	07 30	07 34	07 45
Brockley	d			00 01	00 04	00 14	00 44		07 06	07 20	07 32	07 36	07 47
Honor Oak Park	d			00 03	00 07	00 17	00 47		07 09	07 23	07 35	07 39	07 50
Forest Hill 4	d			00 05	00 10	00 19	00 49		07 12	07 26	07 38	07 42	07 53
Sydenham	d		00 02	00 08	00 12	00 22	00 52		07 14	07 28	07 40	07 44	07 55
Crystal Palace 4	a		00 07	00 11						07 33			
Penge West	d				00 15	00 24	00 54		07 17		07 43	07 47	
Anerley	d	00 01			00 17	00 26	00 56		07 19		07 45	07 49	
Norwood Junction 2	a	00 04			00 20	00 29	00 59		07 22		07 48	07 52	08 00
Norwood Junction	d				00 20				07 22			07 52	08 00
West Croydon 4	a				00 26				07 29			07 58	08 09
Norwood Junction	d	00 05				00 30	01 00				07 52		
East Croydon	a	00 08				00 33	01 03				07 58		
Purley	a	00 18				00 45					08 08		

		LO	SN G	LO	SN	LO	SN G	LO		SN	LO	SN G	LO
London Bridge 4 ⊖	d		07 54		08 09		08 24			08 39		08 54	
Highbury & Islington	d	07 21				07 51		08 07			08 21		08 37
Canonbury	d	07 23				07 53		08 09			08 23		08 39
Dalston Junction	d	07 26		07 42		07 56		08 12			08 26		08 42
Haggerston	d	07 27		07 43		07 57		08 13			08 27		08 43
Hoxton	d	07 29		07 45		07 59		08 15			08 29		08 45
Shoreditch High Street	d	07 32		07 48		08 02		08 18			08 32		08 48
Whitechapel	d	07 34		07 50		08 04		08 20			08 34		08 50
Shadwell	d	07 36		07 52		08 06		08 22			08 36		08 52
Wapping	d	07 38		07 54		08 08		08 24			08 38		08 54
Rotherhithe	d	07 40		07 56		08 10		08 26			08 40		08 56
Canada Water	d	07 42		07 58		08 12		08 28			08 42		08 58
Surrey Quays	d	07 43		07 59		08 13		08 29			08 43		08 59
New Cross Gate 4	d	07 48	08 00	08 03	08 15	08 18	08 30	08 34		08 45	08 48	09 00	09 04
Brockley	d	07 50	08 02	08 06	08 17	08 20	08 32	08 36		08 47	08 50	09 02	09 06
Honor Oak Park	d	07 53	08 05	08 09	08 20	08 23	08 35	08 39		08 50	08 53	09 05	09 09
Forest Hill 4	d	07 56	08 08	08 12	08 23	08 26	08 38	08 42		08 53	08 56	09 08	09 12
Sydenham	d	07 58	08 10	08 14	08 25	08 28	08 40	08 44		08 55	08 58	09 10	09 14
Crystal Palace 4	a	08 03				08 33					09 03		
Penge West	d		08 13	08 17			08 43	08 47				09 13	09 17
Anerley	d		08 15	08 19			08 45	08 49				09 15	09 19
Norwood Junction 2	a		08 18	08 22	08 30		08 48	08 52		09 00		09 18	09 22
Norwood Junction	d			08 22	08 30			08 52		09 00			09 22
West Croydon 4	a			08 29	08 39			08 59		09 09			09 29
Norwood Junction	d		08 22				08 52					09 19	
East Croydon	a		08 26				08 57					09 23	
Purley	a		08 36				09 07					09 33	

A To Caterham
B To London Victoria
C From London Bridge to Caterham
D From Highbury and Islington Ell
E From London Bridge to London Victoria
F From Dalston Junction Stn Ell
G To Tattenham Corner

For Fast trains between London Bridge & New Cross Gate to Norwood Jn & East Croydon, see Table 175

For full service between Highbury & Islington and Surrey Quays, please see Table 178

For Sutton connections at West Croydon, please see table 172

Table 177

Sundays

8 December to 11 May

London Bridge-New Cross Gate,Brockley, Honor Oak Park, Forest Hill, Sydenham, Crystal Palace, Penge West, Anerley-Norwood Junction and Croydon

Network Diagram - see first Page of Table 173

		SN		LO	SN A	LO	SN	LO	SN A	LO	SN	LO		SN A	LO	SN	LO	SN A	LO	SN	LO	SN A		LO	SN
London Bridge 4 ⊖	d	09 09			09 24		09 39		09 54		10 09			10 24		10 39		10 54		11 09		11 24			11 39
Highbury & Islington	d			08 51		09 07		09 21		09 37		09 51			10 07		10 21		10 37		10 51			11 07	
Canonbury	d			08 53		09 09		09 23		09 39		09 53			10 09		10 23		10 39		10 53			11 09	
Dalston Junction	d			08 56		09 12		09 26		09 42		09 56			10 12		10 26		10 42		10 56			11 12	
Haggerston	d			08 57		09 13		09 27		09 43		09 57			10 13		10 27		10 43		10 57			11 13	
Hoxton	d			08 59		09 15		09 29		09 45		09 59			10 15		10 29		10 45		10 59			11 15	
Shoreditch High Street	d			09 02		09 18		09 32		09 48		10 02			10 18		10 32		10 48		11 02			11 18	
Whitechapel	d			09 04		09 20		09 34		09 50		10 04			10 20		10 34		10 50		11 04			11 20	
Shadwell	d			09 06		09 22		09 36		09 52		10 06			10 22		10 36		10 52		11 06			11 22	
Wapping	d			09 08		09 24		09 38		09 54		10 08			10 24		10 38		10 54		11 08			11 24	
Rotherhithe	d			09 10		09 26		09 40		09 56		10 10			10 26		10 40		10 56		11 10			11 26	
Canada Water	d			09 12		09 28		09 42		09 58		10 12			10 28		10 42		10 58		11 12			11 28	
Surrey Quays	d			09 13		09 29		09 43		09 59		10 13			10 29		10 43		10 59		11 13			11 29	
New Cross Gate 4	d	09 15		09 18	09 30	09 34	09 45	09 48	10 00	10 04	10 15	10 18		10 30	10 34	10 45	10 48	11 00	11 04	11 15	11 18	11 30		11 34	11 45
Brockley	d	09 17		09 20	09 32	09 36	09 47	09 50	10 02	10 06	10 17	10 20		10 32	10 36	10 47	10 50	11 02	11 06	11 17	11 20	11 32		11 36	11 47
Honor Oak Park	d	09 20		09 23	09 35	09 39	09 50	09 53	10 05	10 09	10 20	10 23		10 35	10 39	10 50	10 53	11 05	11 09	11 20	11 23	11 35		11 39	11 50
Forest Hill 4	d	09 23		09 26	09 38	09 42	09 53	09 56	10 08	10 12	10 23	10 26		10 38	10 42	10 53	10 56	11 08	11 12	11 23	11 26	11 38		11 42	11 53
Sydenham	d	09 25		09 28	09 40	09 44	09 55	09 58	10 10	10 14	10 25	10 28		10 40	10 44	10 55	10 58	11 10	11 14	11 25	11 28	11 40		11 44	11 55
Crystal Palace 4	a			09 33				10 03				10 33					11 03				11 33				
Penge West	d				09 43	09 47			10 13	10 17				10 43	10 47			11 13	11 17			11 43		11 47	
Anerley	d				09 45	09 49			10 15	10 19				10 45	10 49			11 15	11 19			11 45		11 49	
Norwood Junction 2	a	09 30			09 48	09 52	10 00		10 18	10 22	10 30			10 48	10 52	11 00		11 18	11 22	11 30		11 48		11 52	12 00
Norwood Junction	d	09 30				09 52	10 00			10 22	10 30				10 52	11 00			11 22	11 30				11 52	12 00
West Croydon 4	a	09 39				09 59	10 09			10 29	10 39				10 59	11 09			11 29	11 39				11 59	12 09
Norwood Junction	d				09 49				10 19					10 49				11 19				11 49			
East Croydon	a				09 53				10 23					10 53				11 23				11 53			
Purley	a				10 03				10 33					11 03				11 33				12 03			

		LO	SN A	LO	LO	SN	LO	LO		SN A	LO	LO	SN	LO	LO	SN A	LO	LO	SN	LO	LO	SN A	LO		
London Bridge 4 ⊖	d		11 54			12 09				12 24			12 39			12 54			13 09			13 24			
Highbury & Islington	d	11 21		11 37			11 53				12 08				12 28			12 43			12 58				
Canonbury	d	11 23		11 39			11 55				12 10				12 30			12 45			13 00				
Dalston Junction	d	11 26		11 42	11 48		11 58	12 03			12 13	12 18		12 28	12 33		12 43	12 48		12 58	13 03		13 13		
Haggerston	d	11 27		11 43	11 49		11 59	12 04			12 14	12 19		12 29	12 34		12 44	12 49		12 59	13 04		13 14		
Hoxton	d	11 29		11 45	11 51		12 01	12 06			12 16	12 21		12 31	12 36		12 46	12 51		13 01	13 06		13 16		
Shoreditch High Street	d	11 32		11 48	11 54		12 04	12 09			12 19	12 24		12 34	12 39		12 49	12 54		13 04	13 09		13 19		
Whitechapel	d	11 34		11 50	11 56		12 06	12 11			12 21	12 26		12 36	12 41		12 51	12 56		13 06	13 11		13 21		
Shadwell	d	11 36		11 52	11 58		12 08	12 13			12 23	12 28		12 38	12 43		12 53	12 58		13 08	13 13		13 23		
Wapping	d	11 38		11 54	12 00		12 10	12 15			12 25	12 30		12 40	12 45		12 55	13 00		13 10	13 15		13 25		
Rotherhithe	d	11 40		11 56	12 02		12 12	12 17			12 27	12 32		12 42	12 47		12 57	13 02		13 12	13 17		13 27		
Canada Water	d	11 42		11 58	12 04		12 14	12 19			12 29	12 34		12 44	12 49		12 59	13 04		13 14	13 19		13 29		
Surrey Quays	d	11 43		11 59	12 05		12 15	12 20			12 30	12 35		12 45	12 50		13 00	13 05		13 15	13 20		13 30		
New Cross Gate 4	d	11 48	12 00	12 04	12 10	12 15	12 20	12 25		12 30	12 35	12 40	12 45	12 50	12 55	13 00	13 05	13 10	13 15	13 20	13 25	13 30	13 35		
Brockley	d	11 50	12 02	12 06	12 12	12 17	12 22	12 27		12 32	12 37	12 42	12 47	12 52	12 57	13 02	13 07	13 12	13 17	13 22	13 27	13 32	13 37		
Honor Oak Park	d	11 53	12 05	12 09	12 15	12 20	12 25	12 30		12 35	12 40	12 45	12 50	12 55	13 00	13 05	13 10	13 15	13 20	13 25	13 30	13 35	13 40		
Forest Hill 4	d	11 56	12 08	12 12	12 18	12 23	12 28	12 33		12 38	12 43	12 48	12 53	12 58	13 03	13 08	13 13	13 18	13 23	13 28	13 33	13 38	13 43		
Sydenham	d	11 58	12 10	12 14	12 20	12 25	12 30	12 35		12 40	12 45	12 50	12 55	13 00	13 05	13 10	13 15	13 20	13 25	13 30	13 35	13 40	13 45		
Crystal Palace 4	a	12 03			12 25			12 40				12 55			13 10			13 25			13 40				
Penge West	d		12 13	12 17			12 33			12 43	12 48			13 03		13 13	13 18			13 33		13 43	13 48		
Anerley	d		12 15	12 19			12 35			12 45	12 50			13 05		13 15	13 20			13 35		13 45	13 50		
Norwood Junction 2	a		12 18	12 22		12 30	12 38			12 48	12 53		13 00	13 08		13 18	13 23		13 30	13 38		13 48	13 53		
Norwood Junction	d			12 22		12 30	12 38				12 53		13 00	13 08			13 23		13 30	13 38			13 53		
West Croydon 4	a			12 29		12 39	12 44				12 59		13 09	13 14			13 29		13 39	13 44			13 59		
Norwood Junction	d		12 19							12 49						13 19						13 49			
East Croydon	a		12 23							12 53						13 23						13 53			
Purley	a		12 33							13 03						13 33						14 03			

A To Tattenham Corner

For Fast trains between London Bridge & New Cross Gate to Norwood Jn & East Croydon, see Table 175

For full service between Highbury & Islington and Surrey Quays, please see Table 178

For Sutton connections at West Croydon, please see table 172

Table 177

Sundays

8 December to 11 May

London Bridge-New Cross Gate, Brockley, Honor Oak Park, Forest Hill, Sydenham, Crystal Palace, Penge West, Anerley-Norwood Junction and Croydon

Network Diagram - see first Page of Table 173

		LO		SN	LO	LO	SN A	LO	LO	SN	LO	LO	SN A	LO	LO	SN	LO	LO	SN A	LO	LO	SN	LO
London Bridge 4 ⊖	d			20 39			20 54			21 09			21 24			21 39			21 54			22 09	
Highbury & Islington	d	13 13				20 28			20 43			20 58			21 13			21 28			21 43		
Canonbury	d	13 15				20 30			20 45			21 00			21 15			21 30			21 45		
Dalston Junction	d	13 18			20 28	20 33		20 43	20 48		20 58	21 03		21 13	21 18		21 28	21 33		21 43	21 48		21 58
Haggerston	d	13 19			20 29	20 34		20 44	20 49		20 59	21 04		21 14	21 19		21 29	21 34		21 44	21 49		21 59
Hoxton	d	13 21			20 31	20 36		20 46	20 51		21 01	21 06		21 16	21 21		21 31	21 36		21 46	21 51		22 01
Shoreditch High Street	d	13 24			20 34	20 39		20 49	20 54		21 04	21 09		21 19	21 24		21 34	21 39		21 49	21 54		22 04
Whitechapel	d	13 26			20 36	20 41		20 51	20 56		21 06	21 11		21 21	21 26		21 36	21 41		21 51	21 56		22 06
Shadwell	d	13 28			20 38	20 43		20 53	20 58		21 08	21 13		21 23	21 28		21 38	21 43		21 53	21 58		22 08
Wapping	d	13 30	and at the same minutes past each hour until		20 40	20 45		20 55	21 00		21 10	21 15		21 25	21 30		21 40	21 45		21 55	22 00		22 10
Rotherhithe	d	13 32			20 42	20 47		20 57	21 02		21 12	21 17		21 27	21 32		21 42	21 47		21 57	22 02		22 12
Canada Water	d	13 34			20 44	20 49		20 59	21 04		21 14	21 19		21 29	21 34		21 44	21 49		21 59	22 04		22 14
Surrey Quays	d	13 35			20 45	20 50		21 00	21 05		21 15	21 20		21 30	21 35		21 45	21 50		22 00	22 05		22 15
New Cross Gate 4	d	13 40		20 45	20 50	20 55	21 00	21 05	21 10	21 15	21 20	21 25	21 30	21 35	21 40	21 45	21 50	21 55	22 00	22 05	22 10	22 15	22 20
Brockley	d	13 42		20 47	20 52	20 57	21 02	21 07	21 12	21 17	21 22	21 27	21 32	21 37	21 42	21 47	21 52	21 57	22 02	22 07	22 12	22 17	22 22
Honor Oak Park	d	13 45		20 50	20 55	21 00	21 05	21 10	21 15	21 20	21 25	21 30	21 35	21 40	21 45	21 50	21 55	22 00	22 05	22 10	22 15	22 20	22 25
Forest Hill 4	d	13 48		20 53	20 58	21 03	21 08	21 13	21 18	21 23	21 28	21 33	21 38	21 43	21 48	21 53	21 58	22 03	22 08	22 13	22 18	22 23	22 28
Sydenham	d	13 50		20 55	21 00	21 05	21 10	21 15	21 20	21 25	21 30	21 35	21 40	21 45	21 50	21 55	22 00	22 05	22 10	22 15	22 20	22 25	22 30
Crystal Palace 4	a	13 55				21 10			21 25			21 40			21 55			22 10			22 25		
Penge West	d				21 03		21 13	21 18			21 33		21 43	21 48			22 03		22 13	22 18			22 33
Anerley	d				21 05		21 15	21 20			21 35		21 45	21 50			22 05		22 15	22 20			22 35
Norwood Junction 2	a			21 00	21 08		21 18	21 23		21 30	21 38		21 48	21 53		22 00	22 08		22 18	22 23		22 30	22 38
Norwood Junction	d			21 00	21 08			21 23		21 30	21 38			21 53		22 00	22 08			22 23		22 30	22 38
West Croydon 4 🚋	a			21 09	21 14			21 29		21 39	21 44			21 59		22 09	22 14			22 29		22 39	22 44
Norwood Junction	d						21 19						21 49						22 19				
East Croydon 🚋	a						21 23						21 53						22 23				
Purley	a						21 33						22 03						22 33				

		LO	SN A	LO	LO	SN A	LO	SN	LO	LO	SN B	LO
London Bridge 4 ⊖	d		22 24			22 54		23 09			23 39	
Highbury & Islington	d	21 58		22 13			22 43		22 53	23 13		23 23
Canonbury	d	22 00		22 15			22 45		22 55	23 15		23 25
Dalston Junction	d	22 03		22 18	22 28		22 48		22 58	23 18		23 28
Haggerston	d	22 04		22 19	22 29		22 49		22 59	23 19		23 29
Hoxton	d	22 06		22 21	22 31		22 51		23 01	23 21		23 31
Shoreditch High Street	d	22 09		22 24	22 34		22 54		23 04	23 24		23 34
Whitechapel	d	22 11		22 26	22 36		22 56		23 06	23 26		23 36
Shadwell	d	22 13		22 28	22 38		22 58		23 08	23 28		23 38
Wapping	d	22 15		22 30	22 40		23 00		23 10	23 30		23 40
Rotherhithe	d	22 17		22 32	22 42		23 02		23 12	23 32		23 42
Canada Water	d	22 19		22 34	22 44		23 04		23 14	23 34		23 44
Surrey Quays	d	22 20		22 35	22 45		23 05		23 15	23 35		23 45
New Cross Gate 4	d	22 25	22 30	22 40	22 50	23 00	23 10	23 14	23 20	23 40	23 44	23 50
Brockley	d	22 27	22 32	22 42	22 52	23 02	23 12	23 17	23 22	23 42	23 47	23 52
Honor Oak Park	d	22 30	22 35	22 45	22 55	23 05	23 15	23 20	23 25	23 45	23 50	23 55
Forest Hill 4	d	22 33	22 38	22 48	22 58	23 08	23 18	23 22	23 28	23 48	23 52	23 58
Sydenham	d	22 35	22 40	22 50	23 00	23 10	23 20	23 25	23 30	23 50	23 55	00 01
Crystal Palace 4	a	22 40		22 55			23 25			23 55		
Penge West	d		22 43		23 03	23 13		23 27	23 33		23 57	00 03
Anerley	d		22 45		23 05	23 15		23 29	23 35		23 59	00 05
Norwood Junction 2	a		22 48		23 08	23 18		23 32	23 38		00 02	00 08
Norwood Junction	d				23 08				23 38			00 08
West Croydon 4 🚋	a				23 14				23 44			00 14
Norwood Junction	d		22 49			23 19		23 33			00 03	
East Croydon 🚋	a		22 53			23 23		23 38			00 07	
Purley	a		23 03			23 33					00 17	

A To Tattenham Corner

B To Caterham

For Fast trains between London Bridge & New Cross Gate to Norwood Jn & East Croydon, see Table 175

For full service between Highbury & Islington and Surrey Quays, please see Table 178

For Sutton connections at West Croydon, please see table 172

Table 177R

Mondays to Fridays

9 December to 16 May

Croydon and Norwood Junction-Anerley, Penge West, Crystal Palace, Sydenham, Forest Hill, Honor Oak Park, Brockley, New Cross Gate-London Bridge

Network Diagram - see first Page of Table 173

Miles	Miles	Miles	Miles			LO MX A	SN MX B	LO MX C	SN MX B	SN	LO	LO	SN D	LO	LO	LO	LO	SN E	LO	LO	SN	LO	SN B
0	—	—	—	Purley	d					05 07								06 04					
3	—	—	—	East Croydon	d					05 13								06 13					
4¾	—	—	—	Norwood Junction 2	a					05 17								06 17					
—	0	—	—	West Croydon 4	d							05 39	05 45		05 52		06 09			06 22			
—	1¾	—	—	Norwood Junction	a							05 43	05 50		05 58		06 13			06 28			
—	—	—	—	Norwood Junction	d					05 17		05 43	05 50		05 58		06 13	06 18		06 28	06 32		
6	3	—	—	**Anerley**	d					05 20		05 46	05 53		06 01		06 16	06 21		06 31	06 35		
6¼	3¼	—	—	**Penge West**	d					05 22		05 48	05 55		06 03		06 18	06 23		06 33	06 37		
—	—	0	0	**Crystal Palace 4**	d				00 21		05 43			05 58		06 13			06 28			06 41	06 44
7	4	1¼	1¼	**Sydenham**	d				00 24	05 24	05 46	05 51	05 58	06 01	06 06	06 16	06 21	06 25	06 31	06 36	06 39	06 44	06 48
7¾	4¾	2	2	**Forest Hill 4**	d				00 27	05 27	05 49	05 53	06 00	06 04	06 08	06 19	06 23	06 28	06 34	06 38	06 42	06 47	06 50
8¾	5¾	3	3	**Honor Oak Park**	d				00 29	05 29	05 51	05 56	06 03	06 06	06 11	06 21	06 26	06 30	06 36	06 41	06 44	06 49	06 53
9¾	6¾	4	4	**Brockley**	d		00 02		00 32	05 32	05 54	05 58	06 05	06 09	06 13	06 24	06 28	06 33	06 39	06 43	06 47	06 52	06 55
—	7½	4¾	4¾	New Cross Gate	d		00 04		00 34	05 34	05 56	06 01	06 08	06 11	06 16	06 26	06 31	06 35	06 41	06 46	06 49	06 54	06 58
—	8¾	6	—	Surrey Quays	d						06 00	06 04		06 15	06 20	06 30	06 35		06 45	06 50		07 00	
—	9¼	6½	—	Canada Water	d			00 02			06 02	06 07		06 17	06 22	06 32	06 37		06 47	06 52		07 02	
—	9½	6¾	—	Rotherhithe	d			00 03			06 03	06 08		06 18	06 23	06 33	06 38		06 48	06 53		07 03	
—	9¾	7	—	Wapping	d			00 05			06 05	06 10		06 20	06 25	06 35	06 40		06 50	06 55		07 05	
—	10¼	7½	—	Shadwell	d			00 07			06 07	06 12		06 22	06 27	06 37	06 42		06 52	06 57		07 07	
—	11	8	—	Whitechapel	d			00 09			06 09	06 14		06 24	06 29	06 39	06 44		06 54	06 59		07 09	
—	11¾	8¾	—	Shoreditch High Street	d	00 01		00 11			06 11	06 16		06 26	06 31	06 41	06 46		06 56	07 01		07 11	
—	12½	9½	—	Hoxton	d	00 03		00 13			06 13	06 18		06 28	06 33	06 43	06 48		06 58	07 03		07 13	
—	13	10	—	Haggerston	d	00 05		00 15			06 15	06 20		06 30	06 35	06 45	06 50		07 00	07 05		07 15	
—	13½	10½	—	Dalston Junction	a	00 09		00 17			06 19	06 22		06 32	06 39	06 47	06 54		07 02	07 09		07 17	
—	—	11½	—	Canonbury	a			00 20				06 25		06 35		06 51			07 05			07 20	
—	—	12	—	Highbury & Islington	a			00 25				06 28		06 40		06 56			07 10			07 25	
12½	—	—	7½	London Bridge 4 ⊖	a		00 11		00 41	05 41			06 14					06 44			07 00		07 06

		LO	SN F	LO	LO	SN	LO	SN B	LO	SN F	LO	LO	SN	LO	SN B	LO	SN	LO	LO	SN	LO	SN B	LO
Purley	d																						
East Croydon	d																						
Norwood Junction 2	a																						
West Croydon 4	d	06 39			06 52				07 09			07 22				07 39			07 52				08 09
Norwood Junction	a	06 43			06 58				07 13			07 28				07 43			07 58				08 13
Norwood Junction	d	06 43			06 58	07 02			07 13			07 28	07 32			07 43			07 58	08 03			08 13
Anerley	d	06 46			07 01	07 05			07 16			07 31	07 35			07 46			08 01	08 06			08 16
Penge West	d	06 48			07 03	07 07			07 18			07 33	07 37			07 48			08 03	08 08			08 18
Crystal Palace 4	d		06 53	06 58			07 11	07 15		07 21	07 28			07 41	07 44		07 52	07 58			08 11	08 15	
Sydenham	d	06 51	06 56	07 01	07 06	07 09	07 14	07 18	07 21	07 24	07 31	07 36	07 39	07 44	07 48	07 51	07 56	08 01	08 06	08 10	08 14	08 18	08 21
Forest Hill 4	d	06 53	06 59	07 04	07 08	07 12	07 17	07 21	07 23	07 27	07 34	07 38	07 42	07 47	07 50	07 53	07 58	08 04	08 08	08 13	08 17	08 21	08 23
Honor Oak Park	d	06 56	07 01	07 06	07 11	07 14	07 19	07 23	07 26	07 29	07 36	07 41	07 44	07 49	07 53	07 56	08 01	08 06	08 11	08 15	08 19	08 23	08 26
Brockley	d	06 58	07 04	07 09	07 13	07 17	07 22	07 26	07 28	07 32	07 39	07 43	07 47	07 52	07 55	07 58	08 03	08 09	08 13	08 18	08 22	08 26	08 28
New Cross Gate	d	07 01	07 06	07 11	07 16	07 19	07 24	07 28	07 31	07 34	07 41	07 46	07 49	07 54	07 58	08 01	08 06	08 11	08 16	08 20	08 24	08 28	08 31
Surrey Quays	d	07 05		07 15	07 20		07 30		07 35		07 45	07 50		08 00		08 05		08 15	08 20		08 30		08 35
Canada Water	d	07 07		07 17	07 22		07 32		07 37		07 47	07 52		08 02		08 07		08 17	08 22		08 32		08 37
Rotherhithe	d	07 08		07 18	07 23		07 33		07 38		07 48	07 53		08 03		08 08		08 18	08 23		08 33		08 38
Wapping	d	07 10		07 20	07 25		07 35		07 40		07 50	07 55		08 05		08 10		08 20	08 25		08 35		08 40
Shadwell	d	07 12		07 22	07 27		07 37		07 42		07 52	07 57		08 07		08 12		08 22	08 27		08 37		08 42
Whitechapel	d	07 14		07 24	07 29		07 39		07 44		07 54	07 59		08 09		08 14		08 24	08 29		08 39		08 44
Shoreditch High Street	d	07 16		07 26	07 31		07 41		07 46		07 56	08 01		08 11		08 16		08 26	08 31		08 41		08 46
Hoxton	d	07 18		07 28	07 33		07 43		07 48		07 58	08 03		08 13		08 18		08 28	08 33		08 43		08 48
Haggerston	d	07 20		07 30	07 35		07 45		07 50		08 00	08 05		08 15		08 20		08 30	08 35		08 45		08 50
Dalston Junction	a	07 24		07 32	07 39		07 47		07 54		08 02	08 09		08 17		08 24		08 32	08 39		08 47		08 54
Canonbury	a			07 35			07 50				08 05			08 20				08 35			08 50		
Highbury & Islington	a			07 40			07 55				08 10			08 25				08 40			08 55		
London Bridge 4 ⊖	a		07 17			07 28		07 37		07 43			07 58		08 07		08 15			08 28		08 37	

A From West Croydon
B From London Victoria
C From Crystal Palace
D From Epsom
E From Caterham
F From Streatham Hill

For Fast trains between London Bridge & New Cross Gate to Norwood Jn & East Croydon, see Table 175

For full service between Highbury & Islington and Surrey Quays, please see Table 178

For Sutton connections at West Croydon, please see table 172

Table 177R

Mondays to Fridays

9 December to 16 May

Croydon and Norwood Junction-Anerley, Penge West, Crystal Palace, Sydenham, Forest Hill, Honor Oak Park, Brockley, New Cross Gate-London Bridge

Network Diagram - see first Page of Table 173

		SN A	LO	LO	SN	LO	SN A	LO	SN B	LO	LO	SN	LO	SN B	LO	SN	LO	LO	SN	SN C	LO	LO
Purley	d																			09 21		
East Croydon	d																			09 30		
Norwood Junction 2	a																			09 34		
West Croydon 4	d			08 22				08 39			08 52				09 09			09 22				09 39
Norwood Junction	a			08 28				08 44			08 58				09 13			09 28				09 43
Norwood Junction	d			08 28	08 32			08 44			08 58	09 02			09 13			09 28		09 35		09 43
Anerley	d			08 31	08 35			08 47			09 01	09 05			09 16			09 31		09 38		09 46
Penge West	d			08 33	08 37			08 49			09 03	09 07			09 18			09 33		09 40		09 48
Crystal Palace 4	d	08 25	08 28			08 41	08 44		08 54	08 58			09 11	09 14		09 21	09 28		09 36		09 43	
Sydenham	d	08 28	08 31	08 36	08 39	08 44	08 47	08 51	08 58	09 01	09 06	09 09	09 14	09 18	09 21	09 24	09 31	09 36	09 39	09 42	09 46	09 51
Forest Hill 4	d	08 31	08 34	08 38	08 42	08 47	08 50	08 53	09 00	09 04	09 08	09 12	09 17	09 20	09 23	09 27	09 34	09 38	09 42	09 45	09 49	09 53
Honor Oak Park	d	08 33	08 36	08 41	08 44	08 49	08 52	08 56	09 03	09 06	09 11	09 14	09 19	09 23	09 26	09 29	09 36	09 41	09 44	09 47	09 51	09 56
Brockley	d	08 36	08 39	08 43	08 47	08 52	08 55	08 58	09 05	09 09	09 13	09 17	09 22	09 25	09 28	09 32	09 39	09 43	09 47	09 50	09 54	09 58
New Cross Gate	d	08 38	08 41	08 46	08 49	08 54	08 57	09 01	09 08	09 11	09 16	09 19	09 24	09 28	09 31	09 34	09 41	09 46	09 49	09 52	09 56	10 01
Surrey Quays	d		08 45	08 50		09 00		09 05		09 15	09 20		09 30		09 35		09 45	09 50			10 00	10 05
Canada Water	d		08 47	08 52		09 02		09 07		09 17	09 22		09 32		09 37		09 47	09 52			10 02	10 07
Rotherhithe	d		08 48	08 53		09 03		09 08		09 18	09 23		09 33		09 38		09 48	09 53			10 03	10 08
Wapping	d		08 50	08 55		09 05		09 10		09 20	09 25		09 35		09 40		09 50	09 55			10 05	10 10
Shadwell	d		08 52	08 57		09 07		09 12		09 22	09 27		09 37		09 42		09 52	09 57			10 07	10 12
Whitechapel	d		08 54	08 59		09 09		09 14		09 24	09 29		09 39		09 44		09 54	09 59			10 09	10 14
Shoreditch High Street	d		08 56	09 01		09 11		09 16		09 26	09 31		09 41		09 46		09 56	10 01			10 11	10 16
Hoxton	d		08 58	09 03		09 13		09 18		09 28	09 33		09 43		09 48		09 58	10 03			10 13	10 18
Haggerston	d		09 00	09 05		09 15		09 20		09 30	09 35		09 45		09 50		10 00	10 05			10 15	10 20
Dalston Junction	a		09 02	09 09		09 17		09 24		09 32	09 39		09 47		09 54		10 02	10 09			10 17	10 24
Canonbury	a		09 05			09 20				09 35			09 50				10 05				10 20	
Highbury & Islington	a		09 10			09 25				09 40			09 55				10 10				10 25	
London Bridge 4 ⊖	a	08 47			08 58		09 08		09 14			09 29		09 37		09 43			09 59	09 59		

		SN B	LO	LO	SN C	LO	LO	SN B	LO	LO	SN C	LO	LO	SN B	LO	LO	SN C	LO	LO	SN B	LO	LO	SN C
Purley	d				09 51						10 21						10 51						11 21
East Croydon	d				10 00						10 30						11 00						11 30
Norwood Junction 2	a				10 04						10 34						11 04						11 34
West Croydon 4	d			09 52			10 09			10 22			10 39			10 52			11 09			11 22	
Norwood Junction	a			09 58			10 13			10 28			10 43			10 58			11 13			11 28	
Norwood Junction	d			09 58	10 05		10 13			10 28	10 35		10 43			10 58	11 05		11 13			11 28	11 35
Anerley	d			10 01	10 08		10 16			10 31	10 38		10 46			11 01	11 08		11 16			11 31	11 38
Penge West	d			10 03	10 10		10 18			10 33	10 40		10 48			11 03	11 10		11 18			11 33	11 40
Crystal Palace 4	d	09 51	09 58			10 13		10 21	10 28			10 43		10 51	10 58			11 13		11 21	11 28		
Sydenham	d	09 54	10 01	10 06	10 12	10 16	10 21	10 24	10 31	10 36	10 42	10 46	10 51	10 54	11 01	11 06	11 12	11 16	11 21	11 24	11 31	11 36	11 42
Forest Hill 4	d	09 57	10 04	10 08	10 15	10 19	10 23	10 27	10 34	10 38	10 45	10 49	10 53	10 57	11 04	11 08	11 15	11 19	11 23	11 27	11 34	11 38	11 45
Honor Oak Park	d	09 59	10 06	10 11	10 17	10 21	10 26	10 29	10 36	10 41	10 47	10 51	10 56	10 59	11 06	11 11	11 17	11 21	11 26	11 29	11 36	11 41	11 47
Brockley	d	10 02	10 09	10 13	10 20	10 24	10 28	10 32	10 39	10 43	10 50	10 54	10 58	11 02	11 09	11 13	11 20	11 24	11 28	11 32	11 39	11 43	11 50
New Cross Gate	d	10 04	10 11	10 16	10 22	10 26	10 31	10 34	10 41	10 46	10 52	10 56	11 01	11 04	11 11	11 16	11 22	11 26	11 31	11 34	11 41	11 46	11 52
Surrey Quays	d		10 15	10 20		10 30	10 35		10 45	10 50		11 00	11 05		11 15	11 20		11 30	11 35		11 45	11 50	
Canada Water	d		10 17	10 22		10 32	10 37		10 47	10 52		11 02	11 07		11 17	11 22		11 32	11 37		11 47	11 52	
Rotherhithe	d		10 18	10 23		10 33	10 38		10 48	10 53		11 03	11 08		11 18	11 23		11 33	11 38		11 48	11 53	
Wapping	d		10 20	10 25		10 35	10 40		10 50	10 55		11 05	11 10		11 20	11 25		11 35	11 40		11 50	11 55	
Shadwell	d		10 22	10 27		10 37	10 42		10 52	10 57		11 07	11 12		11 22	11 27		11 37	11 42		11 52	11 57	
Whitechapel	d		10 24	10 29		10 39	10 44		10 54	10 59		11 09	11 14		11 24	11 29		11 39	11 44		11 54	11 59	
Shoreditch High Street	d		10 26	10 31		10 41	10 46		10 56	11 01		11 11	11 16		11 26	11 31		11 41	11 46		11 56	12 01	
Hoxton	d		10 28	10 33		10 43	10 48		10 58	11 03		11 13	11 18		11 28	11 33		11 43	11 48		11 58	12 03	
Haggerston	d		10 30	10 35		10 45	10 50		11 00	11 05		11 15	11 20		11 30	11 35		11 45	11 50		12 00	12 05	
Dalston Junction	a		10 32	10 39		10 47	10 54		11 02	11 09		11 17	11 24		11 32	11 39		11 47	11 54		12 02	12 09	
Canonbury	a		10 35			10 50			11 05			11 20			11 35			11 50			12 05		
Highbury & Islington	a		10 40			10 55			11 10			11 25			11 40			11 55			12 10		
London Bridge 4 ⊖	a	10 11			10 29			10 41			10 59			11 11			11 29			11 41			11 59

A From Streatham Hill
B From London Victoria
C From Caterham

For Fast trains between London Bridge & New Cross Gate to Norwood Jn & East Croydon, see Table 175

For full service between Highbury & Islington and Surrey Quays, please see Table 178

For Sutton connections at West Croydon, please see table 172

Table 177R

Mondays to Fridays

9 December to 16 May

Croydon and Norwood Junction-Anerley, Penge West, Crystal Palace, Sydenham, Forest Hill, Honor Oak Park, Brockley, New Cross Gate-London Bridge

Network Diagram - see first Page of Table 173

Station		LO	LO	SN A	LO	LO	SN B	LO	LO	SN A		LO	LO	SN B	LO	LO	SN A	LO	LO	SN B		LO	LO	SN A	LO
Purley	d						11 51							12 21						12 51					
East Croydon	d						12 00							12 30						13 00					
Norwood Junction 2	a						12 04							12 34						13 04					
West Croydon 4	d		11 39			11 52			12 09				12 22			12 39			12 52				13 09		
Norwood Junction	a		11 43			11 58			12 13				12 28			12 43			12 58				13 13		
Norwood Junction	d		11 43			11 58	12 05		12 13				12 28	12 35		12 43			12 58	13 05			13 13		
Anerley	d		11 46			12 01	12 08		12 16				12 31	12 38		12 46			13 01	13 08			13 16		
Penge West	d		11 48			12 03	12 10		12 18				12 33	12 40		12 48			13 03	13 10			13 18		
Crystal Palace 4	d	11 43		11 51	11 58			12 13		12 21		12 28			12 43		12 51	12 58				13 13		13 21	13 28
Sydenham	d	11 46	11 51	11 54	12 01	12 06	12 12	12 16	12 21	12 24		12 31	12 36	12 42	12 46	12 51	12 54	13 01	13 06	13 12		13 16	13 21	13 24	13 31
Forest Hill 4	d	11 49	11 53	11 57	12 04	12 08	12 15	12 19	12 23	12 27		12 34	12 38	12 45	12 49	12 53	12 57	13 04	13 08	13 15		13 19	13 23	13 27	13 34
Honor Oak Park	d	11 51	11 56	11 59	12 06	12 11	12 17	12 21	12 26	12 29		12 36	12 41	12 47	12 51	12 56	12 59	13 06	13 11	13 17		13 21	13 26	13 29	13 36
Brockley	d	11 54	11 58	12 02	12 09	12 13	12 20	12 24	12 28	12 32		12 39	12 43	12 50	12 54	12 58	13 02	13 09	13 13	13 20		13 24	13 28	13 32	13 39
New Cross Gate	d	11 56	12 01	12 04	12 11	12 16	12 22	12 26	12 31	12 34		12 41	12 46	12 52	12 56	13 01	13 04	13 11	13 16	13 22		13 26	13 31	13 34	13 41
Surrey Quays	d	12 00	12 05		12 15	12 20		12 30	12 35			12 45	12 50		13 00	13 05		13 15	13 20			13 30	13 35		13 45
Canada Water	d	12 02	12 07		12 17	12 22		12 32	12 37			12 47	12 52		13 02	13 07		13 17	13 22			13 32	13 37		13 47
Rotherhithe	d	12 03	12 08		12 18	12 23		12 33	12 38			12 48	12 53		13 03	13 08		13 18	13 23			13 33	13 38		13 48
Wapping	d	12 05	12 10		12 20	12 25		12 35	12 40			12 50	12 55		13 05	13 10		13 20	13 25			13 35	13 40		13 50
Shadwell	d	12 07	12 12		12 22	12 27		12 37	12 42			12 52	12 57		13 07	13 12		13 22	13 27			13 37	13 42		13 52
Whitechapel	d	12 09	12 14		12 24	12 29		12 39	12 44			12 54	12 59		13 09	13 14		13 24	13 29			13 39	13 44		13 54
Shoreditch High Street	d	12 11	12 16		12 26	12 31		12 41	12 46			12 56	13 01		13 11	13 16		13 26	13 31			13 41	13 46		13 56
Hoxton	d	12 13	12 18		12 28	12 33		12 43	12 48			12 58	13 03		13 13	13 18		13 28	13 33			13 43	13 48		13 58
Haggerston	d	12 15	12 20		12 30	12 35		12 45	12 50			13 00	13 05		13 15	13 20		13 30	13 35			13 45	13 50		14 00
Dalston Junction	a	12 17	12 24		12 32	12 39		12 47	12 54			13 02	13 09		13 17	13 24		13 32	13 39			13 47	13 54		14 02
Canonbury	a	12 20			12 35			12 50				13 05			13 20			13 35				13 50			14 05
Highbury & Islington	a	12 25			12 40			12 55				13 10			13 25			13 40				13 55			14 10
London Bridge 4 ⊖	a			12 11			12 29			12 41				12 59			13 11			13 29				13 41	

Station		LO	SN B	LO	LO	SN A		LO	LO	SN B	LO	LO	SN A	LO	LO	SN B		LO	LO	SN A	LO	LO	SN B	LO	LO
Purley	d		13 21							13 51						14 21							14 51		
East Croydon	d		13 30							14 00						14 30							15 00		
Norwood Junction 2	a		13 34							14 04						14 34							15 04		
West Croydon 4	d	13 22			13 39				13 52			14 09			14 22				14 39			14 52			15 09
Norwood Junction	a	13 28			13 43				13 58			14 13			14 28				14 43			14 58			15 13
Norwood Junction	d	13 28	13 35		13 43				13 58	14 05		14 13			14 28	14 35			14 43			14 58	15 05		15 13
Anerley	d	13 31	13 38		13 46				14 01	14 08		14 16			14 31	14 38			14 46			15 01	15 08		15 16
Penge West	d	13 33	13 40		13 48				14 03	14 10		14 18			14 33	14 40			14 48			15 03	15 10		15 18
Crystal Palace 4	d			13 43		13 51		13 58			14 13		14 21	14 28				14 43		14 51	14 58			15 13	
Sydenham	d	13 36	13 42	13 46	13 51	13 54		14 01	14 06	14 12	14 16	14 21	14 24	14 31	14 36	14 42		14 46	14 51	14 54	15 01	15 06	15 12	15 16	15 21
Forest Hill 4	d	13 38	13 45	13 49	13 53	13 57		14 04	14 08	14 15	14 19	14 23	14 27	14 34	14 38	14 45		14 49	14 53	14 57	15 04	15 08	15 15	15 19	15 23
Honor Oak Park	d	13 41	13 47	13 51	13 56	13 59		14 06	14 11	14 17	14 21	14 26	14 29	14 36	14 41	14 47		14 51	14 56	14 59	15 06	15 11	15 17	15 21	15 26
Brockley	d	13 43	13 50	13 54	13 58	14 02		14 09	14 13	14 20	14 24	14 28	14 32	14 39	14 43	14 50		14 54	14 58	15 02	15 09	15 13	15 20	15 24	15 28
New Cross Gate	d	13 46	13 52	13 56	14 01	14 04		14 11	14 16	14 22	14 26	14 31	14 34	14 41	14 46	14 52		14 56	15 01	15 04	15 11	15 16	15 22	15 26	15 31
Surrey Quays	d	13 50		14 00	14 05			14 15	14 20		14 30	14 35		14 45	14 50			15 00	15 05		15 15	15 20		15 30	15 35
Canada Water	d	13 52		14 02	14 07			14 17	14 22		14 32	14 37		14 47	14 52			15 02	15 07		15 17	15 22		15 32	15 37
Rotherhithe	d	13 53		14 03	14 08			14 18	14 23		14 33	14 38		14 48	14 53			15 03	15 08		15 18	15 23		15 33	15 38
Wapping	d	13 55		14 05	14 10			14 20	14 25		14 35	14 40		14 50	14 55			15 05	15 10		15 20	15 25		15 35	15 40
Shadwell	d	13 57		14 07	14 12			14 22	14 27		14 37	14 42		14 52	14 57			15 07	15 12		15 22	15 27		15 37	15 42
Whitechapel	d	13 59		14 09	14 14			14 24	14 29		14 39	14 44		14 54	14 59			15 09	15 14		15 24	15 29		15 39	15 44
Shoreditch High Street	d	14 01		14 11	14 16			14 26	14 31		14 41	14 46		14 56	15 01			15 11	15 16		15 26	15 31		15 41	15 46
Hoxton	d	14 03		14 13	14 18			14 28	14 33		14 43	14 48		14 58	15 03			15 13	15 18		15 28	15 33		15 43	15 48
Haggerston	d	14 05		14 15	14 20			14 30	14 35		14 45	14 50		15 00	15 05			15 15	15 20		15 30	15 35		15 45	15 50
Dalston Junction	a	14 09		14 17	14 24			14 32	14 39		14 47	14 54		15 02	15 09			15 17	15 24		15 32	15 39		15 47	15 54
Canonbury	a			14 20				14 35			14 50			15 05				15 20			15 35			15 50	
Highbury & Islington	a			14 25				14 40			14 55			15 10				15 25			15 40			15 55	
London Bridge 4 ⊖	a		13 59			14 11				14 29			14 41			14 59				15 11			15 29		

A From London Victoria

B From Caterham

For Fast trains between London Bridge & New Cross Gate to Norwood Jn & East Croydon, see Table 175

For full service between Highbury & Islington and Surrey Quays, please see Table 178

For Sutton connections at West Croydon, please see table 172

Table 177R

Mondays to Fridays

9 December to 16 May

Croydon and Norwood Junction-Anerley, Penge West, Crystal Palace, Sydenham, Forest Hill, Honor Oak Park, Brockley, New Cross Gate-London Bridge

Network Diagram - see first Page of Table 173

		SN A	LO	LO	SN B	LO	LO	SN A	LO	LO	SN B	LO	LO	SN A	LO	LO	SN B	LO	LO	SN A	LO	LO	SN B
Purley	d				15 21						15 51						16 21						16 51
East Croydon	d				15 30						16 00						16 30						17 00
Norwood Junction 2	a				15 34						16 04						16 34						17 04
West Croydon 4	d			15 22			15 39			15 52			16 09			16 22			16 39			16 52	
Norwood Junction	a			15 28			15 43			15 58			16 13			16 28			16 43			16 58	
Norwood Junction	d			15 28	15 35		15 43			15 58	16 05		16 13			16 28	16 35		16 43			16 58	17 05
Anerley	d			15 31	15 38		15 46			16 01	16 08		16 16			16 31	16 38		16 46			17 01	17 08
Penge West	d			15 33	15 40		15 48			16 03	16 10		16 18			16 33	16 40		16 48			17 03	17 10
Crystal Palace 4	d	15 21	15 28			15 43		15 51	15 58			16 13		16 21	16 28			16 43		16 50	16 58		
Sydenham	d	15 24	15 31	15 36	15 42	15 46	15 51	15 54	16 01	16 06	16 12	16 16	16 21	16 24	16 31	16 36	16 43	16 46	16 51	16 54	17 01	17 06	17 12
Forest Hill 4	d	15 27	15 34	15 38	15 45	15 49	15 53	15 57	16 04	16 08	16 15	16 19	16 23	16 27	16 34	16 38	16 45	16 49	16 53	16 56	17 04	17 08	17 15
Honor Oak Park	d	15 29	15 36	15 41	15 47	15 51	15 56	15 59	16 06	16 11	16 17	16 21	16 26	16 29	16 36	16 41	16 48	16 51	16 56	16 59	17 06	17 11	17 17
Brockley	d	15 32	15 39	15 43	15 50	15 54	15 58	16 02	16 09	16 13	16 20	16 24	16 28	16 32	16 39	16 43	16 50	16 54	16 58	17 01	17 09	17 13	17 20
New Cross Gate	d	15 34	15 41	15 46	15 52	15 56	16 01	16 04	16 11	16 16	16 22	16 26	16 31	16 34	16 41	16 46	16 53	16 56	17 01	17 04	17 11	17 16	17 22
Surrey Quays	d		15 45	15 50		16 00	16 05		16 15	16 20		16 30	16 35		16 45	16 50		17 00	17 05		17 15	17 20	
Canada Water	d		15 47	15 52		16 02	16 07		16 17	16 22		16 32	16 37		16 47	16 52		17 02	17 07		17 17	17 22	
Rotherhithe	d		15 48	15 53		16 03	16 08		16 18	16 23		16 33	16 38		16 48	16 53		17 03	17 08		17 18	17 23	
Wapping	d		15 50	15 55		16 05	16 10		16 20	16 25		16 35	16 40		16 50	16 55		17 05	17 10		17 20	17 25	
Shadwell	d		15 52	15 57		16 07	16 12		16 22	16 27		16 37	16 42		16 52	16 57		17 07	17 12		17 22	17 27	
Whitechapel	d		15 54	15 59		16 09	16 14		16 24	16 29		16 39	16 44		16 54	16 59		17 09	17 14		17 24	17 29	
Shoreditch High Street	d		15 56	16 01		16 11	16 16		16 26	16 31		16 41	16 46		16 56	17 01		17 11	17 16		17 26	17 31	
Hoxton	d		15 58	16 03		16 13	16 18		16 28	16 33		16 43	16 48		16 58	17 03		17 13	17 18		17 28	17 33	
Haggerston	d		16 00	16 05		16 15	16 20		16 30	16 35		16 45	16 50		17 00	17 05		17 15	17 20		17 30	17 35	
Dalston Junction	a		16 02	16 09		16 17	16 24		16 32	16 39		16 47	16 54		17 02	17 09		17 17	17 24		17 32	17 39	
Canonbury	a		16 05			16 20			16 35			16 50			17 05			17 20			17 35		
Highbury & Islington	a		16 10			16 25			16 40			16 55			17 10			17 25			17 40		
London Bridge 4 ⊖	a	15 41			15 59			16 11			16 29			16 41			17 02			17 12			17 29

		LO	LO	SN A	LO	LO	SN B	LO	LO	SN A	LO	LO	SN	LO	LO	SN A	LO	LO	SN B	LO	LO	SN A
Purley	d						17 21												18 21			
East Croydon	d						17 30												18 30			
Norwood Junction 2	a						17 34												18 34			
West Croydon 4	d		17 09			17 22			17 39			17 52			18 09			18 22			18 39	
Norwood Junction	a		17 13			17 28			17 43			17 58			18 13			18 28			18 43	
Norwood Junction	d		17 13			17 28	17 35		17 43			17 58	18 04		18 13			18 28	18 35		18 43	
Anerley	d		17 16			17 31	17 38		17 46			18 01	18 07		18 16			18 31	18 38		18 46	
Penge West	d		17 18			17 33	17 40		17 48			18 03	18 09		18 18			18 33	18 40		18 48	
Crystal Palace 4	d	17 13		17 21	17 28			17 43		17 48	17 58			18 13		18 20	18 28			18 43		18 51
Sydenham	d	17 16	17 21	17 24	17 31	17 36	17 42	17 46	17 51	17 54	18 01	18 06	18 11	18 16	18 21	18 24	18 31	18 36	18 42	18 46	18 51	18 54
Forest Hill 4	d	17 19	17 23	17 27	17 34	17 38	17 45	17 49	17 53	17 57	18 04	18 08	18 14	18 19	18 23	18 27	18 34	18 38	18 45	18 49	18 53	18 57
Honor Oak Park	d	17 21	17 26	17 29	17 36	17 41	17 47	17 51	17 56	17 59	18 06	18 11	18 16	18 21	18 26	18 29	18 36	18 41	18 47	18 51	18 56	18 59
Brockley	d	17 24	17 28	17 32	17 39	17 43	17 50	17 54	17 58	18 02	18 09	18 13	18 19	18 24	18 28	18 32	18 39	18 43	18 50	18 54	18 58	19 02
New Cross Gate	d	17 26	17 31	17 34	17 41	17 46	17 52	17 56	18 01	18 04	18 11	18 16	18 21	18 26	18 31	18 34	18 41	18 46	18 52	18 56	19 01	19 04
Surrey Quays	d	17 30	17 35		17 45	17 50		18 00	18 05		18 15	18 20		18 30	18 35		18 45	18 50		19 00	19 05	
Canada Water	d	17 32	17 37		17 47	17 52		18 02	18 07		18 17	18 22		18 32	18 37		18 47	18 52		19 02	19 07	
Rotherhithe	d	17 33	17 38		17 48	17 53		18 03	18 08		18 18	18 23		18 33	18 38		18 48	18 53		19 03	19 08	
Wapping	d	17 35	17 40		17 50	17 55		18 05	18 10		18 20	18 25		18 35	18 40		18 50	18 55		19 05	19 10	
Shadwell	d	17 37	17 42		17 52	17 57		18 07	18 12		18 22	18 27		18 37	18 42		18 52	18 57		19 07	19 12	
Whitechapel	d	17 39	17 44		17 54	17 59		18 09	18 14		18 24	18 29		18 39	18 44		18 54	18 59		19 09	19 14	
Shoreditch High Street	d	17 41	17 46		17 56	18 01		18 11	18 16		18 26	18 31		18 41	18 46		18 56	19 01		19 11	19 16	
Hoxton	d	17 43	17 48		17 58	18 03		18 13	18 18		18 28	18 33		18 43	18 48		18 58	19 03		19 13	19 18	
Haggerston	d	17 45	17 50		18 00	18 05		18 15	18 20		18 30	18 35		18 45	18 50		19 00	19 05		19 15	19 20	
Dalston Junction	a	17 47	17 54		18 02	18 09		18 17	18 24		18 32	18 39		18 47	18 54		19 02	19 10		19 17	19 24	
Canonbury	a	17 50			18 05			18 20			18 35			18 50			19 05			19 20		
Highbury & Islington	a	17 55			18 10			18 25			18 40			18 55			19 10			19 25		
London Bridge 4 ⊖	a			17 43			17 59			18 13			18 35			18 45			18 59			19 13

A From London Victoria

B From Caterham

For Fast trains between London Bridge & New Cross Gate to Norwood Jn & East Croydon, see Table 175

For full service between Highbury & Islington and Surrey Quays, please see Table 178

For Sutton connections at West Croydon, please see table 172

Table 177R

Mondays to Fridays

9 December to 16 May

Croydon and Norwood Junction-Anerley, Penge West, Crystal Palace, Sydenham, Forest Hill, Honor Oak Park, Brockley, New Cross Gate-London Bridge

Network Diagram - see first Page of Table 173

		LO	LO	SN A	LO	LO		SN B	LO	LO	SN A	LO	LO	SN B	LO	LO		SN A	LO	LO	SN B	LO	LO	SN A	LO
Purley	d			18 51							19 21							19 51						20 22	
East Croydon 🚊	d			19 00							19 30							20 00						20 31	
Norwood Junction (2)	a			19 04							19 34							20 04						20 35	
West Croydon (4) 🚊	d		18 52			19 09				19 22			19 39			19 52				20 09			20 22		
Norwood Junction	a		18 58			19 13				19 28			19 43			19 58				20 13			20 28		
Norwood Junction	d		18 58	19 05		19 13				19 28	19 35		19 43			19 58		20 05		20 13			20 28	20 35	
Anerley	d		19 01	19 08		19 16				19 31	19 38		19 46			20 01		20 08		20 16			20 31	20 38	
Penge West	d		19 03	19 10		19 18				19 33	19 40		19 48			20 03		20 10		20 18			20 33	20 40	
Crystal Palace (4)	d	18 58			19 13			19 21	19 28			19 43		19 51	19 58				20 13		20 21	20 28			20 43
Sydenham	d	19 01	19 06	19 12	19 16	19 21		19 24	19 31	19 36	19 42	19 46	19 51	19 54	20 01	20 06		20 12	20 16	20 21	20 24	20 31	20 36	20 42	20 46
Forest Hill (4)	d	19 04	19 08	19 15	19 19	19 23		19 27	19 34	19 38	19 45	19 49	19 53	19 57	20 04	20 08		20 15	20 19	20 23	20 27	20 34	20 38	20 45	20 49
Honor Oak Park	d	19 06	19 11	19 17	19 21	19 26		19 29	19 36	19 41	19 47	19 51	19 56	19 59	20 06	20 11		20 17	20 21	20 26	20 29	20 36	20 41	20 47	20 51
Brockley	d	19 09	19 13	19 20	19 24	19 28		19 32	19 39	19 43	19 50	19 54	19 58	20 02	20 09	20 13		20 20	20 24	20 28	20 32	20 39	20 43	20 50	20 54
New Cross Gate	d	19 11	19 16	19 22	19 26	19 31		19 34	19 41	19 46	19 52	19 56	20 01	20 04	20 11	20 16		20 22	20 26	20 31	20 34	20 41	20 46	20 52	20 56
Surrey Quays	d	19 15	19 20		19 30	19 35			19 45	19 50		20 00	20 05		20 15	20 20			20 30	20 35		20 45	20 50		21 00
Canada Water	d	19 17	19 22		19 32	19 37			19 47	19 52		20 02	20 07		20 17	20 22			20 32	20 37		20 47	20 52		21 02
Rotherhithe	d	19 18	19 23		19 33	19 38			19 48	19 53		20 03	20 08		20 18	20 23			20 33	20 38		20 48	20 53		21 03
Wapping	d	19 20	19 25		19 35	19 40			19 50	19 55		20 05	20 10		20 20	20 25			20 35	20 40		20 50	20 55		21 05
Shadwell	d	19 22	19 27		19 37	19 42			19 52	19 57		20 07	20 12		20 22	20 27			20 37	20 42		20 52	20 57		21 07
Whitechapel	d	19 24	19 29		19 39	19 44			19 54	19 59		20 09	20 14		20 24	20 29			20 39	20 44		20 54	20 59		21 09
Shoreditch High Street	d	19 26	19 31		19 41	19 46			19 56	20 01		20 11	20 16		20 26	20 31			20 41	20 46		20 56	21 01		21 11
Hoxton	d	19 28	19 33		19 43	19 48			19 58	20 03		20 13	20 18		20 28	20 33			20 43	20 48		20 58	21 03		21 13
Haggerston	d	19 30	19 35		19 45	19 50			20 00	20 05		20 15	20 20		20 30	20 35			20 45	20 50		21 00	21 05		21 15
Dalston Junction	a	19 32	19 40		19 47	19 54			20 02	20 09		20 17	20 24		20 32	20 39			20 47	20 54		21 02	21 09		21 17
Canonbury	a	19 35			19 50				20 05			20 20			20 35				20 50			21 05			21 20
Highbury & Islington	a	19 40			19 55				20 10			20 25			20 40				20 55			21 10			21 25
London Bridge (4) ⊖	a			19 29				19 41			19 59			20 11				20 29			20 43			20 59	

		LO		SN B	LO	LO	SN A	LO	LO	SN B	LO	LO		SN A	LO	LO	SN B	LO	LO	SN A	LO	LO		SN B	LO
Purley	d						20 51							21 21						21 51					
East Croydon 🚊	d						21 00							21 30						22 00					
Norwood Junction (2)	a						21 04							21 34						22 04					
West Croydon (4) 🚊	d	20 39				20 52			21 09			21 22				21 39			21 52			22 09			
Norwood Junction	a	20 43				20 58			21 13			21 28				21 43			21 58			22 13			
Norwood Junction	d	20 43				20 58	21 05		21 13			21 28		21 35		21 43			21 58	22 05		22 13			
Anerley	d	20 46				21 01	21 08		21 16			21 31		21 38		21 46			22 01	22 08		22 16			
Penge West	d	20 48				21 03	21 10		21 18			21 33		21 40		21 48			22 03	22 10		22 18			
Crystal Palace (4)	d			20 51	20 58			21 13		21 21	21 28				21 43		21 51	21 58			22 13			22 21	22 28
Sydenham	d	20 51		20 54	21 01	21 06	21 12	21 16	21 21	21 27	21 31	21 36		21 42	21 46	21 51	21 54	22 01	22 06	22 12	22 16	22 21		22 24	22 31
Forest Hill (4)	d	20 53		20 57	21 04	21 08	21 15	21 19	21 23	21 29	21 34	21 38		21 45	21 49	21 53	21 57	22 04	22 08	22 15	22 19	22 23		22 27	22 34
Honor Oak Park	d	20 56		20 59	21 06	21 11	21 17	21 21	21 26	21 32	21 36	21 41		21 47	21 51	21 56	21 59	22 06	22 11	22 17	22 21	22 26		22 29	22 36
Brockley	d	20 58		21 02	21 09	21 13	21 20	21 24	21 28	21 34	21 39	21 43		21 50	21 54	21 58	22 02	22 09	22 13	22 20	22 24	22 28		22 32	22 39
New Cross Gate	d	21 01		21 04	21 11	21 16	21 22	21 26	21 31	21 37	21 41	21 46		21 52	21 56	22 01	22 04	22 11	22 16	22 22	22 26	22 31		22 34	22 41
Surrey Quays	d	21 05			21 15	21 20		21 30	21 35		21 45	21 50			22 00	22 05		22 15	22 20		22 30	22 35			22 45
Canada Water	d	21 07			21 17	21 22		21 32	21 37		21 47	21 52			22 02	22 07		22 17	22 22		22 32	22 37			22 47
Rotherhithe	d	21 08			21 18	21 23		21 33	21 38		21 48	21 53			22 03	22 08		22 18	22 23		22 33	22 38			22 48
Wapping	d	21 10			21 20	21 25		21 35	21 40		21 50	21 55			22 05	22 10		22 20	22 25		22 35	22 40			22 50
Shadwell	d	21 12			21 22	21 27		21 37	21 42		21 52	21 57			22 07	22 12		22 22	22 27		22 37	22 42			22 52
Whitechapel	d	21 14			21 24	21 29		21 39	21 44		21 54	21 59			22 09	22 14		22 24	22 29		22 39	22 44			22 54
Shoreditch High Street	d	21 16			21 26	21 31		21 41	21 46		21 56	22 01			22 11	22 16		22 26	22 31		22 41	22 46			22 56
Hoxton	d	21 18			21 28	21 33		21 43	21 48		21 58	22 03			22 13	22 18		22 28	22 33		22 43	22 48			22 58
Haggerston	d	21 20			21 30	21 35		21 45	21 50		22 00	22 05			22 15	22 20		22 30	22 35		22 45	22 50			23 00
Dalston Junction	a	21 24			21 32	21 39		21 47	21 54		22 02	22 09			22 17	22 24		22 32	22 39		22 47	22 52			23 02
Canonbury	a				21 35			21 50			22 05				22 20	22 29		22 35				22 55			23 05
Highbury & Islington	a				21 40			21 55			22 10				22 25	22 34		22 40				22 59			23 10
London Bridge (4) ⊖	a			21 11			21 29			21 43				21 59			22 11			22 29				22 41	

A From Caterham

B From London Victoria

For Fast trains between London Bridge & New Cross Gate to Norwood Jn & East Croydon, see Table 175

For full service between Highbury & Islington and Surrey Quays, please see Table 178

For Sutton connections at West Croydon, please see table 172

Table 177R

Mondays to Fridays

9 December to 16 May

Croydon and Norwood Junction-Anerley, Penge West, Crystal Palace, Sydenham, Forest Hill, Honor Oak Park, Brockley, New Cross Gate-London Bridge

Network Diagram - see first Page of Table 173

		LO	SN A	LO	LO	SN B	LO	SN A	LO	SN B	LO	LO	SN B
Purley	d		22 21					22 52					
East Croydon 🚋	d		22 30					23 01					
Norwood Junction 2	a		22 34					23 05					
West Croydon 4 🚋	d	22 22			22 39		22 52				23 22		
Norwood Junction	a	22 28			22 43		22 58				23 28		
Norwood Junction	d	22 28	22 35		22 43		22 58	23 06			23 28		
Anerley	d	22 31	22 38		22 46		23 01	23 09			23 31		
Penge West	d	22 33	22 40		22 48		23 03	23 11			23 33		
Crystal Palace 4	d			22 43		22 51			23 13	23 21		23 43	23 51
Sydenham	d	22 36	22 42	22 46	22 51	22 54	23 06	23 13	23 16	23 24	23 36	23 46	23 54
Forest Hill 4	d	22 38	22 45	22 49	22 53	22 57	23 08	23 16	23 19	23 27	23 38	23 49	23 57
Honor Oak Park	d	22 41	22 47	22 51	22 56	22 59	23 11	23 18	23 21	23 29	23 41	23 51	23 59
Brockley	d	22 43	22 50	22 54	22 58	23 02	23 13	23 21	23 24	23 32	23 43	23 54	00 02
New Cross Gate	d	22 46	22 52	22 56	23 01	23 04	23 16	23 23	23 26	23 34	23 46	23 56	00 04
Surrey Quays	d	22 50		23 00	23 05		23 20		23 30		23 50	23 59	
Canada Water	d	22 52		23 02	23 07		23 22		23 32		23 52	00 02	
Rotherhithe	d	22 53		23 03	23 08		23 23		23 33		23 53	00 03	
Wapping	d	22 55		23 05	23 10		23 25		23 35		23 55	00 05	
Shadwell	d	22 57		23 07	23 12		23 27		23 37		23 57	00 07	
Whitechapel	d	22 59		23 09	23 14		23 29		23 39		23 59	00 09	
Shoreditch High Street	d	23 01		23 11	23 16		23 31		23 41		00 01	00 11	
Hoxton	d	23 03		23 13	23 18		23 33		23 43		00 03	00 13	
Haggerston	d	23 05		23 15	23 20		23 35		23 45		00 05	00 15	
Dalston Junction	a	23 09		23 17	23 23		23 39		23 47		00 09	00 17	
Canonbury	a				23 25				23 50			00 20	
Highbury & Islington	a				23 28				23 55			00 25	
London Bridge 4 ⊖	a		22 59			23 11		23 30		23 44			00 11

Saturdays

14 December to 17 May

		LO C	SN B	LO D	SN B	LO	LO	LO	LO	LO	LO	LO	SN A	LO	LO	SN	LO	LO	SN A	LO	LO	SN E	LO
Purley	d												06 21						06 51				
East Croydon 🚋	d												06 30			06 43			07 00				
Norwood Junction 2	a												06 34			06 49			07 04				
West Croydon 4 🚋	d					05 39		05 52		06 09		06 22			06 39			06 52			07 09	07 15	
Norwood Junction	a					05 43		05 58		06 13		06 28			06 43			06 58			07 13	07 19	
Norwood Junction	d					05 43		05 58		06 13		06 28	06 35		06 43	06 50		06 58	07 05		07 13	07 20	
Anerley	d					05 46		06 01		06 16		06 31	06 38		06 46			07 01	07 08		07 16		
Penge West	d					05 48		06 03		06 18		06 33	06 40		06 48			07 03	07 10		07 18		
Crystal Palace 4	d				00 21		05 58		06 13		06 28			06 43			06 58			07 13			07 28
Sydenham	d				00 24	05 51	06 01	06 06	06 16	06 21	06 31	06 36	06 42	06 46	06 51	06 54	07 01	07 06	07 12	07 16	07 21	07 24	07 31
Forest Hill 4	d				00 27	05 53	06 04	06 08	06 19	06 23	06 34	06 38	06 45	06 49	06 53	06 57	07 04	07 08	07 15	07 19	07 23	07 27	07 34
Honor Oak Park	d				00 29	05 56	06 06	06 11	06 21	06 26	06 36	06 41	06 47	06 51	06 56	06 59	07 06	07 11	07 17	07 21	07 26	07 29	07 36
Brockley	d		00 02		00 32	05 58	06 09	06 13	06 24	06 28	06 39	06 43	06 50	06 54	06 58	07 02	07 09	07 13	07 20	07 24	07 28	07 32	07 39
New Cross Gate	d		00 04		00 34	06 01	06 11	06 16	06 26	06 31	06 41	06 46	06 52	06 56	07 01	07 04	07 11	07 16	07 22	07 26	07 31	07 34	07 41
Surrey Quays	d					06 05	06 15	06 20	06 30	06 35	06 45	06 50		07 00	07 05		07 15	07 20		07 30	07 35		07 45
Canada Water	d			00 02		06 07	06 17	06 22	06 32	06 37	06 47	06 52		07 02	07 07		07 17	07 22		07 32	07 37		07 47
Rotherhithe	d			00 03		06 08	06 18	06 23	06 33	06 38	06 48	06 53		07 03	07 08		07 18	07 23		07 33	07 38		07 48
Wapping	d			00 05		06 10	06 20	06 25	06 35	06 40	06 50	06 55		07 05	07 10		07 20	07 25		07 35	07 40		07 50
Shadwell	d			00 07		06 12	06 22	06 27	06 37	06 42	06 52	06 57		07 07	07 12		07 22	07 27		07 37	07 42		07 52
Whitechapel	d			00 09		06 14	06 24	06 29	06 39	06 44	06 54	06 59		07 09	07 14		07 24	07 29		07 39	07 44		07 54
Shoreditch High Street	d	00 01		00 11		06 16	06 26	06 31	06 41	06 46	06 56	07 01		07 11	07 16		07 26	07 31		07 41	07 46		07 56
Hoxton	d	00 03		00 13		06 18	06 28	06 33	06 43	06 48	06 58	07 03		07 13	07 18		07 28	07 33		07 43	07 48		07 58
Haggerston	d	00 05		00 15		06 20	06 30	06 35	06 45	06 50	07 00	07 05		07 15	07 20		07 30	07 35		07 45	07 50		08 00
Dalston Junction	a	00 09		00 17		06 24	06 32	06 39	06 47	06 54	07 02	07 09		07 17	07 24		07 32	07 39		07 47	07 54		08 02
Canonbury	a			00 20			06 35		06 51		07 07			07 20			07 35			07 50			08 05
Highbury & Islington	a			00 25			06 40		06 56		07 12			07 25			07 40			07 55			08 10
London Bridge 4 ⊖	a		00 11		00 41								06 59			07 11			07 29			07 43	

A From Caterham
B From London Victoria
C From West Croydon
D From Crystal Palace
E From Sutton (Surrey)

For Fast trains between London Bridge & New Cross Gate to Norwood Jn & East Croydon, see Table 175

For full service between Highbury & Islington and Surrey Quays, please see Table 178

For Sutton connections at West Croydon, please see table 172

Table 177R

Saturdays

14 December to 17 May

Croydon and Norwood Junction-Anerley, Penge West, Crystal Palace, Sydenham, Forest Hill, Honor Oak Park, Brockley, New Cross Gate-London Bridge

Network Diagram - see first Page of Table 173

		LO		SN A	LO	LO	SN B	LO	LO	SN A	LO	LO		SN C	LO	LO	SN A	LO	LO	SN C	LO	LO		SN A	LO
Purley	d			07 21						07 51							08 21							08 51	
East Croydon	d			07 30						08 00							08 30							09 00	
Norwood Junction 2	a			07 34						08 04							08 34							09 04	
West Croydon 4	d	07 22				07 39	07 45		07 52			08 09				08 22			08 39			08 52			
Norwood Junction	a	07 28				07 43	07 49		07 58			08 13				08 28			08 43			08 58			
Norwood Junction	d	07 28		07 35		07 43	07 50		07 58	08 05		08 13				08 28	08 35		08 43			08 58		09 05	
Anerley	d	07 31		07 38		07 46			08 01	08 08		08 16				08 31	08 38		08 46			09 01		09 08	
Penge West	d	07 33		07 40		07 48			08 03	08 10		08 18				08 33	08 40		08 48			09 03		09 10	
Crystal Palace 4	d				07 43			07 58			08 13			08 21	08 28			08 43		08 51	08 58				09 13
Sydenham	d	07 36		07 42	07 46	07 51	07 54	08 01	08 06	08 12	08 16	08 21		08 24	08 31	08 36	08 42	08 46	08 51	08 54	09 01	09 06		09 12	09 16
Forest Hill 4	d	07 38		07 45	07 49	07 53	07 57	08 04	08 08	08 15	08 19	08 23		08 27	08 34	08 38	08 45	08 49	08 53	08 57	09 04	09 08		09 15	09 19
Honor Oak Park	d	07 41		07 47	07 51	07 56	07 59	08 06	08 11	08 17	08 21	08 26		08 29	08 36	08 41	08 47	08 51	08 56	08 59	09 06	09 11		09 17	09 21
Brockley	d	07 43		07 50	07 54	07 58	08 02	08 09	08 13	08 20	08 24	08 28		08 32	08 39	08 43	08 50	08 54	08 58	09 02	09 09	09 13		09 20	09 24
New Cross Gate	d	07 46		07 52	07 56	08 01	08 04	08 11	08 16	08 22	08 26	08 31		08 34	08 41	08 46	08 52	08 56	09 01	09 04	09 11	09 16		09 22	09 26
Surrey Quays	d	07 50			08 00	08 05		08 15	08 20		08 30	08 35			08 45	08 50		09 00	09 05		09 15	09 20			09 30
Canada Water	d	07 52			08 02	08 07		08 17	08 22		08 32	08 37			08 47	08 52		09 02	09 07		09 17	09 22			09 32
Rotherhithe	d	07 53			08 03	08 08		08 18	08 23		08 33	08 38			08 48	08 53		09 03	09 08		09 18	09 23			09 33
Wapping	d	07 55			08 05	08 10		08 20	08 25		08 35	08 40			08 50	08 55		09 05	09 10		09 20	09 25			09 35
Shadwell	d	07 57			08 07	08 12		08 22	08 27		08 37	08 42			08 52	08 57		09 07	09 12		09 22	09 27			09 37
Whitechapel	d	07 59			08 09	08 14		08 24	08 29		08 39	08 44			08 54	08 59		09 09	09 14		09 24	09 29			09 39
Shoreditch High Street	d	08 01			08 11	08 16		08 26	08 31		08 41	08 46			08 56	09 01		09 11	09 16		09 26	09 31			09 41
Hoxton	d	08 03			08 13	08 18		08 28	08 33		08 43	08 48			08 58	09 03		09 13	09 18		09 28	09 33			09 43
Haggerston	d	08 05			08 15	08 20		08 30	08 35		08 45	08 50			09 00	09 05		09 15	09 20		09 30	09 35			09 45
Dalston Junction	a	08 09			08 17	08 24		08 32	08 39		08 47	08 54			09 02	09 09		09 17	09 24		09 32	09 39			09 47
Canonbury	a				08 20			08 35			08 50				09 05			09 20			09 35				09 50
Highbury & Islington	a				08 25			08 40			08 55				09 10			09 25			09 40				09 55
London Bridge 4 ⊖	a			07 59			08 11			08 29				08 41			08 59			09 11				09 29	

		LO	SN C	LO	LO	SN A	LO	LO		SN C	LO	LO	SN A	LO	LO	SN C	LO	LO		SN A	LO	LO	SN C	LO	LO
Purley	d					09 21							09 51							10 21					
East Croydon	d					09 30							10 00							10 30					
Norwood Junction 2	a					09 34							10 04							10 34					
West Croydon 4	d	09 09			09 22			09 39				09 52			10 09			10 22				10 39			10 52
Norwood Junction	a	09 13			09 28			09 43				09 58			10 13			10 28				10 43			10 58
Norwood Junction	d	09 13			09 28	09 35		09 43				09 58	10 05		10 13			10 28		10 35		10 43			10 58
Anerley	d	09 16			09 31	09 38		09 46				10 01	10 08		10 16			10 31		10 38		10 46			11 01
Penge West	d	09 18			09 33	09 40		09 48				10 03	10 10		10 18			10 33		10 40		10 48			11 03
Crystal Palace 4	d		09 21	09 28			09 43			09 51	09 58			10 13		10 21	10 28				10 43		10 51	10 58	
Sydenham	d	09 21	09 24	09 31	09 36	09 42	09 46	09 51		09 54	10 01	10 06	10 12	10 16	10 21	10 24	10 31	10 36		10 42	10 46	10 51	10 54	11 01	11 06
Forest Hill 4	d	09 23	09 27	09 34	09 38	09 45	09 49	09 53		09 57	10 04	10 08	10 15	10 19	10 23	10 27	10 34	10 38		10 45	10 49	10 53	10 57	11 04	11 08
Honor Oak Park	d	09 26	09 29	09 36	09 41	09 47	09 51	09 56		09 59	10 06	10 11	10 17	10 21	10 26	10 29	10 36	10 41		10 47	10 51	10 56	10 59	11 06	11 11
Brockley	d	09 28	09 32	09 39	09 43	09 50	09 54	09 58		10 02	10 09	10 13	10 20	10 24	10 28	10 32	10 39	10 43		10 50	10 54	10 58	11 02	11 09	11 13
New Cross Gate	d	09 31	09 34	09 41	09 46	09 52	09 56	10 01		10 04	10 11	10 16	10 22	10 26	10 31	10 34	10 41	10 46		10 52	10 56	11 01	11 04	11 11	11 16
Surrey Quays	d	09 35		09 45	09 50		10 00	10 05			10 15	10 20		10 30	10 35		10 45	10 50			11 00	11 05		11 15	11 20
Canada Water	d	09 37		09 47	09 52		10 02	10 07			10 17	10 22		10 32	10 37		10 47	10 52			11 02	11 07		11 17	11 22
Rotherhithe	d	09 38		09 48	09 53		10 03	10 08			10 18	10 23		10 33	10 38		10 48	10 53			11 03	11 08		11 18	11 23
Wapping	d	09 40		09 50	09 55		10 05	10 10			10 20	10 25		10 35	10 40		10 50	10 55			11 05	11 10		11 20	11 25
Shadwell	d	09 42		09 52	09 57		10 07	10 12			10 22	10 27		10 37	10 42		10 52	10 57			11 07	11 12		11 22	11 27
Whitechapel	d	09 44		09 54	09 59		10 09	10 14			10 24	10 29		10 39	10 44		10 54	10 59			11 09	11 14		11 24	11 29
Shoreditch High Street	d	09 46		09 56	10 01		10 11	10 16			10 26	10 31		10 41	10 46		10 56	11 01			11 11	11 16		11 26	11 31
Hoxton	d	09 48		09 58	10 03		10 13	10 18			10 28	10 33		10 43	10 48		10 58	11 03			11 13	11 18		11 28	11 33
Haggerston	d	09 50		10 00	10 05		10 15	10 20			10 30	10 35		10 45	10 50		11 00	11 05			11 15	11 20		11 30	11 35
Dalston Junction	a	09 54		10 02	10 09		10 17	10 24			10 32	10 39		10 47	10 54		11 02	11 09			11 17	11 24		11 32	11 39
Canonbury	a			10 05			10 20				10 35			10 50			11 05				11 20			11 35	
Highbury & Islington	a			10 10			10 25				10 40			10 55			11 10				11 25			11 40	
London Bridge 4 ⊖	a		09 41			09 59				10 11			10 29			10 41				10 59			11 11		

A From Caterham **B** From Sutton (Surrey) **C** From London Victoria

For Fast trains between London Bridge & New Cross Gate to Norwood Jn & East Croydon, see Table 175

For full service between Highbury & Islington and Surrey Quays, please see Table 178

For Sutton connections at West Croydon, please see table 172

Table 177R

Saturdays

14 December to 17 May

Croydon and Norwood Junction-Anerley, Penge West, Crystal Palace, Sydenham, Forest Hill, Honor Oak Park, Brockley, New Cross Gate-London Bridge

Network Diagram - see first Page of Table 173

		SN A	LO	LO	SN B	LO	LO	SN A	LO	LO		SN B	LO	LO	SN A	LO	LO	SN B	LO	LO		SN A	LO	LO	SN B
Purley	d	10 51						11 21							11 51							12 21			
East Croydon	d	11 00						11 30							12 00							12 30			
Norwood Junction 2	a	11 04						11 34							12 04							12 34			
West Croydon 4	d			11 09			11 22			11 39				11 52			12 09			12 22				12 39	
Norwood Junction	a			11 13			11 28			11 43				11 58			12 13			12 28				12 43	
Norwood Junction	d	11 05		11 13			11 28	11 35		11 43				11 58	12 05		12 13			12 28		12 35		12 43	
Anerley	d	11 08		11 16			11 31	11 38		11 46				12 01	12 08		12 16			12 31		12 38		12 46	
Penge West	d	11 10		11 18			11 33	11 40		11 48				12 03	12 10		12 18			12 33		12 40		12 48	
Crystal Palace 4	d		11 13		11 21	11 28			11 43			11 51	11 58			12 13		12 21	12 28				12 43		12 51
Sydenham	d	11 12	11 16	11 21	11 24	11 31	11 36	11 42	11 46	11 51		11 54	12 01	12 06	12 12	12 16	12 21	12 24	12 31	12 36		12 42	12 46	12 51	12 54
Forest Hill 4	d	11 15	11 19	11 23	11 27	11 34	11 38	11 45	11 49	11 53		11 57	12 04	12 08	12 15	12 19	12 23	12 27	12 34	12 38		12 45	12 49	12 53	12 57
Honor Oak Park	d	11 17	11 21	11 26	11 29	11 36	11 41	11 47	11 51	11 56		11 59	12 06	12 11	12 17	12 21	12 26	12 29	12 36	12 41		12 47	12 51	12 56	12 59
Brockley	d	11 20	11 24	11 28	11 32	11 39	11 43	11 50	11 54	11 58		12 02	12 09	12 13	12 20	12 24	12 28	12 32	12 39	12 43		12 50	12 54	12 58	13 02
New Cross Gate	d	11 22	11 26	11 31	11 34	11 41	11 46	11 52	11 56	12 01		12 04	12 11	12 16	12 22	12 26	12 31	12 34	12 41	12 46		12 52	12 56	13 01	13 04
Surrey Quays	d		11 30	11 35		11 45	11 50		12 00	12 05			12 15	12 20		12 30	12 35		12 45	12 50			13 00	13 05	
Canada Water	d		11 32	11 37		11 47	11 52		12 02	12 07			12 17	12 22		12 32	12 37		12 47	12 52			13 02	13 07	
Rotherhithe	d		11 33	11 38		11 48	11 53		12 03	12 08			12 18	12 23		12 33	12 38		12 48	12 53			13 03	13 08	
Wapping	d		11 35	11 40		11 50	11 55		12 05	12 10			12 20	12 25		12 35	12 40		12 50	12 55			13 05	13 10	
Shadwell	d		11 37	11 42		11 52	11 57		12 07	12 12			12 22	12 27		12 37	12 42		12 52	12 57			13 07	13 12	
Whitechapel	d		11 39	11 44		11 54	11 59		12 09	12 14			12 24	12 29		12 39	12 44		12 54	12 59			13 09	13 14	
Shoreditch High Street	d		11 41	11 46		11 56	12 01		12 11	12 16			12 26	12 31		12 41	12 46		12 56	13 01			13 11	13 16	
Hoxton	d		11 43	11 48		11 58	12 03		12 13	12 18			12 28	12 33		12 43	12 48		12 58	13 03			13 13	13 18	
Haggerston	d		11 45	11 50		12 00	12 05		12 15	12 20			12 30	12 35		12 45	12 50		13 00	13 05			13 15	13 20	
Dalston Junction	a		11 47	11 54		12 02	12 09		12 17	12 24			12 32	12 39		12 47	12 54		13 02	13 09			13 17	13 24	
Canonbury	a		11 50			12 05			12 20				12 35			12 50			13 05				13 20		
Highbury & Islington	a		11 55			12 10			12 25				12 40			12 55			13 10				13 25		
London Bridge 4 ⊖	a	11 29			11 41			11 59				12 11			12 29			12 41				12 59			13 11

		LO	LO	SN A	LO	LO		SN B	LO	LO	SN A	LO	LO	SN B	LO	LO		SN A	LO	LO	SN B	LO	LO	SN A	LO
Purley	d			12 51							13 21							13 51						14 21	
East Croydon	d			13 00							13 30							14 00						14 30	
Norwood Junction 2	a			13 04							13 34							14 04						14 34	
West Croydon 4	d		12 52			13 09				13 22			13 39			13 52				14 09			14 22		
Norwood Junction	a		12 58			13 13				13 28			13 43			13 58				14 13			14 28		
Norwood Junction	d		12 58	13 05		13 13				13 28	13 35		13 43			13 58		14 05		14 13			14 28	14 35	
Anerley	d		13 01	13 08		13 16				13 31	13 38		13 46			14 01		14 08		14 16			14 31	14 38	
Penge West	d		13 03	13 10		13 18				13 33	13 40		13 48			14 03		14 10		14 18			14 33	14 40	
Crystal Palace 4	d	12 58			13 13			13 21	13 28			13 43		13 51	13 58				14 13		14 21	14 28			14 43
Sydenham	d	13 01	13 06	13 12	13 16	13 21		13 24	13 31	13 36	13 42	13 46	13 51	13 54	14 01	14 06		14 12	14 16	14 21	14 24	14 31	14 36	14 42	14 46
Forest Hill 4	d	13 04	13 08	13 15	13 19	13 23		13 27	13 34	13 38	13 45	13 49	13 53	13 57	14 04	14 08		14 15	14 19	14 23	14 27	14 34	14 38	14 45	14 49
Honor Oak Park	d	13 06	13 11	13 17	13 21	13 26		13 29	13 36	13 41	13 47	13 51	13 56	13 59	14 06	14 11		14 17	14 21	14 26	14 29	14 36	14 41	14 47	14 51
Brockley	d	13 09	13 13	13 20	13 24	13 28		13 32	13 39	13 43	13 50	13 54	13 58	14 02	14 09	14 13		14 20	14 24	14 28	14 32	14 39	14 43	14 50	14 54
New Cross Gate	d	13 11	13 16	13 22	13 26	13 31		13 34	13 41	13 46	13 52	13 56	14 01	14 04	14 11	14 16		14 22	14 26	14 31	14 34	14 41	14 46	14 52	14 56
Surrey Quays	d	13 15	13 20		13 30	13 35			13 45	13 50		14 00	14 05		14 15	14 20			14 30	14 35		14 45	14 50		15 00
Canada Water	d	13 17	13 22		13 32	13 37			13 47	13 52		14 02	14 07		14 17	14 22			14 32	14 37		14 47	14 52		15 02
Rotherhithe	d	13 18	13 23		13 33	13 38			13 48	13 53		14 03	14 08		14 18	14 23			14 33	14 38		14 48	14 53		15 03
Wapping	d	13 20	13 25		13 35	13 40			13 50	13 55		14 05	14 10		14 20	14 25			14 35	14 40		14 50	14 55		15 05
Shadwell	d	13 22	13 27		13 37	13 42			13 52	13 57		14 07	14 12		14 22	14 27			14 37	14 42		14 52	14 57		15 07
Whitechapel	d	13 24	13 29		13 39	13 44			13 54	13 59		14 09	14 14		14 24	14 29			14 39	14 44		14 54	14 59		15 09
Shoreditch High Street	d	13 26	13 31		13 41	13 46			13 56	14 01		14 11	14 16		14 26	14 31			14 41	14 46		14 56	15 01		15 11
Hoxton	d	13 28	13 33		13 43	13 48			13 58	14 03		14 13	14 18		14 28	14 33			14 43	14 48		14 58	15 03		15 13
Haggerston	d	13 30	13 35		13 45	13 50			14 00	14 05		14 15	14 20		14 30	14 35			14 45	14 50		15 00	15 05		15 15
Dalston Junction	a	13 32	13 39		13 47	13 54			14 02	14 09		14 17	14 24		14 32	14 39			14 47	14 54		15 02	15 09		15 17
Canonbury	a	13 35			13 50				14 05			14 20			14 35				14 50			15 05			15 20
Highbury & Islington	a	13 40			13 55				14 10			14 25			14 40				14 55			15 10			15 25
London Bridge 4 ⊖	a			13 29				13 41			13 59			14 11				14 29			14 41			14 59	

A From Caterham

B From London Victoria

For Fast trains between London Bridge & New Cross Gate to Norwood Jn & East Croydon, see Table 175

For full service between Highbury & Islington and Surrey Quays, please see Table 178

For Sutton connections at West Croydon, please see table 172

Table 177R

Saturdays

14 December to 17 May

Croydon and Norwood Junction-Anerley, Penge West, Crystal Palace, Sydenham, Forest Hill, Honor Oak Park, Brockley, New Cross Gate-London Bridge

Network Diagram - see first Page of Table 173

		LO	SN A	LO	LO	SN B	LO	LO		SN A	LO	LO	SN B	LO	LO	SN A	LO	LO		SN B	LO	LO	SN A	LO	LO
Purley	d					14 51							15 21							15 51					
East Croydon	d					15 00							15 30							16 00					
Norwood Junction 2	a					15 04							15 34							16 04					
West Croydon 4	d	14 39			14 52			15 09				15 22			15 39			15 52				16 09			16 22
Norwood Junction	a	14 43			14 58			15 13				15 28			15 43			15 58				16 13			16 28
Norwood Junction	d	14 43			14 58	15 05		15 13				15 28	15 35		15 43			15 58		16 05		16 13			16 28
Anerley	d	14 46			15 01	15 08		15 16				15 31	15 38		15 46			16 01		16 08		16 16			16 31
Penge West	d	14 48			15 03	15 10		15 18				15 33	15 40		15 48			16 03		16 10		16 18			16 33
Crystal Palace 4	d		14 51	14 58			15 13			15 21	15 28			15 43		15 51	15 58				16 13		16 21	16 28	
Sydenham	d	14 51	14 54	15 01	15 06	15 12	15 16	15 21		15 24	15 31	15 36	15 42	15 46	15 51	15 54	16 01	16 06		16 12	16 16	16 21	16 24	16 31	16 36
Forest Hill 4	d	14 53	14 57	15 04	15 08	15 15	15 19	15 23		15 27	15 34	15 38	15 45	15 49	15 53	15 57	16 04	16 08		16 15	16 19	16 23	16 27	16 34	16 38
Honor Oak Park	d	14 56	14 59	15 06	15 11	15 17	15 21	15 26		15 29	15 36	15 41	15 47	15 51	15 56	15 59	16 06	16 11		16 17	16 21	16 26	16 29	16 36	16 41
Brockley	d	14 58	15 02	15 09	15 13	15 20	15 24	15 28		15 32	15 39	15 43	15 50	15 54	15 58	16 02	16 09	16 13		16 20	16 24	16 28	16 32	16 39	16 43
New Cross Gate	d	15 01	15 04	15 11	15 16	15 22	15 26	15 31		15 34	15 41	15 46	15 52	15 56	16 01	16 04	16 11	16 16		16 22	16 26	16 31	16 34	16 41	16 46
Surrey Quays	d	15 05		15 15	15 20		15 30	15 35			15 45	15 50		16 00	16 05		16 15	16 20			16 30	16 35		16 45	16 50
Canada Water	d	15 07		15 17	15 22		15 32	15 37			15 47	15 52		16 02	16 07		16 17	16 22			16 32	16 37		16 47	16 52
Rotherhithe	d	15 08		15 18	15 23		15 33	15 38			15 48	15 53		16 03	16 08		16 18	16 23			16 33	16 38		16 48	16 53
Wapping	d	15 10		15 20	15 25		15 35	15 40			15 50	15 55		16 05	16 10		16 20	16 25			16 35	16 40		16 50	16 55
Shadwell	d	15 12		15 22	15 27		15 37	15 42			15 52	15 57		16 07	16 12		16 22	16 27			16 37	16 42		16 52	16 57
Whitechapel	d	15 14		15 24	15 29		15 39	15 44			15 54	15 59		16 09	16 14		16 24	16 29			16 39	16 44		16 54	16 59
Shoreditch High Street	d	15 16		15 26	15 31		15 41	15 46			15 56	16 01		16 11	16 16		16 26	16 31			16 41	16 46		16 56	17 01
Hoxton	d	15 18		15 28	15 33		15 43	15 48			15 58	16 03		16 13	16 18		16 28	16 33			16 43	16 48		16 58	17 03
Haggerston	d	15 20		15 30	15 35		15 45	15 50			16 00	16 05		16 15	16 20		16 30	16 35			16 45	16 50		17 00	17 05
Dalston Junction	a	15 24		15 32	15 39		15 47	15 54			16 02	16 09		16 17	16 24		16 32	16 39			16 47	16 54		17 02	17 09
Canonbury	a			15 35			15 50				16 05			16 20			16 35				16 50			17 05	
Highbury & Islington	a			15 40			15 55				16 10			16 25			16 40				16 55			17 10	
London Bridge 4 ⊖	a		15 11			15 29				15 41			15 59			16 11				16 29			16 41		

		SN B	LO	LO		SN A	LO	LO	SN B	LO	LO	SN A	LO	LO		SN B	LO	LO	SN A	LO	LO	SN B	LO	LO	
Purley	d	16 21							16 51							17 21						17 51			
East Croydon	d	16 30							17 00							17 30						18 00			
Norwood Junction 2	a	16 34							17 04							17 34						18 04			
West Croydon 4	d			16 39				16 52			17 09			17 22				17 39			17 52			18 09	
Norwood Junction	a			16 43				16 58			17 13			17 28				17 43			17 58			18 13	
Norwood Junction	d	16 35		16 43				16 58	17 05		17 13			17 28		17 35		17 43			17 58	18 05		18 13	
Anerley	d	16 38		16 46				17 01	17 08		17 16			17 31		17 38		17 46			18 01	18 08		18 16	
Penge West	d	16 40		16 48				17 03	17 10		17 18			17 33		17 40		17 48			18 03	18 10		18 18	
Crystal Palace 4	d		16 43			16 51	16 58			17 13		17 21	17 28				17 43		17 51	17 58			18 13		
Sydenham	d	16 42	16 46	16 51		16 54	17 01	17 06	17 12	17 16	17 21	17 24	17 31	17 36		17 42	17 46	17 51	17 54	18 01	18 06	18 12	18 16	18 21	
Forest Hill 4	d	16 45	16 49	16 53		16 57	17 04	17 08	17 15	17 19	17 23	17 27	17 34	17 38		17 45	17 49	17 53	17 57	18 04	18 08	18 15	18 19	18 23	
Honor Oak Park	d	16 47	16 51	16 56		16 59	17 06	17 11	17 17	17 21	17 26	17 29	17 36	17 41		17 47	17 51	17 56	17 59	18 06	18 11	18 17	18 21	18 26	
Brockley	d	16 50	16 54	16 58		17 02	17 09	17 13	17 20	17 24	17 28	17 32	17 39	17 43		17 50	17 54	17 58	18 02	18 09	18 13	18 20	18 24	18 28	
New Cross Gate	d	16 52	16 56	17 01		17 04	17 11	17 16	17 22	17 26	17 31	17 34	17 41	17 46		17 52	17 56	18 01	18 04	18 11	18 16	18 22	18 26	18 31	
Surrey Quays	d		17 00	17 05			17 15	17 20		17 30	17 35		17 45	17 50			18 00	18 05		18 15	18 20		18 30	18 35	
Canada Water	d		17 02	17 07			17 17	17 22		17 32	17 37		17 47	17 52			18 02	18 07		18 17	18 22		18 32	18 37	
Rotherhithe	d		17 03	17 08			17 18	17 23		17 33	17 38		17 48	17 53			18 03	18 08		18 18	18 23		18 33	18 38	
Wapping	d		17 05	17 10			17 20	17 25		17 35	17 40		17 50	17 55			18 05	18 10		18 20	18 25		18 35	18 40	
Shadwell	d		17 07	17 12			17 22	17 27		17 37	17 42		17 52	17 57			18 07	18 12		18 22	18 27		18 37	18 42	
Whitechapel	d		17 09	17 14			17 24	17 29		17 39	17 44		17 54	17 59			18 09	18 14		18 24	18 29		18 39	18 44	
Shoreditch High Street	d		17 11	17 16			17 26	17 31		17 41	17 46		17 56	18 01			18 11	18 16		18 26	18 31		18 41	18 46	
Hoxton	d		17 13	17 18			17 28	17 33		17 43	17 48		17 58	18 03			18 13	18 18		18 28	18 33		18 43	18 48	
Haggerston	d		17 15	17 20			17 30	17 35		17 45	17 50		18 00	18 05			18 15	18 20		18 30	18 35		18 45	18 50	
Dalston Junction	a		17 17	17 24			17 32	17 39		17 47	17 54		18 02	18 09			18 17	18 24		18 32	18 39		18 47	18 54	
Canonbury	a		17 20				17 35			17 50			18 05				18 20			18 35			18 50		
Highbury & Islington	a		17 25				17 40			17 55			18 10				18 25			18 40			18 55		
London Bridge 4 ⊖	a	16 59				17 11			17 30			17 41				17 59			18 11			18 29			

A From London Victoria

B From Caterham

For Fast trains between London Bridge & New Cross Gate to Norwood Jn & East Croydon, see Table 175

For full service between Highbury & Islington and Surrey Quays, please see Table 178

For Sutton connections at West Croydon, please see table 172

Table 177R

Saturdays

14 December to 17 May

Croydon and Norwood Junction-Anerley, Penge West, Crystal Palace, Sydenham, Forest Hill, Honor Oak Park, Brockley, New Cross Gate-London Bridge

Network Diagram - see first Page of Table 173

		SN A	LO	LO	SN B	LO		LO	SN A	LO	LO	SN B	LO	LO	SN A	LO		LO	SN B	LO	LO	SN A	LO	LO	SN B
Purley	d				18 21							18 51							19 21						19 51
East Croydon	d				18 30							19 00							19 30						20 00
Norwood Junction 2	a				18 34							19 04							19 34						20 04
West Croydon 4	d			18 22				18 39			18 52			19 09				19 22			19 39			19 52	
Norwood Junction	a			18 28				18 43			18 58			19 13				19 28			19 43			19 58	
Norwood Junction	d			18 28	18 35			18 43			18 58	19 05		19 13				19 28	19 35		19 43			19 58	20 05
Anerley	d			18 31	18 38			18 46			19 01	19 08		19 16				19 31	19 38		19 46			20 01	20 08
Penge West	d			18 33	18 40			18 48			19 03	19 10		19 18				19 33	19 40		19 48			20 03	20 10
Crystal Palace 4	d	18 21	18 28			18 43			18 51	18 58			19 13		19 21	19 28				19 43		19 51	19 58		
Sydenham	d	18 24	18 31	18 36	18 42	18 46		18 51	18 54	19 01	19 06	19 12	19 16	19 21	19 24	19 31		19 36	19 42	19 46	19 51	19 54	20 01	20 06	20 12
Forest Hill 4	d	18 27	18 34	18 38	18 45	18 49		18 53	18 57	19 04	19 08	19 15	19 19	19 23	19 27	19 34		19 38	19 45	19 49	19 53	19 57	20 04	20 08	20 15
Honor Oak Park	d	18 29	18 36	18 41	18 47	18 51		18 56	18 59	19 06	19 11	19 17	19 21	19 26	19 29	19 36		19 41	19 47	19 51	19 56	19 59	20 06	20 11	20 17
Brockley	d	18 32	18 39	18 43	18 50	18 54		18 58	19 02	19 09	19 13	19 20	19 24	19 28	19 32	19 39		19 43	19 50	19 54	19 58	20 02	20 09	20 13	20 20
New Cross Gate	d	18 34	18 41	18 46	18 52	18 56		19 01	19 04	19 11	19 16	19 22	19 26	19 31	19 34	19 41		19 46	19 52	19 56	20 01	20 04	20 11	20 16	20 22
Surrey Quays	d		18 45	18 50		19 00		19 05		19 15	19 20		19 30	19 35		19 45		19 50		20 00	20 05		20 15	20 20	
Canada Water	d		18 47	18 52		19 02		19 07		19 17	19 22		19 32	19 37		19 47		19 52		20 02	20 07		20 17	20 22	
Rotherhithe	d		18 48	18 53		19 03		19 08		19 18	19 23		19 33	19 38		19 48		19 53		20 03	20 08		20 18	20 23	
Wapping	d		18 50	18 55		19 05		19 10		19 20	19 25		19 35	19 40		19 50		19 55		20 05	20 10		20 20	20 25	
Shadwell	d		18 52	18 57		19 07		19 12		19 22	19 27		19 37	19 42		19 52		19 57		20 07	20 12		20 22	20 27	
Whitechapel	d		18 54	18 59		19 09		19 14		19 24	19 29		19 39	19 44		19 54		19 59		20 09	20 14		20 24	20 29	
Shoreditch High Street	d		18 56	19 01		19 11		19 16		19 26	19 31		19 41	19 46		19 56		20 01		20 11	20 16		20 26	20 31	
Hoxton	d		18 58	19 03		19 13		19 18		19 28	19 33		19 43	19 48		19 58		20 03		20 13	20 18		20 28	20 33	
Haggerston	d		19 00	19 05		19 15		19 20		19 30	19 35		19 45	19 50		20 00		20 05		20 15	20 20		20 30	20 35	
Dalston Junction	a		19 02	19 09		19 17		19 24		19 32	19 39		19 47	19 54		20 02		20 09		20 17	20 24		20 32	20 39	
Canonbury	a		19 05			19 20				19 35			19 50			20 05				20 20			20 35		
Highbury & Islington	a		19 10			19 25				19 40			19 55			20 10				20 25			20 40		
London Bridge 4 ⊖	a	18 41			18 59				19 11			19 29			19 41				19 59			20 11			20 29

		LO		LO	SN A	LO	LO	SN B	LO	LO	SN A	LO		LO	SN B	LO	LO	SN A	LO	LO	SN B	LO		LO	SN A
Purley	d							20 21							20 51						21 21				
East Croydon	d							20 30							21 00						21 30				
Norwood Junction 2	a							20 34							21 04						21 34				
West Croydon 4	d			20 09			20 22			20 39				20 52			21 09			21 22				21 39	
Norwood Junction	a			20 13			20 28			20 43				20 58			21 13			21 28				21 43	
Norwood Junction	d			20 13			20 28	20 35		20 43				20 58	21 05		21 13			21 28	21 35			21 43	
Anerley	d			20 16			20 31	20 38		20 46				21 01	21 08		21 16			21 31	21 38			21 46	
Penge West	d			20 18			20 33	20 40		20 48				21 03	21 10		21 18			21 33	21 40			21 48	
Crystal Palace 4	d	20 13			20 21	20 28			20 43		20 51	20 58				21 13		21 21	21 28			21 43			21 51
Sydenham	d	20 16		20 21	20 24	20 31	20 36	20 42	20 46	20 51	20 54	21 01		21 06	21 12	21 16	21 21	21 24	21 31	21 36	21 42	21 46		21 51	21 54
Forest Hill 4	d	20 19		20 23	20 27	20 34	20 38	20 45	20 49	20 53	20 57	21 04		21 08	21 15	21 19	21 23	21 27	21 34	21 38	21 45	21 49		21 53	21 57
Honor Oak Park	d	20 21		20 26	20 29	20 36	20 41	20 47	20 51	20 56	20 59	21 06		21 11	21 17	21 21	21 26	21 29	21 36	21 41	21 47	21 51		21 56	21 59
Brockley	d	20 24		20 28	20 32	20 39	20 43	20 50	20 54	20 58	21 02	21 09		21 13	21 20	21 24	21 28	21 32	21 39	21 43	21 50	21 54		21 58	22 02
New Cross Gate	d	20 26		20 31	20 34	20 41	20 46	20 52	20 56	21 01	21 04	21 11		21 16	21 22	21 26	21 31	21 34	21 41	21 46	21 52	21 56		22 01	22 04
Surrey Quays	d	20 30		20 35		20 45	20 50		21 00	21 05		21 15		21 20		21 30	21 35		21 45	21 50		22 00		22 05	
Canada Water	d	20 32		20 37		20 47	20 52		21 02	21 07		21 17		21 22		21 32	21 37		21 47	21 52		22 02		22 07	
Rotherhithe	d	20 33		20 38		20 48	20 53		21 03	21 08		21 18		21 23		21 33	21 38		21 48	21 53		22 03		22 08	
Wapping	d	20 35		20 40		20 50	20 55		21 05	21 10		21 20		21 25		21 35	21 40		21 50	21 55		22 05		22 10	
Shadwell	d	20 37		20 42		20 52	20 57		21 07	21 12		21 22		21 27		21 37	21 42		21 52	21 57		22 07		22 12	
Whitechapel	d	20 39		20 44		20 54	20 59		21 09	21 14		21 24		21 29		21 39	21 44		21 54	21 59		22 09		22 14	
Shoreditch High Street	d	20 41		20 46		20 56	21 01		21 11	21 16		21 26		21 31		21 41	21 46		21 56	22 01		22 11		22 16	
Hoxton	d	20 43		20 48		20 58	21 03		21 13	21 18		21 28		21 33		21 43	21 48		21 58	22 03		22 13		22 18	
Haggerston	d	20 45		20 50		21 00	21 05		21 15	21 20		21 30		21 35		21 45	21 50		22 00	22 05		22 15		22 22	
Dalston Junction	a	20 47		20 54		21 02	21 09		21 17	21 24		21 32		21 39		21 47	21 54		22 02	22 09		22 17		22 26	
Canonbury	a	20 50				21 05			21 20			21 35				21 50			22 05			22 20			
Highbury & Islington	a	20 55				21 10			21 25			21 40				21 55			22 10			22 25			
London Bridge 4 ⊖	a				20 41			20 59			21 11				21 29			21 41			21 59				22 11

A From London Victoria

B From Caterham

For Fast trains between London Bridge & New Cross Gate to Norwood Jn & East Croydon, see Table 175

For full service between Highbury & Islington and Surrey Quays, please see Table 178

For Sutton connections at West Croydon, please see table 172

Table 177R

Saturdays

14 December to 17 May

Croydon and Norwood Junction-Anerley, Penge West, Crystal Palace, Sydenham, Forest Hill, Honor Oak Park, Brockley, New Cross Gate-London Bridge

Network Diagram - see first Page of Table 173

		LO	LO	SN A	LO	LO	SN B		LO	LO	SN A	LO	LO	SN B	LO	SN A	LO		SN B	LO	LO	SN B
Purley	d			21 51							22 21					22 52						
East Croydon 🚌	d			22 00							22 30					23 01						
Norwood Junction ■2	a			22 04							22 34					23 05						
West Croydon ■4 🚌	d		21 52			22 09				22 22			22 39		22 52					23 22		
Norwood Junction	a		21 58			22 13				22 28			22 43		22 58					23 28		
Norwood Junction	d		21 58	22 05		22 13				22 28	22 35		22 43		22 58	23 06				23 28		
Anerley	d		22 01	22 08		22 16				22 31	22 38		22 46		23 01	23 09				23 31		
Penge West	d		22 03	22 10		22 18				22 33	22 40		22 48		23 03	23 11				23 33		
Crystal Palace ■4	d	21 58			22 13		22 21		22 28			22 43		22 51			23 13		23 21		23 43	23 51
Sydenham	d	22 01	22 06	22 12	22 16	22 21	22 24		22 31	22 36	22 42	22 46	22 51	22 54	23 06	23 13	23 16		23 24	23 36	23 46	23 54
Forest Hill ■4	d	22 04	22 08	22 15	22 19	22 23	22 27		22 34	22 38	22 45	22 49	22 53	22 57	23 08	23 16	23 19		23 27	23 38	23 49	23 57
Honor Oak Park	d	22 06	22 11	22 17	22 21	22 26	22 29		22 36	22 41	22 47	22 51	22 56	22 59	23 11	23 18	23 21		23 29	23 41	23 51	23 59
Brockley	d	22 09	22 13	22 20	22 24	22 28	22 32		22 39	22 43	22 50	22 54	22 58	23 02	23 13	23 21	23 24		23 32	23 43	23 54	00 02
New Cross Gate	d	22 11	22 16	22 22	22 26	22 31	22 34		22 41	22 46	22 52	22 56	23 01	23 04	23 16	23 23	23 26		23 34	23 46	23 56	00 04
Surrey Quays	d	22 15	22 20		22 30	22 35			22 45	22 50		23 00	23 05		23 20		23 30			23 50	23 59	
Canada Water	d	22 17	22 22		22 32	22 37			22 47	22 52		23 02	23 07		23 22		23 32			23 52	00 02	
Rotherhithe	d	22 18	22 23		22 33	22 38			22 48	22 53		23 03	23 08		23 23		23 33			23 53	00 03	
Wapping	d	22 20	22 25		22 35	22 40			22 50	22 55		23 05	23 10		23 25		23 35			23 55	00 05	
Shadwell	d	22 22	22 27		22 37	22 42			22 52	22 57		23 07	23 12		23 27		23 37			23 57	00 07	
Whitechapel	d	22 24	22 29		22 39	22 44			22 54	22 59		23 09	23 14		23 29		23 39			23 59	00 09	
Shoreditch High Street	d	22 26	22 31		22 41	22 46			22 56	23 01		23 11	23 16		23 31		23 41			00 01	00 11	
Hoxton	d	22 28	22 33		22 43	22 48			22 58	23 03		23 13	23 18		23 33		23 43			00 03	00 13	
Haggerston	d	22 30	22 35		22 45	22 50			23 00	23 05		23 15	23 20		23 35		23 45			00 05	00 15	
Dalston Junction	a	22 32	22 39		22 47	22 52			23 02	23 09		23 17	23 22		23 39		23 47			00 09	00 17	
Canonbury	a	22 35				22 55			23 05				23 25				23 50				00 20	
Highbury & Islington	a	22 40				22 58			23 10				23 27				23 55				00 25	
London Bridge ■4 ⊖	a			22 29			22 41				22 59			23 11		23 30			23 44			00 11

Sundays

8 December to 11 May

		LO C	SN D	LO E	SN D		LO	SN	LO	LO	SN	LO	SN	SN A	LO	LO	SN	LO	SN F	LO		SN	LO	SN F	LO
Purley	d							06 36			07 09			07 32					08 07					08 39	
East Croydon 🚌	d							06 45			07 18			07 41					08 17					08 48	
Norwood Junction ■2	a							06 50			07 24			07 45					08 22					08 52	
West Croydon ■4 🚌	d						06 42			07 12			07 34		07 42		08 04	08 12				08 34	08 42		
Norwood Junction	a						06 47			07 17			07 39		07 47		08 09	08 17				08 39	08 46		
Norwood Junction	d						06 47	06 52		07 17	07 24		07 40	07 45	07 47		08 10	08 17	08 23			08 40	08 46	08 52	
Anerley	d						06 50	06 55		07 20	07 27			07 48	07 50			08 20	08 26				08 49	08 55	
Penge West	d						06 52	06 57		07 22	07 29			07 50	07 52			08 22	08 28				08 51	08 57	
Crystal Palace ■4	d				00 21				07 07			07 37				08 07				08 37					09 07
Sydenham	d				00 24		06 55	06 59	07 10	07 25	07 32	07 40	07 44	07 53	07 55	08 10	08 14	08 25	08 30	08 40		08 44	08 55	09 00	09 10
Forest Hill ■4	d				00 27		06 57	07 02	07 13	07 27	07 34	07 43	07 47	07 55	07 57	08 13	08 17	08 27	08 33	08 43		08 47	08 57	09 02	09 13
Honor Oak Park	d				00 29		07 00	07 04	07 15	07 30	07 37	07 45	07 49	07 58	08 00	08 15	08 19	08 30	08 35	08 45		08 49	09 00	09 05	09 15
Brockley	d		00 02		00 32		07 02	07 07	07 18	07 32	07 39	07 48	07 52	08 00	08 02	08 18	08 22	08 32	08 38	08 48		08 52	09 02	09 07	09 18
New Cross Gate	d		00 04		00 35		07 05	07 09	07 20	07 35	07 42	07 50	07 54	08 03	08 05	08 20	08 24	08 35	08 40	08 50		08 54	09 05	09 10	09 20
Surrey Quays	d						07 09		07 24	07 39		07 54			08 10	08 24		08 39		08 54			09 09		09 24
Canada Water	d			00 02			07 11		07 26	07 41		07 56			08 12	08 26		08 41		08 56			09 11		09 26
Rotherhithe	d			00 03			07 12		07 27	07 42		07 57			08 13	08 27		08 42		08 57			09 12		09 27
Wapping	d			00 05			07 14		07 29	07 44		07 59			08 15	08 29		08 44		08 59			09 14		09 29
Shadwell	d			00 07			07 16		07 31	07 46		08 01			08 17	08 31		08 46		09 01			09 16		09 31
Whitechapel	d			00 09			07 18		07 33	07 48		08 03			08 19	08 33		08 48		09 03			09 18		09 33
Shoreditch High Street	d	00 01		00 11			07 20		07 35	07 50		08 05			08 21	08 35		08 50		09 05			09 20		09 35
Hoxton	d	00 03		00 13			07 22		07 37	07 52		08 07			08 23	08 37		08 52		09 07			09 22		09 37
Haggerston	d	00 05		00 15			07 24		07 39	07 54		08 09			08 25	08 39		08 54		09 09			09 24		09 39
Dalston Junction	a	00 09		00 17			07 26		07 41	07 56		08 11			08 28	08 41		08 56		09 11			09 26		09 41
Canonbury	a			00 20			07 29		07 44	07 59		08 14			08 32	08 44		08 59		09 14			09 29		09 44
Highbury & Islington	a			00 25			07 32		07 49	08 02		08 19			08 34	08 51		09 02		09 19			09 32		09 49
London Bridge ■4 ⊖	a		00 11		00 41			07 17			07 48		08 01	08 12			08 31		08 47			09 01		09 16	

A From Caterham
B From London Victoria
C From West Croydon
D From London Victoria
E From Crystal Palace
F From Tattenham Corner

For Fast trains between London Bridge & New Cross Gate to Norwood Jn & East Croydon, see Table 175

For full service between Highbury & Islington and Surrey Quays, please see Table 178

For Sutton connections at West Croydon, please see table 172

Table 177R

Sundays

8 December to 11 May

Croydon and Norwood Junction-Anerley, Penge West, Crystal Palace, Sydenham, Forest Hill, Honor Oak Park, Brockley, New Cross Gate-London Bridge

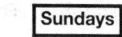

Network Diagram - see first Page of Table 173

		SN		LO	SN A	LO	SN	LO	SN A	LO	SN	LO		SN A	LO	SN	LO	SN A	LO	SN	LO	SN A		LO	SN
Purley	d				09 08				09 38					10 08				10 38				11 08			
East Croydon	d				09 17				09 47					10 17				10 47				11 17			
Norwood Junction 2	a				09 22				09 51					10 21				10 51				11 21			
West Croydon 4	d	09 04		09 12			09 34	09 42			10 04	10 12				10 34	10 42			11 04	11 12				11 34
Norwood Junction	a	09 08		09 17			09 38	09 47			10 08	10 17				10 38	10 47			11 08	11 17				11 38
Norwood Junction	d	09 09		09 17	09 23		09 39	09 47	09 52		10 09	10 17		10 22		10 39	10 47	10 52		11 09	11 17	11 22			11 39
Anerley	d			09 20	09 26			09 50	09 55			10 20		10 25			10 50	10 55			11 20	11 25			
Penge West	d			09 22	09 28			09 52	09 57			10 22		10 27			10 52	10 57			11 22	11 27			
Crystal Palace 4	d					09 37				10 07					10 37				11 07					11 37	
Sydenham	d	09 13		09 25	09 30	09 40	09 43	09 55	10 00	10 10	10 13	10 25		10 30	10 40	10 43	10 55	11 00	11 10	11 13	11 25	11 30		11 40	11 43
Forest Hill 4	d	09 16		09 27	09 33	09 43	09 46	09 57	10 02	10 13	10 16	10 27		10 32	10 43	10 46	10 57	11 02	11 13	11 16	11 27	11 32		11 43	11 46
Honor Oak Park	d	09 18		09 30	09 35	09 45	09 48	10 00	10 05	10 15	10 18	10 30		10 35	10 45	10 48	11 00	11 05	11 15	11 18	11 30	11 35		11 45	11 48
Brockley	d	09 21		09 32	09 38	09 48	09 51	10 02	10 07	10 18	10 21	10 32		10 37	10 48	10 51	11 02	11 07	11 18	11 21	11 32	11 37		11 48	11 51
New Cross Gate	d	09 23		09 35	09 40	09 50	09 53	10 05	10 10	10 20	10 23	10 35		10 40	10 50	10 53	11 05	11 10	11 20	11 23	11 35	11 40		11 50	11 53
Surrey Quays	d			09 39		09 54		10 09		10 24		10 39			10 54		11 09		11 24		11 39			11 54	
Canada Water	d			09 41		09 56		10 11		10 26		10 41			10 56		11 11		11 26		11 41			11 56	
Rotherhithe	d			09 42		09 57		10 12		10 27		10 42			10 57		11 12		11 27		11 42			11 57	
Wapping	d			09 44		09 59		10 14		10 29		10 44			10 59		11 14		11 29		11 44			11 59	
Shadwell	d			09 46		10 01		10 16		10 31		10 46			11 01		11 16		11 31		11 46			12 01	
Whitechapel	d			09 48		10 03		10 18		10 33		10 48			11 03		11 18		11 33		11 48			12 03	
Shoreditch High Street	d			09 50		10 05		10 20		10 35		10 50			11 05		11 20		11 35		11 50			12 05	
Hoxton	d			09 52		10 07		10 22		10 37		10 52			11 07		11 22		11 37		11 52			12 07	
Haggerston	d			09 54		10 09		10 24		10 39		10 54			11 09		11 24		11 39		11 54			12 09	
Dalston Junction	a			09 56		10 11		10 26		10 41		10 56			11 11		11 26		11 41		11 57			12 11	
Canonbury	a			09 59		10 14		10 29		10 44		10 59			11 14		11 29		11 44					12 14	
Highbury & Islington	a			10 02		10 19		10 32		10 49		11 02			11 19		11 32		11 49					12 19	
London Bridge 4 ⊖	a	09 31			09 47		10 01		10 16		10 31			10 46		11 01		11 16		11 31		11 46			12 01

		LO	SN A	LO	SN	LO	LO	SN A		LO	SN	LO	LO	SN A	LO	LO	SN	LO		LO	SN A	LO	LO	SN	LO
Purley	d		11 38					12 08						12 38							13 08				
East Croydon	d		11 47					12 17						12 47							13 17				
Norwood Junction 2	a		11 51					12 21						12 51							13 21				
West Croydon 4	d	11 42			12 04		12 12				12 34		12 42			12 57	13 04			13 12			13 27	13 34	
Norwood Junction	a	11 47			12 08		12 16				12 38		12 46			13 01	13 08			13 16			13 31	13 38	
Norwood Junction	d	11 47	11 52		12 09		12 16	12 22			12 39		12 46	12 52		13 01	13 09			13 16	13 22		13 31	13 39	
Anerley	d	11 50	11 55				12 19	12 25					12 49	12 55		13 04				13 19	13 25		13 34		
Penge West	d	11 52	11 57				12 21	12 27					12 51	12 57		13 06				13 21	13 27		13 36		
Crystal Palace 4	d			12 07		12 16				12 31		12 46			13 01			13 16				13 31			13 46
Sydenham	d	11 55	12 00	12 10	12 13	12 19	12 24	12 30		12 34	12 43	12 49	12 54	13 00	13 04	13 09	13 13	13 19		13 24	13 30	13 34	13 39	13 43	13 49
Forest Hill 4	d	11 57	12 02	12 13	12 16	12 22	12 26	12 32		12 37	12 46	12 52	12 56	13 02	13 07	13 11	13 16	13 22		13 26	13 32	13 37	13 41	13 46	13 52
Honor Oak Park	d	12 00	12 05	12 15	12 18	12 24	12 29	12 35		12 39	12 48	12 54	12 59	13 05	13 09	13 14	13 18	13 24		13 29	13 35	13 39	13 44	13 48	13 54
Brockley	d	12 02	12 07	12 18	12 21	12 27	12 31	12 37		12 42	12 51	12 57	13 01	13 07	13 12	13 16	13 21	13 27		13 31	13 37	13 42	13 46	13 51	13 57
New Cross Gate	d	12 05	12 10	12 20	12 23	12 29	12 34	12 40		12 44	12 53	12 59	13 04	13 10	13 14	13 19	13 23	13 29		13 34	13 40	13 44	13 49	13 53	13 59
Surrey Quays	d	12 09		12 24		12 35	12 38			12 48		13 03	13 08		13 18	13 23		13 33		13 38		13 48	13 53		14 03
Canada Water	d	12 11		12 26		12 37	12 40			12 50		13 05	13 10		13 20	13 25		13 35		13 40		13 50	13 55		14 05
Rotherhithe	d	12 12		12 27		12 39	12 41			12 51		13 06	13 11		13 21	13 26		13 36		13 41		13 51	13 56		14 06
Wapping	d	12 14		12 29		12 40	12 43			12 53		13 08	13 13		13 23	13 28		13 38		13 43		13 53	13 58		14 08
Shadwell	d	12 16		12 31		12 42	12 45			12 55		13 10	13 15		13 25	13 30		13 40		13 45		13 55	14 00		14 10
Whitechapel	d	12 18		12 33		12 45	12 47			12 57		13 12	13 17		13 27	13 32		13 42		13 47		13 57	14 02		14 12
Shoreditch High Street	d	12 20		12 35		12 47	12 49			12 59		13 14	13 19		13 29	13 34		13 44		13 49		13 59	14 04		14 14
Hoxton	d	12 22		12 37		12 49	12 51			13 01		13 16	13 21		13 31	13 36		13 46		13 51		14 01	14 06		14 16
Haggerston	d	12 24		12 39		12 51	12 53			13 03		13 18	13 23		13 33	13 38		13 48		13 53		14 03	14 08		14 18
Dalston Junction	a	12 26		12 41		12 53	12 57			13 05		13 20	13 27		13 35	13 42		13 50		13 57		14 05	14 12		14 20
Canonbury	a	12 29		12 44						13 08		13 23			13 38			13 53				14 08			14 23
Highbury & Islington	a	12 32		12 49						13 13		13 28			13 43			13 58				14 13			14 28
London Bridge 4 ⊖	a		12 16		12 31			12 46			13 01			13 16			13 31				13 46			14 01	

A From Tattenham Corner

For Fast trains between London Bridge & New Cross Gate to Norwood Jn & East Croydon, see Table 175

For full service between Highbury & Islington and Surrey Quays, please see Table 178

For Sutton connections at West Croydon, please see table 172

Table 177R

Sundays

8 December to 11 May

Croydon and Norwood Junction-Anerley, Penge West, Crystal Palace, Sydenham, Forest Hill, Honor Oak Park, Brockley, New Cross Gate-London Bridge

Network Diagram - see first Page of Table 173

		LO	SN A	LO	LO	SN	LO	LO	SN A	LO		LO	SN	LO	LO	SN A	LO	LO	SN	LO		LO	SN A	LO	LO
Purley	d		13 38						14 08							14 38							15 08		
East Croydon	d		13 47						14 17							14 47							15 17		
Norwood Junction [2]	a		13 51						14 21							14 51							15 21		
West Croydon [4]	d	13 42			13 57	14 04		14 12				14 27	14 34		14 42			14 57	15 04			15 12			15 27
Norwood Junction	a	13 46			14 01	14 08		14 16				14 31	14 38		14 46			15 01	15 08			15 16			15 31
Norwood Junction	d	13 46	13 52		14 01	14 09		14 16	14 22			14 31	14 39		14 46	14 52		15 01	15 09			15 16	15 22		15 31
Anerley	d	13 49	13 55		14 04			14 19	14 25			14 34			14 49	14 55		15 04				15 19	15 25		15 34
Penge West	d	13 51	13 57		14 06			14 21	14 27			14 36			14 51	14 57		15 06				15 21	15 27		15 36
Crystal Palace [4]	d			14 01			14 16			14 31				14 46			15 01			15 16				15 31	
Sydenham	d	13 54	14 00	14 04	14 09	14 13	14 19	14 24	14 30	14 34		14 39	14 43	14 49	14 54	15 00	15 04	15 09	15 13	15 19		15 24	15 30	15 34	15 39
Forest Hill [4]	d	13 56	14 02	14 07	14 11	14 16	14 22	14 26	14 32	14 37		14 41	14 46	14 52	14 56	15 02	15 07	15 11	15 16	15 22		15 26	15 32	15 37	15 41
Honor Oak Park	d	13 59	14 05	14 09	14 14	14 18	14 24	14 29	14 35	14 39		14 44	14 48	14 54	14 59	15 05	15 09	15 14	15 18	15 24		15 29	15 35	15 39	15 44
Brockley	d	14 01	14 07	14 12	14 16	14 21	14 27	14 31	14 37	14 42		14 46	14 51	14 57	15 01	15 07	15 12	15 16	15 21	15 27		15 31	15 37	15 42	15 46
New Cross Gate	d	14 04	14 10	14 14	14 19	14 23	14 29	14 34	14 40	14 44		14 49	14 53	14 59	15 04	15 10	15 14	15 19	15 23	15 29		15 34	15 40	15 44	15 49
Surrey Quays	d	14 08		14 18	14 23		14 33	14 38		14 48		14 53		15 03	15 08		15 18	15 23		15 33		15 38		15 48	15 53
Canada Water	d	14 10		14 20	14 25		14 35	14 40		14 50		14 55		15 05	15 10		15 20	15 25		15 35		15 40		15 50	15 55
Rotherhithe	d	14 11		14 21	14 26		14 36	14 41		14 51		14 56		15 06	15 11		15 21	15 26		15 36		15 41		15 51	15 56
Wapping	d	14 13		14 23	14 28		14 38	14 43		14 53		14 58		15 08	15 13		15 23	15 28		15 38		15 43		15 53	15 58
Shadwell	d	14 15		14 25	14 30		14 40	14 45		14 55		15 00		15 10	15 15		15 25	15 30		15 40		15 45		15 55	16 00
Whitechapel	d	14 17		14 27	14 32		14 42	14 47		14 57		15 02		15 12	15 17		15 27	15 32		15 42		15 47		15 57	16 02
Shoreditch High Street	d	14 19		14 29	14 34		14 44	14 49		14 59		15 04		15 14	15 19		15 29	15 34		15 44		15 49		15 59	16 04
Hoxton	d	14 21		14 31	14 36		14 46	14 51		15 01		15 06		15 16	15 21		15 31	15 36		15 46		15 51		16 01	16 06
Haggerston	d	14 23		14 33	14 38		14 48	14 53		15 03		15 08		15 18	15 23		15 33	15 38		15 48		15 53		16 03	16 08
Dalston Junction	a	14 27		14 35	14 42		14 50	14 57		15 05		15 12		15 20	15 27		15 35	15 42		15 50		15 57		16 05	16 12
Canonbury	a			14 38			14 53			15 08				15 23			15 38			15 53				16 08	
Highbury & Islington	a			14 43			14 58			15 13				15 28			15 43			15 58				16 13	
London Bridge [4] ⊖	a		14 16			14 31			14 46				15 01			15 16			15 31				15 46		

		SN	LO	LO	SN A	LO		LO	SN	LO	LO	SN A	LO	LO	SN	LO		LO	SN A	LO	LO	SN	LO	LO	SN A
Purley	d				15 38							16 08							16 38						17 08
East Croydon	d				15 47							16 17							16 47						17 17
Norwood Junction [2]	a				15 51							16 21							16 51						17 21
West Croydon [4]	d	15 34		15 42				15 57	16 04		16 12			16 27	16 34			16 42			16 57	17 04		17 12	
Norwood Junction	a	15 38		15 46				16 01	16 08		16 16			16 31	16 38			16 46			17 01	17 08		17 16	
Norwood Junction	d	15 39		15 46	15 52			16 01	16 09		16 16	16 22		16 31	16 39			16 46	16 52		17 01	17 09		17 16	17 22
Anerley	d			15 49	15 55			16 04			16 19	16 25		16 34				16 49	16 55		17 04			17 19	17 25
Penge West	d			15 51	15 57			16 06			16 21	16 27		16 36				16 51	16 57		17 06			17 21	17 27
Crystal Palace [4]	d		15 46			16 01				16 16			16 31			16 46				17 01			17 16		
Sydenham	d	15 43	15 49	15 54	16 00	16 04		16 09	16 13	16 19	16 24	16 30	16 34	16 39	16 43	16 49		16 54	17 00	17 04	17 09	17 13	17 19	17 24	17 30
Forest Hill [4]	d	15 46	15 52	15 56	16 02	16 07		16 11	16 16	16 22	16 26	16 32	16 37	16 41	16 46	16 52		16 56	17 02	17 07	17 11	17 16	17 22	17 26	17 32
Honor Oak Park	d	15 48	15 54	15 59	16 05	16 09		16 14	16 18	16 24	16 29	16 35	16 39	16 44	16 48	16 54		16 59	17 05	17 09	17 14	17 18	17 24	17 29	17 35
Brockley	d	15 51	15 57	16 01	16 07	16 12		16 16	16 21	16 27	16 31	16 37	16 42	16 46	16 51	16 57		17 01	17 07	17 12	17 16	17 21	17 27	17 31	17 37
New Cross Gate	d	15 53	15 59	16 04	16 10	16 14		16 19	16 23	16 29	16 34	16 40	16 44	16 49	16 53	16 59		17 04	17 10	17 14	17 19	17 23	17 29	17 34	17 40
Surrey Quays	d		16 03	16 08		16 18		16 23		16 33	16 38		16 48	16 53		17 03		17 08		17 18	17 23		17 33	17 38	
Canada Water	d		16 05	16 10		16 20		16 25		16 35	16 40		16 50	16 55		17 05		17 10		17 20	17 25		17 35	17 40	
Rotherhithe	d		16 06	16 11		16 21		16 26		16 36	16 41		16 51	16 56		17 06		17 11		17 21	17 26		17 36	17 41	
Wapping	d		16 08	16 13		16 23		16 28		16 38	16 43		16 53	16 58		17 08		17 13		17 23	17 28		17 38	17 43	
Shadwell	d		16 10	16 15		16 25		16 30		16 40	16 45		16 55	17 00		17 10		17 15		17 25	17 30		17 40	17 45	
Whitechapel	d		16 12	16 17		16 27		16 32		16 42	16 47		16 57	17 02		17 12		17 17		17 27	17 32		17 42	17 47	
Shoreditch High Street	d		16 14	16 19		16 29		16 34		16 44	16 49		16 59	17 04		17 14		17 19		17 29	17 34		17 44	17 49	
Hoxton	d		16 16	16 21		16 31		16 36		16 46	16 51		17 01	17 06		17 16		17 21		17 31	17 36		17 46	17 51	
Haggerston	d		16 18	16 23		16 33		16 38		16 48	16 53		17 03	17 08		17 18		17 23		17 33	17 38		17 48	17 53	
Dalston Junction	a		16 20	16 27		16 35		16 42		16 50	16 57		17 05	17 12		17 20		17 27		17 35	17 42		17 50	17 57	
Canonbury	a		16 23			16 38				16 53			17 08			17 23				17 38			17 53		
Highbury & Islington	a		16 28			16 43				16 56			17 13			17 28				17 43			17 58		
London Bridge [4] ⊖	a	16 01			16 16				16 31			16 46			17 01				17 16			17 31			17 46

A From Tattenham Corner

For Fast trains between London Bridge & New Cross Gate to Norwood Jn & East Croydon, see Table 175

For full service between Highbury & Islington and Surrey Quays, please see Table 178

For Sutton connections at West Croydon, please see table 172

Table 177R

Sundays

8 December to 11 May

Croydon and Norwood Junction-Anerley, Penge West, Crystal Palace, Sydenham, Forest Hill, Honor Oak Park, Brockley, New Cross Gate-London Bridge

Network Diagram - see first Page of Table 173

		LO	LO	SN	LO	LO	SN A	LO		LO	SN	LO	LO	SN A	LO	LO	SN	LO		LO	SN A	LO	LO	SN	LO
Purley	d						17 38							18 08							18 38				
East Croydon	d						17 47							18 17							18 47				
Norwood Junction [2]	a						17 51							18 21							18 51				
West Croydon [4]	d		17 27	17 34		17 42				17 57	18 04		18 12			18 27	18 34			18 42			18 57	19 04	
Norwood Junction	a		17 31	17 38		17 46				18 01	18 08		18 16			18 31	18 38			18 46			19 01	19 08	
Norwood Junction	d		17 31	17 39		17 46	17 52			18 01	18 09		18 16	18 22		18 31	18 39			18 46	18 52		19 01	19 09	
Anerley	d		17 34			17 49	17 55			18 04			18 19	18 25		18 34				18 49	18 55		19 04		
Penge West	d		17 36			17 51	17 57			18 06			18 21	18 27		18 36				18 51	18 57		19 06		
Crystal Palace [4]	d	17 31			17 46			18 01				18 16			18 31			18 46				19 01			19 16
Sydenham	d	17 34	17 39	17 43	17 49	17 54	18 00	18 04		18 09	18 13	18 19	18 24	18 30	18 34	18 39	18 43	18 49		18 54	19 00	19 04	19 09	19 13	19 19
Forest Hill [4]	d	17 37	17 41	17 46	17 52	17 56	18 02	18 07		18 11	18 16	18 22	18 26	18 32	18 37	18 41	18 46	18 52		18 56	19 02	19 07	19 11	19 16	19 22
Honor Oak Park	d	17 39	17 44	17 48	17 54	17 59	18 05	18 09		18 14	18 18	18 24	18 29	18 35	18 39	18 44	18 48	18 54		18 59	19 05	19 09	19 14	19 18	19 24
Brockley	d	17 42	17 46	17 51	17 57	18 01	18 07	18 12		18 16	18 21	18 27	18 31	18 37	18 42	18 46	18 51	18 57		19 01	19 07	19 12	19 16	19 21	19 27
New Cross Gate	d	17 44	17 49	17 53	17 59	18 04	18 10	18 14		18 19	18 23	18 29	18 34	18 40	18 44	18 49	18 53	18 59		19 04	19 10	19 14	19 19	19 23	19 29
Surrey Quays	d	17 48	17 53		18 03	18 08		18 18		18 23		18 33	18 38		18 48	18 53		19 03		19 08		19 18	19 23		19 33
Canada Water	d	17 50	17 55		18 05	18 10		18 20		18 25		18 35	18 40		18 50	18 55		19 05		19 10		19 20	19 25		19 35
Rotherhithe	d	17 51	17 56		18 06	18 11		18 21		18 26		18 36	18 41		18 51	18 56		19 06		19 11		19 21	19 26		19 36
Wapping	d	17 53	17 58		18 08	18 13		18 23		18 28		18 38	18 43		18 53	18 58		19 08		19 13		19 23	19 28		19 38
Shadwell	d	17 55	18 00		18 10	18 15		18 25		18 30		18 40	18 45		18 55	19 00		19 10		19 15		19 25	19 30		19 40
Whitechapel	d	17 57	18 02		18 12	18 17		18 27		18 32		18 42	18 47		18 57	19 02		19 12		19 17		19 27	19 32		19 42
Shoreditch High Street	d	17 59	18 04		18 14	18 19		18 29		18 34		18 44	18 49		18 59	19 04		19 14		19 19		19 29	19 34		19 44
Hoxton	d	18 01	18 06		18 16	18 21		18 31		18 36		18 46	18 51		19 01	19 06		19 16		19 21		19 31	19 36		19 46
Haggerston	d	18 03	18 08		18 18	18 23		18 33		18 38		18 48	18 53		19 03	19 08		19 18		19 23		19 33	19 38		19 48
Dalston Junction	a	18 05	18 12		18 20	18 27		18 35		18 42		18 50	18 57		19 05	19 12		19 20		19 27		19 35	19 42		19 50
Canonbury	a	18 08			18 23			18 38				18 53			19 08			19 23				19 38			19 53
Highbury & Islington	a	18 13			18 28			18 43				18 58			19 13			19 28				19 43			19 58
London Bridge [4] ⊖	a			18 01			18 16				18 31			18 46			19 01				19 16			19 31	

		LO	SN A	LO		LO	SN	LO	LO	SN A	LO	LO	SN	LO		LO	SN A	LO	LO	SN	LO	LO	SN A	LO	
Purley	d		19 08							19 38							20 08						20 38		
East Croydon	d		19 17							19 47							20 17						20 47		
Norwood Junction [2]	a		19 21							19 51							20 21						20 51		
West Croydon [4]	d	19 12				19 27	19 34		19 42			19 57	20 04			20 12			20 27	20 34		20 42			
Norwood Junction	a	19 16				19 31	19 38		19 46			20 01	20 08			20 16			20 31	20 38		20 46			
Norwood Junction	d	19 16	19 22			19 31	19 39		19 46	19 52		20 01	20 09			20 16	20 22		20 31	20 39		20 46	20 52		
Anerley	d	19 19	19 25			19 34			19 49	19 55		20 04				20 19	20 25		20 34			20 49	20 55		
Penge West	d	19 21	19 27			19 36			19 51	19 57		20 06				20 21	20 27		20 36			20 51	20 57		
Crystal Palace [4]	d			19 31				19 46			20 01			20 16				20 31			20 46			21 01	
Sydenham	d	19 24	19 30	19 34		19 39	19 43	19 49	19 54	20 00	20 04	20 09	20 13	20 19		20 24	20 30	20 34	20 39	20 43	20 49	20 54	21 00	21 04	
Forest Hill [4]	d	19 26	19 32	19 37		19 41	19 46	19 52	19 56	20 02	20 07	20 11	20 16	20 22		20 26	20 32	20 37	20 41	20 46	20 52	20 56	21 02	21 07	
Honor Oak Park	d	19 29	19 35	19 39		19 44	19 48	19 54	19 59	20 05	20 09	20 14	20 18	20 24		20 29	20 35	20 39	20 44	20 48	20 54	20 59	21 05	21 09	
Brockley	d	19 31	19 37	19 42		19 46	19 51	19 57	20 01	20 07	20 12	20 16	20 21	20 27		20 31	20 37	20 42	20 46	20 51	20 57	21 01	21 07	21 12	
New Cross Gate	d	19 34	19 40	19 44		19 49	19 53	19 59	20 04	20 10	20 14	20 19	20 23	20 29		20 34	20 40	20 44	20 49	20 53	20 59	21 04	21 10	21 14	
Surrey Quays	d	19 38		19 48		19 53		20 03	20 08		20 18	20 23		20 33		20 38		20 48	20 53		21 03	21 08		21 18	
Canada Water	d	19 40		19 50		19 55		20 05	20 10		20 20	20 25		20 35		20 40		20 50	20 55		21 05	21 10		21 20	
Rotherhithe	d	19 41		19 51		19 56		20 06	20 11		20 21	20 26		20 36		20 41		20 51	20 56		21 06	21 11		21 21	
Wapping	d	19 43		19 53		19 58		20 08	20 13		20 23	20 28		20 38		20 43		20 53	20 58		21 08	21 13		21 23	
Shadwell	d	19 45		19 55		20 00		20 10	20 15		20 25	20 30		20 40		20 45		20 55	21 00		21 10	21 15		21 25	
Whitechapel	d	19 47		19 57		20 02		20 12	20 17		20 27	20 32		20 42		20 47		20 57	21 02		21 12	21 17		21 27	
Shoreditch High Street	d	19 49		19 59		20 04		20 14	20 19		20 29	20 34		20 44		20 49		20 59	21 04		21 14	21 19		21 29	
Hoxton	d	19 51		20 01		20 06		20 16	20 21		20 31	20 36		20 46		20 51		21 01	21 06		21 16	21 21		21 31	
Haggerston	d	19 53		20 03		20 08		20 18	20 23		20 33	20 38		20 48		20 53		21 03	21 08		21 18	21 23		21 33	
Dalston Junction	a	19 57		20 05		20 12		20 20	20 27		20 35	20 42		20 50		20 57		21 05	21 12		21 20	21 27		21 35	
Canonbury	a			20 08				20 23			20 38			20 53				21 08			21 23			21 38	
Highbury & Islington	a			20 13				20 28			20 43			20 58				21 13			21 28			21 43	
London Bridge [4] ⊖	a		19 46				20 01			20 16			20 31				20 46			21 01			21 16		

A From Tattenham Corner

For Fast trains between London Bridge & New Cross Gate to Norwood Jn & East Croydon, see Table 175

For full service between Highbury & Islington and Surrey Quays, please see Table 178

For Sutton connections at West Croydon, please see table 172

Table 177R

Sundays

8 December to 11 May

Croydon and Norwood Junction-Anerley, Penge West, Crystal Palace, Sydenham, Forest Hill, Honor Oak Park, Brockley, New Cross Gate-London Bridge

Network Diagram - see first Page of Table 173

		LO	SN	LO	LO	SN A		LO	LO	SN	LO	LO	SN A	LO	LO	SN		LO	LO	SN A	LO	SN	LO	LO	SN A
Purley	d					21 08							21 38							22 08					22 38
East Croydon 🚌	d					21 17							21 47							22 17					22 47
Norwood Junction 2	a					21 21							21 51							22 21					22 51
West Croydon 4 🚌	d	20 57	21 04		21 12				21 27	21 34		21 42			21 57	22 04			22 12		22 27	22 34		22 42	
Norwood Junction	a	21 01	21 08		21 16				21 31	21 38		21 46			22 01	22 08			22 16		22 31	22 38		22 46	
Norwood Junction	d	21 01	21 09		21 16	21 22			21 31	21 39		21 46	21 52		22 01	22 09			22 16	22 22	22 31	22 39		22 46	22 52
Anerley	d	21 04			21 19	21 25			21 34			21 49	21 55		22 04				22 19	22 25	22 34			22 49	22 55
Penge West	d	21 06			21 21	21 27			21 36			21 51	21 57		22 06				22 21	22 27	22 36			22 51	22 57
Crystal Palace 4	d			21 16				21 31			21 46			22 01				22 16					22 46		
Sydenham	d	21 09	21 13	21 19	21 24	21 30		21 34	21 39	21 43	21 49	21 54	22 00	22 04	22 09	22 13		22 19	22 24	22 30	22 39	22 43	22 49	22 54	23 00
Forest Hill 4	d	21 11	21 16	21 22	21 26	21 32		21 37	21 41	21 46	21 52	21 56	22 02	22 07	22 11	22 16		22 22	22 26	22 32	22 41	22 46	22 52	22 56	23 02
Honor Oak Park	d	21 14	21 18	21 24	21 29	21 35		21 39	21 44	21 48	21 54	21 59	22 05	22 09	22 14	22 18		22 24	22 29	22 35	22 44	22 48	22 54	22 59	23 05
Brockley	d	21 16	21 21	21 27	21 31	21 37		21 42	21 46	21 51	21 57	22 01	22 07	22 12	22 16	22 21		22 27	22 31	22 37	22 46	22 51	22 57	23 01	23 07
New Cross Gate	d	21 19	21 23	21 29	21 34	21 40		21 44	21 49	21 53	21 59	22 04	22 10	22 14	22 19	22 23		22 29	22 34	22 40	22 49	22 53	22 59	23 04	23 10
Surrey Quays	d	21 23		21 33	21 38			21 48	21 53		22 03	22 08		22 18	22 23			22 33	22 38		22 53		23 03	23 08	
Canada Water	d	21 25		21 35	21 40			21 50	21 55		22 05	22 10		22 20	22 25			22 35	22 40		22 55		23 05	23 10	
Rotherhithe	d	21 26		21 36	21 41			21 51	21 56		22 06	22 11		22 21	22 26			22 36	22 41		22 56		23 06	23 11	
Wapping	d	21 28		21 38	21 43			21 53	21 58		22 08	22 13		22 23	22 28			22 38	22 43		22 58		23 08	23 13	
Shadwell	d	21 30		21 40	21 45			21 55	22 00		22 10	22 15		22 25	22 30			22 40	22 45		23 00		23 10	23 15	
Whitechapel	d	21 32		21 42	21 47			21 57	22 02		22 12	22 17		22 27	22 32			22 42	22 47		23 02		23 12	23 17	
Shoreditch High Street	d	21 34		21 44	21 49			21 59	22 04		22 14	22 19		22 29	22 34			22 44	22 49		23 04		23 14	23 19	
Hoxton	d	21 36		21 46	21 51			22 01	22 06		22 16	22 21		22 31	22 36			22 46	22 51		23 06		23 16	23 21	
Haggerston	d	21 38		21 48	21 53			22 03	22 08		22 18	22 23		22 33	22 38			22 48	22 53		23 08		23 18	23 23	
Dalston Junction	a	21 42		21 50	21 57			22 05	22 12		22 20	22 27		22 35	22 42			22 50	22 57		23 12		23 20	23 27	
Canonbury	a			21 53				22 08			22 23			22 38				22 53					23 23		
Highbury & Islington	a			21 58				22 13			22 28			22 43				22 58					23 28		
London Bridge 4 ⊖	a		21 31			21 46				22 01			22 16			22 31				22 46		23 01			23 16

		LO		LO
Purley	d			
East Croydon 🚌	d			
Norwood Junction 2	a			
West Croydon 4 🚌	d	22 57		
Norwood Junction	a	23 01		
Norwood Junction	d	23 01		
Anerley	d	23 04		
Penge West	d	23 06		
Crystal Palace 4	d			23 16
Sydenham	d	23 09		23 19
Forest Hill 4	d	23 11		23 22
Honor Oak Park	d	23 14		23 24
Brockley	d	23 16		23 27
New Cross Gate	d	23 19		23 29
Surrey Quays	d	23 23		23 33
Canada Water	d	23 25		23 35
Rotherhithe	d	23 26		23 36
Wapping	d	23 28		23 38
Shadwell	d	23 30		23 40
Whitechapel	d	23 32		23 42
Shoreditch High Street	d	23 34		23 44
Hoxton	d	23 36		23 46
Haggerston	d	23 38		23 48
Dalston Junction	a	23 42		23 50
Canonbury	a			23 53
Highbury & Islington	a			23 56
London Bridge 4 ⊖	a			

A From Tattenham Corner

For Fast trains between London Bridge & New Cross Gate to Norwood Jn & East Croydon, see Table 175

For full service between Highbury & Islington and Surrey Quays, please see Table 178

For Sutton connections at West Croydon, please see table 172

Table 178

Mondays to Fridays

9 December to 16 May

Highbury & Islington - New Cross, Crystal Palace, West Croydon and Clapham Junction

Network Diagram - see first Page of Table 173

Miles	Miles	Miles	Miles			LO MO A	LO MX A	LO MX A	LO MX B	LO MX A	LO MX A	LO MX	LO	LO	LO	LO	LO	LO	LO	LO	LO	LO	LO
0	0	—	—	Highbury & Islington	d							00 10	05 35		05 47	05 55			06 17	06 25		06 32	
0½	0½	—	—	Canonbury	d						00 01	00 12	05 37		05 49	05 57			06 19	06 27		06 34	
1½	1½	0	0	**Dalston Junction**	d						00 03	00 15	05 40	05 49	05 52	06 00	06 10	06 19	06 22	06 30	06 34	06 37	06 40
2	2	0½	0½	**Haggerston**	d						00 04	00 16	05 41	05 50	05 53	06 01	06 11	06 20	06 23	06 31	06 35	06 38	06 41
2½	2½	1	1	**Hoxton**	d						00 06	00 18	05 43	05 52	05 55	06 03	06 13	06 22	06 25	06 33	06 37	06 40	06 43
3¼	3¼	1¾	1¾	**Shoreditch High Street**	d						00 09	00 21	05 46	05 55	05 58	06 06	06 16	06 25	06 28	06 36	06 40	06 43	06 46
3¾	3¾	2¼	2¼	**Whitechapel**	d						00 11	00 23	05 48	05 57	06 00	06 08	06 18	06 27	06 30	06 38	06 42	06 45	06 48
4½	4½	3	3	**Shadwell**	d						00 13	00 25	05 50	05 59	06 02	06 10	06 20	06 29	06 32	06 40	06 44	06 47	06 50
5	5	3½	3½	**Wapping**	d						00 15	00 27	05 52	06 01	06 04	06 12	06 22	06 31	06 34	06 42	06 46	06 49	06 52
5½	5½	4	4	**Rotherhithe**	d					00 02	00 17	00 29	05 54	06 03	06 06	06 14	06 24	06 33	06 36	06 44	06 48	06 51	06 54
5¾	5¾	4¼	4¼	**Canada Water**	d					00 04	00 19	00 31	05 56	06 05	06 08	06 16	06 26	06 35	06 38	06 46	06 50	06 53	06 56
6	6	4½	4½	**Surrey Quays**	d					00 05	00 20	00 32	05 57	06 06	06 09	06 17	06 27	06 36	06 39	06 47	06 51	06 54	06 57
—	—	—	5¾	New Cross	a									06 11				06 41			06 56		
—	7¼	5¾	—	New Cross Gate [4]	d				00 02	00a09	00a24	00a36	06 02			06 22	06 32			06 52			07 02
—	8	6½	—	Brockley	d				00 04				06 04			06 24	06 34			06 54			07 04
—	9	7½	—	Honor Oak Park	d				00 07				06 07			06 27	06 37			06 57			07 07
—	10	8½	—	Forest Hill [4]	d				00 10				06 10			06 30	06 40			07 00			07 10
—	11¾	9	—	Sydenham	d	00 01	00 02		00 12				06 12			06 32	06 42			07 02			07 12
—	12	—	—	Crystal Palace [4]	a		00 07									06 37				07 07			
—	—	10	—	Penge West	d	00 03			00 15				06 15				06 45						07 15
—	—	10½	—	Anerley	d	00 05			00 17				06 17				06 47						07 17
—	—	11½	—	Norwood Junction [2]	d	00 08			00 20				06 20				06 50						07 20
—	—	13¼	—	West Croydon [4] (tram)	a	00 14			00 27				06 30				07 00						07 30
7½	—	—	—	Queens Rd Peckham	d										06 14				06 44			06 59	
8	—	—	—	Peckham Rye [4]	d			00 02							06 16				06 47			07 02	
9	—	—	—	Denmark Hill [4]	d			00 06							06 21				06 55			07 06	
11	—	—	—	Clapham High Street ⊖	d			00 10							06 24				07 00			07 10	
11¼	—	—	—	Wandsworth Road	d			00 12							06 27				07 01			07 12	
12¾	—	—	—	Clapham Junction	a			00 21							06 35				07 09			07 21	

		LO	LO	LO	LO	LO	LO	LO	LO	LO	LO	LO	LO	LO	LO	LO	LO	LO	LO	LO	LO	LO	LO
Highbury & Islington	d	06 40		06 47		06 55		07 02		07 10		07 17		07 25		07 32		07 40		07 47		07 55	
Canonbury	d	06 42		06 49		06 57		07 04		07 12		07 19		07 27		07 34		07 42		07 49		07 57	
Dalston Junction	d	06 45	06 49	06 52	06 55	07 00	07 04	07 07	07 10	07 15	07 19	07 22	07 25	07 30	07 34	07 37	07 40	07 45	07 49	07 52	07 55	08 00	08 04
Haggerston	d	06 46	06 50	06 53	06 56	07 01	07 05	07 08	07 11	07 16	07 20	07 23	07 26	07 31	07 35	07 38	07 41	07 46	07 50	07 53	07 56	08 01	08 05
Hoxton	d	06 48	06 52	06 55	06 58	07 03	07 07	07 10	07 13	07 18	07 22	07 25	07 28	07 33	07 37	07 40	07 43	07 48	07 52	07 55	07 58	08 03	08 07
Shoreditch High Street	d	06 51	06 55	06 58	07 01	07 06	07 10	07 13	07 16	07 21	07 25	07 28	07 31	07 36	07 40	07 43	07 46	07 51	07 55	07 58	08 01	08 06	08 10
Whitechapel	d	06 53	06 57	07 00	07 03	07 08	07 12	07 15	07 18	07 23	07 27	07 30	07 33	07 38	07 42	07 45	07 48	07 53	07 57	08 00	08 03	08 08	08 12
Shadwell	d	06 55	06 59	07 02	07 05	07 10	07 14	07 17	07 20	07 25	07 29	07 32	07 35	07 40	07 44	07 47	07 50	07 55	07 59	08 02	08 05	08 10	08 14
Wapping	d	06 57	07 01	07 04	07 07	07 12	07 16	07 19	07 22	07 27	07 31	07 34	07 37	07 42	07 46	07 49	07 52	07 57	08 01	08 04	08 07	08 12	08 16
Rotherhithe	d	06 59	07 03	07 06	07 09	07 14	07 18	07 21	07 24	07 29	07 33	07 36	07 39	07 44	07 48	07 51	07 54	07 59	08 03	08 06	08 09	08 14	08 18
Canada Water	d	07 01	07 05	07 08	07 11	07 16	07 20	07 23	07 26	07 31	07 35	07 38	07 41	07 46	07 50	07 53	07 56	08 01	08 05	08 08	08 11	08 16	08 20
Surrey Quays	d	07 02	07 06	07 09	07 12	07 17	07 21	07 24	07 27	07 32	07 36	07 39	07 42	07 47	07 51	07 54	07 57	08 02	08 06	08 09	08 12	08 17	08 21
New Cross	a		07 11				07 26				07 41				07 56				08 11				08 26
New Cross Gate [4]	d	07 07			07 17	07 22			07 32	07 37			07 47	07 52			08 02	08 07			08 17	08 22	
Brockley	d	07 09			07 19	07 24			07 34	07 39			07 49	07 54			08 04	08 09			08 19	08 24	
Honor Oak Park	d	07 12			07 22	07 27			07 37	07 42			07 52	07 57			08 07	08 12			08 22	08 27	
Forest Hill [4]	d	07 15			07 25	07 30			07 40	07 45			07 55	08 00			08 10	08 15			08 25	08 30	
Sydenham	d	07 17			07 27	07 32			07 42	07 47			07 57	08 02			08 12	08 17			08 27	08 32	
Crystal Palace [4]	a	07 22				07 37				07 52				08 07				08 22				08 37	
Penge West	d				07 30				07 45				08 00				08 15				08 30		
Anerley	d				07 32				07 47				08 02				08 17				08 32		
Norwood Junction [2]	d				07 35				07 50				08 05				08 20				08 35		
West Croydon [4] (tram)	a				07 41				08 00				08 11				08 30				08 41		
Queens Rd Peckham	d			07 14				07 29				07 44				07 59				08 14			
Peckham Rye [4]	d			07 17				07 32				07 47				08 02				08 17			
Denmark Hill [4]	d			07 21				07 36				07 51				08 11				08 21			
Clapham High Street ⊖	d			07 25				07 40				07 55				08 16				08 25			
Wandsworth Road	d			07 27				07 42				07 57				08 17				08 27			
Clapham Junction	a			07 36				07 51				08 06				08 24				08 37			

		LO	LO	LO	LO	LO	LO	LO	LO	LO	LO	LO	LO	LO	LO	LO	LO	LO	LO	LO	LO	LO	LO
Highbury & Islington	d	08 02		08 10		08 17		08 25		08 32		08 40		08 47		08 55		09 02		09 10		09 17	
Canonbury	d	08 04		08 12		08 19		08 27		08 34		08 42		08 49		08 57		09 04		09 12		09 19	
Dalston Junction	d	08 07	08 10	08 15	08 19	08 22	08 25	08 30	08 34	08 37	08 40	08 45	08 49	08 52	08 55	09 00	09 04	09 07	09 10	09 15	09 19	09 22	09 25
Haggerston	d	08 08	08 11	08 16	08 20	08 23	08 26	08 31	08 35	08 38	08 41	08 46	08 50	08 53	08 56	09 01	09 05	09 08	09 11	09 16	09 20	09 23	09 26
Hoxton	d	08 10	08 13	08 18	08 22	08 25	08 28	08 33	08 37	08 40	08 43	08 48	08 52	08 55	08 58	09 03	09 07	09 10	09 13	09 18	09 22	09 25	09 28
Shoreditch High Street	d	08 13	08 16	08 21	08 25	08 28	08 31	08 36	08 40	08 43	08 46	08 51	08 55	08 58	09 01	09 06	09 10	09 13	09 16	09 21	09 25	09 28	09 31
Whitechapel	d	08 15	08 18	08 23	08 27	08 30	08 33	08 38	08 42	08 45	08 48	08 53	08 57	09 00	09 03	09 08	09 12	09 15	09 18	09 23	09 27	09 30	09 33
Shadwell	d	08 17	08 20	08 25	08 29	08 32	08 35	08 40	08 44	08 47	08 50	08 55	08 59	09 02	09 05	09 10	09 14	09 17	09 20	09 25	09 29	09 32	09 35
Wapping	d	08 19	08 22	08 27	08 31	08 34	08 37	08 42	08 46	08 49	08 52	08 57	09 01	09 04	09 07	09 12	09 16	09 19	09 22	09 27	09 31	09 34	09 37
Rotherhithe	d	08 21	08 24	08 29	08 33	08 36	08 39	08 44	08 48	08 51	08 54	08 59	09 03	09 06	09 09	09 14	09 18	09 21	09 24	09 29	09 33	09 36	09 39
Canada Water	d	08 23	08 26	08 31	08 35	08 38	08 41	08 46	08 50	08 53	08 56	09 01	09 05	09 08	09 11	09 16	09 20	09 23	09 26	09 31	09 35	09 38	09 41
Surrey Quays	d	08 24	08 27	08 32	08 36	08 39	08 42	08 47	08 51	08 54	08 57	09 02	09 06	09 09	09 12	09 17	09 21	09 24	09 27	09 32	09 36	09 39	09 42
New Cross	a				08 41				08 56				09 11				09 26				09 41		
New Cross Gate [4]	d		08 32	08 37			08 47	08 52			09 02	09 07			09 17	09 22			09 32	09 37			09 47
Brockley	d		08 34	08 39			08 49	08 54			09 04	09 09			09 19	09 24			09 34	09 39			09 49
Honor Oak Park	d		08 37	08 42			08 52	08 57			09 07	09 12			09 22	09 27			09 37	09 42			09 52
Forest Hill [4]	d		08 40	08 45			08 55	09 00			09 10	09 15			09 25	09 30			09 40	09 45			09 55
Sydenham	d		08 42	08 47			08 57	09 02			09 12	09 17			09 27	09 32			09 42	09 47			09 57
Crystal Palace [4]	a			08 52				09 07				09 22				09 37				09 52			
Penge West	d		08 45				09 00				09 15				09 30				09 45				10 00
Anerley	d		08 47				09 02				09 17				09 32				09 47				10 02
Norwood Junction [2]	d		08 50				09 05				09 20				09 35				09 50				10 05
West Croydon [4] (tram)	a		09 00				09 11				09 30				09 41				10 00				10 11
Queens Rd Peckham	d	08 29				08 44				08 59				09 14				09 29				09 44	
Peckham Rye [4]	d	08 32				08 47				09 02				09 17				09 32				09 47	
Denmark Hill [4]	d	08 40				08 51				09 06				09 21				09 36				09 51	
Clapham High Street ⊖	d	08 44				08 55				09 10				09 25				09 40				09 55	
Wandsworth Road	d	08 46				08 57				09 12				09 27				09 42				09 57	
Clapham Junction	a	08 53				09 06				09 22				09 37				09 51				10 07	

A From Highbury and Islington Ell

B From Dalston Junction Stn Ell

Table 178

Mondays to Fridays

9 December to 16 May

Highbury & Islington - New Cross, Crystal Palace, West Croydon and Clapham Junction

Network Diagram - see first Page of Table 173

Station		LO		LO	LO	LO	LO	LO	LO	LO	LO	LO		LO	LO	LO	LO	LO	LO	LO	LO	LO		LO	LO
Highbury & Islington	d	09 25			09 32		09 40		09 47		09 55			10 02		10 10		10 17		10 25		10 32			10 40
Canonbury	d	09 27			09 34		09 42		09 49		09 57			10 04		10 12		10 19		10 27		10 34			10 42
Dalston Junction	d	09 30		09 34	09 37	09 40	09 45	09 49	09 52	09 55	10 00	10 04		10 07	10 10	10 15	10 19	10 22	10 25	10 30	10 34	10 37		10 40	10 45
Haggerston	d	09 31		09 35	09 38	09 41	09 46	09 50	09 53	09 56	10 01	10 05		10 08	10 11	10 16	10 20	10 23	10 26	10 31	10 35	10 38		10 41	10 46
Hoxton	d	09 33		09 37	09 40	09 43	09 48	09 52	09 55	09 58	10 03	10 07		10 10	10 13	10 18	10 22	10 25	10 28	10 33	10 37	10 40		10 43	10 48
Shoreditch High Street	d	09 36		09 40	09 43	09 46	09 51	09 55	09 58	10 01	10 06	10 10		10 13	10 16	10 21	10 25	10 28	10 31	10 36	10 40	10 43		10 46	10 51
Whitechapel	d	09 38		09 42	09 45	09 48	09 53	09 57	10 00	10 03	10 08	10 12		10 15	10 18	10 23	10 27	10 30	10 33	10 38	10 42	10 45		10 48	10 53
Shadwell	d	09 40		09 44	09 47	09 50	09 55	09 59	10 02	10 05	10 10	10 14		10 17	10 20	10 25	10 29	10 32	10 35	10 40	10 44	10 47		10 50	10 55
Wapping	d	09 42		09 46	09 49	09 52	09 57	10 01	10 04	10 07	10 12	10 16		10 19	10 22	10 27	10 31	10 34	10 37	10 42	10 46	10 49		10 52	10 57
Rotherhithe	d	09 44		09 48	09 51	09 54	09 59	10 03	10 06	10 09	10 14	10 18		10 21	10 24	10 29	10 33	10 36	10 39	10 44	10 48	10 51		10 54	10 59
Canada Water	d	09 46		09 50	09 53	09 56	10 01	10 05	10 08	10 11	10 16	10 20		10 23	10 26	10 31	10 35	10 38	10 41	10 46	10 50	10 53		10 56	11 01
Surrey Quays	d	09 47		09 51	09 54	09 57	10 02	10 06	10 09	10 12	10 17	10 21		10 24	10 27	10 32	10 36	10 39	10 42	10 47	10 51	10 54		10 57	11 02
New Cross	a			09 56				10 11				10 26					10 41				10 56				
New Cross Gate [4]	d	09 52				10 02	10 07			10 17	10 22				10 32	10 37			10 47	10 52				11 02	11 07
Brockley	d	09 54				10 04	10 09			10 19	10 24				10 34	10 39			10 49	10 54				11 04	11 09
Honor Oak Park	d	09 57				10 07	10 12			10 22	10 27				10 37	10 42			10 52	10 57				11 07	11 12
Forest Hill [4]	d	10 00				10 10	10 15			10 25	10 30				10 40	10 45			10 55	11 00				11 10	11 15
Sydenham	d	10 02				10 12	10 17			10 27	10 32				10 42	10 47			10 57	11 02				11 12	11 17
Crystal Palace [4]	a	10 07					10 22				10 37					10 52				11 07					11 22
Penge West	d					10 15				10 30					10 45				11 00					11 15	
Anerley	d					10 17				10 32					10 47				11 02					11 17	
Norwood Junction [2]	d					10 20				10 35					10 50				11 05					11 20	
West Croydon [4]	a					10 30				10 41					11 00				11 11					11 30	
Queens Rd Peckham	d				09 59				10 14					10 29				10 44				10 59			
Peckham Rye [4]	d				10 02				10 17					10 32				10 47				11 02			
Denmark Hill [4]	d				10 06				10 21					10 36				10 51				11 06			
Clapham High Street ⊖	d				10 10				10 25					10 40				10 55				11 10			
Wandsworth Road	d				10 12				10 27					10 42				10 57				11 12			
Clapham Junction	a				10 22				10 37					10 51				11 07				11 22			

Station		LO	LO	LO	LO	LO	LO	LO		LO	LO	LO	LO	LO	LO	LO	LO	LO		LO	LO	LO	LO	LO	LO
Highbury & Islington	d		10 47		10 55		11 02			11 10		11 17		11 25		11 32		11 40			11 47		11 55		12 02
Canonbury	d		10 49		10 57		11 04			11 12		11 19		11 27		11 34		11 42			11 49		11 57		12 04
Dalston Junction	d	10 49	10 52	10 55	11 00	11 04	11 07	11 10		11 15	11 19	11 22	11 25	11 30	11 34	11 37	11 40	11 45		11 49	11 52	11 55	12 00	12 04	12 07
Haggerston	d	10 50	10 53	10 56	11 01	11 05	11 08	11 11		11 16	11 20	11 23	11 26	11 31	11 35	11 38	11 41	11 46		11 50	11 53	11 56	12 01	12 05	12 08
Hoxton	d	10 52	10 55	10 58	11 03	11 07	11 10	11 13		11 18	11 22	11 25	11 28	11 33	11 37	11 40	11 43	11 48		11 52	11 55	11 58	12 03	12 07	12 10
Shoreditch High Street	d	10 55	10 58	11 01	11 06	11 10	11 13	11 16		11 21	11 25	11 28	11 31	11 36	11 40	11 43	11 46	11 51		11 55	11 58	12 01	12 06	12 10	12 13
Whitechapel	d	10 57	11 00	11 03	11 08	11 12	11 15	11 18		11 23	11 27	11 30	11 33	11 38	11 42	11 45	11 48	11 53		11 57	12 00	12 03	12 08	12 12	12 15
Shadwell	d	10 59	11 02	11 05	11 10	11 14	11 17	11 20		11 25	11 29	11 32	11 35	11 40	11 44	11 47	11 50	11 55		11 59	12 02	12 05	12 10	12 14	12 17
Wapping	d	11 01	11 04	11 07	11 12	11 16	11 19	11 22		11 27	11 31	11 34	11 37	11 42	11 46	11 49	11 52	11 57		12 01	12 04	12 07	12 12	12 16	12 19
Rotherhithe	d	11 03	11 06	11 09	11 14	11 18	11 21	11 24		11 29	11 33	11 36	11 39	11 44	11 48	11 51	11 54	11 59		12 03	12 06	12 09	12 14	12 18	12 21
Canada Water	d	11 05	11 08	11 11	11 16	11 20	11 23	11 26		11 31	11 35	11 38	11 41	11 46	11 50	11 53	11 56	12 01		12 05	12 08	12 11	12 16	12 20	12 23
Surrey Quays	d	11 06	11 09	11 12	11 17	11 21	11 24	11 27		11 32	11 36	11 39	11 42	11 47	11 51	11 54	11 57	12 02		12 06	12 09	12 12	12 17	12 21	12 24
New Cross	a	11 11				11 26					11 41				11 56					12 11				12 26	
New Cross Gate [4]	d			11 17	11 22			11 32		11 37			11 47	11 52			12 02	12 07				12 17	12 22		
Brockley	d			11 19	11 24			11 34		11 39			11 49	11 54			12 04	12 09				12 19	12 24		
Honor Oak Park	d			11 22	11 27			11 37		11 42			11 52	11 57			12 07	12 12				12 22	12 27		
Forest Hill [4]	d			11 25	11 30			11 40		11 45			11 55	12 00			12 10	12 15				12 25	12 30		
Sydenham	d			11 27	11 32			11 42		11 47			11 57	12 02			12 12	12 17				12 27	12 32		
Crystal Palace [4]	a				11 37					11 52				12 07				12 22					12 37		
Penge West	d			11 30				11 45					12 00				12 15					12 30			
Anerley	d			11 32				11 47					12 02				12 17					12 32			
Norwood Junction [2]	d			11 35				11 50					12 05				12 20					12 35			
West Croydon [4]	a			11 41				12 00					12 11				12 29					12 41			
Queens Rd Peckham	d		11 14				11 29					11 44				11 59					12 14				12 29
Peckham Rye [4]	d		11 17				11 32					11 47				12 02					12 17				12 32
Denmark Hill [4]	d		11 21				11 36					11 51				12 06					12 21				12 36
Clapham High Street ⊖	d		11 25				11 40					11 55				12 10					12 25				12 40
Wandsworth Road	d		11 27				11 42					11 57				12 12					12 27				12 42
Clapham Junction	a		11 36				11 52					12 07				12 22					12 36				12 52

Station		LO	LO	LO		LO	LO	LO	LO	LO	LO	LO	LO	LO		LO	LO	LO	LO	LO	LO	LO	LO	LO	
Highbury & Islington	d		12 10			12 17		12 25		12 32		12 40		12 47			12 55		13 02		13 10		13 17		
Canonbury	d		12 12			12 19		12 27		12 34		12 42		12 49			12 57		13 04		13 12		13 19		
Dalston Junction	d	12 10	12 15	12 19		12 22	12 25	12 30	12 34	12 37	12 40	12 45	12 49	12 52		12 55	13 00	13 04	13 07	13 10	13 15	13 19	13 22	13 25	
Haggerston	d	12 11	12 16	12 20		12 23	12 26	12 31	12 35	12 38	12 41	12 46	12 50	12 53		12 56	13 01	13 05	13 08	13 11	13 16	13 20	13 23	13 26	
Hoxton	d	12 13	12 18	12 22		12 25	12 28	12 33	12 37	12 40	12 43	12 48	12 52	12 55		12 58	13 03	13 07	13 10	13 13	13 18	13 22	13 25	13 28	
Shoreditch High Street	d	12 16	12 21	12 25		12 28	12 31	12 36	12 40	12 43	12 46	12 51	12 55	12 58		13 01	13 06	13 10	13 13	13 16	13 21	13 25	13 28	13 31	
Whitechapel	d	12 18	12 23	12 27		12 30	12 33	12 38	12 42	12 45	12 48	12 53	12 57	13 00		13 03	13 08	13 12	13 15	13 18	13 23	13 27	13 30	13 33	
Shadwell	d	12 20	12 25	12 29		12 32	12 35	12 40	12 44	12 47	12 50	12 55	12 59	13 02		13 05	13 10	13 14	13 17	13 20	13 25	13 29	13 32	13 35	
Wapping	d	12 22	12 27	12 31		12 34	12 37	12 42	12 46	12 49	12 52	12 57	13 01	13 04		13 07	13 12	13 16	13 19	13 22	13 27	13 31	13 34	13 37	
Rotherhithe	d	12 24	12 29	12 33		12 36	12 39	12 44	12 48	12 51	12 54	12 59	13 03	13 06		13 09	13 14	13 18	13 21	13 24	13 29	13 33	13 36	13 39	
Canada Water	d	12 26	12 31	12 35		12 38	12 41	12 46	12 50	12 53	12 56	13 01	13 05	13 08		13 11	13 16	13 20	13 23	13 26	13 31	13 35	13 38	13 41	
Surrey Quays	d	12 27	12 32	12 36		12 39	12 42	12 47	12 51	12 54	12 57	13 02	13 06	13 09		13 12	13 17	13 21	13 24	13 27	13 32	13 36	13 39	13 42	
New Cross	a			12 41					12 56				13 11					13 26				13 41			
New Cross Gate [4]	d	12 32	12 37				12 47	12 52			13 02	13 07				13 17	13 22			13 32	13 37			13 47	
Brockley	d	12 34	12 39				12 49	12 54			13 04	13 09				13 19	13 24			13 34	13 39			13 49	
Honor Oak Park	d	12 37	12 42				12 52	12 57			13 07	13 12				13 22	13 27			13 37	13 42			13 52	
Forest Hill [4]	d	12 40	12 45				12 55	13 00			13 10	13 15				13 25	13 30			13 40	13 45			13 55	
Sydenham	d	12 42	12 47				12 57	13 02			13 12	13 17				13 27	13 32			13 42	13 47			13 57	
Crystal Palace [4]	a		12 52					13 07				13 22					13 37				13 52				
Penge West	d	12 45					13 00				13 15					13 30				13 45				14 00	
Anerley	d	12 47					13 02				13 17					13 32				13 47				14 02	
Norwood Junction [2]	d	12 50					13 05				13 20					13 35				13 50				14 05	
West Croydon [4]	a	13 00					13 11				13 30					13 41				14 00				14 11	
Queens Rd Peckham	d					12 44				12 59				13 14					13 29				13 44		
Peckham Rye [4]	d					12 47				13 02				13 17					13 32				13 47		
Denmark Hill [4]	d					12 51				13 06				13 21					13 36				13 51		
Clapham High Street ⊖	d					12 55				13 10				13 25					13 40				13 55		
Wandsworth Road	d					12 57				13 12				13 27					13 42				13 57		
Clapham Junction	a					13 06				13 22				13 36					13 52				14 06		

Table 178

Mondays to Fridays

9 December to 16 May

Highbury & Islington - New Cross, Crystal Palace, West Croydon and Clapham Junction

Network Diagram - see first Page of Table 173

		LO	LO	LO	LO	LO	LO	LO	LO	LO		LO	LO	LO	LO	LO	LO	LO	LO	LO		LO	LO	LO	LO
Highbury & Islington	d	13 25		13 32		13 40		13 47		13 55			14 02		14 10		14 17		14 25			14 32		14 40	
Canonbury	d	13 27		13 34		13 42		13 49		13 57			14 04		14 12		14 19		14 27			14 34		14 42	
Dalston Junction	d	13 30	13 34	13 37	13 40	13 45	13 49	13 52	13 55	14 00		14 04	14 07	14 10	14 15	14 19	14 22	14 25	14 30	14 34		14 37	14 40	14 45	14 49
Haggerston	d	13 31	13 35	13 38	13 41	13 46	13 50	13 53	13 56	14 01		14 05	14 08	14 11	14 16	14 20	14 23	14 26	14 31	14 35		14 38	14 41	14 46	14 50
Hoxton	d	13 33	13 37	13 40	13 43	13 48	13 52	13 55	13 58	14 03		14 07	14 10	14 13	14 18	14 22	14 25	14 28	14 33	14 37		14 40	14 43	14 48	14 52
Shoreditch High Street	d	13 36	13 40	13 43	13 46	13 51	13 55	13 58	14 01	14 06		14 10	14 13	14 16	14 21	14 25	14 28	14 31	14 36	14 40		14 43	14 46	14 51	14 55
Whitechapel	d	13 38	13 42	13 45	13 48	13 53	13 57	14 00	14 03	14 08		14 12	14 15	14 18	14 23	14 27	14 30	14 33	14 38	14 42		14 45	14 48	14 53	14 57
Shadwell	d	13 40	13 44	13 47	13 50	13 55	13 59	14 02	14 05	14 10		14 14	14 17	14 20	14 25	14 29	14 32	14 35	14 40	14 44		14 47	14 50	14 55	14 59
Wapping	d	13 42	13 46	13 49	13 52	13 57	14 01	14 04	14 07	14 12		14 16	14 19	14 22	14 27	14 31	14 34	14 37	14 42	14 46		14 49	14 52	14 57	15 01
Rotherhithe	d	13 44	13 48	13 51	13 54	13 59	14 03	14 06	14 09	14 14		14 18	14 21	14 24	14 29	14 33	14 36	14 39	14 44	14 48		14 51	14 54	14 59	15 03
Canada Water	d	13 46	13 50	13 53	13 56	14 01	14 05	14 08	14 11	14 16		14 20	14 23	14 26	14 31	14 35	14 38	14 41	14 46	14 50		14 53	14 56	15 01	15 05
Surrey Quays	d	13 47	13 51	13 54	13 57	14 02	14 06	14 09	14 12	14 17		14 21	14 24	14 27	14 32	14 36	14 39	14 42	14 47	14 51		14 54	14 57	15 02	15 06
New Cross	a		13 56				14 11					14 26				14 41				14 56					15 11
New Cross Gate [4]	d	13 52			14 02	14 07			14 17	14 22				14 32	14 37			14 47	14 52				15 02	15 07	
Brockley	d	13 54			14 04	14 09			14 19	14 24				14 34	14 39			14 49	14 54				15 04	15 09	
Honor Oak Park	d	13 57			14 07	14 12			14 22	14 27				14 37	14 42			14 52	14 57				15 07	15 12	
Forest Hill [4]	d	14 00			14 10	14 15			14 25	14 30				14 40	14 45			14 55	15 00				15 10	15 15	
Sydenham	d	14 02			14 12	14 17			14 27	14 32				14 42	14 47			14 57	15 02				15 12	15 17	
Crystal Palace [4]	a	14 07				14 22				14 37					14 52				15 07					15 22	
Penge West	d				14 15				14 30					14 45				15 00					15 15		
Anerley	d				14 17				14 32					14 47				15 02					15 17		
Norwood Junction [2]	d				14 20				14 35					14 50				15 05					15 20		
West Croydon [4] (tram)	a				14 30				14 41					15 00				15 11					15 30		
Queens Rd Peckham	d			13 59				14 14					14 29				14 44					14 59			
Peckham Rye [4]	d			14 02				14 17					14 32				14 47					15 02			
Denmark Hill [4]	d			14 06				14 21					14 36				14 51					15 06			
Clapham High Street ⊖	d			14 10				14 25					14 40				14 55					15 10			
Wandsworth Road	d			14 12				14 27					14 42				14 57					15 12			
Clapham Junction	a			14 22				14 36					14 52				15 07					15 21			

		LO	LO	LO	LO	LO		LO	LO	LO	LO	LO	LO	LO	LO	LO		LO	LO	LO	LO	LO	LO	LO	LO
Highbury & Islington	d	14 47		14 55		15 02			15 10		15 17		15 25		15 32			15 40		15 47		15 55		16 02	
Canonbury	d	14 49		14 57		15 04			15 12		15 19		15 27		15 34			15 42		15 49		15 57		16 04	
Dalston Junction	d	14 52	14 55	15 00	15 04	15 07		15 10	15 15	15 19	15 22	15 25	15 30	15 34	15 37	15 40		15 45	15 49	15 52	15 55	16 00	16 04	16 07	16 10
Haggerston	d	14 53	14 56	15 01	15 05	15 08		15 11	15 16	15 20	15 23	15 26	15 31	15 35	15 38	15 41		15 46	15 50	15 53	15 56	16 01	16 05	16 08	16 11
Hoxton	d	14 55	14 58	15 03	15 07	15 10		15 13	15 18	15 22	15 25	15 28	15 33	15 37	15 40	15 43		15 48	15 52	15 55	15 58	16 03	16 07	16 10	16 13
Shoreditch High Street	d	14 58	15 01	15 06	15 10	15 13		15 16	15 21	15 25	15 28	15 31	15 36	15 40	15 43	15 46		15 51	15 55	15 58	16 01	16 06	16 10	16 13	16 16
Whitechapel	d	15 00	15 03	15 08	15 12	15 15		15 18	15 23	15 27	15 30	15 33	15 38	15 42	15 45	15 48		15 53	15 57	16 00	16 03	16 08	16 12	16 15	16 18
Shadwell	d	15 02	15 05	15 10	15 14	15 17		15 20	15 25	15 29	15 32	15 35	15 40	15 44	15 47	15 50		15 55	15 59	16 02	16 05	16 10	16 14	16 17	16 20
Wapping	d	15 04	15 07	15 12	15 16	15 19		15 22	15 27	15 31	15 34	15 37	15 42	15 46	15 49	15 52		15 57	16 01	16 04	16 07	16 12	16 16	16 19	16 22
Rotherhithe	d	15 06	15 09	15 14	15 18	15 21		15 24	15 29	15 33	15 36	15 39	15 44	15 48	15 51	15 54		15 59	16 03	16 06	16 09	16 14	16 18	16 21	16 24
Canada Water	d	15 08	15 11	15 16	15 20	15 23		15 26	15 31	15 35	15 38	15 41	15 46	15 50	15 53	15 56		16 01	16 05	16 08	16 11	16 16	16 20	16 23	16 26
Surrey Quays	d	15 09	15 12	15 17	15 21	15 24		15 27	15 32	15 36	15 39	15 42	15 47	15 51	15 54	15 57		16 02	16 06	16 09	16 12	16 17	16 21	16 24	16 27
New Cross	a				15 26					15 41				15 56					16 11				16 26		
New Cross Gate [4]	d		15 17	15 22				15 32	15 37			15 47	15 52			16 02		16 07			16 17	16 22			16 32
Brockley	d		15 19	15 24				15 34	15 39			15 49	15 54			16 04		16 09			16 19	16 24			16 34
Honor Oak Park	d		15 22	15 27				15 37	15 42			15 52	15 57			16 07		16 12			16 22	16 27			16 37
Forest Hill [4]	d		15 25	15 30				15 40	15 45			15 55	16 00			16 10		16 15			16 25	16 30			16 40
Sydenham	d		15 27	15 32				15 42	15 47			15 57	16 02			16 12		16 17			16 27	16 32			16 42
Crystal Palace [4]	a			15 37					15 52				16 07					16 22				16 37			
Penge West	d		15 30					15 45				16 00				16 15					16 30				16 45
Anerley	d		15 32					15 47				16 02				16 17					16 32				16 47
Norwood Junction [2]	d		15 35					15 50				16 05				16 20					16 35				16 50
West Croydon [4] (tram)	a		15 41					16 00				16 11				16 30					16 41				17 00
Queens Rd Peckham	d	15 14				15 29					15 44				15 59					16 14				16 29	
Peckham Rye [4]	d	15 17				15 32					15 47				16 02					16 17				16 32	
Denmark Hill [4]	d	15 21				15 36					15 51				16 06					16 21				16 36	
Clapham High Street ⊖	d	15 25				15 40					15 55				16 10					16 25				16 40	
Wandsworth Road	d	15 27				15 42					15 57				16 12					16 27				16 42	
Clapham Junction	a	15 36				15 51					16 06				16 21					16 36				16 51	

		LO		LO	LO	LO	LO	LO	LO	LO	LO	LO		LO	LO	LO	LO	LO	LO	LO	LO	LO		LO	LO
Highbury & Islington	d	16 10			16 17		16 25		16 32		16 40			16 47		16 55		17 02		17 10		17 17			17 25
Canonbury	d	16 12			16 19		16 27		16 34		16 42			16 49		16 57		17 04		17 12		17 19			17 27
Dalston Junction	d	16 15		16 19	16 22	16 25	16 30	16 34	16 37	16 40	16 45	16 49		16 52	16 55	17 00	17 04	17 07	17 10	17 15	17 19	17 22		17 25	17 30
Haggerston	d	16 16		16 20	16 23	16 26	16 31	16 35	16 38	16 41	16 46	16 50		16 53	16 56	17 01	17 05	17 08	17 11	17 16	17 20	17 23		17 26	17 31
Hoxton	d	16 18		16 22	16 25	16 28	16 33	16 37	16 40	16 43	16 48	16 52		16 55	16 58	17 03	17 07	17 10	17 13	17 18	17 22	17 25		17 28	17 33
Shoreditch High Street	d	16 21		16 25	16 28	16 31	16 36	16 40	16 43	16 46	16 51	16 55		16 58	17 01	17 06	17 10	17 13	17 16	17 21	17 25	17 28		17 31	17 36
Whitechapel	d	16 23		16 27	16 30	16 33	16 38	16 42	16 45	16 48	16 53	16 57		17 00	17 03	17 08	17 12	17 15	17 18	17 23	17 27	17 30		17 33	17 38
Shadwell	d	16 25		16 29	16 32	16 35	16 40	16 44	16 47	16 50	16 55	16 59		17 02	17 05	17 10	17 14	17 17	17 20	17 25	17 29	17 32		17 35	17 40
Wapping	d	16 27		16 31	16 34	16 37	16 42	16 46	16 49	16 52	16 57	17 01		17 04	17 07	17 12	17 16	17 19	17 22	17 27	17 31	17 34		17 37	17 42
Rotherhithe	d	16 29		16 33	16 36	16 39	16 44	16 48	16 51	16 54	16 59	17 03		17 06	17 09	17 14	17 18	17 21	17 24	17 29	17 33	17 36		17 39	17 44
Canada Water	d	16 31		16 35	16 38	16 41	16 46	16 50	16 53	16 56	17 01	17 05		17 08	17 11	17 16	17 20	17 23	17 26	17 31	17 35	17 38		17 41	17 46
Surrey Quays	d	16 32		16 36	16 39	16 42	16 47	16 51	16 54	16 57	17 02	17 06		17 09	17 12	17 17	17 21	17 24	17 27	17 32	17 36	17 39		17 42	17 47
New Cross	a			16 41				16 56				17 11					17 26				17 41				
New Cross Gate [4]	d	16 37				16 47	16 52			17 02	17 07				17 17	17 22			17 32	17 37				17 47	17 52
Brockley	d	16 39				16 49	16 54			17 04	17 09				17 19	17 24			17 34	17 39				17 49	17 54
Honor Oak Park	d	16 42				16 52	16 57			17 07	17 12				17 22	17 27			17 37	17 42				17 52	17 57
Forest Hill [4]	d	16 45				16 55	17 00			17 10	17 15				17 25	17 30			17 40	17 45				17 55	18 00
Sydenham	d	16 47				16 57	17 02			17 12	17 17				17 27	17 32			17 42	17 47				17 57	18 02
Crystal Palace [4]	a	16 52					17 07				17 22					17 37				17 52					18 07
Penge West	d					17 00				17 15					17 30				17 45					18 00	
Anerley	d					17 02				17 17					17 32				17 47					18 02	
Norwood Junction [2]	d					17 05				17 20					17 35				17 50					18 05	
West Croydon [4] (tram)	a					17 11				17 30					17 41				17 59					18 11	
Queens Rd Peckham	d				16 44				16 59					17 14				17 29				17 44			
Peckham Rye [4]	d				16 47				17 06					17 17				17 32				17 47			
Denmark Hill [4]	d				16 51				17 07					17 21				17 36				17 51			
Clapham High Street ⊖	d				16 55				17 10					17 25				17 40				17 55			
Wandsworth Road	d				16 57				17 12					17 27				17 42				17 57			
Clapham Junction	a				17 06				17 23					17 35				17 51				18 06			

Table 178

Mondays to Fridays

9 December to 16 May

Highbury & Islington - New Cross, Crystal Palace, West Croydon and Clapham Junction

Network Diagram - see first Page of Table 173

		LO	LO	LO	LO	LO	LO	LO		LO	LO	LO	LO	LO	LO	LO	LO	LO		LO	LO	LO	LO	LO	LO
Highbury & Islington	d		17 32		17 40		17 47			17 55		18 02		18 10		18 17		18 25			18 32		18 40		18 47
Canonbury	d		17 34		17 42		17 49			17 57		18 04		18 12		18 19		18 27			18 34		18 42		18 49
Dalston Junction	d	17 34	17 37	17 40	17 45	17 49	17 52	17 55		18 00	18 04	18 07	18 10	18 15	18 19	18 22	18 25	18 30		18 34	18 37	18 40	18 45	18 49	18 52
Haggerston	d	17 35	17 38	17 41	17 46	17 50	17 53	17 56		18 01	18 05	18 08	18 11	18 16	18 20	18 23	18 26	18 31		18 35	18 38	18 41	18 46	18 50	18 53
Hoxton	d	17 37	17 40	17 43	17 48	17 52	17 55	17 58		18 03	18 07	18 10	18 13	18 18	18 22	18 25	18 28	18 33		18 37	18 40	18 43	18 48	18 52	18 55
Shoreditch High Street	d	17 40	17 43	17 46	17 51	17 55	17 58	18 01		18 06	18 10	18 13	18 16	18 21	18 25	18 28	18 31	18 36		18 40	18 43	18 46	18 51	18 55	18 58
Whitechapel	d	17 42	17 45	17 48	17 53	17 57	18 00	18 03		18 08	18 12	18 15	18 18	18 23	18 27	18 30	18 33	18 38		18 42	18 45	18 48	18 53	18 57	19 00
Shadwell	d	17 44	17 47	17 50	17 55	17 59	18 02	18 05		18 10	18 14	18 17	18 20	18 25	18 29	18 32	18 35	18 40		18 44	18 47	18 50	18 55	18 59	19 02
Wapping	d	17 46	17 49	17 52	17 57	18 01	18 04	18 07		18 12	18 16	18 19	18 22	18 27	18 31	18 34	18 37	18 42		18 46	18 49	18 52	18 57	19 01	19 04
Rotherhithe	d	17 48	17 51	17 54	17 59	18 03	18 06	18 09		18 14	18 18	18 21	18 24	18 29	18 33	18 36	18 39	18 44		18 48	18 51	18 54	18 59	19 03	19 06
Canada Water	d	17 50	17 53	17 56	18 01	18 05	18 08	18 11		18 16	18 20	18 23	18 26	18 31	18 35	18 38	18 41	18 46		18 50	18 53	18 56	19 01	19 05	19 08
Surrey Quays	d	17 51	17 54	17 57	18 02	18 06	18 09	18 12		18 17	18 21	18 24	18 27	18 32	18 36	18 39	18 42	18 47		18 51	18 54	18 57	19 02	19 06	19 09
New Cross	a	17 56				18 11					18 26				18 41					18 56				19 11	
New Cross Gate 4	d			18 02	18 07			18 17		18 22			18 32	18 37			18 47	18 52				19 02	19 07		
Brockley	d			18 04	18 09			18 19		18 24			18 34	18 39			18 49	18 54				19 04	19 09		
Honor Oak Park	d			18 07	18 12			18 22		18 27			18 37	18 42			18 52	18 57				19 07	19 12		
Forest Hill 4	d			18 10	18 15			18 25		18 30			18 40	18 45			18 55	19 00				19 10	19 15		
Sydenham	d			18 12	18 17			18 27		18 32			18 42	18 47			18 57	19 02				19 12	19 17		
Crystal Palace 4	a				18 22					18 37				18 52				19 07					19 22		
Penge West	d			18 15				18 30					18 45				19 00					19 15			
Anerley	d			18 17				18 32					18 47				19 02					19 17			
Norwood Junction 2	d			18 20				18 35					18 50				19 05					19 20			
West Croydon 4	a			18 26				18 42					19 01				19 11					19 30			
Queens Rd Peckham	d		17 59				18 14					18 29				18 44					18 59				19 14
Peckham Rye 4	d		18 02				18 17					18 32				18 47					19 02				19 17
Denmark Hill 4	d		18 06				18 21					18 36				18 51					19 06				19 21
Clapham High Street ⊖	d		18 10				18 25					18 40				18 55					19 10				19 25
Wandsworth Road	d		18 12				18 27					18 42				18 57					19 12				19 27
Clapham Junction	a		18 21				18 36					18 51				19 06					19 21				19 36

		LO	LO	LO		LO	LO	LO	LO	LO	LO	LO	LO	LO		LO	LO	LO	LO	LO	LO	LO	LO	LO	
Highbury & Islington	d		18 55			19 02		19 10		19 17		19 25		19 32			19 40		19 47		19 55		20 02		
Canonbury	d		18 57			19 04		19 12		19 19		19 27		19 34			19 42		19 49		19 57		20 04		
Dalston Junction	d	18 55	19 00	19 04		19 07	19 10	19 15	19 19	19 22	19 25	19 30	19 34	19 37		19 40	19 45	19 49	19 52	19 55	20 00	20 04	20 07	20 10	
Haggerston	d	18 56	19 01	19 05		19 08	19 11	19 16	19 20	19 23	19 26	19 31	19 35	19 38		19 41	19 46	19 50	19 53	19 56	20 01	20 05	20 08	20 11	
Hoxton	d	18 58	19 03	19 07		19 10	19 13	19 18	19 22	19 25	19 28	19 33	19 37	19 40		19 43	19 48	19 52	19 55	19 58	20 03	20 07	20 10	20 13	
Shoreditch High Street	d	19 01	19 06	19 10		19 13	19 16	19 21	19 25	19 28	19 31	19 36	19 40	19 43		19 46	19 51	19 55	19 58	20 01	20 06	20 10	20 13	20 16	
Whitechapel	d	19 03	19 08	19 12		19 15	19 18	19 23	19 27	19 30	19 33	19 38	19 42	19 45		19 48	19 53	19 57	20 00	20 03	20 08	20 12	20 15	20 18	
Shadwell	d	19 05	19 10	19 14		19 17	19 20	19 25	19 29	19 32	19 35	19 40	19 44	19 47		19 50	19 55	19 59	20 02	20 05	20 10	20 14	20 17	20 20	
Wapping	d	19 07	19 12	19 16		19 19	19 22	19 27	19 31	19 34	19 37	19 42	19 46	19 49		19 52	19 57	20 01	20 04	20 07	20 12	20 16	20 19	20 22	
Rotherhithe	d	19 09	19 14	19 18		19 21	19 24	19 29	19 33	19 36	19 39	19 44	19 48	19 51		19 54	19 59	20 03	20 06	20 09	20 14	20 18	20 21	20 24	
Canada Water	d	19 11	19 16	19 20		19 23	19 26	19 31	19 35	19 38	19 41	19 46	19 50	19 53		19 56	20 01	20 05	20 08	20 11	20 16	20 20	20 23	20 26	
Surrey Quays	d	19 12	19 17	19 21		19 24	19 27	19 32	19 36	19 39	19 42	19 47	19 51	19 54		19 57	20 02	20 06	20 09	20 12	20 17	20 21	20 24	20 27	
New Cross	a			19 26					19 41				19 56					20 11				20 26			
New Cross Gate 4	d	19 17	19 22				19 32	19 37			19 47	19 52				20 02	20 07			20 17	20 22			20 32	
Brockley	d	19 19	19 24				19 34	19 39			19 49	19 54				20 04	20 09			20 19	20 24			20 34	
Honor Oak Park	d	19 22	19 27				19 37	19 42			19 52	19 57				20 07	20 12			20 22	20 27			20 37	
Forest Hill 4	d	19 25	19 30				19 40	19 45			19 55	20 00				20 10	20 15			20 25	20 30			20 40	
Sydenham	d	19 27	19 32				19 42	19 47			19 57	20 02				20 12	20 17			20 27	20 32			20 42	
Crystal Palace 4	a		19 37					19 52				20 07					20 22				20 37				
Penge West	d	19 30					19 45				20 00					20 15				20 30				20 45	
Anerley	d	19 32					19 47				20 02					20 17				20 32				20 47	
Norwood Junction 2	d	19 35					19 50				20 05					20 20				20 35				20 50	
West Croydon 4	a	19 41					19 56				20 11					20 26				20 41				21 00	
Queens Rd Peckham	d					19 29				19 44				19 59					20 14				20 29		
Peckham Rye 4	d					19 32				19 47				20 02					20 17				20 32		
Denmark Hill 4	d					19 36				19 51				20 06					20 21				20 36		
Clapham High Street ⊖	d					19 40				19 55				20 10					20 25				20 40		
Wandsworth Road	d					19 42				19 57				20 12					20 27				20 42		
Clapham Junction	a					19 51				20 06				20 21					20 35				20 51		

		LO	LO	LO	LO	LO	LO	LO	LO	LO		LO	LO	LO	LO	LO	LO	LO	LO	LO		LO	LO	LO	LO
Highbury & Islington	d	20 10		20 17		20 25		20 32		20 40			20 47		20 55		21 02		21 10			21 17		21 25	
Canonbury	d	20 12		20 19		20 27		20 34		20 42			20 49		20 57		21 04		21 12			21 19		21 27	
Dalston Junction	d	20 15	20 19	20 22	20 25	20 30	20 34	20 37	20 40	20 45		20 49	20 52	20 55	21 00	21 04	21 07	21 10	21 15	21 19		21 22	21 25	21 30	21 34
Haggerston	d	20 16	20 20	20 23	20 26	20 31	20 35	20 38	20 41	20 46		20 50	20 53	20 56	21 01	21 05	21 08	21 11	21 16	21 20		21 23	21 26	21 31	21 35
Hoxton	d	20 18	20 22	20 25	20 28	20 33	20 37	20 40	20 43	20 48		20 52	20 55	20 58	21 03	21 07	21 10	21 13	21 18	21 22		21 25	21 28	21 33	21 37
Shoreditch High Street	d	20 21	20 25	20 28	20 31	20 36	20 40	20 43	20 46	20 51		20 55	20 58	21 01	21 06	21 10	21 13	21 16	21 21	21 25		21 28	21 31	21 36	21 40
Whitechapel	d	20 23	20 27	20 30	20 33	20 38	20 42	20 45	20 48	20 53		20 57	21 00	21 03	21 08	21 12	21 15	21 18	21 23	21 27		21 30	21 33	21 38	21 42
Shadwell	d	20 25	20 29	20 32	20 35	20 40	20 44	20 47	20 50	20 55		20 59	21 02	21 05	21 10	21 14	21 17	21 20	21 25	21 29		21 32	21 35	21 40	21 44
Wapping	d	20 27	20 31	20 34	20 37	20 42	20 46	20 49	20 52	20 57		21 01	21 04	21 07	21 12	21 16	21 19	21 22	21 27	21 31		21 34	21 37	21 42	21 46
Rotherhithe	d	20 29	20 33	20 36	20 39	20 44	20 48	20 51	20 54	20 59		21 03	21 06	21 09	21 14	21 18	21 21	21 24	21 29	21 33		21 36	21 39	21 44	21 48
Canada Water	d	20 31	20 35	20 38	20 41	20 46	20 50	20 53	20 56	21 01		21 05	21 08	21 11	21 16	21 20	21 23	21 26	21 31	21 35		21 38	21 41	21 46	21 50
Surrey Quays	d	20 32	20 36	20 39	20 42	20 47	20 51	20 54	20 57	21 02		21 06	21 09	21 12	21 17	21 21	21 24	21 27	21 32	21 36		21 39	21 42	21 47	21 51
New Cross	a		20 41				20 56					21 11				21 26				21 41					21 56
New Cross Gate 4	d	20 37			20 47	20 52			21 02	21 07				21 17	21 22			21 32	21 37				21 47	21 52	
Brockley	d	20 39			20 49	20 54			21 04	21 09				21 19	21 24			21 34	21 39				21 49	21 54	
Honor Oak Park	d	20 42			20 52	20 57			21 07	21 12				21 22	21 27			21 37	21 42				21 52	21 57	
Forest Hill 4	d	20 45			20 55	21 00			21 10	21 15				21 25	21 30			21 40	21 45				21 55	22 00	
Sydenham	d	20 47			20 57	21 02			21 12	21 17				21 27	21 32			21 42	21 47				21 57	22 02	
Crystal Palace 4	a	20 52				21 07				21 22					21 37				21 52					22 07	
Penge West	d				21 00				21 15					21 30				21 45					22 00		
Anerley	d				21 02				21 17					21 32				21 47					22 02		
Norwood Junction 2	d				21 05				21 20					21 35				21 50					22 05		
West Croydon 4	a				21 11				21 26					21 41				22 00					22 11		
Queens Rd Peckham	d			20 44				20 59					21 14				21 29					21 44			
Peckham Rye 4	d			20 47				21 02					21 17				21 32					21 47			
Denmark Hill 4	d			20 51				21 06					21 21				21 36					21 51			
Clapham High Street ⊖	d			20 55				21 10					21 25				21 40					21 55			
Wandsworth Road	d			20 57				21 12					21 27				21 42					21 57			
Clapham Junction	a			21 06				21 21					21 36				21 51					22 06			

Table 178

Mondays to Fridays

9 December to 16 May

Highbury & Islington - New Cross, Crystal Palace, West Croydon and Clapham Junction

Network Diagram - see first Page of Table 173

		LO	LO	LO	LO	LO		LO	LO	LO	LO	LO	LO	LO A	LO	LO		LO	LO	LO	LO	LO	LO	LO	LO
Highbury & Islington	d	21 32		21 40		21 47			21 55	22 02		22 10		22 17	22 25	22 32			22 40		22 55	23 02		23 10	
Canonbury	d	21 34		21 42		21 49			21 57	22 04		22 12		22 19	22 27	22 34			22 42		22 57	23 04		23 12	
Dalston Junction	d	21 37	21 40	21 45	21 49	21 52		21 55	22 00	22 07	22 10	22 15	22 19	22 22	22 30	22 37		22 40	22 45	22 52	23 00	23 07	23 10	23 15	23 22
Haggerston	d	21 38	21 41	21 46	21 50	21 53		21 56	22 01	22 08	22 11	22 16	22 20	22 23	22 31	22 38		22 41	22 46	22 53	23 01	23 08	23 11	23 16	23 23
Hoxton	d	21 40	21 43	21 48	21 52	21 55		21 58	22 03	22 10	22 13	22 18	22 22	22 25	22 33	22 40		22 43	22 48	22 55	23 03	23 10	23 13	23 18	23 25
Shoreditch High Street	d	21 43	21 46	21 51	21 55	21 58		22 01	22 06	22 13	22 16	22 21	22 25	22 28	22 36	22 43		22 46	22 51	22 58	23 06	23 13	23 16	23 21	23 28
Whitechapel	d	21 45	21 48	21 53	21 57	22 00		22 03	22 08	22 15	22 18	22 23	22 27	22 30	22 38	22 45		22 48	22 53	23 00	23 08	23 15	23 18	23 23	23 30
Shadwell	d	21 47	21 50	21 55	21 59	22 02		22 05	22 10	22 17	22 20	22 25	22 29	22 32	22 40	22 47		22 50	22 55	23 02	23 10	23 17	23 20	23 25	23 32
Wapping	d	21 49	21 52	21 57	22 01	22 04		22 07	22 12	22 19	22 22	22 27	22 31	22 34	22 42	22 49		22 52	22 57	23 04	23 12	23 19	23 22	23 27	23 34
Rotherhithe	d	21 51	21 54	21 59	22 03	22 06		22 09	22 14	22 21	22 24	22 29	22 33	22 36	22 44	22 51		22 54	22 59	23 06	23 14	23 21	23 24	23 29	23 36
Canada Water	d	21 53	21 56	22 01	22 05	22 08		22 11	22 16	22 23	22 26	22 31	22 35	22 38	22 46	22 53		22 56	23 01	23 08	23 16	23 23	23 26	23 31	23 38
Surrey Quays	d	21 54	21 57	22 02	22 06	22 09		22 12	22 17	22 24	22 27	22 32	22 36	22 39	22 47	22 54		22 57	23 02	23 09	23 17	23 24	23 27	23 32	23 39
New Cross	a				22 11								22 41							23 14					23 44
New Cross Gate [4]	d		22 02	22 07				22 17	22 22		22 32	22 37			22 52			23 02	23 07		23 22		23 32	23 37	
Brockley	d		22 04	22 09				22 19	22 24		22 34	22 39			22 54			23 04	23 09		23 24		23 34	23 39	
Honor Oak Park	d		22 07	22 12				22 22	22 27		22 37	22 42			22 57			23 07	23 12		23 27		23 37	23 42	
Forest Hill [4]	d		22 10	22 15				22 25	22 30		22 40	22 45			23 00			23 10	23 15		23 30		23 40	23 45	
Sydenham	d		22 12	22 17				22 27	22 32		22 42	22 47			23 02			23 12	23 17		23 32		23 42	23 47	
Crystal Palace [4]	a			22 22					22 37			22 52			23 07				23 22		23 37			23 52	
Penge West	d		22 15					22 30			22 45							23 15					23 45		
Anerley	d		22 17					22 32			22 47							23 17					23 47		
Norwood Junction [2]	d		22 20					22 35			22 50							23 20					23 50		
West Croydon [4] (tram)	a		22 30					22 41			23 00							23 30					23 59		
Queens Rd Peckham	d	21 59				22 14				22 29				22 44		22 59						23 29			
Peckham Rye [4]	d	22 02				22 17				22 32				22 47		23 02						23 32			
Denmark Hill [4]	d	22 06				22 21				22 36				22 51		23 06						23 36			
Clapham High Street ⊖	d	22 10				22 25				22 40				22 55		23 10						23 40			
Wandsworth Road	d	22 12				22 27				22 42				22a57		23 12						23 42			
Clapham Junction	a	22 21				22 36				22 51						23 21						23 51			

		LO		LO	LO	LO	LO
Highbury & Islington	d	23 25		23 33		23 42	23 58
Canonbury	d	23 27		23 35		23 44	00 01
Dalston Junction	d	23 30		23 37	23 40	23 48	00 03
Haggerston	d	23 31		23 38	23 41	23 49	00 04
Hoxton	d	23 33		23 40	23 43	23 51	00 06
Shoreditch High Street	d	23 36		23 43	23 46	23 54	00 09
Whitechapel	d	23 38		23 45	23 48	23 56	00 11
Shadwell	d	23 40		23 47	23 50	23 58	00 13
Wapping	d	23 42		23 49	23 52	23 59	00 15
Rotherhithe	d	23 44		23 51	23 54	00 02	00 17
Canada Water	d	23 46		23 53	23 56	00 04	00 19
Surrey Quays	d	23 47		23 54	23 57	00 05	00 20
New Cross	a						
New Cross Gate [4]	d	23 52			00 02	00a09	00a24
Brockley	d	23 54			00 04		
Honor Oak Park	d	23 57			00 07		
Forest Hill [4]	d	23 58			00 10		
Sydenham	d	00 02			00 12		
Crystal Palace [4]	a	00 07					
Penge West	d				00 15		
Anerley	d				00 17		
Norwood Junction [2]	d				00 20		
West Croydon [4] (tram)	a				00 27		
Queens Rd Peckham	d			23 59			
Peckham Rye [4]	d			00 02			
Denmark Hill [4]	d			00 06			
Clapham High Street ⊖	d			00 10			
Wandsworth Road	d			00 12			
Clapham Junction	a			00 21			

A To Battersea Park, arriving at 2259

Table 178

Saturdays

14 December to 17 May

Highbury & Islington - New Cross, Crystal Palace, West Croydon and Clapham Junction

Network Diagram - see first Page of Table 173

		LO A	LO A	LO B	LO A	LO A	LO		LO	LO	LO	LO	LO	LO	LO	LO		LO	LO	LO	LO	LO	LO	LO	LO
Highbury & Islington	d						00 10		05 35		05 47	05 55			06 17	06 25			06 32		06 40		06 47		06 55
Canonbury	d					00 01	00 12		05 37		05 49	05 57			06 19	06 27			06 34		06 42		06 49		06 57
Dalston Junction	d					00 03	00 15		05 40	05 49	05 52	06 00	06 10	06 19	06 22	06 30		06 34	06 37	06 40	06 45	06 49	06 52	06 55	07 00
Haggerston	d					00 04	00 16		05 41	05 50	05 53	06 01	06 11	06 20	06 23	06 31		06 35	06 38	06 41	06 46	06 50	06 53	06 56	07 01
Hoxton	d					00 06	00 18		05 43	05 52	05 55	06 03	06 13	06 22	06 25	06 33		06 37	06 40	06 43	06 48	06 52	06 55	06 58	07 03
Shoreditch High Street	d					00 09	00 21		05 46	05 55	05 58	06 06	06 16	06 25	06 28	06 36		06 40	06 43	06 46	06 51	06 55	06 58	07 01	07 06
Whitechapel	d					00 11	00 23		05 48	05 57	06 00	06 08	06 18	06 27	06 30	06 38		06 42	06 45	06 48	06 53	06 57	07 00	07 03	07 08
Shadwell	d					00 13	00 25		05 50	05 59	06 02	06 10	06 20	06 29	06 32	06 40		06 44	06 47	06 50	06 55	06 59	07 02	07 05	07 10
Wapping	d					00 15	00 27		05 52	06 01	06 04	06 12	06 22	06 31	06 34	06 42		06 46	06 49	06 52	06 57	07 01	07 04	07 07	07 12
Rotherhithe	d				00 02	00 17	00 29		05 54	06 03	06 06	06 14	06 24	06 33	06 36	06 44		06 48	06 51	06 54	06 59	07 03	07 06	07 09	07 14
Canada Water	d				00 04	00 19	00 31		05 56	06 05	06 08	06 16	06 26	06 35	06 38	06 46		06 50	06 53	06 56	07 01	07 05	07 08	07 11	07 16
Surrey Quays	d				00 05	00 20	00 32		05 57	06 06	06 09	06 17	06 27	06 36	06 39	06 47		06 51	06 54	06 57	07 02	07 06	07 09	07 12	07 17
New Cross	a									06 11				06 41				06 56				07 11			
New Cross Gate 4	d			00 02	00a09	00a24	00a36		06 02			06 22	06 32			06 52				07 02	07 07			07 17	07 22
Brockley	d			00 04					06 04			06 24	06 34			06 54				07 04	07 09			07 19	07 24
Honor Oak Park	d			00 07					06 07			06 27	06 37			06 57				07 07	07 12			07 22	07 27
Forest Hill 4	d			00 10					06 10			06 30	06 40			07 00				07 10	07 15			07 25	07 30
Sydenham	d	00 02		00 12					06 12			06 32	06 42			07 02				07 12	07 17			07 27	07 32
Crystal Palace 4	a	00 07										06 37				07 07					07 22				07 37
Penge West	d			00 15					06 15				06 45							07 15				07 30	
Anerley	d			00 17					06 17				06 47							07 17				07 32	
Norwood Junction 2	d			00 20					06 20				06 50							07 20				07 35	
West Croydon 4	a			00 27					06 30				07 00							07 30				07 41	
Queens Rd Peckham	d										06 14				06 44				06 59				07 14		
Peckham Rye 4	d		00 02								06 17				06 47				07 02				07 17		
Denmark Hill 4	d		00 06								06 21				06 49				07 06				07 21		
Clapham High Street ⊖	d		00 10								06 25				06 52				07 10				07 25		
Wandsworth Road	d		00 12								06 27				06 55				07 12				07 27		
Clapham Junction	a		00 21								06 37				07 05				07 21				07 37		

		LO		LO	LO	LO	LO	LO	LO	LO	LO	LO		LO	LO	LO	LO	LO	LO	LO	LO	LO		LO	LO
Highbury & Islington	d			07 02		07 10		07 17		07 25		07 32			07 40		07 47		07 55		08 02			08 10	
Canonbury	d			07 04		07 12		07 19		07 27		07 34			07 42		07 49		07 57		08 04			08 12	
Dalston Junction	d	07 04		07 07	07 10	07 15	07 19	07 22	07 25	07 30	07 34	07 37		07 40	07 45	07 49	07 52	07 55	08 00	08 04	08 07	08 10		08 15	08 19
Haggerston	d	07 05		07 08	07 11	07 16	07 20	07 23	07 26	07 31	07 35	07 38		07 41	07 46	07 50	07 53	07 56	08 01	08 05	08 08	08 11		08 16	08 20
Hoxton	d	07 07		07 10	07 13	07 18	07 22	07 25	07 28	07 33	07 37	07 40		07 43	07 48	07 52	07 55	07 58	08 03	08 07	08 10	08 13		08 18	08 22
Shoreditch High Street	d	07 10		07 13	07 16	07 21	07 25	07 28	07 31	07 36	07 40	07 43		07 46	07 51	07 55	07 58	08 01	08 06	08 10	08 13	08 16		08 21	08 25
Whitechapel	d	07 12		07 15	07 18	07 23	07 27	07 30	07 33	07 38	07 42	07 45		07 48	07 53	07 57	08 00	08 03	08 08	08 12	08 15	08 18		08 23	08 27
Shadwell	d	07 14		07 17	07 20	07 25	07 29	07 32	07 35	07 40	07 44	07 47		07 50	07 55	07 59	08 02	08 05	08 10	08 14	08 17	08 20		08 25	08 29
Wapping	d	07 16		07 19	07 22	07 27	07 31	07 34	07 37	07 42	07 46	07 49		07 52	07 57	08 01	08 04	08 07	08 12	08 16	08 19	08 22		08 27	08 31
Rotherhithe	d	07 18		07 21	07 24	07 29	07 33	07 36	07 39	07 44	07 48	07 51		07 54	07 59	08 03	08 06	08 09	08 14	08 18	08 21	08 24		08 29	08 33
Canada Water	d	07 20		07 23	07 26	07 31	07 35	07 38	07 41	07 46	07 50	07 53		07 56	08 01	08 05	08 08	08 11	08 16	08 20	08 23	08 26		08 31	08 35
Surrey Quays	d	07 21		07 24	07 27	07 32	07 36	07 39	07 42	07 47	07 51	07 54		07 57	08 02	08 06	08 09	08 12	08 17	08 21	08 24	08 27		08 32	08 36
New Cross	a	07 26					07 41				07 56					08 11				08 26					08 41
New Cross Gate 4	d				07 32	07 37			07 47	07 52				08 02	08 07			08 17	08 22			08 32		08 37	
Brockley	d				07 34	07 39			07 49	07 54				08 04	08 09			08 19	08 24			08 34		08 39	
Honor Oak Park	d				07 37	07 42			07 52	07 57				08 07	08 12			08 22	08 27			08 37		08 42	
Forest Hill 4	d				07 40	07 45			07 55	08 00				08 10	08 15			08 25	08 30			08 40		08 45	
Sydenham	d				07 42	07 47			07 57	08 02				08 12	08 17			08 27	08 32			08 42		08 47	
Crystal Palace 4	a					07 52				08 07					08 22				08 37					08 52	
Penge West	d				07 45				08 00					08 15				08 30				08 45			
Anerley	d				07 47				08 02					08 17				08 32				08 47			
Norwood Junction 2	d				07 50				08 05					08 20				08 35				08 50			
West Croydon 4	a				08 00				08 11					08 30				08 41				09 00			
Queens Rd Peckham	d			07 29				07 44				07 59					08 14				08 29				
Peckham Rye 4	d			07 32				07 47				08 02					08 17				08 32				
Denmark Hill 4	d			07 36				07 51				08 06					08 21				08 40				
Clapham High Street ⊖	d			07 40				07 55				08 10					08 25				08 44				
Wandsworth Road	d			07 42				07 57				08 12					08 27				08 46				
Clapham Junction	a			07 52				08 07				08 22					08 37				08 52				

		LO	LO	LO	LO	LO	LO	LO		LO	LO	LO	LO	LO	LO	LO	LO	LO		LO	LO	LO	LO	LO	LO
Highbury & Islington	d	08 17		08 25		08 32		08 40			08 47		08 55		09 02		09 10			09 17		09 25		09 32	
Canonbury	d	08 19		08 27		08 34		08 42			08 49		08 57		09 04		09 12			09 19		09 27		09 34	
Dalston Junction	d	08 22	08 25	08 30	08 34	08 37	08 40	08 45		08 49	08 52	08 55	09 00	09 04	09 07	09 10	09 15	09 19		09 22	09 25	09 30	09 34	09 37	09 40
Haggerston	d	08 23	08 26	08 31	08 35	08 38	08 41	08 46		08 50	08 53	08 56	09 01	09 05	09 08	09 11	09 16	09 20		09 23	09 26	09 31	09 35	09 38	09 41
Hoxton	d	08 25	08 28	08 33	08 37	08 40	08 43	08 48		08 52	08 55	08 58	09 03	09 07	09 10	09 13	09 18	09 22		09 25	09 28	09 33	09 37	09 40	09 43
Shoreditch High Street	d	08 28	08 31	08 36	08 40	08 43	08 46	08 51		08 55	08 58	09 01	09 06	09 10	09 13	09 16	09 21	09 25		09 28	09 31	09 36	09 40	09 43	09 46
Whitechapel	d	08 30	08 33	08 38	08 42	08 45	08 48	08 53		08 57	09 00	09 03	09 08	09 12	09 15	09 18	09 23	09 27		09 30	09 33	09 38	09 42	09 45	09 48
Shadwell	d	08 32	08 35	08 40	08 44	08 47	08 50	08 55		08 59	09 02	09 05	09 10	09 14	09 17	09 20	09 25	09 29		09 32	09 35	09 40	09 44	09 47	09 50
Wapping	d	08 34	08 37	08 42	08 46	08 49	08 52	08 57		09 01	09 04	09 07	09 12	09 16	09 19	09 22	09 27	09 31		09 34	09 37	09 42	09 46	09 49	09 52
Rotherhithe	d	08 36	08 39	08 44	08 48	08 51	08 54	08 59		09 03	09 06	09 09	09 14	09 18	09 21	09 24	09 29	09 33		09 36	09 39	09 44	09 48	09 51	09 54
Canada Water	d	08 38	08 41	08 46	08 50	08 53	08 56	09 01		09 05	09 08	09 11	09 16	09 20	09 23	09 26	09 31	09 35		09 38	09 41	09 46	09 50	09 53	09 56
Surrey Quays	d	08 39	08 42	08 47	08 51	08 54	08 57	09 02		09 06	09 09	09 12	09 17	09 21	09 24	09 27	09 32	09 36		09 39	09 42	09 47	09 51	09 54	09 57
New Cross	a				08 56					09 11				09 26				09 41					09 56		
New Cross Gate 4	d		08 47	08 52			09 02	09 07				09 17	09 22			09 32	09 37				09 47	09 52			10 02
Brockley	d		08 49	08 54			09 04	09 09				09 19	09 24			09 34	09 39				09 49	09 54			10 04
Honor Oak Park	d		08 52	08 57			09 07	09 12				09 22	09 27			09 37	09 42				09 52	09 57			10 07
Forest Hill 4	d		08 55	09 00			09 10	09 15				09 25	09 30			09 40	09 45				09 55	10 00			10 10
Sydenham	d		08 57	09 02			09 12	09 17				09 27	09 32			09 42	09 47				09 57	10 02			10 12
Crystal Palace 4	a			09 07				09 22					09 37				09 52					10 07			
Penge West	d		09 00				09 15					09 30				09 45					10 00				10 15
Anerley	d		09 02				09 17					09 32				09 47					10 02				10 17
Norwood Junction 2	d		09 05				09 20					09 35				09 50					10 05				10 20
West Croydon 4	a		09 11				09 30					09 41				10 00					10 11				10 30
Queens Rd Peckham	d	08 44				08 59					09 14				09 29					09 44				09 59	
Peckham Rye 4	d	08 47				09 02					09 17				09 32					09 47				10 02	
Denmark Hill 4	d	08 51				09 06					09 21				09 36					09 51				10 06	
Clapham High Street ⊖	d	08 55				09 10					09 25				09 40					09 55				10 10	
Wandsworth Road	d	08 57				09 12					09 27				09 42					09 57				10 12	
Clapham Junction	a	09 08				09 22					09 37				09 52					10 07				10 22	

A From Highbury and Islington Ell

B From Dalston Junction Stn Ell

Table 178

Saturdays

14 December to 17 May

Highbury & Islington - New Cross, Crystal Palace, West Croydon and Clapham Junction

Network Diagram - see first Page of Table 173

		LO	LO	LO		LO	LO	LO	LO	LO	LO	LO	LO	LO	LO	LO	LO	LO	LO	LO	LO	LO	LO	LO	
Highbury & Islington	d	09 40		09 47			09 55		10 02		10 10		10 17		10 25		10 32		10 40		10 47		10 55		
Canonbury	d	09 42		09 49			09 57		10 04		10 12		10 19		10 27		10 34		10 42		10 49		10 57		
Dalston Junction	d	09 45	09 49	09 52		09 55	10 00	10 04	10 07	10 10	10 15	10 19	10 22	10 25	10 30	10 34	10 37	10 40	10 45	10 49	10 52	10 55	11 00	11 04	
Haggerston	d	09 46	09 50	09 53		09 56	10 01	10 05	10 08	10 11	10 16	10 20	10 23	10 26	10 31	10 35	10 38	10 41	10 46	10 50	10 53	10 56	11 01	11 05	
Hoxton	d	09 48	09 52	09 55		09 58	10 03	10 07	10 10	10 13	10 18	10 22	10 25	10 28	10 33	10 37	10 40	10 43	10 48	10 52	10 55	10 58	11 03	11 07	
Shoreditch High Street	d	09 51	09 55	09 58		10 01	10 06	10 10	10 13	10 16	10 21	10 25	10 28	10 31	10 36	10 40	10 43	10 46	10 51	10 55	10 58	11 01	11 06	11 10	
Whitechapel	d	09 53	09 57	10 00		10 03	10 08	10 12	10 15	10 18	10 23	10 27	10 30	10 33	10 38	10 42	10 45	10 48	10 53	10 57	11 00	11 03	11 08	11 12	
Shadwell	d	09 55	09 59	10 02		10 05	10 10	10 14	10 17	10 20	10 25	10 29	10 32	10 35	10 40	10 44	10 47	10 50	10 55	10 59	11 02	11 05	11 10	11 14	
Wapping	d	09 57	10 01	10 04		10 07	10 12	10 16	10 19	10 22	10 27	10 31	10 34	10 37	10 42	10 46	10 49	10 52	10 57	11 01	11 04	11 07	11 12	11 16	
Rotherhithe	d	09 59	10 03	10 06		10 09	10 14	10 18	10 21	10 24	10 29	10 33	10 36	10 39	10 44	10 48	10 51	10 54	10 59	11 03	11 06	11 09	11 14	11 18	
Canada Water	d	10 01	10 05	10 08		10 11	10 16	10 20	10 23	10 26	10 31	10 35	10 38	10 41	10 46	10 50	10 53	10 56	11 01	11 05	11 08	11 11	11 16	11 20	
Surrey Quays	d	10 02	10 06	10 09		10 12	10 17	10 21	10 24	10 27	10 32	10 36	10 39	10 42	10 47	10 51	10 54	10 57	11 02	11 06	11 09	11 12	11 17	11 21	
New Cross	a		10 11					10 26				10 41				10 56				11 11				11 26	
New Cross Gate 4	d	10 07				10 17	10 22			10 32	10 37			10 47	10 52			11 02	11 07			11 17	11 22		
Brockley	d	10 09				10 19	10 24			10 34	10 39			10 49	10 54			11 04	11 09			11 19	11 24		
Honor Oak Park	d	10 12				10 22	10 27			10 37	10 42			10 52	10 57			11 07	11 12			11 22	11 27		
Forest Hill 4	d	10 15				10 25	10 30			10 40	10 45			10 55	11 00			11 10	11 15			11 25	11 30		
Sydenham	d	10 17				10 27	10 32			10 42	10 47			10 57	11 02			11 12	11 17			11 27	11 32		
Crystal Palace 4	a	10 22					10 37				10 52				11 07				11 22				11 37		
Penge West	d					10 30				10 45				11 00				11 15				11 30			
Anerley	d					10 32				10 47				11 02				11 17				11 32			
Norwood Junction 2	d					10 35				10 50				11 05				11 20				11 35			
West Croydon 4	a					10 41				11 00				11 11				11 30				11 41			
Queens Rd Peckham	d			10 14					10 29				10 44				10 59				11 14				
Peckham Rye 4	d			10 17					10 32				10 47				11 02				11 17				
Denmark Hill 4	d			10 21					10 36				10 51				11 06				11 21				
Clapham High Street ⊖	d			10 25					10 40				10 55				11 10				11 25				
Wandsworth Road	d			10 27					10 42				10 57				11 12				11 27				
Clapham Junction	a			10 37					10 51				11 07				11 22				11 37				

		LO		LO	LO	LO	LO	LO	LO	LO	LO	LO	LO	LO	LO	LO	LO	LO	LO		LO	LO	LO	LO
Highbury & Islington	d	11 02			15 10		15 17		15 25		15 32		15 40		15 47		15 55		16 02			16 10		16 17
Canonbury	d	11 04			15 12		15 19		15 27		15 34		15 42		15 49		15 57		16 04			16 12		16 19
Dalston Junction	d	11 07		15 10	15 15	15 19	15 22	15 25	15 30	15 34	15 37	15 40	15 45	15 49	15 52	15 55	16 00	16 04	16 07		16 10	16 15	16 19	16 22
Haggerston	d	11 08		15 11	15 16	15 20	15 23	15 26	15 31	15 35	15 38	15 41	15 46	15 50	15 53	15 56	16 01	16 05	16 08		16 11	16 16	16 20	16 23
Hoxton	d	11 10		15 13	15 18	15 22	15 25	15 28	15 33	15 37	15 40	15 43	15 48	15 52	15 55	15 58	16 03	16 07	16 10		16 13	16 18	16 22	16 25
Shoreditch High Street	d	11 13		15 16	15 21	15 25	15 28	15 31	15 36	15 40	15 43	15 46	15 51	15 55	15 58	16 01	16 06	16 10	16 13		16 16	16 21	16 25	16 28
Whitechapel	d	11 15		15 18	15 23	15 27	15 30	15 33	15 38	15 42	15 45	15 48	15 53	15 57	16 00	16 03	16 08	16 12	16 15		16 18	16 23	16 27	16 30
Shadwell	d	11 17		15 20	15 25	15 29	15 32	15 35	15 40	15 44	15 47	15 50	15 55	15 59	16 02	16 05	16 10	16 14	16 17		16 20	16 25	16 29	16 32
Wapping	d	11 19		15 22	15 27	15 31	15 34	15 37	15 42	15 46	15 49	15 52	15 57	16 01	16 04	16 07	16 12	16 16	16 19		16 22	16 27	16 31	16 34
Rotherhithe	d	11 21		15 24	15 29	15 33	15 36	15 39	15 44	15 48	15 51	15 54	15 59	16 03	16 06	16 09	16 14	16 18	16 21		16 24	16 29	16 33	16 36
Canada Water	d	11 23	and at	15 26	15 31	15 35	15 38	15 41	15 46	15 50	15 53	15 56	16 01	16 05	16 08	16 11	16 16	16 20	16 23		16 26	16 31	16 35	16 38
Surrey Quays	d	11 24	the same	15 27	15 32	15 36	15 39	15 42	15 47	15 51	15 54	15 57	16 02	16 06	16 09	16 12	16 17	16 21	16 24		16 27	16 32	16 36	16 39
New Cross	a		minutes			15 41				15 56				16 11				16 26					16 41	
New Cross Gate 4	d		past	15 32	15 37			15 47	15 52			16 02	16 07			16 17	16 22				16 32	16 37		
Brockley	d		each	15 34	15 39			15 49	15 54			16 04	16 09			16 19	16 24				16 34	16 39		
Honor Oak Park	d		hour until	15 37	15 42			15 52	15 57			16 07	16 12			16 22	16 27				16 37	16 42		
Forest Hill 4	d			15 40	15 45			15 55	16 00			16 10	16 15			16 25	16 30				16 40	16 45		
Sydenham	d			15 42	15 47			15 57	16 02			16 12	16 17			16 27	16 32				16 42	16 47		
Crystal Palace 4	a				15 52				16 07				16 22				16 37					16 52		
Penge West	d			15 45				16 00				16 15				16 30					16 45			
Anerley	d			15 47				16 02				16 17				16 32					16 47			
Norwood Junction 2	d			15 50				16 05				16 20				16 35					16 50			
West Croydon 4	a			16 00				16 11				16 30				16 41					17 00			
Queens Rd Peckham	d	11 29					15 44				15 59				16 14				16 29					16 44
Peckham Rye 4	d	11 32					15 47				16 02				16 17				16 32					16 47
Denmark Hill 4	d	11 36					15 51				16 06				16 21				16 36					16 51
Clapham High Street ⊖	d	11 40					15 55				16 10				16 25				16 40					16 55
Wandsworth Road	d	11 42					15 57				16 12				16 27				16 42					16 57
Clapham Junction	a	11 52					16 07				16 22				16 37				16 52					17 07

		LO	LO	LO	LO	LO		LO	LO	LO	LO	LO	LO	LO	LO	LO		LO	LO	LO	LO	LO	LO	LO	LO
Highbury & Islington	d		16 25		16 32			16 40		16 47		16 55		17 02		17 10			17 17		17 25		17 32		17 40
Canonbury	d		16 27		16 34			16 42		16 49		16 57		17 04		17 12			17 19		17 27		17 34		17 42
Dalston Junction	d	16 25	16 30	16 34	16 37	16 40		16 45	16 49	16 52	16 55	17 00	17 04	17 07	17 10	17 15		17 19	17 22	17 25	17 30	17 34	17 37	17 40	17 45
Haggerston	d	16 26	16 31	16 35	16 38	16 41		16 46	16 50	16 53	16 56	17 01	17 05	17 08	17 11	17 16		17 20	17 23	17 26	17 31	17 35	17 38	17 41	17 46
Hoxton	d	16 28	16 33	16 37	16 40	16 43		16 48	16 52	16 55	16 58	17 03	17 07	17 10	17 13	17 18		17 22	17 25	17 28	17 33	17 37	17 40	17 43	17 48
Shoreditch High Street	d	16 31	16 36	16 40	16 43	16 46		16 51	16 55	16 58	17 01	17 06	17 10	17 13	17 16	17 21		17 25	17 28	17 31	17 36	17 40	17 43	17 46	17 51
Whitechapel	d	16 33	16 38	16 42	16 45	16 48		16 53	16 57	17 00	17 03	17 08	17 12	17 15	17 18	17 23		17 27	17 30	17 33	17 38	17 42	17 45	17 48	17 53
Shadwell	d	16 35	16 40	16 44	16 47	16 50		16 55	16 59	17 02	17 05	17 10	17 14	17 17	17 20	17 25		17 29	17 32	17 35	17 40	17 44	17 47	17 50	17 55
Wapping	d	16 37	16 42	16 46	16 49	16 52		16 57	17 01	17 04	17 07	17 12	17 16	17 19	17 22	17 27		17 31	17 34	17 37	17 42	17 46	17 49	17 52	17 57
Rotherhithe	d	16 39	16 44	16 48	16 51	16 54		16 59	17 03	17 06	17 09	17 14	17 18	17 21	17 24	17 29		17 33	17 36	17 39	17 44	17 48	17 51	17 54	17 59
Canada Water	d	16 41	16 46	16 50	16 53	16 56		17 01	17 05	17 08	17 11	17 16	17 20	17 23	17 26	17 31		17 35	17 38	17 41	17 46	17 50	17 53	17 56	18 01
Surrey Quays	d	16 42	16 47	16 51	16 54	16 57		17 02	17 06	17 09	17 12	17 17	17 21	17 24	17 27	17 32		17 36	17 39	17 42	17 47	17 51	17 54	17 57	18 02
New Cross	a			16 56					17 11				17 26					17 41				17 56			
New Cross Gate 4	d	16 47	16 52			17 02		17 07			17 17	17 22			17 32	17 37				17 47	17 52			18 02	18 07
Brockley	d	16 49	16 54			17 04		17 09			17 19	17 24			17 34	17 39				17 49	17 54			18 04	18 09
Honor Oak Park	d	16 52	16 57			17 07		17 12			17 22	17 27			17 37	17 42				17 52	17 57			18 07	18 12
Forest Hill 4	d	16 55	17 00			17 10		17 15			17 25	17 30			17 40	17 45				17 55	18 00			18 10	18 15
Sydenham	d	16 57	17 02			17 12		17 17			17 27	17 32			17 42	17 47				17 57	18 02			18 12	18 17
Crystal Palace 4	a		17 07					17 22				17 37				17 52					18 07				18 22
Penge West	d	17 00				17 15					17 30				17 45					18 00				18 15	
Anerley	d	17 02				17 17					17 32				17 47					18 02				18 17	
Norwood Junction 2	d	17 05				17 20					17 35				17 50					18 05				18 20	
West Croydon 4	a	17 11				17 30					17 41				18 00					18 11				18 30	
Queens Rd Peckham	d				16 59					17 14				17 29					17 44				17 59		
Peckham Rye 4	d				17 02					17 17				17 32					17 47				18 02		
Denmark Hill 4	d				17 06					17 21				17 36					17 51				18 06		
Clapham High Street ⊖	d				17 10					17 25				17 40					17 55				18 10		
Wandsworth Road	d				17 12					17 27				17 42					17 57				18 12		
Clapham Junction	a				17 22					17 36				17 52					18 07				18 22		

Table 178

Saturdays

14 December to 17 May

Highbury & Islington - New Cross, Crystal Palace, West Croydon and Clapham Junction

Network Diagram - see first Page of Table 173

		LO		LO	LO	LO	LO	LO	LO	LO	LO	LO		LO	LO	LO	LO	LO	LO	LO	LO	LO		LO	LO
Highbury & Islington	d			17 47		17 55		18 02		18 10		18 17			18 25		18 32		18 40		18 47			18 55	
Canonbury	d			17 49		17 57		18 04		18 12		18 19			18 27		18 34		18 42		18 49			18 57	
Dalston Junction	d	17 49		17 52	17 55	18 00	18 04	18 07	18 10	18 15	18 19	18 22		18 25	18 30	18 34	18 37	18 40	18 45	18 49	18 52	18 55		19 00	19 04
Haggerston	d	17 50		17 53	17 56	18 01	18 05	18 08	18 11	18 16	18 20	18 23		18 26	18 31	18 35	18 38	18 41	18 46	18 50	18 53	18 56		19 01	19 05
Hoxton	d	17 52		17 55	17 58	18 03	18 07	18 10	18 13	18 18	18 22	18 25		18 28	18 33	18 37	18 40	18 43	18 48	18 52	18 55	18 58		19 03	19 07
Shoreditch High Street	d	17 55		17 58	18 01	18 06	18 10	18 13	18 16	18 21	18 25	18 28		18 31	18 36	18 40	18 43	18 46	18 51	18 55	18 58	19 01		19 06	19 10
Whitechapel	d	17 57		18 00	18 03	18 08	18 12	18 15	18 18	18 23	18 27	18 30		18 33	18 38	18 42	18 45	18 48	18 53	18 57	19 00	19 03		19 08	19 12
Shadwell	d	17 59		18 02	18 05	18 10	18 14	18 17	18 20	18 25	18 29	18 32		18 35	18 40	18 44	18 47	18 50	18 55	18 59	19 02	19 05		19 10	19 14
Wapping	d	18 01		18 04	18 07	18 12	18 16	18 19	18 22	18 27	18 31	18 34		18 37	18 42	18 46	18 49	18 52	18 57	19 01	19 04	19 07		19 12	19 16
Rotherhithe	d	18 03		18 06	18 09	18 14	18 18	18 21	18 24	18 29	18 33	18 36		18 39	18 44	18 48	18 51	18 54	18 59	19 03	19 06	19 09		19 14	19 18
Canada Water	d	18 05		18 08	18 11	18 16	18 20	18 23	18 26	18 31	18 35	18 38		18 41	18 46	18 50	18 53	18 56	19 01	19 05	19 08	19 11		19 16	19 20
Surrey Quays	d	18 06		18 09	18 12	18 17	18 21	18 24	18 27	18 32	18 36	18 39		18 42	18 47	18 51	18 54	18 57	19 02	19 06	19 09	19 12		19 17	19 21
New Cross	a	18 11					18 26				18 41					18 56				19 11					19 26
New Cross Gate 4	d				18 17	18 22			18 32	18 37				18 47	18 52			19 02	19 07			19 17		19 22	
Brockley	d				18 19	18 24			18 34	18 39				18 49	18 54			19 04	19 09			19 19		19 24	
Honor Oak Park	d				18 22	18 27			18 37	18 42				18 52	18 57			19 07	19 12			19 22		19 27	
Forest Hill 4	d				18 25	18 30			18 40	18 45				18 55	19 00			19 10	19 15			19 25		19 30	
Sydenham	d				18 27	18 32			18 42	18 47				18 57	19 02			19 12	19 17			19 27		19 32	
Crystal Palace 4	a					18 37				18 52					19 07				19 22					19 37	
Penge West	d				18 30				18 45					19 00				19 15				19 30			
Anerley	d				18 32				18 47					19 02				19 17				19 32			
Norwood Junction 2	d				18 35				18 50					19 05				19 20				19 35			
West Croydon 4	a				18 41				19 00					19 11				19 30				19 41			
Queens Rd Peckham	d			18 14				18 29				18 44					18 59				19 14				
Peckham Rye 4	d			18 17				18 32				18 47					19 02				19 17				
Denmark Hill 4	d			18 21				18 36				18 51					19 06				19 21				
Clapham High Street ⊖	d			18 25				18 40				18 55					19 10				19 25				
Wandsworth Road	d			18 27				18 42				18 57					19 12				19 27				
Clapham Junction	a			18 37				18 52				19 07					19 22				19 37				

		LO	LO	LO	LO	LO	LO	LO		LO	LO	LO	LO	LO	LO	LO	LO	LO		LO	LO	LO	LO	LO	LO
Highbury & Islington	d	19 02		19 10		19 17		19 25			19 32		19 40		19 47		19 55			20 02		20 10		20 17	
Canonbury	d	19 04		19 12		19 19		19 27			19 34		19 42		19 49		19 57			20 04		20 12		20 19	
Dalston Junction	d	19 07	19 10	19 15	19 19	19 22	19 25	19 30		19 34	19 37	19 40	19 45	19 49	19 52	19 55	20 00	20 04		20 07	20 10	20 15	20 19	20 22	20 25
Haggerston	d	19 08	19 11	19 16	19 20	19 23	19 26	19 31		19 35	19 38	19 41	19 46	19 50	19 53	19 56	20 01	20 05		20 08	20 11	20 16	20 20	20 23	20 26
Hoxton	d	19 10	19 13	19 18	19 22	19 25	19 28	19 33		19 37	19 40	19 43	19 48	19 52	19 55	19 58	20 03	20 07		20 10	20 13	20 18	20 22	20 25	20 28
Shoreditch High Street	d	19 13	19 16	19 21	19 25	19 28	19 31	19 36		19 40	19 43	19 46	19 51	19 55	19 58	20 01	20 06	20 10		20 13	20 16	20 21	20 25	20 28	20 31
Whitechapel	d	19 15	19 18	19 23	19 27	19 30	19 33	19 38		19 42	19 45	19 48	19 53	19 57	20 00	20 03	20 08	20 12		20 15	20 18	20 23	20 27	20 30	20 33
Shadwell	d	19 17	19 20	19 25	19 29	19 32	19 35	19 40		19 44	19 47	19 50	19 55	19 59	20 02	20 05	20 10	20 14		20 17	20 20	20 25	20 29	20 32	20 35
Wapping	d	19 19	19 22	19 27	19 31	19 34	19 37	19 42		19 46	19 49	19 52	19 57	20 01	20 04	20 07	20 12	20 16		20 19	20 22	20 27	20 31	20 34	20 37
Rotherhithe	d	19 21	19 24	19 29	19 33	19 36	19 39	19 44		19 48	19 51	19 54	19 59	20 03	20 06	20 09	20 14	20 18		20 21	20 24	20 29	20 33	20 36	20 39
Canada Water	d	19 23	19 26	19 31	19 35	19 38	19 41	19 46		19 50	19 53	19 56	20 01	20 05	20 08	20 11	20 16	20 20		20 23	20 26	20 31	20 35	20 38	20 41
Surrey Quays	d	19 24	19 27	19 32	19 36	19 39	19 42	19 47		19 51	19 54	19 57	20 02	20 06	20 09	20 12	20 17	20 21		20 24	20 27	20 32	20 36	20 39	20 42
New Cross	a				19 41					19 56				20 11				20 26					20 41		
New Cross Gate 4	d		19 32	19 37			19 47	19 52				20 02	20 07			20 17	20 22				20 32	20 37			20 47
Brockley	d		19 34	19 39			19 49	19 54				20 04	20 09			20 19	20 24				20 34	20 39			20 49
Honor Oak Park	d		19 37	19 42			19 52	19 57				20 07	20 12			20 22	20 27				20 37	20 42			20 52
Forest Hill 4	d		19 40	19 45			19 55	20 00				20 10	20 15			20 25	20 30				20 40	20 45			20 55
Sydenham	d		19 42	19 47			19 57	20 02				20 12	20 17			20 27	20 32				20 42	20 47			20 57
Crystal Palace 4	a			19 52				20 07					20 22				20 37					20 52			
Penge West	d		19 45				20 00					20 15				20 30					20 45				21 00
Anerley	d		19 47				20 02					20 17				20 32					20 47				21 02
Norwood Junction 2	d		19 50				20 05					20 20				20 35					20 50				21 05
West Croydon 4	a		20 00				20 11					20 28				20 41					21 00				21 11
Queens Rd Peckham	d	19 29				19 44					19 59				20 14					20 29				20 44	
Peckham Rye 4	d	19 32				19 47					20 02				20 17					20 32				20 47	
Denmark Hill 4	d	19 36				19 51					20 06				20 21					20 36				20 51	
Clapham High Street ⊖	d	19 40				19 55					20 10				20 25					20 40				20 55	
Wandsworth Road	d	19 42				19 57					20 12				20 27					20 42				20 57	
Clapham Junction	a	19 52				20 07					20 22				20 36					20 52				21 07	

		LO	LO	LO		LO	LO	LO	LO	LO	LO	LO	LO	LO		LO	LO	LO	LO	LO	LO	LO	LO	LO	
Highbury & Islington	d	20 25		20 32			20 40		20 47		20 55		21 02			21 10		21 17		21 25		21 32		21 40	
Canonbury	d	20 27		20 34			20 42		20 49		20 57		21 04			21 12		21 19		21 27		21 34		21 42	
Dalston Junction	d	20 30	20 34	20 37		20 40	20 45	20 49	20 52	20 55	21 00	21 04	21 07	21 10		21 15	21 19	21 22	21 25	21 30	21 34	21 37	21 40	21 45	
Haggerston	d	20 31	20 35	20 38		20 41	20 46	20 50	20 53	20 56	21 01	21 05	21 08	21 11		21 16	21 20	21 23	21 26	21 31	21 35	21 38	21 41	21 46	
Hoxton	d	20 33	20 37	20 40		20 43	20 48	20 52	20 55	20 58	21 03	21 07	21 10	21 13		21 18	21 22	21 25	21 28	21 33	21 37	21 40	21 43	21 48	
Shoreditch High Street	d	20 36	20 40	20 43		20 46	20 51	20 55	20 58	21 01	21 06	21 10	21 13	21 16		21 21	21 25	21 28	21 31	21 36	21 40	21 43	21 46	21 51	
Whitechapel	d	20 38	20 42	20 45		20 48	20 53	20 57	21 00	21 03	21 08	21 12	21 15	21 18		21 23	21 27	21 30	21 33	21 38	21 42	21 45	21 48	21 53	
Shadwell	d	20 40	20 44	20 47		20 50	20 55	20 59	21 02	21 05	21 10	21 14	21 17	21 20		21 25	21 29	21 32	21 35	21 40	21 44	21 47	21 50	21 55	
Wapping	d	20 42	20 46	20 49		20 52	20 57	21 01	21 04	21 07	21 12	21 16	21 19	21 22		21 27	21 31	21 34	21 37	21 42	21 46	21 49	21 52	21 57	
Rotherhithe	d	20 44	20 48	20 51		20 54	20 59	21 03	21 06	21 09	21 14	21 18	21 21	21 24		21 29	21 33	21 36	21 39	21 44	21 48	21 51	21 54	21 59	
Canada Water	d	20 46	20 50	20 53		20 56	21 01	21 05	21 08	21 11	21 16	21 20	21 23	21 26		21 31	21 35	21 38	21 41	21 46	21 50	21 53	21 56	22 01	
Surrey Quays	d	20 47	20 51	20 54		20 57	21 02	21 06	21 09	21 12	21 17	21 21	21 24	21 27		21 32	21 36	21 39	21 42	21 47	21 51	21 54	21 57	22 02	
New Cross	a		20 56					21 11				21 26					21 41				21 56				
New Cross Gate 4	d	20 52				21 02	21 07			21 17	21 22			21 32		21 37			21 47	21 52			22 02	22 07	
Brockley	d	20 54				21 04	21 09			21 19	21 24			21 34		21 39			21 49	21 54			22 04	22 09	
Honor Oak Park	d	20 57				21 07	21 12			21 22	21 27			21 37		21 42			21 52	21 57			22 07	22 12	
Forest Hill 4	d	21 00				21 10	21 15			21 25	21 30			21 40		21 45			21 55	22 00			22 10	22 15	
Sydenham	d	21 02				21 12	21 17			21 27	21 32			21 42		21 47			21 57	22 02			22 12	22 17	
Crystal Palace 4	a	21 07					21 22				21 37					21 52				22 07				22 23	
Penge West	d					21 15				21 30				21 45					22 00				22 15		
Anerley	d					21 17				21 32				21 47					22 02				22 17		
Norwood Junction 2	d					21 20				21 35				21 50					22 05				22 20		
West Croydon 4	a					21 30				21 41				22 00					22 11				22 30		
Queens Rd Peckham	d			20 59					21 14				21 29					21 44				21 59			
Peckham Rye 4	d			21 02					21 17				21 32					21 47				22 02			
Denmark Hill 4	d			21 06					21 21				21 36					21 51				22 06			
Clapham High Street ⊖	d			21 10					21 25				21 40					21 55				22 10			
Wandsworth Road	d			21 12					21 27				21 42					21 57				22 12			
Clapham Junction	a			21 22					21 37				21 52					22 07				22 21			

Table 178

Saturdays

14 December to 17 May

Highbury & Islington - New Cross, Crystal Palace, West Croydon and Clapham Junction

Network Diagram - see first Page of Table 173

		LO	LO	LO	LO	LO	LO	LO	LO	LO		LO	LO	LO	LO	LO	LO	LO	LO	LO		LO	LO	LO	LO
Highbury & Islington	d		21 47		21 55	22 02		22 10		22 25		22 32		22 40		22 55	23 02		23 10			23 25	23 32		23 42
Canonbury	d		21 49		21 57	22 04		22 12		22 27		22 34		22 42		22 57	23 04		23 12			23 27	23 34		23 44
Dalston Junction	d	21 49	21 52	21 55	22 00	22 07	22 10	22 15	22 19	22 30		22 37	22 40	22 45	22 52	23 00	23 07	23 10	23 15	23 22		23 30	23 37	23 40	23 48
Haggerston	d	21 50	21 53	21 56	22 01	22 08	22 11	22 16	22 20	22 31		22 38	22 41	22 46	22 53	23 01	23 08	23 11	23 16	23 23		23 31	23 38	23 41	23 49
Hoxton	d	21 52	21 55	21 58	22 03	22 10	22 13	22 18	22 22	22 33		22 40	22 43	22 48	22 55	23 03	23 10	23 13	23 18	23 25		23 33	23 40	23 43	23 51
Shoreditch High Street	d	21 55	21 58	22 01	22 06	22 13	22 16	22 21	22 25	22 36		22 43	22 46	22 51	22 58	23 06	23 13	23 16	23 21	23 28		23 36	23 43	23 46	23 54
Whitechapel	d	21 57	22 00	22 03	22 08	22 15	22 18	22 23	22 27	22 38		22 45	22 48	22 53	23 00	23 08	23 15	23 18	23 23	23 30		23 38	23 45	23 48	23 56
Shadwell	d	21 59	22 02	22 05	22 10	22 17	22 20	22 25	22 29	22 40		22 47	22 50	22 55	23 02	23 10	23 17	23 20	23 25	23 32		23 40	23 47	23 50	23 58
Wapping	d	22 01	22 04	22 07	22 12	22 19	22 22	22 27	22 31	22 42		22 49	22 52	22 57	23 04	23 12	23 19	23 22	23 27	23 34		23 42	23 49	23 52	23 59
Rotherhithe	d	22 03	22 06	22 09	22 14	22 21	22 24	22 29	22 33	22 44		22 51	22 54	22 59	23 06	23 14	23 21	23 24	23 29	23 36		23 44	23 51	23 54	00 02
Canada Water	d	22 05	22 08	22 11	22 16	22 23	22 26	22 31	22 35	22 46		22 53	22 56	23 01	23 08	23 16	23 23	23 26	23 31	23 38		23 46	23 53	23 56	00 04
Surrey Quays	d	22 06	22 09	22 12	22 17	22 24	22 27	22 32	22 36	22 47		22 54	22 57	23 02	23 09	23 17	23 24	23 27	23 32	23 39		23 47	23 54	23 57	00 06
New Cross	a	22 11							22 42						23 14					23 44					
New Cross Gate 4	d			22 17	22 22		22 32	22 37		22 52			23 02	23 07		23 22		23 32	23 37			23 52		00 02	00a09
Brockley	d			22 19	22 24		22 34	22 39		22 54			23 04	23 09		23 24		23 34	23 39			23 54		00 04	
Honor Oak Park	d			22 22	22 27		22 37	22 42		22 57			23 07	23 12		23 27		23 37	23 42			23 57		00 07	
Forest Hill 4	d			22 25	22 30		22 40	22 45		23 00			23 10	23 15		23 30		23 40	23 45			23 58		00 10	
Sydenham	d			22 27	22 32		22 42	22 47		23 02			23 12	23 17		23 32		23 42	23 47			00 02		00 12	
Crystal Palace 4	a				22 37			22 52		23 07				23 22		23 37			23 53			00 07			
Penge West	d			22 30			22 45						23 15					23 45						00 15	
Anerley	d			22 32			22 47						23 17					23 47						00 17	
Norwood Junction 2	d			22 35			22 50						23 20					23 50						00 20	
West Croydon 4	a			22 41			23 00						23 30					23 59						00 26	
Queens Rd Peckham	d		22 14			22 29						22 59					23 29						23 59		
Peckham Rye 4	d		22 17			22 32						23 02					23 32						00 02		
Denmark Hill 4	d		22 21			22 36						23 06					23 36						00 06		
Clapham High Street ⊖	d		22 25			22 40						23 10					23 40						00 10		
Wandsworth Road	d		22 27			22 42						23 12					23 42						00 12		
Clapham Junction	a		22 37			22 52						23 22					23 52						00 22		

		LO
Highbury & Islington	d	23 58
Canonbury	d	00 01
Dalston Junction	d	00 03
Haggerston	d	00 04
Hoxton	d	00 06
Shoreditch High Street	d	00 09
Whitechapel	d	00 11
Shadwell	d	00 13
Wapping	d	00 15
Rotherhithe	d	00 17
Canada Water	d	00 19
Surrey Quays	d	00 20
New Cross	a	
New Cross Gate 4	d	00a24
Brockley	d	
Honor Oak Park	d	
Forest Hill 4	d	
Sydenham	d	
Crystal Palace 4	a	
Penge West	d	
Anerley	d	
Norwood Junction 2	d	
West Croydon 4	a	
Queens Rd Peckham	d	
Peckham Rye 4	d	
Denmark Hill 4	d	
Clapham High Street ⊖	d	
Wandsworth Road	d	
Clapham Junction	a	

Table 178

Sundays

8 December to 11 May

Highbury & Islington - New Cross, Crystal Palace, West Croydon and Clapham Junction

Network Diagram - see first Page of Table 173

		LO A	LO A	LO B	LO A	LO A	LO		LO	LO	LO	LO	LO	LO	LO	LO		LO	LO	LO	LO	LO	LO	LO	LO
Highbury & Islington	d						00 10		06 51		07 11	07 21		07 41	07 51	08 07		08 11		08 21		08 37	08 41		08 51
Canonbury	d					00 01	00 12		06 53		07 13	07 23		07 43	07 53	08 09		08 13		08 23		08 39	08 43		08 53
Dalston Junction	d					00 03	00 15		06 56	07 12	07 16	07 26	07 42	07 46	07 56	08 12		08 16	08 22	08 26	08 37	08 42	08 46	08 52	08 56
Haggerston	d					00 04	00 16		06 57	07 13	07 17	07 27	07 43	07 47	07 57	08 13		08 17	08 23	08 27	08 38	08 43	08 47	08 53	08 57
Hoxton	d					00 06	00 18		06 59	07 15	07 19	07 29	07 45	07 49	07 59	08 15		08 19	08 25	08 29	08 40	08 45	08 49	08 55	08 59
Shoreditch High Street	d					00 09	00 21		07 02	07 18	07 22	07 32	07 48	07 52	08 02	08 18		08 22	08 28	08 32	08 43	08 48	08 52	08 58	09 02
Whitechapel	d					00 11	00 23		07 04	07 20	07 24	07 34	07 50	07 54	08 04	08 20		08 24	08 30	08 34	08 45	08 50	08 54	09 00	09 04
Shadwell	d					00 13	00 25		07 06	07 22	07 26	07 36	07 52	07 56	08 06	08 22		08 26	08 32	08 36	08 47	08 52	08 56	09 02	09 06
Wapping	d					00 15	00 27		07 08	07 24	07 28	07 38	07 54	07 58	08 08	08 24		08 28	08 34	08 38	08 49	08 54	08 58	09 04	09 08
Rotherhithe	d				00 02	00 17	00 29		07 10	07 26	07 30	07 40	07 56	08 00	08 10	08 26		08 30	08 36	08 40	08 51	08 56	09 00	09 06	09 10
Canada Water	d				00 04	00 19	00 31		07 12	07 28	07 32	07 42	07 58	08 02	08 12	08 28		08 32	08 38	08 42	08 53	08 58	09 02	09 08	09 12
Surrey Quays	d				00 06	00 20	00 32		07 13	07 29	07 33	07 43	07 59	08 03	08 13	08 29		08 33	08 39	08 43	08 54	08 59	09 03	09 09	09 13
New Cross	a																		08 44		08 59			09 14	
New Cross Gate 4	d			00 02	00a09	00a24	00a36		07 18	07 34		07 48	08 03		08 18	08 34				08 48		09 04			09 18
Brockley	d			00 04					07 20	07 36		07 50	08 06		08 20	08 36				08 50		09 06			09 20
Honor Oak Park	d			00 07					07 23	07 39		07 53	08 09		08 23	08 39				08 53		09 09			09 23
Forest Hill 4	d			00 10					07 26	07 42		07 56	08 12		08 26	08 42				08 56		09 12			09 26
Sydenham	d	00 02		00 12					07 28	07 44		07 58	08 14		08 28	08 44				08 58		09 14			09 28
Crystal Palace 4	a	00 07							07 33			08 03			08 33					09 03					09 33
Penge West	d			00 15						07 47			08 17			08 47						09 17			
Anerley	d			00 17						07 49			08 19			08 49						09 19			
Norwood Junction 2	d			00 20						07 52			08 22			08 52						09 22			
West Croydon 4	a			00 26						07 58			08 29			08 59						09 29			
Queens Rd Peckham	d										07 38			08 08				08 38					09 08		
Peckham Rye 4	d		00 02								07 42			08 12				08 42					09 12		
Denmark Hill 4	d		00 06								07 45			08 15				08 45					09 15		
Clapham High Street ⊖	d		00 10								07 49			08 19				08 49					09 19		
Wandsworth Road	d		00 12								07 51			08 21				08 51					09 21		
Clapham Junction	a		00 22								08 01			08 31				09 01					09 31		

		LO		LO	LO	LO	LO	LO	LO	LO	LO	LO		LO	LO	LO	LO	LO	LO	LO	LO	LO		LO	LO
Highbury & Islington	d	08 56			09 07	09 11		09 21	09 26		09 37	09 41			09 51	09 56		10 07	10 11		10 21	10 26			10 37
Canonbury	d	08 58			09 09	09 13		09 23	09 28		09 39	09 43			09 53	09 58		10 09	10 13		10 23	10 28			10 39
Dalston Junction	d	09 01		09 07	09 12	09 16	09 22	09 26	09 31	09 37	09 42	09 46		09 52	09 56	10 01	10 07	10 12	10 16	10 22	10 26	10 31		10 37	10 42
Haggerston	d	09 02		09 08	09 13	09 17	09 23	09 27	09 32	09 38	09 43	09 47		09 53	09 57	10 02	10 08	10 13	10 17	10 23	10 27	10 32		10 38	10 43
Hoxton	d	09 04		09 10	09 15	09 19	09 25	09 29	09 34	09 40	09 45	09 49		09 55	09 59	10 04	10 10	10 15	10 19	10 25	10 29	10 34		10 40	10 45
Shoreditch High Street	d	09 07		09 13	09 18	09 22	09 28	09 32	09 37	09 43	09 48	09 52		09 58	10 02	10 07	10 13	10 18	10 22	10 28	10 32	10 37		10 43	10 48
Whitechapel	d	09 09		09 15	09 20	09 24	09 30	09 34	09 39	09 45	09 50	09 54		10 00	10 04	10 09	10 15	10 20	10 24	10 30	10 34	10 39		10 45	10 50
Shadwell	d	09 11		09 17	09 22	09 26	09 32	09 36	09 41	09 47	09 52	09 56		10 02	10 06	10 11	10 17	10 22	10 26	10 32	10 36	10 41		10 47	10 52
Wapping	d	09 13		09 19	09 24	09 28	09 34	09 38	09 43	09 49	09 54	09 58		10 04	10 08	10 13	10 19	10 24	10 28	10 34	10 38	10 43		10 49	10 54
Rotherhithe	d	09 15		09 21	09 26	09 30	09 36	09 40	09 45	09 51	09 56	10 00		10 06	10 10	10 15	10 21	10 26	10 30	10 36	10 40	10 45		10 51	10 56
Canada Water	d	09 17		09 23	09 28	09 32	09 38	09 42	09 47	09 53	09 58	10 02		10 08	10 12	10 17	10 23	10 28	10 32	10 38	10 42	10 47		10 53	10 58
Surrey Quays	d	09 18		09 24	09 29	09 33	09 39	09 43	09 48	09 54	09 59	10 03		10 09	10 13	10 18	10 24	10 29	10 33	10 39	10 43	10 48		10 54	10 59
New Cross	a			09 29			09 44			09 59				10 14			10 29			10 44				10 59	
New Cross Gate 4	d				09 34			09 48			10 04				10 18			10 34			10 48				11 04
Brockley	d				09 36			09 50			10 06				10 20			10 36			10 50				11 06
Honor Oak Park	d				09 39			09 53			10 09				10 23			10 39			10 53				11 09
Forest Hill 4	d				09 42			09 56			10 12				10 26			10 42			10 56				11 12
Sydenham	d				09 44			09 58			10 14				10 28			10 44			10 58				11 14
Crystal Palace 4	a							10 03							10 33						11 03				
Penge West	d				09 47						10 17							10 47							11 17
Anerley	d				09 49						10 19							10 49							11 19
Norwood Junction 2	d				09 52						10 22							10 52							11 22
West Croydon 4	a				09 59						10 29							10 59							11 29
Queens Rd Peckham	d	09 23				09 38			09 53			10 08				10 23			10 38			10 53			
Peckham Rye 4	d	09 27				09 42			09 57			10 12				10 27			10 42			10 57			
Denmark Hill 4	d	09 30				09 45			10 00			10 15				10 30			10 45			11 00			
Clapham High Street ⊖	d	09 34				09 49			10 04			10 19				10 34			10 49			11 04			
Wandsworth Road	d	09 36				09 51			10 06			10 21				10 36			10 51			11 06			
Clapham Junction	a	09 46				10 01			10 16			10 31				10 46			11 01			11 16			

		LO	LO	LO	LO	LO	LO	LO		LO	LO	LO	LO	LO	LO	LO	LO	LO		LO	LO	LO	LO	LO	LO
Highbury & Islington	d	10 41		10 51	10 56		11 07	11 11			11 21	11 26		11 34	11 37			11 50		11 53			12 05	12 08	
Canonbury	d	10 43		10 53	10 58		11 09	11 13			11 23	11 28		11 36	11 39			11 52		11 55			12 07	12 10	
Dalston Junction	d	10 46	10 52	10 56	11 01	11 07	11 12	11 16		11 22	11 26	11 31	11 37	11 39	11 42	11 48	11 52	11 55		11 58	12 03	12 07	12 10	12 13	12 18
Haggerston	d	10 47	10 53	10 57	11 02	11 08	11 13	11 17		11 23	11 27	11 32	11 38	11 40	11 43	11 49	11 53	11 56		11 59	12 04	12 08	12 11	12 14	12 19
Hoxton	d	10 49	10 55	10 59	11 04	11 10	11 15	11 19		11 25	11 29	11 34	11 40	11 42	11 45	11 51	11 55	11 58		12 01	12 06	12 10	12 13	12 16	12 21
Shoreditch High Street	d	10 52	10 58	11 02	11 07	11 13	11 18	11 22		11 28	11 32	11 37	11 43	11 45	11 48	11 54	11 58	12 01		12 04	12 09	12 13	12 16	12 19	12 24
Whitechapel	d	10 54	11 00	11 04	11 09	11 15	11 20	11 24		11 30	11 34	11 39	11 45	11 47	11 50	11 56	12 00	12 03		12 06	12 11	12 15	12 18	12 21	12 26
Shadwell	d	10 56	11 02	11 06	11 11	11 17	11 22	11 26		11 32	11 36	11 41	11 47	11 49	11 52	11 58	12 02	12 05		12 08	12 13	12 17	12 20	12 23	12 28
Wapping	d	10 58	11 04	11 08	11 13	11 19	11 24	11 28		11 34	11 38	11 43	11 49	11 51	11 54	12 00	12 04	12 07		12 10	12 15	12 19	12 22	12 25	12 30
Rotherhithe	d	11 00	11 06	11 10	11 15	11 21	11 26	11 30		11 36	11 40	11 45	11 51	11 53	11 56	12 02	12 06	12 09		12 12	12 17	12 21	12 24	12 27	12 32
Canada Water	d	11 02	11 08	11 12	11 17	11 23	11 28	11 32		11 38	11 42	11 47	11 53	11 55	11 58	12 04	12 08	12 11		12 14	12 19	12 23	12 26	12 29	12 34
Surrey Quays	d	11 03	11 09	11 13	11 18	11 24	11 29	11 33		11 39	11 43	11 48	11 54	11 56	11 59	12 05	12 09	12 12		12 15	12 20	12 24	12 27	12 30	12 35
New Cross	a		11 14			11 29				11 44			11 59				12 14					12 29			
New Cross Gate 4	d			11 18			11 34				11 48				12 04	12 10				12 20	12 25			12 35	12 40
Brockley	d			11 20			11 36				11 50				12 06	12 12				12 22	12 27			12 37	12 42
Honor Oak Park	d			11 23			11 39				11 53				12 09	12 15				12 25	12 30			12 40	12 45
Forest Hill 4	d			11 26			11 42				11 56				12 12	12 18				12 28	12 33			12 43	12 48
Sydenham	d			11 28			11 44				11 58				12 14	12 20				12 30	12 35			12 45	12 50
Crystal Palace 4	a			11 33							12 03					12 25					12 40				12 55
Penge West	d						11 47								12 17					12 33				12 48	
Anerley	d						11 49								12 19					12 35				12 50	
Norwood Junction 2	d						11 52								12 22					12 38				12 53	
West Croydon 4	a						11 59								12 29					12 44				12 59	
Queens Rd Peckham	d	11 08			11 23			11 38				11 53		12 02				12 17					12 32		
Peckham Rye 4	d	11 12			11 27			11 42				11 57		12 06				12 20					12 36		
Denmark Hill 4	d	11 15			11 30			11 45				12 00		12 09				12 23					12 39		
Clapham High Street ⊖	d	11 19			11 34			11 49				12 04		12 13				12 27					12 43		
Wandsworth Road	d	11 21			11 36			11 51				12 06		12 15				12 29					12 45		
Clapham Junction	a	11 31			11 46			12 01				12 15		12 25				12 39					12 55		

A from Highbury and Islington Ell **B** from Dalston Junction Stn Ell

Table 178

Sundays

8 December to 11 May

Highbury & Islington - New Cross, Crystal Palace, West Croydon and Clapham Junction

Network Diagram - see first Page of Table 173

		LO	LO	LO	LO	LO	LO	LO	LO	LO	LO	LO	LO	LO	LO	LO	LO	LO	LO	LO	LO	LO
Highbury & Islington	d		12 20		12 28		12 35		12 43		12 50		12 58		13 05		13 13		13 20		13 28	
Canonbury	d		12 22		12 30		12 37		12 45		12 52		13 00		13 07		13 15		13 22		13 30	
Dalston Junction	d	12 22	12 25	12 28	12 33	12 37	12 40	12 43	12 48	12 52	12 55	12 58	13 03	13 07	13 10	13 13	13 18	13 22	13 25	13 28	13 33	13 37
Haggerston	d	12 23	12 26	12 29	12 34	12 38	12 41	12 44	12 49	12 53	12 56	12 59	13 04	13 08	13 11	13 14	13 19	13 23	13 26	13 29	13 34	13 38
Hoxton	d	12 25	12 28	12 31	12 36	12 40	12 43	12 46	12 51	12 55	12 58	13 01	13 06	13 10	13 13	13 16	13 21	13 25	13 28	13 31	13 36	13 40
Shoreditch High Street	d	12 28	12 31	12 34	12 39	12 43	12 46	12 49	12 54	12 58	13 01	13 04	13 09	13 13	13 16	13 19	13 24	13 28	13 31	13 34	13 39	13 43
Whitechapel	d	12 30	12 33	12 36	12 41	12 45	12 48	12 51	12 56	13 00	13 03	13 06	13 11	13 15	13 18	13 21	13 26	13 30	13 33	13 36	13 41	13 45
Shadwell	d	12 32	12 35	12 38	12 43	12 47	12 50	12 53	12 58	13 02	13 05	13 08	13 13	13 17	13 20	13 23	13 28	13 32	13 35	13 38	13 43	13 47
Wapping	d	12 34	12 37	12 40	12 45	12 49	12 52	12 55	13 00	13 04	13 07	13 10	13 15	13 19	13 22	13 25	13 30	13 34	13 37	13 40	13 45	13 49
Rotherhithe	d	12 36	12 39	12 42	12 47	12 51	12 54	12 57	13 02	13 06	13 09	13 12	13 17	13 21	13 24	13 27	13 32	13 36	13 39	13 42	13 47	13 51
Canada Water	d	12 38	12 41	12 44	12 49	12 53	12 56	12 59	13 04	13 08	13 11	13 14	13 19	13 23	13 26	13 29	13 34	13 38	13 41	13 44	13 49	13 53
Surrey Quays	d	12 39	12 42	12 45	12 50	12 54	12 57	13 00	13 05	13 09	13 12	13 15	13 20	13 24	13 27	13 30	13 35	13 39	13 42	13 45	13 50	13 54
New Cross	a	12 44				12 59				13 14				13 29				13 44				13 59
New Cross Gate 4	d			12 50	12 55			13 05	13 10			13 20	13 25			13 35	13 40			13 50	13 55	
Brockley	d			12 52	12 57			13 07	13 12			13 22	13 27			13 37	13 42			13 52	13 57	
Honor Oak Park	d			12 55	13 00			13 10	13 15			13 25	13 30			13 40	13 45			13 55	14 00	
Forest Hill 4	d			12 58	13 03			13 13	13 18			13 28	13 33			13 43	13 48			13 58	14 03	
Sydenham	d			13 00	13 05			13 15	13 20			13 30	13 35			13 45	13 50			14 00	14 05	
Crystal Palace 4	a				13 10				13 25				13 40				13 55				14 10	
Penge West	d			13 03				13 18				13 33				13 48				14 03		
Anerley	d			13 05				13 20				13 35				13 50				14 05		
Norwood Junction 2	d			13 08				13 23				13 38				13 53				14 08		
West Croydon 4	a			13 14				13 29				13 44				13 59				14 14		
Queens Rd Peckham	d		12 46				13 02				13 17				13 32				13 47			
Peckham Rye 4	d		12 50				13 06				13 20				13 36				13 50			
Denmark Hill 4	d		12 54				13 09				13 23				13 39				13 53			
Clapham High Street ⊖	d		12 58				13 13				13 27				13 43				13 57			
Wandsworth Road	d		13 00				13 15				13 29				13 45				13 59			
Clapham Junction	a		13 09				13 25				13 39				13 55				14 09			

		LO	LO	LO	LO	LO	LO	LO	LO	LO	LO	LO	LO	LO	LO	LO	LO	LO	LO	LO	LO	LO	LO
Highbury & Islington	d	13 35		13 43		13 50		13 58		14 05		14 13		14 20		14 28		14 35		14 43		14 50	
Canonbury	d	13 37		13 45		13 52		14 00		14 07		14 15		14 22		14 30		14 37		14 45		14 52	
Dalston Junction	d	13 40	13 43	13 48	13 52	13 55	13 58	14 03	14 07	14 10	14 13	14 18	14 22	14 25	14 28	14 33	14 37	14 40	14 43	14 48	14 52	14 55	14 58
Haggerston	d	13 41	13 44	13 49	13 53	13 56	13 59	14 04	14 08	14 11	14 14	14 19	14 23	14 26	14 29	14 34	14 38	14 41	14 44	14 49	14 53	14 56	14 59
Hoxton	d	13 43	13 46	13 51	13 55	13 58	14 01	14 06	14 10	14 13	14 16	14 21	14 25	14 28	14 31	14 36	14 40	14 43	14 46	14 51	14 55	14 58	15 01
Shoreditch High Street	d	13 46	13 49	13 54	13 58	14 01	14 04	14 09	14 13	14 16	14 19	14 24	14 28	14 31	14 34	14 39	14 43	14 46	14 49	14 54	14 58	15 01	15 04
Whitechapel	d	13 48	13 51	13 56	14 00	14 03	14 06	14 11	14 15	14 18	14 21	14 26	14 30	14 33	14 36	14 41	14 45	14 48	14 51	14 56	15 00	15 03	15 06
Shadwell	d	13 50	13 53	13 58	14 02	14 05	14 08	14 13	14 17	14 20	14 23	14 28	14 32	14 35	14 38	14 43	14 47	14 50	14 53	14 58	15 02	15 05	15 08
Wapping	d	13 52	13 55	14 00	14 04	14 07	14 10	14 15	14 19	14 22	14 25	14 30	14 34	14 37	14 40	14 45	14 49	14 52	14 55	15 00	15 04	15 07	15 10
Rotherhithe	d	13 54	13 57	14 02	14 06	14 09	14 12	14 17	14 21	14 24	14 27	14 32	14 36	14 39	14 42	14 47	14 51	14 54	14 57	15 02	15 06	15 09	15 12
Canada Water	d	13 56	13 59	14 04	14 08	14 11	14 14	14 19	14 23	14 26	14 29	14 34	14 38	14 41	14 44	14 49	14 53	14 56	14 59	15 04	15 08	15 11	15 14
Surrey Quays	d	13 57	14 00	14 05	14 09	14 12	14 15	14 20	14 24	14 27	14 30	14 35	14 39	14 42	14 45	14 50	14 54	14 57	15 00	15 05	15 09	15 12	15 15
New Cross	a				14 14				14 29				14 44				14 59				15 14		
New Cross Gate 4	d		14 05	14 10			14 20	14 25			14 35	14 40			14 50	14 55			15 05	15 10			15 20
Brockley	d		14 07	14 12			14 22	14 27			14 37	14 42			14 52	14 57			15 07	15 12			15 22
Honor Oak Park	d		14 10	14 15			14 25	14 30			14 40	14 45			14 55	15 00			15 10	15 15			15 25
Forest Hill 4	d		14 13	14 18			14 28	14 33			14 43	14 48			14 58	15 03			15 13	15 18			15 28
Sydenham	d		14 15	14 20			14 30	14 35			14 45	14 50			15 00	15 05			15 15	15 20			15 30
Crystal Palace 4	a			14 25				14 40				14 55				15 10				15 25			
Penge West	d		14 18				14 33				14 48				15 03				15 18				15 33
Anerley	d		14 20				14 35				14 50				15 05				15 20				15 35
Norwood Junction 2	d		14 23				14 38				14 53				15 08				15 23				15 38
West Croydon 4	a		14 29				14 44				14 59				15 14				15 29				15 44
Queens Rd Peckham	d	14 02				14 17				14 32				14 47				15 02				15 17	
Peckham Rye 4	d	14 06				14 20				14 36				14 50				15 06				15 20	
Denmark Hill 4	d	14 09				14 23				14 39				14 53				15 09				15 23	
Clapham High Street ⊖	d	14 13				14 27				14 43				14 57				15 13				15 27	
Wandsworth Road	d	14 15				14 29				14 45				14 59				15 15				15 29	
Clapham Junction	a	14 25				14 39				14 55				15 09				15 25				15 39	

		LO	LO	LO	LO	LO	LO	LO	LO	LO	LO	LO	LO	LO	LO	LO	LO	LO	LO	LO	LO	LO	LO
Highbury & Islington	d	14 58		15 05		15 13		15 20		15 28		15 35		15 43		15 50		15 58		16 05		16 13	
Canonbury	d	15 00		15 07		15 15		15 22		15 30		15 37		15 45		15 52		16 00		16 07		16 15	
Dalston Junction	d	15 03	15 07	15 10	15 13	15 18	15 22	15 25	15 28	15 33	15 37	15 40	15 43	15 48	15 52	15 55	15 58	16 03	16 07	16 10	16 13	16 18	16 22
Haggerston	d	15 04	15 08	15 11	15 14	15 19	15 23	15 26	15 29	15 34	15 38	15 41	15 44	15 49	15 53	15 56	15 59	16 04	16 08	16 11	16 14	16 19	16 23
Hoxton	d	15 06	15 10	15 13	15 16	15 21	15 25	15 28	15 31	15 36	15 40	15 43	15 46	15 51	15 55	15 58	16 01	16 06	16 10	16 13	16 16	16 21	16 25
Shoreditch High Street	d	15 09	15 13	15 16	15 19	15 24	15 28	15 31	15 34	15 39	15 43	15 46	15 49	15 54	15 58	16 01	16 04	16 09	16 13	16 16	16 19	16 24	16 28
Whitechapel	d	15 11	15 15	15 18	15 21	15 26	15 30	15 33	15 36	15 41	15 45	15 48	15 51	15 56	16 00	16 03	16 06	16 11	16 15	16 18	16 21	16 26	16 30
Shadwell	d	15 13	15 17	15 20	15 23	15 28	15 32	15 35	15 38	15 43	15 47	15 50	15 53	15 58	16 02	16 05	16 08	16 13	16 17	16 20	16 23	16 28	16 32
Wapping	d	15 15	15 19	15 22	15 25	15 30	15 34	15 37	15 40	15 45	15 49	15 52	15 55	16 00	16 04	16 07	16 10	16 15	16 19	16 22	16 25	16 30	16 34
Rotherhithe	d	15 17	15 21	15 24	15 27	15 32	15 36	15 39	15 42	15 47	15 51	15 54	15 57	16 02	16 06	16 09	16 12	16 17	16 21	16 24	16 27	16 32	16 36
Canada Water	d	15 19	15 23	15 26	15 29	15 34	15 38	15 41	15 44	15 49	15 53	15 56	15 59	16 04	16 08	16 11	16 14	16 19	16 23	16 26	16 29	16 34	16 38
Surrey Quays	d	15 20	15 24	15 27	15 30	15 35	15 39	15 42	15 45	15 50	15 54	15 57	16 00	16 05	16 09	16 12	16 15	16 20	16 24	16 27	16 30	16 35	16 39
New Cross	a		15 29				15 44				15 59				16 14				16 29				16 44
New Cross Gate 4	d	15 25			15 35	15 40			15 50	15 55			16 05	16 10			16 20	16 25			16 35	16 40	
Brockley	d	15 27			15 37	15 42			15 52	15 57			16 07	16 12			16 22	16 27			16 37	16 42	
Honor Oak Park	d	15 30			15 40	15 45			15 55	16 00			16 10	16 15			16 25	16 30			16 40	16 45	
Forest Hill 4	d	15 33			15 43	15 48			15 58	16 03			16 13	16 18			16 28	16 33			16 43	16 48	
Sydenham	d	15 35			15 45	15 50			16 00	16 05			16 15	16 20			16 30	16 35			16 45	16 50	
Crystal Palace 4	a	15 40				15 55				16 10				16 25				16 40				16 55	
Penge West	d				15 48				16 03				16 18				16 33				16 48		
Anerley	d				15 50				16 05				16 20				16 35				16 50		
Norwood Junction 2	d				15 53				16 08				16 23				16 38				16 53		
West Croydon 4	a				15 59				16 14				16 29				16 44				16 59		
Queens Rd Peckham	d			15 32				15 47				16 02				16 17				16 32			
Peckham Rye 4	d			15 36				15 50				16 06				16 20				16 36			
Denmark Hill 4	d			15 39				15 53				16 09				16 23				16 39			
Clapham High Street ⊖	d			15 43				15 57				16 13				16 27				16 43			
Wandsworth Road	d			15 45				15 59				16 15				16 29				16 45			
Clapham Junction	a			15 55				16 10				16 24				16 40				16 55			

Table 178

Sundays

8 December to 11 May

Highbury & Islington - New Cross, Crystal Palace, West Croydon and Clapham Junction

Network Diagram - see first Page of Table 173

		LO		LO	LO	LO	LO	LO	LO	LO	LO	LO		LO	LO	LO	LO	LO	LO	LO	LO	LO		LO	LO
Highbury & Islington	d	16 20			16 28		16 35		16 43		16 50			16 58		17 05		17 13		17 20		17 28			17 35
Canonbury	d	16 22			16 30		16 37		16 45		16 52			17 00		17 07		17 15		17 22		17 30			17 37
Dalston Junction	d	16 25		16 28	16 33	16 37	16 40	16 43	16 48	16 52	16 55	16 58		17 03	17 07	17 10	17 13	17 18	17 22	17 25	17 28	17 33		17 37	17 40
Haggerston	d	16 26		16 29	16 34	16 38	16 41	16 44	16 49	16 53	16 56	16 59		17 04	17 08	17 11	17 14	17 19	17 23	17 26	17 29	17 34		17 38	17 41
Hoxton	d	16 28		16 31	16 36	16 40	16 43	16 46	16 51	16 55	16 58	17 01		17 06	17 10	17 13	17 16	17 21	17 25	17 28	17 31	17 36		17 40	17 43
Shoreditch High Street	d	16 31		16 34	16 39	16 43	16 46	16 49	16 54	16 58	17 01	17 04		17 09	17 13	17 16	17 19	17 24	17 28	17 31	17 34	17 39		17 43	17 46
Whitechapel	d	16 33		16 36	16 41	16 45	16 48	16 51	16 56	17 00	17 03	17 06		17 11	17 15	17 18	17 21	17 26	17 30	17 33	17 36	17 41		17 45	17 48
Shadwell	d	16 35		16 38	16 43	16 47	16 50	16 53	16 58	17 02	17 05	17 08		17 13	17 17	17 20	17 23	17 28	17 32	17 35	17 38	17 43		17 47	17 50
Wapping	d	16 37		16 40	16 45	16 49	16 52	16 55	17 00	17 04	17 07	17 10		17 15	17 19	17 22	17 25	17 30	17 34	17 37	17 40	17 45		17 49	17 52
Rotherhithe	d	16 39		16 42	16 47	16 51	16 54	16 57	17 02	17 06	17 09	17 12		17 17	17 21	17 24	17 27	17 32	17 36	17 39	17 42	17 47		17 51	17 54
Canada Water	d	16 41		16 44	16 49	16 53	16 56	16 59	17 04	17 08	17 11	17 14		17 19	17 23	17 26	17 29	17 34	17 38	17 41	17 44	17 49		17 53	17 56
Surrey Quays	d	16 42		16 45	16 50	16 54	16 57	17 00	17 05	17 09	17 12	17 15		17 20	17 24	17 27	17 30	17 35	17 39	17 42	17 45	17 50		17 54	17 57
New Cross	a					16 59				17 14					17 29				17 44					17 59	
New Cross Gate [4]	d			16 50	16 55			17 05	17 10			17 20		17 25			17 35	17 40			17 50	17 55			
Brockley	d			16 52	16 57			17 07	17 12			17 22		17 27			17 37	17 42			17 52	17 57			
Honor Oak Park	d			16 55	17 00			17 10	17 15			17 25		17 30			17 40	17 45			17 55	18 00			
Forest Hill [4]	d			16 58	17 03			17 13	17 18			17 28		17 33			17 43	17 48			17 58	18 03			
Sydenham	d			17 00	17 05			17 15	17 20			17 30		17 35			17 45	17 50			18 00	18 05			
Crystal Palace [4]	a				17 10				17 25					17 40				17 55				18 10			
Penge West	d			17 03				17 18				17 33					17 48				18 03				
Anerley	d			17 05				17 20				17 35					17 50				18 05				
Norwood Junction [2]	d			17 08				17 23				17 38					17 53				18 08				
West Croydon [4]	a			17 14				17 29				17 44					17 59				18 14				
Queens Rd Peckham	d	16 47					17 02				17 17					17 32				17 47					18 02
Peckham Rye [4]	d	16 50					17 06				17 20					17 36				17 50					18 06
Denmark Hill [4]	d	16 53					17 09				17 23					17 39				17 53					18 09
Clapham High Street ⊖	d	16 57					17 13				17 27					17 43				17 57					18 13
Wandsworth Road	d	16 59					17 15				17 29					17 45				17 59					18 15
Clapham Junction	a	17 08					17 24				17 40					17 55				18 10					18 24

		LO	LO	LO	LO	LO	LO	LO		LO	LO	LO	LO	LO	LO	LO	LO	LO		LO	LO	LO	LO	LO	LO
Highbury & Islington	d		17 43		17 50		17 58			18 05		18 13		18 20		18 28		18 35			18 43		18 50		18 58
Canonbury	d		17 45		17 52		18 00			18 07		18 15		18 22		18 30		18 37			18 45		18 52		19 00
Dalston Junction	d	17 43	17 48	17 52	17 55	17 58	18 03	18 07		18 10	18 13	18 18	18 22	18 25	18 28	18 33	18 37	18 40		18 43	18 48	18 52	18 55	18 58	19 03
Haggerston	d	17 44	17 49	17 53	17 56	17 59	18 04	18 08		18 11	18 14	18 19	18 23	18 26	18 29	18 34	18 38	18 41		18 44	18 49	18 53	18 56	18 59	19 04
Hoxton	d	17 46	17 51	17 55	17 58	18 01	18 06	18 10		18 13	18 16	18 21	18 25	18 28	18 31	18 36	18 40	18 43		18 46	18 51	18 55	18 58	19 01	19 06
Shoreditch High Street	d	17 49	17 54	17 58	18 01	18 04	18 09	18 13		18 16	18 19	18 24	18 28	18 31	18 34	18 39	18 43	18 46		18 49	18 54	18 58	19 01	19 04	19 09
Whitechapel	d	17 51	17 56	18 00	18 03	18 06	18 11	18 15		18 18	18 21	18 26	18 30	18 33	18 36	18 41	18 45	18 48		18 51	18 56	19 00	19 03	19 06	19 11
Shadwell	d	17 53	17 58	18 02	18 05	18 08	18 13	18 17		18 20	18 23	18 28	18 32	18 35	18 38	18 43	18 47	18 50		18 53	18 58	19 02	19 05	19 08	19 13
Wapping	d	17 55	18 00	18 04	18 07	18 10	18 15	18 19		18 22	18 25	18 30	18 34	18 37	18 40	18 45	18 49	18 52		18 55	19 00	19 04	19 07	19 10	19 15
Rotherhithe	d	17 57	18 02	18 06	18 09	18 12	18 17	18 21		18 24	18 27	18 32	18 36	18 39	18 42	18 47	18 51	18 54		18 57	19 02	19 06	19 09	19 12	19 17
Canada Water	d	17 59	18 04	18 08	18 11	18 14	18 19	18 23		18 26	18 29	18 34	18 38	18 41	18 44	18 49	18 53	18 56		18 59	19 04	19 08	19 11	19 14	19 19
Surrey Quays	d	18 00	18 05	18 09	18 12	18 15	18 20	18 24		18 27	18 30	18 35	18 39	18 42	18 45	18 50	18 54	18 57		19 00	19 05	19 09	19 12	19 15	19 20
New Cross	a			18 14				18 29					18 44				18 59					19 14			
New Cross Gate [4]	d	18 05	18 10			18 20	18 25				18 35	18 40			18 50	18 55				19 05	19 10			19 20	19 25
Brockley	d	18 07	18 12			18 22	18 27				18 37	18 42			18 52	18 57				19 07	19 12			19 22	19 27
Honor Oak Park	d	18 10	18 15			18 25	18 30				18 40	18 45			18 55	19 00				19 10	19 15			19 25	19 30
Forest Hill [4]	d	18 13	18 18			18 28	18 33				18 43	18 48			18 58	19 03				19 13	19 18			19 28	19 33
Sydenham	d	18 15	18 20			18 30	18 35				18 45	18 50			19 00	19 05				19 15	19 20			19 30	19 35
Crystal Palace [4]	a		18 25				18 40					18 55				19 10					19 25				19 40
Penge West	d	18 18				18 33					18 48				19 03					19 18				19 33	
Anerley	d	18 20				18 35					18 50				19 05					19 20				19 35	
Norwood Junction [2]	d	18 23				18 38					18 53				19 08					19 23				19 38	
West Croydon [4]	a	18 29				18 44					18 59				19 14					19 29				19 44	
Queens Rd Peckham	d			18 17						18 32				18 47				19 02					19 17		
Peckham Rye [4]	d			18 20						18 36				18 50				19 06					19 20		
Denmark Hill [4]	d			18 23						18 39				18 53				19 09					19 23		
Clapham High Street ⊖	d			18 27						18 43				18 57				19 13					19 27		
Wandsworth Road	d			18 29						18 45				18 59				19 15					19 29		
Clapham Junction	a			18 40						18 55				19 10				19 25					19 39		

		LO	LO	LO		LO	LO	LO	LO	LO	LO	LO	LO	LO		LO	LO	LO	LO	LO	LO	LO	LO	LO	
Highbury & Islington	d		19 05			19 13		19 20		19 28		19 35		19 43			19 50		19 58		20 05		20 13		
Canonbury	d		19 07			19 15		19 22		19 30		19 37		19 45			19 52		20 00		20 07		20 15		
Dalston Junction	d	19 07	19 10	19 13		19 18	19 22	19 25	19 28	19 33	19 37	19 40	19 43	19 48		19 52	19 55	19 58	20 03	20 07	20 10	20 13	20 18	20 22	
Haggerston	d	19 08	19 11	19 14		19 19	19 23	19 26	19 29	19 34	19 38	19 41	19 44	19 49		19 53	19 56	19 59	20 04	20 08	20 11	20 14	20 19	20 23	
Hoxton	d	19 10	19 13	19 16		19 21	19 25	19 28	19 31	19 36	19 40	19 43	19 46	19 51		19 55	19 58	20 01	20 06	20 10	20 13	20 16	20 21	20 25	
Shoreditch High Street	d	19 13	19 16	19 19		19 24	19 28	19 31	19 34	19 39	19 43	19 46	19 49	19 54		19 58	20 01	20 04	20 09	20 13	20 16	20 19	20 24	20 28	
Whitechapel	d	19 15	19 18	19 21		19 26	19 30	19 33	19 36	19 41	19 45	19 48	19 51	19 56		20 00	20 03	20 06	20 11	20 15	20 18	20 21	20 26	20 30	
Shadwell	d	19 17	19 20	19 23		19 28	19 32	19 35	19 38	19 43	19 47	19 50	19 53	19 58		20 02	20 05	20 08	20 13	20 17	20 20	20 23	20 28	20 32	
Wapping	d	19 19	19 22	19 25		19 30	19 34	19 37	19 40	19 45	19 49	19 52	19 55	20 00		20 04	20 07	20 10	20 15	20 19	20 22	20 25	20 30	20 34	
Rotherhithe	d	19 21	19 24	19 27		19 32	19 36	19 39	19 42	19 47	19 51	19 54	19 57	20 02		20 06	20 09	20 12	20 17	20 21	20 24	20 27	20 32	20 36	
Canada Water	d	19 23	19 26	19 29		19 34	19 38	19 41	19 44	19 49	19 53	19 56	19 59	20 04		20 08	20 11	20 14	20 19	20 23	20 26	20 29	20 34	20 38	
Surrey Quays	d	19 24	19 27	19 30		19 35	19 39	19 42	19 45	19 50	19 54	19 57	20 00	20 05		20 09	20 12	20 15	20 20	20 24	20 27	20 30	20 35	20 39	
New Cross	a	19 29					19 44				19 59					20 14				20 29				20 44	
New Cross Gate [4]	d			19 35		19 40			19 50	19 55			20 05	20 10				20 20	20 25			20 35	20 40		
Brockley	d			19 37		19 42			19 52	19 57			20 07	20 12				20 22	20 27			20 37	20 42		
Honor Oak Park	d			19 40		19 45			19 55	20 00			20 10	20 15				20 25	20 30			20 40	20 45		
Forest Hill [4]	d			19 43		19 48			19 58	20 03			20 13	20 18				20 28	20 33			20 43	20 48		
Sydenham	d			19 45		19 50			20 00	20 05			20 15	20 20				20 30	20 35			20 45	20 50		
Crystal Palace [4]	a					19 55				20 10				20 25					20 40				20 55		
Penge West	d			19 48					20 03				20 18					20 33				20 48			
Anerley	d			19 50					20 05				20 20					20 35				20 50			
Norwood Junction [2]	d			19 53					20 08				20 23					20 38				20 53			
West Croydon [4]	a			19 59					20 14				20 29					20 44				20 59			
Queens Rd Peckham	d		19 32					19 47				20 02					20 17				20 32				
Peckham Rye [4]	d		19 36					19 50				20 06					20 20				20 36				
Denmark Hill [4]	d		19 39					19 53				20 09					20 23				20 39				
Clapham High Street ⊖	d		19 43					19 57				20 13					20 27				20 43				
Wandsworth Road	d		19 45					19 59				20 15					20 29				20 45				
Clapham Junction	a		19 55					20 09				20 25					20 39				20 55				

Table 178

Sundays

8 December to 11 May

Highbury & Islington - New Cross, Crystal Palace, West Croydon and Clapham Junction

Network Diagram - see first Page of Table 173

		LO	LO	LO	LO	LO	LO	LO	LO	LO	LO	LO	LO	LO	LO	LO	LO	LO	LO	LO	LO	LO	LO
Highbury & Islington	d	20 20		20 28		20 35		20 43		20 50		20 58		21 05		21 13		21 20		21 28		21 35	
Canonbury	d	20 22		20 30		20 37		20 45		20 52		21 00		21 07		21 15		21 22		21 30		21 37	
Dalston Junction	d	20 25	20 28	20 33	20 37	20 40	20 43	20 48	20 52	20 55	20 58	21 03	21 07	21 10	21 13	21 18	21 22	21 25	21 28	21 33	21 37	21 40	21 43
Haggerston	d	20 26	20 29	20 34	20 38	20 41	20 44	20 49	20 53	20 56	20 59	21 04	21 08	21 11	21 14	21 19	21 23	21 26	21 29	21 34	21 38	21 41	21 44
Hoxton	d	20 28	20 31	20 36	20 40	20 43	20 46	20 51	20 55	20 58	21 01	21 06	21 10	21 13	21 16	21 21	21 25	21 28	21 31	21 36	21 40	21 43	21 46
Shoreditch High Street	d	20 31	20 34	20 39	20 43	20 46	20 49	20 54	20 58	21 01	21 04	21 09	21 13	21 16	21 19	21 24	21 28	21 31	21 34	21 39	21 43	21 46	21 49
Whitechapel	d	20 33	20 36	20 41	20 45	20 48	20 51	20 56	21 00	21 03	21 06	21 11	21 15	21 18	21 21	21 26	21 30	21 33	21 36	21 41	21 45	21 48	21 51
Shadwell	d	20 35	20 38	20 43	20 47	20 50	20 53	20 58	21 02	21 05	21 08	21 13	21 17	21 20	21 23	21 28	21 32	21 35	21 38	21 43	21 47	21 50	21 53
Wapping	d	20 37	20 40	20 45	20 49	20 52	20 55	21 00	21 04	21 07	21 10	21 15	21 19	21 22	21 25	21 30	21 34	21 37	21 40	21 45	21 49	21 52	21 55
Rotherhithe	d	20 39	20 42	20 47	20 51	20 54	20 57	21 02	21 06	21 09	21 12	21 17	21 21	21 24	21 27	21 32	21 36	21 39	21 42	21 47	21 51	21 54	21 57
Canada Water	d	20 41	20 44	20 49	20 53	20 56	20 59	21 04	21 08	21 11	21 14	21 19	21 23	21 26	21 29	21 34	21 38	21 41	21 44	21 49	21 53	21 56	21 59
Surrey Quays	d	20 42	20 45	20 50	20 54	20 57	21 00	21 05	21 09	21 12	21 15	21 20	21 24	21 27	21 30	21 35	21 39	21 42	21 45	21 50	21 54	21 57	22 00
New Cross	a				20 59				21 14				21 29				21 44				21 59		
New Cross Gate 4	d		20 50	20 55			21 05	21 10			21 20	21 25			21 35	21 40			21 50	21 55			22 05
Brockley	d		20 52	20 57			21 07	21 12			21 22	21 27			21 37	21 42			21 52	21 57			22 07
Honor Oak Park	d		20 55	21 00			21 10	21 15			21 25	21 30			21 40	21 45			21 55	22 00			22 10
Forest Hill 4	d		20 58	21 03			21 13	21 18			21 28	21 33			21 43	21 48			21 58	22 03			22 13
Sydenham	d		21 00	21 05			21 15	21 20			21 30	21 35			21 45	21 50			22 00	22 05			22 15
Crystal Palace 4	a			21 10				21 25				21 40				21 55				22 10			
Penge West	d		21 03				21 18				21 33				21 48				22 03				22 18
Anerley	d		21 05				21 20				21 35				21 50				22 05				22 20
Norwood Junction 2	d		21 08				21 23				21 38				21 53				22 08				22 23
West Croydon 4 🚌	a		21 14				21 29				21 44				21 59				22 14				22 29
Queens Rd Peckham	d	20 47				21 02				21 17				21 32				21 47				22 02	
Peckham Rye 4	d	20 50				21 06				21 20				21 36				21 50				22 06	
Denmark Hill 4	d	20 53				21 09				21 23				21 39				21 53				22 09	
Clapham High Street ⊖	d	20 57				21 13				21 27				21 43				21 57				22 13	
Wandsworth Road	d	20 59				21 15				21 29				21 45				21 59				22 15	
Clapham Junction	a	21 09				21 25				21 39				21 55				22 09				22 25	

		LO	LO	LO	LO	LO	LO	LO	LO	LO	LO	LO	LO	LO	LO	LO	LO	LO
Highbury & Islington	d	21 43		21 50		21 58		22 05	22 13			22 35	22 43	22 53		23 05	23 13	23 23
Canonbury	d	21 45		21 52		22 00		22 07	22 15			22 37	22 45	22 55		23 07	23 15	23 25
Dalston Junction	d	21 48	21 52	21 55	21 58	22 03	22 07	22 10	22 18	22 28	22 37	22 40	22 48	22 58	23 07	23 10	23 18	23 28
Haggerston	d	21 49	21 53	21 56	21 59	22 04	22 08	22 11	22 19	22 29	22 38	22 41	22 49	22 59	23 08	23 11	23 19	23 29
Hoxton	d	21 51	21 55	21 58	22 01	22 06	22 10	22 13	22 21	22 31	22 40	22 43	22 51	23 01	23 10	23 13	23 21	23 31
Shoreditch High Street	d	21 54	21 58	22 01	22 04	22 09	22 13	22 16	22 24	22 34	22 43	22 46	22 54	23 04	23 13	23 16	23 24	23 34
Whitechapel	d	21 56	22 00	22 03	22 06	22 11	22 15	22 18	22 26	22 36	22 45	22 48	22 56	23 06	23 15	23 19	23 26	23 36
Shadwell	d	21 58	22 02	22 05	22 08	22 13	22 17	22 20	22 28	22 38	22 47	22 50	22 58	23 08	23 17	23 21	23 28	23 38
Wapping	d	22 00	22 04	22 07	22 10	22 15	22 19	22 22	22 30	22 40	22 49	22 52	23 00	23 10	23 19	23 23	23 30	23 40
Rotherhithe	d	22 02	22 06	22 09	22 12	22 17	22 21	22 24	22 32	22 42	22 51	22 54	23 02	23 12	23 21	23 24	23 32	23 42
Canada Water	d	22 04	22 08	22 11	22 14	22 19	22 23	22 26	22 34	22 44	22 53	22 56	23 04	23 14	23 23	23 26	23 34	23 44
Surrey Quays	d	22 05	22 09	22 12	22 15	22 20	22 24	22 28	22 35	22 45	22 54	22 57	23 05	23 15	23 24	23 28	23 35	23 45
New Cross	a		22 14				22 29				22 59				23 29			
New Cross Gate 4	d	22 10			22 20	22 25			22 40	22 50			23 10	23 20			23 40	23 50
Brockley	d	22 12			22 22	22 27			22 42	22 52			23 12	23 22			23 42	23 52
Honor Oak Park	d	22 15			22 25	22 30			22 45	22 55			23 15	23 25			23 45	23 55
Forest Hill 4	d	22 18			22 28	22 33			22 48	22 58			23 18	23 28			23 48	23 58
Sydenham	d	22 20			22 30	22 35			22 50	23 00			23 20	23 30			23 50	00 01
Crystal Palace 4	a	22 25				22 40			22 55				23 25				23 55	
Penge West	d				22 33					23 03				23 33				00 03
Anerley	d				22 35					23 05				23 35				00 05
Norwood Junction 2	d				22 38					23 08				23 38				00 08
West Croydon 4 🚌	a				22 44					23 14				23 44				00 14
Queens Rd Peckham	d			22 17				22 32				23 02				23 32		
Peckham Rye 4	d			22 20				22 36				23 06				23 36		
Denmark Hill 4	d			22 23				22 39				23 09				23 39		
Clapham High Street ⊖	d			22 27				22 43				23 13				23 43		
Wandsworth Road	d			22 29				22 45				23 15				23 45		
Clapham Junction	a			22 39				22 55				23 25				23 55		

Table 178R

Mondays to Fridays

9 December to 16 May

Clapham Junction and West Croydon, Crystal Palace, New Cross - Highbury & Islington

Network Diagram - see first Page of Table 173

Miles	Miles	Miles	Miles			LO MX A	LO MX B	LO MX C	LO	LO	LO	LO	LO	LO	LO	LO	LO	LO D	LO	LO	LO	LO	LO
0	—	—	—	Clapham Junction	d									05 59								06 29	
1½	—	—	—	Wandsworth Road	d									06 05				06 20				06 35	
0¾	—	—	—	Clapham High Street ⊖	d									06 07				06 22				06 37	
3¾	—	—	—	Denmark Hill 4	d									06 12				06 27				06 42	
4¾	—	—	—	Peckham Rye 4	d									06 15				06 29				06 44	
5¼	—	—	—	Queens Rd Peckham	d			00 02						06 17				06 32				06 47	
—	—	0	—	West Croydon 4	d					05 39			05 52				06 09				06 22		
—	—	1¾	—	Norwood Junction 2	d					05 43			05 58				06 13				06 28		
—	—	2¾	—	Anerley	d					05 46			06 01				06 16				06 31		
—	—	3¼	—	Penge West	d					05 48			06 03				06 18				06 33		
—	0	—	—	Crystal Palace 4	d				05 43			05 58				06 13				06 28			
—	1¼	4	—	Sydenham	d				05 46	05 51		06 01	06 06			06 16	06 21			06 31	06 36		
—	2	4¾	—	Forest Hill 4	d				05 49	05 53		06 04	06 08			06 19	06 23			06 34	06 38		
—	3	5¾	—	Honor Oak Park	d				05 51	05 56		06 06	06 11			06 21	06 26			06 36	06 41		
—	4	6¾	—	Brockley	d				05 54	05 58		06 09	06 13			06 24	06 28			06 39	06 43		
—	4¾	7½	—	New Cross Gate	d				05 56	06 01		06 11	06 16			06 26	06 31			06 41	06 46		
—	—	—	0	New Cross 4	d						06 07				06 22				06 37				06 52
6¾	6	8¾	1½	**Surrey Quays**	d			00 08	06 00	06 04	06 11	06 15	06 20	06 23	06 26	06 30	06 35	06 38	06 41	06 45	06 50	06 53	06 56
7	6¼	9¼	1¾	**Canada Water**	d		00 02	00 10	06 02	06 07	06 13	06 17	06 22	06 25	06 28	06 32	06 37	06 40	06 43	06 47	06 52	06 55	06 58
7¼	6½	9½	2	**Rotherhithe**	d		00 03	00 11	06 03	06 08	06 14	06 18	06 23	06 26	06 29	06 33	06 38	06 41	06 44	06 48	06 53	06 56	06 59
7¾	6¾	9¾	2¼	**Wapping**	d		00 05	00 13	06 05	06 10	06 16	06 20	06 25	06 28	06 31	06 35	06 40	06 43	06 46	06 50	06 55	06 58	07 01
8¼	7¼	10¼	2¾	**Shadwell**	d		00 07	00 15	06 07	06 12	06 18	06 22	06 27	06 30	06 33	06 37	06 42	06 45	06 48	06 52	06 57	07 00	07 03
9	8	11	3½	**Whitechapel**	d		00 09	00 17	06 09	06 14	06 20	06 24	06 29	06 32	06 35	06 39	06 44	06 47	06 50	06 54	06 59	07 02	07 05
9¾	8¾	11¾	4¼	**Shoreditch High Street**	d	00 01	00 11	00 19	06 11	06 16	06 22	06 26	06 31	06 34	06 37	06 41	06 46	06 49	06 52	06 56	07 01	07 04	07 07
10¼	9½	12¼	5	**Hoxton**	d	00 03	00 13	00 21	06 13	06 18	06 24	06 28	06 33	06 36	06 39	06 43	06 48	06 51	06 54	06 58	07 03	07 06	07 09
10¾	10	12¾	5½	**Haggerston**	d	00 05	00 15	00 23	06 15	06 20	06 26	06 30	06 35	06 38	06 41	06 45	06 50	06 53	06 56	07 00	07 05	07 08	07 11
11¼	10½	13¼	5¾	**Dalston Junction**	a	00 09	00 17	00 25	06 19	06 22	06 29	06 32	06 39	06 40	06 44	06 47	06 54	06 55	06 59	07 02	07 09	07 10	07 14
12¼	11½	—	—	Canonbury	a		00 20	00 29		06 25		06 35		06 43		06 51		06 58		07 05		07 13	
12¾	12	—	—	Highbury & Islington	a		00 25	00 32		06 28		06 40		06 46		06 56		07 01		07 10		07 16	

		LO	LO	LO	LO	LO	LO	LO	LO	LO	LO	LO	LO	LO	LO	LO	LO	LO	LO	LO	LO	LO	LO
Clapham Junction	d			06 44				06 59				07 14				07 29				07 44			
Wandsworth Road	d			06 50				07 05				07 20				07 35				07 50			
Clapham High Street ⊖	d			06 52				07 07				07 22				07 37				07 52			
Denmark Hill 4	d			06 57				07 12				07 27				07 42				07 57			
Peckham Rye 4	d			06 59				07 14				07 29				07 44				07 59			
Queens Rd Peckham	d			07 02				07 17				07 32				07 47				08 02			
West Croydon 4	d		06 39				06 52				07 09				07 22				07 39				07 52
Norwood Junction 2	d		06 43				06 58				07 13				07 28				07 43				07 58
Anerley	d		06 46				07 01				07 16				07 31				07 46				08 01
Penge West	d		06 48				07 03				07 18				07 33				07 48				08 03
Crystal Palace 4	d	06 41				06 58				07 11				07 28				07 41				07 58	
Sydenham	d	06 44	06 51			07 01	07 06			07 14	07 21			07 31	07 36			07 44	07 51			08 01	08 06
Forest Hill 4	d	06 47	06 53			07 04	07 08			07 17	07 23			07 34	07 38			07 47	07 53			08 04	08 08
Honor Oak Park	d	06 49	06 56			07 06	07 11			07 19	07 26			07 36	07 41			07 49	07 56			08 06	08 11
Brockley	d	06 52	06 58			07 09	07 13			07 22	07 28			07 39	07 43			07 52	07 58			08 09	08 13
New Cross Gate	d	06 54	07 01			07 11	07 16			07 24	07 31			07 41	07 46			07 54	08 01			08 11	08 16
New Cross 4	d				07 07				07 22				07 37				07 52				08 07		
Surrey Quays	d	07 00	07 05	07 08	07 11	07 15	07 20	07 23	07 26	07 30	07 35	07 38	07 41	07 45	07 50	07 53	07 56	08 00	08 05	08 08	08 11	08 15	08 20
Canada Water	d	07 02	07 07	07 10	07 13	07 17	07 22	07 25	07 28	07 32	07 37	07 40	07 43	07 47	07 52	07 55	07 58	08 02	08 07	08 10	08 13	08 17	08 22
Rotherhithe	d	07 03	07 08	07 11	07 14	07 18	07 23	07 26	07 29	07 33	07 38	07 41	07 44	07 48	07 53	07 56	07 59	08 03	08 08	08 11	08 14	08 18	08 23
Wapping	d	07 05	07 10	07 13	07 16	07 20	07 25	07 28	07 31	07 35	07 40	07 43	07 46	07 50	07 55	07 58	08 01	08 05	08 10	08 13	08 16	08 20	08 25
Shadwell	d	07 07	07 12	07 15	07 18	07 22	07 27	07 30	07 33	07 37	07 42	07 45	07 48	07 52	07 57	08 00	08 03	08 07	08 12	08 15	08 18	08 22	08 27
Whitechapel	d	07 09	07 14	07 17	07 20	07 24	07 29	07 32	07 35	07 39	07 44	07 47	07 50	07 54	07 59	08 02	08 05	08 09	08 14	08 17	08 20	08 24	08 29
Shoreditch High Street	d	07 11	07 16	07 19	07 22	07 26	07 31	07 34	07 37	07 41	07 46	07 49	07 52	07 56	08 01	08 04	08 07	08 11	08 16	08 19	08 22	08 26	08 31
Hoxton	d	07 13	07 18	07 21	07 24	07 28	07 33	07 36	07 39	07 43	07 48	07 51	07 54	07 58	08 03	08 06	08 09	08 13	08 18	08 21	08 24	08 28	08 33
Haggerston	d	07 15	07 20	07 23	07 26	07 30	07 35	07 38	07 41	07 45	07 50	07 53	07 56	08 00	08 05	08 08	08 11	08 15	08 20	08 23	08 26	08 30	08 35
Dalston Junction	a	07 17	07 24	07 25	07 29	07 32	07 39	07 40	07 44	07 47	07 54	07 55	07 59	08 02	08 09	08 10	08 14	08 17	08 24	08 25	08 29	08 32	08 39
Canonbury	a	07 20		07 28		07 35		07 43		07 50		07 58		08 05		08 13		08 20		08 28		08 35	
Highbury & Islington	a	07 25		07 31		07 40		07 46		07 55		08 01		08 10		08 16		08 25		08 31		08 40	

A From West Croydon
B From Crystal Palace
C From Clapham Junction Plats 0-2
D From Battersea Park, departing at 0618

Table 178R

Mondays to Fridays

9 December to 16 May

Clapham Junction and West Croydon, Crystal Palace, New Cross - Highbury & Islington

Network Diagram - see first Page of Table 173

		LO		LO	LO	LO	LO	LO	LO	LO	LO	LO		LO	LO	LO	LO	LO	LO	LO	LO	LO		LO	LO
Clapham Junction	d	07 59					08 12				08 29					08 44				08 59					09 14
Wandsworth Road	d	08 05					08 18				08 35					08 50				09 05					09 20
Clapham High Street ⊖	d	08 07					08 20				08 37					08 52				09 07					09 22
Denmark Hill 4	d	08 12					08 25				08 42					08 57				09 12					09 27
Peckham Rye 4	d	08 14					08 28				08 44					08 59				09 14					09 29
Queens Rd Peckham	d	08 17					08 31				08 47					09 02				09 17					09 32
West Croydon 4	d					08 09				08 22					08 39				08 52					09 09	
Norwood Junction 2	d					08 13				08 28					08 44				08 58					09 13	
Anerley	d					08 16				08 31					08 47				09 01					09 16	
Penge West	d					08 18				08 33					08 49				09 03					09 18	
Crystal Palace 4	d				08 11				08 28					08 41				08 58				09 11			
Sydenham	d				08 14	08 21			08 31	08 36				08 44	08 51			09 01	09 06			09 14		09 21	
Forest Hill 4	d				08 17	08 23			08 34	08 38				08 47	08 53			09 04	09 08			09 17		09 23	
Honor Oak Park	d				08 19	08 26			08 36	08 41				08 49	08 56			09 06	09 11			09 19		09 26	
Brockley	d				08 22	08 28			08 39	08 43				08 52	08 58			09 09	09 13			09 22		09 28	
New Cross Gate	d				08 24	08 31			08 41	08 46				08 54	09 01			09 11	09 16			09 24		09 31	
New Cross 4	d			08 22				08 37				08 52					09 07				09 22				
Surrey Quays	d	08 23		08 26	08 30	08 35	08 38	08 41	08 45	08 50	08 53	08 56		09 00	09 05	09 08	09 11	09 15	09 20	09 23	09 26	09 30		09 35	09 38
Canada Water	d	08 25		08 28	08 32	08 37	08 40	08 43	08 47	08 52	08 55	08 58		09 02	09 07	09 10	09 13	09 17	09 22	09 25	09 28	09 32		09 37	09 40
Rotherhithe	d	08 26		08 29	08 33	08 38	08 41	08 44	08 48	08 53	08 56	08 59		09 03	09 08	09 11	09 14	09 18	09 23	09 26	09 29	09 33		09 38	09 41
Wapping	d	08 28		08 31	08 35	08 40	08 43	08 46	08 50	08 55	08 58	09 01		09 05	09 10	09 13	09 16	09 20	09 25	09 28	09 31	09 35		09 40	09 43
Shadwell	d	08 30		08 33	08 37	08 42	08 45	08 48	08 52	08 57	09 00	09 03		09 07	09 12	09 15	09 18	09 22	09 27	09 30	09 33	09 37		09 42	09 45
Whitechapel	d	08 32		08 35	08 39	08 44	08 47	08 50	08 54	08 59	09 02	09 05		09 09	09 14	09 17	09 20	09 24	09 29	09 32	09 35	09 39		09 44	09 47
Shoreditch High Street	d	08 34		08 37	08 41	08 46	08 49	08 52	08 56	09 01	09 04	09 07		09 11	09 16	09 19	09 22	09 26	09 31	09 34	09 37	09 41		09 46	09 49
Hoxton	d	08 36		08 39	08 43	08 48	08 51	08 54	08 58	09 03	09 06	09 09		09 13	09 18	09 21	09 24	09 28	09 33	09 36	09 39	09 43		09 48	09 51
Haggerston	d	08 38		08 41	08 45	08 50	08 53	08 56	09 00	09 05	09 08	09 11		09 15	09 20	09 23	09 26	09 30	09 35	09 38	09 41	09 45		09 50	09 53
Dalston Junction	a	08 40		08 44	08 47	08 54	08 55	08 59	09 02	09 09	09 10	09 14		09 17	09 24	09 25	09 29	09 32	09 39	09 40	09 44	09 47		09 54	09 55
Canonbury	a	08 43			08 50		08 58		09 05		09 13			09 20		09 28		09 35		09 43		09 50			09 58
Highbury & Islington	a	08 47			08 55		09 01		09 10		09 16			09 25		09 31		09 40		09 46		09 55			10 01

		LO	LO	LO	LO	LO	LO	LO		LO	LO	LO	LO	LO	LO	LO	LO	LO		LO	LO	LO	LO	LO	LO
Clapham Junction	d				09 29					09 44				09 59				10 14					10 29		
Wandsworth Road	d				09 35					09 50				10 05				10 20					10 35		
Clapham High Street ⊖	d				09 37					09 52				10 07				10 22					10 37		
Denmark Hill 4	d				09 42					09 57				10 12				10 27					10 42		
Peckham Rye 4	d				09 44					09 59				10 14				10 29					10 44		
Queens Rd Peckham	d				09 47					10 02				10 17				10 32					10 47		
West Croydon 4	d			09 22				09 39					09 52				10 09					10 22			
Norwood Junction 2	d			09 28				09 43					09 58				10 13					10 28			
Anerley	d			09 31				09 46					10 01				10 16					10 31			
Penge West	d			09 33				09 48					10 03				10 18					10 33			
Crystal Palace 4	d		09 28				09 43					09 58				10 13					10 28				10 43
Sydenham	d		09 31	09 36			09 46	09 51				10 01	10 06			10 16	10 21				10 31	10 36			10 46
Forest Hill 4	d		09 34	09 38			09 49	09 53				10 04	10 08			10 19	10 23				10 34	10 38			10 49
Honor Oak Park	d		09 36	09 41			09 51	09 56				10 06	10 11			10 21	10 26				10 36	10 41			10 51
Brockley	d		09 39	09 43			09 54	09 58				10 09	10 13			10 24	10 28				10 39	10 43			10 54
New Cross Gate	d		09 41	09 46			09 56	10 01				10 11	10 16			10 26	10 31				10 41	10 46			10 56
New Cross 4	d	09 37				09 52					10 07				10 22					10 37				10 52	
Surrey Quays	d	09 41	09 45	09 50	09 53	09 56	10 00	10 05		10 08	10 11	10 15	10 20	10 23	10 26	10 30	10 35	10 38		10 41	10 45	10 50	10 53	10 56	11 00
Canada Water	d	09 43	09 47	09 52	09 55	09 58	10 02	10 07		10 10	10 13	10 17	10 22	10 25	10 28	10 32	10 37	10 40		10 43	10 47	10 52	10 55	10 58	11 02
Rotherhithe	d	09 44	09 48	09 53	09 56	09 59	10 03	10 08		10 11	10 14	10 18	10 23	10 26	10 29	10 33	10 38	10 41		10 44	10 48	10 53	10 56	10 59	11 03
Wapping	d	09 46	09 50	09 55	09 58	10 01	10 05	10 10		10 13	10 16	10 20	10 25	10 28	10 31	10 35	10 40	10 43		10 46	10 50	10 55	10 58	11 01	11 05
Shadwell	d	09 48	09 52	09 57	10 00	10 03	10 07	10 12		10 15	10 18	10 22	10 27	10 30	10 33	10 37	10 42	10 45		10 48	10 52	10 57	11 00	11 03	11 07
Whitechapel	d	09 50	09 54	09 59	10 02	10 05	10 09	10 14		10 17	10 20	10 24	10 29	10 32	10 35	10 39	10 44	10 47		10 50	10 54	10 59	11 02	11 05	11 09
Shoreditch High Street	d	09 52	09 56	10 01	10 04	10 07	10 11	10 16		10 19	10 22	10 26	10 31	10 34	10 37	10 41	10 46	10 49		10 52	10 56	11 01	11 04	11 07	11 11
Hoxton	d	09 54	09 58	10 03	10 06	10 09	10 13	10 18		10 21	10 24	10 28	10 33	10 36	10 39	10 43	10 48	10 51		10 54	10 58	11 03	11 06	11 09	11 13
Haggerston	d	09 56	10 00	10 05	10 08	10 11	10 15	10 20		10 23	10 26	10 30	10 35	10 38	10 41	10 45	10 50	10 53		10 56	11 00	11 05	11 08	11 11	11 15
Dalston Junction	a	09 59	10 02	10 09	10 10	10 14	10 17	10 24		10 25	10 29	10 32	10 39	10 40	10 44	10 47	10 54	10 55		10 59	11 02	11 09	11 10	11 14	11 17
Canonbury	a		10 05		10 13		10 20			10 28		10 35		10 43		10 50		10 58			11 05		11 13		11 20
Highbury & Islington	a		10 10		10 16		10 25			10 31		10 40		10 46		10 55		11 01			11 10		11 16		11 25

		LO	LO	LO		LO	LO	LO	LO	LO	LO	LO	LO	LO		LO	LO	LO	LO	LO	LO	LO	LO	LO	
Clapham Junction	d		10 44					10 59				11 14					11 29				11 44				
Wandsworth Road	d		10 50					11 05				11 20					11 35				11 50				
Clapham High Street ⊖	d		10 52					11 07				11 22					11 37				11 52				
Denmark Hill 4	d		10 57					11 12				11 27					11 42				11 57				
Peckham Rye 4	d		10 59					11 14				11 29					11 44				11 59				
Queens Rd Peckham	d		11 02					11 17				11 32					11 47				12 02				
West Croydon 4	d	10 39					10 52				11 09					11 22				11 39				11 52	
Norwood Junction 2	d	10 43					10 58				11 13					11 28				11 43				11 58	
Anerley	d	10 46					11 01				11 16					11 31				11 46				12 01	
Penge West	d	10 48					11 03				11 18					11 33				11 48				12 03	
Crystal Palace 4	d					10 58				11 13				11 28					11 43				11 58		
Sydenham	d	10 51				11 01	11 06			11 16	11 21			11 31		11 36			11 46	11 51			12 01	12 06	
Forest Hill 4	d	10 53				11 04	11 08			11 19	11 23			11 34		11 38			11 49	11 53			12 04	12 08	
Honor Oak Park	d	10 56				11 06	11 11			11 21	11 26			11 36		11 41			11 51	11 56			12 06	12 11	
Brockley	d	10 58				11 09	11 13			11 24	11 28			11 39		11 43			11 54	11 58			12 09	12 13	
New Cross Gate	d	11 01				11 11	11 16			11 26	11 31			11 41		11 46			11 56	12 01			12 11	12 16	
New Cross 4	d			11 07					11 22				11 37					11 52				12 07			
Surrey Quays	d	11 05	11 08	11 11		11 15	11 20	11 23	11 26	11 30	11 35	11 38	11 41	11 45		11 50	11 53	11 56	12 00	12 05	12 08	12 11	12 15	12 20	
Canada Water	d	11 07	11 10	11 13		11 17	11 22	11 25	11 28	11 32	11 37	11 40	11 43	11 47		11 52	11 55	11 58	12 02	12 07	12 10	12 13	12 17	12 22	
Rotherhithe	d	11 08	11 11	11 14		11 18	11 23	11 26	11 29	11 33	11 38	11 41	11 44	11 48		11 53	11 56	11 59	12 03	12 08	12 11	12 14	12 18	12 23	
Wapping	d	11 10	11 13	11 16		11 20	11 25	11 28	11 31	11 35	11 40	11 43	11 46	11 50		11 55	11 58	12 01	12 05	12 10	12 13	12 16	12 20	12 25	
Shadwell	d	11 12	11 15	11 18		11 22	11 27	11 30	11 33	11 37	11 42	11 45	11 48	11 52		11 57	12 00	12 03	12 07	12 12	12 15	12 18	12 22	12 27	
Whitechapel	d	11 14	11 17	11 20		11 24	11 29	11 32	11 35	11 39	11 44	11 47	11 50	11 54		11 59	12 02	12 05	12 09	12 14	12 17	12 20	12 24	12 29	
Shoreditch High Street	d	11 16	11 19	11 22		11 26	11 31	11 34	11 37	11 41	11 46	11 49	11 52	11 56		12 01	12 04	12 07	12 11	12 16	12 19	12 22	12 26	12 31	
Hoxton	d	11 18	11 21	11 24		11 28	11 33	11 36	11 39	11 43	11 48	11 51	11 54	11 58		12 03	12 06	12 09	12 13	12 18	12 21	12 24	12 28	12 33	
Haggerston	d	11 20	11 23	11 26		11 30	11 35	11 38	11 41	11 45	11 50	11 53	11 56	12 00		12 05	12 08	12 11	12 15	12 20	12 23	12 26	12 30	12 35	
Dalston Junction	a	11 24	11 25	11 29		11 32	11 39	11 40	11 44	11 47	11 54	11 55	11 59	12 02		12 09	12 10	12 14	12 17	12 24	12 25	12 29	12 32	12 39	
Canonbury	a		11 28			11 35		11 43		11 50		11 58		12 05			12 13		12 20		12 28		12 35		
Highbury & Islington	a		11 31			11 40		11 46		11 55		12 01		12 10			12 16		12 25		12 31		12 40		

Table 178R

Mondays to Fridays

9 December to 16 May

Clapham Junction and West Croydon, Crystal Palace, New Cross - Highbury & Islington

Network Diagram - see first Page of Table 173

		LO	LO	LO	LO	LO	LO	LO	LO	LO		LO	LO	LO	LO	LO	LO	LO	LO	LO		LO	LO	LO	LO
Clapham Junction	d	11 59				12 14				12 29					12 44				12 59					13 14	
Wandsworth Road	d	12 05				12 20				12 35					12 50				13 05					13 20	
Clapham High Street ⊖	d	12 07				12 22				12 37					12 52				13 07					13 22	
Denmark Hill [4]	d	12 12				12 27				12 42					12 57				13 12					13 27	
Peckham Rye [4]	d	12 14				12 29				12 44					12 59				13 14					13 29	
Queens Rd Peckham	d	12 17				12 32				12 47					13 02				13 17					13 32	
West Croydon [4] 🚊	d				12 09				12 22					12 39				12 52					13 09		
Norwood Junction [2]	d				12 13				12 28					12 43				12 58					13 13		
Anerley	d				12 16				12 31					12 46				13 01					13 16		
Penge West	d				12 18				12 33					12 48				13 03					13 18		
Crystal Palace [4]	d			12 13				12 28					12 43				12 58					13 13			
Sydenham	d			12 16	12 21			12 31	12 36				12 46	12 51			13 01	13 06				13 16	13 21		
Forest Hill [4]	d			12 19	12 23			12 34	12 38				12 49	12 53			13 04	13 08				13 19	13 23		
Honor Oak Park	d			12 21	12 26			12 36	12 41				12 51	12 56			13 06	13 11				13 21	13 26		
Brockley	d			12 24	12 28			12 39	12 43				12 54	12 58			13 09	13 13				13 24	13 28		
New Cross Gate	d			12 26	12 31			12 41	12 46				12 56	13 01			13 11	13 16				13 26	13 31		
New Cross [4]	d		12 22				12 37					12 52				13 07				13 22					13 37
Surrey Quays	d	12 23	12 26	12 30	12 35	12 38	12 41	12 45	12 50	12 53		12 56	13 00	13 05	13 08	13 11	13 15	13 20	13 23	13 26		13 30	13 35	13 38	13 41
Canada Water	d	12 25	12 28	12 32	12 37	12 40	12 43	12 47	12 52	12 55		12 58	13 02	13 07	13 10	13 13	13 17	13 22	13 25	13 28		13 32	13 37	13 40	13 43
Rotherhithe	d	12 26	12 29	12 33	12 38	12 41	12 44	12 48	12 53	12 56		12 59	13 03	13 08	13 11	13 14	13 18	13 23	13 26	13 29		13 33	13 38	13 41	13 44
Wapping	d	12 28	12 31	12 35	12 40	12 43	12 46	12 50	12 55	12 58		13 01	13 05	13 10	13 13	13 16	13 20	13 25	13 28	13 31		13 35	13 40	13 43	13 46
Shadwell	d	12 30	12 33	12 37	12 42	12 45	12 48	12 52	12 57	13 00		13 03	13 07	13 12	13 15	13 18	13 22	13 27	13 30	13 33		13 37	13 42	13 45	13 48
Whitechapel	d	12 32	12 35	12 39	12 44	12 47	12 50	12 54	12 59	13 02		13 05	13 09	13 14	13 17	13 20	13 24	13 29	13 32	13 35		13 39	13 44	13 47	13 50
Shoreditch High Street	d	12 34	12 37	12 41	12 46	12 49	12 52	12 56	13 01	13 04		13 07	13 11	13 16	13 19	13 22	13 26	13 31	13 34	13 37		13 41	13 46	13 49	13 52
Hoxton	d	12 36	12 39	12 43	12 48	12 51	12 54	12 58	13 03	13 06		13 09	13 13	13 18	13 21	13 24	13 28	13 33	13 36	13 39		13 43	13 48	13 51	13 54
Haggerston	d	12 38	12 41	12 45	12 50	12 53	12 56	13 00	13 05	13 08		13 11	13 15	13 20	13 23	13 26	13 30	13 35	13 38	13 41		13 45	13 50	13 53	13 56
Dalston Junction	a	12 40	12 44	12 47	12 54	12 55	12 59	13 02	13 09	13 10		13 14	13 17	13 24	13 25	13 29	13 32	13 39	13 40	13 44		13 47	13 54	13 55	13 59
Canonbury	a	12 43		12 50		12 58		13 05		13 13			13 20		13 28		13 35		13 43			13 50		13 58	
Highbury & Islington	a	12 46		12 55		13 01		13 10		13 16			13 25		13 31		13 40		13 46			13 55		14 01	

		LO	LO	LO	LO	LO		LO	LO	LO	LO	LO	LO	LO	LO	LO		LO	LO	LO	LO	LO	LO	LO	LO
Clapham Junction	d			13 29					13 44				13 59					14 14				14 29			
Wandsworth Road	d			13 35					13 50				14 05					14 20				14 35			
Clapham High Street ⊖	d			13 37					13 52				14 07					14 22				14 37			
Denmark Hill [4]	d			13 42					13 57				14 12					14 27				14 42			
Peckham Rye [4]	d			13 44					13 59				14 14					14 29				14 44			
Queens Rd Peckham	d			13 47					14 02				14 17					14 32				14 47			
West Croydon [4] 🚊	d		13 22					13 39				13 52				14 09					14 22				14 39
Norwood Junction [2]	d		13 28					13 43				13 58				14 13					14 28				14 43
Anerley	d		13 31					13 46				14 01				14 16					14 31				14 46
Penge West	d		13 33					13 48				14 03				14 18					14 33				14 48
Crystal Palace [4]	d	13 28				13 43					13 58				14 13					14 28				14 43	
Sydenham	d	13 31	13 36			13 46		13 51			14 01	14 06			14 16	14 21				14 31	14 36			14 46	14 51
Forest Hill [4]	d	13 34	13 38			13 49		13 53			14 04	14 08			14 19	14 23				14 34	14 38			14 49	14 53
Honor Oak Park	d	13 36	13 41			13 51		13 56			14 06	14 11			14 21	14 26				14 36	14 41			14 51	14 56
Brockley	d	13 39	13 43			13 54		13 58			14 09	14 13			14 24	14 28				14 39	14 43			14 54	14 58
New Cross Gate	d	13 41	13 46			13 56		14 01			14 11	14 16			14 26	14 31				14 41	14 46			14 56	15 01
New Cross [4]	d				13 52					14 07				14 22					14 37				14 52		
Surrey Quays	d	13 45	13 50	13 53	13 56	14 00		14 05	14 08	14 11	14 15	14 20	14 23	14 26	14 30	14 35		14 38	14 41	14 45	14 50	14 53	14 56	15 00	15 05
Canada Water	d	13 47	13 52	13 55	13 58	14 02		14 07	14 10	14 13	14 17	14 22	14 25	14 28	14 32	14 37		14 40	14 43	14 47	14 52	14 55	14 58	15 02	15 07
Rotherhithe	d	13 48	13 53	13 56	13 59	14 03		14 08	14 11	14 14	14 18	14 23	14 26	14 29	14 33	14 38		14 41	14 44	14 48	14 53	14 56	14 59	15 03	15 08
Wapping	d	13 50	13 55	13 58	14 01	14 05		14 10	14 13	14 16	14 20	14 25	14 28	14 31	14 35	14 40		14 43	14 46	14 50	14 55	14 58	15 01	15 05	15 10
Shadwell	d	13 52	13 57	14 00	14 03	14 07		14 12	14 15	14 18	14 22	14 27	14 30	14 33	14 37	14 42		14 45	14 48	14 52	14 57	15 00	15 03	15 07	15 12
Whitechapel	d	13 54	13 59	14 02	14 05	14 09		14 14	14 17	14 20	14 24	14 29	14 32	14 35	14 39	14 44		14 47	14 50	14 54	14 59	15 02	15 05	15 09	15 14
Shoreditch High Street	d	13 56	14 01	14 04	14 07	14 11		14 16	14 19	14 22	14 26	14 31	14 34	14 37	14 41	14 46		14 49	14 52	14 56	15 01	15 04	15 07	15 11	15 16
Hoxton	d	13 58	14 03	14 06	14 09	14 13		14 18	14 21	14 24	14 28	14 33	14 36	14 39	14 43	14 48		14 51	14 54	14 58	15 03	15 06	15 09	15 13	15 18
Haggerston	d	14 00	14 05	14 08	14 11	14 15		14 20	14 23	14 26	14 30	14 35	14 38	14 41	14 45	14 50		14 53	14 56	15 00	15 05	15 08	15 11	15 15	15 20
Dalston Junction	a	14 02	14 09	14 10	14 14	14 17		14 24	14 25	14 29	14 32	14 39	14 40	14 44	14 47	14 54		14 55	14 59	15 02	15 09	15 10	15 14	15 17	15 24
Canonbury	a	14 05		14 13		14 20			14 28		14 35		14 43		14 50			14 58		15 05		15 13		15 20	
Highbury & Islington	a	14 10		14 16		14 25			14 31		14 40		14 46		14 55			15 01		15 10		15 16		15 25	

		LO		LO	LO	LO	LO	LO	LO	LO	LO	LO		LO	LO	LO	LO	LO	LO	LO	LO	LO		LO	LO
Clapham Junction	d	14 44					14 59				15 14					15 29				15 44					15 59
Wandsworth Road	d	14 50					15 05				15 20					15 35				15 50					16 05
Clapham High Street ⊖	d	14 52					15 07				15 22					15 37				15 52					16 07
Denmark Hill [4]	d	14 57					15 12				15 27					15 42				15 57					16 12
Peckham Rye [4]	d	14 59					15 14				15 29					15 44				15 59					16 14
Queens Rd Peckham	d	15 02					15 17				15 32					15 47				16 02					16 17
West Croydon [4] 🚊	d					14 52				15 09					15 22				15 39					15 52	
Norwood Junction [2]	d					14 58				15 13					15 28				15 43					15 58	
Anerley	d					15 01				15 16					15 31				15 46					16 01	
Penge West	d					15 03				15 18					15 33				15 48					16 03	
Crystal Palace [4]	d				14 58				15 13					15 28				15 43				15 58			
Sydenham	d				15 01	15 06			15 16	15 21				15 31	15 36			15 46	15 51			16 01		16 06	
Forest Hill [4]	d				15 04	15 08			15 19	15 23				15 34	15 38			15 49	15 53			16 04		16 08	
Honor Oak Park	d				15 06	15 11			15 21	15 26				15 36	15 41			15 51	15 56			16 06		16 11	
Brockley	d				15 09	15 13			15 24	15 28				15 39	15 43			15 54	15 58			16 09		16 13	
New Cross Gate	d				15 11	15 16			15 26	15 31				15 41	15 46			15 56	16 01			16 11		16 16	
New Cross [4]	d			15 07				15 22				15 37					15 52				16 07				
Surrey Quays	d	15 08		15 11	15 15	15 20	15 23	15 26	15 30	15 35	15 38	15 41		15 45	15 50	15 53	15 56	16 00	16 05	16 08	16 11	16 15		16 20	16 23
Canada Water	d	15 10		15 13	15 17	15 22	15 25	15 28	15 32	15 37	15 40	15 43		15 47	15 52	15 55	15 58	16 02	16 07	16 10	16 13	16 17		16 22	16 25
Rotherhithe	d	15 11		15 14	15 18	15 23	15 26	15 29	15 33	15 38	15 41	15 44		15 48	15 53	15 56	15 59	16 03	16 08	16 11	16 14	16 18		16 23	16 26
Wapping	d	15 13		15 16	15 20	15 25	15 28	15 31	15 35	15 40	15 43	15 46		15 50	15 55	15 58	16 01	16 05	16 10	16 13	16 16	16 20		16 25	16 28
Shadwell	d	15 15		15 18	15 22	15 27	15 30	15 33	15 37	15 42	15 45	15 48		15 52	15 57	16 00	16 03	16 07	16 12	16 15	16 18	16 22		16 27	16 30
Whitechapel	d	15 17		15 20	15 24	15 29	15 32	15 35	15 39	15 44	15 47	15 50		15 54	15 59	16 02	16 05	16 09	16 14	16 17	16 20	16 24		16 29	16 32
Shoreditch High Street	d	15 19		15 22	15 26	15 31	15 34	15 37	15 41	15 46	15 49	15 52		15 56	16 01	16 04	16 07	16 11	16 16	16 19	16 22	16 26		16 31	16 34
Hoxton	d	15 21		15 24	15 28	15 33	15 36	15 39	15 43	15 48	15 51	15 54		15 58	16 03	16 06	16 09	16 13	16 18	16 21	16 24	16 28		16 33	16 36
Haggerston	d	15 23		15 26	15 30	15 35	15 38	15 41	15 45	15 50	15 53	15 56		16 00	16 05	16 08	16 11	16 15	16 20	16 23	16 26	16 30		16 35	16 38
Dalston Junction	a	15 25		15 29	15 32	15 39	15 40	15 44	15 47	15 54	15 55	15 59		16 02	16 09	16 10	16 14	16 17	16 24	16 25	16 29	16 32		16 39	16 40
Canonbury	a	15 28			15 35		15 43		15 50		15 58			16 05		16 13		16 20		16 28		16 35			16 43
Highbury & Islington	a	15 31			15 40		15 46		15 55		16 01			16 10		16 16		16 25		16 31		16 40			16 46

Table 178R

Mondays to Fridays

9 December to 16 May

Clapham Junction and West Croydon, Crystal Palace, New Cross - Highbury & Islington

Network Diagram - see first Page of Table 173

		LO	LO	LO	LO	LO	LO	LO		LO	LO	LO	LO	LO	LO	LO	LO	LO		LO	LO	LO	LO	LO	LO
Clapham Junction	d				16 14					16 29				16 44				16 57					17 14		
Wandsworth Road	d				16 20					16 35				16 50				17 03					17 20		
Clapham High Street ⊖	d				16 22					16 37				16 52				17 05					17 22		
Denmark Hill 4	d				16 27					16 42				16 57				17 10					17 27		
Peckham Rye 4	d				16 29					16 44				16 59				17 13					17 29		
Queens Rd Peckham	d				16 32					16 47				17 02				17 16					17 32		
West Croydon 4	d			16 09				16 22					16 39				16 52					17 09			
Norwood Junction 2	d			16 13				16 28					16 43				16 58					17 13			
Anerley	d			16 16				16 31					16 46				17 01					17 16			
Penge West	d			16 18				16 33					16 48				17 03					17 18			
Crystal Palace 4	d		16 13				16 28					16 43				16 58					17 13				17 28
Sydenham	d		16 16	16 21			16 31	16 36				16 46	16 51			17 01	17 06				17 16	17 21			17 31
Forest Hill 4	d		16 19	16 23			16 34	16 38				16 49	16 53			17 04	17 08				17 19	17 23			17 34
Honor Oak Park	d		16 21	16 26			16 36	16 41				16 51	16 56			17 06	17 11				17 21	17 26			17 36
Brockley	d		16 24	16 28			16 39	16 43				16 54	16 58			17 09	17 13				17 24	17 28			17 39
New Cross Gate	d		16 26	16 31			16 41	16 46				16 56	17 01			17 11	17 16				17 26	17 31			17 41
New Cross 4	d	16 22				16 37					16 52				17 07					17 22				17 37	
Surrey Quays	d	16 26	16 30	16 35	16 38	16 41	16 45	16 50		16 53	16 56	17 00	17 05	17 08	17 11	17 15	17 20	17 23		17 26	17 30	17 35	17 38	17 41	17 45
Canada Water	d	16 28	16 32	16 37	16 40	16 43	16 47	16 52		16 55	16 58	17 02	17 07	17 10	17 13	17 17	17 22	17 25		17 28	17 32	17 37	17 40	17 43	17 47
Rotherhithe	d	16 29	16 33	16 38	16 41	16 44	16 48	16 53		16 56	16 59	17 03	17 08	17 11	17 14	17 18	17 23	17 26		17 29	17 33	17 38	17 41	17 44	17 48
Wapping	d	16 31	16 35	16 40	16 43	16 46	16 50	16 55		16 58	17 01	17 05	17 10	17 13	17 16	17 20	17 25	17 28		17 31	17 35	17 40	17 43	17 46	17 50
Shadwell	d	16 33	16 37	16 42	16 45	16 48	16 52	16 57		17 00	17 03	17 07	17 12	17 15	17 18	17 22	17 27	17 30		17 33	17 37	17 42	17 45	17 48	17 52
Whitechapel	d	16 35	16 39	16 44	16 47	16 50	16 54	16 59		17 02	17 05	17 09	17 14	17 17	17 20	17 24	17 29	17 32		17 35	17 39	17 44	17 47	17 50	17 54
Shoreditch High Street	d	16 37	16 41	16 46	16 49	16 52	16 56	17 01		17 04	17 07	17 11	17 16	17 19	17 22	17 26	17 31	17 34		17 37	17 41	17 46	17 49	17 52	17 56
Hoxton	d	16 39	16 43	16 48	16 51	16 54	16 58	17 03		17 06	17 09	17 13	17 18	17 21	17 24	17 28	17 33	17 36		17 39	17 43	17 48	17 51	17 54	17 58
Haggerston	d	16 41	16 45	16 50	16 53	16 56	17 00	17 05		17 08	17 11	17 15	17 20	17 23	17 26	17 30	17 35	17 38		17 41	17 45	17 50	17 53	17 56	18 00
Dalston Junction	a	16 44	16 47	16 54	16 55	16 59	17 02	17 09		17 10	17 14	17 17	17 24	17 25	17 29	17 32	17 39	17 40		17 44	17 47	17 54	17 55	17 59	18 02
Canonbury	a		16 50		16 58		17 05			17 13		17 20		17 28		17 35		17 43			17 50		17 58		18 05
Highbury & Islington	a		16 55		17 01		17 10			17 16		17 25		17 31		17 40		17 46			17 55		18 01		18 10

		LO	LO	LO		LO	LO	LO	LO	LO	LO	LO	LO	LO		LO	LO	LO	LO	LO	LO	LO	LO	LO	
Clapham Junction	d		17 29					17 44				17 59					18 12				18 29				
Wandsworth Road	d		17 35					17 50				18 05					18 18				18 35				
Clapham High Street ⊖	d		17 37					17 52				18 07					18 20				18 37				
Denmark Hill 4	d		17 42					17 57				18 12					18 25				18 42				
Peckham Rye 4	d		17 44					17 59				18 14					18 28				18 46				
Queens Rd Peckham	d		17 47					18 02				18 17					18 30				18 48				
West Croydon 4	d	17 22					17 39				17 52					18 09				18 22				18 39	
Norwood Junction 2	d	17 28					17 43				17 58					18 13				18 28				18 43	
Anerley	d	17 31					17 46				18 01					18 16				18 31				18 46	
Penge West	d	17 33					17 48				18 03					18 18				18 33				18 48	
Crystal Palace 4	d					17 43				17 58				18 13					18 28				18 43		
Sydenham	d	17 36				17 46	17 51			18 01	18 06			18 16		18 21			18 31	18 36			18 46	18 51	
Forest Hill 4	d	17 38				17 49	17 53			18 04	18 08			18 19		18 23			18 34	18 38			18 49	18 53	
Honor Oak Park	d	17 41				17 51	17 56			18 06	18 11			18 21		18 26			18 36	18 41			18 51	18 56	
Brockley	d	17 43				17 54	17 58			18 09	18 13			18 24		18 28			18 39	18 43			18 54	18 58	
New Cross Gate	d	17 46				17 56	18 01			18 11	18 16			18 26		18 31			18 41	18 46			18 56	19 01	
New Cross 4	d			17 52					18 07				18 22					18 37				18 52			
Surrey Quays	d	17 50	17 53	17 56		18 00	18 05	18 08	18 11	18 15	18 20	18 23	18 26	18 30		18 35	18 38	18 41	18 45	18 50	18 53	18 56	19 00	19 05	
Canada Water	d	17 52	17 55	17 58		18 02	18 07	18 10	18 13	18 17	18 22	18 25	18 28	18 32		18 37	18 40	18 43	18 47	18 52	18 55	18 58	19 02	19 07	
Rotherhithe	d	17 53	17 56	17 59		18 03	18 08	18 11	18 14	18 18	18 23	18 26	18 29	18 33		18 38	18 41	18 44	18 48	18 53	18 56	18 59	19 03	19 08	
Wapping	d	17 55	17 58	18 01		18 05	18 10	18 13	18 16	18 20	18 25	18 28	18 31	18 35		18 40	18 43	18 46	18 50	18 55	18 58	19 01	19 05	19 10	
Shadwell	d	17 57	18 00	18 03		18 07	18 12	18 15	18 18	18 22	18 27	18 30	18 33	18 37		18 42	18 45	18 48	18 52	18 57	19 00	19 03	19 07	19 12	
Whitechapel	d	17 59	18 02	18 05		18 09	18 14	18 17	18 20	18 24	18 29	18 32	18 35	18 39		18 44	18 47	18 50	18 54	18 59	19 02	19 05	19 09	19 14	
Shoreditch High Street	d	18 01	18 04	18 07		18 11	18 16	18 19	18 22	18 26	18 31	18 34	18 37	18 41		18 46	18 49	18 52	18 56	19 01	19 04	19 07	19 11	19 16	
Hoxton	d	18 03	18 06	18 09		18 13	18 18	18 21	18 24	18 28	18 33	18 36	18 39	18 43		18 48	18 51	18 54	18 58	19 03	19 06	19 09	19 13	19 18	
Haggerston	d	18 05	18 08	18 11		18 15	18 20	18 23	18 26	18 30	18 35	18 38	18 41	18 45		18 50	18 53	18 56	19 00	19 05	19 08	19 11	19 15	19 20	
Dalston Junction	a	18 09	18 10	18 14		18 17	18 24	18 25	18 29	18 32	18 39	18 40	18 44	18 47		18 54	18 55	18 59	19 02	19 10	19 10	19 14	19 17	19 24	
Canonbury	a		18 13			18 20		18 28		18 35		18 43		18 50			18 58		19 05		19 13		19 20		
Highbury & Islington	a		18 16			18 25		18 31		18 40		18 46		18 55			19 01		19 10		19 16		19 25		

		LO	LO	LO	LO	LO	LO	LO	LO	LO		LO	LO	LO	LO	LO	LO	LO	LO	LO		LO	LO	LO	LO
Clapham Junction	d	18 44				18 59				19 14					19 29				19 44					19 59	
Wandsworth Road	d	18 50				19 05				19 20					19 35				19 50					20 05	
Clapham High Street ⊖	d	18 52				19 07				19 22					19 37				19 52					20 07	
Denmark Hill 4	d	18 57				19 12				19 27					19 42				19 57					20 12	
Peckham Rye 4	d	18 59				19 14				19 29					19 44				19 59					20 14	
Queens Rd Peckham	d	19 02				19 17				19 32					19 47				20 02					20 17	
West Croydon 4	d				18 52				19 09					19 22				19 39					19 52		
Norwood Junction 2	d				18 58				19 13					19 28				19 43					19 58		
Anerley	d				19 01				19 16					19 31				19 46					20 01		
Penge West	d				19 03				19 18					19 33				19 48					20 03		
Crystal Palace 4	d			18 58				19 13					19 28				19 43					19 58			
Sydenham	d			19 01	19 06			19 16	19 21				19 31	19 36			19 46	19 51				20 01	20 06		
Forest Hill 4	d			19 04	19 08			19 19	19 23				19 34	19 38			19 49	19 53				20 04	20 08		
Honor Oak Park	d			19 06	19 11			19 21	19 26				19 36	19 41			19 51	19 56				20 06	20 11		
Brockley	d			19 09	19 13			19 24	19 28				19 39	19 43			19 54	19 58				20 09	20 13		
New Cross Gate	d			19 11	19 16			19 26	19 31				19 41	19 46			19 56	20 01				20 11	20 16		
New Cross 4	d		19 07				19 22					19 37				19 52				20 07					20 22
Surrey Quays	d	19 08	19 11	19 15	19 20	19 23	19 26	19 30	19 35	19 38		19 41	19 45	19 50	19 53	19 56	20 00	20 05	20 08	20 11		20 15	20 20	20 23	20 26
Canada Water	d	19 10	19 13	19 17	19 22	19 25	19 28	19 32	19 37	19 40		19 43	19 47	19 52	19 55	19 58	20 02	20 07	20 10	20 13		20 17	20 22	20 25	20 28
Rotherhithe	d	19 11	19 14	19 18	19 23	19 26	19 29	19 33	19 38	19 41		19 44	19 48	19 53	19 56	19 59	20 03	20 08	20 11	20 14		20 18	20 23	20 26	20 29
Wapping	d	19 13	19 16	19 20	19 25	19 28	19 31	19 35	19 40	19 43		19 46	19 50	19 55	19 58	20 01	20 05	20 10	20 13	20 16		20 20	20 25	20 28	20 31
Shadwell	d	19 15	19 18	19 22	19 27	19 30	19 33	19 37	19 42	19 45		19 48	19 52	19 57	20 00	20 03	20 07	20 12	20 15	20 18		20 22	20 27	20 30	20 33
Whitechapel	d	19 17	19 20	19 24	19 29	19 32	19 35	19 39	19 44	19 47		19 50	19 54	19 59	20 02	20 05	20 09	20 14	20 17	20 20		20 24	20 29	20 32	20 35
Shoreditch High Street	d	19 19	19 22	19 26	19 31	19 34	19 37	19 41	19 46	19 49		19 52	19 56	20 01	20 04	20 07	20 11	20 16	20 19	20 22		20 26	20 31	20 34	20 37
Hoxton	d	19 21	19 24	19 28	19 33	19 36	19 39	19 43	19 48	19 51		19 54	19 58	20 03	20 06	20 09	20 13	20 18	20 21	20 24		20 28	20 33	20 36	20 39
Haggerston	d	19 23	19 26	19 30	19 35	19 38	19 41	19 45	19 50	19 53		19 56	20 00	20 05	20 08	20 11	20 15	20 20	20 23	20 26		20 30	20 35	20 38	20 41
Dalston Junction	a	19 25	19 29	19 32	19 40	19 40	19 44	19 47	19 54	19 55		19 59	20 02	20 09	20 10	20 14	20 17	20 24	20 25	20 29		20 32	20 39	20 40	20 44
Canonbury	a	19 28		19 35		19 43		19 50		19 58			20 05		20 13		20 20		20 28			20 35		20 43	
Highbury & Islington	a	19 31		19 40		19 46		19 55		20 01			20 10		20 16		20 25		20 31			20 40		20 46	

Table 178R

Mondays to Fridays

9 December to 16 May

Clapham Junction and West Croydon, Crystal Palace, New Cross - Highbury & Islington

Network Diagram - see first Page of Table 173

		LO	LO	LO	LO	LO	LO	LO	LO	LO	LO	LO	LO	LO	LO	LO	LO	LO	LO	LO	LO	LO	LO
Clapham Junction	d			20 14				20 29				20 44				20 59				21 14			
Wandsworth Road	d			20 20				20 35				20 50				21 05				21 20			
Clapham High Street ⊖	d			20 22				20 37				20 52				21 07				21 22			
Denmark Hill 4	d			20 27				20 42				20 57				21 12				21 27			
Peckham Rye 4	d			20 29				20 44				20 59				21 14				21 29			
Queens Rd Peckham	d			20 32				20 47				21 02				21 17				21 32			
West Croydon 4	d		20 09				20 22				20 39				20 52				21 09				21 22
Norwood Junction 2	d		20 13				20 28				20 43				20 58				21 13				21 28
Anerley	d		20 16				20 31				20 46				21 01				21 16				21 31
Penge West	d		20 18				20 33				20 48				21 03				21 18				21 33
Crystal Palace 4	d	20 13				20 28				20 43				20 58				21 13				21 28	
Sydenham	d	20 16	20 21			20 31	20 36			20 46	20 51			21 01	21 06			21 16	21 21			21 31	21 36
Forest Hill 4	d	20 19	20 23			20 34	20 38			20 49	20 53			21 04	21 08			21 19	21 23			21 34	21 38
Honor Oak Park	d	20 21	20 26			20 36	20 41			20 51	20 56			21 06	21 11			21 21	21 26			21 36	21 41
Brockley	d	20 24	20 28			20 39	20 43			20 54	20 58			21 09	21 13			21 24	21 28			21 39	21 43
New Cross Gate	d	20 26	20 31			20 41	20 46			20 56	21 01			21 11	21 16			21 26	21 31			21 41	21 46
New Cross 4	d				20 37				20 52				21 07				21 22				21 37		
Surrey Quays	d	20 30	20 35	20 38	20 41	20 45	20 50	20 53	20 56	21 00	21 05	21 08	21 11	21 15	21 20	21 23	21 26	21 30	21 35	21 38	21 41	21 45	21 50
Canada Water	d	20 32	20 37	20 40	20 43	20 47	20 52	20 55	20 58	21 02	21 07	21 10	21 13	21 17	21 22	21 25	21 28	21 32	21 37	21 40	21 43	21 47	21 52
Rotherhithe	d	20 33	20 38	20 41	20 44	20 48	20 53	20 56	20 59	21 03	21 08	21 11	21 14	21 18	21 23	21 26	21 29	21 33	21 38	21 41	21 44	21 48	21 53
Wapping	d	20 35	20 40	20 43	20 46	20 50	20 55	20 58	21 01	21 05	21 10	21 13	21 16	21 20	21 25	21 28	21 31	21 35	21 40	21 43	21 46	21 50	21 55
Shadwell	d	20 37	20 42	20 45	20 48	20 52	20 57	21 00	21 03	21 07	21 12	21 15	21 18	21 22	21 27	21 30	21 33	21 37	21 42	21 45	21 48	21 52	21 57
Whitechapel	d	20 39	20 44	20 47	20 50	20 54	20 59	21 02	21 05	21 09	21 14	21 17	21 20	21 24	21 29	21 32	21 35	21 39	21 44	21 47	21 50	21 54	21 59
Shoreditch High Street	d	20 41	20 46	20 49	20 52	20 56	21 01	21 04	21 07	21 11	21 16	21 19	21 22	21 26	21 31	21 34	21 37	21 41	21 46	21 49	21 52	21 56	22 01
Hoxton	d	20 43	20 48	20 51	20 54	20 58	21 03	21 06	21 09	21 13	21 18	21 21	21 24	21 28	21 33	21 36	21 39	21 43	21 48	21 51	21 54	21 58	22 03
Haggerston	d	20 45	20 50	20 53	20 56	21 00	21 05	21 08	21 11	21 15	21 20	21 23	21 26	21 30	21 35	21 38	21 41	21 45	21 50	21 53	21 56	22 00	22 05
Dalston Junction	a	20 47	20 54	20 55	20 59	21 02	21 09	21 10	21 14	21 17	21 24	21 25	21 29	21 32	21 39	21 40	21 44	21 47	21 54	21 55	21 59	22 02	22 09
Canonbury	a	20 50		20 58		21 05		21 13		21 20		21 28		21 35		21 43		21 50		21 58		22 05	
Highbury & Islington	a	20 55		21 01		21 10		21 16		21 25		21 31		21 40		21 46		21 55		22 01		22 10	

		LO	LO	LO	LO	LO	LO	LO	LO	LO	LO	LO	LO	LO	LO	LO	LO	LO	LO	LO	LO	LO
Clapham Junction	d	21 29				21 44				21 59			22 14						22 44			
Wandsworth Road	d	21 35				21 50				22 05			22 20						22 50			
Clapham High Street ⊖	d	21 37				21 52				22 07			22 22						22 52			
Denmark Hill 4	d	21 42				21 57				22 12			22 27						22 57			
Peckham Rye 4	d	21 44				21 59				22 14			22 29						22 59			
Queens Rd Peckham	d	21 47				22 02				22 17			22 32						23 02			
West Croydon 4	d				21 39				21 52			22 09				22 22		22 39			22 52	
Norwood Junction 2	d				21 43				21 58			22 13				22 28		22 43			22 58	
Anerley	d				21 46				22 01			22 16				22 31		22 46			23 01	
Penge West	d				21 48				22 03			22 18				22 33		22 48			23 03	
Crystal Palace 4	d			21 43				21 58			22 13				22 28		22 43					23 13
Sydenham	d			21 46	21 51			22 01	22 06		22 16	22 21			22 31	22 36	22 46	22 51			23 06	23 16
Forest Hill 4	d			21 49	21 53			22 04	22 08		22 19	22 23			22 34	22 38	22 49	22 53			23 08	23 19
Honor Oak Park	d			21 51	21 56			22 06	22 11		22 21	22 26			22 36	22 41	22 51	22 56			23 11	23 21
Brockley	d			21 54	21 58			22 09	22 13		22 24	22 28			22 39	22 43	22 54	22 58			23 13	23 24
New Cross Gate	d			21 56	22 01			22 11	22 16		22 26	22 31			22 41	22 46	22 56	23 01			23 16	23 26
New Cross 4	d		21 52				22 07							22 37						23 07		
Surrey Quays	d	21 53	21 56	22 00	22 05	22 08	22 11	22 15	22 20	22 23	22 30	22 35	22 38	22 41	22 45	22 50	23 00	23 05	23 08	23 11	23 20	23 30
Canada Water	d	21 55	21 58	22 02	22 07	22 10	22 13	22 17	22 22	22 25	22 32	22 37	22 40	22 43	22 47	22 52	23 02	23 07	23 10	23 13	23 22	23 32
Rotherhithe	d	21 56	21 59	22 03	22 08	22 11	22 14	22 18	22 23	22 26	22 33	22 38	22 41	22 44	22 48	22 53	23 03	23 08	23 11	23 14	23 23	23 33
Wapping	d	21 58	22 01	22 05	22 10	22 13	22 16	22 20	22 25	22 28	22 35	22 40	22 43	22 46	22 50	22 55	23 05	23 10	23 13	23 16	23 25	23 35
Shadwell	d	22 00	22 03	22 07	22 12	22 15	22 18	22 22	22 27	22 30	22 37	22 42	22 45	22 48	22 52	22 57	23 07	23 12	23 15	23 18	23 27	23 37
Whitechapel	d	22 02	22 05	22 09	22 14	22 17	22 20	22 24	22 29	22 32	22 39	22 44	22 47	22 50	22 54	22 59	23 09	23 14	23 17	23 20	23 29	23 39
Shoreditch High Street	d	22 04	22 07	22 11	22 16	22 19	22 22	22 26	22 31	22 34	22 41	22 46	22 49	22 52	22 56	23 01	23 11	23 16	23 19	23 22	23 31	23 41
Hoxton	d	22 06	22 09	22 13	22 18	22 21	22 24	22 28	22 33	22 36	22 43	22 48	22 51	22 54	22 58	23 03	23 13	23 18	23 21	23 24	23 33	23 43
Haggerston	d	22 08	22 11	22 15	22 20	22 23	22 26	22 30	22 35	22 38	22 45	22 50	22 53	22 56	23 00	23 05	23 15	23 20	23 23	23 26	23 35	23 45
Dalston Junction	a	22 10	22 14	22 17	22 24	22 25	22 29	22 32	22 39	22 40	22 47	22 52	22 55	22 59	23 02	23 09	23 17	23 23	23 25	23 29	23 39	23 47
Canonbury	a	22 13		22 20	22 29			22 35		22 43		22 55		23 01	23 05			23 25	23 28			23 50
Highbury & Islington	a	22 16		22 25	22 34			22 40		22 46		22 59		23 04	23 10			23 28	23 31			23 55

		LO	LO	LO	LO	LO
Clapham Junction	d	23 14				23 44
Wandsworth Road	d	23 20				23 50
Clapham High Street ⊖	d	23 22				23 52
Denmark Hill 4	d	23 27				23 57
Peckham Rye 4	d	23 29				23 59
Queens Rd Peckham	d	23 32				00 02
West Croydon 4	d			23 22		
Norwood Junction 2	d			23 28		
Anerley	d			23 31		
Penge West	d			23 33		
Crystal Palace 4	d				23 43	
Sydenham	d			23 36	23 46	
Forest Hill 4	d			23 38	23 49	
Honor Oak Park	d			23 41	23 51	
Brockley	d			23 43	23 54	
New Cross Gate	d			23 46	23 56	
New Cross 4	d		23 37			
Surrey Quays	d	23 38	23 41	23 50	23 59	00 08
Canada Water	d	23 40	23 43	23 52	00 02	00 10
Rotherhithe	d	23 41	23 44	23 53	00 03	00 11
Wapping	d	23 43	23 46	23 55	00 05	00 13
Shadwell	d	23 45	23 48	23 57	00 07	00 15
Whitechapel	d	23 47	23 50	23 59	00 09	00 17
Shoreditch High Street	d	23 49	23 52	00 01	00 11	00 19
Hoxton	d	23 51	23 54	00 03	00 13	00 21
Haggerston	d	23 53	23 56	00 05	00 15	00 23
Dalston Junction	a	23 55	23 59	00 09	00 17	00 25
Canonbury	a	23 58			00 20	00 29
Highbury & Islington	a	00 03			00 25	00 32

Table 178R

Saturdays

14 December to 17 May

Clapham Junction and West Croydon, Crystal Palace, New Cross - Highbury & Islington

Network Diagram - see first Page of Table 173

		LO A	LO B	LO C		LO	LO	LO	LO	LO	LO	LO	LO	LO	LO	LO	LO	LO	LO	LO		LO	LO	LO	LO
Clapham Junction	d									05 59							06 29					06 44			
Wandsworth Road	d									06 05							06 35					06 50			
Clapham High Street ⊖	d									06 07							06 37					06 52			
Denmark Hill 4	d									06 12							06 42					06 57			
Peckham Rye 4	d									06 14							06 44					07 00			
Queens Rd Peckham	d			00 02						06 17							06 47					07 02			
West Croydon 4	d					05 39			05 52				06 09			06 22				06 39					06 52
Norwood Junction 2	d					05 43			05 58				06 13			06 28				06 43					06 58
Anerley	d					05 46			06 01				06 16			06 31				06 46					07 01
Penge West	d					05 48			06 03				06 18			06 33				06 48					07 03
Crystal Palace 4	d							05 58				06 13			06 28				06 43					06 58	
Sydenham	d					05 51		06 01	06 06			06 16	06 21		06 31	06 36			06 46	06 51				07 01	07 06
Forest Hill 4	d					05 53		06 04	06 08			06 19	06 23		06 34	06 38			06 49	06 53				07 04	07 08
Honor Oak Park	d					05 56		06 06	06 11			06 21	06 26		06 36	06 41			06 51	06 56				07 06	07 11
Brockley	d					05 58		06 09	06 13			06 24	06 28		06 39	06 43			06 54	06 58				07 09	07 13
New Cross Gate	d					06 01		06 11	06 16			06 26	06 31		06 41	06 46			06 56	07 01				07 11	07 16
New Cross 4	d						06 07				06 22			06 37				06 52					07 07		
Surrey Quays	d			00 08		06 05	06 11	06 15	06 20	06 23	06 26	06 30	06 35	06 41	06 45	06 50	06 53	06 56	07 00	07 05		07 08	07 11	07 15	07 20
Canada Water	d		00 02	00 10		06 07	06 13	06 17	06 22	06 25	06 28	06 32	06 37	06 43	06 47	06 52	06 55	06 58	07 02	07 07		07 10	07 13	07 17	07 22
Rotherhithe	d		00 03	00 11		06 08	06 14	06 18	06 23	06 26	06 29	06 33	06 38	06 44	06 48	06 53	06 56	06 59	07 03	07 08		07 11	07 14	07 18	07 23
Wapping	d		00 05	00 13		06 10	06 16	06 20	06 25	06 28	06 31	06 35	06 40	06 46	06 50	06 55	06 58	07 01	07 05	07 10		07 13	07 16	07 20	07 25
Shadwell	d		00 07	00 15		06 12	06 18	06 22	06 27	06 30	06 33	06 37	06 42	06 48	06 52	06 57	07 00	07 03	07 07	07 12		07 15	07 18	07 22	07 27
Whitechapel	d		00 09	00 17		06 14	06 20	06 24	06 29	06 32	06 35	06 39	06 44	06 50	06 54	06 59	07 02	07 05	07 09	07 14		07 17	07 20	07 24	07 29
Shoreditch High Street	d	00 01	00 11	00 19		06 16	06 22	06 26	06 31	06 34	06 37	06 41	06 46	06 52	06 56	07 01	07 04	07 07	07 11	07 16		07 19	07 22	07 26	07 31
Hoxton	d	00 03	00 13	00 21		06 18	06 24	06 28	06 33	06 36	06 39	06 43	06 48	06 54	06 58	07 03	07 06	07 09	07 13	07 18		07 21	07 24	07 28	07 33
Haggerston	d	00 05	00 15	00 23		06 20	06 26	06 30	06 35	06 38	06 41	06 45	06 50	06 56	07 00	07 05	07 08	07 11	07 15	07 20		07 23	07 26	07 30	07 35
Dalston Junction	a	00 09	00 17	00 25		06 24	06 29	06 32	06 39	06 40	06 44	06 47	06 54	06 59	07 02	07 09	07 10	07 14	07 17	07 24		07 25	07 29	07 32	07 39
Canonbury	a		00 20	00 29				06 35		06 43		06 51			07 07		07 13		07 20			07 28		07 35	
Highbury & Islington	a		00 25	00 32				06 40		06 48		06 56			07 12		07 18		07 25			07 33		07 40	

		LO	LO	LO	LO	LO		LO	LO	LO	LO	LO	LO	LO	LO	LO		LO	LO	LO	LO	LO	LO	LO	LO
Clapham Junction	d	06 59				07 14					07 29				07 44					07 59				08 14	
Wandsworth Road	d	07 05				07 20					07 35				07 50					08 05				08 20	
Clapham High Street ⊖	d	07 07				07 22					07 37				07 52					08 07				08 22	
Denmark Hill 4	d	07 12				07 27					07 42				07 57					08 12				08 27	
Peckham Rye 4	d	07 14				07 29					07 44				07 59					08 14				08 29	
Queens Rd Peckham	d	07 17				07 32					07 47				08 02					08 17				08 32	
West Croydon 4	d				07 09					07 22				07 39					07 52				08 09		
Norwood Junction 2	d				07 13					07 28				07 43					07 58				08 13		
Anerley	d				07 16					07 31				07 46					08 01				08 16		
Penge West	d				07 18					07 33				07 48					08 03				08 18		
Crystal Palace 4	d			07 13					07 28				07 43					07 58				08 13			
Sydenham	d			07 16	07 21				07 31	07 36			07 46	07 51				08 01	08 06			08 16	08 21		
Forest Hill 4	d			07 19	07 23				07 34	07 38			07 49	07 53				08 04	08 08			08 19	08 23		
Honor Oak Park	d			07 21	07 26				07 36	07 41			07 51	07 56				08 06	08 11			08 21	08 26		
Brockley	d			07 24	07 28				07 39	07 43			07 54	07 58				08 09	08 13			08 24	08 28		
New Cross Gate	d			07 26	07 31				07 41	07 46			07 56	08 01				08 11	08 16			08 26	08 31		
New Cross 4	d		07 22					07 37				07 52				08 07					08 22				08 37
Surrey Quays	d	07 23	07 26	07 30	07 35	07 38		07 41	07 45	07 50	07 53	07 56	08 00	08 05	08 08	08 11		08 15	08 20	08 23	08 26	08 30	08 35	08 38	08 41
Canada Water	d	07 25	07 28	07 32	07 37	07 40		07 43	07 47	07 52	07 55	07 58	08 02	08 07	08 10	08 13		08 17	08 22	08 25	08 28	08 32	08 37	08 40	08 43
Rotherhithe	d	07 26	07 29	07 33	07 38	07 41		07 44	07 48	07 53	07 56	07 59	08 03	08 08	08 11	08 14		08 18	08 23	08 26	08 29	08 33	08 38	08 41	08 44
Wapping	d	07 28	07 31	07 35	07 40	07 43		07 46	07 50	07 55	07 58	08 01	08 05	08 10	08 13	08 16		08 20	08 25	08 28	08 31	08 35	08 40	08 43	08 46
Shadwell	d	07 30	07 33	07 37	07 42	07 45		07 48	07 52	07 57	08 00	08 03	08 07	08 12	08 15	08 18		08 22	08 27	08 30	08 33	08 37	08 42	08 45	08 48
Whitechapel	d	07 32	07 35	07 39	07 44	07 47		07 50	07 54	07 59	08 02	08 05	08 09	08 14	08 17	08 20		08 24	08 29	08 32	08 35	08 39	08 44	08 47	08 50
Shoreditch High Street	d	07 34	07 37	07 41	07 46	07 49		07 52	07 56	08 01	08 04	08 07	08 11	08 16	08 19	08 22		08 26	08 31	08 34	08 37	08 41	08 46	08 49	08 52
Hoxton	d	07 36	07 39	07 43	07 48	07 51		07 54	07 58	08 03	08 06	08 09	08 13	08 18	08 21	08 24		08 28	08 33	08 36	08 39	08 43	08 48	08 51	08 54
Haggerston	d	07 38	07 41	07 45	07 50	07 53		07 56	08 00	08 05	08 08	08 11	08 15	08 20	08 23	08 26		08 30	08 35	08 38	08 41	08 45	08 50	08 53	08 56
Dalston Junction	a	07 40	07 44	07 47	07 54	07 55		07 59	08 02	08 09	08 10	08 14	08 17	08 24	08 25	08 29		08 32	08 39	08 40	08 44	08 47	08 54	08 55	08 59
Canonbury	a	07 43		07 50		07 58			08 05		08 13		08 20		08 28			08 35		08 43		08 50		08 58	
Highbury & Islington	a	07 48		07 55		08 03			08 10		08 18		08 25		08 33			08 40		08 48		08 55		09 03	

		LO		LO	LO	LO	LO	LO	LO	LO	LO	LO		LO	LO	LO	LO	LO	LO	LO	LO	LO		LO	LO
Clapham Junction	d				08 29				08 44					08 59				09 14				09 29			
Wandsworth Road	d				08 35				08 50					09 05				09 20				09 35			
Clapham High Street ⊖	d				08 37				08 52					09 07				09 22				09 37			
Denmark Hill 4	d				08 42				08 57					09 12				09 27				09 42			
Peckham Rye 4	d				08 44				08 59					09 14				09 29				09 44			
Queens Rd Peckham	d				08 47				09 02					09 17				09 32				09 47			
West Croydon 4	d			08 22				08 39				08 52					09 09				09 22				
Norwood Junction 2	d			08 28				08 43				08 58					09 13				09 28				
Anerley	d			08 31				08 46				09 01					09 16				09 31				
Penge West	d			08 33				08 48				09 03					09 18				09 33				
Crystal Palace 4	d	08 28					08 43				08 58					09 13				09 28					09 43
Sydenham	d	08 31		08 36			08 46	08 51			09 01	09 06				09 16	09 21			09 31	09 36				09 46
Forest Hill 4	d	08 34		08 38			08 49	08 53			09 04	09 08				09 19	09 23			09 34	09 38				09 49
Honor Oak Park	d	08 36		08 41			08 51	08 56			09 06	09 11				09 21	09 26			09 36	09 41				09 51
Brockley	d	08 39		08 43			08 54	08 58			09 09	09 13				09 24	09 28			09 39	09 43				09 54
New Cross Gate	d	08 41		08 46			08 56	09 01			09 11	09 16				09 26	09 31			09 41	09 46				09 56
New Cross 4	d					08 52				09 07					09 22				09 37					09 52	
Surrey Quays	d	08 45		08 50	08 53	08 56	09 00	09 05	09 08	09 11	09 15	09 20		09 23	09 26	09 30	09 35	09 38	09 41	09 45	09 50	09 53		09 56	10 00
Canada Water	d	08 47		08 52	08 55	08 58	09 02	09 07	09 10	09 13	09 17	09 22		09 25	09 28	09 32	09 37	09 40	09 43	09 47	09 52	09 55		09 58	10 02
Rotherhithe	d	08 48		08 53	08 56	08 59	09 03	09 08	09 11	09 14	09 18	09 23		09 26	09 29	09 33	09 38	09 41	09 44	09 48	09 53	09 56		09 59	10 03
Wapping	d	08 50		08 55	08 58	09 01	09 05	09 10	09 13	09 16	09 20	09 25		09 28	09 31	09 35	09 40	09 43	09 46	09 50	09 55	09 58		10 01	10 05
Shadwell	d	08 52		08 57	09 00	09 03	09 07	09 12	09 15	09 18	09 22	09 27		09 30	09 33	09 37	09 42	09 45	09 48	09 52	09 57	10 00		10 03	10 07
Whitechapel	d	08 54		08 59	09 02	09 05	09 09	09 14	09 17	09 20	09 24	09 29		09 32	09 35	09 39	09 44	09 47	09 50	09 54	09 59	10 02		10 05	10 09
Shoreditch High Street	d	08 56		09 01	09 04	09 07	09 11	09 16	09 19	09 22	09 26	09 31		09 34	09 37	09 41	09 46	09 49	09 52	09 56	10 01	10 04		10 07	10 11
Hoxton	d	08 58		09 03	09 06	09 09	09 13	09 18	09 21	09 24	09 28	09 33		09 36	09 39	09 43	09 48	09 51	09 54	09 58	10 03	10 06		10 09	10 13
Haggerston	d	09 00		09 05	09 08	09 11	09 15	09 20	09 23	09 26	09 30	09 35		09 38	09 41	09 45	09 50	09 53	09 56	10 00	10 05	10 08		10 11	10 15
Dalston Junction	a	09 02		09 09	09 10	09 14	09 17	09 24	09 25	09 29	09 32	09 39		09 40	09 44	09 47	09 54	09 55	09 59	10 02	10 09	10 10		10 14	10 17
Canonbury	a	09 05			09 13		09 20		09 28		09 35			09 43		09 50		09 58		10 05		10 13			10 20
Highbury & Islington	a	09 10			09 18		09 25		09 33		09 40			09 48		09 55		10 03		10 10		10 18			10 25

A From West Croydon

B From Crystal Palace

C From Clapham Junction

Table 178R

Saturdays

14 December to 17 May

Clapham Junction and West Croydon, Crystal Palace, New Cross - Highbury & Islington

Network Diagram - see first Page of Table 173

		LO	LO	LO	LO	LO	LO	LO	LO	LO	LO	LO	LO	LO	LO	LO	LO	LO	LO	LO	LO	LO	LO
Clapham Junction	d		09 44				09 59				10 14				10 29				10 44				10 59
Wandsworth Road	d		09 50				10 05				10 20				10 35				10 50				11 05
Clapham High Street ⊖	d		09 52				10 07				10 22				10 37				10 52				11 07
Denmark Hill 4	d		09 57				10 12				10 27				10 42				10 57				11 12
Peckham Rye 4	d		09 59				10 14				10 29				10 44				10 59				11 14
Queens Rd Peckham	d		10 02				10 17				10 32				10 47				11 02				11 17
West Croydon 4	d	09 39				09 52				10 09				10 22				10 39				10 52	
Norwood Junction 2	d	09 43				09 58				10 13				10 28				10 43				10 58	
Anerley	d	09 46				10 01				10 16				10 31				10 46				11 01	
Penge West	d	09 48				10 03				10 18				10 33				10 48				11 03	
Crystal Palace 4	d				09 58				10 13				10 28				10 43				10 58		
Sydenham	d	09 51			10 01	10 06			10 16	10 21			10 31	10 36			10 46	10 51			11 01	11 06	
Forest Hill 4	d	09 53			10 04	10 08			10 19	10 23			10 34	10 38			10 49	10 53			11 04	11 08	
Honor Oak Park	d	09 56			10 06	10 11			10 21	10 26			10 36	10 41			10 51	10 56			11 06	11 11	
Brockley	d	09 58			10 09	10 13			10 24	10 28			10 39	10 43			10 54	10 58			11 09	11 13	
New Cross Gate	d	10 01			10 11	10 16			10 26	10 31			10 41	10 46			10 56	11 01			11 11	11 16	
New Cross 4	d			10 07				10 22				10 37				10 52				11 07			
Surrey Quays	d	10 05	10 08	10 11	10 15	10 20	10 23	10 26	10 30	10 35	10 38	10 41	10 45	10 50	10 53	10 56	11 00	11 05	11 08	11 11	11 15	11 20	11 23
Canada Water	d	10 07	10 10	10 13	10 17	10 22	10 25	10 28	10 32	10 37	10 40	10 43	10 47	10 52	10 55	10 58	11 02	11 07	11 10	11 13	11 17	11 22	11 25
Rotherhithe	d	10 08	10 11	10 14	10 18	10 23	10 26	10 29	10 33	10 38	10 41	10 44	10 48	10 53	10 56	10 59	11 03	11 08	11 11	11 14	11 18	11 23	11 26
Wapping	d	10 10	10 13	10 16	10 20	10 25	10 28	10 31	10 35	10 40	10 43	10 46	10 50	10 55	10 58	11 01	11 05	11 10	11 13	11 16	11 20	11 25	11 28
Shadwell	d	10 12	10 15	10 18	10 22	10 27	10 30	10 33	10 37	10 42	10 45	10 48	10 52	10 57	11 00	11 03	11 07	11 12	11 15	11 18	11 22	11 27	11 30
Whitechapel	d	10 14	10 17	10 20	10 24	10 29	10 32	10 35	10 39	10 44	10 47	10 50	10 54	10 59	11 02	11 05	11 09	11 14	11 17	11 20	11 24	11 29	11 32
Shoreditch High Street	d	10 16	10 19	10 22	10 26	10 31	10 34	10 37	10 41	10 46	10 49	10 52	10 56	11 01	11 04	11 07	11 11	11 16	11 19	11 22	11 26	11 31	11 34
Hoxton	d	10 18	10 21	10 24	10 28	10 33	10 36	10 39	10 43	10 48	10 51	10 54	10 58	11 03	11 06	11 09	11 13	11 18	11 21	11 24	11 28	11 33	11 36
Haggerston	d	10 20	10 23	10 26	10 30	10 35	10 38	10 41	10 45	10 50	10 53	10 56	11 00	11 05	11 08	11 11	11 15	11 20	11 23	11 26	11 30	11 35	11 38
Dalston Junction	a	10 24	10 25	10 29	10 32	10 39	10 40	10 44	10 47	10 54	10 55	10 59	11 02	11 09	11 10	11 14	11 17	11 24	11 25	11 29	11 32	11 39	11 40
Canonbury	a		10 28		10 35		10 43		10 50		10 58		11 05		11 13		11 20		11 28		11 35		11 43
Highbury & Islington	a		10 33		10 40		10 48		10 55		11 03		11 10		11 18		11 25		11 33		11 40		11 48

		LO	LO	LO	LO	LO	LO	LO	LO	LO	LO	LO	LO	LO	LO	LO	LO	LO	LO	LO	LO	LO
Clapham Junction	d				11 14				11 29				11 44				11 59				12 14	
Wandsworth Road	d				11 20				11 35				11 50				12 05				12 20	
Clapham High Street ⊖	d				11 22				11 37				11 52				12 07				12 22	
Denmark Hill 4	d				11 27				11 42				11 57				12 12				12 27	
Peckham Rye 4	d				11 29				11 44				11 59				12 14				12 29	
Queens Rd Peckham	d				11 32				11 47				12 02				12 17				12 32	
West Croydon 4	d			11 09				11 22				11 39				11 52				12 09		
Norwood Junction 2	d			11 13				11 28				11 43				11 58				12 13		
Anerley	d			11 16				11 31				11 46				12 01				12 16		
Penge West	d			11 18				11 33				11 48				12 03				12 18		
Crystal Palace 4	d		11 13				11 28				11 43				11 58				12 13			
Sydenham	d		11 16	11 21			11 31	11 36			11 46	11 51			12 01	12 06			12 16	12 21		
Forest Hill 4	d		11 19	11 23			11 34	11 38			11 49	11 53			12 04	12 08			12 19	12 23		
Honor Oak Park	d		11 21	11 26			11 36	11 41			11 51	11 56			12 06	12 11			12 21	12 26		
Brockley	d		11 24	11 28			11 39	11 43			11 54	11 58			12 09	12 13			12 24	12 28		
New Cross Gate	d		11 26	11 31			11 41	11 46			11 56	12 01			12 11	12 16			12 26	12 31		
New Cross 4	d	11 22				11 37				11 52				12 07				12 22				12 37
Surrey Quays	d	11 26	11 30	11 35	11 38	11 41	11 45	11 50	11 53	11 56	12 00	12 05	12 08	12 11	12 15	12 20	12 23	12 26	12 30	12 35	12 38	12 41
Canada Water	d	11 28	11 32	11 37	11 40	11 43	11 47	11 52	11 55	11 58	12 02	12 07	12 10	12 13	12 17	12 22	12 25	12 28	12 32	12 37	12 40	12 43
Rotherhithe	d	11 29	11 33	11 38	11 41	11 44	11 48	11 53	11 56	11 59	12 03	12 08	12 11	12 14	12 18	12 23	12 26	12 29	12 33	12 38	12 41	12 44
Wapping	d	11 31	11 35	11 40	11 43	11 46	11 50	11 55	11 58	12 01	12 05	12 10	12 13	12 16	12 20	12 25	12 28	12 31	12 35	12 40	12 43	12 46
Shadwell	d	11 33	11 37	11 42	11 45	11 48	11 52	11 57	12 00	12 03	12 07	12 12	12 15	12 18	12 22	12 27	12 30	12 33	12 37	12 42	12 45	12 48
Whitechapel	d	11 35	11 39	11 44	11 47	11 50	11 54	11 59	12 02	12 05	12 09	12 14	12 17	12 20	12 24	12 29	12 32	12 35	12 39	12 44	12 47	12 50
Shoreditch High Street	d	11 37	11 41	11 46	11 49	11 52	11 56	12 01	12 04	12 07	12 11	12 16	12 19	12 22	12 26	12 31	12 34	12 37	12 41	12 46	12 49	12 52
Hoxton	d	11 39	11 43	11 48	11 51	11 54	11 58	12 03	12 06	12 09	12 13	12 18	12 21	12 24	12 28	12 33	12 36	12 39	12 43	12 48	12 51	12 54
Haggerston	d	11 41	11 45	11 50	11 53	11 56	12 00	12 05	12 08	12 11	12 15	12 20	12 23	12 26	12 30	12 35	12 38	12 41	12 45	12 50	12 53	12 56
Dalston Junction	a	11 44	11 47	11 54	11 55	11 59	12 02	12 09	12 10	12 14	12 17	12 24	12 25	12 29	12 32	12 39	12 40	12 44	12 47	12 54	12 55	12 59
Canonbury	a		11 50		11 58		12 05		12 13		12 20		12 28		12 35		12 43		12 50		12 58	
Highbury & Islington	a		11 55		12 03		12 10		12 18		12 25		12 33		12 40		12 48		12 55		13 03	

		LO	LO	LO	LO	LO	LO	LO	LO	LO	LO	LO	LO	LO	LO	LO	LO	LO	LO	LO	LO	LO	LO
Clapham Junction	d			12 29				12 44				12 59				13 14				13 29			
Wandsworth Road	d			12 35				12 50				13 05				13 20				13 35			
Clapham High Street ⊖	d			12 37				12 52				13 07				13 22				13 37			
Denmark Hill 4	d			12 42				12 57				13 12				13 27				13 42			
Peckham Rye 4	d			12 44				12 59				13 14				13 29				13 44			
Queens Rd Peckham	d			12 47				13 02				13 17				13 32				13 47			
West Croydon 4	d		12 22				12 39				12 52				13 09				13 22				13 39
Norwood Junction 2	d		12 28				12 43				12 58				13 13				13 28				13 43
Anerley	d		12 31				12 46				13 01				13 16				13 31				13 46
Penge West	d		12 33				12 48				13 03				13 18				13 33				13 48
Crystal Palace 4	d	12 28				12 43				12 58				13 13				13 28				13 43	
Sydenham	d	12 31	12 36			12 46	12 51			13 01	13 06			13 16	13 21			13 31	13 36			13 46	13 51
Forest Hill 4	d	12 34	12 38			12 49	12 53			13 04	13 08			13 19	13 23			13 34	13 38			13 49	13 53
Honor Oak Park	d	12 36	12 41			12 51	12 56			13 06	13 11			13 21	13 26			13 36	13 41			13 51	13 56
Brockley	d	12 39	12 43			12 54	12 58			13 09	13 13			13 24	13 28			13 39	13 43			13 54	13 58
New Cross Gate	d	12 41	12 46			12 56	13 01			13 11	13 16			13 26	13 31			13 41	13 46			13 56	14 01
New Cross 4	d				12 52				13 07				13 22				13 37				13 52		
Surrey Quays	d	12 45	12 50	12 53	12 56	13 00	13 05	13 08	13 11	13 15	13 20	13 23	13 26	13 30	13 35	13 38	13 41	13 45	13 50	13 53	13 56	14 00	14 05
Canada Water	d	12 47	12 52	12 55	12 58	13 02	13 07	13 10	13 13	13 17	13 22	13 25	13 28	13 32	13 37	13 40	13 43	13 47	13 52	13 55	13 58	14 02	14 07
Rotherhithe	d	12 48	12 53	12 56	12 59	13 03	13 08	13 11	13 14	13 18	13 23	13 26	13 29	13 33	13 38	13 41	13 44	13 48	13 53	13 56	13 59	14 03	14 08
Wapping	d	12 50	12 55	12 58	13 01	13 05	13 10	13 13	13 16	13 20	13 25	13 28	13 31	13 35	13 40	13 43	13 46	13 50	13 55	13 58	14 01	14 05	14 10
Shadwell	d	12 52	12 57	13 00	13 03	13 07	13 12	13 15	13 18	13 22	13 27	13 30	13 33	13 37	13 42	13 45	13 48	13 52	13 57	14 00	14 03	14 07	14 12
Whitechapel	d	12 54	12 59	13 02	13 05	13 09	13 14	13 17	13 20	13 24	13 29	13 32	13 35	13 39	13 44	13 47	13 50	13 54	13 59	14 02	14 05	14 09	14 14
Shoreditch High Street	d	12 56	13 01	13 04	13 07	13 11	13 16	13 19	13 22	13 26	13 31	13 34	13 37	13 41	13 46	13 49	13 52	13 56	14 01	14 04	14 07	14 11	14 16
Hoxton	d	12 58	13 03	13 06	13 09	13 13	13 18	13 21	13 24	13 28	13 33	13 36	13 39	13 43	13 48	13 51	13 54	13 58	14 03	14 06	14 09	14 13	14 18
Haggerston	d	13 00	13 05	13 08	13 11	13 15	13 20	13 23	13 26	13 30	13 35	13 38	13 41	13 45	13 50	13 53	13 56	14 00	14 05	14 08	14 11	14 15	14 20
Dalston Junction	a	13 02	13 09	13 10	13 14	13 17	13 24	13 25	13 29	13 32	13 39	13 40	13 44	13 47	13 54	13 55	13 59	14 02	14 09	14 10	14 14	14 17	14 24
Canonbury	a	13 05		13 13		13 20		13 28		13 35		13 43		13 50		13 58		14 05		14 13		14 20	
Highbury & Islington	a	13 10		13 18		13 25		13 33		13 40		13 48		13 55		14 03		14 10		14 18		14 25	

Table 178R

Saturdays

14 December to 17 May

Clapham Junction and West Croydon, Crystal Palace, New Cross - Highbury & Islington

Network Diagram - see first Page of Table 173

		LO	LO	LO	LO	LO		LO	LO	LO	LO	LO	LO	LO	LO	LO		LO	LO	LO	LO	LO	LO	LO	LO
Clapham Junction	d	13 44				13 59					14 14				14 29					14 44				14 59	
Wandsworth Road	d	13 50				14 05					14 20				14 35					14 50				15 05	
Clapham High Street ⊖	d	13 52				14 07					14 22				14 37					14 52				15 07	
Denmark Hill 4	d	13 57				14 12					14 27				14 42					14 57				15 12	
Peckham Rye 4	d	13 59				14 14					14 29				14 44					14 59				15 14	
Queens Rd Peckham	d	14 02				14 17					14 32				14 47					15 02				15 17	
West Croydon 4	d				13 52					14 09				14 22					14 39				14 52		
Norwood Junction 2	d				13 58					14 13				14 28					14 43				14 58		
Anerley	d				14 01					14 16				14 31					14 46				15 01		
Penge West	d				14 03					14 18				14 33					14 48				15 03		
Crystal Palace 4	d			13 58					14 13				14 28					14 43				14 58			
Sydenham	d			14 01	14 06				14 16	14 21			14 31	14 36				14 46	14 51			15 01	15 06		
Forest Hill 4	d			14 04	14 08				14 19	14 23			14 34	14 38				14 49	14 53			15 04	15 08		
Honor Oak Park	d			14 06	14 11				14 21	14 26			14 36	14 41				14 51	14 56			15 06	15 11		
Brockley	d			14 09	14 13				14 24	14 28			14 39	14 43				14 54	14 58			15 09	15 13		
New Cross Gate	d			14 11	14 16				14 26	14 31			14 41	14 46				14 56	15 01			15 11	15 16		
New Cross 4	d		14 07					14 22				14 37				14 52					15 07				15 22
Surrey Quays	d	14 08	14 11	14 15	14 20	14 23		14 26	14 30	14 35	14 38	14 41	14 45	14 50	14 53	14 56		15 00	15 05	15 08	15 11	15 15	15 20	15 23	15 26
Canada Water	d	14 10	14 13	14 17	14 22	14 25		14 28	14 32	14 37	14 40	14 43	14 47	14 52	14 55	14 58		15 02	15 07	15 10	15 13	15 17	15 22	15 25	15 28
Rotherhithe	d	14 11	14 14	14 18	14 23	14 26		14 29	14 33	14 38	14 41	14 44	14 48	14 53	14 56	14 59		15 03	15 08	15 11	15 14	15 18	15 23	15 26	15 29
Wapping	d	14 13	14 16	14 20	14 25	14 28		14 31	14 35	14 40	14 43	14 46	14 50	14 55	14 58	15 01		15 05	15 10	15 13	15 16	15 20	15 25	15 28	15 31
Shadwell	d	14 15	14 18	14 22	14 27	14 30		14 33	14 37	14 42	14 45	14 48	14 52	14 57	15 00	15 03		15 07	15 12	15 15	15 18	15 22	15 27	15 30	15 33
Whitechapel	d	14 17	14 20	14 24	14 29	14 32		14 35	14 39	14 44	14 47	14 50	14 54	14 59	15 02	15 05		15 09	15 14	15 17	15 20	15 24	15 29	15 32	15 35
Shoreditch High Street	d	14 19	14 22	14 26	14 31	14 34		14 37	14 41	14 46	14 49	14 52	14 56	15 01	15 04	15 07		15 11	15 16	15 19	15 22	15 26	15 31	15 34	15 37
Hoxton	d	14 21	14 24	14 28	14 33	14 36		14 39	14 43	14 48	14 51	14 54	14 58	15 03	15 06	15 09		15 13	15 18	15 21	15 24	15 28	15 33	15 36	15 39
Haggerston	d	14 23	14 26	14 30	14 35	14 38		14 41	14 45	14 50	14 53	14 56	15 00	15 05	15 08	15 11		15 15	15 20	15 23	15 26	15 30	15 35	15 38	15 41
Dalston Junction	a	14 25	14 29	14 32	14 39	14 40		14 44	14 47	14 54	14 55	14 59	15 02	15 09	15 10	15 14		15 17	15 24	15 25	15 29	15 32	15 39	15 40	15 44
Canonbury	a	14 28		14 35		14 43			14 50		14 58		15 05		15 13			15 20		15 28		15 35		15 43	
Highbury & Islington	a	14 33		14 40		14 48			14 55		15 03		15 10		15 18			15 25		15 33		15 40		15 48	

		LO		LO	LO	LO	LO	LO	LO	LO	LO	LO		LO	LO	LO	LO	LO	LO	LO	LO	LO		LO	LO
Clapham Junction	d				15 14				15 29					15 44				15 59				16 14			
Wandsworth Road	d				15 20				15 35					15 50				16 05				16 20			
Clapham High Street ⊖	d				15 22				15 37					15 52				16 07				16 22			
Denmark Hill 4	d				15 27				15 42					15 57				16 12				16 27			
Peckham Rye 4	d				15 29				15 44					15 59				16 14				16 29			
Queens Rd Peckham	d				15 32				15 47					16 02				16 17				16 32			
West Croydon 4	d			15 09				15 22				15 39					15 52				16 09				
Norwood Junction 2	d			15 13				15 28				15 43					15 58				16 13				
Anerley	d			15 16				15 31				15 46					16 01				16 16				
Penge West	d			15 18				15 33				15 48					16 03				16 18				
Crystal Palace 4	d	15 13					15 28				15 43					15 58				16 13					16 28
Sydenham	d	15 16		15 21			15 31	15 36			15 46	15 51				16 01	16 06			16 16	16 21				16 31
Forest Hill 4	d	15 19		15 23			15 34	15 38			15 49	15 53				16 04	16 08			16 19	16 23				16 34
Honor Oak Park	d	15 21		15 26			15 36	15 41			15 51	15 56				16 06	16 11			16 21	16 26				16 36
Brockley	d	15 24		15 28			15 39	15 43			15 54	15 58				16 09	16 13			16 24	16 28				16 39
New Cross Gate	d	15 26		15 31			15 41	15 46			15 56	16 01				16 11	16 16			16 26	16 31				16 41
New Cross 4	d					15 37				15 52					16 07				16 22					16 37	
Surrey Quays	d	15 30		15 35	15 38	15 41	15 45	15 50	15 53	15 56	16 00	16 05		16 08	16 11	16 15	16 20	16 23	16 26	16 30	16 35	16 38		16 41	16 45
Canada Water	d	15 32		15 37	15 40	15 43	15 47	15 52	15 55	15 58	16 02	16 07		16 10	16 13	16 17	16 22	16 25	16 28	16 32	16 37	16 40		16 43	16 47
Rotherhithe	d	15 33		15 38	15 41	15 44	15 48	15 53	15 56	15 59	16 03	16 08		16 11	16 14	16 18	16 23	16 26	16 29	16 33	16 38	16 41		16 44	16 48
Wapping	d	15 35		15 40	15 43	15 46	15 50	15 55	15 58	16 01	16 05	16 10		16 13	16 16	16 20	16 25	16 28	16 31	16 35	16 40	16 43		16 46	16 50
Shadwell	d	15 37		15 42	15 45	15 48	15 52	15 57	16 00	16 03	16 07	16 12		16 15	16 18	16 22	16 27	16 30	16 33	16 37	16 42	16 45		16 48	16 52
Whitechapel	d	15 39		15 44	15 47	15 50	15 54	15 59	16 02	16 05	16 09	16 14		16 17	16 20	16 24	16 29	16 32	16 35	16 39	16 44	16 47		16 50	16 54
Shoreditch High Street	d	15 41		15 46	15 49	15 52	15 56	16 01	16 04	16 07	16 11	16 16		16 19	16 22	16 26	16 31	16 34	16 37	16 41	16 46	16 49		16 52	16 56
Hoxton	d	15 43		15 48	15 51	15 54	15 58	16 03	16 06	16 09	16 13	16 18		16 21	16 24	16 28	16 33	16 36	16 39	16 43	16 48	16 51		16 54	16 58
Haggerston	d	15 45		15 50	15 53	15 56	16 00	16 05	16 08	16 11	16 15	16 20		16 23	16 26	16 30	16 35	16 38	16 41	16 45	16 50	16 53		16 56	17 00
Dalston Junction	a	15 47		15 54	15 55	15 59	16 02	16 09	16 10	16 14	16 17	16 24		16 25	16 29	16 32	16 39	16 40	16 44	16 47	16 54	16 55		16 59	17 02
Canonbury	a	15 50			15 58		16 05		16 13		16 20			16 28		16 35		16 43		16 50		16 58			17 05
Highbury & Islington	a	15 55			16 03		16 10		16 18		16 25			16 33		16 40		16 48		16 55		17 03			17 10

		LO	LO	LO	LO	LO	LO	LO		LO	LO	LO	LO	LO	LO	LO	LO	LO		LO	LO	LO	LO	LO	LO
Clapham Junction	d		16 29				16 44					16 59				17 14					17 29				17 44
Wandsworth Road	d		16 35				16 50					17 05				17 20					17 35				17 50
Clapham High Street ⊖	d		16 37				16 52					17 07				17 22					17 37				17 52
Denmark Hill 4	d		16 42				16 57					17 12				17 27					17 42				17 57
Peckham Rye 4	d		16 44				16 59					17 14				17 29					17 44				17 59
Queens Rd Peckham	d		16 47				17 02					17 17				17 32					17 47				18 02
West Croydon 4	d	16 22				16 39					16 52				17 09					17 22				17 39	
Norwood Junction 2	d	16 28				16 43					16 58				17 13					17 28				17 43	
Anerley	d	16 31				16 46					17 01				17 16					17 31				17 46	
Penge West	d	16 33				16 48					17 03				17 18					17 33				17 48	
Crystal Palace 4	d				16 43					16 58				17 13				17 28					17 43		
Sydenham	d	16 36			16 46	16 51				17 01	17 06			17 16	17 21			17 31		17 36			17 46	17 51	
Forest Hill 4	d	16 38			16 49	16 53				17 04	17 08			17 19	17 23			17 34		17 38			17 49	17 53	
Honor Oak Park	d	16 41			16 51	16 56				17 06	17 11			17 21	17 26			17 36		17 41			17 51	17 56	
Brockley	d	16 43			16 54	16 58				17 09	17 13			17 24	17 28			17 39		17 43			17 54	17 58	
New Cross Gate	d	16 46			16 56	17 01				17 11	17 16			17 26	17 31			17 41		17 46			17 56	18 01	
New Cross 4	d			16 52				17 07					17 22				17 37					17 52			
Surrey Quays	d	16 50	16 53	16 56	17 00	17 05	17 08	17 11		17 15	17 20	17 23	17 26	17 30	17 35	17 38	17 41	17 45		17 50	17 53	17 56	18 00	18 05	18 08
Canada Water	d	16 52	16 55	16 58	17 02	17 07	17 10	17 13		17 17	17 22	17 25	17 28	17 32	17 37	17 40	17 43	17 47		17 52	17 55	17 58	18 02	18 07	18 10
Rotherhithe	d	16 53	16 56	16 59	17 03	17 08	17 11	17 14		17 18	17 23	17 26	17 29	17 33	17 38	17 41	17 44	17 48		17 53	17 56	17 59	18 03	18 08	18 11
Wapping	d	16 55	16 58	17 01	17 05	17 10	17 13	17 16		17 20	17 25	17 28	17 31	17 35	17 40	17 43	17 46	17 50		17 55	17 58	18 01	18 05	18 10	18 13
Shadwell	d	16 57	17 00	17 03	17 07	17 12	17 15	17 18		17 22	17 27	17 30	17 33	17 37	17 42	17 45	17 48	17 52		17 57	18 00	18 03	18 07	18 12	18 15
Whitechapel	d	16 59	17 02	17 05	17 09	17 14	17 17	17 20		17 24	17 29	17 32	17 35	17 39	17 44	17 47	17 50	17 54		17 59	18 02	18 05	18 09	18 14	18 17
Shoreditch High Street	d	17 01	17 04	17 07	17 11	17 16	17 19	17 22		17 26	17 31	17 34	17 37	17 41	17 46	17 49	17 52	17 56		18 01	18 04	18 07	18 11	18 16	18 19
Hoxton	d	17 03	17 06	17 09	17 13	17 18	17 21	17 24		17 28	17 33	17 36	17 39	17 43	17 48	17 51	17 54	17 58		18 03	18 06	18 09	18 13	18 18	18 21
Haggerston	d	17 05	17 08	17 11	17 15	17 20	17 23	17 26		17 30	17 35	17 38	17 41	17 45	17 50	17 53	17 56	18 00		18 05	18 08	18 11	18 15	18 20	18 23
Dalston Junction	a	17 09	17 10	17 14	17 17	17 24	17 25	17 29		17 32	17 39	17 40	17 44	17 47	17 54	17 55	17 59	18 02		18 09	18 10	18 14	18 17	18 24	18 25
Canonbury	a		17 13		17 20		17 28			17 35		17 43		17 50		17 58		18 05			18 13		18 20		18 28
Highbury & Islington	a		17 18		17 25		17 33			17 40		17 48		17 55		18 03		18 10			18 18		18 25		18 33

Table 178R

Saturdays

14 December to 17 May

Clapham Junction and West Croydon, Crystal Palace, New Cross - Highbury & Islington

Network Diagram - see first Page of Table 173

		LO	LO	LO	LO	LO	LO	LO	LO	LO	LO	LO	LO	LO	LO	LO	LO	LO	LO	LO	LO	LO
Clapham Junction	d				17 59				18 14				18 29				18 44				18 59	
Wandsworth Road	d				18 05				18 20				18 35				18 50				19 05	
Clapham High Street ⊖	d				18 07				18 22				18 37				18 52				19 07	
Denmark Hill 4	d				18 12				18 27				18 42				18 57				19 12	
Peckham Rye 4	d				18 14				18 29				18 44				18 59				19 14	
Queens Rd Peckham	d				18 17				18 32				18 47				19 02				19 17	
West Croydon 4	d			17 52				18 09				18 22				18 39				18 52		
Norwood Junction 2	d			17 58				18 13				18 28				18 43				18 58		
Anerley	d			18 01				18 16				18 31				18 46				19 01		
Penge West	d			18 03				18 18				18 33				18 48				19 03		
Crystal Palace 4	d		17 58				18 13				18 28				18 43				18 58			
Sydenham	d		18 01	18 06			18 16	18 21			18 31	18 36			18 46	18 51			19 01	19 06		
Forest Hill 4	d		18 04	18 08			18 19	18 23			18 34	18 38			18 49	18 53			19 04	19 08		
Honor Oak Park	d		18 06	18 11			18 21	18 26			18 36	18 41			18 51	18 56			19 06	19 11		
Brockley	d		18 09	18 13			18 24	18 28			18 39	18 43			18 54	18 58			19 09	19 13		
New Cross Gate	d		18 11	18 16			18 26	18 31			18 41	18 46			18 56	19 01			19 11	19 16		
New Cross 4	d	18 07				18 22				18 37				18 52				19 07				19 22
Surrey Quays	d	18 11	18 15	18 20	18 23	18 26	18 30	18 35	18 38	18 41	18 45	18 50	18 53	18 56	19 00	19 05	19 08	19 11	19 15	19 20	19 23	19 26
Canada Water	d	18 13	18 17	18 22	18 25	18 28	18 32	18 37	18 40	18 43	18 47	18 52	18 55	18 58	19 02	19 07	19 10	19 13	19 17	19 22	19 25	19 28
Rotherhithe	d	18 14	18 18	18 23	18 26	18 29	18 33	18 38	18 41	18 44	18 48	18 53	18 56	18 59	19 03	19 08	19 11	19 14	19 18	19 23	19 26	19 29
Wapping	d	18 16	18 20	18 25	18 28	18 31	18 35	18 40	18 43	18 46	18 50	18 55	18 58	19 01	19 05	19 10	19 13	19 16	19 20	19 25	19 28	19 31
Shadwell	d	18 18	18 22	18 27	18 30	18 33	18 37	18 42	18 45	18 48	18 52	18 57	19 00	19 03	19 07	19 12	19 15	19 18	19 22	19 27	19 30	19 33
Whitechapel	d	18 20	18 24	18 29	18 32	18 35	18 39	18 44	18 47	18 50	18 54	18 59	19 02	19 05	19 09	19 14	19 17	19 20	19 24	19 29	19 32	19 35
Shoreditch High Street	d	18 22	18 26	18 31	18 34	18 37	18 41	18 46	18 49	18 52	18 56	19 01	19 04	19 07	19 11	19 16	19 19	19 22	19 26	19 31	19 34	19 37
Hoxton	d	18 24	18 28	18 33	18 36	18 39	18 43	18 48	18 51	18 54	18 58	19 03	19 06	19 09	19 13	19 18	19 21	19 24	19 28	19 33	19 36	19 39
Haggerston	d	18 26	18 30	18 35	18 38	18 41	18 45	18 50	18 53	18 56	19 00	19 05	19 08	19 11	19 15	19 20	19 23	19 26	19 30	19 35	19 38	19 41
Dalston Junction	a	18 29	18 32	18 39	18 40	18 44	18 47	18 54	18 55	18 59	19 02	19 09	19 10	19 14	19 17	19 24	19 25	19 29	19 32	19 39	19 40	19 44
Canonbury	a		18 35		18 43		18 50		18 58		19 05		19 13		19 20		19 28		19 35		19 43	
Highbury & Islington	a		18 40		18 48		18 55		19 03		19 10		19 18		19 25		19 33		19 40		19 48	

		LO	LO	LO	LO	LO	LO	LO	LO	LO	LO	LO	LO	LO	LO	LO	LO	LO	LO	LO	LO	LO	LO
Clapham Junction	d			19 14				19 29				19 44				19 59				20 14			
Wandsworth Road	d			19 20				19 35				19 50				20 05				20 20			
Clapham High Street ⊖	d			19 22				19 37				19 52				20 07				20 22			
Denmark Hill 4	d			19 27				19 42				19 57				20 12				20 27			
Peckham Rye 4	d			19 29				19 44				19 59				20 14				20 29			
Queens Rd Peckham	d			19 32				19 47				20 02				20 17				20 32			
West Croydon 4	d		19 09				19 22				19 39				19 52				20 09				20 22
Norwood Junction 2	d		19 13				19 28				19 43				19 58				20 13				20 28
Anerley	d		19 16				19 31				19 46				20 01				20 16				20 31
Penge West	d		19 18				19 33				19 48				20 03				20 18				20 33
Crystal Palace 4	d	19 13				19 28				19 43				19 58				20 13				20 28	
Sydenham	d	19 16	19 21			19 31	19 36			19 46	19 51			20 01	20 06			20 16	20 21			20 31	20 36
Forest Hill 4	d	19 19	19 23			19 34	19 38			19 49	19 53			20 04	20 08			20 19	20 23			20 34	20 38
Honor Oak Park	d	19 21	19 26			19 36	19 41			19 51	19 56			20 06	20 11			20 21	20 26			20 36	20 41
Brockley	d	19 24	19 28			19 39	19 43			19 54	19 58			20 09	20 13			20 24	20 28			20 39	20 43
New Cross Gate	d	19 26	19 31			19 41	19 46			19 56	20 01			20 11	20 16			20 26	20 31			20 41	20 46
New Cross 4	d				19 37				19 52				20 07				20 22				20 37		
Surrey Quays	d	19 30	19 35	19 38	19 41	19 45	19 50	19 53	19 56	20 00	20 05	20 08	20 11	20 15	20 20	20 23	20 26	20 30	20 35	20 38	20 41	20 45	20 50
Canada Water	d	19 32	19 37	19 40	19 43	19 47	19 52	19 55	19 58	20 02	20 07	20 10	20 13	20 17	20 22	20 25	20 28	20 32	20 37	20 40	20 43	20 47	20 52
Rotherhithe	d	19 33	19 38	19 41	19 44	19 48	19 53	19 56	19 59	20 03	20 08	20 11	20 14	20 18	20 23	20 26	20 29	20 33	20 38	20 41	20 44	20 48	20 53
Wapping	d	19 35	19 40	19 43	19 46	19 50	19 55	19 58	20 01	20 05	20 10	20 13	20 16	20 20	20 25	20 28	20 31	20 35	20 40	20 43	20 46	20 50	20 55
Shadwell	d	19 37	19 42	19 45	19 48	19 52	19 57	20 00	20 03	20 07	20 12	20 15	20 18	20 22	20 27	20 30	20 33	20 37	20 42	20 45	20 48	20 52	20 57
Whitechapel	d	19 39	19 44	19 47	19 50	19 54	19 59	20 02	20 05	20 09	20 14	20 17	20 20	20 24	20 29	20 32	20 35	20 39	20 44	20 47	20 50	20 54	20 59
Shoreditch High Street	d	19 41	19 46	19 49	19 52	19 56	20 01	20 04	20 07	20 11	20 16	20 19	20 22	20 26	20 31	20 34	20 37	20 41	20 46	20 49	20 52	20 56	21 01
Hoxton	d	19 43	19 48	19 51	19 54	19 58	20 03	20 06	20 09	20 13	20 18	20 21	20 24	20 28	20 33	20 36	20 39	20 43	20 48	20 51	20 54	20 58	21 03
Haggerston	d	19 45	19 50	19 53	19 56	20 00	20 05	20 08	20 11	20 15	20 20	20 23	20 26	20 30	20 35	20 38	20 41	20 45	20 50	20 53	20 56	21 00	21 05
Dalston Junction	a	19 47	19 54	19 55	19 59	20 02	20 09	20 10	20 14	20 17	20 24	20 25	20 29	20 32	20 39	20 40	20 44	20 47	20 54	20 55	20 59	21 02	21 09
Canonbury	a	19 50		19 58		20 05		20 13		20 20		20 28		20 35		20 43		20 50		20 58		21 05	
Highbury & Islington	a	19 55		20 03		20 10		20 18		20 25		20 33		20 40		20 48		20 55		21 03		21 10	

		LO	LO	LO	LO	LO	LO	LO	LO	LO	LO	LO	LO	LO	LO	LO	LO	LO	LO	LO	LO	LO	LO
Clapham Junction	d	20 29				20 44				20 59				21 14				21 29				21 44	
Wandsworth Road	d	20 35				20 50				21 05				21 20				21 35				21 50	
Clapham High Street ⊖	d	20 37				20 52				21 07				21 22				21 37				21 52	
Denmark Hill 4	d	20 42				20 57				21 12				21 27				21 42				21 57	
Peckham Rye 4	d	20 44				20 59				21 14				21 29				21 44				21 59	
Queens Rd Peckham	d	20 47				21 02				21 17				21 32				21 47				22 02	
West Croydon 4	d				20 39				20 52				21 09				21 22				21 39		
Norwood Junction 2	d				20 43				20 58				21 13				21 28				21 43		
Anerley	d				20 46				21 01				21 16				21 31				21 46		
Penge West	d				20 48				21 03				21 18				21 33				21 48		
Crystal Palace 4	d			20 43				20 58				21 13				21 28				21 43			
Sydenham	d			20 46	20 51			21 01	21 06			21 16	21 21			21 31	21 36			21 46	21 51		
Forest Hill 4	d			20 49	20 53			21 04	21 08			21 19	21 23			21 34	21 38			21 49	21 53		
Honor Oak Park	d			20 51	20 56			21 06	21 11			21 21	21 26			21 36	21 41			21 51	21 56		
Brockley	d			20 54	20 58			21 09	21 13			21 24	21 28			21 39	21 43			21 54	21 58		
New Cross Gate	d			20 56	21 01			21 11	21 16			21 26	21 31			21 41	21 46			21 56	22 01		
New Cross 4	d		20 52				21 07				21 22				21 37				21 52				22 07
Surrey Quays	d	20 53	20 56	21 00	21 05	21 08	21 11	21 15	21 20	21 23	21 26	21 30	21 35	21 38	21 41	21 45	21 50	21 53	21 56	22 00	22 05	22 08	22 11
Canada Water	d	20 55	20 58	21 02	21 07	21 10	21 13	21 17	21 22	21 25	21 28	21 32	21 37	21 40	21 43	21 47	21 52	21 55	21 58	22 02	22 07	22 10	22 13
Rotherhithe	d	20 56	20 59	21 03	21 08	21 11	21 14	21 18	21 23	21 26	21 29	21 33	21 38	21 41	21 44	21 48	21 53	21 56	21 59	22 03	22 08	22 11	22 14
Wapping	d	20 58	21 01	21 05	21 10	21 13	21 16	21 20	21 25	21 28	21 31	21 35	21 40	21 43	21 46	21 50	21 55	21 58	22 01	22 05	22 10	22 13	22 16
Shadwell	d	21 00	21 03	21 07	21 12	21 15	21 18	21 22	21 27	21 30	21 33	21 37	21 42	21 45	21 48	21 52	21 57	22 00	22 03	22 07	22 12	22 15	22 18
Whitechapel	d	21 02	21 05	21 09	21 14	21 17	21 20	21 24	21 29	21 32	21 35	21 39	21 44	21 47	21 50	21 54	21 59	22 02	22 05	22 09	22 14	22 17	22 20
Shoreditch High Street	d	21 04	21 07	21 11	21 16	21 19	21 22	21 26	21 31	21 34	21 37	21 41	21 46	21 49	21 52	21 56	22 01	22 04	22 07	22 11	22 16	22 19	22 22
Hoxton	d	21 06	21 09	21 13	21 18	21 21	21 24	21 28	21 33	21 36	21 39	21 43	21 48	21 51	21 54	21 58	22 03	22 06	22 09	22 13	22 18	22 23	22 26
Haggerston	d	21 08	21 11	21 15	21 20	21 23	21 26	21 30	21 35	21 38	21 41	21 45	21 50	21 53	21 56	22 00	22 05	22 08	22 11	22 15	22 22	22 25	22 28
Dalston Junction	a	21 10	21 14	21 17	21 24	21 25	21 29	21 32	21 39	21 40	21 44	21 47	21 54	21 55	21 59	22 02	22 09	22 10	22 14	22 17	22 26	22 27	22 30
Canonbury	a	21 13		21 20		21 28		21 35		21 43		21 50		21 58		22 05		22 13		22 20			22 33
Highbury & Islington	a	21 18		21 25		21 33		21 40		21 48		21 55		22 03		22 10		22 18		22 25			22 35

Table 178R

Saturdays

14 December to 17 May

Clapham Junction and West Croydon, Crystal Palace, New Cross - Highbury & Islington

Network Diagram - see first Page of Table 173

		LO		LO	LO	LO	LO	LO	LO	LO	LO	LO		LO	LO	LO	LO	LO	LO	LO	LO	LO		LO	
Clapham Junction	d				21 59			22 14							22 44				23 14					23 44	
Wandsworth Road	d				22 05			22 20							22 50				23 20					23 50	
Clapham High Street ⊖	d				22 07			22 22							22 52				23 22					23 52	
Denmark Hill 4	d				22 12			22 27							22 57				23 27					23 57	
Peckham Rye 4	d				22 14			22 29							22 59				23 29					23 59	
Queens Rd Peckham	d				22 17			22 32							23 02				23 32					00 02	
West Croydon 4	d			21 52			22 09				22 22			22 39			22 52				23 22				
Norwood Junction 2	d			21 58			22 13				22 28			22 43			22 58				23 28				
Anerley	d			22 01			22 16				22 31			22 46			23 01				23 31				
Penge West	d			22 03			22 18				22 33			22 48			23 03				23 33				
Crystal Palace 4	d	21 58				22 13				22 28		22 43						23 13				23 43			
Sydenham	d	22 01		22 06		22 16	22 21			22 31	22 36	22 46		22 51			23 06	23 16			23 36	23 46			
Forest Hill 4	d	22 04		22 08		22 19	22 23			22 34	22 38	22 49		22 53			23 08	23 19			23 38	23 49			
Honor Oak Park	d	22 06		22 11		22 21	22 26			22 36	22 41	22 51		22 56			23 11	23 21			23 41	23 51			
Brockley	d	22 09		22 13		22 24	22 28			22 39	22 43	22 54		22 58			23 13	23 24			23 43	23 54			
New Cross Gate	d	22 11		22 16		22 26	22 31			22 41	22 46	22 56		23 01			23 16	23 26			23 46	23 56			
New Cross 4	d								22 37							23 07				23 37					
Surrey Quays	d	22 15		22 20	22 23	22 30	22 35	22 38	22 41	22 45	22 50	23 00		23 05	23 08	23 11	23 20	23 30	23 38	23 41	23 50	23 59		00 08	
Canada Water	d	22 17		22 22	22 25	22 32	22 37	22 40	22 43	22 47	22 52	23 02		23 07	23 10	23 13	23 22	23 32	23 40	23 43	23 52	00 02		00 10	
Rotherhithe	d	22 18		22 23	22 26	22 33	22 38	22 41	22 44	22 48	22 53	23 03		23 08	23 11	23 14	23 23	23 33	23 41	23 44	23 53	00 03		00 11	
Wapping	d	22 20		22 25	22 28	22 35	22 40	22 43	22 46	22 50	22 55	23 05		23 10	23 13	23 16	23 25	23 35	23 43	23 46	23 55	00 05		00 13	
Shadwell	d	22 22		22 27	22 30	22 37	22 42	22 45	22 48	22 52	22 57	23 07		23 12	23 15	23 18	23 27	23 37	23 45	23 48	23 57	00 07		00 15	
Whitechapel	d	22 24		22 29	22 32	22 39	22 44	22 47	22 50	22 54	22 59	23 09		23 14	23 17	23 20	23 29	23 39	23 47	23 50	23 59	00 09		00 17	
Shoreditch High Street	d	22 26		22 31	22 34	22 41	22 46	22 49	22 52	22 56	23 01	23 11		23 16	23 19	23 22	23 31	23 41	23 49	23 52	00 01	00 11		00 19	
Hoxton	d	22 28		22 33	22 36	22 43	22 48	22 51	22 54	22 58	23 03	23 13		23 18	23 21	23 24	23 33	23 43	23 51	23 54	00 03	00 13		00 21	
Haggerston	d	22 30		22 35	22 38	22 45	22 50	22 53	22 56	23 00	23 05	23 15		23 20	23 23	23 26	23 35	23 45	23 53	23 56	00 05	00 15		00 23	
Dalston Junction	a	22 32		22 39	22 40	22 47	22 52	22 55	22 59	23 02	23 09	23 17		23 22	23 25	23 29	23 39	23 47	23 55	23 59	00 09	00 17		00 25	
Canonbury	a	22 35			22 43		22 55		23 01	23 05				23 25	23 28			23 50	23 58			00 20		00 29	
Highbury & Islington	a	22 40			22 48		22 58		23 04	23 10				23 27	23 33			23 55	00 03			00 25		00 34	

Sundays

8 December to 11 May

		LO A	LO B	LO C	LO D	LO A	LO	LO	LO	LO	LO	LO	LO	LO	LO	LO	LO	LO	LO	LO	LO	LO	LO	LO	LO
Clapham Junction	d									07 20			07 50				08 20						08 50		
Wandsworth Road	d									07 25			07 55				08 25						08 55		
Clapham High Street ⊖	d									07 27			07 57				08 27						08 57		
Denmark Hill 4	d									07 32			08 02				08 32						09 02		
Peckham Rye 4	d									07 35			08 04				08 34						09 04		
Queens Rd Peckham	d			00 02	00 03					07 38			08 07				08 37						09 07		
West Croydon 4	d						06 42		07 12			07 42				08 12					08 42				
Norwood Junction 2	d						06 47		07 17			07 47				08 17					08 46				
Anerley	d						06 50		07 20			07 50				08 20					08 49				
Penge West	d						06 52		07 22			07 52				08 22					08 51				
Crystal Palace 4	d							07 07			07 37			08 07				08 37						09 07	
Sydenham	d						06 55	07 10	07 25		07 40	07 55		08 10		08 25		08 40			08 55			09 10	
Forest Hill 4	d						06 57	07 13	07 27		07 43	07 57		08 13		08 27		08 43			08 57			09 13	
Honor Oak Park	d						07 00	07 15	07 30		07 45	08 00		08 15		08 30		08 45			09 00			09 15	
Brockley	d						07 02	07 18	07 32		07 48	08 02		08 18		08 32		08 48			09 02			09 18	
New Cross Gate	d						07 05	07 20	07 35		07 50	08 05		08 20		08 35		08 50			09 05			09 20	
New Cross 4	d																		08 55			09 10			09 25
Surrey Quays	d			00 08	00 08		07 09	07 24	07 39	07 47	07 54	08 10	08 17	08 24	08 32	08 39	08 47	08 54	08 59	09 03	09 09	09 14	09 17	09 24	09 29
Canada Water	d		00 02	00 10	00 10		07 11	07 26	07 41	07 49	07 56	08 12	08 19	08 26	08 34	08 41	08 49	08 56	09 01	09 05	09 11	09 16	09 19	09 26	09 31
Rotherhithe	d		00 03	00 11	00 11		07 12	07 27	07 42	07 50	07 57	08 13	08 20	08 27	08 35	08 42	08 50	08 57	09 02	09 06	09 12	09 17	09 20	09 27	09 32
Wapping	d		00 05	00 13	00 13		07 14	07 29	07 44	07 52	07 59	08 15	08 22	08 29	08 37	08 44	08 52	08 59	09 04	09 08	09 14	09 19	09 22	09 29	09 34
Shadwell	d		00 07	00 15	00 15		07 16	07 31	07 46	07 54	08 01	08 17	08 24	08 31	08 39	08 46	08 54	09 01	09 06	09 10	09 16	09 21	09 24	09 31	09 36
Whitechapel	d		00 09	00 17	00 17		07 18	07 33	07 48	07 56	08 03	08 19	08 26	08 33	08 41	08 48	08 56	09 03	09 08	09 12	09 18	09 23	09 26	09 33	09 38
Shoreditch High Street	d	00 01	00 11	00 19	00 19		07 20	07 35	07 50	07 58	08 05	08 21	08 28	08 35	08 43	08 50	08 58	09 05	09 10	09 14	09 20	09 25	09 28	09 35	09 40
Hoxton	d	00 03	00 13	00 21	00 21		07 22	07 37	07 52	08 00	08 07	08 23	08 30	08 37	08 45	08 52	09 00	09 07	09 12	09 16	09 22	09 27	09 30	09 37	09 42
Haggerston	d	00 05	00 15	00 23	00 23		07 24	07 39	07 54	08 02	08 09	08 25	08 32	08 39	08 47	08 54	09 02	09 09	09 14	09 18	09 24	09 29	09 32	09 39	09 44
Dalston Junction	a	00 09	00 17	00 25	00 25		07 26	07 41	07 56	08 04	08 11	08 28	08 34	08 41	08 49	08 56	09 04	09 11	09 16	09 20	09 26	09 32	09 34	09 41	09 46
Canonbury	a		00 20	00 29	00 29		07 29	07 44	07 59	08 08	08 14	08 32	08 37	08 44	08 52	08 59	09 07	09 14		09 23	09 29		09 37	09 44	
Highbury & Islington	a		00 25	00 34	00 34		07 32	07 49	08 02	08 13	08 19	08 34	08 43	08 51	08 55	09 02	09 13	09 19		09 26	09 32		09 43	09 49	

A From West Croydon
B From Crystal Palace
C From Clapham Junction
D From Clapham Junction

Table 178R

Sundays

8 December to 11 May

Clapham Junction and West Croydon, Crystal Palace, New Cross - Highbury & Islington

Network Diagram - see first Page of Table 173

		LO		LO	LO	LO	LO	LO	LO	LO	LO	LO		LO	LO	LO	LO	LO	LO	LO	LO	LO		LO	LO
Clapham Junction	d	09 05				09 20			09 35			09 50				10 05			10 20			10 35			
Wandsworth Road	d	09 10				09 25			09 40			09 55				10 10			10 25			10 40			
Clapham High Street ⊖	d	09 12				09 27			09 42			09 57				10 12			10 27			10 42			
Denmark Hill 4	d	09 17				09 32			09 47			10 02				10 17			10 32			10 47			
Peckham Rye 4	d	09 19				09 34			09 49			10 04				10 19			10 34			10 49			
Queens Rd Peckham	d	09 22				09 37			09 52			10 07				10 22			10 37			10 52			
West Croydon 4	d			09 12						09 42							10 12							10 42	
Norwood Junction 2	d			09 17						09 47							10 17							10 47	
Anerley	d			09 20						09 50							10 20							10 50	
Penge West	d			09 22						09 52							10 22							10 52	
Crystal Palace 4	d						09 37							10 07						10 37					
Sydenham	d			09 25			09 40			09 55				10 10			10 25			10 40				10 55	
Forest Hill 4	d			09 27			09 43			09 57				10 13			10 27			10 43				10 57	
Honor Oak Park	d			09 30			09 45			10 00				10 15			10 30			10 45				11 00	
Brockley	d			09 32			09 48			10 02				10 18			10 32			10 48				11 02	
New Cross Gate	d			09 35			09 50			10 05				10 20			10 35			10 50				11 05	
New Cross 4	d				09 40			09 55			10 10				10 25			10 40			10 55				11 10
Surrey Quays	d	09 32		09 39	09 44	09 47	09 54	09 59	10 02	10 09	10 14	10 17		10 24	10 29	10 32	10 39	10 44	10 47	10 54	10 59	11 02		11 09	11 14
Canada Water	d	09 34		09 41	09 46	09 49	09 56	10 01	10 04	10 11	10 16	10 19		10 26	10 31	10 34	10 41	10 46	10 49	10 56	11 01	11 04		11 11	11 16
Rotherhithe	d	09 35		09 42	09 47	09 50	09 57	10 02	10 05	10 12	10 17	10 20		10 27	10 32	10 35	10 42	10 47	10 50	10 57	11 02	11 05		11 12	11 17
Wapping	d	09 37		09 44	09 49	09 52	09 59	10 04	10 07	10 14	10 19	10 22		10 29	10 34	10 37	10 44	10 49	10 52	10 59	11 04	11 07		11 14	11 19
Shadwell	d	09 39		09 46	09 51	09 54	10 01	10 06	10 09	10 16	10 21	10 24		10 31	10 36	10 39	10 46	10 51	10 54	11 01	11 06	11 09		11 16	11 21
Whitechapel	d	09 41		09 48	09 53	09 56	10 03	10 08	10 11	10 18	10 23	10 26		10 33	10 38	10 41	10 48	10 53	10 56	11 03	11 08	11 11		11 18	11 23
Shoreditch High Street	d	09 43		09 50	09 55	09 58	10 05	10 10	10 13	10 20	10 25	10 28		10 35	10 40	10 43	10 50	10 55	10 58	11 05	11 10	11 13		11 20	11 25
Hoxton	d	09 45		09 52	09 57	10 00	10 07	10 12	10 15	10 22	10 27	10 30		10 37	10 42	10 45	10 52	10 57	11 00	11 07	11 12	11 15		11 22	11 27
Haggerston	d	09 47		09 54	09 59	10 02	10 09	10 14	10 17	10 24	10 29	10 32		10 39	10 44	10 47	10 54	10 59	11 02	11 09	11 14	11 17		11 24	11 29
Dalston Junction	a	09 49		09 56	10 02	10 04	10 11	10 16	10 19	10 26	10 32	10 34		10 41	10 46	10 49	10 56	11 02	11 04	11 11	11 16	11 19		11 26	11 32
Canonbury	a	09 52		09 59		10 07	10 14		10 22	10 29		10 37		10 44		10 52	10 59		11 07	11 14		11 22		11 29	
Highbury & Islington	a	09 58		10 02		10 13	10 19		10 28	10 32		10 40		10 49		10 55	11 02		11 13	11 19		11 28		11 32	

		LO	LO	LO	LO	LO	LO	LO		LO	LO	LO	LO	LO	LO	LO	LO	LO		LO	LO	LO	LO	LO	LO
Clapham Junction	d	10 50				11 05					11 20				11 35					11 50				12 05	
Wandsworth Road	d	10 55				11 10					11 25				11 40					11 55				12 10	
Clapham High Street ⊖	d	10 57				11 12					11 27				11 42					11 57				12 12	
Denmark Hill 4	d	11 02				11 17					11 32				11 47					12 02				12 17	
Peckham Rye 4	d	11 04				11 19					11 34				11 49					12 04				12 19	
Queens Rd Peckham	d	11 07				11 22					11 37				11 52					12 07				12 22	
West Croydon 4	d							11 12									11 42								
Norwood Junction 2	d							11 17									11 47								
Anerley	d							11 20									11 50								
Penge West	d							11 22									11 52								
Crystal Palace 4	d			11 07									11 37									12 07			12 16
Sydenham	d			11 10				11 25					11 40				11 55					12 10			12 19
Forest Hill 4	d			11 13				11 27					11 43				11 57					12 13			12 22
Honor Oak Park	d			11 15				11 30					11 45				12 00					12 15			12 24
Brockley	d			11 18				11 32					11 48				12 02					12 18			12 27
New Cross Gate	d			11 20				11 35					11 50				12 05					12 20			12 29
New Cross 4	d				11 25					11 40				11 55				12 10					12 25		
Surrey Quays	d	11 17	11 21	11 24	11 29	11 32	11 35	11 39		11 44	11 47	11 51	11 54	11 59	12 02	12 05	12 09	12 14		12 17	12 21	12 24	12 29	12 32	12 35
Canada Water	d	11 19	11 23	11 26	11 31	11 34	11 37	11 41		11 46	11 49	11 53	11 56	12 01	12 04	12 07	12 11	12 16		12 19	12 23	12 26	12 31	12 34	12 37
Rotherhithe	d	11 20	11 24	11 27	11 32	11 35	11 38	11 42		11 47	11 50	11 54	11 57	12 02	12 05	12 08	12 12	12 17		12 20	12 24	12 27	12 32	12 35	12 39
Wapping	d	11 22	11 26	11 29	11 34	11 37	11 40	11 44		11 49	11 52	11 56	11 59	12 04	12 07	12 10	12 14	12 19		12 22	12 26	12 29	12 34	12 37	12 40
Shadwell	d	11 24	11 28	11 31	11 36	11 39	11 42	11 46		11 51	11 54	11 58	12 01	12 06	12 09	12 12	12 16	12 21		12 24	12 28	12 31	12 36	12 39	12 42
Whitechapel	d	11 26	11 30	11 33	11 38	11 41	11 44	11 48		11 53	11 56	12 00	12 03	12 08	12 11	12 14	12 18	12 23		12 26	12 30	12 33	12 38	12 41	12 45
Shoreditch High Street	d	11 28	11 32	11 35	11 40	11 43	11 46	11 50		11 55	11 58	12 02	12 05	12 10	12 13	12 16	12 20	12 25		12 28	12 32	12 35	12 40	12 43	12 47
Hoxton	d	11 30	11 34	11 37	11 42	11 45	11 48	11 52		11 57	12 00	12 04	12 07	12 12	12 15	12 18	12 22	12 27		12 30	12 34	12 37	12 42	12 45	12 49
Haggerston	d	11 32	11 36	11 39	11 44	11 47	11 50	11 54		11 59	12 02	12 06	12 09	12 14	12 17	12 20	12 24	12 29		12 32	12 36	12 39	12 44	12 47	12 51
Dalston Junction	a	11 34	11 38	11 41	11 48	11 49	11 52	11 57		12 03	12 04	12 08	12 11	12 18	12 19	12 22	12 26	12 33		12 34	12 38	12 41	12 48	12 49	12 53
Canonbury	a	11 37		11 44		11 52	11 55				12 07		12 14		12 22		12 29			12 37		12 44		12 52	
Highbury & Islington	a	11 43		11 49		11 58	12 00				12 13		12 19		12 28		12 32			12 43		12 49		12 58	

		LO	LO	LO		LO	LO	LO	LO	LO	LO	LO	LO	LO		LO	LO	LO	LO	LO	LO	LO	LO	LO	
Clapham Junction	d		12 17					12 32				12 47					13 02				13 17				
Wandsworth Road	d		12 23					12 38				12 53					13 08				13 23				
Clapham High Street ⊖	d		12 25					12 40				12 55					13 10				13 25				
Denmark Hill 4	d		12 30					12 45				13 00					13 15				13 30				
Peckham Rye 4	d		12 32					12 47				13 02					13 17				13 32				
Queens Rd Peckham	d		12 35					12 50				13 05					13 20				13 35				
West Croydon 4	d	12 12									12 42					12 57				13 12				13 27	
Norwood Junction 2	d	12 16									12 46					13 01				13 16				13 31	
Anerley	d	12 19									12 49					13 04				13 19				13 34	
Penge West	d	12 21									12 51					13 06				13 21				13 36	
Crystal Palace 4	d					12 31				12 46				13 01					13 16				13 31		
Sydenham	d	12 24				12 34				12 49	12 54			13 04		13 09			13 19	13 24			13 34	13 39	
Forest Hill 4	d	12 26				12 37				12 52	12 56			13 07		13 11			13 22	13 26			13 37	13 41	
Honor Oak Park	d	12 29				12 39				12 54	12 59			13 09		13 14			13 24	13 29			13 39	13 44	
Brockley	d	12 31				12 42				12 57	13 01			13 12		13 16			13 27	13 31			13 42	13 46	
New Cross Gate	d	12 34				12 44				12 59	13 04			13 14		13 19			13 29	13 34			13 44	13 49	
New Cross 4	d			12 40					12 55				13 10					13 25				13 40			
Surrey Quays	d	12 38	12 41	12 44		12 48	12 53	12 56	12 59	13 03	13 08	13 11	13 14	13 18		13 23	13 26	13 29	13 33	13 38	13 41	13 44	13 48	13 53	
Canada Water	d	12 40	12 43	12 46		12 50	12 55	12 58	13 01	13 05	13 10	13 13	13 16	13 20		13 25	13 28	13 31	13 35	13 40	13 43	13 46	13 50	13 55	
Rotherhithe	d	12 41	12 44	12 47		12 51	12 56	12 59	13 02	13 06	13 11	13 14	13 17	13 21		13 26	13 29	13 32	13 36	13 41	13 44	13 47	13 51	13 56	
Wapping	d	12 43	12 46	12 49		12 53	12 58	13 01	13 04	13 08	13 13	13 16	13 19	13 23		13 28	13 31	13 34	13 38	13 43	13 46	13 49	13 53	13 58	
Shadwell	d	12 45	12 48	12 51		12 55	13 00	13 03	13 06	13 10	13 15	13 18	13 21	13 25		13 30	13 33	13 36	13 40	13 45	13 48	13 51	13 55	14 00	
Whitechapel	d	12 47	12 50	12 53		12 57	13 02	13 05	13 08	13 12	13 17	13 20	13 23	13 27		13 32	13 35	13 38	13 42	13 47	13 50	13 53	13 57	14 02	
Shoreditch High Street	d	12 49	12 52	12 55		12 59	13 04	13 07	13 10	13 14	13 19	13 22	13 25	13 29		13 34	13 37	13 40	13 44	13 49	13 52	13 55	13 59	14 04	
Hoxton	d	12 51	12 54	12 57		13 01	13 06	13 09	13 12	13 16	13 21	13 24	13 27	13 31		13 36	13 39	13 42	13 46	13 51	13 54	13 57	14 01	14 06	
Haggerston	d	12 53	12 56	12 59		13 03	13 08	13 11	13 14	13 18	13 23	13 26	13 29	13 33		13 38	13 41	13 44	13 48	13 53	13 56	13 59	14 03	14 08	
Dalston Junction	a	12 57	12 58	13 03		13 05	13 12	13 13	13 18	13 20	13 27	13 28	13 33	13 35		13 42	13 43	13 48	13 50	13 57	13 58	14 03	14 05	14 12	
Canonbury	a		13 01			13 08		13 16		13 23		13 31		13 38			13 46		13 53		14 01		14 08		
Highbury & Islington	a		13 07			13 13		13 22		13 28		13 37		13 43			13 52		13 58		14 07		14 13		

Table 178R

Sundays

8 December to 11 May

Clapham Junction and West Croydon, Crystal Palace, New Cross - Highbury & Islington

Network Diagram - see first Page of Table 173

		LO	LO	LO	LO	LO	LO	LO	LO	LO		LO	LO	LO	LO	LO	LO	LO	LO	LO		LO	LO	LO	LO
Clapham Junction	d	13 32				13 47				14 02					14 17				14 32					14 47	
Wandsworth Road	d	13 38				13 53				14 08					14 23				14 38					14 53	
Clapham High Street ⊖	d	13 40				13 55				14 10					14 25				14 40					14 55	
Denmark Hill 4	d	13 45				14 00				14 15					14 30				14 45					15 00	
Peckham Rye 4	d	13 47				14 02				14 17					14 32				14 47					15 02	
Queens Rd Peckham	d	13 50				14 05				14 20					14 35				14 50					15 05	
West Croydon 4	d				13 42				13 57					14 12				14 27					14 42		
Norwood Junction 2	d				13 46				14 01					14 16				14 31					14 46		
Anerley	d				13 49				14 04					14 19				14 34					14 49		
Penge West	d				13 51				14 06					14 21				14 36					14 51		
Crystal Palace 4	d			13 46				14 01					14 16				14 31					14 46			
Sydenham	d			13 49	13 54			14 04	14 09				14 19	14 24			14 34	14 39				14 49	14 54		
Forest Hill 4	d			13 52	13 56			14 07	14 11				14 22	14 26			14 37	14 41				14 52	14 56		
Honor Oak Park	d			13 54	13 59			14 09	14 14				14 24	14 29			14 39	14 44				14 54	14 59		
Brockley	d			13 57	14 01			14 12	14 16				14 27	14 31			14 42	14 46				14 57	15 01		
New Cross Gate	d			13 59	14 04			14 14	14 19				14 29	14 34			14 44	14 49				14 59	15 04		
New Cross 4	d		13 55				14 10					14 25				14 40				14 55					15 10
Surrey Quays	d	13 56	13 59	14 03	14 08	14 11	14 14	14 18	14 23	14 26		14 29	14 33	14 38	14 41	14 44	14 48	14 53	14 56	14 59		15 03	15 08	15 11	15 14
Canada Water	d	13 58	14 01	14 05	14 10	14 13	14 16	14 20	14 25	14 28		14 31	14 35	14 40	14 43	14 46	14 50	14 55	14 58	15 01		15 05	15 10	15 13	15 16
Rotherhithe	d	13 59	14 02	14 06	14 11	14 14	14 17	14 21	14 26	14 29		14 32	14 36	14 41	14 44	14 47	14 51	14 56	14 59	15 02		15 06	15 11	15 14	15 17
Wapping	d	14 01	14 04	14 08	14 13	14 16	14 19	14 23	14 28	14 31		14 34	14 38	14 43	14 46	14 49	14 53	14 58	15 01	15 04		15 08	15 13	15 16	15 19
Shadwell	d	14 03	14 06	14 10	14 15	14 18	14 21	14 25	14 30	14 33		14 36	14 40	14 45	14 48	14 51	14 55	15 00	15 03	15 06		15 10	15 15	15 18	15 21
Whitechapel	d	14 05	14 08	14 12	14 17	14 20	14 23	14 27	14 32	14 35		14 38	14 42	14 47	14 50	14 53	14 57	15 02	15 05	15 08		15 12	15 17	15 20	15 23
Shoreditch High Street	d	14 07	14 10	14 14	14 19	14 22	14 25	14 29	14 34	14 37		14 40	14 44	14 49	14 52	14 55	14 59	15 04	15 07	15 10		15 14	15 19	15 22	15 25
Hoxton	d	14 09	14 12	14 16	14 21	14 24	14 27	14 31	14 36	14 39		14 42	14 46	14 51	14 54	14 57	15 01	15 06	15 09	15 12		15 16	15 21	15 24	15 27
Haggerston	d	14 11	14 14	14 18	14 23	14 26	14 29	14 33	14 38	14 41		14 44	14 48	14 53	14 56	14 59	15 03	15 08	15 11	15 14		15 18	15 23	15 26	15 29
Dalston Junction	a	14 13	14 18	14 20	14 27	14 28	14 33	14 35	14 42	14 43		14 48	14 50	14 57	14 58	15 03	15 05	15 12	15 13	15 18		15 20	15 27	15 28	15 33
Canonbury	a	14 16		14 23		14 31		14 38		14 46			14 53		15 01		15 08		15 16			15 23		15 31	
Highbury & Islington	a	14 19		14 28		14 37		14 43		14 52			14 58		15 07		15 13		15 22			15 28		15 37	

		LO	LO	LO	LO	LO		LO	LO	LO	LO	LO	LO	LO	LO	LO		LO	LO	LO	LO	LO	LO	LO	LO
Clapham Junction	d			15 02					15 17				15 32					15 47				16 02			
Wandsworth Road	d			15 08					15 23				15 38					15 53				16 08			
Clapham High Street ⊖	d			15 10					15 25				15 40					15 55				16 10			
Denmark Hill 4	d			15 15					15 30				15 45					16 00				16 15			
Peckham Rye 4	d			15 17					15 32				15 47					16 02				16 17			
Queens Rd Peckham	d			15 20					15 35				15 50					16 05				16 20			
West Croydon 4	d		14 57					15 12				15 27				15 42					15 57				16 12
Norwood Junction 2	d		15 01					15 16				15 31				15 46					16 01				16 16
Anerley	d		15 04					15 19				15 34				15 49					16 04				16 19
Penge West	d		15 06					15 21				15 36				15 51					16 06				16 21
Crystal Palace 4	d	15 01				15 16					15 31				15 46					16 01				16 16	
Sydenham	d	15 04	15 09			15 19		15 24			15 34	15 39			15 49	15 54				16 04	16 09			16 19	16 24
Forest Hill 4	d	15 07	15 11			15 22		15 26			15 37	15 41			15 52	15 56				16 07	16 11			16 22	16 26
Honor Oak Park	d	15 09	15 14			15 24		15 29			15 39	15 44			15 54	15 59				16 09	16 14			16 24	16 29
Brockley	d	15 12	15 16			15 27		15 31			15 42	15 46			15 57	16 01				16 12	16 16			16 27	16 31
New Cross Gate	d	15 14	15 19			15 29		15 34			15 44	15 49			15 59	16 04				16 14	16 19			16 29	16 34
New Cross 4	d				15 25					15 40				15 55					16 10				16 25		
Surrey Quays	d	15 18	15 23	15 26	15 29	15 33		15 38	15 41	15 44	15 48	15 53	15 56	15 59	16 03	16 08		16 11	16 14	16 18	16 23	16 26	16 29	16 33	16 38
Canada Water	d	15 20	15 25	15 28	15 31	15 35		15 40	15 43	15 46	15 50	15 55	15 58	16 01	16 05	16 10		16 13	16 16	16 20	16 25	16 28	16 31	16 35	16 40
Rotherhithe	d	15 21	15 26	15 29	15 32	15 36		15 41	15 44	15 47	15 51	15 56	15 59	16 02	16 06	16 11		16 14	16 17	16 21	16 26	16 29	16 32	16 36	16 41
Wapping	d	15 23	15 28	15 31	15 34	15 38		15 43	15 46	15 49	15 53	15 58	16 01	16 04	16 08	16 13		16 16	16 19	16 23	16 28	16 31	16 34	16 38	16 43
Shadwell	d	15 25	15 30	15 33	15 36	15 40		15 45	15 48	15 51	15 55	16 00	16 03	16 06	16 10	16 15		16 18	16 21	16 25	16 30	16 33	16 36	16 40	16 45
Whitechapel	d	15 27	15 32	15 35	15 38	15 42		15 47	15 50	15 53	15 57	16 02	16 05	16 08	16 12	16 17		16 20	16 23	16 27	16 32	16 35	16 38	16 42	16 47
Shoreditch High Street	d	15 29	15 34	15 37	15 40	15 44		15 49	15 52	15 55	15 59	16 04	16 07	16 10	16 14	16 19		16 22	16 25	16 29	16 34	16 37	16 40	16 44	16 49
Hoxton	d	15 31	15 36	15 39	15 42	15 46		15 51	15 54	15 57	16 01	16 06	16 09	16 12	16 16	16 21		16 24	16 27	16 31	16 36	16 39	16 42	16 46	16 51
Haggerston	d	15 33	15 38	15 41	15 44	15 48		15 53	15 56	15 59	16 03	16 08	16 11	16 14	16 18	16 23		16 26	16 29	16 33	16 38	16 41	16 44	16 48	16 53
Dalston Junction	a	15 35	15 42	15 43	15 48	15 50		15 57	15 58	16 03	16 05	16 12	16 13	16 18	16 20	16 27		16 28	16 33	16 35	16 42	16 43	16 48	16 50	16 57
Canonbury	a	15 38		15 46		15 53			16 01		16 08		16 16		16 23			16 31		16 38		16 46		16 53	
Highbury & Islington	a	15 43		15 52		15 58			16 07		16 13		16 22		16 28			16 37		16 43		16 52		16 56	

		LO		LO	LO	LO	LO	LO	LO	LO	LO	LO		LO	LO	LO	LO	LO	LO	LO	LO	LO		LO	LO
Clapham Junction	d	16 17					16 32				16 47					17 02				17 17					17 32
Wandsworth Road	d	16 23					16 38				16 53					17 08				17 23					17 38
Clapham High Street ⊖	d	16 25					16 40				16 55					17 10				17 25					17 40
Denmark Hill 4	d	16 30					16 45				17 00					17 15				17 30					17 45
Peckham Rye 4	d	16 32					16 47				17 02					17 17				17 32					17 47
Queens Rd Peckham	d	16 35					16 50				17 05					17 20				17 35					17 50
West Croydon 4	d					16 27				16 42					16 57				17 12					17 27	
Norwood Junction 2	d					16 31				16 46					17 01				17 16					17 31	
Anerley	d					16 34				16 49					17 04				17 19					17 34	
Penge West	d					16 36				16 51					17 06				17 21					17 36	
Crystal Palace 4	d				16 31				16 46					17 01				17 16				17 31			
Sydenham	d				16 34	16 39			16 49	16 54				17 04	17 09			17 19	17 24			17 34		17 39	
Forest Hill 4	d				16 37	16 41			16 52	16 56				17 07	17 11			17 22	17 26			17 37		17 41	
Honor Oak Park	d				16 39	16 44			16 54	16 59				17 09	17 14			17 24	17 29			17 39		17 44	
Brockley	d				16 42	16 46			16 57	17 01				17 12	17 16			17 27	17 31			17 42		17 46	
New Cross Gate	d				16 44	16 49			16 59	17 04				17 14	17 19			17 29	17 34			17 44		17 49	
New Cross 4	d			16 40				16 55				17 10					17 25				17 40				
Surrey Quays	d	16 41		16 44	16 48	16 53	16 56	16 59	17 03	17 08	17 11	17 14		17 18	17 23	17 26	17 29	17 33	17 38	17 41	17 44	17 48		17 53	17 56
Canada Water	d	16 43		16 46	16 50	16 55	16 58	17 01	17 05	17 10	17 13	17 16		17 20	17 25	17 28	17 31	17 35	17 40	17 43	17 46	17 50		17 55	17 58
Rotherhithe	d	16 44		16 47	16 51	16 56	16 59	17 02	17 06	17 11	17 14	17 17		17 21	17 26	17 29	17 32	17 36	17 41	17 44	17 47	17 51		17 56	17 59
Wapping	d	16 46		16 49	16 53	16 58	17 01	17 04	17 08	17 13	17 16	17 19		17 23	17 28	17 31	17 34	17 38	17 43	17 46	17 49	17 53		17 58	18 01
Shadwell	d	16 48		16 51	16 55	17 00	17 03	17 06	17 10	17 15	17 18	17 21		17 25	17 30	17 33	17 36	17 40	17 45	17 48	17 51	17 55		18 00	18 03
Whitechapel	d	16 50		16 53	16 57	17 02	17 05	17 08	17 12	17 17	17 20	17 23		17 27	17 32	17 35	17 38	17 42	17 47	17 50	17 53	17 57		18 02	18 05
Shoreditch High Street	d	16 52		16 55	16 59	17 04	17 07	17 10	17 14	17 19	17 22	17 25		17 29	17 34	17 37	17 40	17 44	17 49	17 52	17 55	17 59		18 04	18 07
Hoxton	d	16 54		16 57	17 01	17 06	17 09	17 12	17 16	17 21	17 24	17 27		17 31	17 36	17 39	17 42	17 46	17 51	17 54	17 57	18 01		18 06	18 09
Haggerston	d	16 56		16 59	17 03	17 08	17 11	17 14	17 18	17 23	17 26	17 29		17 33	17 38	17 41	17 44	17 48	17 53	17 56	17 59	18 03		18 08	18 11
Dalston Junction	a	16 58		17 03	17 05	17 12	17 13	17 18	17 20	17 27	17 28	17 33		17 35	17 42	17 43	17 48	17 50	17 57	17 58	18 03	18 05		18 12	18 13
Canonbury	a	17 01			17 08		17 16		17 23		17 31			17 38		17 46		17 53		18 01		18 08			18 16
Highbury & Islington	a	17 07			17 13		17 22		17 28		17 37			17 43		17 52		17 58		18 07		18 13			18 22

Table 178R

Sundays

8 December to 11 May

Clapham Junction and West Croydon, Crystal Palace, New Cross - Highbury & Islington

Network Diagram - see first Page of Table 173

		LO	LO	LO	LO	LO	LO	LO		LO	LO	LO	LO	LO	LO	LO	LO	LO		LO	LO	LO	LO	LO	LO
Clapham Junction	d				17 47					18 02				18 17				18 32					18 47		
Wandsworth Road	d				17 53					18 08				18 23				18 38					18 53		
Clapham High Street ⊖	d				17 55					18 10				18 25				18 40					18 55		
Denmark Hill 4	d				18 00					18 16				18 30				18 45					19 00		
Peckham Rye 4	d				18 02					18 17				18 32				18 47					19 02		
Queens Rd Peckham	d				18 05					18 20				18 35				18 50					19 05		
West Croydon 4	d			17 42				17 57					18 12				18 27					18 42			
Norwood Junction 2	d			17 46				18 01					18 16				18 31					18 46			
Anerley	d			17 49				18 04					18 19				18 34					18 49			
Penge West	d			17 51				18 06					18 21				18 36					18 51			
Crystal Palace 4	d		17 46				18 01					18 16				18 31					18 46				19 01
Sydenham	d		17 49	17 54			18 04	18 09				18 19	18 24			18 34	18 39				18 49	18 54			19 04
Forest Hill 4	d		17 52	17 56			18 07	18 11				18 22	18 26			18 37	18 41				18 52	18 56			19 07
Honor Oak Park	d		17 54	17 59			18 09	18 14				18 24	18 29			18 39	18 44				18 54	18 59			19 09
Brockley	d		17 57	18 01			18 12	18 16				18 27	18 31			18 42	18 46				18 57	19 01			19 12
New Cross Gate	d		17 59	18 04			18 14	18 19				18 29	18 34			18 44	18 49				18 59	19 04			19 14
New Cross 4	d	17 55				18 10					18 25				18 40					18 55				19 10	
Surrey Quays	d	17 59	18 03	18 08	18 11	18 14	18 18	18 23		18 26	18 29	18 33	18 38	18 41	18 44	18 48	18 53	18 56		18 59	19 03	19 08	19 11	19 14	19 18
Canada Water	d	18 01	18 05	18 10	18 13	18 16	18 20	18 25		18 28	18 31	18 35	18 40	18 43	18 46	18 50	18 55	18 58		19 01	19 05	19 10	19 13	19 16	19 20
Rotherhithe	d	18 02	18 06	18 11	18 14	18 17	18 21	18 26		18 29	18 32	18 36	18 41	18 44	18 47	18 51	18 56	18 59		19 02	19 06	19 11	19 14	19 17	19 21
Wapping	d	18 04	18 08	18 13	18 16	18 19	18 23	18 28		18 31	18 34	18 38	18 43	18 46	18 49	18 53	18 58	19 01		19 04	19 08	19 13	19 16	19 19	19 23
Shadwell	d	18 06	18 10	18 15	18 18	18 21	18 25	18 30		18 33	18 36	18 40	18 45	18 48	18 51	18 55	19 00	19 03		19 06	19 10	19 15	19 18	19 21	19 25
Whitechapel	d	18 08	18 12	18 17	18 20	18 23	18 27	18 32		18 35	18 38	18 42	18 47	18 50	18 53	18 57	19 02	19 05		19 08	19 12	19 17	19 20	19 23	19 27
Shoreditch High Street	d	18 10	18 14	18 19	18 22	18 25	18 29	18 34		18 37	18 40	18 44	18 49	18 52	18 55	18 59	19 04	19 07		19 10	19 14	19 19	19 22	19 25	19 29
Hoxton	d	18 12	18 16	18 21	18 24	18 27	18 31	18 36		18 39	18 42	18 46	18 51	18 54	18 57	19 01	19 06	19 09		19 12	19 16	19 21	19 24	19 27	19 31
Haggerston	d	18 14	18 18	18 23	18 26	18 29	18 33	18 38		18 41	18 44	18 48	18 53	18 56	18 59	19 03	19 08	19 11		19 14	19 18	19 23	19 26	19 29	19 33
Dalston Junction	a	18 18	18 20	18 27	18 28	18 33	18 35	18 42		18 43	18 48	18 50	18 57	18 58	19 03	19 05	19 12	19 13		19 18	19 20	19 27	19 28	19 33	19 35
Canonbury	a		18 23		18 31		18 38			18 46		18 53		19 01		19 08		19 16			19 23		19 31		19 38
Highbury & Islington	a		18 28		18 37		18 43			18 52		18 58		19 07		19 13		19 22			19 28		19 37		19 43

		LO	LO	LO		LO	LO	LO	LO	LO	LO	LO	LO	LO		LO	LO	LO	LO	LO	LO	LO	LO	LO	
Clapham Junction	d		19 02					19 17				19 32					19 47				20 02				
Wandsworth Road	d		19 08					19 23				19 38					19 53				20 08				
Clapham High Street ⊖	d		19 10					19 25				19 40					19 55				20 10				
Denmark Hill 4	d		19 15					19 30				19 45					20 00				20 15				
Peckham Rye 4	d		19 17					19 32				19 47					20 02				20 17				
Queens Rd Peckham	d		19 20					19 35				19 50					20 05				20 20				
West Croydon 4	d	18 57					19 12				19 27					19 42				19 57				20 12	
Norwood Junction 2	d	19 01					19 16				19 31					19 46				20 01				20 16	
Anerley	d	19 04					19 19				19 34					19 49				20 04				20 19	
Penge West	d	19 06					19 21				19 36					19 51				20 06				20 21	
Crystal Palace 4	d					19 16				19 31				19 46					20 01				20 16		
Sydenham	d	19 09				19 19	19 24			19 34	19 39			19 49		19 54			20 04	20 09			20 19	20 24	
Forest Hill 4	d	19 11				19 22	19 26			19 37	19 41			19 52		19 56			20 07	20 11			20 22	20 26	
Honor Oak Park	d	19 14				19 24	19 29			19 39	19 44			19 54		19 59			20 09	20 14			20 24	20 29	
Brockley	d	19 16				19 27	19 31			19 42	19 46			19 57		20 01			20 12	20 16			20 27	20 31	
New Cross Gate	d	19 19				19 29	19 34			19 44	19 49			19 59		20 04			20 14	20 19			20 29	20 34	
New Cross 4	d			19 25					19 40				19 55					20 10				20 25			
Surrey Quays	d	19 23	19 26	19 29		19 33	19 38	19 41	19 44	19 48	19 53	19 56	19 59	20 03		20 08	20 11	20 14	20 18	20 23	20 26	20 29	20 33	20 38	
Canada Water	d	19 25	19 28	19 31		19 35	19 40	19 43	19 46	19 50	19 55	19 58	20 01	20 05		20 10	20 13	20 16	20 20	20 25	20 28	20 31	20 35	20 40	
Rotherhithe	d	19 26	19 29	19 32		19 36	19 41	19 44	19 47	19 51	19 56	19 59	20 02	20 06		20 11	20 14	20 17	20 21	20 26	20 29	20 32	20 36	20 41	
Wapping	d	19 28	19 31	19 34		19 38	19 43	19 46	19 49	19 53	19 58	20 01	20 04	20 08		20 13	20 16	20 19	20 23	20 28	20 31	20 34	20 38	20 43	
Shadwell	d	19 30	19 33	19 36		19 40	19 45	19 48	19 51	19 55	20 00	20 03	20 06	20 10		20 15	20 18	20 21	20 25	20 30	20 33	20 36	20 40	20 45	
Whitechapel	d	19 32	19 35	19 38		19 42	19 47	19 50	19 53	19 57	20 02	20 05	20 08	20 12		20 17	20 20	20 23	20 27	20 32	20 35	20 38	20 42	20 47	
Shoreditch High Street	d	19 34	19 37	19 40		19 44	19 49	19 52	19 55	19 59	20 04	20 07	20 10	20 14		20 19	20 22	20 25	20 29	20 34	20 37	20 40	20 44	20 49	
Hoxton	d	19 36	19 39	19 42		19 46	19 51	19 54	19 57	20 01	20 06	20 09	20 12	20 16		20 21	20 24	20 27	20 31	20 36	20 39	20 42	20 46	20 51	
Haggerston	d	19 38	19 41	19 44		19 48	19 53	19 56	19 59	20 03	20 08	20 11	20 14	20 18		20 23	20 26	20 29	20 33	20 38	20 41	20 44	20 48	20 53	
Dalston Junction	a	19 42	19 43	19 48		19 50	19 57	19 58	20 03	20 05	20 12	20 13	20 18	20 20		20 27	20 28	20 33	20 35	20 42	20 43	20 48	20 50	20 57	
Canonbury	a		19 46			19 53		20 01		20 08		20 16		20 23			20 31		20 38		20 46		20 53		
Highbury & Islington	a		19 52			19 58		20 07		20 13		20 22		20 28			20 37		20 43		20 52		20 58		

		LO	LO	LO	LO	LO	LO	LO	LO	LO		LO	LO	LO	LO	LO	LO	LO	LO	LO		LO	LO	LO	LO
Clapham Junction	d	20 17				20 32				20 47					21 02				21 17					21 32	
Wandsworth Road	d	20 23				20 38				20 53					21 08				21 23					21 38	
Clapham High Street ⊖	d	20 25				20 40				20 55					21 10				21 25					21 40	
Denmark Hill 4	d	20 30				20 45				21 00					21 15				21 30					21 45	
Peckham Rye 4	d	20 32				20 47				21 02					21 17				21 32					21 47	
Queens Rd Peckham	d	20 35				20 50				21 05					21 20				21 35					21 50	
West Croydon 4	d				20 27				20 42					20 57				21 12					21 27		
Norwood Junction 2	d				20 31				20 46					21 01				21 16					21 31		
Anerley	d				20 34				20 49					21 04				21 19					21 34		
Penge West	d				20 36				20 51					21 06				21 21					21 36		
Crystal Palace 4	d			20 31				20 46					21 01				21 16					21 31			
Sydenham	d			20 34	20 39			20 49	20 54				21 04	21 09			21 19	21 24				21 34	21 39		
Forest Hill 4	d			20 37	20 41			20 52	20 56				21 07	21 11			21 22	21 26				21 37	21 41		
Honor Oak Park	d			20 39	20 44			20 54	20 59				21 09	21 14			21 24	21 29				21 39	21 44		
Brockley	d			20 42	20 46			20 57	21 01				21 12	21 16			21 27	21 31				21 42	21 46		
New Cross Gate	d			20 44	20 49			20 59	21 04				21 14	21 19			21 29	21 34				21 44	21 49		
New Cross 4	d		20 40				20 55					21 10				21 25				21 40					21 55
Surrey Quays	d	20 41	20 44	20 48	20 53	20 56	20 59	21 03	21 08	21 11		21 14	21 18	21 23	21 26	21 29	21 33	21 38	21 41	21 44		21 48	21 53	21 56	21 59
Canada Water	d	20 43	20 46	20 50	20 55	20 58	21 01	21 05	21 10	21 13		21 16	21 20	21 25	21 28	21 31	21 35	21 40	21 43	21 46		21 50	21 55	21 58	22 01
Rotherhithe	d	20 44	20 47	20 51	20 56	20 59	21 02	21 06	21 11	21 14		21 17	21 21	21 26	21 29	21 32	21 36	21 41	21 44	21 47		21 51	21 56	21 59	22 02
Wapping	d	20 46	20 49	20 53	20 58	21 01	21 04	21 08	21 13	21 16		21 19	21 23	21 28	21 31	21 34	21 38	21 43	21 46	21 49		21 53	21 58	22 01	22 04
Shadwell	d	20 48	20 51	20 55	21 00	21 03	21 06	21 10	21 15	21 18		21 21	21 25	21 30	21 33	21 36	21 40	21 45	21 48	21 51		21 55	22 00	22 03	22 06
Whitechapel	d	20 50	20 53	20 57	21 02	21 05	21 08	21 12	21 17	21 20		21 23	21 27	21 32	21 35	21 38	21 42	21 47	21 50	21 53		21 57	22 02	22 05	22 08
Shoreditch High Street	d	20 52	20 55	20 59	21 04	21 07	21 10	21 14	21 19	21 22		21 25	21 29	21 34	21 37	21 40	21 44	21 49	21 52	21 55		21 59	22 04	22 07	22 10
Hoxton	d	20 54	20 57	21 01	21 06	21 09	21 12	21 16	21 21	21 24		21 27	21 31	21 36	21 39	21 42	21 46	21 51	21 54	21 57		22 01	22 06	22 09	22 12
Haggerston	d	20 56	20 59	21 03	21 08	21 11	21 14	21 18	21 23	21 26		21 29	21 33	21 38	21 41	21 44	21 48	21 53	21 56	21 59		22 03	22 08	22 11	22 14
Dalston Junction	a	20 58	21 03	21 05	21 12	21 13	21 18	21 20	21 27	21 28		21 33	21 35	21 42	21 43	21 48	21 50	21 57	21 58	22 03		22 05	22 12	22 13	22 18
Canonbury	a	21 01		21 08		21 16		21 23		21 31			21 38		21 46		21 53		22 01			22 08		22 16	
Highbury & Islington	a	21 07		21 13		21 22		21 28		21 37			21 43		21 52		21 58		22 07			22 13		22 22	

Table 178R

Sundays

8 December to 11 May

Clapham Junction and West Croydon, Crystal Palace, New Cross - Highbury & Islington

Network Diagram - see first Page of Table 173

		LO	LO	LO	LO	LO		LO	LO	LO	LO	LO	LO	LO	LO	LO		LO	LO	LO	LO	LO			
Clapham Junction	d			21 47					22 02			22 17						22 47				23 17			
Wandsworth Road	d			21 53					22 08			22 23						22 53				23 23			
Clapham High Street ⊖	d			21 55					22 10			22 25						22 55				23 25			
Denmark Hill 4	d			22 00					22 15			22 30						23 00				23 30			
Peckham Rye 4	d			22 02					22 17			22 32						23 02				23 32			
Queens Rd Peckham	d			22 05					22 20			22 35						23 05				23 35			
West Croydon 4 🚋	d		21 42					21 57			22 12			22 27		22 42				22 57					
Norwood Junction 2	d		21 46					22 01			22 16			22 31		22 46				23 01					
Anerley	d		21 49					22 04			22 19			22 34		22 49				23 04					
Penge West	d		21 51					22 06			22 21			22 36		22 51				23 06					
Crystal Palace 4	d	21 46				22 01				22 16					22 46						23 16				
Sydenham	d	21 49	21 54			22 04		22 09		22 19	22 24			22 39	22 49	22 54				23 09	23 19				
Forest Hill 4	d	21 52	21 56			22 07		22 11		22 22	22 26			22 41	22 52	22 56				23 11	23 22				
Honor Oak Park	d	21 54	21 59			22 09		22 14		22 24	22 29			22 44	22 54	22 59				23 14	23 24				
Brockley	d	21 57	22 01			22 12		22 16		22 27	22 31			22 46	22 57	23 01				23 16	23 27				
New Cross Gate	d	21 59	22 04			22 14		22 19		22 29	22 34			22 49	22 59	23 04				23 19	23 29				
New Cross 4	d				22 10								22 40						23 10						
Surrey Quays	d	22 03	22 08	22 11	22 14	22 18		22 23	22 26	22 33	22 38	22 41	22 44	22 53	23 03	23 08		23 11	23 14	23 23	23 33	23 41			
Canada Water	d	22 05	22 10	22 13	22 16	22 20		22 25	22 28	22 35	22 40	22 43	22 46	22 55	23 05	23 10		23 13	23 16	23 25	23 35	23 43			
Rotherhithe	d	22 06	22 11	22 14	22 17	22 21		22 26	22 29	22 36	22 41	22 44	22 47	22 56	23 06	23 11		23 14	23 17	23 26	23 36	23 44			
Wapping	d	22 08	22 13	22 16	22 19	22 23		22 28	22 31	22 38	22 43	22 46	22 49	22 58	23 08	23 13		23 16	23 19	23 28	23 38	23 46			
Shadwell	d	22 10	22 15	22 18	22 21	22 25		22 30	22 33	22 40	22 45	22 48	22 51	23 00	23 10	23 15		23 18	23 21	23 30	23 40	23 48			
Whitechapel	d	22 12	22 17	22 20	22 23	22 27		22 32	22 35	22 42	22 47	22 50	22 53	23 02	23 12	23 17		23 20	23 23	23 32	23 42	23 50			
Shoreditch High Street	d	22 14	22 19	22 22	22 25	22 29		22 34	22 37	22 44	22 49	22 52	22 55	23 04	23 14	23 19		23 22	23 25	23 34	23 44	23 52			
Hoxton	d	22 16	22 21	22 24	22 27	22 31		22 36	22 39	22 46	22 51	22 54	22 57	23 06	23 16	23 21		23 24	23 27	23 36	23 46	23 54			
Haggerston	d	22 18	22 23	22 26	22 29	22 33		22 38	22 41	22 48	22 53	22 56	22 59	23 08	23 18	23 23		23 26	23 29	23 38	23 48	23 56			
Dalston Junction	a	22 20	22 27	22 28	22 33	22 35		22 42	22 43	22 50	22 57	22 58	23 03	23 12	23 20	23 27		23 28	23 33	23 42	23 50	23 58			
Canonbury	a	22 23		22 31		22 38			22 46	22 53		23 01			23 23			23 31			23 53	00 01			
Highbury & Islington	a	22 28		22 37		22 43			22 52	22 58		23 08			23 28			23 37			23 56	00 04			

Table 179

Thameslink - Wimbledon and Sutton

Mondays to Fridays

9 December to 16 May

Network Diagram - see first Page of Table 173

Miles	Miles			FC MX	FC MX	FC	SN	FC	SN	FC	FC	SN	FC	SN	FC	FC [1]	FC [1] A
0	—	Luton [10]	d							05 08			05 48		06 06	06 34	06 39
1	—	Luton Airport Parkway [7]	d							05 10			05 50		06 08		06 41
10¼	0	St Albans City	d							05 22			06 02		06 20	06 46	06 53
26¼	16	West Hampstead Thameslink	d							05 46	06 04		06 26		06 44		07 08
30¼	20	St Pancras International [15] ⊖	d					05 36		05 54	06 12		06 34		06 52	07 04	07 16
31½	21¼	Farringdon [3] ⊖	d					05 42		06 00	06 18		06 40		06 58	07 10	07 22
31¾	21½	City Thameslink [3]	d					05 44		06 03	06 21		06 43		07 01	07 13	07 25
32¼	22	London Blackfriars [3] ⊖	d					05 47		06 06	06 24		06 46		07 04	07 16	07 28
33½	23¼	Elephant & Castle ⊖	d					05 50		06 09	06 27		06 49		07 07	07 19	07 33
35¼	25	Loughborough Jn	d							06 13	06 31		06 53		07 11	07 23	07 37
36¼	26	Herne Hill [4]	d					05 57		06 17	06 35		06 57		07 15	07 27	07 41
—	—	London Bridge [4] ⊖	d						06 00			06 30		06 58			
37¼	27	Tulse Hill [3]	a					06 01	06 18	06 21	06 39	06 48	07 01	07 16	07 20	07 31	07 45
—	—		d		00 02			06 02	06 19	06 22	06 42	06 48	07 02	07 17	07 20	07 31	07 45
39	28¾	Streatham [4]	d		00 06			06 05	06 22	06 25	06 45	06 51	07 05	07 20	07 23	07 34	07 48
40½	—	**Tooting**	d		00 10			06 10	06 27			06 56	07 11	07 25		07 38	
41¾	—	**Haydons Road**	d		00 13			06 13	06 30			06 59	07 14	07 28		07 41	
42½	—	Wimbledon [6] ⊖	a		00 18			06 15	06 33			07 02	07 17	07 31		07 44	
—	—		d		00 19		05 56	06 16	06 35			07 05	07 17	07 32		07 47	
43½	—	**Wimbledon Chase**	d		00 22		05 59	06 19	06 38			07 07	07 20	07 35		07 50	
44¼	—	**South Merton**	d		00 24		06 01	06 21	06 40			07 09	07 22	07 37		07 52	
44¾	—	**Morden South**	d		00 26		06 03	06 23	06 42			07 11	07 24	07 39		07 54	
45¼	—	**St Helier**	d		00 28		06 05	06 25	06 44			07 13	07 26	07 41		07 56	
46¼	—	**Sutton Common**	d	00 01	00 30		06 07	06 27	06 46			07 16	07 28	07 43		07 58	
47	—	**West Sutton**	d	00 04	00 33		06 10	06 30	06 49				07 31	07 46		08 01	
—	30¼	Mitcham Eastfields	d							06 29	06 49				07 27		07 52
—	31½	Mitcham Junction	d							06 32	06 52				07 30		07 55
—	32½	Hackbridge	d							06 35	06 55				07 33		07 58
—	33½	Carshalton	d							06 38	06 58				07 36		08 01
48	34¾	Sutton (Surrey) [4]	a	00 09	00 39		06 13	06 33	06 52	06 43	07 03	07 19	07 35	07 49	07 39	08 07	08 04
—	—		d			06 05				06 45	07 05				07 40		08 08
—	35¾	**West Sutton**	d			06 08				06 48	07 08				07 43		08 11
—	36½	**Sutton Common**	d			06 10				06 50	07 10				07 45		08 13
—	37½	**St Helier**	d			06 13				06 53	07 13				07 48		08 16
—	38	**Morden South**	d			06 15				06 55	07 15				07 50		08 18
—	38¾	**South Merton**	d			06 17				06 57	07 17				07 52		08 20
—	39¼	**Wimbledon Chase**	a			06 19				06 59	07 19				07 54		08 22

			FC	SN	FC	FC	SN	FC	FC [1]	FC	FC	FC	FC	FC
Luton [10]	d		06 50		07 10	07 30			08 04	08 02			08 54	
Luton Airport Parkway [7]	d		06 52		07 12	07 32				08 04			08 56	
St Albans City	d		07 04		07 24	07 44		07 52	08 16	08 16	08 23	08 43	09 08	09 14
West Hampstead Thameslink	d		07 24		07 44	08 04		08 16		08 36	08 48	09 08	09 26	09 39
St Pancras International [15] ⊖	d		07 32		07 52	08 12		08 24	08 36	08 44	08 56	09 16	09 34	09 48
Farringdon [3] ⊖	d		07 38		07 58	08 18		08 30	08 42	08 50	09 02	09 22	09 40	09 53
City Thameslink [3]	d		07 41		08 01	08 21		08 33	08 45	08 53	09 05	09 25	09 43	09 57
London Blackfriars [3] ⊖	d		07 44		08 04	08 24		08 36	08 48	08 56	09 08	09 28	09 46	10 00
Elephant & Castle ⊖	d		07 47		08 07	08 27		08 39		09 00	09 12	09 31	09 49	10 03
Loughborough Jn	d		07 51		08 11	08 31				09 04	09 16	09 35	09 53	10 07
Herne Hill [4]	d		07 57		08 17	08 36		08 46	08 57	09 11	09 25	09 41	09 57	10 11
London Bridge [4] ⊖	d	07 30		08 00			08 29							
Tulse Hill [3]	a	07 47	08 01	08 18	08 21	08 40	08 46	08 50	09 01	09 15	09 29	09 45	10 01	10 15
	d	07 48	08 05	08 18	08 21	08 40	08 47	08 51	09 01	09 16	09 31	09 46	10 01	10 16
Streatham [4]	d	07 51	08 08	08 21	08 24	08 44	08 50	08 54	09 05	09 20	09 35	09 50	10 05	10 20
Tooting	d	07 56	08 13	08 27		08 48			09 10		09 40		10 10	
Haydons Road	d	07 59	08 16	08 30		08 51			09 13		09 43		10 13	
Wimbledon [6] ⊖	a	08 03	08 18	08 33		08 54			09 16		09 46		10 16	
	d	08 04	08 19	08 35		08 55			09 17		09 47		10 17	
Wimbledon Chase	d	08 07	08 22	08 38		08 58			09 20		09 50		10 20	
South Merton	d	08 09	08 24	08 40		09 00			09 22		09 52		10 22	
Morden South	d	08 11	08 26	08 42		09 02			09 24		09 54		10 24	
St Helier	d	08 13	08 28	08 44		09 04			09 26		09 56		10 26	
Sutton Common	d	08 15	08 30	08 46		09 06			09 28		09 58		10 28	
West Sutton	d	08 18	08 33	08 49		09 09			09 31		10 01		10 31	
Mitcham Eastfields	d				08 28			08 58		09 24		09 54		10 24
Mitcham Junction	d				08 31			09 01		09 27		09 57		10 27
Hackbridge	d				08 34			09 04		09 30		10 00		10 30
Carshalton	d				08 37			09 07		09 33		10 03		10 33
Sutton (Surrey) [4]	a	08 21	08 37	08 21	08 40	09 12	09 02	09 10	09 37	09 36	10 05	10 06	10 35	10 36
	d				08 41			09 11		09 37		10 07		10 37
West Sutton	d				08 44			09 14		09 40		10 10		10 40
Sutton Common	d				08 46			09 16		09 42		10 12		10 42
St Helier	d				08 49			09 19		09 45		10 15		10 45
Morden South	d				08 51			09 21		09 47		10 17		10 47
South Merton	d				08 53			09 23		09 49		10 19		10 49
Wimbledon Chase	a				08 55			09 25		09 51		10 21		10 51

A [1] to London Blackfriars

For other London Bridge connections, please see table 173

Table 179

Thameslink - Wimbledon and Sutton

Mondays to Fridays

9 December to 16 May

Network Diagram - see first Page of Table 173

Station		FC	FC	FC	FC	FC	FC	FC	FC	FC	FC		FC	FC	FC	FC	FC
Luton 10	d	09 14		09 44		10 14		10 44		11 14				14 44		15 14	
Luton Airport Parkway 7	d	09 16		09 46		10 16		10 46		11 16				14 46		15 16	
St Albans City	d	09 29	09 44	09 59	10 14	10 29	10 44	10 59	11 14	11 29	11 44		14 44	14 59	15 14	15 29	15 44
West Hampstead Thameslink	d	09 54	10 10	10 24	10 40	10 54	11 10	11 24	11 39	11 54	12 09		15 09	15 24	15 39	15 54	16 09
St Pancras International 15 ⊖	d	10 04	10 19	10 34	10 49	11 04	11 19	11 34	11 48	12 04	12 18		15 18	15 34	15 48	16 04	16 18
Farringdon 3 ⊖	d	10 09	10 25	10 39	10 55	11 09	11 25	11 39	11 53	12 09	12 23		15 23	15 39	15 53	16 09	16 23
City Thameslink 3	d	10 13	10 27	10 43	10 57	11 13	11 27	11 43	11 57	12 13	12 27		15 27	15 43	15 57	16 13	16 27
London Blackfriars 3 ⊖	d	10 16	10 30	10 46	11 00	11 16	11 30	11 46	12 00	12 16	12 30		15 30	15 46	16 00	16 16	16 30
Elephant & Castle ⊖	d	10 19	10 33	10 49	11 03	11 19	11 33	11 49	12 03	12 19	12 33		15 33	15 49	16 03	16 19	16 33
Loughborough Jn	d	10 23	10 37	10 53	11 07	11 23	11 37	11 53	12 07	12 23	12 37		15 37	15 53	16 07	16 23	16 37
Herne Hill 4	d	10 27	10 41	10 57	11 11	11 27	11 41	11 57	12 11	12 27	12 41		15 41	15 57	16 11	16 27	16 41
London Bridge 4 ⊖	d																
Tulse Hill 3	a	10 31	10 45	11 01	11 15	11 31	11 45	12 01	12 15	12 31	12 45		15 45	16 01	16 15	16 31	16 46
	d	10 31	10 46	11 01	11 16	11 31	11 46	12 01	12 16	12 31	12 46		15 46	16 01	16 16	16 32	16 47
Streatham 4	d	10 35	10 50	11 05	11 20	11 35	11 50	12 05	12 20	12 35	12 50	and at the same minutes past each hour until	15 50	16 05	16 20	16 36	16 51
Tooting	d	10 40		11 10		11 40		12 10		12 40				16 10		16 40	
Haydons Road	d	10 43		11 13		11 43		12 13		12 43				16 13		16 43	
Wimbledon 6 ⊖	a	10 46		11 16		11 46		12 16		12 46				16 16		16 46	
	d	10 47		11 17		11 47		12 17		12 47				16 17		16 47	
Wimbledon Chase	d	10 50		11 20		11 50		12 20		12 50				16 20		16 50	
South Merton	d	10 52		11 22		11 52		12 22		12 52				16 22		16 52	
Morden South	d	10 54		11 24		11 54		12 24		12 54				16 24		16 54	
St Helier	d	10 56		11 26		11 56		12 26		12 56				16 26		16 56	
Sutton Common	d	10 58		11 28		11 58		12 28		12 58				16 28		16 58	
West Sutton	d	11 01		11 31		12 01		12 31		13 01				16 31		17 01	
Mitcham Eastfields	d		10 54		11 24		11 54		12 24		12 54		15 54		16 24		16 55
Mitcham Junction	d		10 57		11 27		11 57		12 27		12 57		15 57		16 27		16 58
Hackbridge	d		11 00		11 30		12 00		12 30		13 00		16 00		16 30		17 01
Carshalton	d		11 03		11 33		12 03		12 33		13 03		16 03		16 33		17 04
Sutton (Surrey) 4	a	11 05	11 06	11 35	11 36	12 05	12 06	12 35	12 36	13 05	13 06		16 06	16 35	16 36	17 05	17 08
	d		11 07		11 37		12 07		12 37		13 07		16 07		16 37		17 11
West Sutton	d		11 10		11 40		12 10		12 40		13 10		16 10		16 40		17 14
Sutton Common	d		11 12		11 42		12 12		12 42		13 12		16 12		16 42		17 16
St Helier	d		11 15		11 45		12 15		12 45		13 15		16 15		16 45		17 19
Morden South	d		11 17		11 47		12 17		12 47		13 17		16 17		16 47		17 21
South Merton	d		11 19		11 49		12 19		12 49		13 19		16 19		16 49		17 23
Wimbledon Chase	a		11 21		11 51		12 21		12 51		13 21		16 21		16 51		17 25

Station		FC	FC	FC	SN	FC	FC	SN	FC	FC	SN	FC 1	FC	SN	FC	FC	FC
Luton 10	d	15 44		16 14			16 44			17 22		17 49			18 06	18 22	
Luton Airport Parkway 7	d	15 46		16 16			16 46			17 24		17 52			18 08	18 24	
St Albans City	d	15 59	16 14	16 29		16 44	17 00		17 20	17 36		18 03	18 06		18 20	18 36	18 52
West Hampstead Thameslink	d	16 24	16 40	16 54		17 08	17 24		17 44	17 56		18 15	18 30		18 40	18 56	19 10
St Pancras International 15 ⊖	d	16 34	16 50	17 02		17 18	17 32		17 52	18 04		18 22	18 38		18 48	19 04	19 18
Farringdon 3 ⊖	d	16 39	16 55	17 07		17 23	17 37		17 57	18 09		18 27	18 43		18 53	19 09	19 23
City Thameslink 3	d	16 43	16 59	17 11		17 27	17 41		18 01	18 13		18 31	18 47		18 57	19 13	19 27
London Blackfriars 3 ⊖	d	16 46	17 02	17 14		17 30	17 44		18 04	18 16		18 34	18 50		19 00	19 16	19 30
Elephant & Castle ⊖	d	16 49	17 06	17 18		17 34	17 48		18 08	18 20		18 38	18 54		19 04	19 19	19 33
Loughborough Jn	d	16 53	17 10	17 22		17 38	17 52		18 12	18 24		18 42	18 58		19 08	19 23	19 37
Herne Hill 4	d	16 57	17 16	17 26		17 43	17 57		18 17	18 28		18 48	19 02		19 12	19 27	19 41
London Bridge 4 ⊖	d				17 20			17 50			18 20			18 50			
Tulse Hill 3	a	17 01	17 20	17 30	17 39	17 47	18 01	18 08	18 21	18 32	18 38	18 52	19 06	19 08	19 16	19 31	19 45
	d	17 02	17 20	17 32	17 39	17 48	18 02	18 09	18 22	18 32	18 38	18 52	19 06	19 09	19 16	19 31	19 46
Streatham 4	d	17 06	17 24	17 36	17 44	17 52	18 06	18 13	18 26	18 36	18 42	18 56	19 10	19 15	19 20	19 35	19 50
Tooting	d	17 10		17 40			18 10			18 40			19 18			19 40	
Haydons Road	d	17 13		17 43			18 13			18 43			19 21			19 43	
Wimbledon 6 ⊖	a	17 16		17 46			18 16			18 46			19 23			19 46	
	d	17 19		17 49			18 17			18 47			19 24			19 49	
Wimbledon Chase	d	17 22		17 52			18 22			18 52			19 27			19 52	
South Merton	d	17 24		17 54			18 24			18 54			19 29			19 54	
Morden South	d	17 26		17 56			18 26			18 56			19 31			19 56	
St Helier	d	17 28		17 58			18 28			18 58			19 33			19 58	
Sutton Common	d	17 30		18 00			18 30			19 00			19 35			20 00	
West Sutton	d	17 33		18 03			18 33			19 03			19 38			20 03	
Mitcham Eastfields	d		17 28		17 48	17 55		18 17	18 29		18 47	18 59		19 19	19 24		19 54
Mitcham Junction	d		17 31		17 51	17 58		18 20	18 32		18 50	19 02		19 22	19 27		19 57
Hackbridge	d		17 34		17 55	18 02		18 24	18 36		18 54	19 06		19 26	19 30		20 00
Carshalton	d		17 37		17 57	18 04		18 26	18 38		18 56	19 08		19 28	19 33		20 03
Sutton (Surrey) 4	a	17 37	17 40	18 07	18 02	18 08	18 37	18 30	18 42	19 07	19 00	19 12	19 41	19 32	19 36	20 07	20 06
	d		17 41		18 03	18 11		18 30	18 43		19 00	19 13			19 37		20 07
West Sutton	d		17 44		18 06	18 14		18 34	18 46		19 04	19 16			19 40		20 10
Sutton Common	d		17 46		18 09	18 16		18 36	18 48		19 06	19 18			19 42		20 12
St Helier	d		17 49		18 11	18 19		18 39	18 51		19 09	19 21			19 45		20 15
Morden South	d		17 51		18 13	18 21		18 41	18 53		19 11	19 23			19 47		20 17
South Merton	d		17 53		18 15	18 23		18 43	18 55		19 13	19 25			19 49		20 19
Wimbledon Chase	a		17 55		18 17	18 25		18 45	18 57		19 15	19 27			19 51		20 21

For other London Bridge connections, please see table 173

Table 179

Mondays to Fridays

9 December to 16 May

Thameslink - Wimbledon and Sutton

Network Diagram - see first Page of Table 173

		FC	FC	FC	FC	FC	FC	FC	FC	FC	FC	FC	FC	FC	FC
Luton 10	d	18 54		19 24	19 32	19 44		20 20		20 50		21 20	21 50	22 20	22 50
Luton Airport Parkway 7	d	18 57		19 27	19 34	19 46		20 22		20 52		21 22	21 52	22 22	22 52
St Albans City	d	19 08	19 22	19 38	19 46	20 00	20 22	20 34		21 04		21 34	22 04	22 34	23 04
West Hampstead Thameslink	d	19 26	19 40	19 56	20 09	20 24	20 40	20 56		21 26		21 56	22 26	22 56	23 29
St Pancras International 15 ⊖	d	19 34	19 48	20 04	20 18	20 34	20 48	21 06		21 36		22 06	22 36	23 06	23 38
Farringdon 3 ⊖	d	19 39	19 53	20 09	20 23	20 39	20 53	21 10		21 40		22 10	22 40	23 10	23 43
City Thameslink 3	d	19 43	19 57	20 13	20 27	20 43	20 57	21 13		21 43		22 13	22 43		
London Blackfriars 3 ⊖	d	19 46	20 00	20 16	20 30	20 46	21 00	21 16		21 46		22 16	22 46	23 16	23 48
Elephant & Castle ⊖	d	19 49	20 03	20 19	20 33	20 49	21 03	21 19		21 49		22 19	22 49	23 19	23 51
Loughborough Jn	d	19 53	20 07	20 23	20 37	20 53	21 07	21 23		21 53		22 23	22 53	23s23	
Herne Hill 4	d	19 57	20 11	20 27	20 41	20 57	21 11	21 27		21 57		22 27	22 57	23 27	23 58
London Bridge 4 ⊖	d														
Tulse Hill 3	a	20 01	20 15	20 31	20 45	21 01	21 15	21 31		22 01		22 31	23 01	23 31	00 02
	d	20 01	20 16	20 31	20 50	21 01	21 20	21 31		22 01		22 31	23 01	23 31	00 02
Streatham 4	d	20 05	20 20	20 35	20 53	21 05	21 23	21 35		22 05		22 35	23 05	23 35	00 06
Tooting	d	20 10		20 40		21 10		21 40		22 10		22 40	23 10	23 40	00 10
Haydons Road	d	20 13		20 43		21 13		21 43		22 13		22 43	23 13	23 43	00 13
Wimbledon 6 ⊖	a	20 16		20 46		21 16		21 46		22 16		22 46	23 16	23 46	00 18
	d	20 19		20 49		21 19		21 49		22 19		22 49	23 17	23 49	00 19
Wimbledon Chase	d	20 22		20 52		21 22		21 52		22 22		22 52	23 20	23 52	00 22
South Merton	d	20 24		20 54		21 24		21 54		22 24		22 54	23 22	23 54	00 24
Morden South	d	20 26		20 56		21 26		21 56		22 26		22 56	23 24	23 56	00 26
St Helier	d	20 28		20 58		21 28		21 58		22 28		22 58	23 26	23 58	00 28
Sutton Common	d	20 30		21 00		21 30		22 00		22 30		23 00	23 28	00 01	00 30
West Sutton	d	20 33		21 03		21 33		22 03		22 33		23 03	23 31	00 04	00 33
Mitcham Eastfields	d		20 24		20 57		21 27								
Mitcham Junction	d		20 27		21 00		21 30								
Hackbridge	d		20 30		21 03		21 33								
Carshalton	d		20 33		21 06		21 36								
Sutton (Surrey) 4	a	20 39	20 36	21 09	21 10	21 39	21 40	22 09		22 39		23 09	23 35	00 09	00 39
	d		20 37				21 47		22 17		22 47				
West Sutton	d		20 40				21 50		22 20		22 50				
Sutton Common	d		20 42				21 52		22 22		22 52				
St Helier	d		20 45				21 55		22 25		22 55				
Morden South	d		20 47				21 57		22 27		22 57				
South Merton	d		20 49				21 59		22 29		22 59				
Wimbledon Chase	a		20 51				22 01		22 31		23 01				

For other London Bridge connections, please see table 173

Table 179

Saturdays

14 December to 17 May

Thameslink - Wimbledon and Sutton

Network Diagram - see first Page of Table 173

		FC	FC	FC	FC	FC	FC	FC	FC	FC	FC	FC	FC	FC	FC	FC
Luton 10	d					05 30		06 00		06 30		07 00	07 14	07 30	07 44	08 00
Luton Airport Parkway 7	d					05 32		06 02		06 32		07 02	07 16	07 32	07 46	08 02
St Albans City	d					05 44		06 14		06 44		07 14	07 29	07 44	07 59	08 14
West Hampstead Thameslink	d			05 40		06 09	06 24	06 39	06 54	07 09	07 24	07 39	07 54	08 09	08 24	08 39
St Pancras International 15 ⊖	d			05 48		06 18	06 34	06 48	07 04	07 18	07 34	07 48	08 04	08 18	08 34	08 48
Farringdon 3 ⊖	d			05 53		06 23	06 39	06 53	07 09	07 23	07 39	07 53	08 09	08 23	08 39	08 53
City Thameslink 3	d															
London Blackfriars 3 ⊖	d			06 00	06 16	06 30	06 46	07 00	07 16	07 30	07 46	08 00	08 16	08 30	08 46	09 00
Elephant & Castle ⊖	d			06 03	06 19	06 33	06 49	07 03	07 19	07 33	07 49	08 03	08 19	08 33	08 49	09 03
Loughborough Jn	d						06 53	07 07	07 23	07 37	07 53	08 07	08 23	08 37	08 53	09 07
Herne Hill 4	d			06 11	06 27	06 41	06 57	07 11	07 27	07 41	07 57	08 11	08 27	08 41	08 57	09 11
London Bridge 4 ⊖	d															
Tulse Hill 3	a			06 15	06 31	06 45	07 01	07 15	07 31	07 45	08 01	08 15	08 31	08 45	09 01	09 15
	d		00 02	06 16	06 31	06 46	07 01	07 16	07 31	07 46	08 01	08 16	08 31	08 46	09 01	09 16
Streatham 4	d		00 06	06 20	06 35	06 50	07 05	07 20	07 35	07 50	08 05	08 20	08 35	08 50	09 05	09 20
Tooting	d		00 10		06 40		07 10		07 40		08 10		08 40		09 10	
Haydons Road	d		00 13		06 43		07 13		07 43		08 13		08 43		09 13	
Wimbledon 6 ⊖	a		00 18		06 46		07 16		07 46		08 16		08 46		09 16	
	d		00 19		06 47		07 17		07 47		08 17		08 47		09 17	
Wimbledon Chase	d		00 22		06 50		07 20		07 50		08 20		08 50		09 20	
South Merton	d		00 24		06 52		07 22		07 52		08 22		08 52		09 22	
Morden South	d		00 26		06 54		07 24		07 54		08 24		08 54		09 24	
St Helier	d		00 28		06 56		07 26		07 56		08 26		08 56		09 26	
Sutton Common	d	00 01	00 30		06 58		07 28		07 58		08 28		08 58		09 28	
West Sutton	d	00 04	00 33		07 01		07 31		08 01		08 31		09 01		09 31	
Mitcham Eastfields	d			06 24		06 54		07 24		07 54		08 24		08 54		09 24
Mitcham Junction	d			06 27		06 57		07 27		07 57		08 27		08 57		09 27
Hackbridge	d			06 30		07 00		07 30		08 00		08 30		09 00		09 30
Carshalton	d			06 33		07 03		07 33		08 03		08 33		09 03		09 33
Sutton (Surrey) 4	a	00 09	00 39	06 36	07 05	07 06	07 35	07 36	08 05	08 06	08 35	08 36	09 05	09 06	09 35	09 36
	d			06 37		07 07		07 37		08 07		08 37		09 07		09 37
West Sutton	d			06 40		07 10		07 40		08 10		08 40		09 10		09 40
Sutton Common	d			06 42		07 12		07 42		08 12		08 42		09 12		09 42
St Helier	d			06 45		07 15		07 45		08 15		08 45		09 15		09 45
Morden South	d			06 47		07 17		07 47		08 17		08 47		09 17		09 47
South Merton	d			06 49		07 19		07 49		08 19		08 49		09 19		09 49
Wimbledon Chase	a			06 51		07 21		07 51		08 21		08 51		09 21		09 51

		FC	FC	FC	FC		FC	FC	FC	FC	FC	FC	FC	FC	FC	FC	FC	FC	FC
Luton 10	d	08 14		08 44				19 14		19 50		20 20		20 50		21 20	21 50	22 20	22 46
Luton Airport Parkway 7	d	08 16		08 46				19 16		19 52		20 22		20 52		21 22	21 52	22 22	22 49
St Albans City	d	08 29	08 44	08 59	09 14		19 14	19 29	19 44	20 04	20 14	20 34		21 04		21 34	22 04	22 34	23 01
West Hampstead Thameslink	d	08 54	09 09	09 24	09 39		19 39	19 54	20 09	20 26	20 39	20 56		21 26		21 56	22 26	22 56	23 24
St Pancras International 15 ⊖	d	09 04	09 18	09 34	09 48		19 48	20 04	20 18	20 36	20 48	21 06		21 36		22 06	22 36	23 06	23 38
Farringdon 3 ⊖	d	09 09	09 23	09 39	09 53		19 53	20 09	20 23	20 40	20 53	21 10		21 40		22 10	22 40	23 10	23 43
City Thameslink 3	d	09 13	09 27	09 43	09 57		19 57	20 13	20 27	20 43	20 57								
London Blackfriars 3 ⊖	d	09 16	09 30	09 46	10 00		20 00	20 16	20 30	20 46	21 00	21 16		21 46		22 16	22 46	23 16	23 48
Elephant & Castle ⊖	d	09 19	09 33	09 49	10 03		20 03	20 19	20 33	20 49	21 03	21 19		21 49		22 19	22 49	23 19	23 50
Loughborough Jn	d	09 23	09 37	09 53	10 07		20 07	20 23	20 37	20 53	21 07	21 23		21 53		22 23	22 53	23 23	
Herne Hill 4	d	09 27	09 41	09 57	10 11		20 11	20 27	20 41	20 57	21 11	21 27		21 57		22 27	22 57	23 27	23 58
London Bridge 4 ⊖	d																		
Tulse Hill 3	a	09 31	09 45	10 01	10 15		20 15	20 31	20 45	21 01	21 15	21 31		22 01		22 31	23 01	23 31	00 02
	d	09 31	09 46	10 01	10 16		20 16	20 31	20 46	21 01	21 16	21 31		22 01		22 31	23 01	23 31	00 02
Streatham 4	d	09 35	09 50	10 05	10 20	and at	20 20	20 35	20 50	21 05	21 20	21 35		22 05		22 35	23 05	23 35	00 06
Tooting	d	09 40		10 10		the same		20 40		21 10		21 40		22 10		22 40	23 10	23 40	00 10
Haydons Road	d	09 43		10 13		minutes		20 43		21 13		21 43		22 13		22 43	23 13	23 43	00 13
Wimbledon 6 ⊖	a	09 46		10 16		past		20 46		21 16		21 46		22 16		22 46	23 16	23 46	00 16
	d	09 47		10 17		each		20 47		21 17		21 47		22 17		22 47	23 17	23 47	00 17
Wimbledon Chase	d	09 50		10 20		hour until		20 50		21 20		21 50		22 20		22 50	23 20	23 50	00 20
South Merton	d	09 52		10 22				20 52		21 22		21 52		22 22		22 52	23 22	23 52	00 22
Morden South	d	09 54		10 24				20 54		21 24		21 54		22 24		22 54	23 24	23 54	00 24
St Helier	d	09 56		10 26				20 56		21 26		21 56		22 26		22 56	23 26	23 56	00 26
Sutton Common	d	09 58		10 28				20 58		21 28		21 58		22 28		22 58	23 28	23 58	00 28
West Sutton	d	10 01		10 31				21 01		21 31		22 01		22 31		23 01	23 31	00 01	00 31
Mitcham Eastfields	d		09 54		10 24		20 24		20 54		21 24								
Mitcham Junction	d		09 57		10 27		20 27		20 57		21 27								
Hackbridge	d		10 00		10 30		20 30		21 00		21 30								
Carshalton	d		10 03		10 33		20 33		21 03		21 33								
Sutton (Surrey) 4	a	10 05	10 06	10 35	10 36		20 36	21 05	21 06	21 35	21 42	22 05	22 15	22 35		23 05	23 35	00 05	00 35
	d		10 07		10 37		20 37		21 15		21 45		22 18		22 45				
West Sutton	d		10 10		10 40		20 40		21 18		21 48		22 20		22 48				
Sutton Common	d		10 12		10 42		20 42		21 20		21 50		22 23		22 50				
St Helier	d		10 15		10 45		20 45		21 23		21 53		22 25		22 53				
Morden South	d		10 17		10 47		20 47		21 25		21 55		22 27		22 55				
South Merton	d		10 19		10 49		20 49		21 27		21 57		22 29		22 57				
Wimbledon Chase	a		10 21		10 51		20 51		21 29		21 59		22 15		22 59				

For other London Bridge connections, please see table 173

Table 179

Sundays

8 December to 11 May

Thameslink - Wimbledon and Sutton

Network Diagram - see first Page of Table 173

Station		FC	FC	FC		FC	FC		FC		FC		FC
Luton 10	d					08 18			08 48		19 48		20 18
Luton Airport Parkway 7	d					08 21			08 51		19 51		20 21
St Albans City	d					08 33			09 03		20 03		20 33
West Hampstead Thameslink	d					08 57			09 27		20 27		20 57
St Pancras International 15 ⊖	d					09 06			09 36		20 36		21 06
Farringdon 3 ⊖	d					09 11			09 41		20 41		21 11
City Thameslink 3	d												
London Blackfriars 3 ⊖	d			08 58		09 16	09 28		09 46		20 46		21 16
Elephant & Castle ⊖	d			09 01		09 19	09 31		09 49		20 49		21 19
Loughborough Jn	d			09 05		09 23	09 35		09 53		20 53		21 23
Herne Hill 4	d			09 09		09 27	09 39		09 57		20 57		21 27
London Bridge 4 ⊖	d												
Tulse Hill 3	a			09 13		09 32	09 43		10 02		21 02		21 32
	d		00 02	09 14		09 32	09 44		10 02		21 02		21 32
Streatham 4	d		00 06	09 18		09 36	09 48		10 06	and at the same minutes past each hour until	21 06		21 36
Tooting	d		00 10			09 42			10 12		21 12		21 42
Haydons Road	d		00 13			09 45			10 15		21 15		21 45
Wimbledon 6 ⊖	a		00 16			09 47			10 17		21 17		21 47
	d		00 17			09 48			10 18		21 18		21 48
Wimbledon Chase	d		00 20			09 51			10 21		21 21		21 51
South Merton	d		00 22			09 53			10 23		21 23		21 53
Morden South	d		00 24			09 55			10 25		21 25		21 55
St Helier	d		00 26			09 57			10 27		21 27		21 57
Sutton Common	d		00 28			09 59			10 29		21 29		21 59
West Sutton	d	00 01	00 31			10 02			10 32		21 32		22 02
Mitcham Eastfields	d			09 22			09 52						
Mitcham Junction	d			09 25			09 55						
Hackbridge	d			09 29			09 59						
Carshalton	d			09 31			10 01						
Sutton (Surrey) 4	a	00 05	00 35	09 35		10 05	10 05		10 35		21 35		22 05
	d			09 37			10 07						
West Sutton	d			09 40			10 10						
Sutton Common	d			09 42			10 12						
St Helier	d			09 45			10 15						
Morden South	d			09 47			10 17						
South Merton	d			09 49			10 19						
Wimbledon Chase	a			09 51			10 21						

For other London Bridge connections, please see table 173

Table 179R

Mondays to Fridays

Wimbledon & Sutton - Thameslink

9 December to 16 May

Network Diagram - see first Page of Table 173

Miles	Miles			FC MX	FC MX	FC MX	FC MX	FC	SN	FC	SN	FC	FC	SN	FC	SN	FC	FC	SN		FC	FC [1]
—	0	**Wimbledon Chase**	d			07 05	00 22				05 59		06 19	06 38			07 05	07 20	07 35			07 50
—	0½	**South Merton**	d			07 07	00 24				06 01		06 21	06 40			07 07	07 22	07 37			07 52
—	1¼	**Morden South**	d			07 09	00 26				06 03		06 23	06 42			07 09	07 24	07 39			07 54
—	1¾	**St Helier**	d			07 11	00 28				06 05		06 25	06 44			07 11	07 26	07 41			07 56
—	2¾	**Sutton Common**	d	00 01		07 13	00 30				06 07		06 27	06 46			07 13	07 28	07 43			07 58
—	3½	**West Sutton**	d	00 04		07 16	00 33				06 10		06 30	06 49			07 16	07 31	07 46			08 01
0	4½	Sutton (Surrey) [4]	d	00a09		07 20	00a39		05 37		06 14	06 05	06 34	06 53	06 45	07 05	07 20	07 36	07 50	07 40		08 08
—	5¾	Carshalton	d			07 23			05 40		06 17		06 37	06 56			07 23	07 39	07 53			08 11
—	6¾	Hackbridge	d			07 25			05 42		06 19		06 39	06 58			07 25	07 41	07 55			08 13
—	7¾	Mitcham Junction	d			07 29			05 46		06 23		06 42	07 02			07 29	07 44	07 59			08 16
—	9	Mitcham Eastfields	d			07 32			05 49		06 26		06 45	07 05			07 32	07 47	08 02			08 19
1	—	**West Sutton**	d									06 08			06 48	07 08				07 43		
2	—	**Sutton Common**	d									06 10			06 50	07 10				07 45		
2¾	—	**St Helier**	d									06 13			06 53	07 13				07 48		
3¼	—	**Morden South**	d									06 15			06 55	07 15				07 50		
4	—	**South Merton**	d									06 17			06 57	07 17				07 52		
4½	—	**Wimbledon Chase**	d									06 19			06 59	07 19				07 54		
5½	—	Wimbledon [6] ⊖	a									06 22			07 05	07 22				07 57		
—	—		d									06 28			07 06	07 26				08 00		
6¼	—	**Haydons Road**	d									06 30			07 08	07 28				08 02		
7½	—	**Tooting**	d									06 33			07 11	07 31				08 06		
9	10½	Streatham [4]	d			07 35		05 46	05 53	06 09	06 30	06 38	06 49	07 10	07 16	07 38	07 35	07 52	08 09	08 12		08 23
10½	12	Tulse Hill [3]	a			07 39		05 50	05 56	06 13	06 34	06 42	06 53	07 13	07 20	07 43	07 39	07 56	08 12	08 16		08 27
—	—		d			07 44		05 51	05 56	06 13	06 34	06 42	06 53	07 14	07 20	07 43	07 44	07 57	08 14	08 16		08 28
—	—	London Bridge [4] ⊖	a			08 03			06 13		06 51			07 33			08 03		08 33			
11¾	13¼	Herne Hill [4]	d					05 55		06 17		06 46	06 57		07 24	07 47		08 01		08 20		08 32
12¾	14¼	Loughborough Jn	d							06 20		06 49	07 00		07 27	07 50		08 04		08 24		08 36
14½	16	Elephant & Castle ⊖	d					06 00		06 24		06 54	07 06		07 32	07 54		08 09		08 29		08 40
15¾	17¼	London Blackfriars [3] ⊖	d					06 04		06 30		06 58	07 12		07 36	07 58		08 13		08 33		08 46
16	17¾	City Thameslink [3]	d					06 07		06 32		07 00	07 14		07 38	08 01		08 15		08 35		08 48
16½	18	Farringdon [3] ⊖	d					06 10		06 36		07 04	07 18		07 42	08 04		08 19		08 39		08 52
17¾	19¼	St Pancras International [15] ⊖	d					06 15		06 40		07 08	07 22		07 46	08 10		08 24		08 44		08 56
21¾	23¼	West Hampstead Thameslink	d					06 22		06 48		07 16	07 30		07 54	08 18		08 34		08 54		09 04
37¾	39¼	St Albans City	d			00 21		06 48		07 12		07 38	07a51		08 09	08a43		08a59		09 18		09a29
47	—	Luton Airport Parkway [7]	d		00 03	00 33		07 00		07 24		07 49			08 21					09 30		08 08
48	—	Luton [10]	a		00 05	00 35		07 03		07 26		07 53			08 23					09 34		08 11

		FC	SN	FC	FC	SN	FC	FC	FC [1]	FC	FC	FC	FC	FC	FC	FC	FC
Wimbledon Chase	d		08 07	08 22		08 38	08 58		09 20		09 50			10 20		10 50	
South Merton	d		08 09	08 24		08 40	09 00		09 22		09 52			10 22		10 52	
Morden South	d		08 11	08 26		08 42	09 02		09 24		09 54			10 24		10 54	
St Helier	d		08 13	08 28		08 44	09 04		09 26		09 56			10 26		10 56	
Sutton Common	d		08 15	08 30		08 46	09 06		09 28		09 58			10 28		10 58	
West Sutton	d		08 18	08 33		08 49	09 09		09 31		10 01			10 31		11 01	
Sutton (Surrey) [4]	d	08 08	08 23	08 39	08 41	08 53	09 13	09 11	09 38	09 37	10 08		10 07	10 38	10 37	11 08	11 07
Carshalton	d		08 26	08 42		08 56	09 16		09 41		10 11			10 41		11 11	
Hackbridge	d		08 28	08 44		08 58	09 18		09 43		10 13			10 43		11 13	
Mitcham Junction	d		08 32	08 47		09 02	09 21		09 46		10 16			10 46		11 16	
Mitcham Eastfields	d		08 35	08 50		09 05	09 24		09 49		10 19			10 49		11 19	
West Sutton	d	08 11			08 44			09 14		09 40			10 10		10 40		11 10
Sutton Common	d	08 13			08 46			09 16		09 42			10 12		10 42		11 12
St Helier	d	08 16			08 49			09 19		09 45			10 15		10 45		11 15
Morden South	d	08 18			08 51			09 21		09 47			10 17		10 47		11 17
South Merton	d	08 20			08 53			09 23		09 49			10 19		10 49		11 19
Wimbledon Chase	d	08 22			08 55			09 25		09 51			10 21		10 51		11 21
Wimbledon [6] ⊖	a	08 25			08 58			09 28		09 54			10 24		10 54		11 24
	d	08 28			08 58			09 28		09 58			10 28		10 58		11 28
Haydons Road	d	08 30			09 00			09 30		10 00			10 30		11 00		11 30
Tooting	d	08 33			09 03			09 33		10 03			10 33		11 03		11 33
Streatham [4]	d	08 39	08 42	08 54	09 08	09 11	09 28	09 38	09 53	10 08	10 23		10 38	10 53	11 08	11 23	11 38
Tulse Hill [3]	a	08 43	08 46	08 58	09 12	09 15	09 32	09 42	09 57	10 12	10 27		10 42	10 57	11 12	11 27	11 42
	d	08 43	08 46	08 58	09 16	09 15	09 32	09 42	09 57	10 12	10 27		10 42	10 57	11 12	11 27	11 42
London Bridge [4] ⊖	a		09 03			09 33											
Herne Hill [4]	d	08 47		09 02	09 20		09 36	09 46	10 01	10 16	10 31		10 46	11 01	11 16	11 31	11 46
Loughborough Jn	d	08 50		09 05	09 23		09 40	09 50	10 04	10 19	10 34		10 49	11 04	11 19	11 34	11 49
Elephant & Castle ⊖	d	08 58		09 10	09 30		09 45	09 55	10 09	10 24	10 39		10 54	11 09	11 24	11 39	11 54
London Blackfriars [3] ⊖	d	09 02		09 14	09 34		09 50	10 00	10 14	10 30	10 44		11 00	11 14	11 30	11 44	12 00
City Thameslink [3]	d	09 04		09 16	09 36		09 52	10 02	10 16	10 32	10 46		11 02	11 16	11 32	11 46	12 02
Farringdon [3] ⊖	d	09 08		09 20	09 40		09 56	10 06	10 19	10 36	10 49		11 06	11 19	11 36	11 49	12 06
St Pancras International [15] ⊖	d	09 12		09 24	09 44		10a00	10 10	10 24	10 40	10 54		11 10	11 24	11 40	11 54	12 10
West Hampstead Thameslink	d	09 20		09 32	09 52			10 20	10 32	10 50	11 02		11 20	11 32	11 50	12 02	12 20
St Albans City	d	09 46		09a53	10 18			10 46	10a57	11 14	11a27		11 44	11a57	12 14	12a27	12 44
Luton Airport Parkway [7]	d	09 57			10 29			10 59		11 25			11 55		12 25		12 55
Luton [10]	a	10 01			10 33			11 03		11 29			11 59		12 29		12 57

For other London Bridge connections, please see table 173

Table 179R

Wimbledon & Sutton - Thameslink

Mondays to Fridays

9 December to 16 May

Network Diagram - see first Page of Table 173

		FC	FC	FC	FC	FC	FC	FC	FC	FC	FC	FC	FC	FC	FC	FC
Wimbledon Chase	d	11 20		11 50		12 20		12 50		13 20		13 50		14 20		14 50
South Merton	d	11 22		11 52		12 22		12 52		13 22		13 52		14 22		14 52
Morden South	d	11 24		11 54		12 24		12 54		13 24		13 54		14 24		14 54
St Helier	d	11 26		11 56		12 26		12 56		13 26		13 56		14 26		14 56
Sutton Common	d	11 28		11 58		12 28		12 58		13 28		13 58		14 28		14 58
West Sutton	d	11 31		12 01		12 31		13 01		13 31		14 01		14 31		15 01
Sutton (Surrey) 4	d	11 38	11 37	12 08	12 07	12 38	12 37	13 08	13 07	13 38	13 37	14 08	14 07	14 38	14 37	15 08
Carshalton	d	11 41		12 11		12 41		13 11		13 41		14 11		14 41		15 11
Hackbridge	d	11 43		12 13		12 43		13 13		13 43		14 13		14 43		15 13
Mitcham Junction	d	11 46		12 16		12 46		13 16		13 46		14 16		14 46		15 16
Mitcham Eastfields	d	11 49		12 19		12 49		13 19		13 49		14 19		14 49		15 19
West Sutton	d		11 40		12 10		12 40		13 10		13 40		14 10		14 40	
Sutton Common	d		11 42		12 12		12 42		13 12		13 42		14 12		14 42	
St Helier	d		11 45		12 15		12 45		13 15		13 45		14 15		14 45	
Morden South	d		11 47		12 17		12 47		13 17		13 47		14 17		14 47	
South Merton	d		11 49		12 19		12 49		13 19		13 49		14 19		14 49	
Wimbledon Chase	d		11 51		12 21		12 51		13 21		13 51		14 21		14 51	
Wimbledon 6 ⊖	a		11 54		12 24		12 54		13 24		13 54		14 24		14 54	
	d		11 58		12 28		12 58		13 28		13 58		14 28		14 58	
Haydons Road	d		12 00		12 30		13 00		13 30		14 00		14 30		15 00	
Tooting	d		12 03		12 33		13 03		13 33		14 03		14 33		15 03	
Streatham 4	d	11 53	12 08	12 23	12 38	12 53	13 08	13 23	13 38	13 53	14 08	14 23	14 38	14 53	15 08	15 23
Tulse Hill 3	a	11 57	12 12	12 27	12 42	12 57	13 12	13 27	13 42	13 57	14 12	14 27	14 42	14 57	15 12	15 27
	d	11 57	12 12	12 27	12 42	12 57	13 12	13 27	13 42	13 57	14 12	14 27	14 42	14 57	15 12	15 27
London Bridge 4 ⊖	a															
Herne Hill 4	d	12 01	12 16	12 31	12 46	13 01	13 16	13 31	13 46	14 01	14 16	14 31	14 46	15 01	15 16	15 31
Loughborough Jn.	d	12 04	12 19	12 34	12 49	13 04	13 19	13 34	13 49	14 04	14 19	14 34	14 49	15 04	15 19	15 34
Elephant & Castle ⊖	d	12 09	12 24	12 39	12 54	13 09	13 24	13 39	13 54	14 09	14 24	14 39	14 54	15 09	15 24	15 39
London Blackfriars 3 ⊖	d	12 14	12 30	12 44	13 00	13 14	13 30	13 44	14 00	14 14	14 30	14 44	15 00	15 14	15 30	15 44
City Thameslink 3	d	12 16	12 32	12 46	13 02	13 16	13 32	13 46	14 02	14 16	14 32	14 46	15 02	15 16	15 32	15 46
Farringdon 3 ⊖	d	12 19	12 36	12 49	13 06	13 19	13 36	13 49	14 06	14 19	14 36	14 49	15 06	15 19	15 36	15 49
St Pancras International 15 ⊖	d	12 24	12 40	12 54	13 10	13 24	13 40	13 54	14 10	14 24	14 40	14 54	15 10	15 24	15 40	15 54
West Hampstead Thameslink	d	12 32	12 50	13 02	13 20	13 32	13 50	14 02	14 20	14 32	14 50	15 02	15 20	15 32	15 50	16 02
St Albans City	d	12a57	13 14	13a27	13 44	13a57	14 14	14a27	14 44	14a57	15 14	15a27	15 44	15a57	16 14	16a27
Luton Airport Parkway 7	d		13 25		13 55		14 25		14 55		15 25		15 55		16 25	
Luton 10	a		13 29		13 59		14 29		14 59		15 29		15 59		16 29	

		FC	FC	FC	FC	FC	FC 1 A	FC	FC	FC	FC	FC	FC	SN	FC	FC
Wimbledon Chase	d		15 20		15 50		16 20		16 50		17 22	17 22			17 52	
South Merton	d		15 22		15 52		16 22		16 52		17 24	17 24			17 54	
Morden South	d		15 24		15 54		16 24		16 54		17 26	17 26			17 56	
St Helier	d		15 26		15 56		16 26		16 56		17 28	17 28			17 58	
Sutton Common	d		15 28		15 58		16 28		16 58		17 30	17 30			18 00	
West Sutton	d		15 31		16 01		16 31		17 01		17 33	17 33			18 03	
Sutton (Surrey) 4	d	15 07	15 38	15 37	16 08	16 07	16 38	16 37	17 08	17 11	17 42	17 42	17 41	18 03	18 08	18 11
Carshalton	d		15 41		16 11		16 41		17 11		17 45	17 45			18 11	
Hackbridge	d		15 43		16 13		16 43		17 13		17 47	17 47			18 13	
Mitcham Junction	d		15 46		16 16		16 46		17 16		17 50	17 50			18 16	
Mitcham Eastfields	d		15 49		16 19		16 49		17 19		17 53	17 53			18 19	
West Sutton	d	15 10		15 40		16 10		16 40		17 14			17 44	18 06		18 14
Sutton Common	d	15 12		15 42		16 12		16 42		17 16			17 46	18 09		18 16
St Helier	d	15 15		15 45		16 15		16 45		17 19			17 49	18 11		18 19
Morden South	d	15 17		15 47		16 17		16 47		17 21			17 51	18 13		18 21
South Merton	d	15 19		15 49		16 19		16 49		17 23			17 53	18 15		18 23
Wimbledon Chase	d	15 21		15 51		16 21		16 51		17 25			17 55	18 17		18 25
Wimbledon 6 ⊖	a	15 24		15 54		16 24		16 54		17 28			17 58	18 20		18 28
	d	15 28		15 58		16 30		17 00		17 30			18 00	18 21		18 30
Haydons Road	d	15 30		16 00		16 32		17 02		17 32			18 02	18 23		18 32
Tooting	d	15 33		16 03		16 35		17 05		17 35			18 05	18 26		18 35
Streatham 4	d	15 38	15 53	16 08	16 23	16 40	16 53	17 10	17 23	17 40	17 57	17 57	18 10	18 31	18 23	18 40
Tulse Hill 3	a	15 42	15 57	16 12	16 27	16 44	16 57	17 14	17 27	17 44	18 01	18 01	18 15	18 35	18 28	18 44
	d	15 42	15 57	16 12	16 27	16 46	16 57	17 16	17 27	17 44	18 01	18 01	18 16	18 36	18 28	18 44
London Bridge 4 ⊖	a													18 53		
Herne Hill 4	d	15 46	16 01	16 16	16 31	16 50	17 01	17 21	17 31	17 48	18 06	18 06	18 20		18 32	18 48
Loughborough Jn.	d	15 49	16 04	16 19	16 34	16 53		17 24	17 34	17 51	18 09	18 09	18 23		18 35	18 51
Elephant & Castle ⊖	d	15 54	16 09	16 24	16 39	17 00	17 08	17 28	17 39	17 56	18 14	18 14	18 28		18 40	18 56
London Blackfriars 3 ⊖	d	16 00	16 14	16 30	16 44	17 04	17 12	17 32	17 46	18 00	18 18	18 18	18 32		18 44	19 00
City Thameslink 3	d	16 02	16 16	16 32	16 46	17 06	17 14	17 34	17 48	18 02	18 20	18 20	18 34		18 46	19 02
Farringdon 3 ⊖	d	16 06	16 19	16 35	16 49	17 09	17 17	17 37	17 51	18 05	18 23	18 23	18 37		18 49	19 05
St Pancras International 15 ⊖	d	16 10	16 24	16 40	16 54	17 14	17 22	17 42	17 56	18 10	18 28	18 28	18 42		18 54	19 10
West Hampstead Thameslink	d	16 20	16 32	16 50	17 02	17 22		17 50	18 04	18 20	18 36	18 36	18 50		19 02	19 18
St Albans City	d	16 44	16a59	17 14	17a29	17a51	17 44	18 16	18a31	18 46	19a03	19a03	19 18		19 22	19 42
Luton Airport Parkway 7	d	16 56		17 25			17 57	18 27		18 58			19 30		19 34	19 54
Luton 10	a	17 00		17 29			18 00	18 31		19 01			19 33		19 36	19 57

A 1 to Farringdon

For other London Bridge connections, please see table 173

Table 179R

Mondays to Fridays

9 December to 16 May

Wimbledon & Sutton - Thameslink

Network Diagram - see first Page of Table 173

		FC	FC	FC	SN	FC	FC	FC	FC	FC	FC	FC	FC	FC	FC	FC	FC
Wimbledon Chase	d		18 22			18 52		19 27		19 52		20 22		20 52		21 22	
South Merton	d		18 24			18 54		19 29		19 54		20 24		20 54		21 24	
Morden South	d		18 26			18 56		19 31		19 56		20 26		20 56		21 26	
St Helier	d		18 28			18 58		19 33		19 58		20 28		20 58		21 28	
Sutton Common	d		18 30			19 00		19 35		20 00		20 30		21 00		21 30	
West Sutton	d		18 33			19 03		19 38		20 03		20 33		21 03		21 33	
Sutton (Surrey) 4	d	18 30	18 38	18 43	19 00	19 08	19 13	19 42	19 37	20 12	20 07	20 42	20 37	21 12	21 17	21a39	21 47
Carshalton	d		18 41			19 11		19 45		20 15		20 45		21 15			
Hackbridge	d		18 43			19 13		19 47		20 17		20 47		21 17			
Mitcham Junction	d		18 46			19 16		19 50		20 20		20 50		21 20			
Mitcham Eastfields	d		18 49			19 19		19 53		20 23		20 53		21 23			
West Sutton	d	18 34		18 46	19 04		19 16		19 40		20 10		20 40		21 20		21 50
Sutton Common	d	18 36		18 48	19 06		19 18		19 42		20 12		20 42		21 22		21 52
St Helier	d	18 39		18 51	19 09		19 21		19 45		20 15		20 45		21 25		21 55
Morden South	d	18 41		18 53	19 11		19 23		19 47		20 17		20 47		21 27		21 57
South Merton	d	18 43		18 55	19 13		19 25		19 49		20 19		20 49		21 29		21 59
Wimbledon Chase	d	18 45		18 57	19 15		19 27		19 51		20 21		20 51		21 31		22 01
Wimbledon 6 ⊖	a	18 50		19 00	19 18		19 30		19 54		20 24		20 54		21 34		22 04
	d	18 51		19 00	19 20		19 30		19 56		20 26		20 56		21 38		22 08
Haydons Road	d	18 53		19 02	19 22		19 32		19 58		20 28		20 58		21 40		22 10
Tooting	d	18 56		19 05	19 26		19 35		20 01		20 31		21 01		21 43		22 13
Streatham 4	d	19 01	18 53	19 10	19 30	19 23	19 40	19 57	20 06	20 27	20 36	20 57	21 06	21 27	21 49		22 19
Tulse Hill 3	a	19 05	18 57	19 14	19 34	19 27	19 44	20 01	20 10	20 31	20 40	21 01	21 10	21 31	21 53		22 23
	d	19 05	18 57	19 14	19 35	19 27	19 44	20 01	20 12	20 31	20 42	21 01	21 12	21 31	21 53		22 23
London Bridge 4 ⊖	a	19 23			19 53												
Herne Hill 4	d		19 02	19 17		19 31	19 47	20 05	20 16	20 35	20 46	21 05	21 16	21 35	21 57		22 27
Loughborough Jn.	d		19 05	19 20		19 34	19 50	20 08	20 19	20 38	20 49	21 08	21 19	21 38	22 00		22 30
Elephant & Castle ⊖	d		19 10	19 25		19 39	19 55	20 13	20 24	20 43	20 54	21 13	21 24	21 43	22 04		22 34
London Blackfriars 3 ⊖	d		19 18	19 30		19 46	20 00	20 18	20 30	20 48	21 00	21 18	21 30	21 48	22 08		22 38
City Thameslink 3	d		19 20	19 32		19 48	20 02	20 20	20 32	20 50	21 02	21 20	21 32	21 50	22 10		22 40
Farringdon 3 ⊖	d		19 23	19 36		19 51	20 06	20 23	20 36	20 53	21 06	21 23	21 36	21 53	22 13		22 43
St Pancras International 15 ⊖	d		19 28	19 40		19 56	20 10	20 28	20 40	20 58	21 10	21 28	21 40	21 58	22 18		22 48
West Hampstead Thameslink	d		19 36	19 50		20 03	20 19	20 35	20 49	21 05	21 19	21 35	21 49	22 05	22 25		22 55
St Albans City	d		20a01	20 14		20a29	20 44	21a01	21 14	21a31	21 44	22a01	22 14	22a31	22 50		23 21
Luton Airport Parkway 7	d			20 25			20 55		21 25		21 55		22 25		23 02		23 33
Luton 10	a			20 29			20 59		21 29		21 59		22 29		23 04		23 35

		FC	FC	FC	FC	FC	FC	FC
Wimbledon Chase	d	21 52		22 22		22 52	23 20	23 52
South Merton	d	21 54		22 24		22 54	23 22	23 54
Morden South	d	21 56		22 26		22 56	23 24	23 56
St Helier	d	21 58		22 28		22 58	23 26	23 58
Sutton Common	d	22 00		22 30		23 00	23 28	00 01
West Sutton	d	22 03		22 33		23 03	23 31	00 04
Sutton (Surrey) 4	d	22a09	22 17	22a39	22 47	23a09	23a35	00a09
Carshalton	d							
Hackbridge	d							
Mitcham Junction	d							
Mitcham Eastfields	d							
West Sutton	d		22 20		22 50			
Sutton Common	d		22 22		22 52			
St Helier	d		22 25		22 55			
Morden South	d		22 27		22 57			
South Merton	d		22 29		22 59			
Wimbledon Chase	d		22 31		23 01			
Wimbledon 6 ⊖	a		22 34		23 04			
	d		22 38		23 08			
Haydons Road	d		22 40		23 10			
Tooting	d		22 43		23 13			
Streatham 4	d		22 49		23 19			
Tulse Hill 3	a		22 53		23 23			
	d		22 53		23 23			
London Bridge 4 ⊖	a							
Herne Hill 4	d		22 57		23 27			
Loughborough Jn.	d		23 00					
Elephant & Castle ⊖	d		23 04		23 34			
London Blackfriars 3 ⊖	d		23 08		23 38			
City Thameslink 3	d							
Farringdon 3 ⊖	d		23 13		23 43			
St Pancras International 15 ⊖	d		23 18		23 48			
West Hampstead Thameslink	d		23 25		23 55			
St Albans City	d		23 51		00 21			
Luton Airport Parkway 7	d		00 03		00 33			
Luton 10	a		00 05		00 35			

For other London Bridge connections, please see table 173

Table 179R

Saturdays

14 December to 17 May

Wimbledon & Sutton - Thameslink

Network Diagram - see first Page of Table 173

		FC	FC	FC	FC	FC	FC	FC	FC	FC	FC	FC	FC	FC	FC	FC	FC
Wimbledon Chase	d				00 22					06 50		07 20		07 50		08 20	
South Merton	d				00 24					06 52		07 22		07 52		08 22	
Morden South	d				00 26					06 54		07 24		07 54		08 24	
St Helier	d				00 28					06 56		07 26		07 56		08 26	
Sutton Common	d	00 01			00 30					06 58		07 28		07 58		08 28	
West Sutton	d	00 04			00 33					07 01		07 31		08 01		08 31	
Sutton (Surrey) 4	d	00a09			00a39				06 37	07 08	07 07	07 38	07 37	08 08	08 07	08 38	08 37
Carshalton	d									07 11		07 41		08 11		08 41	
Hackbridge	d									07 13		07 43		08 13		08 43	
Mitcham Junction	d									07 16		07 46		08 16		08 46	
Mitcham Eastfields	d									07 19		07 49		08 19		08 49	
West Sutton	d								06 40		07 10		07 40		08 10		08 40
Sutton Common	d								06 42		07 12		07 42		08 12		08 42
St Helier	d								06 45		07 15		07 45		08 15		08 45
Morden South	d								06 47		07 17		07 47		08 17		08 47
South Merton	d								06 49		07 19		07 49		08 19		08 49
Wimbledon Chase	d								06 51		07 21		07 51		08 21		08 51
Wimbledon 6	a								06 54		07 24		07 54		08 24		08 54
	d								06 58		07 28		07 58		08 28		08 58
Haydons Road	d								07 00		07 30		08 00		08 30		09 00
Tooting	d								07 03		07 33		08 03		08 33		09 03
Streatham 4	d					05 49	06 19	06 49	07 08	07 23	07 38	07 53	08 08	08 23	08 38	08 53	09 08
Tulse Hill 3	a					05 53	06 23	06 53	07 12	07 27	07 42	07 57	08 12	08 27	08 42	08 57	09 12
	d					05 56	06 26	06 56	07 12	07 27	07 42	07 57	08 12	08 27	08 42	08 57	09 12
London Bridge 4	a																
Herne Hill 4	d					06 02	06 32	07 01	07 16	07 31	07 46	08 01	08 16	08 31	08 46	09 01	09 16
Loughborough Jn.	d						06 35	07 04	07 19	07 34	07 49	08 04	08 19	08 34	08 49	09 04	09 19
Elephant & Castle	d					06 09	06 39	07 09	07 24	07 39	07 54	08 09	08 24	08 39	08 54	09 09	09 24
London Blackfriars 3	d					06 14	06 44	07 14	07 30	07 44	08 00	08 14	08 30	08 44	08 00	09 14	09 30
City Thameslink 3	d														08 02	09 16	09 32
Farringdon 3	d					06 19	06 49	07 19	07 36	07 49	08 06	08 19	08 36	08 49	08 06	09 19	09 36
St Pancras International 15	d					06 24	06 54	07 24	07 40	07 54	08 10	08 24	08 40	08 54	08 10	09 24	09 40
West Hampstead Thameslink	d					06 32	07 02	07 32	07 50	08 02	08 20	08 32	08 50	09 02	08 20	09 32	09 50
St Albans City	d			00 21		06 56	07 26	07 56	08 14	08a27	08 44	08a57	09 14	09a27	08 44	09a57	10 14
Luton Airport Parkway 7	d		00 03	00 33		07 07	07 37	08 07	08 25		08 55		09 25		08 55		10 25
Luton 10	a		00 05	00 35		07 11	07 41	08 10	08 29		08 59		09 29		08 59		10 29

		FC		FC	FC	FC	FC	FC	FC	FC	FC	FC	FC	FC	FC	FC	FC
Wimbledon Chase	d	08 50		17 50		18 20		18 50		19 20		19 50		20 20		20 50	
South Merton	d	08 52		17 52		18 22		18 52		19 22		19 52		20 22		20 52	
Morden South	d	08 54		17 54		18 24		18 54		19 24		19 54		20 24		20 54	
St Helier	d	08 56		17 56		18 26		18 56		19 26		19 56		20 26		20 56	
Sutton Common	d	08 58		17 58		18 28		18 58		19 28		19 58		20 28		20 58	
West Sutton	d	09 01		18 01		18 31		19 01		19 31		20 01		20 31		21 01	
Sutton (Surrey) 4	d	09 08		18 08	18 07	18 38	18 37	19 08	19 07	19 38	19 37	20 08	20 07	20 38	20 37	21 08	21 15
Carshalton	d	09 11		18 11		18 41		19 11		19 41		20 11		20 41		21 11	
Hackbridge	d	09 13		18 13		18 43		19 13		19 43		20 13		20 43		21 13	
Mitcham Junction	d	09 16		18 16		18 46		19 16		19 46		20 16		20 46		21 16	
Mitcham Eastfields	d	09 19		18 19		18 49		19 19		19 49		20 19		20 49		21 19	
West Sutton	d				18 10		18 40		19 10		19 40		20 10		20 40		21 18
Sutton Common	d				18 12		18 42		19 12		19 42		20 12		20 42		21 20
St Helier	d				18 15		18 45		19 15		19 45		20 15		20 45		21 23
Morden South	d		and at		18 17		18 47		19 17		19 47		20 17		20 47		21 25
South Merton	d		the same		18 19		18 49		19 19		19 49		20 19		20 49		21 27
Wimbledon Chase	d		minutes		18 21		18 51		19 21		19 51		20 21		20 51		21 29
Wimbledon 6	a		past		18 24		18 54		19 24		19 54		20 24		20 54		21 32
	d		each		18 28		18 58		19 28		19 58		20 28		20 58		21 38
Haydons Road	d		hour until		18 30		19 00		19 30		20 00		20 30		21 00		21 40
Tooting	d				18 33		19 03		19 33		20 03		20 33		21 03		21 43
Streatham 4	d	09 23		18 23	18 38	18 53	19 08	19 23	19 38	19 53	20 08	20 23	20 38	20 53	21 08	21 23	21 49
Tulse Hill 3	a	09 27		18 27	18 42	18 57	19 12	19 27	19 42	19 57	20 12	20 27	20 42	20 57	21 12	21 27	21 53
	d	09 27		18 27	18 42	18 57	19 12	19 27	19 42	19 57	20 12	20 27	20 42	20 57	21 12	21 27	21 53
London Bridge 4	a																
Herne Hill 4	d	09 31		18 31	18 46	19 01	19 16	19 31	19 46	20 01	20 16	20 31	20 46	21 01	21 16	21 31	21 57
Loughborough Jn.	d	09 34		18 34	18 49	19 04	19 19	19 34	19 49	20 04	20 19	20 34	20 49	21 04	21 19	21 34	22 00
Elephant & Castle	d	09 39		18 39	18 54	19 09	19 24	19 39	19 54	20 09	20 24	20 39	20 54	21 09	21 24	21 39	22 04
London Blackfriars 3	d	09 44		18 44	19 00	19 14	19 30	19 44	20 00	20 14	20 30	20 44	21 00	21 14	21 30	21 44	22 08
City Thameslink 3	d	09 46		18 46	19 02	19 16	19 32	19 46	20 02	20 16	20 32	20 46					
Farringdon 3	d	09 49		18 49	19 06	19 19	19 36	19 49	20 06	20 19	20 36	20 49	21 06	21 19	21 36	21 49	22 13
St Pancras International 15	d	09 54		18 54	19 10	19 24	19 40	19 54	20 10	20 24	20 40	20 54	21 10	21 24	21 40	21 54	22 18
West Hampstead Thameslink	d	10 02		19 02	19 20	19 32	19 50	20 02	20 20	20 32	20 50	21 02	21 20	21 32	21 50	22 02	22 25
St Albans City	d	10a27		19a27	19 44	19a57	20 14	20 27	20 44	20 58	21 14	21a27	21 44	21a57	22 14	22a27	22 50
Luton Airport Parkway 7	d				19 55		20 25	20 41	20 55	21 11	21 25		21 55		22 25		23 02
Luton 10	a				19 59		20 29	20 44	20 59	21 14	21 29		21 59		22 29		23 04

For other London Bridge connections, please see table 173

Table 179R

Saturdays

14 December to 17 May

Wimbledon & Sutton - Thameslink

Network Diagram - see first Page of Table 173

		FC	FC	FC	FC	FC	FC	FC	FC	FC
Wimbledon Chase	d	21 20		21 50		22 20		22 50	23 20	23 50
South Merton	d	21 22		21 52		22 22		22 52	23 22	23 52
Morden South	d	21 24		21 54		22 24		22 54	23 24	23 54
St Helier	d	21 26		21 56		22 26		22 56	23 26	23 56
Sutton Common	d	21 28		21 58		22 28		22 58	23 28	23 58
West Sutton	d	21 31		22 01		22 31		23 01	23 31	00 01
Sutton (Surrey) 4	d	21a35	21 45	22a05	22 15	22a35	22 45	23a05	23a35	00a05
Carshalton	d									
Hackbridge	d									
Mitcham Junction	d									
Mitcham Eastfields	d									
West Sutton	d		21 48		22 18		22 48			
Sutton Common	d		21 50		22 20		22 50			
St Helier	d		21 53		22 23		22 53			
Morden South	d		21 55		22 25		22 55			
South Merton	d		21 57		22 27		22 57			
Wimbledon Chase	d		21 59		22 29		22 59			
Wimbledon 6 ⊖	a		22 02		22 32		23 02			
	d		22 08		22 38		23 08			
Haydons Road	d		22 10		22 40		23 10			
Tooting	d		22 13		22 43		23 13			
Streatham 4	d		22 19		22 49		23 19			
Tulse Hill 3	a		22 23		22 53		23 23			
	d		22 23		22 53		23 23			
London Bridge 4 ⊖	a									
Herne Hill 4	d		22 27		22 57		23 27			
Loughborough Jn.	d		22 30		23 00					
Elephant & Castle ⊖	d		22 34		23 04		23 34			
London Blackfriars 3 ⊖	d		22 38		23 08		23 38			
City Thameslink 3	d									
Farringdon 3 ⊖	d		22 43		23 13		23 43			
St Pancras International 15 ⊖	d		22 48		23 18		23 48			
West Hampstead Thameslink	d		22 55		23 25		23 55			
St Albans City	d		23 21		23 51		00 21			
Luton Airport Parkway 7	d		23 33		00 03		00 33			
Luton 10	a		23 35		00 05		00 35			

Sundays

8 December to 11 May

		FC	FC	FC	FC	FC	FC	FC	FC	FC	FC			FC	FC	FC	FC	FC	FC	FC	FC
Wimbledon Chase	d			00 20			09 51		10 21		10 51				18 21		18 51		19 21		19 51
South Merton	d			00 22			09 53		10 23		10 53				18 23		18 53		19 23		19 53
Morden South	d			00 24			09 55		10 25		10 55				18 25		18 55		19 25		19 55
St Helier	d			00 26			09 57		10 27		10 57				18 27		18 57		19 27		19 57
Sutton Common	d			00 28			09 59		10 29		10 59				18 29		18 59		19 29		19 59
West Sutton	d	00 01		00 31			10 02		10 32		11 02				18 32		19 02		19 32		20 02
Sutton (Surrey) 4	d	00a05		00a35		09 37	10 08	10 07	10 38	10 37	11 08	11 07		18 07	18 38	18 37	19 08	19 07	19 38	19 37	20 08
Carshalton	d						10 11		10 41		11 11				18 41		19 11		19 41		20 11
Hackbridge	d						10 13		10 43		11 13				18 43		19 13		19 43		20 13
Mitcham Junction	d						10 16		10 46		11 16				18 46		19 16		19 46		20 16
Mitcham Eastfields	d						10 19		10 49		11 19				18 49		19 19		19 49		20 19
West Sutton	d					09 40		10 10		10 40		11 10		18 10		18 40		19 10		19 40	
Sutton Common	d					09 42		10 12		10 42		11 12		18 12		18 42		19 12		19 42	
St Helier	d					09 45		10 15		10 45		11 15	and at	18 15		18 45		19 15		19 45	
Morden South	d					09 47		10 17		10 47		11 17	the same	18 17		18 47		19 17		19 47	
South Merton	d					09 49		10 19		10 49		11 19	minutes	18 19		18 49		19 19		19 49	
Wimbledon Chase	d					09 51		10 21		10 51		11 21	past	18 21		18 51		19 21		19 51	
Wimbledon 6 ⊖	a					09 54		10 24		10 54		11 24	each	18 24		18 54		19 24		19 54	
	d					09 56		10 26		10 56		11 26	hour until	18 26		18 56		19 26		19 56	
Haydons Road	d					09 58		10 28		10 58		11 28		18 28		18 58		19 28		19 58	
Tooting	d					10 01		10 31		11 01		11 31		18 31		19 01		19 31		20 01	
Streatham 4	d					10 06	10 23	10 36	10 53	11 06	11 23	11 36		18 36	18 53	19 06	19 23	19 36	19 53	20 06	20 23
Tulse Hill 3	a					10 10	10 27	10 40	10 57	11 10	11 27	11 40		18 40	18 57	19 10	19 27	19 40	19 57	20 10	20 27
	d					10 10	10 27	10 40	10 57	11 10	11 27	11 40		18 40	18 57	19 10	19 27	19 40	19 57	20 10	20 27
London Bridge 4 ⊖	a																				
Herne Hill 4	d					10 14	10 31	10 44	11 01	11 14	11 31	11 44		18 44	19 01	19 14	19 31	19 44	20 01	20 14	20 31
Loughborough Jn.	d					10 17	10 34	10 47	11 04	11 17	11 34	11 47		18 47	19 04	19 17	19 34	19 47	20 04	20 17	20 34
Elephant & Castle ⊖	d					10 22	10 39	10 52	11 09	11 22	11 39	11 52		18 52	19 09	19 22	19 39	19 52	20 09	20 22	20 39
London Blackfriars 3 ⊖	d					10 26	10a43	10 56	11a13	11 26	11a43	11 56		18 56	19a13	19 26	19a43	19 56	20a13	20 26	20a43
City Thameslink 3	d																		19 38		
Farringdon 3 ⊖	d					10 32		11 02		11 32		12 02		19 02		19 32		20 02	19 41	20 32	
St Pancras International 15 ⊖	d					10 36		11 06		11 36		12 06		19 06		19 36		20 06	19 43	20 36	
West Hampstead Thameslink	d					10 44		11 14		11 44		12 14		19 14		19 44		20 14	19 46	20 44	
St Albans City	d				00 21	11 09		11 39		12 09		12 39		19 39		20 09		20 39	19 49	21 09	
Luton Airport Parkway 7	d		00 03		00 33	11 20		11 50		12 20		12 50		19 50		20 20		20 50		21 20	
Luton 10	a		00 05		00 35	11 24		11 54		12 24		12 54		19 54		20 23		20 53		21 23	

For other London Bridge connections, please see table 173

Table 179R

Sundays

8 December to 11 May

Wimbledon & Sutton - Thameslink

Network Diagram - see first Page of Table 173

		FC	FC	FC	FC	FC	FC	FC	FC A	FC	FC B	FC
Wimbledon Chase	d		20 21			20 51			21 21			21 51
South Merton	d		20 23			20 53			21 23			21 53
Morden South	d		20 25			20 55			21 25			21 55
St Helier	d		20 27			20 57			21 27			21 57
Sutton Common	d		20 29			20 59			21 29			21 59
West Sutton	d		20 32			21 02			21 32			22 02
Sutton (Surrey) 4	d	20 07	20 38		20 37	21 08		21 07	21 38		21 38	22 08
Carshalton	d		20 41			21 11			21 41		21 41	22 11
Hackbridge	d		20 43			21 13			21 43		21 43	22 13
Mitcham Junction	d		20 46			21 16			21 46		21 46	22 16
Mitcham Eastfields	d		20 49			21 19			21 49		21 49	22 19
West Sutton	d	20 10			20 40			21 10				
Sutton Common	d	20 12			20 42			21 12				
St Helier	d	20 15			20 45			21 15				
Morden South	d	20 17			20 47			21 17				
South Merton	d	20 19			20 49			21 19				
Wimbledon Chase	d	20 21			20 51			21 21				
Wimbledon 6 ⊖	a	20 24			20 54			21 24				
	d	20 26			20 56			21 26				
Haydons Road	d	20 28			20 58			21 28				
Tooting	d	20 31			21 01			21 31				
Streatham 4	d	20 36	20 53		21 06	21 23		21 36	21 53		21 53	22 23
Tulse Hill 3	a	20 40	20 57		21 10	21 27		21 40	21 57		21 57	22 27
	d	20 40	20 57		21 10	21 27		21 40	21 57		21 57	22 27
London Bridge 4 ⊖	a											
Herne Hill 4	d	20 44	21 01		21 14	21 31		21 44	22 01		22 01	22 31
Loughborough Jn.	d	20 47	21 04		21 17	21 34		21 47	22 04		22 04	22 34
Elephant & Castle ⊖	d	20 52	21 09		21 22	21 39		21 52	22 09		22 09	22 39
London Blackfriars 3 ⊖	d	20 56	21a13		21 26	21a43		21 56	22a13		22 14	22a43
City Thameslink 3	d											
Farringdon 3 ⊖	d	21 02			21 32			22 02			22 20	
St Pancras International 15 ⊖	d	21 06			21 36			22 06			22 24	
West Hampstead Thameslink	d	21 14			21 44			22 14			22 32	
St Albans City	d	21 39			22 09			22 39			22 58	
Luton Airport Parkway 7	d	21 50			22 20			22 50			23 10	
Luton 10	a	21 53			22 23			22 53			23 12	

A until 29 December

B from 5 January

For other London Bridge connections, please see table 173

Network Diagram for Tables 181, 184

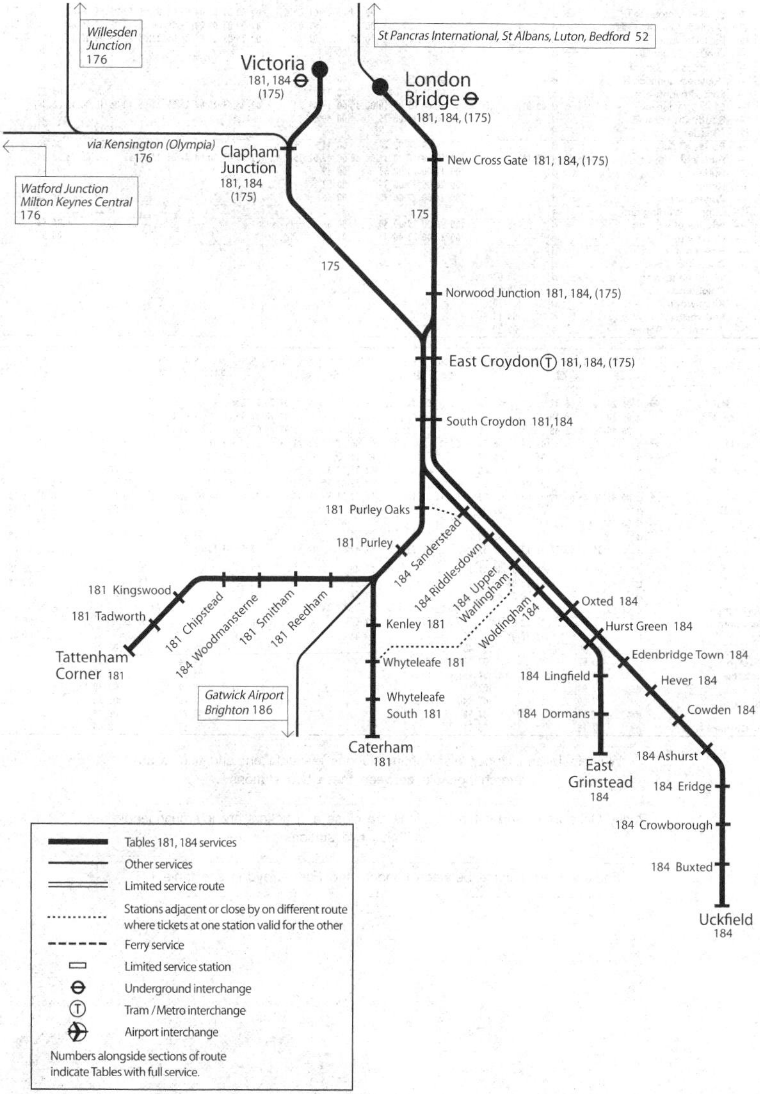

Willesden Junction 176
St Pancras International, St Albans, Luton, Bedford 52
Victoria 181, 184 (175)
London Bridge 181, 184, (175)
via Kensington (Olympia) 176
Clapham Junction 181, 184 (175)
Watford Junction Milton Keynes Central 176
New Cross Gate 181, 184, (175)
175
175
Norwood Junction 181, 184, (175)
East Croydon 181, 184, (175)
South Croydon 181,184
181 Purley Oaks
181 Purley
184 Sanderstead
184 Riddlesdown
184 Upper Warlingham
Woldingham 184
Oxted 184
Hurst Green 184
Edenbridge Town 184
Hever 184
Cowden 184
184 Ashurst
184 Eridge
184 Crowborough
184 Buxted
Uckfield 184
184 Lingfield
184 Dormans
East Grinstead 184
181 Kingswood
181 Tadworth
Tattenham Corner 181
181 Chipstead
184 Woodmansterne
181 Smitham
181 Reedham
Kenley 181
Whyteleafe 181
Whyteleafe South 181
Caterham 181
Gatwick Airport Brighton 186
Tables 181, 184 services
Other services
Limited service route
Stations adjacent or close by on different route where tickets at one station valid for the other
Ferry service
Limited service station
Underground interchange
Tram / Metro interchange
Airport interchange
Numbers alongside sections of route indicate Tables with full service.

TOCs operating on this network - Southern (SN)

Table 181

Mondays to Fridays

9 December to 16 May

London and Croydon - Purley, Caterham and Tattenham Corner

Network Diagram - see first Page of Table 181

Miles	Miles	Miles			SN MX 1	SN MX	SN MX 1	SN MO	SN MX	SN MO	SN 1	SN MX	SN 1		SN 1	SN 1	SN 1	SN 1	SN 1	SN 1	SN 1	SN	SN		SN 1
0	—	0	London Victoria 15 ⊖	d							00 14		01 00		02 00	03 00	04 00	05 01	05 32	05 52	06 02		06 13		06 21
2¾	—	2¾	Clapham Junction 10	d							00 21		01 09		02 09	03 09	04 09	05 08	05 38	05 59	06 08		06 21		06 27
—	—	10½	East Croydon	a							00 35		01 23		02 24	03 24	04 26	05 22	05 48	06 09	06 17		06 45		06 38
—	0	—	London Bridge 4 ⊖	d								00 06										06 06	↪		
—	2¾	—	New Cross Gate 4 ⊖	d								00 11										06 11			
—	8¾	—	Norwood Junction 2	d				00 03	00 05			00 30										06 30			
—	—	—	East Croydon	a				00 07	00 08			00 37										06 33			
10½	10	—	East Croydon	d	00 01		00 05	00 08	00 09	00 18	00 36	00 37	01 24		02 24	03 25	04 26	05 23	05 49	06 10	06 18	06 34			06 38
11½	11	—	**South Croydon 4**	d				00 10	00 11	00 25		00 40										06 37			
—	—	12½	**Sanderstead**	d			00s09													06 14					
12½	12	—	**Purley Oaks**	d				00 14	00 14	00 28		00 43										06 40			
13½	13	—	**Purley 4**	a	00 10			00 17	00 18	00 31	00 40	00 47	01 29		02 29	03 30	04 31	05 27	05 53		06 23	06 44			06 43
—	—	—	**Purley**	d				00 17	00 20	00 31		00 49										06 44			
—	14¼	—	**Kenley**	d				00 20	00 23	00 34		00 52										06 47			
—	15½	—	**Whyteleafe**	d				00 24	00 27	00 38		00 56										06 51			
—	—	15½	**Upper Warlingham**	a			00s16													06 21					
—	16	—	**Whyteleafe South**	d				00 26	00 29	00 40		00 58										06 53			
—	17¾	—	**Caterham**	a				00 30	00 33	00 44		01 02										06 57			
14¼	—	—	**Reedham**	d																					
15	—	—	**Coulsdon Town**	d																					
15¾	—	—	**Woodmansterne**	d		00 02																			
16¾	—	—	**Chipstead**	d		00 05																			
19¼	—	—	**Kingswood**	d		00 10																			
20½	—	—	**Tadworth**	d		00 14																			
21¾	—	—	**Tattenham Corner**	a		00 20																			

		SN 1	SN	SN 1	SN	SN		SN 1	SN 1		SN	SN 1	SN 1	SN	SN	SN 1	SN	SN 1	SN			SN 1	SN	SN 1	SN 1
London Victoria 15 ⊖	d	06 24		06 32					07 02					07 20	07 23			07 32					07 45		
Clapham Junction 10	d	06 30	↤	06 38					07 08					07 28	07 30		↤	07 38					07 51		
East Croydon	a	06 40	06 45	06 48					07 17					07 49	07 46		07 49	07 52					08 12		
London Bridge 4 ⊖	d				06 36	06 54		07 03			07 06	07 19	07 23	↪		07 30			07 36			07 55		07 58	08 00
New Cross Gate 4 ⊖	d				06 41	06 59					07 11					07 36			07 41						08 08
Norwood Junction 2	d				07 00	07 18					07 31	07 30	07 35			07 44			08 00					08 10	08 16
East Croydon	a				07 03	07 21		07 16			07 37	07 33	07 38			07 47			08 03			08 08		08 15	08 19
East Croydon	d	06 41	06 45	06 49	07 04	07 22		07 17	07 18		07 37	07 34	07 39		07 46	07 48	07 49	07 52	08 04			08 09	08 13	08 16	08 21
South Croydon 4	d				07 06	07 26					07 40						07 52		08 06				08 15		
Sanderstead	d	06 45						07 21				07 38						07 57				08 13		08 20	
Purley Oaks	d				07 09	07 29					07 43						07 55		08 09				08 18		
Purley 4	a		06 52	06 55	07 13	07 32			07 23		07 47		07 44		07 54	07 53	07 58		08 13				08 22		08 26
Purley	d		06 52		07 13	07 36	07 38				07 48				07 55		07 59		08 17	08 19			08 25		
Kenley	d				07 16	07 39					07 51				08 00				08 20				08 28		
Whyteleafe	d				07 20	07 42					07 54				08 04				08 23				08 31		
Upper Warlingham	a	06 52						07 28				07 45						08 04				08 20		08 27	
Whyteleafe South	d				07 22	07 44					07 56				08 06				08 25				08 33		
Caterham	a				07 28	07 49					08 01				08 10				08 30				08 39		
Reedham	d		06 55				07 40										08 01			08 21					
Coulsdon Town	d		06 57				07 43										08 04			08 24					
Woodmansterne	d		07 00				07 46										08 07			08 27					
Chipstead	d		07 03				07 49										08 10			08 30					
Kingswood	d		07 09				07 54										08 15			08 35					
Tadworth	d		07 12				07 58										08 19			08 39					
Tattenham Corner	a		07 16				08 01										08 22			08 43					

Whyteleafe and Upper Warlingham stations are adjacent and tickets are interchangeable between these two stations

Purley Oaks and Sanderstead stations are close and tickets are interchangeable between these two stations

For complete service between London and East Croydon see table 175

Table 181

Mondays to Fridays

9 December to 16 May

London and Croydon - Purley, Caterham and Tattenham Corner

Network Diagram - see first Page of Table 181

		SN		SN	SN 1	SN	SN 1	SN	SN	SN 1	SN	SN 1		SN	SN 1	SN	SN 1	SN	SN	SN 1	SN	SN 1		SN	SN
London Victoria 15 ⊖	d					08 15					08 43	08 53							09 13	09 23					
Clapham Junction 10	d					08 23					08 51	08 59		←					09 21	09 29	←				
East Croydon	a					08 44					09 12	09 10		09 12					09 42	09 39	09 42				
London Bridge 4 ⊖	d	08 06		08 14	08 25		08 28	08 34	08 40	08 42	→				09 01	09 06	09 15	09 20	→			09 32			09 36
New Cross Gate 4 ⊖	d	08 11					08 37	08 41		08 48					09 09	09 12						09 38			09 41
Norwood Junction 2	d	08 30		08 27	08 36		08 46	09 00		08 56					09 17	09 30	09 26	09 33				09 46			10 00
East Croydon	a	08 33		08 30	08 40		08 50	09 06	08 55	08 59					09 20	09 33	09 29	09 36				09 50			10 03
East Croydon	d	08 34		08 31	08 41	08 45	08 52	09 07	08 55	09 00		09 11		09 13	09 21	09 34	09 30	09 37		09 40	09 43	09 51			10 04
South Croydon 4	d	08 36				08 47		09 09						09 15		09 36					09 45				10 06
Sanderstead	d				08 45							09 15								09 44					
Purley Oaks	d	08 39				08 50		09 12						09 18		09 39					09 48				10 09
Purley 4	a	08 43		08 38		08 54	08 58	09 16	09 02	09 05				09 22	09 26	09 43	09 35	09 48			09 52	09 56			10 13
Purley	d	08 45		08 39		08 54		09 16	09 06					09 26		09 45		09 48			09 53			10 02	10 13
Kenley	d	08 48				08 57		09 19						09 29		09 48					09 56				10 16
Whyteleafe	d	08 52				09 01		09 23						09 32		09 52					10 00				10 20
Upper Warlingham	a				08 52							09 22								09 51					
Whyteleafe South	d	08 54				09 03		09 25						09 34		09 54					10 02				10 22
Caterham	a	08 58				09 09		09 29						09 40		09 59					10 07				10 29
Reedham	d			08 41					09 08									09 51						10 04	
Coulsdon Town	d			08 44					09 11									09 53						10 07	
Woodmansterne	d			08 47					09 14									09 56						10 10	
Chipstead	d			08 50					09 17									09 59						10 13	
Kingswood	d			08 55					09 22									10 05						10 18	
Tadworth	d			08 59					09 26									10 08						10 22	
Tattenham Corner	a			09 03					09 29									10 12						10 25	

		SN 1	SN	SN	SN 1	SN	SN 1	SN		SN 1	SN	SN	SN 1	SN	SN 1	SN	SN	SN 1		SN	SN	SN 1	SN	SN 1	SN
London Victoria 15 ⊖	d			09 43	09 53							10 13	10 23								10 43	10 53			
Clapham Junction 10	d			09 51	09 59	←						10 21	10 29	←							10 51	10 59	←		
East Croydon	a			10 14	10 09	10 14						10 42	10 39	10 42							11 12	11 09	11 12		
London Bridge 4 ⊖	d	09 45	09 50	→			10 03	10 06		10 15	10 20	→			10 33		10 36	10 45		10 50	→			11 03	11 06
New Cross Gate 4 ⊖	d						10 08	10 11							10 38		10 41							11 08	11 11
Norwood Junction 2	d	09 56	10 03				10 16	10 30		10 26	10 33				10 46		11 00	10 56		11 03				11 16	11 30
East Croydon	a	09 59	10 06				10 20	10 33		10 29	10 36				10 50		11 03	10 59		11 06				11 20	11 33
East Croydon	d	10 00	10 07		10 10	10 14	10 21	10 34		10 30	10 37		10 40	10 43	10 51		11 04	11 00		11 07		11 10	11 13	11 21	11 34
South Croydon 4	d					10 17		10 36						10 45			11 06						11 15		11 36
Sanderstead	d				10 15								10 44									11 14			
Purley Oaks	d					10 20		10 39						10 48			11 09						11 18		11 39
Purley 4	a	10 05	10 16			10 23	10 26	10 43		10 35	10 46			10 52	10 56		11 13	11 06		11 16			11 22	11 26	11 43
Purley	d		10 16			10 24		10 43			10 46			10 52		11 02	11 13			11 16			11 22		11 43
Kenley	d					10 27		10 46						10 55			11 16						11 25		11 46
Whyteleafe	d					10 30		10 50						10 59			11 20						11 29		11 50
Upper Warlingham	a				10 22								10 51									11 21			
Whyteleafe South	d					10 32		10 52						11 01			11 22						11 31		11 52
Caterham	a					10 37		10 58						11 07			11 28						11 37		11 58
Reedham	d		10 18								10 48					11 04				11 18					
Coulsdon Town	d		10 21								10 51					11 07				11 21					
Woodmansterne	d		10 24								10 54					11 10				11 24					
Chipstead	d		10 27								10 57					11 13				11 27					
Kingswood	d		10 32								11 02					11 18				11 32					
Tadworth	d		10 36								11 06					11 22				11 36					
Tattenham Corner	a		10 39								11 09					11 25				11 39					

Whyteleafe and Upper Warlingham stations are adjacent and tickets are interchangeable between these two stations

Purley Oaks and Sanderstead stations are close and tickets are interchangeable between these two stations

For complete service between London and East Croydon see table 175

Table 181

Mondays to Fridays

9 December to 16 May

London and Croydon - Purley, Caterham and Tattenham Corner

Network Diagram - see first Page of Table 181

		SN 1	SN	SN	SN 1	SN	SN 1	SN	SN	SN 1		SN	SN	SN 1	SN	SN 1	SN	SN 1	SN	SN		SN 1	SN	SN 1	SN
London Victoria 15 ⊖	d			11 13	11 23								11 43	11 53						12 13		12 23			
Clapham Junction 10	d			11 21	11 29	←							11 51	11 59	←					12 21		12 29	←		
East Croydon	a			11 42	11 39	11 42							12 12	12 09	12 12					12 42		12 39	12 42		
London Bridge 4 ⊖	d	11 15	11 20	→			11 33		11 36	11 45		11 50	→			12 03	12 06	12 15	12 20	→				12 33	
New Cross Gate 4 ⊖	d						11 38		11 41							12 08	12 11							12 38	
Norwood Junction 2	d	11 26	11 33				11 46		12 00	11 56		12 03				12 16	12 30	12 26	12 33					12 46	
East Croydon	a	11 29	11 36				11 50		12 03	11 59		12 06				12 20	12 33	12 29	12 36					12 50	
East Croydon 🚊	d	11 30	11 37		11 40	11 43	11 51		12 04	12 00		12 07		12 10	12 13	12 21	12 34	12 30	12 37			12 40	12 43	12 51	
South Croydon 4	d					11 45			12 06						12 15		12 36						12 45		
Sanderstead	d				11 44									12 14								12 44			
Purley Oaks	d					11 48			12 09						12 18		12 39						12 48		
Purley 4	a	11 35	11 46			11 52	11 56		12 13	12 05		12 16			12 22	12 26	12 43	12 35	12 46				12 52	12 57	
Purley	d		11 46			11 52		12 02	12 13			12 16			12 22		12 43		12 46				12 52		13 02
Kenley	d					11 55			12 16						12 25		12 46						12 55		
Whyteleafe	d					11 59			12 20						12 29		12 50						12 59		
Upper Warlingham	a				11 51									12 21								12 51			
Whyteleafe South	d					12 01			12 22						12 31		12 52						13 01		
Caterham	a					12 07			12 28						12 37		12 58						13 07		
Reedham	d		11 48					12 04				12 18							12 48						13 04
Coulsdon Town	d		11 51					12 07				12 21							12 51						13 07
Woodmansterne	d		11 54					12 10				12 24							12 54						13 10
Chipstead	d		11 57					12 13				12 27							12 57						13 13
Kingswood	d		12 02					12 18				12 32							13 02						13 18
Tadworth	d		12 06					12 22				12 36							13 06						13 22
Tattenham Corner	a		12 09					12 25				12 39							13 09						13 25

		SN	SN 1	SN	SN	SN 1		SN	SN 1	SN	SN 1	SN	SN	SN 1	SN	SN 1		SN	SN	SN 1	SN	SN	SN 1	SN	SN 1
London Victoria 15 ⊖	d				12 43	12 53							13 13	13 23								13 43	13 53		
Clapham Junction 10	d				12 51	12 59		←					13 21	13 29	←							13 51	13 59	←	
East Croydon	a				13 12	13 09		13 12					13 42	13 39	13 42							14 12	14 09	14 12	
London Bridge 4 ⊖	d	12 36	12 45	12 50	→				13 03	13 06	13 15	13 20	→			13 33			13 36	13 45	13 50	→			14 03
New Cross Gate 4 ⊖	d	12 41							13 08	13 11						13 38			13 41						14 08
Norwood Junction 2	d	13 00	12 56	13 03					13 16	13 30	13 26	13 33				13 46			14 00	13 56	14 03				14 16
East Croydon	a	13 03	12 59	13 06					13 20	13 33	13 29	13 36				13 50			14 03	13 59	14 06				14 20
East Croydon 🚊	d	13 04	13 00	13 07		13 10		13 13	13 21	13 34	13 30	13 37		13 40	13 43	13 51			14 04	14 00	14 07		14 10	14 13	14 21
South Croydon 4	d	13 06						13 15		13 36					13 45				14 06					14 15	
Sanderstead	d					13 14								13 44									14 14		
Purley Oaks	d	13 09						13 18		13 39					13 48				14 09					14 18	
Purley 4	a	13 13	13 05	13 16				13 22	13 26	13 43	13 35	13 46			13 52	13 57			14 13	14 05	14 16			14 22	14 26
Purley	d	13 13		13 16				13 22		13 43		13 46			13 52			14 02	14 13		14 16			14 22	
Kenley	d	13 16						13 25		13 46					13 55				14 16					14 25	
Whyteleafe	d	13 20						13 29		13 50					13 59				14 20					14 29	
Upper Warlingham	a					13 21								13 51									14 21		
Whyteleafe South	d	13 22						13 31		13 52					14 01				14 22					14 31	
Caterham	a	13 28						13 37		13 58					14 07				14 28					14 37	
Reedham	d			13 18								13 48						14 04			14 18				
Coulsdon Town	d			13 21								13 51						14 07			14 21				
Woodmansterne	d			13 24								13 54						14 10			14 24				
Chipstead	d			13 27								13 57						14 13			14 27				
Kingswood	d			13 32								14 02						14 18			14 32				
Tadworth	d			13 36								14 06						14 22			14 36				
Tattenham Corner	a			13 39								14 09						14 25			14 39				

Whyteleafe and Upper Warlingham stations are adjacent and tickets are interchangeable between these two stations

Purley Oaks and Sanderstead stations are close and tickets are interchangeable between these two stations

For complete service between London and East Croydon see table 175

Table 181

Mondays to Fridays

9 December to 16 May

London and Croydon - Purley, Caterham and Tattenham Corner

Network Diagram - see first Page of Table 181

		SN	SN [1]	SN	SN	SN [1]	SN	SN [1]		SN	SN	SN [1]	SN	SN	SN [1]	SN	SN [1]	SN		SN [1]	SN	SN	SN [1]	SN	SN [1]
London Victoria [15]	⊖ d				14 13	14 23								14 43	14 53							15 13	15 23		
Clapham Junction [10]	d				14 21	14 29	←							14 51	14 59	←						15 21	15 29	←	
East Croydon	a				14 42	14 40	14 42							15 12	15 09	15 12						15 42	15 40	15 42	
London Bridge [4]	⊖ d	14 06	14 15	14 20	→			14 33			14 36	14 45	14 50	→			15 03	15 06		15 15	15 20	→			15 33
New Cross Gate [4]	⊖ d	14 11						14 38			14 41						15 08	15 11							15 38
Norwood Junction [2]	d	14 30	14 26	14 33				14 46			15 00	14 56	15 03				15 16	15 30		15 26	15 33				15 46
East Croydon	a	14 33	14 29	14 36				14 50			15 03	14 59	15 06				15 20	15 33		15 29	15 36				15 50
East Croydon	tram d	14 34	14 30	14 37		14 40	14 43	14 51			15 04	15 00	15 07		15 10	15 13	15 21	15 34		15 30	15 36		15 40	15 43	15 51
South Croydon [4]	d	14 36					14 45				15 06					15 15		15 36					15 43	15 45	
Sanderstead	d					14 45									15 14								15 46		
Purley Oaks	d	14 39					14 48				15 09					15 18		15 39						15 48	
Purley [4]	a	14 43	14 35	14 46			14 52	14 56			15 13	15 05	15 16			15 22	15 26	15 43		15 35	15 45			15 52	15 56
Purley	d	14 43		14 46			14 54			15 02	15 13		15 16			15 22		15 43			15 46			15 52	
Kenley	d	14 46					14 57				15 16					15 25		15 46						15 55	
Whyteleafe	d	14 50					15 01				15 20					15 29		15 50						15 59	
Upper Warlingham	a					14 52									15 21								15 53		
Whyteleafe South	d	14 52					15 03				15 22					15 31		15 52						16 01	
Caterham	a	14 58					15 07				15 28					15 37		15 58						16 07	
Reedham	d			14 48						15 04			15 18								15 48				
Coulsdon Town	d			14 51						15 07			15 21								15 51				
Woodmansterne	d			14 54						15 10			15 24								15 54				
Chipstead	d			14 57						15 13			15 27								15 57				
Kingswood	d			15 02						15 18			15 32								16 02				
Tadworth	d			15 06						15 22			15 36								16 06				
Tattenham Corner	a			15 09						15 25			15 39								16 09				

		SN	SN	SN [1]		SN	SN	SN [1]	SN	SN [1]	SN	SN [1]	SN	SN		SN [1]	SN	SN [1]	SN	SN		SN	SN [1]	SN [1]	
London Victoria [15]	⊖ d						15 43	15 53						16 13		16 23			16 39			16 43	16 53		
Clapham Junction [10]	d						15 51	15 59	←					16 21		16 29	←		16 45			16 51	16 59		
East Croydon	a						16 12	16 09	16 12					16 42		16 39	16 42		16 55			17 12	17 09		
London Bridge [4]	⊖ d		15 36	15 45		15 50	→			16 03	16 06	16 15	16 20	→				16 30		16 48		→		16 59	
New Cross Gate [4]	⊖ d		15 41							16 09	16 11							16 36							
Norwood Junction [2]	d		16 00	15 56		16 03				16 17	16 30	16 26	16 33					16 44		17 02				17 10	
East Croydon	a		16 03	15 59		16 06				16 20	16 33	16 29	16 36					16 47		17 05				17 14	
East Croydon	tram d		16 04	16 00		16 07		16 10	16 13	16 21	16 34	16 30	16 37			16 40	16 43	16 48	16 56	17 06			17 10	17 15	
South Croydon [4]	d		16 06					16 12	16 15		16 36					16 42	16 45		16 58	17 08			17 12		
Sanderstead	d							16 15								16 45							17 15		
Purley Oaks	d		16 09						16 18		16 39						16 48		17 01	17 11					
Purley [4]	a		16 13	16 05		16 16			16 22	16 26	16 43	16 35	16 46				16 52	16 54	17 05	17 15				17 19	
Purley	d	16 02	16 13			16 16			16 24		16 43		16 46				16 54		17 05	17 19	17 22				
Kenley	d		16 16						16 27		16 46						16 57		17 08	17 22					
Whyteleafe	d		16 20						16 31		16 50						17 01		17 12	17 25					
Upper Warlingham	a							16 22								16 52							17 22		
Whyteleafe South	d		16 22						16 33		16 52						17 03		17 14	17 27					
Caterham	a		16 28						16 37		16 58						17 07		17 21	17 34					
Reedham	d	16 04				16 18							16 49								17 24				
Coulsdon Town	d	16 07				16 21							16 51								17 27				
Woodmansterne	d	16 10				16 24							16 54								17 30				
Chipstead	d	16 13				16 27							16 57								17 33				
Kingswood	d	16 18				16 32							17 03								17 38				
Tadworth	d	16 22				16 36							17 06								17 42				
Tattenham Corner	a	16 25				16 39							17 12								17 48				

Whyteleafe and Upper Warlingham stations are adjacent and tickets are interchangeable between these two stations

Purley Oaks and Sanderstead stations are close and tickets are interchangeable between these two stations

For complete service between London and East Croydon see table 175

Table 181

Mondays to Fridays

9 December to 16 May

London and Croydon - Purley, Caterham and Tattenham Corner

Network Diagram - see first Page of Table 181

		SN	SN		SN 1	SN			SN 1	SN 1	SN		SN 1	SN		SN 1	SN 1		SN		SN 1	SN	SN		SN 1
London Victoria 15 ⊖	d		17 09						17 23		17 38					17 53			18 08						18 19
Clapham Junction 10	d	←	17 15						17 30		17 44					18 00			18 14			18 02			18 26
East Croydon	a	17 12	17 27						17 40		17 55					18 10			18 27			18 32			18 37
London Bridge 4 ⊖	d				17 15	17 17				17 32			17 44	17 46			17 59				18 16		18 18		
New Cross Gate 4 ⊖	d																								
Norwood Junction 2	d					17 30				17 44				17 59			18 10						18 31		
East Croydon	a				17 29	17 34				17 49			17 57	18 02			18 13				18 30		18 34		
East Croydon	d	17 16	17 27		17 30	17 35			17 41	17 50	17 56		17 58	18 03		18 11	18 14		18 28		18 31	18 33	18 37		18 38
South Croydon 4	d	17 19	17 30		17 32	17 37					17 58		18 01	18 05					18 31		18 33	18 35	18 42		
Sanderstead	d				17 35				17 45				18 04			18 15					18 36				
Purley Oaks	d	17 22	17 33			17 40					18 01			18 08					18 34			18 38	18 45		
Purley 4	a	17 25	17 36			17 45				17 55	18 05			18 13			18 19		18 37			18 40	18 49		18 43
Purley	d	17 28	17 40	17 42		17 49	17 51				18 09	18 11		18 17	18 24				18 41	18 43			18 53	18 55	
Kenley	d	17 31	17 43			17 52					18 12			18 20					18 44				18 56		
Whyteleafe	d	17 34	17 46			17 55					18 15			18 23					18 47				18 59		
Upper Warlingham	a				17 42				17 52				18 11			18 22					18 43				
Whyteleafe South	d	17 36	17 48			17 57					18 17			18 25					18 49				19 01		
Caterham	a	17 43	17 55			18 04					18 24			18 30					18 56				19 08		
Reedham	d			17 44			17 53					18 13			18 26					18 45				18 57	
Coulsdon Town	d			17 47			17 56					18 16			18 29					18 48				19 00	
Woodmansterne	d			17 50			17 59					18 19			18 32					18 51				19 03	
Chipstead	d			17 53			18 02					18 22			18 35					18 54				19 06	
Kingswood	d			17 58			18 07					18 27			18 40					18 59				19 11	
Tadworth	d			18 02			18 11					18 31			18 44					19 03				19 15	
Tattenham Corner	a			18 08			18 17					18 36			18 49					19 09				19 21	

		SN 1	SN 1		SN		SN 1	SN		SN		SN 1	SN			SN 1	SN 1	SN	SN	SN 1	SN	SN 1	SN 1	SN	
London Victoria 15 ⊖	d	18 23			18 38					18 45		18 53					19 10		19 15	19 23			19 40		
Clapham Junction 10	d	18 29			18 44					18 53		19 00	←				19 16		19 23	19 29	←		19 46		
East Croydon	a	18 40			18 57					19 13		19 10	19 13				19 26		19 45	19 39	19 45		19 56		
London Bridge 4 ⊖	d		18 30				18 47	18 49		→						18 59		19 06	→			19 33		19 36	
New Cross Gate 4 ⊖	d															19 07		19 11				19 39		19 41	
Norwood Junction 2	d		18 42					19 02								19 15		19 30				19 47		20 00	
East Croydon	a		18 45				19 00	19 05								19 19		19 33				19 50		20 03	
East Croydon	d	18 41	18 46		18 57		19 01	19 06				19 11	19 14			19 20	19 27	19 34		19 40	19 45	19 51	19 57	20 04	
South Croydon 4	d				19 00		19 03	19 08					19 16					19 36			19 48			20 06	
Sanderstead	d	18 46					19 06					19 15								19 44					
Purley Oaks	d				19 03			19 11					19 19					19 39			19 51			20 09	
Purley 4	a		18 51		19 06			19 15					19 23			19 26	19 32	19 43			19 54	19 56	20 02	20 13	
Purley	d				19 10	19 12		19 19	19 21				19 27	19 29				19 45			19 55			20 15	
Kenley	d				19 13			19 22					19 30					19 48						20 18	
Whyteleafe	d				19 16			19 25					19 33					19 52						20 22	
Upper Warlingham	a	18 53					19 13					19 22								19 51					
Whyteleafe South	d				19 18			19 27					19 35					19 54						20 24	
Caterham	a				19 25			19 34					19 42					19 58						20 28	
Reedham	d					19 14			19 23					19 32							19 57				
Coulsdon Town	d					19 17			19 26					19 35							20 00				
Woodmansterne	d					19 20			19 29					19 38							20 03				
Chipstead	d					19 23			19 32					19 41							20 06				
Kingswood	d					19 28			19 37					19 46							20 11				
Tadworth	d					19 32			19 41					19 50							20 15				
Tattenham Corner	a					19 38			19 45					19 56							20 21				

Whyteleafe and Upper Warlingham stations are adjacent and tickets are interchangeable between these two stations

Purley Oaks and Sanderstead stations are close and tickets are interchangeable between these two stations

For complete service between London and East Croydon see table 175

Table 181

Mondays to Fridays

9 December to 16 May

London and Croydon - Purley, Caterham and Tattenham Corner

Network Diagram - see first Page of Table 181

		SN 1	SN	SN 1	SN	SN 1		SN 1	SN	SN	SN 1	SN	SN 1	SN	SN	SN 1		SN	SN 1	SN 1	SN	SN	SN 1	SN	SN 1
London Victoria 15 ⊖	d		19 45	19 53				20 10		20 15	20 23		20 40		20 45	20 53				21 10		21 15	21 23		21 40
Clapham Junction 10	d		19 53	19 59	←			20 16		20 23	20 29	←	20 46		20 53	21 00		←		21 16		21 23	21 29	←	21 46
East Croydon	a		20 15	20 09	20 15			20 26		20 45	20 39	20 45	20 56		21 15	21 11		21 15		21 26		21 45	21 39	21 45	21 56
London Bridge 4 ⊖	d	19 52	↪			20 04			20 06	↪				20 36	↪				21 04		21 06	↪			
New Cross Gate 4 ⊖	d								20 11					20 41							21 11				
Norwood Junction 2	d	20 03				20 16			20 30					21 00					21 15		21 30				
East Croydon	a	20 06				20 19			20 33					21 03					21 19		21 33				
East Croydon	d	20 07		20 10	20 15	20 20		20 27	20 34		20 40	20 45	20 57	21 04		21 11		21 15	21 19	21 27	21 34		21 40	21 45	21 57
South Croydon 4	d				20 18				20 36			20 48		21 06				21 18			21 36			21 48	
Sanderstead	d			20 14		20 24					20 44					21 16			21 24				21 44		
Purley Oaks	d				20 21				20 39			20 51		21 09				21 21			21 39			21 51	
Purley 4	a	20 12			20 24			20 32	20 43			20 54	21 02	21 13				21 24		21 32	21 43			21 54	22 02
Purley	d				20 25				20 45			20 55		21 15				21 25			21 45			21 55	
Kenley	d								20 48					21 18							21 48				
Whyteleafe	d								20 52					21 22							21 52				
Upper Warlingham	a			20 21		20 30					20 51					21 23			21 29				21 51		
Whyteleafe South	d								20 54					21 24							21 54				
Caterham	a								20 58					21 28							21 58				
Reedham	d				20 27							20 57						21 27						21 57	
Coulsdon Town	d				20 30							21 00						21 30						22 00	
Woodmansterne	d				20 33							21 03						21 33						22 03	
Chipstead	d				20 36							21 06						21 36						22 06	
Kingswood	d				20 41							21 11						21 41						22 11	
Tadworth	d				20 45							21 15						21 45						22 15	
Tattenham Corner	a				20 51							21 21						21 51						22 21	

		SN		SN	SN 1	SN	SN 1	SN 1	SN	SN	SN 1	SN		SN 1	SN	SN	SN 1	SN	SN 1	SN 1	SN	SN		SN 1	SN
London Victoria 15 ⊖	d			21 45	21 53			22 10		22 15	22 23			22 40		22 45	22 53			23 10		23 15		23 24	
Clapham Junction 10	d			21 53	21 59	←		22 16		22 23	22 29	←		22 46		22 53	22 59	←		23 16		23 23		23 30	←
East Croydon	a			22 15	22 09	22 15		22 26		22 44	22 39	22 44		22 56		23 14	23 09	23 14		23 26		23 44		23 40	23 44
London Bridge 4 ⊖	d	21 36		↪			22 04		22 08	↪					22 38	↪			23 04		23 06	↪			
New Cross Gate 4 ⊖	d	21 41							22 13						22 43						23 11				
Norwood Junction 2	d	22 00					22 15		22 32						23 02				23 15		23 30				
East Croydon	a	22 03					22 19		22 35						23 06				23 19		23 33				
East Croydon	d	22 04			22 10	22 15	22 19	22 27	22 36		22 40	22 45		22 57	23 07		23 10	23 14	23 19	23 27	23 34			23 41	23 44
South Croydon 4	d	22 06				22 18			22 38			22 47			23 09			23 18			23 36				23 47
Sanderstead	d				22 14		22 24				22 44						23 14		23 24					23 46	
Purley Oaks	d	22 09				22 21			22 41			22 50			23 12			23 21			23 39				23 50
Purley 4	a	22 13				22 24		22 32	22 45			22 54		23 02	23 16			23 24		23 32	23 43				23 53
Purley	d	22 15				22 25			22 47			22 54			23 16			23 25			23 45				23 54
Kenley	d	22 18							22 50						23 19						23 48				
Whyteleafe	d	22 22							22 54						23 23						23 52				
Upper Warlingham	a				22 21		22 29				22 51						23 21		23 29					23 53	
Whyteleafe South	d	22 24							22 56						23 25						23 54				
Caterham	a	22 28							23 00						23 30						23 58				
Reedham	d					22 27						22 57						23 27							23 56
Coulsdon Town	d					22 30						22 59						23 30							23 59
Woodmansterne	d					22 33						23 02						23 33							00 02
Chipstead	d					22 36						23 05						23 36							00 05
Kingswood	d					22 41						23 11						23 41							00 10
Tadworth	d					22 45						23 14						23 45							00 14
Tattenham Corner	a					22 51						23 20						23 51							00 20

Whyteleafe and Upper Warlingham stations are adjacent and tickets are interchangeable between these two stations

Purley Oaks and Sanderstead stations are close and tickets are interchangeable between these two stations

For complete service between London and East Croydon see table 175

Table 181

Mondays to Fridays

9 December to 16 May

London and Croydon - Purley, Caterham and Tattenham Corner

Network Diagram - see first Page of Table 181

		SN 1	SN FO	SN 1	SN	SN FO
London Victoria 15 ⊖	d	23 40	23 45	23 47		
Clapham Junction 10	d	23 46	23 53	23 53		←
East Croydon	a	23 55	00 14	00 04		00 14
London Bridge 4 ⊖	d		↪		23 41	
New Cross Gate 4 ⊖	d				23 46	
Norwood Junction 2	d				00 05	
East Croydon	a				00 08	
East Croydon	d	00 01		00 05	00 09	00 14
South Croydon 4	d				00 11	00 17
Sanderstead	d			00s09		
Purley Oaks	d				00 14	00 20
Purley 4	a	00 10			00 18	00 23
Purley	d				00 20	00 24
Kenley	d				00 23	
Whyteleafe	d				00 27	
Upper Warlingham	a			00s16		
Whyteleafe South	d				00 29	
Caterham	a				00 33	
Reedham	d					00 26
Coulsdon Town	d					00 29
Woodmansterne	d					00 32
Chipstead	d					00 35
Kingswood	d					00 40
Tadworth	d					00 44
Tattenham Corner	a					00 49

Saturdays

14 December to 17 May

		SN 1	SN	SN 1	SN	SN	SN 1	SN	SN	SN 1		SN 1	SN 1	SN 1	SN 1	SN	SN 1	SN 1	SN	SN	SN	SN 1
London Victoria 15 ⊖	d						00 14		00 17	01 00		04 00	05 02	05 32	06 02		06 23	06 32			06 43	06 53
Clapham Junction 10	d						00 21		00 25	01 09		04 09	05 09	05 38	06 08		06 29	06 38			06 51	06 59
East Croydon	a						00 36		00 45	01 23		04 23	05 23	05 47	06 17		06 39	06 47			07 12	07 09
London Bridge 4 ⊖	d							00 06											06 36	06 50	↪	
New Cross Gate 4 ⊖	d							00 11											06 41			
Norwood Junction 2	d				00 05			00 30								06 33			07 00	07 03		
East Croydon	a				00 08			00 33								06 36			07 03	07 06		
East Croydon	d	00 01		00 05	00 09	00 14	00 36	00 37	00 50	01 24		04 24	05 24	05 48	06 18	06 37	06 40	06 48	07 04	07 07		07 10
South Croydon 4	d				00 11	00 17		00 40	00 53										07 06			
Sanderstead	d			00s09							and						06 44					07 14
Purley Oaks	d				00 14	00 20		00 43	00 56		hourly								07 09			
Purley 4	a	00 10			00 18	00 23	00 41	00 47	00 59	01 29	until	04 29	05 29	05 53	06 23	06 45		06 53	07 12	07 15		
Purley	d				00 20	00 24		00 49	01 00							06 46			07 13	07 16		
Kenley	d				00 23			00 52											07 16			
Whyteleafe	d				00 27			00 56											07 19			
Upper Warlingham	a			00s16													06 51					07 21
Whyteleafe South	d				00 29			00 58											07 21			
Caterham	a				00 33			01 02											07 26			
Reedham	d					00 26			01 02							06 48				07 18		
Coulsdon Town	d					00 29			01 05							06 51				07 21		
Woodmansterne	d		00 02			00 32			01 08							06 54				07 24		
Chipstead	d		00 05			00 35			01 11							06 57				07 27		
Kingswood	d		00 10			00 40			01 16							07 02				07 32		
Tadworth	d		00 14			00 44			01 20							07 06				07 36		
Tattenham Corner	a		00 20			00 49			01 23							07 09				07 39		

Whyteleafe and Upper Warlingham stations are adjacent and tickets are interchangeable between these two stations

Purley Oaks and Sanderstead stations are close and tickets are interchangeable between these two stations

For complete service between London and East Croydon see table 175

Table 181

Saturdays

14 December to 17 May

London and Croydon - Purley, Caterham and Tattenham Corner

Network Diagram - see first Page of Table 181

		SN	SN [1]	SN	SN		SN	SN [1]	SN	SN [1]	SN	SN	SN [1]	SN	SN		SN [1]	SN	SN [1]	SN	SN [1]	SN	SN	SN [1]	SN
London Victoria [15]	⊖ d						07 13	07 23							07 43		07 53						08 13	08 23	
Clapham Junction [10]	d	←					07 21	07 29	←						07 51		07 59	←					08 21	08 29	←
East Croydon	a	07 12					07 42	07 39	07 42						08 12		08 09	08 12					08 42	08 39	08 42
London Bridge [4]	⊖ d		07 03	07 06	07 20		→			07 33		07 36	07 45	07 50	→				08 03	08 06	08 15	08 20	→		
New Cross Gate [4]	⊖ d		07 08	07 11						07 38		07 41							08 08	08 11					
Norwood Junction [2]	d		07 16	07 30	07 33					07 46		08 00	07 56	08 03					08 16	08 30	08 26	08 33			
East Croydon	a		07 20	07 33	07 36					07 50		08 03	07 59	08 06					08 20	08 33	08 29	08 36			
East Croydon	d	07 13	07 21	07 34	07 37			07 40	07 43	07 51		08 04	08 00	08 07			08 10	08 13	08 21	08 34	08 30	08 37		08 40	08 43
South Croydon [4]	d	07 15		07 36					07 45			08 06						08 15		08 36					08 45
Sanderstead	d							07 44									08 14							08 44	
Purley Oaks	d	07 18		07 39					07 48			08 09						08 18		08 39					08 48
Purley [4]	a	07 21	07 26	07 42	07 45				07 51	07 56		08 12	08 05	08 15				08 21	08 26	08 42	08 35	08 45			08 52
Purley	d	07 22		07 43	07 46				07 52		08 02	08 13		08 16				08 22		08 43		08 46			08 52
Kenley	d	07 25		07 46					07 55			08 16						08 25		08 46					08 55
Whyteleafe	d	07 28		07 49					07 58			08 19						08 28		08 49					08 59
Upper Warlingham	a							07 51									08 21							08 51	
Whyteleafe South	d	07 30		07 51					08 00			08 21						08 30		08 51					09 01
Caterham	a	07 35		07 56					08 05			08 26						08 35		08 56					09 05
Reedham	d				07 48						08 04			08 18								08 48			
Coulsdon Town	d				07 51						08 07			08 21								08 51			
Woodmansterne	d				07 54						08 10			08 24								08 54			
Chipstead	d				07 57						08 13			08 27								08 57			
Kingswood	d				08 02						08 18			08 32								09 02			
Tadworth	d				08 06						08 22			08 36								09 06			
Tattenham Corner	a				08 09						08 25			08 39								09 09			

			SN [1]	SN	SN	SN [1]	SN	SN	SN [1]	SN	SN [1]		SN	SN [1]	SN	SN	SN [1]	SN	SN [1]	SN	SN		SN [1]	SN	SN
London Victoria [15]	⊖ d							08 43	08 53							09 13	09 23								09 43
Clapham Junction [10]	d							08 51	08 59	←						09 21	09 29	←							09 51
East Croydon	a							09 12	09 09	09 12						09 42	09 39	09 42							10 12
London Bridge [4]	⊖ d		08 33		08 36	08 45	08 50	→			09 03		09 06	09 15	09 20	→			09 33		09 36		09 45	09 50	→
New Cross Gate [4]	⊖ d		08 38		08 41						09 08		09 11						09 38		09 41				
Norwood Junction [2]	d		08 46		09 00	08 56	09 03				09 16		09 30	09 26	09 33				09 46		10 00		09 56	10 03	
East Croydon	a		08 50		09 03	08 59	09 06				09 20		09 33	09 29	09 36				09 50		10 03		09 59	10 06	
East Croydon	d		08 51		09 04	09 00	09 07		09 10	09 13	09 21		09 34	09 30	09 37		09 40	09 43	09 51		10 04		10 00	10 07	
South Croydon [4]	d				09 06					09 15			09 36					09 45			10 06				
Sanderstead	d								09 14								09 44								
Purley Oaks	d				09 09					09 18			09 39					09 48			10 09				
Purley [4]	a		08 56		09 12	09 05	09 15			09 21	09 26		09 42	09 35	09 45			09 51	09 56		10 12		10 05	10 15	
Purley	d			09 02	09 13		09 16			09 22			09 43		09 46			09 52		10 02	10 13			10 16	
Kenley	d				09 16					09 25			09 46					09 55			10 16				
Whyteleafe	d				09 19					09 28			09 49					09 58			10 19				
Upper Warlingham	a								09 21								09 51								
Whyteleafe South	d				09 21					09 30			09 51					10 00			10 21				
Caterham	a				09 26					09 35			09 56					10 05			10 26				
Reedham	d			09 04			09 18								09 48					10 04				10 18	
Coulsdon Town	d			09 07			09 21								09 51					10 07				10 21	
Woodmansterne	d			09 10			09 24								09 54					10 10				10 24	
Chipstead	d			09 13			09 27								09 57					10 13				10 27	
Kingswood	d			09 18			09 32								10 02					10 18				10 32	
Tadworth	d			09 22			09 36								10 06					10 22				10 36	
Tattenham Corner	a			09 25			09 39								10 09					10 25				10 39	

Whyteleafe and Upper Warlingham stations are adjacent and tickets are interchangeable between these two stations

Purley Oaks and Sanderstead stations are close and tickets are interchangeable between these two stations

For complete service between London and East Croydon see table 175

Table 181

Saturdays

14 December to 17 May

London and Croydon - Purley, Caterham and Tattenham Corner

Network Diagram - see first Page of Table 181

		SN 1	SN		SN 1	SN	SN 1	SN	SN	SN 1	SN	SN 1	SN		SN	SN 1	SN	SN	SN 1	SN	SN 1	SN	SN 1		SN
London Victoria 15 ⊖	d	09 53							10 13	10 23								10 43	10 53						
Clapham Junction 10	d	09 59	←						10 21	10 29	←							10 51	10 59	←					
East Croydon	a	10 09	10 12						10 42	10 39	10 42							11 12	11 09	11 12					
London Bridge 4 ⊖	d				10 03	10 06	10 15	10 20	→			10 33			10 36	10 45	10 50	→			11 03	11 06	11 15		11 20
New Cross Gate 4 ⊖	d				10 08	10 11						10 38			10 41						11 08	11 11			
Norwood Junction 2	d				10 16	10 30	10 26	10 33				10 46			11 00	10 56	11 03				11 16	11 30	11 26		11 33
East Croydon	a				10 20	10 33	10 29	10 36				10 50			11 03	10 59	11 06				11 20	11 33	11 29		11 36
East Croydon	d	10 10	10 13		10 21	10 34	10 30	10 37		10 40	10 43	10 51			11 04	11 00	11 07		11 10	11 13	11 21	11 34	11 30		11 37
South Croydon 4	d		10 15			10 36					10 45				11 06					11 15		11 36			
Sanderstead	d	10 14								10 44									11 14						
Purley Oaks	d		10 18			10 39					10 48				11 09					11 18		11 39			
Purley 4	a		10 21		10 26	10 42	10 35	10 45			10 51	10 56			11 12	11 05	11 15			11 21	11 26	11 42	11 35		11 45
Purley	d		10 22			10 43		10 46			10 52		11 02		11 13		11 16			11 22		11 43			11 46
Kenley	d		10 25			10 46					10 55				11 16					11 25		11 46			
Whyteleafe	d		10 28			10 49					10 58				11 19					11 28		11 49			
Upper Warlingham	a	10 21								10 51									11 21						
Whyteleafe South	d		10 30			10 51					11 00				11 21					11 30		11 51			
Caterham	a		10 35			10 56					11 05				11 26					11 35		11 56			
Reedham	d							10 48					11 04				11 18								11 48
Coulsdon Town	d							10 51					11 07				11 21								11 51
Woodmansterne	d							10 54					11 10				11 24								11 54
Chipstead	d							10 57					11 13				11 27								11 57
Kingswood	d							11 02					11 18				11 32								12 02
Tadworth	d							11 06					11 22				11 36								12 06
Tattenham Corner	a							11 09					11 25				11 39								12 09

		SN	SN 1	SN	SN 1	SN	SN	SN 1	SN		SN	SN 1	SN	SN 1	SN	SN 1	SN	SN	SN 1		SN	SN 1	SN	SN	SN 1
London Victoria 15 ⊖	d	11 13	11 23								11 43	11 53						12 13	12 23						
Clapham Junction 10	d	11 21	11 29	←							11 51	11 59	←					12 21	12 29		←				
East Croydon	a	11 42	11 39	11 42							12 12	12 09	12 12					12 42	12 39		12 42				
London Bridge 4 ⊖	d	→			11 33		11 36	11 45	11 50		→			12 03	12 06	12 15	12 20	→				12 33		12 36	12 45
New Cross Gate 4 ⊖	d				11 38		11 41							12 08	12 11							12 38		12 41	
Norwood Junction 2	d				11 46		12 00	11 56	12 03					12 16	12 30	12 26	12 33					12 46		13 00	12 56
East Croydon	a				11 50		12 03	11 59	12 06					12 20	12 33	12 29	12 36					12 50		13 03	12 59
East Croydon	d		11 40	11 43	11 51		12 04	12 00	12 07			12 10	12 13	12 21	12 34	12 30	12 37		12 40		12 43	12 51		13 04	13 00
South Croydon 4	d			11 45			12 06						12 15		12 36						12 45			13 06	
Sanderstead	d		11 44									12 14							12 44						
Purley Oaks	d			11 48			12 09						12 18		12 39						12 48			13 09	
Purley 4	a			11 51	11 56		12 12	12 05	12 15				12 21	12 26	12 42	12 35	12 45				12 51	12 56		13 12	13 05
Purley	d			11 52		12 02	12 13		12 16				12 22		12 43		12 46				12 52		13 02	13 13	
Kenley	d			11 55			12 16						12 25		12 46						12 55			13 16	
Whyteleafe	d			11 58			12 19						12 28		12 49						12 58			13 19	
Upper Warlingham	a		11 51									12 21							12 51						
Whyteleafe South	d			12 00			12 21						12 30		12 51						13 00			13 21	
Caterham	a			12 05			12 26						12 35		12 56						13 05			13 26	
Reedham	d					12 04			12 18								12 48						13 04		
Coulsdon Town	d					12 07			12 21								12 51						13 07		
Woodmansterne	d					12 10			12 24								12 54						13 10		
Chipstead	d					12 13			12 27								12 57						13 13		
Kingswood	d					12 18			12 32								13 02						13 18		
Tadworth	d					12 22			12 36								13 06						13 22		
Tattenham Corner	a					12 25			12 39								13 09						13 25		

Whyteleafe and Upper Warlingham stations are adjacent and tickets are interchangeable between these two stations

Purley Oaks and Sanderstead stations are close and tickets are interchangeable between these two stations

For complete service between London and East Croydon see table 175

Table 181

Saturdays

14 December to 17 May

London and Croydon - Purley, Caterham and Tattenham Corner

Network Diagram - see first Page of Table 181

			SN	SN	SN 1	SN	SN 1	SN	SN 1	SN	SN		SN 1	SN	SN 1	SN	SN	SN 1	SN	SN	SN 1		SN	SN 1	SN
London Victoria 15 ⊖	d			12 43	12 53						13 13		13 23							13 43	13 53				
Clapham Junction 10	d			12 51	12 59	←					13 21		13 29	←						13 51	13 59		←		
East Croydon	a			13 12	13 09	13 12					13 42		13 39	13 42						14 12	14 09		14 12		
London Bridge 4 ⊖	d		12 50	→			13 03	13 06	13 15	13 20	→				13 33		13 36	13 45	13 50	→				14 03	14 06
New Cross Gate 4 ⊖	d						13 08	13 11							13 38		13 41							14 08	14 11
Norwood Junction 2	d		13 03				13 16	13 30	13 26	13 33					13 46		14 00	13 56	14 03					14 16	14 30
East Croydon	a		13 06				13 20	13 33	13 29	13 36					13 50		14 03	13 59	14 06					14 20	14 33
East Croydon	d		13 07		13 10	13 13	13 21	13 34	13 30	13 37			13 40	13 43	13 51		14 04	14 00	14 07		14 10		14 13	14 21	14 34
South Croydon 4	d					13 15		13 36						13 45			14 06						14 15		14 36
Sanderstead	d				13 14								13 44								14 14				
Purley Oaks	d					13 18		13 39						13 48			14 09						14 18		14 39
Purley 4	a		13 15			13 21	13 26	13 42	13 35	13 45				13 51	13 56		14 12	14 05	14 15				14 22	14 26	14 42
Purley	d		13 16			13 22		13 43		13 46				13 52		14 02	14 13		14 16				14 22		14 43
Kenley	d					13 25		13 46						13 55			14 16						14 25		14 46
Whyteleafe	d					13 28		13 49						13 58			14 19						14 29		14 49
Upper Warlingham	a				13 21								13 51								14 21				
Whyteleafe South	d					13 30		13 51						14 00			14 21						14 31		14 51
Caterham	a					13 35		13 56						14 05			14 26						14 35		14 56
Reedham	d		13 18							13 48						14 04			14 18						
Coulsdon Town	d		13 21							13 51						14 07			14 21						
Woodmansterne	d		13 24							13 54						14 10			14 24						
Chipstead	d		13 27							13 57						14 13			14 27						
Kingswood	d		13 32							14 02						14 18			14 32						
Tadworth	d		13 36							14 06						14 22			14 36						
Tattenham Corner	a		13 39							14 09						14 25			14 39						

		SN 1	SN	SN	SN 1	SN	SN 1		SN	SN	SN 1	SN	SN	SN 1	SN	SN 1	SN		SN 1	SN	SN	SN 1	SN	SN 1	SN
London Victoria 15 ⊖	d			14 13	14 23								14 43	14 53							15 13	15 23			
Clapham Junction 10	d			14 21	14 29	←							14 51	14 59	←						15 21	15 29	←		
East Croydon	a			14 42	14 39	14 42							15 12	15 09	15 12						15 42	15 39	15 42		
London Bridge 4 ⊖	d	14 15	14 20	→			14 33			14 36	14 45	14 50	→			15 03	15 06		15 15	15 20	→			15 33	
New Cross Gate 4 ⊖	d						14 38			14 41						15 08	15 11							15 38	
Norwood Junction 2	d	14 26	14 33				14 46			15 00	14 56	15 03				15 16	15 30		15 26	15 33				15 46	
East Croydon	a	14 29	14 36				14 50			15 03	14 59	15 06				15 20	15 33		15 29	15 36				15 50	
East Croydon	d	14 30	14 37		14 40	14 43	14 51			15 04	15 00	15 07		15 10	15 13	15 21	15 34		15 30	15 37		15 40	15 43	15 51	
South Croydon 4	d					14 45				15 06					15 15		15 36						15 45		
Sanderstead	d				14 44									15 14								15 44			
Purley Oaks	d					14 48				15 09					15 18		15 39						15 48		
Purley 4	a	14 35	14 45			14 52	14 56			15 12	15 05	15 15			15 21	15 26	15 42		15 35	15 45			15 51	15 56	
Purley	d		14 46			14 52			15 02	15 13		15 16			15 22		15 43			15 46			15 52		16 02
Kenley	d					14 55				15 16					15 25		15 46						15 55		
Whyteleafe	d					14 59				15 19					15 28		15 49						15 58		
Upper Warlingham	a				14 51									15 21								15 51			
Whyteleafe South	d					15 01				15 21					15 30		15 51						16 00		
Caterham	a					15 05				15 26					15 35		15 56						16 05		
Reedham	d		14 48						15 04			15 18								15 48					16 04
Coulsdon Town	d		14 51						15 07			15 21								15 51					16 07
Woodmansterne	d		14 54						15 10			15 24								15 54					16 10
Chipstead	d		14 57						15 13			15 27								15 57					16 13
Kingswood	d		15 02						15 18			15 32								16 02					16 18
Tadworth	d		15 06						15 22			15 36								16 06					16 22
Tattenham Corner	a		15 09						15 25			15 39								16 09					16 25

Whyteleafe and Upper Warlingham stations are adjacent and tickets are interchangeable between these two stations

Purley Oaks and Sanderstead stations are close and tickets are interchangeable between these two stations

For complete service between London and East Croydon see table 175

Table 181

Saturdays

14 December to 17 May

London and Croydon - Purley, Caterham and Tattenham Corner

Network Diagram - see first Page of Table 181

Station		SN	SN 1	SN	SN	SN 1	SN	SN 1	SN		SN 1	SN	SN	SN 1	SN	SN 1	SN	SN	SN 1		SN	SN	SN 1	SN	SN 1
London Victoria 15 ⊖	d				15 43	15 53							16 13	16 23								16 43	16 53		
Clapham Junction 10	d				15 51	15 59	←						16 21	16 29	←							16 51	16 59	←	
East Croydon	a				16 12	16 09	16 12						16 42	16 39	16 42							17 12	17 09	17 12	
London Bridge 4 ⊖	d	15 36	15 45	15 50	→			16 03	16 06		16 15	16 20	→			16 33		16 36	16 45		16 50	→			17 03
New Cross Gate 4 ⊖	d	15 41						16 08	16 11							16 38		16 41							17 08
Norwood Junction 2	d	16 00	15 56	16 03				16 16	16 30		16 26	16 33				16 46		17 00	16 56		17 03				17 16
East Croydon	a	16 03	15 59	16 06				16 20	16 33		16 29	16 36				16 50		17 03	16 59		17 06				17 20
East Croydon	d	16 04	16 00	16 07		16 10	16 13	16 21	16 34		16 30	16 37		16 40	16 43	16 51		17 04	17 00		17 07		17 10	17 13	17 21
South Croydon 4	d	16 06					16 15		16 36						16 45			17 06						17 15	
Sanderstead	d					16 14								16 44									17 14		
Purley Oaks	d	16 09					16 18		16 39						16 48			17 09						17 18	
Purley 4	a	16 12	16 05	16 15			16 21	16 26	16 42		16 35	16 45			16 51	16 56		17 12	17 05		17 15			17 21	17 26
Purley	d	16 13		16 16			16 22		16 43			16 46			16 52		17 02	17 13			17 16			17 22	
Kenley	d	16 16					16 25		16 46						16 55			17 16						17 25	
Whyteleafe	d	16 19					16 28		16 49						16 58			17 19						17 28	
Upper Warlingham	a					16 21								16 51									17 21		
Whyteleafe South	d	16 21					16 30		16 51						17 00			17 21						17 30	
Caterham	a	16 26					16 35		16 56						17 05			17 26						17 35	
Reedham	d			16 18								16 48					17 04				17 18				
Coulsdon Town	d			16 21								16 51					17 07				17 21				
Woodmansterne	d			16 24								16 54					17 10				17 24				
Chipstead	d			16 27								16 57					17 13				17 27				
Kingswood	d			16 32								17 02					17 18				17 32				
Tadworth	d			16 36								17 06					17 22				17 36				
Tattenham Corner	a			16 39								17 09					17 25				17 39				

Station		SN	SN 1	SN	SN		SN 1	SN	SN 1	SN	SN	SN 1	SN	SN	SN 1		SN	SN 1	SN	SN 1	SN	SN	SN 1	SN	SN 1
London Victoria 15 ⊖	d				17 13		17 23							17 43	17 53							18 13	18 23		
Clapham Junction 10	d				17 21		17 29	←						17 51	17 59		←					18 21	18 29	←	
East Croydon	a				17 42		17 39	17 42						18 12	18 09		18 12					18 42	18 39	18 42	
London Bridge 4 ⊖	d	17 06	17 15	17 20	→				17 33		17 36	17 45	17 50	→				18 03	18 06	18 15	18 20	→			18 33
New Cross Gate 4 ⊖	d	17 11							17 38		17 41							18 08	18 11						18 38
Norwood Junction 2	d	17 30	17 26	17 33					17 46		18 00	17 56	18 03					18 16	18 30	18 26	18 33				18 46
East Croydon	a	17 33	17 29	17 36					17 50		18 03	17 59	18 06					18 20	18 33	18 29	18 36				18 50
East Croydon	d	17 34	17 30	17 37			17 40	17 43	17 51		18 04	18 00	18 07		18 10		18 13	18 21	18 34	18 30	18 37		18 40	18 43	18 51
South Croydon 4	d	17 36						17 45			18 06						18 15		18 36					18 45	
Sanderstead	d						17 44								18 14								18 44		
Purley Oaks	d	17 39						17 48			18 09						18 18		18 39					18 48	
Purley 4	a	17 42	17 35	17 45				17 51	17 56		18 12	18 05	18 15				18 21	18 26	18 42	18 35	18 45			18 51	18 56
Purley	d	17 43		17 46				17 52		18 02	18 13		18 16				18 22		18 43		18 46			18 52	
Kenley	d	17 46						17 55			18 16						18 25		18 46					18 55	
Whyteleafe	d	17 49						17 58			18 19						18 28		18 49					18 58	
Upper Warlingham	a						17 51								18 21								18 51		
Whyteleafe South	d	17 51						18 00			18 21						18 30		18 51					19 00	
Caterham	a	17 56						18 05			18 26						18 35		18 56					19 05	
Reedham	d			17 48						18 04			18 18								18 48				
Coulsdon Town	d			17 51						18 07			18 21								18 51				
Woodmansterne	d			17 54						18 10			18 24								18 54				
Chipstead	d			17 57						18 13			18 27								18 57				
Kingswood	d			18 02						18 18			18 32								19 02				
Tadworth	d			18 06						18 22			18 36								19 06				
Tattenham Corner	a			18 09						18 25			18 39								19 09				

Whyteleafe and Upper Warlingham stations are adjacent and tickets are interchangeable between these two stations

Purley Oaks and Sanderstead stations are close and tickets are interchangeable between these two stations

For complete service between London and East Croydon see table 175

Table 181

Saturdays

14 December to 17 May

London and Croydon - Purley, Caterham and Tattenham Corner

Network Diagram - see first Page of Table 181

		SN	SN	SN 1	SN	SN	SN 1		SN	SN 1	SN	SN	SN	SN 1	SN	SN 1	SN		SN	SN	SN	SN 1	SN	SN 1	SN
London Victoria 15 ⊖	d					18 43	18 53						19 13	19 23							19 43	19 53		20 10	
Clapham Junction 10	d					18 51	18 59		←				19 21	19 29	←						19 51	19 59	←	20 16	
East Croydon	a					19 12	19 09		19 12				19 42	19 39	19 42						20 12	20 09	20 12	20 29	
London Bridge 4 ⊖	d		18 36	18 45	18 50	→				19 03	19 06	19 20	→			19 33			19 36	19 50	→				20 06
New Cross Gate 4 ⊖	d		18 41							19 08	19 11					19 38			19 41						20 11
Norwood Junction 2	d		19 00	18 56	19 03					19 16	19 30	19 33				19 46			20 00	20 03					20 30
East Croydon	a		19 03	18 59	19 06					19 20	19 33	19 36				19 50			20 03	20 06					20 33
East Croydon	d		19 04	19 00	19 07		19 10		19 13	19 21	19 34	19 37		19 40	19 43	19 51			20 04	20 07		20 10	20 13	20 29	20 34
South Croydon 4	d		19 06						19 15		19 36				19 45				20 06				20 15		20 36
Sanderstead	d						19 14							19 44								20 14			
Purley Oaks	d		19 09						19 18		19 39				19 48				20 09				20 18		20 39
Purley 4	a		19 12	19 05	19 15				19 21	19 26	19 42	19 45			19 51	19 56			20 12	20 15			20 21	20 34	20 42
Purley	d	19 02	19 13		19 16				19 22		19 43	19 46			19 52		20 02		20 13	20 16			20 22		20 43
Kenley	d		19 16						19 25		19 46				19 55				20 16				20 25		20 46
Whyteleafe	d		19 19						19 28		19 49				19 58				20 19				20 28		20 49
Upper Warlingham	a						19 21							19 51								20 21			
Whyteleafe South	d		19 21						19 30		19 51				20 00				20 21				20 30		20 51
Caterham	a		19 26						19 35		19 56				20 05				20 26				20 35		20 56
Reedham	d	19 04			19 18							19 48					20 04			20 18					
Coulsdon Town	d	19 07			19 21							19 51					20 07			20 21					
Woodmansterne	d	19 10			19 24							19 54					20 10			20 24					
Chipstead	d	19 13			19 27							19 57					20 13			20 27					
Kingswood	d	19 18			19 32							20 02					20 18			20 32					
Tadworth	d	19 22			19 36							20 06					20 22			20 36					
Tattenham Corner	a	19 25			19 39							20 09					20 25			20 39					

		SN	SN		SN 1	SN	SN 1	SN	SN	SN	SN	SN 1	SN		SN 1	SN	SN	SN	SN 1	SN	SN 1	SN	SN		SN
London Victoria 15 ⊖	d		20 13		20 23		20 40				20 43	20 53			21 10			21 13	21 23		21 40				
Clapham Junction 10	d		20 21		20 29	←	20 46				20 51	20 59	←		21 16			21 21	21 29	←	21 46				
East Croydon	a		20 42		20 39	20 42	20 57				21 12	21 09	21 12		21 27			21 42	21 39	21 42	21 57				
London Bridge 4 ⊖	d	20 20	→						20 36	20 50	→					21 06	21 20	→					21 36		21 50
New Cross Gate 4 ⊖	d								20 41							21 11							21 41		
Norwood Junction 2	d	20 33							21 00	21 03						21 30	21 33						22 00		22 03
East Croydon	a	20 36							21 03	21 06						21 33	21 36						22 03		22 07
East Croydon	d	20 37			20 40	20 43	20 58		21 04	21 07		21 10	21 13		21 28	21 34	21 37		21 40	21 43	21 58		22 04		22 07
South Croydon 4	d					20 45			21 06				21 15			21 36				21 45			22 06		
Sanderstead	d				20 44							21 14							21 44						
Purley Oaks	d					20 48			21 09				21 18			21 39				21 48			22 09		
Purley 4	a	20 45				20 51	21 03		21 12	21 15			21 21		21 33	21 42	21 45			21 51	22 03		22 12		22 15
Purley	d	20 46				20 52		21 04	21 13	21 16			21 22			21 43	21 46			21 52		22 04	22 13		22 16
Kenley	d					20 55			21 16				21 25			21 46				21 55			22 16		
Whyteleafe	d					20 58			21 19				21 28			21 49				21 58			22 19		
Upper Warlingham	a				20 51							21 21							21 51						
Whyteleafe South	d					21 00			21 21				21 30			21 51				22 00			22 21		
Caterham	a					21 05			21 26				21 35			21 56				22 05			22 26		
Reedham	d	20 48						21 06		21 18							21 48					22 06			22 18
Coulsdon Town	d	20 51						21 09		21 21							21 51					22 09			22 21
Woodmansterne	d	20 54						21 12		21 24							21 54					22 12			22 24
Chipstead	d	20 57						21 15		21 27							21 57					22 15			22 27
Kingswood	d	21 02						21 20		21 32							22 02					22 20			22 32
Tadworth	d	21 06						21 24		21 36							22 06					22 24			22 36
Tattenham Corner	a	21 09						21 27		21 39							22 09					22 27			22 39

Whyteleafe and Upper Warlingham stations are adjacent and tickets are interchangeable between these two stations

Purley Oaks and Sanderstead stations are close and tickets are interchangeable between these two stations

For complete service between London and East Croydon see table 175

Table 181

Saturdays

14 December to 17 May

London and Croydon - Purley, Caterham and Tattenham Corner

Network Diagram - see first Page of Table 181

	SN	SN 1	SN	SN 1		SN	SN	SN	SN 1	SN	SN 1	SN	SN	SN		SN 1	SN	SN 1	SN 1	SN	SN	SN 1	SN	SN 1
London Victoria 15 ⊖ d	21 43	21 53		22 10				22 13	22 23		22 40			22 43		22 53			23 10		23 15	23 24		23 40
Clapham Junction 10 d	21 51	21 59	←	22 16				22 21	22 29	←	22 46			22 51		22 59	←		23 16		23 23	23 30	←	23 46
East Croydon a	22 12	22 09	22 12	22 27				22 43	22 39	22 43	22 57			23 13		23 09	23 13		23 27		23 44	23 40	23 44	23 55
London Bridge 4 ⊖ d	→					22 06	22 20	→				22 36	22 50	→				23 04		23 06	→			
New Cross Gate 4 ⊖ d						22 11						22 41								23 11				
Norwood Junction 2 d						22 30	22 33					23 00	23 03					23 15		23 30				
East Croydon a						22 33	22 36					23 03	23 06					23 19		23 33				
East Croydon d		22 10	22 13	22 28		22 34	22 37		22 40	22 44	22 58	23 04	23 07			23 10	23 14	23 19	23 28	23 34		23 41	23 44	00 01
South Croydon 4 d			22 15			22 36				22 47		23 06					23 16			23 36			23 47	
Sanderstead d		22 14							22 44							23 14		23 24				23 46		
Purley Oaks d			22 18			22 39				22 50		23 09					23 19			23 39			23 50	
Purley 4 a			22 21	22 33		22 42	22 45			22 53	23 03	23 12	23 15				23 22		23 33	23 42			23 53	00 10
Purley d			22 22			22 43	22 46			22 53		23 13	23 16				23 23			23 43			23 53	
Kenley d			22 25			22 46				22 56		23 16					23 26			23 46				
Whyteleafe d			22 28			22 49				23 00		23 19					23 29			23 49				
Upper Warlingham a		22 21							22 51							23 21		23 29				23 53		
Whyteleafe South d			22 30			22 51				23 02		23 21					23 31			23 51				
Caterham a			22 36			22 56				23 06		23 26					23 36			23 56				
Reedham d							22 48						23 18										23 56	
Coulsdon Town d							22 51						23 21										23 58	
Woodmansterne d							22 54						23 24										00 01	
Chipstead d							22 57						23 27										00 04	
Kingswood d							23 02						23 32										00 10	
Tadworth d							23 06						23 36										00 13	
Tattenham Corner a							23 09						23 39										00 17	

	SN	SN 1	SN	SN
London Victoria 15 ⊖ d	23 45	23 47		
Clapham Junction 10 d	23 53	23 53		←
East Croydon a	00 14	00 04		00 14
London Bridge 4 ⊖ d	→		23 41	
New Cross Gate 4 ⊖ d			23 46	
Norwood Junction 2 d			00 05	
East Croydon a			00 08	
East Croydon d		00 04	00 09	00 14
South Croydon 4 d			00 11	00 17
Sanderstead d		00s09		
Purley Oaks d			00 14	00 20
Purley 4 a			00 18	00 23
Purley d			00 20	00 24
Kenley d			00 23	
Whyteleafe d			00 27	
Upper Warlingham a		00s16		
Whyteleafe South d			00 29	
Caterham a			00 33	
Reedham d				00 26
Coulsdon Town d				00 29
Woodmansterne d				00 32
Chipstead d				00 35
Kingswood d				00 40
Tadworth d				00 44
Tattenham Corner a				00 47

Whyteleafe and Upper Warlingham stations are adjacent and tickets are interchangeable between these two stations

Purley Oaks and Sanderstead stations are close and tickets are interchangeable between these two stations

For complete service between London and East Croydon see table 175

Table 181

Sundays

8 December to 11 May

London and Croydon - Purley, Caterham and Tattenham Corner

Network Diagram - see first Page of Table 181

		SN	SN [1]	SN [1]	SN	SN	SN	SN [1]	SN	SN [1]		SN [1]		SN [1]	SN [1]	SN	SN [1]	SN	SN	SN [1]	SN	SN [1]		SN [1]
London Victoria [15] ⊖	d							00 14	00 16	01 00		04 00		05 02	06 32	06 36	07 02	07 06			07 35	07 47		08 02
Clapham Junction [10]	d							00 21	00 24	01 09		04 09		05 09	06 39	06 42	07 09	07 12			07 41	07 54		08 09
East Croydon	a							00 35	00 44	01 25		04 25		05 24	06 54	07 02	07 25	07 32				08 10		08 23
London Bridge [4] ⊖	d						00 06												07 24	07 43				
New Cross Gate [4] ⊖	d						00 11												07 30					
Norwood Junction [2]	d				00 05		00 30												07 52		08 03			
East Croydon	a				00 08		00 33												07 58	07 56	08 07			
East Croydon	d		00 01	00 04	00 09	00 14	00 35	00 36	00 49	01 26		04 26		05 25	06 55	07 05	07 26	07 35	07 58	07 56	08 07	08 10		08 24
South Croydon [4]	d				00 11	00 17	00 39		00 52										08 01					
Sanderstead	d			00 09																		08 15		
Purley Oaks	d				00 14	00 20	00 42		00 55		and hourly until								08 04					
Purley [4]	a		00 10		00 18	00 23	00 45	00 41	00 59	01 31		04 31		05 30	06 59	07 13	07 31	07 43	08 08	08 02	08 14			08 29
Purley	d				00 20	00 24	00 46		00 59							07 13		07 43	08 09		08 14			
Kenley	d				00 23		00 49									07 16		07 46			08 17			
Whyteleafe	d				00 27		00 52									07 20		07 50			08 21			
Upper Warlingham	a			00 16																		08 22		
Whyteleafe South	d				00 29		00 54									07 22		07 52			08 23			
Caterham	a				00 33		00 59									07 26		07 56			08 27			
Reedham	d					00 26			01 02										08 11					
Coulsdon Town	d					00 29			01 04										08 14					
Woodmansterne	d	00 01				00 32			01 07										08 17					
Chipstead	d	00 04				00 35			01 10										08 20					
Kingswood	d	00 10				00 40			01 16										08 25					
Tadworth	d	00 13				00 44			01 19										08 29					
Tattenham Corner	a	00 17				00 47			01 23										08 32					

		SN	SN	SN	SN [1]	SN	SN [1]	SN [1]	SN [1]		SN	SN	SN [1]	SN	SN [1]	SN	SN [1]	SN [1]	SN [1]	SN	SN	SN [1]	SN	SN [1]	SN
London Victoria [15] ⊖	d		08 05			08 35	08 53		09 02			09 08	09 23			09 38	09 53		10 02		10 08	10 23			10 38
Clapham Junction [10]	d		08 12			08 42	08 59		09 08			09 14	09 29			09 44	09 59		10 08		10 14	10 29			10 44
East Croydon	a					09 02	09 09		09 17			09 35	09 39			10 05	10 09		10 17		10 35	10 39			11 05
London Bridge [4] ⊖	d	07 54		08 24	08 35						08 54			09 24	09 35					09 54			10 24	10 35	
New Cross Gate [4] ⊖	d	08 00		08 30							09 00			09 30						10 00			10 30		
Norwood Junction [2]	d	08 22	08 36	08 52	08 46						09 19			09 49	09 46					10 19			10 49	10 46	
East Croydon	a	08 26	08 40	08 57	08 54						09 23			09 53	09 50					10 23			10 53	10 50	
East Croydon	d	08 27	08 41	08 58	08 55	09 03	09 10	09 15	09 18		09 24	09 35	09 40	09 54	09 51	10 05	10 10	10 15	10 17	10 24	10 35	10 40	10 54	10 51	11 05
South Croydon [4]	d	08 30		09 00							09 26			09 56						10 26			10 56		
Sanderstead	d						09 14	09 20					09 44				10 14	10 20				10 44			
Purley Oaks	d	08 33		09 03							09 29			09 59						10 29			10 59		
Purley [4]	a	08 36	08 48	09 07	09 01	09 10			09 23		09 33	09 42		10 03	09 55	10 12			10 23	10 33	10 42		11 03	10 55	11 12
Purley	d	08 37	08 48	09 07		09 10					09 33	09 43		10 03		10 13				10 33	10 43		11 03		11 13
Kenley	d		08 51			09 13						09 46				10 16					10 46				11 16
Whyteleafe	d		08 55			09 17						09 49				10 19					10 49				11 19
Upper Warlingham	a						09 21	09 27					09 51				10 21	10 27				10 51			
Whyteleafe South	d		08 57			09 19						09 51				10 21					10 51				11 21
Caterham	a		09 01			09 23						09 56				10 26					10 56				11 26
Reedham	d	08 39		09 10							09 36			10 06						10 36			11 06		
Coulsdon Town	d	08 42		09 12							09 38			10 08						10 38			11 08		
Woodmansterne	d	08 45		09 15							09 41			10 11						10 41			11 11		
Chipstead	d	08 48		09 18							09 44			10 14						10 44			11 14		
Kingswood	d	08 53		09 24							09 50			10 20						10 50			11 20		
Tadworth	d	08 57		09 27							09 53			10 23						10 53			11 23		
Tattenham Corner	a	09 00		09 31							09 57			10 27						10 57			11 27		

Whyteleafe and Upper Warlingham stations are adjacent and tickets are interchangeable between these two stations

Purley Oaks and Sanderstead stations are close and tickets are interchangeable between these two stations

For complete service between London and East Croydon see table 175

Table 181

Sundays

8 December to 11 May

London and Croydon - Purley, Caterham and Tattenham Corner

Network Diagram - see first Page of Table 181

		SN 1		SN 1	SN	SN	SN 1	SN	SN 1	SN	SN 1		SN 1	SN	SN	SN 1	SN	SN 1	SN	SN 1	SN 1	SN		
London Victoria 15 ⊖	d	10 53	and at the same minutes past each hour until	14 02		14 08	14 23			14 38	14 53		15 02		15 07	15 23			15 38	15 53	16 02			
Clapham Junction 10	d	10 59		14 08		14 14	14 29			14 44	14 59		15 08		15 13	15 29			15 44	15 59	16 08			
East Croydon	a	11 09		14 17		14 35	14 39			15 05	15 09		15 17		15 35	15 39			16 05	16 09	16 17			
London Bridge 4 ⊖	d				13 54			14 24	14 35					14 54			15 24	15 35				15 54		
New Cross Gate 4 ⊖	d				14 00			14 30						15 00			15 30					16 00		
Norwood Junction 2	d				14 19			14 49	14 46					15 19			15 49	15 46				16 19		
East Croydon	a				14 23			14 53	14 50					15 23			15 53	15 50				16 23		
East Croydon	d	11 10		14 17	14 24	14 35	14 40	14 54	14 51	15 05	15 10		15 17	15 24	15 35	15 40	15 54	15 51	16 05	16 10	16 17	16 24		
South Croydon 4	d				14 26			14 56						15 26			15 56					16 26		
Sanderstead	d	11 14					14 44				15 14					15 44				16 14				
Purley Oaks	d				14 29			14 59						15 29			15 59					16 29		
Purley 4	a			14 23	14 33	14 42		15 03	14 55	15 12			15 23	15 33	15 42		16 03	15 55	16 12		16 23	16 33		
Purley	d				14 33	14 43		15 03		15 13				15 33	15 43		16 03		16 13			16 33		
Kenley	d					14 46				15 16					15 46				16 16					
Whyteleafe	d					14 49				15 19					15 49				16 19					
Upper Warlingham	a	11 21					14 51				15 21					15 51				16 21				
Whyteleafe South	d					14 51				15 21					15 51				16 21					
Caterham	a					14 56				15 26					15 56				16 26					
Reedham	d				14 36			15 06						15 36			16 06					16 36		
Coulsdon Town	d				14 38			15 08						15 38			16 08					16 38		
Woodmansterne	d				14 41			15 11						15 41			16 11					16 41		
Chipstead	d				14 44			15 14						15 44			16 14					16 44		
Kingswood	d				14 50			15 20						15 50			16 20					16 50		
Tadworth	d				14 53			15 23						15 53			16 23					16 53		
Tattenham Corner	a				14 57			15 27						15 57			16 27					16 57		

		SN		SN 1	SN	SN 1	SN	SN 1	SN 1	SN	SN		SN	SN 1	SN	SN 1	SN 1	SN	SN	SN	SN 1		SN	SN 1
London Victoria 15 ⊖	d	16 08	and at the same minutes past each hour until	19 23			19 38	19 53	20 02		20 08				20 38	20 53	21 02		21 08				21 38	21 53
Clapham Junction 10	d	16 14		19 29			19 44	19 59	20 08		20 14				20 44	20 59	21 08		21 14				21 44	21 59
East Croydon	a	16 35		19 39			20 05	20 09	20 17		20 35				21 05	21 09	21 17		21 35				22 05	22 09
London Bridge 4 ⊖	d				19 24	19 35				19 54			20 24	20 35				20 54		21 24	21 35			
New Cross Gate 4 ⊖	d				19 30					20 00			20 30					21 00		21 30				
Norwood Junction 2	d				19 49	19 46				20 19			20 49	20 46				21 19		21 49	21 46			
East Croydon	a				19 53	19 50				20 23			20 53	20 50				21 23		21 53	21 50			
East Croydon	d	16 35		19 40	19 54	19 51	20 05	20 10	20 17	20 24	20 35		20 54	20 51	21 05	21 10	21 17	21 24	21 35	21 54	21 51		22 05	22 10
South Croydon 4	d				19 56					20 26			20 56					21 26		21 56				
Sanderstead	d			19 44				20 14								21 14								22 14
Purley Oaks	d				19 59					20 29			20 59					21 29		21 59				
Purley 4	a	16 42			20 03	19 55	20 12		20 23	20 33	20 42		21 03	20 55	21 12		21 23	21 33	21 42	22 03	21 55		22 12	
Purley	d	16 43			20 03		20 13			20 33	20 43		21 03		21 13			21 33	21 43	22 03			22 13	
Kenley	d	16 46					20 16				20 46				21 16				21 46				22 16	
Whyteleafe	d	16 49					20 19				20 49				21 19				21 49				22 19	
Upper Warlingham	a			19 51				20 21								21 21								22 21
Whyteleafe South	d	16 51					20 21				20 51				21 21				21 51				22 21	
Caterham	a	16 56					20 26				20 56				21 26				21 56				22 26	
Reedham	d				20 06					20 36			21 06					21 36		22 06				
Coulsdon Town	d				20 08					20 38			21 08					21 38		22 08				
Woodmansterne	d				20 11					20 41			21 11					21 41		22 11				
Chipstead	d				20 14					20 44			21 14					21 44		22 14				
Kingswood	d				20 20					20 50			21 20					21 50		22 20				
Tadworth	d				20 23					20 53			21 23					21 53		22 23				
Tattenham Corner	a				20 27					20 57			21 27					21 57		22 27				

		SN 1	SN	SN	SN	SN 1	SN 1	SN		SN 1	SN	SN	SN	SN
London Victoria 15 ⊖	d	22 02		22 08			22 36	22 38		23 04		23 08		23 50
Clapham Junction 10	d	22 08		22 14			22 42	22 44		23 10		23 14		23 57
East Croydon	a	22 17		22 35			22 56	23 05		23 21		23 35		00 18
London Bridge 4 ⊖	d		21 54		22 24	22 35					22 54		23 39	
New Cross Gate 4 ⊖	d		22 00		22 30						23 00		23 44	
Norwood Junction 2	d		22 19		22 49	22 46					23 19		00 03	
East Croydon	a		22 23		22 53	22 50					23 23		00 07	
East Croydon	d	22 18	22 24	22 35	22 54	22 51	22 57	23 05		23 22	23 24	23 35	00 08	00 18
South Croydon 4	d		22 26		22 56						23 26	23 38	00 10	00 25
Sanderstead	d						23 01							
Purley Oaks	d		22 29		22 59						23 29	23 41	00 14	00 28
Purley 4	a	22 23	22 33	22 42	23 03	22 55		23 12		23 27	23 33	23 45	00 17	00 31
Purley	d		22 33	22 43	23 03			23 13			23 33	23 45	00 17	00 31
Kenley	d			22 46				23 16				23 48	00 20	00 34
Whyteleafe	d			22 49				23 19				23 52	00 24	00 38
Upper Warlingham	a						23 08							
Whyteleafe South	d			22 51				23 21				23 54	00 26	00 40
Caterham	a			22 56				23 26				23 58	00 30	00 44
Reedham	d		22 36		23 06						23 36			
Coulsdon Town	d		22 38		23 08						23 38			
Woodmansterne	d		22 41		23 11						23 41			
Chipstead	d		22 44		23 14						23 44			
Kingswood	d		22 50		23 20						23 50			
Tadworth	d		22 53		23 23						23 53			
Tattenham Corner	a		22 57		23 27						23 57			

Whyteleafe and Upper Warlingham stations are adjacent and tickets are interchangeable between these two stations

Purley Oaks and Sanderstead stations are close and tickets are interchangeable between these two stations

For complete service between London and East Croydon see table 175

Table 181R

Mondays to Fridays

9 December to 16 May

Tattenham Corner, Caterham and Purley - Croydon and London

Network Diagram - see first Page of Table 181

Miles	Miles	Miles			SN	SN	SN	SN 1	SN	SN		SN 1	SN	SN 1	SN	SN	SN 1	SN	SN	SN 1	SN 1	SN	SN		SN 1
0	—	—	Tattenham Corner	d					05 56						06 32			06 48				07 02			
1¼	—	—	Tadworth	d					05 59						06 35			06 51				07 05			
2½	—	—	Kingswood	d					06 02						06 38			06 54				07 08			
5	—	—	Chipstead	d					06 08						06 44			07 00				07 14			
6	—	—	Woodmansterne	d					06 11						06 47			07 03				07 17			
6¾	—	—	Coulsdon Town	d					06 14						06 50			07 06				07 20			
7½	—	—	Reedham	d					06 16						06 52			07 08				07 22			
—	0	—	Caterham	d			05 52			06 15			06 35			06 45			07 01				07 15		
—	1¾	—	Whyteleafe South	d			05 55			06 18			06 38			06 48			07 04				07 18		
—	—	0	Upper Warlingham	d				06 12				06 40					07 03			07 15					07 31
—	2¼	—	Whyteleafe	d			05 57			06 20			06 40			06 50			07 06				07 20		
—	3½	—	Kenley	d			06 00			06 23			06 43			06 53			07 09				07 23		
—	—	—	Purley	a			06 03		06 19	06 26			06 46		06 55	06 59		07 11	07 15			07 25	07 29		
—	—	—																							
8¼	4¾	—	Purley 4	d	05 07		06 04		06 22	06 27			06 47	06 54	07 02			07 17			07 29	07 31			
9¼	5¾	—	Purley Oaks	d			06 07		06 25	06 30			06 50		07 05			07 20				07 34			
—	—	3¼	Sanderstead	d				06 18			06 38	06 47					07 10			07 22					07 38
10¼	6¾	—	South Croydon 4	d			06 10		06 28	06 33	06 42	06 51	06 53		07 09			07 23		07 25		07 38			
11¼	7¾	5	East Croydon	a	05 12		06 12	06 23	06 30	06 35	06 44	06 53	06 56	06 59	07 11		07 15	07 25		07 28	07 34	07 40			07 44
—	—	—	East Croydon	d	05 13	05 34	06 13	06 24	06 31	06 36	06 45	06 54		07 00	07 12					07 29	07 35	07 41			
—	9	—	Norwood Junction 2	d	05 17	05 38	06 18		06 37	06 40					07 16							07 45			
—	15	—	New Cross Gate 4 ⊖	a	05 34		06 35																		
—	17¾	—	London Bridge 4 ⊖	a	05 41		06 44	06 39	06 49	06 52		07 09		07 17	07 28					07 45	07 52	07 58			
—	—	—	East Croydon	d							06 45		06 57				07 15	07 26							07 44
19	—	13	Clapham Junction 10	a		05 58					07 06		07 06				07 27	07 36							07 54
21¾	—	15½	London Victoria 15 ⊖	a		06 07					07 16		07 15				07 35	07 45							08 03

		SN	SN	SN	SN 1	SN 1	SN	SN	SN 1		SN	SN	SN 1	SN	SN	SN 1	SN	SN	SN 1		SN 1	SN	SN	SN 1	SN
Tattenham Corner	d		07 18				07 32				07 48			08 04			08 16					08 27			
Tadworth	d		07 21				07 35				07 51			08 07			08 19					08 30			
Kingswood	d		07 24				07 38				07 54			08 10			08 22					08 33			
Chipstead	d		07 30				07 44				08 00			08 16			08 28					08 39			
Woodmansterne	d		07 33				07 47				08 03			08 19			08 31					08 42			
Coulsdon Town	d	07 31	07 36				07 50				08 06			08 22			08 34					08 45			
Reedham	d	07 34	07 38				07 52				08 08			08 24			08 36					08 47			
Caterham	d			07 31				07 45				08 01			08 17			08 29					08 40		08 54
Whyteleafe South	d			07 34				07 48				08 04			08 20			08 32					08 43		08 57
Upper Warlingham	d				07 45				08 02				08 15			08 33			08 43					09 02	
Whyteleafe	d			07 36				07 50				08 06			08 22			08 34					08 45		08 59
Kenley	d			07 39				07 53				08 09			08 25			08 37					08 48		09 02
Purley	a	07 37	07 41	07 45			07 55	07 59			08 11	08 13		08 27	08 31		08 39	08 43				08 50	08 54		09 05
Purley 4	d	07 40	07 47			07 55	08 01				08 17			08 34			08 45				08 53	08 56			09 08
Purley Oaks	d	07 43	07 50				08 04				08 20			08 37			08 48					08 59			09 11
Sanderstead	d				07 52				08 09				08 22			08 40			08 49					09 09	
South Croydon 4	d	07 47	07 53		07 56		08 08				08 23		08 26	08 40		08 43	08 51		08 53			09 02			09 14
East Croydon	a	07 49	07 55		07 58	08 01	08 10		08 14		08 26		08 29	08 42		08 45	08 53		08 55		08 58	09 05		09 13	09 16
East Croydon	d				07 59	08 02	08 11						08 29	08 43					08 56		08 59	09 05			
Norwood Junction 2	d						08 16							08 48								09 09			
New Cross Gate 4 ⊖	a																								
London Bridge 4 ⊖	a				08 15	08 17	08 28						08 47	09 00					09 11		09 16	09 25			
East Croydon	d	07 50	07 56						08 15		08 26					08 46	08 54							09 14	09 17
Clapham Junction 10	a	08 13	08 06						08 26		08 38					08 56	09 04							09 26	09 39
London Victoria 15 ⊖	a		08 15						08 35		08 47					09 05	09 13							09 35	09 47

Whyteleafe and Upper Warlingham stations are adjacent and tickets are interchangeable between these two stations

Purley Oaks and Sanderstead stations are close and tickets are interchangeable between these two stations

For complete service between London and East Croydon see table 175

Table 181R

Mondays to Fridays

9 December to 16 May

Tattenham Corner, Caterham and Purley - Croydon and London

Network Diagram - see first Page of Table 181

			SN	SN	SN [1]	SN [1]	SN	SN	SN [1]	SN	SN		SN [1]	SN [1]	SN	SN	SN [1]	SN	SN [1]	SN [1]	SN		SN	SN [1]	SN
Tattenham Corner	d		08 51					09 21			09 33					09 49							10 21		
Tadworth	d		08 54					09 24			09 36					09 52							10 24		
Kingswood	d		08 57					09 27			09 39					09 55							10 27		
Chipstead	d		09 03					09 33			09 45					10 01							10 33		
Woodmansterne	d		09 06					09 36			09 48					10 04							10 36		
Coulsdon Town	d		09 09					09 39			09 51					10 07							10 39		
Reedham	d		09 11					09 41			09 53					10 09							10 41		
Caterham	d			09 07			09 26			09 39					09 56			10 09			10 26				10 39
Whyteleafe South	d			09 10			09 29			09 42					09 59			10 12			10 29				10 42
Upper Warlingham	d					09 32								10 02						10 32					
Whyteleafe	d			09 12			09 31			09 44					10 01			10 14			10 31				10 44
Kenley	d			09 15			09 34			09 47					10 04			10 17			10 34				10 47
Purley	a		09 14	09 18			09 37	09 44		09 50	09 56				10 07	10 12		10 20			10 37		10 44		10 50
Purley [4]	d		09 14	09 21	09 32		09 38	09 45	09 49	09 51			10 02		10 08	10 15	10 19	10 21	10 33		10 38		10 45	10 49	10 51
Purley Oaks	d			09 24			09 41			09 54					10 11			10 24			10 41				10 54
Sanderstead	d					09 39								10 09						10 39					
South Croydon [4]	d			09 27			09 44			09 57					10 14			10 27			10 44				10 57
East Croydon	a		09 21	09 30	09 38	09 43	09 46	09 50	09 54	10 00			10 07	10 13	10 16	10 20	10 24	10 30	10 38	10 43	10 46		10 50	10 54	11 00
East Croydon	d		09 22	09 30	09 39			09 51	09 55	10 00			10 08			10 21	10 25	10 30	10 38				10 51	10 55	11 00
Norwood Junction [2]	d		09 26	09 35	09 43			09 55	09 59	10 05			10 13			10 25	10 30	10 35	10 43				10 55	11 00	11 05
New Cross Gate [4] ⊖	a		09 34	09 52					10 07	10 22							10 38	10 52						11 08	11 22
London Bridge [4] ⊖	a		09 41	09 59	09 55			10 09	10 13	10 29			10 25			10 39	10 44	10 59	10 55				11 09	11 14	11 29
East Croydon	d					09 44	09 47							10 14	10 17					10 44	10 47				
Clapham Junction [10]	a					09 55	10 08							10 25	10 38					10 55	11 08				
London Victoria [15] ⊖	a					10 05	10 17							10 35	10 46					11 02	11 16				

		SN	SN [1]	SN [1]	SN	SN	SN [1]		SN	SN [1]	SN [1]	SN	SN	SN [1]	SN	SN	SN [1]		SN [1]	SN	SN	SN [1]	SN	SN [1]	SN [1]
Tattenham Corner	d	10 33				10 51							11 21			11 33					11 51				
Tadworth	d	10 36				10 54							11 24			11 36					11 54				
Kingswood	d	10 39				10 57							11 27			11 39					11 57				
Chipstead	d	10 45				11 03							11 33			11 45					12 03				
Woodmansterne	d	10 48				11 06							11 36			11 48					12 06				
Coulsdon Town	d	10 51				11 09							11 39			11 51					12 09				
Reedham	d	10 53				11 11							11 41			11 53					12 11				
Caterham	d				10 56				11 09			11 26			11 39					11 56			12 09		
Whyteleafe South	d				10 59				11 12			11 29			11 42					11 59			12 12		
Upper Warlingham	d			11 02							11 32								12 02						12 32
Whyteleafe	d				11 01				11 14			11 31			11 44					12 01			12 14		
Kenley	d				11 04				11 17			11 34			11 47					12 04			12 17		
Purley	a	10 56			11 07	11 14			11 20			11 37	11 44		11 50	11 56				12 07	12 14		12 20		
Purley [4]	d		11 02		11 08	11 15	11 19		11 21	11 32		11 38	11 45	11 49	11 51		12 02			12 08	12 15	12 19	12 21	12 32	
Purley Oaks	d				11 11				11 24			11 41			11 54					12 11			12 24		
Sanderstead	d			11 09							11 39								12 09						12 39
South Croydon [4]	d				11 14				11 27			11 44			11 57					12 14			12 27		
East Croydon	a		11 07	11 13	11 16	11 20	11 24		11 30	11 37	11 43	11 46	11 50	11 54	12 00		12 07		12 13	12 16	12 20	12 24	12 30	12 37	12 43
East Croydon	d		11 07			11 21	11 25		11 30	11 38			11 51	11 55	12 00		12 08				12 21	12 25	12 30	12 38	
Norwood Junction [2]	d		11 13			11 25	11 29		11 35	11 43			11 55	11 59	12 05		12 13				12 25	12 29	12 35	12 43	
New Cross Gate [4] ⊖	a						11 37		11 52					12 07	12 22							12 37	12 52		
London Bridge [4] ⊖	a		11 25			11 39	11 43		11 59	11 55			12 09	12 13	12 29		12 25				12 39	12 43	12 59	12 55	
East Croydon	d			11 14	11 17						11 44	11 47							12 14	12 17					12 44
Clapham Junction [10]	a			11 25	11 38						11 55	12 08							12 25	12 38					12 55
London Victoria [15] ⊖	a			11 32	11 46						12 02	12 16							12 32	12 46					13 02

		SN	SN		SN [1]	SN	SN	SN [1]	SN [1]	SN	SN	SN [1]	SN		SN [1]	SN [1]	SN	SN	SN [1]	SN	SN	SN [1]	SN [1]		SN
Tattenham Corner	d		12 21				12 33				12 51							13 21			13 33				
Tadworth	d		12 24				12 36				12 54							13 24			13 36				
Kingswood	d		12 27				12 39				12 57							13 27			13 39				
Chipstead	d		12 33				12 45				13 03							13 33			13 45				
Woodmansterne	d		12 36				12 48				13 06							13 36			13 48				
Coulsdon Town	d		12 39				12 51				13 09							13 39			13 51				
Reedham	d		12 41				12 53				13 11							13 41			13 53				
Caterham	d	12 26				12 39				12 56			13 09				13 26			13 39					13 56
Whyteleafe South	d	12 29				12 42				12 59			13 12				13 29			13 42					13 59
Upper Warlingham	d								13 02							13 32							14 02		
Whyteleafe	d	12 31				12 44				13 01			13 14				13 31			13 44					14 01
Kenley	d	12 34				12 47				13 04			13 17				13 34			13 47					14 04
Purley	a	12 37	12 44			12 50	12 56			13 07	13 14		13 20				13 37	13 44		13 50	13 56				14 07
Purley [4]	d	12 38	12 45		12 49	12 51		13 02		13 08	13 15	13 19	13 21		13 32		13 38	13 45	13 49	13 51		14 02			14 08
Purley Oaks	d	12 41				12 54				13 11			13 24				13 41			13 54					14 11
Sanderstead	d								13 09							13 39							14 09		
South Croydon [4]	d	12 44				12 57				13 14			13 27				13 44			13 57					14 14
East Croydon	a	12 46	12 50		12 54	13 00		13 07	13 13	13 16	13 20	13 24	13 30		13 37	13 43	13 46	13 50	13 54	14 00		14 07	14 13		14 16
East Croydon	d		12 51		12 55	13 00		13 08			13 21	13 25	13 30		13 38			13 51	13 55	14 00		14 08			
Norwood Junction [2]	d		12 55		13 00	13 05		13 13			13 25	13 29	13 35		13 43			13 55	13 59	14 05		14 13			
New Cross Gate [4] ⊖	a				13 07	13 22						13 37	13 52						14 07	14 22					
London Bridge [4] ⊖	a		13 09		13 14	13 29		13 25			13 39	13 43	13 59		13 55			14 09	14 13	14 29		14 25			
East Croydon	d	12 47							13 14	13 17						13 44	13 47						14 14		14 17
Clapham Junction [10]	a	13 08							13 25	13 38						13 55	14 08						14 25		14 38
London Victoria [15] ⊖	a	13 16							13 32	13 46						14 02	14 16						14 32		14 46

Whyteleafe and Upper Warlingham stations are adjacent and tickets are interchangeable between these two stations

Purley Oaks and Sanderstead stations are close and tickets are interchangeable between these two stations

For complete service between London and East Croydon see table 175

Table 181R

Mondays to Fridays

9 December to 16 May

Tattenham Corner, Caterham and Purley - Croydon and London

Network Diagram - see first Page of Table 181

		SN	SN 1	SN	SN 1	SN 1	SN	SN	SN 1		SN	SN	SN 1	SN 1	SN	SN	SN 1	SN	SN 1		SN 1	SN	SN	SN 1	SN
Tattenham Corner	d	13 51						14 21				14 33				14 51							15 21		
Tadworth	d	13 54						14 24				14 36				14 54							15 24		
Kingswood	d	13 57						14 27				14 39				14 57							15 27		
Chipstead	d	14 03						14 33				14 45				15 03							15 33		
Woodmansterne	d	14 06						14 36				14 48				15 06							15 36		
Coulsdon Town	d	14 09						14 39				14 51				15 09							15 39		
Reedham	d	14 11						14 41				14 53				15 11							15 41		
Caterham	d			14 09			14 26				14 39				14 56			15 09				15 24			15 39
Whyteleafe South	d			14 12			14 29				14 42				14 59			15 12				15 27			15 42
Upper Warlingham	d					14 32								15 02							15 32				
Whyteleafe	d			14 14			14 31				14 44				15 01			15 14				15 29			15 44
Kenley	d			14 17			14 34				14 47				15 04			15 17				15 32			15 47
Purley	a	14 14		14 20			14 37	14 44			14 50	14 56			15 07	15 14		15 20				15 35	15 44		15 50
Purley 4	d	14 15	14 19	14 21	14 32		14 38	14 45	14 49		14 51		15 02		15 08	15 15	15 19	15 21	15 32			15 38	15 45	15 49	15 51
Purley Oaks	d			14 24			14 41				14 54				15 11			15 24				15 41			15 54
Sanderstead	d					14 39								15 09							15 39				
South Croydon 4	d			14 27			14 44				14 57				15 14			15 27				15 44			15 57
East Croydon	a	14 20	14 24	14 30	14 37	14 43	14 46	14 50	14 54		15 00		15 07	15 13	15 16	15 20	15 24	15 30	15 37		15 43	15 46	15 50	15 54	16 00
East Croydon	d	14 21	14 25	14 30	14 38			14 51	14 55		15 00		15 08			15 21	15 25	15 30	15 38				15 51	15 55	16 00
Norwood Junction 2	d	14 25	14 29	14 35	14 43			14 55	14 59		15 05		15 13			15 25	15 29	15 35	15 43				15 55	15 59	16 05
New Cross Gate 4 ⊖	a		14 37	14 52					15 07		15 22						15 37	15 52						16 07	16 22
London Bridge 4 ⊖	a	14 39	14 43	14 59	14 55			15 09	15 13		15 29		15 25			15 39	15 43	15 59	15 55				16 09	16 13	16 29
East Croydon	d					14 44	14 47							15 14	15 17						15 44	15 47			
Clapham Junction 10	a					14 55	15 08							15 25	15 38						15 54	16 08			
London Victoria 15 ⊖	a					15 02	15 16							15 35	15 46						16 05	16 16			

		SN	SN 1	SN 1	SN		SN	SN 1	SN	SN 1	SN 1	SN	SN	SN 1	SN		SN 1	SN	SN	SN	SN 1	SN	SN 1	SN	SN
Tattenham Corner	d	15 33					15 51						16 21					16 33		16 51					17 19
Tadworth	d	15 36					15 54						16 24					16 36		16 54					17 22
Kingswood	d	15 39					15 57						16 27					16 39		16 57					17 25
Chipstead	d	15 45					16 03						16 33					16 45		17 03					17 31
Woodmansterne	d	15 48					16 06						16 36					16 48		17 06					17 34
Coulsdon Town	d	15 51					16 09						16 39					16 51		17 09					17 37
Reedham	d	15 53					16 11						16 41					16 53		17 11					17 39
Caterham	d				15 56				16 07			16 26			16 39				16 52			17 09		17 26	
Whyteleafe South	d				15 59				16 10			16 29			16 42				16 55			17 12		17 29	
Upper Warlingham	d			16 02							16 32						17 02						17 32		
Whyteleafe	d				16 01				16 12			16 31			16 44				16 57			17 14		17 31	
Kenley	d				16 04				16 15			16 34			16 47				17 00			17 17		17 34	
Purley	a	15 56			16 07		16 14		16 18			16 37	16 44		16 50			16 56	17 06	17 14		17 20		17 37	17 42
Purley 4	d		16 02		16 08		16 15	16 18	16 21	16 34		16 38	16 45	16 49	16 51			17 08		17 15	17 19	17 21		17 38	17 45
Purley Oaks	d				16 11				16 24			16 41			16 54			17 11				17 24		17 41	
Sanderstead	d			16 09							16 39						17 09						17 39		
South Croydon 4	d				16 14				16 27			16 44			16 57			17 14				17 27		17 44	
East Croydon	a		16 07	16 13	16 16		16 20	16 23	16 30	16 39	16 43	16 46	16 50	16 54	17 00		17 13	17 16		17 20	17 24	17 30	17 43	17 46	17 50
East Croydon	d		16 08				16 21	16 24	16 30	16 40			16 51	16 55	17 00					17 21	17 25	17 30			17 51
Norwood Junction 2	d		16 13				16 25	16 28	16 35	16 46			16 55	17 01	17 05					17 25	17 31	17 35			17 55
New Cross Gate 4 ⊖	a							16 36	16 53					17 08	17 22						17 38	17 52			
London Bridge 4 ⊖	a		16 25				16 39	16 43	17 02	17 00			17 08	17 14	17 29					17 37	17 49	17 59			18 09
East Croydon	d			16 14	16 17						16 44	16 47					17 14	17 17					17 44	17 47	
Clapham Junction 10	a			16 25	16 38						16 55	17 07					17 26	17 37					17 57	18 08	
London Victoria 15 ⊖	a			16 35	16 46						17 05	17 16					17 33	17 48					18 05	18 16	

Whyteleafe and Upper Warlingham stations are adjacent and tickets are interchangeable between these two stations

Purley Oaks and Sanderstead stations are close and tickets are interchangeable between these two stations

For complete service between London and East Croydon see table 175

Table 181R

Mondays to Fridays

9 December to 16 May

Tattenham Corner, Caterham and Purley - Croydon and London

Network Diagram - see first Page of Table 181

		SN 1	SN	SN 1	SN	SN	SN		SN 1	SN	SN 1	SN	SN 1	SN	SN 1	SN	SN 1		SN	SN 1	SN	SN 1	SN	SN 1	SN
Tattenham Corner	d					17 51				18 12				18 42					19 14				19 42		
Tadworth	d					17 54				18 15				18 45					19 17				19 45		
Kingswood	d					17 57				18 18				18 48					19 20				19 48		
Chipstead	d					18 03				18 24				18 54					19 26				19 54		
Woodmansterne	d					18 06				18 27				18 57					19 29				19 57		
Coulsdon Town	d					18 09				18 30				19 00					19 32				20 00		
Reedham	d					18 11				18 32				19 02					19 34				20 02		
Caterham	d		17 45		17 54		18 09					18 37				19 07					19 39				20 08
Whyteleafe South	d		17 48		17 57		18 12					18 40				19 10					19 42				20 11
Upper Warlingham	d			18 02					18 32		18 43		19 02		19 13		19 32			19 43		20 02		20 13	
Whyteleafe	d		17 50		17 59		18 14					18 42				19 12					19 44				20 13
Kenley	d		17 53		18 02		18 17					18 45				19 15					19 47				20 16
Purley	a		17 56		18 05	18 14	18 20			18 35		18 48		19 05		19 18			19 37		19 50		20 05		20 19
Purley 4	d	17 49	17 59		18 08	18 16	18 21			18 37		18 51		19 08		19 21			19 38		19 51		20 08		20 22
Purley Oaks	d		18 02		18 11		18 24			18 40		18 54		19 11		19 24			19 41		19 54		20 11		20 25
Sanderstead	d			18 09					18 39		18 49		19 09		19 19		19 39			19 49		20 09		20 19	
South Croydon 4	d		18 05		18 14		18 27			18 44		18 57		19 14		19 27			19 44		19 57		20 14		20 28
East Croydon	a	17 54	18 07	18 13	18 16	18 21	18 30		18 43	18 47	18 56	19 00	19 13	19 16	19 25	19 30	19 43		19 46	19 57	20 00	20 13	20 16	20 25	20 30
East Croydon	d	17 55	18 08			18 22	18 30				18 57	19 00				19 30					20 00				20 31
Norwood Junction 2	d	17 59	18 12			18 29	18 35				19 02	19 05				19 35					20 05				20 35
New Cross Gate 4 ⊖	a	18 07					18 52					19 22				19 52					20 22				20 52
London Bridge 4 ⊖	a	18 15	18 24			18 41	18 59				19 15	19 29				19 59					20 29				20 59
East Croydon	d			18 14	18 17				18 44	18 47			19 14	19 17			19 44		19 47			20 14	20 17		
Clapham Junction 10	a			18 25	18 39				18 55	19 08			19 25	19 37			19 55		20 07			20 25	20 37		
London Victoria 15 ⊖	a			18 35	18 46				19 05	19 15			19 35	19 48			20 05		20 18			20 35	20 46		

		SN 1	SN		SN	SN 1	SN	SN	SN 1	SN	SN	SN 1	SN		SN	SN 1	SN	SN	SN 1	SN	SN				
Tattenham Corner	d		20 12				20 42			21 12			21 42				22 12			22 42					
Tadworth	d		20 15				20 45			21 15			21 45				22 15			22 45					
Kingswood	d		20 18				20 48			21 18			21 48				22 18			22 48					
Chipstead	d		20 24				20 54			21 24			21 54				22 24			22 54					
Woodmansterne	d		20 27				20 57			21 27			21 57				22 27			22 57					
Coulsdon Town	d		20 30				21 00			21 30			22 00				22 30			23 00					
Reedham	d		20 32				21 02			21 32			22 02				22 32			23 02					
Caterham	d				20 37			21 07			21 39				22 09			22 38			23 20				
Whyteleafe South	d				20 40			21 10			21 42				22 12			22 41			23 23				
Upper Warlingham	d	20 32				21 02			21 32			22 02				22 32			23 02						
Whyteleafe	d				20 42			21 12			21 44				22 14			22 43			23 25				
Kenley	d				20 45			21 15			21 47				22 17			22 46			23 28				
Purley	a		20 35		20 48		21 05	21 18		21 35	21 50		22 05		22 20		22 35	22 49		23 05	23 31				
Purley 4	d		20 38		20 51		21 08	21 21		21 38	21 51		22 08		22 21		22 38	22 52		23 08	23 34				
Purley Oaks	d		20 41		20 54		21 11	21 24		21 41	21 54		22 11		22 24		22 41	22 55		23 11	23 37				
Sanderstead	d	20 39				21 09			21 39			22 09				22 39			23 09						
South Croydon 4	d		20 44		20 57		21 14	21 27		21 44	21 57		22 14		22 27		22 44	22 58		23 14	23 40				
East Croydon	a	20 43	20 46		21 00	21 13	21 16	21 30	21 43	21 46	22 00	22 13	22 16		22 30	22 43	22 46	23 01	23 13	23 16	23 42				
East Croydon	d				21 00			21 30			22 00				22 30			23 01			23 43				
Norwood Junction 2	d				21 05			21 35			22 05				22 35			23 06			23a47				
New Cross Gate 4 ⊖	a				21 22			21 52			22 22				22 52			23 23							
London Bridge 4 ⊖	a				21 29			21 59			22 29				22 59			23 30							
East Croydon	d	20 44	20 47			21 14	21 17		21 44	21 47		22 14	22 17			22 44	22 47		23 14	23 17					
Clapham Junction 10	a	20 55	21 07			21 25	21 37		21 55	22 07		22 25	22 37			22 55	23 07		23 25	23 37					
London Victoria 15 ⊖	a	21 03	21 18			21 32	21 48		22 02	22 18		22 32	22 48			23 05	23 18		23 35	23 48					

Whyteleafe and Upper Warlingham stations are adjacent and tickets are interchangeable between these two stations

Purley Oaks and Sanderstead stations are close and tickets are interchangeable between these two stations

For complete service between London and East Croydon see table 175

Table 181R

Saturdays

14 December to 17 May

Tattenham Corner, Caterham and Purley - Croydon and London

Network Diagram - see first Page of Table 181

		SN [1]	SN	SN	SN [1]	SN		SN [1]	SN [1]	SN	SN [1]	SN	SN [1]	SN [1]	SN	SN		SN [1]	SN	SN [1]	SN [1]	SN	SN	SN [1]	SN
Tattenham Corner	d			06 12						06 42						07 21							07 51		
Tadworth	d			06 15						06 45						07 24							07 54		
Kingswood	d			06 18						06 48						07 27							07 57		
Chipstead	d			06 24						06 54						07 33							08 03		
Woodmansterne	d			06 27						06 57						07 36							08 06		
Coulsdon Town	d			06 30						07 00						07 39							08 09		
Reedham	d			06 32						07 02						07 41							08 11		
Caterham	d		06 07			06 39						07 09			07 26				07 39			07 56			08 09
Whyteleafe South	d		06 10			06 42						07 12			07 29				07 42			07 59			08 12
Upper Warlingham	d								07 02					07 32							08 02				
Whyteleafe	d		06 12			06 44						07 14			07 31				07 44			08 01			08 14
Kenley	d		06 15			06 47						07 17			07 34				07 47			08 04			08 17
Purley	a		06 18	06 35		06 50				07 05		07 20			07 37	07 44			07 50			08 07	08 14		08 20
Purley [4]	d	06 19	06 21	06 38	06 49	06 51		07 02		07 08	07 19	07 21	07 34		07 38	07 45		07 49	07 51	08 02		08 08	08 15	08 19	08 21
Purley Oaks	d		06 24	06 41		06 54				07 11		07 24			07 41				07 54			08 11			08 24
Sanderstead	d								07 09					07 39							08 09				
South Croydon [4]	d		06 27	06 44		06 57				07 14		07 27			07 44				07 57			08 14			08 27
East Croydon	a	06 24	06 30	06 46	06 54	07 00		07 07	07 13	07 16	07 24	07 30	07 39	07 43	07 46	07 50		07 54	08 00	08 07	08 13	08 16	08 20	08 24	08 30
East Croydon	d	06 25	06 30		06 55	07 00		07 07			07 25	07 30	07 39			07 51		07 55	08 00	08 07			08 21	08 25	08 30
Norwood Junction [2]	d	06 29	06 35		07 00	07 05		07 13			07 29	07 35	07 45			07 55		08 00	08 05	08 13			08 25	08 29	08 35
New Cross Gate [4] ⊖	a	06 37	06 52		07 07	07 22					07 37	07 52						08 07	08 22					08 37	08 52
London Bridge [4] ⊖	a	06 43	06 59		07 13	07 29		07 25			07 43	07 59	07 57			08 09		08 13	08 29	08 25			08 39	08 43	08 59
East Croydon	d			06 47					07 14	07 17				07 44	07 47						08 14	08 17			
Clapham Junction [10]	a			07 08					07 25	07 37				07 55	08 07						08 25	08 37			
London Victoria [15] ⊖	a			07 16					07 32	07 46				08 02	08 16						08 32	08 46			

		SN [1]		SN [1]	SN	SN	SN [1]	SN	SN	SN [1]	SN [1]	SN		SN	SN [1]	SN	SN [1]	SN [1]	SN	SN	SN [1]	SN		SN	SN [1]
Tattenham Corner	d					08 21			08 35					08 51						09 21				09 33	
Tadworth	d					08 24			08 38					08 54						09 24				09 36	
Kingswood	d					08 27			08 41					08 57						09 27				09 39	
Chipstead	d					08 33			08 47					09 03						09 33				09 45	
Woodmansterne	d					08 36			08 50					09 06						09 36				09 48	
Coulsdon Town	d					08 39			08 53					09 09						09 39				09 51	
Reedham	d					08 41			08 55					09 11						09 41				09 53	
Caterham	d				08 26			08 39				08 56				09 09			09 26			09 39			
Whyteleafe South	d				08 29			08 42				08 59				09 12			09 29			09 42			
Upper Warlingham	d			08 32							09 02							09 32							
Whyteleafe	d				08 31			08 44				09 01				09 14			09 31			09 44			
Kenley	d				08 34			08 47				09 04				09 17			09 34			09 47			
Purley	a				08 37	08 44		08 50	08 58			09 07		09 14		09 20			09 37	09 44		09 50		09 56	
Purley [4]	d	08 32			08 38	08 45	08 49	08 51		09 02		09 08		09 15	09 19	09 21	09 32		09 38	09 45	09 49	09 51			10 02
Purley Oaks	d				08 41			08 54				09 11				09 24			09 41			09 54			
Sanderstead	d			08 39							09 09							09 39							
South Croydon [4]	d				08 44			08 57				09 14				09 27			09 44			09 57			
East Croydon	a	08 37		08 43	08 46	08 50	08 54	09 00		09 07	09 13	09 16		09 20	09 24	09 30	09 37	09 43	09 46	09 50	09 54	10 00			10 07
East Croydon	d	08 37				08 51	08 55	09 00		09 07				09 21	09 25	09 30	09 37			09 51	09 55	10 00			10 07
Norwood Junction [2]	d	08 43				08 55	08 59	09 05		09 13				09 25	09 29	09 35	09 43			09 55	09 59	10 05			10 13
New Cross Gate [4] ⊖	a						09 07	09 22							09 37	09 52					10 07	10 22			
London Bridge [4] ⊖	a	08 55				09 09	09 13	09 29		09 25				09 39	09 43	09 59	09 55			10 09	10 13	10 29			10 25
East Croydon	d			08 44	08 47						09 14	09 17						09 44	09 47						
Clapham Junction [10]	a			08 55	09 07						09 25	09 37						09 55	10 07						
London Victoria [15] ⊖	a			09 02	09 16						09 32	09 46						10 02	10 16						

		SN [1]	SN	SN	SN [1]	SN	SN [1]	SN [1]		SN	SN	SN [1]	SN	SN	SN [1]	SN [1]	SN	SN		SN [1]	SN	SN [1]	SN [1]	SN	SN
Tattenham Corner	d			09 51							10 21			10 33				10 51							11 21
Tadworth	d			09 54							10 24			10 36				10 54							11 24
Kingswood	d			09 57							10 27			10 39				10 57							11 27
Chipstead	d			10 03							10 33			10 45				11 03							11 33
Woodmansterne	d			10 06							10 36			10 48				11 06							11 36
Coulsdon Town	d			10 09							10 39			10 51				11 09							11 39
Reedham	d			10 11							10 41			10 53				11 11							11 41
Caterham	d		09 56			10 09				10 26			10 39				10 56				11 09			11 26	
Whyteleafe South	d		09 59			10 12				10 29			10 42				10 59				11 12			11 29	
Upper Warlingham	d	10 02						10 32								11 02							11 32		
Whyteleafe	d		10 01			10 14				10 31			10 44				11 01				11 14			11 31	
Kenley	d		10 04			10 17				10 34			10 47				11 04				11 17			11 34	
Purley	a		10 07	10 14		10 20				10 37	10 44		10 50	10 56			11 07	11 14			11 20			11 37	11 44
Purley [4]	d		10 08	10 15	10 19	10 21	10 32			10 38	10 45	10 49	10 51		11 02		11 08	11 15		11 19	11 21	11 32		11 38	11 45
Purley Oaks	d		10 11			10 24				10 41			10 54				11 11				11 24			11 41	
Sanderstead	d	10 09						10 39								11 09							11 39		
South Croydon [4]	d		10 14			10 27				10 44			10 57				11 14				11 27			11 44	
East Croydon	a	10 13	10 16	10 20	10 24	10 30	10 37	10 43		10 46	10 50	10 54	11 00		11 07	11 13	11 16	11 20		11 24	11 30	11 37	11 43	11 46	11 50
East Croydon	d			10 21	10 25	10 30	10 37				10 51	10 55	11 00		11 07			11 21		11 25	11 30	11 37			11 51
Norwood Junction [2]	d			10 25	10 29	10 35	10 43				10 55	10 59	11 05		11 13			11 25		11 29	11 35	11 43			11 55
New Cross Gate [4] ⊖	a				10 37	10 52						11 07	11 22							11 37	11 52				
London Bridge [4] ⊖	a			10 39	10 43	10 59	10 55				11 09	11 13	11 29		11 25			11 39		11 43	11 59	11 55			12 09
East Croydon	d	10 14	10 17					10 44		10 47						11 14	11 17						11 44	11 47	
Clapham Junction [10]	a	10 25	10 37					10 55		11 07						11 25	11 37						11 55	12 07	
London Victoria [15] ⊖	a	10 32	10 46					11 02		11 16						11 32	11 46						12 02	12 16	

Whyteleafe and Upper Warlingham stations are adjacent and tickets are interchangeable between these two stations

Purley Oaks and Sanderstead stations are close and tickets are interchangeable between these two stations

For complete service between London and East Croydon see table 175

Table 181R

Saturdays

14 December to 17 May

Tattenham Corner, Caterham and Purley - Croydon and London

Network Diagram - see first Page of Table 181

		SN 1	SN	SN		SN 1	SN 1	SN	SN	SN 1	SN	SN 1	SN 1	SN		SN	SN 1	SN	SN	SN 1	SN 1	SN	SN	SN 1	
Tattenham Corner	d			11 33					11 51							12 21			12 33				12 51		
Tadworth	d			11 36					11 54							12 24			12 36				12 54		
Kingswood	d			11 39					11 57							12 27			12 39				12 57		
Chipstead	d			11 45					12 03							12 33			12 45				13 03		
Woodmansterne	d			11 48					12 06							12 36			12 48				13 06		
Coulsdon Town	d			11 51					12 09							12 39			12 51				13 09		
Reedham	d			11 53					12 11							12 41			12 53				13 11		
Caterham	d		11 39					11 56			12 09			12 26				12 39				12 56			
Whyteleafe South	d		11 42					11 59			12 12			12 29				12 42				12 59			
Upper Warlingham	d						12 02						12 32								13 02				
Whyteleafe	d		11 44					12 01			12 14			12 31				12 44				13 01			
Kenley	d		11 47					12 04			12 17			12 34				12 47				13 04			
Purley	a		11 50	11 56				12 07	12 14		12 20			12 37		12 44		12 50	12 56			13 07	13 14		
Purley 4	d	11 49	11 51			12 02		12 08	12 15	12 19	12 21	12 32		12 38		12 45	12 49	12 51		13 02		13 08	13 15	13 19	
Purley Oaks	d		11 54					12 11			12 24			12 41				12 54				13 11			
Sanderstead	d						12 09						12 39								13 09				
South Croydon 4	d		11 57					12 14			12 27			12 44				12 57				13 14			
East Croydon	a	11 54	12 00			12 07	12 13	12 16	12 20	12 24	12 30	12 37	12 43	12 46		12 50	12 54	13 00		13 07	13 13	13 16	13 20	13 24	
East Croydon	d	11 55	12 00			12 07			12 21	12 25	12 30	12 38				12 51	12 55	13 00		13 07			13 21	13 25	
Norwood Junction 2	d	11 59	12 05			12 13			12 25	12 29	12 35	12 43				12 55	12 59	13 05		13 13			13 25	13 29	
New Cross Gate 4 ⊖	a	12 07	12 22							12 37	12 52						13 07	13 22						13 37	
London Bridge 4 ⊖	a	12 13	12 29			12 25			12 39	12 43	12 59	12 55				13 09	13 13	13 29		13 25			13 39	13 43	
East Croydon	d						12 14	12 17					12 44	12 47							13 14	13 17			
Clapham Junction 10	a						12 25	12 37					12 55	13 07							13 25	13 37			
London Victoria 15 ⊖	a						12 32	12 46					13 02	13 16							13 32	13 46			

		SN	SN 1	SN 1	SN	SN	SN 1	SN	SN	SN 1		SN 1	SN	SN	SN 1	SN	SN 1	SN 1	SN	SN		SN 1	SN	SN	SN 1
Tattenham Corner	d					13 21			13 33					13 51						14 21				14 33	
Tadworth	d					13 24			13 36					13 54						14 24				14 36	
Kingswood	d					13 27			13 39					13 57						14 27				14 39	
Chipstead	d					13 33			13 45					14 03						14 33				14 45	
Woodmansterne	d					13 36			13 48					14 06						14 36				14 48	
Coulsdon Town	d					13 39			13 51					14 09						14 39				14 51	
Reedham	d					13 41			13 53					14 11						14 41				14 53	
Caterham	d	13 09			13 26			13 39					13 56			14 09			14 26				14 39		
Whyteleafe South	d	13 12			13 29			13 42					13 59			14 12			14 29				14 42		
Upper Warlingham	d			13 32								14 02						14 32							
Whyteleafe	d	13 14			13 31			13 44					14 01			14 14			14 31				14 44		
Kenley	d	13 17			13 34			13 47					14 04			14 17			14 34				14 47		
Purley	a	13 20			13 37	13 44		13 50	13 56				14 07	14 14		14 20			14 37	14 44			14 50	14 56	
Purley 4	d	13 21	13 32		13 38	13 45	13 49	13 51		14 02			14 08	14 15	14 19	14 21	14 32		14 38	14 45		14 49	14 51		15 02
Purley Oaks	d	13 24			13 41			13 54					14 11			14 24			14 41				14 54		
Sanderstead	d			13 39								14 09						14 39							
South Croydon 4	d	13 27			13 44			13 57					14 14			14 27			14 44				14 57		
East Croydon	a	13 30	13 37	13 43	13 46	13 50	13 54	14 00		14 07		14 13	14 16	14 20	14 24	14 30	14 37	14 43	14 46	14 50		14 54	15 00		15 07
East Croydon	d	13 30	13 37			13 51	13 55	14 00		14 07				14 21	14 25	14 30	14 37			14 51		14 55	15 00		15 07
Norwood Junction 2	d	13 35	13 43			13 55	13 59	14 05		14 13				14 25	14 29	14 35	14 43			14 55		14 59	15 05		15 13
New Cross Gate 4 ⊖	a	13 52					14 07	14 22							14 37	14 52						15 07	15 22		
London Bridge 4 ⊖	a	13 59	13 55			14 09	14 13	14 29		14 25				14 39	14 43	14 59	14 55			15 09		15 13	15 29		15 25
East Croydon	d			13 44	13 47							14 14	14 17					14 44	14 47						
Clapham Junction 10	a			13 55	14 07							14 25	14 37					14 55	15 07						
London Victoria 15 ⊖	a			14 02	14 16							14 32	14 46					15 02	15 16						

		SN 1	SN	SN	SN 1	SN		SN 1	SN 1	SN	SN	SN 1	SN	SN	SN 1	SN 1		SN	SN	SN 1	SN	SN 1	SN 1	SN	SN
Tattenham Corner	d			14 51							15 21			15 33					15 51						16 21
Tadworth	d			14 54							15 24			15 36					15 54						16 24
Kingswood	d			14 57							15 27			15 39					15 57						16 27
Chipstead	d			15 03							15 33			15 45					16 03						16 33
Woodmansterne	d			15 06							15 36			15 48					16 06						16 36
Coulsdon Town	d			15 09							15 39			15 51					16 09						16 39
Reedham	d			15 11							15 41			15 53					16 11						16 41
Caterham	d		14 56			15 09				15 26			15 39					15 56			16 09			16 26	
Whyteleafe South	d		14 59			15 12				15 29			15 42					15 59			16 12			16 29	
Upper Warlingham	d	15 02							15 32							16 02							16 32		
Whyteleafe	d		15 01			15 14				15 31			15 44					16 01			16 14			16 31	
Kenley	d		15 04			15 17				15 34			15 47					16 04			16 17			16 34	
Purley	a		15 07	15 14		15 20				15 37	15 44		15 50	15 56				16 07	16 14		16 20			16 37	16 44
Purley 4	d		15 08	15 15	15 19	15 21		15 32		15 38	15 45	15 49	15 51		16 02			16 08	16 15	16 19	16 21	16 32		16 38	16 45
Purley Oaks	d		15 11			15 24				15 41			15 54					16 11			16 24			16 41	
Sanderstead	d	15 09							15 39							16 09							16 39		
South Croydon 4	d		15 14			15 27				15 44			15 57					16 14			16 27			16 44	
East Croydon	a	15 13	15 16	15 20	15 24	15 30		15 37	15 43	15 46	15 50	15 54	16 00		16 07	16 13		16 16	16 20	16 24	16 30	16 37	16 43	16 46	16 50
East Croydon	d			15 21	15 25	15 30		15 37			15 51	15 55	16 00		16 07				16 21	16 25	16 30	16 37			16 51
Norwood Junction 2	d			15 25	15 29	15 35		15 43			15 55	15 59	16 05		16 13				16 25	16 29	16 35	16 43			16 55
New Cross Gate 4 ⊖	a				15 37	15 52						16 07	16 22							16 37	16 52				
London Bridge 4 ⊖	a			15 39	15 43	15 59		15 55			16 09	16 13	16 29		16 25				16 39	16 43	16 59	16 55			17 09
East Croydon	d	15 14	15 17						15 44	15 47						16 14		16 17					16 44	16 47	
Clapham Junction 10	a	15 25	15 37						15 55	16 07						16 25		16 37					16 55	17 07	
London Victoria 15 ⊖	a	15 32	15 46						16 02	16 16						16 32		16 46					17 02	17 16	

Whyteleafe and Upper Warlingham stations are adjacent and tickets are interchangeable between these two stations

Purley Oaks and Sanderstead stations are close and tickets are interchangeable between these two stations

For complete service between London and East Croydon see table 175

Table 181R

Saturdays

14 December to 17 May

Tattenham Corner, Caterham and Purley - Croydon and London

Network Diagram - see first Page of Table 181

		SN 1		SN	SN	SN 1	SN 1	SN	SN	SN 1	SN	SN 1		SN 1	SN	SN	SN 1	SN	SN	SN 1	SN 1	SN		SN	SN 1
Tattenham Corner	d				16 33				16 51							17 21			17 33					17 51	
Tadworth	d				16 36				16 54							17 24			17 36					17 54	
Kingswood	d				16 39				16 57							17 27			17 39					17 57	
Chipstead	d				16 45				17 03							17 33			17 45					18 03	
Woodmansterne	d				16 48				17 06							17 36			17 48					18 06	
Coulsdon Town	d				16 51				17 09							17 39			17 51					18 09	
Reedham	d				16 53				17 11							17 41			17 53					18 11	
Caterham	d			16 39				16 56			17 09				17 26			17 39				17 56			
Whyteleafe South	d			16 42				16 59			17 12				17 29			17 42				17 59			
Upper Warlingham	d						17 02							17 32							18 02				
Whyteleafe	d			16 44				17 01			17 14				17 31			17 44				18 01			
Kenley	d			16 47				17 04			17 17				17 34			17 47				18 04			
Purley	a			16 50	16 56			17 07	17 14		17 20				17 37	17 44		17 50	17 56			18 07		18 14	
Purley 4	d	16 49		16 51		17 02		17 08	17 15	17 19	17 21	17 32			17 38	17 45	17 49	17 51		18 02		18 08		18 15	18 19
Purley Oaks	d			16 54				17 11			17 24				17 41			17 54				18 11			
Sanderstead	d						17 09							17 39							18 09				
South Croydon 4	d			16 57				17 14			17 27				17 44			17 57				18 14			
East Croydon	a	16 54		17 00		17 07	17 13	17 16	17 20	17 24	17 30	17 37		17 43	17 46	17 50	17 54	18 00		18 07	18 13	18 16		18 21	18 24
East Croydon	d	16 55		17 00		17 07			17 21	17 25	17 30	17 37				17 51	17 55	18 00		18 07				18 22	18 25
Norwood Junction 2	d	16 59		17 05		17 13			17 25	17 29	17 35	17 43				17 55	17 59	18 05		18 13				18 26	18 29
New Cross Gate 4 ⊖	a	17 07		17 22						17 37	17 52						18 07	18 22							18 37
London Bridge 4 ⊖	a	17 13		17 30		17 25			17 39	17 43	17 59	17 55				18 09	18 13	18 29		18 25				18 39	18 43
East Croydon	d						17 14	17 17						17 44	17 47						18 14	18 17			
Clapham Junction 10	a						17 25	17 38						17 55	18 07						18 25	18 37			
London Victoria 15 ⊖	a						17 32	17 47						18 02	18 16						18 32	18 46			

		SN	SN 1	SN 1	SN	SN	SN 1	SN		SN	SN 1	SN 1	SN	SN	SN	SN 1	SN	SN		SN	SN	SN 1	SN	SN	SN
Tattenham Corner	d					18 21				18 33				18 51				19 21			19 33			19 51	
Tadworth	d					18 24				18 36				18 54				19 24			19 36			19 54	
Kingswood	d					18 27				18 39				18 57				19 27			19 39			19 57	
Chipstead	d					18 33				18 45				19 03				19 33			19 45			20 03	
Woodmansterne	d					18 36				18 48				19 06				19 36			19 48			20 06	
Coulsdon Town	d					18 39				18 51				19 09				19 39			19 51			20 09	
Reedham	d					18 41				18 53				19 11				19 41			19 53			20 11	
Caterham	d	18 09			18 26			18 39					18 56		19 09		19 26			19 39			19 56		20 09
Whyteleafe South	d	18 12			18 29			18 42					18 59		19 12		19 29			19 42			19 59		20 12
Upper Warlingham	d			18 32								19 02				19 32						20 02			
Whyteleafe	d	18 14			18 31			18 44					19 01		19 14		19 31			19 44			20 01		20 14
Kenley	d	18 17			18 34			18 47					19 04		19 17		19 34			19 47			20 04		20 17
Purley	a	18 20			18 37	18 44		18 50		18 56			19 07	19 14	19 20		19 37	19 44		19 50	19 56		20 07	20 14	20 20
Purley 4	d	18 21	18 32		18 38	18 45	18 49	18 51			19 02		19 08	19 15	19 21		19 38	19 45		19 51			20 08	20 15	20 21
Purley Oaks	d	18 24			18 41			18 54					19 11		19 24		19 41			19 54			20 11		20 24
Sanderstead	d			18 39								19 09				19 39						20 09			
South Croydon 4	d	18 27			18 44			18 57					19 14		19 27		19 44			19 57			20 14		20 27
East Croydon	a	18 30	18 37	18 43	18 46	18 50	18 54	19 00			19 07	19 13	19 16	19 20	19 30	19 43	19 46	19 50		20 00		20 13	20 16	20 20	20 30
East Croydon	d	18 30	18 37			18 51	18 55	19 00			19 07			19 21	19 30			19 51		20 00				20 21	20 30
Norwood Junction 2	d	18 35	18 43			18 55	18 59	19 05			19 13			19 25	19 35			19 55		20 05				20 25	20 35
New Cross Gate 4 ⊖	a	18 52					19 07	19 22							19 52					20 22					20 52
London Bridge 4 ⊖	a	18 59	18 55			19 09	19 13	19 29			19 25			19 39	19 59			20 09		20 29				20 39	20 59
East Croydon	d			18 44	18 47							19 14	19 17			19 44	19 47					20 14	20 17		
Clapham Junction 10	a			18 55	19 07							19 25	19 37			19 55	20 07					20 25	20 37		
London Victoria 15 ⊖	a			19 02	19 16							19 35	19 46			20 05	20 16					20 32	20 46		

		SN 1	SN	SN		SN	SN	SN 1	SN	SN	SN	SN 1	SN	SN		SN	SN	SN 1	SN	SN	SN	SN 1	SN	SN	
Tattenham Corner	d			20 21			20 33			20 51				21 21			21 33			21 51				22 21	
Tadworth	d			20 24			20 36			20 54				21 24			21 36			21 54				22 24	
Kingswood	d			20 27			20 39			20 57				21 27			21 39			21 57				22 27	
Chipstead	d			20 33			20 45			21 03				21 33			21 45			22 03				22 33	
Woodmansterne	d			20 36			20 48			21 06				21 36			21 48			22 06				22 36	
Coulsdon Town	d			20 39			20 51			21 09				21 39			21 51			22 09				22 39	
Reedham	d			20 41			20 53			21 11				21 41			21 53			22 11				22 41	
Caterham	d		20 26			20 39			20 56		21 09		21 26			21 39			21 56		22 09		22 26		
Whyteleafe South	d		20 29			20 42			20 59		21 12		21 29			21 42			21 59		22 12		22 29		
Upper Warlingham	d	20 32						21 02				21 32						22 02				22 32			
Whyteleafe	d		20 31			20 44			21 01		21 14		21 31			21 44			22 01		22 14		22 31		
Kenley	d		20 34			20 47			21 04		21 17		21 34			21 47			22 04		22 17		22 34		
Purley	a		20 37	20 44		20 50	20 56		21 07	21 14	21 20		21 37	21 44		21 50	21 56		22 07	22 14	22 20		22 37	22 44	
Purley 4	d		20 38	20 45		20 51			21 08	21 15	21 21		21 38	21 45		21 51			22 08	22 15	22 21		22 38	22 45	
Purley Oaks	d		20 41			20 54			21 11		21 24		21 41			21 54			22 11		22 24		22 41		
Sanderstead	d	20 39						21 09				21 39						22 09				22 39			
South Croydon 4	d		20 44			20 57			21 14		21 27		21 44			21 57			22 14		22 27		22 44		
East Croydon	a	20 43	20 46	20 50		21 00		21 13	21 16	21 20	21 30	21 43	21 46	21 50		22 00		22 13	22 16	22 20	22 30	22 43	22 46	22 50	
East Croydon	d			20 51		21 00				21 21	21 30			21 51		22 00				22 21	22 30			22 51	
Norwood Junction 2	d			20 55		21 05				21 25	21 35			21 55		22 05				22 25	22 35			22 55	
New Cross Gate 4 ⊖	a					21 22					21 52					22 22					22 52				
London Bridge 4 ⊖	a			21 09		21 29				21 39	21 59			22 09		22 29				22 39	22 59			23 09	
East Croydon	d	20 44	20 47					21 14	21 17			21 44	21 47					22 14	22 17			22 44	22 47		
Clapham Junction 10	a	20 55	21 07					21 25	21 37			21 55	22 07					22 25	22 37			22 55	23 07		
London Victoria 15 ⊖	a	21 02	21 16					21 32	21 46			22 02	22 16					22 32	22 46			23 02	23 18		

Whyteleafe and Upper Warlingham stations are adjacent and tickets are interchangeable between these two stations

Purley Oaks and Sanderstead stations are close and tickets are interchangeable between these two stations

For complete service between London and East Croydon see table 175

Table 181R

Saturdays

14 December to 17 May

Tattenham Corner, Caterham and Purley - Croydon and London

Network Diagram - see first Page of Table 181

		SN	SN	SN [1]	SN	SN	SN
Tattenham Corner	d		22 33			22 51	
Tadworth	d		22 36			22 54	
Kingswood	d		22 39			22 57	
Chipstead	d		22 45			23 03	
Woodmansterne	d		22 48			23 06	
Coulsdon Town	d		22 51			23 09	
Reedham	d		22 53			23 11	
Caterham	d	22 39			22 56		23 20
Whyteleafe South	d	22 42			22 59		23 23
Upper Warlingham	d			23 02			
Whyteleafe	d	22 44			23 01		23 25
Kenley	d	22 47			23 04		23 28
Purley	a	22 50	22 56		23 07	23 14	23 31
Purley [4]	d	22 52			23 08	23 15	23 34
Purley Oaks	d	22 55			23 11		23 37
Sanderstead	d			23 09			
South Croydon [4]	d	22 58			23 14		23 40
East Croydon	a	23 01		23 13	23 16	23 20	23 42
East Croydon	d	23 01				23 21	23 43
Norwood Junction [2]	d	23 06				23 25	23a47
New Cross Gate [4] ⊖	a	23 23					
London Bridge [4] ⊖	a	23 30				23 39	
East Croydon	d			23 14	23 17		
Clapham Junction [10]	a			23 25	23 37		
London Victoria [15] ⊖	a			23 32	23 48		

Sundays

8 December to 11 May

		SN	SN	SN	SN [1]	SN	SN	SN	SN	SN [1]	SN
Tattenham Corner	d						07 44		08 15		
Tadworth	d						07 47		08 18		
Kingswood	d						07 50		08 21		
Chipstead	d						07 56		08 27		
Woodmansterne	d						07 59		08 30		
Coulsdon Town	d						08 02		08 33		
Reedham	d						08 04		08 35		
Caterham	d			07 20		07 35		08 12			08 37
Whyteleafe South	d			07 23		07 38		08 15			08 40
Upper Warlingham	d										
Whyteleafe	d			07 25		07 40		08 17			08 42
Kenley	d			07 28		07 43		08 20			08 45
Purley	a			07 31		07 46	08 07	08 23	08 38		08 48
Purley [4]	d	06 36	07 09	07 32	07 43	07 48	08 07	08 23	08 39	08 46	08 49
Purley Oaks	d	06 39	07 12	07 35			08 10		08 42		
Sanderstead	d										
South Croydon [4]	d	06 42	07 15	07 38			08 13		08 45		
East Croydon	a	06 44	07 17	07 40	07 48	07 53	08 17	08 29	08 47	08 51	08 54
East Croydon	d	06 45	07 18	07 41	07 48		08 17		08 48	08 52	
Norwood Junction [2]	d	06 52	07 24	07 45	07 54		08 23		08 52	08 56	
New Cross Gate [4] ⊖	a	07 09	07 42	08 03			08 40		09 10		
London Bridge [4] ⊖	a	07 17	07 48	08 12	08 05		08 47		09 16	09 08	
East Croydon	d					07 54		08 30			08 55
Clapham Junction [10]	a					08 14		08 48			09 14
London Victoria [15] ⊖	a					08 22		08 56			09 21

		SN [1]	SN	SN	SN	SN [1]	SN	SN [1]	SN	SN [1]	SN	
Tattenham Corner	d		08 45		09 15				09 45			
Tadworth	d		08 48		09 18				09 48			
Kingswood	d		08 51		09 21				09 51			
Chipstead	d		08 57		09 27				09 57			
Woodmansterne	d		09 00		09 30				10 00			
Coulsdon Town	d		09 03		09 33				10 03			
Reedham	d		09 05		09 35				10 05			
Caterham	d			09 07			09 35				10 05	and at the same minutes past each hour until
Whyteleafe South	d			09 10			09 38				10 08	
Upper Warlingham	d	08 45				09 37				10 07		
Whyteleafe	d			09 12			09 40				10 10	
Kenley	d			09 15			09 43				10 13	
Purley	a		09 08	09 18	09 38		09 46		10 08		10 16	
Purley [4]	d		09 08	09 19	09 38		09 47	09 50	10 08		10 17	
Purley Oaks	d		09 11		09 41				10 11			
Sanderstead	d	08 52				09 44				10 14		
South Croydon [4]	d		09 14		09 44				10 14			
East Croydon	a	08 58	09 16	09 24	09 46	09 49	09 52	09 55	10 16	10 19	10 22	
East Croydon	d		09 17		09 47			09 56	10 17			
Norwood Junction [2]	d		09 23		09 52			10 02	10 22			
New Cross Gate [4] ⊖	a		09 40		10 10				10 40			
London Bridge [4] ⊖	a		09 47		10 16			10 14	10 46			
East Croydon	d	08 59		09 25		09 50	09 53			10 20	10 23	
Clapham Junction [10]	a	09 08		09 44		10 02	10 12			10 32	10 42	
London Victoria [15] ⊖	a	09 15		09 51		10 09	10 20			10 39	10 50	

Whyteleafe and Upper Warlingham stations are adjacent and tickets are interchangeable between these two stations

Purley Oaks and Sanderstead stations are close and tickets are interchangeable between these two stations

For complete service between London and East Croydon see table 175

Table 181R

Sundays

8 December to 11 May

Tattenham Corner, Caterham and Purley - Croydon and London

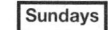

Network Diagram - see first Page of Table 181

		SN	SN 1	SN	SN 1	SN	SN 1	SN
Tattenham Corner	d	19 15				19 45		
Tadworth	d	19 18				19 48		
Kingswood	d	19 21				19 51		
Chipstead	d	19 27				19 57		
Woodmansterne	d	19 30				20 00		
Coulsdon Town	d	19 33				20 03		
Reedham	d	19 35				20 05		
Caterham	d			19 35				20 05
Whyteleafe South	d			19 38				20 08
Upper Warlingham	d		19 37				20 07	
Whyteleafe	d			19 40				20 10
Kenley	d			19 43				20 13
Purley	a	19 38		19 46		20 08		20 16
Purley 4	d	19 38		19 47	19 50	20 08		20 17
Purley Oaks	d	19 41				20 11		
Sanderstead	d		19 44				20 14	
South Croydon 4	d	19 44				20 14		
East Croydon	a	19 46	19 49	19 52	19 55	20 16	20 19	20 22
East Croydon	d	19 47			19 56	20 17		
Norwood Junction 2	d	19 52			20 02	20 22		
New Cross Gate 4 ⊖	a	20 10				20 40		
London Bridge 4 ⊖	a	20 16			20 14	20 46		
East Croydon	d		19 50	19 53			20 20	20 23
Clapham Junction 10	a		20 02	20 12			20 32	20 42
London Victoria 15 ⊖	a		20 09	20 20			20 39	20 50

		SN	SN 1	SN	SN 1	SN	SN	SN	SN 1	SN
Tattenham Corner	d	20 15				20 45		21 15		
Tadworth	d	20 18				20 48		21 18		
Kingswood	d	20 21				20 51		21 21		
Chipstead	d	20 27				20 57		21 27		
Woodmansterne	d	20 30				21 00		21 30		
Coulsdon Town	d	20 33				21 03		21 33		
Reedham	d	20 35				21 05		21 35		
Caterham	d			20 35			21 05			21 35
Whyteleafe South	d			20 38			21 08			21 38
Upper Warlingham	d		20 37						21 37	
Whyteleafe	d			20 40			21 10			21 40
Kenley	d			20 43			21 13			21 43
Purley	a	20 38		20 46		21 08	21 16	21 38		21 46
Purley 4	d	20 38		20 47	20 50	21 08	21 17	21 38		21 47
Purley Oaks	d	20 41				21 11		21 41		
Sanderstead	d		20 44						21 44	
South Croydon 4	d	20 44				21 14		21 44		
East Croydon	a	20 46	20 49	20 52	20 55	21 16	21 22	21 46	21 49	21 52
East Croydon	d	20 47			20 56	21 17		21 47		
Norwood Junction 2	d	20 52			21 02	21 22		21 52		
New Cross Gate 4 ⊖	a	21 10				21 40		22 10		
London Bridge 4 ⊖	a	21 16			21 14	21 46		22 16		
East Croydon	d		20 50	20 53			21 23		21 50	21 53
Clapham Junction 10	a		21 02	21 12			21 42		22 02	22 12
London Victoria 15 ⊖	a		21 09	21 20			21 50		22 09	22 20

		SN 1	SN	SN	SN	SN 1	SN
Tattenham Corner	d		21 45		22 15		
Tadworth	d		21 48		22 18		
Kingswood	d		21 51		22 21		
Chipstead	d		21 57		22 27		
Woodmansterne	d		22 00		22 30		
Coulsdon Town	d		22 03		22 33		
Reedham	d		22 05		22 35		
Caterham	d			22 05			22 35
Whyteleafe South	d			22 08			22 38
Upper Warlingham	d					22 37	
Whyteleafe	d			22 10			22 40
Kenley	d			22 13			22 43
Purley	a		22 08	22 16	22 38		22 46
Purley 4	d	21 50	22 08	22 17	22 38		22 47
Purley Oaks	d		22 11		22 41		
Sanderstead	d					22 44	
South Croydon 4	d		22 14		22 44		
East Croydon	a	21 55	22 16	22 22	22 46	22 49	22 52
East Croydon	d	21 56	22 17		22 47		
Norwood Junction 2	d	22 02	22 22		22 52		
New Cross Gate 4 ⊖	a		22 40		23 10		
London Bridge 4 ⊖	a	22 14	22 46		23 16		
East Croydon	d			22 23		22 50	22 53
Clapham Junction 10	a			22 42		23 02	23 12
London Victoria 15 ⊖	a			22 52		23 09	23 22

		SN	SN	SN 1
Tattenham Corner	d	22 45		
Tadworth	d	22 48		
Kingswood	d	22 51		
Chipstead	d	22 57		
Woodmansterne	d	23 00		
Coulsdon Town	d	23 03		
Reedham	d	23 05		
Caterham	d		23 05	
Whyteleafe South	d		23 08	
Upper Warlingham	d			23 34
Whyteleafe	d		23 10	
Kenley	d		23 13	
Purley	a	23 08	23 16	
Purley 4	d	23 08	23 17	
Purley Oaks	d	23 11	23 20	
Sanderstead	d			23 41
South Croydon 4	d	23 14	23 23	
East Croydon	a	23 16	23 25	23 46
East Croydon	d	23 17		
Norwood Junction 2	d	23a21		
New Cross Gate 4 ⊖	a			
London Bridge 4 ⊖	a			
East Croydon	d			23 47
Clapham Junction 10	a			23 59
London Victoria 15 ⊖	a			00 07

Whyteleafe and Upper Warlingham stations are adjacent and tickets are interchangeable between these two stations

Purley Oaks and Sanderstead stations are close and tickets are interchangeable between these two stations

For complete service between London and East Croydon see table 175

Network Diagram for Table 182

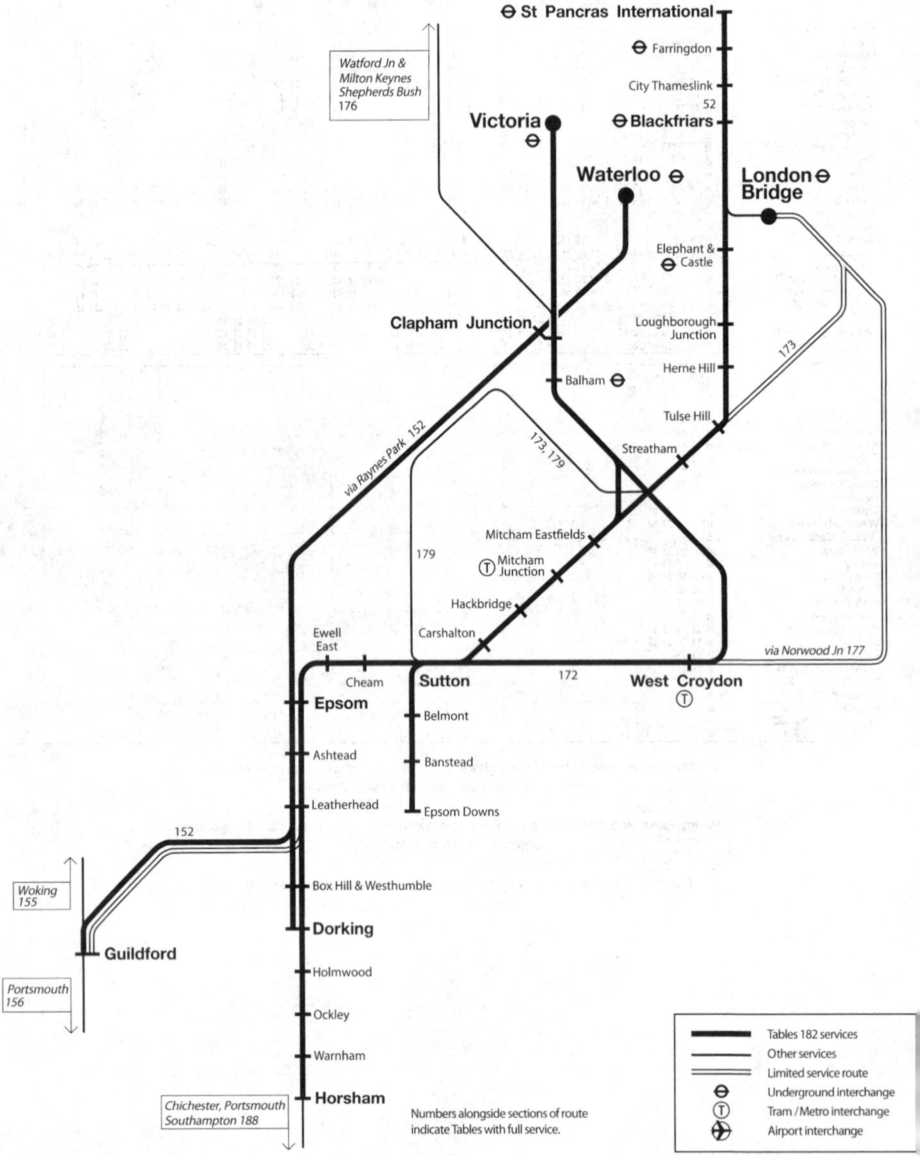

TOCs operating on this network - Southern (SN), First Capital Connect (FC), South West Trains (SW)

Table 182

London - Mitcham, Sutton, Epsom Downs, Epsom, Dorking

Mondays to Fridays

9 December to 16 May

Network Diagram - see first Page of Table 182

Miles	Miles	Miles	Miles			SN	SN	SN	SW	SW	SW	SN	SN	SN		FC	SN	SN	SW	SN	SN	FC	SN	SW	
						MO	MX	MO	MX	MX															
0	—	—	0	London Victoria 15 ⊖	d								05 52				06 00	06 06		06 17			06 30		
—	0	—	—	London Waterloo 15 ⊖	d					00 15	05 47								06 24					06 39	
2¾	3¾	—	2¾	Clapham Junction 10	d					00 25	05 56		05 58				06 08	06 14	06 33	06 24			06 38	06 48	
4¾	—	—	4¾	Balham 4 ⊖	d								06 03				06 14	06 20		06 30			06 44		
—	—	0	—	St Pancras International	d											05 54						06 12			
—	—	1¼	—	Farringdon	d											06 00						06 18			
—	—	1½	—	City Thameslink	d											06 03						06 21			
—	—	2	—	London Blackfriars	d											06 06						06 24			
—	—	3	—	Elephant & Castle	d											06 09						06 27			
—	—	5	—	Loughborough Jn	d											06 13						06 31			
—	—	6	—	Herne Hill	d											06 17						06 35			
—	—	—	—	London Bridge 4 ⊖	d																				
—	—	7	—	Tulse Hill	a											06 21						06 39			
—	—	—	—	Tulse Hill 3	d											06 22						06 42			
—	—	8½	—	Streatham	d											06 25						06 45			
7¾	—	10¼	—	**Mitcham Eastfields**	d								06 12			06 29				06 38		06 49			
8¾	—	11¼	—	**Mitcham Junction**	d								06 15			06 32				06 41		06 52			
10	—	12½	—	**Hackbridge**	d								06 19			06 35				06 45		06 55			
10¾	—	13¼	—	**Carshalton**	d								06 21			06 38				06 47	←	06 58			
—	—	—	10¾	West Croydon	d							05 58					06 32	06 44			06 44		07 03		
12¼	—	14¾	15¼	Sutton (Surrey)	a							06 10	06 25			06 43	06 44	→		06 51	06 56	07 03	07 15		
—	—	—	—	**Sutton (Surrey) 4**	a																				
—	—	—	—		d		00 01	00 04				06 11	06 25	06 39			06 48			06 52	06 57		07 18		
—	—	—	16¼	**Belmont**	d							06 14					06 51						07 21		
—	—	—	17¾	**Banstead**	d							06 18					06 55						07 25		
—	—	—	19¼	**Epsom Downs**	a							06 22					06 58						07 28		
13¼	—	—	—	**Cheam**	d		00 03	00 06					06 28	06 41						06 54	06 59				
14¾	—	—	—	**Ewell East**	d		00 07	00 10					06 31	06 45						06 58	07 03				
16¼	14¼	—	—	**Epsom 3**	a		00 11	00 14		00 50	06 20		06 35	06 49					06 57	07 02	07 08			07 11	
—	—	—	—		d		00 11		00 19		06 21		06 36	06 50					06 58	07 02				07 12	
18¼	16¼	—	—	**Ashtead**	d		00 15		00 23		06 25		06 40						07 02	07 06				07 16	
20	18	—	—	**Leatherhead**	d	00 01	00 18		00 26		06 28		06 43	06 56					07 05	07 09				07a19	
—	31	—	—	Guildford	a				00 53		06 50			07 17											
23¼	—	—	—	**Box Hill & Westhumble**	d	00 05	00 23						06 48												
24¼	—	—	—	**Dorking 4**	a	00 08	00 26						06 50						07 11	07 15					
—	—	—	—		d		00 26						06 51							07 16					
29¼	—	—	—	**Holmwood**	d		00s33						06 58							07 23					
31½	—	—	—	**Ockley**	d		00s37						07 02							07 27					
35¾	—	—	—	**Warnham**	d		00s43						07 08							07 33					
37¾	—	—	—	Horsham 4	a		00 47						07 13							07 38					

		SW	SN	SN	SW	SN	SW	FC	SN	SN		FC	SN	SN	SW	SN	SW	SN	SN	FC		SN	SW	SW	SN
												1 A													
London Victoria 15 ⊖	d		06 36	07 00		07 05				07 08			07 30	07 36		07 47		07 56				08 05			08 19
London Waterloo 15 ⊖	d	06 54			07 09		07 24								07 39		07 54						08 09	08 24	
Clapham Junction 10	d	07 03	06 44	07 08	07 18	07 11	07 33			07 16			07 38	07 44	07 48	07 55	08 03	08 03				08 14	08 18	08 33	08 26
Balham 4 ⊖	d		06 50	07 13		07 16				07 21			07 44	07 50		08 00						08 19			08 31
St Pancras International	d							06 52				07 16								07 52					
Farringdon	d							06 58				07 22								07 58					
City Thameslink	d							07 01				07 25								08 01					
London Blackfriars	d							07 04				07 28								08 04					
Elephant & Castle	d							07 07				07 33								08 07					
Loughborough Jn	d							07 11				07 37								08 11					
Herne Hill	d							07 15				07 41								08 17					
London Bridge 4 ⊖	d																								
Tulse Hill	a							07 20				07 45								08 21					
Tulse Hill 3	d							07 20				07 45								08 21					
Streatham	d							07 23				07 48								08 24					
Mitcham Eastfields	d							07 27				07 52				08 07				08 28					08 37
Mitcham Junction	d					07 24		07 30				07 55				08 10				08 31					08 40
Hackbridge	d					07 27		07 33				07 58				08 13				08 34					08 44
Carshalton	d					07 30		07 36	←			08 01				08 16			←	08 37					08 46
West Croydon	d		07 14	07 32					07 32	07 46			08 04	08 15					08 15			08 36			
Sutton (Surrey)	a		07 26	→		07 35		07 39	07 44	07 58		08 04	08 16	→		08 19		08 22	08 27	08 40		→			08 50
Sutton (Surrey) 4	a																								
	d		07 27			07 36			07 45	07 59			08 16					08 23	08 27						08 50
Belmont	d								07 48				08 20												
Banstead	d								07 52				08 23												
Epsom Downs	a								07 55				08 27												
Cheam	d		07 29			07 38				08 01								08 25	08 30						08 53
Ewell East	d		07 33			07 42				08 05								08 29	08 33						08 56
Epsom 3	a	07 27	07 37		07 42	07 46	07 58			08 09					08 13		08 27	08 33	08 37				08 42	08 57	09 00
	d	07 28	07 37			07 47	07 58								08 17		08 28	08 33	08 38				08 47	08 58	09 01
Ashtead	d	07 32	07 41			07 51	08 02								08 21		08 32	08 37	08 42				08 51	09 02	09 05
Leatherhead	d	07 35	07 44			07 54	08 05								08 24		08 35	08 40	08 45				08 54	09 05	09 08
Guildford	a		08 06												08 50								09 20		
Box Hill & Westhumble	d					07 59													08 50						09 13
Dorking 4	a	07 41				08 01	08 12										08 41	08 46	08 52					09 11	09 15
	d					08 02												08 47							09 16
Holmwood	d					08 09																			09 23
Ockley	d					08 13																			09 27
Warnham	d					08 19																			09 33
Horsham 4	a					08 24												09 05							09 38

A 1 to London Blackfriars

Faster trains London and Clapham Junction to Horsham see table 186

Table 182

Mondays to Fridays

9 December to 16 May

London - Mitcham, Sutton, Epsom Downs, Epsom, Dorking

Network Diagram - see first Page of Table 182

		SN	SN	FC	SN	SW		SW	SN	SN	SN	SN	SW	FC	SN	SW		SN	SN	SN	SN	SW	SW	FC	SN
London Victoria 15	⊖ d				08 31				08 47		08 52	09 01						09 17	09 22	09 31					09 47
London Waterloo 15	⊖ d					08 39		08 54					09 09			09 24						09 39	09 54		
Clapham Junction 10	d				08 40	08 48		09 03	08 54		09 00	09 08	09 18			09 33		09 24	09 30	09 38		09 48	10 03		09 54
Balham 4	⊖ d				08 46				09 00		09 05							09 30	09 35						10 00
St Pancras International	d			08 24										08 44										09 16	
Farringdon	d			08 30										08 50										09 22	
City Thameslink	d			08 33										08 53										09 25	
London Blackfriars	d			08 36										08 56										09 28	
Elephant & Castle	d			08 39										09 00										09 31	
Loughborough Jn	d													09 04										09 35	
Herne Hill	d			08 46										09 11										09 41	
London Bridge 4	⊖ d		08 29																						
Tulse Hill	a		08 46	08 50										09 15										09 45	
Tulse Hill 3	d		08 47	08 51										09 16										09 46	
Streatham	d		08 50	08 54										09 20										09 50	
Mitcham Eastfields	d			08 58					09 06					09 24				09 36						09 54	10 06
Mitcham Junction	d			09 01					09 09					09 27				09 39						09 57	10 09
Hackbridge	d			09 04					09 13					09 30				09 43						10 00	10 13
Carshalton	d	←		09 07					09 15	←				09 33	←			09 45			←			10 03	10 15
West Croydon	d	08 36			09 06					09 06	09 24				09 24				09 54		09 54				
Sutton (Surrey)	a	08 48	09 02	09 10	→				09 19	09 18	→	09 28		09 36	09 39			09 49	→	09 58	10 06			10 06	10 19
Sutton (Surrey) 4	a																								
	d	08 53	09 02						09 19	09 20		09 29			09 40			09 49		09 59	10 07				10 19
Belmont	d	08 56								09 23											10 10				
Banstead	d	09 00								09 27											10 14				
Epsom Downs	a	09 03								09 30											10 17				
Cheam	d		09 05						09 22			09 31			09 42			09 52		10 01					10 22
Ewell East	d		09 08						09 25						09 46			09 55		10 05					10 25
Epsom 3	a		09 12			09 16		09 27	09 29			09 37	09 42		09 50	09 57		09 59		10 09		10 16	10 27		10 29
	d					09 17		09 28				09 37	09 47			09 58				10 09		10 17	10 28		
Ashtead	d					09 21		09 32				09 41	09 51			10 02				10 13		10 21	10 32		
Leatherhead	d					09 24		09 35				09 44	09 54			10 05				10 16		10 24	10 35		
Guildford	a					09 50							10 20									10 50			
Box Hill & Westhumble	d											09 49								10 21					
Dorking 4	a							09 41				09 52				10 11				10 24			10 41		
	d																			10 24					
Holmwood	d																			10 32					
Ockley	d																			10 36					
Warnham	d																			10 41					
Horsham 4	a																			10 47					

		SN		SN	SW	FC	SN	SW	SN	SN	SN	SN		SW	SW	FC	SN	SN	SN	SW	FC	SN		SW	SN
London Victoria 15	⊖ d	09 53		10 01					10 17	10 23	10 31						10 47	10 53	11 01						11 17
London Waterloo 15	⊖ d				10 09			10 24						10 39	10 54					11 09				11 24	
Clapham Junction 10	d	10 00		10 08	10 18			10 33	10 24	10 30	10 38			10 48	11 03		10 54	11 00	11 08	11 18				11 33	11 24
Balham 4	⊖ d	10 05							10 30	10 35							11 00	11 05							11 30
St Pancras International	d					09 48										10 19					10 49				
Farringdon	d					09 53										10 25					10 55				
City Thameslink	d					09 57										10 27					10 57				
London Blackfriars	d					10 00										10 30					11 00				
Elephant & Castle	d					10 03										10 33					11 03				
Loughborough Jn	d					10 07										10 37					11 07				
Herne Hill	d					10 11										10 41					11 11				
London Bridge 4	⊖ d																								
Tulse Hill	a					10 15										10 45					11 15				
Tulse Hill 3	d					10 16										10 46					11 16				
Streatham	d					10 20										10 50					11 20				
Mitcham Eastfields	d					10 24			10 36							10 54	11 06				11 24				11 36
Mitcham Junction	d					10 27			10 39							10 57	11 09				11 27				11 39
Hackbridge	d					10 30			10 43							11 00	11 13				11 30				11 43
Carshalton	d					10 33	←		10 45			←				11 03	11 15				11 33	←			11 45
West Croydon	d	10 24					10 24			10 54		10 54						11 24				11 24			
Sutton (Surrey)	a	→		10 28		10 36	10 39		10 49	→	10 58	11 06				11 06	11 19	→	11 28		11 36	11 39			11 49
Sutton (Surrey) 4	a																								
	d			10 29			10 40		10 49		10 59	11 07					11 19		11 29			11 40			11 49
Belmont	d											11 10													
Banstead	d											11 14													
Epsom Downs	a											11 18													
Cheam	d			10 31			10 42		10 52		11 01						11 22		11 31			11 42			11 52
Ewell East	d						10 46		10 55		11 05						11 25					11 46			11 55
Epsom 3	a			10 37	10 46		10 52	10 57	10 59		11 09			11 16	11 27		11 29		11 37	11 46		11 52		11 57	11 59
	d			10 37	10 47			10 58			11 09			11 17	11 28				11 37	11 47				11 58	
Ashtead	d			10 41	10 51			11 02			11 13			11 21	11 32				11 41	11 51				12 02	
Leatherhead	d			10 44	10 54			11 05			11 16			11 24	11 35				11 44	11 54				12 05	
Guildford	a				11 20									11 50						12 20					
Box Hill & Westhumble	d										11 21														
Dorking 4	a			10 50				11 11			11 24				11 41				11 50					12 11	
	d										11 24														
Holmwood	d										11 32														
Ockley	d										11 36														
Warnham	d										11 41														
Horsham 4	a										11 47														

Faster trains London and Clapham Junction to Horsham see table 186

Table 182

Mondays to Fridays

9 December to 16 May

London - Mitcham, Sutton, Epsom Downs, Epsom, Dorking

Network Diagram - see first Page of Table 182

		SN	SN	SN	SW	SW	FC	SN		SN	SN	SW	FC	SN	SW	SN	SN	SN		SN	SW	SW	FC	SN	SN
London Victoria 15 ⊖	d	11 23	11 31					11 47		11 53	12 01					12 17	12 23	12 31						12 47	12 53
London Waterloo 15 ⊖	d				11 39	11 54						12 09			12 24						12 39	12 54			
Clapham Junction 10	d	11 30	11 38		11 48	12 03		11 54		12 00	12 08	12 18			12 33	12 24	12 30	12 38			12 48	13 03		12 54	13 00
Balham 4 ⊖	d	11 35						12 00		12 05						12 30	12 35							13 00	13 05
St Pancras International	d						11 19						11 48										12 18		
Farringdon	d						11 25						11 53										12 23		
City Thameslink	d						11 27						11 57										12 27		
London Blackfriars	d						11 30						12 00										12 30		
Elephant & Castle	d						11 33						12 03										12 33		
Loughborough Jn	d						11 37						12 07										12 37		
Herne Hill	d						11 41						12 11										12 41		
London Bridge 4 ⊖	d																								
Tulse Hill	a						11 45						12 15										12 45		
Tulse Hill 3	d						11 46						12 16										12 46		
Streatham	d						11 50						12 20										12 50		
Mitcham Eastfields	d						11 54	12 06					12 24			12 36							12 54	13 06	
Mitcham Junction	d						11 57	12 09					12 27			12 39							12 57	13 09	
Hackbridge	d						12 00	12 13					12 30			12 43							13 00	13 13	
Carshalton	d			←			12 03	12 15					12 33	←		12 45				←			13 03	13 15	
West Croydon	d	11 54		11 54						12 24				12 24			12 54			12 54					13 24
Sutton (Surrey)	a	↪	11 58	12 06			12 06	12 19		↪	12 28		12 36	12 39		12 49	↪	12 58		13 06			13 06	13 19	↪
Sutton (Surrey) 4	a																								
	d		11 59	12 07				12 19			12 29			12 40		12 49		12 59		13 07				13 19	
Belmont	d			12 10																13 10					
Banstead	d			12 14																13 14					
Epsom Downs	a			12 18																13 18					
Cheam	d		12 01					12 22			12 31			12 42		12 52		13 01						13 22	
Ewell East	d		12 05					12 25						12 46		12 55		13 05						13 25	
Epsom 3	a		12 09		12 16	12 27		12 29			12 37	12 46		12 52	12 57	12 59		13 09			13 16	13 27		13 29	
	d		12 09		12 17	12 28					12 37	12 47			12 58			13 09			13 17	13 28			
Ashtead	d		12 13		12 21	12 32					12 41	12 51			13 02			13 13			13 21	13 32			
Leatherhead	d		12 16		12 24	12 35					12 44	12 54			13 05			13 16			13 24	13 35			
Guildford	a				12 50							13 20									13 50				
Box Hill & Westhumble	d		12 21															13 21							
Dorking 4	a		12 24			12 41					12 50				13 11			13 24				13 41			
	d		12 24															13 24							
Holmwood	d		12 32															13 32							
Ockley	d		12 36															13 36							
Warnham	d		12 41															13 41							
Horsham 4	a		12 47															13 47							

		SN	SW	FC		SN	SW	SN	SN	SN	SN	SW	SW	FC		SN	SN	SN	SW	FC	SN	SW	SN	SN	
London Victoria 15 ⊖	d	13 01						13 17	13 23	13 31						13 47	13 53	14 01					14 17	14 23	
London Waterloo 15 ⊖	d		13 09				13 24					13 39	13 54						14 09			14 24			
Clapham Junction 10	d	13 08	13 18				13 33	13 24	13 30	13 38		13 48	14 03			13 54	14 00	14 08	14 18			14 33	14 24	14 30	
Balham 4 ⊖	d							13 30	13 35							14 00	14 05						14 30	14 35	
St Pancras International	d			12 48										13 18						13 48					
Farringdon	d			12 53										13 23						13 53					
City Thameslink	d			12 57										13 27						13 57					
London Blackfriars	d			13 00										13 30						14 00					
Elephant & Castle	d			13 03										13 33						14 03					
Loughborough Jn	d			13 07										13 37						14 07					
Herne Hill	d			13 11										13 41						14 11					
London Bridge 4 ⊖	d																								
Tulse Hill	a			13 15										13 45						14 15					
Tulse Hill 3	d			13 16										13 46						14 16					
Streatham	d			13 20										13 50						14 20					
Mitcham Eastfields	d			13 24				13 36						13 54		14 06				14 24			14 36		
Mitcham Junction	d			13 27				13 39						13 57		14 09				14 27			14 39		
Hackbridge	d			13 30				13 43						14 00		14 13				14 30			14 43		
Carshalton	d			13 33		←		13 45			←			14 03		14 15				14 33	←		14 45		
West Croydon	d					13 24			13 54		13 54						14 24				14 24			14 54	
Sutton (Surrey)	a	13 28		13 36		13 39		13 49	↪	13 58	14 06			14 06		14 19	↪	14 28		14 36	14 39		14 49	↪	
Sutton (Surrey) 4	a																								
	d	13 29				13 40		13 49		13 59	14 07					14 19		14 29			14 40		14 49		
Belmont	d										14 10														
Banstead	d										14 14														
Epsom Downs	a										14 18														
Cheam	d	13 31				13 42		13 52		14 01						14 22		14 31			14 42		14 52		
Ewell East	d					13 46		13 55		14 05						14 25					14 46		14 55		
Epsom 3	a	13 37	13 46			13 52	13 57	13 59		14 09		14 16	14 27			14 29		14 37	14 46		14 52	14 57	14 59		
	d	13 37	13 47				13 58			14 09		14 17	14 28					14 37	14 47			14 58			
Ashtead	d	13 41	13 51				14 02			14 13		14 21	14 32					14 41	14 51			15 02			
Leatherhead	d	13 44	13 54				14 05			14 16		14 24	14 35					14 44	14 54			15 05			
Guildford	a		14 20									14 50							15 20						
Box Hill & Westhumble	d									14 21															
Dorking 4	a	13 50					14 11			14 24			14 41					14 50				15 11			
	d									14 24															
Holmwood	d									14 32															
Ockley	d									14 36															
Warnham	d									14 41															
Horsham 4	a									14 47															

Faster trains London and Clapham Junction to Horsham see table 186

Table 182

Mondays to Fridays

9 December to 16 May

London - Mitcham, Sutton, Epsom Downs, Epsom, Dorking

Network Diagram - see first Page of Table 182

Station		SN	SN	SW	SW	FC	SN	SN	SN	SW		FC	SN	SW	SN	SN	SN	SN	SW	SW		FC	SN	SN	SN
London Victoria [15] ⊖	d	14 31					14 47	14 53	15 01						15 17	15 23	15 31						15 47	15 53	16 01
London Waterloo [15] ⊖	d			14 39	14 54					15 09				15 24					15 39	15 54					
Clapham Junction [10]	d	14 38		14 48	15 03		14 54	15 00	15 08	15 18				15 33	15 24	15 30	15 38		15 48	16 03			15 54	16 00	16 07
Balham [4] ⊖	d						15 00	15 05							15 30	15 35							16 00	16 05	
St Pancras International	d					14 18						14 48										15 18			
Farringdon	d					14 23						14 53										15 23			
City Thameslink	d					14 27						14 57										15 27			
London Blackfriars	d					14 30						15 00										15 30			
Elephant & Castle	d					14 33						15 03										15 33			
Loughborough Jn	d					14 37						15 07										15 37			
Herne Hill	d					14 41						15 11										15 41			
London Bridge [4] ⊖	d																								
Tulse Hill	a					14 45						15 15										15 45			
Tulse Hill [3]	d					14 46						15 16										15 46			
Streatham	d					14 50						15 20										15 50			
Mitcham Eastfields	d					14 54	15 06					15 24			15 36							15 54	16 06		
Mitcham Junction	d					14 57	15 09					15 27			15 39							15 57	16 09		16 18
Hackbridge	d					15 00	15 13					15 30			15 43							16 00	16 13		
Carshalton	d		←			15 03	15 15					15 33	←		15 45			←				16 03	16 15		
West Croydon	d		14 54					15 24					15 24			15 54		15 54						16 24	
Sutton (Surrey)	a	14 58	15 06			15 06	15 19	→	15 28			15 36	15 39		15 49	→	15 58	16 06				16 06	16 19	→	16 25
Sutton (Surrey) [4]	a																								
	d	14 59	15 07				15 19		15 29				15 40		15 49		15 59	16 07					16 19		16 26
Belmont	d		15 10															16 10							
Banstead	d		15 14															16 14							
Epsom Downs	a		15 18															16 18							
Cheam	d	15 01					15 22		15 31				15 42		15 52		16 01						16 22		16 28
Ewell East	d	15 05					15 25						15 46		15 55		16 05						16 25		16 32
Epsom [3]	a	15 09		15 16	15 27		15 29		15 37	15 46			15 52	15 57	15 59		16 09		16 15	16 27			16 29		16 36
	d	15 09		15 17	15 28				15 37	15 47				15 58			16 09		16 17	16 28					16 36
Ashtead	d	15 13		15 21	15 32				15 41	15 51				16 02			16 13		16 21	16 32					16 40
Leatherhead	d	15 16		15 24	15 35				15 44	15 54				16 05			16 16		16 24	16 35					16 43
Guildford	a			15 50						16 20									16 50						
Box Hill & Westhumble	d	15 21															16 21								16 48
Dorking [4]	a	15 24			15 41				15 50					16 11			16 24			16 41					16 53
	d	15 24															16 24								
Holmwood	d	15 32															16 32								
Ockley	d	15 36															16 36								
Warnham	d	15 41															16 41								
Horsham [4]	a	15 47															16 47								

Station		SN	SW	SW	FC	SN		SW	SN	FC	SN	SN	SW	SN	SN	SW		SN	FC	SN	SW	SN	SW	SN	SW
London Victoria [15] ⊖	d					16 17			16 31		16 33	16 37		16 47						17 01		17 20			
London Waterloo [15] ⊖	d		16 09	16 24				16 39					16 54			17 09					17 24		17 30		17 39
Clapham Junction [10]	d		16 18	16 33		16 24		16 48	16 38		16 41	16 45	17 03	16 54		17 18				17 09	17 33	17 26	17 39		17 48
Balham [4] ⊖	d					16 30					16 46	16 50		17 00						17 14		17 32			
St Pancras International	d				15 48					16 18									16 50						
Farringdon	d				15 53					16 23									16 55						
City Thameslink	d				15 57					16 27									16 59						
London Blackfriars	d				16 00					16 30									17 02						
Elephant & Castle	d				16 03					16 33									17 06						
Loughborough Jn	d				16 07					16 37									17 10						
Herne Hill	d				16 11					16 41									17 16						
London Bridge [4] ⊖	d																	17 04						17 29	
Tulse Hill	a				16 15					16 46									17 20						
Tulse Hill [3]	d				16 16					16 47									17 20						
Streatham	d				16 20					16 51									17 24						
Mitcham Eastfields	d				16 24	16 36			16 51	16 55				17 07					17 28			17 38			
Mitcham Junction	d				16 27	16 39			16 54	16 58				17 10					17 31			17 41			
Hackbridge	d				16 30	16 43			16 57	17 01				17 13					17 34			17 45			
Carshalton	d	←			16 33	16 45			17 00	17 04				17 16	←				17 37			17 47			
West Croydon	d	16 24									17 04	17 14			17 14			17 22		17 33				17 47	
Sutton (Surrey)	a	16 36			16 36	16 49			17 03	17 08	17 16	→		17 19	17 26			17 34	17 40	17 45		17 51		17 59	
Sutton (Surrey) [4]	a																								
	d	16 38				16 49			17 04		17 16			17 20	17 27			17 34		17 45		17 51		18 00	
Belmont	d	16 41									17 20									17 49					
Banstead	d	16 45									17 23									17 52					
Epsom Downs	a	16 48									17 28									17 58					
Cheam	d					16 52			17 06					17 22	17 29			17 37				17 54		18 02	
Ewell East	d					16 55			17 10					17 26	17 33			17 40				17 57		18 06	
Epsom [3]	a		16 46	16 57		17 01		17 12	17 16				17 27	17 30	17 37	17 42		17 47			17 54	18 01	18 07	18 10	18 15
	d		16 47	16 58		17 02		17 17					17 28	17 31	17 37	17 47					17 54	18 02		18 10	18 17
Ashtead	d		16 51	17 02		17 06		17 21					17 32	17 35	17 41	17 51					17 58	18 06		18 14	18 21
Leatherhead	d		16 54	17 05		17 09		17 24					17 35	17 38	17 44	17a54					18 01	18 09		18 18	18a24
Guildford	a		17 22					17 52							18 13									18 46	
Box Hill & Westhumble	d			17 10		17 14							17 40	17 43							18 06	18 14			
Dorking [4]	a			17 14		17 16							17 44	17 45							18 11	18 16			
	d					17 17								17 46								18 19			
Holmwood	d					17 24								17 53								18 26			
Ockley	d					17 28								17 57								18 30			
Warnham	d					17 34								18 03								18 36			
Horsham [4]	a					17 40								18 09								18 42			

Faster trains London and Clapham Junction to Horsham see table 186

Table 182

Mondays to Fridays

9 December to 16 May

London - Mitcham, Sutton, Epsom Downs, Epsom, Dorking

Network Diagram - see first Page of Table 182

		SN		SN	FC	SN	SW	SN	SW	SN	SN	SW		SN	FC	SN	SW	SN	SW	SN	SN	FC [1]		SN	SW
London Victoria [15] ⊖	d			17 31		17 33		17 50						18 01		18 03		18 20						18 32	
London Waterloo [15] ⊖	d						17 54		18 00			18 09					18 24		18 30						18 39
Clapham Junction [10]	d			17 37		17 41	18 03	17 56	18 09			18 18		18 08		18 11	18 33	18 26	18 39					18 40	18 48
Balham [4] ⊖	d			17 43		17 46		18 02						18 12		18 16		18 32						18 45	
St Pancras International	d				17 18										17 52							18 22			
Farringdon	d				17 23										17 57							18 27			
City Thameslink	d				17 27										18 01							18 31			
London Blackfriars	d				17 30										18 04							18 34			
Elephant & Castle	d				17 34										18 08							18 38			
Loughborough Jn	d				17 38										18 12							18 42			
Herne Hill	d				17 43										18 17							18 48			
London Bridge [4] ⊖	d	17 20								17 50	18 02									18 20	18 32				
Tulse Hill	a	17 39			17 47					18 08					18 21					18 38		18 52			
Tulse Hill [3]	d	17 39			17 48					18 09					18 22					18 38		18 52			
Streatham	d	17 44			17 52					18 13					18 26					18 42		18 56			
Mitcham Eastfields	d	17 48		17 51	17 55			18 08		18 17				18 20	18 29			18 38		18 47		18 59			
Mitcham Junction	d	17 51		17 54	17 58			18 11		18 20				18 23	18 32			18 41		18 50		19 02			
Hackbridge	d	17 55		17 58	18 02			18 15		18 24				18 26	18 36			18 45		18 54		19 06			
Carshalton	d	17 57		18 00	18 04			18 17		18 26				18 29	18 38			18 47		18 56		19 08			
West Croydon	d					18 04					18 21					18 35					18 51			19 04	
Sutton (Surrey)	a	18 02		18 05	18 08	18 16		18 21		18 30	18 33			18 36	18 42	18 47		18 51		19 00	19 03	19 12		19 16	
Sutton (Surrey) [4]	a																								
	d			18 06		18 16		18 21			18 33			18 36		18 48		18 51			19 03			19 17	
Belmont	d					18 20										18 51								19 20	
Banstead	d					18 23										18 55								19 24	
Epsom Downs	a					18 29										19 00								19 28	
Cheam	d			18 08				18 24			18 36			18 39				18 54			19 06				
Ewell East	d			18 12				18 27			18 39			18 42				18 57			19 09				
Epsom [3]	a			18 18			18 24	18 31	18 35		18 43	18 46		18 48			18 54	19 01	19 07		19 13				19 16
	d						18 24	18 34			18 44	18 47					18 54	19 02			19 14				19 17
Ashtead	d						18 28	18 38			18 48	18 51					18 58	19 06			19 18				19 21
Leatherhead	d						18 31	18 41			18 51	18 54					19 01	19 09			19 21				19 24
Guildford	a											19 22													19 52
Box Hill & Westhumble	d						18 36	18 46			18 56						19 06	19 14			19 26				
Dorking [4]	a						18 41	18 48			19 00						19 11	19 16			19 30				
	d							18 49										19 19							
Holmwood	d							18 56										19 26							
Ockley	d							19 00										19 30							
Warnham	d							19 06										19 36							
Horsham [4]	a							19 12										19 42							

		SW	SN	SW	SN	SW	FC	SN		SN	SW	SN	SN	SN	SW	FC	SN	SN		SW	SN	SN	SW	FC	SN
London Victoria [15] ⊖	d		18 50					18 59		19 06		19 20					19 34	19 36			19 50				20 03
London Waterloo [15] ⊖	d	18 54		19 00		19 09					19 24				19 39					19 54			20 09		
Clapham Junction [10]	d	19 03	18 56	19 09		19 18		19 08		19 14	19 33	19 26			19 48		19 41	19 44		20 03	19 56		20 18		20 11
Balham [4] ⊖	d		19 02					19 14		19 20		19 32					19 47	19 50			20 02				20 17
St Pancras International	d						18 48									19 18								19 48	
Farringdon	d						18 53									19 23								19 53	
City Thameslink	d						18 57									19 27								19 57	
London Blackfriars	d						19 00									19 30								20 00	
Elephant & Castle	d						19 04									19 33								20 03	
Loughborough Jn	d						19 08									19 37								20 07	
Herne Hill	d						19 12									19 41								20 11	
London Bridge [4] ⊖	d				18 50									19 30											
Tulse Hill	a				19 08		19 16									19 45								20 15	
Tulse Hill [3]	d				19 09		19 16									19 46								20 16	
Streatham	d				19 15		19 20									19 50								20 20	
Mitcham Eastfields	d		19 08		19 19		19 24					19 38				19 54	19 57				20 08			20 24	20 27
Mitcham Junction	d		19 11		19 22		19 27					19 41				19 57	20 00				20 11			20 27	20 30
Hackbridge	d		19 15		19 26		19 30					19 45				20 00	20 03				20 15			20 30	20 34
Carshalton	d		19 17		19 28		19 33					19 47	←			20 03	20 06				20 17	←		20 33	20 36
West Croydon	d							19 32		19 45			19 45	19 49				20 14				20 14			
Sutton (Surrey)	a		19 21		19 32		19 36	19 44		↪		19 51	19 57	20 01		20 06	20 09	↪			20 21	20 26		20 36	20 40
Sutton (Surrey) [4]	a																								
	d		19 21		19 32			19 45				19 51	19 58	20 02			20 10				20 21	20 27			20 40
Belmont	d												20 01									20 30			
Banstead	d												20 05									20 34			
Epsom Downs	a												20 09									20 38			
Cheam	d		19 24		19 35			19 47				19 54		20 04			20 12				20 24				20 43
Ewell East	d		19 27		19 38			19 51				19 57		20 08			20 16				20 27				20 46
Epsom [3]	a	19 24	19 31	19 35	19 42	19 45		19 55			19 57	20 01		20 12	20 16		20 20			20 27	20 31		20 42		20 50
	d	19 24	19 34			19 47					19 58	20 02		20 12	20 17						20 32		20 43		
Ashtead	d	19 28	19 38			19 51					20 02	20 06		20 16	20 21						20 36		20 47		
Leatherhead	d	19 31	19 41			19 54					20 05	20 09		20 19	20 24						20 39		20 50		
Guildford	a					20 20									20 50										
Box Hill & Westhumble	d	19 36	19 46								20 10	20 14									20 44		20 55		
Dorking [4]	a	19 41	19 50								20 14	20 16		20 25							20 46		20 57		
	d											20 17													
Holmwood	d											20 24													
Ockley	d											20 28													
Warnham	d											20 34													
Horsham [4]	a											20 38													

Faster trains London and Clapham Junction to Horsham see table 186

Table 182

Mondays to Fridays

9 December to 16 May

London - Mitcham, Sutton, Epsom Downs, Epsom, Dorking

Network Diagram - see first Page of Table 182

Station		SN	SW	SN		SN	SW	SN	FC	SN	SW	SN	SN	SW		SN	FC	SN	SW	SN	SN	SW	SN	SN	
London Victoria 15 ⊖	d	20 06		20 20				20 33		20 36		20 50				21 03		21 06		21 20			21 33	21 36	
London Waterloo 15 ⊖	d		20 24				20 39				20 54			21 09					21 24			21 39			
Clapham Junction 10	d	20 14	20 33	20 26			20 48	20 41		20 44	21 03	20 56		21 18		21 11		21 14	21 33	21 26		21 48	21 41	21 44	
Balham 4 ⊖	d	20 20		20 31				20 47		20 50		21 02				21 17		21 20		21 31			21 47	21 50	
St Pancras International	d								20 18								20 48								
Farringdon	d								20 23								20 53								
City Thameslink	d								20 27								20 57								
London Blackfriars	d								20 30								21 00								
Elephant & Castle	d								20 33								21 03								
Loughborough Jn	d								20 37								21 07								
Herne Hill	d								20 41								21 11								
London Bridge 4 ⊖	d																								
Tulse Hill	a								20 45								21 15								
Tulse Hill 3	d								20 50								21 20								
Streatham	d								20 53								21 23								
Mitcham Eastfields	d			20 38				20 54	20 57			21 08				21 24	21 27			21 38			21 54		
Mitcham Junction	d			20 41				20 57	21 00			21 11				21 27	21 30			21 41			21 57		
Hackbridge	d			20 45				21 00	21 03			21 15				21 30	21 33			21 45			22 00		
Carshalton	d			20 47		←		21 03	21 06			21 17	←			21 33	21 36			21 47	←		22 03		
West Croydon	d	20 44				20 44				21 14			21 14					21 44			21 44			22 14	
Sutton (Surrey)	a	↪		20 51		20 56		21 06	21 10	↪		21 21	21 26			21 36	21 40	↪		21 51	21 56		22 06	↪	
Sutton (Surrey) 4	a																								
	d			20 51		20 57		21 07				21 21	21 27			21 37				21 51	21 57		22 07		
Belmont	d												21 30												
Banstead	d												21 34												
Epsom Downs	a												21 38												
Cheam	d			20 54		20 59		21 09				21 24				21 39				21 54	21 59		22 09		
Ewell East	d			20 57		21 03		21 13				21 27				21 43				21 57	22 03		22 13		
Epsom 3	a		20 57	21 01		21 07	21 12	21 17			21 27	21 31		21 42		21 47			21 57	22 01	22 07	22 12	22 17		
	d			21 02			21 13					21 32		21 43						22 02		22 13			
Ashtead	d			21 06			21 17					21 36		21 47						22 06		22 17			
Leatherhead	d			21 09			21 20					21 39		21 50						22 09		22 20			
Guildford	a						21 46															22 46			
Box Hill & Westhumble	d			21 14								21 44		21 55											
Dorking 4	a			21 16								21 46		21 57						22 15					
	d																								
Holmwood	d																								
Ockley	d																								
Warnham	d																								
Horsham 4	a																								

Station		SW	SN	SN	SW	SN	SN	SN	SN	SW		SN	SN	SN	SN	SN	SW	SN	SN	SN		SW			
London Victoria 15 ⊖	d		21 50			22 03	22 06	22 20				22 33	22 36	22 50		23 00		23 03		23 26					
London Waterloo 15 ⊖	d	21 54			22 09					22 39							23 09					23 42			
Clapham Junction 10	d	22 03	21 56		22 18	22 11	22 14	22 26		22 48		22 41	22 46	22 56		23 08	23 18	23 11		23 34		23 51			
Balham 4 ⊖	d		22 02			22 17	22 20	22 32				22 46	22 52	23 01		23 14		23 17		23 40					
St Pancras International	d																								
Farringdon	d																								
City Thameslink	d																								
London Blackfriars	d																								
Elephant & Castle	d																								
Loughborough Jn	d																								
Herne Hill	d																								
London Bridge 4 ⊖	d																								
Tulse Hill	a																								
Tulse Hill 3	d																								
Streatham	d																								
Mitcham Eastfields	d		22 08			22 24		22 38				22 53		23 07				23 24		23 46					
Mitcham Junction	d		22 11			22 27		22 41				22 56		23 10				23 27		23 49					
Hackbridge	d		22 15			22 30		22 45				22 59		23 14				23 30		23 53					
Carshalton	d		22 17	←		22 33		22 47	←			23 02		23 16	←			23 33	←	23 55					
West Croydon	d			22 14			22 44		22 44				23 14		23 14	23 32			23 32						
Sutton (Surrey)	a		22 21	22 26		22 36	↪	22 51	22 56			23 05	↪	23 20	23 26	↪		23 36	23 44	23 59					
Sutton (Surrey) 4	a																								
	d		22 21	22 27		22 37		22 51	22 57			23 06		23 20	23 27			23 37	23 45	00 01					
Belmont	d			22 30											23 30										
Banstead	d			22 34											23 34										
Epsom Downs	a			22 38											23 38										
Cheam	d		22 24			22 39		22 54	22 59			23 08		23 23				23 39	23 47	00 03					
Ewell East	d		22 27			22 43		22 57	23 03			23 12		23 26				23 43	23 51	00 07					
Epsom 3	a	22 27	22 31		22 42	22 47		23 01	23 07	23 12		23 16		23 30			23 42	23 47	23 55	00 11		00 15			
	d		22 32		22 43			23 02		23 13				23 31			23 43			00 11		00 19			
Ashtead	d		22 36		22 47			23 06		23 17				23 35			23 47			00 15		00 23			
Leatherhead	d		22 39		22 50			23 09		23 20				23 38			23 50			00 18		00 26			
Guildford	a									23 46												00 53			
Box Hill & Westhumble	d		22 44		22 55									23 43			23 55			00 23					
Dorking 4	a		22 46		22 57			23 15						23 45			23 57			00 26					
	d																			00 26					
Holmwood	d																			00s33					
Ockley	d																			00s37					
Warnham	d																			00s43					
Horsham 4	a																			00 47					

Faster trains London and Clapham Junction to Horsham see table 186

Table 182

Saturdays

14 December to 17 May

London - Mitcham, Sutton, Epsom Downs, Epsom, Dorking

Network Diagram - see first Page of Table 182

		SN	SW	SW	SN	FC	SN	SN	SW	FC		SN	SW	FC	SN	SW	SN	SN	SN	SN		SW	SW	FC	SN
London Victoria 15 ⊖	d				00 21			06 23				06 47			06 53		07 17	07 23	07 31						07 47
London Waterloo 15 ⊖	d		00 15						06 39				07 09			07 24						07 39	07 54		
Clapham Junction 10	d		00 25		00 28			06 30	06 48			06 54	07 18		07 00	07 33	07 24	07 30	07 38			07 48	08 03		07 54
Balham 4 ⊖	d				00 33			06 35				07 00			07 05		07 30	07 35							08 00
St Pancras International	d					05 48				06 18				06 48										07 18	
Farringdon	d					05 53				06 23				06 53										07 23	
City Thameslink	d																								
London Blackfriars	d					06 00				06 30				07 00										07 30	
Elephant & Castle	d					06 03				06 33				07 03										07 33	
Loughborough Jn	d													07 07										07 37	
Herne Hill	d					06 11				06 41				07 11										07 41	
London Bridge 4 ⊖	d																								
Tulse Hill	a					06 15				06 45				07 15										07 45	
Tulse Hill 3	d					06 16				06 46				07 16										07 46	
Streatham	d					06 20				06 50				07 20										07 50	
Mitcham Eastfields	d				00 39	06 24				06 54		07 06		07 24			07 36							07 54	08 06
Mitcham Junction	d				00 42	06 27				06 57		07 09		07 27			07 39							07 57	08 09
Hackbridge	d				00 46	06 30				07 00		07 13		07 30			07 43							08 00	08 13
Carshalton	d				00 48	06 33				07 03		07 15		07 33			07 45			←				08 03	08 15
West Croydon	d						06 45	06 54							07 24			07 54		07 54					
Sutton (Surrey)	a				00 52	06 36	06 57	07 06		07 06		07 19		07 36	07 39		07 49	→	07 58	08 06				08 06	08 19
Sutton (Surrey) 4	a																								
	d	00 01			00 53		06 57	07 07				07 19			07 40		07 49		07 59	08 07					08 19
Belmont	d							07 10												08 10					
Banstead	d							07 14												08 14					
Epsom Downs	a							07 17												08 17					
Cheam	d	00 03			00 55		07 00					07 22			07 42		07 52		08 01						08 22
Ewell East	d	00 07			00 59		07 03					07 25			07 46		07 55		08 05						08 25
Epsom 3	a	00 11	00 50		01 03		07 07		07 16			07 29	07 46		07 52	07 57	07 59		08 09			08 16	08 27		08 29
	d	00 11		00 19			07 08		07 17			07 30	07 47			07 58			08 09			08 17	08 28		
Ashtead	d	00 15		00 23			07 12		07 21			07 34	07 51			08 02			08 13			08 21	08 32		
Leatherhead	d	00 18		00 26			07 15		07 24			07 37	07 54			08 05			08 16			08 24	08 35		
Guildford	a			00 53					07 50				08 20									08 50			
Box Hill & Westhumble	d	00 23										07 42							08 21						
Dorking 4	a	00 26					07 21					07 44				08 11			08 24				08 41		
	d	00 26																	08 24						
Holmwood	d	00s33																	08 32						
Ockley	d	00s37																	08 36						
Warnham	d	00s43																	08 41						
Horsham 4	a	00 47																	08 45						

		SN	SN	SW	FC	SN		SW	SN	SN	SN	SN	SW	SW	FC	SN		SN	SN	SW	FC	SN	SW	SN	SN
London Victoria 15 ⊖	d	07 53	08 01						08 17	08 23	08 31					08 47		08 53	09 01					09 17	09 23
London Waterloo 15 ⊖	d			08 09				08 24					08 39	08 54						09 09			09 24		
Clapham Junction 10	d	08 00	08 08	08 18				08 33	08 24	08 30	08 38		08 48	09 03		08 54		09 00	09 08	09 18			09 33	09 24	09 30
Balham 4 ⊖	d	08 05							08 30	08 35						09 00		09 05						09 30	09 35
St Pancras International	d				07 48										08 18						08 48				
Farringdon	d				07 53										08 23						08 53				
City Thameslink	d																								
London Blackfriars	d				08 00										08 30						09 00				
Elephant & Castle	d				08 03										08 33						09 03				
Loughborough Jn	d				08 07										08 37						09 07				
Herne Hill	d				08 11										08 41						09 11				
London Bridge 4 ⊖	d																								
Tulse Hill	a				08 15										08 45						09 15				
Tulse Hill 3	d				08 16										08 46						09 16				
Streatham	d				08 20										08 50						09 20				
Mitcham Eastfields	d				08 24				08 36						08 54	09 06					09 24			09 36	
Mitcham Junction	d				08 27				08 39						08 57	09 09					09 27			09 39	
Hackbridge	d				08 30				08 43						09 00	09 13					09 30			09 43	
Carshalton	d				08 33	←			08 45			←			09 03	09 15					09 33	←		09 45	
West Croydon	d	08 24				08 24				08 54		08 54						09 24				09 24			09 54
Sutton (Surrey)	a	→	08 28		08 36	08 39			08 49	→	08 58	09 06			09 06	09 19		→	09 28		09 36	09 39		09 49	→
Sutton (Surrey) 4	a																								
	d		08 29			08 40			08 49		08 59	09 07				09 19			09 29			09 40		09 49	
Belmont	d											09 10													
Banstead	d											09 14													
Epsom Downs	a											09 17													
Cheam	d		08 31			08 42			08 52		09 01					09 22			09 31			09 42		09 52	
Ewell East	d					08 46			08 55		09 05					09 25						09 46		09 55	
Epsom 3	a		08 37	08 46		08 52		08 57	08 59		09 09		09 16	09 27		09 29			09 37	09 46		09 52	09 57	09 59	
	d		08 37	08 47				08 58			09 09		09 17	09 28					09 37	09 47			09 58		
Ashtead	d		08 41	08 51				09 02			09 13		09 21	09 32					09 41	09 51			10 02		
Leatherhead	d		08 44	08 54				09 05			09 16		09 24	09 35					09 44	09 54			10 05		
Guildford	a			09 20									09 50							10 20					
Box Hill & Westhumble	d										09 21														
Dorking 4	a		08 50					09 11			09 24			09 41					09 50				10 11		
	d										09 24														
Holmwood	d										09 32														
Ockley	d										09 36														
Warnham	d										09 41														
Horsham 4	a										09 45														

Faster trains London and Clapham Junction to Horsham see table 186

Table 182

Saturdays

14 December to 17 May

London - Mitcham, Sutton, Epsom Downs, Epsom, Dorking

Network Diagram - see first Page of Table 182

		SN		SN	SW	SW	FC	SN	SN	SN	SW	FC		SN	SW	SN	SN	SN	SN	SW	SW	FC		SN	SN
London Victoria 15 ⊖	d	09 31						09 47	09 53	10 01						10 17	10 23	10 31						10 47	10 53
London Waterloo 15 ⊖	d				09 39	09 54					10 09				10 24					10 39	10 54				
Clapham Junction 10	d	09 38			09 48	10 03		09 54	10 00	10 08	10 18				10 33	10 24	10 30	10 38		10 48	11 03			10 54	11 00
Balham 4 ⊖	d							10 00	10 05							10 30	10 35							11 00	11 05
St Pancras International	d						09 18					09 48										10 18			
Farringdon	d						09 23					09 53										10 23			
City Thameslink	d						09 27					09 57										10 27			
London Blackfriars	d						09 30					10 00										10 30			
Elephant & Castle	d						09 33					10 03										10 33			
Loughborough Jn	d						09 37					10 07										10 37			
Herne Hill	d						09 41					10 11										10 41			
London Bridge 4 ⊖	d																								
Tulse Hill	a						09 45					10 15										10 45			
Tulse Hill 3	d						09 46					10 16										10 46			
Streatham	d						09 50					10 20										10 50			
Mitcham Eastfields	d						09 54	10 06				10 24				10 36						10 54		11 06	
Mitcham Junction	d						09 57	10 09				10 27				10 39						10 57		11 09	
Hackbridge	d						10 00	10 13				10 30				10 43						11 00		11 13	
Carshalton	d			←			10 03	10 15				10 33		←		10 45			←			11 03		11 15	
West Croydon	d			09 54					10 24					10 24			10 54		10 54						11 24
Sutton (Surrey)	a	09 58		10 06			10 06	10 19	→	10 28		10 36		10 39		10 49	→	10 58	11 06			11 06		11 19	→
Sutton (Surrey) 4	a																								
	d	09 59		10 07				10 19		10 29				10 40		10 49		10 59	11 07					11 19	
Belmont	d			10 10															11 10						
Banstead	d			10 14															11 14						
Epsom Downs	a			10 17															11 17						
Cheam	d	10 01						10 22		10 31				10 42		10 52		11 01						11 22	
Ewell East	d	10 05						10 25						10 46		10 55		11 05						11 25	
Epsom 3	a	10 09			10 16	10 27		10 29		10 37	10 46			10 52	10 57	10 59		11 09		11 16	11 27			11 29	
	d	10 09			10 17	10 28				10 37	10 47				10 58			11 09		11 17	11 28				
Ashtead	d	10 13			10 21	10 32				10 41	10 51				11 02			11 13		11 21	11 32				
Leatherhead	d	10 16			10 24	10 35				10 44	10 54				11 05			11 16		11 24	11 35				
Guildford	a				10 50						11 20									11 50					
Box Hill & Westhumble	d	10 21																11 21							
Dorking 4	a	10 24				10 41				10 50					11 11			11 24			11 41				
	d	10 24																11 24							
Holmwood	d	10 32																11 32							
Ockley	d	10 36																11 36							
Warnham	d	10 41																11 41							
Horsham 4	a	10 45																11 45							

		SN	SW	FC	SN	SW	SN	SN		SN	SN	SW	SW	FC	SN	SN	SN	SW		FC	SN	SW	SN	SN	SN
London Victoria 15 ⊖	d	11 01					11 17	11 23		11 31					11 47	11 53	12 01						12 17	12 23	12 31
London Waterloo 15 ⊖	d		11 09			11 24						11 39	11 54					12 09				12 24			
Clapham Junction 10	d	11 08	11 18			11 33	11 24	11 30		11 38		11 48	12 03		11 54	12 00	12 08	12 18				12 33	12 24	12 30	12 38
Balham 4 ⊖	d						11 30	11 35							12 00	12 05							12 30	12 35	
St Pancras International	d			10 48										11 18						11 48					
Farringdon	d			10 53										11 23						11 53					
City Thameslink	d			10 57										11 27						11 57					
London Blackfriars	d			11 00										11 30						12 00					
Elephant & Castle	d			11 03										11 33						12 03					
Loughborough Jn	d			11 07										11 37						12 07					
Herne Hill	d			11 11										11 41						12 11					
London Bridge 4 ⊖	d																								
Tulse Hill	a			11 15										11 45						12 15					
Tulse Hill 3	d			11 16										11 46						12 16					
Streatham	d			11 20										11 50						12 20					
Mitcham Eastfields	d			11 24			11 36							11 54	12 06					12 24			12 36		
Mitcham Junction	d			11 27			11 39							11 57	12 09					12 27			12 39		
Hackbridge	d			11 30			11 43							12 00	12 13					12 30			12 43		
Carshalton	d			11 33	←		11 45				←			12 03	12 15					12 33	←		12 45		
West Croydon	d				11 24			11 54			11 54					12 24					12 24			12 54	
Sutton (Surrey)	a	11 28		11 36	11 39		11 49	→		11 58	12 06			12 06	12 19	→	12 28			12 36	12 39		12 49	→	12 58
Sutton (Surrey) 4	a																								
	d	11 29			11 40		11 49			11 59	12 07				12 19		12 29				12 40		12 49		12 59
Belmont	d										12 10														
Banstead	d										12 14														
Epsom Downs	a										12 17														
Cheam	d	11 31			11 42		11 52			12 01					12 22		12 31				12 42		12 52		13 01
Ewell East	d				11 46		11 55			12 05					12 25						12 46		12 55		13 05
Epsom 3	a	11 37	11 46		11 52	11 57	11 59			12 09		12 16	12 27		12 29		12 37	12 46			12 52	12 57	12 59		13 09
	d	11 37	11 47			11 58				12 09		12 17	12 28				12 37	12 47				12 58			13 09
Ashtead	d	11 41	11 51			12 02				12 13		12 21	12 32				12 41	12 51				13 02			13 13
Leatherhead	d	11 44	11 54			12 05				12 16		12 24	12 35				12 44	12 54				13 05			13 16
Guildford	a		12 20									12 50						13 20							
Box Hill & Westhumble	d									12 21															13 21
Dorking 4	a	11 50				12 11				12 24			12 41				12 50					13 11			13 24
	d									12 24															13 24
Holmwood	d									12 32															13 32
Ockley	d									12 36															13 36
Warnham	d									12 41															13 41
Horsham 4	a									12 45															13 45

Faster trains London and Clapham Junction to Horsham see table 186

Table 182

Saturdays

14 December to 17 May

London - Mitcham, Sutton, Epsom Downs, Epsom, Dorking

Network Diagram - see first Page of Table 182

		SN	SW	SW		FC	SN	SN	SN	SW	FC	SN	SW	SN		SN	SN	SN	SW	SW	FC	SN	SN	SN	
London Victoria 15 ⊖	d						12 47	12 53	13 01					13 17		13 23	13 31					13 47	13 53	14 01	
London Waterloo 15 ⊖	d		12 39	12 54						13 09			13 24						13 39	13 54					
Clapham Junction 10	d		12 48	13 03			12 54	13 00	13 08	13 18			13 33	13 24		13 30	13 38		13 48	14 03		13 54	14 00	14 08	
Balham 4 ⊖	d						13 00	13 05						13 30		13 35						14 00	14 05		
St Pancras International	d					12 18					12 48										13 18				
Farringdon	d					12 23					12 53										13 23				
City Thameslink	d					12 27					12 57										13 27				
London Blackfriars	d					12 30					13 00										13 30				
Elephant & Castle	d					12 33					13 03										13 33				
Loughborough Jn	d					12 37					13 07										13 37				
Herne Hill	d					12 41					13 11										13 41				
London Bridge 4 ⊖	d																								
Tulse Hill	a					12 45					13 15										13 45				
Tulse Hill 3	d					12 46					13 16										13 46				
Streatham	d					12 50					13 20										13 50				
Mitcham Eastfields	d					12 54	13 06				13 24			13 36							13 54	14 06			
Mitcham Junction	d					12 57	13 09				13 27			13 39							13 57	14 09			
Hackbridge	d					13 00	13 13				13 30			13 43							14 00	14 13			
Carshalton	d	←				13 03	13 15				13 33	←		13 45				←			14 03	14 15			
West Croydon	d	12 54						13 24				13 24				13 54		13 54					14 24		
Sutton (Surrey)	a	13 06				13 06	13 19	→	13 28		13 36	13 39		13 49		→	13 58	14 06			14 06	14 19	→	14 28	
Sutton (Surrey) 4	a																								
	d	13 07					13 19		13 29			13 40		13 49			13 59	14 07				14 19		14 29	
Belmont	d	13 10																14 10							
Banstead	d	13 14																14 14							
Epsom Downs	a	13 17																14 17							
Cheam	d						13 22		13 31			13 42		13 52			14 01					14 22		14 31	
Ewell East	d						13 25					13 46		13 55			14 05					14 25			
Epsom 3	a		13 16	13 27			13 29		13 37	13 46		13 52	13 57	13 59			14 09		14 16	14 27		14 29		14 37	
	d		13 17	13 28					13 37	13 47			13 58				14 09		14 17	14 28				14 37	
Ashtead	d		13 21	13 32					13 41	13 51			14 02				14 13		14 21	14 32				14 41	
Leatherhead	d		13 24	13 35					13 44	13 54			14 05				14 16		14 24	14 35				14 44	
Guildford	a		13 50							14 20									14 50						
Box Hill & Westhumble	d																14 21								
Dorking 4	a			13 41					13 50				14 11				14 24			14 41				14 50	
	d																14 24								
Holmwood	d																14 32								
Ockley	d																14 36								
Warnham	d																14 41								
Horsham 4	a																14 45								

		SW	FC	SN	SW	SN	SN	SN	SN	SW		SW	FC	SN	SN	SN	SW	FC	SN	SW		SN	SN	SN	SN
London Victoria 15 ⊖	d					14 17	14 23	14 31						14 47	14 53	15 01						15 17	15 23	15 31	
London Waterloo 15 ⊖	d	14 09			14 24					14 39		14 54					15 09			15 24					
Clapham Junction 10	d	14 18			14 33	14 24	14 30	14 38		14 48		15 03		14 54	15 00	15 08	15 18			15 33		15 24	15 30	15 38	
Balham 4 ⊖	d					14 30	14 35							15 00	15 05							15 30	15 35		
St Pancras International	d		13 48										14 18					14 48							
Farringdon	d		13 53										14 23					14 53							
City Thameslink	d		13 57										14 27					14 57							
London Blackfriars	d		14 00										14 30					15 00							
Elephant & Castle	d		14 03										14 33					15 03							
Loughborough Jn	d		14 07										14 37					15 07							
Herne Hill	d		14 11										14 41					15 11							
London Bridge 4 ⊖	d																								
Tulse Hill	a		14 15										14 45					15 15							
Tulse Hill 3	d		14 16										14 46					15 16							
Streatham	d		14 20										14 50					15 20							
Mitcham Eastfields	d		14 24			14 36							14 54	15 06				15 24				15 36			
Mitcham Junction	d		14 27			14 39							14 57	15 09				15 27				15 39			
Hackbridge	d		14 30			14 43							15 00	15 13				15 30				15 43			
Carshalton	d		14 33	←		14 45			←				15 03	15 15				15 33	←			15 45			←
West Croydon	d			14 24			14 54		14 54						15 24				15 24				15 54		15 54
Sutton (Surrey)	a		14 36	14 39		14 49	→	14 58	15 06				15 06	15 19	→	15 28		15 36	15 39			15 49	→	15 58	16 06
Sutton (Surrey) 4	a																								
	d			14 40		14 49		14 59	15 07					15 19		15 29			15 40			15 49		15 59	16 07
Belmont	d								15 10																16 10
Banstead	d								15 14																16 14
Epsom Downs	a								15 17																16 17
Cheam	d			14 42		14 52		15 01						15 22		15 31			15 42			15 52		16 01	
Ewell East	d			14 46		14 55		15 05						15 25					15 46			15 55		16 05	
Epsom 3	a	14 46		14 52	14 57	14 59		15 09		15 16		15 27		15 29		15 37	15 46		15 52	15 57		15 59		16 09	
	d	14 47			14 58			15 09		15 17		15 28				15 37	15 47			15 58				16 09	
Ashtead	d	14 51			15 02			15 13		15 21		15 32				15 41	15 51			16 02				16 13	
Leatherhead	d	14 54			15 05			15 16		15 24		15 35				15 44	15 54			16 05				16 16	
Guildford	a	15 20								15 50							16 20								
Box Hill & Westhumble	d							15 21																16 21	
Dorking 4	a				15 11			15 24				15 41				15 50				16 11				16 24	
	d							15 24																16 24	
Holmwood	d							15 32																16 32	
Ockley	d							15 36																16 36	
Warnham	d							15 41																16 41	
Horsham 4	a							15 45																16 45	

Faster trains London and Clapham Junction to Horsham see table 186

Table 182

Saturdays

14 December to 17 May

London - Mitcham, Sutton, Epsom Downs, Epsom, Dorking

Network Diagram - see first Page of Table 182

Station		SW	SW	FC	SN	SN		SN	SW	FC	SN	SW	SN	SN	SN	SN		SW	SW	FC	SN	SN	SN	SW	FC
London Victoria 15 ⊖	d				15 47	15 53		16 01					16 17	16 23	16 31						16 47	16 53	17 01		
London Waterloo 15 ⊖	d	15 39	15 54						16 09			16 24						16 39	16 54					17 09	
Clapham Junction 10	d	15 48	16 03		15 54	16 00		16 08	16 18			16 33	16 24	16 30	16 38			16 48	17 03		16 54	17 00	17 08	17 18	
Balham 4 ⊖	d				16 00	16 05							16 30	16 35							17 00	17 05			
St Pancras International	d			15 18						15 48										16 18					16 48
Farringdon	d			15 23						15 53										16 23					16 53
City Thameslink	d			15 27						15 57										16 27					16 57
London Blackfriars	d			15 30						16 00										16 30					17 00
Elephant & Castle	d			15 33						16 03										16 33					17 03
Loughborough Jn	d			15 37						16 07										16 37					17 07
Herne Hill	d			15 41						16 11										16 41					17 11
London Bridge 4 ⊖	d																								
Tulse Hill	a			15 45						16 15										16 45					17 15
Tulse Hill 3	d			15 46						16 16										16 46					17 16
Streatham	d			15 50						16 20										16 50					17 20
Mitcham Eastfields	d			15 54	16 06					16 24			16 36							16 54	17 06				17 24
Mitcham Junction	d			15 57	16 09					16 27			16 39							16 57	17 09				17 27
Hackbridge	d			16 00	16 13					16 30			16 43							17 00	17 13				17 30
Carshalton	d			16 03	16 15					16 33	←		16 45			←				17 03	17 15				17 33
West Croydon	d					16 24					16 24			16 54		16 54						17 24			
Sutton (Surrey)	a			16 06	16 19	→		16 28		16 36	16 39		16 49	→	16 58	17 06				17 06	17 19	→	17 28		17 36
Sutton (Surrey) 4	a																								
	d				16 19			16 29			16 40		16 49		16 59	17 07					17 19		17 29		
Belmont	d															17 10									
Banstead	d															17 14									
Epsom Downs	a															17 17									
Cheam	d				16 22			16 31			16 42		16 52		17 01						17 22		17 31		
Ewell East	d				16 25						16 46		16 55		17 05						17 25				
Epsom 3	a	16 16	16 27		16 29			16 37	16 46		16 52	16 57	16 59		17 09			17 16	17 27		17 29		17 37	17 46	
	d	16 17	16 28					16 37	16 47			16 58			17 09			17 17	17 28				17 37	17 47	
Ashtead	d	16 21	16 32					16 41	16 51			17 02			17 13			17 21	17 32				17 41	17 51	
Leatherhead	d	16 24	16 35					16 44	16 54			17 05			17 16			17 24	17 35				17 44	17 54	
Guildford	a	16 50							17 20									17 50						18 20	
Box Hill & Westhumble	d														17 21										
Dorking 4	a		16 41					16 50				17 11			17 24				17 41				17 50		
	d														17 24										
Holmwood	d														17 32										
Ockley	d														17 36										
Warnham	d														17 41										
Horsham 4	a														17 45										

Station		SN		SW	SN	SN	SN	SN	SW	SW	FC	SN		SN	SN	SW	FC	SN	SW	SN	SN	SN		SN	SW
London Victoria 15 ⊖	d				17 17	17 23	17 31					17 47		17 53	18 01					18 17	18 23	18 31			
London Waterloo 15 ⊖	d			17 24					17 39	17 54						18 09			18 24						18 39
Clapham Junction 10	d			17 33	17 24	17 30	17 38		17 48	18 03		17 54		18 00	18 08	18 18			18 33	18 24	18 30	18 38			18 48
Balham 4 ⊖	d				17 30	17 35						18 00		18 05						18 30	18 35				
St Pancras International	d										17 18						17 48								
Farringdon	d										17 23						17 53								
City Thameslink	d										17 27						17 57								
London Blackfriars	d										17 30						18 00								
Elephant & Castle	d										17 33						18 03								
Loughborough Jn	d										17 37						18 07								
Herne Hill	d										17 41						18 11								
London Bridge 4 ⊖	d																								
Tulse Hill	a										17 45						18 15								
Tulse Hill 3	d										17 46						18 16								
Streatham	d										17 50						18 20								
Mitcham Eastfields	d				17 36						17 54	18 06					18 24			18 36					
Mitcham Junction	d				17 39						17 57	18 09					18 27			18 39					
Hackbridge	d				17 43						18 00	18 13					18 30			18 43					
Carshalton	d	←			17 45			←			18 03	18 15					18 33	←		18 45				←	
West Croydon	d	17 24				17 54		17 54						18 24				18 24			18 54			18 54	
Sutton (Surrey)	a	17 39			17 49	→	17 58	18 06			18 06	18 19		→	18 28		18 36	18 39		18 49	→	18 58		19 06	
Sutton (Surrey) 4	a																								
	d	17 40			17 49		17 59	18 07				18 19			18 29			18 40		18 49		18 59		19 07	
Belmont	d							18 10																19 10	
Banstead	d							18 14																19 14	
Epsom Downs	a							18 17																19 17	
Cheam	d	17 42			17 52		18 01					18 22			18 31			18 42		18 52		19 01			
Ewell East	d	17 46			17 55		18 05					18 25						18 46		18 55		19 05			
Epsom 3	a	17 52		17 57	17 59		18 09		18 16	18 27		18 29			18 37	18 46		18 52	18 57	18 59		19 09			19 16
	d			17 58			18 09		18 17	18 28					18 37	18 47			18 58			19 09			19 17
Ashtead	d			18 02			18 13		18 21	18 32					18 41	18 51			19 02			19 13			19 21
Leatherhead	d			18 05			18 16		18 24	18 35					18 44	18 54			19 05			19 16			19 24
Guildford	a								18 50							19 20									19 50
Box Hill & Westhumble	d						18 21								18 49										
Dorking 4	a			18 11			18 24			18 41					18 52				19 11			19 22			
	d						18 24																		
Holmwood	d						18 32																		
Ockley	d						18 36																		
Warnham	d						18 41																		
Horsham 4	a						18 45																		

Faster trains London and Clapham Junction to Horsham see table 186

Table 182

Saturdays

14 December to 17 May

London - Mitcham, Sutton, Epsom Downs, Epsom, Dorking

Network Diagram - see first Page of Table 182

		SW	FC	SN	SN	SN	SW	FC		SN	SW	SN	SN	SN	SN	SW	SW	FC		SN	SN	SN	SW	FC	SN
London Victoria 15 ⊖	d			18 47	18 53	19 01						19 17	19 23	19 31						19 47	19 53	20 01			
London Waterloo 15 ⊖	d	18 54					19 09				19 24					19 39	19 54						20 09		
Clapham Junction 10	d	19 03		18 54	19 00	19 08	19 18				19 33	19 24	19 30	19 38		19 48	20 03			19 54	20 00	20 08	20 18		
Balham 4 ⊖	d			19 00	19 05							19 30	19 35							20 00	20 05				
St Pancras International	d		18 18					18 48										19 18						19 48	
Farringdon	d		18 23					18 53										19 23						19 53	
City Thameslink	d		18 27					18 57										19 27						19 57	
London Blackfriars	d		18 30					19 00										19 30						20 00	
Elephant & Castle	d		18 33					19 03										19 33						20 03	
Loughborough Jn	d		18 37					19 07										19 37						20 07	
Herne Hill	d		18 41					19 11										19 41						20 11	
London Bridge 4 ⊖	d																								
Tulse Hill	a		18 45					19 15										19 45						20 15	
Tulse Hill 3	d		18 46					19 16										19 46						20 16	
Streatham	d		18 50					19 20										19 50						20 20	
Mitcham Eastfields	d		18 54	19 06				19 24				19 36						19 54		20 06				20 24	
Mitcham Junction	d		18 57	19 09				19 27				19 39						19 57		20 09				20 27	
Hackbridge	d		19 00	19 13				19 30				19 43						20 00		20 13				20 30	
Carshalton	d		19 03	19 15				19 33		←		19 45			←			20 03		20 15				20 33	←
West Croydon	d				19 24					19 24			19 54		19 54						20 25				20 25
Sutton (Surrey)	a		19 06	19 19	→	19 28		19 36		19 39		19 49	→	19 58	20 06			20 06		20 19	→	20 28		20 36	20 39
Sutton (Surrey) 4	a																								
	d			19 19		19 29				19 40		19 49		19 59	20 07					20 19		20 29			20 40
Belmont	d														20 10										
Banstead	d														20 14										
Epsom Downs	a														20 17										
Cheam	d			19 22		19 31				19 42		19 52		20 01						20 22		20 31			20 42
Ewell East	d			19 25						19 46		19 55		20 05						20 25					20 46
Epsom 3	a	19 27		19 29		19 37	19 46			19 52	19 57	19 59		20 09		20 16	20 27			20 29		20 37	20 46		20 52
	d	19 28				19 37	19 47				19 58			20 09		20 17						20 37	20 47		
Ashtead	d	19 32				19 41	19 51				20 02			20 13		20 21						20 41	20 51		
Leatherhead	d	19 35				19 44	19 54				20 05			20 16		20 24						20 44	20 54		
Guildford	a						20 20									20 50									
Box Hill & Westhumble	d					19 49																20 49			
Dorking 4	a	19 41				19 52					20 11			20 22								20 52	21 00		
	d																								
Holmwood	d																								
Ockley	d																								
Warnham	d																								
Horsham 4	a																								

		SW	SN	SN		SN	SW	SW	FC	SN	SN	SN	SN	SW		SN	SW	FC	SN	SN	SN	SN	SW	SW	
London Victoria 15 ⊖	d		20 17	20 23		20 31					20 47	20 53	21 01						21 17	21 23	21 31				
London Waterloo 15 ⊖	d	20 24					20 39	20 54						21 09			21 24						21 39	21 54	
Clapham Junction 10	d	20 33	20 24	20 30		20 38	20 48	21 03			20 54	21 00	21 08	21 18			21 33		21 24	21 30	21 38		21 48	22 03	
Balham 4 ⊖	d		20 30	20 35							21 00	21 05							21 30	21 35					
St Pancras International	d								20 18									20 48							
Farringdon	d								20 23									20 53							
City Thameslink	d								20 27									20 57							
London Blackfriars	d								20 30									21 00							
Elephant & Castle	d								20 33									21 03							
Loughborough Jn	d								20 37									21 07							
Herne Hill	d								20 41									21 11							
London Bridge 4 ⊖	d																								
Tulse Hill	a								20 45									21 15							
Tulse Hill 3	d								20 46									21 16							
Streatham	d								20 50									21 20							
Mitcham Eastfields	d		20 36						20 54		21 06							21 24	21 36						
Mitcham Junction	d		20 39						20 57		21 09							21 27	21 39						
Hackbridge	d		20 43						21 00		21 13							21 30	21 43						
Carshalton	d		20 45						21 03	←	21 15					←		21 33	21 45			←			
West Croydon	d			20 55						20 55		21 25				21 25				21 55		21 55			
Sutton (Surrey)	a		20 49	→		20 58			21 06	21 07	21 19	→	21 28			21 39		21 42	21 49	→	21 58	22 07			
Sutton (Surrey) 4	a																								
	d		20 49			20 59				21 08	21 19		21 29			21 40			21 49		21 59	22 08			
Belmont	d									21 11												22 11			
Banstead	d									21 15												22 15			
Epsom Downs	a									21 18												22 18			
Cheam	d		20 52			21 01					21 22		21 31			21 42			21 52		22 01				
Ewell East	d		20 55			21 05					21 25					21 46			21 55		22 05				
Epsom 3	a	20 57	20 59			21 09	21 16	21 27			21 29		21 37	21 46		21 52	21 57		21 59		22 09		22 16	22 27	
	d					21 09	21 17						21 37	21 47							22 09		22 17		
Ashtead	d					21 13	21 21						21 41	21 51							22 13		22 21		
Leatherhead	d					21 16	21 24						21 44	21 54							22 16		22 24		
Guildford	a						21 50																22 50		
Box Hill & Westhumble	d												21 49												
Dorking 4	a					21 22							21 52	22 00							22 22				
	d																								
Holmwood	d																								
Ockley	d																								
Warnham	d																								
Horsham 4	a																								

Faster trains London and Clapham Junction to Horsham see table 186

Table 182

London - Mitcham, Sutton, Epsom Downs, Epsom, Dorking

Saturdays

14 December to 17 May

Network Diagram - see first Page of Table 182

Station		SN	SN	SN	SW	SN	SN	SN	SN	SN		SN	SW	SN	SN	SN	SN	SN	SW	SN		SN	SW		
London Victoria 15 ⊖	d	21 47	21 53	22 01			22 17	22 23	22 31			22 36		22 47		22 53	23 01					23 26			
London Waterloo 15 ⊖	d				22 09								22 39						23 09				23 42		
Clapham Junction 10	d	21 54	22 00	22 08	22 18		22 24	22 30	22 38			22 44	22 48	22 54		23 00	23 08		23 18			23 32	23 51		
Balham 4 ⊖	d	22 00	22 05				22 30	22 35				22 50		23 00		23 06						23 37			
St Pancras International	d																								
Farringdon	d																								
City Thameslink	d																								
London Blackfriars	d																								
Elephant & Castle	d																								
Loughborough Jn	d																								
Herne Hill	d																								
London Bridge 4 ⊖	d																								
Tulse Hill	a																								
Tulse Hill 3	d																								
Streatham	d																								
Mitcham Eastfields	d	22 06					22 36							23 06								23 43			
Mitcham Junction	d	22 09					22 39							23 09								23 46			
Hackbridge	d	22 13					22 43							23 13								23 50			
Carshalton	d	22 15				←	22 45			←				23 15	←			←		←		23 52			
West Croydon	d		22 24			22 24		22 54		22 54		23 14			23 14	23 24		23 14		23 24					
Sutton (Surrey)	a	22 19	→	22 28		22 39	22 49	→	22 58	23 06		→		23 19	→	→	23 28	23 26		23 39		23 59			
Sutton (Surrey) 4	a																								
	d	22 19		22 29		22 40	22 49		22 59	23 07				23 19			23 29	23 33		23 40		00 01			
Belmont	d									23 10								23 36							
Banstead	d									23 14								23 40							
Epsom Downs	a									23 17								23 43							
Cheam	d	22 22		22 31		22 42	22 52		23 01					23 22			23 31			23 42		00 03			
Ewell East	d	22 25				22 46	22 55		23 05					23 25						23 46		00 07			
Epsom 3	a	22 29		22 37	22 46	22 52	22 59		23 09				23 12	23 29			23 37		23 42	23 52		00 11	00 15		
	d			22 37	22 47				23 09				23 17				23 37		23 47			00 11	00 19		
Ashtead	d			22 41	22 51				23 13				23 21				23 41		23 51			00 15	00 23		
Leatherhead	d			22 44	22 54				23 16				23 24				23 44		23 54			00 18	00 26		
Guildford	a												23 50										00 53		
Box Hill & Westhumble	d			22 49					23 21													00 23			
Dorking 4	a			22 52	23 00				23 24								23 50		00 01			00 26			
	d																								
Holmwood	d																								
Ockley	d																								
Warnham	d																								
Horsham 4	a																								

Sundays

8 December to 11 May

Station		SN A	SW	SW A	SN	SW	SN	SW	SN	SW		SN	FC	SW	SN	SN	FC	SW	SN	SN		FC	SW	SN	SN
London Victoria 15 ⊖	d				06 49		07 37		08 07			08 40			09 10	09 22			09 40	09 52				10 10	10 22
London Waterloo 15 ⊖	d		00 15					08 02		08 33				09 02				09 32					10 02		
Clapham Junction 10	d		00 25		06 57		07 45	08 11	08 15	08 41		08 48		09 11	09 18	09 29		09 41	09 48	09 59			10 11	10 18	10 29
Balham 4 ⊖	d				07 02		07 50		08 20			08 54			09 24	09 33			09 54	10 03				10 24	10 33
St Pancras International	d																								
Farringdon	d																								
City Thameslink	d																								
London Blackfriars	d												08 58				09 28					09 58			
Elephant & Castle	d												09 01				09 31					10 01			
Loughborough Jn	d												09 05				09 35					10 05			
Herne Hill	d												09 09				09 39					10 09			
London Bridge 4 ⊖	d																								
Tulse Hill	a												09 13				09 43					10 13			
Tulse Hill 3	d												09 14				09 44					10 14			
Streatham	d												09 18				09 48					10 18			
Mitcham Eastfields	d						07 57		08 28			09 01	09 22		09 30	09 40	09 52		10 00	10 10		10 22		10 30	10 40
Mitcham Junction	d						08 00		08 31			09 04	09 25		09 33	09 43	09 55		10 03	10 13		10 25		10 33	10 43
Hackbridge	d						08 04		08 34			09 07	09 29		09 37	09 46	09 59		10 07	10 16		10 29		10 37	10 46
Carshalton	d						08 06		08 37			09 10	09 31		09 39	09 49	10 01		10 09	10 19		10 31		10 39	10 49
West Croydon	d				07 20																				
Sutton (Surrey)	a				07 32		08 10		08 40			09 13	09 35		09 43	09 52	10 05		10 13	10 22		10 35		10 43	10 52
Sutton (Surrey) 4	a																								
	d	00 01			07 41		08 10		08 41			09 14			09 43	09 53			10 13	10 23				10 43	10 53
Belmont	d																								
Banstead	d																								
Epsom Downs	a																								
Cheam	d	00 03			07 43		08 13		08 43			09 16			09 46	09 55			10 16	10 25				10 46	10 55
Ewell East	d	00 07			07 47		08 16		08 47			09 20			09 49	09 59			10 19	10 29				10 49	10 59
Epsom 3	a	00 11	00 50		07 51		08 20	08 37	08 51	09 07		09 24		09 36	09 53	10 03		10 06	10 23	10 33			10 36	10 53	11 03
	d	00 11		00 19	07 51	08 08	08 21	08 38	08 51	09 08		09 24		09 38	09 54			10 08	10 24				10 38	10 54	
Ashtead	d	00 15		00 23	07 55	08 12	08 25	08 42	08 55	09 12		09 28		09 42	09 58			10 12	10 28				10 42	10 58	
Leatherhead	d	00 18		00 26	07 58	08 15	08 28	08 45	08 58	09 15		09 31		09 45	10 01			10 15	10 31				10 45	11 01	
Guildford	a			00 53		08 41				09 41								10 41							
Box Hill & Westhumble	d	00 23			08 03		08 33		09 03			09 36			10 06				10 36					11 06	
Dorking 4	a	00 26			08 06		08 36	08 51	09 06			09 39		09 51	10 09				10 39				10 51	11 09	
	d																								
Holmwood	d																								
Ockley	d																								
Warnham	d																								
Horsham 4	a																								

A not 8 December

Faster trains London and Clapham Junction to Horsham see table 186

Table 182

Sundays

8 December to 11 May

London - Mitcham, Sutton, Epsom Downs, Epsom, Dorking

Network Diagram - see first Page of Table 182

Station		FC	SW	SN	SN	FC		SW	SN	SN	FC	SW	SN	SN	FC	SW		SN	SN	FC	SW	SN	SN	FC	SW
London Victoria 15 ⊖	d			10 40	10 52				11 10	11 22			11 40	11 52				12 10	12 22			12 40	12 52		
London Waterloo 15 ⊖	d		10 32					11 02				11 32				12 02					12 32				13 02
Clapham Junction 10	d		10 41	10 48	10 59			11 11	11 18	11 29		11 42	11 48	11 59		12 11		12 18	12 29		12 42	12 48	12 59		13 11
Balham 4 ⊖	d			10 54	11 03				11 24	11 33			11 54	12 03				12 24	12 33			12 54	13 03		
St Pancras International	d																								
Farringdon	d																								
City Thameslink	d																								
London Blackfriars	d	10 28				10 58					11 28				11 58					12 28				12 58	
Elephant & Castle	d	10 31				11 01					11 31				12 01					12 31				13 01	
Loughborough Jn	d	10 35				11 05					11 35				12 05					12 35				13 05	
Herne Hill	d	10 39				11 09					11 39				12 09					12 39				13 09	
London Bridge 4 ⊖	d																								
Tulse Hill	a	10 43				11 13					11 43				12 13					12 43				13 13	
Tulse Hill 3	d	10 44				11 14					11 44				12 14					12 44				13 14	
Streatham	d	10 48				11 18					11 48				12 18					12 48				13 18	
Mitcham Eastfields	d	10 52		11 00	11 10	11 22			11 30	11 40	11 52		12 00	12 10	12 22			12 30	12 40	12 52		13 00	13 10	13 22	
Mitcham Junction	d	10 55		11 03	11 13	11 25			11 33	11 43	11 55		12 03	12 13	12 25			12 33	12 43	12 55		13 03	13 13	13 25	
Hackbridge	d	10 59		11 07	11 16	11 29			11 37	11 46	11 59		12 07	12 16	12 29			12 37	12 46	12 59		13 07	13 16	13 29	
Carshalton	d	11 01		11 09	11 19	11 31			11 39	11 49	12 01		12 09	12 19	12 31			12 39	12 49	13 01		13 09	13 19	13 31	
West Croydon	d																								
Sutton (Surrey)	a	11 05		11 13	11 22	11 35			11 43	11 52	12 05		12 13	12 22	12 35			12 43	12 52	13 05		13 13	13 22	13 35	
Sutton (Surrey) 4	a																								
	d			11 13	11 23				11 43	11 53			12 13	12 23				12 43	12 53			13 13	13 23		
Belmont	d																								
Banstead	d																								
Epsom Downs	a																								
Cheam	d			11 16	11 25				11 46	11 55			12 16	12 25				12 46	12 55			13 16	13 25		
Ewell East	d			11 19	11 29				11 49	11 59			12 19	12 29				12 49	12 59			13 19	13 29		
Epsom 3	a		11 06	11 23	11 33			11 36	11 53	12 03		12 06	12 23	12 33		12 36		12 53	13 05		13 06	13 23	13 33		13 36
	d		11 08	11 24				11 38	11 54			12 08	12 24			12 38		12 54			13 08	13 24			13 38
Ashtead	d		11 12	11 28				11 42	11 58			12 12	12 28			12 42		12 58			13 12	13 28			13 42
Leatherhead	d		11 15	11 31				11 45	12 01			12 15	12 31			12 45		13 01			13 15	13 31			13 45
Guildford	a		11 41									12 41									13 41				
Box Hill & Westhumble	d			11 36					12 06				12 36					13 06				13 36			
Dorking 4	a			11 39				11 51	12 09				12 39			12 51		13 09				13 39			13 51
	d																								
Holmwood	d																								
Ockley	d																								
Warnham	d																								
Horsham 4	a																								

Station		SN	SN	FC	SW		SN	SN	FC	SW	SN	SN	FC	SW		SN	SN	FC	SW	SN	FC	SW	SN	SW
London Victoria 15 ⊖	d	13 10	13 22				18 40	18 52			19 10	19 22				19 40	19 52			20 10			20 40	
London Waterloo 15 ⊖	d				13 32					19 02				19 32					20 02			20 32		21 02
Clapham Junction 10	d	13 18	13 29		13 41		18 48	18 59		19 11	19 18	19 29		19 41		19 48	19 59		20 11	20 18		20 41	20 48	21 11
Balham 4 ⊖	d	13 24	13 33				18 54	19 03			19 24	19 33				19 54	20 03			20 24			20 54	
St Pancras International	d																							
Farringdon	d																							
City Thameslink	d																							
London Blackfriars	d			13 28					18 58				19 28					19 58			20 28			
Elephant & Castle	d			13 31					19 01				19 31					20 01			20 31			
Loughborough Jn	d			13 35					19 05				19 35					20 05			20 35			
Herne Hill	d			13 39					19 09				19 39					20 09			20 39			
London Bridge 4 ⊖	d																							
Tulse Hill	a			13 43					19 13				19 43					20 13			20 43			
Tulse Hill 3	d			13 44					19 14				19 44					20 14			20 44			
Streatham	d			13 48					19 18				19 48					20 18			20 48			
Mitcham Eastfields	d	13 30	13 40	13 52		and at the same minutes past each hour until	19 00	19 10	19 22		19 30	19 40	19 52			20 00	20 10	20 22		20 30	20 52		21 00	
Mitcham Junction	d	13 33	13 43	13 55			19 03	19 13	19 25		19 33	19 43	19 55			20 03	20 13	20 25		20 33	20 55		21 03	
Hackbridge	d	13 37	13 46	13 59			19 07	19 16	19 29		19 37	19 46	19 59			20 07	20 16	20 29		20 37	20 59		21 07	
Carshalton	d	13 39	13 49	14 01			19 09	19 19	19 31		19 39	19 49	20 01			20 09	20 19	20 31		20 39	21 01		21 09	
West Croydon	d																							
Sutton (Surrey)	a	13 43	13 52	14 05			19 13	19 22	19 35		19 43	19 52	20 05			20 13	20 22	20 35		20 43	21 05		21 13	
Sutton (Surrey) 4	a																							
	d	13 43	13 53				19 13	19 23			19 43	19 53				20 13	20 23			20 43			21 13	
Belmont	d																							
Banstead	d																							
Epsom Downs	a																							
Cheam	d	13 46	13 55				19 16	19 25			19 46	19 55				20 16	20 25			20 46			21 16	
Ewell East	d	13 49	13 59				19 19	19 29			19 49	19 59				20 19	20 29			20 49			21 19	
Epsom 3	a	13 53	14 03		14 06		19 23	19 33		19 36	19 53	20 03		20 06		20 23	20 33		20 36	20 53		21 06	21 23	21 36
	d	13 54			14 08		19 24			19 38	19 54			20 08		20 24			20 38	20 54		21 08	21 24	21 38
Ashtead	d	13 58			14 12		19 28			19 42	19 58			20 12		20 28			20 42	20 58		21 12	21 28	21 42
Leatherhead	d	14 01			14 15		19 31			19 45	20 01			20 15		20 31			20 45	21 01		21 15	21 31	21 45
Guildford	a				14 41									20 41								21 41		
Box Hill & Westhumble	d	14 06					19 36				20 06					20 36				21 06			21 36	
Dorking 4	a	14 09					19 39			19 51	20 09					20 39			20 51	21 09			21 39	21 51
	d																							
Holmwood	d																							
Ockley	d																							
Warnham	d																							
Horsham 4	a																							

Faster trains London and Clapham Junction to Horsham see table 186

Table 182

Sundays

8 December to 11 May

London - Mitcham, Sutton, Epsom Downs, Epsom, Dorking

Network Diagram - see first Page of Table 182

		SN	SW	SN	SW	SN	SW	SN	SW	SN		SW	SN
London Victoria 15	⊖ d	21 10		21 40		22 10		22 40		23 10			23 19
London Waterloo 15	⊖ d		21 32		22 02		22 32		23 02			23 32	
Clapham Junction 10	d	21 18	21 41	21 48	22 11	22 18	22 41	22 48	23 11	23 18		23 41	23 27
Balham 4	⊖ d	21 24		21 54		22 24		22 54		23 23			23 32
St Pancras International	d												
Farringdon	d												
City Thameslink	d												
London Blackfriars	d												
Elephant & Castle	d												
Loughborough Jn	d												
Herne Hill	d												
London Bridge 4	⊖ d												
Tulse Hill	a												
Tulse Hill 3	d												
Streatham	d												
Mitcham Eastfields	d	21 30		22 00		22 30		23 00		23 30			
Mitcham Junction	d	21 33		22 03		22 33		23 03		23 33			
Hackbridge	d	21 37		22 07		22 37		23 07		23 36			
Carshalton	d	21 39		22 09		22 39		23 09		23 39			
West Croydon	d												23 50
Sutton (Surrey)	a	21 43		22 13		22 43		23 13		23 42			00 02
Sutton (Surrey) 4	a												
	d	21 43		22 13		22 43		23 13		23 43			00 04
Belmont	d												
Banstead	d												
Epsom Downs	a												
Cheam	d	21 46		22 16		22 46		23 16		23 45			00 06
Ewell East	d	21 49		22 19		22 49		23 19		23 49			00 10
Epsom 3	a	21 53	22 06	22 23	22 36	22 53	23 06	23 23	23 36	23 53		00 06	00 14
	d	21 54	22 08	22 24	22 38	22 54	23 08	23 24		23 53			
Ashtead	d	21 58	22 12	22 28	22 42	22 58	23 12	23 28		23 57			
Leatherhead	d	22 01	22 15	22 31	22 45	23 01	23 15	23 31		00 01			
Guildford	a		22 41				23 41						
Box Hill & Westhumble	d	22 06		22 36		23 06		23 36		00 05			
Dorking 4	a	22 09		22 39	22 51	23 09		23 39		00 08			
	d												
Holmwood	d												
Ockley	d												
Warnham	d												
Horsham 4	a												

Faster trains London and Clapham Junction to Horsham see table 186

Table 182R

Mondays to Fridays

9 December to 16 May

Dorking, Epsom, Epsom Downs, Sutton, Mitcham - London

Network Diagram - see first Page of Table 182

Miles	Miles	Miles	Miles			SN	SN	SW	SN	SN	SW	SN	SW	FC	SN	SW	SW	SN	SN	SN	SN	SW	SN
0	—	—	—	Horsham [4]	d										05 49						06 20		
2	—	—	—	**Warnham**	d										05 53						06 24		
6½	—	—	—	**Ockley**	d										06 00						06 31		
8½	—	—	—	**Holmwood**	d										06 04						06 35		
13½	—	—	—	**Dorking [4]**	a										06 10						06 41		
—	—	—	—		d						05 48				06 11		06 31				06 44		
14½	—	—	—	**Box Hill & Westhumble**	d						05 50				06 13		06 33				06 46		
—	0	—	—	Guildford	d			04 58								05 58						06 28	
17½	13	—	—	**Leatherhead**	d			05 23			05 56				06 18	06 23	06 38				06 51	06 55	
19½	14¾	—	—	**Ashtead**	d			05 27			05 59				06 22	06 27	06 42				06 55	06 58	
21½	16¾	—	—	**Epsom [3]**	a			05 31			06 04				06 26	06 31	06 46				06 59	07 03	
—	—	—	—		d		05 23	05 33	05 39	05 57	06 04		06 18		06 27	06 33	06 47			06 49	07 00	07 03	
23	—	—	—	**Ewell East**	d		05 27		05 43	06 01					06 31					06 53	07 04		
24½	—	—	—	**Cheam**	d		05 30		05 46	06 04					06 34					06 56	07 07		
—	—	—	0	**Epsom Downs**	d													06 34					
—	—	—	1½	**Banstead**	d													06 37					
—	—	—	3	**Belmont**	d													06 40					
25½	—	0	4	**Sutton (Surrey) [4]**	a		05 33		05 49	06 07					06 37			06 43		06 59	07 10		
—	—	—	—		d																		
—	—	—	—	Sutton (Surrey)	d	05 37	05 33		05 49	06 08		06 14		06 34	06 37			06 44	06 53	07 00	07 10		07 20
—	—	—	8½	West Croydon	d		05 45		06 01									06 58		07 14			
26¾	—	1¼	—	**Carshalton**	d	05 40				06 11		06 17		06 37	06 40				06 56		07 13		07 23
27½	—	2	—	**Hackbridge**	d	05 42				06 13		06 19		06 39	06 43				06 58		07 16		07 25
28¾	—	3¼	—	**Mitcham Junction**	d	05 46				06 17		06 23		06 42	06 46				07 02		07 19		07 29
30	—	4½	—	**Mitcham Eastfields**	d	05 49				06 20		06 26		06 45	06 49				07 05		07 22		07 32
—	—	6	—	Streatham	a	05 53						06 30		06 49					07 09				07 35
—	—	7¾	—	Tulse Hill	a	05 56						06 34		06 53					07 13				07 39
—	—	—	—	Tulse Hill [3]	d	05 56						06 34		06 53					07 14				07 44
—	—	—	—	London Bridge [4] ⊖	a	06 13	06 14					06 51							07 33	07 33			08 03
—	—	8¾	—	Herne Hill	a									06 56									
—	—	9¾	—	Loughborough Jn.	a									07 00									
—	—	11½	—	Elephant & Castle	a									07 05									
—	—	12¾	—	London Blackfriars	a									07 09									
—	—	13¼	—	City Thameslink	a									07 14									
—	—	13½	—	Farringdon	a									07 18									
—	—	14¾	—	St Pancras International	a									07 22									
33	—	—	14½	Balham [4] ⊖	a				06 17	06 26					06 57			07 14			07 29		
34¾	27¼	—	16½	Clapham Junction [10]	a			06 01	06 23	06 31	06 30		06 45		07 02	07 00	07 15	07 21			07 34	07 30	
—	31	—	—	London Waterloo [15] ⊖	a			06 11			06 40		06 55			07 12	07 27					07 42	
37½	—	—	19	London Victoria [15] ⊖	a				06 33	06 38					07 10			07 29			07 41		

		SN	SW	SN	SW	SN	FC	SN	SW	SW	SN	SN	SW	SN	SN	FC	SN	SW	SW	SW	SN	SN	SN
Horsham [4]	d							06 54									07 21						
Warnham	d							06 58									07 25						
Ockley	d							07 05									07 32						
Holmwood	d							07 09									07 36						
Dorking [4]	a							07 15									07 42						
	d	06 57	07 01					07 16		07 31							07 46		08 01				
Box Hill & Westhumble	d	07 00	07 03							07 33									08 03				
Guildford	d								06 58						07 23								
Leatherhead	d	07 06	07 08					07 22	07 26	07 38					07 45		07 52	07 55	08 08				
Ashtead	d	07 10	07 12					07 25	07 29	07 42					07 48		07 55	07 59	08 12				
Epsom [3]	a	07 14	07 16					07 30	07 34	07 46					07 53		08 00	08 03	08 16				
	d	07 15	07 17	07 21	07 22			07 30	07 34	07 47		07 49	07 52		07 53		08 02	08 04	08 17	08 22			
Ewell East	d	07 19		07 25								07 53			07 57		08 06						
Cheam	d	07 22		07 28				07 36				07 56			08 01		08 09						
Epsom Downs	d					07 04								07 34							08 04		
Banstead	d					07 07								07 37							08 07		
Belmont	d					07 10								07 40							08 10		
Sutton (Surrey) [4]	a	07 25		07 31		07 13		07 39				07 59		07 43	08 04		08 12				08 13		
	d																						
Sutton (Surrey)	d	07 26		07 32		07 14	07 36	07 42			07 50	07 59		07 45	08 05	08 08	08 12				08 14	08 23	08 29
West Croydon	d			07 44		07 27								07 58	08 15						08 26		
Carshalton	d	07 29					07 39	07 45			07 53	08 02				08 11	08 15					08 26	08 32
Hackbridge	d	07 31					07 41				07 55	08 05				08 13	08 18					08 28	08 34
Mitcham Junction	d	07 35					07 44	07 49			07 59	08 08				08 16	08 21					08 32	08 38
Mitcham Eastfields	d	07 38					07 47	07 52			08 02	08 11				08 19	08 24					08 35	08 41
Streatham	a						07 51				08 08					08 23						08 42	
Tulse Hill	a						07 56				08 12					08 27						08 46	
Tulse Hill [3]	d						07 57				08 14					08 28						08 46	
London Bridge [4] ⊖	a			08 05							08 33				08 33							09 03	
Herne Hill	a						08 01									08 31							
Loughborough Jn.	a						08 04									08 36							
Elephant & Castle	a						08 08									08 40							
London Blackfriars	a						08 12									08 45							
City Thameslink	a						08 15									08 48							
Farringdon	a						08 19									08 52							
St Pancras International	a						08 23									08 56							
Balham [4] ⊖	a	07 46				07 43		08 00				08 18		08 14							08 44		08 48
Clapham Junction [10]	a	07 53	07 42		07 48	07 50		08 04	08 01	08 12		08 24	08 18	08 21			08 35	08 31	08 42	08 48	08 50		08 54
London Waterloo [15] ⊖	a		07 54		08 00				08 13	08 24			08 30					08 43	08 54	09 00			
London Victoria [15] ⊖	a	08 00				07 59		08 12				08 32		08 29			08 42				08 59		09 04

Table 182R

Mondays to Fridays

9 December to 16 May

Dorking, Epsom, Epsom Downs, Sutton, Mitcham - London

Network Diagram - see first Page of Table 182

		SN	SW	FC	SN	SW		SN	SN	SN	SW	FC	SN	SW	SN	SN		SW	FC	SN	SW	SN	SN	SW	FC
Horsham 4	d				07 56																		09 09		
Warnham	d				08 00																		09 13		
Ockley	d				08 07																		09 20		
Holmwood	d				08 11																		09 24		
Dorking 4	a				08 17																		09 30		
	d				08 22	08 31							08 58	09 01							09 35		09 31		
Box Hill & Westhumble	d				08 24	08 33							09 00	09 03									09 33		
Guildford	d		07 58							08 16								08 58						09 28	
Leatherhead	d		08 24		08 29	08 38				08 41	08 56		09 05	09 08				09 23			09 41		09 38	09 53	
Ashtead	d		08 27		08 33	08 42				08 45	08 59		09 09	09 12				09 27			09 44		09 42	09 57	
Epsom 3	a		08 32		08 37	08 46				08 49	09 04		09 13	09 16				09 31			09 49		09 46	10 01	
	d	08 22	08 33		08 38	08 47				08 50	09 04		09 14	09 17	09 20			09 34		09 42	09 49		09 49	10 04	
Ewell East	d	08 26			08 42					08 54			09 18		09 24					09 46			09 53		
Cheam	d	08 29			08 45					08 57			09 21		09 27					09 49			09 56		
Epsom Downs	d							08 34								09 10						09 35			
Banstead	d							08 37								09 13						09 39			
Belmont	d							08 40								09 16						09 42			
Sutton (Surrey) 4	a	08 32			08 48			08 43		09 00			09 24		09 30	09 19				09 52		09 45	09 59		
	d																								
Sutton (Surrey)	d	08 32		08 39	08 48			08 45	08 53	09 00		09 13	09 24		09 30	09 23			09 38	09 52		09 46	09 59		10 08
West Croydon	d	08 44						08 58								09 35						09 58			
Carshalton	d			08 42	08 51				08 56	09 03		09 16			09 33				09 41				10 02		10 11
Hackbridge	d			08 44	08 54				08 58	09 06		09 18			09 36				09 43				10 05		10 13
Mitcham Junction	d			08 47	08 57				09 02	09 09		09 21			09 39				09 46				10 08		10 16
Mitcham Eastfields	d			08 50	09 00				09 05	09 12		09 24	09 33		09 42				09 49				10 11		10 19
Streatham	a			08 54					09 11			09 28							09 53						10 23
Tulse Hill	a			08 58					09 15			09 32							09 57						10 27
Tulse Hill 3	d			08 58					09 15			09 32							09 57						10 27
London Bridge 4 ⊖	a	09 05							09 33																
Herne Hill	a			09 01								09 35							10 01						10 31
Loughborough Jn.	a			09 05								09 40							10 04						10 34
Elephant & Castle	a			09 09								09 44							10 08						10 38
London Blackfriars	a			09 13								09 49							10 12						10 42
City Thameslink	a			09 16								09 52							10 16						10 46
Farringdon	a			09 20								09 56							10 19						10 49
St Pancras International	a			09 24								10 00							10 23						10 53
Balham 4 ⊖	a				09 07			09 14		09 19					09 49	09 52						10 14	10 18		
Clapham Junction 10	a		09 00		09 13	09 15		09 21		09 24	09 30		09 42	09 45	09 53	09 58		10 00		10 11	10 15	10 20	10 23	10 30	
London Waterloo 15 ⊖	a		09 12			09 27					09 42			09 57				10 10			10 25			10 40	
London Victoria 15 ⊖	a				09 20			09 29		09 33			09 52		10 01	10 05				10 22		10 28	10 31		

		SN		SN	SW	SN	SW	FC	SN	SW	SN	SN		SW	FC	SN	SN	SW	SN	SW	FC	SN		SW	SN
Horsham 4	d								10 04													11 04			
Warnham	d								10 08													11 08			
Ockley	d								10 15													11 15			
Holmwood	d								10 19													11 19			
Dorking 4	a								10 25													11 25			
	d			09 57	10 05				10 26	10 35							10 58	11 05				11 26		11 35	
Box Hill & Westhumble	d			09 59					10 28													11 28			
Guildford	d						09 58							10 28						10 58					
Leatherhead	d			10 04	10 11		10 23		10 33	10 41				10 53			11 04	11 11		11 23		11 33		11 41	
Ashtead	d			10 08	10 14		10 27		10 37	10 44				10 57			11 07	11 14		11 27		11 37		11 44	
Epsom 3	a			10 12	10 19		10 31		10 41	10 49				11 01			11 12	11 19		11 31		11 41		11 49	
	d	10 04		10 13	10 19	10 19	10 34		10 42	10 49		10 49		11 04		11 04	11 13	11 19	11 19	11 34		11 42		11 49	
Ewell East	d	10 08		10 17		10 23			10 46			10 53				11 08			11 23			11 46			
Cheam	d	10 11		10 20		10 26			10 49			10 56				11 11	11 18		11 26			11 49			
Epsom Downs	d										10 35														11 35
Banstead	d										10 38														11 38
Belmont	d										10 41														11 41
Sutton (Surrey) 4	a	10 14		10 23		10 29			10 52		10 44	10 59				11 14	11 21		11 29			11 52			11 44
	d																								
Sutton (Surrey)	d	10 15		10 23		10 29		10 38	10 52		10 45	10 59			11 08	11 15	11 22		11 29		11 38	11 52			11 45
West Croydon	d	10 28									10 58					11 28									11 58
Carshalton	d					10 32		10 41				11 02			11 11				11 32		11 41				
Hackbridge	d					10 35		10 43				11 05			11 13				11 35		11 43				
Mitcham Junction	d					10 38		10 46				11 08			11 16				11 38		11 46				
Mitcham Eastfields	d					10 41		10 49				11 11			11 19				11 41		11 49				
Streatham	a							10 53							11 23						11 53				
Tulse Hill	a							10 57							11 27						11 57				
Tulse Hill 3	d							10 57							11 27						11 57				
London Bridge 4 ⊖	a																								
Herne Hill	a							11 01							11 31						12 01				
Loughborough Jn.	a							11 04							11 34						12 04				
Elephant & Castle	a							11 08							11 38						12 08				
London Blackfriars	a							11 12							11 42						12 12				
City Thameslink	a							11 16							11 46						12 16				
Farringdon	a							11 19							11 49						12 19				
St Pancras International	a							11 23							11 53						12 23				
Balham 4 ⊖	a	10 44				10 48					11 14	11 18				11 44			11 48						12 14
Clapham Junction 10	a	10 49		10 41	10 45	10 52	11 00		11 11	11 15	11 20	11 22		11 30		11 49	11 41	11 45	11 52	12 00		12 11		12 15	12 19
London Waterloo 15 ⊖	a				10 55		11 10			11 25				11 40				11 55		12 10				12 25	
London Victoria 15 ⊖	a	10 58		10 48		11 00			11 20		11 28	11 30				11 58	11 48		12 00			12 18			12 28

Table 182R

Mondays to Fridays

9 December to 16 May

Dorking, Epsom, Epsom Downs, Sutton, Mitcham - London

Network Diagram - see first Page of Table 182

		SN	SW	FC	SN	SN	SW	SN		SW	FC	SN	SW	SN	SN	SW	FC	SN		SN	SW	SN	SW	FC	SN
Horsham [4]	d											12 04													13 04
Warnham	d											12 08													13 08
Ockley	d											12 15													13 15
Holmwood	d											12 19													13 19
Dorking [4]	a											12 25													13 25
	d					11 58	12 05					12 26	12 35							12 58	13 05				13 26
Box Hill & Westhumble	d											12 28													13 28
Guildford	d		11 28							11 58						12 28							12 58		
Leatherhead	d		11 53			12 04	12 11			12 23		12 33	12 41			12 53				13 04	13 11		13 23		13 33
Ashtead	d		11 57			12 07	12 14			12 27		12 37	12 44			12 57				13 07	13 14		13 27		13 37
Epsom [3]	a		12 01			12 12	12 19			12 31		12 41	12 49			13 01				13 12	13 19		13 31		13 41
	d	11 49	12 04		12 04	12 13	12 19	12 19		12 34		12 42	12 49		12 49	13 04		13 04		13 13	13 19	13 19	13 34		13 42
Ewell East	d	11 53			12 08			12 23				12 46			12 53			13 08				13 23			13 46
Cheam	d	11 56			12 11	12 18		12 26				12 49			12 56			13 11		13 18		13 26			13 49
Epsom Downs	d													12 35											
Banstead	d													12 38											
Belmont	d													12 41											
Sutton (Surrey) [4]	a	11 59			12 14	12 21		12 29				12 52		12 44	12 59			13 14		13 21		13 29			13 52
	d																								
Sutton (Surrey)	d	11 59		12 08	12 15	12 22		12 29			12 38	12 52		12 45	12 59		13 08	13 15		13 22		13 29		13 38	13 52
West Croydon	d				12 28									12 58				13 28							
Carshalton	d	12 02		12 11				12 32			12 41				13 02		13 11					13 32		13 41	
Hackbridge	d	12 05		12 13				12 35			12 43				13 05		13 13					13 35		13 43	
Mitcham Junction	d	12 08		12 16				12 38			12 46				13 08		13 16					13 38		13 46	
Mitcham Eastfields	d	12 11		12 19				12 41			12 49				13 11		13 19					13 41		13 49	
Streatham	a			12 23							12 53						13 23							13 53	
Tulse Hill	a			12 27							12 57						13 27							13 57	
Tulse Hill [3]	d			12 27							12 57						13 27							13 57	
London Bridge [4] ⊖	a																								
Herne Hill	a			12 31							13 01						13 31							14 01	
Loughborough Jn.	a			12 34							13 04						13 34							14 04	
Elephant & Castle	a			12 38							13 08						13 38							14 08	
London Blackfriars	a			12 42							13 12						13 42							14 12	
City Thameslink	a			12 46							13 16						13 46							14 16	
Farringdon	a			12 49							13 19						13 49							14 19	
St Pancras International	a			12 53							13 23						13 53							14 23	
Balham [4] ⊖	a	12 18			12 44			12 48						13 14	13 18			13 44				13 48			
Clapham Junction [10]	a	12 22	12 30		12 49	12 41	12 45	12 52		13 00		13 11	13 15	13 19	13 22	13 30		13 49		13 41	13 45	13 52	14 00		14 11
London Waterloo [15] ⊖	a		12 40				12 55			13 10			13 25			13 40					13 55		14 10		
London Victoria [15] ⊖	a	12 30			12 58	12 48		13 00				13 20		13 28	13 30			13 58		13 48		14 00			14 18

		SW	SN	SN		SW	FC	SN	SN	SW	SN	SW	FC	SN		SW	SN	SN	SW	FC	SN	SN	SW	SN	
Horsham [4]	d													14 04											
Warnham	d													14 08											
Ockley	d													14 15											
Holmwood	d													14 19											
Dorking [4]	a													14 25											
	d	13 35							13 58	14 05				14 26		14 35						14 58	15 05		
Box Hill & Westhumble	d													14 28											
Guildford	d					13 28						13 58							14 28						
Leatherhead	d	13 41				13 53			14 04	14 11		14 23		14 33		14 41			14 53			15 04	15 11		
Ashtead	d	13 44				13 57			14 07	14 14		14 27		14 37		14 44			14 57			15 07	15 14		
Epsom [3]	a	13 49				14 01			14 12	14 19		14 31		14 41		14 49			15 01			15 12	15 19		
	d	13 49		13 49		14 04		14 04	14 13	14 19	14 19	14 34		14 42		14 49		14 49	15 04		15 04	15 13	15 19	15 19	
Ewell East	d			13 53				14 08			14 23			14 46				14 53			15 08			15 23	
Cheam	d			13 56				14 11	14 18		14 26			14 49				14 56			15 11	15 18		15 26	
Epsom Downs	d		13 35														14 35								
Banstead	d		13 38														14 38								
Belmont	d		13 41														14 41								
Sutton (Surrey) [4]	a		13 44	13 59				14 14	14 21		14 29			14 52			14 44	14 59			15 14	15 21		15 29	
	d																								
Sutton (Surrey)	d		13 45	13 59			14 08	14 15	14 22		14 29		14 38	14 52			14 45	14 59		15 08	15 15	15 22		15 29	
West Croydon	d		13 58					14 28									14 58				15 28				
Carshalton	d			14 02			14 11				14 32		14 41					15 02		15 11				15 32	
Hackbridge	d			14 05			14 13				14 35		14 43					15 05		15 13				15 35	
Mitcham Junction	d			14 08			14 16				14 38		14 46					15 08		15 16				15 38	
Mitcham Eastfields	d			14 11			14 19				14 41		14 49					15 11		15 19				15 41	
Streatham	a						14 23						14 53							15 23					
Tulse Hill	a						14 27						14 57							15 27					
Tulse Hill [3]	d						14 27						14 57							15 27					
London Bridge [4] ⊖	a																								
Herne Hill	a						14 31						15 01							15 31					
Loughborough Jn.	a						14 34						15 04							15 34					
Elephant & Castle	a						14 38						15 08							15 38					
London Blackfriars	a						14 42						15 12							15 42					
City Thameslink	a						14 46						15 16							15 46					
Farringdon	a						14 49						15 19							15 49					
St Pancras International	a						14 53						15 23							15 53					
Balham [4] ⊖	a		14 14	14 18				14 44			14 48						15 14	15 18			15 44			15 48	
Clapham Junction [10]	a	14 15	14 19	14 22		14 30		14 49	14 41	14 45	14 52	15 00		15 11		15 15	15 19	15 22	15 30		15 49	15 41	15 45	15 52	
London Waterloo [15] ⊖	a	14 25				14 40				14 55		15 10				15 25			15 40				15 55		
London Victoria [15] ⊖	a		14 28	14 30				14 58	14 48		15 00			15 22			15 28	15 30			15 58	15 52		16 00	

Table 182R

Mondays to Fridays

9 December to 16 May

Dorking, Epsom, Epsom Downs, Sutton, Mitcham - London

Network Diagram - see first Page of Table 182

		SW	FC	SN	SW	SN	SN	FC	SN	SW		SN	SW	SN	SW	FC 1 A	SN	SW	SN	SN		SW	SW	FC	SN
Horsham 4	d			15 04													16 04								
Warnham	d			15 08													16 08								
Ockley	d			15 15													16 15								
Holmwood	d			15 19													16 19								
Dorking 4	a			15 25													16 25								
	d			15 26	15 35							15 56	16 05				16 26	16 35					17 05		
Box Hill & Westhumble	d			15 28								15 58					16 28								
Guildford	d	14 58								15 28					15 58							16 28			
Leatherhead	d	15 23		15 33	15 41					15 53		16 03	16 11		16 23		16 33	16 41				16 53	17 11		
Ashtead	d	15 27		15 37	15 44					15 57		16 07	16 14		16 27		16 37	16 44				16 57	17 14		
Epsom 3	a	15 31		15 41	15 49					16 01		16 11	16 19		16 31		16 41	16 49				17 01	17 19		
	d	15 34		15 42	15 49		15 49		16 03	16 04		16 12	16 19	16 19	16 34		16 42	16 49		16 49		17 04	17 19		
Ewell East	d			15 46			15 53		16 07			16 16		16 23			16 46			16 53					
Cheam	d			15 49			15 56		16 10			16 19		16 26			16 49			16 56					
Epsom Downs	d					15 35													16 28						17 02
Banstead	d					15 38													16 31						17 05
Belmont	d					15 41													16 34						17 08
Sutton (Surrey) 4	a			15 52		15 44	15 59		16 13			16 22		16 29			16 52		16 37	16 59					17 11
	d																								
Sutton (Surrey)	d		15 38	15 52		15 45	15 59	16 08	16 13			16 22		16 29		16 38	16 52		16 42	16 59				17 08	17 13
West Croydon	d					15 58			16 25										16 55						17 25
Carshalton	d		15 41				16 02	16 11						16 32		16 41				17 02				17 11	
Hackbridge	d		15 43				16 05	16 13						16 35		16 43				17 05				17 13	
Mitcham Junction	d		15 46				16 08	16 16						16 38		16 46				17 08				17 16	
Mitcham Eastfields	d		15 49				16 11	16 19						16 41		16 49				17 11				17 19	
Streatham	a		15 53					16 23								16 53								17 23	
Tulse Hill	a		15 57					16 27								16 57								17 27	
Tulse Hill 3	d		15 57					16 27								16 57								17 27	
London Bridge 4 ⊖	a																								
Herne Hill	a		16 01					16 31								17 01								17 31	
Loughborough Jn	a		16 04					16 34																17 34	
Elephant & Castle	a		16 08					16 38								17 07								17 38	
London Blackfriars	a		16 12					16 42								17 11								17 43	
City Thameslink	a		16 16					16 46								17 14								17 48	
Farringdon	a		16 19					16 49								17 17								17 51	
St Pancras International	a		16 23					16 53								17 21								17 55	
Balham 4 ⊖	a					16 14	16 18		16 42					16 48					17 13	17 19					17 41
Clapham Junction 10	a	16 00		16 11	16 15	16 19	16 23		16 48	16 30		16 41	16 45	16 53	17 00		17 10	17 15	17 19	17 23		17 30	17 45		17 49
London Waterloo 15 ⊖	a	16 10			16 25					16 40			16 55		17 10			17 25				17 40	17 55		
London Victoria 15 ⊖	a			16 18		16 28	16 30		16 58			16 48		17 00			17 18		17 28	17 31					17 58

		SN	SN	SW	FC	SN		SW	SN	SN	SW	FC	SN	SW	SN	SN		SW	FC	SN	SW	SN	SN	SW	FC
Horsham 4	d					17 07							17 34							18 04					
Warnham	d					17 11							17 38							18 08					
Ockley	d					17 18							17 45							18 15					
Holmwood	d					17 22							17 49							18 19					
Dorking 4	a					17 28							17 55							18 25					
	d	17 00				17 31		17 35					17 56	18 05						18 26	18 35			18 50	
Box Hill & Westhumble	d	17 02				17 33							17 58							18 28					
Guildford	d			16 58							17 28							17 58					18 22		
Leatherhead	d	17 07		17 23		17 38		17 41			17 53		18 03	18 11				18 23		18 33	18 41		18 47	18 56	
Ashtead	d	17 11		17 27		17 42		17 44			17 57		18 07	18 14				18 27		18 37	18 44		18 51	18 59	
Epsom 3	a	17 15		17 31		17 46		17 49			18 01		18 14	18 19				18 31		18 41	18 48		18 57	19 03	
	d	17 19	17 23	17 34		17 47		17 49		17 52	18 04		18 17	18 19		18 22		18 34		18 43	18 49		18 57	19 04	
Ewell East	d	17 23	17 27			17 51				17 56			18 23			18 26				18 47					
Cheam	d	17 26	17 30			17 54				17 59			18 26			18 29				18 51					
Epsom Downs	d								17 33						18 02							18 33			
Banstead	d								17 36						18 05							18 36			
Belmont	d								17 39						18 08							18 39			
Sutton (Surrey) 4	a	17 29	17 33			17 57			17 42	18 02			18 29		18 11	18 33				18 55		18 42	19 04		
	d																								
Sutton (Surrey)	d	17 29	17 33		17 42	17 57			17 43	18 03		18 08	18 29		18 12	18 33			18 38	18 56		18 43	19 05		19 08
West Croydon	d		17 48						17 55	18 15					18 26	18 45						18 56	19 18		
Carshalton	d	17 32			17 45	18 01						18 11	18 32						18 41	18 59					19 11
Hackbridge	d	17 35			17 47	18 03						18 13	18 35						18 43	19 01					19 13
Mitcham Junction	d	17 38			17 50	18 07						18 16	18 38						18 46	19 05					19 16
Mitcham Eastfields	d	17 41			17 53	18 10						18 19	18 41						18 49	19 08					19 19
Streatham	a				17 57							18 23							18 53						19 23
Tulse Hill	a				18 01							18 28							18 57						19 27
Tulse Hill 3	d				18 01							18 28							18 57						19 27
London Bridge 4 ⊖	a																								
Herne Hill	a				18 05							18 31							19 01						19 31
Loughborough Jn	a				18 09							18 35							19 05						19 34
Elephant & Castle	a				18 13							18 39							19 09						19 38
London Blackfriars	a				18 17							18 43							19 13						19 42
City Thameslink	a				18 20							18 46							19 20						19 48
Farringdon	a				18 23							18 49							19 23						19 51
St Pancras International	a				18 27							18 53							19 27						19 55
Balham 4 ⊖	a	17 48	18 11			18 17			18 13	18 40			18 48		18 43	19 09				19 14		19 13	19 39		
Clapham Junction 10	a	17 52	18 16	18 00		18 22		18 15	18 19	18 45	18 30		18 52	18 45	18 49	19 14		19 00		19 19	19 16	19 19	19 45	19 30	
London Waterloo 15 ⊖	a			18 10				18 25			18 40			18 55				19 10			19 27			19 41	
London Victoria 15 ⊖	a	18 00	18 25			18 32			18 28	18 54			19 01		18 57	19 25				19 30		19 28	19 54		

A 1 to Farringdon

Table 182R

Mondays to Fridays

9 December to 16 May

Dorking, Epsom, Epsom Downs, Sutton, Mitcham - London

Network Diagram - see first Page of Table 182

Station		SN		SW	SN	SN	SW	FC	SN	SN	SW	SN		SN	SW	FC	SN	SW	SN	SN	SN	SW		FC	SN
Horsham 4	d	18 33								19 04															20 06
Warnham	d	18 37								19 08															20 10
Ockley	d	18 44								19 15															20 17
Holmwood	d	18 48								19 19															20 21
Dorking 4	a	18 54								19 25															20 27
	d	18 55				19 05				19 26	19 33			19 37			19 57	20 05							20 30
Box Hill & Westhumble	d	18 57								19 28							19 59								
Guildford	d								19 04						19 28							19 58			
Leatherhead	d	19 02		19 08		19 11			19 28	19 33	19 39			19 43	19 53		20 04	20 11				20 23			20 36
Ashtead	d	19 06		19 12		19 15			19 32	19 37	19 42			19 46	19 57		20 08	20 14				20 27			20 39
Epsom 3	a	19 10		19 16		19 19			19 36	19 41	19 47			19 51	20 01		20 12	20 19				20 31			20 44
	d	19 11		19 19		19 20	19 34		19 37	19 42	19 49			19 52	20 04		20 13	20 19		20 22	20 25	20 34			20 45
Ewell East	d	19 15				19 24			19 41	19 46				19 56			20 17			20 26	20 29				20 49
Cheam	d	19 18				19 27			19 44	19 49				19 59			20 20			20 29	20 32				20 52
Epsom Downs	d				19 06							19 36							20 13						
Banstead	d				19 09							19 39							20 16						
Belmont	d				19 12							19 42							20 19						
Sutton (Surrey) 4	a	19 22			19 15	19 30			19 47	19 52		19 45		20 02			20 23		20 22	20 32	20 35				20 55
	d																								
Sutton (Surrey)	d	19 22			19 16	19 32		19 42		19 52		19 46		20 03		20 12	20 25		20 23	20 33	20 36			20 42	20 55
West Croydon	d				19 29	19 44						19 59		20 16					20 35	20 45					
Carshalton	d	19 25						19 45		19 55						20 15	20 28				20 39			20 45	20 58
Hackbridge	d	19 28						19 47		19 58						20 17	20 31				20 41			20 47	21 01
Mitcham Junction	d	19 31						19 50		20 01						20 20	20 34				20 45			20 50	21 04
Mitcham Eastfields	d	19 34						19 53		20 04						20 23	20 37				20 48			20 53	21 07
Streatham	a							19 57								20 27								20 57	
Tulse Hill	a							20 01								20 31								21 01	
Tulse Hill 3	d							20 01								20 31								21 01	
London Bridge 4 ⊖	a																								
Herne Hill	a							20 05								20 35								21 05	
Loughborough Jn.	a							20 08								20 38								21 08	
Elephant & Castle	a							20 12								20 42								21 12	
London Blackfriars	a							20 16								20 46								21 16	
City Thameslink	a							20 20								20 50								21 20	
Farringdon	a							20 23								20 53								21 23	
St Pancras International	a							20 27								20 57								21 27	
Balham 4 ⊖	a	19 42			19 45	20 08				20 11		20 15		20 39			20 44		20 51	21 08	20 54				21 14
Clapham Junction 10	a	19 48		19 45	19 51	20 14	20 00			20 17	20 15	20 20		20 44	20 30		20 48	20 45	20 56	21 14	20 59	21 00			21 18
London Waterloo 15 ⊖	a			19 55			20 10				20 25				20 41			20 55				21 10			
London Victoria 15 ⊖	a	19 56			20 00	20 22				20 25		20 29		20 53			20 56		21 04	21 22	21 09				21 26

Station		SW	SN	SW	SN	FC	SN	SW		SN	SN	SW	SN	SW	SN	SN	SN	SW		SN	SN	SN	SW	SN	SN
Horsham 4	d																								
Warnham	d																								
Ockley	d																								
Holmwood	d																								
Dorking 4	a																								
	d	20 35					20 59						21 30	21 35			21 59					22 30	22 35		
Box Hill & Westhumble	d						21 01										22 01								
Guildford	d							20 46										21 46							
Leatherhead	d	20 41					21 06	21 11					21 36	21 41			22 06	22 11				22 36	22 41		
Ashtead	d	20 44					21 10	21 14					21 40	21 44			22 10	22 14				22 40	22 44		
Epsom 3	a	20 49					21 14	21 19					21 44	21 49			22 14	22 19				22 44	22 49		
	d	20 49	20 55	21 04			21 15	21 19		21 21	21 25	21 34	21 45	21 49	21 55		22 15	22 19		22 21	22 25	22 45	22 49	22 55	
Ewell East	d		20 59				21 19			21 25	21 29		21 49		21 59		22 19			22 25	22 29	22 49		22 59	
Cheam	d		21 02				21 22			21 28	21 32		21 52		22 02		22 22			22 28	22 32	22 52		23 02	
Epsom Downs	d				20 54											21 54									22 54
Banstead	d				20 57											21 57									22 57
Belmont	d				21 00											22 00									23 00
Sutton (Surrey) 4	a		21 05		21 03		21 25			21 31	21 35		21 55		22 05	22 03	22 25			22 31	22 35	22 55		23 05	23 03
	d																								
Sutton (Surrey)	d		21 06		21 06	21 12	21 25			21 32	21 36		21 55		22 06	22 05	22 25			22 32	22 36	22 55		23 06	23 06
West Croydon	d				21 18					21 47						22 17				22 47					23 18
Carshalton	d		21 09			21 15	21 28				21 39		21 58		22 09		22 28				22 39	22 58		23 09	
Hackbridge	d		21 11			21 17	21 31				21 41		22 01		22 11		22 31				22 41	23 01		23 11	
Mitcham Junction	d		21 15			21 20	21 34				21 45		22 04		22 15		22 34				22 45	23 04		23 15	
Mitcham Eastfields	d		21 18			21 23	21 37				21 48		22 07		22 18		22 37				22 48	23 07		23 18	
Streatham	a					21 27																			
Tulse Hill	a					21 31																			
Tulse Hill 3	d					21 31																			
London Bridge 4 ⊖	a																								
Herne Hill	a					21 35																			
Loughborough Jn.	a					21 38																			
Elephant & Castle	a					21 42																			
London Blackfriars	a					21 46																			
City Thameslink	a					21 50																			
Farringdon	a					21 53																			
St Pancras International	a					21 57																			
Balham 4 ⊖	a		21 24		21 39		21 44			22 09	21 54		22 14		22 24	22 39	22 44			23 09	22 54	23 14		23 24	23 39
Clapham Junction 10	a	21 15	21 29	21 30	21 44		21 49	21 45		22 14	21 59	22 00	22 19	22 15	22 29	22 44	22 48	22 45		23 15	22 59	23 18	23 15	23 29	23 45
London Waterloo 15 ⊖	a	21 25		21 40				21 55				22 10		22 25				22 55					23 27		
London Victoria 15 ⊖	a		21 37		21 53		21 59			22 23	22 07		22 27		22 38	22 53	22 56			23 25	23 09	23 27		23 37	23 54

Table 182R

Mondays to Fridays

9 December to 16 May

Dorking, Epsom, Epsom Downs, Sutton, Mitcham - London

Network Diagram - see first Page of Table 182

		SN	SW	SN		SN	SN
Horsham 4	d						
Warnham	d						
Ockley	d						
Holmwood	d						
Dorking 4	a						
	d	23 00				23 30	
Box Hill & Westhumble	d	23 02					
Guildford	d		22 46				
Leatherhead	d	23 07	23 11			23 36	
Ashtead	d	23 11	23 14			23 39	
Epsom 3	a	23 15	23 19			23 45	
	d	23 16	23 19	23 27			
Ewell East	d	23 20		23 31			
Cheam	d	23 23		23 35			
Epsom Downs	d						23 43
Banstead	d						23 46
Belmont	d						23 49
Sutton (Surrey) 4	a	23 26		23 40			23 52
	d						
Sutton (Surrey)	d	23 30		23 41			23 53
West Croydon	d	23a41		23a52			00a04
Carshalton	d						
Hackbridge	d						
Mitcham Junction	d						
Mitcham Eastfields	d						
Streatham	a						
Tulse Hill	a						
Tulse Hill 3	d						
London Bridge 4 ⊖	a						
Herne Hill	a						
Loughborough Jn.	a						
Elephant & Castle	a						
London Blackfriars	a						
City Thameslink	a						
Farringdon	a						
St Pancras International	a						
Balham 4 ⊖	a						
Clapham Junction 10	a		23 48				
London Waterloo 15 ⊖	a		23 58				
London Victoria 15 ⊖	a						

Saturdays

14 December to 17 May

		SW	SW	SW	SN	SN	SW	FC	SN	SN		SN	SW	FC	SN	SN	SN	SW	FC	SN		SN	SW	SN	SW
Horsham 4	d																								
Warnham	d																								
Ockley	d																								
Holmwood	d																								
Dorking 4	a																								
	d				06 28					06 57					07 26							07 58	08 05		
Box Hill & Westhumble	d									06 59					07 28										
Guildford	d						06 28						06 58					07 28							07 58
Leatherhead	d				06 34		06 53			07 04			07 23		07 33			07 53				08 04	08 11		08 23
Ashtead	d				06 37		06 57			07 08			07 27		07 37			07 57				08 07	08 14		08 27
Epsom 3	a				06 42		07 01			07 12			07 31		07 41			08 01				08 12	08 19		08 31
	d	05 34	06 04	06 34	06 42	06 49	07 04		07 04	07 13		07 19	07 34		07 42		07 49	08 04		08 04		08 13	08 19	08 19	08 34
Ewell East	d				06 46	06 53			07 08			07 23			07 46		07 53			08 08				08 23	
Cheam	d				06 49	06 56			07 11	07 18		07 26			07 49		07 56			08 11		08 18		08 26	
Epsom Downs	d															07 35									
Banstead	d															07 38									
Belmont	d															07 41									
Sutton (Surrey) 4	a				06 52	06 59			07 14	07 22		07 29			07 52	07 44	07 59			08 14		08 21		08 29	
	d																								
Sutton (Surrey)	d				06 53	06 59		07 08	07 15	07 22		07 29		07 38	07 52	07 45	07 59		08 08	08 15		08 22		08 29	
West Croydon	d								07 28							07 58				08 28					
Carshalton	d					07 02		07 11				07 32		07 41			08 02		08 11					08 32	
Hackbridge	d					07 05		07 13				07 35		07 43			08 05		08 13					08 35	
Mitcham Junction	d					07 08		07 16				07 38		07 46			08 08		08 16					08 38	
Mitcham Eastfields	d					07 11		07 19				07 41		07 49			08 11		08 19					08 41	
Streatham	a							07 23						07 53					08 23						
Tulse Hill	a							07 27						07 57					08 27						
Tulse Hill 3	d							07 27						07 57					08 27						
London Bridge 4 ⊖	a																								
Herne Hill	a							07 31						08 01					08 31						
Loughborough Jn.	a							07 34						08 04					08 34						
Elephant & Castle	a							07 38						08 08					08 38						
London Blackfriars	a							07 42						08 12					08 42						
City Thameslink	a																								
Farringdon	a							07 49						08 19					08 49						
St Pancras International	a							07 53						08 23					08 53						
Balham 4 ⊖	a					07 18			07 44			07 48				08 14	08 18			08 44				08 48	
Clapham Junction 10	a	06 01	06 30	07 00	07 10	07 22	07 30		07 49	07 40		07 52	08 00		08 10	08 19	08 22	08 30		08 49		08 40	08 45	08 52	09 00
London Waterloo 15 ⊖	a	06 11	06 40	07 10			07 40						08 10					08 40					08 55		09 10
London Victoria 15 ⊖	a				07 18	07 30			07 58	07 50		08 00			08 18	08 28	08 30			08 58		08 48		09 00	

Table 182R

Saturdays

14 December to 17 May

Dorking, Epsom, Epsom Downs, Sutton, Mitcham - London

Network Diagram - see first Page of Table 182

		FC	SN	SW	SN	SN		SW	FC	SN	SN	SW	SN	SW	FC	SN		SW	SN	SN	SW	FC	SN	SN	SW
Horsham 4	d		08 04													09 04									
Warnham	d		08 08													09 08									
Ockley	d		08 15													09 15									
Holmwood	d		08 19													09 19									
Dorking 4	a		08 25													09 25									
	d		08 26	08 35							08 58	09 05				09 26		09 35						09 58	10 05
Box Hill & Westhumble	d		08 28													09 28									
Guildford	d							08 28						08 58							09 28				
Leatherhead	d		08 33	08 41				08 53			09 04	09 11		09 23		09 33		09 41			09 53			10 04	10 11
Ashtead	d		08 37	08 44				08 57			09 07	09 14		09 27		09 37		09 44			09 57			10 07	10 14
Epsom 3	a		08 41	08 49				09 01			09 12	09 19		09 31		09 41		09 49			10 01			10 12	10 19
	d		08 42	08 49		08 49		09 04		09 04	09 13	09 19	09 19	09 34		09 42		09 49		09 49	10 04		10 04	10 13	10 19
Ewell East	d		08 46			08 53				09 08			09 23			09 46				09 53			10 08		
Cheam	d		08 49			08 56				09 11	09 18		09 26			09 49				09 56			10 11	10 18	
Epsom Downs	d				08 35														09 35						
Banstead	d				08 38														09 38						
Belmont	d				08 41														09 41						
Sutton (Surrey) 4	a		08 52		08 44	08 59				09 14	09 21		09 29			09 52			09 44	09 59			10 14	10 21	
	d																								
Sutton (Surrey)	d	08 38	08 52		08 45	08 59			09 08	09 15	09 22		09 29		09 38	09 52			09 45	09 59		10 08	10 15	10 22	
West Croydon	d				08 58					09 28									09 58				10 28		
Carshalton	d	08 41				09 02			09 11				09 32		09 41					10 02		10 11			
Hackbridge	d	08 43				09 05			09 13				09 35		09 43					10 05		10 13			
Mitcham Junction	d	08 46				09 08			09 16				09 38		09 46					10 08		10 16			
Mitcham Eastfields	d	08 49				09 11			09 19				09 41		09 49					10 11		10 19			
Streatham	a	08 53							09 23						09 53							10 23			
Tulse Hill	a	08 57							09 27						09 57							10 27			
Tulse Hill 3	d	08 57							09 27						09 57							10 27			
London Bridge 4 ⊖	a																								
Herne Hill	a	09 01							09 31						10 01							10 31			
Loughborough Jn.	a	09 04							09 34						10 04							10 34			
Elephant & Castle	a	09 08							09 38						10 08							10 38			
London Blackfriars	a	09 12							09 42						10 12							10 42			
City Thameslink	a	09 16							09 46						10 16							10 46			
Farringdon	a	09 19							09 49						10 19							10 49			
St Pancras International	a	09 23							09 53						10 23							10 53			
Balham 4 ⊖	a				09 14	09 18				09 44			09 48						10 14	10 18			10 44		
Clapham Junction 10	a		09 10	09 15	09 19	09 22		09 30		09 49	09 40	09 45	09 52	10 00		10 10		10 15	10 19	10 22	10 30		10 49	10 40	10 45
London Waterloo 15 ⊖	a			09 25				09 40				09 55		10 10				10 25			10 40				10 55
London Victoria 15 ⊖	a		09 18		09 28	09 30				09 58	09 48		10 00			10 18			10 28	10 30			10 58	10 48	

		SN		SW	FC	SN	SW	SN	SN	SW	FC	SN		SN	SW	SN	SW	FC	SN	SW	SN	SN		SW	FC
Horsham 4	d					10 04													11 04						
Warnham	d					10 08													11 08						
Ockley	d					10 15													11 15						
Holmwood	d					10 19													11 19						
Dorking 4	a					10 25													11 25						
	d					10 26	10 35							10 58	11 05				11 26	11 35					
Box Hill & Westhumble	d					10 28													11 28						
Guildford	d			09 58						10 28							10 58							11 28	
Leatherhead	d			10 23		10 33	10 41			10 53				11 04	11 11		11 23		11 33	11 41				11 53	
Ashtead	d			10 27		10 37	10 44			10 57				11 07	11 14		11 27		11 37	11 44				11 57	
Epsom 3	a			10 31		10 41	10 49			11 01				11 12	11 19		11 31		11 41	11 49				12 01	
	d	10 19		10 34		10 42	10 49		10 49	11 04		11 04		11 13	11 19	11 19	11 34		11 42	11 49		11 49		12 04	
Ewell East	d	10 23				10 46			10 53			11 08				11 23			11 46			11 53			
Cheam	d	10 26				10 49			10 56			11 11		11 18		11 26			11 49			11 56			
Epsom Downs	d							10 35													11 35				
Banstead	d							10 38													11 38				
Belmont	d							10 41													11 41				
Sutton (Surrey) 4	a	10 29				10 52		10 44	10 59			11 14		11 21		11 29			11 52		11 44	11 59			
	d																								
Sutton (Surrey)	d	10 29			10 38	10 53		10 45	10 59		11 08	11 15		11 22		11 29		11 38	11 52		11 45	11 59			12 08
West Croydon	d							10 58				11 28									11 58				
Carshalton	d	10 32			10 41				11 02		11 11					11 32		11 41				12 02			12 11
Hackbridge	d	10 35			10 43				11 05		11 13					11 35		11 43				12 05			12 13
Mitcham Junction	d	10 38			10 46				11 08		11 16					11 38		11 46				12 08			12 16
Mitcham Eastfields	d	10 41			10 49				11 11		11 19					11 41		11 49				12 11			12 19
Streatham	a				10 53						11 23							11 53							12 23
Tulse Hill	a				10 57						11 27							11 57							12 27
Tulse Hill 3	d				10 57						11 27							11 57							12 27
London Bridge 4 ⊖	a																								
Herne Hill	a				11 01						11 31							12 01							12 31
Loughborough Jn.	a				11 04						11 34							12 04							12 34
Elephant & Castle	a				11 08						11 38							12 08							12 38
London Blackfriars	a				11 12						11 42							12 12							12 42
City Thameslink	a				11 16						11 46							12 16							12 46
Farringdon	a				11 19						11 49							12 19							12 49
St Pancras International	a				11 23						11 53							12 23							12 53
Balham 4 ⊖	a	10 48						11 14	11 18			11 44				11 48					12 14	12 18			
Clapham Junction 10	a	10 52		11 00		11 10	11 15	11 19	11 22	11 30		11 49		11 40	11 45	11 52	12 00		12 10	12 15	12 19	12 22		12 30	
London Waterloo 15 ⊖	a			11 10			11 25			11 40					11 55		12 10			12 25				12 40	
London Victoria 15 ⊖	a	11 00				11 18		11 28	11 30			11 58		11 48		12 00			12 18		12 28	12 30			

Table 182R

Saturdays

14 December to 17 May

Dorking, Epsom, Epsom Downs, Sutton, Mitcham - London

Network Diagram - see first Page of Table 182

		SN	SN	SW	SN	SW	FC	SN		SW	SN	SN	SW	FC	SN	SN	SW	SN		SW	FC	SN	SW	SN	SN
Horsham 4	d							12 04														13 04			
Warnham	d							12 08														13 08			
Ockley	d							12 15														13 15			
Holmwood	d							12 19														13 19			
Dorking 4	a							12 25														13 25			
	d		11 58	12 05				12 26		12 35						12 58	13 05					13 26	13 35		
Box Hill & Westhumble	d							12 28														13 28			
Guildford	d					11 58							12 28							12 58					
Leatherhead	d		12 04	12 11		12 23		12 33		12 41			12 53			13 04	13 11			13 23		13 33	13 41		
Ashtead	d		12 07	12 14		12 27		12 37		12 44			12 57			13 07	13 14			13 27		13 37	13 44		
Epsom 3	a		12 12	12 19		12 31		12 41		12 49			13 01			13 12	13 19			13 31		13 41	13 49		
	d	12 04	12 13	12 19	12 19	12 34		12 42		12 49		12 49	13 04		13 04	13 13	13 19	13 19		13 34		13 42	13 49		13 49
Ewell East	d	12 08			12 23			12 46				12 53			13 08			13 23				13 46			13 53
Cheam	d	12 11	12 18		12 26			12 49				12 56			13 11	13 18		13 26				13 49			13 56
Epsom Downs	d										12 35													13 35	
Banstead	d										12 38													13 38	
Belmont	d										12 41													13 41	
Sutton (Surrey) 4	a	12 14	12 21		12 29			12 52			12 44	12 59			13 14	13 21		13 29				13 52		13 44	13 59
	d																								
Sutton (Surrey)	d	12 15	12 22		12 29		12 38	12 52			12 45	12 59		13 08	13 15	13 22		13 29			13 38	13 52		13 45	13 59
West Croydon	d	12 28									12 58				13 28									13 58	
Carshalton	d				12 32		12 41					13 02		13 11				13 32			13 41				14 02
Hackbridge	d				12 35		12 43					13 05		13 13				13 35			13 43				14 05
Mitcham Junction	d				12 38		12 46					13 08		13 16				13 38			13 46				14 08
Mitcham Eastfields	d				12 41		12 49					13 11		13 19				13 41			13 49				14 11
Streatham	a						12 53							13 23							13 53				
Tulse Hill	a						12 57							13 27							13 57				
Tulse Hill 3	d						12 57							13 27							13 57				
London Bridge 4 ⊖	a																								
Herne Hill	a						13 01							13 31							14 01				
Loughborough Jn	a						13 04							13 34							14 04				
Elephant & Castle	a						13 08							13 38							14 08				
London Blackfriars	a						13 12							13 42							14 12				
City Thameslink	a						13 16							13 46							14 16				
Farringdon	a						13 19							13 49							14 19				
St Pancras International	a						13 23							13 53							14 23				
Balham 4 ⊖	a	12 44			12 48						13 14	13 18			13 44			13 48						14 14	14 18
Clapham Junction 10	a	12 49	12 40	12 45	12 52	13 00		13 10		13 15	13 19	13 22	13 30		13 49	13 40	13 45	13 52		14 00		14 10	14 15	14 19	14 22
London Waterloo 15 ⊖	a			12 55		13 10				13 25			13 40				13 55			14 10			14 25		
London Victoria 15 ⊖	a	12 58	12 48		13 00			13 18			13 28	13 30			13 58	13 48		14 00				14 18		14 28	14 30

		SW	FC	SN		SN	SW	SN	SW	FC	SN	SW	SN	SN		SW	FC	SN	SN	SW	SN	SW	FC	SN	
Horsham 4	d										14 04													15 04	
Warnham	d										14 08													15 08	
Ockley	d										14 15													15 15	
Holmwood	d										14 19													15 19	
Dorking 4	a										14 25													15 25	
	d					13 58	14 05				14 26	14 35							14 58	15 05				15 26	
Box Hill & Westhumble	d										14 28													15 28	
Guildford	d	13 28							13 58							14 28						14 58			
Leatherhead	d	13 53				14 04	14 11		14 23		14 33	14 41				14 53			15 04	15 11		15 23		15 33	
Ashtead	d	13 57				14 07	14 14		14 27		14 37	14 44				14 57			15 07	15 14		15 27		15 37	
Epsom 3	a	14 01				14 12	14 19		14 31		14 41	14 49				15 01			15 12	15 19		15 31		15 41	
	d	14 04		14 04		14 13	14 19	14 19	14 34		14 42	14 49		14 49		15 04		15 04	15 13	15 19	15 19	15 34		15 42	
Ewell East	d			14 08				14 23			14 46			14 53				15 08			15 23			15 46	
Cheam	d			14 11		14 18		14 26			14 49			14 56				15 11	15 18		15 26			15 49	
Epsom Downs	d												14 35												
Banstead	d												14 38												
Belmont	d												14 41												
Sutton (Surrey) 4	a			14 14		14 21		14 29			14 52		14 44	14 59				15 14	15 21		15 29			15 52	
	d																								
Sutton (Surrey)	d		14 08	14 15		14 22		14 29		14 38	14 52		14 45	14 59			15 08	15 15	15 22		15 29		15 38	15 52	
West Croydon	d			14 28									14 58					15 28							
Carshalton	d		14 11					14 32		14 41				15 02			15 11				15 32		15 41		
Hackbridge	d		14 13					14 35		14 43				15 05			15 13				15 35		15 43		
Mitcham Junction	d		14 16					14 38		14 46				15 08			15 16				15 38		15 46		
Mitcham Eastfields	d		14 19					14 41		14 49				15 11			15 19				15 41		15 49		
Streatham	a		14 23							14 53							15 23						15 53		
Tulse Hill	a		14 27							14 57							15 27						15 57		
Tulse Hill 3	d		14 27							14 57							15 27						15 57		
London Bridge 4 ⊖	a																								
Herne Hill	a		14 31							15 01							15 31						16 01		
Loughborough Jn	a		14 34							15 04							15 34						16 04		
Elephant & Castle	a		14 38							15 08							15 38						16 08		
London Blackfriars	a		14 42							15 12							15 42						16 12		
City Thameslink	a		14 46							15 16							15 46						16 16		
Farringdon	a		14 49							15 19							15 49						16 19		
St Pancras International	a		14 53							15 23							15 53						16 23		
Balham 4 ⊖	a			14 44				14 48					15 14	15 18				15 44			15 48				
Clapham Junction 10	a	14 30		14 49		14 40	14 45	14 52	15 00		15 10	15 15	15 19	15 22		15 30		15 49	15 40	15 45	15 52	16 00		16 10	
London Waterloo 15 ⊖	a	14 40					14 55		15 10			15 25				15 40				15 55		16 10			
London Victoria 15 ⊖	a			14 58		14 48		15 00			15 18		15 28	15 30				15 58	15 48		16 00			16 18	

Table 182R

Saturdays

14 December to 17 May

Dorking, Epsom, Epsom Downs, Sutton, Mitcham - London

Network Diagram - see first Page of Table 182

		SW	SN	SN	SW	FC	SN	SN	SW	SN		SW	FC	SN	SW	SN	SN	SW	FC	SN		SN	SW	SN	SW
Horsham 4	d													16 04											
Warnham	d													16 08											
Ockley	d													16 15											
Holmwood	d													16 19											
Dorking 4	a													16 25											
	d	15 35						15 58	16 05					16 26	16 35							16 58	17 05		
Box Hill & Westhumble	d													16 28											
Guildford	d				15 28							15 58						16 28							16 58
Leatherhead	d	15 41			15 53			16 04	16 11			16 23		16 33	16 41			16 53				17 04	17 11		17 23
Ashtead	d	15 44			15 57			16 07	16 14			16 27		16 37	16 44			16 57				17 07	17 14		17 27
Epsom 3	a	15 49			16 01			16 12	16 19			16 31		16 41	16 49			17 01				17 12	17 19		17 31
	d	15 49		15 49	16 04		16 04	16 13	16 19	16 19		16 34		16 42	16 49		16 49	17 04		17 04		17 13	17 19	17 19	17 34
Ewell East	d			15 53			16 08			16 23				16 46			16 53			17 08				17 23	
Cheam	d			15 56			16 11	16 18		16 26				16 49			16 56			17 11		17 18		17 26	
Epsom Downs	d		15 35													16 35									
Banstead	d		15 38													16 38									
Belmont	d		15 41													16 41									
Sutton (Surrey) 4	a		15 44	15 59			16 14	16 21		16 29				16 52		16 44	16 59			17 14		17 21		17 29	
	d																								
Sutton (Surrey)	d		15 45	15 59		16 08	16 15	16 22		16 29			16 38	16 52		16 45	16 59		17 08	17 15		17 22		17 29	
West Croydon	d		15 58				16 28									16 58				17 28					
Carshalton	d			16 02		16 11				16 32			16 41				17 02		17 11					17 32	
Hackbridge	d			16 05		16 13				16 35			16 43				17 05		17 13					17 35	
Mitcham Junction	d			16 08		16 16				16 38			16 46				17 08		17 16					17 38	
Mitcham Eastfields	d			16 11		16 19				16 41			16 49				17 11		17 19					17 41	
Streatham	a					16 23							16 53						17 23						
Tulse Hill	a					16 27							16 57						17 27						
Tulse Hill 3	d					16 27							16 57						17 27						
London Bridge 4 ⊖	a																								
Herne Hill	a					16 31							17 01						17 31						
Loughborough Jn	a					16 34							17 04						17 34						
Elephant & Castle	a					16 38							17 08						17 38						
London Blackfriars	a					16 42							17 12						17 42						
City Thameslink	a					16 46							17 16						17 46						
Farringdon	a					16 49							17 19						17 49						
St Pancras International	a					16 53							17 23						17 53						
Balham 4 ⊖	a		16 14	16 18			16 44			16 48						17 14	17 18			17 44				17 48	
Clapham Junction 10	a	16 15	16 19	16 22	16 30		16 49	16 40	16 45	16 52		17 00		17 10	17 15	17 19	17 22	17 30		17 49		17 41	17 45	17 52	18 00
London Waterloo 15 ⊖	a	16 25			16 40				16 55			17 10			17 25			17 40					17 55		18 10
London Victoria 15 ⊖	a		16 28	16 30			16 58	16 48		17 00				17 18		17 28	17 30			17 58		17 49		18 00	

		FC	SN	SW	SN	SN		SW	FC	SN	SN	SW	SN	SW	FC	SN		SW	SN	SN	SW	FC	SN	SN	SW
Horsham 4	d		17 04													18 04									
Warnham	d		17 08													18 08									
Ockley	d		17 15													18 15									
Holmwood	d		17 19													18 19									
Dorking 4	a		17 25													18 25									
	d		17 26	17 35							17 58	18 05				18 26		18 35						18 58	19 05
Box Hill & Westhumble	d		17 28													18 28								19 00	
Guildford	d							17 28						17 58							18 28				
Leatherhead	d		17 33	17 41				17 53			18 04	18 11		18 23		18 33		18 41			18 53			19 05	19 11
Ashtead	d		17 37	17 44				17 57			18 07	18 14		18 27		18 37		18 44			18 57			19 09	19 14
Epsom 3	a		17 41	17 49				18 01			18 12	18 19		18 31		18 41		18 49			19 01			19 13	19 19
	d		17 42	17 49		17 49		18 04		18 04	18 13	18 19	18 19	18 34		18 42		18 49		18 49	19 04		19 04	19 14	19 19
Ewell East	d		17 46			17 53				18 08			18 23			18 46				18 53			19 08		
Cheam	d		17 49			17 56				18 11	18 18		18 26			18 49				18 56			19 11	19 19	
Epsom Downs	d				17 35														18 35						
Banstead	d				17 38														18 38						
Belmont	d				17 41														18 41						
Sutton (Surrey) 4	a		17 52		17 44	17 59				18 14	18 21		18 29			18 52			18 44	18 59			19 14	19 22	
	d																								
Sutton (Surrey)	d	17 38	17 52		17 45	17 59			18 08	18 15	18 22		18 29		18 38	18 52			18 45	18 59		19 08	19 15	19 23	
West Croydon	d				17 58					18 28									18 58				19 28		
Carshalton	d	17 41				18 02			18 11				18 32		18 41					19 02		19 11			
Hackbridge	d	17 43				18 05			18 13				18 35		18 43					19 05		19 13			
Mitcham Junction	d	17 46				18 08			18 16				18 38		18 46					19 08		19 16			
Mitcham Eastfields	d	17 49				18 11			18 19				18 41		18 49					19 11		19 19			
Streatham	a	17 53							18 23						18 53							19 23			
Tulse Hill	a	17 57							18 27						18 57							19 27			
Tulse Hill 3	d	17 57							18 27						18 57							19 27			
London Bridge 4 ⊖	a																								
Herne Hill	a	18 01							18 31						19 01							19 31			
Loughborough Jn	a	18 04							18 34						19 04							19 34			
Elephant & Castle	a	18 08							18 38						19 08							19 38			
London Blackfriars	a	18 12							18 42						19 12							19 42			
City Thameslink	a	18 16							18 46						19 16							19 46			
Farringdon	a	18 19							18 49						19 19							19 49			
St Pancras International	a	18 23							18 53						19 23							19 53			
Balham 4 ⊖	a				18 14	18 18				18 44			18 48						19 14	19 18			19 44		
Clapham Junction 10	a		18 10	18 15	18 19	18 22		18 30		18 49	18 40	18 45	18 52	19 00		19 10		19 15	19 19	19 22	19 30		19 49	19 40	19 45
London Waterloo 15 ⊖	a			18 25				18 40				18 55		19 10				19 25			19 40				19 55
London Victoria 15 ⊖	a		18 18		18 28	18 30				18 58	18 48		19 00			19 18			19 28	19 30			19 58	19 48	

Table 182R

Saturdays

14 December to 17 May

Dorking, Epsom, Epsom Downs, Sutton, Mitcham - London

Network Diagram - see first Page of Table 182

		SN		SW	FC	SN	SW	SN	SN	SW	FC	SN		SN	SW	SN	SW	FC	SN	SW	SN	SN		FC	SN
Horsham 4	d																								
Warnham	d																								
Ockley	d																								
Holmwood	d																								
Dorking 4	a																								
	d					19 28	19 35							19 58	20 05				20 28	20 35					
Box Hill & Westhumble	d													20 00											
Guildford	d			18 58						19 28							19 58								
Leatherhead	d			19 23		19 34	19 41			19 53				20 05	20 11		20 23		20 34	20 41					
Ashtead	d			19 27		19 37	19 44			19 57				20 09	20 14		20 27		20 37	20 44					
Epsom 3	a			19 31		19 42	19 49			20 01				20 13	20 19		20 31		20 42	20 49					
	d	19 19		19 34		19 42	19 49		19 49	20 04		20 04		20 14	20 19	20 19	20 34		20 42	20 49		20 49			21 03
Ewell East	d	19 23				19 46			19 53			20 08				20 23			20 46			20 53			21 08
Cheam	d	19 26				19 49			19 56			20 11		20 19		20 26			20 49			20 56			21 11
Epsom Downs	d							19 35													20 35				
Banstead	d							19 38													20 38				
Belmont	d							19 41													20 41				
Sutton (Surrey) 4	a	19 29				19 52		19 44	19 59			20 14		20 22		20 29			20 52		20 44	20 59			21 14
	d																								
Sutton (Surrey)	d	19 29			19 38	19 53		19 45	19 59		20 08	20 15		20 23		20 29		20 38	20 53		20 45	20 59		21 08	21 15
West Croydon	d							19 58				20 28									20 58				21 28
Carshalton	d	19 32			19 41				20 02		20 11					20 32		20 41				21 02		21 11	
Hackbridge	d	19 35			19 43				20 05		20 13					20 35		20 43				21 05		21 13	
Mitcham Junction	d	19 38			19 46				20 08		20 16					20 38		20 46				21 08		21 16	
Mitcham Eastfields	d	19 41			19 49				20 11		20 19					20 41		20 49				21 11		21 19	
Streatham	a				19 53						20 23							20 53						21 23	
Tulse Hill	a				19 57						20 27							20 57						21 27	
Tulse Hill 3	d				19 57						20 27							20 57						21 27	
London Bridge 4 ⊖	a																								
Herne Hill	a				20 01						20 31							21 01						21 31	
Loughborough Jn.	a				20 04						20 34							21 04						21 34	
Elephant & Castle	a				20 08						20 38							21 08						21 38	
London Blackfriars	a				20 12						20 42							21 12						21 42	
City Thameslink	a				20 16						20 46														
Farringdon	a				20 19						20 49							21 19						21 49	
St Pancras International	a				20 23						20 53							21 23						21 53	
Balham 4 ⊖	a	19 48						20 14	20 18			20 44				20 48					21 14	21 18			21 44
Clapham Junction 10	a	19 52		20 00		20 10	20 15	20 19	20 22	20 30		20 49		20 40	20 45	20 52	21 00		21 10	21 15	21 19	21 22			21 49
London Waterloo 15 ⊖	a			20 10			20 25			20 40					20 55		21 10			21 25					
London Victoria 15 ⊖	a	20 00				20 18		20 28	20 30			20 58		20 48		21 00			21 18		21 28	21 30			21 58

		SW	SN	SW	SN	SW	SN	SW		SN	SN	SN	SN	SW	SN	SN	SW	SN		SN	SN	SN	SW	SN	SN
Horsham 4	d																								
Warnham	d																								
Ockley	d																								
Holmwood	d																								
Dorking 4	a																								
	d		20 58				21 28	21 35					21 58			22 28	22 35					23 00			23 30
Box Hill & Westhumble	d		21 00										22 00									23 02			
Guildford	d			20 46										21 46									22 46		
Leatherhead	d		21 05	21 11			21 34	21 41					22 05	22 11		22 34	22 41					23 07	23 11		23 36
Ashtead	d		21 09	21 14			21 37	21 44					22 09	22 14		22 37	22 44					23 11	23 14		23 39
Epsom 3	a		21 13	21 19			21 42	21 49					22 13	22 19		22 42	22 49					23 15	23 19		23 45
	d	21 04	21 14	21 19	21 19	21 34	21 42	21 49			21 49	22 04	22 14	22 19	22 19	22 42	22 49			22 49	23 04	23 16	23 19		
Ewell East	d				21 23		21 46				21 53	22 08			22 23	22 46				22 53	23 08	23 20			
Cheam	d		21 19		21 26		21 49				21 56	22 11	22 19		22 26	22 49				22 56	23 11	23 23			
Epsom Downs	d									21 35								22 35						23 23	
Banstead	d									21 38								22 38						23 26	
Belmont	d									21 41								22 41						23 29	
Sutton (Surrey) 4	a		21 22		21 29		21 52			21 44	21 59	22 14	22 22		22 29	22 52		22 44		22 59	23 14	23 26		23 32	
	d																								
Sutton (Surrey)	d		21 23		21 29		21 53			21 45	21 59	22 15	22 23		22 29	22 53		22 45		22 59	23 15	23 30		23 34	
West Croydon	d									21 58		22 28						22 58			23 28	23a41		23a45	
Carshalton	d				21 32						22 02				22 32					23 02					
Hackbridge	d				21 35						22 05				22 35					23 05					
Mitcham Junction	d				21 38						22 08				22 38					23 08					
Mitcham Eastfields	d				21 41						22 11				22 41					23 11					
Streatham	a																								
Tulse Hill	a																								
Tulse Hill 3	d																								
London Bridge 4 ⊖	a																								
Herne Hill	a																								
Loughborough Jn.	a																								
Elephant & Castle	a																								
London Blackfriars	a																								
City Thameslink	a																								
Farringdon	a																								
St Pancras International	a																								
Balham 4 ⊖	a				21 48					22 14	22 18	22 44			22 48			23 14		23 18	23 44				
Clapham Junction 10	a	21 30	21 40	21 45	21 52	22 00	22 10	22 15		22 19	22 22	22 49	22 40	22 45	22 52	23 13	23 15	23 20		23 23	23 49		23 48		
London Waterloo 15 ⊖	a	21 40		21 55		22 10		22 25						22 55			23 25						23 58		
London Victoria 15 ⊖	a		21 48		22 00		22 18			22 28	22 30	22 58	22 48		23 00	23 22		23 29		23 31	23 58				

Table 182R

Saturdays

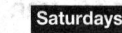

14 December to 17 May

Dorking, Epsom, Epsom Downs, Sutton, Mitcham - London

Network Diagram - see first Page of Table 182

		SN	SN
Horsham 4	d		
Warnham	d		
Ockley	d		
Holmwood	d		
Dorking 4	a		
	d		
Box Hill & Westhumble	d		
Guildford	d		
Leatherhead	d		
Ashtead	d		
Epsom 3	a		
	d	23 35	
Ewell East	d	23 39	
Cheam	d	23 42	
Epsom Downs	d		23 49
Banstead	d		23 52
Belmont	d		23 55
Sutton (Surrey) 4	a	23 45	23 58
	d		
Sutton (Surrey)	d	23 46	23 59
West Croydon	d	23a57	00a10
Carshalton	d		
Hackbridge	d		
Mitcham Junction	d		
Mitcham Eastfields	d		
Streatham	a		
Tulse Hill	a		
Tulse Hill 3	d		
London Bridge 4 ⊖	a		
Herne Hill	a		
Loughborough Jn.	a		
Elephant & Castle	a		
London Blackfriars	a		
City Thameslink	a		
Farringdon	a		
St Pancras International	a		
Balham 4 ⊖	a		
Clapham Junction 10	a		
London Waterloo 15 ⊖	a		
London Victoria 15 ⊖	a		

Sundays

8 December to 11 May

		SN	SN	SW	SN	SW	SN	SW	SN	SN		SW	SN	SN	SW	SN	SN	SW	FC	SN		SN	SW	FC	SN
Horsham 4	d																								
Warnham	d																								
Ockley	d																								
Holmwood	d																								
Dorking 4	a																								
	d				07 16		07 46		08 15				08 45		09 08	09 15				09 45			10 08		10 15
Box Hill & Westhumble	d				07 18		07 48		08 17				08 47			09 17				09 47					10 17
Guildford	d											08 20						09 20							
Leatherhead	d				07 23		07 53		08 22			08 45	08 52		09 15	09 22		09 45		09 52			10 15		10 22
Ashtead	d				07 27		07 57		08 26			08 48	08 56		09 18	09 26		09 48		09 56			10 18		10 26
Epsom 3	a				07 31		08 01		08 30			08 53	09 00		09 23	09 30		09 53		10 00			10 23		10 30
	d	06 44	07 02	07 24	07 32	07 54	08 02	08 24	08 31	08 47		08 54	09 01	09 17	09 24	09 31	09 47	09 54		10 01		10 17	10 24		10 31
Ewell East	d	06 48	07 06		07 36		08 06		08 35	08 51			09 05	09 21		09 35	09 51			10 05		10 21			10 35
Cheam	d	06 51	07 09		07 39		08 09		08 38	08 54			09 08	09 24		09 38	09 54			10 08		10 24			10 38
Epsom Downs	d																								
Banstead	d																								
Belmont	d																								
Sutton (Surrey) 4	a	06 54	07 12		07 42		08 12		08 41	08 57			09 11	09 27		09 41	09 57			10 11		10 27			10 41
	d																								
Sutton (Surrey)	d	06 55	07 13		07 43		08 13		08 42	08 58			09 12	09 28		09 42	09 58		10 08	10 12		10 28		10 38	10 42
West Croydon	d	07 07																							
Carshalton	d		07 16		07 46		08 16		08 45	09 01			09 15	09 31		09 45	10 01		10 11	10 15		10 31		10 41	10 45
Hackbridge	d		07 18		07 48		08 18		08 47	09 03			09 17	09 33		09 47	10 03		10 13	10 17		10 33		10 43	10 47
Mitcham Junction	d		07 22		07 52		08 22		08 51	09 07			09 21	09 37		09 51	10 07		10 16	10 21		10 37		10 46	10 51
Mitcham Eastfields	d		07 25		07 55		08 25		08 54	09 10			09 24	09 40		09 54	10 10		10 19	10 24		10 40		10 49	10 54
Streatham	a																		10 23					10 53	
Tulse Hill	a																		10 27					10 57	
Tulse Hill 3	d																		10 27					10 57	
London Bridge 4 ⊖	a																								
Herne Hill	a																		10 31					11 01	
Loughborough Jn.	a																		10 34					11 04	
Elephant & Castle	a																		10 39					11 09	
London Blackfriars	a																		10 43					11 13	
City Thameslink	a																								
Farringdon	a																								
St Pancras International	a																								
Balham 4 ⊖	a	07 23	07 37		08 05		08 39		09 00	09 18			09 30	09 46		10 00	10 16			10 30		10 46			11 00
Clapham Junction 10	a	07 27	07 41	07 50	08 11	08 21	08 44	08 49	09 06	09 22		09 19	09 36	09 51	09 49	10 06	10 21	10 19		10 36		10 51	10 49		11 06
London Waterloo 15 ⊖	a			08 04		08 34		09 04				09 30			10 04			10 29					11 04		
London Victoria 15 ⊖	a	07 34	07 48		08 19		08 53		09 15	09 29			09 45	09 59		10 15	10 29			10 45		10 59			11 15

Table 182R

Sundays

8 December to 11 May

Dorking, Epsom, Epsom Downs, Sutton, Mitcham - London

Network Diagram - see first Page of Table 182

		SN	SW	FC	SN	SN		SW	FC	SN	SN	SW	FC	SN	SN	SW	FC	SN	SN	SW	FC	SN	SN		
Horsham 4	d																								
Warnham	d																								
Ockley	d																								
Holmwood	d																								
Dorking 4	a																								
	d				10 45			11 08		11 15				11 45		12 08		12 15				12 45			
Box Hill & Westhumble	d				10 47					11 17				11 47				12 17				12 47			
Guildford	d		10 20									11 20								12 20					
Leatherhead	d		10 45		10 52			11 15		11 22		11 45		11 52		12 15		12 22		12 45		12 52			
Ashtead	d		10 48		10 56			11 18		11 26		11 48		11 56		12 18		12 26		12 48		12 56			
Epsom 3	a		10 53		11 00			11 23		11 30		11 53		12 00		12 23		12 30		12 53		13 00			
	d	10 47	10 54		11 01	11 17		11 24		11 31	11 47	11 54		12 01	12 17	12 24		12 31	12 47	12 54		13 01	13 17		
Ewell East	d	10 51			11 05	11 21				11 35	11 51			12 05	12 21			12 35	12 51			13 05	13 21		
Cheam	d	10 54			11 08	11 24				11 38	11 54			12 08	12 24			12 38	12 54			13 08	13 24		
Epsom Downs	d																								
Banstead	d																								
Belmont	d																								
Sutton (Surrey) 4	a	10 57			11 11	11 27				11 41	11 57			12 11	12 27			12 41	12 57			13 11	13 27		
	d																								
Sutton (Surrey)	d	10 58		11 08	11 12	11 28			11 38	11 42	11 58		12 08	12 12	12 28		12 38	12 42	12 58		13 08	13 12	13 28		
West Croydon	d																								
Carshalton	d	11 01		11 11	11 15	11 31			11 41	11 45	12 01		12 11	12 15	12 31		12 41	12 45	13 01		13 11	13 15	13 31		
Hackbridge	d	11 03		11 13	11 17	11 33			11 43	11 47	12 03		12 13	12 17	12 33		12 43	12 47	13 03		13 13	13 17	13 33		
Mitcham Junction	d	11 07		11 16	11 21	11 37			11 46	11 51	12 07		12 16	12 21	12 37		12 46	12 51	13 07		13 16	13 21	13 37		
Mitcham Eastfields	d	11 10		11 19	11 24	11 40			11 49	11 54	12 10		12 19	12 24	12 40		12 49	12 54	13 10		13 19	13 24	13 40		
Streatham	a			11 23					11 53				12 23				12 53				13 23				
Tulse Hill	a			11 27					11 57				12 27				12 57				13 27				
Tulse Hill 3	d			11 27					11 57				12 27				12 57				13 27				
London Bridge 4 ⊖	a																								
Herne Hill	a			11 31					12 01				12 31				13 01				13 31				
Loughborough Jn.	a			11 34					12 04				12 34				13 04				13 34				
Elephant & Castle	a			11 39					12 09				12 39				13 09				13 39				
London Blackfriars	a			11 43					12 13				12 43				13 13				13 43				
City Thameslink	a																								
Farringdon	a																								
St Pancras International	a																								
Balham 4 ⊖	a	11 16			11 30	11 46				12 00	12 16			12 30	12 46			13 00	13 16			13 30	13 46		
Clapham Junction 10	a	11 21	11 19		11 36	11 51		11 49		12 06	12 21	12 19		12 36	12 51	12 49		13 06	13 21	13 19		13 36	13 51		
London Waterloo 15 ⊖	a		11 29					12 04				12 29				13 04				13 29					
London Victoria 15 ⊖	a	11 29			11 45	11 59				12 15	12 29			12 45	12 59			13 15	13 29			13 45	13 59		

		SW		FC	SN	SN	SW	FC	SN	SN	SW		FC	SN	SN	SW	FC	SN	SN	SW	FC		SN	SW
Horsham 4	d																							
Warnham	d																							
Ockley	d																							
Holmwood	d																							
Dorking 4	a																							
	d	13 08			18 15				18 45		19 08			19 15				19 45		20 08			20 15	
Box Hill & Westhumble	d				18 17				18 47					19 17				19 47					20 17	
Guildford	d						18 20									19 20								20 20
Leatherhead	d	13 15			18 22		18 45		18 52		19 15			19 22		19 45		19 52		20 15			20 22	20 45
Ashtead	d	13 18			18 26		18 48		18 56		19 18			19 26		19 48		19 56		20 18			20 26	20 48
Epsom 3	a	13 23			18 30		18 53		19 00		19 23			19 30		19 53		20 00		20 23			20 30	20 53
	d	13 24			18 31	18 47	18 54		19 01	19 17	19 24			19 31	19 47	19 54		20 01	20 17	20 24			20 31	20 54
Ewell East	d				18 35	18 51			19 05	19 21				19 35	19 51			20 05	20 21				20 35	
Cheam	d				18 38	18 54			19 08	19 24				19 38	19 54			20 08	20 24				20 38	
Epsom Downs	d																							
Banstead	d																							
Belmont	d		and at																					
Sutton (Surrey) 4	a		the same		18 41	18 57			19 11	19 27				19 41	19 57			20 11	20 27				20 41	
	d		minutes																					
Sutton (Surrey)	d		past	18 38	18 42	18 58		19 08	19 12	19 28			19 38	19 42	19 58		20 08	20 12	20 28		20 38		20 42	
West Croydon	d		each																					
Carshalton	d		hour until	18 41	18 45	19 01		19 11	19 15	19 31			19 41	19 45	20 01		20 11	20 15	20 31		20 41		20 45	
Hackbridge	d			18 43	18 47	19 03		19 13	19 17	19 33			19 43	19 47	20 03		20 13	20 17	20 33		20 43		20 47	
Mitcham Junction	d			18 46	18 51	19 07		19 16	19 21	19 37			19 46	19 51	20 07		20 16	20 21	20 37		20 46		20 51	
Mitcham Eastfields	d			18 49	18 54	19 10		19 19	19 24	19 40			19 49	19 54	20 10		20 19	20 24	20 40		20 49		20 54	
Streatham	a			18 53				19 23					19 53				20 23				20 53			
Tulse Hill	a			18 57				19 27					19 57				20 27				20 57			
Tulse Hill 3	d			18 57				19 27					19 57				20 27				20 57			
London Bridge 4 ⊖	a																							
Herne Hill	a			19 01				19 31					20 01				20 31				21 01			
Loughborough Jn.	a			19 04				19 34					20 04				20 34				21 04			
Elephant & Castle	a			19 09				19 39					20 09				20 39				21 09			
London Blackfriars	a			19 13				19 43					20 13				20 43				21 13			
City Thameslink	a																							
Farringdon	a																							
St Pancras International	a																							
Balham 4 ⊖	a				19 00	19 16			19 30	19 46				20 00	20 18			20 30	20 48				21 00	
Clapham Junction 10	a	13 49			19 06	19 21	19 19		19 36	19 51	19 49			20 06	20 22	20 19		20 36	20 52	20 49			21 06	21 19
London Waterloo 15 ⊖	a	13 59					19 29				19 59					20 29				21 00				21 29
London Victoria 15 ⊖	a				19 15	19 29			19 45	19 59				20 15	20 29			20 45	20 59				21 15	

Table 182R

Sundays

8 December to 11 May

Dorking, Epsom, Epsom Downs, Sutton, Mitcham - London

Network Diagram - see first Page of Table 182

		FC	SN	SW	FC A	FC B	SN	SW		FC	SN	SW	SN	SW	SN	SW	SN
Horsham [4]	d																
Warnham	d																
Ockley	d																
Holmwood	d																
Dorking [4]	a																
	d		20 45	21 08			21 15				21 45	22 08	22 15		22 45	23 08	23 15
Box Hill & Westhumble	d		20 47				21 17				21 47		22 17		22 47		23 17
Guildford	d							21 20						22 20			
Leatherhead	d		20 52	21 15			21 22	21 45			21 52	22 15	22 22	22 45	22 52	23 15	23 22
Ashtead	d		20 56	21 18			21 26	21 48			21 56	22 18	22 26	22 48	22 56	23 18	23 26
Epsom [3]	a		21 00	21 23			21 30	21 53			22 00	22 23	22 30	22 53	23 00	23 23	23 30
	d		21 01	21 24			21 31	21 54			22 01	22 24	22 31	22 54	23 01	23 24	23 31
Ewell East	d		21 05				21 35				22 05		22 35		23 05		23 35
Cheam	d		21 08				21 38				22 08		22 38		23 08		23 38
Epsom Downs	d																
Banstead	d																
Belmont	d																
Sutton (Surrey) [4]	a		21 11				21 41				22 11		22 41		23 11		23 41
	d																
Sutton (Surrey)	d	21 08	21 12		21 38	21 38	21 42			22 08	22 12		22 42		23 12		23 42
West Croydon	d																
Carshalton	d	21 11	21 15		21 41	21 41	21 45			22 11	22 15		22 45		23 15		23 45
Hackbridge	d	21 13	21 17		21 43	21 43	21 47			22 13	22 17		22 47		23 17		23 47
Mitcham Junction	d	21 16	21 21		21 46	21 46	21 51			22 16	22 21		22 51		23 21		23 51
Mitcham Eastfields	d	21 19	21 24		21 49	21 49	21 54			22 19	22 24		22 54		23 24		23 54
Streatham	a	21 23			21 53	21 53				22 23							
Tulse Hill	a	21 27			21 57	21 57				22 27							
Tulse Hill [3]	d	21 27			21 57	21 57				22 27							
London Bridge [4] ⊖	a																
Herne Hill	a	21 31			22 01	22 01				22 31							
Loughborough Jn.	a	21 34			22 04	22 04				22 34							
Elephant & Castle	a	21 39			22 09	22 09				22 39							
London Blackfriars	a	21 43			22 13	22 13				22 43							
City Thameslink	a																
Farringdon	a					22 19											
St Pancras International	a					22 24											
Balham [4] ⊖	a		21 30				22 00				22 30		23 00		23 30		00 01
Clapham Junction [10]	a		21 36	21 49			22 06	22 19			22 36	22 49	23 06	23 19	23 36	23 49	00 06
London Waterloo [15] ⊖	a			22 00				22 29				23 00		23 29		23 59	
London Victoria [15] ⊖	a		21 45				22 15				22 45		23 15		23 45		00 15

A until 29 December

B from 5 January

Table 184

Mondays to Fridays

9 December to 16 May

London - Oxted, East Grinstead and Uckfield

Network Diagram - see first Page of Table 181

Miles	Miles			SN MX [1]	SN MX [1]	SN [1]	SN [1]	SN [1]	SN [1]	SN [1]	SN [1]	SN [1]		SN [1]	SN [1]	SN [1]	SN [1]	SN [1]	SN [1]	SN [1]	SN [1]	SN [1]		SN [1]	SN [1]
0	—	London Victoria [15] ⊖175,177	d				05 25	05 52		06 24		06 54			07 10		07 32					08 53			09 23
2¾	—	Clapham Junction [10] 175,177	d				05 32	05 59		06 30		07 00			07 16		07 38					08 59			09 29
—	0	London Bridge [4] ⊖175,177	d						06 08		06 38			07 03		07 19		07 55	07 58	08 25	08 30			09 03	
—	8¾	Norwood Junction [2] 175,177	d				05 50									07 30			08 10	08 36					
10½	10¼	East Croydon 175,177	d		00 05	05 26	05 55	06 10	06 23	06 41	06 53	07 11		07 17	07 27	07 34	07 52	08 09	08 16	08 41	08 48	09 11		09 23	09 40
11½	—	South Croydon [4] 175	d				05 57																		
12½	—	**Sanderstead**	d		00s09			06 14		06 45		07 15		07 21	07 31	07 38	07 57	08 13	08 20	08 45		09 15			09 44
13¾	—	**Riddlesdown**	d		00s12			06 17		06 48				07 24		07 41	08 00	08 16	08 23	08 48		09 18			09 47
15½	—	**Upper Warlingham**	d		00s16			06 21		06 52				07 28		07 45	08 04	08 20	08 27	08 52		09 22			09 51
17¼	—	**Woldingham**	d		00s20			06 25		06 56				07 32		07 49	08 08	08 24	08 31	08 56		09 26			09 55
20½	—	**Oxted [3]**	a		00 25	05 42	06 09	06 30	06 36	07 01	07 06	07 26		07 37	07 43	07 54	08 13	08 29	08 36	09 01	09 08	09 31		09 37	10 00
—	—		d	00 02		05 42	06 09	06 31	06 36	07 02	07 07	07 26		07 38	07 43	07 55	08 13	08 30	08 37	09 02		09 32		09 37	10 00
21½	0	**Hurst Green**	d	00 05		05 44	06 11	06 33	06 39	07 04	07 09	07 29		07 40	07 46	07 57	08 17	08 32	08 39	09 04		09 34		09 40	10 03
26¼	—	**Lingfield**	d	00 11			06 17	06 39		07 10		07 35			07 52	08 03	08 23	08 38		09 10		09 40			10 09
28	—	**Dormans**	d	00 14			06 21	06 43		07 14		07 38			07 55	08 07	08 27	08 42		09 14		09 44			10 12
30¼	—	**East Grinstead**	a	00 19			06 25	06 47		07 18		07 43			08 00	08 12	08 31	08 46		09 18		09 48			10 17
—	4¼	**Edenbridge Town**	d			05 50			06 45		07 15			07 46					08 45					09 46	
—	6	**Hever**	d						06 48		07 19			07 50					08 49					09 49	
—	8	**Cowden**	d						06 52		07 23			07 54					08 53					09 53	
—	10¾	**Ashurst**	d						06 57		07 27			07 58					08 57					09 58	
—	14½	**Eridge**	d			06 08			07 02		07 35			08 04					09 03					10 03	
—	17¾	**Crowborough**	d			06 14			07 13		07 41			08 10					09 09					10 09	
—	22½	**Buxted**	d			06 20			07 20		07 48			08 16					09 15					10 16	
—	25	**Uckfield**	a			06 26			07 25		07 53			08 22					09 21					10 21	

		SN [1]	SN [1]	SN [1]	SN [1]	SN [1]	SN [1]	SN [1]		SN [1]	SN [1]	SN [1]	SN [1]	SN [1]	SN [1]	SN [1]	SN [1]	SN [1]		SN [1]	SN [1]	SN [1]	SN [1]	SN [1]	SN [1]
London Victoria [15] ⊖175,177	d	09 53		10 23	10 53		11 23	11 53			12 23	12 53		13 23	13 53		14 23	14 53			15 23		15 53		16 23
Clapham Junction [10] 175,177	d	09 59		10 29	10 59		11 29	11 59			12 29	12 59		13 29	13 59		14 29	14 59			15 29		15 59		16 29
London Bridge [4] ⊖175,177	d		10 08			11 08				12 08			13 08			14 08				15 08		15 38		16 08	
Norwood Junction [2] 175,177	d																								
East Croydon 175,177	d	10 10	10 23	10 40	11 10	11 24	11 40	12 10		12 23	12 40	13 10	13 24	13 40	14 10	14 23	14 40	15 10		15 23	15 40	15 53	16 10	16 24	16 40
South Croydon [4] 175	d																				15 43		16 12		16 42
Sanderstead	d	10 15		10 44	11 14		11 44	12 14			12 44	13 14		13 44	14 14		14 45	15 14			15 46		16 15		16 45
Riddlesdown	d	10 18		10 47	11 17		11 47	12 17			12 47	13 17		13 47	14 17		14 48	15 17			15 49		16 18		16 48
Upper Warlingham	d	10 22		10 51	11 21		11 51	12 21			12 51	13 21		13 51	14 21		14 52	15 21			15 53		16 22		16 52
Woldingham	d	10 26		10 55	11 25		11 55	12 25			12 55	13 25		13 55	14 25		14 56	15 25			15 57		16 26		16 56
Oxted [3]	a	10 31	10 37	11 00	11 30	11 37	12 00	12 30		12 37	13 00	13 30	13 37	14 00	14 30	14 37	15 01	15 30		15 37	16 02	16 07	16 31	16 37	17 01
	d	10 31	10 37	11 00	11 30	11 37	12 00	12 30		12 37	13 00	13 30	13 37	14 00	14 30	14 37	15 01	15 30		15 37	16 02	16 07	16 31	16 37	17 02
Hurst Green	d	10 34	10 40	11 03	11 33	11 40	12 03	12 33		12 40	13 03	13 33	13 40	14 03	14 33	14 40	15 03	15 33		15 40	16 04	16 10	16 34	16 40	17 04
Lingfield	d	10 40		11 09	11 39		12 09	12 39			13 09	13 39		14 09	14 39		15 09	15 39			16 10		16 40		17 10
Dormans	d	10 43		11 12	11 42		12 12	12 42			13 12	13 42		14 12	14 42		15 13	15 42			16 14		16 43		17 14
East Grinstead	a	10 48		11 17	11 47		12 17	12 47			13 17	13 47		14 17	14 47		15 17	15 47			16 18		16 48		17 20
Edenbridge Town	d		10 46			11 46				12 46			13 46			14 46				15 46		16 16		16 46	
Hever	d		10 49			11 49				12 49			13 49			14 49				15 49		16 19		16 49	
Cowden	d		10 53			11 53				12 53			13 53			14 53				15 53		16 23		16 53	
Ashurst	d		10 58			11 58				12 58			13 58			14 58				15 58		16 28		16 58	
Eridge	d		11 03			12 03				13 03			14 03			15 03				16 03		16 33		17 03	
Crowborough	d		11 09			12 09				13 09			14 09			15 09				16 09		16 39		17 09	
Buxted	d		11 16			12 16				13 16			14 16			15 16				16 16		16 46		17 16	
Uckfield	a		11 23			12 23				13 23			14 23			15 23				16 21		16 51		17 21	

		SN [1]	SN [1]	SN [1]		SN [1]	SN [1]	SN [1]	SN [1]	SN [1]	SN [1]	SN [1]	SN [1]	SN [1]		SN [1]	SN [1]	SN [1]	SN [1]	SN [1]	SN [1]	SN [1]	SN [1]	SN [1]	
London Victoria [15] ⊖175,177	d		16 53				17 23			17 53			18 23				18 53		19 23	19 53		20 23	20 53		
Clapham Junction [10] 175,177	d		16 59				17 30			18 00			18 29				19 00		19 29	19 59		20 29	21 00		
London Bridge [4] ⊖175,177	d	16 38		17 08		17 15			17 44		18 08	18 16				18 47		19 08			20 04			21 04	
Norwood Junction [2] 175,177	d																				20 16			21 15	
East Croydon 175,177	d	16 53	17 10	17 23		17 30	17 41		17 58	18 11	18 22	18 31	18 41			19 01	19 11	19 23	19 40	20 10	20 20	20 40	21 11	21 19	
South Croydon [4] 175	d		17 12			17 32			18 01			18 33				19 03									
Sanderstead	d		17 15			17 35	17 45		18 04	18 15		18 36	18 46			19 06	19 15		19 44	20 14	20 24	20 44	21 16	21 24	
Riddlesdown	d		17 18			17 38	17 48		18 07	18 18		18 39	18 49			19 09	19 18		19 47	20 17		20 47	21 19		
Upper Warlingham	d		17 22			17 42	17 52		18 11	18 22		18 43	18 53			19 13	19 22		19 51	20 21	20 30	20 51	21 23	21 29	
Woldingham	d		17 26			17 46	17 56		18 15	18 26		18 47	18 57			19 17	19 26		19 55	20 25		20 55	21 27		
Oxted [3]	a	17 07	17 31	17 37		17 52	18 01		18 20	18 31	18 37	18 53	19 02			19 22	19 31	19 37	20 00	20 30	20 37	21 00	21 32	21 37	
	d	17 07	17 32	17 37		17 53	18 02	18 07	18 20	18 32	18 37	18 54	19 03	19 07		19 23	19 32	19 37	20 00	20 30	20 37	21 00	21 32	21 37	
Hurst Green	d	17 10	17 34	17 40		17 55	18 04	18 09	18 23	18 34	18 40	18 56	19 05	19 09		19 25	19 34	19 40	20 03	20 33	20 40	21 03	21 34	21 40	
Lingfield	d		17 40			18 01	18 10		18 29	18 40		19 02	19 11			19 31	19 40		20 09	20 39		21 09	21 40		
Dormans	d		17 44			18 05	18 14		18 32	18 44		19 06	19 15			19 35	19 44		20 12	20 42		21 12	21 44		
East Grinstead	a		17 50			18 12	18 22		18 40	18 52		19 12	19 22			19 42	19 52		20 17	20 47		21 17	21 49		
Edenbridge Town	d	17 16		17 46				18 16			18 46			19 15				19 46			20 46			21 46	
Hever	d	17 19						18 19						19 19				19 49			20 49			21 49	
Cowden	d	17 23						18 23			18 52			19 23				19 53			20 53			21 53	
Ashurst	d	17 28						18 28						19 27				19 58			20 58			21 58	
Eridge	d	17 33		17 58				18 34			19 00			19 33				20 03			21 03			22 03	
Crowborough	d	17 39		18 04				18 40			19 07			19 39				20 09			21 09			22 09	
Buxted	d	17 46		18 11				18 47			19 14			19 45				20 16			21 16			22 16	
Uckfield	a	17 51		18 18				18 52			19 21			19 51				20 21			21 21			22 21	

Table 184

London - Oxted, East Grinstead and Uckfield

Mondays to Fridays

9 December to 16 May

Network Diagram - see first Page of Table 181

		SN [1]	SN [1]	SN [1]	SN [1]	SN [1]	SN [1]	SN [1]	SN [1]
London Victoria [15] ⊖175,177	d	21 23	21 53		22 23	22 53		23 24	23 47
Clapham Junction [10] 175,177	d	21 29	21 59		22 29	22 59		23 30	23 53
London Bridge [4] ⊖175,177	d			22 04			23 04		
Norwood Junction [2] 175,177	d			22 15			23 15		
East Croydon 175,177 ⛴	d	21 40	22 10	22 19	22 40	23 10	23 19	23 41	00 05
South Croydon [4] 175	d								
Sanderstead	d	21 44	22 14	22 24	22 44	23 14	23 24	23 46	00s09
Riddlesdown	d	21 47	22 17		22 47	23 17		23 49	00s12
Upper Warlingham	d	21 51	22 21	22 29	22 51	23 21	23 29	23 53	00s16
Woldingham	d	21 55	22 25		22 55	23 25		23 57	00s20
Oxted [3]	a	22 00	22 30	22 36	23 00	23 30	23 36	00 02	00 25
	d	22 00	22 30	22 37	23 00	23 30	23 37	00 02	
Hurst Green	d	22 03	22 33	22 39	23 03	23 33	23 39	00 05	
Lingfield	d	22 09	22 39		23 09	23 39		00 11	
Dormans	d	22 12	22 42		23 12	23 42		00 14	
East Grinstead	a	22 17	22 47		23 17	23 47		00 19	
Edenbridge Town	d			22 45			23s45		
Hever	d			22s49					
Cowden	d			22s53					
Ashurst	d			22s57					
Eridge	d			23 03			23s58		
Crowborough	d			23 09			00s04		
Buxted	d			23 15			00s10		
Uckfield	a			23 21			00 16		

Saturdays

14 December to 17 May

		SN [1]	SN [1]	SN [1]	SN [1]	SN [1]	SN [1]		SN [1]	SN [1]	SN [1]	SN [1]	SN [1]	SN [1]	SN [1]	SN [1]	SN [1]	SN [1]	SN [1]	SN [1]	SN [1]	SN [1]
London Victoria [15] ⊖175,177	d			05 23		06 23	06 53	and at the same minutes past each hour until		19 23	19 53		20 23	20 53		21 23	21 53		22 23	22 53		23 24
Clapham Junction [10] 175,177	d			05 29		06 29	06 59			19 29	19 59		20 29	20 59		21 29	21 59		22 29	22 59		23 30
London Bridge [4] ⊖175,177	d				06 08				19 08			20 08			21 08			22 08			23 04	
Norwood Junction [2] 175,177	d			05 46								20 19			21 19			22 19			23 15	
East Croydon 175,177 ⛴	d		00 05	05 50	06 23	06 40	07 10		19 23	19 40	20 10	20 23	20 40	21 10	21 23	21 40	22 10	22 23	22 40	23 10	23 19	23 41
South Croydon [4] 175	d			05 53																		
Sanderstead	d		00s09			06 44	07 14			19 44	20 14		20 44	21 14		21 44	22 14		22 44	23 14	23 24	23 46
Riddlesdown	d		00s12			06 47	07 17			19 47	20 17		20 47	21 17		21 47	22 17		22 47	23 17		23 49
Upper Warlingham	d		00s16			06 51	07 21			19 51	20 21		20 51	21 21		21 51	22 21		22 51	23 21	23 29	23 53
Woldingham	d		00s20			06 55	07 25			19 55	20 25		20 55	21 25		21 55	22 25		22 55	23 25		23 57
Oxted [3]	a		00 25	06 04	06 37	07 00	07 30		19 37	20 00	20 30	20 37	21 00	21 30	21 37	22 00	22 30	22 37	23 00	23 30	23 36	00 02
	d	00 02		06 05	06 37	07 01	07 31		19 37	20 01	20 31	20 37	21 01	21 31	21 37	22 01	22 31	22 37	23 01	23 31	23 37	00 02
Hurst Green	d	00 05		06 07	06 40	07 03	07 33		19 40	20 03	20 33	20 40	21 03	21 33	21 40	22 03	22 33	22 40	23 03	23 33	23 39	00 05
Lingfield	d	00 11		06 13		07 09	07 39			20 09	20 39		21 09	21 39		22 09	22 39		23 09	23 39		00 11
Dormans	d	00 14		06 17		07 13	07 43			20 13	20 43		21 13	21 43		22 13	22 43		23 13	23 43		00 14
East Grinstead	a	00 19		06 21		07 17	07 47			20 17	20 47		21 17	21 47		22 17	22 47		23 17	23 47		00 19
Edenbridge Town	d				06 46				19 46			20 46			21 46			22 46			23s45	
Hever	d				06 49				19 49			20 49			21 49			22s49				
Cowden	d				06 53				19 53			20 53			21 53			22s53				
Ashurst	d				06 58				19 58			20 58			21 58			22s58				
Eridge	d				07 03				20 03			21 03			22 03			23 03			23s58	
Crowborough	d				07 09				20 09			21 09			22 09			23 09			00s04	
Buxted	d				07 16				20 16			21 16			22 16			23 16			00s10	
Uckfield	a				07 21				20 21			21 21			22 21			23 21			00 16	

		SN [1]
London Victoria [15] ⊖175,177	d	23 47
Clapham Junction [10] 175,177	d	23 53
London Bridge [4] ⊖175,177	d	
Norwood Junction [2] 175,177	d	
East Croydon 175,177 ⛴	d	00 04
South Croydon [4] 175	d	
Sanderstead	d	00s09
Riddlesdown	d	00s12
Upper Warlingham	d	00s16
Woldingham	d	00s20
Oxted [3]	a	00 25
	d	
Hurst Green	d	
Lingfield	d	
Dormans	d	
East Grinstead	a	
Edenbridge Town	d	
Hever	d	
Cowden	d	
Ashurst	d	
Eridge	d	
Crowborough	d	
Buxted	d	
Uckfield	a	

Table 184

Sundays

8 December to 11 May

London - Oxted, East Grinstead and Uckfield

Network Diagram - see first Page of Table 181

Station		SN 1	SN 1	SN 1	SN 1	SN 1	SN 1	SN 1	SN 1	SN 1	SN 1	SN 1
London Victoria 15 ⊖175,177	d			07 47	08 53		09 23	09 53		10 23	10 53	
Clapham Junction 10 175,177	d			07 54	08 59		09 29	09 59		10 29	10 59	
London Bridge 4 ⊖175,177	d											
Norwood Junction 2 175,177	d											
East Croydon 175,177	d		00 04	08 10	09 10	09 15	09 40	10 10	10 15	10 40	11 10	
South Croydon 4 175	d											
Sanderstead	d		00 09	08 15	09 14	09 20	09 44	10 14	10 20	10 44	11 14	
Riddlesdown	d		00 12	08 18	09 17		09 47	10 17		10 47	11 17	
Upper Warlingham	d		00 16	08 22	09 21	09 27	09 51	10 21	10 27	10 51	11 21	
Woldingham	d		00 20	08 26	09 25		09 55	10 25		10 55	11 25	
Oxted 3	a		00 25	08 31	09 30	09 36	10 00	10 30	10 36	11 00	11 32	
	d	00 02		08 31	09 30	09 37	10 01	10 31	10 37	11 01	11 33	11 37
Hurst Green	d	00 05		08 34	09 33	09 39	10 03	10 33	10 39	11 03	11 35	11 39
Lingfield	d	00 11		08 40	09 39		10 09	10 39		11 09	11 41	
Dormans	d	00 14		08 43	09 42		10 13	10 43		11 13	11 45	
East Grinstead	a	00 19		08 48	09 47		10 17	10 47		11 17	11 49	
Edenbridge Town	d					09 45			10 45			11 45
Hever	d					09 49			10 49			11 49
Cowden	d					09 53			10 53			11 53
Ashurst	d					09 57			10 57			11 57
Eridge	d					10 03			11 03			12 03
Crowborough	d					10 09			11 09			12 09
Buxted	d					10 15			11 15			12 15
Uckfield	a					10 21			11 21			12 21

Station			SN 1	SN 1	SN 1	SN 1	SN 1	SN 1	SN 1	SN 1
London Victoria 15 ⊖175,177	d	and at the same minutes past each hour until	19 23	19 53		20 53		21 53		22 36
Clapham Junction 10 175,177	d		19 29	19 59		20 59		21 59		22 42
London Bridge 4 ⊖175,177	d									
Norwood Junction 2 175,177	d									
East Croydon 175,177	d		19 40	20 10		21 10		22 10		22 57
South Croydon 4 175	d									
Sanderstead	d		19 44	20 14		21 14		22 14		23 01
Riddlesdown	d		19 47	20 17		21 17		22 17		23 04
Upper Warlingham	d		19 51	20 21		21 21		22 21		23 08
Woldingham	d		19 55	20 25		21 25		22 25		23 12
Oxted 3	a		20 00	20 32		21 32		22 32		23 17
	d		20 01	20 33	20 37	21 33	21 37	22 33	22 37	23 17
Hurst Green	d		20 03	20 35	20 39	21 35	21 39	22 35	22 39	23 20
Lingfield	d		20 09	20 41		21 41		22 41		23 26
Dormans	d		20 13	20 45		21 45		22 45		23 29
East Grinstead	a		20 17	20 49		21 49		22 49		23 34
Edenbridge Town	d				20 45		21 45		22 45	
Hever	d				20 49		21 49		22 49	
Cowden	d				20 53		21 53		22 53	
Ashurst	d				20 57		21 57		22 57	
Eridge	d				21 03		22 03		23 03	
Crowborough	d				21 09		22 09		23 09	
Buxted	d				21 15		22 15		23 15	
Uckfield	a				21 21		22 21		23 21	

Table 184R

Mondays to Fridays

9 December to 16 May

Uckfield, East Grinstead and Oxted - London

Network Diagram - see first Page of Table 181

Miles	Miles			SN 1	SN 1	SN 1	SN 1	SN 1	SN 1	SN 1	SN 1	SN 1	SN 1	SN 1	SN 1	SN 1	SN 1	SN 1	SN 1	SN 1		SN 1	SN 1	SN 1	SN 1
—	0	**Uckfield**	d	05 18			05 42					06 30			07 08			07 34				08 04			08 34
—	2½	**Buxted**	d	05 22			05 47					06 35			07 13			07 38				08 08			08 38
—	7¼	**Crowborough**	d	05 29			05 54					06 43			07 20			07 45				08 15			08 45
—	10½	**Eridge**	d	05 34			06 00					06 49			07 26			07 50				08 20			08 50
—	14¼	**Ashurst**	d									06 55						07 55				08 25			08 55
—	17	**Cowden**	d	05 42			06 08					07 00						08 01				08 30			09 00
—	19	**Hever**	d									07 04						08 06				08 34			09 05
—	20¾	**Edenbridge Town**	d	05 47			06 14					07 08			07 38			08 09				08 38			09 09
0	—	**East Grinstead**	d		05 45	05 58			06 14	06 37	06 49		07 05	07 19		07 36	07 49		08 07	08 17			08 37		
2¼	—	**Dormans**	d		05 49	06 02			06 18	06 41	06 53		07 09	07 23		07 40	07 53		08 11	08 21			08 41		
4	—	**Lingfield**	d		05 52	06 05			06 21	06 44	06 56		07 12	07 26		07 43	07 56		08 14	08 24			08 44		
8¾	—	**Hurst Green**	d		06 00	06 12	06 21		06 28	06 51	07 03	07 15	07 19	07 33	07 45	07 50	08 03	08 17	08 21	08 31		08 46	08 51		09 16
9¾	25	**Oxted** 3	a	05 55	06 02	06 14	06 24		06 30	06 53	07 05	07 18	07 22	07 35	07 48	07 53	08 05	08 20	08 24	08 33		08 49	08 53		09 19
—	—		d	05 55	06 03	06 15	06 25		06 31	06 54	07 06	07 18	07 22	07 36	07 49	07 53	08 06	08 20	08 24	08 34		08 49	08 53	09 14	09 19
13	—	**Woldingham**	d		06 08				06 36	06 59	07 11		07 28	07 41		07 59	08 11		08 30	08 39			08 59		
14¾	—	**Upper Warlingham**	d		06 12				06 40	07 03	07 15		07 31	07 45		08 02	08 15		08 33	08 43			09 02		
16½	—	**Riddlesdown**	d		06 15				06 43	07 06	07 18		07 35	07 48		08 06	08 18		08 37	08 46			09 06		
17¾	—	**Sanderstead**	d		06 18			06 38	06 47	07 10	07 22		07 38	07 52		08 09	08 22		08 40	08 49			09 09		
18¾	—	South Croydon 4 175	d					06 42	06 51		07 25			07 56			08 26		08 43	08 53					
19¾	0	East Croydon 175,177	a	06 09	06 23	06 27	06 38	06 44	06 53	07 15	07 28	07 31	07 44	07 58	08 04	08 14	08 29	08 33	08 45	08 55		09 02	09 13	09 28	09 33
—	1½	Norwood Junction 2 175,177	a																						
—	10¼	London Bridge 4 ⊖175,177	a	06 23	06 39		06 55		07 09		07 45	07 47		08 15	08 23		08 47	08 52		09 11		09 18			09 49
27½	—	Clapham Junction 10 175,177	a			06 37		07 06		07 27			07 54			08 26			08 56				09 26		
30¼	—	London Victoria 15 ⊖175,177	a			06 45		07 16		07 35			08 03			08 35			09 05				09 35		

		SN 1	SN 1	SN 1	SN 1	SN 1		SN 1	SN 1	SN 1		SN 1	SN 1	SN 1	SN 1	SN 1	SN 1	SN 1	SN 1	SN 1		SN 1	SN 1	SN 1
Uckfield	d			09 34				12 34				13 34			14 34			15 34				16 33		17 03
Buxted	d			09 38				12 38				13 38			14 38			15 38				16 37		17 07
Crowborough	d			09 45				12 45				13 45			14 45			15 45				16 45		17 15
Eridge	d			09 50				12 50				13 50			14 50			15 50				16 50		17 20
Ashurst	d			09 55				12 55				13 55			14 55			15 55				16 55		
Cowden	d			10 01				13 01				14 01			15 01			16 01				17 01		
Hever	d			10 05				13 05				14 05			15 05			16 05				17 05		
Edenbridge Town	d			10 09			and at	13 09				14 09			15 09			16 09				17 09		17 34
East Grinstead	d	09 07	09 37		10 07	10 37	the same		13 07	13 37			14 07	14 37		15 07	15 37		16 07	16 37			17 07	
Dormans	d	09 11	09 41		10 11	10 41	minutes		13 11	13 41			14 11	14 41		15 11	15 41		16 11	16 41			17 11	
Lingfield	d	09 14	09 44		10 14	10 44	past		13 14	13 44			14 14	14 44		15 14	15 44		16 14	16 44			17 14	
Hurst Green	d	09 21	09 51	10 16	10 21	10 51	each	13 16	13 21	13 51		14 16	14 21	14 51	15 16	15 21	15 51	16 16	16 21	16 51		17 16	17 21	17 41
Oxted 3	a	09 23	09 53	10 19	10 23	10 53	hour until	13 19	13 23	13 53		14 19	14 23	14 53	15 19	15 23	15 53	16 19	16 23	16 53		17 19	17 23	17 44
	d	09 23	09 53	10 19	10 23	10 53		13 19	13 23	13 53		14 19	14 23	14 53	15 19	15 23	15 53	16 19	16 23	16 53		17 19	17 23	
Woldingham	d	09 29	09 59		10 29	10 59			13 29	13 59			14 29	14 59		15 29	15 59		16 29	16 59			17 29	
Upper Warlingham	d	09 32	10 02		10 32	11 02			13 32	14 02			14 32	15 02		15 32	16 02		16 32	17 02			17 32	
Riddlesdown	d	09 36	10 06		10 36	11 06			13 36	14 06			14 36	15 06		15 36	16 06		16 36	17 06			17 36	
Sanderstead	d	09 39	10 09		10 39	11 09			13 39	14 09			14 39	15 09		15 39	16 09		16 39	17 09			17 39	
South Croydon 4 175	d																							
East Croydon 175,177	a	09 43	10 13	10 32	10 43	11 13		13 32	13 43	14 13		14 32	14 43	15 13	15 32	15 43	16 13	16 32	16 43	17 13		17 35	17 43	
Norwood Junction 2 175,177	a																							
London Bridge 4 ⊖175,177	a			10 49				13 49				14 49			15 49			16 47				17 53		
Clapham Junction 10 175,177	a	09 55	10 25		10 55	11 25			13 55	14 25			14 55	15 25		15 54	16 25		16 55	17 26			17 57	
London Victoria 15 ⊖175,177	a	10 05	10 35		11 02	11 32			14 02	14 32			15 02	15 35		16 05	16 35		17 05	17 33			18 05	

		SN 1	SN 1	SN 1	SN 1	SN 1	SN 1		SN 1	SN 1	SN 1	SN 1	SN 1	SN 1	SN 1	SN 1	SN 1		SN 1	SN 1	SN 1	SN 1	SN 1	SN 1	SN 1
Uckfield	d		17 32			17 58				18 32			19 00			19 33			20 04		20 34			21 34	
Buxted	d		17 36			18 02				18 36			19 04			19 37			20 08		20 38			21 38	
Crowborough	d		17 43			18 15				18 43			19 15			19 45			20 15		20 45			21 45	
Eridge	d		17 48			18 20				18 49			19 20			19 50			20 20		20 50			21 50	
Ashurst	d		17 53							18 54			19 25			19 55					20 55			21 55	
Cowden	d		17 58							18 59			19 30			20 01					21 01			22 01	
Hever	d		18 02							19 04			19 35			20 05					21 05			22 05	
Edenbridge Town	d		18 06			18 34				19 07			19 38			20 09			20 32		21 09			22 09	
East Grinstead	d	17 37		18 07	18 17		18 37		18 47		19 07	19 17		19 37	19 47		20 07			20 37		21 07	21 37		22 07
Dormans	d	17 41		18 11	18 21		18 41		18 51		19 11	19 21		19 41	19 51		20 11			20 41		21 11	21 41		22 11
Lingfield	d	17 44		18 14	18 24		18 44		18 54		19 14	19 24		19 44	19 54		20 14			20 44		21 14	21 44		22 14
Hurst Green	d	17 51	18 13	18 21	18 31	18 41	18 51		19 01	19 14	19 21	19 31	19 45	19 51	20 01	20 16	20 21		20 39	20 51	21 16	21 21	21 51	22 16	22 21
Oxted 3	a	17 53	18 16	18 23	18 33	18 44	18 53		19 03	19 17	19 23	19 33	19 48	19 53	20 03	20 19	20 23		20 42	20 53	21 19	21 23	21 53	22 19	22 23
	d	17 53	18 18	18 23	18 34		18 53		19 04	19 19	19 23	19 34	19 49	19 53	20 04	20 19	20 23		20 42	20 53	21 19	21 23	21 53	22 19	22 23
Woldingham	d	17 59		18 29	18 39		18 59		19 09		19 29	19 39		19 59	20 09		20 29			20 59		21 29	21 59		22 29
Upper Warlingham	d	18 02		18 32	18 43		19 02		19 13		19 32	19 43		20 02	20 13		20 32			21 02		21 32	22 02		22 32
Riddlesdown	d	18 06		18 36	18 46		19 06		19 16		19 36	19 46		20 06	20 16		20 36			21 06		21 36	22 06		22 36
Sanderstead	d	18 09		18 39	18 49		19 09		19 19		19 39	19 49		20 09	20 19		20 39			21 09		21 39	22 09		22 39
South Croydon 4 175	d																								
East Croydon 175,177	a	18 13	18 35	18 43	18 56		19 13		19 25	19 33	19 43	19 57	20 07	20 13	20 25	20 33	20 43		20 55	21 13	21 33	21 43	22 13	22 34	22 43
Norwood Junction 2 175,177	a				19 01																				
London Bridge 4 ⊖175,177	a		18 50		19 15					19 49			20 21			20 48			21 09		21 49			22 49	
Clapham Junction 10 175,177	a	18 25		18 55			19 25				19 55			20 25			20 55			21 25		21 55	22 25		22 55
London Victoria 15 ⊖175,177	a	18 35		19 05			19 35				20 05			20 35			21 03			21 32		22 02	22 32		23 05

Table 184R

Mondays to Fridays

9 December to 16 May

Uckfield, East Grinstead and Oxted - London

Network Diagram - see first Page of Table 181

Station	SN 1	SN 1		SN 1
Uckfield d				22 34
Buxted d				22 38
Crowborough d				22 45
Eridge d				22 50
Ashurst d				
Cowden d				
Hever d				
Edenbridge Town d				23 04
East Grinstead d	22 37	22 54		
Dormans d	22 41			
Lingfield d	22 44			
Hurst Green d	22 51			23 11
Oxted 3 a	22 53	23 06		23 14
Oxted 3 d	22 53	23 07		23 14
Woldingham d	22 59			
Upper Warlingham d	23 02			
Riddlesdown d	23 06			
Sanderstead d	23 09			
South Croydon 4 175 d				
East Croydon 175,177 a	23 13	23 19		23 28
Norwood Junction 2 175,177 a				
London Bridge 4 ⊖175,177 a				
Clapham Junction 10 175,177 a	23 25	23 32		
London Victoria 15 ⊖175,177 a	23 35	23 39		

Saturdays

14 December to 17 May

Station	SN 1	SN 1	SN 1	SN 1	SN 1		SN 1	SN 1	SN 1		SN 1	SN 1	SN 1	SN 1	SN 1	SN 1	SN 1	SN 1	SN 1		SN 1	SN 1	SN 1
Uckfield d		06 34			07 34	and at the same minutes past each hour until			11 34				12 34			13 34			14 34				15 34
Buxted d		06 38			07 38				11 38				12 38			13 38			14 38				15 38
Crowborough d		06 45			07 45				11 45				12 45			13 45			14 45				15 45
Eridge d		06 50			07 50				11 50				12 50			13 50			14 50				15 50
Ashurst d		06 55			07 55				11 55				12 55			13 55			14 56				15 55
Cowden d		07 01			08 01				12 01				13 01			14 01			15 01				16 01
Hever d		07 05			08 05				12 05				13 05			14 05			15 05				16 05
Edenbridge Town d		07 09			08 09				12 09				13 09			14 09			15 09				16 09
East Grinstead d	06 37		07 07	07 37			11 07	11 37			12 07	12 37		13 07	13 37		14 07	14 37			15 07	15 37	
Dormans d	06 41		07 11	07 41			11 11	11 41			12 11	12 41		13 11	13 41		14 11	14 41			15 11	15 41	
Lingfield d	06 44		07 14	07 44			11 14	11 44			12 14	12 44		13 14	13 44		14 14	14 44			15 14	15 44	
Hurst Green d	06 51	07 16	07 21	07 51	08 16		11 21	11 51	12 16		12 21	12 51	13 16	13 21	13 51	14 16	14 21	14 51	15 16		15 21	15 51	16 16
Oxted 3 a	06 53	07 19	07 23	07 53	08 19		11 23	11 53	12 19		12 23	12 53	13 19	13 23	13 53	14 19	14 23	14 53	15 19		15 23	15 53	16 19
Oxted 3 d	06 53	07 19	07 23	07 53	08 19		11 23	11 53	12 19		12 23	12 53	13 19	13 23	13 53	14 19	14 23	14 53	15 19		15 23	15 53	16 19
Woldingham d	06 59		07 29	07 59			11 29	11 59			12 29	12 59		13 29	13 59		14 29	14 59			15 29	15 59	
Upper Warlingham d	07 02		07 32	08 02			11 32	12 02			12 32	13 02		13 32	14 02		14 32	15 02			15 32	16 02	
Riddlesdown d	07 06		07 36	08 06			11 36	12 06			12 36	13 06		13 36	14 06		14 36	15 06			15 36	16 06	
Sanderstead d	07 09		07 39	08 09			11 39	12 09			12 39	13 09		13 39	14 09		14 39	15 09			15 39	16 09	
South Croydon 4 175 d																							
East Croydon 175,177 a	07 13	07 33	07 43	08 13	08 32		11 43	12 13	12 32		12 43	13 13	13 33	13 43	14 13	14 32	14 43	15 13	15 32		15 43	16 13	16 32
Norwood Junction 2 175,177 a																							
London Bridge 4 ⊖175,177 a		07 49			08 49				12 49				13 49			14 49			15 49				16 49
Clapham Junction 10 175,177 a	07 25		07 55	08 25			11 55	12 25			12 55	13 25		13 55	14 25		14 55	15 25			15 55	16 25	
London Victoria 15 ⊖175,177 a	07 32		08 02	08 32			12 02	12 32			13 02	13 32		14 02	14 32		15 02	15 32			16 02	16 32	

Station	SN 1	SN 1	SN 1	SN 1	SN 1	SN 1		SN 1	SN 1	SN 1	SN 1	SN 1	SN 1	SN 1	SN 1	SN 1		SN 1	SN 1	SN 1	SN 1	SN 1	SN 1	
Uckfield d			16 34			17 34				18 34			19 34			20 34				21 34			22 34	
Buxted d			16 38			17 38				18 38			19 38			20 38				21 38			22 38	
Crowborough d			16 45			17 45				18 45			19 45			20 45				21 45			22 45	
Eridge d			16 50			17 50				18 50			19 50			20 50				21 50			22 50	
Ashurst d			16 55			17 55				18 55			19 55			20 55				21 55				
Cowden d			17 01			18 01				19 01			20 01			21 01				22 01				
Hever d			17 05			18 05				19 05			20 05			21 05				22 05				
Edenbridge Town d			17 09			18 09				19 09			20 09			21 09				22 09			23 04	
East Grinstead d	16 07	16 37		17 07	17 37			18 07	18 37		19 07	19 37		20 07	20 37			21 07	21 37		22 07	22 37		
Dormans d	16 11	16 41		17 11	17 41			18 11	18 41		19 11	19 41		20 11	20 41			21 11	21 41		22 11	22 41		
Lingfield d	16 14	16 44		17 14	17 44			18 14	18 44		19 14	19 44		20 14	20 44			21 14	21 44		22 14	22 44		
Hurst Green d	16 21	16 51	17 16	17 21	17 51	18 16		18 21	18 51	19 16	19 21	19 51	20 16	20 21	20 51	21 16		21 21	21 51	22 16	22 21	22 51	23 11	
Oxted 3 a	16 23	16 53	17 19	17 23	17 53	18 19		18 23	18 53	19 19	19 23	19 53	20 19	20 23	20 53	21 19		21 23	21 53	22 19	22 23	22 53	23 14	
Oxted 3 d	16 23	16 53	17 19	17 23	17 53	18 19		18 23	18 53	19 19	19 23	19 53	20 19	20 23	20 53	21 19		21 23	21 53	22 19	22 23	22 53	23 15	
Woldingham d	16 29	16 59		17 29	17 59			18 29	18 59		19 29	19 59		20 29	20 59			21 29	21 59		22 29	22 59		
Upper Warlingham d	16 32	17 02		17 32	18 02			18 32	19 02		19 32	20 02		20 32	21 02			21 32	22 02		22 32	23 02		
Riddlesdown d	16 36	17 06		17 36	18 06			18 36	19 06		19 36	20 06		20 36	21 06			21 36	22 06		22 36	23 06		
Sanderstead d	16 39	17 09		17 39	18 09			18 39	19 09		19 39	20 09		20 39	21 09			21 39	22 09		22 39	23 09		
South Croydon 4 175 d																								
East Croydon 175,177 a	16 43	17 13	17 32	17 43	18 13	18 32		18 43	19 13	19 32	19 43	20 13	20 33	20 43	21 13	21 34		21 43	22 13	22 34	22 43	23 13	23 28	
Norwood Junction 2 175,177 a																								
London Bridge 4 ⊖175,177 a			17 49			18 49				19 49			20 49			21 49				22 49				
Clapham Junction 10 175,177 a	16 55	17 25		17 55	18 25			18 55	19 25		19 55	20 25		20 55	21 25			21 55	22 25		22 55	23 25		
London Victoria 15 ⊖175,177 a	17 02	17 32		18 02	18 32			19 02	19 35		20 05	20 32		21 02	21 32			22 02	22 32		23 02	23 32		

Table 184R

Sundays

8 December to 11 May

Uckfield, East Grinstead and Oxted - London

Network Diagram - see first Page of Table 181

Station		SN 1	SN 1		SN 1	SN 1	SN 1	SN 1		SN 1	SN 1	SN 1	SN 1	SN 1	SN 1	SN 1	SN 1	SN 1	SN 1	SN 1
Uckfield	d					10 34				18 34			19 34		20 34		21 34		22 34	
Buxted	d					10 38				18 38			19 38		20 38		21 38		22 38	
Crowborough	d					10 45				18 45			19 45		20 45		21 45		22 45	
Eridge	d					10 50				18 50			19 50		20 50		21 50		22 50	
Ashurst	d					10 56				18 56			19 56		20 56		21 56		22 56	
Cowden	d					11 00				19 00			20 00		21 00		22 00		23 00	
Hever	d					11 05				19 05			20 05		21 05		22 05		23 05	
Edenbridge Town	d					11 08			and at	19 08			20 08		21 08		22 08		23 08	
East Grinstead	d	08 20	09 12	and	10 42		11 12	11 42	the same		19 12	19 42		20 12		21 12		22 12		23 09
Dormans	d	08 24	09 16	every 30	10 46		11 16	11 46	minutes		19 16	19 46		20 16		21 16		22 16		23 13
Lingfield	d	08 27	09 19	minutes	10 49		11 19	11 49	past		19 19	19 49		20 19		21 19		22 19		23 16
Hurst Green	d	08 34	09 26	until	10 56	11 15	11 26	11 56	each	19 15	19 26	19 56	20 15	20 26	21 15	21 26	22 15	22 26	23 15	23 23
Oxted 3	a	08 36	09 28		10 58	11 18	11 28	11 58	hour until	19 18	19 28	19 58	20 18	20 28	21 18	21 28	22 18	22 28	23 18	23 25
	d	08 36	09 28		10 58		11 28	11 58			19 28	19 58		20 28		21 28		22 28	23 19	23 25
Woldingham	d	08 42	09 34		11 04		11 34	12 04			19 34	20 04		20 34		21 34		22 34		23 31
Upper Warlingham	d	08 45	09 37		11 07		11 37	12 07			19 37	20 07		20 37		21 37		22 37		23 34
Riddlesdown	d	08 49	09 41		11 11		11 41	12 11			19 41	20 11		20 41		21 41		22 41		23 38
Sanderstead	d	08 52	09 44		11 14		11 44	12 14			19 44	20 14		20 44		21 44		22 44		23 41
South Croydon 4 175	d																			
East Croydon 175,177	a	08 58	09 49		11 19		11 49	12 19			19 49	20 19		20 49		21 49		22 49	23 32	23 46
Norwood Junction 2 175,177	a																			
London Bridge 4 ⊖175,177	a																			
Clapham Junction 10 175,177	a	09 08	10 02		11 32		12 02	12 32			20 02	20 32		21 02		22 02		23 02		23 59
London Victoria 15 ⊖175,177	a	09 15	10 09		11 39		12 09	12 39			20 09	20 39		21 09		22 09		23 09		00 07

Table 186

Bedford and London - Brighton

Mondays to Fridays

9 December to 16 May

Network Diagram - see first Page of Table 175

Miles	Miles	Miles			GW MX 1	SN MX 1	FC MO 1	FC MX 1	SN MO 1	SN MX 1	SN MX 1	SN MO 1	SN MO 1	SN MX 1	SN MX 1	FC MX 1	FC MO 1	SN MX 1	SN 1	GW MO 1	SN MX 1
0	—	—	London Victoria 15 ⊖	d															00 02		00 05
2¾	50¾	6¼	Clapham Junction 10	d																	00 12
—	—	—	Bedford	d																	
—	—	—	Luton 10	d																	
—	—	—	Luton Airport Parkway 7 ✈	d																	
—	—	—	St Albans City	d																	
—	—	—	St Pancras International 15 ⊖	d																	
—	—	—	Farringdon 3 ⊖	d																	
—	—	—	City Thameslink 3	d																	
—	—	—	London Blackfriars 3 ⊖	d																	
—	0	—	London Bridge 4 ⊖	d																	
—	—	—	New Cross Gate	d																	
—	9	—	Norwood Junction 2	d																	
10½	10¾	—	East Croydon ⇌	a																	00 26
—	—	—		d														00 01			00 27
13½	—	—	Purley 4	d														00 11			
15½	—	—	**Coulsdon South**	d														00 15			
19	—	—	**Merstham**	d														00 20			
21	0	0	**Redhill**	a														00 24			
—	—	—		d	00 01								00 05	00 05				00 25		00 34	
—	1¾	—	**Reigate**	a																	
—	—	2	**Nutfield**	d																	
—	—	5¾	**Godstone**	d																	
—	—	10½	**Edenbridge**	d											00 06						
—	—	15½	**Penshurst**	d																	
—	—	17¼	**Leigh (Kent)**	d																	
—	—	19¾	Tonbridge 4	a											00 15						
21¾	—	—	**Earlswood (Surrey)**	d																	
23¾	—	—	**Salfords**	d																	
26	—	—	**Horley** 4	d														00 31			
26¾	—	—	**Gatwick Airport** 10 ✈	a	00 11								00 14	00 14				00 34	00 39	00 41	00 45
—	—	—		d									00 15	00 15		00 19	00 20	00 35			00 46
29½	0	—	**Three Bridges** 4	a									00 19	00 20		00 24	00 24	00 39			00 50
—	—	—		d						00 05		00 06	00 20	00 20			00 25	00 39			00 50
—	1½	—	**Crawley**	d					00 03	00 09								00 43			
—	2¾	—	**Ifield**	d					00 05	00 11								00 46			
—	5¼	—	**Faygate**	d																	
—	7½	—	**Littlehaven**	d					00 12	00 18								00 52			
—	8½	—	Horsham 4	a					00 15	00 23								00 57			
34	—	—	**Balcombe**	d									00 26	00 26							
38	—	—	**Haywards Heath**	a								00 15	00 31	00 31			00 34				00 59
—	—	—		d							00 05	00 15	00 31	00 32			00 36				01 03 / 01 05
41	0	—	**Wivelsfield**	d				00 03					00 35	00 36							
—	9¼	—	Lewes 4	a																	01 19
41¾	—	—	**Burgess Hill** 4	d			00 02	00 05			00 11	00 20	00 37	00 38			00 42				
43¾	—	—	**Hassocks** 4	d		00 03	00 06	00 08					00 41	00 41			00 45				
49½	0	—	**Preston Park**	d		00 09		00 15					00 48	00 48							
—	1½	—	Hove 2	a							00 22	00 31									
51	—	—	Brighton 10	a		00 15	00 15	00 19					00 52	00 52			00 55				01s17

		FC 1 A	FC MO 1 B	GW MX 1	SN 1	SN 1	SN 1	FC MO 1 B	FC 1 A	SN 1	FC MO 1	FC MX 1	SN 1	FC 1	SN 1	FC 1	SN 1
London Victoria 15 ⊖	d				00 14		00 32			01 00			02 00		03 00		03 30
Clapham Junction 10	d				00 21					01 09			02 09		03 09		
Bedford	d													00 42		01 42	
Luton 10	d										00 06	00 06		01 06		02 06	
Luton Airport Parkway 7 ✈	d										00 09	00 09		01 09		02 09	
St Albans City	d										00 21	00 21		01 21		02 21	
St Pancras International 15 ⊖	d							00 14	00 24		00 54	00 54		01 54		02 54	
Farringdon 3 ⊖	d							00 19	00 29								
City Thameslink 3	d																
London Blackfriars 3 ⊖	d	00 05						00 25	00 35		01 05	01 05		02 05		03 05	
London Bridge 4 ⊖	d	00 12							00 42								
New Cross Gate	d																
Norwood Junction 2	d																
East Croydon ⇌	a	00 28			00 35			00 56	00 56	01 23	01 34	01 34	02 24	02 34	03 24	03 34	
	d	00 29	00 29		00 36			00 57	00 57	01 24	01 36	01 36	02 24	02 36	03 25	03 36	
Purley 4	d				00 40					01 29			02 30		03 30		
Coulsdon South	d				00 44												
Merstham	d				00 50												
Redhill	a				00 54												
	d			00 54	00 56	05 35											
Reigate	a																
Nutfield	d					05 39											
Godstone	d					05 45											
Edenbridge	d					05 50											
Penshurst	d					05 57											
Leigh (Kent)	d					06 00											
Tonbridge 4	a					06 05											
Earlswood (Surrey)	d																
Salfords	d																
Horley 4	d				01 02					01 45			02 44		03 44		
Gatwick Airport 10 ✈	a	00 48	00 48	01 03	01 05		01 08	01 18	01 18	01 47	01 55	01 55	02 47	02 55	03 47	03 55	04 06
	d	00 49	00 49					01 19	01 19	01 48	01 55	01 56	02 48	02 56	03 48	03 56	
Three Bridges 4	a	00 54	00 54					01 24	01 24	01 53	02 02	02 02	02 53	03 02	03 53	04 02	
	d									01 53							
Crawley	d																
Ifield	d																
Faygate	d																
Littlehaven	d																
Horsham 4	a																
Balcombe	d																
Haywards Heath	a									02 05							
	d									02 06							
Wivelsfield	d																
Lewes 4	a																
Burgess Hill 4	d																
Hassocks 4	d																
Preston Park	d																
Hove 2	a																
Brighton 10	a									02 23							

A until 3 January, MX from 7 January

B from 6 January

Table 186

Mondays to Fridays

9 December to 16 May

Bedford and London - Brighton

Network Diagram - see first Page of Table 175

Station		FC	SN	FC	SN	FC	SN	SN	GW	FC	SN	SN	GW	SN	SN	SN	SN	FC
		1 A	1	1	1	1	1	1	1	1	1	✈	1	1	1 ✈	1		1
London Victoria 15 ⊖	d		04 00		04 30		05 00	05 01				05 15			05 30			
Clapham Junction 10	d		04 09					05 08										
Bedford	d			02 42						03 42								04 08
Luton 10	d			03 06						04 06								04 32
Luton Airport Parkway 7 ✈	d			03 09						04 09								04 35
St Albans City	d			03 21						04 21								04 47
St Pancras International 15 ⊖	d	03 25		03 54		04 24				04 54								05 12
Farringdon 3 ⊖	d									04 59								05 18
City Thameslink 3	d																	05 21
London Blackfriars 3 ⊖	d	03 36		04 05		04 35				05 05								05 24
London Bridge 4 ⊖	d																	05 30
New Cross Gate	d																	
Norwood Junction 2	d																	
East Croydon	a	04 04	04 26	04 34		05 04		05 22		05 31								05 47
	d	04 06	04 26	04 36		05 06		05 23		05 32								05 48
Purley 4	d		04 32					05 27										
Coulsdon South	d							05 31										
Merstham	d							05 36										
Redhill	a							05 40										
	d							05 41	05 43				05 44			05 57		
Reigate	a								05 48									
Nutfield	d															06 01		
Godstone	d															06 07		
Edenbridge	d															06 12		
Penshurst	d															06 19		
Leigh (Kent)	d															06 22		
Tonbridge 4	a															06 27		
Earlswood (Surrey)	d																	
Salfords	d										←							
Horley 4	d		04 48					05 47			05 47							
Gatwick Airport 10 ✈	a	04 25	04 51	04 55	05 07	05 25	05 35	→		05 47	05 49	05 51	05 54		06 00			06 02
	d	04 26	04 52	04 56		05 26				05 48	05 50			05 59				06 04
Three Bridges 4	a	04 32	04 56	05 01		05 31				05 52	05 55			06 03				06 08
	d		04 56	05 02		05 32				05 52	05 55			06 03				06 08
Crawley	d													06 07				
Ifield	d													06 09				
Faygate	d																	
Littlehaven	d													06 16				
Horsham 4	a													06 19				
Balcombe	d										06 01							06 14
Haywards Heath	a		05 05	05 11		05 41				06 01	06 06							06 19
	d		05 06	05 12		05 41				06 02	06 06						06 09	06 19
Wivelsfield	d					05 45					06 10						06 13	06 23
Lewes 4	a																06 26	
Burgess Hill 4	d					05 47				06 07	06 13							06 25
Hassocks 4	d					05 51				06 10	06 16							06 29
Preston Park	d					05 57				06 18	06 23							06 35
Hove 2	a																	
Brighton 10	a		05 21	05 30		06 02				06 22	06 27							06 40

Station		SN	SN	GW	FC MX	FC MO	SN	GW	GW	SN	SN		SN	SN	FC	SN	SN	SN	SN	SN
		✈	1	1	1	1	1 ✈	1	1	1	1		1	1 B ✈	1	1	1	1	1 B ✈	1
London Victoria 15 ⊖	d	05 45	05 32				06 00				06 02		06 06	06 15					06 30	06 21
Clapham Junction 10	d		05 38								06 08		06 12							06 27
Bedford	d				04 20	04 20									05 00					
Luton 10	d				04 44	04 44									05 24					
Luton Airport Parkway 7 ✈	d				04 47	04 47									05 27					
St Albans City	d				04 59	04 59									05 39					
St Pancras International 15 ⊖	d				05 32	05 32									06 02					
Farringdon 3 ⊖	d				05 38	05 38									06 08					
City Thameslink 3	d				05 41	05 41									06 11					
London Blackfriars 3 ⊖	d				05 44	05 44									06 14					
London Bridge 4 ⊖	d				05 50	05 50									06 20					
New Cross Gate	d																			
Norwood Junction 2	d																			
East Croydon	a		05 48		06 05	06 05					06 17		06 22		06 33					06 38
	d		05 49		06 05	06 06					06 18		06 23		06 35					06 38
Purley 4	d		05 53								06 23									06 43
Coulsdon South	d		05 57								06 27									06 47
Merstham	d		06 02								06 32									06 52
Redhill	a		06 06								06 36									06 56
	d		06 07	06 13				06 24	06 33	06 39	06 40	06 42								06 57
Reigate	a			06 18				06 28		06 43										
Nutfield	d											06 46								
Godstone	d											06 52								
Edenbridge	d											06 57								
Penshurst	d											07 04								
Leigh (Kent)	d											07 07								
Tonbridge 4	a											07 12								
Earlswood (Surrey)	d		06 09								06 42									
Salfords	d		06 13								06 46					←				
Horley 4	d		06 16								06 49					06 49				07 03
Gatwick Airport 10 ✈	a	06 15	06 19		06 21	06 21	06 30		06 41		→		06 38	06 45	06 51	06 54			06 59	07 05
	d		06 20		06 23	06 23							06 40	06 48	06 52	06 55			07 04	07 06
Three Bridges 4	a		06 24		06 27	06 27							06 44		06 56	06 59				07 11
	d		06 25		06 27	06 27							06 45		06 56	07 00	07 05			07 11
Crawley	d															07 03	07 08			
Ifield	d																07 11			
Faygate	d																07 15			
Littlehaven	d																07 19			
Horsham 4	a															07 11	07 22			
Balcombe	d				06 34	06 34														
Haywards Heath	a		06 34		06 39	06 39								06 59	07 05				07 15	07 20
	d		06 34		06 39	06 39								07 00	07 06			07 10	07 16	07 21
Wivelsfield	d		06 38		06 43	06 43									07 10			07 14		07 25
Lewes 4	a		06 50															07 29		
Burgess Hill 4	d				06 45	06 45									07 12					07 27
Hassocks 4	d				06 49	06 49									07 16					07 30
Preston Park	d				06 55	06 55									07 22					07 37
Hove 2	a																			
Brighton 10	a				06 59	06 59							07 05	07 13	07 27				07 35	07 41

A 1 from London Blackfriars

B ✈ to Gatwick Airport

Table 186

Mondays to Fridays

9 December to 16 May

Bedford and London - Brighton

Network Diagram - see first Page of Table 175

Station		SN	GW	SN		GW	FC	SN	SN	SN	SN		FC	SN	SN	SN	SN	FC	GW	SN	SN	SN	SN	GW	SN	SN	SN	FC	SN	SN		SN	SN		SN	SN	GW
		1	1	1		1	1	1	1	1	1		1	1	1	1	1	1	1	1	1	1	1	1	1	1	1	1	1	1		1	1		1	1	1
								A 🛒						🛒			🛒						🛒						🛒						🛒		
London Victoria 15 ⊖	d			06 32				06 45	06 47		06 51			07 00		07 02	07 15			07 17			07 30				07 36		07 45	07 47					08 00	08 02	
Clapham Junction 10	d			06 38					06 53		06 57					07 08				07 23							07 42			07 53						08 08	
Bedford	d						05 20						05 40					05 58										06 22									
Luton 10	d						05 44						06 04					06 22										06 46									
Luton Airport Parkway 7 ✈	d						05 46						06 06					06 24										06 48									
St Albans City	d						05 58						06 18					06 36										07 00									
St Pancras International 15 ⊖	d						06 22						06 38					06 58										07 20									
Farringdon 3 ⊖	d						06 28						06 44					07 04										07 26									
City Thameslink 3	d						06 31						06 47					07 07										07 29									
London Blackfriars 3 ⊖	d						06 34						06 50					07 09										07 32									
London Bridge 4 ⊖	d						06 42						07 00					07 16			07 23				07 30			07 42					07 51				
New Cross Gate	d																								07 36												
Norwood Junction 2	d																				07 35				07 44								08 02				
East Croydon 🚌	a			06 48			06 54		07 03		07 06		07 14			07 17		07 30		07 33	07 38				07 47		07 52	07 54		08 03			08 06			08 18	
	d			06 49			06 55		07 04		07 07		07 15			07 18		07 31		07 34	07 39				07 48		07 52	07 55		08 04			08 07			08 18	
Purley 4	d			06 55												07 23					07 45				07 54												
Coulsdon South	d			06 59							07 13					07 26					07 48				07 58												
Merstham	d			07 04							07 19					07 32					07 54				08 03												
Redhill	a			07 08							07 23					07 36				07 47	07 58				08 07								08 19			08 30	
	d	07 00	07 10	07 12	07 14	07 28					07 28	07 30				07 37			07 41	07 47	07 59	08 00		08 08	08 11	08 17							08 23	08 25		08 30	08 33
Reigate	a	07 04	07 15			07 32										07 43						08 04		08 13		08 21											08 37
Nutfield	d				07 18							07 34									08 04													08 29			
Godstone	d				07 24							07 40									08 09													08 35			
Edenbridge	d				07 29							07 45									08 15													08 40			
Penshurst	d				07 36							07 52									08 21													08 47			
Leigh (Kent)	d				07 39							07 55									08 25													08 50			
Tonbridge 4	a				07 44							08 02									08 29													08 55			
Earlswood (Surrey)	d			07 14							07 30									07 50					08 13												
Salfords	d			07 18						←	07 34				←					07 53					08 17							←					
Horley 4	d			07 21						07 21	07 37				07 37					07 57					08 21							08 21					
Gatwick Airport 10 ✈	a			→			07 10	07 16	07 19	07 24	→		07 30	07 31	07 40		07 45	07 46	07 50	07 59			08 03		→		08 07	08 11	08 16	08 18		08 23	08 30		08 31	08 37	
	d						07 11	07 25	07 20	07 25			07 31		07 41			07 47		08 00							08 08	08 12		08 20		08 24	08 31			08 40	
Three Bridges 4	a						07 15		07 24	07 29			07 35		07 45			07 51		08 05							08 12	08 16				08 29	08 35			08 44	
	d						07 15		07 24	07 30			07 35		07 46			07 51		08 05							08 12	08 16				08 30	08 36			08 45	
Crawley	d									07 34					07 50					08 09												08 34				08 48	
Ifield	d									07 36					07 53					08 11												08 36					
Faygate	d																			08 15												08 40					
Littlehaven	d									07 43					07 59					08 19												08 44					
Horsham 4	a									07 46					08 04					08 22												08 48				08 56	
Balcombe	d						07 21											07 57										08 22									
Haywards Heath	a						07 26	07 37	07 33				07 44					08 02									08 21	08 27		08 30			08 45				
	d						07 26	07 38	07 33				07 45					08 02									08 22	08 27		08 34	08 37		08 45				
Wivelsfield	d								07 37				07 49					08 06										08 31		08 38			08 49				
Lewes 4	a								07 52																					08 53							
Burgess Hill 4	d						07 31						07 51					08 08									08 27	08 33					08 51				
Hassocks 4	d						07 35						07 54					08 12										08 37					08 55				
Preston Park	d												08 01					08 18										08 43					09 01				
Hove 2	a																														08 53						
Brighton 10	a						07 44	07 53					08 05					08 23									08 38	08 48					09 05				

A 🛒 to Gatwick Airport

Table 186

Bedford and London - Brighton

Mondays to Fridays

9 December to 16 May

Network Diagram - see first Page of Table 175

		SN 1	SN 1	FC 1	SN 1	SN 1		FC 1	SN 1	GW 1	SN 1		SN 1	SN 1	SN 1	SN 1	SN 1	FC 1	SN 1	GW 1	SN 1	SN 1	SN 1		SN 1	SN 1	FC 1	SN 1	SN 1	GW 1	SN 1	SN	FC 1	SN 1	GW 1	SN 1
					⚒									⚒			⚒				A ⚒	B ⚒	⚒					⚒				⚒		⚒		
London Victoria 15 ⊖	d		08 07		08 15	08 17							08 21	08 30	08 32		08 37				08 45	08 45	08 47		08 49			09 00	09 02			09 06		09 15		
Clapham Junction 10	d		08 13			08 23							08 27		08 38		08 43						08 53		08 56				09 08			09 12				
Bedford	d			06 54				06 58										07 30									07 34						07 48			
Luton 10	d			07 14				07 22										07 50									07 58						08 12			
Luton Airport Parkway 7 ✈	d							07 25																			08 00						08 15			
St Albans City	d			07 26				07 38										08 02									08 11						08 28			
St Pancras International 15 ⊖	d			07 44				07 56										08 20									08 32						08 48			
Farringdon 3 ⊖	d			07 50				08 02										08 26									08 38						08 54			
City Thameslink 3	d			07 53				08 05										08 29									08 41						08 57			
London Blackfriars 3 ⊖	d			07 56				08 08										08 32									08 44						09 00			
London Bridge 4 ⊖	d	08 00						08 18			08 23					08 28			08 42												09 01		09 12			09 15
New Cross Gate	d	08 08														08 37			08 48												09 09					
Norwood Junction 2	d	08 16														08 46			08 56												09 17					09 26
East Croydon	a	08 19	08 22	08 26		08 34		08 37			08 37		08 40		08 48	08 50	08 52	08 57	08 59				09 03		09 07		09 12		09 18		09 20	09 21	09 24			09 29
	d	08 21	08 23	08 26		08 34		08 37			08 38		08 40		08 48	08 52	08 53	08 58	09 00				09 04		09 08		09 12		09 19		09 21	09 22	09 25			09 30
Purley 4	d	08 27														08 59			09 06												09 26					09 36
Coulsdon South	d	08 31									08 48					09 02			09 09												09 30					09 39
Merstham	d	08 36														09 08															09 35					09 45
Redhill	a	08 40									08 55				09 02	09 12			09 17										09 30		09 39					09 49
	d	08 41								08 50	08 59	09 01			09 03	09 12			09 17	09 23									09 30	09 34	09 40				09 51	09 53
Reigate	a											09 05								09 28										09 38						09 58
Nutfield	d										09 03								09 22																	
Godstone	d										09 09								09 27																	
Edenbridge	d										09 14								09 33																	
Penshurst	d										09 21								09 39																	
Leigh (Kent)	d										09 24								09 43																	
Tonbridge 4	a										09 29								09 48																	
Earlswood (Surrey)	d	08 43														09 15															09 42					
Salfords	d	08 47							←							09 18										←					09 46					
Horley 4	d	08 50							08 50							09 22										09 22			09 36		09 50					
Gatwick Airport 10 ✈	a	→		08 41	08 45	08 49		08 52	08 53	08 59			08 56	09 00	09 10	→		09 12			09 15	09 16	09 18		09 22	09 24	09 27	09 30	09 39		→		09 40	09 45	09 59	
	d			08 42		08 50		08 53	08 54				08 57		09 11			09 13					09 20		09 23	09 25	09 28		09 40				09 41			
Three Bridges 4	a		08 41	08 46				08 57	08 58				09 01		09 16			09 17								09 30	09 32		09 44				09 45			
	d		08 42	08 46				08 58	09 00				09 01		09 16			09 17								09 30	09 32		09 45				09 45			
Crawley	d								09 04						09 19											09 34			09 48							
Ifield	d								09 06																	09 36										
Faygate	d								09 10																											
Littlehaven	d								09 14																	09 43										
Horsham 4	a								09 18						09 27											09 46			09 56							
Balcombe	d			08 52																													09 51			
Haywards Heath	a		08 51	08 57		09 00		09 07					09 12					09 26					09 30				09 41						09 56			
	d		08 52	08 58		09 04	09 10	09 08					09 21					09 27					09 35	09 37			09 41						09 56			
Wivelsfield	d			09 02			09 14						09 25																				10 00			
Lewes 4	a						09 25																09 53													
Burgess Hill 4	d			09 04		09 09		09 13					09 27					09 32							09 38								10 02			
Hassocks 4	d			09 07									09 31					09 35							09 42								10 06			
Preston Park	d			09 14		09 18							09 37					09 42															10 12			
Hove 2	a					09 22																		09 53												
Brighton 10	a		09 08	09 18				09 25					09 41				09 28	09 46							09 52		09 55					09 58	10 17			

A until 7 February

B from 10 February

Table 186

Mondays to Fridays

9 December to 16 May

Bedford and London - Brighton

Network Diagram - see first Page of Table 175

		SN	SN	FC	SN	SN	SN	GW	SN	FC	SN	SN	SN	SN	SN	FC	SN	SN
		1	1	1	1	1	1	1	1	1	1	1	1	1	1	1	1	1
		A ☕			☕							☕	☕				☕	
London Victoria 15 ⊖	d	09 17			09 30	09 32			09 36			09 45	09 47	09 51			10 00	10 02
Clapham Junction 10	d	09 23				09 38			09 42				09 53					10 08
Bedford	d			08 04						08 24						08 40		
Luton 10	d			08 28						08 48						09 04		
Luton Airport Parkway 7 ✈	d			08 30						08 50						09 06		
St Albans City	d			08 44						09 02						09 18		
St Pancras International 15 ⊖	d			09 04						09 22						09 40		
Farringdon 3 ⊖	d			09 10						09 28						09 45		
City Thameslink 3	d			09 13						09 31						09 48		
London Blackfriars 3 ⊖	d			09 16						09 34						09 50		
London Bridge 4 ⊖	d			09 27			09 32			09 42	09 45					09 57		
New Cross Gate	d						09 38											
Norwood Junction 2	d						09 46				09 56							
East Croydon ⇌	a	09 32		09 39		09 48	09 50		09 51	09 54	09 59		10 02	10 07		10 09		10 17
	d	09 33		09 41		09 48	09 51		09 52	09 55	10 00		10 03	10 08		10 11		10 18
Purley 4	d						09 56				10 06							
Coulsdon South	d						10 00				10 09							
Merstham	d						10 05											
Redhill	a					10 00	10 09				10 17							10 29
	d					10 00	10 10	10 13			10 17							10 30
Reigate	a							10 18										
Nutfield	d										10 22							
Godstone	d										10 27							
Edenbridge	d										10 33							
Penshurst	d										10 39							
Leigh (Kent)	d										10 43							
Tonbridge 4	a										10 48							
Earlswood (Surrey)	d						10 12											
Salfords	d		←				10 16								←			
Horley 4	d		09 50				10 19								10 19			10 36
Gatwick Airport 10 ✈	a	09 48	09 52	09 56	10 00	10 08	→			10 10		10 15	10 18	10 22	10 23	10 26	10 30	10 38
	d	09 50	09 53	09 57		10 09				10 11			10 20	10 23	10 24	10 27		10 39
Three Bridges 4	a		09 58	10 01		10 14				10 15					10 29	10 31		10 44
	d		10 00	10 02		10 14				10 15					10 30	10 32		10 44
Crawley	d		10 03			10 18									10 33			10 48
Ifield	d		10 06												10 36			
Faygate	d																	
Littlehaven	d		10 12												10 42			
Horsham 4	a		10 18			10 26									10 49			10 56
Balcombe	d									10 21								
Haywards Heath	a	10 00		10 11						10 26			10 30			10 41		
	d	10 05 10 07		10 11						10 27			10 35 10 37			10 41		
Wivelsfield	d	10 11								10 31								
Lewes 4	a	10 22											10 52					
Burgess Hill 4	d	10 10								10 33				10 38				
Hassocks 4	d									10 36				10 42				
Preston Park	d	10 18								10 43								
Hove 2	a	10 22											10 53					
Brighton 10	a			10 25					10 28	10 47				10 52		10 55		

		GW	GW	SN	SN	FC	SN	SN	SN	SN	FC	SN	SN	SN	GW	SN	FC
		1	1	1	1	1	1	1	1	1	1	1	1	1	1	1	1
					☕			☕	A ☕			☕					
London Victoria 15 ⊖	d				10 06			10 15	10 17			10 30	10 32			10 36	
Clapham Junction 10	d				10 12				10 23				10 38			10 42	
Bedford	d					08 54					09 10						09 24
Luton 10	d					09 18					09 34						09 48
Luton Airport Parkway 7 ✈	d					09 20					09 36						09 50
St Albans City	d					09 32					09 48						10 02
St Pancras International 15 ⊖	d					09 54					10 10						10 24
Farringdon 3 ⊖	d					09 59					10 15						10 29
City Thameslink 3	d					10 03					10 18						10 33
London Blackfriars 3 ⊖	d					10 05					10 20						10 35
London Bridge 4 ⊖	d			10 03		10 12	10 15				10 27			10 33			10 42
New Cross Gate	d			10 08										10 38			
Norwood Junction 2	d			10 16			10 26							10 46			
East Croydon ⇌	a			10 20	10 21	10 24	10 29		10 32		10 39		10 48	10 50		10 51	10 54
	d			10 21	10 22	10 25	10 30		10 33		10 41		10 48	10 51		10 52	10 55
Purley 4	d			10 27			10 36							10 56			
Coulsdon South	d			10 30			10 39							11 00			
Merstham	d			10 36			10 45							11 05			
Redhill	a			10 40			10 49						11 00	11 09			
	d	10 34	10 41	10 45			10 52						11 00	11 10	11 13		
Reigate	a	10 38					10 57								11 18		
Nutfield	d																
Godstone	d																
Edenbridge	d																
Penshurst	d																
Leigh (Kent)	d																
Tonbridge 4	a																
Earlswood (Surrey)	d			10 47										11 12			
Salfords	d									←				11 16			
Horley 4	d			10 53						10 53				11 19			
Gatwick Airport 10 ✈	a		10 50	→		10 40		10 45	10 48	10 55	10 56	11 00	11 08	→			11 10
	d					10 41			10 50	10 56	10 57		11 09				11 11
Three Bridges 4	a					10 45				11 01	11 01		11 14				11 15
	d					10 45				11 02	11 02		11 14				11 15
Crawley	d									11 06			11 18				
Ifield	d									11 08							
Faygate	d																
Littlehaven	d									11 15							
Horsham 4	a									11 20			11 26				
Balcombe	d																11 21
Haywards Heath	a					10 54			11 00		11 11						11 26
	d					10 55			11 04 11 07		11 11						11 27
Wivelsfield	d					10 59			11 11								11 31
Lewes 4	a								11 22								
Burgess Hill 4	d					11 01			11 09								11 33
Hassocks 4	d					11 04											11 36
Preston Park	d					11 11			11 18								11 43
Hove 2	a								11 22								
Brighton 10	a				10 58	11 15					11 25					11 28	11 47

A ☕ to Haywards Heath

Table 186

Mondays to Fridays

Bedford and London - Brighton

9 December to 16 May

Network Diagram - see first Page of Table 175

Station		SN 1	SN 1 ✕	SN 1 ✕	SN 1	SN 1	FC 1	SN 1 ✕	SN 1	GW 1	GW 1	SN 1
London Victoria 15 ⊖	d		10 45	10 47	10 51			11 00	11 02			
Clapham Junction 10	d			10 53					11 08			
Bedford	d						09 40					
Luton 10	d						10 04					
Luton Airport Parkway 7 ✈	d						10 06					
St Albans City	d						10 18					
St Pancras International 15 ⊖	d						10 40					
Farringdon 3 ⊖	d						10 45					
City Thameslink 3	d						10 48					
London Blackfriars 3 ⊖	d						10 50					
London Bridge 4 ⊖	d	10 45					10 57					11 03
New Cross Gate	d											11 08
Norwood Junction 2	d	10 56										11 16
East Croydon	a	10 59		11 02	11 07		11 09		11 17			11 20
	d	11 00		11 03	11 08		11 11		11 18			11 21
Purley 4	d	11 07										11 26
Coulsdon South	d	11 10										11 30
Merstham	d											11 36
Redhill	a	11 18							11 29			11 40
	d	11 18							11 30	11 34	11 41	11 45
Reigate	a									11 38		
Nutfield	d	11 23										
Godstone	d	11 28										
Edenbridge	d	11 34										
Penshurst	d	11 40										
Leigh (Kent)	d	11 44										
Tonbridge 4	a	11 48										
Earlswood (Surrey)	d											11 47
Salfords	d					←						
Horley 4	d					11 19			11 36			11 53
Gatwick Airport 10 ✈	a		11 15	11 18	11 22	11 23	11 26	11 30	11 38		11 50	→
	d			11 20	11 23	11 24	11 27		11 39			
Three Bridges 4	a					11 29	11 31		11 44			
	d					11 30	11 32		11 44			
Crawley	d					11 33			11 48			
Ifield	d					11 36						
Faygate	d											
Littlehaven	d					11 42						
Horsham 4	a					11 48			11 56			
Balcombe	d											
Haywards Heath	a			11 30			11 41					
	d			11 35 / 11 37			11 41					
Wivelsfield	d											
Lewes 4	a			11 52								
Burgess Hill 4	d				11 38							
Hassocks 4	d				11 42							
Preston Park	d											
Hove 2	a			11 53								
Brighton 10	a				11 52		11 55					

Station		SN 1	FC 1	SN 1	SN 1 ✕	SN 1	SN 1	FC 1	SN 1 ✕	SN 1	SN 1	GW 1
London Victoria 15 ⊖	d	11 06			11 15	11 17			11 30	11 32		
Clapham Junction 10	d	11 12				11 23				11 38		
Bedford	d		09 54					10 10				
Luton 10	d		10 18					10 34				
Luton Airport Parkway 7 ✈	d		10 20					10 36				
St Albans City	d		10 32					10 48				
St Pancras International 15 ⊖	d		10 54					11 10				
Farringdon 3 ⊖	d		10 59					11 15				
City Thameslink 3	d		11 03					11 18				
London Blackfriars 3 ⊖	d		11 05					11 20				
London Bridge 4 ⊖	d		11 12	11 15				11 27			11 33	
New Cross Gate	d										11 38	
Norwood Junction 2	d			11 26							11 46	
East Croydon	a	11 21	11 24	11 29		11 32		11 39		11 48	11 50	
	d	11 22	11 25	11 30		11 33		11 41		11 48	11 51	
Purley 4	d			11 36							11 56	
Coulsdon South	d			11 39							12 00	
Merstham	d			11 45							12 05	
Redhill	a			11 49						12 00	12 09	
	d			11 52						12 00	12 10	12 13
Reigate	a			11 57								12 18
Nutfield	d											
Godstone	d											
Edenbridge	d											
Penshurst	d											
Leigh (Kent)	d											
Tonbridge 4	a											
Earlswood (Surrey)	d										12 12	
Salfords	d						←				12 16	
Horley 4	d						11 53				12 19	
Gatwick Airport 10 ✈	a		11 40		11 45	11 48	11 55	11 56	12 00	12 08	→	
	d		11 41			11 50	11 56	11 57		12 09		
Three Bridges 4	a		11 45				12 01	12 01		12 14		
	d		11 45				12 02	12 02		12 14		
Crawley	d						12 06			12 18		
Ifield	d						12 08					
Faygate	d						12 12					
Littlehaven	d						12 16					
Horsham 4	a						12 21			12 26		
Balcombe	d											
Haywards Heath	a		11 54			12 00		12 11				
	d		11 55			12 04 / 12 07		12 11				
Wivelsfield	d		11 59			12 11						
Lewes 4	a					12 22						
Burgess Hill 4	d		12 01			12 09						
Hassocks 4	d		12 04									
Preston Park	d		12 11			12 18						
Hove 2	a					12 22						
Brighton 10	a	11 58	12 15					12 25				

Station		SN 1 ✕	FC 1	SN 1	SN 1 ✕	SN 1	SN 1	SN 1	FC 1	SN 1 ✕	SN 1	GW 1
London Victoria 15 ⊖	d	11 36			11 45	11 47	11 51			12 00	12 02	
Clapham Junction 10	d	11 42				11 53					12 08	
Bedford	d		10 24						10 40			
Luton 10	d		10 48						11 04			
Luton Airport Parkway 7 ✈	d		10 50						11 06			
St Albans City	d		11 02						11 18			
St Pancras International 15 ⊖	d		11 24						11 40			
Farringdon 3 ⊖	d		11 29						11 45			
City Thameslink 3	d		11 33						11 48			
London Blackfriars 3 ⊖	d		11 35						11 50			
London Bridge 4 ⊖	d		11 42	11 45					11 57			
New Cross Gate	d											
Norwood Junction 2	d			11 56								
East Croydon	a	11 51	11 54	11 59		12 02	12 07		12 09		12 17	
	d	11 52	11 55	12 00		12 03	12 08		12 11		12 18	
Purley 4	d			12 06								
Coulsdon South	d			12 09								
Merstham	d											
Redhill	a			12 17							12 29	
	d			12 17							12 30	12 34
Reigate	a											12 38
Nutfield	d			12 22								
Godstone	d			12 27								
Edenbridge	d			12 33								
Penshurst	d			12 39								
Leigh (Kent)	d			12 43								
Tonbridge 4	a			12 48								
Earlswood (Surrey)	d											
Salfords	d							←				
Horley 4	d							12 19			12 36	
Gatwick Airport 10 ✈	a		12 10		12 15	12 18	12 22	12 23	12 26	12 30	12 38	
	d		12 11			12 20	12 23	12 24	12 27		12 39	
Three Bridges 4	a		12 15					12 29	12 31		12 44	
	d		12 15					12 30	12 32		12 44	
Crawley	d							12 34			12 48	
Ifield	d							12 36				
Faygate	d											
Littlehaven	d							12 43				
Horsham 4	a							12 48			12 56	
Balcombe	d		12 21									
Haywards Heath	a		12 26			12 30			12 41			
	d		12 27			12 35 / 12 37			12 41			
Wivelsfield	d		12 31									
Lewes 4	a					12 52						
Burgess Hill 4	d		12 33				12 38					
Hassocks 4	d		12 36				12 42					
Preston Park	d		12 43									
Hove 2	a					12 53						
Brighton 10	a	12 28	12 47				12 52		12 55			

Table 186

Mondays to Fridays

9 December to 16 May

Bedford and London - Brighton

Network Diagram - see first Page of Table 175

		GW 1	SN 1	SN 1 trolley	FC 1	SN 1	SN 1 trolley	SN 1	SN 1	FC 1	SN 1 trolley	SN 1	SN 1	GW 1	SN 1 trolley	FC 1	SN 1
London Victoria 15 ⊖	d			12 06			12 15	12 17			12 30	12 32			12 36		
Clapham Junction 10	d			12 12				12 23				12 38			12 42		
Bedford	d				10 54					11 10						11 24	
Luton 10	d				11 18					11 34						11 48	
Luton Airport Parkway 7 ✈	d				11 20					11 36						11 50	
St Albans City	d				11 32					11 48						12 02	
St Pancras International 15 ⊖	d				11 54					12 10						12 24	
Farringdon 3 ⊖	d				11 59					12 15						12 29	
City Thameslink 3	d				12 03					12 18						12 33	
London Blackfriars 3 ⊖	d				12 05					12 20						12 35	
London Bridge 4 ⊖	d		12 03		12 12	12 15				12 27			12 33			12 42	12 45
New Cross Gate	d		12 08										12 38				
Norwood Junction 2	d		12 16			12 26							12 46				12 56
East Croydon	a		12 20	12 21	12 24	12 29		12 32		12 39		12 48	12 50		12 51	12 54	12 59
	d		12 21	12 22	12 25	12 30		12 33		12 41		12 48	12 51		12 52	12 55	13 00
Purley 4	d		12 27			12 36							12 57				13 06
Coulsdon South	d		12 30			12 39							13 01				13 09
Merstham	d		12 36			12 45							13 06				
Redhill	a		12 40			12 49						13 00	13 10				13 17
	d	12 41	12 45			12 52						13 00	13 11	13 13			13 17
Reigate	a					12 57								13 18			
Nutfield	d																13 22
Godstone	d																13 27
Edenbridge	d																13 33
Penshurst	d																13 39
Leigh (Kent)	d																13 43
Tonbridge 4	a																13 48
Earlswood (Surrey)	d		12 47										13 13				
Salfords	d								←				13 17				
Horley 4	d		12 53						12 53				13 20				
Gatwick Airport 10 ✈	a	12 50	→		12 40		12 45	12 48	12 55	12 56	13 00	13 08	→			13 10	
	d				12 41			12 50	12 56	12 57		13 09				13 11	
Three Bridges 4	a				12 45				13 01	13 01		13 14				13 15	
	d				12 45				13 02	13 02		13 14				13 15	
Crawley	d								13 06			13 18					
Ifield	d								13 08								
Faygate	d																
Littlehaven	d								13 15								
Horsham 4	a								13 20			13 26					
Balcombe	d															13 21	
Haywards Heath	a				12 54			13 00		13 11						13 26	
	d				12 55			13 04 / 13 07		13 11						13 27	
Wivelsfield	d				12 59			13 11								13 31	
Lewes 4	a							13 22									
Burgess Hill 4	d				13 01			13 09								13 33	
Hassocks 4	d				13 04											13 36	
Preston Park	d				13 11			13 18								13 43	
Hove 2	a							13 22									
Brighton 10	a			12 58	13 15					13 25					13 28	13 47	

		SN 1 trolley	SN 1	SN 1	SN 1	FC 1	SN 1 trolley	SN 1	GW 1	GW 1	SN 1	SN 1 trolley	FC 1	SN 1	SN 1 trolley	SN 1	SN 1	FC 1
London Victoria 15 ⊖	d	12 45	12 47	12 51			13 00	13 02				13 06			13 15	13 17		
Clapham Junction 10	d		12 53					13 08				13 12				13 23		
Bedford	d					11 40							11 54					12 10
Luton 10	d					12 04							12 18					12 34
Luton Airport Parkway 7 ✈	d					12 06							12 20					12 36
St Albans City	d					12 18							12 32					12 48
St Pancras International 15 ⊖	d					12 40							12 54					13 10
Farringdon 3 ⊖	d					12 45							12 59					13 15
City Thameslink 3	d					12 48							13 03					13 18
London Blackfriars 3 ⊖	d					12 50							13 05					13 20
London Bridge 4 ⊖	d					12 57					13 03		13 12	13 15				13 27
New Cross Gate	d										13 08							
Norwood Junction 2	d										13 16			13 26				
East Croydon	a		13 02	13 07		13 09		13 17			13 20	13 21	13 24	13 29		13 32		13 39
	d		13 03	13 08		13 11		13 18			13 21	13 22	13 25	13 30		13 33		13 41
Purley 4	d										13 27			13 36				
Coulsdon South	d										13 30			13 39				
Merstham	d										13 36			13 45				
Redhill	a							13 29			13 40			13 49				
	d							13 30	13 34	13 41	13 45			13 52				
Reigate	a								13 38					13 57				
Nutfield	d																	
Godstone	d																	
Edenbridge	d																	
Penshurst	d																	
Leigh (Kent)	d																	
Tonbridge 4	a																	
Earlswood (Surrey)	d										13 47							
Salfords	d				←												←	
Horley 4	d				13 20			13 36			13 53						13 53	
Gatwick Airport 10 ✈	a	13 15	13 18	13 22	13 23	13 26	13 30	13 39		13 50	→		13 40		13 45	13 48	13 55	13 56
	d		13 20	13 23	13 24	13 27		13 40					13 41			13 50	13 56	13 57
Three Bridges 4	a				13 29	13 31		13 44					13 45				14 01	14 01
	d				13 30	13 32		13 45					13 45				14 02	14 02
Crawley	d				13 34			13 48									14 06	
Ifield	d				13 36												14 08	
Faygate	d																	
Littlehaven	d				13 43												14 15	
Horsham 4	a				13 48			13 56									14 20	
Balcombe	d																	
Haywards Heath	a		13 30			13 41							13 54			14 00		14 11
	d		13 35 / 13 37			13 41							13 55			14 04 / 14 07		14 11
Wivelsfield	d												13 59			14 11		
Lewes 4	a		13 52													14 22		
Burgess Hill 4	d			13 38									14 01			14 09		
Hassocks 4	d			13 42									14 04					
Preston Park	d												14 11			14 18		
Hove 2	a		13 53													14 22		
Brighton 10	a			13 52		13 55						13 58	14 15					14 25

Table 186

Mondays to Fridays

Bedford and London - Brighton

9 December to 16 May

Network Diagram - see first Page of Table 175

		SN	SN	SN	GW	SN	FC	SN	SN	SN		SN	SN	FC	SN	SN	GW	GW	SN	SN	FC	SN	SN	SN		SN	FC	SN	SN	SN	GW	SN	FC	SN	GW	SN
		1	1	1	1	1	1	1	1	1		1	1	1	1	1	1	1	1	1	1	1	1	1		1	1	1	1	1	1	1	1	1	1	1
		🛒				🛒			🛒						🛒					🛒			🛒					🛒				🛒				🛒
London Victoria 15 ⊖	d	13 30	13 32			13 36			13 45	13 47		13 51			14 00	14 02				14 06			14 15	14 17				14 30	14 32			14 36				14 45
Clapham Junction 10	d		13 38			13 42				13 53						14 08				14 12				14 23					14 38			14 42				
Bedford	d						12 24							12 40							12 54						13 10						13 24			
Luton 10	d						12 48							13 04							13 18						13 34						13 48			
Luton Airport Parkway 7 ✈	d						12 50							13 06							13 20						13 36						13 50			
St Albans City	d						13 02							13 18							13 32						13 48						14 02			
St Pancras International 15 ⊖	d						13 24							13 40							13 54						14 09						14 24			
Farringdon 3 ⊖	d						13 29							13 45							13 59						14 14						14 29			
City Thameslink 3	d						13 33							13 48							14 03						14 18						14 33			
London Blackfriars 3 ⊖	d						13 35							13 50							14 05						14 20						14 35			
London Bridge 4 ⊖	d			13 33			13 42	13 45						13 57					14 03		14 12	14 15					14 27			14 33			14 42	14 45		
New Cross Gate	d			13 38															14 08											14 38						
Norwood Junction 2	d			13 46				13 56											14 16			14 26								14 46				14 56		
East Croydon 🚌	a		13 48	13 50		13 51	13 54	13 59		14 02		14 07		14 09		14 17			14 20	14 21	14 25	14 29		14 32			14 39		14 48	14 50		14 51	14 54	14 59		
	d		13 48	13 51		13 52	13 55	14 00		14 03		14 08		14 11		14 18			14 21	14 22	14 25	14 30		14 33			14 41		14 48	14 51		14 52	14 55	15 00		
Purley 4	d			13 57				14 06											14 27			14 36								14 57				15 06		
Coulsdon South	d			14 01				14 09											14 30			14 39								15 00				15 09		
Merstham	d			14 06															14 36			14 45								15 06						
Redhill	a		14 00	14 10				14 17								14 29			14 40			14 49							15 00	15 09				15 17		
	d		14 00	14 11	14 13			14 17								14 30	14 34	14 41	14 45			14 52							15 00	15 10	15 13			15 17	15 29	
Reigate	a				14 18												14 38					14 57									15 18				15 33	
Nutfield	d							14 22																										15 22		
Godstone	d							14 27																										15 27		
Edenbridge	d							14 33																										15 33		
Penshurst	d							14 39																										15 39		
Leigh (Kent)	d							14 43																										15 43		
Tonbridge 4	a							14 48																										15 48		
Earlswood (Surrey)	d			14 13															14 47											15 12						
Salfords	d			14 17									←													←				15 16						
Horley 4	d			14 20									14 20			14 36			14 53							14 53				15 19						
Gatwick Airport 10 ✈	a	14 00	14 08	→			14 10		14 15	14 18		14 22	14 23	14 26	14 30	14 38		14 50	→		14 40		14 45	14 48		14 55	14 56	15 00	15 08	→			15 10			15 15
	d		14 09				14 11			14 20		14 23	14 24	14 27		14 39					14 41			14 50		14 56	14 57		15 09				15 11			
Three Bridges 4	a		14 14				14 15						14 29	14 31		14 44					14 45					15 01	15 01		15 14				15 15			
	d		14 14				14 15						14 30	14 32		14 44					14 45					15 02	15 02		15 14				15 15			
Crawley	d		14 18										14 34			14 48										15 06			15 18							
Ifield	d												14 36													15 08										
Faygate	d																																			
Littlehaven	d												14 43													15 15										
Horsham 4	a		14 26										14 48			14 56										15 20			15 26							
Balcombe	d						14 21																										15 21			
Haywards Heath	a						14 26			14 30				14 41							14 54			15 00			15 11						15 26			
	d						14 27			14 35	14 37			14 41							14 55			15 04	15 07		15 11						15 27			
Wivelsfield	d						14 31														14 59				15 11								15 31			
Lewes 4	a									14 52															15 22											
Burgess Hill 4	d						14 33					14 38									15 01			15 09									15 33			
Hassocks 4	d						14 36					14 42									15 04												15 36			
Preston Park	d						14 43														15 11			15 18									15 43			
Hove 2	a										14 53													15 22												
Brighton 10	a					14 28	14 47					14 52		14 55						14 58	15 15						15 25					15 28	15 47			

Table 186

Mondays to Fridays

9 December to 16 May

Bedford and London - Brighton

Network Diagram - see first Page of Table 175

Station		SN 1		SN 1	SN 1	FC 1	SN 1	SN 1	GW 1	SN 1	SN 1	FC 1	SN 1	SN 1
							trolley				trolley			trolley
London Victoria 15 ⊖	d	14 47		14 51			15 00	15 02			15 06			15 15
Clapham Junction 10	d	14 53						15 08			15 12			
Bedford	d					13 40						13 54		
Luton 10	d					14 04						14 18		
Luton Airport Parkway 7 ✈	d					14 06						14 20		
St Albans City	d					14 18						14 32		
St Pancras International 15 ⊖	d					14 40						14 54		
Farringdon 3 ⊖	d					14 45						14 59		
City Thameslink 3	d					14 48						15 03		
London Blackfriars 3 ⊖	d					14 50						15 05		
London Bridge 4 ⊖	d					14 57				15 03		15 12	15 15	
New Cross Gate	d									15 08				
Norwood Junction 2	d									15 16			15 26	
East Croydon	a	15 02		15 07		15 09		15 17		15 20	15 21	15 24	15 29	
	d	15 03		15 08		15 11		15 18		15 21	15 22	15 25	15 30	
Purley 4	d									15 27			15 36	
Coulsdon South	d									15 30			15 39	
Merstham	d									15 36			15 45	
Redhill	a							15 29		15 40			15 49	
	d							15 30	15 41	15 45			15 52	
Reigate	a												15 57	
Nutfield	d													
Godstone	d													
Edenbridge	d													
Penshurst	d													
Leigh (Kent)	d													
Tonbridge 4	a													
Earlswood (Surrey)	d									15 47				
Salfords	d				←					15 51				
Horley 4	d				15 19			15 36		15 54				
Gatwick Airport 10 ✈	a	15 18		15 22	15 23	15 26	15 30	15 38	15 50	→		15 40		15 45
	d	15 20		15 23	15 24	15 27		15 39				15 41		
Three Bridges 4	a				15 29	15 31		15 44				15 45		
	d				15 30	15 32		15 44				15 45		
Crawley	d				15 33			15 48						
Ifield	d				15 36									
Faygate	d													
Littlehaven	d				15 42									
Horsham 4	a				15 50			15 56						
Balcombe	d													
Haywards Heath	a	15 30				15 41						15 54		
	d	15 35	15 37			15 41						15 55		
Wivelsfield	d	15 39										15 59		
Lewes 4	a	15 52												
Burgess Hill 4	d			15 38								16 01		
Hassocks 4	d			15 42								16 04		
Preston Park	d											16 11		
Hove 2	a		15 53											
Brighton 10	a			15 52		15 55					15 58	16 15		

Station		SN 1		FC 1	SN 1	SN 1	SN 1	SN 1	GW 1	SN 1	FC 1	SN 1	SN 1
						trolley				trolley			trolley
London Victoria 15 ⊖	d	15 17				15 30	15 32			15 36			15 45
Clapham Junction 10	d	15 23					15 38			15 42			
Bedford	d			14 10							14 24		
Luton 10	d			14 34							14 48		
Luton Airport Parkway 7 ✈	d			14 36							14 50		
St Albans City	d			14 48							15 02		
St Pancras International 15 ⊖	d			15 10							15 24		
Farringdon 3 ⊖	d			15 15							15 29		
City Thameslink 3	d			15 18							15 33		
London Blackfriars 3 ⊖	d			15 20							15 35		
London Bridge 4 ⊖	d			15 27				15 33			15 42	15 45	
New Cross Gate	d							15 38					
Norwood Junction 2	d							15 46				15 56	
East Croydon	a	15 32		15 39			15 47	15 50		15 51	15 54	15 59	
	d	15 33		15 41			15 48	15 51		15 52	15 55	16 00	
Purley 4	d							15 56				16 06	
Coulsdon South	d							16 00				16 09	
Merstham	d							16 05				16 15	
Redhill	a						16 00	16 09				16 19	
	d						16 00	16 10	16 13			16 19	
Reigate	a								16 18				
Nutfield	d											16 24	
Godstone	d											16 29	
Edenbridge	d											16 35	
Penshurst	d											16 41	
Leigh (Kent)	d											16 45	
Tonbridge 4	a											16 49	
Earlswood (Surrey)	d							16 12					
Salfords	d				←			16 16					
Horley 4	d				15 54			16 19					
Gatwick Airport 10 ✈	a	15 48		15 56	15 57	16 00	16 08	→			16 10		16 15
	d	15 50		15 57	15 58		16 09				16 11		
Three Bridges 4	a			16 01	16 02		16 14				16 15		
	d			16 02	16 03		16 14				16 15		
Crawley	d				16 07		16 18						
Ifield	d				16 09								
Faygate	d				16 13								
Littlehaven	d				16 17								
Horsham 4	a				16 20		16 26						
Balcombe	d										16 21		
Haywards Heath	a	16 00		16 11							16 26		
	d	16 04	16 07	16 11							16 27		
Wivelsfield	d		16 11								16 31		
Lewes 4	a		16 22										
Burgess Hill 4	d	16 09									16 33		
Hassocks 4	d										16 36		
Preston Park	d	16 18									16 43		
Hove 2	a	16 22											
Brighton 10	a			16 25						16 28	16 47		

Station		SN 1		SN 1	SN 1	FC 1	SN 1	SN 1	GW 1	SN 1	SN 1	FC 1
							trolley				trolley	
London Victoria 15 ⊖	d	15 47		15 51			16 00	16 02			16 06	
Clapham Junction 10	d	15 53						16 08			16 12	
Bedford	d					14 40						14 54
Luton 10	d					15 04						15 18
Luton Airport Parkway 7 ✈	d					15 06						15 20
St Albans City	d					15 18						15 32
St Pancras International 15 ⊖	d					15 40						15 54
Farringdon 3 ⊖	d					15 45						15 59
City Thameslink 3	d					15 48						16 03
London Blackfriars 3 ⊖	d					15 50						16 05
London Bridge 4 ⊖	d					15 57				16 03		16 12
New Cross Gate	d									16 09		
Norwood Junction 2	d									16 17		
East Croydon	a	16 02		16 07		16 09		16 17		16 20	16 21	16 24
	d	16 03		16 08		16 11		16 18		16 21	16 22	16 25
Purley 4	d									16 26		
Coulsdon South	d									16 30		
Merstham	d									16 35		
Redhill	a							16 29		16 39		
	d							16 30	16 32	16 40		
Reigate	a								16 36			
Nutfield	d											
Godstone	d											
Edenbridge	d											
Penshurst	d											
Leigh (Kent)	d											
Tonbridge 4	a											
Earlswood (Surrey)	d									16 42		
Salfords	d				←					16 46		
Horley 4	d				16 19			16 36		16 50		
Gatwick Airport 10 ✈	a	16 18		16 22	16 23	16 26	16 30	16 38		→		16 40
	d	16 20		16 23	16 24	16 27		16 39				16 41
Three Bridges 4	a				16 29	16 31		16 44				16 45
	d				16 30	16 32		16 44				16 45
Crawley	d				16 34			16 48				
Ifield	d				16 36							
Faygate	d				16 40							
Littlehaven	d				16 44							
Horsham 4	a				16 48			16 56				
Balcombe	d											
Haywards Heath	a	16 30				16 41						16 54
	d	16 35	16 37			16 41						16 55
Wivelsfield	d	16 39										16 59
Lewes 4	a	16 54										
Burgess Hill 4	d			16 38								17 01
Hassocks 4	d			16 42								17 04
Preston Park	d											17 11
Hove 2	a		16 53									
Brighton 10	a			16 52		16 55					16 58	17 15

Table 186

Mondays to Fridays

Bedford and London - Brighton

9 December to 16 May

Network Diagram - see first Page of Table 175

		SN 1	GW 1	SN 1	SN 1 A ⚲		SN 1	SN 1	FC 1	SN 1 ⚲	SN 1		SN 1		GW 1	SN 1 ⚲	SN 1 ⚲
London Victoria 15 ⊖	d	16 15			16 17		16 19			16 30	16 32					16 36	16 45
Clapham Junction 10	d				16 23		16 26				16 38					16 42	
Bedford	d								15 10								
Luton 10	d								15 34								
Luton Airport Parkway 7 ✈	d								15 36								
St Albans City	d								15 48								
St Pancras International 15 ⊖	d								16 10								
Farringdon 3 ⊖	d								16 15								
City Thameslink 3	d								16 18								
London Blackfriars 3 ⊖	d								16 20								
London Bridge 4 ⊖	d			16 15					16 27				16 30				
New Cross Gate	d												16 36				
Norwood Junction 2	d			16 26									16 44				
East Croydon 🚊	a			16 29	16 33		16 36		16 39		16 47		16 47			16 52	
	d			16 30	16 34		16 37		16 41		16 48		16 48			16 52	
Purley 4	d			16 36									16 54				
Coulsdon South	d			16 39									16 58				
Merstham	d			16 45									17 03				
Redhill	a			16 49							16 59		17 07				
	d		16 51	16 53							17 00		17 11	17 13	17 13		
Reigate	a			16 58											17 18		
Nutfield	d													17 17			
Godstone	d													17 23			
Edenbridge	d													17 28			
Penshurst	d													17 35			
Leigh (Kent)	d													17 38			
Tonbridge 4	a													17 43			
Earlswood (Surrey)	d												17 13				
Salfords	d							←					17 17				
Horley 4	d							16 50			17 06		17 21				
Gatwick Airport 10 ✈	a	16 44	16 59		16 48		16 52	16 53	16 56	17 00	17 08		→				17 13
	d	16 49			16 49		16 53	16 55	16 57		17 09						17 18
Three Bridges 4	a	16 54					16 57	17 00	17 01		17 14					17 10	17 22
	d						16 58	17 01	17 02		17 18	17 22				17 10	
Crawley	d						17 02	17 05			17 22	17 26					
Ifield	d							17 07				17 28					
Faygate	d							17 11									
Littlehaven	d							17 15				17 35					
Horsham 4	a						17 12	17 20			17 30	17 38					
Balcombe	d																
Haywards Heath	a				17 00				17 11							17 19	
	d				17 04	17 06			17 11							17 20	
Wivelsfield	d					17 10											
Lewes 4	a					17 21											
Burgess Hill 4	d				17 09				17 17							17 25	
Hassocks 4	d								17 21								
Preston Park	d															17 34	
Hove 2	a				17 20												
Brighton 10	a								17 30							17 38	

		FC 1	SN 1 ⚲	SN 1	SN 1 ⚲	SN 1		SN 1	SN 1		SN 1	SN 1	FC 1	SN 1 ⚲	SN 1	SN 1	SN 1	GW 1	GW 1	SN 1	
London Victoria 15 ⊖	d		16 47		17 00	16 49					17 02	17 06		17 15	17 17					17 21	
Clapham Junction 10	d		16 53			16 56					17 08	17 12			17 23					17 27	
Bedford	d	15 24											15 50								
Luton 10	d	15 48											16 10								
Luton Airport Parkway 7 ✈	d	15 50											16 13								
St Albans City	d	16 02											16 24								
St Pancras International 15 ⊖	d	16 22											16 46								
Farringdon 3 ⊖	d	16 27											16 51								
City Thameslink 3	d	16 31											16 55								
London Blackfriars 3 ⊖	d	16 36											16 58								
London Bridge 4 ⊖	d	16 43						16 57	16 59								17 23				
New Cross Gate	d																				
Norwood Junction 2	d								17 10												
East Croydon 🚊	a	16 59	17 03			17 06		17 09	17 14		17 17	17 21	17 26		17 32		17 35			17 36	
	d	17 00	17 04			17 07		17 10	17 15		17 18	17 23	17 26		17 33		17 36			17 38	
Purley 4	d								17 20												
Coulsdon South	d					17 14			17 24											17 45	
Merstham	d					17 19			17 29											17 50	
Redhill	a					17 23			17 33											17 54	
	d					17 27	17 29		17 37	17 39								17 41	17 43	17 58	18 00
Reigate	a						17 35												17 48		18 04
Nutfield	d									17 43											
Godstone	d									17 49											
Edenbridge	d									17 54											
Penshurst	d									18 01											
Leigh (Kent)	d									18 04											
Tonbridge 4	a									18 09											
Earlswood (Surrey)	d					17 29			17 39											18 00	
Salfords	d			←		17 33			17 43							←				18 04	
Horley 4	d			17 21		17 37			17 47							17 47	17 50			18 07	
Gatwick Airport 10 ✈	a	17 15	17 19	17 23	17 30	17 39			→				17 41	17 45	17 48	17 49		17 54		→	
	d	17 16	17 20	17 24		17 40							17 42		17 49	17 50					
Three Bridges 4	a	17 20	17 24	17 29		17 47		17 28			17 37		17 46			17 55	17 55				
	d	17 21	17 25	17 30				17 29			17 38		17 46			17 55	17 56				
Crawley	d			17 34							17 42					17 59					
Ifield	d			17 36												18 02					
Faygate	d															18 06					
Littlehaven	d			17 43												18 10					
Horsham 4	a			17 48							17 50					18 14					
Balcombe	d	17 27											17 52								
Haywards Heath	a	17 32	17 35					17 38				17 47	17 57		18 00		18 05				
	d	17 32	17 36					17 40				17 48	17 58		18 01		18 05				
Wivelsfield	d	17 37	17 41									17 52					18 10				
Lewes 4	a		17 56														18 21				
Burgess Hill 4	d	17 39						17 46				17 55	18 03		18 08						
Hassocks 4	d	17 43						17 49				17 59	18 07		18 12						
Preston Park	d	17 50						17 56				18 06	18 14								
Hove 2	a							18 00							18 21						
Brighton 10	a	17 54										18 10	18 18								

A ⚲ to Haywards Heath

Table 186

Bedford and London - Brighton

Mondays to Fridays

9 December to 16 May

Network Diagram - see first Page of Table 175

Station		SN	SN	SN	FC	GW	SN		SN	SN	SN	SN	SN	SN	SN	FC	SN
		1	1	1	1	1	1		1	1	1	1	1	1	1	1	1
		🛒	🛒								🛒						
London Victoria [15] ⊖	d	17 27	17 32						17 34		17 44	17 46		17 49			
Clapham Junction [10]	d	17 33							17 40			17 52		17 56			
Bedford	d				16 08											16 24	
Luton [10]	d				16 32											16 48	
Luton Airport Parkway [7] ✈	d				16 34											16 50	
St Albans City	d				16 47											17 02	
St Pancras International [15] ⊖	d				17 08											17 28	
Farringdon [3] ⊖	d				17 13											17 33	
City Thameslink [3]	d				17 17											17 37	
London Blackfriars [3] ⊖	d				17 20											17 40	
London Bridge [4] ⊖	d						17 32			17 42			17 50				17 32
New Cross Gate	d																
Norwood Junction [2]	d						17 44										17 44
East Croydon ⇌	a	17 42			17 47		17 49		17 50	17 54		18 01	18 05	18 06		18 08	17 49
	d	17 43			17 47		17 50		17 51	17 55		18 02	18 06	18 07		18 09	17 50
Purley [4]	d						17 56										17 56
Coulsdon South	d						18 00							18 18			18 00
Merstham	d						18 05							18 23			18 05
Redhill	a				18 02		18 09							18 27			18 09
	d				18 03	18 13	18 13	18 17						18 28	18 32		18 19
Reigate	a					18 18											18 26
Nutfield	d							18 21							18 36		
Godstone	d							18 27							18 42		
Edenbridge	d							18 32							18 47		
Penshurst	d							18 39							18 54		
Leigh (Kent)	d							18 42							18 57		
Tonbridge [4]	a							18 49							19 02		
Earlswood (Surrey)	d						18 15							18 30			
Salfords	d			←			18 19							18 34			
Horley [4]	d			18 07			18 23					18 16		18 38			
Gatwick Airport [10] ✈	a	17 57	18 01	18 10	18 13		→				18 13	18 19		→		18 23	
	d	17 58	18 04	18 11	18 14						18 15	18 20				18 24	
Three Bridges [4]	a			18 17	18 19				18 09			18 24	18 24			18 28	
	d				18 19				18 09			18 25	18 24			18 29	
Crawley	d								18 13				18 28				
Ifield	d												18 31				
Faygate	d																
Littlehaven	d								18 21				18 38				
Horsham [4]	a								18 24				18 41				
Balcombe	d				18 25												
Haywards Heath	a	18 09	18 15		18 30					18 19	18 26	18 34				18 38	
	d	18 09	18 16		18 31					18 21	18 27	18 36				18 38	
Wivelsfield	d	18 14														18 43	
Lewes [4]	a	18 29															
Burgess Hill [4]	d		18 21		18 36					18 27		18 42				18 45	
Hassocks [4]	d				18 40					18 31	18 35	18 46				18 49	
Preston Park	d		18 30		18 47					18 38		18 53				18 56	
Hove [2]	a									18 43		18 57					
Brighton [10]	a		18 35		18 53						18 45					19 01	

Station		SN	SN	SN	SN	SN	SN	SN	SN	SN	FC	GW	SN	SN	GW	SN		SN	SN	FC
		1	1	1	1	1	1	1	1	1	1	1	1	1	1	1		1	1	1
			🛒		🛒				🛒											
London Victoria [15] ⊖	d		17 57		18 02	18 04			18 15				18 17			18 19			18 26	
Clapham Junction [10]	d		18 04			18 11							18 23			18 26			18 32	
Bedford	d										16 40									17 07
Luton [10]	d										17 02									17 31
Luton Airport Parkway [7] ✈	d										17 04									17 34
St Albans City	d										17 16									17 45
St Pancras International [15] ⊖	d										17 40									18 08
Farringdon [3] ⊖	d										17 45									18 13
City Thameslink [3]	d										17 49									18 17
London Blackfriars [3] ⊖	d										17 52									18 20
London Bridge [4] ⊖	d	17 56		17 59				18 12						18 23						18 28
New Cross Gate	d																			
Norwood Junction [2]	d			18 10																
East Croydon ⇌	a	18 10	18 13	18 13		18 20		18 24			18 24		18 32	18 36		18 37			18 41	18 41
	d	18 12	18 14	18 14		18 21		18 25			18 26		18 33	18 37		18 38			18 41	18 43
Purley [4]	d			18 20												18 44				
Coulsdon South	d			18 23												18 48				
Merstham	d			18 29												18 54				
Redhill	a			18 34							18 38					18 58				
	d			18 35							18 39	18 43			18 51	19 01	19 04	19 02		
Reigate	a											18 47						19 06		
Nutfield	d																19 08			
Godstone	d																19 14			
Edenbridge	d																19 19			
Penshurst	d																19 26			
Leigh (Kent)	d																19 29			
Tonbridge [4]	a																19 34			
Earlswood (Surrey)	d			18 37												19 04				
Salfords	d			18 41			←			←						19 07				
Horley [4]	d			18 44			18 38			18 44			18 48			19 11				
Gatwick Airport [10] ✈	a		18 30	→	18 33	18 36	18 40		18 44	18 47	18 49				19 00	→				18 58
	d		18 31		18 36	18 37	18 41		18 47	18 48	18 49									18 59
Three Bridges [4]	a	18 31				18 42	18 46	18 42		18 52	18 56			18 56					18 59	19 03
	d	18 32				18 42		18 43		18 53				18 56					18 59	19 03
Crawley	d					18 46				18 57										
Ifield	d									18 59										
Faygate	d																			
Littlehaven	d									19 06										
Horsham [4]	a					18 54				19 11										
Balcombe	d												18 58							19 10
Haywards Heath	a	18 41	18 44		18 47			18 52	18 58				19 03	19 05					19 08	19 15
	d	18 42	18 45		18 49			18 53	18 59				19 03	19 06					19 09	19 15
Wivelsfield	d		18 51											19 11					19 14	
Lewes [4]	a		19 08											19 27						
Burgess Hill [4]	d	18 49			18 56			18 59					19 09							19 21
Hassocks [4]	d	18 53						19 03	19 07				19 13							19 25
Preston Park	d	19 01			19 05			19 11												
Hove [2]	a							19 14					19 22							
Brighton [10]	a	19 05			19 10				19 17										19 25	19 34

Table 186

Bedford and London - Brighton

Mondays to Fridays

9 December to 16 May

Network Diagram - see first Page of Table 175

		SN 1		SN 1 Trolley	SN 1	SN 1 Trolley	SN 1	FC 1	SN 1 Trolley		SN 1	SN 1	GW 1	FC 1	SN 1 Trolley	SN 1	SN 1	SN 1	SN 1
London Victoria 15 ⊖	d			18 32	18 34	18 44			18 47			18 51			19 00		19 02		
Clapham Junction 10	d				18 41				18 53			18 57					19 08		
Bedford	d							17 20						17 34					
Luton 10	d							17 44						17 58					
Luton Airport Parkway 7 ✈	d							17 46						18 00					
St Albans City	d							17 58						18 12					
St Pancras International 15 ⊖	d							18 18						18 34					
Farringdon 3 ⊖	d							18 23						18 39					
City Thameslink 3	d							18 27						18 43					
London Blackfriars 3 ⊖	d							18 30						18 46					
London Bridge 4 ⊖	d	18 30												18 57					18 59
New Cross Gate	d																		19 07
Norwood Junction 2	d	18 42																	19 15
East Croydon	a	18 45			18 51			19 00	19 03			19 07		19 10			19 18		19 19
	d	18 46			18 52			19 01	19 04			19 08		19 11			19 18		19 20
Purley 4	d	18 51																	19 26
Coulsdon South	d	18 55										19 14							19 30
Merstham	d	19 01										19 20							19 35
Redhill	a	19 06										19 24					19 30		19 39
	d	19 10	19 12									19 24	19 26				19 31	19 36	19 40
Reigate	a		19 17										19 30					19 40	
Nutfield	d																		
Godstone	d																		
Edenbridge	d																		
Penshurst	d																		
Leigh (Kent)	d																		
Tonbridge 4	a																		
Earlswood (Surrey)	d	19 12										19 27							19 42
Salfords	d	19 16					←				←	19 30				←			19 46
Horley 4	d	19 20					19 11		19 18		19 20	19 34				19 34	19 37		19 49
Gatwick Airport 10 ✈	a	→		19 02		19 13	19 14	19 17	19 21		19 22	→		19 25	19 30	19 36	19 40		→
	d			19 07		19 15	19 15	19 18	19 22		19 23			19 26		19 37	19 41		
Three Bridges 4	a				19 10		19 19				19 28			19 30		19 42	19 46		
	d				19 10		19 20				19 28			19 31			19 46		
Crawley	d				19 14		19 24				19 32						19 49		
Ifield	d						19 27				19 35								
Faygate	d										19 39								
Littlehaven	d				19 22		19 34				19 44								
Horsham 4	a				19 25		19 37				19 47						19 57		
Balcombe	d													19 37					
Haywards Heath	a			19 18		19 26		19 29	19 32					19 42					
	d			19 20		19 27		19 30	19 36	19 38				19 42					
Wivelsfield	d								19 40										
Lewes 4	a								19 55										
Burgess Hill 4	d			19 26				19 35		19 43				19 48					
Hassocks 4	d					19 34		19 39		19 47				19 51					
Preston Park	d			19 35				19 46											
Hove 2	a									19 57									
Brighton 10	a			19 40		19 44		19 52						20 01					

		SN 1 Trolley	FC 1	SN 1 Trolley	GW 1	SN 1	SN 1	SN 1 A Trolley		SN 1	FC 1	SN 1	SN 1 Trolley	SN 1	SN 1	SN 1	GW 1	SN 1	FC 1
London Victoria 15 ⊖	d	19 06		19 15		19 10		19 17					19 30	19 32				19 36	
Clapham Junction 10	d	19 12				19 16		19 23						19 38				19 42	
Bedford	d		17 54								18 10								18 24
Luton 10	d		18 18								18 34								18 48
Luton Airport Parkway 7 ✈	d		18 20								18 36								18 50
St Albans City	d		18 32								18 48								19 02
St Pancras International 15 ⊖	d		18 54								19 09								19 24
Farringdon 3 ⊖	d		18 59								19 14								19 29
City Thameslink 3	d		19 03								19 18								19 33
London Blackfriars 3 ⊖	d		19 05								19 20								19 35
London Bridge 4 ⊖	d		19 12								19 27					19 33			19 42
New Cross Gate	d															19 39			
Norwood Junction 2	d															19 47			
East Croydon	a	19 22	19 24			19 26		19 33			19 39			19 48		19 50		19 52	19 54
	d	19 23	19 25			19 27		19 33			19 41			19 48		19 51		19 53	19 55
Purley 4	d					19 33										19 56			
Coulsdon South	d					19 36										20 00			
Merstham	d					19 42										20 05			
Redhill	a					19 46								20 00		20 09			
	d				19 43	19 46	19 51							20 00	20 05	20 10	20 13		
Reigate	a														20 10		20 18		
Nutfield	d						19 55												
Godstone	d						20 01												
Edenbridge	d						20 06												
Penshurst	d						20 13												
Leigh (Kent)	d						20 16												
Tonbridge 4	a						20 21												
Earlswood (Surrey)	d					19 49													
Salfords	d					19 52				←		←							
Horley 4	d					19 56				19 49		19 56				20 16			
Gatwick Airport 10 ✈	a		19 40	19 45	19 56	→		19 48		19 52	19 55	19 58	20 00	20 08		→			20 10
	d		19 41					19 49		19 53	19 57	19 59		20 09					20 11
Three Bridges 4	a		19 45							19 57	20 01	20 04		20 14					20 15
	d		19 45							19 59	20 02	20 04		20 14					20 15
Crawley	d									20 03		20 08		20 18					
Ifield	d									20 05		20 11							
Faygate	d											20 15							
Littlehaven	d									20 12		20 19							
Horsham 4	a									20 15		20 22		20 26					
Balcombe	d		19 51																
Haywards Heath	a	19 47	19 56					20 00			20 11							20 17	20 24
	d	19 48	19 57					20 04	20 07		20 11							20 18	20 25
Wivelsfield	d		20 01						20 11										20 29
Lewes 4	a								20 22										
Burgess Hill 4	d		20 03					20 09			20 16								20 31
Hassocks 4	d		20 06								20 20								20 34
Preston Park	d		20 13																20 41
Hove 2	a							20 21											
Brighton 10	a	20 04	20 17								20 29							20 33	20 45

A Trolley to Haywards Heath

Table 186

Mondays to Fridays

9 December to 16 May

Bedford and London - Brighton

Network Diagram - see first Page of Table 175

Station		SN 1	SN 1 [trolley]	SN 1	SN 1 A [trolley]	SN 1	FC 1	SN 1	SN 1 [trolley]	SN 1	GW 1	SN 1	FC 1	SN 1	GW 1	SN 1	SN 1	SN 1
London Victoria 15 ⊖	d	19 40	19 45		19 47				20 00	20 02		20 06		20 15		20 10		20 17
Clapham Junction 10	d	19 46			19 53					20 08		20 12				20 16		20 23
Bedford	d						18 40						18 54					
Luton 10	d						19 04						19 18					
Luton Airport Parkway 7 ✈	d						19 06						19 20					
St Albans City	d						19 18						19 32					
St Pancras International 15 ⊖	d						19 39						19 54					
Farringdon 3 ⊖	d						19 44						19 59					
City Thameslink 3	d						19 48						20 03					
London Blackfriars 3 ⊖	d						19 50						20 05					
London Bridge 4 ⊖	d					19 52	19 57						20 12					
New Cross Gate	d																	
Norwood Junction 2	d					20 03												
East Croydon	a	19 56			20 03	20 06	20 09			20 19		20 22	20 24			20 26		20 33
	d	19 57			20 03	20 07	20 11			20 19		20 23	20 25			20 27		20 33
Purley 4	d	20 03				20 12										20 33		
Coulsdon South	d	20 06				20 15										20 36		
Merstham	d	20 12				20 21										20 42		
Redhill	a	20 16				20 25				20 30						20 46		
	d	20 16				20 26				20 31	20 34				20 41	20 48	20 51	
Reigate	a					20 31					20 38							
Nutfield	d																20 55	
Godstone	d																21 01	
Edenbridge	d																21 06	
Penshurst	d																21 13	
Leigh (Kent)	d																21 16	
Tonbridge 4	a																21 21	
Earlswood (Surrey)	d	20 19														20 50		
Salfords	d	20 22		←				←										
Horley 4	d	20 26		20 16				20 26								20 56		
Gatwick Airport 10 ✈	a	→	20 15	20 18	20 18		20 25	20 28	20 30	20 38			20 40	20 45	20 50	→		20 48
	d			20 19	20 19		20 27	20 29		20 39			20 41					20 49
Three Bridges 4	a			20 24			20 31	20 34		20 44			20 45					
	d			20 25			20 32	20 35		20 44			20 45					
Crawley	d			20 29				20 39		20 48								
Ifield	d			20 31				20 41										
Faygate	d																	
Littlehaven	d			20 38				20 48										
Horsham 4	a			20 41				20 53		20 56								
Balcombe	d												20 51					
Haywards Heath	a				20 30		20 41					20 47	20 56					21 00
	d				20 34 / 20 36		20 41					20 47	20 57					21 04 / 21 07
Wivelsfield	d				20 40								21 01					21 11
Lewes 4	a				20 55													21 22
Burgess Hill 4	d				20 39		20 46						21 03					21 09
Hassocks 4	d				20 42								21 06					
Preston Park	d				20 49								21 13					
Hove 2	a				20 53													21 21
Brighton 10	a						20 57					21 01	21 17					

Station		SN 1	SN 1	SN 1	SN 1	SN 1	SN 1	FC 1	GW 1	SN 1	SN 1	SN 1	SN 1	SN 1	SN 1	SN 1	SN 1	GW 1
London Victoria 15 ⊖	d			20 30	20 32		20 36			20 40		20 45	20 47			21 00	21 02	
Clapham Junction 10	d				20 38		20 42			20 46			20 53				21 08	
Bedford	d							19 25										
Luton 10	d							19 49										
Luton Airport Parkway 7 ✈	d							19 51										
St Albans City	d							20 03										
St Pancras International 15 ⊖	d							20 24										
Farringdon 3 ⊖	d							20 29										
City Thameslink 3	d							20 33										
London Blackfriars 3 ⊖	d							20 35										
London Bridge 4 ⊖	d	20 28						20 42						20 58				
New Cross Gate	d																	
Norwood Junction 2	d																	
East Croydon	a	20 40			20 48		20 52	20 54		20 56			21 03	21 10			21 18	
	d	20 41			20 48		20 53	20 55		20 57			21 04	21 11			21 18	
Purley 4	d									21 03								
Coulsdon South	d									21 06								
Merstham	d									21 12								
Redhill	a				21 00					21 16							21 30	
	d				21 00	21 05			21 13	21 16	21 22						21 31	21 35
Reigate	a					21 09			21 18		21 26							21 39
Nutfield	d																	
Godstone	d																	
Edenbridge	d																	
Penshurst	d																	
Leigh (Kent)	d																	
Tonbridge 4	a																	
Earlswood (Surrey)	d									21 19								
Salfords	d		←							21 22					←			
Horley 4	d		20 56							21 26					21 26			
Gatwick Airport 10 ✈	a	20 55	20 58	21 00	21 08			21 10		→		21 15	21 18	21 26	21 28	21 30	21 38	
	d	20 56	20 59		21 09			21 11					21 19	21 27	21 29		21 39	
Three Bridges 4	a	21 00	21 04		21 14			21 15						21 31	21 34		21 44	
	d	21 01	21 05		21 14			21 15						21 31	21 35		21 44	
Crawley	d		21 09		21 18										21 39			
Ifield	d		21 11												21 41			
Faygate	d																	
Littlehaven	d		21 18												21 48			
Horsham 4	a		21 23		21 26										21 53			
Balcombe	d																	
Haywards Heath	a	21 10					21 17	21 24					21 30	21 40			21 53	
	d	21 11					21 17	21 25					21 34 / 21 37	21 41			21 53	
Wivelsfield	d							21 29					21 41				21 57	
Lewes 4	a												21 54					
Burgess Hill 4	d							21 31					21 39				21 59	
Hassocks 4	d							21 34					21 42				22 03	
Preston Park	d							21 41					21 49				22 09	
Hove 2	a												21 53					
Brighton 10	a	21 26					21 31	21 45						21 56			22 15	

A [trolley] to Haywards Heath

Table 186

Mondays to Fridays

Bedford and London - Brighton

9 December to 16 May

Network Diagram - see first Page of Table 175

		SN [1]	FC [1]	SN [1]	SN [1]	SN [1]	SN [1]	SN [1]	GW [1]	SN [1]	SN [1]	SN [1]	SN [1]	FC [1]	SN [1]	SN [1]	SN [1]	SN [1]
London Victoria [15] ⊖	d	21 06		21 10	21 15	21 17		21 30			21 32		21 36		21 40		21 45	21 47
Clapham Junction [10]	d	21 12		21 16		21 23					21 38		21 42		21 46			21 53
Bedford	d		19 52											20 22				
Luton [10]	d		20 16											20 46				
Luton Airport Parkway [7] ✈	d		20 18											20 48				
St Albans City	d		20 30											21 00				
St Pancras International [15] ⊖	d		20 54											21 24				
Farringdon [3] ⊖	d		20 59											21 29				
City Thameslink [3]	d		21 03											21 33				
London Blackfriars [3] ⊖	d		21 05											21 35				
London Bridge [4] ⊖	d		21 12											21 42				
New Cross Gate	d																	
Norwood Junction [2]	d																	
East Croydon	a	21 22	21 24	21 26		21 33					21 48		21 51	21 54	21 56			22 03
	d	21 23	21 25	21 27		21 33					21 48		21 52	21 55	21 57			22 03
Purley [4]	d			21 33											22 03			
Coulsdon South	d			21 36											22 06			
Merstham	d			21 42											22 12			
Redhill	a			21 46							22 00				22 16			
	d			21 46					21 53	21 55	22 00	22 05			22 16	22 22		
Reigate	a											22 09				22 26		
Nutfield	d									21 59								
Godstone	d									22 05								
Edenbridge	d									22 10								
Penshurst	d									22 17								
Leigh (Kent)	d									22 20								
Tonbridge [4]	a									22 28								
Earlswood (Surrey)	d			21 49											22 19			
Salfords	d						←								22 22			
Horley [4]	d			21 54			21 54								22 26			
Gatwick Airport [10] ✈	a		21 40	→	21 45	21 48	21 57	22 00	22 06		22 08			22 10	→		22 15	22 18
	d		21 41			21 49	21 58				22 09			22 11				22 19
Three Bridges [4]	a		21 45			21 53	22 03				22 14			22 15				
	d		21 45			21 53	22 05				22 14			22 15				
Crawley	d						22 09				22 18							
Ifield	d						22 11											
Faygate	d																	
Littlehaven	d						22 18											
Horsham [4]	a						22 23				22 26							
Balcombe	d		21 53															
Haywards Heath	a	21 47	21 58			22 02							22 16	22 24				22 30
	d	21 47	21 59			22 06 / 22 08							22 16	22 25				22 34 / 22 37
Wivelsfield	d		22 03			22 12								22 29				22 38
Lewes [4]	a					22 23												22 53
Burgess Hill [4]	d		22 05			22 11								22 31				
Hassocks [4]	d		22 08											22 34				
Preston Park	d		22 15											22 41				
Hove [2]	a					22 22												22 51
Brighton [10]	a	22 01	22 19										22 30	22 45				

		SN [1]	SN [1]	SN [1]	GW [1]	SN [1]	FC [1]	SN [1]	SN [1]	SN [1]	SN [1]	SN [1]	GW [1]	SN [1]	SN [1]	SN [1]	SN [1]	FC [1]
London Victoria [15] ⊖	d		22 00	22 02		22 06		22 10	22 15	22 17		22 30			22 32		22 36	
Clapham Junction [10]	d			22 08		22 12		22 16		22 23					22 38		22 42	
Bedford	d						20 52											21 22
Luton [10]	d						21 16											21 46
Luton Airport Parkway [7] ✈	d						21 18											21 48
St Albans City	d						21 30											22 00
St Pancras International [15] ⊖	d						21 54											22 24
Farringdon [3] ⊖	d						21 59											22 29
City Thameslink [3]	d						22 03											22 33
London Blackfriars [3] ⊖	d						22 05											22 35
London Bridge [4] ⊖	d						22 12											22 42
New Cross Gate	d																	
Norwood Junction [2]	d																	
East Croydon	a			22 18		22 22	22 24	22 26		22 33					22 48		22 51	22 54
	d			22 18		22 22	22 25	22 27		22 34					22 48		22 52	22 55
Purley [4]	d							22 33										
Coulsdon South	d							22 36										
Merstham	d							22 42										
Redhill	a			22 30				22 46							23 00			
	d			22 31	22 33			22 48					22 52	22 55	23 01	23 05		
Reigate	a				22 38											23 09		
Nutfield	d													22 59				
Godstone	d													23 05				
Edenbridge	d													23 10				
Penshurst	d													23 17				
Leigh (Kent)	d													23 20				
Tonbridge [4]	a													23 25				
Earlswood (Surrey)	d							22 50										
Salfords	d	←									←							
Horley [4]	d	22 26						22 56			22 56							
Gatwick Airport [10] ✈	a	22 28	22 30	22 38			22 40	→	22 45	22 48	22 58	23 00	23 06		23 08			23 10
	d	22 29		22 39			22 41			22 49	22 59				23 09			23 11
Three Bridges [4]	a	22 34		22 44			22 45			22 53	23 04				23 15			23 15
	d	22 35		22 44			22 45			22 53	23 05				23 16			23 15
Crawley	d	22 39									23 09				23 19			
Ifield	d	22 41									23 11							
Faygate	d																	
Littlehaven	d	22 48									23 18							
Horsham [4]	a	22 53									23 23				23 27			
Balcombe	d						22 53											
Haywards Heath	a			22 53		22 47	22 58			23 02							23 16	23 24
	d			22 53		22 47	22 59			23 03							23 16	23 25
Wivelsfield	d			22 57			23 03											23 29
Lewes [4]	a																	
Burgess Hill [4]	d			22 59			23 05			23 08								23 31
Hassocks [4]	d			23 03			23 08											23 34
Preston Park	d			23 09			23 15											23 41
Hove [2]	a									23 21								
Brighton [10]	a			23 15		23 01	23 19										23 30	23 45

Table 186

Mondays to Fridays

9 December to 16 May

Bedford and London - Brighton

Network Diagram - see first Page of Table 175

		SN 1	SN 1	SN 1	SN 1	SN 1	SN 1	GW 1	SN 1	FC 1	SN 1	SN 1	SN 1	SN 1	SN 1	SN 1	SN 1	SN 1	FC 1	SN 1	SN 1	FC 1	FC 1	FC 1
London Victoria 15 ⊖	d	22 40	22 45	22 47		23 00	23 02		23 06		23 10		23 15	23 17		23 30	23 32	23 40		23 45				
Clapham Junction 10	d	22 46		22 53			23 08		23 12		23 16			23 23			23 38	23 46						
Bedford	d									21 52									22 22			22 42	23 12	23 42
Luton 10	d									22 16									22 46			23 06	23 36	00 06
Luton Airport Parkway 7 ✈	d									22 18									22 48			23 09	23 39	00 09
St Albans City	d									22 30									23 00			23 21	23 51	00 21
St Pancras International 15 ⊖	d									22 54									23 24			23 54	00 24	00 54
Farringdon 3 ⊖	d									22 59									23 29			23 59	00 29	
City Thameslink 3	d									23 03														
London Blackfriars 3 ⊖	d									23 05									23 35			00 05	00 35	01 05
London Bridge 4 ⊖	d									23 12									23 42			00 12	00 42	
New Cross Gate	d																							
Norwood Junction 2	d																							
East Croydon ⇌	a	22 56		23 03			23 19		23 22	23 24	23 26			23 33			23 48	23 55	23 56			00 28	00 56	01 34
	d	22 57		23 03			23 20		23 23	23 25	23 27			23 33			23 49	00 01	23 57			00 29	00 57	01 36
Purley 4	d	23 03									23 33							00 11						
Coulsdon South	d	23 06									23 36							00 15						
Merstham	d	23 12									23 42							00 20						
Redhill	a	23 16					23 31				23 46						00 04	00 24						
	d	23 16					23 31	23 34			23 46	23 55					00 05	00 25						
Reigate	a							23 38																
Nutfield	d																							
Godstone	d																							
Edenbridge	d											00 06												
Penshurst	d																							
Leigh (Kent)	d																							
Tonbridge 4	a											00 15												
Earlswood (Surrey)	d	23 19									23 49													
Salfords	d	23 22			←						23 52				←						←			
Horley 4	d	23 26			23 26						23 56				23 56			00 31			00 31			
Gatwick Airport 10 ✈	a	→	23 15	23 18	23 28	23 30	23 38			23 40	→		23 45	23 50	23 58	00 05	00 14	→	00 18	00 20	00 34	00 48	01 18	01 55
	d			23 19	23 29		23 39			23 41				23 51	23 59		00 15		00 19		00 35	00 49	01 19	01 56
Three Bridges 4	a				23 34		23 44			23 47				23 55	00 04		00 20		00 24		00 39	00 54	01 24	02 02
	d				23 40		23 44			23 47				23 56	00 05		00 20				00 39			
Crawley	d				23 44										00 09						00 43			
Ifield	d				23 46										00 11						00 46			
Faygate	d																							
Littlehaven	d				23 53										00 18						00 52			
Horsham 4	a				23 58										00 23						00 57			
Balcombe	d									23 53							00 26							
Haywards Heath	a			23 30			23 53		23 47	23 58				00 05			00 31							
	d			23 34 / 23 37			23 53		23 48	23 59				00 05			00 32							
Wivelsfield	d			23 38			23 57			00 03							00 36							
Lewes 4	a			23 51																				
Burgess Hill 4	d						23 59			00 05				00 11			00 38							
Hassocks 4	d						00 03			00 08							00 41							
Preston Park	d						00 09			00 15							00 48							
Hove 2	a			23 51										00 22										
Brighton 10	a						00 15		00 01	00 19							00 52							

Table 186

Bedford and London - Brighton

Saturdays

14 December to 17 May

Network Diagram - see first Page of Table 175

Station		GW 1	SN 1	FC 1	SN 1	SN 1	SN 1	SN 1	FC 1	SN 1
London Victoria 15 ⊖	d									
Clapham Junction 10	d									
Bedford	d									
Luton 10	d									
Luton Airport Parkway 7 ✈	d									
St Albans City	d									
St Pancras International 15 ⊖	d									
Farringdon 3 ⊖	d									
City Thameslink 3	d									
London Blackfriars 3 ⊖	d									
London Bridge 4 ⊖	d									
New Cross Gate	d									
Norwood Junction 2	d									
East Croydon	a									
	d									00 01
Purley 4	d									00 11
Coulsdon South	d									00 15
Merstham	d									00 20
Redhill	a									00 24
	d	00 01					00 05			00 25
Reigate	a									
Nutfield	d									
Godstone	d									
Edenbridge	d							00 06		
Penshurst	d									
Leigh (Kent)	d									
Tonbridge 4	a							00 15		
Earlswood (Surrey)	d									
Salfords	d									
Horley 4	d									00 31
Gatwick Airport 10 ✈	a	00 11					00 14			00 34
	d						00 15		00 19	00 35
Three Bridges 4	a						00 20		00 24	00 39
	d				00 05		00 20			00 39
Crawley	d				00 09					00 43
Ifield	d				00 11					00 46
Faygate	d									
Littlehaven	d				00 18					00 52
Horsham 4	a				00 23					00 57
Balcombe	d						00 26			
Haywards Heath	a						00 31			
	d					00 05	00 32			
Wivelsfield	d			00 03			00 36			
Lewes 4	a									
Burgess Hill 4	d			00 05		00 11	00 38			
Hassocks 4	d		00 03	00 08			00 41			
Preston Park	d		00 09	00 15			00 48			
Hove 2	a					00 22				
Brighton 10	a		00 15	00 19			00 52			

Station		SN 1	SN 1	FC 1	GW 1	SN 1	GW 1	FC 1	SN 1
London Victoria 15 ⊖	d	00 03	00 05			00 14			00 30
Clapham Junction 10	d		00 12			00 21			
Bedford	d								
Luton 10	d								
Luton Airport Parkway 7 ✈	d								
St Albans City	d								
St Pancras International 15 ⊖	d							00 24	
Farringdon 3 ⊖	d							00 29	
City Thameslink 3	d								
London Blackfriars 3 ⊖	d			00 05				00 35	
London Bridge 4 ⊖	d			00 12				00 42	
New Cross Gate	d								
Norwood Junction 2	d								
East Croydon	a		00 26	00 28		00 36		00 56	
	d		00 27	00 29		00 36		00 57	
Purley 4	d					00 41			
Coulsdon South	d					00 46			
Merstham	d					00 51			
Redhill	a					00 55			
	d				00 54	00 56	05 41		
Reigate	a						05 47		
Nutfield	d								
Godstone	d								
Edenbridge	d								
Penshurst	d								
Leigh (Kent)	d								
Tonbridge 4	a								
Earlswood (Surrey)	d								
Salfords	d								
Horley 4	d					01 02			
Gatwick Airport 10 ✈	a	00 39	00 45	00 48	01 03	01 05		01 18	01 20
	d		00 46	00 49				01 19	
Three Bridges 4	a		00 50	00 54				01 24	
	d		00 50						
Crawley	d								
Ifield	d								
Faygate	d								
Littlehaven	d								
Horsham 4	a								
Balcombe	d								
Haywards Heath	a		00 59						
	d		01 03 / 01 05						
Wivelsfield	d								
Lewes 4	a		01 19						
Burgess Hill 4	d								
Hassocks 4	d								
Preston Park	d								
Hove 2	a								
Brighton 10	a		01s17						

Station		SN 1	FC 1	SN 1	FC 1	SN 1	FC 1	SN 1	FC 1	SN 1
London Victoria 15 ⊖	d	01 00		02 00		03 00		03 30		04 00
Clapham Junction 10	d	01 09		02 09		03 09				04 09
Bedford	d				00 42		01 42			
Luton 10	d		00 06		01 06		02 06			
Luton Airport Parkway 7 ✈	d		00 09		01 09		02 09			
St Albans City	d		00 21		01 21		02 21			
St Pancras International 15 ⊖	d		00 54		01 54		02 54		03 25	
Farringdon 3 ⊖	d									
City Thameslink 3	d									
London Blackfriars 3 ⊖	d		01 05		02 05		03 05		03 36	
London Bridge 4 ⊖	d									
New Cross Gate	d									
Norwood Junction 2	d									
East Croydon	a	01 23	01 34	02 23	02 34	03 23	03 34		04 04	04 23
	d	01 24	01 36	02 24	02 36	03 24	03 36		04 06	04 24
Purley 4	d	01 29		02 29		03 29				04 29
Coulsdon South	d									
Merstham	d									
Redhill	a									
	d									
Reigate	a									
Nutfield	d									
Godstone	d									
Edenbridge	d									
Penshurst	d									
Leigh (Kent)	d									
Tonbridge 4	a									
Earlswood (Surrey)	d									
Salfords	d									
Horley 4	d	01 45		02 42		03 42				04 45
Gatwick Airport 10 ✈	a	01 48	01 55	02 45	02 55	03 45	03 55	04 05	04 25	04 48
	d	01 49	01 56	02 46	02 56	03 46	03 56		04 25	04 49
Three Bridges 4	a	01 53	02 02	02 51	03 02	03 51	04 02		04 32	04 54
	d	01 53								04 54
Crawley	d									
Ifield	d									
Faygate	d									
Littlehaven	d									
Horsham 4	a									
Balcombe	d									
Haywards Heath	a	02 05								05 03
	d	02 06								05 03
Wivelsfield	d									
Lewes 4	a									
Burgess Hill 4	d									
Hassocks 4	d									
Preston Park	d									
Hove 2	a									
Brighton 10	a	02 23								05 17

Station		FC 1	SN 1	FC 1	SN 1	SN 1	SN 1	FC 1	GW 1	SN 1
London Victoria 15 ⊖	d		04 30		05 00	05 15	05 02			
Clapham Junction 10	d						05 09			
Bedford	d	02 42		03 12				03 42		
Luton 10	d	03 06		03 36				04 06		
Luton Airport Parkway 7 ✈	d	03 09		03 39				04 09		
St Albans City	d	03 21		03 51				04 21		
St Pancras International 15 ⊖	d	03 54		04 24				04 54		
Farringdon 3 ⊖	d							04 59		
City Thameslink 3	d									
London Blackfriars 3 ⊖	d	04 05		04 35				05 05		
London Bridge 4 ⊖	d									
New Cross Gate	d									
Norwood Junction 2	d									
East Croydon	a	04 34		05 04			05 23	05 31		
	d	04 36		05 06			05 24	05 32		
Purley 4	d						05 29			
Coulsdon South	d						05 33			
Merstham	d						05 38			
Redhill	a						05 42			
	d						05 43		05 49	
Reigate	a									
Nutfield	d									
Godstone	d									
Edenbridge	d									
Penshurst	d									
Leigh (Kent)	d									
Tonbridge 4	a									
Earlswood (Surrey)	d									
Salfords	d									
Horley 4	d						05 49			
Gatwick Airport 10 ✈	a	04 55	05 05	05 25	05 36	05 50	05 52	05 53	05 58	
	d	04 56		05 26			05 53	05 54		05 58
Three Bridges 4	a	05 02		05 31			05 57	05 59		06 02
	d			05 32			05 58	06 00		06 03
Crawley	d									06 06
Ifield	d									06 09
Faygate	d									
Littlehaven	d									06 15
Horsham 4	a									06 18
Balcombe	d			05 38				06 06		
Haywards Heath	a			05 43			06 07	06 11		
	d			05 44			06 07	06 11		
Wivelsfield	d			05 48			06 11	06 15		
Lewes 4	a									
Burgess Hill 4	d			05 50			06 13	06 17		
Hassocks 4	d			05 53			06 17	06 21		
Preston Park	d			06 00			06 23	06 27		
Hove 2	a									
Brighton 10	a			06 05			06 27	06 31		

Table 186

Saturdays

14 December to 17 May

Bedford and London - Brighton

Network Diagram - see first Page of Table 175

		SN 1 ⚯	SN 1	SN 1	SN 1	GW 1	SN 1 ⚯	FC 1	SN 1		SN 1 ⚯	SN 1	GW 1	GW 1	SN 1		FC 1	SN 1 ⚯	SN 1
London Victoria 15 ⊖	d	05 30		05 32	05 32		05 45				06 00				06 02			06 15	
Clapham Junction 10	d			05 38	05 38										06 08				
Bedford	d							04 22									04 52		
Luton 10	d							04 46									05 16		
Luton Airport Parkway 7 ✈	d							04 49									05 19		
St Albans City	d							05 01									05 31		
St Pancras International 15 ⊖	d							05 34									05 53		
Farringdon 3 ⊖	d							05 39									05 59		
City Thameslink 3	d																		
London Blackfriars 3 ⊖	d							05 45									06 05		
London Bridge 4 ⊖	d							05 52									06 12		
New Cross Gate	d																		
Norwood Junction 2	d																		
East Croydon ⇌	a			05 47	05 47			06 04							06 17		06 24		
	d			05 48	05 48			06 05							06 18		06 25		
Purley 4	d			05 53	05 53										06 23				
Coulsdon South	d			05 57	05 57										06 27				
Merstham	d			06 03	06 03										06 32				
Redhill	a			06 07	06 07										06 36				
	d			06 07	06 07	06 13						06 22	06 34	06 41	06 46	06 52			
Reigate	a					06 18							06 38			06 56			
Nutfield	d											06 26							
Godstone	d											06 32							
Edenbridge	d											06 37							
Penshurst	d											06 44							
Leigh (Kent)	d											06 47							
Tonbridge 4	a											06 52							
Earlswood (Surrey)	d			06 11	06 11										06 48				
Salfords	d			06 15	06 15				←						06 52				←
Horley 4	d			06 18	06 18				06 18						06 55				06 55
Gatwick Airport 10 ✈	a	06 00		→	→		06 15	06 19	06 21		06 30			06 50	→		06 40	06 45	06 58
	d		06 12					06 20	06 22								06 41		06 59
Three Bridges 4	a		06 16					06 24	06 26								06 45		07 03
	d		06 17					06 25	06 30	06 34							06 45		07 04
Crawley	d									06 37									07 07
Ifield	d									06 40									07 10
Faygate	d																		
Littlehaven	d									06 46									07 16
Horsham 4	a									06 49									07 19
Balcombe	d							06 31	06 36										
Haywards Heath	a		06 26					06 36	06 41								06 54		
	d		06 26					06 37	06 41								06 55		
Wivelsfield	d		06 30					06 41	06 45								06 59		
Lewes 4	a		06 41																
Burgess Hill 4	d							06 43	06 47								07 01		
Hassocks 4	d							06 46	06 51								07 04		
Preston Park	d							06 53	06 57								07 11		
Hove 2	a																		
Brighton 10	a							06 57	07 02								07 15		

		SN 1 ⚯	SN 1		GW 1	GW 1	FC 1	SN 1 ⚯	SN 1	SN 1	SN 1	FC 1	SN 1 ⚯	GW 1	SN 1		SN 1	FC 1	SN 1 ⚯
London Victoria 15 ⊖	d	06 30	06 32					06 45					07 00				07 06		07 15
Clapham Junction 10	d		06 38														07 12		
Bedford	d						05 22					05 40						05 54	
Luton 10	d						05 46					06 04						06 18	
Luton Airport Parkway 7 ✈	d						05 49					06 06						06 20	
St Albans City	d						06 01					06 18						06 32	
St Pancras International 15 ⊖	d						06 24					06 40						06 54	
Farringdon 3 ⊖	d						06 29					06 45						06 59	
City Thameslink 3	d																		
London Blackfriars 3 ⊖	d						06 35					06 50						07 05	
London Bridge 4 ⊖	d						06 42					06 57			07 03			07 12	
New Cross Gate	d														07 08				
Norwood Junction 2	d														07 16				
East Croydon ⇌	a		06 47				06 54					07 09			07 20		07 22	07 24	
	d		06 48				06 55					07 11			07 21		07 22	07 25	
Purley 4	d		06 53												07 26				
Coulsdon South	d		06 57												07 30				
Merstham	d		07 02												07 35				
Redhill	a		07 06												07 39				
	d		07 10	07 22	07 13	07 34								07 41	07 44	07 52			
Reigate	a				07 18	07 38										07 56			
Nutfield	d			07 26															
Godstone	d			07 32															
Edenbridge	d			07 37															
Penshurst	d			07 44															
Leigh (Kent)	d			07 47															
Tonbridge 4	a			07 52															
Earlswood (Surrey)	d		07 12																
Salfords	d		07 16						←										
Horley 4	d		07 19						07 19						07 51				
Gatwick Airport 10 ✈	a	07 00	→				07 10	07 15	07 23			07 26	07 30	07 50	→			07 40	07 45
	d						07 11		07 24			07 27						07 41	
Three Bridges 4	a						07 15		07 29			07 31						07 45	
	d						07 15		07 30			07 32						07 45	
Crawley	d								07 33										
Ifield	d								07 36										
Faygate	d																		
Littlehaven	d								07 42										
Horsham 4	a								07 45										
Balcombe	d						07 21												
Haywards Heath	a						07 26					07 41						07 54	
	d						07 27			07 33	07 37	07 41						07 55	
Wivelsfield	d						07 31			07 37								07 59	
Lewes 4	a									07 48									
Burgess Hill 4	d						07 33											08 01	
Hassocks 4	d						07 36											08 04	
Preston Park	d						07 43											08 11	
Hove 2	a										07 51								
Brighton 10	a						07 47					07 55					07 57	08 15	

Table 186

Bedford and London - Brighton

Saturdays

14 December to 17 May

Network Diagram - see first Page of Table 175

		SN 1	FC 1	SN 1 ⚯	SN 1	SN 1	GW 1	SN 1	FC 1	SN 1	SN 1 ⚯	SN 1		SN 1	SN 1	FC 1	SN 1 ⚯	SN 1	GW 1
London Victoria 15 ⊖	d			07 30	07 32			07 36			07 45	07 47		07 51			08 00	08 02	
Clapham Junction 10	d				07 38			07 42				07 53						08 08	
Bedford	d		06 10						06 24							06 40			
Luton 10	d		06 34						06 48							07 04			
Luton Airport Parkway 7 ✈	d		06 36						06 50							07 06			
St Albans City	d		06 48						07 02							07 18			
St Pancras International 15 ⊖	d		07 10						07 24							07 40			
Farringdon 3 ⊖	d		07 15						07 29							07 45			
City Thameslink 3	d																		
London Blackfriars 3 ⊖	d		07 20						07 35							07 50			
London Bridge 4 ⊖	d		07 27			07 33			07 42	07 45						07 57			
New Cross Gate	d					07 38													
Norwood Junction 2	d					07 46				07 56									
East Croydon 🚊	a		07 39		07 47	07 50		07 52	07 54	07 59		08 02		08 07		08 09		08 17	
	d		07 41		07 48	07 51		07 52	07 55	08 00		08 03		08 08		08 11		08 18	
Purley 4	d					07 56				08 06									
Coulsdon South	d					08 00				08 09									
Merstham	d					08 05													
Redhill	a				08 00	08 09				08 17								08 30	
	d				08 00	08 10	08 13			08 17								08 30	08 34
Reigate	a						08 18												08 38
Nutfield	d									08 22									
Godstone	d									08 27									
Edenbridge	d									08 33									
Penshurst	d									08 39									
Leigh (Kent)	d									08 43									
Tonbridge 4	a									08 48									
Earlswood (Surrey)	d					08 12													
Salfords	d	←				08 16									←				
Horley 4	d	07 51				08 19									08 19			08 36	
Gatwick Airport 10 ✈	a	07 55	07 56	08 00	08 08	→			08 10		08 15	08 18		08 22	08 23	08 26	08 30	08 39	
	d	07 56	07 57		08 09				08 11			08 20		08 23	08 24	08 27		08 40	
Three Bridges 4	a	08 01	08 01		08 14				08 15						08 29	08 31		08 44	
	d	08 01	08 02		08 14				08 15						08 30	08 32		08 45	
Crawley	d	08 05			08 18										08 33			08 48	
Ifield	d	08 07													08 36				
Faygate	d																		
Littlehaven	d	08 14													08 42				
Horsham 4	a	08 17			08 26										08 45			08 56	
Balcombe	d								08 21										
Haywards Heath	a		08 11						08 26			08 30				08 41			
	d		08 11						08 27			08 35	08 37			08 41			
Wivelsfield	d								08 31										
Lewes 4	a											08 49							
Burgess Hill 4	d								08 33					08 38					
Hassocks 4	d								08 36					08 41					
Preston Park	d								08 43										
Hove 2	a												08 53						
Brighton 10	a		08 25					08 27	08 47					08 52		08 55			

		GW 1	SN 1	SN 1	FC 1	SN 1	SN 1 ⚯	SN 1		SN 1	FC 1	SN 1 ⚯	SN 1	SN 1	GW 1	SN 1	FC 1	SN 1	SN 1 ⚯
London Victoria 15 ⊖	d			08 06			08 15	08 17				08 30	08 32			08 36			08 45
Clapham Junction 10	d			08 12				08 23					08 38			08 42			
Bedford	d				06 54						07 10						07 24		
Luton 10	d				07 18						07 34						07 48		
Luton Airport Parkway 7 ✈	d				07 20						07 36						07 50		
St Albans City	d				07 32						07 48						08 02		
St Pancras International 15 ⊖	d				07 54						08 10						08 24		
Farringdon 3 ⊖	d				07 59						08 15						08 29		
City Thameslink 3	d																		
London Blackfriars 3 ⊖	d				08 05						08 20						08 35		
London Bridge 4 ⊖	d		08 03		08 12	08 15					08 27			08 33			08 42	08 45	
New Cross Gate	d		08 08											08 38					
Norwood Junction 2	d		08 16			08 26								08 46				08 56	
East Croydon 🚊	a		08 20	08 22	08 24	08 29		08 32			08 39		08 47	08 50		08 52	08 54	08 59	
	d		08 21	08 22	08 25	08 30		08 33			08 41		08 48	08 51		08 52	08 55	09 00	
Purley 4	d		08 26			08 36								08 56				09 06	
Coulsdon South	d		08 30			08 39								09 00				09 09	
Merstham	d		08 35			08 45								09 05					
Redhill	a		08 39			08 49							09 00	09 09				09 17	
	d	08 41	08 44			08 52							09 00	09 10	09 13			09 17	
Reigate	a					08 56									09 18				
Nutfield	d																	09 22	
Godstone	d																	09 27	
Edenbridge	d																	09 33	
Penshurst	d																	09 39	
Leigh (Kent)	d																	09 43	
Tonbridge 4	a																	09 48	
Earlswood (Surrey)	d													09 12					
Salfords	d									←				09 16					
Horley 4	d		08 51							08 51				09 19					
Gatwick Airport 10 ✈	a	08 50	→		08 40		08 45	08 48		08 55	08 56	09 00	09 08	→			09 10		09 15
	d				08 41			08 50		08 56	08 57		09 09				09 11		
Three Bridges 4	a				08 45					09 01	09 01		09 14				09 15		
	d				08 45					09 01	09 02		09 14				09 15		
Crawley	d									09 05			09 18						
Ifield	d									09 07									
Faygate	d																		
Littlehaven	d									09 14									
Horsham 4	a									09 17			09 26						
Balcombe	d																09 21		
Haywards Heath	a				08 54			09 00			09 11						09 26		
	d				08 55			09 04	09 07		09 11						09 27		
Wivelsfield	d				08 59				09 11								09 31		
Lewes 4	a								09 22										
Burgess Hill 4	d				09 01			09 09									09 33		
Hassocks 4	d				09 04												09 36		
Preston Park	d				09 11			09 18									09 43		
Hove 2	a							09 22											
Brighton 10	a			08 57	09 15						09 25					09 27	09 47		

Table 186

Saturdays

14 December to 17 May

Bedford and London - Brighton

Network Diagram - see first Page of Table 175

Station		SN 1	SN 1	SN 1	FC 1	SN 1 (trolley)	SN 1	GW 1	GW 1	SN 1	SN 1 (trolley)	FC 1
London Victoria 15 ⊖	d	08 47	08 51			09 00	09 02				09 06	
Clapham Junction 10	d	08 53					09 08				09 12	
Bedford	d				07 40							07 54
Luton 10	d				08 04							08 18
Luton Airport Parkway 7 ✈	d				08 06							08 20
St Albans City	d				08 18							08 32
St Pancras International 15 ⊖	d				08 40							08 54
Farringdon 3 ⊖	d				08 45							08 59
City Thameslink 3	d											09 03
London Blackfriars 3 ⊖	d				08 50							09 05
London Bridge 4 ⊖	d				08 57					09 03		09 12
New Cross Gate	d									09 08		
Norwood Junction 2	d									09 16		
East Croydon	a	09 02	09 07		09 09		09 17			09 20	09 22	09 24
	d	09 03	09 08		09 11		09 18			09 21	09 22	09 25
Purley 4	d									09 26		
Coulsdon South	d									09 30		
Merstham	d									09 35		
Redhill	a						09 30			09 39		
	d						09 30	09 34	09 41	09 44		
Reigate	a							09 38				
Nutfield	d											
Godstone	d											
Edenbridge	d											
Penshurst	d											
Leigh (Kent)	d											
Tonbridge 4	a											
Earlswood (Surrey)	d											
Salfords	d			←								
Horley 4	d			09 19			09 36			09 51		
Gatwick Airport 10 ✈	a	09 18	09 22	09 23	09 26	09 30	09 39		09 50	→		09 40
	d	09 20	09 23	09 24	09 27		09 40					09 41
Three Bridges 4	a			09 29	09 31		09 44					09 45
	d			09 30	09 32		09 45					09 45
Crawley	d			09 33			09 48					
Ifield	d			09 36								
Faygate	d											
Littlehaven	d			09 42								
Horsham 4	a			09 45			09 56					
Balcombe	d											
Haywards Heath	a	09 30			09 41							09 54
	d	09 35 / 09 37			09 41							09 55
Wivelsfield	d											09 59
Lewes 4	a	09 52										
Burgess Hill 4	d		09 38									10 01
Hassocks 4	d		09 41									10 04
Preston Park	d											10 11
Hove 2	a	09 53										
Brighton 10	a		09 52		09 55						09 57	10 15

Station		SN 1	SN 1 (trolley)	SN 1	SN 1	FC 1	SN 1 (trolley)	SN 1	SN 1	GW 1	SN 1 (trolley)	FC 1	SN 1
London Victoria 15 ⊖	d		09 15	09 17			09 30	09 32			09 36		
Clapham Junction 10	d			09 23				09 38			09 42		
Bedford	d					08 10						08 24	
Luton 10	d					08 34						08 48	
Luton Airport Parkway 7 ✈	d					08 36						08 50	
St Albans City	d					08 48						09 02	
St Pancras International 15 ⊖	d					09 10						09 24	
Farringdon 3 ⊖	d					09 15						09 29	
City Thameslink 3	d					09 18						09 33	
London Blackfriars 3 ⊖	d					09 20						09 35	
London Bridge 4 ⊖	d	09 15				09 27			09 33			09 42	09 45
New Cross Gate	d								09 38				
Norwood Junction 2	d	09 26							09 46				09 56
East Croydon	a	09 29		09 32		09 39		09 47	09 50		09 52	09 54	09 59
	d	09 30		09 33		09 41		09 48	09 51		09 52	09 55	10 00
Purley 4	d	09 36							09 56				10 06
Coulsdon South	d	09 39							10 00				10 09
Merstham	d	09 45							10 05				
Redhill	a	09 49						10 00	10 09				10 17
	d	09 52						10 00	10 10	10 13			10 17
Reigate	a	09 56								10 18			
Nutfield	d												10 22
Godstone	d												10 27
Edenbridge	d												10 33
Penshurst	d												10 39
Leigh (Kent)	d												10 43
Tonbridge 4	a												10 48
Earlswood (Surrey)	d								10 12				
Salfords	d				←				10 16				
Horley 4	d				09 51				10 19				
Gatwick Airport 10 ✈	a		09 45	09 48	09 55	09 56	10 00	10 08	→			10 10	
	d			09 50	09 56	09 57		10 09				10 11	
Three Bridges 4	a				10 01	10 01		10 14				10 15	
	d				10 01	10 02		10 14				10 15	
Crawley	d				10 05			10 18					
Ifield	d				10 07								
Faygate	d												
Littlehaven	d				10 14								
Horsham 4	a				10 17			10 26					
Balcombe	d											10 21	
Haywards Heath	a			10 00		10 11						10 26	
	d			10 04 / 10 07		10 11						10 27	
Wivelsfield	d			10 11								10 31	
Lewes 4	a			10 22									
Burgess Hill 4	d			10 09								10 33	
Hassocks 4	d											10 36	
Preston Park	d			10 18								10 43	
Hove 2	a			10 22									
Brighton 10	a					10 25					10 27	10 47	

Station		SN 1 (trolley)	SN 1	SN 1	SN 1	FC 1	SN 1 (trolley)	SN 1	GW 1	GW 1	SN 1	SN 1 (trolley)
London Victoria 15 ⊖	d	09 45	09 47	09 51			10 00	10 02				10 06
Clapham Junction 10	d		09 53					10 08				10 12
Bedford	d					08 40						
Luton 10	d					09 04						
Luton Airport Parkway 7 ✈	d					09 06						
St Albans City	d					09 18						
St Pancras International 15 ⊖	d					09 40						
Farringdon 3 ⊖	d					09 45						
City Thameslink 3	d					09 48						
London Blackfriars 3 ⊖	d					09 50						
London Bridge 4 ⊖	d					09 57					10 03	
New Cross Gate	d										10 08	
Norwood Junction 2	d										10 16	
East Croydon	a		10 02	10 07		10 09		10 17			10 20	10 22
	d		10 03	10 08		10 11		10 18			10 21	10 22
Purley 4	d										10 26	
Coulsdon South	d										10 30	
Merstham	d										10 35	
Redhill	a							10 30			10 39	
	d							10 30	10 34	10 41	10 44	
Reigate	a								10 38			
Nutfield	d											
Godstone	d											
Edenbridge	d											
Penshurst	d											
Leigh (Kent)	d											
Tonbridge 4	a											
Earlswood (Surrey)	d											
Salfords	d				←							
Horley 4	d				10 19			10 36			10 51	
Gatwick Airport 10 ✈	a	10 15	10 18	10 22	10 23	10 26	10 30	10 39		10 50	→	
	d		10 20	10 23	10 24	10 27		10 40				
Three Bridges 4	a				10 29	10 31		10 44				
	d				10 30	10 32		10 45				
Crawley	d				10 33			10 48				
Ifield	d				10 36							
Faygate	d											
Littlehaven	d				10 42							
Horsham 4	a				10 45			10 56				
Balcombe	d											
Haywards Heath	a		10 30			10 41						
	d		10 35 / 10 37			10 41						
Wivelsfield	d											
Lewes 4	a		10 52									
Burgess Hill 4	d			10 38								
Hassocks 4	d			10 41								
Preston Park	d											
Hove 2	a		10 53									
Brighton 10	a			10 52		10 55						10 57

Table 186

Saturdays

14 December to 17 May

Bedford and London - Brighton

Network Diagram - see first Page of Table 175

Station		FC 1	SN 1	SN 1 (trolley)	SN 1		SN 1	FC 1	SN 1 (trolley)	SN 1	SN 1	GW 1	SN 1 (trolley)	FC 1	SN 1	SN 1 (trolley)	SN 1		SN 1
London Victoria 15 ⊖	d			10 15	10 17				10 30	10 32			10 36			10 45	10 47		10 51
Clapham Junction 10	d				10 23					10 38			10 42				10 53		
Bedford	d	08 54						09 10						09 24					
Luton 10	d	09 18						09 34						09 48					
Luton Airport Parkway 7 ✈	d	09 20						09 36						09 50					
St Albans City	d	09 32						09 48						10 02					
St Pancras International 15 ⊖	d	09 54						10 10						10 24					
Farringdon 3 ⊖	d	09 59						10 15						10 29					
City Thameslink 3	d	10 03						10 18						10 33					
London Blackfriars 3 ⊖	d	10 05						10 20						10 35					
London Bridge 4 ⊖	d	10 12	10 15					10 27			10 33			10 42	10 45				
New Cross Gate	d										10 38								
Norwood Junction 2	d		10 26								10 46				10 56				
East Croydon (tram)	a	10 24	10 29		10 32			10 39		10 47	10 50		10 52	10 54	10 59		11 02		11 07
	d	10 25	10 30		10 33			10 41		10 48	10 51		10 52	10 55	11 00		11 03		11 08
Purley 4	d		10 36								10 56				11 06				
Coulsdon South	d		10 39								11 00				11 09				
Merstham	d		10 45								11 05								
Redhill	a		10 49							11 00	11 09				11 17				
	d		10 52							11 00	11 10	11 13			11 17				
Reigate	a		10 56									11 18							
Nutfield	d														11 22				
Godstone	d														11 27				
Edenbridge	d														11 33				
Penshurst	d														11 39				
Leigh (Kent)	d														11 43				
Tonbridge 4	a														11 48				
Earlswood (Surrey)	d										11 12								
Salfords	d						←				11 16								
Horley 4	d						10 51				11 19								
Gatwick Airport 10 ✈	a	10 40		10 45	10 48		10 55	10 56	11 00	11 08	→			11 10		11 15	11 18		11 22
	d	10 41			10 50		10 56	10 57		11 09				11 11			11 20		11 23
Three Bridges 4	a	10 45					11 01	11 01		11 14				11 15					
	d	10 45					11 01	11 02		11 14				11 15					
Crawley	d						11 05			11 18									
Ifield	d						11 07												
Faygate	d																		
Littlehaven	d						11 14												
Horsham 4	a						11 17			11 26									
Balcombe	d													11 21					
Haywards Heath	a	10 54			11 00			11 11						11 26			11 30		
	d	10 55			11 04	11 07		11 11						11 27			11 35	11 37	
Wivelsfield	d	10 59				11 11								11 31					
Lewes 4	a					11 22											11 52		
Burgess Hill 4	d	11 01			11 09									11 33					11 38
Hassocks 4	d	11 04												11 36					11 41
Preston Park	d	11 11			11 18									11 43					
Hove 2	a				11 22													11 53	
Brighton 10	a	11 15						11 25					11 27	11 47					11 52

Station		SN 1	FC 1	SN 1 (trolley)	SN 1	GW 1	GW 1	SN 1	SN 1 (trolley)	FC 1	SN 1	SN 1 (trolley)	SN 1		SN 1	FC 1	SN 1 (trolley)	SN 1	SN 1
London Victoria 15 ⊖	d			11 00	11 02				11 06			11 15	11 17				11 30	11 32	
Clapham Junction 10	d				11 08				11 12				11 23					11 38	
Bedford	d		09 40							09 54						10 10			
Luton 10	d		10 04							10 18						10 34			
Luton Airport Parkway 7 ✈	d		10 06							10 20						10 36			
St Albans City	d		10 18							10 32						10 48			
St Pancras International 15 ⊖	d		10 40							10 54						11 10			
Farringdon 3 ⊖	d		10 45							10 59						11 15			
City Thameslink 3	d		10 48							11 03						11 18			
London Blackfriars 3 ⊖	d		10 50							11 05						11 20			
London Bridge 4 ⊖	d		10 57					11 03		11 12	11 15					11 27			11 33
New Cross Gate	d							11 08											11 38
Norwood Junction 2	d							11 16			11 26								11 46
East Croydon (tram)	a		11 09		11 17			11 20	11 22	11 24	11 29		11 32			11 39		11 47	11 50
	d		11 11		11 18			11 21	11 22	11 25	11 30		11 33			11 41		11 48	11 51
Purley 4	d							11 26			11 36								11 56
Coulsdon South	d							11 30			11 39								12 00
Merstham	d							11 35			11 45								12 05
Redhill	a				11 30			11 39			11 49							12 00	12 09
	d				11 30	11 34	11 41	11 44			11 52							12 00	12 10
Reigate	a					11 38					11 56								
Nutfield	d																		
Godstone	d																		
Edenbridge	d																		
Penshurst	d																		
Leigh (Kent)	d																		
Tonbridge 4	a																		
Earlswood (Surrey)	d																		12 12
Salfords	d	←													←				12 16
Horley 4	d	11 19			11 36			11 51							11 51				12 19
Gatwick Airport 10 ✈	a	11 23	11 26	11 30	11 39		11 50	→		11 40		11 45	11 48		11 55	11 56	12 00	12 08	→
	d	11 24	11 27		11 40					11 41			11 50		11 56	11 57		12 09	
Three Bridges 4	a	11 29	11 31		11 44					11 45					12 01	12 01		12 14	
	d	11 30	11 32		11 45					11 45					12 01	12 02		12 14	
Crawley	d	11 33			11 48										12 05			12 18	
Ifield	d	11 36													12 07				
Faygate	d																		
Littlehaven	d	11 42													12 14				
Horsham 4	a	11 45			11 56										12 17			12 26	
Balcombe	d																		
Haywards Heath	a		11 41							11 54			12 00			12 11			
	d		11 41							11 55			12 04	12 07		12 11			
Wivelsfield	d									11 59				12 11					
Lewes 4	a													12 22					
Burgess Hill 4	d									12 01			12 09						
Hassocks 4	d									12 04									
Preston Park	d									12 11			12 18						
Hove 2	a												12 22						
Brighton 10	a		11 55						11 57	12 15						12 25			

Table 186

Saturdays

14 December to 17 May

Bedford and London - Brighton

Network Diagram - see first Page of Table 175

		GW	SN	FC	SN	SN	SN	SN	SN	FC	SN	SN	GW	GW	SN	SN	FC	SN
		1	1	1	1	1	1	1	1	1	1	1	1	1	1	1	1	1
			🛒			🛒					🛒					🛒		
London Victoria [15] ⊖	d		11 36			11 45	11 47	11 51			12 00	12 02				12 06		
Clapham Junction [10]	d		11 42				11 53					12 08				12 12		
Bedford	d			10 24						10 40							10 54	
Luton [10]	d			10 48						11 04							11 18	
Luton Airport Parkway [7] ✈	d			10 50						11 06							11 20	
St Albans City	d			11 02						11 18							11 32	
St Pancras International [15] ⊖	d			11 24						11 40							11 54	
Farringdon [3] ⊖	d			11 29						11 45							11 59	
City Thameslink [3]	d			11 33						11 48							12 03	
London Blackfriars [3] ⊖	d			11 35						11 50							12 05	
London Bridge [4] ⊖	d			11 42	11 45					11 57					12 03		12 12	12 15
New Cross Gate	d														12 08			
Norwood Junction [2]	d				11 56										12 16			12 26
East Croydon 🚊	a		11 52	11 54	11 59		12 02	12 07		12 09		12 17			12 20	12 22	12 24	12 29
	d		11 52	11 55	12 00		12 03	12 08		12 11		12 18			12 21	12 22	12 25	12 30
Purley [4]	d				12 06										12 26			12 36
Coulsdon South	d				12 09										12 30			12 39
Merstham	d														12 35			12 45
Redhill	a				12 17							12 30			12 39			12 49
	d	12 13			12 17							12 30	12 34	12 41	12 44			12 52
Reigate	a	12 18											12 38					12 56
Nutfield	d				12 22													
Godstone	d				12 27													
Edenbridge	d				12 33													
Penshurst	d				12 39													
Leigh (Kent)	d				12 43													
Tonbridge [4]	a				12 48													
Earlswood (Surrey)	d																	
Salfords	d								←									
Horley [4]	d								12 19			12 36			12 51			
Gatwick Airport [10] ✈	a			12 10		12 15	12 18	12 22	12 23	12 26	12 30	12 39		12 50	→		12 40	
	d			12 11			12 20	12 23	12 24	12 27		12 40					12 41	
Three Bridges [4]	a			12 15					12 29	12 31		12 44					12 45	
	d			12 15					12 30	12 32		12 45					12 45	
Crawley	d								12 33			12 48						
Ifield	d								12 36									
Faygate	d																	
Littlehaven	d								12 42									
Horsham [4]	a								12 45			12 56						
Balcombe	d			12 21														
Haywards Heath	a			12 26			12 30			12 41							12 54	
	d			12 27			12 35 / 12 37			12 41							12 55	
Wivelsfield	d			12 31													12 59	
Lewes [4]	a						12 52											
Burgess Hill [4]	d			12 33				12 38									13 01	
Hassocks [4]	d			12 36				12 41									13 04	
Preston Park	d			12 43													13 11	
Hove [2]	a						12 53											
Brighton [10]	a		12 27	12 47				12 52		12 55						12 57	13 15	

		SN	SN	SN	FC	SN	SN	SN	GW	SN	FC	SN	SN	SN	SN	SN	FC
		1	1	1	1	1	1	1	1	1	1	1	1	1	1	1	1
		🛒				🛒				🛒			🛒				
London Victoria [15] ⊖	d	12 15	12 17			12 30	12 32			12 36			12 45	12 47	12 51		
Clapham Junction [10]	d		12 23				12 38			12 42				12 53			
Bedford	d				11 10						11 24						11 40
Luton [10]	d				11 34						11 48						12 04
Luton Airport Parkway [7] ✈	d				11 36						11 50						12 06
St Albans City	d				11 48						12 02						12 18
St Pancras International [15] ⊖	d				12 10						12 24						12 40
Farringdon [3] ⊖	d				12 15						12 29						12 45
City Thameslink [3]	d				12 18						12 33						12 48
London Blackfriars [3] ⊖	d				12 20						12 35						12 50
London Bridge [4] ⊖	d				12 27			12 33			12 42	12 45					12 57
New Cross Gate	d							12 38									
Norwood Junction [2]	d							12 46				12 56					
East Croydon 🚊	a		12 32		12 39		12 47	12 50		12 52	12 54	12 59		13 02	13 07		13 09
	d		12 33		12 41		12 48	12 51		12 52	12 55	13 00		13 03	13 08		13 11
Purley [4]	d							12 56				13 06					
Coulsdon South	d							13 00				13 09					
Merstham	d							13 05									
Redhill	a						13 00	13 09				13 17					
	d						13 00	13 10	13 13			13 17					
Reigate	a								13 18								
Nutfield	d											13 22					
Godstone	d											13 27					
Edenbridge	d											13 33					
Penshurst	d											13 39					
Leigh (Kent)	d											13 43					
Tonbridge [4]	a											13 48					
Earlswood (Surrey)	d							13 12									
Salfords	d			←				13 16								←	
Horley [4]	d			12 51				13 19								13 19	
Gatwick Airport [10] ✈	a	12 45	12 48	12 55	12 56	13 00	13 08	→			13 10		13 15	13 18	13 22	13 23	13 26
	d		12 50	12 56	12 57		13 09				13 11			13 20	13 23	13 24	13 27
Three Bridges [4]	a			13 01	13 01		13 14				13 15					13 29	13 31
	d			13 01	13 02		13 14				13 15					13 30	13 32
Crawley	d			13 05			13 18									13 33	
Ifield	d			13 07												13 36	
Faygate	d																
Littlehaven	d			13 14												13 42	
Horsham [4]	a			13 17			13 26									13 45	
Balcombe	d										13 21						
Haywards Heath	a		13 00		13 11						13 26			13 30			13 41
	d		13 04 / 13 07		13 11						13 27			13 35 / 13 37			13 41
Wivelsfield	d		13 11								13 31						
Lewes [4]	a		13 22											13 52			
Burgess Hill [4]	d		13 09								13 33				13 38		
Hassocks [4]	d										13 36				13 41		
Preston Park	d		13 18								13 43						
Hove [2]	a		13 22											13 53			
Brighton [10]	a				13 25					13 27	13 47				13 52		13 55

Table 186

Saturdays

Bedford and London - Brighton

14 December to 17 May

Network Diagram - see first Page of Table 175

		SN	SN	GW	GW	SN	SN	FC	SN	SN	SN		SN	FC	SN	SN	SN	GW	SN	FC	SN	SN	SN		SN	SN	FC	SN	SN	GW	GW	SN	SN	FC	SN	SN
		1	1	1	1	1	1	1	1	1	1		1	1	1	1	1	1	1	1	1	1	1		1	1	1	1	1	1	1	1	1	1	1	1
		🚲					🚲			🚲					🚲				🚲			🚲						🚲					🚲			🚲
London Victoria 15 ⊖	d	13 00	13 02				13 06			13 15	13 17				13 30	13 32			13 36			13 45	13 47		13 51			14 00	14 02				14 06			14 15
Clapham Junction 10	d		13 08				13 12				13 23					13 38			13 42				13 53						14 08				14 12			
Bedford	d							11 54						12 10						12 24							12 40							12 54		
Luton 10	d							12 18						12 34						12 48							13 04							13 18		
Luton Airport Parkway 7 ✈	d							12 20						12 36						12 50							13 06							13 20		
St Albans City	d							12 32						12 48						13 02							13 18							13 32		
St Pancras International 15 ⊖	d							12 54						13 10						13 24							13 40							13 54		
Farringdon 3 ⊖	d							12 59						13 15						13 29							13 45							13 59		
City Thameslink 3	d							13 03						13 18						13 33							13 48							14 03		
London Blackfriars 3 ⊖	d							13 05						13 20						13 35							13 50							14 05		
London Bridge 4 ⊖	d					13 03		13 12	13 15					13 27			13 33			13 42	13 45						13 57					14 03		14 12	14 15	
New Cross Gate	d					13 08											13 38															14 08				
Norwood Junction 2	d					13 16			13 26								13 46				13 56											14 16			14 26	
East Croydon	a		13 17			13 20	13 22	13 24	13 29		13 32			13 39		13 47	13 50		13 52	13 54	13 59		14 02		14 07		14 09		14 17			14 20	14 22	14 24	14 29	
	d		13 18			13 21	13 22	13 25	13 30		13 33			13 41		13 48	13 51		13 52	13 55	14 00		14 03		14 08		14 11		14 18			14 21	14 22	14 25	14 30	
Purley 4	d					13 26			13 36								13 56				14 06											14 26			14 36	
Coulsdon South	d					13 30			13 39								14 00				14 09											14 30			14 39	
Merstham	d					13 35			13 45								14 05															14 35			14 45	
Redhill	a		13 30			13 39			13 49							14 00	14 09				14 17								14 30			14 39			14 49	
	d		13 30	13 34	13 41	13 44			13 52							14 00	14 10	14 13			14 17								14 30	14 34	14 41	14 44			14 52	
Reigate	a			13 38					13 56									14 18												14 38					14 56	
Nutfield	d																				14 22															
Godstone	d																				14 27															
Edenbridge	d																				14 33															
Penshurst	d																				14 39															
Leigh (Kent)	d																				14 43															
Tonbridge 4	a																				14 48															
Earlswood (Surrey)	d																14 12																			
Salfords	d												←				14 16									←										
Horley 4	d		13 36			13 51							13 51				14 19									14 19			14 36			14 51				
Gatwick Airport 10 ✈	a	13 30	13 39		13 50	→		13 40		13 45	13 48		13 55	13 56	14 00	14 08	→			14 10		14 15	14 18		14 22	14 23	14 26	14 30	14 39		14 50	→		14 40		14 45
	d		13 40					13 41			13 50		13 56	13 57		14 09				14 11			14 20		14 23	14 24	14 27		14 40					14 41		
Three Bridges 4	a		13 44					13 45					14 01	14 01		14 14				14 15						14 29	14 31		14 44					14 45		
	d		13 45					13 45					14 01	14 02		14 14				14 15						14 30	14 32		14 45					14 45		
Crawley	d		13 48										14 05			14 18										14 33			14 48							
Ifield	d												14 07													14 36										
Faygate	d																																			
Littlehaven	d												14 14													14 42										
Horsham 4	a		13 56										14 17			14 26										14 45			14 56							
Balcombe	d																			14 21																
Haywards Heath	a							13 54			14 00			14 11						14 26			14 30				14 41							14 54		
	d							13 55			14 04	14 07		14 11						14 27			14 35	14 37			14 41							14 55		
Wivelsfield	d							13 59				14 11								14 31														14 59		
Lewes 4	a											14 22											14 52													
Burgess Hill 4	d							14 01			14 09									14 33					14 38									15 01		
Hassocks 4	d							14 04												14 36					14 41									15 04		
Preston Park	d							14 11			14 18									14 43														15 11		
Hove 2	a										14 22													14 53												
Brighton 10	a						13 57	14 15						14 25					14 27	14 47					14 52		14 55						14 57	15 15		

Table 186

Saturdays

14 December to 17 May

Bedford and London - Brighton

Network Diagram - see first Page of Table 175

Station		SN 1		SN 1	FC 1	SN 1 🛒	SN 1	SN 1	GW 1	SN 1 🛒	FC 1	SN 1	SN 1 🛒	SN 1		SN 1	SN 1	FC 1	SN 1 🛒	SN 1	GW 1
London Victoria 15 ⊖	d	14 17				14 30	14 32			14 36			14 45	14 47		14 51			15 00	15 02	
Clapham Junction 10	d	14 23					14 38			14 42				14 53						15 08	
Bedford	d				13 10						13 24							13 40			
Luton 10	d				13 34						13 48							14 04			
Luton Airport Parkway 7 ✈	d				13 36						13 50							14 06			
St Albans City	d				13 48						14 02							14 18			
St Pancras International 15 ⊖	d				14 10						14 24							14 40			
Farringdon 3 ⊖	d				14 15						14 29							14 45			
City Thameslink 3	d				14 18						14 33							14 48			
London Blackfriars 3 ⊖	d				14 20						14 35							14 50			
London Bridge 4 ⊖	d				14 27			14 33			14 42	14 45						14 57			
New Cross Gate	d							14 38													
Norwood Junction 2	d							14 46				14 56									
East Croydon 🚊	a	14 32			14 39		14 47	14 50		14 52	14 54	14 59		15 02		15 07		15 09		15 17	
	d	14 33			14 41		14 48	14 51		14 52	14 55	15 00		15 03		15 08		15 11		15 18	
Purley 4	d							14 56				15 06									
Coulsdon South	d							15 00				15 09									
Merstham	d							15 05													
Redhill	a						15 00	15 09				15 17								15 30	
	d						15 00	15 10	15 13			15 17								15 30	15 34
Reigate	a								15 18												15 38
Nutfield	d											15 22									
Godstone	d											15 27									
Edenbridge	d											15 33									
Penshurst	d											15 39									
Leigh (Kent)	d											15 43									
Tonbridge 4	a											15 48									
Earlswood (Surrey)	d							15 12													
Salfords	d			←				15 16									←				
Horley 4	d			14 51				15 19									15 19			15 36	
Gatwick Airport 10 ✈	a	14 48		14 55	14 56	15 00	15 08	→			15 10		15 15	15 18		15 22	15 23	15 26	15 30	15 39	
	d	14 50		14 56	14 57		15 09				15 11			15 20		15 23	15 24	15 27		15 40	
Three Bridges 4	a			15 01	15 01		15 14				15 15						15 29	15 31		15 44	
	d			15 01	15 02		15 14				15 15						15 30	15 32		15 45	
Crawley	d			15 05			15 18										15 33			15 48	
Ifield	d			15 07													15 36				
Faygate	d																				
Littlehaven	d			15 14													15 42				
Horsham 4	a			15 17			15 26										15 45			15 56	
Balcombe	d										15 21										
Haywards Heath	a	15 00			15 11						15 26			15 30				15 41			
	d	15 04	15 07		15 11						15 27			15 35	15 37			15 41			
Wivelsfield	d		15 11								15 31										
Lewes 4	a		15 22											15 52							
Burgess Hill 4	d	15 09									15 33					15 38					
Hassocks 4	d										15 36					15 41					
Preston Park	d	15 18									15 43										
Hove 2	a	15 22													15 53						
Brighton 10	a				15 25					15 27	15 47					15 52		15 55			

Station		GW 1	SN 1	SN 1 🛒	FC 1	SN 1	SN 1 🛒	SN 1		SN 1	FC 1	SN 1 🛒	SN 1	SN 1	GW 1	SN 1 🛒	FC 1
London Victoria 15 ⊖	d			15 06			15 15	15 17				15 30	15 32			15 36	
Clapham Junction 10	d			15 12				15 23					15 38			15 42	
Bedford	d				13 54						14 10						14 24
Luton 10	d				14 18						14 34						14 48
Luton Airport Parkway 7 ✈	d				14 20						14 36						14 50
St Albans City	d				14 32						14 48						15 02
St Pancras International 15 ⊖	d				14 54						15 10						15 24
Farringdon 3 ⊖	d				14 59						15 15						15 29
City Thameslink 3	d				15 03						15 18						15 33
London Blackfriars 3 ⊖	d				15 05						15 20						15 35
London Bridge 4 ⊖	d		15 03		15 12	15 15					15 27			15 33			15 42
New Cross Gate	d		15 08											15 38			
Norwood Junction 2	d		15 16			15 26								15 46			
East Croydon 🚊	a		15 20	15 22	15 24	15 29		15 32			15 39		15 47	15 50		15 52	15 54
	d		15 21	15 22	15 25	15 30		15 33			15 41		15 48	15 51		15 52	15 55
Purley 4	d		15 26			15 36								15 56			
Coulsdon South	d		15 30			15 39								16 00			
Merstham	d		15 35			15 45								16 05			
Redhill	a		15 39			15 49							16 00	16 09			
	d	15 41	15 44			15 52							16 00	16 10	16 13		
Reigate	a					15 56									16 18		
Nutfield	d																
Godstone	d																
Edenbridge	d																
Penshurst	d																
Leigh (Kent)	d																
Tonbridge 4	a																
Earlswood (Surrey)	d													16 12			
Salfords	d									←				16 16			
Horley 4	d		15 51							15 51				16 19			
Gatwick Airport 10 ✈	a	15 50	→		15 40		15 45	15 48		15 55	15 56	16 00	16 08	→			16 10
	d				15 41			15 50		15 56	15 57		16 09				16 11
Three Bridges 4	a				15 45					16 01	16 01		16 14				16 15
	d				15 45					16 01	16 02		16 14				16 15
Crawley	d									16 05			16 18				
Ifield	d									16 07							
Faygate	d																
Littlehaven	d									16 14							
Horsham 4	a									16 17			16 26				
Balcombe	d																16 21
Haywards Heath	a				15 54			16 00			16 11						16 26
	d				15 55			16 04	16 07		16 11						16 27
Wivelsfield	d				15 59				16 11								16 31
Lewes 4	a								16 22								
Burgess Hill 4	d				16 01			16 09									16 33
Hassocks 4	d				16 04												16 36
Preston Park	d				16 11			16 18									16 43
Hove 2	a							16 22									
Brighton 10	a			15 57	16 15						16 25					16 27	16 47

Table 186

Saturdays

Bedford and London - Brighton

14 December to 17 May

Network Diagram - see first Page of Table 175

		SN 1	SN 1 🚌	SN 1		SN 1	SN 1	FC 1	SN 1 🚌	SN 1	GW 1	GW 1	SN 1	SN 1 🚌	FC 1	SN 1	SN 1 🚌	SN 1	
London Victoria 15 ⊖	d		15 45	15 47		15 51			16 00	16 02				16 06			16 15	16 17	
Clapham Junction 10	d			15 53						16 08				16 12				16 23	
Bedford	d							14 40							14 54				
Luton 10	d							15 04							15 18				
Luton Airport Parkway 7 ✈	d							15 06							15 20				
St Albans City	d							15 18							15 32				
St Pancras International 15 ⊖	d							15 40							15 54				
Farringdon 3 ⊖	d							15 45							15 59				
City Thameslink 3	d							15 48							16 03				
London Blackfriars 3 ⊖	d							15 50							16 05				
London Bridge 4 ⊖	d	15 45						15 57					16 03		16 12	16 15			
New Cross Gate	d												16 08						
Norwood Junction 2	d	15 56											16 16			16 26			
East Croydon	a	15 59		16 02		16 07		16 09		16 17			16 20	16 22	16 24	16 29		16 32	
	d	16 00		16 03		16 08		16 11		16 18			16 21	16 22	16 25	16 30		16 33	
Purley 4	d	16 06											16 26			16 36			
Coulsdon South	d	16 09											16 30			16 39			
Merstham	d												16 35			16 45			
Redhill	a	16 17								16 30			16 39			16 49			
	d	16 17								16 30	16 34	16 41	16 44			16 52			
Reigate	a										16 38					16 56			
Nutfield	d	16 22																	
Godstone	d	16 27																	
Edenbridge	d	16 33																	
Penshurst	d	16 39																	
Leigh (Kent)	d	16 43																	
Tonbridge 4	a	16 48																	
Earlswood (Surrey)	d																		
Salfords	d						←												
Horley 4	d						16 19			16 36			16 51						
Gatwick Airport 10 ✈	a		16 15	16 18		16 22	16 23	16 26	16 30	16 39		16 50	→		16 40		16 45	16 48	
	d			16 20		16 23	16 24	16 27		16 40					16 41			16 50	
Three Bridges 4	a						16 29	16 31		16 44					16 45				
	d						16 30	16 32		16 45					16 45				
Crawley	d						16 33			16 48									
Ifield	d						16 36												
Faygate	d																		
Littlehaven	d						16 42												
Horsham 4	a						16 45			16 56									
Balcombe	d																		
Haywards Heath	a			16 30				16 41							16 54			17 00	
	d			16 35	16 37			16 41							16 55			17 04	17 07
Wivelsfield	d														16 59				17 11
Lewes 4	a			16 52															17 22
Burgess Hill 4	d					16 38									17 01			17 09	
Hassocks 4	d					16 41									17 04				
Preston Park	d														17 11			17 18	
Hove 2	a				16 53													17 22	
Brighton 10	a					16 52		16 55						16 57	17 15				

		SN 1	FC 1	SN 1 🚌	SN 1	SN 1	GW 1	SN 1 🚌	FC 1	SN 1	SN 1 🚌	SN 1		SN 1	SN 1	FC 1	SN 1 🚌	SN 1	GW 1
London Victoria 15 ⊖	d			16 30	16 32			16 36			16 45	16 47		16 51			17 00	17 02	
Clapham Junction 10	d				16 38			16 42				16 53						17 08	
Bedford	d		15 10						15 24							15 40			
Luton 10	d		15 34						15 48							16 04			
Luton Airport Parkway 7 ✈	d		15 36						15 50							16 06			
St Albans City	d		15 48						16 02							16 18			
St Pancras International 15 ⊖	d		16 10						16 24							16 40			
Farringdon 3 ⊖	d		16 15						16 29							16 45			
City Thameslink 3	d		16 18						16 33							16 48			
London Blackfriars 3 ⊖	d		16 20						16 35							16 50			
London Bridge 4 ⊖	d		16 27			16 33			16 42	16 45						16 57			
New Cross Gate	d					16 38													
Norwood Junction 2	d					16 46				16 56									
East Croydon	a		16 39		16 47	16 50		16 52	16 54	16 59		17 02		17 07		17 09		17 17	
	d		16 41		16 48	16 51		16 52	16 55	17 00		17 03		17 08		17 11		17 18	
Purley 4	d					16 56				17 06									
Coulsdon South	d					17 00				17 09									
Merstham	d					17 05													
Redhill	a				17 00	17 09				17 17								17 30	
	d				17 00	17 10	17 13			17 17								17 30	17 34
Reigate	a						17 18												17 38
Nutfield	d									17 22									
Godstone	d									17 27									
Edenbridge	d									17 33									
Penshurst	d									17 39									
Leigh (Kent)	d									17 43									
Tonbridge 4	a									17 48									
Earlswood (Surrey)	d					17 12													
Salfords	d	←				17 16									←				
Horley 4	d	16 51				17 19									17 19			17 36	
Gatwick Airport 10 ✈	a	16 55	16 56	17 00	17 08	→			17 10		17 15	17 18		17 22	17 23	17 26	17 30	17 39	
	d	16 56	16 57		17 09				17 11			17 20		17 23	17 24	17 27		17 40	
Three Bridges 4	a	17 01	17 01		17 14				17 15						17 29	17 31		17 44	
	d	17 01	17 02		17 14				17 15						17 30	17 32		17 45	
Crawley	d	17 05			17 18										17 33			17 48	
Ifield	d	17 07													17 36				
Faygate	d																		
Littlehaven	d	17 14													17 42				
Horsham 4	a	17 17			17 26										17 45			17 56	
Balcombe	d								17 21										
Haywards Heath	a		17 11						17 26			17 30				17 41			
	d		17 11						17 27			17 35	17 37			17 41			
Wivelsfield	d								17 31										
Lewes 4	a											17 52							
Burgess Hill 4	d								17 33					17 38					
Hassocks 4	d								17 36					17 41					
Preston Park	d								17 43										
Hove 2	a												17 53						
Brighton 10	a		17 25					17 27	17 47					17 52		17 55			

Table 186

Saturdays

14 December to 17 May

Bedford and London - Brighton

Network Diagram - see first Page of Table 175

		GW	SN	SN	FC	SN	SN	SN		SN	FC	SN	SN	SN	GW	SN	FC	SN
		1	1	1	1	1	1	1		1	1	1	1	1	1	1	1	1
				✠			✠					✠				✠		
London Victoria 15 ⊖	d			17 06			17 15	17 17				17 30	17 32			17 36		
Clapham Junction 10	d			17 12				17 23					17 38			17 42		
Bedford	d				15 54						16 10						16 24	
Luton 10	d				16 18						16 34						16 48	
Luton Airport Parkway 7 ✈	d				16 20						16 36						16 50	
St Albans City	d				16 32						16 48						17 02	
St Pancras International 15 ⊖	d				16 54						17 10						17 24	
Farringdon 3 ⊖	d				16 59						17 15						17 29	
City Thameslink 3	d				17 03						17 18						17 33	
London Blackfriars 3 ⊖	d				17 05						17 20						17 35	
London Bridge 4 ⊖	d		17 03		17 12	17 15					17 27			17 33			17 42	17 45
New Cross Gate	d		17 08											17 38				
Norwood Junction 2	d		17 16			17 26								17 46				17 56
East Croydon 🚊	a		17 20	17 22	17 24	17 29		17 32			17 39		17 47	17 50		17 52	17 54	17 59
	d		17 21	17 22	17 25	17 30		17 33			17 41		17 48	17 51		17 52	17 55	18 00
Purley 4	d		17 26			17 36								17 56				18 06
Coulsdon South	d		17 30			17 39								18 00				18 09
Merstham	d		17 35			17 45								18 05				
Redhill	a		17 39			17 49							18 00	18 09				18 17
	d	17 41	17 44			17 52							18 00	18 10	18 13			18 17
Reigate	a					17 56									18 18			
Nutfield	d																	18 22
Godstone	d																	18 27
Edenbridge	d																	18 33
Penshurst	d																	18 39
Leigh (Kent)	d																	18 43
Tonbridge 4	a																	18 48
Earlswood (Surrey)	d													18 12				
Salfords	d									←				18 16				
Horley 4	d		17 51							17 51				18 19				
Gatwick Airport 10 ✈	a	17 50	→		17 40		17 45	17 48		17 55	17 56	18 00	18 08	→			18 10	
	d				17 41			17 50		17 56	17 57		18 09				18 11	
Three Bridges 4	a				17 45					18 01	18 01		18 14				18 15	
	d				17 45					18 01	18 02		18 14				18 15	
Crawley	d									18 05			18 18					
Ifield	d									18 07								
Faygate	d																	
Littlehaven	d									18 14								
Horsham 4	a									18 17			18 26					
Balcombe	d																18 21	
Haywards Heath	a				17 54			18 00			18 11						18 26	
	d				17 55			18 04	18 07		18 11						18 27	
Wivelsfield	d				17 59				18 11								18 31	
Lewes 4	a								18 22									
Burgess Hill 4	d				18 01			18 09									18 33	
Hassocks 4	d				18 04												18 36	
Preston Park	d				18 11			18 18									18 43	
Hove 2	a							18 22										
Brighton 10	a			17 57	18 15						18 25					18 27	18 47	

		SN	SN	SN		SN	SN	FC	SN	SN	GW	GW	SN	SN	FC	SN	SN	SN		SN
		1	1	1		1	1	1	1	1	1	1	1	1	1	1	1	1		1
		A	B																	
		✠	✠						✠					✠			✠			
London Victoria 15 ⊖	d	17 45	17 45	17 47		17 51			18 00	18 02				18 06			18 15	18 17		
Clapham Junction 10	d			17 53						18 08				18 12				18 23		
Bedford	d							16 40							16 54					
Luton 10	d							17 04							17 18					
Luton Airport Parkway 7 ✈	d							17 06							17 20					
St Albans City	d							17 18							17 32					
St Pancras International 15 ⊖	d							17 40							17 54					
Farringdon 3 ⊖	d							17 45							17 59					
City Thameslink 3	d							17 48							18 03					
London Blackfriars 3 ⊖	d							17 50							18 05					
London Bridge 4 ⊖	d							17 57					18 03		18 12	18 15				
New Cross Gate	d												18 08							
Norwood Junction 2	d												18 16			18 26				
East Croydon 🚊	a			18 02		18 07		18 09		18 17			18 20	18 22	18 24	18 29		18 32		
	d			18 03		18 08		18 11		18 18			18 21	18 22	18 25	18 30		18 33		
Purley 4	d												18 26			18 36				
Coulsdon South	d												18 30			18 39				
Merstham	d												18 35			18 45				
Redhill	a									18 30			18 39			18 49				
	d									18 30	18 34	18 41	18 44			18 52				
Reigate	a										18 38					18 56				
Nutfield	d																			
Godstone	d																			
Edenbridge	d																			
Penshurst	d																			
Leigh (Kent)	d																			
Tonbridge 4	a																			
Earlswood (Surrey)	d																			
Salfords	d						←													←
Horley 4	d						18 19			18 36			18 51							18 51
Gatwick Airport 10 ✈	a	18 15	18 16	18 18		18 22	18 23	18 26	18 30	18 39		18 50	→		18 40		18 45	18 48		18 55
	d			18 20		18 23	18 24	18 27		18 40					18 41			18 50		18 56
Three Bridges 4	a						18 29	18 31		18 44					18 45					19 01
	d						18 30	18 32		18 45					18 45					19 01
Crawley	d						18 33			18 48										19 05
Ifield	d						18 36													19 07
Faygate	d																			
Littlehaven	d						18 42													19 14
Horsham 4	a						18 47			18 56										19 17
Balcombe	d																			
Haywards Heath	a			18 30				18 41							18 54			19 00		
	d			18 35	18 37			18 41							18 55			19 04	19 07	
Wivelsfield	d														18 59				19 11	
Lewes 4	a			18 52															19 22	
Burgess Hill 4	d					18 38									19 01			19 09		
Hassocks 4	d					18 41									19 04					
Preston Park	d														19 11			19 18		
Hove 2	a				18 52													19 22		
Brighton 10	a					18 52		18 55						18 57	19 15					

A until 8 February

B from 15 February

Table 186

Saturdays

14 December to 17 May

Bedford and London - Brighton

Network Diagram - see first Page of Table 175

Station		FC [1]	SN [1] (trolley)	SN [1]	SN [1]	GW [1]	SN [1] (trolley)	FC [1]	SN [1]	SN [1] (trolley)	SN [1]	SN [1]
London Victoria [15] ⊖	d		18 30	18 32			18 36			18 45	18 47	18 51
Clapham Junction [10]	d			18 38			18 42				18 53	
Bedford	d	17 10						17 24				
Luton [10]	d	17 34						17 48				
Luton Airport Parkway [7] ✈	d	17 36						17 50				
St Albans City	d	17 48						18 02				
St Pancras International [15] ⊖	d	18 10						18 24				
Farringdon [3] ⊖	d	18 15						18 29				
City Thameslink [3]	d	18 18						18 33				
London Blackfriars [3] ⊖	d	18 20						18 35				
London Bridge [4] ⊖	d	18 27			18 33			18 42	18 45			
New Cross Gate	d				18 38							
Norwood Junction [2]	d				18 46				18 56			
East Croydon	a	18 39		18 47	18 50		18 52	18 54	18 59		19 02	19 07
	d	18 41		18 48	18 51		18 52	18 55	19 00		19 03	19 08
Purley [4]	d				18 56				19 06			
Coulsdon South	d				19 00				19 09			
Merstham	d				19 05							
Redhill	a			19 00	19 09				19 17			
	d			19 00	19 10	19 13			19 17			
Reigate	a					19 18						
Nutfield	d								19 22			
Godstone	d								19 27			
Edenbridge	d								19 33			
Penshurst	d								19 39			
Leigh (Kent)	d								19 43			
Tonbridge [4]	a								19 48			
Earlswood (Surrey)	d				19 12							
Salfords	d				19 16							
Horley [4]	d				19 19							
Gatwick Airport [10] ✈	a	18 56	19 00	19 08	→			19 10		19 15	19 18	19 22
	d	18 57		19 09				19 11			19 20	19 23
Three Bridges [4]	a	19 01		19 14				19 15				
	d	19 02		19 14				19 15				
Crawley	d			19 18								
Ifield	d											
Faygate	d											
Littlehaven	d											
Horsham [4]	a			19 26								
Balcombe	d							19 21				
Haywards Heath	a	19 11						19 26			19 30	
	d	19 11						19 27			19 35 / 19 37	
Wivelsfield	d							19 31				
Lewes [4]	a										19 52	
Burgess Hill [4]	d							19 33				19 38
Hassocks [4]	d							19 36				19 41
Preston Park	d							19 43				
Hove [2]	a										19 52	
Brighton [10]	a	19 25					19 27	19 47				19 52

Station		SN [1]	FC [1]	SN [1] (trolley)	SN [1]	GW [1]	GW [1]	SN [1]	SN [1]	SN [1] (trolley)	FC [1]	SN [1] (trolley)
London Victoria [15] ⊖	d			19 00	19 02					19 06		19 15
Clapham Junction [10]	d				19 08					19 12		
Bedford	d		17 40								17 54	
Luton [10]	d		18 04								18 18	
Luton Airport Parkway [7] ✈	d		18 06								18 20	
St Albans City	d		18 18								18 32	
St Pancras International [15] ⊖	d		18 40								18 54	
Farringdon [3] ⊖	d		18 45								18 59	
City Thameslink [3]	d		18 48								19 03	
London Blackfriars [3] ⊖	d		18 50								19 05	
London Bridge [4] ⊖	d		18 57					19 03			19 12	
New Cross Gate	d							19 08				
Norwood Junction [2]	d							19 16				
East Croydon	a		19 09		19 17			19 20		19 22	19 24	
	d		19 11		19 18			19 21		19 22	19 25	
Purley [4]	d							19 26				
Coulsdon South	d							19 30				
Merstham	d							19 35				
Redhill	a				19 30			19 39				
	d				19 30	19 34	19 41	19 46	19 51			
Reigate	a					19 38						
Nutfield	d								19 55			
Godstone	d								20 01			
Edenbridge	d								20 06			
Penshurst	d								20 13			
Leigh (Kent)	d								20 16			
Tonbridge [4]	a								20 21			
Earlswood (Surrey)	d											
Salfords	d	←										
Horley [4]	d	19 19			19 36			19 52				
Gatwick Airport [10] ✈	a	19 23	19 26	19 30	19 39		19 50	→			19 40	19 45
	d	19 24	19 27		19 40						19 41	
Three Bridges [4]	a	19 28	19 31		19 44						19 45	
	d	19 30	19 32		19 45						19 45	
Crawley	d	19 33			19 48							
Ifield	d	19 36										
Faygate	d											
Littlehaven	d	19 42										
Horsham [4]	a	19 45			19 56							
Balcombe	d											
Haywards Heath	a		19 41								19 54	
	d		19 41								19 55	
Wivelsfield	d										19 59	
Lewes [4]	a											
Burgess Hill [4]	d										20 01	
Hassocks [4]	d										20 04	
Preston Park	d										20 11	
Hove [2]	a											
Brighton [10]	a		19 55							19 57	20 15	

Station		SN [1]	SN [1]	FC [1]	SN [1] (trolley)	SN [1]	SN [1]	GW [1]	SN [1]	FC [1]	SN [1] (trolley)	SN [1]
London Victoria [15] ⊖	d	19 17			19 30	19 32			19 36		19 45	19 47
Clapham Junction [10]	d	19 23				19 38			19 42			19 53
Bedford	d			18 10						18 24		
Luton [10]	d			18 34						18 48		
Luton Airport Parkway [7] ✈	d			18 36						18 50		
St Albans City	d			18 48						19 02		
St Pancras International [15] ⊖	d			19 10						19 24		
Farringdon [3] ⊖	d			19 15						19 29		
City Thameslink [3]	d			19 18						19 33		
London Blackfriars [3] ⊖	d			19 20						19 35		
London Bridge [4] ⊖	d			19 27			19 33			19 42		
New Cross Gate	d						19 38					
Norwood Junction [2]	d						19 46					
East Croydon	a	19 33		19 39		19 47	19 50		19 52	19 54		20 02
	d	19 33		19 41		19 48	19 51		19 52	19 55		20 03
Purley [4]	d						19 56					
Coulsdon South	d						20 00					
Merstham	d						20 05					
Redhill	a					20 00	20 09					
	d					20 00	20 10	20 13				
Reigate	a							20 18				
Nutfield	d											
Godstone	d											
Edenbridge	d											
Penshurst	d											
Leigh (Kent)	d											
Tonbridge [4]	a											
Earlswood (Surrey)	d						20 12					
Salfords	d		←				20 16					
Horley [4]	d		19 52				20 19					
Gatwick Airport [10] ✈	a	19 48	19 55	19 56	20 00	20 08	→			20 10	20 15	20 18
	d	19 50	19 56	19 57		20 09				20 11		20 20
Three Bridges [4]	a		20 01	20 01		20 14				20 15		
	d		20 01	20 02		20 14				20 15		
Crawley	d		20 05			20 18						
Ifield	d		20 07									
Faygate	d											
Littlehaven	d		20 14									
Horsham [4]	a		20 17			20 26						
Balcombe	d									20 21		
Haywards Heath	a	20 00		20 11						20 26		20 30
	d	20 04 / 20 07		20 11						20 27		20 35 / 20 37
Wivelsfield	d	20 11								20 31		20 39
Lewes [4]	a	20 22										20 52
Burgess Hill [4]	d	20 09								20 33		
Hassocks [4]	d									20 36		
Preston Park	d	20 18								20 43		
Hove [2]	a	20 22										20 52
Brighton [10]	a			20 25					20 27	20 47		

Table 186

Saturdays

14 December to 17 May

Bedford and London - Brighton

Network Diagram - see first Page of Table 175

Station		SN 1	SN 1	FC 1	SN 1 (bicycle symbol)	SN 1	GW 1	SN 1	FC 1	SN 1	GW 1	SN 1	SN 1	SN 1		SN 1	SN 1	SN 1
London Victoria 15 ⊖	d	19 51			20 00	20 02		20 06		20 15		20 10		20 17		20 21		20 30
Clapham Junction 10	d					20 08		20 12				20 16		20 23				
Bedford	d			18 40					18 54									
Luton 10	d			19 04					19 18									
Luton Airport Parkway 7 ✈	d			19 06					19 20									
St Albans City	d			19 18					19 32									
St Pancras International 15 ⊖	d			19 40					19 54									
Farringdon 3 ⊖	d			19 45					19 59									
City Thameslink 3	d			19 48					20 03									
London Blackfriars 3 ⊖	d			19 50					20 05									
London Bridge 4 ⊖	d			19 57					20 12									
New Cross Gate	d																	
Norwood Junction 2	d																	
East Croydon	a	20 07		20 09		20 17		20 22	20 24			20 29		20 32		20 37		
	d	20 08		20 11		20 18		20 22	20 25			20 29		20 33		20 38		
Purley 4	d											20 34						
Coulsdon South	d											20 38						
Merstham	d											20 44						
Redhill	a					20 30						20 47						
	d					20 30	20 34				20 41	20 48	20 51					
Reigate	a						20 38											
Nutfield	d												20 55					
Godstone	d												21 01					
Edenbridge	d												21 06					
Penshurst	d												21 13					
Leigh (Kent)	d												21 16					
Tonbridge 4	a												21 21					
Earlswood (Surrey)	d																	
Salfords	d		←														←	
Horley 4	d		20 19									20 54					20 54	
Gatwick Airport 10 ✈	a	20 22	20 23	20 26	20 30	20 38			20 40	20 45	20 50	→		20 48		20 52	20 58	21 00
	d	20 23	20 24	20 27		20 40			20 41					20 50		20 53	20 59	
Three Bridges 4	a		20 29	20 31		20 44			20 45								21 03	
	d		20 33	20 32		20 45			20 45								21 04	
Crawley	d		20 36			20 48											21 07	
Ifield	d		20 39														21 10	
Faygate	d																	
Littlehaven	d		20 45														21 16	
Horsham 4	a		20 48			20 56											21 19	
Balcombe	d								20 51									
Haywards Heath	a			20 41					20 56					21 00				
	d			20 41					20 57					21 05	21 07			
Wivelsfield	d								21 01						21 11			
Lewes 4	a														21 22			
Burgess Hill 4	d	20 38							21 03					21 10				
Hassocks 4	d	20 41							21 06							21 11		
Preston Park	d								21 13					21 19				
Hove 2	a													21 22				
Brighton 10	a	20 52		20 55				20 57	21 17							21 22		

Station		SN 1	GW 1	SN 1	FC 1	SN 1	SN 1	SN 1		SN 1	SN 1	SN 1	GW 1	SN 1	FC 1	SN 1	SN 1	SN 1		SN 1
London Victoria 15 ⊖	d	20 32		20 36		20 40	20 45	20 47			21 00	21 02		21 06		21 10	21 15	21 17		
Clapham Junction 10	d	20 38		20 42		20 46		20 53				21 08		21 12		21 16		21 23		
Bedford	d				19 22										19 52					
Luton 10	d				19 46										20 16					
Luton Airport Parkway 7 ✈	d				19 48										20 18					
St Albans City	d				20 00										20 30					
St Pancras International 15 ⊖	d				20 24										20 54					
Farringdon 3 ⊖	d				20 29										20 59					
City Thameslink 3	d				20 33										21 03					
London Blackfriars 3 ⊖	d				20 35										21 05					
London Bridge 4 ⊖	d				20 42										21 12					
New Cross Gate	d																			
Norwood Junction 2	d																			
East Croydon	a	20 47		20 52	20 54	20 57		21 02				21 17		21 22	21 24	21 27		21 33		
	d	20 48		20 52	20 55	20 58		21 03				21 18		21 23	21 25	21 28		21 33		
Purley 4	d					21 03										21 33				
Coulsdon South	d					21 06										21 37				
Merstham	d					21 12										21 42				
Redhill	a	21 00				21 15						21 30				21 46				
	d	21 00	21 13			21 16						21 31	21 36			21 46				
Reigate	a		21 18										21 40							
Nutfield	d																			
Godstone	d																			
Edenbridge	d																			
Penshurst	d																			
Leigh (Kent)	d																			
Tonbridge 4	a																			
Earlswood (Surrey)	d					21 18														
Salfords	d					21 22				←										←
Horley 4	d					21 25				21 25						21 52				21 52
Gatwick Airport 10 ✈	a	21 08			21 10	→	21 15	21 18		21 28	21 30	21 38			21 40	→	21 45	21 48		21 55
	d	21 09			21 11			21 20		21 29		21 39			21 41			21 49		21 56
Three Bridges 4	a	21 14			21 15					21 33		21 44			21 45			21 53		22 00
	d	21 14			21 15					21 36		21 44			21 45			21 53		22 01
Crawley	d	21 18								21 39										22 04
Ifield	d									21 42										22 07
Faygate	d																			
Littlehaven	d									21 48										22 13
Horsham 4	a	21 26								21 52										22 16
Balcombe	d														21 53					
Haywards Heath	a				21 24			21 30				21 53		21 47	21 58			22 02		
	d				21 25			21 34	21 37			21 53		21 47	21 59			22 06	22 08	
Wivelsfield	d				21 29			21 38				21 57			22 03				22 12	
Lewes 4	a							21 51											22 23	
Burgess Hill 4	d				21 31							21 59			22 05			22 11		
Hassocks 4	d				21 34							22 03			22 08					
Preston Park	d				21 41							22 09			22 15					
Hove 2	a								21 51									22 22		
Brighton 10	a			21 27	21 45							22 15		22 01	22 19					

Table 186

Saturdays

Bedford and London - Brighton

14 December to 17 May

Network Diagram - see first Page of Table 175

Station		GW 1	SN 1	SN 1	SN 1	SN 1	FC 1	SN 1	SN 1	SN 1		SN 1	SN 1
London Victoria 15 ⊖	d		21 30		21 32	21 36		21 40	21 45	21 47			22 00
Clapham Junction 10	d				21 38	21 42		21 46		21 53			
Bedford	d						20 22						
Luton 10	d						20 46						
Luton Airport Parkway 7 ✈	d						20 48						
St Albans City	d						21 00						
St Pancras International 15 ⊖	d						21 24						
Farringdon 3 ⊖	d						21 29						
City Thameslink 3	d												
London Blackfriars 3 ⊖	d						21 35						
London Bridge 4 ⊖	d						21 42						
New Cross Gate	d												
Norwood Junction 2	d												
East Croydon	a				21 47	21 52	21 54	21 57		22 03			
	d				21 48	21 53	21 55	21 58		22 03			
Purley 4	d							22 03					
Coulsdon South	d							22 06					
Merstham	d							22 12					
Redhill	a				22 00			22 15					
	d	21 49		21 51	22 00			22 16					
Reigate	a												
Nutfield	d			21 55									
Godstone	d			22 01									
Edenbridge	d			22 06									
Penshurst	d			22 13									
Leigh (Kent)	d			22 16									
Tonbridge 4	a			22 21									
Earlswood (Surrey)	d							22 18					
Salfords	d							22 22				←	
Horley 4	d							22 25				22 25	
Gatwick Airport 10 ✈	a	21 59	22 00		22 08		22 10	→	22 15	22 18		22 28	22 30
	d				22 09		22 11			22 20		22 29	
Three Bridges 4	a				22 14		22 15					22 33	
	d				22 14		22 15					22 36	
Crawley	d				22 18							22 39	
Ifield	d											22 42	
Faygate	d												
Littlehaven	d											22 48	
Horsham 4	a				22 26							22 52	
Balcombe	d												
Haywards Heath	a					22 17	22 24			22 30			
	d					22 17	22 25			22 34	22 37		
Wivelsfield	d						22 29			22 38			
Lewes 4	a									22 51			
Burgess Hill 4	d						22 31						
Hassocks 4	d						22 34						
Preston Park	d						22 41						
Hove 2	a										22 51		
Brighton 10	a					22 31	22 45						

Station		SN 1	GW 1	SN 1	FC 1	SN 1	SN 1	SN 1	SN 1	SN 1
London Victoria 15 ⊖	d	22 02		22 06		22 10		22 15	22 17	
Clapham Junction 10	d	22 08		22 12		22 16			22 23	
Bedford	d				20 52					
Luton 10	d				21 16					
Luton Airport Parkway 7 ✈	d				21 18					
St Albans City	d				21 30					
St Pancras International 15 ⊖	d				21 54					
Farringdon 3 ⊖	d				21 59					
City Thameslink 3	d									
London Blackfriars 3 ⊖	d				22 05					
London Bridge 4 ⊖	d				22 12					
New Cross Gate	d									
Norwood Junction 2	d									
East Croydon	a	22 17		22 22	22 24	22 27			22 33	
	d	22 18		22 23	22 25	22 28			22 33	
Purley 4	d					22 33				
Coulsdon South	d					22 37				
Merstham	d					22 42				
Redhill	a	22 30				22 46				
	d	22 31	22 33			22 46	22 55			
Reigate	a		22 38							
Nutfield	d						22 59			
Godstone	d						23 05			
Edenbridge	d						23 10			
Penshurst	d						23 17			
Leigh (Kent)	d						23 20			
Tonbridge 4	a						23 25			
Earlswood (Surrey)	d									
Salfords	d									←
Horley 4	d					22 52				22 52
Gatwick Airport 10 ✈	a	22 38			22 40	→		22 45	22 48	22 55
	d	22 39			22 41				22 50	22 56
Three Bridges 4	a	22 44			22 45				22 54	23 00
	d	22 44			22 45				22 54	23 01
Crawley	d									23 04
Ifield	d									23 07
Faygate	d									
Littlehaven	d									23 13
Horsham 4	a									23 16
Balcombe	d				22 53					
Haywards Heath	a	22 53		22 47	22 58				23 03	
	d	22 53		22 47	22 59				23 03	
Wivelsfield	d	22 57			23 03					
Lewes 4	a									
Burgess Hill 4	d	22 59			23 05				23 09	
Hassocks 4	d	23 03			23 08					
Preston Park	d	23 09			23 15					
Hove 2	a								23 21	
Brighton 10	a	23 15		23 01	23 19					

Station		SN 1	GW 1	SN 1	SN 1	FC 1	SN 1	GW 1	SN 1	SN 1		SN 1	SN 1	SN 1	SN 1	FC 1
London Victoria 15 ⊖	d	22 30		22 32	22 36		22 40		22 45	22 47			23 00	23 02	23 06	
Clapham Junction 10	d			22 38	22 42		22 46			22 53				23 08	23 12	
Bedford	d					21 22										21 52
Luton 10	d					21 46										22 16
Luton Airport Parkway 7 ✈	d					21 48										22 18
St Albans City	d					22 00										22 30
St Pancras International 15 ⊖	d					22 24										22 54
Farringdon 3 ⊖	d					22 29										22 59
City Thameslink 3	d															
London Blackfriars 3 ⊖	d					22 35										23 05
London Bridge 4 ⊖	d					22 42										23 12
New Cross Gate	d															
Norwood Junction 2	d															
East Croydon	a			22 47	22 52	22 54	22 57			23 03				23 17	23 22	23 24
	d			22 48	22 53	22 55	22 58			23 03				23 18	23 23	23 25
Purley 4	d						23 03									
Coulsdon South	d						23 07									
Merstham	d						23 12									
Redhill	a			23 00			23 16							23 30		
	d		22 56	23 00			23 16	23 28						23 31		
Reigate	a							23 33								
Nutfield	d															
Godstone	d															
Edenbridge	d															
Penshurst	d															
Leigh (Kent)	d															
Tonbridge 4	a															
Earlswood (Surrey)	d						23 19									
Salfords	d						23 22					←				
Horley 4	d						23 26					23 26				
Gatwick Airport 10 ✈	a	23 00	23 05	23 08		23 10	→		23 15	23 18		23 28	23 30	23 38		23 40
	d			23 09		23 11				23 20		23 29		23 39		23 41
Three Bridges 4	a			23 14		23 15						23 34		23 44		23 47
	d			23 15		23 15						23 38		23 44		23 47
Crawley	d			23 18								23 41				
Ifield	d											23 44				
Faygate	d															
Littlehaven	d											23 50				
Horsham 4	a			23 26								23 53				
Balcombe	d															23 53
Haywards Heath	a				23 17	23 24				23 30				23 53	23 47	23 58
	d				23 17	23 25				23 34	23 37			23 53	23 47	23 59
Wivelsfield	d					23 29				23 38				23 57		00 03
Lewes 4	a									23 51						
Burgess Hill 4	d					23 31								23 59		00 05
Hassocks 4	d					23 34								00 03		00 08
Preston Park	d					23 41								00 09		00 15
Hove 2	a										23 51					
Brighton 10	a				23 31	23 45								00 15	00 01	00 19

Table 186

Saturdays

14 December to 17 May

Bedford and London - Brighton

Network Diagram - see first Page of Table 175

		SN 1	SN 1	SN 1	SN 1	SN 1	SN 1	SN 1	SN 1	FC 1	SN	SN 1	FC 1	FC 1	FC 1
London Victoria 15 ⊖	d	23 10		23 15	23 17		23 30	23 32	23 40		23 45				
Clapham Junction 10	d	23 16			23 23			23 38	23 46						
Bedford	d									22 18			22 42	23 12	23 42
Luton 10	d									22 42			23 06	23 36	00 06
Luton Airport Parkway 7 ✈	d									22 44			23 09	23 39	00 09
St Albans City	d									22 56			23 21	23 51	00 21
St Pancras International 15 ⊖	d									23 24			23 54	00 24	00 54
Farringdon 3 ⊖	d									23 29			23 59	00 29	
City Thameslink 3	d														
London Blackfriars 3 ⊖	d									23 35			00 05	00 35	01 05
London Bridge 4 ⊖	d									23 42			00 12	00 42	
New Cross Gate	d														
Norwood Junction 2	d														
East Croydon 🚌	a	23 27			23 32			23 52	23 55	23 56			00 28	00 56	01 34
	d	23 28			23 33			23 52	00 01	23 57			00 29	00 57	01 36
Purley 4	d	23 33							00 11						
Coulsdon South	d	23 37							00 15						
Merstham	d	23 42							00 20						
Redhill	a	23 46						00 04	00 24						
	d	23 46	23 55					00 05	00 25						
Reigate	a														
Nutfield	d														
Godstone	d														
Edenbridge	d		00 06												
Penshurst	d														
Leigh (Kent)	d														
Tonbridge 4	a		00 15												
Earlswood (Surrey)	d	23 49													
Salfords	d	23 52				←						←			
Horley 4	d	23 56				23 56			00 31			00 31			
Gatwick Airport 10 ✈	a	→		23 45	23 49	23 58	00 05	00 14	→	00 18	00 20	00 34	00 48	01 18	01 54
	d				23 50	23 59		00 15		00 19		00 35	00 49	01 19	01 55
Three Bridges 4	a				23 54	00 04		00 20		00 23		00 39	00 54	01 24	02 02
	d				23 55	00 04		00 20		00 24		00 39	00 54		
Crawley	d					00 07						00 43			
Ifield	d					00 10						00 46			
Faygate	d														
Littlehaven	d					00 16						00 52			
Horsham 4	a					00 19						00 55			
Balcombe	d							00 26		00 30					
Haywards Heath	a				00 04			00 31		00 37			01 05		
	d				00 05			00 32		00 38			01 10		
Wivelsfield	d							00 36		00 43					
Lewes 4	a														
Burgess Hill 4	d				00 10			00 38		00 45			01 15		
Hassocks 4	d							00 41		00 48			01 18		
Preston Park	d							00 48		00 55					
Hove 2	a				00 23										
Brighton 10	a							00 52		00 59			01 29		

Table 186

Sundays

Bedford and London - Brighton

8 December to 29 December

Network Diagram - see first Page of Table 175

		GW	SN	FC	SN	SN	SN	SN	FC	SN	SN	SN		FC	GW	SN	GW	SN	FC	SN	FC	SN	SN	SN	SN	SN	SN	SN	SN	SN	SN	SN	SN	SN	SN	SN	SN
		1	1	1	1	1	1	1	1	1	1	1		1	1	1	1	1	1	1	1	1	1	1	1	1	1	1	1	1	1	1	1	1	1	1	1
																													Bus	Bus	Bus			Bus	Bus	Bus	
London Victoria 15 ⊖	d										00 03	00 05				00 14		00 30		01 00		02 00	03 00	03 30	04 00	04 30	05 00	05 02	05 15	05 30	05 45		05 47	06 00	06 15	06 30	06 32
Clapham Junction 10	d											00 12				00 21				01 09		02 09	03 09		04 09			05 09					05 54				06 39
Bedford	d																																				
Luton 10	d																				00 06																
Luton Airport Parkway 7 ✈	d																				00 09																
St Albans City	d																				00 21																
St Pancras International 15 ⊖	d																		00 24		00 54																
Farringdon 3 ⊖	d																		00 29																		
City Thameslink 3	d																																				
London Blackfriars 3 ⊖	d													00 05					00 35		01 05																
London Bridge 4 ⊖	d													00 12					00 42																		
New Cross Gate	d																																				
Norwood Junction 2	d																																				
East Croydon	a											00 27		00 28		00 35			00 56	01 25	01 34	02 25	03 25		04 25			05 24					06 09				06 54
	d									00 01		00 27		00 29		00 36			00 57	01 26	01 36	02 26	03 26		04 26			05 25					06 10				06 55
Purley 4	d									00 11						00 41				01 32		02 32	03 32		04 32			05 30									06 59
Coulsdon South	d									00 15						00 45																					07 03
Merstham	d									00 20						00 51																					07 09
Redhill	a									00 24						00 55																	06 23				07 13
	d	00 03					00 05			00 25					00 52	00 55	06 20																06 23				07 13
Reigate	a																06 24																				
Nutfield	d																																				
Godstone	d																																				
Edenbridge	d							00 06																													
Penshurst	d																																				
Leigh (Kent)	d																																				
Tonbridge 4	a							00 15																													
Earlswood (Surrey)	d																																				
Salfords	d																																				
Horley 4	d									00 31						01 02				01 47		02 49	03 49		04 49			05 46					06 30				07 20
Gatwick Airport 10 ✈	a	00 10					00 14			00 34	00 40	00 45		00 48	01 00	01 04		01 06	01 18	01 50	01 54	02 52	03 52	04 06	04 52	05 06	05 36	05 49	05 53	06 08	06 23		06 32	06 38	06 53	07 08	07 22
	d						00 15		00 19	00 35		00 46		00 49		01 05			01 19	01 51	01 55	02 53	03 53		04 53			05 50				06 30	06 33				07 23
Three Bridges 4	a						00 20		00 23	00 39		00 50		00 54		01 10			01 24	01 55	02 02	02 58	03 58		04 58			05 54				06 34	06 38				07 28
	d				00 04		00 20		00 24	00 39		00 50		00 54						01 56					04 58			05 55				06 43	06 39				07 28
Crawley	d				00 07					00 43																						06 47					
Ifield	d				00 10					00 46																						06 49					
Faygate	d																																				
Littlehaven	d				00 16					00 52																						06 56					
Horsham 4	a				00 19					00 55																						06 59					
Balcombe	d						00 26		00 30																												07 34
Haywards Heath	a						00 31		00 37			00 59		01 05						02 08					05 07			06 04					06 48				07 39
	d					00 05	00 32		00 38			01 03	01 05	01 10						02 08					05 08			06 04					06 48				07 39
Wivelsfield	d			00 03			00 36		00 43																								06 52				07 43
Lewes 4	a												01 19																								
Burgess Hill 4	d			00 05		00 10	00 38		00 45					01 15																			06 54				07 45
Hassocks 4	d		00 03	00 08			00 41		00 48					01 18																			06 58				07 49
Preston Park	d		00 09	00 15			00 48		00 55																								07 04				07 55
Hove 2	a					00 23																															
Brighton 10	a		00 15	00 19			00 52		00 59			01s17		01 29						02 23					05 23			06 20					07 09				07 59

Table 186

Sundays

8 December to 29 December

Bedford and London - Brighton

Network Diagram - see first Page of Table 175

Station		SN 1 🛒	GW 1	SN 1 🛒	FC 1	GW 1	SN 1	SN 1 🛒	SN 1 🛒	SN 1	SN 1	FC 1	SN 1 🛒	SN 1	GW 1	GW 1	SN 1 🛒	FC 1	SN 1	SN 1 🛒	SN 1	SN 1 🛒	SN 1	SN 1	SN 1	GW 1	FC 1	SN 1 🛒	SN 1 🛒	SN 1	SN 1 🛒	SN 1	SN 1	FC 1	SN 1	SN 1 🛒	GW 1
London Victoria 15 ⊖	d	06 45		07 00			07 02	07 15	07 30	07 26			07 45				08 00		08 02	08 15	08 17	08 30	08 32					08 45	08 47		09 00	09 02	09 06			09 15	
Clapham Junction 10	d						07 09			07 33									08 09		08 24		08 39						08 54			09 08	09 12				
Bedford	d											06 10						06 38									07 12							07 50			
Luton 10	d											06 34						07 02									07 36							08 14			
Luton Airport Parkway 7 ✈	d											06 37						07 05									07 39							08 17			
St Albans City	d											06 49						07 17									07 51							08 29			
St Pancras International 15 ⊖	d											07 24						07 50									08 24							08 54			
Farringdon 3 ⊖	d											07 29						07 55									08 29							08 59			
City Thameslink 3	d																																				
London Blackfriars 3 ⊖	d				06 51							07 34						08 00									08 34							09 04			
London Bridge 4 ⊖	d											07 41		07 43				08 09							08 35		08 41							09 11			
New Cross Gate	d																																				
Norwood Junction 2	d																								08 46												
East Croydon 🚊	a				07 23		07 25			07 47		07 54		07 56				08 21	08 23		08 37		08 52		08 54		08 55		09 05			09 17	09 22	09 25			
	d				07 24		07 26			07 47		07 54		07 56				08 21	08 24		08 38		08 53		08 55		08 56		09 06			09 18	09 23	09 26			
Purley 4	d						07 31							08 02					08 29						09 01							09 23					
Coulsdon South	d													08 05											09 05							09 27					
Merstham	d													08 11											09 10												
Redhill	a						07 40			07 59				08 15					08 38				09 04		09 14							09 34					
	d		07 18			07 20	07 41			08 04	08 13			08 19	08 19	08 21			08 39				09 05	09 10	09 15	09 20						09 35					09 37
Reigate	a					07 24									08 23											09 24											
Nutfield	d										08 17													09 14													
Godstone	d										08 23													09 20													
Edenbridge	d										08 28													09 25													
Penshurst	d										08 35													09 32													
Leigh (Kent)	d										08 38													09 35													
Tonbridge 4	a										08 43													09 40													
Earlswood (Surrey)	d																								09 17												
Salfords	d																													←					←		
Horley 4	d						07 47							08 25					08 45						09 23					09 23		09 41			09 41		
Gatwick Airport 10 ✈	a	07 24	07 29	07 39	07 43		07 50	07 53	08 08	08 12		08 16	08 23	08 27		08 31	08 39	08 41	08 48	08 53	08 56	09 08	09 12		→		09 11	09 16	09 20	09 25	09 30	→	09 37	09 41	09 43	09 45	09 47
	d				07 44		07 51			08 13		08 18		08 28				08 42	08 49		08 57		09 13				09 12		09 21	09 26			09 39	09 42	09 44		
Three Bridges 4	a				07 48		07 55			08 17		08 22		08 33				08 46	08 53				09 17				09 16			09 31				09 46	09 49		
	d				07 49		07 55			08 18		08 23		08 33				08 47	08 53				09 19				09 17			09 31				09 47	09 49		
Crawley	d						07 59							08 37					08 57											09 34					09 53		
Ifield	d						08 01							08 39																09 37							
Faygate	d																																				
Littlehaven	d						08 08							08 46																09 43							
Horsham 4	a						08 11							08 49					09 05											09 46					10 01		
Balcombe	d									08 24													09 25														
Haywards Heath	a				07 58					08 29		08 32						08 56			09 09		09 30				09 26		09 32					09 56			
	d				07 58					08 29		08 34						08 56			09 09		09 30				09 26		09 33					09 56			
Wivelsfield	d									08 33													09 35						09 38								
Lewes 4	a																												09 51								
Burgess Hill 4	d				08 03					08 35		08 39						09 01			09 16		09 37				09 33							10 01			
Hassocks 4	d				08 07					08 39		08 43						09 05					09 41				09 37							10 05			
Preston Park	d									08 45													09 47														
Hove 2	a																				09 27																
Brighton 10	a				08 17					08 50		08 53						09 15					09 51				09 47						10 03	10 15			

Table 186

Sundays

8 December to 29 December

Bedford and London - Brighton

Network Diagram - see first Page of Table 175

Station		SN 1	FC 1	SN 1 (trolley)	SN 1	SN 1	SN 1	SN 1	GW 1	FC 1
London Victoria 15 ⊖	d	09 17		09 30	09 27		09 32			
Clapham Junction 10	d	09 23			09 33		09 38			
Bedford	d		08 06							08 20
Luton 10	d		08 30							08 44
Luton Airport Parkway 7 ✈	d		08 33							08 47
St Albans City	d		08 45							08 59
St Pancras International 15 ⊖	d		09 10							09 24
Farringdon 3 ⊖	d		09 15							09 29
City Thameslink 3	d									
London Blackfriars 3 ⊖	d		09 19							09 34
London Bridge 4 ⊖	d		09 26					09 35		09 41
New Cross Gate	d									
Norwood Junction 2	d							09 46		
East Croydon	a	09 32	09 39		09 42		09 48	09 50		09 55
	d	09 33	09 39		09 42		09 49	09 51		09 56
Purley 4	d							09 56		
Coulsdon South	d							09 59		
Merstham	d							10 05		
Redhill	a				09 57			10 09		
	d				09 58	10 10		10 12	10 19	
Reigate	a								10 23	
Nutfield	d					10 14				
Godstone	d					10 20				
Edenbridge	d					10 25				
Penshurst	d					10 32				
Leigh (Kent)	d					10 35				
Tonbridge 4	a					10 40				
Earlswood (Surrey)	d							10 16		
Salfords	d									
Horley 4	d							10 21		
Gatwick Airport 10 ✈	a	09 48	09 54	10 00	10 05			→		10 11
	d	09 49	09 56		10 06					10 12
Three Bridges 4	a		10 01		10 10					10 16
	d				10 11					10 17
Crawley	d									
Ifield	d									
Faygate	d									
Littlehaven	d									
Horsham 4	a									
Balcombe	d				10 17					
Haywards Heath	a	10 00			10 22					10 26
	d	10 00			10 22					10 26
Wivelsfield	d				10 26					
Lewes 4	a									
Burgess Hill 4	d	10 06			10 28					10 33
Hassocks 4	d				10 32					10 37
Preston Park	d				10 38					
Hove 2	a	10 18								
Brighton 10	a				10 43		10 24			10 47

Station		SN 1 (trolley)	SN 1 (trolley)	SN 1	FC 1	SN 1 (trolley)	SN 1	SN 1 (trolley)	FC 1	SN 1
London Victoria 15 ⊖	d	09 45	09 47			10 00	10 02	10 06		
Clapham Junction 10	d		09 53				10 08	10 12		
Bedford	d				08 36				08 50	
Luton 10	d				09 00				09 14	
Luton Airport Parkway 7 ✈	d				09 03				09 17	
St Albans City	d				09 15				09 29	
St Pancras International 15 ⊖	d				09 40				09 54	
Farringdon 3 ⊖	d				09 45				09 59	
City Thameslink 3	d									
London Blackfriars 3 ⊖	d				09 49				10 04	
London Bridge 4 ⊖	d				09 56				10 11	
New Cross Gate	d									
Norwood Junction 2	d									
East Croydon	a		10 02		10 09		10 17	10 22	10 25	
	d		10 02		10 09		10 17	10 23	10 26	
Purley 4	d						10 23			
Coulsdon South	d						10 26			
Merstham	d									
Redhill	a						10 34			
	d						10 34			
Reigate	a									
Nutfield	d									
Godstone	d									
Edenbridge	d									
Penshurst	d									
Leigh (Kent)	d									
Tonbridge 4	a									
Earlswood (Surrey)	d									
Salfords	d			←						←
Horley 4	d			10 21			10 40			10 40
Gatwick Airport 10 ✈	a	10 15	10 18	10 24	10 24	10 30	→	10 37	10 41	10 43
	d		10 19	10 25	10 26			10 39	10 42	10 44
Three Bridges 4	a			10 29	10 33				10 46	10 48
	d			10 30					10 47	10 49
Crawley	d			10 33						10 53
Ifield	d			10 36						
Faygate	d									
Littlehaven	d			10 42						
Horsham 4	a			10 46						11 01
Balcombe	d									
Haywards Heath	a		10 29						10 56	
	d		10 30						10 56	
Wivelsfield	d		10 34							
Lewes 4	a		10 48							
Burgess Hill 4	d								11 01	
Hassocks 4	d								11 05	
Preston Park	d									
Hove 2	a									
Brighton 10	a							11 03	11 15	

Station		SN 1 (trolley)	SN 1	GW 1	FC 1	SN 1 (trolley)	SN 1	SN 1	SN 1 (trolley)	SN 1
London Victoria 15 ⊖	d	10 15	10 17			10 30	10 27		10 32	
Clapham Junction 10	d		10 23				10 33		10 38	
Bedford	d				09 06					
Luton 10	d				09 30					
Luton Airport Parkway 7 ✈	d				09 33					
St Albans City	d				09 45					
St Pancras International 15 ⊖	d				10 10					
Farringdon 3 ⊖	d				10 15					
City Thameslink 3	d									
London Blackfriars 3 ⊖	d				10 19					
London Bridge 4 ⊖	d				10 26					10 35
New Cross Gate	d									
Norwood Junction 2	d									10 46
East Croydon	a		10 32		10 39		10 42		10 48	10 50
	d		10 32		10 39		10 42		10 49	10 51
Purley 4	d									10 56
Coulsdon South	d									10 59
Merstham	d									11 05
Redhill	a						10 57			11 08
	d			10 39			10 58	11 10		11 12
Reigate	a									
Nutfield	d							11 14		
Godstone	d							11 20		
Edenbridge	d							11 25		
Penshurst	d							11 32		
Leigh (Kent)	d							11 35		
Tonbridge 4	a							11 40		
Earlswood (Surrey)	d									11 14
Salfords	d									
Horley 4	d									11 21
Gatwick Airport 10 ✈	a	10 45	10 48	10 48	10 54	11 00	11 05			→
	d		10 49		10 56		11 06			
Three Bridges 4	a				11 01		11 10			
	d						11 11			
Crawley	d									
Ifield	d									
Faygate	d									
Littlehaven	d									
Horsham 4	a									
Balcombe	d						11 17			
Haywards Heath	a		10 59				11 22			
	d		11 00				11 22			
Wivelsfield	d						11 26			
Lewes 4	a									
Burgess Hill 4	d		11 05				11 28			
Hassocks 4	d						11 32			
Preston Park	d						11 38			
Hove 2	a		11 18							
Brighton 10	a						11 43		11 24	

Station		GW 1	FC 1	SN 1 (trolley)	SN 1 (trolley)	SN 1	FC 1	SN 1 (trolley)	SN 1	SN 1 (trolley)
London Victoria 15 ⊖	d			10 45	10 47			11 00	11 02	11 06
Clapham Junction 10	d				10 53				11 08	11 12
Bedford	d		09 20				09 36			
Luton 10	d		09 44				10 00			
Luton Airport Parkway 7 ✈	d		09 47				10 03			
St Albans City	d		09 59				10 15			
St Pancras International 15 ⊖	d		10 24				10 40			
Farringdon 3 ⊖	d		10 29				10 45			
City Thameslink 3	d									
London Blackfriars 3 ⊖	d		10 34				10 49			
London Bridge 4 ⊖	d		10 41				10 56			
New Cross Gate	d									
Norwood Junction 2	d									
East Croydon	a		10 55		11 02		11 09		11 17	11 22
	d		10 56		11 02		11 09		11 17	11 23
Purley 4	d								11 23	
Coulsdon South	d								11 26	
Merstham	d									
Redhill	a								11 34	
	d	11 20							11 34	
Reigate	a	11 24								
Nutfield	d									
Godstone	d									
Edenbridge	d									
Penshurst	d									
Leigh (Kent)	d									
Tonbridge 4	a									
Earlswood (Surrey)	d									
Salfords	d					←				
Horley 4	d					11 21			11 40	
Gatwick Airport 10 ✈	a		11 11	11 15	11 18	11 24	11 24	11 30	→	11 37
	d		11 12		11 19	11 25	11 26			11 39
Three Bridges 4	a		11 16			11 29	11 33			
	d		11 17			11 30				
Crawley	d					11 33				
Ifield	d					11 36				
Faygate	d									
Littlehaven	d					11 42				
Horsham 4	a					11 46				
Balcombe	d									
Haywards Heath	a		11 26		11 29					
	d		11 26		11 30					
Wivelsfield	d				11 34					
Lewes 4	a				11 48					
Burgess Hill 4	d		11 33							
Hassocks 4	d		11 37							
Preston Park	d									
Hove 2	a									
Brighton 10	a		11 47							12 03

Table 186

Sundays

8 December to 29 December

Bedford and London - Brighton

Network Diagram - see first Page of Table 175

Station		FC 1	SN 1	SN 1 (trolley)	GW 1	SN 1	FC 1	SN 1 (trolley)	SN 1	SN 1	SN 1 (trolley)	SN 1	GW 1	FC 1	SN 1 (trolley)	SN 1 (trolley)	SN 1	FC 1	SN 1 (trolley)
London Victoria 15 ⊖	d			11 15		11 17		11 30	11 27		11 32				11 45	11 47			12 00
Clapham Junction 10	d					11 23			11 33		11 38					11 53			
Bedford	d	09 50					10 06							10 20				10 36	
Luton 10	d	10 14					10 30							10 44				11 00	
Luton Airport Parkway 7 ✈	d	10 17					10 33							10 47				11 03	
St Albans City	d	10 29					10 45							10 59				11 15	
St Pancras International 15 ⊖	d	10 54					11 10							11 24				11 40	
Farringdon 3 ⊖	d	10 59					11 15							11 29				11 45	
City Thameslink 3	d																		
London Blackfriars 3 ⊖	d	11 04					11 19							11 34				11 49	
London Bridge 4 ⊖	d	11 11					11 26					11 35		11 41				11 56	
New Cross Gate	d																		
Norwood Junction 2	d											11 46							
East Croydon	a	11 25				11 32	11 39		11 42		11 48	11 50		11 55		12 02		12 09	
	d	11 26				11 33	11 39		11 42		11 49	11 51		11 56		12 02		12 09	
Purley 4	d											11 56							
Coulsdon South	d											11 59							
Merstham	d											12 05							
Redhill	a								11 57			12 08							
	d				11 38				11 58	12 10		12 12	12 19						
Reigate	a												12 23						
Nutfield	d									12 14									
Godstone	d									12 20									
Edenbridge	d									12 25									
Penshurst	d									12 32									
Leigh (Kent)	d									12 35									
Tonbridge 4	a									12 40									
Earlswood (Surrey)	d											12 14							
Salfords	d		←														←		
Horley 4	d		11 40									12 21					12 21		
Gatwick Airport 10 ✈	a	11 41	11 43	11 45	11 47	11 48	11 54	12 00	12 05			→		12 11	12 15	12 18	12 24	12 24	12 30
	d	11 42	11 44			11 49	11 56		12 06					12 12		12 19	12 25	12 26	
Three Bridges 4	a	11 46	11 48				12 01		12 10					12 16			12 29	12 33	
	d	11 47	11 49						12 11					12 17			12 30		
Crawley	d		11 53														12 33		
Ifield	d																12 36		
Faygate	d																		
Littlehaven	d																12 42		
Horsham 4	a		12 01														12 46		
Balcombe	d								12 17										
Haywards Heath	a	11 56				12 00			12 22					12 26		12 29			
	d	11 56				12 00			12 22					12 26		12 30			
Wivelsfield	d								12 26							12 34			
Lewes 4	a															12 48			
Burgess Hill 4	d	12 01				12 06			12 28					12 33					
Hassocks 4	d	12 05							12 32					12 37					
Preston Park	d								12 38										
Hove 2	a					12 18													
Brighton 10	a	12 15							12 43		12 24			12 47					

Station		SN 1	SN 1 (trolley)	FC 1	SN 1	SN 1 (trolley)	SN 1	GW 1	FC 1	SN 1 (trolley)	SN 1	SN 1	SN 1 (trolley)	SN 1	GW 1	FC 1	SN 1 (trolley)	SN 1 (trolley)	SN 1
London Victoria 15 ⊖	d	12 02	12 06			12 15	12 17			12 30	12 27		12 32				12 45	12 47	
Clapham Junction 10	d	12 08	12 12				12 23				12 33		12 38					12 53	
Bedford	d			10 50					11 06							11 20			
Luton 10	d			11 14					11 30							11 44			
Luton Airport Parkway 7 ✈	d			11 17					11 33							11 47			
St Albans City	d			11 29					11 45							11 59			
St Pancras International 15 ⊖	d			11 54					12 10							12 24			
Farringdon 3 ⊖	d			11 59					12 15							12 29			
City Thameslink 3	d																		
London Blackfriars 3 ⊖	d			12 04					12 19							12 34			
London Bridge 4 ⊖	d			12 11					12 26					12 35		12 41			
New Cross Gate	d																		
Norwood Junction 2	d													12 46					
East Croydon	a	12 17	12 22	12 25			12 32		12 39		12 42		12 48	12 50		12 55		13 02	
	d	12 17	12 23	12 26			12 33		12 39		12 42		12 49	12 51		12 56		13 02	
Purley 4	d	12 23												12 56					
Coulsdon South	d	12 26												12 59					
Merstham	d													13 05					
Redhill	a	12 34									12 57			13 08					
	d	12 34						12 39			12 58	13 10		13 12	13 20				
Reigate	a														13 24				
Nutfield	d											13 14							
Godstone	d											13 20							
Edenbridge	d											13 25							
Penshurst	d											13 32							
Leigh (Kent)	d											13 35							
Tonbridge 4	a											13 40							
Earlswood (Surrey)	d													13 14					
Salfords	d				←														←
Horley 4	d	12 40			12 40									13 21					13 21
Gatwick Airport 10 ✈	a	→	12 37	12 41	12 43	12 45	12 48	12 48	12 54	13 00	13 05			→		13 11	13 15	13 18	13 24
	d		12 39	12 42	12 44		12 49		12 56		13 06					13 12		13 19	13 25
Three Bridges 4	a			12 46	12 48				13 01		13 10					13 16			13 29
	d			12 47	12 49						13 11					13 17			13 30
Crawley	d				12 53														13 33
Ifield	d																		13 36
Faygate	d																		
Littlehaven	d																		13 42
Horsham 4	a				13 01														13 46
Balcombe	d										13 17								
Haywards Heath	a			12 56			13 00				13 22					13 26		13 29	
	d			12 56			13 00				13 22					13 26		13 30	
Wivelsfield	d										13 26							13 34	
Lewes 4	a																	13 48	
Burgess Hill 4	d			13 01			13 06				13 28					13 33			
Hassocks 4	d			13 05							13 32					13 37			
Preston Park	d										13 38								
Hove 2	a						13 18												
Brighton 10	a		13 03	13 15							13 43		13 24			13 47			

Table 186

Sundays

Bedford and London - Brighton

8 December to 29 December

Network Diagram - see first Page of Table 175

Station		FC 1	SN 1 🛒	SN 1	SN 1 🛒	FC 1	SN 1	SN 1 🛒	GW 1	SN 1	FC 1	SN 1 🛒	SN 1	SN 1	SN 1 🛒	SN 1	GW 1	FC 1	SN 1 🛒
London Victoria 15 ⊖	d		13 00	13 02	13 06			13 15		13 17		13 30	13 27		13 32				13 45
Clapham Junction 10	d			13 08	13 12					13 23			13 33		13 38				
Bedford	d	11 36				11 50					12 06							12 20	
Luton 10	d	12 00				12 14					12 30							12 44	
Luton Airport Parkway 7 ✈	d	12 03				12 17					12 33							12 47	
St Albans City	d	12 15				12 29					12 45							12 59	
St Pancras International 15 ⊖	d	12 40				12 54					13 10							13 24	
Farringdon 3 ⊖	d	12 45				12 59					13 15							13 29	
City Thameslink 3	d																		
London Blackfriars 3 ⊖	d	12 49				13 04					13 19							13 34	
London Bridge 4 ⊖	d	12 56				13 11					13 26					13 35		13 41	
New Cross Gate	d																		
Norwood Junction 2	d															13 46			
East Croydon 🚌	a	13 09		13 17	13 21	13 25				13 32	13 39		13 42		13 48	13 50		13 55	
	d	13 09		13 17	13 22	13 26				13 33	13 39		13 42		13 49	13 51		13 56	
Purley 4	d			13 23												13 56			
Coulsdon South	d			13 26												13 59			
Merstham	d															14 05			
Redhill	a			13 34									13 57			14 08			
	d			13 34					13 38				13 58	14 10		14 12	14 19		
Reigate	a																14 23		
Nutfield	d													14 14					
Godstone	d													14 20					
Edenbridge	d													14 25					
Penshurst	d													14 32					
Leigh (Kent)	d													14 35					
Tonbridge 4	a													14 40					
Earlswood (Surrey)	d															14 14			
Salfords	d						←												
Horley 4	d			13 40			13 40									14 21			
Gatwick Airport 10 ✈	a	13 24	13 30	→	13 37	13 41	13 43	13 45	13 47	13 48	13 54	14 00	14 05			→		14 11	14 15
	d	13 26			13 38	13 42	13 44			13 49	13 56		14 06					14 12	
Three Bridges 4	a	13 33				13 46	13 48				14 01		14 10					14 16	
	d					13 47	13 49						14 11					14 17	
Crawley	d						13 53												
Ifield	d																		
Faygate	d																		
Littlehaven	d																		
Horsham 4	a						14 01												
Balcombe	d												14 17						
Haywards Heath	a					13 56				14 00			14 22					14 26	
	d					13 56				14 00			14 22					14 26	
Wivelsfield	d												14 26						
Lewes 4	a																		
Burgess Hill 4	d					14 01				14 06			14 28					14 33	
Hassocks 4	d					14 05							14 32					14 37	
Preston Park	d												14 38						
Hove 2	a									14 18									
Brighton 10	a				14 03	14 15							14 43		14 24			14 47	

Station		SN 1 🛒	SN 1	FC 1	SN 1 🛒	SN 1	SN 1 🛒	FC 1	SN 1	SN 1 🛒	SN 1	GW 1	FC 1	SN 1 🛒	SN 1	SN 1	SN 1 🛒	SN 1	GW 1
London Victoria 15 ⊖	d	13 47			14 00	14 02	14 06			14 15	14 17			14 30	14 27		14 32		
Clapham Junction 10	d	13 53				14 08	14 12				14 23				14 33		14 38		
Bedford	d			12 36				12 50					13 06						
Luton 10	d			13 00				13 14					13 30						
Luton Airport Parkway 7 ✈	d			13 03				13 17					13 33						
St Albans City	d			13 15				13 29					13 45						
St Pancras International 15 ⊖	d			13 40				13 54					14 10						
Farringdon 3 ⊖	d			13 45				13 59					14 15						
City Thameslink 3	d																		
London Blackfriars 3 ⊖	d			13 49				14 04					14 19						
London Bridge 4 ⊖	d			13 56				14 11					14 26					14 35	
New Cross Gate	d																		
Norwood Junction 2	d																	14 46	
East Croydon 🚌	a	14 02		14 09		14 17	14 22	14 25			14 32		14 39		14 42		14 48	14 50	
	d	14 02		14 09		14 17	14 23	14 26			14 33		14 39		14 42		14 49	14 51	
Purley 4	d					14 23												14 56	
Coulsdon South	d					14 26												14 59	
Merstham	d																	15 05	
Redhill	a					14 34									14 57			15 08	
	d					14 34						14 39			14 58	15 10		15 12	15 20
Reigate	a																		15 24
Nutfield	d															15 14			
Godstone	d															15 20			
Edenbridge	d															15 25			
Penshurst	d															15 32			
Leigh (Kent)	d															15 35			
Tonbridge 4	a															15 40			
Earlswood (Surrey)	d																	15 14	
Salfords	d		←						←										
Horley 4	d		14 21			14 40			14 40									15 21	
Gatwick Airport 10 ✈	a	14 18	14 24	14 24	14 30	→	14 37	14 41	14 43	14 45	14 48	14 48	14 54	15 00	15 05			→	
	d	14 19	14 25	14 26			14 39	14 42	14 44		14 49		14 56		15 06				
Three Bridges 4	a		14 29	14 33				14 46	14 48				15 01		15 10				
	d		14 30					14 47	14 49						15 11				
Crawley	d		14 33						14 53										
Ifield	d		14 36																
Faygate	d																		
Littlehaven	d		14 42																
Horsham 4	a		14 46						15 01										
Balcombe	d														15 17				
Haywards Heath	a	14 29						14 56			15 00				15 22				
	d	14 30						14 56			15 00				15 22				
Wivelsfield	d	14 34													15 26				
Lewes 4	a	14 48																	
Burgess Hill 4	d							15 01			15 06				15 28				
Hassocks 4	d							15 05							15 32				
Preston Park	d														15 38				
Hove 2	a										15 18								
Brighton 10	a						15 03	15 15							15 43		15 24		

Table 186

Sundays

8 December to 29 December

Bedford and London - Brighton

Network Diagram - see first Page of Table 175

Station		FC 1	SN 1 🛒	SN 1 🛒	SN 1	FC 1	SN 1 🛒	SN 1	SN 1 🛒	FC 1
London Victoria 15 ⊖	d		14 45	14 47			15 00	15 02	15 06	
Clapham Junction 10	d			14 53				15 08	15 12	
Bedford	d	13 20				13 36				13 50
Luton 10	d	13 44				14 00				14 14
Luton Airport Parkway 7 ✈	d	13 47				14 03				14 17
St Albans City	d	13 59				14 15				14 29
St Pancras International 15 ⊖	d	14 24				14 40				14 54
Farringdon 3 ⊖	d	14 29				14 45				14 59
City Thameslink 3	d									
London Blackfriars 3 ⊖	d	14 34				14 49				15 04
London Bridge 4 ⊖	d	14 41				14 56				15 11
New Cross Gate	d									
Norwood Junction 2	d									
East Croydon ⇌	a	14 55		15 02		15 09		15 17	15 22	15 25
	d	14 56		15 02		15 09		15 17	15 23	15 26
Purley 4	d							15 23		
Coulsdon South	d							15 26		
Merstham	d									
Redhill	a							15 34		
	d							15 34		
Reigate	a									
Nutfield	d									
Godstone	d									
Edenbridge	d									
Penshurst	d									
Leigh (Kent)	d									
Tonbridge 4	a									
Earlswood (Surrey)	d									
Salfords	d				←					
Horley 4	d				15 21			15 40		
Gatwick Airport 10 ✈	a	15 11	15 15	15 18	15 24	15 24	15 30	→	15 37	15 41
	d	15 12		15 19	15 25	15 26			15 39	15 42
Three Bridges 4	a	15 16			15 29	15 33				15 46
	d	15 17			15 30					15 47
Crawley	d				15 33					
Ifield	d				15 36					
Faygate	d									
Littlehaven	d				15 42					
Horsham 4	a				15 46					
Balcombe	d									
Haywards Heath	a	15 26		15 29						15 56
	d	15 26		15 30						15 56
Wivelsfield	d			15 34						
Lewes 4	a			15 48						
Burgess Hill 4	d	15 33								16 01
Hassocks 4	d	15 37								16 05
Preston Park	d									
Hove 2	a									
Brighton 10	a	15 47							16 03	16 15

Station		SN 1	SN 1 🛒	GW 1	SN 1	FC 1	SN 1 🛒	SN 1	SN 1	SN 1 🛒
London Victoria 15 ⊖	d		15 15		15 17		15 30	15 27		15 32
Clapham Junction 10	d				15 23			15 33		15 38
Bedford	d					14 06				
Luton 10	d					14 30				
Luton Airport Parkway 7 ✈	d					14 33				
St Albans City	d					14 45				
St Pancras International 15 ⊖	d					15 10				
Farringdon 3 ⊖	d					15 15				
City Thameslink 3	d									
London Blackfriars 3 ⊖	d					15 19				
London Bridge 4 ⊖	d					15 26				
New Cross Gate	d									
Norwood Junction 2	d									
East Croydon ⇌	a				15 32	15 39		15 42		15 48
	d				15 32	15 39		15 42		15 49
Purley 4	d									
Coulsdon South	d									
Merstham	d									
Redhill	a							15 57		
	d			15 38				15 58	16 10	
Reigate	a									
Nutfield	d								16 14	
Godstone	d								16 20	
Edenbridge	d								16 25	
Penshurst	d								16 32	
Leigh (Kent)	d								16 35	
Tonbridge 4	a								16 40	
Earlswood (Surrey)	d									
Salfords	d	←								
Horley 4	d	15 40								
Gatwick Airport 10 ✈	a	15 43	15 45	15 47	15 48	15 54	16 00	16 05		
	d	15 44			15 49	15 56		16 06		
Three Bridges 4	a	15 48				16 01		16 10		
	d	15 49						16 11		
Crawley	d	15 53								
Ifield	d									
Faygate	d									
Littlehaven	d									
Horsham 4	a	16 01								
Balcombe	d							16 17		
Haywards Heath	a				16 00			16 22		
	d				16 00			16 22		
Wivelsfield	d							16 26		
Lewes 4	a									
Burgess Hill 4	d				16 06			16 28		
Hassocks 4	d							16 32		
Preston Park	d							16 38		
Hove 2	a				16 18					
Brighton 10	a							16 43		16 24

Station		SN 1	GW 1	FC 1	SN 1 🛒	SN 1 🛒	SN 1	FC 1	SN 1 🛒	SN 1
London Victoria 15 ⊖	d				15 45	15 47			16 00	16 02
Clapham Junction 10	d					15 53				16 08
Bedford	d			14 20				14 36		
Luton 10	d			14 44				15 00		
Luton Airport Parkway 7 ✈	d			14 47				15 03		
St Albans City	d			14 59				15 15		
St Pancras International 15 ⊖	d			15 24				15 40		
Farringdon 3 ⊖	d			15 29				15 45		
City Thameslink 3	d									
London Blackfriars 3 ⊖	d			15 34				15 49		
London Bridge 4 ⊖	d	15 35		15 41				15 56		
New Cross Gate	d									
Norwood Junction 2	d	15 46								
East Croydon ⇌	a	15 50		15 55		16 02		16 09		16 17
	d	15 51		15 56		16 02		16 09		16 17
Purley 4	d	15 56								16 23
Coulsdon South	d	15 59								16 26
Merstham	d	16 05								
Redhill	a	16 08								16 34
	d	16 12	16 19							16 34
Reigate	a		16 23							
Nutfield	d									
Godstone	d									
Edenbridge	d									
Penshurst	d									
Leigh (Kent)	d									
Tonbridge 4	a									
Earlswood (Surrey)	d	16 14								
Salfords	d						←			
Horley 4	d	16 21					16 21			16 40
Gatwick Airport 10 ✈	a	→		16 11	16 15	16 18	16 24	16 24	16 30	→
	d			16 12		16 19	16 25	16 26		
Three Bridges 4	a			16 16			16 29	16 33		
	d			16 17			16 30			
Crawley	d						16 33			
Ifield	d						16 36			
Faygate	d									
Littlehaven	d						16 42			
Horsham 4	a						16 46			
Balcombe	d									
Haywards Heath	a			16 26		16 29				
	d			16 26		16 30				
Wivelsfield	d					16 34				
Lewes 4	a					16 48				
Burgess Hill 4	d			16 33						
Hassocks 4	d			16 37						
Preston Park	d									
Hove 2	a									
Brighton 10	a			16 47						

Station		SN 1 🛒	FC 1	SN 1	SN 1 🛒	SN 1	GW 1	FC 1	SN 1 🛒	SN 1
London Victoria 15 ⊖	d	16 06			16 15	16 17			16 30	16 27
Clapham Junction 10	d	16 12				16 23				16 33
Bedford	d		14 50					15 06		
Luton 10	d		15 14					15 30		
Luton Airport Parkway 7 ✈	d		15 17					15 33		
St Albans City	d		15 29					15 45		
St Pancras International 15 ⊖	d		15 54					16 10		
Farringdon 3 ⊖	d		15 59					16 15		
City Thameslink 3	d									
London Blackfriars 3 ⊖	d		16 04					16 19		
London Bridge 4 ⊖	d		16 11					16 26		
New Cross Gate	d									
Norwood Junction 2	d									
East Croydon ⇌	a	16 22	16 25			16 32		16 39		16 42
	d	16 23	16 26			16 33		16 39		16 42
Purley 4	d									
Coulsdon South	d									
Merstham	d									
Redhill	a									16 57
	d						16 39			16 58
Reigate	a									
Nutfield	d									
Godstone	d									
Edenbridge	d									
Penshurst	d									
Leigh (Kent)	d									
Tonbridge 4	a									
Earlswood (Surrey)	d									
Salfords	d			←						
Horley 4	d			16 40						
Gatwick Airport 10 ✈	a	16 37	16 41	16 43	16 45	16 48	16 48	16 54	17 00	17 05
	d	16 39	16 42	16 44		16 49		16 56		17 06
Three Bridges 4	a		16 46	16 48				17 01		17 10
	d		16 47	16 49						17 11
Crawley	d			16 53						
Ifield	d									
Faygate	d									
Littlehaven	d									
Horsham 4	a			17 01						
Balcombe	d									17 17
Haywards Heath	a		16 56			17 00				17 22
	d		16 56			17 00				17 22
Wivelsfield	d									17 26
Lewes 4	a									
Burgess Hill 4	d		17 01			17 06				17 28
Hassocks 4	d		17 05							17 32
Preston Park	d									17 38
Hove 2	a					17 18				
Brighton 10	a	17 03	17 15							17 43

Table 186

Sundays

Bedford and London - Brighton

8 December to 29 December

Network Diagram - see first Page of Table 175

		SN 1	SN 1 🛒	SN 1	GW 1	FC 1	SN 1 🛒	SN 1 🛒	SN 1	FC 1	SN 1 🛒	SN 1	SN 1 🛒	FC 1	SN 1	SN 1 🛒	GW 1	SN 1	FC 1
London Victoria 15 ⊖	d		16 32				16 45	16 47			17 00	17 02	17 06			17 15		17 17	
Clapham Junction 10	d		16 38					16 53				17 08	17 12					17 23	
Bedford	d					15 20				15 36				15 50					16 06
Luton 10	d					15 44				16 00				16 14					16 30
Luton Airport Parkway 7 ✈	d					15 47				16 03				16 17					16 33
St Albans City	d					15 59				16 15				16 29					16 45
St Pancras International 15 ⊖	d					16 24				16 40				16 54					17 10
Farringdon 3 ⊖	d					16 29				16 45				16 59					17 15
City Thameslink 3	d																		
London Blackfriars 3 ⊖	d					16 34				16 49				17 04					17 19
London Bridge 4 ⊖	d			16 35		16 41				16 56				17 11					17 26
New Cross Gate	d																		
Norwood Junction 2	d			16 46															
East Croydon 🚋	a		16 48	16 50		16 55		17 02		17 09		17 17	17 22	17 25				17 32	17 39
	d		16 49	16 51		16 56		17 02		17 09		17 17	17 23	17 26				17 33	17 39
Purley 4	d			16 56								17 23							
Coulsdon South	d			16 59								17 26							
Merstham	d			17 05															
Redhill	a			17 08								17 34							
	d	17 10		17 12	17 20							17 34					17 38		
Reigate	a				17 24														
Nutfield	d	17 14																	
Godstone	d	17 20																	
Edenbridge	d	17 25																	
Penshurst	d	17 32																	
Leigh (Kent)	d	17 35																	
Tonbridge 4	a	17 40																	
Earlswood (Surrey)	d			17 14															
Salfords	d								←						←				
Horley 4	d			17 21					17 21			17 40			17 40				
Gatwick Airport 10 ✈	a			→		17 11	17 15	17 18	17 24	17 24	17 30	→	17 37	17 41	17 43	17 45	17 47	17 48	17 54
	d					17 12		17 19	17 25	17 26			17 39	17 42	17 44			17 49	17 56
Three Bridges 4	a					17 16			17 29	17 33				17 46	17 48				18 01
	d					17 17			17 30					17 47	17 49				
Crawley	d								17 33						17 53				
Ifield	d								17 36										
Faygate	d																		
Littlehaven	d								17 42										
Horsham 4	a								17 46						18 01				
Balcombe	d																		
Haywards Heath	a					17 26		17 29						17 56				18 00	
	d					17 26		17 30						17 56				18 00	
Wivelsfield	d							17 34											
Lewes 4	a							17 48											
Burgess Hill 4	d					17 33								18 01				18 06	
Hassocks 4	d					17 37								18 05					
Preston Park	d																		
Hove 2	a																	18 18	
Brighton 10	a		17 24			17 47							18 03	18 15					

		SN 1 🛒	SN 1	SN 1	SN 1 🛒	SN 1	GW 1	FC 1	SN 1 🛒	SN 1 🛒	SN 1	FC 1	SN 1 🛒	SN 1	SN 1 🛒	FC 1	SN 1	SN 1 🛒	SN 1
London Victoria 15 ⊖	d	17 30	17 27		17 32				17 45	17 47			18 00	18 02	18 06			18 15	18 17
Clapham Junction 10	d		17 33		17 38					17 53				18 08	18 12				18 23
Bedford	d							16 20				16 36				16 50			
Luton 10	d							16 44				17 00				17 14			
Luton Airport Parkway 7 ✈	d							16 47				17 03				17 17			
St Albans City	d							16 59				17 15				17 29			
St Pancras International 15 ⊖	d							17 24				17 40				17 54			
Farringdon 3 ⊖	d							17 29				17 45				17 59			
City Thameslink 3	d																		
London Blackfriars 3 ⊖	d							17 34				17 49				18 04			
London Bridge 4 ⊖	d					17 35		17 41				17 56				18 11			
New Cross Gate	d																		
Norwood Junction 2	d					17 46													
East Croydon 🚋	a		17 42		17 48	17 50		17 55		18 02		18 09		18 17	18 22	18 25			18 32
	d		17 42		17 49	17 51		17 56		18 02		18 09		18 17	18 23	18 26			18 33
Purley 4	d					17 56								18 23					
Coulsdon South	d					17 59								18 26					
Merstham	d					18 05													
Redhill	a		17 57			18 08								18 34					
	d		17 58	18 10		18 12	18 19							18 34					
Reigate	a						18 23												
Nutfield	d			18 14															
Godstone	d			18 20															
Edenbridge	d			18 25															
Penshurst	d			18 32															
Leigh (Kent)	d			18 35															
Tonbridge 4	a			18 40															
Earlswood (Surrey)	d					18 14													
Salfords	d										←						←		
Horley 4	d					18 21					18 21			18 40			18 40		
Gatwick Airport 10 ✈	a	18 00	18 05			→		18 11	18 15	18 18	18 24	18 24	18 30	→	18 37	18 41	18 43	18 45	18 48
	d		18 06					18 12		18 19	18 25	18 26			18 39	18 42	18 44		18 49
Three Bridges 4	a		18 10					18 16			18 29	18 33				18 46	18 48		
	d		18 11					18 17			18 30					18 47	18 49		
Crawley	d										18 33						18 53		
Ifield	d										18 36								
Faygate	d																		
Littlehaven	d										18 42								
Horsham 4	a										18 46						19 01		
Balcombe	d		18 17																
Haywards Heath	a		18 22					18 26		18 29						18 56			19 00
	d		18 22					18 26		18 30						18 56			19 00
Wivelsfield	d		18 26							18 34									
Lewes 4	a									18 48									
Burgess Hill 4	d		18 28					18 33								19 01			19 06
Hassocks 4	d		18 32					18 37								19 05			
Preston Park	d		18 38																
Hove 2	a																		19 18
Brighton 10	a		18 43		18 24			18 47							19 03	19 15			

Table 186

Sundays

8 December to 29 December

Bedford and London - Brighton

Network Diagram - see first Page of Table 175

Station		GW 1	FC 1	SN 1	SN 1	SN 1	SN 1	SN 1	GW 1	FC 1	SN 1	SN 1	SN 1	FC 1	SN 1	SN 1	SN 1	FC 1	SN 1
				(bike)			(bike)				(bike)	(bike)			(bike)		(bike)		
London Victoria 15 ⊖	d			18 30	18 27		18 32				18 45	18 47			19 00	19 02	19 06		
Clapham Junction 10	d				18 33		18 38					18 53				19 08	19 12		
Bedford	d		17 06							17 20				17 36				17 50	
Luton 10	d		17 30							17 44				18 00				18 14	
Luton Airport Parkway 7 ✈	d		17 33							17 47				18 03				18 17	
St Albans City	d		17 45							17 59				18 15				18 29	
St Pancras International 15 ⊖	d		18 10							18 24				18 40				18 54	
Farringdon 3 ⊖	d		18 15							18 29				18 45				18 59	
City Thameslink 3	d																		
London Blackfriars 3 ⊖	d		18 19							18 34				18 49				19 04	
London Bridge 4 ⊖	d		18 26					18 35		18 41				18 56				19 11	
New Cross Gate	d																		
Norwood Junction 2	d							18 46											
East Croydon ⇌	a		18 39		18 42		18 48	18 50		18 55		19 02		19 09		19 17	19 22	19 25	
	d		18 39		18 42		18 49	18 51		18 56		19 02		19 09		19 17	19 23	19 26	
Purley 4	d							18 56								19 23			
Coulsdon South	d							18 59								19 26			
Merstham	d							19 05											
Redhill	a				18 57			19 08								19 34			
	d	18 39			18 58	19 10		19 12	19 20							19 34			
Reigate	a								19 24										
Nutfield	d					19 14													
Godstone	d					19 20													
Edenbridge	d					19 25													
Penshurst	d					19 32													
Leigh (Kent)	d					19 35													
Tonbridge 4	a					19 40													
Earlswood (Surrey)	d							19 14											
Salfords	d												←						←
Horley 4	d							19 21					19 21			19 40			19 40
Gatwick Airport 10 ✈	a	18 48	18 54	19 00	19 05			→		19 11	19 15	19 18	19 24	19 24	19 30	→	19 37	19 41	19 43
	d		18 56		19 06					19 12		19 19	19 25	19 26			19 39	19 42	19 44
Three Bridges 4	a		19 01		19 10					19 16			19 29	19 33				19 46	19 48
	d				19 11					19 17			19 30					19 47	19 49
Crawley	d												19 33						19 53
Ifield	d												19 36						
Faygate	d																		
Littlehaven	d												19 42						
Horsham 4	a												19 46						20 01
Balcombe	d				19 17														
Haywards Heath	a				19 22					19 26		19 29						19 56	
	d				19 22					19 26		19 30						19 56	
Wivelsfield	d				19 26							19 34							
Lewes 4	a											19 48							
Burgess Hill 4	d				19 28					19 33								20 01	
Hassocks 4	d				19 32					19 37								20 05	
Preston Park	d				19 38														
Hove 2	a																		
Brighton 10	a				19 43		19 24			19 47							20 03	20 15	

Station		SN 1	GW 1	SN 1	SN 1	SN 1	SN 1	SN 1	SN 1	GW 1	FC 1	SN 1	SN 1	SN 1	SN 1	SN 1	SN 1	FC 1	SN 1
													(bike)						
London Victoria 15 ⊖	d	19 15		19 17	19 30	19 27		19 32				19 45	19 47		20 00	20 02	20 06		
Clapham Junction 10	d			19 23		19 33		19 38					19 53			20 08	20 12		
Bedford	d										18 20							18 50	
Luton 10	d										18 44							19 14	
Luton Airport Parkway 7 ✈	d										18 47							19 17	
St Albans City	d										18 59							19 29	
St Pancras International 15 ⊖	d										19 24							19 54	
Farringdon 3 ⊖	d										19 29							19 59	
City Thameslink 3	d																		
London Blackfriars 3 ⊖	d										19 34							20 04	
London Bridge 4 ⊖	d								19 35		19 41							20 11	
New Cross Gate	d																		
Norwood Junction 2	d								19 46										
East Croydon ⇌	a			19 32		19 42		19 48	19 50		19 55		20 02			20 17	20 22	20 25	
	d			19 33		19 42		19 49	19 51		19 56		20 02			20 17	20 23	20 26	
Purley 4	d								19 56							20 23			
Coulsdon South	d								19 59							20 26			
Merstham	d								20 05										
Redhill	a					19 57			20 08							20 34			
	d		19 38			19 58	20 10		20 12	20 19						20 34			
Reigate	a									20 23									
Nutfield	d						20 14												
Godstone	d						20 20												
Edenbridge	d						20 25												
Penshurst	d						20 32												
Leigh (Kent)	d						20 35												
Tonbridge 4	a						20 40												
Earlswood (Surrey)	d								20 14										
Salfords	d													←					←
Horley 4	d								20 21					20 21		20 40			20 40
Gatwick Airport 10 ✈	a	19 45	19 47	19 48	20 00	20 05			→		20 11	20 15	20 18	20 24	20 30	→	20 37	20 41	20 43
	d			19 49		20 06					20 12		20 19	20 25			20 39	20 42	20 44
Three Bridges 4	a					20 10					20 16			20 29				20 46	20 48
	d					20 11					20 17			20 30				20 47	20 49
Crawley	d													20 33					20 53
Ifield	d													20 36					
Faygate	d																		
Littlehaven	d													20 42					
Horsham 4	a													20 46					21 01
Balcombe	d					20 17													
Haywards Heath	a			20 00		20 22					20 26		20 29					20 56	
	d			20 00		20 22					20 26		20 30					20 56	
Wivelsfield	d					20 26							20 34						
Lewes 4	a												20 48						
Burgess Hill 4	d			20 06		20 28					20 33							21 01	
Hassocks 4	d					20 32					20 37							21 05	
Preston Park	d					20 38													
Hove 2	a			20 18															
Brighton 10	a					20 43		20 24			20 47						21 03	21 15	

Table 186

Sundays

Bedford and London - Brighton

8 December to 29 December

Network Diagram - see first Page of Table 175

		SN 1	SN 1	GW 1	SN 1	SN 1	SN 1	SN 1	SN 1	GW 1	FC 1	SN 1	SN 1	SN 1	SN 1	SN 1	SN 1	FC 1	SN 1
London Victoria 15 ⊖	d	20 15	20 17		20 30	20 27		20 32				20 45	20 47		21 00	21 02	21 06		
Clapham Junction 10	d		20 23			20 33		20 38					20 53			21 08	21 12		
Bedford	d										19 20							19 50	
Luton 10	d										19 44							20 14	
Luton Airport Parkway 7 ✈	d										19 47							20 17	
St Albans City	d										19 59							20 29	
St Pancras International 15 ⊖	d										20 24							20 54	
Farringdon 3 ⊖	d										20 29							20 59	
City Thameslink 3	d																		
London Blackfriars 3 ⊖	d										20 34							21 04	
London Bridge 4 ⊖	d								20 35		20 41							21 11	
New Cross Gate	d																		
Norwood Junction 2	d								20 46										
East Croydon	a		20 32			20 42		20 48	20 50		20 55		21 02			21 17	21 22	21 25	
	d		20 33			20 42		20 49	20 51		20 56		21 03			21 17	21 23	21 26	
Purley 4	d								20 56							21 23			
Coulsdon South	d								20 59							21 26			
Merstham	d								21 05										
Redhill	a					20 57			21 08							21 34			
	d			20 39		20 58	21 10		21 12	21 20						21 34			
Reigate	a									21 24									
Nutfield	d						21 14												
Godstone	d						21 20												
Edenbridge	d						21 25												
Penshurst	d						21 32												
Leigh (Kent)	d						21 35												
Tonbridge 4	a						21 40												
Earlswood (Surrey)	d								21 14										
Salfords	d													←					←
Horley 4	d								21 21					21 21		21 40			21 40
Gatwick Airport 10 ✈	a	20 45	20 48	20 48	21 00	21 05			→		21 11	21 15	21 18	21 24	21 30	→	21 37	21 41	21 43
	d		20 49			21 06					21 12		21 19	21 25			21 39	21 42	21 44
Three Bridges 4	a					21 10					21 16			21 29				21 46	21 48
	d					21 11					21 17			21 30				21 47	21 49
Crawley	d													21 33					21 53
Ifield	d													21 36					
Faygate	d																		
Littlehaven	d													21 42					
Horsham 4	a													21 46					22 01
Balcombe	d					21 17													
Haywards Heath	a		21 00			21 22					21 26		21 30					21 56	
	d		21 00			21 22					21 26		21 30					21 56	
Wivelsfield	d					21 26							21 35						
Lewes 4	a												21 48						
Burgess Hill 4	d		21 06			21 28					21 33							22 01	
Hassocks 4	d					21 32					21 37							22 05	
Preston Park	d					21 38													
Hove 2	a		21 18																
Brighton 10	a					21 43		21 24			21 47						22 03	22 15	

		SN 1	GW 1	SN 1	SN 1	SN 1	SN 1	SN 1	GW 1	FC 1	SN 1	SN 1	SN 1	SN 1	SN 1	FC 1	SN 1	SN 1	SN 1
London Victoria 15 ⊖	d	21 15		21 17	21 30	21 27					21 45	21 47		22 00	22 02			22 15	22 17
Clapham Junction 10	d			21 23		21 33						21 53			22 08				22 23
Bedford	d									20 12						20 42			
Luton 10	d									20 36						21 06			
Luton Airport Parkway 7 ✈	d									20 39						21 09			
St Albans City	d									20 51						21 21			
St Pancras International 15 ⊖	d									21 24						21 54			
Farringdon 3 ⊖	d									21 29						21 59			
City Thameslink 3	d																		
London Blackfriars 3 ⊖	d									21 34						22 04			
London Bridge 4 ⊖	d							21 35		21 41						22 11			
New Cross Gate	d																		
Norwood Junction 2	d							21 46											
East Croydon	a			21 32		21 42		21 50		21 55		22 02			22 17	22 25			22 32
	d			21 33		21 42		21 51		21 56		22 03			22 18	22 26			22 33
Purley 4	d							21 56							22 23				
Coulsdon South	d							21 59							22 27				
Merstham	d							22 05											
Redhill	a					21 57		22 08							22 34				
	d		21 38			21 58	22 10	22 12	22 19						22 35				
Reigate	a								22 23										
Nutfield	d						22 14												
Godstone	d						22 20												
Edenbridge	d						22 25												
Penshurst	d						22 32												
Leigh (Kent)	d						22 35												
Tonbridge 4	a						22 40												
Earlswood (Surrey)	d							22 14											
Salfords	d												←				←		
Horley 4	d							22 21					22 21		22 41		22 41		
Gatwick Airport 10 ✈	a	21 45	21 47	21 48	22 00	22 06		→		22 11	22 15	22 18	22 24	22 30	→	22 41	22 43	22 45	22 48
	d			21 49		22 07				22 12		22 19	22 25			22 42	22 44		22 49
Three Bridges 4	a					22 11				22 16			22 29			22 46	22 49		
	d					22 12				22 17			22 30			22 47	22 49		
Crawley	d												22 33				22 53		
Ifield	d												22 36						
Faygate	d																		
Littlehaven	d												22 42						
Horsham 4	a												22 46				23 02		
Balcombe	d					22 18													
Haywards Heath	a			22 00		22 23				22 26		22 30				22 56			23 00
	d			22 00		22 23				22 26		22 30				22 56			23 01
Wivelsfield	d					22 27						22 35							
Lewes 4	a											22 48							
Burgess Hill 4	d			22 06		22 29				22 33						23 01			23 06
Hassocks 4	d					22 33				22 37						23 05			
Preston Park	d					22 39													
Hove 2	a			22 18															23 21
Brighton 10	a					22 43				22 47						23 15			

Table 186

Sundays

8 December to 29 December

Bedford and London - Brighton

Network Diagram - see first Page of Table 175

		GW 1	SN 1	SN 1	SN 1	SN 1	GW 1	FC 1	SN 1	SN 1	SN 1	SN 1	GW 1	SN 1	FC 1	SN 1	SN 1	SN 1	SN 1	SN 1	FC 1	SN 1	FC 1	FC 1	FC 1
London Victoria 15 ⊖	d		22 30	22 27					22 45	22 47		23 00		23 04		23 15		23 17	23 30	23 32		23 45			
Clapham Junction 10	d			22 33						22 53				23 10				23 23		23 38					
Bedford	d							21 12							21 42						22 12		22 42	23 12	23 42
Luton 10	d							21 36							22 06						22 36		23 06	23 36	00 06
Luton Airport Parkway 7 ✈	d							21 39							22 09						22 39		23 09	23 39	00 09
St Albans City	d							21 51							22 21						22 51		23 21	23 51	00 21
St Pancras International 15 ⊖	d							22 24							22 54						23 24		23 54	00 24	00 54
Farringdon 3 ⊖	d							22 29							22 59						23 29		23 59	00 29	
City Thameslink 3	d																								
London Blackfriars 3 ⊖	d							22 34							23 04						23 34		00 05	00 35	01 05
London Bridge 4 ⊖	d					22 35		22 41							23 11						23 41		00 12	00 42	
New Cross Gate	d																								
Norwood Junction 2	d					22 46																			
East Croydon 🚌	a			22 42		22 50		22 55		23 03				23 21	23 25			23 37		23 52	23 56		00 28	00 56	01 34
	d			22 42		22 51		22 56		23 03				23 22	23 26			23 37		23 53	23 57		00 29	00 57	01 36
Purley 4	d					22 56								23 28											
Coulsdon South	d					22 59								23 32											
Merstham	d					23 05								23 38											
Redhill	a			22 57		23 08								23 41						00 05					
	d	22 39		22 58	23 10	23 12	23 20						23 38	23 41						00 05					
Reigate	a						23 24																		
Nutfield	d				23 14																				
Godstone	d				23 20																				
Edenbridge	d				23 25																				
Penshurst	d				23 32																				
Leigh (Kent)	d				23 35																				
Tonbridge 4	a				23 40																				
Earlswood (Surrey)	d					23 14																			
Salfords	d										←						←								
Horley 4	d					23 21					23 21			23 49			23 49								
Gatwick Airport 10 ✈	a	22 48	23 00	23 05		→		23 11	23 15	23 18	23 24	23 30	23 47	→	23 41	23 50	23 54	23 59	00 05	00 14	00 18	00 20	00 48	01 18	01 55
	d			23 06				23 12		23 19	23 25				23 42		23 55	23 59		00 15	00 20		00 49	01 19	01 55
Three Bridges 4	a			23 10				23 16			23 29				23 46		23 59	00 05		00 19	00 24		00 54	01 24	02 02
	d			23 11				23 17			23 30				23 47		23 59	00 06		00 20	00 25				
Crawley	d										23 33						00 03								
Ifield	d										23 36						00 05								
Faygate	d																								
Littlehaven	d										23 42						00 12								
Horsham 4	a										23 46						00 15								
Balcombe	d			23 17																00 26					
Haywards Heath	a			23 22				23 26		23 30					23 56			00 15		00 31	00 34				
	d			23 22				23 26		23 30					23 56			00 15		00 31	00 36				
Wivelsfield	d			23 26						23 35										00 35					
Lewes 4	a									23 48															
Burgess Hill 4	d			23 28				23 33							00 02			00 20		00 37	00 42				
Hassocks 4	d			23 32				23 37							00 06					00 41	00 45				
Preston Park	d			23 38																00 48					
Hove 2	a																	00 31							
Brighton 10	a			23 43				23 47							00 15					00 52	00 55				

Table 186

Sundays

5 January to 11 May

Bedford and London - Brighton

Network Diagram - see first Page of Table 175

Station		GW 1	SN 1	FC 1	SN 1	SN 1	SN 1	SN 1	FC 1	SN 1	SN 1	SN 1	FC 1	GW 1	SN 1	GW 1	SN 1	FC 1
London Victoria 15 ⊖	d										00 03	00 05			00 14		00 30	
Clapham Junction 10	d											00 12			00 21			
Bedford	d																	
Luton 10	d																	
Luton Airport Parkway 7 ✈	d																	
St Albans City	d																	
St Pancras International 15 ⊖	d																	00 24
Farringdon 3 ⊖	d																	00 29
City Thameslink 3	d																	
London Blackfriars 3 ⊖	d												00 05					00 35
London Bridge 4 ⊖	d												00 12					00 42
New Cross Gate	d																	
Norwood Junction 2	d																	
East Croydon	a											00 27	00 28		00 35			00 56
	d									00 01		00 27	00 29		00 36			00 57
Purley 4	d									00 11					00 41			
Coulsdon South	d									00 15					00 45			
Merstham	d									00 20					00 51			
Redhill	a									00 24					00 55			
	d	00 03					00 05			00 25				00 52	00 55	06 20		
Reigate	a															06 24		
Nutfield	d																	
Godstone	d																	
Edenbridge	d							00 06										
Penshurst	d																	
Leigh (Kent)	d																	
Tonbridge 4	a							00 15										
Earlswood (Surrey)	d																	
Salfords	d																	
Horley 4	d									00 31					01 02			
Gatwick Airport 10 ✈	a	00 10					00 14			00 34	00 40	00 45	00 48	01 00	01 04		01 06	01 18
	d						00 15		00 19	00 35		00 46	00 49		01 05			01 19
Three Bridges 4	a						00 20		00 23	00 39		00 50	00 54		01 10			01 24
	d				00 04		00 20		00 24	00 39		00 50	00 54					
Crawley	d				00 07					00 43								
Ifield	d				00 10					00 46								
Faygate	d																	
Littlehaven	d				00 16					00 52								
Horsham 4	a				00 19					00 55								
Balcombe	d						00 26		00 30									
Haywards Heath	a						00 31		00 37			00 59	01 05					
	d					00 05	00 32		00 38			01 03 / 01 05	01 10					
Wivelsfield	d			00 03			00 36		00 43									
Lewes 4	a											01 19						
Burgess Hill 4	d			00 05		00 10	00 38		00 45				01 15					
Hassocks 4	d		00 03	00 08			00 41		00 48				01 18					
Preston Park	d		00 09	00 15			00 48		00 55									
Hove 2	a					00 23												
Brighton 10	a		00 15	00 19			00 52		00 59			01s17	01 29					

Station		SN 1	FC 1	SN 1	SN 1	SN 1	SN 1	SN 1	SN 1	SN 1	SN 1 🚌	SN 1 🚌	SN 1 🚌	SN 1	SN 1	SN 1 🚌	SN 1 🚌	SN 1 🚌	SN 1
London Victoria 15 ⊖	d	01 00		02 00	03 00	03 30	04 00	04 30	05 00	05 02	05 15	05 30	05 45		05 47	06 00	06 15	06 30	06 32
Clapham Junction 10	d	01 09		02 09	03 09		04 09			05 09					05 54				06 39
Bedford	d																		
Luton 10	d		00 06																
Luton Airport Parkway 7 ✈	d		00 09																
St Albans City	d		00 21																
St Pancras International 15 ⊖	d		00 54																
Farringdon 3 ⊖	d																		
City Thameslink 3	d																		
London Blackfriars 3 ⊖	d		01 05																
London Bridge 4 ⊖	d																		
New Cross Gate	d																		
Norwood Junction 2	d																		
East Croydon	a	01 25	01 34	02 25	03 25		04 25			05 24					06 09				06 54
	d	01 26	01 36	02 26	03 26		04 26			05 25					06 10				06 55
Purley 4	d	01 32		02 32	03 32		04 32			05 30									06 59
Coulsdon South	d																		07 03
Merstham	d																		07 09
Redhill	a														06 23				07 13
	d														06 23				07 13
Reigate	a																		
Nutfield	d																		
Godstone	d																		
Edenbridge	d																		
Penshurst	d																		
Leigh (Kent)	d																		
Tonbridge 4	a																		
Earlswood (Surrey)	d																		
Salfords	d																		
Horley 4	d	01 47		02 49	03 49		04 49			05 46					06 30				07 20
Gatwick Airport 10 ✈	a	01 50	01 54	02 52	03 52	04 06	04 52	05 06	05 36	05 49	05 53	06 08	06 23		06 32	06 38	06 53	07 08	07 22
	d	01 51	01 55	02 53	03 53		04 53			05 50				06 30	06 33				07 23
Three Bridges 4	a	01 55	02 02	02 58	03 58		04 58			05 54				06 34	06 38				07 28
	d	01 56					04 58			05 55				06 43	06 39				07 28
Crawley	d													06 47					
Ifield	d													06 49					
Faygate	d																		
Littlehaven	d													06 56					
Horsham 4	a													06 59					
Balcombe	d																		07 34
Haywards Heath	a	02 08					05 07			06 04					06 48				07 39
	d	02 08					05 08			06 04					06 48				07 39
Wivelsfield	d														06 52				07 43
Lewes 4	a																		
Burgess Hill 4	d														06 54				07 45
Hassocks 4	d														06 58				07 49
Preston Park	d														07 04				07 55
Hove 2	a																		
Brighton 10	a	02 23					05 23			06 20					07 09				07 59

Table 186

Sundays

5 January to 11 May

Bedford and London - Brighton

Network Diagram - see first Page of Table 175

		SN	GW	SN	FC	GW	SN	SN	SN	SN	SN	FC	FC	SN	SN	GW	GW	SN	SN
		1	1	1	1	1	1	1	1	1	1	1	1	1	1	1	1	1	1
												A	B					C	D
		⌶		⌶				⌶	⌶					⌶				⌶	⌶
London Victoria 15 ⊖	d	06 45		07 00			07 02	07 15	07 30	07 26				07 45				08 00	08 00
Clapham Junction 10	d						07 09			07 33									
Bedford	d											05 58							
Luton 10	d											06 22							
Luton Airport Parkway 7 ✈	d											06 25							
St Albans City	d											06 37							
St Pancras International 15 ⊖	d											07 10	07 10						
Farringdon 3 ⊖	d											07 15	07 15						
City Thameslink 3	d																		
London Blackfriars 3 ⊖	d				06 51							07 21	07 21						
London Bridge 4 ⊖	d														07 43				
New Cross Gate	d																		
Norwood Junction 2	d																		
East Croydon ⇌	a				07 23		07 25			07 47		07 52	07 52		07 56				
	d				07 24		07 26			07 47		07 53	07 53		07 56				
Purley 4	d						07 31								08 02				
Coulsdon South	d														08 05				
Merstham	d														08 11				
Redhill	a						07 40			07 59					08 15				
	d		07 18			07 20	07 41			08 04	08 13				08 19	08 19	08 21		
Reigate	a					07 24										08 23			
Nutfield	d										08 17								
Godstone	d										08 23								
Edenbridge	d										08 28								
Penshurst	d										08 35								
Leigh (Kent)	d										08 38								
Tonbridge 4	a										08 43								
Earlswood (Surrey)	d																		
Salfords	d																		
Horley 4	d						07 47								08 25				
Gatwick Airport 10 ✈	a	07 24	07 29	07 39	07 43		07 50	07 53	08 08	08 12		08 16	08 16	08 23	08 27		08 31	08 38	08 39
	d				07 44		07 51			08 13		08 18	08 18		08 28				
Three Bridges 4	a				07 48		07 55			08 17		08 22	08 22		08 33				
	d				07 49		07 55			08 18		08 23	08 23		08 33				
Crawley	d						07 59								08 37				
Ifield	d						08 01								08 39				
Faygate	d																		
Littlehaven	d						08 08								08 46				
Horsham 4	a						08 11								08 49				
Balcombe	d									08 24									
Haywards Heath	a				07 58					08 29		08 32	08 32						
	d				07 58					08 29		08 34	08 34						
Wivelsfield	d									08 33									
Lewes 4	a																		
Burgess Hill 4	d				08 03					08 35		08 39	08 39						
Hassocks 4	d				08 07					08 39		08 43	08 43						
Preston Park	d									08 45									
Hove 2	a																		
Brighton 10	a				08 17					08 50		08 53	08 53						

		FC	FC	SN	SN	SN	SN	SN	SN	SN	SN	GW	FC	FC	SN	SN	SN	SN	SN
		1	1	1	1	1	1	1	1	1	1	1	1	1	1	1	1	1	1
		A	B				C	D					A	B					
					⌶		⌶	⌶							⌶	⌶		⌶	
London Victoria 15 ⊖	d			08 02	08 15	08 17	08 30	08 30	08 32						08 45	08 47		09 00	09 02
Clapham Junction 10	d			08 09		08 24			08 39							08 54			09 08
Bedford	d	06 28											06 58						
Luton 10	d	06 52											07 22						
Luton Airport Parkway 7 ✈	d	06 55											07 25						
St Albans City	d	07 07											07 37						
St Pancras International 15 ⊖	d	07 40	07 40										08 10	08 10					
Farringdon 3 ⊖	d	07 45	07 45										08 15	08 15					
City Thameslink 3	d																		
London Blackfriars 3 ⊖	d	07 51	07 51										08 21	08 21					
London Bridge 4 ⊖	d										08 35								
New Cross Gate	d																		
Norwood Junction 2	d										08 46								
East Croydon ⇌	a	08 21	08 21	08 23		08 37			08 52		08 54		08 55	08 55		09 05			09 17
	d	08 21	08 21	08 24		08 38			08 53		08 55		08 56	08 56		09 06			09 18
Purley 4	d			08 29							09 01								09 23
Coulsdon South	d										09 05								09 27
Merstham	d										09 10								
Redhill	a			08 38					09 04		09 14								09 34
	d			08 39					09 05	09 10	09 15	09 20							09 35
Reigate	a											09 24							
Nutfield	d									09 14									
Godstone	d									09 20									
Edenbridge	d									09 25									
Penshurst	d									09 32									
Leigh (Kent)	d									09 35									
Tonbridge 4	a									09 40									
Earlswood (Surrey)	d										09 17								
Salfords	d																←		
Horley 4	d			08 45							09 23						09 23		09 41
Gatwick Airport 10 ✈	a	08 41	08 41	08 48	08 53	08 56	09 05	09 08	09 12		→		09 11	09 11	09 16	09 20	09 25	09 30	→
	d	08 42	08 42	08 49		08 57			09 13				09 12	09 12		09 21	09 26		
Three Bridges 4	a	08 46	08 46	08 53					09 17				09 16	09 16			09 31		
	d	08 47	08 47	08 53					09 19				09 17	09 17			09 31		
Crawley	d			08 57													09 34		
Ifield	d																09 37		
Faygate	d																		
Littlehaven	d																09 43		
Horsham 4	a			09 05													09 46		
Balcombe	d								09 25										
Haywards Heath	a	08 56	08 56			09 09			09 30				09 26	09 26		09 32			
	d	08 56	08 56			09 09			09 30				09 26	09 26		09 33			
Wivelsfield	d								09 35							09 38			
Lewes 4	a															09 51			
Burgess Hill 4	d	09 01	09 01			09 16			09 37				09 33	09 33					
Hassocks 4	d	09 05	09 05						09 41				09 37	09 37					
Preston Park	d								09 47										
Hove 2	a					09 27													
Brighton 10	a	09 15	09 15						09 51				09 47	09 47					

A from 30 March
B until 23 March
C from 16 February
D until 9 February

Table 186

Sundays

5 January to 11 May

Bedford and London - Brighton

Network Diagram - see first Page of Table 175

		SN 1	FC 1	SN 1	SN 1 🍴	GW 1	SN 1	FC 1	SN 1 🍴	SN 1
London Victoria 15 ⊖	d	09 06			09 15		09 17		09 30	09 27
Clapham Junction 10	d	09 12					09 23			09 33
Bedford	d		07 28					07 50		
Luton 10	d		07 52					08 14		
Luton Airport Parkway 7 ✈	d		07 55					08 17		
St Albans City	d		08 07					08 29		
St Pancras International 15 ⊖	d		08 40					08 54		
Farringdon 3 ⊖	d		08 45					08 59		
City Thameslink 3	d									
London Blackfriars 3 ⊖	d		08 51					09 04		
London Bridge 4 ⊖	d									
New Cross Gate	d									
Norwood Junction 2	d									
East Croydon	a	09 22	09 25				09 32	09 39		09 42
	d	09 23	09 26				09 33	09 39		09 42
Purley 4	d									
Coulsdon South	d									
Merstham	d									
Redhill	a									09 57
	d					09 37				09 58
Reigate	a									
Nutfield	d									
Godstone	d									
Edenbridge	d									
Penshurst	d									
Leigh (Kent)	d									
Tonbridge 4	a									
Earlswood (Surrey)	d									
Salfords	d			←						
Horley 4	d			09 41						
Gatwick Airport 10 ✈	a	09 37	09 41	09 43	09 45	09 47	09 48	09 54	10 00	10 05
	d	09 39	09 42	09 44			09 49	09 56		10 06
Three Bridges 4	a		09 46	09 49				10 01		10 10
	d		09 47	09 49						10 11
Crawley	d			09 53						
Ifield	d									
Faygate	d									
Littlehaven	d									
Horsham 4	a			10 01						
Balcombe	d									10 17
Haywards Heath	a		09 56				10 00			10 22
	d		09 56				10 00			10 22
Wivelsfield	d									10 26
Lewes 4	a									
Burgess Hill 4	d		10 01				10 06			10 28
Hassocks 4	d		10 05							10 32
Preston Park	d									10 38
Hove 2	a						10 18			
Brighton 10	a	10 03	10 15							10 43

		SN 1	SN 1	SN 1	GW 1	FC 1	SN 1 🍴	SN 1 🍴	SN 1	FC 1
London Victoria 15 ⊖	d		09 32				09 45	09 47		
Clapham Junction 10	d		09 38					09 53		
Bedford	d					08 06				08 20
Luton 10	d					08 30				08 44
Luton Airport Parkway 7 ✈	d					08 33				08 47
St Albans City	d					08 45				08 59
St Pancras International 15 ⊖	d					09 10				09 24
Farringdon 3 ⊖	d					09 15				09 29
City Thameslink 3	d									
London Blackfriars 3 ⊖	d					09 21				09 34
London Bridge 4 ⊖	d			09 35						
New Cross Gate	d									
Norwood Junction 2	d			09 46						
East Croydon	a		09 48	09 50		09 55		10 02		10 09
	d		09 49	09 51		09 56		10 02		10 09
Purley 4	d			09 56						
Coulsdon South	d			09 59						
Merstham	d			10 05						
Redhill	a			10 09						
	d	10 10		10 12	10 19					
Reigate	a				10 23					
Nutfield	d	10 14								
Godstone	d	10 20								
Edenbridge	d	10 25								
Penshurst	d	10 32								
Leigh (Kent)	d	10 35								
Tonbridge 4	a	10 40								
Earlswood (Surrey)	d			10 16						
Salfords	d								←	
Horley 4	d			10 21					10 21	
Gatwick Airport 10 ✈	a			→		10 11	10 15	10 18	10 24	10 24
	d					10 12		10 19	10 25	10 26
Three Bridges 4	a					10 16			10 29	10 33
	d					10 17			10 30	
Crawley	d								10 33	
Ifield	d								10 36	
Faygate	d									
Littlehaven	d								10 42	
Horsham 4	a								10 46	
Balcombe	d									
Haywards Heath	a					10 26		10 29		
	d					10 26		10 30		
Wivelsfield	d							10 34		
Lewes 4	a							10 48		
Burgess Hill 4	d					10 33				
Hassocks 4	d					10 37				
Preston Park	d									
Hove 2	a									
Brighton 10	a		10 24			10 47				

		SN 1 🍴	SN 1	SN 1 🍴	FC 1	SN 1	SN 1 🍴	SN 1	GW 1	FC 1
London Victoria 15 ⊖	d	10 00	10 02	10 06			10 15	10 17		
Clapham Junction 10	d		10 08	10 12				10 23		
Bedford	d				08 36					08 50
Luton 10	d				09 00					09 14
Luton Airport Parkway 7 ✈	d				09 03					09 17
St Albans City	d				09 15					09 29
St Pancras International 15 ⊖	d				09 40					09 54
Farringdon 3 ⊖	d				09 45					09 59
City Thameslink 3	d									
London Blackfriars 3 ⊖	d				09 51					10 04
London Bridge 4 ⊖	d									
New Cross Gate	d									
Norwood Junction 2	d									
East Croydon	a		10 17	10 22	10 25			10 32		10 39
	d		10 17	10 23	10 26			10 32		10 39
Purley 4	d		10 23							
Coulsdon South	d		10 26							
Merstham	d									
Redhill	a		10 34							
	d		10 34						10 39	
Reigate	a									
Nutfield	d									
Godstone	d									
Edenbridge	d									
Penshurst	d									
Leigh (Kent)	d									
Tonbridge 4	a									
Earlswood (Surrey)	d									
Salfords	d					←				
Horley 4	d		10 40			10 40				
Gatwick Airport 10 ✈	a	10 30	→	10 37	10 41	10 43	10 45	10 48	10 48	10 54
	d			10 39	10 42	10 44		10 49		10 56
Three Bridges 4	a				10 46	10 48				11 01
	d				10 47	10 49				
Crawley	d					10 53				
Ifield	d									
Faygate	d									
Littlehaven	d									
Horsham 4	a					11 01				
Balcombe	d									
Haywards Heath	a				10 56			10 59		
	d				10 56			11 00		
Wivelsfield	d									
Lewes 4	a									
Burgess Hill 4	d				11 01			11 05		
Hassocks 4	d				11 05					
Preston Park	d									
Hove 2	a							11 18		
Brighton 10	a			11 03	11 15					

		SN 1 🍴	SN 1	SN 1	SN 1 🍴	SN 1	GW 1	FC 1	SN 1 🍴	SN 1 🍴
London Victoria 15 ⊖	d	10 30	10 27		10 32				10 45	10 47
Clapham Junction 10	d		10 33		10 38					10 53
Bedford	d							09 06		
Luton 10	d							09 30		
Luton Airport Parkway 7 ✈	d							09 33		
St Albans City	d							09 45		
St Pancras International 15 ⊖	d							10 10		
Farringdon 3 ⊖	d							10 15		
City Thameslink 3	d									
London Blackfriars 3 ⊖	d							10 21		
London Bridge 4 ⊖	d					10 35				
New Cross Gate	d									
Norwood Junction 2	d					10 46				
East Croydon	a		10 42		10 48	10 50		10 55		11 02
	d		10 42		10 49	10 51		10 56		11 02
Purley 4	d					10 56				
Coulsdon South	d					10 59				
Merstham	d					11 05				
Redhill	a		10 57			11 08				
	d		10 58	11 10		11 12	11 20			
Reigate	a						11 24			
Nutfield	d			11 14						
Godstone	d			11 20						
Edenbridge	d			11 25						
Penshurst	d			11 32						
Leigh (Kent)	d			11 35						
Tonbridge 4	a			11 40						
Earlswood (Surrey)	d					11 14				
Salfords	d									
Horley 4	d					11 21				
Gatwick Airport 10 ✈	a	11 00	11 05			→		11 11	11 15	11 18
	d		11 06					11 12		11 19
Three Bridges 4	a		11 10					11 16		
	d		11 11					11 17		
Crawley	d									
Ifield	d									
Faygate	d									
Littlehaven	d									
Horsham 4	a									
Balcombe	d		11 17							
Haywards Heath	a		11 22					11 26		11 29
	d		11 22					11 26		11 30
Wivelsfield	d		11 26							11 34
Lewes 4	a									11 48
Burgess Hill 4	d		11 28					11 33		
Hassocks 4	d		11 32					11 37		
Preston Park	d		11 38							
Hove 2	a									
Brighton 10	a		11 43		11 24			11 47		

Table 186

Sundays

5 January to 11 May

Bedford and London - Brighton

Network Diagram - see first Page of Table 175

		SN 1	FC 1	SN 1 🛒	SN 1	SN 1 🛒	FC 1	SN 1	SN 1 🛒	GW 1	SN 1	FC 1	SN 1 🛒	SN 1	SN 1	SN 1 🛒	SN 1	GW 1	FC 1
London Victoria 15 ⊖	d			11 00	11 02	11 06			11 15		11 17		11 30	11 27		11 32			
Clapham Junction 10	d				11 08	11 12					11 23			11 33		11 38			
Bedford	d		09 20				09 36					09 50							10 06
Luton 10	d		09 44				10 00					10 14							10 30
Luton Airport Parkway 7 ✈	d		09 47				10 03					10 17							10 33
St Albans City	d		09 59				10 15					10 29							10 45
St Pancras International 15 ⊖	d		10 24				10 40					10 54							11 10
Farringdon 3 ⊖	d		10 29				10 45					10 59							11 15
City Thameslink 3	d																		
London Blackfriars 3 ⊖	d		10 34				10 51					11 04							11 21
London Bridge 4 ⊖	d																11 35		
New Cross Gate	d																		
Norwood Junction 2	d																11 46		
East Croydon	a		11 09		11 17	11 22	11 25				11 32	11 39		11 42		11 48	11 50		11 55
	d		11 09		11 17	11 23	11 26				11 33	11 39		11 42		11 49	11 51		11 56
Purley 4	d				11 23												11 56		
Coulsdon South	d				11 26												11 59		
Merstham	d																12 05		
Redhill	a				11 34									11 57			12 08		
	d				11 34					11 38				11 58	12 10		12 12	12 19	
Reigate	a																	12 23	
Nutfield	d														12 14				
Godstone	d														12 20				
Edenbridge	d														12 25				
Penshurst	d														12 32				
Leigh (Kent)	d														12 35				
Tonbridge 4	a														12 40				
Earlswood (Surrey)	d																12 14		
Salfords	d	←						←											
Horley 4	d	11 21			11 40			11 40									12 21		
Gatwick Airport 10 ✈	a	11 24	11 24	11 30	→	11 37	11 41	11 43	11 45	11 47	11 48	11 54	12 00	12 05			→		12 11
	d	11 25	11 26			11 39	11 42	11 44			11 49	11 56		12 06					12 12
Three Bridges 4	a	11 29	11 33				11 46	11 48				12 01		12 10					12 16
	d	11 30					11 47	11 49						12 11					12 17
Crawley	d	11 33						11 53											
Ifield	d	11 36																	
Faygate	d																		
Littlehaven	d	11 42																	
Horsham 4	a	11 46						12 01											
Balcombe	d													12 17					
Haywards Heath	a						11 56				12 00			12 22					12 26
	d						11 56				12 00			12 22					12 26
Wivelsfield	d													12 26					
Lewes 4	a																		
Burgess Hill 4	d						12 01				12 06			12 28					12 33
Hassocks 4	d						12 05							12 32					12 37
Preston Park	d													12 38					
Hove 2	a										12 18								
Brighton 10	a					12 03	12 15							12 43		12 24			12 47

		SN 1 🛒	SN 1 🛒	SN 1	FC 1	SN 1 🛒	SN 1	SN 1 🛒	FC 1	SN 1	SN 1 🛒	SN 1	GW 1	FC 1	SN 1 🛒	SN 1	SN 1	SN 1 🛒	SN 1
London Victoria 15 ⊖	d	11 45	11 47			12 00	12 02	12 06			12 15	12 17			12 30	12 27		12 32	
Clapham Junction 10	d		11 53				12 08	12 12				12 23				12 33		12 38	
Bedford	d				10 20				10 36					10 50					
Luton 10	d				10 44				11 00					11 14					
Luton Airport Parkway 7 ✈	d				10 47				11 03					11 17					
St Albans City	d				10 59				11 15					11 29					
St Pancras International 15 ⊖	d				11 24				11 40					11 54					
Farringdon 3 ⊖	d				11 29				11 45					11 59					
City Thameslink 3	d																		
London Blackfriars 3 ⊖	d				11 34				11 51					12 04					
London Bridge 4 ⊖	d																		12 35
New Cross Gate	d																		
Norwood Junction 2	d																		12 46
East Croydon	a		12 02		12 09		12 17	12 22	12 25			12 32		12 39		12 42		12 48	12 50
	d		12 02		12 09		12 17	12 23	12 26			12 33		12 39		12 42		12 49	12 51
Purley 4	d						12 23												12 56
Coulsdon South	d						12 26												12 59
Merstham	d																		13 05
Redhill	a						12 34									12 57			13 08
	d						12 34						12 39			12 58	13 10		13 12
Reigate	a																		
Nutfield	d																13 14		
Godstone	d																13 20		
Edenbridge	d																13 25		
Penshurst	d																13 32		
Leigh (Kent)	d																13 35		
Tonbridge 4	a																13 40		
Earlswood (Surrey)	d																		13 14
Salfords	d			←						←									
Horley 4	d			12 21			12 40			12 40									13 21
Gatwick Airport 10 ✈	a	12 15	12 18	12 24	12 24	12 30	→	12 37	12 41	12 43	12 45	12 48	12 48	12 54	13 00	13 05			→
	d		12 19	12 25	12 26			12 39	12 42	12 44		12 49		12 56		13 06			
Three Bridges 4	a			12 29	12 33				12 46	12 48				13 01		13 10			
	d			12 30					12 47	12 49						13 11			
Crawley	d			12 33						12 53									
Ifield	d			12 36															
Faygate	d																		
Littlehaven	d			12 42															
Horsham 4	a			12 46						13 01									
Balcombe	d															13 17			
Haywards Heath	a		12 29						12 56			13 00				13 22			
	d		12 30						12 56			13 00				13 22			
Wivelsfield	d		12 34													13 26			
Lewes 4	a		12 48																
Burgess Hill 4	d								13 01			13 06				13 28			
Hassocks 4	d								13 05							13 32			
Preston Park	d															13 38			
Hove 2	a											13 18							
Brighton 10	a							13 03	13 15							13 43		13 24	

Table 186

Sundays

5 January to 11 May

Bedford and London - Brighton

Network Diagram - see first Page of Table 175

		GW	FC	SN	SN	SN	FC	SN	SN	SN	FC	SN	SN	GW	SN	FC	SN	SN	SN
		1	1	1	1	1	1	1	1	1	1	1	1	1	1	1	1	1	1
				T	T			T		T			T				T		
London Victoria [15] ⊖	d			12 45	12 47			13 00	13 02	13 06			13 15		13 17		13 30	13 27	
Clapham Junction [10]	d				12 53				13 08	13 12					13 23			13 33	
Bedford	d		11 06				11 20				11 36					11 50			
Luton [10]	d		11 30				11 44				12 00					12 14			
Luton Airport Parkway [7] ✈	d		11 33				11 47				12 03					12 17			
St Albans City	d		11 45				11 59				12 15					12 29			
St Pancras International [15] ⊖	d		12 10				12 24				12 40					12 54			
Farringdon [3] ⊖	d		12 15				12 29				12 45					12 59			
City Thameslink [3]	d																		
London Blackfriars [3] ⊖	d		12 21				12 34				12 51					13 04			
London Bridge [4] ⊖	d																		
New Cross Gate	d																		
Norwood Junction [2]	d																		
East Croydon	a		12 55		13 02		13 09		13 17	13 21	13 25				13 32	13 39		13 42	
	d		12 56		13 02		13 09		13 17	13 22	13 26				13 33	13 39		13 42	
Purley [4]	d								13 23										
Coulsdon South	d								13 26										
Merstham	d																		
Redhill	a								13 34									13 57	
	d	13 20							13 34					13 38				13 58	14 10
Reigate	a	13 24																	
Nutfield	d																		14 14
Godstone	d																		14 20
Edenbridge	d																		14 25
Penshurst	d																		14 32
Leigh (Kent)	d																		14 35
Tonbridge [4]	a																		14 40
Earlswood (Surrey)	d																		
Salfords	d					←						←							
Horley [4]	d					13 21			13 40			13 40							
Gatwick Airport [10] ✈	a		13 11	13 15	13 18	13 24	13 24	13 30	→	13 37	13 41	13 43	13 45	13 47	13 48	13 54	14 00	14 05	
	d		13 12		13 19	13 25	13 26			13 38	13 42	13 44			13 49	13 56		14 06	
Three Bridges [4]	a		13 16			13 29	13 33				13 46	13 48				14 01		14 10	
	d		13 17			13 30					13 47	13 49						14 11	
Crawley	d					13 33						13 53							
Ifield	d					13 36													
Faygate	d																		
Littlehaven	d					13 42													
Horsham [4]	a					13 46						14 01							
Balcombe	d																	14 17	
Haywards Heath	a		13 26		13 29						13 56				14 00			14 22	
	d		13 26		13 30						13 56				14 00			14 22	
Wivelsfield	d				13 34													14 26	
Lewes [4]	a				13 48														
Burgess Hill [4]	d		13 33								14 01				14 06			14 28	
Hassocks [4]	d		13 37								14 05							14 32	
Preston Park	d																	14 38	
Hove [2]	a														14 18				
Brighton [10]	a		13 47							14 03	14 15							14 43	

		SN	SN	GW	FC	SN	SN	SN	FC	SN	SN	SN	FC	SN	SN	SN	GW	FC	SN
		1	1	1	1	1	1	1	1	1	1	1	1	1	1	1	1	1	1
		T				T	T			T		T			T				T
London Victoria [15] ⊖	d	13 32				13 45	13 47			14 00	14 02	14 06			14 15	14 17			14 30
Clapham Junction [10]	d	13 38					13 53				14 08	14 12				14 23			
Bedford	d				12 06				12 20				12 36					12 50	
Luton [10]	d				12 30				12 44				13 00					13 14	
Luton Airport Parkway [7] ✈	d				12 33				12 47				13 03					13 17	
St Albans City	d				12 45				12 59				13 15					13 29	
St Pancras International [15] ⊖	d				13 10				13 24				13 40					13 54	
Farringdon [3] ⊖	d				13 15				13 29				13 45					13 59	
City Thameslink [3]	d																		
London Blackfriars [3] ⊖	d				13 21				13 34				13 51					14 04	
London Bridge [4] ⊖	d		13 35																
New Cross Gate	d																		
Norwood Junction [2]	d		13 46																
East Croydon	a	13 48	13 50		13 55		14 02		14 09		14 17	14 22	14 25			14 32		14 39	
	d	13 49	13 51		13 56		14 02		14 09		14 17	14 23	14 26			14 33		14 39	
Purley [4]	d		13 56								14 23								
Coulsdon South	d		13 59								14 26								
Merstham	d		14 05																
Redhill	a		14 08								14 34								
	d		14 12	14 19							14 34						14 39		
Reigate	a			14 23															
Nutfield	d																		
Godstone	d																		
Edenbridge	d																		
Penshurst	d																		
Leigh (Kent)	d																		
Tonbridge [4]	a																		
Earlswood (Surrey)	d		14 14																
Salfords	d							←						←					
Horley [4]	d		14 21					14 21			14 40			14 40					
Gatwick Airport [10] ✈	a		→		14 11	14 15	14 18	14 24	14 24	14 30	→	14 37	14 41	14 43	14 45	14 48	14 48	14 54	15 00
	d				14 12		14 19	14 25	14 26			14 39	14 42	14 44		14 49		14 56	
Three Bridges [4]	a				14 16			14 29	14 33				14 46	14 48				15 01	
	d				14 17			14 30					14 47	14 49					
Crawley	d							14 33						14 53					
Ifield	d							14 36											
Faygate	d																		
Littlehaven	d							14 42											
Horsham [4]	a							14 46						15 01					
Balcombe	d																		
Haywards Heath	a				14 26		14 29						14 56			15 00			
	d				14 26		14 30						14 56			15 00			
Wivelsfield	d						14 34												
Lewes [4]	a						14 48												
Burgess Hill [4]	d				14 33								15 01			15 06			
Hassocks [4]	d				14 37								15 05						
Preston Park	d																		
Hove [2]	a															15 18			
Brighton [10]	a	14 24			14 47							15 03	15 15						

Table 186

Sundays

5 January to 11 May

Bedford and London - Brighton

Network Diagram - see first Page of Table 175

Station		SN 1	SN 1	SN 1 ✠	SN 1	GW 1	FC 1	SN 1 ✠	SN 1 ✠	SN 1	FC 1	SN 1 ✠	SN 1	SN 1 ✠	FC 1	SN 1	SN 1 ✠	GW 1	SN 1
London Victoria 15 ⊖	d	14 27		14 32				14 45	14 47			15 00	15 02	15 06			15 15		15 17
Clapham Junction 10	d	14 33		14 38					14 53				15 08	15 12					15 23
Bedford	d						13 06				13 20				13 36				
Luton 10	d						13 30				13 44				14 00				
Luton Airport Parkway 7 ✈	d						13 33				13 47				14 03				
St Albans City	d						13 45				13 59				14 15				
St Pancras International 15 ⊖	d						14 10				14 24				14 40				
Farringdon 3 ⊖	d						14 15				14 29				14 45				
City Thameslink 3	d																		
London Blackfriars 3 ⊖	d						14 21				14 34				14 51				
London Bridge 4 ⊖	d				14 35														
New Cross Gate	d																		
Norwood Junction 2	d				14 46														
East Croydon	a	14 42		14 48	14 50		14 55		15 02		15 09		15 17	15 22	15 25				15 32
	d	14 42		14 49	14 51		14 56		15 02		15 09		15 17	15 23	15 26				15 32
Purley 4	d				14 56								15 23						
Coulsdon South	d				14 59								15 26						
Merstham	d				15 05														
Redhill	a	14 57			15 08								15 34						
	d	14 58	15 10		15 12	15 20							15 34					15 38	
Reigate	a					15 24													
Nutfield	d		15 14																
Godstone	d		15 20																
Edenbridge	d		15 25																
Penshurst	d		15 32																
Leigh (Kent)	d		15 35																
Tonbridge 4	a		15 40																
Earlswood (Surrey)	d				15 14														
Salfords	d									←						←			
Horley 4	d				15 21					15 21			15 40			15 40			
Gatwick Airport 10 ✈	a	15 05			→		15 11	15 15	15 18	15 24	15 24	15 30	→	15 37	15 41	15 43	15 45	15 47	15 48
	d	15 06					15 12		15 19	15 25	15 26			15 39	15 42	15 44			15 49
Three Bridges 4	a	15 10					15 16			15 29	15 33				15 46	15 48			
	d	15 11					15 17			15 30					15 47	15 49			
Crawley	d									15 33						15 53			
Ifield	d									15 36									
Faygate	d																		
Littlehaven	d									15 42									
Horsham 4	a									15 46						16 01			
Balcombe	d	15 17																	
Haywards Heath	a	15 22					15 26		15 29						15 56				16 00
	d	15 22					15 26		15 30						15 56				16 00
Wivelsfield	d	15 26							15 34										
Lewes 4	a								15 48										
Burgess Hill 4	d	15 28					15 33								16 01				16 06
Hassocks 4	d	15 32					15 37								16 05				
Preston Park	d	15 38																	
Hove 2	a																		16 18
Brighton 10	a	15 43		15 24			15 47							16 03	16 15				

Station		FC 1	SN 1 ✠	SN 1	SN 1	SN 1 ✠	SN 1	GW 1	FC 1	SN 1 ✠	SN 1 ✠	SN 1	FC 1	SN 1 ✠	SN 1	SN 1 ✠	FC 1	SN 1	SN 1 ✠
London Victoria 15 ⊖	d		15 30	15 27		15 32				15 45	15 47			16 00	16 02	16 06			16 15
Clapham Junction 10	d			15 33		15 38					15 53				16 08	16 12			
Bedford	d	13 50							14 06				14 20				14 36		
Luton 10	d	14 14							14 30				14 44				15 00		
Luton Airport Parkway 7 ✈	d	14 17							14 33				14 47				15 03		
St Albans City	d	14 29							14 45				14 59				15 15		
St Pancras International 15 ⊖	d	14 54							15 10				15 24				15 40		
Farringdon 3 ⊖	d	14 59							15 15				15 29				15 45		
City Thameslink 3	d																		
London Blackfriars 3 ⊖	d	15 04							15 21				15 34				15 51		
London Bridge 4 ⊖	d						15 35												
New Cross Gate	d																		
Norwood Junction 2	d						15 46												
East Croydon	a	15 39		15 42		15 48	15 50		15 55		16 02		16 09		16 17	16 22	16 25		
	d	15 39		15 42		15 49	15 51		15 56		16 02		16 09		16 17	16 23	16 26		
Purley 4	d						15 56								16 23				
Coulsdon South	d						15 59								16 26				
Merstham	d						16 05												
Redhill	a			15 57			16 08								16 34				
	d			15 58	16 10		16 12	16 19							16 34				
Reigate	a							16 23											
Nutfield	d				16 14														
Godstone	d				16 20														
Edenbridge	d				16 25														
Penshurst	d				16 32														
Leigh (Kent)	d				16 35														
Tonbridge 4	a				16 40														
Earlswood (Surrey)	d						16 14												
Salfords	d											←						←	
Horley 4	d						16 21					16 21			16 40			16 40	
Gatwick Airport 10 ✈	a	15 54	16 00	16 05			→		16 11	16 15	16 18	16 24	16 24	16 30	→	16 37	16 41	16 43	16 45
	d	15 56		16 06					16 12		16 19	16 25	16 26			16 39	16 42	16 44	
Three Bridges 4	a	16 01		16 10					16 16			16 29	16 33				16 46	16 48	
	d			16 11					16 17			16 30					16 47	16 49	
Crawley	d											16 33						16 53	
Ifield	d											16 36							
Faygate	d																		
Littlehaven	d											16 42							
Horsham 4	a											16 46						17 01	
Balcombe	d			16 17															
Haywards Heath	a			16 22					16 26		16 29						16 56		
	d			16 22					16 26		16 30						16 56		
Wivelsfield	d			16 26							16 34								
Lewes 4	a										16 48								
Burgess Hill 4	d			16 28					16 33								17 01		
Hassocks 4	d			16 32					16 37								17 05		
Preston Park	d			16 38															
Hove 2	a																		
Brighton 10	a			16 43		16 24			16 47							17 03	17 15		

Table 186

Sundays

5 January to 11 May

Bedford and London - Brighton

Network Diagram - see first Page of Table 175

		SN 1	GW 1	FC 1	SN 1 ⊥	SN 1	SN 1	SN 1 ⊥	SN 1	GW 1	FC 1	SN 1 ⊥	SN 1 ⊥	SN 1	FC 1	SN 1 ⊥	SN 1	SN 1 ⊥	FC 1
London Victoria 15 ⊖	d	16 17			16 30	16 27		16 32				16 45	16 47			17 00	17 02	17 06	
Clapham Junction 10	d	16 23				16 33		16 38					16 53				17 08	17 12	
Bedford	d			14 50							15 06				15 20				15 36
Luton 10	d			15 14							15 30				15 44				16 00
Luton Airport Parkway 7 ✈	d			15 17							15 33				15 47				16 03
St Albans City	d			15 29							15 45				15 59				16 15
St Pancras International 15 ⊖	d			15 54							16 10				16 24				16 40
Farringdon 3 ⊖	d			15 59							16 15				16 29				16 45
City Thameslink 3	d																		
London Blackfriars 3 ⊖	d			16 04							16 21				16 34				16 51
London Bridge 4 ⊖	d								16 35										
New Cross Gate	d																		
Norwood Junction 2	d								16 46										
East Croydon 🚊	a	16 32		16 39		16 42		16 48	16 50		16 55		17 02		17 09		17 17	17 22	17 25
	d	16 33		16 39		16 42		16 49	16 51		16 56		17 02		17 09		17 17	17 23	17 26
Purley 4	d								16 56								17 23		
Coulsdon South	d								16 59								17 26		
Merstham	d								17 05										
Redhill	a					16 57			17 08								17 34		
	d		16 39			16 58	17 10		17 12	17 20							17 34		
Reigate	a									17 24									
Nutfield	d						17 14												
Godstone	d						17 20												
Edenbridge	d						17 25												
Penshurst	d						17 32												
Leigh (Kent)	d						17 35												
Tonbridge 4	a						17 40												
Earlswood (Surrey)	d								17 14										
Salfords	d													←					
Horley 4	d								17 21					17 21			17 40		
Gatwick Airport 10 ✈	a	16 48	16 48	16 54	17 00	17 05			→		17 11	17 15	17 18	17 24	17 24	17 30	→	17 37	17 41
	d	16 49		16 56		17 06					17 12		17 19	17 25	17 26			17 39	17 42
Three Bridges 4	a			17 01		17 10					17 16			17 29	17 33				17 46
	d					17 11					17 17			17 30					17 47
Crawley	d													17 33					
Ifield	d													17 36					
Faygate	d																		
Littlehaven	d													17 42					
Horsham 4	a													17 46					
Balcombe	d					17 17													
Haywards Heath	a	17 00				17 22					17 26		17 29						17 56
	d	17 00				17 22					17 26		17 30						17 56
Wivelsfield	d					17 26							17 34						
Lewes 4	a												17 48						
Burgess Hill 4	d	17 06				17 28					17 33								18 01
Hassocks 4	d					17 32					17 37								18 05
Preston Park	d					17 38													
Hove 2	a	17 18																	
Brighton 10	a					17 43		17 24			17 47							18 03	18 15

		SN 1	SN 1 ⊥	GW 1	SN 1	FC 1	SN 1 ⊥	SN 1	SN 1	SN 1 ⊥	SN 1	GW 1	FC 1	SN 1 ⊥	SN 1 ⊥	SN 1	FC 1	SN 1 ⊥	SN 1
London Victoria 15 ⊖	d		17 15		17 17		17 30	17 27		17 32				17 45	17 47			18 00	18 02
Clapham Junction 10	d				17 23			17 33		17 38					17 53				18 08
Bedford	d					15 50							16 06				16 20		
Luton 10	d					16 14							16 30				16 44		
Luton Airport Parkway 7 ✈	d					16 17							16 33				16 47		
St Albans City	d					16 29							16 45				16 59		
St Pancras International 15 ⊖	d					16 54							17 10				17 24		
Farringdon 3 ⊖	d					16 59							17 15				17 29		
City Thameslink 3	d																		
London Blackfriars 3 ⊖	d					17 04							17 21				17 34		
London Bridge 4 ⊖	d										17 35								
New Cross Gate	d																		
Norwood Junction 2	d										17 46								
East Croydon 🚊	a				17 32	17 39		17 42		17 48	17 50		17 55		18 02		18 09		18 17
	d				17 33	17 39		17 42		17 49	17 51		17 56		18 02		18 09		18 17
Purley 4	d										17 56								18 23
Coulsdon South	d										17 59								18 26
Merstham	d										18 05								
Redhill	a							17 57			18 08								18 34
	d			17 38				17 58	18 10		18 12	18 19							18 34
Reigate	a											18 23							
Nutfield	d								18 14										
Godstone	d								18 20										
Edenbridge	d								18 25										
Penshurst	d								18 32										
Leigh (Kent)	d								18 35										
Tonbridge 4	a								18 40										
Earlswood (Surrey)	d										18 14								
Salfords	d	←														←			
Horley 4	d	17 40									18 21					18 21			18 40
Gatwick Airport 10 ✈	a	17 43	17 45	17 47	17 48	17 54	18 00	18 05			→		18 11	18 15	18 18	18 24	18 24	18 30	→
	d	17 44			17 49	17 56		18 06					18 12		18 19	18 25	18 26		
Three Bridges 4	a	17 48				18 01		18 10					18 16			18 29	18 33		
	d	17 49						18 11					18 17			18 30			
Crawley	d	17 53														18 33			
Ifield	d															18 36			
Faygate	d																		
Littlehaven	d															18 42			
Horsham 4	a	18 01														18 46			
Balcombe	d							18 17											
Haywards Heath	a				18 00			18 22					18 26		18 29				
	d				18 00			18 22					18 26		18 30				
Wivelsfield	d							18 26							18 34				
Lewes 4	a														18 48				
Burgess Hill 4	d				18 06			18 28					18 33						
Hassocks 4	d							18 32					18 37						
Preston Park	d							18 38											
Hove 2	a				18 18														
Brighton 10	a							18 43		18 24			18 47						

Table 186

Sundays

5 January to 11 May

Bedford and London - Brighton

Network Diagram - see first Page of Table 175

Station		SN 1 ⌶	FC 1	SN 1	SN 1 ⌶	SN 1	GW 1	FC 1	SN 1 ⌶	SN 1	SN 1	SN 1 ⌶	SN 1	GW 1	FC 1	SN 1 ⌶	SN 1 ⌶	SN 1	FC 1
London Victoria 15 ⊖	d	18 06			18 15	18 17			18 30	18 27		18 32				18 45	18 47		
Clapham Junction 10	d	18 12				18 23				18 33		18 38					18 53		
Bedford	d		16 36					16 50							17 06				17 20
Luton 10	d		17 00					17 14							17 30				17 44
Luton Airport Parkway 7 ✈	d		17 03					17 17							17 33				17 47
St Albans City	d		17 15					17 29							17 45				17 59
St Pancras International 15 ⊖	d		17 40					17 54							18 10				18 24
Farringdon 3 ⊖	d		17 45					17 59							18 15				18 29
City Thameslink 3	d																		
London Blackfriars 3 ⊖	d		17 51					18 04							18 21				18 34
London Bridge 4 ⊖	d												18 35						
New Cross Gate	d																		
Norwood Junction 2	d												18 46						
East Croydon 🚌	a	18 22	18 25			18 32		18 39		18 42		18 48	18 50		18 55		19 02		19 09
	d	18 23	18 26			18 33		18 39		18 42		18 49	18 51		18 56		19 02		19 09
Purley 4	d												18 56						
Coulsdon South	d												18 59						
Merstham	d												19 05						
Redhill	a									18 57			19 08						
	d						18 39			18 58	19 10		19 12	19 20					
Reigate	a													19 24					
Nutfield	d										19 14								
Godstone	d										19 20								
Edenbridge	d										19 25								
Penshurst	d										19 32								
Leigh (Kent)	d										19 35								
Tonbridge 4	a										19 40								
Earlswood (Surrey)	d												19 14						
Salfords	d			←														←	
Horley 4	d			18 40									19 21					19 21	
Gatwick Airport 10 ✈	a	18 37	18 41	18 43	18 45	18 48	18 48	18 54	19 00	19 05			→		19 11	19 15	19 18	19 24	19 24
	d	18 39	18 42	18 44		18 49		18 56		19 06					19 12		19 19	19 25	19 26
Three Bridges 4	a		18 46	18 48				19 01		19 10					19 16			19 29	19 33
	d		18 47	18 49						19 11					19 17			19 30	
Crawley	d			18 53														19 33	
Ifield	d																	19 36	
Faygate	d																		
Littlehaven	d																	19 42	
Horsham 4	a			19 01														19 46	
Balcombe	d									19 17									
Haywards Heath	a		18 56			19 00				19 22					19 26		19 29		
	d		18 56			19 00				19 22					19 26		19 30		
Wivelsfield	d									19 26							19 34		
Lewes 4	a																19 48		
Burgess Hill 4	d		19 01			19 06				19 28					19 33				
Hassocks 4	d		19 05							19 32					19 37				
Preston Park	d									19 38									
Hove 2	a					19 18													
Brighton 10	a	19 03	19 15							19 43		19 24			19 47				

Station		SN 1 ⌶	SN 1	SN 1 ⌶	FC 1	SN 1	SN 1	GW 1	SN 1	SN 1	SN 1	SN 1	SN 1	SN 1	GW 1	FC 1	SN 1	SN 1 ⌶	SN 1
London Victoria 15 ⊖	d	19 00	19 02	19 06			19 15		19 17	19 30	19 27		19 32				19 45	19 47	
Clapham Junction 10	d		19 08	19 12					19 23		19 33		19 38					19 53	
Bedford	d				17 36											18 06			
Luton 10	d				18 00											18 30			
Luton Airport Parkway 7 ✈	d				18 03											18 33			
St Albans City	d				18 15											18 45			
St Pancras International 15 ⊖	d				18 40											19 10			
Farringdon 3 ⊖	d				18 45											19 15			
City Thameslink 3	d																		
London Blackfriars 3 ⊖	d				18 51											19 21			
London Bridge 4 ⊖	d													19 35					
New Cross Gate	d																		
Norwood Junction 2	d													19 46					
East Croydon 🚌	a		19 17	19 22	19 25				19 32		19 42		19 48	19 50		19 55		20 02	
	d		19 17	19 23	19 26				19 33		19 42		19 49	19 51		19 56		20 02	
Purley 4	d		19 23											19 56					
Coulsdon South	d		19 26											19 59					
Merstham	d													20 05					
Redhill	a		19 34								19 57			20 08					
	d		19 34					19 38			19 58	20 10		20 12	20 19				
Reigate	a														20 23				
Nutfield	d											20 14							
Godstone	d											20 20							
Edenbridge	d											20 25							
Penshurst	d											20 32							
Leigh (Kent)	d											20 35							
Tonbridge 4	a											20 40							
Earlswood (Surrey)	d													20 14					
Salfords	d					←													←
Horley 4	d		19 40			19 40								20 21					20 21
Gatwick Airport 10 ✈	a	19 30	→	19 37	19 41	19 43	19 45	19 47	19 48	20 00	20 05			→		20 11	20 15	20 18	20 24
	d			19 39	19 42	19 44			19 49		20 06					20 12		20 19	20 25
Three Bridges 4	a				19 46	19 48					20 10					20 16			20 29
	d				19 47	19 49					20 11					20 17			20 30
Crawley	d					19 53													20 33
Ifield	d																		20 36
Faygate	d																		
Littlehaven	d																		20 42
Horsham 4	a					20 01													20 46
Balcombe	d										20 17								
Haywards Heath	a				19 56				20 00		20 22					20 26		20 29	
	d				19 56				20 00		20 22					20 26		20 30	
Wivelsfield	d										20 26							20 34	
Lewes 4	a																	20 48	
Burgess Hill 4	d				20 01				20 06		20 28					20 33			
Hassocks 4	d				20 05						20 32					20 37			
Preston Park	d										20 38								
Hove 2	a								20 18										
Brighton 10	a			20 03	20 15						20 43		20 24			20 47			

Table 186

Sundays

Bedford and London - Brighton

5 January to 11 May

Network Diagram - see first Page of Table 175

Station		SN 1	SN 1	SN 1	FC 1	SN 1	SN 1	SN 1	GW 1	SN 1
London Victoria 15 ⊖	d	20 00	20 02	20 06			20 15	20 17		20 30
Clapham Junction 10	d		20 08	20 12				20 23		
Bedford	d				18 36					
Luton 10	d				19 00					
Luton Airport Parkway 7 ✈	d				19 03					
St Albans City	d				19 15					
St Pancras International 15 ⊖	d				19 40					
Farringdon 3 ⊖	d				19 45					
City Thameslink 3	d									
London Blackfriars 3 ⊖	d				19 51					
London Bridge 4 ⊖	d									
New Cross Gate	d									
Norwood Junction 2	d									
East Croydon	a		20 17	20 22	20 25			20 32		
	d		20 17	20 23	20 26			20 33		
Purley 4	d		20 23							
Coulsdon South	d		20 26							
Merstham	d									
Redhill	a		20 34							
	d		20 34						20 39	
Reigate	a									
Nutfield	d									
Godstone	d									
Edenbridge	d									
Penshurst	d									
Leigh (Kent)	d									
Tonbridge 4	a									
Earlswood (Surrey)	d									
Salfords	d					←				
Horley 4	d		20 40			20 40				
Gatwick Airport 10 ✈	a	20 30	→	20 37	20 41	20 43	20 45	20 48	20 48	21 00
	d			20 39	20 42	20 44		20 49		
Three Bridges 4	a				20 46	20 48				
	d				20 47	20 49				
Crawley	d					20 53				
Ifield	d									
Faygate	d									
Littlehaven	d									
Horsham 4	a					21 01				
Balcombe	d									
Haywards Heath	a				20 56			21 00		
	d				20 56			21 00		
Wivelsfield	d									
Lewes 4	a									
Burgess Hill 4	d				21 01			21 06		
Hassocks 4	d				21 05					
Preston Park	d									
Hove 2	a							21 18		
Brighton 10	a			21 03	21 15					

Station		SN 1	SN 1	SN 1	SN 1	GW 1	FC 1	SN 1	SN 1	SN 1
London Victoria 15 ⊖	d	20 27		20 32				20 45	20 47	
Clapham Junction 10	d	20 33		20 38					20 53	
Bedford	d						19 06			
Luton 10	d						19 30			
Luton Airport Parkway 7 ✈	d						19 33			
St Albans City	d						19 45			
St Pancras International 15 ⊖	d						20 10			
Farringdon 3 ⊖	d						20 15			
City Thameslink 3	d									
London Blackfriars 3 ⊖	d						20 21			
London Bridge 4 ⊖	d				20 35					
New Cross Gate	d									
Norwood Junction 2	d				20 46					
East Croydon	a	20 42		20 48	20 50		20 55		21 02	
	d	20 42		20 49	20 51		20 56		21 03	
Purley 4	d				20 56					
Coulsdon South	d				20 59					
Merstham	d				21 05					
Redhill	a	20 57			21 08					
	d	20 58	21 10		21 12	21 20				
Reigate	a					21 24				
Nutfield	d		21 14							
Godstone	d		21 20							
Edenbridge	d		21 25							
Penshurst	d		21 32							
Leigh (Kent)	d		21 35							
Tonbridge 4	a		21 40							
Earlswood (Surrey)	d				21 14					
Salfords	d									←
Horley 4	d				21 21					21 21
Gatwick Airport 10 ✈	a	21 05			→		21 11	21 15	21 18	21 24
	d	21 06					21 12		21 19	21 25
Three Bridges 4	a	21 10					21 16			21 29
	d	21 11					21 17			21 30
Crawley	d									21 33
Ifield	d									21 36
Faygate	d									
Littlehaven	d									21 42
Horsham 4	a									21 46
Balcombe	d	21 17								
Haywards Heath	a	21 22					21 26		21 30	
	d	21 22					21 26		21 30	
Wivelsfield	d	21 26							21 35	
Lewes 4	a								21 48	
Burgess Hill 4	d	21 28					21 33			
Hassocks 4	d	21 32					21 37			
Preston Park	d	21 38								
Hove 2	a									
Brighton 10	a	21 43		21 24			21 47			

Station		SN 1	SN 1	SN 1	FC 1	SN 1	SN 1	GW 1	SN 1	SN 1
London Victoria 15 ⊖	d	21 00	21 02	21 06			21 15		21 17	21 30
Clapham Junction 10	d		21 08	21 12					21 23	
Bedford	d				19 36					
Luton 10	d				20 00					
Luton Airport Parkway 7 ✈	d				20 03					
St Albans City	d				20 15					
St Pancras International 15 ⊖	d				20 40					
Farringdon 3 ⊖	d				20 45					
City Thameslink 3	d									
London Blackfriars 3 ⊖	d				20 51					
London Bridge 4 ⊖	d									
New Cross Gate	d									
Norwood Junction 2	d									
East Croydon	a		21 17	21 22	21 25				21 32	
	d		21 17	21 23	21 26				21 33	
Purley 4	d		21 23							
Coulsdon South	d		21 26							
Merstham	d									
Redhill	a		21 34							
	d		21 34					21 38		
Reigate	a									
Nutfield	d									
Godstone	d									
Edenbridge	d									
Penshurst	d									
Leigh (Kent)	d									
Tonbridge 4	a									
Earlswood (Surrey)	d									
Salfords	d					←				
Horley 4	d		21 40			21 40				
Gatwick Airport 10 ✈	a	21 30	→	21 37	21 41	21 43	21 45	21 47	21 48	22 00
	d			21 39	21 42	21 44			21 49	
Three Bridges 4	a				21 46	21 48				
	d				21 47	21 49				
Crawley	d					21 53				
Ifield	d									
Faygate	d									
Littlehaven	d									
Horsham 4	a					22 01				
Balcombe	d									
Haywards Heath	a				21 56				22 00	
	d				21 56				22 00	
Wivelsfield	d									
Lewes 4	a									
Burgess Hill 4	d				22 01				22 06	
Hassocks 4	d				22 05					
Preston Park	d									
Hove 2	a								22 18	
Brighton 10	a			22 03	22 15					

Station		SN 1	SN 1	SN 1	GW 1	FC 1	SN 1	SN 1	SN 1	SN 1
London Victoria 15 ⊖	d	21 27					21 45	21 47		22 00
Clapham Junction 10	d	21 33						21 53		
Bedford	d					20 06				
Luton 10	d					20 30				
Luton Airport Parkway 7 ✈	d					20 33				
St Albans City	d					20 45				
St Pancras International 15 ⊖	d					21 10				
Farringdon 3 ⊖	d					21 15				
City Thameslink 3	d									
London Blackfriars 3 ⊖	d					21 21				
London Bridge 4 ⊖	d			21 35						
New Cross Gate	d									
Norwood Junction 2	d			21 46						
East Croydon	a	21 42		21 50		21 55		22 02		
	d	21 42		21 51		21 56		22 03		
Purley 4	d			21 56						
Coulsdon South	d			21 59						
Merstham	d			22 05						
Redhill	a	21 57		22 08						
	d	21 58	22 10	22 12	22 19					
Reigate	a				22 23					
Nutfield	d		22 14							
Godstone	d		22 20							
Edenbridge	d		22 25							
Penshurst	d		22 32							
Leigh (Kent)	d		22 35							
Tonbridge 4	a		22 40							
Earlswood (Surrey)	d			22 14						
Salfords	d								←	
Horley 4	d			22 21					22 21	
Gatwick Airport 10 ✈	a	22 06		→		22 11	22 15	22 18	22 24	22 30
	d	22 07				22 12		22 19	22 25	
Three Bridges 4	a	22 11				22 16			22 29	
	d	22 12				22 17			22 30	
Crawley	d								22 33	
Ifield	d								22 36	
Faygate	d									
Littlehaven	d								22 42	
Horsham 4	a								22 46	
Balcombe	d	22 18								
Haywards Heath	a	22 23				22 26		22 30		
	d	22 23				22 26		22 30		
Wivelsfield	d	22 27						22 35		
Lewes 4	a							22 48		
Burgess Hill 4	d	22 29				22 33				
Hassocks 4	d	22 33				22 37				
Preston Park	d	22 39								
Hove 2	a									
Brighton 10	a	22 43				22 47				

Table 186

Sundays

5 January to 11 May

Bedford and London - Brighton

Network Diagram - see first Page of Table 175

Station		SN 1	FC 1	SN 1	SN 1	SN 1	GW 1	SN 1	SN 1	SN 1	SN 1	GW 1	FC 1	SN 1	SN 1	SN 1
London Victoria 15 ⊖	d	22 02			22 15	22 17		22 30	22 27					22 45	22 47	
Clapham Junction 10	d	22 08				22 23			22 33						22 53	
Bedford	d		20 28										20 58			
Luton 10	d		20 52										21 22			
Luton Airport Parkway 7 ✈	d		20 55										21 25			
St Albans City	d		21 07										21 37			
St Pancras International 15 ⊖	d		21 40										22 10			
Farringdon 3 ⊖	d		21 45										22 15			
City Thameslink 3	d															
London Blackfriars 3 ⊖	d		21 51										22 21			
London Bridge 4 ⊖	d										22 35					
New Cross Gate	d															
Norwood Junction 2	d										22 46					
East Croydon 🚋	a	22 17	22 25			22 32			22 42		22 50		22 55		23 03	
	d	22 18	22 26			22 33			22 42		22 51		22 56		23 03	
Purley 4	d	22 23									22 56					
Coulsdon South	d	22 27									22 59					
Merstham	d										23 05					
Redhill	a	22 34							22 57		23 08					
	d	22 35					22 39		22 58	23 10	23 12	23 20				
Reigate	a											23 24				
Nutfield	d									23 14						
Godstone	d									23 20						
Edenbridge	d									23 25						
Penshurst	d									23 32						
Leigh (Kent)	d									23 35						
Tonbridge 4	a									23 40						
Earlswood (Surrey)	d										23 14					
Salfords	d			←												←
Horley 4	d	22 41		22 41							23 21					23 21
Gatwick Airport 10 ✈	a	→	22 41	22 43	22 45	22 48	22 48	23 00	23 05		→		23 11	23 15	23 18	23 24
	d		22 42	22 44		22 49			23 06				23 12		23 19	23 25
Three Bridges 4	a		22 46	22 49					23 10				23 16			23 29
	d		22 47	22 49					23 11				23 17			23 30
Crawley	d			22 53												23 33
Ifield	d															23 36
Faygate	d															
Littlehaven	d															23 42
Horsham 4	a			23 02												23 46
Balcombe	d								23 17							
Haywards Heath	a		22 56			23 00			23 22				23 26		23 30	
	d		22 56			23 01			23 22				23 26		23 30	
Wivelsfield	d								23 26						23 35	
Lewes 4	a														23 48	
Burgess Hill 4	d		23 01			23 06			23 28				23 33			
Hassocks 4	d		23 05						23 32				23 37			
Preston Park	d								23 38							
Hove 2	a					23 21										
Brighton 10	a		23 15						23 43				23 47			

Station		SN 1	GW 1	SN 1	FC 1	SN 1	SN 1	SN 1	SN 1	SN 1	FC 1	SN 1	FC 1	FC 1	FC 1
London Victoria 15 ⊖	d	23 00		23 04		23 15		23 17	23 30	23 32		23 45			
Clapham Junction 10	d			23 10				23 23		23 38					
Bedford	d				21 28						21 58		22 28	23 02	23 42
Luton 10	d				21 52						22 22		22 52	23 26	00 06
Luton Airport Parkway 7 ✈	d				21 55						22 25		22 55	23 29	00 09
St Albans City	d				22 07						22 37		23 07	23 41	00 21
St Pancras International 15 ⊖	d				22 40						23 10		23 40	00 14	00 54
Farringdon 3 ⊖	d				22 45						23 15		23 45	00 19	
City Thameslink 3	d														
London Blackfriars 3 ⊖	d				22 51						23 21		23 51	00 25	01 05
London Bridge 4 ⊖	d														
New Cross Gate	d														
Norwood Junction 2	d														
East Croydon 🚋	a			23 21	23 25			23 37		23 52	23 56		00 28	00 56	01 34
	d			23 22	23 26			23 37		23 53	23 57		00 29	00 57	01 36
Purley 4	d			23 28											
Coulsdon South	d			23 32											
Merstham	d			23 38											
Redhill	a			23 41						00 05					
	d		23 38	23 41						00 05					
Reigate	a														
Nutfield	d														
Godstone	d														
Edenbridge	d														
Penshurst	d														
Leigh (Kent)	d														
Tonbridge 4	a														
Earlswood (Surrey)	d														
Salfords	d						←								
Horley 4	d			23 49			23 49								
Gatwick Airport 10 ✈	a	23 30	23 47	→	23 41	23 50	23 54	23 59	00 05	00 14	00 18	00 20	00 48	01 18	01 55
	d				23 42		23 55	23 59		00 15	00 20		00 49	01 19	01 55
Three Bridges 4	a				23 46		23 59	00 05		00 19	00 24		00 54	01 24	02 02
	d				23 47		23 59	00 06		00 20	00 25				
Crawley	d						00 03								
Ifield	d						00 05								
Faygate	d														
Littlehaven	d						00 12								
Horsham 4	a						00 15								
Balcombe	d									00 26					
Haywards Heath	a				23 56			00 15		00 31	00 34				
	d				23 56			00 15		00 31	00 36				
Wivelsfield	d									00 35					
Lewes 4	a														
Burgess Hill 4	d				00 02			00 20		00 37	00 42				
Hassocks 4	d				00 06					00 41	00 45				
Preston Park	d									00 48					
Hove 2	a							00 31							
Brighton 10	a				00 15					00 52	00 55				

Table 186R

Mondays to Fridays

9 December to 16 May

Brighton - London and Bedford

Network Diagram - see first Page of Table 175

Miles	Miles	Miles			FC 1 A	FC MO 1 B	SN 1	SN 1	FC MO 1 C	FC MO 1 B	FC MX 1	SN 1	GW MO 1	SN 1	GW MX 1	SN 1	SN 1	FC 1 D	SN 1	SN 1	FC 1 D	SN 1
0	—	—	Brighton 10	d																		
—	0	—	Hove 2	d																		
1½	1½	—	Preston Park	d																		
7¼	—	—	Hassocks 4	d																		
9¼	—	—	Burgess Hill 4	d																		
—	—	—	Lewes 4	d																		
10	9¼	—	Wivelsfield 4	d																		
13	—	—	Haywards Heath 3	a																		
—	—	—		d					00 01	00 01												
17	—	—	Balcombe	d							00 04											
—	0	—	Horsham 4	d																		
—	1	—	Littlehaven	d																		
—	3¼	—	Faygate	d																		
—	5¾	—	Ifield	d																		
—	7	—	Crawley	d																		
21½	8½	—	Three Bridges 4	a					00 09	00 09	00 10											
—	—	—		d					00 10	00 10	00 10							01 16		01 59	02 16	02 59
24¼	—	—	Gatwick Airport 10 ✈	a					00 14	00 14	00 14							01 20		02 03	02 20	03 03
—	—	—		d				00 06	00 15	00 15	00 15	00 20		00 35		00 50	01 10	01 21	01 35	02 05	02 21	03 05
25	—	—	Horley 4	d													01 12			02 07		03 07
27¼	—	—	Salfords	d																		
29¼	—	—	Earlswood (Surrey)	d																		
—	—	0	Tonbridge 4	d																		
—	—	2½	Leigh (Kent)	d																		
—	—	4¼	Penshurst	d																		
—	—	9¼	Edenbridge	d																		
—	—	14	Godstone	d																		
—	—	17¾	Nutfield	d																		
—	0	—	Reigate	d									00 26		00 45							
30	1¾	19¾	Redhill 5	a					00 23	00 23	00 23		00 30		00 49							
—	—	—		d			00 04		00 24	00 24	00 24											
32	—	—	Merstham	d																		
35½	—	—	Coulsdon South	d																		
37½	—	—	Purley 4	d			00 12										01 26			02 22		03 22
40½	0	—	East Croydon	a			00 17		00 36	00 36	00 36						01 31	01 39		02 27	02 39	03 27
—	—	—		d	00 02	00 02	00 18		00 36	00 36	00 36						01 31	01 40		02 27	02 40	03 28
—	1¼	—	Norwood Junction 2	a																		
—	—	—	New Cross Gate	d																		
—	10¼	—	London Bridge 4 ⊖	a	00 21				00 51		00 52											
—	—	—	London Blackfriars 3 ⊖	a	00 28	00 30			00 58	01 03	00 58							02 08			03 08	
—	—	—	City Thameslink 3	a																		
—	—	—	Farringdon 3 ⊖	a	00 34	00 36																
—	—	—	St Pancras International 15 ⊖	a	00 38	00 40			01 09	01 13	01 08							02 20			03 20	
—	—	—	St Albans City	a	01 11	01 13			01 42	01 47	01 41							02 53			03 53	
—	—	—	Luton Airport Parkway 4 ✈	a	01 23	01 25			01 54	01 59	01 53							03 05			04 05	
—	—	—	Luton 7	a	01 26	01 28			01 57	02 02	01 56							03 08			04 08	
—	—	—	Bedford 10	a	01 52	01 55			02 23	02 29	02 22							03 35			04 35	
48¼	0	0	Clapham Junction 10	a			00 31										01 45			02 41		03 41
51	—	—	London Victoria 15 ⊖	a			00 39	00 41				00 58		01 12		01 26	01 53		02 10	02 49		03 49

Miles	Miles	Miles			FC 1 D	SN 1	FC 1 E	SN 1	FC 1 F	SN 1	SN 1	FC 1	GW 1	GW 1	SN 1	FC 1	SN 1	SN 1	SN 1	SN 1
0	—	—	Brighton 10	d												05 10				05 23
—	0	—	Hove 2	d																
1½	1½	—	Preston Park	d												05 14				
7¼	—	—	Hassocks 4	d												05 20				
9¼	—	—	Burgess Hill 4	d												05 24				05 33
—	—	—	Lewes 4	d																
10	9¼	—	Wivelsfield 4	d												05 26				
13	—	—	Haywards Heath 3	a												05 30				05 38
—	—	—		d												05 31				05 39
17	—	—	Balcombe	d												05 36				05 44
—	0	—	Horsham 4	d											05 16					
—	1	—	Littlehaven	d											05 19					
—	3¼	—	Faygate	d																
—	5¾	—	Ifield	d											05 25					
—	7	—	Crawley	d											05 29					
21½	8½	—	Three Bridges 4	a											05 32	05 42				05 50
—	—	—		d	03 16	03 59	04 16		04 52						05 33	05 42				05 50
24¼	—	—	Gatwick Airport 10 ✈	a	03 20	04 03	04 20		04 56						05 37	05 46				05 54
—	—	—		d	03 21	04 04	04 21	04 35	04 57		05 20	05 27		05 31	05 38	05 47	05 50			05 55
25	—	—	Horley 4	d		04 07									05 40					
27¼	—	—	Salfords	d																
29¼	—	—	Earlswood (Surrey)	d																
—	—	0	Tonbridge 4	d						04 59									05 20	
—	—	2½	Leigh (Kent)	d						05 03									05 24	
—	—	4¼	Penshurst	d						05 07									05 28	
—	—	9¼	Edenbridge	d						05 13									05 34	
—	—	14	Godstone	d						05 20									05 41	
—	—	17¾	Nutfield	d						05 25									05 46	
—	0	—	Reigate	d									05 34					←		
30	1¾	19¾	Redhill 5	a						05 30		05 35	05 39	05 41	05 47			05 47	05 51	
—	—	—		d						05 30		05 35			05 48			05 48		
32	—	—	Merstham	d											→			05 52		
35½	—	—	Coulsdon South	d						05 38								05 57		
37½	—	—	Purley 4	d		04 26				05 41								06 01		
40½	0	—	East Croydon	a	03 39	04 31	04 39		05 15	05 50		05 47				06 01		06 06		06 10
—	—	—		d	03 40	04 32	04 40		05 16	05 50		05 48				06 02		06 06		06 11
—	1¼	—	Norwood Junction 2	a																
—	—	—	New Cross Gate	d																
—	10¼	—	London Bridge 4 ⊖	a					05 34			06 02				06 15				
—	—	—	London Blackfriars 3 ⊖	a	04 08		05 08		05 41			06 10				06 23				
—	—	—	City Thameslink 3	a			05 11		05 44			06 14				06 26				
—	—	—	Farringdon 3 ⊖	a					05 47			06 18				06 30				
—	—	—	St Pancras International 15 ⊖	a	04 20		05 18		05 52			06 22				06 34				
—	—	—	St Albans City	a	04 53		05 53		06 23			06 43				06 57				
—	—	—	Luton Airport Parkway 4 ✈	a	05 05		06 05		06 35			06 55				07 09				
—	—	—	Luton 7	a	05 08		06 08		06 38			06 58				07 12				
—	—	—	Bedford 10	a	05 35		06 37		07 04			07 24				07 40				
48¼	0	0	Clapham Junction 10	a		04 51				06 11								06 18		06 21
51	—	—	London Victoria 15 ⊖	a		04 59		05 11		06 19	05 55						06 20	06 25		06 29

A until 3 January, MX from 7 January
B from 6 January
C until 30 December
D 1 to London Blackfriars
E 1 to City Thameslink
F 1 from Farringdon

Table 186R

Mondays to Fridays

9 December to 16 May

Brighton - London and Bedford

Network Diagram - see first Page of Table 175

Station		GW 1	SN 1	SN 1	SN 1 [trolley]	SN 1	FC 1	SN 1 [trolley]	GW 1	FC 1	SN 1	FC 1
Brighton 10	d						05 40			05 50		
Hove 2	d										05 57	
Preston Park	d						05 44			05 54		
Hassocks 4	d						05 50			06 00		
Burgess Hill 4	d						05 54			06 04		
Lewes 4	d			05 29								
Wivelsfield 4	d						05 56			06 06		
Haywards Heath 3	a			05 46			06 00			06 10	06 12	
	d			05 47			06 01			06 11	06 13	
Balcombe	d						06 06					
Horsham 4	d		05 36									
Littlehaven	d		05 39									
Faygate	d											
Ifield	d		05 45									
Crawley	d		05 49									
Three Bridges 4	a		05 52	05 55			06 12			06 19	06 21	
	d		05 53	05 56			06 12			06 20	06 22	
Gatwick Airport 10 ✈	a		05 57	06 00			06 16			06 24	06 26	
	d	05 56	05 59	06 01	06 05		06 17	06 20		06 25	06 27	
Horley 4	d		06 01									
Salfords	d		06 05									
Earlswood (Surrey)	d		06 09									
Tonbridge 4	d											
Leigh (Kent)	d											
Penshurst	d											
Edenbridge	d											
Godstone	d											
Nutfield	d											
Reigate	d					←			06 24			←
Redhill 5	a	06 07	06 12			06 12			06 29	06 33		06 33
	d		06 13			06 13				06 33		06 33
Merstham	d		→			06 17				→		
Coulsdon South	d					06 22						
Purley 4	d					06 26						
East Croydon	a			06 15		06 30	06 32				06 42	06 44
	d			06 16		06 31	06 32				06 42	06 45
Norwood Junction 2	a											
New Cross Gate	d											
London Bridge 4 ⊖	a						06 46					06 58
London Blackfriars 3 ⊖	a						06 52					07 04
City Thameslink 3	a						06 54					07 08
Farringdon 3 ⊖	a						06 58					07 12
St Pancras International 15 ⊖	a						07 02					07 16
St Albans City	a						07 22					07 41
Luton Airport Parkway 4 ✈	a						07 34					07 53
Luton 7	a						07 37					07 56
Bedford 10	a						08 03					08 23
Clapham Junction 10	a			06 25		06 40					06 51	
London Victoria 15 ⊖	a			06 32	06 35	06 48		06 50			07 00	

Station		SN 1	SN 1 [trolley]	SN 1	SN 1	SN 1	SN 1	SN 1	SN 1	SN 1
Brighton 10	d			06 01						06 17
Hove 2	d									
Preston Park	d									
Hassocks 4	d			06 10						06 25
Burgess Hill 4	d			06 14						06 29
Lewes 4	d				06 06					
Wivelsfield 4	d			06 16						
Haywards Heath 3	a			06 20	06 26					06 34
	d			06 28						06 35
Balcombe	d									
Horsham 4	d	06 09							06 23	
Littlehaven	d	06 12							06 26	
Faygate	d									
Ifield	d	06 19							06 33	
Crawley	d	06 22							06 37	
Three Bridges 4	a	06 26		06 36					06 40	06 46
	d	06 26		06 37					06 48	
Gatwick Airport 10 ✈	a	06 31		06 41					→	
	d	06 32	06 35	06 43						
Horley 4	d	06 34								
Salfords	d	06 38								
Earlswood (Surrey)	d	06 42								
Tonbridge 4	d					06 10				
Leigh (Kent)	d					06 14				
Penshurst	d					06 18				
Edenbridge	d					06 24				
Godstone	d					06 31				
Nutfield	d					06 36				
Reigate	d						←	06 49		
Redhill 5	a	06 45				06 42	06 45	06 53		
	d	06 46				06 43	06 46			
Merstham	d	→					06 50			
Coulsdon South	d					06 50	06 55			
Purley 4	d					06 54	06 59			
East Croydon	a			06 57		06 59	07 04			
	d			06 59		07 00	07 05			
Norwood Junction 2	a									
New Cross Gate	d									
London Bridge 4 ⊖	a			07 13		07 17				
London Blackfriars 3 ⊖	a									
City Thameslink 3	a									
Farringdon 3 ⊖	a									
St Pancras International 15 ⊖	a									
St Albans City	a									
Luton Airport Parkway 4 ✈	a									
Luton 7	a									
Bedford 10	a									
Clapham Junction 10	a						07 16			
London Victoria 15 ⊖	a		07 05				07 28			

Station		FC 1	SN 1 [trolley]	SN 1	GW 1	SN 1	FC 1	SN 1 [trolley]	SN 1	SN 1	SN 1
Brighton 10	d	06 08					06 24	06 30			06 37
Hove 2	d									06 31	
Preston Park	d	06 12					06 28				06 41
Hassocks 4	d	06 19					06 35			06 42	
Burgess Hill 4	d	06 23					06 39	06 42		06 47	
Lewes 4	d										
Wivelsfield 4	d	06 25						06 45			06 52
Haywards Heath 3	a	06 30					06 44	06 50		06 53	06 58
	d	06 30					06 45	06 51		07 00	
Balcombe	d	06 36					06 51				
Horsham 4	d					06 36					
Littlehaven	d					06 39					
Faygate	d					06 43					
Ifield	d					06 48					
Crawley	d			←		06 51					
Three Bridges 4	a	06 41		06 40		06 55	06 56				
	d	06 42		06 48		06 55	06 57		07 04		
Gatwick Airport 10 ✈	a	06 46		06 52		07 00	07 01	07 04	07 08	07 11	
	d	06 47	06 50	06 53	06 58	07 01	07 02	07 06	07 09	07 12	
Horley 4	d			06 56		07 03			07 12		
Salfords	d					07 07			07 16		
Earlswood (Surrey)	d					07 11			07 19		
Tonbridge 4	d										
Leigh (Kent)	d										
Penshurst	d										
Edenbridge	d										
Godstone	d										
Nutfield	d										
Reigate	d										
Redhill 5	a	06 55		07 03	07 07	07 14	07 10		07 23		
	d	06 56		07 04		07 15	07 11		07 23		
Merstham	d					→			→		
Coulsdon South	d										
Purley 4	d										
East Croydon	a	07 08		07 15			07 22			07 26	
	d	07 09		07 15			07 23			07 28	
Norwood Junction 2	a										
New Cross Gate	d										
London Bridge 4 ⊖	a	07 23								07 45	
London Blackfriars 3 ⊖	a	07 30					07 51				
City Thameslink 3	a	07 32					07 56				
Farringdon 3 ⊖	a	07 36					08 00				
St Pancras International 15 ⊖	a	07 40					08 04				
St Albans City	a						08 25				
Luton Airport Parkway 4 ✈	a	08 06					08 37				
Luton 7	a	08 10					08 40				
Bedford 10	a						09 05				
Clapham Junction 10	a			07 24							
London Victoria 15 ⊖	a		07 20	07 32				07 37			

Station		SN 1	SN 1	SN 1 [trolley]	SN 1	SN 1	SN 1
Brighton 10	d			06 40			
Hove 2	d						
Preston Park	d			06 44			
Hassocks 4	d			06 52			
Burgess Hill 4	d			06 56			
Lewes 4	d						
Wivelsfield 4	d						
Haywards Heath 3	a			07 01			
	d			07 03			
Balcombe	d						
Horsham 4	d	06 50					
Littlehaven	d	06 53					
Faygate	d						
Ifield	d	07 00					
Crawley	d	07 04					
Three Bridges 4	a	07 07					
	d	07 08				07 13	07 13
Gatwick Airport 10 ✈	a	07 12		07 15		07 18	07 18
	d	07 14		07 20		07 19	07 19
Horley 4	d	07 16				07 22	07 22
Salfords	d					07 26	07 26
Earlswood (Surrey)	d					07 30	07 30
Tonbridge 4	d				06 47		
Leigh (Kent)	d				06 51		
Penshurst	d				06 55		
Edenbridge	d				07 01		
Godstone	d				07 08		
Nutfield	d				07 13		
Reigate	d		←				
Redhill 5	a		07 14		07 18	07 36	07 36
	d		07 15				07 40
Merstham	d		07 19				→
Coulsdon South	d		07 24				
Purley 4	d		07 29				
East Croydon	a	07 31	07 34				
	d	07 31	07 35				
Norwood Junction 2	a						
New Cross Gate	d						
London Bridge 4 ⊖	a		07 52				
London Blackfriars 3 ⊖	a						
City Thameslink 3	a						
Farringdon 3 ⊖	a						
St Pancras International 15 ⊖	a						
St Albans City	a						
Luton Airport Parkway 4 ✈	a						
Luton 7	a						
Bedford 10	a						
Clapham Junction 10	a	07 40					
London Victoria 15 ⊖	a	07 49		07 50			

Table 186R

Mondays to Fridays

9 December to 16 May

Brighton - London and Bedford

Network Diagram - see first Page of Table 175

		SN 1 ✠	SN 1 A ✠	SN 1	SN 1	GW 1	SN 1	SN 1 ✠	FC 1	SN 1	SN 1	SN 1	SN 1	SN 1	GW 1	SN 1	SN 1	SN 1 ✠	SN 1
Brighton 10	d	06 50						06 56	07 02									07 14	
Hove 2	d									07 11									07 21
Preston Park	d							07 00	07 06									07 19	
Hassocks 4	d								07 13	07 20									07 30
Burgess Hill 4	d	07 00						07 10	07 17									07 28	
Lewes 4	d				06 51														
Wivelsfield 4	d				07 08			07 14	07 20	07 25									07 35
Haywards Heath 3	a	07 05			07 12			07 18	07 24	07 30								07 34	07 40
	d	07 06			07 13			07 20	07 25	07 31								07 35	07 41
Balcombe	d				07 19														
Horsham 4	d		07 04				07 09				07 17	07 25							
Littlehaven	d						07 12				07 20	07 29							
Faygate	d						07 16												
Ifield	d						07 20				07 27								
Crawley	d		07 13				07 23				07 31	07 37							
Three Bridges 4	a	07 16	07 20		07 24		07 27		07 33		07 34	07 40							
	d	07 22			07 25		07 28		07 34		07 35	07 41							
Gatwick Airport 10 ✈	a				07 29		07 32	07 32	07 38		07 39							07 47	
	d				07 30		07 33	07 35	07 39		07 40							07 50	
Horley 4	d						07 36				07 43								
Salfords	d						07 40				07 47								
Earlswood (Surrey)	d						07 43				07 50								
Tonbridge 4	d																		
Leigh (Kent)	d																		
Penshurst	d																		
Edenbridge	d																		
Godstone	d																		
Nutfield	d																		
Reigate	d			←		07 18							07 27	←	07 34	07 40	←		
Redhill 5	a			07 23		07 24	07 49				07 54		07 31	07 36	07 38	07 45	07 49		
	d			07 23			07 51				07 54		07 40			07 51			
Merstham	d			07 28			↳				↳		07 44						
Coulsdon South	d			07 33									07 50						
Purley 4	d			07 37									07 55						
East Croydon	a	07 38		07 42	07 45				07 53	07 56		07 59	08 01			08 03			08 08
	d	07 39		07 42	07 46				07 54	07 57		08 01	08 02			08 04			08 08
Norwood Junction 2	a																		
New Cross Gate	d																		
London Bridge 4 ⊖	a				08 00					08 11			08 17			08 19			
London Blackfriars 3 ⊖	a								08 20										
City Thameslink 3	a								08 23										
Farringdon 3 ⊖	a								08 27										
St Pancras International 15 ⊖	a								08 31										
St Albans City	a								08 52										
Luton Airport Parkway 4 ✈	a								09 01										
Luton 7	a								09 04										
Bedford 10	a								09 26										
Clapham Junction 10	a	07 48		07 51								08 10							08 17
London Victoria 15 ⊖	a	07 57		08 00				08 06				08 19						08 20	08 25

		SN 1	SN 1 ✠	SN 1	SN 1	SN 1	GW 1	FC 1	SN 1 ✠	SN 1	SN 1	SN 1	SN 1	SN 1	SN 1	SN 1	SN 1	SN 1 ✠	FC 1
Brighton 10	d							07 24	07 29				07 32					07 44	07 50
Hove 2	d													07 41					
Preston Park	d							07 28					07 36					07 48	07 54
Hassocks 4	d							07 35	07 39									07 56	08 01
Burgess Hill 4	d							07 39					07 46	07 52				08 00	
Lewes 4	d		07 22												07 42				
Wivelsfield 4	d		07 39						07 46				07 49						
Haywards Heath 3	a		07 44					07 46	07 50				07 54	07 58	08 03			08 05	08 09
	d		07 44					07 47	07 51				07 55	07 59	08 04			08 06	08 09
Balcombe	d												08 01						08 15
Horsham 4	d										07 39	07 47					07 52		
Littlehaven	d										07 42	07 51					07 55		
Faygate	d																07 59		
Ifield	d										07 49	07 58					08 03		
Crawley	d										07 53	08 01					08 07		
Three Bridges 4	a							07 55			07 57	08 05	08 07				08 10		
	d							07 56			07 58	08 06	08 08				08 11		
Gatwick Airport 10 ✈	a							08 00	08 02		08 03						08 15	08 18	08 23
	d					07 43	07 58	08 01	08 05		08 04						08 16	08 20	08 24
Horley 4	d		07 59			07 46					08 06						08 18		
Salfords	d					07 50					08 10						08 22		
Earlswood (Surrey)	d					07 54					08 14						08 26		
Tonbridge 4	d				07 25														
Leigh (Kent)	d				07 29														
Penshurst	d				07 33														
Edenbridge	d				07 39														
Godstone	d				07 46														
Nutfield	d				07 51														
Reigate	d	←		07 52						08 09						←			
Redhill 5	a	07 54		07 56	07 56	08 00	08 05	08 08		08 13	08 17					08 17	08 29		
	d	07 54			08 02			08 09			08 18					08 18	08 30		
Merstham	d	07 59			08 06						↳					08 22	↳		
Coulsdon South	d	08 04			08 11											08 27			
Purley 4	d				08 15											08 31			
East Croydon	a	08 11	08 14		08 20			08 22				08 24	08 26	08 29	08 31	08 36			08 38
	d	08 11	08 14		08 21			08 23				08 25	08 28	08 30	08 33	08 37			08 39
Norwood Junction 2	a																		
New Cross Gate	d																		
London Bridge 4 ⊖	a											08 41	08 43		08 49				
London Blackfriars 3 ⊖	a							08 53											09 09
City Thameslink 3	a							08 56											09 12
Farringdon 3 ⊖	a							09 00											09 16
St Pancras International 15 ⊖	a							09 04											09 20
St Albans City	a							09 25											09 40
Luton Airport Parkway 4 ✈	a							09 37											09 51
Luton 7	a							09 40											09 54
Bedford 10	a							10 07											10 20
Clapham Junction 10	a	08 20	08 23		08 32									08 41		08 48			
London Victoria 15 ⊖	a	08 29	08 32		08 42				08 35					08 50		08 56		08 52	

A ✠ from Three Bridges

Table 186R

Mondays to Fridays

9 December to 16 May

Brighton - London and Bedford

Network Diagram - see first Page of Table 175

Station		SN 1	SN 1 🚲	SN 1 🚲	SN 1	GW 1	SN 1	FC 1	SN 1	SN 1	SN 1	GW 1	SN 1 🚲	SN 1 🚲	FC 1	SN 1	SN 1	SN 1 🚲	SN 1
Brighton 10	d							08 02						08 13	08 16				
Hove 2	d								08 08										
Preston Park	d							08 06	08 12						08 20				
Hassocks 4	d							08 13	08 19						08 27				
Burgess Hill 4	d							08 17	08 23						08 31				
Lewes 4	d			07 55														08 23	
Wivelsfield 4	d			08 11				08 20							08 34			08 39	
Haywards Heath 3	a			08 16				08 24	08 28						08 38			08 44	
	d			08 16				08 25	08 29						08 39			08 44	
Balcombe	d			08 22															
Horsham 4	d	08 09					08 12												08 35
Littlehaven	d						08 15												08 38
Faygate	d						08 19												
Ifield	d						08 23												08 44
Crawley	d	08 18					08 26												08 47
Three Bridges 4	a	08 22		08 28			08 29	08 33	08 37						08 47				08 51
	d	08 22		08 28			08 30	08 34	08 38						08 48				08 51
Gatwick Airport 10 ✈	a						08 34	08 38	08 42					08 46	08 52			08 56	08 56
	d		08 35				08 35	08 39	08 43				08 46	08 50	08 53			08 57	08 57
Horley 4	d	08 28					08 38											08 59	08 59
Salfords	d						08 42												09 03
Earlswood (Surrey)	d						08 45												09 07
Tonbridge 4	d									07 59						08 16			
Leigh (Kent)	d									08 03						08 20			
Penshurst	d									08 07						08 24			
Edenbridge	d									08 13						08 30			
Godstone	d									08 20						08 37			
Nutfield	d									08 25						08 42			
Reigate	d				←	08 24					08 31	08 42					←		
Redhill 5	a				08 29	08 30	08 51			08 33	08 36	08 46				08 47	08 51		09 12
	d				08 30		08 53			08 40						08 53			09 14
Merstham	d						→			08 44						08 57			→
Coulsdon South	d				08 37					08 49						09 02			
Purley 4	d									08 53						09 05			
East Croydon 🚊	a	08 43		08 46	08 50			08 53	08 57	08 58					09 08	09 10		09 14	
	d	08 43		08 50	08 51			08 54	08 58	08 59					09 09	09 11		09 14	
Norwood Junction 2	a																		
New Cross Gate	d																		
London Bridge 4 ⊖	a				09 06			09 08		09 16									
London Blackfriars 3 ⊖	a							09 21							09 37				
City Thameslink 3	a							09 24							09 40				
Farringdon 3 ⊖	a							09 27							09 44				
St Pancras International 15 ⊖	a							09 32							09 48				
St Albans City	a							09 51							10 09				
Luton Airport Parkway 4 ✈	a							10 00							10 20				
Luton 7	a							10 03							10 23				
Bedford 10	a							10 23							10 49				
Clapham Junction 10	a	08 52		09 01					09 07							09 20		09 23	
London Victoria 15 ⊖	a	09 01	09 05	09 09					09 16				09 16	09 20		09 27		09 32	

Station		SN 1 🚲	GW 1	SN 1	FC 1	SN 1	SN 1	SN 1	FC 1	SN 1	SN 1 🚲	GW 1	SN 1	SN 1 🚲	SN 1	FC 1	SN 1 🚲	SN 1 🚲	SN 1
Brighton 10	d	08 30			08 34	08 45										09 00		09 19	
Hove 2	d														08 52				
Preston Park	d				08 38										08 57				
Hassocks 4	d				08 44										09 04	09 09			
Burgess Hill 4	d				08 48										09 08	09 12			
Lewes 4	d													08 48					
Wivelsfield 4	d				08 50				←					09 02					
Haywards Heath 3	a	08 48			08 55	08 58			08 55					09 06	09 13	09 17			
	d	08 49			09 00	08 58			09 00					09 08	09 14	09 18			
Balcombe	d				→				09 06										
Horsham 4	d			08 49									09 00						
Littlehaven	d												09 03						
Faygate	d																		
Ifield	d												09 09						
Crawley	d			08 58									09 13						
Three Bridges 4	a			09 01					09 11				09 16	09 17		09 26			
	d			09 02					09 12				09 18	09 18		09 27			
Gatwick Airport 10 ✈	a	09 01		09 06		09 09			09 16				09 22	09 22	09 26	09 31			
	d	09 05	09 07	09 07		09 10			09 17		09 20		09 23	09 23	09 27	09 32	09 35		
Horley 4	d												09 26						
Salfords	d												09 30						
Earlswood (Surrey)	d												09 33						
Tonbridge 4	d						08 37												
Leigh (Kent)	d						08 41												
Penshurst	d						08 45												
Edenbridge	d						08 51												
Godstone	d						08 58												
Nutfield	d						09 03												
Reigate	d							←		09 14		09 24							←
Redhill 5	a		09 15				09 08	09 12		09 18		09 30	09 36						09 36
	d						09 14			09 19			09 37						09 37
Merstham	d						09 18			09 23			→						09 41
Coulsdon South	d						09 23			09 28									09 46
Purley 4	d									09 32									09 49
East Croydon 🚊	a			09 22		09 25	09 30		09 32	09 38				09 38	09 41	09 46		09 52	09 54
	d			09 23		09 26	09 31		09 32	09 39				09 39	09 42	09 47		09 53	09 55
Norwood Junction 2	a									09 43									09 59
New Cross Gate	d																		10 07
London Bridge 4 ⊖	a								09 46	09 55						10 00			10 13
London Blackfriars 3 ⊖	a								09 53							10 08			
City Thameslink 3	a								09 56							10 10			
Farringdon 3 ⊖	a								10 00							10 14			
St Pancras International 15 ⊖	a								10 04							10 18			
St Albans City	a								10 25							10 39			
Luton Airport Parkway 4 ✈	a								10 37							10 50			
Luton 7	a								10 40							10 53			
Bedford 10	a								11 05							11 19			
Clapham Junction 10	a			09 32		09 35	09 41							09 48	09 51			10 02	
London Victoria 15 ⊖	a	09 35		09 42		09 43	09 50				09 50			09 58	09 58		10 05	10 11	

Table 186R

Mondays to Fridays

9 December to 16 May

Brighton - London and Bedford

Network Diagram - see first Page of Table 175

		GW 1	SN 1	FC 1	SN 1	SN 1	SN 1	SN 1	SN 1	SN 1	FC 1	SN 1	SN 1	GW 1	SN 1	SN 1	FC 1	SN 1	GW 1
						🛒			🛒	A 🛒		🛒			🛒				
Brighton 10	d			09 07			09 25				09 34	09 49					09 37		
Hove 2	d									09 22									
Preston Park	d			09 11													09 41		
Hassocks 4	d			09 17			09 34			09 31							09 47		
Burgess Hill 4	d			09 21			09 38										09 51		
Lewes 4	d								09 17										
Wivelsfield 4	d			09 23					09 33								09 53		
Haywards Heath 3	a			09 28					09 38	09 40	09 47						09 58		
	d			09 31					09 44		09 48						10 01		
Balcombe	d			09 37															
Horsham 4	d		09 20					09 30								09 51			
Littlehaven	d							09 33											
Faygate	d							09 37											
Ifield	d							09 41											
Crawley	d		09 29					09 44								10 00			
Three Bridges 4	a		09 32	09 42				09 48			09 56					10 03	10 11		
	d		09 33	09 42				09 48			09 57					10 04	10 12		
Gatwick Airport 10 ✈	a		09 37	09 46			09 51	09 53	09 55		10 01					10 08	10 16		
	d		09 38	09 47		09 50	09 53	09 54	09 56		10 02			10 03	10 05	10 09	10 17		
Horley 4	d		09 41					09 56											
Salfords	d																		
Earlswood (Surrey)	d							10 02											
Tonbridge 4	d				09 19														
Leigh (Kent)	d				09 23														
Penshurst	d				09 27														
Edenbridge	d				09 33														
Godstone	d				09 40														
Nutfield	d				09 45														
Reigate	d	09 37											←					10 14	10 19
Redhill 5	a	09 42	09 48		09 51			10 05					10 05	10 10		10 16		10 18	10 25
	d		09 48		09 51			10 07					10 07			10 17		10 20	
Merstham	d							↪					10 11					10 24	
Coulsdon South	d				09 58								10 16					10 29	
Purley 4	d				10 02								10 19					10 33	
East Croydon	a		09 59	10 02	10 07		10 08		10 11		10 16	10 22	10 24			10 28	10 31	10 38	
	d		10 00	10 02	10 08		10 08		10 11		10 17	10 23	10 25			10 28	10 32	10 38	
Norwood Junction 2	a				10 13								10 30					10 42	
New Cross Gate	d												10 38						
London Bridge 4 ⊖	a			10 15	10 25						10 30		10 44				10 45	10 55	
London Blackfriars 3 ⊖	a			10 23							10 37						10 52		
City Thameslink 3	a			10 26							10 40						10 56		
Farringdon 3 ⊖	a			10 29							10 44						10 59		
St Pancras International 15 ⊖	a			10 33							10 48						11 03		
St Albans City	a			10 55							11 09						11 25		
Luton Airport Parkway 4 ✈	a			11 06							11 20						11 37		
Luton 7	a			11 09							11 23						11 40		
Bedford 10	a			11 35							11 49						12 05		
Clapham Junction 10	a		10 09				10 17		10 20			10 32				10 37			
London Victoria 15 ⊖	a		10 16			10 20	10 25		10 28			10 40			10 35	10 44			

		SN 1	SN 1	SN 1	SN 1	FC 1	SN 1	SN 1	SN 1	GW 1	SN 1	FC 1	SN 1	SN 1	SN 1	SN 1	SN 1	SN 1	FC 1
		🛒		🛒	A 🛒		🛒	🛒						🛒					
Brighton 10	d					10 04		10 19				10 07			10 25				10 34
Hove 2	d				09 51												10 21		
Preston Park	d				09 55							10 11							
Hassocks 4	d											10 17			10 34				
Burgess Hill 4	d				10 05							10 21			10 38				
Lewes 4	d			09 48														10 19	
Wivelsfield 4	d											10 23						10 35	
Haywards Heath 3	a			10 07	10 12	10 17						10 28					10 35	10 42	10 47
	d			10 14		10 18						10 31					10 44		10 48
Balcombe	d											10 37							
Horsham 4	d		10 00								10 20					10 30			
Littlehaven	d		10 03													10 33			
Faygate	d																		
Ifield	d		10 09													10 39			
Crawley	d		10 13								10 29					10 43			
Three Bridges 4	a		10 16			10 26					10 32	10 42				10 46			10 56
	d		10 18			10 27					10 33	10 42				10 48			10 57
Gatwick Airport 10 ✈	a		10 22	10 25		10 31					10 37	10 46			10 52	10 52	10 55		11 01
	d	10 20	10 23	10 26		10 32	10 35				10 38	10 47		10 50	10 53	10 53	10 56		11 02
Horley 4	d		10 26								10 41					10 56			
Salfords	d		10 30																
Earlswood (Surrey)	d		10 33													11 01			
Tonbridge 4	d												10 19						
Leigh (Kent)	d												10 23						
Penshurst	d												10 27						
Edenbridge	d												10 33						
Godstone	d												10 40						
Nutfield	d												10 45						
Reigate	d								←	10 34									
Redhill 5	a		10 36						10 36	10 38	10 48		10 51			11 05			
	d		10 37						10 37		10 48		10 51			11 07			
Merstham	d		↪						10 41							↪			
Coulsdon South	d								10 46				10 58						
Purley 4	d								10 49				11 02						
East Croydon	a			10 41		10 46		10 52	10 54		10 59	11 02	11 07		11 08		11 11		11 16
	d			10 41		10 47		10 53	10 55		11 00	11 02	11 07		11 08		11 11		11 17
Norwood Junction 2	a								11 00				11 12						
New Cross Gate	d								11 08										
London Bridge 4 ⊖	a					11 00			11 14			11 15	11 25						11 30
London Blackfriars 3 ⊖	a					11 07						11 22							11 37
City Thameslink 3	a					11 10						11 26							11 40
Farringdon 3 ⊖	a					11 14						11 29							11 44
St Pancras International 15 ⊖	a					11 18						11 33							11 48
St Albans City	a					11 39						11 55							12 09
Luton Airport Parkway 4 ✈	a					11 50						12 07							12 20
Luton 7	a					11 53						12 10							12 23
Bedford 10	a					12 19						12 35							12 49
Clapham Junction 10	a			10 50				11 02			11 09				11 17		11 20		
London Victoria 15 ⊖	a	10 50		10 58			11 05	11 10			11 16			11 20	11 24		11 27		

A 🛒 from Haywards Heath

Table 186R

Mondays to Fridays

9 December to 16 May

Brighton - London and Bedford

Network Diagram - see first Page of Table 175

Station		SN 1 (trolley)	SN 1	GW 1	SN 1 (trolley)	SN 1	FC 1	SN 1	GW 1	SN 1 (trolley)	SN 1	SN 1	SN 1	FC 1	SN 1 (trolley)
Brighton 10	d	10 49					10 37							11 04	
Hove 2	d												10 51		
Preston Park	d						10 41						10 55		
Hassocks 4	d						10 47								
Burgess Hill 4	d						10 51						11 04		
Lewes 4	d											10 51			
Wivelsfield 4	d						10 53								
Haywards Heath 3	a						10 58					11 06	11 12	11 17	
	d						11 01					11 14		11 18	
Balcombe	d														
Horsham 4	d					10 50					11 00				
Littlehaven	d										11 03				
Faygate	d														
Ifield	d										11 09				
Crawley	d					10 59					11 13				
Three Bridges 4	a					11 02	11 11				11 16			11 26	
	d					11 03	11 12				11 18			11 27	
Gatwick Airport 10 ✈	a					11 07	11 16				11 22	11 25		11 31	
	d			11 03	11 05	11 08	11 17			11 20	11 23	11 26		11 32	11 35
Horley 4	d										11 26				
Salfords	d										11 30				
Earlswood (Surrey)	d										11 33				
Tonbridge 4	d														
Leigh (Kent)	d														
Penshurst	d														
Edenbridge	d														
Godstone	d														
Nutfield	d														
Reigate	d		←					11 14	11 19						
Redhill 5	a		11 05	11 10		11 16		11 18	11 25		11 36				
	d		11 07			11 16		11 19			11 37				
Merstham	d		11 11					11 23			→				
Coulsdon South	d		11 16					11 28							
Purley 4	d		11 19					11 32							
East Croydon (tram)	a	11 22	11 24			11 27	11 31	11 37				11 40		11 46	
	d	11 23	11 25			11 28	11 32	11 38				11 41		11 47	
Norwood Junction 2	a		11 29					11 42							
New Cross Gate	d		11 37												
London Bridge 4 ⊖	a		11 43				11 45	11 55						12 00	
London Blackfriars 3 ⊖	a						11 52							12 07	
City Thameslink 3	a						11 56							12 10	
Farringdon 3 ⊖	a						11 59							12 14	
St Pancras International 15 ⊖	a						12 03							12 18	
St Albans City	a						12 25							12 39	
Luton Airport Parkway 4 ✈	a						12 37							12 50	
Luton 7	a						12 40							12 53	
Bedford 10	a						13 05							13 19	
Clapham Junction 10	a	11 32				11 37						11 50			
London Victoria 15 ⊖	a	11 41			11 35	11 44				11 50		11 57			12 05

Station		SN 1 (trolley)	SN 1	GW 1	SN 1	FC 1	SN 1	SN 1 (trolley)	SN 1	SN 1
Brighton 10	d	11 19				11 07			11 25	
Hove 2	d									
Preston Park	d					11 11				
Hassocks 4	d					11 17			11 34	
Burgess Hill 4	d					11 21			11 38	
Lewes 4	d									
Wivelsfield 4	d					11 23				
Haywards Heath 3	a					11 28				
	d					11 31				
Balcombe	d					11 37				
Horsham 4	d				11 20					11 30
Littlehaven	d									11 33
Faygate	d									
Ifield	d									11 39
Crawley	d				11 29					11 43
Three Bridges 4	a				11 32	11 42				11 46
	d				11 33	11 42				11 48
Gatwick Airport 10 ✈	a				11 37	11 46			11 52	11 52
	d				11 38	11 47		11 50	11 53	11 53
Horley 4	d				11 41					11 56
Salfords	d									
Earlswood (Surrey)	d									12 01
Tonbridge 4	d						11 19			
Leigh (Kent)	d						11 23			
Penshurst	d						11 27			
Edenbridge	d						11 33			
Godstone	d						11 40			
Nutfield	d						11 45			
Reigate	d		←	11 34						
Redhill 5	a		11 36	11 38	11 48		11 51			12 05
	d		11 37		11 48		11 51			12 07
Merstham	d		11 41							→
Coulsdon South	d		11 46				11 58			
Purley 4	d		11 49				12 02			
East Croydon (tram)	a	11 52	11 54		11 59	12 02	12 07		12 08	
	d	11 53	11 55		12 00	12 02	12 08		12 08	
Norwood Junction 2	a		11 59				12 12			
New Cross Gate	d		12 07							
London Bridge 4 ⊖	a		12 13			12 15	12 25			
London Blackfriars 3 ⊖	a					12 22				
City Thameslink 3	a					12 26				
Farringdon 3 ⊖	a					12 29				
St Pancras International 15 ⊖	a					12 33				
St Albans City	a					12 55				
Luton Airport Parkway 4 ✈	a					13 06				
Luton 7	a					13 09				
Bedford 10	a					13 35				
Clapham Junction 10	a	12 02			12 09				12 17	
London Victoria 15 ⊖	a	12 10			12 18			12 20	12 24	

Station		SN 1	SN 1	FC 1	SN 1 (trolley)	SN 1	GW 1	SN 1 (trolley)	SN 1	FC 1	SN 1	GW 1	SN 1 (trolley)	SN 1
Brighton 10	d			11 34	11 49					11 37				
Hove 2	d	11 21												
Preston Park	d									11 41				
Hassocks 4	d									11 47				
Burgess Hill 4	d									11 51				
Lewes 4	d		11 20											
Wivelsfield 4	d		11 35							11 53				
Haywards Heath 3	a	11 35	11 42	11 47						11 58				
	d	11 44		11 48						12 01				
Balcombe	d													
Horsham 4	d								11 50					12 00
Littlehaven	d													12 03
Faygate	d													
Ifield	d													12 10
Crawley	d								11 59					12 13
Three Bridges 4	a			11 56					12 02	12 11				12 17
	d			11 57					12 03	12 12				12 18
Gatwick Airport 10 ✈	a	11 55		12 01					12 07	12 16				12 22
	d	11 56		12 02			12 03	12 05	12 08	12 17			12 20	12 23
Horley 4	d													12 26
Salfords	d													12 30
Earlswood (Surrey)	d													12 33
Tonbridge 4	d													
Leigh (Kent)	d													
Penshurst	d													
Edenbridge	d													
Godstone	d													
Nutfield	d													
Reigate	d					←					12 14	12 19		
Redhill 5	a					12 05	12 10		12 16		12 18	12 25		12 36
	d					12 07			12 16		12 19			12 37
Merstham	d					12 11					12 23			→
Coulsdon South	d					12 16					12 28			
Purley 4	d					12 19					12 32			
East Croydon (tram)	a	12 11		12 16	12 22	12 24			12 27	12 31	12 37			
	d	12 12		12 17	12 23	12 25			12 28	12 32	12 38			
Norwood Junction 2	a					12 29					12 42			
New Cross Gate	d					12 37								
London Bridge 4 ⊖	a			12 30		12 43				12 45	12 55			
London Blackfriars 3 ⊖	a			12 37						12 52				
City Thameslink 3	a			12 40						12 56				
Farringdon 3 ⊖	a			12 44						12 59				
St Pancras International 15 ⊖	a			12 48						13 03				
St Albans City	a			13 09						13 25				
Luton Airport Parkway 4 ✈	a			13 20						13 37				
Luton 7	a			13 23						13 40				
Bedford 10	a			13 49						14 05				
Clapham Junction 10	a	12 21			12 32				12 37					
London Victoria 15 ⊖	a	12 28			12 40			12 35	12 44				12 50	

Table 186R

Mondays to Fridays

Brighton - London and Bedford

9 December to 16 May

Network Diagram - see first Page of Table 175

		SN 1	SN 1	FC 1	SN 1 🛒	SN 1 🛒	SN 1	GW 1	SN 1	FC 1	SN 1	SN 1 🛒	SN 1	SN 1	SN 1	SN 1
Brighton 10	d			12 04		12 19				12 07			12 25			
Hove 2	d		11 51												12 21	
Preston Park	d		11 55							12 11						
Hassocks 4	d									12 17			12 34			
Burgess Hill 4	d		12 04							12 21			12 38			
Lewes 4	d	11 50														12 20
Wivelsfield 4	d									12 23						12 35
Haywards Heath 3	a	12 05	12 11	12 17						12 28					12 35	12 42
	d	12 13		12 18						12 31					12 44	
Balcombe	d									12 37						
Horsham 4	d								12 20					12 30		
Littlehaven	d													12 33		
Faygate	d													12 37		
Ifield	d													12 41		
Crawley	d								12 29					12 44		
Three Bridges 4	a			12 26					12 32	12 42				12 47		
	d			12 27					12 33	12 42				12 48		
Gatwick Airport 10 ✈	a	12 24		12 31					12 37	12 46			12 52	12 52	12 55	
	d	12 25		12 32	12 35				12 38	12 47		12 50	12 53	12 53	12 56	
Horley 4	d								12 41					12 56		
Salfords	d															
Earlswood (Surrey)	d													13 01		
Tonbridge 4	d										12 19					
Leigh (Kent)	d										12 23					
Penshurst	d										12 27					
Edenbridge	d										12 33					
Godstone	d										12 40					
Nutfield	d										12 45					
Reigate	d						←	12 34								
Redhill 5	a						12 36	12 38	12 48		12 51			13 05		
	d						12 37		12 48		12 51			13 07		
Merstham	d						12 41							↦		
Coulsdon South	d						12 46				12 58					
Purley 4	d						12 49				13 02					
East Croydon 🚊	a	12 40		12 46		12 52	12 54		12 59	13 02	13 07		13 08		13 11	
	d	12 40		12 47		12 53	12 55		13 00	13 02	13 08		13 08		13 11	
Norwood Junction 2	a						13 00				13 12					
New Cross Gate	d						13 07									
London Bridge 4 ⊖	a			13 00			13 14			13 15	13 25					
London Blackfriars 3 ⊖	a			13 07						13 22						
City Thameslink 3	a			13 10						13 26						
Farringdon 3 ⊖	a			13 14						13 29						
St Pancras International 15 ⊖	a			13 18						13 33						
St Albans City	a			13 39						13 55						
Luton Airport Parkway 4 ✈	a			13 50						14 07						
Luton 7	a			13 53						14 10						
Bedford 10	a			14 19						14 35						
Clapham Junction 10	a	12 49				13 02			13 09				13 17		13 20	
London Victoria 15 ⊖	a	12 56			13 05	13 10			13 16			13 20	13 24		13 27	

		FC 1	SN 1 🛒	SN 1	GW 1	SN 1 🛒	SN 1	FC 1	SN 1	GW 1	SN 1 🛒	SN 1	SN 1	SN 1	FC 1	SN 1 🛒	SN 1 🛒	SN 1	GW 1	SN 1	FC 1	SN 1
Brighton 10	d	12 34	12 49					12 37							13 04		13 19				13 07	
Hove 2	d													12 51								
Preston Park	d							12 41						12 55							13 11	
Hassocks 4	d							12 47													13 17	
Burgess Hill 4	d							12 51						13 04							13 21	
Lewes 4	d												12 50									
Wivelsfield 4	d							12 53													13 23	
Haywards Heath 3	a	12 47						12 58					13 05	13 11	13 17						13 28	
	d	12 48						13 01					13 13		13 18						13 31	
Balcombe	d																				13 37	
Horsham 4	d						12 50					13 00								13 20		
Littlehaven	d											13 03										
Faygate	d																					
Ifield	d											13 09										
Crawley	d						12 59					13 13								13 29		
Three Bridges 4	a	12 56					13 02	13 11				13 16			13 26					13 32	13 42	
	d	12 57					13 03	13 12				13 18			13 27					13 33	13 42	
Gatwick Airport 10 ✈	a	13 01					13 07	13 16				13 22	13 24		13 31					13 37	13 46	
	d	13 02			13 03	13 05	13 08	13 17			13 20	13 23	13 25		13 32	13 35				13 38	13 47	
Horley 4	d											13 26								13 41		
Salfords	d											13 30										
Earlswood (Surrey)	d											13 33										
Tonbridge 4	d																					13 19
Leigh (Kent)	d																					13 23
Penshurst	d																					13 27
Edenbridge	d																					13 33
Godstone	d																					13 40
Nutfield	d																					13 45
Reigate	d			←					13 14	13 19								←	13 34			
Redhill 5	a			13 05	13 10		13 16		13 18	13 25		13 36						13 36	13 38	13 48		13 51
	d			13 07			13 16		13 19			13 37						13 37		13 48		13 51
Merstham	d			13 11					13 23			↦						13 41				
Coulsdon South	d			13 16					13 28									13 46				13 58
Purley 4	d			13 19					13 32									13 49				14 02
East Croydon 🚊	a	13 16	13 22	13 24			13 28	13 31	13 37				13 40		13 46		13 52	13 54		13 59	14 02	14 07
	d	13 17	13 23	13 25			13 28	13 32	13 38				13 40		13 47		13 53	13 55		14 00	14 02	14 08
Norwood Junction 2	a			13 29					13 42									13 59				14 12
New Cross Gate	d			13 37														14 07				
London Bridge 4 ⊖	a	13 30		13 43				13 45	13 55						14 00			14 13			14 15	14 25
London Blackfriars 3 ⊖	a	13 37						13 52							14 07						14 22	
City Thameslink 3	a	13 40						13 56							14 10						14 26	
Farringdon 3 ⊖	a	13 44						13 59							14 14						14 29	
St Pancras International 15 ⊖	a	13 48						14 03							14 18						14 33	
St Albans City	a	14 09						14 25							14 39						14 55	
Luton Airport Parkway 4 ✈	a	14 20						14 37							14 50						15 07	
Luton 7	a	14 23						14 40							14 53						15 10	
Bedford 10	a	14 49						15 05							15 19						15 35	
Clapham Junction 10	a		13 32				13 37						13 50				14 02			14 09		
London Victoria 15 ⊖	a		13 40			13 35	13 44				13 50		13 57			14 05	14 10			14 16		

Table 186R

Mondays to Fridays

9 December to 16 May

Brighton - London and Bedford

Network Diagram - see first Page of Table 175

		SN 1 trolley	SN 1	SN 1	SN 1	SN 1	FC 1	SN 1 trolley	SN 1	GW 1	SN 1 trolley	SN 1	FC 1	SN 1	GW 1	SN 1 trolley
Brighton 10	d		13 25				13 34	13 49					13 37			
Hove 2	d				13 21											
Preston Park	d												13 41			
Hassocks 4	d		13 34										13 47			
Burgess Hill 4	d		13 38										13 51			
Lewes 4	d					13 20										
Wivelsfield 4	d					13 35							13 53			
Haywards Heath 3	a				13 35	13 42	13 47						13 58			
	d				13 44		13 48						14 01			
Balcombe	d															
Horsham 4	d			13 30								13 50				
Littlehaven	d			13 33												
Faygate	d															
Ifield	d			13 39												
Crawley	d			13 43								13 59				
Three Bridges 4	a			13 46			13 56					14 02	14 11			
	d			13 48			13 57					14 03	14 12			
Gatwick Airport 10 ✈	a		13 52	13 52	13 55		14 01					14 07	14 16			
	d	13 50	13 53	13 53	13 56		14 02			14 03	14 05	14 08	14 17			14 20
Horley 4	d			13 56												
Salfords	d															
Earlswood (Surrey)	d			14 01												
Tonbridge 4	d															
Leigh (Kent)	d															
Penshurst	d															
Edenbridge	d															
Godstone	d															
Nutfield	d															
Reigate	d								←					14 14	14 19	
Redhill 5	a			14 05					14 05	14 10		14 16		14 18	14 25	
	d			14 07					14 07			14 16		14 19		
Merstham	d			→					14 11					14 23		
Coulsdon South	d								14 16					14 28		
Purley 4	d								14 19					14 32		
East Croydon ⛴	a		14 08		14 11		14 16	14 22	14 24			14 27	14 31	14 37		
	d		14 08		14 11		14 17	14 23	14 25			14 28	14 32	14 38		
Norwood Junction 2	a								14 29					14 42		
New Cross Gate	d								14 37							
London Bridge 4 ⊖	a						14 30		14 43				14 45	14 55		
London Blackfriars 3 ⊖	a						14 37						14 52			
City Thameslink 3	a						14 40						14 56			
Farringdon 3 ⊖	a						14 44						14 59			
St Pancras International 15 ⊖	a						14 48						15 03			
St Albans City	a						15 09						15 25			
Luton Airport Parkway 4 ✈	a						15 20						15 37			
Luton 7	a						15 23						15 40			
Bedford 10	a						15 49						16 05			
Clapham Junction 10	a		14 17		14 20			14 32				14 37				
London Victoria 15 ⊖	a	14 20	14 24		14 28			14 40			14 35	14 44				14 50

		SN 1	SN 1	SN 1	FC 1	SN 1 trolley	SN 1 trolley	SN 1	GW 1	SN 1	FC 1	SN 1	SN 1 trolley	SN 1	SN 1	SN 1	SN 1	FC 1	SN 1 trolley	SN 1	GW 1	SN 1 trolley
Brighton 10	d				14 04		14 19				14 07			14 25				14 34	14 49			
Hove 2	d			13 51												14 21						
Preston Park	d			13 55							14 11											
Hassocks 4	d										14 17			14 34								
Burgess Hill 4	d			14 04							14 21			14 38								
Lewes 4	d		13 50														14 20					
Wivelsfield 4	d										14 23						14 35					
Haywards Heath 3	a		14 05	14 11	14 17						14 28					14 35	14 42	14 47				
	d		14 13		14 18						14 31					14 44		14 48				
Balcombe	d										14 37											
Horsham 4	d	14 00								14 20					14 30							
Littlehaven	d	14 03													14 33							
Faygate	d																					
Ifield	d	14 09													14 39							
Crawley	d	14 13								14 29					14 43							
Three Bridges 4	a	14 16			14 26					14 32	14 42				14 46			14 56				
	d	14 18			14 27					14 33	14 42				14 48			14 57				
Gatwick Airport 10 ✈	a	14 22	14 24		14 31					14 37	14 46			14 52	14 52	14 55		15 01				
	d	14 23	14 25		14 32	14 35				14 38	14 47		14 50	14 53	14 53	14 56		15 02			15 03	15 05
Horley 4	d	14 26								14 41					14 56							
Salfords	d	14 30																				
Earlswood (Surrey)	d	14 33													15 01							
Tonbridge 4	d											14 19										
Leigh (Kent)	d											14 23										
Penshurst	d											14 27										
Edenbridge	d											14 33										
Godstone	d											14 40										
Nutfield	d											14 45										
Reigate	d							←	14 34											←		
Redhill 5	a	14 36						14 36	14 38	14 48		14 51			15 05					15 05	15 10	
	d	14 37						14 37		14 48		14 51			15 07					15 07		
Merstham	d	→						14 41							→					15 11		
Coulsdon South	d							14 46				14 58								15 16		
Purley 4	d							14 49				15 02								15 19		
East Croydon ⛴	a		14 40		14 46		14 52	14 54		14 59	15 02	15 07		15 08		15 11		15 16	15 22	15 24		
	d		14 40		14 47		14 53	14 55		15 00	15 02	15 08		15 08		15 11		15 17	15 23	15 25		
Norwood Junction 2	a							14 59				15 12								15 29		
New Cross Gate	d							15 07												15 37		
London Bridge 4 ⊖	a				15 00			15 13			15 15	15 25						15 30		15 43		
London Blackfriars 3 ⊖	a				15 07						15 22							15 37				
City Thameslink 3	a				15 10						15 26							15 40				
Farringdon 3 ⊖	a				15 14						15 29							15 44				
St Pancras International 15 ⊖	a				15 18						15 33							15 48				
St Albans City	a				15 39						15 55							16 09				
Luton Airport Parkway 4 ✈	a				15 50						16 06							16 20				
Luton 7	a				15 53						16 09							16 23				
Bedford 10	a				16 19						16 35							16 49				
Clapham Junction 10	a		14 49				15 02			15 09				15 17		15 20			15 32			
London Victoria 15 ⊖	a		14 57			15 05	15 10			15 20			15 20	15 24		15 27			15 40			15 35

Table 186R

Brighton - London and Bedford

Mondays to Fridays

9 December to 16 May

Network Diagram - see first Page of Table 175

Station		SN 1	FC 1	SN 1	GW 1	SN 1 (trolley)	SN 1	SN 1 (trolley)	SN 1 A (trolley)	FC 1	SN 1 (trolley)	SN 1 (trolley)	SN 1	GW 1	SN 1	FC 1
Brighton 10	d		14 37							15 04		15 19				15 07
Hove 2	d								14 51							
Preston Park	d		14 41						14 55							15 11
Hassocks 4	d		14 47													15 17
Burgess Hill 4	d		14 51						15 04							15 21
Lewes 4	d							14 50								
Wivelsfield 4	d		14 53													15 23
Haywards Heath 3	a		14 58					15 05	15 11	15 17						15 28
	d		15 01					15 13		15 18						15 31
Balcombe	d															15 37
Horsham 4	d	14 50					15 00								15 20	
Littlehaven	d						15 03									
Faygate	d															
Ifield	d						15 09									
Crawley	d	14 59					15 13								15 29	
Three Bridges 4	a	15 02	15 11				15 16			15 26					15 32	15 42
	d	15 03	15 12				15 18			15 27					15 33	15 42
Gatwick Airport 10 ✈	a	15 07	15 16				15 22	15 24		15 31					15 37	15 46
	d	15 08	15 17			15 20	15 23	15 25		15 32	15 35				15 38	15 47
Horley 4	d						15 26								15 41	
Salfords	d						15 30									
Earlswood (Surrey)	d						15 33									
Tonbridge 4	d															
Leigh (Kent)	d															
Penshurst	d															
Edenbridge	d															
Godstone	d															
Nutfield	d															
Reigate	d			15 14	15 19								←	15 34		
Redhill 5	a	15 16		15 18	15 25		15 36						15 36	15 38	15 48	
	d	15 16		15 19			15 37						15 37		15 48	
Merstham	d			15 23			→						15 41			
Coulsdon South	d			15 28									15 46			
Purley 4	d			15 32									15 49			
East Croydon 🚊	a	15 28	15 31	15 37				15 40		15 46		15 52	15 54		15 59	16 02
	d	15 28	15 32	15 38				15 40		15 47		15 53	15 55		16 00	16 02
Norwood Junction 2	a			15 42									15 59			
New Cross Gate	d												16 07			
London Bridge 4 ⊖	a		15 45	15 55						16 00			16 13			16 15
London Blackfriars 3 ⊖	a		15 52							16 07						16 25
City Thameslink 3	a		15 56							16 10						16 28
Farringdon 3 ⊖	a		15 59							16 13						16 31
St Pancras International 15 ⊖	a		16 03							16 17						16 35
St Albans City	a		16 25							16 38						16 56
Luton Airport Parkway 4 ✈	a		16 37							16 52						17 08
Luton 7	a		16 40							16 55						17 11
Bedford 10	a		17 05							17 20						17 38
Clapham Junction 10	a	15 37						15 49				16 02			16 09	
London Victoria 15 ⊖	a	15 46				15 50		15 57			16 05	16 10			16 16	

Station		SN 1	SN 1 (trolley)	SN 1	SN 1	SN 1 A (trolley)	SN 1 (trolley)	FC 1	SN 1	GW 1	SN 1 (trolley)	SN 1 (trolley)	SN 1	FC 1	SN 1	SN 1 (trolley)	SN 1	SN 1	GW 1	SN 1	SN 1 (trolley)	SN 1 A (trolley)
Brighton 10	d			15 25				15 34				15 49		15 37			15 55					
Hove 2	d					15 21																15 52
Preston Park	d													15 41								15 56
Hassocks 4	d			15 34										15 47			16 06					
Burgess Hill 4	d			15 38										15 51								16 05
Lewes 4	d						15 19														15 50	
Wivelsfield 4	d						15 35							15 53								
Haywards Heath 3	a					15 35	15 42	15 47						15 57							16 05	16 12
	d					15 44		15 48						15 58							16 14	
Balcombe	d																					
Horsham 4	d				15 30								15 50							16 00		
Littlehaven	d				15 33															16 03		
Faygate	d																					
Ifield	d				15 39															16 09		
Crawley	d				15 43								15 59							16 13		
Three Bridges 4	a				15 46			15 56					16 02	16 06						16 16		
	d				15 48			15 57					16 03	16 07						16 18		
Gatwick Airport 10 ✈	a			15 52	15 52	15 55		16 01					16 07	16 11			16 22			16 22	16 25	
	d		15 50	15 53	15 53	15 56		16 02		16 03	16 05		16 08	16 12		16 20	16 23			16 23	16 26	
Horley 4	d				15 56															16 26		
Salfords	d																			16 30		
Earlswood (Surrey)	d				16 01															16 33		
Tonbridge 4	d	15 19																				
Leigh (Kent)	d	15 23																				
Penshurst	d	15 27																				
Edenbridge	d	15 33																				
Godstone	d	15 40																				
Nutfield	d	15 45																				
Reigate	d								←						←			16 14	16 21			
Redhill 5	a	15 51			16 05				16 05	16 10			16 17		16 17			16 18	16 27	16 36		
	d	15 51			16 06				16 06				16 18		16 18			16 21		16 37		
Merstham	d				→				16 10				→					16 25		→		
Coulsdon South	d	15 58							16 15									16 30				
Purley 4	d	16 02							16 18									16 34				
East Croydon 🚊	a	16 07		16 08		16 11		16 16	16 23			16 24		16 27	16 29		16 38	16 39			16 41	
	d	16 08		16 08		16 11		16 17	16 24			16 24		16 28	16 30		16 38	16 40			16 41	
Norwood Junction 2	a	16 12							16 28									16 46				
New Cross Gate	d								16 36													
London Bridge 4 ⊖	a	16 25							16 43									17 00				
London Blackfriars 3 ⊖	a							16 48						16 55								
City Thameslink 3	a							16 54						16 58								
Farringdon 3 ⊖	a							16 57						17 01								
St Pancras International 15 ⊖	a							17 01						17 05								
St Albans City	a							17 19						17 25								
Luton Airport Parkway 4 ✈	a													17 38								
Luton 7	a							17 32						17 41								
Bedford 10	a							17 53						18 06								
Clapham Junction 10	a			16 17		16 20						16 33			16 39		16 47				16 50	
London Victoria 15 ⊖	a		16 22	16 24		16 28					16 35	16 42			16 46	16 52	16 56				16 58	

A (trolley) from Haywards Heath

Table 186R

Mondays to Fridays

9 December to 16 May

Brighton - London and Bedford

Network Diagram - see first Page of Table 175

		FC 1	SN 1	SN 1	SN 1	GW 1	SN 1	FC 1	SN 1	SN 1	SN 1	SN 1	SN 1	FC 1	SN 1	SN 1
			🛒	🛒						🛒			🛒			🛒
Brighton 10	d	16 04		16 19				16 07						16 24		
Hove 2	d											16 21				
Preston Park	d							16 11								
Hassocks 4	d							16 17								
Burgess Hill 4	d							16 21								
Lewes 4	d												16 20			
Wivelsfield 4	d												16 38			←
Haywards Heath 3	a	16 17						16 26				16 35	16 44	16 38		16 35
	d	16 18						16 26				16 46		16 38		16 46
Balcombe	d							16 32				→				
Horsham 4	d						16 20								16 30	
Littlehaven	d														16 33	
Faygate	d														16 37	
Ifield	d														16 41	
Crawley	d						16 29								16 44	
Three Bridges 4	a	16 26					16 32	16 37						16 47	16 47	
	d	16 27					16 33	16 37						16 47	16 48	
Gatwick Airport 10 ✈	a	16 31					16 37	16 41						16 52	16 52	16 57
	d	16 32	16 35				16 38	16 42		16 50				16 53	16 53	16 58
Horley 4	d														16 56	
Salfords	d														17 00	
Earlswood (Surrey)	d														17 03	
Tonbridge 4	d										16 19					
Leigh (Kent)	d										16 23					
Penshurst	d										16 27					
Edenbridge	d										16 33					
Godstone	d										16 40					
Nutfield	d										16 45					
Reigate	d				←	16 38			←							
Redhill 5	a				16 36	16 42	16 46		16 46		16 50				17 06	
	d				16 37		16 47		16 47		16 51				17 07	
Merstham	d				16 41		→								→	
Coulsdon South	d				16 46						16 58					
Purley 4	d				16 49						17 02					
East Croydon	a	16 46		16 54	16 54			16 57	17 01		17 07			17 08		17 12
	d	16 47		16 54	16 55			16 58	17 01		17 07			17 09		17 13
Norwood Junction 2	a				17 01											
New Cross Gate	d				17 08											
London Bridge 4 ⊖	a				17 14									17 27		
London Blackfriars 3 ⊖	a	17 19						17 25						17 35		
City Thameslink 3	a	17 24						17 28						17 38		
Farringdon 3 ⊖	a	17 27						17 31						17 41		
St Pancras International 15 ⊖	a	17 31						17 35						17 45		
St Albans City	a	17 49						17 55						18 06		
Luton Airport Parkway 4 ✈	a							18 08						18 20		
Luton 7	a	18 02						18 11						18 23		
Bedford 10	a	18 23						18 36						18 48		
Clapham Junction 10	a			17 03					17 10		17 18					17 23
London Victoria 15 ⊖	a		17 05	17 12					17 17	17 20	17 26					17 30

		GW 1	SN 1	FC 1	SN 1	SN 1	SN 1	SN 1	SN 1	SN 1	GW 1	SN 1	SN 1	SN 1	SN 1	FC 1	SN 1	SN 1	SN 1	SN 1	FC 1	GW 1
														A								
			🛒			🛒		🛒					🛒	🛒			🛒			🛒		
Brighton 10	d			16 30		16 49									16 55	17 03				17 19	17 07	
Hove 2	d													16 51								
Preston Park	d			16 34											16 58						17 11	
Hassocks 4	d			16 40											17 05						17 17	
Burgess Hill 4	d			16 44										17 02	17 08	17 13					17 21	
Lewes 4	d												16 50									
Wivelsfield 4	d			16 46											17 11			←				
Haywards Heath 3	a			16 50									17 06	17 12	17 15	17 18		17 15			17 26	
	d			16 51									17 14		17 21	17 18		17 21			17 26	
Balcombe	d			16 56											→			17 26				
Horsham 4	d						16 52					17 00										
Littlehaven	d											17 03										
Faygate	d											17 07										
Ifield	d											17 11										
Crawley	d						17 01					17 14										
Three Bridges 4	a			17 02			17 04					17 17				17 27		17 32				
	d			17 02			17 05					17 18				17 27		17 32				
Gatwick Airport 10 ✈	a			17 07			17 09					17 22	17 25			17 31		17 36			17 38	
	d	17 03	17 05	17 08			17 10	17 20				17 23	17 26			17 32	17 35	17 38			17 39	
Horley 4	d											17 26										
Salfords	d											17 30										
Earlswood (Surrey)	d											17 33										
Tonbridge 4	d								16 42													
Leigh (Kent)	d								16 46													
Penshurst	d								16 50													
Edenbridge	d								16 56													
Godstone	d								17 03													
Nutfield	d								17 08													
Reigate	d				←					17 12	17 26								←			17 34
Redhill 5	a	17 10			17 06		17 18		17 13	17 19	17 32	17 36							17 36			17 38
	d				17 07		17 18		17 21			17 37							17 37			
Merstham	d				17 11				17 25			→							17 41			
Coulsdon South	d				17 16				17 30										17 46			
Purley 4	d				17 19														17 49			
East Croydon	a			17 22	17 24	17 25	17 29		17 38				17 41			17 46		17 53	17 54	17 56	17 57	
	d			17 23	17 25	17 25	17 30		17 39				17 42			17 47		17 53	17 55	17 57	17 58	
Norwood Junction 2	a				17 30														17 59			
New Cross Gate	d				17 38														18 07			
London Bridge 4 ⊖	a				17 49											18 13			18 15			
London Blackfriars 3 ⊖	a			17 49												18 21					18 25	
City Thameslink 3	a			17 54												18 24					18 28	
Farringdon 3 ⊖	a			17 57												18 27					18 31	
St Pancras International 15 ⊖	a			18 01												18 31					18 35	
St Albans City	a			18 19												18 49					18 57	
Luton Airport Parkway 4 ✈	a																				19 09	
Luton 7	a			18 32												19 02					19 12	
Bedford 10	a			18 55												19 23					19 38	
Clapham Junction 10	a					17 34	17 39		17 48				17 51					18 02		18 06		
London Victoria 15 ⊖	a		17 37			17 42	17 46	17 52	17 56				17 58				18 07	18 09		18 14		

A 🛒 from Haywards Heath

Table 186R

Mondays to Fridays

Brighton - London and Bedford

9 December to 16 May

Network Diagram - see first Page of Table 175

Station		SN 1	SN 1 T	SN 1	SN 1	SN 1	SN 1 A T	SN 1 T
Brighton [10]	d							
Hove [2]	d						17 21	
Preston Park	d							
Hassocks [4]	d							
Burgess Hill [4]	d							
Lewes [4]	d							17 19
Wivelsfield [4]	d							17 35
Haywards Heath [3]	a						17 35	17 41
	d						17 43 (combined)	
Balcombe	d							
Horsham [4]	d	17 22				17 30		
Littlehaven	d					17 33		
Faygate	d					17 37		
Ifield	d					17 41		
Crawley	d	17 31				17 44		
Three Bridges [4]	a	17 34				17 47		
	d	17 36				17 48		
Gatwick Airport [10]	a	17 41				17 52	17 54	
	d	17 42	17 50			17 53	17 55	
Horley [4]	d					17 56		
Salfords	d					18 00		
Earlswood (Surrey)	d					18 03		
Tonbridge [4]	d				17 21			
Leigh (Kent)	d				17 25			
Penshurst	d				17 29			
Edenbridge	d				17 35			
Godstone	d				17 42			
Nutfield	d				17 47			
Reigate	d			17 44				
Redhill [5]	a	17 49		17 48	17 53	18 06		
	d	17 50		17 57 (combined)		18 07		
Merstham	d					→		
Coulsdon South	d							
Purley [4]	d							
East Croydon	a	18 02		18 08			18 11	
	d	18 02		18 09			18 12	
Norwood Junction [2]	a							
New Cross Gate	d							
London Bridge [4] ⊖	a							
London Blackfriars [3] ⊖	a							
City Thameslink [3]	a							
Farringdon [3] ⊖	a							
St Pancras International [15] ⊖	a							
St Albans City	a							
Luton Airport Parkway [4] ✈	a							
Luton [7]	a							
Bedford [10]	a							
Clapham Junction [10]	a	18 12		18 18			18 21	
London Victoria [15] ⊖	a	18 20	18 22	18 26			18 29	

Station		FC 1	SN 1	SN 1 T	SN 1	GW 1	SN 1 T	SN 1	FC 1	SN 1 T
Brighton [10]	d	17 24		17 49					17 37	
Hove [2]	d									
Preston Park	d	17 28							17 41	
Hassocks [4]	d	17 34							17 47	
Burgess Hill [4]	d	17 38							17 51	
Lewes [4]	d									
Wivelsfield [4]	d	17 40							17 53	
Haywards Heath [3]	a	17 45							17 58	
	d	17 46							18 01	
Balcombe	d								18 07	
Horsham [4]	d							17 52		
Littlehaven	d									
Faygate	d									
Ifield	d									
Crawley	d							18 01		
Three Bridges [4]	a	17 54						18 04	18 12	
	d	17 55						18 05	18 12	
Gatwick Airport [10]	a	17 59						18 09	18 16	
	d	18 00				18 03	18 05	18 10	18 17	18 20
Horley [4]	d									
Salfords	d									
Earlswood (Surrey)	d									
Tonbridge [4]	d									
Leigh (Kent)	d									
Penshurst	d									
Edenbridge	d									
Godstone	d									
Nutfield	d									
Reigate	d		←		←					
Redhill [5]	a		18 06		18 06	18 10		18 18		
	d		18 07		18 07			18 18		
Merstham	d		→		18 11					
Coulsdon South	d				18 16					
Purley [4]	d				18 19					
East Croydon	a	18 15		18 25	18 24			18 30	18 32	
	d	18 16		18 25	18 27			18 31	18 32	
Norwood Junction [2]	a									
New Cross Gate	d									
London Bridge [4] ⊖	a								18 46	
London Blackfriars [3] ⊖	a	18 51							18 55	
City Thameslink [3]	a	18 54							18 58	
Farringdon [3] ⊖	a	18 57							19 01	
St Pancras International [15] ⊖	a	19 01							19 05	
St Albans City	a	19 19							19 28	
Luton Airport Parkway [4] ✈	a								19 39	
Luton [7]	a	19 31							19 42	
Bedford [10]	a	19 55							20 08	
Clapham Junction [10]	a			18 34	18 37			18 40		
London Victoria [15] ⊖	a			18 42	18 44		18 37	18 47		18 50

Station		SN 1	SN 1	GW 1	SN 1	SN 1 T	SN 1 A T	SN 1	FC 1	SN 1 T
Brighton [10]	d							17 55	18 03	
Hove [2]	d						17 51			
Preston Park	d							17 59		
Hassocks [4]	d						18 00	18 05		
Burgess Hill [4]	d						18 04	18 09	18 13	
Lewes [4]	d					17 50				
Wivelsfield [4]	d							18 11		
Haywards Heath [3]	a					18 07	18 13	18 16	18 18	
	d					18 15 (combined)		18 22	18 18	
Balcombe	d							→		
Horsham [4]	d				18 00					
Littlehaven	d				18 03					
Faygate	d				18 07					
Ifield	d				18 11					
Crawley	d				18 14					
Three Bridges [4]	a				18 17				18 27	
	d				18 18				18 27	
Gatwick Airport [10]	a				18 22	18 26			18 31	
	d				18 23	18 27			18 32	18 35
Horley [4]	d				18 26					
Salfords	d				18 30					
Earlswood (Surrey)	d				18 33					
Tonbridge [4]	d		17 49							
Leigh (Kent)	d		17 53							
Penshurst	d		17 57							
Edenbridge	d		18 03							
Godstone	d		18 10							
Nutfield	d		18 15							
Reigate	d	18 14		18 26						
Redhill [5]	a	18 19	18 21	18 32	18 36					
	d	18 24			18 37					
Merstham	d	18 28			→					
Coulsdon South	d	18 33								
Purley [4]	d									
East Croydon	a	18 39				18 42			18 47	
	d	18 40				18 43			18 47	
Norwood Junction [2]	a									
New Cross Gate	d									
London Bridge [4] ⊖	a								19 00	
London Blackfriars [3] ⊖	a								19 09	
City Thameslink [3]	a								19 12	
Farringdon [3] ⊖	a								19 15	
St Pancras International [15] ⊖	a								19 19	
St Albans City	a								19 45	
Luton Airport Parkway [4] ✈	a								19 57	
Luton [7]	a								20 00	
Bedford [10]	a								20 26	
Clapham Junction [10]	a	18 49				18 52				
London Victoria [15] ⊖	a	18 56				18 59				19 05

Station		SN 1	SN 1	SN 1	SN 1	GW 1	SN 1	FC 1	SN 1	SN 1 T	SN 1
Brighton [10]	d			18 19				18 07			
Hove [2]	d										
Preston Park	d							18 11			
Hassocks [4]	d							18 17			
Burgess Hill [4]	d							18 21			
Lewes [4]	d										
Wivelsfield [4]	d	←						18 23			
Haywards Heath [3]	a	18 16						18 28			
	d	18 22						18 31			
Balcombe	d							18 37			
Horsham [4]	d						18 22				18 30
Littlehaven	d										18 33
Faygate	d										18 37
Ifield	d										18 41
Crawley	d						18 31				18 44
Three Bridges [4]	a	18 31					18 34	18 42			18 47
	d	18 31					18 35	18 42			18 48
Gatwick Airport [10]	a	18 36					18 39	18 46			18 52
	d	18 38					18 40	18 47		18 50	18 53
Horley [4]	d										18 56
Salfords	d										19 00
Earlswood (Surrey)	d										19 03
Tonbridge [4]	d								18 23		
Leigh (Kent)	d								18 27		
Penshurst	d								18 31		
Edenbridge	d								18 37		
Godstone	d								18 44		
Nutfield	d								18 49		
Reigate	d		←		18 38	18 42					
Redhill [5]	a		18 36		18 42	18 47	18 48		18 54		19 06
	d		18 37				18 48		18 57		19 07
Merstham	d		18 41								→
Coulsdon South	d		18 46								
Purley [4]	d		18 49								
East Croydon	a	18 53	18 54	18 56			18 59	19 02	19 09		
	d	18 53	18 55	18 57			19 00	19 02	19 10		
Norwood Junction [2]	a								19 13		
New Cross Gate	d										
London Bridge [4] ⊖	a							19 15	19 25		
London Blackfriars [3] ⊖	a							19 22			
City Thameslink [3]	a							19 26			
Farringdon [3] ⊖	a							19 29			
St Pancras International [15] ⊖	a							19 33			
St Albans City	a							19 55			
Luton Airport Parkway [4] ✈	a							20 06			
Luton [7]	a							20 09			
Bedford [10]	a							20 35			
Clapham Junction [10]	a	19 02	19 05	19 08			19 11				
London Victoria [15] ⊖	a	19 09	19 13	19 15			19 18			19 20	

A T from Haywards Heath

Table 186R

Mondays to Fridays

9 December to 16 May

Brighton - London and Bedford

Network Diagram - see first Page of Table 175

		SN	SN	FC	SN	SN	SN	SN	SN	GW	FC	SN	SN
		1	1	1	1	1	1	1	1	1	1	1	1
		🛒	A 🛒		🛒							🛒	
Brighton 10	d			18 34		18 49					18 37		
Hove 2	d		18 21										
Preston Park	d										18 41		
Hassocks 4	d										18 47		
Burgess Hill 4	d		18 34								18 51		
Lewes 4	d	18 18											
Wivelsfield 4	d	18 34									18 53		
Haywards Heath 3	a	18 38	18 43	18 47							18 58		
	d		18 45	18 48							19 01		
Balcombe	d												
Horsham 4	d								18 52				
Littlehaven	d												
Faygate	d												
Ifield	d												
Crawley	d								19 01				
Three Bridges 4	a			18 56					19 04		19 11		
	d			18 57					19 05		19 12		
Gatwick Airport 10 ✈	a		18 56	19 01					19 09		19 16		
	d		18 57	19 02	19 05				19 10	19 13	19 17	19 20	
Horley 4	d												
Salfords	d												
Earlswood (Surrey)	d												
Tonbridge 4	d												18 51
Leigh (Kent)	d												18 55
Penshurst	d												18 59
Edenbridge	d												19 05
Godstone	d												19 12
Nutfield	d												19 17
Reigate	d						←	19 10					
Redhill 5	a						19 06	19 14	19 17	19 20			19 22
	d						19 07		19 18				19 23
Merstham	d						19 11						19 27
Coulsdon South	d						19 16						19 32
Purley 4	d						19 19						
East Croydon	a		19 12	19 16		19 23	19 26		19 29		19 31		19 39
	d		19 12	19 17		19 24	19 26		19 29		19 32		19 39
Norwood Junction 2	a												
New Cross Gate	d												
London Bridge 4 ⊖	a			19 30							19 45		
London Blackfriars 3 ⊖	a			19 37							19 52		
City Thameslink 3	a			19 40							19 56		
Farringdon 3 ⊖	a			19 44							19 59		
St Pancras International 15 ⊖	a			19 48							20 03		
St Albans City	a			20 09							20 25		
Luton Airport Parkway 4 ✈	a			20 20							20 38		
Luton 7	a			20 23							20 41		
Bedford 10	a			20 49							21 06		
Clapham Junction 10	a		19 21			19 33	19 36		19 39				19 48
London Victoria 15 ⊖	a		19 28		19 35	19 41	19 44		19 47			19 50	19 56

		SN	GW	SN	SN	SN	FC	SN	SN	SN	GW	SN	SN
		1	1	1	1	1	1	1	1	1	1	1	1
								🛒					
Brighton 10	d								19 19				
Hove 2	d				18 52								
Preston Park	d												
Hassocks 4	d												
Burgess Hill 4	d												
Lewes 4	d					18 50							
Wivelsfield 4	d					19 06							
Haywards Heath 3	a				19 07	19 10							
	d					19 14							
Balcombe	d												
Horsham 4	d			19 02									19 17
Littlehaven	d			19 05									
Faygate	d												
Ifield	d			19 11									
Crawley	d			19 14									19 26
Three Bridges 4	a			19 18									19 29
	d			19 18			19 27						
Gatwick Airport 10 ✈	a			19 23		19 25	19 31						
	d			19 24		19 26	19 32	19 35					
Horley 4	d			19 26									
Salfords	d			19 30									
Earlswood (Surrey)	d			19 34									
Tonbridge 4	d											19 10	
Leigh (Kent)	d											19 14	
Penshurst	d											19 18	
Edenbridge	d											19 24	
Godstone	d											19 31	
Nutfield	d											19 36	
Reigate	d	19 21	19 30							←	19 36		
Redhill 5	a	19 25	19 35	19 38						19 38	19 40	19 41	
	d			19 39						19 39			
Merstham	d			↪						19 43			
Coulsdon South	d									19 48			
Purley 4	d									19 53			
East Croydon	a					19 42	19 46		19 53	19 58			
	d					19 42	19 47		19 54	19 59			
Norwood Junction 2	a												
New Cross Gate	d												
London Bridge 4 ⊖	a						20 00						
London Blackfriars 3 ⊖	a						20 07						
City Thameslink 3	a						20 10						
Farringdon 3 ⊖	a						20 14						
St Pancras International 15 ⊖	a						20 18						
St Albans City	a						20 39						
Luton Airport Parkway 4 ✈	a						20 50						
Luton 7	a						20 53						
Bedford 10	a						21 19						
Clapham Junction 10	a					19 51			20 03	20 08			
London Victoria 15 ⊖	a					19 59		20 05	20 10	20 15			

		SN	FC	SN	SN	SN	SN	SN	FC	SN	SN	GW	SN
		1	1	1	1	1	1	1	1	1	1	1	1
				🛒	🛒								🛒
Brighton 10	d	18 58	19 07		19 28				19 34	19 49			
Hove 2	d					19 22							
Preston Park	d	19 03	19 11										
Hassocks 4	d	19 09	19 17										
Burgess Hill 4	d	19 13	19 21			19 32							
Lewes 4	d												
Wivelsfield 4	d	19 15	19 23										
Haywards Heath 3	a	19 20	19 28			19 37			19 47				
	d	19 21	19 31			19 44			19 48				
Balcombe	d		19 37										
Horsham 4	d							19 32					
Littlehaven	d							19 35					
Faygate	d												
Ifield	d							19 41					
Crawley	d							19 45					
Three Bridges 4	a	19 33	19 42					19 49	19 56				
	d	19 35	19 42					19 51	19 57				
Gatwick Airport 10 ✈	a	19 39	19 46		19 51	19 55		19 55	20 01				
	d	19 40	19 47	19 50	19 53	19 56		19 56	20 02			20 03	20 05
Horley 4	d							19 59					
Salfords	d												
Earlswood (Surrey)	d												
Tonbridge 4	d												
Leigh (Kent)	d												
Penshurst	d												
Edenbridge	d												
Godstone	d												
Nutfield	d												
Reigate	d						19 51				←		
Redhill 5	a	19 48					19 55	20 05			20 05	20 11	
	d	19 48						20 06			20 06		
Merstham	d							↪			20 10		
Coulsdon South	d										20 15		
Purley 4	d										20 18		
East Croydon	a	20 00	20 02		20 08	20 11			20 16	20 23	20 23		
	d	20 01	20 02		20 09	20 12			20 17	20 24	20 26		
Norwood Junction 2	a												
New Cross Gate	d												
London Bridge 4 ⊖	a		20 15						20 30				
London Blackfriars 3 ⊖	a		20 22						20 37				
City Thameslink 3	a		20 26						20 40				
Farringdon 3 ⊖	a		20 29						20 44				
St Pancras International 15 ⊖	a		20 33						20 48				
St Albans City	a		20 55						21 09				
Luton Airport Parkway 4 ✈	a		21 07						21 20				
Luton 7	a		21 10						21 23				
Bedford 10	a		21 35						21 49				
Clapham Junction 10	a	20 11			20 18	20 21				20 33	20 36		
London Victoria 15 ⊖	a	20 20		20 20	20 26	20 29				20 40	20 44		20 35

A 🛒 from Haywards Heath

Table 186R

Mondays to Fridays

Brighton - London and Bedford

9 December to 16 May

Network Diagram - see first Page of Table 175

		SN 1	FC 1	SN 1	SN 1 🚲	SN 1	SN 1	SN 1	SN 1	FC 1	SN 1 🚲	SN 1	SN 1	GW 1	SN 1	SN 1	FC 1 A	FC 1 B
Brighton 10	d		19 37						19 55	20 03		20 19					20 07	20 07
Hove 2	d						19 50											
Preston Park	d		19 41						19 58								20 11	20 11
Hassocks 4	d		19 47						20 05								20 17	20 17
Burgess Hill 4	d		19 51						20 08	20 13							20 21	20 21
Lewes 4	d							19 50										
Wivelsfield 4	d		19 53					20 04	20 11							←	20 23	20 23
Haywards Heath 3	a		19 58				20 04	20 11	20 15	20 18						20 15	20 28	20 28
	d		20 01				20 13		20 22	20 19						20 22	20 31	20 31
Balcombe	d								→								20 37	20 37
Horsham 4	d	19 52				20 02												
Littlehaven	d					20 05												
Faygate	d																	
Ifield	d					20 11												
Crawley	d	20 01				20 14												
Three Bridges 4	a	20 04	20 11			20 18				20 27						20 32	20 42	20 42
	d	20 05	20 12			20 18				20 27						20 32	20 42	20 42
Gatwick Airport 10 ✈	a	20 10	20 16			20 22	20 24			20 31						20 37	20 46	20 46
	d	20 11	20 17		20 20	20 23	20 25			20 32	20 35					20 38	20 47	20 47
Horley 4	d					20 26												
Salfords	d					20 30												
Earlswood (Surrey)	d					20 33												
Tonbridge 4	d														20 10			
Leigh (Kent)	d														20 14			
Penshurst	d														20 18			
Edenbridge	d														20 24			
Godstone	d														20 31			
Nutfield	d														20 36			
Reigate	d			20 14									←	20 34				
Redhill 5	a	20 18		20 18		20 36							20 36	20 38	20 45	20 47		
	d	20 19				20 37							20 37			20 48		
Merstham	d					→							20 41					
Coulsdon South	d												20 46					
Purley 4	d												20 49					
East Croydon	a	20 30	20 32				20 40			20 47		20 53	20 57			20 59	21 02	21 02
	d	20 30	20 32				20 40			20 47		20 54	20 57			21 00	21 02	21 02
Norwood Junction 2	a																	
New Cross Gate	d																	
London Bridge 4 ⊖	a		20 45							21 00							21 15	21 15
London Blackfriars 3 ⊖	a		20 52							21 07							21 22	21 22
City Thameslink 3	a		20 56							21 10							21 26	21 26
Farringdon 3 ⊖	a		20 59							21 14							21 29	21 29
St Pancras International 15 ⊖	a		21 03							21 18							21 33	21 33
St Albans City	a		21 25							21 38							21 55	21 55
Luton Airport Parkway 4 ✈	a		21 37							21 50							22 07	22 07
Luton 7	a		21 40							21 53							22 10	22 10
Bedford 10	a		22 05							22 19							22 35	22 36
Clapham Junction 10	a	20 40					20 49					21 03	21 07			21 11		
London Victoria 15 ⊖	a	20 50			20 50		20 58				21 05	21 10	21 15			21 18		

		SN 1	SN 1 🚲	SN 1	SN 1	FC 1	SN 1	SN 1	GW 1	SN 1	SN 1	SN 1	FC 1 A	FC 1 B	SN 1	SN 1	SN 1	SN 1	GW 1	SN 1
Brighton 10	d					20 34	20 49						20 37	20 37				21 19		
Hove 2	d			20 22												20 52				
Preston Park	d												20 41	20 41						
Hassocks 4	d												20 47	20 47						
Burgess Hill 4	d			20 33									20 51	20 51						
Lewes 4	d																20 50			
Wivelsfield 4	d												20 53	20 53			21 05			
Haywards Heath 3	a			20 38		20 47							20 58	20 58		21 05	21 11			
	d			20 38		20 48							21 01	21 01		21 13				
Balcombe	d																			
Horsham 4	d				20 32							20 52								21 02
Littlehaven	d				20 35															21 05
Faygate	d																			
Ifield	d				20 41															21 11
Crawley	d				20 45							21 01								21 14
Three Bridges 4	a			20 47	20 48	20 56						21 05	21 11	21 11						21 18
	d			20 47	20 51	20 57						21 05	21 12	21 12						21 18
Gatwick Airport 10 ✈	a			20 51	20 56	21 01						21 10	21 16	21 16		21 25				21 22
	d		20 50	20 53	20 57	21 02			21 03	21 05		21 11	21 17	21 17	21 20	21 26				21 23
Horley 4	d				20 59															21 26
Salfords	d																			21 30
Earlswood (Surrey)	d																			21 33
Tonbridge 4	d																			
Leigh (Kent)	d																			
Penshurst	d																			
Edenbridge	d																			
Godstone	d																			
Nutfield	d																			
Reigate	d	20 50						←			21 13								21 24	
Redhill 5	a	20 54			21 06			21 06	21 10		21 17	21 18							21 30	21 36
	d				21 07			21 07				21 19								21 37
Merstham	d				→			21 11												21 41
Coulsdon South	d							21 16												21 46
Purley 4	d							21 19												21 49
East Croydon	a			21 08		21 16	21 23	21 25				21 30	21 32	21 32		21 41		21 53		21 54
	d			21 09		21 17	21 24	21 26				21 30	21 32	21 32		21 41		21 54		21 57
Norwood Junction 2	a																			
New Cross Gate	d																			
London Bridge 4 ⊖	a					21 30							21 45	21 45						
London Blackfriars 3 ⊖	a					21 37							21 52	21 52						
City Thameslink 3	a					21 40							21 56	21 56						
Farringdon 3 ⊖	a					21 44							21 59	21 59						
St Pancras International 15 ⊖	a					21 48							22 03	22 03						
St Albans City	a					22 08							22 25	22 25						
Luton Airport Parkway 4 ✈	a					22 20							22 37	22 37						
Luton 7	a					22 23							22 40	22 40						
Bedford 10	a					22 49							23 05	23 06						
Clapham Junction 10	a			21 18			21 33	21 37				21 40				21 50		22 03		22 06
London Victoria 15 ⊖	a		21 20	21 28			21 40	21 44		21 35		21 47			21 50	21 58		22 11		22 14

A until 27 December, from 10 February B from 30 December until 7 February

Table 186R

Mondays to Fridays

9 December to 16 May

Brighton - London and Bedford

Network Diagram - see first Page of Table 175

Station		SN 1	SN 1	SN 1	FC 1	GW 1	SN 1	SN 1	SN 1	SN 1	SN 1	SN 1	SN 1	SN 1	SN 1	SN 1	FC 1	SN 1	GW 1	SN 1 ⚒	SN 1 A ⚒	SN 1	SN 1	SN 1	SN 1	SN 1	SN 1	FC 1	GW 1	SN 1	SN 1	SN 1	FC 1	SN 1	FC 1	GW 1	SN 1
Brighton 10	d			21 02	21 11						21 34		21 49				21 37					22 19					22 03	22 07					22 33				
Hove 2	d							21 22													21 52																
Preston Park	d			21 06													21 41										22 06	22 11					22 37				
Hassocks 4	d			21 12	21 20												21 47										22 13	22 17					22 43				
Burgess Hill 4	d			21 16	21 23			21 33									21 51				22 04						22 16	22 21					22 47				
Lewes 4	d																			21 50														22 40			
Wivelsfield 4	d			21 18													21 53			22 02							22 18	22 23					22 49	22 54			
Haywards Heath 3	a			21 23	21 28			21 38			21 47						21 58			22 06	22 12						22 23	22 28					22 53	22 58			
	d			21 23	21 32			21 38			21 47						22 01			22 14							22 23	22 31					22 54	22 59			
Balcombe	d				21 37																							22 37					22 59				
Horsham 4	d									21 32						21 52							22 02														
Littlehaven	d									21 35													22 05														
Faygate	d																																				
Ifield	d									21 41													22 11														
Crawley	d									21 45						22 01							22 14												←		
Three Bridges 4	a			21 32	21 43			21 47		21 48	21 56					22 05	22 11						22 18				22 32	22 42					23 05	23 08	23 05		
	d			21 33	21 43			21 47		21 51	21 56					22 05	22 12						22 19				22 33	22 42					23 12	23 08	23 12		
Gatwick Airport 10 ✈	a			21 37	21 47			21 51		21 55	22 00					22 10	22 16				22 25		22 23				22 37	22 46					→	23 12	23 16		
	d		21 35	21 38	21 47		21 50	21 53		21 56	22 02	22 05				22 11	22 17	22 20	22 22		22 26		22 24			22 35	22 38	22 47		22 50	23 05			23 13	23 17	23 18	23 20
Horley 4	d									21 59													22 27														
Salfords	d																						22 31														
Earlswood (Surrey)	d																						22 34														
Tonbridge 4	d	21 10																							22 10												
Leigh (Kent)	d	21 14																							22 14												
Penshurst	d	21 18																							22 18												
Edenbridge	d	21 24																							22 24												
Godstone	d	21 31																							22 31												
Nutfield	d	21 36																							22 36												
Reigate	d					21 45			21 52					←	22 13									22 33					22 44			23 15					
Redhill 5	a	21 42		21 46		21 49			21 57	22 05				22 05	22 17	22 18			22 30				22 37	22 37	22 42		22 46		22 48			23 19				23 25	
	d			21 46						22 06				22 06		22 19							22 38				22 46										
Merstham	d									→				22 10									22 42														
Coulsdon South	d													22 15									22 47														
Purley 4	d													22 19									22 50														
East Croydon 🚋	a			21 59	22 02			22 08			22 16		22 23	22 24		22 30	22 32				22 40	22 53	22 55				22 59	23 02						23 30	23 32		
	d			22 00	22 02			22 09			22 17		22 24	22 25		22 30	22 32				22 41	22 54	22 56				23 00	23 02						23 30	23 32		
Norwood Junction 2	a																																				
New Cross Gate	d																																				
London Bridge 4 ⊖	a				22 15						22 33						22 45											23 15							23 45		
London Blackfriars 3 ⊖	a				22 22												22 52											23 22							23 51		
City Thameslink 3	a				22 24												22 53																				
Farringdon 3 ⊖	a				22 28												22 58											23 28							23 58		
St Pancras International 15 ⊖	a				22 31												23 02											23 32							00 02		
St Albans City	a				22 56												23 26											23 56							00 26		
Luton Airport Parkway 4 ✈	a				23 08												23 38											00 08							00 38		
Luton 7	a				23 11												23 41											00 11							00 41		
Bedford 10	a				23 38												00 08											00 38							01 08		
Clapham Junction 10	a			22 10				22 18					22 33	22 36		22 40					22 50	23 03	23 06				23 10							23 42			
London Victoria 15 ⊖	a		22 05	22 17			22 20	22 26				22 35	22 41	22 44		22 47		22 50			22 57	23 13	23 15			23 05	23 18			23 20	23 35			23 52			23 55

A ⚒ from Haywards Heath

Table 186R

Mondays to Fridays

Brighton - London and Bedford

9 December to 16 May

Network Diagram - see first Page of Table 175

		SN 1	SN 1	SN 1	GW 1	SN 1	FC 1	SN 1	SN 1	FC 1
Brighton 10	d					23 05	23 11			23 37
Hove 2	d									
Preston Park	d					23 09				23 41
Hassocks 4	d					23 15	23 20			23 47
Burgess Hill 4	d					23 19	23 23			23 51
Lewes 4	d									
Wivelsfield 4	d					23 21				23 53
Haywards Heath 3	a					23 26	23 28			23 58
	d					23 26	23 29			23 59
Balcombe	d									00 04
Horsham 4	d	23 02								
Littlehaven	d	23 05								
Faygate	d									
Ifield	d	23 11								
Crawley	d	23 14							←	
Three Bridges 4	a	23 18				23 35	23 38		23 35	00 10
	d	23 18				23 47	23 38		23 47	00 10
Gatwick Airport 10 ✈	a	23 22				→	23 42		23 52	00 14
	d	23 23		23 35			23 43	23 50	23 53	00 15
Horley 4	d	23 26							23 56	
Salfords	d	23 30								
Earlswood (Surrey)	d	23 33								
Tonbridge 4	d		23 19							
Leigh (Kent)	d		23 23							
Penshurst	d		23 27							
Edenbridge	d		23 33							
Godstone	d		23 40							
Nutfield	d		23 45							
Reigate	d				23 54					
Redhill 5	a	23 36	23 50		23 58				00 03	00 23
	d	23 37							00 04	00 24
Merstham	d	23 41								
Coulsdon South	d	23 46								
Purley 4	d	23 49							00 12	
East Croydon 🚋	a	23 54					00 01		00 17	00 36
	d	23 55					00 02		00 18	00 36
Norwood Junction 2	a									
New Cross Gate	d									
London Bridge 4 ⊖	a						00 21			00 52
London Blackfriars 3 ⊖	a						00 28			00 58
City Thameslink 3	a									
Farringdon 3 ⊖	a						00 34			
St Pancras International 15 ⊖	a						00 38			01 08
St Albans City	a						01 11			01 41
Luton Airport Parkway 4 ✈	a						01 23			01 53
Luton 7	a						01 26			01 56
Bedford 10	a						01 52			02 22
Clapham Junction 10	a	00 10							00 31	
London Victoria 15 ⊖	a	00 18		00 10				00 26	00 39	

Table 186R

Saturdays

14 December to 17 May

Brighton - London and Bedford

Network Diagram - see first Page of Table 175

		FC	SN	SN	FC	SN	SN	GW	SN	SN	FC	SN	SN	FC	SN	FC	SN	FC	SN
		1	1	1	1	1	1	1	1	1	1	1	1	1	1	1	1	1	1
											A			A		A		B	
Brighton 10	d																		
Hove 2	d																		
Preston Park	d																		
Hassocks 4	d																		
Burgess Hill 4	d																		
Lewes 4	d																		
Wivelsfield 4	d																		
Haywards Heath 3	a																		
	d																		
Balcombe	d				00 04														
Horsham 4	d																		
Littlehaven	d																		
Faygate	d																		
Ifield	d																		
Crawley	d																		
Three Bridges 4	a				00 10														
	d				00 10						01 16		01 59	02 16	02 56	03 16	03 56	04 16	
Gatwick Airport 10 ✈	a				00 14						01 20		02 03	02 20	03 00	03 20	04 00	04 20	
	d			00 05	00 15	00 20	00 35		00 50	01 10	01 21	01 35	02 05	02 21	03 05	03 21	04 05	04 21	04 35
Horley 4	d									01 12			02 07		03 07		04 07		
Salfords	d																		
Earlswood (Surrey)	d																		
Tonbridge 4	d																		
Leigh (Kent)	d																		
Penshurst	d																		
Edenbridge	d																		
Godstone	d																		
Nutfield	d																		
Reigate	d							00 45											
Redhill 5	a				00 23			00 49											
	d		00 04		00 24														
Merstham	d																		
Coulsdon South	d																		
Purley 4	d		00 12							01 26			02 22		03 22		04 24		
East Croydon	a		00 17		00 36					01 31	01 39		02 27	02 39	03 27	03 39	04 29	04 39	
	d	00 02	00 18		00 36					01 31	01 40		02 28	02 40	03 28	03 40	04 30	04 40	
Norwood Junction 2	a																		
New Cross Gate	d																		
London Bridge 4 ⊖	a	00 21			00 52														
London Blackfriars 3 ⊖	a	00 28			00 58						02 08			03 08		04 08		05 08	
City Thameslink 3	a																		
Farringdon 3 ⊖	a	00 34																05 15	
St Pancras International 15 ⊖	a	00 38			01 08						02 20			03 20		04 20		05 20	
St Albans City	a	01 11			01 41						02 53			03 53		04 53		05 57	
Luton Airport Parkway 4 ✈	a	01 23			01 53						03 05			04 05		05 05		06 09	
Luton 7	a	01 26			01 56						03 08			04 08		05 08		06 12	
Bedford 10	a	01 52			02 22						03 35			04 35		05 35		06 39	
Clapham Junction 10	a		00 31							01 45			02 41		03 41		04 43		
London Victoria 15 ⊖	a		00 39	00 41		00 56	01 12		01 26	01 53		02 10	02 49		03 49		04 51		05 10

		FC	SN	SN	FC	GW	GW	SN	SN	SN	SN	SN	SN	FC	SN	GW	SN	SN	SN
		1	1	1	1	1	1	1	1	1	1	1	1	1	1	1	1	1	1
		B			B													🚌	🚌
Brighton 10	d		03 50								05 21			05 25					
Hove 2	d																		
Preston Park	d													05 29					
Hassocks 4	d													05 35					
Burgess Hill 4	d										05 31			05 39					
Lewes 4	d												05 26						
Wivelsfield 4	d													05 41					
Haywards Heath 3	a		04 24								05 36		05 41	05 45					
	d		04 25								05 37		05 42	05 46					
Balcombe	d													05 51					
Horsham 4	d											05 30							
Littlehaven	d											05 33							
Faygate	d																		
Ifield	d											05 39							
Crawley	d											05 43					←		
Three Bridges 4	a		04 43								05 45	05 46	05 51	05 57			05 51		
	d	04 52	04 58		05 22			05 33			05 46	05 48	05 58	05 57			05 58		
Gatwick Airport 10 ✈	a	04 56	05 02		05 26			05 37			05 50	05 52	→	06 01			06 05		
	d	04 57	05 03	05 20	05 27	05 31		05 38		05 50	05 53	05 53		06 02		06 03		06 05	06 20
Horley 4	d		05 05					05 40				05 56							
Salfords	d											06 00							
Earlswood (Surrey)	d											06 03							
Tonbridge 4	d								05 24										
Leigh (Kent)	d								05 28										
Penshurst	d								05 32										
Edenbridge	d								05 38										
Godstone	d								05 45										
Nutfield	d								05 50										
Reigate	d						05 34								←				
Redhill 5	a				05 35	05 38	05 39	05 47	05 56			06 06			06 06	06 12			
	d				05 36			05 48				06 07			06 07				
Merstham	d											→			06 11				
Coulsdon South	d														06 16				
Purley 4	d		05 23					05 58							06 19				
East Croydon	a	05 15	05 28		05 47			06 02			06 10			06 16	06 24				
	d	05 16	05 28		05 48			06 07			06 11			06 17	06 25				
Norwood Junction 2	a														06 29				
New Cross Gate	d														06 37				
London Bridge 4 ⊖	a				06 02									06 30	06 43				
London Blackfriars 3 ⊖	a	05 43			06 08									06 37					
City Thameslink 3	a																		
Farringdon 3 ⊖	a	05 50			06 13									06 43					
St Pancras International 15 ⊖	a	05 54			06 18									06 47					
St Albans City	a	06 25			06 40									07 10					
Luton Airport Parkway 4 ✈	a	06 37			06 52									07 21					
Luton 7	a	06 40			06 55									07 24					
Bedford 10	a	07 05			07 20									07 50					
Clapham Junction 10	a		05 47					06 18			06 21								
London Victoria 15 ⊖	a		05 56	05 53				06 26		06 20	06 30							06 35	06 50

A 1 to London Blackfriars

B 1 to Farringdon

Table 186R

Saturdays

14 December to 17 May

Brighton - London and Bedford

Network Diagram - see first Page of Table 175

Station		SN 1	SN 1	SN 1	SN 1	FC 1	SN 1	SN 1	SN 1	GW 1
							trolley			
Brighton 10	d		05 50		05 56	06 02				
Hove 2	d			05 54						
Preston Park	d				06 00					
Hassocks 4	d				06 06					
Burgess Hill 4	d					06 12				
Lewes 4	d									
Wivelsfield 4	d				06 10					
Haywards Heath 3	a		06 03	06 08	06 15	06 17				
	d		06 12		06 15	06 18				
Balcombe	d									
Horsham 4	d	06 00								
Littlehaven	d	06 03								
Faygate	d									
Ifield	d	06 09								
Crawley	d	06 13						←		
Three Bridges 4	a	06 16	06 20		06 24	06 26		06 24		
	d	06 18	06 21		06 30	06 27		06 30		
Gatwick Airport 10 ✈	a	06 22	06 25		→	06 31		06 37		
	d	06 23	06 26			06 32	06 35	06 38		
Horley 4	d	06 26								
Salfords	d	06 30								
Earlswood (Surrey)	d	06 33								
Tonbridge 4	d									
Leigh (Kent)	d									
Penshurst	d									
Edenbridge	d									
Godstone	d									
Nutfield	d									
Reigate	d								←	06 34
Redhill 5	a	06 36							06 36	06 39
	d	06 37							06 37	
Merstham	d	→							06 41	
Coulsdon South	d								06 46	
Purley 4	d								06 49	
East Croydon	a		06 40			06 46		06 52	06 54	
	d		06 41			06 47		06 53	06 55	
Norwood Junction 2	a								06 59	
New Cross Gate	d								07 07	
London Bridge 4 ⊖	a					07 00			07 13	
London Blackfriars 3 ⊖	a					07 07				
City Thameslink 3	a									
Farringdon 3 ⊖	a					07 13				
St Pancras International 15 ⊖	a					07 17				
St Albans City	a					07 40				
Luton Airport Parkway 4 ✈	a					07 51				
Luton 7	a					07 54				
Bedford 10	a					08 20				
Clapham Junction 10	a		06 50					07 02		
London Victoria 15 ⊖	a		06 57				07 05	07 09		

Station		SN 1	SN 1	SN 1	SN 1	SN 1 A	FC 1	SN 1	SN 1	GW 1
			trolley							
Brighton 10	d				06 11		06 25	06 49		
Hove 2	d					06 21				
Preston Park	d				06 15		06 29			
Hassocks 4	d				06 21		06 35			
Burgess Hill 4	d				06 25		06 39			
Lewes 4	d									
Wivelsfield 4	d				06 27		06 41			
Haywards Heath 3	a				06 31	06 35	06 45			
	d				06 40	06 40	06 46			
Balcombe	d						06 51			
Horsham 4	d			06 30						
Littlehaven	d			06 33						
Faygate	d									
Ifield	d			06 39						
Crawley	d			06 43						
Three Bridges 4	a			06 46	06 48	06 48	06 57			
	d			06 48	06 49	06 49	06 57			
Gatwick Airport 10 ✈	a			06 52	06 53	06 53	07 01			
	d		06 50	06 53	06 55	06 55	07 02			07 03
Horley 4	d			06 56						
Salfords	d									
Earlswood (Surrey)	d									
Tonbridge 4	d	06 19								
Leigh (Kent)	d	06 23								
Penshurst	d	06 27								
Edenbridge	d	06 33								
Godstone	d	06 40								
Nutfield	d	06 45								
Reigate	d								←	
Redhill 5	a	06 50		07 02					07 02	07 10
	d	06 51		07 07					07 07	
Merstham	d			→					07 11	
Coulsdon South	d	06 58							07 16	
Purley 4	d	07 02							07 19	
East Croydon	a	07 07			07 09	07 09	07 16	07 22	07 24	
	d	07 07			07 10	07 10	07 17	07 23	07 25	
Norwood Junction 2	a	07 12							07 29	
New Cross Gate	d								07 37	
London Bridge 4 ⊖	a	07 25					07 30		07 43	
London Blackfriars 3 ⊖	a						07 37			
City Thameslink 3	a									
Farringdon 3 ⊖	a						07 44			
St Pancras International 15 ⊖	a						07 48			
St Albans City	a						08 09			
Luton Airport Parkway 4 ✈	a						08 20			
Luton 7	a						08 23			
Bedford 10	a						08 49			
Clapham Junction 10	a				07 19	07 19		07 32		
London Victoria 15 ⊖	a		07 20		07 27	07 27		07 40		

Station		SN 1	SN 1	FC 1	SN 1	GW 1	SN 1	SN 1	SN 1	SN 1
		trolley					trolley			
Brighton 10	d			06 37						
Hove 2	d									06 51
Preston Park	d			06 41						06 55
Hassocks 4	d			06 47						
Burgess Hill 4	d			06 51						07 04
Lewes 4	d								06 50	
Wivelsfield 4	d			06 53						
Haywards Heath 3	a			06 58					07 05	07 09
	d			07 01					07 14	
Balcombe	d									
Horsham 4	d		06 52					07 00		
Littlehaven	d							07 03		
Faygate	d									
Ifield	d							07 09		
Crawley	d		07 01					07 13		
Three Bridges 4	a		07 05	07 11				07 16		
	d		07 05	07 12				07 18		
Gatwick Airport 10 ✈	a		07 10	07 16				07 22	07 25	
	d	07 05	07 11	07 17			07 20	07 23	07 26	
Horley 4	d							07 26		
Salfords	d							07 30		
Earlswood (Surrey)	d							07 33		
Tonbridge 4	d									
Leigh (Kent)	d									
Penshurst	d									
Edenbridge	d									
Godstone	d									
Nutfield	d									
Reigate	d				07 14	07 19				
Redhill 5	a		07 18		07 18	07 25		07 36		
	d		07 18		07 21			07 37		
Merstham	d				07 25			→		
Coulsdon South	d				07 30					
Purley 4	d				07 34					
East Croydon	a		07 29	07 31	07 39				07 41	
	d		07 30	07 32	07 39				07 41	
Norwood Junction 2	a				07 45					
New Cross Gate	d									
London Bridge 4 ⊖	a			07 45	07 57					
London Blackfriars 3 ⊖	a			07 52						
City Thameslink 3	a									
Farringdon 3 ⊖	a			07 59						
St Pancras International 15 ⊖	a			08 03						
St Albans City	a			08 25						
Luton Airport Parkway 4 ✈	a			08 37						
Luton 7	a			08 40						
Bedford 10	a			09 05						
Clapham Junction 10	a		07 39						07 50	
London Victoria 15 ⊖	a	07 35	07 46				07 50		07 58	

Station		FC 1	SN 1	SN 1	SN 1	GW 1	SN 1	FC 1	SN 1	SN 1
			trolley							trolley
Brighton 10	d	07 04		07 19				07 07		
Hove 2	d									
Preston Park	d							07 11		
Hassocks 4	d							07 17		
Burgess Hill 4	d							07 21		
Lewes 4	d									
Wivelsfield 4	d							07 23		
Haywards Heath 3	a	07 17						07 28		
	d	07 18						07 31		
Balcombe	d							07 37		
Horsham 4	d						07 20			
Littlehaven	d									
Faygate	d									
Ifield	d									
Crawley	d						07 29			
Three Bridges 4	a	07 26					07 32	07 42		
	d	07 27					07 33	07 42		
Gatwick Airport 10 ✈	a	07 31					07 37	07 46		
	d	07 32	07 35				07 38	07 47		07 50
Horley 4	d						07 41			
Salfords	d									
Earlswood (Surrey)	d									
Tonbridge 4	d								07 19	
Leigh (Kent)	d								07 23	
Penshurst	d								07 27	
Edenbridge	d								07 33	
Godstone	d								07 40	
Nutfield	d								07 45	
Reigate	d				←	07 34				
Redhill 5	a				07 36	07 39	07 47		07 50	
	d				07 37		07 48		07 51	
Merstham	d				07 41					
Coulsdon South	d				07 46				07 58	
Purley 4	d				07 49				08 02	
East Croydon	a	07 46		07 52	07 54		07 59	08 02	08 07	
	d	07 47		07 53	07 55		07 59	08 02	08 07	
Norwood Junction 2	a				07 59				08 12	
New Cross Gate	d				08 07					
London Bridge 4 ⊖	a	08 00			08 13			08 15	08 25	
London Blackfriars 3 ⊖	a	08 07						08 22		
City Thameslink 3	a									
Farringdon 3 ⊖	a	08 14						08 29		
St Pancras International 15 ⊖	a	08 18						08 33		
St Albans City	a	08 39						08 55		
Luton Airport Parkway 4 ✈	a	08 50						09 07		
Luton 7	a	08 53						09 10		
Bedford 10	a	09 19						09 35		
Clapham Junction 10	a			08 02			08 08			
London Victoria 15 ⊖	a		08 05	08 10			08 16			08 20

A until 8 February

Table 186R

Saturdays

14 December to 17 May

Brighton - London and Bedford

Network Diagram - see first Page of Table 175

Station		SN 1	SN 1	SN 1	SN 1	FC 1	SN 1 ⊼	SN 1	GW 1	SN 1 ⊼	SN 1	FC 1	SN 1	GW 1	SN 1 ⊼	SN 1	SN 1	SN 1	FC 1
Brighton 10	d	07 24				07 34	07 49					07 37							08 04
Hove 2	d			07 22														07 51	
Preston Park	d											07 41						07 55	
Hassocks 4	d	07 34										07 47							
Burgess Hill 4	d	07 38										07 51						08 04	
Lewes 4	d				07 20												07 50		
Wivelsfield 4	d				07 35							07 53							
Haywards Heath 3	a			07 35	07 40	07 47						07 58					08 05	08 09	08 17
	d				07 44	07 48						08 01						08 13	08 18
Balcombe	d																		
Horsham 4	d		07 30								07 50					08 00			
Littlehaven	d		07 33													08 03			
Faygate	d																		
Ifield	d		07 39													08 09			
Crawley	d		07 43								07 59					08 13			
Three Bridges 4	a		07 46			07 56					08 02	08 11				08 16			08 26
	d		07 48			07 57					08 03	08 12				08 18			08 27
Gatwick Airport 10 ✈	a	07 52	07 52		07 55	08 01					08 07	08 16				08 22		08 24	08 31
	d	07 53	07 53		07 56	08 02			08 03	08 05	08 08	08 17			08 20	08 23		08 25	08 32
Horley 4	d		07 56													08 26			
Salfords	d															08 30			
Earlswood (Surrey)	d															08 33			
Tonbridge 4	d																		
Leigh (Kent)	d																		
Penshurst	d																		
Edenbridge	d																		
Godstone	d																		
Nutfield	d																		
Reigate	d							←					08 14	08 19					
Redhill 5	a		08 02					08 02	08 10		08 15		08 18	08 25		08 36			
	d		08 07					08 07			08 16		08 19			08 37			
Merstham	d		→					08 11					08 23			→			
Coulsdon South	d							08 16					08 28						
Purley 4	d							08 19					08 32						
East Croydon	a	08 08			08 11	08 16	08 22	08 24			08 27	08 31	08 37					08 40	08 46
	d	08 08			08 11	08 17	08 23	08 25			08 27	08 32	08 37					08 40	08 47
Norwood Junction 2	a							08 29					08 42						
New Cross Gate	d							08 37											
London Bridge 4 ⊖	a					08 30		08 43				08 45	08 55						09 00
London Blackfriars 3 ⊖	a					08 37						08 52							09 07
City Thameslink 3	a																		09 10
Farringdon 3 ⊖	a					08 44						08 59							09 14
St Pancras International 15 ⊖	a					08 48						09 03							09 18
St Albans City	a					09 09						09 25							09 39
Luton Airport Parkway 4 ✈	a					09 20						09 37							09 50
Luton 7	a					09 23						09 40							09 53
Bedford 10	a					09 49						10 05							10 19
Clapham Junction 10	a	08 17			08 20		08 32				08 36							08 49	
London Victoria 15 ⊖	a	08 24			08 28		08 40			08 35	08 44				08 50			08 57	

Station		SN 1 ⊼	SN 1 ⊼	SN 1	GW 1	SN 1	FC 1	SN 1	SN 1 ⊼	SN 1	SN 1	SN 1	SN 1	FC 1	SN 1 ⊼	SN 1	GW 1	SN 1 ⊼	SN 1
Brighton 10	d		08 19				08 07			08 24				08 34	08 49				
Hove 2	d											08 21							
Preston Park	d						08 11												
Hassocks 4	d						08 17			08 34									
Burgess Hill 4	d						08 21			08 38									
Lewes 4	d												08 20						
Wivelsfield 4	d						08 23						08 35						
Haywards Heath 3	a						08 28					08 35	08 40	08 47					
	d						08 31						08 44	08 48					
Balcombe	d						08 37												
Horsham 4	d					08 20					08 30								08 51
Littlehaven	d										08 33								
Faygate	d																		
Ifield	d										08 39								
Crawley	d					08 29					08 43								08 59
Three Bridges 4	a					08 32	08 42				08 46			08 56					09 03
	d					08 33	08 42				08 48			08 57					09 03
Gatwick Airport 10 ✈	a					08 37	08 46			08 52	08 52		08 55	09 01					09 07
	d	08 35				08 38	08 47		08 50	08 53	08 53		08 56	09 02			09 03	09 05	09 08
Horley 4	d					08 41					08 56								
Salfords	d																		
Earlswood (Surrey)	d																		
Tonbridge 4	d							08 19											
Leigh (Kent)	d							08 23											
Penshurst	d							08 27											
Edenbridge	d							08 33											
Godstone	d							08 40											
Nutfield	d							08 45											
Reigate	d			←	08 34											←			
Redhill 5	a			08 36	08 38	08 47		08 50			09 02					09 02	09 10		09 15
	d			08 37		08 48		08 51			09 07					09 07			09 16
Merstham	d			08 41							→					09 11			
Coulsdon South	d			08 46				08 58								09 16			
Purley 4	d			08 49				09 02								09 19			
East Croydon	a		08 52	08 54		08 59	09 02	09 07		09 08			09 11	09 16	09 22	09 24			09 27
	d		08 53	08 55		08 59	09 02	09 07		09 08			09 11	09 17	09 23	09 25			09 27
Norwood Junction 2	a			08 59				09 12								09 29			
New Cross Gate	d			09 07												09 37			
London Bridge 4 ⊖	a			09 13			09 15	09 25						09 30		09 43			
London Blackfriars 3 ⊖	a						09 22							09 37					
City Thameslink 3	a						09 26							09 40					
Farringdon 3 ⊖	a						09 29							09 44					
St Pancras International 15 ⊖	a						09 33							09 48					
St Albans City	a						09 55							10 09					
Luton Airport Parkway 4 ✈	a						10 07							10 20					
Luton 7	a						10 10							10 23					
Bedford 10	a						10 35							10 49					
Clapham Junction 10	a		09 02			09 08				09 17			09 20		09 32				09 36
London Victoria 15 ⊖	a	09 05	09 10			09 16			09 20	09 24			09 28		09 40			09 35	09 44

Table 186R

Saturdays

Brighton - London and Bedford

14 December to 17 May

Network Diagram - see first Page of Table 175

Station		FC [1]	SN [1]	GW [1]	SN [1] 🛒	SN [1]	SN [1]	SN [1]	FC [1]	SN [1] 🛒
Brighton [10]	d	08 37							09 04	
Hove [2]	d							08 51		
Preston Park	d	08 41						08 55		
Hassocks [4]	d	08 47								
Burgess Hill [4]	d	08 51						09 04		
Lewes [4]	d						08 50			
Wivelsfield [4]	d	08 53								
Haywards Heath [3]	a	08 58					09 05	09 09	09 17	
	d	09 01					09 14		09 18	
Balcombe	d									
Horsham [4]	d					09 00				
Littlehaven	d					09 03				
Faygate	d									
Ifield	d					09 09				
Crawley	d					09 13				
Three Bridges [4]	a	09 11				09 16			09 26	
	d	09 12				09 18			09 27	
Gatwick Airport [10] ✈	a	09 16				09 22	09 25		09 31	
	d	09 17			09 20	09 23	09 26		09 32	09 35
Horley [4]	d					09 26				
Salfords	d					09 30				
Earlswood (Surrey)	d					09 33				
Tonbridge [4]	d									
Leigh (Kent)	d									
Penshurst	d									
Edenbridge	d									
Godstone	d									
Nutfield	d									
Reigate	d		09 14	09 19						
Redhill [5]	a		09 18	09 25		09 36				
	d		09 19			09 37				
Merstham	d		09 23			→				
Coulsdon South	d		09 28							
Purley [4]	d		09 32							
East Croydon	a	09 31	09 37				09 41		09 46	
	d	09 32	09 37				09 41		09 47	
Norwood Junction [2]	a		09 42							
New Cross Gate	d									
London Bridge [4] ⊖	a	09 45	09 55						10 00	
London Blackfriars [3] ⊖	a	09 52							10 07	
City Thameslink [3]	a	09 56							10 10	
Farringdon [3] ⊖	a	09 59							10 14	
St Pancras International [15] ⊖	a	10 03							10 18	
St Albans City	a	10 25							10 39	
Luton Airport Parkway [4] ✈	a	10 37							10 50	
Luton [7]	a	10 40							10 53	
Bedford [10]	a	11 05							11 19	
Clapham Junction [10]	a						09 50			
London Victoria [15] ⊖	a				09 50		09 58			10 05

Station		SN [1] 🛒	SN [1]	GW [1]	SN [1]	FC [1]	SN [1]	SN [1] 🛒	SN [1]	SN [1]
Brighton [10]	d	09 19				09 07			09 24	
Hove [2]	d									
Preston Park	d					09 11				
Hassocks [4]	d					09 17			09 34	
Burgess Hill [4]	d					09 21			09 38	
Lewes [4]	d									
Wivelsfield [4]	d					09 23				
Haywards Heath [3]	a					09 28				
	d					09 31				
Balcombe	d					09 37				
Horsham [4]	d				09 20					09 30
Littlehaven	d									09 33
Faygate	d									
Ifield	d									09 39
Crawley	d				09 29					09 43
Three Bridges [4]	a				09 32	09 42				09 46
	d				09 33	09 42				09 48
Gatwick Airport [10] ✈	a				09 37	09 46			09 52	09 52
	d				09 38	09 47		09 50	09 53	09 53
Horley [4]	d				09 41					09 56
Salfords	d									
Earlswood (Surrey)	d									
Tonbridge [4]	d						09 19			
Leigh (Kent)	d						09 23			
Penshurst	d						09 27			
Edenbridge	d						09 33			
Godstone	d						09 40			
Nutfield	d						09 45			
Reigate	d		←	09 34						
Redhill [5]	a		09 36	09 38	09 47		09 50			10 02
	d		09 37		09 48		09 51			10 07
Merstham	d		09 41							→
Coulsdon South	d		09 46				09 58			
Purley [4]	d		09 49				10 02			
East Croydon	a	09 52	09 54		09 59	10 02	10 07		10 08	
	d	09 53	09 55		09 59	10 02	10 07		10 08	
Norwood Junction [2]	a		09 59				10 12			
New Cross Gate	d		10 07							
London Bridge [4] ⊖	a		10 13			10 15	10 25			
London Blackfriars [3] ⊖	a					10 22				
City Thameslink [3]	a					10 26				
Farringdon [3] ⊖	a					10 29				
St Pancras International [15] ⊖	a					10 33				
St Albans City	a					10 55				
Luton Airport Parkway [4] ✈	a					11 07				
Luton [7]	a					11 10				
Bedford [10]	a					11 35				
Clapham Junction [10]	a	10 02			10 08				10 17	
London Victoria [15] ⊖	a	10 10			10 16			10 20	10 24	

Station		SN [1]	SN [1]	FC [1]	SN [1] 🛒	SN [1]	GW [1]	SN [1] 🛒	SN [1]	FC [1]
Brighton [10]	d			09 34	09 49					09 37
Hove [2]	d	09 21								
Preston Park	d									09 41
Hassocks [4]	d									09 47
Burgess Hill [4]	d									09 51
Lewes [4]	d		09 20							
Wivelsfield [4]	d		09 35							09 53
Haywards Heath [3]	a	09 35	09 40	09 47						09 58
	d	09 44		09 48						10 01
Balcombe	d									
Horsham [4]	d								09 50	
Littlehaven	d									
Faygate	d									
Ifield	d									
Crawley	d								09 59	
Three Bridges [4]	a			09 56					10 02	10 11
	d			09 57					10 03	10 12
Gatwick Airport [10] ✈	a	09 55		10 01					10 07	10 16
	d	09 56		10 02			10 03	10 05	10 08	10 17
Horley [4]	d									
Salfords	d									
Earlswood (Surrey)	d									
Tonbridge [4]	d									
Leigh (Kent)	d									
Penshurst	d									
Edenbridge	d									
Godstone	d									
Nutfield	d									
Reigate	d					←				
Redhill [5]	a					10 02	10 10		10 15	
	d					10 07			10 16	
Merstham	d					10 11				
Coulsdon South	d					10 16				
Purley [4]	d					10 19				
East Croydon	a	10 11		10 16	10 22	10 24			10 27	10 31
	d	10 11		10 17	10 23	10 25			10 27	10 32
Norwood Junction [2]	a					10 29				
New Cross Gate	d					10 37				
London Bridge [4] ⊖	a			10 30		10 43				10 45
London Blackfriars [3] ⊖	a			10 37						10 52
City Thameslink [3]	a			10 40						10 56
Farringdon [3] ⊖	a			10 44						10 59
St Pancras International [15] ⊖	a			10 48						11 03
St Albans City	a			11 09						11 25
Luton Airport Parkway [4] ✈	a			11 20						11 37
Luton [7]	a			11 23						11 40
Bedford [10]	a			11 49						12 05
Clapham Junction [10]	a	10 20			10 32				10 36	
London Victoria [15] ⊖	a	10 28			10 40			10 35	10 44	

Station		SN [1]	GW [1]	SN [1] 🛒	SN [1]	SN [1]	SN [1]	FC [1]	SN [1] 🛒	SN [1] 🛒
Brighton [10]	d							10 04		10 19
Hove [2]	d						09 51			
Preston Park	d						09 55			
Hassocks [4]	d									
Burgess Hill [4]	d						10 04			
Lewes [4]	d					09 50				
Wivelsfield [4]	d									
Haywards Heath [3]	a					10 05	10 09	10 17		
	d					10 13		10 18		
Balcombe	d									
Horsham [4]	d				10 00					
Littlehaven	d				10 03					
Faygate	d									
Ifield	d				10 09					
Crawley	d				10 13					
Three Bridges [4]	a				10 16			10 26		
	d				10 18			10 27		
Gatwick Airport [10] ✈	a				10 22	10 24		10 31		
	d			10 20	10 23	10 25		10 32	10 35	
Horley [4]	d				10 26					
Salfords	d				10 30					
Earlswood (Surrey)	d				10 33					
Tonbridge [4]	d									
Leigh (Kent)	d									
Penshurst	d									
Edenbridge	d									
Godstone	d									
Nutfield	d									
Reigate	d	10 14	10 19							
Redhill [5]	a	10 18	10 25		10 36					
	d	10 19			10 37					
Merstham	d	10 23			→					
Coulsdon South	d	10 28								
Purley [4]	d	10 32								
East Croydon	a	10 37				10 40		10 46		10 52
	d	10 37				10 40		10 47		10 53
Norwood Junction [2]	a	10 42								
New Cross Gate	d									
London Bridge [4] ⊖	a	10 55						11 00		
London Blackfriars [3] ⊖	a							11 07		
City Thameslink [3]	a							11 10		
Farringdon [3] ⊖	a							11 14		
St Pancras International [15] ⊖	a							11 18		
St Albans City	a							11 39		
Luton Airport Parkway [4] ✈	a							11 50		
Luton [7]	a							11 53		
Bedford [10]	a							12 19		
Clapham Junction [10]	a					10 49				11 02
London Victoria [15] ⊖	a			10 50		10 57			11 05	11 10

Table 186R

Saturdays

14 December to 17 May

Brighton - London and Bedford

Network Diagram - see first Page of Table 175

Station		SN 1	GW 1	SN 1	FC 1	SN 1	SN 1 🛒	SN 1	SN 1	SN 1	SN 1	FC 1	SN 1 🛒	SN 1	GW 1	SN 1 🛒	SN 1	FC 1	SN 1	GW 1
Brighton 10	d				10 07			10 24				10 34	10 49					10 37		
Hove 2	d									10 21										
Preston Park	d				10 11													10 41		
Hassocks 4	d				10 17			10 34										10 47		
Burgess Hill 4	d				10 21			10 38										10 51		
Lewes 4	d										10 20									
Wivelsfield 4	d				10 23						10 35							10 53		
Haywards Heath 3	a				10 28					10 35	10 40	10 47						10 58		
	d				10 31						10 44	10 48						11 01		
Balcombe	d				10 37															
Horsham 4	d			10 20					10 30								10 50			
Littlehaven	d								10 33											
Faygate	d																			
Ifield	d								10 39											
Crawley	d			10 29					10 43								10 59			
Three Bridges 4	a			10 32	10 41				10 46			10 56					11 02	11 11		
	d			10 33	10 41				10 48			10 57					11 03	11 12		
Gatwick Airport 10 ✈	a			10 37	10 46			10 52	10 52		10 55	11 01					11 07	11 16		
	d			10 38	10 47		10 50	10 53	10 53		10 56	11 02			11 03	11 05	11 08	11 17		
Horley 4	d			10 41					10 56											
Salfords	d																			
Earlswood (Surrey)	d																			
Tonbridge 4	d					10 19														
Leigh (Kent)	d					10 23														
Penshurst	d					10 27														
Edenbridge	d					10 33														
Godstone	d					10 40														
Nutfield	d					10 45														
Reigate	d	←	10 34											←					11 14	11 19
Redhill 5	a	10 36	10 38	10 47		10 50			11 02					11 02	11 10		11 15		11 18	11 25
	d	10 37		10 48		10 51			11 07					11 07			11 16		11 19	
Merstham	d	10 41							↦					11 11					11 23	
Coulsdon South	d	10 46				10 58								11 16					11 28	
Purley 4	d	10 49				11 02								11 19					11 32	
East Croydon 🚋	a	10 54		10 59	11 02	11 07		11 08			11 11	11 16	11 22	11 24			11 27	11 31	11 37	
	d	10 55		10 59	11 02	11 07		11 08			11 11	11 17	11 23	11 25			11 27	11 32	11 37	
Norwood Junction 2	a	10 59				11 12								11 29					11 42	
New Cross Gate	d	11 07												11 37						
London Bridge 4 ⊖	a	11 13			11 15	11 25						11 30		11 43				11 45	11 55	
London Blackfriars 3 ⊖	a				11 22							11 37						11 52		
City Thameslink 3	a				11 26							11 40						11 56		
Farringdon 3 ⊖	a				11 29							11 44						11 59		
St Pancras International 15 ⊖	a				11 33							11 48						12 03		
St Albans City	a				11 55							12 09						12 25		
Luton Airport Parkway 4 ✈	a				12 07							12 20						12 37		
Luton 7	a				12 10							12 23						12 40		
Bedford 10	a				12 35							12 49						13 05		
Clapham Junction 10	a			11 08				11 17			11 20		11 32				11 36			
London Victoria 15 ⊖	a			11 16			11 20	11 24			11 28		11 40			11 35	11 44			

Station		SN 1 🛒	SN 1	SN 1	SN 1	FC 1	SN 1 🛒	SN 1 🛒	SN 1	GW 1	SN 1	FC 1	SN 1	SN 1 🛒	SN 1	SN 1	SN 1	SN 1	FC 1
Brighton 10	d					11 04		11 19				11 07			11 24				11 34
Hove 2	d				10 51												11 21		
Preston Park	d				10 55							11 11							
Hassocks 4	d											11 17			11 34				
Burgess Hill 4	d				11 04							11 21			11 38				
Lewes 4	d			10 50														11 20	
Wivelsfield 4	d											11 23						11 35	
Haywards Heath 3	a			11 05	11 09	11 17						11 28					11 35	11 40	11 47
	d				11 13	11 18						11 31						11 44	11 48
Balcombe	d											11 37							
Horsham 4	d		11 00								11 20					11 30			
Littlehaven	d		11 03													11 33			
Faygate	d																		
Ifield	d		11 09													11 39			
Crawley	d		11 13								11 29					11 43			
Three Bridges 4	a		11 16			11 26					11 32	11 42				11 46			11 56
	d		11 18			11 27					11 33	11 42				11 48			11 57
Gatwick Airport 10 ✈	a		11 22		11 24	11 31					11 37	11 46			11 52	11 52		11 55	12 01
	d	11 20	11 23		11 25	11 32	11 35				11 38	11 47		11 50	11 53	11 53		11 56	12 02
Horley 4	d		11 26								11 41					11 56			
Salfords	d		11 30																
Earlswood (Surrey)	d		11 33																
Tonbridge 4	d												11 19						
Leigh (Kent)	d												11 23						
Penshurst	d												11 27						
Edenbridge	d												11 33						
Godstone	d												11 40						
Nutfield	d												11 45						
Reigate	d								←	11 34									
Redhill 5	a		11 36						11 36	11 38	11 47		11 50			12 02			
	d		11 37						11 37		11 48		11 51			12 07			
Merstham	d		↦						11 41							↦			
Coulsdon South	d								11 46				11 58						
Purley 4	d								11 49				12 02						
East Croydon 🚋	a				11 40	11 46		11 52	11 54		11 59	12 02	12 07		12 08			12 11	12 16
	d				11 40	11 47		11 53	11 55		11 59	12 02	12 07		12 08			12 11	12 17
Norwood Junction 2	a								11 59				12 12						
New Cross Gate	d								12 07										
London Bridge 4 ⊖	a					12 00			12 13			12 15	12 25						12 30
London Blackfriars 3 ⊖	a					12 07						12 22							12 37
City Thameslink 3	a					12 10						12 26							12 40
Farringdon 3 ⊖	a					12 14						12 29							12 44
St Pancras International 15 ⊖	a					12 18						12 33							12 48
St Albans City	a					12 39						12 55							13 09
Luton Airport Parkway 4 ✈	a					12 50						13 07							13 20
Luton 7	a					12 53						13 10							13 23
Bedford 10	a					13 19						13 35							13 49
Clapham Junction 10	a				11 49			12 02			12 08				12 17			12 20	
London Victoria 15 ⊖	a	11 50			11 57		12 05	12 10			12 16			12 20	12 24			12 28	

Table 186R

Brighton - London and Bedford

Saturdays

14 December to 17 May

Network Diagram - see first Page of Table 175

Station		SN 1 🛒	SN 1	GW 1	SN 1 🛒	SN 1	FC 1	SN 1	GW 1	SN 1 🛒
Brighton 10	d	11 49					11 37			
Hove 2	d									
Preston Park	d						11 41			
Hassocks 4	d						11 47			
Burgess Hill 4	d						11 51			
Lewes 4	d									
Wivelsfield 4	d						11 53			
Haywards Heath 3	a						11 58			
	d						12 01			
Balcombe	d									
Horsham 4	d					11 50				
Littlehaven	d									
Faygate	d									
Ifield	d									
Crawley	d					11 59				
Three Bridges 4	a					12 02	12 11			
	d					12 03	12 12			
Gatwick Airport 10 ✈	a					12 07	12 16			
	d			12 03	12 05	12 08	12 17			12 20
Horley 4	d									
Salfords	d									
Earlswood (Surrey)	d									
Tonbridge 4	d									
Leigh (Kent)	d									
Penshurst	d									
Edenbridge	d									
Godstone	d									
Nutfield	d									
Reigate	d		←					12 14	12 19	
Redhill 5	a		12 02	12 10		12 15		12 18	12 25	
	d		12 07			12 16		12 19		
Merstham	d		12 11					12 23		
Coulsdon South	d		12 16					12 28		
Purley 4	d		12 19					12 32		
East Croydon	a	12 22	12 24			12 27	12 31	12 37		
	d	12 23	12 25			12 27	12 32	12 38		
Norwood Junction 2	a		12 29					12 42		
New Cross Gate	d		12 37							
London Bridge 4 ⊖	a		12 43				12 45	12 55		
London Blackfriars 3 ⊖	a						12 52			
City Thameslink 3	a						12 56			
Farringdon 3 ⊖	a						12 59			
St Pancras International 15 ⊖	a						13 03			
St Albans City	a						13 25			
Luton Airport Parkway 4 ✈	a						13 37			
Luton 7	a						13 40			
Bedford 10	a						14 05			
Clapham Junction 10	a	12 32				12 36				
London Victoria 15 ⊖	a	12 40			12 35	12 44				12 50

Station		SN 1	SN 1	SN 1	FC 1	SN 1 🛒	SN 1 🛒	SN 1	GW 1	SN 1
Brighton 10	d				12 04		12 19			
Hove 2	d			11 51						
Preston Park	d			11 55						
Hassocks 4	d									
Burgess Hill 4	d			12 04						
Lewes 4	d		11 50							
Wivelsfield 4	d									
Haywards Heath 3	a		12 05	12 09	12 17					
	d		12 13		12 18					
Balcombe	d									
Horsham 4	d	12 00								12 20
Littlehaven	d	12 03								
Faygate	d									
Ifield	d	12 09								
Crawley	d	12 13								12 29
Three Bridges 4	a	12 16			12 26					12 32
	d	12 18			12 27					12 33
Gatwick Airport 10 ✈	a	12 22	12 24		12 31					12 37
	d	12 23	12 25		12 32	12 35				12 38
Horley 4	d	12 26								12 41
Salfords	d	12 30								
Earlswood (Surrey)	d	12 33								
Tonbridge 4	d									
Leigh (Kent)	d									
Penshurst	d									
Edenbridge	d									
Godstone	d									
Nutfield	d									
Reigate	d							←	12 34	
Redhill 5	a	12 36						12 36	12 38	12 47
	d	12 37						12 37		12 48
Merstham	d	→						12 41		
Coulsdon South	d							12 46		
Purley 4	d							12 49		
East Croydon	a		12 40		12 46		12 52	12 54		12 59
	d		12 40		12 47		12 53	12 55		12 59
Norwood Junction 2	a							12 59		
New Cross Gate	d							13 07		
London Bridge 4 ⊖	a				13 00			13 13		
London Blackfriars 3 ⊖	a				13 07					
City Thameslink 3	a				13 10					
Farringdon 3 ⊖	a				13 14					
St Pancras International 15 ⊖	a				13 18					
St Albans City	a				13 39					
Luton Airport Parkway 4 ✈	a				13 50					
Luton 7	a				13 53					
Bedford 10	a				14 19					
Clapham Junction 10	a		12 49				13 02			13 08
London Victoria 15 ⊖	a		12 57			13 05	13 10			13 16

Station		FC 1	SN 1	SN 1 🛒	SN 1	SN 1	SN 1	SN 1	FC 1	SN 1 🛒
Brighton 10	d	12 07			12 24				12 34	12 49
Hove 2	d						12 21			
Preston Park	d	12 11								
Hassocks 4	d	12 17			12 34					
Burgess Hill 4	d	12 21			12 38					
Lewes 4	d							12 20		
Wivelsfield 4	d	12 23						12 35		
Haywards Heath 3	a	12 28					12 35	12 40	12 47	
	d	12 31					12 44		12 48	
Balcombe	d	12 37								
Horsham 4	d					12 30				
Littlehaven	d					12 33				
Faygate	d									
Ifield	d					12 39				
Crawley	d					12 43				
Three Bridges 4	a	12 42				12 46			12 56	
	d	12 42				12 48			12 57	
Gatwick Airport 10 ✈	a	12 46			12 52	12 52	12 55		13 01	
	d	12 47		12 50	12 53	12 53	12 56		13 02	
Horley 4	d					12 56				
Salfords	d									
Earlswood (Surrey)	d									
Tonbridge 4	d		12 19							
Leigh (Kent)	d		12 23							
Penshurst	d		12 27							
Edenbridge	d		12 33							
Godstone	d		12 40							
Nutfield	d		12 45							
Reigate	d									
Redhill 5	a		12 50			13 02				
	d		12 51			13 07				
Merstham	d					→				
Coulsdon South	d		12 58							
Purley 4	d		13 02							
East Croydon	a	13 02	13 07		13 08		13 11		13 16	13 22
	d	13 02	13 07		13 08		13 11		13 17	13 23
Norwood Junction 2	a		13 12							
New Cross Gate	d									
London Bridge 4 ⊖	a	13 15	13 25						13 30	
London Blackfriars 3 ⊖	a	13 22							13 37	
City Thameslink 3	a	13 26							13 40	
Farringdon 3 ⊖	a	13 29							13 44	
St Pancras International 15 ⊖	a	13 33							13 48	
St Albans City	a	13 55							14 09	
Luton Airport Parkway 4 ✈	a	14 07							14 20	
Luton 7	a	14 10							14 23	
Bedford 10	a	14 35							14 49	
Clapham Junction 10	a				13 17		13 20			13 32
London Victoria 15 ⊖	a			13 20	13 24		13 28			13 40

Station		SN 1	GW 1	SN 1 🛒	SN 1	FC 1	SN 1	GW 1	SN 1 🛒	SN 1
Brighton 10	d					12 37				
Hove 2	d									
Preston Park	d					12 41				
Hassocks 4	d					12 47				
Burgess Hill 4	d					12 51				
Lewes 4	d									
Wivelsfield 4	d					12 53				
Haywards Heath 3	a					12 58				
	d					13 01				
Balcombe	d									
Horsham 4	d				12 50					13 00
Littlehaven	d									13 03
Faygate	d									
Ifield	d									13 09
Crawley	d				12 59					13 13
Three Bridges 4	a				13 02	13 11				13 16
	d				13 03	13 12				13 18
Gatwick Airport 10 ✈	a				13 07	13 16				13 22
	d		13 03	13 05	13 08	13 17			13 20	13 23
Horley 4	d									13 26
Salfords	d									13 30
Earlswood (Surrey)	d									13 33
Tonbridge 4	d									
Leigh (Kent)	d									
Penshurst	d									
Edenbridge	d									
Godstone	d									
Nutfield	d									
Reigate	d	←					13 14	13 19		
Redhill 5	a	13 02	13 10		13 15		13 18	13 25		13 36
	d	13 07			13 16		13 19			13 37
Merstham	d	13 11					13 23			→
Coulsdon South	d	13 16					13 28			
Purley 4	d	13 19					13 32			
East Croydon	a	13 24			13 27	13 31	13 37			
	d	13 25			13 27	13 32	13 37			
Norwood Junction 2	a	13 29					13 42			
New Cross Gate	d	13 37								
London Bridge 4 ⊖	a	13 43				13 45	13 55			
London Blackfriars 3 ⊖	a					13 52				
City Thameslink 3	a					13 56				
Farringdon 3 ⊖	a					13 59				
St Pancras International 15 ⊖	a					14 03				
St Albans City	a					14 25				
Luton Airport Parkway 4 ✈	a					14 37				
Luton 7	a					14 40				
Bedford 10	a					15 05				
Clapham Junction 10	a				13 36					
London Victoria 15 ⊖	a			13 35	13 44				13 50	

Table 186R

Saturdays

14 December to 17 May

Brighton - London and Bedford

Network Diagram - see first Page of Table 175

Station		SN 1	SN 1	FC 1	SN 1 🛒	SN 1 🛒	SN 1	GW 1	SN 1	FC 1	SN 1	SN 1 🛒	SN 1	SN 1	SN 1	SN 1	FC 1	SN 1 🛒	SN 1
Brighton 10	d			13 04		13 19				13 07			13 24				13 34	13 49	
Hove 2	d		12 51												13 21				
Preston Park	d		12 55							13 11									
Hassocks 4	d									13 17			13 34						
Burgess Hill 4	d		13 04							13 21			13 38						
Lewes 4	d	12 50														13 20			
Wivelsfield 4	d									13 23						13 35			
Haywards Heath 3	a	13 05	13 09	13 17						13 28					13 35	13 40	13 47		
	d		13 13	13 18						13 31					13 44		13 48		
Balcombe	d									13 37									
Horsham 4	d								13 20					13 30					
Littlehaven	d													13 33					
Faygate	d																		
Ifield	d													13 39					
Crawley	d								13 29					13 43					
Three Bridges 4	a			13 26					13 32	13 42				13 46			13 56		
	d			13 27					13 33	13 42				13 48			13 57		
Gatwick Airport 10 ✈	a		13 24	13 31					13 37	13 46			13 52	13 52	13 55		14 01		
	d		13 25	13 32	13 35				13 38	13 47		13 50	13 53	13 53	13 56		14 02		
Horley 4	d								13 41					13 56					
Salfords	d																		
Earlswood (Surrey)	d																		
Tonbridge 4	d										13 19								
Leigh (Kent)	d										13 23								
Penshurst	d										13 27								
Edenbridge	d										13 33								
Godstone	d										13 40								
Nutfield	d										13 45								
Reigate	d						←	13 34											←
Redhill 5	a						13 36	13 38	13 47		13 50			14 02					14 02
	d						13 37		13 48		13 51			14 07					14 07
Merstham	d						13 41							→					14 11
Coulsdon South	d						13 46				13 58								14 16
Purley 4	d						13 49				14 02								14 19
East Croydon	a		13 40	13 46		13 52	13 54		13 59	14 02	14 07		14 08		14 11		14 16	14 22	14 24
	d		13 40	13 47		13 53	13 55		13 59	14 02	14 07		14 08		14 12		14 17	14 23	14 25
Norwood Junction 2	a						13 59				14 12								14 29
New Cross Gate	d						14 07												14 37
London Bridge 4 ⊖	a			14 00			14 13			14 15	14 25						14 30		14 43
London Blackfriars 3 ⊖	a			14 07						14 22							14 37		
City Thameslink 3	a			14 10						14 26							14 40		
Farringdon 3 ⊖	a			14 14						14 29							14 44		
St Pancras International 15 ⊖	a			14 18						14 33							14 48		
St Albans City	a			14 39						14 55							15 09		
Luton Airport Parkway 4 ✈	a			14 50						15 07							15 20		
Luton 7	a			14 53						15 10							15 23		
Bedford 10	a			15 19						15 35							15 49		
Clapham Junction 10	a		13 49			14 02			14 08				14 17		14 21			14 32	
London Victoria 15 ⊖	a		13 57		14 05	14 10			14 16			14 20	14 24		14 28			14 40	

Station		GW 1	SN 1 🛒	SN 1	FC 1	SN 1	GW 1	SN 1 🛒	SN 1	SN 1	SN 1	FC 1	SN 1 🛒	SN 1 🛒	SN 1	GW 1	SN 1	FC 1	SN 1
Brighton 10	d				13 37							14 04		14 19				14 07	
Hove 2	d										13 51								
Preston Park	d				13 41						13 55							14 11	
Hassocks 4	d				13 47													14 17	
Burgess Hill 4	d				13 51						14 04							14 21	
Lewes 4	d									13 50									
Wivelsfield 4	d				13 53													14 23	
Haywards Heath 3	a				13 58					14 05	14 09	14 17						14 28	
	d				14 01						14 13	14 18						14 31	
Balcombe	d																	14 37	
Horsham 4	d			13 50					14 00								14 20		
Littlehaven	d								14 03										
Faygate	d																		
Ifield	d								14 09										
Crawley	d			13 59					14 13								14 29		
Three Bridges 4	a			14 02	14 11				14 16			14 26					14 32	14 42	
	d			14 03	14 12				14 18			14 27					14 33	14 42	
Gatwick Airport 10 ✈	a			14 07	14 16				14 22		14 24	14 31					14 37	14 46	
	d	14 03	14 05	14 08	14 17			14 20	14 23		14 25	14 32	14 35				14 38	14 47	
Horley 4	d								14 26								14 41		
Salfords	d								14 30										
Earlswood (Surrey)	d								14 33										
Tonbridge 4	d																		14 19
Leigh (Kent)	d																		14 23
Penshurst	d																		14 27
Edenbridge	d																		14 33
Godstone	d																		14 40
Nutfield	d																		14 45
Reigate	d					14 14	14 19								←	14 34			
Redhill 5	a	14 10		14 15		14 18	14 25		14 36						14 36	14 38	14 47		14 50
	d			14 16		14 19			14 37						14 37		14 48		14 51
Merstham	d					14 23			→						14 41				
Coulsdon South	d					14 28									14 46				14 58
Purley 4	d					14 32									14 49				15 02
East Croydon	a			14 27	14 31	14 37					14 40	14 46		14 52	14 54		14 59	15 02	15 07
	d			14 28	14 32	14 37					14 40	14 47		14 53	14 55		14 59	15 02	15 07
Norwood Junction 2	a					14 42									14 59				15 12
New Cross Gate	d														15 07				
London Bridge 4 ⊖	a				14 45	14 55						15 00			15 13			15 15	15 25
London Blackfriars 3 ⊖	a				14 52							15 07						15 22	
City Thameslink 3	a				14 56							15 10						15 26	
Farringdon 3 ⊖	a				14 59							15 14						15 29	
St Pancras International 15 ⊖	a				15 03							15 18						15 33	
St Albans City	a				15 25							15 39						15 55	
Luton Airport Parkway 4 ✈	a				15 37							15 50						16 07	
Luton 7	a				15 40							15 53						16 10	
Bedford 10	a				16 05							16 19						16 35	
Clapham Junction 10	a			14 37							14 49			15 02			15 08		
London Victoria 15 ⊖	a		14 35	14 44				14 50			14 57		15 05	15 10			15 16		

Table 186R

Saturdays

Brighton - London and Bedford

14 December to 17 May

Network Diagram - see first Page of Table 175

		SN 1 🚲	SN 1	SN 1	SN 1	SN 1	FC 1	SN 1 🚲	SN 1	GW 1	SN 1 🚲	SN 1	FC 1	SN 1	GW 1	SN 1 🚲	SN 1	SN 1	SN 1	FC 1	SN 1 🚲	SN 1 🚲	SN 1	GW 1	SN 1	FC 1	SN 1	SN 1 🚲	SN 1	SN 1	SN 1	SN 1	FC 1	SN 1 🚲	SN 1	GW 1	SN 1 🚲
Brighton 10	d		14 24				14 34	14 49					14 37							15 04		15 19				15 07			15 24				15 34	15 49			
Hove 2	d				14 21														14 51												15 21						
Preston Park	d												14 41						14 55							15 11											
Hassocks 4	d		14 34										14 47													15 17			15 34								
Burgess Hill 4	d		14 38										14 51						15 04							15 21			15 38								
Lewes 4	d					14 20												14 50														15 20					
Wivelsfield 4	d					14 35							14 53													15 23						15 35					
Haywards Heath 3	a				14 35	14 40	14 47						14 58					15 05	15 09	15 17						15 28					15 35	15 40	15 47				
	d				14 44		14 48						15 01					15 13		15 18						15 31					15 44		15 48				
Balcombe	d																									15 37											
Horsham 4	d			14 30								14 50					15 00								15 20					15 30							
Littlehaven	d			14 33													15 03													15 33							
Faygate	d																																				
Ifield	d			14 39													15 09													15 39							
Crawley	d			14 43								14 59					15 13								15 29					15 43							
Three Bridges 4	a			14 46			14 56					15 02	15 11				15 16			15 26					15 32	15 41				15 46			15 56				
	d			14 48			14 57					15 03	15 12				15 18			15 27					15 33	15 41				15 48			15 57				
Gatwick Airport 10 ✈	a		14 52	14 52	14 55		15 01					15 07	15 16				15 22	15 24		15 31					15 37	15 46			15 52	15 52	15 55		16 01				
	d	14 50	14 53	14 53	14 56		15 02			15 03	15 05	15 08	15 17			15 20	15 23	15 25		15 32	15 35				15 38	15 47		15 50	15 53	15 53	15 56		16 02			16 03	16 05
Horley 4	d			14 56													15 26								15 41					15 56							
Salfords	d																15 30																				
Earlswood (Surrey)	d																15 33																				
Tonbridge 4	d																										15 19										
Leigh (Kent)	d																										15 23										
Penshurst	d																										15 27										
Edenbridge	d																										15 33										
Godstone	d																										15 40										
Nutfield	d																										15 45										
Reigate	d								←					15 14	15 19								←	15 34											←		
Redhill 5	a			15 02					15 02	15 10		15 15		15 18	15 25		15 36						15 36	15 38	15 47		15 50			16 02					16 02	16 10	
	d			15 07					15 07			15 16		15 19			15 37						15 37		15 48		15 51			16 07					16 07		
Merstham	d			→					15 11					15 23			→						15 41							→					16 11		
Coulsdon South	d								15 16					15 28									15 46				15 58								16 16		
Purley 4	d								15 19					15 32									15 49				16 02								16 19		
East Croydon 🚋	a		15 08		15 11		15 16	15 22	15 24			15 28	15 31	15 37				15 40		15 46		15 52	15 54		15 59	16 02	16 07		16 08		16 11		16 16	16 22	16 24		
	d		15 08		15 11		15 17	15 23	15 25			15 28	15 32	15 37				15 40		15 47		15 53	15 55		15 59	16 02	16 07		16 08		16 11		16 17	16 23	16 25		
Norwood Junction 2	a								15 29					15 42									15 59				16 12								16 29		
New Cross Gate	d								15 37														16 07												16 37		
London Bridge 4 ⊖	a						15 30		15 43				15 45	15 55						16 00			16 13			16 15	16 25						16 30		16 43		
London Blackfriars 3 ⊖	a						15 37						15 52							16 07						16 22							16 37				
City Thameslink 3	a						15 40						15 56							16 10						16 26							16 40				
Farringdon 3 ⊖	a						15 44						15 59							16 14						16 29							16 44				
St Pancras International 15 ⊖	a						15 48						16 03							16 18						16 33							16 48				
St Albans City	a						16 09						16 25							16 39						16 55							17 09				
Luton Airport Parkway 4 ✈	a						16 20						16 37							16 50						17 07							17 20				
Luton 7	a						16 23						16 40							16 53						17 10							17 23				
Bedford 10	a						16 49						17 05							17 19						17 35							17 49				
Clapham Junction 10	a		15 17		15 20			15 32				15 37						15 49				16 02			16 08				16 17		16 20			16 32			
London Victoria 15 ⊖	a	15 20	15 24		15 28			15 40			15 35	15 45				15 50		15 57			16 05	16 10			16 16			16 20	16 24		16 28			16 40			16 35

Table 186R

Saturdays

14 December to 17 May

Brighton - London and Bedford

Network Diagram - see first Page of Table 175

Station		SN 1	FC 1	SN 1	GW 1	SN 1 (trolley)	SN 1	SN 1	SN 1	FC 1	SN 1 (trolley)	SN 1 (trolley)	SN 1	GW 1	SN 1	FC 1	SN 1	SN 1 (trolley)	SN 1
Brighton 10	d		15 37							16 04		16 19				16 07			16 24
Hove 2	d								15 51										
Preston Park	d		15 41						15 55							16 11			
Hassocks 4	d		15 47													16 17			16 34
Burgess Hill 4	d		15 51						16 04							16 21			16 38
Lewes 4	d							15 50											
Wivelsfield 4	d		15 53													16 23			
Haywards Heath 3	a		15 58					16 05	16 09	16 17						16 28			
	d		16 01						16 13	16 18						16 31			
Balcombe	d															16 37			
Horsham 4	d	15 50					16 00								16 20				
Littlehaven	d						16 03												
Faygate	d																		
Ifield	d						16 09												
Crawley	d	15 59					16 13								16 29				
Three Bridges 4	a	16 02	16 11				16 16			16 26					16 32	16 42			
	d	16 03	16 12				16 18			16 27					16 33	16 42			
Gatwick Airport 10 ✈	a	16 07	16 16				16 22		16 24	16 31					16 37	16 46			16 52
	d	16 08	16 17			16 20	16 23		16 25	16 32	16 35				16 38	16 47		16 50	16 53
Horley 4	d						16 26								16 41				
Salfords	d						16 30												
Earlswood (Surrey)	d						16 33												
Tonbridge 4	d																16 19		
Leigh (Kent)	d																16 23		
Penshurst	d																16 27		
Edenbridge	d																16 33		
Godstone	d																16 40		
Nutfield	d																16 45		
Reigate	d			16 14	16 19								←	16 34					
Redhill 5	a	16 15		16 18	16 25		16 36						16 36	16 38	16 47		16 50		
	d	16 16		16 19			16 37						16 37		16 48		16 51		
Merstham	d			16 23			→						16 41						
Coulsdon South	d			16 28									16 46				16 58		
Purley 4	d			16 32									16 49				17 02		
East Croydon	a	16 27	16 31	16 37					16 40	16 46		16 52	16 54		16 59	17 02	17 07		17 08
	d	16 27	16 32	16 37					16 40	16 47		16 53	16 55		16 59	17 02	17 07		17 08
Norwood Junction 2	a			16 42									16 59				17 12		
New Cross Gate	d												17 07						
London Bridge 4 ⊖	a		16 45	16 55						17 00			17 13			17 15	17 25		
London Blackfriars 3 ⊖	a		16 52							17 07						17 22			
City Thameslink 3	a		16 56							17 10						17 26			
Farringdon 3 ⊖	a		16 59							17 14						17 29			
St Pancras International 15 ⊖	a		17 03							17 18						17 33			
St Albans City	a		17 25							17 39						17 55			
Luton Airport Parkway 4 ✈	a		17 37							17 50						18 07			
Luton 7	a		17 40							17 53						18 10			
Bedford 10	a		18 05							18 19						18 35			
Clapham Junction 10	a	16 36							16 49			17 02			17 08				17 17
London Victoria 15 ⊖	a	16 44				16 50			16 57		17 05	17 10			17 16			17 20	17 24

Station		SN 1	SN 1	SN 1	FC 1	SN 1 (trolley)	SN 1	GW 1	SN 1 (trolley)	SN 1	FC 1	SN 1	GW 1	SN 1 (trolley)	SN 1	SN 1	SN 1	FC 1	SN 1 (trolley)
Brighton 10	d				16 34	16 49					16 37							17 04	
Hove 2	d		16 21														16 51		
Preston Park	d										16 41						16 55		
Hassocks 4	d										16 47								
Burgess Hill 4	d										16 51						17 04		
Lewes 4	d			16 20												16 50			
Wivelsfield 4	d			16 35							16 53								
Haywards Heath 3	a		16 35	16 40	16 47						16 58					17 05	17 09	17 17	
	d			16 44	16 48						17 01						17 13	17 18	
Balcombe	d																		
Horsham 4	d	16 30								16 50					17 00				
Littlehaven	d	16 33													17 03				
Faygate	d																		
Ifield	d	16 39													17 09				
Crawley	d	16 43								16 59					17 13				
Three Bridges 4	a	16 46			16 56					17 02	17 11				17 16			17 26	
	d	16 48			16 57					17 03	17 12				17 18			17 27	
Gatwick Airport 10 ✈	a	16 52		16 55	17 01					17 07	17 16				17 22		17 24	17 31	
	d	16 53		16 56	17 02			17 03	17 05	17 08	17 17			17 20	17 23		17 25	17 32	17 35
Horley 4	d	16 56													17 26				
Salfords	d														17 30				
Earlswood (Surrey)	d														17 33				
Tonbridge 4	d																		
Leigh (Kent)	d																		
Penshurst	d																		
Edenbridge	d																		
Godstone	d																		
Nutfield	d																		
Reigate	d						←					17 14	17 19						
Redhill 5	a	17 02					17 02	17 10		17 15		17 18	17 25		17 36				
	d	17 07					17 07			17 16		17 19			17 37				
Merstham	d	→					17 11					17 23			→				
Coulsdon South	d						17 16					17 28							
Purley 4	d						17 19					17 32							
East Croydon	a			17 11	17 16	17 22	17 24			17 27	17 31	17 37					17 40	17 46	
	d			17 11	17 17	17 23	17 25			17 27	17 32	17 37					17 40	17 47	
Norwood Junction 2	a						17 29					17 42							
New Cross Gate	d						17 37												
London Bridge 4 ⊖	a				17 30		17 43				17 45	17 55						18 00	
London Blackfriars 3 ⊖	a				17 37						17 52							18 07	
City Thameslink 3	a				17 40						17 56							18 10	
Farringdon 3 ⊖	a				17 44						17 59							18 14	
St Pancras International 15 ⊖	a				17 48						18 03							18 18	
St Albans City	a				18 09						18 25							18 39	
Luton Airport Parkway 4 ✈	a				18 20						18 37							18 50	
Luton 7	a				18 23						18 40							18 53	
Bedford 10	a				18 49						19 05							19 19	
Clapham Junction 10	a			17 20		17 32				17 36							17 49		
London Victoria 15 ⊖	a			17 28		17 40			17 35	17 44				17 50			17 57		18 05

Table 186R

Saturdays

14 December to 17 May

Brighton - London and Bedford

Network Diagram - see first Page of Table 175

Station		SN 1 (trolley)	SN 1	GW 1	SN 1	FC 1	SN 1	SN 1 (trolley)	SN 1	SN 1	SN 1	SN 1
Brighton 10	d	17 19				17 07			17 24			
Hove 2	d										17 21	
Preston Park	d					17 11						
Hassocks 4	d					17 17			17 34			
Burgess Hill 4	d					17 21			17 38			
Lewes 4	d											17 20
Wivelsfield 4	d					17 23						17 35
Haywards Heath 3	a					17 28					17 35	17 40
	d					17 31					17 44	
Balcombe	d					17 37						
Horsham 4	d				17 20					17 30		
Littlehaven	d									17 33		
Faygate	d											
Ifield	d									17 39		
Crawley	d				17 29					17 43		
Three Bridges 4	a				17 32	17 41				17 46		
	d				17 33	17 41				17 48		
Gatwick Airport 10 ✈	a				17 37	17 46			17 52	17 52	17 55	
	d				17 38	17 47		17 50	17 53	17 53	17 56	
Horley 4	d				17 41					17 56		
Salfords	d											
Earlswood (Surrey)	d											
Tonbridge 4	d						17 19					
Leigh (Kent)	d						17 23					
Penshurst	d						17 27					
Edenbridge	d						17 33					
Godstone	d						17 40					
Nutfield	d						17 45					
Reigate	d		←	17 34								
Redhill 5	a		17 36	17 38	17 47		17 50			18 02		
	d		17 37		17 48		17 51			18 07		
Merstham	d		17 41							→		
Coulsdon South	d		17 46				17 58					
Purley 4	d		17 49				18 02					
East Croydon	a	17 52	17 54		17 59	18 02	18 07		18 08		18 11	
	d	17 53	17 55		17 59	18 02	18 07		18 08		18 11	
Norwood Junction 2	a		17 59				18 12					
New Cross Gate	d		18 07									
London Bridge 4 ⊖	a		18 13			18 15	18 25					
London Blackfriars 3 ⊖	a					18 22						
City Thameslink 3	a					18 26						
Farringdon 3 ⊖	a					18 29						
St Pancras International 15 ⊖	a					18 33						
St Albans City	a					18 55						
Luton Airport Parkway 4 ✈	a					19 07						
Luton 7	a					19 10						
Bedford 10	a					19 35						
Clapham Junction 10	a	18 02			18 08				18 17		18 20	
London Victoria 15 ⊖	a	18 10			18 16			18 20	18 24		18 28	

Station		FC 1	SN 1 (trolley)	SN 1	GW 1	SN 1 (trolley)	SN 1	FC 1	SN 1	GW 1	SN 1 (trolley)	SN 1	SN 1	SN 1
Brighton 10	d	17 34	17 49					17 37						
Hove 2	d													17 51
Preston Park	d							17 41						17 55
Hassocks 4	d							17 47						
Burgess Hill 4	d							17 51						18 04
Lewes 4	d												17 50	
Wivelsfield 4	d							17 53						
Haywards Heath 3	a	17 47						17 58					18 05	18 09
	d	17 48						18 01					18 13	
Balcombe	d													
Horsham 4	d						17 50					18 00		
Littlehaven	d											18 03		
Faygate	d													
Ifield	d											18 09		
Crawley	d						17 59					18 13		
Three Bridges 4	a	17 56					18 02	18 11				18 16		
	d	17 57					18 03	18 12				18 18		
Gatwick Airport 10 ✈	a	18 01					18 07	18 16				18 22	18 24	
	d	18 02			18 03	18 05	18 08	18 17			18 20	18 23	18 25	
Horley 4	d											18 26		
Salfords	d											18 30		
Earlswood (Surrey)	d											18 33		
Tonbridge 4	d													
Leigh (Kent)	d													
Penshurst	d													
Edenbridge	d													
Godstone	d													
Nutfield	d													
Reigate	d			←					18 14	18 19				
Redhill 5	a			18 02	18 10		18 15		18 18	18 25		18 36		
	d			18 07			18 16		18 19			18 37		
Merstham	d			18 11					18 23			→		
Coulsdon South	d			18 16					18 28					
Purley 4	d			18 19					18 32					
East Croydon	a	18 16	18 22	18 24			18 27	18 31	18 37				18 40	
	d	18 17	18 23	18 25			18 27	18 32	18 37				18 40	
Norwood Junction 2	a			18 29					18 42					
New Cross Gate	d			18 37										
London Bridge 4 ⊖	a	18 30		18 43				18 45	18 55					
London Blackfriars 3 ⊖	a	18 37						18 52						
City Thameslink 3	a	18 40						18 56						
Farringdon 3 ⊖	a	18 44						18 59						
St Pancras International 15 ⊖	a	18 48						19 03						
St Albans City	a	19 09						19 25						
Luton Airport Parkway 4 ✈	a	19 20						19 37						
Luton 7	a	19 23						19 40						
Bedford 10	a	19 49						20 05						
Clapham Junction 10	a		18 32				18 36						18 49	
London Victoria 15 ⊖	a		18 40			18 35	18 44				18 50		18 57	

Station		FC 1	SN 1 (trolley)	SN 1	SN 1	GW 1	SN 1	FC 1	SN 1	SN 1 (trolley)	SN 1	SN 1
Brighton 10	d	18 04		18 19				18 07			18 24	
Hove 2	d											
Preston Park	d							18 11				
Hassocks 4	d							18 17			18 34	
Burgess Hill 4	d							18 21			18 38	
Lewes 4	d											
Wivelsfield 4	d							18 23				
Haywards Heath 3	a	18 17						18 28				
	d	18 18						18 31				
Balcombe	d							18 37				
Horsham 4	d						18 20					18 32
Littlehaven	d											18 35
Faygate	d											
Ifield	d											18 41
Crawley	d						18 29					18 45
Three Bridges 4	a	18 26					18 32	18 42				18 48
	d	18 27					18 33	18 42				18 50
Gatwick Airport 10 ✈	a	18 31					18 37	18 46			18 52	18 54
	d	18 32	18 35				18 38	18 47		18 50	18 53	18 55
Horley 4	d						18 41					18 58
Salfords	d											
Earlswood (Surrey)	d											
Tonbridge 4	d								18 19			
Leigh (Kent)	d								18 23			
Penshurst	d								18 27			
Edenbridge	d								18 33			
Godstone	d								18 40			
Nutfield	d								18 45			
Reigate	d				←	18 34						
Redhill 5	a				18 36	18 38	18 47		18 50			19 04
	d				18 37		18 48		18 51			19 07
Merstham	d				18 41							→
Coulsdon South	d				18 46				18 58			
Purley 4	d				18 49				19 02			
East Croydon	a	18 46		18 52	18 54		18 59	19 02	19 07		19 08	
	d	18 47		18 53	18 55		18 59	19 02	19 07		19 08	
Norwood Junction 2	a				18 59				19 12			
New Cross Gate	d				19 07							
London Bridge 4 ⊖	a	19 00			19 13			19 15	19 25			
London Blackfriars 3 ⊖	a	19 07						19 22				
City Thameslink 3	a	19 10						19 26				
Farringdon 3 ⊖	a	19 14						19 29				
St Pancras International 15 ⊖	a	19 18						19 33				
St Albans City	a	19 39						19 55				
Luton Airport Parkway 4 ✈	a	19 50						20 07				
Luton 7	a	19 53						20 10				
Bedford 10	a	20 19						20 35				
Clapham Junction 10	a			19 02			19 08				19 17	
London Victoria 15 ⊖	a		19 05	19 10			19 16			19 20	19 24	

Table 186R

Saturdays

14 December to 17 May

Brighton - London and Bedford

Network Diagram - see first Page of Table 175

		SN 1	SN 1	FC 1	SN 1	SN 1	GW 1	SN 1 🚲	SN 1	FC 1	SN	GW 1	SN 1 🚲	SN 1	SN 1	SN 1	SN 1	FC 1	SN 1 🚲
Brighton 10	d			18 34	18 49					18 37				18 54				19 04	
Hove 2	d	18 21															18 51		
Preston Park	d									18 41							18 55		
Hassocks 4	d									18 47				19 06					
Burgess Hill 4	d									18 51							19 04		
Lewes 4	d		18 20													18 50			
Wivelsfield 4	d		18 35							18 53									
Haywards Heath 3	a	18 35	18 40	18 47						18 58						19 05	19 09	19 17	
	d	18 44		18 48						19 01						19 14		19 18	
Balcombe	d																		
Horsham 4	d								18 50						19 02				
Littlehaven	d														19 05				
Faygate	d																		
Ifield	d														19 11				
Crawley	d								18 59						19 14				
Three Bridges 4	a			18 56					19 02	19 11					19 18			19 26	
	d			18 57					19 03	19 12					19 18			19 27	
Gatwick Airport 10 ✈	a	18 55		19 01					19 07	19 16				19 22	19 22	19 25		19 31	
	d	18 56		19 02			19 03	19 05	19 08	19 17			19 20	19 23	19 23	19 26		19 32	19 35
Horley 4	d								19 11						19 26				
Salfords	d														19 30				
Earlswood (Surrey)	d														19 33				
Tonbridge 4	d																		
Leigh (Kent)	d																		
Penshurst	d																		
Edenbridge	d																		
Godstone	d																		
Nutfield	d																		
Reigate	d					←					19 14	19 19							
Redhill 5	a					19 04	19 10		19 17		19 18	19 25			19 36				
	d					19 07			19 18						19 37				
Merstham	d					19 11									→				
Coulsdon South	d					19 16													
Purley 4	d					19 19													
East Croydon 🚊	a	19 11		19 16	19 22	19 25			19 29	19 31				19 38		19 41		19 46	
	d	19 11		19 17	19 23	19 26			19 29	19 32				19 38		19 42		19 47	
Norwood Junction 2	a																		
New Cross Gate	d																		
London Bridge 4 ⊖	a			19 30						19 45								20 00	
London Blackfriars 3 ⊖	a			19 37						19 52								20 07	
City Thameslink 3	a			19 40						19 56								20 10	
Farringdon 3 ⊖	a			19 44						19 59								20 14	
St Pancras International 15 ⊖	a			19 48						20 03								20 18	
St Albans City	a			20 09						20 25								20 39	
Luton Airport Parkway 4 ✈	a			20 20						20 37								20 50	
Luton 7	a			20 23						20 40								20 53	
Bedford 10	a			20 49						21 05								21 19	
Clapham Junction 10	a	19 20			19 32	19 36			19 40					19 47		19 51			
London Victoria 15 ⊖	a	19 28			19 40	19 43		19 35	19 50				19 50	19 54		19 58			20 05

		SN 1	SN 1	GW 1	SN 1	SN 1	FC 1	SN 1 🚲	SN 1	SN 1	SN 1	FC 1	SN 1	SN 1	GW 1	SN 1 🚲	SN 1	FC 1	GW 1
Brighton 10	d	19 19					19 07					19 34	19 49					19 37	
Hove 2	d									19 21									
Preston Park	d						19 11											19 41	
Hassocks 4	d						19 17											19 47	
Burgess Hill 4	d						19 21											19 51	
Lewes 4	d										19 20								
Wivelsfield 4	d						19 23				19 35							19 53	
Haywards Heath 3	a						19 28			19 35	19 40	19 47						19 58	
	d						19 31			19 44		19 48						20 01	
Balcombe	d						19 37												
Horsham 4	d					19 21			19 32								19 52		
Littlehaven	d								19 35										
Faygate	d																		
Ifield	d								19 41										
Crawley	d					19 30			19 45								20 01		
Three Bridges 4	a					19 33	19 42		19 48			19 56					20 05	20 11	
	d					19 34	19 42		19 50			19 57					20 05	20 12	
Gatwick Airport 10 ✈	a					19 38	19 46		19 54	19 55		20 01					20 10	20 16	
	d					19 39	19 47	19 50	19 55	19 56		20 02			20 03	20 05	20 11	20 17	
Horley 4	d								19 58										
Salfords	d																		
Earlswood (Surrey)	d																		
Tonbridge 4	d				19 10														
Leigh (Kent)	d				19 14														
Penshurst	d				19 18														
Edenbridge	d				19 24														
Godstone	d				19 31														
Nutfield	d				19 36														
Reigate	d		←	19 34										←					20 19
Redhill 5	a		19 36	19 38	19 45	19 47			20 04					20 04	20 10		20 18		20 25
	d		19 37			19 48			20 07					20 07			20 18		
Merstham	d		19 41						→					20 11					
Coulsdon South	d		19 46											20 16					
Purley 4	d		19 49											20 19					
East Croydon 🚊	a	19 52	19 54			20 00	20 02			20 11		20 16	20 22	20 25			20 29	20 31	
	d	19 53	19 57			20 00	20 02			20 11		20 17	20 23	20 26			20 30	20 32	
Norwood Junction 2	a																		
New Cross Gate	d																		
London Bridge 4 ⊖	a						20 15					20 30						20 45	
London Blackfriars 3 ⊖	a						20 22					20 37						20 52	
City Thameslink 3	a						20 26					20 40						20 56	
Farringdon 3 ⊖	a						20 29					20 44						20 59	
St Pancras International 15 ⊖	a						20 33					20 48						21 03	
St Albans City	a						20 55					21 09						21 25	
Luton Airport Parkway 4 ✈	a						21 07					21 20						21 37	
Luton 7	a						21 10					21 23						21 40	
Bedford 10	a						21 35					21 49						22 05	
Clapham Junction 10	a	20 02	20 07			20 11				20 20			20 32	20 36			20 40		
London Victoria 15 ⊖	a	20 10	20 14			20 20		20 20		20 27			20 40	20 43		20 35	20 50		

Table 186R

Saturdays

Brighton - London and Bedford

14 December to 17 May

Network Diagram - see first Page of Table 175

		SN 1 🛒	SN 1	SN 1	SN 1	SN 1	FC 1	SN 1 🛒	SN 1	SN 1	GW 1	SN 1	SN 1	FC 1	SN 1 🛒	SN 1	SN 1	FC 1	SN 1	SN 1	GW 1	SN 1	SN 1	FC 1	GW 1	SN 1	SN 1	SN 1	SN 1	SN 1	SN 1	SN 1	GW 1	SN 1	FC 1	SN 1	SN 1
Brighton 10	d					19 54	20 04		20 19					20 07				20 34	20 49					20 37					21 19					21 00	21 07		
Hove 2	d				19 52											20 22												20 52									21 22
Preston Park	d				19 56	19 58								20 11										20 41										21 04	21 11		
Hassocks 4	d					20 04								20 17										20 47										21 10	21 17		
Burgess Hill 4	d				20 04	20 08								20 21										20 51				21 04						21 14	21 21		
Lewes 4	d			19 50																							20 50										
Wivelsfield 4	d			20 02		20 10							←	20 23										20 53			21 04							21 16	21 23		
Haywards Heath 3	a			20 07	20 10	20 14	20 17						20 14	20 28		20 36		20 47						20 58			21 09	21 11						21 21	21 28		21 36
	d			20 14		20 22	20 18						20 22	20 31		20 39		20 48						21 01			21 15							21 22	21 31		21 39
Balcombe	d					→								20 37																					21 37		
Horsham 4	d		20 02														20 32						20 52							21 02							
Littlehaven	d		20 05														20 35													21 05							
Faygate	d																																				
Ifield	d		20 11														20 41													21 11							
Crawley	d		20 14														20 45						21 01							21 14							
Three Bridges 4	a		20 18				20 26						20 32	20 42		20 47	20 48	20 56					21 05	21 11						21 18				21 31	21 42		21 47
	d		20 18				20 27						20 32	20 42		20 48	20 51	20 57					21 05	21 12						21 18				21 32	21 42		21 48
Gatwick Airport 10 ✈	a		20 22	20 25			20 31						20 37	20 46		20 52	20 56	21 01					21 10	21 16			21 26			21 22				21 37	21 46		21 52
	d	20 20	20 23	20 26			20 32	20 35					20 38	20 47	20 50	20 53	20 57	21 02			21 03	21 05	21 11	21 17		21 20	21 27			21 23		21 35		21 38	21 47	21 50	21 53
Horley 4	d		20 26														20 59													21 26							
Salfords	d		20 30																											21 30							
Earlswood (Surrey)	d		20 33																											21 33							
Tonbridge 4	d											20 10																			21 10						
Leigh (Kent)	d											20 14																			21 14						
Penshurst	d											20 18																			21 18						
Edenbridge	d											20 24																			21 24						
Godstone	d											20 31																			21 31						
Nutfield	d											20 36																			21 36						
Reigate	d									←	20 34									←					21 19								21 40				
Redhill 5	a		20 36							20 36	20 38	20 45	20 47				21 06			21 06	21 10		21 18		21 26					21 36	21 41		21 44	21 47			
	d		20 37							20 37			20 48				21 07			21 07			21 18							21 37				21 47			
Merstham	d		→							20 41							→			21 11										21 41							
Coulsdon South	d									20 46										21 16										21 46							
Purley 4	d									20 49										21 19										21 49							
East Croydon 🚋	a			20 41			20 46		20 52	20 54			20 59	21 02		21 08		21 16	21 22	21 25			21 29	21 31			21 41		21 52	21 55				21 59	22 02		22 08
	d			20 41			20 47		20 53	20 56			21 00	21 02		21 09		21 17	21 23	21 26			21 30	21 32			21 42		21 53	21 56				22 00	22 02		22 09
Norwood Junction 2	a																																				
New Cross Gate	d																																				
London Bridge 4 ⊖	a						21 00							21 15				21 30						21 45											22 15		
London Blackfriars 3 ⊖	a						21 07							21 22				21 37						21 52											22 22		
City Thameslink 3	a																																				
Farringdon 3 ⊖	a						21 14							21 29				21 44						21 59											22 28		
St Pancras International 15 ⊖	a						21 18							21 33				21 48						22 03											22 32		
St Albans City	a						21 39							21 55				22 09						22 25											22 56		
Luton Airport Parkway 4 ✈	a						21 50							22 07				22 20						22 37											23 08		
Luton 7	a						21 53							22 10				22 23						22 40											23 11		
Bedford 10	a						22 19							22 35				22 49						23 06											23 38		
Clapham Junction 10	a			20 50					21 02	21 07			21 10			21 18			21 32	21 36			21 41				21 51		22 02	22 06				22 10			22 18
London Victoria 15 ⊖	a	20 50		20 58				21 05	21 10	21 14			21 17		21 20	21 26			21 40	21 43		21 35	21 48			21 50	21 58		22 10	22 13		22 05		22 17		22 20	22 26

Table 186R

Saturdays

14 December to 17 May

Brighton - London and Bedford

Network Diagram - see first Page of Table 175

		SN 1	SN 1	SN 1	SN 1	FC 1	SN 1	GW 1	SN 1	SN 1	SN 1	SN 1	SN 1	SN 1	FC 1	GW 1	SN 1
										A							
									🛒	🛒							
Brighton 10	d	21 49				21 37								22 00	22 07		
Hove 2	d									21 52							
Preston Park	d					21 41								22 04	22 11		
Hassocks 4	d					21 47								22 10	22 17		
Burgess Hill 4	d					21 51				22 04				22 14	22 21		
Lewes 4	d								21 50								
Wivelsfield 4	d					21 53			22 02					22 16	22 23		
Haywards Heath 3	a					21 58			22 06	22 09				22 21	22 28		
	d					22 01			22 13					22 22	22 31		
Balcombe	d														22 37		
Horsham 4	d		21 32		21 52						22 02						
Littlehaven	d		21 35								22 05						
Faygate	d																
Ifield	d		21 41								22 11						
Crawley	d		21 45		22 01						22 14						
Three Bridges 4	a		21 48		22 05	22 11					22 18			22 31	22 42		
	d		21 52		22 05	22 12					22 19			22 32	22 42		
Gatwick Airport 10 ✈	a		21 56		22 10	22 16			22 24		22 23			22 37	22 46		
	d		21 57	22 05	22 11	22 17	22 20	22 22	22 25		22 24		22 35	22 38	22 47		22 50
Horley 4	d		22 00								22 27						
Salfords	d										22 31						
Earlswood (Surrey)	d										22 34						
Tonbridge 4	d											22 10					
Leigh (Kent)	d											22 14					
Penshurst	d											22 18					
Edenbridge	d											22 24					
Godstone	d											22 31					
Nutfield	d											22 36					
Reigate	d															22 48	
Redhill 5	a		22 06		22 18			22 30			22 37	22 42		22 46		22 52	
	d		22 07		22 18						22 38			22 46			
Merstham	d		22 11								22 42						
Coulsdon South	d		22 16								22 47						
Purley 4	d		22 19								22 50						
East Croydon 🚊	a	22 22	22 25		22 30	22 32			22 40		22 55			22 59	23 02		
	d	22 23	22 26		22 31	22 32			22 40		22 56			23 00	23 02		
Norwood Junction 2	a																
New Cross Gate	d																
London Bridge 4 ⊖	a					22 45									23 15		
London Blackfriars 3 ⊖	a					22 52									23 22		
City Thameslink 3	a																
Farringdon 3 ⊖	a					22 58									23 28		
St Pancras International 15 ⊖	a					23 02									23 32		
St Albans City	a					23 26									23 56		
Luton Airport Parkway 4 ✈	a					23 38									00 08		
Luton 7	a					23 41									00 11		
Bedford 10	a					00 08									00 38		
Clapham Junction 10	a	22 32	22 36		22 40				22 49		23 06			23 10			
London Victoria 15 ⊖	a	22 40	22 43	22 35	22 50		22 50		22 57		23 13		23 05	23 20			23 20

		SN 1	FC 1	SN 1	FC 1	GW 1	SN 1	SN 1	SN 1	SN 1	GW 1	SN 1	FC 1	SN 1	SN 1	FC 1
Brighton 10	d		22 33									23 05	23 11			23 37
Hove 2	d															
Preston Park	d		22 37									23 09				23 41
Hassocks 4	d		22 43									23 15	23 20			23 47
Burgess Hill 4	d		22 47									23 19	23 23			23 51
Lewes 4	d			22 40												
Wivelsfield 4	d		22 49	22 54								23 21				23 53
Haywards Heath 3	a		22 53	22 58								23 26	23 28			23 58
	d		22 54	22 59								23 26	23 29			23 59
Balcombe	d		22 59													00 05
Horsham 4	d							23 02								
Littlehaven	d							23 05								
Faygate	d															
Ifield	d							23 11								
Crawley	d				←			23 14							←	
Three Bridges 4	a		23 05	23 08	23 05			23 18				23 35	23 37		23 35	00 10
	d		23 12	23 08	23 12			23 18				23 47	23 38		23 47	00 10
Gatwick Airport 10 ✈	a		→	23 12	23 16			23 22				→	23 42		23 52	00 14
	d	23 05		23 13	23 17	23 18	23 20	23 23		23 35			23 43	23 50	23 53	00 15
Horley 4	d							23 26							23 56	
Salfords	d							23 30								
Earlswood (Surrey)	d							23 33								
Tonbridge 4	d								23 17							
Leigh (Kent)	d								23 21							
Penshurst	d								23 25							
Edenbridge	d								23 31							
Godstone	d								23 38							
Nutfield	d								23 43							
Reigate	d										23 54					
Redhill 5	a					23 25		23 36	23 49		23 58				00 03	00 23
	d							23 37							00 03	00 24
Merstham	d							23 41								
Coulsdon South	d							23 46								
Purley 4	d							23 49							00 12	
East Croydon 🚊	a			23 29	23 32			23 54					00 01		00 17	00 35
	d			23 30	23 32			23 55					00 02		00 17	00 36
Norwood Junction 2	a															
New Cross Gate	d															
London Bridge 4 ⊖	a				23 44								00 21			00 51
London Blackfriars 3 ⊖	a				23 52								00 28			00 58
City Thameslink 3	a															
Farringdon 3 ⊖	a				23 58								00 34			
St Pancras International 15 ⊖	a				00 02								00 38			01 08
St Albans City	a				00 26								01 11			01 41
Luton Airport Parkway 4 ✈	a				00 38								01 23			01 53
Luton 7	a				00 41								01 26			01 56
Bedford 10	a				01 08								01 52			02 22
Clapham Junction 10	a			23 41				00 10							00 33	
London Victoria 15 ⊖	a	23 35		23 52			23 55	00 17		00 08				00 25	00 41	

A 🛒 from Haywards Heath

Table 186R

Sundays

Brighton - London and Bedford

8 December to 29 December

Network Diagram - see first Page of Table 175

		FC	SN	SN	FC	SN	SN	GW	SN	SN	SN	SN	SN	SN	SN	FC	SN	SN	SN
		1	1	1	1	1	1	1	1	1	1	1	1	1	1		1	1	1
Brighton 10	d																		
Hove 2	d																		
Preston Park	d																		
Hassocks 4	d																		
Burgess Hill 4	d																		
Lewes 4	d																		
Wivelsfield 4	d																		
Haywards Heath 3	a																		
	d																		
Balcombe	d				00 05														
Horsham 4	d																		
Littlehaven	d																		
Faygate	d																		
Ifield	d																		
Crawley	d																		
Three Bridges 4	a				00 10														
	d				00 10					01 15		02 10	03 10	04 10		05 13		05 26	
Gatwick Airport 10 ✈	a				00 14					01 19		02 14	03 14	04 14		05 17		05 30	
	d			00 07	00 15	00 20	00 35		00 50	01 20	01 35	02 15	03 15	04 15	04 35	05 18	05 20	05 32	05 50
Horley 4	d									01 23		02 18	03 18	04 18				05 34	
Salfords	d																		
Earlswood (Surrey)	d																		
Tonbridge 4	d																		
Leigh (Kent)	d																		
Penshurst	d																		
Edenbridge	d																		
Godstone	d																		
Nutfield	d																		
Reigate	d							00 45											
Redhill 5	a				00 23			00 49										05 42	
	d		00 03		00 24													05 42	
Merstham	d																		
Coulsdon South	d																		
Purley 4	d		00 12							01 37		02 33	03 33	04 33				05 51	
East Croydon ⇌	a		00 17		00 35					01 43		02 39	03 39	04 39		05 36		05 57	
	d	00 02	00 17		00 36					01 43		02 40	03 40	04 40		05 37		05 58	
Norwood Junction 2	a																		
New Cross Gate	d																		
London Bridge 4 ⊖	a	00 21			00 51														
London Blackfriars 3 ⊖	a	00 28			00 58											06 04			
City Thameslink 3	a																		
Farringdon 3 ⊖	a	00 34																	
St Pancras International 15 ⊖	a	00 38			01 08														
St Albans City	a	01 11			01 41														
Luton Airport Parkway 4 ✈	a	01 23			01 53														
Luton 7	a	01 26			01 56														
Bedford 10	a	01 52			02 22														
Clapham Junction 10	a		00 33							01 57		02 53	03 53	04 55				06 12	
London Victoria 15 ⊖	a		00 41	00 42		00 56	01 11		01 26	02 05	02 10	03 05	04 05	05 05	05 10		05 58	06 21	06 25

		SN	FC	GW	SN	SN	SN	FC	SN	SN	SN	GW	SN	FC	GW	SN	SN	SN	FC
		1		1	1	1	1	1	1	1	1	1	1	1	1	1	1	1	1
		🚲			🚲		🚲		🚲				🚲			🚲		🚲	
Brighton 10	d		05 36					06 06		06 13				06 36					07 04
Hove 2	d																		
Preston Park	d									06 17									
Hassocks 4	d		05 45					06 15		06 23				06 45					07 13
Burgess Hill 4	d		05 48					06 18		06 27				06 48					07 16
Lewes 4	d																		
Wivelsfield 4	d									06 29									
Haywards Heath 3	a		05 53					06 23		06 33				06 53					07 21
	d		05 54					06 24		06 34				06 54					07 24
Balcombe	d																		
Horsham 4	d					06 04					06 28						06 56		
Littlehaven	d					06 07					06 31						06 59		
Faygate	d																		
Ifield	d					06 13					06 37						07 05		
Crawley	d					06 17					06 41						07 09		
Three Bridges 4	a		06 02			06 20		06 32		06 42	06 46			07 02			07 12		07 32
	d		06 02			06 21		06 32		06 43	06 47			07 02			07 13		07 32
Gatwick Airport 10 ✈	a		06 07			06 25		06 37		06 47	06 51			07 07			07 17		07 37
	d	06 05	06 08	06 10	06 20		06 35	06 38	06 45	06 48	06 52		07 05	07 08	07 10	07 15	07 18	07 33	07 38
Horley 4	d										06 54						07 21		
Salfords	d																		
Earlswood (Surrey)	d																		
Tonbridge 4	d																		
Leigh (Kent)	d																		
Penshurst	d																		
Edenbridge	d																		
Godstone	d																		
Nutfield	d																		
Reigate	d											07 05							
Redhill 5	a			06 17							07 01	07 09			07 16		07 29		
	d										07 02						07 29		
Merstham	d										07 06						07 33		
Coulsdon South	d										07 11						07 38		
Purley 4	d										07 15						07 43		
East Croydon ⇌	a		06 26					06 56		07 05	07 20			07 26			07 48		07 56
	d		06 27					06 57		07 06	07 24			07 27			07 48		07 57
Norwood Junction 2	a																07 53		
New Cross Gate	d																		
London Bridge 4 ⊖	a							07 15						07 45			08 05		08 15
London Blackfriars 3 ⊖	a		06 54					07 23						07 53					08 23
City Thameslink 3	a																		
Farringdon 3 ⊖	a							07 30						08 00					08 30
St Pancras International 15 ⊖	a							07 34						08 04					08 34
St Albans City	a							08 07						08 37					09 07
Luton Airport Parkway 4 ✈	a							08 19						08 49					09 19
Luton 7	a							08 22						08 52					09 22
Bedford 10	a							08 49						09 19					09 49
Clapham Junction 10	a									07 18	07 38								
London Victoria 15 ⊖	a	06 40			06 55		07 11		07 20	07 29	07 46		07 42			07 50		08 10	

Table 186R

Sundays

8 December to 29 December

Brighton - London and Bedford

Network Diagram - see first Page of Table 175

		SN 1	SN 1	SN 1 🛒	SN 1 🛒	SN 1	SN 1 🛒	FC 1	GW 1	SN 1	GW 1	SN 1	SN 1 🛒	SN 1 🛒	FC 1	SN 1	SN 1	SN 1 🛒	SN 1 🛒
Brighton 10	d	07 06						07 36							08 04	08 06			
Hove 2	d									07 55									
Preston Park	d	07 10														08 09			
Hassocks 4	d	07 16						07 45							08 13	08 16			
Burgess Hill 4	d	07 20						07 48		08 05					08 16	08 19			
Lewes 4	d				07 20														08 22
Wivelsfield 4	d	07 22			07 35											08 21			08 37
Haywards Heath 3	a	07 26			07 39			07 53		08 10					08 21	08 26			08 41
	d	07 27			07 40			07 54		08 11					08 24	08 26			08 42
Balcombe	d	07 32														08 32			
Horsham 4	d					07 37						07 53							
Littlehaven	d											07 56							
Faygate	d																		
Ifield	d											08 02							
Crawley	d					07 46						08 06							
Three Bridges 4	a	07 38				07 50		08 02				08 09			08 32	08 37			
	d	07 38				07 51		08 02				08 09			08 32	08 38			
Gatwick Airport 10 ✈	a	07 42			07 51	07 55		08 07		08 22		08 14			08 37	08 42			08 53
	d	07 43		07 50	07 52	07 56	08 05	08 08	08 10	08 23		08 15	08 20	08 35	08 38	08 43		08 50	08 54
Horley 4	d					07 59						08 17							
Salfords	d																		
Earlswood (Surrey)	d																		
Tonbridge 4	d		07 23														08 29		
Leigh (Kent)	d		07 27														08 33		
Penshurst	d		07 31														08 37		
Edenbridge	d		07 37														08 43		
Godstone	d		07 44														08 50		
Nutfield	d		07 49														08 55		
Reigate	d										08 13								
Redhill 5	a	07 51	07 54			08 06			08 16		08 18	08 25				08 51	09 00		
	d	07 52				08 07						08 33				08 52			
Merstham	d											08 37							
Coulsdon South	d											08 42							
Purley 4	d					08 16						08 46							
East Croydon 🚊	a	08 04			08 09	08 21		08 26		08 40		08 51			08 55	09 03			09 09
	d	08 04			08 10	08 22		08 27		08 41		08 52			08 56	09 03			09 10
Norwood Junction 2	a											08 56							
New Cross Gate	d																		
London Bridge 4 ⊖	a							08 45				09 08			09 15				
London Blackfriars 3 ⊖	a							08 53							09 23				
City Thameslink 3	a																		
Farringdon 3 ⊖	a							09 00							09 29				
St Pancras International 15 ⊖	a							09 04							09 34				
St Albans City	a							09 37							10 07				
Luton Airport Parkway 4 ✈	a							09 49							10 19				
Luton 7	a							09 52							10 22				
Bedford 10	a							10 19							10 49				
Clapham Junction 10	a	08 17			08 27	08 35				08 57						09 12			09 19
London Victoria 15 ⊖	a	08 25		08 27	08 35	08 43	08 45			09 05			08 58	09 09		09 19		09 21	09 26

		SN 1 🛒	SN 1	SN 1 🛒	GW 1	FC 1	SN 1 🛒	SN 1	FC 1	SN 1 🛒	SN 1	GW 1	SN 1 🛒	SN 1	FC 1	SN 1	SN 1 🛒	SN 1 🛒	SN 1 🛒
Brighton 10	d	08 38				08 44				09 10				09 00	09 14				09 35
Hove 2	d							08 55											
Preston Park	d													09 03					
Hassocks 4	d					08 53								09 10	09 23				
Burgess Hill 4	d					08 57		09 05						09 13	09 27				
Lewes 4	d																	09 20	
Wivelsfield 4	d													09 15				09 34	
Haywards Heath 3	a					09 02		09 10						09 20	09 32			09 38	
	d					09 03		09 11						09 25	09 33			09 41	
Balcombe	d													09 30					
Horsham 4	d		08 44								09 01								
Littlehaven	d										09 04								
Faygate	d																		
Ifield	d										09 10								
Crawley	d		08 53								09 14								
Three Bridges 4	a		08 56			09 11					09 17			09 36	09 41				
	d		08 57			09 12					09 18			09 36	09 42				
Gatwick Airport 10 ✈	a	09 00	09 02			09 16		09 22			09 22			09 40	09 46			09 52	09 56
	d	09 01	09 03	09 05	09 08	09 17	09 20	09 23	09 27		09 23		09 35	09 41	09 47		09 50	09 53	09 57
Horley 4	d		09 05								09 26								
Salfords	d																		
Earlswood (Surrey)	d										09 33								
Tonbridge 4	d															09 29			
Leigh (Kent)	d															09 33			
Penshurst	d															09 37			
Edenbridge	d															09 43			
Godstone	d															09 50			
Nutfield	d															09 55			
Reigate	d											09 30							
Redhill 5	a		09 13		09 16						09 36	09 36		09 48		10 00			
	d		09 14								09 37			09 49					
Merstham	d										09 41								
Coulsdon South	d		09 21								09 46								
Purley 4	d		09 24								09 50								
East Croydon 🚊	a	09 15	09 29			09 32		09 38	09 41	09 45	09 55			10 00	10 02			10 08	10 13
	d	09 16	09 30			09 33		09 39	09 47	09 46	09 56			10 00	10 03			10 09	10 14
Norwood Junction 2	a										10 02								
New Cross Gate	d																		
London Bridge 4 ⊖	a					09 45			10 00		10 14				10 15				
London Blackfriars 3 ⊖	a					09 53			10 07						10 22				
City Thameslink 3	a																		
Farringdon 3 ⊖	a					09 59			10 14						10 28				
St Pancras International 15 ⊖	a					10 04			10 18						10 32				
St Albans City	a					10 37			10 42						10 56				
Luton Airport Parkway 4 ✈	a					10 49			10 55						11 08				
Luton 7	a					10 52			10 58						11 11				
Bedford 10	a					11 19									11 38				
Clapham Junction 10	a	09 25	09 39					09 48		09 55				10 09				10 18	10 23
London Victoria 15 ⊖	a	09 32	09 46	09 35			09 50	09 56		10 03			10 05	10 17			10 20	10 26	10 30

Table 186R

Sundays

Brighton - London and Bedford

8 December to 29 December

Network Diagram - see first Page of Table 175

		FC	SN	SN	GW	FC	SN	SN	FC	SN	SN	GW	SN	SN	FC	SN	SN	SN	SN
		1	1	1 🛒	1	1	1 🛒	1	1	1 🛒	1	1	1 🛒	1	1	1	1 🛒	1 🛒	1 🛒
Brighton [10]	d					09 44				10 10				10 00	10 14				10 35
Hove [2]	d							09 55											
Preston Park	d													10 03					
Hassocks [4]	d					09 53								10 10	10 23				
Burgess Hill [4]	d					09 57		10 05						10 13	10 27				
Lewes [4]	d																	10 20	
Wivelsfield [4]	d													10 15				10 35	
Haywards Heath [3]	a					10 02		10 10						10 20	10 32			10 39	
	d					10 03		10 11						10 25	10 33			10 41	
Balcombe	d													10 30					
Horsham [4]	d		09 44								10 01								
Littlehaven	d										10 04								
Faygate	d																		
Ifield	d										10 10								
Crawley	d		09 53								10 14								
Three Bridges [4]	a		09 56			10 11					10 17			10 36	10 41				
	d		09 57			10 12					10 18			10 36	10 42				
Gatwick Airport [10] ✈	a		10 02			10 16		10 22			10 22			10 40	10 46			10 52	10 56
	d	09 57	10 03	10 05	10 08	10 17	10 20	10 23	10 27		10 23		10 35	10 41	10 47		10 50	10 53	10 57
Horley [4]	d		10 05								10 26								
Salfords	d																		
Earlswood (Surrey)	d										10 33								
Tonbridge [4]	d															10 29			
Leigh (Kent)	d															10 33			
Penshurst	d															10 37			
Edenbridge	d															10 43			
Godstone	d															10 50			
Nutfield	d															10 55			
Reigate	d											10 31							
Redhill [5]	a		10 13		10 16						10 36	10 36		10 48		11 00			
	d		10 14								10 37			10 49					
Merstham	d										10 41								
Coulsdon South	d		10 21								10 46								
Purley [4]	d		10 24								10 50								
East Croydon 🚊	a	10 16	10 29			10 32		10 38	10 42	10 45	10 55			11 00	11 02			11 08	11 13
	d	10 17	10 30			10 33		10 39	10 47	10 46	10 56			11 00	11 03			11 09	11 14
Norwood Junction [2]	a										11 02								
New Cross Gate	d																		
London Bridge [4] ⊖	a	10 30				10 45			11 00		11 14				11 15				
London Blackfriars [3] ⊖	a	10 37				10 52			11 07						11 22				
City Thameslink [3]	a																		
Farringdon [3] ⊖	a	10 44				10 58			11 14						11 28				
St Pancras International [15] ⊖	a	10 48				11 02			11 18						11 32				
St Albans City	a	11 12				11 26			11 42						11 56				
Luton Airport Parkway [4] ✈	a	11 24				11 38			11 54						12 08				
Luton [7]	a	11 27				11 41			11 57						12 11				
Bedford [10]	a	11 54				12 08			12 24						12 38				
Clapham Junction [10]	a		10 39					10 48		10 55				11 09				11 18	11 23
London Victoria [15] ⊖	a		10 46	10 35			10 50	10 56		11 03			11 05	11 17			11 20	11 26	11 30

		FC	SN	SN	GW	FC	SN	SN	SN	FC	SN	SN	GW	SN	SN	FC	SN	SN	SN
		1	1	1 🛒	1	1	1 🛒	1	1	1	1 🛒	1	1	1 🛒	1	1	1	1 🛒	1 🛒
Brighton [10]	d					10 44					11 10				11 00	11 14			
Hove [2]	d							10 55											
Preston Park	d														11 03				
Hassocks [4]	d					10 53									11 10	11 23			
Burgess Hill [4]	d					10 57		11 05							11 13	11 27			
Lewes [4]	d																		11 20
Wivelsfield [4]	d														11 15				11 35
Haywards Heath [3]	a					11 02		11 10							11 20	11 32			11 39
	d					11 03		11 11							11 25	11 33			11 41
Balcombe	d														11 30				
Horsham [4]	d		10 44						11 01										
Littlehaven	d								11 04										
Faygate	d																		
Ifield	d								11 10										
Crawley	d		10 53						11 14										
Three Bridges [4]	a		10 56			11 11			11 17						11 36	11 41			
	d	10 52	10 57			11 12			11 18	11 22					11 36	11 42			
Gatwick Airport [10] ✈	a	10 56	11 02			11 16		11 22	11 22	11 26					11 40	11 46			11 52
	d	10 57	11 03	11 05	11 08	11 17	11 20	11 23	11 23	11 27				11 35	11 41	11 47		11 50	11 53
Horley [4]	d		11 05						11 26										
Salfords	d																		
Earlswood (Surrey)	d								11 33										
Tonbridge [4]	d																11 29		
Leigh (Kent)	d																11 33		
Penshurst	d																11 37		
Edenbridge	d																11 43		
Godstone	d																11 50		
Nutfield	d																11 55		
Reigate	d											←	11 30						
Redhill [5]	a		11 13		11 16				11 36			11 36	11 36		11 48		12 00		
	d		11 14						11 37			11 37			11 49				
Merstham	d								→			11 41							
Coulsdon South	d		11 21									11 46							
Purley [4]	d		11 24									11 50							
East Croydon 🚊	a	11 16	11 29			11 32		11 38		11 41	11 45	11 55			12 00	12 02			12 08
	d	11 17	11 30			11 33		11 39		11 47	11 46	11 56			12 00	12 03			12 09
Norwood Junction [2]	a											12 02							
New Cross Gate	d																		
London Bridge [4] ⊖	a	11 30				11 45				12 00		12 14				12 15			
London Blackfriars [3] ⊖	a	11 37				11 52				12 07						12 22			
City Thameslink [3]	a																		
Farringdon [3] ⊖	a	11 44				11 58				12 14						12 28			
St Pancras International [15] ⊖	a	11 48				12 02				12 18						12 32			
St Albans City	a	12 12				12 26				12 42						12 56			
Luton Airport Parkway [4] ✈	a	12 24				12 38				12 54						13 08			
Luton [7]	a	12 27				12 41				12 57						13 11			
Bedford [10]	a	12 54				13 08				13 24						13 38			
Clapham Junction [10]	a		11 39					11 48			11 55				12 09				12 18
London Victoria [15] ⊖	a		11 46	11 35			11 50	11 56			12 03			12 05	12 17			12 20	12 26

Table 186R

Sundays

8 December to 29 December

Brighton - London and Bedford

Network Diagram - see first Page of Table 175

		SN 1 🛒	FC 1	SN 1	SN 1 🛒	GW 1	FC 1	SN 1 🛒	SN 1	SN 1	FC 1	SN 1 🛒	SN 1	GW 1	SN 1 🛒	SN 1	FC 1	SN 1	SN 1 🛒
Brighton 10	d	11 35					11 44					12 10				12 00	12 14		
Hove 2	d								11 55										
Preston Park	d															12 03			
Hassocks 4	d						11 53									12 10	12 23		
Burgess Hill 4	d						11 57		12 05							12 13	12 27		
Lewes 4	d																		
Wivelsfield 4	d															12 15			
Haywards Heath 3	a						12 02		12 10							12 20	12 32		
	d						12 03		12 11							12 25	12 33		
Balcombe	d															12 30			
Horsham 4	d			11 44						12 01									
Littlehaven	d									12 04									
Faygate	d																		
Ifield	d									12 10									
Crawley	d			11 53						12 14									
Three Bridges 4	a			11 56			12 11			12 17						12 36	12 41		
	d		11 52	11 57			12 12			12 18	12 22					12 36	12 42		
Gatwick Airport 10 ✈	a	11 56	11 56	12 02			12 16		12 22	12 22	12 26					12 40	12 46		
	d	11 57	11 57	12 03	12 05	12 08	12 17	12 20	12 23	12 23	12 27				12 35	12 41	12 47		12 50
Horley 4	d			12 05						12 26									
Salfords	d																		
Earlswood (Surrey)	d									12 33									
Tonbridge 4	d																	12 29	
Leigh (Kent)	d																	12 33	
Penshurst	d																	12 37	
Edenbridge	d																	12 43	
Godstone	d																	12 50	
Nutfield	d																	12 55	
Reigate	d												←	12 31					
Redhill 5	a			12 13		12 16				12 36			12 36	12 36		12 48		13 00	
	d			12 14						12 37			12 37			12 49			
Merstham	d									→			12 41						
Coulsdon South	d			12 21									12 46						
Purley 4	d			12 24									12 50						
East Croydon 🚋	a	12 13	12 16	12 29			12 32		12 38		12 41	12 45	12 55			13 00	13 02		
	d	12 14	12 17	12 30			12 33		12 39		12 47	12 46	12 56			13 00	13 03		
Norwood Junction 2	a												13 02						
New Cross Gate	d																		
London Bridge 4 ⊖	a		12 30				12 45				13 00		13 14				13 15		
London Blackfriars 3 ⊖	a		12 37				12 52				13 07						13 22		
City Thameslink 3	a																		
Farringdon 3 ⊖	a		12 44				12 58				13 14						13 28		
St Pancras International 15 ⊖	a		12 48				13 02				13 18						13 32		
St Albans City	a		13 12				13 26				13 42						13 56		
Luton Airport Parkway 4 ✈	a		13 24				13 38				13 54						14 08		
Luton 7	a		13 27				13 41				13 57						14 11		
Bedford 10	a		13 54				14 08				14 24						14 38		
Clapham Junction 10	a	12 23		12 39					12 48			12 55				13 09			
London Victoria 15 ⊖	a	12 30		12 46	12 35			12 50	12 56			13 03			13 05	13 17			13 20

		SN 1 🛒	SN 1 🛒	FC 1	SN 1	SN 1 🛒	GW 1	FC 1	SN 1 🛒	SN 1	SN 1	FC 1	SN 1 🛒	SN 1	GW 1	SN 1 🛒	SN 1	FC 1	SN 1
Brighton 10	d		12 35					12 44					13 10				13 00	13 14	
Hove 2	d									12 55									
Preston Park	d																13 03		
Hassocks 4	d							12 53									13 10	13 23	
Burgess Hill 4	d							12 57		13 05							13 13	13 27	
Lewes 4	d	12 20																	
Wivelsfield 4	d	12 35															13 15		
Haywards Heath 3	a	12 39						13 02		13 10							13 20	13 32	
	d	12 41						13 03		13 11							13 25	13 33	
Balcombe	d																13 30		
Horsham 4	d				12 44						13 01								
Littlehaven	d										13 04								
Faygate	d																		
Ifield	d										13 10								
Crawley	d				12 53						13 14								
Three Bridges 4	a				12 56			13 11			13 17						13 36	13 41	
	d			12 52	12 57			13 12			13 18	13 22					13 36	13 42	
Gatwick Airport 10 ✈	a	12 52	12 56	12 56	13 02			13 16		13 22	13 22	13 26					13 40	13 46	
	d	12 53	12 57	12 57	13 03	13 05	13 08	13 17	13 20	13 23	13 23	13 27				13 35	13 41	13 47	
Horley 4	d				13 05						13 26								
Salfords	d																		
Earlswood (Surrey)	d										13 33								
Tonbridge 4	d																		13 29
Leigh (Kent)	d																		13 33
Penshurst	d																		13 37
Edenbridge	d																		13 43
Godstone	d																		13 50
Nutfield	d																		13 55
Reigate	d													←	13 30				
Redhill 5	a				13 13		13 16				13 36			13 36	13 36		13 48		14 00
	d				13 14						13 37			13 37			13 49		
Merstham	d										→			13 41					
Coulsdon South	d				13 21									13 46					
Purley 4	d				13 24									13 50					
East Croydon 🚋	a	13 08	13 13	13 16	13 29			13 32		13 38		13 41	13 45	13 55			14 00	14 02	
	d	13 09	13 14	13 17	13 30			13 33		13 39		13 47	13 46	13 56			14 00	14 03	
Norwood Junction 2	a													14 02					
New Cross Gate	d																		
London Bridge 4 ⊖	a			13 30				13 45				14 00		14 14				14 15	
London Blackfriars 3 ⊖	a			13 37				13 52				14 07						14 22	
City Thameslink 3	a																		
Farringdon 3 ⊖	a			13 44				13 58				14 14						14 28	
St Pancras International 15 ⊖	a			13 48				14 02				14 18						14 32	
St Albans City	a			14 12				14 26				14 42						14 56	
Luton Airport Parkway 4 ✈	a			14 24				14 38				14 54						15 08	
Luton 7	a			14 27				14 41				14 57						15 11	
Bedford 10	a			14 54				15 08				15 24						15 38	
Clapham Junction 10	a	13 18	13 23		13 39					13 48			13 55				14 09		
London Victoria 15 ⊖	a	13 26	13 30		13 46	13 35			13 50	13 56			14 03			14 05	14 17		

Table 186R

Sundays

Brighton - London and Bedford

8 December to 29 December

Network Diagram - see first Page of Table 175

		SN 1 ⚲	SN 1 ⚲	SN 1 ⚲	FC 1	SN 1	SN 1 ⚲	GW 1	FC 1	SN 1 ⚲	SN 1	SN 1	FC 1	SN 1 ⚲	SN 1	GW 1	SN 1 ⚲	SN 1	FC 1
Brighton 10	d			13 35					13 44					14 10				14 00	14 14
Hove 2	d										13 55								
Preston Park	d																	14 03	
Hassocks 4	d								13 53									14 10	14 23
Burgess Hill 4	d								13 57		14 05							14 13	14 27
Lewes 4	d		13 20																
Wivelsfield 4	d		13 35															14 15	
Haywards Heath 3	a		13 39						14 02		14 10							14 20	14 32
	d		13 41						14 03		14 11							14 25	14 33
Balcombe	d																	14 30	
Horsham 4	d					13 44						14 01							
Littlehaven	d											14 04							
Faygate	d																		
Ifield	d											14 10							
Crawley	d					13 53						14 14							
Three Bridges 4	a					13 56			14 11			14 17						14 36	14 41
	d				13 52	13 57			14 12			14 18	14 22					14 36	14 42
Gatwick Airport 10 ✈	a		13 52	13 56	13 56	14 02			14 16		14 22	14 22	14 26					14 40	14 46
	d	13 50	13 53	13 57	13 57	14 03	14 05	14 08	14 17	14 20	14 23	14 23	14 27				14 35	14 41	14 47
Horley 4	d					14 05						14 26							
Salfords	d																		
Earlswood (Surrey)	d											14 33							
Tonbridge 4	d																		
Leigh (Kent)	d																		
Penshurst	d																		
Edenbridge	d																		
Godstone	d																		
Nutfield	d																		
Reigate	d														←	14 31			
Redhill 5	a					14 13		14 16				14 36			14 36	14 36		14 48	
	d					14 14						14 37			14 37			14 49	
Merstham	d											→			14 41				
Coulsdon South	d					14 21									14 46				
Purley 4	d					14 24									14 50				
East Croydon	a		14 08	14 13	14 16	14 29			14 32		14 38		14 41	14 45	14 55			15 00	15 02
	d		14 09	14 14	14 17	14 30			14 33		14 39		14 47	14 46	14 56			15 00	15 03
Norwood Junction 2	a														15 02				
New Cross Gate	d																		
London Bridge 4 ⊖	a				14 30				14 45				15 00		15 14				15 15
London Blackfriars 3 ⊖	a				14 37				14 52				15 07						15 22
City Thameslink 3	a																		
Farringdon 3 ⊖	a				14 44				14 58				15 14						15 28
St Pancras International 15 ⊖	a				14 48				15 02				15 18						15 32
St Albans City	a				15 12				15 26				15 42						15 56
Luton Airport Parkway 4 ✈	a				15 24				15 38				15 54						16 08
Luton 7	a				15 27				15 41				15 57						16 11
Bedford 10	a				15 54				16 08				16 24						16 38
Clapham Junction 10	a		14 18	14 23		14 39					14 48			14 55				15 09	
London Victoria 15 ⊖	a	14 20	14 26	14 30		14 46	14 35			14 50	14 56			15 03			15 05	15 17	

		SN 1	SN 1 ⚲	SN 1 ⚲	SN 1 ⚲	FC 1	SN 1	SN 1 ⚲	GW 1	FC 1	SN 1 ⚲	SN 1	SN 1	FC 1	SN 1 ⚲	SN 1	GW 1	SN 1 ⚲	SN 1
Brighton 10	d				14 35					14 44					15 10				15 00
Hove 2	d											14 55							
Preston Park	d																		15 03
Hassocks 4	d									14 53									15 10
Burgess Hill 4	d									14 57		15 05							15 13
Lewes 4	d			14 20															
Wivelsfield 4	d			14 35															15 15
Haywards Heath 3	a			14 39						15 02		15 10							15 20
	d			14 41						15 03		15 11							15 25
Balcombe	d																		15 30
Horsham 4	d						14 44						15 01						
Littlehaven	d												15 04						
Faygate	d																		
Ifield	d												15 10						
Crawley	d						14 53						15 14						
Three Bridges 4	a						14 56			15 11			15 17						15 36
	d					14 52	14 57			15 12			15 18	15 22					15 36
Gatwick Airport 10 ✈	a			14 52	14 56	14 56	15 02			15 16		15 22	15 22	15 26					15 40
	d		14 50	14 53	14 57	14 57	15 03	15 05	15 08	15 17	15 20	15 23	15 23	15 27				15 35	15 41
Horley 4	d						15 05						15 26						
Salfords	d																		
Earlswood (Surrey)	d												15 33						
Tonbridge 4	d	14 29																	
Leigh (Kent)	d	14 33																	
Penshurst	d	14 37																	
Edenbridge	d	14 43																	
Godstone	d	14 50																	
Nutfield	d	14 55																	
Reigate	d															←	15 30		
Redhill 5	a	15 00					15 13		15 16				15 36			15 36	15 36		15 48
	d						15 14						15 37			15 37			15 49
Merstham	d												→			15 41			
Coulsdon South	d						15 21									15 46			
Purley 4	d						15 24									15 50			
East Croydon	a			15 08	15 13	15 16	15 29			15 32		15 38		15 41	15 45	15 55			16 00
	d			15 09	15 14	15 17	15 30			15 33		15 39		15 47	15 46	15 56			16 00
Norwood Junction 2	a															16 02			
New Cross Gate	d																		
London Bridge 4 ⊖	a					15 30				15 45				16 00		16 14			
London Blackfriars 3 ⊖	a					15 37				15 52				16 07					
City Thameslink 3	a																		
Farringdon 3 ⊖	a					15 44				15 58				16 14					
St Pancras International 15 ⊖	a					15 48				16 02				16 18					
St Albans City	a					16 12				16 26				16 42					
Luton Airport Parkway 4 ✈	a					16 24				16 38				16 54					
Luton 7	a					16 27				16 41				16 57					
Bedford 10	a					16 54				17 08				17 24					
Clapham Junction 10	a			15 18	15 23		15 39					15 48			15 55				16 09
London Victoria 15 ⊖	a		15 20	15 26	15 30		15 46	15 35			15 50	15 56			16 03			16 05	16 17

Table 186R

Sundays

8 December to 29 December

Brighton - London and Bedford

Network Diagram - see first Page of Table 175

		FC 1	SN 1	SN 1 ✠	SN 1 ✠	SN 1 ✠	FC 1	SN 1	SN 1 ✠	GW 1	FC 1	SN 1 ✠	SN 1	SN 1	FC 1	SN 1 ✠	SN 1	GW 1	SN 1 ✠
Brighton 10	d	15 14				15 35					15 44					16 10			
Hove 2	d												15 55						
Preston Park	d																		
Hassocks 4	d	15 23									15 53								
Burgess Hill 4	d	15 27									15 57		16 05						
Lewes 4	d				15 20														
Wivelsfield 4	d				15 35														
Haywards Heath 3	a	15 32			15 39						16 02		16 10						
	d	15 33			15 41						16 03		16 11						
Balcombe	d																		
Horsham 4	d							15 44						16 01					
Littlehaven	d													16 04					
Faygate	d																		
Ifield	d													16 10					
Crawley	d							15 53						16 14					
Three Bridges 4	a	15 41						15 56			16 11			16 17					
	d	15 42					15 52	15 57			16 12			16 18	16 22				
Gatwick Airport 10 ✈	a	15 46			15 52	15 56	15 56	16 02			16 16		16 22	16 22	16 26				
	d	15 47		15 50	15 53	15 57	15 57	16 03	16 05	16 08	16 17	16 20	16 23	16 23	16 27				16 35
Horley 4	d							16 05						16 26					
Salfords	d																		
Earlswood (Surrey)	d													16 33					
Tonbridge 4	d		15 29																
Leigh (Kent)	d		15 33																
Penshurst	d		15 37																
Edenbridge	d		15 43																
Godstone	d		15 50																
Nutfield	d		15 55																
Reigate	d																←	16 31	
Redhill 5	a		16 00					16 13		16 16				16 36			16 36	16 36	
	d							16 14						16 37			16 37		
Merstham	d													→			16 41		
Coulsdon South	d							16 21									16 46		
Purley 4	d							16 24									16 50		
East Croydon 🚋	a	16 02			16 08	16 13	16 16	16 29			16 32		16 38		16 41	16 45	16 55		
	d	16 03			16 09	16 14	16 17	16 30			16 33		16 39		16 47	16 46	16 56		
Norwood Junction 2	a																17 02		
New Cross Gate	d																		
London Bridge 4 ⊖	a	16 15					16 30				16 45				17 00		17 14		
London Blackfriars 3 ⊖	a	16 22					16 37				16 52				17 07				
City Thameslink 3	a																		
Farringdon 3 ⊖	a	16 28					16 44				16 58				17 14				
St Pancras International 15 ⊖	a	16 32					16 48				17 02				17 18				
St Albans City	a	16 56					17 12				17 26				17 42				
Luton Airport Parkway 4 ✈	a	17 08					17 24				17 38				17 54				
Luton 7	a	17 11					17 27				17 41				17 57				
Bedford 10	a	17 38					17 54				18 08				18 24				
Clapham Junction 10	a				16 18	16 23		16 39					16 48			16 55			
London Victoria 15 ⊖	a			16 20	16 26	16 30		16 46	16 35			16 50	16 56			17 03			17 05

		SN 1	FC 1	SN 1	SN 1 ✠	SN 1 ✠	SN 1 ✠	FC 1	SN 1	SN 1 ✠	GW 1	FC 1	SN 1 ✠	SN 1	SN 1	FC 1	SN 1 ✠	SN 1	GW 1
Brighton 10	d	16 00	16 14				16 35					16 44					17 10		
Hove 2	d													16 55					
Preston Park	d	16 03																	
Hassocks 4	d	16 10	16 23									16 53							
Burgess Hill 4	d	16 13	16 27									16 57		17 05					
Lewes 4	d					16 20													
Wivelsfield 4	d	16 15				16 35													
Haywards Heath 3	a	16 20	16 32			16 39						17 02		17 10					
	d	16 25	16 33			16 41						17 03		17 11					
Balcombe	d	16 30																	
Horsham 4	d								16 44						17 01				
Littlehaven	d														17 04				
Faygate	d																		
Ifield	d														17 10				
Crawley	d								16 53						17 14				
Three Bridges 4	a	16 36	16 41						16 56			17 11			17 17				
	d	16 36	16 42					16 52	16 57			17 12			17 18	17 22			
Gatwick Airport 10 ✈	a	16 40	16 46			16 52	16 56	16 56	17 02			17 16		17 22	17 22	17 26			
	d	16 41	16 47		16 50	16 53	16 57	16 57	17 03	17 05	17 08	17 17	17 20	17 23	17 23	17 27			
Horley 4	d								17 05						17 26				
Salfords	d																		
Earlswood (Surrey)	d														17 33				
Tonbridge 4	d			16 29															
Leigh (Kent)	d			16 33															
Penshurst	d			16 37															
Edenbridge	d			16 43															
Godstone	d			16 50															
Nutfield	d			16 55															
Reigate	d																	←	17 30
Redhill 5	a	16 48		17 00					17 13		17 16				17 36			17 36	17 36
	d	16 49							17 14						17 37			17 37	
Merstham	d														→			17 41	
Coulsdon South	d								17 21									17 46	
Purley 4	d								17 24									17 50	
East Croydon 🚋	a	17 00	17 02			17 08	17 13	17 16	17 29			17 32		17 38		17 41	17 45	17 55	
	d	17 00	17 03			17 09	17 14	17 17	17 30			17 33		17 39		17 47	17 46	17 56	
Norwood Junction 2	a																	18 02	
New Cross Gate	d																		
London Bridge 4 ⊖	a		17 15					17 30				17 45				18 00		18 14	
London Blackfriars 3 ⊖	a		17 22					17 37				17 52				18 07			
City Thameslink 3	a																		
Farringdon 3 ⊖	a		17 28					17 44				17 58				18 14			
St Pancras International 15 ⊖	a		17 32					17 48				18 02				18 18			
St Albans City	a		17 56					18 12				18 26				18 42			
Luton Airport Parkway 4 ✈	a		18 08					18 24				18 38				18 54			
Luton 7	a		18 11					18 27				18 41				18 57			
Bedford 10	a		18 38					18 54				19 08				19 24			
Clapham Junction 10	a	17 09				17 18	17 23		17 39					17 48			17 55		
London Victoria 15 ⊖	a	17 17			17 20	17 26	17 30		17 46	17 35			17 50	17 56			18 03		

Table 186R

Sundays

Brighton - London and Bedford

8 December to 29 December

Network Diagram - see first Page of Table 175

		SN 1 (bus)	SN 1	FC 1	SN 1	SN 1 (bus)	SN 1 (bus)	SN 1 (bus)	FC 1	SN 1	SN 1 (bus)	GW 1	FC 1	SN 1 (bus)	SN 1	SN 1	FC 1	SN 1	SN 1
Brighton 10	d		17 00	17 14				17 35					17 44					18 10	
Hove 2	d														17 55				
Preston Park	d		17 03																
Hassocks 4	d		17 10	17 23									17 53						
Burgess Hill 4	d		17 13	17 27									17 57		18 05				
Lewes 4	d						17 20												
Wivelsfield 4	d		17 15				17 35												
Haywards Heath 3	a		17 20	17 32			17 39						18 02		18 10				
	d		17 25	17 33			17 41						18 03		18 11				
Balcombe	d		17 30																
Horsham 4	d									17 44						18 01			
Littlehaven	d															18 04			
Faygate	d																		
Ifield	d															18 10			
Crawley	d									17 53						18 14			
Three Bridges 4	a		17 36	17 41						17 56			18 11			18 17			
	d		17 36	17 42					17 52	17 57			18 12			18 18	18 22		
Gatwick Airport 10 ✈	a		17 40	17 46			17 52	17 56	17 56	18 02			18 16		18 22	18 22	18 26		
	d	17 35	17 41	17 47		17 50	17 53	17 57	17 57	18 03	18 05	18 08	18 17	18 20	18 23	18 23	18 27		
Horley 4	d									18 05						18 26			
Salfords	d																		
Earlswood (Surrey)	d															18 33			
Tonbridge 4	d				17 29														
Leigh (Kent)	d				17 33														
Penshurst	d				17 37														
Edenbridge	d				17 43														
Godstone	d				17 50														
Nutfield	d				17 55														
Reigate	d																		←
Redhill 5	a		17 48		18 00					18 13		18 16				18 36			18 36
	d		17 49							18 14						18 37			18 37
Merstham	d															→			18 41
Coulsdon South	d									18 21									18 46
Purley 4	d									18 24									18 50
East Croydon 🚋	a		18 00	18 02			18 08	18 13	18 16	18 29			18 32		18 38		18 41	18 45	18 55
	d		18 00	18 03			18 09	18 14	18 17	18 30			18 33		18 39		18 47	18 46	18 56
Norwood Junction 2	a																		19 02
New Cross Gate	d																		
London Bridge 4 ⊖	a			18 15					18 30				18 45				19 00		19 14
London Blackfriars 3 ⊖	a			18 22					18 37				18 52				19 07		
City Thameslink 3	a																		
Farringdon 3 ⊖	a			18 28					18 44				18 58				19 14		
St Pancras International 15 ⊖	a			18 32					18 48				19 02				19 18		
St Albans City	a			18 56					19 12				19 26				19 42		
Luton Airport Parkway 4 ✈	a			19 08					19 24				19 38				19 54		
Luton 7	a			19 11					19 27				19 41				19 57		
Bedford 10	a			19 38					19 54				20 08				20 24		
Clapham Junction 10	a		18 09				18 18	18 23		18 39					18 48			18 55	
London Victoria 15 ⊖	a	18 05	18 17			18 20	18 26	18 30		18 46	18 35			18 50	18 56			19 03	

		GW 1	SN 1 (bus)	SN 1	FC 1	SN 1	SN 1 (bus)	SN 1 (bus)	SN 1	FC 1	SN 1	SN 1	GW 1	FC 1	SN 1	SN 1	SN 1	SN 1	GW 1
Brighton 10	d			18 00	18 14				18 35					18 44			19 10		
Hove 2	d															18 55			
Preston Park	d			18 03															
Hassocks 4	d			18 10	18 23									18 53					
Burgess Hill 4	d			18 13	18 27									18 57		19 05			
Lewes 4	d							18 20											
Wivelsfield 4	d			18 15				18 35											
Haywards Heath 3	a			18 20	18 32			18 39						19 02		19 10			
	d			18 25	18 33			18 41						19 03		19 11			
Balcombe	d			18 30															
Horsham 4	d										18 44							19 01	
Littlehaven	d																	19 04	
Faygate	d																		
Ifield	d																	19 10	
Crawley	d										18 53							19 14	
Three Bridges 4	a			18 36	18 41						18 56			19 11				19 17	
	d			18 36	18 42					18 52	18 57			19 12				19 18	
Gatwick Airport 10 ✈	a			18 40	18 46			18 52	18 56	18 56	19 02			19 16		19 22		19 22	
	d		18 35	18 41	18 47		18 50	18 53	18 57	18 57	19 03	19 05	19 08	19 17	19 20	19 23		19 23	
Horley 4	d										19 05							19 26	
Salfords	d																		
Earlswood (Surrey)	d																	19 33	
Tonbridge 4	d					18 29													
Leigh (Kent)	d					18 33													
Penshurst	d					18 37													
Edenbridge	d					18 43													
Godstone	d					18 50													
Nutfield	d					18 55													
Reigate	d	18 31																	19 30
Redhill 5	a	18 36		18 48		19 00					19 13		19 16					19 36	19 36
	d			18 49							19 14							19 37	
Merstham	d																	19 41	
Coulsdon South	d										19 21							19 46	
Purley 4	d										19 24							19 50	
East Croydon 🚋	a			19 00	19 02			19 08	19 13	19 16	19 29			19 32		19 38	19 45	19 55	
	d			19 00	19 03			19 09	19 14	19 17	19 30			19 33		19 39	19 46	19 56	
Norwood Junction 2	a																	20 02	
New Cross Gate	d																		
London Bridge 4 ⊖	a				19 15					19 30				19 45				20 14	
London Blackfriars 3 ⊖	a				19 22					19 37				19 52					
City Thameslink 3	a																		
Farringdon 3 ⊖	a				19 28					19 44				19 58					
St Pancras International 15 ⊖	a				19 32					19 48				20 02					
St Albans City	a				19 56					20 12				20 26					
Luton Airport Parkway 4 ✈	a				20 08					20 24				20 38					
Luton 7	a				20 11					20 27				20 41					
Bedford 10	a				20 38					20 54				21 08					
Clapham Junction 10	a			19 09				19 18	19 23		19 39					19 48	19 55		
London Victoria 15 ⊖	a		19 05	19 17			19 20	19 26	19 30		19 46	19 35			19 50	19 56	20 03		

Table 186R

Sundays

8 December to 29 December

Brighton - London and Bedford

Network Diagram - see first Page of Table 175

		SN 1	SN 1	FC 1	SN 1	SN 1	SN 1	SN 1	SN 1	SN 1	GW 1	FC 1	SN 1	SN 1	SN 1	SN 1	GW 1	SN 1	SN 1
Brighton 10	d		19 00	19 14				19 35				19 44			20 10				20 00
Hove 2	d													19 55					
Preston Park	d		19 03																20 03
Hassocks 4	d		19 10	19 23								19 53							20 10
Burgess Hill 4	d		19 13	19 27								19 57		20 05					20 13
Lewes 4	d						19 20												
Wivelsfield 4	d		19 15				19 35												20 15
Haywards Heath 3	a		19 20	19 32			19 39					20 02		20 10					20 20
	d		19 25	19 33			19 41					20 03		20 11					20 25
Balcombe	d		19 30																20 30
Horsham 4	d								19 44							20 01			
Littlehaven	d															20 04			
Faygate	d																		
Ifield	d															20 10			
Crawley	d								19 53							20 14			
Three Bridges 4	a		19 36	19 41					19 56			20 11				20 17			20 36
	d		19 36	19 42					19 57			20 12				20 18			20 36
Gatwick Airport 10 ✈	a		19 40	19 46			19 52	19 56	20 02			20 16		20 22		20 22			20 40
	d	19 35	19 41	19 47		19 50	19 53	19 57	20 03	20 05	20 08	20 17	20 20	20 23		20 23		20 35	20 41
Horley 4	d								20 05							20 26			
Salfords	d																		
Earlswood (Surrey)	d															20 33			
Tonbridge 4	d				19 29														
Leigh (Kent)	d				19 33														
Penshurst	d				19 37														
Edenbridge	d				19 43														
Godstone	d				19 50														
Nutfield	d				19 55														
Reigate	d																20 31		
Redhill 5	a		19 48		20 00				20 13		20 16					20 36	20 36		20 48
	d		19 49						20 14							20 37			20 49
Merstham	d															20 41			
Coulsdon South	d								20 21							20 46			
Purley 4	d								20 24							20 50			
East Croydon 🚋	a		20 00	20 02			20 08	20 13	20 29			20 32		20 38	20 45	20 55			21 00
	d		20 00	20 03			20 09	20 14	20 30			20 33		20 39	20 46	20 56			21 00
Norwood Junction 2	a															21 02			
New Cross Gate	d																		
London Bridge 4 ⊖	a			20 15								20 45				21 14			
London Blackfriars 3 ⊖	a			20 22								20 52							
City Thameslink 3	a																		
Farringdon 3 ⊖	a			20 28								20 58							
St Pancras International 15 ⊖	a			20 32								21 02							
St Albans City	a			20 56								21 26							
Luton Airport Parkway 4 ✈	a			21 08								21 38							
Luton 7	a			21 11								21 41							
Bedford 10	a			21 38								22 08							
Clapham Junction 10	a		20 09				20 18	20 23	20 39					20 48	20 55				21 09
London Victoria 15 ⊖	a	20 05	20 17			20 20	20 26	20 30	20 46	20 35			20 50	20 56	21 05			21 05	21 17

		FC 1	SN 1	SN 1	SN 1	SN 1	SN 1	SN 1	GW 1	FC 1	SN 1	SN 1	SN 1	GW 1	SN 1	SN 1	FC 1	SN 1	SN 1
Brighton 10	d	20 14				20 35				20 44						21 04	21 14		
Hove 2	d											20 55							
Preston Park	d															21 07			
Hassocks 4	d	20 23								20 53						21 14	21 23		
Burgess Hill 4	d	20 27								20 57		21 05				21 17	21 27		
Lewes 4	d				20 20														
Wivelsfield 4	d				20 35											21 19			
Haywards Heath 3	a	20 32			20 39					21 02		21 10				21 24	21 32		
	d	20 33			20 41					21 03		21 11				21 25	21 33		
Balcombe	d															21 30			
Horsham 4	d						20 44						21 01						
Littlehaven	d												21 04						
Faygate	d																		
Ifield	d												21 10						
Crawley	d						20 53						21 14						
Three Bridges 4	a	20 41					20 56			21 11			21 17			21 36	21 41		
	d	20 42					20 57			21 12			21 18			21 36	21 42		
Gatwick Airport 10 ✈	a	20 46			20 52	20 56	21 02			21 16		21 22	21 22			21 40	21 46		
	d	20 47		20 50	20 53	20 57	21 03	21 05	21 08	21 17	21 20	21 23	21 23		21 35	21 41	21 47		21 50
Horley 4	d						21 05						21 26						
Salfords	d																		
Earlswood (Surrey)	d												21 33						
Tonbridge 4	d		20 29															21 29	
Leigh (Kent)	d		20 33															21 33	
Penshurst	d		20 37															21 37	
Edenbridge	d		20 43															21 43	
Godstone	d		20 50															21 50	
Nutfield	d		20 55															21 55	
Reigate	d													21 30					
Redhill 5	a		21 00				21 13		21 16				21 36	21 36		21 48		22 00	
	d						21 14						21 37			21 49			
Merstham	d												21 41						
Coulsdon South	d						21 21						21 46						
Purley 4	d						21 24						21 50						
East Croydon 🚋	a	21 02			21 08	21 13	21 29			21 32		21 38	21 55			22 00	22 02		
	d	21 03			21 09	21 14	21 30			21 33		21 39	21 56			22 00	22 03		
Norwood Junction 2	a												22 02						
New Cross Gate	d																		
London Bridge 4 ⊖	a	21 15								21 45			22 14				22 15		
London Blackfriars 3 ⊖	a	21 22								21 52							22 23		
City Thameslink 3	a																		
Farringdon 3 ⊖	a	21 28								21 58							22 29		
St Pancras International 15 ⊖	a	21 32								22 02							22 34		
St Albans City	a	21 56								22 26							23 07		
Luton Airport Parkway 4 ✈	a	22 08								22 38							23 19		
Luton 7	a	22 11								22 41							23 22		
Bedford 10	a	22 38								23 08							23 49		
Clapham Junction 10	a				21 18	21 23	21 39					21 48				22 09			
London Victoria 15 ⊖	a			21 20	21 26	21 30	21 46	21 35			21 50	21 56			22 05	22 17			22 20

Table 186R

Sundays

Brighton - London and Bedford

8 December to 29 December

Network Diagram - see first Page of Table 175

Station		SN 1	SN 1	SN 1	GW 1	FC 1	SN 1	GW 1	SN 1	SN 1
Brighton 10	d					21 44				
Hove 2	d									
Preston Park	d									
Hassocks 4	d					21 53				
Burgess Hill 4	d					21 57				
Lewes 4	d	21 20								
Wivelsfield 4	d	21 35								
Haywards Heath 3	a	21 39				22 02				
	d	21 41				22 03				
Balcombe	d									
Horsham 4	d		21 44						22 00	
Littlehaven	d								22 03	
Faygate	d									
Ifield	d								22 09	
Crawley	d		21 53						22 13	
Three Bridges 4	a		21 56			22 11			22 16	
	d		21 57			22 12			22 18	
Gatwick Airport 10 ✈	a	21 52	22 02			22 16			22 22	
	d	21 53	22 03	22 05	22 08	22 17	22 20		22 23	22 35
Horley 4	d		22 05						22 26	
Salfords	d									
Earlswood (Surrey)	d								22 33	
Tonbridge 4	d									
Leigh (Kent)	d									
Penshurst	d									
Edenbridge	d									
Godstone	d									
Nutfield	d									
Reigate	d							22 31		
Redhill 5	a		22 13		22 16			22 36	22 37	
	d		22 14						22 37	
Merstham	d								22 41	
Coulsdon South	d		22 21						22 46	
Purley 4	d		22 24						22 50	
East Croydon	a	22 08	22 29			22 32			22 55	
	d	22 09	22 30			22 33			22 56	
Norwood Junction 2	a									
New Cross Gate	d									
London Bridge 4 ⊖	a					22 45				
London Blackfriars 3 ⊖	a					22 53				
City Thameslink 3	a									
Farringdon 3 ⊖	a					22 59				
St Pancras International 15 ⊖	a					23 04				
St Albans City	a					23 37				
Luton Airport Parkway 4 ✈	a					23 49				
Luton 7	a					23 52				
Bedford 10	a					00 19				
Clapham Junction 10	a	22 18	22 39						23 07	
London Victoria 15 ⊖	a	22 26	22 46	22 35			22 50		23 14	23 07

Station		SN 1	FC 1	SN 1	SN 1	SN 1	SN 1	GW 1	FC 1	SN 1
Brighton 10	d	22 04	22 14						22 44	
Hove 2	d									
Preston Park	d	22 07								
Hassocks 4	d	22 14	22 23						22 53	
Burgess Hill 4	d	22 17	22 27						22 57	
Lewes 4	d									
Wivelsfield 4	d	22 19								
Haywards Heath 3	a	22 24	22 32						23 02	
	d	22 25	22 33						23 03	
Balcombe	d	22 30								
Horsham 4	d					22 44				
Littlehaven	d									
Faygate	d									
Ifield	d									
Crawley	d					22 53				
Three Bridges 4	a	22 36	22 41			22 56			23 11	
	d	22 36	22 42			22 57			23 12	
Gatwick Airport 10 ✈	a	22 40	22 46			23 02			23 16	
	d	22 41	22 47		22 50	23 03	23 05	23 08	23 17	23 20
Horley 4	d					23 05				
Salfords	d									
Earlswood (Surrey)	d									
Tonbridge 4	d			22 29						
Leigh (Kent)	d			22 33						
Penshurst	d			22 37						
Edenbridge	d			22 43						
Godstone	d			22 50						
Nutfield	d			22 55						
Reigate	d									
Redhill 5	a	22 48		23 00		23 13		23 16		
	d	22 49				23 14				
Merstham	d									
Coulsdon South	d					23 21				
Purley 4	d					23 24				
East Croydon	a	23 00	23 02			23 29			23 32	
	d	23 00	23 03			23 30			23 33	
Norwood Junction 2	a									
New Cross Gate	d									
London Bridge 4 ⊖	a		23 15						23 45	
London Blackfriars 3 ⊖	a		23 23						23 53	
City Thameslink 3	a									
Farringdon 3 ⊖	a		23 29						23 59	
St Pancras International 15 ⊖	a		23 34						00 03	
St Albans City	a		00 07						00 37	
Luton Airport Parkway 4 ✈	a		00 19						00 49	
Luton 7	a		00 22						00 52	
Bedford 10	a		00 49						01 19	
Clapham Junction 10	a	23 10				23 39				
London Victoria 15 ⊖	a	23 20			23 25	23 46	23 35			23 55

Station		GW 1	SN 1	SN 1	SN 1	FC 1	SN 1	SN 1	FC 1
Brighton 10	d				23 05	23 14			23 42
Hove 2	d								
Preston Park	d				23 09				
Hassocks 4	d				23 15	23 23			23 51
Burgess Hill 4	d				23 19	23 27			23 55
Lewes 4	d								
Wivelsfield 4	d				23 21				
Haywards Heath 3	a				23 26	23 32			23 59
	d				23 26	23 33			00 01
Balcombe	d				23 32				
Horsham 4	d		23 10						
Littlehaven	d		23 13						
Faygate	d								
Ifield	d		23 19						
Crawley	d		23 23						
Three Bridges 4	a		23 26		23 37	23 41			00 09
	d		23 27		23 41	23 42			00 10
Gatwick Airport 10 ✈	a		23 31		23 45	23 46			00 14
	d		23 32	23 35	23 46	23 47	23 50		00 15
Horley 4	d		23 35		23 49				
Salfords	d								
Earlswood (Surrey)	d								
Tonbridge 4	d								
Leigh (Kent)	d								
Penshurst	d								
Edenbridge	d								
Godstone	d								
Nutfield	d								
Reigate	d	23 30						←	
Redhill 5	a	23 36	23 42		23 56			23 56	00 23
	d		23 42		00 04			00 04	00 24
Merstham	d		23 46		→				
Coulsdon South	d		23 51						
Purley 4	d		23 55					00 12	
East Croydon	a		23 59			00 02		00 17	00 36
	d		00 01			00 02		00 18	00 36
Norwood Junction 2	a								
New Cross Gate	d								
London Bridge 4 ⊖	a					00 21			00 51
London Blackfriars 3 ⊖	a					00 28			00 58
City Thameslink 3	a								
Farringdon 3 ⊖	a					00 34			
St Pancras International 15 ⊖	a					00 38			01 09
St Albans City	a					01 11			01 42
Luton Airport Parkway 4 ✈	a					01 23			01 54
Luton 7	a					01 26			01 57
Bedford 10	a					01 52			02 23
Clapham Junction 10	a		00 16					00 31	
London Victoria 15 ⊖	a		00 24	00 10			00 27	00 39	

Table 186R

Sundays

5 January to 11 May

Brighton - London and Bedford

Network Diagram - see first Page of Table 175

Station		FC 1	SN 1	SN 1	FC 1	SN 1	SN 1	GW 1	SN 1	SN 1	SN 1	SN 1	SN 1
Brighton 10	d												
Hove 2	d												
Preston Park	d												
Hassocks 4	d												
Burgess Hill 4	d												
Lewes 4	d												
Wivelsfield 4	d												
Haywards Heath 3	a												
	d												
Balcombe	d				00 05								
Horsham 4	d												
Littlehaven	d												
Faygate	d												
Ifield	d												
Crawley	d												
Three Bridges 4	a				00 10								
	d				00 10					01 15		02 10	03 10
Gatwick Airport 10 ✈	a				00 14					01 19		02 14	03 14
	d			00 07	00 15	00 20	00 35		00 50	01 20	01 35	02 15	03 15
Horley 4	d									01 23		02 18	03 18
Salfords	d												
Earlswood (Surrey)	d												
Tonbridge 4	d												
Leigh (Kent)	d												
Penshurst	d												
Edenbridge	d												
Godstone	d												
Nutfield	d												
Reigate	d							00 45					
Redhill 5	a				00 23			00 49					
	d		00 03		00 24								
Merstham	d												
Coulsdon South	d												
Purley 4	d		00 12							01 37		02 33	03 33
East Croydon 🚌	a		00 17		00 35					01 43		02 39	03 39
	d	00 02	00 17		00 36					01 43		02 40	03 40
Norwood Junction 2	a												
New Cross Gate	d												
London Bridge 4 ⊖	a	00 21			00 51								
London Blackfriars 3 ⊖	a	00 28			00 58								
City Thameslink 3	a												
Farringdon 3 ⊖	a	00 34											
St Pancras International 15 ⊖	a	00 38			01 08								
St Albans City	a	01 11			01 41								
Luton Airport Parkway 4 ✈	a	01 23			01 53								
Luton 7	a	01 26			01 56								
Bedford 10	a	01 52			02 22								
Clapham Junction 10	a		00 33							01 57		02 53	03 53
London Victoria 15 ⊖	a		00 41	00 42		00 56	01 11		01 26	02 05	02 10	03 05	04 05

Station		SN 1	SN 1	FC	SN 1	SN 1	SN 1	SN 1 🚲	FC 1	GW 1	SN 1 🚲	SN 1	SN 1 🚲
Brighton 10	d								05 36				
Hove 2	d												
Preston Park	d												
Hassocks 4	d								05 45				
Burgess Hill 4	d								05 48				
Lewes 4	d												
Wivelsfield 4	d												
Haywards Heath 3	a								05 53				
	d								05 54				
Balcombe	d												
Horsham 4	d											06 04	
Littlehaven	d											06 07	
Faygate	d												
Ifield	d											06 13	
Crawley	d											06 17	
Three Bridges 4	a								06 02			06 20	
	d	04 10		05 13		05 26			06 02			06 21	
Gatwick Airport 10 ✈	a	04 14		05 17		05 30			06 07			06 25	
	d	04 15	04 35	05 18	05 20	05 32	05 50	06 05	06 08	06 10	06 20		06 35
Horley 4	d	04 18				05 34							
Salfords	d												
Earlswood (Surrey)	d												
Tonbridge 4	d												
Leigh (Kent)	d												
Penshurst	d												
Edenbridge	d												
Godstone	d												
Nutfield	d												
Reigate	d												
Redhill 5	a					05 42				06 17			
	d					05 42							
Merstham	d												
Coulsdon South	d												
Purley 4	d	04 33				05 51							
East Croydon 🚌	a	04 39		05 36		05 57			06 26				
	d	04 40		05 37		05 58			06 27				
Norwood Junction 2	a												
New Cross Gate	d												
London Bridge 4 ⊖	a												
London Blackfriars 3 ⊖	a			06 04					06 54				
City Thameslink 3	a												
Farringdon 3 ⊖	a												
St Pancras International 15 ⊖	a												
St Albans City	a												
Luton Airport Parkway 4 ✈	a												
Luton 7	a												
Bedford 10	a												
Clapham Junction 10	a	04 55				06 12							
London Victoria 15 ⊖	a	05 05	05 10		05 58	06 21	06 25	06 40			06 55		07 11

Station		FC 1 A	FC 1 B	SN 1 🚲	SN 1	SN 1	GW 1	SN 1 🚲	FC 1	GW 1	SN 1 🚲	SN 1	SN 1 🚲
Brighton 10	d	06 06	06 06		06 13				06 36				
Hove 2	d												
Preston Park	d				06 17								
Hassocks 4	d	06 15	06 15		06 23				06 45				
Burgess Hill 4	d	06 18	06 18		06 27				06 48				
Lewes 4	d												
Wivelsfield 4	d				06 29								
Haywards Heath 3	a	06 23	06 23		06 33				06 53				
	d	06 24	06 24		06 34				06 54				
Balcombe	d												
Horsham 4	d					06 28						06 56	
Littlehaven	d					06 31						06 59	
Faygate	d												
Ifield	d					06 37						07 05	
Crawley	d					06 41						07 09	
Three Bridges 4	a	06 32	06 32		06 42	06 46			07 02			07 12	
	d	06 32	06 32		06 43	06 47			07 02			07 13	
Gatwick Airport 10 ✈	a	06 37	06 37		06 47	06 51			07 07			07 17	
	d	06 38	06 38	06 45	06 48	06 52		07 05	07 08	07 10	07 15	07 18	07 33
Horley 4	d					06 54						07 21	
Salfords	d												
Earlswood (Surrey)	d												
Tonbridge 4	d												
Leigh (Kent)	d												
Penshurst	d												
Edenbridge	d												
Godstone	d												
Nutfield	d												
Reigate	d						07 05						
Redhill 5	a					07 01	07 09			07 16		07 29	
	d					07 02						07 29	
Merstham	d					07 06						07 33	
Coulsdon South	d					07 11						07 38	
Purley 4	d					07 15						07 43	
East Croydon 🚌	a	06 56	06 56		07 05	07 20			07 26			07 48	
	d	06 57	06 57		07 06	07 24			07 27			07 48	
Norwood Junction 2	a											07 53	
New Cross Gate	d												
London Bridge 4 ⊖	a											08 05	
London Blackfriars 3 ⊖	a	07 23	07 23						07 54				
City Thameslink 3	a												
Farringdon 3 ⊖	a	07 30	07 30						08 00				
St Pancras International 15 ⊖	a	07 34	07 34						08 04				
St Albans City	a		08 07						08 37				
Luton Airport Parkway 4 ✈	a		08 19						08 49				
Luton 7	a		08 22						08 52				
Bedford 10	a		08 49						09 19				
Clapham Junction 10	a				07 18	07 38							
London Victoria 15 ⊖	a			07 20	07 29	07 46		07 42			07 50		08 10

A until 23 March

B from 30 March

Table 186R

Sundays

Brighton - London and Bedford

5 January to 11 May

Network Diagram - see first Page of Table 175

		FC	SN	SN	SN	SN	SN	SN	FC	GW	SN	GW	SN	SN	SN	FC	SN	SN	SN
		1	1	1	1	1	1	1	1	1	1	1	1	1	1	1	1	1	1
					🛒	🛒		🛒						🛒	🛒				🛒
Brighton 10	d	07 04	07 06						07 36							08 04	08 06		
Hove 2	d										07 55								
Preston Park	d		07 10														08 09		
Hassocks 4	d	07 13	07 16						07 45							08 13	08 16		
Burgess Hill 4	d	07 16	07 20						07 48		08 05					08 16	08 19		
Lewes 4	d					07 20													
Wivelsfield 4	d		07 22			07 35											08 21		
Haywards Heath 3	a	07 21	07 26			07 39			07 53		08 10					08 21	08 26		
	d	07 24	07 27			07 40			07 54		08 11					08 24	08 26		
Balcombe	d		07 32														08 32		
Horsham 4	d						07 37						07 53						
Littlehaven	d												07 56						
Faygate	d																		
Ifield	d												08 02						
Crawley	d						07 46						08 06						
Three Bridges 4	a	07 32	07 38				07 50		08 02				08 09			08 32	08 37		
	d	07 32	07 38				07 51		08 02				08 09			08 32	08 38		
Gatwick Airport 10 ✈	a	07 37	07 42			07 51	07 55		08 07		08 22		08 14			08 37	08 42		
	d	07 38	07 43		07 50	07 52	07 56	08 05	08 08	08 10	08 23		08 15	08 20	08 35	08 38	08 43		08 50
Horley 4	d						07 59						08 17						
Salfords	d																		
Earlswood (Surrey)	d																		
Tonbridge 4	d			07 23														08 29	
Leigh (Kent)	d			07 27														08 33	
Penshurst	d			07 31														08 37	
Edenbridge	d			07 37														08 43	
Godstone	d			07 44														08 50	
Nutfield	d			07 49														08 55	
Reigate	d											08 13							
Redhill 5	a		07 51	07 54			08 06			08 16		08 18	08 25				08 51	09 00	
	d		07 52				08 07						08 33				08 52		
Merstham	d												08 37						
Coulsdon South	d												08 42						
Purley 4	d						08 16						08 46						
East Croydon 🚊	a	07 56	08 04			08 09	08 21		08 26		08 40		08 51			08 55	09 03		
	d	07 57	08 04			08 10	08 22		08 27		08 41		08 52			08 56	09 03		
Norwood Junction 2	a												08 56						
New Cross Gate	d																		
London Bridge 4 ⊖	a												09 08						
London Blackfriars 3 ⊖	a	08 24							08 54							09 24			
City Thameslink 3	a																		
Farringdon 3 ⊖	a	08 30							09 00							09 30			
St Pancras International 15 ⊖	a	08 34							09 04							09 34			
St Albans City	a	09 07							09 37							10 07			
Luton Airport Parkway 4 ✈	a	09 19							09 49							10 19			
Luton 7	a	09 22							09 52							10 22			
Bedford 10	a	09 49							10 19							10 49			
Clapham Junction 10	a		08 17			08 27	08 35				08 57						09 12		
London Victoria 15 ⊖	a		08 25		08 27	08 35	08 43	08 45			09 05			08 58	09 09		09 19		09 21

		SN	SN	FC	SN	SN	GW	FC	SN	SN	FC	FC	SN	SN	GW	SN	SN	FC	SN
		1	1	1	1	1	1	1	1	1	1	1	1	1	1	1	1	1	1
											A	B							
		🛒	🛒			🛒			🛒				🛒			🛒			
Brighton 10	d		08 38					08 44					09 10				09 00	09 14	
Hove 2	d									08 55									
Preston Park	d																09 03		
Hassocks 4	d							08 53									09 10	09 23	
Burgess Hill 4	d							08 57		09 05							09 13	09 27	
Lewes 4	d	08 22																	
Wivelsfield 4	d	08 37															09 15		
Haywards Heath 3	a	08 41						09 02		09 10							09 20	09 32	
	d	08 42						09 03		09 11							09 25	09 33	
Balcombe	d																09 30		
Horsham 4	d				08 44									09 01					
Littlehaven	d													09 04					
Faygate	d																		
Ifield	d													09 10					
Crawley	d				08 53									09 14					
Three Bridges 4	a				08 56			09 11						09 17			09 36	09 41	
	d				08 57			09 12						09 18			09 36	09 42	
Gatwick Airport 10 ✈	a	08 53	09 00		09 02			09 16		09 22				09 22			09 40	09 46	
	d	08 54	09 01	08 59	09 03	09 05	09 08	09 17	09 20	09 23	09 27	09 29		09 23		09 35	09 41	09 47	
Horley 4	d				09 05									09 26					
Salfords	d																		
Earlswood (Surrey)	d													09 33					
Tonbridge 4	d																		09 29
Leigh (Kent)	d																		09 33
Penshurst	d																		09 37
Edenbridge	d																		09 43
Godstone	d																		09 50
Nutfield	d																		09 55
Reigate	d														09 30				
Redhill 5	a				09 13		09 16							09 36	09 36		09 48		10 00
	d				09 14									09 37			09 49		
Merstham	d													09 41					
Coulsdon South	d				09 21									09 46					
Purley 4	d				09 24									09 50					
East Croydon 🚊	a	09 09	09 15	09 17	09 29			09 32		09 38	09 41	09 43	09 45	09 55			10 00	10 02	
	d	09 10	09 16	09 17	09 30			09 33		09 39	09 47	09 47	09 46	09 56			10 00	10 03	
Norwood Junction 2	a													10 02					
New Cross Gate	d																		
London Bridge 4 ⊖	a													10 14					
London Blackfriars 3 ⊖	a			09 49				10 07			10 19	10 19						10 37	
City Thameslink 3	a																		
Farringdon 3 ⊖	a			10 00				10 14			10 28	10 28						10 44	
St Pancras International 15 ⊖	a			10 04				10 18			10 32	10 32						10 48	
St Albans City	a			10 37				10 42			10 56	10 56						11 12	
Luton Airport Parkway 4 ✈	a			10 49				10 54			11 08	11 08						11 24	
Luton 7	a			10 52				10 57			11 11	11 11						11 27	
Bedford 10	a			11 19				11 24			11 38	11 38						11 54	
Clapham Junction 10	a	09 19	09 25		09 39					09 48			09 55				10 09		
London Victoria 15 ⊖	a	09 26	09 32		09 46	09 35			09 50	09 56			10 03			10 05	10 17		

A until 9 February

B from 16 February

Table 186R

Sundays

5 January to 11 May

Brighton - London and Bedford

Network Diagram - see first Page of Table 175

		SN	SN	SN	FC	FC	SN	SN	GW	FC
		1	1	1	1	1	1	1	1	1
					A	B				
		🛒	🛒	🛒				🛒		
Brighton [10]	d			09 35						09 44
Hove [2]	d									
Preston Park	d									
Hassocks [4]	d									09 53
Burgess Hill [4]	d									09 57
Lewes [4]	d		09 20							
Wivelsfield [4]	d		09 34							
Haywards Heath [3]	a		09 38							10 02
	d		09 41							10 03
Balcombe	d									
Horsham [4]	d						09 44			
Littlehaven	d									
Faygate	d									
Ifield	d									
Crawley	d						09 53			
Three Bridges [4]	a						09 56			10 11
	d						09 57			10 12
Gatwick Airport [10] ✈	a		09 52	09 56			10 02			10 16
	d	09 50	09 53	09 57	09 57	09 59	10 03	10 05	10 08	10 17
Horley [4]	d						10 05			
Salfords	d									
Earlswood (Surrey)	d									
Tonbridge [4]	d									
Leigh (Kent)	d									
Penshurst	d									
Edenbridge	d									
Godstone	d									
Nutfield	d									
Reigate	d									
Redhill [5]	a						10 13		10 16	
	d						10 14			
Merstham	d									
Coulsdon South	d						10 21			
Purley [4]	d						10 24			
East Croydon	a		10 08	10 13	10 16	10 16	10 29			10 32
	d		10 09	10 14	10 17	10 17	10 30			10 33
Norwood Junction [2]	a									
New Cross Gate	d									
London Bridge [4] ⊖	a									
London Blackfriars [3] ⊖	a				10 49	10 49				11 07
City Thameslink [3]	a									
Farringdon [3] ⊖	a				10 58	10 58				11 14
St Pancras International [15] ⊖	a				11 02	11 02				11 18
St Albans City	a				11 26	11 26				11 42
Luton Airport Parkway [4] ✈	a				11 38	11 38				11 54
Luton [7]	a				11 41	11 41				11 57
Bedford [10]	a				12 08	12 08				12 24
Clapham Junction [10]	a		10 18	10 23			10 39			
London Victoria [15] ⊖	a	10 20	10 26	10 30			10 46	10 35		

		SN	SN	SN	FC	FC	SN	SN	GW	SN
		1	1	1	1	1	1	1	1	1
					A	B				
		🛒					🛒			🛒
Brighton [10]	d						10 10			
Hove [2]	d		09 55							
Preston Park	d									
Hassocks [4]	d									
Burgess Hill [4]	d		10 05							
Lewes [4]	d									
Wivelsfield [4]	d									
Haywards Heath [3]	a		10 10							
	d		10 11							
Balcombe	d									
Horsham [4]	d			10 01						
Littlehaven	d			10 04						
Faygate	d									
Ifield	d			10 10						
Crawley	d			10 14						
Three Bridges [4]	a			10 17						
	d			10 18	10 22	10 24				
Gatwick Airport [10] ✈	a		10 22	10 22	10 26	10 28				
	d	10 20	10 23	10 23	10 27	10 29				10 35
Horley [4]	d			10 26						
Salfords	d									
Earlswood (Surrey)	d			10 33						
Tonbridge [4]	d									
Leigh (Kent)	d									
Penshurst	d									
Edenbridge	d									
Godstone	d									
Nutfield	d									
Reigate	d							←	10 31	
Redhill [5]	a			10 36				10 36	10 36	
	d			10 37				10 37		
Merstham	d			→				10 41		
Coulsdon South	d							10 46		
Purley [4]	d							10 50		
East Croydon	a		10 38		10 41	10 43	10 45	10 55		
	d		10 39		10 47	10 47	10 46	10 56		
Norwood Junction [2]	a							11 02		
New Cross Gate	d									
London Bridge [4] ⊖	a							11 14		
London Blackfriars [3] ⊖	a				11 19	11 19				
City Thameslink [3]	a									
Farringdon [3] ⊖	a				11 28	11 28				
St Pancras International [15] ⊖	a				11 32	11 32				
St Albans City	a				11 56	11 56				
Luton Airport Parkway [4] ✈	a				12 08	12 08				
Luton [7]	a				12 11	12 11				
Bedford [10]	a				12 38	12 38				
Clapham Junction [10]	a		10 48				10 55			
London Victoria [15] ⊖	a	10 50	10 56				11 03			11 05

		SN	FC	SN	SN	SN	SN	FC	FC	SN
		1	1	1	1	1	1	1	1	1
								A	B	
					🛒	🛒	🛒			
Brighton [10]	d	10 00	10 14				10 35			
Hove [2]	d									
Preston Park	d	10 03								
Hassocks [4]	d	10 10	10 23							
Burgess Hill [4]	d	10 13	10 27							
Lewes [4]	d					10 20				
Wivelsfield [4]	d	10 15				10 35				
Haywards Heath [3]	a	10 20	10 32			10 39				
	d	10 25	10 33			10 41				
Balcombe	d	10 30								
Horsham [4]	d									10 44
Littlehaven	d									
Faygate	d									
Ifield	d									
Crawley	d									10 53
Three Bridges [4]	a	10 36	10 41							10 56
	d	10 36	10 42					10 52	10 54	10 57
Gatwick Airport [10] ✈	a	10 40	10 46			10 52	10 56	10 56	10 58	11 02
	d	10 41	10 47		10 50	10 53	10 57	10 57	10 59	11 03
Horley [4]	d									11 05
Salfords	d									
Earlswood (Surrey)	d									
Tonbridge [4]	d			10 29						
Leigh (Kent)	d			10 33						
Penshurst	d			10 37						
Edenbridge	d			10 43						
Godstone	d			10 50						
Nutfield	d			10 55						
Reigate	d									
Redhill [5]	a	10 48		11 00						11 13
	d	10 49								11 14
Merstham	d									
Coulsdon South	d									11 21
Purley [4]	d									11 24
East Croydon	a	11 00	11 02			11 08	11 13	11 16	11 16	11 29
	d	11 00	11 03			11 09	11 14	11 17	11 17	11 30
Norwood Junction [2]	a									
New Cross Gate	d									
London Bridge [4] ⊖	a									
London Blackfriars [3] ⊖	a		11 37					11 49	11 49	
City Thameslink [3]	a									
Farringdon [3] ⊖	a		11 44					11 58	11 58	
St Pancras International [15] ⊖	a		11 48					12 02	12 02	
St Albans City	a		12 12					12 26	12 26	
Luton Airport Parkway [4] ✈	a		12 24					12 38	12 38	
Luton [7]	a		12 27					12 41	12 41	
Bedford [10]	a		12 54					13 08	13 08	
Clapham Junction [10]	a	11 09				11 18	11 23			11 39
London Victoria [15] ⊖	a	11 17			11 20	11 26	11 30			11 46

		SN	GW	FC	SN	SN	SN	FC	FC	SN
		1	1	1	1	1	1	1	1	1
								A	B	
		🛒			🛒					🛒
Brighton [10]	d			10 44						11 10
Hove [2]	d					10 55				
Preston Park	d									
Hassocks [4]	d			10 53						
Burgess Hill [4]	d			10 57		11 05				
Lewes [4]	d									
Wivelsfield [4]	d									
Haywards Heath [3]	a			11 02		11 10				
	d			11 03		11 11				
Balcombe	d									
Horsham [4]	d						11 01			
Littlehaven	d						11 04			
Faygate	d									
Ifield	d						11 10			
Crawley	d						11 14			
Three Bridges [4]	a			11 11			11 17			
	d			11 12			11 18	11 22	11 24	
Gatwick Airport [10] ✈	a			11 16		11 22	11 22	11 26	11 28	
	d	11 05	11 08	11 17	11 20	11 23	11 23	11 27	11 29	
Horley [4]	d						11 26			
Salfords	d									
Earlswood (Surrey)	d						11 33			
Tonbridge [4]	d									
Leigh (Kent)	d									
Penshurst	d									
Edenbridge	d									
Godstone	d									
Nutfield	d									
Reigate	d									
Redhill [5]	a		11 16				11 36			
	d						11 37			
Merstham	d						→			
Coulsdon South	d									
Purley [4]	d									
East Croydon	a			11 32		11 38		11 41	11 43	11 45
	d			11 33		11 39		11 47	11 47	11 46
Norwood Junction [2]	a									
New Cross Gate	d									
London Bridge [4] ⊖	a									
London Blackfriars [3] ⊖	a			12 07				12 19	12 19	
City Thameslink [3]	a									
Farringdon [3] ⊖	a			12 14				12 28	12 28	
St Pancras International [15] ⊖	a			12 18				12 32	12 32	
St Albans City	a			12 42				12 56	12 56	
Luton Airport Parkway [4] ✈	a			12 54				13 08	13 08	
Luton [7]	a			12 57				13 11	13 11	
Bedford [10]	a			13 24				13 38	13 38	
Clapham Junction [10]	a					11 48				11 55
London Victoria [15] ⊖	a	11 35			11 50	11 56				12 03

A until 9 February **B** from 16 February

Table 186R

Sundays

5 January to 11 May

Brighton - London and Bedford

Network Diagram - see first Page of Table 175

Station		SN 1	GW 1	SN 1 trolley	SN 1	FC 1	SN 1	SN 1 trolley	SN 1 trolley	SN 1 trolley	FC 1 A	FC 1 B	SN 1	SN 1 trolley	GW 1	FC 1	SN 1 trolley	SN 1	SN 1
Brighton 10	d				11 00	11 14				11 35						11 44			
Hove 2	d																	11 55	
Preston Park	d				11 03														
Hassocks 4	d				11 10	11 23										11 53			
Burgess Hill 4	d				11 13	11 27										11 57		12 05	
Lewes 4	d								11 20										
Wivelsfield 4	d				11 15				11 35										
Haywards Heath 3	a				11 20	11 32			11 39							12 02		12 10	
	d				11 25	11 33			11 41							12 03		12 11	
Balcombe	d				11 30														
Horsham 4	d												11 44						12 01
Littlehaven	d																		12 04
Faygate	d																		
Ifield	d																		12 10
Crawley	d												11 53						12 14
Three Bridges 4	a				11 36	11 41							11 56			12 11			12 17
	d				11 36	11 42					11 52	11 54	11 57			12 12			12 18
Gatwick Airport 10 ✈	a				11 40	11 46			11 52	11 56	11 56	11 58	12 02			12 16		12 22	12 22
	d			11 35	11 41	11 47		11 50	11 53	11 57	11 57	11 59	12 03	12 05	12 08	12 17	12 20	12 23	12 23
Horley 4	d												12 05						12 26
Salfords	d																		
Earlswood (Surrey)	d																		12 33
Tonbridge 4	d						11 29												
Leigh (Kent)	d						11 33												
Penshurst	d						11 37												
Edenbridge	d						11 43												
Godstone	d						11 50												
Nutfield	d						11 55												
Reigate	d	←	11 30																
Redhill 5	a	11 36	11 36		11 48		12 00						12 13		12 16				12 36
	d	11 37			11 49								12 14						12 37
Merstham	d	11 41																	→
Coulsdon South	d	11 46											12 21						
Purley 4	d	11 50											12 24						
East Croydon	a	11 55			12 00	12 02			12 08	12 13	12 16	12 16	12 29			12 32		12 38	
	d	11 56			12 00	12 03			12 09	12 14	12 17	12 17	12 30			12 33		12 39	
Norwood Junction 2	a	12 02																	
New Cross Gate	d																		
London Bridge 4 ⊖	a	12 14																	
London Blackfriars 3 ⊖	a					12 37					12 49	12 49				13 07			
City Thameslink 3	a																		
Farringdon 3 ⊖	a					12 44					12 58	12 58				13 14			
St Pancras International 15 ⊖	a					12 48					13 02	13 02				13 18			
St Albans City	a					13 12					13 26	13 26				13 42			
Luton Airport Parkway 4 ✈	a					13 24					13 38	13 38				13 54			
Luton 7	a					13 27					13 41	13 41				13 57			
Bedford 10	a					13 54					14 08	14 08				14 24			
Clapham Junction 10	a				12 09				12 18	12 23			12 39					12 48	
London Victoria 15 ⊖	a			12 05	12 17			12 20	12 26	12 30			12 46	12 35			12 50	12 56	

Station		FC 1 A	FC 1 B	SN 1 trolley	SN 1	GW 1	SN 1 trolley	SN 1	FC 1	SN 1	SN 1 trolley	SN 1 trolley	SN 1 trolley	FC 1 A	FC 1 B	SN 1	SN 1 trolley	GW 1	FC 1
Brighton 10	d			12 10				12 00	12 14				12 35						12 44
Hove 2	d																		
Preston Park	d							12 03											
Hassocks 4	d							12 10	12 23										12 53
Burgess Hill 4	d							12 13	12 27										12 57
Lewes 4	d											12 20							
Wivelsfield 4	d							12 15				12 35							
Haywards Heath 3	a							12 20	12 32			12 39							13 02
	d							12 25	12 33			12 41							13 03
Balcombe	d							12 30											
Horsham 4	d															12 44			
Littlehaven	d																		
Faygate	d																		
Ifield	d																		
Crawley	d															12 53			
Three Bridges 4	a							12 36	12 41							12 56			13 11
	d	12 22	12 24					12 36	12 42					12 52	12 54	12 57			13 12
Gatwick Airport 10 ✈	a	12 26	12 28					12 40	12 46			12 52	12 56	12 56	12 58	13 02			13 16
	d	12 27	12 29				12 35	12 41	12 47		12 50	12 53	12 57	12 57	12 59	13 03	13 05	13 08	13 17
Horley 4	d															13 05			
Salfords	d																		
Earlswood (Surrey)	d																		
Tonbridge 4	d									12 29									
Leigh (Kent)	d									12 33									
Penshurst	d									12 37									
Edenbridge	d									12 43									
Godstone	d									12 50									
Nutfield	d									12 55									
Reigate	d				←	12 31													
Redhill 5	a				12 36	12 36		12 48		13 00						13 13		13 16	
	d				12 37			12 49								13 14			
Merstham	d				12 41														
Coulsdon South	d				12 46											13 21			
Purley 4	d				12 50											13 24			
East Croydon	a	12 41	12 43	12 45	12 55			13 00	13 02			13 08	13 13	13 16	13 16	13 29			13 32
	d	12 47	12 47	12 46	12 56			13 00	13 03			13 09	13 14	13 17	13 17	13 30			13 33
Norwood Junction 2	a				13 02														
New Cross Gate	d																		
London Bridge 4 ⊖	a				13 14														
London Blackfriars 3 ⊖	a	13 19	13 19						13 37					13 49	13 49				14 07
City Thameslink 3	a																		
Farringdon 3 ⊖	a	13 28	13 28						13 44					13 58	13 58				14 14
St Pancras International 15 ⊖	a	13 32	13 32						13 48					14 02	14 02				14 18
St Albans City	a	13 56	13 56						14 12					14 26	14 26				14 42
Luton Airport Parkway 4 ✈	a	14 08	14 08						14 24					14 38	14 38				14 54
Luton 7	a	14 11	14 11						14 27					14 41	14 41				14 57
Bedford 10	a	14 38	14 38						14 54					15 08	15 08				15 24
Clapham Junction 10	a			12 55				13 09				13 18	13 23			13 39			
London Victoria 15 ⊖	a			13 03			13 05	13 17			13 20	13 26	13 30			13 46	13 35		

A until 9 February

B from 16 February

Table 186R

Sundays

5 January to 11 May

Brighton - London and Bedford

Network Diagram - see first Page of Table 175

		SN	SN	SN	FC	FC	SN	SN	GW	SN
		1	1	1	1	1	1	1	1	1
					A	B				
		🚌					🚌			🚌
Brighton 10	d						13 10			
Hove 2	d		12 55							
Preston Park	d									
Hassocks 4	d									
Burgess Hill 4	d		13 05							
Lewes 4	d									
Wivelsfield 4	d									
Haywards Heath 3	a		13 10							
	d		13 11							
Balcombe	d									
Horsham 4	d			13 01						
Littlehaven	d			13 04						
Faygate	d									
Ifield	d			13 10						
Crawley	d			13 14						
Three Bridges 4	a			13 17						
	d			13 18	13 22	13 24				
Gatwick Airport 10 ✈	a		13 22	13 22	13 26	13 28				
	d	13 20	13 23	13 23	13 27	13 29				13 35
Horley 4	d			13 26						
Salfords	d									
Earlswood (Surrey)	d			13 33						
Tonbridge 4	d									
Leigh (Kent)	d									
Penshurst	d									
Edenbridge	d									
Godstone	d									
Nutfield	d									
Reigate	d							←	13 30	
Redhill 5	a			13 36				13 36	13 36	
	d			13 37				13 37		
Merstham	d			→				13 41		
Coulsdon South	d							13 46		
Purley 4	d							13 50		
East Croydon 🚊	a		13 38		13 41	13 43	13 45	13 55		
	d		13 39		13 47	13 47	13 46	13 56		
Norwood Junction 2	a							14 02		
New Cross Gate	d									
London Bridge 4 ⊖	a							14 14		
London Blackfriars 3 ⊖	a				14 19	14 19				
City Thameslink 3	a									
Farringdon 3 ⊖	a				14 28	14 28				
St Pancras International 15 ⊖	a				14 32	14 32				
St Albans City	a				14 56	14 56				
Luton Airport Parkway 4 ✈	a				15 08	15 08				
Luton 7	a				15 11	15 11				
Bedford 10	a				15 38	15 38				
Clapham Junction 10	a		13 48				13 55			
London Victoria 15 ⊖	a	13 50	13 56				14 03			14 05

		SN	FC	SN	SN	SN	SN	FC	FC	SN
		1	1	1	1	1	1	1	1	1
								A	B	
					🚌	🚌	🚌			
Brighton 10	d	13 00	13 14				13 35			
Hove 2	d									
Preston Park	d	13 03								
Hassocks 4	d	13 10	13 23							
Burgess Hill 4	d	13 13	13 27							
Lewes 4	d					13 20				
Wivelsfield 4	d	13 15				13 35				
Haywards Heath 3	a	13 20	13 32			13 39				
	d	13 25	13 33			13 41				
Balcombe	d	13 30								
Horsham 4	d									13 44
Littlehaven	d									
Faygate	d									
Ifield	d									
Crawley	d									13 53
Three Bridges 4	a	13 36	13 41							13 56
	d	13 36	13 42					13 52	13 54	13 57
Gatwick Airport 10 ✈	a	13 40	13 46			13 52	13 56	13 56	13 58	14 02
	d	13 41	13 47		13 50	13 53	13 57	13 57	13 59	14 03
Horley 4	d									14 05
Salfords	d									
Earlswood (Surrey)	d									
Tonbridge 4	d			13 29						
Leigh (Kent)	d			13 33						
Penshurst	d			13 37						
Edenbridge	d			13 43						
Godstone	d			13 50						
Nutfield	d			13 55						
Reigate	d									
Redhill 5	a	13 48		14 00						14 13
	d	13 49								14 14
Merstham	d									
Coulsdon South	d									14 21
Purley 4	d									14 24
East Croydon 🚊	a	14 00	14 02			14 08	14 13	14 16	14 16	14 29
	d	14 00	14 03			14 09	14 14	14 17	14 17	14 30
Norwood Junction 2	a									
New Cross Gate	d									
London Bridge 4 ⊖	a									
London Blackfriars 3 ⊖	a		14 37					14 49	14 49	
City Thameslink 3	a									
Farringdon 3 ⊖	a		14 44					14 58	14 58	
St Pancras International 15 ⊖	a		14 48					15 02	15 02	
St Albans City	a		15 12					15 26	15 26	
Luton Airport Parkway 4 ✈	a		15 24					15 38	15 38	
Luton 7	a		15 27					15 41	15 41	
Bedford 10	a		15 54					16 08	16 08	
Clapham Junction 10	a	14 09				14 18	14 23			14 39
London Victoria 15 ⊖	a	14 17			14 20	14 26	14 30			14 46

		SN	GW	FC	SN	SN	SN	FC	FC	SN
		1	1	1	1	1	1	1	1	1
								A	B	
		🚌			🚌					🚌
Brighton 10	d			13 44						14 10
Hove 2	d					13 55				
Preston Park	d									
Hassocks 4	d			13 53						
Burgess Hill 4	d			13 57		14 05				
Lewes 4	d									
Wivelsfield 4	d									
Haywards Heath 3	a			14 02		14 10				
	d			14 03		14 11				
Balcombe	d									
Horsham 4	d						14 01			
Littlehaven	d						14 04			
Faygate	d									
Ifield	d						14 10			
Crawley	d						14 14			
Three Bridges 4	a			14 11			14 17			
	d			14 12			14 18	14 22	14 24	
Gatwick Airport 10 ✈	a			14 16		14 22	14 22	14 26	14 28	
	d	14 05	14 08	14 17	14 20	14 23	14 23	14 27	14 29	
Horley 4	d						14 26			
Salfords	d									
Earlswood (Surrey)	d						14 33			
Tonbridge 4	d									
Leigh (Kent)	d									
Penshurst	d									
Edenbridge	d									
Godstone	d									
Nutfield	d									
Reigate	d									
Redhill 5	a		14 16				14 36			
	d						14 37			
Merstham	d						→			
Coulsdon South	d									
Purley 4	d									
East Croydon 🚊	a			14 32		14 38		14 41	14 43	14 45
	d			14 33		14 39		14 47	14 47	14 46
Norwood Junction 2	a									
New Cross Gate	d									
London Bridge 4 ⊖	a									
London Blackfriars 3 ⊖	a			15 07				15 19	15 19	
City Thameslink 3	a									
Farringdon 3 ⊖	a			15 14				15 28	15 28	
St Pancras International 15 ⊖	a			15 18				15 32	15 32	
St Albans City	a			15 42				15 56	15 56	
Luton Airport Parkway 4 ✈	a			15 54				16 08	16 08	
Luton 7	a			15 57				16 11	16 11	
Bedford 10	a			16 24				16 38	16 38	
Clapham Junction 10	a					14 48				14 55
London Victoria 15 ⊖	a	14 35			14 50	14 56				15 03

		SN	GW	SN	SN	FC	SN	SN	SN	SN
		1	1	1	1	1	1	1	1	1
				🚌				🚌	🚌	🚌
Brighton 10	d				14 00	14 14				14 35
Hove 2	d									
Preston Park	d				14 03					
Hassocks 4	d				14 10	14 23				
Burgess Hill 4	d				14 13	14 27				
Lewes 4	d								14 20	
Wivelsfield 4	d				14 15				14 35	
Haywards Heath 3	a				14 20	14 32			14 39	
	d				14 25	14 33			14 41	
Balcombe	d				14 30					
Horsham 4	d									
Littlehaven	d									
Faygate	d									
Ifield	d									
Crawley	d									
Three Bridges 4	a				14 36	14 41				
	d				14 36	14 42				
Gatwick Airport 10 ✈	a				14 40	14 46			14 52	14 56
	d			14 35	14 41	14 47		14 50	14 53	14 57
Horley 4	d									
Salfords	d									
Earlswood (Surrey)	d									
Tonbridge 4	d						14 29			
Leigh (Kent)	d						14 33			
Penshurst	d						14 37			
Edenbridge	d						14 43			
Godstone	d						14 50			
Nutfield	d						14 55			
Reigate	d	←	14 31							
Redhill 5	a	14 36	14 36		14 48		15 00			
	d	14 37			14 49					
Merstham	d	14 41								
Coulsdon South	d	14 46								
Purley 4	d	14 50								
East Croydon 🚊	a	14 55			15 00	15 02			15 08	15 13
	d	14 56			15 00	15 03			15 09	15 14
Norwood Junction 2	a	15 02								
New Cross Gate	d									
London Bridge 4 ⊖	a	15 14								
London Blackfriars 3 ⊖	a					15 37				
City Thameslink 3	a									
Farringdon 3 ⊖	a					15 44				
St Pancras International 15 ⊖	a					15 48				
St Albans City	a					16 12				
Luton Airport Parkway 4 ✈	a					16 24				
Luton 7	a					16 27				
Bedford 10	a					16 54				
Clapham Junction 10	a				15 09				15 18	15 23
London Victoria 15 ⊖	a			15 05	15 17			15 20	15 26	15 30

A until 9 February

B from 16 February

Table 186R

Sundays

Brighton - London and Bedford

5 January to 11 May

Network Diagram - see first Page of Table 175

		FC 1 A	FC 1 B	SN 1	SN 1 🛒	GW 1	FC 1	SN 1 🛒	SN 1	SN 1	FC 1 A	FC 1 B	SN 1 🛒	SN 1	GW 1	SN 1 🛒	SN 1	FC 1	SN 1
Brighton 10	d						14 44						15 10				15 00	15 14	
Hove 2	d								14 55										
Preston Park	d																15 03		
Hassocks 4	d						14 53										15 10	15 23	
Burgess Hill 4	d						14 57		15 05								15 13	15 27	
Lewes 4	d																		
Wivelsfield 4	d																15 15		
Haywards Heath 3	a						15 02		15 10								15 20	15 32	
	d						15 03		15 11								15 25	15 33	
Balcombe	d																15 30		
Horsham 4	d			14 44						15 01									
Littlehaven	d									15 04									
Faygate	d																		
Ifield	d									15 10									
Crawley	d			14 53						15 14									
Three Bridges 4	a			14 56			15 11			15 17							15 36	15 41	
	d	14 52	14 54	14 57			15 12			15 18	15 22	15 24					15 36	15 42	
Gatwick Airport 10 ✈	a	14 56	14 58	15 02			15 16		15 22	15 22	15 26	15 28					15 40	15 46	
	d	14 57	14 59	15 03	15 05	15 08	15 17	15 20	15 23	15 23	15 27	15 29				15 35	15 41	15 47	
Horley 4	d			15 05						15 26									
Salfords	d																		
Earlswood (Surrey)	d									15 33									
Tonbridge 4	d																		15 29
Leigh (Kent)	d																		15 33
Penshurst	d																		15 37
Edenbridge	d																		15 43
Godstone	d																		15 50
Nutfield	d																		15 55
Reigate	d													←	15 30				
Redhill 5	a			15 13		15 16				15 36				15 36	15 36		15 48		16 00
	d			15 14						15 37				15 37			15 49		
Merstham	d									→				15 41					
Coulsdon South	d			15 21										15 46					
Purley 4	d			15 24										15 50					
East Croydon	a	15 16	15 16	15 29			15 32		15 38		15 41	15 43	15 45	15 55			16 00	16 02	
	d	15 17	15 17	15 30			15 33		15 39		15 47	15 47	15 46	15 56			16 00	16 03	
Norwood Junction 2	a													16 02					
New Cross Gate	d																		
London Bridge 4 ⊖	a													16 14					
London Blackfriars 3 ⊖	a	15 49	15 49				16 07				16 19	16 19						16 37	
City Thameslink 3	a																		
Farringdon 3 ⊖	a	15 58	15 58				16 14				16 28	16 28						16 44	
St Pancras International 15 ⊖	a	16 02	16 02				16 18				16 32	16 32						16 48	
St Albans City	a	16 26	16 26				16 42				16 56	16 56						17 12	
Luton Airport Parkway 4 ✈	a	16 38	16 38				16 54				17 08	17 08						17 24	
Luton 7	a	16 41	16 41				16 57				17 11	17 11						17 27	
Bedford 10	a	17 08	17 08				17 24				17 38	17 38						17 54	
Clapham Junction 10	a			15 39					15 48				15 55				16 09		
London Victoria 15 ⊖	a			15 46	15 35			15 50	15 56				16 03			16 05	16 17		

		SN 1 🛒	SN 1 🛒	SN 1 🛒	FC 1 A	FC 1 B	SN 1	SN 1 🛒	GW 1	FC 1	SN 1 🛒	SN 1	SN 1	FC 1 A	FC 1 B	SN 1 🛒	SN 1	GW 1	SN 1 🛒
Brighton 10	d			15 35						15 44						16 10			
Hove 2	d											15 55							
Preston Park	d																		
Hassocks 4	d									15 53									
Burgess Hill 4	d									15 57		16 05							
Lewes 4	d		15 20																
Wivelsfield 4	d		15 35																
Haywards Heath 3	a		15 39							16 02		16 10							
	d		15 41							16 03		16 11							
Balcombe	d																		
Horsham 4	d						15 44						16 01						
Littlehaven	d												16 04						
Faygate	d																		
Ifield	d												16 10						
Crawley	d						15 53						16 14						
Three Bridges 4	a						15 56			16 11			16 17						
	d				15 52	15 54	15 57			16 12			16 18	16 22	16 24				
Gatwick Airport 10 ✈	a		15 52	15 56	15 56	15 58	16 02			16 16		16 22	16 22	16 26	16 28				
	d	15 50	15 53	15 57	15 57	15 59	16 03	16 05	16 08	16 17	16 20	16 23	16 23	16 27	16 29				16 35
Horley 4	d						16 05						16 26						
Salfords	d																		
Earlswood (Surrey)	d												16 33						
Tonbridge 4	d																		
Leigh (Kent)	d																		
Penshurst	d																		
Edenbridge	d																		
Godstone	d																		
Nutfield	d																		
Reigate	d																←	16 31	
Redhill 5	a						16 13		16 16				16 36				16 36	16 36	
	d						16 14						16 37				16 37		
Merstham	d												→				16 41		
Coulsdon South	d						16 21										16 46		
Purley 4	d						16 24										16 50		
East Croydon	a		16 08	16 13	16 16	16 16	16 29			16 32		16 38		16 41	16 43	16 45	16 55		
	d		16 09	16 14	16 17	16 17	16 30			16 33		16 39		16 47	16 47	16 46	16 56		
Norwood Junction 2	a																17 02		
New Cross Gate	d																		
London Bridge 4 ⊖	a																17 14		
London Blackfriars 3 ⊖	a				16 49	16 49				17 07				17 19	17 19				
City Thameslink 3	a																		
Farringdon 3 ⊖	a				16 58	16 58				17 14				17 28	17 28				
St Pancras International 15 ⊖	a				17 02	17 02				17 18				17 32	17 32				
St Albans City	a				17 26	17 26				17 42				17 56	17 56				
Luton Airport Parkway 4 ✈	a				17 38	17 38				17 54				18 08	18 08				
Luton 7	a				17 41	17 41				17 57				18 11	18 11				
Bedford 10	a				18 08	18 08				18 24				18 38	18 38				
Clapham Junction 10	a		16 18	16 23			16 39					16 48				16 55			
London Victoria 15 ⊖	a	16 20	16 26	16 30			16 46	16 35			16 50	16 56				17 03			17 05

A until 9 February

B from 16 February

Table 186R

Sundays

5 January to 11 May

Brighton - London and Bedford

Network Diagram - see first Page of Table 175

Station		SN 1	FC 1	SN 1	SN 1	SN 1	SN 1	FC 1	FC 1	SN 1
					🛒	🛒	🛒	A	B	
Brighton 10	d	16 00	16 14				16 35			
Hove 2	d									
Preston Park	d	16 03								
Hassocks 4	d	16 10	16 23							
Burgess Hill 4	d	16 13	16 27							
Lewes 4	d					16 20				
Wivelsfield 4	d	16 15				16 35				
Haywards Heath 3	a	16 20	16 32			16 39				
	d	16 25	16 33			16 41				
Balcombe	d	16 30								
Horsham 4	d									16 44
Littlehaven	d									
Faygate	d									
Ifield	d									
Crawley	d									16 53
Three Bridges 4	a	16 36	16 41							16 56
	d	16 36	16 42					16 52	16 54	16 57
Gatwick Airport 10 ✈	a	16 40	16 46			16 52	16 56	16 56	16 58	17 02
	d	16 41	16 47		16 50	16 53	16 57	16 57	16 59	17 03
Horley 4	d									17 05
Salfords	d									
Earlswood (Surrey)	d									
Tonbridge 4	d			16 29						
Leigh (Kent)	d			16 33						
Penshurst	d			16 37						
Edenbridge	d			16 43						
Godstone	d			16 50						
Nutfield	d			16 55						
Reigate	d									
Redhill 5	a	16 48		17 00						17 13
	d	16 49								17 14
Merstham	d									
Coulsdon South	d									17 21
Purley 4	d									17 24
East Croydon (tram)	a	17 00	17 02			17 08	17 13	17 16	17 16	17 29
	d	17 00	17 03			17 09	17 14	17 17	17 17	17 30
Norwood Junction 2	a									
New Cross Gate	d									
London Bridge 4 ⊖	a									
London Blackfriars 3 ⊖	a		17 37					17 49	17 49	
City Thameslink 3	a									
Farringdon 3 ⊖	a		17 44					17 58	17 58	
St Pancras International 15 ⊖	a		17 48					18 02	18 02	
St Albans City	a		18 12					18 26	18 26	
Luton Airport Parkway 4 ✈	a		18 24					18 38	18 38	
Luton 7	a		18 27					18 41	18 41	
Bedford 10	a		18 54					19 08	19 08	
Clapham Junction 10	a	17 09				17 18	17 23			17 39
London Victoria 15 ⊖	a	17 17			17 20	17 26	17 30			17 46

Station		SN 1	GW 1	FC 1	SN 1	SN 1	SN 1	FC 1	FC 1	SN 1
		🛒			🛒			A	B	🛒
Brighton 10	d			16 44						17 10
Hove 2	d					16 55				
Preston Park	d									
Hassocks 4	d			16 53						
Burgess Hill 4	d			16 57		17 05				
Lewes 4	d									
Wivelsfield 4	d									
Haywards Heath 3	a			17 02		17 10				
	d			17 03		17 11				
Balcombe	d									
Horsham 4	d						17 01			
Littlehaven	d						17 04			
Faygate	d									
Ifield	d						17 10			
Crawley	d						17 14			
Three Bridges 4	a			17 11			17 17			
	d			17 12			17 18	17 22	17 24	
Gatwick Airport 10 ✈	a			17 16		17 22	17 22	17 26	17 28	
	d	17 05	17 08	17 17	17 20	17 23	17 23	17 27	17 29	
Horley 4	d						17 26			
Salfords	d									
Earlswood (Surrey)	d						17 33			
Tonbridge 4	d									
Leigh (Kent)	d									
Penshurst	d									
Edenbridge	d									
Godstone	d									
Nutfield	d									
Reigate	d									
Redhill 5	a		17 16				17 36			
	d						17 37			
Merstham	d						→			
Coulsdon South	d									
Purley 4	d									
East Croydon (tram)	a			17 32		17 38		17 41	17 43	17 45
	d			17 33		17 39		17 47	17 47	17 46
Norwood Junction 2	a									
New Cross Gate	d									
London Bridge 4 ⊖	a									
London Blackfriars 3 ⊖	a			18 07				18 19	18 19	
City Thameslink 3	a									
Farringdon 3 ⊖	a			18 14				18 28	18 28	
St Pancras International 15 ⊖	a			18 18				18 32	18 32	
St Albans City	a			18 42				18 56	18 56	
Luton Airport Parkway 4 ✈	a			18 54				19 08	19 08	
Luton 7	a			18 57				19 11	19 11	
Bedford 10	a			19 24				19 38	19 38	
Clapham Junction 10	a					17 48				17 55
London Victoria 15 ⊖	a	17 35			17 50	17 56				18 03

Station		SN 1	GW 1	SN 1	SN 1	FC 1	SN 1	SN 1	SN 1	SN 1
				🛒				🛒	🛒	🛒
Brighton 10	d				17 00	17 14				17 35
Hove 2	d									
Preston Park	d				17 03					
Hassocks 4	d				17 10	17 23				
Burgess Hill 4	d				17 13	17 27				
Lewes 4	d								17 20	
Wivelsfield 4	d				17 15				17 35	
Haywards Heath 3	a				17 20	17 32			17 39	
	d				17 25	17 33			17 41	
Balcombe	d				17 30					
Horsham 4	d									
Littlehaven	d									
Faygate	d									
Ifield	d									
Crawley	d									
Three Bridges 4	a				17 36	17 41				
	d				17 36	17 42				
Gatwick Airport 10 ✈	a				17 40	17 46			17 52	17 56
	d			17 35	17 41	17 47		17 50	17 53	17 57
Horley 4	d									
Salfords	d									
Earlswood (Surrey)	d									
Tonbridge 4	d						17 29			
Leigh (Kent)	d						17 33			
Penshurst	d						17 37			
Edenbridge	d						17 43			
Godstone	d						17 50			
Nutfield	d						17 55			
Reigate	d	←	17 30							
Redhill 5	a	17 36	17 36		17 48		18 00			
	d	17 37			17 49					
Merstham	d	17 41								
Coulsdon South	d	17 46								
Purley 4	d	17 50								
East Croydon (tram)	a	17 55			18 00	18 02			18 08	18 13
	d	17 56			18 00	18 03			18 09	18 14
Norwood Junction 2	a	18 02								
New Cross Gate	d									
London Bridge 4 ⊖	a	18 14								
London Blackfriars 3 ⊖	a					18 37				
City Thameslink 3	a									
Farringdon 3 ⊖	a					18 44				
St Pancras International 15 ⊖	a					18 48				
St Albans City	a					19 12				
Luton Airport Parkway 4 ✈	a					19 24				
Luton 7	a					19 27				
Bedford 10	a					19 54				
Clapham Junction 10	a				18 09				18 18	18 23
London Victoria 15 ⊖	a			18 05	18 17			18 20	18 26	18 30

Station		FC 1	FC 1	SN 1	SN 1	GW 1	FC 1	SN 1	SN 1	SN 1
		A	B		🛒			🛒		
Brighton 10	d						17 44			
Hove 2	d								17 55	
Preston Park	d									
Hassocks 4	d						17 53			
Burgess Hill 4	d						17 57		18 05	
Lewes 4	d									
Wivelsfield 4	d									
Haywards Heath 3	a						18 02		18 10	
	d						18 03		18 11	
Balcombe	d									
Horsham 4	d			17 44						18 01
Littlehaven	d									18 04
Faygate	d									
Ifield	d									18 10
Crawley	d			17 53						18 14
Three Bridges 4	a			17 56			18 11			18 17
	d	17 52	17 54	17 57			18 12			18 18
Gatwick Airport 10 ✈	a	17 56	17 58	18 02			18 16		18 22	18 22
	d	17 57	17 59	18 03	18 05	18 08	18 17	18 20	18 23	18 23
Horley 4	d			18 05						18 26
Salfords	d									
Earlswood (Surrey)	d									18 33
Tonbridge 4	d									
Leigh (Kent)	d									
Penshurst	d									
Edenbridge	d									
Godstone	d									
Nutfield	d									
Reigate	d									
Redhill 5	a			18 13		18 16				18 36
	d			18 14						18 37
Merstham	d									→
Coulsdon South	d			18 21						
Purley 4	d			18 24						
East Croydon (tram)	a	18 16	18 16	18 29			18 32		18 38	
	d	18 17	18 17	18 30			18 33		18 39	
Norwood Junction 2	a									
New Cross Gate	d									
London Bridge 4 ⊖	a									
London Blackfriars 3 ⊖	a	18 49	18 49				19 07			
City Thameslink 3	a									
Farringdon 3 ⊖	a	18 58	18 58				19 14			
St Pancras International 15 ⊖	a	19 02	19 02				19 18			
St Albans City	a	19 26	19 26				19 42			
Luton Airport Parkway 4 ✈	a	19 38	19 38				19 54			
Luton 7	a	19 41	19 41				19 57			
Bedford 10	a	20 08	20 08				20 24			
Clapham Junction 10	a			18 39					18 48	
London Victoria 15 ⊖	a			18 46	18 35			18 50	18 56	

A until 9 February

B from 16 February

Table 186R

Sundays

Brighton - London and Bedford

5 January to 11 May

Network Diagram - see first Page of Table 175

Station		FC 1 A	FC 1 B	SN 1	SN 1	GW 1	SN 1	SN 1	FC 1	SN 1	SN 1	SN 1	SN 1	FC 1 A	FC 1 B	SN 1	SN 1	GW 1	FC 1
Brighton 10	d			18 10				18 00	18 14				18 35						18 44
Hove 2	d																		
Preston Park	d							18 03											
Hassocks 4	d							18 10	18 23										18 53
Burgess Hill 4	d							18 13	18 27										18 57
Lewes 4	d											18 20							
Wivelsfield 4	d							18 15				18 35							
Haywards Heath 3	a							18 20	18 32			18 39							19 02
	d							18 25	18 33			18 41							19 03
Balcombe	d							18 30											
Horsham 4	d															18 44			
Littlehaven	d																		
Faygate	d																		
Ifield	d																		
Crawley	d															18 53			
Three Bridges 4	a							18 36	18 41							18 56			19 11
	d	18 22	18 24					18 36	18 42					18 52	18 54	18 57			19 12
Gatwick Airport 10 ✈	a	18 26	18 28					18 40	18 46			18 52	18 56	18 56	18 58	19 02			19 16
	d	18 27	18 29				18 35	18 41	18 47		18 50	18 53	18 57	18 57	18 59	19 03	19 05	19 08	19 17
Horley 4	d															19 05			
Salfords	d																		
Earlswood (Surrey)	d																		
Tonbridge 4	d									18 29									
Leigh (Kent)	d									18 33									
Penshurst	d									18 37									
Edenbridge	d									18 43									
Godstone	d									18 50									
Nutfield	d									18 55									
Reigate	d				←	18 31													
Redhill 5	a				18 36	18 36		18 48		19 00						19 13		19 16	
	d				18 37			18 49								19 14			
Merstham	d				18 41														
Coulsdon South	d				18 46											19 21			
Purley 4	d				18 50											19 24			
East Croydon	a	18 41	18 43	18 45	18 55			19 00	19 02			19 08	19 13	19 16	19 16	19 29			19 32
	d	18 47	18 47	18 46	18 56			19 00	19 03			19 09	19 14	19 17	19 17	19 30			19 33
Norwood Junction 2	a				19 02														
New Cross Gate	d																		
London Bridge 4 ⊖	a				19 14														
London Blackfriars 3 ⊖	a	19 19	19 19						19 37					19 49	19 49				20 07
City Thameslink 3	a																		
Farringdon 3 ⊖	a	19 28	19 28						19 44					19 58	19 58				20 14
St Pancras International 15 ⊖	a	19 32	19 32						19 48					20 02	20 02				20 18
St Albans City	a	19 56	19 56						20 12					20 26	20 26				20 42
Luton Airport Parkway 4 ✈	a	20 08	20 08						20 24					20 38	20 38				20 54
Luton 7	a	20 11	20 11						20 27					20 41	20 41				20 57
Bedford 10	a	20 38	20 38						20 54					21 08	21 08				21 24
Clapham Junction 10	a			18 55				19 09				19 18	19 23			19 39			
London Victoria 15 ⊖	a			19 03			19 05	19 17			19 20	19 26	19 30			19 46	19 35		

Station		SN 1	SN 1	SN 1	FC 1 A	FC 1 B	SN 1	SN 1	GW 1	SN 1	SN 1	FC 1	SN 1	SN 1	SN 1	SN 1	FC 1 A	FC 1 B	SN 1
Brighton 10	d						19 10				19 00	19 14				19 35			
Hove 2	d		18 55																
Preston Park	d										19 03								
Hassocks 4	d										19 10	19 23							
Burgess Hill 4	d		19 05								19 13	19 27							
Lewes 4	d														19 20				
Wivelsfield 4	d										19 15				19 35				
Haywards Heath 3	a		19 10								19 20	19 32			19 39				
	d		19 11								19 25	19 33			19 41				
Balcombe	d										19 30								
Horsham 4	d			19 01															19 44
Littlehaven	d			19 04															
Faygate	d																		
Ifield	d			19 10															
Crawley	d			19 14															19 53
Three Bridges 4	a			19 17							19 36	19 41							19 56
	d			19 18	19 22	19 24					19 36	19 42					19 52	19 54	19 57
Gatwick Airport 10 ✈	a		19 22	19 22	19 26	19 28					19 40	19 46			19 52	19 56	19 56	19 58	20 02
	d	19 20	19 23	19 23	19 27	19 29				19 35	19 41	19 47		19 50	19 53	19 57	19 57	19 59	20 03
Horley 4	d			19 26															20 05
Salfords	d																		
Earlswood (Surrey)	d			19 33															
Tonbridge 4	d												19 29						
Leigh (Kent)	d												19 33						
Penshurst	d												19 37						
Edenbridge	d												19 43						
Godstone	d												19 50						
Nutfield	d												19 55						
Reigate	d							←	19 30										
Redhill 5	a			19 36				19 36	19 36		19 48		20 00						20 13
	d			19 37				19 37			19 49								20 14
Merstham	d			→				19 41											
Coulsdon South	d							19 46											20 21
Purley 4	d							19 50											20 24
East Croydon	a		19 38		19 41	19 43	19 45	19 55			20 00	20 02			20 08	20 13	20 16	20 16	20 29
	d		19 39		19 47	19 47	19 46	19 56			20 00	20 03			20 09	20 14	20 17	20 17	20 30
Norwood Junction 2	a							20 02											
New Cross Gate	d																		
London Bridge 4 ⊖	a							20 14											
London Blackfriars 3 ⊖	a				20 19	20 19						20 37					20 49	20 49	
City Thameslink 3	a																		
Farringdon 3 ⊖	a				20 28	20 28						20 44					20 58	20 58	
St Pancras International 15 ⊖	a				20 32	20 32						20 48					21 02	21 02	
St Albans City	a				20 56	20 56						21 12					21 26	21 26	
Luton Airport Parkway 4 ✈	a				21 08	21 08						21 24					21 38	21 38	
Luton 7	a				21 11	21 11						21 27					21 41	21 41	
Bedford 10	a				21 38	21 38						21 54					22 08	22 08	
Clapham Junction 10	a		19 48				19 55				20 09				20 18	20 23			20 39
London Victoria 15 ⊖	a	19 50	19 56				20 03			20 05	20 17			20 20	20 26	20 30			20 46

A until 9 February

B from 16 February

Table 186R

Sundays

5 January to 11 May

Brighton - London and Bedford

Network Diagram - see first Page of Table 175

Station		SN 1	GW 1	FC 1	SN 1	SN 1	SN 1	SN 1	GW 1	SN 1
Brighton 10	d			19 44			20 10			
Hove 2	d					19 55				
Preston Park	d									
Hassocks 4	d			19 53						
Burgess Hill 4	d			19 57		20 05				
Lewes 4	d									
Wivelsfield 4	d									
Haywards Heath 3	a			20 02		20 10				
	d			20 03		20 11				
Balcombe	d									
Horsham 4	d							20 01		
Littlehaven	d							20 04		
Faygate	d									
Ifield	d							20 10		
Crawley	d							20 14		
Three Bridges 4	a			20 11				20 17		
	d			20 12				20 18		
Gatwick Airport 10 ✈	a			20 16		20 22		20 22		
	d	20 05	20 08	20 17	20 20	20 23		20 23		20 35
Horley 4	d							20 26		
Salfords	d									
Earlswood (Surrey)	d							20 33		
Tonbridge 4	d									
Leigh (Kent)	d									
Penshurst	d									
Edenbridge	d									
Godstone	d									
Nutfield	d									
Reigate	d								20 31	
Redhill 5	a		20 16					20 36	20 36	
	d							20 37		
Merstham	d							20 41		
Coulsdon South	d							20 46		
Purley 4	d							20 50		
East Croydon	a			20 32		20 38	20 45	20 55		
	d			20 33		20 39	20 46	20 56		
Norwood Junction 2	a							21 02		
New Cross Gate	d									
London Bridge 4 ⊖	a							21 14		
London Blackfriars 3 ⊖	a			21 07						
City Thameslink 3	a									
Farringdon 3 ⊖	a			21 14						
St Pancras International 15 ⊖	a			21 18						
St Albans City	a			21 42						
Luton Airport Parkway 4 ✈	a			21 54						
Luton 7	a			21 57						
Bedford 10	a			22 24						
Clapham Junction 10	a					20 48	20 55			
London Victoria 15 ⊖	a	20 35			20 50	20 56	21 05			21 05

Station		SN 1	FC 1	SN 1	SN 1	SN 1	SN 1	SN 1	SN 1	GW 1
Brighton 10	d	20 00	20 14				20 35			
Hove 2	d									
Preston Park	d	20 03								
Hassocks 4	d	20 10	20 23							
Burgess Hill 4	d	20 13	20 27							
Lewes 4	d					20 20				
Wivelsfield 4	d	20 15				20 35				
Haywards Heath 3	a	20 20	20 32			20 39				
	d	20 25	20 33			20 41				
Balcombe	d	20 30								
Horsham 4	d							20 44		
Littlehaven	d									
Faygate	d									
Ifield	d									
Crawley	d							20 53		
Three Bridges 4	a	20 36	20 41					20 56		
	d	20 36	20 42					20 57		
Gatwick Airport 10 ✈	a	20 40	20 46			20 52	20 56	21 02		
	d	20 41	20 47		20 50	20 53	20 57	21 03	21 05	21 08
Horley 4	d							21 05		
Salfords	d									
Earlswood (Surrey)	d									
Tonbridge 4	d			20 29						
Leigh (Kent)	d			20 33						
Penshurst	d			20 37						
Edenbridge	d			20 43						
Godstone	d			20 50						
Nutfield	d			20 55						
Reigate	d									
Redhill 5	a	20 48		21 00				21 13		21 16
	d	20 49						21 14		
Merstham	d									
Coulsdon South	d							21 21		
Purley 4	d							21 24		
East Croydon	a	21 00	21 02			21 08	21 13	21 29		
	d	21 00	21 03			21 09	21 14	21 30		
Norwood Junction 2	a									
New Cross Gate	d									
London Bridge 4 ⊖	a									
London Blackfriars 3 ⊖	a		21 37							
City Thameslink 3	a									
Farringdon 3 ⊖	a		21 44							
St Pancras International 15 ⊖	a		21 48							
St Albans City	a		22 12							
Luton Airport Parkway 4 ✈	a		22 24							
Luton 7	a		22 27							
Bedford 10	a		22 54							
Clapham Junction 10	a	21 09				21 18	21 23	21 39		
London Victoria 15 ⊖	a	21 17			21 20	21 26	21 30	21 46	21 35	

Station		FC 1	SN 1	SN 1	SN 1	GW 1	SN 1	SN 1	FC 1	SN 1
Brighton 10	d	20 44						21 04	21 14	
Hove 2	d			20 55						
Preston Park	d							21 07		
Hassocks 4	d	20 53						21 14	21 23	
Burgess Hill 4	d	20 57		21 05				21 17	21 27	
Lewes 4	d									
Wivelsfield 4	d							21 19		
Haywards Heath 3	a	21 02		21 10				21 24	21 32	
	d	21 03		21 11				21 25	21 33	
Balcombe	d							21 30		
Horsham 4	d				21 01					
Littlehaven	d				21 04					
Faygate	d									
Ifield	d				21 10					
Crawley	d				21 14					
Three Bridges 4	a	21 11			21 17			21 36	21 41	
	d	21 12			21 18			21 36	21 42	
Gatwick Airport 10 ✈	a	21 16		21 22	21 22			21 40	21 46	
	d	21 17	21 20	21 23	21 23		21 35	21 41	21 47	
Horley 4	d				21 26					
Salfords	d									
Earlswood (Surrey)	d				21 33					
Tonbridge 4	d									21 29
Leigh (Kent)	d									21 33
Penshurst	d									21 37
Edenbridge	d									21 43
Godstone	d									21 50
Nutfield	d									21 55
Reigate	d					21 30				
Redhill 5	a				21 36	21 36		21 48		22 00
	d				21 37			21 49		
Merstham	d				21 41					
Coulsdon South	d				21 46					
Purley 4	d				21 50					
East Croydon	a	21 32		21 38	21 55			22 00	22 02	
	d	21 33		21 39	21 56			22 00	22 03	
Norwood Junction 2	a				22 02					
New Cross Gate	d									
London Bridge 4 ⊖	a				22 14					
London Blackfriars 3 ⊖	a	22 07							22 37	
City Thameslink 3	a									
Farringdon 3 ⊖	a	22 14							22 44	
St Pancras International 15 ⊖	a	22 18							22 48	
St Albans City	a	22 42							23 21	
Luton Airport Parkway 4 ✈	a	22 54							23 33	
Luton 7	a	22 57							23 36	
Bedford 10	a	23 24							00 03	
Clapham Junction 10	a			21 48				22 09		
London Victoria 15 ⊖	a		21 50	21 56			22 05	22 17		

Station		SN 1	SN 1	SN 1	SN 1	GW 1	FC 1	SN 1	GW 1	SN 1
Brighton 10	d						21 44			
Hove 2	d									
Preston Park	d									
Hassocks 4	d						21 53			
Burgess Hill 4	d						21 57			
Lewes 4	d		21 20							
Wivelsfield 4	d		21 35							
Haywards Heath 3	a		21 39				22 02			
	d		21 41				22 03			
Balcombe	d									
Horsham 4	d			21 44						22 00
Littlehaven	d									22 03
Faygate	d									
Ifield	d									22 09
Crawley	d			21 53						22 13
Three Bridges 4	a			21 56			22 11			22 16
	d			21 57			22 12			22 18
Gatwick Airport 10 ✈	a		21 52	22 02			22 16			22 22
	d	21 50	21 53	22 03	22 05	22 08	22 17	22 20		22 23
Horley 4	d			22 05						22 26
Salfords	d									
Earlswood (Surrey)	d									22 33
Tonbridge 4	d									
Leigh (Kent)	d									
Penshurst	d									
Edenbridge	d									
Godstone	d									
Nutfield	d									
Reigate	d								22 31	
Redhill 5	a			22 13		22 16			22 36	22 37
	d			22 14						22 37
Merstham	d									22 41
Coulsdon South	d			22 21						22 46
Purley 4	d			22 24						22 50
East Croydon	a		22 08	22 29			22 32			22 55
	d		22 09	22 30			22 33			22 56
Norwood Junction 2	a									
New Cross Gate	d									
London Bridge 4 ⊖	a									
London Blackfriars 3 ⊖	a						23 07			
City Thameslink 3	a									
Farringdon 3 ⊖	a						23 14			
St Pancras International 15 ⊖	a						23 18			
St Albans City	a						23 51			
Luton Airport Parkway 4 ✈	a						00 03			
Luton 7	a						00 06			
Bedford 10	a						00 33			
Clapham Junction 10	a		22 18	22 39						23 07
London Victoria 15 ⊖	a	22 20	22 26	22 46	22 35			22 50		23 14

Table 186R

Sundays

5 January to 11 May

Brighton - London and Bedford

Network Diagram - see first Page of Table 175

		SN	SN	FC	SN	SN	SN	SN	GW	FC	SN	GW	SN	SN	SN	FC	SN	SN	FC
		1	1	1	1	1	1	1	1	1	1	1	1	1	1	1	1	1	1
Brighton 10	d		22 04	22 14						22 44					23 05	23 14			23 42
Hove 2	d																		
Preston Park	d		22 07												23 09				
Hassocks 4	d		22 14	22 23						22 53					23 15	23 23			23 51
Burgess Hill 4	d		22 17	22 27						22 57					23 19	23 27			23 55
Lewes 4	d																		
Wivelsfield 4	d		22 19												23 21				
Haywards Heath 3	a		22 24	22 32						23 02					23 26	23 32			23 59
	d		22 25	22 33						23 03					23 26	23 33			00 01
Balcombe	d		22 30												23 32				
Horsham 4	d						22 44						23 10						
Littlehaven	d												23 13						
Faygate	d																		
Ifield	d												23 19						
Crawley	d						22 53						23 23						
Three Bridges 4	a		22 36	22 41			22 56			23 11			23 26		23 37	23 41			00 09
	d		22 36	22 42			22 57			23 12			23 27		23 41	23 42			00 10
Gatwick Airport 10 ✈	a		22 40	22 46			23 02			23 16			23 31		23 45	23 46			00 14
	d	22 35	22 41	22 47		22 50	23 03	23 05	23 08	23 17	23 20		23 32	23 35	23 46	23 47	23 50		00 15
Horley 4	d						23 05						23 35		23 49				
Salfords	d																		
Earlswood (Surrey)	d																		
Tonbridge 4	d				22 29														
Leigh (Kent)	d				22 33														
Penshurst	d				22 37														
Edenbridge	d				22 43														
Godstone	d				22 50														
Nutfield	d				22 55														
Reigate	d											23 30						←	
Redhill 5	a		22 48		23 00		23 13		23 16			23 36	23 42		23 56			23 56	00 23
	d		22 49				23 14						23 42		00 04			00 04	00 24
Merstham	d												23 46		→				
Coulsdon South	d						23 21						23 51						
Purley 4	d						23 24						23 55					00 12	
East Croydon 🚋	a		23 00	23 02			23 29			23 32			23 59			00 02		00 17	00 36
	d		23 00	23 03			23 30			23 33			00 01			00 02		00 18	00 36
Norwood Junction 2	a																		
New Cross Gate	d																		
London Bridge 4 ⊖	a																		
London Blackfriars 3 ⊖	a			23 37						00 05						00 30			01 03
City Thameslink 3	a																		
Farringdon 3 ⊖	a			23 44						00 14						00 36			
St Pancras International 15 ⊖	a			23 48						00 18						00 40			01 13
St Albans City	a			00 21						00 51						01 13			01 47
Luton Airport Parkway 4 ✈	a			00 33						01 03						01 25			01 59
Luton 7	a			00 36						01 06						01 28			02 02
Bedford 10	a			01 03						01 33						01 55			02 29
Clapham Junction 10	a		23 10				23 39						00 16					00 31	
London Victoria 15 ⊖	a	23 07	23 20			23 25	23 46	23 35			23 55		00 24	00 10			00 27	00 39	

Table 188

Mondays to Fridays

9 December to 16 May

London, Gatwick Airport, Brighton - Sussex Coast, Portsmouth and Southampton

Network Diagram - see first Page of Table 175

Miles	Miles	Miles			SN MX 1	SN MX 1	SN MX 1	SN MX	SN	SN MX 1	SN MO 1	SN MX 1	SN 1		SN	SN	SN	SN	SN 1	SN 1	SN	SN 1	SN		SN
0	—	0	London Victoria 15 ⊖	d								00 05													
2¾	—	—	Clapham Junction 10	d								00 12													
—	0	—	London Bridge 4 ⊖	d																					
10½	10¼	—	East Croydon	d								00 27													
21	—	—	Redhill 5	d																					
26	—	—	Horley	d																					
26¾	—	—	Gatwick Airport 10 ✈	d								00 46													
29½	—	29½	Three Bridges 4	a								00 50													
—	—	—		d							00 06	00 50													
—	—	31	Crawley	d																					
—	—	38	Horsham 4	a																					
—	—	—		d																					
—	—	40½	**Christs Hospital**	d																					
—	—	45¼	**Billingshurst**	d																					
—	—	50¼	**Pulborough**	d																					
—	—	55	**Amberley**	d																					
—	—	58¾	**Arundel**	d																					
38	—	—	Haywards Heath 3	d						00 05	00 15	01 03													
41¾	—	—	Burgess Hill	d						00 11	00 20														
—	—	—	Preston Park	d																					
—	0	—	Brighton 10	d				00 04	00 10			01s17										05 14			
51	1½	—	**Hove** 2	a				00 07	00 14	00 22	00 31	01s25										05 17			
—	—	—		d				00 08		00 22	00 32											05 18			
—	2	—	**Aldrington**	d				00 10														05 20			
—	3	—	**Portslade**	d				00 12		00s25	00s35	01s28										05 22			
—	3½	—	**Fishersgate**	d				00 14														05 24			
—	4½	—	**Southwick**	d				00 16		00s28	00s38	01s31										05 26			
—	5½	—	**Shoreham-by-Sea**	d			00 01	00 19		00s31	00s41	01s34										05 29			
—	8¼	—	**Lancing**	d			00 05	00 23		00s35	00s45	01s38										05 33			
—	9¾	—	**East Worthing**	d				00 26														05 36			
—	10½	—	**Worthing** 4	a			00 11	00 29		00 41	00 49	01 43										05 39			
—	—	—		d				00 29														05 39			
—	11½	—	**West Worthing**	d				00a32														05 41			
—	12¼	—	**Durrington-on-Sea**	d																		05 44			
—	13	—	**Goring-by-Sea**	d																		05 46			
0	15½	—	**Angmering** 3	d																		05 50			
6	—	—	**Littlehampton** 4	a																					
—	—	—		d																05 35					06 04
8	19¾	61	**Ford** 4	d	00 01															05 39		05 56			06 08
—	—	—	Bognor Regis 4	d												05 13			05 35		05 49		05 55		
0	22½	—	**Barnham**	a	00 06											05 19			05 41	05 43	05 55	06 01	06 02		06 12
—	—	—		d	00 06	00 09							04 58		05 02		05 21	05 36		05 44		06 01			06 13
3½	—	—	**Bognor Regis**	a		00 16												05 44							06 21
—	28¾	—	**Chichester** 4	a	00 14								05 05		05 09		05 28			05 51		06 09			
—	—	—		d									05 06		05 10		05 29			05 52		06 09			
—	30¼	—	**Fishbourne (Sussex)**	d																05 55					
—	31¼	—	**Bosham**	d																05 58					
—	33¼	—	**Nutbourne**	d																06 01					
—	34¼	—	**Southbourne**	d																06 04					
—	35¾	—	**Emsworth**	d																06 07					
—	37	—	**Warblington**	d																06 10					
0	37½	—	Havant	d									05 17		05 21		05 40			06 13		06 20			
—	38¼	—	Bedhampton	a																06 15					
—	41¼	—	Hilsea	a																06 20					
—	44	—	Fratton	a											05 29		05 48			06 24					
—	44¾	—	Portsmouth & Southsea	a											05 33		05 52			06 28					
—	45½	—	Portsmouth Harbour ⛴	a											05 37		05 56			06 32					
4	—	—	Cosham	a									05 23									06 27			
6½	—	—	Portchester	a									05 28												
9¾	—	—	Fareham	a									05 33									06 36			
13½	—	—	Swanwick	a									05 40									06 43			
—	—	—	Eastleigh	a																					
—	—	—	Southampton Airport Parkway	a																					
24¼	—	—	Southampton Central ⛴	a									05 59									07 02			

Table 188

London, Gatwick Airport, Brighton - Sussex Coast, Portsmouth and Southampton

Mondays to Fridays

9 December to 16 May

Network Diagram - see first Page of Table 175

		SN 1	SN 1	SN	SN	SN	SN	SN	SN	SN	SN	SN 1	SN 1		SN	SN 1	SN 1	SN	SN 1	SN 1	SN	SN	SN
London Victoria 15 ⊖	d																						
Clapham Junction 10	d																						
London Bridge 4 ⊖	d																						
East Croydon	d																						
Redhill 5	d																						
Horley	d																						
Gatwick Airport 10 ✈	d												05 59										
Three Bridges 4	a												06 03										
	d												06 03										
Crawley	d												06 07										
Horsham 4	a												06 19										
	d												06 19										
Christs Hospital	d												06 23										
Billingshurst	d												06 29										
Pulborough	d												06 36										
Amberley	d												06 42										
Arundel	d												06 47										
Haywards Heath 3	d																						
Burgess Hill	d																						
Preston Park	d																						
Brighton 10	d		05 30	05 44		05 53				05 57	06 14						06 27		06 35				
Hove 2	a		05 33	05 48		05 56				06 00	06 17						06 30		06 38				
	d		05 34			05 57				06 01	06 18						06 31		06 39				
Aldrington	d		05 36							06 03	06 20												
Portslade	d		05 38							06 05	06 22								06 42				
Fishersgate	d		05 40							06 07	06 24												
Southwick	d		05 42							06 09	06 26								06 45				
Shoreham-by-Sea	d		05 45			06 03				06 12	06 29						06 37		06 48				
Lancing	d		05 49							06 16	06 33								06 52				
East Worthing	d		05 52							06 19	06 36												
Worthing 4	a		05 55			06 09				06 22	06 39						06 43		06 56				
	d		05 55			06 09				06 22	06 39						06 43		06 56				
West Worthing	d		05 57							06 24	06a42						06 45		06 58				
Durrington-on-Sea	d		06 00							06 27							06 48		07 01				
Goring-by-Sea	d		06 02							06 29							06 50		07 03				
Angmering 3	d		06 06							06 33							06 54		07 07				
Littlehampton 4	a									06 43													
	d								06 35									06 58			07 18		
Ford 4	d		06 13						06 39				06 52					07 04	07 13		07 22		
Bognor Regis 4	d	06 06			06 13			06 22				06 41			06 50	06 57				07 17		07 27	
Barnham	a	06 12	06 17		06 19	06 24		06 28	06 43			06 47	06 56		06 56	07 03	07 04	07 08	07 18	07 23	07 26	07 33	
	d		06 18			06 24	06 27		06 48				07 00	07 13			07 05	07 09	07 18		07 27		07 39
Bognor Regis	a						06 36		06 56					07 21									07 47
Chichester 4	a		06 25			06 32							07 07				07 12	07 16	07 26		07 34		
	d		06 26			06 32							07 08				07 13	07 17	07 28		07 35		
Fishbourne (Sussex)	d					06 35												07 20			07 38		
Bosham	d					06 38											07 17				07 41		
Nutbourne	d					06 42												07 25			07 44		
Southbourne	d		06 33			06 44											07 22	07 27			07 47		
Emsworth	d		06 36			06 47											07 25	07 30			07 50		
Warblington	d					06 50											07 28				07 53		
Havant	d		06 40			06 53							07 19				07 31	07 35	07 41		07 58		
Bedhampton	a					06 56												07 37			08 00		
Hilsea	a					07 01												07 42			08 05		
Fratton	a					07 05												07 46	07 49		08 09		
Portsmouth & Southsea	a					07 08												07 50	07 53		08 15		
Portsmouth Harbour ⛴	a					07 12													07 58		08 20		
Cosham	a		06 49										07 25				07 38						
Portchester	a		06 54										07 30										
Fareham	a		06 59										07 35				07 46						
Swanwick	a		07 06										07 42				07 53						
Eastleigh	a																						
Southampton Airport Parkway	a																						
Southampton Central ⛴	a		07 25										08 01				08 13						

Table 188

Mondays to Fridays

9 December to 16 May

London, Gatwick Airport, Brighton - Sussex Coast, Portsmouth and Southampton

Network Diagram - see first Page of Table 175

Station		SN	SN	SN 1	SN 1	SN	SN	SN 1	SN	SN	SN 1	SN	SN 1	SN	SN 1	SN 1	SN	SN	SN	SN	SN	SN	SN
London Victoria 15 ⊖	d				06 02											06 32							
Clapham Junction 10	d				06 08											06 38							
London Bridge 4 ⊖	d																						
East Croydon	d				06 18											06 49							
Redhill 5	d				06 40											07 12							
Horley	d				06 49											07 21							
Gatwick Airport 10 ✈	d				06 55											07 25							
Three Bridges 4	a				06 59											07 29							
	d				07 00											07 30							
Crawley	d				07 03											07 34							
Horsham 4	a				07 11											07 46							
	d				07 12											07 46							
Christs Hospital	d				07 15											07 50							
Billingshurst	d				07 21											07 56							
Pulborough	d				07 28											08 03							
Amberley	d				07 34											08 09							
Arundel	d				07 39											08 14							
Haywards Heath 3	d																						
Burgess Hill	d																						
Preston Park	d																						
Brighton 10	d		06 53	07 06		07 15				07 20	07 30		07 37	07 46			07 50		08 03		08 07	08 14	08 23
Hove 2	a		06 56	07 09		07 18				07 23	07 33		07 40	07 49			07 53		08 06		08 10	08 18	08 26
	d		06 57	07 10		07 19				07 24	07 34		07 41	07 50			07 54		08 07		08 11		08 27
Aldrington	d		06 59							07 26							07 56						08 29
Portslade	d		07 01			07 22				07 28	07 37		07 44	07 53			07 58				08 14		08 31
Fishersgate	d		07 03							07 30							08 00						08 33
Southwick	d		07 05			07 25				07 32	07 40		07 47	07 56			08 02				08 17		08 35
Shoreham-by-Sea	d		07 09	07 16		07 28				07 35	07 43		07 50	08 00			08 06		08 13		08 20		08 39
Lancing	d		07 13			07 32				07 39	07 47		07 54	08 04			08 10				08 24		08 43
East Worthing	d		07 16							07 42							08 13						08 46
Worthing 4	a		07 18	07 22		07 36				07 45	07 51		07 58	08 08			08 15		08 19		08 28		08 48
	d		07 19	07 23		07 36				07 45	07 52		07 59	08 08			08 16		08 20		08 28		08 49
West Worthing	d		07 21	07 25						07 47	07 54		08 01				08 18		08 22		08 30		08a51
Durrington-on-Sea	d		07 23	07 27						07 50	07 56		08 03	08 12			08 20		08 24		08 33		
Goring-by-Sea	d		07 26	07 30						07 52	07 59		08 06				08 23		08 27		08 35		
Angmering 3	d		07 30	07 34			←			07 56	08 03		08 10	08 17			08 27		08 31		08 39		
Littlehampton 4	a		07 38				07 38			08 06						08 21	08 35						
	d		07 48				07 48		07 56							08 26							
Ford 4	d		→		07 44	07 48	07 52		08 00		08 09		08 17			08 30			08 37		08 45		
Bognor Regis 4	d	07 36						07 55				08 13			08 26			08 32					
Barnham	a	07 42		07 43	07 49	07 53	07 56	08 01	08 04		08 13	08 19	08 21	08 27	08 32	08 34		08 38	08 41		08 50		
	d			07 44	07 50	07 53	08 02		08 05		08 14		08 22	08 28		08 35			08 42	08 45	08 52		
Bognor Regis	a				07 58				08 12					08 36						08 52	08 58		
Chichester 4	a			07 51		08 01	08 09				08 21		08 29			08 43			08 49				
	d			07 52		08 01					08 22		08 30						08 50				
Fishbourne (Sussex)	d					08 04																	
Bosham	d					08 07																	
Nutbourne	d					08 11																	
Southbourne	d					08 13					08 29		08 37										
Emsworth	d					08 16					08 32		08 40										
Warblington	d					08 19																	
Havant	d			08 03		08 22					08 37		08 44						09 01				
Bedhampton	a					08 25																	
Hilsea	a					08 30																	
Fratton	a					08 34							08 53						09 11				
Portsmouth & Southsea	a					08 37							08 56						09 17				
Portsmouth Harbour ⛴	a					08 41							09 02						09 21				
Cosham	a			08 09							08 45												
Portchester	a			08 13							08 49												
Fareham	a			08 18							08 54												
Swanwick	a			08 26							09 01												
Eastleigh	a																						
Southampton Airport Parkway	a																						
Southampton Central ⛴	a			08 52							09 19												

Table 188

Mondays to Fridays

9 December to 16 May

London, Gatwick Airport, Brighton - Sussex Coast, Portsmouth and Southampton

Network Diagram - see first Page of Table 175

		SN	SN 1	SN 1	SN	SN	SN	SN 1	SN	SN		SN 1	SN	GW ◇	SN 1	SN 1		SN	SN	SN 1		SN	SN	SN
London Victoria 15 ⊖	d		07 17									07 47				08 02				08 17				
Clapham Junction 10	d		07 23									07 53				08 08				08 23				
London Bridge 4 ⊖	d																							
East Croydon	d		07 34									08 04				08 18				08 34				
Redhill 5	d		07 47													08 30								
Horley	d		07 57																					
Gatwick Airport 10 ✈	d		08 00									08 20				08 40				08 50				
Three Bridges 4	a		08 05													08 44								
	d		08 05													08 45								
Crawley	d		08 09													08 48								
Horsham 4	a		08 22													08 56								
	d		08 23													09 00	09 05							
Christs Hospital	d		08 26														09 08							
Billingshurst	d		08 32														09 14							
Pulborough	d		08 39														09 21							
Amberley	d		08 45														09 27							
Arundel	d		08 50														09 32							
Haywards Heath 3	d											08 37								09 04				
Burgess Hill	d																			09 09				
Preston Park	d																			09 18				
Brighton 10	d							08 33		08 44			08 53	08 59				09 03	09 14			09 23		
Hove 2	a							08 36		08 48		08 53	08 56	09 02				09 07	09 18	09 22		09 26		
	d							08 37				08 53	08 57	09 03				09 08		09 22		09 27		
Aldrington	d												08 59									09 29		
Portslade	d							08 40					09 01					09 11		09 25		09 31		
Fishersgate	d												09 03									09 33		
Southwick	d							08 43					09 05					09 14				09 35		
Shoreham-by-Sea	d							08 46				08 59	09 08	09 13				09 18		09 30		09 39		
Lancing	d							08 50				09 04	09 12					09 22				09 43		
East Worthing	d												09 15									09 46		
Worthing 4	a							08 54				09 08	09 18	09 21				09 26		09 36		09 48		
	d							08 55				09 08	09 18	09 22				09 26		09 37		09 49		
West Worthing	d							08 57				09 10	09a21							09 39		09a51		
Durrington-on-Sea	d							08 59				09 13								09 41				
Goring-by-Sea	d							09 02				09 15								09 44				
Angmering 3	d							09 06				09 19						09 34		09 48				
Littlehampton 4	a											09 29								09 58				
	d				08 54																			
Ford 4	d		08 55		08 59												09 37							
Bognor Regis 4	d	08 48		08 56			09 06								09 30								09 39	
Barnham	a	08 55	08 59	09 02	09 03		09 12	09 16						09 36	09 36	09 26	09 41	09 44					09 45	
	d		09 00		09 04	09 11		09 17	09 19					09 37		09 27	09 42	09 45						09 52
Bognor Regis	a					09 19			09 27								09 48							10 00
Chichester 4	a		09 07		09 11			09 24						09 45		09 34		09 52						
	d		09 08		09 12			09 25						09 46		09 35		09 53						
Fishbourne (Sussex)	d				09 15																			
Bosham	d				09 18																			
Nutbourne	d				09 21																			
Southbourne	d		09 15		09 24			09 32										10 00						
Emsworth	d		09 18		09 27			09 35										10 03						
Warblington	d				09 30																			
Havant	d		09 23		09 33			09 39						09 58		09 46		10 07						
Bedhampton	a				09 36																			
Hilsea	a				09 42																			
Fratton	a				09 46											09 54		10 16						
Portsmouth & Southsea	a				09 50											09 58		10 19						
Portsmouth Harbour ⛴	a															10 02		10 23						
Cosham	a		09 29					09 45						10 04										
Portchester	a																							
Fareham	a		09 37					09 53						10 12										
Swanwick	a		09 44					10 00																
Eastleigh	a																							
Southampton Airport Parkway	a																							
Southampton Central ⛴	a		10 01					10 20						10 40										

Table 188

Mondays to Fridays

9 December to 16 May

London, Gatwick Airport, Brighton - Sussex Coast, Portsmouth and Southampton

Network Diagram - see first Page of Table 175

Station		SN	SN 1	SN 1		SN	SN 1	SN	SN	SN 1 A 🛒	SN	SN 1	SN 1		SN	SN	SN 1 A 🛒	SN	SN	SN	SN	SN 1
London Victoria 15 ⊖	d			08 32						08 47			09 02				09 17					
Clapham Junction 10	d			08 38						08 53			09 08				09 23					
London Bridge 4 ⊖	d																					
East Croydon 🚊	d			08 48						09 04			09 19				09 33					
Redhill 5	d			09 03									09 30									
Horley	d												09 36									
Gatwick Airport 10 ✈	d			09 11						09 20			09 40				09 50					
Three Bridges 4	a			09 16									09 44									
	d			09 16									09 45									
Crawley	d			09 19									09 48									
Horsham 4	a			09 27									09 56									
	d			09 31	09 36								10 00	10 05								
Christs Hospital	d				09 39																	
Billingshurst	d				09 45									10 14								
Pulborough	d				09 52									10 20								
Amberley	d				09 58																	
Arundel	d				10 03									10 29								
Haywards Heath 3	d									09 37							10 05					
Burgess Hill	d																10 10					
Preston Park	d																10 18					
Brighton 10	d						09 33	09 44			09 53				10 03	10 14		10 23				
Hove 2	a						09 36	09 48		09 53	09 56				10 06	10 18	10 22	10 26				
	d						09 37			09 53	09 57				10 07		10 23	10 27				
Aldrington	d										09 59							10 29				
Portslade	d						09 40				10 01				10 10		10 26	10 31				
Fishersgate	d										10 03							10 33				
Southwick	d						09 43				10 05				10 13			10 35				
Shoreham-by-Sea	d						09 46			10 00	10 09				10 16		10 31	10 39				
Lancing	d						09 50			10 04	10 13				10 20			10 43				
East Worthing	d										10 16							10 46				
Worthing 4	a						09 54			10 08	10 18				10 24		10 37	10 48				
	d						09 55			10 08	10 19				10 25		10 37	10 49				
West Worthing	d						09 57			10 10	10a21						10 39	10a51				
Durrington-on-Sea	d						09 59			10 13							10 42					
Goring-by-Sea	d						10 02			10 15							10 44					
Angmering 3	d						10 06			10 19					10 31		10 48					
Littlehampton 4	a									10 29							10 58					
	d	09 54							10 11												10 54	
Ford 4	d	09 58			10 08		10 12		10 16					10 34							10 58	
Bognor Regis 4	d		09 56			10 07						10 30							10 39			10 56
Barnham	a	10 02	10 02	09 57	10 12	10 13	10 16		10 20			10 36	10 26	10 39	10 42				10 45		11 02	11 02
	d	10 03		09 58	10 13		10 17		10 22				10 27	10 39	10 42					10 52	11 03	
Bognor Regis	a				10 19				10 30					10 48						11 00		
Chichester 4	a	10 10		10 05			10 24						10 34		10 50						11 10	
	d	10 11		10 06			10 25						10 35		10 50						11 11	
Fishbourne (Sussex)	d	10 14																			11 14	
Bosham	d	10 17																			11 17	
Nutbourne	d	10 20																			11 20	
Southbourne	d	10 23		10 13											10 57						11 23	
Emsworth	d	10 26		10 16			10 33								11 00						11 26	
Warblington	d	10 29																			11 29	
Havant	d	10 32		10 20			10 37						10 46		11 05						11 32	
Bedhampton	a	10 34																			11 34	
Hilsea	a	10 42																			11 42	
Fratton	a	10 46											10 54		11 13						11 46	
Portsmouth & Southsea	a	10 50											10 58		11 17						11 50	
Portsmouth Harbour ⛴	a												11 02		11 21							
Cosham	a			10 28			10 45															
Portchester	a			10 32																		
Fareham	a			10 37			10 53															
Swanwick	a			10 44			11 00															
Eastleigh	a																					
Southampton Airport Parkway	a																					
Southampton Central ⛴	a			11 01			11 19															

A 🛒 to Haywards Heath

Table 188

Mondays to Fridays

9 December to 16 May

London, Gatwick Airport, Brighton - Sussex Coast, Portsmouth and Southampton

Network Diagram - see first Page of Table 175

		SN 1		SN		SN 1	SN	SN	SN 1 A	SN	SN 1	SN 1		SN		SN	SN 1 A	SN	SN	SN	SN	SN 1	SN 1		
London Victoria 15	d	09 32							09 47			10 02					10 17						10 32		
Clapham Junction 10	d	09 38							09 53			10 08					10 23						10 38		
London Bridge 4	d																								
East Croydon	d	09 48							10 03			10 18					10 33						10 48		
Redhill 5	d	10 00										10 30											11 00		
Horley	d											10 36													
Gatwick Airport 10	d	10 09							10 20			10 39					10 50						11 09		
Three Bridges 4	a	10 14										10 44											11 14		
	d	10 14										10 44											11 14		
Crawley	d	10 18										10 48											11 18		
Horsham 4	a	10 26										10 56											11 26		
	d	10 30	10 35									11 00	11 05										11 30	11 35	
Christs Hospital	d		10 38																					11 38	
Billingshurst	d		10 44										11 14											11 44	
Pulborough	d		10 51										11 20											11 51	
Amberley	d		10 57																					11 57	
Arundel	d		11 02										11 29											12 02	
Haywards Heath 3	d								10 37								11 04								
Burgess Hill	d																11 09								
Preston Park	d																11 18								
Brighton 10	d					10 33	10 44			10 53				11 03		11 14		11 23							
Hove 2	a					10 36	10 48		10 53	10 56				11 06		11 18	11 22	11 26							
	d					10 37			10 53	10 57				11 07			11 22	11 27							
Aldrington	d									10 59								11 29							
Portslade	d					10 40				11 01				11 10			11 25	11 31							
Fishersgate	d									11 03								11 33							
Southwick	d					10 43				11 05				11 13				11 35							
Shoreham-by-Sea	d					10 46			11 00	11 09				11 16			11 30	11 39							
Lancing	d					10 50			11 04	11 13				11 20				11 43							
East Worthing	d									11 16								11 46							
Worthing 4	a					10 54			11 08	11 18				11 24			11 36	11 48							
	d					10 55			11 08	11 19				11 25			11 37	11 49							
West Worthing	d					10 57			11 10	11a21							11 39	11a51							
Durrington-on-Sea	d					10 59			11 13								11 41								
Goring-by-Sea	d					11 02			11 15								11 44								
Angmering 3	d					11 06			11 19					11 31			11 48								
Littlehampton 4	a								11 29								11 58								
	d							11 11													11 54				
Ford 4	d		11 07			11 12		11 16					11 34								11 58			12 07	
Bognor Regis 4	d			11 07							11 30								11 39			11 56			
Barnham	a	10 56	11 11	11 13		11 16		11 20			11 36	11 26	11 39	11 42					11 45		12 02	12 02	11 56	12 11	
	d	10 57	11 12			11 17		11 22				11 27	11 39	11 42						11 52	12 03		11 57	12 12	
Bognor Regis	a		11 18					11 30					11 48							12 00				12 18	
Chichester 4	a	11 04				11 24						11 34		11 50							12 10		12 04		
	d	11 05				11 25						11 35		11 50							12 11		12 05		
Fishbourne (Sussex)	d																				12 14				
Bosham	d																				12 17				
Nutbourne	d																				12 20				
Southbourne	d	11 12												11 57							12 23		12 12		
Emsworth	d	11 15				11 33								12 00							12 26		12 15		
Warblington	d																				12 29				
Havant	d	11 19				11 37						11 46		12 05							12 32		12 19		
Bedhampton	a																				12 34				
Hilsea	a																				12 42				
Fratton	a											11 54		12 13							12 46				
Portsmouth & Southsea	a											11 58		12 17							12 50				
Portsmouth Harbour	a											12 02		12 21											
Cosham	a	11 26				11 45																	12 26		
Portchester	a	11 30																					12 30		
Fareham	a	11 35				11 53																	12 35		
Swanwick	a	11 42				12 00																	12 42		
Eastleigh	a																								
Southampton Airport Parkway	a																								
Southampton Central	a	12 01				12 19																	12 59		

A to Haywards Heath

Table 188

Mondays to Fridays

9 December to 16 May

London, Gatwick Airport, Brighton - Sussex Coast, Portsmouth and Southampton

Network Diagram - see first Page of Table 175

		SN	SN 1	SN	SN	SN 1 A	SN	SN 1	SN 1			SN	SN	SN 1	SN	SN	SN	SN	SN 1	SN 1			SN	SN 1	SN
London Victoria 15 ⊖	d					10 47			11 02					11 17						11 32					
Clapham Junction 10	d					10 53			11 08					11 23						11 38					
London Bridge 4 ⊖	d																								
East Croydon	d					11 03			11 18					11 33						11 48					
Redhill 5	d								11 30											12 00					
Horley	d								11 36																
Gatwick Airport 10 ✈	d					11 20			11 39					11 50						12 09					
Three Bridges 4	a								11 44											12 14					
	d								11 44											12 14					
Crawley	d								11 48											12 18					
Horsham 4	a								11 56											12 26					
	d								12 00	12 05										12 30	12 35				
Christs Hospital	d																				12 38				
Billingshurst	d									12 14											12 44				
Pulborough	d									12 20											12 51				
Amberley	d																				12 57				
Arundel	d									12 29											13 02				
Haywards Heath 3	d					11 37								12 04											
Burgess Hill	d													12 09											
Preston Park	d													12 18											
Brighton 10	d		11 33	11 44			11 53					12 03	12 14		12 23									12 33	12 44
Hove 2	a		11 36	11 48		11 53	11 56					12 06	12 18	12 22	12 26									12 36	12 48
	d		11 37			11 53	11 57					12 07		12 22	12 27									12 37	
Aldrington	d						11 59								12 29										
Portslade	d		11 40				12 01					12 10		12 25	12 31									12 40	
Fishersgate	d						12 03								12 33										
Southwick	d		11 43				12 05					12 13			12 35									12 43	
Shoreham-by-Sea	d		11 46			12 00	12 09					12 16		12 30	12 39									12 46	
Lancing	d		11 50			12 04	12 13					12 20			12 43									12 50	
East Worthing	d						12 16								12 46										
Worthing 4	a		11 54			12 08	12 18					12 24		12 36	12 48									12 54	
	d		11 55			12 08	12 19					12 25		12 37	12 49									12 55	
West Worthing	d		11 57			12 10	12a21							12 39	12a51									12 57	
Durrington-on-Sea	d		11 59			12 13								12 41										12 59	
Goring-by-Sea	d		12 02			12 15								12 44										13 02	
Angmering 3	d		12 06			12 19						12 31		12 48										13 06	
Littlehampton 4	a					12 29								12 58											
	d				12 11													12 54							
Ford 4	d		12 12		12 16					12 34								12 58			13 07			13 12	
Bognor Regis 4	d	12 07						12 30								12 39			12 56				13 07		
Barnham	a	12 13	12 16		12 20			12 36	12 26	12 39		12 42				12 45		13 02	13 02	12 56	13 11		13 13	13 16	
	d		12 17		12 22				12 27	12 39		12 42					12 52	13 03		12 57	13 12			13 17	
Bognor Regis	a				12 30					12 48							13 00				13 18				
Chichester 4	a		12 24						12 34			12 50						13 10		13 04				13 24	
	d		12 25						12 35			12 50						13 11		13 05				13 25	
Fishbourne (Sussex)	d																	13 14							
Bosham	d																	13 17							
Nutbourne	d																	13 20							
Southbourne	d											12 57						13 23		13 12					
Emsworth	d		12 33									13 00						13 26		13 15				13 33	
Warblington	d																	13 29							
Havant	d		12 37						12 46			13 05						13 32		13 19				13 37	
Bedhampton	a																	13 34							
Hilsea	a																	13 42							
Fratton	a								12 54			13 13						13 46							
Portsmouth & Southsea	a								12 58			13 17						13 50							
Portsmouth Harbour ⛴	a								13 02			13 21													
Cosham	a		12 45																	13 26				13 45	
Portchester	a																			13 30					
Fareham	a		12 53																	13 35				13 53	
Swanwick	a		13 00																	13 42				14 00	
Eastleigh	a																							14n37	
Southampton Airport Parkway	a																							14n33	
Southampton Central ⛴	a		13 19																	13 59				14 19	

A to Haywards Heath

n Stops at these stations after Southampton Central

Table 188

Mondays to Fridays

9 December to 16 May

London, Gatwick Airport, Brighton - Sussex Coast, Portsmouth and Southampton

Network Diagram - see first Page of Table 175

		SN	SN 1	SN	SN 1	SN 1			SN	SN	SN 1	SN	SN	SN	SN	SN 1	SN 1			SN	SN 1	SN	SN	SN 1	SN
London Victoria 15 ⊖	d		11 47			12 02					12 17						12 32							12 47	
Clapham Junction 10	d		11 53			12 08					12 23						12 38							12 53	
London Bridge 4 ⊖	d																								
East Croydon	d		12 03			12 18					12 33						12 48							13 03	
Redhill 5	d					12 30											13 00								
Horley	d					12 36																			
Gatwick Airport 10 ✈	d		12 20			12 39					12 50						13 09							13 20	
Three Bridges 4	a					12 44											13 14								
	d					12 44											13 14								
Crawley	d					12 48											13 18								
Horsham 4	a					12 56											13 26								
	d					13 00	13 05										13 30	13 35							
Christs Hospital	d																	13 38							
Billingshurst	d						13 14											13 44							
Pulborough	d						13 20											13 51							
Amberley	d																	13 57							
Arundel	d						13 29											14 02							
Haywards Heath 3	d		12 37								13 04													13 37	
Burgess Hill	d										13 09														
Preston Park	d										13 18														
Brighton 10	d			12 53					13 03	13 14		13 23									13 33	13 44			13 53
Hove 2	a		12 53	12 56					13 06	13 19	13 22	13 26									13 36	13 48		13 53	13 56
	d		12 53	12 57					13 07		13 22	13 27									13 37			13 53	13 57
Aldrington	d			12 59								13 29													13 59
Portslade	d			13 01					13 10		13 25	13 31									13 40				14 01
Fishersgate	d			13 03								13 33													14 03
Southwick	d			13 05					13 13			13 35									13 43				14 05
Shoreham-by-Sea	d		13 00	13 09					13 16		13 30	13 39									13 46			14 00	14 09
Lancing	d		13 04	13 13					13 20			13 43									13 50			14 04	14 13
East Worthing	d			13 16								13 46													14 16
Worthing 4	a		13 08	13 18					13 24		13 36	13 48									13 54			14 08	14 18
	d		13 08	13 19					13 25		13 37	13 49									13 55			14 08	14 19
West Worthing	d		13 10	13a21							13 39	13a51									13 57			14 10	14a21
Durrington-on-Sea	d		13 13								13 41										13 59			14 13	
Goring-by-Sea	d		13 15								13 44										14 02			14 15	
Angmering 3	d		13 19						13 31		13 48										14 06			14 19	
Littlehampton 4	a		13 29								13 58													14 29	
	d	13 11													13 54								14 11		
Ford 4	d	13 16					13 34								13 58			14 07			14 12		14 16		
Bognor Regis 4	d				13 30								13 39			13 56				14 07					
Barnham	a	13 20			13 36	13 26	13 39		13 42				13 45		14 02	14 02	13 56	14 11		14 13	14 16		14 20		
	d	13 22				13 27	13 39		13 42					13 52	14 03		13 57	14 12			14 17		14 22		
Bognor Regis	a	13 30					13 48							14 00				14 18					14 30		
Chichester 4	a					13 34			13 50						14 10		14 04				14 24				
	d					13 35			13 50						14 11		14 05				14 25				
Fishbourne (Sussex)	d														14 14										
Bosham	d														14 17										
Nutbourne	d														14 20										
Southbourne	d								13 57						14 23		14 12								
Emsworth	d								14 00						14 26		14 15				14 33				
Warblington	d														14 29										
Havant	d					13 46			14 05						14 32		14 19				14 37				
Bedhampton	a														14 34										
Hilsea	a														14 42										
Fratton	a					13 54			14 13						14 46										
Portsmouth & Southsea	a					13 58			14 17						14 50										
Portsmouth Harbour ⛴	a					14 02			14 21																
Cosham	a																14 26				14 45				
Portchester	a																14 30								
Fareham	a																14 35				14 53				
Swanwick	a																14 42				15 00				
Eastleigh	a																								
Southampton Airport Parkway	a																								
Southampton Central ⛴	a																14 59				15 19				

Table 188

Mondays to Fridays

9 December to 16 May

London, Gatwick Airport, Brighton - Sussex Coast, Portsmouth and Southampton

Network Diagram - see first Page of Table 175

		SN 1	SN 1			SN	SN	SN 1	SN	SN	SN	SN	SN 1	SN 1			SN	SN 1	SN	SN	SN 1	SN	SN	SN 1	
London Victoria 15 ⊖	d		13 02					13 17						13 32							13 47				
Clapham Junction 10	d		13 08					13 23						13 38							13 53				
London Bridge 4 ⊖	d																								
East Croydon	d		13 18					13 33						13 48							14 03				
Redhill 5	d		13 30											14 00											
Horley	d		13 36																						
Gatwick Airport 10 ✈	d		13 40					13 50						14 09							14 20				
Three Bridges 4	a		13 44											14 14											
	d		13 45											14 14											
Crawley	d		13 48											14 18											
Horsham 4	a		13 56											14 26											
	d		14 00	14 05										14 30	14 35										
Christs Hospital	d														14 38										
Billingshurst	d			14 14											14 44										
Pulborough	d			14 20											14 51										
Amberley	d														14 57										
Arundel	d			14 29											15 02										
Haywards Heath 3	d							14 04													14 37				
Burgess Hill	d							14 09																	
Preston Park	d							14 18																	
Brighton 10	d					14 03	14 14		14 23									14 33	14 44			14 53			
Hove 2	a					14 06	14 18	14 22	14 26									14 36	14 48		14 53	14 56			
	d					14 07		14 22	14 27									14 37			14 53	14 57			
Aldrington	d								14 29													14 59			
Portslade	d					14 10		14 25	14 31									14 40				15 01			
Fishersgate	d								14 33													15 03			
Southwick	d					14 13			14 35									14 43				15 05			
Shoreham-by-Sea	d					14 16		14 30	14 39									14 46			15 00	15 09			
Lancing	d					14 20			14 43									14 50			15 04	15 13			
East Worthing	d								14 46													15 16			
Worthing 4	a					14 24		14 36	14 48									14 54			15 08	15 18			
	d					14 25		14 37	14 49									14 55			15 08	15 19			
West Worthing	d							14 39	14a51									14 57			15 10	15a21			
Durrington-on-Sea	d							14 41										14 59			15 13				
Goring-by-Sea	d							14 44										15 02			15 15				
Angmering 3	d					14 31		14 48										15 06			15 19				
Littlehampton 4	a							14 58													15 29				
	d											14 54								15 11			15 23		
Ford 4	d			14 34								14 58			15 07			15 12		15 16			15 27		
Bognor Regis 4	d	14 30								14 39			14 56				15 07							15 27	
Barnham	a	14 36	14 26	14 39		14 42				14 45		15 02	15 02	14 56	15 11		15 13	15 16		15 20			15 31	15 33	
	d		14 27	14 39		14 42					14 52	15 03		14 57	15 12			15 17		15 22			15 33		
Bognor Regis	a			14 48							15 00				15 18					15 30					
Chichester 4	a		14 34			14 50						15 10		15 04				15 24					15 40		
	d		14 35			14 50						15 11		15 05				15 25					15 41		
Fishbourne (Sussex)	d											15 14											15 44		
Bosham	d											15 17											15 47		
Nutbourne	d											15 20											15 50		
Southbourne	d					14 57						15 23		15 12									15 53		
Emsworth	d					15 00						15 26		15 15				15 33					15 56		
Warblington	d											15 29											15 59		
Havant	d		14 46			15 05						15 32		15 19				15 37					16 02		
Bedhampton	a											15 34											16 04		
Hilsea	a											15 42													
Fratton	a		14 54			15 13						15 46											16 12		
Portsmouth & Southsea	a		14 58			15 17						15 50											16 15		
Portsmouth Harbour ⛴	a		15 02			15 21																	16 21		
Cosham	a													15 26				15 45							
Portchester	a													15 30											
Fareham	a													15 35				15 53							
Swanwick	a													15 42				16 00							
Eastleigh	a																								
Southampton Airport Parkway	a																								
Southampton Central ⛴	a													15 59				16 20							

Table 188

Mondays to Fridays

9 December to 16 May

London, Gatwick Airport, Brighton - Sussex Coast, Portsmouth and Southampton

Network Diagram - see first Page of Table 175

Station		SN 1		SN	SN	SN	SN	SN 1	SN	SN 1	SN 1	SN 1		SN	SN 1	SN	SN	SN 1	SN	SN	SN 1	SN 1	
London Victoria 15 ⊖	d	14 02						14 17				14 32						14 47				15 02	
Clapham Junction 10	d	14 08						14 23				14 38						14 53				15 08	
London Bridge 4 ⊖	d																						
East Croydon	d	14 18						14 33				14 48						15 03				15 18	
Redhill 5	d	14 30										15 00										15 30	
Horley	d	14 36																				15 36	
Gatwick Airport 10 ✈	d	14 39						14 50				15 09						15 20				15 39	
Three Bridges 4	a	14 44										15 14										15 44	
	d	14 44										15 14										15 44	
Crawley	d	14 48										15 18										15 48	
Horsham 4	a	14 56										15 26										15 56	
	d	15 00	15 05									15 30	15 35									16 00	16 05
Christs Hospital	d		15 08										15 38										16 08
Billingshurst	d		15 14										15 44										16 14
Pulborough	d		15 21										15 51										16 21
Amberley	d												15 57										
Arundel	d		15 30										16 02										16 30
Haywards Heath 3	d							15 04										15 37					
Burgess Hill	d							15 09															
Preston Park	d							15 18															
Brighton 10	d				15 03		15 14			15 23					15 33		15 44		15 53				
Hove 2	a				15 06		15 18	15 22		15 26					15 36		15 48	15 53	15 56				
	d				15 07			15 22		15 27					15 37			15 53	15 57				
Aldrington	d									15 29									15 59				
Portslade	d				15 10			15 25		15 31					15 40				16 01				
Fishersgate	d									15 33									16 03				
Southwick	d				15 13					15 35					15 43				16 05				
Shoreham-by-Sea	d				15 16			15 30		15 39					15 46			16 00	16 09				
Lancing	d				15 20					15 43					15 50			16 04	16 13				
East Worthing	d							15 35		15 46									16 16				
Worthing 4	a				15 24			15 38		15 48					15 54			16 08	16 18				
	d				15 25			15 38		15 49					15 55			16 08	16 19				
West Worthing	d				15 27			15 40		15 51					15 57			16 10	16a21				
Durrington-on-Sea	d				15 29			15 43		15 53					15 59			16 13					
Goring-by-Sea	d				15 32			15 45		15 56					16 02			16 15					
Angmering 3	d				15 36			15 49		16 00					16 06			16 19					
Littlehampton 4	a							15 58		16 11								16 29					
	d								15 54											16 22			
Ford 4	d		15 35		15 42				15 58				16 07		16 13					16 26			16 35
Bognor Regis 4	d			15 39							15 56			16 09							16 30		
Barnham	a	15 26	15 39	15 45	15 46				16 02		16 02	15 56	16 11	16 15	16 17					16 30	16 36	16 26	16 39
	d	15 27	15 40		15 47	15 53			16 03			15 57	16 12		16 18	16 24				16 31		16 27	16 40
Bognor Regis	a		15 48			16 00							16 18			16 31							16 48
Chichester 4	a	15 34			15 54				16 10			16 04			16 25					16 38		16 34	
	d	15 35			15 55				16 11			16 05			16 26					16 39		16 35	
Fishbourne (Sussex)	d								16 14											16 42			
Bosham	d								16 17											16 45			
Nutbourne	d								16 20											16 48			
Southbourne	d				16 02				16 23			16 12								16 51			
Emsworth	d				16 05				16 26			16 15			16 34					16 54			
Warblington	d								16 29											16 57			
Havant	d	15 46			16 09				16 32			16 19			16 38					17 00		16 46	
Bedhampton	a								16 34											17 02			
Hilsea	a								16 42											17 07			
Fratton	a	15 54			16 18				16 46											17 11		16 54	
Portsmouth & Southsea	a	15 58			16 21				16 50											17 16		16 58	
Portsmouth Harbour ⛴	a	16 02			16 26															17 20		17 02	
Cosham	a											16 26			16 45								
Portchester	a											16 30											
Fareham	a											16 35			16 53								
Swanwick	a											16 42											
Eastleigh	a														17 11								
Southampton Airport Parkway	a														17 20								
Southampton Central ⛴	a											17 01			17 28								

Table 188

Mondays to Fridays

9 December to 16 May

London, Gatwick Airport, Brighton - Sussex Coast, Portsmouth and Southampton

Network Diagram - see first Page of Table 175

		SN	SN	SN	SN	SN ■1	SN	SN ■1	SN ■1	SN ■1		SN ■1	SN	SN	SN ■1	SN	SN ■1	SN	GW ◇	SN ■1		SN
London Victoria ■15 ⊖	d					15 17				15 32					15 47					16 02		
Clapham Junction ■10	d					15 23				15 38					15 53					16 08		
London Bridge ■4 ⊖	d																					
East Croydon	d					15 33				15 48					16 03					16 18		
Redhill ■5	d									16 00										16 30		
Horley	d																			16 36		
Gatwick Airport ■10 ✈	d					15 50				16 09					16 20					16 39		
Three Bridges ■4	a									16 14										16 44		
	d									16 14										16 44		
Crawley	d									16 18										16 48		
Horsham ■4	a									16 26										16 56		
	d									16 30	16 35									17 00	17 05	
Christs Hospital	d										16 38										17 08	
Billingshurst	d										16 44										17 15	
Pulborough	d										16 51										17 21	
Amberley	d										16 57										17 27	
Arundel	d										17 02										17 32	
Haywards Heath ■3	d					16 04									16 37							
Burgess Hill	d					16 09																
Preston Park	d					16 18																
Brighton ■10	d		16 03		16 14		16 24					16 33	16 44					16 53	16 59			17 03
Hove ■2	a		16 06		16 18	16 22	16 27					16 36	16 48		16 53			16 56	17 02			17 06
	d		16 07			16 22	16 28					16 37			16 53			16 57	17 03			17 07
Aldrington	d						16 30											16 59				
Portslade	d		16 10			16 25	16 32					16 40			16 56			17 01				17 10
Fishersgate	d						16 34											17 03				
Southwick	d		16 13				16 36					16 43						17 05				17 13
Shoreham-by-Sea	d		16 16			16 30	16 40					16 46			17 01			17 08	17 13			17 16
Lancing	d		16 20				16 44					16 50			17 05			17 12				17 20
East Worthing	d						16 47											17 15				
Worthing ■4	a		16 24			16 36	16 49					16 54			17 09			17 18	17 21			17 24
	d		16 25			16 37	16 50					16 55			17 10			17 18	17 22			17 25
West Worthing	d		16 27			16 39	16a52					16 57			17 12			17 20				17 27
Durrington-on-Sea	d		16 29			16 41						16 59			17 14							17 29
Goring-by-Sea	d		16 32			16 44						17 02			17 17							17 32
Angmering ■3	d		16 36			16 48						17 06			17 21							17 36
Littlehampton ■4	a					16 57									17 29			17 33				
	d							16 54						17 11				17 41				
Ford ■4	d		16 42					16 58			17 07	17 12		17 16				↪			17 37	17 42
Bognor Regis ■4	d	16 39							16 56							17 18	17 30					
Barnham	a	16 45	16 46					17 02	17 02	16 56	17 11	17 16		17 20		17 24	17 36		17 38	17 26	17 42	17 46
	d		16 47	16 54				17 03		16 57	17 12	17 17		17 24					17 39	17 27	17 42	17 47
Bognor Regis	a			17 01							17 18			17 31							17 49	
Chichester ■4	a		16 54					17 10		17 04		17 24							17 46	17 34		17 54
	d		16 55					17 11		17 05		17 25							17 47	17 35		17 55
Fishbourne (Sussex)	d							17 14												17 38		
Bosham	d							17 17												17 41		
Nutbourne	d							17 20														
Southbourne	d		17 02					17 23		17 12										17 45		18 04
Emsworth	d		17 05					17 26		17 15		17 33								17 48		18 07
Warblington	d							17 29														18 10
Havant	d		17 09					17 32		17 19		17 37							17 58	17 54		18 13
Bedhampton	a							17 34												17 56		
Hilsea	a							17 42												18 01		
Fratton	a		17 18					17 46												18 05		18 22
Portsmouth & Southsea	a		17 22					17 50												18 09		18 25
Portsmouth Harbour ⛴	a																			18 15		18 31
Cosham	a									17 26		17 45							18 04			
Portchester	a									17 31												
Fareham	a									17 36		17 53							18 12			
Swanwick	a									17 43		18 00										
Eastleigh	a																					
Southampton Airport Parkway	a																					
Southampton Central ⛴	a									18 03		18 20							18 40			

Table 188

Mondays to Fridays

9 December to 16 May

London, Gatwick Airport, Brighton - Sussex Coast, Portsmouth and Southampton

Network Diagram - see first Page of Table 175

		SN	SN	SN 1 A 🚲	SN	SN	SN	SN 1	SN	SN 1		SN 1	SN	SN	SN 1	SN	SN	SN 1		SN 1	SN	SN	SN 1
London Victoria 15 ⊖	d			16 17						16 32								17 02					17 17
Clapham Junction 10	d			16 23						16 38								17 08					17 23
London Bridge 4 ⊖	d														16 57								
East Croydon	d			16 34						16 48					17 10			17 18					17 33
Redhill 5	d									17 00													
Horley	d									17 06													
Gatwick Airport 10 ✈	d			16 49						17 09													17 49
Three Bridges 4	a									17 14					17 28			17 37					
	d									17 18	17 22				17 29			17 38					
Crawley	d									17 22	17 26							17 42					
Horsham 4	a									17 30	17 38							17 50					
	d									17 30	17 38							17 54	17 58				
Christs Hospital	d										17 42								18 01				
Billingshurst	d										17 48								18 07				
Pulborough	d										17 54								18 14				
Amberley	d																		18 20				
Arundel	d										18 03								18 25				
Haywards Heath 3	d			17 04											17 40								18 01
Burgess Hill	d			17 09											17 46								18 08
Preston Park	d														17 56								
Brighton 10	d		17 14				17 23					17 33	17 45	17 53							18 00	18 14	
Hove 2	a		17 18	17 20			17 26					17 36	17 48	17 57	18 00						18 03	18 18	18 21
	d			17 21			17 27					17 37	17 49		18 01						18 04		18 22
Aldrington	d						17 29						17 51								18 06		
Portslade	d			17 24			17 31					17 40	17 53		18 04						18 08		18 25
Fishersgate	d						17 33						17 55								18 10		
Southwick	d						17 35					17 43	17 57								18 12		
Shoreham-by-Sea	d			17 29			17 39					17 46	18 01		18 09						18 16		18 30
Lancing	d			17 33			17 43					17 50	18 05		18 13						18 20		18 34
East Worthing	d						17 46						18 08								18 23		
Worthing 4	a			17 37			17 48					17 54	18 10		18 17						18 25		18 38
	d			17 38			17 49					17 55	18 11		18 17						18 27		18 38
West Worthing	d			17 40			17 51					17 57	18 13		18 19						18 29		18 40
Durrington-on-Sea	d			17 42			17 53					17 59	18 15		18 22						18 31		18 43
Goring-by-Sea	d			17 45			17 56					18 02	18 18		18 24						18 34		18 45
Angmering 3	d	←		17 49			18 00					18 06	18 22		18 28						18 38		18 49
Littlehampton 4	a	17 33		18 00			18 08						18 30		18 39								19 00
	d	17 41				17 54											18 18						
Ford 4	d	17 46				17 58					18 08	18 12					18 22		18 30		18 44		
Bognor Regis 4	d				17 51			17 57								18 19				18 33			
Barnham	a	17 50			17 57	18 02		18 03		17 57	18 13	18 16				18 25	18 26	18 20	18 34	18 39	18 48		
	d	17 54				18 04			18 08	17 57	18 14	18 17					18 27	18 21	18 35		18 49		
Bognor Regis	a	18 02							18 14		18 22						18 34		18 41				
Chichester 4	a					18 11				18 05		18 24						18 28			18 56		
	d					18 12				18 05		18 25						18 29			18 57		
Fishbourne (Sussex)	d					18 15												18 32					
Bosham	d					18 18				18 10								18 35					
Nutbourne	d					18 21												18 38					
Southbourne	d					18 24				18 14								18 41					
Emsworth	d					18 27				18 17		18 33						18 44					
Warblington	d					18 30												18 47					
Havant	d					18 34				18 23		18 37						18 54			19 08		
Bedhampton	a					18 36												18 57					
Hilsea	a					18 42												19 02					
Fratton	a					18 46												19 06			19 17		
Portsmouth & Southsea	a					18 49												19 09			19 21		
Portsmouth Harbour ⛴	a																				19 26		
Cosham	a									18 29		18 44											
Portchester	a									18 34													
Fareham	a									18 39		18 52											
Swanwick	a									18 46		18 59											
Eastleigh	a																						
Southampton Airport Parkway	a																						
Southampton Central ⛴	a									19 04		19 20											

A 🚲 to Haywards Heath

Table 188

Mondays to Fridays

9 December to 16 May

London, Gatwick Airport, Brighton - Sussex Coast, Portsmouth and Southampton

Network Diagram - see first Page of Table 175

		SN	SN	SN	SN 1		SN	SN 1	SN 1	SN	SN 1	SN 1	SN	SN 1		SN 1	SN	SN	SN 1	SN	SN 1	SN 1	
London Victoria 15 ⊖	d				17 34						17 46			18 04							18 17	18 34	
Clapham Junction 10	d				17 40						17 52			18 11							18 23	18 41	
London Bridge 4 ⊖	d								17 42			17 50							18 12				
East Croydon	d				17 51				17 55		18 02	18 06		18 21					18 25		18 33	18 52	
Redhill 5	d																						
Horley	d										18 16										18 48		
Gatwick Airport 10 ✈	d										18 20			18 37									
Three Bridges 4	a				18 09						18 24	18 24		18 42					18 42			19 10	
	d				18 09						18 25	18 24		18 42					18 43			19 10	
Crawley	d				18 13							18 28		18 46								19 14	
Horsham 4	a				18 24							18 41		18 54								19 25	
	d				18 28	18 32						18 41		18 58	19 02							19 29	19 33
Christs Hospital	d					18 35						18 45			19 05								19 36
Billingshurst	d					18 41						18 51			19 11								19 43
Pulborough	d					18 48						18 58			19 18								19 50
Amberley	d											19 04											19 56
Arundel	d					18 57						19 10			19 27								20 01
Haywards Heath 3	d								18 21		18 36								18 53		19 03		
Burgess Hill	d								18 27		18 42								18 59		19 09		
Preston Park	d								18 38		18 53								19 11				
Brighton 10	d							18 28		18 48								19 00		19 15			
Hove 2	a							18 31	18 43	18 53	18 57							19 03	19 14	19 19	19 22		
	d							18 32	18 44		18 57							19 04	19 15		19 23		
Aldrington	d							18 34										19 06					
Portslade	d							18 36	18 47		19 01							19 08	19 18		19 26		
Fishersgate	d							18 38										19 10					
Southwick	d							18 40										19 12					
Shoreham-by-Sea	d							18 44	18 52		19 06							19 16	19 23		19 31		
Lancing	d							18 48	18 57		19 10							19 20	19 28		19 36		
East Worthing	d							18 51										19 23					
Worthing 4	a							18 53	19 01		19 14							19 25	19 32		19 40		
	d							18 54	19 01		19 15							19 26	19 32		19 40		
West Worthing	d								19 03		19 17							19 28	19 34		19 42		
Durrington-on-Sea	d								19 06		19 19							19 30	19 37		19 45		
Goring-by-Sea	d								19 08		19 22							19 33	19 39		19 47		
Angmering 3	d							19 00	19 12		19 26							19 37	19 43		19 51		
Littlehampton 4	a								19 24		19 35								19 54		20 03		
	d			18 48									19 19				19 35						
Ford 4	d			18 53		19 02		19 07					19 25		19 34		19 39	19 43					
Bognor Regis 4	d	18 46					19 03									19 33							
Barnham	a	18 52		18 57	18 54	19 06	19 09	19 11				19 18	19 29	19 24	19 38	19 39	19 43	19 47				19 55	20 09
	d		18 56	19 00	18 55	19 07		19 12				19 19	19 30	19 25	19 39		19 57	19 48				19 56	20 10
Bognor Regis	a		19 04			19 13						19 28	19 38		19 47		20 04						20 16
Chichester 4	a			19 07	19 02			19 19						19 32				19 55				20 03	
	d			19 11	19 03			19 20						19 33				19 56				20 04	
Fishbourne (Sussex)	d			19 14	19 06																	20 07	
Bosham	d			19 17	19 09																	20 10	
Nutbourne	d			19 20																		20 13	
Southbourne	d			19 23	19 13									19 40								20 16	
Emsworth	d			19 26	19 16			19 30						19 43								20 19	
Warblington	d			19 29																		20 22	
Havant	d			19 33	19 21			19 37						19 47				20 07				20 25	
Bedhampton	a			19 35																			
Hilsea	a			19 43																			
Fratton	a			19 47										19 56				20 15					
Portsmouth & Southsea	a			19 50										20 01				20 19					
Portsmouth Harbour ⛴	a													20 07									
Cosham	a				19 29			19 46														20 32	
Portchester	a				19 33																		
Fareham	a				19 38			19 54														20 40	
Swanwick	a				19 45			20 01														20 47	
Eastleigh	a																						
Southampton Airport Parkway	a																						
Southampton Central ⛴	a				20 03			20 18														21 05	

Table 188

Mondays to Fridays

9 December to 16 May

London, Gatwick Airport, Brighton - Sussex Coast, Portsmouth and Southampton

Network Diagram - see first Page of Table 175

		SN		SN	SN	SN	SN	SN	SN		SN	SN		SN	SN	SN	SN		SN	SN	SN	SN		SN	
					1		1	1	1			1			1		1			1		1		1	
							A								A							A			
London Victoria 15	d						18 47		19 02						19 17		19 32					19 47		20 02	
Clapham Junction 10	d						18 53		19 08						19 23		19 38					19 53		20 08	
London Bridge 4	d																								
East Croydon	d						19 04		19 18						19 33		19 48					20 03		20 19	
Redhill 5	d								19 31								20 00							20 31	
Horley	d						19 18		19 37																
Gatwick Airport 10	d						19 22		19 41						19 49		20 09					20 19		20 39	
Three Bridges 4	a								19 46								20 14							20 44	
	d								19 46								20 14							20 44	
Crawley	d								19 49								20 18							20 48	
Horsham 4	a								19 57								20 26							20 56	
	d								20 01	20 06							20 30	20 35						21 00	21 05
Christs Hospital	d									20 09								20 38							21 08
Billingshurst	d									20 15								20 44							21 14
Pulborough	d									20 22								20 51							21 21
Amberley	d									20 28								20 57							21 27
Arundel	d									20 33								21 02							21 32
Haywards Heath 3	d						19 38								20 04							20 34			
Burgess Hill	d						19 43								20 09							20 39			
Preston Park	d																					20 49			
Brighton 10	d				19 30	19 44						20 03		20 14						20 30	20 47				
Hove 2	a				19 33	19 48	19 57					20 06		20 18	20 21					20 33	20 51	20 53			
	d				19 34		19 57					20 07			20 22					20 34		20 54			
Aldrington	d				19 36							20 09								20 36					
Portslade	d				19 38		20 00					20 11			20 25					20 38		20 57			
Fishersgate	d				19 40							20 13								20 40					
Southwick	d				19 42							20 15								20 42					
Shoreham-by-Sea	d				19 46		20 05					20 19			20 30					20 46		21 01			
Lancing	d				19 50		20 09					20 23			20 34					20 50		21 05			
East Worthing	d				19 53							20 26								20 53					
Worthing 4	a				19 55		20 13					20 28			20 38					20 55		21 09			
	d				19 56		20 13					20 29			20 38					20 56		21 10			
West Worthing	d				19 58		20 15					20 31			20 40					20 58		21 12			
Durrington-on-Sea	d				20 00		20 18					20 33			20 43					21 00		21 14			
Goring-by-Sea	d				20 03		20 20					20 36			20 45					21 03		21 17			
Angmering 3	d				20 07		20 24					20 40			20 49					21 07		21 21			
Littlehampton 4	a						20 35								20 58							21 29			
	d			20 06							20 37								21 06						
Ford 4	d			20 10	20 14					20 38	20 42	20 46						21 07	21 10	21 13					21 37
Bognor Regis 4	d	20 05						20 33								21 04									
Barnham	a	20 11		20 14	20 19			20 39	20 27	20 42	20 46	20 50				21 10	20 56	21 11	21 14	21 17				21 26	21 41
	d			20 22	20 19				20 28	20 43	20 52	20 51					20 57	21 12	21 22	21 18				21 27	21 42
Bognor Regis	a			20 30						20 49	20 59							21 18	21 29						21 48
Chichester 4	a				20 27				20 35			20 58					21 04			21 25				21 34	
	d				20 27				20 36			20 59					21 05			21 26				21 35	
Fishbourne (Sussex)	d																21 08								
Bosham	d																21 11								
Nutbourne	d																21 14								
Southbourne	d								20 43								21 17							21 42	
Emsworth	d								20 46								21 20							21 45	
Warblington	d																21 23								
Havant	d				20 38				20 52			21 10					21 26			21 37				21 49	
Bedhampton	a																								
Hilsea	a																								
Fratton	a								21 01			21 18												21 58	
Portsmouth & Southsea	a								21 06			21 23												22 01	
Portsmouth Harbour	a											21 27												22 05	
Cosham	a				20 44												21 33			21 43					
Portchester	a				20 49												21 38								
Fareham	a				20 54												21 43			21 51					
Swanwick	a				21 01												21 49			21 58					
Eastleigh	a																								
Southampton Airport Parkway	a																								
Southampton Central	a				21 19												22 07			22 16					

A to Haywards Heath

Table 188

Mondays to Fridays

9 December to 16 May

London, Gatwick Airport, Brighton - Sussex Coast, Portsmouth and Southampton

Network Diagram - see first Page of Table 175

Station		SN	SN	SN	SN	SN 1	SN	SN 1		SN 1	SN	SN	SN	SN 1	SN	SN	SN	SN	SN 1	SN 1	SN	SN	SN
London Victoria 15 ⊖	d					20 17		20 32						20 47					21 17	21 32			
Clapham Junction 10	d					20 23		20 38						20 53					21 23	21 38			
London Bridge 4 ⊖	d																						
East Croydon	d					20 33		20 48						21 04					21 33	21 48			
Redhill 5	d							21 00												22 00			
Horley	d																						
Gatwick Airport 10 ✈	d					20 49		21 09						21 19					21 49	22 09			
Three Bridges 4	a							21 14											21 53	22 14			
	d							21 14											21 53	22 14			
Crawley	d							21 18												22 18			
Horsham 4	a							21 26												22 26			
	d							21 30	21 35											22 27			
Christs Hospital	d								21 38											22 30			
Billingshurst	d								21 44											22 36			
Pulborough	d								21 51											22 43			
Amberley	d								21 57											22 49			
Arundel	d								22 02											22 54			
Haywards Heath 3	d					21 04								21 34					22 06				
Burgess Hill	d					21 09								21 39					22 11				
Preston Park	d													21 49									
Brighton 10	d		21 03		21 14						21 33		21 44				22 03	22 14				22 33	
Hove 2	a		21 06		21 18	21 21					21 36		21 48	21 53			22 06	22 18	22 22			22 36	
	d		21 07			21 22					21 37			21 54			22 07		22 23			22 37	
Aldrington	d		21 09								21 39						22 09					22 39	
Portslade	d		21 11			21 25					21 41			21 57			22 11		22 26			22 41	
Fishersgate	d		21 13								21 43						22 13					22 43	
Southwick	d		21 15								21 45						22 15					22 45	
Shoreham-by-Sea	d		21 19			21 30					21 49			22 01			22 19		22 31			22 49	
Lancing	d		21 23			21 34					21 53			22 05			22 23		22 35			22 53	
East Worthing	d		21 26								21 56						22 26					22 56	
Worthing 4	a		21 28			21 38					21 58			22 09			22 28		22 39			22 58	
	d		21 29			21 38					21 59			22 10			22 29		22 39			22 59	
West Worthing	d		21 31			21 40					22 01			22 12			22 31		22 41			23 01	
Durrington-on-Sea	d		21 33			21 43					22 03			22 14			22 33		22 44			23 03	
Goring-by-Sea	d		21 36			21 45					22 06			22 17			22 36		22 46			23 06	
Angmering 3	d		21 40			21 49					22 10			22 21			22 40		22 50			23 10	
Littlehampton 4	a					21 58								22 30								23 18	
	d									22 08						22 38						23 23	
Ford 4	d		21 46						22 07	22 12	22 16					22 42	22 46		22 56	23 00		23 27	
Bognor Regis 4	d	21 39					22 00								22 30						23 15		
Barnham	a	21 45	21 50				22 06	21 56	22 11	22 16	22 20				22 36	22 46	22 50		23 01	23 04	23 21	23 31	
	d		21 51	21 52				21 57	22 12	22 17	22 21	22 22				22 52	22 51		23 06	23 05		23 32	23 36
Bognor Regis	a			22 00					22 18			22 30				23 00			23 13				23 44
Chichester 4	a		21 58					22 04		22 25	22 28						22 58			23 12		23 40	
	d		21 59					22 05			22 29						22 59			23 13			
Fishbourne (Sussex)	d							22 08												23 16			
Bosham	d							22 11												23 19			
Nutbourne	d							22 14												23 22			
Southbourne	d							22 17			22 36									23 25			
Emsworth	d							22 20			22 39									23 28			
Warblington	d							22 23												23 31			
Havant	d		22 10					22 26			22 43						23 11			23 34			
Bedhampton	a																						
Hilsea	a																						
Fratton	a		22 18								22 52						23 20			23 47			
Portsmouth & Southsea	a		22 22								22 55						23 23			23 54			
Portsmouth Harbour ⛴	a		22 26								22 59						23 27						
Cosham	a							22 33															
Portchester	a																						
Fareham	a							22 42															
Swanwick	a							22 49															
Eastleigh	a																						
Southampton Airport Parkway	a																						
Southampton Central ⛴	a							23 07															

Table 188

Mondays to Fridays

9 December to 16 May

London, Gatwick Airport, Brighton - Sussex Coast, Portsmouth and Southampton

Network Diagram - see first Page of Table 175

		SN	SN 1	SN	SN		SN 1	SN 1	SN	SN 1	SN 1
London Victoria 15 ⊖	d		21 47				22 17	22 32		22 47	23 17
Clapham Junction 10	d		21 53				22 23	22 38		22 53	23 23
London Bridge 4 ⊖	d										
East Croydon	d		22 03				22 34	22 48		23 03	23 33
Redhill 5	d							23 01			
Horley	d										
Gatwick Airport 10 ✈	d		22 19				22 49	23 09		23 19	23 51
Three Bridges 4	a						22 53	23 15			23 55
	d						22 53	23 16			23 56
Crawley	d							23 19			
Horsham 4	a							23 27			
	d							23 28			
Christs Hospital	d							23 31			
Billingshurst	d							23 37			
Pulborough	d							23 44			
Amberley	d							23 50			
Arundel	d							23 55			
Haywards Heath 3	d		22 37				23 03			23 37	00 05
Burgess Hill	d						23 08				00 11
Preston Park	d										
Brighton 10	d	22 44		23 04	23 14				23 44		
Hove 2	a	22 48	22 51	23 07	23 18		23 21		23 48	23 51	00 22
	d		22 52	23 08			23 22			23 52	00 22
Aldrington	d			23 10							
Portslade	d		22 55	23 12			23 25			23 55	00s25
Fishersgate	d			23 14							
Southwick	d			23 16			23 28			23 58	00s28
Shoreham-by-Sea	d		23 00	23 19			23 31			00 01	00s31
Lancing	d		23 04	23 23			23 35			00 05	00s35
East Worthing	d			23 26							
Worthing 4	a		23 08	23 29			23 39			00 11	00 41
	d		23 08	23 29			23 39				
West Worthing	d		23 10	23a32			23 41				
Durrington-on-Sea	d		23 13				23 44				
Goring-by-Sea	d		23 15				23 46				
Angmering 3	d		23 19				23 50				
Littlehampton 4	a		23 29								
	d										
Ford 4	d						23 56	00 01			
Bognor Regis 4	d										
Barnham	a						00 01	00 06			
	d						00 09	00 06			
Bognor Regis	a						00 16				
Chichester 4	a							00 14			
	d										
Fishbourne (Sussex)	d										
Bosham	d										
Nutbourne	d										
Southbourne	d										
Emsworth	d										
Warblington	d										
Havant	d										
Bedhampton	a										
Hilsea	a										
Fratton	a										
Portsmouth & Southsea	a										
Portsmouth Harbour ⛴	a										
Cosham	a										
Portchester	a										
Fareham	a										
Swanwick	a										
Eastleigh	a										
Southampton Airport Parkway	a										
Southampton Central ⛴	a										

Table 188

Saturdays

14 December to 17 May

London, Gatwick Airport, Brighton - Sussex Coast, Portsmouth and Southampton

Network Diagram - see first Page of Table 175

		SN 1	SN 1	SN 1	SN	SN	SN 1	SN 1	SN 1	SN		SN	SN 1	SN 1	SN 1	SN	SN 1	SN	SN	SN 1		SN	SN	SN	SN
London Victoria 15 ⊖	d							00 05																	
Clapham Junction 10	d							00 12																	
London Bridge 4 ⊖	d																								
East Croydon	d							00 27																	
Redhill 5	d																								
Horley	d																								
Gatwick Airport 10 ✈	d							00 46																	
Three Bridges 4	a							00 50																	
	d							00 50																	
Crawley	d																								
Horsham 4	a																								
	d																								
Christs Hospital	d																								
Billingshurst	d																								
Pulborough	d																								
Amberley	d																								
Arundel	d																								
Haywards Heath 3	d						00 05	01 03																	
Burgess Hill	d						00 11																		
Preston Park	d																								
Brighton 10	d				00 04	00 10		01s17									05 15			05 27		05 44	05 53		
Hove 2	a				00 07	00 14	00 22	01s25									05 18			05 30		05 48	05 56		
	d				00 08		00 22										05 20			05 31			05 57		
Aldrington	d				00 10															05 33			05 59		
Portslade	d				00 12		00s25	01s28									05 23			05 35			06 01		
Fishersgate	d				00 14															05 37			06 03		
Southwick	d				00 16		00s28	01s31												05 39			06 05		
Shoreham-by-Sea	d			00 01	00 19		00s31	01s34									05 27			05 43			06 09		
Lancing	d			00 05	00 23		00s35	01s38									05 31			05 47			06 13		
East Worthing	d				00 26															05 50			06 16		
Worthing 4	a			00 11	00 29		00 41	01 42									05 35			05 52			06 18		
	d				00 29												05 36			05 53			06 19		
West Worthing	d				00a31												05 38			05 55			06a21		
Durrington-on-Sea	d																05 40			05 57					
Goring-by-Sea	d																05 43			06 00					
Angmering 3	d																05 47			06 04					
Littlehampton 4	a																								
	d																	05 54							
Ford 4	d	00 01															05 53	05 58		06 10					
Bognor Regis 4	d											05 13				05 43			06 04					06 13	
Barnham	a	00 06										05 19				05 49	05 57	06 02	06 10	06 14				06 19	
	d	00 06	00 09						04 57	05 15			05 20	05 30	05 38		05 58	06 03		06 15					06 22
Bognor Regis	a		00 16																						06 29
Chichester 4	a	00 14							05 04	05 22			05 27	05 37	05 45		06 05	06 10		06 22					
	d								05 05	05 23			05 28	05 38	05 46		06 06	06 11		06 23					
Fishbourne (Sussex)	d																	06 14							
Bosham	d																06 10	06 17							
Nutbourne	d																	06 20							
Southbourne	d																06 15	06 23		06 30					
Emsworth	d																06 18	06 26		06 33					
Warblington	d																06 21	06 29							
Havant	d								05 16	05 34			05 39	05 49	05 57		06 24	06 32		06 37					
Bedhampton	a																	06 34							
Hilsea	a																	06 42							
Fratton	a									05 42				05 57	06 05			06 46							
Portsmouth & Southsea	a									05 46				06 01	06 09			06 50							
Portsmouth Harbour ⛴	a													06 05	06 16										
Cosham	a								05 22				05 49				06 30			06 45					
Portchester	a								05 27								06 34								
Fareham	a								05 32				05 57				06 39			06 53					
Swanwick	a								05 39				06 04				06 46								
Eastleigh	a																			07 10					
Southampton Airport Parkway	a																			07 17					
Southampton Central ⛴	a								05 58				06 24				07 05			07 27					

Table 188

Saturdays

14 December to 17 May

London, Gatwick Airport, Brighton - Sussex Coast, Portsmouth and Southampton

Network Diagram - see first Page of Table 175

		SN	SN 1	SN 1	SN	SN	SN	SN	SN 1		SN	SN 1	SN	SN 1	SN	SN	SN 1	SN	SN	SN 1	SN	SN	SN
London Victoria 15 ⊖	d																05 32						
Clapham Junction 10	d																05 38						
London Bridge 4 ⊖	d																						
East Croydon	d																05 48						
Redhill 5	d																06 07						
Horley	d																06 18						
Gatwick Airport 10 ✈	d								05 58								06 22						
Three Bridges 4	a								06 02								06 26						
	d								06 03								06 34						
Crawley	d								06 06								06 37						
Horsham 4	a								06 18								06 49						
	d								06 19								06 50						
Christs Hospital	d								06 22								06 53						
Billingshurst	d								06 28								06 59						
Pulborough	d								06 35								07 06						
Amberley	d								06 41								07 12						
Arundel	d								06 46								07 17						
Haywards Heath 3	d																						
Burgess Hill	d																						
Preston Park	d																						
Brighton 10	d			06 01	06 14	06 23								06 33	06 44			06 48	06 53		07 03	07 14	07 23
Hove 2	a			06 04	06 18	06 26								06 36	06 48			06 51	06 56		07 06	07 18	07 26
	d			06 05		06 27								06 37				06 52	06 57		07 07		07 27
Aldrington	d					06 29													06 59				07 29
Portslade	d			06 08		06 31								06 40				06 55	07 01		07 10		07 31
Fishersgate	d					06 33													07 03				07 33
Southwick	d			06 11		06 35								06 43					07 05		07 13		07 35
Shoreham-by-Sea	d			06 14		06 39								06 46				06 59	07 09		07 16		07 39
Lancing	d			06 18		06 43								06 50				07 03	07 13		07 20		07 43
East Worthing	d					06 46													07 16				07 46
Worthing 4	a			06 22		06 48								06 54				07 07	07 18		07 24		07 48
	d			06 23		06 49								06 55				07 08	07 19		07 25		07 49
West Worthing	d			06 25		06a51								06 57				07 10	07a21				07a51
Durrington-on-Sea	d			06 27										06 59				07 12					
Goring-by-Sea	d			06 30										07 02				07 15					
Angmering 3	d			06 34										07 06				07 19			07 31		
Littlehampton 4	a																	07 27					
	d	06 19									06 54					07 11							
Ford 4	d			06 40					06 52		06 58			07 12		07 16	07 22						
Bognor Regis 4	d		06 30				06 39					06 56	07 07							07 30			
Barnham	a	06 26	06 36	06 44			06 45		06 56		07 02	07 02	07 13	07 16		07 20	07 27			07 36	07 41		
	d	06 27		06 45				06 52	07 00	07 05	07 04			07 17		07 22	07 27				07 41		
Bognor Regis	a							06 59		07 12						07 29							
Chichester 4	a	06 34		06 52					07 07		07 11			07 24			07 35				07 49		
	d	06 35		06 53					07 08		07 12			07 25			07 35				07 49		
Fishbourne (Sussex)	d										07 15												
Bosham	d										07 18												
Nutbourne	d										07 21												
Southbourne	d								07 15		07 24										07 56		
Emsworth	d								07 18		07 27			07 33							07 59		
Warblington	d										07 30												
Havant	d	06 46		07 04					07 23		07 33			07 37			07 46				08 04		
Bedhampton	a										07 35												
Hilsea	a										07 42												
Fratton	a	06 54		07 12							07 46						07 55				08 12		
Portsmouth & Southsea	a	06 58		07 16							07 50						07 58				08 16		
Portsmouth Harbour ⛴	a	07 02		07 20													08 02				08 20		
Cosham	a								07 29					07 45									
Portchester	a								07 34														
Fareham	a								07 39					07 53									
Swanwick	a								07 45														
Eastleigh	a													08 10									
Southampton Airport Parkway	a													08 17									
Southampton Central ⛴	a								08 03					08 26									

Table 188

Saturdays

14 December to 17 May

London, Gatwick Airport, Brighton - Sussex Coast, Portsmouth and Southampton

Network Diagram - see first Page of Table 175

		SN		SN	SN 1	SN	SN 1	SN	SN 1	SN	SN	SN 1		SN 1	SN	SN 1	SN	SN	SN	SN	SN	SN		SN 1	
London Victoria 15 ⊖	d				06 02							06 32													
Clapham Junction 10	d				06 08							06 38													
London Bridge 4 ⊖	d																								
East Croydon	d				06 18							06 48													
Redhill 5	d				06 46							07 10													
Horley	d				06 55							07 19													
Gatwick Airport 10 ✈	d				06 59							07 24													
Three Bridges 4	a				07 03							07 29													
	d				07 04							07 30													
Crawley	d				07 07							07 33													
Horsham 4	a				07 19							07 45													
	d				07 20							07 50													
Christs Hospital	d				07 23							07 53													
Billingshurst	d				07 29							07 59													
Pulborough	d				07 36							08 06													
Amberley	d				07 42							08 12													
Arundel	d				07 47							08 17													
Haywards Heath 3	d													07 37											
Burgess Hill	d																								
Preston Park	d																								
Brighton 10	d								07 33	07 44					07 53		08 03	08 14	08 23						
Hove 2	a								07 36	07 48				07 51	07 56		08 06	08 18	08 26						
	d								07 37					07 52	07 57		08 07		08 27						
Aldrington	d														07 59				08 29						
Portslade	d								07 40						08 01		08 10		08 31						
Fishersgate	d														08 03				08 33						
Southwick	d								07 43						08 05		08 13		08 35						
Shoreham-by-Sea	d								07 46					07 58	08 09		08 16		08 39						
Lancing	d								07 50					08 02	08 13		08 20		08 43						
East Worthing	d														08 16				08 46						
Worthing 4	a								07 54					08 06	08 18		08 24		08 48						
	d								07 55					08 07	08 19		08 25		08 49						
West Worthing	d								07 57					08 09	08a21				08a51						
Durrington-on-Sea	d								07 59					08 11											
Goring-by-Sea	d								08 02					08 14											
Angmering 3	d								08 06					08 18			08 31								
Littlehampton 4	a													08 27											
	d					07 54					08 11											08 54			
Ford 4	d				07 53	07 58			08 12		08 16	08 22										08 58			
Bognor Regis 4	d	07 39					07 56	08 07								08 30				08 39				08 56	
Barnham	a	07 45			07 57	08 02	08 02	08 13	08 16		08 20	08 27				08 36	08 41			08 45		09 02		09 02	
	d			07 52	07 58	08 03			08 17		08 22	08 27					08 41				08 52	09 03			
Bognor Regis	a			07 59							08 29										08 59				
Chichester 4	a				08 05	08 10			08 24			08 35					08 49					09 10			
	d				08 06	08 11			08 25			08 35					08 49					09 11			
Fishbourne (Sussex)	d					08 14																09 14			
Bosham	d					08 17																09 17			
Nutbourne	d					08 20																09 20			
Southbourne	d				08 13	08 23											08 56					09 23			
Emsworth	d				08 16	08 26			08 33								08 59					09 26			
Warblington	d					08 29																09 29			
Havant	d				08 20	08 32			08 37			08 46					09 04					09 32			
Bedhampton	a					08 34																09 34			
Hilsea	a					08 42																09 42			
Fratton	a					08 46						08 55					09 12					09 46			
Portsmouth & Southsea	a					08 50						08 58					09 16					09 50			
Portsmouth Harbour ⛴	a											09 02					09 20								
Cosham	a				08 28				08 45																
Portchester	a				08 32																				
Fareham	a				08 37				08 53																
Swanwick	a				08 44				09 00																
Eastleigh	a																								
Southampton Airport Parkway	a																								
Southampton Central ⛴	a				09 01				09 19																

Table 188

Saturdays

14 December to 17 May

London, Gatwick Airport, Brighton - Sussex Coast, Portsmouth and Southampton

Network Diagram - see first Page of Table 175

		SN 1		SN	SN 1	SN	SN	SN 1	SN		SN 1	SN 1		GW ◇	SN	SN	SN 1	SN	SN		SN	SN	SN 1	SN 1	
London Victoria 15 ⊖	d		07 32					07 47					08 02				08 17								08 32
Clapham Junction 10	d		07 38					07 53					08 08				08 23								08 38
London Bridge 4 ⊖	d																								
East Croydon	d		07 48					08 03					08 18				08 33								08 48
Redhill 5	d		08 00										08 30												09 00
Horley	d												08 36												
Gatwick Airport 10 ✈	d		08 09					08 20					08 40				08 50								09 09
Three Bridges 4	a		08 14										08 44												09 14
	d		08 14										08 45												09 14
Crawley	d		08 18										08 48												09 18
Horsham 4	a		08 26										08 56												09 26
	d	08 30	08 35									09 00	09 05											09 30	09 35
Christs Hospital	d		08 38																						09 38
Billingshurst	d		08 44										09 13												09 44
Pulborough	d		08 51										09 19												09 51
Amberley	d		08 57																						09 57
Arundel	d		09 02										09 28												10 02
Haywards Heath 3	d							08 37									09 04								
Burgess Hill	d																09 09								
Preston Park	d																09 18								
Brighton 10	d				08 33	08 44			08 53					09 00	09 03	09 14		09 23							
Hove 2	a				08 36	08 48		08 53	08 56					09 03	09 06	09 18	09 22	09 26							
	d				08 37			08 53	08 57					09 04	09 07		09 22	09 27							
Aldrington	d								08 59									09 29							
Portslade	d				08 40				09 01						09 10		09 25	09 31							
Fishersgate	d								09 03									09 33							
Southwick	d				08 43				09 05						09 13			09 35							
Shoreham-by-Sea	d				08 46			09 00	09 09					09 13	09 17		09 30	09 39							
Lancing	d				08 50			09 04	09 13						09 21			09 43							
East Worthing	d								09 16									09 46							
Worthing 4	a				08 54			09 08	09 18					09 22	09 26		09 36	09 48							
	d				08 55			09 08	09 19					09 22	09 26		09 37	09 49							
West Worthing	d				08 57			09 10	09a21								09 39	09a51							
Durrington-on-Sea	d				08 59			09 13									09 41								
Goring-by-Sea	d				09 02			09 15									09 44								
Angmering 3	d				09 06			09 19							09 34		09 48								
Littlehampton 4	a							09 28									09 57								
	d						09 11															09 54			
Ford 4	d		09 07		09 12		09 16						09 33									09 58			10 07
Bognor Regis 4	d			09 07							09 30								09 39				09 56		
Barnham	a	08 56	09 11	09 13	09 16		09 20				09 36	09 26	09 38	09 40	09 44				09 45			10 02	10 02	09 56	10 11
	d	08 57	09 12		09 17		09 22					09 27	09 38	09 41	09 45						09 52	10 03		09 57	10 12
Bognor Regis	a		09 18				09 29						09 45								09 59				10 18
Chichester 4	a	09 04			09 24							09 34		09 48	09 52							10 10		10 04	
	d	09 05			09 25							09 35		09 49	09 53							10 11		10 05	
Fishbourne (Sussex)	d																					10 14			
Bosham	d																					10 17			
Nutbourne	d																					10 20			
Southbourne	d	09 12													10 00							10 23		10 12	
Emsworth	d	09 15			09 33										10 03							10 26		10 15	
Warblington	d																					10 29			
Havant	d	09 19			09 37							09 46		10 00	10 07							10 32		10 19	
Bedhampton	a																					10 34			
Hilsea	a																					10 43			
Fratton	a											09 54			10 16							10 47			
Portsmouth & Southsea	a											09 58			10 19							10 50			
Portsmouth Harbour ⛴	a											10 02			10 23										
Cosham	a	09 26			09 45									10 06										10 26	
Portchester	a	09 30																						10 30	
Fareham	a	09 35			09 53									10 15										10 35	
Swanwick	a	09 42																						10 42	
Eastleigh	a				10 10																				
Southampton Airport Parkway	a				10 17																				
Southampton Central ⛴	a	09 59			10 27									10 40										10 59	

Table 188

Saturdays

14 December to 17 May

London, Gatwick Airport, Brighton - Sussex Coast, Portsmouth and Southampton

Network Diagram - see first Page of Table 175

		SN	SN 1	SN	SN	SN 1	SN	SN 1	SN 1		SN	SN	SN 1	SN	SN	SN	SN	SN 1	SN 1		SN	SN 1	SN
London Victoria 15 ⊖	d					08 47			09 02				09 17						09 32				
Clapham Junction 10	d					08 53			09 08				09 23						09 38				
London Bridge 4 ⊖	d																						
East Croydon	d					09 03			09 18				09 33						09 48				
Redhill 5	d								09 30										10 00				
Horley	d								09 36														
Gatwick Airport 10 ✈	d					09 20			09 40				09 50						10 09				
Three Bridges 4	a								09 44										10 14				
	d								09 45										10 14				
Crawley	d								09 48										10 18				
Horsham 4	a								09 56										10 26				
	d								10 00	10 05									10 30	10 35			
Christs Hospital	d																			10 38			
Billingshurst	d									10 14										10 44			
Pulborough	d									10 20										10 51			
Amberley	d																			10 57			
Arundel	d									10 29										11 02			
Haywards Heath 3	d					09 37							10 04										
Burgess Hill	d												10 09										
Preston Park	d												10 18										
Brighton 10	d		09 33	09 44			09 53				10 03	10 14		10 23								10 33	10 44
Hove 2	a		09 36	09 48		09 53	09 56				10 06	10 18	10 22	10 26								10 36	10 48
	d		09 37			09 53	09 57				10 07		10 22	10 27								10 37	
Aldrington	d						09 59							10 29									
Portslade	d		09 40				10 01				10 10		10 25	10 31								10 40	
Fishersgate	d						10 03							10 33									
Southwick	d		09 43				10 05				10 13			10 35								10 43	
Shoreham-by-Sea	d		09 46			10 00	10 09				10 16		10 30	10 39								10 46	
Lancing	d		09 50			10 04	10 13				10 20			10 43								10 50	
East Worthing	d						10 16							10 46									
Worthing 4	a		09 54			10 08	10 18				10 24		10 36	10 48								10 54	
	d		09 55			10 08	10 19				10 25		10 37	10 49								10 55	
West Worthing	d		09 57			10 10	10a21						10 39	10a51								10 57	
Durrington-on-Sea	d		09 59			10 13							10 41									10 59	
Goring-by-Sea	d		10 02			10 15							10 44									11 02	
Angmering 3	d		10 06			10 19					10 31		10 48									11 06	
Littlehampton 4	a					10 28							10 57										
	d				10 11												10 54						
Ford 4	d		10 12		10 16					10 34							10 58			11 07		11 12	
Bognor Regis 4	d	10 07						10 30							10 39			10 56			11 07		
Barnham	a	10 13	10 16		10 20			10 36	10 26	10 39	10 42				10 45		11 02	11 02	10 56	11 11	11 13	11 16	
	d		10 17		10 22				10 27	10 39	10 42					10 52	11 03		10 57	11 12		11 17	
Bognor Regis	a				10 29					10 46						10 59				11 18			
Chichester 4	a		10 24						10 34		10 50						11 10		11 04			11 24	
	d		10 25						10 35		10 50						11 11		11 05			11 25	
Fishbourne (Sussex)	d																11 14						
Bosham	d																11 17						
Nutbourne	d																11 20						
Southbourne	d										10 57						11 23		11 12				
Emsworth	d		10 33								11 00						11 26		11 15			11 33	
Warblington	d																11 29						
Havant	d		10 37						10 46		11 05						11 32		11 19			11 37	
Bedhampton	a																11 34						
Hilsea	a																11 42						
Fratton	a								10 54		11 13						11 46						
Portsmouth & Southsea	a								10 58		11 17						11 50						
Portsmouth Harbour ⛴	a								11 02		11 21												
Cosham	a		10 45																11 26			11 45	
Portchester	a																		11 30				
Fareham	a		10 53																11 35			11 53	
Swanwick	a		11 00																11 42				
Eastleigh	a																					12 10	
Southampton Airport Parkway	a																					12 18	
Southampton Central ⛴	a		11 19																11 59			12 27	

Table 188

Saturdays

14 December to 17 May

London, Gatwick Airport, Brighton - Sussex Coast, Portsmouth and Southampton

Network Diagram - see first Page of Table 175

		SN	SN 1	SN	SN 1	SN 1		SN	SN	SN 1	SN	SN	SN	SN	SN 1	SN 1		SN	SN 1	SN	SN	SN 1
London Victoria 15 ⊖	d		09 47			10 02				10 17						10 32						10 47
Clapham Junction 10	d		09 53			10 08				10 23						10 38						10 53
London Bridge 4 ⊖	d																					
East Croydon	d		10 03			10 18				10 33						10 48						11 03
Redhill 5	d					10 30										11 00						
Horley	d					10 36																
Gatwick Airport 10 ✈	d		10 20			10 40				10 50						11 09						11 20
Three Bridges 4	a					10 44										11 14						
	d					10 45										11 14						
Crawley	d					10 48										11 18						
Horsham 4	a					10 56										11 26						
	d					11 00	11 05									11 30	11 35					
Christs Hospital	d																11 38					
Billingshurst	d						11 14										11 44					
Pulborough	d						11 20										11 51					
Amberley	d																11 57					
Arundel	d						11 29										12 02					
Haywards Heath 3	d		10 37							11 04												11 37
Burgess Hill	d									11 09												
Preston Park	d									11 18												
Brighton 10	d			10 53				11 03	11 14		11 23								11 33	11 44		
Hove 2	a		10 53	10 56				11 06	11 18	11 22	11 26								11 36	11 48		11 53
	d		10 53	10 57				11 07		11 22	11 27								11 37			11 53
Aldrington	d			10 59							11 29											
Portslade	d			11 01				11 10		11 25	11 31								11 40			
Fishersgate	d			11 03							11 33											
Southwick	d			11 05				11 13			11 35								11 43			
Shoreham-by-Sea	d		11 00	11 09				11 16		11 30	11 39								11 46			12 00
Lancing	d		11 04	11 13				11 20			11 43								11 50			12 04
East Worthing	d			11 16							11 46											
Worthing 4	a		11 08	11 18				11 24		11 36	11 48								11 54			12 08
	d		11 08	11 19				11 25		11 37	11 49								11 55			12 08
West Worthing	d		11 10	11a21						11 39	11a51								11 57			12 10
Durrington-on-Sea	d		11 13							11 41									11 59			12 13
Goring-by-Sea	d		11 15							11 44									12 02			12 15
Angmering 3	d		11 19					11 31		11 48									12 06			12 19
Littlehampton 4	a		11 28							11 57												12 28
	d	11 11												11 54							12 11	
Ford 4	d	11 16					11 34							11 58			12 07		12 12		12 16	
Bognor Regis 4	d				11 30							11 39			11 56			12 07				
Barnham	a	11 20			11 36	11 26	11 39	11 42				11 45		12 02	12 02	11 56	12 11	12 13	12 16		12 20	
	d	11 22				11 27	11 39	11 42					11 52	12 03		11 57	12 12		12 17		12 22	
Bognor Regis	a	11 29					11 46						11 59				12 18				12 29	
Chichester 4	a					11 34		11 50						12 10		12 04			12 24			
	d					11 35		11 50						12 11		12 05			12 25			
Fishbourne (Sussex)	d													12 14								
Bosham	d													12 17								
Nutbourne	d													12 20								
Southbourne	d							11 57						12 23		12 12						
Emsworth	d							12 00						12 26		12 15			12 33			
Warblington	d													12 29								
Havant	d					11 46		12 05						12 32		12 19			12 37			
Bedhampton	a													12 34								
Hilsea	a													12 42								
Fratton	a					11 54		12 13						12 46								
Portsmouth & Southsea	a					11 58		12 17						12 50								
Portsmouth Harbour ⛴	a					12 02		12 21														
Cosham	a															12 26			12 45			
Portchester	a															12 30						
Fareham	a															12 35			12 53			
Swanwick	a															12 42			13 00			
Eastleigh	a																					
Southampton Airport Parkway	a																					
Southampton Central ⛴	a															12 59			13 19			

Table 188

Saturdays

14 December to 17 May

London, Gatwick Airport, Brighton - Sussex Coast, Portsmouth and Southampton

Network Diagram - see first Page of Table 175

Station		SN	SN 1	SN 1		SN	SN		SN 1	SN	SN	SN	SN	SN 1	SN 1		SN		SN 1	SN	SN	SN 1	SN	SN 1	
London Victoria 15 ⊖	d			11 02					11 17						11 32							11 47			
Clapham Junction 10	d			11 08					11 23						11 38							11 53			
London Bridge 4 ⊖	d																								
East Croydon	d			11 18					11 33						11 48							12 03			
Redhill 5	d			11 30											12 00										
Horley	d			11 36																					
Gatwick Airport 10 ✈	d			11 40					11 50						12 09							12 20			
Three Bridges 4	a			11 44											12 14										
	d			11 45											12 14										
Crawley	d			11 48											12 18										
Horsham 4	a			11 56											12 26										
	d			12 00	12 05										12 30	12 35									
Christs Hospital	d															12 38									
Billingshurst	d				12 14											12 44									
Pulborough	d				12 20											12 51									
Amberley	d															12 57									
Arundel	d				12 29											13 02									
Haywards Heath 3	d								12 04													12 37			
Burgess Hill	d								12 09																
Preston Park	d								12 18																
Brighton 10	d	11 53				12 03	12 14			12 23									12 33	12 44			12 53		
Hove 2	a	11 56				12 06	12 18		12 22	12 26									12 36	12 48		12 53	12 56		
	d	11 57				12 07			12 22	12 27									12 37			12 53	12 57		
Aldrington	d	11 59								12 29													12 59		
Portslade	d	12 01				12 10			12 25	12 31									12 40				13 01		
Fishersgate	d	12 03								12 33													13 03		
Southwick	d	12 05				12 13				12 35									12 43				13 05		
Shoreham-by-Sea	d	12 09				12 16			12 30	12 39									12 46			13 00	13 09		
Lancing	d	12 13				12 20				12 43									12 50			13 04	13 13		
East Worthing	d	12 16								12 46													13 16		
Worthing 4	a	12 18				12 24			12 36	12 48									12 54			13 08	13 18		
	d	12 19				12 25			12 37	12 49									12 55			13 08	13 19		
West Worthing	d	12a21							12 39	12a51									12 57			13 10	13a21		
Durrington-on-Sea	d								12 41										12 59			13 13			
Goring-by-Sea	d								12 44										13 02			13 15			
Angmering 3	d					12 31			12 48										13 06			13 19			
Littlehampton 4	a								12 57													13 28			
	d												12 54								13 11				
Ford 4	d				12 34								12 58			13 07			13 12		13 16				
Bognor Regis 4	d		12 30								12 39			12 56			13 07							13 30	
Barnham	a		12 36	12 26	12 39	12 42					12 45		13 02	13 02	12 56	13 11	13 13		13 16		13 20			13 36	
	d			12 27	12 39	12 42						12 52	13 03		12 57	13 12			13 17		13 22				
Bognor Regis	a				12 46							12 59				13 18					13 29				
Chichester 4	a			12 34		12 50							13 10		13 04				13 24						
	d			12 35		12 50							13 11		13 05				13 25						
Fishbourne (Sussex)	d												13 14												
Bosham	d												13 17												
Nutbourne	d												13 20												
Southbourne	d					12 57							13 23		13 12										
Emsworth	d					13 00							13 26		13 15				13 33						
Warblington	d												13 29												
Havant	d			12 46		13 05							13 32		13 19				13 37						
Bedhampton	a												13 34												
Hilsea	a												13 42												
Fratton	a			12 54		13 13							13 46												
Portsmouth & Southsea	a			12 58		13 17							13 50												
Portsmouth Harbour ⛴	a			13 02		13 21																			
Cosham	a														13 26				13 45						
Portchester	a														13 30										
Fareham	a														13 35				13 53						
Swanwick	a														13 42				14 00						
Eastleigh	a																								
Southampton Airport Parkway	a																								
Southampton Central ⛴	a														13 59				14 19						

Table 188

Saturdays

14 December to 17 May

London, Gatwick Airport, Brighton - Sussex Coast, Portsmouth and Southampton

Network Diagram - see first Page of Table 175

Station		SN 1		SN	SN	SN 1	SN	SN	SN	SN	SN 1	SN 1		SN	SN 1	SN	SN	SN 1	SN	SN 1	SN 1	
London Victoria 15 ⊖	d	12 02				12 17						12 32						12 47			13 02	
Clapham Junction 10	d	12 08				12 23						12 38						12 53			13 08	
London Bridge 4 ⊖	d																					
East Croydon	d	12 18				12 33						12 48						13 03			13 18	
Redhill 5	d	12 30										13 00									13 30	
Horley	d	12 36																			13 36	
Gatwick Airport 10 ✈	d	12 40				12 50						13 09						13 20			13 40	
Three Bridges 4	a	12 44										13 14									13 44	
	d	12 45										13 14									13 45	
Crawley	d	12 48										13 18									13 48	
Horsham 4	a	12 56										13 26									13 56	
	d	13 00	13 05									13 30	13 35								14 00	14 05
Christs Hospital	d												13 38									
Billingshurst	d		13 14										13 44									14 14
Pulborough	d		13 20										13 51									14 20
Amberley	d												13 57									
Arundel	d		13 29										14 02									14 29
Haywards Heath 3	d					13 04												13 37				
Burgess Hill	d					13 09																
Preston Park	d					13 18																
Brighton 10	d			13 03	13 14		13 23								13 33	13 44			13 53			
Hove 2	a			13 06	13 18	13 22	13 26								13 36	13 48		13 53	13 56			
	d			13 07		13 22	13 27								13 37			13 53	13 57			
Aldrington	d						13 29												13 59			
Portslade	d			13 10		13 25	13 31								13 40				14 01			
Fishersgate	d						13 33												14 03			
Southwick	d			13 13			13 35								13 43				14 05			
Shoreham-by-Sea	d			13 16		13 30	13 39								13 46			14 00	14 09			
Lancing	d			13 20			13 43								13 50			14 04	14 13			
East Worthing	d						13 46												14 16			
Worthing 4	a			13 24		13 36	13 48								13 54			14 08	14 18			
	d			13 25		13 37	13 49								13 55			14 08	14 19			
West Worthing	d					13 39	13a51								13 57			14 10	14a21			
Durrington-on-Sea	d					13 41									13 59			14 13				
Goring-by-Sea	d					13 44									14 02			14 15				
Angmering 3	d			13 31		13 48									14 06			14 19				
Littlehampton 4	a					13 57												14 28				
	d									13 54							14 11					
Ford 4	d		13 34							13 58			14 07		14 12		14 16					14 34
Bognor Regis 4	d							13 39			13 56			14 07						14 30		
Barnham	a	13 26	13 39	13 42				13 45		14 02	14 02	13 56	14 11	14 13	14 16		14 20			14 36	14 26	14 39
	d	13 27	13 39	13 42					13 52	14 03		13 57	14 12		14 17		14 22				14 27	14 39
Bognor Regis	a		13 46						13 59				14 18				14 29					14 46
Chichester 4	a	13 34		13 50						14 10		14 04			14 24						14 34	
	d	13 35		13 50						14 11		14 05			14 25						14 35	
Fishbourne (Sussex)	d									14 14												
Bosham	d									14 17												
Nutbourne	d									14 20												
Southbourne	d			13 57						14 23		14 12										
Emsworth	d			14 00						14 26		14 15			14 33							
Warblington	d									14 29												
Havant	d	13 46		14 05						14 32		14 19			14 37						14 46	
Bedhampton	a									14 34												
Hilsea	a									14 42												
Fratton	a	13 54		14 13						14 46											14 54	
Portsmouth & Southsea	a	13 58		14 17						14 50											14 58	
Portsmouth Harbour ⛴	a	14 02		14 21																	15 02	
Cosham	a											14 26			14 45							
Portchester	a											14 30										
Fareham	a											14 35			14 53							
Swanwick	a											14 42			15 00							
Eastleigh	a																					
Southampton Airport Parkway	a																					
Southampton Central ⛴	a											14 59			15 19							

Table 188

Saturdays

14 December to 17 May

London, Gatwick Airport, Brighton - Sussex Coast, Portsmouth and Southampton

Network Diagram - see first Page of Table 175

		SN	SN	SN 1	SN	SN	SN	SN	SN 1	SN 1			SN	SN 1	SN	SN	SN 1	SN	SN 1	SN 1			SN	SN	SN 1
London Victoria 15 ⊖	d			13 17						13 32							13 47			14 02					14 17
Clapham Junction 10	d			13 23						13 38							13 53			14 08					14 23
London Bridge 4 ⊖	d																								
East Croydon	d			13 33						13 48							14 03			14 18					14 33
Redhill 5	d									14 00										14 30					
Horley	d																			14 36					
Gatwick Airport 10 ✈	d			13 50						14 09							14 20			14 40					14 50
Three Bridges 4	a									14 14										14 44					
	d									14 14										14 45					
Crawley	d									14 18										14 48					
Horsham 4	a									14 26										14 56					
	d									14 30	14 35									15 00	15 05				
Christs Hospital	d										14 38														
Billingshurst	d										14 44										15 14				
Pulborough	d										14 51										15 20				
Amberley	d										14 57														
Arundel	d										15 02										15 29				
Haywards Heath 3	d			14 04													14 37								15 04
Burgess Hill	d			14 09																					15 09
Preston Park	d			14 18																					15 18
Brighton 10	d	14 03	14 14		14 23									14 33	14 44			14 53					15 03	15 14	
Hove 2	a	14 06	14 18	14 22	14 26									14 36	14 48		14 53	14 56					15 06	15 18	15 22
	d	14 07		14 22	14 27									14 37			14 53	14 57					15 07		15 22
Aldrington	d				14 29													14 59							
Portslade	d	14 10		14 25	14 31									14 40				15 01					15 10		15 25
Fishersgate	d				14 33													15 03							
Southwick	d	14 13			14 35									14 43				15 05					15 13		
Shoreham-by-Sea	d	14 16		14 30	14 39									14 46			15 00	15 09					15 16		15 30
Lancing	d	14 20			14 43									14 50			15 04	15 13					15 20		
East Worthing	d				14 46													15 16							
Worthing 4	a	14 24		14 36	14 48									14 54			15 08	15 18					15 24		15 36
	d	14 25		14 37	14 49									14 55			15 08	15 19					15 25		15 37
West Worthing	d			14 39	14a51									14 57			15 10	15a21							15 39
Durrington-on-Sea	d			14 41										14 59			15 13								15 41
Goring-by-Sea	d			14 44										15 02			15 15								15 44
Angmering 3	d	14 31		14 48										15 06			15 19						15 31		15 48
Littlehampton 4	a			14 57													15 28								15 58
	d							14 54								15 11									
Ford 4	d							14 58			15 07			15 12		15 16					15 34				
Bognor Regis 4	d					14 39			14 56				15 07						15 30						
Barnham	a	14 42				14 45		15 02	15 02	14 56	15 11		15 13	15 16		15 20			15 36	15 26	15 39		15 42		
	d	14 42					14 52	15 03		14 57	15 12			15 17		15 22				15 27	15 39		15 42		
Bognor Regis	a						14 59				15 18					15 29					15 46				
Chichester 4	a	14 50						15 10		15 04				15 24						15 34			15 50		
	d	14 50						15 11		15 05				15 25						15 35			15 50		
Fishbourne (Sussex)	d							15 14																	
Bosham	d							15 17																	
Nutbourne	d							15 20																	
Southbourne	d	14 57						15 23		15 12													15 57		
Emsworth	d	15 00						15 26		15 15				15 33									16 00		
Warblington	d							15 29																	
Havant	d	15 05						15 32		15 19				15 37						15 46			16 05		
Bedhampton	a							15 34																	
Hilsea	a							15 42																	
Fratton	a	15 13						15 46												15 54			16 13		
Portsmouth & Southsea	a	15 17						15 50												15 58			16 17		
Portsmouth Harbour ⛴	a	15 21																		16 02			16 21		
Cosham	a									15 26				15 45											
Portchester	a									15 30															
Fareham	a									15 35				15 53											
Swanwick	a									15 42															
Eastleigh	a													16 10											
Southampton Airport Parkway	a													16 17											
Southampton Central ⛴	a									15 59				16 27											

Table 188

Saturdays

14 December to 17 May

London, Gatwick Airport, Brighton - Sussex Coast, Portsmouth and Southampton

Network Diagram - see first Page of Table 175

		SN	SN	SN	SN	SN ■1	SN ■1		SN	SN ■1	SN	SN	SN ■1	SN	SN ■1	SN ■1		SN	SN	SN ■1	SN	SN	SN
London Victoria 15 ⊖	d						14 32						14 47			15 02				15 17			
Clapham Junction 10	d						14 38						14 53			15 08				15 23			
London Bridge 4 ⊖	d																						
East Croydon	d						14 48						15 03			15 18				15 33			
Redhill 5	d						15 00									15 30							
Horley	d															15 36							
Gatwick Airport 10 ✈	d						15 09						15 20			15 40				15 50			
Three Bridges 4	a						15 14									15 44							
	d						15 14									15 45							
Crawley	d						15 18									15 48							
Horsham 4	a						15 26									15 56							
	d						15 30	15 35								16 00	16 05						
Christs Hospital	d							15 38															
Billingshurst	d							15 44									16 14						
Pulborough	d							15 51									16 20						
Amberley	d							15 57															
Arundel	d							16 02									16 29						
Haywards Heath 3	d												15 37							16 04			
Burgess Hill	d																			16 09			
Preston Park	d																			16 18			
Brighton 10	d	15 23								15 33	15 44			15 53				16 03	16 14		16 23		
Hove 2	a	15 26								15 36	15 48		15 53	15 56				16 06	16 18	16 22	16 26		
	d	15 27								15 37			15 53	15 57				16 07		16 22	16 27		
Aldrington	d	15 29												15 59							16 29		
Portslade	d	15 31								15 40				16 01				16 10		16 25	16 31		
Fishersgate	d	15 33												16 03							16 33		
Southwick	d	15 35								15 43				16 05				16 13			16 35		
Shoreham-by-Sea	d	15 39								15 46			16 00	16 09				16 16		16 30	16 39		
Lancing	d	15 43								15 50			16 04	16 13				16 20			16 43		
East Worthing	d	15 46												16 16							16 46		
Worthing 4	a	15 48								15 54			16 08	16 18				16 24		16 36	16 48		
	d	15 49								15 55			16 08	16 19				16 25		16 37	16 49		
West Worthing	d	15a51								15 57			16 10	16a21						16 39	16a51		
Durrington-on-Sea	d									15 59			16 13							16 41			
Goring-by-Sea	d									16 02			16 15							16 44			
Angmering 3	d									16 06			16 19					16 31		16 48			
Littlehampton 4	a												16 28							16 57			
	d				15 54							16 11											
Ford 4	d				15 58			16 07		16 12		16 16					16 34						
Bognor Regis 4	d		15 39			15 56			16 07						16 30							16 39	
Barnham	a		15 45		16 02	16 02	15 56	16 11	16 13	16 16		16 20			16 36	16 26	16 39	16 42				16 45	
	d			15 52	16 03		15 57	16 12		16 17		16 22				16 27	16 39	16 42					16 52
Bognor Regis	a			15 59				16 18				16 29					16 46						16 59
Chichester 4	a				16 10		16 04			16 24						16 34		16 50					
	d				16 11		16 05			16 25						16 35		16 50					
Fishbourne (Sussex)	d				16 14																		
Bosham	d				16 17																		
Nutbourne	d				16 20																		
Southbourne	d				16 23		16 12											16 57					
Emsworth	d				16 26		16 15			16 33								17 00					
Warblington	d				16 29																		
Havant	d				16 32		16 19			16 37						16 46		17 05					
Bedhampton	a				16 34																		
Hilsea	a				16 42																		
Fratton	a				16 46											16 54		17 13					
Portsmouth & Southsea	a				16 50											16 58		17 17					
Portsmouth Harbour ⛴	a															17 02		17 22					
Cosham	a						16 26			16 45													
Portchester	a						16 30																
Fareham	a						16 35			16 53													
Swanwick	a						16 42			17 00													
Eastleigh	a																						
Southampton Airport Parkway	a																						
Southampton Central ⛴	a						16 59			17 19													

Table 188

Saturdays

14 December to 17 May

London, Gatwick Airport, Brighton - Sussex Coast, Portsmouth and Southampton

Network Diagram - see first Page of Table 175

Station		SN	SN 1	SN 1		SN	SN 1	SN	SN	SN 1	SN	SN 1	GW ◇	SN 1		SN	SN	SN 1	SN	SN	SN	SN	SN 1
London Victoria 15 ⊖	d			15 32						15 47				16 02				16 17					
Clapham Junction 10	d			15 38						15 53				16 08				16 23					
London Bridge 4 ⊖	d																						
East Croydon	d			15 48						16 03				16 18				16 33					
Redhill 5	d			16 00										16 30									
Horley	d													16 36									
Gatwick Airport 10 ✈	d			16 09						16 20				16 40				16 50					
Three Bridges 4	a			16 14										16 44									
	d			16 14										16 45									
Crawley	d			16 18										16 48									
Horsham 4	a			16 26										16 56									
	d			16 30	16 35									17 00	17 05								
Christs Hospital	d				16 38																		
Billingshurst	d				16 44										17 14								
Pulborough	d				16 51										17 20								
Amberley	d				16 57																		
Arundel	d				17 02										17 29								
Haywards Heath 3	d									16 37								17 04					
Burgess Hill	d																	17 09					
Preston Park	d																	17 18					
Brighton 10	d						16 33	16 44			16 53		17 00			17 03	17 14		17 23				
Hove 2	a						16 36	16 48		16 53	16 56		17 03			17 06	17 18	17 22	17 26				
	d						16 37			16 53	16 57		17 04			17 07		17 22	17 27				
Aldrington	d										16 59								17 29				
Portslade	d						16 40				17 01					17 10		17 25	17 31				
Fishersgate	d										17 03								17 33				
Southwick	d						16 43				17 05					17 13			17 35				
Shoreham-by-Sea	d						16 46			17 00	17 09		17 13			17 17		17 30	17 39				
Lancing	d						16 50			17 04	17 13					17 21			17 43				
East Worthing	d										17 16								17 46				
Worthing 4	a						16 54			17 08	17 18		17 22			17 25		17 36	17 48				
	d						16 55			17 08	17 19		17 22			17 25		17 37	17 49				
West Worthing	d						16 57			17 10	17a21							17 39	17a51				
Durrington-on-Sea	d						16 59			17 13								17 41					
Goring-by-Sea	d						17 02			17 15								17 44					
Angmering 3	d						17 06			17 19						17 34		17 48					
Littlehampton 4	a									17 28								17 57					
	d	16 54							17 11													17 54	
Ford 4	d	16 58			17 07		17 12		17 16						17 36							17 58	
Bognor Regis 4	d		16 56			17 07						17 30								17 39			17 56
Barnham	a	17 02	17 02	16 56	17 11	17 13	17 16		17 20			17 36	17 37	17 26	17 40	17 43				17 45		18 02	18 02
	d	17 03		16 57	17 12		17 17		17 22				17 38	17 27	17 41	17 44					17 52	18 03	
Bognor Regis	a				17 18				17 29						17 47						17 59		
Chichester 4	a	17 10		17 04			17 24						17 45	17 34		17 51						18 10	
	d	17 11		17 05			17 25						17 46	17 35		17 52						18 11	
Fishbourne (Sussex)	d	17 14																				18 14	
Bosham	d	17 17																				18 17	
Nutbourne	d	17 20																				18 20	
Southbourne	d	17 23		17 12												17 59						18 23	
Emsworth	d	17 26		17 15			17 33									18 02						18 26	
Warblington	d	17 29																				18 29	
Havant	d	17 32		17 19			17 37						18 00	17 46		18 06						18 32	
Bedhampton	a	17 34																				18 34	
Hilsea	a	17 42																				18 42	
Fratton	a	17 46												17 54		18 15						18 46	
Portsmouth & Southsea	a	17 50												17 58		18 18						18 50	
Portsmouth Harbour ⛴	a													18 02		18 22							
Cosham	a			17 26			17 45						18 06										
Portchester	a			17 30																			
Fareham	a			17 35			17 53						18 14										
Swanwick	a			17 42																			
Eastleigh	a						18 10																
Southampton Airport Parkway	a						18 17																
Southampton Central ⛴	a			17 59			18 27						18 43										

Table 188

Saturdays

14 December to 17 May

London, Gatwick Airport, Brighton - Sussex Coast, Portsmouth and Southampton

Network Diagram - see first Page of Table 175

		SN 1			SN	SN 1	SN	SN	SN 1	SN 1		SN	SN 1		SN	SN	SN 1	SN	SN	SN	SN	SN	SN 1		
London Victoria 15 ⊖	d	16 32							16 47	17 02							17 17						17 32		
Clapham Junction 10	d	16 38							16 53	17 08							17 23						17 38		
London Bridge 4 ⊖	d																								
East Croydon	d	16 48							17 03	17 18							17 33						17 48		
Redhill 5	d	17 00								17 30													18 00		
Horley	d									17 36															
Gatwick Airport 10 ✈	d	17 09							17 20	17 40							17 50						18 09		
Three Bridges 4	a	17 14								17 44													18 14		
	d	17 14								17 45													18 14		
Crawley	d	17 18								17 48													18 18		
Horsham 4	a	17 26								17 56													18 26		
	d	17 30	17 35							18 00	18 05												18 30	18 35	
Christs Hospital	d		17 38																					18 38	
Billingshurst	d		17 44								18 14													18 44	
Pulborough	d		17 51								18 20													18 51	
Amberley	d		17 57																					18 57	
Arundel	d		18 02								18 29													19 02	
Haywards Heath 3	d								17 37								18 04								
Burgess Hill	d																18 09								
Preston Park	d																18 18								
Brighton 10	d					17 33	17 44					17 53			18 03	18 14					18 23				
Hove 2	a					17 36	17 48		17 53			17 56			18 06	18 18	18 22				18 26				
	d					17 37			17 53			17 57			18 07		18 22				18 27				
Aldrington	d											17 59									18 29				
Portslade	d					17 40						18 01			18 10		18 25				18 31				
Fishersgate	d											18 03									18 33				
Southwick	d					17 43						18 05			18 13						18 35				
Shoreham-by-Sea	d					17 46			18 00			18 09			18 16		18 30				18 39				
Lancing	d					17 50			18 04			18 13			18 20						18 43				
East Worthing	d											18 16									18 46				
Worthing 4	a					17 54			18 08			18 18			18 24		18 36				18 48				
	d					17 55			18 08			18 19			18 25		18 37				18 49				
West Worthing	d					17 57			18 10			18a21					18 39				18 51				
Durrington-on-Sea	d					17 59			18 13								18 41				18 53				
Goring-by-Sea	d					18 02			18 15								18 44				18 56				
Angmering 3	d					18 06			18 19						18 31		18 48				19 00				
Littlehampton 4	a								18 28								18 57				19 11				
	d							18 11												18 54					
Ford 4	d		18 07			18 12		18 16			18 34									18 58				19 07	
Bognor Regis 4	d				18 07								18 33					18 39				19 03			
Barnham	a	17 56	18 11		18 13	18 16		18 20		18 26	18 39		18 40		18 42			18 46		19 02		19 09	18 56	19 11	
	d	17 57	18 12			18 17		18 22		18 27	18 39				18 42				18 52	19 03			18 57	19 12	
Bognor Regis	a		18 18					18 29			18 46								18 59					19 18	
Chichester 4	a	18 04				18 24				18 34					18 50					19 10			19 04		
	d	18 05				18 25				18 35					18 50					19 11			19 05		
Fishbourne (Sussex)	d																			19 14					
Bosham	d																			19 17					
Nutbourne	d																			19 20					
Southbourne	d	18 12													18 57					19 23			19 12		
Emsworth	d	18 15				18 33									19 00					19 26			19 15		
Warblington	d																			19 29					
Havant	d	18 19				18 37				18 46					19 05					19 32			19 19		
Bedhampton	a																			19 34					
Hilsea	a																			19 42					
Fratton	a									18 54					19 13					19 46					
Portsmouth & Southsea	a									18 58					19 17					19 50					
Portsmouth Harbour ⛴	a									19 02					19 21										
Cosham	a	18 26				18 45																	19 26		
Portchester	a	18 30																					19 30		
Fareham	a	18 35				18 53																	19 35		
Swanwick	a	18 42				19 00																	19 42		
Eastleigh	a																								
Southampton Airport Parkway	a																								
Southampton Central ⛴	a	18 59				19 19																	19 59		

Table 188

Saturdays

14 December to 17 May

London, Gatwick Airport, Brighton - Sussex Coast, Portsmouth and Southampton

Network Diagram - see first Page of Table 175

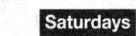

		SN 1	SN	SN	SN 1	SN 1		SN 1	SN	SN 1		SN	SN	SN 1	SN	SN 1		SN 1	SN	SN		SN 1	SN 1		SN 1
London Victoria 15 ⊖	d				17 47	18 02								18 17		18 32						18 47	19 02		
Clapham Junction 10	d				17 53	18 08								18 23		18 38						18 53	19 08		
London Bridge 4 ⊖	d																								
East Croydon	d				18 03	18 18								18 33		18 48						19 03	19 18		
Redhill 5	d					18 30										19 00							19 30		
Horley	d					18 36																	19 36		
Gatwick Airport 10 ✈	d				18 20	18 40								18 50		19 09						19 20	19 40		
Three Bridges 4	a					18 44										19 14							19 44		
	d					18 45										19 14							19 45		
Crawley	d					18 48										19 18							19 48		
Horsham 4	a					18 56										19 26							19 56		
	d					19 00	19 05									19 30	19 35						20 00	20 05	
Christs Hospital	d																19 38								
Billingshurst	d						19 14										19 44							20 14	
Pulborough	d						19 20										19 51							20 20	
Amberley	d																19 57								
Arundel	d						19 29										20 02							20 29	
Haywards Heath 3	d				18 37									19 04								19 37			
Burgess Hill	d													19 09											
Preston Park	d													19 18											
Brighton 10	d	18 33	18 44							19 03			19 14					19 29	19 44						
Hove 2	a	18 36	18 48		18 52					19 06			19 18	19 22				19 32	19 48			19 52			
	d	18 37			18 53					19 07				19 22				19 33				19 53			
Aldrington	d									19 09								19 35							
Portslade	d	18 40			18 56					19 11				19 25				19 37				19 56			
Fishersgate	d									19 13								19 39							
Southwick	d	18 43								19 15								19 41							
Shoreham-by-Sea	d	18 46			19 00					19 19				19 30				19 45				20 00			
Lancing	d	18 50			19 04					19 23				19 34				19 49				20 04			
East Worthing	d									19 26								19 52							
Worthing 4	a	18 54			19 08					19 28				19 38				19 54				20 08			
	d	18 55			19 09					19 29				19 39				19 55				20 09			
West Worthing	d	18 57			19 11					19 31				19 41				19 57				20 11			
Durrington-on-Sea	d	18 59			19 13					19 33				19 43				19 59				20 13			
Goring-by-Sea	d	19 02			19 16					19 36				19 46				20 02				20 16			
Angmering 3	d	19 06			19 20					19 40				19 50				20 06				20 20			
Littlehampton 4	a				19 28									19 58								20 28			
	d			19 11																20 11					
Ford 4	d	19 12		19 16			19 34			19 46							20 07	20 12		20 16				20 34	
Bognor Regis 4	d							19 33	19 39						20 04										20 33
Barnham	a	19 16		19 20		19 26	19 39	19 40	19 46	19 50					20 10	19 56	20 11	20 16		20 20			20 26	20 39	20 39
	d	19 17		19 22		19 27	19 39			19 51		19 52				19 57	20 12	20 17		20 22			20 27	20 39	
Bognor Regis	a			19 29			19 46					19 59					20 18			20 29				20 46	
Chichester 4	a	19 24				19 34				19 58						20 04		20 24					20 34		
	d	19 25				19 35				19 59						20 05		20 25					20 35		
Fishbourne (Sussex)	d															20 08									
Bosham	d															20 11									
Nutbourne	d															20 14									
Southbourne	d															20 17									
Emsworth	d	19 33														20 20		20 33							
Warblington	d															20 23									
Havant	d	19 37				19 46				20 10						20 26		20 37					20 46		
Bedhampton	a																								
Hilsea	a																								
Fratton	a					19 54				20 18													20 54		
Portsmouth & Southsea	a					19 58				20 22													20 58		
Portsmouth Harbour ⛴	a					20 02				20 26													21 02		
Cosham	a	19 45														20 32		20 45							
Portchester	a															20 36									
Fareham	a	19 53														20 41		20 53							
Swanwick	a															20 48		21 01							
Eastleigh	a	20 10																							
Southampton Airport Parkway	a	20 17																							
Southampton Central ⛴	a	20 27														21 05		21 19							

Table 188

Saturdays

14 December to 17 May

London, Gatwick Airport, Brighton - Sussex Coast, Portsmouth and Southampton

Network Diagram - see first Page of Table 175

		SN 1	SN	SN 1	SN	SN		SN	SN 1		SN	SN 1	SN	SN 1	SN 1			SN	SN	SN	SN	SN 1	SN	SN 1	
London Victoria 15 ⊖	d			19 17					19 32					19 47	20 02							20 17		20 32	
Clapham Junction 10	d			19 23					19 38					19 53	20 08							20 23		20 38	
London Bridge 4 ⊖	d																								
East Croydon	d			19 33					19 48					20 03	20 18							20 33		20 48	
Redhill 5	d								20 00						20 30									21 00	
Horley	d																								
Gatwick Airport 10 ✈	d			19 50					20 09					20 20	20 40							20 50		21 09	
Three Bridges 4	a								20 14						20 44									21 14	
	d								20 14						20 45									21 14	
Crawley	d								20 18						20 48									21 18	
Horsham 4	a								20 26						20 56									21 26	
	d								20 30	20 35					21 00	21 05								21 30	21 35
Christs Hospital	d									20 38						21 08									21 38
Billingshurst	d									20 44						21 14									21 44
Pulborough	d									20 51						21 21									21 51
Amberley	d									20 57						21 27									21 57
Arundel	d									21 02						21 32									22 02
Haywards Heath 3	d			20 04										20 37								21 05			
Burgess Hill	d			20 09																		21 10			
Preston Park	d			20 18																		21 19			
Brighton 10	d	19 56	20 14									20 30	20 44						21 03		21 14				
Hove 2	a	19 59	20 18	20 22								20 33	20 48	20 52					21 06		21 18	21 22			
	d	20 00		20 22								20 34		20 53					21 07			21 23			
Aldrington	d	20 02										20 36							21 09						
Portslade	d	20 04		20 25								20 38		20 56					21 11			21 26			
Fishersgate	d	20 06										20 40							21 13						
Southwick	d	20 08										20 42							21 15						
Shoreham-by-Sea	d	20 12		20 30								20 46		21 00					21 19			21 30			
Lancing	d	20 16		20 34								20 50		21 04					21 23			21 34			
East Worthing	d	20 19										20 53							21 26						
Worthing 4	a	20 21		20 38								20 55		21 08					21 28			21 38			
	d	20 22		20 39								20 56		21 09					21 29			21 39			
West Worthing	d	20 24		20 41								20 58		21 11					21 31			21 41			
Durrington-on-Sea	d	20 26		20 43								21 00		21 13					21 33			21 43			
Goring-by-Sea	d	20 29		20 46								21 03		21 16					21 36			21 46			
Angmering 3	d	20 33		20 50								21 07		21 20					21 40			21 50			
Littlehampton 4	a			20 58										21 28								21 58			
	d										21 07														
Ford 4	d	20 39								21 07	21 11	21 15				21 37			21 46						22 07
Bognor Regis 4	d				20 39			21 04										21 39					22 00		
Barnham	a	20 43			20 45			21 10	20 56	21 11	21 15	21 19			21 26	21 41		21 45	21 50				22 06	21 56	22 11
	d	20 44				20 52			20 57	21 12	21 22	21 20			21 27	21 42			21 51	21 52				21 57	22 12
Bognor Regis	a					20 59				21 18	21 29					21 48				21 59					22 18
Chichester 4	a	20 51							21 04			21 27			21 34				21 58					22 04	
	d	20 52							21 05			21 28			21 35				21 59					22 05	
Fishbourne (Sussex)	d	20 55																						22 08	
Bosham	d								21 09															22 11	
Nutbourne	d	21 00																						22 14	
Southbourne	d	21 02							21 14						21 42									22 17	
Emsworth	d	21 05							21 17			21 36			21 45									22 20	
Warblington	d								21 20															22 23	
Havant	d	21 10							21 23			21 40			21 49				22 10					22 26	
Bedhampton	a																								
Hilsea	a																								
Fratton	a	21 18													21 59				22 18						
Portsmouth & Southsea	a	21 22													22 02				22 22						
Portsmouth Harbour ⛴	a	21 26													22 06				22 26						
Cosham	a								21 29			21 46												22 33	
Portchester	a								21 33																
Fareham	a								21 38			21 54												22 41	
Swanwick	a								21 45			22 01												22 48	
Eastleigh	a																								
Southampton Airport Parkway	a																								
Southampton Central ⛴	a								22 02			22 20												23 05	

Table 188

Saturdays

14 December to 17 May

London, Gatwick Airport, Brighton - Sussex Coast, Portsmouth and Southampton

Network Diagram - see first Page of Table 175

		SN ■1		SN	SN	SN	SN ■1	SN	SN	SN	SN	SN ■1		SN ■1	SN	SN	SN	SN	SN ■1	SN	SN	SN ■1		SN ■1	SN
London Victoria 15 ⊖	d						20 47					21 17		21 32					21 47			22 17		22 32	
Clapham Junction 10	d						20 53					21 23		21 38					21 53			22 23		22 38	
London Bridge 4 ⊖	d																								
East Croydon	d						21 03					21 33		21 48					22 03			22 33		22 48	
Redhill 5	d													22 00										23 00	
Horley	d																								
Gatwick Airport 10 ✈	d						21 20					21 49		22 09					22 20			22 50		23 09	
Three Bridges 4	a											21 53		22 14								22 54		23 14	
	d											21 53		22 14								22 54		23 15	
Crawley	d													22 18										23 18	
Horsham 4	a													22 26										23 26	
	d													22 27										23 27	
Christs Hospital	d													22 30										23 30	
Billingshurst	d													22 36										23 36	
Pulborough	d													22 43										23 43	
Amberley	d													22 49										23 49	
Arundel	d													22 54										23 54	
Haywards Heath 3	d						21 37					22 06							22 37			23 03			
Burgess Hill	d											22 11										23 09			
Preston Park	d																								
Brighton 10	d			21 33		21 44				22 03	22 14					22 33		22 44		23 04	23 14				23 44
Hove 2	a			21 36		21 48	21 51			22 06	22 18	22 22				22 36		22 48	22 51	23 07	23 18	23 21			23 48
	d			21 37			21 52			22 07		22 23				22 37			22 52	23 08		23 22			
Aldrington	d			21 39						22 09						22 39				23 10					
Portslade	d			21 41			21 55			22 11		22 26				22 41			22 55	23 12		23 25			
Fishersgate	d			21 43						22 13						22 43				23 14					
Southwick	d			21 45						22 15						22 45				23 16		23 28			
Shoreham-by-Sea	d			21 49			22 00			22 19		22 31				22 49			23 00	23 19		23 31			
Lancing	d			21 53			22 04			22 23		22 35				22 53			23 04	23 23		23 35			
East Worthing	d			21 56						22 26						22 56				23 26					
Worthing 4	a			21 58			22 08			22 28		22 39				22 58			23 08	23 29		23 39			
	d			21 59			22 08			22 29		22 39				22 59			23 08	23 29		23 39			
West Worthing	d			22 01			22 10			22 31		22 41				23 01			23 10	23a31		23 41			
Durrington-on-Sea	d			22 03			22 13			22 33		22 44				23 03			23 13			23 44			
Goring-by-Sea	d			22 06			22 15			22 36		22 46				23 06			23 15			23 46			
Angmering 3	d			22 10			22 19			22 40		22 50				23 10			23 19			23 50			
Littlehampton 4	a						22 28									23 18			23 28						
	d	22 08							22 38							23 23									
Ford 4	d	22 12		22 16					22 42	22 46		22 56		23 00		23 27						23 56		23 59	
Bognor Regis 4	d							22 30							23 15										
Barnham	a	22 16		22 20				22 36	22 46	22 50		23 01		23 04	23 21	23 31						00 01		00 04	
	d	22 17		22 21	22 22				22 52	22 51		23 06		23 05		23 32	23 36					00 09		00 05	
Bognor Regis	a				22 29				22 59			23 12					23 43					00 15			
Chichester 4	a	22 24		22 28						22 58				23 12		23 39								00 12	
	d			22 29						22 59				23 13											
Fishbourne (Sussex)	d													23 16											
Bosham	d													23 19											
Nutbourne	d													23 22											
Southbourne	d			22 36										23 25											
Emsworth	d			22 39										23 28											
Warblington	d													23 31											
Havant	d			22 43						23 10				23 36											
Bedhampton	a																								
Hilsea	a																								
Fratton	a			22 52						23 18				23 48											
Portsmouth & Southsea	a			22 55						23 22				23 51											
Portsmouth Harbour ⛴	a			22 59						23 26															
Cosham	a																								
Portchester	a																								
Fareham	a																								
Swanwick	a																								
Eastleigh	a																								
Southampton Airport Parkway	a																								
Southampton Central ⛴	a																								

Table 188

Saturdays

14 December to 17 May

London, Gatwick Airport, Brighton - Sussex Coast, Portsmouth and Southampton

Network Diagram - see first Page of Table 175

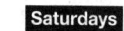

Station		SN 1	SN 1
London Victoria 15 ⊖	d	22 47	23 17
Clapham Junction 10	d	22 53	23 23
London Bridge 4 ⊖	d		
East Croydon	d	23 03	23 33
Redhill 5	d		
Horley	d		
Gatwick Airport 10 ✈	d	23 20	23 50
Three Bridges 4	a		23 54
	d		23 55
Crawley	d		
Horsham 4	a		
	d		
Christs Hospital	d		
Billingshurst	d		
Pulborough	d		
Amberley	d		
Arundel	d		
Haywards Heath 3	d	23 37	00 05
Burgess Hill	d		00 10
Preston Park	d		
Brighton 10	d		
Hove 2	a	23 51	00 23
	d	23 52	00 23
Aldrington	d		
Portslade	d	23 55	00s26
Fishersgate	d		
Southwick	d	23 58	00s29
Shoreham-by-Sea	d	00 01	00s32
Lancing	d	00 05	00s36
East Worthing	d		
Worthing 4	a	00 09	00s40
	d		
West Worthing	d		00s43
Durrington-on-Sea	d		00s45
Goring-by-Sea	d		00s48
Angmering 3	d		00s52
Littlehampton 4	a		
	d		
Ford 4	d		00s58
Bognor Regis 4	d		
Barnham	a		01s02
	d		
Bognor Regis	a		
Chichester 4	a		01 10
	d		
Fishbourne (Sussex)	d		
Bosham	d		
Nutbourne	d		
Southbourne	d		
Emsworth	d		
Warblington	d		
Havant	d		
Bedhampton	a		
Hilsea	a		
Fratton	a		
Portsmouth & Southsea	a		
Portsmouth Harbour ⛴	a		
Cosham	a		
Portchester	a		
Fareham	a		
Swanwick	a		
Eastleigh	a		
Southampton Airport Parkway	a		
Southampton Central ⛴	a		

Table 188

Sundays

8 December to 11 May

London, Gatwick Airport, Brighton - Sussex Coast, Portsmouth and Southampton

Network Diagram - see first Page of Table 175

		SN 1	SN	SN 1	SN 1	SN	SN 1	SN	SN 1	SN 1		SN 1	SN 1	SN 1	SN 1	SN 1	SN 1	SN 1	SN	SN 1		SN 1	SN 1	SN 1	SN 1
London Victoria 15 ⊖	d								00 05														07 02		
Clapham Junction 10	d								00 12														07 09		
London Bridge 4 ⊖	d																								
East Croydon	d								00 27														07 26		
Redhill 5	d																						07 41		
Horley	d																						07 47		
Gatwick Airport 10	d								00 46														07 51		
Three Bridges 4	a								00 50														07 55		
	d								00 50														07 55		
Crawley	d																						07 59		
Horsham 4	a																						08 11		
	d																						08 11		
Christs Hospital	d																								
Billingshurst	d																						08 19		
Pulborough	d																						08 26		
Amberley	d																								
Arundel	d																						08 35		
Haywards Heath 3	d						00 05		01 03																
Burgess Hill	d						00 10																		
Preston Park	d																								
Brighton 10	d		00 04			00 10			01s17							07 15		07 19	07 46					08 00	08 20
Hove 2	a		00 07			00 14	00 23		01s25							07 18		07 22	07 50					08 03	08 23
	d		00 08				00 23									07 19		07 23						08 04	08 24
Aldrington	d		00 10															07 25						08 06	
Portslade	d		00 12				00s26		01s28									07 27						08 08	
Fishersgate	d		00 14															07 29						08 10	
Southwick	d		00 16				00s29		01s31									07 31						08 12	
Shoreham-by-Sea	d	00 01	00 19				00s32		01s34							07 25		07 34						08 15	08 30
Lancing	d	00 05	00 23				00s36		01s38									07 38						08 19	
East Worthing	d		00 26															07 41						08 22	
Worthing 4	a	00 09	00 29				00s40		01 42							07 31		07 44						08 25	08 36
	d		00 29													07 31		07 44						08 25	08 36
West Worthing	d		00a31				00s43											07 46						08 27	
Durrington-on-Sea	d						00s45											07 48						08 30	
Goring-by-Sea	d						00s48											07 51						08 32	
Angmering 3	d						00s52									07 38		07 55						08 36	08 43
Littlehampton 4	a																								
	d									06 42			07 19		07 35		07 54								
Ford 4	d						00s58			06 46			07 23			07 44	07 58	08 01					08 40	08 43	08 49
Bognor Regis 4	d											06 52		07 34						07 59		08 20			
Barnham	a						01s02			06 50		06 58	07 27	07 40	07 43	07 49	08 02	08 05		08 05		08 26	08 44	08 48	08 53
	d			00 05	00 09			06 45		06 51			07 28		07 44	07 49	08 09	08 06					08 45	08 48	08 54
Bognor Regis	a				00 15			06 52					07 34				08 15						08 51		
Chichester 4	a			00 12			01 10			06 58					07 51	07 57		08 13						08 56	09 01
	d									06 59					07 52	07 57		08 14						08 56	09 02
Fishbourne (Sussex)	d																	08 17							
Bosham	d																	08 20							
Nutbourne	d																	08 23							
Southbourne	d															08 04		08 26							09 09
Emsworth	d														08 00	08 07		08 29						09 04	09 12
Warblington	d																	08 32							
Havant	d									07 10					08 04	08 12		08 35						09 08	09 16
Bedhampton	a																	08 37							
Hilsea	a																								
Fratton	a									07 18						08 20		08 45							09 25
Portsmouth & Southsea	a									07 22						08 24		08 48							09 28
Portsmouth Harbour ⛴	a									07 26						08 28		08 52							09 35
Cosham	a														08 10									09 15	
Portchester	a																								
Fareham	a														08 18									09 23	
Swanwick	a														08 25									09 29	
Eastleigh	a																								
Southampton Airport Parkway	a																								
Southampton Central ⛴	a														08 43									09 48	

Table 188

Sundays

8 December to 11 May

London, Gatwick Airport, Brighton - Sussex Coast, Portsmouth and Southampton

Network Diagram - see first Page of Table 175

		SN 1	SN 1	SN 1	SN 1	SN 1		SN 1	SN 1	SN 1		SN 1	SN 1	SN	SN 1	SN 1		SN 1	SN 1	SN 1		SN 1	SN 1	SN	SN 1
London Victoria 15 ⊖	d					08 02				08 17						09 02				09 17					
Clapham Junction 10	d					08 09				08 24						09 08				09 23					
London Bridge 4 ⊖	d																								
East Croydon	d					08 24				08 38						09 18				09 33					
Redhill 5	d					08 39										09 35									
Horley	d					08 45										09 41									
Gatwick Airport 10 ✈	d					08 49				08 57						09 44				09 49					
Three Bridges 4	a					08 53										09 49									
	d					08 53										09 49									
Crawley	d					08 57										09 53									
Horsham 4	a					09 05										10 01									
	d					09 05										10 02									
Christs Hospital	d					09 09										10 06									
Billingshurst	d					09 15										10 12									
Pulborough	d					09 22										10 19									
Amberley	d					09 28										10 25									
Arundel	d					09 33										10 30									
Haywards Heath 3	d									09 09										10 00					
Burgess Hill	d									09 16										10 06					
Preston Park	d																								
Brighton 10	d			08 30				09 00					09 30	09 46				10 00					10 30	10 46	
Hove 2	a			08 33				09 03		09 27			09 33	09 50				10 03		10 18			10 33	10 50	
	d			08 34				09 04		09 28			09 34					10 04		10 19			10 34		
Aldrington	d			08 36				09 06					09 36					10 06					10 36		
Portslade	d			08 38				09 08					09 38					10 08					10 38		
Fishersgate	d			08 40				09 10					09 40					10 10					10 40		
Southwick	d			08 42				09 12					09 42					10 12					10 42		
Shoreham-by-Sea	d			08 45				09 15		09 34			09 45					10 15		10 25			10 45		
Lancing	d			08 49				09 19					09 49					10 19					10 49		
East Worthing	d			08 52				09 22					09 52					10 22					10 52		
Worthing 4	a			08 55				09 25		09 40			09 55					10 25		10 31			10 55		
	d			08 55				09 25		09 44	09 47		09 55					10 25		10 35	10 37		10 55		
West Worthing	d			08 57				09 27			09 49		09 57					10 27			10 39		10 57		
Durrington-on-Sea	d			09 00				09 30			09 51		10 00					10 30			10 42		11 00		
Goring-by-Sea	d			09 02				09 32			09 54		10 02					10 32			10 44		11 02		
Angmering 3	d			09 06				09 36			09 58		10 06					10 36			10 48		11 06		
Littlehampton 4	a										10 06										10 57				
	d	08 54							09 54										10 54						
Ford 4	d	08 58		09 12		09 38		09 42	09 58				10 12			10 36		10 42	10 58				11 12		
Bognor Regis 4	d		08 59		09 20							09 59			10 20							10 59			11 20
Barnham	a	09 02	09 05	09 17	09 26	09 42		09 47	10 02	09 58		10 05	10 17		10 26	10 40		10 47	11 02	10 51		11 05	11 17		11 26
	d	09 03		09 18		09 43		09 48	10 03	09 59			10 18			10 41		10 48	11 03	10 52			11 18		
Bognor Regis	a	09 10				09 49			10 10							10 48			11 10						
Chichester 4	a			09 25				09 55		10 06			10 25					10 55		10 59			11 25		
	d			09 26				09 56		10 07			10 26					10 56		11 00			11 26		
Fishbourne (Sussex)	d			09 29									10 29										11 29		
Bosham	d			09 32									10 32										11 32		
Nutbourne	d			09 35									10 35										11 35		
Southbourne	d			09 38						10 14			10 38							11 07			11 38		
Emsworth	d			09 41				10 04		10 17			10 41					11 04		11 10			11 41		
Warblington	d			09 44									10 44										11 44		
Havant	d			09 48				10 08		10 21			10 48					11 08		11 14			11 47		
Bedhampton	a			09 50									10 50										11 49		
Hilsea	a																								
Fratton	a			09 59						10 32			10 58							11 23			11 57		
Portsmouth & Southsea	a			10 03						10 35			11 03							11 26			12 00		
Portsmouth Harbour ⛴	a			10 07						10 39			11 07							11 30			12 05		
Cosham	a							10 14										11 14							
Portchester	a																								
Fareham	a							10 22										11 22							
Swanwick	a							10 29										11 29							
Eastleigh	a																								
Southampton Airport Parkway	a																								
Southampton Central ⛴	a							10 46										11 46							

Table 188

Sundays

8 December to 11 May

London, Gatwick Airport, Brighton - Sussex Coast, Portsmouth and Southampton

Network Diagram - see first Page of Table 175

		SN 1		SN 1	GW ◇	SN 1	SN 1		SN 1	SN 1	SN	SN 1		SN 1	SN 1	SN 1	SN 1		SN 1	SN 1	SN	SN 1		SN 1	SN 1
London Victoria 15 ⊖	d	10 02					10 17							11 02			11 17							12 02	
Clapham Junction 10	d	10 08					10 23							11 08			11 23							12 08	
London Bridge 4 ⊖	d																								
East Croydon	d	10 17					10 32							11 17			11 33							12 17	
Redhill 5	d	10 34												11 34										12 34	
Horley	d	10 40												11 40										12 40	
Gatwick Airport 10 ✈	d	10 44					10 49							11 44			11 49							12 44	
Three Bridges 4	a	10 48												11 48										12 48	
	d	10 49												11 49										12 49	
Crawley	d	10 53												11 53										12 53	
Horsham 4	a	11 01												12 01										13 01	
	d	11 02												12 02										13 02	
Christs Hospital	d	11 06												12 06										13 06	
Billingshurst	d	11 12												12 12										13 12	
Pulborough	d	11 19												12 19										13 19	
Amberley	d	11 25												12 25										13 25	
Arundel	d	11 30												12 30										13 30	
Haywards Heath 3	d						11 00										12 00								
Burgess Hill	d						11 05										12 06								
Preston Park	d																								
Brighton 10	d			11 00	11 10					11 30	11 46				12 00					12 30	12 46				13 00
Hove 2	a			11 03	11 13		11 18			11 33	11 50				12 03		12 18			12 33	12 50				13 03
	d			11 04	11 14		11 18			11 34					12 04		12 19			12 34					13 04
Aldrington	d			11 06						11 36					12 06					12 36					13 06
Portslade	d			11 08						11 38					12 08					12 38					13 08
Fishersgate	d			11 10						11 40					12 10					12 40					13 10
Southwick	d			11 12						11 42					12 12					12 42					13 12
Shoreham-by-Sea	d			11 15	11 20		11 25			11 45					12 15		12 25			12 45					13 15
Lancing	d			11 19						11 49					12 19					12 49					13 19
East Worthing	d			11 22						11 52					12 22					12 52					13 22
Worthing 4	a			11 25	11 29		11 33			11 55					12 25		12 31			12 55					13 25
	d			11 25	11 29		11 36	11 39		11 55					12 25		12 35	12 37		12 55					13 25
West Worthing	d			11 27				11 41		11 57					12 27			12 39		12 57					13 27
Durrington-on-Sea	d			11 30				11 43		12 00					12 30			12 42		13 00					13 30
Goring-by-Sea	d			11 32				11 46		12 02					12 32			12 44		13 02					13 32
Angmering 3	d			11 36				11 50		12 06					12 36			12 48		13 06					13 36
Littlehampton 4	a							11 58										12 57							
	d					11 54										12 54									
Ford 4	d	11 36		11 42		11 58				12 12				12 36	12 42	12 58				13 12				13 36	13 42
Bognor Regis 4	d								11 59			12 20							12 59			13 20			
Barnham	a	11 40		11 47	11 52	12 02	11 57		12 05	12 17		12 26		12 40	12 47	13 02	12 51		13 06	13 17		13 26		13 40	13 47
	d	11 41		11 48	11 53	12 03	11 57			12 18				12 41	12 48	13 03	12 52			13 18				13 41	13 48
Bognor Regis	a	11 48				12 10								12 48		13 10								13 48	
Chichester 4	a			11 55	12 00		12 05			12 25					12 55		12 59			13 25					13 55
	d			11 56	12 01		12 05			12 26					12 56		13 00			13 26					13 56
Fishbourne (Sussex)	d									12 29										13 29					
Bosham	d									12 32										13 32					
Nutbourne	d									12 35										13 35					
Southbourne	d						12 12			12 38							13 07			13 38					
Emsworth	d			12 04			12 15			12 41					13 04		13 10			13 41					14 04
Warblington	d									12 44										13 44					
Havant	d			12 08	12 12		12 20			12 47					13 08		13 14			13 47					14 08
Bedhampton	a									12 49										13 49					
Hilsea	a																								
Fratton	a						12 28			12 57							13 23			13 57					
Portsmouth & Southsea	a						12 32			13 00							13 26			14 00					
Portsmouth Harbour ⛴	a						12 36			13 05							13 30			14 05					
Cosham	a			12 14	12 19										13 14										14 14
Portchester	a																								
Fareham	a			12 22	12 31										13 22										14 22
Swanwick	a			12 29											13 29										14 29
Eastleigh	a																								
Southampton Airport Parkway	a																								
Southampton Central ⛴	a			12 46	12 53										13 46										14 46

Table 188

Sundays

8 December to 11 May

London, Gatwick Airport, Brighton - Sussex Coast, Portsmouth and Southampton

Network Diagram - see first Page of Table 175

		SN	SN		SN	SN	SN	SN		SN	SN	SN	SN		SN	SN	SN	SN		SN	SN	SN	SN		SN
		1	1		1	1		1		1	1	1	1		1	1		1		1	1	1	1		1
London Victoria 15 ⊖	d		12 17							13 02			13 17							14 02			14 17		
Clapham Junction 10	d		12 23							13 08			13 23							14 08			14 23		
London Bridge 4 ⊖	d																								
East Croydon	d		12 33							13 17			13 33							14 17			14 33		
Redhill 5	d									13 34										14 34					
Horley	d									13 40										14 40					
Gatwick Airport 10 ✈	d		12 49							13 44			13 49							14 44			14 49		
Three Bridges 4	a									13 48										14 48					
	d									13 49										14 49					
Crawley	d									13 53										14 53					
Horsham 4	a									14 01										15 01					
	d									14 02										15 02					
Christs Hospital	d									14 06										15 06					
Billingshurst	d									14 12										15 12					
Pulborough	d									14 19										15 19					
Amberley	d									14 25										15 25					
Arundel	d									14 30										15 30					
Haywards Heath 3	d		13 00										14 00										15 00		
Burgess Hill	d		13 06										14 06										15 06		
Preston Park	d																								
Brighton 10	d					13 30	13 46				14 00					14 30	14 46				15 00				
Hove 2	a		13 18			13 33	13 50				14 03		14 18			14 33	14 50				15 03		15 18		
	d		13 19			13 34					14 04		14 19			14 34					15 04		15 19		
Aldrington	d					13 36					14 06					14 36					15 06				
Portslade	d					13 38					14 08					14 38					15 08				
Fishersgate	d					13 40					14 10					14 40					15 10				
Southwick	d					13 42					14 12					14 42					15 12				
Shoreham-by-Sea	d		13 25			13 45					14 15		14 25			14 45					15 15		15 25		
Lancing	d					13 49					14 19					14 49					15 19				
East Worthing	d					13 52					14 22					14 52					15 22				
Worthing 4	a		13 31			13 55					14 25		14 31			14 55					15 25		15 31		
	d		13 35	13 37		13 55					14 25		14 35	14 37		14 55					15 25		15 35	15 37	
West Worthing	d			13 39		13 57					14 27			14 39		14 57					15 27			15 39	
Durrington-on-Sea	d			13 42		14 00					14 30			14 42		15 00					15 30			15 42	
Goring-by-Sea	d			13 44		14 02					14 32			14 44		15 02					15 32			15 44	
Angmering 3	d			13 48		14 06					14 36			14 48		15 06					15 36			15 48	
Littlehampton 4	a			13 57										14 57										15 57	
	d	13 54										14 54										15 54			
Ford 4	d	13 58				14 12				14 36	14 42	14 58				15 12				15 36	15 42	15 58			
Bognor Regis 4	d				13 59			14 20							14 59			15 20							15 59
Barnham	a	14 02	13 51		14 05	14 17		14 26		14 40	14 47	15 02	14 51		15 05	15 17		15 26		15 40	15 47	16 02	15 51		16 05
	d	14 03	13 52			14 18				14 41	14 48	15 03	14 52			15 18				15 41	15 48	16 03	15 52		
Bognor Regis	a	14 10								14 48		15 10								15 48		16 10			
Chichester 4	a		13 59			14 25					14 55		14 59			15 25					15 55		15 59		
	d		14 00			14 26					14 56		15 00			15 26					15 56		16 00		
Fishbourne (Sussex)	d					14 29										15 29									
Bosham	d					14 32										15 32									
Nutbourne	d					14 35										15 35									
Southbourne	d		14 07			14 38							15 07			15 38							16 07		
Emsworth	d		14 10			14 41					15 04		15 10			15 41					16 04		16 10		
Warblington	d					14 44										15 44									
Havant	d		14 14			14 47					15 08		15 14			15 47					16 08		16 14		
Bedhampton	a					14 49										15 49									
Hilsea	a																								
Fratton	a		14 23			14 57							15 23			15 57							16 23		
Portsmouth & Southsea	a		14 26			15 00							15 26			16 00							16 26		
Portsmouth Harbour ⛴	a		14 30			15 05							15 30			16 05							16 30		
Cosham	a										15 14										16 14				
Portchester	a																								
Fareham	a										15 22										16 22				
Swanwick	a										15 29										16 29				
Eastleigh	a																								
Southampton Airport Parkway	a																								
Southampton Central ⛴	a										15 46										16 46				

Table 188

Sundays

8 December to 11 May

London, Gatwick Airport, Brighton - Sussex Coast, Portsmouth and Southampton

Network Diagram - see first Page of Table 175

		SN	SN	GW		SN	SN	SN	SN	SN		SN	SN	SN		SN	SN	SN	SN	SN		SN	SN	SN	
		1		◇		1	1	1	1	1		1	1			1	1	1	1	1		1	1		
London Victoria [15] ⊖	d						15 02			15 17							16 02			16 17					
Clapham Junction [10]	d						15 08			15 23							16 08			16 23					
London Bridge [4] ⊖	d																								
East Croydon	d						15 17			15 32							16 17			16 33					
Redhill [5]	d						15 34										16 34								
Horley	d						15 40										16 40								
Gatwick Airport [10] ✈	d						15 44			15 49							16 44			16 49					
Three Bridges [4]	a						15 48										16 48								
	d						15 49										16 49								
Crawley	d						15 53										16 53								
Horsham [4]	a						16 01										17 01								
	d						16 02										17 02								
Christs Hospital	d						16 06										17 06								
Billingshurst	d						16 12										17 12								
Pulborough	d						16 19										17 19								
Amberley	d						16 25										17 25								
Arundel	d						16 30										17 30								
Haywards Heath [3]	d									16 00										17 00					
Burgess Hill	d									16 06										17 06					
Preston Park	d																								
Brighton [10]	d	15 30	15 39	15 46				16 00					16 30	16 46				17 00					17 30	17 39	
Hove [2]	a	15 33	15 43	15 49				16 03		16 18			16 33	16 50				17 03		17 18			17 33	17 43	
	d	15 34		15 50				16 04		16 19			16 34					17 04		17 19			17 34		
Aldrington	d	15 36						16 06					16 36					17 06					17 36		
Portslade	d	15 38						16 08					16 38					17 08					17 38		
Fishersgate	d	15 40						16 10					16 40					17 10					17 40		
Southwick	d	15 42						16 12					16 42					17 12					17 42		
Shoreham-by-Sea	d	15 45		15 56				16 15		16 25			16 45					17 15		17 25			17 45		
Lancing	d	15 49						16 19					16 49					17 19					17 49		
East Worthing	d	15 52						16 22					16 52					17 22					17 52		
Worthing [4]	a	15 55		16 03				16 25		16 31			16 55					17 25		17 31			17 55		
	d	15 55		16 08				16 25		16 35	16 37		16 55					17 25		17 35	17 37		17 55		
West Worthing	d	15 57						16 27			16 39		16 57					17 27			17 39		17 57		
Durrington-on-Sea	d	16 00						16 30			16 42		17 00					17 30			17 42		18 00		
Goring-by-Sea	d	16 02						16 32			16 44		17 02					17 32			17 44		18 02		
Angmering [3]	d	16 06						16 36			16 48		17 06					17 36			17 48		18 06		
Littlehampton [4]	a										16 57										17 57				
	d								16 54										17 54						
Ford [4]	d	16 12					16 36	16 42	16 58				17 12				17 36	17 42	17 58				18 12		
Bognor Regis [4]	d					16 20						16 59				17 20						17 59			
Barnham	a	16 17		16 22		16 26	16 40	16 47	17 02	16 51		17 05	17 17			17 26	17 40	17 47	18 02	17 51		18 05	18 17		
	d	16 18		16 23			16 41	16 48	17 03	16 52			17 18				17 41	17 48	18 03	17 52			18 18		
Bognor Regis	a						16 48		17 10								17 48		18 10						
Chichester [4]	a	16 25		16 36				16 55		16 59			17 25					17 55		17 59			18 25		
	d	16 26		16 37				16 56		17 00			17 26					17 56		18 00			18 26		
Fishbourne (Sussex)	d	16 29											17 29										18 29		
Bosham	d	16 32											17 32										18 32		
Nutbourne	d	16 35											17 35										18 35		
Southbourne	d	16 38								17 07			17 38							18 07			18 38		
Emsworth	d	16 41						17 04		17 10			17 41					18 04		18 10			18 41		
Warblington	d	16 44											17 44										18 44		
Havant	d	16 47		16 48				17 08		17 14			17 47					18 08		18 14			18 47		
Bedhampton	a	16 49											17 49										18 49		
Hilsea	a																								
Fratton	a	16 57								17 23			17 57							18 23			18 57		
Portsmouth & Southsea	a	17 00								17 26			18 00							18 26			19 01		
Portsmouth Harbour ⛴	a	17 05								17 30			18 05							18 30			19 05		
Cosham	a			16 55				17 14										18 14							
Portchester	a																								
Fareham	a			17 03				17 22										18 22							
Swanwick	a							17 29										18 29							
Eastleigh	a																								
Southampton Airport Parkway	a																								
Southampton Central ⛴	a			17 24				17 47										18 46							

Table 188

Sundays

8 December to 11 May

London, Gatwick Airport, Brighton - Sussex Coast, Portsmouth and Southampton

Network Diagram - see first Page of Table 175

		GW	SN	SN	SN	SN	SN		SN	SN		SN	SN	SN	SN	SN	SN		SN	SN		SN	SN	SN	SN
		◇	1	1	1	1	1		1	1			1	1	1	1	1		1	1			1	1	1
London Victoria 15 ⊖	d			17 02			17 17							18 02			18 17							19 02	
Clapham Junction 10	d			17 08			17 23							18 08			18 23							19 08	
London Bridge 4 ⊖	d																								
East Croydon	d			17 17			17 33							18 17			18 33							19 17	
Redhill 5	d			17 34										18 34										19 34	
Horley	d			17 40										18 40										19 40	
Gatwick Airport 10 ✈	d			17 44			17 49							18 44			18 49							19 44	
Three Bridges 4	a			17 48										18 48										19 48	
	d			17 49										18 49										19 49	
Crawley	d			17 53										18 53										19 53	
Horsham 4	a			18 01										19 01										20 01	
	d			18 02										19 02										20 02	
Christs Hospital	d			18 06										19 06										20 06	
Billingshurst	d			18 12										19 12										20 12	
Pulborough	d			18 19										19 19										20 19	
Amberley	d			18 25										19 25										20 25	
Arundel	d			18 30										19 30										20 30	
Haywards Heath 3	d						18 00										19 00								
Burgess Hill	d						18 06										19 06								
Preston Park	d																								
Brighton 10	d	17 46			18 00					18 30		18 46			19 00					19 30		19 46			20 00
Hove 2	a	17 49			18 03		18 18			18 33		18 50			19 03		19 18			19 33		19 50			20 03
	d	17 50			18 04		18 19			18 34					19 04		19 19			19 34					20 04
Aldrington	d				18 06					18 36					19 06					19 36					20 06
Portslade	d				18 08					18 38					19 08					19 38					20 08
Fishersgate	d				18 10					18 40					19 10					19 40					20 10
Southwick	d				18 12					18 42					19 12					19 42					20 12
Shoreham-by-Sea	d	17 56			18 15		18 25			18 45					19 15		19 25			19 45					20 15
Lancing	d				18 19					18 49					19 19					19 49					20 19
East Worthing	d				18 22					18 52					19 22					19 52					20 22
Worthing 4	a	18 03			18 25		18 31			18 55					19 25		19 31			19 55					20 25
	d	18 08			18 25		18 35	18 37		18 55					19 25		19 35	19 37		19 55					20 25
West Worthing	d				18 27			18 39		18 57					19 27			19 39		19 57					20 27
Durrington-on-Sea	d				18 30			18 42		19 00					19 30			19 42		20 00					20 30
Goring-by-Sea	d				18 32			18 44		19 02					19 32			19 44		20 02					20 32
Angmering 3	d				18 36			18 48		19 06					19 36			19 48		20 06					20 36
Littlehampton 4	a							18 57										19 57							
	d					18 54										19 54									
Ford 4	d			18 36	18 42	18 58				19 12				19 36	19 42	19 58				20 12				20 36	20 42
Bognor Regis 4	d		18 20						18 59				19 20						19 59				20 26		
Barnham	a	18 22	18 26	18 40	18 47	19 02	18 51		19 05	19 17			19 26	19 40	19 47	20 02	19 51		20 05	20 17			20 32	20 40	20 47
	d	18 23		18 41	18 48	19 03	18 52			19 18				19 41	19 48	20 03	19 52			20 18				20 41	20 48
Bognor Regis	a			18 48		19 10								19 48		20 10								20 48	
Chichester 4	a	18 31			18 55		18 59			19 25					19 55		19 59			20 25					20 55
	d	18 32			18 56		19 00			19 26					19 56		20 00			20 26					20 56
Fishbourne (Sussex)	d									19 29										20 29					
Bosham	d									19 32										20 32					
Nutbourne	d									19 35										20 35					
Southbourne	d						19 07			19 38							20 07			20 38					
Emsworth	d				19 04		19 10			19 41					20 04		20 10			20 41					21 04
Warblington	d									19 44										20 44					
Havant	d	18 50			19 08		19 14			19 47					20 08		20 14			20 47					21 08
Bedhampton	a									19 49										20 49					
Hilsea	a																								
Fratton	a						19 23			19 57							20 23			20 57					
Portsmouth & Southsea	a						19 26			20 00							20 26			21 00					
Portsmouth Harbour ⛴	a						19 30										20 30			21 05					
Cosham	a	18 56			19 14										20 14										21 14
Portchester	a																								
Fareham	a	19 04			19 22										20 22										21 22
Swanwick	a				19 29										20 29										21 29
Eastleigh	a																								
Southampton Airport Parkway	a																								
Southampton Central ⛴	a	19 26			19 47										20 46										21 46

Table 188

Sundays

8 December to 11 May

London, Gatwick Airport, Brighton - Sussex Coast, Portsmouth and Southampton

Network Diagram - see first Page of Table 175

		SN 1	SN 1		SN 1	SN 1		SN 1	SN 1	SN 1	SN 1	SN 1		SN 1	SN 1	GW		SN 1	SN	SN	SN 1	SN	SN	SN 1	
London Victoria 15 ⊖	d		19 17						20 02			20 17									21 02			21 17	
Clapham Junction 10	d		19 23						20 08			20 23									21 08			21 23	
London Bridge 4 ⊖	d																								
East Croydon	d		19 33						20 17			20 33									21 17			21 33	
Redhill 5	d								20 34												21 34				
Horley	d								20 40												21 40				
Gatwick Airport 10 ✈	d		19 49						20 44			20 49									21 44			21 49	
Three Bridges 4	a								20 48												21 48				
	d								20 49												21 49				
Crawley	d								20 53												21 53				
Horsham 4	a								21 01												22 01				
	d								21 02												22 02				
Christs Hospital	d								21 06												22 06				
Billingshurst	d								21 12												22 12				
Pulborough	d								21 19												22 19				
Amberley	d								21 25												22 25				
Arundel	d								21 30												22 30				
Haywards Heath 3	d		20 00									21 00												22 00	
Burgess Hill	d		20 06									21 06												22 06	
Preston Park	d																								
Brighton 10	d					20 30				21 00					21 25	21 46		21 55	22 12						
Hove 2	a		20 18			20 33				21 03		21 18			21 28	21 49		21 58	22 15					22 18	
	d		20 19			20 34				21 04		21 19			21 29	21 50		21 59						22 19	
Aldrington	d					20 36				21 06					21 31			22 01							
Portslade	d					20 38				21 08					21 33			22 03						22 22	
Fishersgate	d					20 40				21 10					21 35			22 05							
Southwick	d					20 42				21 12					21 37			22 07							
Shoreham-by-Sea	d		20 25			20 45				21 15		21 25			21 40	21 56		22 10						22 27	
Lancing	d					20 49				21 19					21 44			22 14							
East Worthing	d					20 52				21 22					21 47			22 17							
Worthing 4	a		20 31			20 55				21 25		21 31			21 50	22 02		22 20						22 33	
	d		20 35	20 37		20 55				21 25		21 35	21 37		21 50	22 03		22 20						22 37	22 39
West Worthing	d			20 39		20 57				21 27			21 39		21 52			22 22							22 41
Durrington-on-Sea	d			20 42		21 00				21 30			21 42		21 55			22 25							22 44
Goring-by-Sea	d			20 44		21 02				21 32			21 44		21 57			22 27							22 46
Angmering 3	d			20 48		21 06				21 36			21 48		22 01			22 31							22 50
Littlehampton 4	a			20 57									21 57					22 41							22 59
	d	20 54									21 54														
Ford 4	d	20 58				21 12			21 36	21 42	21 58				22 07						22 36				
Bognor Regis 4	d				20 59			21 20						21 59						22 13		22 41			
Barnham	a	21 02	20 51		21 05	21 17		21 26	21 40	21 47	22 02	21 51		22 05	22 12	22 17				22 19	22 40	22 47		22 51	
	d	21 03	20 52			21 18			21 41	21 48	22 03	21 52			22 13	22 18					22 41		22 54	22 56	
Bognor Regis	a	21 10							21 48		22 10										22 48		23 01		
Chichester 4	a		20 59			21 25				21 55		21 59			22 20	22 25								23 03	
	d		21 00			21 26				21 56		22 00			22 21	22 26								23 04	
Fishbourne (Sussex)	d					21 29									22 24										
Bosham	d					21 32									22 27									23 08	
Nutbourne	d					21 35									22 30									23 12	
Southbourne	d		21 07			21 38						22 07			22 33									23 14	
Emsworth	d		21 10			21 41				22 04		22 10			22 36									23 17	
Warblington	d					21 44									22 39										
Havant	d		21 14			21 47				22 08		22 14			22 44	22 47								23 22	
Bedhampton	a					21 49									22 46										
Hilsea	a																								
Fratton	a		21 23			21 57						22 23			22 54	22 57								23 31	
Portsmouth & Southsea	a		21 26			22 00						22 26			22 57	23 00								23 34	
Portsmouth Harbour ⛴	a		21 30			22 04						22 30			23 02	23 05								23 38	
Cosham	a									22 14															
Portchester	a																								
Fareham	a									22 22															
Swanwick	a									22 29															
Eastleigh	a																								
Southampton Airport Parkway	a																								
Southampton Central ⛴	a									22 46															

Table 188

Sundays

8 December to 11 May

London, Gatwick Airport, Brighton - Sussex Coast, Portsmouth and Southampton

Network Diagram - see first Page of Table 175

		SN		SN	SN	SN	SN	SN
		1		1	1		1	1
London Victoria 15 ⊖	d			22 02			22 17	23 17
Clapham Junction 10	d			22 08			22 23	23 23
London Bridge 4 ⊖	d							
East Croydon	d			22 18			22 33	23 37
Redhill 5	d			22 35				
Horley	d			22 41				
Gatwick Airport 10 ✈	d			22 44			22 49	23 59
Three Bridges 4	a			22 49				00 05
	d			22 49				00 06
Crawley	d			22 53				
Horsham 4	a			23 02				
	d			23 02				
Christs Hospital	d			23 06				
Billingshurst	d			23 13				
Pulborough	d			23 19				
Amberley	d			23 25				
Arundel	d			23 31				
Haywards Heath 3	d						23 01	00 15
Burgess Hill	d						23 06	00 20
Preston Park	d							
Brighton 10	d				22 45	23 15		
Hove 2	a				22 48	23 19	23 21	00 31
	d				22 49		23 25	00 32
Aldrington	d				22 51			
Portslade	d				22 53		23 28	00s35
Fishersgate	d				22 55			
Southwick	d				22 57		23 31	00s38
Shoreham-by-Sea	d				23 00		23 34	00s41
Lancing	d				23 04		23 38	00s45
East Worthing	d				23 07			
Worthing 4	a				23 10		23 42	00 49
	d				23 10			
West Worthing	d				23 12			
Durrington-on-Sea	d				23 14			
Goring-by-Sea	d				23 17			
Angmering 3	d				23 21			
Littlehampton 4	a				23 30			
	d	23 06			23 34			
Ford 4	d	23 10		23 36	23 39			
Bognor Regis 4	d							
Barnham	a	23 14		23 41	23 44			
	d	23 15		23 46	23 45			
Bognor Regis	a	23 21		23 53				
Chichester 4	a				23 52			
	d							
Fishbourne (Sussex)	d							
Bosham	d							
Nutbourne	d							
Southbourne	d							
Emsworth	d							
Warblington	d							
Havant	d							
Bedhampton	a							
Hilsea	a							
Fratton	a							
Portsmouth & Southsea	a							
Portsmouth Harbour ⛴	a							
Cosham	a							
Portchester	a							
Fareham	a							
Swanwick	a							
Eastleigh	a							
Southampton Airport Parkway	a							
Southampton Central ⛴	a							

Table 188R

Mondays to Fridays

9 December to 16 May

Southampton, Portsmouth and Sussex Coast - Brighton, Gatwick Airport and London

Network Diagram - see first Page of Table 175

Miles	Miles	Miles			SN MX	SN MX	SN MX	SN MX 1	SN MX	SN 1	SN	SN 1	SN		SN	SN	SN 1	SN 1	SN 1	SN	SN 1	SN	SN		SN
—	—	—	Eastleigh	d																					
—	—	—	Southampton Airport Parkway	d																					
0	—	—	Southampton Central	d																					
10¾	—	—	Swanwick	d																					
14½	—	—	Fareham	d																					
17¾	—	—	Portchester	d																					
20¼	—	—	Cosham	d																					
—	0	—	Portsmouth Harbour	d																					
—	0¾	—	Portsmouth & Southsea	d																					
—	1½	—	Fratton	d																					
—	4¼	—	Hilsea	d																					
—	7¼	—	Bedhampton	d																					
24¼	8	—	Havant	d								05 01						05 28							
—	8½	—	**Warblington**	d																					
—	9¾	—	**Emsworth**	d																					
—	11¼	—	**Southbourne**	d																					
—	12¼	—	**Nutbourne**	d																					
—	14	—	**Bosham**	d																					
—	15¼	—	**Fishbourne (Sussex)**	d																					
—	16¾	—	**Chichester** [4]	a								05 14						05 38							
—	—	—		d					00 04			05 15						05 39							
0	—	—	**Bognor Regis** [4]	d							05 13		←				05 35					05 49	05 55		
3½	23	—	**Barnham**	a					00 12		05 19	05 22	05 19				05 41	05 46				05 55	06 02		
—	—	—		d		00 01	00 06	00 09		04 48	05 27	05 23	05 27		05 36		05 42	05 47				05 56	06 02		06 13
—	—	—	Bognor Regis	a				00 16			→				05 44										06 21
0	25¾	0	**Ford** [4]	d		00 05	00 10			04 52			05 31				05 46					06 00	06 07		
2	—	2	**Littlehampton** [4]	a		00 11	00 17			04 57			05 38									06 05			
—	—	—		d						05 02									05 53		05 57				
8	30	—	**Angmering** [3]	d						05 10		05 33					05 53		06 02				06 13		
—	32½	—	**Goring-by-Sea**	d						05 14							05 57		06 06				06 17		
—	33¼	—	**Durrington-on-Sea**	d						05 17							05 59		06 09				06 19		
—	34	—	**West Worthing**	d						05 19							06 01		06 11				06 21		
—	35	—	**Worthing** [4]	a						05 21		05 40					06 04		06 13				06 24		
—	—	—		d						05 22		05 41					06 04		06 14				06 24		
—	35¾	—	**East Worthing**	d	00 01					05 24							06 07						06 27		
—	37¼	—	**Lancing**	d	00 04					05 27		05 45					06 10		06 18				06 30		
—	40	—	**Shoreham-by-Sea**	d	00 08					05 32		05 49					06 14		06 22				06 34		
—	41	—	**Southwick**	d	00 11					05 35							06 17						06 37		
—	42	—	**Fishersgate**	d	00 13					05 37							06 19						06 39		
—	42½	—	**Portslade**	d	00 15					05 39		05 53					06 21		06 27				06 41		
—	43½	—	**Aldrington**	d	00 18					05 41							06 23						06 43		
0	44	—	**Hove** [2]	a	00 21					05 43		05 57					06 25		06 30				06 45		
—	—	—		d	00 21					05 44		05 57				05 59	06 26		06 31	06 38			06 46		
—	45½	—	Brighton [10]	a	00 25					05 48						06 03	06 30			06 42			06 50		
—	—	—	Preston Park	d																					
9¼	—	—	Burgess Hill	a															06 46						
13	—	—	Haywards Heath [3]	a								06 12							06 53						
—	—	2¼	**Arundel**	d														05 55			06 05				
—	—	6	**Amberley**	d																					
—	—	10¾	**Pulborough**	d														06 04			06 15				
—	—	15¾	**Billingshurst**	d														06 11			06 23				
—	—	20½	**Christs Hospital**	d														06 18			06 31				
—	—	23	Horsham [4]	a														06 22			06 35				
—	—	—		d														06 23			06 36				
—	—	30	Crawley	d														06 37			06 51				
21½	—	31½	Three Bridges [4]	a								06 21						06 40			06 55				
24¼	—	—	Gatwick Airport [10]	a								06 26						06 52	07 11		07 00				
—	—	—		d								06 27						06 53	07 12		07 01				
25	—	—	Horley	a														06 56			07 03				
30	—	—	Redhill [5]	a														07 03			07 14				
40½	0	—	East Croydon	a								06 42						07 15	07 26		07 34				
—	10¼	—	London Bridge [4] ⊖	a															07 45		07 52				
48¼	—	—	Clapham Junction [10]	a								06 51						07 24							
51	—	61	Clapham Junction [15] ⊖	a								07 00						07 32							

Table 188R

Mondays to Fridays

9 December to 16 May

Southampton, Portsmouth and Sussex Coast - Brighton, Gatwick Airport and London

Network Diagram - see first Page of Table 175

		SN 1	SN	SN 1	SN	SN 1	SN	SN	SN 1 A	SN 1	SN	SN	SN 1	SN	SN 1	SN	SN	SN 1	SN 1	SN	SN 1	SN	SN
Eastleigh	d																						
Southampton Airport Parkway	d																						
Southampton Central	d																		05 48		06 10		
Swanwick	d																		06 06		06 27		
Fareham	d																		06 13		06 34		
Portchester	d																		06 18		06 40		
Cosham	d																		06 23		06 44		
Portsmouth Harbour	d			05 33					05 47		06 04												
Portsmouth & Southsea	d			05 37					05 51		06 08												
Fratton	d			05 41					05 55		06 12												
Hilsea	d			05 45					05 59														
Bedhampton	d			05 50					06 04										06 34				
Havant	d			05 53					06 07		06 20								06 37		06 53		
Warblington	d			05 55															06 39				
Emsworth	d			05 58					06 11		06 24								06 42		06 57		
Southbourne	d			06 01					06 14		06 27								06 45		07 00		
Nutbourne	d			06 03															06 48				
Bosham	d			06 07					06 18										06 51				
Fishbourne (Sussex)	d			06 10					06 21										06 54				
Chichester 4	a			06 13					06 25		06 34								06 58		07 07		
	d			06 14					06 29		06 35								06 59		07 08		
Bognor Regis 4	d	06 06	06 13					06 22					06 41				06 50	06 57					07 27
Barnham	a	06 12	06 19	06 21				06 28	06 36		06 42		06 47				06 56	07 03	07 07		07 15		07 33
	d	06 13		06 22	06 27			06 29	06 37		06 43	06 48	06 48				06 57	07 11		07 13	07 16		
Bognor Regis	a				06 36							06 56								07 21			
Ford 4	d			06 26				06 33			06 47		06 52				07 01				07 20		
Littlehampton 4	a							06 39									07 07						
	d					06 31				06 41					07 02							07 22	
Angmering 3	d			06 32		06 40				06 50	06 56				07 11						07 26	07 30	
Goring-by-Sea	d			06 36		06 44				06 54	07 00				07 15						07 30	07 34	
Durrington-on-Sea	d			06 39		06 47				06 57	07 03				07 17						07 33	07 37	
West Worthing	d			06 41		06 49				07 00	07 05			07 12	07 20						07 35	07 39	
Worthing 4	a			06 43		06 52				07 02	07 07			07 14	07 22						07 37	07 41	
	d			06 44		06 52				07 03	07 08			07 15	07 23						07 38	07 42	
East Worthing	d			06 46										07 17								07 44	
Lancing	d			06 49		06 57				07 07	07 12			07 20	07 27						07 42	07 47	
Shoreham-by-Sea	d			06 53		07 01				07 12	07 16			07 25	07 31						07 46	07 52	
Southwick	d			06 56							07 19			07 28							07 49	07 55	
Fishersgate	d			06 58										07 30								07 57	
Portslade	d			07 00		07 06				07 17	07 22			07 32	07 36						07 52	07 59	
Aldrington	d			07 03										07 34								08 01	
Hove 2	a			07 05		07 10				07 20	07 25			07 36	07 40						07 55	08 03	
	d			07 05		07 11	07 17			07 21	07 26			07 37	07 41	07 49					07 56	08 04	
Brighton 10	a			07 09			07 21				07 30			07 41		07 54					08 00	08 08	
Preston Park	d																						
Burgess Hill	a														07 51								
Haywards Heath 3	a					07 30				07 40					07 58								
Arundel	d	06 21											06 58					07 19					
Amberley	d	06 26																					
Pulborough	d	06 32											07 07					07 28					
Billingshurst	d	06 39											07 14					07 35					
Christs Hospital	d	06 45											07 20					07 42					
Horsham 4	a	06 49							07 03				07 24					07 46					
	d	06 50							07 04				07 25					07 47					
Crawley	d	07 04							07 13				07 37					08 01					
Three Bridges 4	a	07 07							07 20				07 40					08 05					
Gatwick Airport 10	a	07 12																					
	d	07 14																					
Horley	a	07 16																					
Redhill 5	a																						
East Croydon	a	07 31				07 56			07 38	08 08			07 59		08 29			08 24					
London Bridge 4	a					08 11												08 41					
Clapham Junction 10	a	07 40							07 48	08 17			08 10		08 41								
Clapham Junction 15	a	07 49							07 57	08 25			08 19		08 50								

A from Three Bridges

Table 188R

Mondays to Fridays

9 December to 16 May

Southampton, Portsmouth and Sussex Coast - Brighton, Gatwick Airport and London

Network Diagram - see first Page of Table 175

		SN 1	SN 1	SN	SN 1	GW ♀		SN	SN	SN	SN 1	SN	SN	SN 1	SN 1	SN		SN 1	SN	SN	SN	SN	SN 1	SN	SN 1 A ♀
Eastleigh	d																								
Southampton Airport Parkway	d																								
Southampton Central	d														07 06								07 33		
Swanwick	d														07 24								07 51		
Fareham	d														07 31								07 58		
Portchester	d														07 36										
Cosham	d														07 40								08 07		
Portsmouth Harbour	d		06 46			07 01						07 20													
Portsmouth & Southsea	d		06 50			07 05						07 24													
Fratton	d		06 54			07 11						07 28													
Hilsea	d		06 58																						
Bedhampton	d		07 03																						
Havant	d		07 06			07 19						07 36			07 47								08 13		
Warblington	d		07 08												07 49										
Emsworth	d		07 11												07 52										
Southbourne	d		07 14												07 55										
Nutbourne	d		07 16												07 58										
Bosham	d		07 20												08 01								08 21		
Fishbourne (Sussex)	d		07 23												08 04								08 24		
Chichester 4	a		07 26			07 31						07 47			08 08								08 27		
	d		07 28			07 31						07 47			08 08							08 21	08 28		
Bognor Regis 4	d	07 17								07 36				07 55						08 13				08 32	
Barnham	a	07 23	07 35			07 39				07 42		07 55		08 01	08 16					08 19		08 28	08 35	08 38	
	d	07 24	07 36	07 39		07 39				07 45	07 50	07 55	08 05	08 02	08 16					08 20	08 28	08 29	08 36		
Bognor Regis	a			07 47							07 58		08 12								08 36				
Ford 4	d									07 50		08 00		08 06						08 24		08 33	08 40		
Littlehampton 4	a									07 54												08 38			
	d				07 29				07 45							08 01		08 15							08 45
Angmering 3	d				07 38				07 53			08 06				08 10		08 23		08 30			08 46		08 53
Goring-by-Sea	d				07 42				07 57							08 14		08 27		08 34					08 57
Durrington-on-Sea	d				07 45				08 00			08 12				08 17		08 30		08 37			08 52		09 00
West Worthing	d				07 47				08 02							08 19		08 32		08 39					09 02
Worthing 4	a				07 50	07 56			08 04			08 16				08 21		08 34		08 41			08 56		09 04
	d				07 50	07 59			08 05			08 16				08 22		08 35		08 42			08 56		09 05
East Worthing	d								08 07							08 24				08 44					
Lancing	d				07 54				08 10			08 20				08 27		08 39		08 47			09 00		09 09
Shoreham-by-Sea	d				07 59	08 06			08 15			08 24				08 32		08 43		08 52			09 04		09 13
Southwick	d								08 18			08 27				08 35				08 55			09 07		
Fishersgate	d								08 20							08 37				08 57					
Portslade	d				08 04				08 22			08 31				08 39		08 48		08 59			09 11		09 18
Aldrington	d								08 24							08 41				09 01					
Hove 2	a				08 07	08 13			08 26			08 34				08 43		08 51		09 03			09 14		09 21
	d				08 08	08 13		08 22	08 27			08 34				08 44		08 52	08 54	09 04			09 14		09 22
Brighton 10	a					08 19		08 26	08 31			08 38				08 48			08 58	09 08			09 18		
Preston Park	d				08 12													08 57							
Burgess Hill	a				08 23													09 07							
Haywards Heath 3	a				08 28													09 13							09 40
Arundel	d	07 31												08 11											
Amberley	d	07 36												08 16											
Pulborough	d	07 42												08 22											
Billingshurst	d	07 49												08 29											
Christs Hospital	d	07 55												08 35											
Horsham 4	a	07 59	08 07											08 39	08 47										
	d		08 09												08 49										
Crawley	d		08 18												08 58										
Three Bridges 4	a		08 22		08 37										09 01										
Gatwick Airport 10	a				08 42										09 06			09 26							09 55
	d				08 43										09 07			09 27							09 56
Horley	a		08 28																						
Redhill 5	a																								
East Croydon	a		08 43		08 57										09 22			09 41							10 11
London Bridge 4	a																								
Clapham Junction 10	a		08 52		09 07										09 32			09 51							10 20
Clapham Junction 15	a		09 01		09 16										09 42			09 58							10 28

A ♀ from Haywards Heath

Table 188R

Mondays to Fridays

9 December to 16 May

Southampton, Portsmouth and Sussex Coast - Brighton, Gatwick Airport and London

Network Diagram - see first Page of Table 175

		SN	SN	SN	SN	SN	SN	SN	SN	SN	SN	SN	SN	SN	SN	SN	SN	SN	SN	SN	SN	SN
					1	1						1 A 🚌				1	1		1	1	1	
Eastleigh	d																					
Southampton Airport Parkway	d																					
Southampton Central ⛴	d																08 10		08 33			
Swanwick	d																08 28		08 50			
Fareham	d																08 35		08 57			
Portchester	d																08 40					
Cosham	d																08 44		09 05			
Portsmouth Harbour ⛴	d					08 10				08 29												
Portsmouth & Southsea	d		08 03			08 14				08 33												
Fratton	d		08 07			08 18				08 37												
Hilsea	d		08 11																			
Bedhampton	d		08 16																			
Havant	d		08 19			08 27				08 46							08 51		09 12			
Warblington	d		08 21														08 53					
Emsworth	d		08 24			08 31				08 50							08 56		09 16			
Southbourne	d		08 27							08 53							08 59					
Nutbourne	d		08 29														09 01					
Bosham	d																09 05					
Fishbourne (Sussex)	d																09 08					
Chichester 4	a		08 35			08 40				09 00							09 11		09 24			
	d		08 36			08 41				09 00					09 06		09 12		09 25			
Bognor Regis 4	d				08 26			08 48						09 06		08 56						
Barnham	a		08 43		08 32	08 48		08 55		09 08				09 12	09 14	09 02	09 19		09 32			
	d		08 44	08 45	08 33	08 49	08 52			09 08	09 11			09 15	09 19	09 03	09 20		09 33	09 42		
Bognor Regis	a			08 52			08 58				09 19				09 27					09 48		
Ford 4	d		08 48		08 37									09 19		09 07			09 37			
Littlehampton 4	a		08 53											09 24								
	d											09 15									09 45	
Angmering 3	d									09 17		09 23							09 43		09 54	
Goring-by-Sea	d											09 27							09 47		09 58	
Durrington-on-Sea	d											09 30							09 50		10 00	
West Worthing	d								09 09			09 32						09 39	09 52		10 02	
Worthing 4	a								09 11	09 24		09 34						09 41	09 54		10 05	
	d								09 12	09 26		09 36						09 42	09 56		10 06	
East Worthing	d								09 14									09 44				
Lancing	d								09 17	09 30								09 47	10 00		10 10	
Shoreham-by-Sea	d								09 22	09 34		09 42						09 52	10 04		10 14	
Southwick	d								09 25	09 37								09 55	10 07			
Fishersgate	d								09 27									09 57				
Portslade	d								09 29	09 40		09 47						09 59	10 10			
Aldrington	d								09 31									10 01				
Hove 2	a								09 33	09 43		09 50						10 03	10 13		10 20	
	d	09 24							09 34	09 44		09 51	09 54					10 04	10 14		10 21	10 24
Brighton 10	a	09 28							09 38	09 48			09 58					10 08	10 18			10 28
Preston Park	d											09 55										
Burgess Hill	a											10 04										
Haywards Heath 3	a											10 12									10 35	
Arundel	d				08 42											09 12						
Amberley	d				08 47											09 17						
Pulborough	d				08 53											09 23						
Billingshurst	d				09 00											09 29						
Christs Hospital	d				09 06											09 36						
Horsham 4	a				09 11	09 18										09 40	09 49					
	d				09 20											09 51						
Crawley	d				09 29											10 00						
Three Bridges 4	a				09 32											10 03						
Gatwick Airport 10 ✈	a				09 37							10 25				10 08					10 55	
	d				09 38							10 26				10 09					10 56	
Horley	a				09 41																	
Redhill 5	a				09 48											10 16						
East Croydon 🚊	a				09 59							10 41				10 28					11 11	
London Bridge 4 ⊖	a																					
Clapham Junction 10	a				10 09							10 50				10 37					11 20	
Clapham Junction 15 ⊖	a				10 16							10 58				10 44					11 27	

A 🚌 from Haywards Heath

Table 188R

Mondays to Fridays

9 December to 16 May

Southampton, Portsmouth and Sussex Coast - Brighton, Gatwick Airport and London

Network Diagram - see first Page of Table 175

Station		SN	SN	SN 1	SN 1	SN	SN	SN	SN 1 🚲	SN 1	SN	SN	SN 1	SN 1	SN	SN	SN 1	SN 1 🚲	SN 1	SN	SN	SN
Eastleigh	d																					
Southampton Airport Parkway	d																					
Southampton Central ⛴	d													09 10			09 33					
Swanwick	d													09 28			09 50					
Fareham	d													09 37			09 56					
Portchester	d													09 42								
Cosham	d													09 46			10 05					
Portsmouth Harbour ⛴	d	08 51			09 12			09 29														
Portsmouth & Southsea	d	08 55			09 16			09 33													09 59	
Fratton	d	08 59			09 20			09 37													10 04	
Hilsea	d	09 04																			10 08	
Bedhampton	d	09 13																			10 13	
Havant	d	09 16			09 30			09 46						09 54			10 11				10 16	
Warblington	d	09 18																			10 18	
Emsworth	d	09 21						09 50						10 00			10 15				10 21	
Southbourne	d	09 24						09 53						10 03							10 24	
Nutbourne	d	09 26																			10 26	
Bosham	d	09 30																			10 30	
Fishbourne (Sussex)	d	09 33																			10 33	
Chichester 4	a	09 36			09 40			10 00						10 10			10 23				10 36	
	d	09 37			09 41			10 00						10 11			10 25				10 37	
Bognor Regis 4	d		09 39	09 30								10 07	09 56									10 39
Barnham	a	09 44	09 45	09 36	09 48			10 08				10 13	10 02	10 18			10 32				10 44	10 45
	d	09 45		09 37	09 49	09 52		10 08	10 13			10 15	10 03	10 19	10 22		10 33	10 39			10 45	
Bognor Regis	a					10 00			10 19						10 30			10 48				
Ford 4	d	09 49		09 41								10 19	10 07				10 37				10 49	
Littlehampton 4	a	09 54										10 25									10 54	
	d									10 15									10 45			
Angmering 3	d							10 17		10 23							10 43		10 53			
Goring-by-Sea	d									10 27							10 47		10 57			
Durrington-on-Sea	d									10 30							10 50		11 00			
West Worthing	d						10 09			10 32						10 39	10 52		11 02			
Worthing 4	a						10 11	10 24		10 34						10 41	10 54		11 04			
	d						10 12	10 26		10 36						10 42	10 56		11 06			
East Worthing	d						10 14									10 44						
Lancing	d						10 17	10 30								10 47	11 00		11 10			
Shoreham-by-Sea	d						10 22	10 34		10 42						10 52	11 04		11 14			
Southwick	d						10 25	10 37								10 55	11 07					
Fishersgate	d						10 27									10 57						
Portslade	d						10 29	10 40		10 47						10 59	11 10					
Aldrington	d						10 31									11 01						
Hove 2	a						10 33	10 43		10 50						11 03	11 13		11 20			
	d						10 34	10 44		10 51	10 54					11 04	11 14		11 21	11 24		
Brighton 10	a						10 38	10 48			10 58					11 08	11 18			11 28		
Preston Park	d									10 55												
Burgess Hill	a									11 03												
Haywards Heath 3	a									11 12									11 35			
Arundel	d			09 46									10 12									
Amberley	d												10 17									
Pulborough	d			09 55									10 23									
Billingshurst	d			10 01									10 29									
Christs Hospital	d												10 36									
Horsham 4	a			10 10	10 18								10 40	10 48								
	d			10 20									10 50									
Crawley	d			10 29									10 59									
Three Bridges 4	a			10 32									11 02									
Gatwick Airport 10 ✈	a			10 37						11 25			11 07						11 55			
	d			10 38						11 26			11 08						11 56			
Horley	a			10 41																		
Redhill 5	a			10 48									11 16									
East Croydon 🚌	a			10 59						11 40			11 27						12 11			
London Bridge 4 ⊖	a																					
Clapham Junction 10	a			11 09						11 50			11 37						12 21			
Clapham Junction 15 ⊖	a			11 16						11 57			11 44						12 28			

Table 188R

Mondays to Fridays

9 December to 16 May

Southampton, Portsmouth and Sussex Coast - Brighton, Gatwick Airport and London

Network Diagram - see first Page of Table 175

		SN	SN	SN	SN	SN	SN	SN	SN	SN	SN	SN	SN	SN	SN	SN	SN	SN	SN	SN	SN	SN	SN
		1	1				1 ⚲	1			1	1			1	1 ⚲	1				1	1	
Eastleigh	d																						
Southampton Airport Parkway	d																						
Southampton Central	d											10 13			10 33								
Swanwick	d											10 32			10 50								
Fareham	d											10 39			10 57								
Portchester	d											10 44											
Cosham	d											10 48			11 05								
Portsmouth Harbour	d		10 12			10 29																11 12	
Portsmouth & Southsea	d		10 16			10 33													10 59			11 16	
Fratton	d		10 20			10 37													11 04			11 20	
Hilsea	d																		11 08				
Bedhampton	d																		11 13				
Havant	d		10 30			10 46						10 56			11 12				11 16			11 30	
Warblington	d																		11 18				
Emsworth	d					10 50						11 00			11 16				11 21				
Southbourne	d					10 53						11 03							11 24				
Nutbourne	d																		11 26				
Bosham	d																		11 30				
Fishbourne (Sussex)	d																		11 33				
Chichester 4	a		10 40			11 00						11 10			11 24				11 36			11 40	
	d		10 41			11 00						11 11			11 25				11 37			11 41	
Bognor Regis 4	d	10 30								11 07	10 56									11 39	11 30		
Barnham	a	10 36	10 48			11 08				11 13	11 02	11 18			11 32				11 44	11 45	11 36	11 48	
	d	10 37	10 49	10 52		11 08	11 12			11 15	11 03	11 19	11 22		11 33	11 39			11 45		11 37	11 49	11 52
Bognor Regis	a			11 00			11 18						11 30			11 48							12 00
Ford 4	d	10 41								11 19	11 07				11 37				11 49		11 41		
Littlehampton 4	a									11 25									11 54				
	d							11 15									11 45						
Angmering 3	d					11 17		11 23							11 43		11 53						
Goring-by-Sea	d							11 27							11 47		11 57						
Durrington-on-Sea	d							11 30							11 50		12 00						
West Worthing	d				11 09			11 32						11 39	11 52		12 02						
Worthing 4	a				11 11	11 24		11 34						11 41	11 54		12 04						
	d				11 12	11 26		11 36						11 42	11 56		12 06						
East Worthing	d				11 14									11 44									
Lancing	d				11 17	11 30								11 47	12 00		12 10						
Shoreham-by-Sea	d				11 22	11 34		11 42						11 52	12 04		12 14						
Southwick	d				11 25	11 37								11 55	12 07								
Fishersgate	d				11 27									11 57									
Portslade	d				11 29	11 40		11 47						11 59	12 10								
Aldrington	d				11 31									12 01									
Hove 2	a				11 33	11 43		11 50						12 03	12 13		12 20						
	d				11 34	11 44		11 51	11 54					12 04	12 14		12 21	12 24					
Brighton 10	a				11 38	11 48			11 58					12 08	12 18			12 28					
Preston Park	d							11 55															
Burgess Hill	a							12 03															
Haywards Heath 3	a							12 11									12 35						
Arundel	d	10 46									11 12										11 46		
Amberley	d										11 17												
Pulborough	d	10 55									11 23										11 55		
Billingshurst	d	11 01									11 29										12 01		
Christs Hospital	d										11 36												
Horsham 4	a	11 10	11 18								11 40	11 48									12 10	12 18	
	d		11 20									11 50										12 20	
Crawley	d		11 29									11 59										12 29	
Three Bridges 4	a		11 32									12 02										12 32	
Gatwick Airport 10	a		11 37					12 24				12 07					12 55					12 37	
	d		11 38					12 25				12 08					12 56					12 38	
Horley	a		11 41																			12 41	
Redhill 5	a		11 48									12 16										12 48	
East Croydon	a		11 59					12 40				12 27					13 11					12 59	
London Bridge 4	a																						
Clapham Junction 10	a		12 09					12 49				12 37					13 20					13 09	
Clapham Junction 15	a		12 18					12 56				12 44					13 27					13 16	

Table 188R

Mondays to Fridays

9 December to 16 May

Southampton, Portsmouth and Sussex Coast - Brighton, Gatwick Airport and London

Network Diagram - see first Page of Table 175

		SN	SN	SN 1 🚲	SN 1	SN	SN	SN 1	SN 1	SN	SN	SN 1	SN 1	SN 1	SN	SN	SN	SN 1	SN 1	SN	SN	SN
Eastleigh	d																					
Southampton Airport Parkway	d																					
Southampton Central	d								11 13			11 33										
Swanwick	d								11 33			11 50										
Fareham	d								11 40			11 57										
Portchester	d								11 45													
Cosham	d								11 49			12 05										
Portsmouth Harbour	d		11 29																12 12			12 29
Portsmouth & Southsea	d		11 33													11 59			12 16			12 33
Fratton	d		11 37													12 04			12 20			12 37
Hilsea	d															12 08						
Bedhampton	d															12 13						
Havant	d		11 46						11 56			12 12				12 16			12 30			12 46
Warblington	d															12 18						
Emsworth	d		11 50						12 00			12 16				12 21						12 50
Southbourne	d		11 53						12 03							12 24						12 53
Nutbourne	d															12 26						
Bosham	d															12 30						
Fishbourne (Sussex)	d															12 33						
Chichester 4	a		12 00						12 10			12 24				12 36			12 40			13 00
	d		12 00						12 11			12 25				12 37			12 41			13 00
Bognor Regis 4	d						12 07	11 56									12 39	12 30				
Barnham	a		12 08				12 13	12 02	12 18			12 32				12 44	12 45	12 36	12 48			13 08
	d		12 08	12 12			12 15	12 03	12 19	12 22		12 33	12 39			12 45		12 37	12 49	12 52		13 08
Bognor Regis	a			12 18						12 30			12 48							13 00		
Ford 4	d						12 19	12 07				12 37				12 49		12 41				
Littlehampton 4	a						12 25									12 56						
	d				12 15									12 45								
Angmering 3	d		12 17		12 23							12 43		12 53								13 17
Goring-by-Sea	d				12 27							12 47		12 57								
Durrington-on-Sea	d				12 30							12 50		13 00								
West Worthing	d	12 09			12 32						12 39	12 52		13 02							13 09	
Worthing 4	a	12 11	12 24		12 34						12 41	12 54		13 04							13 11	13 24
	d	12 12	12 26		12 36						12 42	12 56		13 06							13 12	13 26
East Worthing	d	12 14									12 44										13 14	
Lancing	d	12 17	12 30								12 47	13 00		13 10							13 17	13 30
Shoreham-by-Sea	d	12 22	12 34		12 42						12 52	13 04		13 14							13 22	13 34
Southwick	d	12 25	12 37								12 55	13 07									13 25	13 37
Fishersgate	d	12 27									12 57										13 27	
Portslade	d	12 29	12 40		12 47						12 59	13 10									13 29	13 40
Aldrington	d	12 31									13 01										13 31	
Hove 2	a	12 33	12 43		12 50						13 03	13 13		13 20							13 33	13 43
	d	12 34	12 44		12 51	12 54					13 04	13 14		13 21	13 24						13 34	13 44
Brighton 10	a	12 38	12 48			12 58					13 08	13 18			13 28						13 38	13 48
Preston Park	d				12 55																	
Burgess Hill	a				13 03																	
Haywards Heath 3	a				13 11									13 35								
Arundel	d							12 12										12 46				
Amberley	d							12 17														
Pulborough	d							12 23										12 55				
Billingshurst	d							12 29										13 01				
Christs Hospital	d							12 36														
Horsham 4	a							12 40	12 48									13 10	13 18			
	d							12 50										13 20				
Crawley	d							12 59										13 29				
Three Bridges 4	a							13 02										13 32				
Gatwick Airport 10	a				13 24			13 07						13 55				13 37				
	d				13 25			13 08						13 56				13 38				
Horley	a																	13 41				
Redhill 5	a							13 16										13 48				
East Croydon	a				13 40			13 28						14 11				13 59				
London Bridge 4	a																					
Clapham Junction 10	a				13 50			13 37						14 20				14 09				
Clapham Junction 15	a				13 57			13 44						14 28				14 16				

Table 188R

Mondays to Fridays

9 December to 16 May

Southampton, Portsmouth and Sussex Coast - Brighton, Gatwick Airport and London

Network Diagram - see first Page of Table 175

		SN 1	SN 1	SN	SN	SN 1	SN 1	SN	SN	SN 1	SN 1	SN 1	SN	SN	SN	SN 1	SN 1	SN	SN	SN	SN 1	SN 1 A 🚌	SN
Eastleigh	d																						
Southampton Airport Parkway	d																						
Southampton Central ⛴	d						12 13			12 33													
Swanwick	d						12 33			12 50													
Fareham	d						12 40			12 56													
Portchester	d						12 45																
Cosham	d						12 49			13 05													
Portsmouth Harbour ⛴	d																13 12			13 29			
Portsmouth & Southsea	d													12 59			13 16			13 33			
Fratton	d													13 04			13 20			13 37			
Hilsea	d													13 08									
Bedhampton	d													13 13									
Havant	d						12 56			13 11				13 16			13 30			13 46			
Warblington	d													13 18									
Emsworth	d						13 00			13 15				13 21						13 50			
Southbourne	d						13 03							13 24						13 53			
Nutbourne	d													13 26									
Bosham	d													13 30									
Fishbourne (Sussex)	d													13 33									
Chichester 4	a						13 10			13 23				13 36			13 40			14 00			
	d						13 11			13 25				13 37			13 41			14 00			
Bognor Regis 4	d				13 07	12 56									13 39	13 30							
Barnham	a				13 13	13 02	13 18			13 32				13 44	13 45	13 36	13 48			14 08			
	d	13 12			13 15	13 03	13 19	13 22		13 33	13 39			13 45		13 37	13 49	13 52		14 08	14 12		
Bognor Regis	a	13 18						13 30			13 48							14 00			14 18		
Ford 4	d				13 19	13 07				13 37				13 49		13 41							
Littlehampton 4	a				13 25									13 54									
	d		13 15									13 45										14 15	
Angmering 3	d		13 23							13 43		13 53								14 17		14 23	
Goring-by-Sea	d		13 27							13 47		13 57										14 27	
Durrington-on-Sea	d		13 30							13 50		14 00										14 30	
West Worthing	d		13 32						13 39	13 52		14 02							14 09			14 32	
Worthing 4	a		13 34						13 41	13 54		14 04							14 11	14 24		14 34	
	d		13 36						13 42	13 56		14 06							14 12	14 26		14 36	
East Worthing	d								13 44										14 14				
Lancing	d								13 47	14 00		14 10							14 17	14 30			
Shoreham-by-Sea	d		13 42						13 52	14 04		14 14							14 22	14 34		14 42	
Southwick	d								13 55	14 07									14 25	14 37			
Fishersgate	d								13 57										14 27				
Portslade	d		13 47						13 59	14 10									14 29	14 40		14 47	
Aldrington	d								14 01										14 31				
Hove 2	a		13 50						14 03	14 13		14 20							14 33	14 43		14 50	
	d		13 51	13 54					14 04	14 14		14 21	14 24						14 34	14 44		14 51	14 54
Brighton 10	a			13 58					14 08	14 18			14 28						14 38	14 48			14 58
Preston Park	d		13 55																			14 55	
Burgess Hill	a		14 03																			15 03	
Haywards Heath 3	a		14 11									14 35										15 11	
Arundel	d					13 12										13 46							
Amberley	d					13 17																	
Pulborough	d					13 23										13 55							
Billingshurst	d					13 29										14 01							
Christs Hospital	d					13 36																	
Horsham 4	a					13 40	13 48									14 10	14 18						
	d					13 50										14 20							
Crawley	d					13 59										14 29							
Three Bridges 4	a					14 02										14 32							
Gatwick Airport 10 ✈	a		14 24			14 07						14 55				14 37						15 24	
	d		14 25			14 08						14 56				14 38						15 25	
Horley	a															14 41							
Redhill 5	a					14 16										14 48							
East Croydon 🚋	a		14 40			14 27						15 11				14 59						15 40	
London Bridge 4 ⊖	a																						
Clapham Junction 10	a		14 49			14 37						15 20				15 09						15 49	
Clapham Junction 15 ⊖	a		14 57			14 44						15 27				15 20						15 57	

A 🚌 from Haywards Heath

Table 188R

Mondays to Fridays

9 December to 16 May

Southampton, Portsmouth and Sussex Coast - Brighton, Gatwick Airport and London

Network Diagram - see first Page of Table 175

		SN	SN 1	SN 1		SN	SN	SN 1	SN 1	SN 1 A 🚌	SN	SN	SN	SN 1	SN 1		SN	SN	SN	SN 1	SN 1 A 🚌	SN	SN	SN 1	SN 1
Eastleigh	d																								
Southampton Airport Parkway	d																								
Southampton Central 🚢	d			13 13				13 33																	14 13
Swanwick	d			13 33				13 50																	14 33
Fareham	d			13 40				13 56																	14 40
Portchester	d			13 45																					14 45
Cosham	d			13 49				14 05																	14 49
Portsmouth Harbour 🚢	d														14 12				14 29						
Portsmouth & Southsea	d											13 59			14 16				14 33						
Fratton	d											14 04			14 20				14 37						
Hilsea	d											14 08													
Bedhampton	d											14 13													
Havant	d			13 56				14 11				14 16			14 30				14 46						14 56
Warblington	d											14 18													
Emsworth	d			14 00				14 15				14 21							14 50						15 00
Southbourne	d			14 03								14 24							14 53						15 03
Nutbourne	d											14 26													
Bosham	d											14 30													
Fishbourne (Sussex)	d											14 33													
Chichester 4	a			14 10				14 23				14 36			14 40				15 00						15 10
	d			14 11				14 25				14 37			14 41				15 00						15 11
Bognor Regis 4	d	14 07	13 56										14 39	14 30									15 07	14 56	
Barnham	a	14 13	14 02	14 18				14 32				14 44	14 45	14 36	14 48				15 08				15 13	15 02	15 18
	d	14 15	14 03	14 19		14 22		14 33	14 39			14 45		14 37	14 49		14 52		15 08	15 12			15 15	15 03	15 19
Bognor Regis	a					14 30			14 48								15 00			15 18					
Ford 4	d	14 19	14 07					14 37				14 49		14 41									15 19	15 07	
Littlehampton 4	a	14 25										14 56											15 25		
	d									14 45											15 15				
Angmering 3	d							14 43		14 53									15 17		15 23				
Goring-by-Sea	d							14 47		14 57											15 27				
Durrington-on-Sea	d							14 50		15 00											15 30				
West Worthing	d						14 39	14 52		15 02								15 09			15 32				
Worthing 4	a						14 41	14 54		15 04								15 11	15 24		15 34				
	d						14 42	14 56		15 06								15 12	15 26		15 35				
East Worthing	d						14 44											15 14			15 37				
Lancing	d						14 47	15 00		15 10								15 17	15 30						
Shoreham-by-Sea	d						14 52	15 04		15 14								15 22	15 34		15 43				
Southwick	d						14 55	15 07										15 25	15 37						
Fishersgate	d						14 57											15 27							
Portslade	d						14 59	15 10										15 29	15 40		15 48				
Aldrington	d						15 01											15 31							
Hove 2	a						15 03	15 13		15 20								15 33	15 43		15 51				
	d						15 04	15 14		15 21	15 24							15 34	15 44		15 52	15 54			
Brighton 10	a						15 08	15 18			15 28							15 38	15 48			15 58			
Preston Park	d																				15 56				
Burgess Hill	a																				16 04				
Haywards Heath 3	a									15 35											16 12				
Arundel	d		14 12											14 46										15 12	
Amberley	d		14 17																					15 17	
Pulborough	d		14 23											14 55										15 23	
Billingshurst	d		14 29											15 01										15 29	
Christs Hospital	d		14 36																					15 36	
Horsham 4	a		14 40	14 48										15 10	15 18									15 40	15 48
	d		14 50											15 20										15 50	
Crawley	d		14 59											15 29										15 59	
Three Bridges 4	a		15 02											15 32										16 02	
Gatwick Airport 10 ✈	a		15 07							15 55				15 37							16 25			16 07	
	d		15 08							15 56				15 38							16 26			16 08	
Horley	a													15 41											
Redhill 5	a		15 16											15 48										16 17	
East Croydon 🚋	a		15 28							16 11				15 59							16 41			16 29	
London Bridge 4 ⊖	a																								
Clapham Junction 10	a		15 37							16 20				16 09							16 50			16 39	
Clapham Junction 15 ⊖	a		15 46							16 28				16 16							16 58			16 46	

A 🚌 from Haywards Heath

Table 188R

Mondays to Fridays

9 December to 16 May

Southampton, Portsmouth and Sussex Coast - Brighton, Gatwick Airport and London

Network Diagram - see first Page of Table 175

Station		SN	SN	SN	GW	SN	SN	SN	SN	SN	SN	SN	SN	SN	SN	SN	SN	SN	SN	SN	SN	SN
				1	R	1	1		1				1	1			1		1	1		1
									A													A
					⚲				⚲													⚲
Eastleigh	d			14 41																		
Southampton Airport Parkway	d			14n34																		
Southampton Central ⛴	d			14n26	14 34															15 13		
Swanwick	d																			15 33		
Fareham	d			14 56	14 59															15 40		
Portchester	d																			15 45		
Cosham	d				15 07															15 49		
Portsmouth Harbour ⛴	d													15 12		15 29						
Portsmouth & Southsea	d											14 59		15 16		15 33						
Fratton	d											15 04		15 20		15 37						
Hilsea	d											15 08										
Bedhampton	d											15 14										
Havant	d			15 09	15 15							15 17		15 30		15 46				15 58		
Warblington	d											15 19										
Emsworth	d											15 22				15 50				16 02		
Southbourne	d											15 25				15 53				16 05		
Nutbourne	d											15 28										
Bosham	d											15 31										
Fishbourne (Sussex)	d											15 34										
Chichester 4	a			15 19	15 25							15 37		15 41		16 00				16 12		
	d			15 20	15 29							15 38		15 42		16 00				16 13		
Bognor Regis 4	d							15 39					15 27					16 09	15 56			
Barnham	a			15 27	15 36			15 45				15 45	15 33	15 49		16 08		16 15	16 02	16 20		
	d	15 22		15 28	15 37		15 40					15 46	15 34	15 50	15 53	16 08	16 12		16 03	16 21	16 24	
Bognor Regis	a	15 30					15 48								16 00		16 18				16 31	
Ford 4	d			15 32								15 50	15 38						16 07			
Littlehampton 4	a											15 57										
	d								15 45		15 50											16 15
Angmering 3	d			15 39					15 53		16 00					16 17						16 23
Goring-by-Sea	d			15 43					15 57		16 04											16 27
Durrington-on-Sea	d			15 46					16 00		16 07											16 30
West Worthing	d		15 39	15 48		←			16 02		16 09											16 32
Worthing 4	a		15 41	15 51	15 54	15 51			16 04		16 11					16 24						16 34
	d		15 42	15 59	15 55	15 59			16 06		16 12					16 26						16 36
East Worthing	d		15 44	→							16 14											
Lancing	d		15 47			16 03			16 10		16 17					16 30						
Shoreham-by-Sea	d		15 52		16 01	16 07			16 14		16 22					16 34						16 42
Southwick	d		15 55			16 10					16 25					16 37						
Fishersgate	d		15 57								16 27											
Portslade	d		15 59			16 13					16 29					16 40						16 47
Aldrington	d		16 01								16 31											
Hove 2	a		16 03		16 07	16 16			16 20		16 33					16 43						16 50
	d		16 04		16 08	16 17			16 21	16 24	16 34					16 44						16 51
Brighton 10	a		16 08		16 14	16 21				16 28	16 38					16 48						
Preston Park	d																					
Burgess Hill	a																					17 01
Haywards Heath 3	a								16 35													17 12
Arundel	d												15 43						16 12			
Amberley	d																		16 17			
Pulborough	d												15 52						16 23			
Billingshurst	d												15 58						16 29			
Christs Hospital	d												16 05						16 36			
Horsham 4	a												16 10	16 18					16 40	16 50		
	d												16 20						16 52			
Crawley	d												16 29						17 01			
Three Bridges 4	a												16 32						17 04			
Gatwick Airport 10 ✈	a								16 57				16 37						17 09			17 25
	d								16 58				16 38						17 10			17 26
Horley	a																					
Redhill 5	a												16 46						17 18			
East Croydon	a								17 12				17 01						17 29			17 41
London Bridge 4 ⊖	a																					
Clapham Junction 10	a								17 23				17 10						17 39			17 51
Clapham Junction 15 ⊖	a								17 30				17 17						17 46			17 58

A ⚲ from Haywards Heath

n Stops at these stations before Eastleigh

Table 188R

Mondays to Fridays

9 December to 16 May

Southampton, Portsmouth and Sussex Coast - Brighton, Gatwick Airport and London

Network Diagram - see first Page of Table 175

		SN	SN	SN	SN	SN	SN	SN	SN	SN	SN	SN	SN	SN	SN	SN	SN	SN	SN	SN	SN	SN	SN
				1	1	1	1 A 🚲				1	1 B				1	1	1		1 A 🚲			
Eastleigh	d																						
Southampton Airport Parkway	d																						
Southampton Central ⛴	d			15 33														16 12					
Swanwick	d			15 50														16 29					
Fareham	d			15 57														16 36					
Portchester	d																	16 41					
Cosham	d			16 05														16 45					
Portsmouth Harbour ⛴	d										16 12	16 12			16 29								16 40
Portsmouth & Southsea	d								15 59		16 16	16 16			16 33								16 46
Fratton	d								16 04		16 20	16 20			16 37								16 50
Hilsea	d								16 08														16 54
Bedhampton	d								16 13														
Havant	d			16 12					16 16		16 30	16 30			16 46			16 52					17 00
Warblington	d								16 18														17 02
Emsworth	d			16 16					16 21		16 34	16 34			16 50			16 56					17 05
Southbourne	d								16 24						16 53			16 59					17 08
Nutbourne	d								16 26														17 10
Bosham	d								16 30									17 03					17 14
Fishbourne (Sussex)	d								16 33														17 17
Chichester 4	a			16 24					16 36		16 42	16 42			17 00			17 08					17 20
	d			16 25					16 37		16 43	16 43			17 00			17 13					17 21
Bognor Regis 4	d				16 30					16 39							16 56					17 18	
Barnham	a			16 32	16 36				16 44	16 45	16 50	16 50			17 08		17 02	17 20				17 24	17 28
	d			16 33	16 37	16 40			16 45		16 51	16 51	16 54		17 08	17 12	17 03	17 21	17 24			17 25	17 29
Bognor Regis	a					16 48							17 01			17 18			17 31				
Ford 4	d			16 37	16 41				16 49								17 07					17 29	
Littlehampton 4	a								16 54													17 37	
	d						16 45													17 15			
Angmering 3	d			16 43			16 53								17 17					17 23			
Goring-by-Sea	d			16 47			16 57													17 27			
Durrington-on-Sea	d			16 50			17 00													17 30			
West Worthing	d		16 39	16 52			17 02							17 09						17 32			
Worthing 4	a		16 41	16 54			17 04							17 11	17 24					17 34			17 43
	d		16 42	16 56			17 06							17 12	17 26					17 36			17 43
East Worthing	d		16 44											17 14									17 46
Lancing	d		16 47	17 00			17 10							17 17	17 30								17 49
Shoreham-by-Sea	d		16 52	17 04			17 14							17 22	17 34					17 42			17 53
Southwick	d		16 55	17 07										17 25	17 37								17 56
Fishersgate	d		16 57											17 27									17 58
Portslade	d		16 59	17 10										17 29	17 40					17 47			18 00
Aldrington	d		17 01											17 31									18 02
Hove 2	a		17 03	17 13			17 20							17 33	17 43					17 50			18 04
	d	16 54	17 04	17 14			17 21	17 24						17 34	17 44					17 51	18 01		18 05
Brighton 10	a	16 58	17 08	17 18				17 28						17 38	17 48						18 05		18 09
Preston Park	d																						
Burgess Hill	a																			18 03			
Haywards Heath 3	a						17 35													18 13			
Arundel	d				16 46												17 12						
Amberley	d																17 17						
Pulborough	d				16 55												17 23						
Billingshurst	d				17 01												17 29						
Christs Hospital	d				17 08												17 36						
Horsham 4	a				17 12						17 20	17 20					17 40	17 50					
	d				17 22							17 22					17 52						
Crawley	d				17 31							17 31					18 01						
Three Bridges 4	a				17 34							17 34					18 04						
Gatwick Airport 10 ✈	a				17 41		17 54					17 41					18 09			18 26			
	d				17 42		17 55					17 42					18 10			18 27			
Horley	a																						
Redhill 5	a				17 49							17 49					18 18						
East Croydon 🚌	a				18 02		18 11					18 02					18 30			18 42			
London Bridge 4 ⊖	a																						
Clapham Junction 10	a				18 12		18 21					18 12					18 40			18 52			
Clapham Junction 15 ⊖	a				18 20		18 29					18 20					18 47			18 59			

A 🚲 from Haywards Heath

B until 7 February

Table 188R

Mondays to Fridays

9 December to 16 May

Southampton, Portsmouth and Sussex Coast - Brighton, Gatwick Airport and London

Network Diagram - see first Page of Table 175

		SN 1	SN 1	SN 1 A 🚲	SN	SN	SN 1	SN 1	SN	SN	SN	SN	SN 1 🚲	SN 1	SN 1	SN 1	SN	SN	SN	SN	SN 1	SN 1 🚲	SN 1
Eastleigh	d																						
Southampton Airport Parkway	d																						
Southampton Central	d	16 33													17 13						17 33		
Swanwick	d	16 50													17 33						17 50		
Fareham	d	16 57													17 40						17 56		
Portchester	d														17 45								
Cosham	d	17 05													17 49						18 05		
Portsmouth Harbour	d							17 12				17 29											
Portsmouth & Southsea	d					17 00		17 16				17 33								17 46			
Fratton	d					17 04		17 20				17 37								17 50			
Hilsea	d					17 08														17 54			
Bedhampton	d					17 14																	
Havant	d	17 12				17 17		17 30				17 46			17 56					18 00	18 11		
Warblington	d					17 19														18 02			
Emsworth	d	17 17				17 22						17 50			18 00					18 05	18 15		
Southbourne	d					17 25						17 53			18 03					18 08			
Nutbourne	d					17 28														18 10			
Bosham	d					17 31														18 14			
Fishbourne (Sussex)	d					17 34														18 17			
Chichester 4	a	17 25				17 37		17 42				18 00			18 10					18 20	18 24		
	d	17 25				17 38		17 43				18 00			18 13					18 21	18 25		
Bognor Regis 4	d						17 30			17 51				17 57				18 19					18 33
Barnham	a	17 33				17 45	17 36	17 50		17 57		18 08		18 03	18 20			18 25		18 28	18 32		18 39
	d	17 33	17 42			17 46	17 37	17 51	17 54		18 08	18 08	18 14	18 04	18 21				18 27	18 29	18 33	18 35	18 40
Bognor Regis	a		17 49						18 02		18 14		18 22						18 34			18 41	
Ford 4	d	17 38				17 50	17 41							18 08						18 33			18 44
Littlehampton 4	a					17 55														18 42			
	d			17 45												18 15							
Angmering 3	d	17 44		17 53								18 18				18 23					18 42		18 53
Goring-by-Sea	d	17 48		17 57												18 27							18 57
Durrington-on-Sea	d	17 50		18 00												18 30					18 48		19 00
West Worthing	d	17 52		18 02												18 32							19 02
Worthing 4	a	17 55		18 04								18 25				18 34					18 52		19 04
	d	17 56		18 06								18 25				18 35					18 52		19 05
East Worthing	d											18 28									18 55		
Lancing	d	18 00		18 10								18 31				18 39					18 58		19 09
Shoreham-by-Sea	d	18 04		18 14								18 35				18 43					19 02		19 13
Southwick	d	18 07										18 38									19 05		
Fishersgate	d											18 40									19 07		
Portslade	d	18 10										18 42				18 48					19 09		19 18
Aldrington	d											18 44									19 11		
Hove 2	a	18 13		18 20								18 46				18 51					19 13		19 21
	d	18 14		18 21	18 24							18 47				18 52	19 00				19 15		19 22
Brighton 10	a	18 18			18 28							18 51					19 04				19 19		
Preston Park	d																						
Burgess Hill	a			18 33																			19 32
Haywards Heath 3	a			18 43												19 07							19 37
Arundel	d						17 46							18 13									
Amberley	d													18 18									
Pulborough	d						17 55							18 24									
Billingshurst	d						18 01							18 30									
Christs Hospital	d						18 08							18 37									
Horsham 4	a						18 12	18 20						18 42	18 50								
	d						18 22							18 52									
Crawley	d						18 31							19 01									
Three Bridges 4	a						18 34							19 04									
Gatwick Airport 10 ✈	a			18 56			18 39							19 09		19 25							19 55
	d			18 57			18 40							19 10		19 26							19 56
Horley	a																						
Redhill 5	a						18 48							19 17									
East Croydon	a			19 12			18 59							19 29		19 42							20 11
London Bridge 4 ⊖	a																						
Clapham Junction 10	a			19 21			19 11							19 39		19 51							20 21
Clapham Junction 15 ⊖	a			19 28			19 18							19 47		19 59							20 29

A 🚲 from Haywards Heath

Table 188R

Mondays to Fridays

9 December to 16 May

Southampton, Portsmouth and Sussex Coast - Brighton, Gatwick Airport and London

Network Diagram - see first Page of Table 175

		SN		SN 1	SN	SN	SN	SN 1	SN 1	SN 1	SN	SN		SN 1	SN 1	SN	SN	SN 1	SN 1	SN 1	SN	SN		SN	SN
Eastleigh	d																								
Southampton Airport Parkway	d																								
Southampton Central	d													18 11				18 33							
Swanwick	d													18 28				18 50							
Fareham	d													18 35				18 56							
Portchester	d													18 40											
Cosham	d													18 44				19 05							
Portsmouth Harbour	d							18 27								18 37									
Portsmouth & Southsea	d			17 59				18 31								18 42								18 59	
Fratton	d			18 04				18 35								18 46								19 04	
Hilsea	d			18 08												18 50								19 08	
Bedhampton	d			18 13																				19 13	
Havant	d			18 16				18 43						18 51		18 56		19 11						19 16	
Warblington	d			18 18												18 58								19 18	
Emsworth	d			18 21				18 47						18 55		19 01								19 21	
Southbourne	d			18 24				18 50						18 58		19 04								19 24	
Nutbourne	d			18 26												19 07								19 27	
Bosham	d			18 30												19 10								19 30	
Fishbourne (Sussex)	d			18 33												19 13								19 33	
Chichester 4	a			18 36				18 57						19 05		19 17		19 22						19 36	
	d			18 37				18 58						19 06		19 17		19 22						19 40	
Bognor Regis 4	d					18 46						19 03								19 33					
Barnham	a			18 44		18 52		19 05				19 09		19 13		19 25		19 30		19 39				19 47	
	d			18 45		18 53	18 56	19 06	19 07			19 10		19 14	19 19	19 25	19 30	19 30	19 39	19 40				19 48	19 57
Bognor Regis	a						19 04		19 13						19 28		19 38		19 47						20 04
Ford 4	d					18 57						19 14		19 18		19 30				19 44				19 52	
Littlehampton 4	a					19 03						19 20				19 38								19 58	
	d				18 52					19 13												19 49			
Angmering 3	d				19 00			19 15		19 21								19 40		19 53		20 00			
Goring-by-Sea	d				19 04					19 25								19 44		19 57		20 04			
Durrington-on-Sea	d				19 07					19 28								19 46		20 00		20 07			
West Worthing	d				19 09					19 30								19 48		20 02		20 09			
Worthing 4	a				19 11			19 22		19 32								19 51		20 04		20 11			
	d				19 12			19 23		19 33								19 52		20 05		20 12			
East Worthing	d				19 14			19 25										19 55				20 14			
Lancing	d				19 17			19 28		19 37								19 58		20 09		20 17			
Shoreham-by-Sea	d				19 22			19 32		19 41								20 02		20 13		20 22			
Southwick	d				19 25			19 35										20 05				20 25			
Fishersgate	d				19 27			19 37										20 07				20 27			
Portslade	d				19 29			19 39		19 46								20 09		20 18		20 29			
Aldrington	d				19 31			19 42										20 11				20 31			
Hove 2	a				19 33			19 44		19 49								20 13		20 21		20 33			
	d	19 24			19 34			19 44		19 50	19 54							20 14		20 22	20 24	20 34			
Brighton 10	a	19 28			19 38			19 48			19 58							20 18			20 28	20 38			
Preston Park	d																								
Burgess Hill	a																			20 32					
Haywards Heath 3	a									20 04										20 38					
Arundel	d			18 52										19 23											
Amberley	d													19 28											
Pulborough	d			19 01										19 34											
Billingshurst	d			19 08										19 41											
Christs Hospital	d													19 47											
Horsham 4	a			19 16										19 51											
	d			19 17										19 52											
Crawley	d			19 26										20 01											
Three Bridges 4	a			19 29										20 04						20 47					
Gatwick Airport 10	a			19 39						20 24				20 10						20 51					
	d			19 40						20 25				20 11						20 53					
Horley	a																								
Redhill 5	a			19 48										20 18											
East Croydon	a			20 00						20 40				20 30						21 08					
London Bridge 4	a																								
Clapham Junction 10	a			20 11						20 49				20 40						21 18					
Clapham Junction 15	a			20 20						20 58				20 50						21 28					

Table 188R

Mondays to Fridays

9 December to 16 May

Southampton, Portsmouth and Sussex Coast - Brighton, Gatwick Airport and London

Network Diagram - see first Page of Table 175

		SN 1	SN 1	SN 1	SN	SN	SN 1	SN		SN 1	SN 1	SN 1	SN	SN 1 🚲	SN	SN	SN	SN		SN 1 A 🚲	SN	SN	SN 1 🚲	SN 1	SN
Eastleigh	d																								
Southampton Airport Parkway	d																								
Southampton Central ⛴	d						19 12				19 33													20 11	
Swanwick	d						19 29				19 51													20 28	
Fareham	d						19 36				19 57													20 35	
Portchester	d						19 41																	20 40	
Cosham	d						19 46				20 06													20 44	
Portsmouth Harbour ⛴	d									19 40															
Portsmouth & Southsea	d	19 32								19 44						19 59		20 32							
Fratton	d	19 36								19 48						20 04		20 36							
Hilsea	d															20 08									
Bedhampton	d															20 14									
Havant	d	19 46					19 52			19 57	20 12					20 17		20 45						20 51	
Warblington	d									19 59						20 19									
Emsworth	d	19 50					19 56			20 02	20 16					20 22		20 49						20 55	
Southbourne	d	19 53					19 59			20 05						20 25		20 52						20 58	
Nutbourne	d									20 07						20 27									
Bosham	d									20 11						20 31									
Fishbourne (Sussex)	d									20 14						20 34									
Chichester 4	a	20 00					20 06			20 17	20 24					20 37		20 59						21 05	
	d	20 01					20 07			20 18	20 25					20 38		20 59						21 07	
Bognor Regis 4	d					20 05						20 33										21 04			
Barnham	a	20 08				20 11	20 14			20 25	20 32	20 39				20 45		21 07				21 10		21 14	
	d	20 09	20 10			20 12	20 15	20 22		20 27	20 33	20 40		20 43		20 46	20 52	21 07				21 11	21 12	21 15	21 22
Bognor Regis	a		20 16					20 30						20 49			20 59						21 18		21 29
Ford 4	d					20 16	20 19			20 31		20 44				20 50						21 15		21 19	
Littlehampton 4	a					20 22				20 38						20 57						21 21			
	d			20 15											20 52					21 15					
Angmering 3	d	20 18		20 23							20 42	20 53			21 00			21 16		21 23					
Goring-by-Sea	d			20 27								20 57			21 04					21 27					
Durrington-on-Sea	d			20 30							20 48	21 00			21 07					21 30					
West Worthing	d			20 32								21 02			21 09					21 32					
Worthing 4	a	20 25		20 34							20 52	21 04			21 11			21 23		21 34					
	d	20 25		20 35							20 52	21 05			21 12			21 24		21 35					
East Worthing	d	20 28									20 55				21 14			21 26							
Lancing	d	20 31		20 39							20 58	21 09			21 17			21 29		21 39					
Shoreham-by-Sea	d	20 35		20 43							21 02	21 13			21 22			21 33		21 43					
Southwick	d	20 38									21 05				21 25			21 36							
Fishersgate	d	20 40									21 07				21 27			21 38							
Portslade	d	20 42		20 48							21 09	21 18			21 29			21 40		21 48					
Aldrington	d	20 44									21 11				21 31			21 43							
Hove 2	a	20 46		20 51							21 13	21 21			21 33			21 45		21 51					
	d	20 47		20 52	20 55						21 14	21 22	21 24		21 34			21 45		21 52	21 54				
Brighton 10	a	20 51			20 59						21 18		21 28		21 38			21 49			21 58				
Preston Park	d																								
Burgess Hill	a											21 32								22 03					
Haywards Heath 3	a			21 05								21 38								22 12					
Arundel	d						20 24																	21 24	
Amberley	d						20 29																	21 29	
Pulborough	d						20 35																	21 35	
Billingshurst	d						20 41																	21 41	
Christs Hospital	d						20 48																	21 48	
Horsham 4	a						20 52																	21 52	
	d						20 52																	21 52	
Crawley	d						21 01																	22 01	
Three Bridges 4	a						21 05					21 47												22 05	
Gatwick Airport 10 ✈	a			21 25			21 10					21 51								22 25				22 10	
	d			21 26			21 11					21 53								22 26				22 11	
Horley	a																								
Redhill 5	a						21 18																	22 18	
East Croydon 🚊	a			21 41			21 30					22 08								22 40				22 30	
London Bridge 4 ⊖	a																								
Clapham Junction 10	a			21 50			21 40					22 18								22 50				22 40	
Clapham Junction 15 ⊖	a			21 58			21 47					22 26								22 57				22 47	

A 🚲 from Haywards Heath

Table 188R

Mondays to Fridays

9 December to 16 May

Southampton, Portsmouth and Sussex Coast - Brighton, Gatwick Airport and London

Network Diagram - see first Page of Table 175

		SN	SN	SN	SN	SN	SN	SN	SN	SN	SN	SN	SN	SN	SN	SN	SN	SN	SN	SN	SN	SN
		1	1	1 ⚲					1		1		1	1			1	1				1
Eastleigh	d																					
Southampton Airport Parkway	d																					
Southampton Central ⛴	d		20 33										21 13				21 33					
Swanwick	d		20 50										21 33				21 51					
Fareham	d		20 57										21 40				21 58					
Portchester	d												21 45				22 03					
Cosham	d		21 06										21 49				22 07					
Portsmouth Harbour ⛴	d	20 40												21 40							22 15	
Portsmouth & Southsea	d	20 44							21 15					21 44							22 19	
Fratton	d	20 48							21 19					21 48							22 23	
Hilsea	d								21 23					21 52							22 27	
Bedhampton	d								21 28					21 57							22 32	
Havant	d	20 57	21 12						21 31				21 56	22 00			22 14				22 35	
Warblington	d	20 59							21 33								22 16					
Emsworth	d	21 02	21 16						21 36								22 19				22 39	
Southbourne	d	21 05							21 39								22 22				22 42	
Nutbourne	d	21 07							21 41								22 24					
Bosham	d	21 11							21 45								22 28					
Fishbourne (Sussex)	d	21 14							21 48								22 31					
Chichester 4	a	21 17	21 24						21 51				22 06	22 10			22 34				22 49	
	d	21 18	21 25						21 52				22 07	22 11			22 34	22 40			22 52	
Bognor Regis 4	d				21 39					22 00						22 30						
Barnham	a	21 25	21 32		21 45				21 59	22 06			22 14	22 18		22 36	22 42	22 47			22 59	
	d	21 26	21 33	21 42		21 52			22 00		22 12		22 15	22 19	22 22	22 37		22 48	22 52		23 00	23 06
Bognor Regis	a			21 48		22 00					22 18				22 30				23 00			23 13
Ford 4	d	21 30	21 37						22 04				22 19	22 23		22 41		22 52			23 04	
Littlehampton 4	a	21 37											22 24			22 47						
	d							21 52					22 33									
Angmering 3	d		21 43					22 00	22 11				22 41								23 11	
Goring-by-Sea	d		21 47					22 04	22 15				22 45								23 15	
Durrington-on-Sea	d		21 50					22 07	22 18				22 47								23 17	
West Worthing	d		21 52					22 09	22 20				22 49								23 19	
Worthing 4	a		21 54					22 11	22 22				22 52								23 22	
	d		21 55					22 12	22 23				22 52								23 22	
East Worthing	d		21 57					22 14	22 25				22 55								23 25	
Lancing	d		22 00					22 17	22 28				22 58								23 28	
Shoreham-by-Sea	d		22 04					22 22	22 32				23 02								23 32	
Southwick	d		22 07					22 25	22 35				23 05								23 35	
Fishersgate	d		22 09					22 27	22 37				23 07								23 37	
Portslade	d		22 11					22 29	22 39				23 09								23 39	
Aldrington	d		22 14					22 31	22 42				23 11								23 41	
Hove 2	a		22 16					22 33	22 44				23 13								23 43	
	d		22 16				22 24	22 34	22 44			22 54	23 14							23 24	23 44	
Brighton 10	a		22 21				22 28	22 38	22 48			22 58	23 18							23 28	23 48	
Preston Park	d																					
Burgess Hill	a																					
Haywards Heath 3	a																					
Arundel	d													22 28				22 57				
Amberley	d																	23 02				
Pulborough	d													22 37				23 08				
Billingshurst	d													22 43				23 14				
Christs Hospital	d													22 50				23 21				
Horsham 4	a													22 54				23 25				
	d													22 55				23 25				
Crawley	d													23 03				23 38				
Three Bridges 4	a													23 07				23 42				
Gatwick Airport 10 ✈	a																					
	d																					
Horley	a																					
Redhill 5	a																					
East Croydon 🚌	a																					
London Bridge 4 ⊖	a																					
Clapham Junction 10	a																					
Clapham Junction 15 ⊖	a																					

Table 188R

Mondays to Fridays

9 December to 16 May

Southampton, Portsmouth and Sussex Coast - Brighton, Gatwick Airport and London

Network Diagram - see first Page of Table 175

		SN 1	SN	SN	SN	SN 1	SN	SN	SN	SN
Eastleigh	d									
Southampton Airport Parkway	d									
Southampton Central ⛴	d	22 13				22 33				23 12
Swanwick	d	22 30				22 50				
Fareham	d	22 37				22 57				23 38
Portchester	d	22 42								
Cosham	d	22 47				23 05				23 46
Portsmouth Harbour ⛴	d				22 44				23 15	
Portsmouth & Southsea	d				22 48				23 19	
Fratton	d				22 52				23 23	
Hilsea	d				22 56				23 27	
Bedhampton	d				23 01				23 33	
Havant	d	22 57			23 05	23 12			23 36	23 53
Warblington	d								23 38	
Emsworth	d	23 01							23 41	
Southbourne	d	23 04							23 44	
Nutbourne	d								23 47	
Bosham	d								23 50	
Fishbourne (Sussex)	d								23 53	
Chichester 4	a	23 11			23 16	23 22			23 57	00 04
	d	23 12			23 17	23 23		23 52	23 57	00 04
Bognor Regis 4	d		23 15							
Barnham	a	23 19	23 21		23 24	23 30		23 59	00 05	00 12
	d	23 20			23 25	23 31	23 36	00 01	00 06	
Bognor Regis	a						23 44			
Ford 4	d				23 29			00 05	00 10	
Littlehampton 4	a	23 32			23 34	23 42		00 11	00 17	
	d				23 39					
Angmering 3	d				23 47					
Goring-by-Sea	d				23 51					
Durrington-on-Sea	d				23 53					
West Worthing	d				23 55					
Worthing 4	a				23 58					
	d				23 59					
East Worthing	d				00 01					
Lancing	d				00 04					
Shoreham-by-Sea	d				00 08					
Southwick	d				00 11					
Fishersgate	d				00 13					
Portslade	d				00 15					
Aldrington	d				00 18					
Hove 2	a				00 21					
	d			23 54	00 21					
Brighton 10	a			23 58	00 25					
Preston Park	d									
Burgess Hill	a									
Haywards Heath 3	a									
Arundel	d									
Amberley	d									
Pulborough	d									
Billingshurst	d									
Christs Hospital	d									
Horsham 4	a									
	d									
Crawley	d									
Three Bridges 4	a									
Gatwick Airport 10 ✈	a									
	d									
Horley	a									
Redhill 5	a									
East Croydon 🚋	a									
London Bridge 4 ⊖	a									
Clapham Junction 10	a									
Clapham Junction 15 ⊖	a									

Table 188R

Saturdays

14 December to 17 May

Southampton, Portsmouth and Sussex Coast - Brighton, Gatwick Airport and London

Network Diagram - see first Page of Table 175

		SN	SN	SN	SN ■1	SN	SN ■1	SN	SN ■1	SN	SN	SN ■1	SN ■1 A	SN	SN	SN	SN ■1	SN ■1	SN	SN	SN	SN	SN ■1
Eastleigh	d																						
Southampton Airport Parkway	d																						
Southampton Central	d																						
Swanwick	d																						
Fareham	d																						
Portchester	d																						
Cosham	d																						
Portsmouth Harbour	d																						
Portsmouth & Southsea	d								04 56														
Fratton	d								05 00														
Hilsea	d																						
Bedhampton	d																						
Havant	d								05 08								05 52						
Warblington	d																						
Emsworth	d																05 56						
Southbourne	d																05 59						
Nutbourne	d																						
Bosham	d																						
Fishbourne (Sussex)	d																						
Chichester ■4	a								05 19								06 06						
	d					00 04			05 19								06 06						06 25
Bognor Regis ■4	d							05 13		←					05 43	06 04				06 13			
Barnham	a					00 12		05 19	05 27	05 19					05 49	06 10	06 14			06 19			06 32
	d		00 01	00 06	00 09		04 48	05 31	05 27	05 31					05 50		06 14			06 20	06 22		06 33
Bognor Regis	a				00 16			↪													06 29		
Ford ■4	d		00 05	00 10			04 52			05 35					05 54		06 19			06 24			06 37
Littlehampton ■4	a		00 11	00 17			04 57			05 40										06 29			
	d						05 02					05 45	05 45					06 15					
Angmering ■3	d						05 10					05 53	05 53		06 00			06 23					06 43
Goring-by-Sea	d						05 14					05 57	05 57		06 04			06 27					06 47
Durrington-on-Sea	d						05 17					06 00	06 00		06 07			06 30					06 50
West Worthing	d						05 19					06 02	06 02		06 09			06 32				06 39	06 52
Worthing ■4	a						05 21		05 41			06 04	06 04		06 11			06 34				06 41	06 54
	d						05 22		05 42			06 05	06 05		06 12			06 35				06 42	06 56
East Worthing	d	00 01					05 24								06 14							06 44	
Lancing	d	00 04					05 27					06 09	06 09		06 17			06 39				06 47	07 00
Shoreham-by-Sea	d	00 08					05 32		05 48			06 13	06 13		06 22			06 43				06 52	07 04
Southwick	d	00 11					05 35								06 25							06 55	07 07
Fishersgate	d	00 13					05 37								06 27							06 57	
Portslade	d	00 15					05 39					06 17	06 17		06 29			06 47				06 59	07 10
Aldrington	d	00 18					05 41								06 31							07 01	
Hove ■2	a	00 21					05 43		05 54			06 21	06 21		06 33			06 51				07 03	07 13
	d	00 21					05 44		05 54		05 56	06 21	06 21	06 24	06 34			06 51	06 54			07 04	07 14
Brighton ■10	a	00 25					05 48				06 00			06 28	06 38				06 58			07 08	07 18
Preston Park	d																	06 55					
Burgess Hill	a																	07 04					
Haywards Heath ■3	a								06 08			06 35	06 35					07 09					
Arundel	d																06 24						
Amberley	d																06 29						
Pulborough	d																06 35						
Billingshurst	d																06 41						
Christs Hospital	d																06 48						
Horsham ■4	a																06 52						
	d																06 52						
Crawley	d																07 01						
Three Bridges ■4	a								06 20				06 48				07 05						
Gatwick Airport ■10 ✈	a								06 25				06 53				07 10	07 25					
	d								06 26				06 55				07 11	07 26					
Horley	a																						
Redhill ■5	a																07 18						
East Croydon	a								06 40				07 09				07 29	07 41					
London Bridge ■4 ⊖	a																						
Clapham Junction ■10	a								06 50				07 19				07 39	07 50					
Clapham Junction ■15 ⊖	a								06 57				07 27				07 46	07 58					

A until 8 February

Table 188R

Saturdays

14 December to 17 May

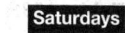

Southampton, Portsmouth and Sussex Coast - Brighton, Gatwick Airport and London

Network Diagram - see first Page of Table 175

		SN 1	SN	SN	SN	SN 1	SN 1	SN	SN 1	SN	SN	SN 1	SN 1	SN	SN	SN 1	SN 1 A	SN	SN	GW	SN 1	SN 1	SN
Eastleigh	d																						
Southampton Airport Parkway	d																						
Southampton Central	d															06 13	06 13				06 33		
Swanwick	d															06 33	06 33				06 50		
Fareham	d															06 40	06 40				06 56		
Portchester	d															06 45	06 45						
Cosham	d															06 49	06 49				07 05		
Portsmouth Harbour	d						06 12					06 29								06 48			
Portsmouth & Southsea	d			05 59			06 16					06 33								06 54			
Fratton	d			06 04			06 20					06 37								06 58			
Hilsea	d			06 08																			
Bedhampton	d			06 13																			
Havant	d			06 16			06 30					06 46				06 56	06 56			07 08	07 11		
Warblington	d			06 18																			
Emsworth	d			06 21								06 50				07 00	07 00				07 15		
Southbourne	d			06 24								06 53				07 03	07 03						
Nutbourne	d			06 26																			
Bosham	d			06 30																			
Fishbourne (Sussex)	d			06 33																			
Chichester 4	a			06 36			06 40					07 00				07 10	07 10			07 19	07 23		
	d			06 37			06 41					07 00				07 11	07 11			07 20	07 25		
Bognor Regis 4	d				06 39	06 30			06 56						07 07								
Barnham	a			06 44	06 45	06 36	06 48		07 02			07 08			07 13	07 18	07 18			07 27	07 32		
	d			06 45		06 37	06 49	06 52	07 03	07 05		07 08			07 15	07 19	07 19	07 22		07 28	07 33		
Bognor Regis	a							06 59		07 12								07 29					
Ford 4	d			06 49		06 41			07 07						07 19						07 37		
Littlehampton 4	a			06 54											07 24								
	d	06 45											07 15									07 45	
Angmering 3	d	06 55										07 17	07 23								07 43	07 53	
Goring-by-Sea	d	06 59											07 27								07 47	07 57	
Durrington-on-Sea	d	07 02											07 30								07 50	08 00	
West Worthing	d	07 04									07 09		07 32						07 39		07 52	08 02	
Worthing 4	a	07 06									07 11	07 24	07 34						07 41	07 45	07 54	08 04	
	d	07 07									07 12	07 26	07 36						07 42	07 50	07 56	08 06	
East Worthing	d										07 14								07 44				
Lancing	d	07 11									07 17	07 30							07 47		08 00	08 10	
Shoreham-by-Sea	d	07 15									07 22	07 34	07 42						07 52	07 57	08 04	08 14	
Southwick	d										07 25	07 37							07 55		08 07		
Fishersgate	d										07 27								07 57				
Portslade	d										07 29	07 40	07 47						07 59		08 10		
Aldrington	d										07 31								08 01				
Hove 2	a	07 21									07 33	07 43	07 50						08 03	08 07	08 13	08 20	
	d	07 22	07 24								07 34	07 44	07 51	07 54					08 04	08 08	08 14	08 21	08 24
Brighton 10	a		07 28								07 38	07 48		07 58					08 08	08 15	08 18		08 28
Preston Park	d												07 55										
Burgess Hill	a												08 03										
Haywards Heath 3	a	07 35											08 09									08 35	
Arundel	d					06 46			07 12														
Amberley	d								07 17														
Pulborough	d					06 55			07 23														
Billingshurst	d					07 01			07 29														
Christs Hospital	d								07 36														
Horsham 4	a					07 10	07 16		07 40							07 46	07 46						
	d					07 20			07 50								07 50						
Crawley	d					07 29			07 59								07 59						
Three Bridges 4	a					07 32			08 02								08 02						
Gatwick Airport 10	a	07 55				07 37			08 07				08 24				08 07					08 55	
	d	07 56				07 38			08 08				08 25				08 08					08 56	
Horley	a					07 41																	
Redhill 5	a					07 47			08 15								08 15						
East Croydon	a	08 11				07 59			08 27				08 40				08 27					09 11	
London Bridge 4	a																						
Clapham Junction 10	a	08 20				08 08			08 36				08 49				08 36					09 20	
Clapham Junction 15	a	08 28				08 16			08 44				08 57				08 44					09 28	

A until 8 February

Table 188R

Saturdays

14 December to 17 May

Southampton, Portsmouth and Sussex Coast - Brighton, Gatwick Airport and London

Network Diagram - see first Page of Table 175

	SN	SN		SN 1	SN 1	SN	SN	SN	SN 1	SN	SN	SN 1	SN 1		SN	SN	SN 1	SN 1	SN	SN	SN	SN 1	SN 1	
Eastleigh d																								
Southampton Airport Parkway d																								
Southampton Central d													07 13				07 33							
Swanwick d													07 33				07 50							
Fareham d													07 40				07 56							
Portchester d													07 45											
Cosham d													07 49				08 05							
Portsmouth Harbour d					07 12			07 29															08 12	
Portsmouth & Southsea d	06 56				07 16			07 33												07 59			08 16	
Fratton d	07 01				07 20			07 37												08 04			08 20	
Hilsea d	07 05																			08 08				
Bedhampton d	07 13																			08 13				
Havant d	07 16				07 30			07 46					07 56				08 11			08 16			08 30	
Warblington d	07 18																			08 18				
Emsworth d	07 21							07 50					08 00				08 15			08 21				
Southbourne d	07 24							07 53					08 03							08 24				
Nutbourne d	07 26																			08 27				
Bosham d	07 30																			08 30				
Fishbourne (Sussex) d	07 33																			08 33				
Chichester 4 a	07 36				07 40			08 00					08 10				08 23			08 36			08 40	
d	07 37				07 41			08 00					08 11				08 25			08 37			08 41	
Bognor Regis 4 d		07 39		07 30							08 07	07 56									08 39	08 30		
Barnham a	07 44	07 45		07 36	07 48			08 08			08 13	08 02	08 18				08 32			08 44	08 45	08 36	08 48	
d	07 45			07 37	07 49	07 52		08 08			08 15	08 03	08 19		08 22		08 33			08 45		08 37	08 49	
Bognor Regis a						07 59									08 29									
Ford 4 d	07 49			07 41							08 19	08 07	08 23				08 37			08 49		08 41		
Littlehampton 4 a	07 54										08 24									08 54				
d									08 15									08 45						
Angmering 3 d								08 17	08 23								08 43	08 53						
Goring-by-Sea d									08 27								08 47	08 57						
Durrington-on-Sea d									08 30								08 50	09 00						
West Worthing d							08 09		08 32							08 39	08 52	09 02						
Worthing 4 a							08 11	08 24	08 34							08 41	08 54	09 04						
d							08 12	08 26	08 36							08 42	08 56	09 06						
East Worthing d							08 14									08 44								
Lancing d							08 17	08 30								08 47	09 00	09 10						
Shoreham-by-Sea d							08 22	08 34	08 42							08 52	09 04	09 14						
Southwick d							08 25	08 37								08 55	09 07							
Fishersgate d							08 27									08 57								
Portslade d							08 29	08 40	08 47							08 59	09 10							
Aldrington d							08 31									09 01								
Hove 2 a							08 33	08 43	08 50							09 03	09 13	09 20						
d							08 34	08 44	08 51	08 54						09 04	09 14	09 21	09 24					
Brighton 10 a							08 38	08 48		08 58						09 08	09 18		09 28					
Preston Park d									08 55															
Burgess Hill a									09 03															
Haywards Heath 3 a									09 09									09 35						
Arundel d				07 46								08 12										08 46		
Amberley d												08 17												
Pulborough d				07 55								08 23										08 55		
Billingshurst d				08 01								08 29										09 01		
Christs Hospital d												08 36												
Horsham 4 a				08 10	08 16							08 40	08 47									09 10	09 16	
d				08 20								08 51										09 20		
Crawley d				08 29								08 59										09 29		
Three Bridges 4 a				08 32								09 03										09 32		
Gatwick Airport 10 a				08 37					09 25			09 07						09 55				09 37		
d				08 38					09 26			09 08						09 56				09 38		
Horley a				08 41																		09 41		
Redhill 5 a				08 47								09 15										09 47		
East Croydon a				08 59					09 41			09 27						10 11				09 59		
London Bridge 4 ⊖ a																								
Clapham Junction 10 a				09 08					09 50			09 36						10 20				10 08		
Clapham Junction 15 ⊖ a				09 16					09 58			09 44						10 28				10 16		

Table 188R

Saturdays

14 December to 17 May

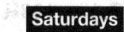

Southampton, Portsmouth and Sussex Coast - Brighton, Gatwick Airport and London

Network Diagram - see first Page of Table 175

		SN	SN	SN	SN 1	SN 1	SN	SN	SN 1	SN 1	SN	SN	SN 1	SN 1	SN 1	SN	SN	SN	SN 1	SN 1	SN	SN	SN
Eastleigh	d																						
Southampton Airport Parkway	d																						
Southampton Central ⛴	d									08 13			08 33										
Swanwick	d									08 33			08 50										
Fareham	d									08 40			08 56										
Portchester	d									08 45													
Cosham	d									08 49			09 05										
Portsmouth Harbour ⛴	d			08 29																09 12			09 29
Portsmouth & Southsea	d			08 33													08 59			09 16			09 33
Fratton	d			08 37													09 04			09 20			09 37
Hilsea	d																09 08						
Bedhampton	d																09 13						
Havant	d			08 46						08 56			09 11				09 16			09 30			09 46
Warblington	d																09 18						
Emsworth	d			08 50						09 00			09 15				09 21						09 50
Southbourne	d			08 53						09 03							09 24						09 53
Nutbourne	d																09 26						
Bosham	d																09 30						
Fishbourne (Sussex)	d																09 33						
Chichester 4	a			09 00						09 10			09 23				09 36			09 40			10 00
	d			09 00						09 11			09 25				09 37			09 41			10 00
Bognor Regis 4	d							09 07	08 56									09 39	09 30				
Barnham	a			09 08				09 13	09 02	09 18			09 32				09 44	09 45	09 36	09 48			10 08
	d	08 52		09 08	09 12			09 15	09 03	09 19	09 22		09 33	09 38			09 45		09 37	09 49	09 52		10 08
Bognor Regis	a	08 59			09 18						09 29			09 45							09 59		
Ford 4	d							09 19	09 07				09 37				09 49		09 41				
Littlehampton 4	a							09 24									09 54						
	d					09 15									09 45								
Angmering 3	d			09 17		09 23							09 43		09 53								10 17
Goring-by-Sea	d					09 27							09 47		09 57								
Durrington-on-Sea	d					09 30							09 50		10 00								
West Worthing	d		09 09			09 32						09 39	09 52		10 02							10 09	
Worthing 4	a		09 11	09 24		09 34						09 41	09 54		10 04							10 11	10 24
	d		09 12	09 26		09 36						09 42	09 56		10 06							10 12	10 26
East Worthing	d		09 14									09 44										10 14	
Lancing	d		09 17	09 30								09 47	10 00		10 10							10 17	10 30
Shoreham-by-Sea	d		09 22	09 34		09 42						09 52	10 04		10 14							10 22	10 34
Southwick	d		09 25	09 37								09 55	10 07									10 25	10 37
Fishersgate	d		09 27									09 57										10 27	
Portslade	d		09 29	09 40		09 47						09 59	10 10									10 29	10 40
Aldrington	d		09 31									10 01										10 31	
Hove 2	a		09 33	09 43		09 50						10 03	10 13		10 20							10 33	10 43
	d		09 34	09 44		09 51	09 54					10 04	10 14		10 21	10 24						10 34	10 44
Brighton 10	a		09 38	09 48			09 58					10 08	10 18			10 28						10 38	10 48
Preston Park	d					09 55																	
Burgess Hill	a					10 03																	
Haywards Heath 3	a					10 09									10 35								
Arundel	d								09 12										09 46				
Amberley	d								09 17														
Pulborough	d								09 23										09 55				
Billingshurst	d								09 29										10 01				
Christs Hospital	d								09 36														
Horsham 4	a								09 40	09 46									10 10	10 16			
	d								09 50										10 20				
Crawley	d								09 59										10 29				
Three Bridges 4	a								10 02										10 32				
Gatwick Airport 10 ✈	a					10 24			10 07						10 55				10 37				
	d					10 25			10 08						10 56				10 38				
Horley	a																		10 41				
Redhill 5	a								10 15										10 47				
East Croydon	a					10 40			10 27						11 11				10 59				
London Bridge 4 ⊖	a																						
Clapham Junction 10	a					10 49			10 36						11 20				11 08				
Clapham Junction 15 ⊖	a					10 57			10 44						11 28				11 16				

Table 188R

Saturdays

14 December to 17 May

Southampton, Portsmouth and Sussex Coast - Brighton, Gatwick Airport and London

Network Diagram - see first Page of Table 175

		SN 1	SN 1	SN	SN	SN 1	SN 1		SN	SN	SN 1	SN 1	SN 1	SN	SN	SN	SN 1	SN 1		SN	SN	SN	SN 1	SN 1	SN
Eastleigh	d																								
Southampton Airport Parkway	d																								
Southampton Central	d						09 13				09 33														
Swanwick	d						09 33				09 50														
Fareham	d						09 40				09 56														
Portchester	d						09 45																		
Cosham	d						09 49				10 05														
Portsmouth Harbour	d																	10 12				10 29			
Portsmouth & Southsea	d														09 59			10 16				10 33			
Fratton	d														10 04			10 20				10 37			
Hilsea	d														10 08										
Bedhampton	d														10 13										
Havant	d						09 56				10 11				10 16			10 30				10 46			
Warblington	d														10 18										
Emsworth	d						10 00				10 15				10 21							10 50			
Southbourne	d						10 03								10 24							10 53			
Nutbourne	d														10 26										
Bosham	d														10 30										
Fishbourne (Sussex)	d														10 33										
Chichester 4	a						10 10				10 23				10 36			10 40				11 00			
	d						10 11				10 25				10 37			10 41				11 00			
Bognor Regis 4	d				10 07	09 56										10 39	10 30								
Barnham	a				10 13	10 02	10 18				10 32				10 44	10 45	10 36	10 48				11 08			
	d	10 12			10 15	10 03	10 19		10 22		10 33	10 39			10 45		10 37	10 49		10 52		11 08	11 12		
Bognor Regis	a	10 18							10 29			10 46								10 59			11 18		
Ford 4	d				10 19	10 07					10 37				10 49		10 41								
Littlehampton 4	a				10 24										10 54										
	d		10 15										10 45											11 15	
Angmering 3	d		10 23								10 43		10 53									11 17		11 23	
Goring-by-Sea	d		10 27								10 47		10 57											11 27	
Durrington-on-Sea	d		10 30								10 50		11 00											11 30	
West Worthing	d		10 32							10 39	10 52		11 02								11 09			11 32	
Worthing 4	a		10 34							10 41	10 54		11 04								11 11	11 24		11 34	
	d		10 36							10 42	10 56		11 06								11 12	11 26		11 36	
East Worthing	d									10 44											11 14				
Lancing	d									10 47	11 00		11 10								11 17	11 30			
Shoreham-by-Sea	d		10 42							10 52	11 04		11 14								11 22	11 34		11 42	
Southwick	d									10 55	11 07										11 25	11 37			
Fishersgate	d									10 57											11 27				
Portslade	d		10 47							10 59	11 10										11 29	11 40		11 47	
Aldrington	d									11 01											11 31				
Hove 2	a		10 50							11 03	11 13		11 20								11 33	11 43		11 50	
	d		10 51	10 54						11 04	11 14		11 21	11 24							11 34	11 44		11 51	11 54
Brighton 10	a			10 58						11 08	11 18			11 28							11 38	11 48			11 58
Preston Park	d		10 55																					11 55	
Burgess Hill	a		11 03																					12 03	
Haywards Heath 3	a		11 09										11 35											12 09	
Arundel	d					10 12											10 46								
Amberley	d					10 17																			
Pulborough	d					10 23											10 55								
Billingshurst	d					10 29											11 01								
Christs Hospital	d					10 36																			
Horsham 4	a					10 40	10 46										11 10	11 16							
	d					10 50											11 20								
Crawley	d					10 59											11 29								
Three Bridges 4	a					11 02											11 32								
Gatwick Airport 10	a		11 24			11 07							11 55				11 37							12 24	
	d		11 25			11 08							11 56				11 38							12 25	
Horley	a																11 41								
Redhill 5	a					11 15											11 47								
East Croydon	a		11 40			11 27							12 11				11 59							12 40	
London Bridge 4	a																								
Clapham Junction 10	a		11 49			11 36							12 20				12 08							12 49	
Clapham Junction 15	a		11 57			11 44							12 28				12 16							12 57	

Table 188R

Saturdays

14 December to 17 May

Southampton, Portsmouth and Sussex Coast - Brighton, Gatwick Airport and London

Network Diagram - see first Page of Table 175

		SN	SN	SN	SN	SN	SN	SN	SN	SN	SN	SN	SN	SN	SN	SN	SN	SN	SN	SN	SN	SN	SN
			1	1			1	1	1				1	1				1	1			1	1
Eastleigh	d																						
Southampton Airport Parkway	d																						
Southampton Central	d			10 13			10 33																11 13
Swanwick	d			10 33			10 50																11 33
Fareham	d			10 40			10 56																11 40
Portchester	d			10 45																			11 45
Cosham	d			10 49			11 05																11 49
Portsmouth Harbour	d													11 12			11 29						
Portsmouth & Southsea	d										10 59			11 16			11 33						
Fratton	d										11 04			11 20			11 37						
Hilsea	d										11 08												
Bedhampton	d										11 13												
Havant	d			10 56			11 11				11 16			11 30			11 46						11 56
Warblington	d										11 18												
Emsworth	d			11 00			11 15				11 21						11 50						12 00
Southbourne	d			11 03							11 24						11 53						12 03
Nutbourne	d										11 26												
Bosham	d										11 30												
Fishbourne (Sussex)	d										11 33												
Chichester 4	a			11 10			11 23				11 36			11 40			12 00						12 10
	d			11 11			11 25				11 37			11 41			12 00						12 11
Bognor Regis 4	d	11 07	10 56									11 39	11 30								12 07	11 56	
Barnham	a	11 13	11 02	11 18			11 32				11 44	11 45	11 36	11 48			12 08				12 13	12 02	12 18
	d	11 15	11 03	11 19	11 22		11 33	11 39			11 45		11 37	11 49	11 52		12 08	12 12			12 15	12 03	12 19
Bognor Regis	a				11 29			11 46							11 59			12 18					
Ford 4	d	11 19	11 07				11 37				11 49		11 41								12 19	12 07	
Littlehampton 4	a	11 24									11 54										12 24		
	d								11 45										12 15				
Angmering 3	d						11 43		11 53								12 17		12 23				
Goring-by-Sea	d						11 47		11 57										12 27				
Durrington-on-Sea	d						11 50		12 00										12 30				
West Worthing	d					11 39	11 52		12 02							12 09			12 32				
Worthing 4	a					11 41	11 54		12 04							12 11	12 24		12 34				
	d					11 42	11 56		12 06							12 12	12 26		12 36				
East Worthing	d					11 44										12 14							
Lancing	d					11 47	12 00		12 10							12 17	12 30						
Shoreham-by-Sea	d					11 52	12 04		12 14							12 22	12 34		12 42				
Southwick	d					11 55	12 07									12 25	12 37						
Fishersgate	d					11 57										12 27							
Portslade	d					11 59	12 10									12 29	12 40		12 47				
Aldrington	d					12 01										12 31							
Hove 2	a					12 03	12 13		12 20							12 33	12 43		12 50				
	d					12 04	12 14		12 21	12 24						12 34	12 44		12 51	12 54			
Brighton 10	a					12 08	12 18			12 28						12 38	12 48			12 58			
Preston Park	d																		12 55				
Burgess Hill	a																		13 03				
Haywards Heath 3	a								12 35										13 09				
Arundel	d		11 12										11 46									12 12	
Amberley	d		11 17																			12 17	
Pulborough	d		11 23										11 55									12 23	
Billingshurst	d		11 29										12 01									12 29	
Christs Hospital	d		11 36																			12 36	
Horsham 4	a		11 40	11 46									12 10	12 16								12 40	12 46
	d		11 50										12 20									12 50	
Crawley	d		11 59										12 29									12 59	
Three Bridges 4	a		12 02										12 32									13 02	
Gatwick Airport 10	a		12 07						12 55				12 37						13 24			13 07	
	d		12 08						12 56				12 38						13 25			13 08	
Horley	a												12 41										
Redhill 5	a		12 15										12 47									13 15	
East Croydon	a		12 27						13 11				12 59						13 40			13 27	
London Bridge 4	a																						
Clapham Junction 10	a		12 36						13 20				13 08						13 49			13 36	
Clapham Junction 15	a		12 44						13 28				13 16						13 57			13 44	

Table 188R

Saturdays

14 December to 17 May

Southampton, Portsmouth and Sussex Coast - Brighton, Gatwick Airport and London

Network Diagram - see first Page of Table 175

		SN	SN	SN ■1	SN ■1 🚲	SN ■1	SN	SN	SN	SN ■1	SN ■1	SN	SN	SN	SN ■1	SN ■1	SN	SN	SN ■1	SN ■1	SN	SN
Eastleigh	d																					
Southampton Airport Parkway	d																					
Southampton Central ⛴	d			11 33																12 13		
Swanwick	d			11 50																12 33		
Fareham	d			11 56																12 40		
Portchester	d																			12 45		
Cosham	d			12 05																12 49		
Portsmouth Harbour ⛴	d										12 12			12 29								
Portsmouth & Southsea	d							11 59			12 16			12 33								
Fratton	d							12 04			12 20			12 37								
Hilsea	d							12 08														
Bedhampton	d							12 13														
Havant	d			12 11				12 16			12 30			12 46						12 56		
Warblington	d							12 18														
Emsworth	d			12 15				12 21						12 50						13 00		
Southbourne	d							12 24						12 53						13 03		
Nutbourne	d							12 26														
Bosham	d							12 30														
Fishbourne (Sussex)	d							12 33														
Chichester ■4	a			12 23				12 36			12 40			13 00						13 10		
	d			12 25				12 37			12 41			13 00						13 11		
Bognor Regis ■4	d								12 39	12 30								13 07	12 56			
Barnham	a			12 32				12 44	12 45	12 36	12 48			13 08				13 13	13 02	13 18		
	d	12 22		12 33	12 39			12 45		12 37	12 49	12 52		13 08	13 12			13 15	13 03	13 19	13 22	
Bognor Regis	a	12 29			12 46							12 59			13 18						13 29	
Ford ■4	d			12 37				12 49		12 41								13 19	13 07			
Littlehampton ■4	a							12 54										13 24				
	d					12 45										13 15						
Angmering ■3	d			12 43		12 53								13 17		13 23						
Goring-by-Sea	d			12 47		12 57										13 27						
Durrington-on-Sea	d			12 50		13 00										13 30						
West Worthing	d		12 39	12 52		13 02							13 09			13 32						13 39
Worthing ■4	a		12 41	12 54		13 04							13 11	13 24		13 34						13 41
	d		12 42	12 56		13 06							13 12	13 26		13 36						13 42
East Worthing	d		12 44										13 14									13 44
Lancing	d		12 47	13 00		13 10							13 17	13 30								13 47
Shoreham-by-Sea	d		12 52	13 04		13 14							13 22	13 34		13 42						13 52
Southwick	d		12 55	13 07									13 25	13 37								13 55
Fishersgate	d		12 57										13 27									13 57
Portslade	d		12 59	13 10									13 29	13 40		13 47						13 59
Aldrington	d		13 01										13 31									14 01
Hove ■2	a		13 03	13 13		13 20							13 33	13 43		13 50						14 03
	d		13 04	13 14		13 21	13 24						13 34	13 44		13 51	13 54					14 04
Brighton ■10	a		13 08	13 18			13 28						13 38	13 48			13 58					14 08
Preston Park	d															13 55						
Burgess Hill	a															14 03						
Haywards Heath ■3	a					13 35										14 09						
Arundel	d									12 46									13 12			
Amberley	d																		13 17			
Pulborough	d									12 55									13 23			
Billingshurst	d									13 01									13 29			
Christs Hospital	d																		13 36			
Horsham ■4	a									13 10	13 16								13 40	13 46		
	d									13 20									13 50			
Crawley	d									13 29									13 59			
Three Bridges ■4	a									13 32									14 02			
Gatwick Airport ■10 ✈	a					13 55				13 37						14 24			14 07			
	d					13 56				13 38						14 25			14 08			
Horley	a									13 41												
Redhill ■5	a									13 47									14 15			
East Croydon 🚋	a					14 11				13 59						14 40			14 27			
London Bridge ■4 ⊖	a																					
Clapham Junction ■10	a					14 21				14 08						14 49			14 37			
Clapham Junction ■15 ⊖	a					14 28				14 16						14 57			14 44			

Table 188R

Saturdays

14 December to 17 May

Southampton, Portsmouth and Sussex Coast - Brighton, Gatwick Airport and London

Network Diagram - see first Page of Table 175

		SN [1]	SN [1] bike	SN [1]	SN	SN	SN	SN [1]	SN [1]		SN	SN	SN	SN [1]	SN [1]	SN	SN	SN [1]	SN [1]		SN	SN	SN [1]	SN [1] bike	SN [1]
Eastleigh	d																								
Southampton Airport Parkway	d																								
Southampton Central (ship)	d	12 33																	13 13				13 33		
Swanwick	d	12 50																	13 33				13 50		
Fareham	d	12 56																	13 40				13 56		
Portchester	d																		13 45						
Cosham	d	13 05																	13 49				14 05		
Portsmouth Harbour (ship)	d								13 12				13 29												
Portsmouth & Southsea	d					12 59			13 16				13 33												
Fratton	d					13 04			13 20				13 37												
Hilsea	d					13 08																			
Bedhampton	d					13 13																			
Havant	d	13 11				13 16			13 30				13 46						13 56				14 11		
Warblington	d					13 18																			
Emsworth	d	13 15				13 21							13 50						14 00				14 15		
Southbourne	d					13 24							13 53						14 03						
Nutbourne	d					13 26																			
Bosham	d					13 30																			
Fishbourne (Sussex)	d					13 33																			
Chichester [4]	a	13 23				13 36			13 40				14 00						14 10				14 23		
	d	13 25				13 37			13 41				14 00						14 11				14 25		
Bognor Regis [4]	d						13 39	13 30									14 07	13 56							
Barnham	a	13 32				13 44	13 45	13 36	13 48				14 08				14 13	14 02	14 18				14 32		
	d	13 33	13 39			13 45		13 37	13 49		13 52		14 08	14 12			14 15	14 03	14 19		14 22		14 33	14 39	
Bognor Regis	a		13 46								13 59			14 18							14 29			14 46	
Ford [4]	d	13 37				13 49		13 41									14 19	14 07					14 37		
Littlehampton [4]	a					13 54											14 24								
	d			13 45											14 15										14 45
Angmering [3]	d	13 43		13 53									14 17		14 23								14 43		14 53
Goring-by-Sea	d	13 47		13 57											14 27								14 47		14 57
Durrington-on-Sea	d	13 50		14 00											14 30								14 50		15 00
West Worthing	d	13 52		14 02								14 09			14 32							14 39	14 52		15 02
Worthing [4]	a	13 54		14 04								14 11	14 24		14 34							14 41	14 54		15 04
	d	13 56		14 06								14 12	14 26		14 36							14 42	14 56		15 06
East Worthing	d											14 14										14 44			
Lancing	d	14 00		14 10								14 17	14 30									14 47	15 00		15 10
Shoreham-by-Sea	d	14 04		14 14								14 22	14 34		14 42							14 52	15 04		15 14
Southwick	d	14 07										14 25	14 37									14 55	15 07		
Fishersgate	d											14 27										14 57			
Portslade	d	14 10										14 29	14 40		14 47							14 59	15 10		
Aldrington	d											14 31										15 01			
Hove [2]	a	14 13		14 20								14 33	14 43		14 50							15 03	15 13		15 20
	d	14 14		14 21	14 24							14 34	14 44		14 51	14 54						15 04	15 14		15 21
Brighton [10]	a	14 18			14 28							14 38	14 48			14 58						15 08	15 18		
Preston Park	d														14 55										
Burgess Hill	a														15 03										
Haywards Heath [3]	a			14 35											15 09										15 35
Arundel	d							13 46										14 12							
Amberley	d																	14 17							
Pulborough	d							13 55										14 23							
Billingshurst	d							14 01										14 29							
Christs Hospital	d																	14 36							
Horsham [4]	a							14 10	14 16									14 40	14 46						
	d							14 20										14 50							
Crawley	d							14 29										14 59							
Three Bridges [4]	a							14 32										15 02							
Gatwick Airport [10] (plane)	a			14 55				14 37							15 24			15 07							15 55
	d			14 56				14 38							15 25			15 08							15 56
Horley	a							14 41																	
Redhill [5]	a							14 47										15 15							
East Croydon (tram)	a			15 11				14 59							15 40			15 28							16 11
London Bridge [4] ⊖	a																								
Clapham Junction [10]	a			15 20				15 08							15 49			15 37							16 20
Clapham Junction [15] ⊖	a			15 28				15 16							15 57			15 45							16 28

Table 188R

Saturdays

14 December to 17 May

Southampton, Portsmouth and Sussex Coast - Brighton, Gatwick Airport and London

Network Diagram - see first Page of Table 175

		SN	SN	SN	SN 1	SN 1	SN	SN	SN	SN 1	SN 1	SN	SN	SN 1	SN 1	SN	SN	GW ◇	SN 1	SN 1 🚲	SN	SN 1	SN
Eastleigh	d																		14 41				
Southampton Airport Parkway	d																		14n34				
Southampton Central ⛴	d														14 13			14 34	14n26				
Swanwick	d														14 33								
Fareham	d														14 40			14 55	15 00				
Portchester	d														14 45								
Cosham	d														14 49			15 03					
Portsmouth Harbour ⛴	d					14 12			14 29														
Portsmouth & Southsea	d		13 59			14 16			14 33														
Fratton	d		14 04			14 20			14 37														
Hilsea	d		14 08																				
Bedhampton	d		14 13																				
Havant	d		14 16			14 30			14 46						14 56			15 10	15 14				
Warblington	d		14 18																				
Emsworth	d		14 21						14 50						15 00								
Southbourne	d		14 24						14 53						15 03								
Nutbourne	d		14 26																				
Bosham	d		14 30																				
Fishbourne (Sussex)	d		14 33																				
Chichester 4	a		14 36			14 40			15 00						15 10			15 21	15 25				
	d		14 37			14 41			15 00						15 11			15 21	15 25				
Bognor Regis 4	d			14 39	14 30								15 07	14 56							15 39		
Barnham	a		14 44	14 45	14 36	14 48			15 08				15 13	15 02	15 18			15 29	15 33		15 45		
	d		14 45		14 37	14 49	14 52		15 08	15 12			15 15	15 03	15 19	15 22		15 29	15 33	15 39			
Bognor Regis	a						14 59			15 18						15 29				15 46			
Ford 4	d		14 49		14 41								15 19	15 07					15 38				
Littlehampton 4	a		14 54										15 24										
	d										15 15											15 45	
Angmering 3	d								15 17		15 23								15 44			15 53	
Goring-by-Sea	d										15 27								15 48			15 57	
Durrington-on-Sea	d										15 30								15 50			16 00	
West Worthing	d							15 09			15 32						15 39		15 52			16 02	
Worthing 4	a							15 11	15 24		15 34						15 41	15 44	15 55			16 04	
	d							15 12	15 26		15 36						15 42	15 48	15 56			16 06	
East Worthing	d							15 14									15 44						
Lancing	d							15 17	15 30								15 47		16 00			16 10	
Shoreham-by-Sea	d							15 22	15 34		15 42						15 52	15 56	16 04			16 14	
Southwick	d							15 25	15 37								15 55		16 07				
Fishersgate	d							15 27									15 57						
Portslade	d							15 29	15 40		15 47						15 59		16 10				
Aldrington	d							15 31									16 01						
Hove 2	a							15 33	15 43		15 50						16 03	16 07	16 13			16 20	
	d	15 24						15 34	15 44		15 51	15 54					16 04	16 08	16 14			16 21	16 24
Brighton 10	a	15 28						15 38	15 48			15 58					16 08	16 14	16 18				16 28
Preston Park	d										15 55												
Burgess Hill	a										16 03												
Haywards Heath 3	a										16 09											16 35	
Arundel	d				14 46									15 12									
Amberley	d													15 17									
Pulborough	d				14 55									15 23									
Billingshurst	d				15 01									15 29									
Christs Hospital	d													15 36									
Horsham 4	a				15 10	15 16								15 40	15 46								
	d				15 20									15 50									
Crawley	d				15 29									15 59									
Three Bridges 4	a				15 32									16 02									
Gatwick Airport 10 ✈	a				15 37						16 24			16 07								16 55	
	d				15 38						16 25			16 08								16 56	
Horley	a				15 41																		
Redhill 5	a				15 47									16 15									
East Croydon	a				15 59						16 40			16 27								17 11	
London Bridge 4 ⊖	a																						
Clapham Junction 10	a				16 08						16 49			16 36								17 20	
Clapham Junction 15 ⊖	a				16 16						16 57			16 44								17 28	

n Stops at these stations before Eastleigh

Table 188R

Saturdays

14 December to 17 May

Southampton, Portsmouth and Sussex Coast - Brighton, Gatwick Airport and London

Network Diagram - see first Page of Table 175

		SN		SN 1	SN 1	SN	SN	SN	SN 1	SN 1	SN	SN		SN 1	SN 1	SN	SN	SN 1	SN 1 (trolley)	SN 1	SN	SN		SN	
Eastleigh	d																								
Southampton Airport Parkway	d																								
Southampton Central ⛴	d														15 13			15 33							
Swanwick	d														15 33			15 50							
Fareham	d														15 40			15 56							
Portchester	d														15 45										
Cosham	d														15 49			16 05							
Portsmouth Harbour ⛴	d				15 12			15 29																	
Portsmouth & Southsea	d	14 59			15 16			15 33														15 59			
Fratton	d	15 04			15 20			15 37														16 04			
Hilsea	d	15 08																				16 08			
Bedhampton	d	15 14																				16 13			
Havant	d	15 17			15 30			15 46							15 56			16 11				16 16			
Warblington	d	15 19																				16 18			
Emsworth	d	15 22						15 50							16 00			16 15				16 21			
Southbourne	d	15 25						15 53							16 03							16 24			
Nutbourne	d	15 28																				16 26			
Bosham	d	15 31																				16 30			
Fishbourne (Sussex)	d	15 34																				16 33			
Chichester 4	a	15 37			15 41			16 00							16 10			16 23				16 36			
	d	15 38			15 42			16 00							16 11			16 25				16 37			
Bognor Regis 4	d			15 30								16 07		15 56										16 39	
Barnham	a	15 45		15 36	15 49			16 08				16 13		16 02	16 18			16 32				16 44		16 45	
	d	15 46		15 37	15 50	15 52		16 08	16 12			16 15		16 03	16 19	16 22		16 33	16 39			16 45			
Bognor Regis	a					15 59			16 18							16 29			16 46						
Ford 4	d	15 50		15 41								16 19		16 07				16 37				16 49			
Littlehampton 4	a	15 55										16 24										16 54			
	d									16 15										16 45					
Angmering 3	d							16 17		16 23								16 43		16 53					
Goring-by-Sea	d									16 27								16 47		16 57					
Durrington-on-Sea	d									16 30								16 50		17 00					
West Worthing	d						16 09			16 32							16 39	16 52		17 02					
Worthing 4	a						16 11	16 24		16 34							16 41	16 54		17 04					
	d						16 12	16 26		16 36							16 42	16 56		17 06					
East Worthing	d						16 14										16 44								
Lancing	d						16 17	16 30									16 47	17 00		17 10					
Shoreham-by-Sea	d						16 22	16 34		16 42							16 52	17 04		17 14					
Southwick	d						16 25	16 37									16 55	17 07							
Fishersgate	d						16 27										16 57								
Portslade	d						16 29	16 40		16 47							16 59	17 10							
Aldrington	d						16 31										17 01								
Hove 2	a						16 33	16 43		16 50							17 03	17 13		17 20					
	d						16 34	16 44		16 51	16 54						17 04	17 14		17 21	17 24				
Brighton 10	a						16 38	16 48			16 58						17 08	17 18			17 28				
Preston Park	d									16 55															
Burgess Hill	a									17 03															
Haywards Heath 3	a									17 09										17 35					
Arundel	d			15 46										16 12											
Amberley	d													16 17											
Pulborough	d			15 55										16 23											
Billingshurst	d			16 01										16 29											
Christs Hospital	d													16 36											
Horsham 4	a			16 10	16 16									16 40	16 46										
	d			16 20										16 50											
Crawley	d			16 29										16 59											
Three Bridges 4	a			16 32										17 02											
Gatwick Airport 10 ✈	a			16 37						17 24				17 07						17 55					
	d			16 38						17 25				17 08						17 56					
Horley	a			16 41																					
Redhill 5	a			16 47										17 15											
East Croydon	a			16 59						17 40				17 27						18 11					
London Bridge 4 ⊖	a																								
Clapham Junction 10	a			17 08						17 49				17 36						18 20					
Clapham Junction 15 ⊖	a			17 16						17 57				17 44						18 28					

Table 188R

Saturdays

14 December to 17 May

Southampton, Portsmouth and Sussex Coast - Brighton, Gatwick Airport and London

Network Diagram - see first Page of Table 175

		SN	SN	SN	SN	SN	SN	SN	SN	SN	SN	SN	SN	SN	SN	SN	SN	SN	SN	SN	SN	SN	SN
		1	1				1	1			1	1			1	1 ⚲	1				1	1	
Eastleigh	d																						
Southampton Airport Parkway	d																						
Southampton Central	d											16 13			16 33								
Swanwick	d											16 33			16 50								
Fareham	d											16 40			16 56								
Portchester	d											16 45											
Cosham	d											16 49			17 05								
Portsmouth Harbour	d		16 12			16 29																17 12	
Portsmouth & Southsea	d		16 16			16 33													16 59			17 16	
Fratton	d		16 20			16 37													17 04			17 20	
Hilsea	d																		17 08				
Bedhampton	d																		17 13				
Havant	d		16 30			16 46						16 56			17 11				17 16			17 30	
Warblington	d																		17 18				
Emsworth	d					16 50						17 00			17 15				17 21				
Southbourne	d					16 53						17 03							17 24				
Nutbourne	d																		17 26				
Bosham	d																		17 30				
Fishbourne (Sussex)	d																		17 33				
Chichester 4	a		16 40			17 00						17 10			17 23				17 36			17 40	
	d		16 41			17 00						17 11			17 25				17 37			17 41	
Bognor Regis 4	d	16 30								17 07	16 56									17 39	17 30		
Barnham	a	16 36	16 48			17 08				17 13	17 02	17 18			17 32				17 44	17 45	17 36	17 48	
	d	16 37	16 49	16 52		17 08	17 12			17 15	17 03	17 19	17 22		17 33	17 41			17 45		17 37	17 49	17 52
Bognor Regis	a			16 59			17 18						17 29			17 47							17 59
Ford 4	d	16 41								17 19	17 07				17 37				17 49		17 41		
Littlehampton 4	a									17 24									17 54				
	d							17 15									17 45						
Angmering 3	d					17 17		17 23							17 43		17 53						
Goring-by-Sea	d							17 27							17 47		17 57						
Durrington-on-Sea	d							17 30							17 50		18 00						
West Worthing	d				17 09			17 32						17 39	17 52		18 02						
Worthing 4	a				17 11	17 24		17 34						17 41	17 54		18 04						
	d				17 12	17 26		17 36						17 42	17 56		18 06						
East Worthing	d				17 14									17 44									
Lancing	d				17 17	17 30								17 47	18 00		18 10						
Shoreham-by-Sea	d				17 22	17 34		17 42						17 52	18 04		18 14						
Southwick	d				17 25	17 37								17 55	18 07								
Fishersgate	d				17 27									17 57									
Portslade	d				17 29	17 40		17 47						17 59	18 10								
Aldrington	d				17 31									18 01									
Hove 2	a				17 33	17 43		17 50						18 03	18 13		18 20						
	d				17 34	17 44		17 51	17 54					18 04	18 14		18 21	18 24					
Brighton 10	a				17 38	17 48			17 58					18 08	18 18			18 28					
Preston Park	d							17 55															
Burgess Hill	a							18 03															
Haywards Heath 3	a							18 09									18 35						
Arundel	d	16 46									17 12										17 46		
Amberley	d										17 17												
Pulborough	d	16 55									17 23										17 55		
Billingshurst	d	17 01									17 29										18 01		
Christs Hospital	d										17 36												
Horsham 4	a	17 10	17 16								17 40	17 46									18 10	18 16	
	d	17 20									17 50										18 20		
Crawley	d	17 29									17 59										18 29		
Three Bridges 4	a	17 32									18 02										18 32		
Gatwick Airport 10 ✈	a	17 37						18 24			18 07						18 55				18 37		
	d	17 38						18 25			18 08						18 56				18 38		
Horley	a	17 41																			18 41		
Redhill 5	a	17 47									18 15										18 47		
East Croydon	a	17 59						18 40			18 27						19 11				18 59		
London Bridge 4 ⊖	a																						
Clapham Junction 10	a	18 08						18 49			18 36						19 20				19 08		
Clapham Junction 15 ⊖	a	18 16						18 57			18 44						19 28				19 16		

Table 188R

Saturdays

14 December to 17 May

Southampton, Portsmouth and Sussex Coast - Brighton, Gatwick Airport and London

Network Diagram - see first Page of Table 175

		SN	SN	SN [1]	SN [1]		SN	SN	SN [1]	SN [1]	SN	SN	SN [1]	SN [1] 🚲	SN [1]		SN	SN [1]	SN	SN	SN	SN	SN	SN [1]	SN
Eastleigh	d																								
Southampton Airport Parkway	d																								
Southampton Central ⛴	d									17 13			17 33												
Swanwick	d									17 33			17 50												
Fareham	d									17 40			17 56												
Portchester	d									17 45															
Cosham	d									17 49			18 05												
Portsmouth Harbour ⛴	d		17 29																			18 12	18 29		
Portsmouth & Southsea	d		17 33															17 59				18 16	18 33		
Fratton	d		17 37															18 04				18 20	18 37		
Hilsea	d																	18 08							
Bedhampton	d																	18 13							
Havant	d		17 46							17 56			18 11					18 16				18 30	18 46		
Warblington	d																	18 18							
Emsworth	d		17 50							18 00			18 15					18 21				18 34	18 50		
Southbourne	d		17 53							18 03								18 24				18 37	18 53		
Nutbourne	d																	18 26							
Bosham	d																	18 30							
Fishbourne (Sussex)	d																	18 33							
Chichester [4]	a		18 00							18 10			18 23					18 36				18 44	19 00		
	d		18 00							18 11			18 25					18 37				18 45	19 00		
Bognor Regis [4]	d							18 07	17 56						18 33				18 39						19 03
Barnham	a		18 08					18 13	18 02	18 18			18 32		18 40			18 44	18 46			18 52	19 08		19 09
	d		18 08	18 12				18 15	18 03	18 19	18 22		18 33	18 39	18 41			18 45		18 52		18 53	19 08	19 12	19 22
Bognor Regis	a			18 18							18 29			18 46						18 59				19 18	→
Ford [4]	d							18 19	18 07				18 37		18 45			18 49				18 57			
Littlehampton [4]	a							18 24														19 02			
	d				18 15																18 51				
Angmering [3]	d		18 17		18 23								18 43		18 53						19 00		19 17		
Goring-by-Sea	d				18 27								18 47		18 57						19 04				
Durrington-on-Sea	d				18 30								18 50		19 00						19 07				
West Worthing	d	18 09			18 32							18 39	18 52		19 02						19 09				
Worthing [4]	a	18 11	18 24		18 34							18 41	18 54		19 04						19 11		19 24		
	d	18 12	18 26		18 36							18 42	18 56		19 06						19 12		19 26		
East Worthing	d	18 14										18 44									19 14				
Lancing	d	18 17	18 30									18 47	19 00		19 10						19 17		19 30		
Shoreham-by-Sea	d	18 22	18 34		18 42							18 52	19 04		19 14						19 22		19 34		
Southwick	d	18 25	18 37									18 55	19 07								19 25		19 37		
Fishersgate	d	18 27										18 57									19 27				
Portslade	d	18 29	18 40		18 47							18 59	19 10								19 29		19 40		
Aldrington	d	18 31										19 01									19 31				
Hove [2]	a	18 33	18 43		18 50							19 03	19 13		19 20						19 33		19 43		
	d	18 34	18 44		18 51		18 54					19 04	19 14		19 21		19 24				19 34		19 44		
Brighton [10]	a	18 38	18 48				18 58					19 08	19 18				19 28				19 38		19 50		
Preston Park	d				18 55																				
Burgess Hill	a				19 03																				
Haywards Heath [3]	a				19 09										19 35										
Arundel	d								18 12									18 54							
Amberley	d								18 17									18 59							
Pulborough	d								18 23									19 05							
Billingshurst	d								18 29									19 11							
Christs Hospital	d								18 36																
Horsham [4]	a								18 40	18 46								19 20							
	d								18 50									19 21							
Crawley	d								18 59									19 30							
Three Bridges [4]	a								19 02									19 33							
Gatwick Airport [10] ✈	a				19 25				19 07						19 55			19 38							
	d				19 26				19 08						19 56			19 39							
Horley	a								19 11																
Redhill [5]	a								19 17									19 47							
East Croydon 🚋	a				19 41				19 29						20 11			20 00							
London Bridge [4] ⊖	a																								
Clapham Junction [10]	a				19 51				19 40						20 20			20 11							
Clapham Junction [15] ⊖	a				19 58				19 50						20 27			20 20							

Table 188R

Saturdays

14 December to 17 May

Southampton, Portsmouth and Sussex Coast - Brighton, Gatwick Airport and London

Network Diagram - see first Page of Table 175

		SN	SN	SN	SN	SN	SN	SN	SN	SN	SN	SN	SN	SN	SN	SN	SN	SN	SN	SN	SN	SN
		1		1			1	1 🛒	1						1		1			1	1	
Eastleigh	d																					
Southampton Airport Parkway	d																					
Southampton Central ⛴	d	18 11					18 33														19 09	
Swanwick	d	18 28					18 50														19 28	
Fareham	d	18 35					18 56														19 35	
Portchester	d	18 40																			19 40	
Cosham	d	18 44					19 05														19 44	
Portsmouth Harbour ⛴	d														19 12	19 29						
Portsmouth & Southsea	d											18 59			19 16	19 33						
Fratton	d											19 04			19 20	19 37						
Hilsea	d											19 08										
Bedhampton	d											19 13										
Havant	d	18 51					19 11					19 16			19 30	19 46					19 52	
Warblington	d											19 18										
Emsworth	d	18 55					19 15					19 21			19 34						19 56	
Southbourne	d	18 58										19 24			19 37						19 59	
Nutbourne	d											19 26										
Bosham	d											19 30										
Fishbourne (Sussex)	d											19 33										
Chichester 4	a	19 05					19 23					19 36			19 44	19 57					20 06	
	d	19 07					19 25					19 37			19 45	19 59					20 07	
Bognor Regis 4	d				⟵				19 33				19 39						20 04			
Barnham	a	19 14			19 09		19 32		19 40			19 44	19 46		19 52	20 06			20 10		20 14	
	d	19 15	19 22		19 22		19 33	19 39	19 41			19 45		19 52	19 53	20 07			20 11	20 12	20 15	20 22
Bognor Regis	a		19 29					19 46						19 59						20 18		20 29
Ford 4	d	19 19			19 26		19 37		19 45			19 49			19 57				20 15		20 19	
Littlehampton 4	a				19 32							19 55			20 02				20 20			
	d			19 15							19 52						20 15					
Angmering 3	d			19 23			19 43		19 53		20 00					20 16	20 23					
Goring-by-Sea	d			19 27					19 57		20 04						20 27					
Durrington-on-Sea	d			19 30			19 49		20 00		20 07						20 30					
West Worthing	d			19 32					20 02		20 09						20 32					
Worthing 4	a			19 34			19 53		20 04		20 11					20 23	20 34					
	d			19 35			19 53		20 05		20 12					20 23	20 35					
East Worthing	d						19 56				20 14					20 26						
Lancing	d			19 39			19 59		20 09		20 17					20 29	20 39					
Shoreham-by-Sea	d			19 43			20 03		20 13		20 22					20 33	20 43					
Southwick	d						20 06				20 25					20 36						
Fishersgate	d						20 08				20 27					20 38						
Portslade	d			19 48			20 10		20 17		20 29					20 40	20 48					
Aldrington	d						20 12				20 31					20 42						
Hove 2	a			19 51			20 14		20 21		20 33					20 44	20 51					
	d			19 52		19 54	20 15		20 22	20 24	20 34					20 45	20 52	20 54				
Brighton 10	a					19 59	20 19			20 28	20 38					20 49		20 58				
Preston Park	d			19 56																		
Burgess Hill	a			20 04													21 03					
Haywards Heath 3	a			20 10					20 36								21 11					
Arundel	d	19 24																			20 24	
Amberley	d	19 29																			20 29	
Pulborough	d	19 35																			20 35	
Billingshurst	d	19 41																			20 41	
Christs Hospital	d	19 48																			20 48	
Horsham 4	a	19 52																			20 52	
	d	19 52																			20 52	
Crawley	d	20 01																			21 01	
Three Bridges 4	a	20 05							20 47												21 05	
Gatwick Airport 10 ✈	a	20 10		20 25					20 52								21 26				21 10	
	d	20 11		20 26					20 53								21 27				21 11	
Horley	a																					
Redhill 5	a	20 18																			21 18	
East Croydon 🚋	a	20 29		20 41					21 08								21 41				21 29	
London Bridge 4 ⊖	a																					
Clapham Junction 10	a	20 40		20 50					21 18								21 51				21 41	
Clapham Junction 15 ⊖	a	20 50		20 58					21 26								21 58				21 48	

Table 188R

Saturdays

14 December to 17 May

Southampton, Portsmouth and Sussex Coast - Brighton, Gatwick Airport and London

Network Diagram - see first Page of Table 175

		SN	SN	SN	SN	SN	SN	SN	SN	SN	SN	SN	SN	SN	SN	SN	SN	SN	SN	SN	SN	SN	SN
		1	1	1						1	1			1	1			1	1				
											A												
			🛒								🛒												
Eastleigh	d																						
Southampton Airport Parkway	d																						
Southampton Central ⛴	d	19 33													20 11			20 33					
Swanwick	d	19 50													20 28			20 50					
Fareham	d	19 56													20 35			20 56					
Portchester	d														20 40								
Cosham	d	20 05													20 44			21 05					
Portsmouth Harbour ⛴	d									20 28							20 40						
Portsmouth & Southsea	d						19 59			20 32							20 45						
Fratton	d						20 04			20 36							20 49						
Hilsea	d						20 08										20 53						
Bedhampton	d						20 13																
Havant	d	20 11					20 16			20 44					20 51		20 59	21 11					
Warblington	d						20 18										21 01						
Emsworth	d	20 15					20 21			20 48					20 55		21 04	21 15					
Southbourne	d						20 24			20 51					20 58		21 07						
Nutbourne	d						20 26										21 09						
Bosham	d						20 30										21 13						
Fishbourne (Sussex)	d						20 33										21 16						
Chichester 4	a	20 23					20 36			20 58					21 05		21 19	21 24					
	d	20 25					20 37			20 59					21 07		21 19	21 25					
Bognor Regis 4	d			20 33				20 39					21 04							21 39			
Barnham	a	20 32		20 39			20 44	20 45		21 06			21 10		21 14		21 27	21 32		21 45			
	d	20 33	20 39	20 40			20 45		20 52	21 07			21 11	21 12	21 15	21 22	21 27	21 33	21 42		21 52		
Bognor Regis	a		20 46						20 59					21 18		21 29			21 48		21 59		
Ford 4	d			20 44			20 49						21 15		21 19		21 32	21 37					
Littlehampton 4	a						20 55						21 20				21 36						
	d					20 52					21 15												21 52
Angmering 3	d	20 42		20 53		21 00				21 16	21 23							21 43					22 00
Goring-by-Sea	d			20 57		21 04					21 27							21 47					22 04
Durrington-on-Sea	d	20 48		21 00		21 07					21 30							21 50					22 07
West Worthing	d			21 02		21 09					21 32							21 52					22 09
Worthing 4	a	20 52		21 04		21 11				21 23	21 34							21 54					22 11
	d	20 52		21 05		21 12				21 23	21 35							21 55					22 12
East Worthing	d	20 55				21 14				21 26								21 57					22 14
Lancing	d	20 58		21 09		21 17				21 29	21 39							22 00					22 17
Shoreham-by-Sea	d	21 02		21 13		21 22				21 33	21 43							22 04					22 22
Southwick	d	21 05				21 25				21 36								22 07					22 25
Fishersgate	d	21 07				21 27				21 38								22 09					22 27
Portslade	d	21 09		21 18		21 29				21 40	21 48							22 11					22 29
Aldrington	d	21 11				21 31				21 42								22 14					22 31
Hove 2	a	21 13		21 21		21 33				21 44	21 51							22 16					22 33
	d	21 14		21 22	21 24	21 34				21 45	21 52	21 54						22 16				22 24	22 34
Brighton 10	a	21 18			21 28	21 38				21 49		21 58						22 21				22 28	22 38
Preston Park	d																						
Burgess Hill	a										22 03												
Haywards Heath 3	a			21 36							22 09												
Arundel	d														21 24								
Amberley	d														21 29								
Pulborough	d														21 35								
Billingshurst	d														21 41								
Christs Hospital	d														21 48								
Horsham 4	a														21 52								
	d														21 52								
Crawley	d														22 01								
Three Bridges 4	a			21 47											22 05								
Gatwick Airport 10 ✈	a			21 52							22 24				22 10								
	d			21 53							22 25				22 11								
Horley	a																						
Redhill 5	a														22 18								
East Croydon 🚌	a			22 08							22 40				22 30								
London Bridge 4 ⊖	a																						
Clapham Junction 10	a			22 18							22 49				22 40								
Clapham Junction 15 ⊖	a			22 26							22 57				22 50								

A 🛒 from Haywards Heath

Table 188R

Saturdays

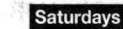

14 December to 17 May

Southampton, Portsmouth and Sussex Coast - Brighton, Gatwick Airport and London

Network Diagram - see first Page of Table 175

Station		SN	SN		SN	SN	SN	SN	SN	SN	SN	SN	SN		SN	SN	SN	SN	SN	SN	SN	SN	SN		SN
		1			1		1	1			1	1				1	1	1				1			
Eastleigh	d																								
Southampton Airport Parkway	d																								
Southampton Central	d						21 13				21 33							22 13				22 33			
Swanwick	d						21 33				21 50							22 31				22 50			
Fareham	d						21 40				21 57							22 39				23 00			
Portchester	d						21 45				22 02							22 44							
Cosham	d						21 49				22 06							22 48				23 08			
Portsmouth Harbour	d	21 11						21 40								22 15					22 44				
Portsmouth & Southsea	d	21 15						21 44								22 19					22 48				
Fratton	d	21 19						21 48								22 23					22 52				
Hilsea	d	21 23						21 52								22 27					22 56				
Bedhampton	d	21 28						21 57								22 32					23 01				
Havant	d	21 31					21 56	22 00			22 13					22 35		22 55			23 05	23 15			
Warblington	d	21 33									22 15														
Emsworth	d	21 36									22 18					22 39		22 59							
Southbourne	d	21 39									22 21					22 42		23 02							
Nutbourne	d	21 41									22 23														
Bosham	d	21 45									22 27														
Fishbourne (Sussex)	d	21 48									22 30														
Chichester 4	a	21 51					22 06	22 10			22 33					22 49		23 09			23 16	23 25			
	d	21 52					22 07	22 11			22 34	22 40				22 52		23 09			23 18	23 26			23 52
Bognor Regis 4	d		22 00							22 30									23 15						
Barnham	a	21 59	22 06				22 14	22 18		22 36	22 41	22 47				22 59		23 17	23 21		23 26	23 33			23 59
	d	22 00			22 12		22 15	22 19	22 22	22 37		22 48	22 52			23 00	23 06	23 17			23 26	23 34	23 36		00 01
Bognor Regis	a				22 18				22 29				22 59				23 12						23 43		
Ford 4	d	22 04					22 19	22 23		22 41		22 52				23 04					23 31				00 05
Littlehampton 4	a						22 24			22 46								23 25			23 35	23 42			00 10
	d						22 33														23 40				
Angmering 3	d	22 11					22 41									23 11					23 48				
Goring-by-Sea	d	22 15					22 45									23 15					23 52				
Durrington-on-Sea	d	22 18					22 47									23 17					23 54				
West Worthing	d	22 20					22 49									23 19					23 56				
Worthing 4	a	22 22					22 52									23 22					23 59				
	d	22 23					22 52									23 22					23 59				
East Worthing	d	22 25					22 55									23 25					00 02				
Lancing	d	22 28					22 58									23 28					00 05				
Shoreham-by-Sea	d	22 32					23 02									23 32					00 09				
Southwick	d	22 35					23 05									23 35					00 12				
Fishersgate	d	22 37					23 07									23 37					00 14				
Portslade	d	22 39					23 09									23 39					00 16				
Aldrington	d	22 42					23 11									23 41					00 18				
Hove 2	a	22 44					23 13									23 43					00 20				
	d	22 44				22 54	23 14								23 24	23 44				23 54	00 21				
Brighton 10	a	22 48				22 58	23 18								23 28	23 48				23 58	00 25				
Preston Park	d																								
Burgess Hill	a																								
Haywards Heath 3	a																								
Arundel	d							22 28				22 57													
Amberley	d											23 02													
Pulborough	d							22 37				23 08													
Billingshurst	d							22 43				23 14													
Christs Hospital	d							22 50				23 21													
Horsham 4	a							22 54				23 25													
	d							22 55				23 25													
Crawley	d							23 03				23 38													
Three Bridges 4	a							23 07				23 42													
Gatwick Airport 10 ✈	a																								
	d																								
Horley	a																								
Redhill 5	a																								
East Croydon	a																								
London Bridge 4 ⊖	a																								
Clapham Junction 10	a																								
Clapham Junction 15 ⊖	a																								

Table 188R

Saturdays

14 December to 17 May

Southampton, Portsmouth and Sussex Coast - Brighton, Gatwick Airport and London

Network Diagram - see first Page of Table 175

Station		SN
Eastleigh	d	
Southampton Airport Parkway	d	
Southampton Central ⛴	d	
Swanwick	d	
Fareham	d	
Portchester	d	
Cosham	d	
Portsmouth Harbour ⛴	d	23 15
Portsmouth & Southsea	d	23 19
Fratton	d	23 23
Hilsea	d	23 27
Bedhampton	d	23 33
Havant	d	23 36
Warblington	d	23 38
Emsworth	d	23 41
Southbourne	d	23 44
Nutbourne	d	23 47
Bosham	d	23 50
Fishbourne (Sussex)	d	23 53
Chichester [4]	a	23 57
	d	23 57
Bognor Regis [4]	d	
Barnham	a	00 05
	d	00 06
Bognor Regis	a	
Ford [4]	d	00 10
Littlehampton [4]	a	00 15
	d	
Angmering [3]	d	
Goring-by-Sea	d	
Durrington-on-Sea	d	
West Worthing	d	
Worthing [4]	a	
	d	
East Worthing	d	
Lancing	d	
Shoreham-by-Sea	d	
Southwick	d	
Fishersgate	d	
Portslade	d	
Aldrington	d	
Hove [2]	a	
	d	
Brighton [10]	a	
Preston Park	d	
Burgess Hill	a	
Haywards Heath [3]	a	
Arundel	d	
Amberley	d	
Pulborough	d	
Billingshurst	d	
Christs Hospital	d	
Horsham [4]	a	
	d	
Crawley	d	
Three Bridges [4]	a	
Gatwick Airport [10] ✈	a	
	d	
Horley	a	
Redhill [5]	a	
East Croydon 🚊	a	
London Bridge [4] ⊖	a	
Clapham Junction [10]	a	
Clapham Junction [15] ⊖	a	

Table 188R

Sundays

8 December to 11 May

Southampton, Portsmouth and Sussex Coast - Brighton, Gatwick Airport and London

Network Diagram - see first Page of Table 175

		SN	SN	SN	SN 1	SN 1	SN	SN 1	SN 1	SN 1		SN	SN	SN 1	SN 1	SN 1	SN 1	SN 1	SN 1	SN 1		SN 1	SN 1	SN 1	SN 1
Eastleigh	d																								
Southampton Airport Parkway	d																								
Southampton Central ⛴	d																						07 30		
Swanwick	d																						07 47		
Fareham	d																						07 54		
Portchester	d																								
Cosham	d																						08 03		
Portsmouth Harbour ⛴	d														07 14				07 44						08 14
Portsmouth & Southsea	d														07 18				07 48						08 18
Fratton	d														07 22				07 52						08 22
Hilsea	d																								
Bedhampton	d														07 30										08 30
Havant	d														07 33				08 01				08 11		08 33
Warblington	d														07 35										08 35
Emsworth	d														07 38				08 05				08 15		08 38
Southbourne	d														07 41				08 08						08 41
Nutbourne	d														07 43										08 43
Bosham	d														07 47										08 47
Fishbourne (Sussex)	d														07 50										08 50
Chichester 4	a														07 53				08 15				08 23		08 53
	d														07 53				08 15				08 23		08 53
Bognor Regis 4	d							06 52						07 34		07 59						08 20			
Barnham	a							06 58						07 40	08 01	08 05			08 23			08 26	08 31		09 01
	d	00 01		00 06	00 09	06 06	06 45	06 59	07 28					07 41	08 02	08 06	08 09		08 23			08 27	08 32	08 45	09 02
Bognor Regis	a				00 15		06 52		07 34								08 15							08 51	
Ford 4	d	00 05		00 10				07 03						07 45	08 06	08 10						08 31	08 36		09 06
Littlehampton 4	a	00 10		00 15		06 13								07 50								08 36			
	d					06 20				07 15			07 40					08 15							
Angmering 3	d									07 23			07 49		08 12			08 23					08 44		09 12
Goring-by-Sea	d									07 27			07 53		08 16			08 27					08 48		09 16
Durrington-on-Sea	d									07 30			07 55		08 19			08 30					08 51		09 19
West Worthing	d									07 32			07 57		08 21			08 32					08 53		09 21
Worthing 4	a					06 33				07 34			08 00		08 23			08 34	08 38				08 55		09 23
	d					06 33				07 36			08 00		08 24			08 42					08 56		09 24
East Worthing	d		00 02										08 03		08 26								08 58		09 26
Lancing	d		00 05			06 37				07 40			08 06		08 29								09 01		09 29
Shoreham-by-Sea	d		00 09			06 41				07 44			08 10		08 33			08 48					09 05		09 33
Southwick	d		00 12			06 44				07 47			08 13		08 36								09 08		09 36
Fishersgate	d		00 14										08 15		08 38								09 10		09 38
Portslade	d		00 16			06 48				07 50			08 17		08 40								09 12		09 40
Aldrington	d		00 18										08 19		08 43								09 15		09 43
Hove 2	a		00 20			06 51				07 54			08 21		08 45			08 54					09 17		09 45
	d		00 21			06 51				07 55		07 56	08 22		08 46			08 55		09 01			09 17		09 46
Brighton 10	a		00 25			06 55						08 00	08 26		08 50					09 05			09 21		09 50
Preston Park	d																								
Burgess Hill	a									08 05								09 05							
Haywards Heath 3	a									08 10								09 10							
Arundel	d							07 08								08 15									
Amberley	d							07 13								08 20									
Pulborough	d							07 19								08 26									
Billingshurst	d							07 26								08 33									
Christs Hospital	d							07 32								08 39									
Horsham 4	a							07 36								08 43									
	d							07 37								08 44									
Crawley	d							07 46								08 53									
Three Bridges 4	a							07 50								08 56									
Gatwick Airport 10 ✈	a							07 55		08 22						09 02		09 22							
	d							07 56		08 23						09 03		09 23							
Horley	a							07 59								09 05									
Redhill 5	a							08 06								09 13									
East Croydon 🚋	a							08 21		08 40						09 29		09 38							
London Bridge 4 ⊖	a																								
Clapham Junction 10	a							08 35		08 57						09 39		09 48							
Clapham Junction 15 ⊖	a							08 43		09 05						09 46		09 56							

Table 188R

Sundays

8 December to 11 May

Southampton, Portsmouth and Sussex Coast - Brighton, Gatwick Airport and London

Network Diagram - see first Page of Table 175

		SN	SN	SN	SN	SN	GW	SN	SN	SN	SN	SN	SN	SN	SN	SN	SN	SN	SN	SN	SN	SN
		1	1	1	1	1		1	1	1	1	1	1	1	1	1	1	1	1	1	1	1
Eastleigh	d								08 48													
Southampton Airport Parkway	d								08n36													
Southampton Central	d						08 31		08n27									09 30				
Swanwick	d																	09 47				
Fareham	d						08 52		09 02									09 54				
Portchester	d																					
Cosham	d						09 00		09 11									10 03				
Portsmouth Harbour	d				08 44						09 14				09 44					10 14		
Portsmouth & Southsea	d				08 48						09 18				09 48					10 18		
Fratton	d				08 52						09 22				09 52					10 22		
Hilsea	d																					
Bedhampton	d										09 30									10 30		
Havant	d				09 01		09 11		09 17		09 33				10 01			10 11		10 33		
Warblington	d										09 35									10 35		
Emsworth	d				09 05				09 21		09 38				10 05			10 15		10 38		
Southbourne	d				09 08						09 41				10 08					10 41		
Nutbourne	d										09 43									10 43		
Bosham	d										09 47									10 47		
Fishbourne (Sussex)	d										09 50									10 50		
Chichester 4	a				09 15		09 22		09 29		09 53				10 15			10 23		10 53		
	d				09 15		09 22		09 30		09 53				10 15			10 23		10 53		
Bognor Regis 4	d		08 59			09 20							09 59				10 20					10 59
Barnham	a		09 05		09 23	09 26	09 30		09 37		10 01		10 05		10 23		10 26	10 31		11 01		11 05
	d	09 03	09 06		09 23	09 27	09 30		09 38	09 43	10 02	10 03	10 06		10 23		10 27	10 32	10 41	11 02	11 03	11 06
Bognor Regis	a	09 10								09 49		10 10							10 48		11 10	
Ford 4	d		09 10			09 31			09 42		10 06		10 10				10 31	10 36		11 06		11 10
Littlehampton 4	a					09 36											10 36					
	d			09 15										10 15								
Angmering 3	d			09 23					09 48		10 12			10 23				10 42		11 12		
Goring-by-Sea	d			09 27					09 52		10 16			10 27				10 46		11 16		
Durrington-on-Sea	d			09 30					09 55		10 19			10 30				10 49		11 19		
West Worthing	d			09 32					09 57		10 21			10 32				10 51		11 21		
Worthing 4	a			09 34	09 38		09 47		09 59		10 23			10 34	10 38			10 53		11 23		
	d			09 42			09 47		10 00		10 24			10 42				10 54		11 24		
East Worthing	d								10 02		10 26							10 56		11 26		
Lancing	d								10 05		10 29							10 59		11 29		
Shoreham-by-Sea	d			09 48			09 54		10 09		10 33			10 48				11 03		11 33		
Southwick	d								10 12		10 36							11 06		11 36		
Fishersgate	d								10 14		10 38							11 08		11 38		
Portslade	d								10 16		10 40							11 10		11 40		
Aldrington	d								10 19		10 43							11 13		11 43		
Hove 2	a			09 54			10 01		10 22		10 45			10 54				11 15		11 45		
	d			09 55			10 01	10 05	10 22		10 46			10 55		11 01		11 16		11 46		
Brighton 10	a						10 07	10 09	10 26		10 50					11 05		11 20		11 50		
Preston Park	d																					
Burgess Hill	a			10 05										11 05								
Haywards Heath 3	a			10 10										11 10								
Arundel	d		09 15										10 15									11 15
Amberley	d		09 20										10 20									11 20
Pulborough	d		09 26										10 26									11 26
Billingshurst	d		09 33										10 33									11 33
Christs Hospital	d		09 39										10 39									11 39
Horsham 4	a		09 43										10 43									11 43
	d		09 44										10 44									11 44
Crawley	d		09 53										10 53									11 53
Three Bridges 4	a		09 56										10 56									11 56
Gatwick Airport 10	a		10 02	10 22									11 02	11 22								12 02
	d		10 03	10 23									11 03	11 23								12 03
Horley	a		10 05										11 05									12 05
Redhill 5	a		10 13										11 13									12 13
East Croydon	a		10 29	10 38									11 29	11 38								12 29
London Bridge 4	a																					
Clapham Junction 10	a		10 39	10 48									11 39	11 48								12 39
Clapham Junction 15	a		10 46	10 56									11 46	11 56								12 46

n Stops at these stations before Eastleigh

Table 188R

Sundays

8 December to 11 May

Southampton, Portsmouth and Sussex Coast - Brighton, Gatwick Airport and London

Network Diagram - see first Page of Table 175

		SN 1	SN 1	SN 1	SN 1	SN 1	SN 1	SN 1	SN 1	SN 1	SN 1	SN 1	SN 1	SN 1	SN 1	SN 1	SN 1	SN 1	SN 1	SN 1	SN 1	SN 1
Eastleigh	d																					
Southampton Airport Parkway	d																					
Southampton Central ⛴	d					10 30									11 30							
Swanwick	d					10 47									11 47							
Fareham	d					10 54									11 54							
Portchester	d																					
Cosham	d					11 03									12 03							
Portsmouth Harbour ⛴	d		10 44					11 14				11 44					12 14				12 44	
Portsmouth & Southsea	d		10 48					11 18				11 48					12 18				12 48	
Fratton	d		10 52					11 22				11 52					12 22				12 52	
Hilsea	d																					
Bedhampton	d							11 30									12 32					
Havant	d		11 01			11 11		11 33				12 01			12 11		12 35				13 01	
Warblington	d							11 35									12 37					
Emsworth	d		11 05			11 15		11 38				12 05			12 15		12 40				13 05	
Southbourne	d		11 08					11 41				12 08					12 43				13 08	
Nutbourne	d							11 43									12 45					
Bosham	d							11 47									12 49					
Fishbourne (Sussex)	d							11 50									12 52					
Chichester 4	a		11 15			11 23		11 53				12 15			12 23		12 55				13 15	
	d		11 15			11 23		11 53				12 15			12 23		12 55				13 15	
Bognor Regis 4	d				11 20					11 59				12 20					12 59			
Barnham	a		11 23		11 26	11 31		12 01		12 05		12 23		12 26	12 31		13 03		13 06		13 23	
	d		11 23		11 27	11 32	11 41	12 02	12 03	12 06		12 23		12 27	12 32	12 41	13 03	13 03	13 06		13 23	
Bognor Regis	a						11 48		12 10							12 48		13 10				
Ford 4	d				11 31	11 36		12 06		12 10				12 31	12 36		13 08		13 11			
Littlehampton 4	a				11 36									12 36								
	d	11 15									12 15									13 15		
Angmering 3	d	11 23				11 42		12 12			12 23				12 42		13 14			13 23		
Goring-by-Sea	d	11 27				11 46		12 16			12 27				12 46		13 18			13 27		
Durrington-on-Sea	d	11 30				11 49		12 19			12 30				12 49		13 20			13 30		
West Worthing	d	11 32				11 51		12 21			12 32				12 51		13 22			13 32		
Worthing 4	a	11 34	11 38			11 53		12 23			12 34	12 38			12 53		13 25			13 34	13 38	
	d	11 42				11 54		12 24			12 42				12 54		13 25			13 42		
East Worthing	d					11 56		12 26							12 56		13 28					
Lancing	d					11 59		12 29							12 59		13 31					
Shoreham-by-Sea	d	11 48				12 03		12 33			12 48				13 03		13 35			13 48		
Southwick	d					12 06		12 36							13 06		13 38					
Fishersgate	d					12 08		12 38							13 08		13 40					
Portslade	d					12 10		12 40							13 10		13 42					
Aldrington	d					12 13		12 43							13 13		13 44					
Hove 2	a	11 54				12 15		12 45			12 54				13 15		13 46			13 54		
	d	11 55		12 01		12 16		12 46			12 55		13 01		13 16		13 47			13 55		14 01
Brighton 10	a			12 05		12 20		12 50					13 05		13 20		13 51					14 05
Preston Park	d																					
Burgess Hill	a	12 05									13 05									14 05		
Haywards Heath 3	a	12 10									13 10									14 10		
Arundel	d									12 15									13 15			
Amberley	d									12 20									13 20			
Pulborough	d									12 26									13 26			
Billingshurst	d									12 33									13 33			
Christs Hospital	d									12 39									13 39			
Horsham 4	a									12 43									13 43			
	d									12 44									13 44			
Crawley	d									12 53									13 53			
Three Bridges 4	a									12 56									13 56			
Gatwick Airport 10 ✈	a	12 22								13 02	13 22								14 02	14 22		
	d	12 23								13 03	13 23								14 03	14 23		
Horley	a									13 05									14 05			
Redhill 5	a									13 13									14 13			
East Croydon	a	12 38								13 29	13 38								14 29	14 38		
London Bridge 4 ⊖	a																					
Clapham Junction 10	a	12 48								13 39	13 48								14 39	14 48		
Clapham Junction 15 ⊖	a	12 56								13 46	13 56								14 46	14 56		

Table 188R

Sundays

8 December to 11 May

Southampton, Portsmouth and Sussex Coast - Brighton, Gatwick Airport and London

Network Diagram - see first Page of Table 175

		SN [1]	SN [1]	SN [1]	SN [1]	SN [1]	SN [1]	GW ◇	SN [1]	SN [1]		SN [1]	SN [1]	SN [1]	SN [1]	SN [1]	SN [1]	SN [1]	SN [1]	SN [1]		SN [1]	SN [1]	SN [1]	SN [1]
Eastleigh	d																								
Southampton Airport Parkway	d																								
Southampton Central ⛴	d		12 30					13 06						13 30										14 30	
Swanwick	d		12 47											13 47										14 47	
Fareham	d		12 54					13 30						13 54										14 54	
Portchester	d																								
Cosham	d		13 03					13 38						14 03										15 03	
Portsmouth Harbour ⛴	d				13 14					13 44						14 14				14 44					
Portsmouth & Southsea	d				13 18					13 48						14 18				14 48					
Fratton	d				13 22					13 52						14 22				14 52					
Hilsea	d																								
Bedhampton	d				13 30											14 30									
Havant	d		13 11		13 33			13 47		14 01				14 11		14 33				15 01				15 11	
Warblington	d				13 35											14 35									
Emsworth	d		13 15		13 38					14 05				14 15		14 38				15 05				15 15	
Southbourne	d				13 41					14 08						14 41				15 08					
Nutbourne	d				13 43											14 43									
Bosham	d				13 47											14 47									
Fishbourne (Sussex)	d				13 50											14 50									
Chichester [4]	a		13 23		13 53			13 57		14 15				14 23		14 53				15 15				15 23	
	d		13 23		13 53			13 58		14 15				14 23		14 53				15 15				15 23	
Bognor Regis [4]	d	13 20					13 59						14 20					14 59					15 20		
Barnham	a	13 26	13 31		14 01		14 05	14 10		14 23			14 26	14 31		15 01		15 05		15 23			15 26	15 31	
	d	13 27	13 32	13 41	14 02	14 03	14 06	14 11		14 23			14 27	14 32	14 41	15 02	15 03	15 06		15 23			15 27	15 32	15 41
Bognor Regis	a			13 48		14 10									14 48		15 10								15 48
Ford [4]	d	13 31	13 36		14 06		14 10						14 31	14 36		15 06		15 10					15 31	15 36	
Littlehampton [4]	a	13 36											14 36										15 36		
	d								14 15										15 15						
Angmering [3]	d		13 42		14 12				14 23					14 42		15 12			15 23					15 42	
Goring-by-Sea	d		13 46		14 16				14 27					14 46		15 16			15 27					15 46	
Durrington-on-Sea	d		13 49		14 19				14 30					14 49		15 19			15 30					15 49	
West Worthing	d		13 51		14 21				14 32					14 51		15 21			15 32					15 51	
Worthing [4]	a		13 53		14 23			14 28	14 34	14 38				14 53		15 23			15 34	15 38				15 53	
	d		13 54		14 24			14 30	14 42					14 54		15 24			15 42					15 54	
East Worthing	d		13 56		14 26									14 56		15 26								15 56	
Lancing	d		13 59		14 29									14 59		15 29								15 59	
Shoreham-by-Sea	d		14 03		14 33			14 38	14 48					15 03		15 33			15 48					16 03	
Southwick	d		14 06		14 36									15 06		15 36								16 06	
Fishersgate	d		14 08		14 38									15 08		15 38								16 08	
Portslade	d		14 10		14 40									15 10		15 40								16 10	
Aldrington	d		14 13		14 43									15 13		15 43								16 13	
Hove [2]	a		14 15		14 45			14 49	14 54					15 15		15 45			15 54					16 15	
	d		14 16		14 46			14 50	14 55			15 00		15 16		15 46			15 55			16 01		16 16	
Brighton [10]	a		14 20		14 50			14 55				15 04		15 20		15 50						16 05		16 20	
Preston Park	d																								
Burgess Hill	a								15 05										16 05						
Haywards Heath [3]	a								15 10										16 10						
Arundel	d						14 15											15 15							
Amberley	d						14 20											15 20							
Pulborough	d						14 26											15 26							
Billingshurst	d						14 33											15 33							
Christs Hospital	d						14 39											15 39							
Horsham [4]	a						14 43											15 43							
	d						14 44											15 44							
Crawley	d						14 53											15 53							
Three Bridges [4]	a						14 56											15 56							
Gatwick Airport [10] ✈	a						15 02		15 22									16 02	16 22						
	d						15 03		15 23									16 03	16 23						
Horley	a						15 05											16 05							
Redhill [5]	a						15 13											16 13							
East Croydon	a						15 29		15 38									16 29	16 38						
London Bridge [4] ⊖	a																								
Clapham Junction [10]	a						15 39		15 48									16 39	16 48						
Clapham Junction [15] ⊖	a						15 46		15 56									16 46	16 56						

Table 188R

Sundays

8 December to 11 May

Southampton, Portsmouth and Sussex Coast - Brighton, Gatwick Airport and London

Network Diagram - see first Page of Table 175

		SN 1	SN 1	SN 1	SN 1	SN 1		SN 1	GW ◇	SN 1	SN 1	SN 1	SN 1	SN 1	SN 1	SN 1	SN 1		SN 1	SN 1	SN 1	SN 1	SN 1	SN 1	SN 1
Eastleigh	d																								
Southampton Airport Parkway	d																								
Southampton Central	d								15 22		15 30										16 30				
Swanwick	d										15 47										16 47				
Fareham	d								15 51		15 59										16 54				
Portchester	d																								
Cosham	d								16 01		16 08										17 03				
Portsmouth Harbour	d	15 14				15 44							16 14				16 44						17 14		
Portsmouth & Southsea	d	15 18				15 48							16 18				16 48						17 18		
Fratton	d	15 22				15 52							16 22				16 52						17 22		
Hilsea	d																								
Bedhampton	d	15 30											16 30										17 30		
Havant	d	15 33				16 01			16 12		16 15		16 33				17 01				17 11		17 33		
Warblington	d	15 35											16 35										17 35		
Emsworth	d	15 38				16 05					16 19		16 38				17 05				17 15		17 38		
Southbourne	d	15 41				16 08							16 41				17 08						17 41		
Nutbourne	d	15 43											16 43										17 43		
Bosham	d	15 47											16 47										17 47		
Fishbourne (Sussex)	d	15 50											16 50										17 50		
Chichester 4	a	15 53				16 15			16 22		16 27		16 53				17 15				17 23		17 53		
	d	15 53				16 15			16 23		16 27		16 53				17 15				17 23		17 53		
Bognor Regis 4	d			15 59				16 20							16 59					17 20					17 59
Barnham	a	16 01		16 05		16 23		16 26	16 30		16 35		17 01		17 05		17 23			17 26	17 31		18 01		18 05
	d	16 02	16 03	16 06		16 23		16 27	16 31		16 36	16 41	17 02	17 03	17 06		17 23			17 27	17 32	17 41	18 02	18 03	18 06
Bognor Regis	a		16 10									16 48		17 10								17 48		18 10	
Ford 4	d	16 06		16 10				16 31			16 40		17 06		17 10					17 31	17 36		18 06		18 10
Littlehampton 4	a							16 36												17 36					
	d				16 15											17 15									
Angmering 3	d	16 12			16 23						16 46		17 12			17 23					17 42		18 12		
Goring-by-Sea	d	16 16			16 27						16 50		17 16			17 27					17 46		18 16		
Durrington-on-Sea	d	16 19			16 30						16 53		17 19			17 30					17 49		18 19		
West Worthing	d	16 21			16 32						16 55		17 21			17 32					17 51		18 21		
Worthing 4	a	16 23			16 34	16 38			16 46		16 57		17 23			17 34	17 38				17 53		18 23		
	d	16 24				16 42			16 46		16 58		17 24				17 42				17 54		18 24		
East Worthing	d	16 26									17 00		17 26								17 56		18 26		
Lancing	d	16 29									17 03		17 29								17 59		18 29		
Shoreham-by-Sea	d	16 33				16 48			16 53		17 07		17 33				17 48				18 03		18 33		
Southwick	d	16 36									17 10		17 36								18 06		18 36		
Fishersgate	d	16 38									17 12		17 38								18 08		18 38		
Portslade	d	16 40									17 14		17 40								18 10		18 40		
Aldrington	d	16 43									17 17		17 43								18 13		18 43		
Hove 2	a	16 45				16 54			16 59		17 19		17 45				17 54				18 15		18 45		
	d	16 46				16 55			17 00	17 04	17 20		17 46				17 55		18 01		18 16		18 46		
Brighton 10	a	16 50							17 05	17 08	17 24		17 50						18 05		18 20		18 50		
Preston Park	d																								
Burgess Hill	a					17 05											18 05								
Haywards Heath 3	a					17 10											18 10								
Arundel	d			16 15											17 15										18 15
Amberley	d			16 20											17 20										18 20
Pulborough	d			16 26											17 26										18 26
Billingshurst	d			16 33											17 33										18 33
Christs Hospital	d			16 39											17 39										18 39
Horsham 4	a			16 43											17 43										18 43
	d			16 44											17 44										18 44
Crawley	d			16 53											17 53										18 53
Three Bridges 4	a			16 56											17 56										18 56
Gatwick Airport 10 ✈	a			17 02		17 22									18 02		18 22								19 02
	d			17 03		17 23									18 03		18 23								19 03
Horley	a			17 05											18 05										19 05
Redhill 5	a			17 13											18 13										19 13
East Croydon	a			17 29		17 38									18 29		18 38								19 29
London Bridge 4 ⊖	a																								
Clapham Junction 10	a			17 39		17 48									18 39		18 48								19 39
Clapham Junction 15 ⊖	a			17 46		17 56									18 46		18 56								19 46

Table 188R

Sundays

8 December to 11 May

Southampton, Portsmouth and Sussex Coast - Brighton, Gatwick Airport and London

Network Diagram - see first Page of Table 175

		SN 1	SN 1		SN 1	SN 1	SN 1	SN 1	SN 1	SN 1	SN 1	SN 1	SN 1		SN 1	SN 1	SN 1	SN 1	SN 1	SN 1	SN 1	SN 1	SN 1		GW ◇
Eastleigh	d																								
Southampton Airport Parkway	d																								
Southampton Central	d						17 30										18 30								19 26
Swanwick	d						17 47										18 47								
Fareham	d						17 54										18 54								19 49
Portchester	d																								
Cosham	d						18 03										19 03								19 58
Portsmouth Harbour	d		17 44						18 14				18 44						19 14				19 44		
Portsmouth & Southsea	d		17 48						18 18				18 48						19 18				19 48		
Fratton	d		17 52						18 22				18 52						19 22				19 52		
Hilsea	d																								
Bedhampton	d								18 30										19 30						
Havant	d		18 01				18 11		18 33				19 01				19 11		19 33				20 01		20 10
Warblington	d								18 35										19 35						
Emsworth	d		18 05				18 15		18 38				19 05				19 15		19 38				20 05		
Southbourne	d		18 08						18 41				19 08						19 41				20 08		
Nutbourne	d								18 43										19 43						
Bosham	d								18 47										19 47						
Fishbourne (Sussex)	d								18 50										19 50						
Chichester 4	a		18 15				18 23		18 53				19 15				19 23		19 53				20 15		20 20
	d		18 15				18 23		18 53				19 15				19 23		19 53				20 15		20 21
Bognor Regis 4	d					18 20					18 59					19 20					19 59				
Barnham	a		18 23			18 26	18 31		19 01		19 05		19 23			19 26	19 31		20 01		20 05		20 23		20 28
	d		18 23			18 27	18 32	18 41	19 02	19 03	19 06		19 23			19 27	19 32	19 41	20 02	20 03	20 06		20 23		20 29
Bognor Regis	a							18 48		19 10								19 48		20 10					
Ford 4	d					18 31	18 36		19 06		19 10					19 31	19 36		20 06		20 10				
Littlehampton 4	a					18 36										19 36									
	d	18 15										19 15										20 15			
Angmering 3	d	18 23					18 42		19 12			19 23					19 42		20 12			20 23			
Goring-by-Sea	d	18 27					18 46		19 16			19 27					19 46		20 16			20 27			
Durrington-on-Sea	d	18 30					18 49		19 19			19 30					19 49		20 19			20 30			
West Worthing	d	18 32					18 51		19 21			19 32					19 51		20 21			20 32			
Worthing 4	a	18 34	18 38				18 53		19 23			19 34	19 38				19 53		20 23			20 34	20 38		20 46
	d	18 42					18 54		19 24			19 42					19 54		20 24			20 42			20 46
East Worthing	d						18 56		19 26								19 56		20 26						
Lancing	d						18 59		19 29								19 59		20 29						
Shoreham-by-Sea	d	18 48					19 03		19 33			19 48					20 03		20 33			20 48			20 53
Southwick	d						19 06		19 36								20 06		20 36						
Fishersgate	d						19 08		19 38								20 08		20 38						
Portslade	d						19 10		19 40								20 10		20 40						
Aldrington	d						19 13		19 43								20 13		20 43						
Hove 2	a	18 54					19 15		19 45			19 54					20 15		20 45			20 54			20 59
	d	18 55			19 01		19 16		19 46			19 55			20 01		20 16		20 46			20 55			21 00
Brighton 10	a				19 05		19 20		19 50						20 05		20 20		20 50						21 04
Preston Park	d																								
Burgess Hill	a	19 05										20 05										21 05			
Haywards Heath 3	a	19 10										20 10										21 10			
Arundel	d										19 15										20 15				
Amberley	d										19 20										20 20				
Pulborough	d										19 26										20 26				
Billingshurst	d										19 33										20 33				
Christs Hospital	d										19 39										20 39				
Horsham 4	a										19 43										20 43				
	d										19 44										20 44				
Crawley	d										19 53										20 53				
Three Bridges 4	a										19 56										20 56				
Gatwick Airport 10 ✈	a	19 22									20 02	20 22									21 02	21 22			
	d	19 23									20 03	20 23									21 03	21 23			
Horley	a										20 05										21 05				
Redhill 5	a										20 13										21 13				
East Croydon	a	19 38									20 29	20 38									21 29	21 38			
London Bridge 4 ⊖	a																								
Clapham Junction 10	a	19 48									20 39	20 48									21 39	21 48			
Clapham Junction 15 ⊖	a	19 56									20 46	20 56									21 46	21 56			

Table 188R

Sundays

8 December to 11 May

Southampton, Portsmouth and Sussex Coast - Brighton, Gatwick Airport and London

Network Diagram - see first Page of Table 175

		SN	SN	SN	SN	SN	SN	SN	SN	SN	SN	SN	SN	SN	SN	SN	SN	SN	SN	SN	SN	SN	SN
		1	1	1	1	1	1	1	1	1	1	1	1	1	1	1	1	1	1	1	1		
Eastleigh	d			19 46							20 46												
Southampton Airport Parkway	d			19n38							20n38												
Southampton Central	d			19n29							20n29								21 30				
Swanwick	d																		21 47				
Fareham	d			20 03							21 02								21 54				
Portchester	d																						
Cosham	d			20 12							21 11								22 03				
Portsmouth Harbour	d								20 43					21 14				21 44					
Portsmouth & Southsea	d					20 15			20 47					21 18				21 48					
Fratton	d					20 19			20 51					21 22				21 52					
Hilsea	d																						
Bedhampton	d					20 26								21 30									
Havant	d			20 18		20 29			21 00		21 17			21 33				22 01	22 11				
Warblington	d					20 31								21 35									
Emsworth	d			20 22		20 34			21 04		21 21			21 38				22 05	22 15				
Southbourne	d					20 37			21 07					21 41				22 08					
Nutbourne	d					20 40								21 43									
Bosham	d					20 43								21 47									
Fishbourne (Sussex)	d					20 46								21 50									
Chichester 4	a			20 30		20 49			21 14		21 29			21 53				22 15	22 23				
	d			20 31		20 50			21 14		21 30			21 53				22 15	22 23				
Bognor Regis 4	d	20 26						20 59		21 20						21 59	22 13					22 41	
Barnham	a	20 32		20 38		20 57		21 05	21 22	21 26	21 37			22 01		22 05	22 19	22 23	22 31			22 47	
	d	20 33		20 39	20 41	20 58	21 03	21 06	21 22	21 27	21 38		21 41	22 02	22 03	22 06	22 20	22 24	22 32		22 41		22 54
Bognor Regis	a				20 48		21 10						21 48		22 10						22 48		23 01
Ford 4	d	20 37		20 43		21 02		21 10	21 27	21 31	21 42			22 06		22 10	22 24	22 28	22 36				
Littlehampton 4	a	20 42				21 07			21 31	21 36							22 29	22 33					
	d					21 14			21 42									22 43					
Angmering 3	d			20 49		21 22			21 52		21 48			22 12				22 52	22 42				
Goring-by-Sea	d			20 53		21 26			21 56		21 52			22 16				22 56	22 46				
Durrington-on-Sea	d			20 56		21 29			21 59		21 55			22 19				22 59	22 49				
West Worthing	d			20 58		21 31			22 01		21 57	←		22 21				23 01	22 51	←			
Worthing 4	a			21 00		21 33			22 03		21 59	22 03		22 23				23 03	22 53	23 03			
	d			21 01		21 34			22 04		22 00	22 04		22 24				23 04	22 54	23 04			
East Worthing	d			21 03		21 36			→		22 02	22 06		22 26				→	22 56	23 06			
Lancing	d			21 06		21 39					22 05	22 09		22 29					22 59	23 09			
Shoreham-by-Sea	d			21 10		21 43					22 09	22 13		22 33					23 03	23 13			
Southwick	d			21 13		21 46					22 12	22 16		22 36					23 06	23 16			
Fishersgate	d			21 15		21 48					22 14	22 18		22 38					23 08	23 18			
Portslade	d			21 17		21 50					22 16	22 20		22 40					23 10	23 20			
Aldrington	d			21 20		21 53					22 19	22 23		22 43					23 13	23 23			
Hove 2	a			21 22		21 55					22 22	22 26		22 45					23 15	23 27			
	d		21 04	21 22		21 55					22 22	22 26		22 46					23 16	23 28			
Brighton 10	a		21 08	21 27		21 59					22 26	22 30		22 50					23 20	23 32			
Preston Park	d																						
Burgess Hill	a																						
Haywards Heath 3	a																						
Arundel	d							21 15								22 15							
Amberley	d							21 20								22 20							
Pulborough	d							21 26								22 26							
Billingshurst	d							21 33								22 33							
Christs Hospital	d							21 39								22 39							
Horsham 4	a							21 43								22 43							
	d							21 44								22 44							
Crawley	d							21 53								22 53							
Three Bridges 4	a							21 56								22 56							
Gatwick Airport 10	a							22 02								23 02							
	d							22 03								23 03							
Horley	a							22 05								23 05							
Redhill 5	a							22 13								23 13							
East Croydon	a							22 29								23 29							
London Bridge 4 ⊖	a																						
Clapham Junction 10	a							22 39								23 39							
Clapham Junction 15 ⊖	a							22 46								23 46							

n Stops at these stations before Eastleigh

Table 188R

Sundays

8 December to 11 May

Southampton, Portsmouth and Sussex Coast - Brighton, Gatwick Airport and London

Network Diagram - see first Page of Table 175

Station		SN [1]	SN [1]	SN [1]	SN [1]		SN [1]	SN [1]	SN [1]
Eastleigh	d								
Southampton Airport Parkway	d								
Southampton Central (ship)	d			22 15					22 52
Swanwick	d			22 32					23 11
Fareham	d			22 39					23 17
Portchester	d								
Cosham	d			22 48					23 26
Portsmouth Harbour (ship)	d	22 14			22 44				
Portsmouth & Southsea	d	22 18			22 48				
Fratton	d	22 22			22 52				
Hilsea	d								
Bedhampton	d	22 30							
Havant	d	22 33		22 54	23 01				23 32
Warblington	d	22 35							
Emsworth	d	22 38		22 58	23 05				23 36
Southbourne	d	22 41			23 08				
Nutbourne	d	22 43							
Bosham	d	22 47							
Fishbourne (Sussex)	d	22 50							
Chichester [4]	a	22 53		23 06	23 15				23 44
	d	22 53		23 07	23 15				23 45
Bognor Regis [4]	d								
Barnham	a	23 01		23 14	23 23				23 52
	d	23 01	23 15	23 15	23 23		23 37	23 46	23 53
Bognor Regis	a		23 21					23 53	
Ford [4]	d	23 06		23 19	23 28		23 42		
Littlehampton [4]	a	23 10		23 27	23 33		23 46		00 01
	d								
Angmering [3]	d								
Goring-by-Sea	d								
Durrington-on-Sea	d								
West Worthing	d								
Worthing [4]	a								
	d								
East Worthing	d								
Lancing	d								
Shoreham-by-Sea	d								
Southwick	d								
Fishersgate	d								
Portslade	d								
Aldrington	d								
Hove [2]	a								
	d								
Brighton [10]	a								
Preston Park	d								
Burgess Hill	a								
Haywards Heath [3]	a								
Arundel	d								
Amberley	d								
Pulborough	d								
Billingshurst	d								
Christs Hospital	d								
Horsham [4]	a								
	d								
Crawley	d								
Three Bridges [4]	a								
Gatwick Airport [10] (plane)	a								
	d								
Horley	a								
Redhill [5]	a								
East Croydon (tram)	a								
London Bridge [4] (Underground)	a								
Clapham Junction [10]	a								
Clapham Junction [15] (Underground)	a								

Network Diagram for Table 189

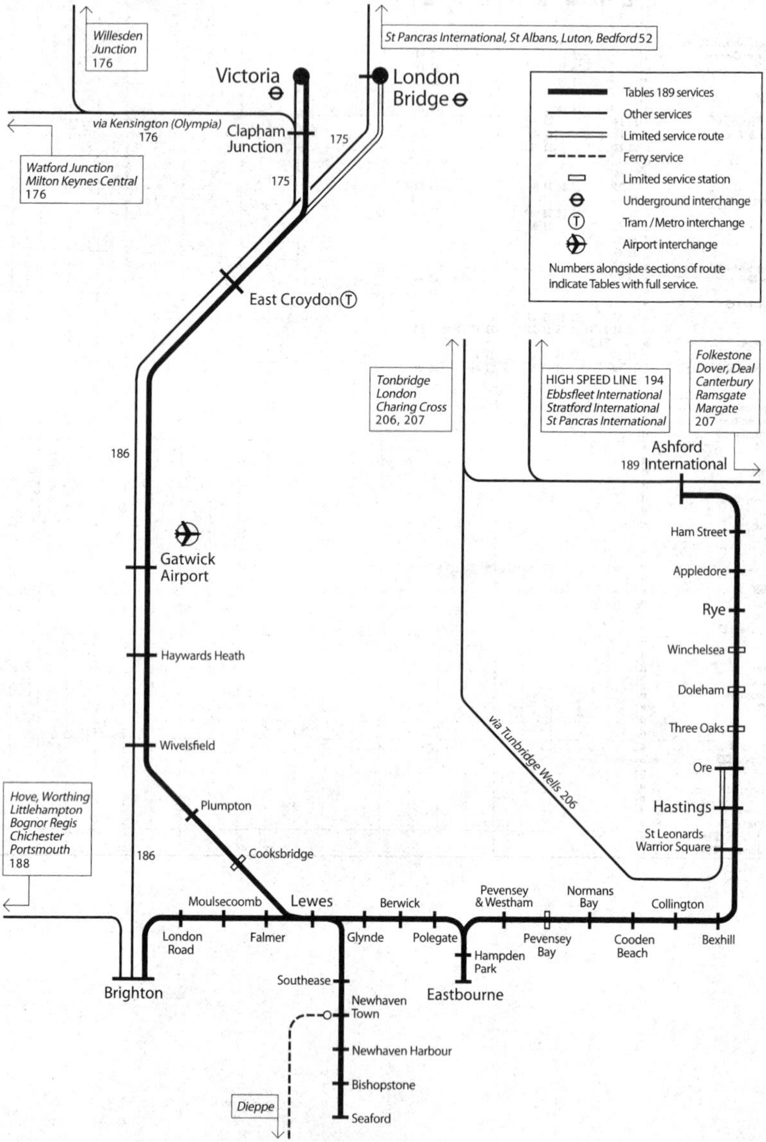
Willesden Junction 176
St Pancras International, St Albans, Luton, Bedford 52
Victoria
London Bridge
via Kensington (Olympia) 176
Clapham Junction
175
175
Watford Junction Milton Keynes Central 176
Tables 189 services
Other services
Limited service route
Ferry service
Limited service station
Underground interchange
Tram / Metro interchange
Airport interchange
Numbers alongside sections of route indicate Tables with full service.
East Croydon
Tonbridge London Charing Cross 206, 207
HIGH SPEED LINE 194 Ebbsfleet International Stratford International St Pancras International
Folkestone Dover, Deal Canterbury Ramsgate Margate 207
Ashford International
189
186
Gatwick Airport
Ham Street
Appledore
Rye
Winchelsea
Doleham
Three Oaks
Haywards Heath
Wivelsfield
via Tunbridge Wells 206
Ore
Hastings
St Leonards Warrior Square
Plumpton
Hove, Worthing Littlehampton Bognor Regis Chichester Portsmouth 188
186
Cooksbridge
Moulsecoomb
Lewes
Berwick
Pevensey & Westham
Normans Bay
Collington
London Road
Falmer
Glynde
Polegate
Pevensey Bay
Cooden Beach
Bexhill
Hampden Park
Brighton
Southease
Eastbourne
Newhaven Town
Newhaven Harbour
Bishopstone
Dieppe
Seaford

TOCs operating on this network - Southern (SN)

Table 189

Mondays to Fridays

9 December to 16 May

London, Haywards Heath and Brighton - Lewes, Seaford, Eastbourne, Hastings and Ashford

Network Diagram - see first Page of Table 189

Miles	Miles			SN MX	SN MX	SN MO	SN	SN	SN	SN	SN	SN	SN	SN	SN	SN	SN	SN	SN	SN
				1		1		1	1			1	1				1	1		1
—	—	London Victoria 15 ⊖	d																	
—	—	Clapham Junction 10	d																	
—	—	London Bridge 4 ⊖	d																	
—	—	East Croydon	d																	
—	—	Gatwick Airport 10 ✈	d																	
—	0	Haywards Heath 3	d																06 09	
—	3	Wivelsfield 4	d																06 13	
—	6¾	Plumpton	d																06 19	
—	9½	Cooksbridge	d																	
0	—	Brighton 10	d										05 12		05 45	06 00				
0¾	—	London Road (Brighton)	d												05 48	06 03				
1¾	—	Moulsecoomb	d												05 50	06 05				
3½	—	Falmer	d												05 54	06 09				
8	12¼	Lewes 4	a										05 23		06 00	06 16			06 26	
—	—		d										05 23		06 03				06 27	
—	15¾	Southease	d																	
—	18½	Newhaven Town ⛴	d		00 04										06 11				06 35	
—	18¾	Newhaven Harbour	d		00 06										06 13				06 37	
—	20¼	Bishopstone	d		00 09										06 16				06 40	
—	21¼	Seaford	a		00 12										06 19				06 43	
11	—	Glynde	d																	
15½	—	Berwick	d	00 02																
19¾	—	Polegate	d	00 07		00 11							05 35							
21¾	—	Hampden Park 4	d	00 11		00 15						05 33					06 08			
23¾	—	Eastbourne 4	a	00 16		00 20						05 38	05 42				06 13			
—	—		d	00 22			04 50	05 08	05 15		05 32	05 43		05 54				06 14		06 24
25¾	—	Hampden Park 4	d					05a12			05a36	05a47						06 18		06a28
28¾	—	Pevensey & Westham	d	00 29					05 22									06 23		
29½	—	Pevensey Bay	d																	
31½	—	Normans Bay	d																	
33¼	—	Cooden Beach	d	00 35														06 29		
34¾	—	Collington	d	00 38														06 32		
35½	—	Bexhill 4	d	00 41			05 05		05 31					06 09				06 34		
39¼	—	St Leonards Warrior Sq 4	d	00 47			05 12		05 37					06 15				06 41		
40	0	Hastings 4	a	00 52			05 15		05 41					06 19				06 44		
—	—		d				05 21			05 47				06 19						
—	1	Ore	d				05 23			05 49										
—	3¾	Three Oaks	d							05 55										
—	5	Doleham	d							05 58										
—	9¼	Winchelsea	d							06 04										
—	11¼	Rye	a				05 44			06 08				06 36						
—	—		d				05 44			06 08				06 37						
—	18	Appledore (Kent)	d				05 53			06 17				06 46						
—	21	Ham Street	d				05 58			06 22				06 51						
—	26½	Ashford International	a				06 06			06 30				06 59						

Miles	Miles			SN	SN	SN	SN	SN	SN	SN	SN	SN	SN	SN	SN	SN	SN	SN	SN	SN
					1	1	1			1	1	1	1					1	1	1
—	—	London Victoria 15 ⊖	d										05 32							
—	—	Clapham Junction 10	d										05 38							
—	—	London Bridge 4 ⊖	d																	
—	—	East Croydon	d										05 49							
—	—	Gatwick Airport 10 ✈	d										06 20							
—	0	Haywards Heath 3	d										06 34							
—	3	Wivelsfield 4	d										06 38							
—	6¾	Plumpton	d																	
—	9½	Cooksbridge	d																	
0	—	Brighton 10	d						06 18		06 26			06 39	06 52	07 00	07 10			
0¾	—	London Road (Brighton)	d								06 29			06 42	06 55	07 03	07 13			
1¾	—	Moulsecoomb	d								06 31			06 44	06 57	07 05	07 15			
3½	—	Falmer	d								06 35			06 48	07 01	07 09	07 19			
8	12¼	Lewes 4	a						06 29		06 41		06 50	06 54	07 08	07 17	07 26			
—	—		d						06 30		06 42		06 51	06 55	07 10					
—	15¾	Southease	d																	
—	18½	Newhaven Town ⛴	d											07 03	07 18					
—	18¾	Newhaven Harbour	d											07 05	07 23					
—	20¼	Bishopstone	d											07 08	07 26					
—	21¼	Seaford	a											07 11	07 29					
11	—	Glynde	d								06 47		06 56							
15½	—	Berwick	d								06 53		07 02							
19¾	—	Polegate	d						06 43		06 58		07 07							
21¾	—	Hampden Park 4	d	06 24			06 42				07 02		07 11					07 15		07 46
23¾	—	Eastbourne 4	a	06 29			06 47		06 50		07 07		07 16					07 20		07 51
—	—		d		06 30	06 47	06 57		06 54	07 02		07 14	07 21						07 38	07 57
25¾	—	Hampden Park 4	d			06a51	07a01			07 06		07a18	07 25						07 42	08a01
28¾	—	Pevensey & Westham	d		06 38					07 11			07 30						07 47	
29½	—	Pevensey Bay	d																07 49	
31½	—	Normans Bay	d		06 43														07 53	
33¼	—	Cooden Beach	d							07 17			07 36						07 56	
34¾	—	Collington	d							07 20			07 39						07 59	
35½	—	Bexhill 4	d		06 50				07 09	07 22			07 41						08 02	
39¼	—	St Leonards Warrior Sq 4	d		06 56				07 16	07 29			07 48						08 08	
40	0	Hastings 4	a		06 59				07 19	07 32			07 51						08 11	
—	—		d						07 20				07 52						08 12	
—	1	Ore	d										07a57						08a15	
—	3¾	Three Oaks	d						07 28											
—	5	Doleham	d																	
—	9¼	Winchelsea	d						07 36											
—	11¼	Rye	a						07 39											
—	—		d					07 06	07 41											
—	18	Appledore (Kent)	d					07 15	07 50											
—	21	Ham Street	d					07 20	07 55											
—	26½	Ashford International	a					07 28	08 03											

Table 189

Mondays to Fridays

9 December to 16 May

London, Haywards Heath and Brighton - Lewes, Seaford, Eastbourne, Hastings and Ashford

Network Diagram - see first Page of Table 189

Station		SN 1	SN 1	SN 1	SN	SN	SN	SN 1	SN 1	SN	SN
London Victoria 15 ⊖	d								06 47		
Clapham Junction 10	d								06 53		
London Bridge 4 ⊖	d										
East Croydon	d								07 04		
Gatwick Airport 10 ✈	d								07 20		
Haywards Heath 3	d	07 10							07 33		
Wivelsfield 4	d	07 14							07 37		
Plumpton	d	07 20							07 43		
Cooksbridge	d	07 24							07 48		
Brighton 10	d			07 17	07 25		07 32			07 40	07 52
London Road (Brighton)	d			07 20						07 43	07 55
Moulsecoomb	d			07 22						07 45	07 57
Falmer	d			07 26						07 49	08 01
Lewes 4	a	07 29		07 32	07 39		07 43		07 52	07 56	08 08
	d	07 31		07 34			07 44		07 53	07 56	08 09
Southease	d										
Newhaven Town ⛴	d			07 42						08 05	
Newhaven Harbour	d			07 44						08 06	
Bishopstone	d			07 47						08 09	
Seaford	a			07 50						08 13	
Glynde	d	07 36									08 14
Berwick	d	07 42									08 20
Polegate	d	07 47					07 57		08 05		08 25
Hampden Park 4	d	07 51						08 06	08 09		08 29
Eastbourne 4	a	07 56					08 04	08 11	08 14		08 34
	d		08 04				08 09		08 21		08 40
Hampden Park 4	d		08a08						08 25		08 44
Pevensey & Westham	d						08 17		08 30		08 49
Pevensey Bay	d								08 32		
Normans Bay	d								08 36		08 53
Cooden Beach	d								08 39		08 57
Collington	d								08 42		09 00
Bexhill 4	d						08 25		08 45		09 02
St Leonards Warrior Sq 4	d						08 32		08 51		09 09
Hastings 4	a						08 35		08 55		09 12
	d						08 36		08 56		09 13
Ore	d								08a59		09a16
Three Oaks	d						08 44				
Doleham	d										
Winchelsea	d										
Rye	a						08 54				
	d					08 14	08 56				
Appledore (Kent)	d					08 23	09 05				
Ham Street	d					08 28	09 10				
Ashford International	a					08 36	09 18				

Station		SN 1	SN 1	SN	SN	SN 1	SN	SN 1	SN	SN	SN	SN 1	SN 1	SN 1	SN 1	SN	SN	SN 1	SN
London Victoria 15 ⊖	d							07 47						08 17					
Clapham Junction 10	d							07 53						08 23					
London Bridge 4 ⊖	d																		
East Croydon	d							08 04						08 34					
Gatwick Airport 10 ✈	d							08 20						08 50					
Haywards Heath 3	d							08 34						09 10					
Wivelsfield 4	d							08 38						09 14					
Plumpton	d							08 44											
Cooksbridge	d							08 49											
Brighton 10	d	08 03		08 10	08 22		08 32			08 37	08 45		08 53			09 10	09 22		09 32
London Road (Brighton)	d	08 06		08 13	08 25					08 40	08 48		08 56			09 13	09 25		
Moulsecoomb	d	08 08		08 15	08 27					08 42	08 50		08 58			09 15	09 27		
Falmer	d	08 12		08 19	08 31					08 46	08 54		09 02			09 19	09 31		
Lewes 4	a	08 18		08 26	08 38		08 43	08 53		08 53	09 00		09 08	09 25		09 25	09 38		09 43
	d	08 19		08 30			08 44	08 54			09 02		09 09	09 25		09 30			09 44
Southease	d															09 36			
Newhaven Town ⛴	d			08 38							09 10					09 40			
Newhaven Harbour	d			08 40							09 12					09 42			
Bishopstone	d			08 43							09 15					09 45			
Seaford	a			08 46							09 18					09 48			
Glynde	d	08 24											09 14						
Berwick	d	08 30											09 20						
Polegate	d	08 35					08 57	09 06					09 25	09 38					09 57
Hampden Park 4	d	08 39				08 52		09 10				09 18	09 29	09 42				09 52	
Eastbourne 4	a	08 44				08 57	09 04	09 15				09 23	09 34	09 47				09 58	10 04
	d		08 56			09 04	09 09	09 20					09 40		09 55			10 03	10 09
Hampden Park 4	d		09a00			09a08		09 24					09 44		09a59			10a07	
Pevensey & Westham	d							09 29					09 49						
Pevensey Bay	d																		
Normans Bay	d												09 53						
Cooden Beach	d							09 35					09 57						
Collington	d							09 38					10 00						
Bexhill 4	d						09 24	09 40					10 02						10 24
St Leonards Warrior Sq 4	d						09 32	09 46					10 09						10 31
Hastings 4	a						09 35	09 49					10 12						10 35
	d						09 36		09 56				10 13						10 36
Ore	d								09a59				10a18						
Three Oaks	d																		10 44
Doleham	d																		
Winchelsea	d						09 50												
Rye	a						09 54												10 54
	d						09 56												10 56
Appledore (Kent)	d						10 05												11 05
Ham Street	d						10 10												11 10
Ashford International	a						10 18												11 18

Station		SN 1 A 🛒	SN	SN 1	SN 1	SN 1 A 🛒	SN 1	SN	SN
London Victoria 15 ⊖	d	08 47				09 17			
Clapham Junction 10	d	08 53				09 23			
London Bridge 4 ⊖	d								
East Croydon	d	09 04				09 33			
Gatwick Airport 10 ✈	d	09 20				09 50			
Haywards Heath 3	d	09 35				10 07			
Wivelsfield 4	d					10 11			
Plumpton	d	09 44							
Cooksbridge	d	09 49							
Brighton 10	d		09 40		09 52			10 10	10 22
London Road (Brighton)	d		09 43		09 55			10 13	10 25
Moulsecoomb	d		09 45		09 57			10 15	10 27
Falmer	d		09 49		10 01			10 19	10 31
Lewes 4	a	09 53	09 55		10 07	10 22		10 25	10 38
	d	09 54	09 58		10 09	10 23		10 28	
Southease	d							10 34	
Newhaven Town ⛴	d		10 06					10 38	
Newhaven Harbour	d		10 08					10 40	
Bishopstone	d		10 11					10 43	
Seaford	a		10 14					10 46	
Glynde	d				10 14				
Berwick	d				10 20				
Polegate	d	10 06			10 25	10 35			
Hampden Park 4	d			10 21	10 29	10 39			
Eastbourne 4	a	10 14		10 26	10 34	10 44			
	d	10 20			10 40		10 58		
Hampden Park 4	d	10 24			10 44		11a02		
Pevensey & Westham	d	10 29			10 49				
Pevensey Bay	d								
Normans Bay	d				10 53				
Cooden Beach	d	10 35			10 57				
Collington	d	10 38			11 00				
Bexhill 4	d	10 40			11 02				
St Leonards Warrior Sq 4	d	10 47			11 09				
Hastings 4	a	10 50			11 12				
	d	10 51			11 13				
Ore	d	10a56			11a18				
Three Oaks	d								
Doleham	d								
Winchelsea	d								
Rye	a								
	d								
Appledore (Kent)	d								
Ham Street	d								
Ashford International	a								

A 🛒 to Lewes

Table 189

Mondays to Fridays

9 December to 16 May

London, Haywards Heath and Brighton - Lewes, Seaford, Eastbourne, Hastings and Ashford

Network Diagram - see first Page of Table 189

		SN	SN	SN 1 A 🚌	SN	SN 1	SN 1	SN 1 A 🚌	SN 1	SN	SN	SN 1	SN	SN 1 A 🚌	SN	SN 1	SN 1	SN 1	SN 1	SN	SN	SN 1	SN	SN 1	SN	SN 1	SN 1	SN 1	SN 1	SN	SN	SN 1	SN	SN 1	SN	SN 1	SN 1
London Victoria 15 ⊖	d			09 47				10 17						10 47				11 17						11 47				12 17						12 47			
Clapham Junction 10	d			09 53				10 23						10 53				11 23						11 53				12 23						12 53			
London Bridge 4 ⊖	d																																				
East Croydon 🚋	d			10 03				10 33						11 03				11 33						12 03				12 33						13 03			
Gatwick Airport 10 ✈	d			10 20				10 50						11 20				11 50						12 20				12 50						13 20			
Haywards Heath 3	d			10 35				11 07						11 35				12 07						12 35				13 07						13 35			
Wivelsfield 4	d							11 11										12 11										13 11									
Plumpton	d			10 44										11 44										12 44										13 44			
Cooksbridge	d																																				
Brighton 10	d		10 32		10 40		10 52			11 10	11 22		11 32		11 40		11 52			12 10	12 22		12 32		12 40		12 52			13 10	13 22		13 32		13 40		13 52
London Road (Brighton)	d				10 43		10 55			11 13	11 25				11 43		11 55			12 13	12 25				12 43		12 55			13 13	13 25				13 43		13 55
Moulsecoomb	d				10 45		10 57			11 15	11 27				11 45		11 57			12 15	12 27				12 45		12 57			13 15	13 27				13 45		13 57
Falmer	d				10 49		11 01			11 19	11 31				11 49		12 01			12 19	12 31				12 49		13 01			13 19	13 31				13 49		14 01
Lewes 4	a		10 43	10 52	10 55		11 07	11 22		11 25	11 38		11 43	11 52	11 55		12 07	12 22		12 25	12 38		12 43	12 52	12 55		13 07	13 22		13 25	13 38		13 43	13 52	13 55		14 07
	d		10 44	10 53	10 58		11 09	11 23		11 28			11 44	11 53	11 58		12 09	12 23		12 28			12 44	12 53	12 58		13 09	13 23		13 28			13 44	13 53	13 58		14 09
Southease	d									11 34										12 34										13 34							
Newhaven Town ⛴	d				11 06					11 38					12 06					12 38					13 06					13 38					14 06		
Newhaven Harbour	d				11 08					11 40					12 08					12 40					13 08					13 40					14 08		
Bishopstone	d				11 11					11 43					12 11					12 43					13 11					13 43					14 11		
Seaford	a				11 14					11 46					12 14					12 46					13 14					13 46					14 14		
Glynde	d						11 14										12 14										13 14										14 14
Berwick	d						11 20										12 20										13 20										14 20
Polegate	d		10 57	11 05			11 25	11 35					11 57	12 05			12 25	12 35					12 57	13 05			13 25	13 35					13 57	14 05			14 25
Hampden Park 4	d	10 52				11 20	11 29	11 39				11 52				12 20	12 29	12 39				12 52				13 20	13 29	13 39				13 52				14 20	14 29
Eastbourne 4	a	10 57	11 04	11 13		11 25	11 34	11 44				11 57	12 04	12 13		12 25	12 34	12 44				12 57	13 04	13 13		13 25	13 34	13 44				13 57	14 04	14 13		14 25	14 34
	d	11 04	11 09	11 19			11 40		11 58			12 04	12 09	12 19			12 40		12 58			13 04	13 09	13 19			13 40		13 58			14 04	14 09	14 19			14 40
Hampden Park 4	d	11a08		11 23			11 44		12a02			12a08		12 23			12 44		13a02			13a08		13 23			13 44		14a02			14a08		14 23			14 44
Pevensey & Westham	d			11 28			11 49							12 28			12 49							13 28			13 49							14 28			14 49
Pevensey Bay	d																																				
Normans Bay	d						11 53										12 53										13 53										14 53
Cooden Beach	d			11 34			11 57							12 34			12 57							13 34			13 57							14 34			14 57
Collington	d			11 37			12 00							12 37			13 00							13 37			14 00							14 37			15 00
Bexhill 4	d		11 24	11 39			12 02						12 24	12 39			13 02						13 24	13 39			14 02						14 24	14 39			15 02
St Leonards Warrior Sq 4	d		11 31	11 46			12 09						12 31	12 46			13 09						13 31	13 46			14 09						14 31	14 46			15 09
Hastings 4	a		11 35	11 49			12 12						12 35	12 49			13 12						13 35	13 49			14 12						14 35	14 49			15 12
	d		11 36	11 50			12 13						12 36	12 50			13 13						13 36	13 50			14 13						14 36	14 50			15 13
Ore	d			11a55			12a18							12a55			13a18							13a55			14a18							14a55			15a18
Three Oaks	d												12 44																				14 44				
Doleham	d																																				
Winchelsea	d		11 50																				13 50														
Rye	a		11 54										12 54										13 54										14 54				
	d		11 56										12 56										13 56										14 56				
Appledore (Kent)	d		12 05										13 05										14 05										15 05				
Ham Street	d		12 10										13 10										14 10										15 10				
Ashford International	a		12 18										13 18										14 18										15 18				

A 🚌 to Lewes

Table 189

Mondays to Fridays

9 December to 16 May

London, Haywards Heath and Brighton - Lewes, Seaford, Eastbourne, Hastings and Ashford

Network Diagram - see first Page of Table 189

		SN ■	SN ■	SN	SN	SN ■	SN	SN ■	SN	SN ■	SN ■	SN ■	SN ■	SN	SN	SN ■	SN	SN ■	SN	SN ■
London Victoria 15 ⊖	d	13 17						13 47				14 17						14 47		
Clapham Junction 10	d	13 23						13 53				14 23						14 53		
London Bridge 4 ⊖	d																			
East Croydon	d	13 33						14 03				14 33						15 03		
Gatwick Airport 10 ✈	d	13 50						14 20				14 50						15 20		
Haywards Heath 3	d	14 07						14 35				15 07						15 35		
Wivelsfield 4	d	14 11										15 11						15 39		
Plumpton	d							14 44										15 45		
Cooksbridge	d																			
Brighton 10	d			14 10	14 22		14 32		14 40		14 52			15 10	15 22		15 32		15 40	
London Road (Brighton)	d			14 13	14 25				14 43		14 55			15 13	15 25				15 43	
Moulsecoomb	d			14 15	14 27				14 45		14 57			15 15	15 27				15 45	
Falmer	d			14 19	14 31				14 49		15 01			15 19	15 31				15 49	
Lewes 4	a	14 22		14 25	14 38		14 43	14 52	14 55		15 07	15 22		15 25	15 38		15 43	15 52	15 55	
	d	14 23		14 28			14 44	14 53	14 58		15 09	15 23		15 28			15 44	15 53	15 58	
Southease	d			14 34										15 34					16 04	
Newhaven Town ⛴	d			14 38					15 06					15 38					16 08	
Newhaven Harbour	d			14 40					15 08					15 40					16 10	
Bishopstone	d			14 43					15 11					15 43					16 13	
Seaford	a			14 46					15 14					15 46					16 16	
Glynde	d										15 14									
Berwick	d										15 20									
Polegate	d	14 35					14 57	15 05			15 25	15 35					15 57	16 05		
Hampden Park 4	d	14 39				14 52				15 20	15 29	15 39				15 52				16 20
Eastbourne 4	a	14 44				14 57	15 04	15 13		15 25	15 34	15 44				15 57	16 04	16 13		16 25
	d		14 58			15 04	15 09	15 19			15 40		15 58			16 04	16 09	16 19		
Hampden Park 4	d		15a02			15a08		15 23			15 44		16a02			16a08		16 23		
Pevensey & Westham	d							15 28			15 49							16 28		
Pevensey Bay	d							15 30												
Normans Bay	d							15 34			15 53									
Cooden Beach	d							15 37			15 57							16 34		
Collington	d							15 40			16 00							16 37		
Bexhill 4	d						15 24	15 43			16 02						16 24	16 39		
St Leonards Warrior Sq 4	d						15 31	15 49			16 09						16 31	16 46		
Hastings 4	a						15 35	15 52			16 12						16 35	16 49		
	d						15 36	15 54			16 13						16 36	16 50		
Ore	d							15a59			16a18							16a55		
Three Oaks	d																16 44			
Doleham	d																			
Winchelsea	d						15 50													
Rye	a						15 54										16 54			
	d						15 56										16 56			
Appledore (Kent)	d						16 05										17 05			
Ham Street	d						16 10										17 10			
Ashford International	a						16 18										17 18			

		SN	SN ■	SN ■	SN	SN	SN	SN ■	SN ■	SN	SN ■	SN	SN ■	SN ■	SN	SN ■ A 🛒	SN ■	SN
London Victoria 15 ⊖	d			15 17							15 47					16 17		
Clapham Junction 10	d			15 23							15 53					16 23		
London Bridge 4 ⊖	d																	
East Croydon	d			15 33							16 03					16 34		
Gatwick Airport 10 ✈	d			15 50							16 20					16 49		
Haywards Heath 3	d			16 07							16 35					17 06		
Wivelsfield 4	d			16 11							16 39					17 10		
Plumpton	d										16 45							
Cooksbridge	d										16 49							
Brighton 10	d		15 52			16 10	16 22			16 32		16 40		16 52	17 02			17 10
London Road (Brighton)	d		15 55			16 13	16 25					16 43		16 55	17 05			17 13
Moulsecoomb	d		15 57			16 15	16 27					16 45		16 57	17 07			17 15
Falmer	d		16 01			16 19	16 31					16 49		17 01	17 11			17 19
Lewes 4	a		16 07	16 22		16 25	16 38			16 43	16 54	16 55		17 07	17 18	17 21		17 25
	d		16 09	16 23		16 28				16 44	16 54	16 58		17 09		17 22		17 28
Southease	d					16 34												17 34
Newhaven Town ⛴	d					16 38						17 06						17 38
Newhaven Harbour	d					16 40						17 08						17 40
Bishopstone	d					16 43						17 11						17 43
Seaford	a					16 46						17 14						17 46
Glynde	d		16 14											17 14				
Berwick	d		16 20								17 03			17 20		17 31		
Polegate	d		16 25	16 35						16 57	17 08			17 25		17 36		
Hampden Park 4	d		16 29	16 39					16 52				17 20	17 29		17 40		
Eastbourne 4	a		16 34	16 44					16 57	17 04	17 16		17 25	17 34		17 48		
	d		16 40		16 45			16 58	17 04	17 09	17 21			17 40			17 57	
Hampden Park 4	d		16 44		16a49			17a02	17a08		17 25			17 44			18a01	
Pevensey & Westham	d		16 49								17 30			17 49				
Pevensey Bay	d										17 32			17 51				
Normans Bay	d		16 53								17 36			17 55				
Cooden Beach	d		16 57								17 39			17 58				
Collington	d		17 00								17 42			18 01				
Bexhill 4	d		17 02							17 25	17 45			18 04				
St Leonards Warrior Sq 4	d		17 09							17 31	17 54			18 10				
Hastings 4	a		17 12							17 35	17 57			18 13				
	d	17 09	17 13							17 36	17 58			18 14				
Ore	d	17 12	17a18								18a03			18a19				
Three Oaks	d	17 18																
Doleham	d	17 21																
Winchelsea	d	17 27								17 50								
Rye	a	17 30								17 54								
	d	17 31								17 56								
Appledore (Kent)	d	17 40								18 05								
Ham Street	d	17 45								18 10								
Ashford International	a	17 53								18 18								

A 🛒 to Lewes

Table 189

Mondays to Fridays

9 December to 16 May

London, Haywards Heath and Brighton - Lewes, Seaford, Eastbourne, Hastings and Ashford

Network Diagram - see first Page of Table 189

		SN 1	SN	SN	SN	SN	SN 1 A	SN	SN 1	SN 1	SN	SN 1	SN 1 A	SN	SN 1	SN 1	SN	SN	SN	SN 1	SN 1	SN 1 A	SN	SN 1	SN	SN	SN 1	SN	SN 1 A	SN	SN 1	SN 1	SN 1 A	SN	SN 1	SN
London Victoria 15	d						16 47						17 27									17 57							18 47				19 17			
Clapham Junction 10	d						16 53						17 33									18 04							18 53				19 23			
London Bridge 4	d											17 23												18 23												
East Croydon	d						17 04					17 36	17 43									18 14		18 37					19 04				19 33			
Gatwick Airport 10	d						17 20						17 58									18 31							19 22				19 49			
Haywards Heath 3	d						17 36					18 05	18 09									18 45		19 06					19 36				20 07			
Wivelsfield 4	d						17 41					18 10	18 14									18 51		19 11					19 40				20 11			
Plumpton	d						17 47						18 20									18 57		19 17					19 46							
Cooksbridge	d						17 51						18 25									19 01		19 22					19 50							
Brighton 10	d		17 20		17 30	17 35		17 45		17 52	18 02			18 22				18 32	18 38		18 51		19 08			19 22		19 32		19 40	19 52			20 10		20 30
London Road (Brighton)	d		17 23			17 39		17 48		17 55	18 05			18 25					18 41		18 54		19 11			19 25				19 43	19 55			20 13		
Moulsecoomb	d		17 25			17 41		17 50		17 57	18 07			18 27					18 43		18 56		19 13			19 27				19 45	19 57			20 15		
Falmer	d		17 29			17 45		17 54		18 01	18 11			18 31					18 47		19 00		19 17		←	19 31				19 49	20 01			20 19		
Lewes 4	a		17 35		17 42	17 52	17 56	18 00		18 07	18 17	18 21	18 29	18 37				18 44	18 53		19 06	19 08	19 23	19 27	19 23	19 37		19 43	19 55	19 55	20 07		20 22	20 25		20 43
	d		17 36		17 44		17 57	18 01		18 08	18 19	18 22	18 30	18 38				18 45	18 54		19 07	19 12 / 19 16	19 31	19 27	19 31	19 40		19 44	19 55	19 59	20 09		20 23	20 28		20 44
Southease	d							18 07											19 00				→		19 37					20 05						
Newhaven Town	d							18 11			18 27			18 46					19 04			19 21			19 41	19 49				20 09				20 36		
Newhaven Harbour	d							18 13											19 06						19 44	19a52				20 11				20 38		
Bishopstone	d							18 16			18 33			18 51					19 09			19 27			19 47					20 14				20 41		
Seaford	a							18 19			18 37			18 55					19 13			19 33			19 50					20 17				20 44		
Glynde	d									18 13		18 27										19 21		19 33								20 14	20 28			
Berwick	d		17 45							18 19		18 33										19 27		19 39								20 20	20 34			
Polegate	d		17 50		17 57		18 09			18 24		18 38	18 44					18 58			19 19	19 32		19 45				19 57	20 08			20 25	20 39			20 57
Hampden Park 4	d	17 52	17 55				18 13		18 20	18 28		18 42				18 52				19 20		19 36		19 50			19 52				20 20	20 29	20 43		20 51	
Eastbourne 4	a	17 57	18 00		18 04		18 18		18 25	18 34		18 49	18 53			18 57		19 05		19 25	19 28	19 41		19 56			19 57	20 04	20 15		20 25	20 34	20 48		20 56	21 04
	d	18 01			18 09		18 25			18 44			18 57		19 00	19 04		19 09				19 51					20 03	20 09	20 20						21 04	21 09
Hampden Park 4	d	18a05					18 29			18 48			19 01		19a04	19a08						19 55					20a07		20 24						21a08	
Pevensey & Westham	d						18 34			18 53			19 07					19 17				20 00							20 29							
Pevensey Bay	d																																			
Normans Bay	d									18 57																										
Cooden Beach	d						18 40			19 01			19 13									20 06							20 35							
Collington	d						18 43			19 04			19 16									20 09							20 38							
Bexhill 4	d				18 24		18 45			19 06			19 18					19 25				20 11						20 24	20 40							21 24
St Leonards Warrior Sq 4	d				18 31		18 56			19 12			19 25					19 32				20 18						20 31	20 46							21 31
Hastings 4	a				18 34		19 00			19 15			19 28					19 36				20 21						20 34	20 49							21 34
	d				18 36					19 16			19 29					19 36				20 22						20 36	20 50							21 35
Ore	d									19a19			19a34									20a27							20a55							21 37
Three Oaks	d				18 44																							20 44								21 43
Doleham	d																																			21 46
Winchelsea	d																	19 50																		21 52
Rye	a				18 54													19 54										20 54								21 56
	d			18 31	18 56												19 33	19 56										20 56								21 56
Appledore (Kent)	d			18 40	19 05												19 42	20 05										21 05								22 05
Ham Street	d			18 45	19 10												19 47	20 10										21 10								22 10
Ashford International	a			18 53	19 18												19 55	20 18										21 18								22 18

A to Lewes

Table 189

Mondays to Fridays

9 December to 16 May

London, Haywards Heath and Brighton - Lewes, Seaford, Eastbourne, Hastings and Ashford

Network Diagram - see first Page of Table 189

		SN ■1 A ⚲	SN	SN ■1	SN	SN ■1	SN	SN ■1	SN ■1	SN	SN ■1	SN	SN	SN ■1	SN	SN ■1	SN	SN	SN ■1	SN	SN ■1	SN ■1	SN	SN	SN ■1	SN	SN ■1
London Victoria ■15 ⊖	d	19 47				20 17					20 47			21 17					21 47						22 47		00 05
Clapham Junction ■10	d	19 53				20 23					20 53			21 23					21 53						22 53		00 12
London Bridge ■4 ⊖	d																										
East Croydon	d	20 03				20 33					21 04			21 33					22 03						23 03		00 27
Gatwick Airport ■10 ✈	d	20 19				20 49					21 19			21 49					22 19						23 19		00 46
Haywards Heath ■3	d	20 36				21 07					21 37			22 08					22 34						23 34		01 05
Wivelsfield ■4	d	20 40				21 11					21 41			22 12					22 38						23 38		
Plumpton	d	20 46									21 47								22 44						23 44		
Cooksbridge	d	20 50																	22 48								
Brighton ■10	d		20 40		21 04					21 30		21 40	22 04				22 28	22 34			23 06		23 28	23 34			
London Road (Brighton)	d		20 43		21 07							21 43	22 07					22 37			23 09			23 37			
Moulsecoomb	d		20 45		21 09							21 45	22 09					22 39			23 11			23 39			
Falmer	d		20 49		21 13		←					21 49	22 13		←			22 43		←	23 15			23 43		←	
Lewes ■4	a	20 55	20 55		21 19	21 22	21 19			21 43	21 54	21 55	22 19	22 23	22 19		22 39	22 49	22 53	22 49	23 21		23 39	23 49	23 51	23 49	01 19
	d	20 55	21 00		21 28	21 23	21 28			21 44	21 55	21 58	22 28	22 23	22 28		22 42	22 57	22 53	22 57	23 22		23 39	23 56	23 53	23 56	01 20
Southease	d				→							22 04	→					→		23 03				→			
Newhaven Town ⛴	d		21 08				21 36					22 08			22 36					23 07						00 04	
Newhaven Harbour	d		21 10				21 38					22 10			22 38					23 09						00 06	
Bishopstone	d		21 13				21 41					22 13			22 41					23 12						00 09	
Seaford	a		21 16				21 44					22 16			22 44					23 15						00 12	
Glynde	d					21 28								22 29							23 27						
Berwick	d					21 34								22 34							23 33				00 02		
Polegate	d	21 08				21 39				21 57	22 07			22 39			22 54		23 06		23 38		23 52		00 07		01s32
Hampden Park ■4	d			21 20		21 43			21 55					22 43		22 55			23 10		23 42	23 47			00 11		01s36
Eastbourne ■4	a	21 15		21 25		21 48			22 00	22 04	22 15			22 48		23 00	23 03		23 15		23 47	23 52	23 59		00 16		01 41
	d	21 21						22 04	22 15	22 09	22 21					23 05			23 20			23 56			00 22		
Hampden Park ■4	d	21 25						22a08	22a19		22 25					23a09			23 24			00a01					
Pevensey & Westham	d	21 30									22 30								23 29						00 29		
Pevensey Bay	d																										
Normans Bay	d																										
Cooden Beach	d	21 36									22 36								23 35						00 35		
Collington	d	21 39									22 39								23 38						00 38		
Bexhill ■4	d	21 41								22 23	22 41								23 40						00 41		
St Leonards Warrior Sq ■4	d	21 48								22 31	22 48								23 47						00 47		
Hastings ■4	a	21 53								22 34	22 52								23 52						00 52		
	d	21 54																									
Ore	d	21a59																									
Three Oaks	d																										
Doleham	d																										
Winchelsea	d																										
Rye	a																										
	d																										
Appledore (Kent)	d																										
Ham Street	d																										
Ashford International	a																										

A ⚲ to Lewes

Table 189

Saturdays

14 December to 17 May

London, Haywards Heath and Brighton - Lewes, Seaford, Eastbourne, Hastings and Ashford

Network Diagram - see first Page of Table 189

Station		SN 1	SN	SN	SN 1	SN 1	SN 1	SN	SN	SN	SN 1	SN	SN 1	SN 1	SN 1	SN 1	SN 1	SN 1
London Victoria 15 ⊖	d																	
Clapham Junction 10	d																	
London Bridge 4 ⊖	d																	
East Croydon	d																	
Gatwick Airport 10 ✈	d																	06 12
Haywards Heath 3	d																	06 26
Wivelsfield 4	d																	06 30
Plumpton	d																	
Cooksbridge	d																	
Brighton 10	d						05 10		05 52			06 10						
London Road (Brighton)	d								05 55			06 13						
Moulsecoomb	d								05 57			06 15						
Falmer	d								06 01			06 19						
Lewes 4	a						05 21		06 07			06 25						06 41
	d						05 21		06 08			06 28						06 53
Southease	d																	→
Newhaven Town	d			00 04					06 16			06 36						
Newhaven Harbour	d			00 06					06 18			06 38						
Bishopstone	d			00 09								06 41						
Seaford	a			00 12					06 23			06 44						
Glynde	d																	
Berwick	d	00 02																
Polegate	d	00 07					05 33											
Hampden Park 4	d	00 11															06 52	
Eastbourne 4	a	00 16					05 41										06 57	
	d	00 22			05 03	05 38		05 48		05 53	06 04		06 18	06 24	06 45	06 58	07 04	
Hampden Park 4	d				05a07			05a52					06 22	06a28		07a02	07a08	
Pevensey & Westham	d	00 29											06 27					
Pevensey Bay	d																	
Normans Bay	d												06 31					
Cooden Beach	d	00 35											06 35					
Collington	d	00 38											06 38					
Bexhill 4	d	00 41				05 52				06 07	06 18		06 40		07 00			
St Leonards Warrior Sq 4	d	00 47				06 00				06 14	06 24		06 49		07 06			
Hastings 4	a	00 52				06 04				06 17	06 28		06 53		07 10			
	d		05 20			06 05				06 18	06 28		06 54		07 11			
Ore	d		05 23			06a08					06a32		06a57		07a14			
Three Oaks	d		05 29							06 26								
Doleham	d		05 32															
Winchelsea	d		05 38															
Rye	a		05 41							06 36								
	d		05 42							06 38								
Appledore (Kent)	d		05 51							06 47								
Ham Street	d		05 56							06 52								
Ashford International	a		06 04							07 00								

Station		SN	SN 1	SN	SN 1	SN 1	SN	SN	SN 1	SN 1	SN	SN 1	SN	SN 1	SN 1	SN	SN	SN 1	SN 1
London Victoria 15 ⊖	d																		
Clapham Junction 10	d																		
London Bridge 4 ⊖	d																		
East Croydon	d																		
Gatwick Airport 10 ✈	d																		
Haywards Heath 3	d											07 33							
Wivelsfield 4	d											07 37							
Plumpton	d																		
Cooksbridge	d																		
Brighton 10	d	06 32		06 40		06 52	07 10	07 22			07 32		07 40		07 52	08 10	08 22		
London Road (Brighton)	d			06 43		06 55	07 13	07 25					07 43		07 55	08 13	08 25		
Moulsecoomb	d			06 45		06 57	07 15	07 27					07 45		07 57	08 15	08 27		
Falmer	d		←	06 49		07 01	07 19	07 31					07 49		08 01	08 19	08 31		
Lewes 4	a	06 43	06 41	06 55		07 07	07 25	07 37			07 43	07 48	07 55		08 07	08 25	08 37		
	d	06 45	06 53	06 58		07 09	07 28				07 44	07 53	07 58		08 09	08 28			
Southease	d																		
Newhaven Town	d			07 06			07 36						08 06			08 36			
Newhaven Harbour	d			07 08			07 38						08 08			08 38			
Bishopstone	d			07 11			07 41						08 11			08 41			
Seaford	a			07 14			07 44						08 14			08 44			
Glynde	d					07 14									08 14				
Berwick	d		07 02			07 20									08 20				
Polegate	d	06 58	07 07			07 25					07 57	08 05			08 25				
Hampden Park 4	d		07 11		07 20	07 29				07 52				08 20	08 29				08 52
Eastbourne 4	a	07 05	07 17		07 25	07 34				07 57	08 05	08 13		08 25	08 34				08 57
	d	07 09	07 21			07 40			07 58	08 04	08 09	08 18			08 40			08 58	09 04
Hampden Park 4	d		07 25			07 44			08a02	08a08		08 22			08 44			09a02	09a08
Pevensey & Westham	d		07 30			07 49						08 28			08 49				
Pevensey Bay	d																		
Normans Bay	d					07 53									08 53				
Cooden Beach	d		07 36			07 57						08 34			08 57				
Collington	d		07 39			08 00						08 37			09 00				
Bexhill 4	d	07 24	07 42			08 02					08 24	08 39			09 02				
St Leonards Warrior Sq 4	d	07 31	07 48			08 09					08 31	08 46			09 09				
Hastings 4	a	07 35	07 51			08 12					08 35	08 50			09 12				
	d	07 36	07 52			08 13					08 36	08 51			09 13				
Ore	d		07a55			08a16						08a54			09a16				
Three Oaks	d										08 44								
Doleham	d																		
Winchelsea	d	07 50																	
Rye	a	07 54									08 54								
	d	07 56									08 56								
Appledore (Kent)	d	08 05									09 05								
Ham Street	d	08 10									09 10								
Ashford International	a	08 18									09 18								

Table 189

Saturdays

14 December to 17 May

London, Haywards Heath and Brighton - Lewes, Seaford, Eastbourne, Hastings and Ashford

Network Diagram - see first Page of Table 189

Station		SN	SN 1	SN	SN 1	SN 1	SN 1	SN 1	SN	SN
London Victoria 15 ⊖	d		07 47				08 17			
Clapham Junction 10	d		07 53				08 23			
London Bridge 4 ⊖	d									
East Croydon	d		08 03				08 33			
Gatwick Airport 10 ✈	d		08 20				08 50			
Haywards Heath 3	d		08 35				09 07			
Wivelsfield 4	d						09 11			
Plumpton	d									
Cooksbridge	d									
Brighton 10	d	08 32		08 40		08 52			09 10	09 22
London Road (Brighton)	d			08 43		08 55			09 13	09 25
Moulsecoomb	d			08 45		08 57			09 15	09 27
Falmer	d			08 49		09 01			09 19	09 31
Lewes 4	a	08 43	08 49	08 55		09 07	09 22		09 25	09 37
	d	08 44	08 53	08 58		09 09	09 23		09 28	
Southease	d								09 34	
Newhaven Town ⛴	d			09 06					09 38	
Newhaven Harbour	d			09 08					09 40	
Bishopstone	d			09 11					09 43	
Seaford	a			09 14					09 46	
Glynde	d					09 14				
Berwick	d					09 20				
Polegate	d	08 57	09 05			09 25	09 35			
Hampden Park 4	d				09 20	09 29	09 39			
Eastbourne 4	a	09 04	09 13		09 25	09 34	09 44			
	d	09 09	09 19			09 40		09 58		
Hampden Park 4	d		09 23			09 44		10a02		
Pevensey & Westham	d		09 28			09 49				
Pevensey Bay	d									
Normans Bay	d					09 53				
Cooden Beach	d		09 34			09 57				
Collington	d		09 37			10 00				
Bexhill 4	d	09 24	09 39			10 02				
St Leonards Warrior Sq 4	d	09 31	09 46			10 09				
Hastings 4	a	09 35	09 49			10 12				
	d	09 36	09 50			10 13				
Ore	d		09a53			10a16				
Three Oaks	d									
Doleham	d									
Winchelsea	d	09 50								
Rye	a	09 54								
	d	09 56								
Appledore (Kent)	d	10 05								
Ham Street	d	10 10								
Ashford International	a	10 18								

Station		SN 1	SN	SN 1	SN	SN 1	SN 1	SN 1	SN 1	SN
London Victoria 15 ⊖	d			08 47				09 17		
Clapham Junction 10	d			08 53				09 23		
London Bridge 4 ⊖	d									
East Croydon	d			09 03				09 33		
Gatwick Airport 10 ✈	d			09 20				09 50		
Haywards Heath 3	d			09 35				10 07		
Wivelsfield 4	d							10 11		
Plumpton	d			09 44						
Cooksbridge	d									
Brighton 10	d		09 32		09 40		09 52			10 10
London Road (Brighton)	d				09 43		09 55			10 13
Moulsecoomb	d				09 45		09 57			10 15
Falmer	d				09 49		10 01			10 19
Lewes 4	a		09 43	09 52	09 55		10 07	10 22		10 25
	d		09 44	09 53	09 58		10 09	10 23		10 28
Southease	d									10 34
Newhaven Town ⛴	d				10 06					10 38
Newhaven Harbour	d				10 08					10 40
Bishopstone	d				10 11					10 43
Seaford	a				10 14					10 46
Glynde	d						10 14			
Berwick	d						10 20			
Polegate	d		09 57	10 05			10 25	10 35		
Hampden Park 4	d	09 52				10 20	10 29	10 39		
Eastbourne 4	a	09 57	10 04	10 13		10 25	10 34	10 44		
	d	10 04	10 09	10 19			10 40		10 58	
Hampden Park 4	d	10a08		10 23			10 44		11a02	
Pevensey & Westham	d			10 28			10 49			
Pevensey Bay	d									
Normans Bay	d						10 53			
Cooden Beach	d			10 34			10 57			
Collington	d			10 37			11 00			
Bexhill 4	d		10 24	10 39			11 02			
St Leonards Warrior Sq 4	d		10 31	10 46			11 09			
Hastings 4	a		10 35	10 49			11 12			
	d		10 36	10 50			11 13			
Ore	d			10a53			11a16			
Three Oaks	d		10 44							
Doleham	d									
Winchelsea	d									
Rye	a		10 54							
	d		10 56							
Appledore (Kent)	d		11 05							
Ham Street	d		11 10							
Ashford International	a		11 18							

Station		SN	SN 1	SN	SN 1	SN	SN 1	SN 1	SN 1	SN 1
London Victoria 15 ⊖	d				09 47				10 17	
Clapham Junction 10	d				09 53				10 23	
London Bridge 4 ⊖	d									
East Croydon	d				10 03				10 33	
Gatwick Airport 10 ✈	d				10 20				10 50	
Haywards Heath 3	d				10 35				11 07	
Wivelsfield 4	d								11 11	
Plumpton	d				10 44					
Cooksbridge	d									
Brighton 10	d	10 22		10 32		10 40		10 52		
London Road (Brighton)	d	10 25				10 43		10 55		
Moulsecoomb	d	10 27				10 45		10 57		
Falmer	d	10 31				10 49		11 01		
Lewes 4	a	10 37		10 43	10 52	10 55		11 07	11 22	
	d			10 44	10 53	10 58		11 09	11 23	
Southease	d									
Newhaven Town ⛴	d					11 06				
Newhaven Harbour	d					11 08				
Bishopstone	d					11 11				
Seaford	a					11 14				
Glynde	d							11 14		
Berwick	d							11 20		
Polegate	d			10 57	11 05			11 25	11 35	
Hampden Park 4	d		10 52				11 20	11 29	11 39	
Eastbourne 4	a		10 57	11 04	11 13		11 25	11 34	11 44	
	d		11 04	11 09	11 19			11 40		11 58
Hampden Park 4	d		11a08		11 23			11 44		12a02
Pevensey & Westham	d				11 28			11 49		
Pevensey Bay	d									
Normans Bay	d							11 53		
Cooden Beach	d				11 34			11 57		
Collington	d				11 37			12 00		
Bexhill 4	d			11 24	11 39			12 02		
St Leonards Warrior Sq 4	d			11 31	11 46			12 09		
Hastings 4	a			11 35	11 49			12 12		
	d			11 36	11 50			12 13		
Ore	d				11a53			12a16		
Three Oaks	d									
Doleham	d									
Winchelsea	d			11 50						
Rye	a			11 54						
	d			11 56						
Appledore (Kent)	d			12 05						
Ham Street	d			12 10						
Ashford International	a			12 18						

Station		SN	SN	SN 1	SN	SN 1	SN	SN 1	SN 1	SN 1
London Victoria 15 ⊖	d					10 47				11 17
Clapham Junction 10	d					10 53				11 23
London Bridge 4 ⊖	d									
East Croydon	d					11 03				11 33
Gatwick Airport 10 ✈	d					11 20				11 50
Haywards Heath 3	d					11 35				12 07
Wivelsfield 4	d									12 11
Plumpton	d					11 44				
Cooksbridge	d									
Brighton 10	d	11 10	11 22		11 32		11 40		11 52	
London Road (Brighton)	d	11 13	11 25				11 43		11 55	
Moulsecoomb	d	11 15	11 27				11 45		11 57	
Falmer	d	11 19	11 31				11 49		12 01	
Lewes 4	a	11 25	11 37		11 43	11 52	11 55		12 07	12 22
	d	11 28			11 44	11 53	11 58		12 09	12 23
Southease	d	11 34								
Newhaven Town ⛴	d	11 38					12 06			
Newhaven Harbour	d	11 40					12 08			
Bishopstone	d	11 43					12 11			
Seaford	a	11 46					12 14			
Glynde	d								12 14	
Berwick	d								12 20	
Polegate	d				11 57	12 05			12 25	12 35
Hampden Park 4	d			11 52				12 20	12 29	12 39
Eastbourne 4	a			11 57	12 04	12 13		12 25	12 34	12 44
	d			12 04	12 09	12 19			12 40	
Hampden Park 4	d			12a08		12 23			12 44	
Pevensey & Westham	d					12 28			12 49	
Pevensey Bay	d									
Normans Bay	d								12 53	
Cooden Beach	d					12 34			12 57	
Collington	d					12 37			13 00	
Bexhill 4	d				12 24	12 39			13 02	
St Leonards Warrior Sq 4	d				12 31	12 46			13 09	
Hastings 4	a				12 35	12 49			13 12	
	d				12 36	12 50			13 13	
Ore	d					12a53			13a16	
Three Oaks	d				12 44					
Doleham	d									
Winchelsea	d									
Rye	a				12 54					
	d				12 56					
Appledore (Kent)	d				13 05					
Ham Street	d				13 10					
Ashford International	a				13 18					

Table 189

Saturdays

14 December to 17 May

London, Haywards Heath and Brighton - Lewes, Seaford, Eastbourne, Hastings and Ashford

Network Diagram - see first Page of Table 189

		SN 1	SN	SN	SN 1	SN	SN 1	SN	SN 1	SN 1	SN 1	SN 1	SN	SN	SN 1	SN	SN 1	SN	SN 1	SN 1	SN 1	SN 1	SN	SN	SN 1	SN	SN 1	SN	SN 1	SN 1	SN 1	SN 1	SN	SN	SN 1	SN	SN 1
London Victoria 15 ⊖	d						11 47				12 17						12 47				13 17						13 47				14 17						14 47
Clapham Junction 10	d						11 53				12 23						12 53				13 23						13 53				14 23						14 53
London Bridge 4 ⊖	d																																				
East Croydon	d						12 03				12 33						13 03				13 33						14 03				14 33						15 03
Gatwick Airport 10 ✈	d						12 20				12 50						13 20				13 50						14 20				14 50						15 20
Haywards Heath 3	d						12 35				13 07						13 35				14 07						14 35				15 07						15 35
Wivelsfield 4	d										13 11										14 11										15 11						
Plumpton	d						12 44										13 44										14 44										15 44
Cooksbridge	d																																				
Brighton 10	d		12 10	12 22		12 32		12 40		12 52			13 10	13 22		13 32		13 40		13 52			14 10	14 22		14 32		14 40		14 52			15 10	15 22		15 32	
London Road (Brighton)	d		12 13	12 25				12 43		12 55			13 13	13 25				13 43		13 55			14 13	14 25				14 43		14 55			15 13	15 25			
Moulsecoomb	d		12 15	12 27				12 45		12 57			13 15	13 27				13 45		13 57			14 15	14 27				14 45		14 57			15 15	15 27			
Falmer	d		12 19	12 31				12 49		13 01			13 19	13 31				13 49		14 01			14 19	14 31				14 49		15 01			15 19	15 31			
Lewes 4	a		12 25	12 37		12 43	12 52	12 55		13 07	13 22		13 25	13 37		13 43	13 52	13 55		14 07	14 22		14 25	14 37		14 43	14 52	14 55		15 07	15 22		15 25	15 37		15 43	15 52
	d		12 28			12 44	12 53	12 58		13 09	13 23		13 28			13 44	13 53	13 58		14 09	14 23		14 28			14 44	14 53	14 58		15 09	15 23		15 28			15 44	15 53
Southease	d		12 34										13 34										14 34										15 34				
Newhaven Town ⛴	d		12 38					13 06					13 38					14 06					14 38					15 06					15 38				
Newhaven Harbour	d		12 40					13 08					13 40					14 08					14 40					15 08					15 40				
Bishopstone	d		12 43					13 11					13 43					14 11					14 43					15 11					15 43				
Seaford	a		12 46					13 14					13 46					14 14					14 46					15 14					15 46				
Glynde	d									13 14										14 14										15 14							
Berwick	d									13 20										14 20										15 20							
Polegate	d					12 57	13 05			13 25	13 35					13 57	14 05			14 25	14 35					14 57	15 05			15 25	15 35					15 57	16 05
Hampden Park 4	d				12 52				13 20	13 29	13 39				13 52				14 20	14 29	14 39				14 52				15 20	15 29	15 39				15 52		
Eastbourne 4	a				12 57	13 04	13 13		13 25	13 34	13 44				13 57	14 04	14 13		14 25	14 34	14 44				14 57	15 04	15 13		15 25	15 34	15 44				15 57	16 04	16 13
	d	12 58			13 04	13 09	13 19			13 40		13 58			14 04	14 09	14 19			14 40		14 58			15 04	15 09	15 19			15 40		15 58			16 04	16 09	16 19
Hampden Park 4	d	13a02			13a08		13 23			13 44		14a02			14a08		14 23			14 44		15a02			15a08		15 23			15 44		16a02			16a08		16 23
Pevensey & Westham	d						13 28			13 49							14 28			14 49							15 28			15 49							16 28
Pevensey Bay	d																																				
Normans Bay	d									13 53										14 53										15 53							
Cooden Beach	d						13 34			13 57							14 34			14 57							15 34			15 57							16 34
Collington	d						13 37			14 00							14 37			15 00							15 37			16 00							16 37
Bexhill 4	d					13 24	13 39			14 02						14 24	14 39			15 02						15 24	15 39			16 02						16 24	16 39
St Leonards Warrior Sq 4	d					13 31	13 46			14 09						14 31	14 46			15 09						15 31	15 46			16 09						16 31	16 46
Hastings 4	a					13 35	13 49			14 12						14 35	14 49			15 12						15 35	15 49			16 12						16 35	16 49
	d					13 36	13 50			14 13						14 36	14 50			15 13						15 36	15 50			16 13						16 36	16 50
Ore	d						13a53			14a16							14a53			15a16							15a53			16a16							16a53
Three Oaks	d															14 44																				16 44	
Doleham	d																																				
Winchelsea	d					13 50																				15 50											
Rye	a					13 54										14 54										15 54										16 54	
	d					13 56										14 56										15 56										16 56	
Appledore (Kent)	d					14 05										15 05										16 05										17 05	
Ham Street	d					14 10										15 10										16 10										17 10	
Ashford International	a					14 18										15 18										16 18										17 18	

Table 189

Saturdays

14 December to 17 May

London, Haywards Heath and Brighton - Lewes, Seaford, Eastbourne, Hastings and Ashford

Network Diagram - see first Page of Table 189

		SN	SN 1	SN 1	SN 1	SN 1	SN	SN	SN 1	SN	SN 1	SN	SN 1	SN 1	SN 1	SN 1	SN	SN	SN 1	SN	SN 1	SN	SN 1	SN 1	SN 1	SN 1	SN	SN	SN 1	SN	SN 1	SN	SN 1	SN 1	SN 1	SN	SN
London Victoria 15 ⊖	d				15 17						15 47				16 17						16 47				17 17						17 47				18 17		
Clapham Junction 10	d				15 23						15 53				16 23						16 53				17 23						17 53				18 23		
London Bridge 4 ⊖	d																																				
East Croydon	d				15 33						16 03				16 33						17 03				17 33						18 03				18 33		
Gatwick Airport 10 ✈	d				15 50						16 20				16 50						17 20				17 50						18 20				18 50		
Haywards Heath 3	d				16 07						16 35				17 07						17 35				18 07						18 35				19 07		
Wivelsfield 4	d				16 11										17 11										18 11										19 11		
Plumpton	d										16 44										17 44										18 44						
Cooksbridge	d																																				
Brighton 10	d	15 40		15 52			16 10	16 22		16 32		16 40		16 52			17 10	17 22		17 32		17 40		17 52			18 10	18 22		18 32		18 40		18 52		19 10	19 22
London Road (Brighton)	d	15 43		15 55			16 13	16 25				16 43		16 55			17 13	17 25				17 43		17 55			18 13	18 25				18 43		18 55		19 13	19 25
Moulsecoomb	d	15 45		15 57			16 15	16 27				16 45		16 57			17 15	17 27				17 45		17 57			18 15	18 27				18 45		18 57		19 15	19 27
Falmer	d	15 49		16 01			16 19	16 31				16 49		17 01			17 19	17 31				17 49		18 01			18 19	18 31				18 49		19 01		19 19	19 31
Lewes 4	a	15 55		16 07	16 22		16 25	16 37		16 43	16 52	16 55		17 07	17 22		17 25	17 37		17 43	17 52	17 55		18 07	18 22		18 25	18 37		18 43	18 52	18 55		19 07	19 22	19 25	19 37
	d	15 58		16 09	16 23		16 28			16 44	16 53	16 58		17 09	17 23		17 28			17 44	17 53	17 58		18 09	18 23		18 28			18 44	18 53	18 58		19 09	19 23	19 28	
Southease	d						16 34										17 34										18 34									19 34	
Newhaven Town ⛴	d	16 06					16 38					17 06					17 38					18 06					18 38					19 06				19 38	
Newhaven Harbour	d	16 08					16 40					17 08					17 40					18 08					18 40					19 08				19 40	
Bishopstone	d	16 11					16 43					17 11					17 43					18 11					18 43					19 11				19 43	
Seaford	a	16 14					16 46					17 14					17 46					18 14					18 46					19 14				19 46	
Glynde	d			16 14										17 14										18 14										19 14			
Berwick	d			16 20										17 20										18 20										19 20			
Polegate	d			16 25	16 35					16 57	17 05			17 25	17 35					17 57	18 05			18 25	18 35					18 57	19 05			19 25	19 35		
Hampden Park 4	d		16 20	16 29	16 39				16 52				17 20	17 29	17 39				17 52				18 20	18 29	18 39				18 52				19 20	19 29	19 39		
Eastbourne 4	a		16 25	16 34	16 44				16 57	17 04	17 13		17 25	17 34	17 44				17 57	18 04	18 13		18 25	18 34	18 44				18 57	19 04	19 13		19 25	19 34	19 44		
	d			16 40		16 58			17 04	17 09	17 19			17 40		17 58			18 04	18 09	18 19			18 40		18 58			19 04	19 09	19 19			19 40			
Hampden Park 4	d			16 44		17a02			17a08		17 23			17 44		18a02			18a08		18 23			18 44		19a02			19a08		19 23			19 44			
Pevensey & Westham	d			16 49							17 28			17 49							18 28			18 49							19 28			19 49			
Pevensey Bay	d																																				
Normans Bay	d			16 53										17 53										18 53										19 53			
Cooden Beach	d			16 57							17 34			17 57							18 34			18 57							19 34			19 57			
Collington	d			17 00							17 37			18 00							18 37			19 00							19 37			20 00			
Bexhill 4	d			17 02						17 24	17 39			18 02						18 24	18 39			19 02						19 24	19 39			20 02			
St Leonards Warrior Sq 4	d			17 09						17 31	17 46			18 09						18 31	18 46			19 09						19 31	19 46			20 09			
Hastings 4	a			17 12						17 35	17 49			18 12						18 35	18 49			19 12						19 35	19 49			20 12			
	d			17 13						17 36	17 50			18 13						18 36	18 50			19 13						19 36	19 50			20 13			
Ore	d			17a16							17a53			18a16							18a53			19a16							19a53			20a16			
Three Oaks	d																			18 44																	
Doleham	d																																				
Winchelsea	d									17 50																				19 50							
Rye	a									17 54										18 54										19 54							
	d									17 56										18 56										19 56							
Appledore (Kent)	d									18 05										19 05										20 05							
Ham Street	d									18 10										19 10										20 10							
Ashford International	a									18 18										19 18										20 18							

Table 189

Saturdays

14 December to 17 May

London, Haywards Heath and Brighton - Lewes, Seaford, Eastbourne, Hastings and Ashford

Network Diagram - see first Page of Table 189

		SN 1	SN	SN 1	SN	SN 1	SN 1	SN 1	SN	SN 1	SN	SN 1	SN	SN 1	SN	SN 1	SN	SN 1	SN
London Victoria 15 ⊖	d			18 47				19 17				19 47				20 17			
Clapham Junction 10	d			18 53				19 23				19 53				20 23			
London Bridge 4 ⊖	d																		
East Croydon	d			19 03				19 33				20 03				20 33			
Gatwick Airport 10 ✈	d			19 20				19 50				20 20				20 50			
Haywards Heath 3	d			19 35				20 07				20 35				21 07			
Wivelsfield 4	d							20 11				20 39				21 11			
Plumpton	d			19 44								20 45							
Cooksbridge	d																		
Brighton 10	d		19 32		19 40		19 52		20 10		20 32		20 40		21 04				21 32
London Road (Brighton)	d				19 43		19 55		20 13				20 43		21 07				
Moulsecoomb	d				19 45		19 57		20 15				20 45		21 09				
Falmer	d				19 49		20 01		20 19				20 49		21 13		←		
Lewes 4	a		19 43	19 52	19 55		20 08	20 22	20 25		20 43	20 52	20 55		21 19	21 22	21 19		21 43
	d		19 44	19 53	19 58		20 09	20 23	20 28		20 44	20 53	20 58		21 28	21 23	21 28		21 44
Southease	d														→				
Newhaven Town ⛴	d				20 06				20 36				21 06				21 36		
Newhaven Harbour	d				20 08				20 38				21 08				21 38		
Bishopstone	d				20 11				20 41				21 11				21 41		
Seaford	a				20 14				20 44				21 14				21 44		
Glynde	d						20 14	20 28								21 28			
Berwick	d						20 20	20 34								21 34			
Polegate	d		19 57	20 05			20 25	20 39			20 57	21 05				21 39			21 57
Hampden Park 4	d	19 52				20 20	20 29	20 43		20 52				21 20		21 43		21 51	
Eastbourne 4	a	19 57	20 04	20 13		20 25	20 34	20 48		20 57	21 04	21 13		21 25		21 48		21 56	22 04
	d	20 04	20 09	20 19				20 54		21 04	21 09	21 19						22 04	22 09
Hampden Park 4	d	20a08		20 23						21a08		21 23						22a08	
Pevensey & Westham	d			20 28				21 01				21 28							
Pevensey Bay	d																		
Normans Bay	d																		
Cooden Beach	d			20 34				21 07				21 34							
Collington	d			20 37								21 37							
Bexhill 4	d		20 24	20 39				21 12			21 23	21 39							22 23
St Leonards Warrior Sq 4	d		20 31	20 46				21 18			21 30	21 46							22 30
Hastings 4	a		20 35	20 49				21 21			21 33	21 49							22 33
	d		20 36	20 50							21 35	21 50							
Ore	d			20a53							21 37	21a53							
Three Oaks	d		20 44								21 43								
Doleham	d										21 46								
Winchelsea	d										21 52								
Rye	a		20 54								21 56								
	d		20 56								21 56								
Appledore (Kent)	d		21 05								22 05								
Ham Street	d		21 10								22 10								
Ashford International	a		21 18								22 18								

		SN 1	SN 1	SN	SN	SN 1	SN	SN 1	SN	SN	SN 1	SN	SN 1	SN 1	SN	SN	SN 1	SN	SN 1
London Victoria 15 ⊖	d		20 47			21 17					21 47						22 47		00 05
Clapham Junction 10	d		20 53			21 23					21 53						22 53		00 12
London Bridge 4 ⊖	d																		
East Croydon	d		21 03			21 33					22 03						23 03		00 27
Gatwick Airport 10 ✈	d		21 20			21 49					22 20						23 20		00 46
Haywards Heath 3	d		21 34			22 08					22 34						23 34		01 05
Wivelsfield 4	d		21 38			22 12					22 38						23 38		
Plumpton	d		21 44								22 44						23 44		
Cooksbridge	d																		
Brighton 10	d			21 40	22 04				22 28	22 34			23 06		23 28	23 34			
London Road (Brighton)	d			21 43	22 07					22 37			23 09			23 37			
Moulsecoomb	d			21 45	22 09					22 39			23 11			23 39			
Falmer	d			21 49	22 13		←			22 43		←	23 15			23 43		←	
Lewes 4	a		21 51	21 55	22 19	22 23	22 19		22 39	22 49	22 51	22 49	23 21		23 39	23 49	23 51	23 49	01 19
	d		21 53	21 58	22 28	22 23	22 28		22 39	22 56	22 53	22 56	23 22		23 39	23 56	23 53	23 56	01 20
Southease	d				→					→						→			
Newhaven Town ⛴	d			22 06			22 36					23 04						00 04	
Newhaven Harbour	d			22 08			22 38					23 06						00 06	
Bishopstone	d			22 11			22 41					23 09						00 09	
Seaford	a			22 14			22 44					23 12						00 12	
Glynde	d					22 29							23 27						
Berwick	d					22 34							23 33				00 02		
Polegate	d		22 05			22 39			22 52		23 05		23 38		23 52		00 07		01s32
Hampden Park 4	d	22 07				22 43		22 55			23 09		23 42	23 47			00 11		01s36
Eastbourne 4	a	22 12	22 15			22 48		23 00	23 03		23 14		23 47	23 52	23 59		00 16		01 41
	d		22 21					23 05	23 10		23 20			23 56			00 22		
Hampden Park 4	d		22 25					23a09			23 24			00a01					
Pevensey & Westham	d		22 30								23 29						00 29		
Pevensey Bay	d																		
Normans Bay	d																		
Cooden Beach	d		22 36								23 35						00 35		
Collington	d		22 39								23 38						00 38		
Bexhill 4	d		22 41						23 24		23 40						00 41		
St Leonards Warrior Sq 4	d		22 48						23 31		23 47						00 47		
Hastings 4	a		22 51						23 34		23 50						00 50		
	d																		
Ore	d																		
Three Oaks	d																		
Doleham	d																		
Winchelsea	d																		
Rye	a																		
	d																		
Appledore (Kent)	d																		
Ham Street	d																		
Ashford International	a																		

Table 189

Sundays

8 December to 11 May

London, Haywards Heath and Brighton - Lewes, Seaford, Eastbourne, Hastings and Ashford

Network Diagram - see first Page of Table 189

	SN 1	SN	SN	SN 1	SN 1	SN 1	SN	SN 1	SN	SN	SN 1	SN
London Victoria 15 ⊖ d				00 05								
Clapham Junction 10 d				00 12								
London Bridge 4 ⊖ d												
East Croydon d				00 27								
Gatwick Airport 10 ✈ d				00 46								
Haywards Heath 3 d				01 05								
Wivelsfield 4 d												
Plumpton d												
Cooksbridge d												
Brighton 10 d								07 09		07 15	07 43	07 49
London Road (Brighton) d								07 12		07 18	07 46	07 52
Moulsecoomb d								07 14		07 20	07 48	07 54
Falmer d								07 18		07 24	07 52	07 58
Lewes 4 a				01 19				07 24		07 31	07 58	08 04
d				01 20				07 25		07 32	07 59	08 05
Southease d												08 11
Newhaven Town d			00 04							07 40		08 15
Newhaven Harbour d			00 06							07 42		08 17
Bishopstone d			00 09							07 45		08 20
Seaford a			00 12							07 49		08 23
Glynde d								07 30				
Berwick d	00 02							07 36				
Polegate d	00 07			01s32				07 41			08 11	
Hampden Park 4 d	00 11			01s36				07 45				
Eastbourne 4 a	00 16			01 41				07 50			08 19	
d	00 22				06 58	07 26	07 30		07 58		08 26	
Hampden Park 4 d					07a02	07 30	07a34				08 30	
Pevensey & Westham d	00 29					07 35					08 35	
Pevensey Bay d												
Normans Bay d												
Cooden Beach d	00 35					07 41					08 41	
Collington d	00 38					07 44					08 44	
Bexhill 4 d	00 41					07 47			08 12		08 46	
St Leonards Warrior Sq 4 d	00 47					07 53			08 18		08 53	
Hastings 4 a	00 50					07 56			08 22		08 56	
d		07 22				07 57			08 22		08 57	
Ore d		07 24				08a00					09a00	
Three Oaks d		07 30										
Doleham d		07 33										
Winchelsea d		07 39										
Rye a		07 43							08 39			
d		07 43							08 41			
Appledore (Kent) d		07 52							08 50			
Ham Street d		07 57							08 55			
Ashford International a		08 06							09 03			

	SN	SN	SN 1	SN	SN 1	SN	SN	SN	SN 1	SN	SN 1 A 🚌
London Victoria 15 ⊖ d											08 47
Clapham Junction 10 d											08 54
London Bridge 4 ⊖ d											
East Croydon d											09 06
Gatwick Airport 10 ✈ d											09 21
Haywards Heath 3 d											09 33
Wivelsfield 4 d											09 38
Plumpton d											09 44
Cooksbridge d											
Brighton 10 d	08 09			08 20	08 43	08 49	09 09			09 20	
London Road (Brighton) d	08 12				08 46	08 52	09 12				
Moulsecoomb d	08 14				08 48	08 54	09 14				
Falmer d	08 18				08 52	08 58	09 18				
Lewes 4 a	08 24			08 31	08 58	09 04	09 24			09 31	09 51
d	08 25			08 32	08 59	09 05	09 25			09 32	09 52
Southease d						09 11					
Newhaven Town d	08 33					09 15	09 33				
Newhaven Harbour d	08 35					09 17	09 35				
Bishopstone d	08 38					09 20	09 38				
Seaford a	08 42					09 23	09 42				
Glynde d				08 37						09 37	
Berwick d				08 43						09 43	
Polegate d				08 49	09 11					09 49	10 04
Hampden Park 4 d			08 46	08 53					09 46	09 53	
Eastbourne 4 a			08 51	08 58	09 19				09 51	09 58	10 12
d		08 34		09 02	09 26			09 34		10 02	10 18
Hampden Park 4 d		08a38			09 30			09a38			10 22
Pevensey & Westham d					09 35						10 27
Pevensey Bay d											
Normans Bay d											
Cooden Beach d					09 41						10 33
Collington d					09 44						10 36
Bexhill 4 d				09 16	09 46					10 16	10 38
St Leonards Warrior Sq 4 d				09 23	09 53					10 23	10 45
Hastings 4 a				09 26	09 56					10 26	10 48
d				09 27	09 57					10 27	10 48
Ore d					10a00						10a51
Three Oaks d											
Doleham d											
Winchelsea d											
Rye a				09 44						10 44	
d				09 46						10 46	
Appledore (Kent) d				09 55						10 55	
Ham Street d				10 00						11 00	
Ashford International a				10 08						11 08	

	SN	SN	SN	SN 1	SN	SN 1 A 🚌		SN	SN	SN	SN 1	SN	SN 1 A 🚌
London Victoria 15 ⊖ d						09 47							19 47
Clapham Junction 10 d						09 53							19 53
London Bridge 4 ⊖ d													
East Croydon d						10 02							20 02
Gatwick Airport 10 ✈ d						10 19							20 19
Haywards Heath 3 d						10 30							20 30
Wivelsfield 4 d						10 34							20 34
Plumpton d						10 40							20 40
Cooksbridge d													
Brighton 10 d	09 47	10 09			10 20			19 47	20 09			20 20	
London Road (Brighton) d	09 50	10 12						19 50	20 12				
Moulsecoomb d	09 52	10 14						19 52	20 14				
Falmer d	09 56	10 18						19 56	20 18				
Lewes 4 a	10 02	10 24			10 31	10 48		20 02	20 24			20 31	20 48
d	10 03	10 25			10 32	10 48		20 03	20 25			20 32	20 48
Southease d	10 09							20 09					
Newhaven Town d	10 13	10 33					and at the same minutes past each hour until	20 13	20 33				
Newhaven Harbour d	10 15	10 35						20 15	20 35				
Bishopstone d	10 18	10 38						20 18	20 38				
Seaford a	10 22	10 42						20 22	20 42				
Glynde d					10 37							20 37	
Berwick d					10 43							20 43	
Polegate d					10 49	11 01						20 49	21 01
Hampden Park 4 d				10 46	10 53						20 46	20 53	
Eastbourne 4 a				10 51	10 58	11 09					20 51	20 58	21 09
d			10 34		11 02	11 14				20 34		21 02	21 14
Hampden Park 4 d			10a38			11 18				20a38			21 18
Pevensey & Westham d						11 23							21 23
Pevensey Bay d													
Normans Bay d													
Cooden Beach d						11 29							21 29
Collington d						11 32							21 32
Bexhill 4 d					11 16	11 35						21 16	21 35
St Leonards Warrior Sq 4 d					11 23	11 42						21 23	21 42
Hastings 4 a					11 26	11 45						21 26	21 45
d					11 27	11 45						21 27	21 45
Ore d						11a48							21a48
Three Oaks d													
Doleham d													
Winchelsea d													
Rye a					11 44							21 44	
d					11 46							21 46	
Appledore (Kent) d					11 55							21 55	
Ham Street d					12 00							22 00	
Ashford International a					12 08							22 08	

A 🚌 to Lewes

Table 189

Sundays

8 December to 11 May

London, Haywards Heath and Brighton - Lewes, Seaford, Eastbourne, Hastings and Ashford

Network Diagram - see first Page of Table 189

		SN	SN	SN	SN ■1	SN	SN ■1	SN	SN	SN	SN ■1	SN	SN ■1	SN	SN	SN ■1	SN	SN ■1	SN
London Victoria 15 ⊖	d						20 47						21 47					22 47	
Clapham Junction 10	d						20 53						21 53					22 53	
London Bridge 4 ⊖	d																		
East Croydon	d						21 03						22 03					23 03	
Gatwick Airport 10 ✈	d						21 19						22 19					23 19	
Haywards Heath 3	d						21 30						22 30					23 30	
Wivelsfield 4	d						21 35						22 35					23 35	
Plumpton	d						21 41						22 41					23 41	
Cooksbridge	d																		
Brighton 10	d	20 47	21 09			21 20		21 47	22 09			22 20		22 39	23 09		23 20		23 39
London Road (Brighton)	d	20 50	21 12					21 50	22 12					22 42	23 12				23 42
Moulsecoomb	d	20 52	21 14					21 52	22 14					22 44	23 14				23 44
Falmer	d	20 56	21 18					21 56	22 18					22 48	23 18				23 48
Lewes 4	a	21 02	21 24			21 31	21 48	22 02	22 24			22 31	22 48	22 54	23 24		23 31	23 48	23 54
	d	21 03	21 25			21 32	21 49	22 03	22 25			22 32	22 59	23 03			23 32	23 59	
Southease	d																		
Newhaven Town ⛴	d	21 11	21 33					22 11	22 33					23 11					
Newhaven Harbour	d	21 15	21 35					22 13	22 35					23 13					
Bishopstone	d	21 18	21 38					22 16	22 38					23 16					
Seaford	a	21 22	21 42					22 20	22 42					23 20					
Glynde	d					21 37						22 37					23 37		
Berwick	d					21 43						22 43					23 43		
Polegate	d					21 49	22 01					22 49	23 11				23 49	00 11	
Hampden Park 4	d				21 43	21 53					22 43	22 53				23 47	23 53	00 15	
Eastbourne 4	a				21 49	21 58	22 09				22 49	22 58	23 19			23 52	23 58	00 20	
	d			21 34		22 02	22 15			22 34			23 26						
Hampden Park 4	d			21a38			22 19			22a38			23 30						
Pevensey & Westham	d						22 24						23 35						
Pevensey Bay	d																		
Normans Bay	d																		
Cooden Beach	d						22 30						23 41						
Collington	d						22 33						23 44						
Bexhill 4	d					22 16	22 36						23 47						
St Leonards Warrior Sq 4	d					22 23	22 42						23 53						
Hastings 4	a					22 26	22 45						23 56						
	d																		
Ore	d																		
Three Oaks	d																		
Doleham	d																		
Winchelsea	d																		
Rye	a																		
	d																		
Appledore (Kent)	d																		
Ham Street	d																		
Ashford International	a																		

Table 189R

Mondays to Fridays

9 December to 16 May

Ashford, Hastings, Eastbourne, Seaford and Lewes - Brighton, Haywards Heath and London

Network Diagram - see first Page of Table 189

Miles	Miles			SN MX [1]	SN MX [1]	SN MO [1]	SN	SN [1]	SN	SN	SN	SN [1]
—	0	Ashford International ⇌	d									
—	5½	Ham Street	d									
—	8½	Appledore (Kent)	d									
—	15¼	Rye	a									
—	—		d									
—	17¾	Winchelsea	d									
—	21½	Doleham	d									
—	22¾	Three Oaks	d									
—	25½	Ore	d									
0	26½	Hastings [4]	a									
—	—		d									05 08
0¾	—	St Leonards Warrior Sq [4]	d									05 11
4½	—	Bexhill [4]	d									05 18
5¼	—	Collington	d									05 20
6¾	—	Cooden Beach	d									05 23
8½	—	Normans Bay	d									
10½	—	Pevensey Bay	d									
11¼	—	Pevensey & Westham	d									05 29
14¼	—	Hampden Park [4]	d		00 11	00 15						05 33
16¼	—	Eastbourne [4]	a		00 16	00 20						05 38
—	—		d					05 08		05 32		05 43
18¼	—	Hampden Park [4]	d	00 01				05 12		05 36		05 47
20¼	—	Polegate	d	00 05				05 16		05 41		05 51
24¼	—	Berwick	d									05 57
29	—	Glynde	d									
—	0	Seaford	d				05 09				05 45	
—	1	Bishopstone	d				05 11				05 47	
—	2½	Newhaven Harbour	d				05 15				05 51	
—	2¾	Newhaven Town ⛴	d				05 16				05 52	
—	5½	Southease	d						←			
32	9	Lewes [4]	a	00 17			05 25	05 28	05 25	05 53	06 01	06 05
—	—											
—	—		d	00 18			05 32	05 29	05 32	05 54	06 09	06 06
36½	—	Falmer	d	00 25			→		05 39	06 01	→	
38¼	—	Moulsecoomb	d	00 28					05 42	06 05		
39¼	—	London Road (Brighton)	d	00 30					05 44	06 07		
40	—	Brighton [10]	a	00 34					05 48	06 11		
—	11¾	Cooksbridge	d									
—	14½	Plumpton	d					05 37				06 14
—	18¼	Wivelsfield [4]	a									
—	21¼	Haywards Heath [3]	a					05 46				06 26
—	—	Gatwick Airport [10] ✈	a					06 00				06 41
—	—	East Croydon 🚋	a					06 15				06 57
—	—	London Bridge [4] ⊖	a									07 13
—	—	Clapham Junction [10]	a					06 25				
—	—	London Victoria [15] ⊖	a					06 32				

Miles	Miles			SN	SN [1]	SN [1]	SN	SN	SN [1]	SN	SN [1]	SN [1] A ✠	SN [1] A ✠
—	0	Ashford International ⇌	d										
—	5½	Ham Street	d										
—	8½	Appledore (Kent)	d										
—	15¼	Rye	a										
—	—		d										
—	17¾	Winchelsea	d										
—	21½	Doleham	d										
—	22¾	Three Oaks	d										
—	25½	Ore	d										
0	26½	Hastings [4]	a										
—	—		d		05 42					05 58			06 15
0¾	—	St Leonards Warrior Sq [4]	d		05 45					06 01			06 18
4½	—	Bexhill [4]	d		05 52					06 12			06 25
5¼	—	Collington	d		05 54								06 27
6¾	—	Cooden Beach	d		05 57								06 30
8½	—	Normans Bay	d										
10½	—	Pevensey Bay	d										
11¼	—	Pevensey & Westham	d		06 04								06 36
14¼	—	Hampden Park [4]	d		06 08					06 24			06 42
16¼	—	Eastbourne [4]	a		06 13					06 29			06 47
—	—		d			06 14			06 24	06 37	06 47		06 57
18¼	—	Hampden Park [4]	d			06a18			06 28		06 51		07 01
20¼	—	Polegate	d						06 33	06 44	06 55		07 05
24¼	—	Berwick	d						06 39		07 00		
29	—	Glynde	d						06 45		07 06		
—	0	Seaford	d					06 30				06 56	
—	1	Bishopstone	d					06 32				06 58	
—	2½	Newhaven Harbour	d					06 36				07 02	
—	2¾	Newhaven Town ⛴	d					06 37				07 03	
—	5½	Southease	d	←								07 08	
32	9	Lewes [4]	a	06 01				06 46	06 50	06 57	07 11	07 14	07 18
—	—												
—	—		d	06 09			06 26	06 47	06 51	06 59	07 12	07 22	
36½	—	Falmer	d	06 16			06 33	06 54		07 06	07 19		
38¼	—	Moulsecoomb	d	06 19			06 36	06 57		07 10	07 22		
39¼	—	London Road (Brighton)	d	06 22			06 38	06 59		07 12	07 24		
40	—	Brighton [10]	a	06 25			06 42	07 03		07 16	07 28		
—	11¾	Cooksbridge	d						06 56			07 27	
—	14½	Plumpton	d						07 01			07 32	
—	18¼	Wivelsfield [4]	a						07 07			07 39	
—	21¼	Haywards Heath [3]	a						07 12			07 44	
—	—	Gatwick Airport [10] ✈	a						07 29				
—	—	East Croydon 🚋	a						07 45			08 14	
—	—	London Bridge [4] ⊖	a						08 00				
—	—	Clapham Junction [10]	a									08 23	
—	—	London Victoria [15] ⊖	a									08 32	

Miles	Miles			SN	SN [1]	SN [1]	SN	SN [1]	SN	SN [1]	SN	SN [1] A ✠	SN [1]	SN	SN	SN	SN	SN [1] A ✠	SN [1]
—	0	Ashford International ⇌	d												06 14	06 35			
—	5½	Ham Street	d												06 22	06 43			
—	8½	Appledore (Kent)	d												06 26	06 47			
—	15¼	Rye	a												06 35	06 56			
—	—		d												06 36				
—	17¾	Winchelsea	d												06 40				
—	21½	Doleham	d												06 46				
—	22¾	Three Oaks	d												06 50				
—	25½	Ore	d												06 55				
0	26½	Hastings [4]	a												06 58				
—	—		d									06 49			07 12			07 20	
0¾	—	St Leonards Warrior Sq [4]	d									06 52			07 15			07 23	
4½	—	Bexhill [4]	d									06 59			07 22			07 31	
5¼	—	Collington	d									07 01						07 33	
6¾	—	Cooden Beach	d									07 04						07 36	
8½	—	Normans Bay	d																
10½	—	Pevensey Bay	d																
11¼	—	Pevensey & Westham	d									07 10						07 42	
14¼	—	Hampden Park [4]	d			07 02				07 11		07 15						07 46	07 51
16¼	—	Eastbourne [4]	a			07 07				07 16		07 20			07 37			07 51	07 56
—	—		d		07 02			07 14		07 21		07 32	07 38		07 47			07 57	
18¼	—	Hampden Park [4]	d		07a06			07 19		07a25			07a42					08 01	
20¼	—	Polegate	d					07 23				07 39			07 54			08 05	
24¼	—	Berwick	d					07 29				07 44						08 11	
29	—	Glynde	d					07 35										08 16	
—	0	Seaford	d				07 16				07 33						07 59		
—	1	Bishopstone	d				07 18				07 35						08 01		
—	2½	Newhaven Harbour	d				07 21				07 38						08 05		
—	2¾	Newhaven Town ⛴	d				07 23				07 40			07 49			08 06		
—	5½	Southease	d				07 27				07 44						08 11		
32	9	Lewes [4]	a				07 33	07 41			07 50	07 53		07 57	08 07		08 17	08 22	
—	—																		
—	—		d	07 23			07 34	07 42	07 45		07 51	07 55		07 58	08 07		08 19	08 23	
36½	—	Falmer	d	07 30			07 41		07 52		07 58			08 05			08 26		
38¼	—	Moulsecoomb	d	07 33			07 44		07 55		08 01			08 08			08 29		
39¼	—	London Road (Brighton)	d	07 35			07 46		07 57		08 03			08 10			08 32		
40	—	Brighton [10]	a	07 39			07 50		08 01		08 07			08 14	08 20		08 36		
—	11¾	Cooksbridge	d					07 48				08 00						08 28	
—	14½	Plumpton	d					07 53				08 05						08 33	
—	18¼	Wivelsfield [4]	a									08 11						08 39	
—	21¼	Haywards Heath [3]	a					08 03				08 16						08 44	
—	—	Gatwick Airport [10] ✈	a															08 56	
—	—	East Croydon 🚋	a					08 31				08 46						09 14	
—	—	London Bridge [4] ⊖	a					08 49											
—	—	Clapham Junction [10]	a									09 01						09 23	
—	—	London Victoria [15] ⊖	a									09 09						09 32	

A ✠ from Lewes

Table 189R

Mondays to Fridays

9 December to 16 May

Ashford, Hastings, Eastbourne, Seaford and Lewes - Brighton, Haywards Heath and London

Network Diagram - see first Page of Table 189

Station		SN ■1	SN	SN ■1 A	SN ■1 A	SN	SN ■1	SN	SN	SN	SN ■1	SN	SN ■1 A	SN ■1	SN ■1	SN	SN ■1 A	SN	SN ■1	SN	SN ■1	SN	SN ■1	SN ■1	SN	SN	SN ■1	SN	SN ■1	SN	SN ■1	SN	SN ■1	SN	SN ■1	SN	SN ■1
Ashford International	d								07 17	07 41										08 33					08 53							09 33					
Ham Street	d								07 25	07 49										08 41					09 01							09 41					
Appledore (Kent)	d								07 29	07 53										08 45					09 05							09 45					
Rye	a								07 38	08 02										08 54					09 15							09 54					
	d								07 45											08 55					09 16							09 55					
Winchelsea	d								07 48																09 19							09 59					
Doleham	d								07 55																09 26												
Three Oaks	d								07 58											09 06					09 29												
Ore	d								08 04					08 22			08 47							09 20	09 35	09 49										10 16	
Hastings ■4	a								08 07					08 25			08 50			09 13				09 23	09 38	09 52						10 13				10 19	
	d				07 38				08 09					08 26			08 52			09 14				09 24					09 56			10 14				10 26	
St Leonards Warrior Sq ■4	d				07 41				08 12					08 29			08 55			09 17				09 27					09 59			10 17				10 29	
Bexhill ■4	d				07 48				08 22					08 35			09 02			09 24				09 35					10 06			10 24				10 35	
Collington	d				07 50									08 37			09 04							09 37					10 08							10 37	
Cooden Beach	d				07 53									08 40			09 07							09 40					10 11							10 40	
Normans Bay	d				07 56									08 43										09 43												10 43	
Pevensey Bay	d				07 59																																
Pevensey & Westham	d				08 02									08 48			09 13							09 48					10 17							10 48	
Hampden Park ■4	d				08 06		08 09	08 29			08 39			08 52	09 10		09 18		09 29		09 42			09 52					10 21		10 29		10 39			10 52	
Eastbourne ■4	a				08 11		08 14	08 34	08 37		08 44			08 57	09 15		09 23		09 34	09 39	09 47			09 58					10 26		10 34	10 39	10 44			10 57	
	d	08 04			08 15		08 21	08 40	08 45				08 56	09 04	09 20		09 28		09 40	09 47			09 55	10 03			10 20		10 32		10 40	10 47			10 58	11 04	11 19
Hampden Park ■4	d	08 08					08a25	08a44					09 00	09 08	09a24				09a44				09 59	10 07			10a24				10a44				11 02	11 08	11a23
Polegate	d	08 12			08 22				08 52				09 04	09 12			09 35			09 54			10 03	10 11					10 38			10 54			11 06	11 12	
Berwick	d	08 18			08 27									09 18									10 09	10 17												11 18	
Glynde	d	08 23			08 33									09 23										10 22												11 23	
Seaford	d			08 18								08 56				09 25						09 58						10 25						10 58			
Bishopstone	d			08 20								08 58				09 27						10 00						10 27						11 00			
Newhaven Harbour	d			08 23								09 01				09 30						10 03						10 30						11 03			
Newhaven Town	d			08 25								09 03				09 32						10 05						10 32						11 05			
Southease	d			08 29												09 36												10 36									
Lewes ■4	a	08 29		08 36	08 39				09 07			09 12	09 16	09 29		09 44	09 47			10 07		10 14	10 18	10 28				10 44	10 50			11 07		11 14	11 19	11 29	
	d	08 30	08 43	08 48		08 58			09 07			09 14	09 17	09 29		09 44	09 48	09 58		10 07		10 14	10 19	10 28				10 44	10 51	10 58		11 07		11 14	11 20	11 29	
Falmer	d	08 37	08 50			09 05						09 21		09 36		09 51		10 05				10 21		10 35				10 51		11 05				11 21		11 36	
Moulsecoomb	d	08 40	08 53			09 08						09 24		09 39		09 54		10 08				10 24		10 38				10 54		11 08				11 24		11 39	
London Road (Brighton)	d	08 42	08 55			09 10						09 27		09 42		09 57		10 10				10 27		10 41				10 57		11 10				11 27		11 42	
Brighton ■10	a	08 46	08 59			09 14			09 20			09 30		09 45		10 00		10 14		10 20		10 30		10 44				11 00		11 14		11 20		11 30		11 45	
Cooksbridge	d												09 22				09 53						10 24														
Plumpton	d												09 27				09 58						10 29												11 28		
Wivelsfield ■4	a			09 01									09 33										10 35												11 35		
Haywards Heath ■3	a			09 06									09 38				10 07						10 42						11 06						11 42		
Gatwick Airport ■10 ✈	a			09 22									09 55				10 25						10 55						11 25						11 55		
East Croydon	a			09 38									10 11				10 41						11 11						11 40						12 11		
London Bridge ■4 ⊖	a																																				
Clapham Junction ■10	a			09 48									10 20				10 50						11 20						11 50						12 21		
London Victoria ■15 ⊖	a			09 58									10 28				10 58						11 27						11 57						12 28		

A [trolley symbol] from Lewes

Table 189R

Mondays to Fridays

9 December to 16 May

Ashford, Hastings, Eastbourne, Seaford and Lewes - Brighton, Haywards Heath and London

Network Diagram - see first Page of Table 189

Station		SN	SN [1]	SN	SN [1]	SN	SN [1]	SN	SN [1]	SN [1]	SN [1]	SN	SN [1]
Ashford International	d					10 33							
Ham Street	d					10 41							
Appledore (Kent)	d					10 45							
Rye	a					10 54							
	d					10 55							
Winchelsea	d												
Doleham	d												
Three Oaks	d					11 06							
Ore	d		10 50							11 22			11 50
Hastings [4]	a		10 53			11 13				11 25			11 53
	d		10 55			11 14				11 26			11 55
St Leonards Warrior Sq [4]	d		10 58			11 17				11 29			11 58
Bexhill [4]	d		11 05			11 24				11 35			12 05
Collington	d		11 07							11 37			12 07
Cooden Beach	d		11 10							11 40			12 10
Normans Bay	d									11 43			
Pevensey Bay	d												
Pevensey & Westham	d		11 16							11 48			12 16
Hampden Park [4]	d		11 20		11 29		11 39			11 52			12 20
Eastbourne [4]	a		11 25		11 34	11 39	11 44			11 57			12 25
	d		11 31		11 40	11 47			11 58	12 04	12 19		12 31
Hampden Park [4]	d				11a44				12 02	12 08	12a23		
Polegate	d		11 37			11 54			12 06	12 12			12 37
Berwick	d									12 18			
Glynde	d									12 23			
Seaford	d	11 25						11 58				12 25	
Bishopstone	d	11 27						12 00				12 27	
Newhaven Harbour	d	11 30						12 03				12 30	
Newhaven Town	d	11 32						12 05				12 32	
Southease	d	11 36										12 36	
Lewes [4]	a	11 44	11 49			12 07		12 14	12 19	12 29		12 44	12 49
	d	11 44	11 50	11 58		12 07		12 14	12 20	12 29		12 44	12 50
Falmer	d	11 51		12 05				12 21		12 36		12 51	
Moulsecoomb	d	11 54		12 08				12 24		12 39		12 54	
London Road (Brighton)	d	11 57		12 10				12 27		12 42		12 57	
Brighton [10]	a	12 00		12 14		12 20		12 30		12 45		13 00	
Cooksbridge	d												
Plumpton	d								12 28				
Wivelsfield [4]	a								12 35				
Haywards Heath [3]	a		12 05						12 42				13 05
Gatwick Airport [10]	a		12 24						12 55				13 24
East Croydon	a		12 40						13 11				13 40
London Bridge [4]	a												
Clapham Junction [10]	a		12 49						13 20				13 50
London Victoria [15]	a		12 56						13 27				13 57

Station		SN	SN [1]	SN	SN [1]	SN	SN [1]	SN [1]	SN [1]	SN	SN [1]	SN	SN [1]
Ashford International	d			11 33									
Ham Street	d			11 41									
Appledore (Kent)	d			11 45									
Rye	a			11 54									
	d			11 55									
Winchelsea	d			11 59									
Doleham	d												
Three Oaks	d												
Ore	d							12 22			12 50		
Hastings [4]	a			12 13				12 25			12 53		
	d			12 14				12 26			12 55		
St Leonards Warrior Sq [4]	d			12 17				12 29			12 58		
Bexhill [4]	d			12 24				12 35			13 05		
Collington	d							12 37			13 07		
Cooden Beach	d							12 40			13 10		
Normans Bay	d							12 43					
Pevensey Bay	d												
Pevensey & Westham	d							12 48			13 16		
Hampden Park [4]	d		12 29		12 39			12 52			13 20		13 29
Eastbourne [4]	a		12 34	12 39	12 44			12 57			13 25		13 34
	d		12 40	12 47			12 58	13 04	13 19		13 31		13 40
Hampden Park [4]	d		12a44				13 02	13 08	13a23				13a44
Polegate	d			12 54			13 06	13 12			13 37		
Berwick	d							13 18					
Glynde	d							13 23					
Seaford	d					12 58				13 25			
Bishopstone	d					13 00				13 27			
Newhaven Harbour	d					13 03				13 30			
Newhaven Town	d					13 05				13 32			
Southease	d									13 36			
Lewes [4]	a			13 07		13 14	13 19	13 29		13 44	13 49		
	d	12 58		13 07		13 14	13 20	13 29		13 44	13 50	13 58	
Falmer	d	13 05				13 21		13 36		13 51		14 05	
Moulsecoomb	d	13 08				13 24		13 39		13 54		14 08	
London Road (Brighton)	d	13 10				13 27		13 42		13 57		14 10	
Brighton [10]	a	13 14		13 20		13 30		13 45		14 00		14 14	
Cooksbridge	d												
Plumpton	d						13 28						
Wivelsfield [4]	a						13 35						
Haywards Heath [3]	a						13 42				14 05		
Gatwick Airport [10]	a						13 55				14 24		
East Croydon	a						14 11				14 40		
London Bridge [4]	a												
Clapham Junction [10]	a						14 20				14 49		
London Victoria [15]	a						14 28				14 57		

Station		SN	SN [1]	SN	SN [1]	SN [1]	SN [1]	SN	SN [1] A	SN	SN [1]	SN	SN [1]
Ashford International	d	12 33										13 33	
Ham Street	d	12 41										13 41	
Appledore (Kent)	d	12 45										13 45	
Rye	a	12 54										13 54	
	d	12 55										13 55	
Winchelsea	d											13 59	
Doleham	d												
Three Oaks	d	13 06											
Ore	d					13 22			13 50				
Hastings [4]	a	13 13				13 25			13 53			14 13	
	d	13 14				13 26			13 55			14 14	
St Leonards Warrior Sq [4]	d	13 17				13 29			13 58			14 17	
Bexhill [4]	d	13 24				13 35			14 05			14 24	
Collington	d					13 37			14 07				
Cooden Beach	d					13 40			14 10				
Normans Bay	d					13 43							
Pevensey Bay	d												
Pevensey & Westham	d					13 48			14 16				
Hampden Park [4]	d		13 39			13 52			14 20		14 29		14 39
Eastbourne [4]	a	13 39	13 44			13 57			14 25		14 34	14 39	14 44
	d	13 47			13 58	14 04	14 19		14 31		14 40	14 47	
Hampden Park [4]	d				14 02	14 08	14a23				14a44		
Polegate	d	13 54			14 06	14 12			14 37			14 54	
Berwick	d					14 18							
Glynde	d					14 23							
Seaford	d			13 58				14 25					
Bishopstone	d			14 00				14 27					
Newhaven Harbour	d			14 03				14 30					
Newhaven Town	d			14 05				14 32					
Southease	d							14 36					
Lewes [4]	a	14 07		14 14	14 19	14 29		14 44	14 49			15 07	
	d	14 07		14 14	14 20	14 29		14 44	14 50	14 58		15 07	
Falmer	d			14 21		14 36		14 51		15 05			
Moulsecoomb	d			14 24		14 39		14 54		15 08			
London Road (Brighton)	d			14 27		14 42		14 57		15 10			
Brighton [10]	a	14 20		14 30		14 45		15 00		15 14		15 20	
Cooksbridge	d												
Plumpton	d				14 28								
Wivelsfield [4]	a				14 35								
Haywards Heath [3]	a				14 42				15 05				
Gatwick Airport [10]	a				14 55				15 24				
East Croydon	a				15 11				15 40				
London Bridge [4]	a												
Clapham Junction [10]	a				15 20				15 49				
London Victoria [15]	a				15 27				15 57				

A from Lewes

Table 189R

Mondays to Fridays

9 December to 16 May

Ashford, Hastings, Eastbourne, Seaford and Lewes - Brighton, Haywards Heath and London

Network Diagram - see first Page of Table 189

		SN	SN 1 A	SN 1	SN 1	SN	SN 1 A	SN	SN 1	SN	SN 1	SN	SN 1 A	SN 1	SN 1	SN	SN 1 A	SN	SN 1	SN	SN 1	SN	SN 1 A	SN	SN 1	SN	SN 1	SN 1 A	SN	SN 1	SN	SN 1	SN	SN 1 A	SN 1	SN	SN 1
Ashford International	d									14 33										15 33											16 33						
Ham Street	d									14 41										15 41											16 41						
Appledore (Kent)	d									14 45										15 45											16 45						
Rye	a									14 54										15 54											16 54						
	d									14 55										15 55											16 55						
Winchelsea	d																			15 59																	
Doleham	d																																				
Three Oaks	d									15 06																					17 06						
Ore	d			14 22			14 50							15 20			15 48								16 22			16 50							17 22		
Hastings 4	a			14 25			14 53			15 13				15 23			15 51			16 13					16 25			16 53			17 13				17 25		
	d			14 26			14 55			15 14				15 24			15 52			16 14					16 26			16 55			17 14				17 26		
St Leonards Warrior Sq 4	d			14 29			14 58			15 17				15 27			15 55			16 17					16 29			16 58			17 17				17 29		
Bexhill 4	d			14 35			15 05			15 24				15 33			16 02			16 24					16 35			17 05			17 24				17 35		
Collington	d			14 37			15 07							15 35			16 04								16 37			17 07							17 37		
Cooden Beach	d			14 40			15 10							15 38			16 07								16 40			17 10							17 40		
Normans Bay	d			14 43										15 41			16 10								16 43										17 43		
Pevensey Bay	d													15 45			16 13																				
Pevensey & Westham	d			14 48			15 16							15 47			16 16								16 48			17 16							17 48		
Hampden Park 4	d			14 52			15 20		15 29		15 39			15 52			16 20		16 29		16 39				16 52			17 20		17 29		17 40			17 52	17 55	18 13
Eastbourne 4	a			14 57			15 25		15 34	15 39	15 44			15 57			16 25		16 34	16 39	16 44				16 57			17 25		17 34	17 39	17 48			17 57	18 00	18 18
	d		14 58	15 04	15 19		15 31		15 40	15 47			15 58	16 04	16 19		16 31		16 40	16 45			16 58		17 04		17 21	17 31		17 40	17 45			17 57	18 01		18 25
Hampden Park 4	d		15 02	15 08	15a23				15a44				16 02	16 08	16a23				16a44	16 49			17 02		17 08		17a25			17a44				18 01	18 05		18a29
Polegate	d		15 06	15 12			15 37			15 54			16 06	16 12			16 37			16 54			17 06		17 12			17 37			17 52			18 05	18 11		
Berwick	d			15 18										16 18											17 18										18 17		
Glynde	d			15 23										16 23											17 23										18 22		
Seaford	d	14 58				15 25						15 58				16 25						16 58				17 20							17 58				
Bishopstone	d	15 00				15 27						16 00				16 27						17 00				17 22							18 00				
Newhaven Harbour	d	15 03				15 30						16 03				16 30						17 03				17 26							18 03				
Newhaven Town ⛴	d	15 05				15 32						16 05				16 32						17 05				17 27							18 05				
Southease	d					15 36										16 36										17 32											
Lewes 4	a	15 14	15 18	15 29		15 44	15 49			16 07		16 14	16 18	16 29		16 44	16 49			17 07		17 14	17 18		17 29	17 39		17 49			18 04		18 14	18 17	18 28		
	d	15 14	15 19	15 29		15 44	15 50	15 58		16 07		16 14	16 20	16 29		16 44	16 50	16 58		17 07		17 14	17 19	17 22	17 29	17 39		17 50	17 57		18 07		18 14	18 18	18 28		
Falmer	d	15 21		15 36		15 51		16 05				16 21		16 36		16 51		17 05				17 21		17 29	17 36	17 46			18 04				18 21		18 35		
Moulsecoomb	d	15 24		15 39		15 54		16 08				16 24		16 39		16 54		17 08				17 24		17 32	17 39	17 49			18 07				18 24		18 38		
London Road (Brighton)	d	15 27		15 42		15 57		16 10				16 27		16 42		16 57		17 10				17 27		17 34	17 42	17 52			18 09				18 27		18 41		
Brighton 10	a	15 30		15 45		16 00		16 14		16 20		16 30		16 45		17 00		17 14		17 20		17 30		17 38	17 45	17 55			18 13		18 20		18 30		18 44		
Cooksbridge	d		15 24										16 25										17 24											18 23			
Plumpton	d		15 29										16 30										17 29					17 58						18 28			
Wivelsfield 4	a		15 35										16 38										17 35											18 34			
Haywards Heath 3	a		15 42				16 05						16 44				17 06						17 41					18 07						18 38			
Gatwick Airport 10 ✈	a		15 55				16 25						16 57				17 25						17 54					18 26						18 56			
East Croydon	a		16 11				16 41						17 12				17 41						18 11					18 42						19 12			
London Bridge 4 ⊖	a																																				
Clapham Junction 10	a		16 20				16 50						17 23				17 51						18 21					18 52						19 21			
London Victoria 15 ⊖	a		16 28				16 58						17 30				17 58						18 29					18 59						19 28			

A from Lewes

Table 189R

Mondays to Fridays
9 December to 16 May

Ashford, Hastings, Eastbourne, Seaford and Lewes - Brighton, Haywards Heath and London

Network Diagram - see first Page of Table 189

		SN	SN 1	SN 1	SN	SN	SN	SN 1	SN 1	SN	SN 1	SN 1	SN	SN 1	SN 1	SN	SN	SN	SN 1
Ashford International	d					17 33	18 00										18 33	19 02	
Ham Street	d					17 41	18 08										18 41	19 10	
Appledore (Kent)	d					17 45	18 12										18 45	19 14	
Rye	a					17 54	18 21										18 54	19 23	
	d					17 55											18 55		
Winchelsea	d					17 59													
Doleham	d																		
Three Oaks	d																19 06		
Ore	d		17 50									18 22		18 50					
Hastings 4	a		17 53			18 13						18 25		18 53			19 13		
	d		17 55			18 14						18 26		18 55			19 14		
St Leonards Warrior Sq 4	d		17 58			18 17						18 29		18 58			19 17		
Bexhill 4	d		18 05			18 24						18 35		19 05			19 24		
Collington	d		18 07									18 37		19 07					
Cooden Beach	d		18 10									18 40		19 10					
Normans Bay	d											18 43							
Pevensey Bay	d																		
Pevensey & Westham	d		18 16									18 48		19 16					
Hampden Park 4	d		18 20	18 28				18 42				18 52		19 20	19 36				19 50
Eastbourne 4	a		18 25	18 34		18 39		18 49				18 57		19 25	19 41		19 44		19 56
	d		18 31	18 44		18 48			18 57		19 00	19 04		19 31	19 51		19 48		
Hampden Park 4	d			18a48					19a01		19 04	19 08			19a55				
Polegate	d		18 37			18 55					19 08	19 12		19 37			19 55		
Berwick	d											19 18							
Glynde	d											19 23							
Seaford	d	18 23			18 41					18 59			19 17			19 37			
Bishopstone	d	18 25			18 43					19 01			19 19			19 39			
Newhaven Harbour	d	18 29											19 23			19 42			
Newhaven Town	d	18 30			18 48					19 06			19 24			19 44			
Southease	d	18 35														19 48			
Lewes 4	a	18 41	18 49		18 56	19 08				19 15	19 20	19 29	19 33	19 49		19 55	20 07		
	d	18 42	18 50		18 57	19 08				19 15	19 21	19 29	19 39	19 50		19 57	20 08		
Falmer	d	18 49			19 04					19 22		19 36	19 46			20 04			
Moulsecoomb	d	18 52			19 07					19 25		19 39	19 49			20 07			
London Road (Brighton)	d	18 54			19 09					19 28		19 42	19 51			20 09			
Brighton 10	a	18 58			19 13	19 21				19 31		19 45	19 55			20 13	20 20		
Cooksbridge	d										19 26								
Plumpton	d		18 58								19 31								
Wivelsfield 4	a		19 06											20 04					
Haywards Heath 3	a		19 10								19 42			20 11					
Gatwick Airport 10	a		19 25											20 24					
East Croydon	a		19 42											20 40					
London Bridge 4	a																		
Clapham Junction 10	a		19 51											20 49					
London Victoria 15	a		19 59											20 58					

		SN	SN 1	SN 1	SN	SN 1	SN	SN 1	SN	SN 1	SN	SN 1	SN	SN 1	SN	SN 1 A 🛒	SN	SN	SN 1
Ashford International	d								19 33				19 59					20 33	
Ham Street	d								19 41				20 07					20 41	
Appledore (Kent)	d								19 45				20 11					20 45	
Rye	a								19 54				20 21					20 54	
	d								19 55				20 22					20 55	
Winchelsea	d								19 59										
Doleham	d																		
Three Oaks	d																	21 06	
Ore	d					19 51						20 22				20 50			
Hastings 4	a					19 54			20 13			20 25	20 39			20 53		21 13	
	d		19 27			19 55			20 14			20 26				20 55		21 14	
St Leonards Warrior Sq 4	d		19 30			19 58			20 17			20 29				20 58		21 17	
Bexhill 4	d		19 37			20 05			20 24			20 35				21 05		21 24	
Collington	d		19 39			20 07						20 37				21 07			
Cooden Beach	d		19 42			20 10						20 40				21 10			
Normans Bay	d																		
Pevensey Bay	d																		
Pevensey & Westham	d		19 48			20 16						20 46				21 16			
Hampden Park 4	d		19 52			20 20		20 29		20 43		20 51				21 20			21 43
Eastbourne 4	a		19 57			20 25		20 34	20 39	20 48		20 56				21 25		21 39	21 48
	d		20 03	20 20		20 31			20 45			21 04		21 21		21 31		21 45	
Hampden Park 4	d		20 07	20a24								21 08		21a25					
Polegate	d		20 11			20 37			20 52			21 12				21 37		21 52	
Berwick	d		20 17									21 18							
Glynde	d		20 22									21 23							
Seaford	d	19 58			20 28						20 58				21 28				
Bishopstone	d	20 00			20 30						21 00				21 30				
Newhaven Harbour	d	20 03			20 33						21 03				21 33				
Newhaven Town	d	20 05			20 35						21 05				21 35				
Southease	d				20 39		←										←		
Lewes 4	a	20 14	20 28		20 46	20 49	20 46		21 07		21 14	21 29			21 44	21 49	21 44	22 07	
	d	20 14	20 28		20 53	20 50	20 53		21 07		21 14	21 29			21 53	21 50	21 53	22 07	
Falmer	d	20 21	20 35		→		21 00				21 21	21 36			→		22 00		
Moulsecoomb	d	20 24	20 38				21 03				21 24	21 39					22 03		
London Road (Brighton)	d	20 27	20 41				21 05				21 27	21 42					22 05		
Brighton 10	a	20 33	20 44				21 09		21 20		21 33	21 45					22 09	22 20	
Cooksbridge	d																		
Plumpton	d					20 58													
Wivelsfield 4	a					21 05										22 02			
Haywards Heath 3	a					21 11										22 06			
Gatwick Airport 10	a					21 25										22 25			
East Croydon	a					21 41										22 40			
London Bridge 4	a																		
Clapham Junction 10	a					21 50										22 50			
London Victoria 15	a					21 58										22 57			

A 🛒 from Lewes

Table 189R

Mondays to Fridays

9 December to 16 May

Ashford, Hastings, Eastbourne, Seaford and Lewes - Brighton, Haywards Heath and London

Network Diagram - see first Page of Table 189

Station		SN	SN [1]	SN	SN [1]	SN	SN [1]	SN	SN [1]	SN	SN [1]	SN	SN [1]	SN	SN [1]	SN [1]
Ashford International	d							21 33				22 34				
Ham Street	d							21 41				22 42				
Appledore (Kent)	d							21 45				22 46				
Rye	a							21 54				22 55				
	d							21 57				22 55				
Winchelsea	d							22 00				22 59				
Doleham	d											23 05				
Three Oaks	d											23 09				
Ore	d				21 22						22 22	23 14				
Hastings [4]	a				21 25			22 14			22 25	23 17				
	d				21 30			22 15			22 26					23 22
St Leonards Warrior Sq [4]	d				21 33			22 18			22 29					23 25
Bexhill [4]	d				21 40			22 25			22 38					23 31
Collington	d				21 42						22 40					23 33
Cooden Beach	d				21 45						22 43					23 36
Normans Bay	d										22 46					
Pevensey Bay	d															
Pevensey & Westham	d				21 51						22 51					23 42
Hampden Park [4]	d				21 55				22 43		22 55		23 10		23 42	23 47
Eastbourne [4]	a				22 00			22 40	22 48		23 00		23 15		23 47	23 52
	d		22 04		22 15		22 21	22 45			23 05		23 20			23 56
Hampden Park [4]	d		22 08		22 19		22a25				23 09		23a24			00 01
Polegate	d		22 12		22 23			22 52			23 13					00 05
Berwick	d		22 18		22 29						23 18					
Glynde	d		22 23								23 24					
Seaford	d	21 58		22 20						22 58				23 25		
Bishopstone	d	22 00		22 22						23 00				23 27		
Newhaven Harbour	d	22 03		22 25						23 03				23 30		
Newhaven Town	d	22 05		22 27						23 05				23 32		
Southease	d					←										
Lewes [4]	a	22 14	22 29	22 35	22 38	22 35		23 07		23 14	23 29			23 40		00 17
	d	22 14	22 29	22 42	22 40	22 42		23 07		23 14	23 30			23 40		00 18
Falmer	d	22 21	22 36	→		22 49				23 21	23 37			23 47		00 25
Moulsecoomb	d	22 24	22 39			22 52				23 24	23 40			23 50		00 28
London Road (Brighton)	d	22 27	22 42			22 54				23 27	23 42			23 53		00 30
Brighton [10]	a	22 31	22 45			22 58		23 20		23 31	23 46			23 56		00 34
Cooksbridge	d															
Plumpton	d				22 48											
Wivelsfield [4]	a				22 54											
Haywards Heath [3]	a				22 58											
Gatwick Airport [10] ✈	a				23 12											
East Croydon	a				23 30											
London Bridge [4] ⊖	a															
Clapham Junction [10]	a				23 42											
London Victoria [15] ⊖	a				23 52											

Table 189R

Saturdays

14 December to 17 May

Ashford, Hastings, Eastbourne, Seaford and Lewes - Brighton, Haywards Heath and London

Network Diagram - see first Page of Table 189

Station		SN [1]	SN [1]	SN	SN [1]	SN	SN	SN [1]	SN	SN [1]
Ashford International	d									
Ham Street	d									
Appledore (Kent)	d									
Rye	a									
	d									
Winchelsea	d									
Doleham	d									
Three Oaks	d									
Ore	d									
Hastings [4]	a									
	d									
St Leonards Warrior Sq [4]	d									
Bexhill [4]	d									
Collington	d									
Cooden Beach	d									
Normans Bay	d									
Pevensey Bay	d									
Pevensey & Westham	d									
Hampden Park [4]	d		00 11							
Eastbourne [4]	a		00 16							
	d				05 03		05 48	06 18		06 24
Hampden Park [4]	d	00 01			05 07		05 52	06a22		06 28
Polegate	d	00 05			05 11		05 57			06 32
Berwick	d									06 38
Glynde	d									06 43
Seaford	d			05 05					06 28	
Bishopstone	d			05 07					06 30	
Newhaven Harbour	d			05 10					06 33	
Newhaven Town	d			05 12					06 35	
Southease	d					←				
Lewes [4]	a	00 17		05 21	05 24	05 21	06 10		06 44	06 49
	d	00 18		05 28	05 26	05 28	06 10		06 44	06 50
Falmer	d	00 25		→		05 35	06 18		06 51	
Moulsecoomb	d	00 28				05 38	06 21		06 54	
London Road (Brighton)	d	00 30				05 40	06 24		06 57	
Brighton [10]	a	00 34				05 44	06 27		07 00	
Cooksbridge	d									
Plumpton	d									
Wivelsfield [4]	a									
Haywards Heath [3]	a				05 41					07 05
Gatwick Airport [10]	a				06 05					07 25
East Croydon	a									07 41
London Bridge [4]	a									
Clapham Junction [10]	a									07 50
London Victoria [15]	a									07 58

Station		SN	SN	SN [1]	SN [1]	SN [1]	SN	SN [1]	SN	SN [1]
Ashford International	d									
Ham Street	d									
Appledore (Kent)	d									
Rye	a									
	d									
Winchelsea	d									
Doleham	d									
Three Oaks	d									
Ore	d				06 22			06 50		
Hastings [4]	a				06 25			06 53		
	d				06 26			06 55		
St Leonards Warrior Sq [4]	d				06 29			06 58		
Bexhill [4]	d				06 35			07 05		
Collington	d				06 37			07 07		
Cooden Beach	d				06 40			07 10		
Normans Bay	d				06 43					
Pevensey Bay	d									
Pevensey & Westham	d				06 48			07 16		
Hampden Park [4]	d				06 52	07 11		07 20		07 29
Eastbourne [4]	a				06 57	07 17		07 25		07 34
	d	06 38		06 58	07 04	07 21		07 31		07 40
Hampden Park [4]	d			07 02	07 08	07a25				07a44
Polegate	d	06 45		07 06	07 12			07 37		
Berwick	d				07 18					
Glynde	d				07 23					
Seaford	d		06 58				07 28			
Bishopstone	d		07 00				07 30			
Newhaven Harbour	d		07 03				07 33			
Newhaven Town	d		07 05				07 35			
Southease	d									
Lewes [4]	a	06 57	07 14	07 18	07 29		07 44	07 49		
	d	06 58	07 14	07 20	07 29		07 44	07 50	07 58	
Falmer	d	07 05	07 21		07 36		07 51		08 05	
Moulsecoomb	d	07 09	07 24		07 39		07 54		08 08	
London Road (Brighton)	d	07 11	07 27		07 42		07 57		08 10	
Brighton [10]	a	07 15	07 30		07 45		08 00		08 14	
Cooksbridge	d									
Plumpton	d			07 28						
Wivelsfield [4]	a			07 35						
Haywards Heath [3]	a			07 40				08 05		
Gatwick Airport [10]	a			07 55				08 24		
East Croydon	a			08 11				08 40		
London Bridge [4]	a									
Clapham Junction [10]	a			08 20				08 49		
London Victoria [15]	a			08 28				08 57		

Station		SN	SN	SN [1]	SN [1]	SN [1]	SN	SN [1]	SN	SN [1]
Ashford International	d	06 15								
Ham Street	d	06 23								
Appledore (Kent)	d	06 27								
Rye	a	06 37								
	d	06 51								
Winchelsea	d	06 54								
Doleham	d	07 01								
Three Oaks	d	07 04								
Ore	d	07 10			07 22			07 50		
Hastings [4]	a	07 13			07 25			07 53		
	d	07 14			07 26			07 55		
St Leonards Warrior Sq [4]	d	07 17			07 29			07 58		
Bexhill [4]	d	07 24			07 35			08 05		
Collington	d				07 37			08 07		
Cooden Beach	d				07 40			08 10		
Normans Bay	d				07 43					
Pevensey Bay	d									
Pevensey & Westham	d				07 48			08 16		
Hampden Park [4]	d				07 52			08 20		08 29
Eastbourne [4]	a	07 39			07 57			08 25		08 34
	d	07 47		07 58	08 04	08 18		08 31		08 40
Hampden Park [4]	d			08 02	08 08	08a22				08a44
Polegate	d	07 54		08 06	08 12			08 37		
Berwick	d				08 18					
Glynde	d				08 23					
Seaford	d		07 58				08 25			
Bishopstone	d		08 00				08 27			
Newhaven Harbour	d		08 03				08 30			
Newhaven Town	d		08 05				08 32			
Southease	d						08 36			
Lewes [4]	a	08 07	08 14	08 18	08 29		08 44	08 49		
	d	08 07	08 14	08 20	08 29		08 44	08 50	08 58	
Falmer	d		08 21		08 36		08 51		09 05	
Moulsecoomb	d		08 24		08 39		08 54		09 08	
London Road (Brighton)	d		08 27		08 42		08 57		09 10	
Brighton [10]	a	08 20	08 30		08 45		09 00		09 14	
Cooksbridge	d									
Plumpton	d			08 28						
Wivelsfield [4]	a			08 35						
Haywards Heath [3]	a			08 40				09 05		
Gatwick Airport [10]	a			08 55				09 25		
East Croydon	a			09 11				09 41		
London Bridge [4]	a									
Clapham Junction [10]	a			09 20				09 50		
London Victoria [15]	a			09 28				09 58		

Station		SN	SN	SN [1]	SN [1]	SN [1]	SN	SN [1]	SN	SN [1]
Ashford International	d	07 33								
Ham Street	d	07 41								
Appledore (Kent)	d	07 45								
Rye	a	07 54								
	d	07 55								
Winchelsea	d	07 59								
Doleham	d									
Three Oaks	d									
Ore	d				08 22			08 50		
Hastings [4]	a	08 13			08 25			08 53		
	d	08 14			08 26			08 55		
St Leonards Warrior Sq [4]	d	08 17			08 29			08 58		
Bexhill [4]	d	08 24			08 35			09 05		
Collington	d				08 37			09 07		
Cooden Beach	d				08 40			09 10		
Normans Bay	d				08 43					
Pevensey Bay	d									
Pevensey & Westham	d				08 48			09 16		
Hampden Park [4]	d				08 52			09 20		09 29
Eastbourne [4]	a	08 39			08 57			09 25		09 34
	d	08 47		08 58	09 04	09 19		09 31		09 40
Hampden Park [4]	d			09 02	09 08	09a23				09a44
Polegate	d	08 54		09 06	09 12			09 37		
Berwick	d				09 18					
Glynde	d				09 23					
Seaford	d		08 58				09 25			
Bishopstone	d		09 00				09 27			
Newhaven Harbour	d		09 03				09 30			
Newhaven Town	d		09 05				09 32			
Southease	d						09 36			
Lewes [4]	a	09 07	09 14	09 18	09 29		09 44	09 49		
	d	09 07	09 14	09 20	09 29		09 44	09 50	09 58	
Falmer	d		09 21		09 36		09 51		10 05	
Moulsecoomb	d		09 24		09 39		09 54		10 08	
London Road (Brighton)	d		09 27		09 42		09 57		10 10	
Brighton [10]	a	09 20	09 30		09 45		10 00		10 14	
Cooksbridge	d									
Plumpton	d			09 28						
Wivelsfield [4]	a			09 35						
Haywards Heath [3]	a			09 40				10 05		
Gatwick Airport [10]	a			09 55				10 24		
East Croydon	a			10 11				10 40		
London Bridge [4]	a									
Clapham Junction [10]	a			10 20				10 49		
London Victoria [15]	a			10 28				10 57		

Table 189R

Saturdays

14 December to 17 May

Ashford, Hastings, Eastbourne, Seaford and Lewes - Brighton, Haywards Heath and London

Network Diagram - see first Page of Table 189

Station		SN	SN 1	SN	SN 1	SN 1	SN 1	SN	SN 1	SN
Ashford International	d	08 33								
Ham Street	d	08 41								
Appledore (Kent)	d	08 45								
Rye	a	08 54								
	d	08 55								
Winchelsea	d									
Doleham	d									
Three Oaks	d	09 06								
Ore	d					09 22			09 50	
Hastings 4	a	09 13				09 25			09 53	
	d	09 14				09 26			09 55	
St Leonards Warrior Sq 4	d	09 17				09 29			09 58	
Bexhill 4	d	09 24				09 35			10 05	
Collington	d					09 37			10 07	
Cooden Beach	d					09 40			10 10	
Normans Bay	d					09 43				
Pevensey Bay	d									
Pevensey & Westham	d					09 48			10 16	
Hampden Park 4	d		09 39			09 52			10 20	
Eastbourne 4	a	09 39	09 44			09 57			10 25	
	d	09 47			09 58	10 04	10 19		10 31	
Hampden Park 4	d				10 02	10 08	10a23			
Polegate	d	09 54			10 06	10 12			10 37	
Berwick	d					10 18				
Glynde	d					10 23				
Seaford	d			09 58				10 25		
Bishopstone	d			10 00				10 27		
Newhaven Harbour	d			10 03				10 30		
Newhaven Town	d			10 05				10 32		
Southease	d							10 36		
Lewes 4	a	10 07		10 14	10 18	10 29		10 44	10 49	
	d	10 07		10 14	10 20	10 29		10 44	10 50	10 58
Falmer	d			10 21		10 36		10 51		11 05
Moulsecoomb	d			10 24		10 39		10 54		11 08
London Road (Brighton)	d			10 27		10 42		10 57		11 10
Brighton 10	a	10 20		10 30		10 45		11 00		11 14
Cooksbridge	d									
Plumpton	d				10 28					
Wivelsfield 4	a				10 35					
Haywards Heath 3	a				10 40				11 05	
Gatwick Airport 10	a				10 55				11 24	
East Croydon	a				11 11				11 40	
London Bridge 4	a									
Clapham Junction 10	a				11 20				11 49	
London Victoria 15	a				11 28				11 57	

Station		SN 1	SN	SN 1	SN	SN 1	SN 1	SN 1	SN	SN 1
Ashford International	d		09 33							
Ham Street	d		09 41							
Appledore (Kent)	d		09 45							
Rye	a		09 54							
	d		09 55							
Winchelsea	d		09 59							
Doleham	d									
Three Oaks	d									
Ore	d						10 22			10 50
Hastings 4	a		10 13				10 25			10 53
	d		10 14				10 26			10 55
St Leonards Warrior Sq 4	d		10 17				10 29			10 58
Bexhill 4	d		10 24				10 35			11 05
Collington	d						10 37			11 07
Cooden Beach	d						10 40			11 10
Normans Bay	d						10 43			
Pevensey Bay	d									
Pevensey & Westham	d						10 48			11 16
Hampden Park 4	d	10 29		10 39			10 52			11 20
Eastbourne 4	a	10 34	10 39	10 44			10 57			11 25
	d	10 40	10 47			10 58	11 04	11 19		11 31
Hampden Park 4	d	10a44				11 02	11 08	11a23		
Polegate	d		10 54			11 06	11 12			11 37
Berwick	d						11 18			
Glynde	d						11 23			
Seaford	d				10 58				11 25	
Bishopstone	d				11 00				11 27	
Newhaven Harbour	d				11 03				11 30	
Newhaven Town	d				11 05				11 32	
Southease	d								11 36	
Lewes 4	a		11 07		11 14	11 18	11 29		11 44	11 49
	d		11 07		11 14	11 20	11 29		11 44	11 50
Falmer	d				11 21		11 36		11 51	
Moulsecoomb	d				11 24		11 39		11 54	
London Road (Brighton)	d				11 27		11 42		11 57	
Brighton 10	a		11 20		11 30		11 45		12 00	
Cooksbridge	d									
Plumpton	d					11 28				
Wivelsfield 4	a					11 35				
Haywards Heath 3	a					11 40				12 05
Gatwick Airport 10	a					11 55				12 24
East Croydon	a					12 11				12 40
London Bridge 4	a									
Clapham Junction 10	a					12 20				12 49
London Victoria 15	a					12 28				12 57

Station		SN	SN 1	SN	SN 1	SN	SN 1	SN 1	SN 1	SN
Ashford International	d			10 33						
Ham Street	d			10 41						
Appledore (Kent)	d			10 45						
Rye	a			10 54						
	d			10 55						
Winchelsea	d									
Doleham	d									
Three Oaks	d			11 06						
Ore	d							11 22		
Hastings 4	a			11 13				11 25		
	d			11 14				11 26		
St Leonards Warrior Sq 4	d			11 17				11 29		
Bexhill 4	d			11 24				11 35		
Collington	d							11 37		
Cooden Beach	d							11 40		
Normans Bay	d							11 43		
Pevensey Bay	d									
Pevensey & Westham	d							11 48		
Hampden Park 4	d		11 29		11 39			11 52		
Eastbourne 4	a		11 34	11 39	11 44			11 57		
	d		11 40	11 47			11 58	12 04	12 19	
Hampden Park 4	d		11a44				12 02	12 08	12a23	
Polegate	d			11 54			12 06	12 12		
Berwick	d							12 18		
Glynde	d							12 23		
Seaford	d					11 58				12 25
Bishopstone	d					12 00				12 27
Newhaven Harbour	d					12 03				12 30
Newhaven Town	d					12 05				12 32
Southease	d									12 36
Lewes 4	a			12 07		12 14	12 18	12 29		12 44
	d	11 58		12 07		12 14	12 20	12 29		12 44
Falmer	d	12 05				12 21		12 36		12 51
Moulsecoomb	d	12 08				12 24		12 39		12 54
London Road (Brighton)	d	12 10				12 27		12 42		12 57
Brighton 10	a	12 14		12 20		12 30		12 45		13 00
Cooksbridge	d									
Plumpton	d						12 28			
Wivelsfield 4	a						12 35			
Haywards Heath 3	a						12 40			
Gatwick Airport 10	a						12 55			
East Croydon	a						13 11			
London Bridge 4	a									
Clapham Junction 10	a						13 20			
London Victoria 15	a						13 28			

Station		SN 1	SN	SN 1	SN	SN 1	SN	SN 1	SN 1	SN 1
Ashford International	d				11 33					
Ham Street	d				11 41					
Appledore (Kent)	d				11 45					
Rye	a				11 54					
	d				11 55					
Winchelsea	d				11 59					
Doleham	d									
Three Oaks	d									
Ore	d	11 50							12 22	
Hastings 4	a	11 53			12 13				12 25	
	d	11 55			12 14				12 26	
St Leonards Warrior Sq 4	d	11 58			12 17				12 29	
Bexhill 4	d	12 05			12 24				12 35	
Collington	d	12 07							12 37	
Cooden Beach	d	12 10							12 40	
Normans Bay	d								12 43	
Pevensey Bay	d									
Pevensey & Westham	d	12 16							12 48	
Hampden Park 4	d	12 20		12 29		12 39			12 52	
Eastbourne 4	a	12 25		12 34	12 39	12 44			12 57	
	d	12 31		12 40	12 47			12 58	13 04	13 19
Hampden Park 4	d			12a44				13 02	13 08	13a23
Polegate	d	12 37			12 54			13 06	13 12	
Berwick	d								13 18	
Glynde	d								13 23	
Seaford	d						12 58			
Bishopstone	d						13 00			
Newhaven Harbour	d						13 03			
Newhaven Town	d						13 05			
Southease	d									
Lewes 4	a	12 49			13 07		13 14	13 19	13 29	
	d	12 50	12 58		13 07		13 14	13 20	13 29	
Falmer	d		13 05				13 21		13 36	
Moulsecoomb	d		13 08				13 24		13 39	
London Road (Brighton)	d		13 10				13 27		13 42	
Brighton 10	a		13 14		13 20		13 30		13 45	
Cooksbridge	d									
Plumpton	d							13 28		
Wivelsfield 4	a							13 35		
Haywards Heath 3	a	13 05						13 40		
Gatwick Airport 10	a	13 24						13 55		
East Croydon	a	13 40						14 11		
London Bridge 4	a									
Clapham Junction 10	a	13 49						14 21		
London Victoria 15	a	13 57						14 28		

Table 189R

Saturdays

14 December to 17 May

Ashford, Hastings, Eastbourne, Seaford and Lewes - Brighton, Haywards Heath and London

Network Diagram - see first Page of Table 189

Station		SN	SN ■	SN	SN ■	SN	SN ■	SN	SN ■	SN ■	SN ■	SN	SN ■	SN	SN ■	SN	SN ■	SN	SN ■
Ashford International	d					12 33										13 33			
Ham Street	d					12 41										13 41			
Appledore (Kent)	d					12 45										13 45			
Rye	a					12 54										13 54			
	d					12 55										13 55			
Winchelsea	d															13 59			
Doleham	d																		
Three Oaks	d					13 06													
Ore	d		12 50							13 22			13 50						
Hastings ■	a		12 53			13 13				13 25			13 53			14 13			
	d		12 55			13 14				13 26			13 55			14 14			
St Leonards Warrior Sq ■	d		12 58			13 17				13 29			13 58			14 17			
Bexhill ■	d		13 05			13 24				13 35			14 05			14 24			
Collington	d		13 07							13 37			14 07						
Cooden Beach	d		13 10							13 40			14 10						
Normans Bay	d									13 43									
Pevensey Bay	d																		
Pevensey & Westham	d		13 16							13 48			14 16						
Hampden Park ■	d		13 20		13 29		13 39			13 52			14 20		14 29		14 39		
Eastbourne ■	a		13 25		13 34	13 39	13 44			13 57			14 25		14 34	14 39	14 44		
	d		13 31		13 40	13 47			13 58	14 04	14 19		14 31		14 40	14 47			14 58
Hampden Park ■	d				13a44				14 02	14 08	14a23				14a44				15 02
Polegate	d		13 37			13 54			14 06	14 12			14 37			14 54			15 06
Berwick	d									14 18									
Glynde	d									14 23									
Seaford	d	13 25						13 58				14 25						14 58	
Bishopstone	d	13 27						14 00				14 27						15 00	
Newhaven Harbour	d	13 30						14 03				14 30						15 03	
Newhaven Town	d	13 32						14 05				14 32						15 05	
Southease	d	13 36										14 36							
Lewes ■	a	13 44	13 49			14 07		14 14	14 19	14 29		14 44	14 49			15 07		15 14	15 19
	d	13 44	13 50	13 58		14 07		14 14	14 20	14 29		14 44	14 50	14 58		15 07		15 14	15 20
Falmer	d	13 51		14 05				14 21		14 36		14 51		15 05				15 21	
Moulsecoomb	d	13 54		14 08				14 24		14 39		14 54		15 08				15 24	
London Road (Brighton)	d	13 57		14 10				14 27		14 42		14 57		15 10				15 27	
Brighton ■	a	14 00		14 14		14 20		14 30		14 45		15 00		15 14		15 20		15 30	
Cooksbridge	d																		
Plumpton	d								14 28										15 28
Wivelsfield ■	a								14 35										15 35
Haywards Heath ■	a		14 05						14 40				15 05						15 40
Gatwick Airport ■	a		14 24						14 55				15 24						15 55
East Croydon	a		14 40						15 11				15 40						16 11
London Bridge ■	a																		
Clapham Junction ■	a		14 49						15 20				15 49						16 20
London Victoria ■	a		14 57						15 28				15 57						16 28

Station		SN ■	SN ■	SN	SN ■	SN	SN ■	SN	SN ■	SN	SN ■	SN ■	SN ■	SN	SN ■	SN	SN ■	SN	SN ■
Ashford International	d							14 33										15 33	
Ham Street	d							14 41										15 41	
Appledore (Kent)	d							14 45										15 45	
Rye	a							14 54										15 54	
	d							14 55										15 55	
Winchelsea	d																	15 59	
Doleham	d																		
Three Oaks	d							15 06											
Ore	d	14 22			14 50							15 22			15 50				
Hastings ■	a	14 25			14 53			15 13				15 25			15 53			16 13	
	d	14 26			14 55			15 14				15 26			15 55			16 14	
St Leonards Warrior Sq ■	d	14 29			14 58			15 17				15 29			15 58			16 17	
Bexhill ■	d	14 35			15 05			15 24				15 35			16 05			16 24	
Collington	d	14 37			15 07							15 37			16 07				
Cooden Beach	d	14 40			15 10							15 40			16 10				
Normans Bay	d	14 43										15 43							
Pevensey Bay	d																		
Pevensey & Westham	d	14 48			15 16							15 48			16 16				
Hampden Park ■	d	14 52			15 20		15 29		15 39			15 52			16 20		16 29		16 39
Eastbourne ■	a	14 57			15 25		15 34	15 39	15 44			15 57			16 25		16 34	16 39	16 44
	d	15 04	15 19		15 31		15 40	15 47			15 58	16 04	16 19		16 31		16 40	16 47	
Hampden Park ■	d	15 08	15a23				15a44				16 02	16 08	16a23				16a44		
Polegate	d	15 12			15 37			15 54			16 06	16 12			16 37			16 54	
Berwick	d	15 18										16 18							
Glynde	d	15 23										16 23							
Seaford	d			15 25						15 58				16 25					
Bishopstone	d			15 27						16 00				16 27					
Newhaven Harbour	d			15 30						16 03				16 30					
Newhaven Town	d			15 32						16 05				16 32					
Southease	d			15 36										16 36					
Lewes ■	a	15 29		15 44	15 49			16 07		16 14	16 18	16 29		16 44	16 49			17 07	
	d	15 29		15 44	15 50	15 58		16 07		16 14	16 20	16 29		16 44	16 50	16 58		17 07	
Falmer	d	15 36		15 51		16 05				16 21		16 36		16 51		17 05			
Moulsecoomb	d	15 39		15 54		16 08				16 24		16 39		16 54		17 08			
London Road (Brighton)	d	15 42		15 57		16 10				16 27		16 42		16 57		17 10			
Brighton ■	a	15 45		16 00		16 14		16 20		16 30		16 45		17 00		17 14		17 20	
Cooksbridge	d																		
Plumpton	d										16 28								
Wivelsfield ■	a										16 35								
Haywards Heath ■	a				16 05						16 40				17 05				
Gatwick Airport ■	a				16 24						16 55				17 24				
East Croydon	a				16 40						17 11				17 40				
London Bridge ■	a																		
Clapham Junction ■	a				16 49						17 20				17 49				
London Victoria ■	a				16 57						17 28				17 57				

Table 189R

Saturdays

14 December to 17 May

Ashford, Hastings, Eastbourne, Seaford and Lewes - Brighton, Haywards Heath and London

Network Diagram - see first Page of Table 189

Station		SN	SN 1	SN 1	SN 1	SN	SN 1	SN	SN 1	SN
Ashford International	d									16 33
Ham Street	d									16 41
Appledore (Kent)	d									16 45
Rye	a									16 54
	d									16 55
Winchelsea	d									
Doleham	d									
Three Oaks	d									17 06
Ore	d			16 22			16 50			
Hastings 4	a			16 25			16 53			17 13
	d			16 26			16 55			17 14
St Leonards Warrior Sq 4	d			16 29			16 58			17 17
Bexhill 4	d			16 35			17 05			17 24
Collington	d			16 37			17 07			
Cooden Beach	d			16 40			17 10			
Normans Bay	d			16 43						
Pevensey Bay	d									
Pevensey & Westham	d			16 48			17 16			
Hampden Park 4	d			16 52			17 20		17 29	
Eastbourne 4	a			16 57			17 25		17 34	17 39
	d		16 58	17 04	17 19		17 31		17 40	17 47
Hampden Park 4	d		17 02	17 08	17a23				17a44	
Polegate	d		17 06	17 12			17 37			17 54
Berwick	d			17 18						
Glynde	d			17 23						
Seaford	d	16 58				17 25				
Bishopstone	d	17 00				17 27				
Newhaven Harbour	d	17 03				17 30				
Newhaven Town	d	17 05				17 32				
Southease	d					17 36				
Lewes 4	a	17 14	17 18	17 29		17 44	17 49			18 07
	d	17 14	17 20	17 29		17 44	17 50	17 58		18 07
Falmer	d	17 21		17 36		17 51		18 05		
Moulsecoomb	d	17 24		17 39		17 54		18 08		
London Road (Brighton)	d	17 27		17 42		17 57		18 10		
Brighton 10	a	17 30		17 45		18 00		18 14		18 20
Cooksbridge	d									
Plumpton	d		17 28							
Wivelsfield 4	a		17 35							
Haywards Heath 3	a		17 40				18 05			
Gatwick Airport 10	a		17 55				18 24			
East Croydon	a		18 11				18 40			
London Bridge 4	a									
Clapham Junction 10	a		18 20				18 49			
London Victoria 15	a		18 28				18 57			

Station		SN 1	SN	SN 1	SN 1	SN 1	SN	SN 1	SN	SN 1
Ashford International	d									
Ham Street	d									
Appledore (Kent)	d									
Rye	a									
	d									
Winchelsea	d									
Doleham	d									
Three Oaks	d									
Ore	d				17 22			17 50		
Hastings 4	a				17 25			17 53		
	d				17 26			17 55		
St Leonards Warrior Sq 4	d				17 29			17 58		
Bexhill 4	d				17 35			18 05		
Collington	d				17 37			18 07		
Cooden Beach	d				17 40			18 10		
Normans Bay	d				17 43					
Pevensey Bay	d									
Pevensey & Westham	d				17 48			18 16		
Hampden Park 4	d	17 39			17 52			18 20		18 29
Eastbourne 4	a	17 44			17 57			18 25		18 34
	d			17 58	18 04	18 19		18 31		18 40
Hampden Park 4	d			18 02	18 08	18a23				18a44
Polegate	d			18 06	18 12			18 37		
Berwick	d				18 18					
Glynde	d				18 23					
Seaford	d		17 58				18 25			
Bishopstone	d		18 00				18 27			
Newhaven Harbour	d		18 03				18 30			
Newhaven Town	d		18 05				18 32			
Southease	d						18 36			
Lewes 4	a		18 14	18 18	18 29		18 44	18 49		
	d		18 14	18 20	18 29		18 44	18 50	18 58	
Falmer	d		18 21		18 36		18 51		19 05	
Moulsecoomb	d		18 24		18 39		18 54		19 08	
London Road (Brighton)	d		18 27		18 42		18 57		19 10	
Brighton 10	a		18 30		18 45		19 00		19 14	
Cooksbridge	d									
Plumpton	d			18 28						
Wivelsfield 4	a			18 35						
Haywards Heath 3	a			18 40				19 05		
Gatwick Airport 10	a			18 55				19 25		
East Croydon	a			19 11				19 41		
London Bridge 4	a									
Clapham Junction 10	a			19 20				19 51		
London Victoria 15	a			19 28				19 58		

Station		SN	SN 1	SN	SN 1	SN 1	SN 1	SN	SN 1	SN
Ashford International	d	17 33								
Ham Street	d	17 41								
Appledore (Kent)	d	17 45								
Rye	a	17 54								
	d	17 55								
Winchelsea	d	17 59								
Doleham	d									
Three Oaks	d									
Ore	d					18 22			18 50	
Hastings 4	a	18 13				18 25			18 53	
	d	18 14				18 26			18 55	
St Leonards Warrior Sq 4	d	18 17				18 29			18 58	
Bexhill 4	d	18 24				18 35			19 05	
Collington	d					18 37			19 07	
Cooden Beach	d					18 40			19 10	
Normans Bay	d					18 43				
Pevensey Bay	d									
Pevensey & Westham	d					18 48			19 16	
Hampden Park 4	d		18 39			18 52			19 20	
Eastbourne 4	a	18 39	18 44			18 57			19 25	
	d	18 47			18 58	19 04	19 19		19 31	
Hampden Park 4	d				19 02	19 08	19a23			
Polegate	d	18 54			19 06	19 12			19 37	
Berwick	d					19 18				
Glynde	d					19 23				
Seaford	d			18 58				19 25		
Bishopstone	d			19 00				19 27		
Newhaven Harbour	d			19 03				19 30		
Newhaven Town	d			19 05				19 32		
Southease	d							19 36		
Lewes 4	a	19 07		19 14	19 18	19 29		19 44	19 49	
	d	19 07		19 14	19 20	19 29		19 44	19 50	19 58
Falmer	d			19 21		19 36		19 51		20 05
Moulsecoomb	d			19 24		19 39		19 54		20 08
London Road (Brighton)	d			19 27		19 42		19 57		20 10
Brighton 10	a	19 20		19 30		19 45		20 00		20 14
Cooksbridge	d									
Plumpton	d				19 28					
Wivelsfield 4	a				19 35				20 02	
Haywards Heath 3	a				19 40				20 07	
Gatwick Airport 10	a				19 55				20 25	
East Croydon	a				20 11				20 41	
London Bridge 4	a									
Clapham Junction 10	a				20 20				20 50	
London Victoria 15	a				20 27				20 58	

Station		SN 1	SN	SN 1	SN	SN 1	SN 1	SN	SN 1	SN
Ashford International	d		18 33							
Ham Street	d		18 41							
Appledore (Kent)	d		18 45							
Rye	a		18 54							
	d		18 55							
Winchelsea	d									
Doleham	d									
Three Oaks	d		19 06							
Ore	d					19 22			19 50	
Hastings 4	a		19 13			19 25			19 53	
	d		19 14			19 26			19 55	
St Leonards Warrior Sq 4	d		19 17			19 29			19 58	
Bexhill 4	d		19 24			19 35			20 05	
Collington	d					19 37			20 07	
Cooden Beach	d					19 40			20 10	
Normans Bay	d					19 43				
Pevensey Bay	d									
Pevensey & Westham	d					19 48			20 16	
Hampden Park 4	d	19 29		19 39		19 52			20 20	
Eastbourne 4	a	19 34	19 39	19 44		19 57			20 25	
	d	19 40	19 47			20 04	20 19		20 31	
Hampden Park 4	d	19a44				20 08	20a23			
Polegate	d		19 54			20 12			20 37	
Berwick	d					20 18				
Glynde	d					20 23				
Seaford	d				19 58			20 28		
Bishopstone	d				20 00			20 30		
Newhaven Harbour	d				20 03			20 33		
Newhaven Town	d				20 05			20 35		
Southease	d									←
Lewes 4	a		20 07		20 14	20 29		20 44	20 49	20 44
	d		20 07		20 14	20 29		20 53	20 50	20 53
Falmer	d				20 21	20 36		→		21 00
Moulsecoomb	d				20 24	20 39				21 03
London Road (Brighton)	d				20 27	20 42				21 05
Brighton 10	a		20 20		20 30	20 45				21 09
Cooksbridge	d									
Plumpton	d									
Wivelsfield 4	a								21 04	
Haywards Heath 3	a								21 09	
Gatwick Airport 10	a								21 26	
East Croydon	a								21 41	
London Bridge 4	a									
Clapham Junction 10	a								21 51	
London Victoria 15	a								21 58	

Table 189R

Saturdays

14 December to 17 May

Ashford, Hastings, Eastbourne, Seaford and Lewes - Brighton, Haywards Heath and London

Network Diagram - see first Page of Table 189

		SN 1	SN	SN 1	SN	SN 1	SN 1	SN	SN 1 A ⚱	SN	SN	SN 1	SN	SN 1	SN	SN 1	SN	SN 1	SN	SN 1	SN	SN 1	SN	SN 1	SN	SN 1	SN 1
Ashford International ⚌	d		19 33								20 33								21 33				22 34				
Ham Street	d		19 41								20 41								21 41				22 42				
Appledore (Kent)	d		19 45								20 45								21 45				22 46				
Rye	a		19 54								20 54								21 54				22 55				
	d		19 55								20 55								21 57				22 55				
Winchelsea	d		19 59																22 00				22 59				
Doleham	d																						23 05				
Three Oaks	d										21 06												23 09				
Ore	d					20 22			20 50					21 22								22 22	23 14				
Hastings 4	a		20 13			20 25			20 53		21 13			21 25					22 14			22 25	23 17				
	d		20 14			20 26			20 55		21 14			21 26		21 42			22 15			22 26					23 22
St Leonards Warrior Sq 4	d		20 17			20 29			20 58		21 17			21 29		21 45			22 18			22 29					23 25
Bexhill 4	d		20 24			20 35			21 05		21 24			21 35		21 52			22 25			22 38					23 31
Collington	d					20 37			21 07					21 37		21 54						22 40					23 33
Cooden Beach	d					20 40			21 10					21 40		21 57						22 43					23 36
Normans Bay	d					20 43																22 46					
Pevensey Bay	d																										
Pevensey & Westham	d					20 48			21 16					21 46		22 03						22 51					23 42
Hampden Park 4	d	20 29		20 43		20 52			21 20			21 43		21 51		22 07				22 43		22 55		23 09		23 42	23 47
Eastbourne 4	a	20 34	20 39	20 48		20 57			21 25		21 39	21 48		21 56		22 12			22 40	22 48		23 00		23 14		23 47	23 52
	d		20 45			21 04	21 19		21 31		21 45			22 04		22 18		22 21	22 45			23 05		23 20			23 56
Hampden Park 4	d					21 08	21a23							22 08				22a25				23 09		23a24			00 01
Polegate	d		20 52			21 12			21 37		21 52			22 12		22 25			22 52			23 13					00 05
Berwick	d					21 18								22 18								23 18					
Glynde	d					21 23								22 23								23 24					
Seaford	d				20 58			21 28					21 58		22 20						22 58				23 25		
Bishopstone	d				21 00			21 30					22 00		22 22						23 00				23 27		
Newhaven Harbour	d				21 03			21 33					22 03		22 25						23 03				23 30		
Newhaven Town ⛴	d				21 05			21 35					22 05		22 27						23 05				23 32		
Southease	d									←							←										
Lewes 4	a		21 07		21 14	21 29		21 44	21 49	21 44	22 07		22 14	22 29	22 35	22 38	22 35		23 07		23 14	23 29			23 40		00 17
	d		21 07		21 14	21 29		21 53	21 50	21 53	22 07		22 14	22 29	22 42	22 40	22 42		23 07		23 14	23 30			23 40		00 18
Falmer	d				21 21	21 36		→		22 00			22 21	22 36	→		22 49				23 21	23 37			23 47		00 25
Moulsecoomb	d				21 24	21 39				22 03			22 24	22 39			22 52				23 24	23 40			23 50		00 28
London Road (Brighton)	d				21 27	21 42				22 05			22 27	22 42			22 54				23 27	23 42			23 53		00 30
Brighton 10	a		21 20		21 30	21 45				22 09	22 20		22 31	22 45			22 58		23 20		23 31	23 46			23 56		00 34
Cooksbridge	d																										
Plumpton	d															22 48											
Wivelsfield 4	a								22 02							22 54											
Haywards Heath 3	a								22 06							22 58											
Gatwick Airport 10 ✈	a								22 24							23 12											
East Croydon 🚌	a								22 40							23 29											
London Bridge 4 ⊖	a																										
Clapham Junction 10	a								22 49							23 41											
London Victoria 15 ⊖	a								22 57							23 52											

A ⚱ from Lewes

Table 189R

Sundays

8 December to 11 May

Ashford, Hastings, Eastbourne, Seaford and Lewes - Brighton, Haywards Heath and London

Network Diagram - see first Page of Table 189

		SN	SN	SN	SN	SN	SN	SN	SN	SN	SN	SN	SN	SN	SN	SN	SN	SN	SN
		1	1	1 A 🛒		1		1		1 A 🛒	1				1 A 🛒			1	
Ashford International	d																		
Ham Street	d																		
Appledore (Kent)	d																		
Rye	a																		
	d																		
Winchelsea	d																		
Doleham	d																		
Three Oaks	d																		
Ore	d														08 15				
Hastings 4	a														08 18				
	d														08 19				
St Leonards Warrior Sq 4	d														08 22				
Bexhill 4	d														08 30				
Collington	d														08 32				
Cooden Beach	d														08 35				
Normans Bay	d																		
Pevensey Bay	d																		
Pevensey & Westham	d														08 41				
Hampden Park 4	d		00 11					07 45							08 46		08 53		
Eastbourne 4	a		00 16					07 50							08 51		08 58		
	d			06 58		07 26	07 30			07 55	08 26		08 34		08 59			09 26	
Hampden Park 4	d	00 01		07 02		07a30	07 34				08a30		08 38					09a30	
Polegate	d	00 05		07 06			07 38			08 02			08 42		09 06				
Berwick	d						07 44						08 48						
Glynde	d						07 49						08 53						
Seaford	d								07 57			08 27		08 57					09 27
Bishopstone	d								07 59			08 29		08 59					09 29
Newhaven Harbour	d								08 03			08 33		09 03					09 33
Newhaven Town	d								08 04			08 34		09 04					09 34
Southease	d								08 09					09 09		←			
Lewes 4	a	00 17		07 18			07 55		08 15	08 18		08 43	08 59	09 15	09 18	09 15			09 43
	d	00 18		07 20	07 22		07 56		08 22	08 22		08 44	09 00	09 22	09 20	09 22			09 44
Falmer	d	00 25			07 29		08 03		08 29			08 51		→		09 29			09 51
Moulsecoomb	d	00 28			07 32		08 07		08 32			08 54				09 32			09 54
London Road (Brighton)	d	00 30			07 34		08 09		08 34			08 56				09 34			09 56
Brighton 10	a	00 34			07 38		08 13		08 38			09 00	09 12			09 38			10 00
Cooksbridge	d																		
Plumpton	d			07 28						08 30					09 28				
Wivelsfield 4	a			07 35						08 37					09 34				
Haywards Heath 3	a			07 39						08 41					09 38				
Gatwick Airport 10 ✈	a			07 51						08 53					09 52				
East Croydon	a			08 09						09 09					10 08				
London Bridge 4 ⊖	a																		
Clapham Junction 10	a			08 27						09 19					10 18				
London Victoria 15 ⊖	a			08 35						09 26					10 26				

		SN	SN	SN	SN	SN	SN	SN	SN	SN	SN	SN	SN	SN		SN	SN	SN	SN	SN
				1 A 🛒			1				1 A 🛒			1					1	
Ashford International	d	08 16							09 22								18 22			
Ham Street	d	08 24							09 30								18 30			
Appledore (Kent)	d	08 28							09 34								18 34			
Rye	a	08 38							09 43								18 43			
	d	08 40							09 45								18 45			
Winchelsea	d	08 43																		
Doleham	d	08 50																		
Three Oaks	d	08 53																		
Ore	d	08 59		09 15							10 15								19 15	
Hastings 4	a	09 02		09 18					10 02		10 18						19 02		19 18	
	d	09 03		09 19					10 03		10 19						19 03		19 19	
St Leonards Warrior Sq 4	d	09 06		09 22					10 06		10 22						19 06		19 22	
Bexhill 4	d	09 13		09 30					10 13		10 30						19 13		19 30	
Collington	d			09 32							10 32								19 32	
Cooden Beach	d			09 35							10 35								19 35	
Normans Bay	d																			
Pevensey Bay	d																			
Pevensey & Westham	d			09 41							10 41				and at the same minutes past each hour until				19 41	
Hampden Park 4	d			09 46		09 53					10 46		10 53						19 46	
Eastbourne 4	a	09 29		09 51		09 58			10 29		10 51		10 58				19 29		19 51	
	d	09 34		09 59			10 18		10 34		10 59			11 14			19 34		19 59	
Hampden Park 4	d	09 38					10a22		10 38					11a18			19 38			
Polegate	d	09 42		10 06					10 42		11 06						19 42		20 06	
Berwick	d	09 48							10 48								19 48			
Glynde	d	09 53							10 53								19 53			
Seaford	d		09 57					10 27		10 57						19 27		19 57		
Bishopstone	d		09 59					10 29		10 59						19 29		19 59		
Newhaven Harbour	d		10 03					10 33		11 03						19 33		20 03		
Newhaven Town	d		10 04					10 34		11 04						19 34		20 04		
Southease	d		10 09		←					11 09		←						20 09		←
Lewes 4	a	09 59	10 15	10 18	10 15			10 43	10 59	11 15	11 18	11 15				19 43	19 59	20 15	20 18	20 15
	d	10 00	10 22	10 20	10 22			10 44	11 00	11 22	11 20	11 22				19 44	20 00	20 22	20 20	20 22
Falmer	d		→		10 29			10 51		→		11 29				19 51		→		20 29
Moulsecoomb	d				10 32			10 54				11 32				19 54				20 32
London Road (Brighton)	d				10 34			10 56				11 34				19 56				20 34
Brighton 10	a	10 12			10 38			11 00	11 12			11 38				20 00	20 12			20 38
Cooksbridge	d																			
Plumpton	d			10 28							11 28								20 28	
Wivelsfield 4	a			10 35							11 35								20 35	
Haywards Heath 3	a			10 39							11 39								20 39	
Gatwick Airport 10 ✈	a			10 52							11 52								20 52	
East Croydon	a			11 08							12 08								21 08	
London Bridge 4 ⊖	a																			
Clapham Junction 10	a			11 18							12 18								21 18	
London Victoria 15 ⊖	a			11 26							12 26								21 26	

A 🛒 from Lewes

Table 189R

Sundays
8 December to 11 May

Ashford, Hastings, Eastbourne, Seaford and Lewes - Brighton, Haywards Heath and London

Network Diagram - see first Page of Table 189

		SN	SN ■	SN	SN	SN	SN ■	SN	SN	SN ■	SN	SN	SN	SN ■	SN	SN ■	SN	SN	SN	SN ■	SN	SN	SN ■	SN ■	SN
Ashford International	d				19 22							20 22						21 22			22 34				
Ham Street	d				19 30							20 30						21 30			22 42				
Appledore (Kent)	d				19 34							20 34						21 34			22 46				
Rye	a				19 43							20 43						21 43			22 55				
	d				19 45							20 45						21 45			22 55				
Winchelsea	d																				22 59				
Doleham	d																				23 05				
Three Oaks	d																				23 09				
Ore	d						20 15							21 14						22 14	23 14				
Hastings 4	a				20 02		20 18					21 02		21 17				22 02		22 17	23 17				
	d				20 03		20 19					21 03		21 18				22 03		22 18				23 22	
St Leonards Warrior Sq 4	d				20 06		20 22					21 06		21 21				22 06		22 21				23 25	
Bexhill 4	d				20 13		20 30					21 13		21 28				22 13		22 28				23 31	
Collington	d						20 32							21 30						22 30				23 33	
Cooden Beach	d						20 35							21 33						22 33				23 36	
Normans Bay	d																								
Pevensey Bay	d																								
Pevensey & Westham	d						20 41							21 39						22 39				23 42	
Hampden Park 4	d	19 53					20 46		20 53					21 43	21 53					22 43		22 53		23 47	23 53
Eastbourne 4	a	19 58			20 29		20 51		20 58			21 29		21 49	21 58			22 29		22 49		22 58		23 52	23 58
	d		20 14		20 34		20 59			21 14		21 34		21 59		22 15		22 34		22 59			23 26		
Hampden Park 4	d		20a18		20 38					21a18		21 38				22a19		22 38					23a30		
Polegate	d				20 42		21 06					21 42		22 06				22 42		23 06					
Berwick	d				20 48							21 48						22 48							
Glynde	d				20 53							21 53						22 53							
Seaford	d			20 27		20 57					21 27		21 53				22 27		22 53						
Bishopstone	d			20 29		20 59					21 29		21 55				22 29		22 55						
Newhaven Harbour	d			20 33		21 03					21 33		21 59				22 33		22 59						
Newhaven Town	d			20 34		21 04					21 34		22 00				22 34		23 00						
Southease	d							←																	
Lewes 4	a			20 43	20 59	21 13	21 18	21 13			21 43	21 59	22 09	22 18			22 43	22 59	23 09	23 18					
	d			20 44	21 00	21 22	21 20	21 22			21 44	22 00	22 10	22 19			22 44	23 00	23 10	23 19					
Falmer	d			20 51		→		21 29			21 51		22 17	22 26			22 51		23 17	23 26					
Moulsecoomb	d			20 54				21 32			21 54		22 20	22 29			22 54		23 20	23 29					
London Road (Brighton)	d			20 56				21 34			21 56		22 22	22 31			22 56		23 22	23 31					
Brighton 10	a			21 00	21 12			21 38			22 00	22 12	22 26	22 35			23 00	23 12	23 26	23 35					
Cooksbridge	d																								
Plumpton	d						21 28																		
Wivelsfield 4	a						21 35																		
Haywards Heath 3	a						21 39																		
Gatwick Airport 10 ✈	a						21 52																		
East Croydon	a						22 08																		
London Bridge 4 ⊖	a																								
Clapham Junction 10	a						22 18																		
London Victoria 15 ⊖	a						22 26																		

Route Diagram for Table 194

HIGH SPEED SERVICES

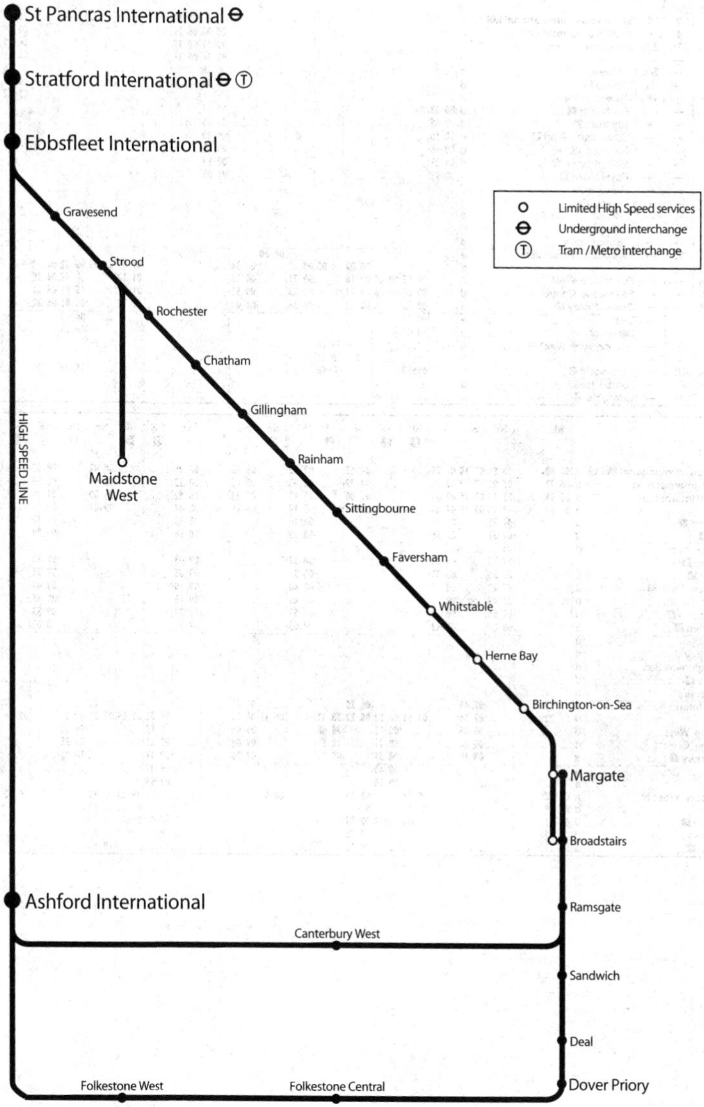

TOCs operating on this network - Southeastern (SE)

Table 194

Mondays to Fridays

9 December to 16 May

St Pancras International - Kent High Speed Domestic Services

Network Diagram - see first Page of Table 194

Miles	Miles	Miles	Miles			SE	SE MX	SE MO	SE MX [1]	SE MX [1]	SE MO [1]	SE	SE MX [1]	SE MX	SE MX		SE MX [1]	SE MX [1]	SE [1]	SE [1]	SE	SE [1]	SE [1]	SE [1]	SE
0	0	0	0	**St Pancras International [15] ⊖**	d										00 12						06 22				
6	6	6	6	**Stratford International ⊖**	d									00 02	00 19						06 29				
22¾	22¾	22¾	22¾	**Ebbsfleet International**	a									00 12	00 30						06 39				
—	—	—	—		d							00 01		00 14	00 31						06 41				
24¾	—	—	24¾	Gravesend [4]	d									00 18							06 46				
32	—	—	32	Strood [4]	d									00 28							06 56				
—	—	—	44¼	Maidstone West	d																07a12				
33	—	—	—	Rochester [4]	d	00 03								00 33											
33½	—	—	—	Chatham [4]	d	00 05								00 35											
35¼	—	—	—	Gillingham (Kent) [4]	d	00 10								00 40											
38¼	—	—	—	Rainham (Kent)	d	00 15								00 45											
44	—	—	—	Sittingbourne [4]	d	00 23								00 53											
51¾	—	—	—	**Faversham [2]**	a	00 33								01 03											
58¾	—	—	—	Whitstable	d																				
62½	—	—	—	Herne Bay	d																				
70½	—	—	—	Birchington-on-Sea	d																				
73½	—	—	—	Margate [4]	d																				
76¾	—	—	—	**Broadstairs**	a																				
—	56	56	—	**Ashford International**	a							00 20			00 50										
—	—	—	—		d				00 02	00 05	00 05		00 34				01 02	01 05	05 32	06 02		06 30	06 33	07 02	07 05
—	69¼	—	—	Folkestone West	d		00 05	00 05	00 18		00 21		00 50				01 18		05 48	06 18		06 46		07 18	
—	70	—	—	Folkestone Central	d		00 08	00 08	00 21		00 23		00 53				01 21		05 51	06 21		06 49		07 21	
—	77¼	—	—	**Dover Priory [4]**	a		00 18	00 20	00 32		00 34		01 04				01 32		06 01	06 32		07 00		07 32	
—	—	—	—	Deal	a		00 34												06 19			07 25		08 00	
—	—	—	—	Sandwich	a		00 41												06 25			07 32		08 06	
—	—	70¼	—	**Canterbury West [4]**	a					00 26								01 26					06 54		07 26
—	—	—	—		d					00 27													06 55		
—	—	87¾	—	Ramsgate [4]	d		00a54			00a48									06a39			07a45	07a17	08a22	
—	—	87¾	—	Broadstairs	d																				
—	—	91	—	**Margate [4]**	a																				

		SE		SE	SE	SE	SE [1]	SE [1]	SE	SE [1]	SE	SE [1]	SE		SE	SE [1]	SE [1]	SE	SE [1]	SE	SE [1]	SE	SE	SE [1]	
St Pancras International [15] ⊖	d	06 40		06 55	07 10	07 25			07 42		07 52		08 10		08 25			08 42		08 52		09 10	09 25		
Stratford International ⊖	d	06 47		07 02	07 17	07 32			07 49		08 02		08 17		08 32			08 49		08 59		09 17	09 32		
Ebbsfleet International	a	06 58		07 12	07 28	07 42			08 00		08 13		08 28		08 42			09 00		09 09		09 28	09 42		
	d	06 59		07 14	07 29	07 44			08 01		08 14		08 29		08 44			09 01		09 14		09 29	09 44		
Gravesend [4]	d			07 21		07 48					08 18				08 48					09 18			09 48		
Strood [4]	d			07 31		07 58					08 28				08 58					09 28			09 58		
Maidstone West	d																								
Rochester [4]	d			07 35		08 03					08 33				09 03					09 33			10 03		
Chatham [4]	d			07 38		08 05					08 35				09 05					09 35			10 05		
Gillingham (Kent) [4]	d			07 42		08 10					08 40				09 10					09 40			10 10		
Rainham (Kent)	d			07 47		08 15					08 45				09 15					09 45			10 15		
Sittingbourne [4]	d			07 56		08 23					08 53				09 23					09 53			10 23		
Faversham [2]	a			08 05		08 33					09 03				09 33					10 03			10 33		
Whitstable	d																								
Herne Bay	d																								
Birchington-on-Sea	d																								
Margate [4]	d																								
Broadstairs	a																								
Ashford International	a	07 18			07 48				08 20				08 48					09 20				09 48			
	d	07 22			07 50		07 53	08 02	08 22	08 32		08 35	08 52			09 02	09 05	09 22	09 36		09 39	09 52		10 02	
Folkestone West	d				08 03			08 18		08 48			09 05			09 18			09 52			10 05		10 18	
Folkestone Central	d				08 06			08 21		08 51			09 08			09 21			09 55			10 08		10 21	
Dover Priory [4]	a				08 18			08 31		09 02			09 20			09 31			10 05			10 20		10 31	
Deal	a							08 49								09 49								10 49	
Sandwich	a							08 55								09 55								10 55	
Canterbury West [4]	a	07 38					08 14		08 38			08 56					09 23	09 38			10 00				
	d	07 39					08 15		08 39								09 24	09 39							
Ramsgate [4]	d	08 01					08a38	09a08	08 59							10a08	09a45	09 59						11a08	
Broadstairs	d	08 06							09 05									10 05							
Margate [4]	a	08 11							09 10									10 10							

Table 194

Mondays to Fridays

9 December to 16 May

St Pancras International - Kent High Speed Domestic Services

Network Diagram - see first Page of Table 194

		SE [1]	SE	SE [1]	SE	SE [1]	SE	SE	SE [1]		SE [1]	SE	SE [1]	SE	SE [1]	SE	SE	SE [1]	SE [1]	SE		SE [1]	SE	SE [1]	SE
St Pancras International [15] ⊖	d		09 42		09 55		10 10	10 22				10 42		10 52		11 12	11 25			11 42			11 55		12 12
Stratford International ⊖	d		09 49		10 02		10 17	10 32				10 49		10 59		11 19	11 32			11 49			12 02		12 19
Ebbsfleet International	a		10 00		10 12		10 28	10 43				11 00		11 09		11 30	11 42			12 00			12 12		12 30
	d		10 01		10 14		10 29	10 44				11 01		11 14		11 31	11 44			12 01			12 14		12 31
Gravesend [4]	d				10 18			10 48						11 18			11 48						12 18		
Strood [4]	d				10 28			10 58						11 28			11 58						12 28		
Maidstone West	d																								
Rochester [4]	d				10 33			11 03						11 33			12 03						12 33		
Chatham [4]	d				10 35			11 05						11 35			12 05						12 35		
Gillingham (Kent) [4]	d				10 40			11 10						11 40			12 10						12 40		
Rainham (Kent)	d				10 45			11 15						11 45			12 15						12 45		
Sittingbourne [4]	d				10 53			11 23						11 53			12 23						12 53		
Faversham [2]	a				11 03			11 33						12 03			12 33						13 03		
Whitstable	d																								
Herne Bay	d																								
Birchington-on-Sea	d																								
Margate [4]	d																								
Broadstairs	a																								
Ashford International	a		10 20				10 48					11 20				11 50				12 20					12 50
	d	10 05	10 22	10 33		10 36	10 52		11 02		11 05	11 22	11 32		11 35	11 52		12 02	12 05	12 22		12 32		12 35	12 52
Folkestone West	d			10 49			11 05		11 18				11 48			12 05		12 18				12 48			13 05
Folkestone Central	d			10 52			11 08		11 21				11 51			12 08		12 21				12 51			13 08
Dover Priory [4]	a			11 02			11 20		11 31				12 02			12 20		12 31				13 02			13 20
Deal	a								11 49									12 49							
Sandwich	a								11 55									12 55							
Canterbury West [4]	a	10 23	10 38			10 57					11 23	11 38			11 56				12 23	12 38				12 56	
	d	10 24	10 39								11 24	11 39							12 24	12 39					
Ramsgate [4]	d	10a45	10 59						12a08		11a45	11 59						13a08	12a45	12 59					
Broadstairs	d		11 05									12 05								13 05					
Margate [4]	a		11 10									12 10								13 10					

		SE	SE [1]	SE [1]	SE	SE [1]	SE		SE [1]	SE	SE	SE [1]	SE [1]	SE	SE [1]	SE	SE [1]	SE		SE	SE [1]	SE [1]	SE	SE [1]	SE
St Pancras International [15] ⊖	d	12 22			12 42		12 52			13 12	13 25			13 42		13 55		14 12		14 25			14 42		14 55
Stratford International ⊖	d	12 32			12 49		12 59			13 19	13 32			13 49		14 02		14 19		14 32			14 49		15 02
Ebbsfleet International	a	12 43			13 00		13 09			13 30	13 42			14 00		14 12		14 30		14 42			15 00		15 12
	d	12 44			13 01		13 14			13 31	13 44			14 01		14 14		14 31		14 44			15 01		15 14
Gravesend [4]	d	12 48					13 18				13 48					14 18				14 48					15 18
Strood [4]	d	12 58					13 28				13 58					14 28				14 58					15 28
Maidstone West	d																								
Rochester [4]	d	13 03					13 33				14 03					14 33				15 03					15 33
Chatham [4]	d	13 05					13 35				14 05					14 35				15 05					15 35
Gillingham (Kent) [4]	d	13 10					13 40				14 10					14 40				15 10					15 40
Rainham (Kent)	d	13 15					13 45				14 15					14 45				15 15					15 45
Sittingbourne [4]	d	13 23					13 53				14 23					14 53				15 23					15 53
Faversham [2]	a	13 33					14 03				14 33					15 03				15 33					16 03
Whitstable	d																								
Herne Bay	d																								
Birchington-on-Sea	d																								
Margate [4]	d																								
Broadstairs	a																								
Ashford International	a				13 20					13 50				14 20				14 50					15 20		
	d		13 02	13 05	13 22	13 32			13 35	13 52		14 02	14 05	14 22	14 32		14 35	14 52			15 02	15 05	15 22	15 32	
Folkestone West	d		13 18			13 48				14 05		14 18			14 48			15 05			15 18			15 48	
Folkestone Central	d		13 21			13 51				14 08		14 21			14 51			15 08			15 21			15 51	
Dover Priory [4]	a		13 31			14 02				14 20		14 31			15 02			15 20			15 31			16 01	
Deal	a		13 49									14 49									15 49			16 19	
Sandwich	a		13 55									14 55									15 55			16 25	
Canterbury West [4]	a			13 23	13 38				13 56				14 23	14 38			14 56					15 23	15 38		
	d			13 24	13 39								14 24	14 39								15 24	15 39		
Ramsgate [4]	d		14a08	13a45	13 59							15a08	14a45	14 59							16a14	15a45	15 59	16a38	
Broadstairs	d				14 05									15 05									16 05		
Margate [4]	a				14 10									15 10									16 10		

Table 194

Mondays to Fridays

9 December to 16 May

St Pancras International - Kent High Speed Domestic Services

Network Diagram - see first Page of Table 194

		SE 1	SE	SE		SE 1	SE 1	SE	SE 1	SE	SE 1	SE	SE	SE 1	SE 1		SE		SE 1	SE	SE	SE 1	SE		SE 1
St Pancras International 15 ⊖	d		15 12	15 25				15 42		15 55		16 10	16 25				16 40			16 58	17 08		17 12		
Stratford International ⊖	d		15 19	15 32				15 49		16 02		16 17	16 32				16 47			17 05	17 15		17 19		
Ebbsfleet International	a		15 30	15 42				16 00		16 12		16 28	16 43				16 58			17 15	17 27				
	d		15 31	15 44				16 01		16 14		16 29	16 44				16 59			17 16					
Gravesend 4	d			15 48						16 18			16 48							17 21					
Strood 4	d			15 58						16 28			16 58							17 31					
Maidstone West	d																								
Rochester 4	d			16 03						16 33			17 03							17 35					
Chatham 4	d			16 05						16 35			17 05							17 38					
Gillingham (Kent) 4	d			16 10						16 40			17 10							17 43					
Rainham (Kent)	d			16 15						16 45			17 15							17 48					
Sittingbourne 4	d			16 23						16 53			17 23							17 57					
Faversham 2	a			16 33						17 03			17 33							18 05					
Whitstable	d																								
Herne Bay	d																								
Birchington-on-Sea	d																								
Margate 4	d																								
Broadstairs	a																								
Ashford International	a		15 50					16 20				16 48					17 18						17 47		
	d	15 35	15 52			16 02	16 05	16 22	16 32		16 35	16 52		17 02	17 05		17 23	17 25	17 32			17 35	17 51	17 54	18 02
Folkestone West	d		16 05			16 18			16 48			17 05		17 18			17 36		17 48				18 04		18 18
Folkestone Central	d		16 08			16 21			16 51			17 08		17 21			17 39		17 51				18 07		18 21
Dover Priory 4	a		16 20			16 31			17 01			17 20		17 31			17 49		18 01				18 18		18 33
Deal	a					16 49			17 19					17 49			18 06		18 19						18 51
Sandwich	a					16 55			17 25					17 55			18 13		18 25						18 57
Canterbury West 4	a	15 56					16 23	16 38			16 56				17 26			17 40				17 58		18 09	
	d						16 24	16 39							17 27			17 41						18 11	
Ramsgate 4	d					17a14	16a46	16 59	17a38					18a08	17a48			18 00	18a40					18 30	19a12
Broadstairs	d							17 05										18 05						18 35	
Margate 4	a							17 10										18 12						18 42	

		SE		SE	SE	SE 1	SE		SE	SE	SE 1	SE 1	SE		SE	SE	SE	SE	SE 1	SE 1	SE		SE 1	SE	
St Pancras International 15 ⊖	d	17 16		17 25	17 38		17 42		17 46	17 55			18 12		18 16	18 19	18 25	18 38			18 42			18 55	
Stratford International ⊖	d	17 23		17 32	17 45		17 49		17 53	18 02			18 19		18 23	18 26	18 32	18 45			18 49			19 02	
Ebbsfleet International	a	17 33		17 42	17 57				18 03	18 12					18 33	18 37	18 42	18 57						19 12	
	d	17 35		17 43					18 05	18 13					18 35	18 37	18 44							19 14	
Gravesend 4	d	17 40							18 10						18 40									19 19	
Strood 4	d	17 50							18 20						18 50									19 29	
Maidstone West	d	18a05							18a35						19a05										
Rochester 4	d			18 01						18 31							19 03							19 34	
Chatham 4	d			18 04						18 34							19 06							19 37	
Gillingham (Kent) 4	d			18 09						18 39							19 11							19 42	
Rainham (Kent)	d			18 14						18 44							19 16							19 47	
Sittingbourne 4	d			18 23						18 52							19 24							19 54	
Faversham 2	a			18 31						19 00							19 32							20 03	
Whitstable	d			18 40						19 09							19 42								
Herne Bay	d			18 46						19 15							19 48								
Birchington-on-Sea	d			18 55						19 24							19 57								
Margate 4	d			19 02						19 30							20 04								
Broadstairs	a			19 08						19 36							20 09								
Ashford International	a						18 17						18 47			18 56					19 16				
	d					18 05	18 21	18 24			18 32	18 44	18 49			18 58			19 04	19 05	19 20	19 23	19 23		
Folkestone West	d						18 34					19 01				19 11				19 21	19 33		19 40		
Folkestone Central	d						18 37					19 04				19 14				19 24	19 36		19a45		
Dover Priory 4	a						18 48					19 15				19 26				19 35	19 48				
Deal	a						19 06					19 34								19 54	20 06				
Sandwich	a						19 13					19 41								20 00	20 13				
Canterbury West 4	a					18 26		18 39			18 53		19 04						19 25			19 38			
	d					18 27		18 41			18 54		19 08						19 26			19 40			
Ramsgate 4	d					18a51		19 00			19a19	19a56	19 32						19a50	20a17		20 00			
Broadstairs	d							19 05					19 37									20 05			
Margate 4	a							19 12					19 42									20 12			

Table 194

Mondays to Fridays

9 December to 16 May

St Pancras International - Kent High Speed Domestic Services

Network Diagram - see first Page of Table 194

		SE 1	SE 1	SE		SE 1	SE	SE 1	SE		SE 1	SE	SE 1	SE	SE	SE 1	SE 1	SE	SE 1	SE		SE	SE	SE 1	SE 1
St Pancras International 15 ⊖	d			19 10			19 28		19 42			19 55		20 12	20 25			20 42		20 55		21 12	21 25		
Stratford International ⊖	d			19 17			19 35		19 49			20 02		20 19	20 32			20 49		21 02		21 19	21 32		
Ebbsfleet International	a			19 28			19 45		20 00			20 12		20 30	20 42			21 00		21 12		21 30	21 42		
	d			19 29			19 46		20 01			20 14		20 31	20 44			21 01		21 14		21 31	21 44		
Gravesend 4	d						19 51					20 18			20 48					21 18			21 48		
Strood 4	d						20 02					20 28			20 58					21 28			21 58		
Maidstone West	d																								
Rochester 4	d						20 07					20 33			21 03					21 33			22 03		
Chatham 4	d						20 09					20 35			21 05					21 35			22 05		
Gillingham (Kent) 4	d						20 15					20 40			21 10					21 40			22 10		
Rainham (Kent)	d						20 20					20 45			21 15					21 45			22 15		
Sittingbourne 4	d						20 27					20 53			21 23					21 53			22 23		
Faversham 2	a						20 36					21 03			21 33					22 03			22 33		
Whitstable	d																								
Herne Bay	d																								
Birchington-on-Sea	d																								
Margate 4	d																								
Broadstairs	a																								
Ashford International	a			19 48					20 20					20 50				21 20				21 50			
	d	19 31	19 37	19 52	19 55	20 07		20 10	20 22		20 35		20 38	20 52		21 02	21 05	21 22	21 32			21 52		22 02	22 05
Folkestone West	d		19 54	20 05		20 23					20 52			21 05		21 18			21 48			22 05		22 18	
Folkestone Central	d		19 57	20 08		20 26					20 55			21 08		21 21			21 51			22 08		22 21	
Dover Priory 4	a		20 08	20 20		20 37					21 08			21 20		21 33			22 02			22 20		22 31	
Deal	a		20 27			20 55										21 51								22 49	
Sandwich	a		20 33			21 01										21 57								22 55	
Canterbury West 4	a	19 53			20 11			20 28	20 38				21 00				21 26	21 38							22 26
	d	19 55			20 12			20 29	20 39								21 27	21 39							22 27
Ramsgate 4	d	20 20	20a48		20 35	21a16		20a53	21 01							22a10	21a48	22 00						23a08	22a48
Broadstairs	d	20 25			20 40				21 06									22 05							
Margate 4	a	20 34			20 45				21 11									22 10							

		SE	SE 1	SE	SE	SE	SE 1		SE 1	SE	SE 1	SE	SE	SE	SE	SE
St Pancras International 15 ⊖	d	21 42		21 55	22 12	22 25				22 42		22 55	23 12	23 25	23 42	23 55
Stratford International ⊖	d	21 49		22 02	22 19	22 32				22 49		23 02	23 19	23 32	23 49	00 02
Ebbsfleet International	a	22 00		22 12	22 30	22 42				23 00		23 12	23 30	23 42	23 59	00 12
	d	22 01		22 14	22 31	22 44				23 01		23 14	23 31	23 44	00 01	00 14
Gravesend 4	d			22 18		22 48						23 18		23 48		00 18
Strood 4	d			22 28		22 58						23 28		23 58		00 28
Maidstone West	d															
Rochester 4	d			22 33		23 03						23 33		00 03		00 33
Chatham 4	d			22 35		23 05						23 35		00 05		00 35
Gillingham (Kent) 4	d			22 40		23 10						23 40		00 10		00 40
Rainham (Kent)	d			22 45		23 15						23 45		00 15		00 45
Sittingbourne 4	d			22 53		23 23						23 53		00 23		00 53
Faversham 2	a			23 03		23 33						00 03		00 33		01 03
Whitstable	d															
Herne Bay	d															
Birchington-on-Sea	d															
Margate 4	d															
Broadstairs	a															
Ashford International	a	22 20			22 50					23 20			23 50		00 20	
	d	22 22	22 34		22 52		23 02		23 05	23 22	23 34		23 52			
Folkestone West	d		22 50		23 05		23 18				23 50		00 05			
Folkestone Central	d		22 53		23 08		23 21				23 53		00 08			
Dover Priory 4	a		23 04		23 20		23 31				00 06		00 18			
Deal	a						23 49				00 24		00 34			
Sandwich	a						23 55				00 30		00 41			
Canterbury West 4	a	22 38							23 26	23 38						
	d	22 39							23 27	23 39						
Ramsgate 4	d	23 00					00a08		23a48	00a01	00a43		00a54			
Broadstairs	d	23 05														
Margate 4	a	23 10														

Table 194

Saturdays

14 December to 17 May

St Pancras International - Kent High Speed Domestic Services

Network Diagram - see first Page of Table 194

		SE	SE	SE 1	SE 1	SE	SE 1	SE	SE		SE 1	SE 1	SE 1	SE 1	SE 1	SE	SE 1	SE	SE 1	SE		SE 1	SE	SE 1	SE
St Pancras International 15 ⊖	d								00 12							06 42		06 51		07 12			07 42		07 55
Stratford International ⊖	d							00 02	00 19							06 49		06 58		07 19			07 49		08 02
Ebbsfleet International	a							00 12	00 30							07 00		07 08		07 30			08 00		08 12
	d					00 01		00 14	00 31							07 01		07 14		07 31			08 01		08 14
Gravesend 4	d							00 18										07 18							08 18
Strood 4	d							00 28										07 28							08 28
Maidstone West	d																								
Rochester 4	d	00 03						00 33										07 33							08 33
Chatham 4	d	00 05						00 35										07 35							08 35
Gillingham (Kent) 4	d	00 10						00 40										07 40							08 40
Rainham (Kent)	d	00 15						00 45										07 45							08 45
Sittingbourne 4	d	00 23						00 53										07 53							08 53
Faversham 2	a	00 33						01 03										08 03							09 03
Whitstable	d																								
Herne Bay	d																								
Birchington-on-Sea	d																								
Margate 4	d																								
Broadstairs	a																								
Ashford International	a					00 20			00 50							07 20				07 51			08 20		
	d			00 02	00 05		00 34				01 02	01 05	06 32	06 35	07 05	07 22	07 32		07 35	07 52		08 05	08 22	08 32	
Folkestone West	d		00 05	00 18			00 50				01 18		06 48				07 48			08 05				08 48	
Folkestone Central	d		00 08	00 21			00 53				01 21		06 51				07 51			08 08				08 51	
Dover Priory 4	a		00 18	00 32			01 04				01 32		07 01				08 01			08 20				09 01	
Deal	a		00 34										07 19				08 19							09 19	
Sandwich	a		00 41										07 25				08 25							09 25	
Canterbury West 4	a				00 26							01 26		06 56	07 23	07 38			07 56			08 23	08 38		
	d				00 27										07 24	07 39						08 24	08 39		
Ramsgate 4	d		00a54		00a48								07a38		07a45	07 59	08a38					08a45	08 59	09a38	
Broadstairs	d															08 05							09 05		
Margate 4	a															08 10							09 10		

		SE 1	SE	SE 1	SE	SE 1	SE		SE 1	SE	SE	SE 1	SE	SE 1	SE	SE 1	SE	SE		SE 1	SE	SE 1	SE	SE 1	SE
St Pancras International 15 ⊖	d		08 12		08 40		08 51			09 12	09 25		09 42		09 55		10 10	10 22			10 42		10 52		11 12
Stratford International ⊖	d		08 19		08 47		09 05			09 19	09 32		09 49		10 02		10 17	10 32			10 49		10 59		11 19
Ebbsfleet International	a		08 30		08 58		09 16			09 30	09 42		10 00		10 12		10 28	10 43			11 00		11 09		11 30
	d		08 31		08 59		09 17			09 31	09 44		10 01		10 14		10 29	10 44			11 01		11 14		11 31
Gravesend 4	d						09 21				09 48				10 18			10 48					11 18		
Strood 4	d						09 31				09 58				10 28			10 58					11 28		
Maidstone West	d																								
Rochester 4	d						09 35				10 03				10 33			11 03					11 33		
Chatham 4	d						09 38				10 05				10 35			11 05					11 35		
Gillingham (Kent) 4	d						09 42				10 10				10 40			11 10					11 40		
Rainham (Kent)	d						09 47				10 15				10 45			11 15					11 45		
Sittingbourne 4	d						09 55				10 23				10 53			11 23					11 53		
Faversham 2	a						10 04				10 33				11 03			11 33					12 03		
Whitstable	d																								
Herne Bay	d																								
Birchington-on-Sea	d																								
Margate 4	d																								
Broadstairs	a																								
Ashford International	a		08 50		09 18					09 50			10 20				10 48				11 20				11 50
	d	08 35	08 52	09 05	09 22	09 32			09 35	09 52		10 05	10 22	10 32		10 35	10 52			11 05	11 22	11 32		11 35	11 52
Folkestone West	d		09 05			09 48				10 05				10 48			11 05					11 48			12 05
Folkestone Central	d		09 08			09 51				10 08				10 51			11 08					11 51			12 08
Dover Priory 4	a		09 20			10 01				10 20				11 01			11 20					12 01			12 20
Deal	a					10 19								11 19								12 19			
Sandwich	a					10 25								11 25								12 25			
Canterbury West 4	a	08 56		09 23	09 38				09 56			10 23	10 38			10 56				11 23	11 38			11 56	
	d			09 24	09 39							10 24	10 39							11 24	11 39				
Ramsgate 4	d			09a48	09 59	10a38						10a45	10 59	11a38						11a45	11 59	12a38			
Broadstairs	d				10 05								11 05								12 05				
Margate 4	a				10 10								11 10								12 10				

Table 194

Saturdays

14 December to 17 May

St Pancras International - Kent High Speed Domestic Services

Network Diagram - see first Page of Table 194

		SE	SE [1]		SE	SE [1]	SE	SE [1]	SE	SE	SE [1]	SE	SE [1]	SE		SE [1]	SE	SE	SE [1]	SE	SE [1]	SE	SE [1]	SE	SE
St Pancras International [15] ⊖	d	11 25			11 42		11 55		12 12	12 22		12 42		12 52			13 12	13 25		13 42		13 55		14 12	14 25
Stratford International ⊖	d	11 32			11 49		12 02		12 19	12 32		12 49		12 59			13 19	13 32		13 49		14 02		14 19	14 32
Ebbsfleet International	a	11 42			12 00		12 12		12 30	12 43		13 00		13 09			13 30	13 42		14 00		14 12		14 30	14 42
	d	11 44			12 01		12 14		12 31	12 44		13 01		13 14			13 31	13 44		14 01		14 14		14 31	14 44
Gravesend [4]	d	11 48					12 18			12 48				13 18				13 48				14 18			14 48
Strood [4]	d	11 58					12 28			12 58				13 28				13 58				14 28			14 58
Maidstone West	d																								
Rochester [4]	d	12 03					12 33			13 03				13 33				14 03				14 33			15 03
Chatham [4]	d	12 05					12 35			13 05				13 35				14 05				14 35			15 05
Gillingham (Kent) [4]	d	12 10					12 40			13 10				13 40				14 10				14 40			15 10
Rainham (Kent)	d	12 15					12 45			13 15				13 45				14 15				14 45			15 15
Sittingbourne [4]	d	12 23					12 53			13 23				13 53				14 23				14 53			15 23
Faversham [2]	a	12 33					13 03			13 33				14 03				14 33				15 03			15 33
Whitstable	d																								
Herne Bay	d																								
Birchington-on-Sea	d																								
Margate [4]	d																								
Broadstairs	a																								
Ashford International	a				12 20				12 50			13 20					13 50			14 20				14 50	
	d		12 05		12 22	12 32		12 35	12 52		13 05	13 22	13 32			13 35	13 52		14 05	14 22	14 32		14 35	14 52	
Folkestone West	d					12 48			13 05				13 48				14 05				14 48			15 05	
Folkestone Central	d					12 51			13 08				13 51				14 08				14 51			15 08	
Dover Priory [4]	a					13 01			13 20				14 01				14 20				15 01			15 20	
Deal	a					13 19							14 19								15 19				
Sandwich	a					13 25							14 25								15 25				
Canterbury West [4]	a		12 23		12 38			12 56			13 23	13 38				13 56			14 23	14 38			14 56		
	d		12 24		12 39						13 24	13 39							14 24	14 39					
Ramsgate [4]	d		12a45		12 59	13a38					13a45	13 59	14a38						14a45	14 59	15a38				
Broadstairs	d				13 05							14 05								15 05					
Margate [4]	a				13 10							14 10								15 10					

			SE [1]	SE	SE [1]	SE	SE [1]	SE	SE	SE [1]	SE	SE [1]		SE	SE [1]	SE	SE	SE [1]	SE	SE [1]	SE	SE [1]	SE		SE
St Pancras International [15] ⊖	d			14 42		14 55		15 12	15 25		15 42			15 55		16 12	16 25		16 40		16 55		17 12		17 25
Stratford International ⊖	d			14 49		15 02		15 19	15 32		15 49			16 02		16 19	16 32		16 47		17 02		17 19		17 32
Ebbsfleet International	a			15 00		15 12		15 30	15 42		16 00			16 12		16 30	16 42		16 58		17 13		17 30		17 42
	d			15 01		15 14		15 31	15 44		16 01			16 14		16 31	16 44		16 58		17 14		17 31		17 44
Gravesend [4]	d					15 18			15 48					16 18			16 48				17 18				17 48
Strood [4]	d					15 28			15 58					16 28			16 58				17 28				17 58
Maidstone West	d																								
Rochester [4]	d					15 33			16 03					16 33			17 03				17 33				18 03
Chatham [4]	d					15 35			16 05					16 35			17 05				17 35				18 05
Gillingham (Kent) [4]	d					15 40			16 10					16 40			17 10				17 40				18 10
Rainham (Kent)	d					15 45			16 15					16 45			17 15				17 45				18 15
Sittingbourne [4]	d					15 53			16 23					16 53			17 23				17 53				18 23
Faversham [2]	a					16 03			16 33					17 03			17 33				18 03				18 33
Whitstable	d																								
Herne Bay	d																								
Birchington-on-Sea	d																								
Margate [4]	d																								
Broadstairs	a																								
Ashford International	a			15 20				15 50			16 20					16 50			17 17				17 50		
	d		15 05	15 22	15 32		15 35	15 52		16 05	16 22	16 32			16 35	16 52		17 05	17 22	17 32		17 35	17 52		
Folkestone West	d				15 48			16 05				16 48				17 05				17 48			18 05		
Folkestone Central	d				15 51			16 08				16 51				17 08				17 51			18 08		
Dover Priory [4]	a				16 01			16 20				17 01				17 20				18 01			18 20		
Deal	a				16 19							17 19								18 19					
Sandwich	a				16 25							17 25								18 25					
Canterbury West [4]	a		15 23	15 38			15 56			16 23	16 38				16 56			17 23	17 38			17 56			
	d		15 24	15 39						16 24	16 39							17 24	17 39						
Ramsgate [4]	d		15a45	15 59	16a38					16a45	16 59	17a38						17a45	17 59	18a38					
Broadstairs	d			16 05							17 05								18 05						
Margate [4]	a			16 10							17 10								18 10						

Table 194

Saturdays

14 December to 17 May

St Pancras International - Kent High Speed Domestic Services

Network Diagram - see first Page of Table 194

		SE [1]	SE	SE [1]	SE	SE [1]	SE	SE		SE [1]	SE	SE [1]	SE	SE	SE	SE [1]	SE	SE [1]	SE		SE	SE	SE [1]	SE	SE [1]
St Pancras International [15] ⊖	d		17 42		17 55		18 12	18 25			18 42		18 55	19 12	19 25		19 42		19 55		20 12	20 25		20 42	
Stratford International ⊖	d		17 49		18 02		18 19	18 32			18 49		19 02	19 19	19 32		19 49		20 02		20 19	20 32		20 49	
Ebbsfleet International	a		18 00		18 12		18 30	18 42			19 00		19 12	19 30	19 42		20 00		20 12		20 30	20 42		21 00	
	d		18 01		18 14		18 31	18 44			19 01		19 14	19 31	19 44		20 01		20 14		20 31	20 44		21 01	
Gravesend [4]	d				18 18			18 48					19 18		19 48				20 18			20 48			
Strood [4]	d				18 28			18 58					19 28		19 58				20 28			20 58			
Maidstone West	d																								
Rochester [4]	d				18 33			19 03					19 33		20 03				20 33			21 03			
Chatham [4]	d				18 35			19 05					19 35		20 05				20 35			21 05			
Gillingham (Kent) [4]	d				18 40			19 10					19 40		20 10				20 40			21 10			
Rainham (Kent)	d				18 45			19 15					19 45		20 15				20 45			21 15			
Sittingbourne [4]	d				18 53			19 23					19 53		20 23				20 53			21 23			
Faversham [2]	a				19 03			19 33					20 03		20 33				21 03			21 33			
Whitstable	d																								
Herne Bay	d																								
Birchington-on-Sea	d																								
Margate [4]	d																								
Broadstairs	a																								
Ashford International	a		18 20				18 50				19 20			19 50			20 20				20 50			21 20	
	d	18 05	18 22	18 32		18 35	18 52			19 05	19 22	19 32		19 52		20 05	20 22	20 32			20 52		21 05	21 22	21 32
Folkestone West	d			18 48			19 05					19 48		20 05				20 48			21 05				21 48
Folkestone Central	d			18 51			19 08					19 51		20 08				20 51			21 08				21 51
Dover Priory [4]	a			19 01			19 20					20 01		20 20				21 01			21 20				22 01
Deal	a			19 19								20 19						21 19							22 19
Sandwich	a			19 25								20 25						21 25							22 25
Canterbury West [4]	a	18 23	18 38			18 56				19 26	19 38					20 26	20 38						21 26	21 38	
	d	18 24	18 39							19 27	19 39					20 27	20 39						21 27	21 39	
Ramsgate [4]	d	18a45	18 59	19a38						19a48	20 01	20a38				20a48	21 01	21a38					21a48	22 01	22a38
Broadstairs	d		19 05								20 06						21 06							22 06	
Margate [4]	a		19 10								20 11						21 11							22 11	

		SE	SE	SE	SE [1]	SE		SE [1]	SE	SE	SE	SE [1]	SE	SE [1]	SE	SE	SE		SE	SE					
St Pancras International [15] ⊖	d	20 55	21 12	21 25		21 42			21 55	22 12	22 25		22 42		22 55	23 12	23 25		23 42	23 55					
Stratford International ⊖	d	21 02	21 19	21 32		21 49			22 02	22 19	22 32		22 49		23 02	23 19	23 32		23 49	00 02					
Ebbsfleet International	a	21 12	21 30	21 42		22 00			22 12	22 30	22 42		23 00		23 12	23 30	23 42		23 59	00 12					
	d	21 14	21 31	21 44		22 01			22 14	22 31	22 44		23 01		23 14	23 31	23 44		00 01	00 14					
Gravesend [4]	d	21 18		21 48					22 18		22 48				23 18		23 48			00 18					
Strood [4]	d	21 28		21 58					22 28		22 58				23 28		23 58			00 28					
Maidstone West	d																								
Rochester [4]	d	21 33		22 03					22 33		23 03				23 33		00 03			00 33					
Chatham [4]	d	21 35		22 05					22 35		23 05				23 35		00 05			00 35					
Gillingham (Kent) [4]	d	21 40		22 10					22 40		23 10				23 40		00 10			00 40					
Rainham (Kent)	d	21 45		22 15					22 45		23 15				23 45		00 15			00 45					
Sittingbourne [4]	d	21 53		22 23					22 53		23 23				23 53		00 23			00 53					
Faversham [2]	a	22 03		22 31					23 01		23 31				00 01		00 31			01 01					
Whitstable	d																								
Herne Bay	d																								
Birchington-on-Sea	d																								
Margate [4]	d																								
Broadstairs	a																								
Ashford International	a		21 50			22 20				22 50			23 20			23 50			00 20						
	d		21 52		22 05	22 22		22 32		22 52		23 05	23 22	23 32		23 52									
Folkestone West	d		22 05					22 48		23 05				23 48		00 05									
Folkestone Central	d		22 08					22 51		23 08				23 51		00 08									
Dover Priory [4]	a		22 20					23 01		23 22				00 01		00 20									
Deal	a							23 19						00 19											
Sandwich	a							23 25						00 25											
Canterbury West [4]	a				22 26	22 38						23 26	23 38												
	d				22 27	22 39						23 27	23 39												
Ramsgate [4]	d				22a48	23 01		23a38				23a48	00a01	00a38											
Broadstairs	d					23 06																			
Margate [4]	a					23 11																			

Table 194

Sundays

8 December to 11 May

St Pancras International - Kent High Speed Domestic Services

Network Diagram - see first Page of Table 194

		SE	SE	SE	SE	SE	SE	SE	SE		SE	SE	SE	SE	SE	SE	SE	SE	SE	SE		SE	SE	SE	SE
			1				1		1		1	1	1	1		1	1			1			1	1	
		A	A	A	A	A	A		A																
St Pancras International 15 ⊖	d							00 12							08 42			09 10	09 25			09 42			10 10
Stratford International ⊖	d				00 02			00 19							08 49			09 17	09 32			09 49			10 17
Ebbsfleet International	a				00 12			00 30							09 00			09 28	09 43			10 00			10 28
	d			00 01	00 14			00 31							09 01			09 29	09 44			10 01			10 29
Gravesend 4	d				00 18														09 48						
Strood 4	d				00 28														09 58						
Maidstone West	d																								
Rochester 4	d	00 03			00 33														10 03						
Chatham 4	d	00 05			00 35														10 05						
Gillingham (Kent) 4	d	00 10			00 40														10 10						
Rainham (Kent)	d	00 15			00 45														10 15						
Sittingbourne 4	d	00 23			00 53														10 23						
Faversham 2	a	00 31			01 01														10 33						
Whitstable	d																								
Herne Bay	d																								
Birchington-on-Sea	d																								
Margate 4	d																								
Broadstairs	a																								
Ashford International	a			00 20				00 50							09 20			09 48				10 20			10 48
	d		00 05				00 32		01 04		01 07	08 32	08 35	09 05	09 22	09 32	09 35	09 52		10 05		10 22	10 32	10 35	10 52
Folkestone West	d					00 05	00 48		01 20			08 48				09 48		10 05					10 48		11 05
Folkestone Central	d					00 08	00 51		01 23			08 51				09 51		10 08					10 51		11 08
Dover Priory 4	a					00 20	01 02		01 34			09 01				10 01		10 20					11 01		11 20
Deal	a											09 19				10 19							11 19		
Sandwich	a											09 25				10 25							11 25		
Canterbury West 4	a		00 26								01 28		08 56	09 23	09 38		09 56			10 23		10 38		10 56	
	d		00 27											09 24	09 39					10 24		10 39			
Ramsgate 4	d		00a48									09a38		09a45	09 59	10a38				10a45		10 59	11a38		
Broadstairs	d														10 05							11 05			
Margate 4	a														10 10							11 10			

		SE	SE	SE	SE	SE	SE		SE	SE	SE	SE	SE	SE	SE	SE	SE	SE		SE	SE	SE	SE	SE	SE
			1		1	1				1		1	1			1		1			1			1	
St Pancras International 15 ⊖	d	10 22		10 42			11 12		11 25		11 42			12 12	12 22		12 42			12 52		13 12	13 25		13 42
Stratford International ⊖	d	10 32		10 49			11 19		11 32		11 49			12 19	12 32		12 49			12 59		13 19	13 32		13 49
Ebbsfleet International	a	10 43		11 00			11 30		11 42		12 00			12 30	12 43		13 00			13 09		13 30	13 42		14 00
	d	10 44		11 01			11 31		11 44		12 01			12 31	12 44		13 01			13 14		13 31	13 44		14 01
Gravesend 4	d	10 48							11 48						12 48					13 18			13 48		
Strood 4	d	10 58							11 58						12 58					13 28			13 58		
Maidstone West	d																								
Rochester 4	d	11 03							12 03						13 03					13 33			14 03		
Chatham 4	d	11 05							12 05						13 05					13 35			14 05		
Gillingham (Kent) 4	d	11 10							12 10						13 10					13 40			14 10		
Rainham (Kent)	d	11 15							12 15						13 15					13 45			14 15		
Sittingbourne 4	d	11 23							12 23						13 22					13 53			14 23		
Faversham 2	a	11 33							12 33						13 33					14 03			14 33		
Whitstable	d																								
Herne Bay	d																								
Birchington-on-Sea	d																								
Margate 4	d																								
Broadstairs	a																								
Ashford International	a			11 20			11 50				12 20			12 50			13 20					13 50			14 20
	d		11 05	11 22	11 32	11 35	11 52			12 05	12 22	12 32	12 35	12 52		13 05	13 22	13 32			13 35	13 52		14 05	14 22
Folkestone West	d				11 48		12 05					12 48		13 05				13 48				14 05			
Folkestone Central	d				11 51		12 08					12 51		13 08				13 51				14 08			
Dover Priory 4	a				12 01		12 20					13 01		13 20				14 01				14 20			
Deal	a				12 19							13 19						14 19							
Sandwich	a				12 25							13 25						14 25							
Canterbury West 4	a		11 23	11 38		11 56				12 23	12 38		12 56			13 23	13 38				13 56			14 23	14 38
	d		11 24	11 39						12 24	12 39					13 24	13 39							14 24	14 39
Ramsgate 4	d		11a45	11 59	12a38					12a45	12 59	13a38				13a45	13 59	14a38						14a45	14 59
Broadstairs	d			12 05							13 05						14 05								15 05
Margate 4	a			12 10							13 10						14 10								15 10

A not 8 December

Table 194

Sundays

8 December to 11 May

St Pancras International - Kent High Speed Domestic Services

Network Diagram - see first Page of Table 194

		SE [1]	SE		SE [1]	SE	SE	SE [1]	SE	SE [1]	SE	SE [1]	SE	SE		SE [1]	SE	SE [1]	SE	SE [1]	SE	SE	SE [1]	SE	SE [1]
St Pancras International [15] ⊖	d		13 55			14 12	14 25		14 42		14 55		15 12	15 25			15 42		15 55		16 10	16 25		16 42	
Stratford International ⊖	d		14 02			14 19	14 32		14 49		15 02		15 19	15 32			15 49		16 02		16 17	16 32		16 49	
Ebbsfleet International	a		14 12			14 30	14 42		15 00		15 12		15 30	15 42			16 00		16 12		16 28	16 43		17 00	
	d		14 14			14 31	14 44		15 01		15 14		15 31	15 44			16 01		16 14		16 29	16 44		17 01	
Gravesend [4]	d		14 18				14 48				15 18			15 48					16 18			16 48			
Strood [4]	d		14 28				14 58				15 28			15 58					16 28			16 58			
Maidstone West	d																								
Rochester [4]	d		14 33				15 03				15 33			16 03					16 33			17 03			
Chatham [4]	d		14 35				15 05				15 35			16 05					16 35			17 05			
Gillingham (Kent) [4]	d		14 40				15 10				15 40			16 10					16 40			17 10			
Rainham (Kent)	d		14 45				15 15				15 45			16 15					16 45			17 15			
Sittingbourne [4]	d		14 53				15 23				15 53			16 23					16 53			17 23			
Faversham [2]	a		15 03				15 33				16 03			16 33					17 03			17 33			
Whitstable	d																								
Herne Bay	d																								
Birchington-on-Sea	d																								
Margate [4]	d																								
Broadstairs	a																								
Ashford International	a					14 50			15 20				15 50				16 20				16 48			17 20	
	d	14 32			14 35	14 52		15 05	15 22	15 32		15 35	15 52			16 05	16 22	16 32		16 35	16 52		17 05	17 22	17 32
Folkestone West	d	14 48				15 05				15 48			16 05					16 48			17 05				17 48
Folkestone Central	d	14 51				15 08				15 51			16 08					16 51			17 08				17 51
Dover Priory [4]	a	15 01				15 20				16 01			16 20					17 01			17 20				18 01
Deal	a	15 19								16 19								17 19							18 19
Sandwich	a	15 25								16 25								17 25							18 25
Canterbury West [4]	a				14 56			15 23	15 38			15 56				16 23	16 38			16 56			17 23	17 38	
	d							15 24	15 39							16 24	16 39						17 24	17 39	
Ramsgate [4]	d	15a38						15a45	15 59	16a38						16a45	16 59	17a38					17a45	17 59	18a38
Broadstairs	d								16 05								17 05							18 05	
Margate [4]	a								16 10								17 10							18 10	

			SE	SE [1]	SE	SE	SE [1]	SE	SE [1]	SE	SE	SE		SE [1]	SE	SE [1]	SE	SE	SE	SE [1]	SE	SE [1]	SE		SE
St Pancras International [15] ⊖	d		16 55		17 12	17 25		17 42		17 52	18 12	18 25			18 42		18 55	19 12	19 25		19 42		19 55		20 12
Stratford International ⊖	d		17 02		17 19	17 32		17 49		18 02	18 19	18 32			18 49		19 02	19 19	19 32		19 49		20 02		20 19
Ebbsfleet International	a		17 12		17 30	17 42		18 00		18 13	18 30	18 42			19 00		19 12	19 30	19 42		20 00		20 12		20 30
	d		17 14		17 31	17 44		18 01		18 14	18 31	18 44			19 01		19 14	19 31	19 44		20 01		20 14		20 31
Gravesend [4]	d		17 18			17 48				18 18		18 48					19 18		19 48				20 18		
Strood [4]	d		17 28			17 58				18 28		18 58					19 28		19 58				20 28		
Maidstone West	d																								
Rochester [4]	d		17 33			18 03				18 33		19 03					19 33		20 03				20 33		
Chatham [4]	d		17 35			18 05				18 35		19 05					19 35		20 05				20 35		
Gillingham (Kent) [4]	d		17 40			18 10				18 40		19 10					19 40		20 10				20 40		
Rainham (Kent)	d		17 45			18 15				18 45		19 15					19 45		20 15				20 45		
Sittingbourne [4]	d		17 53			18 23				18 53		19 23					19 53		20 23				20 53		
Faversham [2]	a		18 03			18 33				19 03		19 33					20 03		20 33				21 03		
Whitstable	d																								
Herne Bay	d																								
Birchington-on-Sea	d																								
Margate [4]	d																								
Broadstairs	a																								
Ashford International	a				17 50			18 20			18 50				19 20			19 50			20 20				20 50
	d			17 35	17 52		18 05	18 22	18 32		18 52			19 05	19 22	19 32		19 52		20 05	20 22	20 32			20 52
Folkestone West	d				18 05				18 48		19 05					19 48		20 05				20 48			21 05
Folkestone Central	d				18 08				18 51		19 08					19 51		20 08				20 51			21 08
Dover Priory [4]	a				18 20				19 01		19 20					20 01		20 20				21 01			21 20
Deal	a								19 19							20 19						21 19			
Sandwich	a								19 25							20 25						21 25			
Canterbury West [4]	a			17 56			18 26	18 38						19 26	19 38					20 26	20 38				
	d						18 27	18 39						19 27	19 39					20 27	20 39				
Ramsgate [4]	d						18a48	19 01	19a38					19a48	20 01	20a38				20a48	21 01	21a38			
Broadstairs	d							19 06							20 06						21 06				
Margate [4]	a							19 11							20 11						21 11				

Table 194

Sundays

8 December to 11 May

St Pancras International - Kent High Speed Domestic Services

Network Diagram - see first Page of Table 194

		SE	SE 1	SE	SE 1	SE	SE	SE	SE 1	SE		SE 1	SE	SE	SE	SE 1	SE	SE 1	SE	SE	SE		SE		
St Pancras International 15 ⊖	d	20 25		20 42		20 55	21 12	21 25		21 42			21 55	22 12	22 25		22 42		22 55	23 12	23 25		23 42		
Stratford International ⊖	d	20 32		20 49		21 02	21 19	21 32		21 49			22 02	22 19	22 32		22 49		23 02	23 19	23 32		23 49		
Ebbsfleet International	a	20 42		21 00		21 12	21 30	21 42		22 00			22 12	22 30	22 42		23 00		23 12	23 30	23 42		23 59		
	d	20 44		21 01		21 14	21 31	21 44		22 01			22 14	22 31	22 44		23 01		23 14	23 31	23 44		00 01		
Gravesend 4	d	20 48				21 18		21 48					22 18		22 48				23 18		23 48				
Strood 4	d	20 58				21 28		21 58					22 28		22 58				23 28		23 58				
Maidstone West	d																								
Rochester 4	d	21 03				21 33		22 03					22 33		23 03				23 33		00 03				
Chatham 4	d	21 05				21 35		22 05					22 35		23 05				23 35		00 05				
Gillingham (Kent) 4	d	21 10				21 40		22 10					22 40		23 10				23 40		00 10				
Rainham (Kent)	d	21 15				21 45		22 15					22 45		23 15				23 45		00 15				
Sittingbourne 4	d	21 23				21 53		22 23					22 53		23 23				23 53		00 23				
Faversham 2	a	21 33				22 03		22 31					23 03		23 31				00 03		00 33				
Whitstable	d																								
Herne Bay	d																								
Birchington-on-Sea	d																								
Margate 4	d																								
Broadstairs	a																								
Ashford International	a			21 20			21 50			22 20				22 50			23 20			23 50			00 20		
	d		21 05	21 22	21 32		21 52		22 05	22 22		22 32		22 52		23 05	23 22	23 32		23 52					
Folkestone West	d				21 48		22 05					22 48		23 05				23 48		00 05					
Folkestone Central	d				21 51		22 08					22 51		23 08				23 51		00 08					
Dover Priory 4	a				22 01		22 20					23 01		23 20				00 01		00 20					
Deal	a				22 19							23 19						00 19							
Sandwich	a				22 25							23 26						00 25							
Canterbury West 4	a		21 26	21 38					22 26	22 38						23 26	23 38								
	d		21 27	21 39					22 27	22 39						23 27	23 39								
Ramsgate 4	d		21a48	22 01	22a38				22a48	23 01		23a40				23a48	00a01	00a38							
Broadstairs	d			22 06						23 06															
Margate 4	a			22 11						23 11															

Table 194R

Mondays to Fridays

9 December to 16 May

Kent - St Pancras International
High Speed Domestic Services

Network Diagram - see first Page of Table 194

Miles	Miles	Miles			SE ■1	SE	SE ■1	SE	SE	SE	SE	SE ■1	SE ■1	SE		SE	SE	SE ■1	SE ■1	SE	SE	SE	SE ■1
—	—	0	Margate ■4	d												05 48							
—	—	3¼	Broadstairs	d												05 54							
—	—	5½	Ramsgate ■4	d			04 51		05 00			05 26	05 36			06 00		06 08					06 12
—	—	20¾	**Canterbury West**	a					05 23				05 58			06 19		06 33					
—	—	—		d					05 25				06 00			06 20		06 34					
—	—	—	Sandwich	d			05 05					05 40					05 52						06 26
—	—	—	Deal	d			05 11					05 46					05 58						06 32
—	0	—	**Dover Priory**	d	04 37		05 28				05 45	06 04					06 12		06 24				06 49
—	7¼	—	Folkestone Central	d	04 49		05 39				05 56	06 15					06 23		06 36				07 00
—	8	—	Folkestone West	d	04 51		05 42				05 58	06 18					06 26		06 38				07 03
—	21¼	—	**Ashford International**	a	05 08		05 59		05 41		06 11	06 35	06 21			06 36	06 39	06 55	06 55				07 20
—	—	—																					
—	—	—		d		05 13			05 43		06 13					06 43							
0	—	—	**Broadstairs**	d																	06 00		
3¼	—	—	Margate ■4	d																	06 05		
6¼	—	—	Birchington-on-Sea	d																	06 10		
14¼	—	—	Herne Bay	d																	06 19		
18¼	—	—	Whitstable	d																	06 25		
25	—	—	**Faversham ■2**	a																	06 33		
—	—	—		d				04 56		05 28				05 58							06 34		
32¾	—	—	Sittingbourne ■4	d				05 07		05 37				06 07							06 42		
38½	—	—	Rainham (Kent)	d				05 15		05 45				06 15							06 50		
41½	—	—	Gillingham (Kent) ■4	d				05 20		05 50				06 20							06 55		
43¼	—	—	Chatham ■4	d				05 24		05 54				06 24							07 00		
43¾	—	—	Rochester ■4	d				05 27		05 57				06 27							07 03		
—	—	—	Maidstone West	d																		06 55	
44¾	—	—	Strood ■4	d				05 32		06 02				06 32								07 11	
52	—	—	Gravesend	d				05 43		06 13				06 42								07 22	
54	54½	68¼	**Ebbsfleet International**	a		05 32		05 46	06 02	06 16	06 32			06 46							07 17	07 25	
—	—	—		d		05 32		05 47	06 02	06 17	06 32			06 47						07 06	07 18	07 26	
70¾	71¼	85	**Stratford International** ⊖	a		05 44		05 59	06 14	06 29	06 44			06 59		07 11				07 17	07 30	07 38	
76¾	77¼	91	**St Pancras International ■4** ⊖	a		05 51		06 06	06 21	06 36	06 51			07 06		07 19				07 24	07 37	07 45	

		SE	SE		SE ■1	SE	SE	SE	SE	SE ■1	SE	SE	SE ■1	SE		SE ■1	SE	SE	SE ■1	SE ■1	SE	SE	SE	SE	SE
Margate ■4	d										06 46												07 49		
Broadstairs	d										06 52												07 55		
Ramsgate ■4	d		06 26		06 42					06 50	06 58		07 10			07 23		07 30		07 40			08 01		
Canterbury West	a		06 45		07 04						07 16		07 32					07 49					08 24		
	d		06 50		07 06						07 18		07 36					07 50	08 00				08 25		
Sandwich	d	06 18							06 52	07 02						07 35	07 22			08 02					
Deal	d	06 24							06 58	07 08						07 41	07 28			08 08					
Dover Priory	d	06 42							07 16	07 25						07 58	07 42			08 25					08 45
Folkestone Central	d	06 53							07 27	07 36						08 09	07 53			08 36					08 56
Folkestone West	d	06 56							07 30	07 38						08 11	07 56			08 38					08 58
Ashford International	a	07 09	07 06		07 27				07 43	07 55	07 34		07 58			08 28	08 09	08 06	08 22	08 55			08 41		09 11
	d	07 13							07 45		07 36						08 13						08 43		09 13
Broadstairs	d						06 30					06 58													
Margate ■4	d						06 35					07 03													
Birchington-on-Sea	d						06 40					07 10													
Herne Bay	d						06 49					07 19													
Whitstable	d						06 55					07 24													
Faversham ■2	a						07 03					07 32													
	d						07 04					07 33										07 58		08 28	
Sittingbourne ■4	d						07 13					07 41										08 07		08 37	
Rainham (Kent)	d						07 21					07 50										08 15		08 45	
Gillingham (Kent) ■4	d						07 26					07 55										08 20		08 50	
Chatham ■4	d						07 30					08 00										08 24		08 54	
Rochester ■4	d						07 33					08 03										08 27		08 57	
Maidstone West	d							07 25						07 55											
Strood ■4	d							07 41						08 11								08 32		09 02	
Gravesend	d							07 52						08 22								08 43		09 13	
Ebbsfleet International	a						07 47	07 55	08 04			08 17		08 25								08 46	09 02	09 16	09 32
	d					07 36	07 48	07 57	08 06			08 18		08 26							08 36	08 48	09 02	09 17	09 32
Stratford International ⊖	a	07 41				07 47	08 00	08 09	08 17		08 04	08 30		08 38			08 41				08 47	09 00	09 14	09 29	09 44
St Pancras International ■4 ⊖	a	07 50				07 54	08 07	08 16	08 24		08 13	08 37		08 45			08 49				08 54	09 07	09 21	09 36	09 51

Table 194R

Mondays to Fridays

9 December to 16 May

Kent - St Pancras International High Speed Domestic Services

Network Diagram - see first Page of Table 194

		SE 1	SE 1	SE 1	SE	SE	SE 1	SE	SE 1	SE	SE 1	SE 1	SE	SE	SE 1	SE	SE 1	SE	SE 1	SE 1	SE	SE
Margate 4	d					08 51								09 53								10 53
Broadstairs	d					08 57								09 59								10 59
Ramsgate 4	d	08 05	08 16	08 40		09 03					09 23	09 40		10 05					10 23	10 40		11 05
Canterbury West	a		08 35	09 02		09 22						10 02		10 24						11 02		11 24
	d		08 36	09 07		09 23			09 36			10 07		10 25			10 36			11 07		11 25
Sandwich	d	08 25									09 35								10 35			
Deal	d	08 31									09 41								10 41			
Dover Priory	d	08 58					09 25			09 45	09 58				10 25			10 45	10 58			
Folkestone Central	d	09 09					09 36			09 56	10 09				10 36			10 56	11 09			
Folkestone West	d	09 11					09 38			09 58	10 11				10 38			10 58	11 11			
Ashford International	a	09 28	08 58	09 25		09 39	09 55		09 58	10 11	10 28	10 25		10 41	10 55		10 58	11 11	11 28	11 25		11 41
	d					09 43				10 13				10 43				11 13				11 43
Broadstairs	d																					
Margate 4	d																					
Birchington-on-Sea	d																					
Herne Bay	d																					
Whitstable	d																					
Faversham 2	a																					
	d				08 58			09 28					09 58			10 28					10 58	
Sittingbourne 4	d				09 07			09 37					10 07			10 37					11 07	
Rainham (Kent)	d				09 15			09 45					10 15			10 45					11 15	
Gillingham (Kent) 4	d				09 20			09 50					10 20			10 50					11 20	
Chatham 4	d				09 24			09 54					10 24			10 54					11 24	
Rochester 4	d				09 27			09 57					10 27			10 57					11 27	
Maidstone West	d																					
Strood 4	d				09 32			10 02					10 32			11 02					11 32	
Gravesend	d				09 43			10 13					10 43			11 13					11 43	
Ebbsfleet International	a				09 46	10 02		10 16		10 32			10 46	11 02		11 16		11 32			11 46	12 02
	d				09 48	10 02		10 17		10 32			10 47	11 02		11 17		11 32			11 47	12 02
Stratford International ⊖	a				10 00	10 14		10 29		10 44			10 59	11 14		11 29		11 44			11 59	12 14
St Pancras International 4 ⊖	a				10 07	10 21		10 36		10 51			11 06	11 21		11 36		11 51			12 06	12 21

		SE 1	SE	SE 1	SE	SE 1	SE 1	SE	SE	SE 1	SE	SE 1	SE	SE 1	SE 1	SE	SE	SE 1	SE	SE 1	SE	SE 1	SE 1
Margate 4	d								11 53								12 53						
Broadstairs	d								11 59								12 59						
Ramsgate 4	d					11 23	11 40		12 05					12 23	12 40		13 05					13 23	13 40
Canterbury West	a						12 02		12 24						13 02		13 24						14 02
	d			11 36			12 07		12 25			12 36			13 07		13 25			13 36			14 07
Sandwich	d					11 35								12 35								13 35	
Deal	d					11 41								12 41								13 41	
Dover Priory	d	11 25			11 45	11 58				12 25			12 45	12 58				13 25			13 45	13 58	
Folkestone Central	d	11 36			11 56	12 09				12 36			12 56	13 09				13 36			13 56	14 09	
Folkestone West	d	11 38			11 58	12 11				12 38			12 58	13 11				13 38			13 58	14 11	
Ashford International	a	11 55		11 58	12 11	12 28	12 25		12 41	12 55		12 58	13 11	13 28	13 25		13 41	13 55		13 58	14 11	14 28	14 25
	d				12 13				12 43				13 13				13 43				14 13		
Broadstairs	d																						
Margate 4	d																						
Birchington-on-Sea	d																						
Herne Bay	d																						
Whitstable	d																						
Faversham 2	a																						
	d		11 28					11 58			12 28					12 58			13 28				
Sittingbourne 4	d		11 37					12 07			12 37					13 07			13 37				
Rainham (Kent)	d		11 45					12 15			12 45					13 15			13 45				
Gillingham (Kent) 4	d		11 50					12 20			12 50					13 20			13 50				
Chatham 4	d		11 54					12 24			12 54					13 24			13 54				
Rochester 4	d		11 57					12 27			12 57					13 27			13 57				
Maidstone West	d																						
Strood 4	d		12 02					12 32			13 02					13 32			14 02				
Gravesend	d		12 13					12 43			13 13					13 43			14 13				
Ebbsfleet International	a		12 16		12 32			12 46	13 02		13 16		13 32			13 46	14 02		14 16		14 32		
	d		12 18		12 32			12 48	13 02		13 18		13 32			13 50	14 02		14 17		14 32		
Stratford International ⊖	a		12 30		12 44			13 00	13 14		13 30		13 44			14 02	14 14		14 29		14 44		
St Pancras International 4 ⊖	a		12 37		12 51			13 07	13 21		13 37		13 51			14 09	14 21		14 36		14 51		

Table 194R

Mondays to Fridays

9 December to 16 May

Kent - St Pancras International High Speed Domestic Services

Network Diagram - see first Page of Table 194

		SE	SE	SE 1	SE	SE 1	SE	SE 1		SE 1	SE	SE	SE 1	SE	SE 1	SE	SE 1	SE 1	SE 1		SE	SE	SE	SE 1	SE
Margate 4	d		13 53									14 53										15 53			
Broadstairs	d		13 59									14 59										15 59			
Ramsgate 4	d		14 05					14 23		14 40		15 05					15 23	15 40	15 50			16 05			
Canterbury West	a		14 24							15 02		15 24						16 02				16 24			
	d		14 25			14 36				15 04		15 25			15 36			16 04				16 25		16 36	
Sandwich	d							14 35									15 35		16 02						
Deal	d							14 41									15 41		16 08						
Dover Priory	d			14 25			14 45	14 58					15 25			15 45	15 58		16 25						16 45
Folkestone Central	d			14 36			14 56	15 09					15 36			15 56	16 09		16 36						16 56
Folkestone West	d			14 38			14 58	15 11					15 38			15 58	16 11		16 38						16 58
Ashford International	a		14 41	14 55		14 58	15 11	15 28		15 22		15 41	15 55		15 58	16 11	16 28	16 22	16 55			16 41		16 58	17 11
	d		14 43				15 13					15 43				16 13						16 43			17 13
Broadstairs	d																								
Margate 4	d																								
Birchington-on-Sea	d																								
Herne Bay	d																								
Whitstable	d																								
Faversham 2	a																								
	d	13 58			14 28						14 58			15 28							15 58		16 28		
Sittingbourne 4	d	14 07			14 37						15 07			15 37							16 07		16 37		
Rainham (Kent)	d	14 15			14 45						15 15			15 45							16 15		16 45		
Gillingham (Kent) 4	d	14 20			14 50						15 20			15 50							16 20		16 50		
Chatham 4	d	14 24			14 54						15 24			15 54							16 24		16 54		
Rochester 4	d	14 27			14 57						15 27			15 57							16 27		16 57		
Maidstone West	d																								
Strood 4	d	14 32			15 02						15 32			16 02							16 32		17 02		
Gravesend	d	14 43			15 13						15 43			16 13							16 43		17 13		
Ebbsfleet International	a	14 46	15 02		15 16		15 32				15 46	16 02		16 16		16 31					16 46	17 02	17 16		17 32
	d	14 47	15 02		15 17		15 32				15 51	16 02		16 17		16 32					16 51	17 02	17 17		17 32
Stratford International ⊖	a	14 59	15 14		15 29		15 44				16 02	16 14		16 29		16 44					17 02	17 14	17 29		17 44
St Pancras International 4 ⊖	a	15 06	15 21		15 36		15 51				16 09	16 21		16 36		16 51					17 09	17 21	17 36		17 51

		SE 1	SE 1	SE 1	SE	SE		SE	SE 1	SE	SE 1	SE 1	SE 1	SE	SE	SE 1	SE		SE	SE	SE 1	SE 1	SE 1	SE	SE
Margate 4	d					16 53									17 53										18 53
Broadstairs	d					16 59									17 59										18 59
Ramsgate 4	d	16 23	16 40	16 50		17 05					17 23	17 40	17 50		18 05						18 23	18 40	18 50		19 05
Canterbury West	a		17 02			17 24						18 02			18 24							19 02			19 24
	d		17 04			17 25			17 36			18 04			18 25	18 36						19 07			19 25
Sandwich	d	16 35		17 02							17 35		18 02								18 35		19 02		
Deal	d	16 41		17 08							17 41		18 08								18 41		19 08		
Dover Priory	d	16 58		17 25						17 45	17 58		18 25							18 45	18 58		19 25		
Folkestone Central	d	17 09		17 36						17 56	18 09		18 36							18 56	19 09		19 36		
Folkestone West	d	17 11		17 38						17 58	18 11		18 38							18 58	19 11		19 38		
Ashford International	a	17 28	17 22	17 55		17 41			17 58	18 11	18 28	18 24	18 55		18 41	18 58				19 11	19 29	19 26	19 55		19 41
	d					17 43				18 13					18 43					19 13					19 43
Broadstairs	d																								
Margate 4	d																								
Birchington-on-Sea	d																								
Herne Bay	d																								
Whitstable	d																								
Faversham 2	a																								
	d				16 58			17 28						17 58					18 28					18 58	
Sittingbourne 4	d				17 07			17 37						18 07					18 37					19 07	
Rainham (Kent)	d				17 15			17 45						18 15					18 45					19 15	
Gillingham (Kent) 4	d				17 20			17 50						18 20					18 50					19 20	
Chatham 4	d				17 24			17 54						18 24					18 54					19 24	
Rochester 4	d				17 27			17 57						18 27					18 57					19 27	
Maidstone West	d																18 42								
Strood 4	d				17 32			18 03						18 32			18 58		19 02					19 32	
Gravesend	d				17 43			18 13						18 43			19 09		19 13					19 43	
Ebbsfleet International	a				17 46	18 03		18 18		18 32				18 46	19 02		19 12		19 16	19 32				19 46	20 02
	d				17 49	18 04		18 18		18 32				18 51	19 02		19 13		19 17	19 34				19 48	20 02
Stratford International ⊖	a				17 59	18 15		18 30		18 44				19 02	19 14		19 25		19 29	19 45				20 00	20 14
St Pancras International 4 ⊖	a				18 07	18 22		18 37		18 51				19 09	19 21		19 32		19 36	19 53				20 07	20 21

Table 194R

Mondays to Fridays

9 December to 16 May

Kent - St Pancras International High Speed Domestic Services

Network Diagram - see first Page of Table 194

		SE	SE 1	SE		SE 1	SE 1	SE 1	SE	SE	SE 1	SE	SE 1
Margate 4	d									19 53			
Broadstairs	d									19 59			
Ramsgate 4	d					19 23		19 40		20 05			
Canterbury West	a							20 02		20 25			
	d		19 36				19 55	20 07		20 25			20 36
Sandwich	d					19 35							
Deal	d					19 41							
Dover Priory	d			19 45		19 58					20 25		
Folkestone Central	d			19 56		20 09					20 36		
Folkestone West	d			19 58		20 11					20 38		
Ashford International	a		19 58	20 13		20 28		20 25		20 41	20 55		20 58
	d			20 16						20 43			
Broadstairs	d						20 25						
Margate 4	d						20a34						
Birchington-on-Sea	d												
Herne Bay	d												
Whitstable	d												
Faversham 2	a												
	d	19 28							19 58			20 28	
Sittingbourne 4	d	19 37							20 07			20 37	
Rainham (Kent)	d	19 45							20 15			20 45	
Gillingham (Kent) 4	d	19 50							20 20			20 50	
Chatham 4	d	19 54							20 24			20 54	
Rochester 4	d	19 57							20 27			20 57	
Maidstone West	d												
Strood 4	d	20 02							20 32			21 02	
Gravesend	d	20 13							20 43			21 13	
Ebbsfleet International	a	20 16		20 35					20 46	21 02		21 16	
	d	20 17		20 36					20 50	21 02		21 17	
Stratford International ⊖	a	20 29		20 47					21 02	21 14		21 29	
St Pancras International 4 ⊖	a	20 36		20 54					21 09	21 21		21 36	

		SE	SE 1		SE 1	SE	SE	SE 1	SE	SE 1	SE	SE 1	SE
Margate 4	d						20 53						
Broadstairs	d						20 59						
Ramsgate 4	d		20 23		20 40		21 05					21 23	
Canterbury West	a				21 02		21 25						
	d				21 07		21 25			21 36			
Sandwich	d		20 35									21 35	
Deal	d		20 41									21 41	
Dover Priory	d	20 45	20 58					21 25			21 45	21 58	
Folkestone Central	d	20 56	21 09					21 36			21 56	22 09	
Folkestone West	d	20 58	21 11					21 38			21 58	22 11	
Ashford International	a	21 11	21 28		21 25		21 41	21 55		21 58	22 11	22 29	
	d	21 13					21 43				22 13		
Broadstairs	d												
Margate 4	d												
Birchington-on-Sea	d												
Herne Bay	d												
Whitstable	d												
Faversham 2	a												
	d					20 58			21 28				21 58
Sittingbourne 4	d					21 07			21 37				22 07
Rainham (Kent)	d					21 15			21 45				22 15
Gillingham (Kent) 4	d					21 20			21 50				22 20
Chatham 4	d					21 24			21 54				22 24
Rochester 4	d					21 27			21 57				22 27
Maidstone West	d												
Strood 4	d					21 32			22 02				22 32
Gravesend	d					21 43			22 13				22 43
Ebbsfleet International	a	21 32				21 46	22 02		22 16		22 32		22 46
	d	21 32				21 48	22 02		22 17		22 32		22 47
Stratford International ⊖	a	21 44				22 00	22 14		22 29		22 44		22 59
St Pancras International 4 ⊖	a	21 51				22 07	22 21		22 36		22 51		23 06

		SE		SE 1	SE	SE 1
Margate 4	d	21 53				
Broadstairs	d	21 59				
Ramsgate 4	d	22 05		22 24		22 50
Canterbury West	a	22 24		22 46		
	d	22 25		22 47		
Sandwich	d					23 02
Deal	d					23 08
Dover Priory	d				22 45	23 25
Folkestone Central	d				22 56	23 36
Folkestone West	d				22 58	23 38
Ashford International	a	22 41		23 08	23 11	23 56
	d	22 43			23 13	
Broadstairs	d					
Margate 4	d					
Birchington-on-Sea	d					
Herne Bay	d					
Whitstable	d					
Faversham 2	a					
	d					
Sittingbourne 4	d					
Rainham (Kent)	d					
Gillingham (Kent) 4	d					
Chatham 4	d					
Rochester 4	d					
Maidstone West	d					
Strood 4	d					
Gravesend	d					
Ebbsfleet International	a	23 02			23 32	
	d	23 02			23 32	
Stratford International ⊖	a	23 14			23 44	
St Pancras International 4 ⊖	a	23 21			23 51	

Table 194R

Saturdays

14 December to 17 May

Kent - St Pancras International
High Speed Domestic Services

Network Diagram - see first Page of Table 194

		SE [1]	SE	SE	SE	SE [1]	SE [1]	SE [1]	SE	SE	SE		SE [1]	SE [1]	SE	SE	SE	SE [1]	SE	SE [1]	SE [1]	SE		SE	SE
Margate [4]	d								05 53							06 53								07 53	
Broadstairs	d								05 59							06 59								07 59	
Ramsgate [4]	d		05 05			05 32		05 50	06 05				06 40	06 50		07 05				07 40	07 50			08 05	
Canterbury West	a		05 24			05 54			06 24				07 02			07 24				08 02				08 24	
	d		05 25			05 56			06 25				07 04			07 25		07 36		08 07				08 25	
Sandwich	d							06 02						07 02							08 02				
Deal	d							06 08						07 08							08 08				
Dover Priory	d	04 51			05 45		05 51	06 25			06 45			07 25					07 45		08 25				
Folkestone Central	d	05 02			05 56		06 02	06 36			06 56			07 36					07 56		08 36				
Folkestone West	d	05 04			05 58		06 04	06 38			06 58			07 38					07 58		08 38				
Ashford International	a	05 21	05 41		06 11	06 17	06 21	06 55	06 41		07 11		07 26	07 55		07 41		07 58	08 11	08 25	08 55			08 41	
	d		05 43		06 13				06 43		07 13					07 43			08 13					08 43	
Broadstairs	d																								
Margate [4]	d																								
Birchington-on-Sea	d																								
Herne Bay	d																								
Whitstable	d																								
Faversham [2]	a																								
	d			05 28						06 28					06 58		07 28					07 58			08 28
Sittingbourne [4]	d			05 37						06 37					07 07		07 37					08 07			08 37
Rainham (Kent)	d			05 45						06 45					07 15		07 45					08 15			08 45
Gillingham (Kent) [4]	d			05 50						06 50					07 20		07 50					08 20			08 50
Chatham [4]	d			05 54						06 54					07 24		07 54					08 24			08 54
Rochester [4]	d			05 57						06 57					07 27		07 57					08 27			08 57
Maidstone West	d																								
Strood [4]	d			06 02						07 02					07 32		08 02					08 32			09 02
Gravesend	d			06 13						07 13					07 43		08 13					08 43			09 13
Ebbsfleet International	a		06 02	06 16	06 32				07 02	07 16	07 32				07 46	08 02	08 16		08 32			08 46		09 02	09 16
	d		06 02	06 17	06 32				07 02	07 17	07 32				07 47	08 02	08 18		08 32			08 47		09 02	09 18
Stratford International ⊖	a		06 14	06 29	06 44				07 14	07 29	07 44				07 59	08 14	08 30		08 44			08 59		09 14	09 30
St Pancras International [4] ⊖	a		06 21	06 36	06 51				07 21	07 36	07 51				08 06	08 21	08 37		08 51			09 06		09 21	09 37

		SE [1]	SE	SE [1]	SE [1]	SE	SE	SE	SE [1]		SE	SE [1]	SE [1]	SE	SE	SE	SE [1]	SE	SE [1]	SE [1]		SE	SE	SE	SE [1]
Margate [4]	d						08 53								09 53								10 53		
Broadstairs	d						08 59								09 59								10 59		
Ramsgate [4]	d			08 40	08 50		09 05					09 40	09 50		10 05				10 40	10 50			11 05		
Canterbury West	a			09 02			09 24					10 02			10 24				11 02				11 24		
	d	08 36		09 07			09 25		09 36			10 07			10 25		10 36		11 07				11 25		11 36
Sandwich	d				09 02								10 02							11 02					
Deal	d				09 08								10 08							11 08					
Dover Priory	d		08 45		09 25						09 45		10 25					10 45		11 25					
Folkestone Central	d		08 56		09 36						09 56		10 36					10 56		11 36					
Folkestone West	d		08 58		09 38						09 58		10 38					10 58		11 38					
Ashford International	a	08 58	09 11	09 28	09 55		09 41		09 58		10 11	10 25	10 55		10 41		10 58	11 11	11 25	11 55			11 41		11 58
	d		09 13				09 43				10 13				10 43			11 13					11 43		
Broadstairs	d																								
Margate [4]	d																								
Birchington-on-Sea	d																								
Herne Bay	d																								
Whitstable	d																								
Faversham [2]	a																								
	d					08 58		09 28						09 58		10 28						10 58		11 28	
Sittingbourne [4]	d					09 07		09 37						10 07		10 37						11 07		11 37	
Rainham (Kent)	d					09 15		09 45						10 15		10 45						11 15		11 45	
Gillingham (Kent) [4]	d					09 20		09 50						10 20		10 50						11 20		11 50	
Chatham [4]	d					09 24		09 54						10 24		10 54						11 24		11 54	
Rochester [4]	d					09 27		09 57						10 27		10 57						11 27		11 57	
Maidstone West	d																								
Strood [4]	d					09 32		10 02						10 32		11 02						11 32		12 02	
Gravesend	d					09 43		10 13						10 43		11 13						11 43		12 13	
Ebbsfleet International	a		09 32			09 46	10 02	10 16			10 32			10 46	11 02	11 16		11 31				11 46	12 02	12 16	
	d		09 32			09 47	10 02	10 17			10 32			10 47	11 02	11 17		11 32				11 47	12 02	12 18	
Stratford International ⊖	a		09 44			09 59	10 14	10 29			10 44			10 59	11 14	11 29		11 44				11 59	12 14	12 30	
St Pancras International [4] ⊖	a		09 51			10 06	10 21	10 36			10 51			11 06	11 21	11 36		11 51				12 06	12 21	12 37	

Table 194R

Saturdays

14 December to 17 May

Kent - St Pancras International High Speed Domestic Services

Network Diagram - see first Page of Table 194

		SE	SE 1	SE 1	SE		SE	SE	SE 1	SE	SE 1	SE 1	SE	SE	SE	SE 1		SE	SE 1	SE 1	SE	SE	SE	SE 1	SE
Margate 4	d						11 53							12 53								13 53			
Broadstairs	d						11 59							12 59								13 59			
Ramsgate 4	d		11 40	11 50			12 05				12 40	12 50		13 05					13 40	13 50		14 05			
Canterbury West	a		12 02				12 24				13 02			13 24					14 02			14 24			
	d		12 07				12 25		12 36		13 07			13 25		13 36			14 07			14 25		14 36	
Sandwich	d			12 02								13 02								14 02					
Deal	d			12 08								13 08								14 08					
Dover Priory	d	11 45		12 25						12 45		13 25						13 45		14 25					14 45
Folkestone Central	d	11 56		12 36						12 56		13 36						13 56		14 36					14 56
Folkestone West	d	11 58		12 38						12 58		13 38						13 58		14 38					14 58
Ashford International	a	12 11	12 25	12 55			12 41		12 58	13 11	13 25	13 55		13 41		13 58		14 11	14 25	14 55		14 41		14 58	15 11
	d	12 13					12 43			13 13				13 43				14 13				14 43			15 13
Broadstairs	d																								
Margate 4	d																								
Birchington-on-Sea	d																								
Herne Bay	d																								
Whitstable	d																								
Faversham 2	a																								
	d				11 58			12 28					12 58		13 28						13 58		14 28		
Sittingbourne 4	d				12 07			12 37					13 07		13 37						14 07		14 37		
Rainham (Kent)	d				12 15			12 45					13 15		13 45						14 15		14 45		
Gillingham (Kent) 4	d				12 20			12 50					13 20		13 50						14 20		14 50		
Chatham 4	d				12 24			12 54					13 24		13 54						14 24		14 54		
Rochester 4	d				12 27			12 57					13 27		13 57						14 27		14 57		
Maidstone West	d																								
Strood 4	d				12 32			13 02					13 32		14 02						14 32		15 02		
Gravesend	d				12 43			13 13					13 43		14 13						14 43		15 13		
Ebbsfleet International	a	12 32			12 46		13 02	13 16		13 32			13 46	14 02	14 16			14 32			14 46	15 02	15 16		15 32
	d	12 32			12 48		13 02	13 17		13 32			13 48	14 02	14 17			14 32			14 47	15 02	15 18		15 32
Stratford International ⊖	a	12 44			13 00		13 14	13 29		13 44			14 00	14 14	14 29			14 44			14 59	15 14	15 30		15 44
St Pancras International 4 ⊖	a	12 51			13 07		13 21	13 36		13 51			14 07	14 21	14 36			14 51			15 06	15 21	15 37		15 51

		SE 1	SE 1		SE	SE	SE	SE 1	SE	SE 1	SE 1	SE	SE	SE		SE 1	SE	SE 1	SE 1	SE	SE	SE	SE 1	SE	SE 1
Margate 4	d					14 53							15 53								16 53				
Broadstairs	d					14 59							15 59								16 59				
Ramsgate 4	d	14 40	14 50			15 05				15 40	15 50		16 05					16 40	16 50		17 05				17 40
Canterbury West	a	15 02				15 24				16 02			16 24					17 02			17 24				18 02
	d	15 07				15 25		15 36		16 07			16 25			16 36		17 07			17 25		17 36		18 07
Sandwich	d		15 02								16 02								17 02						
Deal	d		15 08								16 08								17 08						
Dover Priory	d		15 25						15 45		16 25						16 45		17 25					17 45	
Folkestone Central	d		15 36						15 56		16 36						16 56		17 36					17 56	
Folkestone West	d		15 38						15 58		16 38						16 58		17 38					17 58	
Ashford International	a	15 25	15 55			15 41		15 58	16 11	16 25	16 55		16 41			16 58	17 11	17 26	17 55		17 41		17 58	18 11	18 25
	d					15 46			16 13				16 43				17 13				17 43			18 13	
Broadstairs	d																								
Margate 4	d																								
Birchington-on-Sea	d																								
Herne Bay	d																								
Whitstable	d																								
Faversham 2	a																								
	d				14 58		15 28					15 58		16 28						16 58		17 28			
Sittingbourne 4	d				15 07		15 37					16 07		16 37						17 07		17 37			
Rainham (Kent)	d				15 15		15 45					16 15		16 45						17 15		17 45			
Gillingham (Kent) 4	d				15 20		15 50					16 20		16 50						17 20		17 50			
Chatham 4	d				15 24		15 54					16 24		16 54						17 24		17 54			
Rochester 4	d				15 27		15 57					16 27		16 57						17 27		17 57			
Maidstone West	d																								
Strood 4	d				15 32		16 02					16 32		17 02						17 32		18 02			
Gravesend	d				15 43		16 13					16 43		17 13						17 43		18 13			
Ebbsfleet International	a				15 46	16 05	16 16		16 31			16 46	17 02	17 16			17 32			17 46	18 02	18 16		18 32	
	d				15 51	16 06	16 17		16 32			16 47	17 02	17 17			17 32			17 47	18 02	18 18		18 34	
Stratford International ⊖	a				16 02	16 17	16 29		16 44			16 59	17 14	17 29			17 44			17 59	18 14	18 30		18 45	
St Pancras International 4 ⊖	a				16 10	16 24	16 36		16 51			17 06	17 21	17 36			17 51			18 06	18 21	18 37		18 53	

Table 194R

Saturdays

14 December to 17 May

Kent - St Pancras International High Speed Domestic Services

Network Diagram - see first Page of Table 194

		SE 1	SE	SE	SE	SE 1	SE	SE 1	SE 1	SE		SE	SE	SE 1	SE	SE 1	SE 1	SE	SE	SE	SE		SE 1	SE 1	SE
Margate 4	d			17 53								18 53							19 53						
Broadstairs	d			17 59								18 59							19 59						
Ramsgate 4	d	17 50		18 05				18 40	18 50			19 05				19 40	19 50		20 05				20 40	20 50	
Canterbury West	a			18 24				19 02				19 24				20 02			20 24				21 02		
	d			18 25		18 36		19 07				19 25		19 36		20 04			20 25				21 04		
Sandwich	d	18 02							19 02								20 02							21 02	
Deal	d	18 08							19 08								20 08							21 08	
Dover Priory	d	18 25					18 45		19 25						19 45		20 25				20 45			21 25	
Folkestone Central	d	18 36					18 56		19 36						19 56		20 36				20 56			21 36	
Folkestone West	d	18 38					18 58		19 38						19 58		20 38				20 58			21 38	
Ashford International	a	18 55		18 41		18 58	19 11	19 25	19 55			19 41		19 58	20 11	20 25	20 55		20 41		21 11		21 25	21 55	
	d			18 43			19 13					19 43			20 13				20 43		21 13				
Broadstairs	d																								
Margate 4	d																								
Birchington-on-Sea	d																								
Herne Bay	d																								
Whitstable	d																								
Faversham 2	a																								
	d		17 58		18 28					18 58			19 28					19 58		20 28					20 58
Sittingbourne 4	d		18 07		18 37					19 07			19 37					20 07		20 37					21 07
Rainham (Kent)	d		18 15		18 45					19 15			19 45					20 15		20 45					21 15
Gillingham (Kent) 4	d		18 20		18 50					19 20			19 50					20 20		20 50					21 20
Chatham 4	d		18 24		18 54					19 24			19 54					20 24		20 54					21 24
Rochester 4	d		18 27		18 57					19 27			19 57					20 27		20 57					21 27
Maidstone West	d																								
Strood 4	d		18 32		19 02					19 32			20 02					20 32		21 02					21 32
Gravesend	d		18 43		19 13					19 43			20 13					20 43		21 13					21 43
Ebbsfleet International	a		18 46	19 02	19 16		19 32			19 46		20 02	20 16		20 32			20 46	21 02	21 16	21 32				21 46
	d		18 47	19 02	19 17		19 32			19 47		20 02	20 17		20 32			20 47	21 02	21 17	21 32				21 47
Stratford International ⊖	a		18 59	19 14	19 29		19 44			19 59		20 14	20 29		20 44			20 59	21 14	21 29	21 44				21 59
St Pancras International 4 ⊖	a		19 06	19 21	19 36		19 51			20 06		20 21	20 36		20 51			21 06	21 21	21 36	21 51				22 06

		SE	SE	SE	SE 1	SE	SE	SE 1		SE	SE 1
Margate 4	d	20 53					21 53				
Broadstairs	d	20 59					21 59				
Ramsgate 4	d	21 05			21 23		22 05	22 24			22 50
Canterbury West	a	21 24					22 24	22 46			
	d	21 25					22 25	22 47			
Sandwich	d				21 35						23 02
Deal	d				21 41						23 08
Dover Priory	d			21 45	21 58					22 45	23 25
Folkestone Central	d			21 56	22 09					22 56	23 36
Folkestone West	d			21 58	22 11					22 58	23 38
Ashford International	a	21 41		22 11	22 28		22 41	23 08		23 11	23 56
	d	21 43		22 13			22 43			23 13	
Broadstairs	d										
Margate 4	d										
Birchington-on-Sea	d										
Herne Bay	d										
Whitstable	d										
Faversham 2	a										
	d		21 28			21 58					
Sittingbourne 4	d		21 37			22 07					
Rainham (Kent)	d		21 45			22 15					
Gillingham (Kent) 4	d		21 50			22 20					
Chatham 4	d		21 54			22 24					
Rochester 4	d		21 57			22 27					
Maidstone West	d										
Strood 4	d		22 02			22 32					
Gravesend	d		22 13			22 43					
Ebbsfleet International	a	22 02	22 16	22 32		22 46	23 02			23 32	
	d	22 02	22 17	22 32		22 47	23 02			23 32	
Stratford International ⊖	a	22 14	22 29	22 44		22 59	23 14			23 44	
St Pancras International 4 ⊖	a	22 21	22 36	22 51		23 06	23 21			23 51	

Table 194R

Sundays

8 December to 11 May

Kent - St Pancras International High Speed Domestic Services

Network Diagram - see first Page of Table 194

		SE	SE	SE 1	SE	SE 1	SE 1	SE	SE	SE	SE 1	SE 1	SE	SE	SE 1	SE	SE 1	SE 1	SE	SE	SE 1	SE	SE 1
Margate 4	d								07 53					08 53						09 53			
Broadstairs	d								07 59					08 59						09 59			
Ramsgate 4	d			06 50		07 40	07 50		08 05		08 40	08 50		09 05			09 40	09 50		10 05			10 40
Canterbury West	a					08 02			08 24		09 02			09 24			10 02			10 24			11 02
	d					08 04			08 25		09 04			09 25	09 36		10 07			10 25	10 36		11 07
Sandwich	d			07 02			08 02					09 02						10 02					
Deal	d			07 08			08 08					09 08						10 08					
Dover Priory	d			07 25	07 45		08 25			08 45		09 25				09 45		10 25				10 45	
Folkestone Central	d			07 36	07 56		08 36			08 56		09 36				09 56		10 36				10 56	
Folkestone West	d			07 38	07 58		08 38			08 58		09 38				09 58		10 38				10 58	
Ashford International	a			07 55	08 11	08 25	08 55		08 41	09 11	09 25	09 55		09 41	09 58	10 11	10 25	10 55		10 41	10 58	11 11	11 25
	d		07 43		08 13				08 43	09 13				09 43		10 13				10 43		11 13	
Broadstairs	d																						
Margate 4	d																						
Birchington-on-Sea	d																						
Herne Bay	d																						
Whitstable	d																						
Faversham 2	a																						
	d	06 58						07 58					08 58						09 58				
Sittingbourne 4	d	07 07						08 07					09 07						10 07				
Rainham (Kent)	d	07 15						08 15					09 15						10 15				
Gillingham (Kent) 4	d	07 20						08 20					09 20						10 20				
Chatham 4	d	07 24						08 24					09 24						10 24				
Rochester 4	d	07 27						08 27					09 27						10 27				
Maidstone West	d																						
Strood 4	d	07 32						08 32					09 32						10 32				
Gravesend	d	07 43						08 43					09 43						10 43				
Ebbsfleet International	a	07 47	08 02		08 32			08 47	09 02	09 32			09 46	10 02		10 32			10 46	11 02		11 32	
	d	07 47	08 02		08 32			08 47	09 02	09 32			09 47	10 02		10 32			10 47	11 02		11 32	
Stratford International ⊖	a	07 59	08 14		08 44			08 59	09 14	09 44			09 59	10 14		10 44			10 59	11 14		11 44	
St Pancras International 4 ⊖	a	08 06	08 21		08 51			09 06	09 21	09 51			10 06	10 21		10 51			11 06	11 21		11 51	

		SE 1	SE	SE	SE	SE 1	SE	SE 1	SE 1	SE	SE	SE	SE 1	SE	SE 1	SE 1	SE	SE	SE	SE 1	SE	SE 1	SE 1
Margate 4	d			10 53							11 53							12 53					
Broadstairs	d			10 59							11 59							12 59					
Ramsgate 4	d	10 50		11 05				11 40	11 50		12 05				12 40	12 50		13 05				13 40	13 50
Canterbury West	a			11 24				12 02			12 24				13 02			13 24				14 02	
	d			11 25		11 36		12 07			12 25		12 36		13 07			13 25		13 36		14 07	
Sandwich	d	11 02							12 02							13 02							14 02
Deal	d	11 08							12 08							13 08							14 08
Dover Priory	d	11 25					11 45		12 25					12 45		13 25					13 45		14 25
Folkestone Central	d	11 36					11 56		12 36					12 56		13 36					13 56		14 36
Folkestone West	d	11 38					11 58		12 38					12 58		13 38					13 58		14 38
Ashford International	a	11 55		11 41		11 58	12 11	12 25	12 55		12 41		12 58	13 11	13 25	13 55		13 41		13 58	14 11	14 25	14 55
	d			11 43			12 13				12 43			13 13				13 43			14 13		
Broadstairs	d																						
Margate 4	d																						
Birchington-on-Sea	d																						
Herne Bay	d																						
Whitstable	d																						
Faversham 2	a																						
	d		10 58		11 28					11 58		12 28					12 58		13 28				
Sittingbourne 4	d		11 07		11 37					12 07		12 37					13 07		13 37				
Rainham (Kent)	d		11 15		11 45					12 15		12 45					13 15		13 45				
Gillingham (Kent) 4	d		11 20		11 50					12 20		12 50					13 20		13 50				
Chatham 4	d		11 24		11 54					12 24		12 54					13 24		13 54				
Rochester 4	d		11 27		11 57					12 27		12 57					13 27		13 57				
Maidstone West	d																						
Strood 4	d		11 32		12 02					12 32		13 02					13 32		14 02				
Gravesend	d		11 43		12 13					12 43		13 13					13 43		14 13				
Ebbsfleet International	a		11 46	12 02	12 16		12 32			12 46	13 02	13 16		13 32			13 46	14 02	14 16		14 32		
	d		11 47	12 02	12 18		12 32			12 48	13 02	13 18		13 32			13 47	14 02	14 17		14 32		
Stratford International ⊖	a		11 59	12 14	12 30		12 44			13 00	13 14	13 30		13 44			13 59	14 14	14 29		14 44		
St Pancras International 4 ⊖	a		12 06	12 21	12 37		12 51			13 07	13 21	13 37		13 51			14 06	14 21	14 36		14 51		

Table 194R

Sundays

8 December to 11 May

Kent - St Pancras International High Speed Domestic Services

Network Diagram - see first Page of Table 194

		SE	SE		SE	SE 1	SE	SE 1	SE 1	SE	SE	SE	SE 1	SE		SE 1	SE 1	SE	SE	SE	SE 1	SE	SE 1	SE 1	SE
Margate 4	d		13 53								14 53								15 53						
Broadstairs	d		13 59								14 59								15 59						
Ramsgate 4	d		14 05					14 40	14 50		15 05					15 40	15 50		16 05				16 40	16 50	
Canterbury West	a		14 24					15 02			15 24					16 02			16 24				17 02		
	d		14 25			14 36		15 07			15 25		15 36			16 07			16 25		16 36		17 07		
Sandwich	d								15 02								16 02							17 02	
Deal	d								15 08								16 08							17 08	
Dover Priory	d						14 45		15 25					15 45			16 25					16 45		17 25	
Folkestone Central	d						14 56		15 36					15 56			16 36					16 56		17 36	
Folkestone West	d						14 58		15 38					15 58			16 38					16 58		17 38	
Ashford International	a		14 41			14 58	15 11	15 25	15 55		15 41		15 58	16 11		16 25	16 55		16 41		16 58	17 11	17 25	17 55	
	d		14 43				15 13				15 43			16 13					16 43			17 13			
Broadstairs	d																								
Margate 4	d																								
Birchington-on-Sea	d																								
Herne Bay	d																								
Whitstable	d																								
Faversham 2	a																								
	d	13 58			14 28					14 58		15 28						15 58		16 28					16 58
Sittingbourne 4	d	14 07			14 37					15 07		15 37						16 07		16 37					17 07
Rainham (Kent)	d	14 15			14 45					15 15		15 45						16 15		16 45					17 15
Gillingham (Kent) 4	d	14 20			14 50					15 20		15 50						16 20		16 50					17 20
Chatham 4	d	14 24			14 54					15 24		15 54						16 24		16 54					17 24
Rochester 4	d	14 27			14 57					15 27		15 57						16 27		16 57					17 27
Maidstone West	d																								
Strood 4	d	14 32			15 02					15 32		16 02						16 32		17 02					17 32
Gravesend	d	14 43			15 13					15 43		16 13						16 43		17 13					17 43
Ebbsfleet International	a	14 46	15 02		15 16		15 32			15 46	16 02	16 16		16 32					17 02	17 16		17 32			17 46
	d	14 48	15 02		15 18		15 32			15 51	16 02	16 17		16 32					17 02	17 17		17 32			17 48
Stratford International ⊖	a	15 00	15 14		15 30		15 44			16 02	16 14	16 29		16 44					17 14	17 29		17 44			18 00
St Pancras International 4 ⊖	a	15 07	15 21		15 37		15 51			16 09	16 21	16 36		16 51				17 06	17 21	17 36		17 51			18 07

			SE	SE	SE 1	SE	SE 1	SE 1	SE	SE	SE	SE 1		SE	SE 1	SE 1	SE	SE	SE	SE	SE 1	SE 1	SE		SE
Margate 4	d		16 53							17 53								18 53							19 53
Broadstairs	d		16 59							17 59								18 59							19 59
Ramsgate 4	d		17 05				17 40	17 50		18 05					18 40	18 50		19 05			19 40	19 50			20 05
Canterbury West	a		17 24				18 02			18 24					19 02			19 24			20 02				20 24
	d		17 25		17 36		18 07			18 25		18 36			19 04			19 25			20 04				20 25
Sandwich	d							18 02								19 02						20 02			
Deal	d							18 08								19 08						20 08			
Dover Priory	d					17 45		18 25						18 45		19 25				19 45		20 25			
Folkestone Central	d					17 56		18 36						18 56		19 36				19 56		20 36			
Folkestone West	d					17 58		18 38						18 58		19 38				19 58		20 38			
Ashford International	a		17 41		17 58	18 11	18 25	18 55		18 41		18 58		19 11	19 25	19 55		19 41		20 11	20 25	20 55			20 41
	d		17 43			18 13				18 43				19 13				19 43		20 13					20 43
Broadstairs	d																								
Margate 4	d																								
Birchington-on-Sea	d																								
Herne Bay	d																								
Whitstable	d																								
Faversham 2	a																								
	d			17 28					17 58		18 28						18 58		19 28				19 58		
Sittingbourne 4	d			17 37					18 07		18 37						19 07		19 37				20 07		
Rainham (Kent)	d			17 45					18 15		18 45						19 15		19 45				20 15		
Gillingham (Kent) 4	d			17 50					18 20		18 50						19 20		19 50				20 20		
Chatham 4	d			17 54					18 24		18 54						19 24		19 54				20 24		
Rochester 4	d			17 57					18 27		18 57						19 27		19 57				20 27		
Maidstone West	d																								
Strood 4	d			18 02					18 32		19 02						19 32		20 02				20 32		
Gravesend	d			18 13					18 43		19 13						19 43		20 13				20 43		
Ebbsfleet International	a		18 02	18 16		18 32			18 46	19 02	19 16			19 32			19 46	20 02	20 16	20 32			20 46		21 02
	d		18 02	18 18		18 34			18 48	19 02	19 17			19 32			19 48	20 02	20 17	20 32			20 51		21 02
Stratford International ⊖	a		18 14	18 30		18 45			18 59	19 14	19 29			19 44			20 00	20 14	20 29	20 44			21 02		21 14
St Pancras International 4 ⊖	a		18 21	18 37		18 53			19 07	19 21	19 36			19 51			20 07	20 21	20 36	20 51			21 09		21 21

Table 194R

Sundays

8 December to 11 May

Kent - St Pancras International
High Speed Domestic Services

Network Diagram - see first Page of Table 194

		SE	SE	SE	SE	SE	SE	SE	SE	SE	SE	SE	SE
				1	1					1	1		
Margate 4	d						20 53						21 53
Broadstairs	d						20 59						21 59
Ramsgate 4	d			20 40	20 50		21 05			21 40	21 50		22 05
Canterbury West	a			21 02			21 24			22 02			22 24
	d			21 04			21 25			22 04			22 25
Sandwich	d				21 02						22 02		
Deal	d				21 08						22 08		
Dover Priory	d		20 45		21 25				21 45		22 25		
Folkestone Central	d		20 56		21 36				21 56		22 36		
Folkestone West	d		20 58		21 38				21 58		22 38		
Ashford International	a		21 11	21 25	21 55		21 41		22 11	22 25	22 55		22 41
	d		21 13				21 43		22 13				22 43
Broadstairs	d												
Margate 4	d												
Birchington-on-Sea	d												
Herne Bay	d												
Whitstable	d												
Faversham 2	a												
	d	20 28				20 58		21 28				21 58	
Sittingbourne 4	d	20 37				21 07		21 37				22 07	
Rainham (Kent)	d	20 45				21 15		21 45				22 15	
Gillingham (Kent) 4	d	20 50				21 20		21 50				22 20	
Chatham 4	d	20 54				21 24		21 54				22 24	
Rochester 4	d	20 57				21 27		21 57				22 27	
Maidstone West	d												
Strood 4	d	21 02				21 32		22 02				22 32	
Gravesend	d	21 13				21 43		22 13				22 43	
Ebbsfleet International	a	21 16	21 32			21 46	22 02	22 16	22 32			22 46	23 02
	d	21 17	21 32			21 48	22 02	22 17	22 32			22 47	23 02
Stratford International ⊖	a	21 29	21 44			22 00	22 14	22 29	22 44			22 59	23 14
St Pancras International 4 ⊖	a	21 36	21 51			22 07	22 22	22 36	22 51			23 06	23 21

Network Diagram for Tables 195, 196 | also 199⊙

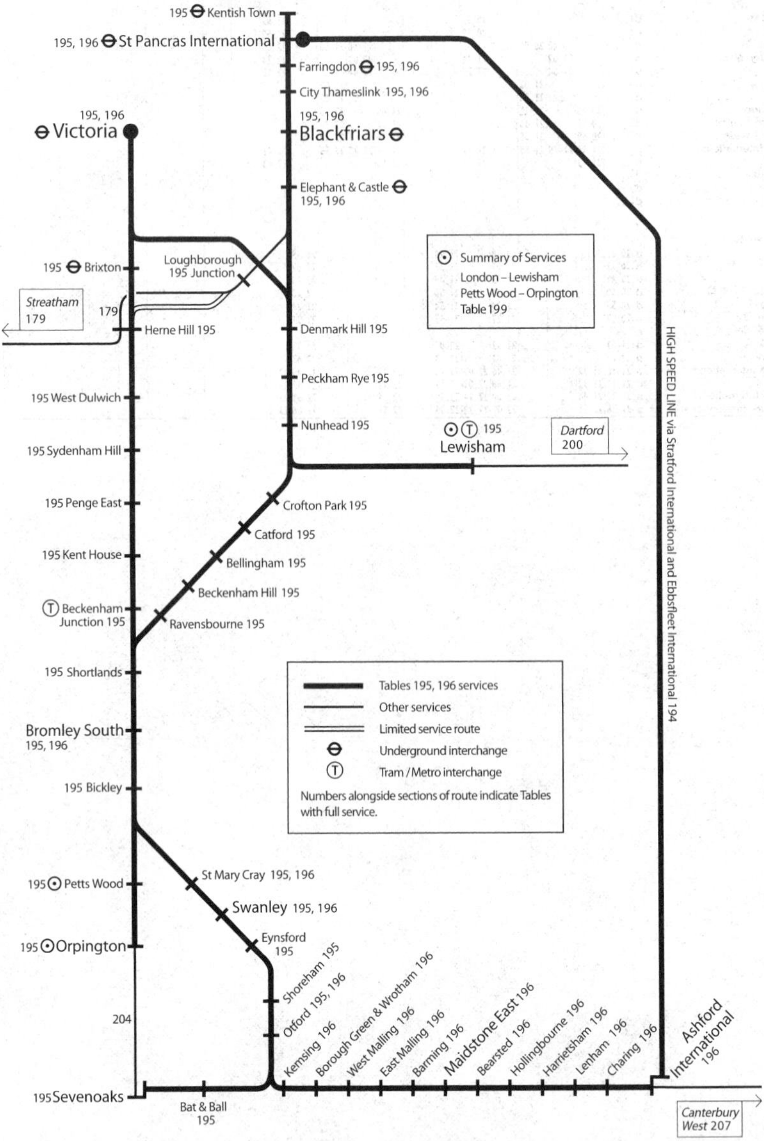

195 Kentish Town
195, 196 St Pancras International
Farringdon 195, 196
City Thameslink 195, 196
195, 196 Blackfriars
195, 196 Victoria
Elephant & Castle 195, 196
195 Brixton
Loughborough 195 Junction
Streatham 179
179
Herne Hill 195
Denmark Hill 195
Peckham Rye 195
Nunhead 195
195 West Dulwich
195 Sydenham Hill
195 Penge East
195 Kent House
Beckenham Junction 195
195 Shortlands
Bromley South 195, 196
195 Bickley
195 Petts Wood
195 Orpington
204
195 Sevenoaks
Bat & Ball 195
Crofton Park 195
Catford 195
Bellingham 195
Beckenham Hill 195
Ravensbourne 195
195 Lewisham
Dartford 200
Summary of Services
London – Lewisham
Petts Wood – Orpington
Table 199
HIGH SPEED LINE via Stratford International and Ebbsfleet International 194
Tables 195, 196 services
Other services
Limited service route
Underground interchange
Tram / Metro interchange
Numbers alongside sections of route indicate Tables with full service.
St Mary Cray 195, 196
Swanley 195, 196
Eynsford 195
Shoreham 195
Otford 195, 196
Kemsing 196
Borough Green & Wrotham 196
West Malling 196
East Malling 196
Barming 196
Maidstone East 196
Bearsted 196
Hollingbourne 196
Harrietsham 196
Lenham 196
Charing 196
Ashford International 196
Canterbury West 207

TOCs operating on this network - Southeastern (SE), First Capital Connect (FC)

Table 195

Mondays to Fridays

9 December to 16 May

London Victoria/Kentish Town - Catford, Beckenham Junction, Bromley South, Orpington, Otford and Sevenoaks

Network Diagram - see first Page of Table 195

Miles	Miles	Miles	Station		SE MO A	SE MX A	SE MO [1] B	SE MX [1] C	SE A	SE D	SE MX [1] E	SE F	SE [1] G	SE	SE	FC H	SE	FC I	SE [1] G	SE	SE [1] E	SE	SE [1] G
0	—	0	**London Victoria** [15] ⊖	d							00 07	00 37	05 22		05 30		05 40		05 52		06 07	06 10	06 22
3¼	—	—	Brixton ⊖	d						00 02							05 47					06 17	
—	—	—	Kentish Town ⊖	d														05 50					
—	—	—	St Pancras International [15] ⊖	d												05 36		05 54					
—	—	—	Farringdon ⊖	d												05 42		06 00					
—	—	—	City Thameslink [3]	d												05 44		06 03					
—	0	—	**London Blackfriars** [3] ⊖	d										05 24		05 47		06 06					
—	1¼	—	Elephant & Castle ⊖	d										05 28		05 50		06 09					
—	—	—	Loughborough Jn	d														06 13					
4	—	—	Herne Hill [4]	d						00 04		00 45				05a57	05 49	06a17				06 19	
5	—	—	West Dulwich	d						00 06							05 51					06 21	
5¾	—	—	Sydenham Hill	d						00 08							05 53					06 23	
7¼	—	—	Penge East	d						00 11		00 50					05 56					06 26	
7¾	—	—	Kent House [4]	d						00 13							05 58					06 28	
8¾	—	—	**Beckenham Junction** [4]	d						00 15		00 52					06 00					06 30	
—	3¾	4¼	Denmark Hill [4]	d										05 34	05 44								
—	4½	5	Peckham Rye [4]	d										05 37	05 46								
—	5¼	5¾	Nunhead [4]	d										05 39									
—	—	7½	Lewisham [4]	a																			
—	6½	—	Crofton Park	d										05 42									
—	7½	—	Catford	d					00 03					05 45									
—	8¼	—	Bellingham	d					00 05					05 47									
—	9	—	Beckenham Hill	d					00 07					05 49									
—	9¾	—	Ravensbourne	d					00 09					05 51									
10	10½	—	Shortlands [4]	d					00 11	00 18				05 53			06 03					06 33	
11	11½	—	**Bromley South** [4]	d			00 02	00 09	00 14	00 21	00 25	00 57	05 39	05 57	05a57		06 06		06 09	06 16	06 23	06 37	06 39
12	12½	—	Bickley [4]	d					00 17	00 24				05 59			06 09			06 18		06 39	
13¾	—	—	Petts Wood [4]	d						00 29							06 14					06 44	
15	—	—	**Orpington** [4]	a						00 32							06 18					06 49	
—	14¾	—	St Mary Cray	d			00 08	00 15	00 21		00 32	01 03	05 45	06 04						06 23	06 30		06 45
—	17½	—	**Swanley** [4]	d			00a12	00a19	00 26		00 36	01a07	05a49	06 09					06a19	06 28	06 34		06a49
—	20½	—	Eynsford	d	00 01				00 30					06 14						06 32			
—	22¾	—	Shoreham (Kent)	d	00 04	00 04			00 34					06 17						06 36			
—	24	—	Otford [4]	d	00 07	00 07			00 37		00a44			06 20						06 39	06a42		
—	25¾	—	Bat & Ball	d	00 10	00 10			00 40					06 23						06 42			
—	27	—	**Sevenoaks** [4]	a	00 13	00 13			00 43					06 27						06 45			

Station		FC	FC J	SE	SE [1] E	SE [1] K	SE	FC I	SE	SE [1] F	SE [1] E	FC [1] L	FC I	FC [1] M	SE	SE [1] G	SE	SE [1] E	FC N	FC [1] O	FC [1] L	FC P	FC Q
London Victoria [15] ⊖	d			06 30	06 37	06 45			06 50	06 58	07 07				07 10	07 22	07 25	07 36					
Brixton ⊖	d			06 37					06 57						07 17		07 32						
Kentish Town ⊖	d	05 54	06 08					06 30					06 48						07 08			07 24	
St Pancras International [15] ⊖	d	05 58	06 12					06 34				06 44	06 52	07 04					07 12	07 16	07 24	07 28	07 32
Farringdon ⊖	d	06 04	06 18					06 40				06 50	06 58	07 10					07 18	07 22	07 30	07 34	07 38
City Thameslink [3]	d	06 07	06 21					06 43				06 53	07 01	07 13					07 21	07 25	07 33	07 37	07 41
London Blackfriars [3] ⊖	d	06 10	06 24				06 42	06 46				06 58	07 04	07 16					07 24	07 28	07 36	07 40	07 44
Elephant & Castle ⊖	d	06 16	06 27				06 46	06 49				07 02	07 07	07 19					07 28	07 33	07 40	07 44	07 47
Loughborough Jn	d		06 31					06 53					07 11	07 23						07 37			07 51
Herne Hill [4]	d		06a35	06 39				06a57	06 59				07a15	07a27	07 19		07 34			07a40			07a55
West Dulwich	d			06 41					07 02						07 21		07 36						
Sydenham Hill	d			06 43					07 04						07 23		07 38						
Penge East	d			06 46					07 07						07 26		07 41						
Kent House [4]	d			06 48					07 09						07 28		07 43						
Beckenham Junction [4]	d			06 50					07 11						07 30		07 45				07a52		
Denmark Hill [4]	d	06 22					06 52					07 09							07 34			07 50	
Peckham Rye [4]	d	06 25					06 55					07 12							07 36			07 53	
Nunhead [4]	d	06 27					06 57					07 14							07 39			07 56	
Lewisham [4]	a																						
Crofton Park	d	06 30					07 00					07 17							07 42				
Catford	d	06 33					07 03					07 20							07 44			08 00	
Bellingham	d	06 35					07 05					07 22							07 47			08 02	
Beckenham Hill	d	06 37					07 07					07 24							07 49				
Ravensbourne	d	06 39					07 09					07 26							07 51				
Shortlands [4]	d	06 41		06 54			07 11		07 14			07 28			07 33		07 48		07 54				
Bromley South [4]	d	06 44		06 57	06 58	07 02	07 14		07 17	07 19	07 23	07 31			07 38	07 40	07 51	07 53	07 57			08a10	
Bickley [4]	d	06 47		07 00			07 17		07 20			07 34			07 40		07 54		08 00				
Petts Wood [4]	d			07 06					07 24						07 49		07 59						
Orpington [4]	a			07 09					07 28						07 53		08 02						
St Mary Cray	d	06 51			07 04	07 08	07 21			07 25	07 30	07 38						08 00	08 04				
Swanley [4]	d	06 56			07 08	07a12	07 26			07a29	07 34	07 46				07a48		08 04	08 10				
Eynsford	d	07 00					07 30					07 50							08 15				
Shoreham (Kent)	d	07 04					07 34					07 54							08 18				
Otford [4]	d	07 07			07a16		07 37				07a42	07 58						08a12	08 22				
Bat & Ball	d	07 10					07 40					08 01							08 25				
Sevenoaks [4]	a	07 14					07 43					08 04							08 28				

A From London Blackfriars
B From London Victoria to Faversham
C From London Victoria to Gillingham (Kent)
D From London Victoria
E To Ashford International
F To Gillingham (Kent)
G To Ramsgate
H To Sutton (Surrey)
I From Luton to Sutton (Surrey)
J From West Hampstead Thameslink to Sutton (Surrey)
K To Dover Priory
L From Bedford
M From Bedford to Sutton (Surrey)
N From St Albans City
O From Bedford to Sutton (Surrey). [1] to London Blackfriars
P From Luton
Q From Flitwick to Sutton (Surrey)

Table 195

Mondays to Fridays

9 December to 16 May

London Victoria/Kentish Town - Catford, Beckenham Junction, Bromley South, Orpington, Otford and Sevenoaks

Network Diagram - see first Page of Table 195

		SE	SE A	SE 1 B	SE	SE 1 C	SE 1 D	FC E	FC F	FC G	SE A	SE	FC 1 E	FC H	FC G	SE 1 I	SE	SE 1 D	FC 1 J	FC K	SE A	SE	FC E
London Victoria 15	⊖ d	07 40	07 43	07 52	07 55	07 58	08 07				08 09	08 10				08 22	08 25	08 37			08 39	08 40	
Brixton	⊖ d	07 47			08 02							08 17					08 32					08 47	
Kentish Town	⊖ d								07 44					08 04						08 20			
St Pancras International 15	⊖ d							07 38	07 48	07 52			08 04	08 08	08 12				08 16	08 24			08 28
Farringdon	⊖ d							07 44	07 54	07 58			08 10	08 14	08 18				08 22	08 30			08 34
City Thameslink 3	d							07 47	07 57	08 01			08 13	08 17	08 21				08 25	08 33			08 37
London Blackfriars 3	⊖ d							07 50	08 00	08 04			08 16	08 20	08 24				08 28	08 36			08 40
Elephant & Castle	⊖ d							07 54	08 04	08 07					08 27				08 32	08 39			08 45
Loughborough Jn.	d									08 11					08 31								
Herne Hill 4	d	07 49			08 04					08a15		08 19			08a36		08 34			08a46		08 49	
West Dulwich	d	07 51			08 06							08 21					08 36					08 51	
Sydenham Hill	d	07 53			08 08							08 23					08 38					08 53	
Penge East	d	07 56			08 11							08 26					08 41					08 56	
Kent House 4	d	07 58			08 13							08 28	08a31				08 43					08 58	
Beckenham Junction 4	d	08 00			08 15							08 30					08 45					09 00	
Denmark Hill 4	d		07 53					08 00	08 10		08 18								08 38		08 48		08 52
Peckham Rye 4	d		07 56					08 03	08 13		08 21								08 41		08 51		08 55
Nunhead 4	d		07 59					08 06	08 15		08 23								08 43		08 53		08 57
Lewisham 4	a		08 07								08 30										09 01		
Crofton Park	d							08 09	08 18										08 46				09 00
Catford	d							08 12	08 21										08 49				09 03
Bellingham	d							08 15	08 23										08 51				09 05
Beckenham Hill	d							08 17	08 25										08 53				09 07
Ravensbourne	d							08 19	08 27										08 55				09 09
Shortlands 4	d	08 03						08 22	08 30			08 33					08 48		08 57			09 03	09 11
Bromley South 4	d	08 06		08a08	08 22	08 28	08 23	08 25	08 33			08 36		08a37		08a39	08 51	08 53	09 00			09 06	09 14
Bickley 4	d	08 09			08 24			08 28	08 35			08 39					08 54		09 03			09 09	09 17
Petts Wood 4	d	08 14			08 29			08 32				08 44					08 59					09 14	
Orpington 4	a	08 19			08 32			08 36				08 47					09 02					09 17	
St Mary Cray	d					08 34	08 30		08 40									09 00	09 07				09 21
Swanley 4	d					08a39	08 34		08 44									09 04	09 12				09 26
Eynsford	d								08 49										09 16				09 30
Shoreham (Kent)	d								08 52										09 20				09 34
Otford 4	d						08a42		08 55									09a12	09 23				09 37
Bat & Ball	d								08 58										09 26				09 40
Sevenoaks 4	a								09 01										09 29				09 45

		FC 1 L	FC H	FC G	FC 1 E	FC K	SE 1 B	SE	SE 1 M	SE 1 D	SE A	SE	FC F	FC K	SE 1 I	SE	SE 1 D	SE A	SE	FC H	FC G	FC K
London Victoria 15	⊖ d						08 52	08 55	08 58	09 07	09 09	09 10			09 22	09 25	09 37	09 39	09 40			
Brixton	⊖ d							09 02				09 17				09 32			09 47			
Kentish Town	⊖ d		08 36			08 52								09 12						09 26		09 44
St Pancras International 15	⊖ d	08 36	08 40	08 44	08 52	08 56							09 00	09 16						09 30	09 34	09 48
Farringdon	⊖ d	08 42	08 46	08 50	08 58	09 02							09 06	09 22						09 36	09 40	09 53
City Thameslink 3	d	08 45	08 49	08 53	09 01	09 05							09 09	09 25						09 39	09 43	09 57
London Blackfriars 3	⊖ d	08 48	08 52	08 56	09 04	09 08							09 12	09 28						09 42	09 46	10 00
Elephant & Castle	⊖ d		08 56	09 00	09a09	09 12							09 16	09 31						09 46	09 49	10 03
Loughborough Jn.	d			09 04		09 16								09 35							09 53	10 07
Herne Hill 4	d	08a57		09a08		09a21		09 04				09 19		09a39		09 34			09 49		09a57	10a11
West Dulwich	d							09 06				09 21				09 36			09 51			
Sydenham Hill	d							09 08				09 23				09 38			09 53			
Penge East	d							09 11				09 26				09 41			09 56			
Kent House 4	d							09 13				09 28				09 43			09 58			
Beckenham Junction 4	d							09 15				09 30				09 45			10 00			
Denmark Hill 4	d		09 02								09 18		09 22					09 48		09 52		
Peckham Rye 4	d										09 21		09 25					09 51		09 55		
Nunhead 4	d										09 23		09 27					09 53		09 57		
Lewisham 4	a										09 31							10 01				
Crofton Park	d												09 30							10 00		
Catford	d		09 09										09 33							10 03		
Bellingham	d												09 35							10 05		
Beckenham Hill	d												09 37							10 07		
Ravensbourne	d												09 39							10 09		
Shortlands 4	d							09 18				09 33	09 41			09 48			10 03	10 11		
Bromley South 4	d		09 18				09a08	09 21	09 19	09 23		09 36	09 44		09a38	09 52	09 53		10 07	10 14		
Bickley 4	d		09 20					09 24				09 39	09 47			09 54			10 09	10 17		
Petts Wood 4	d							09 29				09 44				09 59			10 14			
Orpington 4	a							09 33				09 47				10 02			10 17			
St Mary Cray	d		09 25						09 25				09 51				10 00			10 21		
Swanley 4	d		09 36						09a29	09 33			09 56				10 04			10 26		
Eynsford	d		09 40										10 00							10 30		
Shoreham (Kent)	d		09 44										10 04							10 34		
Otford 4	d		09 47							09a41			10 07				10a12			10 37		
Bat & Ball	d		09 50										10 10							10 40		
Sevenoaks 4	a		09 53										10 13							10 43		

A To Dartford
B To Dover Priory
C To Rochester
D To Ashford International
E From Bedford
F From Luton
G From Luton to Sutton (Surrey)
H From St Albans City
I To Ramsgate
J From Bedford. 1 from London Blackfriars
K From St Albans City to Sutton (Surrey)
L From Bedford to Sutton (Surrey)
M To Gillingham (Kent)

Table 195

Mondays to Fridays

9 December to 16 May

London Victoria/Kentish Town - Catford, Beckenham Junction, Bromley South, Orpington, Otford and Sevenoaks

Network Diagram - see first Page of Table 195

		SE	SE	SE	SE	SE	SE		FC	FC	FC	FC	SE	SE	SE	SE	SE		FC	FC	FC	FC	SE	SE	SE
		1 A		1 B	1 C	D				E	1 F	G	1 H		1 C	D				E	F	G	1 A		1 B
London Victoria 15 ⊖	d	09 52	09 55	09 58	10 07	10 09	10 10						10 22	10 25	10 37	10 39	10 40						10 52	10 55	10 58
Brixton ⊖	d		10 02				10 17							10 32			10 47							11 02	
Kentish Town ⊖	d								09 54	10 00		10 15							10 26	10 30		10 45			
St Pancras International 15 ⊖	d								10 00	10 04	10 15	10 19							10 30	10 34	10 45	10 49			
Farringdon ⊖	d								10 05	10 09	10 21	10 25							10 35	10 39	10 51	10 55			
City Thameslink 3	d								10 09	10 13	10 24	10 27							10 39	10 43	10 54	10 57			
London Blackfriars 3 ⊖	d								10 12	10 16	10 27	10 30							10 42	10 46	10 57	11 00			
Elephant & Castle ⊖	d								10 16	10 19	10a30	10 33							10 46	10 49	11a00	11 03			
Loughborough Jn.	d									10 23		10 37								10 53		11 07			
Herne Hill 4	d		10 04				10 19			10a27		10a41		10 34			10 49			10a57		11a11		11 04	
West Dulwich	d		10 06				10 21							10 36			10 51							11 06	
Sydenham Hill	d		10 08				10 23							10 38			10 53							11 08	
Penge East	d		10 11				10 26							10 41			10 56							11 11	
Kent House 4	d		10 13				10 28							10 43			10 58							11 13	
Beckenham Junction 4	d		10 15				10 30							10 45			11 00							11 15	
Denmark Hill 4	d					10 18			10 22							10 48			10 52						
Peckham Rye 4	d					10 21			10 25							10 51			10 55						
Nunhead 4	d					10 23			10 27							10 53			10 57						
Lewisham 4	a					10 31										11 01									
Crofton Park	d								10 30										11 00						
Catford	d								10 33										11 03						
Bellingham	d								10 35										11 05						
Beckenham Hill	d								10 37										11 07						
Ravensbourne	d								10 39										11 09						
Shortlands 4	d		10 18				10 33		10 41					10 48			11 03		11 11					11 18	
Bromley South 4	d	10a08	10 21	10 19	10 23		10 36		10 44				10a38	10 51	10 53		11 06		11 14				11a08	11 21	11 19
Bickley 4	d		10 24				10 39		10 47					10 54			11 09		11 17					11 24	
Petts Wood 4	d		10 29				10 44							10 59			11 14							11 29	
Orpington 4	a		10 32				10 47							11 02			11 17							11 32	
St Mary Cray	d			10 25					10 51						11 00				11 21						11 25
Swanley 4	d			10a29	10 33				10 56						11 04				11 26						11a29
Eynsford	d								11 00										11 30						
Shoreham (Kent)	d								11 04										11 34						
Otford 4	d				10a41				11 07						11a12				11 37						
Bat & Ball	d								11 10										11 40						
Sevenoaks 4	a								11 13										11 43						

		SE	SE		SE	FC	FC	FC	FC	SE	SE	SE	SE		SE	FC	FC	FC	SE	SE	SE	SE	SE		SE
		1 C	D				E	F	G	1 H		1 C	D				E	G	1 A		1 B	1 C	D		
London Victoria 15 ⊖	d	11 07	11 09		11 10					11 22	11 25	11 37	11 39		11 40				11 52	11 55	11 58	12 07	12 09		12 10
Brixton ⊖	d				11 17						11 32				11 47					12 02					12 17
Kentish Town ⊖	d					10 56	11 00		11 15							11 26	11 30	11 44							
St Pancras International 15 ⊖	d					11 00	11 04	11 15	11 19							11 30	11 34	11 48							
Farringdon ⊖	d					11 05	11 09	11 21	11 25							11 35	11 39	11 53							
City Thameslink 3	d					11 09	11 13	11 24	11 27							11 39	11 43	11 57							
London Blackfriars 3 ⊖	d					11 12	11 16	11 27	11 30							11 42	11 46	12 00							
Elephant & Castle ⊖	d					11 16	11 19	11a30	11 33							11 46	11 49	12 03							
Loughborough Jn.	d						11 23		11 37								11 53	12 07							
Herne Hill 4	d				11 19		11a27		11a41		11 34				11 49		11a57	12a11		12 04					12 19
West Dulwich	d				11 21						11 36				11 51					12 06					12 21
Sydenham Hill	d				11 23						11 38				11 53					12 08					12 23
Penge East	d				11 26						11 41				11 56					12 11					12 26
Kent House 4	d				11 28						11 43				11 58					12 13					12 28
Beckenham Junction 4	d				11 30						11 45				12 00					12 15					12 30
Denmark Hill 4	d		11 18			11 22							11 48			11 52							12 18		
Peckham Rye 4	d		11 21			11 25							11 51			11 55							12 21		
Nunhead 4	d		11 23			11 27							11 53			11 57							12 23		
Lewisham 4	a		11 31										12 01										12 31		
Crofton Park	d					11 30										12 00									
Catford	d					11 33										12 03									
Bellingham	d					11 35										12 05									
Beckenham Hill	d					11 37										12 07									
Ravensbourne	d					11 39										12 09									
Shortlands 4	d				11 33	11 41					11 48				12 03	12 11				12 18					12 33
Bromley South 4	d	11 23			11 36	11 44				11a38	11 51	11 53			12 06	12 14			12a08	12 21	12 19	12 23			12 36
Bickley 4	d				11 39	11 47					11 54				12 09	12 17				12 24					12 39
Petts Wood 4	d				11 44						11 59				12 14					12 29					12 44
Orpington 4	a				11 47						12 02				12 17					12 32					12 47
St Mary Cray	d					11 51						12 00				12 21					12 25				
Swanley 4	d	11 33				11 56						12 04				12 26					12a29	12 33			
Eynsford	d					12 00										12 30									
Shoreham (Kent)	d					12 04										12 34									
Otford 4	d	11a41				12 07						12a12				12 37						12a41			
Bat & Ball	d					12 10										12 40									
Sevenoaks 4	a					12 13										12 43									

A To Dover Priory
B To Gillingham (Kent)
C To Ashford International
D To Dartford
E From Luton to Sutton (Surrey)
F From Bedford
G From St Albans City to Sutton (Surrey)
H To Ramsgate

Table 195

Mondays to Fridays

9 December to 16 May

London Victoria/Kentish Town - Catford, Beckenham Junction, Bromley South, Orpington, Otford and Sevenoaks

Network Diagram - see first Page of Table 195

		FC	FC	FC	SE	SE	SE	SE	SE	FC	FC	FC	SE	SE	SE	SE	SE	SE	FC	FC	FC	SE	SE
					1		1						1		1	1						1	
			A	B	C		D	E			A	B	F		G	D	E			A	B	F	
London Victoria 15 ⊖	d				12 22	12 25	12 37	12 39	12 40				12 52	12 55	12 58	13 07	13 09	13 10				13 22	13 25
Brixton ⊖	d					12 32			12 47					13 02				13 17					13 32
Kentish Town ⊖	d	11 56	12 00	12 14						12 26	12 30	12 44							12 56	13 00	13 14		
St Pancras International 15 ⊖	d	12 00	12 04	12 18						12 30	12 34	12 48							13 00	13 04	13 18		
Farringdon ⊖	d	12 05	12 09	12 23						12 35	12 39	12 53							13 05	13 09	13 23		
City Thameslink 3	d	12 09	12 13	12 27						12 39	12 43	12 57							13 09	13 13	13 27		
London Blackfriars 3 ⊖	d	12 12	12 16	12 30						12 42	12 46	13 00							13 12	13 16	13 30		
Elephant & Castle ⊖	d	12 16	12 19	12 33						12 46	12 49	13 03							13 16	13 19	13 33		
Loughborough Jn	d		12 23	12 37							12 53	13 07								13 23	13 37		
Herne Hill 4	d		12a27	12a41		12 34			12 49		12a57	13a11		13 04				13 19		13a27	13a41		13 34
West Dulwich	d					12 36			12 51					13 06				13 21					13 36
Sydenham Hill	d					12 38			12 53					13 08				13 23					13 38
Penge East	d					12 41			12 56					13 11				13 26					13 41
Kent House 4	d					12 43			12 58					13 13				13 28					13 43
Beckenham Junction 4	d					12 45			13 00					13 15				13 30					13 45
Denmark Hill 4	d	12 22						12 48		12 52							13 18		13 22				
Peckham Rye 4	d	12 25						12 51		12 55							13 21		13 25				
Nunhead 4	d	12 27						12 53		12 57							13 24		13 27				
Lewisham 4	a							13 01									13 31						
Crofton Park	d	12 30								13 00									13 30				
Catford	d	12 33								13 03									13 33				
Bellingham	d	12 35								13 05									13 35				
Beckenham Hill	d	12 37								13 07									13 37				
Ravensbourne	d	12 39								13 09									13 39				
Shortlands 4	d	12 41				12 48			13 03	13 11				13 18				13 33	13 41				13 48
Bromley South 4	d	12 44			12a38	12 51	12 53		13 06	13 14			13a08	13 21	13 19	13 23		13 36	13 44			13a38	13 51
Bickley 4	d	12 47				12 54			13 09	13 17				13 24				13 39	13 47				13 54
Petts Wood 4	d					12 59			13 14					13 29				13 44					13 59
Orpington 4	a					13 02			13 17					13 32				13 47					14 02
St Mary Cray	d	12 51					13 00			13 21					13 25				13 51				
Swanley 4	d	12 56					13 04			13 26					13a29	13 33			13 56				
Eynsford	d	13 00								13 30									14 00				
Shoreham (Kent)	d	13 04								13 34									14 04				
Otford 4	d	13 07					13a12			13 37						13a41			14 07				
Bat & Ball	d	13 10								13 40									14 10				
Sevenoaks 4	a	13 13								13 43									14 13				

		SE	SE	SE	FC	FC	FC	SE	SE	SE	SE	SE	SE	FC	FC	FC	SE	SE	SE	SE	SE	FC	FC
		1						1		1	1						1		1				
		D	E			A	B	F		G	D	E			A	B	C		D	E			A
London Victoria 15 ⊖	d	13 37	13 39	13 40				13 52	13 55	13 58	14 07	14 09	14 10				14 22	14 25	14 37	14 39	14 40		
Brixton ⊖	d			13 47					14 02				14 17					14 32			14 47		
Kentish Town ⊖	d				13 26	13 30	13 44							13 56	14 00	14 14						14 26	14 30
St Pancras International 15 ⊖	d				13 30	13 34	13 48							14 00	14 04	14 18						14 30	14 34
Farringdon ⊖	d				13 35	13 39	13 53							14 05	14 09	14 23						14 35	14 39
City Thameslink 3	d				13 39	13 43	13 57							14 09	14 13	14 27						14 39	14 43
London Blackfriars 3 ⊖	d				13 42	13 46	14 00							14 12	14 16	14 30						14 42	14 46
Elephant & Castle ⊖	d				13 46	13 49	14 03							14 16	14 19	14 33						14 46	14 49
Loughborough Jn	d					13 53	14 07								14 23	14 37							14 53
Herne Hill 4	d			13 49		13a57	14a11		14 04				14 19		14a27	14a41		14 34			14 49		14a57
West Dulwich	d			13 51					14 06				14 21					14 36			14 51		
Sydenham Hill	d			13 53					14 08				14 23					14 38			14 53		
Penge East	d			13 56					14 11				14 26					14 41			14 56		
Kent House 4	d			13 58					14 13				14 28					14 43			14 58		
Beckenham Junction 4	d			14 00					14 15				14 30					14 45			15 00		
Denmark Hill 4	d		13 48		13 52							14 18		14 22						14 48		14 52	
Peckham Rye 4	d		13 51		13 55							14 21		14 25						14 51		14 55	
Nunhead 4	d		13 53		13 57							14 23		14 27						14 53		14 57	
Lewisham 4	a		14 01									14 31								15 01			
Crofton Park	d				14 00									14 30								15 00	
Catford	d				14 03									14 33								15 03	
Bellingham	d				14 05									14 35								15 05	
Beckenham Hill	d				14 07									14 37								15 07	
Ravensbourne	d				14 09									14 39								15 09	
Shortlands 4	d			14 03	14 11				14 18				14 33	14 41				14 48			15 03	15 11	
Bromley South 4	d	13 53		14 06	14 14			14a08	14 21	14 19	14 23		14 36	14 44			14a38	14 51	14 53		15 06	15 14	
Bickley 4	d			14 09	14 17				14 24				14 39	14 47				14 54			15 09	15 17	
Petts Wood 4	d			14 14					14 29				14 44					14 59			15 14		
Orpington 4	a			14 17					14 32				14 47					15 02			15 17		
St Mary Cray	d	14 00			14 21					14 25				14 51					15 00			15 21	
Swanley 4	d	14 04			14 26					14a29	14 33			14 56					15 04			15 26	
Eynsford	d				14 30									15 00								15 30	
Shoreham (Kent)	d				14 34									15 04								15 34	
Otford 4	d	14a12			14 37						14a41			15 07					15a12			15 37	
Bat & Ball	d				14 40									15 10								15 40	
Sevenoaks 4	a				14 43									15 13								15 43	

A From Luton to Sutton (Surrey)
B From St Albans City to Sutton (Surrey)
C To Ramsgate
D To Ashford International
E To Dartford
F To Dover Priory
G To Gillingham (Kent)

Table 195

Mondays to Fridays

9 December to 16 May

London Victoria/Kentish Town - Catford, Beckenham Junction, Bromley South, Orpington, Otford and Sevenoaks

Network Diagram - see first Page of Table 195

		FC A	SE 1 B	SE	SE 1 C	SE 1 D	SE E	SE	FC	FC F	FC A	SE 1 G	SE	SE 1 D	SE E	SE	FC	FC F	FC A	SE 1 B	SE	SE 1 C
London Victoria 15 ⊖	d		14 52	14 55	14 58	15 07	15 09	15 10				15 22	15 25	15 37	15 39	15 40				15 52	15 55	15 58
Brixton ⊖	d			15 02				15 17					15 32			15 47					16 02	
Kentish Town ⊖	d	14 44							14 56	15 00	15 14						15 26	15 30	15 44			
St Pancras International 15 ⊖	d	14 48							15 00	15 04	15 18						15 30	15 34	15 48			
Farringdon ⊖	d	14 53							15 05	15 09	15 23						15 35	15 39	15 53			
City Thameslink 3	d	14 57							15 09	15 13	15 27						15 39	15 43	15 57			
London Blackfriars 3 ⊖	d	15 00							15 12	15 16	15 30						15 42	15 46	16 00			
Elephant & Castle ⊖	d	15 03							15 16	15 19	15 33						15 46	15 49	16 03			
Loughborough Jn.	d	15 07								15 23	15 37							15 53	16 07			
Herne Hill 4	d	15a11		15 04				15 19		15a27	15a41		15 34			15 49		15a57	16a11		16 04	
West Dulwich	d			15 06				15 21					15 36			15 51					16 06	
Sydenham Hill	d			15 08				15 23					15 38			15 53					16 08	
Penge East	d			15 11				15 26					15 41			15 56					16 11	
Kent House 4	d			15 13				15 28					15 43			15 58					16 13	
Beckenham Junction 4	d			15 15				15 30					15 45			16 00					16 15	
Denmark Hill 4	d						15 18		15 22						15 48		15 52					
Peckham Rye 4	d						15 21		15 25						15 51		15 55					
Nunhead 4	d						15 23		15 27						15 53		15 57					
Lewisham 4	a						15 31								16 01							
Crofton Park	d								15 30								16 00					
Catford	d								15 33								16 03					
Bellingham	d								15 35								16 05					
Beckenham Hill	d								15 37								16 07					
Ravensbourne	d								15 39								16 09					
Shortlands 4	d			15 18				15 33	15 41				15 48			16 03	16 11				16 18	
Bromley South 4	d		15a08	15 21	15 19	15 23		15 36	15 44			15a38	15 51	15 53		16 06	16 14			16a08	16 21	16 19
Bickley 4	d			15 24				15 39	15 47				15 54			16 09	16 17				16 24	
Petts Wood 4	d			15 29				15 44					15 59			16 14					16 29	
Orpington 4	a			15 32				15 47					16 02			16 17					16 32	
St Mary Cray	d				15 25				15 51					16 00			16 21					16 25
Swanley 4	d				15a29	15 33			15 56					16 04			16 26					16a29
Eynsford	d								16 00								16 30					
Shoreham (Kent)	d								16 04								16 34					
Otford 4	d					15a41			16 07					16a12			16 37					
Bat & Ball	d								16 10								16 40					
Sevenoaks 4	a								16 13								16 43					

		SE 1 D	SE E	SE	FC	FC F	SE 1 G	SE	SE 1 H	SE 1 D	FC	FC A	SE E	SE	SE 1 D	FC	FC F	FC 1 I	FC 1 J	FC A	SE 1 B	SE	SE E
London Victoria 15 ⊖	d	16 07	16 09	16 10			16 22	16 25	16 28	16 37			16 39	16 40	16 52						16 57	16 59	17 04
Brixton ⊖	d			16 17				16 32						16 47								17 06	
Kentish Town ⊖	d				15 56	16 00					16 10	16 14				16 24	16 30			16 45			
St Pancras International 15 ⊖	d				16 00	16 04					16 14	16 18				16 28	16 34	16 40	16 46	16 50			
Farringdon ⊖	d				16 05	16 09					16 19	16 23				16 33	16 39	16 45	16 51	16 55			
City Thameslink 3	d				16 09	16 13					16 23	16 27				16 37	16 43	16 49	16 55	16 59			
London Blackfriars 3 ⊖	d				16 12	16 16					16 26	16 30				16 42	16 46	16 52	16 58	17 02			
Elephant & Castle ⊖	d				16 16	16 19					16 30	16 33				16 46	16 49	16 56	17a01	17 06			
Loughborough Jn.	d					16 23						16 37					16 53	17 00		17 10			
Herne Hill 4	d			16 19		16a27		16 34				16a41		16 49			16a57	17 06		17a15		17 11	
West Dulwich	d			16 21				16 36						16 51				17 08				17 13	
Sydenham Hill	d			16 23				16 38						16 53				17 10				17 15	
Penge East	d			16 26				16 41						16 56				17 13				17 18	
Kent House 4	d			16 28				16 43						16 58				17 15				17 20	
Beckenham Junction 4	d			16 30				16 45						17 00				17a20				17 23	
Denmark Hill 4	d		16 18		16 22						16 39		16 48			16 52							17 13
Peckham Rye 4	d		16 21		16 25						16 42		16 51			16 55							17 16
Nunhead 4	d		16 23		16 27						16 44		16 53			16 57							17 18
Lewisham 4	a		16 31										16 58										17 23
Crofton Park	d				16 30						16 47					17 00							
Catford	d				16 33						16 50					17 03							
Bellingham	d				16 35						16 52					17 05							
Beckenham Hill	d				16 37						16 54					17 07							
Ravensbourne	d				16 39						16 56					17 09							
Shortlands 4	d			16 33	16 41			16 48			16 58			17 03		17 11						17 26	
Bromley South 4	d	16 23		16 36	16 44		16a38	16 51	16 49	16 53	17 01			17 06	17 09	17 14					17a13	17 29	
Bickley 4	d			16 39	16 47			16 54			17 04			17 09		17 17						17 31	
Petts Wood 4	d			16 44				16 59			17 08			17 14								17 36	
Orpington 4	a			16 49				17 04			17 15			17 19								17 41	
St Mary Cray	d				16 51				16 55	17 00						17 21							
Swanley 4	d	16 33			16 56				16a59	17 04						17 26							
Eynsford	d				17 00											17 30							
Shoreham (Kent)	d				17 04											17 34							
Otford 4	d	16a41			17 07					17a12					17a25	17 37							
Bat & Ball	d				17 10											17 40							
Sevenoaks 4	a				17 14											17 45							

- **A** From St Albans City to Sutton (Surrey)
- **B** To Dover Priory
- **C** To Gillingham (Kent)
- **D** To Ashford International
- **E** To Dartford
- **F** From Luton to Sutton (Surrey)
- **G** To Ramsgate
- **H** To Rochester
- **I** From Bedford
- **J** From Bedford to Brighton

Table 195

Mondays to Fridays

9 December to 16 May

London Victoria/Kentish Town - Catford, Beckenham Junction, Bromley South, Orpington, Otford and Sevenoaks

Network Diagram - see first Page of Table 195

		SE	SE	SE	FC	FC	FC	FC	SE	SE	SE	SE	SE	FC	FC	FC	FC	SE	FC	SE	SE	SE
			1				1		1	1			1			1	1			1		1
		A	B		C	D	E	F	G	H		I	B		D	J	K		L	A	I	M
London Victoria 15 ⊖	d	17 04	17 12	17 15					17 27	17 28	17 30	17 34	17 42					17 45		17 54	17 56	17 57
Brixton ⊖	d			17 22							17 37							17 52				
Kentish Town ⊖	d					16 58		17 12						17 16	17 28							
St Pancras International 15 ⊖	d				16 58	17 02	17 14	17 18						17 22	17 32	17 36	17 40		17 44			
Farringdon ⊖	d				17 03	17 07	17 19	17 23						17 27	17 37	17 41	17 45		17 49			
City Thameslink 3	d				17 07	17 11	17 22	17 27						17 31	17 41	17 45	17 49		17 53			
London Blackfriars 3 ⊖	d				17 10	17 14	17 25	17 30						17 36	17 44	17 48	17 52		17 56			
Elephant & Castle ⊖	d				17 14	17 18	17 29	17 34						17 40	17 48	17 52	17a55		18 00			
Loughborough Jn.	d					17 22		17 38							17 52							
Herne Hill 4	d			17 24		17a25	17 36	17a42			17 39				17a55			17 54	18 07			
West Dulwich	d			17 27							17 42							17 57	18 09			
Sydenham Hill	d			17 29							17 44							17 59	18 11			
Penge East	d			17 32							17 47							18 02	18 14			
Kent House 4	d			17 34							17 49							18 04	18a19			
Beckenham Junction 4	d			17 37							17 51							18 06				
Denmark Hill 4	d				17 20							17 43		17 47							18 06	
Peckham Rye 4	d				17 23							17 46		17 50							18 09	
Nunhead 4	d				17 26							17 49		17 52							18 11	
Lewisham 4	a											17 55									18 17	
Crofton Park	d				17 29									17 55								
Catford	d				17 32									17 58								
Bellingham	d				17 35									18 01								
Beckenham Hill	d				17 37									18 03								
Ravensbourne	d				17 39									18 05								
Shortlands 4	d			17 40	17 43						17 55			18 07				18 10				
Bromley South 4	d	17 24	17 31	17 43	17 46		17 48		17a43	17 50	17 58		17 59	18 10		18 10		18 15		18 19		18a14
Bickley 4	d			17 45			17 50				18 00			18 12				18 18				
Petts Wood 4	d			17 50							18 05							18 26				
Orpington 4	a			17 55							18 10							18 32				
St Mary Cray	d	17 30	17 38				17 55			17 57			18 06	18 22		18 17				18 25		
Swanley 4	d	17a34	17 42		17 55		17a59			18 01			18 11	18 26		18 22				18a29		
Eynsford	d				18 00									18 31								
Shoreham (Kent)	d				18 03									18 34								
Otford 4	d		17a50		18 06					18a09			18a19	18 38		18a30						
Bat & Ball	d				18 14									18 41								
Sevenoaks 4	a				18 23									18 50								

		SE	SE	FC	FC	FC	FC	SE	SE	SE	SE	SE	SE	SE	SE	FC	FC	FC	SE	FC	FC	FC	SE
			1	1						1		1			1		1	1					1
			B	E	N	F	D		I	B	O	P		I	B	Q	R	S		L	F	D	P
London Victoria 15 ⊖	d	18 00	18 03					18 15	18 18	18 18	18 24	18 27	18 30	18 39	18 42				18 45				18 57
Brixton ⊖	d	18 07						18 22					18 37						18 52				
Kentish Town ⊖	d					17 48										18 08				18 23	18 34		
St Pancras International 15 ⊖	d			17 56	17 48	17 52	18 04									18 12	18 18	18 22		18 28	18 38	18 48	
Farringdon ⊖	d			18 01	17 53	17 57	18 09									18 17	18 23	18 27		18 33	18 43	18 53	
City Thameslink 3	d			18 05	17 57	18 01	18 13									18 21	18 27	18 31		18 37	18 47	18 57	
London Blackfriars 3 ⊖	d			18 10	18 00	18 04	18 16									18 24	18 30	18 34		18 42	18 50	19 00	
Elephant & Castle ⊖	d			18 14	18 05	18 08	18 20									18 28	18a33	18 38		18 46	18 54	19 04	
Loughborough Jn.	d					18 12	18 24											18 42			18 58	19 08	
Herne Hill 4	d	18 10		18 21		18a16	18a27	18 24					18 39					18a45	18 54		19a01	19a11	
West Dulwich	d	18 12						18 27					18 42						18 56				
Sydenham Hill	d	18 14						18 29					18 44						18 58				
Penge East	d	18 17						18 32					18 47						19 01				
Kent House 4	d	18 20						18 34					18 49						19 03				
Beckenham Junction 4	d	18 22						18 36					18 51						19 06				
Denmark Hill 4	d				18 15				18 28					18 48		18 34				18 52			
Peckham Rye 4	d				18 18				18 32					18 51		18 38				18 55			
Nunhead 4	d				18 20				18 34					18 54		18 40				18 57			
Lewisham 4	a								18 42					19 02									
Crofton Park	d				18 23											18 43				19 00			
Catford	d				18 26											18 46				19 03			
Bellingham	d				18 29											18 49				19 05			
Beckenham Hill	d				18 31											18 51				19 07			
Ravensbourne	d				18 33											18 53				19 09			
Shortlands 4	d	18 25			18 35			18 39					18 55			18 58			19 09	19 13			
Bromley South 4	d	18 28	18 24	18 31	18 38			18 42		18 39	18 46	18a43	18 58		18 59	19 01			19 12	19 16			19a13
Bickley 4	d	18 31			18 40			18 45					19 00			19 04			19 15	19 19			
Petts Wood 4	d	18 36						18 54					19 07						19 20				
Orpington 4	a	18 41						18 59					19 12						19 25				
St Mary Cray	d			18 38	18 45					18 45	18 52				19 06	19 10				19 23			
Swanley 4	d			18a42	18 53					18 50	18a56				19 11	19 15				19 29			
Eynsford	d				18 57											19 19				19 33			
Shoreham (Kent)	d				19 01											19 23				19 37			
Otford 4	d		18a42		19 04					18a58					19a19	19 26				19 40			
Bat & Ball	d				19 07											19 29				19 43			
Sevenoaks 4	a				19 12											19 37				19 50			

A To Rochester
B To Ashford International
C From Bedford
D From Luton to Sutton (Surrey)
E From Bedford to Rochester
F From St Albans City to Sutton (Surrey)
G To Ramsgate
H To Maidstone East
I To Dartford
J From Bedford to Ashford International
K From Bedford to Three Bridges
L From Luton
M To Margate
N From West Hampstead Thameslink
O To Gillingham (Kent)
P To Dover Priory
Q From St Albans City
R From Bedford to Brighton
S From Bedford to Sutton (Surrey)

Table 195

Mondays to Fridays

9 December to 16 May

London Victoria/Kentish Town - Catford, Beckenham Junction, Bromley South, Orpington, Otford and Sevenoaks

Network Diagram - see first Page of Table 195

Station		SE [1] A	SE	SE [1] B	SE C		SE	FC D	FC E	FC F	SE [1] G	SE	SE A	SE [1] B	SE C		SE	FC H	FC E	FC F	SE [1] I	SE	SE A	SE [1] B	SE C
London Victoria [15] ⊖	d	18 58	19 00	19 07	19 09		19 10				19 22	19 25	19 28	19 37	19 39		19 40				19 52	19 55	19 58	20 07	20 09
Brixton ⊖	d		19 07				19 17					19 32					19 47					20 02			
Kentish Town ⊖	d							18 54										19 26							
St Pancras International [15] ⊖	d							19 00	19 04	19 18								19 30	19 34	19 48					
Farringdon ⊖	d							19 05	19 09	19 23								19 36	19 39	19 53					
City Thameslink [3]	d							19 09	19 13	19 27								19 39	19 43	19 57					
London Blackfriars [3] ⊖	d							19 12	19 16	19 30								19 42	19 46	20 00					
Elephant & Castle ⊖	d							19 16	19 19	19 33								19 46	19 49	20 03					
Loughborough Jn.	d								19 23	19 37									19 53	20 07					
Herne Hill [4]	d		19 09				19 19		19a27	19a41		19 34					19 49		19a57	20a11		20 04			
West Dulwich	d		19 12				19 21					19 36					19 51					20 06			
Sydenham Hill	d		19 14				19 23					19 38					19 53					20 08			
Penge East	d		19 17				19 26					19 41					19 56					20 11			
Kent House [4]	d		19 19				19 28					19 43					19 58					20 13			
Beckenham Junction [4]	d		19 21				19 30					19 45					20 00					20 15			
Denmark Hill [4]	d				19 18			19 22							19 48			19 52							20 18
Peckham Rye [4]	d				19 21			19 25							19 51			19 55							20 21
Nunhead [4]	d				19 23			19 27							19 53			19 57							20 23
Lewisham [4]	a				19 31										20 01										20 31
Crofton Park	d							19 30										20 00							
Catford	d							19 33										20 03							
Bellingham	d							19 35										20 05							
Beckenham Hill	d							19 37										20 07							
Ravensbourne	d							19 39										20 09							
Shortlands [4]	d		19 25				19 33	19 41				19 48					20 03	20 11				20 18			
Bromley South [4]	d	19 21	19 28	19 27			19 36	19 44			19a38	19 51	19 49	19 53			20 06	20 14			20a08	20 21	20 19	20 23	
Bickley [4]	d		19 30				19 39	19 47				19 54					20 09	20 17				20 24			
Petts Wood [4]	d		19 35				19 44					19 59					20 14					20 29			
Orpington [4]	a		19 38				19 48					20 02					20 18					20 32			
St Mary Cray	d	19 27						19 51					19 55	20 00				20 21					20 25		
Swanley [4]	d	19a31		19 36				19 56					19a59	20 04				20 26					20a29	20 33	
Eynsford	d							20 00										20 30							
Shoreham (Kent)	d							20 04										20 34							
Otford [4]	d			19a44				20 07						20a12				20 37						20a41	
Bat & Ball	d							20 10										20 40							
Sevenoaks [4]	a							20 13										20 43							

Station			SE	FC H	FC J	FC E	SE [1] G	SE	SE [1] B	FC	FC J		FC F	SE [1] I	SE	SE [1] A	SE [1] B	FC	FC J	SE [1] I	SE		SE [1] K	SE	FC J
London Victoria [15] ⊖	d		20 10				20 22	20 25	20 37					20 52	20 55	20 58	21 07			21 22	21 25		21 52		
Brixton ⊖	d		20 17					20 32							21 02						21 32				
Kentish Town ⊖	d			19 56		20 14				20 26	20 30							20 56	21 01						21 31
St Pancras International [15] ⊖	d			20 00	20 04	20 18				20 30	20 34		20 48					21 00	21 06						21 36
Farringdon ⊖	d			20 05	20 09	20 23				20 35	20 39		20 53					21 05	21 10						21 40
City Thameslink [3]	d			20 09	20 13	20 27				20 39	20 43		20 57					21 09	21 13						21 43
London Blackfriars [3] ⊖	d			20 12	20 16	20 30				20 42	20 46		21 00					21 12	21 16					21 42	21 46
Elephant & Castle ⊖	d			20 16	20 19	20 33				20 46	20 49		21 03					21 16	21 19					21 46	21 49
Loughborough Jn.	d				20 23	20 37					20 53		21 07						21 23						21 53
Herne Hill [4]	d		20 19		20a27	20a41		20 34			20a57		21a11		21 04				21a27		21 34				21a57
West Dulwich	d		20 21					20 36							21 06						21 36				
Sydenham Hill	d		20 23					20 38							21 08						21 38				
Penge East	d		20 26					20 41							21 11						21 41				
Kent House [4]	d		20 28					20 43							21 13						21 43				
Beckenham Junction [4]	d		20 30					20 45							21 15						21 45				
Denmark Hill [4]	d			20 22						20 52								21 22						21 52	
Peckham Rye [4]	d			20 25						20 55								21 25						21 55	
Nunhead [4]	d			20 27						20 57								21 27						21 57	
Lewisham [4]	a																								
Crofton Park	d			20 30						21 00								21 30						22 00	
Catford	d			20 33						21 03								21 33						22 03	
Bellingham	d			20 35						21 05								21 35						22 05	
Beckenham Hill	d			20 37						21 07								21 37						22 07	
Ravensbourne	d			20 39						21 09								21 39						22 09	
Shortlands [4]	d		20 33	20 41				20 48		21 11					21 18			21 41			21 48			22 11	
Bromley South [4]	d		20 36	20 44			20a38	20 51	20 53	21 14				21a09	21 21	21 19	21 23	21 44		21a38	21 51		22 09	22 14	
Bickley [4]	d		20 39	20 47				20 54		21 17					21 24			21 47			21 54			22 17	
Petts Wood [4]	d		20 44					20 59							21 29						21 59				
Orpington [4]	a		20 47					21 02							21 32						22 02				
St Mary Cray	d			20 51					21 00	21 21						21 25	21 30	21 51					22 15	22 21	
Swanley [4]	d			20 56					21 04	21 26						21a29	21 34	21 56					22a19	22 26	
Eynsford	d			21 00						21 30								22 00						22 30	
Shoreham (Kent)	d			21 04						21 34								22 04						22 34	
Otford [4]	d			21 07					21a12	21 37							21a42	22 07						22 37	
Bat & Ball	d			21 10						21 40								22 10						22 40	
Sevenoaks [4]	a			21 13						21 43								22 13						22 43	

A To Gillingham (Kent)
B To Ashford International
C To Dartford
D From St Albans City
E From Bedford to Sutton (Surrey)
F From St Albans City to Sutton (Surrey)
G To Ramsgate
H From Luton
I To Dover Priory
J From Luton to Sutton (Surrey)
K To Faversham

Table 195

Mondays to Fridays

9 December to 16 May

London Victoria/Kentish Town - Catford, Beckenham Junction, Bromley South, Orpington, Otford and Sevenoaks

Network Diagram - see first Page of Table 195

		SE	SE [1] A	SE	FC B	SE [1] C	SE	SE [1] D	SE	FC B	SE	SE [1] A	SE	FC B	SE [1] C	SE	SE [1] E	SE	FC B	SE
London Victoria [15] ⊖	d	21 55	22 07			22 22	22 25	22 52			22 55	23 07			23 22	23 25	23 52			23 55
Brixton ⊖	d	22 02					22 32				23 02					23 32				00 02
Kentish Town ⊖	d				22 01					22 31				23 01					23 33	
St Pancras International [15] ⊖	d				22 06					22 36				23 06					23 38	
Farringdon ⊖	d				22 10					22 40				23 10					23 43	
City Thameslink [3]	d				22 13					22 43										
London Blackfriars [3] ⊖	d			22 12	22 16				22 42	22 46			23 12	23 16				23 42	23 48	
Elephant & Castle ⊖	d			22 16	22 19				22 46	22 49			23 16	23 19				23 46	23 51	
Loughborough Jn	d				22 23					22 53				23s23						
Herne Hill [4]	d	22 04			22a27		22 34			22a57	23 04			23a27		23 34			23a58	00 04
West Dulwich	d	22 06					22 36				23 06					23 36				00 06
Sydenham Hill	d	22 08					22 38				23 08					23 38				00 08
Penge East	d	22 11					22 41				23 11					23 41				00 11
Kent House [4]	d	22 13					22 43				23 13					23 43				00 13
Beckenham Junction [4]	d	22 15					22 45				23 15					23 45				00 15
Denmark Hill [4]	d			22 22					22 52				23 22					23 52		
Peckham Rye [4]	d			22 25					22 55				23 25					23 55		
Nunhead [4]	d			22 27					22 57				23 27					23 57		
Lewisham [4]	a																			
Crofton Park	d			22 30					23 00				23 30					23 59		
Catford	d			22 33					23 03				23 33					00 03		
Bellingham	d			22 35					23 05				23 35					00 05		
Beckenham Hill	d			22 37					23 07				23 37					00 07		
Ravensbourne	d			22 39					23 09				23 39					00 09		
Shortlands [4]	d	22 18		22 41			22 48		23 11		23 18		23 41			23 48		00 11		00 18
Bromley South [4]	d	22 21	22 23	22 44		22a38	22 51	23 09	23 14		23 21	23 23	23 44		23a38	23 51	00 09	00 14		00 21
Bickley [4]	d	22 24		22 47			22 54		23 17		23 24		23 47			23 54		00 17		00 24
Petts Wood [4]	d	22 29					22 59				23 29					23 59				00 29
Orpington [4]	a	22 32					23 02				23 32					00 02				00 32
St Mary Cray	d		22 30	22 51				23 15	23 21			23 30	23 51				00 15	00 21		
Swanley [4]	d		22 34	22 56				23a19	23 26			23 34	23 56				00a19	00 26		
Eynsford	d			23 00					23 30				23 59					00 30		
Shoreham (Kent)	d			23 04					23 34				00 04					00 34		
Otford [4]	d		22a42	23 07					23 37			23a42	00 07					00 37		
Bat & Ball	d			23 10					23 40				00 10					00 40		
Sevenoaks [4]	a			23 13					23 43				00 13					00 43		

Saturdays

14 December to 17 May

		SE F	SE [1] G	SE F	SE H	SE [1] A	SE E	SE [1] C	FC I	SE	SE [1] A	SE [1] C	SE	FC B	SE	SE	FC I	FC B	SE	SE [1] E	SE [1] A	SE	SE
London Victoria [15] ⊖	d					00 07	00 37	05 22		05 55	06 07	06 22			06 25				06 55	06 58	07 07	07 10	
Brixton ⊖	d				00 02					06 02					06 32				07 02			07 17	
Kentish Town ⊖	d								05 44					06 14			06 28	06 44					
St Pancras International [15] ⊖	d								05 48					06 18			06 34	06 48					
Farringdon ⊖	d								05 53					06 23			06 39	06 53					
City Thameslink [3]	d																						
London Blackfriars [3] ⊖	d								06 00				06 12	06 30		06 42	06 46	07 00					07 12
Elephant & Castle ⊖	d								06 03				06 16	06 33		06 46	06 49	07 03					07 16
Loughborough Jn	d																06 53	07 07					
Herne Hill [4]	d				00 04		00 45		06a11	06 04				06a41	06 34		06a57	07a11	07 04			07 19	
West Dulwich	d				00 06					06 06					06 36				07 06			07 21	
Sydenham Hill	d				00 08					06 08					06 38				07 08			07 23	
Penge East	d				00 11		00 50			06 11					06 41				07 11			07 26	
Kent House [4]	d				00 13					06 13					06 43				07 13			07 28	
Beckenham Junction [4]	d				00 15		00 52			06 15					06 45				07 15			07 30	
Denmark Hill [4]	d												06 22			06 52							07 22
Peckham Rye [4]	d												06 25			06 55							07 25
Nunhead [4]	d												06 27			06 57							07 27
Lewisham [4]	a																						
Crofton Park	d												06 30			07 00							07 30
Catford	d			00 03									06 33			07 03							07 33
Bellingham	d			00 05									06 35			07 05							07 35
Beckenham Hill	d			00 07									06 37			07 07							07 37
Ravensbourne	d			00 09									06 39			07 09							07 39
Shortlands [4]	d			00 11	00 18					06 18			06 41		06 48	07 11			07 18			07 33	07 41
Bromley South [4]	d		00 09	00 14	00 21	00 25	00 57	05 39		06 21	06 23	06 39	06 44		06 51	07 14			07 21	07 19	07 23	07 36	07 44
Bickley [4]	d			00 17	00 24					06 24			06 47		06 54	07 17			07 24			07 39	07 47
Petts Wood [4]	d				00 29					06 29					06 59				07 29			07 44	
Orpington [4]	a				00 32					06 32					07 02				07 32			07 47	
St Mary Cray	d		00 15	00 21		00 32	01 03	05 45			06 30	06 45	06 51			07 21				07 25	07 30		07 51
Swanley [4]	d		00a19	00 26		00 36	01a07	05a49			06 34	06a49	06 56			07 26				07a29	07 34		07 56
Eynsford	d			00 30									07 00			07 30							08 00
Shoreham (Kent)	d	00 04		00 34									07 04			07 34							08 04
Otford [4]	d	00 07		00 37		00a44					06a42		07 07			07 37					07a42		08 07
Bat & Ball	d	00 10		00 40									07 10			07 40							08 10
Sevenoaks [4]	a	00 13		00 43									07 13			07 43							08 13

A To Ashford International
B From Luton to Sutton (Surrey)
C To Ramsgate
D To Faversham
E To Gillingham (Kent)
F From London Blackfriars
G From London Victoria to Gillingham (Kent)
H From London Victoria
I From West Hampstead Thameslink to Sutton (Surrey)

Table 195

Saturdays
14 December to 17 May

London Victoria/Kentish Town - Catford, Beckenham Junction, Bromley South, Orpington, Otford and Sevenoaks

Network Diagram - see first Page of Table 195

		FC A	FC B	SE 1 C	SE	SE 1 D		SE E	SE	SE	FC A	FC B	SE 1 F	SE	SE 1 G	SE 1 D		SE E	SE	SE	FC B	FC B	SE 1 C	SE	SE 1 D
London Victoria 15	⊖ d			07 22	07 25	07 37		07 39	07 40				07 52	07 55	07 58	08 07		08 09	08 10				08 22	08 25	08 37
Brixton	⊖ d				07 32				07 47					08 02					08 17					08 32	
Kentish Town	⊖ d	06 58	07 14								07 28	07 44									07 58	08 14			
St Pancras International 15	⊖ d	07 04	07 18								07 34	07 48									08 04	08 18			
Farringdon	⊖ d	07 09	07 23								07 39	07 53									08 09	08 23			
City Thameslink 3	d																								
London Blackfriars 3	⊖ d	07 16	07 30							07 42	07 46	08 00								08 12	08 16	08 30			
Elephant & Castle	⊖ d	07 19	07 33							07 46	07 49	08 03								08 16	08 19	08 33			
Loughborough Jn.	d	07 23	07 37								07 53	08 07									08 23	08 37			
Herne Hill 4	d	07a27	07a41		07 34				07 49		07a57	08a11		08 04					08 19		08a27	08a41		08 34	
West Dulwich	d				07 36				07 51					08 06					08 21					08 36	
Sydenham Hill	d				07 38				07 53					08 08					08 23					08 38	
Penge East	d				07 41				07 56					08 11					08 26					08 41	
Kent House 4	d				07 43				07 58					08 13					08 28					08 43	
Beckenham Junction 4	⇌ d				07 45				08 00					08 15					08 30					08 45	
Denmark Hill 4	d							07 48		07 52								08 18		08 22					
Peckham Rye 4	d							07 51		07 55								08 21		08 25					
Nunhead 4	d							07 53		07 57								08 23		08 27					
Lewisham 4	⇌ a							08 02										08 31							
Crofton Park	d									08 00										08 30					
Catford	d									08 03										08 33					
Bellingham	d									08 05										08 35					
Beckenham Hill	d									08 07										08 37					
Ravensbourne	d									08 09										08 39					
Shortlands 4	d				07 48				08 03	08 11				08 18					08 33	08 41				08 48	
Bromley South 4	d			07a38	07 51	07 53			08 06	08 14			08a08	08 21	08 19	08 23			08 36	08 44			08a38	08 51	08 53
Bickley 4	d				07 54				08 09	08 17				08 24					08 39	08 47				08 54	
Petts Wood 4	d				07 59				08 14					08 29					08 44					08 59	
Orpington 4	a				08 02				08 17					08 32					08 47					09 02	
St Mary Cray	d					08 00				08 21					08 25					08 51					09 00
Swanley 4	d					08 04				08 26					08a29	08 33				08 56					09 04
Eynsford	d									08 30										09 00					
Shoreham (Kent)	d									08 34										09 04					
Otford 4	d					08a12				08 37						08a41				09 07					09a12
Bat & Ball	d									08 40										09 10					
Sevenoaks 4	a									08 43										09 13					

		SE E		SE	SE	FC B	FC B	SE 1 F	SE	SE 1 G	SE 1 D	SE E	SE	SE	FC B	FC H	SE 1 C	SE	SE 1 D	SE E	SE	SE	FC B		
London Victoria 15	⊖ d	08 39		08 40				08 52	08 55	08 58	09 07	09 09	09 10				09 22	09 25	09 37	09 39	09 40				
Brixton	⊖ d			08 47					09 02				09 17					09 32			09 47				
Kentish Town	⊖ d					08 28	08 44								08 58	09 14							09 28		
St Pancras International 15	⊖ d					08 34	08 48								09 04	09 18							09 34		
Farringdon	⊖ d					08 39	08 53								09 09	09 23							09 39		
City Thameslink 3	d														09 13	09 27							09 43		
London Blackfriars 3	⊖ d				08 42	08 46	09 00							09 12	09 16	09 30						09 42	09 46		
Elephant & Castle	⊖ d				08 46	08 49	09 03							09 16	09 19	09 33						09 46	09 49		
Loughborough Jn.	d					08 53	09 07								09 23	09 37							09 53		
Herne Hill 4	d			08 49		08a57	09a11		09 04				09 19		09a27	09a41		09 34			09 49		09a57		
West Dulwich	d			08 51					09 06				09 21					09 36			09 51				
Sydenham Hill	d			08 53					09 08				09 23					09 38			09 53				
Penge East	d			08 56					09 11				09 26					09 41			09 56				
Kent House 4	d			08 58					09 13				09 28					09 43			09 58				
Beckenham Junction 4	⇌ d			09 00					09 15				09 30					09 45			10 00				
Denmark Hill 4	d	08 48			08 52							09 18		09 22						09 48		09 52			
Peckham Rye 4	d	08 51			08 55							09 21		09 25						09 51		09 55			
Nunhead 4	d	08 53			08 57							09 23		09 27						09 53		09 57			
Lewisham 4	⇌ a	09 01										09 31								10 01					
Crofton Park	d				09 00									09 30								10 00			
Catford	d				09 03									09 33								10 03			
Bellingham	d				09 05									09 35								10 05			
Beckenham Hill	d				09 07									09 37								10 07			
Ravensbourne	d				09 09									09 39								10 09			
Shortlands 4	d			09 03	09 11				09 18				09 33	09 41				09 48			10 03	10 11			
Bromley South 4	d			09 06	09 14			09a08	09 21	09 19	09 23		09 36	09 44			09a38	09 51	09 53		10 06	10 14			
Bickley 4	d			09 09	09 17				09 24				09 39	09 47				09 54			10 09	10 17			
Petts Wood 4	d			09 14					09 29				09 44					09 59			10 14				
Orpington 4	a			09 17					09 32				09 47					10 02			10 17				
St Mary Cray	d				09 21					09 25				09 51					10 00			10 21			
Swanley 4	d				09 26					09a29	09 33			09 56					10 04			10 26			
Eynsford	d				09 30									10 00								10 30			
Shoreham (Kent)	d				09 34									10 04								10 34			
Otford 4	d				09 37						09a41			10 07					10a12			10 37			
Bat & Ball	d				09 40									10 10								10 40			
Sevenoaks 4	a				09 43									10 13								10 43			

A From West Hampstead Thameslink to Sutton (Surrey)
B From Luton to Sutton (Surrey)
C To Ramsgate
D To Ashford International
E To Dartford
F To Dover Priory
G To Gillingham (Kent)
H From St Albans City to Sutton (Surrey)

Table 195

Saturdays
14 December to 17 May

London Victoria/Kentish Town - Catford, Beckenham Junction, Bromley South, Orpington, Otford and Sevenoaks

Network Diagram - see first Page of Table 195

		FC		SE	SE	SE	SE	SE	SE	SE	FC	FC	SE	SE	SE	SE	SE	SE	FC	FC	SE	SE	SE
		A		1 B		1 C	1 D	E			F	A	1 G		1 D	E			F	A	1 B		1 C
London Victoria 15 ⊖	d			17 52	17 55	17 58	18 07	18 09	18 10				18 22	18 25	18 37	18 39	18 40				18 52	18 55	18 58
Brixton ⊖	d				18 02				18 17					18 32			18 47					19 02	
Kentish Town ⊖	d	09 44									17 58	18 14							18 28	18 44			
St Pancras International 15 ⊖	d	09 48									18 04	18 18							18 34	18 48			
Farringdon ⊖	d	09 53									18 09	18 23							18 39	18 53			
City Thameslink 3	d	09 57									18 13	18 27							18 43	18 57			
London Blackfriars 3 ⊖	d	10 00								18 12	18 16	18 30						18 42	18 46	19 00			
Elephant & Castle ⊖	d	10 03								18 16	18 19	18 33						18 46	18 49	19 03			
Loughborough Jn.	d	10 07									18 23	18 37							18 53	19 07			
Herne Hill 4	d	10a11			18 04				18 19		18a27	18a41		18 34			18 49		18a57	19a11		19 04	
West Dulwich	d				18 06				18 21					18 36			18 51					19 06	
Sydenham Hill	d				18 08				18 23					18 38			18 53					19 08	
Penge East	d		and at the same minutes past each hour until		18 11				18 26					18 41			18 56					19 11	
Kent House 4	d				18 13				18 28					18 43			18 58					19 13	
Beckenham Junction 4	d				18 15				18 30					18 45			19 00					19 15	
Denmark Hill 4	d							18 18		18 22						18 48		18 52					
Peckham Rye 4	d							18 21		18 25						18 51		18 55					
Nunhead 4	d							18 23		18 27						18 53		18 57					
Lewisham 4	a							18 31								19 01							
Crofton Park	d									18 30								19 00					
Catford	d									18 33								19 03					
Bellingham	d									18 35								19 05					
Beckenham Hill	d									18 37								19 07					
Ravensbourne	d									18 39								19 09					
Shortlands 4	d				18 18				18 33	18 41				18 48			19 03	19 11				19 18	
Bromley South 4	d			18a08	18 21	18 19	18 23		18 36	18 44			18a38	18 51	18 53		19 06	19 14			19a08	19 21	19 19
Bickley 4	d				18 24				18 39	18 47				18 54			19 09	19 17				19 24	
Petts Wood 4	d				18 29				18 44					18 59			19 14					19 29	
Orpington 4	a				18 32				18 47					19 02			19 17					19 32	
St Mary Cray	d					18 25				18 51					19 00			19 21					19 25
Swanley 4	d					18a29	18 33			18 56					19 04			19 26					19a29
Eynsford	d									19 00								19 30					
Shoreham (Kent)	d									19 04								19 34					
Otford 4	d						18a41			19 07					19a12			19 37					
Bat & Ball	d									19 10								19 40					
Sevenoaks 4	a									19 13								19 43					

		SE	SE	SE	SE	FC	FC	SE	SE	SE	SE	SE	SE	FC	FC	SE	SE	SE	SE	SE	SE	FC	FC
		1 D	E			F	A	1 G		1 D	E			F	A	1 H		1 C	1 D			F	A
London Victoria 15 ⊖	d	19 07	19 09	19 10				19 22	19 25	19 37	19 39	19 40				19 52	19 55	19 58	20 07	20 10			
Brixton ⊖	d			19 17					19 32			19 47					20 02			20 17			
Kentish Town ⊖	d					18 58	19 14							19 28	19 44							19 58	20 14
St Pancras International 15 ⊖	d					19 04	19 18							19 34	19 48							20 04	20 18
Farringdon ⊖	d					19 09	19 23							19 39	19 53							20 09	20 23
City Thameslink 3	d					19 13	19 27							19 43	19 57							20 13	20 27
London Blackfriars 3 ⊖	d				19 12	19 16	19 30						19 42	19 46	20 00						20 12	20 16	20 30
Elephant & Castle ⊖	d				19 16	19 19	19 33						19 46	19 49	20 03						20 16	20 19	20 33
Loughborough Jn.	d					19 23	19 37							19 53	20 07							20 23	20 37
Herne Hill 4	d			19 19		19a27	19a41		19 34			19 49		19a57	20a11		20 04			20 19		20a27	20a41
West Dulwich	d			19 21					19 36			19 51					20 06			20 21			
Sydenham Hill	d			19 23					19 38			19 53					20 08			20 23			
Penge East	d			19 26					19 41			19 56					20 11			20 26			
Kent House 4	d			19 28					19 43			19 58					20 13			20 28			
Beckenham Junction 4	d			19 30					19 45			20 00					20 15			20 30			
Denmark Hill 4	d		19 18		19 22						19 48		19 52								20 22		
Peckham Rye 4	d		19 21		19 25						19 51		19 55								20 25		
Nunhead 4	d		19 23		19 27						19 53		19 57								20 27		
Lewisham 4	a		19 31								20 01												
Crofton Park	d				19 30								20 00								20 30		
Catford	d				19 33								20 03								20 33		
Bellingham	d				19 35								20 05								20 35		
Beckenham Hill	d				19 37								20 07								20 37		
Ravensbourne	d				19 39								20 09								20 39		
Shortlands 4	d			19 33	19 41				19 48			20 03	20 11				20 18			20 33	20 41		
Bromley South 4	d	19 23		19 36	19 44			19a38	19 51	19 53		20 06	20 14			20a08	20 21	20 19	20 23	20 36	20 44		
Bickley 4	d			19 39	19 47				19 54			20 09	20 17				20 24			20 39	20 47		
Petts Wood 4	d			19 44					19 59			20 14					20 29			20 44			
Orpington 4	a			19 48					20 02			20 18					20 32			20 47			
St Mary Cray	d				19 51					20 00			20 21					20 25	20 30		20 51		
Swanley 4	d	19 33			19 56					20 04			20 26					20a29	20 34		20 56		
Eynsford	d				20 00								20 30								21 00		
Shoreham (Kent)	d				20 04								20 34								21 04		
Otford 4	d	19a41			20 07					20a12			20 37						20a42		21 07		
Bat & Ball	d				20 10								20 40								21 10		
Sevenoaks 4	a				20 13								20 43								21 13		

A From St Albans City to Sutton (Surrey)
B To Dover Priory
C To Gillingham (Kent)
D To Ashford International
E To Dartford
F From Luton to Sutton (Surrey)
G To Ramsgate
H To Canterbury East

Table 195

Saturdays
14 December to 17 May

London Victoria/Kentish Town - Catford, Beckenham Junction, Bromley South, Orpington, Otford and Sevenoaks

Network Diagram - see first Page of Table 195

		SE 1 A	SE	SE 1 B	SE	FC C	FC D	SE	SE 1 E	SE	FC C	SE 1 A	SE	SE 1 F	SE	FC C	SE	SE 1 E	SE	FC C	SE 1 G	SE
London Victoria 15	⊖ d	20 22	20 25	20 52				20 55	21 07			21 22	21 25	21 52			21 55	22 07			22 22	22 25
Brixton	⊖ d		20 32					21 02					21 32				22 02					22 32
Kentish Town	⊖ d					20 31	20 44				21 01					21 31				22 01		
St Pancras International 15	⊖ d					20 36	20 48				21 06					21 36				22 06		
Farringdon	⊖ d					20 40	20 53				21 10					21 40				22 10		
City Thameslink 3	d					20 43	20 57															
London Blackfriars 3	⊖ d				20 42	20 46	21 00			21 12	21 16				21 42	21 46			22 12	22 16		
Elephant & Castle	⊖ d				20 46	20 49	21 03			21 16	21 19				21 46	21 49			22 16	22 19		
Loughborough Jn.	d					20 53	21 07				21 23					21 53				22 23		
Herne Hill 4	d		20 34			20a57	21a11	21 04			21a27		21 34			21a57	22 04			22a27		22 34
West Dulwich	d		20 36					21 06					21 36				22 06					22 36
Sydenham Hill	d		20 38					21 08					21 38				22 08					22 38
Penge East	d		20 41					21 11					21 41				22 11					22 41
Kent House 4	d		20 43					21 13					21 43				22 13					22 43
Beckenham Junction 4	d		20 45					21 15					21 45				22 15					22 45
Denmark Hill 4	d				20 52					21 22					21 52				22 22			
Peckham Rye 4	d				20 55					21 25					21 55				22 25			
Nunhead 4	d				20 57					21 27					21 57				22 27			
Lewisham 4	a																					
Crofton Park	d				21 00					21 30					22 00				22 30			
Catford	d				21 03					21 33					22 03				22 33			
Bellingham	d				21 05					21 35					22 05				22 35			
Beckenham Hill	d				21 07					21 37					22 07				22 37			
Ravensbourne	d				21 09					21 39					22 09				22 39			
Shortlands 4	d		20 48		21 11			21 18		21 41			21 48		22 11		22 18		22 41			22 48
Bromley South 4	d	20a38	20 51	21 09	21 14			21 21	21 23	21 44		21a38	21 51	22 09	22 14		22 21	22 23	22 44		22a38	22 51
Bickley 4	d		20 54		21 17			21 24		21 47			21 54		22 17		22 24		22 47			22 54
Petts Wood 4	d		20 59					21 29					21 59				22 29					22 59
Orpington 4	a		21 02					21 32					22 02				22 32					23 02
St Mary Cray	d			21 15	21 21				21 30	21 51				22 15	22 21			22 30	22 51			
Swanley 4	d			21a19	21 26				21 34	21 56				22a19	22 26			22 34	22 56			
Eynsford	d				21 30					22 00					22 30				23 00			
Shoreham (Kent)	d				21 34					22 04					22 34				23 04			
Otford 4	d				21 37				21a42	22 07					22 37			22a42	23 07			
Bat & Ball	d				21 40					22 10					22 40				23 10			
Sevenoaks 4	a				21 43					22 13					22 43				23 13			

		SE 1 F	SE	FC C	SE	SE 1 E	SE	FC C	SE 1 A	SE	SE 1 H	SE	FC C	SE
London Victoria 15	⊖ d	22 52			22 55	23 07			23 22	23 25	23 52			23 55
Brixton	⊖ d				23 02					23 32				00 02
Kentish Town	⊖ d			22 31				23 01					23 30	
St Pancras International 15	⊖ d			22 36				23 06					23 38	
Farringdon	⊖ d			22 40				23 10					23 43	
City Thameslink 3	d													
London Blackfriars 3	⊖ d		22 42	22 46			23 12	23 16				23 42	23 48	
Elephant & Castle	⊖ d		22 46	22 49			23 16	23 19				23 46	23 50	
Loughborough Jn.	d			22 53				23 23						
Herne Hill 4	d			22a57	23 04			23a27		23 34			23a58	00 04
West Dulwich	d				23 06					23 36				00 06
Sydenham Hill	d				23 08					23 38				00 08
Penge East	d				23 11					23 41				00 11
Kent House 4	d				23 13					23 43				00 13
Beckenham Junction 4	d				23 15					23 45				00 15
Denmark Hill 4	d		22 52				23 22					23 52		
Peckham Rye 4	d		22 55				23 25					23 55		
Nunhead 4	d		22 57				23 27					23 57		
Lewisham 4	a													
Crofton Park	d		23 00				23 30					23 59		
Catford	d		23 03				23 33					00 03		
Bellingham	d		23 05				23 35					00 05		
Beckenham Hill	d		23 07				23 37					00 07		
Ravensbourne	d		23 09				23 39					00 09		
Shortlands 4	d		23 11		23 18		23 41			23 48		00 11		00 18
Bromley South 4	d	23 09	23 14		23 21	23 23	23 44		23a38	23 51	00 09	00 14		00 21
Bickley 4	d		23 17		23 24		23 47			23 54		00 17		00 24
Petts Wood 4	d				23 29					23 59				00 29
Orpington 4	a				23 32					00 02				00 32
St Mary Cray	d	23 15	23 21			23 30	23 51				00 15	00 21		
Swanley 4	d	23a19	23 26			23 34	23 56				00a19	00 26		
Eynsford	d		23 30				23 59					00 30		
Shoreham (Kent)	d		23 34				00 04					00 34		
Otford 4	d		23 37			23a42	00 07					00 37		
Bat & Ball	d		23 40				00 10					00 40		
Sevenoaks 4	a		23 43				00 13					00 43		

A To Ramsgate
B To Canterbury East
C From Luton to Sutton (Surrey)
D From St Albans City to Sutton (Surrey)
E To Ashford International
F To Faversham
G To Dover Priory
H To Gillingham (Kent)

Table 195

Sundays

8 December to 11 May

London Victoria/Kentish Town - Catford, Beckenham Junction, Bromley South, Orpington, Otford and Sevenoaks

Network Diagram - see first Page of Table 195

		SE A	SE 1 B	SE A	SE C	SE 1 D	SE E	FC 1 F	SE 1 G	SE 1 D	SE	FC 1 F	SE	SE 1 H ⚯	SE 1 G	SE	FC 1 F	SE	SE 1 D	SE	FC 1 F
London Victoria 15 ⊖	d					00 07	00 37		07 22	07 45			07 55	08 05	08 22			08 25	08 45		
Brixton ⊖	d				00 02								08 02					08 32			
Kentish Town ⊖	d							07 06				07 36					08 06				08 36
St Pancras International 15 ⊖	d							07 10				07 40					08 10				08 40
Farringdon ⊖	d							07 15				07 45					08 15				08 45
City Thameslink 3	d																				
London Blackfriars 3 ⊖	d							07 21			07 42	07 51				08 12	08 21			08 42	08 51
Elephant & Castle ⊖	d							07a25			07 46	07a55				08 16	08a25			08 46	08a55
Loughborough Jn.	d																				
Herne Hill 4	d				00 04		00 45						08 04					08 34			
West Dulwich	d				00 06								08 06					08 36			
Sydenham Hill	d				00 08								08 08					08 38			
Penge East	d				00 11		00 50						08 11					08 41			
Kent House 4	d				00 13								08 13					08 43			
Beckenham Junction 4	d				00 15		00 52						08 15					08 45			
Denmark Hill 4	d										07 52					08 22				08 52	
Peckham Rye 4	d										07 55					08 25				08 55	
Nunhead 4	d										07 57					08 27				08 57	
Lewisham 4	a																				
Crofton Park	d										08 00					08 30				09 00	
Catford	d			00 03							08 03					08 33				09 03	
Bellingham	d			00 05							08 05					08 35				09 05	
Beckenham Hill	d			00 07							08 07					08 37				09 07	
Ravensbourne	d			00 09							08 09					08 39				09 09	
Shortlands 4	d			00 11	00 18						08 11		08 18			08 41		08 48		09 11	
Bromley South 4	d		00 09	00 14	00 21	00 25	00 57		07 39	08 02	08 14		08 21	08a22	08 39	08 44		08 51	09 02	09 14	
Bickley 4	d			00 17	00 24						08 17		08 24			08 47		08 54		09 17	
Petts Wood 4	d				00 29								08 29					08 59			
Orpington 4	a				00 32								08 32					09 02			
St Mary Cray	d		00 15	00 21		00 32	01 03		07 45	08 08	08 21				08 45	08 51			09 08	09 21	
Swanley 4	d		00a19	00 26		00 36	01a07		07a49	08 13	08 26				08a49	08 56			09 13	09 26	
Eynsford	d			00 30							08 30					09 00				09 30	
Shoreham (Kent)	d	00 04		00 34							08 34					09 04				09 34	
Otford 4	d	00 07		00 37		00a44				08a21	08 37					09 07			09a21	09 37	
Bat & Ball	d	00 10		00 40							08 40					09 10				09 40	
Sevenoaks 4	a	00 13		00 43							08 43					09 13				09 43	

		FC 1 I	SE	SE 1 H ⚯	SE 1 G	SE	FC J	FC 1 F	FC 1 I	SE	SE 1 D	SE	FC J	FC 1 F
London Victoria 15 ⊖	d		08 55	09 05	09 22					09 25	09 45			
Brixton ⊖	d		09 02							09 32				
Kentish Town ⊖	d						09 01						09 31	
St Pancras International 15 ⊖	d	08 54					09 06	09 10	09 24				09 36	09 40
Farringdon ⊖	d	08 59					09 11	09 15	09 29				09 41	09 45
City Thameslink 3	d													
London Blackfriars 3 ⊖	d	09 04				09 12	09 16	09 21	09 34			09 42	09 46	09 51
Elephant & Castle ⊖	d	09a08				09 16	09 19	09a25	09a38			09 46	09 49	09a55
Loughborough Jn.	d						09 23						09 53	
Herne Hill 4	d		09 04				09a27			09 34			09a57	
West Dulwich	d		09 06							09 36				
Sydenham Hill	d		09 08							09 38				
Penge East	d		09 11							09 41				
Kent House 4	d		09 13							09 43				
Beckenham Junction 4	d		09 15							09 45				
Denmark Hill 4	d					09 22						09 52		
Peckham Rye 4	d					09 25						09 55		
Nunhead 4	d					09 27						09 57		
Lewisham 4	a													
Crofton Park	d					09 30						10 00		
Catford	d					09 33						10 03		
Bellingham	d					09 35						10 05		
Beckenham Hill	d					09 37						10 07		
Ravensbourne	d					09 39						10 09		
Shortlands 4	d		09 18			09 41				09 48		10 11		
Bromley South 4	d		09 21	09a22	09 39	09 44				09 51	10 02	10 14		
Bickley 4	d		09 24			09 47				09 54		10 17		
Petts Wood 4	d		09 29							09 59				
Orpington 4	a		09 32							10 02				
St Mary Cray	d				09 45	09 51					10 08	10 21		
Swanley 4	d				09a49	09 56					10 13	10 26		
Eynsford	d					10 00						10 30		
Shoreham (Kent)	d					10 04						10 34		
Otford 4	d					10 07					10a21	10 37		
Bat & Ball	d					10 10						10 40		
Sevenoaks 4	a					10 13						10 43		

and at the same minutes past each hour until

		FC 1 I	SE	SE 1 H ⚯	SE 1 G	SE	FC J	FC 1 F	FC 1 I	SE
London Victoria 15 ⊖	d		17 55	18 05	18 22					18 25
Brixton ⊖	d		18 02							18 32
Kentish Town ⊖	d						18 01			
St Pancras International 15 ⊖	d	17 54					18 06	18 10	18 24	
Farringdon ⊖	d	17 59					18 11	18 15	18 29	
City Thameslink 3	d									
London Blackfriars 3 ⊖	d	18 04				18 12	18 16	18 21	18 34	
Elephant & Castle ⊖	d	18a08				18 16	18 19	18a25	18a38	
Loughborough Jn.	d						18 23			
Herne Hill 4	d		18 04				18a27			18 34
West Dulwich	d		18 06							18 36
Sydenham Hill	d		18 08							18 38
Penge East	d		18 11							18 41
Kent House 4	d		18 13							18 43
Beckenham Junction 4	d		18 15							18 45
Denmark Hill 4	d					18 22				
Peckham Rye 4	d					18 25				
Nunhead 4	d					18 27				
Lewisham 4	a									
Crofton Park	d					18 30				
Catford	d					18 33				
Bellingham	d					18 35				
Beckenham Hill	d					18 37				
Ravensbourne	d					18 39				
Shortlands 4	d		18 18			18 41				18 48
Bromley South 4	d		18 21	18a22	18 39	18 44				18 51
Bickley 4	d		18 24			18 47				18 54
Petts Wood 4	d		18 29							18 59
Orpington 4	a		18 32							19 02
St Mary Cray	d				18 45	18 51				
Swanley 4	d				18a49	18 56				
Eynsford	d					19 00				
Shoreham (Kent)	d					19 04				
Otford 4	d					19 07				
Bat & Ball	d					19 10				
Sevenoaks 4	a					19 13				

A not 8 December. From London Blackfriars
B not 8 December. From London Victoria to Gillingham (Kent)
C not 8 December. From London Victoria
D To Ashford International
E To Gillingham (Kent)
F from 5 January. From Bedford to Brighton
G To Canterbury East
H To Ramsgate
I from 5 January. From Bedford to Three Bridges
J From Luton to Sutton (Surrey)

Table 195

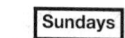

Sundays
8 December to 11 May

London Victoria/Kentish Town - Catford, Beckenham Junction, Bromley South, Orpington, Otford and Sevenoaks

Network Diagram - see first Page of Table 195

		SE [1] A	SE	FC B	FC [1] C	SE	SE [1] D ⚒	SE [1] E	SE	FC B	FC [1] C	SE	SE [1] A	SE	FC B	FC [1] C	SE	SE [1] D ⚒	SE [1] E	SE	FC B	FC [1] C	SE
London Victoria [15] ⊖	d	18 45				18 55	19 05	19 22				19 25	19 45				19 55	20 05	20 22				20 25
Brixton ⊖	d					19 02						19 32					20 02						20 32
Kentish Town ⊖	d			18 31						19 01					19 31						20 01		
St Pancras International [15] ⊖	d			18 36	18 40					19 06	19 10				19 36	19 40					20 06	20 10	
Farringdon ⊖	d			18 41	18 45					19 11	19 15				19 41	19 45					20 11	20 15	
City Thameslink [3]	d																						
London Blackfriars [3] ⊖	d		18 42	18 46	18 51				19 12	19 16	19 21			19 42	19 46	19 51				20 12	20 16	20 21	
Elephant & Castle ⊖	d		18 46	18 49	18a55				19 16	19 19	19a25			19 46	19 49	19a55				20 16	20 19	20a25	
Loughborough Jn.	d			18 53						19 23					19 53						20 23		
Herne Hill [4]	d			18a57		19 04				19a27		19 34			19a57		20 04				20a27		20 34
West Dulwich	d					19 06						19 36					20 06						20 36
Sydenham Hill	d					19 08						19 38					20 08						20 38
Penge East	d					19 11						19 41					20 11						20 41
Kent House [4]	d					19 13						19 43					20 13						20 43
Beckenham Junction [4]	d					19 15						19 45					20 15						20 45
Denmark Hill [4]	d		18 52						19 22					19 52						20 22			
Peckham Rye [4]	d		18 55						19 25					19 55						20 25			
Nunhead [4]	d		18 57						19 27					19 57						20 27			
Lewisham [4]	a																						
Crofton Park	d		19 00						19 30					20 00						20 30			
Catford	d		19 03						19 33					20 03						20 33			
Bellingham	d		19 05						19 35					20 05						20 35			
Beckenham Hill	d		19 07						19 37					20 07						20 37			
Ravensbourne	d		19 09						19 39					20 09						20 39			
Shortlands [4]	d		19 11			19 18			19 41			19 48		20 11			20 18			20 41			20 48
Bromley South [4]	d	19 02	19 14			19 21	19a22	19 39	19 44			19 51	20 02	20 14			20 21	20a22	20 39	20 44			20 51
Bickley [4]	d		19 17			19 24			19 47			19 54		20 17			20 24			20 47			20 54
Petts Wood [4]	d					19 29						19 59					20 29						20 59
Orpington [4]	a					19 32						20 02					20 32						21 02
St Mary Cray	d	19 08	19 21					19 45	19 51				20 08	20 21					20 45	20 51			
Swanley [4]	d	19 13	19 26					19a49	19 56				20 13	20 26					20a49	20 56			
Eynsford	d		19 30						20 00					20 30						21 00			
Shoreham (Kent)	d		19 34						20 04					20 34						21 04			
Otford [4]	d	19a21	19 37						20 07				20a21	20 37						21 07			
Bat & Ball	d		19 40						20 10					20 40						21 10			
Sevenoaks [4]	a		19 43						20 13					20 43						21 13			

		SE [1] A	SE	FC B	FC [1] C	SE	SE [1] D ⚒	SE [1] E	SE	FC B	FC [1] C	SE	SE [1] A	SE	FC [1] C	SE	SE [1] D ⚒	SE [1] E	SE	FC [1] C	SE	SE [1] A
London Victoria [15] ⊖	d	20 45				20 55	21 05	21 22				21 25	21 45			21 55	22 05	22 22			22 25	22 45
Brixton ⊖	d					21 02						21 32				22 02					22 32	
Kentish Town ⊖	d			20 31						21 01					21 36					22 06		
St Pancras International [15] ⊖	d			20 36	20 40					21 06	21 10				21 40					22 10		
Farringdon ⊖	d			20 41	20 45					21 11	21 15				21 45					22 15		
City Thameslink [3]	d																					
London Blackfriars [3] ⊖	d		20 42	20 46	20 51				21 12	21 16	21 21			21 42	21 51				22 12	22 21		
Elephant & Castle ⊖	d		20 46	20 49	20a55				21 16	21 19	21a25			21 46	21a55				22 16	22a25		
Loughborough Jn.	d			20 53						21 23												
Herne Hill [4]	d			20a57		21 04				21a27		21 34				22 04					22 34	
West Dulwich	d					21 06						21 36				22 06					22 36	
Sydenham Hill	d					21 08						21 38				22 08					22 38	
Penge East	d					21 11						21 41				22 11					22 41	
Kent House [4]	d					21 13						21 43				22 13					22 43	
Beckenham Junction [4]	d					21 15						21 45				22 15					22 45	
Denmark Hill [4]	d		20 52						21 22					21 52					22 22			
Peckham Rye [4]	d		20 55						21 25					21 55					22 25			
Nunhead [4]	d		20 57						21 27					21 57					22 27			
Lewisham [4]	a																					
Crofton Park	d		21 00						21 30					22 00					22 30			
Catford	d		21 03						21 33					22 03					22 33			
Bellingham	d		21 05						21 35					22 05					22 35			
Beckenham Hill	d		21 07						21 37					22 07					22 37			
Ravensbourne	d		21 09						21 39					22 09					22 39			
Shortlands [4]	d		21 11			21 18			21 41			21 48		22 11		22 18			22 41		22 48	
Bromley South [4]	d	21 02	21 14			21 21	21a22	21 39	21 44			21 51	22 02	22 14		22 21	22a22	22 39	22 44		22 51	23 02
Bickley [4]	d		21 17			21 24			21 47			21 54		22 17		22 24			22 47		22 54	
Petts Wood [4]	d					21 29						21 59				22 29					22 59	
Orpington [4]	a					21 32						22 02				22 32					23 02	
St Mary Cray	d	21 08	21 21					21 45	21 51				22 08	22 21				22 45	22 51			23 08
Swanley [4]	d	21 13	21 26					21a49	21 56				22 13	22 26				22a49	22 56			23 13
Eynsford	d		21 30						22 00					22 30					23 00			
Shoreham (Kent)	d		21 34						22 04					22 34					23 04			
Otford [4]	d	21a21	21 37						22 07				22a21	22 37					23 07			23a21
Bat & Ball	d		21 40						22 10					22 40					23 10			
Sevenoaks [4]	a		21 43						22 13					22 43					23 13			

A To Ashford International
B From Luton to Sutton (Surrey)
C from 5 January. From Bedford to Brighton
D To Ramsgate
E To Faversham

Table 195

Sundays

8 December to 11 May

London Victoria/Kentish Town - Catford, Beckenham Junction, Bromley South, Orpington, Otford and Sevenoaks

Network Diagram - see first Page of Table 195

Station		SE	FC	SE	SE	SE	FC		SE	SE	SE	SE
			[1]		[1]		[1]			[1]		
			A		B		A			C		
					♿							
London Victoria [15]	⊖ d			22 55	23 05				23 25	23 45		23 55
Brixton	⊖ d			23 02					23 32			00 02
Kentish Town	⊖ d		22 36				23 06					
St Pancras International [15]	⊖ d		22 40				23 10					
Farringdon	⊖ d		22 45				23 15					
City Thameslink [3]	d											
London Blackfriars [3]	⊖ d	22 42	22 51			23 12	23 21				23 42	
Elephant & Castle	⊖ d	22 46	22a55			23 16	23a25				23 46	
Loughborough Jn.	d											
Herne Hill [4]	d			23 04					23 34			00 04
West Dulwich	d			23 06					23 36			00 06
Sydenham Hill	d			23 08					23 38			00 08
Penge East	d			23 11					23 41			00 11
Kent House [4]	d			23 13					23 43			00 13
Beckenham Junction [4]	⇌ d			23 15					23 45			00 15
Denmark Hill [4]	d	22 52				23 22					23 52	
Peckham Rye [4]	d	22 55				23 25					23 55	
Nunhead [4]	d	22 57				23 27					23 57	
Lewisham [4]	⇌ a											
Crofton Park	d	23 00				23 30					23 59	
Catford	d	23 03				23 33					00 03	
Bellingham	d	23 05				23 35					00 05	
Beckenham Hill	d	23 07				23 37					00 07	
Ravensbourne	d	23 09				23 39					00 09	
Shortlands [4]	d	23 11		23 18		23 41			23 48		00 11	00 18
Bromley South [4]	d	23 14		23 21	23a22	23 44			23 51	00 02	00 14	00 21
Bickley [4]	d	23 17		23 24		23 47			23 54		00 17	00 24
Petts Wood [4]	d			23 29					23 59			00 29
Orpington [4]	a			23 32					00 02			00 32
St Mary Cray	d	23 21				23 51				00 08	00 21	
Swanley [4]	d	23 26				23 56				00a12	00 26	
Eynsford	d	23 30				00 01					00 30	
Shoreham (Kent)	d	23 34				00 04					00 34	
Otford [4]	d	23 37				00 07					00 37	
Bat & Ball	d	23 40				00 10					00 40	
Sevenoaks [4]	a	23 43				00 13					00 43	

A from 5 January. From Bedford to Brighton

B To Ramsgate

C To Faversham

Table 195R

Mondays to Fridays

9 December to 16 May

Sevenoaks, Otford, Orpington, Bromley South, Beckenham Junction and Catford - Kentish Town/London Victoria

Network Diagram - see first Page of Table 195

Miles	Miles	Miles			SE MO 1 A	SE MX 1 B	SE	SE	SE	SE	FC C	SE		SE	FC D	SE E	SE 1 B	SE 1 F	SE	SE 1 G	FC H	SE		FC I	SE J
—	0	—	**Sevenoaks 4**	d												05 40									
—	1¼	—	Bat & Ball	d												05 43									
—	3	—	Otford 4	d												05 46				06 16					
—	4¼	—	Shoreham (Kent)	d												05 49									
—	6½	—	Eynsford	d												05 53									
—	9½	—	**Swanley 4**	d		00 10		04 33								05 58		06 02		06 25					
—	12¼	—	St Mary Cray	d		00 14		04 37								06 02		06 06							
0	—	—	**Orpington 4**	d			04 34		04 55	05 10		05 34		05 40					06 10						
1¼	—	—	Petts Wood 4	d			04 37		04 58	05 13		05 37		05 43					06 13						
3	14½	—	Bickley 4	d			04 41	04 41	05 02	05 17		05 41		05 47		06 06			06 17						
4	15½	—	**Bromley South 4**	d	00 18	00 20	04 44	04 50	05 05	05 20		05 44		05 50		06 10	06 12	06 15	06 20	06 33					
5	16½	—	Shortlands 4	d			04 47	04 53	05 08	05 23		05 47		05 53		06 13			06 23						
—	17¼	—	Ravensbourne	d			04 49					05 49				06 15									
—	18	—	Beckenham Hill	d			04 51					05 51				06 17									
—	18¾	—	Bellingham	d			04 53					05 53				06 19									
—	19½	—	Catford	d			04 56					05 56				06 22									
—	20½	—	Crofton Park	d			04 58					05 58				06 25									
—	—	0	Lewisham 4	d																					06 41
—	21¾	1¾	Nunhead 4	d			05 01					06 01				06 27									06 46
—	22½	2½	Peckham Rye 4	d			05 04					06 04				06 30									06 49
—	23¼	3¼	Denmark Hill 4	d			05 07					06 07				06 33									06 52
6¼	—	—	**Beckenham Junction 4**	d				04 56	05 11	05 26				05 56					06 26			06 40			
7¼	—	—	Kent House 4	d				04 58	05 13	05 28				05 58					06 28			06 42			
7¾	—	—	Penge East	d				05 00	05 15	05 30				06 00					06 30			06 44			
9¼	—	—	Sydenham Hill	d				05 03	05 18	05 33				06 03					06 33			06 47			
10	—	—	West Dulwich	d				05 05	05 20	05 35				06 05					06 35			06 49			
11	—	—	Herne Hill 4	d				05 08	05 23	05 38	05 55			06 08	06 17				06 38	06 43	06 46	06 52		06 57	
—	—	—	Loughborough Jn	d											06 20						06 49			07 00	
—	25¾	—	Elephant & Castle ⊖	d			05 13		05 29		06 00	06 13			06 24	06 40					06 54			07 06	
—	27	—	**London Blackfriars 3** ⊖	d			05a17		05 33		06 04	06a17			06 30	06 48					06 58			07 12	
—	—	—	City Thameslink 3	a					05 35		06 06				06 32	06 50					07 00			07 14	
—	—	—	Farringdon ⊖	a					05 38		06 10				06 35	06 54					07 04			07 18	
—	—	—	St Pancras International 15 ⊖	a					05 42		06 14				06 40	06 58					07 08			07 22	
—	—	—	Kentish Town ⊖	a					05 47		06 18				06 44	07 02									
11	—	—	Brixton ⊖	d				05 10		05 40				06 10					06 40			06 54			
15	—	7½	**London Victoria 15** ⊖	a	00 35	00 37		05 17		05 47				06 18			06 30	06 31	06 47	06 51		07 03			07 04

		SE E	SE F	SE 1 A	SE	SE 1 K	SE 1 G	SE 1 F		SE	FC L	SE E	SE M	SE N	SE 1 A	SE 1 O	SE	FC 1 P		SE 1 G	SE F	FC I	SE	SE N	SE J
Sevenoaks 4	d	06 13												06 42											
Bat & Ball	d	06 16												06 48											
Otford 4	d	06 19				06 37	06 47							06 51		07 01				07 14					
Shoreham (Kent)	d	06 22												06 54											
Eynsford	d	06 26												06 58											
Swanley 4	d	06 31	06 35			06 47	06 55	06 57						07 03		07 10				07 22	07 23				
St Mary Cray	d	06 35	06 39					07 01						07 07							07 27				
Orpington 4	d				06 40							06 58					07 08							07 28	
Petts Wood 4	d				06 43							07 01					07 11							07 31	
Bickley 4	d	06 39			06 47							07 05		07 11			07 16							07 35	
Bromley South 4	d	06 42	06 46	06 50	06 50	06 57	07 04	07 08				07 08		07 14	07 16	07 20	07 20			07 31	07 34		07 34	07 38	
Shortlands 4	d	06 45			06 53							07 11		07 17			07 23						07 36	07 41	
Ravensbourne	d	06 47												07 19											
Beckenham Hill	d	06 49												07 21											
Bellingham	d	06 51												07 23											
Catford	d	06 54												07 26											
Crofton Park	d	06 57												07 29											
Lewisham 4	d												07 15												07 46
Nunhead 4	d	06 59											07 20	07 31											07 51
Peckham Rye 4	d	07 02											07 23	07 34											07 54
Denmark Hill 4	d	07 05											07 29	07 37											07 58
Beckenham Junction 4	d				06 56					07 09		07 14					07 26						07 39	07 44	
Kent House 4	d				06 58					07 12		07 17					07 28						07 42	07 47	
Penge East	d				07 00					07 14		07 19					07 30						07 44	07 49	
Sydenham Hill	d				07 03					07 17		07 22					07 33						07 47	07 52	
West Dulwich	d				07 05					07 19		07 24					07 35						07 49	07 54	
Herne Hill 4	d				07 08					07 22	07 24	07 31					07 38	07 41				07 47	07 52	07 57	
Loughborough Jn	d										07 27	07 34										07 50		08 00	
Elephant & Castle ⊖	d	07 12				07 16					07 32	07 38		07 44				07 48				07 54		08 05	
London Blackfriars 3 ⊖	d	07 18				07 24					07 36	07 42		07 48				07 54				07 58		08 09	
City Thameslink 3	a	07 20				07 26					07 38	07 44		07 50				07 56				08 00		08 11	
Farringdon ⊖	a	07 24				07 30					07 42	07 48		07 54				08 00				08 03		08 15	
St Pancras International 15 ⊖	a	07 28				07 34					07 46	07 52		07 58				08 04				08 08		08 19	
Kentish Town ⊖	a	07 32												08 02								08 14			
Brixton ⊖	d				07 10					07 24							07 40						07 54		
London Victoria 15 ⊖	a		07 07	07 09	07 19		07 23	07 30		07 33			07 42		07 38	07 43	07 49			07 53	07 55		08 03		08 11

A From Ramsgate
B From Dover Priory
C From Selhurst to Luton
D From Selhurst to Bedford
E To St Albans City
F From Gillingham (Kent)
G From Ashford International
H From Sutton (Surrey) to Luton
I From Sutton (Surrey) to St Albans City
J From Dartford
K From Ashford International to Bedford
L From Sutton (Surrey) to Bedford
M From Barnehurst
N To Luton
O From Canterbury West
P From Brighton to Bedford

Table 195R

Mondays to Fridays

9 December to 16 May

Sevenoaks, Otford, Orpington, Bromley South, Beckenham Junction and Catford - Kentish Town/London Victoria

Network Diagram - see first Page of Table 195

		SE A	SE 1 B	SE 1 C		FC D	SE	SE 1 E	SE 1 F	SE 1 G	SE H	SE I	FC J	SE		SE	SE 1 K	SE 1 E	SE 1 F	SE 1 C	FC D	SE	SE H	SE 1 G	
Sevenoaks 4	d	07 11														07 36									
Bat & Ball	d	07 14														07 39									
Otford 4	d	07 18	07 23						07 38							07 43			07 56						
Shoreham (Kent)	d	07 21														07 46									
Eynsford	d	07 24														07 49									
Swanley 4	d	07 30	07 32					07 40	07 47							07 54	07 55	08 02	08 05						
St Mary Cray	d	07 34						07 45								07 59	08 00	08 06							
Orpington 4	d						07 38					07 47													
Petts Wood 4	d						07 41					07 50													
Bickley 4	d	07 39					07 46					07 55				08 03									
Bromley South 4	d	07 42	07 40	07 49			07 50	07 53	07 57			07 58		08 04		08 08	08 06	08 12	08 13	08 16				08 18	
Shortlands 4	d	07 44					07 53					08 00		08 06		08 10								08 20	
Ravensbourne	d	07 47														08 13								08 23	
Beckenham Hill	d	07 49														08 15								08 25	
Bellingham	d	07 51										08 05				08 17								08 27	
Catford	d	07 53										08 08				08 20								08 30	
Crofton Park	d	07 56										08 10													
Lewisham 4	⛴ d										08 05												08 25		
Nunhead 4	d	07 58									08 11	08 14											08 30		
Peckham Rye 4	d	08 01									08 13	08 16											08 33	08 36	
Denmark Hill 4	d	08 04									08 17	08 19				08 26		08 30					08 36	08 39	
Beckenham Junction 4	⛴ d						07 56			07 59				08 10								08 22			
Kent House 4	d						07 58			08 02				08 12								08 24			
Penge East	d						08 00			08 04				08 14								08 26			
Sydenham Hill	d						08 03			08 07				08 17								08 29			
West Dulwich	d						08 05			08 09				08 19								08 31			
Herne Hill 4	d					08 01	08 08			08 13			08 20	08 23							08 32	08 34			
Loughborough Jn	d					08 04				08 16			08 24								08 36				
Elephant & Castle	⊖ d	08 13	07 59			08 09				08 21		08 25	08 29			08 35	08 31				08 40			08 45	
London Blackfriars 3	⊖ d	08 17	08 04			08 13				08 25		08 29	08 33			08 42	08 37				08 46			08 50	
City Thameslink 3	a	08 19	08 06			08 15				08 27		08 31	08 35			08 44	08 39				08 48			08 52	
Farringdon	⊖ a	08 23	08 10			08 19				08 30		08 35	08 39			08 48	08 43				08 52			08 56	
St Pancras International 15	⊖ a	08 27	08 14			08 23				08 35		08 39	08 43			08 52	08 47				08 56			09 00	
Kentish Town	⊖ a	08 32				08 29							08 48			08 57					09 00				
Brixton	⊖ d						08 10							08 25								08 36			
London Victoria 15	⊖ a			08 09			08 20	08 17	08 23		08 29			08 35				08 42	08 36	08 39		08 45	08 49		

		FC 1 L	SE	SE F	SE	FC J	SE 1 E	SE 1 G	SE	FC 1 L		SE M	FC D	SE I	SE 1 C	SE	SE 1 G	SE H	SE	SE 1 F		FC J	SE	SE N	SE 1 E
Sevenoaks 4	d		07 53														08 24							08 43	
Bat & Ball	d		07 56														08 27							08 46	
Otford 4	d		08 00	08 10													08 31			08 46				08 49	
Shoreham (Kent)	d		08 03														08 34							08 52	
Eynsford	d		08 06														08 37							08 56	
Swanley 4	d		08 11				08 22										08 42			08 54				09 01	09 05
St Mary Cray	d		08 16				08 27										08 46			08 58				09 05	09 09
Orpington 4	d				08 16				08 26							08 40			08 47				08 55		
Petts Wood 4	d				08 19				08 29							08 43			08 50				08 58		
Bickley 4	d		08 20		08 23				08 33							08 47	08 51		08 55				09 02	09 09	
Bromley South 4	d		08 23	08 26	08 27		08 34		08 36					08 44	08 50	08 50	08 54		08 58	09 05			09 05	09 12	09 15
Shortlands 4	d		08 26		08 29				08 39					08 46		08 53	08 56		09 00				09 08	09 15	
Ravensbourne	d													08 49					09 03					09 17	
Beckenham Hill	d													08 51					09 05					09 19	
Bellingham	d		08 30											08 53			09 01		09 07					09 21	
Catford	d		08 33											08 56			09 04		09 09					09 24	
Crofton Park	d		08 36											08 58					09 12					09 26	
Lewisham 4	⛴ d											08 46						09 07							
Nunhead 4	d		08 38									08 52		09 01				09 12	09 14					09 29	
Peckham Rye 4	d		08 41									08 55		09 04			09 09	09 14	09 17					09 31	
Denmark Hill 4	d		08 45									08 59		09 07			09 12	09 17	09 19					09 34	
Beckenham Junction 4	⛴ d				08 33				08 42							08 56							09 11		
Kent House 4	d				08 36			08 42	08 45							08 58							09 13		
Penge East	d							08 44	08 47							09 00							09 15		
Sydenham Hill	d							08 47	08 50							09 03							09 18		
West Dulwich	d				08 41			08 49	08 52							09 05							09 20		
Herne Hill 4	d	08 41			08 44	08 47		08 52	08 54	08 57			09 02			09 08						09 20	09 23		
Loughborough Jn	d					08 50		08 57					09 05									09 23			
Elephant & Castle	⊖ d	08 50	08 54			08 58		09 02		09 06			09 10	09 14			09 20		09 26			09 30		09 42	
London Blackfriars 3	⊖ d	08 54	08 58			09 02		09 06		09 10			09 14	09 18			09 26		09 30			09 34		09 46	
City Thameslink 3	a	08 56	09 00			09 04		09 08		09 12			09 16	09 20			09 27		09 32			09 36		09 48	
Farringdon	⊖ a	09 00	09 04			09 08		09 12		09 16			09 20	09 24			09 32		09 36			09 40		09 52	
St Pancras International 15	⊖ a	09 04	09 08			09 12		09 16		09 20			09 24	09 28			09 36		09 40			09 44		09 56	
Kentish Town	⊖ a		09 13			09 16								09 34					09 45			09 48		10 00	
Brixton	⊖ d				08 46				08 57							09 10							09 25		
London Victoria 15	⊖ a			08 48	08 56		09 00		09 06			09 11			09 09	09 19		09 30		09 23			09 34		09 38

A To West Hampstead Thameslink
B From Ashford International to Bedford
C From Ramsgate
D From Sutton (Surrey) to St Albans City
E From Gillingham (Kent)
F From Ashford International
G To Bedford
H From Dartford
I To Luton
J From Sutton (Surrey) to Luton
K From Rochester to Bedford
L From Brighton to Bedford
M From London Cannon Street
N To St Albans City

Table 195R

Mondays to Fridays

9 December to 16 May

Sevenoaks, Otford, Orpington, Bromley South, Beckenham Junction and Catford - Kentish Town/London Victoria

Network Diagram - see first Page of Table 195

		SE [1] A	FC B	SE	FC C	SE [1] D	SE E	SE	FC F	SE	SE [1] A	SE	FC C	SE [1] D	SE E	SE	FC F	SE	SE [1] G	SE [1] A	SE	FC C	SE E
Sevenoaks [4]	d									09 13								09 42					
Bat & Ball	d									09 16								09 46					
Otford [4]	d					09 17				09 21				09 46				09 50					
Shoreham (Kent)	d									09 24								09 53					
Eynsford	d									09 28								09 56					
Swanley [4]	d					09 26				09 33				09 54				10 01	10 05				
St Mary Cray	d									09 37				09 58				10 05	10 09				
Orpington [4]	d			09 10				09 25				09 40				09 55					10 10		
Petts Wood [4]	d			09 13				09 28				09 43				09 58					10 13		
Bickley [4]	d			09 17				09 32		09 42		09 47				10 02		10 10			10 17		
Bromley South [4]	d	09 20		09 20		09 34		09 35		09 45	09 50	09 50		10 05		10 05		10 15	10 15	10 20	10 20		
Shortlands [4]	d			09 23				09 38		09 48		09 53				10 08		10 18			10 23		
Ravensbourne	d									09 50								10 20					
Beckenham Hill	d									09 52								10 22					
Bellingham	d									09 54								10 24					
Catford	d									09 57								10 27					
Crofton Park	d									09 59								10 29					
Lewisham [4]	d						09 38								10 08								10 38
Nunhead [4]	d						09 43			10 02					10 13			10 32					10 43
Peckham Rye [4]	d						09 45			10 04					10 15			10 34					10 45
Denmark Hill [4]	d						09 49			10 07					10 19			10 37					10 49
Beckenham Junction [4]	d			09 26				09 41				09 56				10 11					10 26		
Kent House [4]	d			09 28				09 43				09 58				10 13					10 28		
Penge East	d			09 30				09 45				10 00				10 15					10 30		
Sydenham Hill	d			09 33				09 48				10 03				10 18					10 33		
West Dulwich	d			09 35				09 50				10 05				10 20					10 35		
Herne Hill [4]	d		09 36	09 38	09 46			09 53	10 01			10 08	10 16			10 23	10 31				10 38	10 46	
Loughborough Jn	d		09 40		09 50				10 04				10 19				10 34					10 49	
Elephant & Castle ⊖	d		09 45		09 55				10 09	10 14			10 24				10 39	10 44				10 54	
London Blackfriars [3] ⊖	d		09 50		10 00				10 14	10 18			10 30				10 44	10 48				11 00	
City Thameslink [3]	a		09 52		10 02				10 16	10 20			10 32				10 46	10 50				11 02	
Farringdon ⊖	a		09 56		10 06				10 19	10 24			10 35				10 49	10 54				11 06	
St Pancras International [15] ⊖	a		10 00		10 10				10 23	10 28			10 40				10 53	10 58				11 10	
Kentish Town ⊖	a		10 05		10 14				10 27	10 33			10 44				10 57	11 03				11 14	
Brixton ⊖	d			09 40				09 55				10 10				10 25					10 40		
London Victoria [15] ⊖	a	09 43		09 49		09 51	10 00	10 03			10 07	10 17		10 21	10 28	10 32			10 36	10 38	10 47		10 58

		SE	SE [1] D	SE	FC F	SE [1] A	SE	FC C	SE E	SE	SE [1] D	SE	FC F	SE [1] G	SE [1] A	SE	FC H	SE E	SE	SE [1] D	SE	FC F	SE [1] A
Sevenoaks [4]	d	10 02								10 32									11 02				
Bat & Ball	d	10 05								10 35									11 05				
Otford [4]	d	10 08	10 17							10 38	10 46								11 08	11 17			
Shoreham (Kent)	d	10 11								10 41									11 11				
Eynsford	d	10 15								10 45									11 15				
Swanley [4]	d	10 20	10 26							10 50	10 54			11 05					11 20	11 26			
St Mary Cray	d	10 24								10 54	10 58			11 09					11 24				
Orpington [4]	d			10 25			10 40					10 55				11 10					11 25		
Petts Wood [4]	d			10 28			10 43					10 58				11 13					11 28		
Bickley [4]	d	10 28		10 32			10 47			10 58		11 02				11 17			11 28		11 32		
Bromley South [4]	d	10 31	10 35	10 35		10 50	10 50			11 01	11 05	11 05		11 15	11 20	11 20			11 31	11 35	11 35		11 50
Shortlands [4]	d	10 34		10 38			10 53			11 04		11 08				11 23			11 34		11 38		
Ravensbourne	d	10 36								11 06									11 36				
Beckenham Hill	d	10 38								11 08									11 38				
Bellingham	d	10 40								11 10									11 40				
Catford	d	10 43								11 13									11 43				
Crofton Park	d	10 45								11 15									11 45				
Lewisham [4]	d								11 08									11 38					
Nunhead [4]	d	10 48							11 13	11 18								11 43	11 48				
Peckham Rye [4]	d	10 50							11 15	11 20								11 45	11 50				
Denmark Hill [4]	d	10 54							11 19	11 24								11 49	11 54				
Beckenham Junction [4]	d			10 41			10 56					11 11				11 26					11 41		
Kent House [4]	d			10 43			10 58					11 13				11 28					11 43		
Penge East	d			10 45			11 00					11 15				11 30					11 45		
Sydenham Hill	d			10 48			11 03					11 18				11 33					11 48		
West Dulwich	d			10 50			11 05					11 20				11 35					11 50		
Herne Hill [4]	d			10 53	11 01		11 08	11 16				11 23	11 31			11 38	11 46				11 53	12 01	
Loughborough Jn	d				11 04			11 19					11 34				11 49					12 04	
Elephant & Castle ⊖	d	11 00			11 09			11 24		11 30			11 39				11 54		12 00			12 09	
London Blackfriars [3] ⊖	d	11 04			11 14			11 30		11 34			11 44				12 00		12 04			12 14	
City Thameslink [3]	a	11 06			11 16			11 32		11 36			11 46				12 02		12 06			12 16	
Farringdon ⊖	a	11 10			11 19			11 36		11 40			11 49				12 06		12 10			12 19	
St Pancras International [15] ⊖	a	11 14			11 23			11 40		11 44			11 53				12 10		12 14			12 23	
Kentish Town ⊖	a	11 19			11 27			11 44		11 49			11 57				12 14		12 19			12 27	
Brixton ⊖	d			10 55			11 10					11 25				11 40					11 55		
London Victoria [15] ⊖	a		10 51	11 02		11 07	11 17		11 28		11 21	11 32		11 36	11 38	11 47		11 58		11 51	12 02		12 07

A From Ramsgate
B From Sutton (Surrey)
C From Sutton (Surrey) to Luton
D From Ashford International
E From Dartford
F From Sutton (Surrey) to St Albans City
G From Gillingham (Kent)
H From Sutton (Surrey) to Bedford

Table 195R

Mondays to Fridays

9 December to 16 May

Sevenoaks, Otford, Orpington, Bromley South, Beckenham Junction and Catford - Kentish Town/London Victoria

Network Diagram - see first Page of Table 195

Station		SE	FC A	SE B	SE	SE 1 C	SE	FC D	SE 1 E	SE 1 F		SE	FC A	SE B	SE	SE 1 C	SE	FC D	SE 1 F	SE	FC A	SE B	SE	SE 1 C
Sevenoaks 4	d				11 32										14 02								14 32	
Bat & Ball	d				11 35										14 05								14 35	
Otford 4	d				11 38	11 46									14 08	14 17							14 38	14 46
Shoreham (Kent)	d				11 41										14 11								14 41	
Eynsford	d				11 45										14 15								14 45	
Swanley 4	d				11 50	11 54			12 05						14 20	14 26							14 50	14 54
St Mary Cray	d				11 54	11 58			12 09						14 24								14 54	14 58
Orpington 4	d	11 40					11 55					14 10					14 25			14 40				
Petts Wood 4	d	11 43					11 58					14 13					14 28			14 43				
Bickley 4	d	11 47			11 58		12 02					14 17			14 28		14 32			14 47			14 58	
Bromley South 4	d	11 50			12 01	12 05	12 05		12 15	12 20		14 20			14 31	14 35	14 35		14 50	14 50			15 01	15 05
Shortlands 4	d	11 53			12 04		12 08					14 23			14 34		14 38			14 53			15 04	
Ravensbourne	d				12 06						and at the same minutes past each hour until				14 36								15 06	
Beckenham Hill	d				12 08										14 38								15 08	
Bellingham	d				12 10										14 40								15 10	
Catford	d				12 13										14 43								15 13	
Crofton Park	d				12 15										14 45								15 15	
Lewisham 4	d			12 08										14 38								15 08		
Nunhead 4	d			12 13	12 18									14 43	14 48							15 13	15 18	
Peckham Rye 4	d			12 15	12 20									14 45	14 50							15 15	15 20	
Denmark Hill 4	d			12 19	12 24									14 49	14 54							15 19	15 24	
Beckenham Junction 4	d	11 56					12 11					14 26					14 41			14 56				
Kent House 4	d	11 58					12 13					14 28					14 43			14 58				
Penge East	d	12 00					12 15					14 30					14 45			15 00				
Sydenham Hill	d	12 03					12 18					14 33					14 48			15 03				
West Dulwich	d	12 05					12 20					14 35					14 50			15 05				
Herne Hill 4	d	12 08	12 16				12 23	12 31				14 38	14 46				14 53	15 01		15 08	15 16			
Loughborough Jn	d		12 19					12 34					14 49					15 04			15 19			
Elephant & Castle ⊖	d		12 24		12 30			12 39					14 54		15 00			15 09			15 24		15 30	
London Blackfriars 3 ⊖	d		12 30		12 34			12 44					15 00		15 04			15 14			15 30		15 34	
City Thameslink 3	a		12 32		12 36			12 46					15 02		15 06			15 16			15 32		15 36	
Farringdon ⊖	a		12 36		12 40			12 49					15 06		15 10			15 19			15 36		15 40	
St Pancras International 15 ⊖	a		12 40		12 44			12 53					15 10		15 14			15 23			15 40		15 44	
Kentish Town ⊖	a		12 44		12 49			12 57					15 14		15 19			15 27			15 44		15 49	
Brixton ⊖	d	12 10					12 25					14 40					14 55			15 10				
London Victoria 15 ⊖	a	12 17		12 28		12 21	12 32		12 36	12 37		14 47		14 58		14 51	15 02		15 07	15 17		15 28		15 21

Station		SE	FC D	SE 1 E	SE 1 F		SE	FC A	SE B	SE	SE 1 C	SE	FC D	SE 1 F	SE		FC A	SE B	SE 1 G	SE 1 C	SE	FC D	SE E	SE 1 F	SE
Sevenoaks 4	d									15 02									15 32						
Bat & Ball	d									15 05									15 35						
Otford 4	d									15 08	15 17								15 38	15 46					
Shoreham (Kent)	d									15 11									15 41						
Eynsford	d									15 15									15 45						
Swanley 4	d			15 05						15 20	15 26								15 50	15 54			16 05		
St Mary Cray	d			15 09						15 24									15 54	15 58			16 09		
Orpington 4	d	14 55					15 10					15 25			15 40						15 55				16 10
Petts Wood 4	d	14 58					15 13					15 28			15 43						15 58				16 13
Bickley 4	d	15 02					15 17			15 28		15 32			15 47				15 58		16 02				16 17
Bromley South 4	d	15 05		15 15	15 20		15 20			15 31	15 35	15 35		15 50	15 50				16 01	16 05	16 05		16 15	16 20	16 20
Shortlands 4	d	15 08					15 23			15 34		15 38			15 53				16 04		16 08				16 23
Ravensbourne	d									15 36									16 06						
Beckenham Hill	d									15 38									16 08						
Bellingham	d									15 40									16 10						
Catford	d									15 43									16 13						
Crofton Park	d									15 45									16 15						
Lewisham 4	d								15 38									16 08							
Nunhead 4	d								15 43	15 48								16 13	16 18						
Peckham Rye 4	d								15 45	15 50								16 15	16 20						
Denmark Hill 4	d								15 49	15 54								16 19	16 24						
Beckenham Junction 4	d	15 11					15 26					15 41			15 56						16 11				16 26
Kent House 4	d	15 13					15 28					15 43			15 58						16 13				16 28
Penge East	d	15 15					15 30					15 45			16 00						16 15				16 30
Sydenham Hill	d	15 18					15 33					15 48			16 03						16 18				16 33
West Dulwich	d	15 20					15 35					15 50			16 05						16 20				16 35
Herne Hill 4	d	15 23	15 31				15 38	15 46				15 53	16 01		16 08		16 16				16 23	16 31			16 38
Loughborough Jn	d		15 34					15 49					16 04				16 19					16 34			
Elephant & Castle ⊖	d		15 39					15 54		16 00			16 09				16 24		16 30			16 39			
London Blackfriars 3 ⊖	d		15 44					16 00		16 04			16 14				16 30		16 38			16 44			
City Thameslink 3	a		15 46					16 02		16 06			16 16				16 32		16 40			16 46			
Farringdon ⊖	a		15 49					16 06		16 10			16 19				16 35		16 43			16 49			
St Pancras International 15 ⊖	a		15 53					16 10		16 14			16 23				16 39		16 47			16 53			
Kentish Town ⊖	a		15 57					16 14		16 19			16 28				16 44					16 58			
Brixton ⊖	d	15 25					15 40					15 55			16 10						16 25				16 40
London Victoria 15 ⊖	a	15 32		15 36	15 37		15 47		15 58		15 51	16 02		16 07	16 17			16 28		16 21	16 32		16 36	16 38	16 47

A From Sutton (Surrey) to Luton
B From Dartford
C From Ashford International
D From Sutton (Surrey) to St Albans City
E From Gillingham (Kent)
F From Ramsgate
G To Bedford

Table 195R

Mondays to Fridays

9 December to 16 May

Sevenoaks, Otford, Orpington, Bromley South, Beckenham Junction and Catford - Kentish Town/London Victoria

Network Diagram - see first Page of Table 195

Station			FC A	SE B	SE [1] C	SE [1] D	SE	FC [1] E	SE F	SE [1] G	SE		FC H	SE B	SE C	SE [1] D	SE	FC A	SE [1] I	SE [1] G	SE		SE [1] C	SE B	FC H
Sevenoaks [4]	d				16 02				16 22						16 32										
Bat & Ball	d				16 05				16 25						16 35										
Otford [4]	d				16 08	16 17			16 28						16 38	16 46									
Shoreham (Kent)	d				16 11										16 41										
Eynsford	d				16 15										16 45										
Swanley [4]	d				16 20	16 26			16 37						16 50	16 54			17 05						
St Mary Cray	d				16 24				16 41						16 54	16 58			17 09						
Orpington [4]	d						16 25				16 40						16 55				17 10				
Petts Wood [4]	d						16 28				16 43						16 58				17 13				
Bickley [4]	d				16 28		16 32				16 47				16 58		17 02				17 17				
Bromley South [4]	d				16 31	16 35	16 35		16 47	16 50	16 50				17 01	17 05	17 05		17 15	17 20	17 20				
Shortlands [4]	d				16 34		16 38				16 53				17 04		17 08				17 23				
Ravensbourne	d				16 36										17 06										
Beckenham Hill	d				16 38										17 08										
Bellingham	d				16 40				16 52						17 10										
Catford	d				16 43				16 55						17 13										
Crofton Park	d				16 45										17 15										
Lewisham [4]	d			16 38										17 08										17 38	
Nunhead [4]	d			16 43	16 48				16 59					17 13	17 18									17 43	
Peckham Rye [4]	d			16 45	16 50				17 02					17 15	17 20									17 45	
Denmark Hill [4]	d			16 49	16 54				17 05					17 19	17 24									17 49	
Beckenham Junction [4]	d						16 41				16 56						17 11				17 26		17 30		
Kent House [4]	d						16 43				16 58						17 13				17 28		17 33		
Penge East	d						16 45				17 00						17 15				17 30		17 35		
Sydenham Hill	d						16 48				17 03						17 18				17 33		17 38		
West Dulwich	d						16 50				17 05						17 20				17 35		17 40		
Herne Hill [4]	d		16 50				16 53	17 01			17 11		17 21				17 23	17 31			17 38		17 44		17 48
Loughborough Jn	d		16 53										17 24					17 34					17 47		17 51
Elephant & Castle ⊖	d		17 00		17 04			17 08	17 12				17 28		17 34			17 39					17 52		17 56
London Blackfriars [3] ⊖	d		17 04		17 08			17 12	17 16				17 32		17 40			17 46					17 56		18 00
City Thameslink [3]	a		17 06		17 10			17 14	17 18				17 34		17 42			17 48					17 58		18 02
Farringdon ⊖	a		17 09		17 13			17 17	17 23				17 37		17 45			17 51					18 01		18 05
St Pancras International [15] ⊖	a		17 13		17 17			17 21	17 27				17 41		17 49			17 55					18 05		18 09
Kentish Town ⊖	a		17 18						17 32				17 46					18 00							18 14
Brixton ⊖	d						16 55				17 13						17 25				17 40				
London Victoria [15] ⊖	a			17 01		16 51	17 04			17 07	17 20			17 28		17 23	17 33		17 37	17 37	17 48			17 59	

Station		SE [1] C	SE [1] D	SE	SE [1] C	SE [1] I	SE [1] G		FC A	SE	FC H	SE B	SE [1] C	SE [1] D	SE	FC J	SE [1] I		SE [1] G	SE	FC [1] K	SE B	FC H	SE [1] L	SE [1] D
Sevenoaks [4]	d	17 02											17 32											18 02	
Bat & Ball	d	17 05											17 35											18 05	
Otford [4]	d	17 08	17 17										17 38	17 46										18 08	18 17
Shoreham (Kent)	d	17 11											17 41											18 11	
Eynsford	d	17 15											17 45											18 15	
Swanley [4]	d	17 20	17 26			17 35							17 50	17 54			18 05							18 20	18 26
St Mary Cray	d	17 24				17 39							17 54	17 58			18 09							18 24	
Orpington [4]	d			17 24	17 34					17 40					17 55					18 09					
Petts Wood [4]	d			17 28	17 37					17 43					17 58					18 12					
Bickley [4]	d	17 28		17 32	17 42					17 47			17 58		18 02					18 17				18 28	
Bromley South [4]	d	17 31	17 35	17 35	17 45	17 46	17 50			17 50			18 01	18 05	18 05		18 15		18 20	18 20				18 31	18 35
Shortlands [4]	d	17 34		17 38						17 53			18 04		18 08					18 23				18 34	
Ravensbourne	d	17 36											18 06											18 36	
Beckenham Hill	d	17 38											18 08											18 38	
Bellingham	d	17 40											18 10											18 40	
Catford	d	17 43											18 13											18 43	
Crofton Park	d	17 45											18 15											18 45	
Lewisham [4]	d											18 08										18 38			
Nunhead [4]	d	17 48										18 13	18 18									18 43		18 48	
Peckham Rye [4]	d	17 50										18 15	18 20									18 45		18 50	
Denmark Hill [4]	d	17 54										18 19	18 23									18 49		18 54	
Beckenham Junction [4]	d			17 41	17 49					17 56					18 11					18 26					
Kent House [4]	d			17 43						17 58					18 13					18 28					
Penge East	d			17 45						18 00					18 15					18 30					
Sydenham Hill	d			17 48						18 03					18 18					18 33					
West Dulwich	d			17 50						18 05					18 20					18 35					
Herne Hill [4]	d			17 53					18 06	18 09	18 20				18 24	18 32				18 38	18 41		18 48		
Loughborough Jn	d								18 09		18 23					18 35							18 51		
Elephant & Castle ⊖	d	18 01			18 05				18 14		18 28		18 32			18 40					18 48		18 56	19 00	
London Blackfriars [3] ⊖	d	18 06			18 10				18 18		18 32		18 36			18 44					18 52		19 00	19 06	
City Thameslink [3]	a	18 08			18 12				18 20		18 34		18 38			18 46					18 54		19 02	19 08	
Farringdon ⊖	a	18 11			18 15				18 23		18 37		18 41			18 49					18 57		19 05	19 11	
St Pancras International [15] ⊖	a	18 15			18 19				18 27		18 41		18 45			18 53					19 01		19 09	19 15	
Kentish Town ⊖	a								18 32		18 46												19 14		
Brixton ⊖	d			17 55						18 11					18 26					18 40					
London Victoria [15] ⊖	a		17 53	18 03		18 08	18 07			18 18		18 29		18 21	18 33		18 36		18 37	18 48		18 58			18 53

A From Sutton (Surrey) to St Albans City
B From Dartford
C To Bedford
D From Ashford International
E From Sutton (Surrey) to Bedford. [1] to Farringdon
F To St Albans City
G From Ramsgate
H From Sutton (Surrey) to Luton
I From Gillingham (Kent)
J From Sutton (Surrey) to Bedford
K From Brighton to Bedford
L To Bedford. [1] from London Blackfriars

Table 195R

Mondays to Fridays

9 December to 16 May

Sevenoaks, Otford, Orpington, Bromley South, Beckenham Junction and Catford - Kentish Town/London Victoria

Network Diagram - see first Page of Table 195

		SE	FC A		SE	SE 1 B	SE	FC C	SE D	SE	SE 1 E	SE	FC A		SE	SE F	SE 1 G	SE 1 B	SE	FC C	SE	SE 1 E	SE		FC A
Sevenoaks 4	d				18 18					18 32					18 45						19 02				
Bat & Ball	d				18 21					18 35					18 48						19 05				
Otford 4	d				18 24					18 38	18 46				18 51						19 08	19 17			
Shoreham (Kent)	d				18 27					18 41					18 54						19 11				
Eynsford	d				18 31					18 45					18 58						19 15				
Swanley 4	d				18 36					18 50	18 54				19 03	19 05					19 20	19 26			
St Mary Cray	d				18 40					18 54	18 58					19 09					19 24				
Orpington 4	d	18 25					18 40					18 55							19 10				19 25		
Petts Wood 4	d	18 28					18 43					18 58							19 13				19 28		
Bickley 4	d	18 32					18 47			18 58		19 02							19 17		19 28		19 32		
Bromley South 4	d	18 35			18 46	18 50	18 50			19 01	19 05	19 05			19 11	19 15	19 17	19 20	19 20		19 31	19 35	19 35		
Shortlands 4	d	18 38					18 53			19 04		19 08							19 23		19 34		19 38		
Ravensbourne	d									19 06											19 36				
Beckenham Hill	d									19 08											19 38				
Bellingham	d									19 10											19 40				
Catford	d									19 13											19 43				
Crofton Park	d									19 15											19 45				
Lewisham 4	d								19 08																
Nunhead 4	d								19 13	19 18											19 48				
Peckham Rye 4	d								19 15	19 20					19 23						19 50				
Denmark Hill 4	d				18 59				19 19	19 24					19 28						19 54				
Beckenham Junction 4	d	18 41					18 56					19 11							19 26				19 41		
Kent House 4	d	18 43					18 58					19 13							19 28				19 43		
Penge East	d	18 45					19 00					19 15							19 30				19 45		
Sydenham Hill	d	18 48					19 03					19 18							19 33				19 48		
West Dulwich	d	18 50					19 05					19 20							19 35				19 50		
Herne Hill 4	d	18 53	19 02				19 08	19 17				19 23	19 31						19 38	19 47			19 53		20 05
Loughborough Jn	d		19 05					19 20					19 34							19 50					20 08
Elephant & Castle	⊖ d		19 10					19 25		19 30			19 39							19 55	20 00				20 13
London Blackfriars 3	⊖ d		19 18					19 30		19 34			19 46							20 00	20 04				20 18
City Thameslink 3	a		19 20					19 32		19 36			19 48							20 02	20 06				20 20
Farringdon	⊖ a		19 23					19 36		19 40			19 51							20 06	20 10				20 23
St Pancras International 15	⊖ a		19 27					19 40		19 44			19 55							20 10	20 14				20 27
Kentish Town	⊖ a		19 32					19 44		19 49			19 59							20 14	20 19				20 31
Brixton	⊖ d	18 55					19 10					19 25							19 40				19 55		
London Victoria 15	⊖ a	19 03			19 16	19 07	19 17		19 28		19 21	19 32			19 45	19 36	19 37	19 37	19 47			19 51	20 02		

		SE 1 B	SE	FC C	SE	SE 1 E	SE	FC A	SE		SE 1 H	SE 1 B	SE	FC C	SE	SE 1 E	SE 1 B	FC A	SE		FC C	SE	SE 1 E	SE 1 B	FC A
Sevenoaks 4	d				19 32				19 45						20 02							20 32			
Bat & Ball	d				19 35				19 48						20 05							20 35			
Otford 4	d				19 38	19 46			19 51						20 08	20 17						20 38	20 46		
Shoreham (Kent)	d				19 41				19 54						20 11							20 41			
Eynsford	d				19 45				19 58						20 15							20 45			
Swanley 4	d				19 50	19 54			20 03		20 05				20 20	20 26						20 50	20 54	21 10	
St Mary Cray	d				19 54	19 58					20 09				20 24							20 54	20 58	21 14	
Orpington 4	d		19 40				19 55						20 10						20 40						
Petts Wood 4	d		19 43				19 58						20 13						20 43						
Bickley 4	d		19 47		19 58		20 02						20 17		20 28				20 47			20 58			
Bromley South 4	d	19 50	19 50		20 01	20 05	20 05		20a11		20 15	20 20	20 20		20 31	20 35	20 50		20 50			21 01	21 05	21 20	
Shortlands 4	d		19 53		20 04		20 08						20 23		20 34				20 53			21 04			
Ravensbourne	d				20 06										20 36							21 06			
Beckenham Hill	d				20 08										20 38							21 08			
Bellingham	d				20 10										20 40							21 10			
Catford	d				20 13										20 43							21 13			
Crofton Park	d				20 15										20 45							21 15			
Lewisham 4	d																								
Nunhead 4	d				20 18										20 48							21 18			
Peckham Rye 4	d				20 20										20 50							21 20			
Denmark Hill 4	d				20 24										20 54							21 24			
Beckenham Junction 4	d		19 56				20 11						20 26						20 56						
Kent House 4	d		19 58				20 13						20 28						20 58						
Penge East	d		20 00				20 15						20 30						21 00						
Sydenham Hill	d		20 03				20 18						20 33						21 03						
West Dulwich	d		20 05				20 20						20 35						21 05						
Herne Hill 4	d		20 08	20 16			20 23	20 35					20 38	20 46				21 05	21 08		21 16				21 35
Loughborough Jn	d			20 19				20 38						20 49				21 08			21 19				21 38
Elephant & Castle	⊖ d			20 24	20 30			20 43						20 54	21 00			21 13			21 24	21 30			21 43
London Blackfriars 3	⊖ d			20 30	20 34			20 48						21 00	21 04			21 18			21 30	21a34			21 48
City Thameslink 3	a			20 32	20 36			20 50						21 02	21 06			21 20			21 32				21 50
Farringdon	⊖ a			20 36	20 40			20 53						21 06	21 10			21 23			21 36				21 53
St Pancras International 15	⊖ a			20 40	20 44			20 57						21 10	21 14			21 27			21 40				21 57
Kentish Town	⊖ a			20 44	20 49			21 01						21 14	21 19			21 31			21 44				22 01
Brixton	⊖ d		20 10				20 25						20 40						21 10						
London Victoria 15	⊖ a	20 07	20 17			20 21	20 32				20 36	20 38	20 47			20 51	21 07		21 17				21 21	21 37	

A From Sutton (Surrey) to St Albans City
B From Ramsgate
C From Sutton (Surrey) to Luton
D From Dartford
E From Ashford International
F From Gillingham (Kent)
G From Maidstone East
H From Rochester

Table 195R

Mondays to Fridays

9 December to 16 May

Sevenoaks, Otford, Orpington, Bromley South, Beckenham Junction and Catford - Kentish Town/London Victoria

Network Diagram - see first Page of Table 195

		SE	SE	SE	SE	FC	SE	SE	SE	FC	SE	SE	SE	SE	FC	SE	SE	SE	FC	SE	SE	SE
				1	1				1				1	1				1			1	1
				A	B	C			B	C			A	D	C			B	C		A	D
Sevenoaks 4	d		21 02					21 32				22 02					22 32					
Bat & Ball	d		21 05					21 35				22 05					22 35					
Otford 4	d		21 08	21 16				21 38				22 08	22 16				22 38				23 16	
Shoreham (Kent)	d		21 11					21 41				22 11					22 41					
Eynsford	d		21 15					21 45				22 15					22 45					
Swanley 4	d		21 20	21 24				21 50	22 10			22 20	22 24				22 50	23 10			23 24	
St Mary Cray	d		21 24	21 28				21 54	22 14			22 24	22 28				22 54	23 14			23 28	
Orpington 4	d	21 10					21 40				22 10					22 40				23 10		
Petts Wood 4	d	21 13					21 43				22 13					22 43				23 13		
Bickley 4	d	21 17	21 28				21 47	21 58			22 17	22 28				22 47	22 58			23 17		
Bromley South 4	d	21 20	21 31	21 35	21 50		21 50	22 01	22 20		22 20	22 31	22 35	22 50		22 50	23 01	23 20		23 20	23 35	23 50
Shortlands 4	d	21 23	21 34				21 53	22 04			22 23	22 34				22 53	23 04			23 23		
Ravensbourne	d		21 36					22 06				22 36					23 06					
Beckenham Hill	d		21 38					22 08				22 38					23 08					
Bellingham	d		21 40					22 10				22 40					23 10					
Catford	d		21 43					22 13				22 43					23 13					
Crofton Park	d		21 45					22 15				22 45					23 15					
Lewisham 4	d																					
Nunhead 4	d		21 48					22 18				22 48					23 18					
Peckham Rye 4	d		21 50					22 20				22 50					23 20					
Denmark Hill 4	d		21 54					22 24				22 54					23 24					
Beckenham Junction 4	d	21 26					21 56				22 26					22 56				23 26		
Kent House 4	d	21 28					21 58				22 28					22 58				23 28		
Penge East	d	21 30					22 00				22 30					23 00				23 30		
Sydenham Hill	d	21 33					22 03				22 33					23 03				23 33		
West Dulwich	d	21 35					22 05				22 35					23 05				23 35		
Herne Hill 4	d	21 38				21 57	22 08			22 27	22 38				22 57	23 08			23 27	23 38		
Loughborough Jn	d					22 00				22 30					23 00							
Elephant & Castle ⊖	d		22 00			22 04		22 30		22 34		23 00			23 04		23 30		23 34			
London Blackfriars 3 ⊖	d		22a04			22 08		22a34		22 38		23a04			23 08		23a34		23 38			
City Thameslink 3	a					22 10				22 40												
Farringdon ⊖	a					22 13				22 43					23 13				23 43			
St Pancras International 15 ⊖	a					22 17				22 47					23 17				23 47			
Kentish Town ⊖	a					22 21				22 51					23 21				23 51			
Brixton ⊖	d	21 40					22 10				22 40					23 10				23 40		
London Victoria 15 ⊖	a	21 47		21 51	22 07		22 17		22 37		22 47		22 51	23 07		23 17		23 37		23 47	23 51	00 07

Saturdays

14 December to 17 May

		SE	FC	SE	SE	FC	SE	SE	SE	SE	FC	SE	SE	FC	SE	SE	SE	SE	FC	SE	SE	SE	FC
		1			1				1			1					1			1	1		
		B	E		D	E			A		F	D		G	H		A		I	J	D		G
Sevenoaks 4	d			05 32				06 02								06 32							
Bat & Ball	d			05 35				06 05								06 35							
Otford 4	d			05 38				06 08	06 16							06 38	06 46						
Shoreham (Kent)	d			05 41				06 11								06 41							
Eynsford	d			05 45				06 15								06 45							
Swanley 4	d	00 10		05 50	06 05			06 20	06 24							06 50	06 54			07 05			
St Mary Cray	d	00 14		05 54	06 09			06 24	06 28							06 54	06 58			07 09			
Orpington 4	d						06 10			06 25			06 40					06 55				07 10	
Petts Wood 4	d						06 13			06 28			06 43					06 58				07 13	
Bickley 4	d			05 58			06 17	06 28		06 32			06 47			06 58		07 02				07 17	
Bromley South 4	d	00 20		06 01	06 16		06 20	06 31	06 35	06 35		06 50	06 50			07 01	07 05	07 05		07 15	07 20	07 20	
Shortlands 4	d			06 04			06 23	06 34		06 38			06 53			07 04		07 08				07 23	
Ravensbourne	d			06 06				06 36								07 06							
Beckenham Hill	d			06 08				06 38								07 08							
Bellingham	d			06 10				06 40								07 10							
Catford	d			06 13				06 43								07 13							
Crofton Park	d			06 15				06 45								07 15							
Lewisham 4	d														07 08								
Nunhead 4	d			06 18				06 48							07 13	07 18							
Peckham Rye 4	d			06 20				06 50							07 15	07 20							
Denmark Hill 4	d			06 24				06 54							07 19	07 24							
Beckenham Junction 4	d						06 26			06 41			06 56					07 11				07 26	
Kent House 4	d						06 28			06 43			06 58					07 13				07 28	
Penge East	d						06 30			06 45			07 00					07 15				07 30	
Sydenham Hill	d						06 33			06 48			07 03					07 18				07 33	
West Dulwich	d						06 35			06 50			07 05					07 20				07 35	
Herne Hill 4	d		06 02			06 32	06 38			06 53	07 01		07 08	07 16				07 23	07 31			07 38	07 46
Loughborough Jn	d					06 35					07 04			07 19					07 34				07 49
Elephant & Castle ⊖	d		06 09	06 30		06 39		07 00			07 09			07 24		07 30			07 39				07 54
London Blackfriars 3 ⊖	d		06 14	06a34		06 44		07a04			07 14			07 30		07a34			07 44				08 00
City Thameslink 3	a																						
Farringdon ⊖	a		06 19			06 49					07 19			07 36					07 49				08 06
St Pancras International 15 ⊖	a		06 23			06 53					07 23			07 40					07 53				08 10
Kentish Town ⊖	a		06 27			06 57					07 27			07 44					07 57				08 14
Brixton ⊖	d						06 40			06 55			07 10					07 25				07 40	
London Victoria 15 ⊖	a	00 37			06 36		06 47		06 51	07 02		07 07	07 17		07 28		07 21	07 32		07 36	07 37	07 47	

A From Ashford International
B From Dover Priory
C From Sutton (Surrey) to Bedford
D From Ramsgate
E From Selhurst to Luton
F From Selhurst to Bedford
G From Sutton (Surrey) to Luton
H From Dartford
I From Sutton (Surrey) to St Albans City
J From Gillingham (Kent)

Table 195R

Saturdays

14 December to 17 May

Sevenoaks, Otford, Orpington, Bromley South, Beckenham Junction and Catford - Kentish Town/London Victoria

Network Diagram - see first Page of Table 195

		SE	SE	SE	SE	FC		SE	SE	FC	SE	SE	SE	SE	FC	SE	SE	SE	FC	SE	SE	SE	SE	FC	SE
		A		1 B		C		1 D		E	A		1 B		C	1 F	1 D		E	A		1 B		C	1 D
Sevenoaks 4	d		07 02									07 32									08 02				
Bat & Ball	d		07 05									07 35									08 05				
Otford 4	d		07 08	07 17								07 38	07 46								08 08	08 17			
Shoreham (Kent)	d		07 11									07 41									08 11				
Eynsford	d		07 15									07 45									08 15				
Swanley 4	d		07 20	07 26								07 50	07 54			08 05					08 20	08 26			
St Mary Cray	d		07 24									07 54	07 58			08 09					08 24				
Orpington 4	d				07 25				07 40					07 55				08 10					08 25		
Petts Wood 4	d				07 28				07 43					07 58				08 13					08 28		
Bickley 4	d		07 28		07 32				07 47			07 58		08 02				08 17			08 28		08 32		
Bromley South 4	d		07 31	07 35	07 35			07 50	07 50			08 01	08 05	08 05		08 15	08 20	08 20			08 31	08 35	08 35		08 50
Shortlands 4	d		07 34		07 38				07 53			08 04		08 08				08 23			08 34		08 38		
Ravensbourne	d		07 36									08 06									08 36				
Beckenham Hill	d		07 38									08 08									08 38				
Bellingham	d		07 40									08 10									08 40				
Catford	d		07 43									08 13									08 43				
Crofton Park	d		07 45									08 15									08 45				
Lewisham 4	d	07 38									08 08									08 38					
Nunhead 4	d	07 43	07 48								08 13	08 18								08 43	08 48				
Peckham Rye 4	d	07 45	07 50								08 15	08 20								08 45	08 50				
Denmark Hill 4	d	07 49	07 54								08 19	08 24								08 49	08 54				
Beckenham Junction 4	d				07 41				07 56					08 11				08 26					08 41		
Kent House 4	d				07 43				07 58					08 13				08 28					08 43		
Penge East	d				07 45				08 00					08 15				08 30					08 45		
Sydenham Hill	d				07 48				08 03					08 18				08 33					08 48		
West Dulwich	d				07 50				08 05					08 20				08 35					08 50		
Herne Hill 4	d				07 53	08 01			08 08	08 16				08 23	08 31			08 38	08 46				08 53	09 01	
Loughborough Jn	d					08 04				08 19					08 34				08 49					09 04	
Elephant & Castle ⊖	d		08 00			08 09				08 24		08 30			08 39				08 54		09 00			09 09	
London Blackfriars 3 ⊖	d		08a04			08 14				08 30		08a34			08 44				09 00		09a04			09 14	
City Thameslink 3	a																		09 02					09 16	
Farringdon ⊖	a					08 19				08 36					08 49				09 06					09 19	
St Pancras International 15 ⊖	a					08 23				08 40					08 53				09 10					09 23	
Kentish Town ⊖	a					08 27				08 44					08 57				09 14					09 27	
Brixton ⊖	d				07 55				08 10					08 25				08 40					08 55		
London Victoria 15 ⊖	a	07 58		07 51	08 02			08 07	08 17		08 28		08 21	08 32		08 36	08 37	08 47		08 58		08 51	09 02		09 07

		SE	FC	SE	SE	SE	SE	FC		SE	SE	SE	FC	SE	SE	SE	SE	FC	SE	SE	FC	SE	SE	SE
			E	A		1 B		C		1 F	1 D		E	A		1 B		C	1 D		E	A		1 B
Sevenoaks 4	d				08 32										18 02								18 32	
Bat & Ball	d				08 35										18 05								18 35	
Otford 4	d				08 38	08 46									18 08	18 17							18 38	18 46
Shoreham (Kent)	d				08 41										18 11								18 41	
Eynsford	d				08 45										18 15								18 45	
Swanley 4	d				08 50	08 54				18 05					18 20	18 26							18 50	18 54
St Mary Cray	d				08 54	08 58				18 09					18 24								18 54	18 58
Orpington 4	d	08 40					08 55					18 10					18 25			18 40				
Petts Wood 4	d	08 43					08 58					18 13					18 28			18 43				
Bickley 4	d	08 47			08 58		09 02					18 17			18 28		18 32			18 47			18 58	
Bromley South 4	d	08 50			09 01	09 05	09 05			18 15	18 20	18 20			18 31	18 35	18 35		18 50	18 50			19 01	19 05
Shortlands 4	d	08 53			09 04		09 08					18 23			18 34		18 38			18 53			19 04	
Ravensbourne	d				09 06				and at the same minutes past each hour until						18 36								19 06	
Beckenham Hill	d				09 08										18 38								19 08	
Bellingham	d				09 10										18 40								19 10	
Catford	d				09 13										18 43								19 13	
Crofton Park	d				09 15										18 45								19 15	
Lewisham 4	d			09 08										18 38								19 08		
Nunhead 4	d			09 13	09 18									18 43	18 48							19 13	19 18	
Peckham Rye 4	d			09 15	09 20									18 45	18 50							19 15	19 20	
Denmark Hill 4	d			09 19	09 24									18 49	18 54							19 19	19 24	
Beckenham Junction 4	d	08 56					09 11					18 26					18 41			18 56				
Kent House 4	d	08 58					09 13					18 28					18 43			18 58				
Penge East	d	09 00					09 15					18 30					18 45			19 00				
Sydenham Hill	d	09 03					09 18					18 33					18 48			19 03				
West Dulwich	d	09 05					09 20					18 35					18 50			19 05				
Herne Hill 4	d	09 08	09 16				09 23	09 31				18 38	18 46				18 53	19 01		19 08	19 16			
Loughborough Jn	d		09 19					09 34					18 49					19 04			19 19			
Elephant & Castle ⊖	d		09 24		09 30			09 39					18 54		19 00			19 09			19 24		19 30	
London Blackfriars 3 ⊖	d		09 30		09a34			09 44					19 00		19a04			19 14			19 30		19a34	
City Thameslink 3	a		09 32					09 46					19 02					19 16			19 32			
Farringdon ⊖	a		09 36					09 49					19 06					19 19			19 36			
St Pancras International 15 ⊖	a		09 40					09 53					19 10					19 23			19 40			
Kentish Town ⊖	a		09 44					09 57					19 14					19 27			19 44			
Brixton ⊖	d	09 10					09 25					18 40					18 55			19 10				
London Victoria 15 ⊖	a	09 17		09 28		09 21	09 32			18 36	18 37	18 47		18 58		18 51	19 02		19 07	19 17		19 28		19 21

A From Dartford
B From Ashford International
C From Sutton (Surrey) to St Albans City
D From Ramsgate
E From Sutton (Surrey) to Luton
F From Gillingham (Kent)

Table 195R

Saturdays

14 December to 17 May

Sevenoaks, Otford, Orpington, Bromley South, Beckenham Junction and Catford - Kentish Town/London Victoria

Network Diagram - see first Page of Table 195

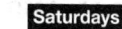

Station		SE	FC A	SE [1] B	SE [1] C	SE	FC D	SE	SE [1] E	SE	FC A	SE [1] C	SE	FC D	SE	SE [1] E	SE	FC F	SE [1] B	SE [1] C	SE	FC D
Sevenoaks	d							19 02							19 32							
Bat & Ball	d							19 05							19 35							
Otford	d							19 08	19 17						19 38	19 46						
Shoreham (Kent)	d							19 11							19 41							
Eynsford	d							19 15							19 45							
Swanley	d			19 05				19 20	19 26						19 50	19 54			20 05			
St Mary Cray	d			19 09				19 24							19 54	19 58			20 09			
Orpington	d	18 55				19 10				19 25			19 40				19 55				20 10	
Petts Wood	d	18 58				19 13				19 28			19 43				19 58				20 13	
Bickley	d	19 02				19 17		19 28		19 32			19 47		19 58		20 02				20 17	
Bromley South	d	19 05		19 15	19 20	19 20		19 31	19 35	19 35		19 50	19 50		20 01	20 05	20 05		20 15	20 20	20 20	
Shortlands	d	19 08				19 23		19 34		19 38			19 53		20 04		20 08				20 23	
Ravensbourne	d							19 36							20 06							
Beckenham Hill	d							19 38							20 08							
Bellingham	d							19 40							20 10							
Catford	d							19 43							20 13							
Crofton Park	d							19 45							20 15							
Lewisham	d																					
Nunhead	d							19 48							20 18							
Peckham Rye	d							19 50							20 20							
Denmark Hill	d							19 54							20 24							
Beckenham Junction	d	19 11				19 26				19 41			19 56				20 11				20 26	
Kent House	d	19 13				19 28				19 43			19 58				20 13				20 28	
Penge East	d	19 15				19 30				19 45			20 00				20 15				20 30	
Sydenham Hill	d	19 18				19 33				19 48			20 03				20 18				20 33	
West Dulwich	d	19 20				19 35				19 50			20 05				20 20				20 35	
Herne Hill	d	19 23	19 31			19 38	19 46			19 53	20 01		20 08	20 16			20 23	20 31			20 38	20 46
Loughborough Jn	d		19 34				19 49				20 04			20 19				20 34				20 49
Elephant & Castle	d		19 39				19 54	20 00			20 09			20 24	20 30			20 39				20 54
London Blackfriars	d		19 44				20 00	20a04			20 14			20 30	20a34			20 44				21 00
City Thameslink	a		19 46				20 02				20 16			20 32				20 46				
Farringdon	a		19 49				20 06				20 19			20 36				20 49				21 06
St Pancras International	a		19 53				20 10				20 23			20 40				20 53				21 10
Kentish Town	a		19 57				20 14				20 27			20 44				20 57				21 14
Brixton	d	19 25				19 40				19 55			20 10				20 25				20 40	
London Victoria	a	19 32		19 36	19 37	19 47			19 51	20 02		20 07	20 17			20 21	20 32		20 36	20 39	20 47	

Station		SE	SE [1] C	FC F	SE	FC D	SE	SE [1] E	SE G	FC F	SE	SE	SE [1] C	FC A	SE	SE	SE [1] E	SE G	FC A	SE	SE	SE [1] C	FC A
Sevenoaks	d	20 02					20 32					21 02				21 32					22 02		
Bat & Ball	d	20 05					20 35					21 05				21 35					22 05		
Otford	d	20 08					20 38	20 46				21 08				21 38	21 46				22 08		
Shoreham (Kent)	d	20 11					20 41					21 11				21 41					22 11		
Eynsford	d	20 15					20 45					21 15				21 45					22 15		
Swanley	d	20 20					20 50	20 54	21 10			21 20				21 50	21 54	22 10			22 20		
St Mary Cray	d	20 24					20 54	20 58	21 14			21 24				21 54	21 58	22 14			22 24		
Orpington	d				20 40						21 10				21 40					22 10			
Petts Wood	d				20 43						21 13				21 43					22 13			
Bickley	d	20 28			20 47		20 58				21 17	21 28			21 47	21 58				22 17	22 28		
Bromley South	d	20 31	20 50		20 50		21 01	21 05	21 20		21 20	21 31	21 50		21 50	22 01	22 05	22 20		22 20	22 31	22 50	
Shortlands	d	20 34			20 53		21 04				21 23	21 34			21 53	22 04				22 23	22 34		
Ravensbourne	d	20 36					21 06					21 36				22 06					22 36		
Beckenham Hill	d	20 38					21 08					21 38				22 08					22 38		
Bellingham	d	20 40					21 10					21 40				22 10					22 40		
Catford	d	20 43					21 13					21 43				22 13					22 43		
Crofton Park	d	20 45					21 15					21 45				22 15					22 45		
Lewisham	d																						
Nunhead	d	20 48					21 18					21 48				22 18					22 48		
Peckham Rye	d	20 50					21 20					21 50				22 20					22 50		
Denmark Hill	d	20 54					21 24					21 54				22 24					22 54		
Beckenham Junction	d				20 56						21 26				21 56					22 26			
Kent House	d				20 58						21 28				21 58					22 28			
Penge East	d				21 00						21 30				22 00					22 30			
Sydenham Hill	d				21 03						21 33				22 03					22 33			
West Dulwich	d				21 05						21 35				22 05					22 35			
Herne Hill	d			21 01	21 08	21 16				21 31	21 38			21 57	22 08				22 27	22 38			22 57
Loughborough Jn	d			21 04		21 19				21 34				22 00					22 30				23 00
Elephant & Castle	d	21 00		21 09		21 24	21 30			21 39		22 00		22 04		22 30			22 34		23 00		23 04
London Blackfriars	d	21a04		21 14		21 30	21a34			21 44		22a04		22 08		22a34			22 38		23a04		23 08
City Thameslink	a																						
Farringdon	a			21 19		21 36				21 49				22 13					22 43				23 13
St Pancras International	a			21 23		21 40				21 53				22 17					22 47				23 17
Kentish Town	a			21 27		21 44				21 57				22 21					22 51				23 21
Brixton	d				21 10						21 40				22 10					22 40			
London Victoria	a		21 07		21 17			21 21	21 37		21 47		22 07		22 17		22 21	22 37		22 47		23 07	

A From Sutton (Surrey) to Bedford
B From Gillingham (Kent)
C From Ramsgate
D From Sutton (Surrey) to Luton
E From Ashford International
F From Sutton (Surrey) to St Albans City
G From Faversham

Table 195R

Saturdays

14 December to 17 May

Sevenoaks, Otford, Orpington, Bromley South, Beckenham Junction and Catford - Kentish Town/London Victoria

Network Diagram - see first Page of Table 195

		SE	SE	SE	FC		SE	SE	SE
								1	1
				A	B			C	D
Sevenoaks 4	d		22 32						
Bat & Ball	d		22 35						
Otford 4	d		22 38					23 16	
Shoreham (Kent)	d		22 41						
Eynsford	d		22 45						
Swanley 4	d		22 50	23 10				23 24	
St Mary Cray	d		22 54	23 14				23 28	
Orpington 4	d	22 40					23 10		
Petts Wood 4	d	22 43					23 13		
Bickley 4	d	22 47	22 58				23 17		
Bromley South 4	d	22 50	23 01	23 20			23 20	23 35	23 50
Shortlands 4	d	22 53	23 04				23 23		
Ravensbourne	d		23 06						
Beckenham Hill	d		23 08						
Bellingham	d		23 10						
Catford	d		23 13						
Crofton Park	d		23 15						
Lewisham 4	d								
Nunhead 4	d		23 18						
Peckham Rye 4	d		23 20						
Denmark Hill 4	d		23 24						
Beckenham Junction 4	d	22 56					23 27		
Kent House 4	d	22 58					23 30		
Penge East	d	23 00					23 32		
Sydenham Hill	d	23 03					23 35		
West Dulwich	d	23 05					23 37		
Herne Hill 4	d	23 08			23 27		23 39		
Loughborough Jn	d								
Elephant & Castle ⊖	d		23 30		23 34				
London Blackfriars 3 ⊖	d		23a34		23 38				
City Thameslink 3	a								
Farringdon ⊖	a				23 43				
St Pancras International 15 ⊖	a				23 47				
Kentish Town ⊖	a				23 51				
Brixton ⊖	d	23 10					23 41		
London Victoria 15 ⊖	a	23 17		23 37			23 48	23 51	00 07

Sundays

8 December to 11 May

		SE	SE	SE	SE	SE	SE	SE	SE	SE		SE	SE	SE	SE	SE	SE	SE	SE	SE		FC	SE
						1		1		1				1		1		1					1
						E		C		D				E		C		D				F	E
																		🚌					
Sevenoaks 4	d						07 32					08 02			08 32				09 02				
Bat & Ball	d						07 35					08 05			08 35				09 05				
Otford 4	d						07 38	07 44				08 08			08 38	08 44			09 08				
Shoreham (Kent)	d						07 41					08 11			08 41				09 11				
Eynsford	d						07 45					08 15			08 45				09 15				
Swanley 4	d					07 37	07 50	07 54				08 20		08 37	08 50	08 54			09 20				09 37
St Mary Cray	d					07 41	07 54	07 58				08 24		08 41	08 54	08 58			09 24				09 41
Orpington 4	d	06 50	06 55	07 20	07 25				07 55				08 25				08 55			09 25			
Petts Wood 4	d	06 53	06 58	07 23	07 28				07 58				08 28				08 58			09 28			
Bickley 4	d	06 58	07 02	07 28	07 32		07 58		08 02			08 28	08 32		08 58		09 02		09 28	09 32			
Bromley South 4	d	07 01	07 05	07 31	07 35	07 48	08 01	08 04	08 05	08 18		08 31	08 35	08 48	09 01	09 04	09 05	09 18	09 31	09 35			09 48
Shortlands 4	d	07 04	07 08	07 34	07 38		08 04		08 08			08 34	08 38		09 04		09 08		09 34	09 38			
Ravensbourne	d	07 06		07 36			08 06					08 36			09 06				09 36				
Beckenham Hill	d	07 08		07 38			08 08					08 38			09 08				09 38				
Bellingham	d	07 10		07 40			08 10					08 40			09 10				09 40				
Catford	d	07 13		07 43			08 13					08 43			09 13				09 43				
Crofton Park	d	07 15		07 45			08 15					08 45			09 15				09 45				
Lewisham 4	d																						
Nunhead 4	d	07 18		07 48			08 18					08 48			09 18				09 48				
Peckham Rye 4	d	07 20		07 50			08 20					08 50			09 20				09 50				
Denmark Hill 4	d	07 24		07 54			08 24					08 54			09 24				09 54				
Beckenham Junction 4	d		07 11		07 41				08 11				08 41				09 11			09 41			
Kent House 4	d		07 13		07 43				08 13				08 43				09 13			09 43			
Penge East	d		07 15		07 45				08 15				08 45				09 15			09 45			
Sydenham Hill	d		07 18		07 48				08 18				08 48				09 18			09 48			
West Dulwich	d		07 20		07 50				08 20				08 50				09 20			09 50			
Herne Hill 4	d		07 23		07 53				08 23				08 53				09 23			09 53		10 14	
Loughborough Jn	d																					10 17	
Elephant & Castle ⊖	d	07 30		08 00			08 30					09 00			09 30				10 00			10 22	
London Blackfriars 3 ⊖	d	07a34		08a04			08a34					09a04			09a34				10a04			10 26	
City Thameslink 3	a																						
Farringdon ⊖	a																					10 32	
St Pancras International 15 ⊖	a																					10 36	
Kentish Town ⊖	a																					10 40	
Brixton ⊖	d		07 25		07 55				08 25				08 55				09 25			09 55			
London Victoria 15 ⊖	a		07 32		08 02	08 05		08 21	08 32	08 35			09 02	09 05		09 21	09 32	09 35		10 02			10 05

A From Canterbury East
B From Sutton (Surrey) to Bedford
C From Ashford International
D From Ramsgate
E From Faversham
F From Sutton (Surrey) to Luton

Table 195R

Sundays

8 December to 11 May

Sevenoaks, Otford, Orpington, Bromley South, Beckenham Junction and Catford - Kentish Town/London Victoria

Network Diagram - see first Page of Table 195

Station		SE	SE 1 A	SE	FC B	SE 1 C	FC D	SE	SE	FC B	SE 1 E	FC D	and at the same minutes past each hour until	SE	SE 1 A	SE	FC B	SE 1 C	FC F	SE	SE	FC B	SE 1 E	FC F
Sevenoaks 4	d	09 32						10 02						19 32						20 02				
Bat & Ball	d	09 35						10 05						19 35						20 05				
Otford 4	d	09 38	09 44					10 08						19 38	19 44					20 08				
Shoreham (Kent)	d	09 41						10 11						19 41						20 11				
Eynsford	d	09 45						10 15						19 45						20 15				
Swanley 4	d	09 50	09 54					10 20			10 37			19 50	19 54					20 20			20 37	
St Mary Cray	d	09 54	09 58					10 24			10 41			19 54	19 58					20 24			20 41	
Orpington 4	d			09 55					10 25							19 55					20 25			
Petts Wood 4	d			09 58					10 28							19 58					20 28			
Bickley 4	d	09 58		10 02				10 28	10 32					19 58		20 02				20 28	20 32			
Bromley South 4	d	10 01	10 04	10 05		10 18		10 31	10 35		10 48			20 01	20 04	20 05		20 18		20 31	20 35		20 48	
Shortlands 4	d	10 04		10 08				10 34	10 38					20 04		20 08				20 34	20 38			
Ravensbourne	d	10 06						10 36						20 06						20 36				
Beckenham Hill	d	10 08						10 38						20 08						20 38				
Bellingham	d	10 10						10 40						20 10						20 40				
Catford	d	10 13						10 43						20 13						20 43				
Crofton Park	d	10 15						10 45						20 15						20 45				
Lewisham 4	d																							
Nunhead 4	d	10 18						10 48						20 18						20 48				
Peckham Rye 4	d	10 20						10 50						20 20						20 50				
Denmark Hill 4	d	10 24						10 54						20 24						20 54				
Beckenham Junction 4	d			10 11					10 41							20 11					20 41			
Kent House 4	d			10 13					10 43							20 13					20 43			
Penge East	d			10 15					10 45							20 15					20 45			
Sydenham Hill	d			10 18					10 48							20 18					20 48			
West Dulwich	d			10 20					10 50							20 20					20 50			
Herne Hill 4	d			10 23	10 31		10 44		10 53	11 01		11 14				20 23	20 31		20 44		20 53	21 01		21 14
Loughborough Jn	d				10 34		10 47			11 04		11 17					20 34		20 47			21 04		21 17
Elephant & Castle ⊖	d	10 30			10 39		10 52	11 00		11 09		11 22		20 30			20 39		20 52	21 00		21 09		21 22
London Blackfriars 3 ⊖	d	10a34			10a43		10 56	11a04		11a13		11 26		20a34			20a43		20 56	21a04		21a13		21 26
City Thameslink 3	a																							
Farringdon ⊖	a						11 02					11 32							21 02					21 32
St Pancras International 15 ⊖	a						11 06					11 36							21 06					21 36
Kentish Town ⊖	a						11 10					11 40							21 10					21 40
Brixton ⊖	d			10 25					10 55							20 25					20 55			
London Victoria 15 ⊖	a		10 21	10 32		10 35			11 02		11 05				20 21	20 32		20 35			21 02		21 05	

Station		SE	SE 1 A	SE	FC B	SE 1 C	FC F	SE	SE	FC G	FC H	SE 1 E	SE	SE 1 A	SE	FC B	SE 1 C	SE	SE	SE 1 I	SE	SE 1 A
Sevenoaks 4	d	20 32						21 02					21 32					22 02			22 32	
Bat & Ball	d	20 35						21 05					21 35					22 05			22 35	
Otford 4	d	20 38	20 44					21 08					21 38	21 44				22 08			22 38	22 44
Shoreham (Kent)	d	20 41						21 11					21 41					22 11			22 41	
Eynsford	d	20 45						21 15					21 45					22 15			22 45	
Swanley 4	d	20 50	20 54					21 20				21 37	21 50	21 54				22 20		22 37	22 50	22 54
St Mary Cray	d	20 54	20 58					21 24				21 41	21 54	21 58				22 24		22 41	22 54	22 58
Orpington 4	d			20 55					21 25						21 55				22 25			
Petts Wood 4	d			20 58					21 28						21 58				22 28			
Bickley 4	d	20 58		21 02				21 28	21 32				21 58		22 02			22 28	22 32		22 58	
Bromley South 4	d	21 01	21 04	21 05		21 18		21 31	21 35			21 48	22 01	22 04	22 05		22 18	22 31	22 35	22 48	23 01	23 04
Shortlands 4	d	21 04		21 08				21 34	21 38				22 04		22 08			22 34	22 38		23 04	
Ravensbourne	d	21 06						21 36					22 06					22 36			23 06	
Beckenham Hill	d	21 08						21 38					22 08					22 38			23 08	
Bellingham	d	21 10						21 40					22 10					22 40			23 10	
Catford	d	21 13						21 43					22 13					22 43			23 13	
Crofton Park	d	21 15						21 45					22 15					22 45			23 15	
Lewisham 4	d																					
Nunhead 4	d	21 18						21 48					22 18					22 48			23 18	
Peckham Rye 4	d	21 20						21 50					22 20					22 50			23 20	
Denmark Hill 4	d	21 24						21 54					22 24					22 54			23 24	
Beckenham Junction 4	d			21 11					21 41						22 11				22 41			
Kent House 4	d			21 13					21 43						22 13				22 43			
Penge East	d			21 15					21 45						22 15				22 45			
Sydenham Hill	d			21 18					21 48						22 18				22 48			
West Dulwich	d			21 20					21 50						22 20				22 50			
Herne Hill 4	d			21 23	21 31		21 44		21 53	22 01	22 01				22 23	22 31			22 53			
Loughborough Jn	d				21 34		21 47			22 04	22 04					22 34						
Elephant & Castle ⊖	d	21 30			21 39		21 52	22 00		22 09	22 09		22 30			22 39		23 00			23 30	
London Blackfriars 3 ⊖	d	21a34			21a43		21 56	22a04		22a13	22 14		22a34			22a43		23a04			23a34	
City Thameslink 3	a																					
Farringdon ⊖	a						22 02				22 19											
St Pancras International 15 ⊖	a						22 06				22 24											
Kentish Town ⊖	a						22 10				22 28											
Brixton ⊖	d			21 25					21 55						22 25				22 55			
London Victoria 15 ⊖	a		21 21	21 32		21 35			22 02			22 05		22 21	22 32		22 35		23 02	23 05		23 21

A From Ashford International
B From Sutton (Surrey)
C From Ramsgate
D From Sutton (Surrey) to Luton
E From Canterbury East
F From Sutton (Surrey) to Bedford
G until 29 December. From Sutton (Surrey)
H from 5 January. From Sutton (Surrey) to Bedford
I From Faversham

Table 195R

Sundays

8 December to 11 May

Sevenoaks, Otford, Orpington, Bromley South, Beckenham Junction and Catford - Kentish Town/London Victoria

Network Diagram - see first Page of Table 195

		SE	SE	SE
			A	B
Sevenoaks	d			
Bat & Ball	d			
Otford	d			
Shoreham (Kent)	d			
Eynsford	d			
Swanley	d			23 37
St Mary Cray	d			23 41
Orpington	d	22 55		
Petts Wood	d	22 58		
Bickley	d	23 02		
Bromley South	d	23 05	23 18	23 48
Shortlands	d	23 08		
Ravensbourne	d			
Beckenham Hill	d			
Bellingham	d			
Catford	d			
Crofton Park	d			
Lewisham	d			
Nunhead	d			
Peckham Rye	d			
Denmark Hill	d			
Beckenham Junction	d	23 11		
Kent House	d	23 13		
Penge East	d	23 15		
Sydenham Hill	d	23 18		
West Dulwich	d	23 20		
Herne Hill	d	23 23		
Loughborough Jn	d			
Elephant & Castle ⊖	d			
London Blackfriars ⊖	d			
City Thameslink	a			
Farringdon ⊖	a			
St Pancras International ⊖	a			
Kentish Town ⊖	a			
Brixton ⊖	d	23 25		
London Victoria ⊖	a	23 32	23 35	00 05

A From Ramsgate

B From Faversham

Table 196

London - Maidstone East and Ashford International

Mondays to Fridays

9 December to 16 May

Network Diagram - see first Page of Table 195

Miles	Miles			SE MO [1] A	SE MX [1] A	SE MX [1]	SE B	SE [1]	SE [1]	SE [1]	SE [1]	SE [1]	SE [1]	SE [1]	SE [1]	SE [1]	SE [1]		SE [1]	SE [1]	SE [1]	SE [1]
0	—	**London Victoria [15]** ⊖	d			00 07		06 07	06 37	07 07	07 36	08 07	08 37	09 07	09 37	10 07	10 37		13 07	13 37	14 07	14 37
—	—	St Pancras International	d																			
—	—	Farringdon	d																			
—	—	City Thameslink	d																			
—	0	**London Blackfriars [3]** ⊖195	d																			
—	1¼	Elephant & Castle ⊖195	d																			
11	11½	Bromley South [4] 195	d			00 25		06 23	06 58	07 23	07 53	08 23	08 53	09 23	09 53	10 23	10 53	and at the same minutes past each hour until	13 23	13 53	14 23	14 53
14¾	—	St Mary Cray 195	d			00 32		06 30	07 04	07 30	08 00	08 30	09 00		10 00		11 00			14 00		15 00
17½	—	Swanley [4] 195	d			00 36		06 34	07 08	07 34	08 04	08 34	09 04	09 33	10 04	10 33	11 04		13 33	14 04	14 33	15 04
24	—	Otford [4] 195	d			00 44		06 42	07 16	07 42	08 12	08 42	09 12	09 41	10 12	10 41	11 12		13 41	14 12	14 41	15 12
27	—	Kemsing	d			00 49		06 47	07 21	07 47	08 17	08 47	09 17		10 17		11 17			14 17		15 17
29½	—	Borough Green & Wrotham	d			00 54		06 52	07 26	07 52	08 22	08 52	09 22	09 48	10 22	10 48	11 22		13 48	14 22	14 48	15 22
34¾	—	West Malling	d			01 00		06 58	07 32	07 58	08 28	08 58	09 28	09 55	10 28	10 55	11 28		13 55	14 28	14 55	15 28
35¾	—	East Malling	d		00 01	01 03		07 01	07 35	08 01	08 31	09 01	09 31		10 31		11 31			14 31		15 31
37½	—	Barming	d		00 05	01 07		07 05	07 39	08 05	08 35	09 05	09 35		10 35		11 35			14 35		15 35
40	—	**Maidstone East [4]**	a		00 09	01 11		07 09	07 43	08 09	08 39	09 10	09 39	10 02	10 39	11 02	11 39		14 02	14 39	15 02	15 39
—	—		d		00 10	01 12	06 34	07 10	07 44	08 10	08 40	09 10	09 40	10 03	10 40	11 03	11 40		14 03	14 40	15 03	15 40
42¾	—	Bearsted	d		00 15	01 17	06 39	07 15	07 49	08 15	08 45	09 15	09 45	10 08	10 45	11 08	11 45		14 08	14 45	15 08	15 45
45	—	Hollingbourne	d		00 18	01 20	06 42	07 18	07 52	08 18	08 48	09 18	09 48		10 48		11 48			14 48		15 48
47½	—	Harrietsham	d		00 22	01 24	06 46	07 22	07 56	08 22	08 52	09 22	09 52		10 52		11 52			14 52		15 52
49¼	—	Lenham	d	00 02	00 25	01 27	06 49	07 25	07 59	08 25	08 55	09 25	09 55		10 55		11 55			14 55		15 55
53¼	—	Charing	d	00 07	00 30	01 32	06 54	07 30	08 04	08 30	09 00	09 30	10 00		11 00		12 00			15 00		16 00
59¼	—	**Ashford International**	a	00 16	00 39	01 41	07 03	07 39	08 13	08 39	09 09	09 40	10 09	10 27	11 11	11 27	12 09		14 27	15 09	15 30	16 09

		SE [1]	SE [1]	SE [1]	SE [1]	SE [1]	SE [1]	SE [1]	SE [1]	FC [1] C	SE [1]	SE [1]	SE [1]	SE [1]	SE [1]	SE [1]	SE [1]	SE [1]	SE [1]	SE [1]
London Victoria [15] ⊖	d	15 07	15 37	16 07	16 37	16 52	17 12	17 28	17 42		18 03	18 18	18 42	19 07	19 37	20 07	20 37	21 07	22 07	23 07
St Pancras International	d									17 36										
Farringdon	d									17 41										
City Thameslink	d									17 45										
London Blackfriars [3] ⊖195	d									17 48										
Elephant & Castle ⊖195	d									17 52										
Bromley South [4] 195	d	15 23	15 53	16 23	16 53	17 09	17 31	17 50	17 59	18 10	18 24	18 39	18 59	19 27	19 53	20 23	20 53	21 23	22 23	23 23
St Mary Cray 195	d		16 00		17 00		17 38	17 57	18 06	18 17		18 45	19 06		20 00		21 00	21 30	22 30	23 30
Swanley [4] 195	d	15 33	16 04	16 33	17 04		17 42	18 01	18 11	18 22		18 50	19 11	19 36	20 04	20 33	21 04	21 34	22 34	23 34
Otford [4] 195	d	15 41	16 12	16 41	17 12	17 26	17 51	18 10	18 19	18 30	18 43	18 58	19 19	19 44	20 12	20 41	21 12	21 42	22 42	23 42
Kemsing	d		16 17		17 17		17 56		18 24	18 35		19 03	19 24		20 17		21 17	21 47	22 47	23 47
Borough Green & Wrotham	d	15 48	16 22	16 48	17 22	17 33	18 00	18 17	18 29	18 40	18 51	19 08	19 29	19 51	20 22	20 48	21 22	21 52	22 52	23 52
West Malling	d	15 55	16 28	16 55	17 28	17 40	18 07	18 24	18 35	18 47	18 57	19 14	19 35	19 57	20 28	20 55	21 28	21 58	22 58	23 58
East Malling	d		16 31		17 31		18 10		18 38	18 50		19 17	19 38		20 31		21 31	22 01	23 01	00 01
Barming	d		16 35		17 35		18 13		18 42	18 53		19 21	19 42		20 35		21 35	22 05	23 05	00 05
Maidstone East [4]	a	16 02	16 39	17 02	17 39	17 47	18 17	18 34	18 46	18 57	19 04	19 25	19 46	20 04	20 39	21 02	21 39	22 09	23 09	00 09
	d	16 03	16 40	17 03	17 40	17 48	18 18		18 47	18 58	19 06	19 26	19 47	20 05	20 40	21 03	21 40	22 10	23 10	00 10
Bearsted	d	16 08	16 45	17 08	17 45	17 53	18 23		18 52	19 04	19 11	19 31	19 52	20 10	20 45	21 08	21 45	22 15	23 15	00 15
Hollingbourne	d	16 11	16 48	17 11	17 48	17 56	18 27		18 55	19 07	19 15	19 34	19 55	20 13	20 48	21 11	21 48	22 18	23 18	00 18
Harrietsham	d	16 15	16 52	17 15	17 52	18 00	18 30		18 59	19 11	19 18	19 38	19 59	20 17	20 52	21 15	21 52	22 22	23 22	00 22
Lenham	d	16 18	16 55	17 18	17 55	18 03	18 34		19 02	19 14	19 22	19 41	20 02	20 20	20 55	21 18	21 55	22 25	23 25	00 25
Charing	d	16 23	17 00	17 23	18 00	18 08	18 39		19 07	19 19	19 27	19 46	20 07	20 25	21 00	21 23	22 00	22 30	23 30	00 30
Ashford International	a	16 32	17 09	17 34	18 11	18 20	18 50		19 18	19 32	19 40	19 59	20 18	20 34	21 09	21 32	22 09	22 39	23 39	00 39

Saturdays

14 December to 17 May

		SE [1] A	SE [1]	SE [1]	SE [1]	SE [1]	SE [1]	SE [1]		SE [1]	SE [1]	SE [1]	SE [1]		SE [1]
London Victoria [15] ⊖	d		00 07		06 07	07 07	07 37	08 07		18 37	19 07	19 37	20 07		23 07
St Pancras International	d														
Farringdon	d														
City Thameslink	d														
London Blackfriars [3] ⊖195	d														
Elephant & Castle ⊖195	d														
Bromley South [4] 195	d		00 25		06 23	07 23	07 53	08 23	and at the same minutes past each hour until	18 53	19 23	19 53	20 23	and hourly until	23 23
St Mary Cray 195	d		00 32		06 30	07 30	08 00			19 00		20 00	20 30		23 30
Swanley [4] 195	d		00 36		06 34	07 34	08 04	08 33		19 04	19 33	20 04	20 34		23 34
Otford [4] 195	d		00 44		06 42	07 42	08 12	08 41		19 12	19 41	20 12	20 42		23 42
Kemsing	d		00 49		06 47	07 47	08 17			19 17		20 17	20 47		23 47
Borough Green & Wrotham	d		00 54		06 52	07 52	08 22	08 48		19 22	19 48	20 22	20 52		23 52
West Malling	d		01 00		06 58	07 58	08 28	08 55		19 28	19 55	20 28	20 58		23 58
East Malling	d	00 01	01 03		07 01	08 01	08 31			19 31		20 31	21 01		00 01
Barming	d	00 05	01 07		07 05	08 05	08 35			19 35		20 35	21 05		00 05
Maidstone East [4]	a	00 09	01 11		07 09	08 09	08 39	09 02		19 39	20 02	20 39	21 09		00 09
	d	00 10	01 12	06 10	07 10	08 10	08 40	09 03		19 40	20 03	20 40	21 10		00 10
Bearsted	d	00 15	01 17	06 15	07 15	08 15	08 45	09 08		19 45	20 08	20 45	21 15		00 15
Hollingbourne	d	00 18	01 20	06 18	07 18	08 18	08 48			19 48		20 48	21 18		00 18
Harrietsham	d	00 22	01 24	06 22	07 22	08 22	08 52			19 52		20 52	21 22		00 22
Lenham	d	00 25	01 27	06 25	07 25	08 25	08 55			19 55		20 55	21 25		00 25
Charing	d	00 30	01 32	06 30	07 30	08 30	09 00			20 00		21 00	21 30		00 30
Ashford International	a	00 39	01 41	06 39	07 39	08 39	09 09	09 27		20 09	20 27	21 09	21 39		00 39

A From London Victoria

B To Canterbury West

C From Bedford

Table 196

Sundays

8 December to 11 May

London - Maidstone East and Ashford International

Network Diagram - see first Page of Table 195

			SE 1 A	SE 1	SE 1		SE 1
London Victoria 15	⊖	d		00 07	07 45		22 45
St Pancras International		d					
Farringdon		d					
City Thameslink		d					
London Blackfriars 3	⊖195	d					
Elephant & Castle	⊖195	d					
Bromley South 4	195	d		00 25	08 02		23 02
St Mary Cray	195	d		00 32	08 08		23 08
Swanley 4	195	d		00 36	08 13	and	23 13
Otford 4	195	d		00 44	08 21	hourly	23 21
Kemsing		d		00 49		until	
Borough Green & Wrotham		d		00 54	08 29		23 29
West Malling		d		01 00	08 35		23 35
East Malling		d	00 01	01 03	08 38		23 38
Barming		d	00 05	01 07	08 42		23 42
Maidstone East 4		a	00 09	01 11	08 46		23 46
		d	00 10	01 12	08 47		23 47
Bearsted		d	00 15	01 17	08 52		23 52
Hollingbourne		d	00 18	01 20	08 55		23 55
Harrietsham		d	00 22	01 24	08 59		23 59
Lenham		d	00 25	01 27	09 02		00 02
Charing		d	00 30	01 32	09 07		00 07
Ashford International		a	00 39	01 41	09 16		00 16

A not 8 December. From London Victoria

Table 196R

Ashford International and Maidstone East to London

Mondays to Fridays

9 December to 16 May

Network Diagram - see first Page of Table 195

Miles	Miles				SE	SE	SE	SE	SE	SE	SE	SE	SE	SE	SE	SE	SE		SE	SE	SE	SE	SE
					[1]	[1]	[1]	[1]	[1]	[1]	[1]	[1]		[1]	[1]	[1]	[1]		[1]	[1]	[1]	[1]	[1]
						A		B		A													
0	—	**Ashford International**		d	05 18	05 43	05 49	06 03	06 16	06 25	06 40	06 57	07 15	07 47	08 26	08 47	09 30		13 47	14 30	14 47	15 24	15 47
6	—	Charing		d	05 27	05 52	05 58	06 11	06 24	06 33	06 48	07 05	07 23	07 55	08 34	08 55			13 55		14 55	15 32	15 55
10	—	Lenham		d	05 32	05 57	06 03	06 16	06 29	06 38	06 53	07 10	07 28	08 00	08 39	09 00			14 00		15 00	15 37	16 00
11¾	—	Harrietsham		d	05 35	06 00	06 06	06 19	06 32	06 41	06 56	07 13	07 31	08 03	08 42	09 03			14 03		15 03	15 40	16 03
14¼	—	Hollingbourne		d	05 39	06 03	06 09	06 23	06 36	06 45	07 00	07 17	07 35	08 07	08 46	09 07			14 07		15 07	15 44	16 07
16½	—	Bearsted		d	05 44	06 08	06 14	06 26	06 39	06 48	07 03	07 21	07 39	08 11	08 49	09 11	09 48		14 11	14 48	15 11	15 48	16 11
19¼	—	**Maidstone East** [4]		a	05 49	06 13	06 19	06 31	06 44	06 53	07 08	07 26	07 44	08 17	08 54	09 17	09 53	and at the same minutes past each hour until	14 17	14 53	15 17	15 53	16 17
—	—			d	05 49	06 14	06 20	06 32	06 45	06 54	07 09	07 27	07 45	08 18	08 55	09 18	09 55		14 18	14 55	15 18	15 55	16 18
21¾	—	Barming		d	05 54		06 25	06 37	06 50	06 59	07 14	07 32	07 50	08 23		09 23			14 23		15 23		16 23
23½	—	East Malling		d	05 58		06 28	06 41	06 54	07 03	07 18	07 36		08 26		09 26			14 26		15 26		16 26
24½	—	West Malling		d	06 01	06 21	06 31	06 44	06 57	07 06	07 21	07 39	07 55	08 29	09 02	09 29	10 02		14 29	15 02	15 29	16 02	16 29
29¾	—	Borough Green & Wrotham		d	06 08	06 29	06 38	06 51	07 04	07 13	07 28	07 46	08 02	08 36	09 09	09 36	10 09		14 36	15 09	15 36	16 09	16 36
32¼	—	Kemsing		d				06 55	07 08	07 17	07 32	07 50		08 40		09 40			14 40		15 40		16 40
35¼	—	Otford [4]	195	a	06 16	06 37	06 46	07 00	07 13	07 22	07 37	07 55	08 10	08 46	09 17	09 46	10 17		14 46	15 17	15 46	16 17	16 46
42	—	Swanley [4]	195	a	06 24	06 46	06 55	07 09	07 22	07 31	07 46	08 04		08 54	09 25	09 54	10 25		14 54	15 25	15 54	16 25	16 54
46¼	—	St Mary Cray	195	a										08 58		09 58			14 58		15 58		16 58
48½	0	Bromley South [4]	195	a	06 33	06 56	07 03	07 19	07 30	07 40	07 57	08 13	08 25	09 04	09 34	10 04	10 34		15 04	15 34	16 04	16 34	17 04
—	10¼	Elephant & Castle	⊖195	a		07 15				07 58													
—	11½	**London Blackfriars** [3]	⊖195	a		07 22				08 03													
—	—	City Thameslink		a		07 26				08 06													
—	—	Farringdon		a		07 30				08 10													
—	—	St Pancras International		a		07 34				08 14													
59¼	—	**London Victoria** [15]	⊖	a	06 51		07 23	07 43	07 53		08 23	08 36	08 48	09 23	09 51	10 21	10 51		15 21	15 51	16 21	16 51	17 23

			SE	SE	SE	SE	SE	SE	SE	SE	SE	SE	SE	SE
			[1]	[1]	[1]	[1]	[1]	[1]	[1]	[1]	[1]	[1]	[1]	[1]
Ashford International		d	16 26	16 47	17 26	17 49		18 26	18 49	19 26	19 47	20 17	21 17	22 17
Charing		d	16 34	16 55	17 34	17 57		18 34	18 57	19 34	19 55	20 25	21 25	22 25
Lenham		d	16 39	17 00	17 39	18 02		18 39	19 02	19 39	20 00	20 30	21 30	22 30
Harrietsham		d	16 42	17 03	17 42	18 05		18 42	19 05	19 42	20 03	20 33	21 33	22 33
Hollingbourne		d	16 46	17 07	17 46	18 09		18 46	19 09	19 46	20 07	20 37	21 37	22 37
Bearsted		d	16 49	17 11	17 49	18 12		18 49	19 12	19 49	20 11	20 41	21 41	22 41
Maidstone East [4]		a	16 54	17 17	17 54	18 17		18 54	19 17	19 54	20 17	20 47	21 47	22 47
		d	16 55	17 18	17 55	18 18	18 40	18 55	19 18	19 55	20 18	20 48	21 48	22 48
Barming		d		17 23		18 23			19 23		20 23	20 53	21 53	22 53
East Malling		d		17 26		18 26			19 26		20 26	20 56	21 56	22 56
West Malling		d	17 02	17 29	18 02	18 29	18 47	19 02	19 29	20 02	20 29	20 59	21 59	22 59
Borough Green & Wrotham		d	17 09	17 36	18 09	18 36	18 54	19 09	19 36	20 09	20 36	21 06	22 06	23 06
Kemsing		d		17 40		18 40			19 40		20 40	21 10	22 10	23 10
Otford [4]	195	a	17 17	17 46	18 17	18 46		19 17	19 46	20 17	20 46	21 16	22 16	23 16
Swanley [4]	195	a	17 25	17 54	18 25	18 54		19 25	19 54	20 25	20 54	21 24	22 24	23 24
St Mary Cray	195	a		17 58		18 58			19 58		20 58	21 28	22 28	23 28
Bromley South [4]	195	a	17 34	18 04	18 34	19 04	19 16	19 34	20 04	20 34	21 04	21 34	22 34	23 34
Elephant & Castle	⊖195	a												
London Blackfriars [3]	⊖195	a												
City Thameslink		a												
Farringdon		a												
St Pancras International		a												
London Victoria [15]	⊖	a	17 53	18 21	18 53	19 21	19 37	19 51	20 21	20 51	21 21	21 51	22 51	23 51

Saturdays

14 December to 17 May

			SE	SE	SE		SE	SE	SE	SE	SE	SE
			[1]	[1]	[1]		[1]	[1]	[1]	[1]	[1]	[1]
Ashford International		d	05 18	05 47	06 30		17 47	18 30	18 47	19 47	20 47	22 17
Charing		d	05 27	05 55			17 55		18 55	19 55	20 55	22 25
Lenham		d	05 32	06 00			18 00		19 00	20 00	21 00	22 30
Harrietsham		d	05 35	06 03			18 03		19 03	20 03	21 03	22 33
Hollingbourne		d	05 39	06 07			18 07		19 07	20 07	21 07	22 37
Bearsted		d	05 44	06 11	06 48		18 11	18 48	19 11	20 11	21 11	22 41
Maidstone East [4]		a	05 49	06 17	06 53	and at the same minutes past each hour until	18 17	18 53	19 17	20 17	21 17	22 47
		d	05 49	06 18	06 55		18 18	18 55	19 18	20 18	21 18	22 48
Barming		d	05 54	06 23			18 23		19 23	20 23	21 23	22 53
East Malling		d	05 58	06 26			18 26		19 26	20 26	21 26	22 56
West Malling		d	06 01	06 29	07 02		18 29	19 02	19 29	20 29	21 29	22 59
Borough Green & Wrotham		d	06 08	06 36	07 09		18 36	19 09	19 36	20 36	21 36	23 06
Kemsing		d		06 40			18 40		19 40	20 40	21 40	23 10
Otford [4]	195	a	06 16	06 46	07 17		18 46	19 17	19 46	20 46	21 46	23 16
Swanley [4]	195	a	06 24	06 54	07 25		18 54	19 25	19 54	20 54	21 54	23 24
St Mary Cray	195	a	06 28	06 58			18 58		19 58	20 58	21 58	23 28
Bromley South [4]	195	a	06 34	07 04	07 34		19 04	19 34	20 04	21 04	22 04	23 34
Elephant & Castle	⊖195	a										
London Blackfriars [3]	⊖195	a										
City Thameslink		a										
Farringdon		a										
St Pancras International		a										
London Victoria [15]	⊖	a	06 51	07 21	07 51		19 21	19 51	20 21	21 21	22 21	23 51

A To Bedford

B From Canterbury West

Table 196R

Sundays

8 December to 11 May

Ashford International and Maidstone East to London

Network Diagram - see first Page of Table 195

			SE 1		SE 1
Ashford International		d	06 47		21 47
Charing		d	06 55		21 55
Lenham		d	07 00		22 00
Harrietsham		d	07 03		22 03
Hollingbourne		d	07 07		22 07
Bearsted		d	07 11		22 11
Maidstone East 4		a	07 17		22 17
		d	07 18		22 18
Barming		d	07 23		22 23
East Malling		d	07 26		22 26
West Malling		d	07 29	and hourly until	22 29
Borough Green & Wrotham		d	07 36		22 36
Kemsing		d			
Otford 4	195	a	07 44		22 44
Swanley 4	195	a	07 53		22 53
St Mary Cray	195	a	07 58		22 58
Bromley South 4	195	a	08 04		23 04
Elephant & Castle	⊖195	a			
London Blackfriars 3	⊖195	a			
City Thameslink		a			
Farringdon		a			
St Pancras International		a			
London Victoria 15	⊖	a	08 21		23 21

Table 199

Mondays to Fridays

9 December to 16 May

London - Lewisham, Hither Green, Petts Wood and Orpington (Summary of Services)

Network Diagram - see first Page of Table 195
Network Diagram - see first Page of Table 200

		SE MO	SE MX	SE MO	SE MX	SE MX	SE MX	SE MX	SE	SE		SE	SE	SE	SE	SE [1]	SE	SE	SE	SE		SE	SE	SE	SE
London Charing Cross [4]	⊖ d			00 01	00 02	00 06	00 10	00 15	00 18	00 48		04 52	05 02		05 20	05 30	05 32	05 36	05 39			05 47	05 52	06 02	06 06
London Waterloo (East) [4]	⊖ d			00 04	00 05	00 09	00 13	00 18	00 21	00 51		04 55	05 05		05 23	05 33	05 35	05 39	05 42			05 50	05 55	06 05	06 09
London Cannon Street [4]	⊖ d																								
London Blackfriars [3]	⊖ d																								
London Bridge [4]	⊖ d			00 09	00 10	00 14	00 18	00 23	00 26	00 56		05 00	05 10		05 30	05 39	05 42	05 44	05 47			05 55	06 00	06 10	06 14
London Victoria [15]	⊖ d																			05 40					
New Cross [4]	⊖ d	00 03	00 05		00 15		00 23		00 31	01 01		05 05	05 15	05 31	05 35		05 48		05 52			06 01	06 05	06 15	
St Johns	d		00 07											05 33								06 03			
Lewisham [4]	a	00 07	00 10	00 17	00 19	00 21	00 27		00 35	01 05		05 09	05 19	05 35	05 39		05 51	05 52	05 56			06 05	06 09	06 19	06 22
Hither Green [4]	a			00 21		00 26	00 31			01 09		05 13			05 43			05 56					06 13		06 27
Petts Wood [4]	a			00 34		00 38				01 22								06 08		06 14					06 39
Orpington [4]	a			00 38		00 42		00 47		01 25						05 54		06 11		06 18					06 42

		SE	SE [1]	SE	SE	SE		SE [1]	SE	SE	SE	SE	SE [1]	SE	SE	SE		SE	SE [1]	SE	SE	SE	SE	SE	SE
London Charing Cross [4]	⊖ d	06 09	06 15		06 17	06 26		06 30		06 32	06 36	06 39	06 45		06 47			06 56	07 00		07 02	07 06			07 12
London Waterloo (East) [4]	⊖ d	06 12	06 18		06 20	06 29		06 33		06 35	06 39	06 42	06 48		06 50			06 59	07 03		07 05	07 09			07 15
London Cannon Street [4]	⊖ d													06 50		07 00								07 10	
London Blackfriars [3]	⊖ d																								
London Bridge [4]	⊖ d	06 17	06 24		06 26	06 34		06 38		06 40	06 44	06 47	06 53	06 54	06 55	07 04		07 05	07 08		07 10	07 14		07 14	07 21
London Victoria [15]	⊖ d			06 10					06 30											06 50			07 09		
New Cross [4]	⊖ d				06 32	06 40				06 46				06 59	07 02	07 09								07 20	
St Johns	d				06 34									07 01	07 04	07 11								07 22	
Lewisham [4]	a	06 26			06 37	06 43				06 49	06 53	06 55		07 04	07 07	07 14					07 18		07 24	07 26	07 29
Hither Green [4]	a					06 48					06 58			07 08				07 18			08 11	07 23		07 31	
Petts Wood [4]	a			06 44					07 06		07 10			07 21						07 24		07 36			
Orpington [4]	a		06 40	06 49				06 53	07 09		07 13		07 09	07 25					07 25	07 28		07 40			

		SE [1]		SE	SE	SE	SE	SE	SE	SE	SE [1]	SE		SE	SE	SE	SE	SE	SE [1]	SE	SE	SE		SE	SE
London Charing Cross [4]	⊖ d	07 15						07 26			07 29				07 36		07 39							07 48	
London Waterloo (East) [4]	⊖ d	07 18						07 29			07 32				07 39		07 42							07 51	
London Cannon Street [4]	⊖ d			07 20		07 24	07 27		07 30	07 32				07 36		07 41		07 44	07 46		07 51				07 54
London Blackfriars [3]	⊖ d																								
London Bridge [4]	⊖ d	07 23		07 24		07 28	07 31	07 34	07 34	07 37	07 38			07 40	07 44	07 45	07 47	07 48	07 51		07 55			07 56	07 58
London Victoria [15]	⊖ d				07 10					09a11		07 25								07 40		07 43			
New Cross [4]	⊖ d					07 33	08a38		07 39							07 50		09a07			08 00				08 04
St Johns	d					07 35			07 41																08 06
Lewisham [4]	a					07 38			07 44					07 48		07 54	07 56				08 04	08 07			08 10
Hither Green [4]	a			07 34		08 31		07 45							07 53	07 58					08 10				
Petts Wood [4]	a				07 49							07 59			08 06					08 14	08 24				
Orpington [4]	a	07 38		07 49	07 53						07 53	08 02			08 09				08 09	08 19	08 27			08 15	

		SE	SE [1]	SE	FC	SE	SE	SE		SE	SE	SE	SE	SE	SE	SE [1]	SE	SE		SE	SE [1]	SE	SE	SE [1]	SE
London Charing Cross [4]	⊖ d		08 00				08 03	08 05			08 11					08 17	08 20	08 23			08 27	08 31		08 33	
London Waterloo (East) [4]	⊖ d		08 03				08 06	08 08			08 14					08 20	08 23	08 26			08 30	08 34		08 36	
London Cannon Street [4]	⊖ d	08 00				08 05				08 09				08 16	08 19					08 29			08 36		
London Blackfriars [3]	⊖ d				07 50																				
London Bridge [4]	⊖ d	08 04	08 09			08 09	08 11	08 13		08 14	08 19			08 20	08 23	08 25	08 29	08 31		08 33	08 35	08 39	08 40	08 41	
London Victoria [15]	⊖ d			07 55								08 09	08 10												08 25
New Cross [4]	⊖ d	08 09				09a33				08 20				09a38	08 28			08 38		08 41			10a03		
St Johns	d	08 11								08 22					08 30			08 40		08 43					
Lewisham [4]	a	08 14					08 18			08 25	08 27	08 30			08 33			08 43		08 45		08 47			
Hither Green [4]	a							08 23		08 29					08 38		08 41								
Petts Wood [4]	a			08 29	08 32			08 36					08 44		08 51										08 59
Orpington [4]	a		08 25	08 32	08 36			08 39					08 47		08 55	08 41					08 53			08 57	09 02

		SE	SE	SE [1]		SE	SE	SE	SE	SE	SE	SE	SE	SE		SE [1]	SE	SE	SE	SE	SE	SE [1]	SE	SE	
London Charing Cross [4]	⊖ d		08 37			08 41					08 49		08 55			09 00		09 02		09 06			09 11		
London Waterloo (East) [4]	⊖ d		08 40			08 44					08 52		08 58			09 03		09 05		09 09			09 14		
London Cannon Street [4]	⊖ d	08 39		08 42					08 44	08 51		08 54		09 00					09 07		09 09	09 14			
London Blackfriars [3]	⊖ d																								
London Bridge [4]	⊖ d	08 43	08 45	08 46		08 49			08 49	08 55	08 57	08 58	09 03	09 04		09 08		09 10	09 11	09 14	09 14	09 18	09 19		
London Victoria [15]	⊖ d						08 39	08 40									08 55							09 09	
New Cross [4]	⊖ d	08 49							10a08	09 00		09 04		09 09					10a33		09 19				
St Johns	d	08 51								09 02		09 06		09 11							09 21				
Lewisham [4]	a	08 54				08 57	09 01			09 05		09 09		09 14				09 18			09 24		09 27	09 31	
Hither Green [4]	a	09 00	08 55							09 10			09 15							09 24	09 28				
Petts Wood [4]	a		09 08					09 14		09 23							09 29			09 37					
Orpington [4]	a		09 11	09 07				09 17		09 27	09 24					09 26	09 33			09 42		09 38			

Table 199

Mondays to Fridays

9 December to 16 May

London - Lewisham, Hither Green, Petts Wood and Orpington (Summary of Services)

Network Diagram - see first Page of Table 195
Network Diagram - see first Page of Table 200

		SE	SE	SE	SE	SE		SE	SE 1	SE	SE	SE	SE	SE	SE	SE		SE	SE 1	SE	SE	SE	SE	SE	SE 1
London Charing Cross 4	⊖ d					09 26			09 30		09 32		09 36		09 39				09 45				09 56		10 00
London Waterloo (East) 4	⊖ d					09 29			09 33		09 35		09 39		09 42				09 48				09 59		10 03
London Cannon Street 4	⊖ d		09 17	09 20	09 24			09 30				09 37		09 40				09 47			09 50	09 54		10 00	
London Blackfriars 3	⊖ d																								
London Bridge 4	⊖ d		09 21	09 24	09 28	09 34		09 34	09 39		09 40	09 41	09 44	09 44	09 47			09 51	09 53		09 54	09 58	10 04	10 04	10 09
London Victoria 15	⊖ d	09 10								09 25						09 39				09 40					
New Cross 4	⊖ d		10a38	09 29	09 33			09 39				11a03		09 49				11a08			09 59	10 03		10 09	
St Johns	d			09 31	09 35			09 41						09 51							10 01	10 05		10 11	
Lewisham 4	a			09 34	09 38			09 44			09 49			09 54	09 56	10 01					10 04	10 08		10 14	
Hither Green 4	a			09 38		09 43							09 53	09 58							10 08		10 13		
Petts Wood 4	a	09 44		09 51						09 59			10 06							10 14	10 21				
Orpington 4	a	09 47		09 55					09 55	10 02			10 09						10 08	10 17	10 24				10 25

		SE		SE	SE	SE	SE	SE	SE	SE	SE 1	SE		SE	SE	SE	SE	SE 1	SE	SE	SE	SE		SE	SE
London Charing Cross 4	⊖ d			10 02		10 06		10 09			10 15					10 26		10 30		10 32		10 36			10 39
London Waterloo (East) 4	⊖ d			10 05		10 09		10 12			10 18					10 29		10 33		10 35		10 39			10 42
London Cannon Street 4	⊖ d				10 07		10 10			10 17				10 20	10 24		10 30				10 37			10 40	
London Blackfriars 3	⊖ d																								
London Bridge 4	⊖ d			10 10	10 11	10 14	10 14	10 17		10 21	10 23			10 24	10 28	10 34	10 34	10 39		10 40	10 41	10 44		10 44	10 47
London Victoria 15	⊖ d	09 55							10 09			10 10							10 25						
New Cross 4	⊖ d				11a33		10 19			11a38				10 29	10 33		10 39				12a03			10 49	
St Johns	d						10 21							10 31	10 35		10 41							10 51	
Lewisham 4	a			10 19			10 24	10 26	10 31					10 34	10 38		10 44			10 49				10 54	10 56
Hither Green 4	a					10 23	10 28							10 38		10 43						10 53		10 58	
Petts Wood 4	a	10 29				10 36						10 44		10 51					10 59			11 06			
Orpington 4	a	10 32				10 39					10 38	10 47		10 54				10 55	11 02			11 09			

		SE	SE	SE 1	SE	SE	SE	SE		SE	SE 1	SE	SE	SE	SE	SE	SE	SE		SE	SE 1	SE	SE	SE	SE
London Charing Cross 4	⊖ d			10 45				10 56			11 00		11 02		11 06		11 09				11 15				11 26
London Waterloo (East) 4	⊖ d			10 48				10 59			11 03		11 05		11 09		11 12				11 18				11 29
London Cannon Street 4	⊖ d		10 47			10 50	10 54			11 00				11 07		11 10				11 17			11 20	11 24	
London Blackfriars 3	⊖ d																								
London Bridge 4	⊖ d		10 51	10 53		10 54	10 58	11 04		11 04	11 09		11 10	11 11	11 14	11 14	11 17			11 21	11 23		11 24	11 28	11 34
London Victoria 15	⊖ d	10 39			10 40							10 55						11 09				11 10			
New Cross 4	⊖ d		12a08			10 59	11 03			11 09				12a33		11 19				12a38			11 29	11 33	
St Johns	d					11 01	11 05			11 11						11 21							11 31	11 35	
Lewisham 4	a	11 01				11 04	11 08			11 14			11 19			11 24	11 26	11 31					11 33	11 38	
Hither Green 4	a					11 08		11 13							11 23	11 28							11 38		11 43
Petts Wood 4	a				11 14	11 21						11 29			11 36							11 44	11 51		
Orpington 4	a			11 08	11 17	11 24					11 25	11 32			11 39						11 38	11 47	11 54		

		SE	SE 1	SE		SE	SE	SE	SE	SE	SE	SE	SE 1	SE		SE	SE	SE	SE	SE 1	SE	SE	SE	SE	
London Charing Cross 4	⊖ d		11 30			11 32		11 36		11 39			11 45					11 56		12 00		12 02		12 06	
London Waterloo (East) 4	⊖ d		11 33			11 35		11 39		11 42			11 48					11 59		12 03		12 05		12 09	
London Cannon Street 4	⊖ d	11 30					11 37		11 40			11 47				11 50	11 54		12 00				12 07		
London Blackfriars 3	⊖ d																								
London Bridge 4	⊖ d	11 34	11 39			11 40	11 41	11 44	11 44	11 47		11 51	11 53			11 54	11 58	12 04	12 04	12 09		12 10	12 11	12 14	
London Victoria 15	⊖ d			11 25							11 39			11 40							11 55				
New Cross 4	⊖ d	11 39					13a03		11 49			13a08				11 59	12 03		12 09				13a33		
St Johns	d	11 41							11 51							12 01	12 05		12 11						
Lewisham 4	a	11 44				11 49			11 54	11 56	12 01					12 03	12 08		12 14			12 19			
Hither Green 4	a							11 53	11 58							12 08		12 13						12 23	
Petts Wood 4	a			11 59				12 06						12 14		12 21					12 29			12 36	
Orpington 4	a		11 55	12 02				12 09					12 08	12 17		12 24				12 25	12 32			12 39	

		SE	SE	SE	SE	SE 1	SE	SE	SE	SE		SE	SE 1	SE	SE	SE	SE	SE	SE	SE		SE	SE 1	SE	SE
London Charing Cross 4	⊖ d		12 09			12 15				12 26			12 30		12 32		12 36		12 39				12 45		
London Waterloo (East) 4	⊖ d		12 12			12 18				12 29			12 33		12 35		12 39		12 42				12 48		
London Cannon Street 4	⊖ d	12 10			12 17			12 20	12 24			12 30				12 37		12 40				12 47			12 50
London Blackfriars 3	⊖ d																								
London Bridge 4	⊖ d	12 14	12 17		12 21	12 23		12 24	12 28	12 34		12 34	12 39		12 40	12 41	12 44	12 44	12 47			12 51	12 53		12 54
London Victoria 15	⊖ d			12 09			12 10							12 25						12 39				12 40	
New Cross 4	⊖ d	12 19			13a38			12 29	12 33			12 39				14a03		12 49				14a08			12 59
St Johns	d	12 21						12 31	12 35			12 41						12 51							13 01
Lewisham 4	a	12 24	12 26	12 31				12 34	12 38			12 44			12 49			12 54	12 56	13 01					13 03
Hither Green 4	a	12 28						12 38		12 43							12 53	12 58							13 08
Petts Wood 4	a						12 44	12 51						12 59			13 06							13 14	13 21
Orpington 4	a					12 38	12 47	12 54					12 55	13 02			13 09						13 08	13 17	13 24

		SE	SE	SE	SE 1	SE		SE	SE	SE	SE	SE	SE	SE	SE 1	SE		SE	SE	SE	SE	SE 1	SE	SE	SE
London Charing Cross 4	⊖ d		12 56		13 00			13 02		13 06		13 09			13 15					13 26		13 30		13 32	
London Waterloo (East) 4	⊖ d		12 59		13 03			13 05		13 09		13 12			13 18					13 29		13 33		13 35	
London Cannon Street 4	⊖ d	12 54		13 00					13 07		13 10			13 17				13 20	13 24		13 30				13 37
London Blackfriars 3	⊖ d																								
London Bridge 4	⊖ d	12 58	13 04	13 04	13 09			13 10	13 11	13 14	13 14	13 17		13 21	13 23			13 24	13 28	13 34	13 34	13 39		13 40	13 41
London Victoria 15	⊖ d					12 55							13 09			13 10							13 25		
New Cross 4	⊖ d	13 03		13 09					14a33		13 19			14a38				13 29	13 33		13 39				15a03
St Johns	d	13 05		13 11							13 21							13 31	13 35		13 41				
Lewisham 4	a	13 08		13 14				13 19			13 24	13 26	13 31					13 34	13 38		13 44			13 49	
Hither Green 4	a		13 13							13 23	13 28							13 38		13 43					
Petts Wood 4	a					13 29				13 36						13 44		13 51					13 59		
Orpington 4	a				13 25	13 32				13 39					13 38	13 47		13 54				13 55	14 02		

Table 199

Mondays to Fridays

9 December to 16 May

London - Lewisham, Hither Green, Petts Wood and Orpington (Summary of Services)

Network Diagram - see first Page of Table 195
Network Diagram - see first Page of Table 200

	SE	SE	SE	SE	SE	SE [1]	SE		SE	SE	SE	SE	SE [1]	SE	SE	SE	SE		SE	SE	SE	SE	SE [1]	SE
London Charing Cross [4] ⊖ d	13 36		13 39			13 45					13 56		14 00		14 02		14 06			14 09			14 15	
London Waterloo (East) [4] ⊖ d	13 39		13 42			13 48					13 59		14 03		14 05		14 09			14 12			14 18	
London Cannon Street [4] ⊖ d		13 40			13 47				13 50	13 54		14 00				14 07			14 10			14 17		
London Blackfriars [3] ⊖ d																								
London Bridge [4] ⊖ d	13 44	13 44	13 47		13 51	13 53			13 54	13 58	14 04	14 04	14 09		14 10	14 11	14 14		14 14	14 17		14 21	14 23	
London Victoria [15] ⊖ d				13 39			13 40							13 55							14 09			14 10
New Cross [4] ⊖ d		13 49			15a08				13 59	14 03		14 09				15a33			14 19			15a38		
St Johns d		13 51							14 01	14 05		14 11							14 21					
Lewisham [4] a		13 54	13 56	14 01					14 04	14 08		14 14			14 19				14 24	14 26	14 31			
Hither Green [4] a	13 53	13 58							14 08		14 13						14 23		14 28					
Petts Wood [4] a	14 06						14 14		14 21					14 29			14 36							14 44
Orpington [4] a	14 09					14 08	14 17		14 24				14 25	14 32			14 39						14 38	14 47

	SE	SE	SE		SE	SE [1]	SE	SE	SE	SE	SE	SE	SE		SE	SE [1]	SE	SE	SE	SE	SE	SE [1]	SE	
London Charing Cross [4] ⊖ d			14 26			14 30		14 32		14 36		14 39				14 45				14 56		15 00		
London Waterloo (East) [4] ⊖ d			14 29			14 33		14 35		14 39		14 42				14 48				14 59		15 03		
London Cannon Street [4] ⊖ d	14 20	14 24			14 30				14 37		14 40				14 47			14 50	14 54		15 00			
London Blackfriars [3] ⊖ d																								
London Bridge [4] ⊖ d	14 24	14 28	14 34		14 34	14 39		14 40	14 41	14 44	14 44	14 47			14 51	14 53		14 54	14 58	15 04	15 04	15 09		
London Victoria [15] ⊖ d							14 25						14 39				14 40						14 55	
New Cross [4] ⊖ d	14 29	14 33			14 39				16a03		14 49				16a08			14 59	15 03		15 09			
St Johns d	14 31	14 35			14 41						14 51							15 01	15 05		15 11			
Lewisham [4] a	14 34	14 38			14 44			14 49			14 54	14 56	15 01					15 04	15 08		15 14			
Hither Green [4] a	14 38		14 43							14 53	14 58							15 08		15 13				
Petts Wood [4] a	14 51						14 59			15 06							15 14	15 21					15 29	
Orpington [4] a	14 54					14 55	15 02			15 09						15 08	15 17	15 24				15 25	15 32	

	SE	SE	SE	SE	SE	SE	SE	SE [1]	SE		SE	SE	SE	SE	SE [1]	SE	SE	SE	SE		SE	SE	SE	SE
London Charing Cross [4] ⊖ d	15 02		15 06		15 09			15 15					15 26		15 30		15 32		15 36			15 39		
London Waterloo (East) [4] ⊖ d	15 05		15 09		15 12			15 18					15 29		15 33		15 35		15 39			15 42		
London Cannon Street [4] ⊖ d		15 07		15 10			15 17				15 20	15 24		15 30				15 37			15 40			15 47
London Blackfriars [3] ⊖ d																								
London Bridge [4] ⊖ d	15 10	15 11	15 14	15 14	15 17		15 21	15 23			15 24	15 28	15 34	15 34	15 39		15 40	15 41	15 44		15 44	15 47		15 51
London Victoria [15] ⊖ d						15 09			15 10							15 25							15 39	
New Cross [4] ⊖ d		16a33		15 19			16a38				15 29	15 33		15 39				17a03			15 49			17a11
St Johns d				15 21							15 31	15 35		15 41							15 51			
Lewisham [4] a	15 19			15 24	15 26	15 31					15 34	15 38		15 44			15 49				15 54	15 56	16 01	
Hither Green [4] a			15 23	15 28							15 38		15 43						15 53		15 58			
Petts Wood [4] a			15 36						15 44		15 51					15 59			16 06					
Orpington [4] a			15 39					15 38	15 47		15 54				15 55	16 02			16 09					

	SE [1]	SE	SE	SE	SE		SE	SE [1]	SE	SE	SE	SE	SE	SE	SE		SE	SE	SE	SE	SE	SE	SE [1]	SE
London Charing Cross [4] ⊖ d	15 45				15 56			16 00		16 02		16 06		16 09							16 26		16 28	
London Waterloo (East) [4] ⊖ d	15 48				15 59			16 03		16 05		16 09		16 12							16 29		16 31	
London Cannon Street [4] ⊖ d			15 50	15 54			16 00				16 07		16 10					16 17	16 20	16 24		16 30		
London Blackfriars [3] ⊖ d																								
London Bridge [4] ⊖ d	15 53		15 54	15 58	16 04		16 04	16 09		16 10	16 11	16 14	16 14	16 17				16 21	16 24	16 28	16 34	16 34	16 36	
London Victoria [15] ⊖ d		15 40							15 55						16 09		16 10							16 25
New Cross [4] ⊖ d			15 59	16 03			16 10				17a33		16 20					17a39	16 30	16 34		16 40		
St Johns d			16 01	16 05			16 12						16 22						16 32	16 36		16 42		
Lewisham [4] a			16 03	16 08			16 14			16 19			16 24	16 26	16 31				16 34	16 38		16 44		
Hither Green [4] a			16 08		16 13							16 23	16 29						16 39		16 43			
Petts Wood [4] a		16 14	16 21						16 29			16 36					16 44		16 51					16 59
Orpington [4] a	16 08	16 17	16 24					16 25	16 32			16 39					16 49		16 57				16 52	17 04

	SE		SE	FC	SE	SE	SE	SE	SE	SE	SE		SE	SE	SE	SE	SE	SE	SE	SE	SE		SE	SE
London Charing Cross [4] ⊖ d	16 30		16 32						16 42	16 45			16 49	16 51					17 03		17 06			17 10
London Waterloo (East) [4] ⊖ d	16 33		16 35						16 45	16 48			16 52	16 54					17 06		17 09			17 13
London Cannon Street [4] ⊖ d					16 39	16 42					16 51				16 56	16 58		17 04					17 12	
London Blackfriars [3] ⊖ d				16 26																				
London Bridge [4] ⊖ d	16 38		16 40		16 43	16 46			16 51	16 53	16 55		16 57	16 59	17 00	17 02		17 08	17 11		17 14		17 16	17 19
London Victoria [15] ⊖ d							16 39	16 40									16 59			17 04				
New Cross [4] ⊖ d					16 49	16 52				18a02	17 01					17 08		17 14					17 22	
St Johns d					16 51						17 03					17 10							17 24	
Lewisham [4] a	16 47				16 53	16 55	16 58		17 00		17 05			17 07		17 12		17 17	17 20	17 23			17 26	
Hither Green [4] a			16 49		16 58	17 57			17 05				17 07			17 17			17 25		18 21			17 28
Petts Wood [4] a			17 03	17 08				17 14	17 18						17 24		17 36		17 39					
Orpington [4] a			17 06	17 15				17 19	17 24						17 27		17 41		17 45					

	SE	SE	SE	SE	SE	SE	SE		SE	SE	SE	SE	SE	SE	SE	SE	SE		SE	SE	SE	SE	SE	SE
London Charing Cross [4] ⊖ d	17 12					17 26				17 32	17 34					17 47				17 54	17 56			
London Waterloo (East) [4] ⊖ d	17 15					17 29				17 35	17 37					17 50				17 57	17 59			
London Cannon Street [4] ⊖ d		17 19		17 21	17 26				17 34				17 41	17 43	17 47				17 56				18 02	
London Blackfriars [3] ⊖ d																								
London Bridge [4] ⊖ d	17 21	17 23		17 25	17 30	17 35			17 39	17 41	17 43		17 45	17 47	17 51	17 55			18 00	18 02	18 04		18 06	
London Victoria [15] ⊖ d			17 15				17 30					17 34					17 45					17 56		18 00
New Cross [4] ⊖ d				17 31	17 36				17 45					17 53	17 58				18 06					
St Johns d				17 33					17 47					17 55					18 08					
Lewisham [4] a	17 30			17 35	17 39	17 43			17 49		17 52	17 55		17 58	18 01	18 04			18 10		18 13	18 17		
Hither Green [4] a				17 40		17 48				17 51				18 03	18 57	18 09				18 12				
Petts Wood [4] a		17 43	17 50			18 01	18 05						18 08			18 23	18 26						18 28	18 35
Orpington [4] a		17 47	17 55			18 07	18 10						18 11			18 29	18 32						18 32	18 41

Table 199

Mondays to Fridays

9 December to 16 May

London - Lewisham, Hither Green, Petts Wood and Orpington (Summary of Services)

Network Diagram - see first Page of Table 195
Network Diagram - see first Page of Table 200

			SE	SE	SE	SE	SE	SE	SE	SE	SE		SE	SE	SE	SE	SE	SE	SE	SE [1]	SE		SE	SE	SE	SE
London Charing Cross [4]	⊖	d			18 09	18 12	18 14		18 18						18 30			18 37	18 39	18 41						
London Waterloo (East) [4]	⊖	d			18 12	18 15	18 17		18 21						18 33			18 40	18 42	18 44						
London Cannon Street [4]	⊖	d	18 04	18 10				18 18		18 23			18 25			18 34	18 40							18 48		18 50
London Blackfriars [3]	⊖	d																								
London Bridge [4]	⊖	d	18 08	18 14	18 17	18 21	18 23	18 23	18 26	18 27			18 29		18 38	18 38	18 44	18 46	18 48	18 50				18 52		18 54
London Victoria [15]	⊖	d									18 15			18 18							18 30		18 39		18 45	
New Cross [4]	⊖	d	18 14	18 20		19a38		18 28					18 35			18 44	18 50		18 55							19 00
St Johns		d	18 16					18 30					18 37			18 46	18 52									19 02
Lewisham [4]		a	18 19	18 23	18 26			18 33	18 35				18 40	18 42		18 48	18 54		18 59				19 02			19 04
Hither Green [4]		a	18 24		18 31		18 35						18 45		18 48			18 55								19 09
Petts Wood [4]		a			18 43					18 49	18 53				19 02						19 06			19 13	19 19	
Orpington [4]		a			18 49					18 53	18 59				19 06					19 06	19 12			19 19	19 25	

			SE	SE	SE	SE	SE [1]		SE	SE	SE	SE	SE	SE	SE [1]	SE	SE		SE	SE	SE	SE [1]	SE	SE	SE	SE
London Charing Cross [4]	⊖	d	18 48		18 56		19 00			19 02	19 06		19 09		19 15					19 26		19 30		19 32	19 36	
London Waterloo (East) [4]	⊖	d	18 51		18 59		19 03			19 05	19 09		19 12		19 18					19 29		19 33		19 35	19 39	
London Cannon Street [4]	⊖	d		18 54		19 00						19 10					19 20		19 24		19 30					19 40
London Blackfriars [3]	⊖	d																								
London Bridge [4]	⊖	d	18 57	18 58	19 04	19 04	19 09			19 10	19 14	19 14	19 17		19 23		19 24		19 28	19 34	19 34	19 39		19 40	19 44	19 44
London Victoria [15]	⊖	d							19 00					19 09		19 10							19 25			
New Cross [4]	⊖	d		19 05		19 09						19 19					19 29		19 33		19 39					19 49
St Johns		d		19 07		19 11						19 21					19 31		19 35		19 41					19 51
Lewisham [4]		a	19 06	19 10		19 14				19 19		19 24	19 26	19 31			19 33		19 38		19 44			19 49		19 55
Hither Green [4]		a			19 14						19 23	19 28					19 38			19 43					19 53	19 59
Petts Wood [4]		a							19 35		19 38					19 44	19 51						19 59		20 06	
Orpington [4]		a					19 27		19 38		19 43				19 38	19 48	19 54					19 55	20 02		20 09	

			SE		SE	SE [1]	SE	SE	SE	SE	SE	SE [1]	SE		SE	SE	SE	SE	SE	SE [1]	SE	SE	SE		SE	SE [1]
London Charing Cross [4]	⊖	d	19 39			19 45				19 56		20 00			20 02	20 06		20 09		20 15			20 17		20 22	20 30
London Waterloo (East) [4]	⊖	d	19 42			19 48				19 59		20 03			20 05	20 09		20 12		20 18			20 20		20 25	20 33
London Cannon Street [4]	⊖	d						19 50	19 54		20 00						20 10					20 20				
London Blackfriars [3]	⊖	d																								
London Bridge [4]	⊖	d	19 47			19 53		19 54	19 58	20 04	20 04	20 09			20 10	20 14	20 14	20 17		20 23		20 24	20 25		20 30	20 39
London Victoria [15]	⊖	d			19 39		19 40						19 55						20 09		20 10					
New Cross [4]	⊖	d						19 59	20 03		20 09						20 19					20 29	20 32		20 35	
St Johns		d						20 01	20 05		20 11						20 21					20 31	20 34			
Lewisham [4]		a	19 56		20 01			20 04	20 08		20 14				20 19		20 25	20 26	20 31			20 34	20 36		20 38	
Hither Green [4]		a						20 08		20 13						20 23	20 29					20 38			20 44	
Petts Wood [4]		a					20 14	20 21					20 29			20 36					20 44	20 51				
Orpington [4]		a				20 08	20 18	20 24				20 25	20 32			20 39				20 38	20 47	20 54				20 55

			SE	SE	SE	SE	SE [1]	SE	SE		SE [1]	SE	SE	SE	SE	SE [1]	SE	SE	SE [1]		SE	SE	SE	SE	SE [1]	SE
London Charing Cross [4]	⊖	d		20 32	20 36	20 39	20 45	20 47	20 52		21 00		21 02	21 06	21 09	21 10	21 17	21 22	21 30			21 32	21 36	21 39	21 45	21 47
London Waterloo (East) [4]	⊖	d		20 35	20 39	20 42	20 48	20 50	20 55		21 03		21 05	21 09	21 12	21 13	21 20	21 25	21 33			21 35	21 39	21 42	21 48	21 50
London Cannon Street [4]	⊖	d																								
London Blackfriars [3]	⊖	d																								
London Bridge [4]	⊖	d		20 40	20 44	20 47	20 53	20 55	21 00		21 09		21 10	21 14	21 17	21 19	21 25	21 30	21 39			21 40	21 44	21 47	21 53	21 55
London Victoria [15]	⊖	d	20 25									20 55									21 25					
New Cross [4]	⊖	d		20 45				21 00	21 05				21 15				21 30	21 35				21 45				22 00
St Johns		d						21 02									21 32									22 02
Lewisham [4]		a		20 49		20 56		21 05	21 09				21 19	21 21	21 26		21 35	21 39				21 49	21 51	21 56		22 05
Hither Green [4]		a			20 53				21 13					21 26				21 43					21 56			
Petts Wood [4]		a	20 59		21 06							21 29		21 38							21 59		22 08			
Orpington [4]		a	21 02		21 09		21 08				21 25	21 32		21 42		21 34			21 55		22 02		22 12		22 08	

			SE	SE [1]	SE		SE	SE	SE	SE [1]	SE	SE	SE [1]	SE	SE		SE	SE	SE [1]	SE	SE	SE [1]	SE	SE	SE	
London Charing Cross [4]	⊖	d	21 52	22 00			22 02	22 06	22 09	22 10	22 17	22 22	22 30		22 32		22 36	22 39	22 45	22 47	22 52	23 00		23 02	23 06	
London Waterloo (East) [4]	⊖	d	21 55	22 03			22 05	22 09	22 12	22 13	22 20	22 25	22 33		22 35		22 39	22 42	22 48	22 50	22 55	23 03		23 05	23 09	
London Cannon Street [4]	⊖	d																								
London Blackfriars [3]	⊖	d																								
London Bridge [4]	⊖	d	22 00	22 09			22 10	22 14	22 17	22 19	22 25	22 30	22 39		22 40		22 44	22 47	22 53	22 55	23 00	23 09		23 10	23 14	
London Victoria [15]	⊖	d			21 55									22 25									22 55			
New Cross [4]	⊖	d	22 05				22 15				22 30	22 35			22 45					23 00	23 05			23 15		
St Johns		d									22 32									23 02						
Lewisham [4]		a	22 09				22 19	22 21	22 26		22 35	22 39			22 49		22 51	22 56		23 05	23 09			23 19	23 21	
Hither Green [4]		a	22 13					22 26				22 43					22 56				23 13				23 26	
Petts Wood [4]		a			22 29			22 38						22 59			23 08						23 29		23 38	
Orpington [4]		a		22 25	22 32			22 42		22 34			22 54	23 02			23 12		23 08			23 24	23 32		23 42	

Table 199

Mondays to Fridays

9 December to 16 May

London - Lewisham, Hither Green, Petts Wood and Orpington (Summary of Services)

Network Diagram - see first Page of Table 195
Network Diagram - see first Page of Table 200

	SE	SE 1	SE	SE	SE 1	SE		SE	SE	SE	SE 1	SE	SE
London Charing Cross 4 ⊖ d	23 09	23 10	23 17	23 22	23 30			23 32	23 36	23 39	23 45	23 52	
London Waterloo (East) 4 ⊖ d	23 12	23 13	23 20	23 25	23 33			23 35	23 39	23 42	23 48	23 55	
London Cannon Street 4 ⊖ d													
London Blackfriars 3 ⊖ d													
London Bridge 4 ⊖ d	23 17	23 19	23 25	23 30	23 39			23 40	23 44	23 47	23 53	23 59	
London Victoria 15 ⊖ d						23 25							23 55
New Cross 4 ⊖ d			23 30	23 35				23 45				00 05	
St Johns d			23 32									00 07	
Lewisham 4 a	23 26		23 35	23 39				23 49	23 51	23 56		00 10	
Hither Green 4 a				23 43					23 56				
Petts Wood 4 a						23 59			00 08				00 29
Orpington 4 a		23 34			23 54	00 02			00 12		00 08		00 32

Saturdays

14 December to 17 May

	SE	SE	SE	SE	SE	SE	SE	SE	SE		SE	SE	SE	SE	SE	SE 1	SE	SE	SE		SE	SE	SE	SE
London Charing Cross 4 ⊖ d		00 02	00 06	00 10	00 15	00 18	00 48	04 52	05 22		05 32	05 36	05 39	05 47	05 52	06 00		06 02	06 06		06 09	06 17	06 22	
London Waterloo (East) 4 ⊖ d		00 05	00 09	00 13	00 18	00 21	00 51	04 55	05 25		05 35	05 39	05 42	05 50	05 55	06 03		06 05	06 09		06 12	06 20	06 25	
London Cannon Street 4 ⊖ d																								
London Blackfriars 3 ⊖ d																								
London Bridge 4 ⊖ d		00 10	00 14	00 18	00 23	00 26	00 56	05 00	05 30		05 40	05 44	05 47	05 55	06 00	06 08		06 10	06 14		06 17	06 25	06 30	
London Victoria 15 ⊖ d																	05 55							06 25
New Cross 4 ⊖ d	00 05	00 15		00 23		00 31	01 01	05 05	05 35		05 45			06 00	06 05			06 15				06 30	06 35	
St Johns d	00 07													06 02								06 32		
Lewisham 4 a	00 10	00 19	00 21	00 27		00 35	01 05	05 09	05 39		05 49	05 52	05 56	06 05	06 09			06 19	06 22		06 26	06 35	06 39	
Hither Green 4 a			00 26	00 31			01 09	05 13	05 43			05 57			06 13				06 27				06 43	
Petts Wood 4 a			00 38				01 22					06 09					06 29		06 39					06 59
Orpington 4 a			00 42		00 47		01 25					06 12				06 23	06 32		06 42					07 02

	SE	SE	SE	SE	SE		SE 1	SE	SE	SE	SE	SE	SE	SE	SE 1		SE	SE	SE	SE	SE	SE 1	SE	SE
London Charing Cross 4 ⊖ d	06 32	06 36	06 39	06 47	06 52		07 00		07 02	07 06	07 09		07 17	07 22	07 30			07 32	07 36	07 39		07 45		07 52
London Waterloo (East) 4 ⊖ d	06 35	06 39	06 42	06 50	06 55		07 03		07 05	07 09	07 12		07 20	07 25	07 33			07 35	07 39	07 42		07 48		07 55
London Cannon Street 4 ⊖ d																								
London Blackfriars 3 ⊖ d																								
London Bridge 4 ⊖ d	06 40	06 44	06 47	06 55	07 00		07 08		07 10	07 14	07 17		07 25	07 30	07 38			07 40	07 44	07 47		07 53		08 00
London Victoria 15 ⊖ d								06 55				07 10					07 25				07 39		07 40	
New Cross 4 ⊖ d	06 45			07 00	07 05				07 15				07 30	07 35				07 45						08 05
St Johns d				07 02									07 32											
Lewisham 4 a	06 49	06 52	06 56	07 05	07 08				07 19	07 22	07 26		07 35	07 39				07 49	07 52	07 56	08 02			08 08
Hither Green 4 a		06 57			07 14					07 27				07 44					07 57					08 14
Petts Wood 4 a		07 09						07 29		07 39		07 44					07 59		08 09				08 14	
Orpington 4 a		07 12					07 23	07 32		07 42		07 47			07 54		08 02		08 12			08 08	08 17	

	SE		SE 1	SE	SE	SE	SE	SE	SE	SE	SE	SE 1	SE	SE	SE	SE	SE	SE 1	SE	SE	SE	SE	SE	SE
London Charing Cross 4 ⊖ d			08 00		08 02		08 06		08 09			08 15				08 26		08 30		08 32		08 36		08 39
London Waterloo (East) 4 ⊖ d			08 03		08 05		08 09		08 12			08 18				08 29		08 33		08 35		08 39		08 42
London Cannon Street 4 ⊖ d	08 00					08 07		08 10			08 17			08 20	08 24		08 30				08 37		08 40	
London Blackfriars 3 ⊖ d																								
London Bridge 4 ⊖ d	08 04		08 08		08 10	08 11	08 14	08 14	08 17		08 21	08 23		08 24	08 28	08 34	08 34	08 39		08 40	08 41	08 44	08 44	08 47
London Victoria 15 ⊖ d				07 55						08 09			08 10						08 25					
New Cross 4 ⊖ d	08 09				08 15	09a33		08 19			09a38			08 29	08 33		08 39				10a03		08 49	
St Johns d	08 11							08 21						08 31	08 35		08 41						08 51	
Lewisham 4 a	08 13				08 19			08 24	08 26	08 31				08 34	08 38		08 44			08 49			08 54	08 56
Hither Green 4 a							08 23	08 28						08 38		08 43						08 53	08 58	
Petts Wood 4 a				08 29			08 36						08 44	08 51					08 59			09 06		
Orpington 4 a			08 23	08 32			08 39					08 38	08 47	08 54				08 55	09 02			09 09		

	SE	SE	SE 1	SE	SE	SE	SE	SE	SE 1	SE	SE		SE	SE	SE	SE	SE	SE	SE 1	SE	SE	SE	SE
London Charing Cross 4 ⊖ d			08 45				08 56		09 00		09 02			17 06		17 09			17 15				17 26
London Waterloo (East) 4 ⊖ d			08 48				08 59		09 03		09 05	and at		17 09		17 12			17 18				17 29
London Cannon Street 4 ⊖ d		08 47			08 50	08 54		09 00				the same	17 07		17 10			17 17			17 20	17 24	
London Blackfriars 3 ⊖ d												minutes											
London Bridge 4 ⊖ d		08 51	08 53		08 54	08 58	09 04	09 04	09 09		09 10	past	17 11	17 14	17 14	17 17		17 21	17 23		17 24	17 28	17 34
London Victoria 15 ⊖ d	08 39			08 40						08 55		each					17 09			17 10			
New Cross 4 ⊖ d		10a08			08 59	09 03		09 09				hour until	18a33		17 19			18a38			17 29	17 33	
St Johns d					09 01	09 05		09 11							17 21						17 31	17 35	
Lewisham 4 a	09 01				09 04	09 08		09 14			09 19				17 24	17 26	17 31				17 34	17 38	
Hither Green 4 a					09 08		09 13							17 23	17 28						17 38		17 43
Petts Wood 4 a				09 14	09 21					09 29				17 36						17 44	17 51		
Orpington 4 a			09 08	09 17	09 24				09 25	09 32				17 39					17 38	17 47	17 54		

Table 199

Saturdays

14 December to 17 May

London - Lewisham, Hither Green, Petts Wood and Orpington (Summary of Services)

Network Diagram - see first Page of Table 195
Network Diagram - see first Page of Table 200

	SE	SE 1	SE	SE	SE	SE	SE	SE	SE	SE	SE 1	SE	SE	SE	SE	SE	SE 1	SE	SE		SE	SE	SE	SE
London Charing Cross 4 ⊖ d		17 30		17 32		17 36		17 39			17 45				17 56		18 00		18 02		18 06		18 09	
London Waterloo (East) 4 ⊖ d		17 33		17 35		17 39		17 42			17 48				17 59		18 03		18 05		18 09		18 12	
London Cannon Street 4 ⊖ d	17 30				17 37		17 40			17 47			17 50	17 54		18 00						18 10		
London Blackfriars 3 ⊖ d																								
London Bridge 4 ⊖ d	17 34	17 39		17 40	17 41	17 44	17 44	17 47		17 51	17 53		17 54	17 58	18 04	18 04	18 09		18 10		18 14	18 14	18 17	
London Victoria 15 ⊖ d			17 25						17 39			17 40						17 55						18 09
New Cross 4 ⊖ d	17 39				19a03		17 49			19a08			17 59	18 03		18 09						18 19		
St Johns d	17 41						17 51						18 01	18 05		18 11						18 21		
Lewisham 4 a	17 44			17 49			17 54	17 56	18 01				18 04	18 08		18 14			18 19			18 24	18 26	18 31
Hither Green 4 a						17 53	17 58						18 08		18 13						18 23	18 28		
Petts Wood 4 a			17 59			18 06						18 14	18 21					18 29			18 36			
Orpington 4 a		17 55	18 02			18 09					18 08	18 17	18 24				18 25	18 32			18 39			

	SE 1	SE	SE	SE	SE		SE	SE 1	SE	SE	SE	SE	SE	SE	SE 1		SE	SE	SE	SE	SE	SE 1	SE	SE
London Charing Cross 4 ⊖ d	18 15				18 26			18 30		18 32	18 36		18 39		18 45					18 56		19 00		19 02
London Waterloo (East) 4 ⊖ d	18 18				18 29			18 33		18 35	18 39		18 42		18 48					18 59		19 03		19 05
London Cannon Street 4 ⊖ d			18 20	18 24			18 30					18 40						18 50	18 54		19 00			
London Blackfriars 3 ⊖ d																								
London Bridge 4 ⊖ d	18 23		18 24	18 28	18 34		18 34	18 39		18 40	18 44	18 44	18 47		18 53			18 54	18 58	19 04	19 04	19 09		19 10
London Victoria 15 ⊖ d		18 10							18 25					18 39			18 40						18 55	
New Cross 4 ⊖ d			18 29	18 33			18 39					18 49						18 59	19 03		19 09			
St Johns d			18 31	18 35			18 41					18 51						19 01	19 05		19 11			
Lewisham 4 a			18 34	18 38			18 44			18 49		18 54	18 56	19 01				19 04	19 08		19 14			19 19
Hither Green 4 a			18 38		18 43						18 53	18 58						19 08		19 13				
Petts Wood 4 a		18 44	18 51						18 59		19 06						19 14	19 21					19 29	
Orpington 4 a	18 38	18 47	18 54					18 55	19 02		19 09				19 08		19 17	19 24				19 25	19 32	

	SE		SE	SE	SE	SE 1	SE	SE	SE	SE	SE		SE 1	SE	SE	SE	SE	SE	SE	SE	SE		SE 1	SE
London Charing Cross 4 ⊖ d	19 06			19 09		19 15			19 17		19 26		19 30		19 32	19 36	19 39			19 47	19 52		19 55	
London Waterloo (East) 4 ⊖ d	19 09			19 12		19 18			19 20		19 29		19 33		19 35	19 39	19 42			19 50	19 55		19 58	
London Cannon Street 4 ⊖ d			19 10					19 20		19 24														
London Blackfriars 3 ⊖ d																								
London Bridge 4 ⊖ d	19 14		19 14	19 17		19 23		19 24	19 25	19 28	19 34		19 39		19 40	19 44	19 47			19 55	20 00		20 03	
London Victoria 15 ⊖ d					19 09		19 10							19 25				19 39	19 40					19 55
New Cross 4 ⊖ d			19 19					19 29		19 33					19 45					20 00	20 05			
St Johns d			19 21					19 31		19 35										20 02				
Lewisham 4 a			19 24	19 26	19 31			19 34	19 37	19 38					19 49	19 51	19 56	20 01		20 05	20 09			
Hither Green 4 a	19 23		19 28					19 38			19 43					19 56					20 13			
Petts Wood 4 a	19 36						19 44	19 51						19 59		20 08			20 14					20 29
Orpington 4 a	19 39					19 38	19 48	19 54					19 55	20 02		20 12			20 18				20 18	20 32

	SE	SE	SE	SE 1	SE	SE	SE		SE 1	SE	SE	SE	SE	SE 1	SE	SE	SE 1		SE	SE	SE	SE	SE 1	SE
London Charing Cross 4 ⊖ d	20 02	20 06	20 09	20 10		20 17	20 22		20 25		20 32	20 36	20 39	20 40	20 47	20 52	20 55			21 02	21 06	21 09	21 10	21 17
London Waterloo (East) 4 ⊖ d	20 05	20 09	20 12	20 13		20 20	20 25		20 28		20 35	20 39	20 42	20 43	20 50	20 55	20 58			21 05	21 09	21 12	21 13	21 20
London Cannon Street 4 ⊖ d																								
London Blackfriars 3 ⊖ d																								
London Bridge 4 ⊖ d	20 10	20 14	20 17	20 19		20 25	20 30		20 33		20 40	20 44	20 47	20 49	20 55	21 00	21 03			21 10	21 14	21 17	21 19	21 25
London Victoria 15 ⊖ d					20 10					20 25									20 55					
New Cross 4 ⊖ d	20 15					20 30	20 35				20 45				21 00	21 05				21 15				21 30
St Johns d						20 32									21 02									21 32
Lewisham 4 a	20 19	20 21	20 26			20 35	20 39				20 49	20 51	20 56		21 05	21 09				21 19	21 21	21 26		21 35
Hither Green 4 a		20 26					20 43					20 56				21 13					21 26			
Petts Wood 4 a		20 38			20 44					20 59		21 08							21 29		21 38			
Orpington 4 a		20 42		20 34	20 47				20 48	21 02		21 12		21 04			21 18		21 32		21 42		21 34	

	SE	SE 1	SE		SE	SE	SE	SE 1	SE	SE	SE 1	SE	SE		SE	SE	SE 1	SE	SE	SE 1	SE	SE	SE	
London Charing Cross 4 ⊖ d	21 22	21 25			21 32	21 36	21 39	21 40	21 47	21 52	21 55		22 02		22 06	22 09	22 10	22 17	22 22	22 25		22 32	22 36	
London Waterloo (East) 4 ⊖ d	21 25	21 28			21 35	21 39	21 42	21 43	21 50	21 55	21 58		22 05		22 09	22 12	22 13	22 20	22 25	22 28		22 35	22 39	
London Cannon Street 4 ⊖ d																								
London Blackfriars 3 ⊖ d																								
London Bridge 4 ⊖ d	21 30	21 33			21 40	21 44	21 47	21 49	21 55	22 00	22 03		22 10		22 14	22 17	22 19	22 25	22 30	22 33		22 40	22 44	
London Victoria 15 ⊖ d			21 25									21 55									22 25			
New Cross 4 ⊖ d	21 35				21 45				22 00	22 05			22 15					22 30	22 35			22 45		
St Johns d									22 02									22 32						
Lewisham 4 a	21 39				21 49	21 51	21 56		22 05	22 09			22 19		22 21	22 26		22 35	22 39			22 49	22 51	
Hither Green 4 a	21 43					21 56				22 13					22 26				22 43				22 56	
Petts Wood 4 a			21 59			22 08						22 29			22 38						22 59		23 08	
Orpington 4 a		21 48	22 02			22 12		22 04			22 18	22 32			22 42		22 34			22 48	23 02		23 12	

Table 199

Saturdays

14 December to 17 May

London - Lewisham, Hither Green, Petts Wood and Orpington (Summary of Services)

Network Diagram - see first Page of Table 195
Network Diagram - see first Page of Table 200

Station	SE	SE 1	SE	SE	SE 1	SE		SE	SE	SE	SE 1	SE	SE	SE 1	SE	SE		SE	SE	SE 1	SE 1	SE	SE	
London Charing Cross 4 ⊖ d	22 39	22 40	22 47	22 52	22 55			23 02	23 06	23 09	23 10	23 17	23 22	23 25		23 32		23 36	23 39	23 40	23 45	23 52		
London Waterloo (East) 4 ⊖ d	22 42	22 43	22 50	22 55	22 58			23 05	23 09	23 12	23 13	23 20	23 25	23 28		23 35		23 39	23 42	23 43	23 48	23 55		
London Cannon Street 4 ⊖ d																								
London Blackfriars 3 ⊖ d																								
London Bridge 4 ⊖ d	22 47	22 49	22 55	23 00	23 03			23 10	23 14	23 17	23 19	23 25	23 30	23 33		23 40		23 44	23 47	23 49	23 53	23 59		
London Victoria 15 ⊖ d						22 55									23 25								23 55	
New Cross 4 ⊖ d			23 00	23 05				23 15				23 30	23 35			23 45						00 05		
St Johns d			23 02									23 32										00 07		
Lewisham 4 a	22 56		23 05	23 09				23 19	23 21	23 26		23 35	23 39			23 49		23 51	23 55			00 10		
Hither Green 4 a				23 13					23 26				23 43					23 56						
Petts Wood 4 a						23 29			23 38						23 59			00 08					00 29	
Orpington 4 a		23 04			23 18	23 32			23 42		23 34			23 48	00 02			00 12		00 04	00 08		00 32	

Sundays

8 December to 11 May

Station	SE A	SE	SE	SE	SE	SE	SE	SE	SE		SE	SE	SE	SE	SE	SE	SE 1	SE	SE	SE 1	SE	SE	SE	SE
London Charing Cross 4 ⊖ d		00 02	00 06	00 10	00 15	00 18	00 48	07 30	07 35		07 50	07 52		08 00	08 05	08 09	08 10	08 20	08 22	08 25		08 30	08 35	08 39
London Waterloo (East) 4 ⊖ d		00 05	00 09	00 13	00 18	00 21	00 51	07 33	07 38		07 53	07 55		08 03	08 08	08 12	08 13	08 23	08 25	08 28		08 33	08 38	08 42
London Cannon Street 4 ⊖ d																								
London Blackfriars 3 ⊖ d																								
London Bridge 4 ⊖ d		00 10	00 14	00 18	00 23	00 26	00 56	07 38	07 43		07 58	08 00		08 08	08 13	08 17	08 19	08 28	08 30	08 33		08 38	08 43	08 47
London Victoria 15 ⊖ d													07 55								08 25			
New Cross 4 ⊖ d	00 05	00 15		00 23		00 31	01 01		07 48		08 03				08 18			08 33					08 48	
St Johns d	00 07								07 50						08 20								08 50	
Lewisham 4 a	00 10	00 19	00 21	00 27		00 35	01 05	07 46	07 53		08 07	08 08		08 17	08 23	08 25		08 37	08 38			08 46	08 53	08 55
Hither Green 4 a			00 26	00 31			01 09	07 51				08 13		08 21					08 43			08 51		
Petts Wood 4 a			00 38				01 22	08 04					08 29	08 34							08 59	09 04		
Orpington 4 a			00 42		00 47		01 25	08 08					08 32	08 38			08 34			08 48	09 02	09 08		

Station	SE 1	SE	SE	SE 1	SE	SE		SE	SE	SE 1 🚲	SE	SE	SE 1	SE	SE	SE	SE	SE 1 🚲	SE	SE	SE 1	SE	SE
London Charing Cross 4 ⊖ d	08 40	08 50	08 52	08 55		09 00	and at the same minutes past each hour until	19 05	19 09	19 10	19 20	19 22	19 25		19 30	19 35	19 39	19 40	19 50	19 52	19 55		20 00
London Waterloo (East) 4 ⊖ d	08 43	08 53	08 55	08 58		09 03		19 08	19 12	19 13	19 23	19 25	19 28		19 33	19 38	19 42	19 43	19 53	19 55	19 58		20 03
London Cannon Street 4 ⊖ d																							
London Blackfriars 3 ⊖ d																							
London Bridge 4 ⊖ d	08 49	08 58	09 00	09 03		09 08		19 13	19 17	19 19	19 28	19 30	19 33		19 38	19 43	19 47	19 49	19 58	20 00	20 03		20 08
London Victoria 15 ⊖ d					08 55									19 25								19 55	
New Cross 4 ⊖ d		09 03						19 18			19 33					19 48			20 03				
St Johns d								19 20								19 50							
Lewisham 4 a		09 07	09 08			09 16		19 23	19 25		19 37	19 38			19 46	19 53	19 55		20 07	20 08			20 16
Hither Green 4 a			09 13			09 21						19 43			19 51					20 13			20 21
Petts Wood 4 a					09 29	09 34								19 59	20 04							20 29	20 34
Orpington 4 a	09 04			09 18	09 32	09 38				19 34			19 48	20 02	20 08			20 04			20 18	20 32	20 38

Station		SE	SE	SE 1 🚲	SE	SE	SE 1	SE	SE	SE		SE	SE 1	SE	SE	SE	SE	SE	SE	SE 1		SE	SE	SE 1
London Charing Cross 4 ⊖ d		20 05	20 09	20 10	20 20	20 22	20 25		20 30	20 35		20 39	20 40	20 50	20 52		21 00	21 05	21 09	21 10		21 20	21 22	21 25
London Waterloo (East) 4 ⊖ d		20 08	20 12	20 13	20 23	20 25	20 28		20 33	20 38		20 42	20 43	20 53	20 55		21 03	21 08	21 12	21 13		21 23	21 25	21 28
London Cannon Street 4 ⊖ d																								
London Blackfriars 3 ⊖ d																								
London Bridge 4 ⊖ d		20 13	20 17	20 19	20 28	20 30	20 33		20 38	20 43		20 47	20 49	20 58	21 00		21 08	21 13	21 17	21 19		21 28	21 30	21 33
London Victoria 15 ⊖ d								20 25								20 55								
New Cross 4 ⊖ d		20 18			20 33					20 48				21 03				21 18				21 33		
St Johns d		20 20								20 50								21 20						
Lewisham 4 a		20 23	20 25		20 37	20 38			20 46	20 53		20 55		21 07	21 08		21 16	21 23	21 25			21 37	21 38	
Hither Green 4 a						20 43			20 51						21 13		21 21						21 43	
Petts Wood 4 a								20 59	21 04							21 29	21 34							
Orpington 4 a				20 34			20 48	21 02	21 08				21 04			21 32	21 38			21 34				21 48

Station	SE	SE	SE	SE	SE 1	SE		SE	SE	SE	SE	SE	SE 1	SE	SE	SE 1		SE	SE	SE	SE	SE 1	SE	SE
London Charing Cross 4 ⊖ d		21 30	21 35	21 39	21 40	21 50		21 52		22 00	22 05	22 09	22 10	22 20	22 22	22 25			22 30	22 35	22 39	22 40	22 50	22 52
London Waterloo (East) 4 ⊖ d		21 33	21 38	21 42	21 43	21 53		21 55		22 03	22 08	22 12	22 13	22 23	22 25	22 28			22 33	22 38	22 42	22 43	22 53	22 55
London Cannon Street 4 ⊖ d																								
London Blackfriars 3 ⊖ d																								
London Bridge 4 ⊖ d		21 38	21 43	21 47	21 49	21 58		22 00		22 08	22 13	22 17	22 19	22 28	22 30	22 33			22 38	22 43	22 47	22 49	22 58	23 00
London Victoria 15 ⊖ d	21 25								21 55									22 25						
New Cross 4 ⊖ d			21 48			22 03					22 18			22 33						22 48			23 03	
St Johns d			21 50								22 20									22 50				
Lewisham 4 a		21 46	21 53	21 55		22 07		22 08		22 16	22 23	22 25		22 37	22 38				22 46	22 53	22 55		23 07	23 08
Hither Green 4 a		21 51						22 13		22 21					22 43				22 51					23 13
Petts Wood 4 a	21 59	22 04							22 29	22 34								22 59	23 04					
Orpington 4 a	22 02	22 08			22 04				22 32	22 38			22 34			22 48		23 02	23 08			23 04		

A not 8 December

Table 199

Sundays

8 December to 11 May

London - Lewisham, Hither Green, Petts Wood and Orpington (Summary of Services)

Network Diagram - see first Page of Table 195
Network Diagram - see first Page of Table 200

		SE	SE	SE	SE	SE 1		SE	SE	SE 1	SE	SE	SE	SE 1	SE	SE		SE							
London Charing Cross 4	⊖ d		23 00	23 05	23 09	23 10		23 20	23 22	23 25		23 30	23 35	23 40	23 50	23 52									
London Waterloo (East) 4	⊖ d		23 03	23 08	23 12	23 13		23 23	23 25	23 28		23 33	23 38	23 43	23 53	23 55									
London Cannon Street 4	⊖ d																								
London Blackfriars 3	⊖ d																								
London Bridge 4	⊖ d		23 08	23 13	23 17	23 19		23 28	23 30	23 33		23 38	23 43	23 49	23 58	23 59									
London Victoria 15	⊖ d	22 55									23 25							23 55							
New Cross 4	⊖ d			23 18				23 33					23 48		00 03										
St Johns	d			23 20									23 50												
Lewisham 4	a		23 16	23 23	23 25			23 37	23 38			23 46	23 53		00 07	00 08									
Hither Green 4	a		23 21						23 43			23 51				00 13									
Petts Wood 4	a	23 29	23 34								23 59	00 04						00 29							
Orpington 4	a	23 32	23 38			23 34				23 48	00 02	00 08		00 04				00 32							

Table 199R

Mondays to Fridays

9 December to 16 May

Orpington, Petts Wood, Hither Green and Lewisham - London (Summary of Services)

Network Diagram - see first Page of Table 195
Network Diagram - see first Page of Table 200

	SE	SE	SE	SE	SE		SE	SE	SE	SE	SE	SE	SE	SE	SE 1		SE	SE	SE	SE	SE 1	SE	SE	SE
Orpington 4 d	04 34	04 55		05 10	05 14			05 15		05 34		05 40			05 54					06 01	06 09	06 10		
Petts Wood 4 d	04 37	04 58		05 13				05 18		05 37		05 43								06 04		06 13		
Hither Green 4 d			05 08				05 23	05 30			05 38							06 08		06 16				06 22
Lewisham 4 d			05 13				05 28	05 36	05 39		05 43		05 50	05 56			06 09	06 13	06 20	06 22			06 25	06 27
St Johns d									05 41								06 11							06 29
New Cross 4 ⊖ d			05 16				05 31	05 39	05 43		05 46		05 53				06 13	06 16		06 25				06 31
London Victoria 15 ⊖ a				05 47								06 18										06 47		
London Bridge 4 ⊖ d			05 22		05 37		05 37	05 46	05 49		05 53		05 59	06 06	06 10		06 19	06 22	06 28	06 32	06 25		06 34	06 37
London Blackfriars 3 ⊖ a	05 17	05 32								06 17														
London Cannon Street 4 ⊖ a							05 41																	
London Waterloo (East) 4 ⊖ d			05 27		05 42			05 50	05 54		05 57		06 04	06 10	06 15		06 24	06 27	06 33	06 36	06 30		06 40	06 42
London Charing Cross 4 ⊖ a			05 30		05 47			05 56	05 57		06 01		06 07	06 14	06 18		06 27	06 30	06 36	06 39	06 33		06 43	06 45

	SE 1		SE	SE	SE	SE	SE 1	SE 1	SE	SE	SE		SE	SE	SE	SE	SE	SE	SE 1	SE	SE		SE	SE
Orpington 4 d	06 20					06 22	06 24	06 39	06 40								06 43	06 52	06 54	06 58				
Petts Wood 4 d						06 25			06 43								06 46	06 55		07 01				
Hither Green 4 d						06 38							06 46		06 56		06 58	07 08						
Lewisham 4 d			06 35	06 39	06 41	06 43				06 48	06 50		06 52	06 55		07 01	07 04				07 08		07 11	07 15
St Johns d				06 41						06 50			06 54			07 03								
New Cross 4 ⊖ d			06 38	06 43						06 52			06 56			07 05					07 11			
London Victoria 15 ⊖ a					07 04				07 19															07 42
London Bridge 4 ⊖ d	06 39		06 44	06 49		06 52	06 40	06 55		07 00	07 01		07 03	07 04	07 07	07 11		07 20	07 10		07 18		07 21	
London Blackfriars 3 ⊖ a																				07 42				
London Cannon Street 4 ⊖ a	06 43		06 48							07 05			07 09			07 17		07 26			07 24			
London Waterloo (East) 4 ⊖ d				06 54		06 57	06 45	07 00			07 06			07 09	07 12		07 17		07 15				07 26	
London Charing Cross 4 ⊖ a				06 57		07 02	06 49	07 05			07 11			07 15	07 17		07 22		07 20				07 31	

	SE	SE	SE	SE	SE	SE	SE 1		SE	SE	SE 1	SE	SE	SE	SE	SE	SE		SE	SE	SE	SE	SE	SE
Orpington 4 d						07 03	07 04		07 08	07 11	07 14					07 22			07 28	07 33	07 38			
Petts Wood 4 d						07 06			07 11	07 15						07 25			07 31	07 36	07 41			
Hither Green 4 d		07 11	07 16			07 19				07 28				07 32	07 36	07 39				07 49				
Lewisham 4 d		07 17		07 20	07 22	07 25						07 30	07 35	07 38		07 44	07 46						07 48	07 50
St Johns d		07 19			07 24									07 40									07 50	
New Cross 4 ⊖ d	07 20	07 21		07 23	07 26								07 38	07 42								07 50	07 53	
London Victoria 15 ⊖ a									07 49								08 11				08 20			
London Bridge 4 ⊖ d	08 38	07 27	07 27	07 29	07 34		07 24			07 38	07 30	07 42	07 44	07 48	07 48	07 54				08 00		09 08	08 02	08 02
London Blackfriars 3 ⊖ a																			08 08					
London Cannon Street 4 ⊖ a		07 33		07 35	07 39		07 30			07 44			07 50	07 54						08 06		09 15	08 08	
London Waterloo (East) 4 ⊖ d	08 43		07 32			07 37					07 35	07 47			07 53	07 59								08 07
London Charing Cross 4 ⊖ a	08 48		07 37			07 42					07 40	07 52			07 58	08 04								08 12

	SE	SE	SE		SE	SE	SE	SE	SE	SE	SE	SE	SE		SE	SE	SE	SE	SE	SE	SE	SE	SE	
Orpington 4 d			07 41			07 47		07 52	07 57								08 01			08 13	08 16			
Petts Wood 4 d			07 44			07 50		07 55	08 00								08 04			08 16	08 19			
Hither Green 4 d		07 52	07 58				08 02									08 12	08 17		08 22					
Lewisham 4 d	07 55	07 57	08 03		08 05						08 08	08 11	08 15			08 17	08 23	08 25				08 28	08 31	
St Johns d		08 00									08 12					08 21						08 30		
New Cross 4 ⊖ d	07 58	08 02								08 04	08 14		08 18		08 20	08 23						08 32		
London Victoria 15 ⊖ a					08 29													08 49			08 56			
London Bridge 4 ⊖ d	08 04	08 09					08 14	08 20		09 18	08 22	08 22	08 26		09 30	08 30			08 34	08 40		08 42	08 42	
London Blackfriars 3 ⊖ a						08 29																		
London Cannon Street 4 ⊖ a	08 10	08 15						08 26			08 28		08 32		09 36	08 36				08 46		08 48		
London Waterloo (East) 4 ⊖ d			08 17				08 19		08 25	09 23		08 27					08 37		08 39				08 47	
London Charing Cross 4 ⊖ a			08 22				08 24		08 30	09 28		08 32					08 42		08 44				08 52	

	SE	SE	SE	SE	SE	SE	SE	SE	SE		SE	SE	SE	SE	SE	SE	SE	SE	SE		SE	SE	SE	SE
Orpington 4 d				08 21		08 26					08 32	08 40						08 43	08 47		08 52	08 55		
Petts Wood 4 d				08 24		08 29					08 35	08 43						08 46	08 50		08 55	08 58		
Hither Green 4 d			08 32	08 37	08 42									08 50	08 55			09 00			09 08			09 14
Lewisham 4 d	08 35		08 37				08 46		08 48				08 52	08 55			09 02	09 05					09 07	
St Johns d			08 39						08 50					08 57				09 08						
New Cross 4 ⊖ d	08 38	08 38	08 41					08 49	08 52					08 59		09 04	09 07	09 10						
London Victoria 15 ⊖ a						09 06	09 11					09 19										09 34	09 30	
London Bridge 4 ⊖ d	08 44	09 51	08 48		08 54			10 01	08 58		09 00		09 01	09 06	09 06	10 21	09 14	09 18			09 21			09 24
London Blackfriars 3 ⊖ a																			09 30					
London Cannon Street 4 ⊖ a	08 50	09 57	08 55					10 06	09 04		09 06			09 13		10 24	09 20	09 24						
London Waterloo (East) 4 ⊖ d				08 53	08 59								09 06		09 11						09 26			09 29
London Charing Cross 4 ⊖ a				08 58	09 04								09 12		09 16						09 31			09 34

	SE	SE	SE	SE	SE 1		SE 1	SE	SE	SE	SE	SE	SE	SE 1	SE		SE	SE	SE	SE	SE	SE	SE 1	SE
Orpington 4 d				09 03	09 04		09 09	09 10					09 21	09 24	09 25							09 33	09 39	09 40
Petts Wood 4 d				09 06				09 13					09 24		09 28							09 36		09 43
Hither Green 4 d				09 19								09 28	09 37					09 42				09 49		
Lewisham 4 d	09 15	09 20		09 24					09 26	09 29		09 34					09 38		09 45	09 50		09 54		
St Johns d	09 17			09 26						09 31		09 36							09 47			09 56		
New Cross 4 ⊖ d	09 19		09 19	09 28						09 33	09 33	09 38							09 49		09 49	09 58		
London Victoria 15 ⊖ a								09 49							10 03		10 00							10 17
London Bridge 4 ⊖ d	09 26	09 30	10 31	09 34	09 23		09 27		09 35	09 39	10 51	09 45	09 49	09 41				09 52	09 55	09 58	11 01	10 04	09 55	
London Blackfriars 3 ⊖ a																								
London Cannon Street 4 ⊖ a	09 32		10 36	09 40	09 29					09 46	10 54	09 51							10 00		11 06	10 08		
London Waterloo (East) 4 ⊖ d		09 35					09 32		09 40				09 55	09 46				09 58		10 04			10 01	
London Charing Cross 4 ⊖ a		09 40					09 37		09 45				10 00	09 51				10 01		10 07			10 04	

Table 199R

Mondays to Fridays

9 December to 16 May

Orpington, Petts Wood, Hither Green and Lewisham - London (Summary of Services)

Network Diagram - see first Page of Table 195
Network Diagram - see first Page of Table 200

		SE	SE	SE	SE	SE	SE 1	SE		SE	SE	SE	SE	SE	SE	SE 1	SE	SE		SE	SE	SE	SE	SE 1	SE
Orpington 4	d					09 51	09 54	09 55							10 03	10 09	10 10						10 21	10 24	10 25
Petts Wood 4	d					09 54		09 58							10 06		10 13						10 24		10 28
Hither Green 4	d				09 58	10 07					10 12				10 19							10 28	10 37		
Lewisham 4	d	09 56	09 59		10 04					10 08		10 14	10 20		10 24			10 26		10 29		10 34			
St Johns	d		10 01		10 06							10 16			10 26					10 31		10 36			
New Cross 4 ⊖	d		10 03	10 03	10 08							10 18		10 19	10 28					10 33	10 33	10 38			
London Victoria 15 ⊖	a							10 32		10 28							10 47								11 02
London Bridge 4 ⊖	d	10 05	10 09	11 21	10 14	10 19	10 11				10 22	10 24	10 28	11 31	10 34	10 25		10 35		10 39	11 51	10 45	10 49	10 41	
London Blackfriars 3 ⊖	a																								
London Cannon Street 4 ⊖	a		10 13	11 24	10 19							10 28		11 36	10 38					10 43	11 54	10 50			
London Waterloo (East) 4 ⊖	d	10 10				10 25	10 16				10 28		10 34			10 31		10 40					10 55	10 46	
London Charing Cross 4 ⊖	a	10 13				10 28	10 19				10 31		10 37			10 34		10 43					10 58	10 49	

		SE	SE	SE		SE	SE	SE	SE 1	SE	SE	SE	SE	SE		SE	SE 1	SE	SE	SE	SE	SE	SE	SE	
Orpington 4	d							10 33	10 39	10 40						10 51	10 54	10 55						11 03	
Petts Wood 4	d							10 36		10 43						10 54		10 58						11 06	
Hither Green 4	d		10 42					10 49						10 58		11 07				11 12				11 19	
Lewisham 4	d	10 38		10 44		10 50		10 54			10 56	10 59		11 04					11 08		11 14	11 20		11 24	
St Johns	d			10 46				10 56				11 01		11 06							11 16			11 26	
New Cross 4 ⊖	d			10 48			10 49	10 58				11 03	11 03	11 08							11 18		11 19	11 28	
London Victoria 15 ⊖	a	10 58								11 17								11 32	11 28						
London Bridge 4 ⊖	d		10 52	10 54		10 58	12 01	11 04	10 55		11 05	11 09	12 21	11 15		11 19	11 11			11 22	11 24	11 28	12 31	11 34	
London Blackfriars 3 ⊖	a																								
London Cannon Street 4 ⊖	a			10 58			12 04	11 08				11 13	12 24	11 19							11 28		12 36	11 38	
London Waterloo (East) 4 ⊖	d		10 58			11 03			11 00		11 10					11 24	11 15			11 27		11 33			
London Charing Cross 4 ⊖	a		11 01			11 06			11 03		11 13					11 27	11 19			11 30		11 36			

		SE 1	SE	SE	SE	SE	SE	SE	SE 1	SE		SE	SE	SE	SE	SE	SE	SE 1	SE	SE		SE	SE	SE	SE
Orpington 4	d	11 09	11 10					11 21	11 24	11 25							11 33	11 39	11 40						11 51
Petts Wood 4	d		11 13					11 24		11 28							11 36		11 43						11 54
Hither Green 4	d						11 28	11 37					11 42				11 49							11 58	12 07
Lewisham 4	d			11 26	11 29		11 34					11 38		11 44	11 50		11 54			11 56		11 59		12 04	
St Johns	d				11 31		11 36							11 46			11 56					12 01		12 06	
New Cross 4 ⊖	d				11 33	11 33	11 38							11 48		11 49	11 58					12 03	12 03	12 08	
London Victoria 15 ⊖	a		11 47							12 02		11 58							12 17						
London Bridge 4 ⊖	d	11 25		11 35	11 39	12 51	11 45	11 49	11 41				11 52	11 54	11 58	13 01	12 04	11 55		12 05		12 09	13 21	12 15	12 19
London Blackfriars 3 ⊖	a																								
London Cannon Street 4 ⊖	a				11 43	12 54	11 49							11 58		13 06	12 08					12 13	13 24	12 19	
London Waterloo (East) 4 ⊖	d	11 30		11 40				11 54	11 45				11 57		12 03			12 00		12 10					12 24
London Charing Cross 4 ⊖	a	11 33		11 43				11 57	11 49				12 00		12 06			12 03		12 13					12 27

		SE 1	SE	SE	SE	SE		SE	SE	SE	SE 1	SE	SE	SE	SE	SE		SE	SE 1	SE	SE	SE	SE	SE	SE
Orpington 4	d	11 54	11 55							12 03	12 09	12 10						12 21	12 24	12 25					
Petts Wood 4	d		11 58							12 06		12 13						12 24		12 28					
Hither Green 4	d				12 12					12 19						12 28		12 37				12 42			
Lewisham 4	d			12 08		12 14		12 20		12 24			12 26	12 29		12 34					12 38		12 44	12 50	
St Johns	d					12 16				12 26				12 31		12 36							12 46		
New Cross 4 ⊖	d					12 18			12 19	12 28				12 33	12 33	12 38							12 48		12 49
London Victoria 15 ⊖	a		12 32	12 28								12 47								13 02	12 58				
London Bridge 4 ⊖	d	12 11			12 22	12 24		12 28	13 31	12 34	12 25		12 35	12 39	13 51	12 45		12 49	12 41			12 52	12 54	12 58	14 01
London Blackfriars 3 ⊖	a																								
London Cannon Street 4 ⊖	a					12 28			13 36	12 38				12 43	13 54	12 50							12 58		14 06
London Waterloo (East) 4 ⊖	d	12 15			12 27			12 33			12 30		12 40					12 54	12 45			12 57		13 03	
London Charing Cross 4 ⊖	a	12 19			12 30			12 36			12 33		12 43					12 57	12 49			13 00		13 06	

		SE		SE 1	SE	SE	SE	SE	SE	SE	SE 1	SE		SE	SE	SE	SE	SE	SE	SE 1	SE	SE		SE	SE
Orpington 4	d	12 33		12 39	12 40					12 51	12 54	12 55							13 03	13 09	13 10				
Petts Wood 4	d	12 36			12 43					12 54		12 58							13 06		13 13				
Hither Green 4	d	12 49							12 58	13 07					13 12				13 19						
Lewisham 4	d	12 54				12 56	12 59		13 04					13 08		13 14	13 20		13 24			13 26		13 29	
St Johns	d	12 56					13 01		13 06							13 16			13 26					13 31	
New Cross 4 ⊖	d	12 58					13 03	13 03	13 08							13 18		13 19	13 28					13 33	13 33
London Victoria 15 ⊖	a				13 17							13 32		13 28							13 47				
London Bridge 4 ⊖	d	13 04		12 55		13 05	13 09	14 21	13 15	13 19	13 11				13 22	13 24	13 28	14 31	13 34	13 25		13 35		13 39	14 51
London Blackfriars 3 ⊖	a																								
London Cannon Street 4 ⊖	a	13 08					13 13	14 24	13 19							13 28		14 36	13 38					13 43	14 54
London Waterloo (East) 4 ⊖	d			13 00		13 10				13 24	13 15				13 27		13 33			13 30		13 40			
London Charing Cross 4 ⊖	a			13 03		13 13				13 27	13 19				13 30		13 36			13 33		13 43			

		SE	SE	SE 1	SE	SE	SE	SE		SE	SE	SE	SE 1	SE	SE	SE	SE	SE		SE	SE 1	SE	SE	SE	SE
Orpington 4	d		13 21	13 24	13 25							13 33	13 39	13 40						13 51	13 54	13 55			
Petts Wood 4	d		13 24		13 28							13 36		13 43						13 54		13 58			
Hither Green 4	d	13 28	13 37				13 42					13 49						13 58		14 07				14 12	
Lewisham 4	d	13 34				13 38		13 44		13 50		13 54			13 56	13 59		14 04					14 08		14 14
St Johns	d	13 36						13 46				13 56				14 01		14 06							14 16
New Cross 4 ⊖	d	13 38						13 48			13 49	13 58				14 03	14 03	14 08							14 18
London Victoria 15 ⊖	a				14 02	13 58								14 17								14 32	14 28		
London Bridge 4 ⊖	d	13 45	13 49	13 41			13 52	13 54		13 58	15 01	14 04	13 55		14 05	14 09	15 21	14 15		14 19	14 11			14 22	14 24
London Blackfriars 3 ⊖	a																								
London Cannon Street 4 ⊖	a	13 49						13 58			15 06	14 08				14 13	15 24	14 19							14 28
London Waterloo (East) 4 ⊖	d		13 54	13 45			13 57			14 03			14 00		14 10					14 24	14 15			14 27	
London Charing Cross 4 ⊖	a		13 57	13 49			14 00			14 06			14 03		14 13					14 27	14 19			14 30	

Table 199R

Mondays to Fridays

9 December to 16 May

Orpington, Petts Wood, Hither Green and Lewisham - London (Summary of Services)

Network Diagram - see first Page of Table 195
Network Diagram - see first Page of Table 200

		SE	SE	SE	SE	SE	SE	SE	SE	SE		SE	SE	SE	SE	SE	SE	SE	SE	SE		SE	SE	SE	SE
					1								1									1			
Orpington 4	d			14 03	14 09	14 10						14 21	14 24	14 25						14 33		14 39	14 40		
Petts Wood 4	d			14 06		14 13						14 24		14 28						14 36			14 43		
Hither Green 4	d			14 19						14 28		14 37				14 42				14 49					
Lewisham 4	d	14 20		14 24			14 26	14 29		14 34					14 38		14 44	14 50		14 54				14 56	14 59
St Johns	d			14 26				14 31		14 36							14 46			14 56					15 01
New Cross 4	d		14 19	14 28				14 33	14 33	14 38							14 48		14 49	14 58					15 03
London Victoria 15	a					14 47								15 02	14 58								15 17		
London Bridge 4	d	14 28	15 31	14 34	14 25		14 35	14 39	15 51	14 45		14 49	14 41			14 52	14 54	14 58	16 01	15 04		14 55		15 05	15 09
London Blackfriars 3	a																								
London Cannon Street 4	a		15 36	14 38				14 43	15 54	14 49							14 58		16 06	15 08					15 13
London Waterloo (East) 4	d	14 33			14 30		14 40					14 54	14 45			14 57		15 03				15 00		15 10	
London Charing Cross 4	a	14 36			14 33		14 43					14 57	14 49			15 00		15 06				15 03		15 13	

		SE	SE	SE	SE	SE		SE	SE	SE	SE	SE	SE	SE	SE	SE		SE	SE	SE	SE	SE	SE	SE	SE
					1									1								1			
Orpington 4	d			14 51	14 54	14 55							15 03	15 09	15 10						15 21	15 24	15 25		
Petts Wood 4	d			14 54		14 58							15 06		15 13						15 24		15 28		
Hither Green 4	d		14 58	15 07					15 12				15 19							15 28	15 37				15 42
Lewisham 4	d		15 04					15 08		15 14	15 20		15 24			15 26		15 29		15 34				15 38	
St Johns	d		15 06							15 16			15 26					15 31		15 36					
New Cross 4	d	15 03	15 08							15 18		15 19	15 28					15 33	15 33	15 38					
London Victoria 15	a					15 32		15 28							15 47								16 02	15 58	
London Bridge 4	d	16 21	15 15	15 19	15 11				15 22	15 24	15 28	16 31	15 34	15 25		15 35		15 39	16 51	15 45	15 50	15 41			15 53
London Blackfriars 3	a																								
London Cannon Street 4	a	16 24	15 19							15 28		16 36	15 38					15 43	16 54	15 49					
London Waterloo (East) 4	d			15 24	15 15				15 27		15 33			15 30		15 40					15 55	15 46			15 58
London Charing Cross 4	a			15 27	15 19				15 30		15 36			15 33		15 43					15 58	15 49			16 01

		SE		SE	SE	SE	SE	SE	SE	SE	SE	SE		SE	SE	SE	SE	SE	SE	SE	SE	SE		SE	SE
							1								1									1	
Orpington 4	d					15 33	15 39	15 40						15 51	15 54	15 55						16 03		16 08	16 10
Petts Wood 4	d					15 36		15 43						15 54		15 58						16 06			16 13
Hither Green 4	d					15 49						15 58		16 07				16 12				16 19			
Lewisham 4	d	15 44		15 50		15 54			15 56	15 59		16 04					16 08		16 14	16 20		16 24			
St Johns	d	15 46				15 56				16 01		16 06							16 16			16 26			
New Cross 4	d	15 48			15 49	15 58				16 03	16 03	16 08							16 18		16 20	16 28			
London Victoria 15	a							16 17								16 32	16 28								16 47
London Bridge 4	d	15 54		15 58	17 01	16 04	15 55		16 05	16 09	17 22	16 15		16 19	16 12			16 22	16 24	16 29	17 31	16 34		16 25	
London Blackfriars 3	a																								
London Cannon Street 4	a	15 58			17 05	16 08				16 13	17 26	16 19							16 28		17 36	16 38			
London Waterloo (East) 4	d			16 03			16 00		16 10					16 25	16 17			16 28		16 34				16 30	
London Charing Cross 4	a			16 06			16 03		16 13					16 28	16 20			16 31		16 37				16 33	

		SE	SE	SE	SE	SE	SE	SE		SE	SE	SE	SE	SE	SE	SE	SE	SE		SE	SE	SE	SE	SE	SE
							1							1											
Orpington 4	d					16 21	16 25	16 25					16 33	16 39	16 40										
Petts Wood 4	d					16 24		16 28					16 36		16 43										
Hither Green 4	d				16 28	16 37					16 42		16 50					16 50		16 56				17 00	17 07
Lewisham 4	d	16 26	16 29		16 34					16 38		16 44				16 50					16 56	16 59		17 05	
St Johns	d		16 31		16 36							16 46						16 54				17 01		17 09	
New Cross 4	d		16 33	16 34	16 38							16 48					16 49	16 56				17 03	17 08	17 11	
London Victoria 15	a							17 04		17 01					17 20										
London Bridge 4	d	16 35	16 39	17 52	16 45	16 49	16 42				16 52	16 54	17 02	16 56		16 59	18 03	17 04		17 06	17 07	17 09	18 21	17 19	17 22
London Blackfriars 3	a																								
London Cannon Street 4	a		16 43	17 56	16 49							16 58					18 07	17 09			17 11	17 15	18 24	17 24	
London Waterloo (East) 4	d	16 40				16 55	16 49				16 57		17 07	17 01		17 04				17 11					17 29
London Charing Cross 4	a	16 44				16 58	16 52				17 00		17 10	17 04		17 07				17 15					17 33

		SE	SE	SE		SE	SE	SE	SE	SE	SE	SE	SE	SE		SE	SE	SE	SE	SE	SE	SE	SE	SE	
			1								1									1		1			
Orpington 4	d	16 51	16 54	16 55						17 03	17 09	17 10	17 13						17 20	17 24	17 24	17 34			
Petts Wood 4	d	16 54		16 58						17 06		17 13							17 24		17 28	17 37			
Hither Green 4	d	17 09								17 19								17 28	17 38						
Lewisham 4	d					17 08		17 14	17 20	17 24				17 27		17 30		17 35					17 38	17 44	
St Johns	d							17 16		17 26								17 37						17 46	
New Cross 4	d						17 14	17 18		17 28						17 33	17 36	17 39						17 48	
London Victoria 15	a			17 33		17 28						17 48									18 03		17 59		
London Bridge 4	d		17 12				18 31	17 25	17 30	17 34	17 28			17 36		17 39	18 51	17 45	17 49	17 42				17 55	
London Blackfriars 3	a																					18 09			
London Cannon Street 4	a						18 35	17 29		17 38	17 32					17 44	18 54	17 49						17 59	
London Waterloo (East) 4	d	17 25	17 16						17 35				17 37	17 41					17 54	17 47					
London Charing Cross 4	a	17 29	17 20						17 38				17 42	17 44					17 57	17 50					

		SE	SE	SE	SE	SE	SE	SE	SE	SE		SE	SE	SE	SE	SE	SE	SE	SE	SE		SE	SE	SE	SE
									1										1					1	
Orpington 4	d							17 37	17 39	17 40								17 50	17 54	17 55			18 03	18 09	18 09
Petts Wood 4	d							17 40		17 43								17 54		17 58			18 06		18 12
Hither Green 4	d					17 41	17 42	17 53				17 58					18 03	18 07				18 12	18 19		
Lewisham 4	d	17 50	17 53	17 56	17 59	18 29						18 05	18 08		18 14	18 20	18 59						18 24		
St Johns	d							17 57				18 07			18 16								18 26		
New Cross 4	d				18 02	18 32		17 59				18 09		18 14	18 18		19 03						18 28		
London Victoria 15	a									18 18			18 29							18 33					18 48
London Bridge 4	d	18 00	19 01	18 04	18 09	18 38	17 54	18 06	17 58			18 16		19 28	18 24	18 28	19 09	18 19	18 10			18 23	18 34	18 25	
London Blackfriars 3	a																								
London Cannon Street 4	a	18 04	19 06		18 13	18 42		18 11				18 20		19 33	18 29		19 13						18 38		
London Waterloo (East) 4	d			18 09			17 59		18 03							18 33		18 24	18 15			18 28		18 30	
London Charing Cross 4	a			18 12			18 03		18 06							18 37		18 27	18 18			18 31		18 35	

Table 199R

Mondays to Fridays

9 December to 16 May

Orpington, Petts Wood, Hither Green and Lewisham - London (Summary of Services)

Network Diagram - see first Page of Table 195
Network Diagram - see first Page of Table 200

		SE		SE	SE	SE	SE	SE	SE	SE	SE	SE		SE 1	SE	SE	SE	SE	SE	SE	SE	SE		SE	SE 1
Orpington 4	d											18 21		18 24	18 25		18 33	18 40						18 50	18 54
Petts Wood 4	d											18 24			18 28		18 36	18 43						18 54	
Hither Green 4	d	18 21					18 28				18 35	18 37				18 42	18 49					18 59		19 07	
Lewisham 4	d			18 26	18 29		18 35	18 38	18 45	18 50	19 29						18 54		18 56		18 59	19 05			
St Johns	d						18 37		18 47								18 56					19 07			
New Cross 4 ⊖	d				18 32	18 35	18 39		18 49		19 32						18 58			19 00	19 03	19 09			
London Victoria 15 ⊖	a							18 58							19 03			19 17							
London Bridge 4 ⊖	d	18 33		18 36	18 38	19 59	18 46		18 55	18 58	19 38	18 49		18 41		18 53	19 05		19 05	20 28	19 09	19 15		19 19	19 10
London Blackfriars 3 ⊖	a																								
London Cannon Street 4 ⊖	a				18 42	20 03	18 51		18 59		19 43						19 10			20 31	19 13	19 20			
London Waterloo (East) 4 ⊖	d	18 38		18 42						19 03		18 54		18 46		18 58			19 10					19 24	19 15
London Charing Cross 4 ⊖	a	18 41		18 45						19 06		18 57		18 49		19 01			19 13					19 27	19 18

		SE	SE	SE	SE	SE	SE	SE 1		SE	SE	SE	SE	SE	SE	SE 1	SE	SE 1		SE	SE	SE	SE	SE	SE
Orpington 4	d	18 55					19 03	19 08		19 10					19 21	19 24	19 25	19 39		19 40					19 51
Petts Wood 4	d	18 58					19 06			19 13					19 24		19 28			19 43					19 54
Hither Green 4	d			19 12			19 19						19 28		19 37						19 42				20 07
Lewisham 4	d		19 08		19 14	19 20	19 24				19 26	19 29	19 34	19 38	19 43						19 48	19 52	19 56	20 08	20 13
St Johns	d				19 16		19 26						19 36	19 40										20 10	
New Cross 4 ⊖	d				19 18		19 28					19 32	19 38	19 42							19 51	19 56		20 12	
London Victoria 15 ⊖	a	19 32	19 28							19 47							20 02			20 17					
London Bridge 4 ⊖	d			19 22	19 24	19 28	19 34	19 25			19 35	19 38	19 45	19 49	19 52	19 41		19 55			19 58	20 04	20 06	20 19	20 22
London Blackfriars 3 ⊖	a																								
London Cannon Street 4 ⊖	a				19 28		19 38					19 43	19 49												
London Waterloo (East) 4 ⊖	d			19 27		19 33		19 30			19 40			19 54	19 57	19 46		20 00			20 03	20 09	20 11	20 24	20 27
London Charing Cross 4 ⊖	a			19 30		19 36		19 33			19 43			19 57	20 00	19 49		20 03			20 06	20 12	20 14	20 27	20 30

		SE 1	SE	SE 1		SE	SE	SE	SE	SE	SE	SE 1	SE	SE		SE	SE	SE	SE	SE 1	SE 1	SE	SE	SE	
Orpington 4	d	19 54	19 55	20 09		20 10					20 21	20 24	20 40						20 51	20 53	21 09	21 10			
Petts Wood 4	d		19 58			20 13					20 24		20 43						20 54			21 13			
Hither Green 4	d						20 12				20 38			20 42					21 07				21 12		
Lewisham 4	d						20 18	20 22	20 26	20 38	20 43			20 48		20 53	20 56	21 08	21 13				21 18	21 23	
St Johns	d									20 40								21 10							
New Cross 4 ⊖	d						20 21	20 26		20 42				20 51		20 56		21 12					21 21	21 26	
London Victoria 15 ⊖	a		20 32			20 47							21 17									21 47			
London Bridge 4 ⊖	d	20 11		20 25			20 28	20 34	20 36	20 49	20 52	20 40		20 58		21 04	21 06	21 19	21 22	21 09	21 25		21 28	21 34	
London Blackfriars 3 ⊖	a																								
London Cannon Street 4 ⊖	a																								
London Waterloo (East) 4 ⊖	d	20 16		20 30			20 33	20 39	20 41	20 54	20 57	20 45		21 03		21 09	21 11	21 24	21 27	21 14	21 30		21 33	21 39	
London Charing Cross 4 ⊖	a	20 19		20 33			20 36	20 42	20 44	20 57	21 00	20 48		21 06		21 12	21 14	21 27	21 30	21 18	21 33		21 36	21 42	

		SE	SE	SE	SE 1	SE	SE	SE	SE	SE		SE	SE 1	SE 1	SE	SE	SE	SE	SE	SE		SE 1	SE	SE	SE
Orpington 4	d			21 21	21 23	21 40						21 51	21 53	22 09	22 10					22 21		22 23	22 40		
Petts Wood 4	d			21 24		21 43						21 54			22 13					22 24			22 43		
Hither Green 4	d			21 37			21 42					22 07				22 12				22 37				22 42	
Lewisham 4	d	21 26	21 38	21 43			21 48	21 53	21 56	22 08		22 13				22 18	22 23	22 26	22 38	22 43				22 48	22 53
St Johns	d		21 40							22 10									22 40						
New Cross 4 ⊖	d		21 42				21 51	21 56		22 12						22 21	22 26		22 42					22 51	22 56
London Victoria 15 ⊖	a					22 17									22 47								23 17		
London Bridge 4 ⊖	d	21 36	21 49	21 52	21 39		21 58	22 03	22 05	22 19		22 22	22 09	22 25		22 28	22 32	22 35	22 49	22 51		22 39		22 58	23 02
London Blackfriars 3 ⊖	a																								
London Cannon Street 4 ⊖	a																								
London Waterloo (East) 4 ⊖	d	21 41	21 54	21 57	21 44		22 03	22 07	22 10	22 24		22 27	22 14	22 30		22 33	22 37	22 40	22 54	22 57		22 44		23 03	23 07
London Charing Cross 4 ⊖	a	21 44	21 57	22 00	21 48		22 06	22 10	22 13	22 27		22 30	22 18	22 33		22 36	22 40	22 43	22 57	23 00		22 48		23 06	23 10

		SE	SE	SE	SE 1	SE 1		SE	SE	SE	SE	SE	SE	SE 1
Orpington 4	d			22 51	22 53	23 09		23 10					23 21	23 37
Petts Wood 4	d			22 54				23 13					23 24	
Hither Green 4	d			23 07					23 12				23 37	
Lewisham 4	d	22 56	23 08	23 13					23 18	23 23	23 26	23 38	23 43	
St Johns	d		23 10									23 40		
New Cross 4 ⊖	d		23 12						23 21	23 26		23 42		
London Victoria 15 ⊖	a							23 47						
London Bridge 4 ⊖	d	23 05	23 19	23 22	23 09	23 25			23 28	23 32	23 35	23 49	23 52	23 55
London Blackfriars 3 ⊖	a													
London Cannon Street 4 ⊖	a													
London Waterloo (East) 4 ⊖	d	23 10	23 24	23 27	23 14	23 30			23 33	23 37	23 40	23 54	23 57	23 59
London Charing Cross 4 ⊖	a	23 13	23 27	23 30	23 18	23 33			23 36	23 40	23 43	23 57	00 01	00 03

Table 199R

Saturdays

14 December to 17 May

Orpington, Petts Wood, Hither Green and Lewisham - London (Summary of Services)

Network Diagram - see first Page of Table 195
Network Diagram - see first Page of Table 200

		SE	SE	SE	SE	SE		SE	SE	SE	SE	SE	SE	SE	SE [1]	SE		SE	SE	SE	SE	SE	SE	SE	SE [1]
Orpington [4]	d							05 51	06 10					06 21	06 24	06 25		06 40						06 51	06 54
Petts Wood [4]	d							05 54	06 13					06 24		06 28		06 43						06 54	
Hither Green [4]	d		05 42					06 07		06 12				06 37					06 42					07 07	
Lewisham [4]	d	05 39	05 48	05 50	05 56	06 02		06 13		06 18	06 20	06 26	06 32	06 43					06 48	06 50	06 56	07 02	07 08	07 13	
St Johns	d	05 41				06 04							06 34									07 04			
New Cross [4]	d	05 43	05 51			06 06				06 21			06 36						06 51			07 06			
London Victoria [15]	a								06 47							07 02		07 17					07 28		
London Bridge [4]	d	05 49	05 57	05 59	06 05	06 12		06 21		06 27	06 29	06 35	06 42	06 51	06 39				06 57	06 59	07 05	07 12		07 21	07 09
London Blackfriars [3]	a																								
London Cannon Street [4]	a																								
London Waterloo (East) [4]	d	05 53	06 02	06 04	06 10	06 17		06 26		06 32	06 34	06 40	06 47	06 56	06 44				07 02	07 04	07 10	07 17		07 26	07 14
London Charing Cross [4]	a	05 56	06 05	06 07	06 13	06 20		06 29		06 35	06 37	06 43	06 50	06 59	06 47				07 05	07 07	07 13	07 20		07 29	07 17

		SE		SE [1]	SE	SE	SE	SE	SE	SE [1]	SE	SE		SE	SE	SE	SE	SE [1]	SE	SE	SE	SE			
Orpington [4]	d	06 55		07 09	07 10				07 21	07 24	07 25						07 33	07 39	07 40						
Petts Wood [4]	d	06 58			07 13				07 24		07 28						07 36		07 43						
Hither Green [4]	d					07 12			07 37						07 42		07 49								
Lewisham [4]	d					07 18	07 20	07 26				07 32		07 38		07 50	07 54			07 56	07 59	07 59			
St Johns	d											07 34					07 56					08 01			
New Cross [4]	d					07 21						07 36					07 58					08 03			
London Victoria [15]	a	07 32			07 47						08 02			07 58					08 17						
London Bridge [4]	d			07 24		07 27	07 29	07 35	07 49	07 39		07 42			07 52	07 58	08 04	07 55		08 05	08 08	08 09			
London Blackfriars [3]	a																								
London Cannon Street [4]	a																08 08					08 13			
London Waterloo (East) [4]	d			07 29		07 32	07 34	07 40	07 54	07 44		07 47			07 57	08 03		08 00		08 10	08 13				
London Charing Cross [4]	a			07 33		07 35	07 40	07 43	07 57	07 48		07 50			08 00	08 06		08 03		08 13	08 16				

		SE	SE	SE [1]	SE	SE	SE	SE	SE	SE	SE	SE [1]	SE	SE	SE	SE	SE	SE	SE [1]	SE	SE	SE	SE	SE	SE
Orpington [4]	d		07 51	07 54	07 55						08 03	08 09	08 10					08 21	08 24	08 25					
Petts Wood [4]	d		07 54		07 58						08 06		08 13					08 24		08 28					
Hither Green [4]	d	07 58	08 07				08 12				08 19						08 28	08 37				08 42			
Lewisham [4]	d	08 04				08 08		08 14	08 20		08 24			08 26	08 29		08 34				08 38		08 44	08 50	
St Johns	d	08 06						08 16			08 26				08 31		08 36						08 46		
New Cross [4]	d	08 08						08 18		08 19	08 28				08 33	08 33	08 38						08 48		08 49
London Victoria [15]	a				08 32	08 28							08 47							09 02	08 58				
London Bridge [4]	d	08 15	08 19	08 11			08 22	08 24	08 28	09 31	08 34	08 25		08 35	08 39	09 51	08 45	08 49	08 41			08 52	08 54	08 58	10 01
London Blackfriars [3]	a																								
London Cannon Street [4]	a	08 19						08 28		09 34	08 38				08 43	09 54	08 49						08 58		10 04
London Waterloo (East) [4]	d		08 24	08 15			08 27		08 33			08 30		08 40				08 54	08 45			08 57		09 03	
London Charing Cross [4]	a		08 27	08 19			08 30		08 36			08 33		08 43				08 57	08 49			09 00		09 06	

		SE	SE [1]	SE	SE	SE	SE	and at the same minutes past each hour until		SE	SE	SE [1]	SE	SE	SE	SE	SE	SE	SE	SE [1]	SE	SE	SE	SE	SE
Orpington [4]	d	08 33	08 39	08 40							15 51	15 54	15 55						16 03	16 09	16 10				
Petts Wood [4]	d	08 36		08 43							15 54		15 58						16 06		16 13				
Hither Green [4]	d	08 49								15 58	16 07				16 12				16 19						16 28
Lewisham [4]	d	08 54			08 56	08 59				16 04				16 08		16 14	16 20		16 24			16 26	16 29		16 34
St Johns	d	08 56				09 01				16 06						16 16			16 26				16 31		16 36
New Cross [4]	d	08 58				09 03	09 03			16 08						16 18		16 19	16 28				16 33	16 33	16 38
London Victoria [15]	a			09 17									16 32	16 28							16 47				
London Bridge [4]	d	09 04	08 55		09 05	09 09	10 21			16 15	16 19	16 11			16 22	16 24	16 28	17 31	16 34	16 25		16 35	16 39	17 51	16 45
London Blackfriars [3]	a																								
London Cannon Street [4]	a	09 08				09 13	10 24			16 19						16 28		17 34	16 38				16 43	17 54	16 49
London Waterloo (East) [4]	d		09 00		09 10						16 24	16 15			16 27		16 33			16 30		16 40			
London Charing Cross [4]	a		09 03		09 13						16 27	16 19			16 30		16 36			16 33		16 43			

		SE	SE [1]	SE	SE	SE	SE	SE	SE	SE	SE [1]	SE	SE	SE	SE		SE	SE	SE [1]	SE	SE	SE	SE	SE	SE
Orpington [4]	d	16 21	16 24	16 25						16 33	16 39	16 40						16 51	16 54	16 55					
Petts Wood [4]	d	16 24		16 28						16 36		16 43						16 54		16 58					
Hither Green [4]	d	16 37				16 42				16 49							16 58	17 07				17 12			
Lewisham [4]	d				16 38		16 44	16 50		16 54			16 56	16 59			17 04				17 08		17 14	17 20	
St Johns	d						16 46			16 56				17 01			17 06						17 16		
New Cross [4]	d						16 48		16 49	16 58				17 03	17 03		17 08						17 18		17 19
London Victoria [15]	a			17 02	16 58							17 17								17 32	17 28				
London Bridge [4]	d	16 49	16 41			16 52	16 54	16 58	18 01	17 04	16 55		17 05	17 09	18 21		17 15	17 19	17 11			17 22	17 24	17 28	18 31
London Blackfriars [3]	a																								
London Cannon Street [4]	a						16 58		18 04	17 08				17 13	18 24		17 19						17 28		18 34
London Waterloo (East) [4]	d	16 54	16 45			16 57		17 03			17 00		17 10					17 24	17 15			17 27		17 33	
London Charing Cross [4]	a	16 57	16 49			17 00		17 06			17 03		17 13					17 27	17 19			17 30		17 36	

			SE	SE [1]	SE	SE	SE	SE	SE	SE	SE [1]		SE	SE	SE	SE	SE	SE	SE	SE [1]	SE		SE	SE	SE
Orpington [4]	d		17 03	17 09	17 10					17 21	17 24		17 25						17 33	17 39	17 40				
Petts Wood [4]	d		17 06		17 13					17 24			17 28						17 36		17 43				
Hither Green [4]	d		17 19						17 28	17 37					17 42				17 49						17 58
Lewisham [4]	d		17 24			17 26	17 29		17 34					17 38		17 44	17 50		17 54				17 56	17 59	18 04
St Johns	d		17 26				17 31		17 36							17 46			17 56					18 01	18 06
New Cross [4]	d		17 28				17 33	17 33	17 38							17 48		17 49	17 58					18 03	18 08
London Victoria [15]	a				17 47								18 02	17 58							18 17				
London Bridge [4]	d		17 34	17 25		17 35	17 39	18 51	17 45	17 49	17 41				17 52	17 54	17 58	19 01	18 04	17 55			18 05	18 09	18 15
London Blackfriars [3]	a																								
London Cannon Street [4]	a		17 38				17 43	18 54	17 49							17 58		19 04	18 08					18 13	18 19
London Waterloo (East) [4]	d			17 30		17 40				17 54	17 45				17 57		18 03			18 00			18 10		
London Charing Cross [4]	a			17 33		17 43				17 57	17 49				18 00		18 06			18 03			18 13		

Table 199R

Saturdays

14 December to 17 May

Orpington, Petts Wood, Hither Green and Lewisham - London (Summary of Services)

Network Diagram - see first Page of Table 195
Network Diagram - see first Page of Table 200

		SE	SE 1		SE	SE	SE	SE	SE	SE	SE	SE 1	SE		SE	SE	SE	SE	SE 1	SE	SE	SE	SE		SE
Orpington 4	d	17 51	17 54		17 55						18 03	18 09	18 10					18 21	18 24	18 25					
Petts Wood 4	d	17 54			17 58						18 06		18 13					18 24		18 28					
Hither Green 4	d	18 07					18 12				18 19						18 28	18 37				18 42			
Lewisham 4	d					18 08		18 14	18 20		18 24				18 26	18 29	18 34				18 38		18 44		18 50
St Johns	d							18 16			18 26					18 31	18 36						18 46		
New Cross 4 ⊖	d							18 18		18 19	18 28					18 33	18 38						18 48		
London Victoria 15 ⊖	a				18 32	18 28							18 47							19 02	18 58				
London Bridge 4 ⊖	d	18 19	18 11				18 22	18 24	18 28	19a30	18 34	18 25			18 35	18 39	18 45	18 49	18 41			18 52	18 54		18 58
London Blackfriars 3 ⊖	a																								
London Cannon Street 4 ⊖	a							18 28			18 38					18 43	18 49						18 58		
London Waterloo (East) 4 ⊖	d	18 24	18 15				18 27		18 33			18 30			18 40			18 54	18 45			18 57			19 03
London Charing Cross 4 ⊖	a	18 27	18 19				18 30		18 36			18 33			18 43			18 57	18 49			19 00			19 06

		SE	SE	SE 1	SE	SE	SE	SE	SE		SE	SE 1	SE	SE	SE 1	SE	SE	SE	SE		SE	SE	SE	SE	SE 1 🚲
Orpington 4	d		18 33	18 39	18 40						18 51	18 54	18 55		19 09	19 10							19 21	19 25	19 28
Petts Wood 4	d		18 36		18 43						18 54		18 58			19 13							19 24	19 28	
Hither Green 4	d		18 49					18 58			19 07						19 12						19 37		
Lewisham 4	d		18 54			18 56	18 59	19 04	19 08		19 12			19 14			19 18		19 20		19 26	19 38	19 43		
St Johns	d		18 56				19 01	19 06						19 16								19 40			
New Cross 4 ⊖	d	18 49	18 58				19 03	19 08						19 18				19 19	19 23			19 42			
London Victoria 15 ⊖	a				19 17				19 28				19 32			19 47								20 02	
London Bridge 4 ⊖	d	20a00	19 04	18 55		19 05	19 09	19 15			19 21	19 11		19a24	19 25		19 28	20a30	19 34		19 37	19 49	19 52		19 44
London Blackfriars 3 ⊖	a																								
London Cannon Street 4 ⊖	a		19 08				19 13	19 19																	
London Waterloo (East) 4 ⊖	d			19 00		19 10					19 26	19 15			19 30		19 32		19 39		19 42	19 54	19 57		19 48
London Charing Cross 4 ⊖	a			19 03		19 13					19 29	19 19			19 33		19 35		19 42		19 45	19 58	20 00		19 51

		SE 1	SE	SE	SE		SE	SE	SE	SE	SE 1	SE 1	SE	SE	SE		SE	SE	SE	SE 1	SE 1	SE	SE	SE	SE
Orpington 4	d	19 39	19 40						19 51	19 55	19 58	20 09	20 10						20 21	20 28	20 39	20 40			
Petts Wood 4	d		19 43						19 54	19 58			20 13						20 24			20 43			
Hither Green 4	d			19 42					20 07					20 12					20 37				20 42		
Lewisham 4	d			19 48	19 53		19 56	20 08	20 13					20 18	20 23		20 26	20 38	20 43				20 48	20 53	20 56
St Johns	d							20 10										20 40							
New Cross 4 ⊖	d			19 51	19 56			20 12						20 21	20 26			20 42					20 51	20 56	
London Victoria 15 ⊖	a		20 17							20 32			20 47									21 17			
London Bridge 4 ⊖	d	19 55		19 58	20 04		20 06	20 19	20 22		20 14	20 25		20 28	20 34		20 36	20 49	20 52	20 44	20 55		20 58	21 04	21 06
London Blackfriars 3 ⊖	a																								
London Cannon Street 4 ⊖	a																								
London Waterloo (East) 4 ⊖	d	20 00		20 04	20 09		20 11	20 24	20 27		20 18	20 30		20 34	20 39		20 41	20 54	20 57	20 48	21 00		21 04	21 09	21 11
London Charing Cross 4 ⊖	a	20 03		20 07	20 12		20 14	20 28	20 30		20 21	20 33		20 37	20 42		20 44	20 58	21 00	20 51	21 03		21 07	21 12	21 14

			SE	SE	SE 1	SE 1	SE	SE	SE	SE	SE		SE	SE 1	SE 1	SE	SE	SE	SE	SE	SE		SE 1	SE 1	SE
Orpington 4	d			20 51	20 58	21 09	21 10						21 21	21 28	21 39	21 40					21 51		21 58	22 09	22 10
Petts Wood 4	d			20 54			21 13						21 24			21 43					21 54				22 13
Hither Green 4	d			21 07				21 12					21 37				21 42				22 07				
Lewisham 4	d		21 08	21 13				21 18	21 23	21 26	21 38		21 43				21 48	21 53	21 56	22 08	22 13				
St Johns	d		21 10								21 40									22 10					
New Cross 4 ⊖	d		21 12					21 21	21 26		21 42						21 51	21 56		22 12					
London Victoria 15 ⊖	a						21 47									22 17									22 47
London Bridge 4 ⊖	d		21 19	21 22	21 14	21 25		21 28	21 34	21 36	21 49		21 52	21 44	21 55		21 58	22 02	22 05	22 19	22 22		22 14	22 25	
London Blackfriars 3 ⊖	a																								
London Cannon Street 4 ⊖	a																								
London Waterloo (East) 4 ⊖	d		21 24	21 27	21 18	21 30		21 34	21 39	21 41	21 54		21 57	21 48	22 00		22 04	22 07	22 10	22 24	22 27		22 18	22 30	
London Charing Cross 4 ⊖	a		21 28	21 30	21 21	21 33		21 37	21 42	21 44	21 58		22 00	21 51	22 03		22 07	22 10	22 13	22 28	22 30		22 21	22 33	

		SE	SE	SE	SE	SE	SE 1		SE 1	SE	SE	SE	SE	SE	SE	SE 1	SE 1		SE	SE	SE	SE	SE	SE	SE 1
Orpington 4	d					22 21	22 28		22 39	22 40					22 51	22 58	23 09		23 10					23 21	23 37
Petts Wood 4	d					22 24				22 43					22 54				23 13					23 24	
Hither Green 4	d	22 12				22 37					22 42				23 07					23 12				23 37	
Lewisham 4	d	22 18	22 23	22 26	22 38	22 43					22 48	22 53	22 56	23 08	23 13					23 18	23 23	23 26	23 38	23 43	
St Johns	d				22 40									23 10									23 40		
New Cross 4 ⊖	d	22 21	22 26		22 42						22 51	22 56		23 12						23 21	23 26		23 42		
London Victoria 15 ⊖	a									23 17									23 48						
London Bridge 4 ⊖	d	22 28	22 32	22 35	22 49	22 52	22 44		22 55		22 58	23 02	23 05	23 19	23 22	23 14	23 25			23 28	23 32	23 35	23 49	23 52	23 55
London Blackfriars 3 ⊖	a																								
London Cannon Street 4 ⊖	a																								
London Waterloo (East) 4 ⊖	d	22 34	22 37	22 40	22 54	22 57	22 48		23 00		23 04	23 07	23 10	23 24	23 27	23 18	23 30			23 34	23 37	23 40	23 54	23 57	23 59
London Charing Cross 4 ⊖	a	22 37	22 40	22 43	22 58	23 00	22 51		23 03		23 07	23 10	23 13	23 27	23 30	23 21	23 33			23 37	23 40	23 43	23 57	00 01	00 03

Table 199R

Sundays

8 December to 11 May

Orpington, Petts Wood, Hither Green and Lewisham - London (Summary of Services)

Network Diagram - see first Page of Table 195
Network Diagram - see first Page of Table 200

		SE	SE	SE	SE	SE	SE	SE	SE	SE 1 (trolley)	SE	SE 1	SE	SE	SE	SE	SE	SE 1 (trolley)	SE	SE 1	SE	SE	SE
Orpington 4	d	06 40		06 50	06 55		07 10	07 20	07 25	07 28		07 40				07 40	07 55	07 58		08 10			
Petts Wood 4	d	06 43		06 53	06 58		07 13	07 23	07 28							07 43	07 58						
Hither Green 4	d	06 56				07 12	07 26						07 42			07 56					08 12		
Lewisham 4	d	07 02	07 12			07 18	07 32				07 42		07 48	07 55	07 57	08 02			08 12		08 18	08 25	08 27
St Johns	d														07 59								08 29
New Cross 4	⊖ d		07 15								07 45				08 01				08 15				08 31
London Victoria 15	⊖ a				07 32				08 02								08 32						
London Bridge 4	⊖ d	07 10	07 21			07 28	07 40			07 43	07 51	07 55	07 58	08 04	08 07	08 10		08 13	08 21	08 25	08 28	08 34	08 37
London Blackfriars 3	⊖ a			07 34				08 04															
London Cannon Street 4	⊖ a																						
London Waterloo (East) 4	⊖ d	07 15	07 26			07 34	07 45			07 48	07 56	08 00	08 04	08 09	08 12	08 15		08 18	08 26	08 30	08 34	08 39	08 42
London Charing Cross 4	⊖ a	07 19	07 30			07 37	07 49			07 52	08 00	08 04	08 07	08 13	08 16	08 19		08 22	08 30	08 34	08 37	08 43	08 46

		SE		SE	SE 1 (trolley)	SE	SE 1	SE	SE	SE	SE	SE	SE 1 (trolley)	SE	SE 1	SE	SE	SE	SE		SE	SE 1 (trolley)	SE	SE
Orpington 4	d	08 10	and at the same minutes past each hour until	19 25	19 28		19 40				19 40	19 55	19 58		20 10				20 10		20 25	20 28		
Petts Wood 4	d	08 13		19 28							19 43	19 58							20 13		20 28			
Hither Green 4	d	08 26						19 42			19 56					20 12			20 26					20 42
Lewisham 4	d	08 32				19 42		19 48	19 55	19 57	20 02			20 12		20 18	20 25	20 27	20 32				20 42	20 48
St Johns	d									19 59								20 29						
New Cross 4	⊖ d					19 45				20 01				20 15				20 31					20 45	
London Victoria 15	⊖ a			20 02								20 32									21 02			
London Bridge 4	⊖ d	08 40			19 43	19 51	19 55	19 58	20 04	20 07	20 10		20 13	20 21	20 25	20 28	20 34	20 37	20 40			20 43	20 51	20 58
London Blackfriars 3	⊖ a																							
London Cannon Street 4	⊖ a																							
London Waterloo (East) 4	⊖ d	08 45			19 48	19 56	20 00	20 04	20 09	20 12	20 15		20 18	20 26	20 30	20 34	20 39	20 42	20 45			20 48	20 56	21 04
London Charing Cross 4	⊖ a	08 49			19 52	20 00	20 04	20 07	20 13	20 16	20 19		20 22	20 30	20 34	20 37	20 43	20 46	20 49			20 52	21 00	21 07

		SE	SE	SE	SE	SE 1 (trolley)		SE	SE 1	SE	SE	SE	SE	SE	SE 1 (trolley)	SE		SE	SE	SE	SE	SE	SE 1 (trolley)	SE	SE 1
Orpington 4	d			20 40	20 55	20 58			21 10				21 10	21 25	21 28						21 40	21 55	21 58		22 10
Petts Wood 4	d			20 43	20 58								21 13	21 28							21 43	21 58			
Hither Green 4	d			20 56						21 12			21 26					21 42			21 56				
Lewisham 4	d	20 55	20 57	21 02				21 12		21 18	21 25	21 27	21 32			21 42		21 48	21 55	21 57	22 02			22 12	
St Johns	d		20 59									21 29								21 59					
New Cross 4	⊖ d		21 01					21 15				21 31				21 45				22 01				22 15	
London Victoria 15	⊖ a				21 32									22 02								22 32			
London Bridge 4	⊖ d	21 04	21 07	21 10		21 13		21 21	21 25	21 28	21 34	21 37	21 40		21 43	21 51		21 58	22 04	22 07	22 10		22 13	22 21	22 25
London Blackfriars 3	⊖ a																								
London Cannon Street 4	⊖ a																								
London Waterloo (East) 4	⊖ d	21 09	21 12	21 15		21 18		21 26	21 30	21 34	21 39	21 42	21 45		21 48	21 56		22 04	22 09	22 12	22 15		22 18	22 26	22 30
London Charing Cross 4	⊖ a	21 13	21 16	21 19		21 22		21 30	21 34	21 37	21 43	21 46	21 49		21 52	22 00		22 07	22 13	22 16	22 19		22 22	22 30	22 34

		SE		SE	SE	SE	SE	SE 1 (trolley)	SE	SE	SE	SE		SE	SE	SE 1 (trolley)	SE	SE 1	SE	SE	SE	SE
Orpington 4	d					22 10	22 25	22 28						22 40	22 55	22 58		23 10				23 10
Petts Wood 4	d					22 13	22 28							22 43	22 58							23 13
Hither Green 4	d	22 12				22 26				22 42				22 56					23 12			23 26
Lewisham 4	d	22 18		22 25	22 27	22 32			22 42	22 48	22 55	22 57		23 02			23 12		23 18	23 25	23 27	23 32
St Johns	d				22 29							22 59									23 29	
New Cross 4	⊖ d				22 31				22 45			23 01					23 15				23 31	
London Victoria 15	⊖ a						23 02								23 32							
London Bridge 4	⊖ d	22 28		22 34	22 37	22 40		22 43	22 51	22 58	23 04	23 07		23 10		23 13	23 21	23 25	23 28	23 34	23 37	23 40
London Blackfriars 3	⊖ a																					
London Cannon Street 4	⊖ a																					
London Waterloo (East) 4	⊖ d	22 34		22 39	22 42	22 45		22 48	22 56	23 04	23 09	23 12		23 15		23 18	23 26	23 30	23 34	23 39	23 42	23 45
London Charing Cross 4	⊖ a	22 37		22 43	22 46	22 49		22 52	23 00	23 07	23 13	23 16		23 19		23 22	23 30	23 34	23 37	23 43	23 46	23 49

Network Diagram for Tables 200, 203, 204 | also 199⊙

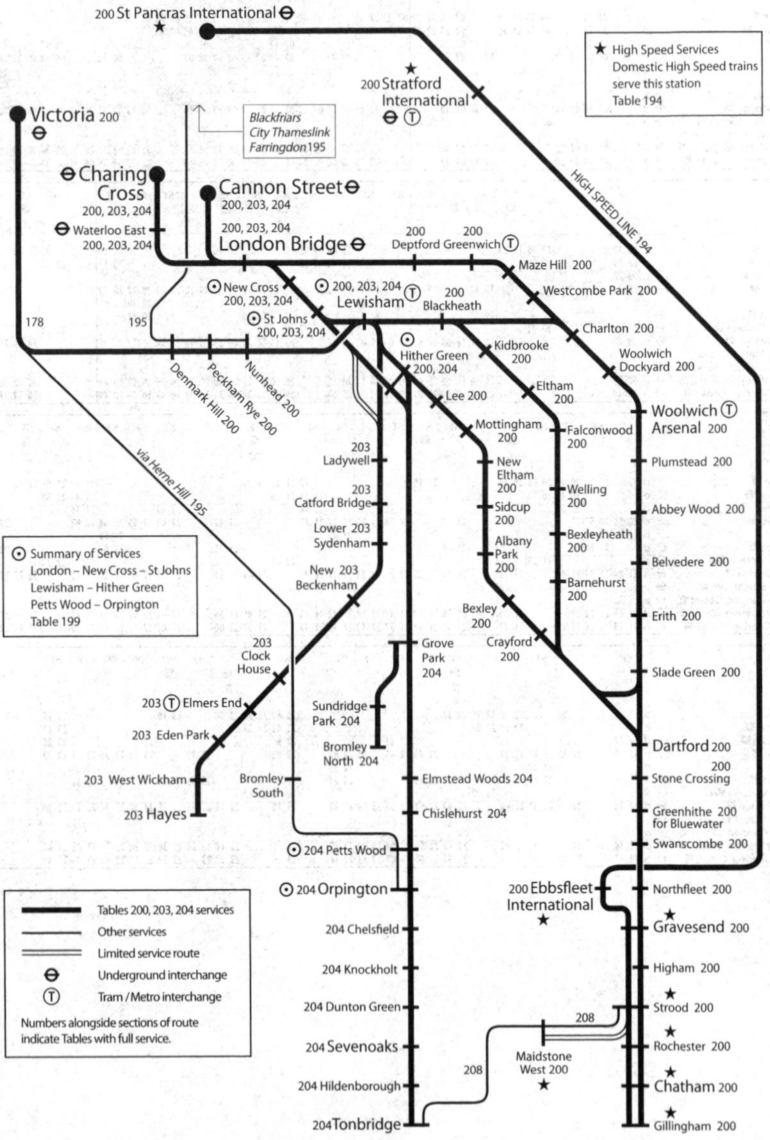

200 St Pancras International
200 Stratford International
High Speed Services
Domestic High Speed trains serve this station
Table 194
HIGH SPEED LINE 194
Victoria 200
Blackfriars
City Thameslink
Farringdon 195
Charing Cross
200, 203, 204
Cannon Street
200, 203, 204
Waterloo East
200, 203, 204
200, 203, 204
London Bridge
200
Deptford
200
Greenwich
Maze Hill 200
Westcombe Park 200
Charlton 200
Woolwich Dockyard 200
Woolwich Arsenal 200
Plumstead 200
Abbey Wood 200
Belvedere 200
Erith 200
Slade Green 200
Dartford 200
200
Stone Crossing
Greenhithe 200 for Bluewater
Swanscombe 200
Northfleet 200
200 Ebbsfleet International
Gravesend 200
Higham 200
Strood 200
Rochester 200
Chatham 200
Gillingham 200
208
Maidstone West 200
New Cross
200, 203, 204
200, 203, 204
Lewisham
200
Blackheath
St Johns
200, 203, 204
178
195
Denmark Hill 200
Peckham Rye 200
Nunhead 200
Hither Green
200, 204
Lee 200
Kidbrooke 200
Eltham 200
Falconwood 200
Welling 200
Bexleyheath 200
Barnehurst 200
Mottingham 200
New Eltham 200
Sidcup 200
Albany Park 200
Bexley 200
Crayford 200
203
Ladywell
203
Catford Bridge
Lower 203
Sydenham
New 203
Beckenham
203
Clock House
203 Elmers End
203 Eden Park
203 West Wickham
203 Hayes
via Herne Hill 195
Summary of Services
London – New Cross – St Johns
Lewisham – Hither Green
Petts Wood – Orpington
Table 199
Grove Park 204
Sundridge Park 204
Bromley North 204
Bromley South
Elmstead Woods 204
Chislehurst 204
204 Petts Wood
204 Orpington
204 Chelsfield
204 Knockholt
204 Dunton Green
204 Sevenoaks
204 Hildenborough
204 Tonbridge
Tables 200, 203, 204 services
Other services
Limited service route
Underground interchange
Tram / Metro interchange
Numbers alongside sections of route indicate Tables with full service.

TOCs operating on this network - Southeastern (SE)

Table 200

Mondays to Fridays

London - Dartford and Gillingham

9 December to 16 May

Network Diagram - see first Page of Table 200

Miles	Miles	Miles	Miles	Miles			SE	SE MX	SE MO	SE MX	SE	SE	SE MX	SE MX	SE MO
—	—	—	—	0	**St Pancras Int'l** 15 ⊖	d									
—	—	—	—	6	**Stratford International** ⊖	d							00 02		
—	—	—	—	22¾	**Ebbsfleet International**	d							00 14		
0	—	0	0	—	**London Charing Cross** 4 ⊖	d									
0¾	—	0¾	0¾	—	**London Waterloo (East)** 4 ⊖	d									
—	0	—	—	—	**London Cannon Street** 4 ⊖	d									
1¾	1¾	1¾	1¾	—	**London Bridge** 4 ⊖	d									
—	3¾	—	—	—	Deptford	d									
—	4¼	—	—	—	Greenwich 4	d									
—	5¼	—	—	—	Maze Hill	d									
—	5¾	—	—	—	Westcombe Park	d									
—	—	—	—	0	**London Victoria** 15 ⊖	d									
—	—	—	—	4¼	Denmark Hill 4	d									
—	—	—	—	5	Peckham Rye 4	d									
—	—	—	—	5¾	Nunhead 4	d									
—	—	4¾	4¾	—	New Cross 4 ⊖	d									00 03
—	—	5½	5½	—	St Johns	d									
6	—	6	6	7½	Lewisham 4	d									00 08
7	—	7	—	8½	Blackheath 4	d									00 10
—	—	8	—	9½	Kidbrooke	d									00 13
—	—	9	—	10½	Eltham	d									00 17
—	—	10¼	—	11¾	Falconwood	d				00 01					00 19
—	—	11¼	—	12¾	Welling	d				00 03					00 22
—	—	12¾	—	14¼	Bexleyheath	d				00 06					00 24
—	—	14	—	15½	Barnehurst 4	d				00 08					00 27
—	—	—	7¼	—	Hither Green 4	d									
—	—	—	8	—	Lee	d									
—	—	—	9½	—	Mottingham	d									
—	—	—	10½	—	New Eltham	d									
—	—	—	12	—	Sidcup 4	d									
—	—	—	13	—	Albany Park	d									
—	—	—	14	—	Bexley	d									
—	—	—	15½	—	Crayford	d	00 03								
9	6½	—	—	—	Charlton 4	d								00 03	
10	7½	—	—	—	Woolwich Dockyard	d									
10¾	8¼	—	—	—	**Woolwich Arsenal** 4	d								00 09	
11¼	8¾	—	—	—	Plumstead	d									
12¾	10¼	—	—	—	Abbey Wood	d		00 01	00 02					00 13	
14¼	11¾	—	—	—	Belvedere	d		00 03	00 05						
15½	13	—	—	—	Erith	d		00 06	00 07						
16¾	14¼	—	—	—	Slade Green 4	d		00 09	00 10						
18¾	16¼	17	17¼	18½	**Dartford** 4	a	00 08	00 14	00 15	00 16				00 24	00 35
—	—	—	—	—		d								00 25	
20¾	—	—	19¼	—	Stone Crossing	d								00 29	
21½	—	—	20	—	Greenhithe for Bluewater	d								00 31	
22¾	—	—	21¼	—	Swanscombe	d						00 04		00 34	
23½	—	—	22	—	Northfleet	d						00 06		00 36	
25½	—	—	24	24¾	**Gravesend** 4	d						00 10	00 18	00 40	
30	—	—	28½	29¼	Higham	d						00 16		00 46	
32¾	—	—	31¼	32	Strood 4	d						00 22	00 28	00 52	
—	—	—	—	—	Maidstone West	d									
33¾	—	—	32¼	33	Rochester 4	d					00 03	00 26	00 33	00 56	
34½	—	—	32¾	33½	**Chatham** 4	d					00 05	00 29	00 35	00 59	
36	—	—	34½	35¼	**Gillingham (Kent)** 4	a					00 09	00 33	00 39	01 03	

		SE MO	SE MX	SE MX	SE MX	SE	SE	SE	SE	SE
St Pancras Int'l 15 ⊖	d									
Stratford International ⊖	d									
Ebbsfleet International	d									
London Charing Cross 4 ⊖	d			00 02	00 10	00 18		04 52	04 56	05 02
London Waterloo (East) 4 ⊖	d			00 05	00 13	00 21		04 55	04 59	05 05
London Cannon Street 4 ⊖	d									
London Bridge 4 ⊖	d		00 04	00 10	00 18	00 26		05 00	05 04	05 10
Deptford	d		00 10						05 10	
Greenwich 4	d		00 12						05 12	
Maze Hill	d		00 15						05 15	
Westcombe Park	d		00 17						05 17	
London Victoria 15 ⊖	d									
Denmark Hill 4	d									
Peckham Rye 4	d									
Nunhead 4	d									
New Cross 4 ⊖	d			00 15	00 23	00 31		05 05		05 15
St Johns	d									
Lewisham 4	d	00 09		00 19	00 27	00 35		05 09		05 19
Blackheath 4	d			00 22		00 38				05 22
Kidbrooke	d			00 25						05 25
Eltham	d			00 28						05 28
Falconwood	d			00 31						05 31
Welling	d			00 33						05 33
Bexleyheath	d			00 36						05 36
Barnehurst 4	d			00 38						05 38
Hither Green 4	d	00 14			00 32			05 14		
Lee	d	00 16			00 34			05 16		
Mottingham	d	00 19			00 37			05 19		
New Eltham	d	00 21			00 39			05 21		
Sidcup 4	d	00 25			00 43			05 25		
Albany Park	d	00 27			00 45			05 27		
Bexley	d	00 29			00 47			05 29		
Crayford	d	00 33			00 51			05 33		
Charlton 4	d		00 20			00 42			05 20	
Woolwich Dockyard	d		00 23						05 23	
Woolwich Arsenal 4	d		00 26			00 47			05 26	
Plumstead	d		00 28			00 49			05 28	
Abbey Wood	d		00 31			00 53			05 31	
Belvedere	d		00 33			00 55			05 33	
Erith	d		00 36			00 58			05 36	
Slade Green 4	d		00 39			01 01			05 40	
Dartford 4	a	00 38	00 44	00 46	00 56	01 06		05 38	05 45	05 47
	d					01 07	05 25	05 39		
Stone Crossing	d							05 43		
Greenhithe for Bluewater	d					01 12	05 30	05 45		
Swanscombe	d							05 48		
Northfleet	d							05 50		
Gravesend 4	d					01 19	05 37	05a55		
Higham	d					01 25	05 43			
Strood 4	d					01 30	05 48			
Maidstone West	d									
Rochester 4	d					01 35	05 53			
Chatham 4	d					01 37	05 55			
Gillingham (Kent) 4	a					01 44	06 00			

		SE	SE	SE	SE	SE	SE	SE	SE	SE	SE	SE	SE	SE	SE
St Pancras Int'l 15 ⊖	d						06 22						06 55		
Stratford International ⊖	d						06 29						07 02		
Ebbsfleet International	d						06 41						07 14		
London Charing Cross 4 ⊖	d		05 20	05 26	05 32	05 39		05 52	05 56	06 02	06 09			06 26	06 32
London Waterloo (East) 4 ⊖	d		05 23	05 29	05 35	05 42		05 55	05 59	06 05	06 12			06 29	06 35
London Cannon Street 4 ⊖	d											06 27			
London Bridge 4 ⊖	d		05 30	05 34	05 42	05 47		06 00	06 04	06 10	06 17	06 31		06 34	06 40
Deptford	d			05 40					06 10			06 37			
Greenwich 4	d			05 42					06 12			06 39			
Maze Hill	d			05 45					06 15			06 42			
Westcombe Park	d			05 47					06 17			06 44			
London Victoria 15 ⊖	d														
Denmark Hill 4	d														
Peckham Rye 4	d														
Nunhead 4	d														
New Cross 4 ⊖	d		05 35		05 48	05 52		06 05		06 15				06 40	06 46
St Johns	d														
Lewisham 4	d		05 39		05 52	05 56		06 09		06 19	06 26			06 44	06 50
Blackheath 4	d				05 54	05 59				06 22	06 29				06 53
Kidbrooke	d				05 57					06 25					06 56
Eltham	d				06 00					06 28					06 59
Falconwood	d				06 03					06 31					07 01
Welling	d				06 05					06 33					07 04
Bexleyheath	d				06 08					06 36					07 06
Barnehurst 4	d				06 10					06 38					07 11
Hither Green 4	d		05 44					06 14						06 48	
Lee	d		05 46					06 16						06 50	
Mottingham	d		05 49					06 19						06 53	
New Eltham	d		05 51					06 21						06 56	
Sidcup 4	d		05 55					06 25						06 59	
Albany Park	d		05 57					06 27						07 01	
Bexley	d		05 59					06 29						07 04	
Crayford	d		06 03					06 33						07 07	
Charlton 4	d			05 50		06 03			06 20		06 33	06 47			
Woolwich Dockyard	d			05 53					06 23			06 50			
Woolwich Arsenal 4	d			05 56		06 09			06 26		06 39	06 53			
Plumstead	d			05 58					06 28			06 55			
Abbey Wood	d			06 01		06 13			06 31		06 43	06 58			
Belvedere	d			06 03					06 33			07 00			
Erith	d			06 06					06 36			07 03			
Slade Green 4	d			06 10		06 19			06 39			07 07			
Dartford 4	a		06 08	06 15	06 17	06 24		06 38	06 45	06 47	06 54	07 12		07 11	07 18
	d	05 55	06 09			06 25		06 39			06 55			07 12	
Stone Crossing	d		06 13					06 43						07 16	
Greenhithe for Bluewater	d	06 00	06 15			06 30		06 45			07 00			07 18	
Swanscombe	d		06 18					06 48						07 21	
Northfleet	d		06 20					06 50						07 23	
Gravesend 4	d	06 07	06a25			06 38	06 46	06a55			07 07		07 21	07a29	
Higham	d	06 13				06 44					07 13				
Strood 4	d	06 18				06 49	06 56				07 18		07 31		
Maidstone West	d						07a12								
Rochester 4	d	06 23				06 53					07 22		07 35		
Chatham 4	d	06 25				06 56					07 25		07 38		
Gillingham (Kent) 4	a	06 30				07 00					07 30		07 42		

Table 200

Mondays to Fridays

9 December to 16 May

London - Dartford and Gillingham

Network Diagram - see first Page of Table 200

		SE	SE	SE	SE	SE	SE	SE	SE	SE	SE	SE	SE	SE
St Pancras Int'l 15 ⊖	d			07 25									07 52	
Stratford International ⊖	d			07 32									08 02	
Ebbsfleet International	d			07 44									08 14	
London Charing Cross 4 ⊖	d	06 39	06 52		06 56	07 02				07 12				07 26
London Waterloo (East) 4 ⊖	d	06 42	06 55		06 59	07 05				07 15				07 29
London Cannon Street 4 ⊖	d							07 10	07 13		07 24	07 27		
London Bridge 4 ⊖	d	06 47	07 00		07 05	07 10		07 14	07 17	07 21	07 28	07 31		07 34
Deptford	d		07 07						07 23					
Greenwich 4	d		07 09						07 25			07 38		
Maze Hill	d		07 12						07 28					
Westcombe Park	d		07 14						07 30					
London Victoria 15 ⊖	d						07 09							
Denmark Hill 4	d													
Peckham Rye 4	d													
Nunhead 4	d													
New Cross 4 ⊖	d							07 20			07 33			
St Johns	d							07 22			07 35			
Lewisham 4	d	06 56				07 18	07 27	07 27		07 30	07 38			
Blackheath 4	d	06 59				07 21	07 29			07 32	07 41			
Kidbrooke	d					07 24					07 44			
Eltham	d					07 27					07 47			
Falconwood	d					07 29					07 50			
Welling	d					07 32					07 52			
Bexleyheath	d					07 34					07 55			
Barnehurst 4	d					07 37	07 40				07 58			
Hither Green 4	d				07 18	08a11		07 31			08a31			07 45
Lee	d				07 20			07 33						07 47
Mottingham	d				07 23			07 36						07 50
New Eltham	d				07 26			07 39						07 53
Sidcup 4	d				07 29			07 42						07 56
Albany Park	d				07 31			07 44						07 58
Bexley	d				07 34			07 47						08 01
Crayford	d				07 37			07 50						08 05
Charlton 4	d	07 03	07 17					08a19	07 33	07 37		07 44		
Woolwich Dockyard	d		07 20						07 36					
Woolwich Arsenal 4	d	07 09	07 23						07 39	07 43		07 49		
Plumstead	d		07 25						07 41					
Abbey Wood	d	07 13	07 28						07 44	07 48		07 53		
Belvedere	d		07 30						07 46					
Erith	d		07 33						07 49					
Slade Green 4	d		07 37						07 52			07a59		
Dartford 4	a	07 23	07 46		07 42		07 48		07 57	07 59				08 11
	d	07 25			07 43					08 00				08 12
Stone Crossing	d				07 47									08 16
Greenhithe for Bluewater	d	07 30			07 49					08 05				08 19
Swanscombe	d				07 52									08 22
Northfleet	d				07 54									08 24
Gravesend 4	d	07 37		07 48	07a58					08 12			08 18	08a28
Higham	d	07 43								08 18				
Strood 4	d	07 48		07 58						08 23			08 28	
Maidstone West	d													
Rochester 4	d	07 53		08 03						08 28			08 33	
Chatham 4	d	07 55		08 05						08 30			08 35	
Gillingham (Kent) 4	a	08 00		08 09						08 37			08 39	

		SE	SE	SE	SE	SE	SE	SE	SE	SE
St Pancras Int'l 15 ⊖	d									08 25
Stratford International ⊖	d									08 32
Ebbsfleet International	d									08 44
London Charing Cross 4 ⊖	d				07 39					
London Waterloo (East) 4 ⊖	d				07 42					
London Cannon Street 4 ⊖	d	07 32	07 36	07 41			07 44	07 54	07 56	
London Bridge 4 ⊖	d	07 37	07 40	07 45	07 47		07 48	07 58	08 01	
Deptford	d	07 43					07 54		08 07	
Greenwich 4	d	07 45					07 59		08 09	
Maze Hill	d	07 48					08 02		08 12	
Westcombe Park	d	07 50					08 04		08 14	
London Victoria 15 ⊖	d					07 43				
Denmark Hill 4	d					07 53				
Peckham Rye 4	d					07 56				
Nunhead 4	d					07 59				
New Cross 4 ⊖	d			07 50				08 04		
St Johns	d							08 06		
Lewisham 4	d		07 49	07 54	07 56	08 08		08 11		
Blackheath 4	d		07 52		07 59	08 10		08 13		
Kidbrooke	d		07 55					08 16		
Eltham	d		07 58					08 20		
Falconwood	d		08 01					08 22		
Welling	d		08 03					08 25		
Bexleyheath	d		08 06					08 27		
Barnehurst 4	d		08 08					08 30		
Hither Green 4	d			07 59						
Lee	d			08 01						
Mottingham	d			08 04						
New Eltham	d			08 07						
Sidcup 4	d			08 13						
Albany Park	d			08 15						
Bexley	d			08 17						
Crayford	d			08 21						
Charlton 4	d	07 53		08a50	08 04		08 07		08 17	
Woolwich Dockyard	d	07 56					08 10		08 20	
Woolwich Arsenal 4	d	07 59			08 09		08 13		08 23	
Plumstead	d	08 01					08 15		08 25	
Abbey Wood	d	08 04			08 13		08 18		08 28	
Belvedere	d	08 06					08 20		08 30	
Erith	d	08 09					08 23		08 33	
Slade Green 4	d	08a12			08 20		08a26	08a37	08 37	
Dartford 4	a		08 15		08 25	08 27			08 42	
	d				08 25					
Stone Crossing	d									
Greenhithe for Bluewater	d				08 30					
Swanscombe	d									
Northfleet	d									
Gravesend 4	d				08 37					08 48
Higham	d				08 43					
Strood 4	d				08 48					08 58
Maidstone West	d									
Rochester 4	d				08 53					09 03
Chatham 4	d				08 55					09 05
Gillingham (Kent) 4	a				09 02					09 09

		SE	SE	SE	SE	SE	SE	SE	SE	SE
St Pancras Int'l 15 ⊖	d								08 52	
Stratford International ⊖	d								08 59	
Ebbsfleet International	d								09 14	
London Charing Cross 4 ⊖	d	07 59		08 03		08 11				08 20
London Waterloo (East) 4 ⊖	d	08 02		08 06		08 14				08 23
London Cannon Street 4 ⊖	d		08 05		08 09			08 16		
London Bridge 4 ⊖	d	08 07	08 09	08 11	08 14	08 19		08 20		08 29
Deptford	d		08 15					08 27		
Greenwich 4	d		08 19					08 29		
Maze Hill	d		08 22					08 32		
Westcombe Park	d		08 24					08 34		
London Victoria 15 ⊖	d						08 09			
Denmark Hill 4	d						08 18			
Peckham Rye 4	d						08 21			
Nunhead 4	d						08 23			
New Cross 4 ⊖	d				08 20					
St Johns	d				08 22					
Lewisham 4	d			08 19	08 25	08 28	08 32			
Blackheath 4	d			08 22		08 30	08 34			
Kidbrooke	d			08 25			08 37			
Eltham	d			08 28			08 41			
Falconwood	d			08 31			08 43			
Welling	d			08 33			08 46			
Bexleyheath	d			08 36			08 48			
Barnehurst 4	d			08 38			08 51			
Hither Green 4	d				08 29					08 44
Lee	d				08 31					08 46
Mottingham	d				08 34					08 49
New Eltham	d	08 21			08 37					08 51
Sidcup 4	d	08 25			08 40					08 55
Albany Park	d	08 27			08 42					08 57
Bexley	d	08 29			08 45					08 59
Crayford	d	08 33			08 48					09 03
Charlton 4	d		08 27		09a13	08 35		08 37		
Woolwich Dockyard	d		08 30					08 40		
Woolwich Arsenal 4	d		08 33			08 40		08 43		
Plumstead	d		08 35					08 45		
Abbey Wood	d		08 38			08 44		08 48		
Belvedere	d		08 40					08 51		
Erith	d		08 43					08 53		
Slade Green 4	d		08a46					08a56		
Dartford 4	a	08 38		08 46		08 54	08 58			09 08
	d	08 39				08 55				09 09
Stone Crossing	d	08 43								09 13
Greenhithe for Bluewater	d	08 45				09 00				09 15
Swanscombe	d	08 48								09 18
Northfleet	d	08 50								09 20
Gravesend 4	d	08a55				09 07			09 18	09a25
Higham	d					09 13				
Strood 4	d					09 18			09 28	
Maidstone West	d									
Rochester 4	d					09 23			09 33	
Chatham 4	d					09 25			09 35	
Gillingham (Kent) 4	a					09 32			09 39	

		SE	SE	SE	SE	SE
St Pancras Int'l 15 ⊖	d					
Stratford International ⊖	d					
Ebbsfleet International	d					
London Charing Cross 4 ⊖	d		08 23	08 31		
London Waterloo (East) 4 ⊖	d		08 26	08 34		
London Cannon Street 4 ⊖	d	08 25			08 36	08 39
London Bridge 4 ⊖	d	08 29	08 31	08 39	08 40	08 43
Deptford	d	08 35			08 47	
Greenwich 4	d	08 39			08 49	
Maze Hill	d	08 42			08 52	
Westcombe Park	d	08 44			08 54	
London Victoria 15 ⊖	d					
Denmark Hill 4	d					
Peckham Rye 4	d					
Nunhead 4	d					
New Cross 4 ⊖	d		08 38			08 49
St Johns	d		08 40			08 51
Lewisham 4	d		08 43	08 49		08 55
Blackheath 4	d		08 46	08 52		
Kidbrooke	d		08 49	08 55		
Eltham	d		08 52	08 58		
Falconwood	d		08 55	09 01		
Welling	d		08 57	09 03		
Bexleyheath	d		09 00	09 06		
Barnehurst 4	d		09 04	09 08		
Hither Green 4	d					09 00
Lee	d					09 02
Mottingham	d					09 05
New Eltham	d					09 08
Sidcup 4	d					09 11
Albany Park	d					09 13
Bexley	d					09 16
Crayford	d					09 19
Charlton 4	d	08 47			08 57	09a45
Woolwich Dockyard	d	08 50			09 00	
Woolwich Arsenal 4	d	08 53			09 03	
Plumstead	d	08 55			09 05	
Abbey Wood	d	08 58			09 08	
Belvedere	d	09 00			09 10	
Erith	d	09 03			09 13	
Slade Green 4	d	09 07	09a12		09a16	
Dartford 4	a	09 12		09 16		
	d					
Stone Crossing	d					
Greenhithe for Bluewater	d					
Swanscombe	d					
Northfleet	d					
Gravesend 4	d					
Higham	d					
Strood 4	d					
Maidstone West	d					
Rochester 4	d					
Chatham 4	d					
Gillingham (Kent) 4	a					

Table 200

London - Dartford and Gillingham

Mondays to Fridays

9 December to 16 May

Network Diagram - see first Page of Table 200

Station		SE	SE	SE	SE	SE	SE	SE	SE	SE	SE	SE	SE	SE	SE	SE	SE	SE	SE
St Pancras Int'l ■15 ⊖	d						09 25										09 55		
Stratford International ⊖ ⛴	d						09 32										10 02		
Ebbsfleet International	d						09 44										10 14		
London Charing Cross ■4 ⊖	d	08 41						08 55	09 02			09 11						09 26	09 32
London Waterloo (East) ■4 ⊖	d	08 44						08 58	09 05			09 14						09 29	09 35
London Cannon Street ■4 ⊖	d			08 44	08 54	08 57				09 07	09 09			09 17	09 24	09 26			
London Bridge ■4 ⊖	d	08 49		08 49	08 58	09 01		09 03	09 10	09 11	09 14	09 19		09 21	09 28	09 31		09 34	09 40
Deptford	d			08 55		09 07				09 17				09 27		09 37			
Greenwich ■4 ⛴	d			08 59		09 09				09 19				09 29		09 39			
Maze Hill	d			09 02		09 12				09 22				09 32		09 42			
Westcombe Park	d			09 04		09 14				09 24				09 34		09 44			
London Victoria ■15 ⊖	d		08 39										09 09						
Denmark Hill ■4	d		08 48										09 18						
Peckham Rye ■4	d		08 51										09 21						
Nunhead ■4	d		08 53										09 23						
New Cross ■4 ⊖	d				09 04						09 19				09 33				
St Johns	d				09 06						09 21				09 35				
Lewisham ■4 ⛴	d	08 58	09 02		09 10				09 19		09 24	09 29	09 32		09 38				09 49
Blackheath ■4	d	09 00	09 04		09 12				09 22			09 31	09 34		09 41				09 52
Kidbrooke	d		09 07		09 15				09 25				09 37		09 44				09 55
Eltham	d		09 11		09 19				09 28				09 41		09 47				09 58
Falconwood	d		09 13		09 21				09 31				09 43		09 50				10 01
Welling	d		09 16		09 24				09 33				09 46		09 52				10 03
Bexleyheath	d		09 18		09 26				09 36				09 48		09 55				10 06
Barnehurst ■4	d		09 21		09 32				09 38				09 51		10 02				10 08
Hither Green ■4	d							09 16			09 29							09 44	
Lee	d							09 18			09 31							09 46	
Mottingham	d							09 21			09 34							09 49	
New Eltham	d							09 23			09 36							09 51	
Sidcup ■4	d							09 27			09 40							09 55	
Albany Park	d							09 29			09 42							09 57	
Bexley	d							09 31			09 44							09 59	
Crayford	d							09 34			09 48							10 03	
Charlton ■4	d	09 05		09 07		09 17				09 27	10a15	09 37		09 40		09 47			
Woolwich Dockyard	d			09 10		09 20				09 30				09 43		09 50			
Woolwich Arsenal ■4 ⛴	d	09 10		09 13		09 23				09 33		09 42		09 46		09 53			
Plumstead	d			09 15		09 25				09 35				09 48		09 55			
Abbey Wood	d	09 14		09 18		09 28				09 38		09 46		09 51		09 58			
Belvedere	d			09 21		09 30				09 40				09 53		10 00			
Erith	d			09 23		09 33				09 43				09 56		10 03			
Slade Green ■4	d			09a26	09a42	09 37				09a46				09a59	10a12	10 07			
Dartford ■4	a	09 24	09 29			09 42		09 39	09 46			09 54	09 58			10 12		10 08	10 15
	d	09 25						09 39				09 55						10 09	
Stone Crossing	d							09 43										10 13	
Greenhithe for Bluewater	d	09 30						09 46				10 00						10 15	
Swanscombe	d							09 49										10 18	
Northfleet	d							09 51										10 20	
Gravesend ■4	d	09 37					09 48	09a55				10 07					10 18	10a25	
Higham	d	09 43										10 13							
Strood ■4	d	09 48					09 58					10 18					10 28		
Maidstone West	d																		
Rochester ■4	d	09 53					10 03					10 23					10 33		
Chatham ■4	d	09 55					10 05					10 25					10 35		
Gillingham (Kent) ■4	a	10 02					10 09					10 32					10 39		

Station		SE	SE	SE	SE	SE	SE	SE	SE	SE	SE	SE	SE	SE	SE	SE	SE	SE	SE
St Pancras Int'l ■15 ⊖	d								10 22										10 52
Stratford International ⊖ ⛴	d								10 32										10 59
Ebbsfleet International	d								10 44										11 14
London Charing Cross ■4 ⊖	d			09 39						09 56	10 02			10 09					
London Waterloo (East) ■4 ⊖	d			09 42						09 59	10 05			10 12					
London Cannon Street ■4 ⊖	d	09 37	09 40			09 47	09 54	09 57				10 07	10 10			10 17	10 24	10 27	
London Bridge ■4 ⊖	d	09 41	09 44	09 47		09 51	09 58	10 01		10 04	10 10	10 11	10 14	10 17		10 21	10 28	10 31	
Deptford	d	09 47				09 57		10 07				10 17				10 27		10 37	
Greenwich ■4 ⛴	d	09 49				09 59		10 09				10 19				10 29		10 39	
Maze Hill	d	09 52				10 02		10 12				10 22				10 32		10 42	
Westcombe Park	d	09 54				10 04		10 14				10 24				10 34		10 44	
London Victoria ■15 ⊖	d				09 39										10 09				
Denmark Hill ■4	d				09 48										10 18				
Peckham Rye ■4	d				09 51										10 21				
Nunhead ■4	d				09 53										10 23				
New Cross ■4 ⊖	d		09 49				10 03						10 19				10 33		
St Johns	d		09 51				10 05						10 21				10 35		
Lewisham ■4 ⛴	d		09 54	09 56	10 02		10 08				10 19		10 24	10 26	10 32		10 38		
Blackheath ■4	d			09 59	10 04		10 11				10 22			10 29	10 34		10 41		
Kidbrooke	d				10 07		10 14				10 25				10 37		10 44		
Eltham	d				10 11		10 17				10 28				10 41		10 47		
Falconwood	d				10 13		10 20				10 31				10 43		10 50		
Welling	d				10 16		10 22				10 33				10 46		10 52		
Bexleyheath	d				10 18		10 25				10 36				10 48		10 55		
Barnehurst ■4	d				10 21		10 32				10 38				10 51		11 02		
Hither Green ■4	d		09 59							10 14			10 29						
Lee	d		10 01							10 16			10 31						
Mottingham	d		10 04							10 19			10 34						
New Eltham	d		10 06							10 21			10 36						
Sidcup ■4	d		10 10							10 25			10 40						
Albany Park	d		10 12							10 27			10 42						
Bexley	d		10 14							10 29			10 44						
Crayford	d		10 18							10 33			10 48						
Charlton ■4	d	09 57	10a45	10 03		10 07		10 17				10 27	11a15	10 33		10 37		10 47	
Woolwich Dockyard	d	10 00				10 10		10 20				10 30				10 40		10 50	
Woolwich Arsenal ■4 ⛴	d	10 03		10 09		10 13		10 23				10 33		10 39		10 43		10 53	
Plumstead	d	10 05				10 15		10 25				10 35				10 45		10 55	
Abbey Wood	d	10 08		10 13		10 18		10 28				10 38		10 43		10 48		10 58	
Belvedere	d	10 10				10 20		10 30				10 40				10 50		11 00	
Erith	d	10 13				10 23		10 33				10 43				10 53		11 03	
Slade Green ■4	d	10a16				10a25	10a42	10 37				10a46				10a55	11a12	11 07	
Dartford ■4	a			10 24	10 28			10 42		10 38	10 45			10 54	10 58			11 12	
	d			10 25						10 39				10 55					
Stone Crossing	d									10 43									
Greenhithe for Bluewater	d			10 30						10 45				11 00					
Swanscombe	d									10 48									
Northfleet	d									10 50									
Gravesend ■4	d			10 37					10 48	10a55				11 07					11 18
Higham	d			10 43										11 13					
Strood ■4	d			10 48					10 58					11 18					11 28
Maidstone West	d																		
Rochester ■4	d			10 53					11 03					11 23					11 33
Chatham ■4	d			10 55					11 05					11 26					11 35
Gillingham (Kent) ■4	a			11 00					11 09					11 30					11 39

Table 200

Mondays to Fridays

9 December to 16 May

London - Dartford and Gillingham

Network Diagram - see first Page of Table 200

		SE	SE	SE	SE	SE	SE	SE	SE	SE	SE	SE	SE	SE	SE	SE	SE	SE	SE	SE	SE	SE	SE	SE	SE	SE	SE	SE	SE	SE	SE	SE	SE	SE	SE	SE	SE
St Pancras Int'l [15] ⊖	d										11 25									11 55										12 22						
Stratford International ⊖	d										11 32									12 02										12 32						
Ebbsfleet International	d										11 44									12 14										12 44						
London Charing Cross [4] ⊖	d	10 26	10 32			10 39						10 56	11 02			11 09						11 26	11 32			11 39						11 56	12 02			12 09	
London Waterloo (East) [4] ⊖	d	10 29	10 35			10 42						10 59	11 05			11 12						11 29	11 35			11 42						11 59	12 05			12 12	
London Cannon Street [4] ⊖	d			10 37	10 40			10 47	10 54	10 57				11 07	11 10			11 17	11 24	11 27				11 37	11 40			11 47	11 54	11 57				12 07	12 10		
London Bridge [4] ⊖	d	10 34	10 40	10 41	10 44	10 47		10 51	10 58	11 01		11 04	11 10	11 11	11 14	11 17		11 21	11 28	11 31		11 34	11 40	11 41	11 44	11 47		11 51	11 58	12 01		12 04	12 10	12 11	12 14	12 17	
Deptford	d			10 47				10 57		11 07				11 17				11 27		11 37				11 47				11 57		12 07				12 17			
Greenwich [4]	d			10 49				10 59		11 09				11 19				11 29		11 39				11 49				11 59		12 09				12 19			
Maze Hill	d			10 52				11 02		11 12				11 22				11 32		11 42				11 52				12 02		12 12				12 22			
Westcombe Park	d			10 54				11 04		11 14				11 24				11 34		11 44				11 54				12 04		12 14				12 24			
London Victoria [15] ⊖	d						10 39										11 09										11 39										12 09
Denmark Hill [4]	d						10 48										11 18										11 48										12 18
Peckham Rye [4]	d						10 51										11 21										11 51										12 21
Nunhead [4]	d						10 53										11 23										11 53										12 23
New Cross [4] ⊖	d				10 49				11 03						11 19				11 33						11 49				12 03						12 19		
St Johns	d				10 51				11 05						11 21				11 35						11 51				12 05						12 21		
Lewisham [4]	d		10 49		10 54	10 56	11 02		11 08		11 19				11 24	11 26	11 32		11 38				11 49		11 54	11 56	12 02		12 08				12 19		12 24	12 26	12 32
Blackheath [4]	d		10 52			10 59	11 04		11 11		11 22					11 29	11 34		11 41				11 52			11 59	12 04		12 11				12 22			12 29	12 34
Kidbrooke	d		10 55				11 07		11 14		11 25						11 37		11 44				11 55				12 07		12 14				12 25				12 37
Eltham	d		10 58				11 11		11 17		11 28						11 41		11 47				11 58				12 11		12 17				12 28				12 41
Falconwood	d		11 01				11 13		11 20		11 31						11 43		11 50				12 01				12 13		12 20				12 31				12 43
Welling	d		11 03				11 16		11 22		11 33						11 46		11 52				12 03				12 16		12 22				12 33				12 46
Bexleyheath	d		11 06				11 18		11 25		11 36						11 48		11 55				12 06				12 18		12 25				12 36				12 48
Barnehurst [4]	d		11 08				11 21		11 32		11 38						11 51		12 02				12 08				12 21		12 32				12 38				12 51
Hither Green [4]	d	10 44			10 59							11 14			11 29							11 44			11 59							12 14			12 29		
Lee	d	10 46			11 01							11 16			11 31							11 46			12 01							12 16			12 31		
Mottingham	d	10 49			11 04							11 19			11 34							11 49			12 04							12 19			12 34		
New Eltham	d	10 51			11 06							11 21			11 36							11 51			12 06							12 21			12 36		
Sidcup [4]	d	10 55			11 10							11 25			11 40							11 55			12 10							12 25			12 40		
Albany Park	d	10 57			11 12							11 27			11 42							11 57			12 12							12 27			12 42		
Bexley	d	10 59			11 14							11 29			11 44							11 59			12 14							12 29			12 44		
Crayford	d	11 03			11 18							11 33			11 48							12 03			12 18							12 33			12 48		
Charlton [4]	d			10 57	11a45	11 03		11 07		11 17				11 27	12a15	11 33		11 37		11 47				11 57	12a45	12 03		12 07		12 17				12 27	13a15	12 33	
Woolwich Dockyard	d			11 00				11 10		11 20				11 30				11 40		11 50				12 00				12 10		12 20				12 30			
Woolwich Arsenal [4]	d			11 03		11 09		11 13		11 23				11 33		11 39		11 43		11 53				12 03		12 09		12 13		12 23				12 33		12 39	
Plumstead	d			11 05				11 15		11 25				11 35				11 45		11 55				12 05				12 15		12 25				12 35			
Abbey Wood	d			11 08		11 13		11 18		11 28				11 38		11 43		11 48		11 58				12 08		12 13		12 18		12 28				12 38		12 43	
Belvedere	d			11 10				11 20		11 30				11 40				11 50		12 00				12 10				12 20		12 30				12 40			
Erith	d			11 13				11 23		11 33				11 43				11 53		12 03				12 13				12 23		12 33				12 43			
Slade Green [4]	d			11a16				11a25	11a42	11 37				11a46				11a55	12a12	12 07				12a16				12a25	12a42	12 37				12a46			
Dartford [4]	a	11 08	11 15			11 24	11 28			11 42		11 38	11 45			11 54	11 58			12 12		12 08	12 15			12 24	12 28			12 42		12 38	12 45			12 54	12 58
	d	11 09				11 25						11 39				11 55						12 09				12 25						12 39				12 55	
Stone Crossing	d	11 13										11 43										12 13										12 43					
Greenhithe for Bluewater	d	11 15				11 30						11 45				12 00						12 15				12 30						12 45				13 00	
Swanscombe	d	11 18										11 48										12 18										12 48					
Northfleet	d	11 20										11 50										12 20										12 50					
Gravesend [4]	d	11a25				11 37					11 48	11a55				12 07					12 18	12a25				12 37					12 48	12a55				13 07	
Higham	d					11 43										12 13										12 43										13 13	
Strood [4]	d					11 48					11 58					12 18					12 28					12 48					12 58					13 18	
Maidstone West	d																																				
Rochester [4]	d					11 53					12 03					12 23					12 33					12 53					13 03					13 23	
Chatham [4]	d					11 55					12 05					12 25					12 35					12 55					13 05					13 25	
Gillingham (Kent) [4]	a					12 00					12 09					12 30					12 39					13 00					13 09					13 30	

Table 200

Mondays to Fridays

London - Dartford and Gillingham

9 December to 16 May

Network Diagram - see first Page of Table 200

Station		SE	SE	SE	SE	SE	SE	SE	SE	SE	SE	SE	SE	SE
St Pancras Int'l ⊖	d				12 52									
Stratford International ⊖	d				12 59									
Ebbsfleet International	d				13 14									
London Charing Cross ⊖	d					12 26	12 32			12 39				
London Waterloo (East) ⊖	d					12 29	12 35			12 42				
London Cannon Street ⊖	d	12 17	12 24	12 27				12 37	12 40			12 47	12 54	12 57
London Bridge ⊖	d	12 21	12 28	12 31		12 34	12 40	12 41	12 44	12 47		12 51	12 58	13 01
Deptford	d	12 27		12 37				12 47				12 57		13 07
Greenwich	d	12 29		12 39				12 49				12 59		13 09
Maze Hill	d	12 32		12 42				12 52				13 02		13 12
Westcombe Park	d	12 34		12 44				12 54				13 04		13 14
London Victoria ⊖	d										12 39			
Denmark Hill	d										12 48			
Peckham Rye	d										12 51			
Nunhead	d										12 53			
New Cross ⊖	d		12 33						12 49				13 03	
St Johns	d		12 35						12 51				13 05	
Lewisham	d		12 38				12 49		12 54	12 56	13 02		13 08	
Blackheath	d		12 41				12 52			12 59	13 04		13 11	
Kidbrooke	d		12 44				12 55				13 07		13 14	
Eltham	d		12 47				12 58				13 11		13 17	
Falconwood	d		12 50				13 01				13 13		13 20	
Welling	d		12 52				13 03				13 16		13 22	
Bexleyheath	d		12 55				13 06				13 18		13 25	
Barnehurst	d		13 02				13 08				13 21		13 32	
Hither Green	d					12 44			12 59					
Lee	d					12 46			13 01					
Mottingham	d					12 49			13 04					
New Eltham	d					12 51			13 06					
Sidcup	d					12 55			13 10					
Albany Park	d					12 57			13 12					
Bexley	d					12 59			13 14					
Crayford	d					13 03			13 18					
Charlton	d	12 37		12 47				12 57	13a45	13 03		13 07		13 17
Woolwich Dockyard	d	12 40		12 50				13 00				13 10		13 20
Woolwich Arsenal	d	12 43		12 53				13 03		13 09		13 13		13 23
Plumstead	d	12 45		12 55				13 05				13 15		13 25
Abbey Wood	d	12 48		12 58				13 08		13 13		13 18		13 28
Belvedere	d	12 50		13 00				13 10				13 20		13 30
Erith	d	12 53		13 03				13 13				13 23		13 33
Slade Green	d	12a55	13a12	13 07				13a16				13a25	13a42	13 37
Dartford	a			13 12		13 08	13 15			13 24	13 28			13 42
	d					13 09				13 25				
Stone Crossing	d					13 13								
Greenhithe for Bluewater	d					13 15				13 30				
Swanscombe	d					13 18								
Northfleet	d					13 20								
Gravesend	d				13 18	13a25				13 37				
Higham	d									13 43				
Strood	d				13 28					13 48				
Maidstone West	d													
Rochester	d				13 33					13 53				
Chatham	d				13 35					13 55				
Gillingham (Kent)	a				13 39					14 00				

Station		SE	SE	SE	SE	SE	SE	SE	SE	SE
St Pancras Int'l ⊖	d	13 25								
Stratford International ⊖	d	13 32								
Ebbsfleet International	d	13 44								
London Charing Cross ⊖	d		12 56	13 02			13 09			
London Waterloo (East) ⊖	d		12 59	13 05			13 12			
London Cannon Street ⊖	d				13 07	13 10			13 17	13 24
London Bridge ⊖	d		13 04	13 10	13 11	13 14	13 17		13 21	13 28
Deptford	d				13 17				13 27	
Greenwich	d				13 19				13 29	
Maze Hill	d				13 22				13 32	
Westcombe Park	d				13 24				13 34	
London Victoria ⊖	d							13 09		
Denmark Hill	d							13 18		
Peckham Rye	d							13 21		
Nunhead	d							13 24		
New Cross ⊖	d					13 19				13 33
St Johns	d					13 21				13 35
Lewisham	d			13 19		13 24	13 26	13 32		13 38
Blackheath	d			13 22			13 29	13 34		13 41
Kidbrooke	d			13 25				13 37		13 44
Eltham	d			13 28				13 41		13 47
Falconwood	d			13 31				13 43		13 50
Welling	d			13 33				13 46		13 52
Bexleyheath	d			13 36				13 48		13 55
Barnehurst	d			13 38				13 51		14 02
Hither Green	d		13 14			13 29				
Lee	d		13 16			13 31				
Mottingham	d		13 19			13 34				
New Eltham	d		13 21			13 36				
Sidcup	d		13 25			13 40				
Albany Park	d		13 27			13 42				
Bexley	d		13 29			13 44				
Crayford	d		13 33			13 48				
Charlton	d				13 27	14a15	13 33		13 37	
Woolwich Dockyard	d				13 30				13 40	
Woolwich Arsenal	d				13 33		13 39		13 43	
Plumstead	d				13 35				13 45	
Abbey Wood	d				13 38		13 43		13 48	
Belvedere	d				13 40				13 50	
Erith	d				13 43				13 53	
Slade Green	d				13a46				13a55	14a12
Dartford	a		13 38	13 45			13 54	13 58		
	d		13 39				13 55			
Stone Crossing	d		13 43							
Greenhithe for Bluewater	d		13 45				14 00			
Swanscombe	d		13 48							
Northfleet	d		13 50							
Gravesend	d	13 48	13a55				14 07			
Higham	d						14 13			
Strood	d	13 58					14 18			
Maidstone West	d									
Rochester	d	14 03					14 23			
Chatham	d	14 05					14 25			
Gillingham (Kent)	a	14 09					14 30			

Station		SE	SE	SE	SE	SE	SE	SE	SE	SE	SE	SE	SE	SE	SE
St Pancras Int'l ⊖	d		13 55										14 25		
Stratford International ⊖	d		14 02										14 32		
Ebbsfleet International	d		14 14										14 44		
London Charing Cross ⊖	d			13 26	13 32			13 39						13 56	14 02
London Waterloo (East) ⊖	d			13 29	13 35			13 42						13 59	14 05
London Cannon Street ⊖	d	13 27				13 37	13 40			13 47	13 54	13 57			
London Bridge ⊖	d	13 31		13 34	13 40	13 41	13 44	13 47		13 51	13 58	14 01		14 04	14 10
Deptford	d	13 37				13 47				13 57		14 07			
Greenwich	d	13 39				13 49				13 59		14 09			
Maze Hill	d	13 42				13 52				14 02		14 12			
Westcombe Park	d	13 44				13 54				14 04		14 14			
London Victoria ⊖	d								13 39						
Denmark Hill	d								13 48						
Peckham Rye	d								13 51						
Nunhead	d								13 53						
New Cross ⊖	d						13 49				14 03				
St Johns	d						13 51				14 05				
Lewisham	d				13 49		13 54	13 56	14 02		14 08				14 19
Blackheath	d				13 52			13 59	14 04		14 11				14 22
Kidbrooke	d				13 55				14 07		14 14				14 25
Eltham	d				13 58				14 11		14 17				14 28
Falconwood	d				14 01				14 13		14 20				14 31
Welling	d				14 03				14 16		14 22				14 33
Bexleyheath	d				14 06				14 18		14 25				14 36
Barnehurst	d				14 08				14 21		14 32				14 38
Hither Green	d			13 44			13 59							14 14	
Lee	d			13 46			14 01							14 16	
Mottingham	d			13 49			14 04							14 19	
New Eltham	d			13 51			14 06							14 21	
Sidcup	d			13 55			14 10							14 25	
Albany Park	d			13 57			14 12							14 27	
Bexley	d			13 59			14 14							14 29	
Crayford	d			14 03			14 18							14 33	
Charlton	d	13 47				13 57	14a45	14 03		14 07		14 17			
Woolwich Dockyard	d	13 50				14 00				14 10		14 20			
Woolwich Arsenal	d	13 53				14 03		14 09		14 13		14 23			
Plumstead	d	13 55				14 05				14 15		14 25			
Abbey Wood	d	13 58				14 08		14 13		14 18		14 28			
Belvedere	d	14 00				14 10				14 20		14 30			
Erith	d	14 03				14 13				14 23		14 33			
Slade Green	d	14 07				14a16				14a25	14a42	14 37			
Dartford	a	14 12		14 08	14 15			14 24	14 28			14 42		14 38	14 45
	d			14 09				14 25						14 39	
Stone Crossing	d			14 13										14 43	
Greenhithe for Bluewater	d			14 15				14 30						14 45	
Swanscombe	d			14 18										14 48	
Northfleet	d			14 20										14 50	
Gravesend	d		14 18	14a25				14 37					14 48	14a55	
Higham	d							14 43							
Strood	d		14 28					14 48					14 58		
Maidstone West	d														
Rochester	d		14 33					14 53					15 03		
Chatham	d		14 35					14 55					15 05		
Gillingham (Kent)	a		14 39					15 00					15 09		

Table 200

Mondays to Fridays

9 December to 16 May

London - Dartford and Gillingham

Network Diagram - see first Page of Table 200

		SE	SE	SE	SE	SE	SE	SE	SE	SE	SE	SE	SE	SE	SE	SE	SE	SE	SE	SE	SE	SE	SE	SE	SE	SE	SE	SE	SE	SE	SE	SE	SE	SE	SE	SE	SE
St Pancras Int'l 15 ⊖	d								14 55										15 25										15 55								
Stratford International ⊖ ⛴	d								15 02										15 32										16 02								
Ebbsfleet International	d								15 14										15 44										16 14								
London Charing Cross 4 ⊖	d			14 09						14 26	14 32			14 39						14 56	15 02			15 09						15 26	15 32			15 39			
London Waterloo (East) 4 ⊖	d			14 12						14 29	14 35			14 42						14 59	15 05			15 12						15 29	15 35			15 42			
London Cannon Street 4 ⊖	d	14 07	14 10			14 17	14 24	14 27				14 37	14 40			14 47	14 54	14 57				15 07	15 10			15 17	15 24	15 27				15 37	15 40			15 47	15 54
London Bridge 4 ⊖	d	14 11	14 14	14 17		14 21	14 28	14 31		14 34	14 40	14 41	14 44	14 47		14 51	14 58	15 01		15 04	15 10	15 11	15 14	15 17		15 21	15 28	15 31		15 34	15 40	15 41	15 44	15 47		15 51	15 58
Deptford	d	14 17				14 27		14 37				14 47				14 57		15 07				15 17				15 27		15 37				15 47				15 57	
Greenwich 4 ⛴	d	14 19				14 29		14 39				14 49				14 59		15 09				15 19				15 29		15 39				15 49				15 59	
Maze Hill	d	14 22				14 32		14 42				14 52				15 02		15 12				15 22				15 32		15 42				15 52				16 02	
Westcombe Park	d	14 24				14 34		14 44				14 54				15 04		15 14				15 24				15 34		15 44				15 54				16 04	
London Victoria 15 ⊖	d				14 09										14 39										15 09										15 39		
Denmark Hill 4	d				14 18										14 48										15 18										15 48		
Peckham Rye 4	d				14 21										14 51										15 21										15 51		
Nunhead 4	d				14 23										14 53										15 23										15 53		
New Cross 4 ⊖	d		14 19				14 33						14 49				15 03						15 19				15 33						15 49				16 03
St Johns	d		14 21				14 35						14 51				15 05						15 21				15 35						15 51				16 05
Lewisham 4 ⛴	d		14 24	14 26	14 32		14 38				14 49		14 54	14 56	15 02		15 08				15 19		15 24	15 26	15 32		15 38				15 49		15 54	15 56	16 02		16 08
Blackheath 4	d			14 29	14 34		14 41				14 52			14 59	15 04		15 11				15 22			15 29	15 34		15 41				15 52			15 59	16 04		16 11
Kidbrooke	d				14 37		14 44				14 55				15 07		15 14				15 25				15 37		15 44				15 55				16 07		16 14
Eltham	d				14 41		14 47				14 58				15 11		15 17				15 28				15 41		15 47				15 58				16 11		16 17
Falconwood	d				14 43		14 50				15 01				15 13		15 20				15 31				15 43		15 50				16 01				16 13		16 20
Welling	d				14 46		14 52				15 03				15 16		15 22				15 33				15 46		15 52				16 03				16 16		16 22
Bexleyheath	d				14 48		14 55				15 06				15 18		15 25				15 36				15 48		15 55				16 06				16 18		16 25
Barnehurst 4	d				14 51		15 02				15 08				15 21		15 32				15 38				15 51		16 02				16 08				16 21		16 32
Hither Green 4	d		14 29							14 44			14 59							15 14			15 29							15 44			15 59				
Lee	d		14 31							14 46			15 01							15 16			15 31							15 46			16 01				
Mottingham	d		14 34							14 49			15 04							15 19			15 34							15 49			16 04				
New Eltham	d		14 36							14 51			15 06							15 21			15 36							15 51			16 06				
Sidcup 4	d		14 40							14 55			15 10							15 25			15 40							15 55			16 10				
Albany Park	d		14 42							14 57			15 12							15 27			15 42							15 57			16 12				
Bexley	d		14 44							14 59			15 14							15 29			15 44							15 59			16 14				
Crayford	d		14 48							15 03			15 18							15 33			15 48							16 03			16 18				
Charlton 4	d	14 27	15a15	14 33		14 37		14 47				14 57	15a45	15 03		15 07		15 17				15 27	16a15	15 33		15 37		15 47				15 57	16a45	16 03		16 07	
Woolwich Dockyard	d	14 30				14 40		14 50				15 00				15 10		15 20				15 30				15 40		15 50				16 00				16 10	
Woolwich Arsenal 4 ⛴	d	14 33		14 39		14 43		14 53				15 03		15 09		15 13		15 23				15 33		15 39		15 43		15 53				16 03		16 09		16 13	
Plumstead	d	14 35				14 45		14 55				15 05				15 15		15 25				15 35				15 45		15 55				16 05				16 15	
Abbey Wood	d	14 38		14 43		14 48		14 58				15 08		15 13		15 18		15 28				15 38		15 43		15 48		15 58				16 08		16 13		16 18	
Belvedere	d	14 40				14 50		15 00				15 10				15 20		15 30				15 40				15 50		16 00				16 10				16 20	
Erith	d	14 43				14 53		15 03				15 13				15 23		15 33				15 43				15 53		16 03				16 13				16 23	
Slade Green 4	d	14a46				14a55	15a12	15 07				15a16				15a25	15a42	15 37				15a46				15a55	16a12	16 07				16a16				16a25	16a42
Dartford 4	a			14 54	14 58			15 12		15 08	15 15			15 24	15 28			15 42		15 38	15 45			15 54	15 58			16 12		16 08	16 15			16 24	16 28		
	d			14 55						15 09				15 25						15 39				15 55						16 09				16 25			
Stone Crossing	d									15 13										15 43										16 13							
Greenhithe for Bluewater	d			15 00						15 15				15 30						15 45				16 00						16 15				16 30			
Swanscombe	d									15 18										15 48										16 18							
Northfleet	d									15 20										15 50										16 20							
Gravesend 4	d			15 07					15 18	15a25				15 37					15 48	15a55				16 07					16 18	16a25				16 37			
Higham	d			15 13										15 43										16 13										16 43			
Strood 4	d			15 18					15 28					15 48					15 58					16 18					16 28					16 48			
Maidstone West	d																																				
Rochester 4	d			15 23					15 33					15 53					16 03					16 23					16 33					16 53			
Chatham 4	d			15 25					15 35					15 55					16 05					16 25					16 35					16 55			
Gillingham (Kent) 4	a			15 30					15 39					16 00					16 09					16 30					16 39					17 00			

Table 200

Mondays to Fridays

9 December to 16 May

London - Dartford and Gillingham

Network Diagram - see first Page of Table 200

	SE	SE	SE	SE	SE	SE	SE	SE	SE	SE	SE	SE	SE	SE	SE	SE	SE	SE	SE	SE	SE	SE	SE	SE	SE	SE	SE	SE	SE	SE	SE	SE	SE	SE	SE	SE
St Pancras Int'l 15 ⊖ d		16 25										16 58													17 16										17 46	
Stratford International ⊖ ⛴ d		16 32										17 05													17 23										17 53	
Ebbsfleet International d		16 44										17 16													17 35										18 05	
London Charing Cross 4 ⊖ d			15 56	16 02			16 09						16 26	16 30						16 45	16 49		16 51			16 55				17 06	17 10		17 12			17 17
London Waterloo (East) 4 ⊖ d			15 59	16 05			16 12						16 29	16 33						16 48	16 52		16 54			16 58				17 09	17 13		17 15			17 20
London Cannon Street 4 ⊖ d	15 57				16 07	16 10			16 17	16 24	16 27				16 35	16 39	16 42	16 44				16 54		16 58			17 04	17 06				17 16		17 21		
London Bridge 4 ⊖ d	16 01		16 04	16 10	16 11	16 14	16 17		16 21	16 28	16 31		16 34	16 38	16 39	16 43	16 46	16 48		16 53	16 57	16 58	16 59	17 02		17 04	17 08	17 10		17 14	17 19	17 20	17 21	17 25		17 26
Deptford d	16 07				16 17				16 27		16 37				16 45					16 59		17 04								17 20		17 26				
Greenwich 4 ⛴ d	16 09				16 20				16 30		16 40				16 48			16 56		17 02		17 07						17 18		17 23		17 29				
Maze Hill d	16 12				16 23				16 33		16 43				16 51					17 05		17 10								17 26		17 32				
Westcombe Park d	16 14				16 25				16 35		16 45				16 53					17 07		17 12								17 28		17 34				
London Victoria 15 ⊖ d								16 09											16 39										17 04							
Denmark Hill 4 d								16 18											16 48										17 13							
Peckham Rye 4 d								16 21											16 51										17 16							
Nunhead 4 d								16 23											16 53										17 18							
New Cross 4 ⊖ d						16 20				16 34						16 49	16 52							17 08			17 14							17 31		
St Johns d						16 22				16 36						16 51								17 10										17 33		
Lewisham 4 ⛴ d				16 19		16 25	16 27	16 32		16 39				16 49		16 54	16 56		17 02				17 08	17 13			17 18		17 25				17 30	17 36		
Blackheath 4 d				16 22			16 29	16 34		16 42				16 53			16 59		17 04				17 10				17 22		17 28				17 34			
Kidbrooke d				16 25				16 37		16 45				16 56			17 02		17 07				17 13				17 25		17 31				17 37			
Eltham d				16 29				16 41		16 48				16 59			17 06		17 11				17 17				17 29		17 34				17 40			
Falconwood d				16 31				16 43		16 51				17 02			17 08		17 13				17 19				17 31		17 37				17 43			
Welling d				16 34				16 46		16 53				17 04			17 11		17 16				17 22				17 34		17 39				17 45			
Bexleyheath d				16 36				16 48		16 56				17 07			17 13		17 18				17 24				17 36		17 42				17 48			
Barnehurst 4 d				16 39				16 51		17 02				17 10			17 17		17 21				17 27				17 41		17 45				17 51			
Hither Green 4 d			16 14			16 29							16 44			16 58	17a57				17 07			17 18							17 29			17 41		
Lee d			16 16			16 31							16 46			17 00					17 09			17 20							17 31			17 43		
Mottingham d			16 19			16 34							16 49			17 03					17 12			17 23							17 34			17 46		
New Eltham d			16 21			16 37							16 51			17 06					17 15			17 26		17 20					17 36			17 48		17 42
Sidcup 4 d			16 25			16 40							16 55			17 09					17a20			17 30		17 26					17a41			17 52		17 47
Albany Park d			16 27			16 42							16 57			17 11								17 32		17 28								17 54		17 49
Bexley d			16 29			16 45							16 59			17 14								17 35		17 30								17 57		17 52
Crayford d			16 33			16 48							17 03			17 17								17 39		17 34								18a00		17 55
Charlton 4 d	16 17				16 27	17a15	16 34		16 37		16 47				16 55	17a45		17 02		17 10		17 15		18a05				17 24		17 30		17 37				
Woolwich Dockyard d	16 20				16 30				16 40		16 50				16 58					17 13		17 18								17 33		17 40				
Woolwich Arsenal 4 ⛴ d	16 23				16 33		16 39		16 43		16 53				17 01			17 07		17 16		17 21						17 29		17 36		17 43				
Plumstead d	16 25				16 35				16 45		16 55				17 03					17 18		17 23								17 38		17 45				
Abbey Wood d	16 28				16 39		16 43		16 48		16 59				17 07			17 11		17 21		17 26						17 33		17 42		17 48				
Belvedere d	16 30				16 41				16 51		17 01				17 09					17 24		17 29								17 44		17 51				
Erith d	16 33				16 44				16 53		17 04				17 12					17 26		17 31								17 47		17 53				
Slade Green 4 d	16 37				16a46				16a56	17a14	17 07				17 15					17a29		17 34					17a52			17a49		17 56				
Dartford 4 a	16 45		16 38	16 48			16 54	17 00			17 14		17 08	17 23	17 22			17 22	17 31			17 43	17 38			17 39		17 44	17 54			18 06	18 00			18 00
d			16 39				16 55						17 09					17 23								17 40		17 46								18 02
Stone Crossing d			16 43										17 13													17 44										18 06
Greenhithe for Bluewater d			16 45				17 00						17 15					17 28								17 46		17 51								18 08
Swanscombe d			16 48										17 18													17 49										18 11
Northfleet d			16 50										17 20													17 51										18 13
Gravesend 4 d		16 48	16a55				17 07					17 21	17a27					17 35							17 40	17a57		18 00							18 10	18 20
Higham d							17 13											17 41										18 06								18 26
Strood 4 d		16 58					17 18					17 31						17 46							17 50			18 12							18 20	18a34
Maidstone West d																									18a05										18a35	
Rochester 4 d		17 03					17 23					17 35						17 54										18 20								
Chatham 4 d		17 05					17 25					17 38						17 57										18 23								
Gillingham (Kent) 4 a		17 09					17 32					17 42						18 05										18 30								

Table 200

Mondays to Fridays

9 December to 16 May

London - Dartford and Gillingham

Network Diagram - see first Page of Table 200

Station		SE	SE	SE	SE	SE	SE	SE	SE	SE	SE	SE	SE	SE
St Pancras Int'l 15 ⊖	d												18 16	
Stratford International ⊖ ⛴	d												18 23	
Ebbsfleet International	d												18 35	
London Charing Cross 4 ⊖	d			17 29	17 30	17 32		17 34			17 39			
London Waterloo (East) 4 ⊖	d			17 32	17 33	17 35		17 37			17 42			
London Cannon Street 4 ⊖	d	17 26	17 28				17 39			17 43		17 47		17 50
London Bridge 4 ⊖	d	17 30	17 32	17 37		17 41	17 43	17 43		17 47	17 48	17 51		17 54
Deptford	d			17 43			17 49							
Greenwich 4 ⛴	d		17 40	17 46			17 52							18 02
Maze Hill	d			17 49			17 55							
Westcombe Park	d			17 51			17 57							
London Victoria 15 ⊖	d								17 34					
Denmark Hill 4	d								17 43					
Peckham Rye 4	d								17 46					
Nunhead 4	d								17 49					
New Cross 4 ⊖	d	17 36								17 53		17 58		
St Johns	d									17 55				
Lewisham 4 ⛴	d	17 40						17 53	17 56	17 59		18 02		
Blackheath 4	d	17 43			17 49			17 56	18 00			18 05		
Kidbrooke	d	17 46			17 52			17 59	18 03			18 08		
Eltham	d	17 50			17 56			18 02	18 06			18 12		
Falconwood	d	17 52			17 58			18 05	18 09			18 14		
Welling	d	17 55			18 01			18 07	18 11			18 17		
Bexleyheath	d	17 58			18 04			18 10	18 14			18 20		
Barnehurst 4	d	18 02			18 07			18 12	18 16			18 23		
Hither Green 4	d					17 51				18 03		18a57		
Lee	d					17 53				18 05				
Mottingham	d					17 56				18 08				
New Eltham	d					17 59				18 11	18 04			
Sidcup 4	d					18a04				18 15	18 08			
Albany Park	d									18 17	18 10			
Bexley	d									18 20	18 13			
Crayford	d									18a23	18 16			
Charlton 4	d		17 46	17 53			18 00							18 08
Woolwich Dockyard	d			17 56			18 03							
Woolwich Arsenal 4 ⛴	d		17 51	17 59			18 06							18 13
Plumstead	d			18 01			18 08							
Abbey Wood	d		17 55	18 05			18 11							18 17
Belvedere	d			18 07			18 14							
Erith	d			18 10			18 16							
Slade Green 4	d	18a12		18a14			18 19	18a22						
Dartford 4	a		18 05		18 16		18 27		18 25		18 21			18 29
	d		18 08								18 22			18 31
Stone Crossing	d		18 12											18 35
Greenhithe for Bluewater	d		18 14								18 27			18 37
Swanscombe	d		18 17											18 40
Northfleet	d		18 19											18 42
Gravesend 4	d		18a27								18 34		18 40	18a53
Higham	d										18 40			
Strood 4	d										18 45		18 50	
Maidstone West	d												19a05	
Rochester 4	d										18 51			
Chatham 4	d										18 54			
Gillingham (Kent) 4	a										19 02			

Station		SE	SE	SE	SE	SE	SE	SE	SE	SE
St Pancras Int'l 15 ⊖	d									
Stratford International ⊖ ⛴	d									
Ebbsfleet International	d									
London Charing Cross 4 ⊖	d	17 50	17 52	17 54	17 56				18 01	
London Waterloo (East) 4 ⊖	d	17 53	17 55	17 57	17 59				18 04	
London Cannon Street 4 ⊖	d					18 00		18 04		18 10
London Bridge 4 ⊖	d	17 58		18 02	18 04	18 04		18 08	18 10	18 14
Deptford	d	18 04				18 10				
Greenwich 4 ⛴	d	18 07				18 13				
Maze Hill	d	18 10				18 16				
Westcombe Park	d	18 12				18 18				
London Victoria 15 ⊖	d						17 56			
Denmark Hill 4	d						18 06			
Peckham Rye 4	d						18 09			
Nunhead 4	d						18 11			
New Cross 4 ⊖	d							18 14		18 20
St Johns	d							18 16		
Lewisham 4 ⛴	d				18 14		18 18	18 20		18 24
Blackheath 4	d		18 09		18 17		18 23			18 27
Kidbrooke	d		18 12		18 20		18 26			18 30
Eltham	d		18 16		18 23		18 30			18 34
Falconwood	d		18 18		18 26		18 32			18 36
Welling	d		18 21		18 28		18 35			18 39
Bexleyheath	d		18 24		18 31		18 38			18 42
Barnehurst 4	d		18 27		18a36		18 41			18a47
Hither Green 4	d			18 13				18 25		
Lee	d			18 16				18 27		
Mottingham	d			18 19				18 30		
New Eltham	d			18 22				18 32	18 26	
Sidcup 4	d			18 26				18 36	18 30	
Albany Park	d							18 38	18 32	
Bexley	d							18 40	18 35	
Crayford	d			18a33				18 44	18 39	
Charlton 4	d	18 15				18 21		19a10		
Woolwich Dockyard	d	18 18				18 24				
Woolwich Arsenal 4 ⛴	d	18 21				18 27				
Plumstead	d	18 23				18 29				
Abbey Wood	d	18 26				18 32				
Belvedere	d	18 29				18 35				
Erith	d	18 31				18 37				
Slade Green 4	d	18a36				18 41				
Dartford 4	a		18 36			18 48	18 53		18 44	
	d								18 45	
Stone Crossing	d								18 49	
Greenhithe for Bluewater	d								18 51	
Swanscombe	d								18 54	
Northfleet	d								18 56	
Gravesend 4	d								19 02	
Higham	d								19 08	
Strood 4	d								19 14	
Maidstone West	d									
Rochester 4	d								19 19	
Chatham 4	d								19 22	
Gillingham (Kent) 4	a								19 29	

Station		SE	SE	SE	SE	SE	SE	SE	SE	SE	SE	SE	SE	SE	SE
St Pancras Int'l 15 ⊖	d							18 55							
Stratford International ⊖ ⛴	d							19 02							
Ebbsfleet International	d							19 14							
London Charing Cross 4 ⊖	d		18 12	18 14		18 18			18 23				18 34	18 37	18 39
London Waterloo (East) 4 ⊖	d		18 15	18 17		18 21			18 26				18 37	18 40	18 42
London Cannon Street 4 ⊖	d	18 12			18 21		18 25			18 30		18 34			
London Bridge 4 ⊖	d	18 16	18 21	18 23	18 25	18 26	18 29		18 32	18 34		18 38	18 42	18 46	18 48
Deptford	d		18 27		18 31								18 48		
Greenwich 4 ⛴	d	18 24	18 29		18 34					18 42			18 51		
Maze Hill	d		18 32		18 37								18 54		
Westcombe Park	d		18 34		18 39								18 56		
London Victoria 15 ⊖	d										18 18				
Denmark Hill 4	d										18 28				
Peckham Rye 4	d										18 32				
Nunhead 4	d										18 34				
New Cross 4 ⊖	d						18 35					18 44			18 55
St Johns	d						18 37					18 46			
Lewisham 4 ⛴	d					18 36	18 41				18 43	18 49			18 59
Blackheath 4	d					18 39					18 46	18 52			19 02
Kidbrooke	d					18 42					18 49	18 55			19 05
Eltham	d					18 46					18 53	18 59			19 09
Falconwood	d					18 48					18 55	19 01			19 11
Welling	d					18 51					18 58	19 04			19 14
Bexleyheath	d					18 54					19 01	19 07			19 16
Barnehurst 4	d					18 57					19 04	19a12			19a21
Hither Green 4	d			18 35			18 46							18 56	
Lee	d			18 37			18 48							18 58	
Mottingham	d			18 40			18 51							19 01	
New Eltham	d			18 43			18 54		18 48					19 04	
Sidcup 4	d			18 47			18 58		18 51					19 08	
Albany Park	d			18 49			19 00		18 53					19 10	
Bexley	d			18 51			19 03		18 56					19 13	
Crayford	d			18a54			19 10		18 59					19 16	
Charlton 4	d	18 30	18 37		18 41		19a40			18 48			18 59		
Woolwich Dockyard	d		18 40		18 44								19 02		
Woolwich Arsenal 4 ⛴	d	18 35	18 43		18 47					18 53			19 05		
Plumstead	d		18 45		18 49								19 07		
Abbey Wood	d	18 40	18 48		18 53					18 57			19 10		
Belvedere	d		18 50		18 55								19 13		
Erith	d		18 53		18 58								19 15		
Slade Green 4	d		18a55		19 01								19 18		
Dartford 4	a	18 52			19 09	19 06			19 04	19 09	19 13		19 28	19 21	
	d	18 53							19 05	19 10				19 22	
Stone Crossing	d								19 09	19 14				19 26	
Greenhithe for Bluewater	d	18 58							19 11	19 16				19 29	
Swanscombe	d								19 14	19 19				19 32	
Northfleet	d								19 16	19 21				19 34	
Gravesend 4	d	19a07						19 19	19a24	19 26				19 38	
Higham	d									19 32				19 44	
Strood 4	d							19 29		19 38				19a53	
Maidstone West	d														
Rochester 4	d							19 34		19 45					
Chatham 4	d							19 37		19 48					
Gillingham (Kent) 4	a							19 41		19 55					

Table 200

Mondays to Fridays

London - Dartford and Gillingham

9 December to 16 May

Network Diagram - see first Page of Table 200

Station		SE	SE	SE	SE	SE	SE	SE	SE	SE	SE	SE	SE	SE
St Pancras Int'l 15 ⊖	d							19 28						
Stratford International ⊖ ⛴	d							19 35						
Ebbsfleet International	d							19 46						
London Charing Cross 4 ⊖	d				18 48				18 56	19 02			19 09	
London Waterloo (East) 4 ⊖	d				18 51				18 59	19 05			19 12	
London Cannon Street 4 ⊖	d		18 46	18 50		18 54	18 57				19 07	19 10		
London Bridge 4 ⊖	d		18 50	18 54	18 57	18 58	19 01		19 04	19 10	19 11	19 14	19 17	
Deptford	d		18 56				19 07				19 17			
Greenwich 4 ⛴	d		18 59				19 10				19 19			
Maze Hill	d		19 02				19 13				19 22			
Westcombe Park	d		19 04				19 15				19 24			
London Victoria 15 ⊖	d	18 39												19 09
Denmark Hill 4	d	18 48												19 18
Peckham Rye 4	d	18 51												19 21
Nunhead 4	d	18 54												19 23
New Cross 4 ⊖	d			19 00		19 05						19 19		
St Johns	d			19 02		19 07						19 21		
Lewisham 4 ⛴	d	19 03		19 05	19 07	19 11				19 19		19 24	19 26	19 32
Blackheath 4	d	19 06			19 10	19 14				19 22			19 29	19 34
Kidbrooke	d	19 09				19 17				19 25				19 37
Eltham	d	19 13				19 21				19 29				19 41
Falconwood	d	19 16				19 23				19 31				19 43
Welling	d	19 18				19 26				19 34				19 46
Bexleyheath	d	19 21				19 29				19 36				19 48
Barnehurst 4	d	19 25				19a34				19 39				19 51
Hither Green 4	d			19 09					19 14			19 29		
Lee	d			19 11					19 16			19 31		
Mottingham	d			19 14					19 19			19 34		
New Eltham	d			19 17					19 22			19 36		
Sidcup 4	d			19 20					19 25			19 40		
Albany Park	d			19 22					19 27			19 42		
Bexley	d			19 25					19 30			19 44		
Crayford	d			19 29					19 33			19 48		
Charlton 4	d		19 06	20a10	19 15		19 18				19 27		19 33	
Woolwich Dockyard	d		19 09				19 21				19 30			
Woolwich Arsenal 4 ⛴	d		19 12		19 20		19 24				19 33		19 39	
Plumstead	d		19 14				19 26				19 35			
Abbey Wood	d		19 17		19 24		19 29				19 38		19 43	
Belvedere	d		19 19				19 32				19 40			
Erith	d		19 22				19 34				19 43			
Slade Green 4	d		19a26				19 37				19a45			
Dartford 4	a	19 34			19 34		19 44		19 38	19 48		19 54	19 55	19 58
	d				19 35				19 39				19 55	
Stone Crossing	d								19 43					
Greenhithe for Bluewater	d				19 40				19 45				20 00	
Swanscombe	d								19 48					
Northfleet	d								19 50					
Gravesend 4	d				19 47			19 51	19a57				20 07	
Higham	d				19 53								20 13	
Strood 4	d				19 58			20 02					20 18	
Maidstone West	d													
Rochester 4	d				20 03			20 07					20 23	
Chatham 4	d				20 05			20 09					20 25	
Gillingham (Kent) 4	a				20 13			20 14					20 30	

Station		SE	SE	SE	SE	SE	SE	SE	SE	SE
St Pancras Int'l 15 ⊖	d				19 55					
Stratford International ⊖ ⛴	d				20 02					
Ebbsfleet International	d				20 14					
London Charing Cross 4 ⊖	d					19 26	19 32			19 39
London Waterloo (East) 4 ⊖	d					19 29	19 35			19 42
London Cannon Street 4 ⊖	d	19 17	19 24	19 27				19 37	19 40	
London Bridge 4 ⊖	d	19 21	19 28	19 31		19 34	19 40	19 41	19 44	19 47
Deptford	d	19 27		19 37				19 47		
Greenwich 4 ⛴	d	19 29		19 39				19 49		
Maze Hill	d	19 32		19 42				19 52		
Westcombe Park	d	19 34		19 44				19 54		
London Victoria 15 ⊖	d									
Denmark Hill 4	d									
Peckham Rye 4	d									
Nunhead 4	d									
New Cross 4 ⊖	d		19 33						19 49	
St Johns	d		19 35						19 51	
Lewisham 4 ⛴	d		19 38				19 49		19 55	19 56
Blackheath 4	d		19 41				19 52			19 59
Kidbrooke	d		19 44				19 55			
Eltham	d		19 47				19 58			
Falconwood	d		19 50				20 01			
Welling	d		19 52				20 03			
Bexleyheath	d		19 55				20 06			
Barnehurst 4	d		19a58				20 08			
Hither Green 4	d					19 44			20 00	
Lee	d					19 46			20 02	
Mottingham	d					19 49			20 05	
New Eltham	d					19 51			20 07	
Sidcup 4	d					19 55			20 11	
Albany Park	d					19 57			20 13	
Bexley	d					19 59			20 15	
Crayford	d					20 03			20 18	
Charlton 4	d	19 37		19 47				19 57		20 03
Woolwich Dockyard	d	19 40		19 50				20 00		
Woolwich Arsenal 4 ⛴	d	19 43		19 53				20 03		20 09
Plumstead	d	19 45		19 55				20 05		
Abbey Wood	d	19 48		19 58				20 08		20 13
Belvedere	d	19 50		20 00				20 10		
Erith	d	19 53		20 03				20 13		
Slade Green 4	d	19a55		20 07				20a15		
Dartford 4	a			20 13		20 08	20 15		20 23	20 25
	d					20 09				20 25
Stone Crossing	d					20 13				
Greenhithe for Bluewater	d					20 15				20 30
Swanscombe	d					20 18				
Northfleet	d					20 20				
Gravesend 4	d				20 18	20a25				20 37
Higham	d									20 43
Strood 4	d				20 28					20 48
Maidstone West	d									
Rochester 4	d				20 33					20 53
Chatham 4	d				20 35					20 55
Gillingham (Kent) 4	a				20 39					21 00

Station		SE	SE	SE	SE	SE	SE	SE	SE	SE	SE	SE	SE	SE	SE
St Pancras Int'l 15 ⊖	d					20 25							20 55		
Stratford International ⊖ ⛴	d					20 32							21 02		
Ebbsfleet International	d					20 44							21 14		
London Charing Cross 4 ⊖	d						19 56	20 02		20 09				20 22	
London Waterloo (East) 4 ⊖	d						19 59	20 05		20 12				20 25	
London Cannon Street 4 ⊖	d		19 47	19 54	19 57				20 10			20 17			20 27
London Bridge 4 ⊖	d		19 51	19 58	20 01		20 04	20 10	20 14	20 17		20 21		20 30	20 31
Deptford	d		19 57		20 07							20 27			20 37
Greenwich 4 ⛴	d		19 59		20 09							20 29			20 39
Maze Hill	d		20 02		20 12							20 32			20 42
Westcombe Park	d		20 04		20 14							20 34			20 44
London Victoria 15 ⊖	d	19 39									20 09				
Denmark Hill 4	d	19 48									20 18				
Peckham Rye 4	d	19 51									20 21				
Nunhead 4	d	19 53									20 23				
New Cross 4 ⊖	d			20 03					20 19					20 35	
St Johns	d			20 05					20 21						
Lewisham 4 ⛴	d	20 02		20 08				20 19	20 25	20 26	20 32			20 39	
Blackheath 4	d	20 04		20 11				20 22		20 29	20 34				
Kidbrooke	d	20 07		20 14				20 25			20 37				
Eltham	d	20 11		20 17				20 28			20 41				
Falconwood	d	20 13		20 20				20 31			20 43				
Welling	d	20 16		20 22				20 33			20 46				
Bexleyheath	d	20 18		20 25				20 36			20 48				
Barnehurst 4	d	20 21		20a28				20 38			20 51				
Hither Green 4	d						20 14		20 30					20 44	
Lee	d						20 16		20 32					20 46	
Mottingham	d						20 19		20 35					20 49	
New Eltham	d						20 21		20 37					20 51	
Sidcup 4	d						20 25		20 41					20 55	
Albany Park	d						20 27		20 43					20 57	
Bexley	d						20 29		20 45					20 59	
Crayford	d						20 33		20 48					21 03	
Charlton 4	d		20 07		20 17					20 33		20 37			20 47
Woolwich Dockyard	d		20 10		20 20							20 40			20 50
Woolwich Arsenal 4 ⛴	d		20 13		20 23					20 39		20 43			20 53
Plumstead	d		20 15		20 25							20 45			20 55
Abbey Wood	d		20 18		20 28					20 43		20 48			20 58
Belvedere	d		20 20		20 30							20 50			21 00
Erith	d		20 23		20 33							20 53			21 03
Slade Green 4	d		20a25		20 37							20a56			21 07
Dartford 4	a	20 28			20 43		20 38	20 45	20 53	20 54	20 58			21 08	21 12
	d						20 39			20 55				21 09	
Stone Crossing	d						20 43							21 13	
Greenhithe for Bluewater	d						20 45			21 00				21 15	
Swanscombe	d						20 48							21 18	
Northfleet	d						20 50							21 20	
Gravesend 4	d					20 48	20a55			21 07			21 18	21a25	
Higham	d									21 13					
Strood 4	d					20 58				21 18			21 28		
Maidstone West	d														
Rochester 4	d					21 03				21 23			21 33		
Chatham 4	d					21 05				21 25			21 35		
Gillingham (Kent) 4	a					21 09				21 30			21 39		

Table 200

Mondays to Fridays

9 December to 16 May

London - Dartford and Gillingham

Network Diagram - see first Page of Table 200

Station		SE	SE	SE	SE	SE	SE	SE	SE	SE	SE	SE	SE	SE
St Pancras Int'l 15 ⊖	d				21 25						21 55			
Stratford International ⊖ ⛴	d				21 32						22 02			
Ebbsfleet International	d				21 44						22 14			
London Charing Cross 4 ⊖	d	20 32	20 39			20 52		21 02	21 09			21 22	21 26	21 32
London Waterloo (East) 4 ⊖	d	20 35	20 42			20 55		21 05	21 12			21 25	21 29	21 35
London Cannon Street 4 ⊖	d			20 47			20 57							
London Bridge 4 ⊖	d	20 40	20 47	20 51		21 00	21 01	21 10	21 17	21 20		21 30	21 34	21 40
Deptford	d			20 57			21 07			21 26			21 40	
Greenwich 4 ⛴	d			20 59			21 09			21 28			21 42	
Maze Hill	d			21 02			21 12			21 31			21 45	
Westcombe Park	d			21 04			21 14			21 33			21 47	
London Victoria 15 ⊖	d													
Denmark Hill 4	d													
Peckham Rye 4	d													
Nunhead 4	d													
New Cross 4 ⊖	d	20 45				21 05		21 15				21 35		21 45
St Johns	d													
Lewisham 4 ⛴	d	20 49	20 56			21 09		21 19	21 26			21 39		21 49
Blackheath 4	d	20 52	20 59					21 22	21 29					21 52
Kidbrooke	d	20 55						21 25						21 55
Eltham	d	20 58						21 28						21 58
Falconwood	d	21 01						21 31						22 01
Welling	d	21 03						21 33						22 03
Bexleyheath	d	21 06						21 36						22 06
Barnehurst 4	d	21 08						21 38						22 08
Hither Green 4	d					21 14						21 44		
Lee	d					21 16						21 46		
Mottingham	d					21 19						21 49		
New Eltham	d					21 21						21 51		
Sidcup 4	d					21 25						21 55		
Albany Park	d					21 27						21 57		
Bexley	d					21 29						21 59		
Crayford	d					21 33						22 03		
Charlton 4	d		21 03	21 07			21 17		21 33	21 36			21 50	
Woolwich Dockyard	d			21 10			21 20			21 39			21 53	
Woolwich Arsenal 4 ⛴	d		21 09	21 13			21 23		21 39	21 42			21 56	
Plumstead	d			21 15			21 25			21 44			21 58	
Abbey Wood	d		21 13	21 18			21 28		21 43	21 47			22 01	
Belvedere	d			21 20			21 30			21 50			22 03	
Erith	d			21 23			21 33			21 52			22 06	
Slade Green 4	d			21 27			21 37			21 56			22 09	
Dartford 4	a	21 15	21 24	21 32		21 38	21 42	21 45	21 54	22 00		22 08	22 14	22 16
	d		21 25			21 39			21 55			22 09		
Stone Crossing	d					21 43						22 13		
Greenhithe for Bluewater	d		21 30			21 45			22 00			22 15		
Swanscombe	d					21 48						22 18		
Northfleet	d					21 50						22 20		
Gravesend 4	d		21 37		21 48	21a55			22 07		22 18	22a25		
Higham	d		21 43						22 13					
Strood 4	d		21 48		21 58				22 18		22 28			
Maidstone West	d													
Rochester 4	d		21 53		22 03				22 23		22 33			
Chatham 4	d		21 55		22 05				22 25		22 35			
Gillingham (Kent) 4	a		22 00		22 09				22 30		22 39			

Station		SE	SE	SE	SE	SE	SE	SE	SE	SE
St Pancras Int'l 15 ⊖	d			22 25						22 55
Stratford International ⊖ ⛴	d			22 32						23 02
Ebbsfleet International	d			22 44						23 14
London Charing Cross 4 ⊖	d	21 39			21 52	21 56	22 02	22 09		
London Waterloo (East) 4 ⊖	d	21 42			21 55	21 59	22 05	22 12		
London Cannon Street 4 ⊖	d									
London Bridge 4 ⊖	d	21 47	21 50		22 00	22 04	22 10	22 17	22 20	
Deptford	d		21 56			22 10			22 26	
Greenwich 4 ⛴	d		21 58			22 12			22 28	
Maze Hill	d		22 01			22 15			22 31	
Westcombe Park	d		22 03			22 17			22 33	
London Victoria 15 ⊖	d									
Denmark Hill 4	d									
Peckham Rye 4	d									
Nunhead 4	d									
New Cross 4 ⊖	d				22 05		22 15			
St Johns	d									
Lewisham 4 ⛴	d	21 56			22 09		22 19	22 26		
Blackheath 4	d	21 59					22 22	22 29		
Kidbrooke	d						22 25			
Eltham	d						22 28			
Falconwood	d						22 31			
Welling	d						22 33			
Bexleyheath	d						22 36			
Barnehurst 4	d						22 38			
Hither Green 4	d				22 14					
Lee	d				22 16					
Mottingham	d				22 19					
New Eltham	d				22 21					
Sidcup 4	d				22 25					
Albany Park	d				22 27					
Bexley	d				22 29					
Crayford	d				22 33					
Charlton 4	d	22 03	22 06			22 20		22 33	22 36	
Woolwich Dockyard	d		22 09			22 23			22 39	
Woolwich Arsenal 4 ⛴	d	22 09	22 12			22 26		22 39	22 42	
Plumstead	d		22 14			22 28			22 44	
Abbey Wood	d	22 13	22 17			22 31		22 43	22 47	
Belvedere	d		22 20			22 33			22 50	
Erith	d		22 22			22 36			22 52	
Slade Green 4	d		22 26			22 39			22 56	
Dartford 4	a	22 24	22 30		22 38	22 44	22 46	22 54	23 00	
	d	22 25			22 39			22 55		
Stone Crossing	d				22 43					
Greenhithe for Bluewater	d	22 30			22 45			23 00		
Swanscombe	d				22 48					
Northfleet	d				22 50					
Gravesend 4	d	22 37		22 48	22a55			23 07		23 18
Higham	d	22 43						23 13		
Strood 4	d	22 48		22 58				23 18		23 28
Maidstone West	d									
Rochester 4	d	22 53		23 03				23 23		23 33
Chatham 4	d	22 55		23 05				23 25		23 35
Gillingham (Kent) 4	a	23 00		23 09				23 30		23 39

Station		SE	SE	SE	SE	SE	SE	SE	SE	SE	SE	SE	SE	SE	SE
St Pancras Int'l 15 ⊖	d									23 25					23 55
Stratford International ⊖ ⛴	d									23 32					00 02
Ebbsfleet International	d									23 44					00 14
London Charing Cross 4 ⊖	d	22 22	22 26	22 32	22 39		22 52	22 56	23 02		23 09	23 22	23 26	23 32	
London Waterloo (East) 4 ⊖	d	22 25	22 29	22 35	22 42		22 55	22 59	23 05		23 12	23 25	23 29	23 35	
London Cannon Street 4 ⊖	d														
London Bridge 4 ⊖	d	22 30	22 34	22 40	22 47	22 50	23 00	23 04	23 10		23 17	23 30	23 34	23 40	
Deptford	d		22 40			22 56		23 10					23 40		
Greenwich 4 ⛴	d		22 42			22 58		23 12					23 42		
Maze Hill	d		22 45			23 01		23 15					23 45		
Westcombe Park	d		22 47			23 03		23 17					23 47		
London Victoria 15 ⊖	d														
Denmark Hill 4	d														
Peckham Rye 4	d														
Nunhead 4	d														
New Cross 4 ⊖	d	22 35		22 45			23 05		23 15			23 35		23 45	
St Johns	d														
Lewisham 4 ⛴	d	22 39		22 49	22 56		23 09		23 19		23 26	23 39		23 49	
Blackheath 4	d			22 52	22 59				23 22		23 29			23 52	
Kidbrooke	d			22 55					23 25					23 55	
Eltham	d			22 58					23 28					23 58	
Falconwood	d			23 01					23 31					00 01	
Welling	d			23 03					23 33					00 03	
Bexleyheath	d			23 06					23 36					00 06	
Barnehurst 4	d			23 08					23 38					00 08	
Hither Green 4	d	22 44					23 14					23 44			
Lee	d	22 46					23 16					23 46			
Mottingham	d	22 49					23 19					23 49			
New Eltham	d	22 51					23 21					23 51			
Sidcup 4	d	22 55					23 25					23 55			
Albany Park	d	22 57					23 27					23 57			
Bexley	d	22 59					23 29					23 59			
Crayford	d	23 03					23 33					00 03			
Charlton 4	d		22 50		23 03	23 06		23 20			23 33		23 50		
Woolwich Dockyard	d		22 53			23 09		23 23					23 53		
Woolwich Arsenal 4 ⛴	d		22 56		23 09	23 12		23 26			23 39		23 56		
Plumstead	d		22 58			23 14		23 28					23 58		
Abbey Wood	d		23 01		23 13	23 17		23 31			23 43		00 01		
Belvedere	d		23 03			23 20		23 33					00 03		
Erith	d		23 06			23 22		23 36					00 06		
Slade Green 4	d		23 09			23 26		23 39					00 09		
Dartford 4	a	23 08	23 14	23 16	23 24	23 30	23 38	23 44	23 46		23 54	00 08	00 14	00 16	
	d	23 09			23 25						23 55				
Stone Crossing	d	23 13			23 29						23 58				
Greenhithe for Bluewater	d	23 15			23 31						23 59				
Swanscombe	d	23 18			23 34						00 04				
Northfleet	d	23 20			23 36						00 06				
Gravesend 4	d	23a25			23 40					23 48	00 10				00 18
Higham	d				23 46						00 16				
Strood 4	d				23 52					23 58	00 22				00 28
Maidstone West	d														
Rochester 4	d				23 56					00 03	00 26				00 33
Chatham 4	d				23 59					00 05	00 29				00 35
Gillingham (Kent) 4	a				00 03					00 09	00 33				00 39

Table 200

London - Dartford and Gillingham

Mondays to Fridays

9 December to 16 May

Network Diagram - see first Page of Table 200

			SE	SE
St Pancras Int'l 15	⊖	d		
Stratford International	⊖ ⛴	d		
Ebbsfleet International		d		
London Charing Cross 4	⊖	d	23 39	23 56
London Waterloo (East) 4	⊖	d	23 42	23 59
London Cannon Street 4	⊖	d		
London Bridge 4	⊖	d	23 47	00 04
Deptford		d		00 10
Greenwich 4	⛴	d		00 12
Maze Hill		d		00 15
Westcombe Park		d		00 17
London Victoria 15	⊖	d		
Denmark Hill 4		d		
Peckham Rye 4		d		
Nunhead 4		d		
New Cross 4	⊖	d		
St Johns		d		
Lewisham 4	⛴	d	23 56	
Blackheath 4		d	23 59	
Kidbrooke		d		
Eltham		d		
Falconwood		d		
Welling		d		
Bexleyheath		d		
Barnehurst 4		d		
Hither Green 4		d		
Lee		d		
Mottingham		d		
New Eltham		d		
Sidcup 4		d		
Albany Park		d		
Bexley		d		
Crayford		d		
Charlton 4		d	00 03	00 20
Woolwich Dockyard		d		00 23
Woolwich Arsenal 4	⛴	d	00 09	00 26
Plumstead		d		00 28
Abbey Wood		d	00 13	00 31
Belvedere		d		00 33
Erith		d		00 36
Slade Green 4		d		00 39
Dartford 4		a	00 24	00 44
		d	00 25	
Stone Crossing		d	00 29	
Greenhithe for Bluewater		d	00 31	
Swanscombe		d	00 34	
Northfleet		d	00 36	
Gravesend 4		d	00 40	
Higham		d	00 46	
Strood 4		d	00 52	
Maidstone West		d		
Rochester 4		d	00 56	
Chatham 4		d	00 59	
Gillingham (Kent) 4		a	01 03	

Table 200

Saturdays

14 December to 17 May

London - Dartford and Gillingham

Network Diagram - see first Page of Table 200

Station		SE	SE	SE	SE	SE	SE	SE	SE	SE
St Pancras Int'l	d									
Stratford International	d						00 02			
Ebbsfleet International	d						00 14			
London Charing Cross	d									00 02
London Waterloo (East)	d									00 05
London Cannon Street	d									
London Bridge	d								00 04	00 10
Deptford	d								00 10	
Greenwich	d								00 12	
Maze Hill	d								00 15	
Westcombe Park	d								00 17	
London Victoria	d									
Denmark Hill	d									
Peckham Rye	d									
Nunhead	d									
New Cross	d									00 15
St Johns	d									
Lewisham	d									00 19
Blackheath	d									00 22
Kidbrooke	d									00 25
Eltham	d									00 28
Falconwood	d			00 01						00 31
Welling	d			00 03						00 33
Bexleyheath	d			00 06						00 36
Barnehurst	d			00 08						00 38
Hither Green	d									
Lee	d									
Mottingham	d									
New Eltham	d									
Sidcup	d									
Albany Park	d									
Bexley	d									
Crayford	d	00 03								
Charlton	d							00 03	00 20	
Woolwich Dockyard	d								00 23	
Woolwich Arsenal	d							00 09	00 26	
Plumstead	d								00 28	
Abbey Wood	d		00 01					00 13	00 31	
Belvedere	d		00 03						00 33	
Erith	d		00 06						00 36	
Slade Green	d		00 09						00 39	
Dartford	a	00 08	00 14	00 16				00 24	00 44	00 46
	d							00 25		
Stone Crossing	d							00 29		
Greenhithe for Bluewater	d							00 31		
Swanscombe	d					00 04		00 34		
Northfleet	d					00 06		00 36		
Gravesend	d					00 10	00 18	00 40		
Higham	d					00 16		00 46		
Strood	d					00 22	00 28	00 52		
Maidstone West	d									
Rochester	d				00 03	00 26	00 33	00 56		
Chatham	d				00 05	00 29	00 35	00 59		
Gillingham (Kent)	a				00 09	00 33	00 39	01 03		

Station		SE	SE	SE	SE	SE	SE	SE	SE	SE
St Pancras Int'l	d									
Stratford International	d									
Ebbsfleet International	d									
London Charing Cross	d	00 10	00 18	04 52		05 22	05 26	05 32	05 39	05 52
London Waterloo (East)	d	00 13	00 21	04 55		05 25	05 29	05 35	05 42	05 55
London Cannon Street	d									
London Bridge	d	00 18	00 26	05 00		05 30	05 34	05 40	05 47	06 00
Deptford	d						05 40			
Greenwich	d						05 42			
Maze Hill	d						05 45			
Westcombe Park	d						05 47			
London Victoria	d									
Denmark Hill	d									
Peckham Rye	d									
Nunhead	d									
New Cross	d	00 23	00 31	05 05		05 35		05 45		06 05
St Johns	d									
Lewisham	d	00 27	00 35	05 09		05 39		05 49	05 56	06 09
Blackheath	d		00 38					05 52	05 59	
Kidbrooke	d							05 55		
Eltham	d							05 58		
Falconwood	d							06 01		
Welling	d							06 03		
Bexleyheath	d							06 06		
Barnehurst	d							06 08		
Hither Green	d	00 32		05 14		05 44				06 14
Lee	d	00 34		05 16		05 46				06 16
Mottingham	d	00 37		05 19		05 49				06 19
New Eltham	d	00 39		05 21		05 51				06 21
Sidcup	d	00 43		05 25		05 55				06 25
Albany Park	d	00 45		05 27		05 57				06 27
Bexley	d	00 47		05 29		05 59				06 29
Crayford	d	00 51		05 33		06 03				06 33
Charlton	d		00 42				05 50		06 03	
Woolwich Dockyard	d						05 53			
Woolwich Arsenal	d		00 47				05 56		06 09	
Plumstead	d		00 49				05 58			
Abbey Wood	d		00 53				06 01		06 13	
Belvedere	d		00 55				06 03			
Erith	d		00 58				06 06			
Slade Green	d		01 01				06 09			
Dartford	a	00 56	01 06	05 38		06 08	06 14	06 16	06 24	06 38
	d		01 07	05 39	05 55	06 09			06 25	06 39
Stone Crossing	d			05 43		06 13				06 43
Greenhithe for Bluewater	d		01 12	05 45	06 00	06 15			06 30	06 45
Swanscombe	d			05 48		06 18				06 48
Northfleet	d			05 50		06 20				06 50
Gravesend	d		01 19	05a55	06 07	06a25			06 37	06a55
Higham	d		01 25		06 13				06 43	
Strood	d		01 30		06 18				06 48	
Maidstone West	d									
Rochester	d		01 35		06 23				06 53	
Chatham	d		01 37		06 25				06 55	
Gillingham (Kent)	a		01 44		06 30				07 00	

Station		SE	SE	SE	SE	SE	SE	SE	SE	SE
St Pancras Int'l	d				06 51					
Stratford International	d				06 58					
Ebbsfleet International	d				07 14					
London Charing Cross	d	05 56	06 02	06 09		06 22	06 26	06 32	06 39	06 52
London Waterloo (East)	d	05 59	06 05	06 12		06 25	06 29	06 35	06 42	06 55
London Cannon Street	d									
London Bridge	d	06 04	06 10	06 17		06 30	06 34	06 40	06 47	07 00
Deptford	d	06 10					06 40			
Greenwich	d	06 12					06 42			
Maze Hill	d	06 15					06 45			
Westcombe Park	d	06 17					06 47			
London Victoria	d									
Denmark Hill	d									
Peckham Rye	d									
Nunhead	d									
New Cross	d		06 15			06 35		06 45		07 05
St Johns	d									
Lewisham	d		06 19	06 26		06 39		06 49	06 56	07 09
Blackheath	d		06 22	06 29				06 52	06 59	
Kidbrooke	d		06 25					06 55		
Eltham	d		06 28					06 58		
Falconwood	d		06 31					07 01		
Welling	d		06 33					07 03		
Bexleyheath	d		06 36					07 06		
Barnehurst	d		06 38					07 08		
Hither Green	d					06 44				07 14
Lee	d					06 46				07 16
Mottingham	d					06 49				07 19
New Eltham	d					06 51				07 21
Sidcup	d					06 55				07 25
Albany Park	d					06 57				07 27
Bexley	d					06 59				07 29
Crayford	d					07 03				07 33
Charlton	d	06 20		06 33			06 50		07 03	
Woolwich Dockyard	d	06 23					06 53			
Woolwich Arsenal	d	06 26		06 39			06 56		07 09	
Plumstead	d	06 28					06 58			
Abbey Wood	d	06 31		06 43			07 01		07 13	
Belvedere	d	06 33					07 03			
Erith	d	06 36					07 06			
Slade Green	d	06 39					07 09			
Dartford	a	06 44	06 46	06 54		07 08	07 14	07 16	07 24	07 38
	d			06 55		07 09			07 25	07 39
Stone Crossing	d					07 13				07 43
Greenhithe for Bluewater	d			07 00		07 15			07 30	07 45
Swanscombe	d					07 18				07 48
Northfleet	d					07 20				07 50
Gravesend	d			07 07	07 18	07a25			07 37	07a55
Higham	d			07 13					07 43	
Strood	d			07 18	07 28				07 48	
Maidstone West	d									
Rochester	d			07 23	07 33				07 53	
Chatham	d			07 25	07 35				07 55	
Gillingham (Kent)	a			07 30	07 39				08 00	

Station		SE	SE	SE	SE	SE	SE	SE	SE	SE
St Pancras Int'l	d				07 55					
Stratford International	d				08 02					
Ebbsfleet International	d				08 14					
London Charing Cross	d	06 56	07 02	07 09		07 22	07 26	07 32	07 39	
London Waterloo (East)	d	06 59	07 05	07 12		07 25	07 29	07 35	07 42	
London Cannon Street	d									
London Bridge	d	07 04	07 10	07 17		07 30	07 34	07 40	07 47	
Deptford	d	07 10					07 40			
Greenwich	d	07 12					07 42			
Maze Hill	d	07 15					07 45			
Westcombe Park	d	07 17					07 47			
London Victoria	d									07 39
Denmark Hill	d									07 48
Peckham Rye	d									07 51
Nunhead	d									07 53
New Cross	d		07 15			07 35		07 45		
St Johns	d									
Lewisham	d		07 19	07 26		07 39		07 49	07 56	08 02
Blackheath	d		07 22	07 29				07 52	07 59	08 04
Kidbrooke	d		07 25					07 55		08 07
Eltham	d		07 28					07 58		08 11
Falconwood	d		07 31					08 01		08 13
Welling	d		07 33					08 03		08 16
Bexleyheath	d		07 36					08 06		08 18
Barnehurst	d		07 38					08 08		08 21
Hither Green	d					07 44				
Lee	d					07 46				
Mottingham	d					07 49				
New Eltham	d					07 51				
Sidcup	d					07 55				
Albany Park	d					07 57				
Bexley	d					07 59				
Crayford	d					08 03				
Charlton	d	07 20		07 33			07 50		08 03	
Woolwich Dockyard	d	07 23					07 53			
Woolwich Arsenal	d	07 26		07 39			07 56		08 09	
Plumstead	d	07 28					07 58			
Abbey Wood	d	07 31		07 43			08 01		08 13	
Belvedere	d	07 33					08 03			
Erith	d	07 36					08 06			
Slade Green	d	07 39					08 09			
Dartford	a	07 44	07 46	07 54		08 08	08 14	08 16	08 24	08 29
	d			07 55		08 09			08 25	
Stone Crossing	d					08 13				
Greenhithe for Bluewater	d			08 00		08 15			08 30	
Swanscombe	d					08 18				
Northfleet	d					08 20				
Gravesend	d			08 07	08 18	08a25			08 37	
Higham	d			08 13					08 43	
Strood	d			08 18	08 28				08 48	
Maidstone West	d									
Rochester	d			08 23	08 33				08 53	
Chatham	d			08 25	08 35				08 55	
Gillingham (Kent)	a			08 30	08 39				09 00	

Table 200

Saturdays

14 December to 17 May

London - Dartford and Gillingham

Network Diagram - see first Page of Table 200

Station		SE	SE	SE	SE	SE	SE	SE	SE	SE	SE	SE	SE	SE	SE	SE	SE	SE	SE
St Pancras Int'l 15 ⊖	d											08 51							
Stratford International ⊖	d											09 05							
Ebbsfleet International	d											09 17							
London Charing Cross 4 ⊖	d	07 52	07 56	08 02			08 09						08 26	08 32			08 39		
London Waterloo (East) 4 ⊖	d	07 55	07 59	08 05			08 12						08 29	08 35			08 42		
London Cannon Street 4 ⊖	d				08 07	08 10			08 17	08 24	08 27				08 37	08 40			08 47
London Bridge 4 ⊖	d	08 00	08 04	08 10	08 11	08 14	08 17		08 21	08 28	08 31		08 34	08 40	08 41	08 44	08 47		08 51
Deptford	d		08 10		08 17				08 27		08 37				08 47				08 57
Greenwich 4	d		08 12		08 19				08 29		08 39				08 49				08 59
Maze Hill	d		08 15		08 22				08 32		08 42				08 52				09 02
Westcombe Park	d		08 17		08 24				08 34		08 44				08 54				09 04
London Victoria 15 ⊖	d							08 09										08 39	
Denmark Hill 4	d							08 18										08 48	
Peckham Rye 4	d							08 21										08 51	
Nunhead 4	d							08 23										08 53	
New Cross 4 ⊖	d	08 05		08 15		08 19				08 33						08 49			
St Johns	d					08 21				08 35						08 51			
Lewisham 4	d	08 09		08 19		08 24	08 26	08 32		08 38				08 49		08 54	08 56	09 02	
Blackheath 4	d			08 22			08 29	08 34		08 41				08 52			08 59	09 04	
Kidbrooke	d			08 25				08 37		08 44				08 55				09 07	
Eltham	d			08 28				08 41		08 47				08 58				09 11	
Falconwood	d			08 31				08 43		08 50				09 01				09 13	
Welling	d			08 33				08 46		08 52				09 03				09 16	
Bexleyheath	d			08 36				08 48		08 55				09 06				09 18	
Barnehurst 4	d			08 38				08 51		09 02				09 08				09 21	
Hither Green 4	d	08 14				08 29							08 44			08 59			
Lee	d	08 16				08 31							08 46			09 01			
Mottingham	d	08 19				08 34							08 49			09 04			
New Eltham	d	08 21				08 36							08 51			09 06			
Sidcup 4	d	08 25				08 40							08 55			09 10			
Albany Park	d	08 27				08 42							08 57			09 12			
Bexley	d	08 29				08 44							08 59			09 14			
Crayford	d	08 33				08 48							09 03			09 18			
Charlton 4	d		08 20		08 27	09a15	08 33		08 37		08 47				08 57	09a45	09 03		09 07
Woolwich Dockyard	d		08 23		08 30				08 40		08 50				09 00				09 10
Woolwich Arsenal 4	d		08 26		08 33		08 39		08 43		08 53				09 03		09 09		09 13
Plumstead	d		08 28		08 35				08 45		08 55				09 05				09 15
Abbey Wood	d		08 31		08 38		08 43		08 48		08 58				09 08		09 13		09 18
Belvedere	d		08 33		08 40				08 50		09 00				09 10				09 20
Erith	d		08 36		08 43				08 53		09 03				09 13				09 23
Slade Green 4	d		08 39		08a46				08a55	09a12	09 07				09a16				09a25
Dartford 4	a	08 38	08 44	08 46			08 54	08 58			09 12		09 08	09 15			09 24	09 28	
	d	08 39					08 55						09 09				09 25		
Stone Crossing	d	08 43											09 13						
Greenhithe for Bluewater	d	08 45					09 00						09 15				09 30		
Swanscombe	d	08 48											09 18						
Northfleet	d	08 50											09 20						
Gravesend 4	d	08a55					09 07					09 21	09a25				09 37		
Higham	d						09 13										09 43		
Strood 4	d						09 18					09 31					09 48		
Maidstone West	d																		
Rochester 4	d						09 23					09 35					09 53		
Chatham 4	d						09 25					09 38					09 55		
Gillingham (Kent) 4	a						09 30					09 42					10 00		

Station		SE	SE	SE	SE	SE	SE	SE	SE	SE	SE	SE	SE	SE	SE	SE	SE	SE	SE
St Pancras Int'l 15 ⊖	d			09 25										09 55					
Stratford International ⊖	d			09 32										10 02					
Ebbsfleet International	d			09 44										10 14					
London Charing Cross 4 ⊖	d				08 56	09 02			09 09						09 26	09 32			09 39
London Waterloo (East) 4 ⊖	d				08 59	09 05			09 12						09 29	09 35			09 42
London Cannon Street 4 ⊖	d	08 54	08 57				09 07	09 10			09 17	09 24	09 27				09 37	09 40	
London Bridge 4 ⊖	d	08 58	09 01		09 04	09 10	09 11	09 14	09 17		09 21	09 28	09 31		09 34	09 40	09 41	09 44	09 47
Deptford	d		09 07				09 17				09 27		09 37				09 47		
Greenwich 4	d		09 09				09 19				09 29		09 39				09 49		
Maze Hill	d		09 12				09 22				09 32		09 42				09 52		
Westcombe Park	d		09 14				09 24				09 34		09 44				09 54		
London Victoria 15 ⊖	d									09 09									
Denmark Hill 4	d									09 18									
Peckham Rye 4	d									09 21									
Nunhead 4	d									09 23									
New Cross 4 ⊖	d	09 03						09 19				09 33						09 49	
St Johns	d	09 05						09 21				09 35						09 51	
Lewisham 4	d	09 08				09 19		09 24	09 26	09 32		09 38				09 49		09 54	09 56
Blackheath 4	d	09 11				09 22			09 29	09 34		09 41				09 52			09 59
Kidbrooke	d	09 14				09 25				09 37		09 44				09 55			
Eltham	d	09 17				09 28				09 41		09 47				09 58			
Falconwood	d	09 20				09 31				09 43		09 50				10 01			
Welling	d	09 22				09 33				09 46		09 52				10 03			
Bexleyheath	d	09 25				09 36				09 48		09 55				10 06			
Barnehurst 4	d	09 32				09 38				09 51		10 02				10 08			
Hither Green 4	d				09 14			09 29							09 44			09 59	
Lee	d				09 16			09 31							09 46			10 01	
Mottingham	d				09 19			09 34							09 49			10 04	
New Eltham	d				09 21			09 36							09 51			10 06	
Sidcup 4	d				09 25			09 40							09 55			10 10	
Albany Park	d				09 27			09 42							09 57			10 12	
Bexley	d				09 29			09 44							09 59			10 14	
Crayford	d				09 33			09 48							10 03			10 18	
Charlton 4	d		09 17				09 27	10a15	09 33		09 37		09 47				09 57	10a45	10 03
Woolwich Dockyard	d		09 20				09 30				09 40		09 50				10 00		
Woolwich Arsenal 4	d		09 23				09 33		09 39		09 43		09 53				10 03		10 09
Plumstead	d		09 25				09 35				09 45		09 55				10 05		
Abbey Wood	d		09 28				09 38		09 43		09 48		09 58				10 08		10 13
Belvedere	d		09 30				09 40				09 50		10 00				10 10		
Erith	d		09 33				09 43				09 53		10 03				10 13		
Slade Green 4	d	09a42	09 37				09a46				09a55	10a12	10 07				10a16		
Dartford 4	a		09 42		09 38	09 45			09 54	09 58			10 12		10 08	10 15			10 24
	d				09 39				09 55						10 09				10 25
Stone Crossing	d				09 43										10 13				
Greenhithe for Bluewater	d				09 45				10 00						10 15				10 30
Swanscombe	d				09 48										10 18				
Northfleet	d				09 50										10 20				
Gravesend 4	d			09 48	09a55				10 07					10 18	10a25				10 37
Higham	d								10 13										10 43
Strood 4	d			09 58					10 18					10 28					10 48
Maidstone West	d																		
Rochester 4	d			10 03					10 23					10 33					10 53
Chatham 4	d			10 05					10 25					10 35					10 55
Gillingham (Kent) 4	a			10 09					10 30					10 39					11 00

Table 200

Saturdays

14 December to 17 May

London - Dartford and Gillingham

Network Diagram - see first Page of Table 200

Station		SE	SE	SE	SE	SE	SE	SE	SE	SE	SE	SE	SE	SE	SE	SE	SE	SE	SE
St Pancras Int'l 15 ⊖	d					10 22										10 52			
Stratford International ⊖ ⛴	d					10 32										10 59			
Ebbsfleet International	d					10 44										11 14			
London Charing Cross 4 ⊖	d						09 56	10 02			10 09						10 26	10 32	
London Waterloo (East) 4 ⊖	d						09 59	10 05			10 12						10 29	10 35	
London Cannon Street 4 ⊖	d		09 47	09 54	09 57				10 07	10 10			10 17	10 24	10 27				10 37
London Bridge 4 ⊖	d		09 51	09 58	10 01		10 04	10 10	10 11	10 14	10 17		10 21	10 28	10 31		10 34	10 40	10 41
Deptford	d		09 57		10 07				10 17				10 27		10 37				10 47
Greenwich 4 ⛴	d		09 59		10 09				10 19				10 29		10 39				10 49
Maze Hill	d		10 02		10 12				10 22				10 32		10 42				10 52
Westcombe Park	d		10 04		10 14				10 24				10 34		10 44				10 54
London Victoria 15 ⊖	d	09 39										10 09							
Denmark Hill 4	d	09 48										10 18							
Peckham Rye 4	d	09 51										10 21							
Nunhead 4	d	09 53										10 23							
New Cross 4 ⊖	d			10 03						10 19				10 33					
St Johns	d			10 05						10 21				10 35					
Lewisham 4 ⛴	d	10 02		10 08				10 19		10 24	10 26	10 32		10 38				10 49	
Blackheath 4	d	10 04		10 11				10 22			10 29	10 34		10 41				10 52	
Kidbrooke	d	10 07		10 14				10 25				10 37		10 44				10 55	
Eltham	d	10 11		10 17				10 28				10 41		10 47				10 58	
Falconwood	d	10 13		10 20				10 31				10 43		10 50				11 01	
Welling	d	10 16		10 22				10 33				10 46		10 52				11 03	
Bexleyheath	d	10 18		10 25				10 36				10 48		10 55				11 06	
Barnehurst 4	d	10 21		10 32				10 38				10 51		11 02				11 08	
Hither Green 4	d						10 14			10 29							10 44		
Lee	d						10 16			10 31							10 46		
Mottingham	d						10 19			10 34							10 49		
New Eltham	d						10 21			10 36							10 51		
Sidcup 4	d						10 25			10 40							10 55		
Albany Park	d						10 27			10 42							10 57		
Bexley	d						10 29			10 44							10 59		
Crayford	d						10 33			10 48							11 03		
Charlton 4	d		10 07		10 17				10 27	11a15	10 33		10 37		10 47				10 57
Woolwich Dockyard	d		10 10		10 20				10 30				10 40		10 50				11 00
Woolwich Arsenal 4 ⛴	d		10 13		10 23				10 33		10 39		10 43		10 53				11 03
Plumstead	d		10 15		10 25				10 35				10 45		10 55				11 05
Abbey Wood	d		10 18		10 28				10 38		10 43		10 48		10 58				11 08
Belvedere	d		10 20		10 30				10 40				10 50		11 00				11 10
Erith	d		10 23		10 33				10 43				10 53		11 03				11 13
Slade Green 4	d		10a25	10a42	10 37				10a46				10a55	11a12	11 07				11a16
Dartford 4	a	10 28			10 42		10 38	10 45			10 54	10 58			11 12		11 08	11 15	
	d						10 39				10 55						11 09		
Stone Crossing	d						10 43										11 13		
Greenhithe for Bluewater	d						10 45				11 00						11 15		
Swanscombe	d						10 48										11 18		
Northfleet	d						10 50										11 20		
Gravesend 4	d					10 48	10a55				11 07					11 18	11a25		
Higham	d										11 13								
Strood 4	d					10 58					11 18					11 28			
Maidstone West	d																		
Rochester 4	d					11 03					11 23					11 33			
Chatham 4	d					11 05					11 25					11 35			
Gillingham (Kent) 4	a					11 09					11 30					11 39			

Station		SE	SE	SE	SE	SE	SE	SE	SE	SE	SE	SE	SE	SE	SE	SE	SE	SE	SE
St Pancras Int'l 15 ⊖	d							11 25										11 55	
Stratford International ⊖ ⛴	d							11 32										12 02	
Ebbsfleet International	d							11 44										12 14	
London Charing Cross 4 ⊖	d		10 39						10 56	11 02			11 09						11 26
London Waterloo (East) 4 ⊖	d		10 42						10 59	11 05			11 12						11 29
London Cannon Street 4 ⊖	d	10 40			10 47	10 54	10 57				11 07	11 10			11 17	11 24	11 27		
London Bridge 4 ⊖	d	10 44	10 47		10 51	10 58	11 01		11 04	11 10	11 11	11 14	11 17		11 21	11 28	11 31		11 34
Deptford	d				10 57		11 07				11 17				11 27		11 37		
Greenwich 4 ⛴	d				10 59		11 09				11 19				11 29		11 39		
Maze Hill	d				11 02		11 12				11 22				11 32		11 42		
Westcombe Park	d				11 04		11 14				11 24				11 34		11 44		
London Victoria 15 ⊖	d			10 39										11 09					
Denmark Hill 4	d			10 48										11 18					
Peckham Rye 4	d			10 51										11 21					
Nunhead 4	d			10 53										11 23					
New Cross 4 ⊖	d	10 49				11 03						11 19				11 33			
St Johns	d	10 51				11 05						11 21				11 35			
Lewisham 4 ⛴	d	10 54	10 56	11 02		11 08				11 19		11 24	11 26	11 32		11 38			
Blackheath 4	d		10 59	11 04		11 11				11 22			11 29	11 34		11 41			
Kidbrooke	d			11 07		11 14				11 25				11 37		11 44			
Eltham	d			11 11		11 17				11 28				11 41		11 47			
Falconwood	d			11 13		11 20				11 31				11 43		11 50			
Welling	d			11 16		11 22				11 33				11 46		11 52			
Bexleyheath	d			11 18		11 25				11 36				11 48		11 55			
Barnehurst 4	d			11 21		11 32				11 38				11 51		12 02			
Hither Green 4	d	10 59							11 14			11 29							11 44
Lee	d	11 01							11 16			11 31							11 46
Mottingham	d	11 04							11 19			11 34							11 49
New Eltham	d	11 06							11 21			11 36							11 51
Sidcup 4	d	11 10							11 25			11 40							11 55
Albany Park	d	11 12							11 27			11 42							11 57
Bexley	d	11 14							11 29			11 44							11 59
Crayford	d	11 18							11 33			11 48							12 03
Charlton 4	d	11a45	11 03		11 07		11 17				11 27	12a15	11 33		11 37		11 47		
Woolwich Dockyard	d				11 10		11 20				11 30				11 40		11 50		
Woolwich Arsenal 4 ⛴	d		11 09		11 13		11 23				11 33		11 39		11 43		11 53		
Plumstead	d				11 15		11 25				11 35				11 45		11 55		
Abbey Wood	d		11 13		11 18		11 28				11 38		11 43		11 48		11 58		
Belvedere	d				11 20		11 30				11 40				11 50		12 00		
Erith	d				11 23		11 33				11 43				11 53		12 03		
Slade Green 4	d				11a25	11a42	11 37				11a46				11a55	12a12	12 07		
Dartford 4	a		11 24	11 28			11 42		11 38	11 45			11 54	11 58			12 12		12 08
	d		11 25						11 39				11 55						12 09
Stone Crossing	d								11 43										12 13
Greenhithe for Bluewater	d		11 30						11 45				12 00						12 15
Swanscombe	d								11 48										12 18
Northfleet	d								11 50										12 20
Gravesend 4	d		11 37					11 48	11a55				12 07					12 18	12a25
Higham	d		11 43										12 13						
Strood 4	d		11 48					11 58					12 18					12 28	
Maidstone West	d																		
Rochester 4	d		11 53					12 03					12 23					12 33	
Chatham 4	d		11 55					12 05					12 25					12 35	
Gillingham (Kent) 4	a		12 00					12 09					12 30					12 39	

Table 200

Saturdays

London - Dartford and Gillingham

14 December to 17 May

Network Diagram - see first Page of Table 200

Station		SE	SE	SE	SE	SE	SE	SE	SE	SE
St Pancras Int'l 15 ⊖	d									12 22
Stratford International ⊖ ⛴	d									12 32
Ebbsfleet International	d									12 44
London Charing Cross 4 ⊖	d	11 32			11 39					
London Waterloo (East) 4 ⊖	d	11 35			11 42					
London Cannon Street 4 ⊖	d		11 37	11 40			11 47	11 54	11 57	
London Bridge 4 ⊖	d	11 40	11 41	11 44	11 47		11 51	11 58	12 01	
Deptford	d		11 47				11 57		12 07	
Greenwich 4 ⛴	d		11 49				11 59		12 09	
Maze Hill	d		11 52				12 02		12 12	
Westcombe Park	d		11 54				12 04		12 14	
London Victoria 15 ⊖	d					11 39				
Denmark Hill 4	d					11 48				
Peckham Rye 4	d					11 51				
Nunhead 4	d					11 53				
New Cross 4 ⊖	d			11 49				12 03		
St Johns	d			11 51				12 05		
Lewisham 4 ⛴	d	11 49		11 54	11 56	12 02		12 08		
Blackheath 4	d	11 52			11 59	12 04		12 11		
Kidbrooke	d	11 55				12 07		12 14		
Eltham	d	11 58				12 11		12 17		
Falconwood	d	12 01				12 13		12 20		
Welling	d	12 03				12 16		12 22		
Bexleyheath	d	12 06				12 18		12 25		
Barnehurst 4	d	12 08				12 21		12 32		
Hither Green 4	d			11 59						
Lee	d			12 01						
Mottingham	d			12 04						
New Eltham	d			12 06						
Sidcup 4	d			12 10						
Albany Park	d			12 12						
Bexley	d			12 14						
Crayford	d			12 18						
Charlton 4	d		11 57	12a45	12 03		12 07		12 17	
Woolwich Dockyard	d		12 00				12 10		12 20	
Woolwich Arsenal 4 ⛴	d		12 03		12 09		12 13		12 23	
Plumstead	d		12 05				12 15		12 25	
Abbey Wood	d		12 08		12 13		12 18		12 28	
Belvedere	d		12 10				12 20		12 30	
Erith	d		12 13				12 23		12 33	
Slade Green 4	d		12a16				12a25	12a42	12 37	
Dartford 4	a	12 15			12 24	12 28			12 42	
	d				12 25					
Stone Crossing	d									
Greenhithe for Bluewater	d				12 30					
Swanscombe	d									
Northfleet	d									
Gravesend 4	d				12 37					12 48
Higham	d				12 43					
Strood 4	d				12 48					12 58
Maidstone West	d									
Rochester 4	d				12 53					13 03
Chatham 4	d				12 55					13 05
Gillingham (Kent) 4	a				13 00					13 09

Station		SE	SE	SE	SE	SE	SE	SE	SE	SE
St Pancras Int'l 15 ⊖	d									
Stratford International ⊖ ⛴	d									
Ebbsfleet International	d									
London Charing Cross 4 ⊖	d	11 56	12 02			12 09				
London Waterloo (East) 4 ⊖	d	11 59	12 05			12 12				
London Cannon Street 4 ⊖	d			12 07	12 10			12 17	12 24	12 27
London Bridge 4 ⊖	d	12 04	12 10	12 11	12 14	12 17		12 21	12 28	12 31
Deptford	d			12 17				12 27		12 37
Greenwich 4 ⛴	d			12 19				12 29		12 39
Maze Hill	d			12 22				12 32		12 42
Westcombe Park	d			12 24				12 34		12 44
London Victoria 15 ⊖	d						12 09			
Denmark Hill 4	d						12 18			
Peckham Rye 4	d						12 21			
Nunhead 4	d						12 23			
New Cross 4 ⊖	d				12 19				12 33	
St Johns	d				12 21				12 35	
Lewisham 4 ⛴	d		12 19		12 24	12 26	12 32		12 38	
Blackheath 4	d		12 22			12 29	12 34		12 41	
Kidbrooke	d		12 25				12 37		12 44	
Eltham	d		12 28				12 41		12 47	
Falconwood	d		12 31				12 43		12 50	
Welling	d		12 33				12 46		12 52	
Bexleyheath	d		12 36				12 48		12 55	
Barnehurst 4	d		12 38				12 51		13 02	
Hither Green 4	d	12 14			12 29					
Lee	d	12 16			12 31					
Mottingham	d	12 19			12 34					
New Eltham	d	12 21			12 36					
Sidcup 4	d	12 25			12 40					
Albany Park	d	12 27			12 42					
Bexley	d	12 29			12 44					
Crayford	d	12 33			12 48					
Charlton 4	d			12 27	13a15	12 33		12 37		12 47
Woolwich Dockyard	d			12 30				12 40		12 50
Woolwich Arsenal 4 ⛴	d			12 33		12 39		12 43		12 53
Plumstead	d			12 35				12 45		12 55
Abbey Wood	d			12 38		12 43		12 48		12 58
Belvedere	d			12 40				12 50		13 00
Erith	d			12 43				12 53		13 03
Slade Green 4	d			12a46				12a55	13a12	13 07
Dartford 4	a	12 38	12 45			12 54	12 58			13 12
	d	12 39				12 55				
Stone Crossing	d	12 43								
Greenhithe for Bluewater	d	12 45				13 00				
Swanscombe	d	12 48								
Northfleet	d	12 50								
Gravesend 4	d	12a55				13 07				
Higham	d					13 13				
Strood 4	d					13 18				
Maidstone West	d									
Rochester 4	d					13 23				
Chatham 4	d					13 25				
Gillingham (Kent) 4	a					13 30				

Station		SE	SE	SE	SE	SE	SE	SE	SE	SE
St Pancras Int'l 15 ⊖	d	12 52								
Stratford International ⊖ ⛴	d	12 59								
Ebbsfleet International	d	13 14								
London Charing Cross 4 ⊖	d		12 26	12 32			12 39			
London Waterloo (East) 4 ⊖	d		12 29	12 35			12 42			
London Cannon Street 4 ⊖	d				12 37	12 40			12 47	12 54
London Bridge 4 ⊖	d		12 34	12 40	12 41	12 44	12 47		12 51	12 58
Deptford	d				12 47				12 57	
Greenwich 4 ⛴	d				12 49				12 59	
Maze Hill	d				12 52				13 02	
Westcombe Park	d				12 54				13 04	
London Victoria 15 ⊖	d							12 39		
Denmark Hill 4	d							12 48		
Peckham Rye 4	d							12 51		
Nunhead 4	d							12 53		
New Cross 4 ⊖	d					12 49				13 03
St Johns	d					12 51				13 05
Lewisham 4 ⛴	d			12 49		12 54	12 56	13 02		13 08
Blackheath 4	d			12 52			12 59	13 04		13 11
Kidbrooke	d			12 55				13 07		13 14
Eltham	d			12 58				13 11		13 17
Falconwood	d			13 01				13 13		13 20
Welling	d			13 03				13 16		13 22
Bexleyheath	d			13 06				13 18		13 25
Barnehurst 4	d			13 08				13 21		13 32
Hither Green 4	d		12 44			12 59				
Lee	d		12 46			13 01				
Mottingham	d		12 49			13 04				
New Eltham	d		12 51			13 06				
Sidcup 4	d		12 55			13 10				
Albany Park	d		12 57			13 12				
Bexley	d		12 59			13 14				
Crayford	d		13 03			13 18				
Charlton 4	d				12 57	13a45	13 03		13 07	
Woolwich Dockyard	d				13 00				13 10	
Woolwich Arsenal 4 ⛴	d				13 03		13 09		13 13	
Plumstead	d				13 05				13 15	
Abbey Wood	d				13 08		13 13		13 18	
Belvedere	d				13 10				13 20	
Erith	d				13 13				13 23	
Slade Green 4	d				13a16				13a25	13a42
Dartford 4	a		13 08	13 15			13 24	13 28		
	d		13 09				13 25			
Stone Crossing	d		13 13							
Greenhithe for Bluewater	d		13 15				13 30			
Swanscombe	d		13 18							
Northfleet	d		13 20							
Gravesend 4	d	13 18	13a25				13 37			
Higham	d						13 43			
Strood 4	d	13 28					13 48			
Maidstone West	d									
Rochester 4	d	13 33					13 53			
Chatham 4	d	13 35					13 55			
Gillingham (Kent) 4	a	13 39					14 00			

Station		SE	SE	SE	SE	SE	SE	SE	SE	SE
St Pancras Int'l 15 ⊖	d		13 25							
Stratford International ⊖ ⛴	d		13 32							
Ebbsfleet International	d		13 44							
London Charing Cross 4 ⊖	d			12 56	13 02			13 09		
London Waterloo (East) 4 ⊖	d			12 59	13 05			13 12		
London Cannon Street 4 ⊖	d	12 57				13 07	13 10			13 17
London Bridge 4 ⊖	d	13 01		13 04	13 10	13 11	13 14	13 17		13 21
Deptford	d	13 07				13 17				13 27
Greenwich 4 ⛴	d	13 09				13 19				13 29
Maze Hill	d	13 12				13 22				13 32
Westcombe Park	d	13 14				13 24				13 34
London Victoria 15 ⊖	d								13 09	
Denmark Hill 4	d								13 18	
Peckham Rye 4	d								13 21	
Nunhead 4	d								13 23	
New Cross 4 ⊖	d						13 19			
St Johns	d						13 21			
Lewisham 4 ⛴	d				13 19		13 24	13 26	13 32	
Blackheath 4	d				13 22			13 29	13 34	
Kidbrooke	d				13 25				13 37	
Eltham	d				13 28				13 41	
Falconwood	d				13 31				13 43	
Welling	d				13 33				13 46	
Bexleyheath	d				13 36				13 48	
Barnehurst 4	d				13 38				13 51	
Hither Green 4	d			13 14			13 29			
Lee	d			13 16			13 31			
Mottingham	d			13 19			13 34			
New Eltham	d			13 21			13 36			
Sidcup 4	d			13 25			13 40			
Albany Park	d			13 27			13 42			
Bexley	d			13 29			13 44			
Crayford	d			13 33			13 48			
Charlton 4	d	13 17				13 27	14a15	13 33		13 37
Woolwich Dockyard	d	13 20				13 30				13 40
Woolwich Arsenal 4 ⛴	d	13 23				13 33		13 39		13 43
Plumstead	d	13 25				13 35				13 45
Abbey Wood	d	13 28				13 38		13 43		13 48
Belvedere	d	13 30				13 40				13 50
Erith	d	13 33				13 43				13 53
Slade Green 4	d	13 37				13a46				13a55
Dartford 4	a	13 42		13 38	13 45			13 54	13 58	
	d			13 39				13 55		
Stone Crossing	d			13 43						
Greenhithe for Bluewater	d			13 45				14 00		
Swanscombe	d			13 48						
Northfleet	d			13 50						
Gravesend 4	d		13 48	13a55				14 07		
Higham	d							14 13		
Strood 4	d		13 58					14 18		
Maidstone West	d									
Rochester 4	d		14 03					14 23		
Chatham 4	d		14 05					14 25		
Gillingham (Kent) 4	a		14 09					14 30		

Table 200

Saturdays

14 December to 17 May

London - Dartford and Gillingham

Network Diagram - see first Page of Table 200

Station		SE	SE	SE	SE	SE	SE	SE	SE	SE	SE	SE	SE	SE	SE	SE	SE	SE	SE
St Pancras Int'l 15 ⊖	d			13 55										14 25					
Stratford International ⊖ ⛴	d			14 02										14 32					
Ebbsfleet International	d			14 14										14 44					
London Charing Cross 4 ⊖	d				13 26	13 32			13 39						13 56	14 02			14 09
London Waterloo (East) 4 ⊖	d				13 29	13 35			13 42						13 59	14 05			14 12
London Cannon Street 4 ⊖	d	13 24	13 27				13 37	13 40			13 47	13 54	13 57				14 07	14 10	
London Bridge 4 ⊖	d	13 28	13 31		13 34	13 40	13 41	13 44	13 47		13 51	13 58	14 01		14 04	14 10	14 11	14 14	14 17
Deptford	d		13 37				13 47				13 57		14 07				14 17		
Greenwich 4 ⛴	d		13 39				13 49				13 59		14 09				14 19		
Maze Hill	d		13 42				13 52				14 02		14 12				14 22		
Westcombe Park	d		13 44				13 54				14 04		14 14				14 24		
London Victoria 15 ⊖	d									13 39									
Denmark Hill 4	d									13 48									
Peckham Rye 4	d									13 51									
Nunhead 4	d									13 53									
New Cross 4 ⊖	d	13 33						13 49				14 03						14 19	
St Johns	d	13 35						13 51				14 05						14 21	
Lewisham 4 ⛴	d	13 38				13 49		13 54	13 56	14 02		14 08				14 19		14 24	14 26
Blackheath 4	d	13 41				13 52			13 59	14 04		14 11				14 22			14 29
Kidbrooke	d	13 44				13 55				14 07		14 14				14 25			
Eltham	d	13 47				13 58				14 11		14 17				14 28			
Falconwood	d	13 50				14 01				14 13		14 20				14 31			
Welling	d	13 52				14 03				14 16		14 22				14 33			
Bexleyheath	d	13 55				14 06				14 18		14 25				14 36			
Barnehurst 4	d	14 02				14 08				14 21		14 32				14 38			
Hither Green 4	d				13 44			13 59							14 14			14 29	
Lee	d				13 46			14 01							14 16			14 31	
Mottingham	d				13 49			14 04							14 19			14 34	
New Eltham	d				13 51			14 06							14 21			14 36	
Sidcup 4	d				13 55			14 10							14 25			14 40	
Albany Park	d				13 57			14 12							14 27			14 42	
Bexley	d				13 59			14 14							14 29			14 44	
Crayford	d				14 03			14 18							14 33			14 48	
Charlton 4	d		13 47				13 57	14a45	14 03		14 07		14 17				14 27	15a15	14 33
Woolwich Dockyard	d		13 50				14 00				14 10		14 20				14 30		
Woolwich Arsenal 4 ⛴	d		13 53				14 03		14 09		14 13		14 23				14 33		14 39
Plumstead	d		13 55				14 05				14 15		14 25				14 35		
Abbey Wood	d		13 58				14 08		14 13		14 18		14 28				14 38		14 43
Belvedere	d		14 00				14 10				14 20		14 30				14 40		
Erith	d		14 03				14 13				14 23		14 33				14 43		
Slade Green 4	d	14a12	14 07				14a16				14a25	14a42	14 37				14a46		
Dartford 4	a		14 12		14 08	14 15			14 24	14 28			14 42		14 38	14 45			14 54
	d				14 09				14 25						14 39				14 55
Stone Crossing	d				14 13										14 43				
Greenhithe for Bluewater	d				14 15				14 30						14 45				15 00
Swanscombe	d				14 18										14 48				
Northfleet	d				14 20										14 50				
Gravesend 4	d			14 18	14a25				14 37					14 48	14a55				15 07
Higham	d								14 43										15 13
Strood 4	d			14 28					14 48					14 58					15 18
Maidstone West	d																		
Rochester 4	d			14 33					14 53					15 03					15 23
Chatham 4	d			14 35					14 55					15 05					15 25
Gillingham (Kent) 4	a			14 39					15 00					15 09					15 30

Station		SE	SE	SE	SE	SE	SE	SE	SE	SE	SE	SE	SE	SE	SE	SE	SE	SE	SE
St Pancras Int'l 15 ⊖	d					14 55										15 25			
Stratford International ⊖ ⛴	d					15 02										15 32			
Ebbsfleet International	d					15 14										15 44			
London Charing Cross 4 ⊖	d						14 26	14 32			14 39						14 56	15 02	
London Waterloo (East) 4 ⊖	d						14 29	14 35			14 42						14 59	15 05	
London Cannon Street 4 ⊖	d		14 17	14 24	14 27				14 37	14 40			14 47	14 54	14 57				15 07
London Bridge 4 ⊖	d		14 21	14 28	14 31		14 34	14 40	14 41	14 44	14 47		14 51	14 58	15 01		15 04	15 10	15 11
Deptford	d		14 27		14 37				14 47				14 57		15 07				15 17
Greenwich 4 ⛴	d		14 29		14 39				14 49				14 59		15 09				15 19
Maze Hill	d		14 32		14 42				14 52				15 02		15 12				15 22
Westcombe Park	d		14 34		14 44				14 54				15 04		15 14				15 24
London Victoria 15 ⊖	d	14 09										14 39							
Denmark Hill 4	d	14 18										14 48							
Peckham Rye 4	d	14 21										14 51							
Nunhead 4	d	14 23										14 53							
New Cross 4 ⊖	d			14 33						14 49				15 03					
St Johns	d			14 35						14 51				15 05					
Lewisham 4 ⛴	d	14 32		14 38				14 49		14 54	14 56	15 02		15 08				15 19	
Blackheath 4	d	14 34		14 41				14 52			14 59	15 04		15 11				15 22	
Kidbrooke	d	14 37		14 44				14 55				15 07		15 14				15 25	
Eltham	d	14 41		14 47				14 58				15 11		15 17				15 28	
Falconwood	d	14 43		14 50				15 01				15 13		15 20				15 31	
Welling	d	14 46		14 52				15 03				15 16		15 22				15 33	
Bexleyheath	d	14 48		14 55				15 06				15 18		15 25				15 36	
Barnehurst 4	d	14 51		15 02				15 08				15 21		15 32				15 38	
Hither Green 4	d						14 44			14 59							15 14		
Lee	d						14 46			15 01							15 16		
Mottingham	d						14 49			15 04							15 19		
New Eltham	d						14 51			15 06							15 21		
Sidcup 4	d						14 55			15 10							15 25		
Albany Park	d						14 57			15 12							15 27		
Bexley	d						14 59			15 14							15 29		
Crayford	d						15 03			15 18							15 33		
Charlton 4	d		14 37		14 47				14 57	15a45	15 03		15 07		15 17				15 27
Woolwich Dockyard	d		14 40		14 50				15 00				15 10		15 20				15 30
Woolwich Arsenal 4 ⛴	d		14 43		14 53				15 03		15 09		15 13		15 23				15 33
Plumstead	d		14 45		14 55				15 05				15 15		15 25				15 35
Abbey Wood	d		14 48		14 58				15 08		15 13		15 18		15 28				15 38
Belvedere	d		14 50		15 00				15 10				15 20		15 30				15 40
Erith	d		14 53		15 03				15 13				15 23		15 33				15 43
Slade Green 4	d		14a55	15a12	15 07				15a16				15a25	15a42	15 37				15a46
Dartford 4	a	14 58			15 12		15 08	15 15			15 24	15 28			15 42		15 38	15 45	
	d						15 09				15 25						15 39		
Stone Crossing	d						15 13										15 43		
Greenhithe for Bluewater	d						15 15				15 30						15 45		
Swanscombe	d						15 18										15 48		
Northfleet	d						15 20										15 50		
Gravesend 4	d					15 18	15a25				15 37					15 48	15a55		
Higham	d										15 43								
Strood 4	d					15 28					15 48					15 58			
Maidstone West	d																		
Rochester 4	d					15 33					15 53					16 03			
Chatham 4	d					15 35					15 55					16 05			
Gillingham (Kent) 4	a					15 39					16 00					16 09			

Table 200

Saturdays

London - Dartford and Gillingham

14 December to 17 May

Network Diagram - see first Page of Table 200

Station		SE	SE	SE	SE	SE	SE	SE	SE	SE	SE	SE	SE	SE	SE	SE	SE	SE	SE
St Pancras Int'l 15 ⊖	d							15 55										16 25	
Stratford International ⊖	d							16 02										16 32	
Ebbsfleet International	d							16 14										16 44	
London Charing Cross 4 ⊖	d		15 09						15 26	15 32			15 39						15 56
London Waterloo (East) 4 ⊖	d		15 12						15 29	15 35			15 42						15 59
London Cannon Street 4 ⊖	d	15 10			15 17	15 24	15 27				15 37	15 40			15 47	15 54	15 57		
London Bridge 4 ⊖	d	15 14	15 17		15 21	15 28	15 31		15 34	15 40	15 41	15 44	15 47		15 51	15 58	16 01		16 04
Deptford	d				15 27		15 37				15 47				15 57		16 07		
Greenwich 4	d				15 29		15 39				15 49				15 59		16 09		
Maze Hill	d				15 32		15 42				15 52				16 02		16 12		
Westcombe Park	d				15 34		15 44				15 54				16 04		16 14		
London Victoria 15 ⊖	d			15 09										15 39					
Denmark Hill 4	d			15 18										15 48					
Peckham Rye 4	d			15 21										15 51					
Nunhead 4	d			15 23										15 53					
New Cross 4 ⊖	d	15 19				15 33						15 49				16 03			
St Johns	d	15 21				15 35						15 51				16 05			
Lewisham 4	d	15 24	15 26	15 32		15 38				15 49		15 54	15 56	16 02		16 08			
Blackheath 4	d		15 29	15 34		15 41				15 52			15 59	16 04		16 11			
Kidbrooke	d			15 37		15 44				15 55				16 07		16 14			
Eltham	d			15 41		15 47				15 58				16 11		16 17			
Falconwood	d			15 43		15 50				16 01				16 13		16 20			
Welling	d			15 46		15 52				16 03				16 16		16 22			
Bexleyheath	d			15 48		15 55				16 06				16 18		16 25			
Barnehurst 4	d			15 51		16 02				16 08				16 21		16 32			
Hither Green 4	d	15 29							15 44			15 59							16 14
Lee	d	15 31							15 46			16 01							16 16
Mottingham	d	15 34							15 49			16 04							16 19
New Eltham	d	15 36							15 51			16 06							16 21
Sidcup 4	d	15 40							15 55			16 10							16 25
Albany Park	d	15 42							15 57			16 12							16 27
Bexley	d	15 44							15 59			16 14							16 29
Crayford	d	15 48							16 03			16 18							16 33
Charlton 4	d	16a15	15 33		15 37		15 47				15 57	16a45	16 03		16 07		16 17		
Woolwich Dockyard	d				15 40		15 50				16 00				16 10		16 20		
Woolwich Arsenal 4	d		15 39		15 43		15 53				16 03		16 09		16 13		16 23		
Plumstead	d				15 45		15 55				16 05				16 15		16 25		
Abbey Wood	d		15 43		15 48		15 58				16 08		16 13		16 18		16 28		
Belvedere	d				15 50		16 00				16 10				16 20		16 30		
Erith	d				15 53		16 03				16 13				16 23		16 33		
Slade Green 4	d				15a55	16a12	16 07				16a16				16a25	16a42	16 37		
Dartford 4	a		15 54	15 58			16 12		16 08	16 15			16 24	16 28			16 42		16 38
	d		15 55						16 09				16 25						16 39
Stone Crossing	d								16 13										16 43
Greenhithe for Bluewater	d		16 00						16 15				16 30						16 45
Swanscombe	d								16 18										16 48
Northfleet	d								16 20										16 50
Gravesend 4	d		16 07					16 18	16a25				16 37					16 48	16a55
Higham	d		16 13										16 43						
Strood 4	d		16 18					16 28					16 48					16 58	
Maidstone West	d																		
Rochester 4	d		16 23					16 33					16 53					17 03	
Chatham 4	d		16 25					16 35					16 55					17 05	
Gillingham (Kent) 4	a		16 30					16 39					17 00					17 09	

Station		SE	SE	SE	SE	SE	SE	SE	SE	SE	SE	SE	SE	SE	SE	SE	SE	SE	SE
St Pancras Int'l 15 ⊖	d									16 55									
Stratford International ⊖	d									17 02									
Ebbsfleet International	d									17 14									
London Charing Cross 4 ⊖	d	16 02			16 09						16 26	16 32			16 39				
London Waterloo (East) 4 ⊖	d	16 05			16 12						16 29	16 35			16 42				
London Cannon Street 4 ⊖	d		16 07	16 10			16 17	16 24	16 27				16 37	16 40			16 47	16 54	16 57
London Bridge 4 ⊖	d	16 10	16 11	16 14	16 17		16 21	16 28	16 31		16 34	16 40	16 41	16 44	16 47		16 51	16 58	17 01
Deptford	d		16 17				16 27		16 37				16 47				16 57		17 07
Greenwich 4	d		16 19				16 29		16 39				16 49				16 59		17 09
Maze Hill	d		16 22				16 32		16 42				16 52				17 02		17 12
Westcombe Park	d		16 24				16 34		16 44				16 54				17 04		17 14
London Victoria 15 ⊖	d					16 09										16 39			
Denmark Hill 4	d					16 18										16 48			
Peckham Rye 4	d					16 21										16 51			
Nunhead 4	d					16 23										16 53			
New Cross 4 ⊖	d			16 19				16 33						16 49				17 03	
St Johns	d			16 21				16 35						16 51				17 05	
Lewisham 4	d	16 19		16 24	16 26	16 32		16 38				16 49		16 54	16 56	17 02		17 08	
Blackheath 4	d	16 22			16 29	16 34		16 41				16 52			16 59	17 04		17 11	
Kidbrooke	d	16 25				16 37		16 44				16 55				17 07		17 14	
Eltham	d	16 28				16 41		16 47				16 58				17 11		17 17	
Falconwood	d	16 31				16 43		16 50				17 01				17 13		17 20	
Welling	d	16 33				16 46		16 52				17 03				17 16		17 22	
Bexleyheath	d	16 36				16 48		16 55				17 06				17 18		17 25	
Barnehurst 4	d	16 38				16 51		17 02				17 08				17 21		17 32	
Hither Green 4	d			16 29							16 44			16 59					
Lee	d			16 31							16 46			17 01					
Mottingham	d			16 34							16 49			17 04					
New Eltham	d			16 36							16 51			17 06					
Sidcup 4	d			16 40							16 55			17 10					
Albany Park	d			16 42							16 57			17 12					
Bexley	d			16 44							16 59			17 14					
Crayford	d			16 48							17 03			17 18					
Charlton 4	d		16 27	17a15	16 33		16 37		16 47				16 57	17a45	17 03		17 07		17 17
Woolwich Dockyard	d		16 30				16 40		16 50				17 00				17 10		17 20
Woolwich Arsenal 4	d		16 33		16 39		16 43		16 53				17 03		17 09		17 13		17 23
Plumstead	d		16 35				16 45		16 55				17 05				17 15		17 25
Abbey Wood	d		16 38		16 43		16 48		16 58				17 08		17 13		17 18		17 28
Belvedere	d		16 40				16 50		17 00				17 10				17 20		17 30
Erith	d		16 43				16 53		17 03				17 13				17 23		17 33
Slade Green 4	d		16a46				16a55	17a12	17 07				17a16				17a25	17a42	17 37
Dartford 4	a	16 45			16 54	16 58			17 12		17 08	17 15			17 24	17 28			17 42
	d				16 55						17 09				17 25				
Stone Crossing	d										17 13								
Greenhithe for Bluewater	d				17 00						17 15				17 30				
Swanscombe	d										17 18								
Northfleet	d										17 20								
Gravesend 4	d				17 07					17 18	17a25				17 37				
Higham	d				17 13										17 43				
Strood 4	d				17 18					17 28					17 48				
Maidstone West	d																		
Rochester 4	d				17 23					17 33					17 53				
Chatham 4	d				17 25					17 35					17 55				
Gillingham (Kent) 4	a				17 30					17 39					18 00				

Table 200

Saturdays

14 December to 17 May

London - Dartford and Gillingham

Network Diagram - see first Page of Table 200

Station		SE	SE	SE	SE	SE	SE	SE	SE	SE
St Pancras Int'l 15	d	17 25								
Stratford International	d	17 32								
Ebbsfleet International	d	17 44								
London Charing Cross 4	d		16 56	17 02			17 09			
London Waterloo (East) 4	d		16 59	17 05			17 12			
London Cannon Street 4	d				17 07	17 10			17 17	17 24
London Bridge 4	d		17 04	17 10	17 11	17 14	17 17		17 21	17 28
Deptford	d				17 17				17 27	
Greenwich 4	d				17 19				17 29	
Maze Hill	d				17 22				17 32	
Westcombe Park	d				17 24				17 34	
London Victoria 15	d							17 09		
Denmark Hill 4	d							17 18		
Peckham Rye 4	d							17 21		
Nunhead 4	d							17 23		
New Cross 4	d					17 19				17 33
St Johns	d					17 21				17 35
Lewisham 4	d			17 19		17 24	17 26	17 32		17 38
Blackheath 4	d			17 22			17 29	17 34		17 41
Kidbrooke	d			17 25				17 37		17 44
Eltham	d			17 28				17 41		17 47
Falconwood	d			17 31				17 43		17 50
Welling	d			17 33				17 46		17 52
Bexleyheath	d			17 36				17 48		17 55
Barnehurst 4	d			17 38				17 51		18 02
Hither Green 4	d		17 14			17 29				
Lee	d		17 16			17 31				
Mottingham	d		17 19			17 34				
New Eltham	d		17 21			17 36				
Sidcup 4	d		17 25			17 40				
Albany Park	d		17 27			17 42				
Bexley	d		17 29			17 44				
Crayford	d		17 33			17 48				
Charlton 4	d				17 27	18a15	17 33		17 37	
Woolwich Dockyard	d				17 30				17 40	
Woolwich Arsenal 4	d				17 33		17 39		17 43	
Plumstead	d				17 35				17 45	
Abbey Wood	d				17 38		17 43		17 48	
Belvedere	d				17 40				17 50	
Erith	d				17 43				17 53	
Slade Green 4	d				17a46				17a55	18a12
Dartford 4	a		17 38	17 45			17 54	17 58		
	d		17 39				17 55			
Stone Crossing	d		17 43							
Greenhithe for Bluewater	d		17 45				18 00			
Swanscombe	d		17 48							
Northfleet	d		17 50							
Gravesend 4	d	17 48	17a55				18 07			
Higham	d						18 13			
Strood 4	d	17 58					18 18			
Maidstone West	d									
Rochester 4	d	18 03					18 23			
Chatham 4	d	18 05					18 25			
Gillingham (Kent) 4	a	18 09					18 30			

Station		SE	SE	SE	SE	SE	SE	SE	SE	SE
St Pancras Int'l 15	d		17 55							
Stratford International	d		18 02							
Ebbsfleet International	d		18 14							
London Charing Cross 4	d			17 26	17 32			17 39		
London Waterloo (East) 4	d			17 29	17 35			17 42		
London Cannon Street 4	d	17 27				17 37	17 40			17 47
London Bridge 4	d	17 31		17 34	17 40	17 41	17 44	17 47		17 51
Deptford	d	17 37				17 47				17 57
Greenwich 4	d	17 39				17 49				17 59
Maze Hill	d	17 42				17 52				18 02
Westcombe Park	d	17 44				17 54				18 04
London Victoria 15	d								17 39	
Denmark Hill 4	d								17 48	
Peckham Rye 4	d								17 51	
Nunhead 4	d								17 53	
New Cross 4	d						17 49			
St Johns	d						17 51			
Lewisham 4	d				17 49		17 54	17 56	18 02	
Blackheath 4	d				17 52			17 59	18 04	
Kidbrooke	d				17 55				18 07	
Eltham	d				17 58				18 11	
Falconwood	d				18 01				18 13	
Welling	d				18 03				18 16	
Bexleyheath	d				18 06				18 18	
Barnehurst 4	d				18 08				18 21	
Hither Green 4	d			17 44			17 59			
Lee	d			17 46			18 01			
Mottingham	d			17 49			18 04			
New Eltham	d			17 51			18 06			
Sidcup 4	d			17 55			18 10			
Albany Park	d			17 57			18 12			
Bexley	d			17 59			18 14			
Crayford	d			18 03			18 18			
Charlton 4	d	17 47				17 57	18a45	18 03		18 07
Woolwich Dockyard	d	17 50				18 00				18 10
Woolwich Arsenal 4	d	17 53				18 03		18 09		18 13
Plumstead	d	17 55				18 05				18 15
Abbey Wood	d	17 58				18 08		18 13		18 18
Belvedere	d	18 00				18 10				18 20
Erith	d	18 03				18 13				18 23
Slade Green 4	d	18 07				18a16				18a25
Dartford 4	a	18 12		18 08	18 15			18 24	18 28	
	d			18 09				18 25		
Stone Crossing	d			18 13						
Greenhithe for Bluewater	d			18 15				18 30		
Swanscombe	d			18 18						
Northfleet	d			18 20						
Gravesend 4	d		18 18	18a25				18 37		
Higham	d							18 43		
Strood 4	d		18 28					18 48		
Maidstone West	d									
Rochester 4	d		18 33					18 53		
Chatham 4	d		18 35					18 55		
Gillingham (Kent) 4	a		18 39					19 00		

Station		SE	SE	SE	SE	SE	SE	SE	SE	SE
St Pancras Int'l 15	d			18 25						
Stratford International	d			18 32						
Ebbsfleet International	d			18 44						
London Charing Cross 4	d				17 56	18 02			18 09	
London Waterloo (East) 4	d				17 59	18 05			18 12	
London Cannon Street 4	d	17 54	17 57				18 07	18 10		
London Bridge 4	d	17 58	18 01		18 04	18 10	18 11	18 14	18 17	
Deptford	d		18 07				18 17			
Greenwich 4	d		18 09				18 19			
Maze Hill	d		18 12				18 22			
Westcombe Park	d		18 14				18 24			
London Victoria 15	d									18 09
Denmark Hill 4	d									18 18
Peckham Rye 4	d									18 21
Nunhead 4	d									18 23
New Cross 4	d	18 03						18 19		
St Johns	d	18 05						18 21		
Lewisham 4	d	18 08				18 19		18 24	18 26	18 32
Blackheath 4	d	18 11				18 22			18 29	18 34
Kidbrooke	d	18 14				18 25				18 37
Eltham	d	18 17				18 28				18 41
Falconwood	d	18 20				18 31				18 43
Welling	d	18 22				18 33				18 46
Bexleyheath	d	18 25				18 36				18 48
Barnehurst 4	d	18a28				18 38				18 51
Hither Green 4	d				18 14			18 29		
Lee	d				18 16			18 31		
Mottingham	d				18 19			18 34		
New Eltham	d				18 21			18 36		
Sidcup 4	d				18 25			18 40		
Albany Park	d				18 27			18 42		
Bexley	d				18 29			18 44		
Crayford	d				18 33			18 48		
Charlton 4	d		18 17				18 27	19a15	18 33	
Woolwich Dockyard	d		18 20				18 30			
Woolwich Arsenal 4	d		18 23				18 33		18 39	
Plumstead	d		18 25				18 35			
Abbey Wood	d		18 28				18 38		18 43	
Belvedere	d		18 30				18 40			
Erith	d		18 33				18 43			
Slade Green 4	d		18 37				18a45			
Dartford 4	a		18 42		18 38	18 45			18 54	18 58
	d				18 39				18 55	
Stone Crossing	d				18 43					
Greenhithe for Bluewater	d				18 45				19 00	
Swanscombe	d				18 48					
Northfleet	d				18 50					
Gravesend 4	d			18 48	18a55				19 07	
Higham	d								19 13	
Strood 4	d			18 58					19 18	
Maidstone West	d									
Rochester 4	d			19 03					19 23	
Chatham 4	d			19 05					19 25	
Gillingham (Kent) 4	a			19 09					19 30	

Station		SE	SE	SE	SE	SE	SE	SE	SE	SE
St Pancras Int'l 15	d				18 55					
Stratford International	d				19 02					
Ebbsfleet International	d				19 14					
London Charing Cross 4	d					18 26	18 32			18 39
London Waterloo (East) 4	d					18 29	18 35			18 42
London Cannon Street 4	d	18 17	18 24	18 27				18 37	18 40	
London Bridge 4	d	18 21	18 28	18 31		18 34	18 40	18 41	18 44	18 47
Deptford	d	18 27		18 37				18 47		
Greenwich 4	d	18 29		18 39				18 49		
Maze Hill	d	18 32		18 42				18 52		
Westcombe Park	d	18 34		18 44				18 54		
London Victoria 15	d									
Denmark Hill 4	d									
Peckham Rye 4	d									
Nunhead 4	d									
New Cross 4	d		18 33						18 49	
St Johns	d		18 35						18 51	
Lewisham 4	d		18 38				18 49		18 54	18 56
Blackheath 4	d		18 41				18 52			18 59
Kidbrooke	d		18 44				18 55			
Eltham	d		18 47				18 58			
Falconwood	d		18 50				19 01			
Welling	d		18 52				19 03			
Bexleyheath	d		18 55				19 06			
Barnehurst 4	d		18a58				19 08			
Hither Green 4	d					18 44			18 59	
Lee	d					18 46			19 01	
Mottingham	d					18 49			19 04	
New Eltham	d					18 51			19 06	
Sidcup 4	d					18 55			19 10	
Albany Park	d					18 57			19 12	
Bexley	d					18 59			19 14	
Crayford	d					19 03			19 18	
Charlton 4	d	18 37		18 47				18 57	19a45	19 03
Woolwich Dockyard	d	18 40		18 50				19 00		
Woolwich Arsenal 4	d	18 43		18 53				19 03		19 09
Plumstead	d	18 45		18 55				19 05		
Abbey Wood	d	18 48		18 58				19 08		19 13
Belvedere	d	18 50		19 00				19 10		
Erith	d	18 53		19 03				19 13		
Slade Green 4	d	18a56		19 07				19a15		
Dartford 4	a			19 12		19 08	19 15			19 24
	d					19 09				19 25
Stone Crossing	d					19 13				
Greenhithe for Bluewater	d					19 15				19 30
Swanscombe	d					19 18				
Northfleet	d					19 20				
Gravesend 4	d				19 18	19a25				19 37
Higham	d									19 43
Strood 4	d				19 28					19 48
Maidstone West	d									
Rochester 4	d				19 33					19 53
Chatham 4	d				19 35					19 55
Gillingham (Kent) 4	a				19 39					20 00

Table 200

Saturdays

14 December to 17 May

London - Dartford and Gillingham

Network Diagram - see first Page of Table 200

Station		SE	SE	SE	SE	SE	SE	SE	SE	SE	SE	SE	SE	SE	SE	SE	SE	SE	SE
St Pancras Int'l 15 ⊖	d					19 25									19 55				
Stratford International ⊖ ⛴	d					19 32									20 02				
Ebbsfleet International	d					19 44									20 14				
London Charing Cross 4 ⊖	d						18 56	19 02			19 09					19 26	19 32	19 39	
London Waterloo (East) 4 ⊖	d						18 59	19 05			19 12					19 29	19 35	19 42	
London Cannon Street 4 ⊖	d		18 47	18 54	18 57				19 07	19 10			19 24	19 27					
London Bridge 4 ⊖	d		18 51	18 58	19 01		19 04	19 10	19 11	19 14	19 17		19 28	19 31		19 34	19 40	19 47	
Deptford	d		18 57		19 07				19 17					19 37					
Greenwich 4 ⛴	d		18 59		19 09				19 19					19 39					
Maze Hill	d		19 02		19 12				19 22					19 42					
Westcombe Park	d		19 04		19 14				19 24					19 44					
London Victoria 15 ⊖	d	18 39										19 09							19 39
Denmark Hill 4	d	18 48										19 18							19 48
Peckham Rye 4	d	18 51										19 21							19 51
Nunhead 4	d	18 53										19 23							19 53
New Cross 4 ⊖	d			19 03						19 19			19 33				19 45		
St Johns	d			19 05						19 21			19 35						
Lewisham 4 ⛴	d	19 02		19 08				19 19		19 24	19 26	19 32	19 38				19 49	19 56	20 02
Blackheath 4	d	19 04		19 11				19 22			19 29	19 34	19 41				19 52	19 59	20 04
Kidbrooke	d	19 07		19 14				19 25				19 37	19 44				19 55		20 07
Eltham	d	19 11		19 17				19 28				19 41	19 47				19 58		20 11
Falconwood	d	19 13		19 20				19 31				19 43	19 50				20 01		20 13
Welling	d	19 16		19 22				19 33				19 46	19 52				20 03		20 16
Bexleyheath	d	19 18		19 25				19 36				19 48	19 55				20 06		20 18
Barnehurst 4	d	19 21		19a28				19 38				19 51	19a58				20 08		20 21
Hither Green 4	d						19 14			19 29						19 44			
Lee	d						19 16			19 31						19 46			
Mottingham	d						19 19			19 34						19 49			
New Eltham	d						19 21			19 36						19 51			
Sidcup 4	d						19 25			19 40						19 55			
Albany Park	d						19 27			19 42						19 57			
Bexley	d						19 29			19 44						19 59			
Crayford	d						19 33			19 48						20 03			
Charlton 4	d		19 07		19 17				19 27	20a15	19 33			19 47				20 03	
Woolwich Dockyard	d		19 10		19 20				19 30					19 50					
Woolwich Arsenal 4 ⛴	d		19 13		19 23				19 33		19 39			19 53				20 09	
Plumstead	d		19 15		19 25				19 35					19 55					
Abbey Wood	d		19 18		19 28				19 38		19 43			19 58				20 13	
Belvedere	d		19 20		19 30				19 40					20 00					
Erith	d		19 23		19 33				19 43					20 03					
Slade Green 4	d		19a26		19 37				19 46					20 07					
Dartford 4	a	19 28			19 42		19 38	19 45	19 52		19 54	19 58		20 12		20 08	20 15	20 24	20 28
	d						19 39				19 55					20 09		20 25	
Stone Crossing	d						19 43									20 13			
Greenhithe for Bluewater	d						19 45				20 00					20 15		20 30	
Swanscombe	d						19 48									20 18			
Northfleet	d						19 50									20 20			
Gravesend 4	d					19 48	19a55				20 07				20 18	20a25		20 37	
Higham	d										20 13							20 43	
Strood 4	d					19 58					20 18				20 28			20 48	
Maidstone West	d																		
Rochester 4	d					20 03					20 23				20 33			20 53	
Chatham 4	d					20 05					20 25				20 35			20 55	
Gillingham (Kent) 4	a					20 09					20 30				20 39			21 00	

Station		SE	SE	SE	SE	SE	SE	SE	SE	SE	SE	SE	SE	SE	SE	SE	SE	SE	SE
St Pancras Int'l 15 ⊖	d		20 25						20 55						21 25				
Stratford International ⊖ ⛴	d		20 32						21 02						21 32				
Ebbsfleet International	d		20 44						21 14						21 44				
London Charing Cross 4 ⊖	d			19 52	19 56	20 02	20 09			20 22	20 26	20 32	20 39			20 52	20 56	21 02	21 09
London Waterloo (East) 4 ⊖	d			19 55	19 59	20 05	20 12			20 25	20 29	20 35	20 42			20 55	20 59	21 05	21 12
London Cannon Street 4 ⊖	d																		
London Bridge 4 ⊖	d	19 50		20 00	20 05	20 10	20 17	20 20		20 30	20 35	20 40	20 47	20 50		21 00	21 05	21 10	21 17
Deptford	d	19 56			20 11			20 26			20 41			20 56			21 11		
Greenwich 4 ⛴	d	19 58			20 13			20 28			20 43			20 58			21 13		
Maze Hill	d	20 01			20 16			20 31			20 46			21 01			21 16		
Westcombe Park	d	20 03			20 18			20 33			20 48			21 03			21 18		
London Victoria 15 ⊖	d																		
Denmark Hill 4	d																		
Peckham Rye 4	d																		
Nunhead 4	d																		
New Cross 4 ⊖	d			20 05		20 15				20 35		20 45				21 05		21 15	
St Johns	d																		
Lewisham 4 ⛴	d			20 09		20 19	20 26			20 39		20 49	20 56			21 09		21 19	21 26
Blackheath 4	d					20 22	20 29					20 52	20 59					21 22	21 29
Kidbrooke	d					20 25						20 55						21 25	
Eltham	d					20 28						20 58						21 28	
Falconwood	d					20 31						21 01						21 31	
Welling	d					20 33						21 03						21 33	
Bexleyheath	d					20 36						21 06						21 36	
Barnehurst 4	d					20 38						21 08						21 38	
Hither Green 4	d			20 14						20 44						21 14			
Lee	d			20 16						20 46						21 16			
Mottingham	d			20 19						20 49						21 19			
New Eltham	d			20 21						20 51						21 21			
Sidcup 4	d			20 25						20 55						21 25			
Albany Park	d			20 27						20 57						21 27			
Bexley	d			20 29						20 59						21 29			
Crayford	d			20 33						21 03						21 33			
Charlton 4	d	20 06			20 20		20 33	20 36			20 50		21 03	21 06			21 20		21 33
Woolwich Dockyard	d	20 09			20 23			20 39			20 53			21 09			21 23		
Woolwich Arsenal 4 ⛴	d	20 12			20 26		20 39	20 42			20 56		21 09	21 12			21 26		21 39
Plumstead	d	20 14			20 28			20 44			20 58			21 14			21 28		
Abbey Wood	d	20 17			20 31		20 43	20 47			21 01		21 13	21 17			21 31		21 43
Belvedere	d	20 20			20 34			20 50			21 04			21 20			21 34		
Erith	d	20 22			20 36			20 52			21 06			21 22			21 36		
Slade Green 4	d	20 26			20 39			20 56			21 09			21 26			21 39		
Dartford 4	a	20 31		20 38	20 44	20 46	20 54	21 01		21 08	21 14	21 16	21 24	21 31		21 38	21 44	21 46	21 54
	d			20 39			20 55			21 09			21 25			21 39			21 55
Stone Crossing	d			20 43						21 13						21 43			
Greenhithe for Bluewater	d			20 45			21 00			21 15			21 30			21 45			22 00
Swanscombe	d			20 48						21 18						21 48			
Northfleet	d			20 50						21 20						21 50			
Gravesend 4	d		20 48	20a55			21 07		21 18	21a25			21 37		21 48	21a55			22 07
Higham	d						21 13						21 43						22 13
Strood 4	d		20 58				21 18		21 28				21 48		21 58				22 18
Maidstone West	d																		
Rochester 4	d		21 03				21 23		21 33				21 53		22 03				22 23
Chatham 4	d		21 05				21 25		21 35				21 55		22 05				22 25
Gillingham (Kent) 4	a		21 09				21 30		21 39				22 00		22 09				22 30

Table 200

Saturdays

14 December to 17 May

London - Dartford and Gillingham

Network Diagram - see first Page of Table 200

Station		SE	SE	SE	SE	SE	SE	SE	SE	SE	SE	SE	SE	SE	SE	SE	SE	SE	SE	SE	SE	SE	SE	SE	SE	SE	SE
St Pancras Int'l 15 ⊖	d	21 55								22 25					22 55					23 25					23 55		
Stratford International ⊖ ⛴	d	22 02								22 32					23 02					23 32					00 02		
Ebbsfleet International	d	22 14								22 44					23 14					23 44					00 14		
London Charing Cross 4 ⊖	d		21 22	21 26	21 32	21 39	21 52	21 56	22 02		22 09	22 22	22 26	22 32		22 39	22 52	22 56	23 02		23 09	23 22	23 26	23 32		23 39	23 56
London Waterloo (East) 4 ⊖	d		21 25	21 29	21 35	21 42	21 55	21 59	22 05		22 12	22 25	22 29	22 35		22 42	22 55	22 59	23 05		23 12	23 25	23 29	23 35		23 42	23 59
London Cannon Street 4 ⊖	d																										
London Bridge 4 ⊖	d		21 30	21 35	21 40	21 47	22 00	22 05	22 10		22 17	22 30	22 35	22 40		22 47	23 00	23 05	23 10		23 17	23 30	23 35	23 40		23 47	00 05
Deptford	d			21 41				22 11					22 41					23 11					23 41				00 11
Greenwich 4 ⛴	d			21 43				22 13					22 43					23 13					23 43				00 13
Maze Hill	d			21 46				22 16					22 46					23 16					23 46				00 16
Westcombe Park	d			21 48				22 18					22 48					23 18					23 48				00 18
London Victoria 15 ⊖	d																										
Denmark Hill 4	d																										
Peckham Rye 4	d																										
Nunhead 4	d																										
New Cross 4 ⊖	d		21 35		21 45		22 05		22 15			22 35		22 45			23 05		23 15			23 35		23 45			
St Johns	d																										
Lewisham 4 ⛴	d		21 39		21 49	21 56	22 09		22 19		22 26	22 39		22 49		22 56	23 09		23 19		23 26	23 39		23 49		23 56	
Blackheath 4	d				21 52	21 59			22 22		22 29			22 52		22 59			23 22		23 29			23 52		23 58	
Kidbrooke	d				21 55				22 25					22 55					23 25					23 55			
Eltham	d				21 58				22 28					22 58					23 28					23 58			
Falconwood	d				22 01				22 31					23 01					23 31					00 01			
Welling	d				22 03				22 33					23 03					23 33					00 03			
Bexleyheath	d				22 06				22 36					23 06					23 36					00 06			
Barnehurst 4	d				22 08				22 38					23 08					23 38					00 08			
Hither Green 4	d		21 44				22 14					22 44					23 14					23 44					
Lee	d		21 46				22 16					22 46					23 16					23 46					
Mottingham	d		21 49				22 19					22 49					23 19					23 49					
New Eltham	d		21 51				22 21					22 51					23 21					23 51					
Sidcup 4	d		21 55				22 25					22 55					23 25					23 55					
Albany Park	d		21 57				22 27					22 57					23 27					23 57					
Bexley	d		21 59				22 29					22 59					23 29					23 59					
Crayford	d		22 03				22 33					23 03					23 33					00 03					
Charlton 4	d			21 50		22 03		22 20			22 33		22 50			23 03		23 20			23 33		23 50			00 03	00 20
Woolwich Dockyard	d			21 53				22 23					22 53					23 23					23 53				00 23
Woolwich Arsenal 4 ⛴	d			21 56		22 09		22 26			22 39		22 56			23 09		23 26			23 39		23 56			00 09	00 26
Plumstead	d			21 58				22 28					22 58					23 28					23 58				00 28
Abbey Wood	d			22 01		22 13		22 31			22 43		23 01			23 13		23 31			23 43		00 01			00 13	00 31
Belvedere	d			22 04				22 34					23 04					23 34					00 04				00 34
Erith	d			22 06				22 36					23 06					23 36					00 06				00 36
Slade Green 4	d			22 09				22 39					23 09					23 39					00 09				00 39
Dartford 4	a		22 08	22 14	22 16	22 24	22 38	22 44	22 46		22 54	23 08	23 14	23 16		23 24	23 38	23 44	23 46		23 54	00 08	00 14	00 16		00 24	00 44
	d		22 09			22 25					22 55					23 25					23 55					00 25	
Stone Crossing	d		22 13			22 29					22 59					23 29					23 58					00 29	
Greenhithe for Bluewater	d		22 15			22 31					23 01					23 31					23 59					00 31	
Swanscombe	d		22 18			22 34					23 04					23 34					00 04					00 34	
Northfleet	d		22 20			22 36					23 06					23 36					00 06					00 36	
Gravesend 4	d	22 18	22a25			22 40				22 48	23 10				23 18	23 40				23 48	00 10				00 18	00 40	
Higham	d					22 46					23 16					23 46					00 16					00 46	
Strood 4	d	22 28				22 52				22 58	23 22				23 28	23 52				23 58	00 22				00 28	00 52	
Maidstone West	d																										
Rochester 4	d	22 33				22 56				23 03	23 26				23 33	23 56				00 03	00 26				00 33	00 56	
Chatham 4	d	22 35				22 59				23 05	23 29				23 35	23 59				00 05	00 29				00 35	00 59	
Gillingham (Kent) 4	a	22 39				23 03				23 09	23 33				23 39	00 03				00 09	00 33				00 39	01 03	

Table 200

Sundays

London - Dartford and Gillingham

8 December to 11 May

Network Diagram - see first Page of Table 200

Station		SE A	SE A	SE A	SE A	SE A	SE A	SE A	SE A	SE
St Pancras Int'l ⊖	d									
Stratford International ⊖	d						00 02			
Ebbsfleet International	d						00 14			
London Charing Cross ⊖	d									00 02
London Waterloo (East) ⊖	d									00 05
London Cannon Street ⊖	d									
London Bridge ⊖	d								00 05	00 10
Deptford	d								00 11	
Greenwich	d								00 13	
Maze Hill	d								00 16	
Westcombe Park	d								00 18	
London Victoria ⊖	d									
Denmark Hill	d									
Peckham Rye	d									
Nunhead	d									
New Cross ⊖	d									00 15
St Johns	d									
Lewisham	d									00 19
Blackheath	d									00 22
Kidbrooke	d									00 25
Eltham	d									00 28
Falconwood	d			00 01						00 31
Welling	d			00 03						00 33
Bexleyheath	d			00 06						00 36
Barnehurst	d			00 08						00 38
Hither Green	d									
Lee	d									
Mottingham	d									
New Eltham	d									
Sidcup	d									
Albany Park	d									
Bexley	d									
Crayford	d	00 03								
Charlton	d							00 03	00 20	
Woolwich Dockyard	d								00 23	
Woolwich Arsenal	d							00 09	00 26	
Plumstead	d								00 28	
Abbey Wood	d		00 01					00 13	00 31	
Belvedere	d		00 04						00 34	
Erith	d		00 06						00 36	
Slade Green	d		00 09						00 39	
Dartford	a	00 08	00 14	00 16				00 24	00 44	00 46
	d							00 25		
Stone Crossing	d							00 29		
Greenhithe for Bluewater	d							00 31		
Swanscombe	d					00 04		00 34		
Northfleet	d					00 06		00 36		
Gravesend	d					00 10	00 18	00 40		
Higham	d					00 16		00 46		
Strood	d					00 22	00 28	00 52		
Maidstone West	d									
Rochester	d				00 03	00 26	00 33	00 56		
Chatham	d				00 05	00 29	00 35	00 59		
Gillingham (Kent)	a				00 09	00 33	00 39	01 03		

Station		SE	SE	SE	SE	SE	SE	SE	SE	SE
St Pancras Int'l ⊖	d									
Stratford International ⊖	d									
Ebbsfleet International	d									
London Charing Cross ⊖	d	00 10	00 18		07 26		07 50	07 52	07 56	08 09
London Waterloo (East) ⊖	d	00 13	00 21		07 29		07 53	07 55	07 59	08 12
London Cannon Street ⊖	d									
London Bridge ⊖	d	00 18	00 26		07 35		07 58	08 00	08 05	08 17
Deptford	d				07 41				08 11	
Greenwich	d				07 43				08 13	
Maze Hill	d				07 46				08 16	
Westcombe Park	d				07 48				08 18	
London Victoria ⊖	d									
Denmark Hill	d									
Peckham Rye	d									
Nunhead	d									
New Cross ⊖	d	00 23	00 31				08 03			
St Johns	d									
Lewisham	d	00 27	00 35				08 08	08 09		08 26
Blackheath	d		00 38				08 10			08 28
Kidbrooke	d						08 13			
Eltham	d						08 17			
Falconwood	d						08 19			
Welling	d						08 22			
Bexleyheath	d						08 24			
Barnehurst	d						08 27			
Hither Green	d	00 32						08 14		
Lee	d	00 34						08 16		
Mottingham	d	00 37						08 19		
New Eltham	d	00 39						08 21		
Sidcup	d	00 43						08 25		
Albany Park	d	00 45						08 27		
Bexley	d	00 47						08 29		
Crayford	d	00 51						08 33		
Charlton	d		00 42		07 51				08 21	08 33
Woolwich Dockyard	d				07 54				08 24	
Woolwich Arsenal	d		00 47		07 57				08 27	08 39
Plumstead	d		00 49		07 59				08 29	
Abbey Wood	d		00 53		08 02				08 32	08 43
Belvedere	d		00 55		08 05				08 35	
Erith	d		00 58		08 07				08 37	
Slade Green	d		01 01		08 10				08 40	
Dartford	a	00 56	01 06		08 15		08 35	08 38	08 45	08 54
	d		01 07	07 55		08 25		08 39		08 55
Stone Crossing	d			07 59		08 29		08 43		
Greenhithe for Bluewater	d		01 12	08 01		08 31		08 45		09 00
Swanscombe	d			08 04		08 34		08 48		
Northfleet	d			08 06		08 36		08 50		
Gravesend	d		01 19	08 10		08 40		08a55		09 07
Higham	d		01 25	08 16		08 46				09 13
Strood	d		01 30	08 22		08 52				09 18
Maidstone West	d									
Rochester	d		01 35	08 26		08 56				09 23
Chatham	d		01 37	08 29		08 59				09 25
Gillingham (Kent)	a		01 42	08 33		09 07				09 30

Station		SE	SE	SE	SE	SE	SE	SE	SE	SE
St Pancras Int'l ⊖	d						09 25			
Stratford International ⊖	d						09 32			
Ebbsfleet International	d						09 44			
London Charing Cross ⊖	d	08 20	08 22	08 26	08 39	08 50		08 52	08 56	09 09
London Waterloo (East) ⊖	d	08 23	08 25	08 29	08 42	08 53		08 55	08 59	09 12
London Cannon Street ⊖	d									
London Bridge ⊖	d	08 28	08 30	08 35	08 47	08 58		09 00	09 05	09 17
Deptford	d			08 41					09 11	
Greenwich	d			08 43					09 13	
Maze Hill	d			08 46					09 16	
Westcombe Park	d			08 48					09 18	
London Victoria ⊖	d									
Denmark Hill	d									
Peckham Rye	d									
Nunhead	d									
New Cross ⊖	d	08 33				09 03				
St Johns	d									
Lewisham	d	08 38	08 39		08 56	09 08		09 09		09 26
Blackheath	d	08 40			08 58	09 10				09 28
Kidbrooke	d	08 43				09 13				
Eltham	d	08 47				09 17				
Falconwood	d	08 49				09 19				
Welling	d	08 52				09 22				
Bexleyheath	d	08 54				09 24				
Barnehurst	d	08 57				09 27				
Hither Green	d		08 44					09 14		
Lee	d		08 46					09 16		
Mottingham	d		08 49					09 19		
New Eltham	d		08 51					09 21		
Sidcup	d		08 55					09 25		
Albany Park	d		08 57					09 27		
Bexley	d		08 59					09 29		
Crayford	d		09 03					09 33		
Charlton	d			08 51	09 03				09 21	09 33
Woolwich Dockyard	d			08 54					09 24	
Woolwich Arsenal	d			08 57	09 09				09 27	09 39
Plumstead	d			08 59					09 29	
Abbey Wood	d			09 02	09 13				09 32	09 43
Belvedere	d			09 05					09 35	
Erith	d			09 07					09 37	
Slade Green	d			09 10					09 40	
Dartford	a	09 05	09 08	09 15	09 24	09 35		09 38	09 45	09 54
	d		09 09		09 25			09 39		09 55
Stone Crossing	d		09 13					09 43		
Greenhithe for Bluewater	d		09 15		09 30			09 45		10 00
Swanscombe	d		09 18					09 48		
Northfleet	d		09 20					09 50		
Gravesend	d		09a25		09 37		09 48	09a55		10 07
Higham	d				09 43					10 13
Strood	d				09 48		09 58			10 18
Maidstone West	d									
Rochester	d				09 53		10 03			10 23
Chatham	d				09 55		10 05			10 25
Gillingham (Kent)	a				10 00		10 09			10 30

Station		SE	SE	SE	SE	SE	SE	SE	SE	SE
St Pancras Int'l ⊖	d								10 22	
Stratford International ⊖	d								10 32	
Ebbsfleet International	d								10 44	
London Charing Cross ⊖	d		09 20	09 22	09 26	09 39		09 50		09 52
London Waterloo (East) ⊖	d		09 23	09 25	09 29	09 42		09 53		09 55
London Cannon Street ⊖	d									
London Bridge ⊖	d	09 20	09 28	09 30	09 35	09 47	09 50	09 58		10 00
Deptford	d	09 26			09 41		09 56			
Greenwich	d	09 28			09 43		09 58			
Maze Hill	d	09 31			09 46		10 01			
Westcombe Park	d	09 33			09 48		10 03			
London Victoria ⊖	d									
Denmark Hill	d									
Peckham Rye	d									
Nunhead	d									
New Cross ⊖	d		09 33					10 03		
St Johns	d									
Lewisham	d		09 38	09 39		09 56		10 08		10 09
Blackheath	d		09 40			09 58		10 10		
Kidbrooke	d		09 43					10 13		
Eltham	d		09 47					10 17		
Falconwood	d		09 49					10 19		
Welling	d		09 52					10 22		
Bexleyheath	d		09 54					10 24		
Barnehurst	d		09 57					10 27		
Hither Green	d			09 44						10 14
Lee	d			09 46						10 16
Mottingham	d			09 49						10 19
New Eltham	d			09 51						10 21
Sidcup	d			09 55						10 25
Albany Park	d			09 57						10 27
Bexley	d			09 59						10 29
Crayford	d			10 03						10 33
Charlton	d	09 36			09 51	10 03	10 06			
Woolwich Dockyard	d	09 39			09 54		10 09			
Woolwich Arsenal	d	09 42			09 57	10 09	10 12			
Plumstead	d	09a45			09 59		10a15			
Abbey Wood	d				10 02	10 13				
Belvedere	d				10 05					
Erith	d				10 07					
Slade Green	d				10 10					
Dartford	a		10 05	10 08	10 15	10 24		10 35		10 38
	d			10 09		10 25				10 39
Stone Crossing	d			10 13						10 43
Greenhithe for Bluewater	d			10 15		10 30				10 45
Swanscombe	d			10 18						10 48
Northfleet	d			10 20						10 50
Gravesend	d			10a25		10 37			10 48	10a55
Higham	d					10 43				
Strood	d					10 48			10 58	
Maidstone West	d									
Rochester	d					10 53			11 03	
Chatham	d					10 55			11 05	
Gillingham (Kent)	a					11 00			11 09	

A not 8 December

Table 200

Sundays

8 December to 11 May

London - Dartford and Gillingham

Network Diagram - see first Page of Table 200

		SE	SE	SE	SE	SE	SE	SE	SE	SE	SE	SE	SE	SE	SE	SE	SE	SE	SE
St Pancras Int'l ⊖	d										11 25								
Stratford International ⊖	d										11 32								
Ebbsfleet International	d										11 44								
London Charing Cross ⊖	d	09 56	10 09		10 20	10 22	10 26	10 39		10 50		10 52	10 56	11 09		11 20	11 22	11 26	11 39
London Waterloo (East) ⊖	d	09 59	10 12		10 23	10 25	10 29	10 42		10 53		10 55	10 59	11 12		11 23	11 25	11 29	11 42
London Cannon Street ⊖	d																		
London Bridge ⊖	d	10 05	10 17	10 20	10 28	10 30	10 35	10 47	10 50	10 58		11 00	11 05	11 17	11 20	11 28	11 30	11 35	11 47
Deptford	d	10 11		10 26			10 41		10 56				11 11		11 26			11 41	
Greenwich	d	10 13		10 28			10 43		10 58				11 13		11 28			11 43	
Maze Hill	d	10 16		10 31			10 46		11 01				11 16		11 31			11 46	
Westcombe Park	d	10 18		10 33			10 48		11 03				11 18		11 33			11 48	
London Victoria ⊖	d																		
Denmark Hill	d																		
Peckham Rye	d																		
Nunhead	d																		
New Cross ⊖	d				10 33					11 03						11 33			
St Johns	d																		
Lewisham	d		10 26		10 38	10 39		10 56		11 08		11 09		11 26		11 38	11 39		11 56
Blackheath	d		10 28		10 40			10 58		11 10				11 28		11 40			11 58
Kidbrooke	d				10 43					11 13						11 43			
Eltham	d				10 47					11 17						11 47			
Falconwood	d				10 49					11 19						11 49			
Welling	d				10 52					11 22						11 52			
Bexleyheath	d				10 54					11 24						11 54			
Barnehurst	d				10 57					11 27						11 57			
Hither Green	d					10 44						11 14					11 44		
Lee	d					10 46						11 16					11 46		
Mottingham	d					10 49						11 19					11 49		
New Eltham	d					10 51						11 21					11 51		
Sidcup	d					10 55						11 25					11 55		
Albany Park	d					10 57						11 27					11 57		
Bexley	d					10 59						11 29					11 59		
Crayford	d					11 03						11 33					12 03		
Charlton	d	10 21	10 33	10 36			10 51	11 03	11 06				11 21	11 33	11 36			11 51	12 03
Woolwich Dockyard	d	10 24		10 39			10 54		11 09				11 24		11 39			11 54	
Woolwich Arsenal	d	10 27	10 39	10 42			10 57	11 09	11 12				11 27	11 39	11 42			11 57	12 09
Plumstead	d	10 29		10a45			10 59		11a15				11 29		11a45			11 59	
Abbey Wood	d	10 32	10 43				11 02	11 13					11 32	11 43				12 02	12 13
Belvedere	d	10 35					11 05						11 35					12 05	
Erith	d	10 37					11 07						11 37					12 07	
Slade Green	d	10 40					11 10						11 40					12 10	
Dartford	a	10 45	10 54		11 05	11 08	11 15	11 24		11 35		11 38	11 45	11 54		12 05	12 08	12 15	12 24
	d		10 55			11 09		11 25				11 39		11 55			12 09		12 25
Stone Crossing	d					11 13						11 43					12 13		
Greenhithe for Bluewater	d		11 00			11 15		11 30				11 45		12 00			12 15		12 30
Swanscombe	d					11 18						11 48					12 18		
Northfleet	d					11 20						11 50					12 20		
Gravesend	d		11 07			11a25		11 37			11 48	11a55		12 07			12a25		12 37
Higham	d		11 13					11 43						12 13					12 43
Strood	d		11 18					11 48			11 58			12 18					12 48
Maidstone West	d																		
Rochester	d		11 23					11 53			12 03			12 23					12 53
Chatham	d		11 25					11 55			12 05			12 25					12 55
Gillingham (Kent)	a		11 30					12 00			12 09			12 30					13 00

		SE	SE	SE	SE	SE	SE	SE	SE	SE	SE	SE	SE	SE	SE	SE	SE	SE	SE
St Pancras Int'l ⊖	d			12 22						12 52						13 25			
Stratford International ⊖	d			12 32						12 59						13 32			
Ebbsfleet International	d			12 44						13 14						13 44			
London Charing Cross ⊖	d		11 50		11 52	11 56	12 09		12 20		12 22	12 26	12 39		12 50		12 52	12 56	13 09
London Waterloo (East) ⊖	d		11 53		11 55	11 59	12 12		12 23		12 25	12 29	12 42		12 53		12 55	12 59	13 12
London Cannon Street ⊖	d																		
London Bridge ⊖	d	11 50	11 58		12 00	12 05	12 17	12 20	12 28		12 30	12 35	12 47	12 50	12 58		13 00	13 05	13 17
Deptford	d	11 56				12 11		12 26				12 41		12 56				13 11	
Greenwich	d	11 58				12 13		12 28				12 43		12 58				13 13	
Maze Hill	d	12 01				12 16		12 31				12 46		13 01				13 16	
Westcombe Park	d	12 03				12 18		12 33				12 48		13 03				13 18	
London Victoria ⊖	d																		
Denmark Hill	d																		
Peckham Rye	d																		
Nunhead	d																		
New Cross ⊖	d		12 03						12 33						13 03				
St Johns	d																		
Lewisham	d		12 08		12 09		12 26		12 38		12 39		12 56		13 08		13 09		13 26
Blackheath	d		12 10				12 28		12 40				12 58		13 10				13 28
Kidbrooke	d		12 13						12 43						13 13				
Eltham	d		12 17						12 47						13 17				
Falconwood	d		12 19						12 49						13 19				
Welling	d		12 22						12 52						13 22				
Bexleyheath	d		12 24						12 54						13 24				
Barnehurst	d		12 27						12 57						13 27				
Hither Green	d				12 14						12 44						13 14		
Lee	d				12 16						12 46						13 16		
Mottingham	d				12 19						12 49						13 19		
New Eltham	d				12 21						12 51						13 21		
Sidcup	d				12 25						12 55						13 25		
Albany Park	d				12 27						12 57						13 27		
Bexley	d				12 29						12 59						13 29		
Crayford	d				12 33						13 03						13 33		
Charlton	d	12 06				12 21	12 33	12 36				12 51	13 03	13 06				13 21	13 33
Woolwich Dockyard	d	12 09				12 24		12 39				12 54		13 09				13 24	
Woolwich Arsenal	d	12 12				12 27	12 39	12 42				12 57	13 09	13 12				13 27	13 39
Plumstead	d	12a15				12 29		12a45				12 59		13a15				13 29	
Abbey Wood	d					12 32	12 43					13 02	13 13					13 32	13 43
Belvedere	d					12 35						13 05						13 35	
Erith	d					12 37						13 07						13 37	
Slade Green	d					12 40						13 10						13 40	
Dartford	a		12 35		12 38	12 45	12 54		13 05		13 08	13 15	13 24		13 35		13 38	13 45	13 54
	d				12 39		12 55				13 09		13 25				13 39		13 55
Stone Crossing	d				12 43						13 13						13 43		
Greenhithe for Bluewater	d				12 45		13 00				13 15		13 30				13 45		14 00
Swanscombe	d				12 48						13 18						13 48		
Northfleet	d				12 50						13 20						13 50		
Gravesend	d			12 48	12a55		13 07			13 18	13a25		13 37			13 48	13a55		14 07
Higham	d						13 13						13 43						14 13
Strood	d			12 58			13 18			13 28			13 48			13 58			14 18
Maidstone West	d																		
Rochester	d			13 03			13 23			13 33			13 53			14 03			14 23
Chatham	d			13 05			13 25			13 35			13 55			14 05			14 25
Gillingham (Kent)	a			13 09			13 30			13 39			14 00			14 09			14 30

Table 200

Sundays

8 December to 11 May

London - Dartford and Gillingham

Network Diagram - see first Page of Table 200

Station		SE	SE	SE	SE	SE	SE	SE	SE	SE	SE	SE	SE	SE	SE	SE	SE	SE	SE
St Pancras Int'l 15 ⊖	d			13 55						14 25						14 55			
Stratford International ⊖	d			14 02						14 32						15 02			
Ebbsfleet International	d			14 14						14 44						15 14			
London Charing Cross 4 ⊖	d		13 20		13 22	13 26	13 39		13 50		13 52	13 56	14 09		14 20		14 22	14 26	14 39
London Waterloo (East) 4 ⊖	d		13 23		13 25	13 29	13 42		13 53		13 55	13 59	14 12		14 23		14 25	14 29	14 42
London Cannon Street 4 ⊖	d																		
London Bridge 4 ⊖	d	13 20	13 28		13 30	13 35	13 47	13 50	13 58		14 00	14 05	14 17	14 20	14 28		14 30	14 35	14 47
Deptford	d	13 26				13 41		13 56				14 11		14 26				14 41	
Greenwich 4	d	13 28				13 43		13 58				14 13		14 28				14 43	
Maze Hill	d	13 31				13 46		14 01				14 16		14 31				14 46	
Westcombe Park	d	13 33				13 48		14 03				14 18		14 33				14 48	
London Victoria 15 ⊖	d																		
Denmark Hill 4	d																		
Peckham Rye 4	d																		
Nunhead 4	d																		
New Cross 4 ⊖	d		13 33						14 03						14 33				
St Johns	d																		
Lewisham 4	d		13 38		13 39		13 56		14 08		14 09		14 26		14 38		14 39		14 56
Blackheath 4	d		13 40				13 58		14 10				14 28		14 40				14 58
Kidbrooke	d		13 43						14 13						14 43				
Eltham	d		13 47						14 17						14 47				
Falconwood	d		13 49						14 19						14 49				
Welling	d		13 52						14 22						14 52				
Bexleyheath	d		13 54						14 24						14 54				
Barnehurst 4	d		13 57						14 27						14 57				
Hither Green 4	d				13 44						14 14						14 44		
Lee	d				13 46						14 16						14 46		
Mottingham	d				13 49						14 19						14 49		
New Eltham	d				13 51						14 21						14 51		
Sidcup 4	d				13 55						14 25						14 55		
Albany Park	d				13 57						14 27						14 57		
Bexley	d				13 59						14 29						14 59		
Crayford	d				14 03						14 33						15 03		
Charlton 4	d	13 36				13 51	14 03	14 06				14 21	14 33	14 36				14 51	15 03
Woolwich Dockyard	d	13 39				13 54		14 09				14 24		14 39				14 54	
Woolwich Arsenal 4	d	13 42				13 57	14 09	14 12				14 27	14 39	14 42				14 57	15 09
Plumstead	d	13a45				13 59		14a15				14 29		14a45				14 59	
Abbey Wood	d					14 02	14 13					14 32	14 43					15 02	15 13
Belvedere	d					14 05						14 35						15 05	
Erith	d					14 07						14 37						15 07	
Slade Green 4	d					14 10						14 40						15 10	
Dartford 4	a		14 05		14 08	14 15	14 24		14 35		14 38	14 45	14 54		15 05		15 08	15 15	15 24
	d				14 09		14 25				14 39		14 55				15 09		15 25
Stone Crossing	d				14 13						14 43						15 13		
Greenhithe for Bluewater	d				14 15		14 30				14 45		15 00				15 15		15 30
Swanscombe	d				14 18						14 48						15 18		
Northfleet	d				14 20						14 50						15 20		
Gravesend 4	d			14 18	14a25		14 37			14 48	14a55		15 07			15 18	15a25		15 37
Higham	d						14 43						15 13						15 43
Strood 4	d			14 28			14 48			14 58			15 18			15 28			15 48
Maidstone West	d																		
Rochester 4	d			14 33			14 53			15 03			15 23			15 33			15 53
Chatham 4	d			14 35			14 55			15 05			15 25			15 35			15 55
Gillingham (Kent) 4	a			14 39			15 00			15 09			15 30			15 39			16 00

Station		SE	SE	SE	SE	SE	SE	SE	SE	SE	SE	SE	SE	SE	SE	SE	SE	SE	SE
St Pancras Int'l 15 ⊖	d			15 25						15 55						16 25			
Stratford International ⊖	d			15 32						16 02						16 32			
Ebbsfleet International	d			15 44						16 14						16 44			
London Charing Cross 4 ⊖	d		14 50		14 52	14 56	15 09		15 20		15 22	15 26	15 39		15 50		15 52	15 56	16 09
London Waterloo (East) 4 ⊖	d		14 53		14 55	14 59	15 12		15 23		15 25	15 29	15 42		15 53		15 55	15 59	16 12
London Cannon Street 4 ⊖	d																		
London Bridge 4 ⊖	d	14 50	14 58		15 00	15 05	15 17	15 20	15 28		15 30	15 35	15 47	15 50	15 58		16 00	16 05	16 17
Deptford	d	14 56				15 11		15 26				15 41		15 56				16 11	
Greenwich 4	d	14 58				15 13		15 28				15 43		15 58				16 13	
Maze Hill	d	15 01				15 16		15 31				15 46		16 01				16 16	
Westcombe Park	d	15 03				15 18		15 33				15 48		16 03				16 18	
London Victoria 15 ⊖	d																		
Denmark Hill 4	d																		
Peckham Rye 4	d																		
Nunhead 4	d																		
New Cross 4 ⊖	d		15 03						15 33						16 03				
St Johns	d																		
Lewisham 4	d		15 08		15 09		15 26		15 38		15 39		15 56		16 08		16 09		16 26
Blackheath 4	d		15 10				15 28		15 40				15 58		16 10				16 28
Kidbrooke	d		15 13						15 43						16 13				
Eltham	d		15 17						15 47						16 17				
Falconwood	d		15 19						15 49						16 19				
Welling	d		15 22						15 52						16 22				
Bexleyheath	d		15 24						15 54						16 24				
Barnehurst 4	d		15 27						15 57						16 27				
Hither Green 4	d				15 14						15 44						16 14		
Lee	d				15 16						15 46						16 16		
Mottingham	d				15 19						15 49						16 19		
New Eltham	d				15 21						15 51						16 21		
Sidcup 4	d				15 25						15 55						16 25		
Albany Park	d				15 27						15 57						16 27		
Bexley	d				15 29						15 59						16 29		
Crayford	d				15 33						16 03						16 33		
Charlton 4	d	15 06				15 21	15 33	15 36				15 51	16 03	16 06				16 21	16 33
Woolwich Dockyard	d	15 09				15 24		15 39				15 54		16 09				16 24	
Woolwich Arsenal 4	d	15 12				15 27	15 39	15 42				15 57	16 09	16 12				16 27	16 39
Plumstead	d	15a15				15 29		15a45				15 59		16a15				16 29	
Abbey Wood	d					15 32	15 43					16 02	16 13					16 32	16 43
Belvedere	d					15 35						16 05						16 35	
Erith	d					15 37						16 07						16 37	
Slade Green 4	d					15 40						16 10						16 40	
Dartford 4	a		15 35		15 38	15 45	15 54		16 05		16 08	16 15	16 24		16 35		16 38	16 45	16 54
	d				15 39		15 55				16 09		16 25				16 39		16 55
Stone Crossing	d				15 43						16 13						16 43		
Greenhithe for Bluewater	d				15 45		16 00				16 15		16 30				16 45		17 00
Swanscombe	d				15 48						16 18						16 48		
Northfleet	d				15 50						16 20						16 50		
Gravesend 4	d			15 48	15a55		16 07			16 18	16a25		16 37			16 48	16a55		17 07
Higham	d						16 13						16 43						17 13
Strood 4	d			15 58			16 18			16 28			16 48			16 58			17 18
Maidstone West	d																		
Rochester 4	d			16 03			16 23			16 33			16 53			17 03			17 23
Chatham 4	d			16 05			16 25			16 35			16 55			17 05			17 25
Gillingham (Kent) 4	a			16 09			16 30			16 39			17 00			17 09			17 30

Table 200

Sundays

8 December to 11 May

London - Dartford and Gillingham

Network Diagram - see first Page of Table 200

Station		SE	SE	SE	SE	SE	SE	SE	SE	SE
St Pancras Int'l 15 ⊖	d			16 55						17 25
Stratford International ⊖ ⛴	d			17 02						17 32
Ebbsfleet International	d			17 14						17 44
London Charing Cross 4 ⊖	d		16 20		16 22	16 26	16 39		16 50	
London Waterloo (East) 4 ⊖	d		16 23		16 25	16 29	16 42		16 53	
London Cannon Street 4 ⊖	d									
London Bridge 4 ⊖	d	16 20	16 28		16 30	16 35	16 47	16 50	16 58	
Deptford	d	16 26				16 41		16 56		
Greenwich 4 ⛴	d	16 28				16 43		16 58		
Maze Hill	d	16 31				16 46		17 01		
Westcombe Park	d	16 33				16 48		17 03		
London Victoria 15 ⊖	d									
Denmark Hill 4	d									
Peckham Rye 4	d									
Nunhead 4	d									
New Cross 4 ⊖	d		16 33						17 03	
St Johns	d									
Lewisham 4 ⛴	d		16 38		16 39		16 56		17 08	
Blackheath 4	d		16 40				16 58		17 10	
Kidbrooke	d		16 43						17 13	
Eltham	d		16 47						17 17	
Falconwood	d		16 49						17 19	
Welling	d		16 52						17 22	
Bexleyheath	d		16 54						17 24	
Barnehurst 4	d		16 57						17 27	
Hither Green 4	d				16 44					
Lee	d				16 46					
Mottingham	d				16 49					
New Eltham	d				16 51					
Sidcup 4	d				16 55					
Albany Park	d				16 57					
Bexley	d				16 59					
Crayford	d				17 03					
Charlton 4	d	16 36				16 51	17 03	17 06		
Woolwich Dockyard	d	16 39				16 54		17 09		
Woolwich Arsenal 4 ⛴	d	16 42				16 57	17 09	17 12		
Plumstead	d	16a45				16 59		17a15		
Abbey Wood	d					17 02	17 13			
Belvedere	d					17 05				
Erith	d					17 07				
Slade Green 4	d					17 10				
Dartford 4	a		17 05		17 08	17 15	17 24		17 35	
	d				17 09		17 25			
Stone Crossing	d				17 13					
Greenhithe for Bluewater	d				17 15		17 30			
Swanscombe	d				17 18					
Northfleet	d				17 20					
Gravesend 4	d			17 18	17a25		17 37			17 48
Higham	d						17 43			
Strood 4	d			17 28			17 48			17 58
Maidstone West	d									
Rochester 4	d			17 33			17 53			18 03
Chatham 4	d			17 35			17 55			18 05
Gillingham (Kent) 4	a			17 39			18 00			18 09

Station		SE	SE	SE	SE	SE	SE	SE	SE	SE
St Pancras Int'l 15 ⊖	d						17 52			
Stratford International ⊖ ⛴	d						18 02			
Ebbsfleet International	d						18 14			
London Charing Cross 4 ⊖	d	16 52	16 56	17 09		17 20		17 22	17 26	17 39
London Waterloo (East) 4 ⊖	d	16 55	16 59	17 12		17 23		17 25	17 29	17 42
London Cannon Street 4 ⊖	d									
London Bridge 4 ⊖	d	17 00	17 05	17 17	17 20	17 28		17 30	17 35	17 47
Deptford	d		17 11		17 26				17 41	
Greenwich 4 ⛴	d		17 13		17 28				17 43	
Maze Hill	d		17 16		17 31				17 46	
Westcombe Park	d		17 18		17 33				17 48	
London Victoria 15 ⊖	d									
Denmark Hill 4	d									
Peckham Rye 4	d									
Nunhead 4	d									
New Cross 4 ⊖	d					17 33				
St Johns	d									
Lewisham 4 ⛴	d	17 09		17 26		17 38		17 39		17 56
Blackheath 4	d			17 28		17 40				17 58
Kidbrooke	d					17 43				
Eltham	d					17 47				
Falconwood	d					17 49				
Welling	d					17 52				
Bexleyheath	d					17 54				
Barnehurst 4	d					17 57				
Hither Green 4	d	17 14						17 44		
Lee	d	17 16						17 46		
Mottingham	d	17 19						17 49		
New Eltham	d	17 21						17 51		
Sidcup 4	d	17 25						17 55		
Albany Park	d	17 27						17 57		
Bexley	d	17 29						17 59		
Crayford	d	17 33						18 03		
Charlton 4	d		17 21	17 33	17 36				17 51	18 03
Woolwich Dockyard	d		17 24		17 39				17 54	
Woolwich Arsenal 4 ⛴	d		17 27	17 39	17 42				17 57	18 09
Plumstead	d		17 29		17a45				17 59	
Abbey Wood	d		17 32	17 43					18 02	18 13
Belvedere	d		17 35						18 05	
Erith	d		17 37						18 07	
Slade Green 4	d		17 40						18 10	
Dartford 4	a	17 38	17 45	17 54		18 05		18 08	18 15	18 24
	d	17 39		17 55				18 09		18 25
Stone Crossing	d	17 43						18 13		
Greenhithe for Bluewater	d	17 45		18 00				18 15		18 30
Swanscombe	d	17 48						18 18		
Northfleet	d	17 50						18 20		
Gravesend 4	d	17a55		18 07			18 18	18a25		18 37
Higham	d			18 13						18 43
Strood 4	d			18 18			18 28			18 48
Maidstone West	d									
Rochester 4	d			18 23			18 33			18 53
Chatham 4	d			18 25			18 35			18 55
Gillingham (Kent) 4	a			18 30			18 39			19 00

Station		SE	SE	SE	SE	SE	SE	SE	SE	SE
St Pancras Int'l 15 ⊖	d			18 25						18 55
Stratford International ⊖ ⛴	d			18 32						19 02
Ebbsfleet International	d			18 44						19 14
London Charing Cross 4 ⊖	d		17 50		17 52	17 56	18 09		18 20	
London Waterloo (East) 4 ⊖	d		17 53		17 55	17 59	18 12		18 23	
London Cannon Street 4 ⊖	d									
London Bridge 4 ⊖	d	17 50	17 58		18 00	18 05	18 17	18 20	18 28	
Deptford	d	17 56				18 11		18 26		
Greenwich 4 ⛴	d	17 58				18 13		18 28		
Maze Hill	d	18 01				18 16		18 31		
Westcombe Park	d	18 03				18 18		18 33		
London Victoria 15 ⊖	d									
Denmark Hill 4	d									
Peckham Rye 4	d									
Nunhead 4	d									
New Cross 4 ⊖	d		18 03						18 33	
St Johns	d									
Lewisham 4 ⛴	d		18 08		18 09		18 26		18 38	
Blackheath 4	d		18 10				18 28		18 40	
Kidbrooke	d		18 13						18 43	
Eltham	d		18 17						18 47	
Falconwood	d		18 19						18 49	
Welling	d		18 22						18 52	
Bexleyheath	d		18 24						18 54	
Barnehurst 4	d		18 27						18 57	
Hither Green 4	d				18 14					
Lee	d				18 16					
Mottingham	d				18 19					
New Eltham	d				18 21					
Sidcup 4	d				18 25					
Albany Park	d				18 27					
Bexley	d				18 29					
Crayford	d				18 33					
Charlton 4	d	18 06				18 21	18 33	18 36		
Woolwich Dockyard	d	18 09				18 24		18 39		
Woolwich Arsenal 4 ⛴	d	18 12				18 27	18 39	18 42		
Plumstead	d	18a15				18 29		18a45		
Abbey Wood	d					18 32	18 43			
Belvedere	d					18 35				
Erith	d					18 37				
Slade Green 4	d					18 40				
Dartford 4	a		18 35		18 38	18 45	18 54		19 05	
	d				18 39		18 55			
Stone Crossing	d				18 43					
Greenhithe for Bluewater	d				18 45		19 00			
Swanscombe	d				18 48					
Northfleet	d				18 50					
Gravesend 4	d			18 48	18a55		19 07			19 18
Higham	d						19 13			
Strood 4	d			18 58			19 18			19 28
Maidstone West	d									
Rochester 4	d			19 03			19 23			19 33
Chatham 4	d			19 05			19 25			19 35
Gillingham (Kent) 4	a			19 09			19 30			19 39

Station		SE	SE	SE	SE	SE	SE	SE	SE	SE
St Pancras Int'l 15 ⊖	d						19 25			
Stratford International ⊖ ⛴	d						19 32			
Ebbsfleet International	d						19 44			
London Charing Cross 4 ⊖	d	18 22	18 26	18 39		18 50		18 52	18 56	19 09
London Waterloo (East) 4 ⊖	d	18 25	18 29	18 42		18 53		18 55	18 59	19 12
London Cannon Street 4 ⊖	d									
London Bridge 4 ⊖	d	18 30	18 35	18 47	18 50	18 58		19 00	19 05	19 17
Deptford	d		18 41		18 56				19 11	
Greenwich 4 ⛴	d		18 43		18 58				19 13	
Maze Hill	d		18 46		19 01				19 16	
Westcombe Park	d		18 48		19 03				19 18	
London Victoria 15 ⊖	d									
Denmark Hill 4	d									
Peckham Rye 4	d									
Nunhead 4	d									
New Cross 4 ⊖	d					19 03				
St Johns	d									
Lewisham 4 ⛴	d	18 39		18 56		19 08		19 09		19 26
Blackheath 4	d			18 58		19 10				19 28
Kidbrooke	d					19 13				
Eltham	d					19 17				
Falconwood	d					19 19				
Welling	d					19 22				
Bexleyheath	d					19 24				
Barnehurst 4	d					19 27				
Hither Green 4	d	18 44						19 14		
Lee	d	18 46						19 16		
Mottingham	d	18 49						19 19		
New Eltham	d	18 51						19 21		
Sidcup 4	d	18 55						19 25		
Albany Park	d	18 57						19 27		
Bexley	d	18 59						19 29		
Crayford	d	19 03						19 33		
Charlton 4	d		18 51	19 03	19 06				19 21	19 33
Woolwich Dockyard	d		18 54		19 09				19 24	
Woolwich Arsenal 4 ⛴	d		18 57	19 09	19 12				19 27	19 39
Plumstead	d		18 59		19a15				19 29	
Abbey Wood	d		19 02	19 13					19 32	19 43
Belvedere	d		19 05						19 35	
Erith	d		19 07						19 37	
Slade Green 4	d		19 10						19 40	
Dartford 4	a	19 08	19 15	19 24		19 35		19 38	19 45	19 54
	d	19 09		19 25				19 39		19 55
Stone Crossing	d	19 13						19 43		
Greenhithe for Bluewater	d	19 15		19 30				19 45		20 00
Swanscombe	d	19 18						19 48		
Northfleet	d	19 20						19 50		
Gravesend 4	d	19a25		19 37			19 48	19a55		20 07
Higham	d			19 43						20 13
Strood 4	d			19 48			19 58			20 18
Maidstone West	d									
Rochester 4	d			19 53			20 03			20 23
Chatham 4	d			19 55			20 05			20 25
Gillingham (Kent) 4	a			20 00			20 09			20 30

Table 200

Sundays

8 December to 11 May

London - Dartford and Gillingham

Network Diagram - see first Page of Table 200

Station		SE	SE	SE	SE	SE	SE	SE	SE	SE
St Pancras Int'l 15 ⊖	d			19 55						20 25
Stratford International ⊖	d			20 02						20 32
Ebbsfleet International	d			20 14						20 44
London Charing Cross 4 ⊖	d		19 20		19 22	19 26	19 39		19 50	
London Waterloo (East) 4 ⊖	d		19 23		19 25	19 29	19 42		19 53	
London Cannon Street 4 ⊖	d									
London Bridge 4 ⊖	d	19 20	19 28		19 30	19 35	19 47	19 50	19 58	
Deptford	d	19 26				19 41		19 56		
Greenwich 4	d	19 28				19 43		19 58		
Maze Hill	d	19 31				19 46		20 01		
Westcombe Park	d	19 33				19 48		20 03		
London Victoria 15 ⊖	d									
Denmark Hill 4	d									
Peckham Rye 4	d									
Nunhead 4	d									
New Cross 4 ⊖	d		19 33						20 03	
St Johns	d									
Lewisham 4	d		19 38		19 39		19 56		20 08	
Blackheath 4	d		19 40				19 58		20 10	
Kidbrooke	d		19 43						20 13	
Eltham	d		19 47						20 17	
Falconwood	d		19 49						20 19	
Welling	d		19 52						20 22	
Bexleyheath	d		19 54						20 24	
Barnehurst 4	d		19 57						20 27	
Hither Green 4	d				19 44					
Lee	d				19 46					
Mottingham	d				19 49					
New Eltham	d				19 51					
Sidcup 4	d				19 55					
Albany Park	d				19 57					
Bexley	d				19 59					
Crayford	d				20 03					
Charlton 4	d	19 36				19 51	20 03	20 06		
Woolwich Dockyard	d	19 39				19 54		20 09		
Woolwich Arsenal 4	d	19 42				19 57	20 09	20 12		
Plumstead	d	19a45				19 59		20a15		
Abbey Wood	d					20 02	20 13			
Belvedere	d					20 05				
Erith	d					20 07				
Slade Green 4	d					20 10				
Dartford 4	a		20 05		20 08	20 15	20 24		20 35	
	d				20 09		20 25			
Stone Crossing	d				20 13					
Greenhithe for Bluewater	d				20 15		20 30			
Swanscombe	d				20 18					
Northfleet	d				20 20					
Gravesend 4	d			20 18	20a25		20 37			20 48
Higham	d						20 43			
Strood 4	d			20 28			20 48			20 58
Maidstone West	d									
Rochester 4	d			20 33			20 53			21 03
Chatham 4	d			20 35			20 55			21 05
Gillingham (Kent) 4	a			20 39			21 00			21 09

Station		SE	SE	SE	SE	SE	SE	SE	SE	SE
St Pancras Int'l 15 ⊖	d					20 55				
Stratford International ⊖	d					21 02				
Ebbsfleet International	d					21 14				
London Charing Cross 4 ⊖	d	19 52	19 56	20 09	20 20		20 22	20 26	20 39	20 50
London Waterloo (East) 4 ⊖	d	19 55	19 59	20 12	20 23		20 25	20 29	20 42	20 53
London Cannon Street 4 ⊖	d									
London Bridge 4 ⊖	d	20 00	20 05	20 17	20 28		20 30	20 35	20 47	20 58
Deptford	d		20 11					20 41		
Greenwich 4	d		20 13					20 43		
Maze Hill	d		20 16					20 46		
Westcombe Park	d		20 18					20 48		
London Victoria 15 ⊖	d									
Denmark Hill 4	d									
Peckham Rye 4	d									
Nunhead 4	d									
New Cross 4 ⊖	d				20 33					21 03
St Johns	d									
Lewisham 4	d	20 09		20 26	20 38		20 39		20 56	21 08
Blackheath 4	d			20 28	20 40				20 58	21 10
Kidbrooke	d				20 43					21 13
Eltham	d				20 47					21 17
Falconwood	d				20 49					21 19
Welling	d				20 52					21 22
Bexleyheath	d				20 54					21 24
Barnehurst 4	d				20 57					21 27
Hither Green 4	d	20 14					20 44			
Lee	d	20 16					20 46			
Mottingham	d	20 19					20 49			
New Eltham	d	20 21					20 51			
Sidcup 4	d	20 25					20 55			
Albany Park	d	20 27					20 57			
Bexley	d	20 29					20 59			
Crayford	d	20 33					21 03			
Charlton 4	d		20 21	20 33				20 51	21 03	
Woolwich Dockyard	d		20 24					20 54		
Woolwich Arsenal 4	d		20 27	20 39				20 57	21 09	
Plumstead	d		20 29					20 59		
Abbey Wood	d		20 32	20 43				21 02	21 13	
Belvedere	d		20 35					21 05		
Erith	d		20 37					21 07		
Slade Green 4	d		20 40					21 10		
Dartford 4	a	20 38	20 45	20 54	21 05		21 08	21 15	21 24	21 35
	d	20 39		20 55			21 09		21 25	
Stone Crossing	d	20 43					21 13			
Greenhithe for Bluewater	d	20 45		21 00			21 15		21 30	
Swanscombe	d	20 48					21 18			
Northfleet	d	20 50					21 20			
Gravesend 4	d	20a55		21 07		21 18	21a25		21 37	
Higham	d			21 13					21 43	
Strood 4	d			21 18		21 28			21 48	
Maidstone West	d									
Rochester 4	d			21 23		21 33			21 53	
Chatham 4	d			21 25		21 35			21 55	
Gillingham (Kent) 4	a			21 30		21 39			22 00	

Station		SE	SE	SE	SE	SE	SE	SE	SE	SE
St Pancras Int'l 15 ⊖	d	21 25					21 55			
Stratford International ⊖	d	21 32					22 02			
Ebbsfleet International	d	21 44					22 14			
London Charing Cross 4 ⊖	d		20 52	20 56	21 09	21 20		21 22	21 26	21 39
London Waterloo (East) 4 ⊖	d		20 55	20 59	21 12	21 23		21 25	21 29	21 42
London Cannon Street 4 ⊖	d									
London Bridge 4 ⊖	d		21 00	21 05	21 17	21 28		21 30	21 35	21 47
Deptford	d			21 11					21 41	
Greenwich 4	d			21 13					21 43	
Maze Hill	d			21 16					21 46	
Westcombe Park	d			21 18					21 48	
London Victoria 15 ⊖	d									
Denmark Hill 4	d									
Peckham Rye 4	d									
Nunhead 4	d									
New Cross 4 ⊖	d					21 33				
St Johns	d									
Lewisham 4	d		21 09		21 26	21 38		21 39		21 56
Blackheath 4	d				21 28	21 40				21 58
Kidbrooke	d					21 43				
Eltham	d					21 47				
Falconwood	d					21 49				
Welling	d					21 52				
Bexleyheath	d					21 54				
Barnehurst 4	d					21 57				
Hither Green 4	d		21 14					21 44		
Lee	d		21 16					21 46		
Mottingham	d		21 19					21 49		
New Eltham	d		21 21					21 51		
Sidcup 4	d		21 25					21 55		
Albany Park	d		21 27					21 57		
Bexley	d		21 29					21 59		
Crayford	d		21 33					22 03		
Charlton 4	d			21 21	21 33				21 51	22 03
Woolwich Dockyard	d			21 24					21 54	
Woolwich Arsenal 4	d			21 27	21 39				21 57	22 09
Plumstead	d			21 29					21 59	
Abbey Wood	d			21 32	21 43				22 02	22 13
Belvedere	d			21 35					22 05	
Erith	d			21 37					22 07	
Slade Green 4	d			21 40					22 10	
Dartford 4	a		21 38	21 45	21 54	22 05		22 08	22 15	22 24
	d		21 39		21 55			22 09		22 25
Stone Crossing	d		21 43					22 13		22 29
Greenhithe for Bluewater	d		21 45		22 00			22 15		22 31
Swanscombe	d		21 48					22 18		22 34
Northfleet	d		21 50					22 20		22 36
Gravesend 4	d	21 48	21a55		22 07		22 18	22a25		22 40
Higham	d				22 13					22 46
Strood 4	d	21 58			22 18		22 28			22 52
Maidstone West	d									
Rochester 4	d	22 03			22 23		22 33			22 56
Chatham 4	d	22 05			22 25		22 35			22 59
Gillingham (Kent) 4	a	22 09			22 30		22 39			23 03

Station		SE	SE	SE	SE	SE	SE	SE	SE	SE
St Pancras Int'l 15 ⊖	d				22 25					22 55
Stratford International ⊖	d				22 32					23 02
Ebbsfleet International	d				22 44					23 14
London Charing Cross 4 ⊖	d	21 50	21 52	21 56		22 09	22 20	22 22	22 26	
London Waterloo (East) 4 ⊖	d	21 53	21 55	21 59		22 12	22 23	22 25	22 29	
London Cannon Street 4 ⊖	d									
London Bridge 4 ⊖	d	21 58	22 00	22 05		22 17	22 28	22 30	22 35	
Deptford	d			22 11					22 41	
Greenwich 4	d			22 13					22 43	
Maze Hill	d			22 16					22 46	
Westcombe Park	d			22 18					22 48	
London Victoria 15 ⊖	d									
Denmark Hill 4	d									
Peckham Rye 4	d									
Nunhead 4	d									
New Cross 4 ⊖	d	22 03					22 33			
St Johns	d									
Lewisham 4	d	22 08	22 09			22 26	22 38	22 39		
Blackheath 4	d	22 10				22 28	22 40			
Kidbrooke	d	22 13					22 43			
Eltham	d	22 17					22 47			
Falconwood	d	22 19					22 49			
Welling	d	22 22					22 52			
Bexleyheath	d	22 24					22 54			
Barnehurst 4	d	22 27					22 57			
Hither Green 4	d		22 14					22 44		
Lee	d		22 16					22 46		
Mottingham	d		22 19					22 49		
New Eltham	d		22 21					22 51		
Sidcup 4	d		22 25					22 55		
Albany Park	d		22 27					22 57		
Bexley	d		22 29					22 59		
Crayford	d		22 33					23 03		
Charlton 4	d			22 21		22 33			22 51	
Woolwich Dockyard	d			22 24					22 54	
Woolwich Arsenal 4	d			22 27		22 39			22 57	
Plumstead	d			22 29					22 59	
Abbey Wood	d			22 32		22 43			23 02	
Belvedere	d			22 35					23 05	
Erith	d			22 37					23 07	
Slade Green 4	d			22 40					23 10	
Dartford 4	a	22 35	22 38	22 45		22 54	23 05	23 08	23 15	
	d					22 55				
Stone Crossing	d					22 59				
Greenhithe for Bluewater	d					23 01				
Swanscombe	d					23 04				
Northfleet	d					23 06				
Gravesend 4	d				22 48	23 10				23 18
Higham	d					23 16				
Strood 4	d				22 58	23 22				23 28
Maidstone West	d									
Rochester 4	d				23 03	23 26				23 33
Chatham 4	d				23 05	23 29				23 35
Gillingham (Kent) 4	a				23 09	23 33				23 39

Table 200

Sundays

8 December to 11 May

London - Dartford and Gillingham

Network Diagram - see first Page of Table 200

		SE	SE	SE	SE	SE	SE	SE	SE	SE	SE	SE
St Pancras Int'l 15 ⊖	d					23 25						
Stratford International ⊖ ⛴	d					23 32						
Ebbsfleet International	d					23 44						
London Charing Cross 4 ⊖	d	22 39	22 50	22 52	22 56		23 09	23 20	23 22	23 26	23 50	23 52
London Waterloo (East) 4 ⊖	d	22 42	22 53	22 55	22 59		23 12	23 23	23 25	23 29	23 53	23 55
London Cannon Street 4 ⊖	d											
London Bridge 4 ⊖	d	22 47	22 58	23 00	23 05		23 17	23 28	23 30	23 35	23 58	23 59
Deptford	d				23 11					23 41		
Greenwich 4 ⛴	d				23 13					23 43		
Maze Hill	d				23 16					23 46		
Westcombe Park	d				23 18					23 48		
London Victoria 15 ⊖	d											
Denmark Hill 4	d											
Peckham Rye 4	d											
Nunhead 4	d											
New Cross 4 ⊖	d		23 03					23 33			00 03	
St Johns	d											
Lewisham 4 ⛴	d	22 56	23 08	23 09			23 26	23 38	23 39		00 08	00 09
Blackheath 4	d	22 58	23 10				23 28	23 40			00 10	
Kidbrooke	d		23 13					23 43			00 13	
Eltham	d		23 17					23 47			00 17	
Falconwood	d		23 19					23 49			00 19	
Welling	d		23 22					23 52			00 22	
Bexleyheath	d		23 24					23 54			00 24	
Barnehurst 4	d		23 27					23 57			00 27	
Hither Green 4	d			23 14					23 44			00 14
Lee	d			23 16					23 46			00 16
Mottingham	d			23 19					23 49			00 19
New Eltham	d			23 21					23 51			00 21
Sidcup 4	d			23 25					23 55			00 25
Albany Park	d			23 27					23 57			00 27
Bexley	d			23 29					23 59			00 29
Crayford	d			23 33					00 03			00 33
Charlton 4	d	23 03			23 21		23 33			23 51		
Woolwich Dockyard	d				23 24					23 54		
Woolwich Arsenal 4 ⛴	d	23 09			23 27		23 39			23 57		
Plumstead	d				23 29					23 59		
Abbey Wood	d	23 13			23 32		23 43			00 02		
Belvedere	d				23 35					00 05		
Erith	d				23 37					00 07		
Slade Green 4	d				23 40					00 10		
Dartford 4	a	23 24	23 35	23 38	23 45		23 54	00 05	00 08	00 15	00 35	00 38
	d	23 25					23 55					
Stone Crossing	d	23 29					23 58					
Greenhithe for Bluewater	d	23 31					23 59					
Swanscombe	d	23 34					00 04					
Northfleet	d	23 36					00 06					
Gravesend 4	d	23 40				23 48	00 10					
Higham	d	23 46					00 16					
Strood 4	d	23 52				23 58	00 22					
Maidstone West	d											
Rochester 4	d	23 56				00 03	00 26					
Chatham 4	d	23 59				00 05	00 29					
Gillingham (Kent) 4	a	00 03				00 09	00 33					

Table 200R

Mondays to Fridays

9 December to 16 May

Gillingham and Dartford - London

Network Diagram - see first Page of Table 200

Miles	Miles	Miles	Miles	Miles			SE	SE	SE	SE	SE	SE	SE	SE	SE	SE	SE	SE	SE	SE	SE	SE	SE	SE	SE	SE	SE	SE	SE	SE	SE	SE	SE	SE	SE	SE	SE	SE
0	—	—	0	0	**Gillingham (Kent)** [4]	d	04 09			04 34		04 54			05 20			05 24	05 45							05 50		05 54					06 07					06 20
1¾	—	—	1¾	1¾	**Chatham** [4]	d	04 13			04 38		04 58			05 24			05 28	05 49							05 54		05 58					06 11					06 24
2¼	—	—	2¼	2¼	Rochester [4]	d	04 15			04 40		05 00			05 27			05 30	05 51							05 57		06 00					06 13					06 27
—	—	—	—	—	Maidstone West	d																																
3¼	—	—	3¼	3¼	Strood [4]	d	04 20			04 45		05 05			05 32			05 35								06 02		06 05					06 18					06 32
6	—	—	6	6	Higham	d	04 25			04 50		05 10						05 40										06 10					06 23					
10½	—	—	10½	10½	**Gravesend** [4]	d	04 33			04 58		05 18		05 28	05 43			05 48							06 05	06 13		06 18					06 31				06 34	06 42
12½	—	—	12½	—	Northfleet	d				05 02				05 32											06 09												06 38	
13¼	—	—	13¼	—	Swanscombe	d				05 04				05 34											06 11												06 40	
14½	—	—	14½	—	Greenhithe for Bluewater	d	04 38			05 07		05 23		05 37				05 53							06 14			06 23					06 37				06 43	
15¼	—	—	15¼	—	Stone Crossing	d				05 09				05 39											06 16												06 45	
17¼	0	0	17¼	0	**Dartford** [4]	a	04 43			05 13		05 28		05 43				05 58							06 20			06 28					06 41				06 49	
—	—	—	—	—		d	04 44		05 01	05 14	05 22	05 29	05 31	05 44		05 52	05 56	05 59		06 01		06 13	06 16		06 21			06 29	06 31		06 31	06 39	06 42				06 50	
19¼	2	—	—	—	Slade Green [4]	d			05 05				05 35							06 05			06 20								06 36							
20½	3¼	—	—	—	Erith	d			05 08				05 38							06 08			06 23								06 39							
21¾	4½	—	—	—	Belvedere	d			05 10				05 40							06 10			06 25								06 41							
23¼	6	—	—	—	Abbey Wood	d			05 13			05 38	05 43					06 08		06 13			06 28					06 38			06 45		06 51					
24¾	7½	—	—	—	Plumstead	d			05 16				05 46							06 16			06 31								06 48							
25¼	8	—	—	—	**Woolwich Arsenal** [4] ⛴	d			05 19			05 43	05 49					06 13		06 19			06 34					06 43			06 51		06 56					
26	8¾	—	—	—	Woolwich Dockyard	d			05 22				05 52							06 22			06 37								06 53							
27	9¾	—	—	—	Charlton [4]	d			05 25			05 47	05 55					06 17		06 25			06 40					06 47			06 57							
—	—	—	19	—	Crayford	d	04 48			05 18				05 48			06 01										06 25		06 35							06 50	06 55	
—	—	—	20½	—	Bexley	d	04 51			05 21				05 51			06 04										06 28		06 38							06 53	06 58	
—	—	—	21½	—	Albany Park	d	04 54			05 24				05 54			06 07										06 31		06 41							06 56	07 01	
—	—	—	22½	—	Sidcup [4]	d	04 57			05 27				05 57			06 10										06 34		06 44							06 59	07 04	
—	—	—	24	—	New Eltham	d	05 00			05 30				06 00			06 13										06 38		06 47							07 02	07 07	
—	—	—	25	—	Mottingham	d	05 02			05 32				06 02			06 16										06 40		06 50							07 05	07 10	
—	—	—	26½	—	Lee	d	05 05			05 35				06 05			06 19										06 43		06 53							07 08	07 13	
—	—	—	27¼	—	Hither Green [4]	d	05 08	05 23		05 38				06 08			06 22										06 46		06 56						07 08	07 11	07 16	
—	—	3	—	3	Barnehurst [4]	d					05 29					05 59					06 14	06 20			06 28					06 39		06 49		06 53				
—	—	4¼	—	4¼	Bexleyheath	d					05 31					06 01					06 16	06 22			06 31					06 41		06 52		06 56				
—	—	5¾	—	5¾	Welling	d					05 34					06 04					06 19	06 25			06 34					06 44		06 55		06 59				
—	—	6¾	—	6¾	Falconwood	d					05 37					06 07					06 22	06 28			06 37					06 47		06 57		07 01				
—	—	8	—	8	Eltham	d					05 40					06 10					06 25	06 31			06 40					06 50		07 00		07 04				
—	—	9	—	9	Kidbrooke	d					05 43					06 13					06 28	06 34			06 43					06 53		07 03		07 07				
29	—	10	—	10	Blackheath [4]	d					05 46	05 52				06 16		06 22			06 31	06 37			06 47			06 52		06 57		07 08	07 05	07 11				
30	—	11	28½	11	Lewisham [4] ⛴	d	05 13	05 28		05 43	05 50	05 56		06 13		06 20	06 27	06 25			06 35	06 41		06 48	06 50		06 52	06 55		07 01		07 11	07 08	07 15		07 17		
—	—	11½	29	—	St Johns	d											06 29							06 50			06 54			07 03						07 19		
—	—	12¼	29¾	—	New Cross [4] ⊖	d	05 16	05 31		05 46	05 53			06 16			06 31				06 38			06 52			06 56			07 05			07 11			07 21		
—	—	—	—	12¾	Nunhead [4]	d																06 46												07 20				
—	—	—	—	13½	Peckham Rye [4]	d																06 49												07 23				
—	—	—	—	14¼	Denmark Hill [4]	d																06 52												07 29				
—	—	—	—	18½	**London Victoria** [15] ⊖	a																07 04												07 42				
—	10½	—	—	—	Westcombe Park	d			05 27				05 57							06 27			06 42								06 59							
—	11	—	—	—	Maze Hill	d			05 29				05 59							06 29			06 44								07 01							
—	12	—	—	—	Greenwich [4] ⛴	d			05 32				06 02							06 32			06 47								07 05							
—	12½	—	—	—	**Deptford**	a			05 34				06 04							06 34			06 49								07 07							
34¼	15½	15¼	32¾	—	London Bridge [4] ⊖	a	05 22	05 36	05 41	05 52	05 58	06 05	06 12	06 22		06 28	06 37	06 34	06 27	06 42	06 43		06 56	06 58	07 00		07 02	07 03	07 06	07 10	07 14	07 20	07 17		07 18	07 26	07 26	
—	16¼	—	—	—	**London Cannon Street** [4] ⊖	a		05 41											06 32		06 48		07 03	07 05			07 09			07 17	07 21		07 24		07 26	07 33		
35¼	—	16¼	33¾	—	**London Waterloo (East)** [4] ⊖	a	05 26		05 46	05 57	06 03	06 10	06 18	06 26		06 32	06 41	06 39		06 48					07 06			07 09	07 12			07 25					07 31	
—	—	—	—	—	**London Charing Cross** [4] ⊖	a	05 30		05 50	06 01	06 07	06 14	06 21	06 30		06 36	06 45	06 43		06 52					07 11			07 15	07 17			07 31					07 37	
—	—	—	—	12½	**Ebbsfleet International**	a									05 46											06 16												06 46
—	—	—	—	29¼	**Stratford International** ⊖ ⛴	a									05 59											06 29												06 59
—	—	—	—	35¼	**St Pancras Int'l** [15] ⊖	a									06 06											06 36												07 06

Table 200R

Mondays to Fridays

9 December to 16 May

Gillingham and Dartford - London

Network Diagram - see first Page of Table 200

Station		SE 1	SE	SE	SE	SE	SE	SE	SE	SE	SE	SE	SE 1	SE	SE	SE	SE	SE	SE
Gillingham (Kent) 4	d	06 34										06 38	07 02						
Chatham 4	d	06 38										06 42	07 07						
Rochester 4	d	06 41										06 44	07 09						
Maidstone West	d																		
Strood 4	d											06 49						06 58	
Higham	d											06 54						07 03	
Gravesend 4	d						06 47					07 02						07 10	
Northfleet	d						06 51												
Swanscombe	d						06 53												
Greenhithe for Bluewater	d						06 56					07 07						07 16	
Stone Crossing	d						06 58												
Dartford 4	a						07 02					07 12						07 21	
	d					07 00	07 03			07 05		07 12		07 17			07 20	07 23	
Slade Green 4	d			06 55						07 09					07 19				
Erith	d			06 57						07 12					07 22				
Belvedere	d			07 00						07 14					07 24				
Abbey Wood	d			07 03			07 12			07 18					07 28			07 34	
Plumstead	d			07 06						07 21					07 31				
Woolwich Arsenal 4	d			07 09			07 17			07 24					07 34			07 39	
Woolwich Dockyard	d			07 12						07 26					07 36				
Charlton 4	d			07 15			07 22			07 30					07 40			07 44	
Crayford	d										07 10	07 17							
Bexley	d										07 13	07 20							
Albany Park	d										07 16	07 22							
Sidcup 4	d										07 19	07 25							
New Eltham	d										07 23	07 28							
Mottingham	d										07 25	07 31							
Lee	d										07 28	07 34							
Hither Green 4	d							07 28			07 32	07 36							07 49
Barnehurst 4	d				07 00	07 08			07 13					07 24			07 28		
Bexleyheath	d				07 03	07 11			07 16					07 26			07 31		
Welling	d				07 06	07 14			07 19					07 29			07 34		
Falconwood	d				07 08	07 16			07 21					07 32			07 36		
Eltham	d				07 11	07 19			07 24					07 35			07 39		
Kidbrooke	d				07 14	07 22			07 27					07 38			07 42		
Blackheath 4	d				07 18	07 27			07 31					07 42			07 47		
Lewisham 4	d		07 20		07 22	07 30			07 35		07 38			07 46		07 48	07 50		
St Johns	d				07 24						07 40					07 50			
New Cross 4 ⊖	d		07 23		07 26				07 38		07 42					07 53			
Nunhead 4	d													07 51					
Peckham Rye 4	d													07 54					
Denmark Hill 4	d													07 58					
London Victoria 15 ⊖	a													08 11					
Westcombe Park	d			07 17						07 32					07 42				
Maze Hill	d			07 19						07 34					07 44				
Greenwich 4	d			07 23			07 28			07 37					07 47			07 51	
Deptford	a			07 25						07 39					07 49				
London Bridge 4 ⊖	a	07 20	07 28	07 33	07 33	07 40	07 35	07 37	07 43	07 45	07 47	07 47	07 51		07 57	08 01	08 00	07 57	07 59
London Cannon Street 4 ⊖	a	07 28	07 35		07 39		07 42	07 44	07 50	07 52	07 54		07 58			08 08		08 04	08 06
London Waterloo (East) 4 ⊖	a			07 38		07 46						07 52			08 02		08 06		
London Charing Cross 4 ⊖	a			07 44		07 52						07 58			08 08		08 12		
Ebbsfleet International	a																		
Stratford International ⊖	a																		
St Pancras Int'l 15 ⊖	a																		

Station		SE	SE	SE	SE	SE	SE	SE	SE	SE	SE	SE	SE	SE	SE	SE	SE	SE 1	SE
Gillingham (Kent) 4	d																07 12	07 19	
Chatham 4	d																07 16	07 24	
Rochester 4	d																07 18		
Maidstone West	d					06 55													
Strood 4	d					07 11							07 18				07 23		
Higham	d												07 23				07 28		
Gravesend 4	d				07 17	07 22							07 31				07 36		
Northfleet	d				07 21												07 40		
Swanscombe	d				07 23												07 42		
Greenhithe for Bluewater	d				07 26								07 37				07 45		
Stone Crossing	d				07 28												07 47		
Dartford 4	a				07 33								07 42				07 51		
	d		07 25		07 34			07 36				07 40	07 43		07 45		07 52		
Slade Green 4	d		07 29							07 39					07 50				
Erith	d		07 32							07 42					07 52				
Belvedere	d		07 34							07 44					07 55				
Abbey Wood	d		07 38							07 48			07 52		07 58				
Plumstead	d		07 41							07 51					08 01				
Woolwich Arsenal 4	d		07 44							07 54			07 57		08 05				
Woolwich Dockyard	d		07 46							07 56					08 07				
Charlton 4	d		07 50							08 00			08 03		08 11				
Crayford	d			07 30	07 38											07 50	07 56		
Bexley	d			07 33	07 41											07 53	07 59		
Albany Park	d			07 36	07 44											07 56	08 02		
Sidcup 4	d			07 39	07 47				07 51							07 59	08 05		
New Eltham	d			07 43	07 50				07 54							08 03	08 09		
Mottingham	d			07 45					07 56							08 05			
Lee	d			07 48					07 59							08 08			
Hither Green 4	d			07 52					08 02							08 12			
Barnehurst 4	d	07 33					07 38	07 44				07 48		07 53					07 58
Bexleyheath	d	07 36					07 41	07 46				07 51		07 56					08 01
Welling	d	07 39					07 44	07 49				07 54		07 59					08 04
Falconwood	d	07 41					07 46	07 52				07 56		08 01					08 06
Eltham	d	07 44					07 49	07 55				07 59		08 04					08 09
Kidbrooke	d	07 47					07 52	07 58				08 02		08 07					08 12
Blackheath 4	d	07 51					07 57	08 02				08 07		08 11					08 17
Lewisham 4	d	07 55		07 57				08 05			08 08	08 11		08 15		08 17			
St Johns	d			08 00							08 12					08 21			
New Cross 4 ⊖	d	07 58		08 02							08 14			08 18		08 23			
Nunhead 4	d							08 11											
Peckham Rye 4	d							08 13											
Denmark Hill 4	d							08 17											
London Victoria 15 ⊖	a							08 29											
Westcombe Park	d		07 52							08 02					08 13				
Maze Hill	d		07 54							08 04					08 15				
Greenwich 4	d		07 57							08 07			08 11		08 19				
Deptford	a		07 59							08 09					08 21				
London Bridge 4 ⊖	a	08 03	08 05	08 08	08 05				08 13	08 16	08 21	08 20	08 17	08 25	08 27	08 29	08 25	08 09	
London Cannon Street 4 ⊖	a	08 10	08 12	08 15							08 28		08 24	08 32	08 35	08 36		08 17	
London Waterloo (East) 4 ⊖	a				08 10		08 12		08 18	08 22		08 26					08 30		08 32
London Charing Cross 4 ⊖	a				08 16		08 18		08 24	08 28		08 32					08 36		08 39
Ebbsfleet International	a					07 25													
Stratford International ⊖	a					07 38													
St Pancras Int'l 15 ⊖	a					07 45													

Table 200R

Mondays to Fridays

9 December to 16 May

Gillingham and Dartford - London

Network Diagram - see first Page of Table 200

Station		SE	SE	SE	SE	SE	SE	SE	SE	SE	SE	SE	SE	SE
Gillingham (Kent) 4	d													07 38
Chatham 4	d													07 42
Rochester 4	d													07 44
Maidstone West	d							07 25						
Strood 4	d							07 41						07 49
Higham	d													07 54
Gravesend 4	d						07 47	07 52						08 02
Northfleet	d						07 51							
Swanscombe	d						07 53							
Greenhithe for Bluewater	d						07 56							08 08
Stone Crossing	d						07 58							
Dartford 4	a						08 03							08 12
	d	07 56				08 02	08 04					08 06		08 13
Slade Green 4	d			07 59					08 00		08 00	08 10		
Erith	d			08 02								08 13		
Belvedere	d			08 04								08 15		
Abbey Wood	d			08 08			08 14					08 18		
Plumstead	d			08 11								08 21		
Woolwich Arsenal 4	d			08 14			08 19					08 24		
Woolwich Dockyard	d			08 16								08 27		
Charlton 4	d			08 20			08 24					08 30		
Crayford	d												08 10	08 17
Bexley	d												08 13	08 20
Albany Park	d												08 16	08 23
Sidcup 4	d		08 11										08 19	08 26
New Eltham	d		08 14										08 23	08 30
Mottingham	d		08 16										08 25	
Lee	d		08 19										08 28	
Hither Green 4	d		08 22										08 32	
Barnehurst 4	d	08 04				08 09			08a12	08 13	08 13			
Bexleyheath	d	08 06				08 11				08 16	08 16			
Welling	d	08 09				08 14				08 19	08 19			
Falconwood	d	08 12				08 17				08 21	08 21			
Eltham	d	08 15				08 20				08 24	08 24			
Kidbrooke	d	08 18				08 23				08 27	08 27			
Blackheath 4	d	08 22				08 27				08 31	08 31			
Lewisham 4	d	08 25			08 28	08 31				08 35	08 35		08 37	
St Johns	d				08 30								08 39	
New Cross 4 ⊖	d				08 32					08 38	08 38		08 41	
Nunhead 4	d	08 30												
Peckham Rye 4	d	08 33												
Denmark Hill 4	d	08 36												
London Victoria 15 ⊖	a	08 49												
Westcombe Park	d			08 22								08 32		
Maze Hill	d			08 24								08 34		
Greenwich 4	d			08 27			08 31					08 37		
Deptford	a			08 29								08 39		
London Bridge 4 ⊖	a		08 33	08 37	08 41	08 40	08 37			08 43	08 43	08 45	08 47	08 45
London Cannon Street 4 ⊖	a				08 48		08 44			08 50	08 50	08 52	08 55	
London Waterloo (East) 4 ⊖	a		08 38	08 42		08 46								08 50
London Charing Cross 4 ⊖	a		08 44	08 48		08 52								08 56
Ebbsfleet International	a							07 55						
Stratford International ⊖	a							08 09						
St Pancras Int'l 15 ⊖	a							08 16						

Station		SE 1	SE 1	SE	SE	SE	SE	SE	SE	SE
Gillingham (Kent) 4	d	07 46	08 04							
Chatham 4	d	07 50	08 08							
Rochester 4	d		08 11							
Maidstone West	d									
Strood 4	d									
Higham	d									
Gravesend 4	d								08 17	
Northfleet	d									
Swanscombe	d									
Greenhithe for Bluewater	d								08 23	
Stone Crossing	d									
Dartford 4	a								08 28	
	d								08 29	
Slade Green 4	d			08 17		08 17				
Erith	d					08 19				
Belvedere	d					08 22				
Abbey Wood	d					08 25				
Plumstead	d					08 28				
Woolwich Arsenal 4	d					08 31				
Woolwich Dockyard	d					08 34				
Charlton 4	d					08 37				
Crayford	d							08 28	08 34	
Bexley	d							08 31	08 37	
Albany Park	d							08 34	08 40	
Sidcup 4	d				08 31			08 37	08 43	
New Eltham	d				08 34			08 41	08 46	
Mottingham	d				08 36			08 43	08 49	
Lee	d				08 39			08 46	08 52	
Hither Green 4	d				08 42			08 50	08 55	09 00
Barnehurst 4	d			08 24						
Bexleyheath	d			08 27						
Welling	d			08 30						
Falconwood	d			08 32						
Eltham	d			08 35						
Kidbrooke	d			08 38						
Blackheath 4	d			08 42						
Lewisham 4	d			08 46			08 48	08 55		09 05
St Johns	d						08 50	08 57		09 08
New Cross 4 ⊖	d						08 52	08 59		09 10
Nunhead 4	d			08 52						
Peckham Rye 4	d			08 55						
Denmark Hill 4	d			08 59						
London Victoria 15 ⊖	a			09 11						
Westcombe Park	d					08 39				
Maze Hill	d					08 41				
Greenwich 4	d					08 45				
Deptford	a					08 47				
London Bridge 4 ⊖	a	08 31	08 49		08 52	08 56	08 57	09 05	09 05	09 17
London Cannon Street 4 ⊖	a	08 38	08 57				09 04	09 13		09 24
London Waterloo (East) 4 ⊖	a				08 58	09 02			09 10	
London Charing Cross 4 ⊖	a				09 04	09 08			09 16	
Ebbsfleet International	a									
Stratford International ⊖	a									
St Pancras Int'l 15 ⊖	a									

Station		SE	SE	SE	SE	SE	SE	SE	SE	SE 1
Gillingham (Kent) 4	d		08 08				08 20			08 24
Chatham 4	d		08 12				08 24			08 28
Rochester 4	d		08 14				08 27			08 31
Maidstone West	d	07 55								
Strood 4	d	08 11	08 19				08 32			
Higham	d		08 24							
Gravesend 4	d	08 22	08 33			08 05	08 43			
Northfleet	d		08 37			08 09				
Swanscombe	d		08 39			08 11				
Greenhithe for Bluewater	d		08 42			08 14				
Stone Crossing	d		08 44			08 16				
Dartford 4	a		08 49			08 21				
	d		08 49			08 22		08 24		
Slade Green 4	d					08 27			08 31	
Erith	d								08 33	
Belvedere	d								08 36	
Abbey Wood	d					08 34			08 39	
Plumstead	d								08 42	
Woolwich Arsenal 4	d					08 40			08 45	
Woolwich Dockyard	d								08 47	
Charlton 4	d				08 37	08 45			08 50	
Crayford	d		08 54		09 07					
Bexley	d		08 57		09 10					
Albany Park	d		09 00		09 13					
Sidcup 4	d		09 03		09 16					
New Eltham	d		09 06		09 19					
Mottingham	d		09 08		09 21					
Lee	d		09 11		09 24					
Hither Green 4	d		09 14	09 19	09 28					
Barnehurst 4	d							08 30		
Bexleyheath	d							08 33		
Welling	d							08 36		
Falconwood	d							08 38		
Eltham	d							08 41		
Kidbrooke	d							08 44		
Blackheath 4	d							08 48		
Lewisham 4	d			09 24	09 34			08 52		
St Johns	d			09 26	09 36					
New Cross 4 ⊖	d			09 28	09 38					
Nunhead 4	d									
Peckham Rye 4	d									
Denmark Hill 4	d									
London Victoria 15 ⊖	a									
Westcombe Park	d								08 52	
Maze Hill	d								08 54	
Greenwich 4	d					08 51			08 58	
Deptford	a								09 00	
London Bridge 4 ⊖	a		09 23	09 33	09 44	09 00		09 00	09 07	09 09
London Cannon Street 4 ⊖	a			09 40	09 51	09 08			09 15	09 18
London Waterloo (East) 4 ⊖	a		09 28					09 05		
London Charing Cross 4 ⊖	a		09 34					09 12		
Ebbsfleet International	a	08 25					08 46			
Stratford International ⊖	a	08 38					09 00			
St Pancras Int'l 15 ⊖	a	08 45					09 07			

Station		SE	SE	SE	SE	SE
Gillingham (Kent) 4	d					
Chatham 4	d					
Rochester 4	d					
Maidstone West	d					
Strood 4	d					
Higham	d					
Gravesend 4	d					
Northfleet	d					
Swanscombe	d					
Greenhithe for Bluewater	d					
Stone Crossing	d					
Dartford 4	a					
	d				08 38	
Slade Green 4	d	08 31		08 31		08 39
Erith	d					08 41
Belvedere	d					08 44
Abbey Wood	d					08 47
Plumstead	d					08 50
Woolwich Arsenal 4	d					08 53
Woolwich Dockyard	d					08 56
Charlton 4	d					08 59
Crayford	d					
Bexley	d					
Albany Park	d					
Sidcup 4	d					
New Eltham	d					
Mottingham	d					
Lee	d					
Hither Green 4	d					
Barnehurst 4	d	08a38	08 39	08 39	08 45	
Bexleyheath	d		08 42	08 42	08 47	
Welling	d		08 45	08 45	08 50	
Falconwood	d		08 47	08 47	08 53	
Eltham	d		08 50	08 50	08 56	
Kidbrooke	d		08 53	08 53	08 59	
Blackheath 4	d		08 58	08 58	09 03	
Lewisham 4	d		09 02	09 02	09 07	
St Johns	d					
New Cross 4 ⊖	d		09 07	09 07		
Nunhead 4	d				09 12	
Peckham Rye 4	d				09 14	
Denmark Hill 4	d				09 17	
London Victoria 15 ⊖	a				09 30	
Westcombe Park	d					09 01
Maze Hill	d					09 03
Greenwich 4	d					09 07
Deptford	a					09 09
London Bridge 4 ⊖	a		09 13	09 13		09 17
London Cannon Street 4 ⊖	a		09 20	09 20		
London Waterloo (East) 4 ⊖	a					09 22
London Charing Cross 4 ⊖	a					09 28
Ebbsfleet International	a					
Stratford International ⊖	a					
St Pancras Int'l 15 ⊖	a					

Table 200R

Mondays to Fridays

Gillingham and Dartford - London

9 December to 16 May

Network Diagram - see first Page of Table 200

Station		SE	SE	SE	SE	SE	SE	SE	SE	SE	SE	SE	SE	SE	SE	SE	SE	SE	SE	SE	SE	SE	SE	SE	SE	SE	SE	SE	SE	SE	SE	SE	SE	SE	SE	SE	SE
Gillingham (Kent) [4]	d									08 50													08 54	09 20												09 24	09 50
Chatham [4]	d									08 54													08 58	09 24												09 28	09 54
Rochester [4]	d									08 57													09 00	09 27												09 30	09 57
Maidstone West	d																																			
Strood [4]	d									09 02													09 05	09 32												09 35	10 02
Higham	d																						09 10													09 40	
Gravesend [4]	d				09 02				08 48	09 13									09 32				09 18	09 43								10 02				09 48	10 13
Northfleet	d				09 06														09 36													10 06					
Swanscombe	d				09 08														09 38													10 08					
Greenhithe for Bluewater	d				09 11				08 53										09 41				09 23									10 11				09 53	
Stone Crossing	d				09 13														09 43													10 13					
Dartford [4]	a				09 17				08 58										09 47				09 28									10 17				09 58	
	d		08 52		09 18				08 59			09 01	09 08			09 22			09 48				09 29			09 31	09 38			09 52		10 18				09 59	
Slade Green [4]	d			08 47				08 54				09 05		09 15			09 17	09 17				09 25				09 35		09 45			09 47				09 55		
Erith	d							08 56				09 08		09 18								09 28				09 38		09 48							09 58		
Belvedere	d							08 59				09 10		09 20								09 30				09 40		09 50							10 00		
Abbey Wood	d							09 02	09 08			09 13		09 23								09 33	09 38			09 43		09 53							10 03	10 08	
Plumstead	d							09 05				09 16		09 26								09 36				09 46		09 56							10 06		
Woolwich Arsenal [4]	d							09 08	09 13			09 19		09 29								09 39	09 43			09 49		09 59							10 09	10 13	
Woolwich Dockyard	d							09 10				09 22										09 42				09 52		10 02							10 12		
Charlton [4]	d						09 07	09 13	09 17			09 25		09 35							09 40	09 45	09 47			09 55		10 05						10 07	10 15	10 17	
Crayford	d				09 22		09 37												09 52		10 07											10 22		10 37			
Bexley	d				09 25		09 40												09 55		10 10											10 25		10 40			
Albany Park	d				09 28		09 43												09 58		10 13											10 28		10 43			
Sidcup [4]	d				09 31		09 46												10 01		10 16											10 31		10 46			
New Eltham	d				09 34		09 49												10 04		10 19											10 34		10 49			
Mottingham	d				09 36		09 51												10 06		10 21											10 36		10 51			
Lee	d				09 39		09 54												10 09		10 24											10 39		10 54			
Hither Green [4]	d				09 42	09 49	09 58												10 12	10 19	10 28											10 42	10 49	10 58			
Barnehurst [4]	d		08 59	09 08							09 08		09 16			09 29	09a34	09 38							09 38		09 46			09 59	10 08						
Bexleyheath	d		09 01	09 10							09 10		09 19			09 31		09 40							09 40		09 49			10 01	10 10						
Welling	d		09 04	09 13							09 13		09 22			09 34		09 43							09 43		09 52			10 04	10 13						
Falconwood	d		09 07	09 16							09 16		09 24			09 37		09 46							09 46		09 54			10 07	10 16						
Eltham	d		09 10	09 19							09 19		09 27			09 40		09 49							09 49		09 57			10 10	10 19						
Kidbrooke	d		09 13	09 22							09 22		09 30			09 43		09 52							09 52		10 00			10 13	10 22						
Blackheath [4]	d		09 16	09 25					09 22		09 25		09 34			09 46		09 55					09 52		09 55		10 04			10 16	10 25					10 22	
Lewisham [4]	d	09 15	09 20	09 29		09 54	10 04		09 26		09 29		09 38		09 45	09 50		09 59		10 24	10 34		09 56		09 59		10 08		10 14	10 20	10 29		10 54	11 04		10 26	
St Johns	d	09 17		09 31		09 56	10 06				09 31				09 47			10 01		10 26	10 36				10 01				10 16		10 31		10 56	11 06			
New Cross [4] ⊖	d	09 19		09 33		09 58	10 08				09 33				09 49			10 03		10 28	10 38				10 03				10 18		10 33		10 58	11 08			
Nunhead [4]	d													09 43														10 13										
Peckham Rye [4]	d													09 45														10 15										
Denmark Hill [4]	d													09 49														10 19										
London Victoria [15] ⊖	a													10 00														10 28										
Westcombe Park	d							09 15				09 27		09 37								09 47				09 57		10 07							10 17		
Maze Hill	d							09 17				09 29		09 39								09 49				09 59		10 09							10 19		
Greenwich [4]	d							09 21				09 32		09 42								09 52				10 02		10 12							10 22		
Deptford	a							09 23				09 34		09 44								09 54				10 04		10 14							10 24		
London Bridge [4] ⊖	a	09 25	09 29	09 38	09 52	10 04	10 14	09 29	09 34		09 38	09 41		09 50	09 54	09 58		10 08	10 22	10 34	10 44	10 00	10 05		10 08	10 11		10 20	10 24	10 28	10 38	10 52	11 04	11 14	10 30	10 35	
London Cannon Street [4] ⊖	a	09 32		09 46		10 08	10 19	09 36			09 46	09 48		09 57	10 00			10 13		10 38	10 50	10 06			10 13	10 15		10 24	10 28		10 43		11 08	11 19	10 36		
London Waterloo (East) [4] ⊖	a		09 34		09 56				09 39							10 02			10 26				10 09							10 32		10 56				10 39	
London Charing Cross [4] ⊖	a		09 40		10 01				09 45							10 07			10 31				10 13							10 37		11 01				10 43	
Ebbsfleet International	a									09 16														09 46													10 16
Stratford International ⊖	a									09 29														10 00													10 29
St Pancras Int'l [15] ⊖	a									09 36														10 07													10 36

Table 200R

Mondays to Fridays

9 December to 16 May

Gillingham and Dartford - London

Network Diagram - see first Page of Table 200

		SE	SE	SE	SE	SE	SE	SE	SE	SE
Gillingham (Kent) 4	d									
Chatham 4	d									
Rochester 4	d									
Maidstone West	d									
Strood 4	d									
Higham	d									
Gravesend 4	d									10 32
Northfleet	d									10 36
Swanscombe	d									10 38
Greenhithe for Bluewater	d									10 41
Stone Crossing	d									10 43
Dartford 4	a									10 47
	d		10 01	10 08			10 22			10 48
Slade Green 4	d		10 05		10 15			10 17	10 17	
Erith	d		10 08		10 18					
Belvedere	d		10 10		10 20					
Abbey Wood	d		10 13		10 23					
Plumstead	d		10 16		10 26					
Woolwich Arsenal 4	d		10 19		10 29					
Woolwich Dockyard	d		10 22		10 32					
Charlton 4	d		10 25		10 35					
Crayford	d									10 52
Bexley	d									10 55
Albany Park	d									10 58
Sidcup 4	d									11 01
New Eltham	d									11 04
Mottingham	d									11 06
Lee	d									11 09
Hither Green 4	d									11 12
Barnehurst 4	d	10 08		10 16			10 29	10a34	10 38	
Bexleyheath	d	10 10		10 19			10 31		10 40	
Welling	d	10 13		10 22			10 34		10 43	
Falconwood	d	10 16		10 24			10 37		10 46	
Eltham	d	10 19		10 27			10 40		10 49	
Kidbrooke	d	10 22		10 30			10 43		10 52	
Blackheath 4	d	10 25		10 34			10 46		10 55	
Lewisham 4	d	10 29		10 38		10 44	10 50		10 59	
St Johns	d	10 31				10 46			11 01	
New Cross 4 ⊖	d	10 33				10 48			11 03	
Nunhead 4	d			10 43						
Peckham Rye 4	d			10 45						
Denmark Hill 4	d			10 49						
London Victoria 15 ⊖	a			10 58						
Westcombe Park	d		10 27		10 37					
Maze Hill	d		10 29		10 39					
Greenwich 4	d		10 32		10 42					
Deptford	a		10 34		10 44					
London Bridge 4 ⊖	a	10 38	10 41		10 50	10 54	10 58		11 08	11 22
London Cannon Street 4 ⊖	a	10 43	10 45		10 54	10 58			11 13	
London Waterloo (East) 4 ⊖	a						11 02			11 26
London Charing Cross 4 ⊖	a						11 06			11 30
Ebbsfleet International	a									
Stratford International ⊖	a									
St Pancras Int'l 15 ⊖	a									

		SE	SE	SE	SE	SE	SE	SE	SE	SE
Gillingham (Kent) 4	d				09 54	10 20				
Chatham 4	d				09 58	10 24				
Rochester 4	d				10 00	10 27				
Maidstone West	d									
Strood 4	d				10 05	10 32				
Higham	d				10 10					
Gravesend 4	d				10 18	10 43				
Northfleet	d									
Swanscombe	d									
Greenhithe for Bluewater	d				10 23					
Stone Crossing	d									
Dartford 4	a				10 28					
	d				10 29			10 31	10 38	
Slade Green 4	d			10 25				10 35		10 45
Erith	d			10 28				10 38		10 48
Belvedere	d			10 30				10 40		10 50
Abbey Wood	d			10 33	10 38			10 43		10 53
Plumstead	d			10 36				10 46		10 56
Woolwich Arsenal 4	d			10 39	10 43			10 49		10 59
Woolwich Dockyard	d			10 42				10 52		11 02
Charlton 4	d		10 37	10 45	10 47			10 55		11 05
Crayford	d		11 07							
Bexley	d		11 10							
Albany Park	d		11 13							
Sidcup 4	d		11 16							
New Eltham	d		11 19							
Mottingham	d		11 21							
Lee	d		11 24							
Hither Green 4	d	11 19	11 28							
Barnehurst 4	d						10 38		10 46	
Bexleyheath	d						10 40		10 49	
Welling	d						10 43		10 52	
Falconwood	d						10 46		10 54	
Eltham	d						10 49		10 57	
Kidbrooke	d						10 52		11 00	
Blackheath 4	d				10 52		10 55		11 04	
Lewisham 4	d	11 24	11 34		10 56		10 59		11 08	
St Johns	d	11 26	11 36				11 01			
New Cross 4 ⊖	d	11 28	11 38				11 03			
Nunhead 4	d								11 13	
Peckham Rye 4	d								11 15	
Denmark Hill 4	d								11 19	
London Victoria 15 ⊖	a								11 28	
Westcombe Park	d			10 47				10 57		11 07
Maze Hill	d			10 49				10 59		11 09
Greenwich 4	d			10 52				11 02		11 12
Deptford	a			10 54				11 04		11 14
London Bridge 4 ⊖	a	11 34	11 44	11 00	11 05		11 08	11 11		11 20
London Cannon Street 4 ⊖	a	11 38	11 49	11 06			11 13	11 15		11 24
London Waterloo (East) 4 ⊖	a				11 09					
London Charing Cross 4 ⊖	a				11 13					
Ebbsfleet International	a					10 46				
Stratford International ⊖	a					10 59				
St Pancras Int'l 15 ⊖	a					11 06				

		SE	SE	SE	SE	SE	SE	SE	SE	SE
Gillingham (Kent) 4	d								10 24	10 50
Chatham 4	d								10 28	10 54
Rochester 4	d								10 30	10 57
Maidstone West	d									
Strood 4	d								10 35	11 02
Higham	d								10 40	
Gravesend 4	d				11 02				10 48	11 13
Northfleet	d				11 06					
Swanscombe	d				11 08					
Greenhithe for Bluewater	d				11 11				10 53	
Stone Crossing	d				11 13					
Dartford 4	a				11 17				10 58	
	d		10 52		11 18				10 59	
Slade Green 4	d			10 47				10 55		
Erith	d							10 58		
Belvedere	d							11 00		
Abbey Wood	d							11 03	11 08	
Plumstead	d							11 06		
Woolwich Arsenal 4	d							11 09	11 13	
Woolwich Dockyard	d							11 12		
Charlton 4	d						11 07	11 15	11 17	
Crayford	d				11 22		11 37			
Bexley	d				11 25		11 40			
Albany Park	d				11 28		11 43			
Sidcup 4	d				11 31		11 46			
New Eltham	d				11 34		11 49			
Mottingham	d				11 36		11 51			
Lee	d				11 39		11 54			
Hither Green 4	d				11 42	11 49	11 58			
Barnehurst 4	d		10 59	11 08						
Bexleyheath	d		11 01	11 10						
Welling	d		11 04	11 13						
Falconwood	d		11 07	11 16						
Eltham	d		11 10	11 19						
Kidbrooke	d		11 13	11 22						
Blackheath 4	d		11 16	11 25					11 22	
Lewisham 4	d	11 14	11 20	11 29		11 54	12 04		11 26	
St Johns	d	11 16		11 31		11 56	12 06			
New Cross 4 ⊖	d	11 18		11 33		11 58	12 08			
Nunhead 4	d									
Peckham Rye 4	d									
Denmark Hill 4	d									
London Victoria 15 ⊖	a									
Westcombe Park	d							11 17		
Maze Hill	d							11 19		
Greenwich 4	d							11 22		
Deptford	a							11 24		
London Bridge 4 ⊖	a	11 24	11 28	11 38	11 52	12 04	12 14	11 30	11 35	
London Cannon Street 4 ⊖	a	11 28		11 43		12 08	12 19	11 36		
London Waterloo (East) 4 ⊖	a		11 32		11 56				11 39	
London Charing Cross 4 ⊖	a		11 36		12 00				11 43	
Ebbsfleet International	a									11 16
Stratford International ⊖	a									11 29
St Pancras Int'l 15 ⊖	a									11 36

		SE	SE	SE	SE	SE	SE	SE	SE	SE
Gillingham (Kent) 4	d									
Chatham 4	d									
Rochester 4	d									
Maidstone West	d									
Strood 4	d									
Higham	d									
Gravesend 4	d								11 32	
Northfleet	d								11 36	
Swanscombe	d								11 38	
Greenhithe for Bluewater	d								11 41	
Stone Crossing	d								11 43	
Dartford 4	a								11 47	
	d		11 01	11 08			11 22		11 48	
Slade Green 4	d		11 05		11 15			11 17		
Erith	d		11 08		11 18					
Belvedere	d		11 10		11 20					
Abbey Wood	d		11 13		11 23					
Plumstead	d		11 16		11 26					
Woolwich Arsenal 4	d		11 19		11 29					
Woolwich Dockyard	d		11 22		11 32					
Charlton 4	d		11 25		11 35					
Crayford	d								11 52	
Bexley	d								11 55	
Albany Park	d								11 58	
Sidcup 4	d								12 01	
New Eltham	d								12 04	
Mottingham	d								12 06	
Lee	d								12 09	
Hither Green 4	d								12 12	12 19
Barnehurst 4	d	11 08		11 16			11 29	11 38		
Bexleyheath	d	11 10		11 19			11 31	11 40		
Welling	d	11 13		11 22			11 34	11 43		
Falconwood	d	11 16		11 24			11 37	11 46		
Eltham	d	11 19		11 27			11 40	11 49		
Kidbrooke	d	11 22		11 30			11 43	11 52		
Blackheath 4	d	11 25		11 34			11 46	11 55		
Lewisham 4	d	11 29		11 38		11 44	11 50	11 59		12 24
St Johns	d	11 31				11 46		12 01		12 26
New Cross 4 ⊖	d	11 33				11 48		12 03		12 28
Nunhead 4	d			11 43						
Peckham Rye 4	d			11 45						
Denmark Hill 4	d			11 49						
London Victoria 15 ⊖	a			11 58						
Westcombe Park	d		11 27		11 37					
Maze Hill	d		11 29		11 39					
Greenwich 4	d		11 32		11 42					
Deptford	a		11 34		11 44					
London Bridge 4 ⊖	a	11 38	11 41		11 50	11 54	11 58	12 08	12 22	12 34
London Cannon Street 4 ⊖	a	11 43	11 45		11 54	11 58		12 13		12 38
London Waterloo (East) 4 ⊖	a						12 02		12 26	
London Charing Cross 4 ⊖	a						12 06		12 30	
Ebbsfleet International	a									
Stratford International ⊖	a									
St Pancras Int'l 15 ⊖	a									

Table 200R

Mondays to Fridays

9 December to 16 May

Gillingham and Dartford - London

Network Diagram - see first Page of Table 200

Station		SE	SE	SE	SE	SE	SE	SE	SE	SE	SE	SE	SE	SE	SE	SE	SE	SE	SE
Gillingham (Kent) [4]	d			10 54	11 20												11 24	11 50	
Chatham [4]	d			10 58	11 24												11 28	11 54	
Rochester [4]	d			11 00	11 27												11 30	11 57	
Maidstone West	d																		
Strood [4]	d			11 05	11 32												11 35	12 02	
Higham	d			11 10													11 40		
Gravesend [4]	d			11 18	11 43								12 02				11 48	12 13	
Northfleet	d												12 06						
Swanscombe	d												12 08						
Greenhithe for Bluewater	d			11 23									12 11				11 53		
Stone Crossing	d												12 13						
Dartford [4]	a			11 28									12 17				11 58		
	d			11 29			11 31	11 38			11 52		12 18				11 59		
Slade Green [4]	d		11 25				11 35		11 45			11 47				11 55			
Erith	d		11 28				11 38		11 48							11 58			
Belvedere	d		11 30				11 40		11 50							12 00			
Abbey Wood	d		11 33	11 38			11 43		11 53							12 03	12 08		
Plumstead	d		11 36				11 46		11 56							12 06			
Woolwich Arsenal [4] ⛴	d		11 39	11 43			11 49		11 59							12 09	12 13		
Woolwich Dockyard	d		11 42				11 52		12 02							12 12			
Charlton [4]	d	11 37	11 45	11 47			11 55		12 05						12 07	12 15	12 17		
Crayford	d	12 07											12 22		12 37				
Bexley	d	12 10											12 25		12 40				
Albany Park	d	12 13											12 28		12 43				
Sidcup [4]	d	12 16											12 31		12 46				
New Eltham	d	12 19											12 34		12 49				
Mottingham	d	12 21											12 36		12 51				
Lee	d	12 24											12 39		12 54				
Hither Green [4]	d	12 28											12 42	12 49	12 58				
Barnehurst [4]	d					11 38		11 46			11 59	12 08							12 08
Bexleyheath	d					11 40		11 49			12 01	12 10							12 10
Welling	d					11 43		11 52			12 04	12 13							12 13
Falconwood	d					11 46		11 54			12 07	12 16							12 16
Eltham	d					11 49		11 57			12 10	12 19							12 19
Kidbrooke	d					11 52		12 00			12 13	12 22							12 22
Blackheath [4]	d			11 52		11 55		12 04			12 16	12 25					12 22		12 25
Lewisham [4] ⛴	d	12 34		11 56		11 59		12 08		12 14	12 20	12 29		12 54	13 04		12 26		12 29
St Johns	d	12 36				12 01				12 16		12 31		12 56	13 06				12 31
New Cross [4] ⊖	d	12 38				12 03				12 18		12 33		12 58	13 08				12 33
Nunhead [4]	d							12 13											
Peckham Rye [4]	d							12 15											
Denmark Hill [4]	d							12 19											
London Victoria [15] ⊖	a							12 28											
Westcombe Park	d		11 47				11 57		12 07							12 17			
Maze Hill	d		11 49				11 59		12 09							12 19			
Greenwich [4] ⛴	d		11 52				12 02		12 12							12 22			
Deptford	a		11 54				12 04		12 14							12 24			
London Bridge [4] ⊖	a	12 44	12 00	12 05		12 08	12 11		12 20	12 24	12 28	12 38	12 52	13 04	13 14	12 30	12 35		12 38
London Cannon Street [4] ⊖	a	12 50	12 04			12 13	12 15		12 24	12 28		12 43		13 08	13 19	12 36			12 43
London Waterloo (East) [4] ⊖	a			12 09							12 32		12 56				12 39		
London Charing Cross [4] ⊖	a			12 13							12 36		13 00				12 43		
Ebbsfleet International	a				11 46													12 16	
Stratford International ⊖ ⛴	a				11 59													12 30	
St Pancras Int'l [15] ⊖	a				12 06													12 37	

Station		SE	SE	SE	SE	SE	SE	SE	SE	SE	SE	SE	SE	SE	SE	SE	SE	SE	SE
Gillingham (Kent) [4]	d											11 54	12 20						
Chatham [4]	d											11 58	12 24						
Rochester [4]	d											12 00	12 27						
Maidstone West	d																		
Strood [4]	d											12 05	12 32						
Higham	d											12 10							
Gravesend [4]	d							12 32				12 18	12 43						
Northfleet	d							12 36											
Swanscombe	d							12 38											
Greenhithe for Bluewater	d							12 41				12 23							
Stone Crossing	d							12 43											
Dartford [4]	a							12 47				12 28							
	d	12 01	12 08			12 22		12 48				12 29			12 31	12 38			12 52
Slade Green [4]	d	12 05		12 15			12 17				12 25				12 35		12 45		
Erith	d	12 08		12 18							12 28				12 38		12 48		
Belvedere	d	12 10		12 20							12 30				12 40		12 50		
Abbey Wood	d	12 13		12 23							12 33	12 38			12 43		12 53		
Plumstead	d	12 16		12 26							12 36				12 46		12 56		
Woolwich Arsenal [4] ⛴	d	12 19		12 29							12 39	12 43			12 49		12 59		
Woolwich Dockyard	d	12 22		12 32							12 42				12 52		13 02		
Charlton [4]	d	12 25		12 35						12 37	12 45	12 47			12 55		13 05		
Crayford	d							12 52		13 07									
Bexley	d							12 55		13 10									
Albany Park	d							12 58		13 13									
Sidcup [4]	d							13 01		13 16									
New Eltham	d							13 04		13 19									
Mottingham	d							13 06		13 21									
Lee	d							13 09		13 24									
Hither Green [4]	d							13 12	13 19	13 28									
Barnehurst [4]	d		12 16			12 29	12 38							12 38		12 46			12 59
Bexleyheath	d		12 19			12 31	12 40							12 40		12 49			13 01
Welling	d		12 22			12 34	12 43							12 43		12 52			13 04
Falconwood	d		12 24			12 37	12 46							12 46		12 54			13 07
Eltham	d		12 27			12 40	12 49							12 49		12 57			13 10
Kidbrooke	d		12 30			12 43	12 52							12 52		13 00			13 13
Blackheath [4]	d		12 34			12 46	12 55					12 52		12 55		13 04			13 16
Lewisham [4] ⛴	d		12 38		12 44	12 50	12 59		13 24	13 34		12 56		12 59		13 08		13 14	13 20
St Johns	d				12 46		13 01		13 26	13 36				13 01				13 16	
New Cross [4] ⊖	d				12 48		13 03		13 28	13 38				13 03				13 18	
Nunhead [4]	d		12 43													13 13			
Peckham Rye [4]	d		12 45													13 15			
Denmark Hill [4]	d		12 49													13 19			
London Victoria [15] ⊖	a		12 58													13 28			
Westcombe Park	d	12 27		12 37							12 47				12 57		13 07		
Maze Hill	d	12 29		12 39							12 49				12 59		13 09		
Greenwich [4] ⛴	d	12 32		12 42							12 52				13 02		13 12		
Deptford	a	12 34		12 44							12 54				13 04		13 14		
London Bridge [4] ⊖	a	12 41		12 50	12 54	12 58	13 08	13 22	13 34	13 44	13 00	13 05		13 08	13 11		13 20	13 24	13 28
London Cannon Street [4] ⊖	a	12 45		12 54	12 58		13 13		13 38	13 49	13 06			13 13	13 15		13 24	13 28	
London Waterloo (East) [4] ⊖	a					13 02		13 26				13 09							13 32
London Charing Cross [4] ⊖	a					13 06		13 30				13 13							13 36
Ebbsfleet International	a												12 46						
Stratford International ⊖ ⛴	a												13 00						
St Pancras Int'l [15] ⊖	a												13 07						

Table 200R

Mondays to Fridays

Gillingham and Dartford - London

9 December to 16 May

Network Diagram - see first Page of Table 200

Station		SE	SE	SE	SE	SE	SE	SE	SE	SE	SE	SE	SE	SE	SE	SE	SE	SE	SE
Gillingham (Kent) ■	d						12 24	12 50											
Chatham ■	d						12 28	12 54											
Rochester ■	d						12 30	12 57											
Maidstone West	d																		
Strood ■	d						12 35	13 02											
Higham	d						12 40												
Gravesend ■	d		13 02				12 48	13 13								13 32			
Northfleet	d		13 06													13 36			
Swanscombe	d		13 08													13 38			
Greenhithe for Bluewater	d		13 11				12 53									13 41			
Stone Crossing	d		13 13													13 43			
Dartford ■	a		13 17				12 58									13 47			
	d		13 18				12 59			13 01	13 08			13 22		13 48			
Slade Green ■	d	12 47				12 55				13 05		13 15			13 17				13 25
Erith	d					12 58				13 08		13 18							13 28
Belvedere	d					13 00				13 10		13 20							13 30
Abbey Wood	d					13 03	13 08			13 13		13 23							13 33
Plumstead	d					13 06				13 16		13 26							13 36
Woolwich Arsenal ■	d					13 09	13 13			13 19		13 29							13 39
Woolwich Dockyard	d					13 12				13 22		13 32							13 42
Charlton ■	d				13 07	13 15	13 17			13 25		13 35						13 37	13 45
Crayford	d		13 22		13 37											13 52		14 07	
Bexley	d		13 25		13 40											13 55		14 10	
Albany Park	d		13 28		13 43											13 58		14 13	
Sidcup ■	d		13 31		13 46											14 01		14 16	
New Eltham	d		13 34		13 49											14 04		14 19	
Mottingham	d		13 36		13 51											14 06		14 21	
Lee	d		13 39		13 54											14 09		14 24	
Hither Green ■	d		13 42	13 49	13 58											14 12	14 19	14 28	
Barnehurst ■	d	13 08							13 08		13 16			13 29	13 38				
Bexleyheath	d	13 10							13 10		13 19			13 31	13 40				
Welling	d	13 13							13 13		13 22			13 34	13 43				
Falconwood	d	13 16							13 16		13 24			13 37	13 46				
Eltham	d	13 19							13 19		13 27			13 40	13 49				
Kidbrooke	d	13 22							13 22		13 30			13 43	13 52				
Blackheath ■	d	13 25					13 22		13 25		13 34			13 46	13 55				
Lewisham ■	d	13 29		13 54	14 04		13 26		13 29		13 38		13 44	13 50	13 59		14 24	14 34	
St Johns	d	13 31		13 56	14 06				13 31				13 46		14 01		14 26	14 36	
New Cross ■	d	13 33		13 58	14 08				13 33				13 48		14 03		14 28	14 38	
Nunhead ■	d										13 43								
Peckham Rye ■	d										13 45								
Denmark Hill ■	d										13 49								
London Victoria ■	a										13 58								
Westcombe Park	d					13 17				13 27		13 37							13 47
Maze Hill	d					13 19				13 29		13 39							13 49
Greenwich ■	d					13 22				13 32		13 42							13 52
Deptford	a					13 24				13 34		13 44							13 54
London Bridge ■	a	13 38	13 52	14 04	14 14	13 30	13 35		13 38	13 41		13 50	13 54	13 58	14 08	14 22	14 34	14 44	14 00
London Cannon Street ■	a	13 43		14 08	14 19	13 36			13 43	13 45		13 54	13 58		14 13		14 38	14 49	14 06
London Waterloo (East) ■	a		13 56				13 39							14 02		14 26			
London Charing Cross ■	a		14 00				13 43							14 06		14 30			
Ebbsfleet International	a							13 16											
Stratford International	a							13 30											
St Pancras Int'l ■	a							13 37											

Station		SE	SE	SE	SE	SE	SE	SE	SE	SE	SE	SE	SE	SE	SE	SE	SE	SE	SE
Gillingham (Kent) ■	d	12 54	13 20												13 24	13 50			
Chatham ■	d	12 58	13 24												13 28	13 54			
Rochester ■	d	13 00	13 27												13 30	13 57			
Maidstone West	d																		
Strood ■	d	13 05	13 32												13 35	14 02			
Higham	d	13 10													13 40				
Gravesend ■	d	13 18	13 43								14 02				13 48	14 13			
Northfleet	d										14 06								
Swanscombe	d										14 08								
Greenhithe for Bluewater	d	13 23									14 11				13 53				
Stone Crossing	d										14 13								
Dartford ■	a	13 28									14 17				13 58				
	d	13 29			13 31	13 38			13 52		14 18				13 59			14 01	14 08
Slade Green ■	d				13 35		13 45			13 47				13 55				14 05	
Erith	d				13 38		13 48							13 58				14 08	
Belvedere	d				13 40		13 50							14 00				14 10	
Abbey Wood	d	13 38			13 43		13 53							14 03	14 08			14 13	
Plumstead	d				13 46		13 56							14 06				14 16	
Woolwich Arsenal ■	d	13 43			13 49		13 59							14 09	14 13			14 19	
Woolwich Dockyard	d				13 52		14 02							14 12				14 22	
Charlton ■	d	13 47			13 55		14 05						14 07	14 15	14 17			14 25	
Crayford	d										14 22		14 37						
Bexley	d										14 25		14 40						
Albany Park	d										14 28		14 43						
Sidcup ■	d										14 31		14 46						
New Eltham	d										14 34		14 49						
Mottingham	d										14 36		14 51						
Lee	d										14 39		14 54						
Hither Green ■	d										14 42	14 49	14 58						
Barnehurst ■	d			13 38		13 46			13 59	14 08							14 08		14 16
Bexleyheath	d			13 40		13 49			14 01	14 10							14 10		14 19
Welling	d			13 43		13 52			14 04	14 13							14 13		14 22
Falconwood	d			13 46		13 54			14 07	14 16							14 16		14 24
Eltham	d			13 49		13 57			14 10	14 19							14 19		14 27
Kidbrooke	d			13 52		14 00			14 13	14 22							14 22		14 30
Blackheath ■	d	13 52		13 55		14 04			14 16	14 25					14 22		14 25		14 34
Lewisham ■	d	13 56		13 59		14 08		14 14	14 20	14 29		14 54	15 04		14 26		14 29		14 38
St Johns	d			14 01				14 16		14 31		14 56	15 06				14 31		
New Cross ■	d			14 03				14 18		14 33		14 58	15 08				14 33		
Nunhead ■	d					14 13													14 43
Peckham Rye ■	d					14 15													14 45
Denmark Hill ■	d					14 19													14 49
London Victoria ■	a					14 28													14 58
Westcombe Park	d				13 57		14 07							14 17				14 27	
Maze Hill	d				13 59		14 09							14 19				14 29	
Greenwich ■	d				14 02		14 12							14 22				14 32	
Deptford	a				14 04		14 14							14 24				14 34	
London Bridge ■	a	14 05		14 08	14 11		14 20	14 24	14 28	14 38	14 52	15 04	15 14	14 30	14 35		14 38	14 41	
London Cannon Street ■	a			14 13	14 15		14 24	14 28		14 43		15 08	15 19	14 36			14 43	14 45	
London Waterloo (East) ■	a	14 09							14 32		14 56				14 39				
London Charing Cross ■	a	14 13							14 36		15 00				14 43				
Ebbsfleet International	a		13 46													14 16			
Stratford International	a		14 02													14 29			
St Pancras Int'l ■	a		14 09													14 36			

Table 200R

Mondays to Fridays

9 December to 16 May

Gillingham and Dartford - London

Network Diagram - see first Page of Table 200

Station		SE	SE	SE	SE	SE	SE	SE	SE	SE	SE	SE	SE	SE
Gillingham (Kent) [4]	d									13 54	14 20			
Chatham [4]	d									13 58	14 24			
Rochester [4]	d									14 00	14 27			
Maidstone West	d													
Strood [4]	d									14 05	14 32			
Higham	d									14 10				
Gravesend [4]	d					14 32				14 18	14 43			
Northfleet	d					14 36								
Swanscombe	d					14 38								
Greenhithe for Bluewater	d					14 41				14 23				
Stone Crossing	d					14 43								
Dartford [4]	a					14 47				14 28				
	d			14 22		14 48				14 29			14 31	14 38
Slade Green [4]	d	14 15			14 17				14 25				14 35	
Erith	d	14 18							14 28				14 38	
Belvedere	d	14 20							14 30				14 40	
Abbey Wood	d	14 23							14 33	14 38			14 43	
Plumstead	d	14 26							14 36				14 46	
Woolwich Arsenal [4] ⛴	d	14 29							14 39	14 43			14 49	
Woolwich Dockyard	d	14 32							14 42				14 52	
Charlton [4]	d	14 35						14 37	14 45	14 47			14 55	
Crayford	d					14 52		15 07						
Bexley	d					14 55		15 10						
Albany Park	d					14 58		15 13						
Sidcup [4]	d					15 01		15 16						
New Eltham	d					15 04		15 19						
Mottingham	d					15 06		15 21						
Lee	d					15 09		15 24						
Hither Green [4]	d					15 12	15 19	15 28						
Barnehurst [4]	d			14 29	14 38							14 38		14 46
Bexleyheath	d			14 31	14 40							14 40		14 49
Welling	d			14 34	14 43							14 43		14 52
Falconwood	d			14 37	14 46							14 46		14 54
Eltham	d			14 40	14 49							14 49		14 57
Kidbrooke	d			14 43	14 52							14 52		15 00
Blackheath [4]	d			14 46	14 55					14 52		14 55		15 04
Lewisham [4] ⛴	d		14 44	14 50	14 59		15 24	15 34		14 56		14 59		15 08
St Johns	d		14 46		15 01		15 26	15 36				15 01		
New Cross [4] ⊖	d		14 48		15 03		15 28	15 38				15 03		
Nunhead [4]	d													15 13
Peckham Rye [4]	d													15 15
Denmark Hill [4]	d													15 19
London Victoria [15] ⊖	a													15 28
Westcombe Park	d	14 37							14 47				14 57	
Maze Hill	d	14 39							14 49				14 59	
Greenwich [4] ⛴	d	14 42							14 52				15 02	
Deptford	a	14 44							14 54				15 04	
London Bridge [4] ⊖	a	14 50	14 54	14 58	15 08	15 22	15 34	15 44	15 00	15 05		15 08	15 11	
London Cannon Street [4] ⊖	a	14 54	14 58		15 13		15 38	15 49	15 06			15 13	15 15	
London Waterloo (East) [4] ⊖	a			15 02		15 26				15 09				
London Charing Cross [4] ⊖	a			15 06		15 30				15 13				
Ebbsfleet International	a										14 46			
Stratford International ⊖ ⛴	a										14 59			
St Pancras Int'l [15] ⊖	a										15 06			

Station		SE	SE	SE	SE	SE	SE	SE	SE	SE
Gillingham (Kent) [4]	d									14 24
Chatham [4]	d									14 28
Rochester [4]	d									14 30
Maidstone West	d									
Strood [4]	d									14 35
Higham	d									14 40
Gravesend [4]	d					15 02				14 48
Northfleet	d					15 06				
Swanscombe	d					15 08				
Greenhithe for Bluewater	d					15 11				14 53
Stone Crossing	d					15 13				
Dartford [4]	a					15 17				14 58
	d			14 52		15 18				14 59
Slade Green [4]	d	14 45			14 47				14 55	
Erith	d	14 48							14 58	
Belvedere	d	14 50							15 00	
Abbey Wood	d	14 53							15 03	15 08
Plumstead	d	14 56							15 06	
Woolwich Arsenal [4] ⛴	d	14 59							15 09	15 13
Woolwich Dockyard	d	15 02							15 12	
Charlton [4]	d	15 05						15 07	15 15	15 17
Crayford	d					15 22		15 37		
Bexley	d					15 25		15 40		
Albany Park	d					15 28		15 43		
Sidcup [4]	d					15 31		15 46		
New Eltham	d					15 34		15 49		
Mottingham	d					15 36		15 51		
Lee	d					15 39		15 54		
Hither Green [4]	d					15 42	15 49	15 58		
Barnehurst [4]	d			14 59	15 08					
Bexleyheath	d			15 01	15 10					
Welling	d			15 04	15 13					
Falconwood	d			15 07	15 16					
Eltham	d			15 10	15 19					
Kidbrooke	d			15 13	15 22					
Blackheath [4]	d			15 16	15 25					15 22
Lewisham [4] ⛴	d		15 14	15 20	15 29		15 54	16 04		15 26
St Johns	d		15 16		15 31		15 56	16 06		
New Cross [4] ⊖	d		15 18		15 33		15 58	16 08		
Nunhead [4]	d									
Peckham Rye [4]	d									
Denmark Hill [4]	d									
London Victoria [15] ⊖	a									
Westcombe Park	d	15 07							15 17	
Maze Hill	d	15 09							15 19	
Greenwich [4] ⛴	d	15 12							15 22	
Deptford	a	15 14							15 24	
London Bridge [4] ⊖	a	15 20	15 24	15 28	15 38	15 52	16 04	16 15	15 30	15 35
London Cannon Street [4] ⊖	a	15 24	15 28		15 43		16 08	16 19	15 36	
London Waterloo (East) [4] ⊖	a			15 32		15 57				15 39
London Charing Cross [4] ⊖	a			15 36		16 01				15 43
Ebbsfleet International	a									
Stratford International ⊖ ⛴	a									
St Pancras Int'l [15] ⊖	a									

Station		SE	SE	SE	SE	SE	SE	SE	SE	SE
Gillingham (Kent) [4]	d	14 50								
Chatham [4]	d	14 54								
Rochester [4]	d	14 57								
Maidstone West	d									
Strood [4]	d	15 02								
Higham	d									
Gravesend [4]	d	15 13								15 32
Northfleet	d									15 36
Swanscombe	d									15 38
Greenhithe for Bluewater	d									15 41
Stone Crossing	d									15 43
Dartford [4]	a									15 47
	d			15 01	15 08			15 22		15 48
Slade Green [4]	d			15 05		15 15			15 17	
Erith	d			15 08		15 18				
Belvedere	d			15 10		15 20				
Abbey Wood	d			15 13		15 23				
Plumstead	d			15 16		15 26				
Woolwich Arsenal [4] ⛴	d			15 19		15 29				
Woolwich Dockyard	d			15 22		15 32				
Charlton [4]	d			15 25		15 35				
Crayford	d									15 52
Bexley	d									15 55
Albany Park	d									15 58
Sidcup [4]	d									16 01
New Eltham	d									16 04
Mottingham	d									16 06
Lee	d									16 09
Hither Green [4]	d									16 12
Barnehurst [4]	d		15 08		15 16			15 29	15 38	
Bexleyheath	d		15 10		15 19			15 31	15 40	
Welling	d		15 13		15 22			15 34	15 43	
Falconwood	d		15 16		15 24			15 37	15 46	
Eltham	d		15 19		15 27			15 40	15 49	
Kidbrooke	d		15 22		15 30			15 43	15 52	
Blackheath [4]	d		15 25		15 34			15 46	15 55	
Lewisham [4] ⛴	d		15 29		15 38		15 44	15 50	15 59	
St Johns	d		15 31				15 46		16 01	
New Cross [4] ⊖	d		15 33				15 48		16 03	
Nunhead [4]	d				15 43					
Peckham Rye [4]	d				15 45					
Denmark Hill [4]	d				15 49					
London Victoria [15] ⊖	a				15 58					
Westcombe Park	d			15 27		15 37				
Maze Hill	d			15 29		15 39				
Greenwich [4] ⛴	d			15 32		15 42				
Deptford	a			15 34		15 44				
London Bridge [4] ⊖	a		15 38	15 41		15 50	15 54	15 58	16 09	16 22
London Cannon Street [4] ⊖	a		15 43	15 45		15 54	15 58		16 13	
London Waterloo (East) [4] ⊖	a							16 02		16 27
London Charing Cross [4] ⊖	a							16 06		16 31
Ebbsfleet International	a	15 16								
Stratford International ⊖ ⛴	a	15 29								
St Pancras Int'l [15] ⊖	a	15 36								

Station		SE	SE	SE	SE	SE
Gillingham (Kent) [4]	d				14 54	15 20
Chatham [4]	d				14 58	15 24
Rochester [4]	d				15 00	15 27
Maidstone West	d					
Strood [4]	d				15 05	15 32
Higham	d				15 10	
Gravesend [4]	d				15 18	15 43
Northfleet	d					
Swanscombe	d					
Greenhithe for Bluewater	d				15 23	
Stone Crossing	d					
Dartford [4]	a				15 28	
	d				15 29	
Slade Green [4]	d			15 25		
Erith	d			15 28		
Belvedere	d			15 30		
Abbey Wood	d			15 33	15 38	
Plumstead	d			15 36		
Woolwich Arsenal [4] ⛴	d			15 39	15 43	
Woolwich Dockyard	d			15 42		
Charlton [4]	d		15 37	15 45	15 47	
Crayford	d		16 07			
Bexley	d		16 10			
Albany Park	d		16 13			
Sidcup [4]	d		16 16			
New Eltham	d		16 19			
Mottingham	d		16 21			
Lee	d		16 24			
Hither Green [4]	d	16 19	16 28			
Barnehurst [4]	d					
Bexleyheath	d					
Welling	d					
Falconwood	d					
Eltham	d					
Kidbrooke	d					
Blackheath [4]	d				15 52	
Lewisham [4] ⛴	d	16 24	16 34		15 56	
St Johns	d	16 26	16 36			
New Cross [4] ⊖	d	16 28	16 38			
Nunhead [4]	d					
Peckham Rye [4]	d					
Denmark Hill [4]	d					
London Victoria [15] ⊖	a					
Westcombe Park	d			15 47		
Maze Hill	d			15 49		
Greenwich [4] ⛴	d			15 52		
Deptford	a			15 54		
London Bridge [4] ⊖	a	16 34	16 44	16 00	16 05	
London Cannon Street [4] ⊖	a	16 38	16 49	16 06		
London Waterloo (East) [4] ⊖	a				16 09	
London Charing Cross [4] ⊖	a				16 13	
Ebbsfleet International	a					15 46
Stratford International ⊖ ⛴	a					16 02
St Pancras Int'l [15] ⊖	a					16 09

Table 200R

Mondays to Fridays

9 December to 16 May

Gillingham and Dartford - London

Network Diagram - see first Page of Table 200

Station		SE	SE	SE	SE	SE	SE	SE	SE	SE	SE	SE	SE	SE	SE	SE	SE	SE	SE	SE	SE	SE	SE	SE	SE	SE	SE	SE	SE	SE	SE	SE	SE	SE	SE	SE	SE
Gillingham (Kent) 4	d												15 24	15 50												15 54							16 20			16 24
Chatham 4	d												15 28	15 54												15 58							16 24			16 28
Rochester 4	d												15 30	15 57												16 00							16 27			16 30
Maidstone West	d																																			
Strood 4	d												15 35	16 02												16 05							16 32			16 35
Higham	d												15 40													16 10										16 40
Gravesend 4	d								16 02				15 48	16 13												16 18						16 32	16 43			16 48
Northfleet	d								16 06																							16 36				
Swanscombe	d								16 08																							16 38				
Greenhithe for Bluewater	d								16 11				15 53													16 23						16 41				16 53
Stone Crossing	d								16 13																							16 43				
Dartford 4	a								16 17				15 58													16 28						16 48				16 58
	d		15 31	15 38			15 52		16 18				15 59			16 01	16 08			16 22			16 42				16 29		16 31	16 38			16 52				16 59
Slade Green 4	d		15 35		15 45			15 47				15 55				16 05		16 15			16 17	16 17				16 25			16 35		16 44				16 47	16 55	
Erith	d		15 38		15 48							15 58				16 08		16 18								16 28			16 38		16 46					16 58	
Belvedere	d		15 40		15 50							16 00				16 10		16 20								16 30			16 40		16 49					17 00	
Abbey Wood	d		15 43		15 53							16 03	16 08			16 13		16 23								16 33	16 38		16 43		16 52					17 03	17 08
Plumstead	d		15 46		15 56							16 06				16 16		16 26								16 36			16 46		16 55					17 06	
Woolwich Arsenal 4 ⛴	d		15 49		15 59							16 09	16 13			16 19		16 29								16 39	16 43		16 49		16 58					17 09	17 13
Woolwich Dockyard	d		15 52		16 02							16 12				16 22		16 32								16 42			16 52		17 00					17 12	
Charlton 4	d		15 55		16 05						16 07	16 15	16 17			16 25		16 35							16 37	16 45	16 47		16 55		17 03					17 15	17 17
Crayford	d								16 22		16 37												16 46		17 07												
Bexley	d								16 25		16 40												16 49		17 10												
Albany Park	d								16 28		16 43												16 52		17 13												
Sidcup 4	d								16 31	16 38	16 46												16 55		17 16												
New Eltham	d								16 34	16 41	16 49												16 58		17 19												
Mottingham	d								16 36	16 43	16 51												17 00		17 21												
Lee	d								16 39	16 46	16 54												17 03		17 24												
Hither Green 4	d								16 42	16 50	17 00												17 07	17 19	17 28												
Barnehurst 4	d	15 38		15 46			15 59	16 08							16 08		16 16			16 29	16a34	16 38						16 38		16 46			16 59		17 08		
Bexleyheath	d	15 40		15 49			16 01	16 10							16 10		16 19			16 31		16 40						16 40		16 49			17 01		17 10		
Welling	d	15 43		15 52			16 04	16 13							16 13		16 22			16 34		16 43						16 43		16 52			17 04		17 13		
Falconwood	d	15 46		15 54			16 07	16 16							16 16		16 24			16 37		16 46						16 46		16 54			17 07		17 16		
Eltham	d	15 49		15 57			16 10	16 19							16 19		16 27			16 40		16 49						16 49		16 57			17 10		17 19		
Kidbrooke	d	15 52		16 00			16 13	16 22							16 22		16 30			16 43		16 52						16 52		17 00			17 13		17 22		
Blackheath 4	d	15 55		16 04			16 16	16 25					16 22		16 25		16 34			16 46		16 55					16 52	16 55		17 04			17 16		17 25		17 22
Lewisham 4 ⛴	d	15 59		16 08		16 14	16 20	16 29			17 05		16 26		16 29		16 38		16 44	16 50		16 59		17 24	17 35		16 56	16 59		17 08		17 14	17 20		17 30		17 27
St Johns	d	16 01				16 16		16 31		16 54	17 09				16 31				16 46			17 01		17 26	17 37			17 01				17 16					
New Cross 4 ⊖	d	16 03				16 18		16 33		16 56	17 11				16 33				16 48			17 03		17 28	17 39			17 03				17 18			17 33		
Nunhead 4	d			16 13													16 43													17 13							
Peckham Rye 4	d			16 15													16 45													17 15							
Denmark Hill 4	d			16 19													16 49													17 19							
London Victoria 15 ⊖	a			16 28													17 01													17 28							
Westcombe Park	d		15 57		16 07							16 17				16 27		16 37								16 47			16 57		17 05					17 17	
Maze Hill	d		15 59		16 09							16 19				16 29		16 39								16 49			16 59		17 07					17 19	
Greenwich 4 ⛴	d		16 02		16 12							16 22				16 32		16 42								16 52			17 02		17 11					17 22	
Deptford	a		16 04		16 14							16 24				16 34		16 44								16 54			17 04		17 13					17 24	
London Bridge 4 ⊖	a	16 09	16 12		16 20	16 24	16 29	16 39	16 52	17 04	17 18	16 30	16 35		16 39	16 42		16 50	16 54	16 58		17 09	17 21	17 34	17 45	17 01	17 07	17 09	17 13		17 21	17 24	17 29		17 39	17 31	17 35
London Cannon Street 4 ⊖	a	16 13	16 16		16 24	16 28		16 43		17 09	17 24	16 36			16 43	16 46		16 54	16 58			17 15		17 38	17 49	17 05	17 11	17 15	17 17		17 26	17 29			17 44	17 36	
London Waterloo (East) 4 ⊖	a						16 33		16 56				16 39							17 03			17 28										17 34				17 40
London Charing Cross 4 ⊖	a						16 37		17 00				16 44							17 07			17 33										17 38				17 44
Ebbsfleet International	a													16 16																				16 46			
Stratford International ⊖ ⛴	a													16 29																				17 02			
St Pancras Int'l 15 ⊖	a													16 36																				17 09			

Table 200R

Mondays to Fridays

9 December to 16 May

Gillingham and Dartford - London

Network Diagram - see first Page of Table 200

		SE	SE	SE	SE	SE	SE	SE	SE	SE	SE	SE	SE	SE	SE	SE	SE	SE	SE	SE	SE	SE	SE	SE	SE	SE	SE	SE	SE	SE	SE	SE	SE	SE	SE	SE	SE
Gillingham (Kent) [4]	d							16 50											16 54	17 20							17 24									17 50
Chatham [4]	d							16 54											16 58	17 24							17 28									17 54
Rochester [4]	d							16 57											17 00	17 27							17 30									17 57
Maidstone West	d																																			
Strood [4]	d							17 02											17 05	17 32							17 35									18 03
Higham	d																		17 10								17 40									
Gravesend [4]	d						17 02	17 13						17 32					17 18	17 43							17 48								18 02	18 13
Northfleet	d						17 06							17 36																					18 06	
Swanscombe	d						17 08							17 38																					18 08	
Greenhithe for Bluewater	d						17 11							17 41					17 23								17 53								18 11	
Stone Crossing	d						17 13							17 43																					18 13	
Dartford [4]	a						17 17							17 47					17 28								17 58								18 17	
	d		17 01	17 08			17 18		17 22					17 48					17 29			17 31	17 38			17 52		17 59		18 01		18 08				18 18	
Slade Green [4]	d		17 05														17 15	17 25			17 29	17 35		17 45			17 55			18 05			18 15				
Erith	d		17 08														17 18	17 28				17 38		17 48			17 57			18 08			18 18				
Belvedere	d		17 10														17 20	17 30				17 40		17 50			18 00			18 10			18 20				
Abbey Wood	d		17 13														17 23	17 33	17 38			17 43		17 53			18 03	18 08		18 13			18 23				
Plumstead	d		17 16														17 26	17 36				17 46		17 56			18 06			18 16			18 26				
Woolwich Arsenal [4]	d		17 19														17 29	17 39	17 43			17 49		17 59			18 09	18 13		18 19			18 29				
Woolwich Dockyard	d		17 22														17 32	17 42				17 52		18 02			18 11			18 22			18 32				
Charlton [4]	d		17 25													17 30	17 35	17 45	17 47			17 55		18 05			18 14	18 17		18 25			18 35				
Crayford	d						17 22					17 37		17 52		18 01																				18 22	
Bexley	d						17 25					17 40		17 55		18 04																				18 25	
Albany Park	d						17 28					17 43		17 58		18 07																				18 28	
Sidcup [4]	d						17 31					17 46		18 01		18 10															18 20					18 31	
New Eltham	d						17 34					17 49		18 04		18 13															18 23					18 34	
Mottingham	d						17 36					17 51		18 06		18 15																				18 36	
Lee	d						17 39					17 54		18 09		18 18																				18 39	
Hither Green [4]	d					17 41	17 42			17 53		17 58	18 03	18 12	18 19	18 21															18 28				18 35	18 42	
Barnehurst [4]	d	17 08		17 16		18 10			17 29		17 38		18 38								17 38		17 46			17 59			18 10			18 16			19 08		
Bexleyheath	d	17 10		17 19		18 12			17 31		17 40		18 40								17 40		17 49			18 01			18 12			18 19			19 10		
Welling	d	17 13		17 22		18 15			17 34		17 43		18 43								17 43		17 52			18 04			18 15			18 22			19 13		
Falconwood	d	17 16		17 24		18 18			17 37		17 46		18 46								17 46		17 54			18 07			18 18			18 24			19 16		
Eltham	d	17 19		17 27		18 20			17 40		17 49		18 49								17 49		17 57			18 10			18 20			18 27			19 19		
Kidbrooke	d	17 22		17 30		18 23			17 43		17 52		18 52								17 52		18 00			18 13			18 23			18 30			19 22		
Blackheath [4]	d	17 25		17 34					17 46		17 55		18 55						17 52		17 55		18 04			18 16		18 22				18 34			19 25		
Lewisham [4]	d	17 30		17 38	17 44	18 29			17 50		17 59	18 05	18 59		18 24				17 56		17 59		18 08		18 14	18 20		18 26	18 29		18 35	18 38		18 45	19 29		
St Johns	d				17 46					17 57		18 07			18 26										18 16						18 37			18 47			
New Cross [4] ⊖	d	17 33			17 48	18 32				17 59	18 02	18 09	19 03		18 28						18 02				18 18				18 32		18 39			18 49	19 32		
Nunhead [4]	d			17 43																			18 13									18 43					
Peckham Rye [4]	d			17 45																			18 15									18 45					
Denmark Hill [4]	d			17 49																			18 19									18 49					
London Victoria [15] ⊖	a			17 59																			18 29									18 58					
Westcombe Park	d		17 27														17 37	17 47				17 57		18 07			18 16			18 27			18 37				
Maze Hill	d		17 29														17 39	17 49				17 59		18 09			18 18			18 29			18 39				
Greenwich [4]	d		17 32														17 42	17 52				18 02		18 12			18 22			18 32			18 42				
Deptford	a		17 34														17 44	17 54				18 04		18 14			18 24			18 34			18 44				
London Bridge [4] ⊖	a	17 39	17 42		17 55	18 38	17 53		18 00	18 06	18 09	18 16	19 08	18 22	18 34	18 33	17 52	18 03	18 04		18 09	18 13		18 20	18 24	18 28	18 31	18 35	18 38	18 43	18 46		18 50	18 55	19 38	18 52	
London Cannon Street [4] ⊖	a	17 44	17 46		17 59	18 42			18 04	18 11	18 13	18 20	19 13		18 38		17 56	18 07			18 13	18 17		18 24	18 29		18 35		18 42	18 47	18 51		18 54	18 59	19 43		
London Waterloo (East) [4] ⊖	a						17 58							18 27		18 37			18 08							18 32		18 41								18 57	
London Charing Cross [4] ⊖	a						18 03							18 31		18 41			18 12							18 37		18 45								19 01	
Ebbsfleet International	a							17 16												17 46																	18 18
Stratford International ⊖	a							17 29												17 59																	18 30
St Pancras Int'l [15] ⊖	a							17 36												18 07																	18 37

Gillingham and Dartford - London

9 December to 16 May

Network Diagram - see first Page of Table 200

		SE	SE	SE	SE	SE	SE	SE	SE	SE	SE	SE	SE	SE	SE	SE	SE	SE	SE
Gillingham (Kent) 4	d								17 54	18 20							18 24		
Chatham 4	d								17 58	18 24							18 28		
Rochester 4	d								18 00	18 27							18 30		
Maidstone West	d																		
Strood 4	d								18 05	18 32							18 35		
Higham	d								18 10								18 40		
Gravesend 4	d				18 32				18 18	18 43							18 48		
Northfleet	d				18 36														
Swanscombe	d				18 38														
Greenhithe for Bluewater	d				18 41				18 23								18 53		
Stone Crossing	d				18 43														
Dartford 4	a				18 47				18 28								18 58		
	d	18 22			18 48				18 29			18 31	18 38			18 52	18 59		19 01
Slade Green 4	d							18 25				18 35			18 51				19 05
Erith	d							18 28				18 38			18 53				19 08
Belvedere	d							18 30				18 40			18 56				19 10
Abbey Wood	d							18 33	18 38			18 43			18 59		19 08		19 13
Plumstead	d							18 36				18 46			19 02				19 16
Woolwich Arsenal 4	d							18 39	18 43			18 49			19 05		19 13		19 19
Woolwich Dockyard	d							18 42				18 52			19 07				19 22
Charlton 4	d						18 37	18 45	18 47			18 55			19 10		19 17		19 25
Crayford	d			18 37	18 52		19 07												
Bexley	d			18 40	18 55		19 10												
Albany Park	d			18 43	18 58		19 12												
Sidcup 4	d			18 46	19 01		19 15												
New Eltham	d			18 49	19 04		19 18												
Mottingham	d			18 51	19 06		19 21												
Lee	d			18 54	19 09		19 24												
Hither Green 4	d		18 49	18 59	19 12	19 19	19 28												
Barnehurst 4	d	18 29									18 38		18 46			18 59		19 08	
Bexleyheath	d	18 31									18 40		18 49			19 01		19 10	
Welling	d	18 34									18 43		18 52			19 04		19 13	
Falconwood	d	18 37									18 46		18 54			19 07		19 16	
Eltham	d	18 40									18 49		18 57			19 10		19 19	
Kidbrooke	d	18 43									18 52		19 00			19 13		19 22	
Blackheath 4	d	18 46							18 52		18 55		19 04			19 16	19 22	19 25	
Lewisham 4	d	18 50	18 54	19 05		19 24	19 34		18 56		18 59		19 08	19 14		19 20	19 26	19 29	
St Johns	d		18 56	19 07		19 26	19 36							19 16					
New Cross 4 ⊖	d		18 58	19 09		19 28	19 38				19 03			19 18				19 32	
Nunhead 4	d												19 13						
Peckham Rye 4	d												19 15						
Denmark Hill 4	d												19 19						
London Victoria 15 ⊖	a												19 28						
Westcombe Park	d							18 47				18 57			19 12				19 27
Maze Hill	d							18 49				18 59			19 14				19 29
Greenwich 4	d							18 52				19 02			19 18				19 32
Deptford	a							18 54				19 04			19 20				19 34
London Bridge 4 ⊖	a	18 58	19 04	19 15	19 22	19 34	19 44	19 00	19 05		19 08	19 11		19 24	19 27	19 28	19 35	19 38	19 41
London Cannon Street 4 ⊖	a		19 10	19 20		19 38	19 49	19 06			19 13	19 16		19 28	19 33			19 43	19 45
London Waterloo (East) 4 ⊖	a	19 02			19 26				19 09							19 32	19 39		
London Charing Cross 4 ⊖	a	19 06			19 30				19 13							19 36	19 43		
Ebbsfleet International	a									18 46									
Stratford International ⊖	a									19 02									
St Pancras Int'l 15 ⊖	a									19 09									

		SE	SE	SE	SE	SE	SE	SE	SE	SE	SE	SE	SE	SE	SE	SE	SE	SE	SE
Gillingham (Kent) 4	d			18 50			18 54			19 20			19 24				19 50		19 54
Chatham 4	d			18 54			18 58			19 24			19 28				19 54		19 58
Rochester 4	d			18 57			19 00			19 27			19 30				19 57		20 00
Maidstone West	d		18 42																
Strood 4	d		18 58	19 02			19 05			19 32			19 35				20 02		20 05
Higham	d						19 10						19 40						20 10
Gravesend 4	d	19 02	19 09	19 13			19 18		19 32	19 43			19 48			20 02	20 13		20 18
Northfleet	d	19 06							19 36							20 06			
Swanscombe	d	19 08							19 38							20 08			
Greenhithe for Bluewater	d	19 11					19 23		19 41				19 53			20 11			20 23
Stone Crossing	d	19 13							19 43							20 13			
Dartford 4	a	19 17					19 28		19 47				19 58			20 17			20 28
	d	19 18				19 22	19 29	19 31	19 48			19 55	19 59	20 01	20 16	20 18		20 25	20 29
Slade Green 4	d				19 20			19 35			19 50			20 05	20 20				
Erith	d				19 23			19 38			19 53			20 08	20 23				
Belvedere	d				19 25			19 40			19 55			20 10	20 25				
Abbey Wood	d				19 28		19 38	19 43			19 58		20 08	20 13	20 28				20 38
Plumstead	d				19 31			19 46			20 01			20 16	20 31				
Woolwich Arsenal 4	d				19 34		19 43	19 49			20 04		20 13	20 19	20 34				20 43
Woolwich Dockyard	d				19 37			19 52			20 07			20 22	20 37				
Charlton 4	d				19 40		19 47	19 55			20 10		20 17	20 25	20 40				20 47
Crayford	d	19 22							19 52							20 22			
Bexley	d	19 25							19 55							20 25			
Albany Park	d	19 28							19 58							20 28			
Sidcup 4	d	19 31							20 01							20 31			
New Eltham	d	19 34							20 04							20 34			
Mottingham	d	19 36							20 06							20 36			
Lee	d	19 39							20 09							20 39			
Hither Green 4	d	19 42							20 12							20 42			
Barnehurst 4	d					19 30						20 02						20 32	
Bexleyheath	d					19 32						20 04						20 34	
Welling	d					19 35						20 07						20 37	
Falconwood	d					19 38						20 10						20 40	
Eltham	d					19 41						20 12						20 42	
Kidbrooke	d					19 44						20 15						20 45	
Blackheath 4	d					19 48	19 52					20 19	20 22					20 49	20 52
Lewisham 4	d	19 48				19 52	19 56		20 18			20 22	20 26			20 48		20 53	20 56
St Johns	d																		
New Cross 4 ⊖	d	19 51				19 56			20 21			20 26				20 51		20 56	
Nunhead 4	d																		
Peckham Rye 4	d																		
Denmark Hill 4	d																		
London Victoria 15 ⊖	a																		
Westcombe Park	d				19 42			19 57			20 12			20 27	20 42				
Maze Hill	d				19 44			19 59			20 14			20 29	20 44				
Greenwich 4	d				19 47			20 02			20 17			20 32	20 47				
Deptford	a				19 49			20 04			20 19			20 34	20 49				
London Bridge 4 ⊖	a	19 57			19 59	20 03	20 06	20 11	20 27		20 27	20 33	20 36	20 41	20 57	20 57		21 03	21 06
London Cannon Street 4 ⊖	a				20 03			20 15			20 31			20 45					
London Waterloo (East) 4 ⊖	a	20 02				20 08	20 11		20 32			20 38	20 40			21 02		21 08	21 10
London Charing Cross 4 ⊖	a	20 06				20 12	20 14		20 36			20 42	20 44			21 06		21 12	21 14
Ebbsfleet International	a		19 12	19 16						19 46							20 16		
Stratford International ⊖	a		19 25	19 29						20 00							20 29		
St Pancras Int'l 15 ⊖	a		19 32	19 36						20 07							20 36		

Table 200R

Mondays to Fridays

9 December to 16 May

Gillingham and Dartford - London

Network Diagram - see first Page of Table 200

		SE	SE	SE	SE	SE	SE	SE	SE	SE	SE	SE	SE	SE	SE	SE	SE	SE	SE	SE	SE	SE	SE	SE	SE	SE	SE	SE	SE	SE	SE
Gillingham (Kent) 4	d				20 20		20 24				20 50		20 54				21 20		21 24			21 50		21 54			22 20		22 24		22 54
Chatham 4	d				20 24		20 28				20 54		20 58				21 24		21 28			21 54		21 58			22 24		22 28		22 58
Rochester 4	d				20 27		20 30				20 57		21 00				21 27		21 30			21 57		22 00			22 27		22 30		23 00
Maidstone West	d																														
Strood 4	d				20 32		20 35				21 02		21 05				21 32		21 35			22 02		22 05			22 32		22 35		23 05
Higham	d						20 40						21 10						21 40					22 10					22 40		23 10
Gravesend 4	d			20 32	20 43		20 48			21 02	21 13		21 18			21 32	21 43		21 48		22 02	22 13		22 18		22 32	22 43		22 48		23 18
Northfleet	d			20 36						21 06						21 36					22 06					22 36					
Swanscombe	d			20 38						21 08						21 38					22 08					22 38					
Greenhithe for Bluewater	d			20 41			20 53			21 11			21 23			21 41			21 53		22 11			22 23		22 41			22 53		23 23
Stone Crossing	d			20 43						21 13						21 43					22 13					22 43					
Dartford 4	a			20 47			20 58			21 17			21 28			21 47			21 58		22 17			22 28		22 47			22 58		23 28
	d	20 31	20 46	20 48		20 55	20 59	21 01	21 16	21 18		21 25	21 29	21 31	21 46	21 48		21 55	21 59	22 01	22 18		22 25	22 29	22 31	22 48		22 55	22 59	23 01	
Slade Green 4	d	20 35	20 50					21 05	21 20					21 35	21 50					22 05					22 35					23 05	
Erith	d	20 38	20 53					21 08	21 23					21 38	21 53					22 08					22 38					23 08	
Belvedere	d	20 40	20 55					21 10	21 25					21 40	21 55					22 10					22 40					23 10	
Abbey Wood	d	20 43	20 58				21 08	21 13	21 28				21 38	21 43	21 58				22 08	22 13				22 38	22 43				23 08	23 13	
Plumstead	d	20 46	21 01					21 16	21 31					21 46	22 01					22 16					22 46					23 16	
Woolwich Arsenal 4 ⛴	d	20 49	21 04				21 13	21 19	21 34				21 43	21 49	22 04				22 13	22 19				22 43	22 49				23 13	23 19	
Woolwich Dockyard	d	20 52	21 07					21 22	21 37					21 52	22 07					22 22					22 52					23 22	
Charlton 4	d	20 55	21 10				21 17	21 25	21 40				21 47	21 55	22 10				22 17	22 25				22 47	22 55				23 17	23 25	
Crayford	d			20 52						21 22						21 52					22 22					22 52					
Bexley	d			20 55						21 25						21 55					22 25					22 55					
Albany Park	d			20 58						21 28						21 58					22 28					22 58					
Sidcup 4	d			21 01						21 31						22 01					22 31					23 01					
New Eltham	d			21 04						21 34						22 04					22 34					23 04					
Mottingham	d			21 06						21 36						22 06					22 36					23 06					
Lee	d			21 09						21 39						22 09					22 39					23 09					
Hither Green 4	d			21 12						21 42						22 12					22 42					23 12					
Barnehurst 4	d					21 02						21 32						22 02					22 32					23 02			
Bexleyheath	d					21 04						21 34						22 04					22 34					23 04			
Welling	d					21 07						21 37						22 07					22 37					23 07			
Falconwood	d					21 10						21 40						22 10					22 40					23 10			
Eltham	d					21 12						21 42						22 12					22 42					23 12			
Kidbrooke	d					21 15						21 45						22 15					22 45					23 15			
Blackheath 4	d					21 19	21 22					21 49	21 52					22 19	22 22				22 49	22 52				23 19	23 22		
Lewisham 4 ⛴	d			21 18		21 23	21 26			21 48		21 53	21 56			22 18		22 23	22 26		22 48		22 53	22 56		23 18		23 23	23 26		
St Johns	d																														
New Cross 4 ⊖	d			21 21		21 26				21 51		21 56				22 21		22 26			22 51		22 56			23 21		23 26			
Nunhead 4	d																														
Peckham Rye 4	d																														
Denmark Hill 4	d																														
London Victoria 15 ⊖	a																														
Westcombe Park	d	20 57	21 12					21 27	21 42					21 57	22 12					22 27					22 57					23 27	
Maze Hill	d	20 59	21 14					21 29	21 44					21 59	22 14					22 29					22 59					23 29	
Greenwich 4 ⛴	d	21 02	21 17					21 32	21 47					22 02	22 17					22 32					23 02					23 32	
Deptford	a	21 04	21 19					21 34	21 49					22 04	22 19					22 34					23 04					23 34	
London Bridge 4 ⊖	a	21 11	21 27	21 27		21 33	21 36	21 41	21 57	21 57		22 02	22 05	22 11	22 27	22 27		22 31	22 35	22 41	22 57		23 01	23 05	23 11	23 27		23 31	23 35	23 41	
London Cannon Street 4 ⊖	a																														
London Waterloo (East) 4 ⊖	a	21 15		21 32		21 39	21 41	21 45		22 02		22 07	22 09	22 15		22 32		22 36	22 39	22 45	23 02		23 06	23 09	23 15	23 32		23 36	23 39	23 45	
London Charing Cross 4 ⊖	a	21 19		21 36		21 42	21 44	21 49		22 06		22 10	22 13	22 19		22 36		22 40	22 43	22 49	23 06		23 10	23 13	23 19	23 36		23 40	23 43	23 49	
Ebbsfleet International	a				20 46						21 16						21 46					22 16					22 46				
Stratford International ⊖ ⛴	a				21 02						21 29						22 00					22 29					22 59				
St Pancras Int'l 15 ⊖	a				21 09						21 36						22 07					22 36					23 06				

Table 200R

Saturdays

14 December to 17 May

Gillingham and Dartford - London

Network Diagram - see first Page of Table 200

Station		SE	SE	SE	SE	SE	SE	SE	SE	SE
Gillingham (Kent) 4	d				04 48				05 18	
Chatham 4	d				04 52				05 22	
Rochester 4	d				04 54				05 24	
Maidstone West	d									
Strood 4	d				04 59				05 29	
Higham	d				05 04				05 34	
Gravesend 4	d				05 12				05 42	
Northfleet	d				05 15				05 45	
Swanscombe	d				05 17				05 47	
Greenhithe for Bluewater	d				05 21				05 51	
Stone Crossing	d				05 23				05 53	
Dartford 4	a				05 27				05 57	
	d	05 05	05 18	05 22	05 29	05 35	05 48	05 52	05 59	06 05
Slade Green 4	d	05 10				05 40				06 10
Erith	d	05 12				05 42				06 12
Belvedere	d	05 15				05 45				06 15
Abbey Wood	d	05 18			05 38	05 48			06 08	06 18
Plumstead	d	05 21				05 51				06 21
Woolwich Arsenal 4 ⛴	d	05 24			05 43	05 54			06 13	06 24
Woolwich Dockyard	d	05 26				05 56				06 26
Charlton 4	d	05 29			05 47	05 59			06 17	06 29
Crayford	d		05 22				05 52			
Bexley	d		05 25				05 55			
Albany Park	d		05 28				05 58			
Sidcup 4	d		05 31				06 01			
New Eltham	d		05 34				06 04			
Mottingham	d		05 36				06 06			
Lee	d		05 39				06 09			
Hither Green 4	d		05 42				06 12			
Barnehurst 4	d			05 29				05 59		
Bexleyheath	d			05 31				06 01		
Welling	d			05 34				06 04		
Falconwood	d			05 37				06 07		
Eltham	d			05 40				06 10		
Kidbrooke	d			05 43				06 13		
Blackheath 4	d			05 46	05 52			06 16	06 22	
Lewisham 4 ⛴	d		05 48	05 50	05 56		06 18	06 20	06 26	
St Johns	d									
New Cross 4 ⊖	d		05 51				06 21			
Nunhead 4	d									
Peckham Rye 4	d									
Denmark Hill 4	d									
London Victoria 15 ⊖	a									
Westcombe Park	d	05 31				06 01				06 31
Maze Hill	d	05 33				06 03				06 33
Greenwich 4 ⛴	d	05 37				06 07				06 37
Deptford	a	05 39				06 09				06 39
London Bridge 4 ⊖	a	05 45	05 56	05 59	06 05	06 15	06 26	06 29	06 35	06 45
London Cannon Street 4 ⊖	a									
London Waterloo (East) 4 ⊖	a	05 49	06 01	06 03	06 09	06 19	06 31	06 33	06 39	06 49
London Charing Cross 4 ⊖	a	05 53	06 05	06 07	06 13	06 25	06 35	06 37	06 43	06 55
Ebbsfleet International	a									
Stratford International ⊖ ⛴	a									
St Pancras Int'l 15 ⊖	a									

Station		SE	SE	SE	SE	SE	SE	SE	SE	SE
Gillingham (Kent) 4	d		05 50		05 54					06 24
Chatham 4	d		05 54		05 58					06 28
Rochester 4	d		05 57		06 00					06 30
Maidstone West	d									
Strood 4	d		06 02		06 05					06 35
Higham	d				06 10					06 40
Gravesend 4	d	06 02	06 13		06 18			06 32		06 48
Northfleet	d	06 06						06 36		
Swanscombe	d	06 08						06 38		
Greenhithe for Bluewater	d	06 11			06 23			06 41		06 53
Stone Crossing	d	06 13						06 43		
Dartford 4	a	06 17			06 28			06 47		06 58
	d	06 18		06 22	06 29	06 35	06 38	06 48	06 52	06 59
Slade Green 4	d					06 40				
Erith	d					06 42				
Belvedere	d					06 45				
Abbey Wood	d				06 38	06 48				07 08
Plumstead	d					06 51				
Woolwich Arsenal 4 ⛴	d				06 43	06 54				07 13
Woolwich Dockyard	d					06 56				
Charlton 4	d				06 47	06 59				07 17
Crayford	d	06 22						06 52		
Bexley	d	06 25						06 55		
Albany Park	d	06 28						06 58		
Sidcup 4	d	06 31						07 01		
New Eltham	d	06 34						07 04		
Mottingham	d	06 36						07 06		
Lee	d	06 39						07 09		
Hither Green 4	d	06 42						07 12		
Barnehurst 4	d			06 29			06 46		06 59	
Bexleyheath	d			06 31			06 49		07 01	
Welling	d			06 34			06 52		07 04	
Falconwood	d			06 37			06 54		07 07	
Eltham	d			06 40			06 57		07 10	
Kidbrooke	d			06 43			07 00		07 13	
Blackheath 4	d			06 46	06 52		07 04		07 16	07 22
Lewisham 4 ⛴	d	06 48		06 50	06 56		07 08	07 18	07 20	07 26
St Johns	d									
New Cross 4 ⊖	d	06 51						07 21		
Nunhead 4	d						07 13			
Peckham Rye 4	d						07 15			
Denmark Hill 4	d						07 19			
London Victoria 15 ⊖	a						07 28			
Westcombe Park	d					07 01				
Maze Hill	d					07 03				
Greenwich 4 ⛴	d					07 07				
Deptford	a					07 09				
London Bridge 4 ⊖	a	06 56		06 59	07 05	07 15		07 26	07 29	07 35
London Cannon Street 4 ⊖	a									
London Waterloo (East) 4 ⊖	a	07 01		07 03	07 09	07 19		07 31	07 33	07 39
London Charing Cross 4 ⊖	a	07 05		07 07	07 13	07 25		07 35	07 40	07 43
Ebbsfleet International	a		06 16							
Stratford International ⊖ ⛴	a		06 29							
St Pancras Int'l 15 ⊖	a		06 36							

Station		SE	SE	SE	SE	SE	SE	SE	SE	SE
Gillingham (Kent) 4	d				06 50				06 54	
Chatham 4	d				06 54				06 58	
Rochester 4	d				06 57				07 00	
Maidstone West	d									
Strood 4	d				07 02				07 05	
Higham	d								07 10	
Gravesend 4	d			07 02	07 13				07 18	
Northfleet	d			07 06						
Swanscombe	d			07 08						
Greenhithe for Bluewater	d			07 11					07 23	
Stone Crossing	d			07 13						
Dartford 4	a			07 17					07 28	
	d	07 01	07 08	07 18		07 22			07 29	
Slade Green 4	d	07 05					07 25			
Erith	d	07 08					07 28			
Belvedere	d	07 10					07 30			
Abbey Wood	d	07 13					07 33		07 38	
Plumstead	d	07 16					07 36			
Woolwich Arsenal 4 ⛴	d	07 19					07 39		07 43	
Woolwich Dockyard	d	07 22					07 42			
Charlton 4	d	07 25					07 45		07 47	
Crayford	d			07 22						
Bexley	d			07 25						
Albany Park	d			07 28						
Sidcup 4	d			07 31						
New Eltham	d			07 34						
Mottingham	d			07 36						
Lee	d			07 39						
Hither Green 4	d			07 42				07 49		
Barnehurst 4	d		07 16			07 29				07 38
Bexleyheath	d		07 19			07 31				07 40
Welling	d		07 22			07 34				07 43
Falconwood	d		07 24			07 37				07 46
Eltham	d		07 27			07 40				07 49
Kidbrooke	d		07 30			07 43				07 52
Blackheath 4	d		07 34			07 46			07 52	07 55
Lewisham 4 ⛴	d		07 38			07 50		07 54	07 56	07 59
St Johns	d							07 56		08 01
New Cross 4 ⊖	d							07 58		08 03
Nunhead 4	d		07 43							
Peckham Rye 4	d		07 45							
Denmark Hill 4	d		07 49							
London Victoria 15 ⊖	a		07 58							
Westcombe Park	d	07 27					07 47			
Maze Hill	d	07 29					07 49			
Greenwich 4 ⛴	d	07 32					07 52			
Deptford	a	07 34					07 54			
London Bridge 4 ⊖	a	07 41		07 52		07 58	08 00	08 04	08 05	08 08
London Cannon Street 4 ⊖	a	07 45					08 04	08 08		08 13
London Waterloo (East) 4 ⊖	a			07 56		08 02			08 09	
London Charing Cross 4 ⊖	a			08 00		08 06			08 13	
Ebbsfleet International	a				07 16					
Stratford International ⊖ ⛴	a				07 29					
St Pancras Int'l 15 ⊖	a				07 36					

Station		SE	SE	SE	SE	SE	SE	SE	SE	SE
Gillingham (Kent) 4	d						07 20			
Chatham 4	d						07 24			
Rochester 4	d						07 27			
Maidstone West	d									
Strood 4	d						07 32			
Higham	d									
Gravesend 4	d					07 32	07 43			
Northfleet	d					07 36				
Swanscombe	d					07 38				
Greenhithe for Bluewater	d					07 41				
Stone Crossing	d					07 43				
Dartford 4	a					07 47				
	d	07 31		07 38		07 48			07 52	
Slade Green 4	d	07 35			07 45					07 55
Erith	d	07 38			07 48					07 58
Belvedere	d	07 40			07 50					08 00
Abbey Wood	d	07 43			07 53					08 03
Plumstead	d	07 46			07 56					08 06
Woolwich Arsenal 4 ⛴	d	07 49			07 59					08 09
Woolwich Dockyard	d	07 52			08 02					08 12
Charlton 4	d	07 55			08 05					08 15
Crayford	d		07 37			07 52				
Bexley	d		07 40			07 55				
Albany Park	d		07 43			07 58				
Sidcup 4	d		07 46			08 01				
New Eltham	d		07 49			08 04				
Mottingham	d		07 51			08 06				
Lee	d		07 54			08 09				
Hither Green 4	d		07 58			08 12				
Barnehurst 4	d			07 46					07 59	
Bexleyheath	d			07 49					08 01	
Welling	d			07 52					08 04	
Falconwood	d			07 54					08 07	
Eltham	d			07 57					08 10	
Kidbrooke	d			08 00					08 13	
Blackheath 4	d			08 04					08 16	
Lewisham 4 ⛴	d		08 04	08 08				08 14	08 20	
St Johns	d		08 06					08 16		
New Cross 4 ⊖	d		08 08					08 18		
Nunhead 4	d			08 13						
Peckham Rye 4	d			08 15						
Denmark Hill 4	d			08 19						
London Victoria 15 ⊖	a			08 28						
Westcombe Park	d	07 57			08 07					08 17
Maze Hill	d	07 59			08 09					08 19
Greenwich 4 ⛴	d	08 02			08 12					08 22
Deptford	a	08 04			08 14					08 24
London Bridge 4 ⊖	a	08 11	08 14		08 20	08 22		08 24	08 28	08 30
London Cannon Street 4 ⊖	a	08 15	08 19		08 24			08 28		08 34
London Waterloo (East) 4 ⊖	a					08 26			08 32	
London Charing Cross 4 ⊖	a					08 30			08 36	
Ebbsfleet International	a						07 46			
Stratford International ⊖ ⛴	a						07 59			
St Pancras Int'l 15 ⊖	a						08 06			

Table 200R

Saturdays

14 December to 17 May

Gillingham and Dartford - London

Network Diagram - see first Page of Table 200

Station		SE	SE	SE	SE	SE	SE	SE	SE	SE
Gillingham (Kent)	d		07 24							07 50
Chatham	d		07 28							07 54
Rochester	d		07 30							07 57
Maidstone West	d									
Strood	d		07 35							08 02
Higham	d		07 40							
Gravesend	d		07 48						08 02	08 13
Northfleet	d								08 06	
Swanscombe	d								08 08	
Greenhithe for Bluewater	d		07 53						08 11	
Stone Crossing	d								08 13	
Dartford	a		07 58						08 17	
	d		07 59		08 01		08 08		08 18	
Slade Green	d				08 05			08 15		
Erith	d				08 08			08 18		
Belvedere	d				08 10			08 20		
Abbey Wood	d		08 08		08 13			08 23		
Plumstead	d				08 16			08 26		
Woolwich Arsenal	d		08 13		08 19			08 29		
Woolwich Dockyard	d				08 22			08 32		
Charlton	d		08 17		08 25			08 35		
Crayford	d					08 07			08 22	
Bexley	d					08 10			08 25	
Albany Park	d					08 13			08 28	
Sidcup	d					08 16			08 31	
New Eltham	d					08 19			08 34	
Mottingham	d					08 21			08 36	
Lee	d					08 24			08 39	
Hither Green	d	08 19				08 28			08 42	
Barnehurst	d			08 08			08 16			
Bexleyheath	d			08 10			08 19			
Welling	d			08 13			08 22			
Falconwood	d			08 16			08 24			
Eltham	d			08 19			08 27			
Kidbrooke	d			08 22			08 30			
Blackheath	d		08 22	08 25			08 34			
Lewisham	d	08 24	08 26	08 29		08 34	08 38			
St Johns	d	08 26		08 31		08 36				
New Cross	d	08 28		08 33		08 38				
Nunhead	d						08 43			
Peckham Rye	d						08 45			
Denmark Hill	d						08 49			
London Victoria	a						08 58			
Westcombe Park	d				08 27			08 37		
Maze Hill	d				08 29			08 39		
Greenwich	d				08 32			08 42		
Deptford	a				08 34			08 44		
London Bridge	a	08 34	08 35	08 38	08 41	08 44		08 50	08 52	
London Cannon Street	a	08 38		08 43	08 45	08 49		08 54		
London Waterloo (East)	a		08 39						08 56	
London Charing Cross	a		08 43						09 00	
Ebbsfleet International	a									08 16
Stratford International	a									08 30
St Pancras Int'l	a									08 37

Station		SE	SE	SE	SE	SE	SE	SE	SE	SE
Gillingham (Kent)	d									07 54
Chatham	d									07 58
Rochester	d									08 00
Maidstone West	d									
Strood	d									08 05
Higham	d									08 10
Gravesend	d					08 32				08 18
Northfleet	d					08 36				
Swanscombe	d					08 38				
Greenhithe for Bluewater	d					08 41				08 23
Stone Crossing	d					08 43				
Dartford	a					08 47				08 28
	d		08 22			08 48				08 29
Slade Green	d								08 25	
Erith	d								08 28	
Belvedere	d								08 30	
Abbey Wood	d								08 33	08 38
Plumstead	d								08 36	
Woolwich Arsenal	d								08 39	08 43
Woolwich Dockyard	d								08 42	
Charlton	d							08 37	08 45	08 47
Crayford	d				08 37	08 52		09 07		
Bexley	d				08 40	08 55		09 10		
Albany Park	d				08 43	08 58		09 13		
Sidcup	d				08 46	09 01		09 16		
New Eltham	d				08 49	09 04		09 19		
Mottingham	d				08 51	09 06		09 21		
Lee	d				08 54	09 09		09 24		
Hither Green	d			08 49	08 58	09 12	09 19	09 28		
Barnehurst	d		08 29							
Bexleyheath	d		08 31							
Welling	d		08 34							
Falconwood	d		08 37							
Eltham	d		08 40							
Kidbrooke	d		08 43							
Blackheath	d		08 46							08 52
Lewisham	d	08 44	08 50	08 54	09 04		09 24	09 34		08 56
St Johns	d	08 46		08 56	09 06		09 26	09 36		
New Cross	d	08 48		08 58	09 08		09 28	09 38		
Nunhead	d									
Peckham Rye	d									
Denmark Hill	d									
London Victoria	a									
Westcombe Park	d								08 47	
Maze Hill	d								08 49	
Greenwich	d								08 52	
Deptford	a								08 54	
London Bridge	a	08 54	08 58	09 04	09 14	09 22	09 34	09 44	09 00	09 05
London Cannon Street	a	08 58		09 08	09 19		09 38	09 49	09 04	
London Waterloo (East)	a		09 02			09 26				09 09
London Charing Cross	a		09 06			09 30				09 13
Ebbsfleet International	a									
Stratford International	a									
St Pancras Int'l	a									

Station		SE	SE	SE	SE	SE	SE	SE	SE	SE
Gillingham (Kent)	d	08 20								
Chatham	d	08 24								
Rochester	d	08 27								
Maidstone West	d									
Strood	d	08 32								
Higham	d									
Gravesend	d	08 43								09 02
Northfleet	d									09 06
Swanscombe	d									09 08
Greenhithe for Bluewater	d									09 11
Stone Crossing	d									09 13
Dartford	a									09 17
	d			08 31	08 38			08 52		09 18
Slade Green	d			08 35		08 45			08 47	
Erith	d			08 38		08 48				
Belvedere	d			08 40		08 50				
Abbey Wood	d			08 43		08 53				
Plumstead	d			08 46		08 56				
Woolwich Arsenal	d			08 49		08 59				
Woolwich Dockyard	d			08 52		09 02				
Charlton	d			08 55		09 05				
Crayford	d									09 22
Bexley	d									09 25
Albany Park	d									09 28
Sidcup	d									09 31
New Eltham	d									09 34
Mottingham	d									09 36
Lee	d									09 39
Hither Green	d									09 42
Barnehurst	d		08 38		08 46			08 59	09 08	
Bexleyheath	d		08 40		08 49			09 01	09 10	
Welling	d		08 43		08 52			09 04	09 13	
Falconwood	d		08 46		08 54			09 07	09 16	
Eltham	d		08 49		08 57			09 10	09 19	
Kidbrooke	d		08 52		09 00			09 13	09 22	
Blackheath	d		08 55		09 04			09 16	09 25	
Lewisham	d		08 59		09 08		09 14	09 20	09 29	
St Johns	d		09 01				09 16		09 31	
New Cross	d		09 03				09 18		09 33	
Nunhead	d				09 13					
Peckham Rye	d				09 15					
Denmark Hill	d				09 19					
London Victoria	a				09 28					
Westcombe Park	d			08 57		09 07				
Maze Hill	d			08 59		09 09				
Greenwich	d			09 02		09 12				
Deptford	a			09 04		09 14				
London Bridge	a		09 08	09 11		09 20	09 24	09 28	09 38	09 52
London Cannon Street	a		09 13	09 15		09 24	09 28		09 43	
London Waterloo (East)	a							09 32		09 56
London Charing Cross	a							09 36		10 00
Ebbsfleet International	a	08 46								
Stratford International	a	08 59								
St Pancras Int'l	a	09 06								

Station		SE	SE	SE	SE	SE	SE	SE	SE	SE
Gillingham (Kent)	d				08 24	08 50				
Chatham	d				08 28	08 54				
Rochester	d				08 30	08 57				
Maidstone West	d									
Strood	d				08 35	09 02				
Higham	d				08 40					
Gravesend	d				08 48	09 13				
Northfleet	d									
Swanscombe	d									
Greenhithe for Bluewater	d				08 53					
Stone Crossing	d									
Dartford	a				08 58					
	d				08 59			09 01	09 08	
Slade Green	d			08 55				09 05		09 15
Erith	d			08 58				09 08		09 18
Belvedere	d			09 00				09 10		09 20
Abbey Wood	d			09 03	09 08			09 13		09 23
Plumstead	d			09 06				09 16		09 26
Woolwich Arsenal	d			09 09	09 13			09 19		09 29
Woolwich Dockyard	d			09 12				09 22		09 32
Charlton	d		09 07	09 15	09 17			09 25		09 35
Crayford	d		09 37							
Bexley	d		09 40							
Albany Park	d		09 43							
Sidcup	d		09 46							
New Eltham	d		09 49							
Mottingham	d		09 51							
Lee	d		09 54							
Hither Green	d	09 49	09 58							
Barnehurst	d						09 08		09 16	
Bexleyheath	d						09 10		09 19	
Welling	d						09 13		09 22	
Falconwood	d						09 16		09 24	
Eltham	d						09 19		09 27	
Kidbrooke	d						09 22		09 30	
Blackheath	d				09 22		09 25		09 34	
Lewisham	d	09 54	10 04		09 26		09 29		09 38	
St Johns	d	09 56	10 06				09 31			
New Cross	d	09 58	10 08				09 33			
Nunhead	d								09 43	
Peckham Rye	d								09 45	
Denmark Hill	d								09 49	
London Victoria	a								09 58	
Westcombe Park	d			09 17				09 27		09 37
Maze Hill	d			09 19				09 29		09 39
Greenwich	d			09 22				09 32		09 42
Deptford	a			09 24				09 34		09 44
London Bridge	a	10 04	10 14	09 30	09 35		09 38	09 41		09 50
London Cannon Street	a	10 08	10 19	09 34			09 43	09 45		09 54
London Waterloo (East)	a				09 39					
London Charing Cross	a				09 43					
Ebbsfleet International	a					09 16				
Stratford International	a					09 30				
St Pancras Int'l	a					09 37				

Table 200R

Saturdays

14 December to 17 May

Gillingham and Dartford - London

Network Diagram - see first Page of Table 200

		SE	SE	SE	SE	SE	SE	SE	SE	SE	SE	SE	SE	SE	SE	SE	SE	SE	SE
Gillingham (Kent)	d								08 54	09 20									
Chatham	d								08 58	09 24									
Rochester	d								09 00	09 27									
Maidstone West	d																		
Strood	d								09 05	09 32									
Higham	d								09 10										
Gravesend	d				09 32				09 18	09 43								10 02	
Northfleet	d				09 36													10 06	
Swanscombe	d				09 38													10 08	
Greenhithe for Bluewater	d				09 41				09 23									10 11	
Stone Crossing	d				09 43													10 13	
Dartford	a				09 47				09 28									10 17	
	d		09 22		09 48				09 29			09 31	09 38			09 52		10 18	
Slade Green	d			09 17				09 25				09 35		09 45			09 47		
Erith	d							09 28				09 38		09 48					
Belvedere	d							09 30				09 40		09 50					
Abbey Wood	d							09 33	09 38			09 43		09 53					
Plumstead	d							09 36				09 46		09 56					
Woolwich Arsenal	d							09 39	09 43			09 49		09 59					
Woolwich Dockyard	d							09 42				09 52		10 02					
Charlton	d						09 37	09 45	09 47			09 55		10 05					
Crayford	d				09 52		10 07											10 22	
Bexley	d				09 55		10 10											10 25	
Albany Park	d				09 58		10 13											10 28	
Sidcup	d				10 01		10 16											10 31	
New Eltham	d				10 04		10 19											10 34	
Mottingham	d				10 06		10 21											10 36	
Lee	d				10 09		10 24											10 39	
Hither Green	d				10 12	10 19	10 28											10 42	10 49
Barnehurst	d		09 29	09 38							09 38		09 46			09 59	10 08		
Bexleyheath	d		09 31	09 40							09 40		09 49			10 01	10 10		
Welling	d		09 34	09 43							09 43		09 52			10 04	10 13		
Falconwood	d		09 37	09 46							09 46		09 54			10 07	10 16		
Eltham	d		09 40	09 49							09 49		09 57			10 10	10 19		
Kidbrooke	d		09 43	09 52							09 52		10 00			10 13	10 22		
Blackheath	d		09 46	09 55					09 52		09 55		10 04			10 16	10 25		
Lewisham	d	09 44	09 50	09 59		10 24	10 34		09 56		09 59		10 08		10 14	10 20	10 29		10 54
St Johns	d	09 46		10 01		10 26	10 36				10 01				10 16		10 31		10 56
New Cross	d	09 48		10 03		10 28	10 38				10 03				10 18		10 33		10 58
Nunhead	d												10 13						
Peckham Rye	d												10 15						
Denmark Hill	d												10 19						
London Victoria	a												10 28						
Westcombe Park	d							09 47				09 57		10 07					
Maze Hill	d							09 49				09 59		10 09					
Greenwich	d							09 52				10 02		10 12					
Deptford	a							09 54				10 04		10 14					
London Bridge	a	09 54	09 58	10 08	10 22	10 34	10 44	10 00	10 05		10 08	10 11		10 20	10 24	10 28	10 38	10 52	11 04
London Cannon Street	a	09 58		10 13		10 38	10 49	10 04			10 13	10 15		10 24	10 28		10 43		11 08
London Waterloo (East)	a		10 02		10 26				10 09							10 32		10 56	
London Charing Cross	a		10 06		10 30				10 13							10 36		11 00	
Ebbsfleet International	a									09 46									
Stratford International	a									09 59									
St Pancras Int'l	a									10 06									

		SE	SE	SE	SE	SE	SE	SE	SE	SE	SE	SE	SE	SE	SE	SE	SE	SE	SE
Gillingham (Kent)	d			09 24	09 50												09 54	10 20	
Chatham	d			09 28	09 54												09 58	10 24	
Rochester	d			09 30	09 57												10 00	10 27	
Maidstone West	d																		
Strood	d			09 35	10 02												10 05	10 32	
Higham	d			09 40													10 10		
Gravesend	d			09 48	10 13								10 32				10 18	10 43	
Northfleet	d												10 36						
Swanscombe	d												10 38						
Greenhithe for Bluewater	d			09 53									10 41				10 23		
Stone Crossing	d												10 43						
Dartford	a			09 58									10 47				10 28		
	d			09 59			10 01	10 08			10 22		10 48				10 29		
Slade Green	d		09 55				10 05		10 15			10 17				10 25			
Erith	d		09 58				10 08		10 18							10 28			
Belvedere	d		10 00				10 10		10 20							10 30			
Abbey Wood	d		10 03	10 08			10 13		10 23							10 33	10 38		
Plumstead	d		10 06				10 16		10 26							10 36			
Woolwich Arsenal	d		10 09	10 13			10 19		10 29							10 39	10 43		
Woolwich Dockyard	d		10 12				10 22		10 32							10 42			
Charlton	d	10 07	10 15	10 17			10 25		10 35						10 37	10 45	10 47		
Crayford	d	10 37											10 52		11 07				
Bexley	d	10 40											10 55		11 10				
Albany Park	d	10 43											10 58		11 13				
Sidcup	d	10 46											11 01		11 16				
New Eltham	d	10 49											11 04		11 19				
Mottingham	d	10 51											11 06		11 21				
Lee	d	10 54											11 09		11 24				
Hither Green	d	10 58											11 12	11 19	11 28				
Barnehurst	d					10 08		10 16			10 29	10 38							10 38
Bexleyheath	d					10 10		10 19			10 31	10 40							10 40
Welling	d					10 13		10 22			10 34	10 43							10 43
Falconwood	d					10 16		10 24			10 37	10 46							10 46
Eltham	d					10 19		10 27			10 40	10 49							10 49
Kidbrooke	d					10 22		10 30			10 43	10 52							10 52
Blackheath	d			10 22		10 25		10 34			10 46	10 55					10 52		10 55
Lewisham	d	11 04		10 26		10 29		10 38		10 44	10 50	10 59		11 24	11 34		10 56		10 59
St Johns	d	11 06				10 31				10 46		11 01		11 26	11 36				11 01
New Cross	d	11 08				10 33				10 48		11 03		11 28	11 38				11 03
Nunhead	d							10 43											
Peckham Rye	d							10 45											
Denmark Hill	d							10 49											
London Victoria	a							10 58											
Westcombe Park	d		10 17				10 27		10 37							10 47			
Maze Hill	d		10 19				10 29		10 39							10 49			
Greenwich	d		10 22				10 32		10 42							10 52			
Deptford	a		10 24				10 34		10 44							10 54			
London Bridge	a	11 14	10 30	10 35		10 38	10 41		10 50	10 54	10 58	11 08	11 22	11 34	11 44	11 00	11 05		11 08
London Cannon Street	a	11 19	10 34			10 43	10 45		10 54	10 58		11 13		11 38	11 49	11 04			11 13
London Waterloo (East)	a			10 39							11 02		11 26				11 09		
London Charing Cross	a			10 43							11 06		11 30				11 13		
Ebbsfleet International	a				10 16													10 46	
Stratford International	a				10 29													10 59	
St Pancras Int'l	a				10 36													11 06	

Table 200R

Saturdays

14 December to 17 May

Gillingham and Dartford - London

Network Diagram - see first Page of Table 200

		SE	SE	SE	SE	SE	SE	SE	SE	SE	SE	SE	SE	SE	SE	SE	SE	SE	SE
Gillingham (Kent) [4]	d											10 24	10 50						
Chatham [4]	d											10 28	10 54						
Rochester [4]	d											10 30	10 57						
Maidstone West	d																		
Strood [4]	d											10 35	11 02						
Higham	d											10 40							
Gravesend [4]	d							11 02				10 48	11 13						
Northfleet	d							11 06											
Swanscombe	d							11 08											
Greenhithe for Bluewater	d							11 11				10 53							
Stone Crossing	d							11 13											
Dartford [4]	a							11 17				10 58							
	d	10 31	10 38			10 52		11 18				10 59			11 01	11 08			11 22
Slade Green [4]	d	10 35		10 45			10 47				10 55				11 05		11 15		
Erith	d	10 38		10 48							10 58				11 08		11 18		
Belvedere	d	10 40		10 50							11 00				11 10		11 20		
Abbey Wood	d	10 43		10 53							11 03	11 08			11 13		11 23		
Plumstead	d	10 46		10 56							11 06				11 16		11 26		
Woolwich Arsenal [4]	d	10 49		10 59							11 09	11 13			11 19		11 29		
Woolwich Dockyard	d	10 52		11 02							11 12				11 22		11 32		
Charlton [4]	d	10 55		11 05						11 07	11 15	11 17			11 25		11 35		
Crayford	d							11 22		11 37									
Bexley	d							11 25		11 40									
Albany Park	d							11 28		11 43									
Sidcup [4]	d							11 31		11 46									
New Eltham	d							11 34		11 49									
Mottingham	d							11 36		11 51									
Lee	d							11 39		11 54									
Hither Green [4]	d							11 42	11 49	11 58									
Barnehurst [4]	d		10 46			10 59	11 08							11 08		11 16			11 29
Bexleyheath	d		10 49			11 01	11 10							11 10		11 19			11 31
Welling	d		10 52			11 04	11 13							11 13		11 22			11 34
Falconwood	d		10 54			11 07	11 16							11 16		11 24			11 37
Eltham	d		10 57			11 10	11 19							11 19		11 27			11 40
Kidbrooke	d		11 00			11 13	11 22							11 22		11 30			11 43
Blackheath [4]	d		11 04			11 16	11 25					11 22		11 25		11 34			11 46
Lewisham [4]	d		11 08		11 14	11 20	11 29		11 54	12 04		11 26		11 29		11 38		11 44	11 50
St Johns	d				11 16		11 31		11 56	12 06				11 31				11 46	
New Cross [4] ⊖	d				11 18		11 33		11 58	12 08				11 33				11 48	
Nunhead [4]	d		11 13													11 43			
Peckham Rye [4]	d		11 15													11 45			
Denmark Hill [4]	d		11 19													11 49			
London Victoria [15] ⊖	a		11 28													11 58			
Westcombe Park	d	10 57		11 07							11 17				11 27		11 37		
Maze Hill	d	10 59		11 09							11 19				11 29		11 39		
Greenwich [4]	d	11 02		11 12							11 22				11 32		11 42		
Deptford	a	11 04		11 14							11 24				11 34		11 44		
London Bridge [4] ⊖	a	11 11		11 20	11 24	11 28	11 38	11 52	12 04	12 14	11 30	11 35		11 38	11 41		11 50	11 54	11 58
London Cannon Street [4] ⊖	a	11 15		11 24	11 28		11 43		12 08	12 19	11 34			11 43	11 45		11 54	11 58	
London Waterloo (East) [4] ⊖	a					11 32		11 56				11 39							12 02
London Charing Cross [4] ⊖	a					11 36		12 00				11 43							12 06
Ebbsfleet International	a												11 16						
Stratford International ⊖	a												11 29						
St Pancras Int'l [15] ⊖	a												11 36						

		SE	SE	SE	SE	SE	SE	SE	SE	SE	SE	SE	SE	SE	SE	SE	SE	SE	SE
Gillingham (Kent) [4]	d						10 54	11 20											
Chatham [4]	d						10 58	11 24											
Rochester [4]	d						11 00	11 27											
Maidstone West	d																		
Strood [4]	d						11 05	11 32											
Higham	d						11 10												
Gravesend [4]	d		11 32				11 18	11 43								12 02			
Northfleet	d		11 36													12 06			
Swanscombe	d		11 38													12 08			
Greenhithe for Bluewater	d		11 41				11 23									12 11			
Stone Crossing	d		11 43													12 13			
Dartford [4]	a		11 47				11 28									12 17			
	d		11 48				11 29			11 31	11 38			11 52		12 18			
Slade Green [4]	d	11 17				11 25				11 35		11 45			11 47				11 55
Erith	d					11 28				11 38		11 48							11 58
Belvedere	d					11 30				11 40		11 50							12 00
Abbey Wood	d					11 33	11 38			11 43		11 53							12 03
Plumstead	d					11 36				11 46		11 56							12 06
Woolwich Arsenal [4]	d					11 39	11 43			11 49		11 59							12 09
Woolwich Dockyard	d					11 42				11 52		12 02							12 12
Charlton [4]	d				11 37	11 45	11 47			11 55		12 05						12 07	12 15
Crayford	d		11 52		12 07											12 22		12 37	
Bexley	d		11 55		12 10											12 25		12 40	
Albany Park	d		11 58		12 13											12 28		12 43	
Sidcup [4]	d		12 01		12 16											12 31		12 46	
New Eltham	d		12 04		12 19											12 34		12 49	
Mottingham	d		12 06		12 21											12 36		12 51	
Lee	d		12 09		12 24											12 39		12 54	
Hither Green [4]	d		12 12	12 19	12 28											12 42	12 49	12 58	
Barnehurst [4]	d	11 38							11 38		11 46			11 59	12 08				
Bexleyheath	d	11 40							11 40		11 49			12 01	12 10				
Welling	d	11 43							11 43		11 52			12 04	12 13				
Falconwood	d	11 46							11 46		11 54			12 07	12 16				
Eltham	d	11 49							11 49		11 57			12 10	12 19				
Kidbrooke	d	11 52							11 52		12 00			12 13	12 22				
Blackheath [4]	d	11 55						11 52	11 55		12 04			12 16	12 25				
Lewisham [4]	d	11 59		12 24	12 34			11 56	11 59		12 08		12 14	12 20	12 29		12 54	13 04	
St Johns	d	12 01		12 26	12 36				12 01				12 16		12 31		12 56	13 06	
New Cross [4] ⊖	d	12 03		12 28	12 38				12 03				12 18		12 33		12 58	13 08	
Nunhead [4]	d										12 13								
Peckham Rye [4]	d										12 15								
Denmark Hill [4]	d										12 19								
London Victoria [15] ⊖	a										12 28								
Westcombe Park	d					11 47				11 57		12 07							12 17
Maze Hill	d					11 49				11 59		12 09							12 19
Greenwich [4]	d					11 52				12 02		12 12							12 22
Deptford	a					11 54				12 04		12 14							12 24
London Bridge [4] ⊖	a	12 08	12 22	12 34	12 44	12 00	12 05		12 08	12 11		12 20	12 24	12 28	12 38	12 52	13 04	13 14	12 30
London Cannon Street [4] ⊖	a	12 13		12 38	12 49	12 04			12 13	12 15		12 24	12 28		12 43		13 08	13 19	12 34
London Waterloo (East) [4] ⊖	a		12 26				12 09							12 32		12 56			
London Charing Cross [4] ⊖	a		12 30				12 13							12 36		13 00			
Ebbsfleet International	a							11 46											
Stratford International ⊖	a							11 59											
St Pancras Int'l [15] ⊖	a							12 06											

Table 200R

Saturdays

14 December to 17 May

Gillingham and Dartford - London

Network Diagram - see first Page of Table 200

Station		SE	SE	SE	SE	SE	SE	SE	SE	SE
Gillingham (Kent) 4	d	11 24	11 50							
Chatham 4	d	11 28	11 54							
Rochester 4	d	11 30	11 57							
Maidstone West	d									
Strood 4	d	11 35	12 02							
Higham	d	11 40								
Gravesend 4	d	11 48	12 13							
Northfleet	d									
Swanscombe	d									
Greenhithe for Bluewater	d	11 53								
Stone Crossing	d									
Dartford 4	a	11 58								
	d	11 59			12 01	12 08			12 22	
Slade Green 4	d				12 05		12 15			12 17
Erith	d				12 08		12 18			
Belvedere	d				12 10		12 20			
Abbey Wood	d	12 08			12 13		12 23			
Plumstead	d				12 16		12 26			
Woolwich Arsenal 4 ⛴	d	12 13			12 19		12 29			
Woolwich Dockyard	d				12 22		12 32			
Charlton 4	d	12 17			12 25		12 35			
Crayford	d									
Bexley	d									
Albany Park	d									
Sidcup 4	d									
New Eltham	d									
Mottingham	d									
Lee	d									
Hither Green 4	d									
Barnehurst 4	d			12 08		12 16			12 29	12 38
Bexleyheath	d			12 10		12 19			12 31	12 40
Welling	d			12 13		12 22			12 34	12 43
Falconwood	d			12 16		12 24			12 37	12 46
Eltham	d			12 19		12 27			12 40	12 49
Kidbrooke	d			12 22		12 30			12 43	12 52
Blackheath 4	d	12 22		12 25		12 34			12 46	12 55
Lewisham 4 ⛴	d	12 26		12 29		12 38		12 44	12 50	12 59
St Johns	d			12 31				12 46		13 01
New Cross 4 ⊖	d			12 33				12 48		13 03
Nunhead 4	d					12 43				
Peckham Rye 4	d					12 45				
Denmark Hill 4	d					12 49				
London Victoria 15 ⊖	a					12 58				
Westcombe Park	d				12 27		12 37			
Maze Hill	d				12 29		12 39			
Greenwich 4 ⛴	d				12 32		12 42			
Deptford	a				12 34		12 44			
London Bridge 4 ⊖	a	12 35		12 38	12 41		12 50	12 54	12 58	13 08
London Cannon Street 4 ⊖	a			12 43	12 45		12 54	12 58		13 13
London Waterloo (East) 4 ⊖	a	12 39							13 02	
London Charing Cross 4 ⊖	a	12 43							13 06	
Ebbsfleet International	a		12 16							
Stratford International ⊖ ⛴	a		12 30							
St Pancras Int'l 15 ⊖	a		12 37							

Station		SE	SE	SE	SE	SE	SE	SE	SE	SE
Gillingham (Kent) 4	d					11 54	12 20			
Chatham 4	d					11 58	12 24			
Rochester 4	d					12 00	12 27			
Maidstone West	d									
Strood 4	d					12 05	12 32			
Higham	d					12 10				
Gravesend 4	d	12 32				12 18	12 43			
Northfleet	d	12 36								
Swanscombe	d	12 38								
Greenhithe for Bluewater	d	12 41				12 23				
Stone Crossing	d	12 43								
Dartford 4	a	12 47				12 28				
	d	12 48				12 29			12 31	12 38
Slade Green 4	d				12 25				12 35	
Erith	d				12 28				12 38	
Belvedere	d				12 30				12 40	
Abbey Wood	d				12 33	12 38			12 43	
Plumstead	d				12 36				12 46	
Woolwich Arsenal 4 ⛴	d				12 39	12 43			12 49	
Woolwich Dockyard	d				12 42				12 52	
Charlton 4	d			12 37	12 45	12 47			12 55	
Crayford	d	12 52		13 07						
Bexley	d	12 55		13 10						
Albany Park	d	12 58		13 13						
Sidcup 4	d	13 01		13 16						
New Eltham	d	13 04		13 19						
Mottingham	d	13 06		13 21						
Lee	d	13 09		13 24						
Hither Green 4	d	13 12	13 19	13 28						
Barnehurst 4	d							12 38		12 46
Bexleyheath	d							12 40		12 49
Welling	d							12 43		12 52
Falconwood	d							12 46		12 54
Eltham	d							12 49		12 57
Kidbrooke	d							12 52		13 00
Blackheath 4	d					12 52		12 55		13 04
Lewisham 4 ⛴	d		13 24	13 34		12 56		12 59		13 08
St Johns	d		13 26	13 36				13 01		
New Cross 4 ⊖	d		13 28	13 38				13 03		
Nunhead 4	d									13 13
Peckham Rye 4	d									13 15
Denmark Hill 4	d									13 19
London Victoria 15 ⊖	a									13 28
Westcombe Park	d				12 47				12 57	
Maze Hill	d				12 49				12 59	
Greenwich 4 ⛴	d				12 52				13 02	
Deptford	a				12 54				13 04	
London Bridge 4 ⊖	a	13 22	13 34	13 44	13 00	13 05		13 08	13 11	
London Cannon Street 4 ⊖	a		13 38	13 49	13 04			13 13	13 15	
London Waterloo (East) 4 ⊖	a	13 26				13 09				
London Charing Cross 4 ⊖	a	13 30				13 13				
Ebbsfleet International	a						12 46			
Stratford International ⊖ ⛴	a						13 00			
St Pancras Int'l 15 ⊖	a						13 07			

Station		SE	SE	SE	SE	SE	SE	SE	SE	SE
Gillingham (Kent) 4	d									12 24
Chatham 4	d									12 28
Rochester 4	d									12 30
Maidstone West	d									
Strood 4	d									12 35
Higham	d									12 40
Gravesend 4	d					13 02				12 48
Northfleet	d					13 06				
Swanscombe	d					13 08				
Greenhithe for Bluewater	d					13 11				12 53
Stone Crossing	d					13 13				
Dartford 4	a					13 17				12 58
	d			12 52		13 18				12 59
Slade Green 4	d	12 45			12 47				12 55	
Erith	d	12 48							12 58	
Belvedere	d	12 50							13 00	
Abbey Wood	d	12 53							13 03	13 08
Plumstead	d	12 56							13 06	
Woolwich Arsenal 4 ⛴	d	12 59							13 09	13 13
Woolwich Dockyard	d	13 02							13 12	
Charlton 4	d	13 05						13 07	13 15	13 17
Crayford	d					13 22		13 37		
Bexley	d					13 25		13 40		
Albany Park	d					13 28		13 43		
Sidcup 4	d					13 31		13 46		
New Eltham	d					13 34		13 49		
Mottingham	d					13 36		13 51		
Lee	d					13 39		13 54		
Hither Green 4	d					13 42	13 49	13 58		
Barnehurst 4	d			12 59	13 08					
Bexleyheath	d			13 01	13 10					
Welling	d			13 04	13 13					
Falconwood	d			13 07	13 16					
Eltham	d			13 10	13 19					
Kidbrooke	d			13 13	13 22					
Blackheath 4	d			13 16	13 25					13 22
Lewisham 4 ⛴	d		13 14	13 20	13 29		13 54	14 04		13 26
St Johns	d		13 16		13 31		13 56	14 06		
New Cross 4 ⊖	d		13 18		13 33		13 58	14 08		
Nunhead 4	d									
Peckham Rye 4	d									
Denmark Hill 4	d									
London Victoria 15 ⊖	a									
Westcombe Park	d	13 07							13 17	
Maze Hill	d	13 09							13 19	
Greenwich 4 ⛴	d	13 12							13 22	
Deptford	a	13 14							13 24	
London Bridge 4 ⊖	a	13 20	13 24	13 28	13 38	13 52	14 04	14 14	13 30	13 35
London Cannon Street 4 ⊖	a	13 24	13 28		13 43		14 08	14 19	13 34	
London Waterloo (East) 4 ⊖	a			13 33		13 56				13 39
London Charing Cross 4 ⊖	a			13 36		14 00				13 43
Ebbsfleet International	a									
Stratford International ⊖ ⛴	a									
St Pancras Int'l 15 ⊖	a									

Station		SE	SE	SE	SE	SE	SE	SE	SE	SE
Gillingham (Kent) 4	d	12 50								
Chatham 4	d	12 54								
Rochester 4	d	12 57								
Maidstone West	d									
Strood 4	d	13 02								
Higham	d									
Gravesend 4	d	13 13								13 32
Northfleet	d									13 36
Swanscombe	d									13 38
Greenhithe for Bluewater	d									13 41
Stone Crossing	d									13 43
Dartford 4	a									13 47
	d			13 01	13 08			13 22		13 48
Slade Green 4	d			13 05		13 15			13 17	
Erith	d			13 08		13 18				
Belvedere	d			13 10		13 20				
Abbey Wood	d			13 13		13 23				
Plumstead	d			13 16		13 26				
Woolwich Arsenal 4 ⛴	d			13 19		13 29				
Woolwich Dockyard	d			13 22		13 32				
Charlton 4	d			13 25		13 35				
Crayford	d									13 52
Bexley	d									13 55
Albany Park	d									13 58
Sidcup 4	d									14 01
New Eltham	d									14 04
Mottingham	d									14 06
Lee	d									14 09
Hither Green 4	d									14 12
Barnehurst 4	d		13 08		13 16			13 29	13 38	
Bexleyheath	d		13 10		13 19			13 31	13 40	
Welling	d		13 13		13 22			13 34	13 43	
Falconwood	d		13 16		13 24			13 37	13 46	
Eltham	d		13 19		13 27			13 40	13 49	
Kidbrooke	d		13 22		13 30			13 43	13 52	
Blackheath 4	d		13 25		13 34			13 46	13 55	
Lewisham 4 ⛴	d		13 29		13 38		13 44	13 50	13 59	
St Johns	d		13 31				13 46		14 01	
New Cross 4 ⊖	d		13 33				13 48		14 03	
Nunhead 4	d				13 43					
Peckham Rye 4	d				13 45					
Denmark Hill 4	d				13 49					
London Victoria 15 ⊖	a				13 58					
Westcombe Park	d			13 27		13 37				
Maze Hill	d			13 29		13 39				
Greenwich 4 ⛴	d			13 32		13 42				
Deptford	a			13 34		13 44				
London Bridge 4 ⊖	a		13 38	13 41		13 50	13 54	13 58	14 08	14 22
London Cannon Street 4 ⊖	a		13 43	13 45		13 54	13 58		14 13	
London Waterloo (East) 4 ⊖	a							14 02		14 26
London Charing Cross 4 ⊖	a							14 06		14 30
Ebbsfleet International	a	13 16								
Stratford International ⊖ ⛴	a	13 29								
St Pancras Int'l 15 ⊖	a	13 36								

Table 200R

Saturdays

14 December to 17 May

Gillingham and Dartford - London

Network Diagram - see first Page of Table 200

		SE	SE	SE	SE	SE	SE	SE	SE	SE	SE	SE	SE	SE	SE	SE	SE	SE	SE	SE	SE	SE	SE	SE	SE	SE	SE	SE	SE	SE	SE	SE	SE	SE	SE	SE	SE
Gillingham (Kent) 4	d				12 54	13 20												13 24	13 50												13 54	14 20					
Chatham 4	d				12 58	13 24												13 28	13 54												13 58	14 24					
Rochester 4	d				13 00	13 27												13 30	13 57												14 00	14 27					
Maidstone West	d																																				
Strood 4	d				13 05	13 32												13 35	14 02												14 05	14 32					
Higham	d				13 10													13 40													14 10						
Gravesend 4	d				13 18	13 43								14 02				13 48	14 13								14 32				14 18	14 43					
Northfleet	d													14 06													14 36										
Swanscombe	d													14 08													14 38										
Greenhithe for Bluewater	d				13 23									14 11				13 53									14 41				14 23						
Stone Crossing	d													14 13													14 43										
Dartford 4	a				13 28									14 17				13 58									14 47				14 28						
	d				13 29			13 31	13 38			13 52		14 18				13 59			14 01	14 08			14 22		14 48				14 29			14 31	14 38		
Slade Green 4	d			13 25				13 35		13 45			13 47				13 55				14 05		14 15			14 17				14 25				14 35		14 45	
Erith	d			13 28				13 38		13 48							13 58				14 08		14 18							14 28				14 38		14 48	
Belvedere	d			13 30				13 40		13 50							14 00				14 10		14 20							14 30				14 40		14 50	
Abbey Wood	d			13 33	13 38			13 43		13 53							14 03	14 08			14 13		14 23							14 33	14 38			14 43		14 53	
Plumstead	d			13 36				13 46		13 56							14 06				14 16		14 26							14 36				14 46		14 56	
Woolwich Arsenal 4 ⛴	d			13 39	13 43			13 49		13 59							14 09	14 13			14 19		14 29							14 39	14 43			14 49		14 59	
Woolwich Dockyard	d			13 42				13 52		14 02							14 12				14 22		14 32							14 42				14 52		15 02	
Charlton 4	d		13 37	13 45	13 47			13 55		14 05						14 07	14 15	14 17			14 25		14 35						14 37	14 45	14 47			14 55		15 05	
Crayford	d		14 07											14 22		14 37											14 52		15 07								
Bexley	d		14 10											14 25		14 40											14 55		15 10								
Albany Park	d		14 13											14 28		14 43											14 58		15 13								
Sidcup 4	d		14 16											14 31		14 46											15 01		15 16								
New Eltham	d		14 19											14 34		14 49											15 04		15 19								
Mottingham	d		14 21											14 36		14 51											15 06		15 21								
Lee	d		14 24											14 39		14 54											15 09		15 24								
Hither Green 4	d	14 19	14 28											14 42	14 49	14 58											15 12	15 19	15 28								
Barnehurst 4	d						13 38		13 46			13 59	14 08							14 08		14 16			14 29	14 38							14 38		14 46		
Bexleyheath	d						13 40		13 49			14 01	14 10							14 10		14 19			14 31	14 40							14 40		14 49		
Welling	d						13 43		13 52			14 04	14 13							14 13		14 22			14 34	14 43							14 43		14 52		
Falconwood	d						13 46		13 54			14 07	14 16							14 16		14 24			14 37	14 46							14 46		14 54		
Eltham	d						13 49		13 57			14 10	14 19							14 19		14 27			14 40	14 49							14 49		14 57		
Kidbrooke	d						13 52		14 00			14 13	14 22							14 22		14 30			14 43	14 52							14 52		15 00		
Blackheath 4	d				13 52		13 55		14 04			14 16	14 25					14 22		14 25		14 34			14 46	14 55					14 52		14 55		15 04		
Lewisham 4 ⛴	d	14 24	14 34		13 56		13 59		14 08		14 14	14 20	14 29		14 54	15 04		14 26		14 29		14 38		14 44	14 50	14 59		15 24	15 34		14 56		14 59		15 08		15 14
St Johns	d	14 26	14 36				14 01				14 16		14 31		14 56	15 06				14 31				14 46		15 01		15 26	15 36				15 01				15 16
New Cross 4 ⊖	d	14 28	14 38				14 03				14 18		14 33		14 58	15 08				14 33				14 48		15 03		15 28	15 38				15 03				15 18
Nunhead 4	d								14 13													14 43													15 13		
Peckham Rye 4	d								14 15													14 45													15 15		
Denmark Hill 4	d								14 19													14 49													15 19		
London Victoria 15 ⊖	a								14 28													14 58													15 28		
Westcombe Park	d			13 47				13 57		14 07							14 17				14 27		14 37							14 47				14 57		15 07	
Maze Hill	d			13 49				13 59		14 09							14 19				14 29		14 39							14 49				14 59		15 09	
Greenwich 4 ⛴	d			13 52				14 02		14 12							14 22				14 32		14 42							14 52				15 02		15 12	
Deptford	a			13 54				14 04		14 14							14 24				14 34		14 44							14 54				15 04		15 14	
London Bridge 4 ⊖	a	14 34	14 44	14 00	14 05		14 08	14 11		14 20	14 24	14 28	14 38	14 52	15 04	15 14	14 30	14 35		14 38	14 41		14 50	14 54	14 58	15 08	15 22	15 34	15 44	15 00	15 05		15 08	15 11		15 20	15 24
London Cannon Street 4 ⊖	a	14 38	14 49	14 04			14 13	14 15		14 24	14 28		14 43		15 08	15 19	14 34			14 43	14 45		14 54	14 58		15 13		15 38	15 49	15 04			15 13	15 15		15 24	15 28
London Waterloo (East) 4 ⊖	a				14 09							14 32		14 56				14 39							15 02		15 26				15 09						
London Charing Cross 4 ⊖	a				14 13							14 36		15 00				14 43							15 06		15 30				15 13						
Ebbsfleet International	a					13 46													14 16													14 46					
Stratford International ⊖ ⛴	a					14 00													14 29													14 59					
St Pancras Int'l 15 ⊖	a					14 07													14 36													15 06					

Table 200R

Saturdays

14 December to 17 May

Gillingham and Dartford - London

Network Diagram - see first Page of Table 200

Station		SE	SE	SE	SE	SE	SE	SE	SE	SE
Gillingham (Kent) 4	d							14 24	14 50	
Chatham 4	d							14 28	14 54	
Rochester 4	d							14 30	14 57	
Maidstone West	d									
Strood 4	d							14 35	15 02	
Higham	d							14 40		
Gravesend 4	d			15 02				14 48	15 13	
Northfleet	d			15 06						
Swanscombe	d			15 08						
Greenhithe for Bluewater	d			15 11				14 53		
Stone Crossing	d			15 13						
Dartford 4	a			15 17				14 58		
	d	14 52		15 18				14 59		
Slade Green 4	d		14 47				14 55			
Erith	d						14 58			
Belvedere	d						15 00			
Abbey Wood	d						15 03	15 08		
Plumstead	d						15 06			
Woolwich Arsenal 4	d						15 09	15 13		
Woolwich Dockyard	d						15 12			
Charlton 4	d					15 07	15 15	15 17		
Crayford	d			15 22		15 37				
Bexley	d			15 25		15 40				
Albany Park	d			15 28		15 43				
Sidcup 4	d			15 31		15 46				
New Eltham	d			15 34		15 49				
Mottingham	d			15 36		15 51				
Lee	d			15 39		15 54				
Hither Green 4	d			15 42	15 49	15 58				
Barnehurst 4	d	14 59	15 08							15 08
Bexleyheath	d	15 01	15 10							15 10
Welling	d	15 04	15 13							15 13
Falconwood	d	15 07	15 16							15 16
Eltham	d	15 10	15 19							15 19
Kidbrooke	d	15 13	15 22							15 22
Blackheath 4	d	15 16	15 25					15 22		15 25
Lewisham 4	d	15 20	15 29		15 54	16 04		15 26		15 29
St Johns	d		15 31		15 56	16 06				15 31
New Cross 4 ⊖	d		15 33		15 58	16 08				15 33
Nunhead 4	d									
Peckham Rye 4	d									
Denmark Hill 4	d									
London Victoria 15 ⊖	a									
Westcombe Park	d						15 17			
Maze Hill	d						15 19			
Greenwich 4	d						15 22			
Deptford	a						15 24			
London Bridge 4 ⊖	a	15 28	15 38	15 52	16 04	16 14	15 30	15 35		15 38
London Cannon Street 4 ⊖	a		15 43		16 08	16 19	15 34			15 43
London Waterloo (East) 4 ⊖	a	15 32		15 56				15 39		
London Charing Cross 4 ⊖	a	15 36		16 00				15 43		
Ebbsfleet International	a								15 16	
Stratford International ⊖	a								15 30	
St Pancras Int'l 15 ⊖	a								15 37	

Station		SE	SE	SE	SE	SE	SE	SE	SE	SE
Gillingham (Kent) 4	d									
Chatham 4	d									
Rochester 4	d									
Maidstone West	d									
Strood 4	d									
Higham	d									
Gravesend 4	d							15 32		
Northfleet	d							15 36		
Swanscombe	d							15 38		
Greenhithe for Bluewater	d							15 41		
Stone Crossing	d							15 43		
Dartford 4	a							15 47		
	d	15 01	15 08			15 22		15 48		
Slade Green 4	d	15 05		15 15			15 17			
Erith	d	15 08		15 18						
Belvedere	d	15 10		15 20						
Abbey Wood	d	15 13		15 23						
Plumstead	d	15 16		15 26						
Woolwich Arsenal 4	d	15 19		15 29						
Woolwich Dockyard	d	15 22		15 32						
Charlton 4	d	15 25		15 35						15 37
Crayford	d							15 52		16 07
Bexley	d							15 55		16 10
Albany Park	d							15 58		16 13
Sidcup 4	d							16 01		16 16
New Eltham	d							16 04		16 19
Mottingham	d							16 06		16 21
Lee	d							16 09		16 24
Hither Green 4	d							16 12	16 19	16 28
Barnehurst 4	d		15 16			15 29	15 38			
Bexleyheath	d		15 19			15 31	15 40			
Welling	d		15 22			15 34	15 43			
Falconwood	d		15 24			15 37	15 46			
Eltham	d		15 27			15 40	15 49			
Kidbrooke	d		15 30			15 43	15 52			
Blackheath 4	d		15 34			15 46	15 55			
Lewisham 4	d		15 38		15 44	15 50	15 59		16 24	16 34
St Johns	d				15 46		16 01		16 26	16 36
New Cross 4 ⊖	d				15 48		16 03		16 28	16 38
Nunhead 4	d		15 43							
Peckham Rye 4	d		15 45							
Denmark Hill 4	d		15 49							
London Victoria 15 ⊖	a		15 58							
Westcombe Park	d	15 27		15 37						
Maze Hill	d	15 29		15 39						
Greenwich 4	d	15 32		15 42						
Deptford	a	15 34		15 44						
London Bridge 4 ⊖	a	15 41		15 50	15 54	15 58	16 08	16 22	16 34	16 44
London Cannon Street 4 ⊖	a	15 45		15 54	15 58		16 13		16 38	16 49
London Waterloo (East) 4 ⊖	a					16 02		16 26		
London Charing Cross 4 ⊖	a					16 06		16 30		
Ebbsfleet International	a									
Stratford International ⊖	a									
St Pancras Int'l 15 ⊖	a									

Station		SE	SE	SE	SE	SE	SE	SE	SE	SE
Gillingham (Kent) 4	d		14 54	15 20						
Chatham 4	d		14 58	15 24						
Rochester 4	d		15 00	15 27						
Maidstone West	d									
Strood 4	d		15 05	15 32						
Higham	d		15 10							
Gravesend 4	d		15 18	15 43						
Northfleet	d									
Swanscombe	d									
Greenhithe for Bluewater	d		15 23							
Stone Crossing	d									
Dartford 4	a		15 28							
	d		15 29			15 31	15 38			15 52
Slade Green 4	d	15 25				15 35		15 45		
Erith	d	15 28				15 38		15 48		
Belvedere	d	15 30				15 40		15 50		
Abbey Wood	d	15 33	15 38			15 43		15 53		
Plumstead	d	15 36				15 46		15 56		
Woolwich Arsenal 4	d	15 39	15 43			15 49		15 59		
Woolwich Dockyard	d	15 42				15 52		16 02		
Charlton 4	d	15 45	15 47			15 55		16 05		
Crayford	d									
Bexley	d									
Albany Park	d									
Sidcup 4	d									
New Eltham	d									
Mottingham	d									
Lee	d									
Hither Green 4	d									
Barnehurst 4	d				15 38		15 46			15 59
Bexleyheath	d				15 40		15 49			16 01
Welling	d				15 43		15 52			16 04
Falconwood	d				15 46		15 54			16 07
Eltham	d				15 49		15 57			16 10
Kidbrooke	d				15 52		16 00			16 13
Blackheath 4	d		15 52		15 55		16 04			16 16
Lewisham 4	d		15 56		15 59		16 08		16 14	16 20
St Johns	d				16 01				16 16	
New Cross 4 ⊖	d				16 03				16 18	
Nunhead 4	d						16 13			
Peckham Rye 4	d						16 15			
Denmark Hill 4	d						16 19			
London Victoria 15 ⊖	a						16 28			
Westcombe Park	d	15 47				15 57		16 07		
Maze Hill	d	15 49				15 59		16 09		
Greenwich 4	d	15 52				16 02		16 12		
Deptford	a	15 54				16 04		16 14		
London Bridge 4 ⊖	a	16 00	16 05		16 08	16 11		16 20	16 24	16 28
London Cannon Street 4 ⊖	a	16 04			16 13	16 15		16 24	16 28	
London Waterloo (East) 4 ⊖	a		16 09							16 32
London Charing Cross 4 ⊖	a		16 13							16 36
Ebbsfleet International	a			15 46						
Stratford International ⊖	a			16 02						
St Pancras Int'l 15 ⊖	a			16 10						

Station		SE	SE	SE	SE	SE	SE	SE	SE	SE
Gillingham (Kent) 4	d						15 24	15 50		
Chatham 4	d						15 28	15 54		
Rochester 4	d						15 30	15 57		
Maidstone West	d									
Strood 4	d						15 35	16 02		
Higham	d						15 40			
Gravesend 4	d		16 02				15 48	16 13		
Northfleet	d		16 06							
Swanscombe	d		16 08							
Greenhithe for Bluewater	d		16 11				15 53			
Stone Crossing	d		16 13							
Dartford 4	a		16 17				15 58			
	d		16 18				15 59			16 01
Slade Green 4	d	15 47				15 55				16 05
Erith	d					15 58				16 08
Belvedere	d					16 00				16 10
Abbey Wood	d					16 03	16 08			16 13
Plumstead	d					16 06				16 16
Woolwich Arsenal 4	d					16 09	16 13			16 19
Woolwich Dockyard	d					16 12				16 22
Charlton 4	d				16 07	16 15	16 17			16 25
Crayford	d		16 22		16 37					
Bexley	d		16 25		16 40					
Albany Park	d		16 28		16 43					
Sidcup 4	d		16 31		16 46					
New Eltham	d		16 34		16 49					
Mottingham	d		16 36		16 51					
Lee	d		16 39		16 54					
Hither Green 4	d		16 42	16 49	16 58					
Barnehurst 4	d	16 08							16 08	
Bexleyheath	d	16 10							16 10	
Welling	d	16 13							16 13	
Falconwood	d	16 16							16 16	
Eltham	d	16 19							16 19	
Kidbrooke	d	16 22							16 22	
Blackheath 4	d	16 25					16 22		16 25	
Lewisham 4	d	16 29		16 54	17 04		16 26		16 29	
St Johns	d	16 31		16 56	17 06				16 31	
New Cross 4 ⊖	d	16 33		16 58	17 08				16 33	
Nunhead 4	d									
Peckham Rye 4	d									
Denmark Hill 4	d									
London Victoria 15 ⊖	a									
Westcombe Park	d					16 17				16 27
Maze Hill	d					16 19				16 29
Greenwich 4	d					16 22				16 32
Deptford	a					16 24				16 34
London Bridge 4 ⊖	a	16 38	16 52	17 04	17 14	16 30	16 35		16 38	16 41
London Cannon Street 4 ⊖	a	16 43		17 08	17 19	16 34			16 43	16 45
London Waterloo (East) 4 ⊖	a		16 56				16 39			
London Charing Cross 4 ⊖	a		17 00				16 43			
Ebbsfleet International	a							16 16		
Stratford International ⊖	a							16 29		
St Pancras Int'l 15 ⊖	a							16 36		

Table 200R

Saturdays

14 December to 17 May

Gillingham and Dartford - London

Network Diagram - see first Page of Table 200

		SE	SE	SE	SE	SE	SE	SE	SE	SE	SE	SE	SE	SE	SE	SE	SE	SE	SE
Gillingham (Kent) 4	d										15 54	16 20							
Chatham 4	d										15 58	16 24							
Rochester 4	d										16 00	16 27							
Maidstone West	d																		
Strood 4	d										16 05	16 32							
Higham	d										16 10								
Gravesend 4	d						16 32				16 18	16 43							
Northfleet	d						16 36												
Swanscombe	d						16 38												
Greenhithe for Bluewater	d						16 41				16 23								
Stone Crossing	d						16 43												
Dartford 4	a						16 47				16 28								
	d	16 08			16 22		16 48				16 29			16 31	16 38			16 52	
Slade Green 4	d		16 15			16 17				16 25				16 35		16 45			16 47
Erith	d		16 18							16 28				16 38		16 48			
Belvedere	d		16 20							16 30				16 40		16 50			
Abbey Wood	d		16 23							16 33	16 38			16 43		16 53			
Plumstead	d		16 26							16 36				16 46		16 56			
Woolwich Arsenal 4 ⛴	d		16 29							16 39	16 43			16 49		16 59			
Woolwich Dockyard	d		16 32							16 42				16 52		17 02			
Charlton 4	d		16 35						16 37	16 45	16 47			16 55		17 05			
Crayford	d						16 52		17 07										
Bexley	d						16 55		17 10										
Albany Park	d						16 58		17 13										
Sidcup 4	d						17 01		17 16										
New Eltham	d						17 04		17 19										
Mottingham	d						17 06		17 21										
Lee	d						17 09		17 24										
Hither Green 4	d						17 12	17 19	17 28										
Barnehurst 4	d	16 16			16 29	16 38							16 38		16 46			16 59	17 08
Bexleyheath	d	16 19			16 31	16 40							16 40		16 49			17 01	17 10
Welling	d	16 22			16 34	16 43							16 43		16 52			17 04	17 13
Falconwood	d	16 24			16 37	16 46							16 46		16 54			17 07	17 16
Eltham	d	16 27			16 40	16 49							16 49		16 57			17 10	17 19
Kidbrooke	d	16 30			16 43	16 52							16 52		17 00			17 13	17 22
Blackheath 4	d	16 34			16 46	16 55					16 52		16 55		17 04			17 16	17 25
Lewisham 4 ⛴	d	16 38		16 44	16 50	16 59		17 24	17 34		16 56		16 59		17 08		17 14	17 20	17 29
St Johns	d			16 46		17 01		17 26	17 36				17 01				17 16		17 31
New Cross 4 ⊖	d			16 48		17 03		17 28	17 38				17 03				17 18		17 33
Nunhead 4	d	16 43													17 13				
Peckham Rye 4	d	16 45													17 15				
Denmark Hill 4	d	16 49													17 19				
London Victoria 15 ⊖	a	16 58													17 28				
Westcombe Park	d		16 37							16 47				16 57		17 07			
Maze Hill	d		16 39							16 49				16 59		17 09			
Greenwich 4 ⛴	d		16 42							16 52				17 02		17 12			
Deptford	a		16 44							16 54				17 04		17 14			
London Bridge 4 ⊖	a		16 50	16 54	16 58	17 08	17 22	17 34	17 44	17 00	17 05		17 08	17 11		17 20	17 24	17 28	17 38
London Cannon Street 4 ⊖	a		16 54	16 58		17 13		17 38	17 49	17 04			17 13	17 15		17 24	17 28		17 43
London Waterloo (East) 4 ⊖	a				17 02		17 26				17 09							17 32	
London Charing Cross 4 ⊖	a				17 06		17 30				17 13							17 36	
Ebbsfleet International	a											16 46							
Stratford International ⊖ ⛴	a											16 59							
St Pancras Int'l 15 ⊖	a											17 06							

		SE	SE	SE	SE	SE	SE	SE	SE	SE	SE	SE	SE	SE	SE	SE	SE	SE	SE
Gillingham (Kent) 4	d					16 24	16 50												16 54
Chatham 4	d					16 28	16 54												16 58
Rochester 4	d					16 30	16 57												17 00
Maidstone West	d																		
Strood 4	d					16 35	17 02												17 05
Higham	d					16 40													17 10
Gravesend 4	d	17 02				16 48	17 13								17 32				17 18
Northfleet	d	17 06													17 36				
Swanscombe	d	17 08													17 38				
Greenhithe for Bluewater	d	17 11				16 53									17 41				17 23
Stone Crossing	d	17 13													17 43				
Dartford 4	a	17 17				16 58									17 47				17 28
	d	17 18				16 59			17 01	17 08			17 22		17 48				17 29
Slade Green 4	d				16 55				17 05		17 15			17 17				17 25	
Erith	d				16 58				17 08		17 18							17 28	
Belvedere	d				17 00				17 10		17 20							17 30	
Abbey Wood	d				17 03	17 08			17 13		17 23							17 33	17 38
Plumstead	d				17 06				17 16		17 26							17 36	
Woolwich Arsenal 4 ⛴	d				17 09	17 13			17 19		17 29							17 39	17 43
Woolwich Dockyard	d				17 12				17 22		17 32							17 42	
Charlton 4	d			17 07	17 15	17 17			17 25		17 35						17 37	17 45	17 47
Crayford	d	17 22		17 37											17 52		18 07		
Bexley	d	17 25		17 40											17 55		18 10		
Albany Park	d	17 28		17 43											17 58		18 13		
Sidcup 4	d	17 31		17 46											18 01		18 16		
New Eltham	d	17 34		17 49											18 04		18 19		
Mottingham	d	17 36		17 51											18 06		18 21		
Lee	d	17 39		17 54											18 09		18 24		
Hither Green 4	d	17 42	17 49	17 58											18 12	18 19	18 28		
Barnehurst 4	d							17 08		17 16			17 29	17 38					
Bexleyheath	d							17 10		17 19			17 31	17 40					
Welling	d							17 13		17 22			17 34	17 43					
Falconwood	d							17 16		17 24			17 37	17 46					
Eltham	d							17 19		17 27			17 40	17 49					
Kidbrooke	d							17 22		17 30			17 43	17 52					
Blackheath 4	d					17 22		17 25		17 34			17 46	17 55					17 52
Lewisham 4 ⛴	d		17 54	18 04		17 26		17 29		17 38		17 44	17 50	17 59		18 24	18 34		17 56
St Johns	d		17 56	18 06				17 31				17 46		18 01		18 26	18 36		
New Cross 4 ⊖	d		17 58	18 08				17 33				17 48		18 03		18 28	18 38		
Nunhead 4	d									17 43									
Peckham Rye 4	d									17 45									
Denmark Hill 4	d									17 49									
London Victoria 15 ⊖	a									17 58									
Westcombe Park	d				17 17				17 27		17 37							17 47	
Maze Hill	d				17 19				17 29		17 39							17 49	
Greenwich 4 ⛴	d				17 22				17 32		17 42							17 52	
Deptford	a				17 24				17 34		17 44							17 54	
London Bridge 4 ⊖	a	17 52	18 04	18 14	17 30	17 35		17 38	17 41		17 50	17 54	17 58	18 08	18 22	18 34	18 44	18 00	18 05
London Cannon Street 4 ⊖	a		18 08	18 19	17 34			17 43	17 45		17 54	17 58		18 13		18 38	18 49	18 04	
London Waterloo (East) 4 ⊖	a	17 56				17 39							18 02		18 26				18 09
London Charing Cross 4 ⊖	a	18 00				17 43							18 06		18 30				18 13
Ebbsfleet International	a						17 16												
Stratford International ⊖ ⛴	a						17 29												
St Pancras Int'l 15 ⊖	a						17 36												

Table 200R

Saturdays

14 December to 17 May

Gillingham and Dartford - London

Network Diagram - see first Page of Table 200

		SE	SE	SE	SE	SE	SE	SE	SE	SE	SE	SE	SE
Gillingham (Kent) [4]	d	17 20											
Chatham [4]	d	17 24											
Rochester [4]	d	17 27											
Maidstone West	d												
Strood [4]	d	17 32											
Higham	d												
Gravesend [4]	d	17 43								18 02			
Northfleet	d									18 06			
Swanscombe	d									18 08			
Greenhithe for Bluewater	d									18 11			
Stone Crossing	d									18 13			
Dartford [4]	a									18 17			
	d			17 31	17 38			17 52		18 18			
Slade Green [4]	d			17 35		17 45			17 47				17 55
Erith	d			17 38		17 48							17 58
Belvedere	d			17 40		17 50							18 00
Abbey Wood	d			17 43		17 53							18 03
Plumstead	d			17 46		17 56							18 06
Woolwich Arsenal [4]	d			17 49		17 59							18 09
Woolwich Dockyard	d			17 52		18 02							18 12
Charlton [4]	d			17 55		18 05						18 07	18 15
Crayford	d									18 22		18 37	
Bexley	d									18 25		18 40	
Albany Park	d									18 28		18 43	
Sidcup [4]	d									18 31		18 46	
New Eltham	d									18 34		18 49	
Mottingham	d									18 36		18 51	
Lee	d									18 39		18 54	
Hither Green [4]	d									18 42	18 49	18 58	
Barnehurst [4]	d		17 38		17 46			17 59	18 08				
Bexleyheath	d		17 40		17 49			18 01	18 10				
Welling	d		17 43		17 52			18 04	18 13				
Falconwood	d		17 46		17 54			18 07	18 16				
Eltham	d		17 49		17 57			18 10	18 19				
Kidbrooke	d		17 52		18 00			18 13	18 22				
Blackheath [4]	d		17 55		18 04			18 16	18 25				
Lewisham [4]	d		17 59		18 08		18 14	18 20	18 29		18 54	19 04	
St Johns	d		18 01				18 16		18 31		18 56	19 06	
New Cross [4] ⊖	d		18 03				18 18		18 33		18 58	19 08	
Nunhead [4]	d				18 13								
Peckham Rye [4]	d				18 15								
Denmark Hill [4]	d				18 19								
London Victoria [15] ⊖	a				18 28								
Westcombe Park	d			17 57		18 07							18 17
Maze Hill	d			17 59		18 09							18 19
Greenwich [4]	d			18 02		18 12							18 22
Deptford	a			18 04		18 14							18 24
London Bridge [4] ⊖	a		18 08	18 11		18 20	18 24	18 28	18 38	18 52	19 04	19 14	18 30
London Cannon Street [4] ⊖	a		18 13	18 15		18 24	18 28		18 43		19 08	19 19	18 34
London Waterloo (East) [4] ⊖	a							18 32		18 56			
London Charing Cross [4] ⊖	a							18 36		19 00			
Ebbsfleet International	a	17 46											
Stratford International ⊖	a	17 59											
St Pancras Int'l [15] ⊖	a	18 06											

		SE	SE	SE	SE	SE	SE	SE	SE	SE	SE	SE	SE
Gillingham (Kent) [4]	d	17 24	17 50									17 54	
Chatham [4]	d	17 28	17 54									17 58	
Rochester [4]	d	17 30	17 57									18 00	
Maidstone West	d												
Strood [4]	d	17 35	18 02									18 05	
Higham	d	17 40										18 10	
Gravesend [4]	d	17 48	18 13									18 18	
Northfleet	d												
Swanscombe	d												
Greenhithe for Bluewater	d	17 53										18 23	
Stone Crossing	d												
Dartford [4]	a	17 58										18 28	
	d	17 59			18 01	18 08			18 22			18 29	
Slade Green [4]	d				18 05		18 15			18 17	18 25		
Erith	d				18 08		18 18				18 28		
Belvedere	d				18 10		18 20				18 30		
Abbey Wood	d	18 08			18 13		18 23				18 33	18 38	
Plumstead	d				18 16		18 26				18 36		
Woolwich Arsenal [4]	d	18 13			18 19		18 29				18 39	18 43	
Woolwich Dockyard	d				18 22		18 32				18 42		
Charlton [4]	d	18 17			18 25		18 35				18 45	18 47	
Crayford	d												
Bexley	d												
Albany Park	d												
Sidcup [4]	d												
New Eltham	d												
Mottingham	d												
Lee	d												
Hither Green [4]	d												
Barnehurst [4]	d			18 08		18 16			18 29	18 38			18 38
Bexleyheath	d			18 10		18 19			18 31	18 40			18 40
Welling	d			18 13		18 22			18 34	18 43			18 43
Falconwood	d			18 16		18 24			18 37	18 46			18 46
Eltham	d			18 19		18 27			18 40	18 49			18 49
Kidbrooke	d			18 22		18 30			18 43	18 52			18 52
Blackheath [4]	d	18 22		18 25		18 34			18 46	18 55		18 52	18 55
Lewisham [4]	d	18 26		18 29		18 38		18 44	18 50	18 59		18 56	18 59
St Johns	d			18 31				18 46		19 01			19 01
New Cross [4] ⊖	d			18 33				18 48		19 03			19 03
Nunhead [4]	d					18 43							
Peckham Rye [4]	d					18 45							
Denmark Hill [4]	d					18 49							
London Victoria [15] ⊖	a					18 58							
Westcombe Park	d				18 27		18 37				18 47		
Maze Hill	d				18 29		18 39				18 49		
Greenwich [4]	d				18 32		18 42				18 52		
Deptford	a				18 34		18 44				18 54		
London Bridge [4] ⊖	a	18 35		18 38	18 41		18 50	18 54	18 58	19 08	19 00	19 05	19 08
London Cannon Street [4] ⊖	a			18 43	18 45		18 54	18 58		19 13	19 04		19 13
London Waterloo (East) [4] ⊖	a	18 39							19 02			19 09	
London Charing Cross [4] ⊖	a	18 43							19 06			19 13	
Ebbsfleet International	a		18 16										
Stratford International ⊖	a		18 30										
St Pancras Int'l [15] ⊖	a		18 37										

		SE	SE	SE	SE	SE	SE	SE	SE	SE	SE	SE	SE
Gillingham (Kent) [4]	d				18 20			18 24			18 50		
Chatham [4]	d				18 24			18 28			18 54		
Rochester [4]	d				18 27			18 30			18 57		
Maidstone West	d												
Strood [4]	d				18 32			18 35			19 02		
Higham	d							18 40					
Gravesend [4]	d			18 32	18 43			18 48		19 02	19 13		
Northfleet	d			18 36						19 06			
Swanscombe	d			18 38						19 08			
Greenhithe for Bluewater	d			18 41				18 53		19 11			
Stone Crossing	d			18 43						19 13			
Dartford [4]	a			18 47				18 58		19 17			
	d	18 31	18 38	18 48			18 52	18 59	19 01	19 18			19 25
Slade Green [4]	d	18 35				18 55			19 05			19 25	
Erith	d	18 38				18 58			19 08			19 28	
Belvedere	d	18 40				19 00			19 10			19 30	
Abbey Wood	d	18 43				19 03		19 08	19 13			19 33	
Plumstead	d	18 46				19 06			19 16			19 36	
Woolwich Arsenal [4]	d	18 49				19 09		19 13	19 19			19 39	
Woolwich Dockyard	d	18 52				19 12			19 22			19 42	
Charlton [4]	d	18 55				19 15		19 17	19 25			19 45	
Crayford	d			18 52						19 22			
Bexley	d			18 55						19 25			
Albany Park	d			18 58						19 28			
Sidcup [4]	d			19 01						19 31			
New Eltham	d			19 04						19 34			
Mottingham	d			19 06						19 36			
Lee	d			19 09						19 39			
Hither Green [4]	d			19 12						19 42			
Barnehurst [4]	d		18 46				18 59						19 32
Bexleyheath	d		18 49				19 01						19 34
Welling	d		18 52				19 04						19 37
Falconwood	d		18 54				19 07						19 40
Eltham	d		18 57				19 10						19 42
Kidbrooke	d		19 00				19 13						19 45
Blackheath [4]	d		19 04				19 16	19 22					19 49
Lewisham [4]	d		19 08	19 18			19 20	19 26		19 48			19 53
St Johns	d												
New Cross [4] ⊖	d						19 23			19 51			19 56
Nunhead [4]	d		19 13										
Peckham Rye [4]	d		19 15										
Denmark Hill [4]	d		19 19										
London Victoria [15] ⊖	a		19 28										
Westcombe Park	d	18 57				19 17			19 27			19 47	
Maze Hill	d	18 59				19 19			19 29			19 49	
Greenwich [4]	d	19 02				19 22			19 32			19 52	
Deptford	a	19 04				19 24			19 34			19 54	
London Bridge [4] ⊖	a	19 11		19 27		19 30	19 33	19 36	19 41	19 57		20 00	20 03
London Cannon Street [4] ⊖	a	19 15											
London Waterloo (East) [4] ⊖	a			19 32			19 39	19 42	19 45	20 04			20 08
London Charing Cross [4] ⊖	a			19 35			19 42	19 45	19 49	20 07			20 12
Ebbsfleet International	a				18 46						19 16		
Stratford International ⊖	a				18 59						19 29		
St Pancras Int'l [15] ⊖	a				19 06						19 36		

Table 200R

Saturdays

14 December to 17 May

Gillingham and Dartford - London

Network Diagram - see first Page of Table 200

		SE	SE	SE	SE	SE	SE	SE	SE	SE	SE	SE	SE	SE	SE	SE	SE	SE	SE
Gillingham (Kent) 4	d	18 54			19 20			19 24			19 50		19 54			20 20		20 24	
Chatham 4	d	18 58			19 24			19 28			19 54		19 58			20 24		20 28	
Rochester 4	d	19 00			19 27			19 30			19 57		20 00			20 27		20 30	
Maidstone West	d																		
Strood 4	d	19 05			19 32			19 35			20 02		20 05			20 32		20 35	
Higham	d	19 10						19 40					20 10					20 40	
Gravesend 4	d	19 18		19 32	19 43			19 48		20 02	20 13		20 18		20 32	20 43		20 48	
Northfleet	d			19 36						20 06					20 36				
Swanscombe	d			19 38						20 08					20 38				
Greenhithe for Bluewater	d	19 23		19 41				19 53		20 11			20 23		20 41			20 53	
Stone Crossing	d			19 43						20 13					20 43				
Dartford 4	a	19 28		19 47				19 58		20 17			20 28		20 47			20 58	
	d	19 29	19 31	19 48			19 55	19 59	20 01	20 18		20 25	20 29	20 31	20 48		20 55	20 59	21 01
Slade Green 4	d		19 35			19 55			20 05					20 35					21 05
Erith	d		19 38			19 58			20 08					20 38					21 08
Belvedere	d		19 40			20 00			20 10					20 40					21 10
Abbey Wood	d	19 38	19 43			20 03		20 08	20 13				20 38	20 43				21 08	21 13
Plumstead	d		19 46			20 06			20 16					20 46					21 16
Woolwich Arsenal 4	d	19 43	19 49			20 09		20 13	20 19				20 43	20 49				21 13	21 19
Woolwich Dockyard	d		19 52			20 12			20 22					20 52					21 22
Charlton 4	d	19 47	19 55			20 15		20 17	20 25				20 47	20 55				21 17	21 25
Crayford	d			19 52						20 22					20 52				
Bexley	d			19 55						20 25					20 55				
Albany Park	d			19 58						20 28					20 58				
Sidcup 4	d			20 01						20 31					21 01				
New Eltham	d			20 04						20 34					21 04				
Mottingham	d			20 06						20 36					21 06				
Lee	d			20 09						20 39					21 09				
Hither Green 4	d			20 12						20 42					21 12				
Barnehurst 4	d						20 02					20 32					21 02		
Bexleyheath	d						20 04					20 34					21 04		
Welling	d						20 07					20 37					21 07		
Falconwood	d						20 10					20 40					21 10		
Eltham	d						20 12					20 42					21 12		
Kidbrooke	d						20 15					20 45					21 15		
Blackheath 4	d	19 52					20 19	20 22				20 49	20 52				21 19	21 22	
Lewisham 4	d	19 56		20 18			20 23	20 26		20 48		20 53	20 56		21 18		21 23	21 26	
St Johns	d																		
New Cross 4 ⊖	d			20 21			20 26			20 51		20 56			21 21		21 26		
Nunhead 4	d																		
Peckham Rye 4	d																		
Denmark Hill 4	d																		
London Victoria 15 ⊖	a																		
Westcombe Park	d		19 57			20 17			20 27					20 57					21 27
Maze Hill	d		19 59			20 19			20 29					20 59					21 29
Greenwich 4	d		20 02			20 22			20 32					21 02					21 32
Deptford	a		20 04			20 24			20 34					21 04					21 34
London Bridge 4 ⊖	a	20 06	20 11	20 27		20 30	20 33	20 36	20 41	20 57		21 03	21 06	21 11	21 27		21 33	21 36	21 41
London Cannon Street 4 ⊖	a																		
London Waterloo (East) 4 ⊖	a	20 10	20 15	20 34			20 38	20 40	20 45	21 04		21 08	21 10	21 15	21 34		21 38	21 40	21 45
London Charing Cross 4 ⊖	a	20 14	20 19	20 37			20 42	20 44	20 49	21 07		21 12	21 14	21 19	21 37		21 42	21 44	21 49
Ebbsfleet International	a				19 46						20 16					20 46			
Stratford International ⊖	a				19 59						20 29					20 59			
St Pancras Int'l 15 ⊖	a				20 06						20 36					21 06			

		SE	SE	SE	SE	SE	SE	SE	SE	SE	SE	SE	SE	SE	SE	SE	SE	SE	SE
Gillingham (Kent) 4	d		20 50		20 54			21 20		21 24			21 50		21 54			22 20	
Chatham 4	d		20 54		20 58			21 24		21 28			21 54		21 58			22 24	
Rochester 4	d		20 57		21 00			21 27		21 30			21 57		22 00			22 27	
Maidstone West	d																		
Strood 4	d		21 02		21 05			21 32		21 35			22 02		22 05			22 32	
Higham	d				21 10					21 40					22 10				
Gravesend 4	d	21 02	21 13		21 18		21 32	21 43		21 48		22 02	22 13		22 18		22 32	22 43	
Northfleet	d	21 06					21 36					22 06					22 36		
Swanscombe	d	21 08					21 38					22 08					22 38		
Greenhithe for Bluewater	d	21 11			21 23		21 41			21 53		22 11			22 23		22 41		
Stone Crossing	d	21 13					21 43					22 13					22 43		
Dartford 4	a	21 17			21 28		21 47			21 58		22 17			22 28		22 47		
	d	21 18		21 25	21 29	21 31	21 48		21 55	21 59	22 01	22 18		22 25	22 29	22 31	22 48		22 55
Slade Green 4	d					21 35					22 05					22 35			
Erith	d					21 38					22 08					22 38			
Belvedere	d					21 40					22 10					22 40			
Abbey Wood	d				21 38	21 43				22 08	22 13				22 38	22 43			
Plumstead	d					21 46					22 16					22 46			
Woolwich Arsenal 4	d				21 43	21 49				22 13	22 19				22 43	22 49			
Woolwich Dockyard	d					21 52					22 22					22 52			
Charlton 4	d				21 47	21 55				22 17	22 25				22 47	22 55			
Crayford	d	21 22					21 52					22 22					22 52		
Bexley	d	21 25					21 55					22 25					22 55		
Albany Park	d	21 28					21 58					22 28					22 58		
Sidcup 4	d	21 31					22 01					22 31					23 01		
New Eltham	d	21 34					22 04					22 34					23 04		
Mottingham	d	21 36					22 06					22 36					23 06		
Lee	d	21 39					22 09					22 39					23 09		
Hither Green 4	d	21 42					22 12					22 42					23 12		
Barnehurst 4	d			21 32					22 02					22 32					23 02
Bexleyheath	d			21 34					22 04					22 34					23 04
Welling	d			21 37					22 07					22 37					23 07
Falconwood	d			21 40					22 10					22 40					23 10
Eltham	d			21 42					22 12					22 42					23 12
Kidbrooke	d			21 45					22 15					22 45					23 15
Blackheath 4	d			21 49	21 52				22 19	22 22				22 49	22 52				23 19
Lewisham 4	d	21 48		21 53	21 56		22 18		22 23	22 26		22 48		22 53	22 56		23 18		23 23
St Johns	d																		
New Cross 4 ⊖	d	21 51		21 56			22 21		22 26			22 51		22 56			23 21		23 26
Nunhead 4	d																		
Peckham Rye 4	d																		
Denmark Hill 4	d																		
London Victoria 15 ⊖	a																		
Westcombe Park	d					21 57					22 27					22 57			
Maze Hill	d					21 59					22 29					22 59			
Greenwich 4	d					22 02					22 32					23 02			
Deptford	a					22 04					22 34					23 04			
London Bridge 4 ⊖	a	21 57		22 01	22 05	22 11	22 27		22 31	22 35	22 41	22 57		23 01	23 05	23 11	23 27		23 31
London Cannon Street 4 ⊖	a																		
London Waterloo (East) 4 ⊖	a	22 04		22 06	22 09	22 15	22 34		22 36	22 39	22 45	23 04		23 06	23 09	23 15	23 34		23 36
London Charing Cross 4 ⊖	a	22 07		22 10	22 13	22 19	22 37		22 40	22 43	22 49	23 07		23 10	23 13	23 20	23 37		23 40
Ebbsfleet International	a		21 16					21 46					22 16					22 46	
Stratford International ⊖	a		21 29					21 59					22 29					22 59	
St Pancras Int'l 15 ⊖	a		21 36					22 06					22 36					23 06	

Table 200R

Saturdays

14 December to 17 May

Gillingham and Dartford - London

Network Diagram - see first Page of Table 200

Station		SE	SE	SE
Gillingham (Kent) 4	d	22 24		22 54
Chatham 4	d	22 28		22 58
Rochester 4	d	22 30		23 00
Maidstone West	d			
Strood 4	d	22 35		23 05
Higham	d	22 40		23 10
Gravesend 4	d	22 48		23 18
Northfleet	d			
Swanscombe	d			
Greenhithe for Bluewater	d	22 53		23 23
Stone Crossing	d			
Dartford 4	a	22 58		23 28
	d	22 59	23 01	
Slade Green 4	d		23 05	
Erith	d		23 08	
Belvedere	d		23 10	
Abbey Wood	d	23 08	23 13	
Plumstead	d		23 16	
Woolwich Arsenal 4 ⛴	d	23 13	23 19	
Woolwich Dockyard	d		23 22	
Charlton 4	d	23 17	23 25	
Crayford	d			
Bexley	d			
Albany Park	d			
Sidcup 4	d			
New Eltham	d			
Mottingham	d			
Lee	d			
Hither Green 4	d			
Barnehurst 4	d			
Bexleyheath	d			
Welling	d			
Falconwood	d			
Eltham	d			
Kidbrooke	d			
Blackheath 4	d	23 22		
Lewisham 4 ⛴	d	23 26		
St Johns	d			
New Cross 4 ⊖	d			
Nunhead 4	d			
Peckham Rye 4	d			
Denmark Hill 4	d			
London Victoria 15 ⊖	a			
Westcombe Park	d		23 27	
Maze Hill	d		23 29	
Greenwich 4 ⛴	d		23 32	
Deptford	a		23 34	
London Bridge 4 ⊖	a	23 35	23 41	
London Cannon Street 4 ⊖	a			
London Waterloo (East) 4 ⊖	a	23 39	23 45	
London Charing Cross 4 ⊖	a	23 43	23 49	
Ebbsfleet International	a			
Stratford International ⊖ ⛴	a			
St Pancras Int'l 15 ⊖	a			

Table 200R

Sundays

8 December to 11 May

Gillingham and Dartford - London

Network Diagram - see first Page of Table 200

Station		SE	SE	SE	SE	SE	SE	SE	SE	SE	SE	SE	SE	SE	SE	SE	SE	SE	SE
Gillingham (Kent) [4]	d							06 48				07 16		07 20				07 48	
Chatham [4]	d							06 52				07 20		07 24				07 52	
Rochester [4]	d							06 54				07 22		07 27				07 54	
Maidstone West	d																		
Strood [4]	d							06 59				07 28		07 32				07 59	
Higham	d							07 04				07 33						08 04	
Gravesend [4]	d							07 12				07 40		07 43				08 12	
Northfleet	d							07 15				07 44						08 15	
Swanscombe	d							07 17				07 46						08 17	
Greenhithe for Bluewater	d							07 21				07 49						08 21	
Stone Crossing	d							07 23				07 51						08 23	
Dartford [4]	a							07 27				07 56						08 27	
	d	06 36	06 44	06 48	07 06	07 14	07 18	07 29	07 36	07 44	07 48	07 59	08 06		08 14	08 18		08 29	08 36
Slade Green [4]	d	06 41			07 11				07 41				08 11						08 41
Erith	d	06 43			07 13				07 43				08 13						08 43
Belvedere	d	06 46			07 16				07 46				08 16						08 46
Abbey Wood	d	06 49			07 19			07 38	07 49			08 08	08 19					08 38	08 49
Plumstead	d	06 52			07 22				07 52				08 22				08 36		08 52
Woolwich Arsenal [4] ⛴	d	06 55			07 25			07 43	07 55			08 13	08 25				08 39	08 43	08 55
Woolwich Dockyard	d	06 57			07 27				07 57				08 27				08 41		08 57
Charlton [4]	d	07 00			07 30			07 47	08 00			08 17	08 30				08 44	08 47	09 00
Crayford	d			06 52			07 22				07 52					08 22			
Bexley	d			06 55			07 25				07 55					08 25			
Albany Park	d			06 58			07 28				07 58					08 28			
Sidcup [4]	d			07 01			07 31				08 01					08 31			
New Eltham	d			07 04			07 34				08 04					08 34			
Mottingham	d			07 06			07 36				08 06					08 36			
Lee	d			07 09			07 39				08 09					08 39			
Hither Green [4]	d			07 12			07 42				08 12					08 42			
Barnehurst [4]	d		06 51			07 21				07 51					08 21				
Bexleyheath	d		06 53			07 23				07 53					08 23				
Welling	d		06 56			07 26				07 56					08 26				
Falconwood	d		06 59			07 29				07 59					08 29				
Eltham	d		07 02			07 32				08 02					08 32				
Kidbrooke	d		07 05			07 35				08 05					08 35				
Blackheath [4]	d		07 08			07 38		07 52		08 08		08 22			08 38			08 52	
Lewisham [4] ⛴	d		07 12	07 18		07 42	07 48	07 55		08 12	08 18	08 25			08 42	08 48		08 55	
St Johns	d																		
New Cross [4] ⊖	d		07 15			07 45				08 15					08 45				
Nunhead [4]	d																		
Peckham Rye [4]	d																		
Denmark Hill [4]	d																		
London Victoria [15] ⊖	a																		
Westcombe Park	d	07 02			07 32				08 02				08 32				08 46		09 02
Maze Hill	d	07 04			07 34				08 04				08 34				08 48		09 04
Greenwich [4] ⛴	d	07 08			07 38				08 08				08 38				08 52		09 08
Deptford	a	07 10			07 40				08 10				08 40				08 54		09 10
London Bridge [4] ⊖	a	07 18	07 21	07 28	07 48	07 51	07 58	08 04	08 18	08 21	08 28	08 34	08 48		08 51	08 58	09 01	09 04	09 18
London Cannon Street [4] ⊖	a																		
London Waterloo (East) [4] ⊖	a	07 23	07 26	07 33	07 53	07 56	08 03	08 09	08 23	08 26	08 33	08 39	08 53		08 56	09 03		09 09	09 23
London Charing Cross [4] ⊖	a	07 26	07 30	07 37	07 56	08 00	08 07	08 13	08 26	08 30	08 37	08 43	08 56		09 00	09 07		09 13	09 26
Ebbsfleet International	a													07 47					
Stratford International ⊖ ⛴	a													07 59					
St Pancras Int'l [15] ⊖	a													08 06					

Station		SE	SE	SE	SE	SE	SE	SE	SE	SE	SE	SE	SE	SE	SE	SE	SE	SE	SE
Gillingham (Kent) [4]	d				08 16		08 20				08 54				09 20		09 24		
Chatham [4]	d				08 20		08 24				08 58				09 24		09 28		
Rochester [4]	d				08 22		08 27				09 00				09 27		09 30		
Maidstone West	d																		
Strood [4]	d				08 28		08 32				09 05				09 32		09 35		
Higham	d				08 33						09 10						09 40		
Gravesend [4]	d				08 40		08 43		09 02		09 18			09 32	09 43		09 48		
Northfleet	d				08 44				09 06					09 36					
Swanscombe	d				08 46				09 08					09 38					
Greenhithe for Bluewater	d				08 49				09 11		09 23			09 41			09 53		
Stone Crossing	d				08 51				09 13					09 43					
Dartford [4]	a				08 56				09 17		09 28			09 47			09 58		
	d	08 44	08 48		08 59	09 06		09 14	09 18		09 29	09 36	09 44	09 48			09 59	10 06	10 14
Slade Green [4]	d					09 11						09 41						10 11	
Erith	d					09 13						09 43						10 13	
Belvedere	d					09 16						09 46						10 16	
Abbey Wood	d				09 08	09 19					09 38	09 49					10 08	10 19	
Plumstead	d			09 06		09 22				09 36		09 52				10 06		10 22	
Woolwich Arsenal [4] ⛴	d			09 09	09 13	09 25				09 39	09 43	09 55				10 09	10 13	10 25	
Woolwich Dockyard	d			09 11		09 27				09 41		09 57				10 11		10 27	
Charlton [4]	d			09 14	09 17	09 30				09 44	09 47	10 00				10 14	10 17	10 30	
Crayford	d		08 52						09 22					09 52					
Bexley	d		08 55						09 25					09 55					
Albany Park	d		08 58						09 28					09 58					
Sidcup [4]	d		09 01						09 31					10 01					
New Eltham	d		09 04						09 34					10 04					
Mottingham	d		09 06						09 36					10 06					
Lee	d		09 09						09 39					10 09					
Hither Green [4]	d		09 12						09 42					10 12					
Barnehurst [4]	d	08 51						09 21					09 51						10 21
Bexleyheath	d	08 53						09 23					09 53						10 23
Welling	d	08 56						09 26					09 56						10 26
Falconwood	d	08 59						09 29					09 59						10 29
Eltham	d	09 02						09 32					10 02						10 32
Kidbrooke	d	09 05						09 35					10 05						10 35
Blackheath [4]	d	09 08			09 22			09 38			09 52		10 08				10 22		10 38
Lewisham [4] ⛴	d	09 12	09 18		09 25			09 42	09 48		09 55		10 12	10 18			10 25		10 42
St Johns	d																		
New Cross [4] ⊖	d	09 15						09 45					10 15						10 45
Nunhead [4]	d																		
Peckham Rye [4]	d																		
Denmark Hill [4]	d																		
London Victoria [15] ⊖	a																		
Westcombe Park	d			09 16		09 32				09 46		10 02				10 16		10 32	
Maze Hill	d			09 18		09 34				09 48		10 04				10 18		10 34	
Greenwich [4] ⛴	d			09 22		09 38				09 52		10 08				10 22		10 38	
Deptford	a			09 24		09 40				09 54		10 10				10 24		10 40	
London Bridge [4] ⊖	a	09 21	09 28	09 31	09 34	09 48		09 51	09 58	10 01	10 04	10 18	10 21	10 28		10 31	10 34	10 48	10 51
London Cannon Street [4] ⊖	a																		
London Waterloo (East) [4] ⊖	a	09 26	09 33		09 39	09 53		09 56	10 03		10 09	10 23	10 26	10 33			10 39	10 53	10 56
London Charing Cross [4] ⊖	a	09 30	09 37		09 43	09 56		10 00	10 07		10 13	10 26	10 30	10 37			10 43	10 56	11 00
Ebbsfleet International	a						08 47								09 46				
Stratford International ⊖ ⛴	a						08 59								09 59				
St Pancras Int'l [15] ⊖	a						09 06								10 06				

Table 200R

Sundays

8 December to 11 May

Gillingham and Dartford - London

Network Diagram - see first Page of Table 200

Station		SE	SE	SE	SE	SE	SE	SE	SE	SE
Gillingham (Kent) [4]	d			09 54				10 20		10 24
Chatham [4]	d			09 58				10 24		10 28
Rochester [4]	d			10 00				10 27		10 30
Maidstone West	d									
Strood [4]	d			10 05				10 32		10 35
Higham	d			10 10						10 40
Gravesend [4]	d	10 02		10 18			10 32	10 43		10 48
Northfleet	d	10 06					10 36			
Swanscombe	d	10 08					10 38			
Greenhithe for Bluewater	d	10 11		10 23			10 41			10 53
Stone Crossing	d	10 13					10 43			
Dartford [4]	a	10 17		10 28			10 47			10 58
	d	10 18		10 29	10 36	10 44	10 48			10 59
Slade Green [4]	d				10 41					
Erith	d				10 43					
Belvedere	d				10 46					
Abbey Wood	d			10 38	10 49					11 08
Plumstead	d		10 36		10 52				11 06	
Woolwich Arsenal [4]	d		10 39	10 43	10 55				11 09	11 13
Woolwich Dockyard	d		10 41		10 57				11 11	
Charlton [4]	d		10 44	10 47	11 00				11 14	11 17
Crayford	d	10 22					10 52			
Bexley	d	10 25					10 55			
Albany Park	d	10 28					10 58			
Sidcup [4]	d	10 31					11 01			
New Eltham	d	10 34					11 04			
Mottingham	d	10 36					11 06			
Lee	d	10 39					11 09			
Hither Green [4]	d	10 42					11 12			
Barnehurst [4]	d					10 51				
Bexleyheath	d					10 53				
Welling	d					10 56				
Falconwood	d					10 59				
Eltham	d					11 02				
Kidbrooke	d					11 05				
Blackheath [4]	d			10 52		11 08				11 22
Lewisham [4]	d	10 48		10 55		11 12	11 18			11 25
St Johns	d									
New Cross [4] ⊖	d					11 15				
Nunhead [4]	d									
Peckham Rye [4]	d									
Denmark Hill [4]	d									
London Victoria [15] ⊖	a									
Westcombe Park	d		10 46		11 02				11 16	
Maze Hill	d		10 48		11 04				11 18	
Greenwich [4]	d		10 52		11 08				11 22	
Deptford	a		10 54		11 10				11 24	
London Bridge [4] ⊖	a	10 58	11 01	11 04	11 18	11 21	11 28		11 31	11 34
London Cannon Street [4] ⊖	a									
London Waterloo (East) [4] ⊖	a	11 03		11 09	11 23	11 26	11 33			11 39
London Charing Cross [4] ⊖	a	11 07		11 13	11 26	11 30	11 37			11 43
Ebbsfleet International	a							10 46		
Stratford International ⊖	a							10 59		
St Pancras Int'l [15] ⊖	a							11 06		

Station		SE	SE	SE	SE	SE	SE	SE	SE	SE
Gillingham (Kent) [4]	d					10 54				11 20
Chatham [4]	d					10 58				11 24
Rochester [4]	d					11 00				11 27
Maidstone West	d									
Strood [4]	d					11 05				11 32
Higham	d					11 10				
Gravesend [4]	d			11 02		11 18			11 32	11 43
Northfleet	d			11 06					11 36	
Swanscombe	d			11 08					11 38	
Greenhithe for Bluewater	d			11 11		11 23			11 41	
Stone Crossing	d			11 13					11 43	
Dartford [4]	a			11 17		11 28			11 47	
	d	11 06	11 14	11 18		11 29	11 36	11 44	11 48	
Slade Green [4]	d	11 11					11 41			
Erith	d	11 13					11 43			
Belvedere	d	11 16					11 46			
Abbey Wood	d	11 19				11 38	11 49			
Plumstead	d	11 22			11 36		11 52			
Woolwich Arsenal [4]	d	11 25			11 39	11 43	11 55			
Woolwich Dockyard	d	11 27			11 41		11 57			
Charlton [4]	d	11 30			11 44	11 47	12 00			
Crayford	d			11 22					11 52	
Bexley	d			11 25					11 55	
Albany Park	d			11 28					11 58	
Sidcup [4]	d			11 31					12 01	
New Eltham	d			11 34					12 04	
Mottingham	d			11 36					12 06	
Lee	d			11 39					12 09	
Hither Green [4]	d			11 42					12 12	
Barnehurst [4]	d		11 21					11 51		
Bexleyheath	d		11 23					11 53		
Welling	d		11 26					11 56		
Falconwood	d		11 29					11 59		
Eltham	d		11 32					12 02		
Kidbrooke	d		11 35					12 05		
Blackheath [4]	d		11 38			11 52		12 08		
Lewisham [4]	d		11 42	11 48		11 55		12 12	12 18	
St Johns	d									
New Cross [4] ⊖	d		11 45					12 15		
Nunhead [4]	d									
Peckham Rye [4]	d									
Denmark Hill [4]	d									
London Victoria [15] ⊖	a									
Westcombe Park	d	11 32			11 46		12 02			
Maze Hill	d	11 34			11 48		12 04			
Greenwich [4]	d	11 38			11 52		12 08			
Deptford	a	11 40			11 54		12 10			
London Bridge [4] ⊖	a	11 48	11 51	11 58	12 01	12 04	12 18	12 21	12 28	
London Cannon Street [4] ⊖	a									
London Waterloo (East) [4] ⊖	a	11 53	11 56	12 03		12 09	12 23	12 26	12 33	
London Charing Cross [4] ⊖	a	11 56	12 00	12 07		12 13	12 26	12 30	12 37	
Ebbsfleet International	a									11 46
Stratford International ⊖	a									11 59
St Pancras Int'l [15] ⊖	a									12 06

Station		SE	SE	SE	SE	SE	SE	SE	SE	SE
Gillingham (Kent) [4]	d		11 24				11 50		11 54	
Chatham [4]	d		11 28				11 54		11 58	
Rochester [4]	d		11 30				11 57		12 00	
Maidstone West	d									
Strood [4]	d		11 35				12 02		12 05	
Higham	d		11 40						12 10	
Gravesend [4]	d		11 48			12 02	12 13		12 18	
Northfleet	d					12 06				
Swanscombe	d					12 08				
Greenhithe for Bluewater	d		11 53			12 11			12 23	
Stone Crossing	d					12 13				
Dartford [4]	a		11 58			12 17			12 28	
	d		11 59	12 06	12 14	12 18			12 29	12 36
Slade Green [4]	d			12 11						12 41
Erith	d			12 13						12 43
Belvedere	d			12 16						12 46
Abbey Wood	d		12 08	12 19					12 38	12 49
Plumstead	d	12 06		12 22				12 36		12 52
Woolwich Arsenal [4]	d	12 09	12 13	12 25				12 39	12 43	12 55
Woolwich Dockyard	d	12 11		12 27				12 41		12 57
Charlton [4]	d	12 14	12 17	12 30				12 44	12 47	13 00
Crayford	d					12 22				
Bexley	d					12 25				
Albany Park	d					12 28				
Sidcup [4]	d					12 31				
New Eltham	d					12 34				
Mottingham	d					12 36				
Lee	d					12 39				
Hither Green [4]	d					12 42				
Barnehurst [4]	d				12 21					
Bexleyheath	d				12 23					
Welling	d				12 26					
Falconwood	d				12 29					
Eltham	d				12 32					
Kidbrooke	d				12 35					
Blackheath [4]	d		12 22		12 38				12 52	
Lewisham [4]	d		12 25		12 42	12 48			12 55	
St Johns	d									
New Cross [4] ⊖	d				12 45					
Nunhead [4]	d									
Peckham Rye [4]	d									
Denmark Hill [4]	d									
London Victoria [15] ⊖	a									
Westcombe Park	d	12 16		12 32				12 46		13 02
Maze Hill	d	12 18		12 34				12 48		13 04
Greenwich [4]	d	12 22		12 38				12 52		13 08
Deptford	a	12 24		12 40				12 54		13 10
London Bridge [4] ⊖	a	12 31	12 34	12 48	12 51	12 58		13 01	13 04	13 18
London Cannon Street [4] ⊖	a									
London Waterloo (East) [4] ⊖	a		12 39	12 53	12 56	13 03			13 09	13 23
London Charing Cross [4] ⊖	a		12 43	12 56	13 00	13 07			13 13	13 26
Ebbsfleet International	a						12 16			
Stratford International ⊖	a						12 30			
St Pancras Int'l [15] ⊖	a						12 37			

Station		SE	SE	SE	SE	SE	SE	SE	SE	SE
Gillingham (Kent) [4]	d			12 20		12 24				12 50
Chatham [4]	d			12 24		12 28				12 54
Rochester [4]	d			12 27		12 30				12 57
Maidstone West	d									
Strood [4]	d			12 32		12 35				13 02
Higham	d					12 40				
Gravesend [4]	d		12 32	12 43		12 48			13 02	13 13
Northfleet	d		12 36						13 06	
Swanscombe	d		12 38						13 08	
Greenhithe for Bluewater	d		12 41			12 53			13 11	
Stone Crossing	d		12 43						13 13	
Dartford [4]	a		12 47			12 58			13 17	
	d	12 44	12 48			12 59	13 06	13 14	13 18	
Slade Green [4]	d						13 11			
Erith	d						13 13			
Belvedere	d						13 16			
Abbey Wood	d					13 08	13 19			
Plumstead	d				13 06		13 22			
Woolwich Arsenal [4]	d				13 09	13 13	13 25			
Woolwich Dockyard	d				13 11		13 27			
Charlton [4]	d				13 14	13 17	13 30			
Crayford	d		12 52						13 22	
Bexley	d		12 55						13 25	
Albany Park	d		12 58						13 28	
Sidcup [4]	d		13 01						13 31	
New Eltham	d		13 04						13 34	
Mottingham	d		13 06						13 36	
Lee	d		13 09						13 39	
Hither Green [4]	d		13 12						13 42	
Barnehurst [4]	d	12 51						13 21		
Bexleyheath	d	12 53						13 23		
Welling	d	12 56						13 26		
Falconwood	d	12 59						13 29		
Eltham	d	13 02						13 32		
Kidbrooke	d	13 05						13 35		
Blackheath [4]	d	13 08				13 22		13 38		
Lewisham [4]	d	13 12	13 18			13 25		13 42	13 48	
St Johns	d									
New Cross [4] ⊖	d	13 15						13 45		
Nunhead [4]	d									
Peckham Rye [4]	d									
Denmark Hill [4]	d									
London Victoria [15] ⊖	a									
Westcombe Park	d				13 16		13 32			
Maze Hill	d				13 18		13 34			
Greenwich [4]	d				13 22		13 38			
Deptford	a				13 24		13 40			
London Bridge [4] ⊖	a	13 21	13 28		13 31	13 34	13 48	13 51	13 58	
London Cannon Street [4] ⊖	a									
London Waterloo (East) [4] ⊖	a	13 26	13 33			13 39	13 53	13 56	14 03	
London Charing Cross [4] ⊖	a	13 30	13 37			13 43	13 56	14 00	14 07	
Ebbsfleet International	a			12 46						13 16
Stratford International ⊖	a			13 00						13 30
St Pancras Int'l [15] ⊖	a			13 07						13 37

Table 200R

Sundays

8 December to 11 May

Gillingham and Dartford - London

Network Diagram - see first Page of Table 200

Station		SE	SE	SE	SE	SE	SE	SE	SE	SE
Gillingham (Kent) [4]	d		12 54				13 20		13 24	
Chatham [4]	d		12 58				13 24		13 28	
Rochester [4]	d		13 00				13 27		13 30	
Maidstone West	d									
Strood [4]	d		13 05				13 32		13 35	
Higham	d		13 10						13 40	
Gravesend [4]	d		13 18			13 32	13 43		13 48	
Northfleet	d					13 36				
Swanscombe	d					13 38				
Greenhithe for Bluewater	d		13 23			13 41			13 53	
Stone Crossing	d					13 43				
Dartford [4]	a		13 28			13 47			13 58	
	d		13 29	13 36	13 44	13 48			13 59	14 06
Slade Green [4]	d			13 41						14 11
Erith	d			13 43						14 13
Belvedere	d			13 46						14 16
Abbey Wood	d		13 38	13 49					14 08	14 19
Plumstead	d	13 36		13 52				14 06		14 22
Woolwich Arsenal [4] ⛴	d	13 39	13 43	13 55				14 09	14 13	14 25
Woolwich Dockyard	d	13 41		13 57				14 11		14 27
Charlton [4]	d	13 44	13 47	14 00				14 14	14 17	14 30
Crayford	d					13 52				
Bexley	d					13 55				
Albany Park	d					13 58				
Sidcup [4]	d					14 01				
New Eltham	d					14 04				
Mottingham	d					14 06				
Lee	d					14 09				
Hither Green [4]	d					14 12				
Barnehurst [4]	d				13 51					
Bexleyheath	d				13 53					
Welling	d				13 56					
Falconwood	d				13 59					
Eltham	d				14 02					
Kidbrooke	d				14 05					
Blackheath [4]	d		13 52		14 08				14 22	
Lewisham [4] ⛴	d		13 55		14 12	14 18			14 25	
St Johns	d									
New Cross [4] ⊖	d				14 15					
Nunhead [4]	d									
Peckham Rye [4]	d									
Denmark Hill [4]	d									
London Victoria [15] ⊖	a									
Westcombe Park	d	13 46		14 02				14 16		14 32
Maze Hill	d	13 48		14 04				14 18		14 34
Greenwich [4] ⛴	d	13 52		14 08				14 22		14 38
Deptford	a	13 54		14 10				14 24		14 40
London Bridge [4] ⊖	a	14 01	14 04	14 18	14 21	14 28		14 31	14 34	14 48
London Cannon Street [4] ⊖	a									
London Waterloo (East) [4] ⊖	a		14 09	14 23	14 26	14 33			14 39	14 53
London Charing Cross [4] ⊖	a		14 13	14 26	14 30	14 37			14 43	14 56
Ebbsfleet International	a						13 46			
Stratford International ⊖ ⛴	a						13 59			
St Pancras Int'l [15] ⊖	a						14 06			

Station		SE	SE	SE	SE	SE	SE	SE	SE	SE
Gillingham (Kent) [4]	d			13 50		13 54				14 20
Chatham [4]	d			13 54		13 58				14 24
Rochester [4]	d			13 57		14 00				14 27
Maidstone West	d									
Strood [4]	d			14 02		14 05				14 32
Higham	d					14 10				
Gravesend [4]	d		14 02	14 13		14 18			14 32	14 43
Northfleet	d		14 06						14 36	
Swanscombe	d		14 08						14 38	
Greenhithe for Bluewater	d		14 11			14 23			14 41	
Stone Crossing	d		14 13						14 43	
Dartford [4]	a		14 17			14 28			14 47	
	d	14 14	14 18			14 29	14 36	14 44	14 48	
Slade Green [4]	d						14 41			
Erith	d						14 43			
Belvedere	d						14 46			
Abbey Wood	d					14 38	14 49			
Plumstead	d				14 36		14 52			
Woolwich Arsenal [4] ⛴	d				14 39	14 43	14 55			
Woolwich Dockyard	d				14 41		14 57			
Charlton [4]	d				14 44	14 47	15 00			
Crayford	d		14 22						14 52	
Bexley	d		14 25						14 55	
Albany Park	d		14 28						14 58	
Sidcup [4]	d		14 31						15 01	
New Eltham	d		14 34						15 04	
Mottingham	d		14 36						15 06	
Lee	d		14 39						15 09	
Hither Green [4]	d		14 42						15 12	
Barnehurst [4]	d	14 21						14 51		
Bexleyheath	d	14 23						14 53		
Welling	d	14 26						14 56		
Falconwood	d	14 29						14 59		
Eltham	d	14 32						15 02		
Kidbrooke	d	14 35						15 05		
Blackheath [4]	d	14 38				14 52		15 08		
Lewisham [4] ⛴	d	14 42	14 48			14 55		15 12	15 18	
St Johns	d									
New Cross [4] ⊖	d	14 45						15 15		
Nunhead [4]	d									
Peckham Rye [4]	d									
Denmark Hill [4]	d									
London Victoria [15] ⊖	a									
Westcombe Park	d				14 46		15 02			
Maze Hill	d				14 48		15 04			
Greenwich [4] ⛴	d				14 52		15 08			
Deptford	a				14 54		15 10			
London Bridge [4] ⊖	a	14 51	14 58		15 01	15 04	15 18	15 21	15 28	
London Cannon Street [4] ⊖	a									
London Waterloo (East) [4] ⊖	a	14 56	15 03			15 09	15 23	15 26	15 33	
London Charing Cross [4] ⊖	a	15 00	15 07			15 13	15 26	15 30	15 37	
Ebbsfleet International	a			14 16						14 46
Stratford International ⊖ ⛴	a			14 29						15 00
St Pancras Int'l [15] ⊖	a			14 36						15 07

Station		SE	SE	SE	SE	SE	SE	SE	SE	SE
Gillingham (Kent) [4]	d		14 24				14 50		14 54	
Chatham [4]	d		14 28				14 54		14 58	
Rochester [4]	d		14 30				14 57		15 00	
Maidstone West	d									
Strood [4]	d		14 35				15 02		15 05	
Higham	d		14 40						15 10	
Gravesend [4]	d		14 48			15 02	15 13		15 18	
Northfleet	d					15 06				
Swanscombe	d					15 08				
Greenhithe for Bluewater	d		14 53			15 11			15 23	
Stone Crossing	d					15 13				
Dartford [4]	a		14 58			15 17			15 28	
	d		14 59	15 06	15 14	15 18			15 29	15 36
Slade Green [4]	d			15 11						15 41
Erith	d			15 13						15 43
Belvedere	d			15 16						15 46
Abbey Wood	d		15 08	15 19					15 38	15 49
Plumstead	d	15 06		15 22				15 36		15 52
Woolwich Arsenal [4] ⛴	d	15 09	15 13	15 25				15 39	15 43	15 55
Woolwich Dockyard	d	15 11		15 27				15 41		15 57
Charlton [4]	d	15 14	15 17	15 30				15 44	15 47	16 00
Crayford	d					15 22				
Bexley	d					15 25				
Albany Park	d					15 28				
Sidcup [4]	d					15 31				
New Eltham	d					15 34				
Mottingham	d					15 36				
Lee	d					15 39				
Hither Green [4]	d					15 42				
Barnehurst [4]	d				15 21					
Bexleyheath	d				15 23					
Welling	d				15 26					
Falconwood	d				15 29					
Eltham	d				15 32					
Kidbrooke	d				15 35					
Blackheath [4]	d		15 22		15 38				15 52	
Lewisham [4] ⛴	d		15 25		15 42	15 48			15 55	
St Johns	d									
New Cross [4] ⊖	d				15 45					
Nunhead [4]	d									
Peckham Rye [4]	d									
Denmark Hill [4]	d									
London Victoria [15] ⊖	a									
Westcombe Park	d	15 16		15 32				15 46		16 02
Maze Hill	d	15 18		15 34				15 48		16 04
Greenwich [4] ⛴	d	15 22		15 38				15 52		16 08
Deptford	a	15 24		15 40				15 54		16 10
London Bridge [4] ⊖	a	15 31	15 34	15 48	15 51	15 58		16 01	16 04	16 18
London Cannon Street [4] ⊖	a									
London Waterloo (East) [4] ⊖	a		15 39	15 53	15 56	16 03			16 09	16 23
London Charing Cross [4] ⊖	a		15 43	15 56	16 00	16 07			16 13	16 26
Ebbsfleet International	a						15 16			
Stratford International ⊖ ⛴	a						15 30			
St Pancras Int'l [15] ⊖	a						15 37			

Station		SE	SE	SE	SE	SE	SE	SE	SE	SE
Gillingham (Kent) [4]	d			15 20		15 24				15 50
Chatham [4]	d			15 24		15 28				15 54
Rochester [4]	d			15 27		15 30				15 57
Maidstone West	d									
Strood [4]	d			15 32		15 35				16 02
Higham	d					15 40				
Gravesend [4]	d		15 32	15 43		15 48			16 02	16 13
Northfleet	d		15 36						16 06	
Swanscombe	d		15 38						16 08	
Greenhithe for Bluewater	d		15 41			15 53			16 11	
Stone Crossing	d		15 43						16 13	
Dartford [4]	a		15 47			15 58			16 17	
	d	15 44	15 48			15 59	16 06	16 14	16 18	
Slade Green [4]	d						16 11			
Erith	d						16 13			
Belvedere	d						16 16			
Abbey Wood	d					16 08	16 19			
Plumstead	d				16 06		16 22			
Woolwich Arsenal [4] ⛴	d				16 09	16 13	16 25			
Woolwich Dockyard	d				16 11		16 27			
Charlton [4]	d				16 14	16 17	16 30			
Crayford	d		15 52						16 22	
Bexley	d		15 55						16 25	
Albany Park	d		15 58						16 28	
Sidcup [4]	d		16 01						16 31	
New Eltham	d		16 04						16 34	
Mottingham	d		16 06						16 36	
Lee	d		16 09						16 39	
Hither Green [4]	d		16 12						16 42	
Barnehurst [4]	d	15 51						16 21		
Bexleyheath	d	15 53						16 23		
Welling	d	15 56						16 26		
Falconwood	d	15 59						16 29		
Eltham	d	16 02						16 32		
Kidbrooke	d	16 05						16 35		
Blackheath [4]	d	16 08				16 22		16 38		
Lewisham [4] ⛴	d	16 12	16 18			16 25		16 42	16 48	
St Johns	d									
New Cross [4] ⊖	d	16 15						16 45		
Nunhead [4]	d									
Peckham Rye [4]	d									
Denmark Hill [4]	d									
London Victoria [15] ⊖	a									
Westcombe Park	d				16 16		16 32			
Maze Hill	d				16 18		16 34			
Greenwich [4] ⛴	d				16 22		16 38			
Deptford	a				16 24		16 40			
London Bridge [4] ⊖	a	16 21	16 28		16 31	16 34	16 48	16 51	16 58	
London Cannon Street [4] ⊖	a									
London Waterloo (East) [4] ⊖	a	16 26	16 33			16 39	16 53	16 56	17 03	
London Charing Cross [4] ⊖	a	16 30	16 37			16 43	16 56	17 00	17 07	
Ebbsfleet International	a			15 46						16 16
Stratford International ⊖ ⛴	a			16 02						16 29
St Pancras Int'l [15] ⊖	a			16 09						16 36

Table 200R

Sundays

Gillingham and Dartford - London

8 December to 11 May

Network Diagram - see first Page of Table 200

		SE	SE	SE	SE	SE	SE	SE	SE	SE
Gillingham (Kent) 4	d		15 54				16 20		16 24	
Chatham 4	d		15 58				16 24		16 28	
Rochester 4	d		16 00				16 27		16 30	
Maidstone West	d									
Strood 4	d		16 05				16 32		16 35	
Higham	d		16 10						16 40	
Gravesend 4	d		16 18			16 32	16 43		16 48	
Northfleet	d					16 36				
Swanscombe	d					16 38				
Greenhithe for Bluewater	d		16 23			16 41			16 53	
Stone Crossing	d					16 43				
Dartford 4	a		16 28			16 47			16 58	
	d		16 29	16 36	16 44	16 48			16 59	17 06
Slade Green 4	d			16 41						17 11
Erith	d			16 43						17 13
Belvedere	d			16 46						17 16
Abbey Wood	d		16 38	16 49					17 08	17 19
Plumstead	d	16 36		16 52				17 06		17 22
Woolwich Arsenal 4	d	16 39	16 43	16 55				17 09	17 13	17 25
Woolwich Dockyard	d	16 41		16 57				17 11		17 27
Charlton 4	d	16 44	16 47	17 00				17 14	17 17	17 30
Crayford	d					16 52				
Bexley	d					16 55				
Albany Park	d					16 58				
Sidcup 4	d					17 01				
New Eltham	d					17 04				
Mottingham	d					17 06				
Lee	d					17 09				
Hither Green 4	d					17 12				
Barnehurst 4	d				16 51					
Bexleyheath	d				16 53					
Welling	d				16 56					
Falconwood	d				16 59					
Eltham	d				17 02					
Kidbrooke	d				17 05					
Blackheath 4	d		16 52		17 08				17 22	
Lewisham 4	d		16 55		17 12	17 18			17 25	
St Johns	d									
New Cross 4 ⊖	d				17 15					
Nunhead 4	d									
Peckham Rye 4	d									
Denmark Hill 4	d									
London Victoria 15 ⊖	a									
Westcombe Park	d	16 46		17 02				17 16		17 32
Maze Hill	d	16 48		17 04				17 18		17 34
Greenwich 4	d	16 52		17 08				17 22		17 38
Deptford	a	16 54		17 10				17 24		17 40
London Bridge 4 ⊖	a	17 01	17 04	17 18	17 21	17 28		17 31	17 34	17 48
London Cannon Street 4 ⊖	a									
London Waterloo (East) 4 ⊖	a		17 09	17 23	17 26	17 33			17 39	17 53
London Charing Cross 4 ⊖	a		17 13	17 26	17 30	17 37			17 43	17 56
Ebbsfleet International	a									
Stratford International ⊖	a									
St Pancras Int'l 15 ⊖	a						17 06			

		SE	SE	SE	SE	SE	SE	SE	SE	SE
Gillingham (Kent) 4	d			16 50		16 54				17 20
Chatham 4	d			16 54		16 58				17 24
Rochester 4	d			16 57		17 00				17 27
Maidstone West	d									
Strood 4	d			17 02		17 05				17 32
Higham	d					17 10				
Gravesend 4	d		17 02	17 13		17 18			17 32	17 43
Northfleet	d		17 06						17 36	
Swanscombe	d		17 08						17 38	
Greenhithe for Bluewater	d		17 11			17 23			17 41	
Stone Crossing	d		17 13						17 43	
Dartford 4	a		17 17			17 28			17 47	
	d	17 14	17 18			17 29	17 36	17 44	17 48	
Slade Green 4	d						17 41			
Erith	d						17 43			
Belvedere	d						17 46			
Abbey Wood	d					17 38	17 49			
Plumstead	d				17 36		17 52			
Woolwich Arsenal 4	d				17 39	17 43	17 55			
Woolwich Dockyard	d				17 41		17 57			
Charlton 4	d				17 44	17 47	18 00			
Crayford	d		17 22						17 52	
Bexley	d		17 25						17 55	
Albany Park	d		17 28						17 58	
Sidcup 4	d		17 31						18 01	
New Eltham	d		17 34						18 04	
Mottingham	d		17 36						18 06	
Lee	d		17 39						18 09	
Hither Green 4	d		17 42						18 12	
Barnehurst 4	d	17 21						17 51		
Bexleyheath	d	17 23						17 53		
Welling	d	17 26						17 56		
Falconwood	d	17 29						17 59		
Eltham	d	17 32						18 02		
Kidbrooke	d	17 35						18 05		
Blackheath 4	d	17 38				17 52		18 08		
Lewisham 4	d	17 42	17 48			17 55		18 12	18 18	
St Johns	d									
New Cross 4 ⊖	d	17 45						18 15		
Nunhead 4	d									
Peckham Rye 4	d									
Denmark Hill 4	d									
London Victoria 15 ⊖	a									
Westcombe Park	d				17 46		18 02			
Maze Hill	d				17 48		18 04			
Greenwich 4	d				17 52		18 08			
Deptford	a				17 54		18 10			
London Bridge 4 ⊖	a	17 51	17 58		18 01	18 04	18 18	18 21	18 28	
London Cannon Street 4 ⊖	a									
London Waterloo (East) 4 ⊖	a	17 56	18 03			18 09	18 23	18 26	18 33	
London Charing Cross 4 ⊖	a	18 00	18 07			18 13	18 26	18 30	18 37	
Ebbsfleet International	a			17 16						17 46
Stratford International ⊖	a			17 29						18 00
St Pancras Int'l 15 ⊖	a			17 36						18 07

		SE	SE	SE	SE	SE	SE	SE	SE	SE
Gillingham (Kent) 4	d		17 24				17 50		17 54	
Chatham 4	d		17 28				17 54		17 58	
Rochester 4	d		17 30				17 57		18 00	
Maidstone West	d									
Strood 4	d		17 35				18 02		18 05	
Higham	d		17 40						18 10	
Gravesend 4	d		17 48			18 02	18 13		18 18	
Northfleet	d					18 06				
Swanscombe	d					18 08				
Greenhithe for Bluewater	d		17 53			18 11			18 23	
Stone Crossing	d					18 13				
Dartford 4	a		17 58			18 17			18 28	
	d		17 59	18 06	18 14	18 18			18 29	18 36
Slade Green 4	d			18 11						18 41
Erith	d			18 13						18 43
Belvedere	d			18 16						18 46
Abbey Wood	d		18 08	18 19					18 38	18 49
Plumstead	d	18 06		18 22				18 36		18 52
Woolwich Arsenal 4	d	18 09	18 13	18 25				18 39	18 43	18 55
Woolwich Dockyard	d	18 11		18 27				18 41		18 57
Charlton 4	d	18 14	18 17	18 30				18 44	18 47	19 00
Crayford	d					18 22				
Bexley	d					18 25				
Albany Park	d					18 28				
Sidcup 4	d					18 31				
New Eltham	d					18 34				
Mottingham	d					18 36				
Lee	d					18 39				
Hither Green 4	d					18 42				
Barnehurst 4	d				18 21					
Bexleyheath	d				18 23					
Welling	d				18 26					
Falconwood	d				18 29					
Eltham	d				18 32					
Kidbrooke	d				18 35					
Blackheath 4	d		18 22		18 38				18 52	
Lewisham 4	d		18 25		18 42	18 48			18 55	
St Johns	d									
New Cross 4 ⊖	d				18 45					
Nunhead 4	d									
Peckham Rye 4	d									
Denmark Hill 4	d									
London Victoria 15 ⊖	a									
Westcombe Park	d	18 16		18 32				18 46		19 02
Maze Hill	d	18 18		18 34				18 48		19 04
Greenwich 4	d	18 22		18 38				18 52		19 08
Deptford	a	18 24		18 40				18 54		19 10
London Bridge 4 ⊖	a	18 31	18 34	18 48	18 51	18 58		19 01	19 04	19 18
London Cannon Street 4 ⊖	a									
London Waterloo (East) 4 ⊖	a		18 39	18 53	18 56	19 03			19 09	19 23
London Charing Cross 4 ⊖	a		18 43	18 56	19 00	19 07			19 13	19 26
Ebbsfleet International	a						18 16			
Stratford International ⊖	a						18 30			
St Pancras Int'l 15 ⊖	a						18 37			

		SE	SE	SE	SE	SE	SE	SE	SE	SE
Gillingham (Kent) 4	d			18 20		18 24				18 50
Chatham 4	d			18 24		18 28				18 54
Rochester 4	d			18 27		18 30				18 57
Maidstone West	d									
Strood 4	d			18 32		18 35				19 02
Higham	d					18 40				
Gravesend 4	d		18 32	18 43		18 48			19 02	19 13
Northfleet	d		18 36						19 06	
Swanscombe	d		18 38						19 08	
Greenhithe for Bluewater	d		18 41			18 53			19 11	
Stone Crossing	d		18 43						19 13	
Dartford 4	a		18 47			18 58			19 17	
	d	18 44	18 48			18 59	19 06	19 14	19 18	
Slade Green 4	d						19 11			
Erith	d						19 13			
Belvedere	d						19 16			
Abbey Wood	d					19 08	19 19			
Plumstead	d				19 06		19 22			
Woolwich Arsenal 4	d				19 09	19 13	19 25			
Woolwich Dockyard	d				19 11		19 27			
Charlton 4	d				19 14	19 17	19 30			
Crayford	d		18 52						19 22	
Bexley	d		18 55						19 25	
Albany Park	d		18 58						19 28	
Sidcup 4	d		19 01						19 31	
New Eltham	d		19 04						19 34	
Mottingham	d		19 06						19 36	
Lee	d		19 09						19 39	
Hither Green 4	d		19 12						19 42	
Barnehurst 4	d	18 51						19 21		
Bexleyheath	d	18 53						19 23		
Welling	d	18 56						19 26		
Falconwood	d	18 59						19 29		
Eltham	d	19 02						19 32		
Kidbrooke	d	19 05						19 35		
Blackheath 4	d	19 08				19 22		19 38		
Lewisham 4	d	19 12	19 18			19 25		19 42	19 48	
St Johns	d									
New Cross 4 ⊖	d	19 15						19 45		
Nunhead 4	d									
Peckham Rye 4	d									
Denmark Hill 4	d									
London Victoria 15 ⊖	a									
Westcombe Park	d				19 16		19 32			
Maze Hill	d				19 18		19 34			
Greenwich 4	d				19 22		19 38			
Deptford	a				19 24		19 40			
London Bridge 4 ⊖	a	19 21	19 28		19 31	19 34	19 48	19 51	19 58	
London Cannon Street 4 ⊖	a									
London Waterloo (East) 4 ⊖	a	19 26	19 33			19 39	19 53	19 56	20 03	
London Charing Cross 4 ⊖	a	19 30	19 37			19 43	19 56	20 00	20 07	
Ebbsfleet International	a			18 46						19 16
Stratford International ⊖	a			18 59						19 29
St Pancras Int'l 15 ⊖	a			19 07						19 36

Table 200R

Sundays

8 December to 11 May

Gillingham and Dartford - London

Network Diagram - see first Page of Table 200

Station		SE	SE	SE	SE	SE	SE	SE	SE	SE
Gillingham (Kent)	d	18 54				19 20	19 24			
Chatham	d	18 58				19 24	19 28			
Rochester	d	19 00				19 27	19 30			
Maidstone West	d									
Strood	d	19 05				19 32	19 35			
Higham	d	19 10					19 40			
Gravesend	d	19 18			19 32	19 43	19 48			20 02
Northfleet	d				19 36					20 06
Swanscombe	d				19 38					20 08
Greenhithe for Bluewater	d	19 23			19 41		19 53			20 11
Stone Crossing	d				19 43					20 13
Dartford	a	19 28			19 47		19 58			20 17
	d	19 29	19 36	19 44	19 48		19 59	20 06	20 14	20 18
Slade Green	d		19 41					20 11		
Erith	d		19 43					20 13		
Belvedere	d		19 46					20 16		
Abbey Wood	d	19 38	19 49				20 08	20 19		
Plumstead	d		19 52					20 22		
Woolwich Arsenal	d	19 43	19 55				20 13	20 25		
Woolwich Dockyard	d		19 57					20 27		
Charlton	d	19 47	20 00				20 17	20 30		
Crayford	d				19 52					20 22
Bexley	d				19 55					20 25
Albany Park	d				19 58					20 28
Sidcup	d				20 01					20 31
New Eltham	d				20 04					20 34
Mottingham	d				20 06					20 36
Lee	d				20 09					20 39
Hither Green	d				20 12					20 42
Barnehurst	d			19 51					20 21	
Bexleyheath	d			19 53					20 23	
Welling	d			19 56					20 26	
Falconwood	d			19 59					20 29	
Eltham	d			20 02					20 32	
Kidbrooke	d			20 05					20 35	
Blackheath	d	19 52		20 08			20 22		20 38	
Lewisham	d	19 55		20 12	20 18		20 25		20 42	20 48
St Johns	d									
New Cross	d			20 15					20 45	
Nunhead	d									
Peckham Rye	d									
Denmark Hill	d									
London Victoria	a									
Westcombe Park	d		20 02					20 32		
Maze Hill	d		20 04					20 34		
Greenwich	d		20 08					20 38		
Deptford	a		20 10					20 40		
London Bridge	a	20 04	20 18	20 21	20 28		20 34	20 48	20 51	20 58
London Cannon Street	a									
London Waterloo (East)	a	20 09	20 23	20 26	20 33		20 39	20 53	20 56	21 03
London Charing Cross	a	20 13	20 26	20 30	20 37		20 43	20 56	21 00	21 07
Ebbsfleet International	a					19 46				
Stratford International	a					20 00				
St Pancras Int'l	a					20 07				

Station		SE	SE	SE	SE	SE	SE	SE	SE	SE
Gillingham (Kent)	d	19 50	19 54				20 20	20 24		
Chatham	d	19 54	19 58				20 24	20 28		
Rochester	d	19 57	20 00				20 27	20 30		
Maidstone West	d									
Strood	d	20 02	20 05				20 32	20 35		
Higham	d		20 10					20 40		
Gravesend	d	20 13	20 18			20 32	20 43	20 48		
Northfleet	d					20 36				
Swanscombe	d					20 38				
Greenhithe for Bluewater	d		20 23			20 41		20 53		
Stone Crossing	d					20 43				
Dartford	a		20 28			20 47		20 58		
	d		20 29	20 36	20 44	20 48		20 59	21 06	21 14
Slade Green	d			20 41					21 11	
Erith	d			20 43					21 13	
Belvedere	d			20 46					21 16	
Abbey Wood	d		20 38	20 49				21 08	21 19	
Plumstead	d			20 52					21 22	
Woolwich Arsenal	d		20 43	20 55				21 13	21 25	
Woolwich Dockyard	d			20 57					21 27	
Charlton	d		20 47	21 00				21 17	21 30	
Crayford	d					20 52				
Bexley	d					20 55				
Albany Park	d					20 58				
Sidcup	d					21 01				
New Eltham	d					21 04				
Mottingham	d					21 06				
Lee	d					21 09				
Hither Green	d					21 12				
Barnehurst	d				20 51					21 21
Bexleyheath	d				20 53					21 23
Welling	d				20 56					21 26
Falconwood	d				20 59					21 29
Eltham	d				21 02					21 32
Kidbrooke	d				21 05					21 35
Blackheath	d		20 52		21 08			21 22		21 38
Lewisham	d		20 55		21 12	21 18		21 25		21 42
St Johns	d									
New Cross	d				21 15					21 45
Nunhead	d									
Peckham Rye	d									
Denmark Hill	d									
London Victoria	a									
Westcombe Park	d			21 02					21 32	
Maze Hill	d			21 04					21 34	
Greenwich	d			21 08					21 38	
Deptford	a			21 10					21 40	
London Bridge	a		21 04	21 18	21 21	21 28		21 34	21 48	21 51
London Cannon Street	a									
London Waterloo (East)	a		21 09	21 23	21 26	21 33		21 39	21 53	21 56
London Charing Cross	a		21 13	21 26	21 30	21 37		21 43	21 56	22 00
Ebbsfleet International	a	20 16					20 46			
Stratford International	a	20 29					21 02			
St Pancras Int'l	a	20 36					21 09			

Station		SE	SE	SE	SE	SE	SE	SE	SE	SE
Gillingham (Kent)	d		20 50	20 54				21 20	21 24	
Chatham	d		20 54	20 58				21 24	21 28	
Rochester	d		20 57	21 00				21 27	21 30	
Maidstone West	d									
Strood	d		21 02	21 05				21 32	21 35	
Higham	d			21 10					21 40	
Gravesend	d	21 02	21 13	21 18			21 32	21 43	21 48	
Northfleet	d	21 06					21 36			
Swanscombe	d	21 08					21 38			
Greenhithe for Bluewater	d	21 11		21 23			21 41		21 53	
Stone Crossing	d	21 13					21 43			
Dartford	a	21 17		21 28			21 47		21 58	
	d	21 18		21 29	21 36	21 44	21 48		21 59	22 06
Slade Green	d				21 41					22 11
Erith	d				21 43					22 13
Belvedere	d				21 46					22 16
Abbey Wood	d			21 38	21 49				22 08	22 19
Plumstead	d				21 52					22 22
Woolwich Arsenal	d			21 43	21 55				22 13	22 25
Woolwich Dockyard	d				21 57					22 27
Charlton	d			21 47	22 00				22 17	22 30
Crayford	d	21 22					21 52			
Bexley	d	21 25					21 55			
Albany Park	d	21 28					21 58			
Sidcup	d	21 31					22 01			
New Eltham	d	21 34					22 04			
Mottingham	d	21 36					22 06			
Lee	d	21 39					22 09			
Hither Green	d	21 42					22 12			
Barnehurst	d					21 51				
Bexleyheath	d					21 53				
Welling	d					21 56				
Falconwood	d					21 59				
Eltham	d					22 02				
Kidbrooke	d					22 05				
Blackheath	d			21 52		22 08			22 22	
Lewisham	d	21 48		21 55		22 12	22 18		22 25	
St Johns	d									
New Cross	d					22 15				
Nunhead	d									
Peckham Rye	d									
Denmark Hill	d									
London Victoria	a									
Westcombe Park	d				22 02					22 32
Maze Hill	d				22 04					22 34
Greenwich	d				22 08					22 38
Deptford	a				22 10					22 40
London Bridge	a	21 58		22 04	22 18	22 21	22 28		22 34	22 48
London Cannon Street	a									
London Waterloo (East)	a	22 03		22 09	22 23	22 26	22 33		22 39	22 53
London Charing Cross	a	22 07		22 13	22 26	22 30	22 37		22 43	22 56
Ebbsfleet International	a		21 16					21 46		
Stratford International	a		21 29					22 00		
St Pancras Int'l	a		21 36					22 07		

Station		SE	SE	SE	SE	SE	SE	SE	SE	SE
Gillingham (Kent)	d			21 50	21 54				22 20	22 24
Chatham	d			21 54	21 58				22 24	22 28
Rochester	d			21 57	22 00				22 27	22 30
Maidstone West	d									
Strood	d			22 02	22 05				22 32	22 35
Higham	d				22 10					22 40
Gravesend	d		22 02	22 13	22 18			22 32	22 43	22 48
Northfleet	d		22 06					22 36		
Swanscombe	d		22 08					22 38		
Greenhithe for Bluewater	d		22 11		22 23			22 41		22 53
Stone Crossing	d		22 13					22 43		
Dartford	a		22 17		22 28			22 47		22 58
	d	22 14	22 18		22 29	22 36	22 44	22 48		22 59
Slade Green	d					22 41				
Erith	d					22 43				
Belvedere	d					22 46				
Abbey Wood	d				22 38	22 49				23 08
Plumstead	d					22 52				
Woolwich Arsenal	d				22 43	22 55				23 13
Woolwich Dockyard	d					22 57				
Charlton	d				22 47	23 00				23 17
Crayford	d		22 22					22 52		
Bexley	d		22 25					22 55		
Albany Park	d		22 28					22 58		
Sidcup	d		22 31					23 01		
New Eltham	d		22 34					23 04		
Mottingham	d		22 36					23 06		
Lee	d		22 39					23 09		
Hither Green	d		22 42					23 12		
Barnehurst	d	22 21					22 51			
Bexleyheath	d	22 23					22 53			
Welling	d	22 26					22 56			
Falconwood	d	22 29					22 59			
Eltham	d	22 32					23 02			
Kidbrooke	d	22 35					23 05			
Blackheath	d	22 38			22 52		23 08			23 22
Lewisham	d	22 42	22 48		22 55		23 12	23 18		23 25
St Johns	d									
New Cross	d	22 45					23 15			
Nunhead	d									
Peckham Rye	d									
Denmark Hill	d									
London Victoria	a									
Westcombe Park	d					23 02				
Maze Hill	d					23 04				
Greenwich	d					23 08				
Deptford	a					23 10				
London Bridge	a	22 51	22 58		23 04	23 18	23 21	23 28		23 34
London Cannon Street	a									
London Waterloo (East)	a	22 56	23 03		23 09	23 23	23 26	23 33		23 39
London Charing Cross	a	23 00	23 07		23 13	23 26	23 30	23 37		23 43
Ebbsfleet International	a			22 16					22 46	
Stratford International	a			22 29					22 59	
St Pancras Int'l	a			22 36					23 06	

Table 200R

Sundays

8 December to 11 May

Gillingham and Dartford - London

Network Diagram - see first Page of Table 200

Station		SE
Gillingham (Kent) 4	d	22 54
Chatham 4	d	22 58
Rochester 4	d	23 00
Maidstone West	d	
Strood 4	d	23 05
Higham	d	23 10
Gravesend 4	d	23 18
Northfleet	d	
Swanscombe	d	
Greenhithe for Bluewater	d	23 23
Stone Crossing	d	
Dartford 4	a	23 28
	d	
Slade Green 4	d	
Erith	d	
Belvedere	d	
Abbey Wood	d	
Plumstead	d	
Woolwich Arsenal 4 ⛴	d	
Woolwich Dockyard	d	
Charlton 4	d	
Crayford	d	
Bexley	d	
Albany Park	d	
Sidcup 4	d	
New Eltham	d	
Mottingham	d	
Lee	d	
Hither Green 4	d	
Barnehurst 4	d	
Bexleyheath	d	
Welling	d	
Falconwood	d	
Eltham	d	
Kidbrooke	d	
Blackheath 4	d	
Lewisham 4 ⛴	d	
St Johns	d	
New Cross 4 ⊖	d	
Nunhead 4	d	
Peckham Rye 4	d	
Denmark Hill 4	d	
London Victoria 15 ⊖	a	
Westcombe Park	d	
Maze Hill	d	
Greenwich 4 ⛴	d	
Deptford	a	
London Bridge 4 ⊖	a	
London Cannon Street 4 ⊖	a	
London Waterloo (East) 4 ⊖	a	
London Charing Cross 4 ⊖	a	
Ebbsfleet International	a	
Stratford International ⊖ ⛴	a	
St Pancras Int'l 15 ⊖	a	

Table 203

Mondays to Fridays

9 December to 16 May

London - Hayes (Kent) via Catford Bridge

Network Diagram - see first Page of Table 200

Miles	Miles			SE MO	SE MX	SE	SE	SE	SE	SE	SE	SE	SE	SE	SE	SE	SE	SE	SE	SE	SE
0	—	**London Charing Cross** 4	⊖ d				05 47	06 17	06 47		07 17		07 44		08 15		08 44			09 17	
0¾	—	**London Waterloo (East)** 4	⊖ d				05 50	06 20	06 50		07 20		07 47		08 18		08 47			09 20	
—	0	**London Cannon Street** 4	⊖ d							07 00		07 30		08 00		08 29		09 00	09 02		09 30
1¾	0¾	**London Bridge** 4	⊖ d				05 55	06 26	06 55	07 04	07 25	07 34	07 53	08 04	08 23	08 33	08 53	09 04		09 25	09 34
4¾	—	New Cross 4	⊖ d		00 05	05 31	06 01	06 32	07 02	07 09		07 39		08 09		08 41		09 09			09 39
5½	—	St Johns	d		00 07	05 33	06 03	06 34	07 04	07 11		07 41		08 11		08 43		09 11			09 41
6	—	**Lewisham** 4	⇌ d		00 10	05 36	06 06	06 38	07 08	07 16		07 44		08 17		08 46		09 14			09 44
6¾	—	Ladywell	d		00 13	05 39	06 09	06 41	07 11	07 19	07 34	07 47	08 04	08 20	08 34	08 49	09 04	09 17	09 22	09 34	09 47
7½	—	**Catford Bridge**	d		00 15	05 41	06 11	06 43	07 13	07 21	07 36	07 49	08 06	08 22	08 36	08 51	09 06	09 19	09 24	09 36	09 49
9	—	Lower Sydenham	d	00 02	00 18	05 44	06 14	06 46	07 16	07 24	07 39	07 52	08 09	08 25	08 39	08 54	09 09	09 22	09 27	09 39	09 52
9½	—	New Beckenham 4	d	00 04	00 20	05 46	06 16	06 48	07 18	07 26	07 41	07 54	08 11	08 27	08 41	08 56	09 11	09 24	09a29	09 41	09 54
10¼	—	Clock House	d	00 06	00 23	05 48	06 18	06 50	07 20	07 29	07 43	07 57	08 13	08 29	08 43	08 58	09 13	09 27		09 43	09 57
11	—	Elmers End 4	⇌ d	00 09	00 25	05 51	06 21	06 53	07 23	07 31	07 46	07 59	08 16	08 32	08 46	09 01	09 16	09 29		09 46	09 59
12½	—	Eden Park	d	00 12	00 29	05 54	06 24	06 56	07 26	07 35	07 49	08 03	08 19	08 35	08 49	09 04	09 19	09 33		09 49	10 03
13¼	—	West Wickham	d	00 15	00 31	05 57	06 27	06 59	07 29	07 37	07 52	08 05	08 22	08 38	08 52	09 07	09 22	09 35		09 52	10 05
14½	—	**Hayes (Kent)**	a	00 19	00 34	06 00	06 30	07 02	07 32	07 42	07 56	08 10	08 25	08 41	08 55	09 11	09 26	09 39		09 56	10 09

		SE	SE	SE	SE		SE	SE	SE	SE	SE	SE	SE	SE	SE	SE	SE	SE	SE	SE	SE	SE
London Charing Cross 4	⊖ d	09 47		10 17		and at the same minutes past each hour until	14 47		15 17		15 47		16 20		16 39		16 59		17 21		17 43	
London Waterloo (East) 4	⊖ d	09 50		10 20			14 50		15 20		15 50		16 23		16 42		17 02		17 24		17 46	
London Cannon Street 4	⊖ d		10 00		10 30			15 00		15 30		16 00		16 30		16 51		17 12		17 34		17 56
London Bridge 4	⊖ d	09 55	10 04	10 25	10 34		14 55	15 04	15 25	15 34	15 55	16 04	16 29	16 34	16 47	16 55	17 07	17 16	17 29	17 39	17 52	18 00
New Cross 4	⊖ d		10 09		10 39			15 09		15 39		16 10		16 40		17 01		17 22		17 45		18 06
St Johns	d		10 11		10 41			15 11		15 41		16 12		16 42		17 03		17 24		17 47		18 08
Lewisham 4	⇌ d		10 14		10 44			15 14		15 44		16 15		16 45		17 06		17 27		17 50		18 11
Ladywell	d	10 04	10 17	10 34	10 47		15 04	15 17	15 34	15 47	16 04	16 18	16 38	16 48	16 57	17 09	17 17	17 30	17 40	17 53	18 01	18 14
Catford Bridge	d	10 06	10 19	10 36	10 49		15 06	15 19	15 36	15 49	16 06	16 20	16 40	16 50	16 59	17 11	17 19	17 32	17 42	17 55	18 03	18 16
Lower Sydenham	d	10 09	10 22	10 39	10 52		15 09	15 22	15 39	15 52	16 09	16 23	16 43	16 53	17 02	17 14	17 22	17 35	17 45	17 58	18 06	18 19
New Beckenham 4	d	10 11	10 24	10 41	10 54		15 11	15 24	15 41	15 54	16 11	16 25	16 45	16 55	17 04	17 16	17 24	17 37	17 47	18 00	18 08	18 21
Clock House	d	10 13	10 27	10 43	10 57		15 13	15 27	15 43	15 57	16 13	16 27	16 48	16 57	17 07	17 18	17 27	17 39	17 49	18 02	18 11	18 23
Elmers End 4	⇌ d	10 16	10 29	10 46	10 59		15 16	15 29	15 46	15 59	16 16	16 30	16 51	17 00	17 10	17 21	17 30	17 42	17 52	18 05	18 14	18 26
Eden Park	d	10 19	10 33	10 49	11 03		15 19	15 33	15 49	16 03	16 19	16 34	16 54	17 04	17 13	17 25	17 33	17 46	17 56	18 09	18 17	18 30
West Wickham	d	10 22	10 35	10 52	11 05		15 22	15 35	15 52	16 05	16 22	16 36	16 57	17 06	17 16	17 27	17 36	17 48	17 58	18 11	18 20	18 32
Hayes (Kent)	a	10 25	10 38	10 55	11 08		15 25	15 38	15 55	16 08	16 25	16 42	17 02	17 12	17 21	17 32	17 42	17 54	18 03	18 16	18 26	18 38

		SE	SE	SE	SE	SE	SE	SE	SE	SE	SE	SE	SE		SE	SE
London Charing Cross 4	⊖ d	18 05		18 27		18 52		19 17		19 47		20 17	20 47	and every 30 minutes until	23 17	23 52
London Waterloo (East) 4	⊖ d	18 08		18 30		18 55		19 20		19 50		20 20	20 50		23 20	23 55
London Cannon Street 4	⊖ d		18 18		18 40		19 00		19 30		20 00					
London Bridge 4	⊖ d	18 13	18 23	18 35	18 44	19 00	19 04	19 25	19 34	19 55	20 04	20 25	20 55		23 25	23 59
New Cross 4	⊖ d		18 28		18 50		19 09		19 39		20 09	20 32	21 00		23 30	00 05
St Johns	d		18 30		18 52		19 11		19 41		20 11	20 34	21 02		23 32	00 07
Lewisham 4	⇌ d		18 33		18 55		19 14		19 44		20 14	20 37	21 05		23 35	00 10
Ladywell	d	18 23	18 36	18 45	18 58	19 09	19 17	19 34	19 47	20 04	20 17	20 40	21 08		23 38	00 13
Catford Bridge	d	18 25	18 38	18 47	19 00	19 11	19 19	19 36	19 49	20 06	20 19	20 42	21 10		23 40	00 15
Lower Sydenham	d	18 28	18 41	18 50	19 03	19 14	19 22	19 39	19 52	20 09	20 22	20 45	21 13		23 43	00 18
New Beckenham 4	d	18 30	18 43	18 52	19 05	19 16	19 24	19 41	19 54	20 11	20 24	20 47	21 15		23 45	00 20
Clock House	d	18 33	18 46	18 55	19 07	19 19	19 27	19 43	19 57	20 13	20 27	20 50	21 18		23 48	00 23
Elmers End 4	⇌ d	18 36	18 49	18 58	19 10	19 22	19 29	19 46	19 59	20 16	20 29	20 52	21 20		23 50	00 25
Eden Park	d	18 39	18 52	19 01	19 14	19 25	19 33	19 49	20 03	20 19	20 33	20 56	21 24		23 54	00 29
West Wickham	d	18 42	18 55	19 04	19 16	19 28	19 35	19 52	20 05	20 22	20 35	20 58	21 26		23 56	00 31
Hayes (Kent)	a	18 47	19 00	19 10	19 22	19 33	19 39	19 55	20 09	20 25	20 39	21 01	21 29		23 59	00 34

Saturdays

14 December to 17 May

		SE	SE		SE	SE	SE	SE	SE	SE	SE		SE	SE	SE	SE	SE	SE		SE	SE
London Charing Cross 4	⊖ d		05 47	and every 30 minutes until	07 17	07 47		08 17		08 47		and at the same minutes past each hour until	18 17		18 47		19 17	19 47	and every 30 minutes until	23 17	23 52
London Waterloo (East) 4	⊖ d		05 50		07 20	07 50		08 20		08 50			18 20		18 50		19 20	19 50		23 20	23 55
London Cannon Street 4	⊖ d						08 00		08 30		09 00			18 30		19 00					
London Bridge 4	⊖ d		05 55		07 25	07 55	08 04	08 25	08 34	08 55	09 04		18 25	18 34	18 55	19 04	19 25	19 55		23 25	23 59
New Cross 4	⊖ d	00 05	06 00		07 30		08 09		08 39		09 09			18 39		19 09		20 00		23 30	00 05
St Johns	d	00 07	06 02		07 32		08 11		08 41		09 11			18 41		19 11		20 02		23 32	00 07
Lewisham 4	⇌ d	00 10	06 05		07 35		08 14		08 44		09 14			18 44		19 14	19 37	20 05		23 35	00 10
Ladywell	d	00 13	06 08		07 38	08 04	08 17	08 34	08 47	09 04	09 17		18 34	18 47	19 04	19 17	19 40	20 08		23 38	00 13
Catford Bridge	d	00 15	06 10		07 40	08 06	08 19	08 36	08 49	09 06	09 19		18 36	18 49	19 06	19 19	19 42	20 10		23 40	00 15
Lower Sydenham	d	00 18	06 13		07 43	08 09	08 22	08 39	08 52	09 09	09 22		18 39	18 52	19 09	19 22	19 45	20 13		23 43	00 18
New Beckenham 4	d	00 20	06 15		07 45	08 11	08 24	08 41	08 54	09 11	09 24		18 41	18 54	19 11	19 24	19 47	20 15		23 45	00 20
Clock House	d	00 23	06 18		07 48	08 13	08 27	08 43	08 57	09 13	09 27		18 43	18 57	19 13	19 27	19 50	20 18		23 48	00 23
Elmers End 4	⇌ d	00 25	06 20		07 50	08 16	08 29	08 46	08 59	09 16	09 29		18 46	18 59	19 16	19 29	19 52	20 20		23 50	00 25
Eden Park	d	00 29	06 24		07 54	08 19	08 33	08 49	09 03	09 19	09 33		18 49	19 03	19 19	19 33	19 56	20 24		23 54	00 29
West Wickham	d	00 31	06 26		07 56	08 22	08 35	08 52	09 05	09 22	09 35		18 52	19 05	19 22	19 35	19 58	20 26		23 56	00 31
Hayes (Kent)	a	00 34	06 29		07 59	08 25	08 41	08 55	09 08	09 25	09 38		18 55	19 08	19 25	19 38	20 01	20 29		23 59	00 34

Table 203

Sundays

8 December to 11 May

London - Hayes (Kent) via Catford Bridge

Network Diagram - see first Page of Table 200

			SE A	SE		SE
London Charing Cross 4	⊖	d		07 35		23 35
London Waterloo (East) 4	⊖	d		07 38		23 38
London Cannon Street 4	⊖	d				
London Bridge 4	⊖	d		07 43		23 43
New Cross 4	⊖	d	00 05	07 48	and every 30 minutes until	23 48
St Johns		d	00 07	07 50		23 50
Lewisham 4	🚌	d	00 10	07 54		23 54
Ladywell		d	00 13	07 57		23 57
Catford Bridge		d	00 15	07 59		23 59
Lower Sydenham		d	00 18	08 02		00 02
New Beckenham 4		d	00 20	08 04		00 04
Clock House		d	00 23	08 06		00 06
Elmers End 4	🚌	d	00 25	08 09		00 09
Eden Park		d	00 29	08 12		00 12
West Wickham		d	00 31	08 15		00 15
Hayes (Kent)		a	00 34	08 19		00 19

A not 8 December

Table 203R

Mondays to Fridays

9 December to 16 May

Hayes (Kent) - London via Catford Bridge

Network Diagram - see first Page of Table 200

Miles	Miles			SE	SE	SE	SE	SE	SE	SE	SE	SE	SE	SE	SE	SE	SE	SE	SE	SE	SE	SE	SE
0	—	**Hayes (Kent)**	d	05 15	05 45	06 15	06 23	06 45	06 55	07 13	07 23	07 33	07 43	07 53	08 03	08 13	08 23	08 33	08 50	09 08	09 20	09 38	09 50
1¼	—	West Wickham	d	05 18	05 48	06 18	06 26	06 48	06 58	07 16	07 26	07 36	07 46	07 56	08 06	08 16	08 26	08 36	08 53	09 11	09 23	09 41	09 53
2	—	Eden Park	d	05 20	05 50	06 20	06 28	06 50	07 00	07 18	07 28	07 38	07 48	07 58	08 08	08 18	08 28	08 38	08 55	09 13	09 25	09 43	09 55
3½	—	Elmers End	d	05 24	05 54	06 24	06 32	06 54	07 04	07 22	07 32	07 42	07 52	08 02	08 12	08 22	08 32	08 42	08 59	09 17	09 29	09 47	09 59
4¼	—	Clock House	d	05 26	05 56	06 26	06 34	06 56	07 06	07 24	07 34	07 44	07 54	08 04	08 14	08 24	08 34	08 44	09 01	09 19	09 31	09 49	10 01
5	—	New Beckenham	d	05 28	05 58	06 28	06 37	06 59	07 09	07 27	07 37	07 47	07 57	08 07	08 17	08 27	08 37	08 47	09 04	09 21	09 34	09 51	10 03
5½	—	Lower Sydenham	d	05 30	06 00	06 30	06 39	07 01	07 11	07 29	07 39	07 49	07 59	08 09	08 19	08 29	08 39	08 49	09 06	09 23	09 36	09 53	10 05
7	—	**Catford Bridge**	d	05 33	06 03	06 33	06 42	07 04	07 14	07 32	07 42	07 52	08 02	08 12	08 22	08 32	08 42	08 52	09 09	09 26	09 39	09 56	10 08
7¾	—	Ladywell	d	05 35	06 05	06 35	06 44	07 06	07 16	07 34	07 44	07 54	08 04	08 14	08 24	08 34	08 44	08 54	09 11	09 28	09 41	09 58	10 10
8½	—	**Lewisham**	d	05 39	06 09	06 39	06 48		07 20		07 48		08 08		08 28		08 48		09 15		09 45		10 14
9	—	St Johns	a	05 41	06 11	06 41	06 50				07 50		08 12		08 30		08 50		09 17		09 47		10 16
9¾	—	New Cross	a	05 43	06 13	06 43	06 52		07 23		07 52		08 14		08 32		08 52		09 19		09 49		10 18
12¾	0	**London Bridge**	a	05 48	06 18	06 48	06 58	07 17	07 28	07 44	08 01		08 21		08 41		08 57		09 25	09 37	09 54	10 07	10 24
—	0¾	**London Cannon Street**	a				07 05		07 35		08 08		08 28		08 48		09 04		09 32		10 00		10 28
13¾	—	**London Waterloo (East)**	a	05 53	06 24	06 53		07 22		07 50		08 08		08 28		08 48		09 07		09 42		10 12	
14½	—	**London Charing Cross**	a	05 57	06 27	06 57		07 28		07 56		08 14		08 34		08 54		09 13		09 48		10 16	

		SE	SE	SE	SE	SE		SE	SE	SE	SE	SE	SE	SE	SE	SE	SE	SE	SE	SE	SE	SE
Hayes (Kent)	d	10 08	10 20	10 38	10 50	11 08	and at the same minutes past each hour until	14 20	14 38	14 50	15 08	15 20	15 38	15 50		16 08	16 20	16 38	16 50	17 08	17 20	17 37
West Wickham	d	10 11	10 23	10 41	10 53	11 11		14 23	14 41	14 53	15 11	15 23	15 41	15 53		16 11	16 23	16 41	16 53	17 11	17 23	17 40
Eden Park	d	10 13	10 25	10 43	10 55	11 13		14 25	14 43	14 55	15 13	15 25	15 43	15 55		16 13	16 25	16 43	16 55	17 13	17 25	17 42
Elmers End	d	10 17	10 29	10 47	10 59	11 17		14 29	14 47	14 59	15 17	15 29	15 47	15 59		16 17	16 29	16 47	16 59	17 17	17 29	17 46
Clock House	d	10 19	10 31	10 49	11 01	11 19		14 31	14 49	15 01	15 19	15 31	15 49	16 01		16 19	16 31	16 49	17 01	17 19	17 31	17 48
New Beckenham	d	10 21	10 33	10 51	11 03	11 21		14 33	14 51	15 03	15 21	15 33	15 51	16 03	16 15	16 21	16 33	16 51	17 03	17 21	17 33	17 50
Lower Sydenham	d	10 23	10 35	10 53	11 05	11 23		14 35	14 53	15 05	15 23	15 35	15 53	16 05	16 17	16 23	16 35	16 53	17 05	17 23	17 35	17 52
Catford Bridge	d	10 26	10 38	10 56	11 08	11 26		14 38	14 56	15 08	15 26	15 38	15 56	16 08	16 20	16 26	16 38	16 56	17 08	17 26	17 38	17 55
Ladywell	d	10 28	10 40	10 58	11 10	11 28		14 40	14 58	15 10	15 28	15 40	15 58	16 10	16 22	16 28	16 40	16 58	17 10	17 28	17 40	17 57
Lewisham	d		10 44		11 14			14 44		15 14		15 44		16 14			16 44		17 14		17 44	
St Johns	a		10 46		11 16			14 46		15 16		15 46		16 16			16 46		17 16		17 46	
New Cross	a		10 48		11 18			14 48		15 18		15 48		16 18			16 48		17 18		17 48	
London Bridge	a	10 37	10 54	11 07	11 24	11 37		14 54	15 07	15 24	15 37	15 54	16 09	16 24	16 32	16 37	16 54	17 08	17 24	17 38	17 55	18 07
London Cannon Street	a		10 58		11 28			14 58		15 28		15 58		16 28			16 58		17 29		17 59	
London Waterloo (East)	a	10 42		11 12		11 42			15 12		15 42		16 13		16 37	16 42		17 13		17 42		18 12
London Charing Cross	a	10 47		11 16		11 46			15 16		15 46		16 18		16 42	16 46		17 18		17 46		18 16

		SE	SE	SE	SE	SE	SE	SE		SE
Hayes (Kent)	d	17 47	18 08	18 21	18 38	18 50	19 05	19 14	and every 30 minutes until	23 14
West Wickham	d	17 50	18 11	18 24	18 41	18 53	19 08	19 17		23 17
Eden Park	d	17 52	18 13	18 26	18 43	18 55	19 10	19 19		23 19
Elmers End	d	17 56	18 17	18 30	18 47	18 59	19 17	19 23		23 23
Clock House	d	17 58	18 19	18 32	18 49	19 01	19 19	19 25		23 25
New Beckenham	d	18 00	18 21	18 34	18 51	19 03	19 21	19 27		23 27
Lower Sydenham	d	18 02	18 23	18 36	18 53	19 05	19 23	19 29		23 29
Catford Bridge	d	18 05	18 26	18 39	18 56	19 08	19 26	19 32		23 32
Ladywell	d	18 07	18 28	18 41	18 58	19 10	19 28	19 34		23 34
Lewisham	d	18 14		18 45		19 14		19 38		23 38
St Johns	a	18 16		18 47		19 16		19 40		23 40
New Cross	a	18 18		18 49		19 18		19 42		23 42
London Bridge	a	18 24	18 38	18 55	19 07	19 24	19 37	19 49		23 49
London Cannon Street	a	18 29		18 59		19 28				
London Waterloo (East)	a		18 44		19 12		19 42	19 53		23 53
London Charing Cross	a		18 48		19 16		19 46	19 57		23 57

Saturdays

14 December to 17 May

		SE	SE		SE	SE	SE	SE	SE	SE		SE	SE	SE	SE	SE	SE		SE	SE	SE
Hayes (Kent)	d	05 15	05 38	and every 30 minutes until	07 08	07 36	07 50	08 08	08 20	08 38	and at the same minutes past each hour until	17 50	18 08	18 20	18 38	18 50	19 14	and every 30 minutes until	21 44	22 14	22 44
West Wickham	d	05 18	05 41		07 11	07 39	07 53	08 11	08 23	08 41		17 53	18 11	18 23	18 41	18 53	19 17		21 47	22 17	22 47
Eden Park	d	05 20	05 43		07 13	07 41	07 55	08 13	08 25	08 43		17 55	18 13	18 25	18 43	18 55	19 19		21 49	22 19	22 49
Elmers End	d	05 24	05 47		07 17	07 45	07 59	08 17	08 29	08 47		17 59	18 17	18 29	18 47	18 59	19 23		21 53	22 23	22 53
Clock House	d	05 26	05 49		07 19	07 47	08 01	08 19	08 31	08 49		18 01	18 19	18 31	18 49	19 01	19 25		21 55	22 25	22 55
New Beckenham	d	05 28	05 51		07 21	07 49	08 03	08 21	08 33	08 51		18 03	18 21	18 33	18 51	19 03	19 27		21 57	22 27	22 57
Lower Sydenham	d	05 30	05 53		07 23	07 51	08 05	08 23	08 35	08 53		18 05	18 23	18 35	18 53	19 05	19 29		21 59	22 29	22 59
Catford Bridge	d	05 33	05 56		07 26	07 54	08 08	08 26	08 38	08 56		18 08	18 26	18 38	18 56	19 08	19 32		22 02	22 32	23 02
Ladywell	d	05 35	05 58		07 28	07 56	08 10	08 28	08 40	08 58		18 10	18 28	18 40	18 58	19 10	19 34		22 04	22 34	23 04
Lewisham	d	05 39	06 02		07 32	07 59	08 14		08 44			18 14		18 44		19 14	19 38		22 08	22 38	23 08
St Johns	a	05 41	06 04		07 34		08 16		08 46			18 16		18 46		19 16	19 40		22 10	22 40	23 10
New Cross	a	05 43	06 06		07 36		08 18		08 48			18 18		18 48		19 18	19 42		22 12	22 42	23 12
London Bridge	a	05 48	06 12		07 42	08 07	08 24	08 37	08 54	09 07		18 24	18 37	18 54	19 07	19 24	19 49		22 19	22 49	23 19
London Cannon Street	a						08 28		08 58			18 28		18 58							
London Waterloo (East)	a	05 53	06 16		07 46	08 12		08 42		09 12			18 42		19 12		19 53		22 23	22 54	23 23
London Charing Cross	a	05 56	06 20		07 50	08 16		08 46		09 16			18 46		19 16		19 58		22 28	22 58	23 27

		SE
Hayes (Kent)	d	23 14
West Wickham	d	23 17
Eden Park	d	23 19
Elmers End	d	23 23
Clock House	d	23 25
New Beckenham	d	23 27
Lower Sydenham	d	23 29
Catford Bridge	d	23 32
Ladywell	d	23 34
Lewisham	d	23 38
St Johns	a	23 40
New Cross	a	23 42
London Bridge	a	23 49
London Cannon Street	a	
London Waterloo (East)	a	23 53
London Charing Cross	a	23 57

Table 203R

Sundays

8 December to 11 May

Hayes (Kent) - London via Catford Bridge

Network Diagram - see first Page of Table 200

		SE		SE
Hayes (Kent)	d	07 32		23 02
West Wickham	d	07 35		23 05
Eden Park	d	07 37		23 07
Elmers End 4 ⇌	d	07 41		23 11
Clock House	d	07 43		23 13
New Beckenham 4	d	07 45	and	23 15
Lower Sydenham	d	07 47	every 30	23 17
Catford Bridge	d	07 50	minutes	23 20
Ladywell	d	07 52	until	23 22
Lewisham 4 ⇌	d	07 57		23 27
St Johns	a	07 59		23 29
New Cross 4	a	08 01		23 31
London Bridge 4 ⊖	a	08 07		23 37
London Cannon Street 4 ⊖	a			
London Waterloo (East) 4 ⊖	a	08 12		23 42
London Charing Cross 4 ⊖	a	08 16		23 46

Table 204

Mondays to Fridays

9 December to 16 May

London Charing Cross/Cannon Street - Grove Park, Orpington, Sevenoaks and Tonbridge, Grove Park - Bromley North

Network Diagram - see first Page of Table 200

Miles	Miles			SE MO 1	SE MX 1	SE MX	SE MX 1	SE MO 1	SE MO	SE MX 1	SE MX	SE MO		SE MX	SE MX	SE MX	SE	SE 1	SE	SE	SE	SE		SE 1	SE 1
0	—	**London Charing Cross 4** ⊖	d									00 01		00 06		00 15	00 48	05 30	05 36		06 06			06 15	06 30
0¾	—	**London Waterloo (East) 4** ⊖	d									00 04		00 09		00 18	00 51	05 33	05 39		06 09			06 18	06 33
—	—	**London Cannon Street 4** ⊖	d																						
1¾	—	**London Bridge 4** ⊖	d									00 09		00 14		00 23	00 56	05 39	05 44		06 14			06 24	06 38
4¾	—	New Cross 4 ⊖	d														01 01								
5½	—	St Johns	d																						
6	—	**Lewisham 4**	d									00 17		00 22			01 05		05 52		06 23				
7¼	—	Hither Green 4	d									00 22		00 26			01 09		05 56		06 27				
9	0	**Grove Park 4**	d			00 07						00 26		00 30	00 37		01 13		06 00	06 16	06 30	06 36			
—	1¼	Sundridge Park	d			00 10									00 40					06 19		06 39			
—	1¾	**Bromley North**	a			00 12									00 42					06 21		06 41			
10¼	—	Elmstead Woods	d								00 03	00 29		00 33			01 16		06 03		06 33				
11¼	—	Chislehurst	d						00 01		00 05	00 31		00 35			01 19		06 05		06 36				
12¾	—	Petts Wood 4	d						00 04		00 08	00 34		00 38			01 22		06 08		06 39				
13¾	—	**Orpington 4**	a						00 08		00 12	00 38		00 42		00 47	01 25	05 54	06 11		06 42			06 40	06 53
—	—		d					00 05		00 09						00 48		05 55	06 12		06 44			06 40	06 54
15¼	—	Chelsfield 3	d													00 51		05 58	06 15		06 47				
16½	—	Knockholt	d																06 18		06 50				
20½	—	Dunton Green	d													00 57			06 23		06 55				
22	—	**Sevenoaks 4**	a					00 14		00 18						01 00		06 05	06 26		06 59			06 49	07 03
—	—		d		00 05		00 12	00 15		00 19						01 01		06 06						06 50	07 03
27	—	Hildenborough	d	00 06	00 11											01 07		06 12							07 09
29½	—	**Tonbridge 4**	a	00 10	00 15		00 20	00 23		00 27						01 12		06 16						06 58	07 13

		SE	SE	SE 1	SE	SE	SE 1	SE		SE 1	SE 1	SE	SE	SE 1	SE 1	SE	SE	SE 1		SE	SE 1	SE 1	SE	SE	SE
London Charing Cross 4 ⊖	d	06 36		06 45			07 00	07 06		07 10	07 15			07 29		07 36		07 40		07 48	07 52	08 00			08 05
London Waterloo (East) 4 ⊖	d	06 39		06 48			07 03	07 09		07 13	07 18			07 32		07 39		07 43		07 51	07 55	08 03			08 08
London Cannon Street 4 ⊖	d				06 50							07 20			07 46								07 51		
London Bridge 4 ⊖	d	06 44		06 53	06 54		07 08	07 14		07 19	07 23	07 24		07 38	07 51	07 44		07 49		07 56	08 01	08 09	07 55		08 13
New Cross 4 ⊖	d				06 59																		08 00		
St Johns	d				07 01																				
Lewisham 4	d	06 53			07 04																		08 05		
Hither Green 4	d	06 58			07 08			07 23				07 35				07 53							08 10		08 23
Grove Park 4	d	07 02	07 06		07 12	07 25		07 27				07 39	07 46			07 57	08 06						08 14	08 26	08 27
Sundridge Park	d		07 09			07 28							07 49				08 09							08 29	
Bromley North	a		07 11			07 30							07 51				08 11							08 31	
Elmstead Woods	d	07 05			07 15			07 30				07 42				08 00							08 17		08 30
Chislehurst	d	07 07			07 18			07 33				07 44				08 03							08 20		08 32
Petts Wood 4	d	07 10			07 21			07 36								08 06							08 24		08 36
Orpington 4	a	07 13		07 09	07 25		07 25	07 40			07 38	07 49		07 53	08 09	08 09				08 15		08 25	08 27		08 39
	d	07 14		07 10			07 26	07 42			07 39			07 54	08 09	08 12						08 26			08 45
Chelsfield 3	d	07 17						07 45						07 57		08 15									08 48
Knockholt	d	07 20						07 48						08 00											08 51
Dunton Green	d	07 25						07 53								08 21									08 56
Sevenoaks 4	a	07 28		07 19			07 35	08 00		07 41	07 48			08 06	08 18	08 24		08 11				08 35			08 59
	d			07 19			07 35			07 42	07 49			08 07	08 19			08 12				08 35			
Hildenborough	d						07 41							08 13								08 41			
Tonbridge 4	a			07 27			07 45			07 51	07 58			08 17	08 27			08 20			08 37	08 47			

		SE 1	SE 1	SE 1		SE	SE	SE 1	SE 1	SE	SE	SE	SE 1	SE 1		SE	SE 1	SE	SE	SE 1	SE	SE	SE 1	SE	
London Charing Cross 4 ⊖	d	08 13	08 17	08 27				08 33		08 37		08 49	08 53	09 00				09 06		09 13			09 30	09 36	
London Waterloo (East) 4 ⊖	d	08 16	08 20	08 30				08 36		08 40		08 52	08 56	09 03				09 09		09 16			09 33	09 39	
London Cannon Street 4 ⊖	d					08 19			08 42							08 51	09 14				09 20				
London Bridge 4 ⊖	d	08 21	08 25	08 35		08 23		08 41	08 46	08 45		08 57	09 01	09 08		08 55	09 18	09 14		09 21	09 24		09 39	09 44	
New Cross 4 ⊖	d					08 28										09 00					09 29				
St Johns	d					08 30										09 02					09 31				
Lewisham 4	d					08 34										09 06					09 34				
Hither Green 4	d					08 38				08 55						09 10		09 24			09 38			09 53	
Grove Park 4	d					08 42	08 46			08 59	09 06					09 14		09 29	09 35		09 42	09 55		09 57	
Sundridge Park	d						08 49				09 09								09 38			09 58			
Bromley North	a						08 51				09 11								09 40			10 00			
Elmstead Woods	d					08 45				09 02						09 17		09 32			09 45			10 00	
Chislehurst	d					08 48				09 05						09 20		09 34			09 48			10 03	
Petts Wood 4	d					08 51				09 08						09 23		09 37			09 51			10 06	
Orpington 4	a		08 41	08 53		08 55		08 57	09 07	09 11		09 24		09 26		09 27	09 38	09 42			09 55		09 55	10 09	
	d		08 42	08 54				08 58	09 07	09 12				09 26			09 39	09 43					09 56	10 12	
Chelsfield 3	d									09 15								09 46						10 15	
Knockholt	d									09 18								09 49						10 18	
Dunton Green	d									09 23								09 54						10 23	
Sevenoaks 4	a	08 44	08 51	09 03				09 07	09 17	09 26				09 35			09 48	09 57		09 43			10 05	10 26	
	d	08 45	08 52	09 03				09 08	09 17					09 35			09 49			09 44			10 05		
Hildenborough	d			09 09										09 41									10 11		
Tonbridge 4	a	08 53	09 00	09 13				09 19	09 25				09 36	09 47			09 57			09 52			10 15		

Table 204

Mondays to Fridays

9 December to 16 May

London Charing Cross/Cannon Street - Grove Park, Orpington, Sevenoaks and Tonbridge, Grove Park - Bromley North

Network Diagram - see first Page of Table 200

Station		SE 1	SE 1	SE	SE	SE 1		SE	SE	SE 1 ⊤	SE 1	SE	SE	SE 1	SE	SE 1 ⊤		SE 1	SE	SE	SE 1	SE	SE	SE 1 ⊤	SE 1
London Charing Cross 4 ⊖	d	09 40	09 45			10 00		10 06		10 10	10 15			10 30	10 36	10 40		10 45			11 00	11 06		11 10	11 15
London Waterloo (East) 4 ⊖	d	09 43	09 48			10 03		10 09		10 13	10 18			10 33	10 39	10 43		10 48			11 03	11 09		11 13	11 18
London Cannon Street 4 ⊖	d			09 50								10 20							10 50						
London Bridge 4 ⊖	d	09 49	09 53	09 54		10 09		10 14		10 19	10 23	10 24		10 39	10 44	10 49		10 53	10 54		11 09	11 14		11 19	11 23
New Cross 4 ⊖	d			09 59								10 29							10 59						
St Johns	d			10 01								10 31							11 01						
Lewisham 4	d			10 04								10 34							11 04						
Hither Green 4	d			10 08				10 23				10 38			10 53				11 08			11 23			
Grove Park 4	d			10 12	10 15			10 27	10 35			10 42	10 55		10 57				11 12	11 15		11 27	11 35		
Sundridge Park	d				10 18				10 38				10 58							11 18			11 38		
Bromley North	a				10 20				10 40				11 00							11 20			11 40		
Elmstead Woods	d			10 15				10 30				10 45			11 00				11 15			11 30			
Chislehurst	d			10 18				10 33				10 48			11 03				11 18			11 33			
Petts Wood 4	d			10 21				10 36				10 51			11 06				11 21			11 36			
Orpington 4	a		10 08	10 24		10 25		10 39			10 38	10 54		10 55	11 09			11 08	11 24		11 25	11 39			11 38
	d		10 09			10 26		10 42			10 39			10 56	11 12			11 09			11 26	11 42			11 39
Chelsfield 3	d							10 45							11 15							11 45			
Knockholt	d							10 48							11 18							11 48			
Dunton Green	d							10 53							11 23							11 53			
Sevenoaks 4	a	10 11	10 18			10 35		10 56		10 41	10 48			11 05	11 26	11 11		11 18			11 35	11 56		11 41	11 48
	d	10 12	10 19			10 35				10 42	10 49			11 05		11 12		11 19			11 35			11 42	11 49
Hildenborough	d					10 41								11 11							11 41				
Tonbridge 4	a	10 20	10 27			10 45				10 50	10 57			11 15		11 20		11 27			11 45			11 50	11 57

Station		SE		SE	SE 1	SE	SE 1 ⊤	SE 1	SE	SE	SE 1	SE		SE	SE 1 ⊤	SE 1	SE	SE	SE 1	SE	SE 1 ⊤	SE 1		SE	SE
London Charing Cross 4 ⊖	d				11 30	11 36	11 40	11 45			12 00	12 06			12 10	12 15			12 30	12 36	12 40	12 45			
London Waterloo (East) 4 ⊖	d				11 33	11 39	11 43	11 48			12 03	12 09			12 13	12 18			12 33	12 39	12 43	12 48			
London Cannon Street 4 ⊖	d	11 20							11 50								12 20							12 50	
London Bridge 4 ⊖	d	11 24			11 39	11 44	11 49	11 53	11 54		12 09	12 14			12 19	12 23	12 24		12 39	12 44	12 49	12 53		12 54	
New Cross 4 ⊖	d	11 29							11 59								12 29							12 59	
St Johns	d	11 31							12 01								12 31							13 01	
Lewisham 4	d	11 34							12 04								12 34							13 04	
Hither Green 4	d	11 38				11 53			12 08			12 23					12 38			12 53				13 08	
Grove Park 4	d	11 42		11 55		11 57			12 12	12 15		12 27		12 35			12 42	12 55		12 57				13 12	13 15
Sundridge Park	d			11 58						12 18				12 38				12 58							13 18
Bromley North	a			12 00						12 20				12 40				13 00							13 20
Elmstead Woods	d	11 45				12 00			12 15			12 30					12 45			13 00				13 15	
Chislehurst	d	11 48				12 03			12 18			12 33					12 48			13 03				13 18	
Petts Wood 4	d	11 51				12 06			12 21			12 36					12 51			13 06				13 21	
Orpington 4	a	11 54			11 55	12 09		12 08	12 24		12 25	12 39				12 38	12 54		12 55	13 09		13 08		13 24	
	d				11 56	12 12		12 09			12 26	12 42				12 39			12 56	13 12		13 09			
Chelsfield 3	d					12 15						12 45								13 15					
Knockholt	d					12 18						12 48								13 18					
Dunton Green	d					12 23						12 53								13 23					
Sevenoaks 4	a				12 05	12 26	12 11	12 18			12 35	12 56			12 41	12 48			13 05	13 26	13 11	13 18			
	d				12 05		12 12	12 19			12 35				12 42	12 49			13 05		13 12	13 19			
Hildenborough	d				12 11						12 41								13 11						
Tonbridge 4	a				12 15		12 20	12 27			12 45				12 50	12 57			13 15		13 20	13 27			

Station		SE 1	SE	SE	SE 1 ⊤	SE 1	SE	SE		SE 1	SE	SE 1 ⊤	SE 1	SE	SE	SE 1	SE	SE		SE 1 ⊤	SE 1	SE	SE	SE 1	SE
London Charing Cross 4 ⊖	d	13 00	13 06		13 10	13 15				13 30	13 36	13 40	13 45			14 00	14 06			14 10	14 15			14 30	14 36
London Waterloo (East) 4 ⊖	d	13 03	13 09		13 13	13 18				13 33	13 39	13 43	13 48			14 03	14 09			14 13	14 18			14 33	14 39
London Cannon Street 4 ⊖	d						13 20							13 50								14 20			
London Bridge 4 ⊖	d	13 09	13 14		13 19	13 23	13 24			13 39	13 44	13 49	13 53	13 54		14 09	14 14			14 19	14 23	14 24		14 39	14 44
New Cross 4 ⊖	d						13 29							13 59								14 29			
St Johns	d						13 31							14 01								14 31			
Lewisham 4	d						13 34							14 04								14 34			
Hither Green 4	d		13 23				13 38				13 53			14 08			14 23					14 38			14 53
Grove Park 4	d		13 27	13 35			13 42	13 55			13 57			14 12	14 15		14 27	14 35				14 42	14 55		14 57
Sundridge Park	d			13 38				13 58							14 18			14 38					14 58		
Bromley North	a			13 40				14 00							14 20			14 40					15 00		
Elmstead Woods	d		13 30				13 45				14 00			14 15			14 30					14 45			15 00
Chislehurst	d		13 33				13 48				14 03			14 18			14 33					14 48			15 03
Petts Wood 4	d		13 36				13 51				14 06			14 21			14 36					14 51			15 06
Orpington 4	a	13 25	13 39			13 38	13 54			13 55	14 09		14 08	14 24		14 25	14 39				14 38	14 54		14 55	15 09
	d	13 26	13 42			13 39				13 56	14 12		14 09			14 26	14 42				14 39			14 56	15 12
Chelsfield 3	d		13 45								14 15						14 45								15 15
Knockholt	d		13 48								14 18						14 48								15 18
Dunton Green	d		13 53								14 23						14 53								15 23
Sevenoaks 4	a	13 35	13 56		13 41	13 48				14 05	14 26	14 11	14 18			14 35	14 56			14 41	14 48			15 05	15 26
	d	13 35			13 42	13 49				14 05		14 12	14 19			14 35				14 42	14 49			15 05	
Hildenborough	d	13 41								14 11						14 41								15 11	
Tonbridge 4	a	13 45			13 50	13 57				14 15		14 20	14 27			14 45				14 50	14 57			15 16	

Table 204

Mondays to Fridays

9 December to 16 May

London Charing Cross/Cannon Street - Grove Park, Orpington, Sevenoaks and Tonbridge, Grove Park - Bromley North

Network Diagram - see first Page of Table 200

Station		SE 1 🚲	SE 1	SE	SE	SE 1	SE	SE	SE 1 🚲	SE 1		SE	SE	SE 1	SE	SE 1 🚲	SE 1	SE	SE	SE 1		SE	SE	SE 1 🚲	SE 1
London Charing Cross 4 ⊖	d	14 40	14 45			15 00	15 06		15 10	15 15				15 30	15 36	15 40	15 45			16 00		16 06		16 10	16 15
London Waterloo (East) 4 ⊖	d	14 43	14 48			15 03	15 09		15 13	15 18				15 33	15 39	15 43	15 48			16 03		16 09		16 13	16 18
London Cannon Street 4 ⊖	d			14 50								15 20						15 50							
London Bridge 4 ⊖	d	14 49	14 53	14 54		15 09	15 14		15 19	15 23		15 24		15 39	15 44	15 49	15 53	15 54		16 09		16 14		16 19	16 23
New Cross 4 ⊖	d			14 59								15 29						15 59							
St Johns	d			15 01								15 31						16 01							
Lewisham 4	d			15 04								15 34						16 04							
Hither Green 4	d			15 08			15 23					15 38			15 53			16 08				16 23			
Grove Park 4	d			15 12	15 15		15 27	15 35				15 42	15 55		15 57			16 12	16 15			16 27	16 35		
Sundridge Park	d				15 18			15 38					15 58						16 18				16 38		
Bromley North	a				15 20			15 40					16 00						16 20				16 40		
Elmstead Woods	d			15 15			15 30					15 45			16 00			16 15				16 30			
Chislehurst	d			15 18			15 33					15 48			16 03			16 18				16 33			
Petts Wood 4	d			15 21			15 36					15 51			16 06			16 21				16 36			
Orpington 4	a		15 08	15 24		15 25	15 39			15 38		15 54		15 55	16 09		16 08	16 24		16 25		16 39			
	d		15 09			15 26	15 42			15 39				15 56	16 12		16 09			16 26		16 42			
Chelsfield 3	d						15 45								16 15							16 45			
Knockholt	d						15 48								16 18							16 48			
Dunton Green	d						15 53								16 23							16 53			
Sevenoaks 4	a	15 11	15 18			15 35	15 56		15 41	15 48				16 05	16 26	16 11	16 18			16 35		16 58		16 42	16 46
	d	15 12	15 19			15 35			15 42	15 49				16 05		16 12	16 19			16 35				16 42	16 47
Hildenborough	d					15 41								16 11						16 41					
Tonbridge 4	a	15 20	15 27			15 45			15 50	15 57				16 15		16 20	16 27			16 45				16 50	16 55

Station		SE 1	SE	SE	SE	SE 1 🚲		SE 1	SE	SE 1	SE	SE	SE 1	SE 1	SE	SE 1 🚲		SE	SE	SE 1	SE 1	SE	SE 1 🚲	SE	SE
London Charing Cross 4 ⊖	d	16 28		16 32		16 37		16 41	16 42	16 57				17 01	17 03	17 14					17 23	17 26	17 41		
London Waterloo (East) 4 ⊖	d	16 31		16 35		16 40		16 44	16 45	17 00				17 04	17 06	17 18					17 26	17 29	17 44		
London Cannon Street 4 ⊖	d		16 20								16 56		17 02					17 19		17 24				17 41	
London Bridge 4 ⊖	d	16 36	16 24	16 40		16 45		16 49	16 51		17 00		17 06	17 09	17 11			17 23		17 28	17 31	17 35		17 45	
New Cross 4 ⊖	d		16 30																						
St Johns	d		16 32																						
Lewisham 4	d		16 35						17 01						17 21							17 44			
Hither Green 4	d		16 39	16 50					17 06						17 26							17 49			
Grove Park 4	d		16 43	16 54	17 00				17 10		17 15	17 20			17 30			17 35	17 40			17 53		17 59	18 05
Sundridge Park	d				17 03							17 23							17 43						18 08
Bromley North	a				17 05							17 25							17 45						18 10
Elmstead Woods	d		16 46	16 57					17 13		17 18				17 33			17 38				17 56		18 02	
Chislehurst	d		16 48	17 00					17 15		17 21				17 35			17 40				17 58		18 05	
Petts Wood 4	d		16 51	17 03					17 19		17 24				17 40			17 44				18 02		18 08	
Orpington 4	a	16 52	16 57	17 06					17 24		17 27				17 45			17 47				18 07		18 11	
	d	16 53		17 07							17 28							17 50						18 12	
Chelsfield 3	d			17 10							17 31			17 28				17 53			17 50			18 15	
Knockholt	d			17 13							17 34							17 56						18 18	
Dunton Green	d			17 18							17 39							18 01						18 23	
Sevenoaks 4	a	17 02		17 23		17 09		17 13		17 27	17 44		17 31	17 37		17 45		18 07		17 53	17 59		18 11	18 28	
	d	17 03				17 10		17 14		17 27			17 32	17 37		17 46				17 54	17 59		18 11		
Hildenborough	d	17 09												17 43						18 00	18 05				
Tonbridge 4	a	17 13				17 18		17 22		17 35			17 40	17 48		17 54				18 04	18 09		18 19		

Station		SE 1		SE 1	SE	SE 1	SE	SE	SE 1	SE 1	SE	SE 1 🚲		SE	SE	SE 1	SE	SE 1	SE 1 🚲	SE	SE	SE 1		SE 1	SE 1
London Charing Cross 4 ⊖	d			17 45	17 47	18 03				18 07	18 09	18 21					18 30	18 32	18 41			18 45			19 00
London Waterloo (East) 4 ⊖	d			17 48	17 50	18 06				18 10	18 12	18 24					18 33	18 35	18 44			18 48			19 03
London Cannon Street 4 ⊖	d	17 45					18 02		18 08					18 23		18 32				18 48				19 04	
London Bridge 4 ⊖	d	17 49		17 53	17 55		18 06		18 12	18 15	18 17			18 27		18 36	18 38	18 40	18 50	18 52		18 53		19 09	19 09
New Cross 4 ⊖	d																								
St Johns	d																								
Lewisham 4	d				18 05						18 27														
Hither Green 4	d				18 10						18 31						18 49								
Grove Park 4	d				18 14		18 20	18 25			18 35			18 41	18 46		18 53			19 05	19 10				
Sundridge Park	d							18 28							18 49						19 13				
Bromley North	a							18 30							18 51						19 15				
Elmstead Woods	d				18 17		18 23				18 38			18 44			18 56			19 08					
Chislehurst	d				18 20		18 25				18 40			18 46			18 58			19 10					
Petts Wood 4	d				18 23		18 29				18 44			18 50			19 03			19 14					
Orpington 4	a				18 29		18 32				18 49			18 53			19 06		19 06	19 19					19 27
	d						18 34							18 58			19 12		19 07						19 28
Chelsfield 3	d			18 12			18 37			18 34				19 01			19 15	18 58							19 31
Knockholt	d						18 40							19 04			19 18								
Dunton Green	d						18 45							19 09			19 23								
Sevenoaks 4	a	18 15		18 21		18 33	18 50		18 37	18 42		18 52		19 14		19 00	19 28	19 06	19 16			19 20		19 32	19 38
	d	18 16		18 21		18 34			18 38	18 43		18 52				19 01		19 06	19 17			19 21		19 33	19 39
Hildenborough	d			18 27					18 44	18 49								19 12						19 40	19 45
Tonbridge 4	a	18 24		18 32		18 42			18 48	18 54		19 00				19 09		19 17	19 25			19 29		19 44	19 52

Table 204

Mondays to Fridays

9 December to 16 May

London Charing Cross/Cannon Street - Grove Park, Orpington, Sevenoaks and Tonbridge, Grove Park - Bromley North

Network Diagram - see first Page of Table 200

		SE	SE	SE 1 🚲		SE 1	SE	SE	SE 1	SE	SE 1 🚲	SE 1	SE	SE		SE 1	SE	SE	SE 1 🚲	SE 1	SE	SE 1	SE	SE	
London Charing Cross 4 ⊖	d	19 06		19 10		19 15			19 30	19 36	19 40	19 45				20 00	20 06		20 10	20 15		20 30	20 36		
London Waterloo (East) 4 ⊖	d	19 09		19 13		19 18			19 33	19 39	19 43	19 48				20 03	20 09		20 13	20 18		20 33	20 39		
London Cannon Street 4 ⊖	d						19 20						19 50								20 20				
London Bridge 4 ⊖	d	19 14		19 19		19 23	19 24		19 39	19 44	19 49	19 53	19 54			20 09	20 14		20 19	20 23	20 24	20 39	20 44		
New Cross 4 ⊖	d						19 29						19 59								20 29				
St Johns	d						19 31						20 01								20 31				
Lewisham 4	d						19 34						20 04								20 34				
Hither Green 4	d	19 23					19 38			19 53			20 08				20 23				20 38		20 53		
Grove Park 4	d	19 27	19 32				19 42	19 52		19 57			20 12	20 17			20 27	20 37			20 42		20 57	21 07	
Sundridge Park	d		19 35					19 55						20 20				20 40						21 10	
Bromley North	a		19 37					19 57						20 22				20 42						21 12	
Elmstead Woods	d	19 30					19 45			20 00			20 15				20 30				20 45		21 00		
Chislehurst	d	19 33					19 48			20 03			20 18				20 33				20 48		21 03		
Petts Wood 4	d	19 38					19 51			20 06			20 21				20 36				20 51		21 06		
Orpington 4	a	19 43				19 38	19 54		19 55	20 09		20 08	20 24			20 25	20 39			20 38	20 54	20 55	21 09		
	d	19 44				19 39			19 56	20 12		20 09				20 26	20 42			20 39		20 56	21 12		
Chelsfield 3	d	19 47								20 15							20 45						21 15		
Knockholt	d	19 50								20 18							20 48						21 18		
Dunton Green	d	19 55								20 23							20 53						21 23		
Sevenoaks 4	a	19 58		19 41		19 48			20 05	20 26	20 11	20 18				20 35	20 56		20 41	20 48		21 05	21 26		
	d			19 42		19 49			20 05		20 12	20 19				20 35			20 42	20 49		21 05			
Hildenborough	d								20 11							20 41						21 11			
Tonbridge 4	a			19 53		19 57			20 15		20 20	20 27				20 45			20 50	20 57		21 15			

		SE 1	SE 1	SE 1	SE	SE	SE 1	SE 1	SE	SE		SE 1	SE 1	SE 1	SE	SE	SE 1	SE 1	SE	SE		SE 1	SE 1	SE 1	SE
London Charing Cross 4 ⊖	d	20 40	20 45	21 00	21 06		21 10	21 30	21 36			21 40	21 45	22 00	22 06		22 10	22 30	22 36			22 40	22 45	23 00	23 06
London Waterloo (East) 4 ⊖	d	20 43	20 48	21 03	21 09		21 13	21 33	21 39			21 43	21 48	22 03	22 09		22 13	22 33	22 39			22 43	22 48	23 03	23 09
London Cannon Street 4 ⊖	d																								
London Bridge 4 ⊖	d	20 49	20 53	21 09	21 14		21 19	21 39	21 44			21 49	21 53	22 09	22 14		22 19	22 39	22 44			22 49	22 53	23 09	23 14
New Cross 4 ⊖	d																								
St Johns	d																								
Lewisham 4	d				21 22				21 52						22 22				22 52						23 22
Hither Green 4	d				21 26				21 56						22 26				22 56						23 26
Grove Park 4	d				21 30	21 37			22 00	22 07					22 30	22 37			23 00	23 07					23 30
Sundridge Park	d					21 40				22 10						22 40				23 10					
Bromley North	a					21 42				22 12						22 42				23 12					
Elmstead Woods	d				21 33				22 03						22 33				23 03						23 33
Chislehurst	d				21 35				22 05						22 35				23 05						23 35
Petts Wood 4	d				21 38				22 08						22 38				23 08						23 38
Orpington 4	a		21 08	21 25	21 42		21 34	21 55	22 12				22 08	22 25	22 42		22 34	22 54	23 12				23 08	23 24	23 42
	d		21 09	21 26	21 43		21 35	21 56					22 09	22 26			22 35	22 54					23 09	23 24	
Chelsfield 3	d				21 46			21 59						22 29				22 57						23 27	
Knockholt	d				21 49																				
Dunton Green	d				21 54																				
Sevenoaks 4	a	21 11	21 18	21 35	21 57		21 44	22 06				22 11	22 18	22 36			22 44	23 05				23 11	23 18	23 35	
	d	21 12	21 19	21 35			21 44	22 07				22 12	22 19	22 37			22 44	23 05				23 12	23 19	23 35	
Hildenborough	d			21 41				22 13						22 43				23 11						23 41	
Tonbridge 4	a	21 20	21 27	21 45			21 52	22 17				22 20	22 27	22 47			22 52	23 15				23 20	23 27	23 45	

		SE	SE 1	SE 1	SE	SE 1		SE 1
London Charing Cross 4 ⊖	d		23 10	23 30	23 36	23 40		23 45
London Waterloo (East) 4 ⊖	d		23 13	23 33	23 39	23 43		23 48
London Cannon Street 4 ⊖	d							
London Bridge 4 ⊖	d		23 19	23 39	23 44	23 49		23 53
New Cross 4 ⊖	d							
St Johns	d							
Lewisham 4	d				23 52			
Hither Green 4	d				23 56			
Grove Park 4	d	23 37			23 59			
Sundridge Park	d	23 40						
Bromley North	a	23 42						
Elmstead Woods	d				00 03			
Chislehurst	d				00 05			
Petts Wood 4	d				00 08			
Orpington 4	a		23 34	23 54	00 12			00 08
	d		23 35	23 54				00 09
Chelsfield 3	d			23 57				
Knockholt	d							
Dunton Green	d							
Sevenoaks 4	a		23 44	00 05		00 11		00 18
	d		23 44	00 05		00 12		00 19
Hildenborough	d			00 11				
Tonbridge 4	a		23 52	00 15		00 20		00 27

Table 204

Saturdays

14 December to 17 May

London Charing Cross/Cannon Street - Grove Park, Orpington, Sevenoaks and Tonbridge, Grove Park - Bromley North

Network Diagram - see first Page of Table 200

		SE 1	SE	SE 1	SE 1	SE		SE	SE	SE	SE	SE	SE	SE 1	SE	SE		SE	SE	SE 1	SE	SE	SE 1	SE	SE
London Charing Cross 4 ⊖	d							00 06		00 15	00 48	05 36		06 00	06 06			06 36		07 00	07 06		07 30		07 36
London Waterloo (East) 4 ⊖	d							00 09		00 18	00 51	05 39		06 03	06 09			06 39		07 03	07 09		07 33		07 39
London Cannon Street 4 ⊖	d																								
London Bridge 4 ⊖	d							00 14		00 23	00 56	05 44		06 08	06 14			06 44		07 08	07 14		07 38		07 44
New Cross 4 ⊖	d										01 01														
St Johns	d																								
Lewisham 4	d							00 22			01 05	05 53			06 23			06 53			07 23				07 53
Hither Green 4	d							00 26			01 09	05 57			06 27			06 57			07 27				07 57
Grove Park 4	d		00 07					00 30	00 37		01 13	06 01	06 07		06 31	06 37		07 01	07 07		07 31	07 35		07 55	08 01
Sundridge Park	d		00 10						00 40				06 10			06 40			07 10			07 38		07 58	
Bromley North	a		00 12						00 42				06 12			06 42			07 12			07 40		08 00	
Elmstead Woods	d					00 03		00 33			01 16	06 04			06 34			07 04			07 34				08 04
Chislehurst	d					00 05		00 35			01 19	06 06			06 36			07 06			07 36				08 06
Petts Wood 4	d					00 08		00 38			01 22	06 09			06 39			07 09			07 39				08 09
Orpington 4	a					00 12		00 42		00 47	01 25	06 12		06 23	06 42			07 12		07 23	07 42		07 54		08 12
	d				00 09					00 48		06 13		06 24	06 43			07 13		07 24	07 43		07 54		08 13
Chelsfield 3	d									00 51		06 16			06 46			07 16			07 46				08 16
Knockholt	d											06 19			06 49			07 19			07 49				08 19
Dunton Green	d									00 57		06 24			06 54			07 24			07 54				08 24
Sevenoaks 4	a				00 18					01 00		06 27		06 33	06 57			07 27		07 33	07 57		08 02		08 27
	d	00 05		00 12	00 19					01 01				06 33						07 33			08 03		
Hildenborough	d	00 11								01 07				06 39						07 39			08 09		
Tonbridge 4	a	00 15		00 20	00 27					01 12				06 43						07 43			08 14		

		SE		SE 1	SE 1	SE	SE	SE 1	SE	SE	SE 1	SE		SE 1	SE 1	SE	SE	SE 1	SE	SE	SE 1	SE 1		SE	SE
London Charing Cross 4 ⊖	d			07 45	08 00	08 06		08 15			08 30	08 36		08 40	08 45			09 00	09 06		09 10	09 15			
London Waterloo (East) 4 ⊖	d			07 48	08 03	08 09		08 18			08 33	08 39		08 43	08 48			09 03	09 09		09 13	09 18			
London Cannon Street 4 ⊖	d								08 20							08 50								09 20	
London Bridge 4 ⊖	d			07 53	08 08	08 14		08 23	08 24		08 39	08 44		08 49	08 53	08 54		09 09	09 14		09 19	09 23		09 24	
New Cross 4 ⊖	d								08 29							08 59								09 29	
St Johns	d								08 31							09 01								09 31	
Lewisham 4	d								08 34							09 04								09 34	
Hither Green 4	d					08 23			08 38			08 53				09 08			09 23					09 38	
Grove Park 4	d	08 15				08 27	08 35		08 42	08 55		08 57				09 12	09 15		09 27	09 35				09 42	09 55
Sundridge Park	d	08 18					08 38			08 58							09 18			09 38					09 58
Bromley North	a	08 20					08 40			09 00							09 20			09 40					10 00
Elmstead Woods	d					08 30			08 45			09 00				09 15			09 30					09 45	
Chislehurst	d					08 33			08 48			09 03				09 18			09 33					09 48	
Petts Wood 4	d					08 36			08 51			09 06				09 21			09 36					09 51	
Orpington 4	a			08 08	08 23	08 39		08 38	08 54		08 55	09 09			09 08	09 24		09 25	09 39			09 38		09 54	
	d			08 09	08 24	08 42		08 39			08 56	09 12			09 09			09 26	09 42			09 39			
Chelsfield 3	d					08 45						09 15							09 45						
Knockholt	d					08 48						09 18							09 48						
Dunton Green	d					08 53						09 23							09 53						
Sevenoaks 4	a			08 18	08 33	08 56		08 48			09 05	09 26		09 11	09 19			09 35	09 56		09 41	09 48			
	d			08 19	08 33			08 49			09 05			09 12	09 20			09 35			09 42	09 49			
Hildenborough	d				08 39						09 11							09 41							
Tonbridge 4	a			08 27	08 43			08 57			09 15			09 20	09 28			09 45			09 50	09 57			

		SE 1	SE	SE 1	SE 1	SE	SE	SE 1		SE	SE	SE 1 (cycle)	SE 1	SE	SE	SE 1	SE	SE 1 (cycle)		SE 1	SE	SE	SE 1	SE	SE
London Charing Cross 4 ⊖	d	09 30	09 36	09 40	09 45			10 00		10 06		10 10	10 15			10 30	10 36	10 40		10 45			11 00	11 06	
London Waterloo (East) 4 ⊖	d	09 33	09 39	09 43	09 48			10 03		10 09		10 13	10 18			10 33	10 39	10 43		10 48			11 03	11 09	
London Cannon Street 4 ⊖	d					09 50								10 20							10 50				
London Bridge 4 ⊖	d	09 39	09 44	09 49	09 53	09 54		10 09		10 14		10 19	10 23	10 24		10 39	10 44	10 49		10 53	10 54		11 09	11 14	
New Cross 4 ⊖	d					09 59								10 29							10 59				
St Johns	d					10 01								10 31							11 01				
Lewisham 4	d					10 04								10 34							11 04				
Hither Green 4	d		09 53			10 08				10 23				10 38			10 53				11 08			11 23	
Grove Park 4	d		09 57			10 12	10 15			10 27	10 35			10 42	10 55		10 57				11 12	11 15		11 27	11 35
Sundridge Park	d						10 18				10 38				10 58							11 18			11 38
Bromley North	a						10 20				10 40				11 00							11 20			11 40
Elmstead Woods	d		10 00			10 15				10 30				10 45			11 00				11 15			11 30	
Chislehurst	d		10 03			10 18				10 33				10 48			11 03				11 18			11 33	
Petts Wood 4	d		10 06			10 21				10 36				10 51			11 06				11 21			11 36	
Orpington 4	a	09 55	10 09		10 08	10 24		10 25		10 39			10 38	10 54		10 55	11 09			11 08	11 24		11 25	11 39	
	d	09 56	10 12		10 09			10 26		10 42			10 39			10 56	11 12			11 09			11 26	11 42	
Chelsfield 3	d		10 15							10 45							11 15							11 45	
Knockholt	d		10 18							10 48							11 18							11 48	
Dunton Green	d		10 23							10 53							11 23							11 53	
Sevenoaks 4	a	10 05	10 26	10 11	10 18			10 35		10 56		10 41	10 48			11 05	11 26	11 11		11 18			11 35	11 56	
	d	10 05		10 12	10 19			10 35				10 42	10 49			11 05		11 12		11 19			11 35		
Hildenborough	d	10 11						10 41								11 11							11 41		
Tonbridge 4	a	10 15		10 20	10 27			10 45				10 50	10 57			11 15		11 20		11 27			11 45		

Table 204

Saturdays

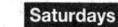

14 December to 17 May

London Charing Cross/Cannon Street - Grove Park, Orpington, Sevenoaks and Tonbridge, Grove Park - Bromley North

Network Diagram - see first Page of Table 200

		SE	SE	SE	SE	SE	SE	SE	SE	SE		SE	SE	SE	SE	SE	SE	SE	SE	SE		SE	SE	SE	SE
		1 🛒	1			1		1 🛒	1				1			1 🛒	1			1			1 🛒	1	
London Charing Cross 4 ⊖	d	11 10	11 15			11 30	11 36	11 40	11 45				12 00	12 06		12 10	12 15			12 30		12 36	12 40	12 45	
London Waterloo (East) 4 ⊖	d	11 13	11 18			11 33	11 39	11 43	11 48				12 03	12 09		12 13	12 18			12 33		12 39	12 43	12 48	
London Cannon Street 4 ⊖	d			11 20						11 50								12 20							12 50
London Bridge 4 ⊖	d	11 19	11 23	11 24		11 39	11 44	11 49	11 53	11 54			12 09	12 14		12 19	12 23	12 24		12 39		12 44	12 49	12 53	12 54
New Cross 4 ⊖	d			11 29						11 59								12 29							12 59
St Johns	d			11 31						12 01								12 31							13 01
Lewisham 4 🚋	d			11 34						12 04								12 34							13 04
Hither Green 4	d			11 38			11 53			12 08				12 23				12 38				12 53			13 08
Grove Park 4	d			11 42	11 55		11 57			12 12		12 15		12 27	12 35			12 42	12 55			12 57			13 12
Sundridge Park	d				11 58							12 18			12 38				12 58						
Bromley North	a				12 00							12 20			12 40				13 00						
Elmstead Woods	d			11 45			12 00			12 15				12 30				12 45				13 00			13 15
Chislehurst	d			11 48			12 03			12 18				12 33				12 48				13 03			13 18
Petts Wood 4	d			11 51			12 06			12 21				12 36				12 51				13 06			13 21
Orpington 4	a		11 38	11 54		11 55	12 09		12 08	12 24			12 25	12 39			12 38	12 54		12 55		13 09		13 08	13 24
	d		11 39			11 56	12 12		12 09				12 26	12 42			12 39			12 56		13 12		13 09	
Chelsfield 3	d						12 15							12 45								13 15			
Knockholt	d						12 18							12 48								13 18			
Dunton Green	d						12 23							12 53								13 23			
Sevenoaks 4	a	11 41	11 48			12 05	12 26	12 11	12 18				12 35	12 56		12 41	12 48			13 05		13 26	13 11	13 18	
	d	11 42	11 49			12 05		12 12	12 19				12 35			12 42	12 49			13 05			13 12	13 19	
Hildenborough	d					12 11							12 41							13 11					
Tonbridge 4	a	11 50	11 57			12 15		12 20	12 27				12 45			12 50	12 57			13 15			13 20	13 27	

		SE	SE	SE	SE	SE		SE	SE	SE	SE	SE	SE	SE	SE	SE		SE	SE	SE	SE	SE	SE	SE	SE
			1			1 🛒		1			1		1 🛒	1				1			1 🛒	1			1
London Charing Cross 4 ⊖	d		13 00	13 06		13 10		13 15			13 30	13 36	13 40	13 45				14 00	14 06		14 10	14 15			14 30
London Waterloo (East) 4 ⊖	d		13 03	13 09		13 13		13 18			13 33	13 39	13 43	13 48				14 03	14 09		14 13	14 18			14 33
London Cannon Street 4 ⊖	d								13 20						13 50								14 20		
London Bridge 4 ⊖	d		13 09	13 14		13 19		13 23	13 24		13 39	13 44	13 49	13 53	13 54			14 09	14 14		14 19	14 23	14 24		14 39
New Cross 4 ⊖	d								13 29						13 59								14 29		
St Johns	d								13 31						14 01								14 31		
Lewisham 4 🚋	d								13 34						14 04								14 34		
Hither Green 4	d			13 23					13 38			13 53			14 08				14 23				14 38		
Grove Park 4	d	13 15		13 27	13 35				13 42	13 55		13 57			14 12	14 15			14 27	14 35			14 42	14 55	
Sundridge Park	d	13 18			13 38					13 58						14 18				14 38				14 58	
Bromley North	a	13 20			13 40					14 00						14 20				14 40				15 00	
Elmstead Woods	d			13 30					13 45			14 00			14 15				14 30				14 45		
Chislehurst	d			13 33					13 48			14 03			14 18				14 33				14 48		
Petts Wood 4	d			13 36					13 51			14 06			14 21				14 36				14 51		
Orpington 4	a		13 25	13 39				13 38	13 54		13 55	14 09		14 08	14 24			14 25	14 39			14 38	14 54		14 55
	d		13 26	13 42				13 39			13 56	14 12		14 09				14 26	14 42			14 39			14 56
Chelsfield 3	d			13 45								14 15							14 45						
Knockholt	d			13 48								14 18							14 48						
Dunton Green	d			13 53								14 23							14 53						
Sevenoaks 4	a		13 35	13 56		13 41		13 48			14 05	14 26	14 11	14 18				14 35	14 56		14 41	14 48			15 05
	d		13 35			13 42		13 49			14 05		14 12	14 19				14 35			14 42	14 49			15 05
Hildenborough	d		13 41								14 11							14 41							15 11
Tonbridge 4	a		13 45			13 50		13 57			14 15		14 20	14 27				14 45			14 50	14 57			15 15

		SE		SE	SE	SE	SE	SE	SE	SE	SE	SE		SE	SE	SE	SE	SE	SE	SE	SE	SE		SE	SE
				1 🛒	1			1			1 🛒	1				1		1 🛒	1			1			
London Charing Cross 4 ⊖	d	14 36		14 40	14 45			15 00	15 06		15 10	15 15				15 30	15 36	15 40	15 45			16 00		16 06	
London Waterloo (East) 4 ⊖	d	14 39		14 43	14 48			15 03	15 09		15 13	15 18				15 33	15 39	15 43	15 48			16 03		16 09	
London Cannon Street 4 ⊖	d					14 50								15 20						15 50					
London Bridge 4 ⊖	d	14 44		14 49	14 53	14 54		15 09	15 14		15 19	15 23		15 24		15 39	15 44	15 49	15 53	15 54		16 09		16 14	
New Cross 4 ⊖	d					14 59								15 29						15 59					
St Johns	d					15 01								15 31						16 01					
Lewisham 4 🚋	d					15 04								15 34						16 04					
Hither Green 4	d	14 53				15 08			15 23					15 38			15 53			16 08				16 23	
Grove Park 4	d	14 57				15 12	15 15		15 27	15 35				15 42	15 55		15 57			16 12	16 15			16 27	16 35
Sundridge Park	d						15 18			15 38					15 58						16 18				16 38
Bromley North	a						15 20			15 40					16 00						16 20				16 40
Elmstead Woods	d	15 00				15 15			15 30					15 45			16 00			16 15				16 30	
Chislehurst	d	15 03				15 18			15 33					15 48			16 03			16 18				16 33	
Petts Wood 4	d	15 06				15 21			15 36					15 51			16 06			16 21				16 36	
Orpington 4	a	15 09			15 08	15 24		15 25	15 39			15 38		15 54		15 55	16 09		16 08	16 24		16 25		16 39	
	d	15 12			15 09			15 26	15 42			15 39				15 56	16 12		16 09			16 26		16 42	
Chelsfield 3	d	15 15							15 45								16 15							16 45	
Knockholt	d	15 18							15 48								16 18							16 48	
Dunton Green	d	15 23							15 53								16 23							16 53	
Sevenoaks 4	a	15 26		15 11	15 18			15 35	15 56		15 41	15 48				16 05	16 26	16 11	16 18			16 35		16 56	
	d			15 12	15 19			15 35			15 42	15 49				16 05		16 12	16 19			16 35			
Hildenborough	d							15 41								16 11						16 41			
Tonbridge 4	a			15 20	15 27			15 45			15 50	15 57				16 15		16 20	16 27			16 45			

Table 204

Saturdays

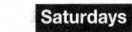

14 December to 17 May

London Charing Cross/Cannon Street - Grove Park, Orpington, Sevenoaks and Tonbridge, Grove Park - Bromley North

Network Diagram - see first Page of Table 200

	SE 1 ⚲	SE 1	SE		SE	SE 1	SE	SE 1 ⚲	SE 1	SE	SE	SE 1	SE		SE	SE 1 ⚲	SE 1	SE	SE	SE 1	SE	SE 1 ⚲	SE 1	
London Charing Cross 4 ⊖ d	16 10	16 15				16 30	16 36	16 40	16 45			17 00	17 06			17 10	17 15			17 30	17 36	17 40	17 45	
London Waterloo (East) 4 ⊖ d	16 13	16 18				16 33	16 39	16 43	16 48			17 03	17 09			17 13	17 18			17 33	17 39	17 43	17 48	
London Cannon Street 4 ⊖ d			16 20							16 50								17 20						
London Bridge 4 ⊖ d	16 19	16 23	16 24			16 39	16 44	16 49	16 53	16 54		17 09	17 14			17 19	17 23	17 24		17 39	17 44	17 49	17 53	
New Cross 4 ⊖ d			16 29							16 59								17 29						
St Johns d			16 31							17 01								17 31						
Lewisham 4 ⇌ d			16 34							17 04								17 34						
Hither Green 4 d			16 38				16 53			17 08			17 23					17 38			17 53			
Grove Park 4 d			16 42		16 55		16 57			17 12	17 15		17 27		17 35			17 42	17 55		17 57			
Sundridge Park d					16 58						17 18				17 38				17 58					
Bromley North a					17 00						17 20				17 40				18 00					
Elmstead Woods d			16 45				17 00			17 15			17 30					17 45			18 00			
Chislehurst d			16 48				17 03			17 18			17 33					17 48			18 03			
Petts Wood 4 d			16 51				17 06			17 21			17 36					17 51			18 06			
Orpington 4 a		16 38	16 54			16 55	17 09		17 08	17 24		17 25	17 39				17 38	17 54		17 55	18 09		18 08	
d		16 39				16 56	17 12		17 09			17 26	17 42				17 39			17 56	18 12		18 09	
Chelsfield 3 d							17 15						17 45								18 15			
Knockholt d							17 18						17 48								18 18			
Dunton Green d							17 23						17 53								18 23			
Sevenoaks 4 a	16 41	16 48				17 05	17 26	17 11	17 18			17 35	17 56			17 41	17 48			18 05	18 26	18 11	18 18	
d	16 42	16 49				17 05		17 12	17 19			17 35				17 42	17 49			18 05		18 12	18 19	
Hildenborough d						17 11						17 41								18 11				
Tonbridge 4 a	16 50	16 57				17 15		17 20	17 27			17 45				17 50	17 57			18 15		18 20	18 27	

	SE	SE	SE 1	SE	SE	SE 1 ⚲	SE 1	SE	SE		SE 1	SE	SE 1 ⚲	SE 1	SE	SE	SE 1	SE	SE		SE 1 ⚲	SE 1	SE	SE
London Charing Cross 4 ⊖ d			18 00	18 06		18 10	18 15				18 30	18 36	18 40	18 45			19 00	19 06			19 10	19 15		
London Waterloo (East) 4 ⊖ d			18 03	18 09		18 13	18 18				18 33	18 39	18 43	18 48			19 03	19 09			19 13	19 18		
London Cannon Street 4 ⊖ d	17 50							18 20							18 50								19 20	
London Bridge 4 ⊖ d	17 54		18 09	18 14		18 19	18 23	18 24			18 39	18 44	18 49	18 53	18 54		19 09	19 14			19 19	19 23	19 24	
New Cross 4 ⊖ d	17 59							18 29							18 59								19 29	
St Johns d	18 01							18 31							19 01								19 31	
Lewisham 4 ⇌ d	18 04							18 34							19 04								19 34	
Hither Green 4 d	18 08			18 23				18 38				18 53			19 09			19 23					19 38	
Grove Park 4 d	18 12	18 15		18 27	18 35			18 42	18 55			18 57			19 12	19 15		19 27	19 35				19 42	19 55
Sundridge Park d		18 18			18 38				18 58							19 18			19 38					19 58
Bromley North a		18 20			18 40				19 00							19 20			19 40					20 00
Elmstead Woods d	18 15			18 30				18 45				19 00			19 15			19 30					19 45	
Chislehurst d	18 18			18 33				18 48				19 03			19 18			19 33					19 48	
Petts Wood 4 d	18 21			18 36				18 51				19 06			19 21			19 36					19 51	
Orpington 4 a	18 24		18 25	18 39			18 38	18 54			18 55	19 09		19 08	19 24		19 25	19 39				19 38	19 54	
d			18 26	18 42			18 39				18 56	19 12		19 09			19 26	19 42				19 39		
Chelsfield 3 d				18 45								19 15						19 45						
Knockholt d				18 48								19 18						19 48						
Dunton Green d				18 53								19 23						19 53						
Sevenoaks 4 a			18 35	18 56		18 41	18 48				19 05	19 26	19 11	19 18			19 35	19 56			19 41	19 49		
d			18 35			18 42	18 49				19 05		19 12	19 19			19 35				19 42	19 49		
Hildenborough d			18 41								19 11						19 41							
Tonbridge 4 a			18 45			18 50	18 58				19 15		19 20	19 27			19 45				19 50	19 58		

	SE 1	SE	SE	SE 1 ⚲	SE 1		SE	SE	SE 1 ⚲	SE 1	SE	SE	SE 1	SE 1	SE		SE	SE 1	SE 1	SE	SE	SE 1	SE 1	SE
London Charing Cross 4 ⊖ d	19 30	19 36		19 40	19 55		20 06		20 10	20 25	20 36		20 40	20 55	21 06			21 10	21 25	21 36		21 40	21 55	22 06
London Waterloo (East) 4 ⊖ d	19 33	19 39		19 43	19 58		20 09		20 13	20 28	20 39		20 43	20 58	21 09			21 13	21 28	21 39		21 43	21 58	22 09
London Cannon Street 4 ⊖ d																								
London Bridge 4 ⊖ d	19 39	19 44		19 49	20 03		20 14		20 19	20 33	20 44		20 49	21 03	21 14			21 19	21 33	21 44		21 49	22 03	22 14
New Cross 4 ⊖ d																								
St Johns d																								
Lewisham 4 ⇌ d		19 52					20 22				20 52				21 22					21 52				22 22
Hither Green 4 d		19 56					20 26				20 56				21 26					21 56				22 26
Grove Park 4 d		20 00	20 15				20 30	20 37			21 00	21 07			21 30		21 37			22 00	22 07			22 30
Sundridge Park d			20 18					20 40				21 10					21 40				22 10			
Bromley North a			20 20					20 42				21 12					21 42				22 12			
Elmstead Woods d		20 03					20 33				21 03				21 33					22 03				22 33
Chislehurst d		20 05					20 35				21 05				21 35					22 05				22 35
Petts Wood 4 d		20 08					20 38				21 08				21 38					22 08				22 38
Orpington 4 a	19 55	20 12			20 18		20 42		20 34	20 48	21 12		21 04	21 18	21 42			21 34	21 48	22 12		22 04	22 18	22 42
d	19 56	20 13			20 21		20 43		20 35	20 51	21 13		21 05	21 21	21 43			21 35	21 51			22 05	22 21	
Chelsfield 3 d		20 16					20 46				21 16				21 46									
Knockholt d		20 19					20 49				21 19				21 49									
Dunton Green d		20 24					20 54				21 24				21 54									
Sevenoaks 4 a	20 05	20 27		20 11	20 30		20 57		20 44	21 00	21 27		21 14	21 30	21 57			21 44	22 00			22 14	22 30	
d	20 05			20 12	20 31				20 44	21 01			21 14	21 31				21 44	22 01			22 14	22 31	
Hildenborough d	20 11									21 07									22 07					
Tonbridge 4 a	20 15			20 20	20 39				20 52	21 11			21 22	21 39				21 52	22 11			22 22	22 39	

Table 204

Saturdays

14 December to 17 May

London Charing Cross/Cannon Street - Grove Park, Orpington, Sevenoaks and Tonbridge, Grove Park - Bromley North

Network Diagram - see first Page of Table 200

		SE	SE 1	SE 1	SE	SE	SE 1	SE 1	SE	SE	SE 1	SE 1	SE	SE 1	SE 1
London Charing Cross 4 ⊖	d		22 10	22 25	22 36		22 40	22 55	23 06		23 10	23 25	23 36	23 40	23 45
London Waterloo (East) 4 ⊖	d		22 13	22 28	22 39		22 43	22 58	23 09		23 13	23 28	23 39	23 43	23 48
London Cannon Street 4 ⊖	d														
London Bridge 4 ⊖	d		22 19	22 33	22 44		22 49	23 03	23 14		23 19	23 33	23 44	23 49	23 53
New Cross 4 ⊖	d														
St Johns	d														
Lewisham 4	d				22 52				23 22				23 52		
Hither Green 4	d				22 56				23 26				23 56		
Grove Park 4	d	22 37			23 00	23 07			23 30	23 37			23 59		
Sundridge Park	d	22 40				23 10				23 40					
Bromley North	a	22 42				23 12				23 42					
Elmstead Woods	d				23 03				23 33				00 03		
Chislehurst	d				23 05				23 35				00 05		
Petts Wood 4	d				23 08				23 38				00 08		
Orpington 4	a		22 34	22 48	23 12		23 04	23 18	23 42		23 34	23 48	00 12	00 04	00 08
	d		22 35	22 49			23 05	23 19			23 35	23 49		00 05	00 09
Chelsfield 3	d			22 52								23 52			
Knockholt	d														
Dunton Green	d														
Sevenoaks 4	a		22 44	22 59			23 14	23 28			23 43	23 59		00 14	00 18
	d		22 44	23 00			23 14	23 28			23 44	23 59		00 14	00 19
Hildenborough	d			23 06								00 06			
Tonbridge 4	a		22 52	23 10			23 22	23 36			23 53	00 10		00 23	00 27

Sundays

8 December to 11 May

		SE 1 A	SE 1 A	SE	SE 1 A	SE A	SE	SE	SE	SE	SE	SE	SE 1	SE 1	SE	SE 1	SE 1		SE	SE 1 🛒	SE 1	SE	SE 1 🛒
London Charing Cross 4 ⊖	d						00 06		00 15	00 48	07 30	08 00	08 10	08 25	08 30	08 40	08 55		19 00	19 10	19 25	19 30	19 40
London Waterloo (East) 4 ⊖	d						00 09		00 18	00 51	07 33	08 03	08 13	08 28	08 33	08 43	08 58		19 03	19 13	19 28	19 33	19 43
London Cannon Street 4 ⊖	d																						
London Bridge 4 ⊖	d						00 14		00 23	00 56	07 38	08 08	08 19	08 33	08 38	08 49	09 03		19 08	19 19	19 33	19 38	19 49
New Cross 4 ⊖	d									01 01													
St Johns	d																						
Lewisham 4	d						00 22			01 05	07 47	08 17			08 47			and at	19 17			19 47	
Hither Green 4	d						00 26			01 09	07 52	08 22			08 52			the same	19 22			19 52	
Grove Park 4	d			00 07			00 30	00 37		01 13	07 56	08 26			08 56			minutes	19 26			19 56	
Sundridge Park	d			00 10				00 40										past					
Bromley North	a			00 12				00 42										each					
Elmstead Woods	d					00 03	00 33			01 16	07 59	08 29			08 59			hour until	19 29			19 59	
Chislehurst	d					00 05	00 35			01 19	08 01	08 31			09 01				19 31			20 01	
Petts Wood 4	d					00 08	00 38			01 22	08 04	08 34			09 04				19 34			20 04	
Orpington 4	a					00 12	00 42		00 47	01 25	08 08	08 38	08 34	08 48	09 08	09 04	09 18		19 38	19 34	19 48	20 08	20 04
	d		00 05		00 09				00 48			08 39	08 35	08 49		09 05	09 19		19 39	19 35	19 49		20 05
Chelsfield 3	d								00 51			08 42							19 42				
Knockholt	d											08 45							19 45				
Dunton Green	d								00 57			08 50							19 50				
Sevenoaks 4	a		00 14		00 18				01 00			08 54	08 44	08 58		09 14	09 28		19 54	19 44	19 58		20 14
	d		00 14		00 19				01 01				08 45	08 59		09 15	09 29			19 45	19 59		20 15
Hildenborough	d	00 06							01 07								09 35						
Tonbridge 4	a	00 10	00 23		00 27				01 12				08 53	09 07		09 23	09 39			19 53	20 07		20 23

		SE 1	SE	SE 1 🛒	SE 1	SE	SE 1	SE	SE 1	SE 1	SE	SE 1	SE	SE 1	SE 1	SE	SE 1	SE	SE 1	SE 1	SE	SE 1
London Charing Cross 4 ⊖	d	19 55	20 00	20 10	20 25	20 30	20 40	21 00	21 10	21 25	21 30	21 40	22 00	22 10	22 25	22 30	22 40	23 00	23 10	23 25	23 30	23 40
London Waterloo (East) 4 ⊖	d	19 58	20 03	20 13	20 28	20 33	20 43	21 03	21 13	21 28	21 33	21 43	22 03	22 13	22 28	22 33	22 43	23 03	23 13	23 28	23 33	23 43
London Cannon Street 4 ⊖	d																					
London Bridge 4 ⊖	d	20 03	20 08	20 19	20 33	20 38	20 49	21 08	21 19	21 33	21 38	21 49	22 08	22 19	22 33	22 38	22 49	23 08	23 19	23 33	23 38	23 49
New Cross 4 ⊖	d																					
St Johns	d																					
Lewisham 4	d		20 17			20 47		21 17			21 47		22 17			22 47		23 17			23 47	
Hither Green 4	d		20 22			20 52		21 22			21 52		22 22			22 52		23 22			23 52	
Grove Park 4	d		20 26			20 56		21 26			21 56		22 26			22 56		23 26			23 56	
Sundridge Park	d																					
Bromley North	a																					
Elmstead Woods	d		20 29			20 59		21 29			21 59		22 29			22 59		23 29			23 59	
Chislehurst	d		20 31			21 01		21 31			22 01		22 31			23 01		23 31			00 01	
Petts Wood 4	d		20 34			21 04		21 34			22 04		22 34			23 04		23 34			00 04	
Orpington 4	a	20 18	20 38	20 34	20 48	21 08	21 04	21 38	21 34	21 48	22 08	22 04	22 38	22 34	22 48	23 08	23 04	23 38	23 34	23 48	00 08	00 04
	d	20 19	20 39	20 35	20 49		21 05	21 39	21 35	21 49		22 05		22 35	22 49		23 05		23 35	23 49		00 05
Chelsfield 3	d		20 42					21 42		21 52					22 52					23 52		
Knockholt	d		20 45					21 45														
Dunton Green	d		20 50					21 50														
Sevenoaks 4	a	20 28	20 54	20 44	20 58		21 14	21 54	21 44	21 59		22 14		22 44	22 59		23 14		23 44	23 58		00 14
	d	20 29		20 45	20 59		21 15		21 45	22 00		22 15		22 45	23 00		23 15		23 45	23 59		00 15
Hildenborough	d	20 35			21 05					22 06					23 06					00 06		
Tonbridge 4	a	20 39		20 53	21 09		21 23		21 53	22 10		22 23		22 53	23 10		23 23		23 53	00 10		00 23

A not 8 December

Table 204R

Mondays to Fridays

9 December to 16 May

Bromley North to Grove Park, Tonbridge, Sevenoaks, Orpington and Grove Park - London Cannon Street/Charing Cross

Network Diagram - see first Page of Table 200

Miles	Miles			SE MX	SE	SE	SE [1]	SE	SE [1]	SE		SE	SE [1]	SE [1]	SE [1]	SE	SE	SE	SE [1]	SE [1]		SE	SE [1]	SE	SE
0	—	**Tonbridge [4]**	d		04 52		05 32		05 50				06 00	06 06	06 17				06 32	06 40			06 44		
2½	—	Hildenborough	d		04 56		05 36						06 04		06 21				06 36						
7½	—	**Sevenoaks [4]**	a		05 02		05 42		05 58				06 10	06 14	06 28				06 43	06 48			06 52		
—	—		d		05 03		05 43		05 59			06 02	06 11	06 15	06 30			06 36	06 44	06 49			06 53		06 56
1½	—	Dunton Green	d									06 05						06 39							06 59
5½	—	Knockholt	d									06 10						06 44							07 04
6¾	—	Chelsfield [3]	d		05 10		05 50					06 13						06 47							07 07
8¼	—	**Orpington [4]**	a		05 13		05 53		06 08			06 16	06 19	06 23	06 38			06 50	06 53				07 02		07 10
—	—		d		05 14	05 15	05 54	06 01	06 09			06 22	06 20	06 24	06 39		06 43	06 52	06 54			07 03	07 04		07 11
9¼	—	Petts Wood [4]	d			05 18		06 04				06 25					06 46	06 55				07 06			07 15
10¾	—	Chislehurst	d			05 21		06 07				06 28					06 49	06 58				07 09			07 18
11¾	—	Elmstead Woods	d			05 23		06 09				06 30					06 51	07 00				07 11			07 20
—	0	**Bromley North**	d	00 23						06 25						06 45								07 15	
—	0½	Sundridge Park	d	00 25						06 27						06 47								07 17	
13	1¾	**Grove Park [4]**	d	00a28		05 27		06 12		06a30		06 34				06a50	06 54	07 04				07 15		07a20	07 24
14¾	—	Hither Green [4]	d			05 30		06 16				06 38					06 58	07 08				07 19			07 28
16	—	**Lewisham [4]**	d			05 36		06 22				06 43					07 04					07 25			
16½	—	St Johns	a																						
17¼	—	New Cross [4] ⊖	a			05 39		06 25																	
20¼	—	**London Bridge [4]** ⊖	a		05 37	05 45	06 09	06 31	06 24			06 51	06 38	06 39	06 54			07 18	07 09	07 14			07 22		07 37
—	—	**London Cannon Street [4]** ⊖	a										06 43					07 26					07 30		07 44
21¼	—	**London Waterloo (East) [4]** ⊖	a		05 41	05 50	06 14	06 36	06 29			06 56		06 44	06 59		07 16		07 14	07 19		07 36			
22	—	**London Charing Cross [4]** ⊖	a		05 47	05 56	06 18	06 39	06 33			07 02		06 49	07 05		07 22		07 20	07 25		07 42			

		SE [1]	SE [1]	SE [1]	SE	SE		SE	SE [1]	SE [1]	SE [1]	SE	SE	SE	SE [1]	SE [1]		SE	SE [1]	SE	SE	SE	SE [1]	SE [1]	SE
Tonbridge [4]	d	06 51	07 02	07 11					07 15	07 23	07 31				07 35	07 42			07 51				07 59	08 04	
Hildenborough	d	06 55		07 15					07 20		07 35				07 40				07 55						
Sevenoaks [4]	a	07 02	07 10	07 22					07 26	07 31	07 42				07 46	07 50			08 02				08 07	08 12	
	d	07 03	07 11	07 23				07 17	07 27	07 32	07 43			07 37	07 47	07 51			08 03			07 57	08 08	08 12	
Dunton Green	d							07 20						07 40								08 00			
Knockholt	d							07 25						07 45								08 05			
Chelsfield [3]	d			07 32				07 28			07 52			07 48					08 12			08 08			
Orpington [4]	a	07 13						07 31						07 51								08 12			
	d	07 14			07 22			07 33				07 41		07 52				07 57		08 01		08 13			08 21
Petts Wood [4]	d				07 25			07 36				07 44		07 55				08 00		08 04		08 16			08 24
Chislehurst	d				07 28			07 39				07 47		07 59				08 03		08 07		08 20			08 27
Elmstead Woods	d				07 31			07 41				07 50		08 01				08 06		08 10		08 22			08 29
Bromley North	d					07 35							07 55								08 15				
Sundridge Park	d					07 37							07 57								08 17				
Grove Park [4]	d				07 35	07a40		07 45				07 53	08a00	08 05				08 09		08 13	08a20	08 26			08 33
Hither Green [4]	d				07 39			07 49				07 58								08 17					08 37
Lewisham [4]	d				07 44							08 03								08 23					
St Johns	a																								
New Cross [4] ⊖	a																								
London Bridge [4] ⊖	a	07 29	07 36	07 50	07 53			07 59	07 53		08 09			08 18	08 13				08 29			08 39	08 33		
London Cannon Street [4] ⊖	a							08 06	08 00					08 26	08 20							08 46	08 40		
London Waterloo (East) [4] ⊖	a	07 34	07 41	07 55	07 58					08 00	08 14	08 16				08 20		08 24	08 34	08 36				08 40	08 52
London Charing Cross [4] ⊖	a	07 40	07 47	08 01	08 04					08 06	08 20	08 22				08 26		08 30	08 40	08 42				08 46	08 58

		SE		SE	SE [1]	SE [1]	SE [1]	SE [1]	SE [1]	SE	SE	SE		SE	SE [1]	SE [1]	SE	SE	SE [1]	SE [1] 🚲	SE	SE [1]		SE	SE
Tonbridge [4]	d				08 11	08 15	08 22	08 35	08 40						08 43	08 50			09 02	09 10		09 20			
Hildenborough	d				08 15	08 20		08 39							08 48				09 06						
Sevenoaks [4]	a				08 22	08 26	08 30	08 45	08 48						08 54	08 58			09 13	09 18		09 28			
	d			08 17	08 23	08 27	08 31	08 45	08 49			08 37			08 55	08 59		09 06	09 14	09 19		09 29			09 36
Dunton Green	d			08 20								08 40						09 09							09 39
Knockholt	d			08 25								08 45						09 14							09 44
Chelsfield [3]	d			08 28	08 32			08 53				08 48						09 17							09 47
Orpington [4]	a			08 31								08 51			09 03	09 08		09 20	09 24			09 38			09 50
	d			08 32						08 43		08 52		09 03	09 04	09 09		09 21	09 24		09 33	09 39			09 51
Petts Wood [4]	d			08 35						08 46		08 55		09 06				09 24			09 36				09 54
Chislehurst	d			08 39						08 50		08 58		09 09				09 27			09 39				09 57
Elmstead Woods	d			08 41						08 52		09 00		09 11				09 30			09 41				09 59
Bromley North	d	08 35									08 55						09 25							09 45	
Sundridge Park	d	08 37									08 57						09 27							09 47	
Grove Park [4]	d	08a40		08 45						08 56	09a00	09 04		09 15			09a30	09 33			09 45			09a50	10 03
Hither Green [4]	d									09 00		09 08		09 19				09 37			09 49				10 07
Lewisham [4]	d									09 05				09 24							09 54				
St Johns	a									09 08				09 26							09 56				
New Cross [4] ⊖	a									09 10				09 28							09 58				
London Bridge [4] ⊖	a			08 59	08 49	08 55		09 11	09 14	09 17		09 20		09 33	09 22	09 26		09 49	09 40	09 43	10 04	09 55			10 19
London Cannon Street [4] ⊖	a			09 06		09 02				09 24				09 40	09 29						10 08				
London Waterloo (East) [4] ⊖	a				08 54		09 00	09 16	09 19			09 25				09 31		09 53	09 45	09 48		09 59			10 23
London Charing Cross [4] ⊖	a				09 00		09 06	09 22	09 25			09 31				09 37		10 00	09 51	09 54		10 04			10 28

Table 204R

Mondays to Fridays

9 December to 16 May

Bromley North to Grove Park, Tonbridge, Sevenoaks, Orpington and Grove Park - London Cannon Street/Charing Cross

Network Diagram - see first Page of Table 200

		SE ■1	SE ■1 🚲	SE		SE	SE ■1	SE	SE	SE ■1	SE ■1 🚲	SE	SE ■1	SE		SE	SE ■1	SE ■1 🚲	SE	SE	SE ■1	SE	SE	SE ■1	
Tonbridge 4	d	09 32	09 40				09 50			10 02	10 10		10 20				10 32	10 40			10 50			11 02	
Hildenborough	d	09 36								10 06							10 36							11 06	
Sevenoaks 4	a	09 43	09 48				09 58			10 13	10 18		10 28				10 43	10 48			10 58			11 13	
	d	09 44	09 49				09 59		10 06	10 14	10 19		10 29			10 36	10 44	10 49			10 59		11 06	11 14	
Dunton Green	d								10 09							10 39							11 09		
Knockholt	d								10 14							10 44							11 14		
Chelsfield 3	d								10 17							10 47							11 17		
Orpington 4	a	09 53					10 08		10 20	10 23			10 38			10 50	10 53				11 08		11 20	11 23	
	d	09 54				10 03	10 09		10 21	10 24		10 33	10 39			10 51	10 54			11 03	11 09		11 21	11 24	
Petts Wood 4	d					10 06			10 24			10 36				10 54				11 06			11 24		
Chislehurst	d					10 09			10 27			10 39				10 57				11 09			11 27		
Elmstead Woods	d					10 11			10 29			10 41				10 59				11 11			11 29		
Bromley North	d			10 05				10 25						10 45					11 05			11 25			
Sundridge Park	d			10 07				10 27						10 47					11 07			11 27			
Grove Park 4	d			10a10		10 15		10a30	10 33			10 45		10a50		11 03			11a10	11 15		11a30	11 33		
Hither Green 4	d					10 19			10 37			10 49				11 07				11 19			11 37		
Lewisham 4	d					10 24						10 54								11 24					
St Johns	a					10 26						10 56								11 26					
New Cross 4 ⊖	a					10 28						10 58								11 28					
London Bridge 4 ⊖	a	10 10	10 13			10 34	10 25		10 49	10 40	10 43	11 04	10 55			11 19	11 10	11 13		11 34	11 25		11 49	11 40	
London Cannon Street 4 ⊖	a					10 38						11 08								11 38					
London Waterloo (East) 4 ⊖	a	10 15	10 18				10 29		10 53	10 45	10 48		10 59			11 23	11 15	11 18			11 29		11 53	11 45	
London Charing Cross 4 ⊖	a	10 19	10 22				10 34		10 58	10 49	10 52		11 03			11 27	11 19	11 22			11 33		11 57	11 49	

		SE ■1 🚲	SE	SE ■1	SE	SE	SE ■1	SE ■1 🚲	SE	SE		SE ■1	SE	SE	SE ■1	SE ■1 🚲	SE	SE ■1	SE	SE		SE ■1	SE ■1 🚲	SE	SE
Tonbridge 4	d	11 10		11 20			11 32	11 40				11 50			12 02	12 10		12 20				12 32	12 40		
Hildenborough	d						11 36								12 06							12 36			
Sevenoaks 4	a	11 18		11 28			11 43	11 48				11 58			12 13	12 18		12 28				12 43	12 48		
	d	11 19		11 29		11 36	11 44	11 49				11 59		12 06	12 14	12 19		12 29		12 36		12 44	12 49		
Dunton Green	d					11 39								12 09						12 39					
Knockholt	d					11 44								12 14						12 44					
Chelsfield 3	d					11 47								12 17						12 47					
Orpington 4	a			11 38		11 50	11 53					12 08		12 20	12 23			12 38		12 50		12 53			
	d		11 33	11 39		11 51	11 54			12 03		12 09		12 21	12 24		12 33	12 39		12 51		12 54			13 03
Petts Wood 4	d		11 36			11 54				12 06				12 24			12 36			12 54					13 06
Chislehurst	d		11 39			11 57				12 09				12 27			12 39			12 57					13 09
Elmstead Woods	d		11 41			11 59				12 11				12 29			12 41			12 59					13 11
Bromley North	d				11 45				12 05				12 25						12 45					13 05	
Sundridge Park	d				11 47				12 07				12 27						12 47					13 07	
Grove Park 4	d		11 45		11a50	12 03			12a10	12 15			12a30	12 33			12 45		12a50	13 03				13a10	13 15
Hither Green 4	d		11 49			12 07				12 19				12 37			12 49			13 07					13 19
Lewisham 4	d		11 54							12 24							12 54								13 24
St Johns	a		11 56							12 26							12 56								13 26
New Cross 4 ⊖	a		11 58							12 28							12 58								13 28
London Bridge 4 ⊖	a	11 43	12 04	11 55		12 19	12 10	12 13		12 34		12 25		12 49	12 40	12 43	13 04	12 55		13 19		13 10	13 13		13 34
London Cannon Street 4 ⊖	a		12 08							12 38							13 08								13 38
London Waterloo (East) 4 ⊖	a	11 48		11 59		12 23	12 15	12 18				12 29		12 53	12 45	12 48		12 59		13 23		13 15	13 18		
London Charing Cross 4 ⊖	a	11 52		12 03		12 27	12 19	12 22				12 33		12 57	12 49	12 52		13 03		13 27		13 19	13 22		

		SE ■1	SE	SE	SE ■1	SE ■1 🚲		SE	SE ■1	SE	SE	SE ■1	SE ■1 🚲	SE	SE	SE ■1		SE	SE	SE ■1	SE ■1 🚲	SE	SE ■1	SE	SE
Tonbridge 4	d	12 50			13 02	13 10			13 20			13 32	13 40			13 50				14 02	14 10		14 20		
Hildenborough	d				13 06							13 36								14 06					
Sevenoaks 4	a	12 58			13 13	13 18			13 28			13 43	13 48			13 58				14 13	14 18		14 28		
	d	12 59		13 06	13 14	13 19			13 29		13 36	13 44	13 49			13 59			14 06	14 14	14 19		14 29		14 36
Dunton Green	d			13 09							13 39								14 09						14 39
Knockholt	d			13 14							13 44								14 14						14 44
Chelsfield 3	d			13 17							13 47								14 17						14 47
Orpington 4	a	13 08		13 20	13 23				13 38		13 50	13 53				14 08			14 20	14 23			14 38		14 50
	d	13 09		13 21	13 24			13 33	13 39		13 51	13 54			14 03	14 09			14 21	14 24		14 33	14 39		14 51
Petts Wood 4	d			13 24				13 36			13 54				14 06				14 24			14 36			14 54
Chislehurst	d			13 27				13 39			13 57				14 09				14 27			14 39			14 57
Elmstead Woods	d			13 29				13 41			13 59				14 11				14 29			14 41			14 59
Bromley North	d		13 25							13 45				14 05				14 25						14 45	
Sundridge Park	d		13 27							13 47				14 07				14 27						14 47	
Grove Park 4	d		13a30	13 33				13 45		13a50	14 03			14a10	14 15			14a30	14 33			14 45		14a50	15 03
Hither Green 4	d			13 37				13 49			14 07				14 19				14 37			14 49			15 07
Lewisham 4	d							13 54							14 24							14 54			
St Johns	a							13 56							14 26							14 56			
New Cross 4 ⊖	a							13 58							14 28							14 58			
London Bridge 4 ⊖	a	13 25		13 49	13 40	13 43		14 04	13 55		14 19	14 10	14 13		14 34	14 25			14 49	14 40	14 43	15 04	14 55		15 19
London Cannon Street 4 ⊖	a							14 08							14 38							15 08			
London Waterloo (East) 4 ⊖	a	13 29		13 53	13 45	13 48			13 59		14 23	14 15	14 18			14 29			14 53	14 45	14 48		14 59		15 23
London Charing Cross 4 ⊖	a	13 33		13 57	13 49	13 52			14 03		14 27	14 19	14 22			14 33			14 57	14 49	14 52		15 03		15 27

Table 204R

Mondays to Fridays

9 December to 16 May

Bromley North to Grove Park, Tonbridge, Sevenoaks, Orpington and Grove Park - London Cannon Street/Charing Cross

Network Diagram - see first Page of Table 200

		SE	SE	SE	SE	SE	SE	SE		SE	SE	SE	SE	SE	SE	SE	SE	SE		SE	SE	SE	SE	SE	SE
		1	1 🚲			1				1	1 🚲		1			1	1 🚲				1			1	1 🚲
Tonbridge 4	d	14 32	14 40			14 50				15 02	15 10		15 20			15 32	15 40				15 50			16 02	16 10
Hildenborough	d	14 36								15 06						15 36								16 06	
Sevenoaks 4	a	14 43	14 48			14 58				15 13	15 18		15 28			15 43	15 48				15 58			16 13	16 18
	d	14 44	14 49			14 59		15 06		15 14	15 19		15 29		15 36	15 44	15 49				15 59		16 06	16 14	16 19
Dunton Green	d							15 09							15 39								16 09		
Knockholt	d							15 14							15 44								16 14		
Chelsfield 3	d							15 17							15 47								16 17	16 21	
Orpington 4	a	14 53				15 08		15 20		15 23			15 38		15 50	15 53					16 07		16 20	16 24	
	d	14 54			15 03	15 09		15 21		15 24		15 33	15 39		15 51	15 54				16 03	16 08		16 21	16 25	
Petts Wood 4	d				15 06			15 24				15 36			15 54					16 06			16 24		
Chislehurst	d				15 09			15 27				15 39			15 57					16 09			16 27		
Elmstead Woods	d				15 11			15 29				15 41			15 59					16 11			16 29		
Bromley North	d			15 05			15 25							15 45				16 05				16 25			
Sundridge Park	d			15 07			15 27							15 47				16 07				16 27			
Grove Park 4	d			15a10	15 15		15a30	15 33				15 45		15a50	16 03			16a10		16 15		16a30	16 33		
Hither Green 4	d				15 19			15 37				15 49			16 07					16 19			16 37		
Lewisham 4 ⛴	d				15 24							15 54								16 24					
St Johns	a				15 26							15 56								16 26					
New Cross 4 ⊖	a				15 28							15 58								16 28					
London Bridge 4 ⊖	a	15 10	15 13		15 34	15 25		15 49		15 40	15 43	16 04	15 55		16 19	16 11	16 14			16 34	16 25		16 48	16 42	16 46
London Cannon Street 4 ⊖	a				15 38							16 08								16 38					
London Waterloo (East) 4 ⊖	a	15 15	15 18			15 29		15 55		15 45	15 48		15 59		16 24	16 16	16 20				16 29		16 54	16 48	16 52
London Charing Cross 4 ⊖	a	15 19	15 22			15 33		15 58		15 49	15 52		16 03		16 28	16 20	16 24				16 33		16 58	16 52	16 56

		SE	SE	SE		SE	SE	SE	SE	SE	SE	SE	SE	SE		SE	SE	SE	SE	SE	SE	SE	SE	SE	
			1				1	1 🚲		1				1		1 🚲			1			1	1 🚲		
Tonbridge 4	d		16 20				16 32	16 40		16 50				17 02		17 10			17 20			17 32	17 40		
Hildenborough	d						16 36							17 06								17 36			
Sevenoaks 4	a		16 28				16 43	16 48		16 58				17 13		17 18			17 28			17 43	17 48		
	d		16 29			16 36	16 44	16 52		16 59			17 05	17 14		17 19			17 29		17 35	17 44	17 49		
Dunton Green	d					16 39							17 08								17 38				
Knockholt	d					16 44							17 13								17 43				
Chelsfield 3	d					16 47							17 16								17 46				
Orpington 4	a		16 38			16 50	16 53			17 08			17 19	17 23					17 38		17 49	17 53			
	d	16 33	16 39			16 51	16 54		17 03	17 09		17 13	17 20	17 24				17 37	17 39		17 50	17 54		18 03	
Petts Wood 4	d	16 36				16 54			17 06				17 24					17 40			17 54			18 06	
Chislehurst	d	16 39				16 57			17 09				17 27					17 43			17 57			18 09	
Elmstead Woods	d	16 41				16 59			17 11				17 29					17 45			17 59			18 11	
Bromley North	d			16 45							17 10						17 30			17 50					
Sundridge Park	d			16 47							17 12						17 32			17 52					
Grove Park 4	d	16 45		16a50		17 03			17 15		17a15		17 34				17a35	17 49		17a55	18 03			18 15	
Hither Green 4	d	16 50				17 09			17 19				17 38					17 53			18 07			18 19	
Lewisham 4 ⛴	d								17 24															18 24	
St Johns	a								17 26									17 57						18 26	
New Cross 4 ⊖	a								17 28									17 59						18 28	
London Bridge 4 ⊖	a	17 01	16 56				17 11	17 17	17 34	17 27			17 49	17 41		17 44		18 06	17 58		18 18	18 09	18 16	18 34	
London Cannon Street 4 ⊖	a								17 38	17 32								18 11						18 38	
London Waterloo (East) 4 ⊖	a	17 06	17 00			17 24	17 16	17 22				17 36	17 53	17 46		17 50			18 02		18 23	18 14	18 20		
London Charing Cross 4 ⊖	a	17 10	17 04			17 29	17 20	17 26				17 42	17 57	17 50		17 53			18 06		18 27	18 18	18 25		

		SE	SE	SE	SE	SE	SE	SE	SE	SE		SE	SE	SE	SE	SE	SE	SE	SE	SE		SE	SE	SE	SE
		1			1	1 🚲	1						1	1 🚲		1			1	1 🚲		1			1
Tonbridge 4	d	17 50			18 02	18 10	18 23						18 32	18 40		18 50			19 02	19 10		19 20			19 32
Hildenborough	d				18 06								18 36						19 06						19 36
Sevenoaks 4	a	17 58			18 13	18 18	18 31						18 43	18 48		18 59			19 13	19 18		19 28			19 43
	d	17 59		18 05	18 14	18 19	18 32					18 35	18 44	18 49		18 59		19 06	19 14	19 19		19 29		19 36	19 44
Dunton Green	d			18 08								18 38						19 09						19 39	
Knockholt	d			18 13								18 43						19 14						19 44	
Chelsfield 3	d			18 16								18 46						19 17						19 47	
Orpington 4	a	18 08		18 19	18 23							18 49	18 53			19 08		19 20	19 23			19 38		19 50	19 53
	d	18 09		18 21	18 24				18 33			18 50	18 54		19 03	19 08		19 21	19 24			19 39		19 51	19 54
Petts Wood 4	d			18 24					18 36			18 54			19 06			19 24						19 54	
Chislehurst	d			18 27					18 39			18 57			19 09			19 27						19 57	
Elmstead Woods	d			18 29					18 41			18 59			19 11			19 29						19 59	
Bromley North	d		18 15					18 35		18 56							19 20						19 42		
Sundridge Park	d		18 17					18 37		18 58							19 22						19 44		
Grove Park 4	d		18a20	18 33				18a40	18 45	19a01		19 03			19 15		19a25	19 33					19a47	20 03	
Hither Green 4	d			18 37					18 49			19 07			19 19			19 37						20 07	
Lewisham 4 ⛴	d								18 54						19 24			19 43						20 13	
St Johns	a								18 56						19 26										
New Cross 4 ⊖	a								18 58						19 28										
London Bridge 4 ⊖	a	18 25		18 48	18 40	18 43	18 55		19 04			19 19	19 10	19 13	19 34	19 25		19 52	19 40	19 43		19 54		20 22	20 10
London Cannon Street 4 ⊖	a								19 10						19 38										
London Waterloo (East) 4 ⊖	a	18 29		18 53	18 45	18 48	18 59					19 23	19 14	19 17		19 29		19 56	19 45	19 48		19 59		20 26	20 15
London Charing Cross 4 ⊖	a	18 35		18 57	18 49	18 52	19 04					19 27	19 18	19 21		19 33		20 00	19 49	19 52		20 03		20 30	20 19

Table 204R

Mondays to Fridays

9 December to 16 May

Bromley North to Grove Park, Tonbridge, Sevenoaks, Orpington and Grove Park - London Cannon Street/Charing Cross

Network Diagram - see first Page of Table 200

		SE ■1		SE ■1	SE	SE	SE	SE ■1	SE ■1	SE	SE	SE ■1		SE ■1	SE ■1	SE	SE	SE ■1	SE ■1	SE	SE	SE ■1		SE ■1	SE ■1
Tonbridge ■4	d	19 40		19 51				20 02	20 10			20 32		20 40	20 50			21 02	21 10			21 32		21 40	21 50
Hildenborough	d							20 06				20 36						21 06				21 36			
Sevenoaks ■4	a	19 48		19 59				20 13	20 18			20 43		20 48	20 58			21 13	21 18			21 43		21 48	21 58
	d	19 49		20 00			20 06	20 14	20 19		20 35	20 44		20 49	20 59		21 05	21 14	21 19		21 35	21 44		21 49	21 59
Dunton Green	d						20 09				20 38						21 08				21 38				
Knockholt	d						20 14				20 43						21 13				21 43				
Chelsfield ■3	d						20 17				20 46						21 16				21 46				
Orpington ■4	a			20 08			20 20	20 23			20 49	20 52			21 08		21 19	21 22			21 49	21 52			22 08
	d			20 09			20 21	20 24			20 51	20 53			21 09		21 21	21 23			21 51	21 53			22 09
Petts Wood ■4	d						20 24				20 54						21 24				21 54				
Chislehurst	d						20 27				20 57						21 27				21 57				
Elmstead Woods	d						20 29				20 59						21 29				21 59				
Bromley North	d				20 02	20 27				20 53						21 23				21 53					
Sundridge Park	d				20 04	20 29				20 55						21 25				21 55					
Grove Park ■4	d				20a07	20a32	20 34			20a58	21 03					21a28	21 33			21a58	22 03				
Hither Green ■4	d						20 38				21 07						21 37				22 07				
Lewisham ■4	d						20 43				21 13						21 43				22 13				
St Johns	a																								
New Cross ■4	a																								
London Bridge ■4	a	20 13		20 24			20 52	20 39	20 42		21 22	21 08		21 13	21 24		21 52	21 38	21 43		22 22	22 08		22 13	22 24
London Cannon Street ■4	a																								
London Waterloo (East) ■4	a	20 18		20 29			20 56	20 44	20 47		21 26	21 13		21 18	21 29		21 56	21 43	21 48		22 26	22 13		22 18	22 29
London Charing Cross ■4	a	20 22		20 33			21 00	20 48	20 51		21 30	21 18		21 22	21 33		22 00	21 48	21 52		22 30	22 18		22 22	22 33

		SE	SE	SE ■1	SE ■1	SE	SE	SE ■1		SE ■1	SE ■1	SE	SE	SE ■1	SE
Tonbridge ■4	d			22 02	22 10			22 31		22 40	22 50			23 14	
Hildenborough	d			22 06				22 35						23 18	
Sevenoaks ■4	a			22 13	22 18			22 41		22 48	22 58			23 24	
	d		22 05	22 14	22 19			22 42		22 49	22 59			23 25	
Dunton Green	d		22 08												
Knockholt	d		22 13												
Chelsfield ■3	d		22 16					22 49						23 32	
Orpington ■4	a		22 19	22 22				22 52			23 08			23 36	
	d		22 21	22 23			22 51	22 53			23 09		23 21	23 37	
Petts Wood ■4	d		22 24				22 54						23 24		
Chislehurst	d		22 27				22 57						23 27		
Elmstead Woods	d		22 29				22 59						23 29		
Bromley North	d	22 23				22 53						23 23			23 53
Sundridge Park	d	22 25				22 55						23 25			23 55
Grove Park ■4	d	22a28	22 33			22a58	23 03					23a28	23 33		23a58
Hither Green ■4	d		22 37				23 07						23 37		
Lewisham ■4	d		22 43				23 13						23 43		
St Johns	a														
New Cross ■4	a														
London Bridge ■4	a		22 51	22 38	22 43		23 22	23 08		23 13	23 24		23 52	23 54	
London Cannon Street ■4	a														
London Waterloo (East) ■4	a		22 56	22 43	22 48		23 26	23 13		23 18	23 29		23 56	23 59	
London Charing Cross ■4	a		23 00	22 48	22 52		23 30	23 18		23 22	23 33		00 01	00 03	

Saturdays

14 December to 17 May

		SE	SE	SE	SE	SE ■1	SE	SE	SE ■1	SE ■1		SE	SE	SE ■1	SE	SE ■1	SE	SE	SE ■1	SE ■1		SE	SE	SE ■1	SE
Tonbridge ■4	d					06 02			06 32	06 50				07 02		07 20			07 32	07 40				07 50	
Hildenborough	d					06 06			06 36					07 06					07 36						
Sevenoaks ■4	a					06 13			06 43	06 58				07 13		07 28			07 43	07 48				07 58	
	d		05 36		06 06	06 14		06 36	06 44	06 59			07 06	07 14		07 29		07 36	07 44	07 49				07 59	
Dunton Green	d		05 39		06 09			06 39					07 09					07 39							
Knockholt	d		05 44		06 14			06 44					07 14					07 44							
Chelsfield ■3	d		05 47		06 17			06 47					07 17					07 47							
Orpington ■4	a		05 50		06 20	06 23		06 50	06 53	07 08			07 20	07 23		07 38		07 50	07 53					08 08	
	d		05 51		06 21	06 24		06 51	06 54	07 09			07 21	07 24	07 33	07 39		07 51	07 54				08 03	08 09	
Petts Wood ■4	d		05 54		06 24			06 54					07 24		07 36			07 54					08 06		
Chislehurst	d		05 57		06 27			06 57					07 27		07 39			07 57					08 09		
Elmstead Woods	d		05 59		06 29			06 59					07 29		07 41			07 59					08 11		
Bromley North	d	00 23		06 23			06 53					07 23					07 45					08 05			08 25
Sundridge Park	d	00 25		06 25			06 55					07 25					07 47					08 07			08 27
Grove Park ■4	d	00a28	06 03	06a28	06 33		06a58	07 03				07a28	07 33		07 45		07a50	08 03				08a10	08 15		08a30
Hither Green ■4	d		06 07		06 37			07 07					07 37		07 49			08 07					08 19		
Lewisham ■4	d		06 13		06 43			07 13							07 54								08 24		
St Johns	a														07 56								08 26		
New Cross ■4	a														07 58								08 28		
London Bridge ■4	a		06 21		06 51	06 39		07 21	07 09	07 24			07 49	07 39	08 04	07 55		08 19	08 10	08 13			08 34	08 25	
London Cannon Street ■4	a														08 08								08 38		
London Waterloo (East) ■4	a		06 25		06 55	06 43		07 25	07 13	07 29			07 53	07 43		07 59		08 23	08 15	08 19				08 29	
London Charing Cross ■4	a		06 29		06 59	06 47		07 29	07 17	07 33			07 57	07 48		08 03		08 27	08 19	08 22				08 33	

Table 204R

Saturdays

14 December to 17 May

Bromley North to Grove Park, Tonbridge, Sevenoaks, Orpington and Grove Park - London Cannon Street/Charing Cross

Network Diagram - see first Page of Table 200

		SE		SE 1	SE 1	SE	SE 1	SE	SE	SE 1	SE 1	SE		SE	SE 1	SE	SE	SE 1	SE 1 🚲	SE	SE 1	SE		SE	SE 1
Tonbridge 4	d			08 02	08 10		08 20			08 32	08 40				08 50			09 02	09 10		09 20				09 32
Hildenborough	d			08 06						08 36								09 06							09 36
Sevenoaks 4	a			08 13	08 18		08 28			08 43	08 48				08 58			09 13	09 18		09 28				09 43
	d	08 06		08 14	08 19		08 29		08 36	08 44	08 49				08 59		09 06	09 14	09 19		09 29			09 36	09 44
Dunton Green	d	08 09							08 39								09 09							09 39	
Knockholt	d	08 14							08 44								09 14							09 44	
Chelsfield 3	d	08 17							08 47								09 17							09 47	
Orpington 4	a	08 20		08 23			08 38		08 50	08 53					09 08		09 20	09 23			09 38			09 50	09 53
	d	08 21		08 24		08 33	08 39		08 51	08 54				09 03	09 09		09 21	09 24		09 33	09 39			09 51	09 54
Petts Wood 4	d	08 24				08 36			08 54					09 06			09 24			09 36				09 54	
Chislehurst	d	08 27				08 39			08 57					09 09			09 27			09 39				09 57	
Elmstead Woods	d	08 29				08 41			08 59					09 11			09 29			09 41				09 59	
Bromley North	d							08 45				09 05				09 25						09 45			
Sundridge Park	d							08 47				09 07				09 27						09 47			
Grove Park 4	d	08 33				08 45		08a50	09 03			09a10		09 15		09a30	09 33			09 45		09a50		10 03	
Hither Green 4	d	08 37				08 49			09 07					09 19			09 37			09 49				10 07	
Lewisham 4	d					08 54								09 24						09 54					
St Johns	a					08 56								09 26						09 56					
New Cross 4 ⊖	a					08 58								09 28						09 58					
London Bridge 4 ⊖	a	08 49		08 40	08 43	09 04	08 55		09 19	09 10	09 13			09 34	09 25		09 49	09 40	09 43	10 04	09 55			10 19	10 10
London Cannon Street 4 ⊖	a					09 08								09 38						10 08					
London Waterloo (East) 4 ⊖	a	08 53		08 45	08 49		08 59		09 23	09 15	09 19				09 29		09 53	09 45	09 49		09 59			10 23	10 15
London Charing Cross 4 ⊖	a	08 57		08 49	08 52		09 03		09 27	09 19	09 22				09 33		09 57	09 49	09 52		10 03			10 27	10 19

		SE 1 🚲	SE	SE	SE 1	SE	SE	SE 1		SE 1 🚲	SE	SE 1	SE	SE	SE 1	SE 1 🚲	SE	SE		SE 1	SE	SE	SE 1	SE 1 🚲	SE
Tonbridge 4	d	09 40			09 50			10 02		10 10		10 20			10 32	10 40				10 50			11 02	11 10	
Hildenborough	d							10 06							10 36								11 06		
Sevenoaks 4	a	09 48			09 58			10 13		10 18		10 28			10 43	10 48				10 58			11 13	11 18	
	d	09 49			09 59		10 06	10 14		10 19		10 29		10 36	10 44	10 49				10 59		11 06	11 14	11 19	
Dunton Green	d						10 09							10 39								11 09			
Knockholt	d						10 14							10 44								11 14			
Chelsfield 3	d						10 17							10 47								11 17			
Orpington 4	a				10 08		10 20	10 23				10 38		10 50	10 53					11 08		11 20	11 23		
	d			10 03	10 09		10 21	10 24			10 33	10 39		10 51	10 54			11 03		11 09		11 21	11 24		11 33
Petts Wood 4	d			10 06			10 24				10 36			10 54				11 06				11 24			11 36
Chislehurst	d			10 09			10 27				10 39			10 57				11 09				11 27			11 39
Elmstead Woods	d			10 11			10 29				10 41			10 59				11 11				11 29			11 41
Bromley North	d		10 05			10 25							10 45				11 05				11 25				
Sundridge Park	d		10 07			10 27							10 47				11 07				11 27				
Grove Park 4	d		10a10	10 15		10a30	10 33				10 45		10a50	11 03			11a10	11 15			11a30	11 33			11 45
Hither Green 4	d			10 19			10 37				10 49			11 07				11 19				11 37			11 49
Lewisham 4	d			10 24							10 54							11 24							11 54
St Johns	a			10 26							10 56							11 26							11 56
New Cross 4 ⊖	a			10 28							10 58							11 28							11 58
London Bridge 4 ⊖	a	10 13		10 34	10 25		10 49	10 40		10 43	11 04	10 55		11 19	11 10	11 13		11 34		11 25		11 49	11 40	11 43	12 04
London Cannon Street 4 ⊖	a			10 38							11 08							11 38							12 08
London Waterloo (East) 4 ⊖	a	10 19			10 29		10 53	10 45		10 49		10 59		11 23	11 15	11 19				11 29		11 53	11 45	11 49	
London Charing Cross 4 ⊖	a	10 22			10 33		10 57	10 49		10 52		11 03		11 27	11 19	11 22				11 33		11 57	11 49	11 52	

		SE 1	SE	SE		SE 1	SE 1 🚲	SE	SE	SE 1	SE	SE	SE 1	SE 1 🚲		SE	SE 1	SE	SE	SE 1	SE 1 🚲	SE	SE	SE 1	
Tonbridge 4	d	11 20				11 32	11 40			11 50			12 02	12 10			12 20			12 32	12 40			12 50	
Hildenborough	d					11 36							12 06							12 36					
Sevenoaks 4	a	11 28				11 43	11 48			11 58			12 13	12 18			12 28			12 43	12 48			12 58	
	d	11 29		11 36		11 44	11 49			11 59		12 06	12 14	12 19			12 29		12 36	12 44	12 49			12 59	
Dunton Green	d			11 39								12 09							12 39						
Knockholt	d			11 44								12 14							12 44						
Chelsfield 3	d			11 47								12 17							12 47						
Orpington 4	a	11 38		11 50		11 53				12 08		12 20	12 23				12 38		12 50	12 53				13 08	
	d	11 39		11 51		11 54			12 03	12 09		12 21	12 24			12 33	12 39		12 51	12 54			13 03	13 09	
Petts Wood 4	d			11 54					12 06			12 24				12 36			12 54				13 06		
Chislehurst	d			11 57					12 09			12 27				12 39			12 57				13 09		
Elmstead Woods	d			11 59					12 11			12 29				12 41			12 59				13 11		
Bromley North	d		11 45					12 05			12 25							12 45				13 05			
Sundridge Park	d		11 47					12 07			12 27							12 47				13 07			
Grove Park 4	d		11a50	12 03				12a10	12 15		12a30	12 33				12 45		12a50	13 03			13a10	13 15		
Hither Green 4	d			12 07					12 19			12 37				12 49			13 07				13 19		
Lewisham 4	d								12 24							12 54							13 24		
St Johns	a								12 26							12 56							13 26		
New Cross 4 ⊖	a								12 28							12 58							13 28		
London Bridge 4 ⊖	a	11 55		12 19		12 10	12 13		12 34	12 25		12 49	12 40	12 43		13 04	12 55		13 19	13 10	13 13		13 34	13 25	
London Cannon Street 4 ⊖	a								12 38							13 08							13 38		
London Waterloo (East) 4 ⊖	a	11 59		12 23		12 15	12 19			12 29		12 53	12 45	12 49			12 59		13 23	13 15	13 19			13 29	
London Charing Cross 4 ⊖	a	12 03		12 27		12 19	12 22			12 33		12 57	12 49	12 52			13 03		13 27	13 19	13 22			13 33	

Table 204R

Saturdays

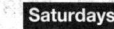

14 December to 17 May

Bromley North to Grove Park, Tonbridge, Sevenoaks, Orpington and Grove Park - London Cannon Street/Charing Cross

Network Diagram - see first Page of Table 200

		SE	SE	SE 1	SE 1 trolley	SE		SE 1	SE	SE	SE 1	SE 1 trolley	SE	SE	SE 1	SE		SE	SE 1	SE 1 trolley	SE	SE 1	SE	SE	SE 1
Tonbridge 4	d			13 02	13 10			13 20			13 32	13 40			13 50				14 02	14 10		14 20			14 32
Hildenborough	d			13 06							13 36								14 06						14 36
Sevenoaks 4	a			13 13	13 18			13 28			13 43	13 48			13 58				14 13	14 18		14 28			14 43
	d		13 06	13 14	13 19			13 29		13 36	13 44	13 49			13 59			14 06	14 14	14 19		14 29		14 36	14 44
Dunton Green	d		13 09							13 39								14 09						14 39	
Knockholt	d		13 14							13 44								14 14						14 44	
Chelsfield 3	d		13 17							13 47								14 17						14 47	
Orpington 4	a		13 20	13 23				13 38		13 50	13 53				14 08			14 20	14 23			14 38		14 50	14 53
	d		13 21	13 24		13 33		13 39		13 51	13 54			14 03	14 09			14 21	14 24		14 33	14 39		14 51	14 54
Petts Wood 4	d		13 24			13 36				13 54				14 06				14 24			14 36			14 54	
Chislehurst	d		13 27			13 39				13 57				14 09				14 27			14 39			14 57	
Elmstead Woods	d		13 29			13 41				13 59				14 11				14 29			14 41			14 59	
Bromley North	d	13 25							13 45				14 05			14 25							14 45		
Sundridge Park	d	13 27							13 47				14 07			14 27							14 47		
Grove Park 4	d	13a30	13 33			13 45			13a50	14 03			14a10	14 15		14a30		14 33			14 45		14a50	15 03	
Hither Green 4	d		13 37			13 49				14 07				14 19				14 37			14 49			15 07	
Lewisham 4	d					13 54								14 24							14 54				
St Johns	a					13 56								14 26							14 56				
New Cross 4 ⊖	a					13 58								14 28							14 58				
London Bridge 4 ⊖	a		13 49	13 40	13 43	14 04		13 55		14 19	14 10	14 13		14 34	14 25			14 49	14 40	14 43	15 04	14 55		15 19	15 10
London Cannon Street 4 ⊖	a					14 08								14 38							15 08				
London Waterloo (East) 4 ⊖	a		13 53	13 45	13 49			13 59		14 23	14 15	14 19			14 29			14 53	14 45	14 49		14 59		15 23	15 15
London Charing Cross 4 ⊖	a		13 57	13 49	13 52			14 03		14 27	14 19	14 22			14 33			14 57	14 49	14 52		15 03		15 27	15 19

		SE 1 trolley		SE	SE	SE 1	SE	SE	SE 1	SE 1 trolley	SE	SE 1		SE	SE	SE 1	SE 1 trolley	SE	SE	SE 1	SE	SE		SE 1	SE 1 trolley
Tonbridge 4	d	14 40				14 50			15 02	15 10		15 20				15 32	15 40			15 50				16 02	16 10
Hildenborough	d								15 06							15 36								16 06	
Sevenoaks 4	a	14 48				14 58			15 13	15 18		15 28				15 43	15 48			15 58				16 13	16 18
	d	14 49				14 59		15 06	15 14	15 19		15 29			15 36	15 44	15 49			15 59		16 06		16 14	16 19
Dunton Green	d							15 09							15 39							16 09			
Knockholt	d							15 14							15 44							16 14			
Chelsfield 3	d							15 17							15 47							16 17			
Orpington 4	a					15 08		15 20	15 23			15 38			15 50	15 53				16 08		16 20		16 23	
	d				15 03	15 09		15 21	15 24		15 33	15 39			15 51	15 54			16 03	16 09		16 21		16 24	
Petts Wood 4	d				15 06			15 24			15 36				15 54				16 06			16 24			
Chislehurst	d				15 09			15 27			15 39				15 57				16 09			16 27			
Elmstead Woods	d				15 11			15 29			15 41				15 59				16 11			16 29			
Bromley North	d			15 05			15 25							15 45				16 05			16 25				
Sundridge Park	d			15 07			15 27							15 47				16 07			16 27				
Grove Park 4	d			15a10	15 15		15a30	15 33			15 45			15a50	16 03			16a10	16 15		16a30	16 33			
Hither Green 4	d				15 19			15 37			15 49				16 07				16 19			16 37			
Lewisham 4	d				15 24						15 54								16 24						
St Johns	a				15 26						15 56								16 26						
New Cross 4 ⊖	a				15 28						15 58								16 28						
London Bridge 4 ⊖	a	15 13			15 34	15 25		15 49	15 40	15 43	16 04	15 55			16 19	16 10	16 13		16 34	16 25		16 49		16 40	16 43
London Cannon Street 4 ⊖	a				15 38						16 08								16 38						
London Waterloo (East) 4 ⊖	a	15 19				15 29		15 53	15 45	15 49		15 59			16 23	16 15	16 19			16 29		16 53		16 45	16 49
London Charing Cross 4 ⊖	a	15 22				15 33		15 57	15 49	15 52		16 03			16 27	16 19	16 22			16 33		16 57		16 49	16 52

		SE	SE 1	SE	SE	SE 1	SE 1 trolley	SE		SE	SE 1	SE	SE	SE 1	SE 1 trolley	SE	SE 1	SE		SE	SE 1	SE 1 trolley	SE	SE	SE 1
Tonbridge 4	d		16 20			16 32	16 40				16 50			17 02	17 10		17 20				17 32	17 40			17 50
Hildenborough	d					16 36								17 06							17 36				
Sevenoaks 4	a		16 28			16 43	16 48				16 58			17 13	17 18		17 28				17 43	17 48			17 58
	d		16 29		16 36	16 44	16 49				16 59		17 06	17 14	17 19		17 29			17 36	17 44	17 49			17 59
Dunton Green	d				16 39								17 09							17 39					
Knockholt	d				16 44								17 14							17 44					
Chelsfield 3	d				16 47								17 17							17 47					
Orpington 4	a		16 38		16 50	16 53					17 08		17 20	17 23			17 38			17 50	17 53				18 08
	d	16 33	16 39		16 51	16 54				17 03	17 09		17 21	17 24		17 33	17 39			17 51	17 54			18 03	18 09
Petts Wood 4	d	16 36			16 54					17 06			17 24			17 36				17 54				18 06	
Chislehurst	d	16 39			16 57					17 09			17 27			17 39				17 57				18 09	
Elmstead Woods	d	16 41			16 59					17 11			17 29			17 41				17 59				18 11	
Bromley North	d			16 45				17 05				17 25						17 45					18 05		
Sundridge Park	d			16 47				17 07				17 27						17 47					18 07		
Grove Park 4	d	16 45		16a50	17 03			17a10		17 15		17a30	17 33			17 45		17a50		18 03			18a10	18 15	
Hither Green 4	d	16 49			17 07					17 19			17 37			17 49				18 07				18 19	
Lewisham 4	d	16 54								17 24						17 54								18 24	
St Johns	a	16 56								17 26						17 56								18 26	
New Cross 4 ⊖	a	16 58								17 28						17 58								18 28	
London Bridge 4 ⊖	a	17 04	16 55		17 19	17 10	17 13			17 34	17 25		17 49	17 40	17 43	18 04	17 55			18 19	18 10	18 13		18 34	18 25
London Cannon Street 4 ⊖	a	17 08								17 38						18 08								18 38	
London Waterloo (East) 4 ⊖	a		16 59		17 23	17 15	17 19				17 29		17 53	17 45	17 49		17 59			18 23	18 15	18 19			18 29
London Charing Cross 4 ⊖	a		17 03		17 27	17 19	17 22				17 33		17 57	17 49	17 52		18 03			18 27	18 19	18 22			18 33

Table 204R

Saturdays

14 December to 17 May

Bromley North to Grove Park, Tonbridge, Sevenoaks, Orpington and Grove Park - London Cannon Street/Charing Cross

Network Diagram - see first Page of Table 200

		SE	SE	SE [1]	SE [1] 🚲	SE	SE [1]	SE	SE	SE [1]		SE [1] 🚲	SE [1]	SE	SE	SE	SE [1] 🚲	SE [1]	SE	SE		SE [1]	SE [1]	SE	SE
Tonbridge [4]	d			18 02	18 10		18 20			18 32		18 40	18 50				19 10	19 18				19 40	19 50		
Hildenborough	d			18 06						18 36								19 22							
Sevenoaks [4]	a			18 13	18 18		18 28			18 43		18 48	18 58				19 18	19 28				19 48	19 58		
	d		18 06	18 14	18 19		18 29		18 36	18 44		18 49	18 59			19 06	19 19	19 29		19 36		19 49	19 59		
Dunton Green	d		18 09						18 39							19 09				19 39					
Knockholt	d		18 14						18 44							19 14				19 44					
Chelsfield [3]	d		18 17						18 47							19 17				19 47					
Orpington [4]	a		18 20	18 23			18 38		18 50	18 53			19 08			19 20	19 27	19 38		19 50		19 57	20 08		
	d		18 21	18 24		18 33	18 39		18 51	18 54			19 09			19 21	19 28	19 39		19 51		19 58	20 09		
Petts Wood [4]	d		18 24			18 36			18 54							19 24				19 54					
Chislehurst	d		18 27			18 39			18 57							19 27				19 57					
Elmstead Woods	d		18 29			18 41			18 59							19 29				19 59					
Bromley North	d	18 25						18 45						19 05	19 25				19 45					20 05	20 25
Sundridge Park	d	18 27						18 47						19 07	19 27				19 47					20 07	20 27
Grove Park [4]	d	18a30	18 33			18 45		18a50	19 03					19a10	19a30	19 33			19a50	20 03				20a10	20a30
Hither Green [4]	d		18 37			18 49			19 07							19 37				20 07					
Lewisham [4]	d					18 54			19 12							19 43				20 13					
St Johns	a					18 56																			
New Cross [4] ⊖	a					18 58																			
London Bridge [4] ⊖	a		18 49	18 40	18 43	19 04	18 55		19 21	19 10		19 13	19 24			19 52	19 43	19 54		20 22		20 13	20 24		
London Cannon Street [4] ⊖	a					19 08																			
London Waterloo (East) [4] ⊖	a		18 53	18 45	18 49		18 59		19 25	19 15		19 19	19 29			19 56	19 48	19 59		20 26		20 18	20 29		
London Charing Cross [4] ⊖	a		18 57	18 49	18 52		19 03		19 29	19 19		19 22	19 33			20 00	19 51	20 03		20 30		20 21	20 33		

		SE	SE [1]	SE [1]	SE	SE		SE [1]	SE [1]	SE	SE	SE [1]	SE [1]	SE	SE	SE [1]		SE [1]	SE	SE	SE [1]	SE [1]	SE	SE	SE [1]
Tonbridge [4]	d		20 10	20 18				20 40	20 50			21 10	21 18			21 40		21 50			22 10	22 18			22 40
Hildenborough	d			20 22									21 22									22 22			
Sevenoaks [4]	a		20 18	20 28				20 48	20 58			21 18	21 28			21 48		21 58			22 18	22 28			22 48
	d	20 06	20 19	20 29		20 36		20 49	20 59		21 06	21 19	21 29		21 36	21 49		21 59		22 06	22 19	22 29			22 49
Dunton Green	d	20 09				20 39					21 09				21 39					22 09					
Knockholt	d	20 14				20 44					21 14				21 44					22 14					
Chelsfield [3]	d	20 17				20 47					21 17				21 47					22 17					
Orpington [4]	a	20 20	20 27	20 38		20 50		20 57	21 08		21 20	21 27	21 38		21 50	21 57		22 08		22 20	22 27	22 38			22 57
	d	20 21	20 28	20 39		20 51		20 58	21 09		21 21	21 28	21 39		21 51	21 58		22 09		22 21	22 28	22 39		22 51	22 58
Petts Wood [4]	d	20 24				20 54					21 24				21 54					22 24				22 54	
Chislehurst	d	20 27				20 57					21 27				21 57					22 27				22 57	
Elmstead Woods	d	20 29				20 59					21 29				21 59					22 29				22 59	
Bromley North	d				20 53					21 23				21 53					22 23				22 53		
Sundridge Park	d				20 55					21 25				21 55					22 25				22 55		
Grove Park [4]	d	20 33			20a58	21 03				21a28	21 33			21a58	22 03				22a28	22 33			22a58	23 03	
Hither Green [4]	d	20 37				21 07					21 37				22 07					22 37				23 07	
Lewisham [4]	d	20 43				21 13					21 43				22 13					22 43				23 13	
St Johns	a																								
New Cross [4] ⊖	a																								
London Bridge [4] ⊖	a	20 52	20 43	20 54		21 22		21 13	21 24		21 52	21 43	21 54		22 22	22 13		22 24		22 52	22 43	22 54		23 22	23 13
London Cannon Street [4] ⊖	a																								
London Waterloo (East) [4] ⊖	a	20 56	20 48	20 59		21 26		21 18	21 29		21 56	21 48	21 59		22 26	22 18		22 29		22 56	22 48	22 59		23 26	23 18
London Charing Cross [4] ⊖	a	21 00	20 51	21 03		21 30		21 21	21 33		22 00	21 51	22 03		22 30	22 21		22 33		23 00	22 51	23 03		23 30	23 21

		SE [1]		SE	SE	SE [1]	SE
Tonbridge [4]	d	22 50				23 14	
Hildenborough	d					23 18	
Sevenoaks [4]	a	22 58				23 24	
	d	22 59				23 25	
Dunton Green	d						
Knockholt	d						
Chelsfield [3]	d					23 32	
Orpington [4]	a	23 08				23 36	
	d	23 09			23 21	23 37	
Petts Wood [4]	d				23 24		
Chislehurst	d				23 27		
Elmstead Woods	d				23 29		
Bromley North	d			23 23			23 53
Sundridge Park	d			23 25			23 55
Grove Park [4]	d			23a28	23 33		23a58
Hither Green [4]	d				23 37		
Lewisham [4]	d				23 43		
St Johns	a						
New Cross [4] ⊖	a						
London Bridge [4] ⊖	a	23 24			23 52	23 54	
London Cannon Street [4] ⊖	a						
London Waterloo (East) [4] ⊖	a	23 29			23 56	23 59	
London Charing Cross [4] ⊖	a	23 33			00 01	00 03	

Table 204R

Sundays

8 December to 11 May

Bromley North to Grove Park, Tonbridge, Sevenoaks, Orpington and Grove Park - London Cannon Street/Charing Cross

Network Diagram - see first Page of Table 200

		SE	SE	SE	SE 1 🚲	SE 1	SE	SE 1 🚲	SE 1	SE	SE 1 🚲	SE	SE 1		SE 1 🚲	SE 1	SE	SE 1 🚲	SE	SE 1		SE 1 🚲	SE 1	SE
Tonbridge 4	d				07 10	07 18		07 40	07 49		08 10		08 20		18 40	18 49		19 10		19 20		19 40	19 49	
Hildenborough	d								07 53							18 53							19 53	
Sevenoaks 4	a				07 18	07 27		07 48	07 59		08 18		08 29		18 48	18 59		19 18		19 29		19 48	19 59	
	d				07 19	07 28		07 49	08 00		08 19	08 22	08 30		18 49	19 00		19 19	19 22	19 30		19 49	20 00	
Dunton Green	d											08 25							19 25					
Knockholt	d											08 30							19 30					
Chelsfield 3	d					07 35						08 33		and at					19 33					
Orpington 4	a				07 27	07 39		07 57	08 09		08 27	08 37	08 39	the same	18 57	19 09		19 27	19 37	19 39		19 57	20 09	
	d		06 40	07 10	07 28	07 40	07 40	07 58	08 10	08 10	08 28	08 40	08 40	minutes	18 58	19 10	19 10	19 28	19 40	19 40		19 58	20 10	20 10
Petts Wood 4	d		06 43	07 13			07 43			08 13		08 43		past			19 13		19 43					20 13
Chislehurst	d		06 46	07 16			07 46			08 16		08 46		each			19 16		19 46					20 16
Elmstead Woods	d		06 48	07 18			07 48			08 18		08 48		hour until			19 18		19 48					20 18
Bromley North	d	00 23																						
Sundridge Park	d	00 25																						
Grove Park 4	d	00a28	06 52	07 22			07 52			08 22		08 52					19 22		19 52					20 22
Hither Green 4	d		06 56	07 26			07 56			08 26		08 56					19 26		19 56					20 26
Lewisham 4	d		07 02	07 32			08 02			08 32		09 02					19 32		20 02					20 32
St Johns	a																							
New Cross 4 ⊖	a																							
London Bridge 4 ⊖	a		07 10	07 40	07 43	07 55	08 10	08 13	08 25	08 40	08 43	09 10	08 55		19 13	19 25	19 40	19 43	20 10	19 55		20 13	20 25	20 40
London Cannon Street 4 ⊖	a																							
London Waterloo (East) 4 ⊖	a		07 15	07 45	07 48	08 00	08 15	08 18	08 30	08 45	08 48	09 15	09 00		19 18	19 30	19 45	19 48	20 15	20 00		20 18	20 30	20 45
London Charing Cross 4 ⊖	a		07 19	07 49	07 52	08 04	08 19	08 22	08 34	08 49	08 52	09 19	09 04		19 22	19 34	19 49	19 52	20 19	20 04		20 22	20 34	20 49

		SE 1 🚲	SE	SE 1 🚲	SE 1	SE	SE 1 🚲		SE	SE 1 🚲	SE 1	SE	SE 1 🚲	SE	SE 1 🚲	SE 1	SE
Tonbridge 4	d	20 10		20 40	20 49		21 10			21 40	21 49		22 10		22 40	22 49	
Hildenborough	d				20 53						21 53					22 53	
Sevenoaks 4	a	20 18		20 48	20 59		21 18			21 48	21 59		22 18		22 48	22 59	
	d	20 19	20 22	20 49	21 00		21 19		21 22	21 49	22 00		22 19	22 22	22 49	23 00	
Dunton Green	d		20 25						21 25					22 25			
Knockholt	d		20 30						21 30					22 30			
Chelsfield 3	d		20 33						21 33					22 33			
Orpington 4	a	20 27	20 37	20 57	21 09		21 27		21 37	21 57	22 09		22 27	22 37	22 57	23 09	
	d	20 28	20 40	20 58	21 10	21 10	21 28		21 40	21 58	22 10	22 10	22 28	22 40	22 58	23 10	23 10
Petts Wood 4	d		20 43			21 13			21 43			22 13		22 43			23 13
Chislehurst	d		20 46			21 16			21 46			22 16		22 46			23 16
Elmstead Woods	d		20 48			21 18			21 48			22 18		22 48			23 18
Bromley North	d																
Sundridge Park	d																
Grove Park 4	d		20 52			21 22			21 52			22 22		22 52			23 22
Hither Green 4	d		20 56			21 26			21 56			22 26		22 56			23 26
Lewisham 4	d		21 02			21 32			22 02			22 32		23 02			23 32
St Johns	a																
New Cross 4 ⊖	a																
London Bridge 4 ⊖	a	20 43	21 10	21 13	21 25	21 40	21 43		22 10	22 13	22 25	22 40	22 43	23 10	23 13	23 25	23 40
London Cannon Street 4 ⊖	a																
London Waterloo (East) 4 ⊖	a	20 48	21 15	21 18	21 30	21 45	21 48		22 15	22 18	22 30	22 45	22 48	23 15	23 18	23 30	23 45
London Charing Cross 4 ⊖	a	20 52	21 19	21 22	21 34	21 49	21 52		22 19	22 22	22 34	22 49	22 52	23 19	23 22	23 34	23 49

Network Diagram for Tables 206, 207, 208

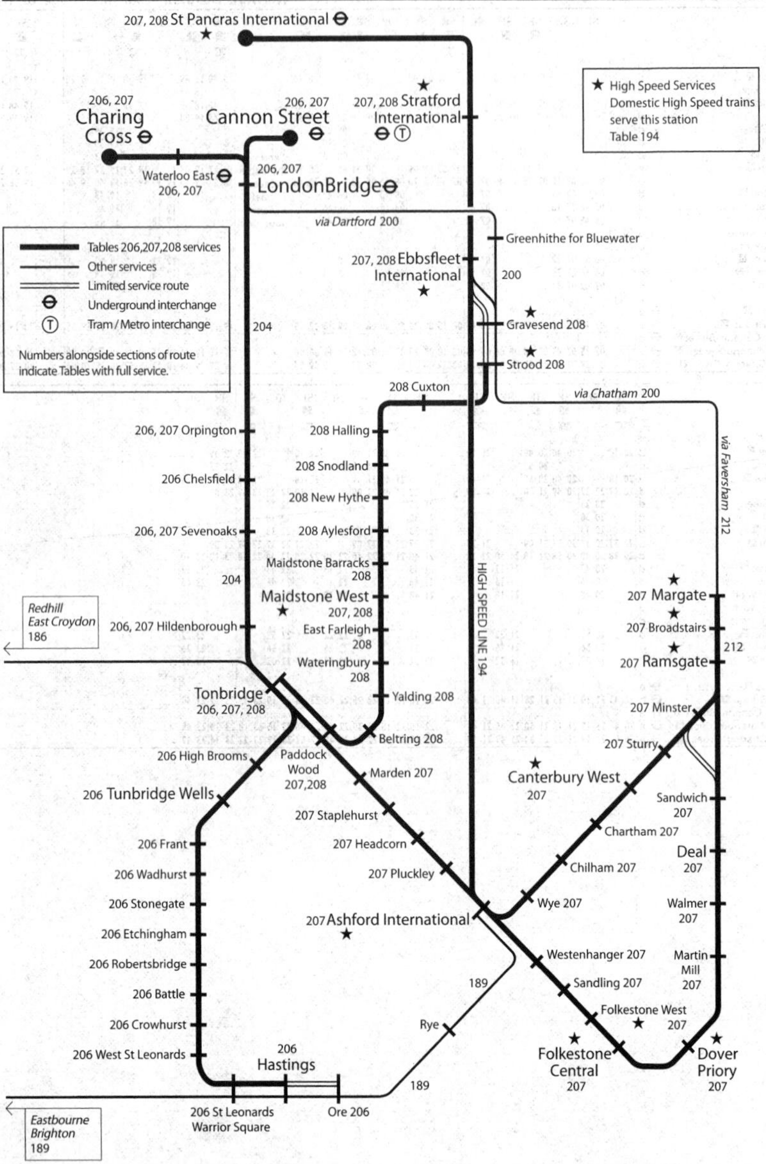
207, 208 St Pancras International
206, 207 Charing Cross
206, 207 Cannon Street
207, 208 Stratford International
High Speed Services
Domestic High Speed trains serve this station
Table 194
Waterloo East
206, 207
206, 207
LondonBridge
via Dartford 200
Greenhithe for Bluewater
207, 208 Ebbsfleet International
200
Tables 206,207,208 services
Other services
Limited service route
Underground interchange
Tram / Metro interchange
Numbers alongside sections of route indicate Tables with full service.
204
Gravesend 208
Strood 208
208 Cuxton
via Chatham 200
206, 207 Orpington
208 Halling
208 Snodland
206 Chelsfield
208 New Hythe
via Faversham 212
206, 207 Sevenoaks
208 Aylesford
Maidstone Barracks
208
204
HIGH SPEED LINE 194
Maidstone West
207, 208
207 Margate
Redhill
East Croydon
186
206, 207 Hildenborough
East Farleigh
208
207 Broadstairs
Wateringbury
208
207 Ramsgate
212
Tonbridge
206, 207, 208
Yalding 208
207 Minster
Beltring 208
206 High Brooms
Paddock Wood
207,208
207 Sturry
Marden 207
206 Tunbridge Wells
Canterbury West
207
Sandwich
207
207 Staplehurst
Chartham 207
206 Frant
207 Headcorn
Deal
207
206 Wadhurst
207 Pluckley
Chilham 207
206 Stonegate
Wye 207
Walmer
207
207 Ashford International
206 Etchingham
Westenhanger 207
Martin Mill
207
206 Robertsbridge
189
Sandling 207
206 Battle
Folkestone West
207
206 Crowhurst
Rye
206 West St Leonards
206
Hastings
Folkestone Central
207
Dover Priory
207
189
206 St Leonards Warrior Square
Ore 206
Eastbourne
Brighton
189

TOCs operating on this network - Southeastern (SE)

Table 206

Mondays to Fridays

9 December to 16 May

London and Tonbridge - Tunbridge Wells and Hastings

Network Diagram - see first Page of Table 206

Miles	Station		SE MO 1	SE MX 1	SE MO 1	SE MX 1	SE MX 1	SE 1	SE 1	SE 1	SE 1	SE 1	SE 1	SE 1	SE 1	SE 1	SE 1	SE 1	SE 1	SE 1	SE 1	SE 1	SE 1
—	**London Charing Cross 4** ⊖	d											06 15		06 45	07 00	07 15	07 29		08 00	08 17	08 27	
0¾	**London Waterloo (East) 4** ⊖	d											06 18		06 48	07 03	07 18	07 32		08 03	08 20	08 30	
—	**London Cannon Street 4** ⊖	d																	07 46				08 42
1¾	**London Bridge 4** ⊖	d											06 24		06 53	07 08	07 23	07 38	07 51	08 09	08 25	08 35	08 46
13¾	Orpington 4	d					00 09						06 40		07 10	07 26	07 39	07 54	08 09	08 26	08 42	08 54	09 07
15¼	Chelsfield	d																07 57					
22	Sevenoaks 4	d				00 05	00 19						06 50		07 19	07 35	07 49	08 07	08 19	08 35	08 52	09 03	09 17
27	Hildenborough	d			00 06	00 11										07 41		08 13		08 41		09 09	
29½	**Tonbridge 4**	a			00 10	00 15	00 27						06 58		07 27	07 45	07 58	08 17	08 27	08 47	09 00	09 13	09 25
—		d			00 11	00 17	00 29	05 00	05 30	06 08	06 20	06 35	06 58	07 19	07 31	07 47	07 59	08 17	08 27	08 48	09 00	09 16	09 29
33	High Brooms	d			00 17	00 23	00 35	05 06	05 36	06 14	06 26	06 41	07 04	07 25	07 37	07 55	08 05	08 23	08 34	08 54	09 06	09 23	09 35
34½	**Tunbridge Wells 4**	a			00 20	00 27	00 39	05 10	05 40	06 17	06 30	06 45	07 08	07 28	07 41	08 02	08 08	08 30	08 40	08 58	09 10	09 27	09 39
—		d			00 21		00 40			06 18		06 46			07 42		08 17		08 49		09 14		09 42
36¾	Frant	d			00 25		00 45			06 22		06 50			07 46		08 21				09 18		
39¼	Wadhurst	d			00 29		00 50			06 27		06 56			07 51		08 26		08 56		09 25		09 49
43¼	Stonegate	d			00 36		00 56			06 33		07 03			07 57		08 32				09 31		
47½	Etchingham	d		00 01	00 41		01 00			06 37		07 08			08 02		08 36		09 05		09 35		
49¼	Robertsbridge	d		00 05	00 46		01 04			06 41		07 12			08 06		08 40		09 09		09 39		
55½	Battle	d		00 13	00 54		01 12			06 50		07 20			08 14		08 48		09 17		09 47		10 05
57½	Crowhurst	d		00 16	00 57		01 16			06 53		07 24			08 18		08 52				09 51		
60¾	West St Leonards	d	00 03	00 22	01 03		01 21			06 59		07 31			08 23		08 57				09 57		
—	St Leonards Warrior Sq 4	d	00 06	00 25	01 06		01 25			07 03		07 34			08 26		09 00		09 28		10 00		10 16
62½	**Hastings 4**	a	00 10	00 28	01 10		01 29			07 07		07 38			08 30		09 04		09 32		10 03		10 20
63½	Ore	a								07 12													

Station		SE 1	SE 1	SE 1	SE 1	SE 1	SE 1	SE 1	SE 1	SE 1	SE 1		SE 1	SE 1	SE 1	SE 1	SE 1	SE 1	SE 1	SE 1	SE 1	SE 1	SE 1
London Charing Cross 4 ⊖	d	09 00		09 30	09 45	10 00	10 15	10 30	10 45	11 00	11 15		13 30	13 45	14 00	14 15	14 30	14 45	15 00	15 15	15 30	15 45	16 00
London Waterloo (East) 4 ⊖	d	09 03		09 33	09 48	10 03	10 18	10 33	10 48	11 03	11 18		13 33	13 48	14 03	14 18	14 33	14 48	15 03	15 18	15 33	15 48	16 03
London Cannon Street 4 ⊖	d		09 14																				
London Bridge 4 ⊖	d	09 08	09 18	09 39	09 53	10 09	10 23	10 39	10 53	11 09	11 23		13 39	13 53	14 09	14 23	14 39	14 53	15 09	15 23	15 39	15 53	16 09
Orpington 4	d	09 26	09 39	09 56	10 09	10 26	10 39	10 56	11 09	11 26	11 39		13 56	14 09	14 26	14 39	14 56	15 09	15 26	15 39	15 56	16 09	16 26
Chelsfield	d																						
Sevenoaks 4	d	09 35	09 49	10 05	10 19	10 35	10 49	11 05	11 19	11 35	11 49		14 05	14 19	14 35	14 49	15 05	15 19	15 35	15 49	16 05	16 19	16 35
Hildenborough	d	09 41		10 11		10 41		11 11		11 41		and at	14 11		14 41		15 11		15 41		16 11		16 41
Tonbridge 4	a	09 47	09 57	10 15	10 27	10 45	10 57	11 15	11 27	11 45	11 57	the same	14 15	14 27	14 45	14 57	15 16	15 27	15 45	15 57	16 15	16 27	16 45
	d	09 47	09 59	10 17	10 29	10 47	11 01	11 17	11 29	11 47	11 59	minutes	14 17	14 29	14 47	14 59	15 17	15 29	15 47	15 59	16 17	16 29	16 47
High Brooms	d	09 53	10 05	10 24	10 35	10 54	11 07	11 23	11 35	11 53	12 05	past	14 23	14 35	14 53	15 05	15 23	15 35	15 53	16 05	16 23	16 35	16 53
Tunbridge Wells 4	a	09 57	10 09	10 27	10 39	10 57	11 11	11 27	11 39	11 57	12 09	each	14 27	14 39	14 57	15 09	15 27	15 39	15 57	16 09	16 27	16 39	16 59
	d		10 10		10 40		11 12		11 40		12 10	hour until		14 40		15 10		15 40		16 14		16 40	
Frant	d		10 15				11 17				12 15					15 15				16 18		16 44	
Wadhurst	d		10 20		10 48		11 21		11 48		12 20			14 48		15 20		15 47		16 24		16 49	
Stonegate	d		10 26				11 27				12 26					15 26				16 30		16 55	
Etchingham	d		10 30				11 32				12 30					15 30				16 35		16 59	
Robertsbridge	d		10 34				11 36				12 34					15 34				16 39		17 03	
Battle	d		10 42		11 04		11 44		12 04		12 42			15 04		15 42		16 03		16 46		17 11	
Crowhurst	d		10 46				11 47				12 46					15 46				16 50		17 15	
West St Leonards	d		10 51				11 53				12 51					15 51		16 12		16 55		17 21	
St Leonards Warrior Sq 4	d		10 55		11 15		11 56		12 15		12 55			15 15		15 55		16 15		16 58		17 24	
Hastings 4	a		11 01		11 18		12 00		12 18		12 59			15 18		15 59		16 18		17 01		17 28	
Ore	a																						

Station		SE 1	SE 1	SE 1	SE 1	SE 1	SE 1	SE 1	SE 1		SE 1	SE 1	SE 1	SE 1	SE 1	SE 1	SE 1	SE 1	SE 1	SE 1	SE 1	SE 1
London Charing Cross 4 ⊖	d	16 15	16 28	16 41		17 01	17 19	17 23			17 45	17 59	18 07		18 32	18 45		19 15	19 30	19 45	20 00	20 15
London Waterloo (East) 4 ⊖	d	16 18	16 31	16 44		17 04	17 22	17 26			17 48	18 02	18 10		18 35	18 48		19 18	19 33	19 48	20 03	20 18
London Cannon Street 4 ⊖	d				17 02				17 37					18 28			19 04					
London Bridge 4 ⊖	d	16 23	16 36	16 49	17 06	17 09		17 31	17 42		17 53		18 15	18 32	18 40	18 53	19 09	19 23	19 39	19 53	20 09	20 23
Orpington 4	d		16 53															19 39	19 56	20 09	20 26	20 39
Chelsfield	d					17 28		17 50			18 12		18 34		18 58							
Sevenoaks 4	d	16 47	17 03	17 14	17 32	17 37		17 59			18 21		18 43		19 06	19 21	19 33	19 49	20 05	20 19	20 35	20 49
Hildenborough	d		17 09			17 43		18 05			18 27		18 49		19 12		19 40		20 11		20 41	
Tonbridge 4	a	16 55	17 13	17 22	17 40	17 48		18 09			18 32		18 54		19 17	19 29	19 44	19 57	20 15	20 27	20 45	20 57
	d	16 56	17 13	17 22	17 41	17 48		18 11			18 32		18 54		19 17	19 30	19 46	19 59	20 17	20 29	20 47	20 59
High Brooms	d	17 02	17 21	17 28	17 47	17 54	18 04	18 17	18 21		18 38	18 42	19 00	19 09	19 23	19 36	19 53	20 05	20 23	20 35	20 53	21 05
Tunbridge Wells 4	a	17 05	17 26	17 32	17 50	18 00	18 08	18 22	18 24		18 44	18 46	19 06	19 13	19 29	19 39	19 56	20 09	20 27	20 39	20 57	21 09
	d	17 06		17 38	17 52		18 08		18 29	18 33		18 49		19 20		19 41	19 57	20 11		20 40		21 10
Frant	d	17 11			17 56		18 13			18 37		18 53		19 24		19 45	20 02	20 15		20 45		21 15
Wadhurst	d	17 15		17 45	18 01		18 17		18 36	18 42		18 58		19 29		19 50	20 06	20 20		20 50		21 20
Stonegate	d	17 21			18 07		18 23			18 48		19 04		19 35		19 56	20 12	20 26		20 56		21 26
Etchingham	d	17 26		17 54	18 12		18 28		18 45	18 53		19 09		19 40		20 00	20 17	20 31		21 00		21 31
Robertsbridge	d	17 30		17 58	18 16		18 32			18 58		19 14		19 44		20 04	20 21	20 35		21 04		21 35
Battle	d	17 37		18 06	18 24		18 39		18 55	19 05		19 22		19 52		20 12	20 29	20 43		21 12		21 43
Crowhurst	d	17 41			18 28		18 43			19 09		19 25		19 56		20 16		20 47		21 16		21 47
West St Leonards	d	17 46			18 34		18 48			19 15		19 34		20 01		20 21		20 53		21 21		21 52
St Leonards Warrior Sq 4	d	17 49		18 17	18 37		18 51		19 06	19 18		19 37		20 05		20 25	20 39	20 56		21 25		21 56
Hastings 4	a	17 55		18 24	18 43		18 54		19 12	19 23		19 42		20 08		20 30	20 43	21 00		21 29		21 59
Ore	a						19 00							20 15								

Table 206

Mondays to Fridays

9 December to 16 May

London and Tonbridge - Tunbridge Wells and Hastings

Network Diagram - see first Page of Table 206

		SE 1	SE 1	SE 1	SE 1	SE 1	SE 1	SE 1	SE 1	SE 1	SE 1	SE 1
London Charing Cross 4 ⊖	d	20 30	20 45	21 00	21 30	21 45	22 00	22 30	22 45	23 00	23 30	23 45
London Waterloo (East) 4 ⊖	d	20 33	20 48	21 03	21 33	21 48	22 03	22 33	22 48	23 03	23 33	23 48
London Cannon Street 4 ⊖	d											
London Bridge 4 ⊖	d	20 39	20 53	21 09	21 39	21 53	22 09	22 39	22 53	23 09	23 39	23 53
Orpington 4	d	20 56	21 09	21 26	21 56	22 09	22 26	22 54	23 09	23 24	23 54	00 09
Chelsfield	d				21 59		22 29	22 57		23 27	23 57	
Sevenoaks 4	d	21 05	21 19	21 35	22 07	22 19	22 37	23 05	23 19	23 35	00 05	00 19
Hildenborough	d	21 11		21 41	22 13		22 43	23 11		23 41	00 11	
Tonbridge 4	a	21 15	21 27	21 45	22 17	22 27	22 47	23 15	23 27	23 45	00 15	00 27
	d	21 17	21 29	21 47	22 17	22 29	22 47	23 17	23 29	23 47	00 17	00 29
High Brooms	d	21 23	21 35	21 53	22 24	22 35	22 54	23 23	23 35	23 53	00 23	00 35
Tunbridge Wells 4	a	21 27	21 39	21 57	22 27	22 39	22 58	23 27	23 39	23 57	00 27	00 39
	d		21 40			22 40			23 40			00 40
Frant	d		21 45			22 45			23 45			00 45
Wadhurst	d		21 50			22 50			23 50			00 50
Stonegate	d		21 56			22 56			23 56			00 56
Etchingham	d		22 00			23 00			00 01			01 00
Robertsbridge	d		22 04			23 04			00 05			01 04
Battle	d		22 12			23 12			00 13			01 12
Crowhurst	d		22 16			23 16			00 16			01 16
West St Leonards	d		22 21			23 21			00 22			01 21
St Leonards Warrior Sq 4	d		22 25			23 25			00 25			01 25
Hastings 4	a		22 29			23 29			00 28			01 29
Ore	a											

Saturdays

14 December to 17 May

		SE 1	SE 1	SE 1	SE 1	SE 1	SE 1	SE 1	SE 1	SE 1	SE 1	SE 1	SE 1	SE 1	SE 1		SE 1	SE 1	SE 1	SE 1	SE 1	SE 1
London Charing Cross 4 ⊖	d							07 45	08 15	08 30	08 45	09 00	09 15	09 30	09 45		17 00	17 15	17 30	17 45	18 00	18 15
London Waterloo (East) 4 ⊖	d							07 48	08 18	08 33	08 48	09 03	09 18	09 33	09 48		17 03	17 18	17 33	17 48	18 03	18 18
London Cannon Street 4 ⊖	d																					
London Bridge 4 ⊖	d							07 53	08 23	08 39	08 53	09 09	09 23	09 39	09 53		17 09	17 23	17 39	17 53	18 09	18 23
Orpington 4	d			00 09				08 09	08 39	08 56	09 09	09 26	09 39	09 56	10 09		17 26	17 39	17 56	18 09	18 26	18 39
Chelsfield	d																					
Sevenoaks 4	d		00 05	00 19				08 19	08 49	09 05	09 20	09 35	09 49	10 05	10 19		17 35	17 49	18 05	18 19	18 35	18 49
Hildenborough	d		00 11							09 11		09 41		10 11		and at	17 41		18 11		18 41	
Tonbridge 4	a		00 15	00 27				08 27	08 57	09 15	09 28	09 45	09 57	10 15	10 27	the same	17 45	17 57	18 15	18 27	18 45	18 58
	d		00 17	00 29	06 58	07 29	07 59	08 29	08 59	09 17	09 29	09 47	09 59	10 17	10 29	minutes	17 47	17 59	18 17	18 29	18 47	18 59
High Brooms	d		00 23	00 35	07 05	07 35	08 05	08 35	09 05	09 23	09 35	09 53	10 05	10 23	10 35	past	17 53	18 05	18 23	18 35	18 53	19 05
Tunbridge Wells 4	a		00 27	00 39	07 09	07 39	08 09	08 39	09 09	09 27	09 39	09 57	10 09	10 27	10 39	each	17 57	18 09	18 27	18 39	18 57	19 09
	d			00 40	07 10		08 10	08 40	09 10		09 40		10 10		10 40	hour until		18 10		18 40		19 10
Frant	d			00 45	07 15		08 15	08 45	09 15				10 15					18 15				19 15
Wadhurst	d			00 50	07 20		08 20	08 50	09 20		09 48		10 20		10 48			18 20		18 48		19 20
Stonegate	d			00 56	07 26		08 26	08 56	09 26				10 26					18 26				19 26
Etchingham	d	00 01		01 00	07 30		08 30	09 00	09 30				10 30					18 30				19 30
Robertsbridge	d	00 05		01 04	07 34		08 34	09 04	09 34				10 34					18 34				19 34
Battle	d	00 13		01 12	07 42		08 42	09 12	09 42		10 04		10 42		11 04			18 42		19 04		19 42
Crowhurst	d	00 16		01 16	07 46		08 46	09 16	09 46				10 46					18 46				19 46
West St Leonards	d	00 22		01 21	07 51		08 51	09 21	09 51				10 51					18 51				19 51
St Leonards Warrior Sq 4	d	00 25		01 25	07 55		08 55	09 25	09 55		10 15		10 55		11 15			18 55		19 15		19 55
Hastings 4	a	00 28		01 29	07 59		08 59	09 29	09 59		10 18		10 59		11 18			18 59		19 18		19 59
Ore	a																					

		SE 1	SE 1	SE 1	SE 1	SE 1	SE 1	SE 1	SE 1	SE 1	SE 1	SE 1	SE 1	SE 1	SE 1
London Charing Cross 4 ⊖	d	18 30	18 45	19 00	19 15	19 30	19 55	20 25	20 55	21 25	21 55	22 25	22 55	23 25	23 45
London Waterloo (East) 4 ⊖	d	18 33	18 48	19 03	19 18	19 33	19 58	20 28	20 58	21 28	21 58	22 28	22 58	23 28	23 48
London Cannon Street 4 ⊖	d														
London Bridge 4 ⊖	d	18 39	18 53	19 09	19 23	19 39	20 03	20 33	21 03	21 33	22 03	22 33	23 03	23 33	23 53
Orpington 4	d	18 56	19 09	19 26	19 39	19 56	20 21	20 51	21 21	21 51	22 21	22 49	23 19	23 49	00 09
Chelsfield	d											22 52		23 52	
Sevenoaks 4	d	19 05	19 19	19 35	19 49	20 05	20 31	21 01	21 31	22 01	22 31	23 00	23 28	23 59	00 19
Hildenborough	d	19 11		19 41		20 11		21 07		22 07		23 06		00 06	
Tonbridge 4	a	19 15	19 27	19 45	19 58	20 15	20 39	21 11	21 39	22 11	22 39	23 10	23 36	00 10	00 27
	d	19 17	19 29	19 47	19 59	20 17	20 40	21 13	21 40	22 13	22 40	23 11	23 37	00 11	00 29
High Brooms	d	19 23	19 35	19 53	20 05	20 23	20 46	21 19	21 46	22 19	22 46	23 17	23 43	00 17	00 35
Tunbridge Wells 4	a	19 27	19 39	19 57	20 09	20 27	20 50	21 23	21 50	22 23	22 50	23 21	23 47	00 21	00 39
	d		19 40		20 10		20 51		21 51		22 51		23 48		00 40
Frant	d				20 15		20 56		21 56		22 56		23 53		00 45
Wadhurst	d		19 48		20 20		21 01		22 01		23 01		23 58		00 50
Stonegate	d				20 26		21 07		22 07		23 07		00 04		00 56
Etchingham	d				20 30		21 11		22 11		23 11		00 08		01 00
Robertsbridge	d				20 34		21 15		22 15		23 15		00 12		01 04
Battle	d		20 04		20 42		21 23		22 23		23 23		00 20		01 12
Crowhurst	d				20 46		21 27		22 27		23 27		00 24		01 16
West St Leonards	d				20 51		21 32		22 32		23 33		00 29		01 21
St Leonards Warrior Sq 4	d		20 15		20 55		21 36		22 36		23 36		00 33		01 25
Hastings 4	a		20 18		20 59		21 39		22 39		23 39		00 36		01 29
Ore	a														

Table 206

Sundays

8 December to 11 May

London and Tonbridge - Tunbridge Wells and Hastings

Network Diagram - see first Page of Table 206

		SE 1 A	SE 1 A	SE 1 A	SE 1	SE 1	SE 1	SE 1		SE 1	SE 1	SE 1	SE 1	SE 1	SE 1	SE 1
London Charing Cross 4 ⊖	d					08 25	08 55	09 25		18 55	19 25	19 55	20 25	21 25	22 25	23 25
London Waterloo (East) 4 ⊖	d					08 28	08 58	09 28		18 58	19 28	19 58	20 28	21 28	22 28	23 28
London Cannon Street 4 ⊖	d															
London Bridge 4 ⊖	d					08 33	09 03	09 33		19 03	19 33	20 03	20 33	21 33	22 33	23 33
Orpington 4	d			00 09		08 49	09 19	09 49		19 19	19 49	20 19	20 49	21 49	22 49	23 49
Chelsfield	d													21 52	22 52	23 52
Sevenoaks 4	d			00 19		08 59	09 29	09 59		19 29	19 59	20 29	20 59	22 00	23 00	23 59
Hildenborough	d		00 06				09 35		and at	19 35		20 35	21 05	22 06	23 06	00 06
Tonbridge 4	a		00 10	00 27		09 07	09 39	10 07	the same	19 39	20 07	20 39	21 09	22 10	23 10	00 10
	d		00 11	00 29	08 40	09 09	09 40	10 09	minutes	19 40	20 09	20 40	21 10	22 11	23 11	00 11
High Brooms	d		00 17	00 35	08 46	09 15	09 46	10 15	past	19 46	20 15	20 46	21 16	22 17	23 17	00 17
Tunbridge Wells 4	a		00 21	00 39	08 49	09 19	09 49	10 19	each	19 49	20 19	20 49	21 19	22 20	23 20	00 20
	d			00 40	08 51	09 22	09 51	10 22	hour until	19 51	20 22	20 51	21 21	22 21	23 21	00 21
Frant	d			00 45	08 55		09 55			19 55		20 55	21 25	22 25	23 25	00 25
Wadhurst	d			00 50	09 00	09 30	10 00	10 30		20 00	20 30	21 00	21 30	22 30	23 30	00 29
Stonegate	d	00 04		00 56	09 06		10 06			20 06		21 06	21 36	22 36	23 36	00 36
Etchingham	d	00 08		01 00	09 11		10 11			20 11		21 11	21 41	22 41	23 41	00 41
Robertsbridge	d	00 12		01 04	09 16		10 16			20 16		21 16	21 46	22 46	23 46	00 46
Battle	d	00 20		01 12	09 24	09 46	10 24	10 46		20 24	20 46	21 24	21 54	22 54	23 54	00 54
Crowhurst	d	00 24		01 16	09 27		10 27			20 27		21 27	21 57	22 57	23 57	00 57
West St Leonards	d	00 29		01 21	09 33		10 33			20 33		21 33	22 03	23 03	00 03	01 03
St Leonards Warrior Sq 4	d	00 33		01 25	09 36	09 59	10 36	10 57		20 36	20 57	21 36	22 06	23 06	00 06	01 06
Hastings 4	a	00 36		01 29	09 40	10 02	10 40	11 00		20 40	21 00	21 40	22 10	23 10	00 10	01 10
Ore	a															

A not 8 December

Table 206R

Mondays to Fridays

9 December to 16 May

Hastings and Tunbridge Wells - Tonbridge and London

Network Diagram - see first Page of Table 206

Miles			SE	SE	SE	SE	SE	SE	SE	SE	SE	SE	SE	SE	SE	SE	SE	SE	SE	SE	SE	SE	SE
			1	1	1	1	1	1	1	1	1	1	1	1	1	1	1	1	1	1	1	1	1
												A	B										
0	Ore	d										06 12			06 39						07 40		
1	**Hastings 4**	d			05 17		05 37	05 48		06 05		06 20	06 28		06 43		07 03		07 27		07 44		08 14
1¾	St Leonards Warrior Sq 4	d			05 20		05 40	05 51		06 08		06 23	06 31		06 46		07 06		07 30		07 47		08 17
2¾	West St Leonards	d			05 24		05 44			06 12			06 35		06 50		07 10		07 34		07 51		08 21
6	Crowhurst	d			05 29		05 49			06 17			06 40		06 55		07 15		07 39		07 56		08 26
8	Battle	d			05 34		05 54	06 02		06 22		06 34	06 45		07 00		07 20		07 44		08 01		08 31
14¼	Robertsbridge	d			05 41		06 01			06 29		06 41			07 07		07 27		07 51		08 08		08 39
16	Etchingham	d			05 44		06 04	06 11		06 33		06 45	06 54		07 11		07 31		07 54		08 12		08 42
19¾	Stonegate	d			05 49		06 09			06 38		06 50			07 17		07 37		08 00		08 17		08 47
24¼	Wadhurst	d			05 56		06 16	06 21		06 45		06 57	07 04		07 24		07 44		08 07		08 24		08 54
26¾	Frant	d			06 00		06 20			06 49		07 01			07 28		07 48		08 11		08 28		08 58
29	**Tunbridge Wells 4**	a			06 05		06 25	06 29		06 54		07 06	07 12		07 34		07 54		08 16		08 33		09 03
—		d	05 21	05 50	06 07	06 21	06 34		06 40	06 56	07 00	07 16		07 20	07 36	07 40	07 56	08 00	08 18	08 25	08 40	08 51	09 09
30½	High Brooms	d	05 24	05 53	06 10	06 24	06 37		06 44	07 00	07 04	07 20		07 24	07 40	07 44	08 00	08 04	08 22	08 28	08 43	08 54	09 12
34	**Tonbridge 4**	a	05 30	05 59	06 16	06 30	06 44		06 50		07 10			07 30		07 50		08 10		08 34	08 49	09 00	09 18
36½	Hildenborough	d	05 36	06 04	06 21	06 36			06 55		07 15			07 35		07 55		08 15		08 39		09 06	
41½	Sevenoaks 4	a	05 42	06 10	06 28	06 43	06 52		07 02		07 22			07 42		08 02		08 22		08 45	08 58	09 13	09 28
48¼	Chelsfield	d	05 50								07 32			07 52		08 12		08 32		08 53			
49¾	Orpington 4	a	05 53	06 19	06 38	06 53	07 02		07 13												09 08	09 24	09 38
61¾	**London Bridge 4** ⊖	a	06 09	06 38	06 54	07 09	07 22		07 29		07 50			08 09	08 23	08 29		08 49	09 03	09 11	09 26	09 40	09 55
—	**London Cannon Street 4** ⊖	a		06 43			07 30								08 30				09 10				
62¾	**London Waterloo (East) 4** ⊖	a	06 14		06 59	07 14			07 34	07 44	07 55	08 04		08 14		08 34	08 44	08 54		09 16	09 31	09 45	09 59
63½	**London Charing Cross 4** ⊖	a	06 18		07 05	07 20			07 40	07 50	08 01	08 08		08 20		08 40	08 50	09 00		09 22	09 37	09 51	10 04

		SE	SE	SE	SE	SE	SE	SE	SE	SE	SE		SE	SE	SE	SE	SE	SE	SE	SE	SE	SE
		1	1	1	1	1	1	1	1	1	1		1	1	1	1	1	1	1	1	1	1
Ore	d											and at the same minutes past each hour until										
Hastings 4	d		08 47		09 29		09 50		10 31		10 50			13 31		13 50		14 31		14 50		15 31
St Leonards Warrior Sq 4	d		08 50		09 32		09 53		10 34		10 53			13 34		13 53		14 34		14 53		15 34
West St Leonards	d		08 53				09 57				10 57					13 57				14 57		
Crowhurst	d		08 59				10 02				11 02					14 02				15 02		
Battle	d		09 03		09 42		10 07		10 44		11 07			13 44		14 07		14 44		15 07		15 44
Robertsbridge	d		09 10				10 14				11 14					14 14				15 14		
Etchingham	d		09 13				10 18				11 18					14 18				15 18		
Stonegate	d		09 18				10 23				11 23					14 23				15 23		
Wadhurst	d		09 25		09 58		10 29		11 00		11 29			14 00		14 29		15 00		15 29		16 00
Frant	d		09 29				10 33				11 33					14 33				15 33		
Tunbridge Wells 4	a		09 34		10 06		10 38		11 08		11 38			14 08		14 38		15 08		15 38		16 08
	d	09 21	09 39	09 51	10 09	10 21	10 39	10 51	11 09	11 21	11 39		13 51	14 09	14 21	14 39	14 51	15 09	15 21	15 39	15 51	16 09
High Brooms	d	09 24	09 42	09 54	10 13	10 24	10 43	10 54	11 12	11 24	11 42		13 54	14 12	14 24	14 42	14 54	15 12	15 24	15 42	15 54	16 12
Tonbridge 4	a	09 30	09 48	10 00	10 19	10 30	10 49	11 00	11 18	11 30	11 48		14 00	14 18	14 30	14 48	15 00	15 18	15 30	15 48	16 00	16 18
Hildenborough	d	09 36		10 06		10 36		11 06		11 36			14 06		14 36		15 06		15 36		16 06	
Sevenoaks 4	a	09 43	09 58	10 13	10 28	10 43	10 58	11 13	11 28	11 43	11 58		14 13	14 28	14 43	14 58	15 13	15 28	15 43	15 58	16 13	16 28
Chelsfield	d																				16 21	
Orpington 4	a	09 53	10 08	10 23	10 38	10 53	11 08	11 23	11 38	11 53	12 08		14 23	14 38	14 53	15 08	15 23	15 38	15 53	16 07	16 24	16 38
London Bridge 4 ⊖	a	10 10	10 25	10 40	10 55	11 10	11 25	11 40	11 55	12 10	12 25		14 40	14 55	15 10	15 25	15 40	15 55	16 11	16 25	16 42	16 56
London Cannon Street 4 ⊖	a																					
London Waterloo (East) 4 ⊖	a	10 15	10 29	10 45	10 59	11 15	11 29	11 45	11 59	12 15	12 29		14 45	14 59	15 15	15 29	15 45	15 59	16 16	16 29	16 48	17 00
London Charing Cross 4 ⊖	a	10 19	10 34	10 49	11 03	11 19	11 33	11 49	12 03	12 19	12 33		14 49	15 03	15 19	15 33	15 49	16 03	16 20	16 33	16 52	17 04

		SE	SE	SE	SE	SE	SE	SE	SE	SE	SE	SE	SE	SE	SE	SE	SE	SE	SE	SE	SE	SE
		1	1	1	1	1	1	1	1	1	1	1	1	1	1	1	1	1	1	1	1	1
Ore	d																					
Hastings 4	d		15 45		16 19		16 50		17 19		17 50		18 19		18 46			19 50			20 50	
St Leonards Warrior Sq 4	d		15 48		16 22		16 53		17 22		17 53		18 22		18 49			19 53			20 53	
West St Leonards	d		15 52		16 25		16 57		17 26		17 57		18 26		18 53			19 57			20 57	
Crowhurst	d		15 57		16 31		17 02		17 31		18 02		18 31		18 58			20 02			21 02	
Battle	d		16 02		16 35		17 07		17 36		18 07		18 36		19 02			20 07			21 07	
Robertsbridge	d		16 09		16 42		17 14		17 43		18 14		18 43		19 09			20 14			21 14	
Etchingham	d		16 13		16 45		17 18		17 47		18 18		18 46		19 13			20 18			21 18	
Stonegate	d		16 18		16 50		17 23		17 52		18 23		18 51		19 18			20 23			21 23	
Wadhurst	d		16 25		16 57		17 29		17 59		18 29		18 58		19 24			20 29			21 29	
Frant	d		16 29		17 01		17 33		18 03		18 33		19 02		19 28			20 33			21 33	
Tunbridge Wells 4	a		16 34		17 06		17 38		18 08		18 39		19 07		19 33			20 38			21 38	
	d	16 21	16 39	16 51	17 06	17 21	17 39	17 49	18 13	18 19	18 39	18 51	19 09	19 21	19 38	19 51	20 21	20 39	20 51	21 21	21 39	21 51
High Brooms	d	16 24	16 42	16 55	17 10	17 24	17 42	17 52	18 16	18 22	18 42	18 54	19 12	19 24	19 41	19 54	20 24	20 42	20 54	21 24	21 42	21 54
Tonbridge 4	a	16 30	16 48	17 01	17 16	17 30	17 49	17 59	18 22	18 28	18 50	19 00	19 18	19 30	19 47	20 00	20 30	20 48	21 00	21 30	21 48	22 00
Hildenborough	d	16 36		17 06		17 36		18 06		18 36		19 06		19 36		20 06	20 36		21 06	21 36		22 06
Sevenoaks 4	a	16 43	16 58	17 13	17 28	17 43	17 58	18 13	18 31	18 43	18 59	19 13	19 28	19 43	19 59	20 13	20 43	20 58	21 13	21 43	21 58	22 13
Chelsfield	d																					
Orpington 4	a	16 53	17 08	17 23	17 38	17 53	18 08	18 23		18 53	19 08	19 23	19 38	19 53	20 08	20 23	20 52	21 08	21 22	21 52	22 08	22 22
London Bridge 4 ⊖	a	17 11	17 27	17 41	17 58	18 09	18 25	18 40	18 55	19 10	19 25	19 40	19 54	20 10	20 24	20 39	21 08	21 24	21 38	22 08	22 24	22 38
London Cannon Street 4 ⊖	a		17 32																			
London Waterloo (East) 4 ⊖	a	17 16		17 46	18 02	18 14	18 29	18 45	18 59	19 14	19 29	19 45	19 59	20 15	20 29	20 44	21 13	21 29	21 43	22 13	22 29	22 43
London Charing Cross 4 ⊖	a	17 20		17 50	18 06	18 18	18 35	18 49	19 04	19 18	19 33	19 49	20 03	20 19	20 33	20 48	21 18	21 33	21 48	22 18	22 33	22 48

A from Hastings

B from Tunbridge Wells

Table 206R

Mondays to Fridays

9 December to 16 May

Hastings and Tunbridge Wells - Tonbridge and London

Network Diagram - see first Page of Table 206

		SE 1	SE 1	SE 1	SE 1
Ore	d				
Hastings 4	d		21 50	22 10	
St Leonards Warrior Sq 4	d		21 53	22 13	
West St Leonards	d		21 57	22 17	
Crowhurst	d		22 02	22 22	
Battle	d		22 07	22 27	
Robertsbridge	d		22 14	22 34	
Etchingham	d		22 18	22 37	
Stonegate	d		22 23	22 42	
Wadhurst	d		22 29	22 49	
Frant	d		22 33	22 53	
Tunbridge Wells 4	a		22 38	22 58	
	d	22 21	22 39	22 59	23 34
High Brooms	d	22 24	22 42	23 02	23 37
Tonbridge 4	a	22 30	22 48	23 08	23 44
Hildenborough	d	22 35		23 18	
Sevenoaks 4	a	22 41	22 58	23 24	
Chelsfield	d	22 49		23 32	
Orpington 4	a	22 52	23 08	23 36	
London Bridge 4 ⊖	a	23 08	23 24	23 54	
London Cannon Street 4 ⊖	a				
London Waterloo (East) 4 ⊖	a	23 13	23 29	23 59	
London Charing Cross 4 ⊖	a	23 18	23 33	00 03	

Saturdays

14 December to 17 May

		SE 1	SE 1	SE 1	SE 1	SE 1	SE 1	SE 1	SE 1	SE 1		SE 1	SE 1	SE 1	SE 1	SE 1	SE 1		SE 1	SE 1	SE 1	SE 1		SE 1
Ore	d																							
Hastings 4	d		05 50	06 20		06 50		07 20		07 50			08 20		08 50		09 31			15 50		16 31		
St Leonards Warrior Sq 4	d		05 53	06 23		06 53		07 23		07 53			08 23		08 53		09 34			15 53		16 34		
West St Leonards	d		05 57	06 27		06 57		07 27		07 57			08 27		08 57					15 57				
Crowhurst	d		06 02	06 32		07 02		07 32		08 02			08 32		09 02					16 02				
Battle	d		06 07	06 37		07 07		07 37		08 07			08 37		09 07		09 44			16 07		16 44		
Robertsbridge	d		06 14	06 44		07 14		07 44		08 14			08 44		09 14			and at		16 14				
Etchingham	d		06 18	06 48		07 18		07 48		08 18			08 48		09 18			the same		16 18				
Stonegate	d		06 23	06 53		07 23		07 53		08 23			08 53		09 23			minutes		16 23				
Wadhurst	d		06 29	06 59		07 29		07 59		08 29			08 59		09 29		10 00	past		16 29		17 00		
Frant	d		06 33	07 03		07 33		08 03		08 33			09 03		09 33			each		16 33				
Tunbridge Wells 4	a		06 38	07 08		07 38		08 08		08 38			09 08		09 38		10 08	hour until		16 38		17 08		
	d	05 48	06 39	07 09	07 21	07 39	07 51	08 09	08 21	08 39		08 51	09 09	09 21	09 39	09 51	10 09		16 21	16 39	16 51	17 09		17 21
High Brooms	d	05 51	06 42	07 12	07 24	07 42	07 54	08 12	08 24	08 42		08 54	09 12	09 24	09 42	09 54	10 12		16 24	16 42	16 54	17 12		17 24
Tonbridge 4	a	05 57	06 48	07 18	07 30	07 48	08 00	08 18	08 30	08 48		09 00	09 18	09 30	09 48	10 00	10 18		16 30	16 48	17 00	17 18		17 30
Hildenborough	d				07 36		08 06		08 36			09 06		09 36		10 06			16 36		17 06			17 36
Sevenoaks 4	a		06 58	07 28	07 43	07 58	08 13	08 28	08 43	08 58		09 13	09 28	09 43	09 58	10 13	10 28		16 43	16 58	17 13	17 28		17 43
Chelsfield	d																							
Orpington 4	a		07 08	07 38	07 53	08 08	08 23	08 38	08 53	09 08		09 23	09 38	09 53	10 08	10 23	10 38		16 53	17 08	17 23	17 38		17 53
London Bridge 4 ⊖	a		07 24	07 55	08 10	08 25	08 40	08 55	09 10	09 25		09 40	09 55	10 10	10 25	10 40	10 55		17 10	17 25	17 40	17 55		18 10
London Cannon Street 4 ⊖	a																							
London Waterloo (East) 4 ⊖	a		07 29	07 59	08 15	08 29	08 45	08 59	09 15	09 29		09 45	09 59	10 15	10 29	10 45	10 59		17 15	17 29	17 45	17 59		18 15
London Charing Cross 4 ⊖	a		07 33	08 03	08 19	08 33	08 49	09 03	09 19	09 33		09 49	10 03	10 19	10 33	10 49	11 03		17 19	17 33	17 49	18 03		18 19

		SE 1	SE 1	SE 1	SE 1	SE 1	SE 1	SE 1	SE 1		SE 1	SE 1	SE 1	SE 1	SE 1	SE 1	SE 1
Ore	d																
Hastings 4	d	16 50		17 20		17 50		18 50			19 50		20 50		21 50	22 10	
St Leonards Warrior Sq 4	d	16 53		17 23		17 53		18 53			19 53		20 53		21 53	22 13	
West St Leonards	d	16 57		17 27		17 57		18 57			19 57		20 57		21 57	22 17	
Crowhurst	d	17 02		17 32		18 02		19 02			20 02		21 02		22 02	22 22	
Battle	d	17 07		17 37		18 07		19 07			20 07		21 07		22 07	22 27	
Robertsbridge	d	17 14		17 44		18 14		19 14			20 14		21 14		22 14	22 34	
Etchingham	d	17 18		17 48		18 18		19 18			20 18		21 18		22 18	22 37	
Stonegate	d	17 23		17 53		18 23		19 23			20 23		21 23		22 23	22 42	
Wadhurst	d	17 29		17 59		18 29		19 29			20 29		21 29		22 29	22 49	
Frant	d	17 33		18 03		18 33		19 33			20 33		21 33		22 33	22 53	
Tunbridge Wells 4	a	17 38		18 08		18 38		19 38			20 38		21 38		22 38	22 58	
	d	17 39	17 51	18 09	18 21	18 39	19 08	19 39	20 08		20 39	21 05	21 39	22 05	22 39	22 59	23 34
High Brooms	d	17 42	17 54	18 12	18 24	18 42	19 11	19 42	20 11		20 42	21 08	21 42	22 08	22 42	23 02	23 37
Tonbridge 4	a	17 48	18 00	18 18	18 30	18 48	19 17	19 48	20 17		20 48	21 14	21 48	22 14	22 48	23 08	23 44
Hildenborough	d		18 06		18 36		19 22		20 22			21 22		22 22		23 18	
Sevenoaks 4	a	17 58	18 13	18 28	18 43	18 58	19 28	19 58	20 28		20 58	21 28	21 58	22 28	22 58	23 24	
Chelsfield	d															23 32	
Orpington 4	a	18 08	18 23	18 38	18 53	19 08	19 38	20 08	20 38		21 08	21 38	22 08	22 38	23 08	23 36	
London Bridge 4 ⊖	a	18 25	18 40	18 55	19 10	19 24	19 54	20 24	20 54		21 24	21 54	22 24	22 54	23 24	23 54	
London Cannon Street 4 ⊖	a																
London Waterloo (East) 4 ⊖	a	18 29	18 45	18 59	19 15	19 29	19 59	20 29	20 59		21 29	21 59	22 29	22 59	23 29	23 59	
London Charing Cross 4 ⊖	a	18 33	18 49	19 03	19 19	19 33	20 03	20 33	21 03		21 33	22 03	22 33	23 03	23 33	00 03	

Table 206R

Sundays

8 December to 11 May

Hastings and Tunbridge Wells - Tonbridge and London

Network Diagram - see first Page of Table 206

		SE 1	SE 1	SE 1		SE 1	SE 1		SE 1		SE 1		SE 1
Ore	d												
Hastings 4	d	07 20	07 50	08 31		17 50	18 31		18 50		21 50		22 30
St Leonards Warrior Sq 4	d	07 23	07 53	08 34		17 53	18 34		18 53		21 53		22 33
West St Leonards	d	07 27	07 57			17 57			18 57		21 57		22 37
Crowhurst	d	07 32	08 02			18 02			19 02		22 02		22 42
Battle	d	07 37	08 07	08 44		18 07	18 44		19 07		22 07		22 47
Robertsbridge	d	07 44	08 14			18 14			19 14		22 14		22 56
Etchingham	d	07 48	08 18		and at the same minutes past each hour until	18 18			19 18		22 18		23 00
Stonegate	d	07 53	08 23			18 23			19 23	and hourly until	22 23		23 05
Wadhurst	d	07 59	08 29	09 00		18 29	19 00		19 29		22 29		23 11
Frant	d	08 03	08 33			18 33			19 33		22 33		23 15
Tunbridge Wells 4	a	08 08	08 38	09 08		18 38	19 08		19 38		22 38		23 20
	d	08 09	08 39	09 09		18 39	19 09		19 39		22 39		23 21
High Brooms	d	08 12	08 42	09 12		18 42	19 12		19 42		22 42		23 24
Tonbridge 4	a	08 18	08 48	09 18		18 48	19 18		19 48		22 48		23 30
Hildenborough	d		08 53			18 53			19 53		22 53		
Sevenoaks 4	a	08 29	08 59	09 29		18 59	19 29		19 59		22 59		
Chelsfield	d												
Orpington 4	a	08 39	09 09	09 39		19 09	19 39		20 09		23 09		
London Bridge 4 ⊖	a	08 55	09 25	09 55		19 25	19 55		20 25		23 25		
London Cannon Street 4 ⊖	a												
London Waterloo (East) 4 ⊖	a	09 00	09 30	10 00		19 30	20 00		20 30		23 30		
London Charing Cross 4 ⊖	a	09 04	09 34	10 04		19 34	20 04		20 34		23 34		

Table 207

Mondays to Fridays

9 December to 16 May

London and Tonbridge - Ashford International, Folkestone, Dover, Canterbury West, Ramsgate and Margate

Network Diagram - see first Page of Table 206

Miles	Miles	Miles	Miles			SE	SE MO 1	SE MX 1	SE MX	SE MO	SE MX 1	SE MX 1	SE MO 1	SE MX 1		SE MO 1	SE MX	SE MX 1		SE MO 1	SE 1	SE	SE 1	SE	
—	—	—	0	**St Pancras Intl.** 15 ⊖	d												00 12								
—	—	—	6	**Stratford International** ⊖	d												00 19								
—	—	—	22¾	**Ebbsfleet International**	d	00 01											00 31								
0	—	—	—	**London Charing Cross** 4 ⊖	d																				
0¾	—	—	—	**London Waterloo (East)** 4 ⊖	d																				
—	—	—	—	**London Cannon Street** 4 ⊖	d																				
1¾	—	—	—	**London Bridge** 4 ⊖	d																				
13¾	—	—	—	Orpington 4	d															00 05					
22	—	—	—	Sevenoaks 4	d													00 12		00 15					
27	—	—	—	Hildenborough	d																				
29½	—	—	—	**Tonbridge** 4	a													00 20		00 23					
—	—	—	—		d													00 21		00 24	04 51				
34¾	—	—	—	Paddock Wood 4	d											00 01		00 28		00 31	04 58	05 41		06 18	
—	—	—	—	Maidstone West 4 194	a																	06 02		06 39	
39½	—	—	—	Marden	d									00 06		00 07		00 34		00 37	05 04				
41¾	—	—	—	Staplehurst	d									00 10		00 11		00 38		00 41	05 08				
45¼	—	—	—	Headcorn	d									00 15		00 16		00 43		00 46	05 13				
50½	—	—	—	Pluckley	d									00 21				00 49		00 52	05 19				
56	0	—	56	**Ashford International**	a	00 20								00 30		00 28	00 50	00 58		01 01	05 28				
—	—	—	—																						
—	—	—	—		d						00 02	00 05	00 05	00 34				01 02	01 05		05 32		06 02		
—	4¼	—	—	Wye	d							00 11							01 11						
—	9	—	—	Chilham	d							00 17							01 17						
—	11	—	—	Chartham	d							00 21							01 21						
—	14¼	—	—	**Canterbury West** 4	d							00 27							01a26						
—	16½	—	—	Sturry	d							00 31													
64¼	—	—	—	Westenhanger	d						00 10			00 42				01 10			05 40		06 10		
65½	—	—	—	Sandling	d						00 13		00 15	00 45				01 13			05 43		06 13		
69¼	—	—	—	Folkestone West	d				00 05	00 05	00 18		00 21	00 50				01 18			05 48		06 18		
70	—	—	—	**Folkestone Central**	d				00 08	00 08	00 21		00 23	00 53				01 21			05 51		06 21		
77¼	—	—	—	**Dover Priory** 4	a				00 18	00 20	00 32		00 34	01 04				01 32			06 01		06 32		
—	—	—	—		d		00 02	00 07	00 19												06 02				
82¼	—	—	—	Martin Mill	d		00 11	00 16													06 11				
85	—	—	—	Walmer	d		00 15	00 20													06 15				
86½	—	—	—	**Deal**	d		00 19	00 24	00 35												06 19				
90¾	—	—	—	Sandwich	d		00 26	00 31	00 41												06 26				
—	25½	4¾	—	Minster 4	d							00 42													
99	29½	—	—	**Ramsgate** 4	a		00 38	00 43	00 54			00 48									06 39				
101¼	31¾	—	—	Broadstairs	a																				
104½	35	—	—	**Margate** 4	a																				

		SE 1	SE 1	SE 1	SE	SE	SE	SE	SE	SE 1		SE	SE 1	SE	SE 1		SE	SE	SE 1			SE	SE 1		SE
St Pancras Intl. 15 ⊖	d						06 22	06 40	07 10					07 42				08 10				08 42			
Stratford International ⊖	d						06 29	06 47	07 17					07 49				08 17				08 49			
Ebbsfleet International	d						06 41	06 59	07 29					08 01				08 29				09 01			
London Charing Cross 4 ⊖	d			05 30						06 30					07 10				07 40				08 13		
London Waterloo (East) 4 ⊖	d			05 33						06 33					07 13				07 43				08 16		
London Cannon Street 4 ⊖	d																								
London Bridge 4 ⊖	d			05 39						06 38					07 19				07 49				08 21		
Orpington 4	d			05 55						06 54															
Sevenoaks 4	d			06 06						07 03					07 42				08 12				08 45		
Hildenborough	d			06 12						07 09															
Tonbridge 4	a			06 16						07 13					07 51				08 20				08 53		
	d			06 21						07 14					07 51				08 21				08 53		09 04
Paddock Wood 4	d			06 28		06 48				07 22		07 41			07 58		08 11		08 28				09 01		09 11
Maidstone West 4 194	a					07 09	07 12					08 02					08 32								09 32
Marden	d			06 34						07 27					08 04				08 34				09 06		
Staplehurst	d			06 38						07 31					08 08				08 38				09 10		
Headcorn	d			06 43						07 37					08 13				08 43				09 16		
Pluckley	d			06 49						07 43					08 19				08 49				09 22		
Ashford International	a			06 58				07 18	07 48	07 51				08 20	08 28			08 48	08 58			09 20	09 32		
	d	06 30	06 33	07 02	07 05			07 22	07 50	07 53			08 02	08 22	08 32	08 35		08 52	09 02	09 05		09 22	09 36	09 39	
Wye	d		06 39		07 11					07 59						08 41				09 11				09 45	
Chilham	d		06 45		07 17					08 05						08 47								09 51	
Chartham	d		06 49		07 21					08 09						08 51								09 55	
Canterbury West 4	d		06 55		07a26			07 39		08 15				08 39		08a56				09 24		09 39		10a00	
Sturry	d		06 59					07 44		08 19										09 28					
Westenhanger	d	06 38		07 10									08 10		08 40				09 10				09 44		
Sandling	d	06 41		07 13									08 13		08 43				09 13				09 47		
Folkestone West	d	06 46		07 18					08 03				08 18		08 48			09 05	09 18				09 52		
Folkestone Central	d	06 49		07 21					08 06				08 21		08 51			09 08	09 21				09 55		
Dover Priory 4	a	07 00		07 32					08 18				08 31		09 02			09 20	09 31				10 05		
	d	07 08		07 42									08 32						09 32						
Martin Mill	d	07 17		07 51									08 41						09 41						
Walmer	d	07 21		07 56									08 45						09 45						
Deal	d	07 26		08 00									08 49						09 49						
Sandwich	d	07 33		08 09									08 56						09 56						
Minster 4	d		07 11					07 55		08 31										09 39					
Ramsgate 4	a	07 45	07 17	08 22				08 00		08 38			09 08	08 59					10 08	09 45		09 59			
Broadstairs	a							08 06						09 04								10 04			
Margate 4	a							08 11						09 10								10 10			

Table 207

Mondays to Fridays

9 December to 16 May

London and Tonbridge - Ashford International, Folkestone, Dover, Canterbury West, Ramsgate and Margate

Network Diagram - see first Page of Table 206

		SE	SE ■1		SE ■1	SE	SE ■1		SE	SE	SE ■1		SE	SE ■1 A		SE	SE	and at the same minutes past each hour until	SE ■1 A		SE
St Pancras Intl. ■15 ⊖	d	09 10				09 42				10 10			10 42				11 12				13 42
Stratford International ⊖	d	09 17				09 49				10 17			10 49				11 19				13 49
Ebbsfleet International	d	09 29				10 01				10 29			11 01				11 31				14 01
London Charing Cross ■4 ⊖	d		08 33		08 53		09 13				09 40			10 10					12 40		
London Waterloo (East) ■4 ⊖	d		08 36		08 56		09 16				09 43			10 13					12 43		
London Cannon Street ■4 ⊖	d																				
London Bridge ■4 ⊖	d		08 41		09 01		09 21				09 49			10 19					12 49		
Orpington ■4	d		08 58																		
Sevenoaks ■4	d		09 08				09 44				10 12			10 42					13 12		
Hildenborough	d																				
Tonbridge ■4	a		09 19		09 36		09 52				10 20			10 50					13 20		
	d		09 21		09 37		09 52		10 04		10 21			10 51		11 04			13 21		
Paddock Wood ■4	d		09 28				10 00		10 11		10 28			10 58		11 11			13 28		
Maidstone West ■4 194	a								10 32							11 32					
Marden	d		09 34				10 05				10 34			11 04					13 34		
Staplehurst	d		09 38				10 09				10 38			11 08					13 38		
Headcorn	d		09 43				10 15				10 43			11 13					13 43		
Pluckley	d		09 49				10 21				10 49			11 19					13 49		
Ashford International	a	09 48	09 58		10 07	10 20	10 29			10 48	10 58		11 20	11 28			11 50		13 58		14 20
	d	09 52	10 02	10 05		10 22	10 33	10 36		10 52	11 02	11 05	11 22	11 32	11 35		11 52		14 02	14 05	14 22
Wye	d			10 11				10 42				11 11			11 41					14 11	
Chilham	d							10 48							11 47						
Chartham	d							10 52							11 51						
Canterbury West ■4	d			10 24		10 39		10a57				11 24	11 39		11a56					14 24	14 39
Sturry	d			10 28								11 28								14 28	
Westenhanger	d		10 10				10 41				11 10			11 40					14 10		
Sandling	d		10 13				10 44				11 13			11 43					14 13		
Folkestone West	d	10 05	10 18				10 49			11 05	11 18			11 48			12 05		14 18		
Folkestone Central	d	10 08	10 21				10 52			11 08	11 21			11 51			12 08		14 21		
Dover Priory ■4	a	10 20	10 31				11 02			11 20	11 31			12 02			12 20		14 31		
	d		10 32								11 32								14 32		
Martin Mill	d		10 41								11 41								14 41		
Walmer	d		10 45								11 45								14 45		
Deal	d		10 49								11 49								14 49		
Sandwich	d		10 56								11 56								14 56		
Minster ■4	d			10 39								11 39								14 39	
Ramsgate ■4	a		11 08	10 45		10 59					12 08	11 45	11 59						15 08	14 45	14 59
Broadstairs	a					11 04							12 04								15 04
Margate ■4	a					11 10							12 10								15 10

		SE ■1 A		SE	SE	SE ■1 A		SE	SE ■1 A		SE	SE	SE ■1 A		SE	SE ■1 A		SE	SE	SE ■1 A		SE	
St Pancras Intl. ■15 ⊖	d				14 12			14 42				15 12			15 42				16 10			16 40	
Stratford International ⊖	d				14 19			14 49				15 19			15 49				16 17			16 47	
Ebbsfleet International	d				14 31			15 01				15 31			16 01				16 29			16 59	
London Charing Cross ■4 ⊖	d	13 10				13 40			14 10				14 40			15 10				15 40			
London Waterloo (East) ■4 ⊖	d	13 13				13 43			14 13				14 43			15 13				15 43			
London Cannon Street ■4 ⊖	d																						
London Bridge ■4 ⊖	d	13 19				13 49			14 19				14 49			15 19				15 49			
Orpington ■4	d																						
Sevenoaks ■4	d	13 42				14 12			14 42				15 12			15 42				16 12			
Hildenborough	d																						
Tonbridge ■4	a	13 50				14 20			14 50				15 20			15 50				16 20			
	d	13 51		14 04		14 21			14 51		15 04		15 21			15 51		16 04		16 21			
Paddock Wood ■4	d	13 58		14 11		14 28			14 58		15 11		15 28			15 58		16 11		16 28			
Maidstone West ■4 194	a			14 32							15 32							16 32					
Marden	d	14 04				14 34			15 04				15 34			16 04				16 34			
Staplehurst	d	14 08				14 38			15 08				15 38			16 08				16 38			
Headcorn	d	14 13				14 43			15 13				15 43			16 13				16 43			
Pluckley	d	14 19				14 49			15 19				15 49			16 19				16 49			
Ashford International	a	14 28			14 50	14 58		15 20	15 28			15 50	15 58		16 20	16 28			16 48	16 58		17 18	
	d	14 32	14 35		14 52	15 02	15 05	15 22	15 32	15 35		15 52	16 02	16 05	16 22	16 32	16 35		16 52	17 02	17 05	17 23	17 25
Wye	d		14 41				15 11			15 41				16 11			16 41				17 11		
Chilham	d		14 47							15 47							16 47				17 17		
Chartham	d		14 51							15 51							16 51				17 21		
Canterbury West ■4	d		14a56				15 24	15 39		15a56				16 24	16 39		16a56				17 27		17 41
Sturry	d						15 28							16 28							17 31		
Westenhanger	d	14 40				15 10			15 40				16 10			16 40				17 10			
Sandling	d	14 43				15 13			15 43				16 13			16 43				17 13			
Folkestone West	d	14 48			15 05	15 18			15 48			16 05	16 18			16 48			17 05	17 18		17 36	
Folkestone Central	d	14 51			15 08	15 21			15 51			16 08	16 21			16 51			17 08	17 21		17 39	
Dover Priory ■4	a	15 02			15 20	15 31			16 01			16 20	16 31			17 01			17 20	17 31		17 49	
	d					15 32			16 02				16 32			17 02				17 32		17 50	
Martin Mill	d					15 41			16 11				16 41			17 11				17 41			
Walmer	d					15 45			16 15				16 45			17 15				17 45			
Deal	d					15 49			16 19				16 49			17 19				17 49		18 07	
Sandwich	d					15 56			16 26				16 56			17 26				17 56		18a13	
Minster ■4	d					16 08	15 39						17 08	16 40							17 42		
Ramsgate ■4	a					16 14	15 45	15 59	16 38				17 14	16 46	16 59	17 38				18 08	17 48		17 59
Broadstairs	a							16 04							17 04								18 05
Margate ■4	a							16 10							17 10								18 12

A to Ashford International

Table 207

Mondays to Fridays

9 December to 16 May

London and Tonbridge - Ashford International, Folkestone, Dover, Canterbury West, Ramsgate and Margate

Network Diagram - see first Page of Table 206

Station		SE 1 A ⚲		SE	SE		SE 1 A ⚲		SE	SE 1	SE 1	SE 1	SE	SE	SE		SE	SE 1 A ⚲	SE 1	SE 1	SE	SE
St Pancras Intl. 15 ⊖	d				17 12								17 16	17 25	17 42						17 46	17 55
Stratford International ⊖	d				17 19								17 23	17 32	17 49						17 53	18 02
Ebbsfleet International	d												17 35	17 43							18 05	18 13
London Charing Cross 4 ⊖	d	16 10					16 37				16 57							17 14				
London Waterloo (East) 4 ⊖	d	16 13					16 40				17 00							17 18				
London Cannon Street 4 ⊖	d									16 46		17 08							17 24	17 30		
London Bridge 4 ⊖	d	16 19					16 45			16 50		17 12							17 28	17 34		
Orpington 4	d																					
Sevenoaks 4	d	16 42					17 10				17 27							17 46	17 54			
Hildenborough	d																		18 00			
Tonbridge 4	a	16 50					17 18				17 35							17 54	18 04			
	d	16 51					17 19				17 36							17 55	18 05			
Paddock Wood 4	d	16 58		17 04			17 27		17 34		17 43						17 52	18 03	18 12			
Maidstone West 4 194	a			17 25					17 55				18 05				18 15				18 35	
Marden	d	17 04					17 32				17 49							18 08	18 18			
Staplehurst	d	17 08					17 36				17 53							18 12	18 22			
Headcorn	d	17 13					17 42				17 59							18 18	18 28			
Pluckley	d	17 19					17 48				18 05								18 34			
Ashford International	a	17 28			17 47		17 57				18 16				18 17			18 30	18 42			
	d	17 32	17 35		17 51	17 54	18 02	18 05							18 21	18 24		18 32	18 44			
Wye	d		17 41					18 11										18 38				
Chilham	d		17 47					18 17										18 44				
Chartham	d		17 51					18 21										18 48				
Canterbury West 4	d		17a58			18 11		18 27								18 41		18 54				
Sturry	d							18 31										18 59				
Westenhanger	d	17 40					18 10												18 53			
Sandling	d	17 43					18 13												18 56			
Folkestone West	d	17 48			18 04		18 18								18 34				19 01			
Folkestone Central	d	17 51			18 07		18 21								18 37				19 04			
Dover Priory 4	a	18 01			18 18		18 33								18 48				19 15			
	d	18 02					18 34								18 50				19 16			
Martin Mill	d	18 11					18 43												19 26			
Walmer	d	18 15					18 47												19 30			
Deal	d	18 19					18 51								19 07				19 35			
Sandwich	d	18 26					18 58								19a13				19 41			
Minster 4	d							18 42										19 10				
Ramsgate 4	a	18 40				18 29	19 12	18 51								18 59		19 19	19 56			
Broadstairs	a					18 35										19 05						
Margate 4	a					18 42				18 28		18 55		19 01		19 12				19 19		19 29

Station		SE	SE	SE	SE 1	SE 1 A ⚲	SE	SE 1	SE	SE 1	SE		SE 1	SE 1	SE 1 A ⚲	SE	SE 1	SE 1	SE		SE 1 A ⚲		SE
St Pancras Intl. 15 ⊖	d	18 12	18 16	18 19					18 25		18 42								19 10				
Stratford International ⊖	d	18 19	18 23	18 26					18 32		18 49								19 17				
Ebbsfleet International	d		18 35	18 37					18 44										19 29				
London Charing Cross 4 ⊖	d					17 41				18 03					18 21						18 41		
London Waterloo (East) 4 ⊖	d					17 44				18 06					18 24						18 44		
London Cannon Street 4 ⊖	d				17 45			17 52					18 08	18 14			18 32	18 44					
London Bridge 4 ⊖	d				17 49			17 56					18 12	18 18			18 36	18 48			18 50		
Orpington 4	d																				19 07		
Sevenoaks 4	d				18 16	18 11				18 34			18 38		18 52		19 01				19 17		
Hildenborough	d												18 44										
Tonbridge 4	a				18 24	18 19				18 42			18 48		19 00		19 09				19 25		
	d				18 25	18 21				18 43			18 49		19 01		19 10				19 26		
Paddock Wood 4	d				18 32	18 28	18 42			18 51			18 56		19 09	19 12	19 18				19 33		19 42
Maidstone West 4 194	a		19 05				19 03									19 33							20 03
Marden	d				18 38	18 34				18 57			19 02				19 24				19 39		
Staplehurst	d				18 42	18 38				19 01			19 06		19 17		19 28				19 43		
Headcorn	d				18 48	18 44				19 07			19 12		19 23		19 34				19 49		
Pluckley	d				18 54	18 50							19 19				19 40				19 55		
Ashford International	a	18 47		18 56	19 02	18 59				19 19	19 16		19 29		19 35		19 52		19 48		20 03		
	d	18 49		18 58	19 04	19 05				19 23	19 20	19 23	19 31		19 37				19 52	19 55	20 07	20 10	
Wye	d				19 10								19 37									20 16	
Chilham	d				19 16								19 44										
Chartham	d				19 20								19 48										
Canterbury West 4	d	19 08			19 26							19 40	19 55							20 12		20 29	
Sturry	d				19 30								20 00									20 33	
Westenhanger	d					19 13				19 31					19 45						20 15		
Sandling	d					19 16				19 34					19 48						20 18		
Folkestone West	d			19 11		19 21				19 40	19 33				19 54				20 05		20 23		
Folkestone Central	d			19 14		19 24				19a45	19 36				19 57				20 08		20 26		
Dover Priory 4	a			19 26		19 35					19 48				20 08				20 20		20 37		
	d					19 36					19 50				20 09						20 38		
Martin Mill	d					19 46									20 18						20 47		
Walmer	d					19 50									20 23						20 51		
Deal	d					19 54					20 07				20 27						20 55		
Sandwich	d					20 01					20a13				20 34						21 02		
Minster 4	d				19 42								20 11									20 44	
Ramsgate 4	a	19 31			19 50	20 17						19 59	20 18		20 48					20 34	21 16	20 53	
Broadstairs	a	19 37										20 05	20 25							20 40			
Margate 4	a	19 42						19 36	20 03			20 12	20 34	19 59				20 31		20 45			

A ⚲ to Ashford International

Table 207

Mondays to Fridays

9 December to 16 May

London and Tonbridge - Ashford International, Folkestone, Dover, Canterbury West, Ramsgate and Margate

Network Diagram - see first Page of Table 206

		SE	SE 1 A ⚯		SE	SE 1 A ⚯		SE	SE	SE 1 A ⚯	SE	SE 1		SE	SE	SE 1	SE	SE 1		SE	SE	SE 1
St Pancras Intl. 15 ⊖	d	19 42			20 12				20 42		21 12				21 42		22 12				22 42	
Stratford International ⊖	d	19 49			20 19				20 49		21 19				21 49		22 19				22 49	
Ebbsfleet International	d	20 01			20 31				21 01		21 31				22 01		22 31				23 01	
London Charing Cross 4 ⊖	d		19 10			19 40				20 10		20 40				21 10		21 40				22 10
London Waterloo (East) 4 ⊖	d		19 13			19 43				20 13		20 43				21 13		21 43				22 13
London Cannon Street 4 ⊖	d																					
London Bridge 4 ⊖	d		19 19			19 49				20 19		20 49				21 19		21 49				22 19
Orpington 4	d															21 35						22 35
Sevenoaks 4	d		19 42			20 12				20 42		21 12				21 44		22 12				22 44
Hildenborough	d																					
Tonbridge 4	a		19 53			20 20				20 50		21 20				21 52		22 20				22 52
	d		19 54			20 21		20 34		20 51		21 21		21 34		21 53		22 21		22 34		22 53
Paddock Wood 4	d		20 01			20 28		20 41		20 58		21 28		21 41		22 00		22 28		22 41		23 00
Maidstone West 4 194	a							21 02						22 02						23 02		
Marden	d		20 07			20 34				21 04		21 34				22 06		22 34				23 06
Staplehurst	d		20 11			20 38				21 08		21 38				22 10		22 38				23 10
Headcorn	d		20 17			20 43				21 13		21 43				22 15		22 43				23 15
Pluckley	d		20 23			20 49				21 19		21 49				22 21		22 49				23 21
Ashford International	a	20 20	20 31		20 50	20 58			21 20	21 28	21 50	21 58			22 20	22 30	22 50	22 58			23 20	23 30
	d	20 22	20 35	20 38	20 52	21 02	21 05		21 22	21 32	21 52	22 02	22 05		22 22	22 34	22 52	23 02	23 05		23 22	23 34
Wye	d			20 44			21 11						22 11						23 11			
Chilham	d			20 50			21 17						22 17						23 17			
Chartham	d			20 54			21 21						22 21						23 21			
Canterbury West 4	d	20 39		21a00			21 27		21 39				22 27		22 39				23 27		23 39	
Sturry	d						21 31						22 31						23 31			
Westenhanger	d		20 43			21 10				21 40		22 10				22 42		23 10				23 42
Sandling	d		20 46			21 13				21 43		22 13				22 45		23 13				23 45
Folkestone West	d		20 52		21 05	21 18				21 48	22 05	22 18				22 50	23 05	23 18				23 50
Folkestone Central	d		20 55		21 08	21 21				21 51	22 08	22 21				22 53	23 08	23 21				23 53
Dover Priory 4	a		21 08		21 20	21 33				22 02	22 20	22 31				23 04	23 20	23 31				00 06
	d					21 34						22 32						23 32				00 07
Martin Mill	d					21 43						22 41						23 41				00 16
Walmer	d					21 47						22 45						23 45				00 20
Deal	d					21 51						22 49						23 49				00 24
Sandwich	d					21 58						22 56						23 56				00 31
Minster 4	d						21 42						22 42						23 42			
Ramsgate 4	a	21 00				22 10	21 48		21 59			23 08	22 48		22 59			00 08	23 48		00 01	00 43
Broadstairs	a	21 06							22 05						23 05							
Margate 4	a	21 11							22 10						23 10							

		SE	SE 1		SE 1	SE 1		SE
St Pancras Intl. 15 ⊖	d	23 12						23 42
Stratford International ⊖	d	23 19						23 49
Ebbsfleet International	d	23 31						00 01
London Charing Cross 4 ⊖	d		22 40		23 10	23 40		
London Waterloo (East) 4 ⊖	d		22 43		23 13	23 43		
London Cannon Street 4 ⊖	d							
London Bridge 4 ⊖	d		22 49		23 19	23 49		
Orpington 4	d				23 35			
Sevenoaks 4	d		23 12		23 44	00 12		
Hildenborough	d							
Tonbridge 4	a		23 20		23 52	00 20		
	d		23 21		23 53	00 21		
Paddock Wood 4	d		23 28		23 59	00 28		
Maidstone West 4 194	a							
Marden	d		23 34		00 06	00 34		
Staplehurst	d		23 38		00 10	00 38		
Headcorn	d		23 43		00 15	00 43		
Pluckley	d		23 49		00 21	00 49		
Ashford International	a	23 50	23 58		00 30	00 58		00 20
	d	23 52	00 02	00 05	00 34	01 02	01 05	
Wye	d			00 11			01 11	
Chilham	d			00 17			01 17	
Chartham	d			00 21			01 21	
Canterbury West 4	d			00 27			01a26	
Sturry	d			00 31				
Westenhanger	d		00 10		00 42	01 10		
Sandling	d		00 13		00 45	01 13		
Folkestone West	d	00 05	00 18		00 50	01 18		
Folkestone Central	d	00 08	00 21		00 53	01 21		
Dover Priory 4	a	00 18	00 32		01 04	01 32		
	d	00 19						
Martin Mill	d							
Walmer	d							
Deal	d	00 35						
Sandwich	d	00 41						
Minster 4	d			00 42				
Ramsgate 4	a	00 54		00 48				
Broadstairs	a							
Margate 4	a							

A ⚯ to Ashford International

Table 207

Saturdays

14 December to 17 May

London and Tonbridge - Ashford International, Folkestone, Dover, Canterbury West, Ramsgate and Margate

Network Diagram - see first Page of Table 206

		SE	SE [1]	SE	SE [1]	SE [1]	SE [1]	SE	SE [1]	SE [1]			SE	SE [1]	SE [1]	SE [1]	SE	SE [1]	SE [1]	SE	SE		SE [1]	SE	
St Pancras Intl. [15] ⊖	d							00 12									06 42				07 12			07 42	
Stratford International ⊖	d							00 19									06 49				07 19			07 49	
Ebbsfleet International	d	00 01						00 31									07 01				07 31			08 01	
London Charing Cross [4] ⊖	d																	06 00							
London Waterloo (East) [4] ⊖	d																	06 03							
London Cannon Street [4] ⊖	d																								
London Bridge [4] ⊖	d																	06 08							
Orpington [4]	d																	06 24							
Sevenoaks [4]	d									00 12								06 33							
Hildenborough	d																	06 39							
Tonbridge [4]	a									00 20								06 43							
	d									00 21			06 04			06 21		06 51		07 04					
Paddock Wood [4]	d									00 28			06 11			06 28		06 58		07 11					
Maidstone West [4] 194	a												06 32							07 32					
Marden	d						00 06			00 34						06 34		07 04							
Staplehurst	d						00 10			00 38						06 38		07 08							
Headcorn	d						00 15			00 43						06 43		07 13							
Pluckley	d						00 21			00 49						06 49		07 19							
Ashford International	a	00 20					00 30	00 50		00 58						06 58	07 20	07 28			07 51			08 20	
	d				00 02	00 05	00 34		01 05	01 02	01 05			06 32	06 35	07 05	07 22	07 32	07 35		07 52		08 05	08 22	
Wye	d					00 11			01 11		01 11				06 41	07 11			07 41				08 11		
Chilham	d					00 17			01 17		01 17				06 47				07 47						
Chartham	d					00 21			01 21		01 21				06 51				07 51						
Canterbury West [4]	d					00 27			01a26		01a26				06a56	07 24	07 39		07a56				08 24	08 39	
Sturry	d					00 31										07 28							08 28		
Westenhanger	d				00 10		00 42			01 10				06 40				07 40							
Sandling	d				00 13		00 45			01 13				06 43				07 43							
Folkestone West	d			00 05	00 18		00 50			01 18				06 48				07 48			08 05				
Folkestone Central	d			00 08	00 21		00 53			01 21				06 51				07 51			08 08				
Dover Priory [4]	a			00 18	00 32		01 04			01 32				07 01				08 01			08 20				
	d		00 07	00 19										07 02				08 02							
Martin Mill	d		00 16											07 11				08 11							
Walmer	d		00 20											07 15				08 15							
Deal	d		00 24	00 35										07 19				08 19							
Sandwich	d		00 31	00 41										07 26				08 26							
Minster [4]	d					00 42										07 39							08 39		
Ramsgate [4]	a		00 43	00 54		00 48								07 38		07 45	07 59	08 38					08 45	08 59	
Broadstairs	a																08 04							09 04	
Margate [4]	a																08 10							09 10	

		SE [1]		SE	SE	SE [1]	SE	SE [1]			SE	SE	SE [1]	SE	SE [1]		SE	SE	SE [1]	SE	SE [1] A		SE		
St Pancras Intl. [15] ⊖	d				08 12		08 40					09 12		09 42				10 10		10 42					
Stratford International ⊖	d				08 19		08 47					09 19		09 49				10 17		10 49					
Ebbsfleet International	d				08 31		08 59					09 31		10 01				10 29		11 01					
London Charing Cross [4] ⊖	d	07 00				07 30		08 00					08 40		09 10				09 40		10 10				
London Waterloo (East) [4] ⊖	d	07 03				07 33		08 03					08 43		09 13				09 43		10 13				
London Cannon Street [4] ⊖	d																								
London Bridge [4] ⊖	d	07 08				07 38		08 08					08 49		09 19				09 49		10 19				
Orpington [4]	d	07 24				07 54		08 24																	
Sevenoaks [4]	d	07 33				08 03		08 33					09 12		09 42				10 12		10 42				
Hildenborough	d	07 39				08 09		08 39																	
Tonbridge [4]	a	07 43				08 14		08 43					09 20		09 50				10 20		10 50				
	d	07 51		08 04		08 21		08 51			09 04		09 21		09 51		10 04		10 21		10 51		11 04		
Paddock Wood [4]	d	07 58		08 11		08 28		08 58			09 11		09 28		09 58		10 11		10 28		10 58		11 11		
Maidstone West [4] 194	a			08 32							09 32						10 32						11 32		
Marden	d	08 04				08 34		09 04					09 34		10 04				10 34		11 04				
Staplehurst	d	08 08				08 38		09 08					09 38		10 08				10 38		11 08				
Headcorn	d	08 13				08 43		09 13					09 43		10 13				10 43		11 13				
Pluckley	d	08 19				08 49		09 19					09 49		10 19				10 49		11 19				
Ashford International	a	08 28			08 50	08 58	09 18	09 28				09 50	09 58	10 20	10 28			10 48	10 58	11 20	11 28				
	d	08 32	08 35		08 52	09 05	09 22	09 32	09 35			09 52	10 05	10 22	10 32	10 35		10 52	11 05	11 22	11 32	11 35			
Wye	d		08 41			09 11			09 41				10 11			10 41			11 11			11 41			
Chilham	d		08 47						09 47							10 47						11 47			
Chartham	d		08 51						09 51							10 51						11 51			
Canterbury West [4]	d		08a56			09 24	09 39		09a56				10 24	10 39		10a56			11 24	11 39		11a56			
Sturry	d					09 28							10 28						11 28						
Westenhanger	d	08 40						09 40							10 40						11 40				
Sandling	d	08 43						09 43							10 43						11 43				
Folkestone West	d	08 48			09 05			09 48				10 05			10 48			11 05			11 48				
Folkestone Central	d	08 51			09 08			09 51				10 08			10 51			11 08			11 51				
Dover Priory [4]	a	09 01			09 20			10 01				10 20			11 01			11 20			12 01				
	d	09 02						10 02							11 02						12 02				
Martin Mill	d	09 11						10 11							11 11						12 11				
Walmer	d	09 15						10 15							11 15						12 15				
Deal	d	09 19						10 19							11 19						12 19				
Sandwich	d	09 26						10 26							11 26						12 26				
Minster [4]	d					09 39							10 39						11 39						
Ramsgate [4]	a	09 38				09 48	09 59	10 38					10 45	10 59	11 38				11 45	11 59	12 38				
Broadstairs	a						10 04							11 04						12 04					
Margate [4]	a						10 10							11 10						12 10					

A ⚮ to Ashford International

Table 207

Saturdays

14 December to 17 May

London and Tonbridge - Ashford International, Folkestone, Dover, Canterbury West, Ramsgate and Margate

Network Diagram - see first Page of Table 206

		SE		SE 1 A 🛒	SE	SE 1 A 🛒		SE	SE	SE 1 A 🛒	SE	SE 1 A 🛒		SE	SE	SE 1 A 🛒	SE	SE 1 A 🛒		SE	SE	SE 1 A 🛒
St Pancras Intl. 15 ⊖	d	11 12			15 42				16 12		16 40				17 12		17 42				18 12	
Stratford International ⊖	d	11 19			15 49				16 19		16 47				17 19		17 49				18 19	
Ebbsfleet International	d	11 31			16 01				16 31		16 58				17 31		18 01				18 31	
London Charing Cross 4 ⊖	d			14 40		15 10				15 40		16 10				16 40		17 10				17 40
London Waterloo (East) 4 ⊖	d			14 43		15 13				15 43		16 13				16 43		17 13				17 43
London Cannon Street 4 ⊖	d																					
London Bridge 4 ⊖	d			14 49		15 19				15 49		16 19				16 49		17 19				17 49
Orpington 4	d																					
Sevenoaks 4	d			15 12		15 42				16 12		16 42				17 12		17 42				18 12
Hildenborough	d																					
Tonbridge 4	a			15 20		15 50				16 20		16 50				17 20		17 50				18 20
	d			15 21		15 51		16 04		16 21		16 51		17 04		17 21		17 51		18 04		18 21
Paddock Wood 4	d			15 28		15 58		16 11		16 28		16 58		17 11		17 28		17 58		18 11		18 28
Maidstone West 4 194	a							16 32						17 32						18 32		
Marden	d		and at	15 34		16 04				16 34		17 04				17 34		18 04				18 34
Staplehurst	d		the same	15 38		16 08				16 38		17 08				17 38		18 08				18 38
Headcorn	d		minutes	15 43		16 13				16 43		17 13				17 43		18 13				18 43
Pluckley	d		past	15 49		16 19				16 49		17 19				17 49		18 19				18 49
Ashford International	a	11 50	each	15 58	16 20	16 28			16 50	16 58	17 17	17 28			17 50	17 58	18 20	18 28			18 50	18 58
	d	11 52	hour until	16 05	16 22	16 32	16 35		16 52	17 05	17 22	17 32	17 35		17 52	18 05	18 22	18 32	18 35		18 52	19 05
Wye	d			16 11			16 41			17 11			17 41			18 11			18 41			19 11
Chilham	d						16 47						17 47						18 47			19 17
Chartham	d						16 51						17 51						18 51			19 21
Canterbury West 4	d			16 24	16 39		16a56			17 24	17 39		17a56			18 24	18 39		18a56			19 27
Sturry	d			16 28						17 28						18 28						19 31
Westenhanger	d					16 40						17 40						18 40				
Sandling	d					16 43						17 43						18 43				
Folkestone West	d	12 05				16 48			17 05			17 48			18 05			18 48			19 05	
Folkestone Central	d	12 08				16 51			17 08			17 51			18 08			18 51			19 08	
Dover Priory 4	a	12 20				17 01			17 20			18 01			18 20			19 01			19 20	
	d					17 02						18 02						19 02				
Martin Mill	d					17 11						18 11						19 11				
Walmer	d					17 15						18 15						19 15				
Deal	d					17 19						18 19						19 19				
Sandwich	d					17 26						18 26						19 26				
Minster 4	d			16 39						17 39						18 39						19 42
Ramsgate 4	a			16 45	16 59	17 38				17 45	17 59	18 38				18 45	18 59	19 38				19 48
Broadstairs	a				17 04						18 04						19 04					
Margate 4	a				17 10						18 10						19 10					

		SE	SE 1 A 🛒	SE	SE	SE 1 A 🛒	SE	SE 1 A 🛒	SE	SE	SE 1 A 🛒	SE	SE 1 A 🛒	SE	SE	SE 1	SE	SE 1	SE	SE	SE 1	SE	SE 1
St Pancras Intl. 15 ⊖	d	18 42			19 12		19 42			20 12		20 42			21 12		21 42			22 12		22 42	
Stratford International ⊖	d	18 49			19 19		19 49			20 19		20 49			21 19		21 49			22 19		22 49	
Ebbsfleet International	d	19 01			19 31		20 01			20 31		21 01			21 31		22 01			22 31		23 01	
London Charing Cross 4 ⊖	d		18 10			18 40		19 10			19 40		20 10			20 40		21 10			21 40		22 10
London Waterloo (East) 4 ⊖	d		18 13			18 43		19 13			19 43		20 13			20 43		21 13			21 43		22 13
London Cannon Street 4 ⊖	d																						
London Bridge 4 ⊖	d		18 19			18 49		19 19			19 49		20 19			20 49		21 19			21 49		22 19
Orpington 4	d												20 35			21 05		21 35			22 05		22 35
Sevenoaks 4	d		18 42			19 12		19 42			20 12		20 44			21 14		21 44			22 14		22 44
Hildenborough	d																						
Tonbridge 4	a		18 50			19 20		19 50			20 20		20 52			21 22		21 52			22 22		22 52
	d		18 51	19 04		19 21		19 51	20 04		20 21		20 53	21 04		21 23		21 53	22 04		22 23		22 53
Paddock Wood 4	d		18 58	19 11		19 28		19 58	20 11		20 28		21 00	21 11		21 30		22 00	22 11		22 30		23 00
Maidstone West 4 194	a			19 32					20 32					21 32					22 32				
Marden	d		19 04			19 34		20 04			20 34		21 05			21 36		22 05			22 36		23 05
Staplehurst	d		19 08			19 38		20 08			20 38		21 09			21 40		22 09			22 40		23 09
Headcorn	d		19 13			19 43		20 13			20 43		21 14			21 45		22 14			22 45		23 14
Pluckley	d		19 19			19 49		20 19			20 49		21 20			21 51		22 20			22 51		23 20
Ashford International	a	19 20	19 28		19 50	19 58	20 20	20 28		20 50	20 58	21 20	21 29		21 50	22 00	22 20	22 29		22 50	23 00	23 20	23 29
	d	19 22	19 32		19 52	20 05	20 22	20 32		20 52	21 05	21 22	21 32		21 52	22 05	22 22	22 32		22 52	23 05	23 22	23 32
Wye	d					20 11					21 11					22 11					23 11		
Chilham	d					20 17					21 17					22 17					23 17		
Chartham	d					20 21					21 21					22 21					23 21		
Canterbury West 4	d	19 39				20 27	20 39				21 27	21 39				22 27	22 39				23 27	23 39	
Sturry	d					20 31					21 31					22 31					23 31		
Westenhanger	d		19 40					20 40					21 41					22 41					23 41
Sandling	d		19 43					20 43					21 43					22 43					23 43
Folkestone West	d		19 48		20 05			20 48		21 05			21 48		22 05			22 48		23 05			23 48
Folkestone Central	d		19 51		20 08			20 51		21 08			21 51		22 08			22 51		23 08			23 51
Dover Priory 4	a		20 01		20 20			21 01		21 20			22 01		22 20			23 01		23 22			00 01
	d		20 02					21 02					22 02					23 02					00 02
Martin Mill	d		20 11					21 11					22 11					23 11					00 11
Walmer	d		20 15					21 15					22 15					23 15					00 15
Deal	d		20 19					21 19					22 19					23 19					00 19
Sandwich	d		20 26					21 26					22 26					23 26					00 26
Minster 4	d					20 42					21 42					22 42					23 42		
Ramsgate 4	a	20 00	20 38			20 48	21 00	21 38			21 48	22 00	22 38			22 48	23 00	23 38			23 48	00 01	00 38
Broadstairs	a	20 06					21 06					22 06					23 06						
Margate 4	a	20 11					21 11					22 11					23 11						

A 🛒 to Ashford International

Table 207

Saturdays
14 December to 17 May

London and Tonbridge - Ashford International, Folkestone, Dover, Canterbury West, Ramsgate and Margate

Network Diagram - see first Page of Table 206

		SE	SE ■1	SE ■1	SE ■1	SE ■1 A	SE
St Pancras Intl. ■15 ⊖	d	23 12					23 42
Stratford International ⊖	d	23 19					23 49
Ebbsfleet International	d	23 31					00 01
London Charing Cross ■4 ⊖	d		22 40	23 10	23 40	23 40	
London Waterloo (East) ■4 ⊖	d		22 43	23 13	23 43	23 43	
London Cannon Street ■4 ⊖	d						
London Bridge ■4 ⊖	d		22 49	23 19	23 49	23 49	
Orpington ■4	d		23 05	23 35	00 05	00 05	
Sevenoaks ■4	d		23 14	23 44	00 14	00 14	
Hildenborough	d						
Tonbridge ■4	a		23 22	23 53	00 23	00 23	
	d		23 23	23 53	00 23	00 23	
Paddock Wood ■4	d		23 30	00 01	00 30	00 30	
Maidstone West ■4 194	a						
Marden	d		23 36	00 05	00 36	00 36	
Staplehurst	d		23 40	00 09	00 40	00 40	
Headcorn	d		23 45	00 15	00 45	00 45	
Pluckley	d		23 51	00 21	00 51	00 51	
Ashford International	a	23 50	23 59	00 29	01 00	01 00	00 20
	d	23 52	00 05	00 32	01 04	01 07	
Wye	d		00 11			01 13	
Chilham	d		00 17			01 19	
Chartham	d		00 21			01 23	
Canterbury West ■4	d		00 27			01a28	
Sturry	d		00 31				
Westenhanger	d			00 41	01 12		
Sandling	d			00 43	01 15		
Folkestone West	d	00 05		00 48	01 20		
Folkestone Central	d	00 08		00 51	01 23		
Dover Priory ■4	a	00 20		01 02	01 34		
	d						
Martin Mill	d						
Walmer	d						
Deal	d						
Sandwich	d						
Minster ■4	d		00 42				
Ramsgate ■4	a		00 48				
Broadstairs	a						
Margate ■4	a						

Sundays
8 December to 11 May

		SE B	SE ■1 B	SE ■1 B	SE B	SE ■1 B	SE ■1	SE ■1 B		SE	SE ■1	SE	SE	SE ■1	SE ■1	SE	SE	SE ■1		SE	SE ■1	SE	SE
St Pancras Intl. ■15 ⊖	d									00 12							08 42			09 10			09 42
Stratford International ⊖	d									00 19							08 49			09 17			09 49
Ebbsfleet International	d	00 01								00 31							09 01			09 29			10 01
London Charing Cross ■4 ⊖	d																	08 10			08 40		
London Waterloo (East) ■4 ⊖	d																	08 13			08 43		
London Cannon Street ■4 ⊖	d																						
London Bridge ■4 ⊖	d																	08 19			08 49		
Orpington ■4	d							00 05										08 35			09 05		
Sevenoaks ■4	d							00 14										08 45			09 15		
Hildenborough	d																						
Tonbridge ■4	a							00 23										08 53			09 23		
	d							00 23				06 32	07 32		08 24	08 34		08 54			09 24	09 34	
Paddock Wood ■4	d					00 01		00 30				06 39	07 39		08 31	08 41		09 01			09 31	09 41	
Maidstone West ■4 194	a											07 00	08 00			09 02						10 02	
Marden	d					00 05		00 36							08 37			09 07			09 37		
Staplehurst	d					00 09		00 40							08 41			09 11			09 41		
Headcorn	d					00 15		00 45							08 46			09 16			09 46		
Pluckley	d					00 21		00 51							08 52						09 52		
Ashford International	a	00 20				00 29		01 00		00 50					09 01		09 20	09 28		09 48	10 01		10 20
	d			00 05		00 32	01 07	01 04	01 07		08 32			08 35	09 05		09 22	09 32	09 35	09 52	10 05		10 22
Wye	d			00 11			01 13		01 13					08 41	09 11				09 41		10 11		
Chilham	d			00 17			01 19		01 19					08 47					09 47				
Chartham	d			00 21			01 23		01 23					08 51					09 51				
Canterbury West ■4	d			00 27			01a28		01a28					08a56	09 24		09 39		09a56		10 24		10 39
Sturry	d			00 31											09 28						10 28		
Westenhanger	d					00 41		01 12			08 40							09 40					
Sandling	d					00 43		01 15			08 43							09 43					
Folkestone West	d				00 05	00 48		01 20			08 48							09 48		10 05			
Folkestone Central	d				00 08	00 51		01 23			08 51							09 51		10 08			
Dover Priory ■4	a				00 20	01 02		01 34			09 01							10 01		10 20			
	d		00 02								09 02							10 02					
Martin Mill	d		00 11								09 11							10 11					
Walmer	d		00 15								09 15							10 15					
Deal	d		00 19								09 19							10 19					
Sandwich	d		00 26								09 26							10 26					
Minster ■4	d			00 42											09 39						10 39		
Ramsgate ■4	a		00 38	00 48							09 38				09 45		09 59	10 38			10 45		10 59
Broadstairs	a																10 04						11 04
Margate ■4	a																10 10						11 10

A until 16 May
B not 8 December

Table 207

Sundays

8 December to 11 May

London and Tonbridge - Ashford International, Folkestone, Dover, Canterbury West, Ramsgate and Margate

Network Diagram - see first Page of Table 206

		SE 1		SE	SE 1	SE	SE	SE 1 A		SE		SE 1 A	SE	SE	SE 1 A		SE	SE 1 A	SE	SE	SE 1 A		SE
St Pancras Intl. 15 ⊖	d			10 10			10 42			11 12				14 42			15 12			15 42			16 10
Stratford International ⊖	d			10 17			10 49			11 19				14 49			15 19			15 49			16 17
Ebbsfleet International	d			10 29			11 01			11 31				15 01			15 31			16 01			16 29
London Charing Cross 4 ⊖	d	09 10			09 40			10 10				13 40			14 10			14 40			15 10		
London Waterloo (East) 4 ⊖	d	09 13			09 43			10 13				13 43			14 13			14 43			15 13		
London Cannon Street 4 ⊖	d																						
London Bridge 4 ⊖	d	09 19			09 49			10 19				13 49			14 19			14 49			15 19		
Orpington 4	d	09 35			10 05			10 35				14 05			14 35			15 05			15 35		
Sevenoaks 4	d	09 45			10 15			10 45				14 15			14 45			15 15			15 45		
Hildenborough	d																						
Tonbridge 4	a	09 53			10 23			10 53				14 23			14 53			15 23			15 53		
	d	09 54			10 24	10 34		10 54				14 24	14 34		14 54			15 24	15 34		15 54		
Paddock Wood 4	d	10 01			10 31	10 41		11 01				14 31	14 41		15 01			15 31	15 41		16 01		
Maidstone West 4 194	a					11 02							15 02						16 02				
Marden	d	10 07			10 37			11 07			and at	14 37			15 07			15 37			16 07		
Staplehurst	d	10 11			10 41			11 11			the same	14 41			15 11			15 41			16 11		
Headcorn	d	10 16			10 46			11 16			minutes	14 46			15 16			15 46			16 16		
Pluckley	d				10 52						past	14 52						15 52					
Ashford International	a	10 28		10 48	11 01		11 20	11 28		11 50	each	15 01		15 20	15 28		15 50	16 01		16 20	16 28		16 48
	d	10 32	10 35	10 52	11 05		11 22	11 32	11 35	11 52	hour until	15 05		15 22	15 32	15 35	15 52	16 05		16 22	16 32	16 35	16 52
Wye	d		10 41		11 11				11 41			15 11				15 41		16 11				16 41	
Chilham	d		10 47						11 47							15 47						16 47	
Chartham	d		10 51						11 51							15 51						16 51	
Canterbury West 4	d		10a56		11 24		11 39		11a56			15 24		15 39		15a56		16 24		16 39		16a56	
Sturry	d				11 28							15 28						16 28					
Westenhanger	d	10 40						11 40							15 40						16 40		
Sandling	d	10 43						11 43							15 43						16 43		
Folkestone West	d	10 48		11 05				11 48		12 05					15 48		16 05				16 48		17 05
Folkestone Central	d	10 51		11 08				11 51		12 08					15 51		16 08				16 51		17 08
Dover Priory 4	a	11 01		11 20				12 01		12 20					16 01		16 20				17 01		17 20
	d	11 02						12 02							16 02						17 02		
Martin Mill	d	11 11						12 11							16 11						17 11		
Walmer	d	11 15						12 15							16 15						17 15		
Deal	d	11 19						12 19							16 19						17 19		
Sandwich	d	11 26						12 26							16 26						17 26		
Minster 4	d				11 39							15 39						16 39					
Ramsgate 4	a	11 38			11 45		11 59	12 38				15 45		15 59	16 38			16 45		16 59	17 38		
Broadstairs	a						12 04							16 04						17 04			
Margate 4	a						12 10							16 10						17 10			

		SE 1 A	SE	SE	SE 1 A		SE	SE 1 A	SE	SE	SE 1 A		SE	SE 1 A	SE	SE	SE 1 A	SE	SE 1	SE	SE	SE 1
St Pancras Intl. 15 ⊖	d			16 42			17 12			17 42			20 12			20 42		21 12			21 42	
Stratford International ⊖	d			16 49			17 19			17 49			20 19			20 49		21 19			21 49	
Ebbsfleet International	d			17 01			17 31			18 01			20 31			21 01		21 31			22 01	
London Charing Cross 4 ⊖	d	15 40			16 10			16 40			17 10			19 40			20 10		20 40			21 10
London Waterloo (East) 4 ⊖	d	15 43			16 13			16 43			17 13			19 43			20 13		20 43			21 13
London Cannon Street 4 ⊖	d																					
London Bridge 4 ⊖	d	15 49			16 19			16 49			17 19			19 49			20 19		20 49			21 19
Orpington 4	d	16 05			16 35			17 05			17 35			20 05			20 35		21 05			21 35
Sevenoaks 4	d	16 15			16 45			17 15			17 45			20 15			20 45		21 15			21 45
Hildenborough	d																					
Tonbridge 4	a	16 23			16 53			17 23			17 53			20 23			20 53		21 23			21 53
	d	16 24	16 34		16 54			17 24	17 34		17 54			20 24	20 34		20 54		21 24	21 34		21 54
Paddock Wood 4	d	16 31	16 41		17 01			17 31	17 41		18 01			20 31	20 41		21 01		21 31	21 41		22 01
Maidstone West 4 194	a		17 02						18 02						21 02					22 02		
Marden	d	16 37			17 07			17 37			18 07	and at		20 37			21 07		21 37			22 07
Staplehurst	d	16 41			17 11			17 41			18 11	the same		20 41			21 11		21 41			22 11
Headcorn	d	16 46			17 16			17 46			18 16	minutes		20 46			21 16		21 46			22 16
Pluckley	d	16 52						17 52				past		20 52					21 52			
Ashford International	a	17 01		17 20	17 28		17 50	18 01		18 20	18 28	each	20 50	21 01		21 20	21 28	21 50	22 01		22 20	22 28
	d	17 05		17 22	17 32	17 35	17 52	18 05		18 22	18 32	hour until	20 52	21 05		21 22	21 32	21 52	22 05		22 22	22 32
Wye	d	17 11				17 41		18 11						21 11					22 11			
Chilham	d					17 47		18 17						21 17					22 17			
Chartham	d					17 51		18 21						21 21					22 21			
Canterbury West 4	d	17 24		17 39		17a56		18 27		18 39				21 27		21 39			22 27		22 39	
Sturry	d	17 28						18 31						21 31					22 31			
Westenhanger	d				17 40						18 40						21 40					22 40
Sandling	d				17 43						18 43						21 43					22 43
Folkestone West	d				17 48		18 05				18 48		21 05				21 48	22 05				22 48
Folkestone Central	d				17 51		18 08				18 51		21 08				21 51	22 08				22 51
Dover Priory 4	a				18 01		18 20				19 01		21 20				22 01	22 20				23 01
	d				18 02						19 02						22 02					23 02
Martin Mill	d				18 11						19 11						22 11					23 11
Walmer	d				18 15						19 15						22 15					23 15
Deal	d				18 19						19 19						22 19					23 19
Sandwich	d				18 26						19 26						22 26					23 26
Minster 4	d	17 39						18 42						21 42					22 42			
Ramsgate 4	a	17 45		17 59	18 38			18 48		19 00	19 38			21 48		22 00	22 38		22 48		23 00	23 40
Broadstairs	a			18 04						19 06						22 06					23 06	
Margate 4	a			18 10						19 11						22 11					23 11	

A to Ashford International

Table 207

Sundays

8 December to 11 May

London and Tonbridge - Ashford International, Folkestone, Dover, Canterbury West, Ramsgate and Margate

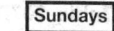

Network Diagram - see first Page of Table 206

Station			SE	SE 1	SE	SE 1	SE	SE 1	SE 1	SE 1	SE
St Pancras Intl. 15	⊖	d	22 12		22 42		23 12				23 42
Stratford International	⊖	d	22 19		22 49		23 19				23 49
Ebbsfleet International		d	22 31		23 01		23 31				00 01
London Charing Cross 4	⊖	d		21 40		22 10		22 40	23 10	23 40	
London Waterloo (East) 4	⊖	d		21 43		22 13		22 43	23 13	23 43	
London Cannon Street 4	⊖	d									
London Bridge 4	⊖	d		21 49		22 19		22 49	23 19	23 49	
Orpington 4		d		22 05		22 35		23 05	23 35	00 05	
Sevenoaks 4		d		22 15		22 45		23 15	23 45	00 15	
Hildenborough		d									
Tonbridge 4		a		22 23		22 53		23 23	23 53	00 23	
		d		22 24		22 54		23 24	23 54	00 24	
Paddock Wood 4		d		22 31		23 01		23 31	00 01	00 31	
Maidstone West 4	194	a									
Marden		d		22 37		23 07		23 37	00 07	00 37	
Staplehurst		d		22 41		23 11		23 41	00 11	00 41	
Headcorn		d		22 46		23 16		23 46	00 16	00 46	
Pluckley		d		22 52				23 52		00 52	
Ashford International		a	22 50	23 01	23 20	23 28	23 50	00 01	00 28	01 01	00 20
		d	22 52	23 05	23 22	23 32	23 52	00 05			
Wye		d		23 11							
Chilham		d		23 17							
Chartham		d		23 21							
Canterbury West 4		d		23 27	23 39						
Sturry		d		23 31							
Westenhanger		d				23 40					
Sandling		d				23 43		00 15			
Folkestone West		d	23 05			23 48	00 05	00 21			
Folkestone Central		d	23 08			23 51	00 08	00 23			
Dover Priory 4		a	23 20			00 01	00 20	00 34			
		d				00 02					
Martin Mill		d				00 11					
Walmer		d				00 15					
Deal		d				00 19					
Sandwich		d				00 26					
Minster 4		d		23 42							
Ramsgate 4		a		23 48	00 01	00 38					
Broadstairs		a									
Margate 4		a									

Table 207R

Mondays to Fridays

9 December to 16 May

Margate, Ramsgate, Canterbury West, Dover, Folkestone, Ashford International - Tonbridge and London

Network Diagram - see first Page of Table 206

Miles	Miles	Miles	Miles			SE	SE ■1	SE	SE ■1	SE	SE ■1	SE	SE ■1	SE	SE	SE ■1	SE ■1	SE ■1	SE	SE	SE ■1	SE	SE
0	0	—	—	**Margate ■4**	d														05 48				
3¼	3¼	—	—	Broadstairs	d														05 54				
5½	5½	—	—	**Ramsgate ■4**	d					05 00			04 51			05 36		05 26	06 00				
—	9½	0	—	Minster ■4	d					05 06						05 42							
13¾	—	4¾	—	Sandwich	d								05 05					05 40		05 52			
18	—	—	—	**Deal**	d								05 11					05 46		05 58			
19½	—	—	—	Walmer	d								05 14					05 49					
22¼	—	—	—	Martin Mill	d								05 18					05 53					
27¼	—	—	—	**Dover Priory ■4**	a								05 27					06 02		06 12			
—	—	—	—		d		04 37						05 28	05 45			05 45	06 04		06 12			
34½	—	—	—	**Folkestone Central**	d		04 49						05 39	05 56				06 15		06 23			
35¼	—	—	—	Folkestone West	d		04 51						05 42	05 58				06 18		06 26			
39	—	—	—	Sandling	d		04 56						05 47					06 23					
40¼	—	—	—	Westenhanger	d		04 59						05 49					06 26					
—	18½	—	—	Sturry	d					05 18						05 54							
—	20¾	—	—	**Canterbury West ■4**	d					05 25	05 36					06 00			06 20				
—	24	—	—	Chartham	d						05 41					06 05							
—	26	—	—	Chilham	d						05 44					06 08							
—	30¾	—	—	Wye	d						05 51					06 15							
48½	35	—	0	**Ashford International** ≡	a		05 08			05 41	05 57		05 59	06 11		06 21		06 35	06 36	06 39			
—	—	—	—																				
—	—	—	—		d		05 12	05 13	05 29	05 43			06 03	06 13		06 24		06 38	06 43		06 45		
54	—	—	—	Pluckley	d		05 18		05 35				06 09			06 30		06 44			06 51		
59¼	—	—	—	Headcorn	d		05 25		05 42				06 16			06 37		06 51			06 58		
62¾	—	—	—	Staplehurst	d		05 30		05 47				06 21			06 42		06 56			07 03		
65	—	—	—	Marden	d		05 34		05 51				06 25			06 46		07 00			07 07		
—	—	—	—	Maidstone West ■4 194	d	05 14						05 54			06 24							06 55	07 01
69¾	—	—	—	Paddock Wood ■4	d	05a34	05 41		05 58			06a13	06 32		06a43	06 53		07 07			07 14		07a20
75	—	—	—	**Tonbridge ■4**	a		05 49		06 05				06 39			07 01		07 14			07 21		
—	—	—	—		d		05 50		06 06				06 40			07 02		07 15			07 23		
77½	—	—	—	Hildenborough	a													07 19					
82¼	—	—	—	Sevenoaks ■4	a		05 58		06 14				06 48			07 10		07 26			07 31		
90¾	—	—	—	Orpington ■4	a		06 08		06 23														
102¾	—	—	—	**London Bridge ■4** ⊖	a		06 24		06 39				07 14			07 36	07 51	07 53					
—	—	—	—	**London Cannon Street ■4** ⊖	a												07 58	08 00					
103¾	—	—	—	**London Waterloo (East) ■4** ⊖	a		06 29		06 44				07 19			07 41					08 00		
104½	—	—	—	**London Charing Cross ■4** ⊖	a		06 33		06 49				07 25			07 47					08 06		
—	—	—	33¼	**Ebbsfleet International**	a			05 32		06 02				06 32								07 25	
—	—	—	50	**Stratford International** ⊖	a			05 44		06 14				06 44					07 11			07 38	
—	—	—	56	**St Pancras Intl. ■15** ⊖	a			05 51		06 21				06 51					07 19			07 45	

		SE ■1	SE ■1	SE	SE	SE ■1	SE ■1	SE	SE	SE	SE ■1	SE	SE ■1	SE ■1	SE ■1	SE ■1	SE ■1	SE	SE	SE	SE	SE ■1 A ⚲	SE ■1 A ⚲
Margate ■4	d							06 46															
Broadstairs	d							06 52															
Ramsgate ■4	d	06 08		06 26		06 12	06 42	06 58						06 57	06 50	07 10	07 19		07 30				07 23
Minster ■4	d	06 17					06 48									07 16							
Sandwich	d				06 18	06 26						06 52			07 02					07 22			07 35
Deal	d				06 24	06 32						06 58			07 08					07 28			07 41
Walmer	d					06 35									07 11								07 44
Martin Mill	d					06 39									07 16								07 49
Dover Priory ■4	a				06 39	06 48						07 12			07 24					07 42			07 57
	d		06 24		06 42	06 49						07 16			07 25					07 42			07 58
Folkestone Central	d		06 36		06 53	07 00					07 16	07 27			07 36					07 53			08 09
Folkestone West	d		06 38		06 56	07 03					07 19	07 30			07 38					07 56			08 11
Sandling	d		06 43			07 08					07 24				07 43								08 16
Westenhanger	d		06 46			07 11					07 27				07 46								08 19
Sturry	d	06 29					07 00									07 28							
Canterbury West ■4	d	06 34		06 50			07 06	07 18								07 36			07 50			08 00	
Chartham	d	06 39					07 11									07 41						08 05	
Chilham	d	06 42					07 14									07 44						08 08	
Wye	d	06 49					07 21									07 51						08 15	
Ashford International ≡	a	06 55	06 55	07 06	07 09	07 20	07 27	07 34			07 36	07 43			07 55	07 58			08 06	08 09		08 22	08 28
	d	06 57	07 03	07 13		07 22	07 29	07 36			07 38	07 45	07 45		08 03				08 13			08 33	
Pluckley	d	07 04	07 09			07 28					07 44		07 51		08 09							08 39	
Headcorn	d	07 11	07 16			07 35	07 40				07 51		07 58		08 16							08 46	
Staplehurst	d	07 16	07 22			07 40	07 45				07 56		08 03		08 21							08 51	
Marden	d	07 20	07 26			07 44	07 49				08 00		08 07		08 25							08 55	
Maidstone West ■4 194	d								07 25	07 42								07 55			08 18		
Paddock Wood ■4	d	07 27	07 33			07 51	07 55			08a01	08 07		08 14		08 31						08 37	09 01	
Tonbridge ■4	a	07 34	07 41			07 58	08 03				08 14		08 21		08 39						08 45	09 09	
	d	07 35	07 42			07 59	08 04				08 15		08 22		08 40							09 10	
Hildenborough	a	07 39									08 19												
Sevenoaks ■4	a	07 46	07 50			08 07	08 12				08 26		08 30		08 48							09 18	
Orpington ■4	a																						
London Bridge ■4 ⊖	a	08 13				08 33					08 55			08 49	09 14		09 09					09 43	
London Cannon Street ■4 ⊖	a	08 20				08 40					09 02			08 57			09 18						
London Waterloo (East) ■4 ⊖	a		08 20				08 40						09 00		09 19							09 48	
London Charing Cross ■4 ⊖	a		08 26				08 46						09 06		09 25							09 54	
Ebbsfleet International	a								07 55			08 04						08 25					
Stratford International ⊖	a			07 41				08 04	08 09			08 17						08 38	08 41				
St Pancras Intl. ■15 ⊖	a			07 50				08 13	08 16			08 24						08 45	08 49				

A ⚲ from Ashford International

Table 207R

Mondays to Fridays

9 December to 16 May

Margate, Ramsgate, Canterbury West, Dover, Folkestone, Ashford International - Tonbridge and London

Network Diagram - see first Page of Table 206

Station		SE	SE [1] A 🛒	SE [1] A 🛒	SE	SE	SE [1] A 🛒	SE [1] A 🛒	SE	SE [1] A 🛒	SE [1] A 🛒	SE	SE	SE [1] A 🛒	SE [1] A 🛒	SE	SE [1] A 🛒	SE [1] A 🛒	SE	SE	SE [1] A 🛒	SE [1] A 🛒	SE
Margate [4]	d	07 49							08 51							09 53							10 53
Broadstairs	d	07 55							08 57							09 59							10 59
Ramsgate [4]	d	08 01	07 40	08 16			08 40	08 05	09 03					09 40	09 23	10 05					10 40	10 23	11 05
Minster [4]	d	08 07	07 54				08 46	08 16						09 46							10 46		
Sandwich	d		08 02					08 25							09 35							10 35	
Deal	d		08 08					08 31							09 41							10 41	
Walmer	d		08 11					08 34							09 44							10 44	
Martin Mill	d		08 16					08 38							09 49							10 49	
Dover Priory [4]	a		08 24					08 48							09 57							10 57	
	d		08 25		08 45			08 58		09 25		09 45			09 58		10 25		10 45			10 58	
Folkestone Central	d		08 36		08 56			09 09		09 36		09 56			10 09		10 36		10 56			11 09	
Folkestone West	d		08 38		08 58			09 11		09 38		09 58			10 11		10 38		10 58			11 11	
Sandling	d		08 43					09 16		09 43					10 16		10 43					11 16	
Westenhanger	d		08 46					09 19		09 46					10 19		10 46					11 19	
Sturry	d	08 19					08 58							09 58							10 58		
Canterbury West [4]	d	08 25		08 36			09 07		09 23		09 36			10 07		10 25		10 36			11 07		11 25
Chartham	d			08 41							09 41							10 41					
Chilham	d			08 44							09 44							10 44					
Wye	d			08 51			09 19				09 51			10 19				10 51			11 19		
Ashford International	a	08 41	08 55	08 58	09 11		09 25	09 28	09 39	09 55	09 58	10 11		10 25	10 28	10 41	10 55	10 58	11 11		11 25	11 28	11 41
	d	08 43	09 03		09 13		09 33		09 43	10 03		10 13		10 33		10 43	11 03		11 13		11 33		11 43
Pluckley	d		09 09				09 39			10 09				10 39			11 09				11 39		
Headcorn	d		09 16				09 46			10 16				10 46			11 16				11 46		
Staplehurst	d		09 21				09 51			10 21				10 51			11 21				11 51		
Marden	d		09 25				09 55			10 25				10 55			11 25				11 55		
Maidstone West [4] 194	d					09 28							10 28							11 28			
Paddock Wood [4]	d		09 31			09 47	10 01			10 31			10 47	11 01			11 31			11 47	12 01		
Tonbridge [4]	a		09 39			09 55	10 09			10 39			10 55	11 09			11 39			11 55	12 09		
	d		09 40				10 10			10 40				11 10			11 40				12 10		
Hildenborough	a																						
Sevenoaks [4]	a		09 48				10 18			10 48				11 18			11 48				12 18		
Orpington [4]	a																						
London Bridge [4] ⊖	a		10 13				10 43			11 13				11 43			12 13				12 43		
London Cannon Street [4] ⊖	a																						
London Waterloo (East) [4] ⊖	a		10 18				10 48			11 18				11 48			12 18				12 48		
London Charing Cross [4] ⊖	a		10 22				10 52			11 22				11 52			12 22				12 52		
Ebbsfleet International	a	09 02			09 32				10 02			10 32				11 02			11 32				12 02
Stratford International ⊖	a	09 14			09 44				10 14			10 44				11 14			11 44				12 14
St Pancras Intl. [15] ⊖	a	09 21			09 51				10 21			10 51				11 21			11 51				12 21

Station		SE [1] A 🛒	SE [1] A 🛒	SE	SE	SE [1] A 🛒	SE [1] A 🛒	SE	SE [1] A 🛒	SE [1] A 🛒	SE	SE	SE [1] A 🛒	SE [1] A 🛒	SE	SE [1] A 🛒	SE [1] A 🛒	SE	SE	SE [1] A 🛒	SE [1] A 🛒	SE
Margate [4]	d							11 53							12 53							13 53
Broadstairs	d							11 59							12 59							13 59
Ramsgate [4]	d					11 40	11 23	12 05					12 40	12 23	13 05					13 40	13 23	14 05
Minster [4]	d					11 46							12 46							13 46		
Sandwich	d						11 35							12 35							13 35	
Deal	d						11 41							12 41							13 41	
Walmer	d						11 44							12 44							13 44	
Martin Mill	d						11 49							12 49							13 49	
Dover Priory [4]	a						11 57							12 57							13 57	
	d	11 25		11 45			11 58		12 25		12 45			12 58		13 25		13 45			13 58	
Folkestone Central	d	11 36		11 56			12 09		12 36		12 56			13 09		13 36		13 56			14 09	
Folkestone West	d	11 38		11 58			12 11		12 38		12 58			13 11		13 38		13 58			14 11	
Sandling	d	11 43					12 16		12 43					13 16		13 43					14 16	
Westenhanger	d	11 46					12 19		12 46					13 19		13 46					14 19	
Sturry	d					11 58							12 58							13 58		
Canterbury West [4]	d		11 36			12 07		12 25		12 36			13 07		13 25		13 36			14 07		14 25
Chartham	d		11 41							12 41							13 41					
Chilham	d		11 44							12 44							13 44					
Wye	d		11 51			12 19				12 51			13 19				13 51			14 19		
Ashford International	a	11 55	11 58	12 11		12 25	12 28	12 41	12 55	12 58	13 11		13 25	13 28	13 41	13 55	13 58	14 11		14 25	14 28	14 41
	d	12 03		12 13		12 33		12 43	13 03		13 13		13 33		13 43	14 03		14 13		14 33		14 43
Pluckley	d	12 09				12 39			13 09				13 39			14 09				14 39		
Headcorn	d	12 16				12 46			13 16				13 46			14 16				14 46		
Staplehurst	d	12 21				12 51			13 21				13 51			14 21				14 51		
Marden	d	12 25				12 55			13 25				13 55			14 25				14 55		
Maidstone West [4] 194	d				12 28							13 28							14 28			
Paddock Wood [4]	d	12 31			12 47	13 01			13 31			13 47	14 01			14 31			14 47	15 01		
Tonbridge [4]	a	12 39			12 58	13 09			13 39			13 55	14 09			14 39			14 55	15 09		
	d	12 40				13 10			13 40				14 10			14 40				15 10		
Hildenborough	a																					
Sevenoaks [4]	a	12 48				13 18			13 48				14 18			14 48				15 18		
Orpington [4]	a																					
London Bridge [4] ⊖	a	13 13				13 43			14 13				14 43			15 13				15 43		
London Cannon Street [4] ⊖	a																					
London Waterloo (East) [4] ⊖	a	13 18				13 48			14 18				14 48			15 18				15 48		
London Charing Cross [4] ⊖	a	13 22				13 52			14 22				14 52			15 22				15 52		
Ebbsfleet International	a			12 32				13 02			13 32				14 02			14 32				15 02
Stratford International ⊖	a			12 44				13 14			13 44				14 14			14 44				15 14
St Pancras Intl. [15] ⊖	a			12 51				13 21			13 51				14 21			14 51				15 21

A 🛒 from Ashford International

Table 207R

Mondays to Fridays

9 December to 16 May

Margate, Ramsgate, Canterbury West, Dover, Folkestone, Ashford International - Tonbridge and London

Network Diagram - see first Page of Table 206

		SE [1] A [trolley]	SE [1] A [trolley]	SE	SE	SE [1] A [trolley]	SE [1] A [trolley]	SE	SE [1] A [trolley]	SE [1] A [trolley]	SE	SE	SE [1] A [trolley]	SE [1] A [trolley]	SE	SE	SE [1] A [trolley]	SE [1] A [trolley]	SE	SE	SE [1] A [trolley]	SE [1] A [trolley]
Margate [4]	d							14 53							15 53							
Broadstairs	d							14 59							15 59							
Ramsgate [4]	d					14 40	14 23	15 05					15 40	15 23	16 05		15 50				16 40	16 23
Minster [4]	d					14 46							15 46								16 46	
Sandwich	d						14 35							15 35			16 02					16 35
Deal	d						14 41							15 41			16 08					16 41
Walmer	d						14 44							15 44			16 11					16 44
Martin Mill	d						14 49							15 49			16 16					16 49
Dover Priory [4]	a						14 57							15 57			16 24					16 57
	d	14 25		14 45			14 58		15 25		15 45			15 58			16 25		16 45			16 58
Folkestone Central	d	14 36		14 56			15 09		15 36		15 56			16 09			16 36		16 56			17 09
Folkestone West	d	14 38		14 58			15 11		15 38		15 58			16 11			16 38		16 58			17 11
Sandling	d	14 43					15 16		15 43					16 16			16 43					17 16
Westenhanger	d	14 46					15 19		15 46					16 19			16 46					17 19
Sturry	d					14 58							15 58								16 58	
Canterbury West [4]	d		14 36			15 04		15 25		15 36			16 04		16 25			16 36			17 04	
Chartham	d		14 41							15 41								16 41				
Chilham	d		14 44							15 44								16 44				
Wye	d		14 51			15 16				15 51			16 16					16 51			17 16	
Ashford International ≡	a	14 55	14 58	15 11		15 22	15 28	15 41	15 55	15 58	16 11		16 22	16 28	16 41		16 55	16 58	17 11		17 22	17 28
	d	15 03		15 13		15 33		15 43	16 03		16 13		16 33		16 43		17 03		17 13		17 33	
Pluckley	d	15 09				15 39			16 09				16 39				17 09				17 39	
Headcorn	d	15 16				15 46			16 16				16 46				17 16				17 46	
Staplehurst	d	15 21				15 51			16 21				16 51				17 21				17 51	
Marden	d	15 25				15 55			16 25				16 55				17 25				17 55	
Maidstone West [4] 194	d				15 28							16 28				16 58				17 28		
Paddock Wood [4]	d	15 31			15 47	16 01			16 31			16a47	17 01			17a17	17 31			17a47	18 01	
Tonbridge [4]	a	15 39			15 55	16 09			16 39				17 09				17 39				18 09	
	d	15 40				16 10			16 40				17 10				17 40				18 10	
Hildenborough	a																					
Sevenoaks [4]	a	15 48				16 18			16 48				17 18				17 48				18 18	
Orpington [4]	a																					
London Bridge [4] ⊖	a	16 14				16 46			17 17				17 44				18 16				18 43	
London Cannon Street [4] ⊖	a																					
London Waterloo (East) [4] ⊖	a	16 20				16 52			17 22				17 50				18 20				18 48	
London Charing Cross [4] ⊖	a	16 24				16 56			17 26				17 53				18 25				18 52	
Ebbsfleet International	a			15 32				16 02			16 31				17 02				17 32			
Stratford International ⊖	a			15 44				16 14			16 44				17 14				17 44			
St Pancras Intl. [15] ⊖	a			15 51				16 21			16 51				17 21				17 51			

		SE	SE [1] A [trolley]	SE [1] A [trolley]	SE	SE	SE [1] A [trolley]	SE [1] A [trolley]	SE	SE	SE	SE [1]	SE [1]	SE	SE	SE [1]	SE [1]	SE	SE	SE [1]	SE [1]	SE
Margate [4]	d	16 53							17 53									18 53				
Broadstairs	d	16 59							17 59									18 59				
Ramsgate [4]	d	17 05	16 50				17 40	17 23	18 05			17 50				18 40	18 23	19 05		18 50		
Minster [4]	d						17 46									18 46						
Sandwich	d		17 02					17 35				18 02					18 35			19 02		
Deal	d		17 08					17 41				18 08					18 41			19 08		
Walmer	d		17 11					17 44				18 11					18 44			19 11		
Martin Mill	d		17 16					17 49				18 16					18 49			19 16		
Dover Priory [4]	a		17 24					17 57				18 24					18 57			19 24		
	d		17 25		17 45			17 58				18 25		18 45			18 58			19 25		19 45
Folkestone Central	d		17 36		17 56			18 09				18 36		18 56			19 09			19 36		19 56
Folkestone West	d		17 38		17 58			18 11				18 38		18 58			19 11			19 38		19 58
Sandling	d		17 43					18 16				18 43					19 16			19 43		
Westenhanger	d		17 46					18 19				18 46					19 19			19 46		
Sturry	d						17 58									18 58						
Canterbury West [4]	d	17 25		17 36			18 04		18 25				18 36			19 07		19 25			19 36	
Chartham	d			17 41									18 41								19 41	
Chilham	d			17 44									18 44								19 44	
Wye	d			17 51			18 16						18 51			19 19					19 51	
Ashford International ≡	a	17 41	17 55	17 58	18 11		18 24	18 28	18 41			18 55	18 58	19 11		19 26	19 29	19 41		19 55	19 58	20 13
	d	17 43	18 03		18 13		18 33		18 43			19 03		19 13		19 33		19 43		20 03		20 16
Pluckley	d		18 09				18 39					19 09				19 39				20 09		
Headcorn	d		18 16				18 46					19 16				19 46				20 16		
Staplehurst	d		18 21				18 51					19 21				19 51				20 21		
Marden	d		18 25				18 55					19 25				19 55				20 25		
Maidstone West [4] 194	d					18 18				18 42	18 48				19 18				19 58			
Paddock Wood [4]	d		18 31			18a37	19 01				19a07	19 31			19a37	20 01			20 17	20 31		
Tonbridge [4]	a		18 39				19 09					19 39				20 09			20 25	20 39		
	d		18 40				19 10					19 40				20 10				20 40		
Hildenborough	a																					
Sevenoaks [4]	a		18 48				19 18					19 48				20 18				20 48		
Orpington [4]	a																					
London Bridge [4] ⊖	a		19 13				19 43					20 13				20 42				21 13		
London Cannon Street [4] ⊖	a																					
London Waterloo (East) [4] ⊖	a		19 17				19 48					20 18				20 47				21 18		
London Charing Cross [4] ⊖	a		19 21				19 52					20 22				20 51				21 22		
Ebbsfleet International	a	18 03			18 32				19 02	19 12				19 32				20 02				20 35
Stratford International ⊖	a	18 15			18 44				19 14	19 25				19 45				20 14				20 47
St Pancras Intl. [15] ⊖	a	18 22			18 51				19 21	19 32				19 53				20 21				20 54

A [trolley] from Ashford International

Table 207R

Mondays to Fridays

9 December to 16 May

Margate, Ramsgate, Canterbury West, Dover, Folkestone, Ashford International - Tonbridge and London

Network Diagram - see first Page of Table 206

		SE 1	SE 1	SE	SE	SE 1	SE 1		SE	SE 1	SE 1	SE	SE	SE 1	SE 1	SE	SE 1		SE	SE 1	SE	SE 1		
Margate 4	d			19 53								20 53							21 53					
Broadstairs	d			19 59								20 59							21 59					
Ramsgate 4	d	19 40	19 23	20 05						20 40	20 23	21 05					21 23		22 05	22 24		22 50		
Minster 4	d	19 46								20 46										22 30				
Sandwich	d		19 35								20 35						21 35					23 02		
Deal	d		19 41								20 41						21 41					23 08		
Walmer	d		19 44								20 44						21 44					23 11		
Martin Mill	d		19 49								20 49						21 49					23 16		
Dover Priory 4	a		19 57								20 57						21 57					23 24		
	d		19 58			20 25			20 45		20 58			21 25		21 45	21 58				22 45	23 25		
Folkestone Central	d		20 09			20 36			20 56		21 09			21 36		21 56	22 09				22 56	23 36		
Folkestone West	d		20 11			20 38			20 58		21 11			21 38		21 58	22 11				22 58	23 38		
Sandling	d		20 16			20 43					21 16			21 43			22 16					23 43		
Westenhanger	d		20 19			20 46					21 19			21 46			22 19					23 46		
Sturry	d	19 58								20 58										22 42				
Canterbury West 4	d	20 07		20 25			20 36			21 07		21 25			21 36				22 25	22 47				
Chartham	d						20 41								21 41					22 52				
Chilham	d						20 44								21 44					22 55				
Wye	d	20 19					20 51			21 19					21 51					23 02				
Ashford International	a	20 25	20 28	20 41		20 55	20 58		21 11	21 25	21 28	21 41		21 55	21 58	22 11	22 29		22 41	23 08	23 11	23 56		
	d	20 33		20 43		21 03			21 13	21 33		21 43		22 03		22 13	22 33		22 43		23 13			
Pluckley	d	20 39				21 09				21 39				22 09			22 39							
Headcorn	d	20 46				21 16				21 46				22 16			22 46							
Staplehurst	d	20 51				21 21				21 51				22 21			22 51							
Marden	d	20 55				21 25				21 55				22 25			22 55							
Maidstone West 4 194	d				20 58								21 58											
Paddock Wood 4	d	21 01			21 17	21 31				22 01			22 17	22 31			23 01							
Tonbridge 4	a	21 09			21 25	21 39				22 09			22 25	22 39			23 10							
	d	21 10				21 40				22 10				22 40			23 14							
Hildenborough	a																23 18							
Sevenoaks 4	a	21 18				21 48				22 18				22 48			23 24							
Orpington 4	a																23 36							
London Bridge 4 ⊖	a	21 43				22 13				22 43				23 13			23 54							
London Cannon Street 4 ⊖	a																							
London Waterloo (East) 4 ⊖	a	21 48				22 18				22 48				23 18			23 59							
London Charing Cross 4 ⊖	a	21 52				22 22				22 52				23 22			00 03							
Ebbsfleet International	a			21 02					21 32			22 02				22 32			23 02		23 32			
Stratford International ⊖	a			21 14					21 44			22 14				22 44			23 14		23 44			
St Pancras Intl. 15 ⊖	a			21 21					21 51			22 21				22 51			23 21		23 51			

Saturdays

14 December to 17 May

		SE 1	SE	SE	SE	SE 1	SE 1	SE	SE 1	SE		SE	SE 1	SE	SE 1	SE 1	SE	SE	SE 1 A	SE		SE 1 A	SE 1 A	SE	SE
Margate 4	d							05 53						06 53						07 53					
Broadstairs	d							05 59						06 59						07 59					
Ramsgate 4	d		05 05			05 32		06 05	05 50				06 40	07 05	06 50				07 40	08 05		07 50			
Minster 4	d					05 38							06 46						07 46						
Sandwich	d								06 02						07 02							08 02			
Deal	d								06 08						07 08							08 08			
Walmer	d								06 11						07 11							08 11			
Martin Mill	d								06 16						07 16							08 16			
Dover Priory 4	a								06 24						07 24							08 24			
	d	04 51		05 45			05 51		06 25	06 45					07 25		07 45					08 25		08 45	
Folkestone Central	d	05 02		05 56			06 02		06 36	06 56					07 36		07 56					08 36		08 56	
Folkestone West	d	05 04		05 58			06 04		06 38	06 58					07 38		07 58					08 38		08 58	
Sandling	d	05 09					06 09		06 43						07 43							08 43			
Westenhanger	d	05 12					06 12		06 46						07 46							08 46			
Sturry	d					05 50							06 58						07 58						
Canterbury West 4	d		05 25			05 56		06 25					07 04	07 25		07 36			08 07	08 25			08 36		
Chartham	d					06 01							07 09			07 41							08 41		
Chilham	d					06 04							07 12			07 44							08 44		
Wye	d					06 11							07 19			07 51			08 19				08 51		
Ashford International	a	05 21	05 41	06 11		06 17	06 21	06 41	06 55	07 11			07 26	07 41	07 55	07 58	08 11		08 25	08 41		08 55	08 58	09 11	
	d	05 25	05 43	06 13		06 25		06 43	07 03	07 13			07 33	07 43	08 03		08 13		08 33	08 43		09 03		09 13	
Pluckley	d	05 31				06 31			07 09				07 39		08 09				08 39			09 09			
Headcorn	d	05 38				06 38			07 16				07 46		08 16				08 46			09 16			
Staplehurst	d	05 43				06 43			07 21				07 51		08 21				08 51			09 21			
Marden	d	05 47				06 47			07 25				07 55		08 25				08 55			09 25			
Maidstone West 4 194	d				06 28							07 28						08 28							09 28
Paddock Wood 4	d	05 53			06 47	06 53			07 31			07 47	08 01		08 31			08 47	09 01			09 31			09 47
Tonbridge 4	a	06 01			06 55	07 01			07 39			07 55	08 09		08 39			08 55	09 09			09 39			09 55
	d	06 02				07 02			07 40				08 10		08 40				09 10			09 40			
Hildenborough	a	06 06				07 06																			
Sevenoaks 4	a	06 13				07 13			07 48				08 18		08 48				09 18			09 48			
Orpington 4	a	06 23				07 23																			
London Bridge 4 ⊖	a	06 39				07 39			08 13				08 43		09 13				09 43			10 13			
London Cannon Street 4 ⊖	a																								
London Waterloo (East) 4 ⊖	a	06 43				07 43			08 19				08 49		09 19				09 49			10 19			
London Charing Cross 4 ⊖	a	06 47				07 48			08 22				08 52		09 22				09 52			10 22			
Ebbsfleet International	a		06 02	06 32				07 02		07 32				08 02			08 32			09 02				09 32	
Stratford International ⊖	a		06 14	06 44				07 14		07 44				08 14			08 44			09 14				09 44	
St Pancras Intl. 15 ⊖	a		06 21	06 51				07 21		07 51				08 21			08 51			09 21				09 51	

A from Ashford International

Table 207R

Saturdays

14 December to 17 May

Margate, Ramsgate, Canterbury West, Dover, Folkestone, Ashford International - Tonbridge and London

Network Diagram - see first Page of Table 206

		SE 1 A	SE	SE 1 A	SE 1 A	SE	SE	SE 1 A	SE	SE 1 A	SE 1 A	SE	SE	SE 1 A	SE	SE 1 A	SE 1 A	SE		SE	SE 1 A	SE
Margate 4	d		08 53						09 53						10 53							13 53
Broadstairs	d		08 59						09 59						10 59							13 59
Ramsgate 4	d	08 40	09 05	08 50				09 40	10 05	09 50				10 40	11 05	10 50					13 40	14 05
Minster 4	d	08 46						09 46						10 46							13 46	
Sandwich	d			09 02						10 02						11 02						
Deal	d			09 08						10 08						11 08						
Walmer	d			09 11						10 11						11 11						
Martin Mill	d			09 16						10 16						11 16						
Dover Priory 4	a			09 24						10 24						11 24						
	d			09 25		09 45				10 25		10 45				11 25		11 45				
Folkestone Central	d			09 36		09 56				10 36		10 56				11 36		11 56				
Folkestone West	d			09 38		09 58				10 38		10 58				11 38		11 58				
Sandling	d			09 43						10 43						11 43						
Westenhanger	d			09 46						10 46						11 46						
Sturry	d	08 58						09 58						10 58					and at		13 58	
Canterbury West 4	d	09 07	09 25		09 36			10 07	10 25		10 36			11 07	11 25		11 36		the same		14 07	14 25
Chartham	d				09 41						10 41						11 41		minutes			
Chilham	d				09 44						10 44						11 44		past			
Wye	d	09 19			09 51			10 19			10 51			11 19			11 51		each		14 19	
Ashford International	a	09 28	09 41	09 55	09 58	10 11		10 25	10 41	10 55	10 58	11 11		11 25	11 41	11 55	11 58	12 11	hour until		14 25	14 41
	d	09 33	09 43	10 03		10 13		10 33	10 43	11 03		11 13		11 33	11 43	12 03		12 13			14 33	14 43
Pluckley	d	09 39		10 09				10 39		11 09				11 39		12 09					14 39	
Headcorn	d	09 46		10 16				10 46		11 16				11 46		12 16					14 46	
Staplehurst	d	09 51		10 21				10 51		11 21				11 51		12 21					14 51	
Marden	d	09 55		10 25				10 55		11 25				11 55		12 25					14 55	
Maidstone West 4 194	d						10 28						11 28							14 28		
Paddock Wood 4	d	10 01		10 31			10 47	11 01		11 31			11 47	12 01		12 31				14 47	15 01	
Tonbridge 4	a	10 09		10 39			10 55	11 09		11 39			11 55	12 09		12 39				14 55	15 09	
	d	10 10		10 40				11 10		11 40				12 10		12 40					15 10	
Hildenborough	a																					
Sevenoaks 4	a	10 18		10 48				11 18		11 48				12 18		12 48					15 18	
Orpington 4	a																					
London Bridge 4 ⊖	a	10 43		11 13				11 43		12 13				12 43		13 13					15 43	
London Cannon Street 4 ⊖	a																					
London Waterloo (East) 4 ⊖	a	10 49		11 19				11 49		12 19				12 49		13 19					15 49	
London Charing Cross 4 ⊖	a	10 52		11 22				11 52		12 22				12 52		13 22					15 52	
Ebbsfleet International	a		10 02			10 32			11 02			11 31			12 02			12 32				15 02
Stratford International ⊖	a		10 14			10 44			11 14			11 44			12 14			12 44				15 14
St Pancras Intl. 15 ⊖	a		10 21			10 51			11 21			11 51			12 21			12 51				15 21

		SE 1 A	SE 1 A	SE	SE	SE 1 A	SE	SE 1 A	SE 1 A	SE	SE	SE 1 A	SE	SE 1 A	SE 1 A	SE	SE	SE 1 A	SE	SE 1 A	SE 1 A	SE
Margate 4	d						14 53						15 53						16 53			
Broadstairs	d						14 59						15 59						16 59			
Ramsgate 4	d	13 50				14 40	15 05	14 50				15 40	16 05	15 50				16 40	17 05	16 50		
Minster 4	d					14 46						15 46						16 46				
Sandwich	d	14 02						15 02						16 02						17 02		
Deal	d	14 08						15 08						16 08						17 08		
Walmer	d	14 11						15 11						16 11						17 11		
Martin Mill	d	14 16						15 16						16 16						17 16		
Dover Priory 4	a	14 24						15 24						16 24						17 24		
	d	14 25		14 45				15 25		15 45				16 25		16 45				17 25		17 45
Folkestone Central	d	14 36		14 56				15 36		15 56				16 36		16 56				17 36		17 56
Folkestone West	d	14 38		14 58				15 38		15 58				16 38		16 58				17 38		17 58
Sandling	d	14 43						15 43						16 43						17 43		
Westenhanger	d	14 46						15 46						16 46						17 46		
Sturry	d					14 58						15 58						16 58				
Canterbury West 4	d		14 36			15 07	15 25		15 36			16 07	16 25		16 36			17 07	17 25		17 36	
Chartham	d		14 41						15 41						16 41						17 41	
Chilham	d		14 44						15 44						16 44						17 44	
Wye	d		14 51			15 19			15 51			16 19			16 51			17 19			17 51	
Ashford International	a	14 55	14 58	15 11		15 25	15 41	15 55	15 58	16 11		16 25	16 41	16 55	16 58	17 11		17 26	17 41	17 55	17 58	18 11
	d	15 03		15 13		15 33	15 46	16 03		16 13		16 33	16 43	17 03		17 13		17 33	17 43	18 03		18 13
Pluckley	d	15 09				15 39		16 09				16 39		17 09				17 39		18 09		
Headcorn	d	15 16				15 46		16 16				16 46		17 16				17 46		18 16		
Staplehurst	d	15 21				15 51		16 21				16 51		17 21				17 51		18 21		
Marden	d	15 25				15 55		16 25				16 55		17 25				17 55		18 25		
Maidstone West 4 194	d				15 28						16 28						17 28					
Paddock Wood 4	d	15 31			15 47	16 01		16 31			16 47	17 01		17 31			17 47	18 01		18 31		
Tonbridge 4	a	15 39			15 55	16 09		16 39			16 55	17 09		17 39			17 55	18 09		18 39		
	d	15 40				16 10		16 40				17 10		17 40				18 10		18 40		
Hildenborough	a																					
Sevenoaks 4	a	15 48				16 18		16 48				17 18		17 48				18 18		18 48		
Orpington 4	a																					
London Bridge 4 ⊖	a	16 13				16 43		17 13				17 43		18 13				18 43		19 13		
London Cannon Street 4 ⊖	a																					
London Waterloo (East) 4 ⊖	a	16 19				16 49		17 19				17 49		18 19				18 49		19 19		
London Charing Cross 4 ⊖	a	16 22				16 52		17 22				17 52		18 22				18 52		19 22		
Ebbsfleet International	a			15 32			16 05			16 31			17 02			17 32			18 02			18 32
Stratford International ⊖	a			15 44			16 17			16 44			17 14			17 44			18 14			18 45
St Pancras Intl. 15 ⊖	a			15 51			16 24			16 51			17 21			17 51			18 21			18 53

A ✠ from Ashford International

Table 207R

Saturdays

14 December to 17 May

Margate, Ramsgate, Canterbury West, Dover, Folkestone, Ashford International - Tonbridge and London

Network Diagram - see first Page of Table 206

		SE	SE [1] A [trolley]	SE	SE [1]	SE [1]	SE	SE	SE [1]	SE	SE [1]	SE [1]	SE	SE	SE [1]	SE	SE [1]	SE	SE	SE [1]	SE	SE [1]	SE
Margate [4]	d			17 53						18 53						19 53					20 53		
Broadstairs	d			17 59						18 59						19 59					20 59		
Ramsgate [4]	d		17 40	18 05	17 50				18 40	19 05	18 50				19 40	20 05	19 50			20 40	21 05	20 50	
Minster [4]	d		17 46						18 46						19 46					20 46			
Sandwich	d				18 02						19 02						20 02					21 02	
Deal	d				18 08						19 08						20 08					21 08	
Walmer	d				18 11						19 11						20 11					21 11	
Martin Mill	d				18 16						19 16						20 16					21 16	
Dover Priory [4]	a				18 24						19 24						20 24					21 24	
	d				18 25		18 45				19 25		19 45				20 25	20 45				21 25	21 45
Folkestone Central	d				18 36		18 56				19 36		19 56				20 36	20 56				21 36	21 56
Folkestone West	d				18 38		18 58				19 38		19 58				20 38	20 58				21 38	21 58
Sandling	d				18 43						19 43						20 43					21 43	
Westenhanger	d				18 46						19 46						20 46					21 46	
Sturry	d		17 58						18 58						19 58					20 58			
Canterbury West [4]	d		18 07	18 25		18 36			19 07	19 25		19 36			20 04	20 25				21 04	21 25		
Chartham	d					18 41						19 41			20 09					21 09			
Chilham	d					18 44						19 44			20 12					21 12			
Wye	d		18 19			18 51			19 19			19 51			20 19					21 19			
Ashford International	a		18 25	18 41	18 55	18 58	19 11		19 25	19 41	19 55	19 58	20 11		20 25	20 41	20 55	21 11		21 25	21 41	21 55	22 11
	d		18 33	18 43	19 03		19 13		19 33	19 43	20 03		20 13		20 33	20 43	21 03	21 13		21 33	21 43	22 03	22 13
Pluckley	d		18 39		19 09				19 39		20 09				20 39		21 09			21 39		22 09	
Headcorn	d		18 46		19 16				19 46		20 16				20 46		21 16			21 46		22 16	
Staplehurst	d		18 51		19 21				19 51		20 21				20 51		21 21			21 51		22 21	
Marden	d		18 55		19 25				19 55		20 25				20 55		21 25			21 55		22 25	
Maidstone West [4] 194	d	18 28						19 28						20 28					21 28				
Paddock Wood [4]	d	18 47	19 01		19 31			19 47	20 01		20 31			20 47	21 01		21 31		21 47	22 01		22 31	
Tonbridge [4]	a	18 55	19 09		19 39			19 55	20 09		20 39			20 55	21 09		21 39		21 55	22 09		22 39	
	d		19 10		19 40				20 10		20 40				21 10		21 40			22 10		22 40	
Hildenborough	a																						
Sevenoaks [4]	a		19 18		19 48				20 18		20 48				21 18		21 48			22 18		22 48	
Orpington [4]	a		19 27		19 57				20 27		20 57				21 27		21 57			22 27		22 57	
London Bridge [4] ⊖	a		19 43		20 13				20 43		21 13				21 43		22 13			22 43		23 13	
London Cannon Street [4] ⊖	a																						
London Waterloo (East) [4] ⊖	a		19 48		20 18				20 48		21 18				21 48		22 18			22 48		23 18	
London Charing Cross [4] ⊖	a		19 51		20 21				20 51		21 21				21 51		22 21			22 51		23 21	
Ebbsfleet International	a			19 02			19 32			20 02			20 32			21 02		21 32			22 02		22 32
Stratford International ⊖	a			19 14			19 44			20 14			20 44			21 14		21 44			22 14		22 44
St Pancras Intl. [15] ⊖	a			19 21			19 51			20 21			20 51			21 21		21 51			22 21		22 51

		SE	SE [1]	SE	SE [1]	SE	SE [1]
Margate [4]	d			21 53			
Broadstairs	d			21 59			
Ramsgate [4]	d		21 23	22 05	22 24		22 50
Minster [4]	d				22 30		
Sandwich	d		21 35				23 02
Deal	d		21 41				23 08
Walmer	d		21 44				23 11
Martin Mill	d		21 49				23 16
Dover Priory [4]	a		21 57				23 24
	d		21 58			22 45	23 25
Folkestone Central	d		22 09			22 56	23 36
Folkestone West	d		22 11			22 58	23 38
Sandling	d		22 16				23 43
Westenhanger	d		22 19				23 46
Sturry	d				22 42		
Canterbury West [4]	d			22 25	22 47		
Chartham	d				22 52		
Chilham	d				22 55		
Wye	d				23 02		
Ashford International	a		22 28	22 41	23 08	23 11	23 56
	d		22 33	22 43		23 13	
Pluckley	d		22 39				
Headcorn	d		22 46				
Staplehurst	d		22 51				
Marden	d		22 55				
Maidstone West [4] 194	d	22 28					
Paddock Wood [4]	d	22 47	23 01				
Tonbridge [4]	a	22 55	23 10				
	d		23 14				
Hildenborough	a		23 18				
Sevenoaks [4]	a		23 24				
Orpington [4]	a		23 36				
London Bridge [4] ⊖	a		23 54				
London Cannon Street [4] ⊖	a						
London Waterloo (East) [4] ⊖	a		23 59				
London Charing Cross [4] ⊖	a		00 03				
Ebbsfleet International	a			23 02		23 32	
Stratford International ⊖	a			23 14		23 44	
St Pancras Intl. [15] ⊖	a			23 21		23 51	

A [trolley] from Ashford International

Table 207R

Sundays

8 December to 11 May

Margate, Ramsgate, Canterbury West, Dover, Folkestone, Ashford International - Tonbridge and London

Network Diagram - see first Page of Table 206

		SE 1 🛒	SE	SE 1 🛒	SE 1 🛒	SE	SE	SE 1 A 🛒	SE	SE 1 A 🛒	SE	SE	SE 1 A 🛒	SE	SE 1 A 🛒	SE	SE	SE 1 A 🛒	SE 1 A 🛒	SE	SE 1 A 🛒	
Margate 4	d										07 53					08 53						
Broadstairs	d										07 59					08 59						
Ramsgate 4	d							06 50		07 40	08 05		07 50		08 40	09 05		08 50			09 40	
Minster 4	d									07 46					08 46						09 46	
Sandwich	d							07 02					08 02					09 02				
Deal	d							07 08					08 08					09 08				
Walmer	d							07 11					08 11					09 11				
Martin Mill	d							07 16					08 16					09 16				
Dover Priory 4	a							07 24					08 24					09 24				
	d							07 25	07 45				08 25	08 45				09 25		09 45		
Folkestone Central	d							07 36	07 56				08 36	08 56				09 36		09 56		
Folkestone West	d							07 38	07 58				08 38	08 58				09 38		09 58		
Sandling	d							07 43					08 43					09 43				
Westenhanger	d							07 46					08 46					09 46				
Sturry	d									07 58					08 58						09 58	and at
Canterbury West 4	d									08 04	08 25				09 04	09 25			09 36		10 07	the same
Chartham	d									08 09					09 09				09 41			minutes
Chilham	d									08 12					09 12				09 44			past
Wye	d									08 19					09 19				09 51		10 19	each
Ashford International	a							07 55	08 11	08 25	08 41		08 55	09 11	09 25	09 41		09 55	09 58	10 11	10 25	hour until
	d	06 33		07 05	07 33	07 43		08 05	08 13	08 33	08 43		09 05	09 13	09 33	09 43		10 05		10 13	10 33	
Pluckley	d	06 39			07 39					08 39					09 39						10 39	
Headcorn	d	06 46		07 16	07 46			08 16		08 46			09 16		09 46			10 16			10 46	
Staplehurst	d	06 51		07 21	07 51			08 21		08 51			09 21		09 51			10 21			10 51	
Marden	d	06 55		07 25	07 55			08 25		08 55			09 25		09 55			10 25			10 55	
Maidstone West 4 194	d		07 00				08 00					09 00					10 00					
Paddock Wood 4	d	07 01	07 19	07 31	08 01		08 19	08 31		09 01		09 19	09 31		10 01		10 19	10 31			11 01	
Tonbridge 4	a	07 09	07 27	07 39	08 09		08 27	08 39		09 09		09 27	09 39		10 09		10 27	10 39			11 09	
	d	07 10		07 40	08 10			08 40		09 10			09 40		10 10			10 40			11 10	
Hildenborough	a																					
Sevenoaks 4	a	07 18		07 48	08 18			08 48		09 18			09 48		10 18			10 48			11 18	
Orpington 4	a	07 27		07 57	08 27			08 57		09 27			09 57		10 27			10 57			11 27	
London Bridge 4 ⊖	a	07 43		08 13	08 43			09 13		09 43			10 13		10 43			11 13			11 43	
London Cannon Street 4 ⊖	a																					
London Waterloo (East) 4 ⊖	a	07 48		08 18	08 48			09 18		09 48			10 18		10 48			11 18			11 48	
London Charing Cross 4 ⊖	a	07 52		08 22	08 52			09 22		09 52			10 22		10 52			11 22			11 52	
Ebbsfleet International	a					08 02			08 32		09 02			09 32		10 02				10 32		
Stratford International ⊖	a					08 14			08 44		09 14			09 44		10 14				10 44		
St Pancras Intl. 15 ⊖	a					08 21			08 51		09 21			09 51		10 21				10 51		

		SE	SE	SE 1 A 🛒	SE 1 A 🛒	SE	SE 1 A 🛒	SE	SE	SE 1 A 🛒	SE 1 A 🛒	SE	SE 1 A 🛒	SE	SE	SE 1 A 🛒	SE 1 A 🛒	SE	SE 1 A 🛒	SE	SE	SE 1 A 🛒	SE
Margate 4	d	15 53						16 53						17 53						18 53			
Broadstairs	d	15 59						16 59						17 59						18 59			
Ramsgate 4	d	16 05		15 50			16 40	17 05		16 50			17 40	18 05		17 50			18 40	19 05		18 50	
Minster 4	d						16 46						17 46						18 46				
Sandwich	d			16 02						17 02						18 02						19 02	
Deal	d			16 08						17 08						18 08						19 08	
Walmer	d			16 11						17 11						18 11						19 11	
Martin Mill	d			16 16						17 16						18 16						19 16	
Dover Priory 4	a			16 24						17 24						18 24						19 24	
	d			16 25		16 45				17 25		17 45				18 25		18 45				19 25	19 45
Folkestone Central	d			16 36		16 56				17 36		17 56				18 36		18 56				19 36	19 56
Folkestone West	d			16 38		16 58				17 38		17 58				18 38		18 58				19 38	19 58
Sandling	d			16 43						17 43						18 43						19 43	
Westenhanger	d			16 46						17 46						18 46						19 46	
Sturry	d						16 58						17 58						18 58				
Canterbury West 4	d	16 25			16 36		17 07	17 25			17 36		18 07	18 25			18 36		19 04	19 25			
Chartham	d				16 41						17 41						18 41		19 09				
Chilham	d				16 44						17 44						18 44		19 12				
Wye	d				16 51		17 19				17 51		18 19				18 51		19 19				
Ashford International	a	16 41		16 55	16 58	17 11	17 25	17 41		17 55	17 58	18 11	18 25	18 41		18 55	18 58	19 11	19 25	19 41		19 55	20 11
	d	16 43		17 05		17 13	17 33	17 43		18 05		18 13	18 33	18 43		19 05		19 13	19 33	19 43		20 05	20 13
Pluckley	d						17 39						18 39						19 39				
Headcorn	d			17 16			17 46			18 16			18 46			19 16			19 46			20 16	
Staplehurst	d			17 21			17 51			18 21			18 51			19 21			19 51			20 21	
Marden	d			17 25			17 55			18 25			18 55			19 25			19 55			20 25	
Maidstone West 4 194	d		17 00						18 00						19 00						20 00		
Paddock Wood 4	d		17 19	17 31			18 01		18 19	18 31			19 01		19 19	19 31			20 01		20 19	20 31	
Tonbridge 4	a		17 27	17 39			18 09		18 27	18 39			19 09		19 27	19 39			20 09		20 27	20 39	
	d			17 40			18 10			18 40			19 10			19 40			20 10			20 40	
Hildenborough	a																						
Sevenoaks 4	a			17 48			18 18			18 48			19 18			19 48			20 18			20 48	
Orpington 4	a			17 57			18 27			18 57			19 27			19 57			20 27			20 57	
London Bridge 4 ⊖	a			18 13			18 43			19 13			19 43			20 13			20 43			21 13	
London Cannon Street 4 ⊖	a																						
London Waterloo (East) 4 ⊖	a			18 18			18 48			19 18			19 48			20 18			20 48			21 18	
London Charing Cross 4 ⊖	a			18 22			18 52			19 22			19 52			20 22			20 52			21 22	
Ebbsfleet International	a	17 02				17 32		18 02				18 32		19 02				19 32		20 02			20 32
Stratford International ⊖	a	17 14				17 44		18 14				18 45		19 14				19 44		20 14			20 44
St Pancras Intl. 15 ⊖	a	17 21				17 51		18 21				18 53		19 21				19 51		20 21			20 51

A 🛒 from Ashford International

Table 207R

Sundays

8 December to 11 May

Margate, Ramsgate, Canterbury West, Dover, Folkestone, Ashford International - Tonbridge and London

Network Diagram - see first Page of Table 206

		SE [1] A 🛒	SE	SE	SE [1] A 🛒	SE	SE [1] A 🛒	SE	SE	SE [1] A 🛒	SE	SE [1]	SE	SE [1]
Margate [4]	d		19 53					20 53					21 53	
Broadstairs	d		19 59					20 59					21 59	
Ramsgate [4]	d	19 40	20 05		19 50		20 40	21 05		20 50		21 40	22 05	21 50
Minster [4]	d	19 46					20 46					21 46		
Sandwich	d				20 02					21 02				22 02
Deal	d				20 08					21 08				22 08
Walmer	d				20 11					21 11				22 11
Martin Mill	d				20 16					21 16				22 16
Dover Priory [4]	a				20 24					21 24				22 24
	d				20 25	20 45				21 25	21 45			22 25
Folkestone Central	d				20 36	20 56				21 36	21 56			22 36
Folkestone West	d				20 38	20 58				21 38	21 58			22 38
Sandling	d				20 43					21 43				22 43
Westenhanger	d				20 46					21 46				22 46
Sturry	d	19 58					20 58					21 58		
Canterbury West [4]	d	20 04	20 25				21 04	21 25				22 04	22 25	
Chartham	d	20 09					21 09					22 09		
Chilham	d	20 12					21 12					22 12		
Wye	d	20 19					21 19					22 19		
Ashford International	a	20 25	20 41		20 55	21 11	21 25	21 41		21 55	22 11	22 25	22 41	22 55
	d	20 33	20 43		21 05	21 13	21 33	21 43		22 05	22 13		22 43	
Pluckley	d	20 39					21 39							
Headcorn	d	20 46			21 16		21 46			22 16				
Staplehurst	d	20 51			21 21		21 51			22 21				
Marden	d	20 55			21 25		21 55			22 25				
Maidstone West [4] 194	d			21 00					22 00					
Paddock Wood [4]	d	21 01		21 19	21 31		22 01		22 19	22 31				
Tonbridge [4]	a	21 09		21 27	21 39		22 09		22 27	22 39				
	d	21 10			21 40		22 10			22 40				
Hildenborough	a													
Sevenoaks [4]	a	21 18			21 48		22 18			22 48				
Orpington [4]	a	21 27			21 57		22 27			22 57				
London Bridge [4] ⊖	a	21 43			22 13		22 43			23 13				
London Cannon Street [4] ⊖	a													
London Waterloo (East) [4] ⊖	a	21 48			22 18		22 48			23 18				
London Charing Cross [4] ⊖	a	21 52			22 22		22 52			23 22				
Ebbsfleet International	a		21 02			21 32		22 02			22 32		23 02	
Stratford International ⊖	a		21 14			21 44		22 14			22 44		23 14	
St Pancras Intl. [15] ⊖	a		21 21			21 51		22 22			22 51		23 21	

A 🛒 from Ashford International

Table 208

Strood - Maidstone West and Paddock Wood

Network Diagram - see first Page of Table 206

Mondays to Fridays

9 December to 16 May

Miles			SE	SE	SE	SE	SE	SE	SE	SE	SE		SE	SE	SE	SE	SE	SE	SE	SE	SE		SE	SE	SE
0	St Pancras International	d					06 22																		
5¼	Stratford International	d					06 29																		
22	Ebbsfleet International	d					06 41																		
25	Gravesend	d					06 46																		
33	**Strood** 4	d	04 50	05 30	06 00	06 36	06 56	07 18	07 54	08 34	09 04		09 34	10 04	10 34	11 04	11 34	12 04	12 34	13 04	13 34		14 04	14 34	15 04
35¼	Cuxton	d	04 54	05 34	06 04	06 40		07 22	07 58	08 38	09 08		09 38	10 08	10 38	11 08	11 38	12 08	12 38	13 08	13 38		14 08	14 38	15 08
37	Halling	d	04 58	05 38	06 08	06 44		07 26	08 02	08 42	09 12		09 42	10 12	10 42	11 12	11 42	12 12	12 42	13 12	13 42		14 12	14 42	15 12
38½	Snodland	d	05 01	05 41	06 11	06 47		07 29	08 05	08 45	09 15		09 45	10 15	10 45	11 15	11 45	12 15	12 45	13 15	13 45		14 15	14 45	15 15
39¾	New Hythe	d	05 03	05 43	06 13	06 49		07 31	08 07	08 47	09 17		09 47	10 17	10 47	11 17	11 47	12 17	12 47	13 17	13 47		14 17	14 47	15 17
40¾	Aylesford	d	05 06	05 46	06 16	06 52		07 34	08 10	08 50	09 20		09 50	10 20	10 50	11 20	11 50	12 20	12 50	13 20	13 50		14 20	14 50	15 20
43¾	Maidstone Barracks	d	05 11	05 51	06 21	06 57		07 39	08 15	08 55	09 25		09 55	10 25	10 55	11 25	11 55	12 25	12 55	13 25	13 55		14 25	14 55	15 25
44¼	**Maidstone West** 4 194	a	05 13	05 53	06 23	06 59	07 12	07 41	08 17	08 57	09 27		09 57	10 27	10 57	11 27	11 57	12 27	12 57	13 27	13 57		14 27	14 57	15 27
—		d	05 14	05 54	06 24	07 01		07 42	08 18		09 28			10 28		11 28		12 28		13 28			14 28		15 28
46	East Farleigh	d	05 17	05 57	06 27	07 04		07 45	08 21		09 31			10 31		11 31		12 31		13 31			14 31		15 31
49	Wateringbury	d	05 22	06 02	06 32	07 09		07 50	08 26		09 36			10 36		11 36		12 36		13 36			14 36		15 36
50¾	Yalding	d	05 26	06 06	06 36	07 13		07 54	08 30		09 40			10 40		11 40		12 40		13 40			14 40		15 40
52¼	Beltring	d	05 29	06 09	06 39	07 16		07 57	08 33		09 43			10 43		11 43		12 43		13 43			14 43		15 43
54¼	**Paddock Wood** 4	a	05 34	06 13	06 43	07 20		08 01	08 37		09 47			10 47		11 47		12 47		13 47			14 47		15 47
59½	Tonbridge 4	a							08 45		09 55			10 55		11 55		12 58		13 55			14 55		15 55

		SE	SE	SE	SE	SE	SE		SE	SE	SE	SE	SE	SE	SE	SE	SE		SE	SE
St Pancras International	d					17 16			17 46		18 16									
Stratford International	d					17 23			17 53		18 23									
Ebbsfleet International	d					17 35			18 05		18 35									
Gravesend	d					17 40			18 10		18 40									
Strood 4	d	15 34	16 04	16 34	17 04	17 50	17 54		18 20	18 24	18 50	18 54	19 34	20 04	20 34	21 04	21 34		22 04	22 34
Cuxton	d	15 38	16 08	16 38	17 08		17 58			18 28		18 58	19 38	20 08	20 38	21 08	21 38		22 08	22 38
Halling	d	15 42	16 12	16 42	17 12		18 02			18 32		19 02	19 42	20 12	20 42	21 12	21 42		22 12	22 42
Snodland	d	15 45	16 15	16 45	17 15		18 05			18 35		19 05	19 45	20 15	20 45	21 15	21 45		22 15	22 45
New Hythe	d	15 47	16 17	16 47	17 17		18 07			18 37		19 07	19 47	20 17	20 47	21 17	21 47		22 17	22 47
Aylesford	d	15 50	16 20	16 50	17 20		18 10			18 40		19 10	19 50	20 20	20 50	21 20	21 50		22 20	22 50
Maidstone Barracks	d	15 55	16 25	16 55	17 25		18 15			18 45		19 15	19 55	20 25	20 55	21 25	21 55		22 25	22 55
Maidstone West 4 194	a	15 57	16 27	16 57	17 27	18 05	18 17		18 35	18 47	19 05	19 17	19 57	20 27	20 57	21 27	21 57		22 27	22 57
	d		16 28	16 58	17 28		18 18			18 48		19 18	19 58		20 58		21 58			
East Farleigh	d		16 31	17 01	17 31		18 21			18 51		19 21	20 01		21 01		22 01			
Wateringbury	d		16 36	17 06	17 36		18 26			18 56		19 26	20 06		21 06		22 06			
Yalding	d		16 40	17 10	17 40		18 30			19 00		19 30	20 10		21 10		22 10			
Beltring	d		16 43	17 13	17 43		18 33			19 03		19 33	20 13		21 13		22 13			
Paddock Wood 4	a		16 47	17 17	17 47		18 37			19 07		19 37	20 17		21 17		22 17			
Tonbridge 4	a												20 25		21 25		22 25			

Saturdays

14 December to 17 May

		SE	SE		SE	SE
St Pancras International	d					
Stratford International	d					
Ebbsfleet International	d					
Gravesend	d					
Strood 4	d	06 04	06 34		22 04	22 34
Cuxton	d	06 08	06 38	and at	22 08	22 38
Halling	d	06 12	06 42	the same	22 12	22 42
Snodland	d	06 15	06 45	minutes	22 15	22 45
New Hythe	d	06 17	06 47	past	22 17	22 47
Aylesford	d	06 20	06 50	each	22 20	22 50
Maidstone Barracks	d	06 25	06 55	hour until	22 25	22 55
Maidstone West 4 194	a	06 27	06 57		22 27	22 57
	d	06 28			22 28	
East Farleigh	d	06 31			22 31	
Wateringbury	d	06 36			22 36	
Yalding	d	06 40			22 40	
Beltring	d	06 43			22 43	
Paddock Wood 4	a	06 47			22 47	
Tonbridge 4	a	06 55			22 55	

Sundays

8 December to 11 May

		SE		SE
St Pancras International	d			
Stratford International	d			
Ebbsfleet International	d			
Gravesend	d			
Strood 4	d	06 35		21 35
Cuxton	d	06 39		21 39
Halling	d	06 43		21 43
Snodland	d	06 46	and	21 46
New Hythe	d	06 48	hourly	21 48
Aylesford	d	06 51	until	21 51
Maidstone Barracks	d	06 56		21 56
Maidstone West 4 194	a	06 58		21 58
	d	07 00		22 00
East Farleigh	d	07 03		22 03
Wateringbury	d	07 08		22 08
Yalding	d	07 12		22 12
Beltring	d	07 15		22 15
Paddock Wood 4	a	07 19		22 19
Tonbridge 4	a	07 27		22 27

Table 208R

Mondays to Fridays

9 December to 16 May

Paddock Wood and Maidstone West - Strood

Network Diagram - see first Page of Table 206

Miles			SE	SE	SE	SE	SE	SE	SE	SE	SE	SE		SE	SE	SE	SE	SE	SE	SE	SE	SE	SE
0	Tonbridge 4	d										09 04			16 04								
5¼	**Paddock Wood 4**	d	05 41	06 18		06 48			07 41	08 11		09 11			16 11	17 04	17 34	17 52		18 42	19 12	19 42	
7	Beltring	d	05 45	06 22		06 52			07 45	08 15		09 15			16 15	17 08	17 38	17 56		18 46	19 16	19 46	
8¾	Yalding	d	05 49	06 26		06 56			07 49	08 19		09 19			16 19	17 12	17 42	18 00		18 50	19 20	19 50	
10½	Wateringbury	d	05 52	06 29		06 59			07 52	08 22		09 22			16 22	17 15	17 45	18 03		18 53	19 23	19 53	
13½	East Farleigh	d	05 57	06 34		07 04			07 57	08 27		09 27	and at		16 27	17 20	17 50	18 08		18 58	19 28	19 58	
15¼	**Maidstone West 4** 194	a	06 02	06 39		07 09			08 02	08 32		09 32	the same		16 32	17 25	17 55	18 15		19 03	19 33	20 03	
—		d	06 03	06 40	06 55	07 10	07 25	07 55	08 03	08 33	09 03	09 33	minutes	16 03	16 33	17 26	17 56	18 16	18 42	19 04	19 34	20 04	20 33
15½	Maidstone Barracks	d	06 05	06 42		07 12			08 05	08 35	09 05	09 35	past	16 05	16 35	17 28	17 58	18 18		19 06	19 36	20 06	20 35
18¾	Aylesford	d	06 10	06 47		07 17			08 10	08 40	09 10	09 40	each	16 10	16 40	17 33	18 03	18 23		19 11	19 41	20 11	20 40
19½	New Hythe	d	06 12	06 49		07 19			08 12	08 42	09 12	09 42	hour until	16 12	16 42	17 35	18 05	18 25		19 13	19 43	20 13	20 42
21	Snodland	d	06 15	06 52		07 22			08 15	08 45	09 15	09 45		16 15	16 45	17 38	18 08	18 28		19 16	19 46	20 16	20 45
22½	Halling	d	06 18	06 55		07 25			08 18	08 48	09 18	09 48		16 18	16 48	17 41	18 11	18 31		19 19	19 49	20 19	20 48
24¼	Cuxton	d	06 22	06 59		07 29			08 22	08 52	09 22	09 52		16 22	16 52	17 45	18 15	18 35		19 23	19 53	20 23	20 52
26½	**Strood 4**	a	06 26	07 03	07 10	07 33	07 40	08 10	08 26	08 56	09 26	09 56		16 26	16 56	17 49	18 19	18 39	18 57	19 27	19 57	20 27	20 56
34½	Gravesend	d			07 22		07 52	08 22											19 09				
37½	Ebbsfleet International	d			07 26		07 57	08 26											19 13				
54¼	Stratford International	d			07 38		08 09	08 38											19 25				
59½	St Pancras International	a			07 45		08 16	08 45											19 32				

		SE		SE	SE	SE	SE
Tonbridge 4	d	20 34			21 34		22 34
Paddock Wood 4	d	20 41			21 41		22 41
Beltring	d	20 45			21 45		22 45
Yalding	d	20 49			21 49		22 49
Wateringbury	d	20 52			21 52		22 52
East Farleigh	d	20 57			21 57		22 57
Maidstone West 4 194	a	21 02			22 02		23 02
	d	21 03		21 33	22 03	22 33	23 03
Maidstone Barracks	d	21 05		21 35	22 05	22 35	23 05
Aylesford	d	21 10		21 40	22 10	22 40	23 10
New Hythe	d	21 12		21 42	22 12	22 42	23 12
Snodland	d	21 15		21 45	22 15	22 45	23 15
Halling	d	21 18		21 48	22 18	22 48	23 18
Cuxton	d	21 22		21 52	22 22	22 52	23 22
Strood 4	a	21 26		21 56	22 26	22 56	23 26
Gravesend	d						
Ebbsfleet International	d						
Stratford International	d						
St Pancras International	a						

Saturdays

14 December to 17 May

		SE	SE		SE	SE
Tonbridge 4	d	06 04			22 04	
Paddock Wood 4	d	06 11			22 11	
Beltring	d	06 15			22 15	
Yalding	d	06 19			22 19	
Wateringbury	d	06 22			22 22	
East Farleigh	d	06 27		and at	22 27	
Maidstone West 4 194	a	06 32		the same	22 32	
	d	06 33	07 03	minutes	22 33	23 03
Maidstone Barracks	d	06 35	07 05	past	22 35	23 05
Aylesford	d	06 40	07 10	each	22 40	23 10
New Hythe	d	06 42	07 12	hour until	22 42	23 12
Snodland	d	06 45	07 15		22 45	23 15
Halling	d	06 48	07 18		22 48	23 18
Cuxton	d	06 52	07 22		22 52	23 22
Strood 4	a	06 56	07 26		22 56	23 26
Gravesend	d					
Ebbsfleet International	d					
Stratford International	d					
St Pancras International	a					

Sundays

8 December to 11 May

		SE	SE	SE		SE
Tonbridge 4	d	06 32	07 32	08 34		21 34
Paddock Wood 4	d	06 39	07 39	08 41		21 41
Beltring	d	06 43	07 43	08 45		21 45
Yalding	d	06 47	07 47	08 49		21 49
Wateringbury	d	06 50	07 50	08 52		21 52
East Farleigh	d	06 55	07 55	08 57		21 57
Maidstone West 4 194	a	07 00	08 00	09 02		22 02
	d	07 01	08 01	09 03	and	22 03
Maidstone Barracks	d	07 03	08 03	09 05	hourly	22 05
Aylesford	d	07 08	08 08	09 10	until	22 10
New Hythe	d	07 10	08 10	09 12		22 12
Snodland	d	07 13	08 13	09 15		22 15
Halling	d	07 16	08 16	09 18		22 18
Cuxton	d	07 20	08 20	09 22		22 22
Strood 4	a	07 24	08 24	09 26		22 26
Gravesend	d					
Ebbsfleet International	d					
Stratford International	d					
St Pancras International	a					

Network Diagram for Table 212

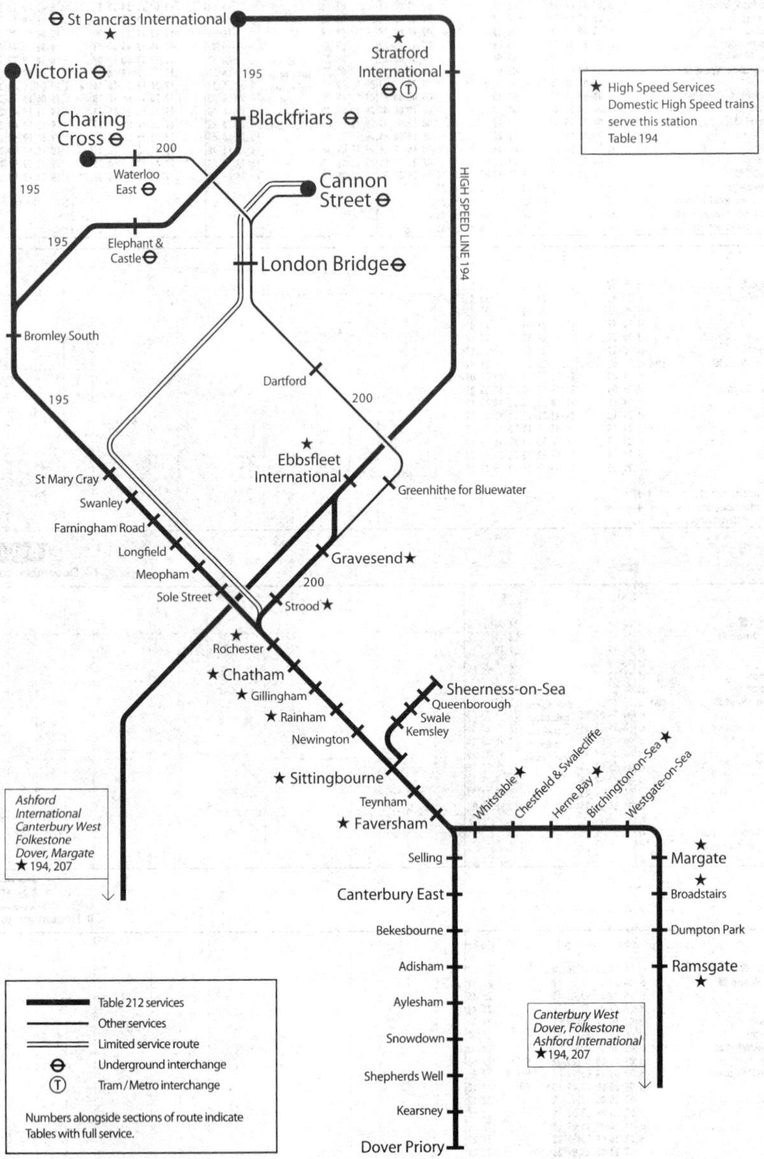

St Pancras International
Victoria
Charing Cross
Waterloo East
Elephant & Castle
Blackfriars
Stratford International
Cannon Street
London Bridge
HIGH SPEED LINE 194
195
200
Bromley South
Dartford
Ebbsfleet International
Greenhithe for Bluewater
St Mary Cray
Swanley
Farningham Road
Longfield
Meopham
Sole Street
Gravesend
Strood
Rochester
Chatham
Gillingham
Rainham
Newington
Sittingbourne
Teynham
Faversham
Sheerness-on-Sea
Queenborough
Swale
Kemsley
Whitstable
Chestfield & Swalecliffe
Herne Bay
Birchington-on-Sea
Westgate-on-Sea
Margate
Broadstairs
Dumpton Park
Ramsgate
Selling
Canterbury East
Bekesbourne
Adisham
Aylesham
Snowdown
Shepherds Well
Kearsney
Dover Priory
★ High Speed Services Domestic High Speed trains serve this station Table 194
Ashford International Canterbury West Folkestone Dover, Margate ★194, 207
Canterbury West Dover, Folkestone Ashford International ★194, 207
Table 212 services
Other services
Limited service route
Underground interchange
Tram/Metro interchange
Numbers alongside sections of route indicate Tables with full service.

TOCs operating on this network - Southeastern (SE)

Table 212

Mondays to Fridays

9 December to 16 May

London - Medway, Sheerness-on-Sea, Dover and Ramsgate

Network Diagram - see first Page of Table 212

Miles	Miles	Miles	Miles	Miles			SE MX [1] A	SE MO [1] A	SE MX [1] A	SE MX	SE B	SE MX [1] A	SE C	SE MX B	SE MO [1]		SE MX [1]	SE MX [1]	SE [1]	SE MX	SE MX C	SE	SE	SE	SE
—	—	—	—	0	**St Pancras Internatnl** 15 ⊖	d														00 12					
—	—	—	—	6	Stratford International ⊖	d								00 02						00 19					
—	—	—	—	22¾	Ebbsfleet International	d								00 14						00a30					
—	—	—	—	—	Farringdon	d																			
—	—	—	—	—	City Thameslink	d																			
—	—	—	—	—	London Blackfriars 3 ⊖	d																			
—	—	—	—	—	Elephant & Castle ⊖	d																			
0	0	—	—	—	**London Victoria** 15 ⊖	d												00 10				00 37			
11	11	—	—	—	Bromley South 4	d									00 02		00 09					00 57			
14¾	14¾	—	—	—	St Mary Cray	d									00 08		00 15					01 03			
17½	17½	—	—	—	Swanley 4	d									00 13		00 19					01 07			
20½	20½	—	—	—	Farningham Road	d									00 18		00 24					01 12			
23½	23½	—	—	—	Longfield	d									00 22		00 28					01 16			
26	26	—	—	—	Meopham	d									00 26		00 32					01 20			
27	27	—	—	—	Sole Street	d									00 29		00 35								
—	—	—	0	—	**London Charing Cross** 4 ⊖	d																	00 18		
—	—	—	0¾	—	**London Waterloo (East)** 4 ⊖	d																	00 21		
—	—	—	—	—	**London Cannon Street** 4 ⊖	d																			
—	—	—	1¾	—	**London Bridge** 4 ⊖	d																	00 26		
—	—	—	18¾	—	Dartford 4	d															00 25		01 07		
—	—	—	21½	—	Greenhithe for Bluewater	d															00 31		01 12		
—	—	—	25½	24¾	Gravesend 4	d							00 10	00 18							00 40		01 19		
—	—	—	32¾	32	Strood 4	d							00 22	00 28							00 52		01 30		
33¾	33¾	—	33¾	33	Rochester 4	d					00 03	00 09	00 26	00 33	00 39		00 45	00 49			00 56	01 31	01 35		
34¼	34¼	—	34¼	33½	**Chatham** 4	d					00 05	00 12	00 29	00 35	00 42		00 47	00 52			00 59	01 34	01 37		
36	36	—	36	35¼	**Gillingham (Kent)** 4	d					00 10	00 17	00a33	00 40	00 46		00a52	00 57			01a03	01a38	01a44	04 56	
39	39	—	—	38¼	Rainham (Kent)	d					00 15	00 21		00 45	00 51			01 01						05 01	
41½	41½	—	—	40¾	Newington	d			00 01						00 55			01 05						05 05	
44¾	44¾	0	—	44	**Sittingbourne** 4	a			00 06		00 22	00 28		00 52	01 00			01 10							
—	—	—	—	—		d		00 06	00 07	00 15	00 23	00 29		00 53	01 00			01 11							05 22
—	—	2	—	—	Kemsley	d				00 20														05 12	05 27
—	—	4	—	—	Swale	d				00 23														05 16	05 30
—	—	6	—	—	Queenborough	d				00 27														05 20	05 37
—	—	8	—	—	**Sheerness-on-Sea**	a				00 32														05 26	05 42
47½	47½	—	—	46¾	Teynham	d						00 33			01 05			01 15							
52	52	—	—	51¾	**Faversham** 2	a		00 14	00 15		00 33	00 39		01 03	01 12			01 23							
—	—	—	—	—		d		00 18				00 43						01 24	05 16						
—	55¼	—	—	—	Selling	d													05 20						
—	61¾	—	—	—	**Canterbury East** 4	d													05 29						
—	64¾	—	—	—	Bekesbourne	d													05 34						
—	67¾	—	—	—	Adisham	d													05 38						
—	68¾	—	—	—	Aylesham	d													05 40						
—	69¾	—	—	—	Snowdown	d													05 43						
—	71¾	—	—	—	Shepherds Well	d													05 47						
—	75	—	—	—	Kearsney	d													05 51						
—	77¼	—	—	—	**Dover Priory** 4	a													05 56						
59	—	—	—	—	Whitstable	d		00 26				00 51						01 32							
60½	—	—	—	—	Chestfield & Swalecliffe	d		00 29				00 54						01 35							
62¾	—	—	—	—	**Herne Bay**	d		00 33				00 58						01 39							
70¾	—	—	—	—	Birchington-on-Sea	d	00 07	00 41				01 07						01 48							
72½	—	—	—	—	Westgate-on-Sea	d	00 10	00 45				01 10						01 51							
73¾	—	—	—	—	**Margate** 4	d	00 14	00 49				01 14						01 55							
77	—	—	—	—	Broadstairs	d	00 20	00 54				01 20						02 01							
78¼	—	—	—	—	Dumpton Park	d	00 23	00 57				01 23						02 04							
79¼	—	—	—	—	**Ramsgate** 4	a	00 26	01 01				01 26						02 07							

A from London Victoria
B from St Pancras International
C from London Charing Cross

For further services to St Pancras International, Blackfriars and Elephant & Castle and onwards to Bromley South, St Mary Cray and Swanley please see table 52

Table 212

Mondays to Fridays

9 December to 16 May

London - Medway, Sheerness-on-Sea, Dover and Ramsgate

Network Diagram - see first Page of Table 212

		SE 1	SE	SE	SE	SE	SE	SE 1	SE 1	SE 1	SE	SE	SE	SE 1	SE	SE	SE	SE	SE 1	SE 1	SE	SE
St Pancras Internatnl 15 ⊖	d																06 22					
Stratford International ⊖	d																06 29					
Ebbsfleet International	d																06 41					
Farringdon	d																					
City Thameslink	d																					
London Blackfriars 3 ⊖	d																					
Elephant & Castle ⊖	d																					
London Victoria 15 ⊖	d								05 22		05 30			05 52					06 22			
Bromley South 4	d								05 39		05a57			06 09					06 39			
St Mary Cray	d								05 45										06 45			
Swanley 4	d								05 49					06 20					06 49			
Farningham Road	d								05 54										06 54			
Longfield	d								05 58					06 26					06 58			
Meopham	d								06 02					06 30					07 02			
Sole Street	d								06 05										07 05			
London Charing Cross 4 ⊖	d															05 39					06 09	
London Waterloo (East) 4 ⊖	d															05 42					06 12	
London Cannon Street 4 ⊖	d																					
London Bridge 4 ⊖	d															05 47					06 17	
Dartford 4	d			05 25								05 55				06 25					06 55	
Greenhithe for Bluewater	d			05 30								06 00				06 30					07 00	
Gravesend 4	d			05 37								06 07				06 38	06 46				07 07	
Strood 4	d			05 48								06 18				06 49	06a55				07 18	
Rochester 4	d			05 53					06 15			06 23		06 41		06 53			07 15		07 22	
Chatham 4	d			05 55					06 17			06 25		06 44		06 56			07 17		07 25	
Gillingham (Kent) 4	d	05 47		06a00					06 22			06a30		06 48		07a00			07 22		07a30	
Rainham (Kent)	d	05 51							06 26					06 53					07 26			
Newington	d	05 55							06 30					06 57					07 30			
Sittingbourne 4	a	06 00							06 35					07 02					07 37			
	d	06 01	06 03			06 22			06 36				06 53	07 02	07 09				07 38			07 44
Kemsley	d		06 08			06 27							06 58		07 14							07 49
Swale	d		06 11			06 30							07 01		07 17							07 52
Queenborough	d		06 15			06 35							07 05		07 22							07 56
Sheerness-on-Sea	a		06 20			06 40							07 10		07 27							08 01
Teynham	d	06 05							06 40					07 07					07 42			
Faversham 2	a	06 11							06 46					07 13					07 48			
	d	06 12						06 15	06 47	06 55				07 13					07 49	07 52		
Selling	d	06 16								06 59										07 56		
Canterbury East 4	d	06 26								07 09										08 07		
Bekesbourne	d	06 30								07 14										08 11		
Adisham	d	06 34								07 18										08 15		
Aylesham	d	06 37								07 21										08 18		
Snowdown	d	06 39								07 23										08 20		
Shepherds Well	d	06 43								07 27										08 24		
Kearsney	d	06 48								07 32										08 29		
Dover Priory 4	a	06 53								07 38										08 35		
Whitstable	d							06 23	06 55					07 21					07 57			
Chestfield & Swalecliffe	d							06 26	06 58					07 24					08 00			
Herne Bay	d							06 30	07 02					07 28					08 04			
Birchington-on-Sea	d							06 39	07 11					07 37					08 13			
Westgate-on-Sea	d							06 42	07 14					07 41					08 17			
Margate 4	d				05 48		06 46	06 50	07 18					07 45				07 49	08 21			
Broadstairs	d				05 54		06 52	06 56	07 24					07 50				07 55	08 26			
Dumpton Park	d							06 59	07 27					07 53					08 29			
Ramsgate 4	a				05 59		06 57	07 02	07 30					07 56				08 00	08 32			

For further services to St Pancras International, Blackfriars and Elephant & Castle and onwards to Bromley South, St Mary Cray and Swanley please see table 52

Table 212

Mondays to Fridays

9 December to 16 May

London - Medway, Sheerness-on-Sea, Dover and Ramsgate

Network Diagram - see first Page of Table 212

		SE	SE 1	SE	SE	SE 1	SE		SE	SE 1	SE	SE 1		SE	SE	SE	SE		SE 1		SE	SE	SE 1	SE	SE
St Pancras Internatnl 15 ⊖	d	06 55							07 25								07 52							08 25	
Stratford International ⊖	d	07 02							07 32								08 02							08 32	
Ebbsfleet International	d	07 14							07 44								08 14							08 44	
Farringdon	d																								
City Thameslink	d																								
London Blackfriars 3 ⊖	d																								
Elephant & Castle ⊖	d																								
London Victoria 15 ⊖	d		06 45			06 58	07 09					07 22				07 43			07 52				07 58		
Bromley South 4	d		07 02			07 19						07 40							08 09				08 28		
St Mary Cray	d		07 08			07 25																	08 34		
Swanley 4	d		07 13			07 29						07 49											08 39		
Farningham Road	d		07 18			07 34																	08 44		
Longfield	d		07 22			07 38						07 55							08 22				08 49		
Meopham	d		07 26			07 42						07 59							08 27				08 53		
Sole Street	d		07 28			07 45																	08 56		
London Charing Cross 4 ⊖	d				06 39										07 12							07 39			
London Waterloo (East) 4 ⊖	d				06 42										07 15							07 42			
London Cannon Street 4 ⊖	d																								
London Bridge 4 ⊖	d				06 47										07 21							07 47			
Dartford 4	d				07 25		07a48								08 00	08a27						08 25			
Greenhithe for Bluewater	d				07 30										08 05							08 30			
Gravesend 4	d	07 21			07 37				07 48						08 12		08 18					08 37		08 48	
Strood 4	d	07 31			07 48				07 58						08 23		08 28					08 48		08 58	
Rochester 4	d	07 35	07 40		07 53	07 56			08 03			08 11			08 28		08 33		08 40			08 53	09a07	09 03	
Chatham 4	d	07 38	07 43		07 55	07 59			08 05			08 13			08 30		08 35		08 42			08 55		09 05	
Gillingham (Kent) 4	d	07 42	07 47		08a00	08a03			08 10			08 18			08a37		08 40		08 47			09a02		09 10	
Rainham (Kent)	d	07 47	07 52						08 15			08 22					08 45		08 51					09 15	
Newington	d		07 56									08 26							08 55						
Sittingbourne 4	a	07 55	08 01						08 22			08 31					08 52		09 00					09 22	
	d	07 56	08 01	08 14					08 23			08 32		08 40			08 53		09 01		09 10			09 23	
Kemsley	d			08 19										08 45							09 15				
Swale	d			08 22										08 48							09 18				
Queenborough	d			08 26										08 52							09 22				
Sheerness-on-Sea	a			08 31										08 57							09 27				
Teynham	d		08 06									08 36													
Faversham 2	a	08 05	08 12						08 33			08 42					09 03		09 09					09 33	
	d		08 13							08 16		08 46	08 50						09 13	09 15					
Selling	d		08 17										08 54												
Canterbury East 4	d		08 27										09 03							09 29					
Bekesbourne	d		08 31										09 08												
Adisham	d		08 35										09 12												
Aylesham	d		08 38										09 14												
Snowdown	d		08 40										09 17												
Shepherds Well	d		08 44										09 20												
Kearsney	d		08 49										09 25												
Dover Priory 4	a		08 54										09 29							09 48					
Whitstable	d									08 24		08 54							09 21						
Chestfield & Swalecliffe	d									08 27		08 57													
Herne Bay	d									08 31		09 01							09 26						
Birchington-on-Sea	d									08 39		09 10							09 35						
Westgate-on-Sea	d									08 43		09 13													
Margate 4	d									08 47	08 51	09 17							09 41						09 53
Broadstairs	d									08 52	08 57	09 23							09 46						09 59
Dumpton Park	d									08 55		09 26													
Ramsgate 4	a									08 58	09 02	09 29							09 51						10 04

For further services to St Pancras International, Blackfriars and Elephant & Castle and onwards to Bromley South, St Mary Cray and Swanley please see table 52

Table 212

Mondays to Fridays

9 December to 16 May

London - Medway, Sheerness-on-Sea, Dover and Ramsgate

Network Diagram - see first Page of Table 212

		SE 1		SE	SE	SE	SE 1		SE	SE	SE 1	SE	SE	SE 1 A		SE	SE	SE	SE 1 A		SE	SE
St Pancras Internatnl 15 ⊖	d					08 52						09 25						09 55				
Stratford International ⊖	d					08 59						09 32						10 02				
Ebbsfleet International	d					09 14						09 44						10 14				
Farringdon	d																					
City Thameslink	d																					
London Blackfriars 3 ⊖	d																					
Elephant & Castle ⊖	d																					
London Victoria 15 ⊖	d	08 22					08 52				08 58			09 22					09 52			
Bromley South 4	d	08 39					09 09				09 19			09 39					10 09			
St Mary Cray	d										09 25											
Swanley 4	d										09 29											
Farningham Road	d										09 34											
Longfield	d	08 52					09 22				09 38			09 52					10 22			
Meopham	d	08 57					09 27				09 42			09 57					10 27			
Sole Street	d										09 45											
London Charing Cross 4 ⊖	d				08 11					08 41							09 11					09 39
London Waterloo (East) 4 ⊖	d				08 14					08 44							09 14					09 42
London Cannon Street 4 ⊖	d																					
London Bridge 4 ⊖	d				08 19					08 49							09 19					09 47
Dartford 4	d				08 55					09 25							09 55					10 25
Greenhithe for Bluewater	d				09 00					09 30							10 00					10 30
Gravesend 4	d				09 07	09 18				09 37		09 48					10 07	10 18				10 37
Strood 4	d				09 18	09 28				09 48		09 58					10 18	10 28				10 48
Rochester 4	d	09 09			09 23	09 33	09 39			09 53	09 56	10 03		10 09			10 23	10 33	10 39			10 53
Chatham 4	d	09 12			09 25	09 35	09 42			09 55	09 59	10 05		10 12			10 25	10 35	10 42			10 55
Gillingham (Kent) 4	d	09 17			09a32	09 40	09 47			10a02	10a03	10 10		10 17			10a32	10 40	10 47			11a00
Rainham (Kent)	d	09 21				09 45	09 51					10 15		10 21				10 45	10 51			
Newington	d						09 55												10 55			
Sittingbourne 4	a	09 28				09 52	10 00					10 22		10 28				10 52	11 00			
	d	09 29		09 40		09 53	10 01		10 10			10 23		10 29		10 40		10 53	11 01		11 10	
Kemsley	d			09 45					10 15							10 45					11 15	
Swale	d			09 48					10 18							10 48					11 18	
Queenborough	d			09 52					10 22							10 52					11 22	
Sheerness-on-Sea	a			09 57					10 27							10 57					11 27	
Teynham	d	09 33												10 33								
Faversham 2	a	09 39				10 03	10 09					10 33		10 39				11 03	11 09			
	d	09 43	09 45				10 13	10 15						10 43	10 45				11 13	11 15		
Selling	d		09 49												10 49							
Canterbury East 4	d		09 59					10 29							10 59					11 29		
Bekesbourne	d		10 03												11 03							
Adisham	d		10 07												11 07							
Aylesham	d		10 10												11 10							
Snowdown	d		10 12												11 12							
Shepherds Well	d		10 16												11 16							
Kearsney	d		10 21												11 21							
Dover Priory 4	a		10 26					10 48							11 26					11 48		
Whitstable	d	09 51					10 21							10 51					11 21			
Chestfield & Swalecliffe	d	09 54												10 54								
Herne Bay	d	09 58					10 26							10 58					11 26			
Birchington-on-Sea	d	10 07					10 35							11 07					11 35			
Westgate-on-Sea	d	10 10												11 10								
Margate 4	d	10 14					10 41						10 53	11 14					11 41			
Broadstairs	d	10 20					10 46						10 59	11 20					11 46			
Dumpton Park	d	10 23												11 23								
Ramsgate 4	a	10 26					10 51						11 04	11 26					11 51			

A to Margate

For further services to St Pancras International, Blackfriars and Elephant & Castle and onwards to Bromley South, St Mary Cray and Swanley please see table 52

Table 212

Mondays to Fridays

9 December to 16 May

London - Medway, Sheerness-on-Sea, Dover and Ramsgate

Network Diagram - see first Page of Table 212

		SE	SE	SE	SE	SE	SE	SE	SE	SE	SE	SE	SE	SE	SE	SE	SE	SE	SE
		1			1				1			1			1				1
					A 🛒				A 🛒						A 🛒				A 🛒
St Pancras Internatnl [15] ⊖	d		10 22					10 52					11 25					11 55	
Stratford International ⊖	d		10 32					10 59					11 32					12 02	
Ebbsfleet International	d		10 44					11 14					11 44					12 14	
Farringdon	d																		
City Thameslink	d																		
London Blackfriars [3] ⊖	d																		
Elephant & Castle ⊖	d																		
London Victoria [15] ⊖	d	09 58			10 22				10 52			10 58			11 22				11 52
Bromley South [4]	d	10 19			10 39				11 09			11 19			11 39				12 09
St Mary Cray	d	10 25										11 25							
Swanley [4]	d	10 29										11 29							
Farningham Road	d	10 34										11 34							
Longfield	d	10 38			10 52				11 22			11 38			11 52				12 22
Meopham	d	10 42			10 57				11 27			11 42			11 57				12 27
Sole Street	d	10 45										11 45							
London Charing Cross [4] ⊖	d						10 09				10 39						11 09		
London Waterloo (East) [4] ⊖	d						10 12				10 42						11 12		
London Cannon Street [4] ⊖	d																		
London Bridge [4] ⊖	d						10 17				10 47						11 17		
Dartford [4]	d						10 55				11 25						11 55		
Greenhithe for Bluewater	d						11 00				11 30						12 00		
Gravesend [4]	d		10 48				11 07	11 18			11 37		11 48				12 07	12 18	
Strood [4]	d		10 58				11 18	11 28			11 48		11 58				12 18	12 28	
Rochester [4]	d	10 56	11 03		11 09		11 23	11 33	11 39		11 53	11 56	12 03		12 09		12 23	12 33	12 39
Chatham [4]	d	10 59	11 05		11 12		11 26	11 35	11 42		11 55	11 59	12 05		12 12		12 25	12 35	12 42
Gillingham (Kent) [4]	d	11a03	11 10		11 17		11a30	11 40	11 47		12a00	12a03	12 10		12 17		12a30	12 40	12 47
Rainham (Kent)	d		11 15		11 21			11 45	11 51				12 15		12 21			12 45	12 51
Newington	d								11 55										12 55
Sittingbourne [4]	a		11 22		11 28			11 52	12 00				12 22		12 28			12 52	13 00
	d		11 23		11 29	11 40		11 53	12 01	12 10			12 23		12 29	12 40		12 53	13 01
Kemsley	d					11 45				12 15						12 45			
Swale	d					11 48				12 18						12 48			
Queenborough	d					11 52				12 22						12 52			
Sheerness-on-Sea	a					11 57				12 27						12 57			
Teynham	d				11 33										12 33				
Faversham [2]	a		11 33		11 39			12 03	12 09				12 33		12 39			13 03	13 09
	d				11 43 11 45				12 13 12 15						12 43 12 45				13 13 13 15
Selling	d				11 49										12 49				
Canterbury East [4]	d				11 59				12 29						12 59				13 29
Bekesbourne	d				12 03										13 03				
Adisham	d				12 07										13 07				
Aylesham	d				12 10										13 10				
Snowdown	d				12 12										13 12				
Shepherds Well	d				12 16										13 16				
Kearsney	d				12 21										13 21				
Dover Priory [4]	a				12 26				12 48						13 26				13 48
Whitstable	d				11 51				12 21						12 51				13 21
Chestfield & Swalecliffe	d				11 54										12 54				
Herne Bay	d				11 58				12 26						12 58				13 26
Birchington-on-Sea	d				12 07				12 35						13 07				13 35
Westgate-on-Sea	d				12 10										13 10				
Margate [4]	d			11 53	12 14				12 41					12 53	13 14				13 41
Broadstairs	d			11 59	12 20				12 46					12 59	13 20				13 46
Dumpton Park	d				12 23										13 23				
Ramsgate [4]	a			12 04	12 26				12 51					13 04	13 26				13 51

A 🛒 to Margate

For further services to St Pancras International, Blackfriars and Elephant & Castle and onwards to Bromley South, St Mary Cray and Swanley please see table 52

Table 212

Mondays to Fridays

9 December to 16 May

London - Medway, Sheerness-on-Sea, Dover and Ramsgate

Network Diagram - see first Page of Table 212

		SE	SE	SE [1]	SE	SE	SE [1] A [trolley]		SE	SE	SE	SE [1] A [trolley]		SE	SE	SE [1]	SE	SE	SE [1] A [trolley]		SE	SE	SE
St Pancras Internatnl [15] ⊖	d				12 22						12 52						13 25						13 55
Stratford International ⊖	d				12 32						12 59						13 32						14 02
Ebbsfleet International	d				12 44						13 14						13 44						14 14
Farringdon	d																						
City Thameslink	d																						
London Blackfriars [3] ⊖	d																						
Elephant & Castle ⊖	d																						
London Victoria [15] ⊖	d			11 58			12 22					12 52				12 58			13 22				
Bromley South [4]	d			12 19			12 39					13 09				13 19			13 39				
St Mary Cray	d			12 25												13 25							
Swanley [4]	d			12 29												13 29							
Farningham Road	d			12 34												13 34							
Longfield	d			12 38			12 52					13 22				13 38			13 52				
Meopham	d			12 42			12 57					13 27				13 42			13 57				
Sole Street	d			12 45												13 45							
London Charing Cross [4] ⊖	d		11 39							12 09					12 39							13 09	
London Waterloo (East) [4] ⊖	d		11 42							12 12					12 42							13 12	
London Cannon Street [4] ⊖	d																						
London Bridge [4] ⊖	d		11 47							12 17					12 47							13 17	
Dartford [4]	d		12 25							12 55					13 25							13 55	
Greenhithe for Bluewater	d		12 30							13 00					13 30							14 00	
Gravesend [4]	d		12 37		12 48					13 07	13 18				13 37		13 48					14 07	14 18
Strood [4]	d		12 48		12 58					13 18	13 28				13 48		13 58					14 18	14 28
Rochester [4]	d		12 53	12 56	13 03		13 09			13 23	13 33	13 39			13 53	13 56	14 03		14 09			14 23	14 33
Chatham [4]	d		12 55	12 59	13 05		13 12			13 25	13 35	13 42			13 55	13 59	14 05		14 12			14 25	14 35
Gillingham (Kent) [4]	d		13a00	13a03	13 10		13 17			13a30	13 40	13 47			14a00	14a03	14 10		14 17			14a30	14 40
Rainham (Kent)	d				13 15		13 21				13 45	13 51					14 15		14 21				14 45
Newington	d											13 55											
Sittingbourne [4]	a				13 22		13 28				13 52	14 00					14 22		14 28				14 52
	d	13 10			13 23		13 28		13 40		13 53	14 01		14 10			14 23		14 29		14 40		14 53
Kemsley	d	13 15							13 45					14 15							14 45		
Swale	d	13 18							13 48					14 18							14 48		
Queenborough	d	13 22							13 52					14 22							14 52		
Sheerness-on-Sea	a	13 27							13 57					14 27							14 57		
Teynham	d						13 33												14 33				
Faversham [2]	a				13 33		13 39				14 03	14 09					14 33		14 39				15 03
	d						13 43	13 45				14 13	14 15						14 43	14 45			
Selling	d							13 49												14 49			
Canterbury East [4]	d							13 59					14 29							14 59			
Bekesbourne	d							14 03												15 03			
Adisham	d							14 07												15 07			
Aylesham	d							14 10												15 10			
Snowdown	d							14 12												15 12			
Shepherds Well	d							14 16												15 16			
Kearsney	d							14 21												15 21			
Dover Priory [4]	a							14 26					14 48							15 26			
Whitstable	d						13 51					14 21							14 51				
Chestfield & Swalecliffe	d						13 54												14 54				
Herne Bay	d						13 58					14 26							14 58				
Birchington-on-Sea	d						14 07					14 35							15 07				
Westgate-on-Sea	d						14 10												15 10				
Margate [4]	d					13 53	14 14					14 41						14 53	15 14				
Broadstairs	d					13 59	14 20					14 46						14 59	15 20				
Dumpton Park	d						14 23												15 23				
Ramsgate [4]	a					14 04	14 26					14 51						15 04	15 26				

A [trolley] to Margate

For further services to St Pancras International, Blackfriars and Elephant & Castle and onwards to Bromley South, St Mary Cray and Swanley please see table 52

Table 212

London - Medway, Sheerness-on-Sea, Dover and Ramsgate

Mondays to Fridays

9 December to 16 May

Network Diagram - see first Page of Table 212

Station		SE	SE	SE	SE	SE	SE	SE	SE	SE	SE	SE	SE	SE	SE	SE	SE	SE
		[1] A 🚲			[1]			[1] A 🚲				[1] A 🚲			[1]			[1] A 🚲
St Pancras Internatnl [15] ⊖	d					14 25					14 55					15 25		
Stratford International ⊖	d					14 32					15 02					15 32		
Ebbsfleet International	d					14 44					15 14					15 44		
Farringdon	d																	
City Thameslink	d																	
London Blackfriars [3] ⊖	d																	
Elephant & Castle ⊖	d																	
London Victoria [15] ⊖	d	13 52			13 58			14 22				14 52			14 58			15 22
Bromley South [4]	d	14 09			14 19			14 39				15 09			15 19			15 39
St Mary Cray	d				14 25										15 25			
Swanley [4]	d				14 29										15 29			
Farningham Road	d				14 34										15 34			
Longfield	d	14 22			14 38			14 52				15 22			15 38			15 52
Meopham	d	14 27			14 42			14 57				15 27			15 42			15 57
Sole Street	d				14 45										15 45			
London Charing Cross [4] ⊖	d			13 39						14 09				14 39				
London Waterloo (East) [4] ⊖	d			13 42						14 12				14 42				
London Cannon Street [4] ⊖	d																	
London Bridge [4] ⊖	d			13 47						14 17				14 47				
Dartford [4]	d			14 25						14 55				15 25				
Greenhithe for Bluewater	d			14 30						15 00				15 30				
Gravesend [4]	d			14 37		14 48				15 07	15 18			15 37		15 48		
Strood [4]	d			14 48		14 58				15 18	15 28			15 48		15 58		
Rochester [4]	d	14 39		14 53	14 56	15 03		15 09		15 23	15 33	15 39		15 53	15 56	16 03		16 09
Chatham [4]	d	14 42		14 55	14 59	15 05		15 12		15 25	15 35	15 42		15 55	15 59	16 05		16 12
Gillingham (Kent) [4]	d	14 47		15a00	15a03	15 10		15 17		15a30	15 40	15 47		16a00	16a03	16 10		16 17
Rainham (Kent)	d	14 51				15 15		15 20			15 45	15 51				16 15		16 21
Newington	d	14 55										15 55						
Sittingbourne [4]	a	15 00				15 22		15 28			15 52	16 00				16 22		16 28
	d	15 01	15 10			15 23		15 29	15 40		15 53	16 01	16 10			16 23		16 29
Kemsley	d		15 15						15 45				16 15					
Swale	d		15 18						15 48				16 18					
Queenborough	d		15 22						15 52				16 22					
Sheerness-on-Sea	a		15 27						15 57				16 27					
Teynham	d							15 33										16 33
Faversham [2]	a	15 09				15 33		15 39			16 03	16 09				16 33		16 39
	d	15 13 / 15 15						15 43 / 15 45				16 13 / 16 15						16 43 / 16 45
Selling	d							15 49				16 19						16 49
Canterbury East [4]	d	15 29						15 59				16 28						16 59
Bekesbourne	d							16 03				16 33						17 03
Adisham	d							16 07				16 37						17 07
Aylesham	d							16 10				16 39						17 10
Snowdown	d							16 12										17 12
Shepherds Well	d	15 39						16 16				16 44						17 16
Kearsney	d							16 21										17 21
Dover Priory [4]	a	15 48						16 27				16 52						17 27
Whitstable	d	15 21						15 51				16 21						16 51
Chestfield & Swalecliffe	d							15 54				16 24						16 54
Herne Bay	d	15 26						15 58				16 28						16 58
Birchington-on-Sea	d	15 35						16 07				16 37						17 07
Westgate-on-Sea	d							16 10				16 40						17 10
Margate [4]	d	15 41					15 53	16 14				16 44					16 53	17 14
Broadstairs	d	15 46					15 59	16 20				16 50					16 59	17 20
Dumpton Park	d							16 23				16 53						17 23
Ramsgate [4]	a	15 51					16 04	16 26				16 56					17 04	17 26

A 🚲 to Margate

For further services to St Pancras International, Blackfriars and Elephant & Castle and onwards to Bromley South, St Mary Cray and Swanley please see table 52

Table 212

Mondays to Fridays

9 December to 16 May

London - Medway, Sheerness-on-Sea, Dover and Ramsgate

Network Diagram - see first Page of Table 212

		SE	SE	SE	SE [1] A 🛒		SE	SE	SE [1]	SE	SE	SE [1] A 🛒		SE	SE	SE [1]	SE [1]	SE	SE [1] A 🛒		SE	SE	SE
St Pancras Internatnl [15] ⊖	d			15 55						16 25								16 58				17 08	
Stratford International ⊖	d			16 02						16 32								17 05				17 15	
Ebbsfleet International	d			16 14						16 44								17 16				17a27	
Farringdon	d																						
City Thameslink	d																						
London Blackfriars [3] ⊖	d																						
Elephant & Castle ⊖	d																						
London Victoria [15] ⊖	d				15 52				15 58			16 22				16 28			16 57		17 04		
Bromley South [4]	d				16 09				16 19			16 39				16 49			17 13		17 24		
St Mary Cray	d								16 25							16 55					17 30		
Swanley [4]	d								16 29							16 59					17 34		
Farningham Road	d								16 34							17 04					17 39		
Longfield	d				16 22				16 38			16 52				17 08					17 44		
Meopham	d				16 27				16 42			16 57				17 12					17 48		
Sole Street	d								16 45							17 15					17 51		
London Charing Cross [4] ⊖	d		15 09					15 39							16 09								
London Waterloo (East) [4] ⊖	d		15 12					15 42							16 12								
London Cannon Street [4] ⊖	d																16 46						
London Bridge [4] ⊖	d		15 17					15 47							16 17		16 50						
Dartford [4]	d		15 55					16 25							16 55								
Greenhithe for Bluewater	d		16 00					16 30							17 00								
Gravesend [4]	d		16 07	16 18				16 37		16 48					17 07			17 21					
Strood [4]	d		16 18	16 28				16 48		16 58					17 18			17 31					
Rochester [4]	d		16 23	16 33	16 39			16 53	16 56	17 03		17 10			17 23	17a27	17 29	17 35	17 40		18a04		
Chatham [4]	d		16 25	16 35	16 42			16 55	16 59	17 05		17 13			17 25		17 31	17 38	17 43				
Gillingham (Kent) [4]	d		16a30	16 40	16 47			17a00	17a03	17 10		17 18			17a32		17 36	17 43	17 48				
Rainham (Kent)	d			16 45	16 51					17 15		17 23					17 41	17 48	17 53				
Newington	d				16 55							17 27							17 57				
Sittingbourne [4]	a			16 52	17 00					17 22		17 32					17 48	17 56	18 02				
	d	16 40		16 53	17 01		17 10			17 23		17 33		17 40			17 48	17 57	18 03				
Kemsley	d	16 45					17 15							17 45									
Swale	d	16 48					17 18							17 48									
Queenborough	d	16 52					17 22							17 52									
Sheerness-on-Sea	a	16 57					17 27							17 57									
Teynham	d				17 05							17 37							18 07				
Faversham [2]	a			17 03	17 11					17 33		17 43					17 56	18 05	18 13				
	d				17 15	17 19						17 47	17 49				17 57		18 17	18 19			
Selling	d					17 23							17 53							18 23			
Canterbury East [4]	d					17 32							18 03							18 32			
Bekesbourne	d												18 07										
Adisham	d												18 11										
Aylesham	d					17 40							18 14							18 40			
Snowdown	d												18 16										
Shepherds Well	d					17 45							18 20							18 45			
Kearsney	d												18 25										
Dover Priory [4]	a					17 53							18 32							18 55			
Whitstable	d				17 23							17 55					18 05		18 25				
Chestfield & Swalecliffe	d				17 26							17 58					18 08		18 28				
Herne Bay	d				17 30							18 02					18 12		18 32				
Birchington-on-Sea	d				17 39							18 11					18 21		18 41				
Westgate-on-Sea	d				17 42							18 15					18 25		18 45				
Margate [4]	d				17 46						17 53	18 19					18 29		18 49				18 53
Broadstairs	d				17 52						17 59	18 24					18 35		18 55				18 59
Dumpton Park	d				17 55							18 27					18 38		18 58				
Ramsgate [4]	a				17 58						18 04	18 32					18 46		19 03				19 04

A 🛒 to Margate

For further services to St Pancras International, Blackfriars and Elephant & Castle and onwards to Bromley South, St Mary Cray and Swanley please see table 52

Table 212

Mondays to Fridays

9 December to 16 May

London - Medway, Sheerness-on-Sea, Dover and Ramsgate

Network Diagram - see first Page of Table 212

		SE	SE	SE	SE	SE	SE	SE		SE	SE	SE	FC	SE	SE	SE	SE	SE	FC	SE	SE	SE		SE	SE
		1						1		1							1			1		1			
				B				A ⚲					B						B			A ⚲			
St Pancras Internatnl 15 ⊖	d			17 14		17 16	17 25							17 38	17 46			17 55	17 56						
Stratford International ⊖	d					17 23	17 32							17 45	17 53			18 02							
Ebbsfleet International	d					17 35	17 43							17a57	18 05			18 13							
Farringdon	d			17 19															18 01						
City Thameslink	d			17 22															18 05						
London Blackfriars 3 ⊖	d			17 25															18 10						
Elephant & Castle ⊖	d			17 29															18 14						
London Victoria 15 ⊖	d							17 27					←				17 54					17 57			
Bromley South 4	d			17 48				17 44					17 48				18 19		18 31			18 15			
St Mary Cray	d			↪									17 55				18 25		↪						
Swanley 4	d												18 00				18 30								
Farningham Road	d												18 05				18 35								
Longfield	d												18 09									18 28			
Meopham	d												18 13				18 41								
Sole Street	d												18 15				18 44								
London Charing Cross 4 ⊖	d															17 17									17 39
London Waterloo (East) 4 ⊖	d															17 20									17 42
London Cannon Street 4 ⊖	d	17 08			16 44					17 30		17 06								17 52					
London Bridge 4 ⊖	d	17 12			16 48					17 34		17 10				17 26				17 56					17 48
Dartford 4	d				17 23							17 46				18 02									18 22
Greenhithe for Bluewater	d				17 28							17 51				18 08									18 27
Gravesend 4	d				17 35	17 40						18 00			18 10	18 20									18 34
Strood 4	d				17 46	17a49						18 12			18a19	18a34									18 45
Rochester 4	d	17 49			17 54		18 01	18 10		18 15		18 20	18a28				18a56	18 31		18 38		18 43			18 51
Chatham 4	d	17 52			17 57		18 04	18 13		18 18		18 23						18 34		18 41		18 46			18 54
Gillingham (Kent) 4	d	17 57			18a05		18 09	18 18		18 24		18a30						18 39		18 46		18 51			19a02
Rainham (Kent)	d	18 02					18 14	18 23		18 29								18 44		18 51		18 56			
Newington	d	18 06								18 33												19 00			
Sittingbourne 4	a	18 11					18 22	18 30		18 38								18 51		18 58		19 05			
	d	18 12	18 15				18 23	18 30		18 38	18 44							18 52		18 59		19 06		19 10	
Kemsley	d		18 20								18 49													19 15	
Swale	d		18 23								18 54													19 18	
Queenborough	d		18 27								18 58													19 22	
Sheerness-on-Sea	a		18 32								19 02													19 27	
Teynham	d	18 16						18 35														19 10			
Faversham 2	a	18 22					18 31	18 41		18 47								19 00		19 07		19 16			
	d	18 24					18 32	18 44	18 50	18 49								19 01		19 08		19 20	19 22		
Selling	d								18 54														19 26		
Canterbury East 4	d								19 04														19 36		
Bekesbourne	d								19 08																
Adisham	d								19 12																
Aylesham	d								19 15																
Snowdown	d								19 17																
Shepherds Well	d								19 21																
Kearsney	d								19 25																
Dover Priory 4	a								19 32														19 54		
Whitstable	d	18 32					18 40	18 52		18 57								19 09		19 16		19 28			
Chestfield & Swalecliffe	d	18 35						18 55		19 00												19 31			
Herne Bay	d	18 39					18 46	18 59		19 04								19 15		19 22		19 35			
Birchington-on-Sea	d	18 48					18 55	19 08		19 12								19 24		19 31		19 44			
Westgate-on-Sea	d	18 52						19 11		19 16												19 48			
Margate 4	d	18 56					19 02	19 15		19 20								19 30		19 37	19 53	19a54			
Broadstairs	d	19a03					19a08	19 21		19 26								19a36		19a45	19 59				
Dumpton Park	d							19 24		19 29															
Ramsgate 4	a							19 30		19 34											20 04				

A ⚲ to Margate

B from Bedford to Rochester

For further services to St Pancras International, Blackfriars and Elephant & Castle and onwards to Bromley South, St Mary Cray and Swanley please see table 52

Table 212

Mondays to Fridays

9 December to 16 May

London - Medway, Sheerness-on-Sea, Dover and Ramsgate

Network Diagram - see first Page of Table 212

		SE 1	SE	SE	FC B	SE	SE 1 A	SE	SE	SE	SE 1	SE	SE 1 A	SE	SE	SE	SE 1		SE	SE	SE	SE 1 A
St Pancras Internatnl 15 ⊖	d		18 16	18 25						18 38		18 55								19 28		
Stratford International ⊖	d		18 23	18 32						18 45		19 02								19 35		
Ebbsfleet International	d		18 35	18 44						18a57		19 14								19 46		
Farringdon	d																					
City Thameslink	d																					
London Blackfriars 3 ⊖	d																					
Elephant & Castle ⊖	d																					
London Victoria 15 ⊖	d				←	18 24	18 27						18 57				18 58					19 22
Bromley South 4	d				18 31	18 46	18 44						19 14				19 21					19 39
St Mary Cray	d				18 38	18 52											19 27					
Swanley 4	d				18 43	18 57											19 31					
Farningham Road	d				18 48	19 02											19 36					
Longfield	d				18 52	19 06											19 40					19 52
Meopham	d				18 56	19 11											19 44					19 57
Sole Street	d				18 58	19 13											19 47					
London Charing Cross 4 ⊖	d								18 01							18 37			18 48			
London Waterloo (East) 4 ⊖	d								18 04							18 40			18 51			
London Cannon Street 4 ⊖	d	18 14									18 44				18 30							
London Bridge 4 ⊖	d	18 18							18 10		18 48				18 34	18 46			18 57			
Dartford 4	d								18 45						19 10	19 22			19 35			
Greenhithe for Bluewater	d								18 51						19 16	19 29			19 40			
Gravesend 4	d		18 40						19 02			19 19			19 26	19 38			19 47	19 51		
Strood 4	d		18a49						19 14			19 29			19 38	19a53			19 58	20 02		
Rochester 4	d			19 03	19a10	19 23	19 12		19 19		19 27	19 34	19 40		19 45		19 57		20 03	20 07		20 13
Chatham 4	d	19 00		19 06		19 26	19 15		19 22		19 30	19 37	19 43		19 48		19 59		20 05	20 09		20 16
Gillingham (Kent) 4	d	19 05		19 11		19a32	19 20		19a29		19 34	19 42	19 49		19a55		20a06		20a13	20 15		20 21
Rainham (Kent)	d	19 10		19 16			19 25				19 39	19 47	19 54							20 20		20 25
Newington	d	19 14									19 43		19 58									
Sittingbourne 4	a	19 19		19 24			19 32				19 48	19 54	20 03							20 27		20 32
	d	19 19		19 24			19 33	19 40			19 49	19 54	20 03	20 10						20 27		20 33
Kemsley	d							19 45						20 15								
Swale	d							19 48						20 18								
Queenborough	d							19 52						20 22								
Sheerness-on-Sea	a							19 57						20 27								
Teynham	d						19 37				19 53											20 37
Faversham 2	a	19 27		19 32			19 43				19 59	20 03	20 11							20 36		20 43
	d	19 28		19 33			19 47 / 19 49				20 00		20 15 / 20 17									20 47 / 20 49
Selling	d						19 53						20 21									20 53
Canterbury East 4	d						20 03						20 30									21 03
Bekesbourne	d						20 07						20 35									21 07
Adisham	d						20 11						20 39									21 11
Aylesham	d						20 14						20 41									21 14
Snowdown	d						20 16															21 16
Shepherds Well	d						20 20						20 46									21 20
Kearsney	d						20 25															21 25
Dover Priory 4	a						20 32						20 56									21 32
Whitstable	d	19 36		19 42			19 55				20 08		20 23									20 55
Chestfield & Swalecliffe	d	19 39					19 58				20 11		20 26									20 58
Herne Bay	d	19 43		19 48			20 02				20 15		20 30									21 02
Birchington-on-Sea	d	19 52		19 57			20 11				20 24		20 39									21 11
Westgate-on-Sea	d	19 55					20 15				20 27		20 43									21 15
Margate 4	d	19 59		20 04			20 19				20 31		20 47								20 53	21 19
Broadstairs	d	20 05		20a09			20 25				20 37		20 53								20 59	21 24
Dumpton Park	d	20 08					20 28				20 40		20 56									21 27
Ramsgate 4	a	20 14					20 33				20 46		21 01								21 04	21 32

A to Margate

B from Bedford

For further services to St Pancras International, Blackfriars and Elephant & Castle and onwards to Bromley South, St Mary Cray and Swanley please see table 52

Table 212

Mondays to Fridays

9 December to 16 May

London - Medway, Sheerness-on-Sea, Dover and Ramsgate

Network Diagram - see first Page of Table 212

		SE	SE	SE	SE	SE [1]		SE	SE	SE	SE	SE	SE [1]		SE	SE	SE	SE [1]		SE	SE [1]	SE
St Pancras Internatnl [15] ⊖	d				19 55						20 25						20 55					21 25
Stratford International ⊖	d				20 02						20 32						21 02					21 32
Ebbsfleet International	d				20 14						20 44						21 14					21 44
Farringdon	d																					
City Thameslink	d																					
London Blackfriars [3] ⊖	d																					
Elephant & Castle ⊖	d																					
London Victoria [15] ⊖	d			19 28		19 52				19 58			20 22					20 52			20 58	
Bromley South [4]	d			19 49		20 09				20 19			20 39					21 09			21 19	
St Mary Cray	d			19 55						20 25											21 25	
Swanley [4]	d			19 59						20 29											21 29	
Farningham Road	d			20 04						20 34											21 34	
Longfield	d			20 08		20 22				20 38			20 52					21 22			21 38	
Meopham	d			20 12		20 27				20 42			20 57					21 27			21 42	
Sole Street	d			20 15						20 45											21 45	
London Charing Cross [4] ⊖	d		19 09						19 39							20 09				20 39		
London Waterloo (East) [4] ⊖	d		19 12						19 42							20 12				20 42		
London Cannon Street [4] ⊖	d																					
London Bridge [4] ⊖	d		19 17						19 47							20 17				20 47		
Dartford [4]	d		19 55						20 25							20 55				21 25		
Greenhithe for Bluewater	d		20 00						20 30							21 00				21 30		
Gravesend [4]	d		20 07		20 18				20 37		20 48					21 07	21 18			21 37		21 48
Strood [4]	d		20 18		20 28				20 48		20 58					21 18	21 28			21 48		21 58
Rochester [4]	d		20 23	20 26	20 33	20 39			20 53	20 56	21 03		21 09			21 23	21 33	21 39		21 53	21 56	22 03
Chatham [4]	d		20 25	20 29	20 35	20 42			20 55	20 59	21 05		21 12			21 25	21 35	21 42		21 55	21 59	22 05
Gillingham (Kent) [4]	d		20a30	20a33	20 40	20 47			21a00	21a03	21 10		21 17			21a30	21 40	21 47		22a00	22a03	22 10
Rainham (Kent)	d				20 45	20 51					21 15		21 21				21 45	21 51				22 15
Newington	d					20 55												21 55				
Sittingbourne [4]	a				20 52	21 00					21 22		21 28				21 52	22 00				22 22
	d	20 40			20 53	21 01		21 10			21 23		21 29		21 40		21 53	22 01				22 23
Kemsley	d	20 45						21 15							21 45							
Swale	d	20 48						21 18							21 48							
Queenborough	d	20 52						21 22							21 52							
Sheerness-on-Sea	a	20 57						21 27							21 57							
Teynham	d												21 33									
Faversham [2]	a				21 03	21 09					21 33		21 39				22 03	22 09				22 33
	d					21 13	21 15						21 43	21 45				22 13	22 15			
Selling	d						21 19							21 49					22 19			
Canterbury East [4]	d						21 28							21 59					22 28			
Bekesbourne	d						21 33							22 03					22 33			
Adisham	d						21 37							22 07					22 37			
Aylesham	d						21 39							22 10					22 39			
Snowdown	d													22 12								
Shepherds Well	d						21 44							22 16					22 44			
Kearsney	d													22 21								
Dover Priory [4]	a						21 52							22 26					22 52			
Whitstable	d					21 21							21 51					22 21				
Chestfield & Swalecliffe	d					21 24							21 54					22 24				
Herne Bay	d					21 28							21 58					22 28				
Birchington-on-Sea	d					21 37							22 07					22 37				
Westgate-on-Sea	d					21 40							22 10					22 40				
Margate [4]	d					21 44						21 53	22 14					22 44				
Broadstairs	d					21 50						21 59	22 20					22 50				
Dumpton Park	d					21 53							22 23					22 53				
Ramsgate [4]	a					21 56						22 04	22 26					22 56				

For further services to St Pancras International, Blackfriars and Elephant & Castle and onwards to Bromley South, St Mary Cray and Swanley please see table 52

Table 212

Mondays to Fridays

9 December to 16 May

London - Medway, Sheerness-on-Sea, Dover and Ramsgate

Network Diagram - see first Page of Table 212

		SE 1		SE	SE	SE	SE 1	SE	SE	SE 1		SE	SE	SE	SE 1	SE	SE	SE 1	SE	SE	SE	SE 1
St Pancras Internatnl 15 ⊖	d					21 55			22 25					22 55			23 25			23 42	23 55	
Stratford International ⊖	d					22 02			22 32					23 02			23 32			23 49	00 02	
Ebbsfleet International	d					22 14			22 44					23 14			23 44			23a59	00 14	
Farringdon	d																					
City Thameslink	d																					
London Blackfriars 3 ⊖	d																					
Elephant & Castle ⊖	d																					
London Victoria 15 ⊖	d	21 22					21 52			22 22					22 52			23 22				23 52
Bromley South 4	d	21 39					22 09			22 39					23 09			23 39				00 09
St Mary Cray	d						22 15								23 15							00 15
Swanley 4	d						22 19								23 19							00 19
Farningham Road	d						22 24								23 24							00 24
Longfield	d	21 52					22 28			22 52					23 28			23 52				00 28
Meopham	d	21 57					22 32			22 57					23 32			23 57				00 32
Sole Street	d						22 35								23 35							00 35
London Charing Cross 4 ⊖	d				21 09			21 39					22 09			22 39			23 09			
London Waterloo (East) 4 ⊖	d				21 12			21 42					22 12			22 42			23 12			
London Cannon Street 4 ⊖	d																					
London Bridge 4 ⊖	d				21 17			21 47					22 17			22 47			23 17			
Dartford 4	d				21 55			22 25					22 55			23 25			23 55			
Greenhithe for Bluewater	d				22 00			22 30					23 00			23 31			23 59			
Gravesend 4	d				22 07	22 18		22 37	22 48				23 07	23 18		23 40	23 48		00 10		00 18	
Strood 4	d				22 18	22 28		22 48	22 58				23 18	23 28		23 52	23 58		00 22		00 28	
Rochester 4	d	22 09			22 23	22 33	22 45	22 53	23 03	23 09			23 23	23 33	23 45	23 56	00 03	00 09	00 26		00 33	00 45
Chatham 4	d	22 12			22 25	22 35	22 47	22 55	23 05	23 12			23 25	23 35	23 47	23 59	00 05	00 12	00 29		00 35	00 47
Gillingham (Kent) 4	d	22 17			22a30	22 40	22 52	23a00	23 10	23 17			23a30	23 40	23 52	00a03	00 10	00 17	00a33		00 40	00a52
Rainham (Kent)	d	22 21				22 45	22 56		23 15	23 21				23 45	23 56		00 15	00 21			00 45	
Newington	d						23 00								00 01							
Sittingbourne 4	a	22 28				22 52	23 05		23 22	23 28				23 52	00 06		00 22	00 28			00 52	
	d	22 29		22 40		22 53	23 06		23 23	23 29		23 32		23 53	00 07		00 23	00 29			00 53	
Kemsley	d			22 45								23 37										
Swale	d			22 48								23 40										
Queenborough	d			22 52								23 44										
Sheerness-on-Sea	a			22 57								23 49										
Teynham	d	22 33								23 33								00 33				
Faversham 2	a	22 39				23 03	23 17		23 33	23 39				00 03	00 15		00 33	00 39			01 03	
	d	22 43	22 45							23 43	23 45							00 43				
Selling	d		22 49								23s49											
Canterbury East 4	d		22 59								23 59											
Bekesbourne	d		23 03								00s03											
Adisham	d		23 07								00s07											
Aylesham	d		23 10								00s10											
Snowdown	d		23 12								00s12											
Shepherds Well	d		23 16								00s16											
Kearsney	d		23 21								00s21											
Dover Priory 4	a		23 26								00 27											
Whitstable	d	22 51								23 51								00 51				
Chestfield & Swalecliffe	d	22 54								23 54								00 54				
Herne Bay	d	22 58								23 58								00 58				
Birchington-on-Sea	d	23 07								00 07								01 07				
Westgate-on-Sea	d	23 10								00 10								01 10				
Margate 4	d	23 14								00 14								01 14				
Broadstairs	d	23 20								00 20								01 20				
Dumpton Park	d	23 23								00 23								01 23				
Ramsgate 4	a	23 26								00 26								01 26				

For further services to St Pancras International, Blackfriars and Elephant & Castle and onwards to Bromley South, St Mary Cray and Swanley please see table 52

Table 212

Mondays to Fridays

9 December to 16 May

London - Medway, Sheerness-on-Sea, Dover and Ramsgate

Network Diagram - see first Page of Table 212

Station		SE
St Pancras Internatnl [15] ⊖	d	
Stratford International ⊖	d	
Ebbsfleet International	d	
Farringdon	d	
City Thameslink	d	
London Blackfriars [3] ⊖	d	
Elephant & Castle ⊖	d	
London Victoria [15] ⊖	d	
Bromley South [4]	d	
St Mary Cray	d	
Swanley [4]	d	
Farningham Road	d	
Longfield	d	
Meopham	d	
Sole Street	d	
London Charing Cross [4] ⊖	d	23 39
London Waterloo (East) [4] ⊖	d	23 42
London Cannon Street [4] ⊖	d	
London Bridge [4] ⊖	d	23 47
Dartford [4]	d	00 25
Greenhithe for Bluewater	d	00 31
Gravesend [4]	d	00 40
Strood [4]	d	00 52
Rochester [4]	d	00 56
Chatham [4]	d	00 59
Gillingham (Kent) [4]	d	01a03
Rainham (Kent)	d	
Newington	d	
Sittingbourne [4]	a	
	d	
Kemsley	d	
Swale	d	
Queenborough	d	
Sheerness-on-Sea	a	
Teynham	d	
Faversham [2]	a	
	d	
Selling	d	
Canterbury East [4]	d	
Bekesbourne	d	
Adisham	d	
Aylesham	d	
Snowdown	d	
Shepherds Well	d	
Kearsney	d	
Dover Priory [4]	a	
Whitstable	d	
Chestfield & Swalecliffe	d	
Herne Bay	d	
Birchington-on-Sea	d	
Westgate-on-Sea	d	
Margate [4]	d	
Broadstairs	d	
Dumpton Park	d	
Ramsgate [4]	a	

For further services to St Pancras International, Blackfriars and Elephant & Castle and onwards to Bromley South, St Mary Cray and Swanley please see table 52

Table 212

Saturdays

14 December to 17 May

London - Medway, Sheerness-on-Sea, Dover and Ramsgate

Network Diagram - see first Page of Table 212

		SE 1 A	SE	SE B	SE 1 A	SE 1 A	SE C	SE B	SE 1	SE 1	SE	SE C	SE	SE	SE 1	SE	SE	SE 1	SE	SE 1	SE 1	SE	SE
St Pancras Internatnl 15 ⊖	d										00 12												
Stratford International ⊖	d							00 02			00 19												
Ebbsfleet International	d							00 14			00a30												
Farringdon	d																						
City Thameslink	d																						
London Blackfriars 3 ⊖	d																						
Elephant & Castle ⊖	d																						
London Victoria 15 ⊖	d									00 10			00 37							05 22			
Bromley South 4	d								00 09				00 57							05 39			
St Mary Cray	d								00 15				01 03							05 45			
Swanley 4	d								00 19				01 07							05 49			
Farningham Road	d								00 24				01 12							05 54			
Longfield	d								00 28				01 16							05 58			
Meopham	d								00 32				01 20							06 02			
Sole Street	d								00 35											06 05			
London Charing Cross 4 ⊖	d													00 18									05 39
London Waterloo (East) 4 ⊖	d													00 21									05 42
London Cannon Street 4 ⊖	d																						
London Bridge 4 ⊖	d													00 26									05 47
Dartford 4	d											00 25		01 07								05 55	06 25
Greenhithe for Bluewater	d											00 31		01 12								06 00	06 30
Gravesend 4	d						00 10	00 18				00 40		01 19								06 07	06 37
Strood 4	d						00 22	00 28				00 52		01 30								06 18	06 48
Rochester 4	d			00 03		00 09	00 26	00 33	00 45	00 49		00 56	01 31	01 35						06 15		06 23	06 53
Chatham 4	d			00 05		00 12	00 29	00 35	00 47	00 52		00 59	01 34	01 37						06 17		06 25	06 55
Gillingham (Kent) 4	d			00 10		00 17	00a33	00 40	00a52	00 57		01a03	01a38	01a44	05 47					06 22		06a30	07a00
Rainham (Kent)	d			00 15		00 21		00 45		01 01					05 51					06 26			
Newington	d	00 01								01 05					05 55					06 30			
Sittingbourne 4	a	00 06		00 22		00 28		00 52		01 10					06 00					06 35			
	d	00 07	00 15	00 23		00 29		00 53		01 11					06 01	06 10				06 36			
Kemsley	d		00 20													06 15							
Swale	d		00 23													06 18							
Queenborough	d		00 27													06 22							
Sheerness-on-Sea	a		00 32													06 27							
Teynham	d					00 33				01 15					06 05					06 40			
Faversham 2	a	00 15		00 33		00 39		01 03		01 23					06 11					06 46			
	d					00 43				01 24					06 12			06 17		06 47	06 50		
Selling	d														06 16						06 54		
Canterbury East 4	d														06 26						07 04		
Bekesbourne	d														06 30						07 08		
Adisham	d														06 34						07 12		
Aylesham	d														06 37						07 15		
Snowdown	d														06 39						07 17		
Shepherds Well	d														06 43						07 21		
Kearsney	d														06 48						07 26		
Dover Priory 4	a														06 53						07 31		
Whitstable	d					00 51				01 32								06 25		06 55			
Chestfield & Swalecliffe	d					00 54				01 35								06 28		06 58			
Herne Bay	d					00 58				01 39								06 32		07 02			
Birchington-on-Sea	d				00 07	01 07				01 48								06 41		07 11			
Westgate-on-Sea	d				00 10	01 10				01 51								06 44		07 14			
Margate 4	d				00 14	01 14				01 55							05 53	06 48	06 53	07 18			
Broadstairs	d				00 20	01 20				02 01							05 59	06 54	06 59	07 24			
Dumpton Park	d				00 23	01 23				02 04								06 57		07 27			
Ramsgate 4	a				00 26	01 26				02 07							06 04	07 00	07 04	07 30			

A from London Victoria
B from St Pancras International
C from London Charing Cross

For further services to St Pancras International, Blackfriars and Elephant & Castle and onwards to Bromley South, St Mary Cray and Swanley please see table 52

Table 212

Saturdays

14 December to 17 May

London - Medway, Sheerness-on-Sea, Dover and Ramsgate

Network Diagram - see first Page of Table 212

		SE	SE	SE	SE ■1	SE ■1		SE	SE	SE	SE ■1	SE	SE ■1	SE	SE ■1	SE		SE ■1		SE	SE	SE	SE ■1		SE
St Pancras Internatnl ■15 ⊖	d									06 51												07 55			
Stratford International ⊖	d									06 58												08 02			
Ebbsfleet International	d									07 14												08 14			
Farringdon	d																								
City Thameslink	d																								
London Blackfriars ■3 ⊖	d																								
Elephant & Castle ⊖	d																								
London Victoria ■15 ⊖	d				06 22								06 58					07 22					07 52		
Bromley South ■4	d				06 39								07 19					07 39					08 09		
St Mary Cray	d				06 45								07 25												
Swanley ■4	d				06 49								07 29												
Farningham Road	d				06 54								07 34												
Longfield	d				06 58								07 38					07 52					08 22		
Meopham	d				07 02								07 42					07 57					08 27		
Sole Street	d				07 05								07 45												
London Charing Cross ■4 ⊖	d							06 09				06 39									07 09				
London Waterloo (East) ■4 ⊖	d							06 12				06 42									07 12				
London Cannon Street ■4 ⊖	d																								
London Bridge ■4 ⊖	d							06 17				06 47									07 17				
Dartford ■4	d							06 55				07 25									07 55				
Greenhithe for Bluewater	d							07 00				07 30									08 00				
Gravesend ■4	d							07 07		07 18		07 37									08 07	08 18			
Strood ■4	d							07 18		07 28		07 48									08 18	08 28			
Rochester ■4	d				07 15			07 23		07 33		07 53	07 56					08 09			08 23	08 33	08 39		
Chatham ■4	d				07 17			07 25		07 35		07 55	07 59					08 12			08 25	08 35	08 42		
Gillingham (Kent) ■4	d				07 22			07a30		07 40		08a00	08a03					08 17			08a30	08 40	08 47		
Rainham (Kent)	d				07 26					07 45								08 21				08 45	08 51		
Newington	d				07 30													08 25					08 55		
Sittingbourne ■4	a				07 35					07 52								08 30				08 52	09 00		
	d	06 40	07 10		07 36				07 40	07 53				08 10				08 31		08 40		08 53	09 01		09 10
Kemsley	d	06 45	07 15						07 45					08 15						08 45					09 15
Swale	d	06 48	07 18						07 48					08 18						08 48					09 18
Queenborough	d	06 52	07 22						07 52					08 22						08 52					09 22
Sheerness-on-Sea	a	06 57	07 27						07 57					08 27						08 57					09 27
Teynham	d				07 40													08 35							
Faversham ■2	a				07 46					08 03								08 41				09 03	09 09		
	d				07 47	07 50					08 13				08 15			08 45	08 50				09 13	09 15	
Selling	d					07 54													08 54						
Canterbury East ■4	d					08 04									08 29				09 04					09 29	
Bekesbourne	d					08 08													09 08						
Adisham	d					08 12													09 12						
Aylesham	d					08 15													09 15						
Snowdown	d					08 17													09 17						
Shepherds Well	d					08 21													09 21						
Kearsney	d					08 26													09 26						
Dover Priory ■4	a					08 31									08 48				09 31					09 48	
Whitstable	d				07 55						08 21							08 53					09 21		
Chestfield & Swalecliffe	d				07 58													08 56							
Herne Bay	d				08 02						08 26							09 00					09 26		
Birchington-on-Sea	d				08 11						08 35							09 09					09 35		
Westgate-on-Sea	d				08 14													09 12							
Margate ■4	d			07 53	08 18						08 41					08 53		09 16					09 41		
Broadstairs	d			07 59	08 24						08 46					08 59		09 22					09 46		
Dumpton Park	d				08 27													09 25							
Ramsgate ■4	a			08 04	08 30						08 51					09 04		09 28					09 51		

For further services to St Pancras International, Blackfriars and Elephant & Castle and onwards to Bromley South, St Mary Cray and Swanley please see table 52

Table 212

Saturdays

14 December to 17 May

London - Medway, Sheerness-on-Sea, Dover and Ramsgate

Network Diagram - see first Page of Table 212

		SE	SE 1	SE	SE 1		SE	SE	SE	SE 1		SE	SE	SE 1	SE	SE	SE 1		SE	SE	SE
St Pancras Internatnl 15 ⊖	d								08 51						09 25						09 55
Stratford International ⊖	d								09 05						09 32						10 02
Ebbsfleet International	d								09 17						09 44						10 14
Farringdon	d																				
City Thameslink	d																				
London Blackfriars 3 ⊖	d																				
Elephant & Castle ⊖	d																				
London Victoria 15 ⊖	d		07 58		08 22					08 52				08 58			09 22				
Bromley South 4	d		08 19		08 39					09 09				09 19			09 39				
St Mary Cray	d		08 25											09 25							
Swanley 4	d		08 29											09 29							
Farningham Road	d		08 34											09 34							
Longfield	d		08 38		08 52					09 22				09 38			09 52				
Meopham	d		08 42		08 57					09 27				09 42			09 57				
Sole Street	d		08 45											09 45							
London Charing Cross 4 ⊖	d	07 39						08 09					08 39							09 09	
London Waterloo (East) 4 ⊖	d	07 42						08 12					08 42							09 12	
London Cannon Street 4 ⊖	d																				
London Bridge 4 ⊖	d	07 47						08 17					08 47							09 17	
Dartford 4	d	08 25						08 55					09 25							09 55	
Greenhithe for Bluewater	d	08 30						09 00					09 30							10 00	
Gravesend 4	d	08 37						09 07	09 21				09 37		09 48					10 07	10 18
Strood 4	d	08 48						09 18	09 31				09 48		09 58					10 18	10 28
Rochester 4	d	08 53	08 56		09 09			09 23	09 35	09 39			09 53	09 56	10 03		10 09			10 23	10 33
Chatham 4	d	08 55	08 59		09 12			09 25	09 38	09 42			09 55	09 59	10 05		10 12			10 25	10 35
Gillingham (Kent) 4	d	09a00	09a03		09 17			09a30	09 42	09 47			10a00	10a03	10 10		10 17			10a30	10 40
Rainham (Kent)	d				09 21				09 47	09 51					10 15		10 21				10 45
Newington	d									09 55											
Sittingbourne 4	a				09 28				09 54	10 00					10 22		10 28				10 52
	d				09 29		09 40		09 55	10 01		10 10			10 23		10 29		10 40		10 53
Kemsley	d						09 45					10 15							10 45		
Swale	d						09 48					10 18							10 48		
Queenborough	d						09 52					10 22							10 52		
Sheerness-on-Sea	a						09 57					10 27							10 57		
Teynham	d				09 33												10 33				
Faversham 2	a				09 39				10 04	10 09					10 33		10 39				11 03
	d				09 43	09 45				10 13	10 15						10 43	10 45			
Selling	d					09 49												10 49			
Canterbury East 4	d					09 59					10 29							10 59			
Bekesbourne	d					10 03												11 03			
Adisham	d					10 07												11 07			
Aylesham	d					10 10												11 10			
Snowdown	d					10 12												11 12			
Shepherds Well	d					10 16												11 16			
Kearsney	d					10 21												11 21			
Dover Priory 4	a					10 27					10 48							11 27			
Whitstable	d				09 51					10 21							10 51				
Chestfield & Swalecliffe	d				09 54												10 54				
Herne Bay	d				09 58					10 26							10 58				
Birchington-on-Sea	d				10 07					10 35							11 07				
Westgate-on-Sea	d				10 10												11 10				
Margate 4	d			09 53	10 14					10 41						10 53	11 14				
Broadstairs	d			09 59	10 20					10 46						10 59	11 20				
Dumpton Park	d				10 23												11 23				
Ramsgate 4	a			10 04	10 26					10 51						11 04	11 26				

For further services to St Pancras International, Blackfriars and Elephant & Castle and onwards to Bromley South, St Mary Cray and Swanley please see table 52

Table 212

Saturdays

14 December to 17 May

London - Medway, Sheerness-on-Sea, Dover and Ramsgate

Network Diagram - see first Page of Table 212

		SE 1 A (trolley)		SE	SE	SE 1	SE	SE	SE 1 A (trolley)		SE	SE	SE	SE 1 A (trolley)		SE	SE	SE 1	SE	SE	SE 1 A (trolley)		SE
St Pancras Internatnl 15 ⊖	d						10 22						10 52						11 25				
Stratford International ⊖	d						10 32						10 59						11 32				
Ebbsfleet International	d						10 44						11 14						11 44				
Farringdon	d																						
City Thameslink	d																						
London Blackfriars 3 ⊖	d																						
Elephant & Castle ⊖	d																						
London Victoria 15 ⊖	d	09 52				09 58			10 22					10 52				10 58			11 22		
Bromley South 4	d	10 09				10 19			10 39					11 09				11 19			11 39		
St Mary Cray	d					10 25												11 25					
Swanley 4	d					10 29												11 29					
Farningham Road	d					10 34												11 34					
Longfield	d	10 22				10 38			10 52					11 22				11 38			11 52		
Meopham	d	10 27				10 42			10 57					11 27				11 42			11 57		
Sole Street	d					10 45												11 45					
London Charing Cross 4 ⊖	d				09 39							10 09					10 39						
London Waterloo (East) 4 ⊖	d				09 42							10 12					10 42						
London Cannon Street 4 ⊖	d																						
London Bridge 4 ⊖	d				09 47							10 17					10 47						
Dartford 4	d				10 25							10 55					11 25						
Greenhithe for Bluewater	d				10 30							11 00					11 30						
Gravesend 4	d				10 37		10 48					11 07	11 18				11 37		11 48				
Strood 4	d				10 48		10 58					11 18	11 28				11 48		11 58				
Rochester 4	d	10 39			10 53	10 56	11 03		11 09			11 23	11 33	11 39			11 53	11 56	12 03		12 09		
Chatham 4	d	10 42			10 55	10 59	11 05		11 12			11 25	11 35	11 42			11 55	11 59	12 05		12 12		
Gillingham (Kent) 4	d	10 47			11a00	11a03	11 10		11 17			11a30	11 40	11 47			12a00	12a03	12 10		12 17		
Rainham (Kent)	d	10 51					11 15		11 21				11 45	11 51					12 15		12 21		
Newington	d	10 55												11 55									
Sittingbourne 4	a	11 00					11 22		11 28				11 52	12 00					12 22		12 28		
	d	11 01		11 10			11 23		11 29		11 40		11 53	12 01		12 10			12 23		12 29		12 40
Kemsley	d			11 15							11 45					12 15							12 45
Swale	d			11 18							11 48					12 18							12 48
Queenborough	d			11 22							11 52					12 22							12 52
Sheerness-on-Sea	a			11 27							11 57					12 27							12 57
Teynham	d								11 33												12 33		
Faversham 2	a	11 09					11 33		11 39				12 03	12 09					12 33		12 39		
	d	11 13	11 15						11 43	11 45				12 13	12 15						12 43	12 45	
Selling	d									11 49												12 49	
Canterbury East 4	d		11 29							11 59					12 29							12 59	
Bekesbourne	d									12 03												13 03	
Adisham	d									12 07												13 07	
Aylesham	d									12 10												13 10	
Snowdown	d									12 12												13 12	
Shepherds Well	d									12 16												13 16	
Kearsney	d									12 21												13 21	
Dover Priory 4	a		11 48							12 27					12 48							13 27	
Whitstable	d	11 21							11 51					12 21							12 51		
Chestfield & Swalecliffe	d								11 54												12 54		
Herne Bay	d	11 26							11 58					12 26							12 58		
Birchington-on-Sea	d	11 35							12 07					12 35							13 07		
Westgate-on-Sea	d								12 10												13 10		
Margate 4	d	11 41						11 53	12 14					12 41						12 53	13 14		
Broadstairs	d	11 46						11 59	12 20					12 46						12 59	13 20		
Dumpton Park	d								12 23												13 23		
Ramsgate 4	a	11 51						12 04	12 26					12 51						13 04	13 26		

A (trolley) to Margate

For further services to St Pancras International, Blackfriars and Elephant & Castle and onwards to Bromley South, St Mary Cray and Swanley please see table 52

Table 212

Saturdays

14 December to 17 May

London - Medway, Sheerness-on-Sea, Dover and Ramsgate

Network Diagram - see first Page of Table 212

		SE	SE	SE 1 A ⚯		SE		SE	SE 1	SE	SE	SE 1 A ⚯		SE	SE	SE		SE 1 A ⚯		SE	SE	SE 1	SE	SE	
St Pancras Internatnl 15 ⊖	d		11 55							12 22						12 52							13 25		
Stratford International ⊖	d		12 02							12 32						12 59							13 32		
Ebbsfleet International	d		12 14							12 44						13 14							13 44		
Farringdon	d																								
City Thameslink	d																								
London Blackfriars 3 ⊖	d																								
Elephant & Castle ⊖	d																								
London Victoria 15 ⊖	d			11 52					11 58			12 22						12 52				12 58			
Bromley South 4	d			12 09					12 19			12 39						13 09				13 19			
St Mary Cray	d								12 25													13 25			
Swanley 4	d								12 29													13 29			
Farningham Road	d								12 34													13 34			
Longfield	d			12 22					12 38			12 52						13 22				13 38			
Meopham	d			12 27					12 42			12 57						13 27				13 42			
Sole Street	d								12 45													13 45			
London Charing Cross 4 ⊖	d	11 09						11 39							12 09						12 39				
London Waterloo (East) 4 ⊖	d	11 12						11 42							12 12						12 42				
London Cannon Street 4 ⊖	d																								
London Bridge 4 ⊖	d	11 17						11 47							12 17						12 47				
Dartford 4	d	11 55						12 25							12 55						13 25				
Greenhithe for Bluewater	d	12 00						12 30							13 00						13 30				
Gravesend 4	d	12 07	12 18					12 37		12 48					13 07	13 18					13 37		13 48		
Strood 4	d	12 18	12 28					12 48		12 58					13 18	13 28					13 48		13 58		
Rochester 4	d	12 23	12 33	12 39				12 53	12 56	13 03		13 09			13 23	13 33		13 39			13 53	13 56	14 03		
Chatham 4	d	12 25	12 35	12 42				12 55	12 59	13 05		13 12			13 25	13 35		13 42			13 55	13 59	14 05		
Gillingham (Kent) 4	d	12a30	12 40	12 47				13a00	13a03	13 10		13 17			13a30	13 40		13 47			14a00	14a03	14 10		
Rainham (Kent)	d		12 45	12 51						13 15		13 21				13 45		13 51					14 15		
Newington	d			12 55														13 55							
Sittingbourne 4	a		12 52	13 00						13 22		13 29				13 52		14 00					14 22		
	d		12 53	13 01		13 10				13 23		13 29		13 40		13 53		14 01		14 10			14 23		
Kemsley	d					13 15								13 45						14 15					
Swale	d					13 18								13 48						14 18					
Queenborough	d					13 22								13 52						14 22					
Sheerness-on-Sea	a					13 27								13 57						14 27					
Teynham	d											13 33													
Faversham 2	a		13 03	13 09						13 33		13 39				14 03		14 09					14 33		
	d			13 13	13 15							13 43	13 45					14 13	14 15						
Selling	d												13 49												
Canterbury East 4	d				13 29								13 59						14 29						
Bekesbourne	d												14 03												
Adisham	d												14 07												
Aylesham	d												14 10												
Snowdown	d												14 12												
Shepherds Well	d												14 16												
Kearsney	d												14 21												
Dover Priory 4	a				13 48								14 27						14 48						
Whitstable	d			13 21								13 51						14 21							
Chestfield & Swalecliffe	d											13 54													
Herne Bay	d			13 26								13 58						14 26							
Birchington-on-Sea	d			13 35								14 07						14 35							
Westgate-on-Sea	d											14 10													
Margate 4	d			13 41							13 53	14 14						14 41						14 53	
Broadstairs	d			13 46							13 59	14 20						14 46						14 59	
Dumpton Park	d											14 23													
Ramsgate 4	a			13 51							14 04	14 26						14 51						15 04	

A ⚯ to Margate

For further services to St Pancras International, Blackfriars and Elephant & Castle and onwards to Bromley South, St Mary Cray and Swanley please see table 52

Table 212

Saturdays

14 December to 17 May

London - Medway, Sheerness-on-Sea, Dover and Ramsgate

Network Diagram - see first Page of Table 212

		SE [1] A 🛒			SE	SE	SE	SE [1] A 🛒		SE	SE	SE [1]	SE		SE	SE [1] A 🛒		SE	SE	SE	SE [1] A 🛒		SE		SE
St Pancras Internatnl [15] ⊖	d						13 55						14 25							14 55					
Stratford International ⊖	d						14 02						14 32							15 02					
Ebbsfleet International	d						14 14						14 44							15 14					
Farringdon	d																								
City Thameslink	d																								
London Blackfriars [3] ⊖	d																								
Elephant & Castle ⊖	d																								
London Victoria [15] ⊖	d	13 22						13 52				13 58				14 22					14 52				
Bromley South [4]	d	13 39						14 09				14 19				14 39					15 09				
St Mary Cray	d											14 25													
Swanley [4]	d											14 29													
Farningham Road	d											14 34													
Longfield	d	13 52						14 22				14 38				14 52					15 22				
Meopham	d	13 57						14 27				14 42				14 57					15 27				
Sole Street	d											14 45													
London Charing Cross [4] ⊖	d					13 09					13 39								14 09						14 39
London Waterloo (East) [4] ⊖	d					13 12					13 42								14 12						14 42
London Cannon Street [4] ⊖	d																								
London Bridge [4] ⊖	d					13 17					13 47								14 17						14 47
Dartford [4]	d					13 55					14 25								14 55						15 25
Greenhithe for Bluewater	d					14 00					14 30								15 00						15 30
Gravesend [4]	d					14 07	14 18				14 37		14 48						15 07	15 18					15 37
Strood [4]	d					14 18	14 28				14 48		14 58						15 18	15 28					15 48
Rochester [4]	d	14 09				14 23	14 33	14 39			14 53	14 56	15 03			15 09			15 23	15 33	15 39				15 53
Chatham [4]	d	14 12				14 25	14 35	14 42			14 55	14 59	15 05			15 12			15 25	15 35	15 42				15 55
Gillingham (Kent) [4]	d	14 17				14a30	14 40	14 47			15a00	15a03	15 10			15 17			15a30	15 40	15 47				16a00
Rainham (Kent)	d	14 21					14 45	14 51					15 15			15 21				15 45	15 51				
Newington	d							14 55													15 55				
Sittingbourne [4]	a	14 28					14 52	15 00					15 22			15 28				15 52	16 00				
	d	14 29			14 40		14 53	15 01		15 10			15 23			15 29		15 40		15 53	16 01		16 10		
Kemsley	d				14 45					15 15								15 45					16 15		
Swale	d				14 48					15 18								15 48					16 18		
Queenborough	d				14 52					15 22								15 52					16 22		
Sheerness-on-Sea	a				14 57					15 27								15 57					16 27		
Teynham	d	14 33														15 33									
Faversham [2]	a	14 39					15 03	15 09					15 33			15 39				16 03	16 09				
	d	14 43	14 45					15 13	15 15							15 43	15 45				16 13	16 15			
Selling	d		14 49														15 49								
Canterbury East [4]	d		14 59						15 29								15 59					16 29			
Bekesbourne	d		15 03														16 03								
Adisham	d		15 07														16 07								
Aylesham	d		15 10														16 10								
Snowdown	d		15 12														16 12								
Shepherds Well	d		15 16														16 16								
Kearsney	d		15 21														16 21								
Dover Priory [4]	a		15 27						15 48								16 27					16 48			
Whitstable	d	14 51						15 21								15 51					16 21				
Chestfield & Swalecliffe	d	14 54														15 54									
Herne Bay	d	14 58						15 26								15 58					16 26				
Birchington-on-Sea	d	15 07						15 35								16 07					16 35				
Westgate-on-Sea	d	15 10														16 10									
Margate [4]	d	15 14						15 41								16 14					16 41				
Broadstairs	d	15 20						15 46							15 53	16 20					16 46				
Dumpton Park	d	15 23													15 59	16 23									
Ramsgate [4]	a	15 26						15 51							16 04	16 26					16 51				

A 🛒 to Margate

For further services to St Pancras International, Blackfriars and Elephant & Castle and onwards to Bromley South, St Mary Cray and Swanley please see table 52

Table 212

Saturdays

14 December to 17 May

London - Medway, Sheerness-on-Sea, Dover and Ramsgate

Network Diagram - see first Page of Table 212

		SE 1	SE	SE	SE 1 A		SE	SE	SE	SE 1 A		SE	SE	SE 1	SE	SE	SE 1 A		SE	SE	SE	SE 1 A	
St Pancras Internatnl 15 ⊖	d		15 25						15 55						16 25						16 55		
Stratford International ⊖	d		15 32						16 02						16 32						17 02		
Ebbsfleet International	d		15 44						16 14						16 44						17 14		
Farringdon	d																						
City Thameslink	d																						
London Blackfriars 3 ⊖	d																						
Elephant & Castle ⊖	d																						
London Victoria 15 ⊖	d	14 58			15 22					15 52				15 58			16 22					16 52	
Bromley South 4	d	15 19			15 39					16 09				16 19			16 39					17 09	
St Mary Cray	d	15 25												16 25									
Swanley 4	d	15 29												16 29									
Farningham Road	d	15 34												16 34									
Longfield	d	15 38			15 52					16 22				16 38			16 52					17 22	
Meopham	d	15 42			15 57					16 27				16 42			16 57					17 27	
Sole Street	d	15 45												16 45									
London Charing Cross 4 ⊖	d							15 09					15 39							16 09			
London Waterloo (East) 4 ⊖	d							15 12					15 42							16 12			
London Cannon Street 4 ⊖	d																						
London Bridge 4 ⊖	d							15 17					15 47							16 17			
Dartford 4	d							15 55					16 25							16 55			
Greenhithe for Bluewater	d							16 00					16 30							17 00			
Gravesend 4	d		15 48					16 07	16 18				16 37		16 48					17 07	17 18		
Strood 4	d		15 58					16 18	16 28				16 48		16 58					17 18	17 28		
Rochester 4	d	15 56	16 03		16 09			16 23	16 33	16 39			16 53	16 56	17 03		17 09			17 23	17 33	17 39	
Chatham 4	d	15 59	16 05		16 12			16 25	16 35	16 42			16 55	16 59	17 05		17 12			17 25	17 35	17 42	
Gillingham (Kent) 4	d	16a03	16 10		16 17			16a30	16 40	16 47			17a00	17a03	17 10		17 17			17a30	17 40	17 47	
Rainham (Kent)	d		16 15		16 21				16 45	16 51					17 15		17 21				17 45	17 51	
Newington	d									16 55												17 55	
Sittingbourne 4	a		16 22		16 28				16 52	17 00					17 22		17 28				17 52	18 00	
	d		16 23		16 29		16 40		16 53	17 01		17 10			17 23		17 29		17 40		17 53	18 01	
Kemsley	d						16 45					17 15							17 45				
Swale	d						16 48					17 18							17 48				
Queenborough	d						16 52					17 22							17 52				
Sheerness-on-Sea	a						16 57					17 27							17 57				
Teynham	d				16 33												17 33						
Faversham 2	a		16 33		16 39				17 03	17 09					17 33		17 39				18 03	18 09	
	d				16 43	16 45				17 13	17 15						17 43	17 45				18 13	18 15
Selling	d					16 49												17 49					
Canterbury East 4	d					16 59					17 29							17 59					18 29
Bekesbourne	d					17 03												18 03					
Adisham	d					17 07												18 07					
Aylesham	d					17 10												18 10					
Snowdown	d					17 12												18 12					
Shepherds Well	d					17 16												18 16					
Kearsney	d					17 21												18 21					
Dover Priory 4	a					17 27					17 48							18 27					18 48
Whitstable	d				16 51					17 21							17 51					18 21	
Chestfield & Swalecliffe	d				16 54												17 54						
Herne Bay	d				16 58					17 26							17 58					18 26	
Birchington-on-Sea	d				17 07					17 35							18 07					18 35	
Westgate-on-Sea	d				17 10												18 10						
Margate 4	d			16 53	17 14					17 41						17 53	18 14					18 41	
Broadstairs	d			16 59	17 20					17 46						17 59	18 20					18 46	
Dumpton Park	d				17 23												18 23						
Ramsgate 4	a			17 04	17 26					17 51						18 04	18 26					18 51	

A 🛒 to Margate

For further services to St Pancras International, Blackfriars and Elephant & Castle and onwards to Bromley South, St Mary Cray and Swanley please see table 52

Table 212

Saturdays

14 December to 17 May

London - Medway, Sheerness-on-Sea, Dover and Ramsgate

Network Diagram - see first Page of Table 212

		SE	SE	SE [1]	SE		SE	SE [1] A 🛒		SE	SE	SE	SE [1] A 🛒		SE		SE	SE [1]	SE	SE	SE [1] A 🛒		SE	SE	SE
St Pancras Internatnl [15] ⊖	d				17 25							17 55							18 25						18 55
Stratford International ⊖	d				17 32							18 02							18 32						19 02
Ebbsfleet International	d				17 44							18 14							18 44						19 14
Farringdon	d																								
City Thameslink	d																								
London Blackfriars [3] ⊖	d																								
Elephant & Castle ⊖	d																								
London Victoria [15] ⊖	d			16 58				17 22					17 52					17 58			18 22				
Bromley South [4]	d			17 19				17 39					18 09					18 19			18 39				
St Mary Cray	d			17 25														18 25							
Swanley [4]	d			17 29														18 29							
Farningham Road	d			17 34														18 34							
Longfield	d			17 38				17 52					18 22					18 38			18 52				
Meopham	d			17 42				17 57					18 27					18 42			18 57				
Sole Street	d			17 45														18 45							
London Charing Cross [4] ⊖	d		16 39								17 09						17 39							18 09	
London Waterloo (East) [4] ⊖	d		16 42								17 12						17 42							18 12	
London Cannon Street [4] ⊖	d																								
London Bridge [4] ⊖	d		16 47								17 17						17 47							18 17	
Dartford [4]	d		17 25								17 55						18 25							18 55	
Greenhithe for Bluewater	d		17 30								18 00						18 30							19 00	
Gravesend [4]	d		17 37		17 48						18 07	18 18					18 37		18 48					19 07	19 18
Strood [4]	d		17 48		17 58						18 18	18 28					18 48		18 58					19 18	19 28
Rochester [4]	d		17 53	17 56	18 03			18 09			18 23	18 33	18 39				18 53	18 56	19 03		19 09			19 23	19 33
Chatham [4]	d		17 55	17 59	18 05			18 12			18 25	18 35	18 42				18 55	18 59	19 05		19 12			19 25	19 35
Gillingham (Kent) [4]	d		18a00	18a03	18 10			18 17			18a30	18 40	18 47				19a00	19a03	19 10		19 17			19a30	19 40
Rainham (Kent)	d				18 15			18 21				18 45	18 51						19 15		19 21				19 45
Newington	d												18 55												
Sittingbourne [4]	a				18 22			18 28				18 52	19 00						19 22		19 28				19 52
	d	18 10			18 23			18 29		18 40		18 53	19 01		19 10				19 23		19 29		19 40		19 53
Kemsley	d	18 15								18 45					19 15								19 45		
Swale	d	18 18								18 48					19 18								19 48		
Queenborough	d	18 22								18 52					19 22								19 52		
Sheerness-on-Sea	a	18 27								18 57					19 27								19 57		
Teynham	d							18 33													19 33				
Faversham [2]	a				18 33			18 39				19 03	19 09						19 33		19 39				20 03
	d							18 43	18 45				19 13	19 15							19 43	19 45			
Selling	d								18 49													19 49			
Canterbury East [4]	d								18 59					19 29								19 59			
Bekesbourne	d								19 03													20 03			
Adisham	d								19 07													20 07			
Aylesham	d								19 10													20 10			
Snowdown	d								19 12													20 12			
Shepherds Well	d								19 16													20 16			
Kearsney	d								19 21													20 21			
Dover Priory [4]	a								19 27					19 48								20 27			
Whitstable	d							18 51					19 21								19 51				
Chestfield & Swalecliffe	d							18 54													19 54				
Herne Bay	d							18 58					19 26								19 58				
Birchington-on-Sea	d							19 07					19 35								20 07				
Westgate-on-Sea	d							19 10													20 10				
Margate [4]	d						18 53	19 14					19 41							19 53	20 14				
Broadstairs	d						18 59	19 20					19 46							19 59	20 20				
Dumpton Park	d							19 23													20 23				
Ramsgate [4]	a						19 04	19 26					19 51							20 04	20 26				

A 🛒 to Margate

For further services to St Pancras International, Blackfriars and Elephant & Castle and onwards to Bromley South, St Mary Cray and Swanley please see table 52

Table 212

Saturdays

14 December to 17 May

London - Medway, Sheerness-on-Sea, Dover and Ramsgate

Network Diagram - see first Page of Table 212

			SE 1		SE	SE	SE 1	SE	SE	SE 1			SE	SE	SE	SE 1		SE	SE 1	SE	SE		SE 1		SE
St Pancras Internatnl 15 ⊖	d							19 25							19 55					20 25					
Stratford International ⊖	d							19 32							20 02					20 32					
Ebbsfleet International	d							19 44							20 14					20 44					
Farringdon	d																								
City Thameslink	d																								
London Blackfriars 3 ⊖	d																								
Elephant & Castle ⊖	d																								
London Victoria 15 ⊖	d		18 52				18 58			19 22						19 52			19 58				20 22		
Bromley South 4	d		19 09				19 19			19 39						20 09			20 19				20 39		
St Mary Cray	d						19 25												20 25						
Swanley 4	d						19 29												20 29						
Farningham Road	d						19 34												20 34						
Longfield	d		19 22				19 38			19 52						20 22			20 38				20 52		
Meopham	d		19 27				19 42			19 57						20 27			20 42				20 57		
Sole Street	d						19 45												20 45						
London Charing Cross 4 ⊖	d					18 39								19 09				19 39							
London Waterloo (East) 4 ⊖	d					18 42								19 12				19 42							
London Cannon Street 4 ⊖	d																								
London Bridge 4 ⊖	d					18 47								19 17				19 47							
Dartford 4	d					19 25								19 55				20 25							
Greenhithe for Bluewater	d					19 30								20 00				20 30							
Gravesend 4	d					19 37		19 48						20 07	20 18			20 37		20 48					
Strood 4	d					19 48		19 58						20 18	20 28			20 48		20 58					
Rochester 4	d		19 39			19 53	19 56	20 03		20 09				20 23	20 33	20 39		20 53	20 56	21 03			21 09		
Chatham 4	d		19 42			19 55	19 59	20 05		20 12				20 25	20 35	20 42		20 55	20 59	21 05			21 12		
Gillingham (Kent) 4	d		19 47			20a00	20a03	20 10		20 17				20a30	20 40	20 47		21a00	21a03	21 10			21 17		
Rainham (Kent)	d		19 51					20 15		20 21					20 45	20 51				21 15			21 21		
Newington	d		19 55													20 55									
Sittingbourne 4	a		20 00					20 22		20 28					20 52	21 00				21 22			21 28		
	d		20 01		20 10			20 23		20 29			20 40		20 53	21 01				21 23			21 29		21 40
Kemsley	d				20 15								20 45												21 45
Swale	d				20 18								20 48												21 48
Queenborough	d				20 22								20 52												21 52
Sheerness-on-Sea	a				20 27								20 57												21 57
Teynham	d									20 33													21 33		
Faversham 2	a		20 09					20 33		20 39					21 03	21 09				21 33			21 39		
	d		20 13	20 15						20 43	20 45					21 13	21 15						21 43	21 45	
Selling	d										20 49													21 49	
Canterbury East 4	d			20 29							20 59						21a27							21 59	
Bekesbourne	d										21 03													22 03	
Adisham	d										21 07													22 07	
Aylesham	d										21 10													22 10	
Snowdown	d										21 12													22 12	
Shepherds Well	d										21 16													22 16	
Kearsney	d										21 21													22 21	
Dover Priory 4	a			20 48							21 27													22 27	
Whitstable	d		20 21							20 51						21 21							21 51		
Chestfield & Swalecliffe	d									20 54													21 54		
Herne Bay	d		20 26							20 58						21 26							21 58		
Birchington-on-Sea	d		20 35							21 07						21 35							22 07		
Westgate-on-Sea	d									21 10													22 10		
Margate 4	d		20 41						20 53	21 14						21 41					21 53		22 14		
Broadstairs	d		20 46						20 59	21 20						21 46					21 59		22 20		
Dumpton Park	d									21 23													22 23		
Ramsgate 4	a		20 51						21 04	21 26						21 51					22 04		22 26		

For further services to St Pancras International, Blackfriars and Elephant & Castle and onwards to Bromley South, St Mary Cray and Swanley please see table 52

Table 212

Saturdays

14 December to 17 May

London - Medway, Sheerness-on-Sea, Dover and Ramsgate

Network Diagram - see first Page of Table 212

		SE	SE	SE ■1	SE	SE	SE ■1			SE	SE	SE	SE ■1	SE	SE	SE ■1		SE		SE	SE	SE ■1	SE	SE	SE ■1
St Pancras Internatnl ■15 ⊖	d		20 55			21 25						21 55			22 25						22 55			23 25	
Stratford International ⊖	d		21 02			21 32						22 02			22 32						23 02			23 32	
Ebbsfleet International	d		21 14			21 44						22 14			22 44						23 14			23 44	
Farringdon	d																								
City Thameslink	d																								
London Blackfriars ■3 ⊖	d																								
Elephant & Castle ⊖	d																								
London Victoria ■15 ⊖	d			20 52			21 22						21 52			22 22						22 52			23 22
Bromley South ■4	d			21 09			21 39						22 09			22 39						23 09			23 39
St Mary Cray	d			21 15									22 15									23 15			
Swanley ■4	d			21 19									22 19									23 19			
Farningham Road	d			21 24									22 24									23 24			
Longfield	d			21 28			21 52						22 28			22 52						23 28			23 52
Meopham	d			21 32			21 57						22 32			22 57						23 32			23 57
Sole Street	d			21 35									22 35									23 35			
London Charing Cross ■4 ⊖	d	20 09			20 39						21 09			21 39						22 09			22 39		
London Waterloo (East) ■4 ⊖	d	20 12			20 42						21 12			21 42						22 12			22 42		
London Cannon Street ■4 ⊖	d																								
London Bridge ■4 ⊖	d	20 17			20 47						21 17			21 47						22 17			22 47		
Dartford ■4	d	20 55			21 25						21 55			22 25						22 55			23 25		
Greenhithe for Bluewater	d	21 00			21 30						22 00			22 31						23 01			23 31		
Gravesend ■4	d	21 07	21 18		21 37	21 48					22 07	22 18		22 40	22 48					23 10	23 18		23 40	23 48	
Strood ■4	d	21 18	21 28		21 48	21 58					22 18	22 28		22 52	22 58					23 22	23 28		23 52	23 58	
Rochester ■4	d	21 23	21 33	21 45	21 53	22 03	22 09				22 23	22 33	22 45	22 56	23 03	23 09				23 26	23 33	23 45	23 56	00 03	00 09
Chatham ■4	d	21 25	21 35	21 47	21 55	22 05	22 12				22 25	22 35	22 47	22 59	23 05	23 12				23 29	23 35	23 47	23 59	00 05	00 12
Gillingham (Kent) ■4	d	21a30	21 40	21 52	22a00	22 10	22 17				22a30	22 40	22 52	23a03	23 10	23 17				23a33	23 40	23 52	00a03	00 10	00 17
Rainham (Kent)	d		21 45	21 56		22 15	22 21					22 45	22 56		23 15	23 21					23 45	23 56		00 15	00 21
Newington	d			22 00									23 00									00 01			
Sittingbourne ■4	a		21 52	22 05		22 22	22 28					22 52	23 05		23 22	23 28					23 52	00 06		00 22	00 28
	d		21 53	22 06		22 23	22 29			22 40		22 53	23 06		23 23	23 29		23 32			23 53	00 07		00 23	00 29
Kemsley	d									22 45								23 37							
Swale	d									22 48								23 40							
Queenborough	d									22 52								23 44							
Sheerness-on-Sea	a									22 57								23 49							
Teynham	d						22 33									23 33									00 33
Faversham ■2	a		22 03	22 14		22 31	22 39					23 01	23 14		23 31	23 39					00 01	00 16		00 31	00 39
	d			22 15			22 43	22 45								23 43	23 45								00 43
Selling	d							22 49									23s49								
Canterbury East ■4	d			22a26				22 59									23 59								
Bekesbourne	d							23 03									00s03								
Adisham	d							23 07									00s07								
Aylesham	d							23 10									00s10								
Snowdown	d							23 12									00s12								
Shepherds Well	d							23 16									00s16								
Kearsney	d							23 21									00s21								
Dover Priory ■4	a							23 27									00 26								
Whitstable	d						22 51									23 51									00 51
Chestfield & Swalecliffe	d						22 54									23 54									00 54
Herne Bay	d						22 58									23 58									00 58
Birchington-on-Sea	d						23 07									00 07									01 07
Westgate-on-Sea	d						23 10									00 10									01 10
Margate ■4	d						23 14									00 14									01 14
Broadstairs	d						23 20									00 20									01 20
Dumpton Park	d						23 23									00 23									01 23
Ramsgate ■4	a						23 26									00 26									01 26

For further services to St Pancras International, Blackfriars and Elephant & Castle and onwards to Bromley South, St Mary Cray and Swanley please see table 52

Table 212

Saturdays

14 December to 17 May

London - Medway, Sheerness-on-Sea, Dover and Ramsgate

Network Diagram - see first Page of Table 212

Station		SE	SE	SE	SE [1]	SE
St Pancras Internatnl [15] ⊖	d		23 42	23 55		
Stratford International ⊖	d		23 49	00 02		
Ebbsfleet International	d		23a59	00 14		
Farringdon	d					
City Thameslink	d					
London Blackfriars [3] ⊖	d					
Elephant & Castle ⊖	d					
London Victoria [15] ⊖	d				23 52	
Bromley South [4]	d				00 09	
St Mary Cray	d				00 15	
Swanley [4]	d				00 19	
Farningham Road	d				00 24	
Longfield	d				00 28	
Meopham	d				00 32	
Sole Street	d				00 35	
London Charing Cross [4] ⊖	d	23 09				23 39
London Waterloo (East) [4] ⊖	d	23 12				23 42
London Cannon Street [4] ⊖	d					
London Bridge [4] ⊖	d	23 17				23 47
Dartford [4]	d	23 55				00 25
Greenhithe for Bluewater	d	23 59				00 31
Gravesend [4]	d	00 10		00 18		00 40
Strood [4]	d	00 22		00 28		00 52
Rochester [4]	d	00 26		00 33	00 45	00 56
Chatham [4]	d	00 29		00 35	00 47	00 59
Gillingham (Kent) [4]	d	00a33		00 40	00a52	01a03
Rainham (Kent)	d			00 45		
Newington	d					
Sittingbourne [4]	a			00 52		
	d			00 53		
Kemsley	d					
Swale	d					
Queenborough	d					
Sheerness-on-Sea	a					
Teynham	d					
Faversham [2]	a			01 01		
	d					
Selling	d					
Canterbury East [4]	d					
Bekesbourne	d					
Adisham	d					
Aylesham	d					
Snowdown	d					
Shepherds Well	d					
Kearsney	d					
Dover Priory [4]	a					
Whitstable	d					
Chestfield & Swalecliffe	d					
Herne Bay	d					
Birchington-on-Sea	d					
Westgate-on-Sea	d					
Margate [4]	d					
Broadstairs	d					
Dumpton Park	d					
Ramsgate [4]	a					

For further services to St Pancras International, Blackfriars and Elephant & Castle and onwards to Bromley South, St Mary Cray and Swanley please see table 52

Table 212

Sundays

8 December to 11 May

London - Medway, Sheerness-on-Sea, Dover and Ramsgate

Network Diagram - see first Page of Table 212

		SE	SE	SE	SE	SE	SE	SE	SE	SE		SE	SE	SE	SE	SE	SE	SE	SE	SE		SE		SE	SE
		1			1	1			1	1							1					1			
		A		A	A	A	A	A	A					A											
St Pancras Internatnl 15 ⊖	d												00 12												
Stratford International ⊖	d							00 02					00 19												
Ebbsfleet International	d							00 14					00a30												
Farringdon	d																								
City Thameslink	d																								
London Blackfriars 3 ⊖	d																								
Elephant & Castle ⊖	d																								
London Victoria 15 ⊖	d									00 10					00 37		07 22					08 05			
Bromley South 4	d								00 09						00 57		07 39					08 23			
St Mary Cray	d								00 15						01 03		07 45								
Swanley 4	d								00 19						01 07		07 50								
Farningham Road	d								00 24						01 12		07 55								
Longfield	d								00 28						01 16		07 59								
Meopham	d								00 32						01 20		08 03								
Sole Street	d								00 35								08 06								
London Charing Cross 4 ⊖	d															00 18									
London Waterloo (East) 4 ⊖	d															00 21									
London Cannon Street 4 ⊖	d																								
London Bridge 4 ⊖	d															00 26									
Dartford 4	d													00 25		01 07			07 55						08 25
Greenhithe for Bluewater	d													00 31		01 12			08 01						08 31
Gravesend 4	d						00 10	00 18						00 40		01 19			08 10						08 40
Strood 4	d						00 22	00 28						00 52		01 30			08 22						08 52
Rochester 4	d			00 03		00 09	00 26	00 33	00 45	00 49				00 56	01 31	01 35	08 16		08 26			08 47			08 56
Chatham 4	d			00 05		00 12	00 29	00 35	00 47	00 52				00 59	01 34	01 37	08 19		08 29			08 50			08 59
Gillingham (Kent) 4	d			00 10		00 17	00a33	00 40	00a52	00 57				01a03	01a38	01a42	08 23		08a33			08 54			09a07
Rainham (Kent)	d			00 15		00 21		00 45		01 01							08 28					08 59			
Newington	d	00 01								01 05							08 32								
Sittingbourne 4	a	00 06		00 22		00 28		00 52		01 10							08 37					09 06			
	d	00 07	00 15	00 23		00 29		00 53		01 11		08 12					08 37					09 06		09 12	
Kemsley	d		00 20									08 17												09 17	
Swale	d		00 23									08 20												09 20	
Queenborough	d		00 27									08 24												09 24	
Sheerness-on-Sea	a		00 32									08 29												09 29	
Teynham	d					00 33				01 15							08 42								
Faversham 2	a	00 16		00 31		00 39		01 01		01 23							08 48					09 14			
	d					00 43				01 24							08 49					09 18	09 22		
Selling	d																						09 26		
Canterbury East 4	d																09a01						09 36		
Bekesbourne	d																						09 40		
Adisham	d																						09 44		
Aylesham	d																						09 47		
Snowdown	d																						09 49		
Shepherds Well	d																						09 53		
Kearsney	d																						09 58		
Dover Priory 4	a																						10 05		
Whitstable	d					00 51				01 32												09 26			
Chestfield & Swalecliffe	d					00 54				01 35												09 29			
Herne Bay	d					00 58				01 39												09 33			
Birchington-on-Sea	d				00 07	01 07				01 48												09 41			
Westgate-on-Sea	d				00 10	01 10				01 51												09 45			
Margate 4	d				00 14	01 14				01 55								07 53		08 53		09 49			
Broadstairs	d				00 20	01 20				02 01								07 59		08 59		09 54			
Dumpton Park	d				00 23	01 23				02 04												09 57			
Ramsgate 4	a				00 26	01 26				02 07								08 04		09 04		10 01			

A not 8 December

B to Margate

For further services to St Pancras International, Blackfriars and Elephant & Castle and onwards to Bromley South, St Mary Cray and Swanley please see table 52

Table 212

Sundays

8 December to 11 May

London - Medway, Sheerness-on-Sea, Dover and Ramsgate

Network Diagram - see first Page of Table 212

		SE 1	SE	SE	SE 1		SE	SE	SE	SE 1	SE	SE	SE 1 A 🚲		SE	SE	SE	SE 1	SE	SE	SE 1 A 🚲		SE
St Pancras Internatnl 15 ⊖	d								09 25								10 22						
Stratford International ⊖	d								09 32								10 32						
Ebbsfleet International	d								09 44								10 44						
Farringdon	d																						
City Thameslink	d																						
London Blackfriars 3 ⊖	d																						
Elephant & Castle ⊖	d																						
London Victoria 15 ⊖	d	08 22			09 05					09 22			10 05					10 22			11 05		
Bromley South 4	d	08 39			09 23					09 39			10 23					10 39			11 23		
St Mary Cray	d	08 45								09 45								10 45					
Swanley 4	d	08 50								09 50								10 50					
Farningham Road	d	08 55								09 55								10 55					
Longfield	d	08 59								09 59								10 59					
Meopham	d	09 03								10 03								11 03					
Sole Street	d	09 06								10 06								11 06					
London Charing Cross 4 ⊖	d		08 09					08 39			09 09					09 39			10 09				
London Waterloo (East) 4 ⊖	d		08 12					08 42			09 12					09 42			10 12				
London Cannon Street 4 ⊖	d																						
London Bridge 4 ⊖	d		08 17					08 47			09 17					09 47			10 17				
Dartford 4	d		08 55					09 25			09 55					10 25			10 55				
Greenhithe for Bluewater	d		09 00					09 30			10 00					10 30			11 00				
Gravesend 4	d		09 07					09 37	09 48		10 07					10 37	10 48		11 07				
Strood 4	d		09 18					09 48	09 58		10 18					10 48	10 58		11 18				
Rochester 4	d	09 16	09 23		09 47			09 53	10 03	10 16	10 23		10 47			10 53	11 03	11 16	11 23		11 47		
Chatham 4	d	09 19	09 25		09 50			09 55	10 05	10 19	10 25		10 50			10 55	11 05	11 19	11 25		11 50		
Gillingham (Kent) 4	d	09 23	09a30		09 54			10a00	10 10	10 23	10a30		10 54			11a00	11 10	11 23	11a30		11 54		
Rainham (Kent)	d	09 28			09 59				10 15	10 28			10 59				11 15	11 28			11 59		
Newington	d	09 32								10 32								11 32					
Sittingbourne 4	a	09 37			10 06				10 22	10 37			11 06				11 22	11 37			12 06		
	d	09 37			10 06		10 12		10 23	10 37			11 06		11 12		11 23	11 37			12 06		12 12
Kemsley	d						10 17								11 17								12 17
Swale	d						10 20								11 20								12 20
Queenborough	d						10 24								11 24								12 24
Sheerness-on-Sea	a						10 29								11 29								12 29
Teynham	d	09 42								10 42								11 42					
Faversham 2	a	09 48			10 14				10 33	10 48			11 14				11 33	11 48			12 14		
	d	09 49			10 18	10 22				10 49			11 18	11 22				11 49			12 18	12 22	
Selling	d					10 26								11 26								12 26	
Canterbury East 4	d	10a01				10 36				11a01				11 36				12a01				12 36	
Bekesbourne	d					10 40								11 40								12 40	
Adisham	d					10 44								11 44								12 44	
Aylesham	d					10 47								11 47								12 47	
Snowdown	d					10 49								11 49								12 49	
Shepherds Well	d					10 53								11 53								12 53	
Kearsney	d					10 58								11 58								12 58	
Dover Priory 4	a					11 05								12 05								13 05	
Whitstable	d				10 26								11 26								12 26		
Chestfield & Swalecliffe	d				10 29								11 29								12 29		
Herne Bay	d				10 33								11 33								12 33		
Birchington-on-Sea	d				10 41								11 41								12 41		
Westgate-on-Sea	d				10 45								11 45								12 45		
Margate 4	d			09 53	10 49							10 53	11 49							11 53	12 49		
Broadstairs	d			09 59	10 54							10 59	11 54							11 59	12 54		
Dumpton Park	d				10 57								11 57								12 57		
Ramsgate 4	a			10 04	11 01							11 04	12 01							12 04	13 01		

A 🚲 to Margate

For further services to St Pancras International, Blackfriars and Elephant & Castle and onwards to Bromley South, St Mary Cray and Swanley please see table 52

Table 212

Sundays

8 December to 11 May

London - Medway, Sheerness-on-Sea, Dover and Ramsgate

Network Diagram - see first Page of Table 212

		SE		SE	SE 1	SE	SE	SE 1 A		SE	SE	SE		SE 1	SE	SE	SE	SE 1 A		SE	SE	SE	SE 1	SE	
St Pancras Internatnl 15	⊖ d			11 25								12 22				12 52						13 25			
Stratford International	⊖ d			11 32								12 32				12 59						13 32			
Ebbsfleet International	d			11 44								12 44				13 14						13 44			
Farringdon	d																								
City Thameslink	d																								
London Blackfriars 3	⊖ d																								
Elephant & Castle	⊖ d																								
London Victoria 15	⊖ d				11 22			12 05						12 22				13 05					13 22		
Bromley South 4	d				11 39			12 23						12 39				13 23					13 39		
St Mary Cray	d				11 45									12 45									13 45		
Swanley 4	d				11 50									12 50									13 50		
Farningham Road	d				11 55									12 55									13 55		
Longfield	d				11 59									12 59									13 59		
Meopham	d				12 03									13 03									14 03		
Sole Street	d				12 06									13 06									14 06		
London Charing Cross 4	⊖ d	10 39				11 09					11 39				12 09						12 39			13 09	
London Waterloo (East) 4	⊖ d	10 42				11 12					11 42				12 12						12 42			13 12	
London Cannon Street 4	⊖ d																								
London Bridge 4	⊖ d	10 47				11 17					11 47				12 17						12 47			13 17	
Dartford 4	d	11 25				11 55					12 25				12 55						13 25			13 55	
Greenhithe for Bluewater	d	11 30				12 00					12 30				13 00						13 30			14 00	
Gravesend 4	d	11 37		11 48		12 07					12 37	12 48			13 07	13 18					13 37	13 48		14 07	
Strood 4	d	11 48		11 58		12 18					12 48	12 58			13 18	13 28					13 48	13 58		14 18	
Rochester 4	d	11 53		12 03	12 16	12 23		12 47			12 53	13 03		13 16	13 23	13 33		13 47			13 53	14 03	14 16	14 23	
Chatham 4	d	11 55		12 05	12 19	12 25		12 50			12 55	13 05		13 19	13 25	13 35		13 50			13 55	14 05	14 19	14 25	
Gillingham (Kent) 4	d	12a00		12 10	12 23	12a30		12 54			13a00	13 10		13 23	13a30	13 40		13 54			14a00	14 10	14 23	14a30	
Rainham (Kent)	d			12 15	12 28			12 59				13 15		13 28		13 45		13 59				14 15	14 28		
Newington	d				12 32									13 32									14 32		
Sittingbourne 4	a			12 22	12 37			13 06				13 22		13 37		13 52		14 06				14 22	14 37		
	d			12 23	12 37			13 06		13 12		13 22		13 37		13 53		14 06		14 12		14 23	14 37		
Kemsley	d									13 17										14 17					
Swale	d									13 20										14 20					
Queenborough	d									13 24										14 24					
Sheerness-on-Sea	a									13 29										14 29					
Teynham	d				12 42									13 42									14 42		
Faversham 2	a			12 33	12 48			13 14				13 33		13 48		14 03		14 14				14 33	14 48		
	d				12 49			13 18	13 22					13 49				14 18	14 22				14 49		
Selling	d								13 26										14 26						
Canterbury East 4	d				13a01				13 36					14a01					14 36				15a01		
Bekesbourne	d								13 40										14 40						
Adisham	d								13 44										14 44						
Aylesham	d								13 47										14 47						
Snowdown	d								13 49										14 49						
Shepherds Well	d								13 53										14 53						
Kearsney	d								13 58										14 58						
Dover Priory 4	a								14 05										15 05						
Whitstable	d							13 26										14 26							
Chestfield & Swalecliffe	d							13 29										14 29							
Herne Bay	d							13 33										14 33							
Birchington-on-Sea	d							13 41										14 41							
Westgate-on-Sea	d							13 45										14 45							
Margate 4	d						12 53	13 49									13 53	14 49							
Broadstairs	d						12 59	13 54									13 59	14 54							
Dumpton Park	d							13 57										14 57							
Ramsgate 4	a						13 04	14 01									14 04	15 01							

A to Margate

For further services to St Pancras International, Blackfriars and Elephant & Castle and onwards to Bromley South, St Mary Cray and Swanley please see table 52

Table 212

Sundays

8 December to 11 May

London - Medway, Sheerness-on-Sea, Dover and Ramsgate

Network Diagram - see first Page of Table 212

		SE		SE	SE [1] A 🛒		SE	SE	SE	SE [1]	SE	SE		SE	SE [1] A 🛒		SE	SE	SE	SE [1]	SE	SE		SE
St Pancras Internatnl [15] ⊖	d	13 55							16 25			16 55							17 25			17 52		
Stratford International ⊖	d	14 02							16 32			17 02							17 32			18 02		
Ebbsfleet International	d	14 14							16 44			17 14							17 44			18 14		
Farringdon	d																							
City Thameslink	d																							
London Blackfriars [3] ⊖	d																							
Elephant & Castle ⊖	d																							
London Victoria [15] ⊖	d				16 05					16 22					17 05					17 22				
Bromley South [4]	d				16 23					16 39					17 23					17 39				
St Mary Cray	d									16 45										17 45				
Swanley [4]	d									16 50										17 50				
Farningham Road	d									16 55										17 55				
Longfield	d									16 59										17 59				
Meopham	d									17 03										18 03				
Sole Street	d									17 06										18 06				
London Charing Cross [4] ⊖	d							15 39			16 09							16 39			17 09			
London Waterloo (East) [4] ⊖	d							15 42			16 12							16 42			17 12			
London Cannon Street [4] ⊖	d																							
London Bridge [4] ⊖	d							15 47			16 17							16 47			17 17			
Dartford [4]	d							16 25			16 55							17 25			17 55			
Greenhithe for Bluewater	d							16 30			17 00							17 30			18 00			
Gravesend [4]	d	14 18						16 37	16 48		17 07	17 18						17 37	17 48		18 07	18 18		
Strood [4]	d	14 28	and at the same minutes past each hour until					16 48	16 58		17 18	17 28						17 48	17 58		18 18	18 28		
Rochester [4]	d	14 33			16 47			16 53	17 03	17 16	17 23	17 33			17 47			17 53	18 03	18 16	18 23	18 33		
Chatham [4]	d	14 35			16 50			16 55	17 05	17 19	17 25	17 35			17 50			17 55	18 05	18 19	18 25	18 35		
Gillingham (Kent) [4]	d	14 40			16 54			17a00	17 10	17 23	17a30	17 40			17 54			18a00	18 10	18 23	18a30	18 40		
Rainham (Kent)	d	14 45			16 59				17 15	17 28		17 45			17 59				18 15	18 28		18 45		
Newington	d									17 32										18 32				
Sittingbourne [4]	a	14 52			17 06				17 22	17 37		17 52			18 06				18 22	18 37		18 52		
	d	14 53			17 06		17 12		17 23	17 37		17 53			18 06		18 12		18 23	18 37		18 53		
Kemsley	d						17 17										18 17							
Swale	d						17 20										18 20							
Queenborough	d						17 24										18 24							
Sheerness-on-Sea	a						17 29										18 29							
Teynham	d									17 42										18 42				
Faversham [2]	a	15 03			17 14				17 33	17 48		18 03			18 14				18 33	18 48		19 03		
	d				17 18	17 22				17 49					18 18	18 22				18 49				
Selling	d					17 26										18 26								
Canterbury East [4]	d					17 36				18a01						18 36				19a01				
Bekesbourne	d					17 40										18 40								
Adisham	d					17 44										18 44								
Aylesham	d					17 47										18 47								
Snowdown	d					17 49										18 49								
Shepherds Well	d					17 53										18 53								
Kearsney	d					17 58										18 58								
Dover Priory [4]	a					18 05										19 05								
Whitstable	d				17 26										18 26									
Chestfield & Swalecliffe	d				17 29										18 29									
Herne Bay	d				17 33										18 33									
Birchington-on-Sea	d				17 41										18 41									
Westgate-on-Sea	d				17 45										18 45									
Margate [4]	d			16 53	17 49									17 53	18 49									18 53
Broadstairs	d			16 59	17 54									17 59	18 54									18 59
Dumpton Park	d				17 57										18 57									
Ramsgate [4]	a			17 04	18 01									18 04	19 01									19 04

A 🛒 to Margate

For further services to St Pancras International, Blackfriars and Elephant & Castle and onwards to Bromley South, St Mary Cray and Swanley please see table 52

Table 212

Sundays

8 December to 11 May

London - Medway, Sheerness-on-Sea, Dover and Ramsgate

Network Diagram - see first Page of Table 212

		SE 1 A [trolley]		SE	SE	SE	SE 1	SE	SE		SE	SE 1 A [trolley]		SE	SE	SE	SE 1	SE	SE		SE	SE 1		SE	SE
St Pancras Internatnl 15 ⊖	d					18 25			18 55							19 25			19 55						
Stratford International ⊖	d					18 32			19 02							19 32			20 02						
Ebbsfleet International	d					18 44			19 14							19 44			20 14						
Farringdon	d																								
City Thameslink	d																								
London Blackfriars 3 ⊖	d																								
Elephant & Castle ⊖	d																								
London Victoria 15 ⊖	d	18 05					18 22					19 05					19 22					20 05			
Bromley South 4	d	18 23					18 39					19 23					19 39					20 23			
St Mary Cray	d						18 45										19 45								
Swanley 4	d						18 50										19 50								
Farningham Road	d						18 55										19 55								
Longfield	d						18 59										19 59								
Meopham	d						19 03										20 03								
Sole Street	d						19 06										20 06								
London Charing Cross 4 ⊖	d				17 39			18 09							18 39			19 09							19 39
London Waterloo (East) 4 ⊖	d				17 42			18 12							18 42			19 12							19 42
London Cannon Street 4 ⊖	d																								
London Bridge 4 ⊖	d				17 47			18 17							18 47			19 17							19 47
Dartford 4	d				18 25			18 55							19 25			19 55							20 25
Greenhithe for Bluewater	d				18 30			19 00							19 30			20 00							20 30
Gravesend 4	d				18 37	18 48		19 07	19 18						19 37	19 48		20 07	20 18						20 37
Strood 4	d				18 48	18 58		19 18	19 28						19 48	19 58		20 18	20 28						20 48
Rochester 4	d	18 47			18 53	19 03	19 16	19 23	19 33			19 47			19 53	20 03	20 16	20 23	20 33			20 47			20 53
Chatham 4	d	18 50			18 55	19 05	19 19	19 25	19 35			19 50			19 55	20 05	20 19	20 25	20 35			20 50			20 55
Gillingham (Kent) 4	d	18 54			19a00	19 10	19 23	19a30	19 40			19 54			20a00	20 10	20 23	20a30	20 40			20 54			21a00
Rainham (Kent)	d	18 59				19 15	19 28		19 45			19 59				20 15	20 28		20 45			20 59			
Newington	d						19 32										20 32								
Sittingbourne 4	a	19 06				19 22	19 37		19 52			20 06				20 22	20 37		20 52			21 06			
	d	19 06		19 12		19 23	19 37		19 53			20 06		20 12		20 23	20 37		20 53			21 06		21 12	
Kemsley	d			19 17										20 17										21 17	
Swale	d			19 20										20 20										21 20	
Queenborough	d			19 24										20 24										21 24	
Sheerness-on-Sea	a			19 29										20 29										21 29	
Teynham	d						19 42										20 42								
Faversham 2	a	19 14				19 33	19 48		20 03			20 14				20 33	20 49		21 03			21 14			
	d	19 18	19 22				19 49					20 18	20 22									21 18	21 22		
Selling	d		19 26										20 26										21 26		
Canterbury East 4	d		19 36				20a01						20 36										21 36		
Bekesbourne	d		19 40										20 40										21 40		
Adisham	d		19 44										20 44										21 44		
Aylesham	d		19 47										20 47										21 47		
Snowdown	d		19 49										20 49										21 49		
Shepherds Well	d		19 53										20 53										21 53		
Kearsney	d		19 58										20 58										21 58		
Dover Priory 4	a		20 05										21 05										22 05		
Whitstable	d	19 26										20 26										21 26			
Chestfield & Swalecliffe	d	19 29										20 29										21 29			
Herne Bay	d	19 33										20 33										21 33			
Birchington-on-Sea	d	19 41										20 41										21 41			
Westgate-on-Sea	d	19 45										20 45										21 45			
Margate 4	d	19 49									19 53	20 49									20 53	21 49			
Broadstairs	d	19 54									19 59	20 54									20 59	21 54			
Dumpton Park	d	19 57										20 57										21 57			
Ramsgate 4	a	20 01									20 04	21 01									21 04	22 01			

A [trolley] to Margate

For further services to St Pancras International, Blackfriars and Elephant & Castle and onwards to Bromley South, St Mary Cray and Swanley please see table 52

Table 212

Sundays
8 December to 11 May

London - Medway, Sheerness-on-Sea, Dover and Ramsgate

Network Diagram - see first Page of Table 212

		SE	SE ■1	SE	SE	SE	SE ■1		SE	SE	SE	SE ■1	SE	SE	SE		SE	SE	SE	SE ■1	SE	SE	SE ■1
St Pancras Internatnl ■15 ⊖	d	20 25			20 55						21 25			21 55					22 25			22 55	
Stratford International ⊖	d	20 32			21 02						21 32			22 02					22 32			23 02	
Ebbsfleet International	d	20 44			21 14						21 44			22 14					22 44			23 14	
Farringdon	d																						
City Thameslink	d																						
London Blackfriars ■3 ⊖	d																						
Elephant & Castle ⊖	d																						
London Victoria ■15 ⊖	d		20 22				21 05					21 22			22 05					22 22			23 05
Bromley South ■4	d		20 39				21 23					21 39			22 23					22 39			23 23
St Mary Cray	d		20 45									21 45								22 45			
Swanley ■4	d		20 50									21 50								22 50			
Farningham Road	d		20 55									21 55								22 55			
Longfield	d		20 59									21 59								22 59			
Meopham	d		21 03									22 03								23 03			
Sole Street	d		21 06									22 06								23 06			
London Charing Cross ■4 ⊖	d			20 09						20 39			21 09					21 39			22 09		
London Waterloo (East) ■4 ⊖	d			20 12						20 42			21 12					21 42			22 12		
London Cannon Street ■4 ⊖	d																						
London Bridge ■4 ⊖	d			20 17						20 47			21 17					21 47			22 17		
Dartford ■4	d			20 55						21 25			21 55					22 25			22 55		
Greenhithe for Bluewater	d			21 00						21 30			22 00					22 31			23 01		
Gravesend ■4	d	20 48		21 07	21 18					21 37	21 48		22 07	22 18				22 40	22 48		23 10	23 18	
Strood ■4	d	20 58		21 18	21 28					21 48	21 58		22 18	22 28				22 52	22 58		23 22	23 28	
Rochester ■4	d	21 03	21 16	21 23	21 33		21 47			21 53	22 03	22 16	22 23	22 33	22 47			22 56	23 03	23 16	23 26	23 33	23 47
Chatham ■4	d	21 05	21 19	21 25	21 35		21 50			21 55	22 05	22 19	22 25	22 35	22 50			22 59	23 05	23 19	23 29	23 35	23 50
Gillingham (Kent) ■4	d	21 10	21 23	21a30	21 40		21 54			22a00	22 10	22 23	22a30	22 40	22 54			23a03	23 10	23 23	23a33	23 40	23 54
Rainham (Kent)	d	21 15	21 28		21 45		21 59				22 15	22 28		22 45	22 59				23 15	23 28		23 45	23 59
Newington	d		21 32									22 32								23 32			
Sittingbourne ■4	a	21 22	21 37		21 52		22 06				22 22	22 37		22 52	23 06				23 22	23 37		23 52	00 06
	d	21 23	21 37		21 53		22 06		22 12		22 23	22 37		22 53	23 06		23 12		23 23	23 37		23 53	00 06
Kemsley	d								22 17								23 17						
Swale	d								22 20								23 20						
Queenborough	d								22 24								23 24						
Sheerness-on-Sea	a								22 29								23 29						
Teynham	d		21 42									22 42								23 42			
Faversham ■2	a	21 33	21 49		22 03		22 14				22 31	22 49		23 03	23 14				23 31	23 49		00 03	00 14
	d						22 18	22 22							23 18	23 22							00 18
Selling	d							22 26								23 26							
Canterbury East ■4	d							22 36								23 36							
Bekesbourne	d							22 40								23 40							
Adisham	d							22 44								23 44							
Aylesham	d							22 47								23 47							
Snowdown	d							22 49								23 49							
Shepherds Well	d							22 53								23 53							
Kearsney	d							22 58								23 58							
Dover Priory ■4	a							23 05								00 05							
Whitstable	d						22 26								23 26								00 26
Chestfield & Swalecliffe	d						22 29								23 29								00 29
Herne Bay	d						22 33								23 33								00 33
Birchington-on-Sea	d						22 41								23 41								00 41
Westgate-on-Sea	d						22 45								23 45								00 45
Margate ■4	d					21 53	22 49								23 49								00 49
Broadstairs	d					21 59	22 54								23 54								00 54
Dumpton Park	d						22 57								23 57								00 57
Ramsgate ■4	a					22 04	23 01								00 01								01 01

A ⚯ to Margate

For further services to St Pancras International, Blackfriars and Elephant & Castle and onwards to Bromley South, St Mary Cray and Swanley please see table 52

Table 212

Sundays

8 December to 11 May

London - Medway, Sheerness-on-Sea, Dover and Ramsgate

Network Diagram - see first Page of Table 212

		SE	SE	SE	SE	SE 1
St Pancras Internatnl 15 ⊖	d		23 25		23 42	
Stratford International ⊖	d		23 32		23 49	
Ebbsfleet International	d		23 44		23a59	
Farringdon	d					
City Thameslink	d					
London Blackfriars 3 ⊖	d					
Elephant & Castle ⊖	d					
London Victoria 15 ⊖	d					23 45
Bromley South 4	d					00 02
St Mary Cray	d					00 08
Swanley 4	d					00 13
Farningham Road	d					00 18
Longfield	d					00 22
Meopham	d					00 26
Sole Street	d					00 29
London Charing Cross 4 ⊖	d	22 39		23 09		
London Waterloo (East) 4 ⊖	d	22 42		23 12		
London Cannon Street 4 ⊖	d					
London Bridge 4 ⊖	d	22 47		23 17		
Dartford 4	d	23 25		23 55		
Greenhithe for Bluewater	d	23 31		23 59		
Gravesend 4	d	23 40	23 48	00 10		
Strood 4	d	23 52	23 58	00 22		
Rochester 4	d	23 56	00 03	00 26		00 39
Chatham 4	d	23 59	00 05	00 29		00 42
Gillingham (Kent) 4	d	00a03	00 10	00a33		00 46
Rainham (Kent)	d		00 15			00 51
Newington	d					00 55
Sittingbourne 4	a		00 22			01 00
	d		00 23			01 00
Kemsley	d					
Swale	d					
Queenborough	d					
Sheerness-on-Sea	a					
Teynham	d					01 05
Faversham 2	a		00 33			01 12
	d					
Selling	d					
Canterbury East 4	d					
Bekesbourne	d					
Adisham	d					
Aylesham	d					
Snowdown	d					
Shepherds Well	d					
Kearsney	d					
Dover Priory 4	a					
Whitstable	d					
Chestfield & Swalecliffe	d					
Herne Bay	d					
Birchington-on-Sea	d					
Westgate-on-Sea	d					
Margate 4	d					
Broadstairs	d					
Dumpton Park	d					
Ramsgate 4	a					

For further services to St Pancras International, Blackfriars and Elephant & Castle and onwards to Bromley South, St Mary Cray and Swanley please see table 52

Table 212R

Mondays to Fridays

9 December to 16 May

Ramsgate, Dover, Sheerness-on-Sea and Medway - London

Network Diagram - see first Page of Table 212

Miles	Miles	Miles	Miles	Miles			SE MX [1] A	SE	SE MX B	SE MX [1]	SE	SE	SE	SE	SE [1]		SE [1]	SE [1]	SE [1]	SE	SE	SE	SE	SE	SE
0	—	—	—	—	**Ramsgate [4]**	d												04 32							
1	—	—	—	—	Dumpton Park	d												04 35							
2¼	—	—	—	—	Broadstairs	d												04 38							
5½	—	—	—	—	**Margate [4]**	d												04 43							
6¾	—	—	—	—	Westgate-on-Sea	d												04 46							
8½	—	—	—	—	Birchington-on-Sea	d												04 50							
16¼	—	—	—	—	**Herne Bay**	d												04 59							
18½	—	—	—	—	Chestfield & Swalecliffe	d												05 03							
20½	—	—	—	—	Whitstable	d												05 06							
—	0	—	—	—	**Dover Priory [4]**	d											04 30		05 04						
—	2¼	—	—	—	Kearsney	d											04 34		05 08						
—	5½	—	—	—	Shepherds Well	d											04 40		05 13						
—	7½	—	—	—	Snowdown	d											04 43		05 17						
—	8½	—	—	—	Aylesham	d											04 46		05 19						
—	9½	—	—	—	Adisham	d											04 49		05 22						
—	12½	—	—	—	Bekesbourne	d											04 53		05 26						
—	15½	—	—	—	**Canterbury East [4]**	d											04 59		05 31						
—	22	—	—	—	Selling	d											05 08		05 40						
27¼	25¼	—	—	0	**Faversham [2]**	a											05 13	05 15	05 45						
—	—	—	—	—		d							04 56				05 19				05 28				
31¾	29¾	—	—	4½	Teynham	d																			
—	—	0	—	—	**Sheerness-on-Sea**	d																05 32			
—	—	2	—	—	Queenborough	d																05 36			
—	—	4	—	—	Swale	d			00 01													05 40			
—	—	6	—	—	Kemsley	d			00 05													05 44			
34½	32½	8	—	7¼	**Sittingbourne [4]**	a			00 10				05 06				05 26				05 36	05 49			
—	—	—	—	—		d	00 03						05 07				05 27				05 37				
37¼	35¾	—	—	10½	Newington	d	00 08																		
40¼	38¼	—	—	13	Rainham (Kent)	d	00 12						05 15				05 35				05 45				
43¼	41¼	—	0	16	**Gillingham (Kent) [4]**	d	00a17	04 09			04 34	04 54	05 20	05 24	05 30		05 40			05 45	05 50		05 54	06 02	06 07
45	43	—	1¾	17¾	**Chatham [4]**	d		04 13			04 38	04 58	05 24	05 28	05 34		05 44			05 49	05 54		05 58	06 06	06 11
45½	43½	—	2¼	18¼	Rochester [4]	d		04 15			04 40	05 00	05 27	05 30	05 36		05 47			05 51	05 57		06 00	06 09	06 13
—	—	—	3¼	19¼	Strood [4]	a		04 20			04 45	05 05	05 31	05 35							06 01		06 05		06 18
—	—	—	10½	26½	Gravesend [4]	a		04 32			04 57	05 17	05 42	05 47							06 12		06 17		06 30
—	—	—	14½	—	Greenhithe for Bluewater	a		04 38			05 07	05 23		05 53									06 23		06 36
—	—	—	17¼	—	Dartford [4]	a		04 43			05 13	05 28		05 58									06 28		06 41
—	—	—	34¼	—	**London Bridge [4]** ⊖	a		05 22			05 52	06 05		06 34						06 27			07 03		07 17
—	—	—	—	—	**London Cannon Street [4]** ⊖	a														06 32					07 24
—	—	—	35¼	—	**London Waterloo (East) [4]** ⊖	a		05 26			05 57	06 10		06 39									07 09		
—	—	—	36	—	**London Charing Cross [4]** ⊖	a		05 30			06 01	06 14		06 43									07 15		
52¼	50¼	—	—	—	Sole Street	d									05 47									06 19	
53¼	51¼	—	—	—	Meopham	d									05 49									06 22	
55¼	53¼	—	—	—	Longfield	d									05 53									06 26	
58¾	56¾	—	—	—	Farningham Road	d				00 04					05 57									06 29	
61¾	59¾	—	—	—	Swanley [4]	a				00 09					06 02									06 34	
64½	62½	—	—	—	St Mary Cray	a				00 14					06 06									06 39	
68¼	66¼	—	—	—	Bromley South [4]	a				00 20					06 14		06 12							06 45	
79¼	77¼	—	—	—	**London Victoria [15]** ⊖	a				00 37					06 31		06 30							07 07	
—	—	—	—	—	Elephant & Castle ⊖	a																			
—	—	—	—	—	London Blackfriars [3] ⊖	a																			
—	—	—	—	—	City Thameslink	a																			
—	—	—	—	—	Farringdon	a																			
—	—	—	—	28½	Ebbsfleet International	a							05 46								06 16				
—	—	—	—	45¼	Stratford International ⊖	a							05 59								06 29				
—	—	—	—	—	St Pancras International	a							06 06								06 36				

A from Ramsgate

B from Sheerness on Sea

For further services to St Pancras International, Blackfriars and Elephant & Castle and onwards to Bromley South, St Mary Cray and Swanley please see table 52

Table 212R

Mondays to Fridays

9 December to 16 May

Ramsgate, Dover, Sheerness-on-Sea and Medway - London

Network Diagram - see first Page of Table 212

		SE [1]	SE	SE	SE [1]	SE [1]	SE	SE	SE [1]	SE	SE [1]	SE	SE [1]	SE	SE [1]	SE	SE [1]	SE [1]	SE	SE [1] A	SE [1] B	SE
Ramsgate [4]	d	05 06							05 40								06 08					
Dumpton Park	d	05 09							05 43								06 11					
Broadstairs	d	05 12							05 46			06 00					06 14	06 25				06 30
Margate [4]	d	05 17							05 51			06 05					06 19	06 30				06 35
Westgate-on-Sea	d	05 20							05 54								06 22					
Birchington-on-Sea	d	05 24							05 58			06 10					06 26	06 35				06 40
Herne Bay	d	05 33							06 07			06 19					06 35	06 44				06 49
Chestfield & Swalecliffe	d	05 36							06 10								06 38					
Whitstable	d	05 40							06 14			06 25					06 42	06 49				06 55
Dover Priory [4]	d										05 45		06 05									
Kearsney	d										05 50		06 09									
Shepherds Well	d										05 55		06 14									
Snowdown	d										05 59		06 18									
Aylesham	d										06 02		06 20									
Adisham	d										06 04		06 23									
Bekesbourne	d										06 09		06 27									
Canterbury East [4]	d										06 15		06 32									
Selling	d										06 24		06 41									
Faversham [2]	a	05 48							06 22		06 29	06 33	06 46				06 50	06 57				07 03
	d	05 49	05 58			06 07			06 23		06 38	06 34					06 51	06 58				07 04
Teynham	d	05 55				06 13					06 44											
Sheerness-on-Sea	d			05 57										06 29					06 46			
Queenborough	d			06 01										06 35					06 50			
Swale	d			06 05										06 39					06 54			
Kemsley	d			06 09										06 42					06 58			
Sittingbourne [4]	a	05 59	06 06	06 14		06 17			06 30		06 48	06 41		06 47			06 58	07 05	07 05			07 12
	d	06 00	06 07			06 18			06 31		06 49	06 42					06 59	07 06				07 13
Newington	d	06 05				06 24											07 05					
Rainham (Kent)	d	06 10	06 15			06 29			06 39		06 57	06 50					07 10	07 14				07 21
Gillingham (Kent) [4]	d	06 15	06 20		06 24	06 34		06 38	06 44	06 50	07 02	06 55			07 08	07 12	07 15	07 19				07 26
Chatham [4]	d	06 19	06 24		06 28	06 38		06 42	06 48	06 54	07 07	07 00			07 12	07 16	07 20	07 24				07 30
Rochester [4]	d	06 22	06 27		06 31	06 41		06 44		06 57	07 09	07 03			07 15	07 18					07 28	07 33
Strood [4]	a		06 31					06 49								07 23						
Gravesend [4]	a		06 42					07 01								07 35						
Greenhithe for Bluewater	a							07 07								07 45						
Dartford [4]	a							07 12								07 51						
London Bridge [4] ⊖	a					07 20	07d37	07 47			07 51					08 25		08 09				
London Cannon Street [4] ⊖	a					07 28					07 58							08 17				
London Waterloo (East) [4] ⊖	a							07 52								08 30						
London Charing Cross [4] ⊖	a							07 58								08 36						
Sole Street	d				06 41					07 07					07 25						07 38	
Meopham	d				06 44					07 10					07 28						07 41	
Longfield	d				06 48					07 14							07 35				07 46	
Farningham Road	d				06 51					07 17					07 33						07 50	
Swanley [4]	a				06 56					07 22					07 38						07 55	
St Mary Cray	a				07 01					07 27					07 44						07 59	
Bromley South [4]	a	06 49			07 07				07 15	07 33					07 52		07 49				08 06	
London Victoria [15] ⊖	a	07 09			07 30		09 11		07 38	07 55					08 17		08 09					
Elephant & Castle ⊖	a																			08d21	08 30	
London Blackfriars [3] ⊖	a																			08 25	08 36	
City Thameslink	a																			08 27	08 39	
Farringdon	a																			08 30	08 43	
Ebbsfleet International	a		06 46									07 17										07 47
Stratford International ⊖	a		06 59									07 30										08 00
St Pancras International	a		07 06									07 37								08 35	08 47	08 07

A from Beckenham Junction to Bedford

B to Bedford

For further services to St Pancras International, Blackfriars and Elephant & Castle and onwards to Bromley South, St Mary Cray and Swanley please see table 52

Table 212R

Mondays to Fridays

9 December to 16 May

Ramsgate, Dover, Sheerness-on-Sea and Medway - London

Network Diagram - see first Page of Table 212

		SE 1	SE	SE 1	SE 1	SE 1	SE		SE 1	SE	SE 1	SE	SE	SE 1	SE 1	SE 1 A	SE		SE 1	SE	SE 1	SE 1 B	SE 1 C	SE	SE 1 D
Ramsgate [4]	d			06 32							06 57				07 05				07 19				07 35	08 01	
Dumpton Park	d			06 35							07 00				07 08				07 22				07 38		
Broadstairs	d			06 38		06 48				06 58	07 03				07 11				07 25				07 41	08 06	
Margate [4]	d			06 43		06 53				07 03	07 08				07 16				07 30				07 46	08a11	
Westgate-on-Sea	d			06 46		06 56					07 11				07 20				07 33				07 50		
Birchington-on-Sea	d			06 50		07 00				07 10	07 15				07 24				07 37				07 54		
Herne Bay	d			06 59		07 09				07 19	07 24				07 33				07 46				08 03		
Chestfield & Swalecliffe	d			07 02		07 12					07 28				07 36				07 49				08 06		
Whitstable	d			07 06		07 16				07 24	07 31				07 39				07 53				08 09		
Dover Priory [4]	d				06 39									07 05								07 35			
Kearsney	d				06 43									07 09								07 39			
Shepherds Well	d				06 48									07 14								07 44			
Snowdown	d				06 52									07 18								07 48			
Aylesham	d				06 54									07 20								07 50			
Adisham	d				06 57									07 23								07 53			
Bekesbourne	d				07 01									07 27								08 02			
Canterbury East [4]	d				07 06									07 33								08 11			
Selling	d				07 15									07 42											
Faversham [2]	a			07 14	07 20	07 24				07 32	07 39			07 46	07 48				08 01			08 16	08 18		
	d			07 16		07 25				07 33	07 40			07 52			07 58		08 03			08 22			
Teynham	d			07 22										07 58											
Sheerness-on-Sea	d						07 16					07 35								08 07					
Queenborough	d						07 22					07 39								08 11					
Swale	d						07 26					07 43								08 15					
Kemsley	d						07 29					07 47								08 19					
Sittingbourne [4]	a			07 26		07 32	07 34			07 40	07 47	07 52		08 02			08 06		08 10	08 25		08 29			
	d			07 27		07 33				07 41	07 48			08 03			08 07		08 11			08 30			
Newington	d			07 32							07 54											08 35			
Rainham (Kent)	d			07 37		07 41				07 50	07 59			08 10			08 15		08 19			08 40			
Gillingham (Kent) [4]	d	07 33	07 38	07 42		07 46			07 50	07 55	08 04		08 08	08 15			08 20		08 24		08 32	08 45			
Chatham [4]	d	07 37	07 42	07 46		07 50			07 54	08 00	08 08		08 12	08 20			08 24		08 28		08 36	08 50			
Rochester [4]	d	07 40	07 44						07 56	08 03	08 11		08 14	08 22			08 27		08 31		08 39	08 52			
Strood [4]	a		07 49										08 19				08 31								
Gravesend [4]	a		08 01										08 31				08 42								
Greenhithe for Bluewater	a		08 07										08 42												
Dartford [4]	a		08 12										08 49												
London Bridge [4] ⊖	a		08 45			08 31					08 49		09 23						09 09						
London Cannon Street [4] ⊖	a					08 38					08 57								09 18						
London Waterloo (East) [4] ⊖	a		08 50										09 28												
London Charing Cross [4] ⊖	a		08 56										09 34												
Sole Street	d								08 07												08 49				
Meopham	d	07 51							08 09					08 33							08 52	09 03			
Longfield	d	07 55							08 13					08 37							08 56	09 07			
Farningham Road	d								08 17												08 59				
Swanley [4]	a	08 01							08 22												09 04				
St Mary Cray	a	08 06							08 26												09 09				
Bromley South [4]	a	08 12		08 15					08 33					08 50							09 15	09 20			
London Victoria [15] ⊖	a	08 42		08 39					09 00					09 09							09 38	09 43			
Elephant & Castle ⊖	a															08d45									09d02
London Blackfriars [3] ⊖	a															08 50									09 06
City Thameslink	a															08 52									09 08
Farringdon	a															08 56									09 12
Ebbsfleet International	a									08 17							08 46								
Stratford International ⊖	a									08 30							09 00								
St Pancras International	a									08 37						09 00	09 07								09 16

A from Bromley South to Bedford
B from Faversham
C from Margate
D from Kent House to Bedford

For further services to St Pancras International, Blackfriars and Elephant & Castle and onwards to Bromley South, St Mary Cray and Swanley please see table 52

Table 212R

Mondays to Fridays

9 December to 16 May

Ramsgate, Dover, Sheerness-on-Sea and Medway - London

Network Diagram - see first Page of Table 212

		SE	SE	SE	SE	SE	SE	SE	SE	SE	SE	SE	SE	SE	SE	SE	SE	SE	SE	SE	SE	SE
						1	1				1	1	1					1	1			
		A				B	C					B	C					B	C			
						⊥	⊥					⊥	⊥					⊥	⊥			
Ramsgate 4	d						08 05						08 40	08 59					09 05			
Dumpton Park	d						08 08												09 08			
Broadstairs	d						08 11						08 45	09 05					09 11			
Margate 4	d						08 16						08 50	09a10					09 16			
Westgate-on-Sea	d						08 20												09 20			
Birchington-on-Sea	d						08 24						08 55						09 24			
Herne Bay	d						08 33						09 04						09 33			
Chestfield & Swalecliffe	d						08 36												09 36			
Whitstable	d						08 39						09 09						09 39			
Dover Priory 4	d					08 05						08 45						09 05				
Kearsney	d					08 09												09 09				
Shepherds Well	d					08 14												09 14				
Snowdown	d					08 18												09 18				
Aylesham	d					08 20												09 20				
Adisham	d					08 23												09 23				
Bekesbourne	d					08 27												09 27				
Canterbury East 4	d					08 32						09 02						09 32				
Selling	d					08 41												09 41				
Faversham 2	a					08 46	08 48					09 14	09 18					09 46	09 48			
	d		08 28				08 52	08 58					09 22		09 28				09 52	09 58		
Teynham	d						08 58												09 58			
Sheerness-on-Sea	d			08 36					09 02							09 32					10 02	
Queenborough	d			08 40					09 06							09 36					10 06	
Swale	d			08 44					09 10							09 40					10 10	
Kemsley	d			08 48					09 14							09 44					10 14	
Sittingbourne 4	a		08 36	08 56			09 02	09 06	09 19				09 29		09 36	09 49			10 02	10 06	10 19	
	d		08 37				09 03	09 07					09 30		09 37				10 03	10 07		
Newington	d												09 35									
Rainham (Kent)	d		08 45				09 10	09 15					09 40		09 45				10 10	10 15		
Gillingham (Kent) 4	d		08 50		08 54		09 15	09 20		09 24	09 32		09 45		09 50		09 54		10 15	10 20		10 24
Chatham 4	d		08 54		08 58		09 20	09 24		09 28	09 36		09 50		09 54		09 58		10 20	10 24		10 28
Rochester 4	d		08 57		09 00		09 22	09 27		09 30	09 39		09 52		09 57		10 00		10 22	10 27		10 30
Strood 4	a		09 01		09 05			09 31		09 35					10 01		10 05			10 31		10 35
Gravesend 4	a		09 12		09 17			09 42		09 47					10 12		10 17			10 42		10 47
Greenhithe for Bluewater	a				09 23					09 53							10 23					10 53
Dartford 4	a				09 28					09 58							10 28					10 58
London Bridge 4 ⊖	a				10 05					10 35							11 05					11 35
London Cannon Street 4 ⊖	a																					
London Waterloo (East) 4 ⊖	a				10 09					10 39							11 09					11 39
London Charing Cross 4 ⊖	a				10 13					10 43							11 13					11 43
Sole Street	d										09 49											
Meopham	d						09 33				09 52		10 03						10 33			
Longfield	d						09 37				09 56		10 07						10 37			
Farningham Road	d										09 59											
Swanley 4	a										10 04											
St Mary Cray	a										10 09											
Bromley South 4	a						09 50				10 15		10 20						10 50			
London Victoria 15 ⊖	a						10 07				10 36		10 38						11 07			
Elephant & Castle ⊖	a	09d14																				
London Blackfriars 3 ⊖	a	09 18																				
City Thameslink	a	09 20																				
Farringdon	a	09 24																				
Ebbsfleet International	a		09 16					09 46							10 16					10 46		
Stratford International ⊖	a		09 29					10 00							10 29					10 59		
St Pancras International	a	09 28	09 36					10 07							10 36					11 06		

A from Bromley South to Luton

B ⊥ from Faversham

C ⊥ from Margate

For further services to St Pancras International, Blackfriars and Elephant & Castle and onwards to Bromley South, St Mary Cray and Swanley please see table 52

Table 212R

Mondays to Fridays

9 December to 16 May

Ramsgate, Dover, Sheerness-on-Sea and Medway - London

Network Diagram - see first Page of Table 212

		SE [1]	SE [1] A 🛒	SE [1] B 🛒	SE	SE	SE	SE	SE [1] A 🛒	SE [1] B 🛒		SE	SE	SE	SE [1]	SE [1] A 🛒	SE [1] B 🛒	SE	SE	SE		SE	SE [1] A 🛒	SE [1] B 🛒	SE
Ramsgate [4]	d			09 40	09 59					10 05							10 40	10 59						11 05	
Dumpton Park	d									10 08														11 08	
Broadstairs	d			09 45	10 05					10 11							10 45	11 05						11 11	
Margate [4]	d			09 50	10a10					10 16							10 50	11a10						11 16	
Westgate-on-Sea	d									10 20														11 20	
Birchington-on-Sea	d			09 55						10 24							10 55							11 24	
Herne Bay	d			10 04						10 33							11 04							11 33	
Chestfield & Swalecliffe	d									10 36														11 36	
Whitstable	d			10 09						10 39							11 09							11 39	
Dover Priory [4]	d		09 45						10 05							10 45							11 05		
Kearsney	d								10 09														11 09		
Shepherds Well	d								10 14														11 14		
Snowdown	d								10 18														11 18		
Aylesham	d								10 20														11 20		
Adisham	d								10 23														11 23		
Bekesbourne	d								10 27														11 27		
Canterbury East [4]	d		10 02						10 32							11 02							11 32		
Selling	d								10 41														11 41		
Faversham [2]	a		10 14	10 18					10 46	10 48						11 14	11 18						11 46	11 48	
	d		10 22			10 28			10 52			10 58				11 22			11 28				11 52		11 58
Teynham	d								10 58														11 58		
Sheerness-on-Sea	d						10 32						11 02							11 32					
Queenborough	d						10 36						11 06							11 36					
Swale	d						10 40						11 10							11 40					
Kemsley	d						10 44						11 14							11 44					
Sittingbourne [4]	a			10 29		10 36	10 49			11 02		11 06	11 19				11 29		11 36	11 49				12 02	12 06
	d			10 30		10 37				11 03		11 07					11 30		11 37					12 03	12 07
Newington	d			10 35													11 35								
Rainham (Kent)	d			10 40		10 45				11 10		11 15					11 40		11 45					12 10	12 15
Gillingham (Kent) [4]	d	10 32		10 45		10 50		10 54		11 15		11 20		11 24	11 32		11 45		11 50			11 54		12 15	12 20
Chatham [4]	d	10 36		10 50		10 54		10 58		11 20		11 24		11 28	11 36		11 50		11 54			11 58		12 20	12 24
Rochester [4]	d	10 39		10 52		10 57		11 00		11 22		11 27		11 30	11 39		11 52		11 57			12 00		12 22	12 27
Strood [4]	a					11 01		11 05				11 31		11 35					12 01			12 05			12 31
Gravesend [4]	a					11 12		11 17				11 42		11 47					12 12			12 17			12 42
Greenhithe for Bluewater	a							11 23						11 53								12 23			
Dartford [4]	a							11 28						11 58								12 28			
London Bridge [4] ⊖	a							12 05						12 35								13 05			
London Cannon Street [4] ⊖	a																								
London Waterloo (East) [4] ⊖	a							12 09						12 39								13 09			
London Charing Cross [4] ⊖	a							12 13						12 43								13 13			
Sole Street	d	10 49													11 49										
Meopham	d	10 52		11 03						11 33					11 52		12 03							12 33	
Longfield	d	10 56		11 07						11 37					11 56		12 07							12 37	
Farningham Road	d	10 59													11 59										
Swanley [4]	a	11 04													12 04										
St Mary Cray	a	11 09													12 09										
Bromley South [4]	a	11 15		11 20						11 50					12 15		12 20							12 50	
London Victoria [15] ⊖	a	11 36		11 38						12 07					12 36		12 37							13 07	
Elephant & Castle ⊖	a																								
London Blackfriars [3] ⊖	a																								
City Thameslink	a																								
Farringdon	a																								
Ebbsfleet International	a					11 16						11 46							12 16						12 46
Stratford International ⊖	a					11 29						11 59							12 30						13 00
St Pancras International	a					11 36						12 06							12 37						13 07

A 🛒 from Faversham

B 🛒 from Margate

For further services to St Pancras International, Blackfriars and Elephant & Castle and onwards to Bromley South, St Mary Cray and Swanley please see table 52

Table 212R

Mondays to Fridays

9 December to 16 May

Ramsgate, Dover, Sheerness-on-Sea and Medway - London

Network Diagram - see first Page of Table 212

		SE	SE	SE	SE	SE	SE	SE	SE	SE	SE	SE	SE	SE	SE	SE	SE	SE	SE	SE	SE	SE
				1	1	1					1	1				1	1	1				
					A	B					A	B					A	B				
					🛒	🛒					🛒	🛒					🛒	🛒				
Ramsgate 4	d					11 40	11 59					12 05						12 40	12 59			
Dumpton Park	d											12 08										
Broadstairs	d					11 45	12 05					12 11						12 45	13 05			
Margate 4	d					11 50	12a10					12 16						12 50	13a10			
Westgate-on-Sea	d											12 20										
Birchington-on-Sea	d					11 55						12 24						12 55				
Herne Bay	d					12 04						12 33						13 04				
Chestfield & Swalecliffe	d											12 36										
Whitstable	d					12 09						12 39						13 09				
Dover Priory 4	d				11 45						12 05						12 45					
Kearsney	d										12 09											
Shepherds Well	d										12 14											
Snowdown	d										12 18											
Aylesham	d										12 20											
Adisham	d										12 23											
Bekesbourne	d										12 27											
Canterbury East 4	d				12 02						12 32						13 02					
Selling	d										12 41											
Faversham 2	a				12 14	12 18					12 46	12 48					13 14	13 18				
	d				12 22			12 28			12 52		12 58				13 22			13 28		
Teynham	d										12 58											
Sheerness-on-Sea	d	12 02							12 32					13 02							13 32	
Queenborough	d	12 06							12 36					13 06							13 36	
Swale	d	12 10							12 40					13 10							13 40	
Kemsley	d	12 14							12 44					13 14							13 44	
Sittingbourne 4	a	12 19			12 29			12 36	12 49		13 02		13 06	13 19			13 29			13 36	13 49	
	d				12 30			12 37			13 03		13 07				13 30			13 37		
Newington	d				12 35												13 35					
Rainham (Kent)	d				12 40			12 45			13 10		13 15				13 40			13 45		
Gillingham (Kent) 4	d		12 24	12 32	12 45			12 50		12 54	13 15		13 20		13 24	13 32	13 45			13 50		13 54
Chatham 4	d		12 28	12 36	12 50			12 54		12 58	13 20		13 24		13 28	13 36	13 50			13 54		13 58
Rochester 4	d		12 30	12 39	12 52			12 57		13 00	13 22		13 27		13 30	13 39	13 52			13 57		14 00
Strood 4	a		12 35					13 01		13 05			13 31		13 35					14 01		14 05
Gravesend 4	a		12 47					13 12		13 17			13 42		13 47					14 12		14 17
Greenhithe for Bluewater	a		12 53							13 23					13 53							14 23
Dartford 4	a		12 58							13 28					13 58							14 28
London Bridge 4 ⊖	a		13 35							14 05					14 35							15 05
London Cannon Street 4 ⊖	a																					
London Waterloo (East) 4 ⊖	a		13 39							14 09					14 39							15 09
London Charing Cross 4 ⊖	a		13 43							14 13					14 43							15 13
Sole Street	d			12 49												13 49						
Meopham	d			12 52	13 03						13 33					13 52	14 03					
Longfield	d			12 56	13 07						13 37					13 56	14 07					
Farningham Road	d			12 59												13 59						
Swanley 4	a			13 04												14 04						
St Mary Cray	a			13 09												14 09						
Bromley South 4	a			13 15	13 20						13 50					14 15	14 20					
London Victoria 15 ⊖	a			13 36	13 37						14 07					14 36	14 37					
Elephant & Castle ⊖	a																					
London Blackfriars 3 ⊖	a																					
City Thameslink	a																					
Farringdon	a																					
Ebbsfleet International	a							13 16					13 46							14 16		
Stratford International ⊖	a							13 30					14 02							14 29		
St Pancras International	a							13 37					14 09							14 36		

A 🛒 from Faversham

B 🛒 from Margate

For further services to St Pancras International, Blackfriars and Elephant & Castle and onwards to Bromley South, St Mary Cray and Swanley please see table 52

Table 212R

Mondays to Fridays

9 December to 16 May

Ramsgate, Dover, Sheerness-on-Sea and Medway - London

Network Diagram - see first Page of Table 212

		SE [1] A 🛒	SE [1] B 🛒	SE	SE	SE	SE [1]	SE [1] A 🛒	SE [1] B 🛒	SE	SE	SE	SE	SE [1] A 🛒	SE [1] B 🛒	SE	SE	SE	SE	SE [1] A 🛒	SE [1] B 🛒	SE
Ramsgate [4]	d		13 05						13 40	13 59					14 05						14 40	14 59
Dumpton Park	d		13 08												14 08							
Broadstairs	d		13 11						13 45	14 05					14 11						14 45	15 05
Margate [4]	d		13 16						13 50	14a10					14 16						14 50	15a10
Westgate-on-Sea	d		13 20												14 20							
Birchington-on-Sea	d		13 24						13 55						14 24						14 55	
Herne Bay	d		13 33						14 04						14 33						15 04	
Chestfield & Swalecliffe	d		13 36												14 36							
Whitstable	d		13 39						14 09						14 39						15 09	
Dover Priory [4]	d	13 05						13 45						14 05						14 45		
Kearsney	d	13 09												14 09								
Shepherds Well	d	13 14												14 14								
Snowdown	d	13 18												14 18								
Aylesham	d	13 20												14 20								
Adisham	d	13 23												14 23								
Bekesbourne	d	13 27												14 27								
Canterbury East [4]	d	13 32						14 02						14 32						15 02		
Selling	d	13 41												14 41								
Faversham [2]	a	13 46	13 48					14 14	14 18					14 46	14 48					15 14	15 18	
	d	13 52		13 58				14 22			14 28			14 52		14 58				15 22		
Teynham	d	13 58												14 58								
Sheerness-on-Sea	d				14 02							14 32					15 02					
Queenborough	d				14 06							14 36					15 06					
Swale	d				14 10							14 40					15 10					
Kemsley	d				14 14							14 44					15 14					
Sittingbourne [4]	a	14 02		14 06	14 19			14 29			14 36	14 49		15 02		15 06	15 19			15 29		
	d	14 03		14 07				14 30			14 37			15 03		15 07				15 30		
Newington	d							14 35												15 35		
Rainham (Kent)	d	14 10		14 15				14 40			14 45			15 10		15 15				15 40		
Gillingham (Kent) [4]	d	14 15		14 20		14 24	14 32	14 45			14 50		14 54	15 15		15 20		15 24	15 32	15 45		
Chatham [4]	d	14 20		14 24		14 28	14 36	14 50			14 54		14 58	15 20		15 24		15 28	15 36	15 50		
Rochester [4]	d	14 22		14 27		14 30	14 39	14 52			14 57		15 00	15 22		15 27		15 30	15 39	15 52		
Strood [4]	a			14 31		14 35					15 01		15 05			15 31		15 35				
Gravesend [4]	a			14 42		14 47					15 12		15 17			15 42		15 47				
Greenhithe for Bluewater	a					14 53							15 23					15 53				
Dartford [4]	a					14 58							15 28					15 58				
London Bridge [4] ⊖	a					15 35							16 05					16 35				
London Cannon Street [4] ⊖	a																					
London Waterloo (East) [4] ⊖	a					15 39							16 09					16 39				
London Charing Cross [4] ⊖	a					15 43							16 13					16 44				
Sole Street	d						14 49												15 49			
Meopham	d	14 33					14 52	15 03						15 33					15 52	16 03		
Longfield	d	14 37					14 56	15 07						15 37					15 56	16 07		
Farningham Road	d						14 59												15 59			
Swanley [4]	a						15 04												16 04			
St Mary Cray	a						15 09												16 09			
Bromley South [4]	a	14 50					15 15	15 20						15 50					16 15	16 20		
London Victoria [15] ⊖	a	15 07					15 36	15 37						16 07					16 36	16 38		
Elephant & Castle ⊖	a																					
London Blackfriars [3] ⊖	a																					
City Thameslink	a																					
Farringdon	a																					
Ebbsfleet International	a			14 46							15 16					15 46						
Stratford International ⊖	a			14 59							15 29					16 02						
St Pancras International	a			15 06							15 36					16 09						

A 🛒 from Faversham

B 🛒 from Margate

For further services to St Pancras International, Blackfriars and Elephant & Castle and onwards to Bromley South, St Mary Cray and Swanley please see table 52

Table 212R

Mondays to Fridays

9 December to 16 May

Ramsgate, Dover, Sheerness-on-Sea and Medway - London

Network Diagram - see first Page of Table 212

		SE	SE	SE	SE [1] A [trolley]	SE [1] B [trolley]	SE	SE	SE		SE [1]	SE [1] A [trolley]	SE [1] B [trolley]	SE	SE	SE	SE	SE [1]	SE [1] A [trolley]	SE [1] B [trolley]		SE [1]	SE	SE	SE
Ramsgate [4]	d					15 05							15 35		15 59					16 05					
Dumpton Park	d					15 08							15 38							16 08					
Broadstairs	d					15 11							15 41		16 05					16 11					
Margate [4]	d					15 16							15 46		16a10					16 16					
Westgate-on-Sea	d					15 20							15 50							16 20					
Birchington-on-Sea	d					15 24							15 54							16 24					
Herne Bay	d					15 33							16 03							16 33					
Chestfield & Swalecliffe	d					15 36							16 06							16 36					
Whitstable	d					15 39							16 09							16 39					
Dover Priory [4]	d				15 05							15 39							16 05						
Kearsney	d				15 09							15 43							16 09						
Shepherds Well	d				15 14							15 48							16 14						
Snowdown	d				15 18														16 18						
Aylesham	d				15 20							15 52							16 20						
Adisham	d				15 23							15 55							16 23						
Bekesbourne	d				15 27														16 27						
Canterbury East [4]	d				15 32							16 02							16 32						
Selling	d				15 41							16 11							16 41						
Faversham [2]	a				15 46	15 48						16 16	16 18						16 46	16 48					
	d	15 28				15 52	15 58						16 22	16 28						16 52			16 58		
Teynham	d					15 58														16 58					
Sheerness-on-Sea	d		15 32					16 02								16 32								17 02	
Queenborough	d		15 36					16 06								16 36								17 06	
Swale	d		15 40					16 10								16 40								17 10	
Kemsley	d		15 44					16 14								16 44								17 14	
Sittingbourne [4]	a	15 36	15 49			16 02	16 06	16 19					16 29	16 36		16 49				17 02			17 06	17 19	
	d	15 37				16 03	16 07						16 30	16 37						17 03			17 07		
Newington	d												16 35												
Rainham (Kent)	d	15 45				16 10	16 15						16 40	16 45						17 10			17 15		
Gillingham (Kent) [4]	d	15 50		15 54		16 15	16 20		16 24		16 32		16 45	16 50			16 54	17 02		17 15			17 20		17 24
Chatham [4]	d	15 54		15 58		16 20	16 24		16 28		16 36		16 50	16 54			16 58	17 06		17 20			17 24		17 28
Rochester [4]	d	15 57		16 00		16 22	16 27		16 30		16 39		16 52	16 57			17 00	17 09		17 22			17 27		17 30
Strood [4]	a	16 01		16 05			16 31		16 35					17 01			17 05						17 31		17 35
Gravesend [4]	a	16 12		16 17			16 42		16 47					17 12			17 17						17 42		17 47
Greenhithe for Bluewater	a			16 23					16 53								17 23								17 53
Dartford [4]	a			16 28					16 58								17 28								17 58
London Bridge [4] ⊖	a			17 07					17 35								18 04								18 35
London Cannon Street [4] ⊖	a			17 11																					
London Waterloo (East) [4] ⊖	a								17 40								18 08								18 41
London Charing Cross [4] ⊖	a								17 44								18 12								18 45
Sole Street	d										16 49							17 19							
Meopham	d					16 33					16 52		17 03					17 22		17 33					
Longfield	d					16 37					16 56		17 07					17 26		17 37					
Farningham Road	d										16 59							17 29							
Swanley [4]	a										17 04							17 34							
St Mary Cray	a										17 09							17 39							
Bromley South [4]	a					16 50					17 15		17 20					17 45		17 50					
London Victoria [15] ⊖	a					17 07					17 37		17 37					18 08		18 07					
Elephant & Castle ⊖	a																					17d52			
London Blackfriars [3] ⊖	a																					17 55			
City Thameslink	a																					17 58			
Farringdon	a																					18 01			
Ebbsfleet International	a	16 16					16 46							17 16									17 46		
Stratford International ⊖	a	16 29					17 02							17 29									17 59		
St Pancras International	a	16 36					17 09							17 36								18 05	18 07		

A [trolley] from Faversham

B [trolley] from Margate

For further services to St Pancras International, Blackfriars and Elephant & Castle and onwards to Bromley South, St Mary Cray and Swanley please see table 52

Table 212R

Mondays to Fridays

9 December to 16 May

Ramsgate, Dover, Sheerness-on-Sea and Medway - London

Network Diagram - see first Page of Table 212

		SE [1]	SE [1] A 🛒	SE [1] B 🛒	SE	SE		SE	SE	SE [1]	SE [1]	SE	SE	SE	SE	SE [1]	SE [1]		SE	SE	SE	SE	SE [1]	SE [1]	SE
Ramsgate [4]	d			16 35		16 59					17 05						17 35			18 00				18 05	
Dumpton Park	d			16 38							17 08						17 38							18 08	
Broadstairs	d			16 41		17 05					17 11						17 41			18 05				18 11	
Margate [4]	d			16 46		17a10					17 16						17 46			18a12				18 16	
Westgate-on-Sea	d			16 50							17 20						17 50							18 20	
Birchington-on-Sea	d			16 54							17 24						17 54							18 24	
Herne Bay	d			17 03							17 33						18 03							18 33	
Chestfield & Swalecliffe	d			17 06							17 36						18 06							18 36	
Whitstable	d			17 09							17 39						18 09							18 39	
Dover Priory [4]	d		16 39							17 05						17 39							18 05		
Kearsney	d		16 43							17 09						17 43							18 09		
Shepherds Well	d		16 48							17 14						17 48							18 14		
Snowdown	d									17 18													18 18		
Aylesham	d		16 52							17 20						17 52							18 20		
Adisham	d		16 55							17 23						17 55							18 23		
Bekesbourne	d									17 27													18 27		
Canterbury East [4]	d		17 02							17 32						18 02							18 32		
Selling	d		17 11							17 41						18 11							18 41		
Faversham [2]	a		17 16	17 18						17 46	17 48					18 16	18 18						18 46	18 48	
	d		17 22		17 28					17 52		17 58				18 22			18 28				18 52		18 58
Teynham	d									17 58													18 58		
Sheerness-on-Sea	d							17 32					18 02								18 37				
Queenborough	d							17 36					18 06								18 41				
Swale	d							17 40					18 10								18 45				
Kemsley	d							17 44					18 14								18 49				
Sittingbourne [4]	a		17 29		17 36			17 52		18 02		18 06	18 19			18 29			18 36		18 54		19 02		19 06
	d		17 30		17 37					18 03		18 07				18 30			18 37				19 03		19 07
Newington	d		17 35													18 35									
Rainham (Kent)	d		17 40		17 45					18 10		18 15				18 40			18 45				19 10		19 15
Gillingham (Kent) [4]	d	17 32	17 45		17 50				17 54	18 15		18 20		18 24	18 32	18 45			18 50			18 54	19 15		19 20
Chatham [4]	d	17 36	17 50		17 54				17 58	18 20		18 24		18 28	18 36	18 50			18 54			18 58	19 20		19 24
Rochester [4]	d	17 39	17 52		17 57				18 00	18 22		18 27		18 30	18 39	18 52			18 57			19 00	19 22		19 27
Strood [4]	a				18 02				18 05			18 31		18 35					19 01			19 05			19 31
Gravesend [4]	a				18 13				18 18			18 42		18 47					19 12			19 17			19 42
Greenhithe for Bluewater	a								18 23					18 53								19 23			
Dartford [4]	a								18 28					18 58								19 28			
London Bridge [4] ⊖	a								19 05					19 35								20 06			
London Cannon Street [4] ⊖	a																								
London Waterloo (East) [4] ⊖	a								19 09					19 39								20 11			
London Charing Cross [4] ⊖	a								19 13					19 43								20 14			
Sole Street	d	17 49													18 49										
Meopham	d	17 52	18 03							18 33					18 52	19 03							19 33		
Longfield	d	17 56	18 07							18 37					18 56	19 07							19 37		
Farningham Road	d	17 59													18 59										
Swanley [4]	a	18 04													19 04										
St Mary Cray	a	18 09													19 09										
Bromley South [4]	a	18 15	18 20							18 50					19 15	19 20							19 50		
London Victoria [15] ⊖	a	18 36	18 37							19 07					19 36	19 37							20 07		
Elephant & Castle ⊖	a																								
London Blackfriars [3] ⊖	a																								
City Thameslink	a																								
Farringdon	a																								
Ebbsfleet International	a				18 18							18 46							19 16						19 46
Stratford International ⊖	a				18 30							19 02							19 29						20 00
St Pancras International	a				18 37							19 09							19 36						20 07

A 🛒 from Faversham

B 🛒 from Margate

For further services to St Pancras International, Blackfriars and Elephant & Castle and onwards to Bromley South, St Mary Cray and Swanley please see table 52

Table 212R

Mondays to Fridays

9 December to 16 May

Ramsgate, Dover, Sheerness-on-Sea and Medway - London

Network Diagram - see first Page of Table 212

		SE	SE		SE	SE	SE	SE	SE	SE	SE	SE	SE		SE	SE	SE	SE	SE	SE	SE	SE	SE		SE
					1	1	1					1	1						1	1					
																				A					
Ramsgate 4	d	18 30					18 35		19 00				19 05							19 25		19 32	20 00		
Dumpton Park	d						18 38						19 08							19 28					
Broadstairs	d	18 35					18 41		19 05				19 11							19 31		19 37	20 05		
Margate 4	d	18a42					18 46		19a12				19 16							19 38		19a42	20a12		
Westgate-on-Sea	d						18 50						19 20							19 41					
Birchington-on-Sea	d						18 54						19 24							19 45					
Herne Bay	d						19 03						19 33							19 54					
Chestfield & Swalecliffe	d						19 06						19 36							19 58					
Whitstable	d						19 09						19 39							20 01					
Dover Priory 4	d					18 39						19 05							19 40						
Kearsney	d					18 43						19 09													
Shepherds Well	d					18 48						19 14													
Snowdown	d											19 18													
Aylesham	d					18 52						19 20													
Adisham	d					18 55						19 23													
Bekesbourne	d											19 27													
Canterbury East 4	d					19 02						19 32							19 57						
Selling	d					19 11						19 41													
Faversham 2	a					19 16	19 18					19 46	19 48						20 08	20 10					
	d						19 22	19 28					19 52		19 58					20 14	20 28				
Teynham	d												19 58												
Sheerness-on-Sea	d									19 16						19 46	20 02								20 32
Queenborough	d									19 23						19 53	20 06								20 36
Swale	d									19 27						19 57	20 10								20 40
Kemsley	d									19 31						20 01	20 14								20 44
Sittingbourne 4	a						19 29	19 36		19 36			20 02		20 06	20 06	20 19			20 21	20 36				20 49
	d						19 30	19 37					20 03		20 07					20 22	20 37				
Newington	d						19 35													20 27					
Rainham (Kent)	d						19 40	19 45					20 10		20 15					20 31	20 45				
Gillingham (Kent) 4	d		19 24				19 45	19 50			19 54		20 15		20 20			20 24		20 36	20 50				
Chatham 4	d		19 28				19 50	19 54			19 58		20 20		20 24			20 28		20 41	20 54				
Rochester 4	d		19 30		19 39		19 52	19 57			20 00		20 22		20 27			20 30		20 43	20 57				
Strood 4	a		19 35					20 01			20 05				20 31			20 35			21 01				
Gravesend 4	a		19 47					20 12			20 17				20 42			20 47			21 12				
Greenhithe for Bluewater	a		19 53								20 23							20 53							
Dartford 4	a		19 58								20 28							20 58							
London Bridge 4 ⊖	a		20 36								21 06							21 36							
London Cannon Street 4 ⊖	a																								
London Waterloo (East) 4 ⊖	a		20 40								21 10							21 41							
London Charing Cross 4 ⊖	a		20 44								21 14							21 44							
Sole Street	d				19 49															20 54					
Meopham	d				19 52		20 03						20 33							20 56					
Longfield	d				19 56		20 07						20 37							21 00					
Farningham Road	d				19 59															21 04					
Swanley 4	a				20 04															21 09					
St Mary Cray	a				20 09															21 14					
Bromley South 4	a				20 15		20 20						20 50							21 20					
London Victoria 15 ⊖	a				20 36		20 38						21 07							21 37					
Elephant & Castle ⊖	a																								
London Blackfriars 3 ⊖	a																								
City Thameslink	a																								
Farringdon	a																								
Ebbsfleet International	a							20 16							20 46						21 16				
Stratford International ⊖	a							20 29							21 02						21 29				
St Pancras International	a							20 36							21 09						21 36				

A 1 from Faversham

For further services to St Pancras International, Blackfriars and Elephant & Castle and onwards to Bromley South, St Mary Cray and Swanley please see table 52

Table 212R

Mondays to Fridays

9 December to 16 May

Ramsgate, Dover, Sheerness-on-Sea and Medway - London

Network Diagram - see first Page of Table 212

		SE	SE ■1	SE ■1	SE	SE ■1	SE	SE	SE		SE	SE ■1	SE	SE	SE	SE ■1	SE ■1	SE	SE		SE	SE	SE ■1	SE ■1	SE
Ramsgate ■4	d			20 05		20 20	20 35	21 01									21 05		22 00						
Dumpton Park	d			20 08													21 08								
Broadstairs	d			20 11		20 25	20 40	21 06									21 11		22 05						
Margate ■4	d			20 16		20a34	20a45	21a11									21 16		22a10						
Westgate-on-Sea	d			20 20													21 20								
Birchington-on-Sea	d			20 24													21 24								
Herne Bay	d			20 33													21 33								
Chestfield & Swalecliffe	d			20 36													21 36								
Whitstable	d			20 39													21 39								
Dover Priory ■4	d		20 05									20 45				21 05							21 45	22 05	
Kearsney	d		20 09													21 09								22 09	
Shepherds Well	d		20 14													21 14								22 14	
Snowdown	d		20 18													21 18								22 18	
Aylesham	d		20 20													21 20								22 20	
Adisham	d		20 23													21 23								22 23	
Bekesbourne	d		20 27													21 27								22 27	
Canterbury East ■4	d		20 32									21 02				21 32							22 02	22 32	
Selling	d		20 41													21 41								22 41	
Faversham ■2	a		20 46	20 48								21 13				21 46	21 48						22 13	22 46	
	d		20 52		20 58							21 14	21 28			21 52		21 58					22 14		
Teynham	d		20 58													21 58									
Sheerness-on-Sea	d								21 02						21 32						22 02				
Queenborough	d								21 06						21 36						22 06				
Swale	d								21 10						21 40						22 10				
Kemsley	d								21 14						21 44						22 14				
Sittingbourne ■4	a		21 02		21 06				21 19			21 21	21 36			22 02		22 06			22 19		22 21		
	d		21 03		21 07							21 22	21 37			22 03		22 07					22 22		
Newington	d											21 27			21 51								22 27		
Rainham (Kent)	d		21 10		21 15							21 31	21 45		21 55	22 10		22 15					22 31		
Gillingham (Kent) ■4	d	20 54	21 15		21 20						21 24	21 36	21 50	21 54	22a02	22 15		22 20				22 24	22 36		22 54
Chatham ■4	d	20 58	21 20		21 24						21 28	21 41	21 54	21 58		22 20		22 24				22 28	22 41		22 58
Rochester ■4	d	21 00	21 22		21 27						21 30	21 43	21 57	22 00		22 22		22 27				22 30	22 43		23 00
Strood ■4	a	21 05			21 31						21 35		22 01	22 05				22 31				22 35			23 05
Gravesend ■4	a	21 17			21 42						21 47		22 12	22 17				22 42				22 47			23 17
Greenhithe for Bluewater	a	21 23									21 53			22 23								22 53			23 23
Dartford ■4	a	21 28									21 58			22 28								22 58			23 28
London Bridge ■4 ⊖	a	22 05									22 35			23 05								23 35			
London Cannon Street ■4 ⊖	a																								
London Waterloo (East) ■4 ⊖	a	22 09									22 39			23 09								23 39			
London Charing Cross ■4 ⊖	a	22 13									22 43			23 13								23 43			
Sole Street	d											21 54											22 54		
Meopham	d		21 33									21 56				22 33							22 56		
Longfield	d		21 37									22 00				22 37							23 00		
Farningham Road	d											22 04											23 04		
Swanley ■4	a											22 09											23 09		
St Mary Cray	a											22 14											23 14		
Bromley South ■4	a		21 50									22 20				22 50							23 20		
London Victoria ■15 ⊖	a		22 07									22 37				23 07							23 37		
Elephant & Castle ⊖	a																								
London Blackfriars ■3 ⊖	a																								
City Thameslink	a																								
Farringdon	a																								
Ebbsfleet International	a				21 46								22 16					22 46							
Stratford International ⊖	a				22 00								22 29					22 59							
St Pancras International	a				22 07								22 36					23 06							

For further services to St Pancras International, Blackfriars and Elephant & Castle and onwards to Bromley South, St Mary Cray and Swanley please see table 52

Table 212R

Mondays to Fridays

9 December to 16 May

Ramsgate, Dover, Sheerness-on-Sea and Medway - London

Network Diagram - see first Page of Table 212

		SE [1]	SE	SE	SE [1]		SE [1]	SE [1]	SE
Ramsgate [4]	d	22 05	23 00					23 05	
Dumpton Park	d	22 08						23 08	
Broadstairs	d	22 11	23 05					23 11	
Margate [4]	d	22 16	23a10					23 16	
Westgate-on-Sea	d	22 20						23 20	
Birchington-on-Sea	d	22 24						23 24	
Herne Bay	d	22 33						23 33	
Chestfield & Swalecliffe	d	22 36						23 36	
Whitstable	d	22 39						23 39	
Dover Priory [4]	d				22 45		23 05		
Kearsney	d						23 09		
Shepherds Well	d						23 14		
Snowdown	d						23 18		
Aylesham	d						23 20		
Adisham	d						23 23		
Bekesbourne	d						23 27		
Canterbury East [4]	d				23 02		23 32		
Selling	d						23 41		
Faversham [2]	a	22 48			23 13		23 46	23 48	
	d	22 52			23 14			23 52	
Teynham	d	22 58						23 58	
Sheerness-on-Sea	d			23 02					23 53
Queenborough	d			23 06					23 57
Swale	d			23 10					00 01
Kemsley	d			23 14					00 05
Sittingbourne [4]	a	23 02		23 19	23 21			00 02	00 10
	d	23 03			23 22			00 03	
Newington	d				23 27			00 08	
Rainham (Kent)	d	23 10			23 31			00 12	
Gillingham (Kent) [4]	d	23 15			23 36			00a17	
Chatham [4]	d	23 20			23 41				
Rochester [4]	d	23 22			23 43				
Strood [4]	a								
Gravesend [4]	a								
Greenhithe for Bluewater	a								
Dartford [4]	a								
London Bridge [4] ⊖	a								
London Cannon Street [4] ⊖	a								
London Waterloo (East) [4] ⊖	a								
London Charing Cross [4] ⊖	a								
Sole Street	d				23 54				
Meopham	d	23 33			23 56				
Longfield	d	23 37			23 59				
Farningham Road	d				00 04				
Swanley [4]	a				00 09				
St Mary Cray	a				00 14				
Bromley South [4]	a	23 50			00 20				
London Victoria [15] ⊖	a	00 07			00 37				
Elephant & Castle ⊖	a								
London Blackfriars [3] ⊖	a								
City Thameslink	a								
Farringdon	a								
Ebbsfleet International	a								
Stratford International ⊖	a								
St Pancras International	a								

For further services to St Pancras International, Blackfriars and Elephant & Castle and onwards to Bromley South, St Mary Cray and Swanley please see table 52

Table 212R

Saturdays

14 December to 17 May

Ramsgate, Dover, Sheerness-on-Sea and Medway - London

Network Diagram - see first Page of Table 212

		SE	SE	SE	SE	SE	SE	SE	SE	SE	SE		SE	SE	SE	SE	SE	SE	SE	SE	SE		SE	SE	SE
		1			1		1			1	1			1	1	1				1	1				
		A		B																					
Ramsgate [4]	d						04 32				05 05					05 40					06 05				
Dumpton Park	d										05 08										06 08				
Broadstairs	d						04 37				05 11					05 45					06 11				
Margate [4]	d						04 42				05 16					05 50					06 16				
Westgate-on-Sea	d										05 20										06 20				
Birchington-on-Sea	d						04 47				05 24					05 55					06 24				
Herne Bay	d						04 56				05 33					06 04					06 33				
Chestfield & Swalecliffe	d										05 36										06 36				
Whitstable	d						05 01				05 39					06 09					06 39				
Dover Priory [4]	d									05 05					05 45					06 05					
Kearsney	d									05 09										06 09					
Shepherds Well	d									05 14										06 14					
Snowdown	d									05 18										06 18					
Aylesham	d									05 20										06 20					
Adisham	d									05 23										06 23					
Bekesbourne	d									05 27										06 27					
Canterbury East [4]	d									05 32					06 02					06 32					
Selling	d									05 41										06 41					
Faversham [2]	a						05 09			05 46	05 48				06 14	06 18				06 46	06 48				
	d						05 09	05 28		05 52					06 22		06 28			06 52			06 58		
Teynham	d									05 58										06 58					
Sheerness-on-Sea	d																	06 32						07 02	
Queenborough	d																	06 36						07 06	
Swale	d			00 01														06 40						07 10	
Kemsley	d			00 05														06 44						07 14	
Sittingbourne [4]	a			00 10			05 17	05 36		06 02					06 29		06 36	06 49		07 02			07 06	07 19	
	d	00 03					05 17	05 37		06 03					06 30		06 37			07 03			07 07		
Newington	d	00 08					05 23								06 35										
Rainham (Kent)	d	00 12					05 27	05 45		06 10					06 40		06 45			07 10			07 15		
Gillingham (Kent) [4]	d	00a17	04 48			05 18	05 32	05 50	05 54	06 15			06 24	06 32	06 45		06 50		06 54	07 15			07 20		07 24
Chatham [4]	d		04 52			05 22	05 36	05 54	05 58	06 20			06 28	06 36	06 50		06 54		06 58	07 20			07 24		07 28
Rochester [4]	d		04 54			05 24	05 39	05 57	06 00	06 22			06 30	06 39	06 52		06 57		07 00	07 22			07 27		07 30
Strood [4]	a		04 59			05 29		06 01	06 05				06 35				07 01		07 05				07 31		07 35
Gravesend [4]	a		05 11			05 41		06 12	06 17				06 47				07 12		07 17				07 42		07 47
Greenhithe for Bluewater	a		05 20			05 50			06 23				06 53						07 23						07 53
Dartford [4]	a		05 27			05 57			06 28				06 58						07 28						07 58
London Bridge [4] ⊖	a		06 05			06 35			07 05				07 35						08 05						08 35
London Cannon Street [4] ⊖	a																								
London Waterloo (East) [4] ⊖	a		06 09			06 39			07 09				07 39						08 09						08 39
London Charing Cross [4] ⊖	a		06 13			06 43			07 13				07 43						08 13						08 43
Sole Street	d						05 49							06 49											
Meopham	d						05 52			06 33				06 52	07 03					07 33					
Longfield	d						05 56			06 37				06 56	07 07					07 37					
Farningham Road	d				00 04		06 00							06 59											
Swanley [4]	a				00 09		06 05							07 04											
St Mary Cray	a				00 14		06 09							07 09											
Bromley South [4]	a				00 20		06 15			06 50				07 15	07 20					07 50					
London Victoria [15] ⊖	a				00 37		06 36			07 07				07 36	07 37					08 07					
Elephant & Castle ⊖	a																								
London Blackfriars [3] ⊖	a																								
City Thameslink	a																								
Farringdon	a																								
Ebbsfleet International	a							06 16									07 16						07 46		
Stratford International ⊖	a							06 29									07 29						07 59		
St Pancras International	a							06 36									07 36						08 06		

A from Ramsgate

B from Sheerness on Sea

For further services to St Pancras International, Blackfriars and Elephant & Castle and onwards to Bromley South, St Mary Cray and Swanley please see table 52

Table 212R

Saturdays

14 December to 17 May

Ramsgate, Dover, Sheerness-on-Sea and Medway - London

Network Diagram - see first Page of Table 212

		SE	SE	SE	SE	SE	SE		SE	SE	SE	SE	SE	SE	SE	SE	SE		SE	SE	SE	SE	SE	SE	SE
		1	1	1					1	1				1	1	1						1	1		
															A	B							B		
															Trolley	Trolley						Trolley	Trolley		
Ramsgate 4	d			06 40						07 05						07 40	07 59						08 05		
Dumpton Park	d									07 08													08 08		
Broadstairs	d			06 45						07 11						07 45	08 05						08 11		
Margate 4	d			06 50						07 16						07 50	08a10						08 16		
Westgate-on-Sea	d									07 20													08 20		
Birchington-on-Sea	d			06 55						07 24						07 55							08 24		
Herne Bay	d			07 04						07 33						08 04							08 33		
Chestfield & Swalecliffe	d									07 36													08 36		
Whitstable	d			07 09						07 39						08 09							08 39		
Dover Priory 4	d		06 45						07 05						07 45							08 05			
Kearsney	d								07 09													08 09			
Shepherds Well	d								07 14													08 14			
Snowdown	d								07 18													08 18			
Aylesham	d								07 20													08 20			
Adisham	d								07 23													08 23			
Bekesbourne	d								07 27													08 27			
Canterbury East 4	d		07 02						07 32						08 02							08 32			
Selling	d								07 41													08 41			
Faversham 2	a		07 14	07 18					07 46	07 48					08 14	08 18						08 46	08 48		
	d		07 22		07 28				07 52		07 58				08 22				08 28			08 52		08 58	
Teynham	d								07 58													08 58			
Sheerness-on-Sea	d					07 32						08 02								08 32					09 02
Queenborough	d					07 36						08 06								08 36					09 06
Swale	d					07 40						08 10								08 40					09 10
Kemsley	d					07 44						08 14								08 44					09 14
Sittingbourne 4	a		07 29		07 36	07 49			08 02		08 06	08 19			08 29				08 36	08 49		09 02		09 06	09 19
	d		07 30		07 37				08 03		08 07				08 30				08 37			09 03		09 07	
Newington	d		07 35												08 35										
Rainham (Kent)	d		07 40		07 45				08 10		08 15				08 40				08 45			09 10		09 15	
Gillingham (Kent) 4	d	07 32	07 45		07 50		07 54		08 15		08 20		08 24	08 32	08 45				08 50		08 54	09 15		09 20	
Chatham 4	d	07 36	07 50		07 54		07 58		08 20		08 24		08 28	08 36	08 50				08 54		08 58	09 20		09 24	
Rochester 4	d	07 39	07 52		07 57		08 00		08 22		08 27		08 30	08 39	08 52				08 57		09 00	09 22		09 27	
Strood 4	a				08 01		08 05				08 31		08 35						09 01		09 05			09 31	
Gravesend 4	a				08 12		08 17				08 42		08 47						09 12		09 17			09 42	
Greenhithe for Bluewater	a						08 23						08 53								09 23				
Dartford 4	a						08 28						08 58								09 28				
London Bridge 4 ⊖	a						09 05						09 35								10 05				
London Cannon Street 4 ⊖	a																								
London Waterloo (East) 4 ⊖	a						09 09						09 39								10 09				
London Charing Cross 4 ⊖	a						09 13						09 43								10 13				
Sole Street	d	07 49												08 49											
Meopham	d	07 52	08 03						08 33					08 52	09 03							09 33			
Longfield	d	07 56	08 07						08 37					08 56	09 07							09 37			
Farningham Road	d	07 59												08 59											
Swanley 4	a	08 04												09 04											
St Mary Cray	a	08 09												09 09											
Bromley South 4	a	08 15	08 20						08 50					09 15	09 20							09 50			
London Victoria 15 ⊖	a	08 36	08 37						09 07					09 36	09 37							10 07			
Elephant & Castle ⊖	a																								
London Blackfriars 3 ⊖	a																								
City Thameslink	a																								
Farringdon	a																								
Ebbsfleet International	a				08 16						08 46								09 16					09 46	
Stratford International ⊖	a				08 30						08 59								09 30					09 59	
St Pancras International	a				08 37						09 06								09 37					10 06	

A Trolley from Faversham

B Trolley from Margate

For further services to St Pancras International, Blackfriars and Elephant & Castle and onwards to Bromley South, St Mary Cray and Swanley please see table 52

Table 212R

Saturdays

14 December to 17 May

Ramsgate, Dover, Sheerness-on-Sea and Medway - London

Network Diagram - see first Page of Table 212

		SE	SE	SE	SE	SE	SE	SE	SE	SE	SE	SE	SE	SE	SE	SE	SE	SE	SE	SE	SE
			[1]	[1]	[1]					[1]	[1]				[1]	[1]	[1]				
					A						A						A				
				⛾	⛾					⛾	⛾					⛾	⛾				
Ramsgate [4]	d				08 40	08 59					09 05						09 40	09 59			
Dumpton Park	d										09 08										
Broadstairs	d				08 45	09 05					09 11						09 45	10 05			
Margate [4]	d				08 50	09a10					09 16						09 50	10a10			
Westgate-on-Sea	d										09 20										
Birchington-on-Sea	d				08 55						09 24						09 55				
Herne Bay	d				09 04						09 33						10 04				
Chestfield & Swalecliffe	d										09 36										
Whitstable	d				09 09						09 39						10 09				
Dover Priory [4]	d			08 45						09 05						09 45					
Kearsney	d									09 09											
Shepherds Well	d									09 14											
Snowdown	d									09 18											
Aylesham	d									09 20											
Adisham	d									09 23											
Bekesbourne	d									09 27											
Canterbury East [4]	d			09 02						09 32						10 02					
Selling	d									09 41											
Faversham [2]	a			09 14	09 18					09 46	09 48					10 14	10 18				
	d				09 22		09 28				09 52	09 58					10 22		10 28		
Teynham	d										09 58										
Sheerness-on-Sea	d							09 32					10 02							10 32	
Queenborough	d							09 36					10 06							10 36	
Swale	d							09 40					10 10							10 40	
Kemsley	d							09 44					10 14							10 44	
Sittingbourne [4]	a				09 29		09 36	09 49			10 02	10 06	10 19				10 29		10 36	10 49	
	d				09 30		09 37				10 03	10 07					10 30		10 37		
Newington	d				09 35												10 35				
Rainham (Kent)	d				09 40		09 45				10 10	10 15					10 40		10 45		
Gillingham (Kent) [4]	d	09 24	09 32		09 45		09 50		09 54		10 15	10 20		10 24	10 32		10 45		10 50		10 54
Chatham [4]	d	09 28	09 36		09 50		09 54		09 58		10 20	10 24		10 28	10 36		10 50		10 54		10 58
Rochester [4]	d	09 30	09 39		09 52		09 57		10 00		10 22	10 27		10 30	10 39		10 52		10 57		11 00
Strood [4]	a	09 35					10 01		10 05			10 31		10 35					11 01		11 05
Gravesend [4]	a	09 47					10 12		10 17			10 42		10 47					11 12		11 17
Greenhithe for Bluewater	a	09 53							10 23					10 53							11 23
Dartford [4]	a	09 58							10 28					10 58							11 28
London Bridge [4] ⊖	a	10 35							11 05					11 35							12 05
London Cannon Street [4] ⊖	a																				
London Waterloo (East) [4] ⊖	a	10 39							11 09					11 39							12 09
London Charing Cross [4] ⊖	a	10 43							11 13					11 43							12 13
Sole Street	d		09 49												10 49						
Meopham	d		09 52		10 03						10 33				10 52		11 03				
Longfield	d		09 56		10 07						10 37				10 56		11 07				
Farningham Road	d		09 59												10 59						
Swanley [4]	a		10 04												11 04						
St Mary Cray	a		10 09												11 09						
Bromley South [4]	a		10 15		10 20						10 50				11 15		11 20				
London Victoria [15] ⊖	a		10 36		10 37						11 07				11 36		11 37				
Elephant & Castle ⊖	a																				
London Blackfriars [3] ⊖	a																				
City Thameslink	a																				
Farringdon	a																				
Ebbsfleet International	a						10 16					10 46							11 16		
Stratford International ⊖	a						10 29					10 59							11 29		
St Pancras International	a						10 36					11 06							11 36		

A ⛾ from Margate

For further services to St Pancras International, Blackfriars and Elephant & Castle and onwards to Bromley South, St Mary Cray and Swanley please see table 52

Table 212R

Saturdays

14 December to 17 May

Ramsgate, Dover, Sheerness-on-Sea and Medway - London

Network Diagram - see first Page of Table 212

		SE	SE	SE	SE	SE	SE	SE	SE	SE	SE	SE	SE	SE	SE	SE	SE	SE	SE	SE	SE	SE	SE
		[1]	[1]				[1]	[1]	[1]					[1]	[1]				[1]	[1]	[1]		
			A						A						A						A		
		🛒	🛒					🛒	🛒					🛒	🛒					🛒	🛒		
Ramsgate [4]	d		10 05						10 40	10 59					11 05						11 40	11 59	
Dumpton Park	d		10 08												11 08								
Broadstairs	d		10 11						10 45	11 05					11 11						11 45	12 05	
Margate [4]	d		10 16						10 50	11a10					11 16						11 50	12a10	
Westgate-on-Sea	d		10 20												11 20								
Birchington-on-Sea	d		10 24						10 55						11 24						11 55		
Herne Bay	d		10 33						11 04						11 33						12 04		
Chestfield & Swalecliffe	d		10 36												11 36								
Whitstable	d		10 39						11 09						11 39						12 09		
Dover Priory [4]	d	10 05						10 45						11 05						11 45			
Kearsney	d	10 09												11 09									
Shepherds Well	d	10 14												11 14									
Snowdown	d	10 18												11 18									
Aylesham	d	10 20												11 20									
Adisham	d	10 23												11 23									
Bekesbourne	d	10 27												11 27									
Canterbury East [4]	d	10 32						11 02						11 32						12 02			
Selling	d	10 41												11 41									
Faversham [2]	a	10 46	10 48					11 14	11 18					11 46	11 48					12 14	12 18		
	d	10 52		10 58				11 22			11 28			11 52		11 58				12 22			12 28
Teynham	d	10 58												11 58									
Sheerness-on-Sea	d				11 02							11 32					12 02						
Queenborough	d				11 06							11 36					12 06						
Swale	d				11 10							11 40					12 10						
Kemsley	d				11 14							11 44					12 14						
Sittingbourne [4]	a	11 02		11 06	11 19			11 29			11 36	11 49		12 02		12 06	12 19			12 29			12 36
	d	11 03		11 07				11 30			11 37			12 03		12 07				12 30			12 37
Newington	d							11 35												12 35			
Rainham (Kent)	d	11 10		11 15				11 40			11 45			12 10		12 15				12 40			12 45
Gillingham (Kent) [4]	d	11 15		11 20		11 24	11 32	11 45			11 50		11 54	12 15		12 20		12 24	12 32	12 45			12 50
Chatham [4]	d	11 20		11 24		11 28	11 36	11 50			11 54		11 58	12 20		12 24		12 28	12 36	12 50			12 54
Rochester [4]	d	11 22		11 27		11 30	11 39	11 52			11 57		12 00	12 22		12 27		12 30	12 39	12 52			12 57
Strood [4]	a			11 31		11 35					12 01		12 05			12 31		12 35					13 01
Gravesend [4]	a			11 42		11 47					12 12		12 17			12 42		12 47					13 12
Greenhithe for Bluewater	a					11 53							12 23					12 53					
Dartford [4]	a					11 58							12 28					12 58					
London Bridge [4] ⊖	a					12 35							13 05					13 35					
London Cannon Street [4] ⊖	a																						
London Waterloo (East) [4] ⊖	a					12 39							13 09					13 39					
London Charing Cross [4] ⊖	a					12 43							13 13					13 43					
Sole Street	d						11 49												12 49				
Meopham	d	11 33					11 52	12 03						12 33					12 52	13 03			
Longfield	d	11 37					11 56	12 07						12 37					12 56	13 07			
Farningham Road	d						11 59												12 59				
Swanley [4]	a						12 04												13 04				
St Mary Cray	a						12 09												13 09				
Bromley South [4]	a	11 50					12 15	12 20						12 50					13 15	13 20			
London Victoria [15] ⊖	a	12 07					12 36	12 37						13 07					13 36	13 37			
Elephant & Castle ⊖	a																						
London Blackfriars [3] ⊖	a																						
City Thameslink	a																						
Farringdon	a																						
Ebbsfleet International	a			11 46							12 16					12 46							13 16
Stratford International ⊖	a			11 59							12 30					13 00							13 29
St Pancras International	a			12 06							12 37					13 07							13 36

A 🛒 from Margate

For further services to St Pancras International, Blackfriars and Elephant & Castle and onwards to Bromley South, St Mary Cray and Swanley please see table 52

Table 212R

Saturdays

14 December to 17 May

Ramsgate, Dover, Sheerness-on-Sea and Medway - London

Network Diagram - see first Page of Table 212

		SE	SE	SE	SE	SE		SE	SE	SE	SE	SE	SE	SE	SE	SE		SE	SE	SE	SE	SE	SE	SE	SE
				[1]	[1]					[1]	[1]	[1]						[1]	[1]				[1]	[1]	[1]
					A							A							A						A
				🛒	🛒						🛒	🛒						🛒	🛒					🛒	🛒
Ramsgate [4]	d				12 05							12 40	12 59						13 05						13 40
Dumpton Park	d				12 08														13 08						
Broadstairs	d				12 11							12 45	13 05						13 11						13 45
Margate [4]	d				12 16							12 50	13a10						13 16						13 50
Westgate-on-Sea	d				12 20														13 20						
Birchington-on-Sea	d				12 24							12 55							13 24						13 55
Herne Bay	d				12 33							13 04							13 33						14 04
Chestfield & Swalecliffe	d				12 36														13 36						
Whitstable	d				12 39							13 09							13 39						14 09
Dover Priory [4]	d			12 05							12 45							13 05						13 45	
Kearsney	d			12 09														13 09							
Shepherds Well	d			12 14														13 14							
Snowdown	d			12 18														13 18							
Aylesham	d			12 20														13 20							
Adisham	d			12 23														13 23							
Bekesbourne	d			12 27														13 27							
Canterbury East [4]	d			12 32							13 02							13 32						14 02	
Selling	d			12 41														13 41							
Faversham [2]	a			12 46	12 48						13 14	13 18						13 46	13 48					14 14	14 18
	d			12 52		12 58					13 22			13 28				13 52		13 58				14 22	
Teynham	d			12 58														13 58							
Sheerness-on-Sea	d	12 32						13 02							13 32						14 02				
Queenborough	d	12 36						13 06							13 36						14 06				
Swale	d	12 40						13 10							13 40						14 10				
Kemsley	d	12 44						13 14							13 44						14 14				
Sittingbourne [4]	a	12 49		13 02		13 06		13 19			13 29			13 36	13 49			14 02		14 06	14 19			14 29	
	d			13 03		13 07					13 30			13 37				14 03		14 07				14 30	
Newington	d										13 35													14 35	
Rainham (Kent)	d			13 10		13 15					13 40			13 45				14 10		14 15				14 40	
Gillingham (Kent) [4]	d		12 54	13 15		13 20			13 24	13 32	13 45			13 50		13 54		14 15		14 20		14 24	14 32	14 45	
Chatham [4]	d		12 58	13 20		13 24			13 28	13 36	13 50			13 54		13 58		14 20		14 24		14 28	14 36	14 50	
Rochester [4]	d		13 00	13 22		13 27			13 30	13 39	13 52			13 57		14 00		14 22		14 27		14 30	14 39	14 52	
Strood [4]	a		13 05			13 31			13 35					14 01		14 05				14 31		14 35			
Gravesend [4]	a		13 17			13 42			13 47					14 12		14 17				14 42		14 47			
Greenhithe for Bluewater	a		13 23						13 53							14 23						14 53			
Dartford [4]	a		13 28						13 58							14 28						14 58			
London Bridge [4] ⊖	a		14 05						14 35							15 05						15 35			
London Cannon Street [4] ⊖	a																								
London Waterloo (East) [4] ⊖	a		14 09						14 39							15 09						15 39			
London Charing Cross [4] ⊖	a		14 13						14 43							15 13						15 43			
Sole Street	d									13 49													14 49		
Meopham	d			13 33						13 52	14 03							14 33					14 52	15 03	
Longfield	d			13 37						13 56	14 07							14 37					14 56	15 07	
Farningham Road	d									13 59													14 59		
Swanley [4]	a									14 04													15 04		
St Mary Cray	a									14 09													15 09		
Bromley South [4]	a			13 50						14 15	14 20							14 50					15 15	15 20	
London Victoria [15] ⊖	a			14 07						14 36	14 37							15 07					15 36	15 37	
Elephant & Castle ⊖	a																								
London Blackfriars [3] ⊖	a																								
City Thameslink	a																								
Farringdon	a																								
Ebbsfleet International	a					13 46								14 16						14 46					
Stratford International ⊖	a					14 00								14 29						14 59					
St Pancras International	a					14 07								14 36						15 06					

A 🛒 from Margate

For further services to St Pancras International, Blackfriars and Elephant & Castle and onwards to Bromley South, St Mary Cray and Swanley please see table 52

Table 212R

Saturdays

14 December to 17 May

Ramsgate, Dover, Sheerness-on-Sea and Medway - London

Network Diagram - see first Page of Table 212

		SE		SE	SE	SE	SE	SE	SE	SE	SE	SE		SE	SE	SE	SE	SE	SE	SE	SE	SE		SE	SE
							[1]	[1]				[1]		[1]	[1]					[1]	[1]				
								A							A						A				
							🚲	🚲						🚲	🚲					🚲	🚲				
Ramsgate [4]	d	13 59						14 05							14 40	14 59					15 05				
Dumpton Park	d							14 08													15 08				
Broadstairs	d	14 05						14 11							14 45	15 05					15 11				
Margate [4]	d	14a10						14 16							14 50	15a10					15 16				
Westgate-on-Sea	d							14 20													15 20				
Birchington-on-Sea	d							14 24							14 55						15 24				
Herne Bay	d							14 33							15 04						15 33				
Chestfield & Swalecliffe	d							14 36													15 36				
Whitstable	d							14 39							15 09						15 39				
Dover Priory [4]	d						14 05							14 45						15 05					
Kearsney	d						14 09													15 09					
Shepherds Well	d						14 14													15 14					
Snowdown	d						14 18													15 18					
Aylesham	d						14 20													15 20					
Adisham	d						14 23													15 23					
Bekesbourne	d						14 27													15 27					
Canterbury East [4]	d						14 32							15 02						15 32					
Selling	d						14 41													15 41					
Faversham [2]	a						14 46	14 48						15 14	15 18					15 46	15 48				
	d			14 28			14 52		14 58					15 22			15 28			15 52		15 58			
Teynham	d						14 58													15 58					
Sheerness-on-Sea	d				14 32					15 02								15 32						16 02	
Queenborough	d				14 36					15 06								15 36						16 06	
Swale	d				14 40					15 10								15 40						16 10	
Kemsley	d				14 44					15 14								15 44						16 14	
Sittingbourne [4]	a			14 36	14 49		15 02		15 06	15 19				15 29			15 36	15 49		16 02		16 06		16 19	
	d			14 37			15 03		15 07					15 30			15 37			16 03		16 07			
Newington	d													15 35											
Rainham (Kent)	d			14 45			15 10		15 15					15 40			15 45			16 10		16 15			
Gillingham (Kent) [4]	d			14 50		14 54	15 15		15 20		15 24	15 32		15 45			15 50		15 54	16 15		16 20			16 24
Chatham [4]	d			14 54		14 58	15 20		15 24		15 28	15 36		15 50			15 54		15 58	16 20		16 24			16 28
Rochester [4]	d			14 57		15 00	15 22		15 27		15 30	15 39		15 52			15 57		16 00	16 22		16 27			16 30
Strood [4]	a			15 01		15 05			15 31		15 35						16 01		16 05			16 31			16 35
Gravesend [4]	a			15 12		15 17			15 42		15 47						16 12		16 17			16 42			16 47
Greenhithe for Bluewater	a					15 23					15 53								16 23						16 53
Dartford [4]	a					15 28					15 58								16 28						16 58
London Bridge [4] ⊖	a					16 05					16 35								17 05						17 35
London Cannon Street [4] ⊖	a																								
London Waterloo (East) [4] ⊖	a					16 09					16 39								17 09						17 39
London Charing Cross [4] ⊖	a					16 13					16 43								17 13						17 43
Sole Street	d											15 49													
Meopham	d						15 33					15 52		16 03						16 33					
Longfield	d						15 37					15 56		16 07						16 37					
Farningham Road	d											15 59													
Swanley [4]	a											16 04													
St Mary Cray	a											16 09													
Bromley South [4]	a						15 50					16 15		16 20						16 50					
London Victoria [15] ⊖	a						16 07					16 36		16 37						17 07					
Elephant & Castle ⊖	a																								
London Blackfriars [3] ⊖	a																								
City Thameslink	a																								
Farringdon	a																								
Ebbsfleet International	a			15 16					15 46								16 16					16 46			
Stratford International ⊖	a			15 30					16 02								16 29					16 59			
St Pancras International	a			15 37					16 10								16 36					17 06			

A 🚲 from Margate

For further services to St Pancras International, Blackfriars and Elephant & Castle and onwards to Bromley South, St Mary Cray and Swanley please see table 52

Table 212R

Saturdays

14 December to 17 May

Ramsgate, Dover, Sheerness-on-Sea and Medway - London

Network Diagram - see first Page of Table 212

		SE ■1	SE ■1 🚲	SE ■1 A 🚲	SE	SE	SE	SE		SE ■1 🚲	SE ■1 A 🚲	SE	SE	SE	SE ■1	SE ■1	SE ■1	SE		SE	SE	SE	SE ■1	SE ■1	SE
Ramsgate ■4	d			15 40	15 59						16 05						16 40	16 59						17 05	
Dumpton Park	d										16 08													17 08	
Broadstairs	d			15 45	16 05						16 11						16 45	17 05						17 11	
Margate ■4	d			15 50	16a10						16 16						16 50	17a10						17 16	
Westgate-on-Sea	d										16 20													17 20	
Birchington-on-Sea	d			15 55							16 24						16 55							17 24	
Herne Bay	d			16 04							16 33						17 04							17 33	
Chestfield & Swalecliffe	d										16 36													17 36	
Whitstable	d			16 09							16 39						17 09							17 39	
Dover Priory ■4	d		15 45							16 05						16 45							17 05		
Kearsney	d									16 09													17 09		
Shepherds Well	d									16 14													17 14		
Snowdown	d									16 18													17 18		
Aylesham	d									16 20													17 20		
Adisham	d									16 23													17 23		
Bekesbourne	d									16 27													17 27		
Canterbury East ■4	d		16 02							16 32						17 02							17 32		
Selling	d									16 41													17 41		
Faversham ■2	a		16 14	16 18						16 46	16 48					17 14	17 18						17 46	17 48	
	d		16 22			16 28				16 52		16 58				17 22				17 28			17 52		17 58
Teynham	d									16 58													17 58		
Sheerness-on-Sea	d						16 32						17 02								17 32				
Queenborough	d						16 36						17 06								17 36				
Swale	d						16 40						17 10								17 40				
Kemsley	d						16 44						17 14								17 44				
Sittingbourne ■4	a		16 29			16 36	16 49			17 02		17 06	17 19			17 29				17 36	17 49		18 02		18 06
	d		16 30			16 37				17 03		17 07				17 30				17 37			18 03		18 07
Newington	d		16 35													17 35									
Rainham (Kent)	d		16 40			16 45				17 10		17 15				17 40				17 45			18 10		18 15
Gillingham (Kent) ■4	d	16 32	16 45			16 50		16 54		17 15		17 20		17 24	17 32	17 45				17 50		17 54	18 15		18 20
Chatham ■4	d	16 36	16 50			16 54		16 58		17 20		17 24		17 28	17 36	17 50				17 54		17 58	18 20		18 24
Rochester ■4	d	16 39	16 52			16 57		17 00		17 22		17 27		17 30	17 39	17 52				17 57		18 00	18 22		18 27
Strood ■4	a					17 01		17 05				17 31		17 35						18 01		18 05			18 31
Gravesend ■4	a					17 12		17 17				17 42		17 47						18 12		18 17			18 42
Greenhithe for Bluewater	a							17 23						17 53								18 23			
Dartford ■4	a							17 28						17 58								18 28			
London Bridge ■4 ⊖	a							18 05						18 35								19 05			
London Cannon Street ■4 ⊖	a																								
London Waterloo (East) ■4 ⊖	a							18 09						18 39								19 09			
London Charing Cross ■4 ⊖	a							18 13						18 43								19 13			
Sole Street	d	16 49													17 49										
Meopham	d	16 52	17 03							17 33					17 52	18 03							18 33		
Longfield	d	16 56	17 07							17 37					17 56	18 07							18 37		
Farningham Road	d	16 59													17 59										
Swanley ■4	a	17 04													18 04										
St Mary Cray	a	17 09													18 09										
Bromley South ■4	a	17 15	17 20							17 50					18 15	18 20							18 50		
London Victoria ■15 ⊖	a	17 36	17 37							18 07					18 36	18 37							19 07		
Elephant & Castle ⊖	a																								
London Blackfriars ■3 ⊖	a																								
City Thameslink	a																								
Farringdon	a																								
Ebbsfleet International	a					17 16						17 46								18 16					18 46
Stratford International ⊖	a					17 29						17 59								18 30					18 59
St Pancras International	a					17 36						18 06								18 37					19 06

A 🚲 from Margate

For further services to St Pancras International, Blackfriars and Elephant & Castle and onwards to Bromley South, St Mary Cray and Swanley please see table 52

Table 212R

Saturdays

14 December to 17 May

Ramsgate, Dover, Sheerness-on-Sea and Medway - London

Network Diagram - see first Page of Table 212

		SE	SE	SE [1]	SE [1]	SE [1]	SE	SE	SE	SE	SE [1]	SE [1]	SE	SE	SE	SE [1]	SE [1]	SE [1]	SE	SE	SE	SE
Ramsgate [4]	d					17 40	17 59					18 05						18 40	18 59			
Dumpton Park	d											18 08										
Broadstairs	d					17 45	18 05					18 11						18 45	19 05			
Margate [4]	d					17 50	18a10					18 16						18 50	19a10			
Westgate-on-Sea	d											18 20										
Birchington-on-Sea	d					17 55						18 24						18 55				
Herne Bay	d					18 04						18 33						19 04				
Chestfield & Swalecliffe	d											18 36										
Whitstable	d					18 09						18 39						19 09				
Dover Priory [4]	d				17 45						18 05						18 45					
Kearsney	d										18 09											
Shepherds Well	d										18 14											
Snowdown	d										18 18											
Aylesham	d										18 20											
Adisham	d										18 23											
Bekesbourne	d										18 27											
Canterbury East [4]	d				18 02						18 32						19 02					
Selling	d										18 41											
Faversham [2]	a				18 14	18 18					18 46	18 48					19 14	19 18				
	d				18 22			18 28			18 52		18 58				19 22			19 28		
Teynham	d										18 58											
Sheerness-on-Sea	d	18 02							18 32					19 02							19 32	
Queenborough	d	18 06							18 36					19 06							19 36	
Swale	d	18 10							18 40					19 10							19 40	
Kemsley	d	18 14							18 44					19 14							19 44	
Sittingbourne [4]	a	18 19			18 29			18 36	18 49		19 02		19 06	19 19			19 29			19 36	19 49	
	d				18 30			18 37			19 03		19 07				19 30			19 37		
Newington	d				18 35												19 35					
Rainham (Kent)	d				18 40			18 45			19 10		19 15				19 40			19 45		
Gillingham (Kent) [4]	d		18 24	18 32	18 45			18 50		18 54	19 15		19 20		19 24	19 32	19 45			19 50		19 54
Chatham [4]	d		18 28	18 36	18 50			18 54		18 58	19 20		19 24		19 28	19 36	19 50			19 54		19 58
Rochester [4]	d		18 30	18 39	18 52			18 57		19 00	19 22		19 27		19 30	19 39	19 52			19 57		20 00
Strood [4]	a		18 35					19 01		19 05			19 31		19 35					20 01		20 05
Gravesend [4]	a		18 47					19 12		19 17			19 42		19 47					20 12		20 17
Greenhithe for Bluewater	a		18 53							19 23					19 53							20 23
Dartford [4]	a		18 58							19 28					19 58							20 28
London Bridge [4] ⊖	a		19 36							20 06					20 36							21 06
London Cannon Street [4] ⊖	a																					
London Waterloo (East) [4] ⊖	a		19 42							20 10					20 40							21 10
London Charing Cross [4] ⊖	a		19 45							20 14					20 44							21 14
Sole Street	d			18 49												19 49						
Meopham	d			18 52	19 03						19 33					19 52	20 03					
Longfield	d			18 56	19 07						19 37					19 56	20 07					
Farningham Road	d			18 59												19 59						
Swanley [4]	a			19 04												20 04						
St Mary Cray	a			19 09												20 09						
Bromley South [4]	a			19 15	19 20						19 50					20 15	20 20					
London Victoria [15] ⊖	a			19 36	19 37						20 07					20 36	20 39					
Elephant & Castle ⊖	a																					
London Blackfriars [3] ⊖	a																					
City Thameslink	a																					
Farringdon	a																					
Ebbsfleet International	a							19 16					19 46							20 16		
Stratford International ⊖	a							19 29					19 59							20 29		
St Pancras International	a							19 36					20 06							20 36		

For further services to St Pancras International, Blackfriars and Elephant & Castle and onwards to Bromley South, St Mary Cray and Swanley please see table 52

Table 212R

Saturdays

14 December to 17 May

Ramsgate, Dover, Sheerness-on-Sea and Medway - London

Network Diagram - see first Page of Table 212

		SE 1	SE 1	SE	SE	SE	SE	SE	SE	SE	SE	SE 1	SE 1	SE	SE	SE	SE	SE	SE	SE	SE 1	SE 1	SE
Ramsgate 4	d		19 05		20 01								20 05		21 01							21 05	
Dumpton Park	d		19 08										20 08									21 08	
Broadstairs	d		19 11		20 06								20 11		21 06							21 11	
Margate 4	d		19 16		20a11								20 16		21a11							21 16	
Westgate-on-Sea	d		19 20										20 20									21 20	
Birchington-on-Sea	d		19 24										20 24									21 24	
Herne Bay	d		19 33										20 33									21 33	
Chestfield & Swalecliffe	d		19 36										20 36									21 36	
Whitstable	d		19 39										20 39									21 39	
Dover Priory 4	d	19 05										20 05									21 05		
Kearsney	d	19 09										20 09									21 09		
Shepherds Well	d	19 14										20 14									21 14		
Snowdown	d	19 18										20 18									21 18		
Aylesham	d	19 20										20 20									21 20		
Adisham	d	19 23										20 23									21 23		
Bekesbourne	d	19 27										20 27									21 27		
Canterbury East 4	d	19 32										20 32									21 32		
Selling	d	19 41										20 41									21 41		
Faversham 2	a	19 46	19 48									20 46	20 48								21 46	21 48	
	d		19 52	19 58				20 14	20 28				20 52	20 58				21 14	21 28			21 52	21 58
Teynham	d		19 58										20 58									21 58	
Sheerness-on-Sea	d					20 02				20 32						21 02							
Queenborough	d					20 06				20 36						21 06							
Swale	d					20 10				20 40						21 10							
Kemsley	d					20 14				20 44						21 14							
Sittingbourne 4	a		20 02	20 06		20 19		20 21	20 36	20 49			21 02	21 06		21 19		21 21	21 36			22 02	22 06
	d		20 03	20 07				20 22	20 37				21 03	21 07				21 22	21 37			22 03	22 07
Newington	d							20 27										21 27					
Rainham (Kent)	d		20 10	20 15				20 31	20 45				21 10	21 15				21 31	21 45			22 10	22 15
Gillingham (Kent) 4	d		20 15	20 20			20 24	20 36	20 50		20 54		21 15	21 20			21 24	21 36	21 50	21 54		22 15	22 20
Chatham 4	d		20 20	20 24			20 28	20 41	20 54		20 58		21 20	21 24			21 28	21 41	21 54	21 58		22 20	22 24
Rochester 4	d		20 22	20 27			20 30	20 43	20 57		21 00		21 22	21 27			21 30	21 43	21 57	22 00		22 22	22 27
Strood 4	a			20 31			20 35		21 01		21 05			21 31			21 35		22 01	22 05			22 31
Gravesend 4	a			20 42			20 47		21 12		21 17			21 42			21 47		22 12	22 17			22 42
Greenhithe for Bluewater	a						20 53				21 23						21 53			22 23			
Dartford 4	a						20 58				21 28						21 58			22 28			
London Bridge 4 ⊖	a						21 36				22 05						22 35			23 05			
London Cannon Street 4 ⊖	a																						
London Waterloo (East) 4 ⊖	a						21 40				22 09						22 39			23 09			
London Charing Cross 4 ⊖	a						21 44				22 13						22 43			23 13			
Sole Street	d							20 54										21 54					
Meopham	d		20 33					20 56					21 33					21 56				22 33	
Longfield	d		20 37					21 00					21 37					22 00				22 37	
Farningham Road	d							21 04										22 04					
Swanley 4	a							21 09										22 09					
St Mary Cray	a							21 14										22 14					
Bromley South 4	a		20 50					21 20					21 50					22 20				22 50	
London Victoria 15 ⊖	a		21 07					21 37					22 07					22 37				23 07	
Elephant & Castle ⊖	a																						
London Blackfriars 3 ⊖	a																						
City Thameslink	a																						
Farringdon	a																						
Ebbsfleet International	a			20 46					21 16					21 46					22 16				22 46
Stratford International ⊖	a			20 59					21 29					21 59					22 29				22 59
St Pancras International	a			21 06					21 36					22 06					22 36				23 06

For further services to St Pancras International, Blackfriars and Elephant & Castle and onwards to Bromley South, St Mary Cray and Swanley please see table 52

Table 212R

Saturdays

14 December to 17 May

Ramsgate, Dover, Sheerness-on-Sea and Medway - London

Network Diagram - see first Page of Table 212

		SE	SE	SE	SE	SE [1]		SE	SE [1]	SE	SE	SE [1]	SE [1]	SE
Ramsgate [4]	d	22 01							22 05	23 01			23 05	
Dumpton Park	d								22 08				23 08	
Broadstairs	d	22 06							22 11	23 06			23 11	
Margate [4]	d	22a11							22 16	23a11			23 16	
Westgate-on-Sea	d								22 20				23 20	
Birchington-on-Sea	d								22 24				23 24	
Herne Bay	d								22 33				23 33	
Chestfield & Swalecliffe	d								22 36				23 36	
Whitstable	d								22 39				23 39	
Dover Priory [4]	d					22 05						23 05		
Kearsney	d					22 09						23 09		
Shepherds Well	d					22 14						23 14		
Snowdown	d					22 18						23 18		
Aylesham	d					22 20						23 20		
Adisham	d					22 23						23 23		
Bekesbourne	d					22 27						23 27		
Canterbury East [4]	d				22 02	22 32						23 32		
Selling	d					22 41						23 41		
Faversham [2]	a				22 13	22 46			22 48			23 46	23 49	
	d				22 14				22 52				23 52	
Teynham	d								22 58				23 58	
Sheerness-on-Sea	d		22 02								23 02			23 53
Queenborough	d		22 06								23 06			23 57
Swale	d		22 10								23 10			00 01
Kemsley	d		22 14								23 14			00 05
Sittingbourne [4]	a		22 19		22 21				23 02		23 19		00 02	00 10
	d				22 22				23 03				00 03	
Newington	d				22 27								00 08	
Rainham (Kent)	d				22 31				23 10				00 12	
Gillingham (Kent) [4]	d			22 24	22 36			22 54	23 15				00a17	
Chatham [4]	d			22 28	22 41			22 58	23 20					
Rochester [4]	d			22 30	22 43			23 00	23 22					
Strood [4]	a			22 35				23 05						
Gravesend [4]	a			22 47				23 17						
Greenhithe for Bluewater	a			22 53				23 23						
Dartford [4]	a			22 58				23 28						
London Bridge [4] ⊖	a			23 35										
London Cannon Street [4] ⊖	a													
London Waterloo (East) [4] ⊖	a			23 39										
London Charing Cross [4] ⊖	a			23 43										
Sole Street	d				22 54									
Meopham	d				22 56				23 33					
Longfield	d				23 00				23 37					
Farningham Road	d				23 04									
Swanley [4]	a				23 09									
St Mary Cray	a				23 14									
Bromley South [4]	a				23 20				23 50					
London Victoria [15] ⊖	a				23 37				00 07					
Elephant & Castle ⊖	a													
London Blackfriars [3] ⊖	a													
City Thameslink	a													
Farringdon	a													
Ebbsfleet International	a													
Stratford International ⊖	a													
St Pancras International	a													

For further services to St Pancras International, Blackfriars and Elephant & Castle and onwards to Bromley South, St Mary Cray and Swanley please see table 52

Table 212R

Sundays

8 December to 11 May

Ramsgate, Dover, Sheerness-on-Sea and Medway - London

Network Diagram - see first Page of Table 212

		SE [1] A	SE	SE B	SE [1]	SE	SE	SE [1]	SE	SE [1]		SE	SE	SE [1] 🚌	SE [1] C 🚌	SE	SE [1]	SE	SE	SE		SE [1] 🚌	SE [1] C 🚌	SE	SE [1]
Ramsgate [4]	d							06 35							07 35								08 35		
Dumpton Park	d							06 38							07 38								08 38		
Broadstairs	d							06 41							07 41								08 41		
Margate [4]	d							06 46							07 46								08 46		
Westgate-on-Sea	d							06 50							07 50								08 50		
Birchington-on-Sea	d							06 54							07 54								08 54		
Herne Bay	d							07 03							08 03								09 03		
Chestfield & Swalecliffe	d							07 06							08 06								09 06		
Whitstable	d							07 09							08 09								09 09		
Dover Priory [4]	d													07 35								08 35			
Kearsney	d													07 39								08 39			
Shepherds Well	d													07 44								08 44			
Snowdown	d													07 48								08 48			
Aylesham	d													07 50								08 50			
Adisham	d													07 53								08 53			
Bekesbourne	d													07 57								08 57			
Canterbury East [4]	d													08 02								09 02			09 25
Selling	d													08 11								09 11			
Faversham [2]	a							07 18						08 16	08 18							09 16	09 18		09 37
	d				06 38		06 58	07 22		07 38			07 58	08 22			08 38		08 58			09 22			09 38
Teynham	d				06 44					07 44							08 44								09 44
Sheerness-on-Sea	d																	08 42							
Queenborough	d																	08 46							
Swale	d			00 01														08 50							
Kemsley	d			00 05														08 54							
Sittingbourne [4]	a			00 10	06 48		07 06	07 29		07 48			08 06	08 29			08 48	08 59	09 06			09 29			09 48
	d	00 03			06 49		07 07	07 30		07 49			08 07	08 30			08 49		09 07			09 30			09 49
Newington	d	00 08			06 54					07 54							08 54								09 54
Rainham (Kent)	d	00 12			06 59		07 15	07 38		07 59			08 15	08 38			08 59		09 15			09 38			09 59
Gillingham (Kent) [4]	d	00a17	06 48		07 04	07 16	07 20	07 43	07 48	08 04		08 16	08 20	08 43		08 54	09 04		09 20	09 24		09 43		09 54	10 04
Chatham [4]	d		06 52		07 08	07 20	07 24	07 48	07 52	08 08		08 20	08 24	08 48		08 58	09 08		09 24	09 28		09 48		09 58	10 08
Rochester [4]	d		06 54		07 11	07 22	07 27	07 50	07 54	08 11		08 22	08 27	08 50		09 00	09 11		09 27	09 30		09 50		10 00	10 11
Strood [4]	a		06 59			07 27	07 31		07 59			08 27	08 31			09 05			09 31	09 35				10 05	
Gravesend [4]	a		07 11			07 40	07 43		08 11			08 40	08 43			09 17			09 42	09 47				10 17	
Greenhithe for Bluewater	a		07 20			07 49			08 20			08 49				09 23				09 53				10 23	
Dartford [4]	a		07 27			07 56			08 27			08 56				09 28				09 58				10 28	
London Bridge [4] ⊖	a		08 04			08 34			09 04			09 34				10 04				10 34				11 04	
London Cannon Street [4] ⊖	a																								
London Waterloo (East) [4] ⊖	a		08 09			08 39			09 09			09 39				10 09				10 39				11 09	
London Charing Cross [4] ⊖	a		08 13			08 43			09 13			09 43				10 13				10 43				11 13	
Sole Street	d				07 21					08 21							09 21								10 21
Meopham	d				07 24					08 24							09 24								10 24
Longfield	d				07 28					08 28							09 28								10 28
Farningham Road	d				07 32					08 32							09 32								10 32
Swanley [4]	a				07 37					08 37							09 37								10 37
St Mary Cray	a				07 41					08 41							09 41								10 41
Bromley South [4]	a				07 47			08 16		08 47				09 16			09 47					10 16			10 47
London Victoria [15] ⊖	a				08 05			08 35		09 05				09 35			10 05					10 35			11 05
Elephant & Castle ⊖	a																								
London Blackfriars [3] ⊖	a																								
City Thameslink	a																								
Farringdon	a																								
Ebbsfleet International	a						07 47						08 47						09 46						
Stratford International ⊖	a						07 59						08 59						09 59						
St Pancras International	a						08 06						09 06						10 06						

A from Ramsgate
B from Sheerness on Sea
C 🚌 from Margate

For further services to St Pancras International, Blackfriars and Elephant & Castle and onwards to Bromley South, St Mary Cray and Swanley please see table 52

Table 212R

Sundays

8 December to 11 May

Ramsgate, Dover, Sheerness-on-Sea and Medway - London

Network Diagram - see first Page of Table 212

		SE	SE	SE	SE	SE	SE	SE	SE	SE	SE	SE	SE	SE	SE	SE	SE	SE	SE	SE	SE	SE	SE
					[1]	[1]			[1]				[1]	[1]				[1]				[1]	[1]
						A								A									A
					⚲	⚲							⚲	⚲								⚲	⚲
Ramsgate [4]	d					09 35	09 59							10 35		10 59							11 35
Dumpton Park	d					09 38								10 38									11 38
Broadstairs	d					09 41	10 05							10 41		11 05							11 41
Margate [4]	d					09 46	10a10							10 46		11a10							11 46
Westgate-on-Sea	d					09 50								10 50									11 50
Birchington-on-Sea	d					09 54								10 54									11 54
Herne Bay	d					10 03								11 03									12 03
Chestfield & Swalecliffe	d					10 06								11 06									12 06
Whitstable	d					10 09								11 09									12 09
Dover Priory [4]	d				09 35								10 35									11 35	
Kearsney	d				09 39								10 39									11 39	
Shepherds Well	d				09 44								10 44									11 44	
Snowdown	d				09 48								10 48									11 48	
Aylesham	d				09 50								10 50									11 50	
Adisham	d				09 53								10 53									11 53	
Bekesbourne	d				09 57								10 57									11 57	
Canterbury East [4]	d				10 02				10 25				11 02					11 25				12 02	
Selling	d				10 11								11 11									12 11	
Faversham [2]	a				10 16	10 18			10 37				11 16	11 18				11 37				12 16	12 18
	d		09 58		10 22				10 38		10 58		11 22		11 28			11 38		11 58		12 22	
Teynham	d								10 44									11 44					
Sheerness-on-Sea	d	09 42								10 42									11 42				
Queenborough	d	09 46								10 46									11 46				
Swale	d	09 50								10 50									11 50				
Kemsley	d	09 54								10 54									11 54				
Sittingbourne [4]	a	09 59	10 06		10 29				10 48	10 59	11 06		11 29		11 36			11 48	11 59	12 06		12 29	
	d		10 07		10 30				10 49		11 07		11 30		11 37			11 49		12 07		12 30	
Newington	d								10 54									11 54					
Rainham (Kent)	d		10 15		10 38				10 59		11 15		11 38		11 45			11 59		12 15		12 38	
Gillingham (Kent) [4]	d		10 20	10 24	10 43			10 54	11 04		11 20	11 24	11 43		11 50		11 54	12 04		12 20	12 24	12 43	
Chatham [4]	d		10 24	10 28	10 48			10 58	11 08		11 24	11 28	11 48		11 54		11 58	12 08		12 24	12 28	12 48	
Rochester [4]	d		10 27	10 30	10 50			11 00	11 11		11 27	11 30	11 50		11 57		12 00	12 11		12 27	12 30	12 50	
Strood [4]	a		10 31	10 35				11 05			11 31	11 35			12 01		12 05			12 31	12 35		
Gravesend [4]	a		10 42	10 47				11 17			11 42	11 47			12 12		12 17			12 42	12 47		
Greenhithe for Bluewater	a			10 53				11 23				11 53					12 23				12 53		
Dartford [4]	a			10 58				11 28				11 58					12 28				12 58		
London Bridge [4] ⊖	a			11 34				12 04				12 34					13 04				13 34		
London Cannon Street [4] ⊖	a																						
London Waterloo (East) [4] ⊖	a			11 39				12 09				12 39					13 09				13 39		
London Charing Cross [4] ⊖	a			11 43				12 13				12 43					13 13				13 43		
Sole Street	d								11 21									12 21					
Meopham	d								11 24									12 24					
Longfield	d								11 28									12 28					
Farningham Road	d								11 32									12 32					
Swanley [4]	a								11 37									12 37					
St Mary Cray	a								11 41									12 41					
Bromley South [4]	a				11 16				11 47				12 16					12 47				13 16	
London Victoria [15] ⊖	a				11 35				12 05				12 35					13 05				13 35	
Elephant & Castle ⊖	a																						
London Blackfriars [3] ⊖	a																						
City Thameslink	a																						
Farringdon	a																						
Ebbsfleet International	a		10 46								11 46				12 16					12 46			
Stratford International ⊖	a		10 59								11 59				12 30					13 00			
St Pancras International	a		11 06								12 06				12 37					13 07			

A ⚲ from Margate

For further services to St Pancras International, Blackfriars and Elephant & Castle and onwards to Bromley South, St Mary Cray and Swanley please see table 52

Table 212R

Sundays

8 December to 11 May

Ramsgate, Dover, Sheerness-on-Sea and Medway - London

Network Diagram - see first Page of Table 212

		SE		SE	SE	SE	SE	SE	SE	SE	SE	SE		SE	SE	SE	SE	SE	SE	SE	SE	SE		SE	SE
						1				1	1					1				1	1				
											A										A				
										🚲	🚲									🚲	🚲				
Ramsgate 4	d			11 59							12 35			12 59							13 35			13 59	
Dumpton Park	d										12 38										13 38				
Broadstairs	d			12 05							12 41			13 05							13 41			14 05	
Margate 4	d			12a10							12 46			13a10							13 46			14a10	
Westgate-on-Sea	d										12 50										13 50				
Birchington-on-Sea	d										12 54										13 54				
Herne Bay	d										13 03										14 03				
Chestfield & Swalecliffe	d										13 06										14 06				
Whitstable	d										13 09										14 09				
Dover Priory 4	d									12 35										13 35					
Kearsney	d									12 39										13 39					
Shepherds Well	d									12 44										13 44					
Snowdown	d									12 48										13 48					
Aylesham	d									12 50										13 50					
Adisham	d									12 53										13 53					
Bekesbourne	d									12 57										13 57					
Canterbury East 4	d					12 25				13 02						13 25				14 02					
Selling	d									13 11										14 11					
Faversham 2	a					12 37				13 16	13 18					13 37				14 16	14 18				
	d	12 28				12 38		12 58		13 22		13 28				13 38		13 58		14 22		14 28			
Teynham	d					12 44										13 44									
Sheerness-on-Sea	d						12 42										13 42								
Queenborough	d						12 46										13 46								
Swale	d						12 50										13 50								
Kemsley	d						12 54										13 54								
Sittingbourne 4	a	12 36				12 48	12 59	13 06		13 29		13 36				13 48	13 59	14 06		14 29		14 36			
	d	12 37				12 49		13 07		13 30		13 37				13 49		14 07		14 30		14 37			
Newington	d					12 54										13 54									
Rainham (Kent)	d	12 45				12 59		13 15		13 38		13 45				13 59		14 15		14 38		14 45			
Gillingham (Kent) 4	d	12 50			12 54	13 04		13 20	13 24	13 43		13 50			13 54	14 04		14 20	14 24	14 43		14 50			14 54
Chatham 4	d	12 54			12 58	13 08		13 24	13 28	13 48		13 54			13 58	14 08		14 24	14 28	14 48		14 54			14 58
Rochester 4	d	12 57			13 00	13 11		13 27	13 30	13 50		13 57			14 00	14 11		14 27	14 30	14 50		14 57			15 00
Strood 4	a	13 01			13 05			13 31	13 35			14 01			14 05			14 31	14 35			15 01			15 05
Gravesend 4	a	13 12			13 17			13 42	13 47			14 12			14 17			14 42	14 47			15 12			15 17
Greenhithe for Bluewater	a				13 23				13 53						14 23				14 53						15 23
Dartford 4	a				13 28				13 58						14 28				14 58						15 28
London Bridge 4 ⊖	a				14 04				14 34						15 04				15 34						16 04
London Cannon Street 4 ⊖	a																								
London Waterloo (East) 4 ⊖	a				14 09				14 39						15 09				15 39						16 09
London Charing Cross 4 ⊖	a				14 13				14 43						15 13				15 43						16 13
Sole Street	d					13 21										14 21									
Meopham	d					13 24										14 24									
Longfield	d					13 28										14 28									
Farningham Road	d					13 32										14 32									
Swanley 4	a					13 37										14 37									
St Mary Cray	a					13 41										14 41									
Bromley South 4	a					13 47				14 16						14 47				15 16					
London Victoria 15 ⊖	a					14 05				14 35						15 05				15 35					
Elephant & Castle ⊖	a																								
London Blackfriars 3 ⊖	a																								
City Thameslink	a																								
Farringdon	a																								
Ebbsfleet International	a	13 16						13 46				14 16						14 46				15 16			
Stratford International ⊖	a	13 30						13 59				14 29						15 00				15 30			
St Pancras International	a	13 37						14 06				14 36						15 07				15 37			

A 🚲 from Margate

For further services to St Pancras International, Blackfriars and Elephant & Castle and onwards to Bromley South, St Mary Cray and Swanley please see table 52

Table 212R

Sundays

8 December to 11 May

Ramsgate, Dover, Sheerness-on-Sea and Medway - London

Network Diagram - see first Page of Table 212

		SE	SE	SE	SE	SE	SE	SE		SE	SE	SE	SE	SE	SE	SE	SE	SE		SE	SE	SE	SE	SE	SE
		[1]				[1]	[1]					[1]				[1]	[1]					[1]			
							A										A								
						🚌	🚌									🚌	🚌								
Ramsgate [4]	d						14 35			14 59							15 35			15 59					
Dumpton Park	d						14 38										15 38								
Broadstairs	d						14 41			15 05							15 41			16 05					
Margate [4]	d						14 46			15a10							15 46			16a10					
Westgate-on-Sea	d						14 50										15 50								
Birchington-on-Sea	d						14 54										15 54								
Herne Bay	d						15 03										16 03								
Chestfield & Swalecliffe	d						15 06										16 06								
Whitstable	d						15 09										16 09								
Dover Priory [4]	d					14 35										15 35									
Kearsney	d					14 39										15 39									
Shepherds Well	d					14 44										15 44									
Snowdown	d					14 48										15 48									
Aylesham	d					14 50										15 50									
Adisham	d					14 53										15 53									
Bekesbourne	d					14 57										15 57									
Canterbury East [4]	d	14 25				15 02						15 25				16 02						16 25			
Selling	d					15 11										16 11									
Faversham [2]	a	14 37				15 16	15 18					15 37				16 16	16 18					16 37			
	d	14 38		14 58		15 22		15 28				15 38		15 58		16 22		16 28				16 38		16 58	
Teynham	d	14 44										15 44										16 44			
Sheerness-on-Sea	d		14 42										15 42										16 42		
Queenborough	d		14 46										15 46										16 46		
Swale	d		14 50										15 50										16 50		
Kemsley	d		14 54										15 54										16 54		
Sittingbourne [4]	a	14 48	14 59	15 06		15 29		15 36				15 48	15 59	16 06		16 29		16 36				16 48	16 59	17 06	
	d	14 49		15 07		15 30		15 37				15 49		16 07		16 30		16 37				16 49		17 07	
Newington	d	14 54										15 54										16 54			
Rainham (Kent)	d	14 59		15 15		15 38		15 45				15 59		16 15		16 38		16 45				16 59		17 15	
Gillingham (Kent) [4]	d	15 04		15 20	15 24	15 43		15 50			15 54	16 04		16 20	16 24	16 43		16 50			16 54	17 04		17 20	17 24
Chatham [4]	d	15 08		15 24	15 28	15 48		15 54			15 58	16 08		16 24	16 28	16 48		16 54			16 58	17 08		17 24	17 28
Rochester [4]	d	15 11		15 27	15 30	15 50		15 57			16 00	16 11		16 27	16 30	16 50		16 57			17 00	17 11		17 27	17 30
Strood [4]	a			15 31	15 35			16 01			16 05			16 31	16 35			17 01			17 05			17 31	17 35
Gravesend [4]	a			15 42	15 47			16 12			16 17			16 42	16 47			17 12			17 17			17 42	17 47
Greenhithe for Bluewater	a				15 53						16 23				16 53						17 23				17 53
Dartford [4]	a				15 58						16 28				16 58						17 28				17 58
London Bridge [4] ⊖	a				16 34						17 04				17 34						18 04				18 34
London Cannon Street [4] ⊖	a																								
London Waterloo (East) [4] ⊖	a				16 39						17 09				17 39						18 09				18 39
London Charing Cross [4] ⊖	a				16 43						17 13				17 43						18 13				18 43
Sole Street	d	15 21										16 21										17 21			
Meopham	d	15 24										16 24										17 24			
Longfield	d	15 28										16 28										17 28			
Farningham Road	d	15 32										16 32										17 32			
Swanley [4]	a	15 37										16 37										17 37			
St Mary Cray	a	15 41										16 41										17 41			
Bromley South [4]	a	15 47				16 16						16 47				17 16						17 47			
London Victoria [15] ⊖	a	16 05				16 35						17 05				17 35						18 05			
Elephant & Castle ⊖	a																								
London Blackfriars [3] ⊖	a																								
City Thameslink	a																								
Farringdon	a																								
Ebbsfleet International	a			15 46				16 16										17 16						17 46	
Stratford International ⊖	a			16 02				16 29										17 29						18 00	
St Pancras International	a			16 09				16 36						17 06				17 36						18 07	

A 🚌 from Margate

For further services to St Pancras International, Blackfriars and Elephant & Castle and onwards to Bromley South, St Mary Cray and Swanley please see table 52

Table 212R

Sundays

8 December to 11 May

Ramsgate, Dover, Sheerness-on-Sea and Medway - London

Network Diagram - see first Page of Table 212

		SE 1 ⛴	SE 1 A ⛴	SE		SE	SE	SE 1	SE	SE	SE	SE 1	SE 1	SE		SE	SE	SE 1	SE	SE	SE	SE 1	SE 1	SE	
Ramsgate 4	d		16 35			16 59							17 35			17 59							18 35		
Dumpton Park	d		16 38										17 38										18 38		
Broadstairs	d		16 41			17 05							17 41			18 05							18 41		
Margate 4	d		16 46			17a10							17 46			18a10							18 46		
Westgate-on-Sea	d		16 50										17 50										18 50		
Birchington-on-Sea	d		16 54										17 54										18 54		
Herne Bay	d		17 03										18 03										19 03		
Chestfield & Swalecliffe	d		17 06										18 06										19 06		
Whitstable	d		17 09										18 09										19 09		
Dover Priory 4	d	16 35										17 35										18 35			
Kearsney	d	16 39										17 39										18 39			
Shepherds Well	d	16 44										17 44										18 44			
Snowdown	d	16 48										17 48										18 48			
Aylesham	d	16 50										17 50										18 50			
Adisham	d	16 53										17 53										18 53			
Bekesbourne	d	16 57										17 57										18 57			
Canterbury East 4	d	17 02						17 25				18 02						18 25				19 02			
Selling	d	17 11										18 11										19 11			
Faversham 2	a	17 16	17 18					17 37				18 16	18 18					18 37				19 16	19 18		
	d		17 22	17 28				17 38		17 58			18 22	18 28				18 38		18 58			19 22	19 28	
Teynham	d							17 44										18 44							
Sheerness-on-Sea	d								17 42										18 42						
Queenborough	d								17 46										18 46						
Swale	d								17 50										18 50						
Kemsley	d								17 54										18 54						
Sittingbourne 4	a		17 29	17 36				17 48	17 59	18 06			18 29	18 36				18 48	18 59	19 06			19 29	19 36	
	d		17 30	17 37				17 49		18 07			18 30	18 37				18 49		19 07			19 30	19 37	
Newington	d							17 54										18 54							
Rainham (Kent)	d		17 38	17 45				17 59		18 15			18 38	18 45				18 59		19 15			19 38	19 45	
Gillingham (Kent) 4	d		17 43	17 50			17 54	18 04		18 20	18 24		18 43	18 50			18 54	19 04		19 20	19 24		19 43	19 50	
Chatham 4	d		17 48	17 54			17 58	18 08		18 24	18 28		18 48	18 54			18 58	19 08		19 24	19 28		19 48	19 54	
Rochester 4	d		17 50	17 57			18 00	18 11		18 27	18 30		18 50	18 57			19 00	19 11		19 27	19 30		19 50	19 57	
Strood 4	a			18 01			18 05			18 31	18 35			19 01			19 05			19 31	19 35			20 01	
Gravesend 4	a			18 12			18 17			18 42	18 47			19 12			19 17			19 42	19 47			20 12	
Greenhithe for Bluewater	a						18 23				18 53						19 23				19 53				
Dartford 4	a						18 28				18 58						19 28				19 58				
London Bridge 4 ⊖	a						19 04				19 34						20 04				20 34				
London Cannon Street 4 ⊖	a																								
London Waterloo (East) 4 ⊖	a						19 09				19 39						20 09				20 39				
London Charing Cross 4 ⊖	a						19 13				19 43						20 13				20 43				
Sole Street	d							18 21										19 21							
Meopham	d							18 24										19 24							
Longfield	d							18 28										19 28							
Farningham Road	d							18 32										19 32							
Swanley 4	a							18 37										19 37							
St Mary Cray	a							18 41										19 41							
Bromley South 4	a		18 16					18 47					19 16					19 47					20 16		
London Victoria 15 ⊖	a		18 35					19 05					19 35					20 05					20 35		
Elephant & Castle ⊖	a																								
London Blackfriars 3 ⊖	a																								
City Thameslink	a																								
Farringdon	a																								
Ebbsfleet International	a			18 16						18 46				19 16						19 46				20 16	
Stratford International ⊖	a			18 30						18 59				19 29						20 00				20 29	
St Pancras International	a			18 37						19 07				19 36						20 07				20 36	

A ⛴ from Margate

For further services to St Pancras International, Blackfriars and Elephant & Castle and onwards to Bromley South, St Mary Cray and Swanley please see table 52

Table 212R

Sundays

8 December to 11 May

Ramsgate, Dover, Sheerness-on-Sea and Medway - London

Network Diagram - see first Page of Table 212

		SE	SE	SE 1	SE	SE	SE	SE 1	SE 1	SE		SE	SE	SE 1	SE	SE	SE	SE 1	SE 1	SE		SE	SE	SE 1	SE
Ramsgate 4	d	19 01							19 35			20 01							20 35			21 01			
Dumpton Park	d								19 38										20 38						
Broadstairs	d	19 06							19 41			20 06							20 41			21 06			
Margate 4	d	19a11							19 46			20a11							20 46			21a11			
Westgate-on-Sea	d								19 50										20 50						
Birchington-on-Sea	d								19 54										20 54						
Herne Bay	d								20 03										21 03						
Chestfield & Swalecliffe	d								20 06										21 06						
Whitstable	d								20 09										21 09						
Dover Priory 4	d							19 35										20 35							
Kearsney	d							19 39										20 39							
Shepherds Well	d							19 44										20 44							
Snowdown	d							19 48										20 48							
Aylesham	d							19 50										20 50							
Adisham	d							19 53										20 53							
Bekesbourne	d							19 57										20 57							
Canterbury East 4	d			19 25				20 02						20 25				21 02							
Selling	d							20 11										21 11							
Faversham 2	a			19 37				20 16	20 18					20 37				21 16	21 18						
	d			19 38		19 58		20 22		20 28				20 38		20 58		21 22		21 28				21 38	
Teynham	d			19 44										20 44										21 44	
Sheerness-on-Sea	d				19 42										20 42										21 42
Queenborough	d				19 46										20 46										21 46
Swale	d				19 50										20 50										21 50
Kemsley	d				19 54										20 54										21 54
Sittingbourne 4	a			19 48	19 59	20 06		20 29		20 36				20 48	20 59	21 06		21 29		21 36				21 48	21 59
	d			19 49		20 07		20 30		20 37				20 49		21 07		21 30		21 37				21 49	
Newington	d			19 54										20 54										21 54	
Rainham (Kent)	d			19 59		20 15		20 38		20 45				20 59		21 15		21 38		21 45				21 59	
Gillingham (Kent) 4	d		19 54	20 04		20 20	20 24	20 43		20 50			20 54	21 04		21 20	21 24	21 43		21 50			21 54	22 04	
Chatham 4	d		19 58	20 08		20 24	20 28	20 48		20 54			20 58	21 08		21 24	21 28	21 48		21 54			21 58	22 08	
Rochester 4	d		20 00	20 11		20 27	20 30	20 50		20 57			21 00	21 11		21 27	21 30	21 50		21 57			22 00	22 11	
Strood 4	a		20 05			20 31	20 35			21 01			21 05			21 31	21 35			22 01			22 05		
Gravesend 4	a		20 17			20 42	20 47			21 12			21 17			21 42	21 47			22 12			22 17		
Greenhithe for Bluewater	a		20 23				20 53						21 23				21 53						22 23		
Dartford 4	a		20 28				20 58						21 28				21 58						22 28		
London Bridge 4 ⊖	a		21 04				21 34						22 04				22 34						23 04		
London Cannon Street 4 ⊖	a																								
London Waterloo (East) 4 ⊖	a		21 09				21 39						22 09				22 39						23 09		
London Charing Cross 4 ⊖	a		21 13				21 43						22 13				22 43						23 13		
Sole Street	d			20 21										21 21										22 21	
Meopham	d			20 24										21 24										22 24	
Longfield	d			20 28										21 28										22 28	
Farningham Road	d			20 32										21 32										22 32	
Swanley 4	a			20 37										21 37										22 37	
St Mary Cray	a			20 41										21 41										22 41	
Bromley South 4	a			20 47				21 16						21 47				22 16						22 47	
London Victoria 15 ⊖	a			21 05				21 35						22 05				22 35						23 05	
Elephant & Castle ⊖	a																								
London Blackfriars 3 ⊖	a																								
City Thameslink	a																								
Farringdon	a																								
Ebbsfleet International	a					20 46				21 16						21 46				22 16					
Stratford International ⊖	a					21 02				21 29						22 00				22 29					
St Pancras International	a					21 09				21 36						22 07				22 36					

For further services to St Pancras International, Blackfriars and Elephant & Castle and onwards to Bromley South, St Mary Cray and Swanley please see table 52

Table 212R

Sundays

8 December to 11 May

Ramsgate, Dover, Sheerness-on-Sea and Medway - London

Network Diagram - see first Page of Table 212

		SE	SE	SE ■1	SE ■1	SE	SE ■1	SE	SE ■1	SE	SE ■1	SE	SE
Ramsgate ■4	d				21 35	22 01					22 35	23 01	
Dumpton Park	d				21 38						22 38		
Broadstairs	d				21 41	22 06					22 41	23 06	
Margate ■4	d				21 46	22a11					22 46	23a11	
Westgate-on-Sea	d				21 50						22 50		
Birchington-on-Sea	d				21 54						22 54		
Herne Bay	d				22 03						23 03		
Chestfield & Swalecliffe	d				22 06						23 06		
Whitstable	d				22 09						23 09		
Dover Priory ■4	d			21 35			22 35						
Kearsney	d			21 39			22 39						
Shepherds Well	d			21 44			22 44						
Snowdown	d			21 48			22 48						
Aylesham	d			21 50			22 50						
Adisham	d			21 53			22 53						
Bekesbourne	d			21 57			22 57						
Canterbury East ■4	d			22 02			23 02						
Selling	d			22 11			23 11						
Faversham ■2	a			22 16	22 18		23 16				23 18		
	d	21 58		22 22					22 38		23 22		
Teynham	d								22 44				
Sheerness-on-Sea	d									22 42			23 42
Queenborough	d									22 46			23 46
Swale	d									22 50			23 50
Kemsley	d									22 54			23 54
Sittingbourne ■4	a	22 06		22 29					22 48	22 59	23 29		23 59
	d	22 07		22 30					22 49		23 30		
Newington	d								22 54				
Rainham (Kent)	d	22 15		22 38					22 59		23 38		
Gillingham (Kent) ■4	d	22 20	22 24	22 43				22 54	23 04		23 43		
Chatham ■4	d	22 24	22 28	22 48				22 58	23 08		23 48		
Rochester ■4	d	22 27	22 30	22 50				23 00	23 11		23 50		
Strood ■4	a	22 31	22 35					23 05					
Gravesend ■4	a	22 42	22 47					23 17					
Greenhithe for Bluewater	a		22 53					23 23					
Dartford ■4	a		22 58					23 28					
London Bridge ■4 ⊖	a		23 34										
London Cannon Street ■4 ⊖	a												
London Waterloo (East) ■4 ⊖	a		23 39										
London Charing Cross ■4 ⊖	a		23 43										
Sole Street	d								23 21				
Meopham	d								23 24				
Longfield	d								23 28				
Farningham Road	d								23 32				
Swanley ■4	a								23 37				
St Mary Cray	a								23 41				
Bromley South ■4	a			23 16					23 47		00 16		
London Victoria ■15 ⊖	a			23 35					00 05		00 35		
Elephant & Castle ⊖	a												
London Blackfriars ■3 ⊖	a												
City Thameslink	a												
Farringdon	a												
Ebbsfleet International	a	22 46											
Stratford International ⊖	a	22 59											
St Pancras International	a	23 06											

For further services to St Pancras International, Blackfriars and Elephant & Castle and onwards to Bromley South, St Mary Cray and Swanley please see table 52

Network Diagram for Tables 216, 217, 218, 219, 221, 222

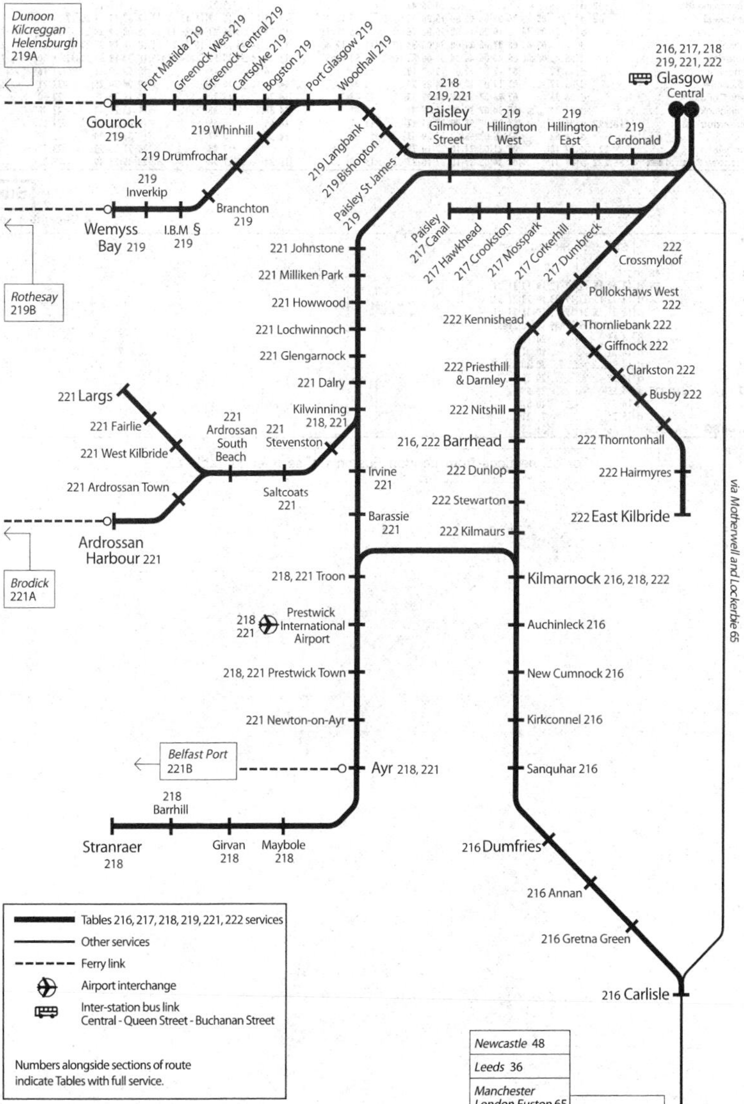

Dunoon
Kilcreggan
Helensburgh
219A
Fort Matilda 219
Greenock West 219
Greenock Central 219
Cartsdyke 219
Bogston 219
Port Glasgow 219
Woodhall 219
216, 217, 218
219, 221, 222
Glasgow
Central
Gourock
219
219 Whinhill
219 Drumfrochar
219
Inverkip
Wemyss
Bay 219
I.B.M §
219
Branchton
219
219 Langbank
219 Bishopton
Paisley St James
219
218
219, 221
Paisley
Gilmour
Street
219
Hillington
West
219
Hillington
East
219
Cardonald
Rothesay
219B
221 Johnstone
221 Milliken Park
221 Howwood
221 Lochwinnoch
221 Glengarnock
221 Dalry
Paisley
217 Canal
217 Hawkhead
217 Crookston
217 Mosspark
217 Corkerhill
217 Dumbreck
222
Crossmyloof
Pollokshaws West
222
222 Kennishead
Thornliebank 222
Giffnock 222
Clarkston 222
Busby 222
222 Priesthill
& Darnley
222 Nitshill
216, 222 Barrhead
222 Thorntonhall
222 Hairmyres
222 Dunlop
222 Stewarton
222 Kilmaurs
222 East Kilbride
221 Largs
221 Fairlie
221 West Kilbride
221
Ardrossan
South
Beach
221
Stevenston
Kilwinning
218, 221
221 Ardrossan Town
Saltcoats
221
Irvine
221
Barassie
221
Ardrossan
Harbour 221
Brodick
221A
218, 221 Troon
Kilmarnock 216, 218, 222
218
221
Prestwick
International
Airport
Auchinleck 216
218, 221 Prestwick Town
New Cumnock 216
221 Newton-on-Ayr
Kirkconnel 216
Belfast Port
221B
Ayr 218, 221
Sanquhar 216
218
Barrhill
Stranraer
218
Girvan
218
Maybole
218
216 Dumfries
216 Annan
216 Gretna Green
216 Carlisle
via Motherwell and Lockerbie 65
Tables 216, 217, 218, 219, 221, 222 services
Other services
Ferry link
Airport interchange
Inter-station bus link
Central - Queen Street - Buchanan Street
Numbers alongside sections of route
indicate Tables with full service.
Newcastle 48
Leeds 36
Manchester
London Euston 65

§ For authorized access to I.B.M only

TOCs operating on this network - ScotRail (SR)

Table 216

Mondays to Saturdays

9 December to 17 May

Carlisle and Dumfries - Kilmarnock and Glasgow Central

Network Diagram - refer to first Page of Table 216

Miles	Miles			SR	SR	SR SO	SR SX	NT SO	NT SX	SR SO	SR	SR SO	SR	SR SO	NT	SR	SR SO	SR	NT	SR SO	SR	SR
—	—	Newcastle 8	48 d					06 30	06 47						13 22				17 16			
0	0	**Carlisle 8**	65 d		05 23	06 08	06 08	08 15	08 15	09 55	11 15	12 20	13 12	14 22	15 12	16 17	17 12	17 57	19 17	20 22	21 12	23 10
9¾	9¾	Gretna Green	d		05 34	06 19	06 19	08 26	08 26	10 06	11 26	12 31	13 23	14 33	15 23	16 28	17 23	18 08	19 28	20 33	21 23	23 21
17½	17½	Annan	d		05 43	06 27	06 27	08 34	08 34	10 14	11 34	12 40	13 31	14 41	15 31	16 36	17 31	18 16	19 37	20 41	21 31	23 29
33	33	**Dumfries**	d	05 46	06a00	06 46	06 46	08 53	08 53	10a32	11 53	12a57	13 48	14a59	15 50	16a54	17a49	18 33	19 55	20a59	21 50	23a47
59¼	59¼	Sanquhar	d	06 12		07 12	07 12	09 19	09 19		12 19		14 16		16 16			18 59	20 21		22 16	
62½	62½	Kirkconnel	d	06 17		07 17	07 17	09 24	09 24		12 24		14 21		16 21			19 04	20 26		22 21	
69¾	69¾	New Cumnock	d	06 26		07 26	07 26	09 33	09 33		12 33		14 30		16 30			19 15	20 35		22 30	
77¼	77¼	Auchinleck	d	06 34		07 34	07 34	09 41	09 41		12 41		14 38		16 38			19 23	20 44		22 38	
91	91	**Kilmarnock 3**	218,222 a	06 51		07 55	07 55	09 57	09 57		12 57		14 55		16 55			19 40	21 00		22 55	
—	—		d	06 52		07 55	07 55	09 57	09 57		12 57		14 57		16 57			19 57	21 00		22 57	
107¾	—	Barrhead	222 d	07 18		08 21	08 21	10 22	10 22						17 22			20 21	21 25		23 22	
115¼	—	**Glasgow Central 15**	65,222 a	07 31		08 34	08 37	10 37	10 37		13 35		15 34		17 36			20 35	21 39		23 36	

Sundays

8 December to 11 May

		SR	SR	SR	SR	SR
Newcastle 8	48 d					
Carlisle 8	65 d	13 12	15 12	17 12	19 12	21 22
Gretna Green	d	13 23	15 23	17 23	19 23	21 33
Annan	d	13 31	15 31	17 31	19 31	21 41
Dumfries	d	13 50	15a49	17a49	19 50	21a59
Sanquhar	d	14 16			20 16	
Kirkconnel	d	14 21			20 21	
New Cumnock	d	14 30			20 30	
Auchinleck	d	14 38			20 38	
Kilmarnock 3	218,222 a	14 55			20 55	
	d	14 57			20 57	
Barrhead	222 d	15 21			21 21	
Glasgow Central 15	65,222 a	15 36			21 35	

For connections from London Euston please refer to Table 65

Table 216R

Mondays to Saturdays

9 December to 17 May

Glasgow Central and Kilmarnock - Dumfries and Carlisle

Network Diagram - refer to first Page of Table 216

Miles	Miles		SR MO	NT MO	SR MX	SR	SR	SR SO	SR SX	SR	SR	SR SO	SR	SR SO	SR	SR	SR SO	SR	SR	SR SO	SR	SR
0	—	**Glasgow Central [15]** 65,222 d								07 08	08 37		10 12		12 12	13 12			16 12		17 42	19 12
7½	—	Barrhead 222 d								07 22	08 51								16 24		17 56	19 24
24¼	74½	**Kilmarnock [3]** 218,222 a								07 50	09 18		10 51		12 50	13 50			16 51		18 22	19 51
—	—	d								07 50	09 18		10 51		12 50	13 50			16 51		18 26	19 51
38	89¼	Auchinleck d			00 18					08 07	09 35		11 08		13 07	14 07			17 08		18 42	20 08
45½	96¾	New Cumnock d			00 26					08 15	09 43		11 16		13 15	14 15			17 16		18 51	20 16
52¾	104½	Kirkconnel d			00 39					08 24	09 52		11 25		13 24	14 24			17 25		18 59	20 25
56	107¾	Sanquhar d			00 44					08 29	09 57		11 30		13 29	14 29			17 30		19 04	20 30
82¼	135	**Dumfries** d			01a15	04 58	06 17	07 43	07 45	08 58	10 25	11 02	11 58	13 10	13 57	14 57	16 02	17 07	17 58	18 41	19 33	20 57
97¾	150½	Annan d	00 11	00 11		05 13	06 32	07 58	08 00	09 13	10 40	11 17	12 13	13 25	14 13	15 12	16 17	17 22	18 13	18 56	19 48	21 12
105½	158	Gretna Green d	00 20	00 20		05 22	06 41	08 07	08 09	09 22	10 49	11 26	12 22	13 34	14 21	15 21	16 26	17 31	18 22	19 05	19 57	21 21
115½	168	**Carlisle [8]** 65 a	00 34	00 34		05 35	06 54	08 20	08 22	09 37	11 02	11 39	12 35	13 52	14 35	15 34	16 39	17 44	18 35	19 18	20 11	21 43
—	—	Newcastle [8] 48 a					08 58		09 59	11 07					15 57				20 16			

	SR SO	SR SX	SR SO	SR SX
Glasgow Central [15] 65,222 d		21 12	22 12	23 12
Barrhead 222 d		21 26	22 23	23 33
Kilmarnock [3] 218,222 a		21 53	22 50	23 59
d		21 53	22 51	23 59
Auchinleck d		22 10	23 07	00 18
New Cumnock d		22 18	23 16	00 26
Kirkconnel d		22 27	23 24	00 39
Sanquhar d		22 32	23 29	00 44
Dumfries d	22 13	23 00	23 57	01a15
Annan d	22 28	23 15	00 12	
Gretna Green d	22 37	23 24	00 21	
Carlisle [8] 65 a	22 50	23 37	00 34	
Newcastle [8] 48 a				

Sundays

8 December to 11 May

	SR A	SR	SR	SR	SR	SR
Glasgow Central [15] 65,222 d				15 12		22 12
Barrhead 222 d				15 26		22 23
Kilmarnock [3] 218,222 a				15 52		22 48
d				15 53		22 49
Auchinleck d				16 10		23 06
New Cumnock d				16 18		23 14
Kirkconnel d				16 27		23 23
Sanquhar d				16 32		23 28
Dumfries d		13 00	15 01	17 00	19 01	23 56
Annan d	00 12	13 15	15 16	17 15	19 16	00 11
Gretna Green d	00 21	13 24	15 25	17 24	19 25	00 20
Carlisle [8] 65 a	00 34	13 37	15 42	17 37	19 38	00 34
Newcastle [8] 48 a						

A not 8 December

For connections to London Euston please see Table 65

Table 217

Mondays to Saturdays

9 December to 17 May

Network Diagram - refer to first Page of Table 216

Glasgow Central - Paisley Canal

Miles			SR SO	SR		SR
0	**Glasgow Central** 15	d	00 12	06 12	and every 30 minutes until	23 12
1¾	Dumbreck	d	00 17	06 17		23 17
3¼	Corkerhill	d	00 20	06 20		23 20
3¾	Mosspark	d	00 22	06 22		23 22
4½	Crookston	d	00 24	06 24		23 24
6½	Hawkhead	d	00 27	06 27		23 27
7	**Paisley Canal**	a	00 30	06 30		23 30

No Sunday Service

Table 217R

Mondays to Saturdays

9 December to 17 May

Network Diagram - refer to first Page of Table 216

Paisley Canal - Glasgow Central

Miles			SR	SR	SR	SR	SR		SR	SR	SR	SR	SR	SR	SR	SR	SR	SR	SR	SR	SR	SR
0	**Paisley Canal**	d	06 35	07 05	07 35	08 05	08 35	and every 30 minutes until	15 05	15 35	16 05	16 35	17 05	17 35	18 05	18 35	19 05	19 35	20 05	20 35	21 05	21 35
0½	Hawkhead	d	06 37	07 07	07 37	08 07	08 37		15 07	15 37	16 07	16 37	17 07	17 37	18 07	18 37	19 07	19 37	20 07	20 37	21 07	21 37
2½	Crookston	d	06 40	07 10	07 40	08 10	08 40		15 10	15 40	16 10	16 40	17 10	17 40	18 10	18 40	19 10	19 40	20 10	20 40	21 10	21 40
3¼	Mosspark	d	06 43	07 13	07 43	08 13	08 43		15 13	15 43	16 13	16 43	17 13	17 43	18 13	18 43	19 13	19 43	20 13	20 43	21 13	21 43
3¾	Corkerhill	d	06 45	07 15	07 45	08 15	08 45		15 15	15 45	16 15	16 45	17 15	17 45	18 15	18 45	19 15	19 45	20 15	20 45	21 15	21 45
5¼	Dumbreck	d	06 48	07 18	07 48	08 18	08 48		15 18	15 48	16 18	16 48	17 18	17 48	18 18	18 48	19 18	19 48	20 18	20 48	21 18	21 48
7	**Glasgow Central** 15	a	06 56	07 26	07 57	08 25	08 54		15 24	15 57	16 25	16 56	17 27	17 56	18 24	18 54	19 27	19 56	20 25	20 56	21 27	21 56

		SR	SR	SR
Paisley Canal	d	22 05	22 35	23 05
Hawkhead	d	22 07	22 37	23 07
Crookston	d	22 10	22 40	23 10
Mosspark	d	22 13	22 43	23 13
Corkerhill	d	22 15	22 45	23 15
Dumbreck	d	22 18	22 48	23 18
Glasgow Central 15	a	22 26	22 56	23 29

No Sunday Service

Table 218

Mondays to Saturdays

9 December to 17 May

Glasgow Central and Kilmarnock - Girvan, Stranraer

Network Diagram - refer to first Page of Table 216

Miles	Miles			SR MX	SR	SR	SR	SR	SR ◇	SR	SR ◇	SR	SR	SR	SR	SR	SR	SR	SR SX	SR SO
0	—	**Glasgow Cen.** 15 219,221,222	d				*07c30*	*08c00*	09 38	*10c25*	11 50	*12c25*	*13c25*	15 12	*16c30*	17 12	*18c25*	*20c30*	22 12	*22c30*
7¼	—	Paisley Gilmour St. 219,221	d						09 50		12 03									
—	—	Kilwinning 4 221	d						10 14		12 21									
—	0	**Kilmarnock** 3 222	a											15 50		17 51			22 50	
—	—		d					08 37		11 04		13 04	14 04	16 03	17 04	18 03	19 05	21 10	23 06	23 06
35	10¾	Troon 221	d					08 49		11 16		13 16	14 16	16 16	17 16	18 17	19 16	21 21	23 18	23 18
37¾	11¾	Prestwick Int. Airport 221	d					08 54		11 21		13 21	14 21	16 21	17 21	18 21	19 21	21 26	23 23	23 23
38¼	12½	Prestwick Town 221	d					08 56		11 23		13 23	14 23	16 23	17 23	18 23	19 23	21 28	23 25	23 25
41½	15½	**Ayr** 221	a					09 03	10 38	11 28	12 41	13 29	14 30	16 30	17 31	18 30	19 31	21 34	23 30	23 30
—	—		d		05 28	06 35	08 37	09 05	10 39	11 29	12 42	13 34	14 31	16 31	17 31	18 31	19 32	21 35	23 31	23 31
50½	24½	Maybole	d		05 39	06 46	08 48	09 16	10 49	11 41	12 53	13 46	14 42	16 43	17 42	18 42	19 44	21 46	23 42	23 42
62¾	36½	**Girvan**	d		05a55	07a02	09 03	09a32	11 04	11a57	13 08	14a10	14a58	16a59	17 58	18a58	20 03	22a02	23 57	23 57
75	51¼	Barrhill	d	00 16			09 22		11 24		13 27				18 18		20 23		00 16	00 16
101	77¼	**Stranraer**	a	00 52			09 58		12 00		14 04				18 54		20 59		00 52	00 52

Sundays

8 December to 11 May

		SR A	SR ◇	SR ◇	SR
Glasgow Cen. 15 219,221,222	d		11 55	15 22	17 54
Paisley Gilmour St. 219,221	d		12 06	15 33	18 05
Kilwinning 4 221	d		12 23	15 50	18 22
Kilmarnock 3 222	a				
	d				
Troon 221	d				
Prestwick Int. Airport 221	d				
Prestwick Town 221	d				
Ayr 221	a		12 41	16 08	18 40
	d		12 42	16 14	18 42
Maybole	d		12 53	16 25	18 53
Girvan	d		13 08	16 40	19 08
Barrhill	d	00 16	13 27	16 59	19 27
Stranraer	a	00 52	14 04	17 35	20 04

A not 8 December

c Change at Ayr (Table 221)

Table 218R

Mondays to Saturdays

9 December to 17 May

Stranraer and Girvan - Kilmarnock and Glasgow Central

Network Diagram - refer to first Page of Table 216

Miles	Miles			SR	SR	SR ◇	SR	SR ◇	SR	SR ◇	SR	SR SO	SR SX	SR ◇	SR	SR	SR ◇	SR ◇	SR
0	—	**Stranraer**	d			07 01		10 10		12 50				14 43			19 08	21 13	
26	—	Barrhill	d			07 35		10 44		13 30				15 17			19 43	21 48	
38¼	—	**Girvan**	d	06 00	07 07	07 53	09 44	11 06	12 43	13 48	14 33	15 03	15 07	15 35	17 33	19 10	20 01	22 06	22 27
50½	—	Maybole	d	06 16	07 23	08 09	10 00	11 22	13 07	14 04	14 56	15 19	15 23	15 51	17 57	19 26	20 17	22 22	22 43
59¼	—	**Ayr**	a	06 28	07 35	08 21	10 12	11 35	13 19	14 16	15 11	15 31	15 35	16 04	18 08	19 38	20 30	22 34	22 55
—	—		d		07 36		10 13	11 35	13 20	14 17	15 18	15 32	15 36	16 05	18 15	19 39	20 30	22 35	
62½	—	Prestwick Town 221	a		07 41		10 18	11 40	13 25		15 23			16 10	18 20	19 44		22 40	
63	—	Prestwick Int. Airport 221	a				10 21	11 43	13 27		15 25			16 12	18 22	19 46			
63¼	0	Troon 221	a		07 47		10 26	11 48	13 32		15 30			16 17	18 29	19 51		22 45	
—	10¾	**Kilmarnock** 3	a		08 07		10 41	12 04	13 48		15 47			16 34	18 46	20 07			
—	—		d								15 57								
—	—	Glengarnock	d																
74¼	—	Kilwinning 4 221	a							14 37		15 53	15 53				20 58	22 55	
93¾	—	Paisley Gilmour St. 219,221	a							14 58		16 16	16 16				21 18	23 14	
101	—	**Glasgow Cen.** 15 219,221,222	a	*07c38*	*08c31*	*09c22*	*11c06*	*12c44*	*14c07*	15 12	16 33	16 36	16 36	*17c09*	*19c15*	*20c37*	21 31	23 25	*00c01*

Sundays

8 December to 11 May

		SR ◇	SR ◇	SR ◇
Stranraer	d	10 40	14 40	19 40
Barrhill	d	11 14	15 14	20 19
Girvan	d	11 32	15 32	20 37
Maybole	d	11 48	15 48	20 53
Ayr	a	12 01	16 01	21 06
	d	12 01	16 01	21 06
Prestwick Town 221	a			
Prestwick Int. Airport 221	a			
Troon 221	a			
Kilmarnock 3	a			
	d			
Glengarnock	d			
Kilwinning 4 221	a	12 16	16 16	21 21
Paisley Gilmour St. 219,221	a	12 35	16 36	21 40
Glasgow Cen. 15 219,221,222	a	12 49	16 50	21 54

c Change at Ayr (Table 221)

Table 219

Mondays to Saturdays

9 December to 17 May

Glasgow Central - Wemyss Bay and Gourock

Network Diagram - refer to first Page of Table 216

Miles	Miles			SR	SR MX	SR	SR	SR	SR	SR	SR	SR		SR	SR	SR SX	SR SO	SR	SR	SR	SR	SR		SR	SR
0	0	**Glasgow Central** 15 221	d			05 55	06 05	06 25	06 32	06 54	07 06	07 21		07 39	07 50	08 03	08 03	08 25	08 40	08 55	09 08	09 25		09 36	09 55
3¾	3¾	Cardonald	d						06 39		07 13	07 28		07 46		08 10	08 10		08 47		09 15			09 43	
4½	4½	Hillington East	d				06 12		06 41		07 15	07 30		07 48		08 12	08 12		08 49		09 17			09 45	
5	5	Hillington West	d		00 01	06 03	06 14		06 43	07 02	07 17	07 32		07 50	07 59	08 14	08 14		08 51		09 19			09 47	
7¼	7¼	Paisley Gilmour Street 221 ⇐	a		00 05	06 08	06 18	06 35	06 47	07 06	07 22	07 36		07 53	08 03	08 18	08 18	08 35	08 56	09 05	09 23	09 34		09 53	10 05
—	—		d		00 05	06 08	06 19	06 36	06 47	07 06	07 22	07 36		07 53	08 04	08 18	08 18	08 36	08 56	09 07	09 23	09 35		09 53	10 06
8	8	Paisley St James	d		00 07			06 38			07 24			07 55		08 20	08 20		08 58		09 25			09 55	
12¼	12¼	Bishopton	d		00 12	06 14	06 24	06 43	06 53	07 13	07 29	07 43		08 00	08 10	08 25	08 25	08 41	09 03	09 11	09 30	09 40		10 00	10 11
16¼	16¼	Langbank	d		00 18			06 48			07 35			08 07		08 31	08 31		09 09		09 36			10 06	
19	19	Woodhall	d		00 22		06 32	06 52	07 00		07 39	07 50		08 11		08 35	08 35		09 13		09 40			10 10	
20¼	20¼	Port Glasgow	d		00 25	06 23	06 35	06 55	07 04	07 22	07 42	07 53		08 15	08 19	08 38	08 38	08 50	09 15	09 20	09 43	09 49		10 13	10 20
—	22½	Whinhill	d				06 39		07 08						08 23					09 24					10 24
—	23	Drumfrochar	d				06 41		07 10						08 26					09 28					10 27
—	24¾	Branchton	d				06 44		07 13						08 29					09 31					10 30
—	25½	I.B.M.	d				06 47		07 16						08 31					09 32					10 32
—	28¾	Inverkip	d				06 52		07 27						08 36					09 37					10 37
—	31	**Wemyss Bay**	a				06 57		07 33						08 41					09 44					10 43
21¼	—	Bogston	d		00 27			06 57		07 24	07 44	07 55		08 17		08 40	08 40		09 17		09 45			10 15	
22	—	Cartsdyke	d		00 29	06 26		07 00		07 26	07 46	07 57		08 19		08 42	08 42		09 19		09 47			10 17	
23	—	Greenock Central	d	00 01	00 31	06 28		07 02		07 28	07 48	07 59		08 21		08 44	08 44	08 55	09 21		09 49	09 54		10 19	
23¾	—	Greenock West	d	00 03	00 33	06 30		07 04		07 30	07 50	08 01		08 23		08 46	08 46	08 57	09 23		09 51	09 56		10 21	
25	—	Fort Matilda	d	00 06	00 36			07 07		07 33	07 53	08 04		08 26		08 49	08 49	09 00	09 26		09 54	09 59		10 24	
26¼	—	**Gourock**	a	00 11	00 40	06 36		07 11		07 37	07 58	08 09		08 30		08 54	08 55	09 04	09 32		09 59	10 04		10 28	

		SR	SR	SR	SR	SR	SR	SR		SR	SR	SR	SR	SR	SR	SR	SR	SR		SR	SR	SR	SR	SR	SR
Glasgow Central 15 221	d	10 06	10 25	10 36	10 55	11 06	11 25	11 36		11 55	12 06	12 25	12 36	12 55	13 06	13 25	13 36	13 55		14 06	14 25	14 36	14 55	15 06	15 25
Cardonald	d	10 13		10 43		11 13		11 43			12 13		12 43		13 13		13 43			14 13		14 43		15 13	
Hillington East	d	10 15		10 45		11 15		11 45			12 15		12 45		13 15		13 45			14 15		14 45		15 15	
Hillington West	d	10 17		10 47		11 17		11 47			12 17		12 47		13 17		13 47			14 17		14 47		15 17	
Paisley Gilmour Street 221 ⇐	a	10 21	10 35	10 51	11 05	11 21	11 35	11 51		12 05	12 21	12 36	12 51	13 05	13 24	13 36	13 51	14 06		14 21	14 35	14 51	15 06	15 21	15 36
	d	10 21	10 36	10 51	11 06	11 21	11 36	11 51		12 06	12 21	12 36	12 51	13 06	13 25	13 36	13 51	14 06		14 21	14 36	14 51	15 06	15 21	15 37
Paisley St James	d	10 23		10 53		11 23		11 53			12 23		12 53		13 27		13 53			14 23		14 53		15 23	
Bishopton	d	10 28	10 41	10 58	11 11	11 28	11 41	11 58		12 11	12 28	12 41	12 58	13 11	13 32	13 41	13 58	14 11		14 28	14 41	14 58	15 11	15 28	15 42
Langbank	d	10 34		11 04		11 34		12 04			12 34		13 04		13 37		14 04			14 34		15 04		15 34	
Woodhall	d	10 38		11 08		11 38		12 08			12 38		13 08		13 41		14 08			14 38		15 08		15 38	
Port Glasgow	d	10 41	10 50	11 11	11 20	11 41	11 50	12 11		12 20	12 41	12 50	13 11	13 20	13 44	13 50	14 11	14 20		14 41	14 50	15 11	15 20	15 41	15 51
Whinhill	d				11 24					12 24				13 24				14 24					15 24		
Drumfrochar	d				11 27					12 27				13 27				14 27					15 27		
Branchton	d				11 30					12 30				13 30				14 30					15 30		
I.B.M.	d				11 32					12 32				13 32				14 32					15 32		
Inverkip	d				11 37					12 37				13 37				14 37					15 37		
Wemyss Bay	a				11 43					12 43				13 43				14 43					15 43		
Bogston	d	10 43		11 13		11 43		12 13			12 43		13 13		13 46		14 13			14 43		15 13		15 43	
Cartsdyke	d	10 45		11 15		11 45		12 15			12 45		13 15		13 49		14 15			14 45		15 15		15 45	
Greenock Central	d	10 47	10 55	11 17		11 47	11 55	12 17			12 47	12 55	13 17		13 51	13 55	14 17			14 47	14 55	15 17		15 47	15 56
Greenock West	d	10 49	10 57	11 19		11 49	11 57	12 19			12 49	12 57	13 19		13 53	13 57	14 19			14 49	14 57	15 19		15 49	15 58
Fort Matilda	d	10 52	11 00	11 22		11 52	12 00	12 22			12 52	13 00	13 22		13 56	14 00	14 22			14 52	15 00	15 22		15 52	16 01
Gourock	a	10 57	11 04	11 27		11 59	12 04	12 27			12 58	13 04	13 27		13 59	14 04	14 27			14 58	15 04	15 27		15 57	16 05

		SR	SR	SR		SR	SR	SR	SR	SR	SR	SR	SR	SR		SR	SR	SR	SR	SR	SR	SR	SR	SR	
Glasgow Central 15 221	d	15 36	15 47	16 06		16 18	16 32	16 55	17 06	17 16	17 25	17 37	17 55	18 06		18 25	18 38	18 55	19 06	19 25	19 36	19 50	20 06	20 36	
Cardonald	d	15 44		16 13		16 25	16 41		17 13	17 23		17 44		18 13			18 45		19 13		19 43		20 13	20 43	
Hillington East	d	15 46		16 15		16 27	16 43		17 15	17 25		17 46		18 15			18 47		19 15		19 45		20 15	20 45	
Hillington West	d	15 48	15 55	16 17		16 29	16 45	17 03	17 17			17 48		18 17			18 49		19 17		19 47		20 17	20 47	
Paisley Gilmour Street 221 ⇐	a	15 51	15 58	16 21		16 33	16 49	17 07	17 21	17 30	17 36	17 52	18 06	18 21		18 37	18 53	19 05	19 22	19 35	19 51	20 00	20 21	20 51	
	d	15 51	15 59	16 21		16 34	16 49	17 08	17 21	17 30	17 37	17 52	18 06	18 21		18 37	18 53	19 06	19 22	19 36	19 51	20 01	20 21	20 51	
Paisley St James	d	15 53		16 23		16 36			17 23			17 54		18 23			18 55		19 24		19 53		20 23	20 53	
Bishopton	d	15 58	16 05	16 28		16 41	16 55	17 13	17 28	17 36		17 59	18 12	18 28		18 43	19 00	19 11	19 29	19 41	19 58	20 06	20 28	20 58	
Langbank	d	16 04		16 34		16 46			17 34			18 05		18 34			19 06		19 35		20 04		20 34	21 04	
Woodhall	d	16 08		16 38		16 50			17 38			18 09		18 38			19 10		19 39		20 08		20 38	21 08	
Port Glasgow	d	16 11	16 15	16 41		16 53	17 04	17 22	17 41	17 46	17 50	18 12	18 21	18 41		18 52	19 15	19 20	19 42	19 50	20 11	20 16	20 41	21 11	
Whinhill	d		16 19				17 08			17 50			18 25				19 19				20 15			21 15	
Drumfrochar	d		16 21				17 11			17 52			18 27				19 22				20 17			21 17	
Branchton	d		16 24				17 14			17 55			18 30				19 25				20 20			21 20	
I.B.M.	d		16 27							17 58			18 33				19 27				20 23			21 23	
Inverkip	d		16 32				17 19			18 03			18 38				19 32				20 28			21 28	
Wemyss Bay	a		16 38				17 24			18 07			18 43				19 37				20 33			21 33	
Bogston	d	16 13		16 43		16 55		17 24	17 43			18 14		18 43				19 22	19 44				20 43		
Cartsdyke	d	16 16		16 45		16 58		17 27	17 45			18 16		18 45				19 25	19 46			20 19	20 45		
Greenock Central	d	16 18		16 47		17 00		17 29	17 47		17 54	18 18		18 47		18 56		19 27	19 48	19 55		20 21	20 47		
Greenock West	d	16 20		16 49		17 02		17 31	17 49		17 56	18 20		18 49		18 58		19 29	19 50	19 57		20 23	20 49		
Fort Matilda	d	16 23		16 52		17 05		17 34	17 52		17 59	18 23		18 52		19 01		19 32	19 53	20 00		20 26	20 52		
Gourock	a	16 27		16 57		17 09		17 38	17 57		18 03	18 28		18 57		19 05		19 36	19 58	20 04		20 30	20 57		

Table 219

Glasgow Central - Wemyss Bay and Gourock

Mondays to Saturdays

9 December to 17 May

Network Diagram - refer to first Page of Table 216

Station		SR	SR	SR	SR	SR	SR	SR	SR	SR
Glasgow Central 15 221	d	20 50	21 06	21 36	21 50	22 06	22 36	22 50	23 20	23 50
Cardonald	d		21 13	21 43		22 13	22 43		23 27	23 57
Hillington East	d		21 15	21 45		22 15	22 45		23 29	23 59
Hillington West	d		21 17	21 47		22 17	22 47		23 31	00 01
Paisley Gilmour Street 221 ✈	a	21 00	21 21	21 51	22 00	22 21	22 51	23 00	23 35	00 05
	d	21 01	21 21	21 51	22 01	22 21	22 51	23 01	23 35	00 05
Paisley St James	d		21 23	21 53		22 23	22 53		23 37	00 07
Bishopton	d	21 06	21 28	21 58	22 06	22 28	22 58	23 06	23 42	00 12
Langbank	d		21 34	22 04		22 34	23 04		23 48	00 18
Woodhall	d		21 38	22 08		22 38	23 08		23 52	00 22
Port Glasgow	d	21 15	21 41	22 11	22 16	22 41	23 11	23 15	23 55	00 25
Whinhill	d			22 15			23 15			
Drumfrochar	d			22 17			23 17			
Branchton	d			22 20			23 20			
I.B.M.	d			22 23			23 23			
Inverkip	d			22 28			23 28			
Wemyss Bay	a			22 33			23 33			
Bogston	d		21 43			22 43			23 57	00 27
Cartsdyke	d	21 18	21 45		22 19	22 45		23 18	23 59	00 29
Greenock Central	d	21 20	21 47		22 21	22 47		23 20	00 01	00 31
Greenock West	d	21 22	21 49		22 23	22 49		23 22	00 03	00 33
Fort Matilda	d	21 25	21 52		22 26	22 52		23 25	00 06	00 36
Gourock	a	21 30	21 57		22 30	22 57		23 30	00 11	00 40

Sundays

8 December to 11 May

Station		SR A	SR A	SR	SR	SR		SR	SR	SR	SR	SR	SR	SR	SR	SR	SR		SR	SR	SR
Glasgow Central 15 221	d			07 20	07 50	08 20		11 50	12 20	12 50	13 20	13 50	14 20	14 50	15 20	15 50	16 20		19 50	20 20	21 20
Cardonald	d			07 27		08 27			12 27		13 27		14 27		15 27		16 27			20 27	21 27
Hillington East	d			07 29	07 57	08 29		11 57	12 29	12 57	13 29	13 57	14 29	14 57	15 29	15 57	16 29		19 57	20 29	21 29
Hillington West	d		00 01	07 31		08 31			12 31	12 59	13 31		14 31		15 31		16 31			20 31	21 31
Paisley Gilmour Street 221 ✈	a		00 05	07 35	08 02	08 35		12 02	12 35	13 02	13 35	14 02	14 35	15 02	15 35	16 02	16 35		20 02	20 35	21 35
	d		00 05	07 35	08 02	08 35		12 02	12 35	13 02	13 35	14 02	14 35	15 02	15 36	16 02	16 35		20 02	20 35	21 35
Paisley St James	d		00 07			08 37			12 37		13 37		14 37		15 38		16 37			20 37	21 37
Bishopton	d		00 12	07 42	08 08	08 42	and at	12 08	12 42	13 08	13 42	14 08	14 42	15 08	15 43	16 08	16 42	and at	20 08	20 42	21 42
Langbank	d		00 18			08 48	the same		12 48		13 48		14 48		15 48		16 48	the same		20 48	21 48
Woodhall	d		00 22	07 49		08 52	minutes		12 52		13 52		14 52		15 52		16 52	minutes		20 52	21 52
Port Glasgow	d		00 25	07 52	08 17	08 55	past	12 17	12 55	13 17	13 55	14 17	14 55	15 17	15 55	16 17	16 55	past	20 17	20 55	21 55
Whinhill	d				08 21		each	12 21		13 21		14 21		15 21		16 21		each	20 21		
Drumfrochar	d				08 23		hour until	12 23		13 23		14 23		15 23		16 23		hour until	20 23		
Branchton	d				08 26			12 26		13 26		14 26		15 26		16 26			20 26		
I.B.M.	d				08 29			12 29		13 29		14 29		15 29		16 29			20 29		
Inverkip	d				08 34			12 34		13 34		14 34		15 34		16 34			20 34		
Wemyss Bay	a				08 39			12 39		13 40		14 39		15 39		16 39			20 39		
Bogston	d		00 27	07 54		08 57			12 57		13 57		14 57		15 57		16 57			20 57	21 57
Cartsdyke	d		00 29	07 57		08 59			12 59		13 59		14 59		16 00		16 59			20 59	21 59
Greenock Central	d	00 01	00 31	07 59		09 01			13 01		14 01		15 01		16 02		17 01			21 01	22 01
Greenock West	d	00 03	00 33	08 01		09 03			13 03		14 03		15 03		16 04		17 03			21 03	22 03
Fort Matilda	d	00 06	00 36			09 06			13 06		14 06		15 06		16 07		17 06			21 06	22 06
Gourock	a	00 11	00 40	08 06		09 11			13 11		14 11		15 11		16 11		17 11			21 11	22 11

Station		SR	SR
Glasgow Central 15 221	d	22 20	23 20
Cardonald	d	22 27	23 27
Hillington East	d	22 29	23 29
Hillington West	d	22 31	23 31
Paisley Gilmour Street 221 ✈	a	22 35	23 35
	d	22 35	23 35
Paisley St James	d	22 37	23 37
Bishopton	d	22 42	23 42
Langbank	d	22 48	23 48
Woodhall	d	22 52	23 52
Port Glasgow	d	22 55	23 55
Whinhill	d		
Drumfrochar	d		
Branchton	d		
I.B.M.	d		
Inverkip	d		
Wemyss Bay	a		
Bogston	d	22 57	23 57
Cartsdyke	d	22 59	23 59
Greenock Central	d	23 01	00 01
Greenock West	d	23 03	00 03
Fort Matilda	d	23 06	00 06
Gourock	a	23 11	00 11

A not 8 December

Table 219R

Mondays to Saturdays

9 December to 17 May

Network Diagram - refer to first Page of Table 216

Gourock and Wemyss Bay - Glasgow Central

Miles	Miles	Station		SR MX	SR	SR	SR SX	SR SO	SR SX	SR SX		SR SO	SR	SR SX	SR SO	SR SX	SR	SR	SR SX	SR		SR	SR	SR	SR
0	—	**Gourock**	d		05 20	06 05	06 25	06 38	06 47	07 07		07 08		07 28	07 38	07 47	07 51		08 10	08 23		08 38		09 08	09 24
1¼	—	Fort Matilda	d		05 23	06 08	06 28	06 41	06 50	07 10		07 11		07 31	07 41		07 54		08 13	08 26		08 41		09 11	09 27
2½	—	Greenock West	d		05 26	06 11	06 31	06 44	06 53	07 13		07 14		07 34	07 44	07 52	07 57		08 16	08 29		08 44		09 14	09 30
3¼	—	Greenock Central	d		05 28	06 13	06 33	06 46	06 55	07 15		07 16		07 36	07 46	07 54	07 59		08 18	08 31		08 46		09 16	09 32
4¼	—	Cartsdyke	d		05 31	06 16	06 36	06 49	06 58	07 18		07 19		07 39	07 49		08 02			08 34		08 49		09 19	
5	—	Bogston	d		05 33		06 38	06 51	07 00	07 20		07 21		07 41	07 51		08 04			08 36		08 51		09 21	
—	0	**Wemyss Bay**	d										07 16					07 54					08 57		
—	2¼	Inverkip	d										07 20					07 58					09 01		
—	4¾	I.B.M.	d										07 25					08 03					09 06		
—	6¼	Branchton	d										07 27					08 05					09 08		
—	8	Drumfrochar	d										07 30					08 08					09 11		
—	8½	Whinhill	d										07 32					08 10					09 13		
6	10¾	Port Glasgow	d		05 35	06 19	06 40	06 53	07 02	07 22		07 23	07 37	07 43	07 53	07 59	08 06	08 15	08 23	08 38		08 53	09 18	09 23	09 37
7¼	12	Woodhall	d		05 38		06 43	06 56	07 05			07 26	07 39	07 46	07 56		08 09	08 17		08 41		08 56		09 26	
10	14¾	Langbank	d		05 42		06 47	07 00	07 09			07 30		07 50	08 00			08 21		08 45		09 00		09 30	
14	18¾	Bishopton	d		05 47	06 28	06 52	07 05	07 14	07 31		07 35	07 47	07 55	08 05	08 08	08 16	08 27	08 32	08 50		09 05	09 27	09 35	09 46
18¼	23	Paisley St James	d		05 52	06 33	06 57	07 10	07 19			07 40		08 00	08 10			08 32		08 55		09 10		09 40	
19	23¾	Paisley Gilmour Street 221	a		05 55	06 36	07 00	07 13	07 22	07 37		07 43	07 53	08 03	08 13	08 14	08 22	08 34	08 38	08 58		09 13	09 33	09 43	09 52
—	—		d		05 55	06 36	07 00	07 13	07 22	07 38		07 43	07 54	08 04	08 14	08 14	08 23	08 35	08 38	08 58		09 13	09 33	09 43	09 52
21¼	26	Hillington West	d	00 02	05 59	06 40	07 04	07 17	07 26	07 41		07 47	07 57	08 07	08 18	08 18	08 26			09 02		09 17		09 47	
21¾	26½	Hillington East	d	00 04	06 01	06 42	07 06	07 19	07 28	07 43		07 49	07 59	08 09	08 20	08 20	08 28			09 04		09 19		09 49	
22½	27¼	Cardonald	d	00 06	06 03	06 44	07 08	07 21	07 30	07 45		07 51	08 01	08 11	08 22	08 22	08 30			09 06		09 21		09 51	
26½	31	**Glasgow Central** 15 221	a	00 14	06 11	06 52	07 16	07 29	07 38	07 54		07 59	08 09	08 19	08 31	08 31	08 42	08 47	08 50	09 16		09 29	09 44	09 59	10 03

Station		SR	SR	SR	SR	SR		SR	SR	SR	SR	SR	SR	SR	SR	SR		SR	SR	SR	SR	SR	SR	SR	SR
Gourock	d	09 38		10 08	10 24	10 38			11 08	11 24	11 38		12 08	12 24	12 38			13 08	13 24	13 38		14 08	14 24	14 38	
Fort Matilda	d	09 41		10 11	10 27	10 41			11 11	11 27	11 41		12 11	12 27	12 41			13 11	13 27	13 41		14 11	14 27	14 41	
Greenock West	d	09 44		10 14	10 30	10 44			11 14	11 30	11 44		12 14	12 30	12 44			13 14	13 30	13 44		14 14	14 30	14 44	
Greenock Central	d	09 46		10 16	10 32	10 46			11 16	11 32	11 46		12 16	12 32	12 46			13 16	13 32	13 46		14 16	14 32	14 46	
Cartsdyke	d	09 49		10 19		10 49			11 19		11 49		12 19		12 49			13 19		13 49		14 19		14 49	
Bogston	d	09 51		10 21		10 51			11 21		11 51		12 21		12 51			13 21		13 51		14 21		14 51	
Wemyss Bay	d		09 57					10 57				11 57				12 57					13 57				14 57
Inverkip	d		10 01					11 01				12 01				13 01					14 01				15 01
I.B.M.	d		10 06					11 06				12 06				13 06					14 06				15 06
Branchton	d		10 08					11 08				12 08				13 08					14 08				15 08
Drumfrochar	d		10 11					11 11				12 11				13 11					14 11				15 11
Whinhill	d		10 13					11 13				12 13				13 13					14 13				15 13
Port Glasgow	d	09 53	10 18	10 23	10 37	10 53		11 18	11 23	11 37	11 53	12 18	12 23	12 37	12 53	13 18		13 23	13 37	13 53	14 18	14 23	14 37	14 53	15 18
Woodhall	d	09 56		10 26		10 56			11 26		11 56		12 26		12 56			13 26		13 56		14 26		14 56	
Langbank	d	10 00		10 30		11 00			11 30		12 00		12 30		13 00			13 30		14 00		14 30		15 00	
Bishopton	d	10 05	10 27	10 35	10 46	11 05		11 27	11 35	11 46	12 05	12 27	12 35	12 46	13 05	13 27		13 35	13 46	14 05	14 27	14 35	14 46	15 05	15 27
Paisley St James	d	10 10		10 40		11 10			11 40		12 10		12 40		13 10			13 40		14 10		14 40		15 10	
Paisley Gilmour Street 221	a	10 13	10 33	10 43	10 52	11 13		11 33	11 43	11 52	12 13	12 33	12 43	12 52	13 13	13 33		13 43	13 52	14 13	14 33	14 43	14 52	15 13	15 33
	d	10 13	10 34	10 43	10 52	11 13		11 33	11 43	11 52	12 13	12 33	12 43	12 52	13 13	13 33		13 43	13 52	14 13	14 33	14 43	14 52	15 13	15 33
Hillington West	d	10 17		10 47		11 17			11 47		12 17		12 47		13 17			13 47		14 17		14 47		15 17	
Hillington East	d	10 19		10 49		11 19			11 49		12 19		12 49		13 19			13 49		14 19		14 49		15 19	
Cardonald	d	10 21		10 51		11 21			11 51		12 21		12 51		13 21			13 51		14 21		14 51		15 21	
Glasgow Central 15 221	a	10 29	10 44	10 59	11 03	11 29		11 44	11 59	12 03	12 29	12 44	12 59	13 03	13 29	13 44		13 59	14 04	14 29	14 44	14 59	15 03	15 30	15 46

Station		SR		SR	SR	SR	SR	SR	SR	SR SX	SR SO	SR		SR	SR	SR	SR	SR	SR	SR	SR	SR		SR	SR
Gourock	d	15 08		15 24	15 38		16 08	16 24	16 38			17 08		17 24	17 43		18 08	18 24		18 38		19 08		19 24	19 48
Fort Matilda	d	15 11		15 27	15 41		16 11	16 27	16 41			17 11		17 27	17 46		18 11	18 27		18 41		19 11		19 27	19 51
Greenock West	d	15 14		15 30	15 44		16 14	16 30	16 44			17 14		17 30	17 49		18 14	18 30		18 44		19 14		19 30	19 54
Greenock Central	d	15 16		15 32	15 46		16 16	16 32	16 46			17 16		17 32	17 51		18 16	18 32		18 46		19 16		19 32	19 56
Cartsdyke	d	15 19			15 49		16 19		16 49			17 19			17 54		18 19			18 49		19 19		19 35	19 59
Bogston	d	15 21			15 51		16 21		16 51			17 21			17 56		18 21			18 51		19 21		19 37	
Wemyss Bay	d					15 57				16 45	16 45					17 49			18 24		18 56				
Inverkip	d					16 01				16 49	16 49					17 53			18 28		19 00				
I.B.M.	d					16 06				16 54	16 54					18 03			18 38		19 05				
Branchton	d					16 08				16 56	16 56					18 06			18 40		19 07				
Drumfrochar	d					16 11				16 59	16 59					18 08			18 43		19 10				
Whinhill	d					16 13				17 01	17 01					18 11			18 45		19 12				
Port Glasgow	d	15 23		15 37	15 53	16 17	16 23	16 37	16 53	17 06	17 06	17 23		17 37	17 58	18 17	18 23	18 37	18 50	18 54	19 17	19 23		19 39	20 02
Woodhall	d	15 26			15 56		16 26		16 56			17 26			18 01		18 26			18 56		19 26		19 41	
Langbank	d	15 30			16 00		16 30		17 00			17 30			18 05		18 30			19 00		19 30		19 45	
Bishopton	d	15 35		15 46	16 05	16 26	16 35	16 46	17 05	17 15	17 15	17 35		17 46	18 10	18 26	18 35	18 46	18 59	19 06	19 26	19 35		19 51	20 11
Paisley St James	d	15 40			16 10		16 40		17 11			17 40			18 15		18 40			19 11		19 40		19 56	
Paisley Gilmour Street 221	a	15 43		15 52	16 13	16 32	16 43	16 52	17 14	17 21	17 21	17 43		17 52	18 18	18 32	18 43	18 52	19 05	19 13	19 32	19 43		19 59	20 17
	d	15 43		15 52	16 13	16 32	16 43	16 52	17 16	17 21	17 21	17 43		17 52	18 18	18 33	18 43	18 52	19 05	19 14	19 32	19 43		19 59	20 18
Hillington West	d	15 47		15 56	16 17		16 47	16 56	17 20			17 47			18 22		18 47			19 17		19 47		20 02	
Hillington East	d	15 49			16 19		16 49		17 22			17 49			18 24		18 49			19 19		19 49		20 04	
Cardonald	d	15 51			16 21		16 51		17 24			17 51			18 26		18 51			19 21		19 51		20 06	
Glasgow Central 15 221	a	16 00		16 06	16 31	16 46	16 59	17 04	17 32	17 35	17 36	17 59		18 03	18 34	18 44	19 01	19 04	19 19	19 29	19 44	19 59		20 14	20 29

Table 219R

Mondays to Saturdays

9 December to 17 May

Network Diagram - refer to first Page of Table 216

Gourock and Wemyss Bay - Glasgow Central

		SR	SR	SR	SR	SR	SR	SR SX	SR SO	SR	SR	SR	SR SO
Gourock	d		20 24	20 48		21 24	21 48			22 24		23 24	
Fort Matilda	d		20 27	20 51		21 27	21 51			22 27		23 27	
Greenock West	d		20 30	20 54		21 30	21 54			22 30		23 30	
Greenock Central	d		20 32	20 56		21 32	21 56			22 32		23 32	
Cartsdyke	d		20 35	20 59		21 35	21 59			22 35		23 35	
Bogston	d		20 37			21 37				22 37		23 37	
Wemyss Bay	d	19 47			20 47			21 47	21 52		22 47		23 39
Inverkip	d	19 51			20 51			21 51	21 56		22 51		23 43
I.B.M.	d	19 56			20 56			21 56	22 01		22 56		23 48
Branchton	d	19 58			20 58			21 58	22 03		22 58		23 50
Drumfrochar	d	20 01			21 01			22 01	22 06		23 01		23 53
Whinhill	d	20 03			21 03			22 03	22 08		23 03		23 55
Port Glasgow	d	20 08	20 39	21 02	21 08	21 39	22 02	22 08	22 13	22 39	23 08	23 39	00 02
Woodhall	d	20 10	20 41		21 10	21 41		22 10	22 15	22 41	23 10	23 41	
Langbank	d	20 14	20 45		21 14	21 45		22 14	22 19	22 45	23 14	23 45	
Bishopton	d	20 20	20 51	21 11	21 20	21 51	22 11	22 20	22 25	22 51	23 20	23 51	00 10
Paisley St James	d	20 25	20 56		21 25	21 56		22 25	22 30	22 56	23 25	23 56	
Paisley Gilmour Street 221 ✈	a	20 27	20 59	21 17	21 27	21 59	22 17	22 27	22 32	22 59	23 27	23 59	00 16
	d	20 28	20 59	21 18	21 28	21 59	22 18	22 28	22 33	22 59	23 28	23 59	00 17
Hillington West	d	20 31	21 02		21 31	22 02		22 31	22 36	23 02	23 31	00 02	
Hillington East	d	20 33	21 04		21 33	22 04		22 33	22 38	23 04	23 33	00 04	
Cardonald	d	20 35	21 06		21 35	22 06		22 35	22 40	23 06	23 35	00 06	
Glasgow Central 15 221	a	20 44	21 14	21 29	21 44	22 19	22 30	22 44	22 49	23 14	23 44	00 14	00 27

Sundays

8 December to 11 May

		SR A	SR A	SR	SR	SR	SR	SR	SR	SR	SR	SR	SR	SR	SR	SR	SR	SR	SR	SR	SR	SR	SR
Gourock	d			08 23		09 23		10 23		11 23		12 23		13 23		14 23		15 23		16 23		17 23	
Fort Matilda	d			08 26		09 26		10 26		11 26		12 26		13 26		14 26		15 26		16 26		17 26	
Greenock West	d			08 29		09 29		10 29		11 29		12 29		13 29		14 29		15 29		16 29		17 29	
Greenock Central	d			08 31		09 31		10 31		11 31		12 31		13 31		14 31		15 31		16 31		17 31	
Cartsdyke	d			08 34		09 34		10 34		11 34		12 34		13 34		14 34		15 34		16 34		17 34	
Bogston	d			08 36		09 36		10 36		11 36		12 36		13 36		14 36		15 36		16 36		17 36	
Wemyss Bay	d				08 50		09 50		10 55		11 50		12 50		13 50		14 50		15 55		16 50		17 50
Inverkip	d				08 54		09 54		10 59		11 54		12 54		13 54		14 54		15 59		16 54		17 54
I.B.M.	d				08 59		09 59		11 04		11 59		12 59		13 59		15 00		16 04		16 59		17 59
Branchton	d				09 01		10 01		11 06		12 01		13 01		14 01		15 02		16 06		17 01		18 01
Drumfrochar	d				09 04		10 04		11 09		12 04		13 04		14 04		15 05		16 09		17 04		18 04
Whinhill	d				09 06		10 06		11 11		12 06		13 06		14 06		15 07		16 11		17 06		18 06
Port Glasgow	d		00 02	08 38	09 11	09 38	10 11	10 38	11 16	11 38	12 11	12 38	13 11	13 38	14 11	14 38	15 12	15 38	16 16	16 38	17 11	17 38	18 11
Woodhall	d			08 41		09 41		10 41		11 41		12 41		13 41		14 41		15 41		16 41		17 41	
Langbank	d			08 45		09 45		10 45		11 45		12 45		13 45		14 45		15 45		16 45		17 45	
Bishopton	d		00 10	08 50	09 20	09 50	10 20	10 50	11 25	11 50	12 20	12 50	13 20	13 50	14 20	14 50	15 21	15 50	16 25	16 50	17 20	17 50	18 20
Paisley St James	d			08 55		09 55		10 55		11 55		12 55		13 55		14 55		15 55		16 55		17 55	
Paisley Gilmour Street 221 ✈	a		00 16	08 58	09 26	09 58	10 26	10 58	11 31	11 58	12 26	12 58	13 26	13 58	14 26	14 58	15 27	15 58	16 31	16 58	17 26	17 58	18 26
	d		00 17	08 58	09 26	09 58	10 26	10 58	11 31	11 58	12 26	12 58	13 26	13 58	14 26	14 58	15 27	15 58	16 31	16 58	17 26	17 58	18 26
Hillington West	d	00 02		09 02		10 02		11 02		12 02		13 02		14 02		15 02		16 02		17 02		18 02	
Hillington East	d	00 04		09 04	09 30	10 04	10 30	11 04	11 35	12 04	12 30	13 04	13 30	14 04	14 30	15 04	15 31	16 04	16 35	17 04	17 30	18 04	18 30
Cardonald	d	00 06		09 06		10 06		11 06		12 06		13 06		14 06		15 06		16 06		17 06		18 06	
Glasgow Central 15 221	a	00 14	00 27	09 14	09 39	10 14	10 39	11 14	11 44	12 14	12 39	13 14	13 39	14 14	14 39	15 14	15 39	16 14	16 44	17 14	17 39	18 14	18 39

		SR	SR	SR	SR	SR	SR	SR	SR
Gourock	d	18 23		19 23		20 23		21 23	22 23
Fort Matilda	d	18 26		19 26		20 26		21 26	22 26
Greenock West	d	18 29		19 29		20 29		21 29	22 29
Greenock Central	d	18 31		19 31		20 31		21 31	22 31
Cartsdyke	d	18 34		19 34		20 34		21 34	22 34
Bogston	d	18 36		19 36		20 36		21 36	22 36
Wemyss Bay	d		18 55		19 50		20 50		
Inverkip	d		18 59		19 54		20 54		
I.B.M.	d		19 04		19 59		20 59		
Branchton	d		19 06		20 01		21 01		
Drumfrochar	d		19 09		20 04		21 04		
Whinhill	d		19 11		20 06		21 06		
Port Glasgow	d	18 38	19 16	19 38	20 11	20 38	21 11	21 38	22 38
Woodhall	d	18 41		19 41		20 41		21 41	22 41
Langbank	d	18 45		19 45		20 45		21 45	22 45
Bishopton	d	18 50	19 25	19 50	20 20	20 50	21 20	21 50	22 50
Paisley St James	d	18 55		19 55		20 55		21 55	22 55
Paisley Gilmour Street 221 ✈	a	18 58	19 31	19 58	20 26	20 58	21 26	21 58	22 58
	d	18 58	19 31	19 58	20 26	20 58	21 26	21 58	22 58
Hillington West	d	19 02		20 02		21 02		22 02	23 02
Hillington East	d	19 04	19 35	20 04	20 30	21 04	21 30	22 04	23 04
Cardonald	d	19 06		20 06		21 06		22 06	23 06
Glasgow Central 15 221	a	19 14	19 44	20 14	20 39	21 16	21 39	22 14	23 14

A not 8 December

Table 219A SHIPPING SERVICES

Mondays to Saturdays

until 03 April 2014

Glasgow and Gourock - Dunoon and Kilcreggan (in association with ScotRail)

All Dunoon sailings are operated by Argyll Ferries Ltd

All Kilcreggan sailings are operated by Clydelink Ltd on behalf of Strathclyde Partnership for Transport

			SX		SX		SO		SX			SO	SX		SO										
Glasgow Central 15	219 d	05 55	05 55	06 25	06 25	06 54	07 06	07 21	07 21	07 39	....	07 39	08 25	08 25	08 40	08 40	09 25	09 25	09 36	10 25	10 25	10 36	....	11 25	11 36
Paisley Gilmour Street	219 d	06 08	06 08	06 36	06 36	07 06	07 22	07 36	07 36	07 53	.	07 53	08 36	08 36	08 56	08 56	09 35	09 35	09 53	10 36	10 36	10 51	.	11 36	11 51
Gourock	219 a	06 36	06 36	07 11	07 11	07 37	07 58	08 09	08 09	08 30	....	08 30	09 04	09 04	09 32	09 32	10 04	10 04	10 28	11 04	11 04	11 27	....	12 04	12 27
Gourock	⛴ d	06 45	06 45	07 20	07 29	07 50	08 04	08 20	08 20	08 50	.	08 52	09 18	09 20	09 36	09 50	10 18	10 20	10 50	11 18	11 20	11 50	.	12 20	12 56
Dunoon	⛴ a	07 10	....	07 45	....	08 15	....	08 45	....	09 15	....	....	....	09 45	....	10 15	....	10 45	11 15	....	11 45	12 15	....	12 45	....
Kilcreggan	⛴ a	.	06 57	.	07 41	.	08 16		08 32	.	.	09 04	09 30	.	09 48	.	10 30	.	.	11 30			.	.	13 08

													B									FSO	A
Glasgow Central 15	219 d	12 25	12 36	13 25	13 25	14 25	14 25	14 36	15 25	15 25	15 36	16 18	16 18	16 55	17 25	17 25	17 37	18 25	18 55	19 25	20 06	20 50	21 50	22 50	23 50
Paisley Gilmour Street	219 d	12 36	12 51	13 36	13 36	14 36	14 36	14 51	15 37	15 37	15 51	16 34	16 34	17 08	17 37	17 37	17 52	18 37	19 06	19 36	20 21	21 01	22 01	23 01	00 05
Gourock	219 a	13 04	13 27	14 04	14 04	15 04	15 04	15 27	16 05	16 05	16 27	17 09	17 09	17 38	18 03	18 03	18 28	19 05	19 36	20 04	20 57	21 30	22 30	23 30	00 40
Gourock	⛴ d	13 20	13 40	14 20	14 24	15 18	15 20	15 50	16 18	16 20	16 50	17 20	17 28	17 50	18 12	18 20	18 50	19 20	19 50	20 20	21 20	21 40	22 40	23 40	01 00
Dunoon	⛴ a	13 45	....	14 45	....	....	15 45	16 15	....	16 45	17 15	17 45	....	18 15	....	18 45	19 15	19 45	20 15	20 45	21 45	22 05	23 05	00 05	01 25
Kilcreggan	⛴ a	.	13 52	.	14 36	15 30	.	.	16 30	.	.		17 40	.	18 24	.	.	.	.	.	.	.	.	.	.

Sundays

until 30 March 2014

Glasgow Central 15	219 d	07 20	08 20	09 20	10 20	11 20	12 20	13 20	14 20	15 20	16 20	....	17 20	18 20	19 20	20 20	21 20	....	....	....	....	....	....	....	....
Paisley Gilmour Street	219 d	07 35	08 35	09 35	10 35	11 35	12 35	13 35	14 35	15 36	16 35	.	17 35	18 35	19 35	20 35	21 35	.	.	.	.	.	.	.	.
Gourock	219 a	08 06	09 11	10 11	11 11	12 11	13 11	14 11	15 11	16 11	17 11	....	18 11	19 11	20 11	21 11	22 11	....	....	....	....	....	....	....	....
Gourock	⛴ d	08 20	09 20	10 20	11 20	12 20	13 20	14 20	15 20	16 20	17 20	.	18 20	19 20	20 20	21 20	22 20	.	.	.	.	.	.	.	.
Dunoon	⛴ a	08 45	09 45	10 45	11 45	12 45	13 45	14 45	15 45	16 45	17 45	....	18 45	19 45	20 45	21 45	22 45	....	....	....	....	....	....	....	....
Kilcreggan	⛴ a	....	.	.	.	....	.	....	.	.	.	.	.	.	.	.	.	.	.	.	.	.	.	.	.

A Saturday and Sunday morning only

B The ferry service will be held until 1825 in the event of a late-running train

No Sunday service to Kilcreggan

For details of Dunoon sailings from 4 April 2014 please telephone 08000 66 5000 or visit www.argyllferries.co.uk

For details of Kilcreggan sailings from 4 April 2014 please telephone 0871 705 0888. For information on Sunday services from 6 April 2014 please telephone Clyde Marine Transport Ltd on 01475 721 281 (open Monday to Friday only).

Table 219A SHIPPING SERVICES

Mondays to Saturdays

until 03 April 2014

Kilcreggan and Dunoon - Gourock and Glasgow (in association with ScotRail)

All Dunoon sailings are operated by Argyll Ferries Ltd

All Kilcreggan sailings are operated by Clydelink Ltd on behalf of Strathclyde Partnership for Transport

		SX	SO	SX		SX		SO			SX		SO												
Kilcreggan	d	.		07 07	.	07 51	.	08 30	.	.	08 42	.	09 14			09 56	.	.	10 56	.	.	11 40	.	.	.
Dunoon	d	06 45	06 45	....	07 15	....	07 50	....	....	08 20	....	08 50	....	09 20	09 50	....	10 20	10 50	....	....	11 20	....	11 50	12 20	12 50
Gourock	a	07 15	07 15	07 19	07 40	08 03	08 15	08 42	.	08 45	08 54	09 15	09 26	09 45	10 15	10 08	10 45	11 15	11 08	.	11 45	11 52	12 15	12 45	13 15
Gourock	219 d	07 28	07 38	07 28	07 51	08 10	08 23	09 08	....	09 08	09 08	09 24	09 38	10 08	10 24	10 24	11 08	11 24	11 24	....	12 08	12 08	12 24	13 08	13 24
Paisley Gilmour Street	219 a	08 03	08 13	08 03	08 22	08 38	08 58	09 43	.	09 43	09 43	09 52	10 13	10 43	10 52	10 52	11 43	11 52	11 52	.	12 43	12 43	12 52	13 43	13 52
Glasgow Central 15	219 a	08 19	08 31	08 19	08 42	08 50	09 16	09 59	....	09 59	09 59	10 03	10 29	10 59	11 03	11 03	11 59	12 03	12 03	....	12 59	12 59	13 03	13 59	14 04

Kilcreggan	d	13 18	.	14 02	.	14 56	.	15 56	.	.	.	17 06	.	17 50	.	.	18 35	.	.	.	.	.	.	.	.
Dunoon	d	....	13 50	....	14 50	....	15 50	....	16 20	....	16 50	....	17 20	....	17 50	18 20	....	18 50	19 50	20 50	....	21 45	22 10	....	....
Gourock	a	13 30	14 15	14 14	15 15	15 08	16 15	16 08	16 45	.	17 15	17 18	17 45	18 02	18 15	18 45	18 47	19 15	20 15	21 15	.	22 15	22 35	.	.
Gourock	219 d	13 38	14 24	14 24	15 24	15 24	16 24	16 24	17 08	....	17 24	17 24	18 08	18 08	18 24	19 08	19 08	19 24	20 24	21 24	....	22 24	23 24	....	....
Paisley Gilmour Street	219 a	14 13	14 52	14 52	15 52	15 52	16 52	16 52	17 43	.	17 52	17 52	18 43	18 43	18 52	19 43	19 43	19 59	20 59	21 59	.	22 59	23 59	.	.
Glasgow Central 15	219 a	14 29	15 03	15 03	16 06	16 06	17 04	17 04	17 59	....	18 03	18 03	19 01	19 01	19 04	19 59	19 59	20 14	21 14	22 19	....	23 14	00 14	....	....

Sundays

until 30 March 2014

Kilcreggan	d	.	.	.	.	.	.	.	.	.	.	.	.	.	.	.	.	.	.	.	.	.	.	.	.
Dunoon	d	08 50	09 50	10 50	11 50	12 50	13 50	14 50	15 50	16 50	....	17 50	18 50	19 50	20 50	21 50	....	....	....	....	....	....	....	....	....
Gourock	a	09 15	10 15	11 15	12 15	13 15	14 15	15 15	16 15	17 15	.	18 15	19 15	20 15	21 15	22 15	.	.	.	.	.	.	.	.	.
Gourock	219 d	09 23	10 23	11 23	12 23	13 23	14 23	15 23	16 23	17 23	....	18 23	19 23	20 23	21 23	22 23	....	....	....	....	....	....	....	....	....
Paisley Gilmour Street	219 a	09 58	10 58	11 58	12 58	13 58	14 58	15 58	16 58	17 58	.	18 58	19 58	20 58	21 58	22 58	.	.	.	.	.	.	.	.	.
Glasgow Central 15	219 a	10 14	11 14	12 14	13 14	14 14	15 14	16 14	17 14	18 14	....	19 14	20 14	21 16	22 14	23 14	....	....	....	....	....	....	....	....	....

No Sunday service from Kilcreggan

For details of Dunoon sailings from 4 April 2014 please telephone 08000 66 5000 or visit www.argyllferries.co.uk

For details of Kilcreggan sailings from 4 April 2014 please telephone 0871 705 0888. For information on Sunday services from 6 April 2014 please telephone Clyde Marine Transport Ltd on 01475 721 281 (open Monday to Friday only).

Table 219B

Mondays to Saturdays

until 03 April 2014

Glasgow and Wemyss Bay - Rothesay (Bute)

Caledonian MacBrayne Ltd. in association with ScotRail

		SX		SX														
Glasgow Central 15	219 d	06 05		06 32	07 50	08 55	09 55	10 55	11 55	12 55		13 55	14 55	15 47	16 32	17 16	17 55	18 38
Paisley Gilmour Street	219 d	06 19		06 47	08 04	09 07	10 06	11 06	12 06	13 06		14 06	15 06	15 59	16 49	17 30	18 06	18 53
Wemyss Bay	219 a	06 57		07 33	08 41	09 44	10 43	11 43	12 43	13 43		14 43	15 43	16 38	17 24	18 07	18 43	19 37
Wemyss Bay	d	07 15		07 55	08 45	10 15	11 00	12 00	13 05	14 05		15 00	16 00	16 45	17 30	18 15	19 00	19 45
Rothesay	a	07 50		08 30	09 20	10 50	11 35	12 35	13 40	14 40		15 35	16 35	17 20	18 05	18 50	19 35	20 20

Sundays

until 30 March 2014

Glasgow Central 15	219 d	07 50	08 50	10 50	11 50	12 50	13 50	14 50	15 50	16 50		17 50	18 50
Paisley Gilmour Street	219 d	08 02	09 02	11 02	12 02	13 02	14 02	15 02	16 02	17 02		18 02	19 02
Wemyss Bay	219 a	08 39	09 39	11 39	12 39	13 40	14 39	15 39	16 39	17 39		18 39	19 39
Wemyss Bay	d	08 45	10 15	12 00	13 00	14 00	15 00	16 00	17 00	18 00		19 00	19 45
Rothesay	a	09 20	10 50	12 35	13 35	14 35	15 35	16 35	17 35	18 35		19 35	20 20

For details of sailings from 4 April 2014 please telephone 08000 66 5000 or visit www.calmac.co.uk

Table 219B

Mondays to Saturdays

until 03 April 2014

Rothesay (Bute) - Wemyss Bay and Glasgow

Caledonian MacBrayne Ltd. in association with ScotRail

		SX	SX														
Rothesay	d	06 25	07 00	08 00	08 40	10 10	11 00	12 00	13 00	14 00		15 00	16 00	16 45	17 30	18 15	19 00
Wemyss Bay	a	07 00	07 35	08 35	09 15	10 45	11 35	12 35	13 35	14 35		15 35	16 35	17 20	18 05	18 50	19 35
Wemyss Bay	219 d	07 16	07 54	08 57	09 57	10 57	11 57	12 57	13 57	14 57		15 57	16 45	17 49	18 24	18 56	19 47
Paisley Gilmour Street	219 a	07 53	08 34	09 33	10 33	11 33	12 33	13 33	14 33	15 33		16 32	17 21	18 32	19 05	19 32	20 27
Glasgow Central 15	219 a	08 09	08 47	09 44	10 44	11 44	12 44	13 44	14 44	15 46		16 46	17b35	18 44	19 19	19 44	20 44

Sundays

until 30 March 2014

Rothesay	d	08 00	09 30	10 45	12 00	13 00	14 00	15 00	16 00	17 00		18 00	19 00
Wemyss Bay	a	08 35	10 05	11 20	12 35	13 35	14 35	15 35	16 35	17 35		18 35	19 35
Wemyss Bay	219 d	08 50	10 55	11 50	12 50	13 50	14 50	15 55	16 50	17 50		18 55	19 50
Paisley Gilmour Street	219 a	09 26	11 31	12 26	13 26	14 26	15 27	16 31	17 26	18 26		19 31	20 26
Glasgow Central 15	219 a	09 39	11 44	12 39	13 39	14 39	15 39	16 44	17 39	18 39		19 44	20 39

b Arrives 1 minute later on Saturdays

For details of sailings from 4 April 2014 please telephone 08000 66 5000 or visit www.calmac.co.uk

Network Diagram for Tables 220, 223, 224, 226, 232

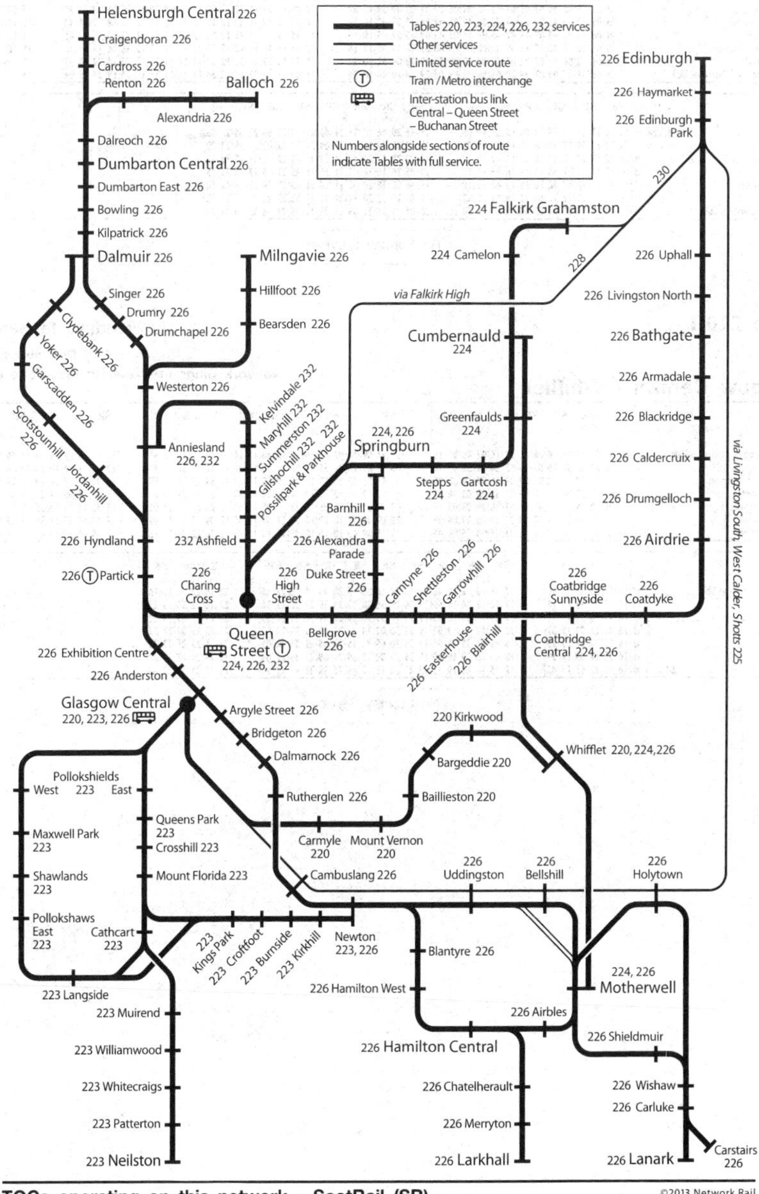

TOCs operating on this network - ScotRail (SR)

Table 220

Mondays to Saturdays

9 December to 17 May

Network Diagram - refer to first Page of Table 220

Whifflet - Glasgow Central

Miles			SR	SR	SR	SR	SR	SR	SR	SR	SR		SR	SR	SR	SR	SR	SR	SR	SR	SR		SR	SR	SR
0	**Whifflet** 224,226	d	06 06	06 36	07 06	07 36	08 06	08 36	09 06	09 36	10 06		10 36	11 06	11 36	12 06	12 36	13 06	13 36	14 06	14 36		15 06	15 36	16 06
2½	Kirkwood	d	06 09	06 39	07 09	07 39	08 09	08 39	09 09	09 39	10 09		10 39	11 09	11 39	12 09	12 39	13 09	13 39	14 09	14 39		15 09	15 39	16 09
3¼	Bargeddie	d	06 12	06 42	07 12	07 42	08 12	08 42	09 12	09 42	10 12		10 42	11 12	11 42	12 12	12 42	13 12	13 42	14 12	14 42		15 12	15 42	16 12
4½	Baillieston	d	06 15	06 45	07 15	07 45	08 15	08 45	09 15	09 45	10 15		10 45	11 15	11 45	12 15	12 45	13 15	13 45	14 15	14 45		15 15	15 45	16 15
5¾	Mount Vernon	d	06 18	06 48	07 18	07 48	08 18	08 48	09 18	09 48	10 18		10 48	11 18	11 48	12 18	12 48	13 18	13 48	14 18	14 48		15 18	15 48	16 18
7	Carmyle	d	06 22	06 52	07 22	07 52	08 22	08 52	09 22	09 52	10 22		10 52	11 22	11 52	12 22	12 52	13 22	13 52	14 22	14 52		15 22	15 52	16 22
12½	**Glasgow Central** 15	a	06 35	07 04	07 34	08 04	08 36	09 04	09 34	10 04	10 34		11 04	11 34	12 04	12 34	13 04	13 34	14 04	14 34	15 04		15 34	16 04	16 35

		SR	SR	SR	SR	SR	SR		SR	SR	SR	SR	SR	SR	SR	SR								
Whifflet 224,226	d	16 36	17 06	17 36	18 06	18 36	19 06		19 36	20 06	20 36	21 06	21 36	22 06	22 36	23 06								
Kirkwood	d	16 39	17 09	17 39	18 09	18 39	19 09		19 39	20 09	20 39	21 09	21 39	22 09	22 39	23 09								
Bargeddie	d	16 42	17 12	17 42	18 12	18 42	19 12		19 42	20 12	20 42	21 12	21 42	22 12	22 42	23 12								
Baillieston	d	16 45	17 15	17 45	18 15	18 45	19 15		19 45	20 15	20 45	21 15	21 45	22 15	22 45	23 15								
Mount Vernon	d	16 48	17 18	17 48	18 18	18 48	19 18		19 48	20 18	20 48	21 18	21 48	22 18	22 48	23 18								
Carmyle	d	16 52	17 22	17 52	18 22	18 52	19 22		19 52	20 22	20 52	21 22	21 52	22 22	22 52	23 22								
Glasgow Central 15	a	17 04	17 34	18 04	18 34	19 04	19 34		20 06	20 35	21 05	21 35	22 04	22 34	23 04	23 34								

No Sunday Service

Table 220R

Mondays to Saturdays

9 December to 17 May

Network Diagram - refer to first Page of Table 220

Glasgow Central - Whifflet

Miles			SR SO	SR	SR	SR	SR	SR		SR	SR	SR	SR	SR	SR	SR	SR	SR		SR	SR	SR	SR	SR	SR
0	**Glasgow Central** 15	d	00 16	06 18	06 46	07 16	07 46	08 16		08 46	09 16	09 46	10 16	10 46	11 16	11 46	12 16	12 46		13 16	13 46	14 16	14 46	15 16	15 46
5½	Carmyle	d	00 26	06 29	06 56	07 26	07 56	08 26		08 56	09 26	09 56	10 26	10 56	11 26	11 56	12 26	12 56		13 26	13 56	14 26	14 56	15 26	15 56
6¾	Mount Vernon	d	00 29	06 32	06 59	07 29	07 59	08 29		08 59	09 29	09 59	10 29	10 59	11 29	11 59	12 29	12 59		13 29	13 59	14 29	14 59	15 29	15 59
8	Baillieston	d	00 32	06 35	07 02	07 32	08 02	08 32		09 02	09 32	10 02	10 32	11 02	11 32	12 02	12 32	13 02		13 32	14 02	14 32	15 02	15 32	16 02
9¼	Bargeddie	d	00 35	06 39	07 05	07 35	08 05	08 35		09 05	09 35	10 05	10 35	11 05	11 35	12 05	12 35	13 05		13 35	14 05	14 35	15 05	15 35	16 05
10	Kirkwood	d	00 39	06 42	07 09	07 39	08 09	08 39		09 09	09 39	10 09	10 39	11 09	11 39	12 09	12 39	13 09		13 39	14 09	14 39	15 09	15 39	16 09
12½	**Whifflet** 224,226	a	00 45	06 47	07 15	07 45	08 15	08 45		09 15	09 45	10 15	10 45	11 15	11 45	12 16	12 45	13 15		13 45	14 15	14 45	15 15	15 45	16 15

		SR	SR	SR		SR	SR	SR	SR	SR	SR	SR	SR	SR		SR	SR	SR						
Glasgow Central 15	d	16 16	16 46	17 16		17 46	18 16	18 46	19 16	19 46	20 16	20 46	21 16	21 46		22 16	22 46	23 16						
Carmyle	d	16 26	16 56	17 26		17 56	18 26	18 56	19 26	19 56	20 26	20 56	21 26	21 56		22 26	22 56	23 26						
Mount Vernon	d	16 29	16 59	17 29		17 59	18 29	18 59	19 29	19 59	20 29	20 59	21 29	21 59		22 29	22 59	23 29						
Baillieston	d	16 32	17 02	17 32		18 02	18 32	19 02	19 32	20 02	20 32	21 02	21 32	22 02		22 32	23 02	23 32						
Bargeddie	d	16 35	17 05	17 35		18 05	18 35	19 05	19 35	20 05	20 35	21 05	21 35	22 05		22 35	23 05	23 35						
Kirkwood	d	16 39	17 09	17 39		18 09	18 39	19 09	19 39	20 09	20 39	21 09	21 39	22 09		22 39	23 09	23 39						
Whifflet 224,226	a	16 45	17 15	17 45		18 15	18 45	19 15	19 45	20 15	20 45	21 15	21 45	22 15		22 45	23 15	23 45						

No Sunday Service

Table 221

Mondays to Saturdays

9 December to 17 May

Network Diagram - refer to first Page of Table 216

Glasgow Central - Ardrossan, Largs and Ayr

Miles	Miles	Miles			SR MX A	SR SO A	SR MSX A	SR SO A	SR MSX A	SR MX	SR	SR	SR		SR	SR	SR	SR	SR	SR	SR SX B	SR C	SR		SR
0	0	—	**Glasgow Central** 15 219	d						00 15	06 00	06 15	06 30		06 45	07 00	07 15	07 30	07 45	08 00	08 15		08 30		08 34
7¼	7¼	—	Paisley Gilmour Street 219	a						00 24	06 10	06 24	06 39		06 54	07 09	07 24	07 39	07 57	08 10	08 24				08 43
—	—	—		d						00 25	06 10	06 25	06 40		06 55	07 10	07 25	07 40	07 57	08 11	08 25				08 44
10¾	10¾	—	Johnstone	d						00 29	06 14	06 29	06 44		06 59	07 14	07 29	07 44	08 01	08 15	08 29				08 48
11½	11½	—	Milliken Park	d				00 02	00 02			06 32			07 02		07 32		08 04		08 32				
13	13	—	Howwood	d				00 04	00 04			06 34			07 04		07 34		08 07		08 34				
16½	16½	—	Lochwinnoch	d				00 08	00 08			06 38			07 08		07 38		08 11		08 38				
20½	20½	—	Glengarnock	d				00 13	00 13			06 43			07 13		07 43		08 15	08 23					
23¼	23¼	—	Dalry	d				00 17	00 17			06 47			07 17		07 47		08 19	08 27					
26¾	26¾	—	Kilwinning 4	d				00 21	00 21	00 42	06 28	06 51	06 57		07 21	07 27	07 51	07 57	08 23	08 31	08 47		08 54		09 01
—	29	—	Stevenston	d				00 25	00 25			06 55			07 25		07 55				08 51				09 05
—	30¼	—	Saltcoats	d				00 28	00 28			06 59			07 28		07 58				08 54				09 09
—	31¼	—	Ardrossan South Beach	d		00 02	00 02	00 30	00a31			07 01			07 30		08 00				08 56				09 11
—	—	31¾	Ardrossan Town	d		00a04									07 33						08a59				09 14
—	—	32¼	**Ardrossan Harbour**	a											07 36										09 20
—	35¾	—	West Kilbride	d			00 07	00 36				07 07					08 06								
—	39¾	—	Fairlie	d			00 12	00 41				07 12					08 11								
—	42¼	—	**Largs**	a			00 18	00 47				07 18					08 20								
30	—	—	Irvine	d	00 01					00 46	06 32		07 01			07 31		08 01	08 27	08 35			08 58		
33¾	—	—	Barassie	d	00 06					00 51	06 36		07 06			07 36		08 06		08 40					
35	—	—	Troon	d	00 09					00 54	06 39		07 09			07 39		08 09	08 34	08 43		08 49	09 05		
37¾	—	—	Prestwick Int. Airport ✈	d	00 13					00 58	06 43		07 13			07 43		08 13	08 38	08 47		08 54	09 09		
38¼	—	—	Prestwick Town	d	00 14					00 59	06 45		07 14			07 44		08 14	08 39	08 48		08 56	09 10		
40¼	—	—	Newton-on-Ayr	d	00 18					01 03	06 48		07 18			07 48		08 18		08 54					
41½	—	—	**Ayr**	a	00 21					01 09	06 54		07 23			07 53		08 23	08 45	08 57		09 03	09 18		

		SR	SR	SR	SR SX	SR SO	SR	SR	SR		SR ◇ D	SR	SR	SR SX	SR SO	SR	SR	SR C	SR		SR	SR	SR SX	SR SO	SR
Glasgow Central 15 219	d	08 38	08 48	09 00	09 04	09 04	09 18	09 30	09 34		09 38	09 48	10 00	10 04	10 04	10 18	10 30		10 34		10 48	11 00	11 04	11 04	11 18
Paisley Gilmour Street 219	a	08 47	08 58		09 13	09 13	09 27		09 43		09 50	09 57		10 13	10 13	10 27			10 43		10 57		11 13	11 13	11 27
	d	08 48	08 59		09 14	09 14	09 28		09 44		09 50	09 58		10 14	10 14	10 28			10 44		10 58		11 14	11 14	11 28
Johnstone	d	08 52	09 03		09 18	09 18	09 32		09 48			10 02		10 18	10 18	10 32			10 48		11 02		11 18	11 18	11 32
Milliken Park	d	08 55			09 21	09 21			09 51					10 21	10 21				10 51				11 21	11 21	
Howwood	d	08 57			09 23	09 23			09 53					10 23	10 23				10 53				11 23	11 23	
Lochwinnoch	d	09 01			09 27	09 27			09 57					10 27	10 27				10 57				11 27	11 27	
Glengarnock	d	09 06	09 11		09 32	09 32			10 02			10 10		10 32	10 32				11 02		11 10		11 32	11 32	
Dalry	d	09 10			09 36	09 36	09 43		10 06					10 36	10 36	10 43			11 06				11 36	11 36	11 44
Kilwinning 4	d	09 14	09 17	09 26	09 40	09 40	09 47	09 56	10 10		10 14	10 17	10 25	10 40	10 40	10 47	10 54		11 10		11 17	11 27	11 40	11 40	11 48
Stevenston	d		09 21				09 51					10 21				10 51					11 21				11 52
Saltcoats	d		09 24				09 54					10 24				10 54					11 24				11 55
Ardrossan South Beach	d		09 26				09 56					10 26				10 56					11 26				11 57
Ardrossan Town	d						09 59									10 59									12 00
Ardrossan Harbour	a						10 02									11 02									12 02
West Kilbride	d		09 32									10 32									11 32				
Fairlie	d		09 37									10 37									11 37				
Largs	a		09 44									10 44									11 44				
Irvine	d	09 18		09 30	09a44	09 44		10 00	10 14				10 29	10a44	10 44		10 58		11 14			11 31	11a44	11 44	
Barassie	d	09 22		09 35		09 48			10 18				10 34		10 48				11 18			11 36		11 48	
Troon	d	09 25		09 38		09 51		10 07	10 21				10 37		10 51		11 06	11 16	11 21			11 39		11 51	
Prestwick Int. Airport ✈	d	09 29		09 42		09 55		10 11	10 25				10 41		10 55		11 10	11 21	11 25			11 43		11 55	
Prestwick Town	d	09 31		09 43		09 57		10 12	10 27				10 42		10 57		11 11	11 23	11 27			11 44		11 57	
Newton-on-Ayr	d	09 34		09 47		10 01			10 30				10 46		11 00				11 30			11 48		12 00	
Ayr	a	09 39		09 51		10 08		10 18	10 34		10 38		10 52		11 05		11 17	11 28	11 34			11 51		12 05	

		SR	SR	SR	SR ◇ D		SR	SR SX	SR SO	SR	SR	SR C	SR	SR	SR		SR SX	SR SO	SR	SR	SR C	SR SO	SR SX	SR	SR
Glasgow Central 15 219	d	11 30	11 34	11 48	11 50		12 00	12 04	12 04	12 18	12 30		12 34	12 48	13 00		13 04	13 04	13 18	13 30		13 34	13 34	13 48	14 00
Paisley Gilmour Street 219	a		11 43	11 57	12 02			12 14	12 14	12 27			12 43	12 57			13 13	13 13	13 27			13 43	13 43	13 57	
	d		11 44	11 58	12 03			12 15	12 15	12 28			12 44	12 58			13 14	13 14	13 28			13 44	13 44	13 58	
Johnstone	d		11 48	12 02				12 20	12 20	12 32			12 48	13 02			13 18	13 18	13 32			13 48	13 48	14 02	
Milliken Park	d		11 51					12 23	12 23				12 51				13 21	13 21				13 51	13 51		
Howwood	d		11 53					12 25	12 25				12 53				13 23	13 23				13 53	13 53		
Lochwinnoch	d		11 57					12 29	12 29				12 57				13 27	13 27				13 57	13 57		
Glengarnock	d		12 02	12 10				12 34	12 34				13 02	13 10			13 32	13 32				14 02	14 02	14 10	
Dalry	d		12 06					12 38	12 38	12 43			13 06				13 36	13 36	13 44			14 06	14 06		
Kilwinning 4	d	11 56	12 10	12 18	12 21		12 25	12 42	12 42	12 47	12 55		13 10	13 17	13 25		13 40	13 40	13 48	13 54		14 10	14 10	14 17	14 28
Stevenston	d			12 22						12 51				13 21					13 52					14 21	
Saltcoats	d			12 25						12 54				13 24					13 55					14 24	
Ardrossan South Beach	d			12 27						12 56				13 26					13 58					14 26	
Ardrossan Town	d									12 59									14 01						
Ardrossan Harbour	a									13 02									14 04						
West Kilbride	d			12 33										13 32										14 32	
Fairlie	d			12 38										13 37										14 37	
Largs	a			12 44										13 44										14 44	
Irvine	d	12 00	12 14				12 29	12a46	12 46		12 59		13 14		13 29		13a44	13 44		13 58		14 14	14 14		14 32
Barassie	d		12 18				12 33		12 50				13 18		13 34			13 48				14 18	14 21		14 35
Troon	d	12 07	12 21				12 36		12 53		13 06	13 16	13 21		13 37			13 51		14 05	14 16	14 21	14 24		14 38
Prestwick Int. Airport ✈	d	12 11	12 25				12 40		12 57		13 10	13 21	13 25		13 41			13 55		14 09	14 21	14 25	14 28		14 42
Prestwick Town	d	12 12	12 27				12 42		12 59		13 11	13 23	13 27		13 42			13 57		14 10	14 23	14 27	14 29		14 44
Newton-on-Ayr	d		12 30				12 48		13 02				13 30		13 46			14 00				14 30	14 33		14 47
Ayr	a	12 18	12 35		12 41		12 53		13 08		13 18	13 29	13 35		13 53			14 05		14 19	14 30	14 35	14 38		14 53

A From Glasgow Central
B not 25 December, 26 December, 1 January, 2 January
C From Kilmarnock to Girvan
D To Stranraer

Table 221

Mondays to Saturdays

9 December to 17 May

Network Diagram - refer to first Page of Table 216

Glasgow Central - Ardrossan, Largs and Ayr

			SR SX	SR SO	SR	SR	SR	SR	SR	SR SX	SR SO		SR A	SR	SR	SR B	SR	SR	SR	SR SX	SR SO		SR	SR	SR
Glasgow Central 15	219 d		14 04	14 04	14 18	14 30	14 34	14 48	15 00	15 04	15 04		15 12	15 18	15 30		15 34	15 45	16 00	16 04	16 04		16 14	16 27	16 30
Paisley Gilmour Street	219 a		14 13	14 13	14 27		14 43	14 57		15 13	15 13			15 27			15 46	15 55		16 13	16 13		16 24		16 39
	d		14 14	14 14	14 28		14 44	14 58		15 14	15 14			15 28			15 47	15 55		16 14	16 14		16 24		16 40
Johnstone	d		14 18	14 18	14 32		14 48	15 02		15 18	15 18			15 32			15 52	15 59		16 18	16 18		16 28		16 44
Milliken Park	d		14 21	14 21			14 51			15 21	15 21						15 55			16 21	16 21				
Howwood	d		14 23	14 23			14 53			15 23	15 23						15 57			16 23	16 23				
Lochwinnoch	d		14 27	14 27			14 57			15 27	15 27						16 01			16 27	16 27				
Glengarnock	d		14 32	14 32			15 02	15 10		15 32	15 32						16 06	16 09		16 32	16 32		16 37		
Dalry	d		14 36	14 36	14 43		15 06			15 36	15 36			15 43			16 10			16 36	16 36		16 41		
Kilwinning 4	d		14 40	14 40	14 47	14 55	15 10	15 17	15 25	15 40	15 40			15 47	15 55		16 14	16 17	16 26	16 40	16 40		16 46	16 51	16 58
Stevenston	d				14 51			15 21						15 51				16 21					16 50		17 02
Saltcoats	d				14 54			15 24						15 54				16 24					16 53		17 05
Ardrossan South Beach	d				14 56			15 26						15 57				16 26					16 55		17 07
Ardrossan Town	d				14 59									16 00									16 58		
Ardrossan Harbour	a				15 03									16 03									17 02		
West Kilbride	d							15 33										16 30							17 13
Fairlie	d							15 38										16 35							17 18
Largs	a							15 44										16 42							17 27
Irvine	d		14a44	14 44		14 59	15 14		15 29	15a44	15 44				15 59		16 18		16 30	16a44	16 44			16 55	
Barassie	d			14 48			15 18		15 34		15 48					←	16 22		16 35		16 48			17 00	
Troon	d			14 51		15 05	15 21		15 37		15 51		16 16		16 06	16 16	16 24		16 38		16 51			17 03	
Prestwick Int. Airport ✈	d			14 55		15 09	15 25		15 41		15 55		→		16 10	16 21	16 27		16 42		16 55			17 07	
Prestwick Town	d			14 57		15 11	15 27		15 42		15 57				16 11	16 23	16 30		16 43		16 57			17 08	
Newton-on-Ayr	d			15 00			15 30		15 46		16 00						16 32		16 47		17 00			17 12	
Ayr	a			15 08		15 18	15 35		15 53		16 08				16 18	16 30	16 39		16 50		17 04			17 17	

		SR C	SR	SR	SR SO	SR SX	SR		SR A	SR SO	SR SX	SR SX	SR SX	SR SO	SR B	SR SX	SR SO		SR SX	SR	SR	SR SX	SR SO	SR	SR
Glasgow Central 15	219 d		16 40	16 50	17 00	17 00	17 04		17 12	17 14	17 14	17 21	17 28	17 30		17 31	17 34		17 45	17 49	18 00	18 04	18 04	18 18	18 30
Paisley Gilmour Street	219 a		16 51	16 59			17 13			17 24	17 24	17 32		17 39		17 43	17 43		17 55	17 58		18 13	18 13	18 27	
	d		16 52	17 00			17 14			17 24	17 24	17 32		17 40		17 45	17 45		17 55	17 59		18 14	18 14	18 28	
Johnstone	d		16 56	17 04			17 18			17 28	17 29	17 36				17 49	17 49			18 03		18 18	18 18	18 32	
Milliken Park	d		16 59				17 21			17 31		17 39				17 52	17 52					18 21	18 21		
Howwood	d		17 01				17 23			17 34	17 33					17 55	17 55					18 23	18 23		
Lochwinnoch	d		17 05				17 27									17 59	17 59					18 27	18 27		
Glengarnock	d		17 10	17 13			17 32			17 40	17 39					18 03	18 03			18 11		18 32	18 32		
Dalry	d		17 14	17 17			17 36			17 44	17 43					18 07	18 07					18 36	18 36	18 43	
Kilwinning 4	d		17 18	17 21	17 24	17 24	17 40			17 52	17 48	17 52	17 55	17 55		18 11	18 11			18 18	18 26	18 40	18 40	18 48	18 58
Stevenston	d			17 25						17 56		17 56				18 15	18 15			18 22				18 52	
Saltcoats	d			17 28						17 59		17 59				18 18	18 18			18 25				18 55	
Ardrossan South Beach	d			17 30						18 01		18 01				18 20	18 20			18 27				18 57	
Ardrossan Town	d			17 33												18 23	18 23							19 00	
Ardrossan Harbour	a			17 36												18 26	18 26							19 03	
West Kilbride	d									18 07		18 07								18 33					
Fairlie	d									18 12		18 12								18 38					
Largs	a									18 17		18 17								18 44					
Irvine	d		17 22		17 28	17 28	17 44				17 52		18 00	18 00					18 17		18 30	18a44	18 44		19 02
Barassie	d				17 33	17 39					17 57		18 04	18 04	←				18 23		18 36		18 48		
Troon	d	17 16	17 28		17 36	17 42	17 50		18 17		18 00		18 07	18 07	18 17				18 26		18 39		18 51		19 09
Prestwick Int. Airport ✈	d	17 21	17 32		17 40	17 46	17 54		→		18 04		18 11	18 11	18 21				18 30		18 43		18 55		19 13
Prestwick Town	d	17 23	17 34		17 41	17 47	17 56				18 05		18 13	18 13	18 23				18 31		18 44		18 57		19 14
Newton-on-Ayr	d				17 46	17 51					18 09		18 16	18 16					18 35		18 48		19 00		
Ayr	a	17 31	17 41		17 49	17 54	18 03				18 12		18 21	18 21	18 30				18 38		18 53		19 05		19 22

		SR C	SR		SR SO	SR SX	SR	SR	SR	SR	SR	SR	SR		SR	SR D	SR	SR	SR	SR	SR	SR SX E	SR		SR
Glasgow Central 15	219 d		18 34		18 48	18 48	19 00	19 15	19 30	19 45	20 00	20 15	20 30		20 45		21 00	21 15	21 30	21 45	22 00	22 12	22 15		22 30
Paisley Gilmour Street	219 a		18 43		18 57	18 57	19 09	19 24	19 39	19 54	20 10	20 24	20 39		20 54		21 09	21 24	21 39	21 54	22 09		22 24		22 39
	d		18 44		18 58	18 58	19 10	19 25	19 40	19 55	20 10	20 25	20 40		20 55		21 10	21 25	21 40	21 55	22 10		22 25		22 40
Johnstone	d		18 48		19 02	19 02	19 14	19 29	19 44	19 59	20 14	20 29	20 44		20 59		21 14	21 29	21 44	21 59	22 14		22 29		22 44
Milliken Park	d		18 51					19 32		20 02		20 32			21 02			21 32		22 02			22 32		
Howwood	d		18 53					19 34				20 34						21 34					22 34		
Lochwinnoch	d		18 57					19 38				20 38						21 38					22 38		
Glengarnock	d		19 02		19 10	19 10		19 43		20 09		20 43			21 09			21 43		22 09			22 43		
Dalry	d		19 06					19 47		20 13		20 47			21 13			21 47		22 13			22 47		
Kilwinning 4	d		19 10		19 17	19 17	19 27	19 51	19 58	20 17	20 28	20 51	20 57		21 17		21 27	21 51	21 57	22 17	22 27		22 51		22 57
Stevenston	d				19 21	19 21		19 55		20 21		20 55			21 21			21 55		22 21			22 55		
Saltcoats	d				19 24	19 24		19 58		20 24		20 58			21 24			21 58		22 24			22 58		
Ardrossan South Beach	d				19 26	19 26		20 00		20 26		21 00			21 26			22 00		22 26			23 00		
Ardrossan Town	d							20 03				21 03						22 03					23a03		
Ardrossan Harbour	a							20 06				21 06						22 06							
West Kilbride	d				19 32	19 32				20 32					21 32					22 32					
Fairlie	d				19 37	19 37				20 37					21 37					22 37					
Largs	a				19 42	19 44				20 44					21 44					22 44					
Irvine	d		19 15				19 31		20 02		20 32		21 01				21 31		22 01		22 31				23 01
Barassie	d		19 20				19 36				20 37						21 36				22 36				
Troon	d	19 16	19 23				19 39		20 08		20 40		21 08			21 21	21 39		22 08		22 39	23 18			23 10
Prestwick Int. Airport ✈	d	19 21	19 27				19 43		20 12		20 44		21 12			21 26	21 43		22 12		22 43	→			23 14
Prestwick Town	d	19 23	19 29				19 44		20 14		20 45		21 13			21 28	21 44		22 13		22 44				23 15
Newton-on-Ayr	d		19 32				19 48				20 49						21 48				22 50				
Ayr	a	19 31	19 37				19 51		20 21		20 54		21 21			21 34	21 53		22 21		22 55				23 21

A To Girvan
B From Glasgow Central to Girvan
C From Kilmarnock to Stranraer
D From Kilmarnock to Girvan
E To Stranraer

Table 221

Glasgow Central - Ardrossan, Largs and Ayr

Mondays to Saturdays

9 December to 17 May

Network Diagram - refer to first Page of Table 216

			SR	SR	SR	SR	SR	SR	SR	SR	SR
			SX	SO			FO	FX		FO	FSX
			A	B							
Glasgow Central 15	219	d			22 45	23 00	23 15	23 15	23 30	23 45	23 45
Paisley Gilmour Street	219	a			22 54	23 09	23 24	23 24	23 39	23 54	23 54
		d			22 55	23 10	23 26	23 26	23 40	23 55	23 55
Johnstone		d			22 59	23 14	23 30	23 30	23 44	23 59	23 59
Milliken Park		d			23 02		23 33	23 33		00 02	00 02
Howwood		d					23 35	23 35		00 04	00 04
Lochwinnoch		d					23 39	23 39		00 08	00 08
Glengarnock		d			23 09		23 44	23 44		00 13	00 13
Dalry		d			23 13		23 48	23 48		00 17	00 17
Kilwinning 4		d			23 17	23 27	23 52	23 52	23 57	00 21	00 21
Stevenston		d			23 21		23 56	23 56		00 25	00 25
Saltcoats		d			23 26		23 59	23 59		00 28	00 28
Ardrossan South Beach		d			23 28		00 02	00 02		00 30	00a31
Ardrossan Town		d					00a04				
Ardrossan Harbour		a									
West Kilbride		d			23 35			00 07		00 36	
Fairlie		d			23 40			00 12		00 41	
Largs		a			23 47			00 18		00 47	
Irvine		d				23 31			00 01		
Barassie		d	←			23 36			00 06		
Troon		d	23 18	23 18		23 39			00 09		
Prestwick Int. Airport ✈		d	23 23	23 23		23 43			00 13		
Prestwick Town		d	23 25	23 25		23 44			00 14		
Newton-on-Ayr		d				23 48			00 18		
Ayr		a	23 30	23 30		23 51			00 21		

Sundays

8 December to 11 May

			SR	SR	SR	SR	SR	SR	SR	SR	SR	SR	SR	SR	SR	SR	SR	SR	SR	SR	SR	SR	SR	SR
																◇								
			C	C												D								
Glasgow Central 15	219	d			08 40	09 00	09 30	09 40	10 00	10 30	10 40	11 00	11 15	11 30	11 40	11 55	12 00	12 30	12 40	13 00	13 30	13 40	14 00	14 05
Paisley Gilmour Street	219	a			08 49	09 09	09 39	09 49	10 09	10 39	10 49	11 09	11 24	11 39	11 49	12 05	12 09	12 39	12 49	13 09	13 39	13 49	14 09	14 14
		d			08 50	09 10	09 40	09 50	10 10	10 40	10 50	11 10	11 25	11 40	11 50	12 06	12 10	12 40	12 50	13 10	13 40	13 50	14 10	14 15
Johnstone		d			08 54	09 14	09 44	09 54	10 14	10 44	10 54	11 14	11 29	11 44	11 54		12 14	12 44	12 54	13 14	13 44	13 54	14 14	14 19
Milliken Park		d			08 57			09 57			10 57		11 32		11 57				12 57			13 57		14 22
Howwood		d						09 59			10 59				11 59				12 59			13 59		
Lochwinnoch		d						10 03			11 03				12 03				13 03			14 03		
Glengarnock		d			09 04			10 08			11 08				12 08				13 08			14 08		
Dalry		d			09 08			10 12			11 12				12 12				13 12			14 12		
Kilwinning 4		d			09 13	09 28	09 58	10 16	10 28	10 58	11 16	11 28	11 45	11 58	12 17	12 23	12 28	12 58	13 16	13 28	13 58	14 16	14 28	14 35
Stevenston		d			09 17			10 20			11 20		11 49		12 21				13 20			14 20		14 39
Saltcoats		d			09 20			10 23			11 23		11 52		12 24				13 23			14 23		14 42
Ardrossan South Beach		d		00 02	09 22			10 25			11 25		11 54		12 26				13 25			14 25		14 44
Ardrossan Town		d																						
Ardrossan Harbour		a			09 29								12 01											14 51
West Kilbride		d		00 07				10 31			11 31				12 32				13 31			14 31		
Fairlie		d		00 12				10 36			11 36				12 37				13 36			14 36		
Largs		a		00 18				10 43			11 43				12 46				13 43			14 43		
Irvine		d	00 01			09 32	10 02		10 32	11 02		11 32		12 02			12 32	13 02		13 32	14 02		14 32	
Barassie		d	00 06			09 36			10 36			11 36					12 36			13 36			14 36	
Troon		d	00 09			09 39	10 08		10 39	11 08		11 39		12 08			12 39	13 08		13 39	14 08		14 39	
Prestwick Int. Airport ✈		d	00 13			09 43	10 12		10 43	11 12		11 43		12 12			12 43	13 12		13 43	14 12		14 43	
Prestwick Town		d	00 14			09 45	10 14		10 45	11 14		11 45		12 14			12 45	13 14		13 45	14 14		14 45	
Newton-on-Ayr		d	00 18			09 48			10 48			11 48					12 48			13 48			14 48	
Ayr		a	00 21			09 53	10 21		10 53	11 21		11 53		12 21		12 41	12 53	13 21		13 53	14 21		14 53	

			SR	SR	SR	SR	SR	SR	SR	SR	SR	SR	SR	SR	SR	SR	SR	SR	SR	SR	SR	SR	SR	SR
						◇																		
						D										D								
Glasgow Central 15	219	d	14 30	14 40	15 00	15 22	15 30	15 40	16 00	16 30	16 40	16 55	17 00	17 30	17 40	17 54	18 00	18 30	18 40	19 00	19 40	20 00	20 40	21 00
Paisley Gilmour Street	219	a	14 39	14 49	15 09	15 32	15 39	15 49	16 09	16 39	16 49	17 04	17 09	17 39	17 49	18 04	18 09	18 39	18 49	19 09	19 49	20 09	20 49	21 09
		d	14 40	14 50	15 10	15 33	15 40	15 50	16 10	16 40	16 50	17 05	17 10	17 40	17 50	18 05	18 10	18 40	18 50	19 10	19 50	20 10	20 50	21 10
Johnstone		d	14 44	14 54	15 14		15 44	15 54	16 14	16 44	16 54	17 09	17 14	17 44	17 54		18 14	18 44	18 54	19 14	19 54	20 14	20 54	21 14
Milliken Park		d		14 57				15 57			16 57	17 12			17 57				18 57		19 57		20 57	
Howwood		d		14 59				15 59			16 59				17 59				18 59		19 59		20 59	
Lochwinnoch		d		15 03				16 03			17 03				18 03				19 03		20 03		21 03	
Glengarnock		d		15 08				16 08			17 08				18 08				19 08		20 08		21 08	
Dalry		d		15 12				16 12			17 12				18 12				19 12		20 12		21 12	
Kilwinning 4		d	14 58	15 16	15 28	15 50	15 58	16 18	16 28	16 58	17 16	17 25	17 28	17 58	18 16	18 22	18 28	18 58	19 16	19 28	20 16	20 28	21 16	21 28
Stevenston		d		15 20				16 22			17 20	17 29			18 20				19 20		20 20		21 20	
Saltcoats		d		15 23				16 25			17 23	17 32			18 23				19 23		20 23		21 23	
Ardrossan South Beach		d		15 25				16 27			17 25	17 34			18 25				19 25		20 25		21 25	
Ardrossan Town		d																						
Ardrossan Harbour		a										17 41												
West Kilbride		d		15 31				16 33			17 31				18 31				19 31		20 31		21 31	
Fairlie		d		15 36				16 38			17 36				18 36				19 36		20 36		21 36	
Largs		a		15 43				16 46			17 43				18 43				19 43		20 43		21 43	
Irvine		d	15 02		15 32		16 02		16 32	17 02			17 32	18 02			18 32	19 02		19 32		20 32		21 32
Barassie		d			15 36				16 36				17 36				18 36			19 36		20 36		21 36
Troon		d	15 08		15 39		16 08		16 39	17 08			17 39	18 08			18 39	19 08		19 39		20 39		21 39
Prestwick Int. Airport ✈		d	15 12		15 43		16 12		16 43	17 12			17 43	18 12			18 43	19 12		19 43		20 43		21 43
Prestwick Town		d	15 14		15 45		16 14		16 45	17 14			17 45	18 14			18 45	19 14		19 45		20 45		21 45
Newton-on-Ayr		d			15 48				16 48				17 48				18 48			19 48		20 48		21 48
Ayr		a	15 21		15 53	16 08	16 21		16 53	17 21			17 54	18 21		18 40	18 53	19 21		19 53		20 53		21 53

A From Glasgow Central to Stranraer
B From Kilmarnock to Stranraer
C not 8 December. From Glasgow Central
D To Stranraer

Table 221

Sundays

8 December to 11 May

Network Diagram - refer to first Page of Table 216

Glasgow Central - Ardrossan, Largs and Ayr

			SR	SR	SR	SR
Glasgow Central 15	219	d	21 40	22 00	22 42	23 00
Paisley Gilmour Street	219	a	21 49	22 09	22 51	23 09
		d	21 50	22 10	22 52	23 10
Johnstone		d	21 54	22 14	22 56	23 14
Milliken Park		d	21 57		22 59	
Howwood		d	21 59		23 01	
Lochwinnoch		d	22 03		23 05	
Glengarnock		d	22 08		23 10	
Dalry		d	22 12		23 14	
Kilwinning 4		d	22 16	22 28	23 26	23 30
Stevenston		d	22 20		23 30	
Saltcoats		d	22 23		23 33	
Ardrossan South Beach		d	22 25		23 35	
Ardrossan Town		d				
Ardrossan Harbour		a				
West Kilbride		d	22 31		23 41	
Fairlie		d	22 36		23 46	
Largs		a	22 43		23 51	
Irvine		d		22 32		23 34
Barassie		d		22 36		23 38
Troon		d		22 39		23 41
Prestwick Int. Airport ✈		d		22 43		23 45
Prestwick Town		d		22 45		23 47
Newton-on-Ayr		d		22 48		23 50
Ayr		a		22 53		23 54

Table 221R

Mondays to Saturdays

9 December to 17 May

Network Diagram - refer to first Page of Table 216

Ayr, Largs and Ardrossan - Glasgow Central

Miles	Miles	Miles	Station		SR	SR	SR	SR SX	SR	SR	SR	SR		SR SX	SR SO	SR	SR SX	SR SX	SR A	SR	SR SX	SR SO		SR SX	SR SX
0	—	—	**Ayr**	d	05 13	05 40	06 02	06 20		06 33		06 50		07 05	07 05	07 19		07 32	07 36	07 40					08 05
1¼	—	—	Newton-on-Ayr	d	05 15	05 42	06 04			06 35		06 52		07 07	07 07	07 21				07 42					08 07
3¼	—	—	Prestwick Town	d	05 18	05 45	06 07	06 25		06 38		06 55		07 10	07 10	07 24		07 37	07 41	07 46					08 10
3¾	—	—	Prestwick Int. Airport ✈	d	05 20	05 47	06 09	06 26		06 40		06 57		07 12	07 12	07 26		07 38		07 47					08 12
6½	—	—	Troon	d	05 24	05 51	06 13	06 30		06 44		07 01		07 16	07 16	07 30		07 43	07a47	07 52					08 16
7¾	—	—	Barassie	d	05 26	05 54	06 15			06 46		07 03		07 18	07 18	07 32				07 54					08 18
11½	—	—	Irvine	d	05 31	05 58	06 20	06 36		06 51		07 08		07 23	07 23	07 37		07 49		07 59					08 23
—	0	—	**Largs**	d							06 40						07 22				07 42	07 42			
—	3	—	Fairlie	d							06 45						07 27				07 47	07 47			
—	7	—	West Kilbride	d							06 50						07 32				07 52	07 52			
—	—	0	**Ardrossan Harbour**	d					06 31																
—	—	0½	Ardrossan Town	d					06 33																
—	11½	1	Ardrossan South Beach	d					06 36		06 57						07 39				07 59	07 59			
—	12½	2	Saltcoats	d					06 38		06 59						07 41				08 01	08 01			
—	13¾	3¼	Stevenston	d					06 40		07 01						07 43				08 03	08 03			
14¾	16	5½	Kilwinning 4	d	05 35	06 02	06 24	06 40	06 44	06 55	07 05	07 12		07 27	07 27	07 41	07 49	07 54		08 03	08 07	08 07		08 12	08 28
18½	19¾	9¼	Dalry	d	05 39	06 07	06 28		06 48	07 01	07 09			07 31	07 31	07 46						08 11		08 16	
21	22¼	11¾	Glengarnock	d	05 43	06 11	06 32			07 05	07 13			07 35	07 35	07 50	07 55					08 15		08 20	
25	26¼	15¾	Lochwinnoch	d	05 48	06 15	06 37			07 10				07 40	07 40			08 04				08 20		08 25	
28½	29¾	19¼	Howwood	d	05 52	06 19	06 41			07 14				07 44	07 44			08 08				08 24		08 29	
30	31¼	20¾	Milliken Park	d	05 54	06 22	06 43			07 16		07 25		07 46	07 46			08 10				08 26		08 31	
30¾	32	21½	Johnstone	d	05 57	06 25	06 46		06 59	07 19	07 23	07 28		07 49	07 49	07 59	08 04			08 17	08 20	08 29		08 34	08 41
34¼	35½	25	Paisley Gilmour Street 219	a	06 02	06 29	06 51	06 55	07 03	07 24	07 28	07 32		07 53	07 53	08 03	08 08	08 15		08 21	08 24	08 33		08 38	08 45
—	—	—		d	06 02	06 29	06 52	06 56	07 05	07 24	07 28	07 32		07 53	07 54	08 03	08 10	08 17		08 21	08 25	08 35		08 39	08 46
41½	42¾	32¼	**Glasgow Central** 15 219	a	06 14	06 40	07 04	07 07	07 19	07 36	07 41	07 44		08 07	08 07	08 14	08 21	08 27		08 33	08 36	08 48		08 52	08 59

Station		SR SO	SR SX	SR	SR SX	SR SO	SR B	SR SO		SR SX	SR	SR	SR	SR SO	SR SX	SR	SR	SR		SR A	SR	SR	SR SO	SR SX	SR
Ayr	d	08 05		08 28			08 50				09 05	09 23		09 36		09 50		10 05		10 13	10 23		10 36		10 50
Newton-on-Ayr	d	08 07		08 30			08 52				09 07			09 38		09 52		10 07					10 38		10 52
Prestwick Town	d	08 10		08 33			08 56				09 10	09 28		09 41		09 55		10 10		10 18	10 28		10 41		10 55
Prestwick Int. Airport ✈	d	08 12		08 35			08 58				09 12	09 29		09 43		09 57		10 12		10 21	10 29		10 43		10 57
Troon	d	08 16		08 39			09 02				09 16	09 33		09 47		10 01		10 16		10a26	10 33		10 47		11 01
Barassie	d	08 18		08 41			09 04				09 18			09 49		10 03		10 18					10 49		11 03
Irvine	d	08 23		08 46			09 09				09 23	09 39		09 53	09 53	10 08		10 23			10 39		10 53	10 53	11 08
Largs	d				08 33			08 53									09 53								
Fairlie	d				08 38			08 58									09 58								
West Kilbride	d				08 43			09 03									10 03								
Ardrossan Harbour	d		08 19			08 45							09 36									10 36			
Ardrossan Town	d		08 21			08 47				09 07			09 39									10 38			
Ardrossan South Beach	d		08 24		08 50	08 50		09 10		09 10			09 42				10 10					10 41			
Saltcoats	d		08 26		08 52	08 52		09 13		09 13			09 44				10 13					10 43			
Stevenston	d		08 28		08 54	08 54		09 15		09 15			09 46				10 15					10 45			
Kilwinning 4	d	08 27	08 32	08 51	08 58	08 58	09 13	09 19		09 19	09 27	09 43	09 50	09 57	09 57	10 12	10 19	10 27			10 43	10 49	10 57	10 57	11 12
Dalry	d	08 31	08 37		09 02	09 02					09 31		09 54	10 03	10 03			10 31				10 53	11 02	11 02	
Glengarnock	d	08 35	08 41		09 06	09 06		09 25		09 25	09 35			10 07	10 07		10 25	10 35					11 06	11 06	
Lochwinnoch	d	08 40	08 45		09 10	09 10					09 40			10 11	10 11			10 40					11 11	11 11	
Howwood	d	08 44	08 49		09 14	09 14					09 44			10 15	10 15			10 44					11 15	11 15	
Milliken Park	d	08 46	08 52		09 17	09 17					09 46			10 19	10 19			10 46					11 19	11 19	
Johnstone	d	08 49	08 55	09 07	09 20	09 20		09 34		09 34	09 49		10 05	10 22	10 22		10 34	10 49				11 04	11 22	11 22	
Paisley Gilmour Street 219	a	08 53	08 59	09 11	09 24	09 24		09 38		09 38	09 54		10 09	10 26	10 26		10 39	10 54				11 08	11 26	11 26	
	d	08 54	08 59	09 11	09 25	09 25		09 39		09 39	09 55		10 10	10 26	10 26		10 40	10 55				11 09	11 26	11 26	
Glasgow Central 15 219	a	09 05	09 11	09 22	09 37	09 37	09 39	09 52		09 52	10 06	10 10	10 22	10 36	10 36	10 39	10 52	11 06			11 10	11 22	11 37	11 37	11 40

Station		SR	SR	SR		SR	SR SO	SR SX	SR ◇ C	SR	SR	SR	SR	SR		SR SO	SR SX	SR	SR	SR	SR A	SR	SR	SR SO	
Ayr	d		11 07	11 23			11 31		11 35	11 52		12 02	12 23			12 37		12 50		13 05	13 20	13 25		13 36	
Newton-on-Ayr	d		11 09				11 33			11 54		12 04				12 39		12 52		13 07				13 38	
Prestwick Town	d		11 12	11 28			11 36		11 40	11 57		12 07	12 28			12 42		12 55		13 10	13 25	13 30		13 41	
Prestwick Int. Airport ✈	d		11 14	11 29			11 38		11 43	11 59		12 09	12 29			12 44		12 57		13 12	13 27	13 31		13 43	
Troon	d		11 18	11 33			11 43		11a48	12 03		12 13	12 33			12 48		13 01		13 16	13a32	13 34		13 47	
Barassie	d		11 20				11 47			12 05		12 15				12 50		13 03		13 18				13 49	
Irvine	d		11 25	11 39			11 53	11 53		12 10		12 20	12 39			12 54	12 54	13 08		13 23		13 41		13 53	
Largs	d	10 53									11 53								12 53						
Fairlie	d	10 58									11 58								12 58						
West Kilbride	d	11 03									12 03								13 03						
Ardrossan Harbour	d					11 36								12 36									13 36		
Ardrossan Town	d					11 38								12 38									13 38		
Ardrossan South Beach	d	11 10				11 41					12 10			12 41					13 10				13 40		
Saltcoats	d	11 13				11 43					12 13			12 43					13 13				13 43		
Stevenston	d	11 15				11 45					12 15			12 45					13 15				13 45		
Kilwinning 4	d	11 19	11 29	11 43		11 50	11 56	11 56		12 14	12 19	12 24	12 43	12 49		12 58	12 58	13 12	13 19	13 26		13 45	13 49	13 57	
Dalry	d		11 33			11 56	12 01	12 01				12 28		12 53		13 03	13 03			13 32			13 53	14 02	
Glengarnock	d	11 25	11 37				12 05	12 05			12 25	12 32				13 07	13 07		13 25	13 36				14 06	
Lochwinnoch	d		11 42				12 09	12 09				12 37				13 11	13 11			13 39				14 10	
Howwood	d		11 46				12 13	12 13				12 41				13 15	13 15			13 43				14 14	
Milliken Park	d		11 48				12 16	12 16				12 43				13 19	13 19			13 47				14 17	
Johnstone	d	11 34	11 51			12 05	12 19	12 19			12 34	12 46		13 04		13 22	13 22		13 34	13 50			14 04	14 20	
Paisley Gilmour Street 219	a	11 38	11 55			12 09	12 24	12 24			12 38	12 53		13 08		13 26	13 26		13 38	13 54			14 08	14 24	
	d	11 39	11 56			12 10	12 25	12 25			12 39	12 54		13 09		13 26	13 26		13 39	13 54			14 09	14 25	
Glasgow Central 15 219	a	11 52	12 07	12 14		12 22	12 36	12 36		12 41	12 52	13 06	13 10	13 22		13 37	13 37	13 42	13 52	14 07		14 10	14 22	14 36	

A From Girvan to Kilmarnock
B not 9 December
C From Stranraer to Kilmarnock

Table 221R

Mondays to Saturdays

9 December to 17 May

Network Diagram - refer to first Page of Table 216

Ayr, Largs and Ardrossan - Glasgow Central

		SR SX	SR	SR	SR	SR ◇ A	SR	SR	SR SO	SR SX		SR	SR	SR	SR B	SR	SR	SR SO B	SR SX B	SR SO		SR SX	SR	SR	SR
Ayr	d		13 50		14 05	14 17	14 25		14 36			14 50		15 05	15 18	15 24		15 32	15 36	15 36			15 48		16 00
Newton-on-Ayr	d		13 52		14 07				14 38			14 52		15 07						15 38			15 50		16 02
Prestwick Town	d		13 55		14 10		14 30		14 41			14 55		15 10	15 23	15 29				15 41			15 53		16 06
Prestwick Int. Airport ✈	d		13 57		14 12		14 31		14 43			14 57		15 12	15 25	15 30				15 43			15 55		16 08
Troon	d		14 01		14 16		14 35		14 47			15 01		15 16	15 30	15 34				15 47			15 59		16 13
Barassie	d		14 03		14 18				14 49			15 03		15 18						15 49			16 01		16 15
Irvine	d	13 53	14 08		14 23		14 41		14 53	14 53		15 08		15 23		15 40				15 53		15 53	16 06		16 20
Largs	d			13 53									14 53											15 53	
Fairlie	d			13 58									14 58											15 58	
West Kilbride	d			14 03									15 03											16 03	
Ardrossan Harbour	d							14 36									15 36								
Ardrossan Town	d							14 38									15 38								
Ardrossan South Beach	d			14 10				14 41					15 10				15 41							16 10	
Saltcoats	d			14 13				14 43					15 12				15 43							16 13	
Stevenston	d			14 15				14 45					15 14				15 45							16 15	
Kilwinning ④	d	13 57	14 12	14 19	14 28	14 37	14 45	14 49	14 57	14 57		15 12	15 18	15 26		15 44	15 49	15 53	15 53	15 57		15 57	16 10	16 19	16 25
Dalry	d	14 02			14 32			14 53	15 02	15 02				15 32			15 53			16 03		16 03			16 29
Glengarnock	d	14 06		14 26	14 36				15 06	15 06			15 24	15 36						16 07		16 07		16 25	16 33
Lochwinnoch	d	14 10			14 41				15 11	15 11				15 39						16 10		16 10			16 38
Howwood	d	14 14			14 45				15 15	15 15				15 43						16 14		16 14			16 42
Milliken Park	d	14 17			14 47				15 19	15 19				15 47						16 18		16 18			16 44
Johnstone	d	14 20		14 37	14 50			15 04	15 22	15 22			15 34	15 50			16 04			16 21		16 21		16 34	16 47
Paisley Gilmour Street 219	a	14 24		14 41	14 54	14 58		15 08	15 26	15 26			15 38	15 54			16 08	16 16	16 16	16 25		16 25		16 38	16 51
	d	14 25		14 42	14 55	14 59		15 09	15 26	15 26			15 39	15 54			16 09	16 20	16 20	16 25		16 25		16 39	16 55
Glasgow Central ⑮ 219	a	14 36	14 39	14 52	15 08	15 12	15 16	15 22	15 36	15 36		15 42	15 52	16 08	16 33	16 13	16 20	16 36	16 36	16 38		16 38	16 40	16 54	17 09

		SR ◇ C	SR	SR	SR SO	SR SX		SR	SR	SR	SR	SR	SR	SR	SR	SR		SR D	SR	SR	SR SO	SR SX	SR	SR	SR
Ayr	d	16 05	16 23		16 36				16 54	17 05		17 23		17 53		18 05		18 15	18 25		18 39		18 50		19 15
Newton-on-Ayr	d				16 38				16 56	17 07		17 25		17 55		18 07					18 41		18 52		
Prestwick Town	d	16 10	16 28		16 41				16 59	17 10		17 28		17 58		18 10		18 20	18 30		18 44		18 55		19 20
Prestwick Int. Airport ✈	d	16 12	16 29		16 43				17 01	17 12		17 30		18 00		18 12		18 22	18 31		18 46		18 57		19 21
Troon	d	16a17	16 33		16 47				17 05	17 16		17 34		18 04		18 16		18a29	18 35		18 50		19 01		19 25
Barassie	d				16 49				17 07	17 18		17 36		18 06		18 18					18 52		19 03		
Irvine	d		16 39		16 53	16 53			17 12	17 23		17 41		18 11		18 23			18 41		18 57	18 57	19 08		19 31
Largs	d							16 48					17 33											18 52	
Fairlie	d							16 53					17 38											18 57	
West Kilbride	d							16 58					17 43											19 02	
Ardrossan Harbour	d			16 36							17 21				18 07					18 36					
Ardrossan Town	d			16 38							17 23				18 09					18 38					
Ardrossan South Beach	d			16 41				17 05			17 26		17 50		18 11					18 41				19 09	
Saltcoats	d			16 43				17 07			17 30		17 52		18 13					18 43				19 11	
Stevenston	d			16 45				17 09			17 32		17 54		18 16					18 45				19 13	
Kilwinning ④	d		16 43	16 49	16 57	16 57		17 12	17 17	17 27	17 41	17 45	17 57	18 15	18 19	18 27			18 45	18 49	19 01	19 01	19 12	19 17	19 35
Dalry	d			16 53	17 04	17 04			17 21	17 31		17 50	18 02			18 31				18 53	19 05	19 05		19 21	
Glengarnock	d				17 08	17 08			17 25	17 35	17 48		18 06		18 26	18 35					19 09	19 09		19 25	
Lochwinnoch	d				17 14	17 14				17 40			18 10			18 40					19 14	19 14			
Howwood	d				17 18	17 18				17 44			18 14			18 44					19 18	19 18			
Milliken Park	d				17 20	17 20				17 46			18 17			18 46					19 20	19 20		19 33	
Johnstone	d			17 04	17 23	17 23			17 34	17 49		18 00	18 20		18 34	18 49				19 04	19 23	19 23		19 36	19 48
Paisley Gilmour Street 219	a			17 09	17 27	17 27		17 31	17 42	17 54	18 00	18 05	18 24	18 30	18 38	18 54			19 00	19 08	19 28	19 28	19 32	19 40	19 52
	d			17 10	17 28	17 28		17 31	17 43	17 55	18 00	18 06	18 25	18 31	18 39	18 55			19 01	19 09	19 28	19 28	19 35	19 40	19 53
Glasgow Central ⑮ 219	a		17 11	17 22	17 39	17 39		17 41	17 53	18 06	18 10	18 17	18 36	18 42	18 52	19 06			19 15	19 24	19 40	19 40	19 46	19 52	20 04

		SR		SR SO	SR D	SR	SR	SR	SR	SR ◇ A	SR	SR		SR	SR	SR	SR	SR	SR ◇ A	SR	SR				
Ayr	d			19 32	19 39	19 45		20 15		20 30	20 45			21 15		21 45		22 15	22 35		23 00				
Newton-on-Ayr	d			19 34		19 47					20 47					21 47		22 17			23 02				
Prestwick Town	d			19 37	19 44	19 50		20 20			20 50			21 20		21 50		22 20	22 40		23 05				
Prestwick Int. Airport ✈	d			19 39	19 46	19 52		20 21			20 52			21 21		21 52		22 22			23 07				
Troon	d			19 43	19a51	19 55		20 25			20 56			21 25		21 56		22 26	22 45		23 11				
Barassie	d			19 45		19 59					20 58					21 58		22 28			23 13				
Irvine	d			19 50		20 02		20 31			21 03			21 31		22 03		22 33			23 18				
Largs	d						19 52					20 52					21 52			22 52					
Fairlie	d						19 57					20 57					21 57			22 57					
West Kilbride	d						20 02					21 02					22 02			23 02					
Ardrossan Harbour	d	19 31							20 31						21 31										
Ardrossan Town	d	19 33							20 34						21 33										
Ardrossan South Beach	d	19 36					20 09		20 36			21 09			21 36		22 09			23 09					
Saltcoats	d	19 38					20 11		20 38			21 11			21 38		22 11			23 11					
Stevenston	d	19 40					20 13		20 41			21 13			21 40		22 13			23 13					
Kilwinning ④	d	19 44		19 54		20 06	20 17	20 35	20 44	20 58	21 07	21 17		21 35	21 44	22 08	22 17	22 37	22 55	23 17	23 22				
Dalry	d	19 48		19 59			20 21		20 52			21 22			21 48		22 21				23 26				
Glengarnock	d	19 52		20 03			20 25		20 56			21 26			21 52		22 25				23 30				
Lochwinnoch	d	19 57		20 07					20 59						21 57						23 35				
Howwood	d	20 01		20 11					21 03						22 01						23 39				
Milliken Park	d	20 03		20 14			20 33		21 05			21 35			22 03		22 33				23 41				
Johnstone	d	20 06		20 17		20 21	20 36	20 48	21 08		21 20	21 38		21 48	22 06	22 21	22 36	22 50		23 30	23 44				
Paisley Gilmour Street 219	a	20 09		20 21		20 24	20 40	20 52	21 11	21 18	21 25	21 41		21 53	22 09	22 25	22 40	22 55	23 14	23 35	23 49				
	d	20 10		20 21		20 25	20 40	20 53	21 12	21 18	21 25	21 41		21 53	22 10	22 26	22 40	22 55	23 14	23 35	23 49				
Glasgow Central ⑮ 219	a	20 22		20 31		20 37	20 54	21 04	21 25	21 31	21 37	21 54		22 06	22 22	22 37	22 54	23 07	23 25	23 46	00 01				

A From Stranraer
B From Girvan
C From Stranraer to Kilmarnock
D From Girvan to Kilmarnock

Table 221R

Sundays

8 December to 11 May

Network Diagram - refer to first Page of Table 216

Ayr, Largs and Ardrossan - Glasgow Central

		SR	SR	SR	SR	SR	SR	SR	SR	SR		SR	SR	SR	SR	SR	SR	SR	SR	SR		SR	SR	SR	SR
													◇ A												
Ayr	d	08 45		09 15	09 45		10 15	10 45		11 15		11 45	12 01		12 15		12 45		13 15	13 45			14 15	14 45	
Newton-on-Ayr	d	08 47			09 47			10 47				11 47					12 47			13 47				14 47	
Prestwick Town	d	08 50		09 20	09 50		10 20	10 50		11 20		11 50			12 20		12 50		13 20	13 50			14 20	14 50	
Prestwick Int. Airport ✈	d	08 52		09 21	09 52		10 21	10 52		11 21		11 52			12 21		12 52		13 21	13 52			14 21	14 52	
Troon	d	08 56		09 25	09 56		10 25	10 56		11 25		11 56			12 25		12 56		13 25	13 56			14 25	14 56	
Barassie	d	08 58			09 58			10 58				11 58					12 58			13 58				14 58	
Irvine	d	09 03		09 31	10 03		10 31	11 03		11 31		12 03			12 31		13 03		13 31	14 03			14 31	15 03	
Largs	d		08 54			09 54			10 54					11 54				12 54				13 54			
Fairlie	d		08 59			09 59			10 59					11 59				12 59				13 59			
West Kilbride	d		09 04			10 04			11 04					12 04				13 04				14 04			
Ardrossan Harbour	d															12 35									15 03
Ardrossan Town	d																								
Ardrossan South Beach	d		09 11			10 11			11 11					12 11		12 38		13 11				14 11			15 06
Saltcoats	d		09 13			10 13			11 13					12 13		12 40		13 13				14 13			15 08
Stevenston	d		09 15			10 15			11 15					12 15		12 43		13 15				14 15			15 11
Kilwinning 4	d	09 07	09 19	09 35	10 07	10 19	10 35	11 07	11 19	11 35		12 07	12 16	12 19	12 35	12 47	13 07	13 19	13 35	14 07		14 19	14 35	15 07	15 15
Dalry	d		09 24			10 24			11 24					12 24				13 24				14 24			
Glengarnock	d		09 28			10 28			11 28					12 28				13 28				14 28			
Lochwinnoch	d		09 32			10 32			11 32					12 32				13 32				14 32			
Howwood	d		09 36			10 36			11 36					12 36				13 36				14 36			
Milliken Park	d		09 39			10 39			11 39					12 39		12 59		13 39				14 39			15 27
Johnstone	d	09 21	09 42	09 49	10 21	10 42	10 49	11 21	11 42	11 49		12 21		12 42	12 49	13 02	13 21	13 42	13 49	14 21		14 42	14 49	15 21	15 30
Paisley Gilmour Street 219	a	09 25	09 46	09 53	10 25	10 46	10 53	11 25	11 46	11 53		12 25	12 35	12 46	12 53	13 06	13 25	13 46	13 53	14 25		14 46	14 53	15 25	15 34
	d	09 25	09 46	09 53	10 25	10 46	10 53	11 25	11 46	11 53		12 25	12 36	12 46	12 53	13 07	13 25	13 46	13 53	14 25		14 46	14 53	15 25	15 35
Glasgow Central 15 219	a	09 36	09 58	10 05	10 36	10 58	11 05	11 36	11 58	12 05		12 36	12 49	12 58	13 05	13 18	13 36	13 58	14 05	14 36		14 58	15 06	15 36	15 46

		SR	SR	SR	SR	SR		SR	SR	SR	SR	SR	SR	SR	SR	SR		SR	SR	SR	SR	SR	SR	SR	SR
					◇ A																			◇ A	
Ayr	d		15 15	15 45	16 01			16 15	16 45		17 15	17 45			18 15	18 45			19 15	19 45			20 45	21 06	
Newton-on-Ayr	d			15 47					16 47			17 47				18 47				19 47			20 47		
Prestwick Town	d		15 20	15 50				16 20	16 50		17 20	17 50			18 20	18 50			19 20	19 50			20 50		
Prestwick Int. Airport ✈	d		15 21	15 52				16 21	16 52		17 21	17 52			18 21	18 52			19 21	19 52			20 52		
Troon	d		15 25	15 56				16 25	16 56		17 25	17 56			18 25	18 56			19 25	19 56			20 56		
Barassie	d			15 58					16 58			17 58				18 58				19 58			20 58		
Irvine	d		15 31	16 03				16 31	17 03		17 31	18 03			18 31	19 03			19 31	20 03			21 03		
Largs	d	14 54				15 54				16 54				17 54				18 54			19 54				20 54
Fairlie	d	14 59				15 59				16 59				17 59				18 59			19 59				20 59
West Kilbride	d	15 04				16 04				17 04				18 04				19 04			20 04				21 04
Ardrossan Harbour	d												18 00									20 31			
Ardrossan Town	d																								
Ardrossan South Beach	d	15 11				16 11				17 11			18 03	18 11				19 11			20 11	20 34			21 11
Saltcoats	d	15 13				16 13				17 13			18 05	18 13				19 13			20 13	20 36			21 13
Stevenston	d	15 15				16 15				17 15			18 08	18 15				19 15			20 15	20 39			21 15
Kilwinning 4	d	15 19	15 35	16 07	16 17	16 19		16 35	17 07	17 19	17 35	18 07	18 12	18 19	18 35	19 07		19 19	19 35	20 07	20 19	20 43	21 07	21 21	21 24
Dalry	d	15 24				16 24				17 24				18 24				19 24			20 24				21 29
Glengarnock	d	15 28				16 28				17 28				18 28				19 28			20 28				21 33
Lochwinnoch	d	15 32				16 32				17 32				18 32				19 32			20 32				21 37
Howwood	d	15 36				16 36				17 36				18 36				19 36			20 36				21 41
Milliken Park	d	15 39				16 39				17 39			18 24	18 39				19 39			20 39	20 55			21 44
Johnstone	d	15 42	15 49	16 21		16 42		16 49	17 21	17 42	17 49	18 21	18 27	18 42	18 49	19 21		19 42	19 49	20 21	20 42	20 58	21 21		21 47
Paisley Gilmour Street 219	a	15 46	15 53	16 25	16 36	16 45		16 53	17 25	17 46	17 53	18 25	18 31	18 46	18 53	19 25		19 46	19 53	20 25	20 46	21 02	21 25	21 40	21 51
	d	15 46	15 53	16 25	16 36	16 47		16 53	17 25	17 46	17 53	18 25	18 32	18 46	18 53	19 25		19 46	19 53	20 25	20 46	21 03	21 25	21 41	21 51
Glasgow Central 15 219	a	15 58	16 05	16 36	16 50	16 58		17 05	17 36	17 58	18 05	18 36	18 44	18 58	19 05	19 36		19 58	20 05	20 36	20 58	21 14	21 36	21 54	22 04

		SR		SR	SR	SR
Ayr	d	21 45			23 00	
Newton-on-Ayr	d	21 47			23 02	
Prestwick Town	d	21 50			23 05	
Prestwick Int. Airport ✈	d	21 52			23 07	
Troon	d	21 56			23 11	
Barassie	d	21 58			23 13	
Irvine	d	22 03			23 18	
Largs	d			21 54		23 00
Fairlie	d			21 59		23 05
West Kilbride	d			22 04		23 10
Ardrossan Harbour	d					
Ardrossan Town	d					
Ardrossan South Beach	d			22 11		23 17
Saltcoats	d			22 13		23 19
Stevenston	d			22 15		23 21
Kilwinning 4	d	22 07		22 19	23 22	23 26
Dalry	d			22 24		23 30
Glengarnock	d			22 28		23 34
Lochwinnoch	d			22 32		23 39
Howwood	d			22 36		23 43
Milliken Park	d			22 39		23 45
Johnstone	d	22 21		22 42	23 36	23 48
Paisley Gilmour Street 219	a	22 25		22 46	23 40	23 52
	d	22 25		22 46	23 40	23 53
Glasgow Central 15 219	a	22 36		22 58	23 51	00 04

A From Stranraer

Table 221A

Mondays to Saturdays

until 3 April 2014

Glasgow and Ardrossan - Brodick (Arran)

Caledonian MacBrayne Ltd in association with ScotRail — **Network Diagram - see first Page of Table 216**

Glasgow Central 15	221	d	*08 34*	*11 18*	*14 18*	*16 50*
Paisley Gilmour Street	221	d	*08 44*	*11 28*	*14 28*	*17 00*
Ardrossan Harbour	221	a	*09 20*	*12 02*	*15 03*	*17 36*
Ardrossan Harbour	⛴	d	**09 45**	**12 30**	**15 15**	**18 00**
Brodick	⛴	a	**10 40**	**13 25**	**16 10**	**18 55**

Sundays

until 30 March 2014

Glasgow Central 15	221	d	*08 40*	*11 15*	*14 05*	*16 55*
Paisley Gilmour Street	221	d	*08 50*	*11 25*	*14 15*	*17 05*
Ardrossan Harbour	221	a	*09 29*	*12 01*	*14 51*	*17 41*
Ardrossan Harbour	⛴	d	**09 45**	**12 30**	**15 15**	**18 00**
Brodick	⛴	a	**10 40**	**13 25**	**16 10**	**18 55**

For details of sailings from 4 April 2014 please telephone 08000 66 5000 or visit www.calmac.co.uk

Table 221A

Mondays to Saturdays

until 3 April 2014

Brodick (Arran) - Ardrossan and Glasgow

Caledonian MacBrayne Ltd in association with ScotRail — **Network Diagram - see first Page of Table 216**

Brodick	⛴	d	**08 20**	**11 05**	**13 50**	**16 40**	**19 20**
Ardrossan Harbour	⛴	a	**09 15**	**12 00**	**14 45**	**17 35**	**20 15**
Ardrossan Harbour	221	d	*09 36*	*12 36*	*15 36*	*18 07*	*20 31*
Paisley Gilmour Street	221	a	*10 09*	*13 08*	*16 08*	*18 38*	*21 11*
Glasgow Central 15	221	a	*10 22*	*13 22*	*16 20*	*18 52*	*21 25*

Sundays

until 30 March 2014

Brodick	⛴	d	**11 05**	**13 50**	**16 40**	**19 20**
Ardrossan Harbour	⛴	a	**12 00**	**14 45**	**17 35**	**20 15**
Ardrossan Harbour	221	d	*12 35*	*15 03*	*18 00*	*20 31*
Paisley Gilmour Street	221	a	*13 06*	*15 34*	*18 31*	*21 02*
Glasgow Central 15	221	a	*13 18*	*15 46*	*18 44*	*21 14*

For details of sailings from 4 April 2014 please telephone 08000 66 5000 or visit www.calmac.co.uk

Table 221B

Mondays to Saturdays

9 December to 17 May

Network Diagram - refer to first Page of Table 216

Cairnryan (Loch Ryan Port) - Belfast Port

		SR	SR	SR	SR	SR	SR	SR	SR	SR
				🚌	B	🚌	B	🚌	B	
Ayr	d			08 40		12 35		17 05		
Cairnryan (Loch Ryan Port)	a			09 55		13 50		18 20		
Cairnryan (Loch Ryan Port)	d	03 45	07 30		11 30		15 30		19 30	23 30
Belfast Port	a	06 00	09 45		13 45		17 45		21 45	01 45

Sundays

8 December to 11 May

		SR	SR	SR	SR	SR	SR	SR
			🚌	B	🚌	B	🚌	B
Ayr	d		08 40		12 40		17 05	
Cairnryan (Loch Ryan Port)	a		09 55		13 55		18 20	
Cairnryan (Loch Ryan Port)	d	05 30		11 30		15 30		19 30
Belfast Port	a	07 45		13 45		17 45		21 45

Ferry service operated by Stena Line. Please telephone 08705 70 70 70 or visit www.stenaline.co.uk for details

Table 221B-R

Mondays to Saturdays

9 December to 17 May

Network Diagram - refer to first Page of Table 216

Belfast Port - Cairnryan (Loch Ryan Port)

		SR	SR	SR	SR	SR	SR	SR	SR	SR
			B	🚌	B	🚌	B	🚌		
Belfast Port	d	03 30	07 30		11 30		15 30		19 30	23 30
Cairnryan (Loch Ryan Port)	a	05 45	09 45		13 45		17 45		21 45	01 45
Cairnryan (Loch Ryan Port)	d			10 15		14 15		18 25		
Ayr	a			11 30		15 30		19 35		

Sundays

8 December to 11 May

		SR	SR	SR	SR	SR	SR	SR
		B	🚌	B	🚌	B	🚌	
Belfast Port	d	07 30		11 30		15 30		21 00
Cairnryan (Loch Ryan Port)	a	09 45		13 45		17 45		23 45
Cairnryan (Loch Ryan Port)	d		10 15		14 15		18 25	
Ayr	a		11 30		15 30		19 35	

Ferry service operated by Stena Line. Please telephone 08705 70 70 70 or visit www.stenaline.co.uk for details

Table 222

Mondays to Saturdays

9 December to 17 May

Kilmarnock, Barrhead and East Kilbride - Glasgow Central

Network Diagram - refer to first Page of Table 216

Miles	Miles			SR A	SR	SR SX	SR	SR	SR B	SR SX	SR SO	SR SO		SR SX	SR SX	SR SO	SR SX	SR SX	SR SO	SR SX	SR SO C	SR SX C		SR SX	SR SO
0	—	**Kilmarnock 3**	d		05 22		06 22		06 52						07 22	07 22					07 55	07 55			
2¼	—	Kilmaurs	d		05 26		06 26		06 56						07 26	07 26					08 00	08 00			
5½	—	Stewarton	d		05 31		06 31		07 02						07 31	07 31					08 06	08 06			
7¾	—	Dunlop	d		05 36		06 36		07 06						07 36	07 36					08 10	08 10			
16¾	—	**Barrhead**	d		05 46		06 46		07 18	07 24	07 27				07 49	07 47		07 56			08 21	08 21			08 27
18½	—	Nitshill	d		05 49		06 49			07 27	07 30					07 50		07 59							08 30
19½	—	Priesthill & Darnley	d		05 52		06 52			07 29	07 32					07 52		08 01							08 32
20	—	Kennishead	d		05 54		06 54			07 31	07 34					07 54		08 03							08 34
—	0	**East Kilbride**	d			06 17		06 54				07 24		07 24			07 42		07 58	07 58				08 10	
—	1½	Hairmyres	d			06 21		06 58				07 28		07 28			07 46		08 02	08 02				08 18	
—	3	Thorntonhall	d	00 02		06 24		07 01				07 31		07 31					08 05	08 05					
—	4¼	Busby	d	00 05		06 27		07 04				07 35		07 35					08 09	08 09				08 23	
—	5	Clarkston	d	00 08		06 30		07 07				07 38		07 38			07 54		08 12	08 12				08 26	
—	6¼	Giffnock	d	00 11		06 34		07 11				07 41		07 41					08 15	08 15				08 29	
—	7¼	Thornliebank	d	00 14		06 36		07 13				07 45		07 45					08 18	08 18				08 31	
21¼	8¼	Pollokshaws West	d	00 17	05 57	06 40	06 57	07 17		07 35	07 38	07 48		07 48		07 58		08 07	08 21	08 21				08 35	08 38
22¼	9¼	Crossmyloof	d	00 20	06 00	06 43	07 00	07 20		07 38	07 41	07 51		07 51		08 00		08 10	08 24	08 24				08 39	08 41
24¼	11½	**Glasgow Central 15**	a	00 27	06 08	06 49	07 10	07 27	07 31	07 45	07 47	07 58		07 59	08 00	08 09	08 09	08 16	08 30	08 32	08 34	08 37		08 45	08 50

		SR SX	SR	SR	SR	SR	SR	SR		SR	SR	SR	SR	NT D	SR	SR	SR	SR		SR	SR	SR	SR	SR	SR
Kilmarnock 3	d			08 23			08 57				09 27			09 57			10 27				10 57			11 27	
Kilmaurs	d			08 27			09 01				09 31			10 01			10 31				11 01			11 31	
Stewarton	d			08 32			09 06				09 36			10 06			10 36				11 06			11 36	
Dunlop	d			08 37			09 11				09 41			10 11			10 41				11 11			11 41	
Barrhead	d	08 27		08 50	08 57		09 22	09 27			09 52	09 57		10 22	10 27		10 52	10 57				11 27		11 52	11 57
Nitshill	d	08 30			09 00			09 30				10 00			10 30			11 00				11 30			12 00
Priesthill & Darnley	d	08 32			09 02			09 32				10 02			10 32			11 02				11 32			12 02
Kennishead	d	08 34			09 04			09 34				10 04			10 34			11 04				11 34			12 04
East Kilbride	d		08 26			08 56				09 26			09 55			10 26				10 55			11 26		
Hairmyres	d		08 30			09 00				09 30			09 59			10 30				10 59			11 30		
Thorntonhall	d		08 33			09 03							10 02							11 02					
Busby	d		08 36			09 06				09 35			10 05			10 35				11 05			11 35		
Clarkston	d		08 39			09 09				09 38			10 08			10 38				11 08			11 38		
Giffnock	d		08 43			09 13				09 41			10 11			10 41				11 11			11 41		
Thornliebank	d		08 45			09 15				09 44			10 14			10 44				11 14			11 44		
Pollokshaws West	d	08 39	08 48		09 08	09 18		09 38		09 47		10 08	10 17		10 38	10 47		11 08		11 17		11 38	11 47		12 08
Crossmyloof	d	08 42	08 51		09 11	09 21		09 41		09 50		10 11	10 20		10 41	10 50		11 11		11 20		11 41	11 50		12 11
Glasgow Central 15	a	08 50	08 58	09 03	09 17	09 27	09 36	09 47		09 57	10 07	10 17	10 27	10 37	10 47	10 57	11 06	11 17		11 27	11 35	11 47	11 57	12 06	12 18

		SR	SR	SR		SR	SR	SR	SR	SR C	SR	SR	SR	SR		SR	SR	SR	SR	SR	SR	SR	SR C	SR	
Kilmarnock 3	d		11 57				12 27			12 57			13 27				13 57			14 27			14 57		
Kilmaurs	d		12 01				12 31			13 01			13 31				14 01			14 31			15 01		
Stewarton	d		12 06				12 36			13 06			13 36				14 06			14 36			15 06		
Dunlop	d		12 11				12 41			13 11			13 41				14 11			14 41			15 11		
Barrhead	d			12 27			12 52	12 57			13 27		13 52	13 57				14 27		14 52	14 57			15 27	
Nitshill	d			12 30				13 00			13 30			14 00				14 30			15 00			15 30	
Priesthill & Darnley	d			12 32				13 02			13 32			14 02				14 32			15 02			15 32	
Kennishead	d			12 34				13 04			13 34			14 04				14 34			15 04			15 34	
East Kilbride	d	11 55				12 26			12 55			13 26				13 55			14 26			14 55			
Hairmyres	d	11 59				12 30			12 59			13 30				13 59			14 30			14 59			
Thorntonhall	d	12 02							13 02							14 02						15 02			
Busby	d	12 05				12 35			13 05			13 35				14 05			14 35			15 05			
Clarkston	d	12 08				12 38			13 08			13 38				14 08			14 38			15 08			
Giffnock	d	12 11				12 41			13 11			13 41				14 11			14 41			15 11			
Thornliebank	d	12 14				12 44			13 14			13 44				14 14			14 44			15 14			
Pollokshaws West	d	12 17		12 38		12 47		13 08	13 17		13 38	13 47		14 08		14 17		14 38	14 47		15 08	15 17		15 38	
Crossmyloof	d	12 20		12 41		12 50		13 11	13 20		13 41	13 50		14 11		14 20		14 41	14 50		15 11	15 20		15 41	
Glasgow Central 15	a	12 27	12 35	12 47		12 57	13 05	13 17	13 27	13 35	13 47	13 57	14 05	14 17		14 27	14 34	14 47	14 57	15 05	15 19	15 27	15 34	15 47	

		SR	SR	SR	SR	SR E	SR	SR	SR	SR		SR	NT D	SR	SR	SR	SR	SR SO	SR SX	SR		SR	SR SO	SR SX	SR
Kilmarnock 3	d		15 27			15 57			16 27				16 57			17 27				17 59					18 28
Kilmaurs	d		15 31			16 01			16 31				17 01			17 31				18 03					18 32
Stewarton	d		15 36			16 06			16 36				17 06			17 36				18 08					18 37
Dunlop	d		15 41			16 11			16 41				17 11			17 41				18 13					18 42
Barrhead	d		15 52	15 57			16 27		16 52	16 57			17 22	17 27		17 52	17 57			18 23		18 27			18 54
Nitshill	d			16 00			16 30			17 00				17 30			18 00					18 30			
Priesthill & Darnley	d			16 02			16 32			17 02				17 32			18 02					18 33			
Kennishead	d			16 04			16 34			17 04				17 34			18 04					18 35			
East Kilbride	d	15 26			15 55			16 26				16 56			17 26			17 56	17 56				18 26	18 26	
Hairmyres	d	15 30			15 59			16 30				17 00			17 31			18 00	18 05				18 30	18 36	
Thorntonhall	d				16 02							17 03						18 03	18 08						
Busby	d	15 35			16 05			16 35				17 06			17 36			18 06	18 11				18 35	18 41	
Clarkston	d	15 38			16 08			16 38				17 09			17 39			18 09	18 14				18 38	18 44	
Giffnock	d	15 41			16 12			16 41				17 13			17 42			18 13	18 18				18 41	18 47	
Thornliebank	d	15 44			16 14			16 44				17 15			17 45			18 15	18 20				18 44	18 50	
Pollokshaws West	d	15 47		16 08	16 18		16 38	16 47		17 08		17 18		17 38	17 48		18 08	18 18	18 23			18 38	18 47	18 53	
Crossmyloof	d	15 50		16 11	16 21		16 41	16 50		17 11		17 21		17 41	17 51		18 11	18 21	18 26			18 41	18 50	18 56	
Glasgow Central 15	a	15 57	16 06	16 17	16 27	16 33	16 48	16 57	17 05	17 18		17 29	17 36	17 49	17 58	18 06	18 17	18 27	18 33	18 37		18 47	18 57	19 03	19 07

A From East Kilbride
B From Dumfries
C From Carlisle
D From Newcastle
E From Girvan

Table 222

Kilmarnock, Barrhead and East Kilbride - Glasgow Central

Mondays to Saturdays

9 December to 17 May

Network Diagram - refer to first Page of Table 216

		SR		SR	SR	SR	SR	SR	SR	SR A	SR	SR		SR	NT B	SR	SR	SR	SR	SR	SR	SR		SR A	SR
Kilmarnock 3	d				18 57			19 27		19 57		20 27			21 00		21 27		21 57		22 27			22 57	
Kilmaurs	d				19 01			19 31		20 01		20 31			21 04		21 31		22 01		22 31			23 01	
Stewarton	d				19 06			19 36		20 06		20 36			21 10		21 36		22 06		22 36			23 06	
Dunlop	d				19 11			19 41		20 11		20 41			21 14		21 41		22 11		22 41			23 11	
Barrhead	d	18 57			19 22	19 27		19 51		20 21		20 51			21 25		21 51		22 22		22 51			23 22	
Nitshill	d	19 00				19 30		19 54				20 54					21 54				22 54				
Priesthill & Darnley	d	19 02				19 32		19 57				20 57					21 57				22 57				
Kennishead	d	19 04				19 34		19 59				20 59					21 59				22 59				
East Kilbride	d			18 55			19 26		19 55		20 26			20 55		21 26		21 55		22 26		22 55			23 26
Hairmyres	d			18 59			19 30		19 59		20 30			20 59		21 30		21 59		22 30		22 59			23 30
Thorntonhall	d			19 02					20 02					21 02				22 02				23 02			
Busby	d			19 05			19 35		20 05		20 35			21 05		21 35		22 05		22 35		23 05			23 35
Clarkston	d			19 07			19 38		20 08		20 38			21 08		21 38		22 08		22 38		23 08			23 38
Giffnock	d			19 11			19 41		20 11		20 41			21 11		21 41		22 11		22 41		23 11			23 41
Thornliebank	d			19 14			19 44		20 14		20 44			21 14		21 44		22 14		22 44		23 14			23 44
Pollokshaws West	d	19 07		19 17		19 37	19 47	20 02	20 17		20 47	21 02		21 17		21 47	22 02	22 17		22 47	23 02	23 17			23 47
Crossmyloof	d	19 11		19 20		19 41	19 50	20 05	20 20		20 50	21 05		21 20		21 50	22 05	22 20		22 50	23 05	23 20			23 50
Glasgow Central 15	a	19 19		19 27	19 37	19 48	19 57	20 13	20 27	20 35	20 57	21 13		21 27	21 39	21 57	22 13	22 27	22 37	22 57	23 13	23 27		23 36	23 57

		SR
Kilmarnock 3	d	
Kilmaurs	d	
Stewarton	d	
Dunlop	d	
Barrhead	d	
Nitshill	d	
Priesthill & Darnley	d	
Kennishead	d	
East Kilbride	d	23 55
Hairmyres	d	23 59
Thorntonhall	d	00 02
Busby	d	00 05
Clarkston	d	00 08
Giffnock	d	00 11
Thornliebank	d	00 14
Pollokshaws West	d	00 17
Crossmyloof	d	00 20
Glasgow Central 15	a	00 27

Sundays

8 December to 11 May

		SR C	SR	SR	SR	SR	SR	SR	SR	SR	SR		SR	SR	SR A			NT A	SR	SR	
Kilmarnock 3	d				08 57			09 57			10 57	and at the same minutes past each hour until			14 57			14 57			and at the same minutes past each hour until
Kilmaurs	d				09 01			10 01			11 01				15 01			15 01			
Stewarton	d				09 06			10 06			11 06				15 06			15 06			
Dunlop	d				09 11			10 11			11 11				15 11			15 11			
Barrhead	d				09 21			10 21			11 21				15 21			15 21			
Nitshill	d																				
Priesthill & Darnley	d																				
Kennishead	d																				
East Kilbride	d		08 26	08 55		09 26	09 55		10 26	10 55			14 26	14 55					15 26	15 55	
Hairmyres	d		08 29	08 59		09 30	09 59		10 30	10 59			14 30	14 59					15 30	15 59	
Thorntonhall	d	00 02		09 02			10 02			11 02				15 02						16 02	
Busby	d	00 05	08 35	09 05		09 35	10 05		10 35	11 05			14 35	15 05					15 35	16 05	
Clarkston	d	00 08	08 38	09 08		09 38	10 08		10 38	11 08			14 38	15 08					15 38	16 08	
Giffnock	d	00 11	08 41	09 11		09 41	10 11		10 41	11 11			14 41	15 11					15 41	16 11	
Thornliebank	d	00 14	08 44	09 14		09 44	10 14		10 44	11 14			14 44	15 14					15 44	16 14	
Pollokshaws West	d	00 17	08 47	09 17	09 27	09 47	10 17	10 27	10 47	11 17	11 27		14 47	15 17	15 27			15 27	15 47	16 17	
Crossmyloof	d	00 20	08 50	09 20		09 50	10 20		10 50	11 20			14 50	15 20					15 50	16 20	
Glasgow Central 15	a	00 27	08 57	09 27	09 36	09 57	10 27	10 40	10 57	11 27	11 36		14 57	15 27	15 36			15 36	15 57	16 27	

		SR	SR	SR	SR A		SR	SR	SR	SR	SR	SR
Kilmarnock 3	d	19 57			20 57							
Kilmaurs	d	20 01			21 01							
Stewarton	d	20 06			21 06							
Dunlop	d	20 11			21 11							
Barrhead	d	20 21			21 21							
Nitshill	d											
Priesthill & Darnley	d											
Kennishead	d											
East Kilbride	d		20 26	20 55			21 26	21 55	22 26	22 55	23 26	23 55
Hairmyres	d		20 30	20 59			21 30	21 59	22 30	22 59	23 30	23 59
Thorntonhall	d			21 02				22 02		23 02		00 02
Busby	d		20 35	21 05			21 35	22 05	22 35	23 05	23 35	00 05
Clarkston	d		20 38	21 08			21 38	22 08	22 38	23 08	23 38	00 08
Giffnock	d		20 41	21 11			21 41	22 11	22 41	23 11	23 41	00 11
Thornliebank	d		20 44	21 14			21 44	22 14	22 44	23 14	23 44	00 14
Pollokshaws West	d	20 27	20 47	21 17			21 47	22 17	22 47	23 17	23 47	00 17
Crossmyloof	d		20 50	21 20			21 50	22 20	22 50	23 20	23 50	00 20
Glasgow Central 15	a	20 36	20 57	21 27	21 35		21 57	22 27	22 57	23 27	23 57	00 27

A From Carlisle B From Newcastle C not 8 December. From East Kilbride

Table 222R

Mondays to Saturdays

9 December to 17 May

Glasgow Central - East Kilbride, Barrhead and Kilmarnock

Network Diagram - refer to first Page of Table 216

Miles	Miles			SR SO	SR SO	SR	SR	SR	SR	SR A		SR SX	SR SO	SR SX	SR	SR SX	SR SO	SR	SR	SR SX		SR SO	SR	SR B	SR
0	0	**Glasgow Central** 15	d	00 12	00 18	06 12	06 30	06 48	06 52	07 08		07 12	07 18	07 23	07 37	07 43	07 48	07 52	08 07	08 17		08 18	08 23	08 37	08 48
2¼	2¼	Crossmyloof	d	00 18	00 24	06 18	06 36	06 54	06 58			07 18	07 24	07 29		07 49	07 54	07 58		08 24		08 24	08 29		08 55
3¼	3¼	Pollokshaws West	d	00 21	00 27	06 21	06 39	06 57	07 01			07 21	07 27	07 32		07 52	07 57	08 01		08 27		08 27	08 32		08 57
—	4¼	Thornliebank	d		00 30	06 24		07 00				07 24	07 30			07 55	08 00			08 30		08 30			09 00
—	5¼	Giffnock	d		00 33	06 27		07 03				07 27	07 33			07 58	08 03			08 33		08 33			09 04
—	6½	Clarkston	d		00 37	06 31		07 07				07 31	07 37			08 02	08 07			08 37		08 37			09 08
—	7¼	Busby	d		00 40	06 34		07 10				07 35	07 40			08 09	08 10			08 40		08 40			09 11
—	8½	Thorntonhall	d		00 43	06 37											08 13			08 43					09 14
—	10	Hairmyres	d		00 46	06 41		07 16				07 41	07 45			08 14	08 16			08 45		08 45			09 17
—	11½	**East Kilbride**	a		00 51	06 45		07 19				07 50	07 50			08 18	08 21			08 51		08 51			09 21
4½	—	Kennishead	d	00 24			06 42		07 04					07 35				08 04					08 35		
5	—	Priesthill & Darnley	d	00 26			06 44		07 06					07 37				08 06					08 37		
5¾	—	Nitshill	d	00 29			06 47		07 09					07 40				08 09					08 40		
7½	—	**Barrhead**	d	00 33			06 51		07a14	07 22				07a44	07 50			08a15	08 22				08a46	08 51	
16½	—	Dunlop	d	00 45			07 03			07 34					08 02				08 34					09 03	
18¾	—	Stewarton	d	00 49			07 07			07 38					08 06				08 38					09 07	
22	—	Kilmaurs	d	00 53			07 11			07 44					08 10				08 42					09 12	
24¼	—	**Kilmarnock** 3	a	00 59			07 17			07 50					08 16				08 50					09 18	

		SR	SR	SR	SR	SR		SR	SR	SR B	SR	SR	SR	SR	SR	SR		SR	SR	SR	SR	SR	SR A	SR	SR
Glasgow Central 15	d	08 57	09 12	09 18	09 27	09 42		09 48	09 57	10 12	10 18	10 27	10 42	10 48	10 57	11 12		11 18	11 27	11 42	11 48	11 57	12 12	12 18	12 27
Crossmyloof	d	09 03		09 24	09 33			09 54	10 03		10 24	10 33		10 54	11 03			11 24	11 33		11 54	12 03		12 24	12 33
Pollokshaws West	d	09 06		09 27	09 36			09 57	10 06		10 27	10 36		10 57	11 06			11 27	11 36		11 57	12 06		12 27	12 36
Thornliebank	d			09 30				10 00			10 30			11 00				11 30			12 00			12 30	
Giffnock	d			09 33				10 03			10 33			11 03				11 33			12 03			12 33	
Clarkston	d			09 37				10 07			10 37			11 07				11 37			12 07			12 37	
Busby	d			09 40				10 10			10 40			11 10				11 40			12 10			12 40	
Thorntonhall	d							10 13						11 13							12 13				
Hairmyres	d			09 45				10 16			10 45			11 16				11 45			12 16			12 45	
East Kilbride	a			09 50				10 21			10 50			11 21				11 50			12 21			12 50	
Kennishead	d	09 09			09 39				10 09			10 39			11 09				11 39			12 09			12 39
Priesthill & Darnley	d	09 11			09 41				10 11			10 41			11 11				11 41			12 11			12 41
Nitshill	d	09 14			09 44				10 14			10 44			11 14				11 44			12 14			12 44
Barrhead	d	09a19			09a49	09 54			10a19			10a48	10 54		11a19				11a48	11 54		12a19			12a48
Dunlop	d		09 35			10 05				10 35			11 05			11 35				12 05			12 35		
Stewarton	d		09 39			10 09				10 39			11 09			11 39				12 09			12 39		
Kilmaurs	d		09 43			10 14				10 44			11 14			11 44				12 14			12 44		
Kilmarnock 3	a		09 49			10 21				10 51			11 21			11 50				12 21			12 50		

		SR		SR	SR	SR B	SR	SR	SR	SR	SR	SR		SR	SR	SR	SR	SR	SR C	SR	SR	SR		SR	SR
Glasgow Central 15	d	12 42		12 48	12 57	13 12	13 18	13 27	13 42	13 48	13 57	14 12		14 18	14 27	14 42	14 48	14 57	15 12	15 18	15 27	15 42		15 48	15 57
Crossmyloof	d			12 54	13 03		13 24	13 33		13 54	14 03			14 24	14 33		14 54	15 03		15 24	15 33			15 54	16 03
Pollokshaws West	d			12 57	13 06		13 27	13 36		13 57	14 06			14 27	14 36		14 57	15 06		15 27	15 36			15 57	16 06
Thornliebank	d			13 00			13 30			14 00				14 30			15 00			15 30				16 00	
Giffnock	d			13 03			13 33			14 03				14 33			15 03			15 33				16 03	
Clarkston	d			13 07			13 37			14 07				14 37			15 07			15 37				16 07	
Busby	d			13 10			13 40			14 10				14 40			15 10			15 40				16 10	
Thorntonhall	d			13 13						14 13							15 13							16 13	
Hairmyres	d			13 16			13 45			14 16				14 45			15 16			15 45				16 16	
East Kilbride	a			13 21			13 50			14 21				14 50			15 21			15 50				16 21	
Kennishead	d				13 09			13 39			14 09				14 39			15 09			15 39				16 09
Priesthill & Darnley	d				13 11			13 41			14 11				14 41			15 11			15 41				16 11
Nitshill	d				13 14			13 44			14 14				14 44			15 14			15 44				16 14
Barrhead	d	12 54			13a18			13a48	13 54		14a19				14a48	14 54		15a19			15a48	15 54			16a18
Dunlop	d	13 05				13 35			14 05			14 35				15 05			15 35			16 05			
Stewarton	d	13 09				13 39			14 09			14 39				15 09			15 39			16 09			
Kilmaurs	d	13 14				13 44			14 14			14 44				15 14			15 44			16 14			
Kilmarnock 3	a	13 20				13 50			14 21			14 50				15 21			15 50			16 21			

		SR A	SR	SR	SR	SR	SR	SR SX		SR C	SR SO	SR SX	SR	SR SX	SR B	SR SO	SR SX	SR		SR SX	SR	SR	SR	SR	SR
Glasgow Central 15	d	16 12	16 18	16 27	16 42	16 48	16 57	17 01		17 12	17 18	17 21	17 27	17 32	17 42	17 48	17 48	17 57		18 03	18 12	18 18	18 27	18 42	18 48
Crossmyloof	d		16 24	16 33		16 54	17 03	17 07			17 24		17 33	17 38		17 54	17 56	18 03		18 09		18 25	18 35		18 54
Pollokshaws West	d		16 27	16 36		16 57	17 06	17 10			17 27		17 36	17 41		17 57	17 58	18 06		18 12		18 28	18 37		18 57
Thornliebank	d		16 30			17 00		17 13			17 30			17 44		18 00	18 01			18 15		18 31			19 00
Giffnock	d		16 33			17 03		17 16			17 33			17 47		18 03	18 05			18 18		18 35			19 03
Clarkston	d		16 37			17 07		17 20			17 37	17 34		17 51		18 07	18 09			18 22		18 39			19 07
Busby	d		16 40			17 10		17 23			17 40			17 54		18 10	18 12			18 25		18 42			19 10
Thorntonhall	d		16 43			17 13					17 43			17 57		18 13				18 28					19 13
Hairmyres	d		16 47			17 17		17 28			17 46	17 44		18 00		18 17	18 17			18 31		18 47			19 16
East Kilbride	a		16 51			17 21		17 34			17 51	17 48		18 05		18 21	18 21			18 36		18 51			19 21
Kennishead	d			16 39			17 09						17 39					18 09					18 40		
Priesthill & Darnley	d			16 41			17 11						17 41					18 11					18 42		
Nitshill	d			16 44			17 14						17 44					18 14					18 45		
Barrhead	d	16 24		16a48	16 53		17a18			17 24			17a48		17 56			18a19			18 25		18a50	18 56	
Dunlop	d	16 36			17 05					17 36					18 08						18 37			19 08	
Stewarton	d	16 40			17 09					17 41					18 12						18 41			19 12	
Kilmaurs	d	16 45			17 14					17 45					18 16						18 45			19 16	
Kilmarnock 3	a	16 51			17 20					17 51					18 22						18 51			19 22	

A To Newcastle **B** To Carlisle **C** To Girvan

Table 222R

Mondays to Saturdays

9 December to 17 May

Glasgow Central - East Kilbride, Barrhead and Kilmarnock

Network Diagram - refer to first Page of Table 216

		SR	SR A		SR	SR	SR	SR	SR	SR	SR	SR	SR		SR	SR	SR A	SR	SR	SR	SR B	SR			
Glasgow Central 15	d	18 57	19 12		19 18	19 33	19 48	20 12	20 18	20 33	20 48	21 12	21 18		21 33	21 48	22 12	22 18	22 33	22 48	23 12	23 18			
Crossmyloof	d	19 03			19 24	19 39	19 54		20 24	20 39	20 54		21 24		21 39	21 54		22 24	22 39	22 54	23 18	23 24			
Pollokshaws West	d	19 06			19 27	19 42	19 57		20 27	20 42	20 57		21 27		21 42	21 57		22 27	22 42	22 57	23 21	23 27			
Thornliebank	d				19 30		20 00		20 30		21 00		21 30			22 00		22 30		23 00		23 30			
Giffnock	d				19 33		20 03		20 33		21 03		21 33			22 03		22 33		23 03		23 33			
Clarkston	d				19 37		20 07		20 37		21 07		21 37			22 07		22 37		23 07		23 37			
Busby	d				19 40		20 10		20 40		21 10		21 40			22 10		22 40		23 10		23 40			
Thorntonhall	d						20 13				21 13					22 13				23 13		23 43			
Hairmyres	d				19 45		20 16		20 45		21 16		21 45			22 16		22 45		23 16		23 45			
East Kilbride	a				19 50		20 21		20 50		21 21		21 50			22 21		22 50		23 21		23 51			
Kennishead	d	19 09				19 45				20 45					21 45				22 45		23 24				
Priesthill & Darnley	d	19 11				19 47				20 47					21 47				22 47		23 26				
Nitshill	d	19 14				19 50				20 50					21 50				22 50		23 29				
Barrhead	d	19a18	19 24			19 54		20 24		20 54		21 26			21 54		22 23		22 54		23 33				
Dunlop	d		19 35			20 05		20 35		21 05		21 38			22 05		22 35		23 05		23 45				
Stewarton	d		19 39			20 09		20 39		21 09		21 42			22 09		22 39		23 09		23 49				
Kilmaurs	d		19 44			20 14		20 44		21 14		21 47			22 14		22 44		23 14		23 53				
Kilmarnock 3	a		19 51			20 20		20 51		21 21		21 53			22 20		22 50		23 20		23 59				

Sundays

8 December to 11 May

		SR	SR	SR		SR	SR	SR	SR A	NT A	SR	SR		SR	SR	SR		SR	SR	SR	SR	SR A	NT A
Glasgow Central 15	d	08 12	08 18	08 48	and at the same minutes past each hour until	14 12	14 18	14 48	15 12	15 12	15 18	15 48	and at the same minutes past each hour until	19 12	19 18	19 48		20 18	20 48	21 18	21 48	22 12	22 12
Crossmyloof	d		08 24	08 54			14 24	14 54			15 24	15 54			19 24	19 54		20 24	20 54	21 24	21 54		
Pollokshaws West	d	08 20	08 27	08 57		14 20	14 27	14 57	15 20	15 20	15 27	15 57		19 20	19 27	19 57		20 27	20 57	21 27	21 57		
Thornliebank	d		08 30	09 00			14 30	15 00			15 30	16 00			19 30	20 00		20 30	21 00	21 30	22 00		
Giffnock	d		08 33	09 03			14 33	15 03			15 33	16 03			19 33	20 03		20 33	21 03	21 33	22 03		
Clarkston	d		08 37	09 07			14 37	15 07			15 37	16 07			19 37	20 07		20 37	21 07	21 37	22 07		
Busby	d		08 40	09 10			14 40	15 10			15 40	16 10			19 40	20 10		20 40	21 10	21 40	22 10		
Thorntonhall	d			09 13				15 13				16 13				20 13			21 13		22 13		
Hairmyres	d		08 45	09 16			14 45	15 16			15 45	16 16			19 45	20 16		20 45	21 16	21 45	22 16		
East Kilbride	a		08 50	09 21			14 50	15 21			15 50	16 21			19 50	20 21		20 50	21 21	21 50	22 21		
Kennishead	d																						
Priesthill & Darnley	d																						
Nitshill	d																						
Barrhead	d	08 26				14 26			15 26	15 26				19 26								22 23	22 23
Dunlop	d	08 38				14 38			15 38	15 38				19 38								22 35	22 35
Stewarton	d	08 42				14 42			15 42	15 42				19 42								22 39	22 39
Kilmaurs	d	08 46				14 46			15 46	15 46				19 46								22 44	22 44
Kilmarnock 3	a	08 52				14 52			15 52	15 52				19 52								22 48	22 48

		SR	SR	SR
Glasgow Central 15	d	22 18	22 48	23 18
Crossmyloof	d	22 24	22 54	23 24
Pollokshaws West	d	22 27	22 57	23 27
Thornliebank	d	22 30	23 00	23 30
Giffnock	d	22 33	23 03	23 33
Clarkston	d	22 37	23 07	23 37
Busby	d	22 40	23 10	23 40
Thorntonhall	d		23 13	23 43
Hairmyres	d	22 45	23 16	23 45
East Kilbride	a	22 50	23 21	23 51
Kennishead	d			
Priesthill & Darnley	d			
Nitshill	d			
Barrhead	d			
Dunlop	d			
Stewarton	d			
Kilmaurs	d			
Kilmarnock 3	a			

A To Carlisle

B To Dumfries

Table 223

Mondays to Saturdays

9 December to 17 May

Newton, Neilston, Cathcart Circle and Glasgow Central

Network Diagram - refer to first Page of Table 220

Miles	Miles	Miles		SR SO	SR	SR	SR	SR	SR SX	SR	SR SX	SR SX		SR SO	SR SX	SR SO	SR SX	SR SX	SR SX	SR SO	SR SX	SR SX		SR
0	0	—	**Newton** 226 d			06 22		06 49			07 15			07 20				07 37		07 50	07 50			
1½	1½	—	Kirkhill d			06 25		06 52			07 18			07 23				07 44		07 53	07 53			
2¾	2¾	—	Burnside d			06 28		06 55			07 21			07 26				07 47		07 56	07 56			
3¾	3¾	—	Croftfoot d			06 30		06 57			07 23			07 28				07 49		07 58	07 58			
4¼	4¼	—	Kings Park d			06 32		06 59			07 25			07 30				07 52		08 00	08 02			
—	—	—	**Neilston** d				06 30			07 00					07 26	07 30			07 41					07 56
—	—	3¾	Patterton d				06 36			07 06					07 32	07 36			07 47					08 02
—	—	4¾	Whitecraigs d				06 38			07 08					07 34	07 38			07 49					08 05
—	—	5½	Williamwood d				06 40			07 10					07 36	07 40			07 51					08 07
—	—	7	Muirend d				06 43			07 13					07 39	07 43			07 54					08 10
4¾	—	7¾	Cathcart d	00 37	06 30		06 47		07 04	07 17		07 32			07 42	07 47	07 47		07 58			08 10		08 14
—	5½	8½	Mount Florida d	00 39	06 32		06 49	07 03		07 19		07 34			07 44	07 49		07 55	08 01	08 04		08 12		08 17
—	6	9	Crosshill d	00 41	06 34		06 51	07 05		07 21		07 36			07 46	07 51		07 57	08 03	08 06		08 14		08 19
—	6½	9½	Queens Park d	00 43	06 36		06 53	07 07		07 23		07 38			07 48	07 53		07 59	08 05	08 08		08 16		08 21
—	6¾	9¾	Pollokshields East d	00 44	06 37		06 54	07 08		07 24		07 42			07 50	07 54		08 01	08 07	08 09		08 18		08 23
5¼	—	—	Langside d			06 37			07 06		07 29			07 35			07 50				08 06			
6¼	—	—	Pollokshaws East d			06 39			07 08		07 31			07 37			07 52				08 08			
6¾	—	—	Shawlands d			06 42			07 10		07 33			07 39			07 54				08 10			
7½	—	—	Maxwell Park d			06 44			07 12		07 35			07 41			07 56				08 12			
8	—	—	Pollokshields West d			06 48			07 14		07 37			07 44			07 58				08 14			
10	8¾	11¾	**Glasgow Central** 15 226 a	00 49	06 43	06 54	06 59	07 13	07 20	07 29	07 43	07 47		07 50	07 55	08 00	08 05	08 07	08 12	08 14	08 21	08 23		08 28

	SR SX	SR SX	SR SX	SR SX	SR SO	SR SX	SR SX	SR SO		SR SX	SR SX	SR SX	SR SO	SR	SR SO	SR SX	SR SX	SR	SR	SR	SR	SR	SR	
Newton 226 d				08 21	08 21						08 33		08 49			09 05			09 20		09 49			
Kirkhill d				08 24	08 24						08 36		08 52			09 08			09 23		09 52			
Burnside d				08 27	08 27						08 39		08 55			09 11			09 26		09 55			
Croftfoot d				08 29	08 29						08 42		08 57			09 13			09 28		09 57			
Kings Park d				08 31	08 31						08 44		08 59			09 15			09 30		09 59			
Neilston d	08 07						08 21	08 30				08 43			09 00		09 04			09 30			10 00	
Patterton d	08 13						08 27	08 36				08 49			09 06		09 10			09 36			10 06	
Whitecraigs d	08 15						08 30	08 38				08 51			09 08		09 12			09 38			10 08	
Williamwood d	08 17						08 32	08 40				08 53			09 10		09 14			09 40			10 10	
Muirend d	08 21						08 35	08 43				08 56			09 13		09 17			09 43			10 13	
Cathcart d		08 27	08 24			08 33	08 39	08 47		08 50		09 00		09 04	09 17		09 21	09 32		09 46		10 03	10 16	
Mount Florida d		08 29		08 35			08 42	08 49		08 52		09 02	09 03		09 19	09 19	09 23	09 34		09 48	10 03		10 18	
Crosshill d		08 31		08 37			08 44	08 51		08 54		09 04	09 05		09 21	09 21	09 25	09 36		09 50	10 05		10 20	
Queens Park d		08 33		08 39			08 46	08 53		08 56		09 06	09 07		09 23	09 23	09 27	09 38		09 52	10 07		10 22	
Pollokshields East d		08 34		08 42			08 48	08 54		08 58		09 07	09 08		09 24	09 24	09 28	09 39		09 53	10 08		10 23	
Langside d			08 27		08 35	08 36					08 49			09 06					09 35			10 05		
Pollokshaws East d			08 29		08 37	08 38					08 51			09 08					09 37			10 07		
Shawlands d			08 31		08 39	08 40					08 54			09 10					09 39			10 09		
Maxwell Park d			08 33		08 41	08 42					08 56			09 12					09 41			10 11		
Pollokshields West d			08 35		08 44	08 45					09 00			09 14					09 43			10 13		
Glasgow Central 15 226 a	08 34	08 39	08 43	08 47	08 50	08 52	08 55	08 59		09 03	09 06	09 12	09 13	09 22	09 29	09 29	09 34	09 44	09 50	09 59	10 13	10 20	10 29	

	SR	and at the same minutes past each hour until	SR	SR	SR	SR	SR	SR		SR	SR	SR SX	SR SO	SR	SR	SR	SR	SR		SR	SR	SR	SR
Newton 226 d			12 20		12 49					13 20		13 49	13 49				14 20			14 49			
Kirkhill d			12 23		12 52					13 23		13 52	13 52				14 23			14 52			
Burnside d			12 26		12 55					13 26		13 55	13 55				14 26			14 55			
Croftfoot d			12 28		12 57					13 28		13 57	13 57				14 28			14 57			
Kings Park d			12 30		12 59					13 30		13 59	13 59				14 30			14 59			
Neilston d				12 30			13 00				13 30				14 00			14 30				15 00	
Patterton d				12 36			13 06				13 36				14 06			14 36				15 06	
Whitecraigs d				12 38			13 08				13 38				14 08			14 38				15 08	
Williamwood d				12 40			13 10				13 40				14 10			14 40				15 10	
Muirend d				12 43			13 13				13 43				14 13			14 43				15 13	
Cathcart d	10 31			12 46		13 03	13 16	13 31			13 46			14 03	14 16	14 31		14 46			15 03	15 16	15 31
Mount Florida d	10 33			12 48	13 03		13 18	13 33			13 48	14 03	14 03		14 18	14 33		14 48		15 03		15 18	15 33
Crosshill d	10 35			12 50	13 05		13 20	13 35			13 50	14 05	14 05		14 20	14 35		14 50		15 05		15 20	15 35
Queens Park d	10 37			12 52	13 07		13 22	13 37			13 52	14 07	14 07		14 22	14 37		14 52		15 07		15 22	15 37
Pollokshields East d	10 38			12 53	13 08		13 23	13 38			13 53	14 08	14 08		14 23	14 38		14 53		15 08		15 23	15 38
Langside d			12 35			13 05				13 35				14 05			14 35				15 05		
Pollokshaws East d			12 37			13 07				13 37				14 07			14 37				15 07		
Shawlands d			12 39			13 09				13 39				14 09			14 39				15 09		
Maxwell Park d			12 41			13 11				13 41				14 11			14 41				15 11		
Pollokshields West d			12 43			13 13				13 43				14 13			14 43				15 13		
Glasgow Central 15 226 a	10 44		12 50	12 59	13 13	13 20	13 29	13 44		13 50	13 59	14 13	14 14	14 20	14 29	14 44	14 50	14 59		15 14	15 21	15 29	15 44

Table 223

Newton, Neilston, Cathcart Circle and Glasgow Central

Mondays to Saturdays

9 December to 17 May

Network Diagram - refer to first Page of Table 220

	SR		SR	SR SX	SR SO	SR SO	SR SX	SR	SR	SR	SR		SR	SR	SR SX	SR SO	SR SX	SR SX	SR SO	SR	SR SX		SR SO	SR SX
Newton 226 d	15 20			15 49	15 49					16 20			16 49							17 20				
Kirkhill d	15 23			15 52	15 52					16 23			16 52							17 23				
Burnside d	15 26			15 55	15 55					16 26			16 55							17 26				
Croftfoot d	15 28			15 57	15 57					16 28			16 57							17 28				
Kings Park d	15 30			15 59	15 59					16 30			16 59							17 30				
Neilston d			15 30					16 00			16 30				16 53	17 00		17 14					17 30	17 39
Patterton d			15 36					16 06			16 36				16 59	17 06		17 20					17 36	17 45
Whitecraigs d			15 38					16 08			16 38				17 01	17 08		17 22					17 38	17 47
Williamwood d			15 40					16 10			16 40				17 03	17 10		17 24					17 40	17 49
Muirend d			15 43					16 13			16 43				17 06	17 13		17 27					17 43	17 52
Cathcart d			15 46			16 03	16 06	16 16	16 31		16 46			17 04	17 10	17 17	17 22	17 30	17 31		17 41		17 46	17 56
Mount Florida d			15 48	16 03	16 03			16 18	16 33		16 48		17 03		17 12	17 19	17 24	17 32	17 33		17 43		17 48	17 58
Crosshill d			15 50	16 05	16 05			16 20	16 35		16 50		17 05		17 14	17 21	17 26	17 34	17 35		17 45		17 50	18 00
Queens Park d			15 52	16 07	16 07			16 22	16 37		16 52		17 07		17 16	17 23	17 28	17 36	17 37		17 47		17 52	18 02
Pollokshields East d			15 53	16 08	16 08			16 24	16 39		16 54		17 08		17 17	17 24	17 29	17 38	17 39		17 48		17 54	18 03
Langside d	15 35					16 07	16 09			16 35				17 06						17 35				
Pollokshaws East d	15 37					16 09	16 11			16 37				17 08						17 37				
Shawlands d	15 39					16 11	16 13			16 39				17 10						17 39				
Maxwell Park d	15 41					16 13	16 15			16 41				17 12						17 41				
Pollokshields West d	15 43					16 16	16 18			16 43				17 14						17 43				
Glasgow Central 15 226 a	15 50		15 59	16 13	16 14	16 22	16 24	16 29	16 44	16 53	16 59		17 16	17 22	17 23	17 29	17 38	17 43	17 44	17 51	17 55		17 59	18 08

	SR	SR	SR SX	SR SO	SR SX	SR	SR		SR	SR	SR	SR	SR	SR	SR	SR	SR	SR	SR	SR			
Newton 226 d	17 49						18 20			18 49				19 20		19 49				20 20	and at the same minutes past each hour until		
Kirkhill d	17 52						18 23			18 52				19 23		19 52				20 23			
Burnside d	17 55						18 26			18 55				19 26		19 55				20 26			
Croftfoot d	17 57						18 28			18 58				19 28		19 57				20 28			
Kings Park d	17 59						18 30			19 00				19 30		19 59				20 30			
Neilston d			17 56	18 00	18 04				18 30			19 00			19 30			20 00					
Patterton d			18 02	18 06	18 10				18 36			19 06			19 36			20 06					
Whitecraigs d			18 04	18 08	18 12				18 38			19 08			19 38			20 08					
Williamwood d			18 06	18 10	18 14				18 40			19 10			19 40			20 10					
Muirend d			18 09	18 13	18 17				18 43			19 13			19 43			20 13					
Cathcart d		18 04	18 12	18 16	18 21	18 31			18 46		19 04	19 16	19 31		19 46		20 03	20 16	20 31				
Mount Florida d	18 03		18 14	18 18	18 23	18 33			18 48	19 03		19 18	19 33		19 48	20 03		20 18	20 33				
Crosshill d	18 05		18 16	18 20	18 25	18 35			18 50	19 05		19 20	19 35		19 50	20 05		20 20	20 35				
Queens Park d	18 07		18 18	18 22	18 27	18 37			18 52	19 07		19 22	19 37		19 52	20 07		20 22	20 37				
Pollokshields East d	18 08		18 20	18 24	18 28	18 39			18 54	19 09		19 23	19 38		19 53	20 08		20 23	20 38				
Langside d		18 06					18 35				19 06			19 35			20 05			20 35			
Pollokshaws East d		18 08					18 37				19 08			19 37			20 07			20 37			
Shawlands d		18 10					18 39				19 10			19 39			20 09			20 39			
Maxwell Park d		18 12					18 41				19 12			19 41			20 11			20 41			
Pollokshields West d		18 14					18 43				19 14			19 43			20 13			20 43			
Glasgow Central 15 226 a	18 13	18 20	18 25	18 29	18 35	18 44	18 50		18 59	19 14	19 21	19 29	19 44	19 52	19 59	20 15	20 20	20 29	20 44	20 50			

	SR	SR	SR	SR	SR	SR		SR
Newton 226 d		22 49				23 20		
Kirkhill d		22 52				23 23		
Burnside d		22 55				23 26		
Croftfoot d		22 57				23 28		
Kings Park d		22 59				23 30		
Neilston d	22 30			23 00				23 30
Patterton d	22 36			23 06				23 36
Whitecraigs d	22 38			23 08				23 38
Williamwood d	22 40			23 10				23 40
Muirend d	22 43			23 13				23 43
Cathcart d	22 46		23 03	23 16	23 31			23 46
Mount Florida d	22 48	23 03		23 18	23 33			23 48
Crosshill d	22 50	23 05		23 20	23 35			23 50
Queens Park d	22 52	23 07		23 22	23 37			23 52
Pollokshields East d	22 53	23 08		23 23	23 38			23 53
Langside d			23 05			23 35		
Pollokshaws East d			23 07			23 37		
Shawlands d			23 09			23 39		
Maxwell Park d			23 11			23 41		
Pollokshields West d			23 13			23 43		
Glasgow Central 15 226 a	22 59	23 15	23 20	23 29	23 44	23 50		23 59

Table 223

Sundays

8 December to 11 May

Newton, Neilston, Cathcart Circle and Glasgow Central

Network Diagram - refer to first Page of Table 220

		SR	SR	SR	SR		SR	SR	SR	SR	SR	SR	SR	SR	SR	SR	SR
Newton 226	d		09 09		09 39	and at the same minutes past each hour until		21 09		21 39		22 09		22 39		23 09	
Kirkhill	d		09 12		09 42			21 12		21 42		22 12		22 42		23 12	
Burnside	d		09 15		09 45			21 15		21 45		22 15		22 45		23 15	
Croftfoot	d		09 17		09 47			21 17		21 47		22 17		22 47		23 17	
Kings Park	d		09 19		09 49			21 19		21 49		22 19		22 49		23 19	
Neilston	d	08 48		09 19			20 48		21 19		21 48		22 19		22 48		23 19
Patterton	d	08 54		09 25			20 54		21 25		21 54		22 25		22 54		23 25
Whitecraigs	d	08 56		09 27			20 56		21 27		21 56		22 27		22 56		23 27
Williamwood	d	08 58		09 29			20 58		21 29		21 58		22 29		22 58		23 29
Muirend	d	09 01		09 32			21 01		21 32		22 01		22 32		23 01		23 32
Cathcart	d	09 05		09 36			21 05		21 36		22 05		22 36		23 05		23 36
Mount Florida	d	09 07		09 38	09 53		21 07		21 38	21 53	22 07		22 38	22 53	23 07		23 38
Crosshill	d	09 09		09 40	09 55		21 09		21 40	21 55	22 09		22 40	22 55	23 09		23 40
Queens Park	d	09 11		09 42	09 57		21 11		21 42	21 57	22 11		22 42	22 57	23 11		23 42
Pollokshields East	d	09 12		09 43	09 58		21 12		21 43	21 58	22 12		22 43	22 58	23 12		23 43
Langside	d		09 23					21 23				22 23				23 23	
Pollokshaws East	d		09 25					21 25				22 25				23 25	
Shawlands	d		09 27					21 27				22 27				23 27	
Maxwell Park	d		09 29					21 29				22 29				23 29	
Pollokshields West	d		09 31					21 31				22 31				23 31	
Glasgow Central 15 226	a	09 17	09 38	09 48	10 03		21 17	21 38	21 48	22 03	22 17	22 37	22 48	23 03	23 17	23 37	23 48

Table 223R

Mondays to Saturdays

9 December to 17 May

Glasgow Central, Cathcart Circle, Neilston and Newton

Network Diagram - refer to first Page of Table 220

Miles	Miles	Miles			SR SO	SR SO	SR SO	SR	SR	SR	SR	SR SX		SR SO	SR SX	SR SX	SR SX	SR SO	SR SX	SR SX	SR	SR SX		SR SO	SR SX
0	0	0	**Glasgow Central** 15 226	d		00 05	00 20	06 14	06 17	06 20	06 34	06 36		06 45	06 50	06 58	07 03	07 06	07 06	07 14	07 20	07 29		07 35	07 35
2¼	—	—	Pollokshields West	d			00 27	06 20				06 42		06 51			07 09			07 20					
2¾	—	—	Maxwell Park	d			00 29	06 22				06 44		06 53			07 11			07 22					
3½	—	—	Shawlands	d			00 31	06 24				06 46		06 55			07 13			07 24					
3¾	—	—	Pollokshaws East	d			00 32	06 25				06 48		06 56			07 14			07 25					
4¼	—	—	Langside	d			00 34	06 27				06 50		06 59			07 16			07 27					
—	1¾	1¾	Pollokshields East	d		00 10			06 22	06 25	06 39				06 55	07 03		07 11	07 11		07 25	07 34		07 40	07 40
—	2¼	2¼	Queens Park	d		00 11			06 23	06 27	06 40				06 56	07 04		07 12	07 12		07 26	07 35		07 41	07 41
—	2½	2½	Crosshill	d		00 13			06 25	06 29	06 42				06 58	07 06		07 14	07 14		07 28	07 37		07 43	07 43
—	3¼	3¼	Mount Florida	d		00 15			06 27	06 31	06 44				07 00	07 08		07 16	07 16		07 30	07 39		07 45	07 45
5¼	—	4	Cathcart	d		00 17	00a37	06a30	06 29		06 46				07a04	07 10		07 20	07 20	07a30		07 41		07 47	07a47
—	—	4¾	Muirend	d		00 20			06 32		06 49					07 13		07 23	07 23			07 44		07 50	
—	—	6	Williamwood	d		00 23			06 35		06 52					07 16		07 26	07 26			07 47		07 53	
—	—	6¾	Whitecraigs	d		00 25			06 37		06 54					07 18		07 28	07 28			07 49		07 55	
—	—	7¾	Patterton	d		00 28			06 40		06 57					07 21		07 31	07 31			07 52		07 58	
—	—	11¾	**Neilston**	a		00 34			06 46		07 03					07 27		07 37	07 38			07 58		08 04	
5¾	4½	—	Kings Park	d	00 04					06 34		06 54		07 05			07 20				07 33				
6	4¾	—	Croftfoot	d	00 06					06 36		06 56		07 07			07 22				07 35				
7	5¾	—	Burnside	d	00 08					06 38		06 58		07 09			07 25				07 38				
8½	7¼	—	Kirkhill	a	00 11					06 41		07 01		07 12			07 28				07 41				
10	8¾	—	**Newton** 226	a	00 14					06 44		07 04		07 15			07 31				07 44				

		SR	SR SX	SR SX	SR SX	SR SX	SR SO	SR SX		SR SX	SR SX	SR	SR SX	SR SX	SR SO	SR SX	SR	SR		SR SO	SR SX	SR
Glasgow Central 15 226	d	07 45	07 48	07 54	07 56	08 01	08 05	08 10		08 12	08 15	08 20	08 26	08 33	08 35	08 39	08 45	08 50		09 05	09 08	09 14
Pollokshields West	d	07 51		08 00				08 16						08 39			08 51					09 21
Maxwell Park	d	07 53		08 02				08 18						08 41			08 53					09 23
Shawlands	d	07 55		08 04				08 20						08 43			08 55					09 25
Pollokshaws East	d	07 56		08 06				08 21						08 45			08 56					09 26
Langside	d	07 58		08 08				08 23						08 47			08 58					09 28
Pollokshields East	d				08 01	08 06	08 10			08 17	08 21	08 25	08 31		08 40	08 44		08 55		09 10	09 13	
Queens Park	d				08 02	08 07	08 11			08 18	08 22	08 26	08 32		08 41	08 45		08 57		09 11	09 14	
Crosshill	d				08 04	08 09	08 13			08 20	08 24	08 28	08 34		08 43	08 47		08 59		09 13	09 16	
Mount Florida	d				08 06	08 11	08 15			08 22	08 26	08 30	08 36		08 45	08 49		09 01		09 15	09 18	
Cathcart	d			08a10		08 13	08 17	08a27		08a24	08a28		08 38	08a49	08 47	08 51		09a04		09 17	09 20	09a31
Muirend	d		07 58			08 16	08 20						08 41		08 50	08 54				09 20	09 23	
Williamwood	d		08 01			08 19	08 23						08 44		08 53	08 57				09 23	09 26	
Whitecraigs	d		08 03			08 21	08 25						08 46		08 55	08 59				09 25	09 28	
Patterton	d		08 06			08 24	08 28						08 49		08 58	09 02				09 28	09 31	
Neilston	a		08 12			08 30	08 34						08 55		09 04	09 08				09 34	09 37	
Kings Park	d	08 04			08 09							08 34					09 04					
Croftfoot	d	08 06			08 11							08 36					09 06					
Burnside	d	08 08			08 14							08 38					09 08					
Kirkhill	a	08 11			08 17							08 41					09 11					
Newton 226	a	08 16			08 20							08 44					09 15					

		SR	SR	SR	SR	SR	SR		SR	SR	SR	SR	SR	SR		SR	SR	SR	SR SO	SR SX	SR	SR	SR	SR
Glasgow Central 15 226	d	09 20	09 35	09 45	09 50	10 05	10 15		14 20	14 35	14 45	14 50	15 05	15 15		15 20	15 35	15 45	15 50	15 50	16 07	16 15	16 20	16 35
Pollokshields West	d			09 51			10 21				14 51			15 21				15 51				16 21		
Maxwell Park	d			09 53			10 23				14 53			15 23				15 53				16 23		
Shawlands	d			09 55			10 25				14 55			15 25				15 55				16 25		
Pollokshaws East	d			09 56			10 26				14 56			15 26				15 56				16 26		
Langside	d			09 58			10 28				14 58			15 28				15 58				16 28		
Pollokshields East	d	09 25	09 40		09 55	10 10		and at the same minutes past each hour until	14 25	14 40		14 55	15 10			15 25	15 40		15 55	15 55	16 12		16 25	16 40
Queens Park	d	09 26	09 41		09 56	10 11			14 26	14 41		14 56	15 11			15 26	15 41		15 57	15 57	16 13		16 27	16 41
Crosshill	d	09 28	09 43		09 58	10 13			14 28	14 43		14 58	15 13			15 28	15 43		15 58	16 03	16 15		16 29	16 43
Mount Florida	d	09 30	09 45		10 00	10 15			14 30	14 45		15 00	15 15			15 30	15 45		16 00	16 05	16 17		16 31	16 45
Cathcart	d		09 47		10a03	10 17	10a31			14 47		15a03	15 17	15a31			15 47		16a03	16a06	16 19	16a31		16 47
Muirend	d		09 50			10 20				14 50			15 20				15 50				16 22			16 50
Williamwood	d		09 53			10 23				14 53			15 23				15 53				16 25			16 53
Whitecraigs	d		09 55			10 25				14 55			15 25				15 55				16 27			16 55
Patterton	d		09 58			10 28				14 58			15 28				15 58				16 30			16 58
Neilston	a		10 04			10 34				15 04			15 34				16 04				16 36			17 04
Kings Park	d	09 34		10 04					14 34		15 04					15 34		16 04					16 34	
Croftfoot	d	09 36		10 06					14 36		15 06					15 36		16 06					16 36	
Burnside	d	09 38		10 08					14 38		15 08					15 38		16 08					16 38	
Kirkhill	a	09 41		10 11					14 41		15 11					15 41		16 11					16 41	
Newton 226	a	09 44		10 14					14 44		15 14					15 44		16 14					16 44	

Table 223R

Mondays to Saturdays

9 December to 17 May

Glasgow Central, Cathcart Circle, Neilston and Newton

Network Diagram - refer to first Page of Table 220

		SR	SR	SR SX	SR SX	SR SO	SR SX		SR SX	SR SO	SR SX	SR SO	SR SX	SR SX	SR SO	SR SX	SR		SR	SR	SR	SR	SR	SR	SR
Glasgow Central 15 226	d	16 45	16 50	16 59	17 06	17 07	17 08		17 14	17 15	17 19	17 20	17 23	17 28	17 35	17 38	17 45		17 51	18 07	18 15	18 20	18 35	18 45	18 51
Pollokshields West	d	16 51			17 12					17 21			17 29				17 51				18 21			18 51	
Maxwell Park	d	16 53			17 14					17 23			17 32				17 53				18 23			18 53	
Shawlands	d	16 55			17 16					17 25			17 34				17 55				18 25			18 55	
Pollokshaws East	d	16 56			17 17					17 26			17 35				17 56				18 26			18 56	
Langside	d	16 58			17 19					17 28			17 37				17 58				18 28			18 59	
Pollokshields East	d		16 55	17 04		17 12	17 13				17 24	17 25		17 34	17 40	17 43			17 56	18 12		18 25	18 40		18 56
Queens Park	d		16 56	17 05		17 13	17 14				17 25	17 26		17 35	17 41	17 44			17 58	18 13		18 26	18 41		18 57
Crosshill	d		16 58	17 07		17 15	17 16				17 27	17 28		17 37	17 43	17 46			18 00	18 15		18 28	18 43		18 59
Mount Florida	d		17 00	17 09		17 17	17 18				17 29	17 30		17 39	17 45	17 48			18 02	18 17		18 30	18 45		19 01
Cathcart	d		17a04	17 11	17a22	17 19				17a31	17 31		17a40		17 47	17 50			18a04	18 19	18a31		18 47		19a04
Muirend	d			17 14		17 22			17 25		17 34				17 50	17 53				18 22			18 50		
Williamwood	d			17 17		17 25			17 28		17 38				17 53	17 56				18 25			18 53		
Whitecraigs	d			17 19		17 27			17 30		17 40				17 55	17 58				18 27			18 55		
Patterton	d			17 22		17 30			17 33		17 43				17 58	18 01				18 30			18 58		
Neilston	a			17 28		17 36			17 39		17 50				18 04	18 07				18 36			19 04		
Kings Park	d	17 04					17 21					17 34		17 42			18 04					18 34		19 04	
Croftfoot	d	17 06					17 23					17 36		17 44			18 06					18 36		19 06	
Burnside	d	17 08					17 26					17 38		17 47			18 08					18 38		19 09	
Kirkhill	a	17 11					17 29					17 41		17 50			18 11					18 41		19 12	
Newton 226	a	17 14					17 32					17 44		17 53			18 14					18 45		19 15	

		SR	SR		SR	SR	SR	SR	SR	SR	SR	SR	SR		SR	SR	SR	SR	SR	SR	SR	SR	SR		SR
Glasgow Central 15 226	d	19 05	19 15		19 20	19 35	19 45	19 50	20 05	20 15	20 20	20 35	20 45		20 50	21 05	21 15	21 20	21 35	21 45	21 50	22 05	22 15		22 20
Pollokshields West	d		19 21				19 51			20 21			20 51				21 21			21 51			22 21		
Maxwell Park	d		19 23				19 53			20 23			20 53				21 23			21 53			22 23		
Shawlands	d		19 25				19 55			20 25			20 55				21 25			21 55			22 25		
Pollokshaws East	d		19 26				19 56			20 26			20 56				21 26			21 56			22 26		
Langside	d		19 28				19 58			20 28			20 58				21 28			21 58			22 28		
Pollokshields East	d	19 10			19 25	19 40		19 55	20 10		20 25	20 40			20 55	21 10		21 25	21 40		21 55	22 10			22 25
Queens Park	d	19 11			19 26	19 41		19 56	20 11		20 26	20 41			20 56	21 11		21 26	21 41		21 56	22 11			22 26
Crosshill	d	19 13			19 28	19 43		19 58	20 13		20 28	20 43			20 58	21 13		21 28	21 43		21 58	22 13			22 28
Mount Florida	d	19 15			19 30	19 45		20 00	20 15		20 30	20 45			21 00	21 15		21 30	21 45		22 00	22 15			22 30
Cathcart	d	19 17	19a31			19 47		20a03	20 17	20a31		20 47			21a03	21 17	21a31		21 47		22a03	22 17	22a31		
Muirend	d	19 20				19 50			20 20			20 50				21 20			21 50			22 20			
Williamwood	d	19 23				19 53			20 23			20 53				21 23			21 53			22 23			
Whitecraigs	d	19 25				19 55			20 25			20 55				21 25			21 55			22 25			
Patterton	d	19 28				19 58			20 28			20 58				21 28			21 58			22 28			
Neilston	a	19 34				20 04			20 36			21 04				21 34			22 04			22 34			
Kings Park	d				19 34		20 04				20 34		21 04					21 34		22 04					22 34
Croftfoot	d				19 36		20 06				20 36		21 06					21 36		22 06					22 36
Burnside	d				19 38		20 08				20 38		21 08					21 38		22 08					22 38
Kirkhill	a				19 41		20 11				20 41		21 11					21 41		22 11					22 41
Newton 226	a				19 45		20 15				20 44		21 15					21 44		22 14					22 44

		SR	SR	SR	SR	SR	SR	SR FO
Glasgow Central 15 226	d	22 35	22 45	22 50	23 05	23 15	23 20	23 50
Pollokshields West	d		22 51			23 21		
Maxwell Park	d		22 53			23 23		
Shawlands	d		22 55			23 25		
Pollokshaws East	d		22 56			23 26		
Langside	d		22 58			23 28		
Pollokshields East	d	22 40		22 55	23 10		23 25	23 55
Queens Park	d	22 41		22 56	23 11		23 26	23 56
Crosshill	d	22 43		22 58	23 13		23 28	23 58
Mount Florida	d	22 45		23 00	23 15		23 30	23 59
Cathcart	d	22 47		23a03	23 17	23a31		
Muirend	d	22 50			23 20			
Williamwood	d	22 53			23 23			
Whitecraigs	d	22 55			23 25			
Patterton	d	22 58			23 28			
Neilston	a	23 04			23 34			
Kings Park	d		23 04				23 34	00 04
Croftfoot	d		23 06				23 36	00 06
Burnside	d		23 08				23 38	00 08
Kirkhill	a		23 11				23 41	00 11
Newton 226	a		23 14				23 44	00 14

Table 223R

Sundays

8 December to 11 May

Glasgow Central, Cathcart Circle, Neilston and Newton

Network Diagram - refer to first Page of Table 220

		SR	SR	SR	SR		SR	SR	SR	SR	SR	SR	SR	SR	SR	SR	SR		SR	SR	SR	SR
Glasgow Central 15 226	d	08 23	08 36	08 53	09 08	and at the same minutes past each hour until	11 23	11 36	11 53	12 08	12 23	12 36	12 59	13 08	13 23	13 36	13 53	and at the same minutes past each hour until	22 08	22 23	22 36	22 53
Pollokshields West	d		08 42					11 42				12 42				13 42					22 42	
Maxwell Park	d		08 44					11 44				12 44				13 44					22 44	
Shawlands	d		08 46					11 46				12 46				13 46					22 46	
Pollokshaws East	d		08 47					11 47				12 47				13 47					22 47	
Langside	d		08 49					11 49				12 49				13 49					22 49	
Pollokshields East	d	08 28		08 58	09 13		11 28		11 58	12 13	12 28		13 04	13 13	13 28		13 58		22 13	22 28		22 58
Queens Park	d	08 29		08 59	09 14		11 29		11 59	12 14	12 29		13 05	13 14	13 29		13 59		22 14	22 29		22 59
Crosshill	d	08 31		09 01	09 16		11 31		12 01	12 16	12 31		13 07	13 16	13 31		14 01		22 16	22 31		23 01
Mount Florida	d	08 33		09 03	09 18		11 33		12 03	12 18	12 33		13 09	13 18	13 33		14 03		22 18	22 33		23 03
Cathcart	d	08 35		09 05			11 35		12 05		12 35		13 11		13 35		14 05			22 35		23 05
Muirend	d	08 38		09 08			11 38		12 08		12 38		13 14		13 38		14 08			22 38		23 08
Williamwood	d	08 41		09 11			11 41		12 11		12 41		13 17		13 41		14 11			22 41		23 11
Whitecraigs	d	08 43		09 13			11 43		12 13		12 43		13 19		13 43		14 13			22 43		23 13
Patterton	d	08 46		09 16			11 46		12 16		12 46		13 22		13 46		14 16			22 46		23 16
Neilston	a	08 52		09 22			11 52		12 22		12 52		13 28		13 52		14 22			22 52		23 22
Kings Park	d		08 53		09 21			11 53		12 21		12 53		13 21		13 53			22 21		22 53	
Croftfoot	d		08 55		09 23			11 55		12 23		12 55		13 23		13 55			22 23		22 55	
Burnside	d		08 58		09 26			11 58		12 26		12 58		13 26		13 58			22 26		22 58	
Kirkhill	a		09 01		09 29			12 01		12 29		13 01		13 29		14 01			22 29		23 01	
Newton 226	a		09 04		09 32			12 04		12 32		13 04		13 32		14 04			22 32		23 04	

		SR
Glasgow Central 15 226	d	23 08
Pollokshields West	d	
Maxwell Park	d	
Shawlands	d	
Pollokshaws East	d	
Langside	d	
Pollokshields East	d	23 13
Queens Park	d	23 14
Crosshill	d	23 16
Mount Florida	d	23 18
Cathcart	d	
Muirend	d	
Williamwood	d	
Whitecraigs	d	
Patterton	d	
Neilston	a	
Kings Park	d	23 21
Croftfoot	d	23 23
Burnside	d	23 26
Kirkhill	a	23 29
Newton 226	a	23 32

Table 224

Mondays to Saturdays

9 December to 1 March

Motherwell and Glasgow Queen Street - Cumbernauld and Falkirk Grahamston

Network Diagram - refer to first Page of Table 220

Miles	Miles			SR	SR	SR	SR	SR	SR	SR	SR	SR		SR	SR	SR	SR	SR	SR	SR	SR	SR		SR	SR
				ThFO	ThFO	TWO	SO	ThFO	ThFO	TWO															
				🚌	🚌	🚌			🚌	🚌															
—	0	**Motherwell** 226	d														07 37			08 38				09 37	
—	4½	Whifflet 220,226	d											06 44			07 47			08 47				09 47	
—	5¼	**Coatbridge Central**	d											06 46			07 49			08 50				09 50	
0	—	**Glasgow Queen Street** [10]	d								05 52	06 22			06 52	07 23		07 52	08 24		08 52	09 22			09 52
1¼	—	Springburn	d								05 57	06 27			06 57	07 29		07 57	08 29		08 57	09 27			09 57
5¼	—	Stepps	d				00 04	00 04			06 04	06 34			07 04	07 36		08 04	08 36		09 04	09 34			10 04
7¾	—	Gartcosh	d			00 05	00 08	00a09	00 14		06 08	06 38			07 08	07 40		08 08	08 40		09 08	09 38			10 08
13¾	11	Greenfaulds	d		00 02	00 23	00 15		00 32		06 15	06 45		06 54	07 15	07 47	07 57	08 15	08 47	08 58	09 15	09 45		09 58	10 15
14	11¾	**Cumbernauld**	d		00a07	00a28	00a20		00a37		06a19	06 48		06a57	07a19	07 50	08a00	08a19	08 50	09a01	09a20	09 48		10a01	10a19
22½	—	Camelon [4]	d	00 02						00 22		07 01				08 08			09 04			10 04			
24	—	**Falkirk Grahamston**	a	00 08						00 29		07 04				08 11			09 07			10 07			

		SR	SR	SR	SR	SR	SR	SR		SR	SR	SR	SR	SR	SR	SR	SR	SR		SR	SR	SR	SR	SR	SR
																									SX
Motherwell 226	d		10 37			11 37				12 37			13 37			14 37				15 37			16 37		
Whifflet 220,226	d		10 47			11 47				12 47			13 47			14 47				15 47			16 47		
Coatbridge Central	d		10 50			11 50				12 50			13 50			14 50				15 50			16 50		
Glasgow Queen Street [10]	d	10 22		10 52	11 22		11 52	12 23			12 52	13 22		13 52	14 22		14 52	15 22			15 52	16 22		16 52	17 03
Springburn	d	10 27		10 57	11 30		11 57	12 27			12 57	13 27		13 57	14 27		14 57	15 27			15 58	16 27		16 58	
Stepps	d	10 34		11 04	11 37		12 04	12 34			13 04	13 34		14 04	14 34		15 04	15 34			16 05	16 34		17 05	
Gartcosh	d	10 38		11 08	11 40		12 08	12 38			13 08	13 38		14 08	14 38		15 08	15 38			16 08	16 38		17 08	
Greenfaulds	d	10 45	10 58	11 15	11 48	11 58	12 15	12 45		12 58	13 15	13 45	13 58	14 15	14 45	14 58	15 15	15 45		15 58	16 16	16 45	16 58	17 16	
Cumbernauld	d	10 48	11a01	11a19	11 51	12a01	12a19	12 48		13a01	13a19	13 48	14a01	14a19	14 48	15a01	15a19	15 48		16a01	16a21	16 48	17a01	17a19	
Camelon [4]	d	11 04			12 05			13 04				14 04			15 04			16 04				17 04			17 31
Falkirk Grahamston	a	11 07			12 08			13 07				14 07			15 07			16 07				17 07			17 33

		SR	SR	SR		SR	SR	SR	SR	SR	SR	SR	SR	SR		SR	SR	SR	SR	SR	SR	SR	SR	SR	
		SX									W	W	FSO	W		W	MTO	FSO	W	W	W	MTO	W	FSO	
											ThX	ThO		ThO		ThO			ThO	ThX	ThO		ThO		
														🚌		🚌	🚌				🚌	🚌			
Motherwell 226	d			17 37				18 37			19 37			19 37						20 37					
Whifflet 220,226	d			17 47				18 47			19 47			19 58						20 47					
Coatbridge Central	d			17 50				18 50			19 50			20 03						20 50					
Glasgow Queen Street [10]	d	17 33	17 22			17 52	18 24		18 52	19 22		19 52	19 52				19 52	20 22	20 22			20 22	20 52	20 52	
Springburn	d		17 28			17 57	18 29		18 57	19 27		19 57	19 57				20 03	20 27	20 27			20 33	20 57	20 57	
Stepps	d		17 35			18 04	18 36		19 04	19 34		20 04	20 04				20 21	20 34	20 34			20 51	21 04	21 04	
Gartcosh	d		17 39			18 08	18 40		19 08	19 38		20a08	20 08			20 14	20 35	20 38	20a39		20 44	21 05	21a08	21 08	
Greenfaulds	d		17 46	17 58		18 15	18 48	18 58	19 15	19 45	19 58		20 15	20 24		20 32	20 53	20 45		20 58	21 02	21 23		21 15	
Cumbernauld	d		17 49	18a01		18a19	18 50	19a01	19a19	19a49	20a01		20 18	20a29		20 38	20 59	20a49		21a01	21a07	21a28		21 18	
Camelon [4]	d	18 01	18 09				19 04						20 31			21 01	21 22							21 31	
Falkirk Grahamston	a	18 03	18 12				19 07						20 34			21 08	21 29							21 34	

		SR	SR	SR	SR	SR	SR	SR	SR	SR		SR	SR	SR	SR	SR	SR	SR	SR	SR		SR	SR	SR	SR
		W	W	MTO	W	FSO	MT	SO	W	MTO		W	FSO	W	W	MTO	W	FSO	W	MTO		W	FSO	W	MTO
		ThO	ThO		ThO		FO		ThO			ThO		ThO	ThO		ThO		ThO			ThO		ThO	
		🚌	🚌	🚌					🚌	🚌				🚌	🚌	🚌			🚌	🚌				🚌	🚌
Motherwell 226	d	20 37					21 37	21 37						21 37											
Whifflet 220,226	d	20 58					21 47	21 47						21 58											
Coatbridge Central	d	21 03					21 50	21 50						22 03											
Glasgow Queen Street [10]	d			20 52	21 22	21 22				21 22		21 52	21 52			21 52	22 22	22 22		22 22		22 52	22 52		22 52
Springburn	d			21 03	21 27	21 27				21 33		21 57	21 57			22 03	22 27	22 27		22 33		22 57	22 57		23 03
Stepps	d			21 21	21 34	21 34				21 51		22 04	22 04			22 21	22 34	22 34		22 51		23 04	23 04		23 21
Gartcosh	d		21 14	21 35	21a38	21 38			21 44	22 05		22a08	22 08		22 14	22 35	22a38	22 38	22 44	23 05		23a08	23 08	23 14	23 35
Greenfaulds	d	21 24	21 32	21 53		21 45	21 57	21 59	22 02	22 23			22 15	22 24	22 32	22 53		22 45	23 02	23 23			23 15	23 32	23 53
Cumbernauld	d	21a29	21 38	21 59		21a49	22a01	22a01	22a07	22a28			22 18	22a29	22 38	22 59		22a49	23a07	23a28			23 18	23 38	23 59
Camelon [4]	d		22 01	22 22									22 31		23 01	23 22							23 31	00 02	00 22
Falkirk Grahamston	a		22 08	22 29									22 34		23 08	23 29							23 36	00 08	00 29

		SR	SR	SR	SR	SR		SR
		W	FSO	W	MTO	FSO		W
		ThO		ThO				ThO
				🚌	🚌			
Motherwell 226	d							
Whifflet 220,226	d							
Coatbridge Central	d							
Glasgow Queen Street [10]	d	23 22	23 22		23 22	23 52		23 52
Springburn	d	23 27	23 27		23 33	23 57		23 57
Stepps	d	23 34	23 34		23 51	00 04		00 04
Gartcosh	d	23a38	23 38	23 44	00 05	00 08		00a09
Greenfaulds	d		23 45	00 02	00 23	00 15		
Cumbernauld	d		23a49	00a07	00a28	00a20		
Camelon [4]	d							
Falkirk Grahamston	a							

Table 224

Mondays to Saturdays

3 March to 17 May

Motherwell and Glasgow Queen Street - Cumbernauld and Falkirk Grahamston

Network Diagram - refer to first Page of Table 220

Station			SR MX	SR	SR	SR	SR		SR	SR	SR	SR	SR	SR	SR	SR	SR		SR	SR	SR	SR	SR	SR	SR	SR
Motherwell	226	d								07 37			08 38			09 37				10 37			11 37			12 37
Whifflet	220,226	d				06 44				07 47			08 47			09 47				10 47			11 47			12 47
Coatbridge Central		d				06 46				07 49			08 50			09 50				10 50			11 50			12 50
Glasgow Queen Street 10		d		05 52	06 22		06 52		07 23		07 52	08 24		08 52	09 22		09 52		10 22		10 52	11 22		11 52	12 23	
Springburn		d		05 57	06 27		06 57		07 29		07 57	08 29		08 57	09 27		09 57		10 27		10 57	11 30		11 57	12 27	
Stepps		d	00 04	06 04	06 34		07 04		07 36		08 04	08 36		09 04	09 34		10 04		10 34		11 04	11 37		12 04	12 34	
Gartcosh		d	00 08	06 08	06 38		07 08		07 40		08 08	08 40		09 08	09 38		10 08		10 38		11 08	11 40		12 08	12 38	
Greenfaulds		d	00 15	06 15	06 45	06 54	07 15		07 47	07 57	08 15	08 47	08 58	09 15	09 45	09 58	10 15		10 45	10 58	11 15	11 48	11 58	12 15	12 45	12 58
Cumbernauld		d	00a20	06a19	06 48	06a57	07a19		07 50	08a00	08a19	08 50	09a01	09a20	09 48	10a01	10a19		10 48	11a01	11a19	11 51	12a01	12a19	12 48	13a01
Camelon 4		d			07 01				08 08			09 04			10 04				11 04			12 05			13 04	
Falkirk Grahamston		a			07 04				08 11			09 07			10 07				11 07			12 08			13 07	

Station			SR		SR	SR	SR	SR	SR	SR	SR	SR	SR		SR	SR	SR	SR SX	SR SX	SR	SR	SR	SR		SR	SR
Motherwell	226	d				13 37			14 37			15 37				16 37					17 37				18 37	
Whifflet	220,226	d				13 47			14 47			15 47				16 47					17 47				18 47	
Coatbridge Central		d				13 50			14 50			15 50				16 50					17 50				18 50	
Glasgow Queen Street 10		d	12 52		13 22		13 52	14 22		14 52	15 22		15 52		16 22		16 52	17 03	17 33	17 22		17 52	18 24			18 52
Springburn		d	12 57		13 27		13 57	14 27		14 57	15 27		15 58		16 27		16 58			17 28		17 57	18 29			18 57
Stepps		d	13 04		13 34		14 04	14 34		15 04	15 34		16 05		16 34		17 05			17 35		18 04	18 36			19 04
Gartcosh		d	13 08		13 38		14 08	14 38		15 08	15 38		16 08		16 38		17 08			17 39		18 08	18 40			19 08
Greenfaulds		d	13 15		13 45	13 58	14 15	14 45	14 58	15 15	15 45	15 58	16 16		16 45	16 58	17 16			17 46	17 58	18 15	18 48		18 58	19 15
Cumbernauld		d	13a19		13 48	14a01	14a19	14 48	15a01	15a19	15 48	16a01	16a21		16 48	17a01	17a19			17 49	18a01	18a19	18 50		19a01	19a19
Camelon 4		d			14 04			15 04			16 04				17 04			17 31	18 01	18 09			19 04			
Falkirk Grahamston		a			14 07			15 07			16 07				17 07			17 33	18 03	18 12			19 07			

Station			SR	SR	SR	SR	SR	SR	SR		SR SX	SR SO	SR	SR	SR	SR	SR
Motherwell	226	d		19 37			20 37				21 37	21 37					
Whifflet	220,226	d		19 47			20 47				21 47	21 47					
Coatbridge Central		d		19 50			20 50				21 50	21 50					
Glasgow Queen Street 10		d	19 22		19 52	20 22		20 52	21 22				21 52	22 22	22 52	23 22	23 52
Springburn		d	19 27		19 57	20 27		20 57	21 27				21 57	22 27	22 57	23 27	23 57
Stepps		d	19 34		20 04	20 34		21 04	21 34				22 04	22 34	23 04	23 34	00 04
Gartcosh		d	19 38		20 08	20 38		21 08	21 38				22 08	22 38	23 08	23 38	00 08
Greenfaulds		d	19 45	19 58	20 15	20 45	20 58	21 15	21 45		21 57	21 59	22 15	22 45	23 15	23 45	00 15
Cumbernauld		d	19a49	20a01	20 18	20a49	21a01	21 18	21a49		22a01	22a01	22 18	22a49	23 18	23a49	00a20
Camelon 4		d			20 31			21 31					22 31		23 31		
Falkirk Grahamston		a			20 34			21 34					22 34		23 36		

Sundays

8 December to 23 February

Station			SR A	SR	SR	SR	SR	SR	SR	SR	SR		SR	SR	SR	SR	SR 🚌	SR 🚌	SR 🚌
Motherwell	226	d																	
Whifflet	220,226	d																	
Coatbridge Central		d																	
Glasgow Queen Street 10		d		08 19	09 22	10 22	11 22	12 22	13 22	14 22	15 22		16 22	17 22	18 22	19 22	20 22	21 22	22 22
Springburn		d		08 24	09 27	10 27	11 27	12 27	13 27	14 27	15 27		16 27	17 27	18 27	19 27	20 33	21 33	22 33
Stepps		d	00 04	08 31	09 34	10 34	11 34	12 34	13 34	14 34	15 34		16 34	17 34	18 34	19 34	20 51	21 51	22 51
Gartcosh		d	00 08	08 35	09 38	10 38	11 38	12 38	13 38	14 38	15 38		16 38	17 38	18 38	19 38	21 05	22 05	23 05
Greenfaulds		d	00 15	08 42	09 45	10 45	11 45	12 45	13 45	14 45	15 45		16 45	17 45	18 45	19 45	21 23	22 23	23 23
Cumbernauld		d	00a20	08a46	09a49	10a50	11a49	12a50	13a49	14a49	15a50		16a49	17a49	18a50	19a49	21a28	22a28	23a28
Camelon 4		d																	
Falkirk Grahamston		a																	

Sundays

2 March to 11 May

Station			SR	SR	SR	SR	SR	SR	SR	SR	SR		SR	SR	SR	SR		SR
Motherwell	226	d																
Whifflet	220,226	d																
Coatbridge Central		d																
Glasgow Queen Street 10		d		08 19	09 22	10 22	11 22	12 22	13 22	14 22	15 22		16 22	17 22	18 22	19 22	and hourly until	22 22
Springburn		d		08 24	09 27	10 27	11 27	12 27	13 27	14 27	15 27		16 27	17 27	18 27	19 27		22 27
Stepps		d	00 04	08 31	09 34	10 34	11 34	12 34	13 34	14 34	15 34		16 34	17 34	18 34	19 34		22 34
Gartcosh		d	00 08	08 35	09 38	10 38	11 38	12 38	13 38	14 38	15 38		16 38	17 38	18 38	19 38		22 38
Greenfaulds		d	00 15	08 42	09 45	10 45	11 45	12 45	13 45	14 45	15 45		16 45	17 45	18 45	19 45		22 45
Cumbernauld		d	00a20	08a46	09a49	10a50	11a49	12a50	13a49	14a49	15a50		16a49	17a49	18a50	19a49		22a49
Camelon 4		d																
Falkirk Grahamston		a																

A not 8 December

Table 224R

Mondays to Saturdays

9 December to 1 March

Falkirk Grahamston and Cumbernauld - Glasgow Queen Street and Motherwell

Network Diagram - refer to first Page of Table 220

Miles	Miles			SR TWO 🚌	SR	SR	SR	SR	SR	SR	SR SX		SR	SR	SR	SR	SR	SR	SR	SR	SR		SR	SR	
0	—	**Falkirk Grahamston**	d		05 43			06 43					07 45			08 43			09 43				10 43		
1½	—	Camelon 4	d		05 46			06 46					07 48			08 46			09 46				10 46		
10	—	**Cumbernauld**	d		05 58	06 28		06 58	07 10	07 28			08 01	08 10	08 29	08 58	09 10	09 28	09 58	10 10	10 28		10 58	11 10	
10¾	0¾	Greenfaulds	d		06 00	06 30		07 00	07 12	07 30			08 03	08 12	08 31	09 00	09 12	09 30	10 00	10 12	10 30		11 00	11 12	
16¼	—	Gartcosh	d		06 07	06 37		07 07		07 37			08 10		08 38	09 07		09 37	10 07		10 37		11 07		
18¾	—	Stepps	d		06 11	06 41		07 11		07 41			08 14		08 42	09 11		09 41	10 11		10 41		11 11		
22¾	—	Springburn	d	00 06	06 17	06 47		07 17		07 47			08 21		08 48	09 17		09 47	10 17		10 47		11 17		
24	—	**Glasgow Queen Street 10**	a	00 16	06 25	06 55		07 29		07 55			08 30		08 59	09 25		09 55	10 25		10 55		11 25		
—	6¼	**Coatbridge Central**	d				06 42		07 21		07 39			08 21			09 21			10 21				11 21	
—	7¼	Whifflet 220,226	d				06 44		07 23		07 41			08 23			09 23			10 23				11 23	
—	11¾	**Motherwell** 226	a				06 51		07 32		07 49			08 33			09 32			10 32				11 33	

		SR	SR	SR		SR	SR	SR		SR	SR	SR	SR	SR SX	SR	SR SX	SR	SR		SR SX	SR	SR	SR	SR W ThO 🚌
Falkirk Grahamston	d		11 43		and at the same minutes past each hour until		15 43				16 43				17 44						18 43			19 08
Camelon 4	d		11 46				15 46				16 46				17 47						18 47			19 15
Cumbernauld	d	11 28	11 58	12 10		15 28	15 58	16 10		16 30	16 58	17 10	17 28		17 59		18 10	18 28			18 59	19 10	19 28	19 39
Greenfaulds	d	11 30	12 00	12 12		15 30	16 00	16 12		16 32	17 00	17 12	17 30		18 01		18 12	18 30			19 01	19 12	19 30	19 44
Gartcosh	d	11 37	12 07			15 37	16 07			16 39	17 07		17 37		18 08			18 37			19 09		19 37	20a02
Stepps	d	11 41	12 11			15 41	16 11			16 43	17 11		17 41		18 12			18 41			19 13		19 41	
Springburn	d	11 47	12 17			15 47	16 17			16 49	17 17		17 47		18 19			18 47			19 19		19 47	
Glasgow Queen Street 10	a	11 55	12 25			15 55	16 25			16 59	17 29		17 55		18 27			18 55			19 29		19 55	
Coatbridge Central	d			12 21				16 21				17 21		17 31		17 58	18 21			18 34		19 20		
Whifflet 220,226	d			12 23				16 23				17 23		17 33		18 01	18 23			18 36		19 23		
Motherwell 226	a			12 32				16 32				17 32		17 40		18 08	18 32			18 43		19 32		

		SR MTO 🚌	SR FSO	SR W ThO	SR W ThO 🚌		SR MTO 🚌	SR W ThX	SR W ThO 🚌	SR FSO	SR W ThO	SR W ThO 🚌	SR MTO 🚌	SR FSO	SR W ThO		SR W ThO 🚌	SR MTO 🚌	SR W ThX	SR W ThO 🚌	SR FSO	SR W ThO	SR W ThO 🚌	SR MTO 🚌	SR FSO
Falkirk Grahamston	d	19 08	19 43		19 38		19 38					20 08	20 08								21 13		21 08	21 08	
Camelon 4	d	19 15	19 46		19 45		19 45					20 15	20 15								21 16		21 15	21 15	
Cumbernauld	d	19 39	19 58		20 09		20 09	20 10	20 10	20 28		20 39	20 39	20 58			21 09	21 09	21 10	21 10	21 28		21 39	21 39	21 58
Greenfaulds	d	19 44	20 00		20 14		20 14	20 12	20 15	20 30		20 44	20 44	21 00			21 14	21 14	21 12	21 15	21 30		21 44	21 44	22 00
Gartcosh	d	20 03	20 07	20 07	20a32		20 33			20 37	20 37	21a02	21 03	21 07	21 07		21a32	21 33			21 37	21 37	22a02	22 03	22 07
Stepps	d	20 16	20 11	20 11			20 46			20 41	20 41		21 16	21 11	21 11			21 46			21 41	21 41		22 16	22 11
Springburn	d	20 36	20 17	20 17			21 06			20 47	20 47		21 36	21 17	21 17			22 06			21 47	21 47		22 36	22 17
Glasgow Queen Street 10	a	20 46	20 25	20 25			21 16			20 55	20 55		21 46	21 25	21 25			22 16			21 55	21 55		22 46	22 26
Coatbridge Central	d							20 21	20 36										21 21	21 36					
Whifflet 220,226	d							20 23	20 41										21 23	21 41					
Motherwell 226	a							20 32	21 01										21 32	22 01					

			SR W ThO	SR W ThO 🚌	SR MTO 🚌	SR W ThX	SR W ThO 🚌	SR FSO	SR W ThO	SR W ThO 🚌	SR MTO 🚌		SR FSO	SR W ThO	SR W ThO 🚌	SR MTO 🚌	SR FSO	SR W ThO
Falkirk Grahamston	d							22 13		22 08	22 08						23 13	
Camelon 4	d							22 16		22 15	22 15						23 16	
Cumbernauld	d			22 09	22 09	22 10	22 10	22 28		22 39	22 39		22 58		23 09	23 09	23 28	
Greenfaulds	d			22 14	22 14	22 12	22 15	22 30		22 44	22 44		23 00		23 14	23 14	23 30	
Gartcosh	d		22 07	22a32	22 33			22 37	22 37	23a02	23 03		23 07	23 07	23a32	23 33	23 37	23 37
Stepps	d		22 11		22 46			22 41	22 41		23 16		23 11	23 11		23 46	23 41	23 41
Springburn	d		22 17		23 06			22 47	22 47		23 36		23 17	23 17		00 06	23 47	23 47
Glasgow Queen Street 10	a		22 26		23 16			22 55	22 55		23 46		23 25	23 25		00 16	23 55	23 55
Coatbridge Central	d					22 21	22 36											
Whifflet 220,226	d					22 23	22 41											
Motherwell 226	a					22 32	23 01											

Mondays to Saturdays

3 March to 17 May

		SR	SR	SR	SR	SR	SR	SR SX	SR	SR		SR	SR	SR	SR	SR	SR	SR	SR	SR	SR	SR	SR	
Falkirk Grahamston	d	05 43			06 43				07 45				08 43			09 43			10 43			11 43		and at the same minutes past each hour until
Camelon 4	d	05 46			06 46				07 48				08 46			09 46			10 46			11 46		
Cumbernauld	d	05 58	06 28		06 58	07 10	07 28		08 01	08 10		08 29	08 58	09 10	09 28	09 58	10 10	10 28	10 58	11 10	11 28	11 58	12 10	
Greenfaulds	d	06 00	06 30		07 00	07 12	07 30		08 03	08 12		08 31	09 00	09 12	09 30	10 00	10 12	10 30	11 00	11 12	11 30	12 00	12 12	
Gartcosh	d	06 07	06 37		07 07		07 37		08 10			08 38	09 07		09 37	10 07		10 37	11 07		11 37	12 07		
Stepps	d	06 11	06 41		07 11		07 41		08 14			08 42	09 11		09 41	10 11		10 41	11 11		11 41	12 11		
Springburn	d	06 17	06 47		07 17		07 47		08 21			08 48	09 17		09 47	10 17		10 47	11 17		11 47	12 17		
Glasgow Queen Street 10	a	06 25	06 55		07 29		07 55		08 30			08 59	09 25		09 55	10 25		10 55	11 25		11 55	12 25		
Coatbridge Central	d			06 42		07 21		07 39		08 21				09 21			10 21			11 21			12 21	
Whifflet 220,226	d			06 44		07 23		07 41		08 23				09 23			10 23			11 23			12 23	
Motherwell 226	a			06 51		07 32		07 49		08 33				09 32			10 32			11 33			12 32	

Table 224R

Mondays to Saturdays

3 March to 17 May

Falkirk Grahamston and Cumbernauld - Glasgow Queen Street and Motherwell

Network Diagram - refer to first Page of Table 220

		SR	SR	SR	SR	SR	SR	SR	SR SX	SR		SR SX	SR	SR	SR SX	SR	SR	SR	SR	SR		SR	SR	SR	SR
Falkirk Grahamston	d		15 43			16 43				17 44						18 43			19 43						21 13
Camelon ■4	d		15 46			16 46				17 47						18 47			19 46						21 16
Cumbernauld	d	15 28	15 58	16 10	16 30	16 58	17 10	17 28		17 59			18 10	18 28		18 59	19 10	19 28	19 58	20 10		20 28	20 58	21 10	21 28
Greenfaulds	d	15 30	16 00	16 12	16 32	17 00	17 12	17 30		18 01			18 12	18 30		19 01	19 12	19 30	20 00	20 12		20 30	21 00	21 12	21 30
Gartcosh	d	15 37	16 07		16 39	17 07		17 37		18 08				18 37		19 09		19 37	20 07			20 37	21 07		21 37
Stepps	d	15 41	16 11		16 43	17 11		17 41		18 12				18 41		19 13		19 41	20 11			20 41	21 11		21 41
Springburn	d	15 47	16 17		16 49	17 17		17 47		18 19				18 47		19 19		19 47	20 17			20 47	21 17		21 47
Glasgow Queen Street ■10	a	15 55	16 25		16 59	17 29		17 55		18 27				18 55		19 29		19 55	20 25			20 55	21 25		21 55
Coatbridge Central	d			16 21			17 21		17 31			17 58	18 21		18 34		19 20			20 21				21 21	
Whifflet 220,226	d			16 23			17 23		17 33			18 01	18 23		18 36		19 23			20 23				21 23	
Motherwell 226	a			16 32			17 32		17 40			18 08	18 32		18 43		19 32			20 32				21 32	

		SR	SR	SR	SR	SR
Falkirk Grahamston	d			22 13		23 13
Camelon ■4	d			22 16		23 16
Cumbernauld	d	21 58	22 10	22 28	22 58	23 28
Greenfaulds	d	22 00	22 12	22 30	23 00	23 30
Gartcosh	d	22 07		22 37	23 07	23 37
Stepps	d	22 11		22 41	23 11	23 41
Springburn	d	22 17		22 47	23 17	23 47
Glasgow Queen Street ■10	a	22 26		22 55	23 25	23 55
Coatbridge Central	d		22 21			
Whifflet 220,226	d		22 23			
Motherwell 226	a		22 32			

Sundays

8 December to 23 February

		SR	SR	SR	SR	SR	SR	SR	SR	SR		SR	SR	SR 🚌		SR 🚌
Falkirk Grahamston	d															
Camelon ■4	d															
Cumbernauld	d	08 55	09 58	10 58	11 58	12 58	13 58	14 58	15 58	16 58		17 58	18 58	19 58	and hourly until	22 58
Greenfaulds	d	08 57	10 00	11 00	12 00	13 00	14 00	15 00	16 00	17 00		18 00	19 00	20 03		23 03
Gartcosh	d	09 04	10 07	11 07	12 07	13 07	14 07	15 07	16 07	17 07		18 07	19 07	20 22		23 22
Stepps	d	09 08	10 11	11 11	12 11	13 11	14 11	15 11	16 11	17 11		18 11	19 11	20 35		23 35
Springburn	d	09 16	10 17	11 17	12 17	13 17	14 17	15 17	16 17	17 17		18 17	19 17	20 55		23 55
Glasgow Queen Street ■10	a	09 22	10 25	11 25	12 25	13 26	14 25	15 25	16 26	17 25		18 25	19 25	21 05		00 05
Coatbridge Central	d															
Whifflet 220,226	d															
Motherwell 226	a															

Sundays

2 March to 11 May

		SR	SR	SR	SR	SR	SR	SR	SR	SR		SR		SR	SR	SR
Falkirk Grahamston	d															
Camelon ■4	d															
Cumbernauld	d	08 55	09 58	10 58	11 58	12 58	13 58	14 58	15 58	16 58	and hourly until	19 58		20 58	21 58	22 58
Greenfaulds	d	08 57	10 00	11 00	12 00	13 00	14 00	15 00	16 00	17 00		20 00		21 00	22 00	23 00
Gartcosh	d	09 04	10 07	11 07	12 07	13 07	14 07	15 07	16 07	17 07		20 07		21 07	22 07	23 07
Stepps	d	09 08	10 11	11 11	12 11	13 11	14 11	15 11	16 11	17 11		20 11		21 11	22 11	23 11
Springburn	d	09 16	10 17	11 17	12 17	13 17	14 17	15 17	16 17	17 17		20 17		21 17	22 17	23 17
Glasgow Queen Street ■10	a	09 22	10 25	11 25	12 25	13 26	14 25	15 25	16 26	17 25		20 25		21 26	22 25	23 25
Coatbridge Central	d															
Whifflet 220,226	d															
Motherwell 226	a															

Network Diagram for Tables 225, 228, 229, 230, 238, 240, 242

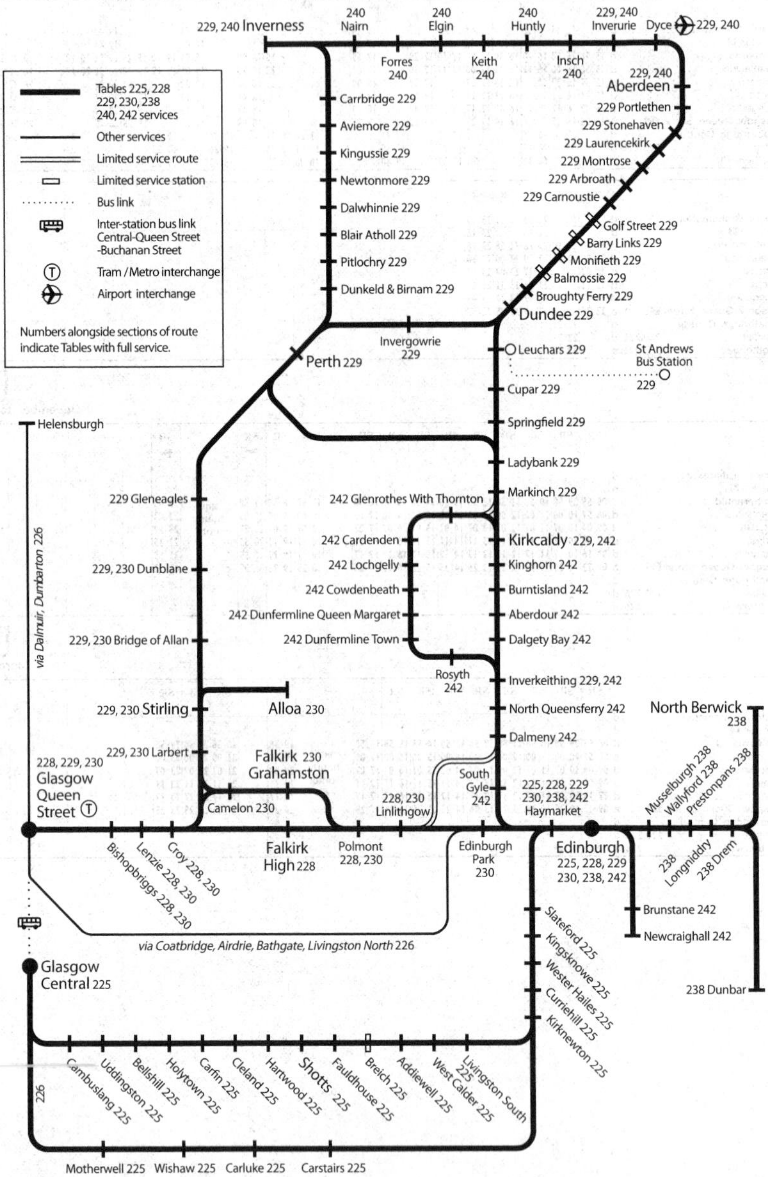
Tables 225, 228 229, 230, 238 240, 242 services
Other services
Limited service route
Limited service station
Bus link
Inter-station bus link Central-Queen Street -Buchanan Street
Tram / Metro interchange
Airport interchange
Numbers alongside sections of route indicate Tables with full service.
229, 240 Inverness
240 Nairn
240 Elgin
240 Huntly
229, 240 Inverurie
Dyce 229, 240
Forres 240
Keith 240
Insch 240
229, 240 Aberdeen
229 Portlethen
229 Stonehaven
229 Laurencekirk
229 Montrose
229 Arbroath
229 Carnoustie
Golf Street 229
Barry Links 229
Monifieth 229
Balmossie 229
Broughty Ferry 229
Dundee 229
Carrbridge 229
Aviemore 229
Kingussie 229
Newtonmore 229
Dalwhinnie 229
Blair Atholl 229
Pitlochry 229
Dunkeld & Birnam 229
Invergowrie 229
Perth 229
Leuchars 229
St Andrews Bus Station
229
Cupar 229
Springfield 229
Ladybank 229
Markinch 229
242 Glenrothes With Thornton
Kirkcaldy 229, 242
Kinghorn 242
Burntisland 242
Aberdour 242
Dalgety Bay 242
242 Cardenden
242 Lochgelly
242 Cowdenbeath
242 Dunfermline Queen Margaret
242 Dunfermline Town
Rosyth 242
Inverkeithing 229, 242
North Queensferry 242
Dalmeny 242
Helensburgh
via Dalmuir, Dumbarton 226
229 Gleneagles
229, 230 Dunblane
229, 230 Bridge of Allan
229, 230 Stirling
Alloa 230
229, 230 Larbert
Falkirk Grahamston 230
Camelon 230
228, 229, 230 Glasgow Queen Street
228, 230 Linlithgow
South Gyle 242
225, 228, 229 230, 238, 242 Haymarket
North Berwick 238
Musselburgh 238
Wallyford 238
Prestonpans 238
Bishopbriggs 228, 230
Lenzie 228, 230
Croy 228, 230
Falkirk High 228
Polmont 228, 230
Edinburgh Park 230
Edinburgh 225, 228, 229 230, 238, 242
238 Longniddry
238 Drem
Brunstane 242
Newcraighall 242
238 Dunbar
via Coatbridge, Airdrie, Bathgate, Livingston North 226
Glasgow Central 225
Slateford 225
Kingsknowe 225
Wester Hailes 225
Curriehill 225
Kirknewton 225
226
Cambuslang 225
Uddingston 225
Bellshill 225
Holytown 225
Carfin 225
Cleland 225
Hartwood 225
Shotts 225
Fauldhouse 225
Breich 225
Addiewell 225
West Calder 225
Livingston South 225
Motherwell 225
Wishaw 225
Carluke 225
Carstairs 225

TOCs operating on this network - ScotRail (SR), Cross Country (XC) East Coast (GR)

Table 225

Mondays to Saturdays

9 December to 17 May

Edinburgh - Shotts, Carstairs, Motherwell and Glasgow Central

Network Diagram - refer to first page of Table 225

Miles	Miles		SR MX A	SR MX B	SR	XC SX ◇1	XC SO ◇1	SR	SR SX C	SR B	XC SX ◇1 D		XC SO ◇1	SR E	SR	SR	SR	XC SO ◇1 F	XC SX ◇1 F	SR	SR		SR SO	SR SX
0	0	**Edinburgh** 10 230,238,242 d			05 51	06 24	06 26	06 40		06 55	07 26		07 26	07 54	07 57	08 25	08 57	09 11	09 11	09 26	09 56		10 16	10 20
1¼	1¼	Haymarket 230,238,242 d			05 55		06 30	06 45		07 00	07 30		07 31	07 59	08 02	08 30	09 01	09 17	09 17	09 30	10 00		10 20	10 24
3	3	Slateford d			05 59					07 04						08 35				09 35				
3¾	3¾	Kingsknowe d			06 03					07 07						08 38				09 38				
4¾	4¾	Wester Hailes d			06 05					07 10						08 41				09 41				
7½	7½	Curriehill d			06 09					07 13						08 45				09 45				
11	11	Kirknewton d			06 16					07 21						08 52				09 52				
14	—	Livingston South d			06 22			06 59		07 26					08 19	08 58	09 16			09 59	10 16			
16¾	—	West Calder d			06 27			07 05		07 31					08 25	09 03	09 21			10 04	10 21			
18½	—	Addiewell d			06 31					07 34						09 06				10 07				
21	—	Breich d																						
23¼	—	Fauldhouse d			06 38					07 41						09 13				10 14				
26¾	—	**Shotts** d			06 44			07 18		07 46					08 38	09 19	09 34			10 20	10 34			
28¼	—	Hartwood d			06 47					07 49						09 22				10 23				
31½	—	Cleland d			06 53					07 54						09 27				10 28				
33¼	—	Carfin d			06 57					07 58						09 30				10 31				
34¼	—	Holytown d	00 01		06 59					08 00						09 32				10 33				
—	28½	Carstairs d		00 04										08 32									11 09	11 09
—	—	Carluke 226 d		00 13										08 41									11 19	11 19
—	—	Wishaw 226 d		00 24										08 55									11 26	11 26
—	44½	**Motherwell** 226 a		00 29		07 04	07 04				08 09		08 14	09 00				09 52	10 00				11 32	11 32
—	—	d				07 05	07 05		07 47		08 10		08 15	09 00				09 53	10 01				11 34	11 34
36	—	Bellshill 226 d	00 04		07 07			07 30	07 54	08 04					08 49	09 37	09 47			10 37	10 47			
38¾	—	Uddingston 226 d	00 08		07 13				07 58	08 08						09 41				10 41				
42	—	Cambuslang 226 d	00 14		07 18				08a03															
47¼	57¼	**Glasgow Central** 15 226 a	00 25		07 29	07 22	07 22	07 52		08 26	08 28		08 32	09 26	09 10	09 58	10 10	10 15	10 27	10 58	11 10		11 55	11 55

	SR SO	SR SX	SR	XC ◇1 G	SR SX	SR SO	SR		SR	SR SX	SR SO	SR	XC SO ◇1 H	XC SX ◇1 I	SR	SR	SR		SR SX	SR SO	SR SX	SR SO	XC ◇1 J	SR
Edinburgh 10 230,238,242 d	10 26	10 26	10 56	11 11	11 26	11 26	11 51		11 56	12 26	12 26	12 56	13 12	13 13	13 26	13 51	13 56		14 26	14 26	14 56	14 56	15 11	15 26
Haymarket 230,238,242 d	10 30	10 30	11 00	11 16	11 30	11 30	11 58		12 00	12 30	12 30	13 00	13 16	13 18	13 30	13 56	14 00		14 29	14 31	15 00	15 01	15 16	15 30
Slateford d	10 35	10 36			11 35	11 35				12 35	12 35				13 35				14 35	14 35				15 35
Kingsknowe d	10 39	10 38			11 38	11 39				12 38	12 39				13 39				14 38	14 38				15 38
Wester Hailes d	10 41	10 41			11 41	11 41				12 41	12 41				13 41				14 41	14 41				15 41
Curriehill d	10 45	10 45			11 45	11 45				12 45	12 45				13 45				14 45	14 45				15 45
Kirknewton d	10 52	10 52			11 52	11 52				12 52	12 52				13 52				14 52	14 52				15 52
Livingston South d	10 58	10 58	11 16		11 58	11 58			12 18	12 58	12 58	13 16			13 58		14 16		14 58	14 58	15 16	15 16		15 58
West Calder d	11 03	11 03	11 21		12 03	12 03			12 23	13 03	13 03	13 21			14 03		14 21		15 03	15 03	15 21	15 21		16 03
Addiewell d	11 06	11 06			12 06	12 06				13 06	13 06				14 06				15 06	15 06				16 06
Breich d																								
Fauldhouse d	11 13	11 13			12 13	12 13				13 13	13 13				14 13				15 13	15 13				16 13
Shotts d	11 19	11 19	11 34		12 19	12 19			12 36	13 19	13 19	13 34			14 19		14 34		15 19	15 19	15 34	15 34		16 19
Hartwood d	11 22	11 22			12 22	12 22				13 22	13 22				14 22				15 22	15 22				16 22
Cleland d	11 27	11 27			12 27	12 27				13 27	13 27				14 27				15 27	15 27				16 27
Carfin d	11 30	11 30			12 30	12 30				13 30	13 30				14 30				15 30	15 30				16 30
Holytown d	11 32	11 32			12 32	12 32				13 32	13 32				14 32				15 32	15 32				16 32
Carstairs d							12 33									14 34								
Carluke 226 d							12 43									14 42								
Wishaw 226 d							12 48									14 47								
Motherwell 226 a				11 52			12 54						13 52	13 52		14 53							15 52	
d				11 53			12 54						13 53	13 53		14 53							15 53	
Bellshill 226 d	11 37	11 37	11 47		12 37	12 37			12 49	13 37	13 37	13 48			14 37		14 47		15 37	15 37	15 47	15 47		16 37
Uddingston 226 d	11 41	11 41			12 41	12 41				13 41	13 41				14 41				15 41	15 41				16 43
Cambuslang 226 d																								
Glasgow Central 15 226 a	11 58	11 58	12 10	12 11	12 58	12 58	13 27		13 10	13 58	13 58	14 10	14 12	14 12	14 58	15 14	15 10		15 58	15 58	16 10	16 10	16 12	16 58

A From Edinburgh
B From Newcraighall
C To Anderston
D From Dunbar
E From North Berwick
F From Newcastle
G From Birmingham New Street
H From Bristol Temple Meads
I From Bath Spa
J From Plymouth

Table 225

Mondays to Saturdays

9 December to 17 May

Edinburgh - Shotts, Carstairs, Motherwell and Glasgow Central

Network Diagram - refer to first page of Table 225

			SR SX	SR SO	SR SX	SR SO	SR	SR	XC SX ◇1 A	XC SO ◇1 A	SR		SR SX	SR SO	SR SX	SR SO	SR SX	SR SO	SR SX	SR B	SR		XC SX ◇1 A	XC SO ◇1 A	SR	GR SX R 1 C
Edinburgh 10	230,238,242	d	15 48	15 48	15 56	15 56	16 26	16 56	17 11	17 11	17 18		17 42	17 42	17 47	17 47	17 56	17 56		18 26	18 56		19 11	19 12	19 26	20 17
Haymarket	230,238,242	d	15 53	15 53	16 00	16 00	16 30	17 00	17 15	17 16	17 23		17 46	17 46	17 52	17 52	18 01	18 02		18 30	19 00		19 16	19 16	19 30	20 22
Slateford		d					16 35				17 28				17 57	17 57				18 33					19 35	
Kingsknowe		d					16 38				17 32				18 00	18 00				18 36					19 38	
Wester Hailes		d					16 41				17 34				18 03	18 03	18 09	18 09		18 39					19 41	
Curriehill		d					16 45				17 38						18 12	18 12		18 42					19 45	
Kirknewton		d					16 52				17 45						18 20	18 20		18 49					19 52	
Livingston South		d			16 15	16 15	16 58	17 15			17 51				18 14	18 14	18 25	18 25			19 17				19 58	
West Calder		d			16 20	16 20	17 03	17 20			17 56				18 19	18 19	18 30	18 30			19 22				20 03	
Addiewell		d					17 06				18 00						18 33	18 33							20 06	
Breich		d															18 38	18 38								
Fauldhouse		d					17 13				18 07						18 42	18 42							20 13	
Shotts		d			16 32	16 32	17 19	17 32			18 13				18 32	18 32	18 47	18 47			19 35				20 19	
Hartwood		d					17 22				18 16						18 50	18 50							20 22	
Cleland		d					17 27				18 21						18 55	18 55							20 27	
Carfin		d					17 30				18 25						18 59	18 59							20 30	
Holytown		d					17 32				18 28						19 01	19 01							20 32	
Carstairs		d	16 29	16 29									18 11	18 11					18 29	19 13						
Carluke	226	d	16 39	16 39									18 21	18 21					18 37	19 22						
Wishaw	226	d	16 48	16 48									18 27	18 27					18 44	19 27						
Motherwell	226	a	16 55	16 55					17 52	17 52	18 35		18 33	18 33					18 52	19 33			19 56	19 52		21 03
		d	16 56	16 56					17 53	17 53			18 34	18 34						19 34			19 57	19 53		21 04
Bellshill	226	d			16 43	16 43	17 36	17 43							18 43	18 43	19 05	19 05			19 47				20 37	
Uddingston	226	d					17 40										19 13	19 13							20 41	
Cambuslang	226	d					17 47								18 50	19 00	19 18	19 18								
Glasgow Central 15	226	a	17 18	17 23	17 05	17 06	17 58	18 06	18 11	18 11			18 51	18 52	19 01	19 11	19 31	19 31		19 54	20 04		20 15	20 09	20 57	21 25

			XC SO ◇1 D	XC SX ◇1 D	SR FO	SR FX	VT SO ◇1 E		SR	SR SO F	SR SX F
Edinburgh 10	230,238,242	d	21 13	21 14	21 26	21 26			22 56	23 21	23 21
Haymarket	230,238,242	d	21 18	21 19	21 30	21 30			23 00	23 25	23 25
Slateford		d			21 35	21 35			23 04	23 29	23 29
Kingsknowe		d			21 38	21 39			23 07	23 32	23 32
Wester Hailes		d			21 41	21 41			23 10	23 34	23 34
Curriehill		d			21 45	21 45			23 14	23 37	23 37
Kirknewton		d			21 52	21 52			23 21	23 44	23 44
Livingston South		d			21 58	21 58			23 26		
West Calder		d			22 03	22 03			23 31		
Addiewell		d			22 06	22 06			23 35		
Breich		d									
Fauldhouse		d			22 13	22 13			23 42		
Shotts		d			22 19	22 19			23 47		
Hartwood		d			22 22	22 22			23 50		
Cleland		d			22 27	22 27			23 55		
Carfin		d			22 30	22 30			23 58		
Holytown		d			22 32	22 32			00 01		
Carstairs		d								00 04	00 04
Carluke	226	d								00 13	00 13
Wishaw	226	d								00 20	00 24
Motherwell	226	a	21 56	22 04						00 25	00 29
		d	21 57	22 05			22 53				
Bellshill	226	d			22 37	22 37			00 04		
Uddingston	226	d			22 41	22 41			00 08		
Cambuslang	226	d							00 14		
Glasgow Central 15	226	a	22 21	22 28	22 58	22 58	23 13		00 25		

A From Penzance
B From North Berwick
C From London Kings Cross
D From Plymouth
E from 4 January until 8 February. From Carlisle
F From Newcraighall

Table 225

Sundays

8 December to 11 May

Edinburgh - Shotts, Carstairs, Motherwell and Glasgow Central

Network Diagram - refer to first page of Table 225

Station			SR	SR	SR		XC	SR	XC	SR	XC	SR	XC	SR	XC		SR	XC	GR
							◇1		◇1		◇1		◇1		◇1			◇1	R 1
			A	B			C 🍴		D		E		F		G			G	H 🍴
Edinburgh 10	230,238,242	d			10 26		12 17	12 26	13 10	14 27	15 10	16 26	17 11	18 26	19 18		20 26	21 12	21 22
Haymarket	230,238,242	d			10 30		12 21	12 30	13 14	14 31	15 15	16 30	17 15	18 30	19 23		20 30	21 17	21 26
Slateford		d			10 34			12 34		14 35		16 34		18 34			20 34		
Kingsknowe		d			10 38			12 38		14 39		16 38		18 38			20 38		
Wester Hailes		d			10 40			12 40		14 41		16 40		18 40			20 40		
Curriehill		d			10 44			12 44		14 45		16 44		18 44			20 44		
Kirknewton		d			10 51			12 51		14 52		16 51		18 51			20 51		
Livingston South		d			10 57			12 57		14 57		16 57		18 57			20 57		
West Calder		d			11 02			13 02		15 02		17 02		19 02			21 02		
Addiewell		d			11 06			13 06		15 06		17 06		19 06			21 06		
Breich		d																	
Fauldhouse		d			11 13			13 13		15 13		17 13		19 13			21 13		
Shotts		d			11 18			13 18		15 18		17 18		19 18			21 18		
Hartwood		d			11 21			13 21		15 21		17 21		19 21			21 21		
Cleland		d			11 26			13 26		15 26		17 26		19 26			21 26		
Carfin		d			11 30			13 30		15 30		17 30		19 30			21 30		
Holytown		d	00 01		11 32			13 32		15 32		17 32		19 32			21 32		
Carstairs		d		00 04															
Carluke	226	d		00 13															
Wishaw	226	d		00 20															
Motherwell	226	a		00 25			12 55		13 50		15 52		17 52		19 58			21 53	22 05
		d					12 56		13 51		15 53		17 53		20 00			21 54	22 06
Bellshill	226	d	00 04		11 36			13 36		15 36		17 36		19 36			21 36		
Uddingston	226	d	00 08		11 39			13 39		15 39		17 39		19 39			21 39		
Cambuslang	226	d	00 14																
Glasgow Central 15	226	a	00 25		11 58		13 14	13 58	14 09	15 58	16 13	17 58	18 12	19 58	20 21		21 58	22 14	22 26

A not 8 December. From Edinburgh
B not 8 December. From Newcraighall
C From Leeds
D From Sheffield
E From Birmingham New Street
F From Bristol Temple Meads
G From Plymouth
H From London Kings Cross

Table 225R

Mondays to Saturdays

9 December to 17 May

Glasgow Central, Motherwell, Carstairs and Shotts - Edinburgh

Network Diagram - refer to first page of Table 225

Miles	Miles			SR	SR	SR	XC	SR	SR	GR	SR	SR	SR	XC	SR	SR	SR	SR	XC	XC	SR	SR	SR
				MX	SO			SX							SO	SX	SO	SX	SO	SX	SX	SO	SX
							◇1			R 1				◇1					◇1	◇1			
				A			B			C		D		B					E	E			
0	0	**Glasgow Central** 15	226 d		00 06		06 01		06 16	06 50	07 00	07 05	07 13	07 50	08 05	08 05	08 18	08 20	09 00	09 00	09 05	09 05	09 18
5¼	—	Cambuslang	226 d		00 15				06 25				07 23										
8½	—	Uddingston	226 d		00 20				06 30				07 30				08 32	08 32					09 30
11¼	—	Bellshill	226 d		00 25				06 35		07 15		07 34		08 19	08 20	08 36	08 36			09 19	09 19	09 34
—	12¼	**Motherwell**	226 a				06 16			07 05		07 19		08 04					09 14	09 14			
—	—		d			06 00	06 17	07 01		07 06		07 20		08 05					09 15	09 15			
—	—	Wishaw	226 d					07 10				07 28											
—	—	Carluke	226 d					07 17				07 34											
—	28½	Carstairs	d					07a26				07 47											
13¼	—	Holytown	d		00 29	06 09			06 39				07 39				08 41	08 41					09 39
14	—	Carfin	d		00 31	06 11			06 41				07 41				08 43	08 43					09 41
15¾	—	Cleland	d		00 35	06 15			06 45				07 45				08 47	08 47					09 45
19	—	Hartwood	d		00 41	06 21			06 51				07 51				08 53	08 53					09 50
20½	—	**Shotts**	d		00 44	06 25			06 55		07 28		07 55		08 32	08 32	08 57	08 57			09 32	09 32	09 54
24	—	Fauldhouse	d		00 50	06 31			07 01				08 01				09 03	09 03					10 00
26¼	—	Breich	d										08 04										
28¾	—	Addiewell	d		00 56	06 37			07 07				08 08				09 09	09 09					10 06
30½	—	West Calder	d		00 59	06 40			07 10		07 40		08 12		08 44	08 44	09 12	09 12			09 44	09 44	10 10
33¼	—	Livingston South	d	00 04	01 04	06 44			07 15		07 44		08 17		08 49	08 49	09 17	09 17			09 48	09 48	10 15
36¼	46¼	Kirknewton	d	00 09		06 50			07 22		07 49	08 04	08 22				09 22	09 22					10 20
40¾	49¾	Curriehill	d	00 15		06 56			07 28		07 55	08 09	08 28				09 28	09 28					10 26
42½	52½	Wester Hailes	d	00 19		07 00			07 31			08 12	08 31				09 32	09 32					10 30
43½	53½	Kingsknowe	d	00 21		07 02			07 34			08 14	08 34				09 34	09 34					10 33
44¼	54¼	Slateford	d	00 24		07 05			07 37			08 17	08 36				09 37	09 37					10 35
46	56	Haymarket	230,238,242 d	00 30	01 18	07 11	06 57		07 43	07 48	08 05	08 23	08 43	08 51	09 05	09 05	09 42	09 42	09 57	09 58	10 05	10 06	10 42
47¼	57¼	**Edinburgh** 10	230,238,242 a	00 34	01 23	07 16	07 02		07 47	07 52	08 10	08 28	08 48	08 56	09 14	09 14	09 47	09 47	10 02	10 04	10 13	10 13	10 47

		SR	SR	SR	SR	SR	SR	XC	XC	SR	SR	SR	SR	SR	SR	SR	XC	XC	SR	SR	SR	SR	SR
		SO	SX	SO		SO	SX	SO	SX		SO	SX			SO	SX	SX	SO	SX	SO			
								◇1	◇1								◇1	◇1					
								E	E								B	B					
Glasgow Central 15	226 d	09 18	09 30	09 48	10 05	10 18	10 18	11 00	11 00	11 05	11 18	11 18	11 48	12 05	12 18	12 18	13 00	13 00	13 05	13 05	13 18	13 43	14 05
Cambuslang	226 d																						
Uddingston	226 d	09 30				10 30	10 30				11 30	11 30			12 30	12 30					13 30		
Bellshill	226 d	09 34			10 19	10 34	10 34			11 19	11 34	11 34		12 19	12 34	12 34			13 19	13 19	13 34		14 19
Motherwell	226 a		09 58	10 05				11 13	11 13				12 08				13 13	13 13				14 06	
	d		09 59	10 06				11 14	11 14				12 09				13 14	13 14				14 07	
Wishaw	226 d		10 05	10 14									12 14									14 14	
Carluke	226 d		10 11	10 21									12 22									14 22	
Carstairs	d		10 20	10 32									12 32									14 34	
Holytown	d	09 39				10 39	10 39				11 39	11 39			12 39	12 39					13 39		
Carfin	d	09 41				10 41	10 41				11 41	11 41			12 41	12 42					13 41		
Cleland	d	09 45				10 45	10 45				11 45	11 45			12 45	12 45					13 45		
Hartwood	d	09 50				10 50	10 50				11 50	11 50			12 50	12 50					13 50		
Shotts	d	09 54			10 32	10 54	10 54			11 32	11 54	11 54		12 32	12 54	12 54			13 32	13 32	13 54		14 32
Fauldhouse	d	10 00				11 00	11 00				12 00	12 00			13 00	13 00					14 00		
Breich	d																						
Addiewell	d	10 06				11 06	11 06				12 06	12 06			13 06	13 06					14 06		
West Calder	d	10 10			10 44	11 10	11 10			11 44	12 10	12 10		12 44	13 10	13 10			13 44	13 44	14 10		14 44
Livingston South	d	10 15			10 48	11 15	11 15			11 48	12 15	12 15		12 48	13 15	13 15			13 48	13 48	14 15		14 48
Kirknewton	d	10 20				11 20	11 20				12 20	12 20			13 20	13 20					14 20		
Curriehill	d	10 26				11 26	11 26				12 26	12 26			13 26	13 26					14 26		
Wester Hailes	d	10 30				11 30	11 30				12 30	12 30			13 30	13 30					14 30		
Kingsknowe	d	10 33				11 33	11 33				12 33	12 33			13 33	13 33					14 33		
Slateford	d	10 35				11 35	11 35				12 35	12 35			13 35	13 35					14 35		
Haymarket	230,238,242 d	10 42	10 49	11 12	11 04	11 41	11 42	11 52	11 53	12 04	12 41	12 42	12 57	13 04	13 42	13 42			14 03	14 04	14 42	15 18	15 04
Edinburgh 10	230,238,242 a	10 48	10 53	11 19	11 10	11 47	11 47	11 57	11 56	12 10	12 48	12 48	13 04	13 11	13 47	13 47	13 54	13 55	14 11	14 10	14 48	15 25	15 10

A From Glasgow Central
B To Plymouth
C To London Kings Cross
D To North Berwick
E To Penzance

Table 225R

Mondays to Saturdays

9 December to 17 May

Glasgow Central, Motherwell, Carstairs and Shotts - Edinburgh

Network Diagram - refer to first page of Table 225

		SR SO	SR SX	XC SX ◇1 A	XC SO ◇1 A 🚲	SR SX	SR SO	SR SO		SR SX	SR B	SR SX	SR SO	SR	XC ◇1 C	SR	SR SO	SR SX		SR	SR	XC ◇1	SR	SR	SR
Glasgow Central 15	226 d	14 18	14 18	15 00	15 00	15 05	15 05	15 18		15 18	15 50	16 05	16 05	16 18	16 52	17 08	17 18	17 18		18 05	18 18	19 00	19 05	19 18	19 49
Cambuslang	226 d																				18 27				
Uddingston	226 d	14 30	14 30					15 30		15 30				16 30			17u32	17u32			18 32			19 32	
Bellshill	226 d	14 34	14 34			15 19	15 19	15 34		15 34		16 20	16 20	16 35		17 23	17 36	17 36		18 19	18 37		19 19	19 36	
Motherwell	226 a			15 13	15 13						16 07				17 05							19 13			20 04
	d			15 14	15 14						16 07				17 06							19 14			20 05
Wishaw	226 d										16 13														20 12
Carluke	226 d										16 26														20 18
Carstairs	d										16 35														20 27
Holytown	d	14 39	14 39					15 39		15 39				16 40			17 40	17 41			18 41			19 41	
Carfin	d	14 41	14 41					15 41		15 41				16 42			17 43	17 43			18 44			19 43	
Cleland	d	14 45	14 45					15 45		15 45				16 46			17 47	17 47			18 48			19 47	
Hartwood	d	14 50	14 50					15 50		15 50				16 52			17 53	17 53			18 53			19 53	
Shotts	d	14 54	14 54			15 32	15 32	15 54		15 54		16 33	16 33	16 56		17 36	17 57	17 57		18 32	18 57		19 32	19 57	
Fauldhouse	d	15 00	15 00					16 00		16 00				17 02			18 03	18 03			19 03			20 03	
Breich	d																								
Addiewell	d	15 06	15 06					16 06		16 07				17 08			18 09	18 09			19 09			20 09	
West Calder	d	15 10	15 10			15 44	15 44	16 10		16 10		16 46	16 46	17 11		17 48	18 12	18 12		18 44	19 13		19 44	20 12	
Livingston South	d	15 15	15 15			15 48	15 49	16 15		16 16		16 51	16 51	17 16		17 53	18 17	18 17		18 48	19 18		19 48	20 17	
Kirknewton	d	15 20	15 20					16 20		16 21				17 22			18 22	18 22			19 23			20 22	
Curriehill	d	15 26	15 26					16 26		16 27				17 28			18 28	18 28			19 29			20 28	
Wester Hailes	d	15 30	15 30					16 30		16 31				17 31			18 31	18 31			19 32			20 32	
Kingsknowe	d	15 33	15 33					16 33		16 34				17 34			18 34	18 34			19 35			20 34	
Slateford	d	15 35	15 35					16 35		16 37				17 36			18 36	18 36			19 37			20 37	
Haymarket	230,238,242 d	15 42	15 42	15 56	15 57	16 05	16 05	16 47		16 47	17 05	17 09	17 10	17 42	17 53	18 10	18 47	18 47		19 05	19 43	19 53	20 04	20 43	20 53
Edinburgh 10	230,238,242 a	15 47	15 48	16 00	16 01	16 11	16 11	16 52		16 52	17 09	17 13	17 14	17 47	17 57	18 17	18 52	18 52		19 11	19 48	19 57	20 10	20 47	20 58

		XC SX ◇1	SR	SR
Glasgow Central 15	226 d	21 05	21 18	23 06
Cambuslang	226 d			23 15
Uddingston	226 d		21 30	23 20
Bellshill	226 d		21 35	23 25
Motherwell	226 a	21 22		
	d	21 23		
Wishaw	226 d			
Carluke	226 d			
Carstairs	d			
Holytown	d		21 40	23 29
Carfin	d		21 42	23 31
Cleland	d		21 46	23 35
Hartwood	d		21 52	23 41
Shotts	d		21 56	23 45
Fauldhouse	d		22 02	23 51
Breich	d			
Addiewell	d		22 08	23 57
West Calder	d		22 11	23 59
Livingston South	d		22 16	00 04
Kirknewton	d		22 21	00 09
Curriehill	d		22 27	00 15
Wester Hailes	d		22 31	00 19
Kingsknowe	d		22 33	00 21
Slateford	d		22 36	00 24
Haymarket	230,238,242 d		22 43	00 30
Edinburgh 10	230,238,242 a	22 23	22 48	00 34

A To Bristol Temple Meads
B To North Berwick
C To Birmingham New Street

Table 225R

Sundays

8 December to 11 May

Glasgow Central, Motherwell, Carstairs and Shotts - Edinburgh

Network Diagram - refer to first page of Table 225

		SR	SR	XC	XC	SR	XC	XC	SR	XC	SR	XC	SR	XC	SR	XC
		A		B	B		C	D		E		E		F		
Glasgow Central	226 d		10 18	10 55	11 51	12 18	13 49	13 49	14 18	14 55	16 18	16 55	18 18	18 57	20 18	20 58
Cambuslang	226 d															
Uddingston	226 d		10 31			12 31			14 31		16 31		18 31		20 31	
Bellshill	226 d		10 36			12 36			14 36		16 36		18 36		20 36	
Motherwell	226 a			11 09	12 05		14 03	14 03		15 10		17 10		19 10		21 17
	d			11 10	12 08		14 04	14 04		15 11		17 11		19 11		21 18
Wishaw	226 d															
Carluke	226 d															
Carstairs	d															
Holytown	d		10 40			12 40			14 40		16 40		18 40		20 40	
Carfin	d		10 42			12 42			14 42		16 42		18 42		20 42	
Cleland	d		10 46			12 46			14 46		16 46		18 46		20 46	
Hartwood	d		10 52			12 52			14 52		16 52		18 52		20 52	
Shotts	d		10 56			12 56			14 56		16 56		18 56		20 56	
Fauldhouse	d		11 02			13 02			15 02		17 02		19 02		21 02	
Breich	d															
Addiewell	d		11 08			13 08			15 08		17 08		19 08		21 08	
West Calder	d		11 11			13 11			15 11		17 11		19 11		21 11	
Livingston South	d	00 04	11 15			13 15			15 15		17 15		19 16		21 16	
Kirknewton	d	00 09	11 20			13 20			15 23		17 23		19 23		21 23	
Curriehill	d	00 15	11 26			13 26			15 29		17 29		19 29		21 29	
Wester Hailes	d	00 19	11 30			13 30			15 32		17 32		19 32		21 33	
Kingsknowe	d	00 21	11 32			13 32			15 35		17 35		19 35		21 35	
Slateford	d	00 24	11 35			13 35			15 37		17 37		19 37		21 38	
Haymarket	230,238,242 d	00 30	11 41	11 51	12 49	13 41	14 42	14 42	15 44	15 51	17 44	17 51	19 44	19 51	21 44	22 04
Edinburgh	230,238,242 a	00 34	11 45	11 56	12 54	13 45	14 47	14 47	15 48	15 56	17 48	17 56	19 48	19 55	21 48	22 08

A not 8 December. From Glasgow Central
B To Reading
C until 23 March. To Guildford
D from 30 March. To Plymouth
E To Birmingham New Street
F To Newcastle

Table 226

Mondays to Saturdays

9 December to 17 May

Edinburgh, Lanark, Coatbridge, Motherwell, Larkhall, Hamilton, Bathgate, Airdrie and Springburn-Glasgow-Milngavie, Dalmuir, Balloch and Helensburgh

Network Diagram - refer to first Page of Table 220

Miles	Miles	Miles	Miles	Miles			SR MO A	SR MX B	SR MSX B	SR MX C	SR SO B	SR MO C	SR SO D	SR MX C	SR MX E	SR SO F	SR MX C	SR MX C	SR R G ✕	SR	SR	SR	SR	SR
—	—	—	0	—	Edinburgh	d													04 50					
—	—	—	1¼	—	Haymarket	d																		
0	—	—	—	—	**Lanark**	d																		
—	—	—	—	—	Carstairs	d									00 04									
8½	—	—	—	—	Carluke	d									00 13									
13	—	—	—	—	Wishaw	d									00 24									
14½	—	—	—	—	Holytown	d											00 01							
15	—	—	—	—	Shieldmuir	d																		
—	—	—	—	0	**Coatbridge Central**	d																		
—	—	—	—	1	Whifflet 220,224	d																		
16¼	0	0	—	5½	**Motherwell**	a									00 29									
—	—	—	—	—		d																		
—	3	—	—	—	Bellshill	d											00 04							
20½	5½	—	—	—	Uddingston	d											00 08							
—	—	0¾	—	—	Airbles	d																		
—	—	—	—	0	**Larkhall**	d																	06 06	
—	—	—	—	1½	Merryton	d																	06 08	
—	—	—	—	2¾	Chatelherault	d																	06 11	
—	—	3	—	5¼	**Hamilton Central**	d																	06 15	
—	—	3¾	—	—	Hamilton West	d																	06 17	
—	—	5¾	—	—	Blantyre	d																	06 21	
22½	—	8¼	—	—	Newton	d																		
24	9	—	—	—	Cambuslang	d											00 14							
25¾	10¾	—	—	—	Rutherglen	d																	06 29	
26½	11½	—	—	—	Dalmarnock	d																		
27	12	—	—	—	Bridgeton	d																		
—	—	—	3¾	—	Edinburgh Park	d																		
—	—	—	12½	—	Uphall	d												00 08						
—	—	—	15½	—	Livingston North	d												00 11						
—	—	—	18½	—	**Bathgate**	a												00 16						
—	—	—	—	—		d																05 35		05 50
—	—	—	21	—	Armadale	d																05 39		05 54
—	—	—	23¼	—	Blackridge	d																05 42		05 57
—	—	—	28¾	—	Caldercruix	d																05 49		06 04
—	—	—	31¾	—	Drumgelloch	d																05 52		06 07
—	—	—	33¼	—	**Airdrie**	d														05 34		05 56		06 11
—	—	—	34¼	—	Coatdyke	d														05 36		05 58		06 13
—	—	—	35¼	—	Coatbridge Sunnyside	d														05 39		06 01		06 16
—	—	—	35¾	—	Blairhill	d														05 42		06 04		06 19
—	—	—	38½	—	Easterhouse	d														05 46		06 08		06 23
—	—	—	39½	—	Garrowhill	d														05 48		06 10		06 25
—	—	—	40¾	—	Shettleston	d														05 51		06 13		06 28
—	—	—	41½	—	Carntyne	d														05 53		06 15		06 30
—	—	—	—	0	**Springburn**	d																		
—	—	—	—	0¼	Barnhill	d																		
—	—	—	—	1½	Alexandra Parade	d																		
—	—	—	—	1¾	Duke Street	d																		
—	—	—	43¼	2¼	Bellgrove	d														05 56		06 18		06 33
—	—	—	43¾	2¾	High Street	d								00 02						05 58		06 20		06 35
—	—	—	44¼	3¼	**Glasgow Queen St** 10 ⛴	a								00 04						06 00		06 22		06 37
—	—	—	—	—		d								00 04						06 01		06 23		06 41
—	—	—	45	4	Charing Cross	d								00 06						06 03		06 25		06 43
28¼	13¼	—	—	—	Argyle Street	d										00 04							06 34	
28¾	13¾	—	—	—	**Glasgow Central** 15	a										00 06	00b25						06 35	
—	—	—	—	—		d										00 06							06 36	
29¼	14¼	—	—	—	Anderston	d							00 01			00 08							06 38	
29¾	14¾	—	—	—	Exhibition Centre	d							00 03			00 10							06 40	
31	16	—	47	6	**Partick** ⛴	d						00 01	00 05	00 11		00 14				06 07		06 29	06 44	06 49
31½	16½	0	47½	6½	Hyndland 3	d			00 02		00 02	00 03	00 08	00 13		00 16				06 10		06 32	06 46	06 51
—	—	0½	—	—	Jordanhill	d			00 04			00 05		00 15						06 12				
—	—	1½	—	—	Scotstounhill	d			00 06			00 07		00 17						06 15				
—	—	2	—	—	Garscadden	d			00a08			00 09		00a19						06 17				06 55
—	—	3	—	—	Yoker	d				00 03		00 12								06 19				
—	—	4	—	—	Clydebank	d				00 05		00 14								06 21				
32½	17½	—	48½	7½	Anniesland	d					00 05		00 11			00 20						06 35	06 50	
33¾	18¾	—	49¾	8¾	Westerton	d					00 08		00 14			00 23			05 54			06 38	06 53	
35	—	—	—	—	Bearsden	d							00 16											
35¾	—	—	—	—	Hillfoot	d							00 18											
37¼	—	—	—	—	**Milngavie**	a							00 22											
—	20	—	51	10	Drumchapel	d					00 10					00 25						06 40	06 55	
—	20¾	—	51¾	10¾	Drumry	d					00 12					00 27						06 42	06 57	
—	21¾	—	52¾	11¾	Singer	d					00 15					00 30						06 45	07 00	
—	22¼	5¼	53½	12½	**Dalmuir**	a				00 08	00 18	00 18				00 32			06 00	06 24		06 47	07 02	07 00
—	—	—	—	—		d				00 08	00 18								06 01	06 24	06 30	06 48		07 00
—	—	—	54¾	13¾	Kilpatrick	d					00 21										06 32	06 51		
—	—	—	56½	15½	Bowling	d					00 24										06 35	06 54		
—	—	—	59¼	18¼	Dumbarton East	d				00 16	00 28									06 32	06 39	06 58		07 08
—	—	—	60	19	Dumbarton Central	d		00 01		00 18	00 31								06 12	06 34	06 42	07 01		07 10
—	—	—	60¼	19¼	Dalreoch	d	00 01	00 02		00 19	00 32									06 35	06 43	07 02		07 11
—	—	—	—	20¾	Renton	d		00 05			00 35									06 38		07 05		
—	—	—	—	22	Alexandria	d		00 07			00 37									06 40		07 07		
—	—	—	—	23	**Balloch**	a		00 11			00 41									06 44		07 11		
—	—	—	63½	—	Cardross	d	00 06			00 24											06 48			07 16
—	—	—	67¼	—	Craigendoran	d	00 12			00 30											06 54			07 22
—	—	—	68¼	—	**Helensburgh Central**	a	00 15			00 33									06c26		06 57			07 25

A From Airdrie
B From Springburn
C From Edinburgh
D From Motherwell
E From Newcraighall
F From Larkhall
G To Fort William
b Glasgow Central High Level
c Helensburgh Upper

Table 226

Mondays to Saturdays

9 December to 17 May

Edinburgh, Lanark, Coatbridge, Motherwell, Larkhall, Hamilton, Bathgate, Airdrie and Springburn-Glasgow-Milngavie, Dalmuir, Balloch and Helensburgh

Network Diagram - refer to first Page of Table 220

		SR	SR SX	SR SO	SR	SR SX	SR	SR	SR	SR SX	SR	SR SX	SR SO	SR	SR SX	SR	SR	XC SX	XC SO	SR SX	SR SX	SR
																		◇1	◇1			
Edinburgh	d							05 51		06 07							06 21	06 24	06 26	06 37		
Haymarket	d							05 55		06 12							06 25		06 30	06 41		
Lanark	d										06 22										06 54	
Carstairs	d																					
Carluke	d										06 32										07 04	
Wishaw	d										06 37										07 10	
Holytown	d							06 59														
Shieldmuir	d										06 41										07 13	
Coatbridge Central	d													06 42								
Whifflet 220,224	d													06 44								
Motherwell	a										06 45			06 51				07 04	07 04		07 17	
	d	06 18			06 23						06 46			06 53				07 05	07 05		07 18	07 20
Bellshill	d	06 24						07 07			06 52											07 26
Uddingston	d	06 28						07 13			06 56											07 30
Airbles	d				06 25									06 55								
Larkhall	d						06 36									07 06						
Merryton	d						06 38									07 08						
Chatelherault	d						06 41									07 11						
Hamilton Central	d				06 30		06 45							07 00		07 15						
Hamilton West	d				06 33		06 47							07 03		07 17						
Blantyre	d				06 36		06 51							07 06		07 21						
Newton	d				06 40									07 12								
Cambuslang	d	06 33			06 44			07 18			07 01			07 15								07 35
Rutherglen	d	06 38			06 48		06 59				07 06			07 19		07 32					07 28	07 39
Dalmarnock	d	06 40			06 50						07 08			07 21								07 41
Bridgeton	d	06 42			06 52						07 10			07 23								07 43
Edinburgh Park	d									06 16							06 31			06 46		
Uphall	d									06 24							06 39			06 55		
Livingston North	d									06 28							06 42			06 59		
Bathgate	a									06 32							06 47			07 03		
	d								06 20	06 34							06 48			07 04		
Armadale	d								06 24								06 52					
Blackridge	d								06 27								06 56					
Caldercruix	d								06 34								07 02					
Drumgelloch	d								06 37	06 46							07 06			07 16		
Airdrie	d		06 26						06 42	06 50		06 57					07 11			07 20		
Coatdyke	d		06 28						06 44			06 59					07 13			07 22		
Coatbridge Sunnyside	d		06 31						06 47	06 53		07 01					07 16			07 24		
Blairhill	d		06 34						06 49			07 04					07 19			07 27		
Easterhouse	d		06 38						06 53			07 08					07 23					
Garrowhill	d		06 40						06 56			07 10					07 25					
Shettleston	d		06 43						06 58			07 13					07 28					
Carntyne	d		06 45						07 00			07 15					07 30					
Springburn	d			06 40		06 49							07 10		07 19							
Barnhill	d			06 41		06 50							07 11		07 20							
Alexandra Parade	d			06 44		06 53							07 14		07 23							
Duke Street	d			06 46		06 55							07 16		07 25							
Bellgrove	d		06 48	06 48		06 57			07 04			07 18	07 18		07 27		07 33					
High Street	d		06 50	06 50		06 59			07 06	07 12		07 20	07 20		07 29		07 35			07 42		
Glasgow Queen St 10	a		06 52	06 52		07 01			07 08	07 14		07 22	07 22		07 31		07 37			07 44		
	d		06 53	06 53		07 02			07 11	07 14		07 23	07 23		07 33		07 41			07 44		
Charing Cross	d		06 55	06 55		07 04			07 13	07 17		07 25	07 25		07 35		07 43			07 47		
Argyle Street	d	06 46			06 56		07 04				07 14			07 27		07 37					07 33	07 47
Glasgow Central 15	a	06 47			06 57		07 05	07b29			07 16			07 28		07 39		07b22	07b22		07 35	07 48
	d	06 48			06 58		07 06				07 18			07 29		07 39					07 35	07 49
Anderston	d	06 49			06 59		07 08				07 19			07 30		07 41					07a37	07 50
Exhibition Centre	d	06 52			07 02		07 10				07 21			07 32		07 43						07 52
Partick	d	06 55	06 59	06 59	07 05	07 08	07 14		07 17	07 21	07 25	07 29	07 29	07 36	07 39	07 46	07 49			07 51		07 56
Hyndland 3	d	06 58	07 02	07 02	07 08	07 11	07 16		07 19	07 23	07 28	07 32	07 32	07 38	07 41	07 48	07 51			07 53		07 58
Jordanhill	d	07 00				07 13					07 30				07 43							08 00
Scotstounhill	d	07 02				07 15					07 32				07 46							08 02
Garscadden	d	07 05				07 17					07 34				07 48							08 05
Yoker	d	07 07				07 20					07 37				07 51							08 07
Clydebank	d	07 09				07 22					07 39				07 53							08 09
Anniesland	d		07 05	07 05	07 11		07 20			07 26		07 35	07 35	07 41		07 51				07 56		
Westerton	d		07 08	07 08	07 14		07 23			07 29		07 38	07 38	07 44		07 54				07 59		
Bearsden	d				07 16					07 31				07 46						08 02		
Hillfoot	d				07 18					07 33				07 48						08 04		
Milngavie	a				07 22					07 37				07 52						08 07		
Drumchapel	d		07 10	07 10			07 25					07 40	07 40			07 57						
Drumry	d		07 12	07 12			07 27					07 42	07 42			07 59						
Singer	d		07 15	07 15			07 30					07 45	07 45			08 01						
Dalmuir	a	07 13	07 17	07 18		07 26	07 32		07 29		07 42	07 47	07 47		07 57	08 04	08 00					08 13
	d		07 18	07 18					07 29			07 48	07 48				08 00					
Kilpatrick	d		07 21	07 21								07 51	07 51									
Bowling	d		07 24	07 24								07 54	07 54									
Dumbarton East	d		07 28	07 28					07 37			07 58	07 58				08 08					
Dumbarton Central	d		07 31	07 31					07 39			08 01	08 01				08 10					
Dalreoch	d		07 32	07 32					07 40			08 02	08 02				08 11					
Renton	d		07 35	07 35								08 05	08 05									
Alexandria	d		07 37	07 37								08 07	08 07									
Balloch	a		07 41	07 41								08 11	08 11									
Cardross	d								07 45								08 16					
Craigendoran	d								07 51								08 22					
Helensburgh Central	a								07 54								08 25					

b Glasgow Central High Level

Table 226

Mondays to Saturdays

9 December to 17 May

Edinburgh, Lanark, Coatbridge, Motherwell, Larkhall, Hamilton, Bathgate, Airdrie and Springburn-Glasgow-Milngavie, Dalmuir, Balloch and Helensburgh

Network Diagram - refer to first Page of Table 220

		SR	SR SX	SR SO	SR	SR A	SR SX		SR SO	SR SX	SR SX	SR	SR B	SR SX	SR ◇ C	SR SX	SR SO		SR SX	SR SO	SR SX	SR SO	SR SX	SR SX	SR SO
Edinburgh	d	06 40										06 48	06 55	07 07											
Haymarket	d	06 45										06 52	07 00	07 11											
Lanark	d									07 22							07 23							07 48	
Carstairs	d																								
Carluke	d									07 32							07 33							07 59	
Wishaw	d									07 37							07 38							08 06	
Holytown	d												08 00												
Shieldmuir	d									07 41							07 42							08 11	
Coatbridge Central	d					07 21															07 39				
Whifflet 220,224	d					07 23															07 41				
Motherwell	a					07 32				07 44							07 46				07 49			08 14	
	d				07 23					07 44	07 47						07 47				07 53	07 53		08 14	
Bellshill	d	07 30									07 54		08 04				07 54								
Uddingston	d									07 51	07 58		08 08				07 58							08 20	
Airbles	d				07 25																07 55	07 55			
Larkhall	d								07 36							07 36									08 06
Merryton	d								07 38							07 38									08 08
Chatelherault	d								07 41							07 41									08 11
Hamilton Central	d				07 30				07 45							07 45					08 00	08 00			08 15
Hamilton West	d				07 33				07 47							07 47					08 03	08 03			08 17
Blantyre	d				07 36				07 51							07 51					08 06	08 06			08 21
Newton	d				07 40											07 56					08 10	08 10			
Cambuslang	d				07 44						08 04					07 59	08 04				08 14	08 14			
Rutherglen	d				07 48				07 59	08 00	08 08					08 04	08 08				08 18	08 18		08 28	08 31
Dalmarnock	d				07 50						08 10					08 06	08 10				08 20	08 20			
Bridgeton	d				07 52						08 12					08 08	08 12				08 22	08 22			
Edinburgh Park	d											06 59		07 18											
Uphall	d											07 07		07 26											
Livingston North	d											07 10		07 30											
Bathgate	a											07 15		07 34											
	d											07 18		07 35											
Armadale	d											07 22													
Blackridge	d											07 26													
Caldercruix	d											07 32													
Drumgelloch	d											07 36		07 47											
Airdrie	d		07 26									07 41		07 51					07 56						
Coatdyke	d		07 28									07 43		07 53					07 58						
Coatbridge Sunnyside	d		07 31									07 46		07 55					08 01						
Blairhill	d		07 34									07 49		07 58					08 04						
Easterhouse	d		07 38									07 53							08 08						
Garrowhill	d		07 40									07 55							08 10						
Shettleston	d		07 43									07 58							08 13						
Carntyne	d		07 45									08 00							08 15						
Springburn	d			07 40			07 49													08 10			08 19		
Barnhill	d			07 41			07 50													08 11			08 20		
Alexandra Parade	d			07 44			07 53													08 14			08 23		
Duke Street	d			07 46			07 55													08 16			08 25		
Bellgrove	d		07 48	07 48			07 57					08 03							08 18	08 18			08 27		
High Street	d		07 50	07 50			07 59					08 05		08 12					08 20	08 20			08 29		
Glasgow Queen St 10	a		07 52	07 52			08 01					08 07		08 14					08 22	08 22			08 31		
	d		07 53	07 53			08 03					08 11		08 14	08c21				08 23	08 23			08 33		
Charing Cross	d		07 55	07 55			08 05					08 13		08 17					08 25	08 25			08 35		
Argyle Street	d				07 56				08 04	08 05	08 19					08 13	08 16				08 26	08 26		08 33	08 36
Glasgow Central 15	a	07b52			07 57				08 06	08 07	08 20		08b26			08 14	08 17				08 27	08 27		08 35	08 38
	d				07 58				08 07	08 07	08 22					08 18	08 18				08 28	08 28		08 38	08 38
Anderston	d				07 59				08 08	08 09	08a23					08 19	08 19				08 30	08 30		08 40	08 40
Exhibition Centre	d				08 01				08 11	08 11						08 21	08 21				08 32	08 32		08 42	08 42
Partick	d		08 00	08 00	08 05		08 10		08 14	08 14		08 17		08 21		08 25	08 25		08 30	08 30	08 36	08 36	08 39	08 45	08 45
Hyndland 3	d		08 02	08 02	08 10		08 12		08 17	08 17		08 19		08 24		08 28	08 28		08 33	08 33	08 38	08 38	08 41	08 47	08 47
Jordanhill	d						08 14									08 30	08 30						08 43		
Scotstounhill	d						08 17									08 32	08 32						08 46		
Garscadden	d						08 19									08 35	08 35						08 48		
Yoker	d						08 21									08 37	08 37						08 50		
Clydebank	d						08 23									08 39	08 39						08 52		
Anniesland	d		08 05	08 05	08 13				08 20	08 20				08 27					08 36	08 36	08 41	08 41		08 50	08 50
Westerton	d		08 09	08 09	08 20				08 23	08 24				08 31					08 39	08 39	08 44	08 44		08 53	08 53
Bearsden	d				08 23									08 33							08 47	08 47			
Hillfoot	d				08 25									08 35							08 49	08 49			
Milngavie	a				08 28									08 39							08 52	08 52			
Drumchapel	d		08 11	08 11					08 25	08 26									08 41	08 41				08 56	08 56
Drumry	d		08 13	08 13					08 27	08 28									08 43	08 43				08 58	08 58
Singer	d		08 16	08 16					08 30	08 31									08 46	08 46				09 00	09 00
Dalmuir	a		08 18	08 18			08 27		08 32	08 33		08 30			08 39	08 43	08 43		08 48	08 48			08 56	09 03	09 03
	d		08 18	08 19								08 30			08 39				08 49	08 49					
Kilpatrick	d		08 21	08 21															08 51	08 51					
Bowling	d		08 24	08 24															08 54	08 54					
Dumbarton East	d		08 28	08 29								08 38							08 59	08 59					
Dumbarton Central	d		08 31	08 31								08 40			08 49				09 01	09 01					
Dalreoch	d		08 32	08 32								08 41							09 02	09 02					
Renton	d		08 35	08 35															09 05	09 05					
Alexandria	d		08 37	08 37															09 07	09 07					
Balloch	a		08 41	08 41															09 11	09 11					
Cardross	d											08 46													
Craigendoran	d											08 52													
Helensburgh Central	a											08 55			09e03										

A From Cumbernauld
B From Newcraighall
C To Oban
b Glasgow Central High Level
c Glasgow Queen St High Level
e Helensburgh Upper

Table 226

Mondays to Saturdays

9 December to 17 May

Edinburgh, Lanark, Coatbridge, Motherwell, Larkhall, Hamilton, Bathgate, Airdrie and Springburn-Glasgow-Milngavie, Dalmuir, Balloch and Helensburgh

Network Diagram - refer to first Page of Table 220

		SR	XC SX ◇1 A	XC SO ◇1	SR SX	SR SX	SR	SR SX	SR SX	SR SO	SR SO	SR SX	SR B	SR SX ◇ C	SR SX	SR SX	SR	SR SX	SR SO	SR D	SR	SR SX
Edinburgh	d	07 21	07 26	07 26	07 37													07 48	07 48	07 54	07 57	08 08
Haymarket	d	07 25	07 30	07 31	07 42													07 53	07 53	07 59	08 02	08 12
Lanark	d										07 53					08 23						
Carstairs	d							08 06												08 32		
Carluke	d							08 16			08 03					08 33				08 41		
Wishaw	d							08 23			08 08					08 38				08 55		
Holytown	d										08 13											
Shieldmuir	d							08 26								08 42						
Coatbridge Central	d												08 21									
Whifflet 220,224	d												08 23									
Motherwell	a		08 09	08 14				08 29			08 20		08 33			08 46				09 00		
	d		08 10	08 15			08 18	08 30			08 23	08 23				08 46				09 00		
Bellshill	d						08 24														08 49	
Uddingston	d						08 28	08 35														
Airbles	d										08 25	08 25										
Larkhall	d					08 06											08 36					
Merryton	d					08 08											08 38					
Chatelherault	d					08 11											08 41					
Hamilton Central	d					08 15					08 30	08 30					08 45					
Hamilton West	d					08 17					08 33	08 33					08 47					
Blantyre	d					08 21					08 36	08 36					08 51					
Newton	d										08 40	08 40										
Cambuslang	d					08 28	08 33				08 44	08 44										
Rutherglen	d						08 37				08 48	08 48				08 58	09 01					
Dalmarnock	d						08 39				08 50	08 50										
Bridgeton	d						08 41				08 52	08 52										
Edinburgh Park	d	07 32			07 47													08 01	08 02			08 17
Uphall	d	07 40			07 55													08 10	08 10			08 25
Livingston North	d	07 44			07 58													08 13	08 13			08 29
Bathgate	a	07 48			08 03													08 18	08 18			08 33
	d	07 49			08 04													08 20	08 20			08 35
Armadale	d	07 53																08 24	08 24			
Blackridge	d	07 56																08 28	08 28			
Caldercruix	d	08 03																08 34	08 34			
Drumgelloch	d	08 06			08 16													08 38	08 38			08 47
Airdrie	d	08 11			08 20				08 26									08 42	08 42			08 53
Coatdyke	d	08 13			08 22				08 28									08 45	08 45			
Coatbridge Sunnyside	d	08 16			08 24				08 31									08 48	08 48			08 56
Blairhill	d	08 19			08 27				08 34									08 50	08 50			
Easterhouse	d	08 23							08 38									08 54	08 54			
Garrowhill	d	08 25							08 40									08 58	08 58			
Shettleston	d	08 28							08 43									09 00	09 00			
Carntyne	d	08 30							08 45									09 02	09 02			
Springburn	d									08 40					08 49							
Barnhill	d									08 41					08 50							
Alexandra Parade	d									08 44					08 53							
Duke Street	d									08 46					08 55							
Bellgrove	d	08 33							08 48	08 48					08 57			09 06	09 06			
High Street	d	08 35			08 42				08 50	08 50					08 59			09 08	09 08			09 12
Glasgow Queen St 10	a	08 37			08 44				08 52	08 52					09 01			09 10	09 10			09 14
	d	08 40			08 44				08 53	08 53				09c03	09 03			09 11	09 11			09 14
Charing Cross	d	08 42			08 46				08 56	08 56					09 05			09 13	09 13			09 17
Argyle Street	d					08 39	08 45	08 49			08 56	08 56				09 03	09 06					
Glasgow Central 15	a		08b28	08b32		08 40	08 47	08 50			08 59	08 59				09 05	09 08			09b26	09b10	
	d					08 41	08 48	08 50			08 59	08 59				09 05	09 08					
Anderston	d					08a42	08 49	08 52			09 00	09 00				09 06	09 10					
Exhibition Centre	d						08 51	08 54			09 02	09 02				09 08	09 12					
Partick	d	08 49			08 51		08 55	08 57	09 00	09 00	09 06	09 06			09 09	09 12	09 16	09 18	09 18			09 21
Hyndland 3	d	08 51			08 53		08 57	09 00	09 02	09 02	09 08	09 08			09 11	09 15	09 18	09 20	09 20			09 23
Jordanhill	d						08 59	09 02							09 13	09 17						
Scotstounhill	d						09 01	09 05							09 16	09 19						
Garscadden	d						09 04	09a07							09 18	09a21						
Yoker	d						09 06								09 21							
Clydebank	d						09 08								09 23							
Anniesland	d				08 56				09 05	09 05	09 11	09 11					09 21					09 26
Westerton	d				08 59				09 08	09 08	09 14	09 14					09 24					09 29
Bearsden	d				09 02						09 17	09 17										09 32
Hillfoot	d				09 04						09 19	09 19										09 34
Milngavie	a				09 07						09 22	09 22										09 37
Drumchapel	d								09 11	09 11							09 26					
Drumry	d								09 13	09 13							09 28					
Singer	d								09 15	09 15							09 31					
Dalmuir	a	09 00					09 12		09 18	09 18				09 23	09 27		09 33	09 30	09 30			
	d	09 00							09 18	09 18				09 24				09 30	09 30			
Kilpatrick	d								09 21	09 21												
Bowling	d								09 24	09 24												
Dumbarton East	d	09 08							09 28	09 28								09 38	09 38			
Dumbarton Central	d	09 10							09 31	09 31				09 36				09 40	09 40			
Dalreoch	d	09 11							09 32	09 32								09 41	09 41			
Renton	d								09 35	09 35												
Alexandria	d								09 37	09 37												
Balloch	a								09 41	09 41												
Cardross	d	09 16																09 46	09 46			
Craigendoran	d	09 22																09 52	09 52			
Helensburgh Central	a	09 25												09e50				09 55	09 55			

A From Dunbar
B From Cumbernauld
C from 31 March. To Mallaig
D From North Berwick
b Glasgow Central High Level
c Glasgow Queen St High Level
e Helensburgh Upper

Table 226

Mondays to Saturdays

9 December to 17 May

Edinburgh, Lanark, Coatbridge, Motherwell, Larkhall, Hamilton, Bathgate, Airdrie and Springburn-Glasgow-Milngavie, Dalmuir, Balloch and Helensburgh

Network Diagram - refer to first Page of Table 220

		SR SO	SR SO	SR SX	SR SX	SR SO	SR	SR	SR	SR	SR	SR	SR	SR	SR SO	SR SX	SR A	SR	SR	SR	SR	SR	SR
Edinburgh	d									08 21	08 25	08 40								08 48	08 57	09 07	
Haymarket	d									08 25	08 30	08 45								08 52	09 01	09 12	
Lanark	d		08 23												08 53								09 23
Carstairs	d																						
Carluke	d		08 33												09 03								09 33
Wishaw	d		08 38												09 08								09 38
Holytown	d										09 32				09 13								
Shieldmuir	d		08 42																				09 42
Coatbridge Central	d																09 21						
Whifflet 220,224	d																09 23						
Motherwell	a		08 46												09 21		09 32						09 48
	d		08 48	08 48			08 53						09 18		09 23	09 23							09 48
Bellshill	d		08 54	08 54							09 37		09 24								09 47		09 54
Uddingston	d		09 00	09 00							09 41		09 28										09 58
Airbles	d						08 55								09 25	09 25							
Larkhall	d								09 06										09 36				
Merryton	d								09 08										09 38				
Chatelherault	d								09 11										09 41				
Hamilton Central	d						09 00		09 15						09 30	09 30			09 45				
Hamilton West	d						09 03		09 17						09 33	09 33			09 47				
Blantyre	d						09 06		09 21						09 36	09 36			09 51				
Newton	d						09 10								09 40	09 40							
Cambuslang	d		09 05	09 05			09 14						09 33		09 44	09 44							10 03
Rutherglen	d		09 09	09 09			09 18		09 29				09 37		09 48	09 48			09 59				10 08
Dalmarnock	d		09 11	09 11			09 20						09 39		09 50	09 50							10 10
Bridgeton	d		09 13	09 13			09 22						09 41		09 52	09 52							10 12
Edinburgh Park	d									08 31		08 49								08 57		09 17	
Uphall	d									08 39		08 57								09 06		09 25	
Livingston North	d									08 42		09 01								09 09		09 28	
Bathgate	a									08 47		09 05								09 15		09 33	
	d	08 35								08 48		09 06								09 18		09 34	
Armadale	d									08 52										09 22			
Blackridge	d									08 56										09 26			
Caldercruix	d									09 02										09 32			
Drumgelloch	d	08 47								09 06		09 18								09 36		09 46	
Airdrie	d	08 53			08 56					09 11		09 22		09 26						09 41		09 50	
Coatdyke	d				08 58					09 13				09 28						09 43			
Coatbridge Sunnyside	d	08 56			09 01					09 16		09 25		09 31						09 46		09 54	
Blairhill	d				09 04					09 19				09 34						09 49			
Easterhouse	d				09 08					09 23				09 38						09 53			
Garrowhill	d				09 10					09 25				09 40						09 55			
Shettleston	d				09 13					09 28				09 43						09 58			
Carntyne	d				09 15					09 30				09 45						10 00			
Springburn	d					09 09		09 19										09 49					
Barnhill	d					09 10		09 20										09 50					
Alexandra Parade	d					09 13		09 23										09 53					
Duke Street	d					09 17		09 25										09 55					
Bellgrove	d				09 18	09 18		09 27		09 33				09 48				09 57		10 03			
High Street	d	09 12			09 20	09 20		09 29		09 35		09 42		09 50				09 59		10 05		10 12	
Glasgow Queen St 10 ⛴	a	09 14			09 22	09 23		09 31		09 37		09 44		09 52				10 01		10 07		10 14	
	d	09 14			09 24	09 24		09 33		09 41		09 44		09 53				10 03		10 11		10 14	
Charing Cross	d	09 17			09 26	09 26		09 35		09 43		09 46		09 55				10 04		10 13		10 16	
Argyle Street	d		09 17	09 17			09 26		09 34				09 45		09 56	09 56			10 04				10 15
Glasgow Central 15	a		09 18	09 18			09 28		09 35		09b58		09 47		09 58	09 58			10 05		10b10		10 17
	d		09 19	09 19			09 28		09 36				09 48		09 58	09 58			10 06				10 18
Anderston	d		09 20	09 20			09 30		09 38				09 49		10 00	10 00			10 08				10 19
Exhibition Centre	d		09 22	09 22			09 32		09 40				09 51		10 02	10 02			10 10				10 21
Partick ⛴	d	09 21	09 26	09 26	09 30	09 30	09 35	09 39	09 44	09 47		09 50	09 54	09 59	10 05	10 05		10 09	10 14	10 17		10 20	10 24
Hyndland 3	d	09 23	09 28	09 28	09 32	09 32	09 38	09 41	09 46	09 49		09 53	09 56	10 02	10 08	10 08		10 11	10 16	10 19		10 23	10 26
Jordanhill	d		09 30	09 30				09 43					09 58					10 13					10 28
Scotstounhill	d		09 33	09 33				09 46					10 01					10 16					10 31
Garscadden	d		09 35	09 35				09 48					10 03					10 18					10 33
Yoker	d		09 37	09 37				09 51					10 05					10 21					10 36
Clydebank	d		09 39	09 39				09 53					10 08					10 23					10 38
Anniesland	d	09 26			09 36	09 36	09 41		09 50			09 56		10 05	10 11	10 11			10 20			10 26	
Westerton	d	09 29			09 39	09 39	09 44		09 53			09 59		10 08	10 14	10 14			10 23			10 29	
Bearsden	d	09 32					09 46					10 01			10 16	10 16						10 31	
Hillfoot	d	09 34					09 48					10 03			10 18	10 18						10 33	
Milngavie	a	09 37					09 52					10 07			10 22	10 22						10 37	
Drumchapel	d				09 40	09 40			09 55					10 10					10 25				
Drumry	d				09 42	09 42			09 57					10 12					10 27				
Singer	d				09 45	09 45			10 00					10 15					10 30				
Dalmuir	a		09 43	09 43	09 48	09 48		09 57	10 02	10 00			10 13	10 17				10 27	10 32	10 30			10 43
	d				09 49	09 49				10 00				10 18						10 30			
Kilpatrick	d				09 51	09 51								10 21									
Bowling	d				09 54	09 54								10 24									
Dumbarton East	d				09 58	09 58				10 08				10 28						10 38			
Dumbarton Central	d				10 01	10 01				10 10				10 31						10 40			
Dalreoch	d				10 02	10 02				10 11				10 32						10 41			
Renton	d				10 05	10 05								10 35									
Alexandria	d				10 07	10 07								10 37									
Balloch	a				10 11	10 11								10 41									
Cardross	d									10 16										10 46			
Craigendoran	d									10 22										10 52			
Helensburgh Central	a									10 25										10 55			

A From Cumbernauld

b Glasgow Central High Level

Table 226

Mondays to Saturdays

9 December to 17 May

Edinburgh, Lanark, Coatbridge, Motherwell, Larkhall, Hamilton, Bathgate, Airdrie and Springburn-Glasgow-Milngavie, Dalmuir, Balloch and Helensburgh

Network Diagram - refer to first Page of Table 220

		XC	SR	SR	XC	SR	SR	SR	SR	SR	SR	SR	SR	SR	SR	SR	SR	SR	SR	SR	SR	SR	SR
		SO			SX	SO					SO	SX							SX	SO			
		◇1			◇1	◇																	
		A			A	B										C							
Edinburgh	d	09 11			09 11				09 21	09 26	09 37	09 37							09 47	09 48	09 56	10 07	
Haymarket	d	09 17			09 17				09 25	09 30	09 40	09 41							09 53	09 53	10 00	10 11	
Lanark	d														09 53								10 23
Carstairs	d																						
Carluke	d														10 03								10 33
Wishaw	d														10 08								10 38
Holytown	d									10 33					10 13								
Shieldmuir	d																						10 42
Coatbridge Central	d															10 21							
Whifflet 220,224	d															10 23							
Motherwell	a	09 52			10 00										10 20	10 32							10 48
	d	09 53		09 53	10 01								10 18		10 23								10 48
Bellshill	d									10 37			10 24								10 47		10 54
Uddingston	d									10 41			10 28										10 58
Airbles	d			09 55											10 25								
Larkhall	d							10 06										10 36					
Merryton	d							10 08										10 38					
Chatelherault	d							10 11										10 41					
Hamilton Central	d			10 00				10 15							10 30			10 45					
Hamilton West	d			10 03				10 17							10 33			10 47					
Blantyre	d			10 06				10 21							10 36			10 51					
Newton	d			10 10											10 40								
Cambuslang	d			10 14									10 33		10 44								11 03
Rutherglen	d			10 18				10 29					10 37		10 48			10 59					11 08
Dalmarnock	d			10 20									10 39		10 50								11 10
Bridgeton	d			10 22									10 41		10 52								11 12
Edinburgh Park	d								09 34		09 46	09 46							09 58	09 58		10 16	
Uphall	d								09 42		09 54	09 54							10 06	10 06		10 24	
Livingston North	d								09 45		09 57	09 57							10 09	10 09		10 27	
Bathgate	a								09 50		10 03	10 03							10 14	10 14		10 33	
	d								09 50		10 04	10 04							10 18	10 18		10 34	
Armadale	d								09 54										10 22	10 22			
Blackridge	d								09 58										10 26	10 26			
Caldercruix	d								10 04										10 32	10 32			
Drumgelloch	d								10 08		10 16	10 16							10 36	10 36		10 46	
Airdrie	d		09 56						10 11		10 20	10 20		10 26					10 41	10 41		10 50	
Coatdyke	d		09 58						10 13					10 28					10 43	10 43			
Coatbridge Sunnyside	d		10 01						10 16		10 23	10 23		10 31					10 46	10 46		10 53	
Blairhill	d		10 04						10 19					10 34					10 49	10 49			
Easterhouse	d		10 08						10 23					10 38					10 53	10 53			
Garrowhill	d		10 10						10 25					10 40					10 55	10 55			
Shettleston	d		10 13						10 28					10 43					10 58	10 58			
Carntyne	d		10 15						10 30					10 45					11 00	11 00			
Springburn	d						10 19										10 49						
Barnhill	d						10 20										10 50						
Alexandra Parade	d						10 23										10 53						
Duke Street	d						10 25										10 55						
Bellgrove	d		10 18				10 27		10 33					10 48			10 57		11 03	11 03			
High Street	d		10 20				10 29		10 35		10 42	10 42		10 50			10 59		11 05	11 05		11 12	
Glasgow Queen St 10	a		10 22				10 31		10 38		10 43	10 43		10 52			11 01		11 07	11 07		11 14	
	d		10 23			10c37	10 33		10 41		10 44	10 44		10 53			11 03		11 11	11 11		11 14	
Charing Cross	d		10 25				10 34		10 43		10 46	10 46		10 55			11 04		11 13	11 13		11 16	
Argyle Street	d			10 26				10 34					10 45		10 56			11 04					11 15
Glasgow Central 15	a	10b15		10 28	10b27			10 35		10b58			10 47		10 58			11 05			11b10		11 17
	d			10 28				10 36					10 48		10 58			11 06					11 18
Anderston	d			10 30				10 38					10 49		11 00			11 08					11 19
Exhibition Centre	d			10 32				10 40					10 51		11 02			11 10					11 21
Partick	d		10 29	10 35			10 39	10 44	10 47		10 50	10 50	10 54	10 59	11 05		11 09	11 14	11 17	11 17		11 20	11 24
Hyndland 3	d		10 31	10 38			10 41	10 46	10 49		10 53	10 53	10 56	11 01	11 08		11 11	11 16	11 19	11 19		11 23	11 26
Jordanhill	d						10 43						10 58				11 13						11 28
Scotstounhill	d						10 46						11 01				11 16						11 31
Garscadden	d						10 48						11 03				11 18						11 33
Yoker	d						10 51						11 06				11 21						11 36
Clydebank	d						10 53						11 08				11 23						11 38
Anniesland	d		10 35	10 41				10 50			10 56	10 56		11 05	11 11			11 20				11 26	
Westerton	d		10 38	10 44				10 53			10 59	10 59		11 08	11 14			11 23				11 29	
Bearsden	d			10 46							11 01	11 01			11 16							11 31	
Hillfoot	d			10 48							11 03	11 03			11 18							11 33	
Milngavie	a			10 52							11 07	11 07			11 22							11 37	
Drumchapel	d		10 40					10 55						11 10				11 25					
Drumry	d		10 42					10 57						11 12				11 27					
Singer	d		10 45					11 00						11 15				11 30					
Dalmuir	a		10 47			10 52	10 57	11 02	11 00				11 13	11 17			11 27	11 32	11 30	11 30			11 43
	d		10 48			10 52			11 00					11 18					11 30	11 30			
Kilpatrick	d		10 51											11 21									
Bowling	d		10 54											11 24									
Dumbarton East	d		10 58						11 08					11 28					11 38	11 38			
Dumbarton Central	d		11 01			11 05			11 10					11 31					11 40	11 40			
Dalreoch	d		11 02						11 11					11 32					11 41	11 41			
Renton	d		11 05											11 35									
Alexandria	d		11 07											11 37									
Balloch	a		11 11											11 41									
Cardross	d								11 16										11 46	11 46			
Craigendoran	d								11 22										11 52	11 52			
Helensburgh Central	a					11e19			11 25										11 55	11 55			

A From Newcastle
B from 29 March. To Oban
C From Cumbernauld
b Glasgow Central High Level
c Glasgow Queen St High Level
e Helensburgh Upper

Table 226

Mondays to Saturdays

9 December to 17 May

Edinburgh, Lanark, Coatbridge, Motherwell, Larkhall, Hamilton, Bathgate, Airdrie and Springburn-Glasgow-Milngavie, Dalmuir, Balloch and Helensburgh

Network Diagram - refer to first Page of Table 220

		SR	SR	SR	SR	SR SO	SR SX	SR SX	SR SO	SR		SR	SR	SR	SR	SR	SR	SR	SR	SR		SR	SR	SR
																A							◇ B 🚌	
Edinburgh	d					10 16	10 20	10 21	10 21	10 26		10 37							10 48	10 56		11 07		
Haymarket	d					10 20	10 24	10 26	10 27	10 30		10 41							10 53	11 00		11 11		
Lanark	d														10 53									11 23
Carstairs	d					11 09	11 09																	
Carluke	d					11 19	11 19								11 03									11 33
Wishaw	d					11 26	11 26								11 08									11 38
Holytown	d									11 32					11 13									
Shieldmuir	d																							11 42
Coatbridge Central	d															11 21								
Whifflet 220,224	d															11 23								
Motherwell	a					11 32	11 32								11 20	11 33								11 48
	d		10 53			11 34	11 34						11 18		11 23									11 48
Bellshill	d									11 37			11 24							11 47				11 54
Uddingston	d									11 41			11 28											11 58
Airbles	d		10 55												11 25									
Larkhall	d				11 06													11 36						
Merryton	d				11 08													11 38						
Chatelherault	d				11 11													11 41						
Hamilton Central	d		11 00		11 15										11 30			11 45						
Hamilton West	d		11 03		11 17										11 33			11 47						
Blantyre	d		11 06		11 21										11 36			11 51						
Newton	d		11 10												11 40									
Cambuslang	d		11 14										11 33		11 44									12 03
Rutherglen	d		11 18		11 29								11 37		11 48			11 59						12 07
Dalmarnock	d		11 20										11 39		11 50									12 09
Bridgeton	d		11 22										11 42		11 52									12 11
Edinburgh Park	d							10 31	10 31			10 46							10 58			11 16		
Uphall	d							10 39	10 39			10 54							11 06			11 24		
Livingston North	d							10 42	10 42			10 57							11 09			11 27		
Bathgate	a							10 46	10 46			11 03							11 14			11 33		
	d							10 48	10 48			11 04							11 18			11 34		
Armadale	d							10 52	10 52										11 22					
Blackridge	d							10 56	10 56										11 26					
Caldercruix	d							11 02	11 02										11 32					
Drumgelloch	d							11 06	11 06			11 16							11 36			11 46		
Airdrie	d	10 56						11 11	11 11			11 20		11 26					11 41			11 50		
Coatdyke	d	10 58						11 13	11 13					11 28					11 43					
Coatbridge Sunnyside	d	11 01						11 16	11 16			11 23		11 31					11 46			11 53		
Blairhill	d	11 04						11 19	11 19					11 34					11 49					
Easterhouse	d	11 08						11 23	11 23					11 38					11 53					
Garrowhill	d	11 10						11 25	11 25					11 40					11 55					
Shettleston	d	11 13						11 28	11 28					11 43					11 58					
Carntyne	d	11 15						11 30	11 30					11 45					12 00					
Springburn	d			11 19													11 49							
Barnhill	d			11 20													11 50							
Alexandra Parade	d			11 23													11 53							
Duke Street	d			11 25													11 55							
Bellgrove	d	11 18		11 27				11 33	11 33					11 48			11 57		12 03					
High Street	d	11 20		11 29				11 35	11 35			11 42		11 50			11 59		12 05			12 12		
Glasgow Queen St 10 🚢	a	11 22		11 31				11 37	11 37			11 43		11 52			12 01		12 07			12 13		
	d	11 23		11 33				11 41	11 41			11 44		11 53			12 03		12 11			12 14	12c21	
Charing Cross	d	11 25		11 34				11 43	11 43			11 46		11 55			12 04		12 13			12 16		
Argyle Street	d		11 26		11 34								11 46		11 56			12 04						12 15
Glasgow Central 15	a		11 28		11 35	11b55	11b55			11b58			11 48		11 58			12 05		12b10				12 17
	d		11 28		11 36								11 49		11 58			12 06						12 18
Anderston	d		11 30		11 38								11 50		12 00			12 08						12 19
Exhibition Centre	d		11 32		11 40								11 52		12 02			12 10						12 21
Partick 🚢	d	11 29	11 35	11 39	11 44			11 47	11 47			11 50	11 55	11 59	12 05		12 09	12 14	12 17			12 20		12 24
Hyndland 3	d	11 31	11 38	11 41	11 46			11 49	11 49			11 53	11 57	12 01	12 08		12 11	12 16	12 19			12 23		12 26
Jordanhill	d			11 43									11 59				12 13							12 28
Scotstounhill	d			11 46									12 02				12 16							12 31
Garscadden	d			11 48									12 04				12 18							12 33
Yoker	d			11 51									12 07				12 21							12 36
Clydebank	d			11 53									12 09				12 23							12 38
Anniesland	d	11 35	11 41		11 50							11 56		12 05	12 11			12 20				12 26		
Westerton	d	11 38	11 44		11 53							11 59		12 08	12 14			12 23				12 29		
Bearsden	d		11 46									12 01			12 16							12 31		
Hillfoot	d		11 48									12 03			12 18							12 33		
Milngavie	a		11 52									12 07			12 22							12 37		
Drumchapel	d	11 40			11 55									12 10				12 25						
Drumry	d	11 42			11 57									12 12				12 27						
Singer	d	11 45			12 00									12 15				12 30						
Dalmuir	a	11 47		11 57	12 02			12 00	12 00				12 14	12 17			12 27	12 32	12 30				12 38	12 43
	d	11 48						12 00	12 00					12 18					12 30				12 42	
Kilpatrick	d	11 51												12 21										
Bowling	d	11 54												12 24										
Dumbarton East	d	11 58						12 08	12 08					12 28					12 38					
Dumbarton Central	d	12 01						12 10	12 10					12 31					12 40				12 48	
Dalreoch	d	12 02						12 11	12 11					12 32					12 41					
Renton	d	12 05												12 35										
Alexandria	d	12 07												12 37										
Balloch	a	12 12												12 41										
Cardross	d							12 16	12 16										12 46					
Craigendoran	d							12 22	12 22										12 52					
Helensburgh Central	a							12 25	12 25										12 55				13e03	

A From Cumbernauld
B To Oban
b Glasgow Central High Level
c Glasgow Queen St High Level
e Helensburgh Upper

Table 226

Mondays to Saturdays

9 December to 17 May

Edinburgh, Lanark, Coatbridge, Motherwell, Larkhall, Hamilton, Bathgate, Airdrie and Springburn-Glasgow-Milngavie, Dalmuir, Balloch and Helensburgh

Network Diagram - refer to first Page of Table 220

		XC	SR	SR	SR	SR	SR	SR	SR	SR	SR	SR	SR	SR	SR	SR	SR	SR	SR	SR	SR	SR	SR
		◇1 A											B										
Edinburgh	d	11 11					11 21	11 26	11 37							11 48	11 51	11 56	12 07				
Haymarket	d	11 16					11 25	11 30	11 41							11 53	11 58	12 00	12 11				
Lanark	d											11 53								12 23			
Carstairs	d																12 33						
Carluke	d											12 03					12 43			12 33			
Wishaw	d											12 08					12 48			12 38			
Holytown	d							12 32				12 13											
Shieldmuir	d																			12 42			
Coatbridge Central	d												12 21										
Whifflet 220,224	d												12 23										
Motherwell	a	11 52										12 20	12 32				12 54			12 48			
	d	11 53		11 53						12 18		12 23					12 54			12 48		12 53	
Bellshill	d							12 37		12 24								12 49		12 54			
Uddingston	d							12 41		12 28										12 58			
Airbles	d			11 55								12 25										12 55	
Larkhall	d					12 06									12 36								
Merryton	d					12 08									12 38								
Chatelherault	d					12 11									12 41								
Hamilton Central	d			12 00		12 15						12 30			12 45							13 00	
Hamilton West	d			12 03		12 17						12 33			12 47							13 03	
Blantyre	d			12 06		12 21						12 36			12 51							13 06	
Newton	d			12 10								12 40										13 10	
Cambuslang	d			12 14						12 33		12 44								13 03		13 14	
Rutherglen	d			12 18		12 29				12 37		12 48			12 59					13 07		13 18	
Dalmarnock	d			12 20						12 39		12 50								13 09		13 20	
Bridgeton	d			12 22						12 41		12 52								13 11		13 22	
Edinburgh Park	d						11 31		11 46							11 58			12 16				
Uphall	d						11 39		11 54							12 06			12 24				
Livingston North	d						11 42		11 57							12 09			12 27				
Bathgate	a						11 46		12 03							12 14			12 33				
	d						11 48		12 04							12 18			12 34				
Armadale	d						11 52									12 22							
Blackridge	d						11 56									12 26							
Caldercruix	d						12 02									12 32							
Drumgelloch	d						12 06		12 16							12 36			12 46				
Airdrie	d		11 56				12 11		12 20		12 26					12 41			12 50		12 56		
Coatdyke	d		11 58				12 13				12 28					12 43					12 58		
Coatbridge Sunnyside	d		12 01				12 16		12 23		12 31					12 46			12 53		13 01		
Blairhill	d		12 04				12 19				12 34					12 49					13 04		
Easterhouse	d		12 08				12 23				12 38					12 53					13 08		
Garrowhill	d		12 10				12 25				12 40					12 55					13 10		
Shettleston	d		12 13				12 28				12 43					12 58					13 13		
Carntyne	d		12 15				12 30				12 45					13 00					13 15		
Springburn	d				12 19									12 49									13 19
Barnhill	d				12 20									12 50									13 20
Alexandra Parade	d				12 23									12 53									13 23
Duke Street	d				12 25									12 55									13 25
Bellgrove	d		12 18		12 27		12 33				12 48			12 57		13 03					13 18		13 27
High Street	d		12 20		12 29		12 35		12 42		12 50			12 59		13 05			13 12		13 20		13 29
Glasgow Queen St 10	a		12 22		12 31		12 38		12 43		12 52			13 01		13 08			13 13		13 22		13 31
	d		12 23		12 33		12 41		12 44		12 53			13 03		13 11			13 14		13 23		13 33
Charing Cross	d		12 25		12 34		12 43		12 46		12 55			13 04		13 13			13 16		13 25		13 34
Argyle Street	d			12 26		12 34				12 45		12 56			13 04					13 15		13 26	
Glasgow Central 15	a	12b11		12 28		12 35		12b58		12 47		12 58			13 06		13b27	13b10		13 17		13 28	
	d			12 28		12 36				12 48		12 58			13 06					13 18		13 28	
Anderston	d			12 30		12 38				12 49		13 00			13 08					13 19		13 30	
Exhibition Centre	d			12 32		12 40				12 51		13 02			13 10					13 21		13 32	
Partick	d		12 29	12 35	12 39	12 44	12 47		12 50	12 54	12 59	13 05		13 09	13 14	13 17			13 20	13 24	13 29	13 35	13 39
Hyndland 3	d		12 31	12 38	12 41	12 46	12 49		12 53	12 56	13 01	13 08		13 11	13 16	13 19			13 23	13 26	13 31	13 38	13 41
Jordanhill	d				12 43					12 58				13 13						13 28			13 43
Scotstounhill	d				12 46					13 01				13 16						13 31			13 46
Garscadden	d				12 48					13 03				13 18						13 33			13 48
Yoker	d				12 51					13 06				13 21						13 36			13 50
Clydebank	d				12 53					13 08				13 23						13 38			13 52
Anniesland	d		12 35	12 41		12 50			12 56		13 05	13 11			13 20				13 26		13 35	13 41	
Westerton	d		12 38	12 44		12 53			12 59		13 08	13 14			13 23				13 29		13 38	13 44	
Bearsden	d			12 46					13 01			13 16							13 31			13 46	
Hillfoot	d			12 48					13 03			13 18							13 33			13 48	
Milngavie	a			12 52					13 07			13 22							13 37			13 52	
Drumchapel	d		12 40			12 55					13 10				13 25						13 40		
Drumry	d		12 42			12 57					13 12				13 27						13 42		
Singer	d		12 45			13 00					13 15				13 30						13 45		
Dalmuir	a		12 47		12 57	13 02	13 00			13 13	13 17			13 27	13 32	13 30				13 43	13 47		13 56
	d		12 48				13 00				13 18					13 30					13 48		
Kilpatrick	d		12 51								13 21										13 51		
Bowling	d		12 54								13 24										13 54		
Dumbarton East	d		12 58				13 08				13 28					13 38					13 58		
Dumbarton Central	d		13 01				13 10				13 31					13 40					14 01		
Dalreoch	d		13 02				13 11				13 32					13 41					14 02		
Renton	d		13 05								13 35										14 05		
Alexandria	d		13 07								13 37										14 07		
Balloch	a		13 11								13 41										14 11		
Cardross	d						13 16									13 46							
Craigendoran	d						13 22									13 52							
Helensburgh Central	a						13 25									13 55							

A From Birmingham New Street

B From Cumbernauld

b Glasgow Central High Level

Table 226

Mondays to Saturdays

9 December to 17 May

Edinburgh, Lanark, Coatbridge, Motherwell, Larkhall, Hamilton, Bathgate, Airdrie and Springburn-Glasgow-Milngavie, Dalmuir, Balloch and Helensburgh

Network Diagram - refer to first Page of Table 220

		SR	SR	SR	SR	SR	SR	SR	SR	SR	SR	SR	SR	SR	SR	XC	XC	SR	SR	SR	SR	SR
																SO ◇1	SX ◇1					
									A							B	C					
Edinburgh	d		12 21	12 26	12 37							12 48	12 56	13 07		13 12	13 13					13 21
Haymarket	d		12 25	12 30	12 41							12 53	13 00	13 11		13 16	13 18					13 25
Lanark	d							12 53							13 23							
Carstairs	d																					
Carluke	d							13 03							13 33							
Wishaw	d							13 08							13 38							
Holytown	d			13 32				13 13														
Shieldmuir	d														13 42							
Coatbridge Central	d								13 21													
Whifflet 220,224	d								13 23													
Motherwell	a							13 21	13 32						13 48	13 52	13 52					
	d					13 18		13 23							13 48	13 53	13 53		13 53			
Bellshill	d			13 37		13 24							13 48		13 54							
Uddingston	d			13 41		13 28									13 58							
Airbles	d							13 25											13 55			
Larkhall	d	13 06									13 36										14 06	
Merryton	d	13 08									13 38										14 08	
Chatelherault	d	13 11									13 41										14 11	
Hamilton Central	d	13 15						13 30			13 45								14 00		14 15	
Hamilton West	d	13 17						13 33			13 47								14 03		14 17	
Blantyre	d	13 21						13 36			13 51								14 06		14 21	
Newton	d							13 40											14 10			
Cambuslang	d					13 33		13 44							14 03				14 14			
Rutherglen	d	13 29				13 37		13 48			13 59				14 07				14 18		14 29	
Dalmarnock	d					13 39		13 50							14 09				14 20			
Bridgeton	d					13 41		13 52							14 11				14 22			
Edinburgh Park	d		12 31		12 46							12 58		13 16								13 31
Uphall	d		12 39		12 54							13 06		13 24								13 39
Livingston North	d		12 42		12 57							13 09		13 27								13 42
Bathgate	a		12 46		13 03							13 14		13 33								13 46
	d		12 48		13 04							13 18		13 34								13 48
Armadale	d		12 52									13 22										13 52
Blackridge	d		12 56									13 26										13 56
Caldercruix	d		13 02									13 32										14 02
Drumgelloch	d		13 06		13 16							13 36		13 46								14 06
Airdrie	d		13 11		13 20		13 26					13 41		13 50				13 56				14 11
Coatdyke	d		13 13				13 28					13 43						13 58				14 13
Coatbridge Sunnyside	d		13 16		13 23		13 31					13 46		13 53				14 01				14 16
Blairhill	d		13 19				13 34					13 49						14 04				14 19
Easterhouse	d		13 23				13 38					13 53						14 08				14 23
Garrowhill	d		13 25				13 40					13 55						14 10				14 25
Shettleston	d		13 28				13 43					13 58						14 13				14 28
Carntyne	d		13 30				13 45					14 00						14 15				14 30
Springburn	d									13 49										14 19		
Barnhill	d									13 50										14 20		
Alexandra Parade	d									13 53										14 23		
Duke Street	d									13 55										14 25		
Bellgrove	d		13 33				13 48			13 57		14 03						14 18		14 27		14 33
High Street	d		13 35		13 42		13 50			13 59		14 05		14 12				14 20		14 29		14 35
Glasgow Queen St 10 ⛴	a		13 37		13 43		13 52			14 01		14 07		14 13				14 22		14 31		14 37
	d		13 41		13 44		13 53			14 03		14 11		14 14				14 23		14 33		14 41
Charing Cross	d		13 43		13 46		13 55			14 04		14 13		14 16				14 25		14 34		14 43
Argyle Street	d	13 34				13 45		13 56			14 04				14 15				14 26		14 34	
Glasgow Central 15	a	13 35		13b58		13 47		13 58			14 05		14b10		14 17	14b12	14b12		14 28		14 35	
	d	13 36				13 48		13 58			14 06				14 18				14 28		14 36	
Anderston	d	13 38				13 49		14 00			14 08				14 19				14 30		14 38	
Exhibition Centre	d	13 40				13 51		14 02			14 10				14 21				14 32		14 40	
Partick ⛴	d	13 44	13 47		13 50	13 54	13 59	14 05		14 09	14 14	14 17		14 20	14 24			14 29	14 35	14 39	14 44	14 47
Hyndland 3	d	13 46	13 49		13 53	13 56	14 01	14 08		14 11	14 16	14 19		14 23	14 26			14 31	14 38	14 41	14 46	14 49
Jordanhill	d					13 58				14 13					14 28					14 43		
Scotstounhill	d					14 01				14 16					14 31					14 46		
Garscadden	d					14 03				14 18					14 33					14 48		
Yoker	d					14 06				14 21					14 36					14 51		
Clydebank	d					14 08				14 23					14 38					14 53		
Anniesland	d	13 50			13 56		14 05	14 11			14 20			14 26				14 35	14 41		14 50	
Westerton	d	13 53			13 59		14 08	14 14			14 23			14 29				14 38	14 44		14 53	
Bearsden	d				14 01			14 16						14 31					14 46			
Hillfoot	d				14 03			14 18						14 33					14 48			
Milngavie	a				14 07			14 22						14 37					14 52			
Drumchapel	d	13 55					14 10				14 25							14 40			14 55	
Drumry	d	13 57					14 12				14 27							14 42			14 57	
Singer	d	14 00					14 15				14 30							14 45			15 00	
Dalmuir	a	14 02	14 00			14 13	14 17			14 27	14 32	14 30			14 43			14 47		14 57	15 02	15 00
	d		14 00				14 18					14 30						14 48				15 00
Kilpatrick	d						14 21											14 51				
Bowling	d						14 24											14 54				
Dumbarton East	d		14 08				14 28					14 38						14 58				15 08
Dumbarton Central	d		14 10				14 31					14 40						15 01				15 10
Dalreoch	d		14 11				14 32					14 41						15 02				15 11
Renton	d						14 35											15 05				
Alexandria	d						14 37											15 07				
Balloch	a						14 41											15 11				
Cardross	d		14 16									14 46										15 16
Craigendoran	d		14 22									14 52										15 22
Helensburgh Central	a		14 25									14 55										15 26

A From Cumbernauld
B From Bristol Temple Meads
C From Bath Spa
b Glasgow Central High Level

Table 226

Mondays to Saturdays

9 December to 17 May

Edinburgh, Lanark, Coatbridge, Motherwell, Larkhall, Hamilton, Bathgate, Airdrie and Springburn-Glasgow-Milngavie, Dalmuir, Balloch and Helensburgh

Network Diagram - refer to first Page of Table 220

Station		SR	SR	SR	SR	SR	SR	SR	SR		SR	SR	SR	SR	SR	SR	SR	SR	SR		SR	SR	SR	SR	SR
											SO	SX			SX	SO								SX	SO
							A																		
Edinburgh	d	13 26	13 37								13 48	13 48	13 51	13 56	14 07	14 09							14 21	14 26	14 26
Haymarket	d	13 30	13 41								13 53	13 53	13 56	14 00	14 13	14 13							14 25	14 29	14 31
Lanark	d					13 53											14 23								
Carstairs	d												14 34												
Carluke	d					14 03							14 42				14 33								
Wishaw	d					14 08							14 47				14 38								
Holytown	d	14 32				14 13																		15 32	15 32
Shieldmuir	d																14 42								
Coatbridge Central	d						14 21																		
Whifflet 220,224	d						14 23																		
Motherwell	a					14 20	14 32						14 53				14 48								
	d			14 18		14 23							14 53				14 48		14 53						
Bellshill	d	14 37		14 24										14 47			14 54							15 37	15 37
Uddingston	d	14 41		14 28													15 01							15 41	15 41
Airbles	d					14 25													14 55						
Larkhall	d								14 36													15 06			
Merryton	d								14 38													15 08			
Chatelherault	d								14 41													15 11			
Hamilton Central	d					14 30			14 45										15 00			15 15			
Hamilton West	d					14 33			14 47										15 03			15 17			
Blantyre	d					14 36			14 51										15 06			15 21			
Newton	d					14 40													15 10						
Cambuslang	d			14 33		14 44											15 03		15 14						
Rutherglen	d			14 37		14 48			14 59								15 07		15 18			15 29			
Dalmarnock	d			14 39		14 50											15 09		15 20						
Bridgeton	d			14 41		14 52											15 11		15 22						
Edinburgh Park	d		13 46								13 58	13 58			14 18	14 18							14 31		
Uphall	d		13 54								14 06	14 06			14 26	14 26							14 39		
Livingston North	d		13 57								14 09	14 09			14 29	14 29							14 42		
Bathgate	a		14 03								14 14	14 14			14 33	14 33							14 46		
	d		14 04								14 18	14 18			14 34	14 34							14 48		
Armadale	d										14 22	14 22											14 52		
Blackridge	d										14 26	14 26											14 56		
Caldercruix	d										14 32	14 32											15 02		
Drumgelloch	d		14 16								14 36	14 36			14 46	14 46							15 06		
Airdrie	d		14 20		14 26						14 41	14 41			14 50	14 50		14 56					15 11		
Coatdyke	d				14 28						14 43	14 43						14 58					15 13		
Coatbridge Sunnyside	d		14 23		14 31						14 46	14 46			14 53	14 53		15 01					15 16		
Blairhill	d				14 34						14 49	14 49						15 04					15 19		
Easterhouse	d				14 38						14 53	14 53						15 08					15 23		
Garrowhill	d				14 40						14 55	14 55						15 10					15 25		
Shettleston	d				14 43						14 58	14 58						15 13					15 28		
Carntyne	d				14 45						15 00	15 00						15 15					15 30		
Springburn	d							14 49													15 19				
Barnhill	d							14 50													15 20				
Alexandra Parade	d							14 53													15 23				
Duke Street	d							14 55													15 25				
Bellgrove	d				14 48			14 57			15 03	15 03						15 18			15 27		15 33		
High Street	d		14 42		14 50			14 59			15 05	15 05			15 12	15 12		15 20			15 29		15 35		
Glasgow Queen St 10	a		14 43		14 52			15 02			15 07	15 07			15 13	15 13		15 22			15 32		15 37		
	d		14 44		14 53			15 03			15 11	15 11			15 14	15 14		15 23			15 33		15 41		
Charing Cross	d		14 46		14 55			15 04			15 13	15 13			15 16	15 16		15 25			15 34		15 43		
Argyle Street	d			14 45		14 56			15 04								15 15		15 26			15 34			
Glasgow Central 15	a	14b58		14 47		14 58			15 06				15b14	15b10			15 18		15 28			15 35		15b58	15b58
	d			14 48		14 58			15 06								15 18		15 28			15 36			
Anderston	d			14 49		15 00			15 09								15 19		15 30			15 38			
Exhibition Centre	d			14 51		15 02			15 10								15 21		15 32			15 40			
Partick	d		14 50	14 54	14 59	15 05		15 09	15 14		15 17	15 17			15 20	15 20	15 24	15 29	15 35		15 39	15 44	15 47		
Hyndland 3	d		14 53	14 56	15 01	15 08		15 11	15 16		15 19	15 19			15 23	15 23	15 26	15 31	15 38		15 41	15 46	15 49		
Jordanhill	d			14 58				15 13									15 28				15 43				
Scotstounhill	d			15 01				15 16									15 31				15 46				
Garscadden	d			15 03				15 18									15 33				15 48				
Yoker	d			15 06				15 21									15 36				15 51				
Clydebank	d			15 08				15 23									15 38				15 53				
Anniesland	d		14 56		15 05	15 11			15 20						15 26	15 26		15 35	15 41			15 50			
Westerton	d		14 59		15 08	15 14			15 23						15 29	15 29		15 38	15 44			15 53			
Bearsden	d		15 01			15 16									15 31	15 31			15 46						
Hillfoot	d		15 03			15 18									15 33	15 33			15 48						
Milngavie	a		15 07			15 24									15 37	15 37			15 52						
Drumchapel	d				15 10				15 25									15 40				15 55			
Drumry	d				15 12				15 27									15 42				15 57			
Singer	d				15 15				15 30									15 45				16 00			
Dalmuir	a			15 13	15 17			15 27	15 32		15 30	15 30					15 43	15 47			15 57	16 02	16 00		
	d				15 18						15 30	15 30						15 48					16 00		
Kilpatrick	d				15 21													15 51							
Bowling	d				15 24													15 54							
Dumbarton East	d				15 28						15 38	15 38						15 58					16 08		
Dumbarton Central	d				15 31						15 40	15 40						16 01					16 10		
Dalreoch	d				15 32						15 41	15 45						16 02					16 11		
Renton	d				15 35													16 05							
Alexandria	d				15 37													16 07							
Balloch	a				15 41													16 11							
Cardross	d										15 46	15 50											16 16		
Craigendoran	d										15 52	15 55											16 22		
Helensburgh Central	a										15 55	15 58											16 25		

A From Cumbernauld

b Glasgow Central High Level

Table 226

Mondays to Saturdays

9 December to 17 May

Edinburgh, Lanark, Coatbridge, Motherwell, Larkhall, Hamilton, Bathgate, Airdrie and Springburn-Glasgow-Milngavie, Dalmuir, Balloch and Helensburgh

Network Diagram - refer to first Page of Table 220

		SR	SR	SR	SR	SR A	SR	SR	SR	SR SX	SR SO	SR	SR	XC ◇1 B	SR	SR	SR	SR	SR	SR	SR	SR	SR
Edinburgh	d	14 37							14 48	14 56	14 56	15 07		15 11					15 21	15 26	15 37		
Haymarket	d	14 41							14 53	15 00	15 01	15 11		15 16					15 25	15 30	15 41		
Lanark	d				14 53								15 23										
Carstairs	d																						
Carluke	d				15 03								15 33										
Wishaw	d				15 08								15 38										
Holytown	d				15 13															16 32			
Shieldmuir	d												15 44										
Coatbridge Central	d					15 21																	
Whifflet 220,224	d					15 23																	
Motherwell	a				15 21	15 32							15 48	15 52									
	d		15 18		15 23								15 48	15 53		15 53						16 18	
Bellshill	d		15 24							15 47	15 47		15 54							16 37		16 24	
Uddingston	d		15 28										16 01							16 43		16 28	
Airbles	d				15 25											15 55							
Larkhall	d							15 36										16 06					
Merryton	d							15 38										16 08					
Chatelherault	d							15 41										16 11					
Hamilton Central	d				15 30			15 45								16 00		16 15					
Hamilton West	d				15 33			15 47								16 03		16 17					
Blantyre	d				15 36			15 51								16 06		16 21					
Newton	d				15 40											16 10							
Cambuslang	d		15 33		15 44								16 06			16 14						16 33	
Rutherglen	d		15 37		15 48			15 59					16 10			16 18		16 29				16 37	
Dalmarnock	d		15 39		15 50								16 12			16 20						16 39	
Bridgeton	d		15 41		15 52								16 14			16 22						16 41	
Edinburgh Park	d	14 46							14 58			15 16							15 31		15 46		
Uphall	d	14 54							15 06			15 24							15 39		15 54		
Livingston North	d	14 57							15 09			15 27							15 42		15 57		
Bathgate	a	15 03							15 14			15 33							15 46		16 03		
	d	15 04							15 18			15 34							15 48		16 04		
Armadale	d								15 22										15 52				
Blackridge	d								15 26										15 56				
Caldercruix	d								15 32										16 02				
Drumgelloch	d	15 16							15 36			15 46							16 06		16 16		
Airdrie	d	15 20		15 26					15 41			15 50			15 56				16 11		16 21		16 26
Coatdyke	d			15 28					15 43						15 58				16 13				16 28
Coatbridge Sunnyside	d	15 23		15 31					15 46			15 53			16 01				16 16		16 24		16 31
Blairhill	d			15 34					15 49						16 04				16 19				16 34
Easterhouse	d			15 38					15 53						16 08				16 23				16 38
Garrowhill	d			15 40					15 55						16 10				16 25				16 40
Shettleston	d			15 43					15 58						16 13				16 28				16 43
Carntyne	d			15 45					16 00						16 15				16 30				16 45
Springburn	d						15 49										16 19						
Barnhill	d						15 50										16 20						
Alexandra Parade	d						15 53										16 23						
Duke Street	d						15 55										16 25						
Bellgrove	d			15 48			15 57		16 03						16 18		16 27		16 33				16 48
High Street	d	15 42		15 50			15 59		16 05			16 12			16 20		16 29		16 35		16 42		16 50
Glasgow Queen St 10	a	15 43		15 52			16 01		16 07			16 13			16 22		16 31		16 37		16 44		16 52
	d	15 44		15 53			16 03		16 11			16 14			16 23		16 33		16 41		16 44		16 53
Charing Cross	d	15 46		15 55			16 05		16 13			16 16			16 25		16 35		16 43		16 46		16 55
Argyle Street	d		15 45		15 56			16 04					16 17			16 26		16 34				16 45	
Glasgow Central 15	a		15 47		15 58			16 05		16b10	16b10		16 19	16b12		16 28		16 35		16b58		16 46	
	d		15 48		15 58			16 06					16 19			16 28		16 36				16 48	
Anderston	d		15 49		16 00			16 08					16 20			16 30		16 38				16 49	
Exhibition Centre	d		15 51		16 02			16 10					16 22			16 32		16 40				16 51	
Partick	d	15 50	15 54	16 00	16 05		16 09	16 14	16 17			16 20	16 26		16 30	16 35	16 39	16 44	16 48		16 50	16 55	17 00
Hyndland 3	d	15 53	15 56	16 02	16 08		16 11	16 16	16 20			16 23	16 28		16 32	16 38	16 41	16 46	16 50		16 53	16 58	17 02
Jordanhill	d		15 58				16 13						16 30				16 43					17 00	
Scotstounhill	d		16 01				16 16						16 32				16 46					17 02	
Garscadden	d		16 03				16 18						16 35				16 48					17 05	
Yoker	d		16 06				16 21						16 37				16 51					17 07	
Clydebank	d		16 08				16 23						16 39				16 53					17 09	
Anniesland	d	15 56		16 05	16 11			16 20				16 26			16 35	16 41		16 50			16 56		17 05
Westerton	d	15 59		16 08	16 14			16 23				16 29			16 38	16 44		16 53			16 59		17 08
Bearsden	d	16 01			16 16							16 31				16 46					17 01		
Hillfoot	d	16 03			16 18							16 33				16 48					17 03		
Milngavie	a	16 07			16 22							16 37				16 52					17 07		
Drumchapel	d			16 10				16 25							16 40			16 55					17 10
Drumry	d			16 12				16 27							16 42			16 57					17 12
Singer	d			16 15				16 30							16 45			17 00					17 15
Dalmuir	a		16 13	16 17			16 27	16 32	16 30				16 43		16 47		16 57	17 02	17 00			17 13	17 17
	d			16 18					16 30						16 48				17 00				17 18
Kilpatrick	d			16 21											16 51								17 21
Bowling	d			16 24											16 54								17 24
Dumbarton East	d			16 28					16 38						16 58				17 08				17 28
Dumbarton Central	d			16 31					16 40						17 01				17 10				17 31
Dalreoch	d			16 32					16 41						17 02				17 11				17 32
Renton	d			16 35											17 05								17 35
Alexandria	d			16 37											17 07								17 37
Balloch	a			16 41											17 11								17 41
Cardross	d								16 46										17 16				
Craigendoran	d								16 52										17 22				
Helensburgh Central	a								16 55										17 25				

A From Cumbernauld

B From Plymouth

b Glasgow Central High Level

Table 226

Mondays to Saturdays

9 December to 17 May

Edinburgh, Lanark, Coatbridge, Motherwell, Larkhall, Hamilton, Bathgate, Airdrie and Springburn-Glasgow-Milngavie, Dalmuir, Balloch and Helensburgh

Network Diagram - refer to first Page of Table 220

		SR	SR A	SR	SR	SR SX	SR SO	SR	SR SX	SR SO	SR	SR SX	SR	SR SO	SR SX	SR	SR SX	SR	SR	SR	SR	SR
Edinburgh	d					15 48	15 48	15 51	15 56	15 56	16 08									16 22	16 26	16 37
Haymarket	d					15 53	15 53	15 56	16 00	16 00	16 12									16 26	16 30	16 42
Lanark	d	15 53											16 23									
Carstairs	d					16 29	16 29															
Carluke	d	16 03				16 39	16 39						16 33									
Wishaw	d	16 08				16 48	16 48						16 38									
Holytown	d	16 13																			17 32	
Shieldmuir	d												16 44									
Coatbridge Central	d		16 21																			
Whifflet 220,224	d		16 23																			
Motherwell	a	16 20	16 32			16 55	16 55						16 48									
	d	16 23				16 56	16 56						16 48			16 53						
Bellshill	d								16 43	16 43			16 54								17 36	
Uddingston	d												16 58								17 40	
Airbles	d	16 25														16 55						
Larkhall	d				16 37														17 06			
Merryton	d				16 39														17 08			
Chatelherault	d				16 42														17 11			
Hamilton Central	d	16 30			16 46											17 00			17 15			
Hamilton West	d	16 33			16 49											17 03			17 17			
Blantyre	d	16 36			16 53											17 06			17 21			
Newton	d	16 40														17 10						
Cambuslang	d	16 44											17 03			17 14					17 47	
Rutherglen	d	16 48			17 02								17 07			17 18			17 29			
Dalmarnock	d	16 50											17 09			17 20						
Bridgeton	d	16 52											17 11			17 22						
Edinburgh Park	d							16 01			16 18									16 31		16 50
Uphall	d							16 09			16 26									16 39		16 58
Livingston North	d							16 12			16 29									16 42		17 02
Bathgate	a							16 17			16 34									16 47		17 06
	d							16 18			16 34									16 48		17 07
Armadale	d							16 22												16 52		
Blackridge	d							16 26												16 56		
Caldercruix	d							16 32												17 02		
Drumgelloch	d							16 36			16 47									17 06		17 19
Airdrie	d							16 41			16 50			16 56	16 56					17 11		17 23
Coatdyke	d							16 43						16 58	16 58					17 13		
Coatbridge Sunnyside	d							16 46			16 54			17 01	17 01					17 16		17 26
Blairhill	d							16 49						17 04	17 04					17 19		
Easterhouse	d							16 53						17 08	17 08					17 23		
Garrowhill	d							16 55						17 10	17 10					17 25		
Shettleston	d							16 58						17 13	17 13					17 28		
Carntyne	d							17 00						17 15	17 15					17 30		
Springburn	d			16 49														17 22				
Barnhill	d			16 50														17 23				
Alexandra Parade	d			16 53														17 26				
Duke Street	d			16 55														17 28				
Bellgrove	d			16 57				17 03				17 13		17 18	17 18		17 27	17 30		17 33		
High Street	d			16 59				17 05			17 12	17 15		17 21	17 21		17 29	17 32		17 36		17 42
Glasgow Queen St 10	a			17 01				17 07			17 14	17 17		17 23	17 23		17 31	17 34		17 38		17 44
	d			17 03				17 11			17 14	17 18		17 23	17 23		17 31	17 35		17 41		17 45
Charing Cross	d			17 05				17 13			17 16	17 20		17 25	17 25		17 34	17 37		17 43		17 47
Argyle Street	d	16 56			17 07								17 15			17 26			17 34			
Glasgow Central 15	a	16 58			17 09	17b18	17b23		17b05	17b06			17 17			17 27			17 35		17b58	
	d	16 58			17 09								17 20			17 28			17 37			
Anderston	d	17 00			17 11								17 21			17 30			17 38			
Exhibition Centre	d	17 02			17 13								17 23			17 32			17 41			
Partick	d	17 05		17 09	17 17			17 19			17 22	17 24	17 27	17 30	17 30	17 35	17 38	17 41	17 44	17 47		17 51
Hyndland 3	d	17 08		17 11	17 19			17 22			17 24		17 30	17 32	17 32	17 38		17 43	17 47	17 49		17 53
Jordanhill	d			17 13									17 32					17 45				
Scotstounhill	d			17 16									17 34					17 47				
Garscadden	d			17 18									17 36					17 49				
Yoker	d			17 21									17 39					17 52				
Clydebank	d			17 23									17 41					17 54				
Anniesland	d	17 11			17 22						17 27			17 35	17 35	17 41			17 50			17 56
Westerton	d	17 14			17 25						17 30			17 38	17 38	17 44			17 53			17 59
Bearsden	d	17 17									17 33					17 46						18 02
Hillfoot	d	17 19									17 35					17 48						18 04
Milngavie	a	17 22									17 39					17 52						18 07
Drumchapel	d				17 27									17 41	17 41				17 55			
Drumry	d				17 29									17 43	17 43				17 57			
Singer	d				17 32									17 45	17 45				18 00			
Dalmuir	a			17 27	17 34			17 30					17 45	17 48	17 48			17 58	18 02	18 02		
	d							17 30						17 48	17 53					18 02		
Kilpatrick	d													17 51	17 55							
Bowling	d													17 54	17 58							
Dumbarton East	d							17 38						17 58	18 03					18 10		
Dumbarton Central	d							17 40				17 45		18 01	18 05		18 01			18 12		
Dalreoch	d							17 41				17 46		18 02	18 06		18 02			18 13		
Renton	d													18 05			18 05					
Alexandria	d													18 07			18 07					
Balloch	a													18 11			18 11					
Cardross	d							17 46				17 51			18 11					18 18		
Craigendoran	d							17 52				17 57			18 17					18 24		
Helensburgh Central	a							17 55				18 00			18 20					18 27		

A From Cumbernauld

b Glasgow Central High Level

Table 226

Mondays to Saturdays

9 December to 17 May

Edinburgh, Lanark, Coatbridge, Motherwell, Larkhall, Hamilton, Bathgate, Airdrie and Springburn-Glasgow-Milngavie, Dalmuir, Balloch and Helensburgh

Network Diagram - refer to first Page of Table 220

		SR	SR	SR	SR	SR	SR		SR	SR	SR	SR	SR	SR	SR	SR	SR		SR	XC	XC	SR	SR	SR	SR
		SX	SO		SO	SX						SO	SX						SX	SX	SO	SO	SX		
							A								◇ B					◇**1** C	◇**1** C				
Edinburgh	d									16 48	16 56			17 07						17 11	17 11			17 18	
Haymarket	d									16 53	17 00			17 11						17 15	17 16			17 23	
Lanark	d	16 53			16 53											17 23									
Carstairs	d																								
Carluke	d	17 03			17 03											17 33									
Wishaw	d	17 08			17 08											17 38									
Holytown	d				17 13																			18 28	
Shieldmuir	d	17 13														17 44									
Coatbridge Central	d						17 21												17 31				17 58		
Whifflet 220,224	d						17 23												17 33				18 01		
Motherwell	a	17 17			17 20		17 32									17 48			17 40	17 52	17 52		18 08	18 35	
	d	17 18	17 18		17 23	17 23										17 48			17 53	17 53	17 53	17 53			
Bellshill	d	17 24	17 24								17 43					17 54									
Uddingston	d	17 28	17 28													18 01									
Airbles	d				17 25	17 25													17 55			17 55			
Larkhall	d											17 39	17 41												
Merryton	d											17 41	17 43												
Chatelherault	d											17 44	17 47												
Hamilton Central	d				17 30	17 30						17 48	17 52						18 00			18 00			
Hamilton West	d				17 33	17 33						17 50	17 54						18 03			18 03			
Blantyre	d				17 36	17 36						17 54	17 58						18 06			18 06			
Newton	d				17 40	17 40													18 10			18 10			
Cambuslang	d	17 33	17 33		17 44	17 44										18 06			18 14			18 14			
Rutherglen	d	17 39	17 39		17 48	17 48						18 02	18 06			18 10			18 18			18 18			
Dalmarnock	d	17 41	17 41		17 50	17 50										18 12			18 20			18 20			
Bridgeton	d	17 43	17 43		17 52	17 52										18 14			18 22			18 22			
Edinburgh Park	d									16 59				17 18											
Uphall	d									17 07				17 26											
Livingston North	d									17 11				17 30											
Bathgate	a									17 15				17 34											
	d									17 18				17 35											
Armadale	d									17 22															
Blackridge	d									17 26															
Caldercruix	d									17 32															
Drumgelloch	d									17 36				17 48											
Airdrie	d			17 27						17 41				17 51			17 56								
Coatdyke	d			17 29						17 43							17 58								
Coatbridge Sunnyside	d			17 31						17 46				17 55			18 01								
Blairhill	d			17 34						17 49							18 04								
Easterhouse	d			17 38						17 53							18 08								
Garrowhill	d			17 40						17 55							18 10								
Shettleston	d			17 43						17 58							18 13								
Carntyne	d			17 45						18 00							18 15								
Springburn	d								17 49																18 19
Barnhill	d								17 50																18 20
Alexandra Parade	d								17 53																18 23
Duke Street	d								17 55																18 25
Bellgrove	d			17 48					17 57	18 03							18 18								18 27
High Street	d			17 51					17 59	18 05				18 12			18 20								18 29
Glasgow Queen St **10**	a			17 53					18 01	18 07				18 14			18 22								18 31
	d			17 53					18 03	18 11				18 15	18c21		18 23								18 33
Charing Cross	d			17 56					18 05	18 13				18 17			18 25								18 35
Argyle Street	d	17 47	17 47		17 56	17 56						18 07	18 11			18 17			18 26			18 26			
Glasgow Central **15**	a	17 48	17 48		17 58	17 58					18b06	18 09	18 12			18 19			18 27	18b11	18b11	18 27			
	d	17 49	17 49		17 58	17 58						18 12	18 12			18 19			18 28			18 28			
Anderston	d	17 50	17 50		18 00	18 00						18 14	18 14			18 21			18 30			18 30			
Exhibition Centre	d	17 52	17 52		18 02	18 02						18 16	18 16			18 23			18 32			18 32			
Partick	d	17 56	17 56	18 00	18 05	18 05			18 09	18 17		18 19	18 19	18 23		18 26	18 29		18 35			18 35			18 40
Hyndland **3**	d	17 58	17 58	18 02	18 08	18 08			18 11	18 19		18 21	18 21	18 25		18 28	18 32		18 38			18 38			18 42
Jordanhill	d	18 00	18 00						18 13							18 30									18 44
Scotstounhill	d	18 02	18 02						18 16							18 33									18 46
Garscadden	d	18 05	18 05						18 18							18 35									18a48
Yoker	d	18 07	18 07						18 21							18 37									
Clydebank	d	18 09	18 09						18 23							18 39									
Anniesland	d			18 05	18 11	18 11						18 24	18 24	18 28			18 35		18 41			18 41			
Westerton	d			18 08	18 14	18 14						18 27	18 27	18 31			18 38		18 44			18 44			
Bearsden	d				18 16	18 16								18 34					18 46			18 46			
Hillfoot	d				18 18	18 18								18 36					18 48			18 48			
Milngavie	a				18 22	18 22								18 39					18 52			18 52			
Drumchapel	d			18 11								18 30	18 30				18 40								
Drumry	d			18 13								18 32	18 32				18 42								
Singer	d			18 15								18 34	18 34				18 45								
Dalmuir	a	18 13	18 13	18 18					18 27	18 30		18 37	18 37		18 42	18 43	18 47								
	d			18 19						18 30					18 42		18 48								
Kilpatrick	d			18 21													18 51								
Bowling	d			18 24													18 54								
Dumbarton East	d			18 29						18 38							18 58								
Dumbarton Central	d			18 31						18 40					18 51		19 01								
Dalreoch	d			18 32						18 41							19 02								
Renton	d			18 35													19 05								
Alexandria	d			18 37													19 07								
Balloch	a			18 41													19 11								
Cardross	d									18 46															
Craigendoran	d									18 52															
Helensburgh Central	a									18 55					19e03										

A From Cumbernauld
B To Oban
C From Penzance
b Glasgow Central High Level
c Glasgow Queen St High Level
e Helensburgh Upper

Table 226

Mondays to Saturdays

9 December to 17 May

Edinburgh, Lanark, Coatbridge, Motherwell, Larkhall, Hamilton, Bathgate, Airdrie and Springburn-Glasgow-Milngavie, Dalmuir, Balloch and Helensburgh

Network Diagram - refer to first Page of Table 220

		SR	SR		SR	SR SO	SR SX	SR	SR SO	SR SX	SR A	SR SX	SR SO		SR SX	SR	SR	SR SO	SR SO	SR SX	SR SX	SR SO	SR SO		SR SX
Edinburgh	d		17 21		17 38							17 42	17 42		17 47			17 47	17 51	17 53	17 56	17 56	18 05		18 07
Haymarket	d		17 26		17 42							17 46	17 46		17 52			17 52	17 56	17 57	18 01	18 02	18 10		18 11
Lanark	d								17 53																
Carstairs	d											18 11	18 11												
Carluke	d								18 03			18 21	18 21												
Wishaw	d								18 08			18 27	18 27												
Holytown	d								18 13												19 01	19 01			
Shieldmuir	d																								
Coatbridge Central	d										18 21														
Whifflet 220,224	d										18 23														
Motherwell	a								18 20		18 32	18 33	18 33												
	d					18 18	18 18		18 23	18 23		18 34	18 34												
Bellshill	d					18 24	18 24								18 43			18 43			19 05	19 05			
Uddingston	d					18 28	18 28														19 13	19 13			
Airbles	d								18 25	18 25															
Larkhall	d	18 05															18 36								
Merryton	d	18 07															18 38								
Chatelherault	d	18 13															18 41								
Hamilton Central	d	18 17							18 30	18 30							18 45								
Hamilton West	d	18 20							18 33	18 33							18 47								
Blantyre	d	18 23							18 36	18 36							18 51								
Newton	d								18 41	18 41															
Cambuslang	d					18 33	18 33		18 45	18 45					18 50			19 00			19 18	19 18			
Rutherglen	d	18 31				18 37	18 37		18 49	18 49							18 59								
Dalmarnock	d					18 39	18 39		18 51	18 51															
Bridgeton	d					18 41	18 41		18 53	18 53															
Edinburgh Park	d		17 31		17 48														18 01	18 03			18 17		18 18
Uphall	d		17 39		17 56														18 09	18 11			18 26		18 26
Livingston North	d		17 42		17 59														18 12	18 14			18 30		18 30
Bathgate	a		17 47		18 04														18 17	18 19			18 34		18 34
	d		17 48		18 05														18 17	18 19			18 35		18 35
Armadale	d		17 52																18 21	18 23					
Blackridge	d		17 56																18 25	18 27					
Caldercruix	d		18 02																18 31	18 33					
Drumgelloch	d		18 06		18 17														18 35	18 37			18 47		18 47
Airdrie	d		18 11		18 21			18 26											18 41	18 41			18 51		18 51
Coatdyke	d		18 13					18 28											18 43	18 43					
Coatbridge Sunnyside	d		18 16		18 24			18 31											18 46	18 46			18 54		18 54
Blairhill	d		18 19					18 34											18 49	18 49					
Easterhouse	d		18 23					18 38											18 53	18 53					
Garrowhill	d		18 25					18 40											18 55	18 55					
Shettleston	d		18 28					18 43											18 58	18 58					
Carntyne	d		18 30					18 45											19 00	19 00					
Springburn	d															18 49									
Barnhill	d															18 50									
Alexandra Parade	d															18 53									
Duke Street	d															18 55									
Bellgrove	d		18 33					18 48								18 57			19 03	19 03					
High Street	d		18 35		18 42			18 50								18 59			19 05	19 05			19 12		19 12
Glasgow Queen St 10	a		18 37		18 44			18 52								19 01			19 07	19 07			19 14		19 14
	d		18 41		18 44			18 53								19 03			19 11	19 11			19 14		19 14
Charing Cross	d		18 43		18 47			18 55								19 05			19 13	19 13			19 17		19 17
Argyle Street	d	18 36				18 44	18 45		18 56	18 56							19 04								
Glasgow Central 15	a	18 38				18 46	18 47		18 58	18 58		18b51	18b52		19b01		19 05	19b11			19b31	19b31			
	d	18 38				18 48	18 48		18 59	18 59							19 07								
Anderston	d	18 39				18 49	18 49		19 00	19 00							19 08								
Exhibition Centre	d	18 41				18 51	18 51		19 02	19 02							19 11								
Partick	d	18 45	18 48		18 51	18a55	18a55	18 59	19 06	19 06						19 10	19 14		19 17	19 17			19 21		19 21
Hyndland 3	d	18 47	18 50		18 53			19 01	19 08	19 08						19 12	19 16		19 20	19 20			19 24		19 24
Jordanhill	d		18 52													19 14			19 22	19 22			19 26		19 26
Scotstounhill	d		18 55													19 16			19 24	19 24			19 28		19 28
Garscadden	d		18 57													19a18			19 27	19 27			19a30		19a30
Yoker	d		19 00																19 30	19 30					
Clydebank	d		19 02																19 32	19 32					
Anniesland	d	18 50			18 56			19 06	19 11	19 11							19 20								
Westerton	d	18 53			18 59			19 09	19 14	19 14							19 23								
Bearsden	d				19 02				19 16	19 16															
Hillfoot	d				19 04				19 18	19 18															
Milngavie	a				19 07				19 22	19 22															
Drumchapel	d	18 55						19 10									19 25								
Drumry	d	18 57						19 12									19 27								
Singer	d	19 00						19 15									19 30								
Dalmuir	a	19 02	19 05					19 17									19 32		19 35	19 35					
	d		19 05					19 18											19 35	19 35					
Kilpatrick	d							19 21																	
Bowling	d							19 24																	
Dumbarton East	d		19 13					19 28											19 43	19 43					
Dumbarton Central	d		19 15					19 31											19 45	19 45					
Dalreoch	d		19 16					19 32											19 46	19 46					
Renton	d							19 35																	
Alexandria	d							19 37																	
Balloch	a							19 41																	
Cardross	d		19 21																19 51	19 51					
Craigendoran	d		19 27																19 57	19 57					
Helensburgh Central	a		19 30																20 00	20 00					

A From Cumbernauld

b Glasgow Central High Level

Table 226

Mondays to Saturdays

9 December to 17 May

Edinburgh, Lanark, Coatbridge, Motherwell, Larkhall, Hamilton, Bathgate, Airdrie and Springburn-Glasgow-Milngavie, Dalmuir, Balloch and Helensburgh

Network Diagram - refer to first Page of Table 220

		SR SO	SR SX	SR	SR SX	SR SX	SR SO	SR	SR		SR A	SR	SR	SR	SR	SR B	SR	SR	SR		SR	SR	SR	SR	XC SX ◇1 C
Edinburgh	d								18 22		18 26	18 37						18 48	18 56		19 07				19 11
Haymarket	d								18 26		18 30	18 41						18 53	19 00		19 11				19 16
Lanark	d	18 23	18 23												18 53							19 23			
Carstairs	d					18 29					19 13														
Carluke	d	18 33	18 33			18 37					19 22				19 03							19 33			
Wishaw	d	18 38	18 38			18 44					19 27				19 08							19 38			
Holytown	d														19 13										
Shieldmuir	d	18 42	18 43			18 47																19 42			
Coatbridge Central	d				18 34											19 20									
Whifflet 220,224	d				18 36											19 23									
Motherwell	a	18 48	18 48		18 43	18 52					19 33				19 21	19 32						19 48			19 56
	d	18 48	18 48		18 53		18 53				19 34		19 18		19 23							19 48		19 53	19 57
Bellshill	d	18 54	18 54										19 24						19 47			19 54			
Uddingston	d	18 58	18 58										19 28									19 58			
Airbles	d				18 55		18 55								19 25									19 55	
Larkhall	d							19 06									19 36								
Merryton	d							19 08									19 38								
Chatelherault	d							19 11									19 41								
Hamilton Central	d				19 00		19 00	19 15							19 30		19 45							20 00	
Hamilton West	d				19 03		19 03	19 17							19 33		19 47							20 03	
Blantyre	d				19 06		19 06	19 21							19 36		19 51							20 06	
Newton	d				19 10		19 10								19 40									20 10	
Cambuslang	d	19 03	19 03		19 14		19 14						19 33		19 44							20 03		20 14	
Rutherglen	d	19 07	19 07		19 18		19 18	19 29					19 37		19 48		19 59					20 07		20 18	
Dalmarnock	d	19 09	19 09		19 20		19 20						19 39		19 50							20 09		20 20	
Bridgeton	d	19 11	19 11		19 22		19 22						19 41		19 52							20 11		20 22	
Edinburgh Park	d								18 31			18 48						18 58			19 19				
Uphall	d								18 39			18 56						19 06			19 27				
Livingston North	d								18 42			18 59						19 10			19 30				
Bathgate	a								18 47			19 04						19 14			19 35				
	d								18 48			19 04						19 18							
Armadale	d								18 52									19 22							
Blackridge	d								18 56									19 26							
Caldercruix	d								19 02									19 32							
Drumgelloch	d								19 06			19 17						19 36							
Airdrie	d								19 11			19 20						19 41							
Coatdyke	d								19 13									19 43							
Coatbridge Sunnyside	d								19 16			19 24						19 46							
Blairhill	d								19 19									19 49							
Easterhouse	d								19 23									19 53							
Garrowhill	d								19 25									19 55							
Shettleston	d								19 28									19 58							
Carntyne	d								19 30									20 00							
Springburn	d			19 09										19 39									20 09		
Barnhill	d			19 10										19 40									20 10		
Alexandra Parade	d			19 13										19 43									20 13		
Duke Street	d			19 15										19 45									20 15		
Bellgrove	d			19 17					19 33					19 47				20 03					20 17		
High Street	d			19 19					19 35			19 42		19 49				20 05					20 19		
Glasgow Queen St 10 ⛴	a			19 21					19 37			19 44		19 51				20 07					20 21		
	d			19 23					19 41			19 44		19 53				20 11					20 23		
Charing Cross	d			19 25					19 43			19 46		19 55				20 13					20 25		
Argyle Street	d	19 15	19 15		19 26		19 26	19 34					19 45		19 56		20 04					20 15		20 26	
Glasgow Central 15	a	19 17	19 17		19 28		19 28	19 35			19b54		19 47		19 58		20 06		20b04			20 17		20 28	20b15
	d	19 18	19 18		19 28		19 28	19 36					19 48		19 58		20 06					20 18		20 28	
Anderston	d	19 19	19 19		19 30		19 30	19 38					19 49		20 00		20 08					20 19		20 30	
Exhibition Centre	d	19 21	19 21		19 32		19 32	19 40					19 51		20 02		20 10					20 21		20 32	
Partick ⛴	d	19a25	19a25	19 29	19 35		19 35	19 44	19 47			19 51	19a55	19 59	20 05		20 14	20 17				20a25	20 29	20 35	
Hyndland 3	d			19 31	19 38		19 38	19 46	19 50			19 53		20 01	20 08		20 16	20 20					20 31	20 38	
Jordanhill	d								19 52			19 55						20 22							
Scotstounhill	d								19 54			19 58						20 24							
Garscadden	d								19 57			20a00						20 27							
Yoker	d								20 00									20 30							
Clydebank	d								20 02									20 32							
Anniesland	d			19 35	19 41		19 41	19 50						20 05	20 11		20 20						20 35	20 41	
Westerton	d			19 38	19 44		19 44	19 53						20 08	20 14		20 23						20 38	20 44	
Bearsden	d				19 46		19 46								20 17									20 46	
Hillfoot	d				19 48		19 48								20 19									20 48	
Milngavie	a				19 52		19 52								20 22									20 52	
Drumchapel	d			19 40				19 55						20 10			20 25						20 40		
Drumry	d			19 42				19 57						20 12			20 27						20 42		
Singer	d			19 45				20 00						20 15			20 30						20 45		
Dalmuir	a			19 47				20 02	20 05					20 17			20 32	20 35					20 47		
	d			19 48					20 05					20 18				20 35					20 48		
Kilpatrick	d			19 51										20 21									20 51		
Bowling	d			19 54										20 24									20 54		
Dumbarton East	d			19 58					20 13					20 28				20 43					20 58		
Dumbarton Central	d			20 01					20 15					20 31				20 45					21 01		
Dalreoch	d			20 02					20 16					20 32				20 46					21 02		
Renton	d			20 05										20 35									21 05		
Alexandria	d			20 07										20 37									21 07		
Balloch	a			20 11										20 41									21 11		
Cardross	d								20 21									20 51							
Craigendoran	d								20 27									20 57							
Helensburgh Central	a								20 30									21 00							

A From North Berwick
B From Cumbernauld
C From Penzance
b Glasgow Central High Level

Table 226

Mondays to Saturdays

9 December to 17 May

Edinburgh, Lanark, Coatbridge, Motherwell, Larkhall, Hamilton, Bathgate, Airdrie and Springburn-Glasgow-Milngavie, Dalmuir, Balloch and Helensburgh

Network Diagram - refer to first Page of Table 220

		XC	SR	SR	SR	SR	SR	SR	SR	SR	SR	SR	SR	SR	SR	SR	SR	GR	SR	SR	SR	SR	SR
		SO											SX	SO			W ThO	SX					
		◇1 A								B							C	1 D					
Edinburgh	d	19 12		19 21				19 26	19 39			19 51						20 17		20 21			
Haymarket	d	19 16		19 25				19 30	19 41			19 55						20 22		20 25			
Lanark	d						19 53						20 23	20 23									20 53
Carstairs	d																						
Carluke	d						20 03						20 33	20 33									21 03
Wishaw	d						20 08						20 38	20 39									21 08
Holytown	d						20 13	20 32															21 13
Shieldmuir	d												20 44	20 44									
Coatbridge Central	d									20 21							20 36						
Whifflet 220,224	d									20 23							20 41						
Motherwell	a	19 52					20 20			20 32			20 48	20 48			21 01	21 03					21 20
	d	19 53			20 18		20 23						20 48	20 48		20 53		21 04			21 18		21 23
Bellshill	d				20 24			20 37					20 54	20 54							21 24		
Uddingston	d				20 28			20 41					20 58	20 58							21 28		
Airbles	d						20 25									20 55							21 25
Larkhall	d		20 06								20 36								21 06				
Merryton	d		20 08								20 38								21 08				
Chatelherault	d		20 11								20 41								21 11				
Hamilton Central	d		20 15				20 30				20 45					21 00			21 15				21 30
Hamilton West	d		20 17				20 33				20 47					21 03			21 17				21 33
Blantyre	d		20 21				20 36				20 51					21 06			21 21				21 36
Newton	d						20 41									21 10							21 40
Cambuslang	d				20 33		20 44						21 03	21 03		21 14					21 33		21 44
Rutherglen	d		20 29		20 37		20 48				20 59		21 07	21 07		21 18			21 29		21 37		21 48
Dalmarnock	d				20 39		20 50						21 09	21 09		21 20					21 39		21 50
Bridgeton	d				20 41		20 52						21 11	21 11		21 22					21 41		21 52
Edinburgh Park	d			19 31					19 47			20 01								20 31			
Uphall	d			19 39					19 54			20 09								20 39			
Livingston North	d			19 42					19 58			20 12								20 42			
Bathgate	a			19 47					20 04			20 17								20 47			
	d			19 48								20 18								20 48			
Armadale	d			19 52								20 22								20 52			
Blackridge	d			19 56								20 26								20 56			
Caldercruix	d			20 02								20 32								21 02			
Drumgelloch	d			20 06								20 36								21 06			
Airdrie	d			20 11								20 41								21 11			
Coatdyke	d			20 13								20 43								21 13			
Coatbridge Sunnyside	d			20 16								20 46								21 16			
Blairhill	d			20 19								20 49								21 19			
Easterhouse	d			20 23								20 53								21 23			
Garrowhill	d			20 25								20 55								21 25			
Shettleston	d			20 28								20 58								21 28			
Carntyne	d			20 30								21 00								21 30			
Springburn	d					20 39									21 09							21 39	
Barnhill	d					20 40									21 10							21 40	
Alexandra Parade	d					20 43									21 13							21 43	
Duke Street	d					20 45									21 15							21 45	
Bellgrove	d			20 33		20 47						21 03			21 17					21 33		21 47	
High Street	d			20 35		20 49						21 05			21 19					21 35		21 49	
Glasgow Queen St 10	a			20 37		20 51						21 07			21 21					21 37		21 51	
	d			20 41		20 53						21 11			21 23					21 41		21 53	
Charing Cross	d			20 43		20 55						21 13			21 25					21 43		21 55	
Argyle Street	d		20 34		20 45		20 56				21 04		21 15	21 15		21 26			21 34		21 45		21 56
Glasgow Central 15	a	20b09	20 35		20 47		20 58	20b57			21 05		21 17	21 17		21 28		21b25	21 36		21 47		21 58
	d		20 36		20 48		20 58				21 06		21 18	21 18		21 28			21 36		21 48		21 58
Anderston	d		20 38		20 49		21 00				21 08		21 19	21 19		21 30			21 38		21 49		22 00
Exhibition Centre	d		20 40		20 51		21 02				21 10		21 21	21 21		21 32			21 40		21 51		22 02
Partick	d		20 44	20 47	20a55	20 59	21 05				21 14	21 17	21a26	21a26	21 29	21 35			21 44	21 47	21a55	21 59	22 05
Hyndland 3	d		20 46	20 50		21 01	21 08				21 16	21 20			21 31	21 38			21 46	21 50		22 01	22 08
Jordanhill	d			20 52								21 22								21 52			
Scotstounhill	d			20 54								21 24								21 54			
Garscadden	d			20 57								21 27								21 57			
Yoker	d			21 00								21 30								22 00			
Clydebank	d			21 02								21 32								22 02			
Anniesland	d		20 50			21 05	21 11				21 20				21 35	21 41			21 50			22 05	22 11
Westerton	d		20 53			21 08	21 14				21 23				21 38	21 44			21 53			22 08	22 14
Bearsden	d						21 16									21 46							22 16
Hillfoot	d						21 18									21 48							22 18
Milngavie	a						21 23									21 52							22 22
Drumchapel	d		20 55			21 10					21 25				21 40				21 55			22 10	
Drumry	d		20 57			21 12					21 27				21 42				21 57			22 12	
Singer	d		21 00			21 15					21 30				21 45				22 00			22 15	
Dalmuir	a		21 02	21 05		21 17					21 32	21 35			21 47				22 02	22 05		22 17	
	d			21 05		21 18						21 35			21 48					22 05		22 18	
Kilpatrick	d					21 21									21 51							22 21	
Bowling	d					21 24									21 54							22 24	
Dumbarton East	d			21 13		21 28						21 43			21 58					22 13		22 28	
Dumbarton Central	d			21 15		21 31						21 45			22 01					22 15		22 31	
Dalreoch	d			21 16		21 32						21 46			22 02					22 16		22 32	
Renton	d					21 35									22 05							22 35	
Alexandria	d					21 37									22 07							22 37	
Balloch	a					21 41									22 11							22 41	
Cardross	d			21 21								21 51								22 21			
Craigendoran	d			21 27								21 57								22 27			
Helensburgh Central	a			21 30								22 00								22 30			

A From Penzance
b Glasgow Central High Level
B WThX until 25 February, from 28 February. From Cumbernauld
C until 27 February. From Cumbernauld
D From London Kings Cross

Table 226

Mondays to Saturdays

9 December to 17 May

Edinburgh, Lanark, Coatbridge, Motherwell, Larkhall, Hamilton, Bathgate, Airdrie and Springburn-Glasgow-Milngavie, Dalmuir, Balloch and Helensburgh

Network Diagram - refer to first Page of Table 220

		VT SX	SR	VT SX	SR	SR	SR	SR	SR	XC SO	SR W ThO	XC SX	SR	SR	SR	SR	SR	SR	SR	SR	SR	SR
		◇1 A ⊠	B	◇1 A ⊠						◇1 C	D	◇1 C							B			
Edinburgh	d					20 51				21 13		21 14		21 21				21 26			21 51	
Haymarket	d					20 55				21 18		21 19		21 25				21 30			21 55	
Lanark	d						21 23										21 53					22 23
Carstairs	d																					
Carluke	d						21 33										22 03					22 33
Wishaw	d						21 41										22 08					22 38
Holytown	d																22 13	22 32				
Shieldmuir	d						21 46															22 42
Coatbridge Central	d		21 21								21 36								22 21			
Whifflet 220,224	d		21 23								21 41								22 23			
Motherwell	a		21 32				21 50			21 56	22 01	22 04					22 21		22 32			22 48
	d	21 27		21 44			21 51		21 53	21 57		22 05			22 18		22 23					22 48
Bellshill	d						21 57								22 24			22 37				22 54
Uddingston	d						22 01								22 28			22 41				22 58
Airbles	d								21 55								22 25					
Larkhall	d				21 36								22 06							22 36		
Merryton	d				21 38								22 08							22 38		
Chatelherault	d				21 41								22 11							22 41		
Hamilton Central	d				21 45				22 00				22 15				22 30			22 45		
Hamilton West	d				21 47				22 03				22 17				22 33			22 47		
Blantyre	d				21 51				22 06				22 21				22 36			22 51		
Newton	d								22 10								22 40					
Cambuslang	d						22 06		22 14						22 33		22 44					23 03
Rutherglen	d				21 59		22 09		22 18				22 29		22 37		22 48			22 59		23 07
Dalmarnock	d						22 11		22 20						22 39		22 50					23 09
Bridgeton	d						22 12		22 22						22 41		22 52					23 11
Edinburgh Park	d					21 01								21 31							22 01	
Uphall	d					21 09								21 39							22 09	
Livingston North	d					21 12								21 42							22 12	
Bathgate	a					21 17								21 47							22 17	
	d					21 18								21 48							22 18	
Armadale	d					21 22								21 52							22 22	
Blackridge	d					21 26								21 56							22 26	
Caldercruix	d					21 32								22 02							22 32	
Drumgelloch	d					21 36								22 06							22 36	
Airdrie	d					21 41								22 11							22 41	
Coatdyke	d					21 43								22 13							22 43	
Coatbridge Sunnyside	d					21 46								22 16							22 46	
Blairhill	d					21 49								22 19							22 49	
Easterhouse	d					21 53								22 23							22 53	
Garrowhill	d					21 55								22 25							22 55	
Shettleston	d					21 58								22 28							22 58	
Carntyne	d					22 00								22 30							23 00	
Springburn	d							22 09								22 39						
Barnhill	d							22 10								22 40						
Alexandra Parade	d							22 13								22 43						
Duke Street	d							22 15								22 45						
Bellgrove	d					22 03		22 17						22 33		22 47					23 03	
High Street	d					22 05		22 19						22 35		22 49					23 05	
Glasgow Queen St 10 ⛴	a					22 07		22 21						22 37		22 51					23 07	
	d					22 11		22 23						22 41		22 53					23 11	
Charing Cross	d					22 13		22 25						22 43		22 55					23 13	
Argyle Street	d				22 04		22 15		22 26				22 34		22 45		22 56			23 04		23 15
Glasgow Central 15	a	21b48		22b02	22 06		22 17		22 28	22b21		22b28	22 35		22 47		22 58	22b58		23 05		23 18
	d				22 06		22 18		22 28				22 36		22 49		22 58			23 06		23 18
Anderston	d				22 08		22 19		22 30				22 38		22 50		23 00			23 08		23 20
Exhibition Centre	d				22 10		22 21		22 32				22 40		22 52		23 02			23 10		23 22
Partick ⛴	d				22 14	22 17	22a26	22 29	22 35				22 44	22 47	22a56	22 59	23 05			23 14	23 17	23 26
Hyndland 3	d				22 16	22 20		22 31	22 38				22 46	22 50		23 01	23 08			23 16	23 20	23 28
Jordanhill	d					22 22								22 52							23 22	23 30
Scotstounhill	d					22 24								22 54							23 24	23 32
Garscadden	d					22 27								22 57							23 27	23a34
Yoker	d					22 30								23 00							23 30	
Clydebank	d					22 32								23 02							23 32	
Anniesland	d				22 20			22 35	22 41				22 50			23 05	23 11			23 20		
Westerton	d				22 23			22 38	22 44				22 53			23 08	23 14			23 23		
Bearsden	d								22 46								23 16					
Hillfoot	d								22 48								23 18					
Milngavie	a								22 52								23 22					
Drumchapel	d				22 25			22 40					22 55			23 10				23 25		
Drumry	d				22 27			22 42					22 57			23 12				23 27		
Singer	d				22 30			22 45					23 00			23 15				23 30		
Dalmuir	a				22 32	22 35		22 47					23 02	23 05		23 17				23 32	23 35	
	d					22 35		22 48						23 05		23 18					23 35	
Kilpatrick	d							22 51								23 21						
Bowling	d							22 54								23 24						
Dumbarton East	d					22 43		22 58						23 13		23 28					23 43	
Dumbarton Central	d					22 45		23 01						23 15		23 31					23 45	
Dalreoch	d					22 46		23 02						23 16		23 32					23 46	
Renton	d							23 05								23 35						
Alexandria	d							23 07								23 37						
Balloch	a							23 11								23 41						
Cardross	d					22 51								23 21							23 51	
Craigendoran	d					22 57								23 27							23 57	
Helensburgh Central	a					23 00								23 30							00 01	

A From London Euston
b Glasgow Central High Level
B WThX until 25 February, from 28 February. From Cumbernauld
C From Plymouth
D until 27 February. From Cumbernauld

Table 226

Mondays to Saturdays

9 December to 17 May

Edinburgh, Lanark, Coatbridge, Motherwell, Larkhall, Hamilton, Bathgate, Airdrie and Springburn-Glasgow-Milngavie, Dalmuir, Balloch and Helensburgh

Network Diagram - refer to first Page of Table 220

		VT	VT	SR	SR	SR	SR	SR	SR	SR	SR	SR	SR	SR	SR	SR	SR	SR	SR	SR
		SX	SO			W ThO	SX			FX	FO	FO		FO			SO	SX		
		◇1	◇1																	
		A	A			B											C	C		
		⊠	☕			🚌														
Edinburgh	d								22 21				22 51		22 56	23 07	23 21	23 21	23 37	23 51
Haymarket	d								22 25				22 55		23 00	23 11	23 25	23 25	23 42	23 55
Lanark	d						22 59													
Carstairs	d																00 04	00 04		
Carluke	d						23 09										00 13	00 13		
Wishaw	d																00 20	00 24		
Holytown	d														00 01					
Shieldmuir	d						23 18													
Coatbridge Central	d					22 36														
Whifflet 220,224	d					22 41														
Motherwell	a					23 01	23 22										00 25	00 29		
	d	22 53	22 53		22 53							23 23								
Bellshill	d														00 04					
Uddingston	d														00 08					
Airbles	d				22 55							23 25								
Larkhall	d							23 06						23 36						
Merryton	d							23 08						23 38						
Chatelherault	d							23 11						23 41						
Hamilton Central	d				23 00			23 15				23 30		23 45						
Hamilton West	d				23 03			23 17				23 33		23 47						
Blantyre	d				23 06			23 21				23 36		23 51						
Newton	d				23 10							23 40								
Cambuslang	d				23 14							23 44			00 14					
Rutherglen	d				23 18			23 29				23 48		23 59						
Dalmarnock	d				23 20							23 50								
Bridgeton	d				23 22							23 52								
Edinburgh Park	d								22 31				23 01			23 16			23 47	23 59
Uphall	d								22 39				23 09			23 24			23 55	00 08
Livingston North	d								22 42				23 12			23 27			23 59	00 11
Bathgate	a								22 47				23 16			23 32			00 04	00 16
	d								22 48				23 17			23 33				
Armadale	d								22 52				23 21			23 37				
Blackridge	d								22 56				23 25			23 41				
Caldercruix	d								23 02				23 31			23 47				
Drumgelloch	d								23 06				23 35			23 51				
Airdrie	d								23 11				23 38			23a54				
Coatdyke	d								23 13				23 40							
Coatbridge Sunnyside	d								23 16				23 43							
Blairhill	d								23 19				23 45							
Easterhouse	d								23 23				23 49							
Garrowhill	d								23 25				23 52							
Shettleston	d								23 28				23 54							
Carntyne	d								23 30				23 56							
Springburn	d			23 09						23 39	23 39									
Barnhill	d			23 10						23 40	23 40									
Alexandra Parade	d			23 13						23 43	23 43									
Duke Street	d			23 15						23 45	23 45									
Bellgrove	d			23 17					23 33	23 47	23 47		23 59							
High Street	d			23 19					23 35	23 49	23 49		00 02							
Glasgow Queen St 10	a			23 21					23 37	23 51	23 51		00 04							
	d			23 23					23 44	23 53	23 53		00 04							
Charing Cross	d			23 25					23 46	23 55	23 55		00 06							
Argyle Street	d				23 26			23 34				23 56		00 04						
Glasgow Central 15	a	23b11	23b13		23 28			23 36				23 58		00 06	00b25					
	d				23 28			23 37				23 58		00 06						
Anderston	d				23 30			23 38				00 01		00 08						
Exhibition Centre	d				23 32			23 41				00 03		00 10						
Partick	d			23 29	23 35			23 44	23 50	23 59	23 59	00 05	00 11	00 14						
Hyndland 3	d			23 31	23 38			23 47	23 53	00 02	00 02	00 08	00 13	00 16						
Jordanhill	d							23 49	23 55	00 04			00 15							
Scotstounhill	d							23 51	23 57	00 06			00 17							
Garscadden	d							23a53	23 59	00a08			00a19							
Yoker	d								00 03											
Clydebank	d								00 05											
Anniesland	d			23 35	23 41						00 05	00 11		00 20						
Westerton	d			23 38	23 44						00 08	00 14		00 23						
Bearsden	d				23 46							00 16								
Hillfoot	d				23 48							00 18								
Milngavie	a				23 52							00 22								
Drumchapel	d			23 40							00 10			00 25						
Drumry	d			23 42							00 12			00 27						
Singer	d			23 45							00 15			00 30						
Dalmuir	a			23 47					00 08		00 18			00 32						
	d			23 48					00 08		00 18									
Kilpatrick	d			23 51							00 21									
Bowling	d			23 54							00 24									
Dumbarton East	d			23 58					00 15		00 28									
Dumbarton Central	d			00 01					00 18		00 31									
Dalreoch	d			00 02					00 19		00 32									
Renton	d			00 05							00 35									
Alexandria	d			00 07							00 37									
Balloch	a			00 11							00 41									
Cardross	d								00 24											
Craigendoran	d								00 30											
Helensburgh Central	a								00 33											

A From London Euston
B until 27 February. From Cumbernauld
C From Newcraighall
b Glasgow Central High Level

Table 226

Sundays

8 December to 11 May

Edinburgh, Lanark, Coatbridge, Motherwell, Larkhall, Hamilton, Bathgate, Airdrie and Springburn-Glasgow-Milngavie, Dalmuir, Balloch and Helensburgh

Network Diagram - refer to first Page of Table 220

		SR	SR	SR	SR	SR	SR	SR	SR	SR	SR	SR	SR	SR	SR	SR	SR	SR	SR	SR	SR	SR	SR
		A	B	B	A	A	C	A									◇ D						
Edinburgh	d																	08 38			09 06		
Haymarket	d																	08 42			09 10		
Lanark	d																						
Carstairs	d						00 04																
Carluke	d						00 13																
Wishaw	d						00 20																
Holytown	d	00 01																					
Shieldmuir	d																						
Coatbridge Central	d																						
Whifflet 220,224	d																						
Motherwell	a						00 25																
	d												08 34	08 40		09 10			09 34	09 40		10 04	10 10
Bellshill	d	00 04											08 40						09 40			10 10	
Uddingston	d	00 08											08 44						09 44			10 14	
Airbles	d													08 42		09 12				09 42			10 12
Larkhall	d																						
Merryton	d																						
Chatelherault	d																						
Hamilton Central	d													08 47		09 17				09 47			10 17
Hamilton West	d													08 50		09 20				09 50			10 20
Blantyre	d													08 53		09 23				09 53			10 23
Newton	d													08 57		09 27				09 57			10 27
Cambuslang	d	00 14											08 49	09 01		09 31			09 49	10 01		10 19	10 31
Rutherglen	d												08 53	09 05		09 35			09 53	10 05		10 23	10 35
Dalmarnock	d																						
Bridgeton	d												08 57	09 09		09 39			09 57	10 09		10 27	10 39
Edinburgh Park	d																	08 47			09 20		
Uphall	d							00 08										08 58			09 28		
Livingston North	d							00 11										09 01			09 31		
Bathgate	a							00 16										09 06			09 36		
	d											08 06						09 06			09 36		
Armadale	d											08 10						09 10			09 40		
Blackridge	d											08 14						09 14			09 44		
Caldercruix	d											08 20						09 20			09 50		
Drumgelloch	d											08 24						09 24			09 54		
Airdrie	d									07 57		08 27			08 57			09 27			09 58		
Coatdyke	d									07 59		08 29			08 59			09 29			10 00		
Coatbridge Sunnyside	d									08 02		08 32			09 02			09 32			10 02		
Blairhill	d									08 05		08 35			09 05			09 35			10 05		
Easterhouse	d									08 09		08 39			09 09			09 39			10 09		
Garrowhill	d									08 11		08 41			09 11			09 41			10 11		
Shettleston	d									08 14		08 44			09 14			09 44			10 14		
Carntyne	d									08 16		08 46			09 16			09 46			10 16		
Springburn	d																						
Barnhill	d																						
Alexandra Parade	d																						
Duke Street	d																						
Bellgrove	d									08 19		08 49			09 19			09 49			10 19		
High Street	d				00 02					08 21		08 51			09 21			09 51			10 21		
Glasgow Queen St 10	a				00 04					08 23		08 53			09 23			09 53			10 23		
	d				00 04					08 24		08 54			09 24		09c56	09 54			10 24		
Charing Cross	d				00 06					08 27		08 57			09 27			09 57			10 27		
Argyle Street	d																		10 01	10 13		10 31	10 43
Glasgow Central 15	a	00b25											09 02	09 14		09 44			10 02	10 14		10 32	10 44
	d												09 05	09 15		09 45			10 05	10 15		10 35	10 45
Anderston	d																						
Exhibition Centre	d												09 08	09 18		09 48			10 08	10 18		10 38	10 48
Partick	d				00 11					08 32		09 02	09 12	09 22	09 32	09 52		10 02	10 12	10 22	10 32	10 42	10 52
Hyndland 3	d			00 02	00 13					08 34		09 04	09 15	09 24	09 34	09 54		10 04	10 15	10 24	10 34	10 45	10 54
Jordanhill	d			00 04	00 15									09 26		09 56				10 26			10 56
Scotstounhill	d			00 06	00 17									09 28		09 58				10 28			10 58
Garscadden	d			00a08	00a19									09 30		10 00				10 30			11 00
Yoker	d					00 03			08 33		09 03			09 33		10 03				10 33			11 03
Clydebank	d					00 05			08 35		09 05			09 35		10 05				10 35			11 05
Anniesland	d									08 37		09 07	09 18		09 37			10 07	10 18		10 37	10 48	
Westerton	d									08 40		09 10	09 21		09 40			10 10	10 21		10 40	10 51	
Bearsden	d												09 25						10 25			10 55	
Hillfoot	d												09 27						10 27			10 57	
Milngavie	a												09 30						10 30			11 00	
Drumchapel	d									08 42		09 12			09 42			10 12			10 42		
Drumry	d									08 44		09 14			09 44			10 14			10 44		
Singer	d									08 47		09 17			09 47			10 17			10 47		
Dalmuir	a					00 08			08 38	08 49	09 09	09 19		09 39	09 49	10 09	10 12	10 19		10 39	10 49		11 09
	d					00 08			08 39	08 50	09 09	09 20		09 39	09 50	10 09	10 16	10 20		10 39	10 50		11 09
Kilpatrick	d								08 41		09 11			09 41		10 11				10 41			11 11
Bowling	d								08 44		09 14			09 44		10 14				10 44			11 14
Dumbarton East	d					00 15			08 49	08 58	09 19	09 28		09 49	09 58	10 19		10 28		10 49	10 58		11 19
Dumbarton Central	d		00 01			00 18			08 51	09 00	09 21	09 30		09 51	10 00	10 21	10 25	10 30		10 51	11 00		11 21
Dalreoch	d		00 02			00 19			08 52	09 01	09 22	09 31		09 52	10 01	10 22		10 31		10 52	11 01		11 22
Renton	d		00 05						08 55		09 25			09 55		10 25				10 55			11 25
Alexandria	d		00 07						08 58		09 28			09 58		10 28				10 58			11 28
Balloch	a		00 11						09 02		09 32			10 01		10 31				11 01			11 31
Cardross	d					00 24				09 06		09 36			10 06			10 36			11 06		
Craigendoran	d					00 30				09 12		09 42			10 12			10 42			11 12		
Helensburgh Central	a					00 33				09 15		09 45			10 15		10e37	10 45			11 15		

A not 8 December. From Edinburgh
B not 8 December. From Springburn
C not 8 December. From Newcraighall
D from 30 March. To Oban
b Glasgow Central High Level
c Glasgow Queen St High Level
e Helensburgh Upper

Table 226

Sundays

8 December to 11 May

Edinburgh, Lanark, Coatbridge, Motherwell, Larkhall, Hamilton, Bathgate, Airdrie and Springburn-Glasgow-Milngavie, Dalmuir, Balloch and Helensburgh

Network Diagram - refer to first Page of Table 220

Station		SR	SR	SR	SR	SR	SR	SR	SR	SR	SR	SR	SR	SR	SR	SR	SR	SR	SR	XC	SR	SR	SR
											◇ A									◇1 B			
Edinburgh	d	09 38			10 14			10 26	10 40				11 10			11 40			12 10	12 17			12 26
Haymarket	d	09 42			10 18			10 30	10 44				11 14			11 44			12 14	12 21			12 30
Lanark	d		10 12							11 12							12 12						
Carstairs	d																						
Carluke	d		10 22							11 22							12 22						
Wishaw	d		10 27							11 27							12 27						
Holytown	d							11 32															13 32
Shieldmuir	d		10 31							11 31							12 31						
Coatbridge Central	d																						
Whifflet 220,224	d																						
Motherwell	a		10 34							11 34							12 34			12 55			
	d		10 34	10 40		11 04	11 10			11 34		11 40		12 04	12 10		12 34	12 40		12 56	13 04	13 10	
Bellshill	d		10 40			11 10		11 36		11 40				12 10			12 40				13 10		13 36
Uddingston	d		10 44			11 14		11 39		11 44				12 14			12 44				13 14		13 39
Airbles	d			10 42			11 12					11 42			12 12			12 42				13 12	
Larkhall	d																						
Merryton	d																						
Chatelherault	d																						
Hamilton Central	d			10 47			11 17					11 47			12 17			12 47				13 17	
Hamilton West	d			10 50			11 20					11 50			12 20			12 50				13 20	
Blantyre	d			10 53			11 23					11 53			12 23			12 53				13 23	
Newton	d			10 57			11 27					11 57			12 27			12 57				13 27	
Cambuslang	d		10 49	11 01		11 19	11 31			11 49		12 01		12 19	12 31		12 49	13 01			13 19	13 31	
Rutherglen	d		10 53	11 05		11 23	11 35			11 53		12 05		12 23	12 35		12 53	13 05			13 23	13 35	
Dalmarnock	d		10 55	11 07		11 25	11 37			11 55		12 07		12 25	12 37		12 55	13 07			13 25	13 37	
Bridgeton	d		10 57	11 09		11 27	11 39			11 57		12 09		12 27	12 39		12 57	13 09			13 27	13 39	
Edinburgh Park	d	09 47			10 23				10 49				11 19			11 49			12 19				
Uphall	d	09 58			10 31				10 57				11 27			11 57			12 27				
Livingston North	d	10 01			10 35				11 00				11 30			12 00			12 30				
Bathgate	a	10 06			10 39				11 05				11 35			12 05			12 36				
	d	10 06			10 40				11 06				11 36			12 06			12 36				
Armadale	d	10 10			10 44				11 10				11 40			12 10			12 40				
Blackridge	d	10 14			10 47				11 14				11 44			12 14			12 44				
Caldercruix	d	10 20			10 54				11 20				11 50			12 20			12 50				
Drumgelloch	d	10 24			10 57				11 24				11 54			12 24			12 54				
Airdrie	d	10 27			11 02				11 27				11 58			12 27			12 57				
Coatdyke	d	10 29			11 04				11 29				12 00			12 29			12 59				
Coatbridge Sunnyside	d	10 32			11 06				11 32				12 02			12 32			13 02				
Blairhill	d	10 35			11 09				11 35				12 05			12 35			13 05				
Easterhouse	d	10 39			11 13				11 39				12 09			12 39			13 09				
Garrowhill	d	10 41			11 15				11 41				12 11			12 41			13 11				
Shettleston	d	10 44			11 18				11 44				12 14			12 44			13 14				
Carntyne	d	10 46			11 20				11 46				12 16			12 46			13 16				
Springburn	d																						
Barnhill	d																						
Alexandra Parade	d																						
Duke Street	d																						
Bellgrove	d	10 49			11 23				11 49				12 19			12 49			13 19				
High Street	d	10 51			11 25				11 51				12 21			12 51			13 21				
Glasgow Queen St 10	a	10 53			11 27				11 53				12 23			12 53			13 23				
	d	10 54			11 28				11 54		12c20		12 24			12 54			13 24				
Charing Cross	d	10 57			11 31				11 57				12 27			12 57			13 27				
Argyle Street	d		11 01	11 13		11 31	11 43			12 01		12 13		12 31	12 43		13 01	13 13			13 31	13 43	
Glasgow Central 15	a		11 02	11 14		11 32	11 44	11b58		12 02		12 14		12 32	12 44		13 02	13 14		13b14	13 32	13 44	13b58
	d		11 05	11 15		11 35	11 45			12 05		12 15		12 35	12 45		13 05	13 15			13 35	13 45	
Anderston	d																						
Exhibition Centre	d		11 08	11 18		11 38	11 48			12 08		12 18		12 38	12 48		13 08	13 18			13 38	13 48	
Partick	d	11 02	11 12	11 22	11 36	11 42	11 52		12 02	12 11		12 22	12 32	12 42	12 52	13 02	13 12	13 22	13 32		13 42	13 52	
Hyndland 3	d	11 04	11 15	11 24	11 38	11 45	11 54		12 04	12 15		12 24	12 34	12 45	12 54	13 04	13 15	13 24	13 34		13 45	13 54	
Jordanhill	d			11 26			11 56					12 26			12 56			13 26				13 56	
Scotstounhill	d			11 28			11 58					12 28			12 58			13 28				13 58	
Garscadden	d			11 30			12 00					12 30			13 00			13 30				14 00	
Yoker	d			11 33			12 03					12 33			13 03			13 33				14 03	
Clydebank	d			11 35			12 05					12 35			13 05			13 35				14 05	
Anniesland	d	11 07	11 18		11 41	11 48			12 07	12 18			12 37	12 48		13 07	13 18		13 37		13 48		
Westerton	d	11 10	11 21		11 44	11 51			12 10	12 21			12 40	12 51		13 10	13 21		13 40		13 51		
Bearsden	d		11 25			11 55				12 25				12 55			13 25				13 55		
Hillfoot	d		11 27			11 57				12 27				12 57			13 27				13 57		
Milngavie	a		11 30			12 00				12 30				13 00			13 30				14 00		
Drumchapel	d	11 12			11 46				12 12				12 42			13 12			13 42				
Drumry	d	11 14			11 48				12 14				12 44			13 14			13 44				
Singer	d	11 17			11 51				12 17				12 47			13 17			13 47				
Dalmuir	a	11 19		11 39	11 53		12 09		12 19		12 34	12 39	12 49		13 09	13 19		13 39	13 49			14 09	
	d	11 20		11 39	11 54		12 09		12 20		12 34	12 39	12 50		13 09	13 20		13 39	13 50			14 09	
Kilpatrick	d			11 41			12 11					12 41			13 11			13 41				14 11	
Bowling	d			11 44			12 14					12 44			13 14			13 44				14 14	
Dumbarton East	d	11 28		11 49	12 02		12 19		12 28			12 49	12 58		13 19	13 28		13 49	13 58			14 19	
Dumbarton Central	d	11 30		11 51	12 04		12 21		12 30		12 44	12 51	13 00		13 21	13 30		13 51	14 00			14 21	
Dalreoch	d	11 31		11 52	12 05		12 22		12 31			12 52	13 01		13 22	13 31		13 52	14 01			14 22	
Renton	d			11 55			12 25					12 55			13 25			13 55				14 25	
Alexandria	d			11 58			12 28					12 58			13 28			13 58				14 28	
Balloch	a			12 01			12 31					13 01			13 31			14 01				14 31	
Cardross	d	11 36			12 10				12 36				13 06			13 36			14 06				
Craigendoran	d	11 42			12 15				12 42				13 12			13 42			14 12				
Helensburgh Central	a	11 45			12 18				12 45		12e59		13 15			13 45			14 15				

A from 30 March. To Oban
B From Leeds
b Glasgow Central High Level
c Glasgow Queen St High Level
e Helensburgh Upper

Table 226

Sundays

8 December to 11 May

Edinburgh, Lanark, Coatbridge, Motherwell, Larkhall, Hamilton, Bathgate, Airdrie and Springburn-Glasgow-Milngavie, Dalmuir, Balloch and Helensburgh

Network Diagram - refer to first Page of Table 220

		SR		SR	SR	XC	SR	SR	SR	SR	SR	SR		SR	SR	SR	SR	SR	SR	SR	SR	XC		SR	SR
						◇1 A																◇1 B			
Edinburgh	d	12 40				13 10	13 10			13 40				14 10			14 27	14 40			15 10	15 10			
Haymarket	d	12 44				13 14	13 14			13 44				14 14			14 31	14 44			15 14	15 15			
Lanark	d			13 12							14 12								15 12						
Carstairs	d																								
Carluke	d			13 22							14 22								15 22						
Wishaw	d			13 27							14 27								15 29						
Holytown	d																15 32								
Shieldmuir	d			13 31							14 31								15 32						
Coatbridge Central	d																								
Whifflet 220,224	d																								
Motherwell	a			13 34		13 50					14 34								15 35			15 52			
	d			13 34	13 40	13 51		14 04	14 10		14 34	14 40			15 04	15 10			15 35	15 40		15 53		16 04	16 10
Bellshill	d			13 40				14 10			14 40				15 10		15 36		15 41					16 10	
Uddingston	d			13 44				14 14			14 44				15 14		15 39		15 45					16 14	
Airbles	d				13 42				14 12			14 42				15 12				15 42					16 12
Larkhall	d																								
Merryton	d																								
Chatelherault	d																								
Hamilton Central	d				13 47				14 17			14 47				15 17				15 47					16 17
Hamilton West	d				13 50				14 20			14 50				15 20				15 50					16 20
Blantyre	d				13 53				14 23			14 53				15 23				15 53					16 23
Newton	d				13 57				14 27			14 57				15 27				15 57					16 27
Cambuslang	d			13 49	14 01			14 19	14 31		14 49	15 01			15 19	15 31			15 50	16 01				16 19	16 31
Rutherglen	d			13 53	14 05			14 23	14 35		14 53	15 05			15 23	15 35			15 54	16 05				16 23	16 35
Dalmarnock	d			13 55	14 07			14 25	14 37		14 55	15 07			15 25	15 37			15 56	16 07				16 25	16 37
Bridgeton	d			13 57	14 09			14 27	14 39		14 57	15 09			15 27	15 39			15 58	16 09				16 27	16 39
Edinburgh Park	d	12 49					13 19			13 49				14 19				14 49			15 19				
Uphall	d	12 57					13 27			13 57				14 27				14 57			15 27				
Livingston North	d	13 00					13 30			14 00				14 30				15 00			15 30				
Bathgate	a	13 05					13 36			14 05				14 36				15 05			15 36				
	d	13 06					13 36			14 06				14 36				15 06			15 36				
Armadale	d	13 10					13 40			14 10				14 41				15 10			15 40				
Blackridge	d	13 14					13 44			14 14				14 44				15 14			15 44				
Caldercruix	d	13 20					13 50			14 20				14 51				15 20			15 50				
Drumgelloch	d	13 24					13 54			14 24				14 54				15 24			15 54				
Airdrie	d	13 27					13 57			14 27				14 57				15 27			15 57				
Coatdyke	d	13 29					13 59			14 29				14 59				15 29			15 59				
Coatbridge Sunnyside	d	13 32					14 02			14 32				15 02				15 32			16 02				
Blairhill	d	13 35					14 05			14 35				15 05				15 35			16 05				
Easterhouse	d	13 39					14 09			14 39				15 09				15 39			16 09				
Garrowhill	d	13 41					14 11			14 41				15 11				15 41			16 11				
Shettleston	d	13 44					14 14			14 44				15 14				15 44			16 14				
Carntyne	d	13 46					14 16			14 46				15 16				15 46			16 16				
Springburn	d																								
Barnhill	d																								
Alexandra Parade	d																								
Duke Street	d																								
Bellgrove	d	13 49					14 19			14 49				15 19				15 49			16 19				
High Street	d	13 51					14 21			14 51				15 21				15 51			16 21				
Glasgow Queen St 10 ⛴	a	13 53					14 23			14 53				15 23				15 53			16 23				
	d	13 54					14 24			14 54				15 24				15 54			16 24				
Charing Cross	d	13 57					14 27			14 57				15 27				15 57			16 27				
Argyle Street	d			14 01	14 13			14 31	14 43		15 01	15 13			15 31	15 43			16 02	16 13				16 31	16 43
Glasgow Central 15	a			14 02	14 14	14b09		14 32	14 44		15 02	15 14			15 32	15 44	15b58		16 03	16 14		16b13		16 32	16 44
	d			14 05	14 15			14 35	14 45		15 05	15 15			15 35	15 45			16 05	16 15				16 35	16 45
Anderston	d																								
Exhibition Centre	d			14 08	14 18			14 38	14 48		15 08	15 18			15 38	15 48			16 08	16 18				16 38	16 48
Partick ⛴	d	14 02		14 12	14 22		14 32	14 42	14 52	15 02	15 12	15 22		15 32	15 42	15 52		16 02	16 12	16 22	16 32			16 42	16 52
Hyndland 3	d	14 04		14 15	14 24		14 34	14 45	14 54	15 04	15 15	15 24		15 34	15 45	15 54		16 04	16 15	16 24	16 34			16 45	16 54
Jordanhill	d				14 26				14 56			15 26				15 56				16 26					16 56
Scotstounhill	d				14 28				14 58			15 28				15 58				16 28					16 58
Garscadden	d				14 31				15 00			15 30				16 00				16 30					17 00
Yoker	d				14 33				15 03			15 33				16 03				16 33					17 03
Clydebank	d				14 35				15 05			15 35				16 05				16 35					17 05
Anniesland	d	14 07		14 18			14 37	14 48		15 07	15 18			15 37	15 48			16 07	16 18		16 37			16 48	
Westerton	d	14 10		14 21			14 40	14 51		15 10	15 21			15 40	15 51			16 10	16 21		16 40			16 51	
Bearsden	d			14 25				14 55			15 25				15 55				16 25					16 55	
Hillfoot	d			14 27				14 57			15 27				15 57				16 27					16 57	
Milngavie	a			14 30				15 00			15 30				16 00				16 30					17 00	
Drumchapel	d	14 12					14 42			15 12				15 42				16 12			16 42				
Drumry	d	14 14					14 44			15 14				15 44				16 14			16 44				
Singer	d	14 17					14 47			15 17				15 47				16 17			16 47				
Dalmuir	a	14 19			14 38		14 49		15 09	15 19		15 39		15 49		16 09		16 19		16 39	16 49				17 09
	d	14 20			14 39		14 50		15 09	15 20		15 39		15 50		16 09		16 20		16 39	16 50				17 09
Kilpatrick	d				14 41				15 11			15 41				16 11				16 41					17 11
Bowling	d				14 44				15 14			15 44				16 14				16 44					17 14
Dumbarton East	d	14 28			14 49		14 58		15 19	15 28		15 49		15 58		16 19		16 28		16 49	16 58				17 19
Dumbarton Central	d	14 30			14 51		15 00		15 21	15 30		15 51		16 00		16 21		16 30		16 51	17 00				17 21
Dalreoch	d	14 31			14 52		15 01		15 22	15 31		15 52		16 01		16 22		16 31		16 52	17 01				17 22
Renton	d				14 55				15 25			15 55				16 25				16 55					17 25
Alexandria	d				14 58				15 28			15 58				16 28				16 58					17 28
Balloch	a				15 01				15 31			16 01				16 31				17 01					17 31
Cardross	d	14 36					15 06			15 36				16 06				16 36			17 06				
Craigendoran	d	14 42					15 12			15 42				16 12				16 42			17 12				
Helensburgh Central	a	14 45					15 15			15 45				16 15				16 45			17 15				

A From Sheffield

B From Birmingham New Street

b Glasgow Central High Level

Table 226

Sundays

8 December to 11 May

Edinburgh, Lanark, Coatbridge, Motherwell, Larkhall, Hamilton, Bathgate, Airdrie and Springburn-Glasgow-Milngavie, Dalmuir, Balloch and Helensburgh

Network Diagram - refer to first Page of Table 220

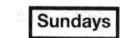

		SR	SR	SR	SR	SR	SR	SR	SR	SR	SR	SR	SR	XC	SR	SR	SR	SR	SR	SR	SR	SR	SR
											◇ A			◇1 B									
Edinburgh	d	15 40			16 10			16 26	16 40				17 10	17 11			17 40			18 10			18 26
Haymarket	d	15 44			16 14			16 30	16 44				17 14	17 15			17 44			18 14			18 30
Lanark	d		16 12							17 12								18 12					
Carstairs	d																						
Carluke	d		16 22							17 22								18 22					
Wishaw	d		16 27							17 27								18 27					
Holytown	d							17 32															19 32
Shieldmuir	d		16 31							17 31								18 31					
Coatbridge Central	d																						
Whifflet 220,224	d																						
Motherwell	a		16 34							17 34				17 52				18 34					
	d		16 34	16 40		17 04	17 10			17 34		17 40		17 53	18 04	18 10		18 34	18 40		19 04	19 10	
Bellshill	d		16 40			17 10		17 36		17 40					18 10			18 40			19 10		19 36
Uddingston	d		16 44			17 14		17 39		17 49					18 14			18 47			19 14		19 39
Airbles	d			16 42			17 12					17 42				18 12			18 42			19 12	
Larkhall	d																						
Merryton	d																						
Chatelherault	d																						
Hamilton Central	d			16 47			17 17					17 47				18 17			18 47			19 17	
Hamilton West	d			16 50			17 20					17 50				18 20			18 50			19 20	
Blantyre	d			16 53			17 23					17 53				18 23			18 53			19 23	
Newton	d			16 57			17 27					17 57				18 27			18 57			19 27	
Cambuslang	d		16 49	17 01		17 19	17 31			17 54		18 01			18 19	18 31		18 52	19 01		19 19	19 31	
Rutherglen	d		16 53	17 05		17 23	17 35			17 58		18 05			18 23	18 35		18 56	19 06		19 23	19 35	
Dalmarnock	d		16 55	17 07		17 25	17 37			18 00		18 07											
Bridgeton	d		16 57	17 09		17 27	17 39			18 02		18 09			18 27	18 39		18 59	19 11		19 27	19 39	
Edinburgh Park	d	15 49			16 19				16 49				17 19				17 49			18 19			
Uphall	d	15 57			16 27				16 57				17 27				17 57			18 27			
Livingston North	d	16 00			16 30				17 00				17 30				18 00			18 30			
Bathgate	a	16 05			16 36				17 05				17 36				18 05			18 36			
	d	16 06			16 36				17 06				17 36				18 06			18 36			
Armadale	d	16 10			16 40				17 10				17 40				18 10			18 40			
Blackridge	d	16 14			16 44				17 14				17 44				18 14			18 44			
Caldercruix	d	16 20			16 50				17 20				17 50				18 20			18 50			
Drumgelloch	d	16 24			16 54				17 24				17 54				18 24			18 54			
Airdrie	d	16 27			16 57				17 27				17 57				18 27			18 57			
Coatdyke	d	16 29			16 59				17 29				17 59				18 29			18 59			
Coatbridge Sunnyside	d	16 32			17 02				17 32				18 02				18 32			19 02			
Blairhill	d	16 35			17 05				17 35				18 05				18 35			19 05			
Easterhouse	d	16 39			17 09				17 39				18 09				18 39			19 09			
Garrowhill	d	16 41			17 11				17 41				18 11				18 41			19 11			
Shettleston	d	16 44			17 14				17 44				18 14				18 44			19 14			
Carntyne	d	16 46			17 16				17 46				18 16				18 46			19 16			
Springburn	d																						
Barnhill	d																						
Alexandra Parade	d																						
Duke Street	d																						
Bellgrove	d	16 49			17 19				17 49				18 19				18 49			19 19			
High Street	d	16 51			17 21				17 51				18 21				18 51			19 21			
Glasgow Queen St 10	a	16 53			17 23				17 53				18 23				18 53			19 23			
	d	16 54			17 24				17 54		18c20		18 24				18 54			19 24			
Charing Cross	d	16 57			17 27				17 57				18 27				18 57			19 27			
Argyle Street	d		17 01	17 13		17 31	17 43			18 06		18 13											
Glasgow Central 15	a		17 02	17 14		17 32	17 44	17b58		18 07		18 14		18b12	18 32	18 44		19 01	19 15		19 32	19 44	19b58
	d		17 05	17 15		17 35	17 45			18 08		18 15			18 35	18 45		19 05	19 15		19 34	19 45	
Anderston	d																						
Exhibition Centre	d		17 08	17 18		17 38	17 48			18 10		18 18			18 38	18 48		19 08	19 18		19 38	19 48	
Partick	d	17 02	17 12	17 22	17 32	17 42	17 52		18 02	18 14		18 22	18 32		18 42	18 52	19 02	19 12	19 22	19 32	19 42	19 52	
Hyndland 3	d	17 04	17 15	17 24	17 34	17 45	17 54		18 04	18 16		18 24	18 34		18 45	18 54	19 04	19 15	19 24	19 34	19 45	19 54	
Jordanhill	d			17 26			17 56					18 26				18 56			19 26			19 56	
Scotstounhill	d			17 28			17 58					18 28				18 58			19 28			19 58	
Garscadden	d			17 30			18 00					18 30				19 00			19 30			20 00	
Yoker	d			17 33			18 03					18 33				19 03			19 33			20 03	
Clydebank	d			17 35			18 05					18 35				19 05			19 35			20 05	
Anniesland	d	17 07	17 18		17 37	17 48			18 07	18 19			18 37		18 48		19 07	19 18		19 37	19 48		
Westerton	d	17 10	17 21		17 40	17 51			18 10	18 22			18 40		18 51		19 10	19 21		19 40	19 51		
Bearsden	d		17 25			17 55				18 25					18 55			19 25			19 55		
Hillfoot	d		17 27			17 57				18 27					18 57			19 27			19 57		
Milngavie	a		17 30			18 00				18 30					19 00			19 31			20 00		
Drumchapel	d	17 12			17 42				18 12				18 42				19 12			19 42			
Drumry	d	17 14			17 44				18 14				18 44				19 14			19 44			
Singer	d	17 17			17 47				18 17				18 47				19 17			19 47			
Dalmuir	a	17 19		17 39	17 49		18 09		18 19		18 34	18 39	18 49			19 09	19 19		19 39	19 49		20 09	
	d	17 20		17 39	17 50		18 09		18 20		18 34	18 39	18 50			19 09	19 20		19 39	19 50		20 09	
Kilpatrick	d			17 41			18 11					18 41				19 11			19 41			20 11	
Bowling	d			17 44			18 14					18 44				19 14			19 44			20 14	
Dumbarton East	d	17 28		17 49	17 58		18 19		18 28			18 49	18 58			19 19	19 28		19 49	19 58		20 19	
Dumbarton Central	d	17 30		17 51	18 00		18 21		18 30		18 44	18 51	19 00			19 21	19 30		19 51	20 00		20 21	
Dalreoch	d	17 31		17 52	18 01		18 22		18 31			18 52	19 01			19 22	19 31		19 52	20 01		20 22	
Renton	d			17 55			18 25					18 55				19 25			19 55			20 25	
Alexandria	d			17 58			18 28					18 58				19 28			19 58			20 28	
Balloch	a			18 01			18 31					19 01				19 31			20 01			20 31	
Cardross	d	17 36			18 06				18 36				19 06				19 36			20 06			
Craigendoran	d	17 42			18 12				18 42				19 12				19 42			20 12			
Helensburgh Central	a	17 45			18 15				18 45		18e59		19 15				19 45			20 15			

A To Oban
B From Bristol Temple Meads
b Glasgow Central High Level
c Glasgow Queen St High Level
e Helensburgh Upper

Table 226

Sundays

8 December to 11 May

Edinburgh, Lanark, Coatbridge, Motherwell, Larkhall, Hamilton, Bathgate, Airdrie and Springburn-Glasgow-Milngavie, Dalmuir, Balloch and Helensburgh

Network Diagram - refer to first Page of Table 220

		SR	SR	SR	SR	XC ◇1 A	SR	SR	SR	SR	SR	SR	SR	SR	SR	SR	SR	SR	SR	SR	XC ◇1 A	SR
Edinburgh	d	18 40	19 10			19 18				19 40	20 10						20 26	20 40			21 12	
Haymarket	d	18 44	19 14			19 23				19 44	20 14						20 30	20 44			21 17	
Lanark	d			19 12								20 13							21 12			
Carstairs	d																					
Carluke	d			19 22								20 23							21 22			
Wishaw	d			19 27								20 30							21 27			
Holytown	d																21 32					
Shieldmuir	d			19 31								20 33							21 31			
Coatbridge Central	d																					
Whifflet 220,224	d																					
Motherwell	a			19 34		19 58						20 36							21 34		21 53	
	d			19 34	19 40	20 00		20 06	20 10			20 37	20 40		21 04	21 10			21 34	21 40	21 54	
Bellshill	d			19 40				20 12				20 43			21 10		21 36		21 40			
Uddingston	d			19 44				20 16				20 46			21 14		21 39		21 44			
Airbles	d				19 42				20 12				20 42			21 12				21 42		
Larkhall	d																					
Merryton	d																					
Chatelherault	d																					
Hamilton Central	d				19 47				20 17				20 47			21 17				21 47		
Hamilton West	d				19 50				20 20				20 50			21 20				21 50		
Blantyre	d				19 53				20 23				20 53			21 23				21 53		
Newton	d				19 57				20 27				20 57			21 27				21 57		
Cambuslang	d			19 49	20 01			20 21	20 31			20 51	21 01		21 19	21 31			21 49	22 01		
Rutherglen	d			19 53	20 05			20 25	20 35			20 55	21 05		21 23	21 35			21 53	22 05		
Dalmarnock	d																					
Bridgeton	d			19 57	20 09			20 28	20 39			20 59	21 09		21 27	21 39			21 57	22 09		
Edinburgh Park	d	18 49	19 19							19 49	20 19							20 49				
Uphall	d	18 57	19 27							19 57	20 27							20 57				
Livingston North	d	19 00	19 30							20 00	20 30							21 00				
Bathgate	a	19 05	19 35							20 05	20 35							21 05				
	d	19 06								20 06								21 06				
Armadale	d	19 10								20 10								21 10				
Blackridge	d	19 14								20 14								21 14				
Caldercruix	d	19 20								20 20								21 20				
Drumgelloch	d	19 24								20 24								21 24				
Airdrie	d	19 27					19 57			20 27				20 57				21 27				21 57
Coatdyke	d	19 29					19 59			20 29				20 59				21 29				21 59
Coatbridge Sunnyside	d	19 32					20 02			20 32				21 02				21 32				22 02
Blairhill	d	19 35					20 05			20 35				21 05				21 35				22 05
Easterhouse	d	19 39					20 09			20 39				21 09				21 39				22 09
Garrowhill	d	19 41					20 11			20 41				21 11				21 41				22 11
Shettleston	d	19 44					20 14			20 44				21 14				21 44				22 14
Carntyne	d	19 46					20 16			20 46				21 16				21 46				22 16
Springburn	d																					
Barnhill	d																					
Alexandra Parade	d																					
Duke Street	d																					
Bellgrove	d	19 49					20 19			20 49				21 19				21 49				22 19
High Street	d	19 51					20 21			20 51				21 21				21 51				22 21
Glasgow Queen St 10	a	19 53					20 23			20 53				21 23				21 53				22 23
	d	19 54					20 24			20 54				21 24				21 54				22 24
Charing Cross	d	19 57					20 27			20 57				21 27				21 57				22 27
Argyle Street	d																					
Glasgow Central 15	a			20 02	20 15	20b21		20 34	20 44			21 03	21 14		21 34	21 44	21b58		22 02	22 14	22b14	
	d			20 05	20 15			20 34	20 45			21 05	21 15		21 35	21 45			22 05	22 15		
Anderston	d																					
Exhibition Centre	d			20 08	20 18			20 38	20 48			21 08	21 18		21 38	21 48			22 08	22 18		
Partick	d	20 02		20 12	20 22		20 32	20 42	20 52	21 02		21 12	21 22	21 32	21 42	21 52		22 02	22 12	22 22		22 32
Hyndland 3	d	20 04		20 15	20 24		20 34	20 45	20 54	21 04		21 15	21 24	21 34	21 45	21 54		22 04	22 15	22 24		22 34
Jordanhill	d				20 26				20 56				21 26			21 56				22 26		
Scotstounhill	d				20 28				20 58				21 28			21 58				22 28		
Garscadden	d				20 30				21 00				21 30			22 00				22 30		
Yoker	d				20 33				21 03				21 33			22 03				22 33		
Clydebank	d				20 35				21 05				21 35			22 05				22 35		
Anniesland	d	20 07		20 18			20 37	20 48		21 07		21 18		21 37	21 48			22 07	22 18			22 37
Westerton	d	20 10		20 21			20 40	20 51		21 14		21 21		21 40	21 51			22 10	22 21			22 40
Bearsden	d			20 25				20 55				21 25			21 55				22 25			
Hillfoot	d			20 27				20 57				21 27			21 57				22 27			
Milngavie	a			20 30				21 00				21 30			22 00				22 30			
Drumchapel	d	20 12					20 42			21 16				21 42				22 12				22 42
Drumry	d	20 14					20 44			21 18				21 44				22 14				22 44
Singer	d	20 17					20 47			21 21				21 47				22 17				22 47
Dalmuir	a	20 19			20 39		20 49		21 09	21 23			21 39	21 49		22 09		22 19		22 39		22 49
	d	20 20			20 39		20 50		21 09	21 23			21 39	21 50		22 09		22 20		22 39		22 50
Kilpatrick	d				20 41				21 11				21 41			22 11				22 41		
Bowling	d				20 44				21 14				21 44			22 14				22 44		
Dumbarton East	d	20 28			20 49		20 58		21 19	21 31			21 49	21 58		22 19		22 28		22 49		22 58
Dumbarton Central	d	20 30			20 51		21 00		21 21	21 33			21 51	22 00		22 21		22 30		22 51		23 00
Dalreoch	d	20 31			20 52		21 01		21 22	21 34			21 52	22 01		22 22		22 31		22 52		23 01
Renton	d				20 55				21 25				21 55			22 25				22 55		
Alexandria	d				20 58				21 28				21 58			22 28				22 58		
Balloch	a				21 02				21 31				22 01			22 31				23 01		
Cardross	d	20 36					21 06			21 39				22 06				22 36				23 06
Craigendoran	d	20 42					21 12			21 45				22 12				22 42				23 12
Helensburgh Central	a	20 45					21 15			21 48				22 15				22 45				23 15

A From Plymouth

b Glasgow Central High Level

Table 226

Sundays
8 December to 11 May

Edinburgh, Lanark, Coatbridge, Motherwell, Larkhall, Hamilton, Bathgate, Airdrie and Springburn-Glasgow-Milngavie, Dalmuir, Balloch and Helensburgh

Network Diagram - refer to first Page of Table 220

		SR	GR	SR	SR	SR	SR	VT	SR	VT	SR	SR	SR	SR
			R 1 A					◇1 B		R 1 B				
Edinburgh	d		21 22		21 40								22 40	23 18
Haymarket	d		21 26		21 44								22 44	23 22
Lanark	d					22 12								
Carstairs	d													
Carluke	d					22 22								
Wishaw	d					22 27								
Holytown	d													
Shieldmuir	d					22 31								
Coatbridge Central	d													
Whifflet 220,224	d													
Motherwell	a		22 05			22 34								
	d	22 03	22 06	22 10		22 34	22 40	22 49		23 04	23 04	23 10		
Bellshill	d	22 10				22 40					23 10			
Uddingston	d	22 14				22 44					23 14			
Airbles	d			22 12			22 42					23 12		
Larkhall	d													
Merryton	d													
Chatelherault	d													
Hamilton Central	d			22 17			22 47					23 17		
Hamilton West	d			22 20			22 50					23 20		
Blantyre	d			22 23			22 53					23 23		
Newton	d			22 27			22 57					23 27		
Cambuslang	d	22 19		22 31		22 49	23 01				23 19	23 31		
Rutherglen	d	22 23		22 35		22 53	23 05				23 23	23 35		
Dalmarnock	d													
Bridgeton	d	22 27		22 39		22 57	23 09				23 27	23 39		
Edinburgh Park	d				21 49								22 49	23 27
Uphall	d				21 57								22 57	23 35
Livingston North	d				22 00								23 00	23 38
Bathgate	a				22 05								23 05	23 43
	d				22 06								23 06	
Armadale	d				22 10								23 10	
Blackridge	d				22 14								23 14	
Caldercruix	d				22 20								23 20	
Drumgelloch	d				22 24								23 24	
Airdrie	d				22 27				22 57				23 27	
Coatdyke	d				22 29				22 59				23 29	
Coatbridge Sunnyside	d				22 32				23 02				23 32	
Blairhill	d				22 35				23 05				23 35	
Easterhouse	d				22 39				23 09				23 39	
Garrowhill	d				22 41				23 11				23 41	
Shettleston	d				22 44				23 14				23 44	
Carntyne	d				22 46				23 16				23 46	
Springburn	d													
Barnhill	d													
Alexandra Parade	d													
Duke Street	d													
Bellgrove	d				22 49				23 19				23 49	
High Street	d				22 51				23 21				23 51	
Glasgow Queen St 10	a				22 53				23 23				23 53	
	d				22 54				23 24				23 54	
Charing Cross	d				22 57				23 27				23 57	
Argyle Street	d													
Glasgow Central 15	a	22 32	22b26	22 44		23 02	23 14	23b09		23b20	23 33	23 44		
	d	22 35		22 45		23 05	23 15				23 35	23 45		
Anderston	d													
Exhibition Centre	d	22 38		22 48		23 08	23 18				23 38	23 48		
Partick	d	22 42		22 52	23 02	23 12	23 22		23 32		23 42	23 52	00 01	
Hyndland 3	d	22 45		22 54	23 04	23 15	23 24		23 34		23 44	23 54	00 03	
Jordanhill	d			22 56			23 26				23 46	23 56	00 05	
Scotstounhill	d			22 58			23 28				23 48	23 58	00 07	
Garscadden	d			23 00			23 30				23a50	00a01	00 09	
Yoker	d			23 03			23 33						00 12	
Clydebank	d			23 05			23 35						00 14	
Anniesland	d	22 48			23 07	23 18			23 37					
Westerton	d	22 51			23 10	23 21			23 40					
Bearsden	d	22 55				23 25								
Hillfoot	d	22 57				23 27								
Milngavie	a	23 00				23 30								
Drumchapel	d				23 12				23 42					
Drumry	d				23 14				23 44					
Singer	d				23 17				23 47					
Dalmuir	a			23 09	23 19		23 39		23 49				00 18	
	d			23 09	23 20		23 39		23 50					
Kilpatrick	d			23 11			23 41							
Bowling	d			23 14			23 44							
Dumbarton East	d			23 19	23 28		23 49		23 58					
Dumbarton Central	d			23 21	23 30		23 51		23 59					
Dalreoch	d			23 22	23 31		23 52		00 01					
Renton	d			23 25			23 55							
Alexandria	d			23 28			23 58							
Balloch	a			23 31			00 01							
Cardross	d				23 36				00 06					
Craigendoran	d				23 42				00 12					
Helensburgh Central	a				23 45				00 15					

A From London Kings Cross
B From London Euston
b Glasgow Central High Level

Table 226R

Mondays to Saturdays

9 December to 17 May

Helensburgh, Balloch, Dalmuir and Milngavie - Glasgow - Springburn, Airdrie, Bathgate, Hamilton, Larkhall, Motherwell, Coatbridge, Lanark and Edinburgh

Network Diagram - refer to first Page of Table 220

Miles	Miles	Miles	Miles	Miles			SR SO A	SR MSX B	SR MX C	SR MX C	SR SO D	SR SO	SR SO E	SR	SR		SR SX	SR SO	SR	SR	SR SX	SR SO	SR	SR SX	SR
0	—	—	—	—	**Helensburgh Central**	d																			
1¼	—	—	—	—	Craigendoran	d																			
4¼	—	—	—	—	Cardross	d																			
—	0	—	—	—	**Balloch**	d																			
—	1	—	—	—	Alexandria	d																			
—	2¼	—	—	—	Renton	d																			
8	3¾	—	—	—	Dalreoch	d																			
8¼	4	—	—	—	Dumbarton Central	d																			
9	4¾	—	—	—	Dumbarton East	d																			
11¾	7½	—	—	—	Bowling	d																			
13½	9¼	—	—	—	Kilpatrick	d																			
14¾	10½	0	0	—	**Dalmuir**	a																			
—	—	—	—	—		d															05 47	05 47			
15½	11¼	—	0¾	—	Singer	d																			
16½	12¼	—	1¾	—	Drumry	d																			
17¼	13	—	2½	—	Drumchapel	d																			
—	—	—	—	0	**Milngavie**	d																			
—	—	—	—	1½	Hillfoot	d																			
—	—	—	—	2¼	Bearsden	d																			
18½	14¼	—	3¾	3½	Westerton	d																			
19¾	15½	—	5	4¾	Anniesland	d																			
—	—	1¼	—	—	Clydebank	d															05 49	05 49			
—	—	2¼	—	—	Yoker	d															05 51	05 51			
—	—	3¼	—	—	Garscadden	d													05 42		05 54	05 54			
—	—	3¾	—	—	Scotstounhill	d													05 44		05 57	05 57			
—	—	4¾	—	—	Jordanhill	d													05 46		05 59	05 59			
20¾	16½	5¼	6	5¾	Hyndland 3	d													05 48		06 01	06 01			
21¼	17	—	6½	6¼	**Partick**	d													05 51		06 04	06 04			
—	—	—	8¼	7½	Exhibition Centre	d							00 02												
—	—	—	8¼	8	Anderston	d							00 04												
—	—	—	8¾	8½	**Glasgow Central 15**	a							00 05												
—	—	—	—	—		d						00b06	00 07												06b16
—	—	—	9¼	9	Argyle Street	d							00 09												
23¼	19	—	—	—	Charing Cross	d													05 55		06 08	06 08			
24	19¾	—	—	—	**Glasgow Queen St 10**	a													05 57		06 10	06 10			
—	—	—	—	—		d													05 58		06 12	06 15			
24½	20¼	—	—	—	High Street	d			00 02										06 00		06 14	06 17			
25	20¾	—	—	—	Bellgrove	d			00 04										06 02		06 16	06 19			
—	21¼	—	—	—	Duke Street	d																06 21			
—	21½	—	—	—	Alexandra Parade	d																06 22			
—	22¾	—	—	—	Barnhill	d																06 25			
—	23	—	—	—	**Springburn**	a																06 27			
26¾	—	—	—	—	Carntyne	d			00 07										06 05		06 19				
27½	—	—	—	—	Shettleston	d			00 10										06 08		06 22				
28¾	—	—	—	—	Garrowhill	d			00 12										06 10		06 24				
29¾	—	—	—	—	Easterhouse	d		00 02	00 15										06 13		06 27				
32½	—	—	—	—	Blairhill	d		00 05	00 19										06 17		06 31				
33	—	—	—	—	Coatbridge Sunnyside	d		00 07	00 21										06 19		06 33				
34	—	—	—	—	Coatdyke	d		00 10	00 24										06 22		06 36				
35	—	—	—	—	**Airdrie**	d		00a13	00a28										06 25		06 45				
36½	—	—	—	—	Drumgelloch	d													06 28		06 48				
39½	—	—	—	—	Caldercruix	d				00 03									06 32						
45	—	—	—	—	Blackridge	d				00 09									06 38						
47¼	—	—	—	—	Armadale	d				00 13									06 41						
49¾	—	—	—	—	**Bathgate**	a				00 17									06 45		07 00				
—	—	—	—	—		d									05 47		06 17	06 17	06 47		07 02				
52¾	—	—	—	—	Livingston North	d									05 51		06 21	06 21	06 51		07 06				
55¾	—	—	—	—	Uphall	d									05 54		06 24	06 24	06 54		07 09				
64½	—	—	—	—	Edinburgh Park	a									06 02		06 32	06 32	07 02		07 19				
—	—	—	10½	10¼	Bridgeton	d							00 12												
—	—	—	11	10¾	Dalmarnock	d							00 14												
—	—	—	11¾	11½	Rutherglen	d					00 04		00 16												
—	—	—	13½	13¼	Cambuslang	d	00 01					00 15	00 20												06 25
—	—	0	—	14¾	Newton	d							00 23												
—	—	2½	—	—	Blantyre	d					00 13		00 27												
—	—	4½	—	—	Hamilton West	d					00 16		00 30												
0	—	5¼	—	—	**Hamilton Central**	d					00 19		00 33												
2¼	—	—	—	—	Chatelherault	d					00 23														
3¾	—	—	—	—	Merryton	d					00 26														
5¼	—	—	—	—	**Larkhall**	a					00 30														
0	—	7½	—	—	Airbles	d							00 38												
—	—	—	17	16¾	Uddingston	d	00 05					00 20													06 30
—	—	—	19½	—	Bellshill	d	00 09					00 25													06 35
—	0	8¼	22½	21	**Motherwell**	a	00 17						00 41												
—	—	—	—	—		d	00 17							05 47						06 00			06 11	06 25	
—	4½	—	—	—	Whifflet	a																	06 17		
—	5¼	—	—	—	**Coatbridge Central**	a																	06 20		
—	—	—	—	22½	Shieldmuir	d	00 20							05 50										06 28	
—	—	—	—	—	Holytown	d						00 29								06 09					06 39
—	—	—	—	24¼	Wishaw	d	00 24							05 53										06 32	
—	—	—	—	28¾	Carluke	d	00 31							06 01										06 38	
—	—	—	—	—	Carstairs	a																			
—	—	—	—	37¼	**Lanark**	a	00 42							06 12										06 49	
67	—	—	—	—	Haymarket	a						01 17			06 07		06 37	06 38	07 07	07 10	07 24				07 42
68¼	—	—	—	—	Edinburgh	a						01 23			06 12		06 43	06 46	07 13	07 16	07 29				07 47

A From Partick
B From Balloch
C From Helensburgh Central
D From Dalmuir
E From Milngavie
b Glasgow Central High Level

Table 226R

Mondays to Saturdays

9 December to 17 May

Helensburgh, Balloch, Dalmuir and Milngavie - Glasgow - Springburn, Airdrie, Bathgate, Hamilton, Larkhall, Motherwell, Coatbridge, Lanark and Edinburgh

Network Diagram - refer to first Page of Table 220

		SR SX	SR	SR SX	SR	SR	SR SX	SR SO	SR SX	SR SX		SR SO	SR SO	SR	SR SX	SR SX	SR	SR	SR SX	SR	SR A	SR B	SR SX	SR SO
Helensburgh Central	d																06 10							
Craigendoran	d																06 13							
Cardross	d																06 18							
Balloch	d																							
Alexandria	d																							
Renton	d																							
Dalreoch	d																06 23							
Dumbarton Central	d																06 25							
Dumbarton East	d																06 27							
Bowling	d																							
Kilpatrick	d																							
Dalmuir	a																06 34							
	d				06 01					06 16		06 16		06 23			06 35	06 31						
Singer	d				06 03					06 18		06 18						06 33						
Drumry	d				06 05					06 20		06 20						06 35						
Drumchapel	d				06 08					06 23		06 23						06 38						
Milngavie	d																						06 42	06 42
Hillfoot	d																						06 45	06 45
Bearsden	d																						06 47	06 47
Westerton	d				06 10					06 25		06 25						06 40					06 50	06 50
Anniesland	d				06 14					06 28		06 28						06 44					06 53	06 53
Clydebank	d													06 25										
Yoker	d													06 27										
Garscadden	d		06 00	06 08		06 13		06 19	06 19					06 31					06 46					
Scotstounhill	d		06 02	06 10		06 15		06 21	06 21					06 33					06 48					
Jordanhill	d		06 05	06 12		06 18		06 23	06 23					06 35					06 50					
Hyndland	d		06 07	06 14	06 17	06 20		06 25	06 25	06 31		06 31		06 37	06 41		06 44	06 48	06 52				06 57	06 57
Partick	d		06 10	06 17	06 20	06 22		06 27	06 27	06 34		06 34		06 40	06 43		06 47	06 50	06 55				06 59	06 59
Exhibition Centre	d		06 13		06 23			06 30	06 30					06 43				06 53					07 02	07 02
Anderston	d		06 15		06 25			06 32	06 32					06 45				06 55					07 04	07 04
Glasgow Central 15	a		06 17		06 26			06 34	06 34					06 46				06 56					07 05	07 05
	d		06 18		06 28			06 35	06 35					06 48		06 50		06 57		07b00	07b05		07 07	07 07
Argyle Street	d		06 19		06 30			06 37	06 37					06 49				06 58					07 08	07 08
Charing Cross	d			06 21		06 26				06 38		06 38			06 49		06 55		06 59					
Glasgow Queen St 10	a			06 23		06 28				06 40		06 40			06 51		06 57		07 01					
	d			06 24		06 29				06 42		06 46			06 54		06 58		07 02					
High Street	d			06 26		06 31				06 44		06 48			06 56		07 00		07 04					
Bellgrove	d			06 28		06 33				06 46		06 51					07 02		07 06					
Duke Street	d			06 30								06 53							07 08					
Alexandra Parade	d			06 31								06 54							07 09					
Barnhill	d			06 34								06 57							07 12					
Springburn	a			06 36								06 59							07 14					
Carntyne	d					06 36				06 49							07 06							
Shettleston	d					06 39				06 52							07 08							
Garrowhill	d					06 41				06 54							07 11							
Easterhouse	d					06 44				06 57							07 13							
Blairhill	d					06 48				07 01							07 17							
Coatbridge Sunnyside	d					06 50				07 03					07 10		07 20							
Coatdyke	d					06 53				07 06							07 22							
Airdrie	d					06 56				07a10					07 15		07 25							
Drumgelloch	d					06 59									07 18		07 28							
Caldercruix	d					07 03											07 32							
Blackridge	d					07 09											07 38							
Armadale	d					07 12											07 42							
Bathgate	a					07 16									07 30		07 46							
	d					07 17									07 32		07 46							
Livingston North	d					07 21									07 36		07 51							
Uphall	d					07 24									07 39		07 54							
Edinburgh Park	a					07 32									07 48		08 02							
Bridgeton	d		06 22					06 40	06 40					06 52									07 11	07 11
Dalmarnock	d		06 24					06 42	06 42					06 54									07 13	07 13
Rutherglen	d		06 27		06 35			06 44	06 44					06 57				07 03					07 17	07 17
Cambuslang	d		06 30					06 48	06 48					07 00									07 20	07 20
Newton	d							06 51	06 51														07 24	07 24
Blantyre	d				06 44			06 55	06 55									07 13					07 28	07 28
Hamilton West	d				06 47			06 58	06 58									07 16					07 31	07 31
Hamilton Central	d				06 50			07 01	07 01									07 19					07 33	07 33
Chatelherault	d				06 53													07 23						
Merryton	d				06 56													07 26						
Larkhall	a				07 00													07 30						
Airbles	d							07 06	07 06														07 38	07 38
Uddingston	d		06 35											07 05										
Bellshill	d		06 39											07 10						07 15				
Motherwell	a		06 48					07 09	07 09					07 16		07 06					07 19		07 41	07 41
	d	06 37	06 48				07 01		07 09				07 10								07 20	07 37		07 42
Whifflet	a								07 17													07 47		
Coatbridge Central	a								07 21													07 49		
Shieldmuir	d		06 52				07 05						07 13											
Holytown	d	06 43																						07 49
Wishaw	d	06 49	06 55				07 10						07 17								07 28			07 55
Carluke	d	06 55	07 02				07 17						07 23								07 34			08 03
Carstairs	a						07 26														07 46			
Lanark	a	07 06	07 13										07 34											08 13
Haymarket	a					07 37									07 52	07 48	08 08			08 04	08 22			
Edinburgh	a					07 44									07 58	08 00	08 13			08 10	08 28			

A To North Berwick **B** To Cumbernauld **b** Glasgow Central High Level

Table 226R

Mondays to Saturdays

9 December to 17 May

Helensburgh, Balloch, Dalmuir and Milngavie - Glasgow - Springburn, Airdrie, Bathgate, Hamilton, Larkhall, Motherwell, Coatbridge, Lanark and Edinburgh

Network Diagram - refer to first Page of Table 220

		SR SX	SR SO	SR	SR SO	SR SX	SR SX	SR SO	SR	SR	SR SX	SR	SR SX	SR SO	SR SO	SR SX	SR A	SR SX	SR SO	SR	SR	SR SX	SR SO
Helensburgh Central	d								06 40											07 10			
Craigendoran	d								06 43											07 13			
Cardross	d								06 48											07 18			
Balloch	d	06 23	06 23										06 53	06 53									
Alexandria	d	06 25	06 25										06 55	06 55									
Renton	d	06 28	06 28										06 58	06 58									
Dalreoch	d	06 31	06 31						06 53				07 01	07 01						07 23			
Dumbarton Central	d	06 32	06 32						06 55				07 02	07 02						07 25			
Dumbarton East	d	06 34	06 34						06 57				07 04	07 04						07 27			
Bowling	d	06 39	06 39										07 09	07 09									
Kilpatrick	d	06 42	06 42										07 12	07 12									
Dalmuir	a	06 45	06 45						07 04				07 15	07 15						07 34			
	d	06 46	06 46		06 53	06 53			07 05	07 01			07 16	07 16	07 22	07 22				07 35	07 31	07 38	
Singer	d	06 48	06 48							07 03			07 18	07 18							07 33		
Drumry	d	06 50	06 50							07 05			07 20	07 20							07 35		
Drumchapel	d	06 53	06 53							07 08			07 23	07 23							07 38		
Milngavie	d						06 57					07 12						07 27					
Hillfoot	d						07 00					07 15						07 30					
Bearsden	d						07 04					07 17						07 32					
Westerton	d	06 55	06 55				07 07			07 10		07 20	07 25	07 25				07 35			07 40		
Anniesland	d	06 59	06 59				07 10			07 15		07 23	07 28	07 28				07 38			07 44		
Clydebank	d				06 55	06 55									07 25	07 25						07 40	
Yoker	d				06 57	06 57									07 27	07 27						07 42	
Garscadden	d				07 01	07 01					07 16				07 31	07 31						07 46	
Scotstounhill	d				07 03	07 03					07 18				07 33	07 33						07 48	
Jordanhill	d				07 05	07 05					07 20				07 35	07 35						07 50	
Hyndland 3	d	07 02	07 02		07 07	07 07	07 13		07 15	07 18	07 22	07 27	07 31	07 31	07 37	07 37		07 41		07 44	07 47	07 52	
Partick	d	07 05	07 05		07 10	07 10	07 15	07 15	07 17	07 20	07 25	07 29	07 34	07 34	07 40	07 40		07 44	07 44	07 47	07 50	07 55	
Exhibition Centre	d				07 13	07 13				07 23		07 32			07 43	07 43					07 53		
Anderston	d				07 15	07 15				07 25		07 34			07 45	07 45					07 55		
Glasgow Central 15	a				07 16	07 16				07 27		07 35			07 46	07 46					07 56		
	d			07b13	07 18	07 18				07 28		07 37			07 48	07 48					07 58		08b05
Argyle Street	d				07 19	07 19				07 30		07 39			07 49	07 49					08 00		
Charing Cross	d	07 09	07 09				07 19	07 19	07 25		07 29		07 38	07 38				07 49	07 49	07 55		07 59	
Glasgow Queen St 10	a	07 11	07 11				07 21	07 21	07 27		07 31		07 40	07 40				07 51	07 51	07 57		08 01	
	d	07 12	07 16				07 24	07 24	07 28		07 32		07 42	07 46				07 54	07 54	07 58		08 02	
High Street	d	07 14	07 19				07 26	07 26	07 30		07 34		07 44	07 49				07 56	07 56	08 00		08 04	
Bellgrove	d	07 16	07 21						07 32		07 36		07 46	07 51						08 02		08 06	
Duke Street	d		07 23								07 38			07 53								08 08	
Alexandra Parade	d		07 24								07 39			07 54								08 09	
Barnhill	d		07 27								07 42			07 57								08 12	
Springburn	a		07 29								07 44			07 59								08 14	
Carntyne	d	07 19							07 35				07 49							08 06			
Shettleston	d	07 22							07 38				07 52							08 08			
Garrowhill	d	07 24							07 40				07 54							08 11			
Easterhouse	d	07 27							07 43				07 57							08 13			
Blairhill	d	07 31							07 47				08 01							08 17			
Coatbridge Sunnyside	d	07 33					07 39	07 39	07 49				08 03					08 09	08 09	08 20			
Coatdyke	d	07 36							07 52				08 06							08 22			
Airdrie	d	07a40					07 45	07 45	07 55				08a10					08 15	08 15	08 25			
Drumgelloch	d						07 48	07 48	07 58									08 18	08 18	08 28			
Caldercruix	d								08 02											08 32			
Blackridge	d								08 08											08 38			
Armadale	d								08 11											08 42			
Bathgate	a						08 00	08 00	08 15									08 30	08 30	08 46			
	d						08 01	08 01	08 18									08 32	08 32	08 47			
Livingston North	d						08 06	08 06	08 23									08 36	08 36	08 52			
Uphall	d						08 09	08 09	08 26									08 39	08 39	08 55			
Edinburgh Park	a						08 18	08 18	08 38									08 47	08 47	09 04			
Bridgeton	d				07 22	07 22						07 42			07 52	07 52							
Dalmarnock	d				07 24	07 24						07 44			07 54	07 54							
Rutherglen	d				07 27	07 27				07 35		07 46			07 57	07 57					08 05		
Cambuslang	d			07 23	07 30	07 30						07 50			08 01	08 01							
Newton	d											07 53											
Blantyre	d									07 43		07 58									08 14		
Hamilton West	d									07 46		08 01									08 17		
Hamilton Central	d									07 49		08 03									08 20		
Chatelherault	d									07 53											08 23		
Merryton	d									07 56											08 26		
Larkhall	a									08 00											08 30		
Airbles	d											08 08											
Uddingston	d			07 30	07 35	07 35									08 05	08 05							
Bellshill	d			07 34	07 40	07 40									08 10	08 10							08 19
Motherwell	a				07 46	07 46						08 11			08 17	08 18							
	d					07 47									08 17		08 38						
Whifflet	a																08 47						
Coatbridge Central	a																08 49						
Shieldmuir	d					07 51									08 21								
Holytown	d			07 39																			
Wishaw	d					07 55									08 25								
Carluke	d					08 03									08 31								
Carstairs	a																						
Lanark	a					08 15									08 42								
Haymarket	a			08 43			08 26	08 26	08 45									08 55	08 55	09 11			09 05
Edinburgh	a			08 48			08 31	08 31	08 49									09 00	09 00	09 17			09 14

A To Cumbernauld

b Glasgow Central High Level

Table 226R

Mondays to Saturdays

9 December to 17 May

Helensburgh, Balloch, Dalmuir and Milngavie - Glasgow - Springburn, Airdrie, Bathgate, Hamilton, Larkhall, Motherwell, Coatbridge, Lanark and Edinburgh

Network Diagram - refer to first Page of Table 220

		SR SX	SR SO	SR SX	SR SX	SR SO	SR SO	SR SO	SR SX	SR SO	SR SX	SR SO	SR SX	SR SX	SR	SR SX A	SR SX	SR SX	SR	SR SX	SR SO	SR SX
Helensburgh Central	d										07 34	07 40				07c42						08 00
Craigendoran	d										07 37	07 43										08 03
Cardross	d										07 42	07 48				07 51						08 08
Balloch	d				07 23	07 23											07 53				07 53	
Alexandria	d				07 25	07 25											07 55				07 55	
Renton	d				07 28	07 28											07 58				07 58	
Dalreoch	d				07 31	07 31					07 47	07 53					08 01				08 01	
Dumbarton Central	d				07 32	07 32					07 49	07 55				07 57	08 03				08 02	08 14
Dumbarton East	d				07 34	07 34					07 51	07 57									08 04	
Bowling	d				07 39	07 39					07 56										08 09	
Kilpatrick	d				07 42	07 42					07 59										08 12	
Dalmuir	a				07 45	07 45					08 02	08 04									08 15	
	d				07 46	07 46		07 53	07 53		08 02	08 05			08 01			08 08			08 16	
Singer	d				07 48	07 48									08 03	08 09					08 18	
Drumry	d				07 50	07 50									08 05						08 20	
Drumchapel	d				07 53	07 53									08 08						08 23	
Milngavie	d		07 42	07 42										07 59					08 12	08 18		
Hillfoot	d		07 45	07 45										08 02					08 15	08 21		
Bearsden	d		07 47	07 47										08 04					08 17	08 24		
Westerton	d		07 50	07 50	07 55	07 55								08 07	08 10				08 20		08 25	
Anniesland	d		07 53	07 53	07 58	07 58								08 10	08 14				08 23		08 28	
Clydebank	d							07 55	07 55		08 05							08 10				
Yoker	d							07 57	07 57									08 12				
Garscadden	d							08 01	08 01									08 16				
Scotstounhill	d							08 03	08 03									08 18				08 27
Jordanhill	d							08 05	08 05									08 21				
Hyndland 3	d		07 57	07 57	08 01	08 01		08 07	08 07		08 11	08 14		08 14	08 17			08 23	08 27		08 31	08 33
Partick	d		07 59	07 59	08 04	08 04		08 10	08 10	08 14	08 14	08 17		08 17	08 20		08 23	08 26	08 29		08 34	08 35
Exhibition Centre	d		08 02	08 02				08 13	08 13					08 20	08 23				08 32			
Anderston	d		08 04	08 04				08 15	08 15					08 22	08 25				08 34			
Glasgow Central 15	a		08 05	08 05				08 16	08 17					08 23	08 26				08 35			
	d	08b05	08 08	08 08			08b18	08 18	08 18				08b20	08 24	08 28				08 37			
Argyle Street	d		08 10	08 10				08 20	08 20					08 26	08 31				08 39			
Charing Cross	d				08 08	08 08				08 19	08 19	08 24					08 27	08 30		08 35	08 38	08 40
Glasgow Queen St 10	a				08 10	08 10				08 21	08 21	08 26				08e37	08 29	08 32		08 37	08 40	08 42
	d				08 12	08 16				08 24	08 22	08 28					08 29	08 34		08 38	08 46	08 42
High Street	d				08 14	08 19				08 26	08 25	08 30					08 31	08 36		08 40	08 49	08 44
Bellgrove	d				08 16	08 21					08 27	08 32					08 33	08 38			08 51	08 46
Duke Street	d					08 23											08 35	08 40			08 53	
Alexandra Parade	d					08 24											08 37	08 41			08 54	
Barnhill	d					08 27											08 40	08 44			08 57	
Springburn	a					08 29											08 42	08 46			08 59	
Carntyne	d				08 19						08 30	08 36										08 50
Shettleston	d				08 22						08 33	08 38										08 52
Garrowhill	d				08 24						08 35	08 41										08 55
Easterhouse	d				08 27						08 38	08 43										08 57
Blairhill	d				08 31						08 42	08 47										09 01
Coatbridge Sunnyside	d				08 33					08 39	08 44	08 50								08 52		09 04
Coatdyke	d				08 36						08 47	08 52										09 06
Airdrie	d				08 44					08 44	08a51	08 57								08 57		09a10
Drumgelloch	d				08 47					08 47		09 00								09 00		
Caldercruix	d											09 04								09 04		
Blackridge	d											09 10								09 10		
Armadale	d											09 13								09 13		
Bathgate	a				09 00					09 00		09 17								09 17		
	d				09 02					09 02		09 18								09 18		
Livingston North	d				09 06					09 06		09 22								09 22		
Uphall	d				09 09					09 09		09 25								09 25		
Edinburgh Park	a				09 18					09 18		09 33								09 33		
Bridgeton	d		08 13	08 13				08 23	08 23					08 29					08 42			
Dalmarnock	d		08 15	08 15				08 25	08 25					08 31					08 44			
Rutherglen	d		08 17	08 17				08 27	08 27					08 33	08 36				08 46			
Cambuslang	d		08 21	08 21				08 31	08 31										08 50			
Newton	d		08 26	08 26															08 53			
Blantyre	d		08 30	08 30											08 44				08 57			
Hamilton West	d		08 33	08 33											08 47				09 00			
Hamilton Central	d		08 36	08 36											08 50				09 03			
Chatelherault	d														08 53							
Merryton	d														08 56							
Larkhall	a														09 00							
Airbles	d		08 41	08 41															09 08			
Uddingston	d						08 32	08 35	08 35				08 32									
Bellshill	d	08 20					08 36	08 41	08 41				08 36									
Motherwell	a		08 43	08 44				08 47	08 47					08 45					09 11			
	d		08 44						08 48													
Whifflet	a																					
Coatbridge Central	a																					
Shieldmuir	d								08 51													
Holytown	d		08 50				08 41						08 41									
Wishaw	d		08 56						08 55													
Carluke	d		09 02						09 02													
Carstairs	a																					
Lanark	a		09 13						09 13													
Haymarket	a	09 05			09 22		09 42			09 25		09 38	09 42							09 38		
Edinburgh	a	09 14			09 27		09 47			09 30		09 44	09 47							09 44		

A From Arrochar & Tarbet
b Glasgow Central High Level
c Helensburgh Upper
e Glasgow Queen St High Level

Table 226R

Mondays to Saturdays

9 December to 17 May

Helensburgh, Balloch, Dalmuir and Milngavie - Glasgow - Springburn, Airdrie, Bathgate, Hamilton, Larkhall, Motherwell, Coatbridge, Lanark and Edinburgh

Network Diagram - refer to first Page of Table 220

		SR	SR	SR	SR	SR	SR	SR	SR	SR	SR	SR	SR	SR	SR	SR	SR	SR	SR	SR	SR	SR	SR
		SX	SX			SX	SO			SX	SO				SX	SO		SX	SO				SX
			A		B																		
Helensburgh Central	d	07 55						08 10												08 40			
Craigendoran	d	07 58						08 13												08 43			
Cardross	d	08 03						08 18												08 48			
Balloch	d													08 23									
Alexandria	d													08 25									
Renton	d													08 28									
Dalreoch	d	08 08						08 23						08 31						08 53			
Dumbarton Central	d	08 10						08 25						08 32						08 55			
Dumbarton East	d	08 12						08 27						08 34						08 57			
Bowling	d							08 31						08 39									
Kilpatrick	d							08 34						08 42									
Dalmuir	a	08 19						08 37						08 45						09 04			
	d	08 19		08 24				08 37	08 31	08 40				08 46			08 53			09 05	09 01	09 09	
Singer	d	08 21							08 33					08 48							09 03		
Drumry	d	08 24							08 35					08 50							09 05		
Drumchapel	d	08 26							08 38					08 53							09 08		
Milngavie	d					08 27							08 42					08 57	08 57				
Hillfoot	d					08 30							08 45					09 00	09 00				
Bearsden	d					08 32							08 47					09 02	09 02				
Westerton	d	08 30				08 35			08 42				08 50	08 55				09 05	09 05		09 10		
Anniesland	d	08 33				08 38			08 46				08 53	08 58				09 08	09 08		09 14		
Clydebank	d			08 27						08 42							08 56					09 11	
Yoker	d			08 29						08 44							08 58					09 13	
Garscadden	d			08 31						08 47	08 47						09 01					09 16	
Scotstounhill	d			08 33						08 49	08 49						09 03					09 18	
Jordanhill	d			08 36						08 51	08 51						09 07					09 21	
Hyndland 3	d	08 36		08 38		08 41		08 46	08 49	08 53	08 53		08 57	09 01			09 09	09 11	09 11	09 14	09 17	09 23	
Partick	d	08 38		08 40		08 44	08 44	08 48	08 51	08 55	08 55		08 59	09 04			09 11	09 14	09 14	09 17	09 20	09 25	
Exhibition Centre	d			08 43					08 54				09 02				09 14				09 23		
Anderston	d		08 38	08 45					08 56				09 04				09 16				09 25		
Glasgow Central 15	a		08 39	08 47					08 57				09 06				09 17				09 26		
	d		08 40	08 48					08 58			09b05	09 07		09b18	09b18	09 18				09 28		09b30
Argyle Street	d		08 42	08 49					09 00				09 09				09 19				09 30		
Charing Cross	d	08 43				08 49	08 49	08 55		08 59	08 59			09 08				09 19	09 19	09 24		09 29	
Glasgow Queen St 10	a	08 45				08 51	08 51	08 57		09 01	09 01			09 10				09 21	09 21	09 26		09 31	
	d	08 46				08 54	08 54	08 58		09 02	09 02			09 12				09 24	09 24	09 28		09 32	
High Street	d	08a48				08 56	08 56	09 00		09 04	09 04			09 14				09 26	09 26	09 30		09 34	
Bellgrove	d							09 02		09 06	09 06			09 16						09 32		09 36	
Duke Street	d									09 08	09 08											09 38	
Alexandra Parade	d									09 09	09 09											09 39	
Barnhill	d									09 12	09 12											09 42	
Springburn	a									09 14	09 14											09 44	
Carntyne	d							09 06						09 19						09 36			
Shettleston	d							09 08						09 22						09 40			
Garrowhill	d							09 11						09 24						09 42			
Easterhouse	d							09 13						09 27						09 45			
Blairhill	d							09 17						09 31						09 49			
Coatbridge Sunnyside	d					09 09	09 09	09 20						09 33				09 39	09 39	09 51			
Coatdyke	d							09 22						09 36						09 53			
Airdrie	d					09 14	09 14	09 25						09a40				09 44	09 44	09 55			
Drumgelloch	d					09 17	09 17	09 28										09 47	09 47	09 58			
Caldercruix	d							09 32												10 02			
Blackridge	d							09 38												10 08			
Armadale	d							09 42												10 12			
Bathgate	a					09 30	09 30	09 46										10 00	10 00	10 16			
	d					09 31	09 31	09 47										10 01	10 01	10 17			
Livingston North	d					09 35	09 36	09 51										10 06	10 06	10 21			
Uphall	d					09 38	09 39	09 54										10 09	10 09	10 24			
Edinburgh Park	a					09 47	09 47	10 02										10 17	10 17	10 32			
Bridgeton	d		08 45	08 52									09 12				09 22						
Dalmarnock	d		08 48	08 54									09 14				09 24						
Rutherglen	d		08 54	08 57					09 05				09 16				09 27				09 35		
Cambuslang	d		08 57	09 00									09 20				09 30						
Newton	d												09 23										
Blantyre	d								09 15				09 27								09 43		
Hamilton West	d								09 18				09 30								09 46		
Hamilton Central	d								09 20				09 33								09 49		
Chatelherault	d								09 24												09 53		
Merryton	d								09 27												09 56		
Larkhall	a								09 30												10 00		
Airbles	d												09 38										
Uddingston	d		09 02	09 05											09 30	09 30	09 35						
Bellshill	d			09 09								09 19			09 34	09 34	09 39						
Motherwell	a		09 09	09 17									09 41				09 47						09 58
	d			09 18	09 37								09 41										09 59
Whifflet	a				09 47																		
Coatbridge Central	a				09 49																		
Shieldmuir	d			09 21																			
Holytown	d												09 49		09 39	09 39							
Wishaw	d			09 25									09 55										10 05
Carluke	d			09 31									10 01										10 11
Carstairs	a																						10 20
Lanark	a			09 42									10 14										
Haymarket	a					09 52	09 52	10 07				10 05			10 41	10 41		10 23	10 24	10 37			10 48
Edinburgh	a					09 57	09 57	10 16				10 13			10 47	10 48		10 32	10 32	10 44			10 53

A Forms tight booked connection into 2F23.

B To Cumbernauld

b Glasgow Central High Level

Table 226R

Mondays to Saturdays

9 December to 17 May

Helensburgh, Balloch, Dalmuir and Milngavie - Glasgow - Springburn, Airdrie, Bathgate, Hamilton, Larkhall, Motherwell, Coatbridge, Lanark and Edinburgh

Network Diagram - refer to first Page of Table 220

		SR	SR	SR SO	SR	SR A	SR	SR	SR	SR	SR	SR	SR	SR	SR	SR	SR	SR	SR	SR	SR	SR	SR A
Helensburgh Central	d							09 10									09 40						
Craigendoran	d							09 13									09 43						
Cardross	d							09 18									09 48						
Balloch	d		08 53										09 23								09 53		
Alexandria	d		08 55										09 25								09 55		
Renton	d		08 58										09 28								09 58		
Dalreoch	d		09 01					09 23					09 31				09 53				10 01		
Dumbarton Central	d		09 02					09 25					09 32				09 55				10 02		
Dumbarton East	d		09 04					09 27					09 34				09 57				10 04		
Bowling	d		09 09										09 39								10 09		
Kilpatrick	d		09 12										09 42								10 12		
Dalmuir	a		09 15					09 34					09 46				10 04				10 15		
	d		09 16		09 23			09 35	09 31	09 38			09 46		09 53		10 05	10 01	10 08		10 16	10 23	
Singer	d		09 18						09 33				09 48					10 03			10 18		
Drumry	d		09 20						09 35				09 50					10 05			10 20		
Drumchapel	d		09 23						09 38				09 53					10 08			10 23		
Milngavie	d	09 12					09 27					09 42				09 57				10 12			
Hillfoot	d	09 15					09 30					09 45				10 00				10 15			
Bearsden	d	09 18					09 32					09 47				10 02				10 17			
Westerton	d	09 21	09 25				09 35		09 40			09 50	09 55			10 05		10 10		10 20	10 25		
Anniesland	d	09 24	09 28				09 38		09 44			09 53	09 58			10 08		10 14		10 23	10 28		
Clydebank	d				09 25					09 40					09 55				10 10			10 25	
Yoker	d				09 27					09 42					09 57				10 12			10 27	
Garscadden	d				09 31					09 46					10 01				10 16			10 31	
Scotstounhill	d				09 33					09 48					10 03				10 18			10 33	
Jordanhill	d				09 35					09 50					10 05				10 20			10 35	
Hyndland 3	d	09 28	09 31		09 37		09 42	09 44	09 47	09 52		09 57	10 01		10 07	10 11	10 14	10 17	10 22	10 27	10 31	10 37	
Partick	d	09 30	09 34		09 40		09 44	09 47	09 50	09 55		09 59	10 04		10 10	10 14	10 17	10 20	10 25	10 29	10 34	10 40	
Exhibition Centre	d	09 33			09 43				09 53			10 02			10 13			10 23		10 32		10 43	
Anderston	d	09 35			09 45				09 55			10 04			10 15			10 25		10 34		10 45	
Glasgow Central 15	a	09 36			09 46				09 56			10 05			10 16			10 26		10 35		10 46	
	d	09 37		09b48	09 48				09 58		10b05	10 07		10b18	10 18			10 28		10 37		10 48	
Argyle Street	d	09 39			09 49				10 00			10 09			10 19			10 30		10 39		10 49	
Charing Cross	d		09 38				09 49	09 54		09 59			10 08			10 19	10 24		10 29		10 38		
Glasgow Queen St 10	a		09 40				09 51	09 56		10 01			10 10			10 21	10 26		10 31		10 40		
	d		09 42				09 54	09 58		10 02			10 12			10 24	10 28		10 32		10 42		
High Street	d		09 44				09 56	10 00		10 04			10 14			10 26	10 30		10 34		10 44		
Bellgrove	d		09 46					10 02		10 06			10 16				10 32		10 36		10 46		
Duke Street	d									10 08									10 38				
Alexandra Parade	d									10 09									10 39				
Barnhill	d									10 12									10 42				
Springburn	a									10 14									10 44				
Carntyne	d		09 49					10 06					10 19				10 36				10 49		
Shettleston	d		09 52					10 08					10 22				10 38				10 52		
Garrowhill	d		09 54					10 11					10 24				10 41				10 54		
Easterhouse	d		09 57					10 13					10 27				10 43				10 57		
Blairhill	d		10 01					10 17					10 31				10 47				11 01		
Coatbridge Sunnyside	d		10 03				10 09	10 20					10 33			10 39	10 50				11 03		
Coatdyke	d		10 06					10 22					10 36				10 52				11 06		
Airdrie	d		10a10				10 14	10 25					10a40			10 44	10 55				11a10		
Drumgelloch	d						10 17	10 28								10 47	10 58						
Caldercruix	d							10 32									11 02						
Blackridge	d							10 38									11 08						
Armadale	d							10 42									11 12						
Bathgate	a						10 30	10 46								11 00	11 16						
	d						10 31	10 47								11 01	11 17						
Livingston North	d						10 36	10 51								11 06	11 21						
Uphall	d						10 39	10 54								11 09	11 24						
Edinburgh Park	a						10 47	11 02								11 17	11 32						
Bridgeton	d	09 42			09 52							10 12			10 22					10 42		10 52	
Dalmarnock	d	09 44			09 54							10 14			10 24					10 44		10 54	
Rutherglen	d	09 46			09 57				10 05			10 16			10 27			10 35		10 46		10 57	
Cambuslang	d	09 50			10 00							10 20			10 30					10 49		11 00	
Newton	d	09 53										10 23								10 53			
Blantyre	d	09 57							10 13			10 27						10 43		10 57			
Hamilton West	d	10 00							10 16			10 30						10 46		11 00			
Hamilton Central	d	10 03							10 19			10 33						10 49		11 03			
Chatelherault	d								10 23									10 53					
Merryton	d								10 26									10 56					
Larkhall	a								10 30									11 00					
Airbles	d	10 08										10 38								11 07			
Uddingston	d				10 05									10 30	10 35							11 05	
Bellshill	d				10 09						10 19			10 34	10 39							11 09	
Motherwell	a	10 11		10 05	10 17							10 41			10 47					11 11		11 17	
	d			10 06	10 17	10 37						10 44										11 17	11 37
Whifflet	a					10 47																	11 47
Coatbridge Central	a					10 49																	11 49
Shieldmuir	d				10 21																	11 21	
Holytown	d											10 49		10 39									
Wishaw	d			10 14	10 25							10 55										11 25	
Carluke	d			10 21	10 31							11 01										11 31	
Carstairs	a			10 32																			
Lanark	a				10 43							11 14										11 43	
Haymarket	a			11 11			10 52	11 07			11 04			11 41		11 22	11 37						
Edinburgh	a			11 19			10 58	11 14			11 10			11 47		11 28	11 44						

A To Cumbernauld

b Glasgow Central High Level

Table 226R

Mondays to Saturdays

9 December to 17 May

Helensburgh, Balloch, Dalmuir and Milngavie - Glasgow - Springburn, Airdrie, Bathgate, Hamilton, Larkhall, Motherwell, Coatbridge, Lanark and Edinburgh

Network Diagram - refer to first Page of Table 220

		SR	SR	SR	SR	SR	SR	SR	SR	SR	SR	SR	SR	SR	SR	SR	SR	SR	SR	SR	SR	SR
																		SO	SX	SX	SO	
																◇ A (train symbol)						B
Helensburgh Central	d		10 10									10 40				10c44						
Craigendoran	d		10 13									10 43										
Cardross	d		10 18									10 48										
Balloch	d							10 23									10 53					
Alexandria	d							10 25									10 55					
Renton	d							10 28									10 58					
Dalreoch	d		10 23					10 31				10 53					11 01					
Dumbarton Central	d		10 25					10 32				10 55				10 59	11 02					
Dumbarton East	d		10 27					10 34				10 57					11 04					
Bowling	d							10 39									11 09					
Kilpatrick	d							10 42									11 12					
Dalmuir	a		10 34					10 45				11 04				11 10	11 15					
	d		10 35	10 31	10 38			10 46		10 53		11 05	11 01	11 08		11 10	11 16			11 23	11 23	
Singer	d			10 33				10 48					11 03				11 18					
Drumry	d			10 35				10 50					11 05				11 20					
Drumchapel	d			10 38				10 53					11 08				11 23					
Milngavie	d	10 27					10 42				10 57				11 12							
Hillfoot	d	10 30					10 45				11 00				11 15							
Bearsden	d	10 32					10 47				11 02				11 17							
Westerton	d	10 35		10 40			10 50	10 55			11 05		11 10		11 20		11 25					
Anniesland	d	10 38		10 44			10 53	10 58			11 08		11 14		11 23		11 28					
Clydebank	d				10 40					10 55				11 10						11 25	11 25	
Yoker	d				10 42					10 57				11 12						11 27	11 27	
Garscadden	d				10 46					11 01				11 16						11 31	11 31	
Scotstounhill	d				10 48					11 03				11 18						11 33	11 33	
Jordanhill	d				10 50					11 05				11 20						11 35	11 35	
Hyndland 3	d	10 42	10 44	10 47	10 52		10 57	11 01		11 07	11 12	11 14	11 17	11 22	11 27		11 31			11 37	11 37	
Partick	d	10 44	10 47	10 50	10 55		10 59	11 04		11 10	11 14	11 17	11 20	11 25	11 29		11 34			11 40	11 40	
Exhibition Centre	d			10 53			11 02			11 13			11 23		11 32					11 43	11 43	
Anderston	d			10 55			11 04			11 15			11 25		11 34					11 45	11 45	
Glasgow Central 15	a			10 56			11 05			11 16			11 26		11 35					11 46	11 46	
	d			10 58		11b05	11 07		11b18	11 18			11 28		11 37			11b48	11b48	11 48	11 48	
Argyle Street	d			11 00			11 09			11 19			11 29		11 39					11 49	11 49	
Charing Cross	d	10 49	10 54		10 59			11 08			11 19	11 24		11 29			11 38					
Glasgow Queen St 10	a	10 51	10 56		11 01			11 11			11 21	11 26		11 31		11e30	11 40					
	d	10 54	10 58		11 02			11 12			11 24	11 28		11 32			11 42					
High Street	d	10 56	11 00		11 04			11 14			11 26	11 30		11 34			11 44					
Bellgrove	d		11 02		11 06			11 16				11 32		11 36			11 46					
Duke Street	d				11 08									11 38								
Alexandra Parade	d				11 09									11 39								
Barnhill	d				11 12									11 42								
Springburn	a				11 14									11 44								
Carntyne	d		11 06					11 19				11 36					11 49					
Shettleston	d		11 08					11 22				11 38					11 52					
Garrowhill	d		11 11					11 24				11 41					11 54					
Easterhouse	d		11 13					11 27				11 43					11 57					
Blairhill	d		11 17					11 31				11 47					12 01					
Coatbridge Sunnyside	d	11 09	11 20					11 33			11 39	11 50					12 03					
Coatdyke	d		11 22					11 36				11 52					12 06					
Airdrie	d	11 14	11 25					11a40			11 44	11 55					12a10					
Drumgelloch	d	11 17	11 28								11 47	11 58										
Caldercruix	d		11 32									12 02										
Blackridge	d		11 38									12 08										
Armadale	d		11 42									12 12										
Bathgate	a	11 30	11 46								12 00	12 16										
	d	11 31	11 47								12 01	12 17										
Livingston North	d	11 36	11 51								12 06	12 21										
Uphall	d	11 39	11 54								12 09	12 24										
Edinburgh Park	a	11 47	12 02								12 17	12 32										
Bridgeton	d						11 12			11 22					11 42					11 52	11 52	
Dalmarnock	d						11 14			11 24					11 44					11 54	11 54	
Rutherglen	d			11 05			11 16			11 27			11 34		11 46					11 57	11 57	
Cambuslang	d						11 20			11 30					11 50					12 00	12 00	
Newton	d						11 23								11 53							
Blantyre	d			11 13			11 27						11 43		11 57							
Hamilton West	d			11 16			11 30						11 46		12 00							
Hamilton Central	d			11 19			11 33						11 49		12 03							
Chatelherault	d			11 23									11 53									
Merryton	d			11 26									11 56									
Larkhall	a			11 30									12 00									
Airbles	d						11 38								12 08							
Uddingston	d								11 30	11 35										12 05	12 05	
Bellshill	d					11 19			11 34	11 39										12 09	12 09	
Motherwell	a						11 41			11 48					12 11			12 08	12 08	12 17	12 17	
	d						11 41											12 09	12 09	12 17	12 17	12 37
Whifflet	a																					12 47
Coatbridge Central	a																					12 49
Shieldmuir	d																			12 21	12 21	
Holytown	d						11 49		11 39													
Wishaw	d						11 55											12 14	12 14	12 25	12 25	
Carluke	d						12 01											12 22	12 22	12 31	12 31	
Carstairs	a																	12 31	12 32			
Lanark	a						12 12													12 42	12 45	
Haymarket	a	11 56	12 08			12 04			12 41		12 22	12 37						12 57	12 57			
Edinburgh	a	12 02	12 13			12 10			12 48		12 28	12 43						13 04	13 04			

A From Mallaig
B To Cumbernauld
b Glasgow Central High Level
c Helensburgh Upper
e Glasgow Queen St High Level

Table 226R

Mondays to Saturdays

9 December to 17 May

Helensburgh, Balloch, Dalmuir and Milngavie - Glasgow - Springburn, Airdrie, Bathgate, Hamilton, Larkhall, Motherwell, Coatbridge, Lanark and Edinburgh

Network Diagram - refer to first Page of Table 220

		SR	SR SO	SR SX	SR	SR	SR	SR	SR	SR	SR	SR	SR	SR	SR	SR	SR	SR	SR A	SR	SR	SR	SR
Helensburgh Central	d		11 10	11 10									11 40								12 10		
Craigendoran	d		11 13	11 13									11 43								12 13		
Cardross	d		11 18	11 18									11 48								12 18		
Balloch	d								11 23								11 53						
Alexandria	d								11 25								11 55						
Renton	d								11 28								11 58						
Dalreoch	d		11 23	11 23					11 31				11 53				12 01				12 23		
Dumbarton Central	d		11 25	11 25					11 32				11 55				12 02				12 25		
Dumbarton East	d		11 27	11 27					11 34				11 57				12 04				12 27		
Bowling	d								11 39								12 09						
Kilpatrick	d								11 42								12 12						
Dalmuir	a		11 34	11 34					11 45				12 04				12 15				12 34		
	d		11 35	11 35	11 31	11 38			11 46		11 53		12 05	12 01	12 08		12 16	12 23			12 35	12 31	12 38
Singer	d				11 33				11 48					12 03			12 18					12 33	
Drumry	d				11 35				11 50					12 05			12 20					12 35	
Drumchapel	d				11 38				11 53					12 08			12 23					12 38	
Milngavie	d	11 27						11 42				11 57				12 12				12 27			
Hillfoot	d	11 30						11 45				12 00				12 15				12 30			
Bearsden	d	11 32						11 47				12 02				12 17				12 32			
Westerton	d	11 35			11 40			11 50	11 55			12 05		12 10		12 20	12 25			12 35		12 40	
Anniesland	d	11 38			11 44			11 53	11 58			12 08		12 14		12 23	12 28			12 38		12 44	
Clydebank	d					11 40					11 55				12 10			12 25					12 40
Yoker	d					11 42					11 57				12 12			12 27					12 42
Garscadden	d					11 46					12 01				12 16			12 31					12 46
Scotstounhill	d					11 48					12 03				12 18			12 33					12 48
Jordanhill	d					11 50					12 05				12 20			12 35					12 50
Hyndland 3	d	11 42	11 44	11 44	11 47	11 52		11 57	12 01		12 07	12 12	12 14	12 17	12 22	12 27	12 31	12 37		12 42	12 44	12 47	12 52
Partick	d	11 44	11 47	11 47	11 50	11 55		11 59	12 04		12 10	12 14	12 17	12 20	12 25	12 29	12 34	12 40		12 44	12 47	12 50	12 55
Exhibition Centre	d				11 53			12 02			12 13			12 23		12 32		12 43				12 53	
Anderston	d				11 55			12 04			12 15			12 25		12 34		12 45				12 55	
Glasgow Central 15	a				11 56			12 05			12 16			12 26		12 35		12 46				12 56	
	d				11 58		12b05	12 07		12b18	12 18			12 28		12 37		12 48				12 58	
Argyle Street	d				12 00			12 09			12 19			12 30		12 39		12 49				13 00	
Charing Cross	d	11 49	11 54	11 54		11 59			12 08			12 19	12 24		12 29		12 38			12 49	12 54		12 59
Glasgow Queen St 10	a	11 51	11 56	11 56		12 01			12 10			12 21	12 26		12 31		12 40			12 51	12 56		13 01
	d	11 54	11 58	11 58		12 02			12 12			12 24	12 28		12 32		12 42			12 54	12 58		13 02
High Street	d	11 56	12 00	12 00		12 04			12 14			12 26	12 30		12 34		12 44			12 56	13 00		13 04
Bellgrove	d		12 02	12 02		12 06			12 16				12 32		12 36		12 46				13 02		13 06
Duke Street	d					12 08									12 38								13 08
Alexandra Parade	d					12 09									12 39								13 09
Barnhill	d					12 12									12 42								13 12
Springburn	a					12 14									12 44								13 14
Carntyne	d		12 06	12 06					12 19				12 36				12 49				13 06		
Shettleston	d		12 08	12 08					12 22				12 38				12 52				13 08		
Garrowhill	d		12 11	12 11					12 24				12 41				12 54				13 11		
Easterhouse	d		12 13	12 13					12 27				12 43				12 57				13 13		
Blairhill	d		12 17	12 17					12 31				12 47				13 01				13 17		
Coatbridge Sunnyside	d	12 09	12 20	12 20					12 33			12 39	12 50				13 03			13 09	13 20		
Coatdyke	d		12 22	12 22					12 36				12 52				13 06				13 22		
Airdrie	d	12 14	12 25	12 25					12a40			12 44	12 55				13a10			13 14	13 25		
Drumgelloch	d	12 17	12 28	12 28								12 47	12 58							13 17	13 28		
Caldercruix	d		12 32	12 32									13 02								13 32		
Blackridge	d		12 38	12 38									13 08								13 38		
Armadale	d		12 42	12 42									13 12								13 42		
Bathgate	a	12 30	12 46	12 46								13 00	13 16							13 30	13 46		
	d	12 31	12 47	12 47								13 01	13 17							13 31	13 47		
Livingston North	d	12 36	12 51	12 51								13 06	13 21							13 36	13 51		
Uphall	d	12 39	12 54	12 54								13 09	13 24							13 39	13 54		
Edinburgh Park	a	12 47	13 02	13 02								13 17	13 32							13 47	14 02		
Bridgeton	d							12 12			12 22					12 42		12 52					
Dalmarnock	d							12 14			12 24					12 44		12 54					
Rutherglen	d				12 05			12 16			12 27			12 35		12 46		12 57				13 05	
Cambuslang	d							12 20			12 30					12 50		13 00					
Newton	d							12 23								12 53							
Blantyre	d				12 13			12 27						12 43		12 57						13 13	
Hamilton West	d				12 16			12 30						12 46		13 00						13 16	
Hamilton Central	d				12 19			12 33						12 49		13 03						13 19	
Chatelherault	d				12 23									12 53								13 23	
Merryton	d				12 26									12 56								13 26	
Larkhall	a				12 30									13 00								13 30	
Airbles	d							12 38								13 08							
Uddingston	d									12 30	12 35							13 05					
Bellshill	d						12 19			12 34	12 39							13 09					
Motherwell	a							12 41			12 48					13 11		13 17					
	d							12 41										13 17	13 37				
Whifflet	a																		13 47				
Coatbridge Central	a																		13 49				
Shieldmuir	d																	13 21					
Holytown	d							12 49		12 39													
Wishaw	d							12 55										13 25					
Carluke	d							13 01										13 31					
Carstairs	a																						
Lanark	a							13 12										13 43					
Haymarket	a	12 52	13 07	13 07			13 04			13 42		13 22	13 37							13 52	14 07		
Edinburgh	a	13 00	13 14	13 17			13 11			13 47		13 28	13 44							13 59	14 13		

A To Cumbernauld

b Glasgow Central High Level

Table 226R

Mondays to Saturdays

9 December to 17 May

Helensburgh, Balloch, Dalmuir and Milngavie - Glasgow - Springburn, Airdrie, Bathgate, Hamilton, Larkhall, Motherwell, Coatbridge, Lanark and Edinburgh

Network Diagram - refer to first Page of Table 220

		SR SX	SR SO	SR	SR	SR	SR	SR	SR	SR	SR	SR	SR	SR	SR	SR A	SR SX	SR SO	SR SO	SR SX	SR	SR
Helensburgh Central	d								12 40										13 10	13 10		
Craigendoran	d								12 43										13 13	13 13		
Cardross	d								12 48										13 18	13 18		
Balloch	d				12 23								12 53									
Alexandria	d				12 25								12 55									
Renton	d				12 28								12 58									
Dalreoch	d				12 31				12 53				13 01						13 23	13 23		
Dumbarton Central	d				12 32				12 55				13 02						13 25	13 25		
Dumbarton East	d				12 34				12 57				13 04						13 27	13 27		
Bowling	d				12 39								13 09									
Kilpatrick	d				12 42								13 12									
Dalmuir	a				12 45				13 04				13 15						13 34	13 34		
	d				12 46		12 53		13 05	13 01	13 08		13 16		13 23				13 35	13 35	13 31	13 38
Singer	d				12 48					13 03			13 18								13 33	
Drumry	d				12 50					13 05			13 20								13 35	
Drumchapel	d				12 53					13 08			13 23								13 38	
Milngavie	d			12 42				12 57				13 12					13 27	13 27				
Hillfoot	d			12 45				13 00				13 15					13 30	13 30				
Bearsden	d			12 47				13 02				13 17					13 32	13 32				
Westerton	d			12 50	12 55			13 05		13 10		13 20	13 25				13 35	13 35			13 40	
Anniesland	d			12 53	12 58			13 08		13 14		13 23	13 28				13 38	13 38			13 44	
Clydebank	d						12 55				13 10				13 25							13 40
Yoker	d						12 57				13 12				13 27							13 42
Garscadden	d						13 01				13 16				13 31							13 46
Scotstounhill	d						13 03				13 18				13 33							13 48
Jordanhill	d						13 05				13 20				13 35							13 50
Hyndland 3	d			12 57	13 01		13 07	13 12	13 14	13 17	13 22	13 27	13 31		13 37		13 42	13 42	13 44	13 44	13 47	13 52
Partick	d			12 59	13 04		13 10	13 14	13 17	13 20	13 25	13 29	13 34		13 40		13 44	13 44	13 47	13 47	13 50	13 55
Exhibition Centre	d			13 02			13 13			13 23		13 32			13 43						13 53	
Anderston	d			13 04			13 15			13 25		13 34			13 45						13 55	
Glasgow Central 15	a			13 05			13 16			13 26		13 35			13 46						13 56	
	d	13b05	13b05	13 07		13b18	13 18			13 28		13 37		13b43	13 48						13 58	
Argyle Street	d			13 09			13 19			13 30		13 39			13 49						14 00	
Charing Cross	d				13 08			13 19	13 24		13 29		13 38				13 49	13 49	13 54	13 54		13 59
Glasgow Queen St 10	a				13 10			13 21	13 26		13 31		13 40				13 51	13 51	13 56	13 56		14 01
	d				13 12			13 24	13 28		13 32		13 42				13 54	13 54	13 58	13 58		14 02
High Street	d				13 14			13 26	13 30		13 34		13 44				13 56	13 56	14 00	14 00		14 04
Bellgrove	d				13 16				13 32		13 36		13 46						14 02	14 02		14 06
Duke Street	d										13 38											14 08
Alexandra Parade	d										13 39											14 09
Barnhill	d										13 42											14 12
Springburn	a										13 44											14 14
Carntyne	d				13 19				13 36				13 49						14 06	14 06		
Shettleston	d				13 22				13 38				13 52						14 08	14 08		
Garrowhill	d				13 24				13 41				13 54						14 11	14 11		
Easterhouse	d				13 27				13 43				13 57						14 13	14 13		
Blairhill	d				13 31				13 47				14 01						14 17	14 17		
Coatbridge Sunnyside	d				13 33			13 39	13 50				14 03				14 09	14 09	14 20	14 20		
Coatdyke	d				13 36				13 52				14 06						14 22	14 22		
Airdrie	d				13a40			13 44	13 55				14a10				14 14	14 14	14 25	14 25		
Drumgelloch	d							13 47	13 58								14 17	14 17	14 28	14 28		
Caldercruix	d								14 02										14 32	14 32		
Blackridge	d								14 08										14 38	14 38		
Armadale	d								14 12										14 42	14 42		
Bathgate	a							14 00	14 16								14 30	14 30	14 46	14 46		
	d							14 01	14 17								14 31	14 31	14 47	14 47		
Livingston North	d							14 06	14 21								14 36	14 36	14 51	14 51		
Uphall	d							14 09	14 24								14 39	14 39	14 54	14 54		
Edinburgh Park	a							14 17	14 32								14 47	14 47	15 02	15 02		
Bridgeton	d			13 12			13 22					13 42			13 52							
Dalmarnock	d			13 14			13 24					13 44			13 54							
Rutherglen	d			13 16			13 27			13 35		13 46			13 57						14 05	
Cambuslang	d			13 20			13 30					13 50			14 00							
Newton	d			13 23								13 53										
Blantyre	d			13 27						13 43		13 57									14 13	
Hamilton West	d			13 30						13 46		14 00									14 16	
Hamilton Central	d			13 33						13 49		14 03									14 19	
Chatelherault	d									13 53											14 23	
Merryton	d									13 56											14 26	
Larkhall	a									14 00											14 30	
Airbles	d			13 38								14 08										
Uddingston	d					13 30	13 35								14 05							
Bellshill	d	13 19	13 19			13 34	13 39								14 09							
Motherwell	a			13 41			13 47					14 11		14 06	14 17							
	d			13 41										14 07	14 17	14 37						
Whifflet	a															14 47						
Coatbridge Central	a															14 49						
Shieldmuir	d														14 21							
Holytown	d			13 49		13 39																
Wishaw	d			13 55										14 14	14 25							
Carluke	d			14 01										14 22	14 31							
Carstairs	a													14 34								
Lanark	a			14 12											14 43							
Haymarket	a	14 03	14 04			14 42		14 25	14 37					15 18			14 52	14 52	15 07	15 10		
Edinburgh	a	14 11	14 10			14 48		14 30	14 45					15 25			14 57	14 58	15 15	15 15		

A To Cumbernauld

b Glasgow Central High Level

Table 226R

Mondays to Saturdays

9 December to 17 May

Helensburgh, Balloch, Dalmuir and Milngavie - Glasgow - Springburn, Airdrie, Bathgate, Hamilton, Larkhall, Motherwell, Coatbridge, Lanark and Edinburgh

Network Diagram - refer to first Page of Table 220

		SR	SR	SR	SR	SR	SR	SR	SR	SR	SR	SR	SR	SR	SR	SR	SR	SR	SR	SR	SR	SR	SR
					SO	SX									A						SO	SX	
Helensburgh Central	d								13 40								14 10						
Craigendoran	d								13 43								14 13						
Cardross	d								13 48								14 18						
Balloch	d			13 23									13 53										14 23
Alexandria	d			13 25									13 55										14 25
Renton	d			13 28									13 58										14 28
Dalreoch	d			13 31					13 53				14 01				14 23						14 31
Dumbarton Central	d			13 32					13 55				14 02				14 25						14 32
Dumbarton East	d			13 34					13 57				14 04				14 27						14 34
Bowling	d			13 39									14 09										14 39
Kilpatrick	d			13 42									14 12										14 42
Dalmuir	a			13 45					14 04				14 15				14 34						14 45
	d			13 46			13 53		14 05	14 01	14 08		14 16	14 23			14 35	14 31	14 38				14 46
Singer	d			13 48						14 03			14 18					14 33					14 48
Drumry	d			13 50						14 05			14 20					14 35					14 50
Drumchapel	d			13 53						14 08			14 23					14 38					14 53
Milngavie	d		13 42					13 57				14 12				14 27					14 42	14 42	
Hillfoot	d		13 45					14 00				14 15				14 30					14 45	14 45	
Bearsden	d		13 47					14 02				14 17				14 32					14 47	14 47	
Westerton	d		13 50	13 55				14 05		14 10		14 20	14 25			14 35		14 40			14 50	14 50	14 55
Anniesland	d		13 53	13 58				14 08		14 14		14 23	14 28			14 38		14 44			14 53	14 53	14 58
Clydebank	d						13 55				14 10			14 25					14 40				
Yoker	d						13 57				14 12			14 27					14 42				
Garscadden	d						14 01				14 16			14 31					14 46				
Scotstounhill	d						14 03				14 18			14 33					14 48				
Jordanhill	d						14 05				14 20			14 35					14 50				
Hyndland 3	d		13 57	14 01			14 07	14 12	14 14	14 17	14 22	14 27	14 31	14 37		14 42	14 44	14 47	14 52		14 57	14 57	15 01
Partick	d		13 59	14 04			14 10	14 14	14 17	14 20	14 25	14 29	14 34	14 40		14 44	14 47	14 50	14 55		14 59	14 59	15 04
Exhibition Centre	d		14 02				14 13			14 23		14 32		14 43				14 53			15 02	15 02	
Anderston	d		14 04				14 15			14 25		14 34		14 45				14 55			15 04	15 04	
Glasgow Central 15	a		14 05				14 16			14 26		14 35		14 46				14 56			15 05	15 05	
	d	14b05	14 07		14b18	14b18	14 18			14 28		14 37		14 48				14 58		15b05	15 07	15 07	
Argyle Street	d		14 09				14 19			14 30		14 39		14 49				15 00			15 09	15 09	
Charing Cross	d			14 08				14 19	14 24		14 29		14 38			14 49	14 54		14 59				15 08
Glasgow Queen St 10	a			14 10				14 21	14 26		14 31		14 40			14 51	14 56		15 01				15 10
	d			14 12				14 24	14 28		14 32		14 42			14 54	14 58		15 02				15 12
High Street	d			14 14				14 26	14 30		14 34		14 44			14 56	15 00		15 04				15 14
Bellgrove	d			14 16					14 32		14 36		14 46				15 02		15 06				15 16
Duke Street	d										14 38								15 08				
Alexandra Parade	d										14 39								15 09				
Barnhill	d										14 42								15 12				
Springburn	a										14 44								15 14				
Carntyne	d			14 19					14 36				14 49				15 06						15 19
Shettleston	d			14 22					14 38				14 52				15 08						15 22
Garrowhill	d			14 24					14 41				14 54				15 11						15 24
Easterhouse	d			14 27					14 43				14 57				15 13						15 27
Blairhill	d			14 31					14 47				15 01				15 17						15 31
Coatbridge Sunnyside	d			14 33				14 39	14 50				15 03			15 09	15 20						15 33
Coatdyke	d			14 36					14 52				15 06				15 22						15 36
Airdrie	d			14a40				14 44	14 55				15a10			15 14	15 25						15a40
Drumgelloch	d							14 47	14 58							15 17	15 28						
Caldercruix	d								15 02								15 32						
Blackridge	d								15 08								15 38						
Armadale	d								15 12								15 42						
Bathgate	a							15 00	15 16							15 30	15 46						
	d							15 01	15 17							15 31	15 47						
Livingston North	d							15 06	15 21							15 36	15 51						
Uphall	d							15 09	15 24							15 39	15 54						
Edinburgh Park	a							15 17	15 32							15 47	16 02						
Bridgeton	d		14 12				14 22					14 42		14 52							15 12	15 12	
Dalmarnock	d		14 14				14 24					14 44		14 54							15 14	15 14	
Rutherglen	d		14 16				14 27			14 35		14 46		14 57				15 06			15 16	15 16	
Cambuslang	d		14 20				14 30					14 50		15 00							15 20	15 20	
Newton	d		14 23									14 53									15 23	15 23	
Blantyre	d		14 27							14 43		14 57						15 13			15 27	15 27	
Hamilton West	d		14 30							14 46		15 00						15 16			15 30	15 30	
Hamilton Central	d		14 33							14 49		15 03						15 19			15 33	15 33	
Chatelherault	d									14 53								15 23					
Merryton	d									14 56								15 26					
Larkhall	a									15 00								15 30					
Airbles	d		14 38									15 08									15 38	15 38	
Uddingston	d				14 30	14 30	14 35							15 05									
Bellshill	d	14 19			14 34	14 34	14 39							15 09						15 19			
Motherwell	a		14 41				14 47					15 11		15 17							15 40	15 41	
	d		14 41											15 17	15 37						15 41	15 41	
Whifflet	a														15 47								
Coatbridge Central	a														15 49								
Shieldmuir	d													15 21									
Holytown	d		14 49		14 39	14 39															15 49	15 49	
Wishaw	d		14 55											15 25							15 55	15 55	
Carluke	d		15 01											15 31							16 01	16 01	
Carstairs	a																						
Lanark	a		15 12											15 42							16 12	16 12	
Haymarket	a	15 04			15 42	15 42		15 22	15 37							15 52	16 07			16 04			
Edinburgh	a	15 10			15 47	15 48		15 28	15 44							15 58	16 14			16 11			

A To Cumbernauld

b Glasgow Central High Level

Table 226R

Mondays to Saturdays

9 December to 17 May

Helensburgh, Balloch, Dalmuir and Milngavie - Glasgow - Springburn, Airdrie, Bathgate, Hamilton, Larkhall, Motherwell, Coatbridge, Lanark and Edinburgh

Network Diagram - refer to first Page of Table 220

		SR	SR	SR	SR		SR	SR SX ◇ A	SR ◇ B	SR	SR	SR	SR	SR	SR C		SR D	SR	SR	SR SX ◇ E	SR	SR SX	SR SO	SR SX	SR SO
Helensburgh Central	d				14 40			14c40	14c40									15 10		15c15					
Craigendoran	d				14 43													15 13							
Cardross	d				14 48													15 18							
Balloch	d											14 53													
Alexandria	d											14 55													
Renton	d											14 58													
Dalreoch	d				14 53							15 01						15 23							
Dumbarton Central	d				14 55			14 58	14 58			15 02						15 25		15 29					
Dumbarton East	d				14 57							15 04						15 27							
Bowling	d											15 09													
Kilpatrick	d											15 12													
Dalmuir	a				15 04			15 07	15 07			15 15						15 34		15 38					
	d		14 53		15 05		15 01	15 07	15 07	15 08		15 16	15 23					15 35	15 30	15 38	15 38				
Singer	d						15 03					15 18							15 32						
Drumry	d						15 05					15 20							15 34						
Drumchapel	d						15 08					15 23							15 37						
Milngavie	d			14 57							15 12			15 27										15 42	15 42
Hillfoot	d			15 00							15 15			15 30										15 45	15 45
Bearsden	d			15 02							15 17			15 32										15 47	15 48
Westerton	d			15 05			15 10				15 20	15 25		15 35					15 39					15 50	15 50
Anniesland	d			15 08			15 14				15 23	15 28		15 38					15 44					15 53	15 53
Clydebank	d		14 55							15 10			15 25								15 40				
Yoker	d		14 57							15 12			15 27								15 42				
Garscadden	d		15 01							15 16			15 31								15 46				
Scotstounhill	d		15 03							15 18			15 33								15 48				
Jordanhill	d		15 05							15 20			15 35								15 50				
Hyndland 3	d		15 07	15 12	15 14		15 17			15 22	15 27	15 31	15 37	15 42				15 44	15 47		15 52			15 57	15 57
Partick	d		15 10	15 14	15 17		15 20			15 25	15 29	15 34	15 40	15 44				15 47	15 50		15 55			15 59	15 59
Exhibition Centre	d		15 13				15 23				15 32		15 43						15 53					16 02	16 02
Anderston	d		15 15				15 25				15 34		15 45						15 55					16 04	16 04
Glasgow Central 15	a		15 16				15 26				15 37		15 46						15 56					16 05	16 05
	d	15b18	15 18				15 28				15 37		15 48		15b50				15 58			16b05	16b05	16 07	16 07
Argyle Street	d		15 19				15 30				15 38		15 49						16 00					16 09	16 09
Charing Cross	d			15 19	15 24					15 29		15 38		15 49				15 54			15 59				
Glasgow Queen St 10	a			15 21	15 26			15e30	15e30	15 31		15 40		15 51				15 56		15e59	16 01				
	d			15 24	15 28					15 32		15 42		15 54				15 58			16 02				
High Street	d			15 26	15 30					15 34		15 44		15 56				16 00			16 04				
Bellgrove	d				15 32					15 36		15 46						16 02			16 06				
Duke Street	d									15 38											16 08				
Alexandra Parade	d									15 39											16 09				
Barnhill	d									15 42											16 12				
Springburn	a									15 44											16 14				
Carntyne	d				15 36							15 49						16 06							
Shettleston	d				15 38							15 52						16 08							
Garrowhill	d				15 41							15 54						16 11							
Easterhouse	d				15 43							15 57						16 13							
Blairhill	d				15 47							16 01						16 17							
Coatbridge Sunnyside	d			15 39	15 50							16 03		16 09				16 20							
Coatdyke	d				15 52							16 06						16 22							
Airdrie	d			15 44	15 55							16a10		16 14				16 25							
Drumgelloch	d			15 47	15 58									16 17				16 28							
Caldercruix	d				16 02													16 32							
Blackridge	d				16 08													16 38							
Armadale	d				16 12													16 42							
Bathgate	a			16 00	16 16									16 30				16 46							
	d			16 01	16 17									16 31				16 47							
Livingston North	d			16 06	16 21									16 36				16 51							
Uphall	d			16 09	16 24									16 39				16 54							
Edinburgh Park	a			16 17	16 32									16 48				17 02							
Bridgeton	d		15 22								15 41		15 52											16 12	16 12
Dalmarnock	d		15 24								15 43		15 54											16 14	16 14
Rutherglen	d		15 27				15 35				15 46		15 57						16 05					16 16	16 16
Cambuslang	d		15 30								15 49		16 00											16 20	16 20
Newton	d										15 53													16 23	16 23
Blantyre	d						15 43				15 57								16 14					16 27	16 27
Hamilton West	d						15 46				16 00								16 17					16 30	16 30
Hamilton Central	d						15 49				16 02								16 20					16 33	16 33
Chatelherault	d						15 53												16 23						
Merryton	d						15 56												16 26						
Larkhall	a						16 00												16 30						
Airbles	d										16 07													16 38	16 38
Uddingston	d	15 30	15 35										16 06												
Bellshill	d	15 34	15 39										16 10									16 20	16 20		
Motherwell	a		15 48								16 11		16 17		16 07									16 41	16 41
	d												16 17		16 07		16 37							16 44	16 44
Whifflet	a																16 47							16 55	
Coatbridge Central	a																16 49							16 58	
Shieldmuir	d												16 21												
Holytown	d	15 39																							16 51
Wishaw	d												16 25		16 13										16 57
Carluke	d												16 31		16 26										17 04
Carstairs	a														16 35										
Lanark	a												16 42												17 15
Haymarket	a	16 46		16 22	16 37									16 52	17 04			17 14				17 08	17 09		
Edinburgh	a	16 52		16 28	16 43									16 57	17 09			17 19				17 13	17 14		

A from 31 March. From Mallaig
B until 29 March, SO from 5 April. From Mallaig
C To North Berwick
D To Cumbernauld
E from 31 March. From Oban
b Glasgow Central High Level
c Helensburgh Upper
e Glasgow Queen St High Level

Table 226R

Mondays to Saturdays

9 December to 17 May

Helensburgh, Balloch, Dalmuir and Milngavie - Glasgow - Springburn, Airdrie, Bathgate, Hamilton, Larkhall, Motherwell, Coatbridge, Lanark and Edinburgh

Network Diagram - refer to first Page of Table 220

		SR	SR	SR	SR	SR	SR SX	SR	SR	SR SO	SR SX	SR	SR SX	SR SO	SR	SR SO	SR SX	SR	SR	SR SO	SR SX	SR A
Helensburgh Central	d					15 40										16 10	16 10					
Craigendoran	d					15 43										16 13	16 13					
Cardross	d					15 48										16 18	16 18					
Balloch	d	15 23										15 53										
Alexandria	d	15 25										15 55										
Renton	d	15 28										15 58										
Dalreoch	d	15 31				15 53						16 01				16 23	16 23					
Dumbarton Central	d	15 32				15 55						16 02				16 25	16 25					
Dumbarton East	d	15 34				15 57						16 04				16 27	16 27					
Bowling	d	15 39										16 09										
Kilpatrick	d	15 42										16 12										
Dalmuir	a	15 45				16 06						16 15				16 34	16 34					
	d	15 46		15 53		16 07		16 01	16 09			16 16	16 23	16 23		16 35	16 35	16 31	16 38			
Singer	d	15 48						16 03				16 18						16 33				
Drumry	d	15 50						16 05				16 20						16 35				
Drumchapel	d	15 53						16 08				16 23						16 38				
Milngavie	d				15 57					16 12	16 12				16 27					16 42		
Hillfoot	d				16 00					16 15	16 15				16 30					16 45		
Bearsden	d				16 02					16 17	16 17				16 32					16 47		
Westerton	d	15 55			16 05			16 10		16 20	16 20	16 25			16 35			16 40		16 50		
Anniesland	d	15 59			16 08			16 14		16 23	16 23	16 29			16 38			16 44		16 53		
Clydebank	d			15 55					16 11				16 25	16 25					16 40			
Yoker	d			15 57					16 13				16 27	16 27					16 42			
Garscadden	d			16 01					16 16				16 31	16 31					16 46			
Scotstounhill	d			16 03					16 18				16 33	16 33					16 48			
Jordanhill	d			16 05					16 21				16 35	16 35					16 51			
Hyndland 3	d	16 02		16 07	16 12	16 15		16 17	16 23	16 27	16 27	16 32	16 37	16 37	16 42	16 44	16 44	16 47	16 53	16 57		
Partick ⛴	d	16 05		16 10	16 14	16 17		16 20	16 25	16 29	16 29	16 35	16 40	16 40	16 44	16 47	16 47	16 50	16 55	16 59		
Exhibition Centre	d			16 13				16 24		16 32	16 32		16 43	16 43				16 53		17 02		
Anderston	d			16 15			16 22	16 26		16 34	16 34		16 45	16 45				16 55		17 04	17 05	
Glasgow Central 15	a			16 16			16 23	16 27		16 35	16 35		16 46	16 46				16 56		17 05	17 06	
	d		16b18	16 18			16 24	16 28		16 37	16 37		16 48	16 48				16 58		17 07	17 07	
Argyle Street	d			16 19			16 26	16 29		16 39	16 39		16 50	16 50				17 00		17 09	17 09	
Charing Cross	d	16 10			16 19	16 24			16 29			16 39			16 49	16 54	16 54		16 59			
Glasgow Queen St 10 ⛴	a	16 12			16 21	16 26			16 31			16 41			16 51	16 56	16 56		17 01			
	d	16 12			16 24	16 28			16 32			16 42			16 54	16 58	16 58		17 02			
High Street	d	16 14			16 26	16 30			16 34			16 44			16 56	17 00	17 00		17 04			
Bellgrove	d	16 16				16 32			16 36			16 46				17 02	17 02		17 06			
Duke Street	d								16 38										17 08			
Alexandra Parade	d								16 39										17 09			
Barnhill	d								16 42										17 12			
Springburn	a								16 44										17 14			
Carntyne	d	16 20				16 36						16 49				17 06	17 06					
Shettleston	d	16 22				16 38						16 52				17 08	17 08					
Garrowhill	d	16 25				16 41						16 54				17 11	17 11					
Easterhouse	d	16 27				16 43						16 57				17 13	17 13					
Blairhill	d	16 31			16 38	16 47						17 01			17 08	17 17	17 17					
Coatbridge Sunnyside	d	16 34			16 40	16 50						17 03			17 10	17 20	17 20					
Coatdyke	d	16 36			16 43	16 52						17 06			17 13	17 22	17 22					
Airdrie	d	16a40			16 46	16 55						17a10			17 16	17 25	17 25					
Drumgelloch	d				16 49	16 58									17 19	17 28	17 28					
Caldercruix	d					17 02										17 32	17 32					
Blackridge	d					17 08										17 38	17 38					
Armadale	d					17 12										17 42	17 42					
Bathgate	a				17 02	17 16									17 31	17 46	17 46					
	d				17 02	17 17									17 32	17 47	17 47					
Livingston North	d				17 07	17 21									17 36	17 51	17 51					
Uphall	d				17 10	17 24									17 39	17 54	17 54					
Edinburgh Park	a				17 18	17 34									17 49	18 02	18 03					
Bridgeton	d			16 22						16 42	16 42		16 53	16 53						17 12	17 12	
Dalmarnock	d			16 24						16 44	16 44		16 55	16 55						17 14		
Rutherglen	d			16 27			16 31	16 34		16 46	16 46		16 57	16 57				17 05		17 16		
Cambuslang	d			16 30						16 50	16 50		17 02	17 02				17 08		17 20		
Newton	d									16 53	16 53									17 23		
Blantyre	d							16 43		16 57	16 57							17 15		17 27		
Hamilton West	d							16 46		17 00	17 00							17 19		17 30		
Hamilton Central	d							16 49		17 03	17 03							17 22		17 33		
Chatelherault	d							16 53										17 25				
Merryton	d							16 56										17 28				
Larkhall	a							17 00										17 31				
Airbles	d									17 08	17 08									17 38		
Uddingston	d		16 30	16 35									17 06	17 06							17 22	
Bellshill	d		16 35	16 39									17 11	17 11								
Motherwell	a			16 47			16 44			17 11	17 11		17 17	17 17						17 40	17 28	
	d						16 44				17 13			17 17						17 41	17 29	17 37
Whifflet	a										17 20											17 47
Coatbridge Central	a										17 22											17 49
Shieldmuir	d						16 54							17 21							17 32	
Holytown	d		16 40																	17 50		
Wishaw	d						16 57							17 25						17 55	17 36	
Carluke	d						17 04							17 31						18 02	17 44	
Carstairs	a																					
Lanark	a						17 15							17 42						18 12	17 54	
Haymarket	a		17 42		17 23	17 38									17 56	18 07	18 09					
Edinburgh	a		17 47		17 28	17 43									18 03	18 12	18 14					

A To Cumbernauld

b Glasgow Central High Level

Table 226R

Mondays to Saturdays

9 December to 17 May

Helensburgh, Balloch, Dalmuir and Milngavie - Glasgow - Springburn, Airdrie, Bathgate, Hamilton, Larkhall, Motherwell, Coatbridge, Lanark and Edinburgh

Network Diagram - refer to first Page of Table 220

		SR	SR SX	SR	SR SO	SR SX	SR SO		SR SX	SR	SR	SR SX	SR SO	SR	SR SX	SR SO	SR SX		SR	SR SX	SR SO	SR A	SR	SR	SR
Helensburgh Central	d										16 40													17 10	
Craigendoran	d										16 43													17 13	
Cardross	d										16 48													17 18	
Balloch	d			16 23															16 53						
Alexandria	d			16 25															16 55						
Renton	d			16 28															16 58						
Dalreoch	d			16 31							16 53								17 01					17 23	
Dumbarton Central	d			16 32							16 55								17 02					17 25	
Dumbarton East	d			16 34							16 57								17 04					17 27	
Bowling	d			16 39															17 09						
Kilpatrick	d			16 42															17 12						
Dalmuir	a			16 45							17 06								17 15					17 34	
	d			16 46			16 53		16 53		17 06	17 01	17 01	17 09					17 16	17 23	17 23			17 35	17 31
Singer	d			16 48								17 03	17 03						17 18						17 33
Drumry	d			16 50								17 05	17 05						17 20						17 35
Drumchapel	d			16 53								17 08	17 08						17 23						17 38
Milngavie	d		16 42							16 57						17 12	17 12						17 27		
Hillfoot	d		16 45							17 00						17 15	17 15						17 30		
Bearsden	d		16 47							17 02						17 18	17 18						17 33		
Westerton	d		16 50	16 55						17 05		17 10	17 10			17 21	17 21		17 25				17 36		17 40
Anniesland	d		16 53	16 58						17 08		17 14	17 14			17 24	17 24		17 28				17 39		17 44
Clydebank	d						16 55		16 55					17 11						17 25	17 25				
Yoker	d						16 57		16 57					17 13						17 27	17 27				
Garscadden	d						17 01		17 01					17 16						17 31	17 31				
Scotstounhill	d						17 03		17 03					17 18						17 33	17 33				
Jordanhill	d						17 05		17 05					17 21						17 35	17 35				
Hyndland 3	d		16 57	17 01			17 07		17 07	17 11	17 14	17 17	17 17	17 23		17 27	17 27		17 31	17 37	17 37		17 42	17 45	17 48
Partick	d		16 59	17 04			17 10		17 10	17 14	17 17	17 20	17 20	17 25		17 29	17 29		17 34	17 40	17 40		17 44	17 47	17 50
Exhibition Centre	d		17 06				17 13		17 13			17 23	17 23			17 32	17 34			17 43	17 43				17 53
Anderston	d		17 08				17 15		17 15			17 25	17 25		17 34	17 34	17 37			17 45	17 45				17 55
Glasgow Central 15	a		17 09				17 16		17 16			17 26	17 26		17 35	17 35	17 38			17 46	17 46				17 56
	d	17b08	17 10		17b18	17b18	17 18		17 18			17 28	17 28		17 36	17 37	17 39			17 48	17 48				17 58
Argyle Street	d		17 12				17 19		17 20			17 29	17 30		17 38	17 39	17 40			17 49	17 49				18 00
Charing Cross	d			17 08						17 19	17 24			17 29					17 38				17 49	17 55	
Glasgow Queen St 10	a			17 10						17 21	17 26			17 31					17 40				17 51	17 57	
	d			17 12						17 24	17 28			17 32					17 42				17 54	17 58	
High Street	d			17 14						17 26	17 30			17 34					17 44				17 56	18 00	
Bellgrove	d			17 16							17 32			17 36					17 46					18 02	
Duke Street	d													17 38											
Alexandra Parade	d													17 39											
Barnhill	d													17 42											
Springburn	a													17 44											
Carntyne	d			17 19							17 36								17 49					18 06	
Shettleston	d			17 22							17 38								17 52					18 08	
Garrowhill	d			17 24							17 41								17 54					18 11	
Easterhouse	d			17 27							17 43								17 57					18 13	
Blairhill	d			17 31						17 39	17 47								18 01					18 17	
Coatbridge Sunnyside	d			17 33						17 41	17 50								18 03				18 09	18 20	
Coatdyke	d			17 36						17 44	17 52								18 06					18 22	
Airdrie	d			17a40						17 47	17 55								18a10				18 14	18 25	
Drumgelloch	d									17 50	17 58												18 17	18 28	
Caldercruix	d										18 02													18 32	
Blackridge	d										18 08													18 38	
Armadale	d										18 12													18 42	
Bathgate	a									18 02	18 16												18 30	18 46	
	d									18 04	18 17												18 31	18 47	
Livingston North	d									18 08	18 21												18 36	18 51	
Uphall	d									18 11	18 24												18 39	18 54	
Edinburgh Park	a									18 19	18 33												18 48	19 04	
Bridgeton	d		17 15				17 22		17 23			17 32				17 42	17 43			17 52	17 52				
Dalmarnock	d		17 17				17 24		17 25			17 34				17 44	17 45			17 54	17 54				
Rutherglen	d		17 19				17 27		17 27			17 37	17 35		17 45	17 46	17 49			17 57	17 57				18 05
Cambuslang	d		17 23				17 30		17 31			17 40				17 50	17 53			18 00	18 00				
Newton	d		17 26						17 35							17 54	17 56								
Blantyre	d		17 30						17 39				17 43			17 58	18 00								18 14
Hamilton West	d		17 33						17 42				17 46			18 01	18 03								18 17
Hamilton Central	d		17 36						17 44				17 49			18 04	18 06								18 20
Chatelherault	d		17 39										17 53				18 09								18 23
Merryton	d		17 48										17 56				18 12								18 26
Larkhall	a		17 51										18 00				18 15								18 30
Airbles	d								17 49							18 09									
Uddingston	d				17u32	17u32	17 35					17 45								18 05	18 05				
Bellshill	d	17 23			17 36	17 36	17 39					17 49								18 09	18 09				
Motherwell	a						17 48		17 52			18 01			17 57	18 11				18 17	18 17				
	d								17 57			18 01			17 57						18 18	18 37			
Whifflet	a								18 09													18 47			
Coatbridge Central	a								18 11													18 49			
Shieldmuir	d											18 05			18 01						18 21				
Holytown	d				17 40	17 41																			
Wishaw	d											18 08			18 04						18 25				
Carluke	d											18 15			18 11						18 31				
Carstairs	a											18 24													
Lanark	a														18 21						18 42				
Haymarket	a	18 09			18 47	18 47				18 24	18 38												18 53	19 09	
Edinburgh	a	18 17			18 52	18 52				18 29	18 43												18 59	19 14	

A To Cumbernauld

b Glasgow Central High Level

Table 226R

Mondays to Saturdays

9 December to 17 May

Helensburgh, Balloch, Dalmuir and Milngavie - Glasgow - Springburn, Airdrie, Bathgate, Hamilton, Larkhall, Motherwell, Coatbridge, Lanark and Edinburgh

Network Diagram - refer to first Page of Table 220

		SR	SR	SR	SR	SR	SR	SR	SR	SR	SR	SR	SR	SR	SR	XC	SR	SR	SR	SR	SR	SR
																SO		W ThO				
																◇1	A	B				
Helensburgh Central	d								17 40											18 10		
Craigendoran	d								17 43											18 13		
Cardross	d								17 48											18 18		
Balloch	d				17 23								17 53									18 23
Alexandria	d				17 25								17 55									18 25
Renton	d				17 28								17 58									18 29
Dalreoch	d				17 31				17 53				18 01							18 23		18 32
Dumbarton Central	d				17 32				17 55				18 02							18 25		18 33
Dumbarton East	d				17 34				17 57				18 04							18 27		18 35
Bowling	d				17 39								18 09									18 40
Kilpatrick	d				17 42								18 12									18 43
Dalmuir	a				17 45				18 04				18 15							18 34		18 46
	d	17 38			17 46		17 54		18 05	18 01	18 08		18 16	18 23	18 31					18 35		18 47
Singer	d				17 48					18 03			18 18		18 33							18 49
Drumry	d				17 50					18 06			18 20		18 35							18 51
Drumchapel	d				17 53					18 08			18 23		18 38							18 54
Milngavie	d			17 42				17 57				18 12									18 42	
Hillfoot	d			17 45				18 00				18 15									18 45	
Bearsden	d			17 47				18 02				18 17									18 47	
Westerton	d			17 50	17 55			18 05		18 11		18 20	18 25		18 40						18 50	18 56
Anniesland	d			17 53	17 58			18 08		18 14		18 23	18 28		18 44						18 53	19 00
Clydebank	d	17 40					17 56				18 10			18 25						18 38		
Yoker	d	17 42					17 58				18 12			18 27						18 40		
Garscadden	d	17 46					18 01				18 16			18 31						18 43		
Scotstounhill	d	17 48					18 03				18 18			18 33						18 45		
Jordanhill	d	17 50					18 06				18 20			18 35						18 50		
Hyndland 3	d	17 52		17 57	18 01		18 08	18 12	18 14	18 17	18 22	18 27	18 31	18 37	18 47					18 52	18 57	19 03
Partick	d	17 55		17 59	18 04		18 10	18 14	18 17	18 20	18 25	18 29	18 34	18 40	18 50					18 54	18 59	19 05
Exhibition Centre	d			18 02			18 13			18 23		18 32		18 43	18 53						19 02	
Anderston	d			18 04			18 15			18 25		18 34		18 45	18 55						19 04	
Glasgow Central 15	a			18 05			18 16			18 26		18 35		18 46	18 56						19 05	
	d		18b05	18 07		18b18	18 18			18 28		18 37		18 48	18 58	19b00			19b05		19 07	
Argyle Street	d			18 09			18 19			18 30		18 39		18 49	19 00						19 09	
Charing Cross	d	17 59			18 08			18 19	18 24		18 29		18 38							18 58		19 09
Glasgow Queen St 10	a	18 01			18 10			18 21	18 26		18 31		18 42							19 00		19 11
	d	18 02			18 12			18 24	18 28		18 32		18 45							19 00		19 15
High Street	d	18 04			18 14			18 26	18 30		18 34		18 48							19 02		19 18
Bellgrove	d	18 06			18 16			18 29	18 32		18 36		18 50							19 04		19 20
Duke Street	d	18 08									18 38		18 52									19 22
Alexandra Parade	d	18 09									18 39		18 53									19 23
Barnhill	d	18 12									18 42		18 56									19 26
Springburn	a	18 14									18 44		18 58									19 28
Carntyne	d				18 19				18 36											19 08		
Shettleston	d				18 22				18 38											19 10		
Garrowhill	d				18 24				18 41											19 13		
Easterhouse	d				18 27				18 43											19 15		
Blairhill	d				18 31				18 47											19 19		
Coatbridge Sunnyside	d				18 33			18 40	18 50											19 22		
Coatdyke	d				18 36				18 52											19 24		
Airdrie	d				18a40			18 44	18 55											19 27		
Drumgelloch	d							18 47	18 58											19 30		
Caldercruix	d								19 02											19 34		
Blackridge	d								19 08											19 40		
Armadale	d								19 12											19 44		
Bathgate	a							19 00	19 16											19 47		
	d							19 01	19 17											19 49		
Livingston North	d							19 06	19 21											19 53		
Uphall	d							19 09	19 24											19 56		
Edinburgh Park	a							19 18	19 32											20 04		
Bridgeton	d			18 12			18 22					18 42		18 52							19 12	
Dalmarnock	d			18 14			18 24					18 44		18 54							19 14	
Rutherglen	d			18 16			18 27			18 35		18 46		18 57	19 05						19 16	
Cambuslang	d			18 20		18 27	18 30					18 50		19 00							19 20	
Newton	d			18 23								18 53									19 23	
Blantyre	d			18 27						18 43		18 57			19 13						19 27	
Hamilton West	d			18 30						18 46		19 00			19 16						19 30	
Hamilton Central	d			18 33						18 49		19 03			19 19						19 33	
Chatelherault	d									18 53					19 22							
Merryton	d									18 56					19 25							
Larkhall	a									19 00					19 30							
Airbles	d			18 38								19 08									19 38	
Uddingston	d					18 32	18 35							19 05								
Bellshill	d		18 19			18 37	18 39							19 09					19 19			
Motherwell	a			18 40			18 47					19 11		19 17		19 13					19 40	
	d			18 41										19 17		19 14	19 37	19 37			19 40	
Whifflet	a																19 47	19 57				
Coatbridge Central	a																19 49	20 02				
Shieldmuir	d													19 20								
Holytown	d			18 50		18 41															19 49	
Wishaw	d			18 57										19 24							19 54	
Carluke	d			19 04										19 31							20 01	
Carstairs	a																					
Lanark	a			19 14										19 42							20 12	
Haymarket	a		19 05			19 43		19 22	19 37							19 52			20 04	20 09		
Edinburgh	a		19 11			19 48		19 27	19 45							19 57			20 10	20 14		

A WThX until 25 February, from 28 February. To Cumbernauld

B until 27 February. To Cumbernauld

b Glasgow Central High Level

Table 226R

Mondays to Saturdays

9 December to 17 May

Helensburgh, Balloch, Dalmuir and Milngavie - Glasgow - Springburn, Airdrie, Bathgate, Hamilton, Larkhall, Motherwell, Coatbridge, Lanark and Edinburgh

Network Diagram - refer to first Page of Table 220

Station		SR SO ◇ A	SR	SR	SR	SR	SR	SR	SR	SR	SR B	SR	SR	SR W ThO C	SR	SR	SR	SR	SR	SR	SR	SR	SR
Helensburgh Central	d	18b34				18 40							19 10						19 40				
Craigendoran	d					18 43							19 13						19 43				
Cardross	d					18 48							19 18						19 48				
Balloch	d							18 53								19 23					19 53		
Alexandria	d							18 55								19 25					19 55		
Renton	d							18 58								19 28					19 58		
Dalreoch	d					18 53		19 01					19 23			19 31			19 53		20 01		
Dumbarton Central	d	18 45				18 55		19 02					19 25			19 32			19 55		20 02		
Dumbarton East	d					18 57		19 04					19 27			19 34			19 57		20 04		
Bowling	d							19 09								19 39					20 09		
Kilpatrick	d							19 12								19 42					20 12		
Dalmuir	a	18 56				19 04		19 15					19 34			19 45			20 04		20 15		
	d	18 56			19 01	19 05		19 16				19 31	19 35			19 46		20 01	20 05		20 16		20 31
Singer	d				19 03			19 18				19 33				19 48		20 03			20 18		20 33
Drumry	d				19 05			19 20				19 35				19 50		20 05			20 20		20 35
Drumchapel	d				19 08			19 23				19 38				19 53		20 08			20 23		20 38
Milngavie	d						19 12								19 42					20 12			
Hillfoot	d						19 15								19 45					20 15			
Bearsden	d						19 17								19 47					20 17			
Westerton	d				19 10		19 20	19 25				19 40			19 50	19 55		20 10		20 20	20 25		20 40
Anniesland	d				19 14		19 23	19 28				19 44			19 53	19 58		20 14		20 23	20 28		20 44
Clydebank	d					19 07							19 37						20 07				
Yoker	d					19 09							19 39						20 09				
Garscadden	d					19 13							19 43						20 13				
Scotstounhill	d					19 15							19 45						20 15				
Jordanhill	d					19 17							19 47						20 17				
Hyndland 3	d				19 17	19 21	19 27	19 31				19 47	19 51		19 57	20 01		20 17	20 21	20 27	20 31		20 47
Partick	d			19 10	19 20	19 23	19 29	19 34	19 40			19 50	19 53		19 59	20 04	20 10	20 20	20 23	20 29	20 34	20 40	20 50
Exhibition Centre	d			19 13	19 23		19 32		19 43			19 53			20 02		20 13	20 23		20 32		20 43	20 53
Anderston	d			19 15	19 25		19 34		19 45			19 55			20 04		20 15	20 25		20 34		20 45	20 55
Glasgow Central 15	a			19 16	19 26		19 36		19 46			19 56			20 05		20 16	20 26		20 36		20 46	20 56
	d		19e18	19 18	19 28		19 37		19 48	19e49		19 58			20 07		20 18	20 28		20 37		20 48	20 58
Argyle Street	d			19 19	19 30		19 38		19 49			20 00			20 09		20 19	20 30		20 39		20 49	21 00
Charing Cross	d					19 27		19 38					19 57			20 08			20 27		20 38		
Glasgow Queen St 10	a	19c19				19 29		19 42					19 59			20 12			20 29		20 42		
	d					19 30		19 45					20 00			20 15			20 30		20 45		
High Street	d					19 32		19 48					20 02			20 18			20 32		20 48		
Bellgrove	d					19 34		19 50					20 04			20 20			20 34		20 50		
Duke Street	d							19 52								20 22					20 52		
Alexandra Parade	d							19 53								20 23					20 53		
Barnhill	d							19 56								20 26					20 56		
Springburn	a							19 58								20 28					20 58		
Carntyne	d					19 37							20 07						20 37				
Shettleston	d					19 40							20 10						20 40				
Garrowhill	d					19 42							20 12						20 42				
Easterhouse	d					19 45							20 15						20 45				
Blairhill	d					19 49							20 19						20 49				
Coatbridge Sunnyside	d					19 51							20 21						20 51				
Coatdyke	d					19 54							20 24						20 54				
Airdrie	d					19 57							20 27						20 57				
Drumgelloch	d					20 00							20 30						21 00				
Caldercruix	d					20 04							20 34						21 04				
Blackridge	d					20 10							20 40						21 10				
Armadale	d					20 13							20 43						21 13				
Bathgate	a					20 17							20 47						21 17				
	d					20 19							20 49						21 19				
Livingston North	d					20 23							20 53						21 23				
Uphall	d					20 26							20 56						21 26				
Edinburgh Park	a					20 34							21 04						21 34				
Bridgeton	d			19 22			19 41		19 52						20 12		20 22			20 42		20 52	
Dalmarnock	d			19 24			19 43		19 54						20 14		20 24			20 44		20 54	
Rutherglen	d			19 27	19 35		19 46		19 57			20 05			20 16		20 27	20 35		20 46		20 57	21 05
Cambuslang	d			19 30			19 49		20 00						20 20		20 30			20 50		21 00	
Newton	d						19 53								20 23					20 53			
Blantyre	d				19 43		19 57					20 13			20 27			20 43		20 57			21 13
Hamilton West	d				19 46		20 00					20 16			20 30			20 46		21 00			21 16
Hamilton Central	d				19 49		20 03					20 19			20 33			20 49		21 03			21 19
Chatelherault	d				19 53							20 23						20 53					21 23
Merryton	d				19 56							20 26						20 56					21 26
Larkhall	a				20 00							20 30						21 00					21 30
Airbles	d						20 08								20 38					21 08			
Uddingston	d		19 32	19 35					20 05								20 35					21 05	
Bellshill	d		19 36	19 39					20 09								20 41					21 09	
Motherwell	a			19 47			20 11		20 17	20 04					20 40		20 48			21 11		21 17	
	d								20 17	20 05	20 37			20 37	20 40							21 17	
Whifflet	a										20 47			20 57									
Coatbridge Central	a										20 49			21 02									
Shieldmuir	d								20 20													21 20	
Holytown	d		19 41												20 49								
Wishaw	d								20 24	20 12					20 54							21 24	
Carluke	d								20 31	20 18					21 01							21 31	
Carstairs	a									20 27													
Lanark	a								20 42						21 12							21 43	
Haymarket	a		20 42			20 39				20 53			21 09						21 39				
Edinburgh	a		20 47			20 44				20 58			21 14						21 44				

A from 29 March. From Oban
B WThX until 25 February, from 28 February. To Cumbernauld
C until 27 February. To Cumbernauld
b Helensburgh Upper
c Glasgow Queen St High Level
e Glasgow Central High Level

Table 226R

Mondays to Saturdays

9 December to 17 May

Helensburgh, Balloch, Dalmuir and Milngavie - Glasgow - Springburn, Airdrie, Bathgate, Hamilton, Larkhall, Motherwell, Coatbridge, Lanark and Edinburgh

Network Diagram - refer to first Page of Table 220

Station		XC SO ◇1	SR	XC SX ◇1	SR A	SR W ThO B	SR	SR	SR SX ◇ C	SR ◇ D	SR	SR
Helensburgh Central	d		20 10						20c38	20c38		
Craigendoran	d		20 13									
Cardross	d		20 18									
Balloch	d							20 23				
Alexandria	d							20 25				
Renton	d							20 28				
Dalreoch	d		20 23					20 31				
Dumbarton Central	d		20 25					20 32	20 51	20 51		
Dumbarton East	d		20 27					20 34				
Bowling	d							20 39				
Kilpatrick	d							20 42				
Dalmuir	a		20 34					20 45	21 00	21 00		
	d		20 35					20 46	21 00	21 00		
Singer	d							20 48				
Drumry	d							20 50				
Drumchapel	d							20 53				
Milngavie	d						20 42					
Hillfoot	d						20 45					
Bearsden	d						20 47					
Westerton	d						20 50	20 55				
Anniesland	d						20 53	20 58				
Clydebank	d		20 37									
Yoker	d		20 39									
Garscadden	d		20 43									
Scotstounhill	d		20 45									
Jordanhill	d		20 47									
Hyndland 3	d		20 51				20 57	21 01				
Partick	d		20 53				20 59	21 04				21 10
Exhibition Centre	d						21 02					21 13
Anderston	d						21 04					21 15
Glasgow Central 15	a						21 05					21 16
	d	21b05		21b05			21 07				21b18	21 18
Argyle Street	d						21 08					21 19
Charing Cross	d		20 57					21 08				
Glasgow Queen St 10	a		20 59					21 12	21e18	21e18		
	d		21 00					21 15				
High Street	d		21 02					21 18				
Bellgrove	d		21 04					21 20				
Duke Street	d							21 22				
Alexandra Parade	d							21 23				
Barnhill	d							21 26				
Springburn	a							21 28				
Carntyne	d		21 07									
Shettleston	d		21 10									
Garrowhill	d		21 12									
Easterhouse	d		21 15									
Blairhill	d		21 19									
Coatbridge Sunnyside	d		21 21									
Coatdyke	d		21 24									
Airdrie	d		21 27									
Drumgelloch	d		21 30									
Caldercruix	d		21 34									
Blackridge	d		21 40									
Armadale	d		21 43									
Bathgate	a		21 47									
	d		21 49									
Livingston North	d		21 53									
Uphall	d		21 56									
Edinburgh Park	a		22 04									
Bridgeton	d						21 11					21 22
Dalmarnock	d						21 13					21 24
Rutherglen	d						21 16					21 27
Cambuslang	d						21 19					21 30
Newton	d						21 23					
Blantyre	d						21 27					
Hamilton West	d						21 30					
Hamilton Central	d						21 32					
Chatelherault	d											
Merryton	d											
Larkhall	a											
Airbles	d						21 37					
Uddingston	d										21 30	21 35
Bellshill	d										21 35	21 39
Motherwell	a			21 22			21 39					21 48
	d			21 23	21 37	21 37	21 40					
Whifflet	a				21 47	21 57						
Coatbridge Central	a				21 49	22 02						
Shieldmuir	d											
Holytown	d						21 49				21 40	
Wishaw	d						21 54					
Carluke	d						22 01					
Carstairs	a											
Lanark	a						22 13					
Haymarket	a	21 54	22 09								22 42	
Edinburgh	a	21 59	22 14	22 23							22 48	

Station		SR	SR	SR	SR	SR	SR	SR	SR	SR	SR	SR
Helensburgh Central	d		20 40					21 10				
Craigendoran	d		20 43					21 13				
Cardross	d		20 48					21 18				
Balloch	d				20 53					21 23		
Alexandria	d				20 55					21 25		
Renton	d				20 58					21 28		
Dalreoch	d		20 53		21 01			21 23		21 31		
Dumbarton Central	d		20 55		21 02			21 25		21 32		
Dumbarton East	d		20 57		21 04			21 27		21 34		
Bowling	d				21 09					21 39		
Kilpatrick	d				21 12					21 42		
Dalmuir	a		21 04		21 15			21 34		21 45		
	d	21 01	21 05		21 16		21 31	21 35		21 46		22 01
Singer	d	21 03			21 18		21 33			21 48		22 03
Drumry	d	21 05			21 20		21 35			21 50		22 05
Drumchapel	d	21 08			21 23		21 38			21 53		22 08
Milngavie	d			21 12					21 42			
Hillfoot	d			21 15					21 45			
Bearsden	d			21 17					21 47			
Westerton	d	21 10		21 20	21 25		21 40		21 50	21 55		22 10
Anniesland	d	21 14		21 23	21 28		21 44		21 53	21 58		22 14
Clydebank	d		21 07					21 37				
Yoker	d		21 09					21 39				
Garscadden	d		21 13					21 43				
Scotstounhill	d		21 15					21 45				
Jordanhill	d		21 17					21 47				
Hyndland 3	d	21 17	21 21	21 27	21 31		21 47	21 51	21 57	22 01		22 17
Partick	d	21 20	21 23	21 29	21 34	21 40	21 50	21 53	21 59	22 04	22 10	22 20
Exhibition Centre	d	21 23		21 32		21 43	21 53		22 02		22 13	22 23
Anderston	d	21 25		21 34		21 45	21 55		22 04		22 15	22 25
Glasgow Central 15	a	21 26		21 35		21 46	21 56		22 05		22 16	22 26
	d	21 28		21 37		21 48	21 58		22 07		22 18	22 28
Argyle Street	d	21 30		21 39		21 49	22 00		22 09		22 19	22 30
Charing Cross	d		21 27		21 38			21 57		22 08		
Glasgow Queen St 10	a		21 29		21 42			21 59		22 12		
	d		21 30		21 45			22 00		22 15		
High Street	d		21 32		21 48			22 02		22 18		
Bellgrove	d		21 34		21 50			22 04		22 20		
Duke Street	d				21 52					22 22		
Alexandra Parade	d				21 53					22 23		
Barnhill	d				21 56					22 26		
Springburn	a				21 58					22 28		
Carntyne	d		21 37					22 07				
Shettleston	d		21 40					22 10				
Garrowhill	d		21 42					22 12				
Easterhouse	d		21 45					22 15				
Blairhill	d		21 49					22 19				
Coatbridge Sunnyside	d		21 51					22 21				
Coatdyke	d		21 54					22 24				
Airdrie	d		21 57					22 27				
Drumgelloch	d		22 00					22 30				
Caldercruix	d		22 04					22 34				
Blackridge	d		22 10					22 40				
Armadale	d		22 13					22 43				
Bathgate	a		22 17					22 47				
	d		22 19					22 49				
Livingston North	d		22 23					22 53				
Uphall	d		22 26					22 56				
Edinburgh Park	a		22 34					23 04				
Bridgeton	d			21 42		21 52			22 12		22 23	
Dalmarnock	d			21 44		21 54			22 14		22 25	
Rutherglen	d	21 35		21 46		21 57	22 05		22 16		22 28	22 35
Cambuslang	d			21 50		22 00			22 20		22 30	
Newton	d			21 53					22 23			
Blantyre	d	21 43		21 57			22 13		22 27			22 43
Hamilton West	d	21 46		22 00			22 16		22 30			22 46
Hamilton Central	d	21 49		22 03			22 19		22 33			22 49
Chatelherault	d	21 53					22 23					22 53
Merryton	d	21 56					22 26					22 56
Larkhall	a	22 00					22 30					23 00
Airbles	d			22 08					22 38			
Uddingston	d					22 05					22 35	
Bellshill	d					22 09					22 39	
Motherwell	a			22 11		22 17			22 41		22 47	
	d					22 17			22 42			
Whifflet	a								22 49			
Coatbridge Central	a								22 51			
Shieldmuir	d					22 20						
Holytown	d											
Wishaw	d					22 24						
Carluke	d					22 31						
Carstairs	a											
Lanark	a					22 42						
Haymarket	a		22 39					23 09				
Edinburgh	a		22 44					23 14				

A WThX until 25 February, from 28 February. To Cumbernauld
B until 27 February. To Cumbernauld
C from 31 March. From Mallaig
D until 29 March, SO from 5 April. From Mallaig
b Glasgow Central High Level
c Helensburgh Upper
e Glasgow Queen St High Level

Table 226R

Mondays to Saturdays

9 December to 17 May

Helensburgh, Balloch, Dalmuir and Milngavie - Glasgow - Springburn, Airdrie, Bathgate, Hamilton, Larkhall, Motherwell, Coatbridge, Lanark and Edinburgh

Network Diagram - refer to first Page of Table 220

		SR	SR	SR	SR	SR	SR	SR	SR	SR	SR	SR	SR	SR FX	SR FO	SR FO	SR FO	SR	SR	SR FO	SR SX R A ✕
Helensburgh Central	d	21 40					22 10						22 40					23 10			23c24
Craigendoran	d	21 43					22 13						22 43					23 13			
Cardross	d	21 48					22 18						22 48					23 18			
Balloch	d			21 53						22 23				22 53	22 53				23 23		
Alexandria	d			21 55						22 25				22 55	22 55				23 25		
Renton	d			21 58						22 28				22 58	22 58				23 28		
Dalreoch	d	21 53		22 01			22 23			22 31			22 53	23 01	23 01			23 23	23 31		
Dumbarton Central	d	21 55		22 02			22 25			22 32			22 55	23 02	23 02			23 25	23 32		23 39
Dumbarton East	d	21 57		22 04			22 27			22 34			22 57	23 04	23 04			23 27	23 34		
Bowling	d			22 09						22 39				23 09	23 09				23 39		
Kilpatrick	d			22 12						22 42				23 12	23 12				23 42		
Dalmuir	a	22 04		22 15			22 35			22 45			23 05	23 15	23 15			23 34	23 45		23 50
	d	22 05		22 16		22 31	22 35			22 46		23 01	23 05	23 16	23 16		23 31	23 35			23 51
Singer	d			22 18		22 33				22 48		23 03		23 18	23 18		23 33				
Drumry	d			22 20		22 35				22 50		23 05		23 20	23 20		23 35				
Drumchapel	d			22 23		22 38				22 53		23 08		23 23	23 23		23 38				
Milngavie	d		22 12						22 42											23 42	
Hillfoot	d		22 15						22 45											23 45	
Bearsden	d		22 17						22 47											23 47	
Westerton	d		22 20	22 25		22 40			22 50	22 55		23 10		23 25	23 25		23 40			23 50	23 59
Anniesland	d		22 23	22 28		22 44			22 53	22 58		23 14		23 28	23 28		23 44			23 53	
Clydebank	d	22 07					22 37						23 07					23 37			
Yoker	d	22 09					22 39						23 09					23 39			
Garscadden	d	22 13					22 43						23 13					23 43			
Scotstounhill	d	22 15					22 45						23 15					23 45			
Jordanhill	d	22 17					22 47						23 17					23 47			
Hyndland 3	d	22 21	22 27	22 31		22 47	22 51		22 57	23 01		23 17	23 21	23 31	23 31		23 47	23 51		23 57	
Partick ⛴	d	22 23	22 29	22 34	22 40	22 50	22 53		22 59	23 04	23 10	23 20	23 23	23 34	23 34	23 40	23 50	23 53		23 59	
Exhibition Centre	d		22 32		22 43	22 53			23 02		23 13	23 23				23 43	23 53			00 02	
Anderston	d		22 34		22 45	22 55			23 04		23 15	23 25				23 45	23 55			00 04	
Glasgow Central 15	a		22 35		22 46	22 56			23 05		23 16	23 26				23 46	23 56			00 05	
	d		22 37		22 48	22 58		23b06	23 07		23 18	23 28				23 48	23 58			00 07	
Argyle Street	d		22 39		22 49	23 00			23 09		23 19	23 30				23 49	23 59			00 09	
Charing Cross	d	22 27		22 38			22 57			23 08			23 27	23 38	23 38			23 57			
Glasgow Queen St 10 ⛴	a	22 29		22 42			22 59			23 12			23 29	23 40	23 40			23 59			
	d	22 30		22 45			23 00			23 15			23 30	23 45	23 45			23 59			
High Street	d	22 32		22 48			23 02			23 18			23 32	23 48	23 48			00 02			
Bellgrove	d	22 34		22 50			23 04			23 20			23 34	23 50	23 50			00 04			
Duke Street	d			22 52						23 22					23 52						
Alexandra Parade	d			22 53						23 23					23 53						
Barnhill	d			22 56						23 26					23 56						
Springburn	a			22 58						23 28					23 58						
Carntyne	d	22 37					23 07						23 37	23 53				00 07			
Shettleston	d	22 40					23 10						23 40	23 56				00 10			
Garrowhill	d	22 42					23 12						23 42	23 58				00 12			
Easterhouse	d	22 45					23 15						23 45	00 02				00 15			
Blairhill	d	22 49					23 19						23 49	00 05				00 19			
Coatbridge Sunnyside	d	22 51					23 21						23 51	00 07				00 21			
Coatdyke	d	22 54					23 24						23 54	00 10				00 24			
Airdrie	d	22 57					23 27						23 57	00a13				00a28			
Drumgelloch	d	23 00					23 30						23 59								
Caldercruix	d	23 04					23 34						00 03								
Blackridge	d	23 10					23 40						00 09								
Armadale	d	23 13					23 43						00 13								
Bathgate	a	23 17					23 47						00 17								
	d	23 18																			
Livingston North	d	23 23																			
Uphall	d	23 26																			
Edinburgh Park	a	23 34																			
Bridgeton	d		22 42		22 52				23 12		23 22					23 53				00 12	
Dalmarnock	d		22 44		22 54				23 14		23 24					23 55				00 14	
Rutherglen	d		22 46		22 57	23 05			23 16		23 27	23 35				23 58	00 04			00 16	
Cambuslang	d		22 50		23 00			23 15	23 20		23 30					00 01				00 20	
Newton	d		22 53						23 23											00 23	
Blantyre	d		22 57			23 13			23 27			23 43					00 13			00 27	
Hamilton West	d		23 00			23 16			23 30			23 46					00 16			00 30	
Hamilton Central	d		23 03			23 19			23 33			23 49					00 19			00 33	
Chatelherault	d					23 23						23 53					00 23				
Merryton	d					23 26						23 56					00 26				
Larkhall	a					23 30						23 59					00 30				
Airbles	d		23 08						23 38											00 38	
Uddingston	d				23 05			23 20			23 35					00 05					
Bellshill	d				23 09			23 25			23 39					00 09					
Motherwell	a		23 11		23 17				23 41		23 47					00 17				00 41	
	d				23 17											00 17					
Whifflet	a																				
Coatbridge Central	a																				
Shieldmuir	d				23 20											00 20					
Holytown	d							23 29													
Wishaw	d				23 24											00 24					
Carluke	d				23 31											00 31					
Carstairs	a																				
Lanark	a				23 42											00 42					
Haymarket	a	23 39						00 29													
Edinburgh	a	23 44						00 34													00 50

A From Fort William

b Glasgow Central High Level

c Helensburgh Upper

Table 226R

Sundays

8 December to 11 May

Helensburgh, Balloch, Dalmuir and Milngavie - Glasgow - Springburn, Airdrie, Bathgate, Hamilton, Larkhall, Motherwell, Coatbridge, Lanark and Edinburgh

Network Diagram - refer to first Page of Table 220

		SR	SR	SR	SR	SR	SR	SR	SR	SR	SR	SR	SR	SR	SR	SR	SR	SR	SR	SR	SR	SR	SR
		A	B	B																			
Helensburgh Central	d							07 55			08 25				08 55			09 25					09 55
Craigendoran	d							07 58			08 28				08 58			09 28					09 58
Cardross	d							08 03			08 33				09 03			09 33					10 03
Balloch	d								08 09			08 39				09 09				09 39			
Alexandria	d								08 11			08 41				09 11				09 41			
Renton	d								08 14			08 44				09 14				09 44			
Dalreoch	d							08 08	08 17		08 38	08 47			09 08	09 17		09 38		09 47			10 08
Dumbarton Central	d							08 10	08 18		08 40	08 48			09 10	09 18		09 40		09 48			10 10
Dumbarton East	d							08 12	08 20		08 42	08 50			09 12	09 20		09 42		09 50			10 12
Bowling	d								08 25			08 55				09 25				09 55			
Kilpatrick	d								08 28			08 58				09 28				09 58			
Dalmuir	a							08 19	08 31		08 49	09 01			09 19	09 31		09 49		10 01			10 19
	d					07 45	08 01	08 20	08 31		08 50	09 01			09 20	09 31		09 50		10 01			10 20
Singer	d					07 47		08 22			08 52				09 22			09 52					10 22
Drumry	d					07 49		08 25			08 55				09 25			09 55					10 25
Drumchapel	d					07 52		08 27			08 57				09 27			09 57					10 27
Milngavie	d												09 11				09 41				10 11		
Hillfoot	d												09 14				09 44				10 14		
Bearsden	d												09 16				09 46				10 16		
Westerton	d					07 54		08 30			09 00		09 19		09 30		09 49	10 00			10 19		10 30
Anniesland	d					07 57		08 33			09 03		09 22		09 33		09 52	10 03			10 22		10 33
Clydebank	d						08 03		08 33			09 03				09 33				10 03			
Yoker	d						08 05		08 35			09 05				09 35				10 05			
Garscadden	d						08 09		08 39			09 09				09 39				10 09			
Scotstounhill	d						08 11		08 41			09 11				09 41				10 11			
Jordanhill	d						08 13		08 43			09 13				09 43				10 13			
Hyndland 3	d					08 00	08 15	08 35	08 45	08 55	09 05	09 15	09 25		09 35	09 45	09 55	10 05		10 15	10 25		10 35
Partick	d					08 03	08 18	08 38	08 48	08 58	09 08	09 18	09 28	09 36	09 38	09 48	09 58	10 08		10 18	10 28	10 36	10 38
Exhibition Centre	d						08 21		08 51	09 01		09 21	09 31	09 39		09 51	10 01			10 21	10 31	10 39	
Anderston	d																						
Glasgow Central 15	a						08 23		08 53	09 03		09 23	09 33	09 41		09 53	10 03			10 23	10 33	10 41	
	d						08 24		08 54	09 04		09 24	09 34	09 43		09 54	10 04		10b18	10 24	10 34	10 43	
Argyle Street	d															09 55	10 06			10 25	10 36	10 45	
Charing Cross	d					08 07		08 43			09 13				09 43			10 13					10 43
Glasgow Queen St 10	a					08 09		08 45			09 15				09 45			10 15					10 45
	d					08 10		08 45			09 15				09 45			10 15					10 45
High Street	d		00 02			08 12		08 47			09 17				09 47			10 17					10 47
Bellgrove	d		00 04			08 14		08 49			09 19				09 49			10 19					10 49
Duke Street	d																						
Alexandra Parade	d																						
Barnhill	d																						
Springburn	a																						
Carntyne	d		00 07			08 18		08 53			09 23				09 53			10 23					10 53
Shettleston	d		00 10			08 20		08 55			09 25				09 55			10 25					10 55
Garrowhill	d		00 12			08 23		08 58			09 28				09 58			10 28					10 58
Easterhouse	d	00 02	00 15			08 25		09 00			09 30				10 00			10 30					11 00
Blairhill	d	00 05	00 19			08 29		09 04			09 34				10 04			10 34					11 04
Coatbridge Sunnyside	d	00 07	00 21			08 32		09 07			09 37				10 07			10 37					11 07
Coatdyke	d	00 10	00 24			08 34		09 09			09 39				10 09			10 39					11 09
Airdrie	d	00a13	00a28			08 37		09 12			09 42				10 12			10 42					11 12
Drumgelloch	d					08 40		09 15			09 45				10 15			10 45					11 15
Caldercruix	d			00 03		08 44		09 19			09 49				10 19			10 49					11 19
Blackridge	d			00 09		08 50		09 25			09 55				10 25			10 55					11 25
Armadale	d			00 13		08 54		09 29			09 59				10 29			10 59					11 29
Bathgate	a			00 17		08 58		09 33			10 03				10 33			11 03					11 33
	d				07 55	08 59		09 34			10 03				10 34			11 04					11 34
Livingston North	d				07 59	09 04		09 38			10 08				10 38			11 08					11 38
Uphall	d				08 02	09 07		09 41			10 11				10 41			11 11					11 41
Edinburgh Park	a				08 10	09 15		09 53			10 22				10 49			11 23					11 49
Bridgeton	d						08 28		08 58	09 09		09 28	09 39			09 58	10 09			10 28	10 39		
Dalmarnock	d																				10 41		
Rutherglen	d						08 33		09 03	09 14		09 33	09 44	09 50		10 03	10 14			10 33	10 44	10 50	
Cambuslang	d						08 36		09 06	09 17		09 36	09 47			10 06	10 17			10 36	10 47		
Newton	d								09 10			09 40				10 10				10 40			
Blantyre	d								09 14			09 44		09 58		10 14				10 44		10 58	
Hamilton West	d								09 17			09 47		10 01		10 17				10 47		11 01	
Hamilton Central	d								09 19			09 49		10 04		10 19				10 49		11 04	
Chatelherault	d													10 07								11 07	
Merryton	d													10 10								11 10	
Larkhall	a													10 14								11 14	
Airbles	d								09 24			09 54				10 24				10 54			
Uddingston	d						08 41			09 22			09 52				10 22		10 31		10 52		
Bellshill	d						08 45			09 26			09 56				10 26		10 36		10 56		
Motherwell	a						08 52		09 27	09 33		09 57	10 03			10 27	10 33			10 57	11 03		
	d									09 34							10 34						
Whifflet	a																						
Coatbridge Central	a																						
Shieldmuir	d									09 37							10 37						
Holytown	d																		10 40				
Wishaw	d									09 41							10 41						
Carluke	d									09 47							10 47						
Carstairs	a																						
Lanark	a									09 59							10 59						
Haymarket	a				08 20	09 24		10 02			10 30				10 54			11 30	11 40				11 54
Edinburgh	a				08 25	09 29		10 07			10 35				10 59			11 35	11 45				11 59

A not 8 December. From Balloch
B not 8 December. From Helensburgh Central
b Glasgow Central High Level

Table 226R

Sundays

8 December to 11 May

Helensburgh, Balloch, Dalmuir and Milngavie - Glasgow - Springburn, Airdrie, Bathgate, Hamilton, Larkhall, Motherwell, Coatbridge, Lanark and Edinburgh

Network Diagram - refer to first Page of Table 220

		SR	SR	SR	SR	SR		SR	SR	SR	SR	SR	SR	SR	SR	SR		SR	SR	SR	SR	SR	SR	SR	SR
Helensburgh Central	d			10 25					10 55			11 25						11 55			12 25				12 55
Craigendoran	d			10 28					10 58			11 28						11 58			12 28				12 58
Cardross	d			10 33					11 03			11 33						12 03			12 33				13 03
Balloch	d	10 09			10 39					11 09				11 39					12 09			12 39			
Alexandria	d	10 11			10 41					11 11				11 41					12 11			12 41			
Renton	d	10 14			10 44					11 14				11 44					12 14			12 44			
Dalreoch	d	10 17		10 38	10 47				11 08	11 17		11 38		11 47				12 08	12 17		12 38	12 47			13 08
Dumbarton Central	d	10 18		10 40	10 48				11 10	11 18		11 40		11 48				12 10	12 18		12 40	12 48			13 10
Dumbarton East	d	10 20		10 42	10 50				11 12	11 20		11 42		11 50				12 12	12 20		12 42	12 50			13 12
Bowling	d	10 25			10 55					11 25				11 55					12 25			12 55			
Kilpatrick	d	10 28			10 58					11 28				11 58					12 28			12 58			
Dalmuir	a	10 31		10 49	11 01				11 19	11 31		11 49		12 01				12 19	12 31		12 49	13 01			13 19
	d	10 31		10 50	11 01				11 20	11 31		11 50		12 01				12 20	12 31		12 50	13 01			13 20
Singer	d			10 52					11 22			11 52						12 22			12 52				13 22
Drumry	d			10 55					11 25			11 55						12 25			12 55				13 25
Drumchapel	d			10 57					11 27			11 57						12 27			12 57				13 27
Milngavie	d		10 41			11 11					11 41				12 11					12 41			13 11		
Hillfoot	d		10 44			11 14					11 44				12 14					12 44			13 14		
Bearsden	d		10 46			11 16					11 46				12 16					12 46			13 16		
Westerton	d		10 49	11 00		11 19			11 30		11 49	12 00			12 19			12 30		12 49	13 00		13 19		13 30
Anniesland	d		10 52	11 03		11 22			11 33		11 52	12 03			12 22			12 33		12 52	13 03		13 22		13 33
Clydebank	d	10 33			11 03					11 33				12 03					12 33			13 03			
Yoker	d	10 35			11 05					11 35				12 05					12 35			13 05			
Garscadden	d	10 39			11 09					11 39				12 09					12 39			13 09			
Scotstounhill	d	10 41			11 11					11 41				12 11					12 41			13 11			
Jordanhill	d	10 43			11 13					11 43				12 13					12 43			13 13			
Hyndland 3	d	10 45	10 55	11 05	11 15	11 26			11 35	11 45	11 55	12 05		12 15	12 25			12 35	12 45	12 55	13 05	13 15	13 25		13 35
Partick	d	10 48	10 58	11 08	11 18	11 28		11 36	11 38	11 48	11 58	12 08		12 18	12 28	12 36		12 38	12 48	12 58	13 08	13 18	13 28	13 36	13 38
Exhibition Centre	d	10 51	11 01		11 21	11 31		11 39		11 51	12 01			12 21	12 31	12 39			12 51	13 01		13 21	13 31	13 39	
Anderston	d																								
Glasgow Central 15	a	10 53	11 03		11 23	11 33		11 41		11 53	12 03			12 23	12 33	12 41			12 53	13 03		13 23	13 33	13 41	
	d	10 54	11 04		11 24	11 34		11 43		11 54	12 04		12b18	12 24	12 34	12 43			12 54	13 04		13 24	13 34	13 43	
Argyle Street	d	10 55	11 06		11 25	11 36		11 45		11 55	12 06			12 25	12 35	12 45			12 55	13 06		13 25	13 36	13 45	
Charing Cross	d			11 13					11 43			12 13						12 43			13 13				13 43
Glasgow Queen St 10	a			11 15					11 45			12 15						12 45			13 15				13 45
	d			11 15					11 45			12 15						12 45			13 15				13 45
High Street	d			11 17					11 47			12 17						12 47			13 17				13 47
Bellgrove	d			11 19					11 49			12 19						12 49			13 19				13 49
Duke Street	d																								
Alexandra Parade	d																								
Barnhill	d																								
Springburn	a																								
Carntyne	d			11 23					11 53			12 23						12 53			13 23				13 53
Shettleston	d			11 25					11 55			12 25						12 55			13 25				13 55
Garrowhill	d			11 28					11 58			12 28						12 58			13 28				13 58
Easterhouse	d			11 30					12 00			12 30						13 00			13 30				14 00
Blairhill	d			11 34					12 04			12 34						13 04			13 34				14 04
Coatbridge Sunnyside	d			11 37					12 07			12 37						13 07			13 37				14 07
Coatdyke	d			11 39					12 09			12 39						13 09			13 39				14 09
Airdrie	d			11 43					12 12			12 42						13 12			13 42				14 12
Drumgelloch	d			11 46					12 15			12 45						13 15			13 45				14 15
Caldercruix	d			11 50					12 19			12 49						13 19			13 49				14 19
Blackridge	d			11 56					12 25			12 55						13 25			13 55				14 25
Armadale	d			12 00					12 29			12 59						13 29			13 59				14 29
Bathgate	a			12 04					12 33			13 03						13 33			14 03				14 33
	d			12 04					12 34			13 04						13 34			14 04				14 34
Livingston North	d			12 08					12 38			13 08						13 38			14 08				14 38
Uphall	d			12 11					12 41			13 11						13 41			14 11				14 41
Edinburgh Park	a			12 19					12 49			13 19						13 49			14 19				14 49
Bridgeton	d	10 58	11 09		11 28	11 39				11 58	12 09			12 28	12 38				12 58	13 09		13 28	13 39		
Dalmarnock	d	11 00	11 11		11 30	11 41				12 00	12 11			12 30	12 40				13 00	13 11		13 30	13 41		
Rutherglen	d	11 03	11 14		11 33	11 44		11 50		12 03	12 14			12 33	12 43	12 51			13 03	13 14		13 33	13 44	13 50	
Cambuslang	d	11 06	11 17		11 36	11 47				12 06	12 17			12 36	12 45				13 06	13 17		13 36	13 47		
Newton	d	11 10			11 40					12 10				12 40					13 10			13 40			
Blantyre	d	11 14			11 44			11 58		12 14				12 44		12 59			13 14			13 44		13 58	
Hamilton West	d	11 17			11 47			12 01		12 17				12 47		13 02			13 17			13 47		14 01	
Hamilton Central	d	11 19			11 49			12 04		12 19				12 49		13 05			13 19			13 49		14 04	
Chatelherault	d							12 07								13 08								14 07	
Merryton	d							12 10								13 11								14 10	
Larkhall	a							12 14								13 14								14 14	
Airbles	d	11 24			11 54					12 24				12 54					13 24			13 54			
Uddingston	d		11 22			11 52					12 22		12 31		12 50					13 22			13 52		
Bellshill	d		11 26			11 56					12 26		12 36		12 54					13 26			13 57		
Motherwell	a	11 27	11 33		11 57	12 03				12 29	12 33			12 57	13 03				13 27	13 33		13 57	14 06		
	d		11 34								12 34									13 34					
Whifflet	a																								
Coatbridge Central	a																								
Shieldmuir	d		11 37								12 37									13 37					
Holytown	d												12 40												
Wishaw	d		11 41								12 41									13 41					
Carluke	d		11 47								12 47									13 47					
Carstairs	a																								
Lanark	a		11 59								12 59									13 59					
Haymarket	a			12 27					12 54			13 24	13 40					13 54			14 25				14 54
Edinburgh	a			12 32					12 59			13 29	13 45					13 59			14 30				14 59

b Glasgow Central High Level

Table 226R

Sundays

8 December to 11 May

Helensburgh, Balloch, Dalmuir and Milngavie - Glasgow - Springburn, Airdrie, Bathgate, Hamilton, Larkhall, Motherwell, Coatbridge, Lanark and Edinburgh

Network Diagram - refer to first Page of Table 220

		SR		SR	SR	SR	SR	SR	SR	SR	SR	SR		SR	SR	SR	SR	SR ◇ A	SR	SR	SR	SR		SR	SR
Helensburgh Central	d				13 25					13 55				14 25				14c40	14 55			15 25			
Craigendoran	d				13 28					13 58				14 28					14 58			15 28			
Cardross	d				13 33					14 03				14 33					15 03			15 33			
Balloch	d	13 09					13 39				14 09				14 39					15 09					15 39
Alexandria	d	13 11					13 41				14 11				14 41					15 11					15 41
Renton	d	13 14					13 44				14 14				14 44					15 14					15 44
Dalreoch	d	13 17			13 38		13 47			14 08	14 17			14 38	14 47				15 08	15 17		15 38			15 47
Dumbarton Central	d	13 18			13 40		13 48			14 10	14 18			14 40	14 48			14 57	15 10	15 18		15 40			15 48
Dumbarton East	d	13 20			13 42		13 50			14 12	14 20			14 42	14 50				15 12	15 20		15 42			15 50
Bowling	d	13 25					13 55				14 25				14 55					15 25					15 55
Kilpatrick	d	13 28					13 58				14 28				14 58					15 28					15 58
Dalmuir	a	13 31			13 49		14 01			14 19	14 31			14 49	15 01			15 06	15 19	15 31		15 49			16 01
	d	13 31			13 50		14 01			14 20	14 31			14 50	15 01			15 06	15 20	15 31		15 50			16 01
Singer	d				13 52					14 22				14 52					15 22			15 52			
Drumry	d				13 55					14 25				14 55					15 25			15 55			
Drumchapel	d				13 57					14 27				14 57					15 27			15 57			
Milngavie	d			13 41				14 11				14 41				15 11					15 41				
Hillfoot	d			13 44				14 14				14 44				15 14					15 44				
Bearsden	d			13 46				14 16				14 46				15 16					15 46				
Westerton	d			13 49	14 00			14 19		14 30		14 49		15 00		15 19			15 30		15 49	16 00			
Anniesland	d			13 52	14 03			14 22		14 33		14 52		15 03		15 22			15 33		15 52	16 03			
Clydebank	d	13 33					14 03				14 33				15 03					15 33					16 03
Yoker	d	13 35					14 05				14 35				15 05					15 35					16 05
Garscadden	d	13 39					14 09				14 39				15 09					15 39					16 09
Scotstounhill	d	13 41					14 11				14 41				15 11					15 41					16 11
Jordanhill	d	13 43					14 13				14 43				15 13					15 43					16 13
Hyndland 3	d	13 45		13 55	14 05		14 15	14 25		14 35	14 45	14 55		15 05	15 15	15 25			15 35	15 45	15 55	16 05			16 15
Partick	d	13 48		13 58	14 08		14 18	14 28	14 36	14 38	14 48	14 58		15 08	15 18	15 28	15 36		15 38	15 48	15 58	16 08			16 18
Exhibition Centre	d	13 51		14 01			14 21	14 31	14 39		14 51	15 01			15 21	15 31	15 39			15 51	16 01				16 21
Anderston	d																								
Glasgow Central 15	a	13 53		14 03			14 23	14 33	14 41		14 53	15 03			15 23	15 33	15 41			15 53	16 03				16 23
	d	13 54		14 04		14b18	14 24	14 34	14 43		14 54	15 04			15 24	15 34	15 43			15 54	16 04			16b18	16 24
Argyle Street	d	13 55		14 06			14 25	14 36	14 45		14 55	15 06			15 25	15 36	15 45			15 55	16 06				16 25
Charing Cross	d				14 13					14 43				15 13					15 43			16 13			
Glasgow Queen St 10	a				14 15					14 45				15 15				15e30	15 45			16 15			
	d				14 15					14 45				15 15					15 45			16 15			
High Street	d				14 17					14 47				15 17					15 47			16 17			
Bellgrove	d				14 19					14 49				15 19					15 49			16 19			
Duke Street	d																								
Alexandra Parade	d																								
Barnhill	d																								
Springburn	a																								
Carntyne	d				14 23					14 53				15 23					15 53			16 23			
Shettleston	d				14 25					14 55				15 25					15 55			16 25			
Garrowhill	d				14 28					14 58				15 28					15 58			16 28			
Easterhouse	d				14 30					15 00				15 30					16 00			16 30			
Blairhill	d				14 34					15 04				15 34					16 04			16 34			
Coatbridge Sunnyside	d				14 37					15 07				15 37					16 07			16 37			
Coatdyke	d				14 39					15 09				15 39					16 09			16 39			
Airdrie	d				14 42					15 12				15 42					16 12			16 42			
Drumgelloch	d				14 45					15 15				15 45					16 15			16 45			
Caldercruix	d				14 49					15 19				15 49					16 19			16 49			
Blackridge	d				14 55					15 25				15 55					16 25			16 55			
Armadale	d				14 59					15 29				15 59					16 29			16 59			
Bathgate	a				15 03					15 33				16 03					16 33			17 03			
	d				15 04					15 34				16 04					16 34			17 04			
Livingston North	d				15 08					15 38				16 08					16 38			17 08			
Uphall	d				15 11					15 41				16 11					16 41			17 11			
Edinburgh Park	a				15 19					15 49				16 19					16 49			17 19			
Bridgeton	d	13 58		14 09			14 28	14 39			14 58	15 09			15 28	15 39				15 58	16 09				16 28
Dalmarnock	d	14 00		14 11			14 30	14 41			15 00	15 11			15 30	15 41				16 00	16 11				16 30
Rutherglen	d	14 03		14 14			14 33	14 44	14 50		15 03	15 14			15 33	15 44	15 50			16 03	16 14				16 33
Cambuslang	d	14 06		14 17			14 36	14 47			15 06	15 17			15 36	15 47				16 06	16 17				16 36
Newton	d	14 10					14 40				15 10				15 40					16 10					16 40
Blantyre	d	14 14					14 44		14 58		15 14				15 44		15 58			16 14					16 44
Hamilton West	d	14 17					14 47		15 01		15 17				15 47		16 01			16 17					16 47
Hamilton Central	d	14 19					14 49		15 04		15 19				15 49		16 04			16 19					16 49
Chatelherault	d								15 07								16 07								
Merryton	d								15 10								16 10								
Larkhall	a								15 14								16 14								
Airbles	d	14 24					14 54				15 24				15 54					16 24					16 54
Uddingston	d			14 22		14 31		14 52				15 22				15 52					16 22			16 31	
Bellshill	d			14 26		14 36		14 56				15 26				15 56					16 26			16 36	
Motherwell	a	14 27		14 33			14 57	15 03			15 27	15 33			15 57	16 03				16 28	16 33				16 57
	d			14 34								15 34									16 34				
Whifflet	a																								
Coatbridge Central	a																								
Shieldmuir	d			14 37								15 37									16 37				
Holytown	d					14 40																		16 40	
Wishaw	d			14 41								15 41									16 41				
Carluke	d			14 47								15 47									16 47				
Carstairs	a																								
Lanark	a			14 59								15 59									16 59				
Haymarket	a				15 24	15 43				15 54				16 24					16 54			17 24		17 43	
Edinburgh	a				15 29	15 48				15 59				16 29					16 59			17 29		17 48	

A from 30 March. From Mallaig
b Glasgow Central High Level
c Helensburgh Upper
e Glasgow Queen St High Level

Table 226R

Sundays

8 December to 11 May

Helensburgh, Balloch, Dalmuir and Milngavie - Glasgow - Springburn, Airdrie, Bathgate, Hamilton, Larkhall, Motherwell, Coatbridge, Lanark and Edinburgh

Network Diagram - refer to first Page of Table 220

		SR	SR	SR	SR	SR	SR	SR	SR	SR	SR	SR	SR	SR	SR	SR	SR	SR	SR	SR	SR	SR	SR
																							◇ A
Helensburgh Central	d			15 55			16 25				16 55			17 25					17 55			18 25	18c34
Craigendoran	d			15 58			16 28				16 58			17 28					17 58			18 28	
Cardross	d			16 03			16 33				17 03			17 33					18 03			18 33	
Balloch	d				16 09			16 39				17 09				17 39				18 09			
Alexandria	d				16 11			16 41				17 11				17 41				18 11			
Renton	d				16 14			16 44				17 14				17 44				18 14			
Dalreoch	d			16 08	16 17		16 38	16 47			17 08	17 17		17 38		17 47			18 08	18 17		18 38	
Dumbarton Central	d			16 10	16 18		16 40	16 48			17 10	17 18		17 40		17 48			18 10	18 18		18 40	18 45
Dumbarton East	d			16 12	16 20		16 42	16 50			17 12	17 20		17 42		17 50			18 12	18 20		18 42	
Bowling	d				16 25			16 55				17 25				17 55				18 25			
Kilpatrick	d				16 28			16 58				17 28				17 58				18 28			
Dalmuir	a			16 19	16 31		16 49	17 01			17 19	17 31		17 49		18 01			18 19	18 31		18 49	18 56
	d			16 20	16 31		16 50	17 01			17 20	17 31		17 50		18 01			18 20	18 31		18 50	18 56
Singer	d			16 22			16 52				17 22			17 52					18 22			18 52	
Drumry	d			16 25			16 55				17 25			17 55					18 25			18 55	
Drumchapel	d			16 27			16 57				17 27			17 57					18 27			18 57	
Milngavie	d	16 11				16 41			17 11				17 41				18 11				18 41		
Hillfoot	d	16 14				16 44			17 14				17 44				18 14				18 44		
Bearsden	d	16 16				16 46			17 16				17 46				18 16				18 46		
Westerton	d	16 19		16 30		16 49	17 00		17 19		17 30		17 49	18 00			18 19		18 30		18 49	19 00	
Anniesland	d	16 22		16 33		16 52	17 03		17 22		17 33		17 52	18 03			18 22		18 33		18 52	19 03	
Clydebank	d				16 33			17 03				17 33				18 03				18 33			
Yoker	d				16 35			17 05				17 35				18 05				18 35			
Garscadden	d				16 39			17 09				17 39				18 09				18 39			
Scotstounhill	d				16 41			17 11				17 41				18 11				18 41			
Jordanhill	d				16 43			17 13				17 43				18 13				18 43			
Hyndland 3	d	16 25		16 35	16 45	16 55	17 05	17 15	17 25		17 35	17 45	17 55	18 05		18 15	18 25		18 35	18 45	18 55	19 05	
Partick	d	16 28	16 36	16 38	16 48	16 58	17 08	17 18	17 28	17 36	17 38	17 48	17 58	18 08		18 18	18 28	18 36	18 38	18 48	18 58	19 08	
Exhibition Centre	d	16 31	16 39		16 51	17 01		17 21	17 31	17 39		17 51	18 01			18 21	18 31	18 39		18 51	19 01		
Anderston	d																						
Glasgow Central 15	a	16 33	16 41		16 53	17 03		17 23	17 33	17 41		17 53	18 03			18 23	18 33	18 41		18 53	19 03		
	d	16 34	16 43		16 54	17 04		17 24	17 34	17 43		17 54	18 04		18b18	18 24	18 34	18 43		18 54	19 04		
Argyle Street	d	16 36	16 45		16 55	17 06		17 25	17 36	17 45		17 55	18 06										
Charing Cross	d			16 43			17 13				17 43			18 13					18 43			19 13	
Glasgow Queen St 10	a			16 45			17 15				17 45			18 15					18 45			19 15	19e15
	d			16 45			17 15				17 45			18 15					18 45			19 15	
High Street	d			16 47			17 17				17 47			18 17					18 47			19 17	
Bellgrove	d			16 49			17 19				17 49			18 19					18 49			19 19	
Duke Street	d																						
Alexandra Parade	d																						
Barnhill	d																						
Springburn	a																						
Carntyne	d			16 53			17 23				17 53			18 23					18 53			19 23	
Shettleston	d			16 55			17 25				17 55			18 25					18 55			19 25	
Garrowhill	d			16 58			17 28				17 58			18 28					18 58			19 28	
Easterhouse	d			17 00			17 30				18 00			18 30					19 00			19 30	
Blairhill	d			17 04			17 34				18 04			18 34					19 04			19 34	
Coatbridge Sunnyside	d			17 07			17 37				18 07			18 37					19 07			19 37	
Coatdyke	d			17 09			17 39				18 09			18 39					19 09			19 39	
Airdrie	d			17 12			17 42				18 12			18 42					19 12			19a43	
Drumgelloch	d			17 15			17 45				18 15			18 45					19 15				
Caldercruix	d			17 19			17 49				18 19			18 49					19 19				
Blackridge	d			17 25			17 55				18 25			18 55					19 25				
Armadale	d			17 29			17 59				18 29			18 59					19 29				
Bathgate	a			17 33			18 03				18 33			19 03					19 33				
	d			17 34			18 04				18 34			19 04					19 34				
Livingston North	d			17 38			18 08				18 38			19 08					19 38				
Uphall	d			17 41			18 11				18 41			19 11					19 41				
Edinburgh Park	a			17 49			18 19				18 49			19 19					19 49				
Bridgeton	d	16 39			16 58	17 09		17 28	17 39			17 58	18 09			18 28	18 39			18 58	19 09		
Dalmarnock	d	16 41			17 00	17 11		17 30	17 41			18 00	18 11										
Rutherglen	d	16 44	16 50		17 03	17 14		17 33	17 44	17 50		18 03	18 14			18 33	18 44	18 50		19 03	19 14		
Cambuslang	d	16 50			17 06	17 17		17 36	17 47			18 06	18 17			18 36	18 47			19 06	19 17		
Newton	d				17 10			17 40				18 10				18 40				19 10			
Blantyre	d		16 58		17 14			17 44		17 59		18 14				18 44		18 58		19 14			
Hamilton West	d		17 01		17 17			17 47		18 02		18 17				18 47		19 01		19 17			
Hamilton Central	d		17 04		17 19			17 49		18 04		18 19				18 49		19 04		19 19			
Chatelherault	d		17 07							18 08								19 07					
Merryton	d		17 10							18 11								19 10					
Larkhall	a		17 14							18 14								19 14					
Airbles	d				17 24			17 54				18 24				18 54				19 24			
Uddingston	d	16 54				17 22			17 52				18 22		18 31		18 52				19 22		
Bellshill	d	16 59				17 26			17 56				18 26		18 36		18 56				19 26		
Motherwell	a	17 05			17 27	17 33		17 57	18 03			18 27	18 33			18 57	19 03			19 27	19 33		
	d					17 34							18 34								19 34		
Whifflet	a																						
Coatbridge Central	a																						
Shieldmuir	d					17 37							18 37								19 37		
Holytown	d														18 40								
Wishaw	d					17 41							18 41								19 41		
Carluke	d					17 47							18 47								19 47		
Carstairs	a																						
Lanark	a					17 59							18 59								19 59		
Haymarket	a			17 54			18 24				18 54			19 24	19 43				19 54				
Edinburgh	a			17 59			18 29				18 59			19 29	19 48				19 59				

A from 30 March. From Oban
b Glasgow Central High Level
c Helensburgh Upper
e Glasgow Queen St High Level

Table 226R

Sundays

8 December to 11 May

Helensburgh, Balloch, Dalmuir and Milngavie - Glasgow - Springburn, Airdrie, Bathgate, Hamilton, Larkhall, Motherwell, Coatbridge, Lanark and Edinburgh

Network Diagram - refer to first Page of Table 220

		SR	SR	SR	SR	SR	SR	SR	SR	SR	SR	SR	SR	SR	XC	SR	SR	SR	SR	SR	SR	SR
															◇1						◇ A	
Helensburgh Central	d				18 55			19 25					19 55				20 25				20c38	20 55
Craigendoran	d				18 58			19 28					19 58				20 28					20 58
Cardross	d				19 03			19 33					20 03				20 33					21 03
Balloch	d	18 39				19 09				19 39				20 09				20 39				
Alexandria	d	18 41				19 11				19 41				20 11				20 41				
Renton	d	18 44				19 14				19 44				20 14				20 44				
Dalreoch	d	18 47			19 08	19 17		19 38		19 47			20 08	20 17			20 38	20 47				21 08
Dumbarton Central	d	18 48			19 10	19 18		19 40		19 48			20 10	20 18			20 40	20 48			20 54	21 10
Dumbarton East	d	18 50			19 12	19 20		19 42		19 50			20 12	20 20			20 42	20 50				21 12
Bowling	d	18 55				19 25				19 55				20 25				20 55				
Kilpatrick	d	18 58				19 28				19 58				20 28				20 58				
Dalmuir	a	19 01			19 19	19 31		19 49		20 01			20 19	20 31			20 49	21 01			21 05	21 19
	d	19 01			19 20	19 31		19 50		20 01			20 20	20 31			20 50	21 01			21 05	21 20
Singer	d				19 22			19 52					20 22				20 52					21 22
Drumry	d				19 25			19 55					20 25				20 55					21 25
Drumchapel	d				19 27			19 57					20 27				20 57					21 27
Milngavie	d		19 11				19 41				20 11					20 41			21 11			
Hillfoot	d		19 14				19 44				20 14					20 44			21 14			
Bearsden	d		19 16				19 46				20 16					20 46			21 16			
Westerton	d		19 19		19 30		19 49	20 00			20 19		20 30			20 49	21 00		21 19			21 30
Anniesland	d		19 22		19 33		19 52	20 03			20 22		20 33			20 52	21 03		21 22			21 33
Clydebank	d	19 03				19 33				20 03				20 33				21 03				
Yoker	d	19 05				19 35				20 05				20 35				21 05				
Garscadden	d	19 09				19 39				20 09				20 39				21 09				
Scotstounhill	d	19 11				19 41				20 11				20 41				21 11				
Jordanhill	d	19 13				19 43				20 13				20 43				21 13				
Hyndland 3	d	19 15	19 25		19 35	19 45	19 55	20 05		20 15	20 25		20 35	20 45		20 55	21 05	21 15	21 25			21 35
Partick	d	19 18	19 28	19 36	19 38	19 48	19 58	20 08		20 18	20 28	20 36	20 38	20 48		20 58	21 08	21 18	21 28	21 36		21 38
Exhibition Centre	d	19 21	19 31	19 39		19 51	20 01			20 21	20 31	20 39		20 51		21 01		21 21	21 31	21 39		
Anderston	d																					
Glasgow Central 15	a	19 24	19 33	19 41		19 53	20 03			20 23	20 33	20 41		20 53		21 03		21 23	21 33	21 41		
	d	19 24	19 34	19 43		19 54	20 04		20b18	20 24	20 34	20 43		20 54	20b58	21 04		21 24	21 34	21 43		
Argyle Street	d																					
Charing Cross	d				19 43			20 13					20 43				21 13					21 43
Glasgow Queen St 10	a				19 45			20 15					20 45				21 15				21e20	21 45
	d				19 45			20 15					20 45				21 15					21 45
High Street	d				19 47			20 17					20 47				21 17					21 47
Bellgrove	d				19 49			20 19					20 49				21 19					21 49
Duke Street	d																					
Alexandra Parade	d																					
Barnhill	d																					
Springburn	a																					
Carntyne	d				19 53			20 23					20 53				21 23					21 53
Shettleston	d				19 55			20 25					20 55				21 25					21 55
Garrowhill	d				19 58			20 28					20 58				21 28					21 58
Easterhouse	d				20 00			20 30					21 00				21 30					22 00
Blairhill	d				20 04			20 34					21 04				21 34					22 04
Coatbridge Sunnyside	d				20 07			20 37					21 07				21 37					22 07
Coatdyke	d				20 09			20 39					21 09				21 39					22 09
Airdrie	d				20 12			20a43					21 12				21a43					22 12
Drumgelloch	d				20 15								21 15									22 15
Caldercruix	d				20 19								21 19									22 19
Blackridge	d				20 25								21 25									22 25
Armadale	d				20 29								21 29									22 29
Bathgate	a				20 33								21 33									22 33
	d				20 34								21 34									22 34
Livingston North	d				20 38								21 38									22 38
Uphall	d				20 41								21 41									22 41
Edinburgh Park	a				20 49								21 49									22 49
Bridgeton	d	19 28	19 39			19 58	20 09			20 28	20 39			20 58		21 09		21 28	21 39			
Dalmarnock	d																					
Rutherglen	d	19 33	19 44	19 50		20 03	20 14			20 33	20 44	20 50		21 03		21 14		21 33	21 44	21 50		
Cambuslang	d	19 36	19 47			20 06	20 17			20 36	20 47			21 06		21 17		21 36	21 47			
Newton	d	19 40				20 10				20 40				21 10				21 40				
Blantyre	d	19 44		19 58		20 14				20 44		20 58		21 14				21 44		21 58		
Hamilton West	d	19 47		20 01		20 17				20 47		21 01		21 17				21 47		22 01		
Hamilton Central	d	19 49		20 04		20 19				20 49		21 04		21 19				21 49		22 04		
Chatelherault	d			20 07								21 07								22 07		
Merryton	d			20 10								21 10								22 10		
Larkhall	a			20 14								21 14								22 14		
Airbles	d	19 54				20 24				20 54				21 24				21 54				
Uddingston	d		19 52				20 22		20 31		20 52					21 22			21 52			
Bellshill	d		19 56				20 26		20 36		20 56					21 26			21 56			
Motherwell	a	19 57	20 03			20 27	20 33			20 57	21 03			21 27	21 17	21 33		21 57	22 03			
	d						20 34								21 18	21 34						
Whifflet	a																					
Coatbridge Central	a																					
Shieldmuir	d						20 37									21 37						
Holytown	d								20 40													
Wishaw	d						20 41									21 41						
Carluke	d						20 47									21 47						
Carstairs	a																					
Lanark	a						20 59									22 00						
Haymarket	a				20 54				21 43				21 54		22 03							22 54
Edinburgh	a				20 59				21 48				21 59		22 08							22 59

A From Mallaig
b Glasgow Central High Level
c Helensburgh Upper
e Glasgow Queen St High Level

Table 226R

Sundays

8 December to 11 May

Helensburgh, Balloch, Dalmuir and Milngavie - Glasgow - Springburn, Airdrie, Bathgate, Hamilton, Larkhall, Motherwell, Coatbridge, Lanark and Edinburgh

Network Diagram - refer to first Page of Table 220

		SR	SR	SR	SR	SR	SR	SR	SR	SR	SR	SR	SR R A ✕	SR R B ✕	SR	SR
Helensburgh Central	d			21 25				21 55			22 25		22b37	22b37	22 55	
Craigendoran	d			21 28				21 58			22 28				22 58	
Cardross	d			21 33				22 03			22 33				23 03	
Balloch	d	21 09			21 39				22 09			22 39				23 09
Alexandria	d	21 11			21 41				22 11			22 41				23 11
Renton	d	21 14			21 44				22 14			22 44				23 14
Dalreoch	d	21 17		21 38	21 47			22 08	22 17		22 38	22 47			23 08	23 17
Dumbarton Central	d	21 18		21 40	21 48			22 10	22 18		22 40	22 48	22 53	22 53	23 10	23 18
Dumbarton East	d	21 20		21 42	21 50			22 12	22 20		22 42	22 50			23 12	23 20
Bowling	d	21 25			21 55				22 25			22 55				23 25
Kilpatrick	d	21 28			21 58				22 28			22 58				23 28
Dalmuir	a	21 31		21 49	22 01			22 19	22 31		22 49	23 01	23 04	23 04	23 19	23 31
	d	21 31		21 50	22 01			22 20	22 31		22 50	23 01	23 05	23 05		23 31
Singer	d			21 52				22 22			22 52					
Drumry	d			21 55				22 25			22 55					
Drumchapel	d			21 57				22 27			22 57					
Milngavie	d		21 41			22 11				22 41						
Hillfoot	d		21 44			22 14				22 44						
Bearsden	d		21 46			22 16				22 46						
Westerton	d		21 49	22 00		22 19		22 30		22 49	23 00		23a13	23 14		
Anniesland	d		21 52	22 03		22 22		22 33		22 52	23 03					
Clydebank	d	21 33			22 03				22 33			23 03				23 33
Yoker	d	21 35			22 05				22 35			23a05				23a35
Garscadden	d	21 39			22 09				22 39							
Scotstounhill	d	21 41			22 11				22 41							
Jordanhill	d	21 43			22 13				22 43							
Hyndland 3	d	21 45	21 55	22 05	22 15	22 25		22 35	22 45	22 55	23 05					
Partick ⛴	d	21 48	21 58	22 08	22 18	22 28	22 36	22 38	22 48	22 58	23 08					
Exhibition Centre	d	21 51	22 01		22 21	22 31	22 39		22 51	23 01						
Anderston	d															
Glasgow Central 15	a	21 53	22 03		22 23	22 33	22 41		22 53	23 03						
	d	21 54	22 04		22 24	22 34	22 43		22 54	23 04						
Argyle Street	d															
Charing Cross	d			22 13				22 43			23 13					
Glasgow Queen St 10 ⛴	a			22 15				22 45			23 15					
	d			22 15				22 45			23 15					
High Street	d			22 17				22 47			23 17					
Bellgrove	d			22 19				22 49			23 19					
Duke Street	d															
Alexandra Parade	d															
Barnhill	d															
Springburn	a															
Carntyne	d			22 23				22 53			23 23					
Shettleston	d			22 25				22 55			23 25					
Garrowhill	d			22 28				22 58			23 28					
Easterhouse	d			22 30				23 00			23 30					
Blairhill	d			22 34				23 04			23 34					
Coatbridge Sunnyside	d			22 37				23 07			23 37					
Coatdyke	d			22 39				23 09			23 39					
Airdrie	d			22a43				23 12			23a43					
Drumgelloch	d							23 15								
Caldercruix	d							23 19								
Blackridge	d							23 25								
Armadale	d							23 29								
Bathgate	a							23 33								
	d															
Livingston North	d															
Uphall	d															
Edinburgh Park	a															
Bridgeton	d	21 58	22 09		22 28	22 39			22 58	23 09						
Dalmarnock	d															
Rutherglen	d	22 03	22 14		22 33	22 44	22 50		23 03	23 14						
Cambuslang	d	22 06	22 17		22 36	22 47			23 06	23 17						
Newton	d	22 10			22 40				23 10							
Blantyre	d	22 14			22 44		22 58		23 14							
Hamilton West	d	22 17			22 47		23 01		23 17							
Hamilton Central	d	22 19			22 49		23 04		23 19							
Chatelherault	d						23 07									
Merryton	d						23 10									
Larkhall	a						23 14									
Airbles	d	22 24			22 54				23 24							
Uddingston	d		22 22			22 52				23 22						
Bellshill	d		22 26			22 56				23 26						
Motherwell	a	22 27	22 33		22 57	23 03			23 27	23 33						
	d		22 34													
Whifflet	a															
Coatbridge Central	a															
Shieldmuir	d		22 37													
Holytown	d															
Wishaw	d		22 41													
Carluke	d		22 47													
Carstairs	a															
Lanark	a		22 59													
Haymarket	a															
Edinburgh	a													00 13		

A until 9 February. From Fort William to London Euston

B from 16 February. From Fort William

b Helensburgh Upper

Network Diagram for Tables 227, 239

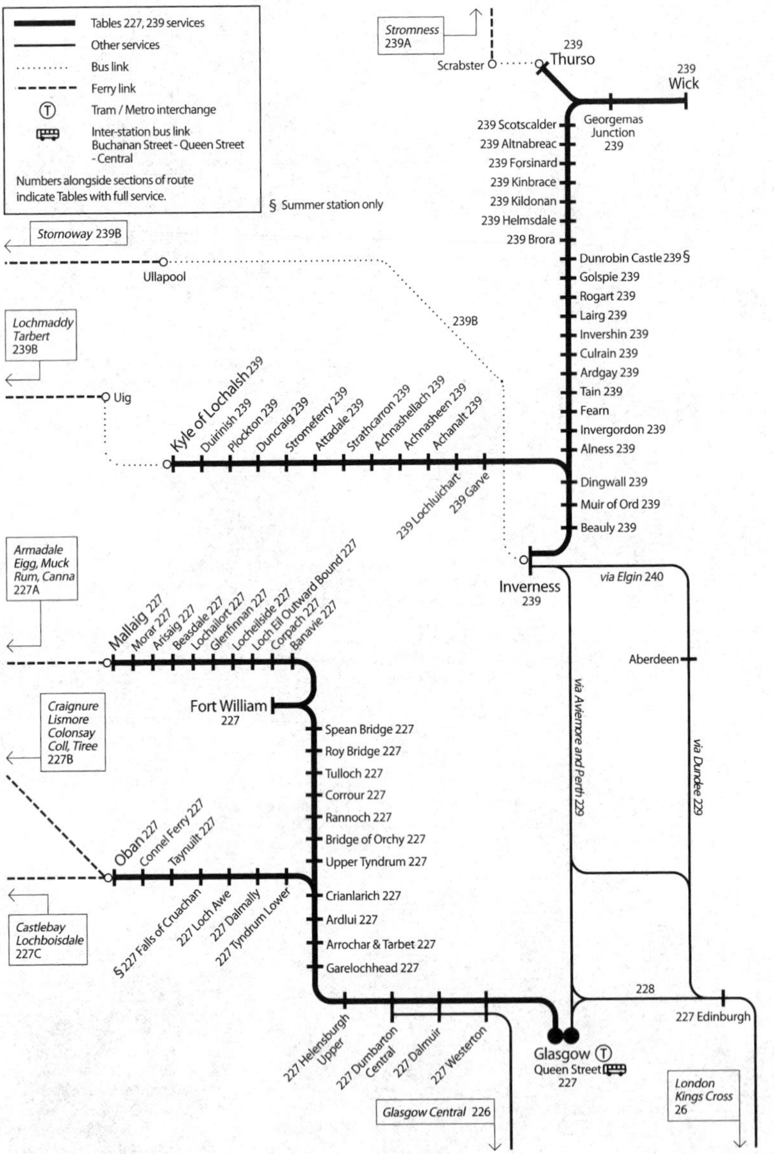

Tables 227, 239 services
Other services
Bus link
Ferry link
Tram / Metro interchange
Inter-station bus link Buchanan Street - Queen Street - Central
Numbers alongside sections of route indicate Tables with full service.
§ Summer station only
Stromness 239A
Scrabster
239 Thurso
239 Wick
Georgemas Junction 239
239 Scotscalder
239 Altnabreac
239 Forsinard
239 Kinbrace
239 Kildonan
239 Helmsdale
239 Brora
Dunrobin Castle 239 §
Golspie 239
Rogart 239
Lairg 239
Invershin 239
Culrain 239
Ardgay 239
Tain 239
Fearn
Invergordon 239
Alness 239
Dingwall 239
Muir of Ord 239
Beauly 239
Inverness 239
Stornoway 239B
Ullapool
239B
Lochmaddy Tarbert 239B
Uig
Kyle of Lochalsh 239
Duirinish 239
Plockton 239
Duncraig 239
Stromeferry 239
Attadale 239
Strathcarron 239
Achnashellach 239
Achnasheen 239
Achanalt 239
239 Lochluichart
239 Garve
via Elgin 240
Aberdeen
via Aviemore and Perth 229
via Dundee 229
Armadale Eigg, Muck Rum, Canna 227A
Mallaig 227
Morar 227
Arisaig 227
Beasdale 227
Lochailort 227
Glenfinnan 227
Locheilside 227
Loch Eil Outward Bound 227
Corpach 227
Banavie 227
Fort William 227
Spean Bridge 227
Roy Bridge 227
Tulloch 227
Corrour 227
Rannoch 227
Bridge of Orchy 227
Upper Tyndrum 227
Craignure Lismore Colonsay Coll, Tiree 227B
Oban 227
Connel Ferry 227
Taynuilt 227
§ 227 Falls of Cruachan
227 Loch Awe
227 Dalmally
227 Tyndrum Lower
Castlebay Lochboisdale 227C
Crianlarich 227
Ardlui 227
Arrochar & Tarbet 227
Garelochhead 227
227 Helensburgh Upper
227 Dumbarton Central
227 Dalmuir
227 Westerton
Glasgow Central 226
Glasgow Queen Street 227
228
227 Edinburgh
London Kings Cross 26

TOCs operating on this network - ScotRail (SR), West Coast Railways (WR)

Table 227

Glasgow Queen Street - Oban, Fort William and Mallaig

Mondays to Fridays

9 December to 28 March

Network Diagram - refer to first Page of Table 227

Miles	Miles			SR	SR	SR	SR		SR		SR	
						[R]						
					◇		◇		◇		◇	
									A		A	
					🛒	✕ 🛏	🛒		🛒		🛒	
—	—	Edinburgh 228	d			04 50	*07 15*		*11 15*		*17 15*	
0	0	**Glasgow Queen St.** 10 226 ⛴	d	05 30			08 21		12 21		18 21	
5½	5½	Westerton 226	d	05a43		05 54						
10	10	Dalmuir 226	d			06 01	08 39		12 42		18 42	
16½	16½	Dumbarton Central 226	d			06 12	08 49		12 48		18 51	
25½	25½	Helensburgh Upper	a			06 26	09 03		13 03		19 03	
—	—		d			06 29	09 06		13 06		19 06	
32¼	32¼	Garelochhead	d			06 42	09 17		13 17		19 17	
43	43	Arrochar & Tarbet	d			07 08	09 37		13 37		19 36	
51	51	Ardlui	d			07x22	09 53		13 53		19 23	
59¾	59¾	**Crianlarich**	a			07 43	10 09		14 09		20 08	
—	—											
—	—		d			07 45	10 15	10 21	14 15	14 21	20 14	20 17
64¾	—	Tyndrum Lower	d				10 24		14 24		20 23	
76¾	—	Dalmally	d				10 42		14 42		20 40	
79½	—	Loch Awe	d				10 47		14 47		20 45	
83½	—	Falls of Cruachan §	d									
88½	—	Taynuilt	d				11 03		15 03		21 01	
95¼	—	Connel Ferry	d				11 14		15 14		21 11	
101½	—	**Oban**	a				11 27		15 27		21 24	
—	64½	Upper Tyndrum	d			07 58		10 32		14 32		20 28
—	72¼	Bridge of Orchy	d			08 15		10 48		14 46		20 42
—	87¾	Rannoch	d			08 46		11 09		15 09		21 05
—	95	Corrour	d			08x59		11 21		15 21		21 17
—	105	Tulloch	d			09 20		11 37		15 38		21 33
—	110¾	Roy Bridge	d			09x31		11 47		15 48		21 43
—	114	Spean Bridge	d			09 39		11 54		15 56		21 53
—	122¾	**Fort William**	a			09 55		12 07		16 09		22 06
—	—		d		08 30			12 12		16 19		22 14
—	125	Banavie	d		08 36			12 18		16 25		22 20
—	126	Corpach	d		08 42			12 23		16 30		22 25
—	129	Loch Eil Outward Bound	d		08 49			12 29		16 36		22 31
—	132¾	Locheilside	d		08x54			12x34		16x41		22x36
—	139¼	Glenfinnan	d		09 05			12 46		16 55		22 47
—	148½	Lochailort	d		09x20			13x01		17x10		23x03
—	153¼	Beasdale	d		09x29			13x10		17x19		23x12
—	156¾	Arisaig	d		09 38			13 18		17 27		23 20
—	161¼	Morar	d		09 46			13 26		17 36		23 28
—	164¼	**Mallaig**	a		09 53			13 34		17 43		23 35

Mondays to Fridays

31 March to 16 May

		SR	SR	SR	SR	WR	SR	SR			SR	
				[R]								
			◇		◇	◇	◇	◇			◇	
						B		A			A	
			🛒	✕ 🛏	🛒	🛒	🛒	🛒			🛒	
Edinburgh 228	d			04 50	*07 15*		*07 45*	*11 15*			*17 15*	
Glasgow Queen St. 10 226 ⛴	d	05 30			08 21		09 03	12 21			18 21	
Westerton 226	d	05a43		05 54								
Dalmuir 226	d			06 01	08 39		09 24	12 42			18 42	
Dumbarton Central 226	d			06 12	08 49		09 36	12 48			18 51	
Helensburgh Upper	a			06 26	09 03		09 50	13 03			19 03	
	d			06 29	09 06		09 52	13 06			19 06	
Garelochhead	d			06 42	09 17		10 04	13 17			19 17	
Arrochar & Tarbet	d			07 08	09 37		10 27	13 37			19 36	
Ardlui	d			07x22	09 53		10x39	13 53			19 52	
Crianlarich	a			07 43	10 09		10 55	14 09			20 08	
	d			07 45	10 15		10 58	14 15	14 21		20 14	20 17
Tyndrum Lower	d				10 24			14 24			20 23	
Dalmally	d				10 42			14 42			20 40	
Loch Awe	d				10 47			14 47			20 45	
Falls of Cruachan §	d				10 52			14 52			20 50	
Taynuilt	d				11 03			15 03			21 01	
Connel Ferry	d				11 14			15 14			21 11	
Oban	a				11 27			15 27			21 24	
Upper Tyndrum	d			07 58			11 10		14 32			20 28
Bridge of Orchy	d			08 15			11 24		14 46			20 42
Rannoch	d			08 46			11 45		15 09			21 05
Corrour	d			08x59			11 57		15 21			21 17
Tulloch	d			09 20			12 14		15 38			21 33
Roy Bridge	d			09x31			12 24		15 48			21 43
Spean Bridge	d			09 39			12 31		15 56			21 53
Fort William	a			09 55			12 44		16 09			22 06
	d		08 30			10 15	12 48		16 19			22 14
Banavie	d		08 36				12 55		16 25			22 20
Corpach	d		08 42				12 59		16 30			22 25
Loch Eil Outward Bound	d		08 49				13 06		16 36			22 31
Locheilside	d		08x54				13x11		16x41			22x36
Glenfinnan	d		09 05			11c22	13 22		16 55			22 47
Lochailort	d		09x20				13x37		17x10			23x03
Beasdale	d		09x29				13x46		17x19			23x12
Arisaig	d		09 38				13 54		17 27			23 20
Morar	d		09 46				14 03		17 36			23 28
Mallaig	a		09 53			12 26	14 10		17 43			23 35

§ Summer station only

B **The Jacobite,** from 12 May

B 🛒 to Oban and Fort William

c arrives at Glenfinnan at 1054

Table 227

Saturdays

14 December to 22 March

Glasgow Queen Street - Oban, Fort William and Mallaig

Network Diagram - refer to first Page of Table 227

		SR	SR	SR	SR		SR		SR	
				B						
			◇		◇		◇		◇	
							A		A	
			🛒	✕ 🛏	🛒		🛒		🛒	
Edinburgh 228	d			04 50	*07 15*		*11 15*		*17 15*	
Glasgow Queen St. [10] 226 ⛴	d	05 30			08 21		12 21		18 21	
Westerton 226	d	05a43		05 54						
Dalmuir 226	d			06 01	08 39		12 42		18 42	
Dumbarton Central 226	d			06 12	08 49		12 48		18 51	
Helensburgh Upper	a			06 26	09 03		13 03		19 03	
	d			06 29	09 06		13 06		19 06	
Garelochhead	d			06 42	09 17		13 17		19 17	
Arrochar & Tarbet	d			07 08	09 37		13 37		19 36	
Ardlui	d			07x22	09 53		13 53		19 52	
Crianlarich	a			07 43	10 09		14 09		20 08	
	d			07 45	10 15	10 21	14 15	14 21	20 14	20 17
Tyndrum Lower	d				10 24		14 24		20 23	
Dalmally	d				10 42		14 42		20 40	
Loch Awe	d				10 47		14 47		20 45	
Falls of Cruachan §	d									
Taynuilt	d				11 03		15 03		21 01	
Connel Ferry	d				11 14		15 14		21 11	
Oban	a				11 27		15 27		21 24	
Upper Tyndrum	d			07 58		10 32		14 32		20 28
Bridge of Orchy	d			08 15		10 48		14 46		20 42
Rannoch	d			08 46		11 09		15 09		21 05
Corrour	d			08x59		11 21		15 21		21 17
Tulloch	d			09 20		11 37		15 38		21 33
Roy Bridge	d			09x31		11 47		15 48		21 43
Spean Bridge	d			09 39		11 54		15 56		21 53
Fort William	a			09 55		12 07		16 09		22 06
	d		08 30			12 12		16 19		22 14
Banavie	d		08 36			12 18		16 25		22 20
Corpach	d		08 42			12 23		16 30		22 25
Loch Eil Outward Bound	d		08 49			12 29		16 36		22 31
Locheilside	d		08x54			12x34		16x41		22x36
Glenfinnan	d		09 05			12 46		16 55		22 47
Lochailort	d		09x20			13x01		17x10		23x03
Beasdale	d		09x29			13x10		17x19		23x12
Arisaig	d		09 38			13 18		17 27		23 20
Morar	d		09 46			13 26		17 36		23 28
Mallaig	a		09 53			13 34		17 43		23 35

Saturdays

29 March to 17 May

		SR	SR		SR	SR			SR	SR		SR	
					B								
			◇			◇			◇	◇		◇	
			🛒		✕	🛒			🛒	🛒		🛒	
										A		A	
Edinburgh 228	d				04 50	*07 15*			*09 30*	*11 15*		*17 15*	
Glasgow Queen St. [10] 226 ⛴	d	05 30				08 21			10 37	12 21		18 21	
Westerton 226	d	05a43			05 54								
Dalmuir 226	d				06 01	08 39			10 52	12 42		18 42	
Dumbarton Central 226	d				06 12	08 49			11 05	12 48		18 51	
Helensburgh Upper	a				06 26	09 03			11 19	13 03		19 03	
	d				06 29	09 06			11 22	13 06		19 06	
Garelochhead	d				06 42	09 17			11 34	13 17		19 17	
Arrochar & Tarbet	d				07 08	09 37			11 54	13 37		19 36	
Ardlui	d				07x22	09 53			12 08	13 53		19 52	
Crianlarich	a				07 43	10 09			12 24	14 09		20 08	
	d				07 45	10 15	10 21		12 26	14 15	14 21	20 14	20 17
Tyndrum Lower	d					10 24			12 35	14 24		20 23	
Dalmally	d					10 42			12 57	14 42		20 40	
Loch Awe	d					10 47			13 02	14 47		20 45	
Falls of Cruachan §	d					10 52			13 08	14 52		20 50	
Taynuilt	d					11 03			13 18	15 03		21 01	
Connel Ferry	d					11 14			13 29	15 14		21 11	
Oban	a					11 27			13 42	15 27		21 24	
Upper Tyndrum	d				07 58		10 32				14 32		20 28
Bridge of Orchy	d				08 15		10 48				14 46		20 42
Rannoch	d				08 46		11 09				15 09		21 05
Corrour	d				08x59		11 21				15 21		21 17
Tulloch	d				09 20		11 37				15 38		21 33
Roy Bridge	d				09x31		11 47				15 48		21 43
Spean Bridge	d				09 39		11 54				15 56		21 53
Fort William	a				09 55		12 07				16 09		22 06
	d		08 30				12 12				16 19		22 14
Banavie	d		08 36				12 18				16 25		22 20
Corpach	d		08 42				12 23				16 30		22 25
Loch Eil Outward Bound	d		08 49				12 29				16 36		22 31
Locheilside	d		08x54				12x34				16x41		22x36
Glenfinnan	d		09 05				12 46				16 55		22 47
Lochailort	d		09x20				13x01				17x10		23x03
Beasdale	d		09x29				13x10				17x19		23x12
Arisaig	d		09 38				13 18				17 27		23 20
Morar	d		09 46				13 26				17 36		23 28
Mallaig	a		09 53				13 34				17 43		23 35

§ Summer station only

A 🛒 to Oban and Fort William

Table 227

Glasgow Queen Street - Oban, Fort William and Mallaig

Sundays

8 December to 23 March

Network Diagram - refer to first Page of Table 227

		SR ◇ 🛒 B	
Edinburgh 228	d	*17 00*	
Glasgow Queen St. **10** 226 ⛴	d	18 20	
Westerton 226	d		
Dalmuir 226	d	18 34	
Dumbarton Central 226	d	18 44	
Helensburgh Upper	a	18 59	
	d	19 05	
Garelochhead	d	19 16	
Arrochar & Tarbet	d	19 36	
Ardlui	d	19 52	
Crianlarich	a	20 08	
	d	20 14	20 17
Tyndrum Lower	d	20 23	
Dalmally	d	20 40	
Loch Awe	d	20 45	
Falls of Cruachan §	d		
Taynuilt	d	21 01	
Connel Ferry	d	21 11	
Oban	a	21 24	
Upper Tyndrum	d		20 28
Bridge of Orchy	d		20 42
Rannoch	d		21 07
Corrour	d		21 19
Tulloch	d		21 35
Roy Bridge	d		21 45
Spean Bridge	d		21 52
Fort William	a		22 05
	d		22 14
Banavie	d		22 20
Corpach	d		22 25
Loch Eil Outward Bound	d		22 31
Locheilside	d		22x36
Glenfinnan	d		22 47
Lochailort	d		23x03
Beasdale	d		23x12
Arisaig	d		23 20
Morar	d		23 28
Mallaig	a		23 35

Sundays

30 March to 11 May

		SR ◇ 🛒	SR ◇	SR ◇ 🛒 A		SR ◇ 🛒 A	
Edinburgh 228	d	*08 30*		*11 00*		*17 00*	
Glasgow Queen St. **10** 226 ⛴	d	09 56		12 20		18 20	
Westerton 226	d						
Dalmuir 226	d	10 16		12 34		18 34	
Dumbarton Central 226	d	10 25		12 44		18 44	
Helensburgh Upper	a	10 37		12 59		18 59	
	d	10 40		13 06		19 05	
Garelochhead	d	10 51		13 17		19 16	
Arrochar & Tarbet	d	11 11		13 37		19 36	
Ardlui	d	11 27		13 53		19 52	
Crianlarich	a	11 44		14 09		20 08	
	d	11 46		14 15	14 21	20 14	20 17
Tyndrum Lower	d	11 55		14 24		20 23	
Dalmally	d	12 14		14 42		20 40	
Loch Awe	d	12 19		14 47		20 45	
Falls of Cruachan §	d	12 24		14 52		20 50	
Taynuilt	d	12 40		15 03		21 01	
Connel Ferry	d	12 51		15 14		21 11	
Oban	a	13 04		15 27		21 24	
Upper Tyndrum	d				14 32		20 28
Bridge of Orchy	d				14 46		20 42
Rannoch	d				15 09		21 07
Corrour	d				15 21		21 19
Tulloch	d				15 38		21 35
Roy Bridge	d				15 48		21 45
Spean Bridge	d				15 56		21 52
Fort William	a				16 09		22 05
	d		12 12		16 19		22 14
Banavie	d		12 18		16 25		22 20
Corpach	d		12 23		16 30		22 25
Loch Eil Outward Bound	d		12 29		16 36		22 31
Locheilside	d		12x34		16x41		22x36
Glenfinnan	d		12 46		16 55		22 47
Lochailort	d		13x01		17x10		23x03
Beasdale	d		13x10		17x19		23x12
Arisaig	d		13 18		17 27		23 20
Morar	d		13 26		17 36		23 28
Mallaig	a		13 34		17 43		23 35

§ Summer station only

A 🛒 to Oban and Fort William

B 🛒 from Crianlarich to Oban and Fort William

Table 227R

Mondays to Fridays

9 December to 28 March

Mallaig, Fort William and Oban - Glasgow Queen Street

Network Diagram - refer to first Page of Table 227

Miles	Miles			SR	SR	SR	SR	SR	SR	SR	SR	SR	SR
				MX									R
						◇	◇	◇	◇	◇	◇	◇	
							A						sleeper
						trolley	trolley	trolley	trolley	trolley	trolley		✕
—	0	**Mallaig**	d				06 03		10 10	16 05		18 15	
—	3	Morar	d				06 09		10 17	16 12		18 22	
—	7½	Arisaig	d				06 19		10 26	16 21		18 31	
—	11	Beasdale	d				06x25		10x33	16x28		18x38	
—	15¾	Lochailort	d				06x34		10x42	16x37		18x47	
—	25	Glenfinnan	d				06 51		10 59	16 54		19 04	
—	31½	Locheilside	d				07x01		11x09	17x03		19x13	
—	35¼	Loch Eil Outward Bound	d				07 07		11 15	17 10		19 20	
—	38¼	Corpach	d				07 13		11 21	17 16		19 26	
—	39¼	Banavie	d				07 17		11 25	17 20		19 30	
—	41½	**Fort William**	a				07 25		11 32	17 28		19 37	
—	—		d				07 42		11 40	17 37			19 50
—	50¼	Spean Bridge	d				07 55		11 55	17 51			20 10
—	53½	Roy Bridge	d				08 02		12 02	17 57			20x17
—	59¼	Tulloch	d				08 13		12 14	18 09			20 31
—	69¼	Corrour	d				08 30		12 31	18 25			20x52
—	76½	Rannoch	d				08 43		12 42	18 37			21 06
—	92	Bridge of Orchy	d				09 03		13 03	18 57			21 34
—	99¾	Upper Tyndrum	d				09 19		13 19	19 13			21 52
0	—	**Oban**	d			08 11		12 11			18 11		
6¼	—	Connel Ferry	d			08 23		12 23			18 23		
13	—	Taynuilt	d			08 35		12 35			18 35		
18½	—	Falls of Cruachan §	d										
22	—	Loch Awe	d			08 50		12 50			18 50		
24¾	—	Dalmally	d			08 55		12 55			18 56		
36¾	—	Tyndrum Lower	d			09 14		13 14			19 14		
42	104½	**Crianlarich**	a			09 29	09 30	13 29	13 30	19 25	19 26		22 04
—	—												
—	—		d			09 36		13 36		19 33			22 05
50¾	113¼	Ardlui	d			09 52		13 52		19 53			22x26
58¾	121¼	Arrochar & Tarbet	d		07 10	10 07		14 07		20 07			22 44
69½	132	Garelochhead	d		07 30	10 32		14 28		20 27			23 10
76¼	138¾	Helensburgh Upper	a		07 41	10 42		14 39		20 37			23 23
—	—		d		07 42	10 44		14 40		20 38			23 24
85¼	147¾	Dumbarton Central 226	a		07 57	10 59		14 58		20 51			23 38
92½	154¼	Dalmuir 226	a			11 10		15 07		21 00			23 50
96	157¾	Westerton 226	a	00d05									23 58
101½	164¼	**Glasgow Queen St.** 10 226	a	00 20	08e37	11 30		15 30		21 18			
—	—	Edinburgh 228	a		*09 54*	*12 50*		*16 52*		*22 23*			00 50

§ Summer station only

A trolley from Fort William

e by changing at Dumbarton Central passengers can arrive at Glasgow Queen Street LL at 0829

Table 227R

Mondays to Fridays

31 March to 16 May

Mallaig, Fort William and Oban - Glasgow Queen Street

Network Diagram - refer to first Page of Table 227

		SR MX	SR	SR	SR	SR	SR	WR	SR	SR	SR	SR
				◇	◇ A	◇	◇	◇ C	◇	◇	◇	R
				trolley	trolley	trolley	trolley		trolley	trolley		sleeper ✕
Mallaig	d				06 03	10 10		14 09	16 05		18 15	
Morar	d				06 09	10 17			16 12		18 22	
Arisaig	d				06 19	10 26			16 21		18 31	
Beasdale	d				06x25	10x33			16x28		18x38	
Lochailort	d				06x34	10x42			16x37		18x47	
Glenfinnan	d				06 51	10 59			16 54		19 04	
Locheilside	d				07x01	11x09			17x03		19x13	
Loch Eil Outward Bound	d				07 07	11 15			17 10		19 20	
Corpach	d				07 13	11 21			17 16		19 26	
Banavie	d				07 17	11 25			17 20		19 30	
Fort William	a				07 25	11 32		16 03	17 28		19 37	
	d				07 42	11 40			17 37			19 50
Spean Bridge	d				07 55	11 55			17 51			20 10
Roy Bridge	d				08 02	12 02			17 57			20x17
Tulloch	d				08 13	12 14			18 09			20 31
Corrour	d				08 30	12 31			18 25			20x52
Rannoch	d				08 43	12 42			18 37			21 06
Bridge of Orchy	d				09 03	13 03			18 57			21 34
Upper Tyndrum	d				09 19	13 19			19 13			21 52
Oban	d			08 11			12 56			18 11		
Connel Ferry	d			08 23			13 08			18 23		
Taynuilt	d			08 35			13 20			18 35		
Falls of Cruachan §	d			08 43			13 28			18 44		
Loch Awe	d			08 50			13 35			18 50		
Dalmally	d			08 55			13 41			18 56		
Tyndrum Lower	d			09 14			14 00			19 14		
Crianlarich	a			09 29	09 30	13 30	14 10		19 25	19 26		22 04
	d			09 36		13 36	14 12		19 33			22 05
Ardlui	d			09 52		13 52	14 28		19 53			22x26
Arrochar & Tarbet	d		07 10	10 07		14 07	14 43		20 07			22 44
Garelochhead	d		07 30	10 32		14 28	15 03		20 27			23 10
Helensburgh Upper	a		07 41	10 42		14 39	15 14		20 37			23 23
	d		07 42	10 44		14 40	15 15		20 38			23 24
Dumbarton Central 226	a		07 57	10 59		14 58	15 29		20 51			23 38
Dalmuir 226	a			11 10		15 07	15 38		21 00			23 50
Westerton 226	a	00d05										23 58
Glasgow Queen St. 10 226	a	00 20	08e37	11 30		15 30	15 59		21 18			
Edinburgh 228	a		*09 51*	*12 35*		*16 36*	*17 06*		*22 22*			00 50

Saturdays

14 December to 22 March

		SR	SR	SR	SR	SR	SR	SR	SR
			◇	◇ A	◇	◇ A	◇ A	◇	◇
			trolley	trolley	trolley	trolley	trolley	trolley	
Mallaig	d			06 03		10 10	16 05		18 15
Morar	d			06 09		10 17	16 12		18 22
Arisaig	d			06 19		10 26	16 21		18 31
Beasdale	d			06x25		10x33	16x28		18x38
Lochailort	d			06x34		10x42	16x37		18x47
Glenfinnan	d			06 51		10 59	16 54		19 04
Locheilside	d			07x01		11x09	17x03		19x13
Loch Eil Outward Bound	d			07 07		11 15	17 10		19 20
Corpach	d			07 13		11 21	17 16		19 26
Banavie	d			07 17		11 25	17 20		19 30
Fort William	a			07 25		11 32	17 28		19 37
	d			07 42		11 40	17 37		
Spean Bridge	d			07 55		11 55	17 51		
Roy Bridge	d			08 02		12 02	17 57		
Tulloch	d			08 13		12 14	18 09		
Corrour	d			08 30		12 31	18 25		
Rannoch	d			08 43		12 42	18 37		
Bridge of Orchy	d			09 03		13 03	18 57		
Upper Tyndrum	d			09 19		13 19	19 13		
Oban	d		08 11		12 11			18 11	
Connel Ferry	d		08 23		12 23			18 23	
Taynuilt	d		08 35		12 35			18 35	
Falls of Cruachan §	d								
Loch Awe	d		08 50		12 50			18 50	
Dalmally	d		08 55		12 55			18 56	
Tyndrum Lower	d		09 14		13 14			19 14	
Crianlarich	a		09 29	09 30	13 29	13 30	19 25	19 26	
	d		09 36		13 36		19 33		
Ardlui	d		09 52		13 52		19 53		
Arrochar & Tarbet	d		10 07		14 07		20 07		
Garelochhead	d		10 32		14 28		20 27		
Helensburgh Upper	a		10 42		14 39		20 37		
	d		10 44		14 40		20 38		
Dumbarton Central 226	a		10 59		14 58		20 51		
Dalmuir 226	a		11 10		15 07		21 00		
Westerton 226	a	00d05							
Glasgow Queen St. 10 226	a	00 20	11 30		15 30		21 18		
Edinburgh 228	a		*12 35*		*16 36*		*22 22*		

§ Summer station only

C **The Jacobite,** from 12 May

e by changing at Dumbarton Central passengers can arrive at Glasgow Queen Street LL at 0829

A trolley from Fort William

Table 227R

Saturdays

29 March to 17 May

Mallaig, Fort William and Oban - Glasgow Queen Street

Network Diagram - refer to first Page of Table 227

		SR	SR	SR	SR	SR	SR	SR	SR	SR
			◇	◇	◇	◇	◇	◇	◇	◇
				A		A		A		
			🛒	🛒	🛒	🛒	🛒	🛒	🛒	
Mallaig	d			06 03		10 10		16 05		18 15
Morar	d			06 09		10 17		16 12		18 22
Arisaig	d			06 19		10 26		16 21		18 31
Beasdale	d			06x25		10x33		16x28		18x38
Lochailort	d			06x34		10x42		16x37		18x47
Glenfinnan	d			06 51		10 59		16 54		19 04
Locheilside	d			07x01		11x09		17x03		19x13
Loch Eil Outward Bound	d			07 07		11 15		17 10		19 20
Corpach	d			07 13		11 21		17 16		19 26
Banavie	d			07 17		11 25		17 20		19 30
Fort William	a			07 25		11 32		17 28		19 37
	d			07 42		11 40		17 37		
Spean Bridge	d			07 55		11 55		17 51		
Roy Bridge	d			08 02		12 02		17 57		
Tulloch	d			08 13		12 14		18 09		
Corrour	d			08 30		12 31		18 25		
Rannoch	d			08 43		12 42		18 37		
Bridge of Orchy	d			09 03		13 03		18 57		
Upper Tyndrum	d			09 19		13 19		19 13		
Oban	d		08 11		12 11		16 11		18 11	
Connel Ferry	d		08 23		12 23		16 23		18 23	
Taynuilt	d		08 35		12 35		16 35		18 35	
Falls of Cruachan §	d		08 43		12 43		16 44		18 44	
Loch Awe	d		08 50		12 50		16 50		18 50	
Dalmally	d		08 55		12 55		16 56		18 56	
Tyndrum Lower	d		09 14		13 14		17 14		19 14	
Crianlarich	a		09 29	09 30	13 29	13 30	17 25	19 25	19 26	
	d			09 36		13 36	17 31	19 33		
Ardlui	d			09 52		13 52	17 48	19 53		
Arrochar & Tarbet	d			10 07		14 07	18 02	20 07		
Garelochhead	d			10 32		14 28	18 23	20 27		
Helensburgh Upper	a			10 42		14 39	18 33	20 37		
	d			10 44		14 40	18 34	20 38		
Dumbarton Central 226	a			10 59		14 58	18 45	20 51		
Dalmuir 226	a			11 10		15 07	18 56	21 00		
Westerton 226	a	00d05								
Glasgow Queen St. 10 226 ⛴	a	00 20		11 30		15 30	19 19	21 18		
Edinburgh 228	a			*12 35*		*16 36*	*20 21*	*22 22*		

§ Summer station only

A 🛒 from Fort William

Table 227R

Sundays

Mallaig, Fort William and Oban - Glasgow Queen Street

8 December to 23 March

Network Diagram - refer to first Page of Table 227

		SR	SR	SR		SR
				🅁		
		◇	◇			
		A	D	B		
		⛟	⛟	✕		
Mallaig	d	16 05				
Morar	d	16 12				
Arisaig	d	16 21				
Beasdale	d	16x28				
Lochailort	d	16x37				
Glenfinnan	d	16 54				
Locheilside	d	17x03				
Loch Eil Outward Bound	d	17 10				
Corpach	d	17 16				
Banavie	d	17 20				
Fort William	a	17 28				
	d	17 37		19 00		
Spean Bridge	d	17 51		19 20		
Roy Bridge	d	17 57		19x27		
Tulloch	d	18 09		19 40		
Corrour	d	18 25		20x01		
Rannoch	d	18 37		20 15		
Bridge of Orchy	d	18 57		20 47		
Upper Tyndrum	d	19 13		21 05		
Oban	d		18 11			
Connel Ferry	d		18 23			
Taynuilt	d		18 35			
Falls of Cruachan §	d					
Loch Awe	d		18 50			
Dalmally	d		18 56			
Tyndrum Lower	d		19 14			
Crianlarich	a	19 25	19 26	21 16		
	d	19 33		21 18		
Ardlui	d	19 53		21x39		
Arrochar & Tarbet	d	20 07		21 57		
Garelochhead	d	20 27		22 23		
Helensburgh Upper	a	20 37		22 35		
	d	20 38		22 37		
Dumbarton Central 226	a	20 54		22 52		
Dalmuir 226	a	21 05		23 04		
Westerton 226	a			23 13		23d28
Glasgow Queen St. 10 226 ⛴	a	21 20				23 49
Edinburgh 228	a	*22 23*		00 13		

§ Summer station only

A ⛟ from Fort William to Crianlarich

B from 16 February

C until 9 February

D ⛟ from Oban to Crianlarich

Table 227R

Sundays

30 March to 11 May

Mallaig, Fort William and Oban - Glasgow Queen Street

Network Diagram - refer to first Page of Table 227

			SR	SR	SR	SR	SR	SR	SR	SR
								B		
			◇	◇	◇	◇	◇		◇	
						A				
			⌶	⌶	⌶	⌶	⌶	✕	⌶	
Mallaig		d		10 10		16 05			18 15	
Morar		d		10 17		16 12			18 22	
Arisaig		d		10 26		16 21			18 31	
Beasdale		d		10x33		16x28			18x38	
Lochailort		d		10x42		16x37			18x47	
Glenfinnan		d		10 59		16 54			19 04	
Locheilside		d		11x09		17x03			19x13	
Loch Eil Outward Bound		d		11 15		17 10			19 20	
Corpach		d		11 21		17 16			19 26	
Banavie		d		11 25		17 20			19 30	
Fort William		a		11 32		17 28			19 37	
		d		11 40		17 37		19 00		
Spean Bridge		d		11 55		17 51		19 20		
Roy Bridge		d		12 02		17 57		19x27		
Tulloch		d		12 14		18 09		19 40		
Corrour		d		12 31		18 25		20x01		
Rannoch		d		12 42		18 37		20 15		
Bridge of Orchy		d		13 03		18 57		20 47		
Upper Tyndrum		d		13 19		19 13		21 05		
Oban		d	12 11		16 11		18 11			
Connel Ferry		d	12 23		16 23		18 23			
Taynuilt		d	12 35		16 35		18 35			
Falls of Cruachan §		d	12 43		16 44		18 44			
Loch Awe		d	12 50		16 50		18 50			
Dalmally		d	12 55		16 56		18 56			
Tyndrum Lower		d	13 14		17 14		19 14			
Crianlarich		a	13 29	13 32	17 25	19 25	19 26	21 16		
		d		13 36	17 31	19 33		21 18		
Ardlui		d		13 52	17 48	19 53		21x39		
Arrochar & Tarbet		d		14 07	18 02	20 07		21 57		
Garelochhead		d		14 28	18 23	20 27		22 23		
Helensburgh Upper		a		14 39	18 33	20 37		22 35		
		d		14 40	18 34	20 38		22 37		
Dumbarton Central	226	a		14 56	18 45	20 54		22 52		
Dalmuir	226	a		15 06	18 56	21 05		23 04		
Westerton	226	a						23 13		23d28
Glasgow Queen St. 10	226 ⛴	a		15 30	19 15	21 20				23 49
Edinburgh	228	a		*16 52*	*20 21*	*22 23*		00 13		

§ Summer station only

A ⌶ from Fort William

Table 227A - Shipping Services

Mallaig - Armadale (Skye) and Small Isles

Caledonian MacBrayne Ltd. in association with ScotRail

Mondays to Saturdays

9 December to 3 April

			WFO	TThO	MO	SO A	
Glasgow Queen St. 10	227	d					08c21
Fort William	227	d	08 30	08 30	08 30	08 30	12c12
Mallaig	227	a	09 53	09 53	09 53	09 53	13c34
Mallaig		d	10 20	10 20	10 20	10 20	16 00
Armadale		a					16 30
Eigg		a	11 40		11 40	14 00	
Muck		a	12 35		12 35	13 10	
Rum		a		11 35	14 00	11 35	
Canna		a		12 50			

Sundays

8 December to 30 March

			C
Glasgow Queen St. 10	227	d	
Fort William	227	d	12 12
Mallaig	227	a	13 34
Mallaig		d	16 00
Armadale		a	16 30
Eigg		a	
Muck		a	
Rum		a	
Canna		a	

A Sails via Rum
C 30 March only
c From 31 March 2014 train departs Glasgow 0903, Fort William 1248 and arrives Mallaig 1410

For details of sailings from 4 April 2014, please telephone 08000 66 5000 or visit www.calmac.co.uk

Table 227A-R - Shipping Services

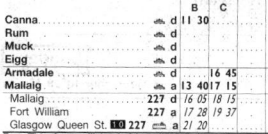

Small Isles and Armadale (Skye) - Mallaig

Operated by Caledonian MacBrayne Ltd

Mondays to Saturdays

9 December to 3 April

				WFO	SO	MO		TThO	
Canna		d						13 10	
Rum		d			11 50	14 20		14 25	
Muck		d		12 50	13 25				
Eigg		d		13 40	14 15				
Armadale		d	09 25						16 45
Mallaig		a	09 55	15 00	15 25	15 40		15 40	17 15
Mallaig	227	d	10 10	16 05	16 05	16 05		16 05	18 15
Fort William	227	a	11 32	17 28	17 28	17 28		17 28	19 37
Glasgow Queen St. 10	227	a	15 30	21 18	21 18	21 18		21 18	00b20

Sundays

8 December to 30 March

			B	C
Canna		d	11 30	
Rum		d		
Muck		d		
Eigg		d		
Armadale		d		16 45
Mallaig		a	13 40	17 15
Mallaig	227	d	16 05	18 15
Fort William	227	a	17 28	19 37
Glasgow Queen St. 10	227	a	21 20	

B This ferry will be held until 1330 (arriving 1540) on request which must be made by 1600 the previous day. Please telephone 01687 462 403
b Tuesday to Saturday mornings only. Change at Fort William and Westerton. Reservations compulsory from Fort William
C 30 March only

For details of sailings from 4 April 2014, please telephone 08000 66 5000 or visit www.calmac.co.uk

Table 227B - Shipping Services

Mondays to Saturdays

9 December to 3 April

Oban - Craignure (Mull), Lismore, Colonsay, Coll and Tiree

Caledonian MacBrayne Ltd. in association with ScotRail

		MO C	TThSO D	WFX B	TThSO C		TThSO	MWO	SO	SX	SO			SO	SX	FSO
Glasgow Queen St. 10 227	d	*18b20*	*18b21*	*18c20*	*18b21*		*08 21*	*08 21*	*08 21*	*08 21*	*08 21*		*12 21*	*12 21*	*12 21*	*18 21*
Oban 227	a	*21b24*	*21b24*	*21c24*	*21b24*		*11 27*	*11 27*	*11 27*	*11 27*	*11 27*		*15 27*	*15 27*	*15 27*	*21 24*
Oban	d	06 30	06 45	07 15	07 15		12 00	12 00	13 30	14 00	14 15		16 00	17 00	17 15	21 45
Craignure	a						12 46						16 46			22 31
Lismore	a									14 50	15 05			17 50	18 05	
Colonsay	a							14 20	15 50							
Coll	a	09 40	09 40	09 55	10 25											
Tiree	a	10 55	10 45	11 00	11 40											

Sundays

8 December to 30 March

		D	B	C		A	A
Glasgow Queen St. 10 227	d	*18b21*	*18b21*	*18b21*		*09 56*	*12 20*
Oban 227	a	*21b24*	*21b24*	*21b24*		*13 04*	*15 27*
Oban	d	06 30	10 30	10 30		15 00	16 00
Craignure	a						16 46
Lismore	a					15 50	
Colonsay	a						
Coll	a						
Tiree	a	10 10	13 50	14 30			

A 30 March only
B Until 31 December
C From 2 January until 24 January and from 16 February until 3 April
D From 25 January until 15 February
b Previous Evening
c Previous evening. Departs 1820 on Sundays and 1821 on all other nights

For details of sailings from 4 April 2014, please telephone 08000 66 5000 or visit www.calmac.co.uk

Table 227B-R - Shipping Services

Mondays to Saturdays

9 December to 3 April

Tiree, Coll, Colonsay, Lismore and Craignure (Mull) - Oban

Caledonian MacBrayne Ltd. in association with ScotRail

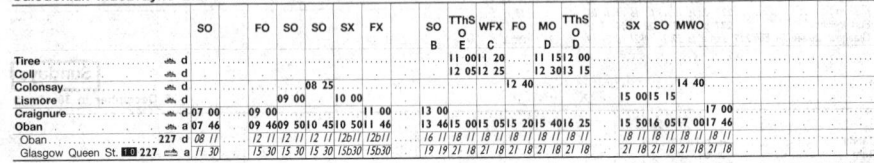

		SO		FO	SO	SO	SX	FX		SO B	TThSO E	WFX C	FO	MO D	TThSO D		SX	SO	MWO	
Tiree	d										11 00	11 20		11 15	12 00					
Coll	d										12 05	12 25		12 30	13 15					
Colonsay	d					08 25							12 40						14 40	
Lismore	d				09 00		10 00										15 00	15 15		
Craignure	d	07 00		09 00				11 00		13 00										17 00
Oban	a	07 46		09 46	09 50	10 45	10 50	11 46		13 46	15 00	15 05	15 20	15 40	16 25		15 50	16 05	17 00	17 46
Oban 227	d	*08 11*		*12 11*	*12 11*	*12 11*	*12b11*	*12b11*		*16 11*	*18 11*	*18 11*	*18 11*	*18 11*	*18 11*		*18 11*	*18 11*	*18 11*	*18 11*
Glasgow Queen St. 10 227	a	*11 30*		*15 30*	*15 30*	*15 30*	*15b30*	*15b30*		*19 19*	*21 18*	*21 18*	*21 18*	*21 18*	*21 18*		*21 18*	*21 18*	*21 18*	*21 18*

Sundays

8 December to 30 March

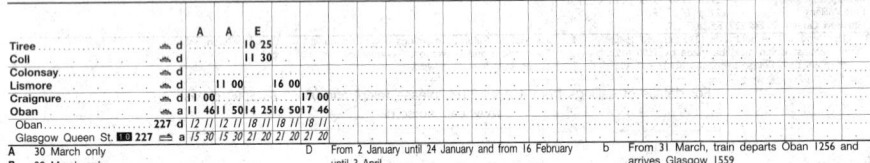

		A	A	E		
Tiree	d			10 25		
Coll	d			11 30		
Colonsay	d					
Lismore	d		11 00		16 00	
Craignure	d	11 00				17 00
Oban	a	11 46	11 50	14 25	16 50	17 46
Oban 227	d	*12 11*	*12 11*	*18 11*	*18 11*	*18 11*
Glasgow Queen St. 10 227	a	*15 30*	*15 30*	*21 20*	*21 20*	*21 20*

A 30 March only
B 29 March only
C Until 31 December
D From 2 January until 24 January and from 16 February until 3 April
E From 25 January until 15 February
b From 31 March, train departs Oban 1256 and arrives Glasgow 1559

For details of sailings from 4 April 2014, please telephone 08000 66 5000 or visit www.calmac.co.uk

Table 227C - Shipping Services

Mondays to Saturdays

9 December to 3 April

Oban - Castlebay (Barra) and Lochboisdale (South Uist)

Caledonian MacBrayne Ltd. in association with ScotRail

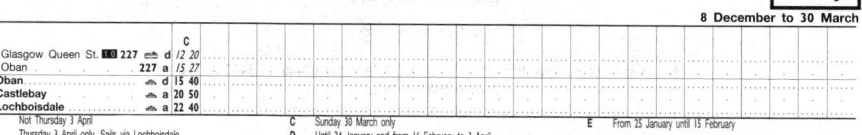

		MWFO D		ThO A D	TThO E	ThO B
Glasgow Queen St. 10 227	d	08 21		12 21	12 21	12 21
Oban 227	a	11 27		15 27	15 27	15 27
Oban	d	13 40		15 40	15 40	15 40
Castlebay	a	18 50		20 50	20 50	22 40
Lochboisdale	a	20 40		22 40	22 40	20 50

Sundays

8 December to 30 March

		C
Glasgow Queen St. 10 227	d	12 20
Oban 227	a	15 27
Oban	d	15 40
Castlebay	a	20 50
Lochboisdale	a	22 40

A Not Thursday 3 April
B Thursday 3 April only. Sails via Lochboisdale
C Sunday 30 March only
D Until 24 January and from 16 February to 3 April
E From 25 January until 15 February

For details of sailings from 4 April 2014 please telephone 08000 66 5000 or visit www.calmac.co.uk

Table 227C-R - Shipping Services

Mondays to Saturdays

9 December to 3 April

Lochboisdale (South Uist) and Castlebay (Barra) - Oban

Caledonian MacBrayne Ltd. in association with ScotRail

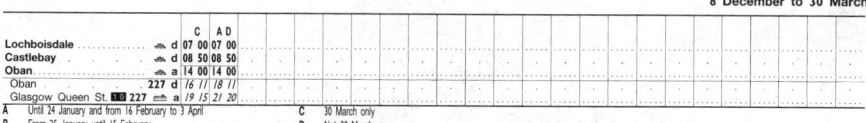

		MWFO A	MWO B	ThO A		ThO B
Lochboisdale	d	06 00	07 00	07 00		23 00
Castlebay	d	07 50	08 45	08 50		
Oban	a	13 00	13 55	14 00		06 00
Oban 227	d	18 11	18 11	18 11		08 11
Glasgow Queen St. 10 227	a	21 18	21 18	21 18		11 30

Sundays

8 December to 30 March

		C	A D
Lochboisdale	d	07 00	07 00
Castlebay	d	08 50	08 50
Oban	a	14 00	14 00
Oban 227	d	16 11	18 11
Glasgow Queen St. 10 227	a	19 15	21 20

A Until 24 January and from 16 February to 3 April
B From 25 January until 15 February
C 30 March only
D Not 30 March

For details of sailings from 4 April 2014 please telephone 08000 66 5000 or visit www.calmac.co.uk

Table 227D - Shipping Services

Mondays to Saturdays

Until 21 January and from 18 February to 1 April

Mallaig - Lochboisdale (South Uist)

Caledonian MacBrayne Ltd in association with ScotRail

			TSO
Glasgow Queen Street 10	227	d	12 21
Fort William	227	d	16 19
Mallaig	227	a	17 43
Mallaig	⛴	d	18 15
Lochboisdale	⛴	a	21 45

Please note there is no Mallaig to Lochboisdale service between 22 January and 17 February 2014

No Sunday Service

For details of sailings from 4 April please telephone 08000 66 5000 or visit www.calmac.co.uk

Table 227D - Shipping Services

Mondays to Saturdays

Until 21 January and from 18 February to 1 April

Lochboisdale (South Uist) - Mallaig

Caledonian MacBrayne Ltd in association with ScotRail

			TSO		TO	SO
Lochboisdale	⛴	d	06 00		14 00	14 00
Mallaig	⛴	a	09 30		17 30	17 30
Mallaig	227	d	10 10		18 15	18 15
Fort William	227	a	11 32		19 37	19 37
Glasgow Queen Street 10	227	a	15 30		00b20	

b Change at Fort William and Westerton. Reservations compulsory from Fort William.

Please note there is no Lochboisdale to Mallaig service between 22 January and 17 February 2014

No Sunday Service

For details of sailings from 4 April please telephone 08000 66 5000 or visit www.calmac.co.uk

Table 228

Edinburgh - Falkirk High - Glasgow Queen Street

Mondays to Saturdays

9 December to 17 May

Network Diagram - refer to first page of Table 225

Miles																									
			SR	SR	SR	SR	SR	SR	SR	SR	SR		SR	SR	SR	SR	SR	SR	SR	SR	SR		SR	SR	SR
					SX				SX	SO	SX		SX												
			1	1	1	1	1	1		1	1			1	1	1	1	1	1	1	1		1	1	1
						trolley	trolley	trolley		trolley	trolley			trolley	trolley	trolley	trolley	trolley	trolley	trolley	trolley		trolley	trolley	trolley
0	**Edinburgh 10**	225,230,242 d	05 55	06 30	06 45	07 00	07 15	07 30		07 45	07 45			08 00	08 15	08 30	08 45	09 00	09 15	09 30	09 45		10 00	10 15	10 30
1¼	Haymarket	225,230,242 d	05 59	06 34	06 49	07 04	07 19	07 35		07 49	07 49			08 05	08 19	08 34	08 49	09 05	09 19	09 34	09 49		10 04	10 19	10 34
17½	Linlithgow	230 d	06 14	06 49	07 04		07 34	07 50	08 01	08 06	08 06				08 35		09 05		09 35		10 04			10 34	
22¼	Polmont 3	230 d	06 20	06 56		07 22		07 56						08 25	08 42		09 12		09 41		10 10			10 40	
25½	**Falkirk High 3**	d	06 25	07 01	07 13	07 27	07 43	08 01	08b12	08 15	08 15			08 30	08 47	08 55	09 17	09 25	09 46	09 54	10 15		10 24	10 45	10 54
35¾	Croy 3	230 a	06 34	07 10	07 23		07 53	08 11					←	08 39		09 04		09 36		10 03			10 34		11 03
41	Lenzie 3	230 a							08 31	08 27	08 27		08 31												
44	Bishopbriggs	230 a							→	08 32			08 36												
47¼	**Glasgow Queen Street 10**	230 a	06 49	07 25	07 37	07 50	08 07	08 25		08 40	08 40		08 48	08 55	09 07	09 19	09 37	09 50	10 06	10 19	10 36		10 49	11 06	11 19

		SR	SR	SR	SR	SR	SR		SR	SR	SR	SR	SR	SR	SR	SR	SR		SR	SR	SR	SR	SR	SR	SR
		SO	SX										SO	SX	SO	SX							SO	SX	
		1	1	1	1	1	1		1	1	1	1	1	1	1	1	1		1	1	1	1	1	1	1
		trolley	trolley	trolley	trolley	trolley	trolley		trolley	trolley	trolley	trolley	trolley	trolley	trolley	trolley	trolley		trolley	trolley	trolley	trolley	trolley	trolley	trolley
Edinburgh 10	225,230,242 d	10 45	10 45	11 00	11 15	11 30	11 45		12 00	12 15	12 30	12 45	13 00	13 00	13 15	13 15	13 30		13 45	14 00	14 15	14 30	14 45	14 45	15 00
Haymarket	225,230,242 d	10 49	10 49	11 04	11 19	11 34	11 51		12 04	12 19	12 34	12 49	13 04	13 05	13 19	13 20	13 34		13 49	14 04	14 19	14 34	14 49	14 49	15 04
Linlithgow	230 d	11 04	11 04		11 34		12 06			12 34		13 04			13 34	13 34			14 04		14 34		15 04	15 06	
Polmont 3	230 d	11 10	11 10		11 40		12 12			12 40		13 10			13 40	13 40			14 10		14 40		15 10	15 13	
Falkirk High 3	d	11 15	11 15	11 24	11 45	11 54	12 17		12 24	12 45	12 54	13 15	13 24	13 24	13 45	13 45	13 55		14 15	14 24	14 45	14 54	15 15	15 17	15 24
Croy 3	230 a			11 34		12 03			12 34		13 03		13 34	13 34			14 04			14 33		15 03			15 34
Lenzie 3	230 a																								
Bishopbriggs	230 a																								
Glasgow Queen Street 10	230 a	11 37	11 38	11 50	12 06	12 20	12 37		12 49	13 06	13 19	13 37	13 51	13 51	14 07	14 07	14 19		14 36	14 49	15 07	15 21	15 38	15 38	15 51

		SR	SR		SR	SR	SR	SR	SR	SR	SR	SR	SR		SR	SR	SR	SR	SR	SR	SR	SR	SR		SR
						SO	SX			SO	SX						SO	SX		SX	SO		SO		SX
		1	1		1	1	1	1	1	1	1	1	1		1	1	1	1	1	1	1	1	1		1
		trolley	trolley		trolley	trolley	trolley	trolley	trolley	trolley	trolley	trolley	trolley		trolley	trolley	trolley	trolley	trolley	trolley	trolley	trolley	trolley		
Edinburgh 10	225,230,242 d	15 15	15 30		15 45	16 00	16 00	16 15	16 30	16 45	16 45	17 00	17 15		17 30	17 45	18 00	18 00	18 15	18 30	18 30	18 45	19 00		19 00
Haymarket	225,230,242 d	15 19	15 34		15 49	16 04	16 05	16 19	16 34	16 49	16 50	17 04	17 19		17 34	17 49	18 04	18 05	18 19	18 34	18 34	18 49	19 04		19 04
Linlithgow	230 d	15 34			16 04			16 34		17 06	17 06		17 34			18 05			18 36			19 04			
Polmont 3	230 d	15 41			16 10			16 41		17 13	17 13		17 41			18 12			18 43			19 10			
Falkirk High 3	d	15 45	15 54		16 15	16 26	16 26	16 46	16 55	17 18	17 18	17 26	17 46		17 56	18 17	18 26	18 26	18 48	18 54	18 54	19 15	19 24		19 24
Croy 3	230 a		16 03			16 36	16 36		17 05			17 36			18 06		18 35	18 35		19 04	19 04		19 34		19 34
Lenzie 3	230 a														18 12										
Bishopbriggs	230 a																								
Glasgow Queen Street 10	230 a	16 06	16 19		16 36	16 51	16 51	17 07	17 21	17 39	17 40	17 51	18 06		18 23	18 37	18 50	18 50	19 08	19 20	19 22	19 36	19 49		19 49

		SR	SR	SR	SR	SR	SR	SR	SR		SR	SR	SR	SR
		SX	SO						SX		SO			
		1	1	1	1	1	1	1	1		1	1	1	1
Edinburgh 10	225,230,242 d	19 15	19 15	19 30	20 00	20 30	21 00	21 30	22 00		22 00	22 30	23 00	23 30
Haymarket	225,230,242 d	19 19	19 20	19 34	20 04	20 34	21 04	21 34	22 04		22 04	22 34	23 04	23 34
Linlithgow	230 d	19 34	19 34	19 49	20 19	20 49	21 19	21 49	22 19		22 19	22 49	23 19	23 49
Polmont 3	230 d	19 40	19 40		20 25		21 25		22 25		22 25		23 24	23 54
Falkirk High 3	d	19 45	19 45	19 58	20 30	20 58	21 30	21 58	22 30		22 30	22 58	23 30	23 59
Croy 3	230 a			20 07		21 07		22 07				23 07	23 38	00 10
Lenzie 3	230 a												23 44	00 15
Bishopbriggs	230 a												23 49	
Glasgow Queen Street 10	230 a	20 07	20 07	20 22	20 51	21 21	21 51	22 23	22 51		22 52	23 22	23 58	00 27

Sundays

8 December to 11 May

		SR	SR	SR	SR	SR	SR	SR	SR	SR		SR	SR	SR	SR	SR	SR	SR	SR	SR		SR	SR	SR	SR
		1	1	1	1	1	1	1	1	1		1	1	1	1	1	1	1	1	1		1	1	1	1
			trolley	trolley	trolley	trolley	trolley	trolley	trolley	trolley		trolley	trolley	trolley	trolley		trolley	trolley	trolley	trolley		trolley		trolley	trolley
Edinburgh 10	225,230,242 d	08 00	08 30	09 00	09 30	10 00	10 30	11 00	11 30	12 00		12 30	13 00	13 30	14 00	14 30	15 00	15 30	16 00	16 30		17 00	17 30	18 00	18 30
Haymarket	225,230,242 d	08 04	08 34	09 04	09 34	10 04	10 34	11 04	11 34	12 04		12 33	13 04	13 34	14 04	14 35	15 04	15 34	16 04	16 34		17 04	17 34	18 04	18 34
Linlithgow	230 d	08 23	08 53	09 23	09 53	10 23	10 49	11 19	11 49	12 19		12 49	13 19	13 49	14 19	14 49	15 19	15 49	16 19	16 49		17 19	17 49	18 19	18 49
Polmont 3	230 d	08 29		09 29		10 29		11 25		12 25			13 25		14 25		15 25		16 25			17 25		18 25	
Falkirk High 3	d	08 34	09 02	09 34	10 02	10 34	10 58	11 30	11 58	12 30		12 58	13 30	13 58	14 30	14 58	15 30	15 58	16 30	16 58		17 30	17 58	18 30	18 58
Croy 3	230 a	08 43	09 11		10 11		11 07		12 07			13 07		14 07		15 06		16 07		17 07			18 07		19 07
Lenzie 3	230 a																								
Bishopbriggs	230 a																								
Glasgow Queen Street 10	230 a	08 58	09 25	09 54	10 28	10 55	11 21	11 51	12 21	12 52		13 22	13 51	14 21	14 51	15 22	15 51	16 22	16 51	17 22		17 51	18 22	18 52	19 22

		SR	SR	SR	SR	SR		SR	SR	SR	SR	SR
		1	1	1	1	1		1	1	1	1	1
		trolley										
Edinburgh 10	225,230,242 d	19 00	19 30	20 00	20 30	21 00		21 30	22 00	22 30	23 00	23 30
Haymarket	225,230,242 d	19 04	19 34	20 04	20 34	21 04		21 34	22 04	22 34	23 04	23 34
Linlithgow	230 d	19 19	19 49	20 19	20 49	21 19		21 49	22 19	22 49	23 19	23 49
Polmont 3	230 d	19 25		20 25		21 25			22 25		23 25	23 55
Falkirk High 3	d	19 30	19 58	20 30	20 58	21 30		21 58	22 30	22 58	23 30	23 59
Croy 3	230 a		20 07		21 07			22 07		23 07	23 40	00 09
Lenzie 3	230 a											
Bishopbriggs	230 a											
Glasgow Queen Street 10	230 a	19 51	20 22	20 51	21 23	21 51		22 21	22 51	23 21	23 54	00 24

b Falkirk Grahamston

Table 228R

Mondays to Saturdays

9 December to 17 May

Glasgow Queen Street - Falkirk High - Edinburgh

Network Diagram - refer to first page of Table 225

Miles																						
		SR	SR SX	SR SO	SR SX	SR	SR	SR	SR	SR	SR	SR	SR SX	SR SO	SR	SR	SR	SR SX	SR SO	SR	SR	SR
		1	1	1	1	1 trolley	1 trolley	1 trolley	1	1 trolley	1 trolley	1 trolley	1 trolley	1 trolley	1 trolley	1 trolley	1 trolley	1 trolley	1	1 trolley	1 trolley	1 trolley
0	**Glasgow Queen Street [10]** 230 d	06 00	06 30	06 30	06 45	07 00	07 15	07 30	07 45	08 00	08 15	08 30	08 45	08 45	09 00	09 15	09 30	09 45	09 45	10 00	10 15	10 30
3¼	Bishopbriggs 230 d																					
6¼	Lenzie [3] 230 d		06 38	06 38		07 09																
11½	Croy [3] 230 d			06 44	06 57			07 43		08 12		08 43			09 12		09 42			10 12		10 42
21¾	**Falkirk High [3]** d	06 18	06 52	06 54	07 07	07 22	07 34	07 53	08 04	08 22	08 34	08 53	09 04	09 04	09 22	09 35	09 52	10 03	10 03	10 22	10 33	10 52
25	Polmont [3] 230 a	06 23	06 56	06 58		07 26	07 38		08 10	08 27			09 09	09 09		09 40		10 08	10 08		10 38	
29¾	Linlithgow 230 a	06 29	07 03	07 05	07 15	07 33	07 45	08 00	08 16		08 43		09 15	09 15		09 46		10 14	10 14		10 44	
46	Haymarket 225,230,242 a	06s45	07s20	07s20	07s32	07s50	08s02	08s19	08s31	08s46	09s01	09s14	09s33	09s33	09s46	10s02	10s12	10s31	10s31	10s44	11s00	11s14
47¼	**Edinburgh [10]** 225,230,242 a	06 50	07 25	07 25	07 37	07 55	08 07	08 25	08 36	08 51	09 07	09 20	09 37	09 39	09 51	10 10	10 19	10 37	10 37	10 50	11 07	11 21

	SR	SR	SR	SR	SR	SR	SR	SR	SR	SR	SR SX	SR SO	SR	SR	SR	SR	SR	SR	SR	SR	SR
	1 trolley	1 trolley	1 trolley	1 trolley	1 trolley	1 trolley	1 trolley	1 trolley	1 trolley	1 trolley	1 trolley	1 trolley	1 trolley	1 trolley	1 trolley	1 trolley	1 trolley	1 trolley	1 trolley	1 trolley	1 trolley
Glasgow Queen Street [10] 230 d	10 45	11 00	11 15	11 30	11 45	12 00	12 15	12 30	12 45	13 00	13 15	13 15	13 30	13 45	14 00	14 15	14 30	14 45	15 00	15 15	15 30
Bishopbriggs 230 d																					
Lenzie [3] 230 d																					
Croy [3] 230 d		11 12		11 42		12 12		12 42		13 12			13 42		14 12		14 42		15 12		15 42
Falkirk High [3] d	11 03	11 22	11 33	11 52	12 03	12 22	12 33	12 52	13 03	13 22	13 33	13 33	13 52	14 03	14 22	14 33	14 52	15 03	15 22	15 33	15 52
Polmont [3] 230 a	11 08		11 38		12 08		12 38		13 08		13 38	13 38		14 08		14 38		15 08		15 38	
Linlithgow 230 a	11 14		11 44		12 14		12 44		13 14		13 44	13 44		14 14		14 44		15 14		15 44	
Haymarket 225,230,242 a	11s30	11s45	12s00	12s12	12s30	12s45	13s01	13s14	13s30	13s45	14s00	14s01	14s11	14s32	14s45	15s00	15s14	15s29	15s45	16s01	16s13
Edinburgh [10] 225,230,242 a	11 35	11 51	12 07	12 19	12 35	12 52	13 07	13 20	13 35	13 50	14 07	14 07	14 19	14 37	14 51	15 05	15 20	15 36	15 50	16 08	16 18

	SR	SR	SR	SR	SR SX	SR SO	SR	SR	SR	SR	SR	SR	SR	SR	SR	SR	SR	SR	SR	SR	SR	SR
	1 trolley	1 trolley	1 trolley	1 trolley	1 trolley	1	1 trolley	1 trolley	1 trolley	1 trolley	1 trolley	1 trolley	1 trolley	1 trolley	1 trolley	1	1	1	1	1	1	1
Glasgow Queen Street [10] 230 d	15 45	16 00	16 15	16 30	16 45	16 45	17 00	17 15	17 30	17 45	18 00	18 15	18 30	18 45	19 00	19 15	19 30	20 00	20 30	21 00	21 30	22 00
Bishopbriggs 230 d																						
Lenzie [3] 230 d																						
Croy [3] 230 d		16 12		16 42			17 12		17 42		18 13		18 43		19 12			20 12		21 12		22 12
Falkirk High [3] d	16 03	16 22	16 34	16 52	17 06	17 06	17 22	17 36	17 52	18 05	18 23	18 34	18 53	19 03	19 22	19 33	19 48	20 22	20 48	21 22	21 48	22 22
Polmont [3] 230 a	16 08		16 39		17 11	17 11	17 27		17 57	18 10		18 39		19 08		19 38	19 53		20 53		21 53	
Linlithgow 230 a	16 14		16 45		17 17	17 17		17 44	18 04	18 16		18 45		19 14		19 44	19 58	20 29	20 59	21 29	21 59	22 29
Haymarket 225,230,242 a	16s30	16s43	17s00	17s17	17s34	17s34	17s46	18s02	18s19	18s32	18s43	19s02	19s14	19s31	19s46	20s00	20s15	20s45	21s15	21s45	22s15	22s46
Edinburgh [10] 225,230,242 a	16 36	16 48	17 06	17 22	17 40	17 40	17 52	18 08	18 25	18 38	18 49	19 07	19 20	19 39	19 51	20 06	20 21	20 51	21 20	21 50	22 22	22 51

	SR	SR	SR
	1	1	1
Glasgow Queen Street [10] 230 d	22 30	23 00	23 30
Bishopbriggs 230 d			
Lenzie [3] 230 d			
Croy [3] 230 d		23 12	23 42
Falkirk High [3] d	22 48	23 22	23 52
Polmont [3] 230 a	22 53	23 26	23 56
Linlithgow 230 a	22 59	23 33	00 03
Haymarket 225,230,242 a	23s15	23s49	00s20
Edinburgh [10] 225,230,242 a	23 20	23 55	00 25

Sundays

8 December to 11 May

	SR	SR	SR	SR	SR	SR	SR	SR	SR	SR	SR	SR	SR	SR	SR	SR	SR	SR	SR	SR	SR
	1	1 trolley	1 trolley	1 trolley	1 trolley	1 trolley	1 trolley	1 trolley	1 trolley	1 trolley	1 trolley	1	1 trolley	1 trolley	1	1	1 trolley	1 trolley	1 trolley	1 trolley	1 trolley	1 trolley
Glasgow Queen Street [10] 230 d	07 50	08 30	09 00	09 30	10 00	10 30	11 00	11 30	12 00	12 30	13 00	13 30	14 00	14 30	15 00	15 30	16 00	16 30	17 00	17 30	18 00	18 30
Bishopbriggs 230 d																						
Lenzie [3] 230 d																						
Croy [3] 230 d	08 02		09 12		10 12		11 12		12 12		13 12		14 12		15 12		16 12		17 12		18 12	
Falkirk High [3] d	08 12	08 48	09 22	09 48	10 22	10 48	11 22	11 48	12 22	12 48	13 22	13 48	14 22	14 48	15 22	15 48	16 22	16 48	17 22	17 48	18 22	18 48
Polmont [3] 230 a	08 17	08 53		09 53		10 53		11 53		12 58		13 53		14 53		15 53		16 53		17 53		18 53
Linlithgow 230 a	08 23	08 59	09 29	09 59	10 29	10 59	11 29	11 59	12 29	13 05	13 29	13 59	14 29	14 59	15 29	15 59	16 29	16 59	17 29	17 59	18 29	18 59
Haymarket 225,230,242 a	08 44	09s19	09s49	10s19	10s45	11s15	11s47	12s15	12s45	13s19	13s47	14s17	14s47	15s15	15s47	16s18	16s47	17s15	17s47	18s17	18s47	19s16
Edinburgh [10] 225,230,242 a	08 49	09 24	09 54	10 24	10 50	11 20	11 52	12 20	12 50	13 24	13 52	14 22	14 52	15 20	15 52	16 24	16 52	17 20	17 52	18 22	18 52	19 21

	SR	SR	SR	SR	SR	SR	SR	SR	SR	SR
	1 trolley	1 trolley	1	1	1	1	1	1	1	1
Glasgow Queen Street [10] 230 d	19 00	19 30	20 00	20 30	21 00	21 30	22 00	22 30	23 00	23 30
Bishopbriggs 230 d										
Lenzie [3] 230 d										
Croy [3] 230 d	19 12		20 12		21 12		22 12		23 12	23 42
Falkirk High [3] d	19 22	19 48	20 22	20 48	21 22	21 48	22 22	22 48	23 22	23 52
Polmont [3] 230 a		19 53		20 53		21 53		22 53		23 56
Linlithgow 230 a	19 29	19 59	20 29	20 59	21 29	21 59	22 29	22 59	23 29	00 03
Haymarket 225,230,242 a	19s47	20s16	20s45	21s15	21s46	22s18	22s45	23s15	23s45	00s19
Edinburgh [10] 225,230,242 a	19 52	20 21	20 50	21 20	21 52	22 23	22 50	23 20	23 50	00 24

Table 229

Mondays to Saturdays

9 December to 17 May

Edinburgh and Glasgow Queen Street - Perth, Inverness, Dundee, Aberdeen, Dyce and Inverurie

Network Diagram - refer to first page of Table 225

Miles	Miles	Miles	Miles	Miles	Station		SR MX	SR MO	SR MX	SR MX	SR	SR MO	SR SX	SR SO	SR
											B	B			
							◇1	◇1	◇	◇			◇1	◇1	1
							A	A	A	B	C	D			
								(trolley)			(sleeper) ✕	(sleeper) ✕			
—	0	—	0	0	**Edinburgh** 10	242 d									
—	1¼	—	1¼	1¼	Haymarket	242 d									
—	13¼	—	13¼	—	Inverkeithing	242 d									
—	26	—	26	—	Kirkcaldy	242 d									
—	33¼	—	33¼	—	Markinch	d				00 03					
—	39¼	—	39¼	—	Ladybank	d				00 10					
—	42¼	—	—	—	Springfield	d									
—	44½	—	—	—	Cupar	d				00 17					
—	—	—	—	—	Leuchars 5	a				00 23					
—	—	—	—	—	St Andrews Bus Station (bus)	a									
—	—	—	—	—	St Andrews Bus Station (bus)	d									
—	51	—	—	—	Leuchars 3	d				00 24					
0	—	0	—	—	**Glasgow Queen St.** 10	230 (ship) d									
21	—	21	—	28¼	Larbert	230 d									
29	—	29	—	36½	Stirling	230 d									
—	—	—	—	—	Bridge of Allan	230 d									
34½	—	34½	—	42	Dunblane	230 d									
46¾	—	46¾	—	54¼	Gleneagles	d									
62½	—	62½	57	70¾	**Perth**	a									
—	—	—	—	—		d			00 13						06 00
79¾	—	—	—	—	Invergowrie	d									
83¾	59¼	—	—	—	**Dundee**	a			00 36	00 40					06 24
—	—	—	—	—		d							05 39		06 25
87¼	63¼	—	—	—	Broughty Ferry	d							05 46		06 32
89	65	—	—	—	Balmossie	d									
89¾	65¾	—	—	—	Monifieth	d									
92¾	68¾	—	—	—	Barry Links	d									
93½	69½	—	—	—	Golf Street	d									
94	70	—	—	—	Carnoustie	d							05 57		06 40
100¼	76¼	—	—	—	Arbroath	d							06 04		06 47
114	90	—	—	—	Montrose	d							06 25	06 25	07 02
124	100	—	—	—	Laurencekirk	d							06 36	06 36	
138¼	114¼	—	—	—	Stonehaven	d	00 05	00 05					06 50	06 50	07 25
146½	122½	—	—	—	Portlethen	d							06 59	06 59	07 34
154½	130½	—	—	—	**Aberdeen**	a	00 25	00 25					07 14	07 14	07 47
—	—	—	—	—		d							07 15	07 15	07 48
160¾	136¾	—	—	—	Dyce	240 (plane) a							07 25	07 25	07 57
171½	147½	—	—	—	**Inverurie**	240 a							07 40	07 40	08 11
—	—	78	72½	86¼	Dunkeld & Birnam	d									
—	—	91	85½	99¼	Pitlochry	d									
—	—	97¾	92¼	106	Blair Atholl	d									
—	—	121	116¼	130¼	Dalwhinnie	d									
—	—	131¼	126¾	140½	Newtonmore	d									
—	—	134	129½	143¼	Kingussie	d					07 19	07 21			
—	—	145¾	141¼	155	Aviemore	d					07 43	07 41			
—	—	152¾	148¼	162	Carrbridge	d					07 56	07 53			
—	—	180	175	188¾	**Inverness**	a					08 36	08 37	09 35	09 35	

Station		XC	SR	SR	SR SX	SR SO	SR	SR	SR	SR
		◇1	◇1	◇1	◇1	◇	◇	◇1	◇1	◇1
				E					E	
				(trolley)				(trolley)	(trolley)	(trolley)
Edinburgh 10	242 d		05 30		06 33	06 33	07 00		07 28	
Haymarket	242 d		05 34		06 37	06 37	07 04		07 32	
Inverkeithing	242 d		05 47		06 50	06 50	07 20			
Kirkcaldy	242 d		06 03		07 06	07 06	07 36		08 03	
Markinch	d		06 12		07 15	07 15	07 47			
Ladybank	d		06 20		07 22	07 22	07 55			
Springfield	d									
Cupar	d		06 26				08 01			
Leuchars 5	a		06 33				08 08		08 26	
St Andrews Bus Station (bus)	a		*07 01*				*08 31*			
St Andrews Bus Station (bus)	d		*06 00*				*07 43*			
Leuchars 3	d		06 33				08 08		08 26	
Glasgow Queen St. 10	230 (ship) d			05 56				07 10		07 41
Larbert	230 d			06 16						
Stirling	230 d			06 25				07 36		08u09
Bridge of Allan	230 d									
Dunblane	230 d			06 31				07 43		08 15
Gleneagles	d			06 43						
Perth	a			06 59	07 45	07 45		08 09		08 41
	d			07 00	07 46	07 46		08 10		08 42
Invergowrie	d				08 04	08 04				
Dundee	a		06 46	07 22	08 12	08 12	08 24		08 41	09 03
	d	06 40	06 52	07 23					08 42	09 04
Broughty Ferry	d									
Balmossie	d									
Monifieth	d									
Barry Links	d									
Golf Street	d									
Carnoustie	d		07 04	07 35						09 16
Arbroath	d	07 00	07 12	07 42					08 59	09 23
Montrose	d	07 15	07 26	07 57					09 13	09 38
Laurencekirk	d		07 37	08 08						
Stonehaven	d	07 36	07 51	08 21					09 35	
Portlethen	d		07 59	08 30						
Aberdeen	a	07 57	08 14	08 47					09 54	10 17
	d			08 52					09 58	
Dyce	240 (plane) a			09 01					10 06	
Inverurie	240 a								10 21	
Dunkeld & Birnam	d							08 30		
Pitlochry	d							08 43		
Blair Atholl	d							08 52		
Dalwhinnie	d							09 17		
Newtonmore	d							09 27		
Kingussie	d							09 36		
Aviemore	d							09 50		
Carrbridge	d							09 58		
Inverness	a							10 27		

Station		SR	SR	SR	SR	SR	SR	SR	SR SX	SR SO
		◇	◇1	◇1	◇1	◇1	◇1	◇1	◇1	◇1
				E						
				(trolley)		(trolley)	(trolley)		(trolley)	(trolley)
Edinburgh 10	242 d	07 33	08 00	08 28			08 34	09 00	09 28	09 28
Haymarket	242 d	07 38	08 04	08 32			08 38	09 04	09 34	09 34
Inverkeithing	242 d	07 53	08 17					09 17		
Kirkcaldy	242 d	08 09	08 33				09 07	09 33		
Markinch	d	08 19	08 42				09 16	09 42		
Ladybank	d	08 27	08 49					09 49		
Springfield	d		08 55							
Cupar	d		08 59					09 55		
Leuchars 5	a		09 06	09 22				10 02		10 25
St Andrews Bus Station (bus)	a		*09 34*	*09 42*				*10 22*		*10 42*
St Andrews Bus Station (bus)	d		*08 45*	*09 05*				*09 45*		*10 05*
Leuchars 3	d		09 06	09 22				10 02		10 25
Glasgow Queen St. 10	230 (ship) d				08 06	08 41				
Larbert	230 d									
Stirling	230 d				08 36	09 08				
Bridge of Allan	230 d				08 40					
Dunblane	230 d				08 44					
Gleneagles	d				08 56					
Perth	a	08 54			09 12	09 39	09 46			
	d				09 15	09 40	09 47			
Invergowrie	d				09 39					
Dundee	a		09 22	09 37	09 44	10 04		10 19	10 33	10 38
	d			09 38		10 05			10 34	10 39
Broughty Ferry	d			09 45						
Balmossie	d									
Monifieth	d									
Barry Links	d									
Golf Street	d									
Carnoustie	d									
Arbroath	d			09 58		10 21			10 51	10 56
Montrose	d					10 40			11 05	11 10
Laurencekirk	d			10 21						
Stonehaven	d			10 34		11 02			11 26	11 31
Portlethen	d					11 11				
Aberdeen	a			10 54		11 24			11 46	11 51
	d			11 03						
Dyce	240 (plane) a			11 11						
Inverurie	240 a			11 28						
Dunkeld & Birnam	d									
Pitlochry	d						10 19			
Blair Atholl	d						10 28			
Dalwhinnie	d						10 54			
Newtonmore	d									
Kingussie	d						11 07			
Aviemore	d						11 22			
Carrbridge	d									
Inverness	a						11 57			

Station		SR	SR SO	SR SX	SR	SR
		◇	◇1	◇1	◇	◇1
			(trolley)	(trolley)		
Edinburgh 10	242 d				09 35	10 00
Haymarket	242 d				09 40	10 04
Inverkeithing	242 d				09 54	10 17
Kirkcaldy	242 d				10 10	10 33
Markinch	d				10 19	10 42
Ladybank	d				10 27	10 49
Springfield	d					
Cupar	d					10 55
Leuchars 5	a					11 02
St Andrews Bus Station (bus)	a					*11 22*
St Andrews Bus Station (bus)	d					*10 45*
Leuchars 3	d					11 02
Glasgow Queen St. 10	230 (ship) d	09 08	09 41	09 41		
Larbert	230 d					
Stirling	230 d	09 35	10 08	10 08		
Bridge of Allan	230 d					
Dunblane	230 d	09 41				
Gleneagles	d	09 53				
Perth	a	10 09	10 37	10 37	10 52	
	d	10 15	10 40	10 40		
Invergowrie	d	10 34				
Dundee	a	10 43	11 01	11 01		11 20
	d		11 02	11 02		
Broughty Ferry	d		11 09	11 09		
Balmossie	d					
Monifieth	d					
Barry Links	d					
Golf Street	d					
Carnoustie	d		11 17	11 17		
Arbroath	d		11 24	11 24		
Montrose	d		11 38	11 40		
Laurencekirk	d		11 49	11 58		
Stonehaven	d		12 03	12 12		
Portlethen	d					
Aberdeen	a		12 23	12 35		
	d					
Dyce	240 (plane) a					
Inverurie	240 a					
Dunkeld & Birnam	d					
Pitlochry	d					
Blair Atholl	d					
Dalwhinnie	d					
Newtonmore	d					
Kingussie	d					
Aviemore	d					
Carrbridge	d					
Inverness	a					

A From Glasgow Queen Street
B From Edinburgh
C until 15 February, MX from 18 February until 22 March, from 25 March. From London Euston
D from 17 February until 24 March. From London Euston
E (trolley) to Aberdeen

Table 229

Mondays to Saturdays

9 December to 17 May

Edinburgh and Glasgow Queen Street - Perth, Inverness, Dundee, Aberdeen, Dyce and Inverurie

Network Diagram - refer to first page of Table 225

	SR	GR	SR	SR	VT SO	SR SO	SR SX	SR	SR	SR	SR	SR	SR
	◇1	R 1	◇1	◇1	◇1	◇1	◇	◇1	◇1	◇	◇1	◇1	◇1
		A			B								C
	🛒	🍽🛒	🛒	🛒	🍽			🛒	🛒			🛒	🛒
Edinburgh 10 242 d		10 28		10 35	10 52	11 00	11 00	11 28		11 35	12 00		12 28
Haymarket 242 d		10 33		10u40	10a56	11 04	11 04	11 33		11 40	12 04		12 32
Inverkeithing 242 d		10 48		10u54		11 17	11 17			11 54	12 17		
Kirkcaldy 242 d		11 05		11u10		11 33	11 33			12 10	12 33		
Markinch d				11 19		11 42	11 42			12 19	12 42		
Ladybank d				11 27		11 49	11 49			12 27	12 49		
Springfield d													
Cupar d						11 55	11 55				12 55		
Leuchars 5 a		11 28				12 02	12 02	12 25			13 02		13 23
St Andrews Bus Station 🚌 a		*11 52*				*12 22*	*12 22*	*12 42*			*13 22*		*13 42*
St Andrews Bus Station 🚌 d		*11 05*				*11 45*	*11 45*	*12 45*			*12 45*		*13 05*
Leuchars 3 d		11 30				12 02	12 02	12 26			13 02		13 23
Glasgow Queen St. 10 230 ⛴ d	10 10		10 41						11 41			12 10	
Larbert 230 d													
Stirling 230 d	10 37		11 09						12 08			12 36	
Bridge of Allan 230 d	10 41											12 41	
Dunblane 230 d	10 46											12 45	
Gleneagles d	10 58												
Perth a	11 15		11 38	11 52					12 37	12 52		13 12	
d	11 16		11 39	11 53					12 38			13 13	
Invergowrie d													
Dundee a		11 43	12 01			12 19	12 19	12 39	13 00		13 19		13 38
d		11 44	12 02					12 40	13 01				13 39
Broughty Ferry d													
Balmossie d													
Monifieth d													
Barry Links d													
Golf Street d													
Carnoustie d									13 13				
Arbroath d		12 02	12 18					12 56	13 20				13 55
Montrose d		12 18	12 33						13 34				14 10
Laurencekirk d									13 45				
Stonehaven d		12 41						13 30					14 31
Portlethen d													
Aberdeen a		13 03	13 13					13 50	14 16				14 50
d													14 57
Dyce 240 ✈ a													15 05
Inverurie 240 a													15 19
Dunkeld & Birnam d	11 36											13 29	
Pitlochry d	11 49			12 22								13 42	
Blair Atholl d				12 31								13 52	
Dalwhinnie d				12 59									
Newtonmore d				13 09									
Kingussie d	12 34			13 15								14 28	
Aviemore d	12 45			13 32								14 39	
Carrbridge d				13 40									
Inverness a	13 28			14 10								15 21	

	SR	SR	VT SO	SR	SR SX	SR SO	SR	SR	SR	GR	SR	SR
	◇1	◇	◇1	◇1	◇1	◇1	◇1	◇1	◇1	R 1	◇1	◇
			B		D	C				E		
	🛒		🍽		🛒	🛒	🛒	🛒		🍽🛒	🛒	
Edinburgh 10 242 d		12 35	12 52	13 00	13 28	13 28		13 35	14 00	14 28		14 35
Haymarket 242 d		12 40	12a56	13 04	13 32	13 32		13u40	14 04	14 33		14 40
Inverkeithing 242 d		12 54		13 17					14 17	14 48		14 54
Kirkcaldy 242 d		13 10		13 33				14u10	14 33	15 05		15 10
Markinch d		13 19		13 42				14 19	14 42			15 20
Ladybank d		13 27		13 49					14 49			15 27
Springfield d												
Cupar d				13 55					14 55			
Leuchars 5 a				14 02	14 23	14 23			15 02	15 28		
St Andrews Bus Station 🚌 a				*14 22*	*14 42*	*14 42*			*15 22*	*15 52*		
St Andrews Bus Station 🚌 d				*13 45*	*14 05*	*14 05*			*14 45*	*14 45*		
Leuchars 3 d				14 02	14 23	14 23			15 02	15 30		
Glasgow Queen St. 10 230 ⛴ d	12 41						13 41				14 41	
Larbert 230 d												
Stirling 230 d	13 07						14 07				15 07	
Bridge of Allan 230 d												
Dunblane 230 d												
Gleneagles d	13 22											
Perth a	13 38	13 52					14 37	14 50			15 39	15 53
d	13 39						14 38	14 51			15 40	
Invergowrie d												
Dundee a	14 01			14 19	14 36	14 36	15 01		15 19	15 46	16 01	
d	14 02				14 37	14 37	15 02			15 48	16 02	
Broughty Ferry d							15 09					
Balmossie d												
Monifieth d												
Barry Links d												
Golf Street d												
Carnoustie d							15 17				16 14	
Arbroath d	14 18				14 54	14 54	15 24			16 05	16 21	
Montrose d	14 33						15 41			16 21	16 36	
Laurencekirk d							15 52					
Stonehaven d	14 54				15 27	15 27				16 44		
Portlethen d							16 12					
Aberdeen a	15 14					15 47	16 26			17 06	17 15	
d						15 52						
Dyce 240 ✈ a					16 00	16 00						
Inverurie 240 a					16 16	16 16						
Dunkeld & Birnam d								15 08				
Pitlochry d								15 21				
Blair Atholl d								15 30				
Dalwhinnie d								15 55				
Newtonmore d												
Kingussie d								16 08				
Aviemore d								16 19				
Carrbridge d												
Inverness a								16 54				

	VT SO	SR	SR	SR	SR	SR	SR SX	SR SO	SR	SR	SR SO
	◇1	◇1	◇1	◇1	◇1	◇	◇	◇1	◇1	1	◇1
	B			C					F	D	
	🍽		🛒	🛒	🛒				🛒		🛒
Edinburgh 10 242 d	14 52	15 00		15 28		15 35	16 00	16 00	16 28		
Haymarket 242 d	14a56	15 04		15 33		15 40	16 04	16 04	16u33		
Inverkeithing 242 d		15 17				15 54	16 17	16 17			
Kirkcaldy 242 d		15 33				16 10	16 33	16 33			
Markinch d		15 42				16 19	16 42	16 42			
Ladybank d		15 49				16 27	16 50	16 50			
Springfield d											
Cupar d		15 55					16 56	16 56	17 19		
Leuchars 5 a		16 02		16 24			17 03	17 03	17 25		
St Andrews Bus Station 🚌 a		*16 22*		*16 42*			*17 24*	*17 22*	*17c46*		
St Andrews Bus Station 🚌 d		*15c05*		*16 05*			*16 45*	*16 45*	*17 05*		
Leuchars 3 d		16 02		16 25			17 03	17 03	17 26		
Glasgow Queen St. 10 230 ⛴ d			15 10		15 41					16 11	16 41
Larbert 230 d											
Stirling 230 d			15 36							16 39	17 10
Bridge of Allan 230 d			15 41							16 44	
Dunblane 230 d			15 45							16 49	
Gleneagles d										17 02	
Perth a			16 12		16 34	16 53				17 18	17 39
d			16 16		16 37					17 19	17 40
Invergowrie d										17 38	
Dundee a		16 21		16 38	16 59		17 19	17 19	17 39	17 45	18 02
d				16 39	17 00				17 40	17 46	18 03
Broughty Ferry d										17 52	
Balmossie d											
Monifieth d										17 57	
Barry Links d											
Golf Street d											
Carnoustie d					17 12					18 03	18 15
Arbroath d				16 55	17 19				17 56	18a10	18 22
Montrose d				17 09	17 33				18 11		
Laurencekirk d				17 20					18 21		
Stonehaven d				17 33	17 55				18 35		18 55
Portlethen d									18 43		
Aberdeen a				17 53	18 15				18 57		19 15
d				17 54					19 10		
Dyce 240 ✈ a				18 02					19 18		
Inverurie 240 a				18 19					19 40		
Dunkeld & Birnam d			16 34								
Pitlochry d			16 47								
Blair Atholl d			16 56								
Dalwhinnie d											
Newtonmore d			17 28								
Kingussie d			17 33								
Aviemore d			17 44								
Carrbridge d			17 52								
Inverness a			18 21								

A From Leeds
B from 4 January until 8 February. To Carlisle
C 🛒 to Aberdeen
D not 25 December, 26 December, 1 January, 2 January
E From London Kings Cross. The Northern Lights
F not 25 December, 26 December, 1 January, 2 January. 🛒 to Aberdeen

Table 229

Edinburgh and Glasgow Queen Street - Perth, Inverness, Dundee, Aberdeen, Dyce and Inverurie

Mondays to Saturdays

9 December to 17 May

Network Diagram - refer to first page of Table 225

	SR SX	SR	GR	VT SO	SR SX	SR SO	SR SX	SR SO	SR SO	SR SX	SR	SR	SR SX	XC SO	XC SX	SR	GR	SR	SR	VT SO
	◇1 ⊥		R 1 A ⊓⊥	◇1 B ⊓	1		◇1 ⊥	◇1 ⊥	◇	◇	◇1 ⊥	◇1 ⊥	◇	◇1 C ⊥	◇1 C	◇1 ⊥	R 1 D ⊓⊥	◇1 ⊥	◇	◇1 B ⊓
Edinburgh 10 242 d		16 33	16 33	16ʃ52	17 00	17 00	17 35	17 36				17 41	18 00	18 11	18 11		18 33		18 40	18ʃ52
Haymarket 242 d		16 37	16 39	16a56	17 04	17 04	17 40	17 40				17u46	18 04	18 15	18 15		18 38		18 46	18a55
Inverkeithing 242 d		16 53			17 22	17 22							18 23	18 29	18 29		18 55		19 02	
Kirkcaldy 242 d		17 09			17 39	17 39						18 15	18 40	18 44	18 47		19 13		19 19	
Markinch d		17 18			17 48	17 48						18 25	18 50	18 53	18 57				19 29	
Ladybank d		17 27			17 55	17 55						18 32	18 57	19 00	19 04				19 36	
Springfield d					18 00	18 00														
Cupar d					18 04	18 04	18 27	18 27					19 04	19 07	19 16					
Leuchars 5 a					18 11	18 11	18 33	18 33					19 10	19 13	19 22		19 37			
St Andrews Bus Station a					*18 32*	*18 32*	*18 58*	*18 58*					*19 31*	*19 31*	*20 01*		*20 01*			
St Andrews Bus Station d					*17 45*	*17 45*	*17 45*	*18 45*					*18 32*	*18 32*	*19 02*		*19 10*			
Leuchars 3 d					18 11	18 11	18 34	18 34					19 11	19 14	19 23		19 38			
Glasgow Queen St. 10 230 d	16 41								17 03	17 11	17 41					18 11		18 41		
Larbert 230 d									17 34	17 34						18 31				
Stirling 230 d			17 23						17 45	17 45	18 16					18 42		19 07		
Bridge of Allan 230 d									17 49	17 49						18 46				
Dunblane 230 d									17 54	17 54	18 23					18 50		19 14		
Gleneagles d			17 40						18 07	18 07	18 36					19 02		19 26		
Perth a	17 39	17 52	17 57						18 23	18 23	18 52	18 57				19 19		19 42	20 01	
d	17 40		18 02						18 25	18 25	18 55	18 58				19 21		19 42		
Invergowrie d									18 44	18 44										
Dundee a	18 02				18 27	18 27	18 49	18 49	18 53	18 53	19 17		19 27	19 29	19 35		19 53	20 03		
d	18 03						18 49	18 49	18 54	18 54	19 18			19 30	19 36		19 55	20 04		
Broughty Ferry d									19 00	19 00								20 12		
Balmossie d									19 04	19 04										
Monifieth d									19 06	19 06										
Barry Links d									19 11	19 11										
Golf Street d									19 13	19 13										
Carnoustie d	18 15								19a17	19a17	19 29							20 19		
Arbroath d	18 22						19 05	19 05			19 36			19 49	19 52		20 12	20 26		
Montrose d							19 22	19 22			19 51			20 03	20 06		20 28	20 41		
Laurencekirk d											20 02									
Stonehaven d	18 55						19 44	19 44			20 15			20 24	20 27		20 51			
Portlethen d							19 53	19 53												
Aberdeen a	19 15						20 07	20 07			20 36			20 42	20 48		21 13	21 22		
d																				
Dyce 240 a																				
Inverurie 240 a																				
Dunkeld & Birnam d												19 18				19 38				
Pitlochry d			18 31									19 31				19 51				
Blair Atholl d																20 01				
Dalwhinnie d																20 24				
Newtonmore d																20 34				
Kingussie d			19 16									20 14				20 39				
Aviemore d			19 29									20 26				20 51				
Carrbridge d																				
Inverness a			20 06									21 01				21 26				

	SR SX	SR SO	SR	SR	SR	SR	SR	XC SX	XC SO	GR SX	SR		SR	SR	SR	SR	SR	SR	SR SX	SR
	◇	◇1	◇	◇1 E ⊥	◇1 ⊥	◇1 F ⊥	◇	◇1 C	◇1 C	R 1 D ⊓⊥	◇1		◇	◇	◇1	◇1	◇	◇	◇	◇
Edinburgh 10 242 d	19 00	19 00		19 28		19 44	20 00	20 14	20 14	20 32			20 45	21 08	21 40		22 08	22 38		23 08
Haymarket 242 d	19 04	19 04		19 32		19 48	20 04	20 17	20 18	20 37			20 49	21 13	21 44		22 13	22 43		23 13
Inverkeithing 242 d	19 17	19 17				20 01	20 23	20 31	20 35	20 52			21 03	21 32			22 32	23 02		23 32
Kirkcaldy 242 d	19 33	19 33				20 17	20 45		20 52	21 09			21 19	21 54	22 12		22 54	23 24		23 54
Markinch d	19 42	19 42				20 26	20 54	21 03	21 02				21 28	22 03			23 03	23 33		00 03
Ladybank d	19 49	19 49				20 33	21 01	21 11	21 10				21 35	22 10			23 10	23 40		00 10
Springfield d																	23 17			
Cupar d	19 55	19 55		20 22			21 08	21 19	21 19					22 17			23 21			00 17
Leuchars 5 a	20 02	20 02		20 28			21 14	21 25	21 25	21 36				22 24	22 34		23 27			00 23
St Andrews Bus Station a	*20 18*	*20 18*		*21 01*			*21 31*	*22 01*	*22 01*	*22 01*				*23 01*	*23 01*		*23 45*			*00 39*
St Andrews Bus Station d	*19 40*	*19 40*		*20 02*			*20 40*	*21 02*	*21 02*	*21 02*				*22 02*	*22 02*		*23 02*			*23 50*
Leuchars 3 d	20 02	20 02		20 29			21 15	21 26	21 27	21 37				22 24	22 35		23 28			00 24
Glasgow Queen St. 10 230 d			19 09		19 41						20 41					21 41			22 48	
Larbert 230 d																			23 20	
Stirling 230 d			19 36		20 07						21 07					22 07			23 31	
Bridge of Allan 230 d			19 40																23 37	
Dunblane 230 d			19 44								21 14								23 42	
Gleneagles d			19 56								21 26								23 53	
Perth a			20 12		20 37	20 58					21 42		22 00			22 37		00 05	00 09	
d			20 13		20 38	21 01					21 43					22 41			00 13	
Invergowrie d			20 30																	
Dundee a	20 18	20 18	20 36	20 42	20 59		21 31	21 41	21 42	21 50	22 03			22 40	22 49	23 02	23 44		00 36	00 40
d				20 43	21 00					21 52	22 05				22 50	23 03				
Broughty Ferry d																23 10				
Balmossie d																				
Monifieth d																23 14				
Barry Links d																				
Golf Street d																				
Carnoustie d											22 17					23 20				
Arbroath d				20 59	21 17					22 09	22 24				23 06	23 27				
Montrose d				21 14	21 31					22 25	22 38				23 20	23 41				
Laurencekirk d					21 42											23 52				
Stonehaven d				21 35	21 55					22 48	22 59				23 41	00 05				
Portlethen d															23 50					
Aberdeen a				21 55	22 15					23 10	23 19				00 04	00 25				
d				21 56																
Dyce 240 a				22 04																
Inverurie 240 a				22 17																
Dunkeld & Birnam d						21 18														
Pitlochry d						21 33														
Blair Atholl d						21 42														
Dalwhinnie d						22 07														
Newtonmore d						22 17														
Kingussie d						22 22														
Aviemore d						22 34														
Carrbridge d						22 42														
Inverness a				00 07		23 10														

A From London Kings Cross. The Highland Chieftain
B from 4 January until 8 February. To Carlisle
C From Plymouth
D From London Kings Cross
E ⊥ to Aberdeen
F ⊥ from Perth

Table 229

Sundays
8 December to 11 May

Edinburgh and Glasgow Queen Street - Perth, Inverness, Dundee, Aberdeen, Dyce and Inverurie

Network Diagram - refer to first page of Table 225

Station			SR	SR	XC	GR	SR	SR	SR	SR	VT
			◇ A	◇1 B	◇	1	◇1	◇1	◇1	◇1	◇1 C
Edinburgh 10	242	d			08 04	09 10	09 15		09 33	10 50	10 51
Haymarket	242	d			08 08	09 15	09 19		09 37	10 54	10a54
Inverkeithing	242	d			08 25	09 33	09 38		09 53	11 07	
Kirkcaldy	242	d			08 40	09 50	10 00		10 09	11 23	
Markinch		d	00 03				10 12		10 18		
Ladybank		d	00 10				10 20		10 26		
Springfield		d									
Cupar		d	00 17		08 57		10 26				
Leuchars 5		a	00 23		09 05	10 13	10 33			11 46	
St Andrews Bus Station		a			*09 29*	*10 29*	*10 58*			*12 17*	
St Andrews Bus Station		d			*08 30*	*09 50*	*10 15*			*11 35*	
Leuchars 3		d	00 24		09 06	10 14	10 34			11 47	
Glasgow Queen St. 10	230	d						09 37			
Larbert	230	d						10 01			
Stirling	230	d						10 10			
Bridge of Allan	230	d									
Dunblane	230	d						10 17			
Gleneagles		d						10 30			
Perth		a						10 46	10 50		
		d						10 47	10 51		
Invergowrie		d									
Dundee		a	00 40		09 18	10 27	10 47	11 10		12 00	
		d			09 20	10 29	10 48	11 11		12 07	
Broughty Ferry		d						11 18			
Balmossie		d									
Monifieth		d									
Barry Links		d									
Golf Street		d									
Carnoustie		d						11 26			
Arbroath		d			09 36	10 46	11 04	11 33		12 23	
Montrose		d			09 50	11 02	11 20	11 48		12 38	
Laurencekirk		d						11 59			
Stonehaven		d		00 05	10 10	11 25	11 42	12 13		12 59	
Portlethen		d					11 51			13 08	
Aberdeen		a		00 25	10 29	11 47	12 05	12 34		13 22	
		d									
Dyce	240	a									
Inverurie	240	a									
Dunkeld & Birnam		d							11 08		
Pitlochry		d							11 21		
Blair Atholl		d							11 30		
Dalwhinnie		d							11 54		
Newtonmore		d							12 04		
Kingussie		d							12 09		
Aviemore		d							12 20		
Carrbridge		d							12 28		
Inverness		a							12 57		

Station			SR	SR	SR	SR	VT	SR	SR	SR	GR
			◇1	◇	◇1	◇1	◇1 C	◇	◇1	◇1	1 D
Edinburgh 10	242	d		11 34		12 40	12 51	13 31		13 56	14 33
Haymarket	242	d		11 38		12 44	12a54	13 35		14 00	14 39
Inverkeithing	242	d		11 52		12 57		13 49		14 14	14 54
Kirkcaldy	242	d		12 08		13 13		14 08		14 30	15 11
Markinch		d		12 18				14 18			
Ladybank		d		12 25				14 25			
Springfield		d									
Cupar		d		12 32				14 32			
Leuchars 5		a		12 39		13 36		14 39			15 34
St Andrews Bus Station		a		*12 57*		*13 55*		*14 55*			*15 55*
St Andrews Bus Station		d		*12 15*		*13 15*		*14 15*			*15 15*
Leuchars 3		d		12 39		13 37		14 39			15 36
Glasgow Queen St. 10	230	d	11 10		11 45				13 45		
Larbert	230	d	11 30								
Stirling	230	d	11 40		12 11				14 13		
Bridge of Allan	230	d									
Dunblane	230	d	11 46		12 18				14 20		
Gleneagles		d	11 58		12 29				14 33		
Perth		a	12 15		12 45				14 49	15 07	
		d	12 16		12 46				14 50	15 11	
Invergowrie		d									
Dundee		a		12 55	13 08	13 50		14 55	15 12		15 49
		d			13 10	13 51			15 13		15 50
Broughty Ferry		d									
Balmossie		d									
Monifieth		d									
Barry Links		d									
Golf Street		d									
Carnoustie		d							15 25		
Arbroath		d			13 26	14 07			15 32		16 08
Montrose		d			13 41	14 21			15 48		16 24
Laurencekirk		d				14 32					
Stonehaven		d			14 02	14 45			16 10		16 47
Portlethen		d							16 20		
Aberdeen		a			14 22	15 05			16 33		17 08
		d									
Dyce	240	a									
Inverurie	240	a									
Dunkeld & Birnam		d	12 34							15 29	
Pitlochry		d	12 47							15 42	
Blair Atholl		d								15 51	
Dalwhinnie		d								16 22	
Newtonmore		d								16 32	
Kingussie		d	13 34							16 37	
Aviemore		d	13 46							16 49	
Carrbridge		d	13 59							16 58	
Inverness		a	14 27							17 27	

Station			SR	SR	SR	SR	SR	GR	SR	SR	SR
			◇1 E		◇1	◇1	◇1	1 F	◇1		◇1
Edinburgh 10	242	d		15 34		15 50	16 05	16 32	17 05	17 34	
Haymarket	242	d		15 38		15 54	16 09	16 37	17 09	17 38	
Inverkeithing	242	d		15 52		16 07	16 23		17 23	17 52	
Kirkcaldy	242	d		16 08		16 23	16 39		17 39	18 08	
Markinch		d		16 18		16 32	16 48			18 18	
Ladybank		d		16 25		16 40				18 25	
Springfield		d									
Cupar		d		16 32			17 01			18 32	
Leuchars 5		a		16 39			17 08		18 03	18 39	
St Andrews Bus Station		a		*16 55*			*17 37*		*18 37*	*18 55*	
St Andrews Bus Station		d		*16 15*			*16 35*		*17 35*	*18 00*	
Leuchars 3		d		16 39			17 08		18 04	18 39	
Glasgow Queen St. 10	230	d	14 40		15 45						17 45
Larbert	230	d	15 00								
Stirling	230	d	15 09		16 12			17 20			18 13
Bridge of Allan	230	d									
Dunblane	230	d	15 16		16 18						
Gleneagles		d	15 28		16 30			17 38			
Perth		a	15 45		16 46	17 04		17 55			18 44
		d	15 46		16 47	17 05		18 01			18 45
Invergowrie		d									
Dundee		a		16 55	17 09		17 21		18 17	18 55	19 08
		d			17 10		17 22		18 18		19 09
Broughty Ferry		d					17 29				
Balmossie		d									
Monifieth		d									
Barry Links		d									
Golf Street		d									
Carnoustie		d					17 37				19 21
Arbroath		d			17 26		17 43		18 35		19 28
Montrose		d			17 41		17 59		18 50		19 44
Laurencekirk		d			17 52						19 55
Stonehaven		d			18 05		18 21		19 12		20 09
Portlethen		d							19 21		
Aberdeen		a			18 25		18 42		19 35		20 29
		d									
Dyce	240	a									
Inverurie	240	a									
Dunkeld & Birnam		d				17 22					
Pitlochry		d	16 13			17 35		18 32			
Blair Atholl		d									
Dalwhinnie		d									
Newtonmore		d									
Kingussie		d	16 56			18 18		19 16			
Aviemore		d	17 10			18 29		19 30			
Carrbridge		d									
Inverness		a	17 45			19 05		20 08			

Station			SR	SR	XC	GR	SR	SR	SR	SR	SR
			◇1	◇1 E	◇1 G	1 H	◇ I	◇1 J	◇1	◇1	◇
Edinburgh 10	242	d	17 50		18 13	18 36	19 15		21 00		22 25
Haymarket	242	d	17 54		18 16	18 41	19 19		21 05		22 29
Inverkeithing	242	d	18 07		18 30	18 56	19 38		21 19		22 48
Kirkcaldy	242	d	18 23		18 45	19 13	19 59		21 35		23 10
Markinch		d	18 32		18 54		20 09		21 44		23 19
Ladybank		d			19 02		20 16		21 51		23 26
Springfield		d									
Cupar		d			19 08		20 23		21 58		23 33
Leuchars 5		a			19 14	19 36	20 30		22 05		23 40
St Andrews Bus Station		a			*19 37*	*19 55*	*20 55*		*22 31*		
St Andrews Bus Station		d			*18 32*	*19 15*	*20 02*		*21 32*		*22 32*
Leuchars 3		d			19 15	19 37	20 30		22 05		23 40
Glasgow Queen St. 10	230	d		18 10				19 45		21 45	
Larbert	230	d		18 30							
Stirling	230	d		18 40				20 12		22 12	
Bridge of Allan	230	d									
Dunblane	230	d		18 47				20 18		22 18	
Gleneagles		d		18 59				20 30		22 30	
Perth		a	19 04	19 16				20 46		22 46	
		d		19 17				20 47		22 47	
Invergowrie		d									
Dundee		a			19 29	19 50	20 46	21 09	22 18	23 09	23 56
		d			19 31	19 52		21 10	22 21	23 10	
Broughty Ferry		d							22 28		
Balmossie		d									
Monifieth		d									
Barry Links		d									
Golf Street		d									
Carnoustie		d								23 22	
Arbroath		d			19 47	20 09		21 26	22 40	23 29	
Montrose		d			20 01	20 25		21 41	22 55	23 44	
Laurencekirk		d						21 52			
Stonehaven		d			20 23	20 48		22 05	23 16	00 05	
Portlethen		d							23 25		
Aberdeen		a			20 42	21 10		22 25	23 39	00 25	
		d									
Dyce	240	a									
Inverurie	240	a									
Dunkeld & Birnam		d		19 33							
Pitlochry		d		19 46							
Blair Atholl		d		19 56							
Dalwhinnie		d		20 19							
Newtonmore		d		20 30							
Kingussie		d		20 35							
Aviemore		d		20 46							
Carrbridge		d		20 54							
Inverness		a		21 24							

A not 8 December. From Edinburgh
B not 8 December. From Glasgow Queen Street
C from 5 January until 9 February. To Carlisle
D From London Kings Cross. The Northern Lights
E To Elgin
F From London Kings Cross. The Highland Chieftain
G From Plymouth
H From London Kings Cross
I Forms tight booked connection into IT88.
J from Dundee

Table 229R

Mondays to Saturdays

9 December to 17 May

Inverurie, Dyce, Aberdeen, Dundee, Inverness and Perth - Glasgow Queen Street and Edinburgh

Network Diagram - refer to first page of Table 225

Miles	Miles	Miles	Miles	Miles	Station		SR SO	SR SX	SR	SR SO	SR	SR	SR	XC SO	XC SX	SR	SR	SR SX	SR SX	SR SO	SR SO	SR SX	SR SX	SR SO	SR SO	SR SX	SR	SR	SR SX	SR SO	SR	SR SX	SR SO	SR	SR SX	SR SO	GR SX	GR SO
							1 A	◇	◇	B	◇		◇1	◇1 C	◇1 C				◇1	◇1 [trolley]	◇1 [trolley]	◇1 [trolley]		1	◇1	1 B		◇1 [trolley]	◇1	◇	◇1 D [trolley]	◇	◇	◇1 [trolley]	◇1 E	◇1 D [trolley]	1 F [restaurant]	1 F [restaurant]
—	—	0	0	0	**Inverness**	d																									04 53			06 50				
—	—	28	28	28	Carrbridge	d																																
—	—	34¾	34¾	34¾	Aviemore	d																												07 25				
—	—	46½	46½	46½	Kingussie	d																												07 37				
—	—	49¼	49¼	49¼	Newtonmore	d																																
—	—	59½	59½	59½	Dalwhinnie	d																																
—	—	82¾	82¾	82¾	Blair Atholl	d																					07 12											
—	—	89½	89½	89½	Pitlochry	d																					07 26							08 17				
—	—	102½	102½	102½	Dunkeld & Birnam	d																					07 39							08 30				
0	0	—	—	—	**Inverurie** 240	d																									06 38				07 13	07 13		
10¾	10¾	—	—	—	Dyce 240 ✈	d																									06 50					07 26		
6¼	6¼	—	—	—	**Aberdeen** 240	a																									07 02					07 37		
—	—	—	—	—		d													05 26	05 26	05 46	05 46						06 33			07 03					07 40	07 52	07 52
14¼	14¼	—	—	—	Portlethen	d													05 37	05 37								06 43										
22½	22½	—	—	—	Stonehaven	d													05 45	05 45	06 02	06 02						06 52			07 20				07 56	07 56	08 10	08 10
36¾	36¾	—	—	—	Laurencekirk	d													05 59	05 59											07 34							
46¾	46¾	—	—	—	Montrose	d	00 06												06 10	06 10	06 24	06 24						07 13			07 44				08 17	08 17	08 33	08 33
60½	60½	—	—	—	Arbroath	d	00 20												06 25	06 25	06 38	06 38						07 27			07 58				08 31	08 31	08 49	08 49
66¾	66¾	—	—	—	Carnoustie	d	00 27					06 00									06 45	06 45						07 34			08 05				08 38	08 38		
67¼	67¼	—	—	—	Golf Street	d						06 02																										
68	68	—	—	—	Barry Links	d						06 05																										
71	71	—	—	—	Monifieth	d						06 10																			08 11							
71¾	71¾	—	—	—	Balmossie	d						06 13																										
73¼	73¼	—	—	—	Broughty Ferry	d	00 34					06 16																07 41										
77½	77½	—	—	—	**Dundee**	a	00 44					06 23							06 45	06 45	06 57	06 57						07 51			08 20				08 53	08 53	09 05	09 05
—	—	—	—	—		d	00 45				05 53		06 05	06 32	06 32				06 50	06 50	06 58	06 58	07 09	07 09	07 36	07 36		07 52	08 17	08 17	08 22	08 29	08 29		08 54	08 54	09 07	09 07
81	—	—	—	—	Invergowrie	d	00 50				05 59																		08 22	08 22								
98¼	—	118	118	118	**Perth**	a	01 09				06 17								07 12	07 12							07 58	08 12	08 40	08 40				08 49	09 14	09 14		
—	—	—	—	—		d		05 13	05 18	05 37	06 19					06 39	06 55	07 01	07 15	07 15							08 02	08 13	08 41	08 41				08 50	09 15	09 15		
114	—	133¾	—	133¾	Gleneagles	d			05 33		06 34					06 54		07 17	07 30	07 30								08 28	08 56	08 56								
121¼	—	146	—	146	Dunblane 230	d			05 46		06 47					07 08		07 31	07 44	07 44									09 07	09 07								
—	—	—	—	—	Bridge of Allan 230	d			05 49		06 50					07 11		07 34	07 48	07 48									09 11	09 11								
131¾	—	151½	—	151½	Stirling 230	d			05 54		06 55					07 17		07 39	07 53	07 53								08 44	09 15	09 15					09 43	09 43		
139¾	—	159½	—	159½	Larbert 230	d			06 03		07 04					07 26		07 47	08 03	08 03																		
160¾	—	180½	—	—	**Glasgow Queen St.** 10 230	a			06 34		07 34							08 19	08 34	08 34								09 16	09 46	09 46					10 14	10 14		
—	85¾	—	—	—	Leuchars 5	a							06 17	06 44	06 44						07 12	07 12	07 22	07 22	07 48	07 48						08 41	08 41				09 19	09 19
—	—	—	—	—	St Andrews Bus Station 🚌	a							*06c41*	*07 01*	*07 01*						*07e31*	*08 02*	*08 02*	*08 02*	*08 12*	*08 12*						*09c02*	*09c02*				*09 42*	*09 42*
—	—	—	—	—	St Andrews Bus Station 🚌	d							*06 00*	*06 30*	*06 30*						*06f30*	*07 00*	*07 00*	*07 00*	*07 30*	*07 30*						*08e25*	*08e25*				*08 55*	*08 55*
—	—	—	—	—	Leuchars 5	d							06 18	06 46	06 46						07 12	07 12	07 23	07 23	07 49	07 49						08 42	08 42				09 21	09 21
—	92¼	—	—	—	Cupar	d							06 25	06 54	06 54						07 19	07 19	07 30	07 30	07 56	07 56						08 49	08 49					
—	94½	—	—	—	Springfield	d																	07 35	07 35														
—	97½	—	135¾	—	Ladybank	d		05 36		05 59			06 33	07 03	07 03		07 31						07 39	07 39			08 23					08 57	08 57					
—	103½	—	141	—	Markinch	d		05 44		06 07			06 40	07 11	07 11		07 38						07 47	07 47	08 09	08 09	08 31					09 04	09 04					
—	110¾	—	149	—	Kirkcaldy 242	d		05 53		06 16			06 50	07 21	07 21		07 48				07 41	07 41	07 57	07 57	08 19	08 19	08 41					09 14	09 14	09 25			09 45	09 45
—	123½	—	161¾	—	Inverkeithing 242	d		06 17		06 39			07 12	07 38	07 41		08 04						08 20	08 20	08 35	08 35	08 57					09 36	09 36				10 01	10 01
—	135½	—	173¾	186½	Haymarket 242	a		06 41		07 01			07 33	07 55	07 58	08 12	08 19				08 14	08 14	08 41	08 41	08 54	08 54	09 17				09 24	09 52	09 54	09 57			10 18	10 18
—	136¾	—	175	187¾	**Edinburgh** 10 242	a		06 46		07 06			07 40	08 01	08 04	08 19	08 24				08 21	08 22	08 46	08 46	09 01	09 01	09 22				09 32	09 59	09 59	10 04			10 24	10 25

A From Aberdeen
B To Newcraighall
C To Plymouth
D [trolley] from Aberdeen
E not 25 December, 26 December, 1 January, 2 January
F To London Kings Cross

Table 229R

Mondays to Saturdays

9 December to 17 May

Inverurie, Dyce, Aberdeen, Dundee, Inverness and Perth - Glasgow Queen Street and Edinburgh

Network Diagram - refer to first page of Table 225

		XC	XC	SR	GR	SR	SR	SR	SR	SR	SR	SR	SR	GR
		SX	SO						SX	SO				
		■ 1	◇1	◇1	■ 1	◇	◇1	◇1	◇1	◇1	◇1	◇	◇1	■ 1
		A	A		B								C	D
					🍽		☕	☕	☕	☕			☕	🍽
Inverness	d				07 55			08 45						
Carrbridge	d							09 16						
Aviemore	d				08 30			09 24						
Kingussie	d				08 43			09 36						
Newtonmore	d							09 40						
Dalwhinnie	d													
Blair Atholl	d													
Pitlochry	d				09 24			10 19						
Dunkeld & Birnam	d													
Inverurie 240	d													
Dyce 240 ✈	d												09 08	
Aberdeen 240	a												09 19	
	d	08 20	08 20				08 42		09 07	09 07			09 35	09 52
Portlethen	d												09 45	
Stonehaven	d	08 38	08 38										09 53	10 10
Laurencekirk	d								09 35	09 35				
Montrose	d	08 59	08 59				09 18		09 46	09 46			10 15	10 33
Arbroath	d	09 15	09 15				09 32		10 00	10 00			10 29	10 49
Carnoustie	d						09 39						10 36	
Golf Street	d													
Barry Links	d													
Monifieth	d													
Balmossie	d													
Broughty Ferry	d												10 43	
Dundee	a	09 31	09 31				09 52		10 15	10 15			10 52	11 05
	d	09 32	09 32	09 41			09 53		10 17	10 17	10 34		10 52	11 08
Invergowrie	d													
Perth	a				09 54		10 14	10 49					11 14	
	d				09 57	10 02	10 15	10 53				11 00	11 14	
Gleneagles	d				10 13			11 08						
Dunblane 230	d							11 20						
Bridge of Allan 230	d							11 23						
Stirling 230	d				10 32		10 43	11 29					11 43	
Larbert 230	d													
Glasgow Queen St. 10 230 ⛴	a						11 14	12 09					12 15	
Leuchars 5	a	09 46	09 46	09 53					10 29	10 29	10 47			11 20
St Andrews Bus Station 🚌	a	*10 02*	*10 02*	*10 12*					*10 52*	*10 52*	*11 02*			*11 42*
St Andrews Bus Station 🚌	d	*09 25*	*09 25*	*09 35*					*10 05*	*10 05*	*10 25*			*11 05*
Leuchars 5	d	09 47	09 47	09 54					10 29	10 30	10 47			11 23
Cupar	d	09 54	09 54	10 01							10 53			
Springfield	d													
Ladybank	d	10 01	10 01	10 09		10 21					11 01	11 21		
Markinch	d	10 09	10 09	10 16		10 29					11 08	11 29		
Kirkcaldy 242	d	10 17	10 17	10 26		10 42					11 18	11 38		11 47
Inverkeithing 242	d	10 32	10 32	10 44		10 59					11 34	11 55		12 03
Haymarket 242	a	10 47	10 51	11 06	11 11	11 20			11 23	11 24	11 50	12 16		12 20
Edinburgh 10 242	a	10 55	10 58	11 11	11 17	11 25			11 32	11 31	12 00	12 22		12 26

		SR	SR	SR	SR	SR	SR	SR	SR	SR	SR	SR	SR
		SO	SX				SO	SX	SO	SX			
		◇1	◇1	◇1	◇1	◇1	◇1	◇1	◇1	◇	◇1	◇1	◇1
							E	E					E
				☕	☕		☕	☕			☕	☕	☕
Inverness	d			09 41							10 45		
Carrbridge	d												
Aviemore	d			10 26							11 23		
Kingussie	d			10 38							11 36		
Newtonmore	d												
Dalwhinnie	d			10 52									
Blair Atholl	d			11 13									
Pitlochry	d			11 23							12 22		
Dunkeld & Birnam	d			11 36							12 35		
Inverurie 240	d						10 38	10 38					11 33
Dyce 240 ✈	d						10 50	10 50					11 45
Aberdeen 240	a						11 01	11 01					11 56
	d				10 38		11 03	11 03				11 42	12 06
Portlethen	d												12 16
Stonehaven	d						11 20	11 20					12 24
Laurencekirk	d						11 34	11 34					
Montrose	d				11 14		11 44	11 44				12 18	
Arbroath	d				11 28		11 58	11 58				12 32	12 59
Carnoustie	d				11 35							12 39	
Golf Street	d												
Barry Links	d												
Monifieth	d												
Balmossie	d												
Broughty Ferry	d												
Dundee	a				11 49		12 14	12 14				12 52	13 14
	d	11 30	11 30		11 50	12 13	12 15	12 15	12 34	12 34		12 53	13 15
Invergowrie	d					12 18							
Perth	a			11 55	12 11	12 36					12 55	13 14	
	d			12 02	12 12	12 38					13 02	13 15	
Gleneagles	d					12 53							
Dunblane 230	d					13 05							
Bridge of Allan 230	d					13 08							
Stirling 230	d				12 43	13 13						13 43	
Larbert 230	d												
Glasgow Queen St. 10 230 ⛴	a				13 14	13 47						14 14	
Leuchars 5	a	11 42	11 42				12 27	12 27	12 47	12 47			13 28
St Andrews Bus Station 🚌	a	*12 02*	*12 02*				*12 52*	*13 02*	*13 02*	*13 02*			*13 52*
St Andrews Bus Station 🚌	d	*11 25*	*11 25*				*12 05*	*13 05*	*12 25*	*12 25*			*13 05*
Leuchars 5	d	11 44	11 44				12 28	12 28	12 47	12 47			13 28
Cupar	d	11 52	11 52						12 53	12 53			
Springfield	d												
Ladybank	d	11 59	11 59	12 21					13 01	13 01			
Markinch	d	12 06	12 06	12 29					13 08	13 08	13 29		
Kirkcaldy 242	d	12 16	12 16	12 38					13 18	13 18	13 38		
Inverkeithing 242	d	12 32	12 32	12 55					13 34	13 34			
Haymarket 242	a	12 48	12 52	13 17			13 22	13 22	13 50	13 50	14 18		14 21
Edinburgh 10 242	a	12 54	12 57	13 23			13 28	13 32	13 57	13 57	14 24		14 29

		SR	SR	SR	SR	SR	SR	SR	SR	SR	SR	SR
		◇1	◇	◇1	◇1	◇1	◇1	◇1	◇	◇1	◇1	◇
				☕	☕		☕	☕		☕		
Inverness	d						12 53					
Carrbridge	d						13 23					
Aviemore	d						13 32					
Kingussie	d						13 45					
Newtonmore	d						13 49					
Dalwhinnie	d											
Blair Atholl	d						14 20					
Pitlochry	d						14 31					
Dunkeld & Birnam	d						14 43					
Inverurie 240	d											
Dyce 240 ✈	d											
Aberdeen 240	a											
	d			12 40	13 09			13 38		14 04		
Portlethen	d							13 48				
Stonehaven	d			12 56	13 25			13 56		14 20		
Laurencekirk	d			13 10						14 34		
Montrose	d			13 20	13 47			14 18				
Arbroath	d			13 34	14 01			14 32		14 57		
Carnoustie	d							14 39				
Golf Street	d											
Barry Links	d											
Monifieth	d											
Balmossie	d											
Broughty Ferry	d									15 08		
Dundee	a			13 53	14 15			14 53		15 15		
	d	13 34		13 53	14 17	14 34		14 53	15 13	15 16	15 34	
Invergowrie	d								15 18			
Perth	a			14 14			15 03	15 15	15 36			
	d		14 02	14 15			15 04	15 15	15 37			16 00
Gleneagles	d								15 52			
Dunblane 230	d								16 05			
Bridge of Allan 230	d								16 09			
Stirling 230	d			14 43				15 43	16 14			
Larbert 230	d											
Glasgow Queen St. 10 230 ⛴	a			15 14				16 14	16 48			
Leuchars 5	a	13 46			14 30	14 46				15 28	15 47	
St Andrews Bus Station 🚌	a	*14 02*			*14 52*	*15 02*				*15 52*	*16 12*	
St Andrews Bus Station 🚌	d	*13 25*			*14 05*	*14 25*				*15 05*	*15 25*	
Leuchars 5	d	13 47			14 30	14 47				15 29	15 47	
Cupar	d	13 53				14 53					15 53	
Springfield	d											
Ladybank	d	14 01	14 21			15 01					16 01	16 21
Markinch	d	14 08	14 29			15 08	15 32				16 08	16 29
Kirkcaldy 242	d	14 18	14 38			15 18	15 42				16 18	16 38
Inverkeithing 242	d	14 34	14 55			15 34	15 58				16 34	16 55
Haymarket 242	a	14 49	15 17		15 24	15 53	16 16			16 24	16 51	17 15
Edinburgh 10 242	a	14 54	15 22		15 34	15 58	16 22			16 29	16 59	17 20

A To Penzance
B To London Kings Cross. The Highland Chieftain
C not 25 December, 26 December, 1 January, 2 January. ☕ from Aberdeen
D To London Kings Cross. The Northern Lights
E ☕ from Aberdeen

Table 229R

Mondays to Saturdays

9 December to 17 May

Inverurie, Dyce, Aberdeen, Dundee, Inverness and Perth - Glasgow Queen Street and Edinburgh

Network Diagram - refer to first page of Table 225

Station	SR ◇1 🛒	SR ◇1 🛒	GR 1 A 🍴🛒	SR ◇ B	SR ◇1 🛒	SR ◇	SR ◇ C	SR ◇1 D 🛒	SR SX ◇	SR SO ◇1	SR ◇1 🛒	SR ◇1 🛒	SR ◇1 E 🛒	SR ◇	SR 1 F	SR SO	SR ◇	SR ◇1 🛒
Inverness d		14 47									15 51							
Carrbridge d											16 27							
Aviemore d		15 23									16 35							
Kingussie d		15 35									16 47							
Newtonmore d											16 51							
Dalwhinnie d		15 49																
Blair Atholl d											17 22							
Pitlochry d		16 19									17 32							
Dunkeld & Birnam d		16 34									17 44							
Inverurie 240 d								15 24					16 38					
Dyce 240 ✈ d								15 38					16 53		17 05			
Aberdeen 240 a								15 49					17 04		17 16			
d	14 39		14 52		15 33			16 02				16 37	17 09		17 18			17 36
Portlethen d												16 47			17 29			
Stonehaven d			15 10		15 49			16 19				16 55			17a37			17 52
Laurencekirk d								16 32					17 39					18 06
Montrose d	15 15		15 33		16 10							17 17	17 49					18 17
Arbroath d	15 29		15 49		16 24			16 55				17 31	18 03	18 19				18 31
Carnoustie d	15 36							17 02						18 25				18 38
Golf Street d																		
Barry Links d																		
Monifieth d														18 31				
Balmossie d																		
Broughty Ferry d					16 36									18 35				
Dundee a	15 50		16 05		16 45			17 15				17 49	18 19	18 42				18 52
d	15 51		16 07		16 46	16 49		17 16	17 26	17 26		17 50	18 19	18 43				18 53
Invergowrie d					16 52													
Perth a	16 11	16 53			17 10						18 04	18 13						19 14
d	16 13	16 54		17 02	17 11						18 05	18 14				18 28	19 11	19 15
Gleneagles d		17 09			17 26													
Dunblane 230 d		17 21			17 37							18 38				18 49		
Bridge of Allan 230 d		17 24														18 52		
Stirling 230 d	16s41	17 29			17 43							18 43				18a59		19 43
Larbert 230 d																		
Glasgow Queen St. 10 230 ⛴ a	17 18	18 09			18 15							19 16						20 15
Leuchars 5 a			16 19			17 01		17 29	17 38	17 38			18 32	18 55				
St Andrews Bus Station 🚌 a			*16c37*			*17d24*		*17e46*	*18 02*	*18 02*				*19f16*				
St Andrews Bus Station 🚌 d			*16 05*			*16 45*		*18 32*	*17 17*	*17 17*				*18 32*				
Leuchars 5 d			16 22			17 02		17 29	17 39	17 39			18 32	18 56				
Cupar d						17 09			17 46	17 46				19 03				
Springfield d							←		17 51	17 51								
Ladybank d				17 23		17 16	17 23		17 56	17 56	18 26			19 10			19 32	
Markinch d				→		17 23	17 31		18 03	18 03	18 34			19 17			19 44	
Kirkcaldy 242 d			16 46			17 33	17 48		18 13	18 13	18 44			19 27			19 54	
Inverkeithing 242 d			17 03			17 55	18 04		18 29	18 29	19 00			19 43				
Haymarket 242 a			17 20			18 17	18 20	18 25	18 44	18 44	19 16		19 29	20 04			20 23	
Edinburgh 10 242 a			17 26			18 23	18 26	18 32	18 49	18 49	19 21		19 34	20 09			20 29	

Station	SR ◇1 🛒	SR SO ◇1 🛒	GR SX 1 G 🍴	SR ◇	SR ◇1 🛒	SR ◇1 D 🛒	SR ◇	SR ◇1 🛒	SR ◇1 🛒	SR ◇ D 🛒	SR ◇1	SR ◇1	SR ◇1	XC SO ◇1	XC SX ◇1	SR FSX 1	SR SO 1	SR FO 1
Inverness d	17 30							18 46				20 15						
Carrbridge d	18 06							19 16				20 59						
Aviemore d	18 14							19 28				21 06						
Kingussie d	18 26							19 40				21 18						
Newtonmore d								19 45				21 22						
Dalwhinnie d								19 57				21 34						
Blair Atholl d								20 18				21 55						
Pitlochry d	19 05							20 28				22 05						
Dunkeld & Birnam d	19 18							20 41				22 17						
Inverurie 240 d						18 42				19 45								
Dyce 240 ✈ d						18 55				19 56								
Aberdeen 240 a						19 07				20 08								
d		18 18	18 18		18 30	19 09			19 47	20 09	20 42		21 05	21 17	21 31	22 27	22 27	23 23
Portlethen d					18 40				19 57							22 37	22 37	23 33
Stonehaven d		18 36	18 36		18 49	19 26			20 05	20 25	20 58		21 21	21 35	21 49	22 46	22 46	23 42
Laurencekirk d						19 40							21 35			22 59	22 59	23 55
Montrose d		18 59	18 59		19 12	19 50			20 27	20 46	21 20		21 45	21 56	22 10	23 10	23 10	00 06
Arbroath d		19 15	19 15		19 26	20 04			20 41	21 00	21 34		21 59	22 12	22 26	23 24	23 24	00 20
Carnoustie d					19 33					21 07						23 31	23 31	00 27
Golf Street d																		
Barry Links d																		
Monifieth d																		
Balmossie d																		
Broughty Ferry d																23 38	23 38	00 34
Dundee a		19 31	19 31		19 47	20 19			20 59	21 18	21 53		22 15	22 28	22 42	23 48	23 48	00 44
d		19 32	19 33		19 49	20 20	20 41		21 00	21 19	21 53		22 16	22 30	22 43	23 49		00 45
Invergowrie d																23 54		00 50
Perth a	19 38				20 09			21 00	21 21		22 14	22 36				00 13		01 09
d	19 39			20 02	20 11			21 02	21 21		22 15	22 37						
Gleneagles d	19 54				20 26						22 32							
Dunblane 230 d	20 05											23 02						
Bridge of Allan 230 d	20 09											23 05						
Stirling 230 d	20 14				20 42				21 49		22 48	23 09						
Larbert 230 d																		
Glasgow Queen St. 10 230 ⛴ a	20 45				21 14				22 20		23 19	23 43						
Leuchars 5 a		19 45	19 45			20 33	20 53			21 32			22 28	22 42	22 55			
St Andrews Bus Station 🚌 a		*20 01*	*20 01*			*21 01*	*21 15*			*22 01*			*23 01*	*23 01*	*23 31*			
St Andrews Bus Station 🚌 d		*20 02*	*20 02*			*20 02*	*20 32*			*21 02*			*22 02*	*22 02*	*22 32*			
Leuchars 5 d		19 46	19 47			20 33	20 54			21 32			22 29	22 43	22 56			
Cupar d							21 01			21 39			22 36	22 50	23 03			
Springfield d																		
Ladybank d				20 24			21 09			21 47			22 43	22 57	23 10			
Markinch d				20 32			21 16	21 32		21 54			22 50	23 05	23 18			
Kirkcaldy 242 d		20 10	20 11	20 41			21 26	21 41		22 03			22 59	23 14	23 26			
Inverkeithing 242 d		20 26	20 27	20 59			21 49			22 25			23 22	23 31	23 42			
Haymarket 242 a		20 44	20 44	21 15		21 26	22 10	22 14		22 47			23 43	23 50	23 57			
Edinburgh 10 242 a		20 50	20 50	21 20		21 31	22 17	22 19		22 52			23 49	23 55	00 05			

A To London Kings Cross
B To Edinburgh
C From Perth
D 🛒 from Aberdeen
E not 25 December, 26 December, 1 January, 2 January. 🛒 from Aberdeen
F not 25 December, 26 December, 1 January, 2 January
G To Leeds

Table 229R

Sundays

8 December to 11 May

Inverurie, Dyce, Aberdeen, Dundee, Inverness and Perth - Glasgow Queen Street and Edinburgh

Network Diagram - refer to first page of Table 225

Station		SR	SR	SR	SR	SR	SR	SR	SR	GR
		◇		◇	◇1	◇		◇	◇1	R 1
										A
									trolley	restaurant trolley
Inverness	d									
Carrbridge	d									
Aviemore	d									
Kingussie	d									
Newtonmore	d									
Dalwhinnie	d									
Blair Atholl	d									
Pitlochry	d									
Dunkeld & Birnam	d									
Inverurie 240	d									
Dyce 240 ✈	d									
Aberdeen 240	a									
	d								09 24	09 47
Portlethen	d									
Stonehaven	d								09 41	10 05
Laurencekirk	d								09 55	
Montrose	d								10 05	10 28
Arbroath	d								10 20	10 44
Carnoustie	d								10 27	
Golf Street	d									
Barry Links	d									
Monifieth	d									
Balmossie	d									
Broughty Ferry	d								10 34	
Dundee	a								10 44	11 00
	d	07 24			08 45		09 24		10 44	11 03
Invergowrie	d									
Perth	a				09 05				11 06	
	d			08 45	09 06	09 16		10 10	11 06	
Gleneagles	d				09 21	09 31		10 25	11 23	
Dunblane 230	d				09 33	09 43		10 38	11 34	
Bridge of Allan 230	d					09 47		10 41		
Stirling 230	d		09 05		09 39	09 51		10 46	11 43	
Larbert 230	d		09 13		09 47	10 00		10 55		
Glasgow Queen St. 10 230 ⛴	a				10 14				12 14	
Leuchars 5	a	07 36					09 36			11 15
St Andrews Bus Station 🚌	a						*09 55*			*11 55*
St Andrews Bus Station 🚌	d						*09 15*			*10 55*
Leuchars 5	d	07 37					09 37			11 17
Cupar	d	07 44					09 44			
Springfield	d									
Ladybank	d	07 52		09 07			09 52			
Markinch	d	07 59		09 15			09 59			
Kirkcaldy 242	d	08 07		09 25			10 07			11 41
Inverkeithing 242	d	08 30		09 47			10 30			11 57
Haymarket 242	a	08 56	09 59	10 12		10 40	10 58	11 35		12 14
Edinburgh 10 242	a	09 01	10 04	10 17		10 45	11 03	11 40		12 20

Station		SR	SR	GR	SR	XC	SR	SR	GR	SR
		◇		R 1		◇1	◇1	◇1	R 1	
				B		C		D	E	
				restaurant trolley			trolley	trolley	restaurant trolley	
Inverness	d			09 40			10 50			
Carrbridge	d			10 11						
Aviemore	d			10 19			11 25			
Kingussie	d			10 32			11 37			
Newtonmore	d			10 37						
Dalwhinnie	d						11 51			
Blair Atholl	d			11 09						
Pitlochry	d			11 23			12 19			
Dunkeld & Birnam	d			11 37			12 34			
Inverurie 240	d							11 02		
Dyce 240 ✈	d							11 14		
Aberdeen 240	a							11 25		
	d					11 08		11 29	11 47	
Portlethen	d									
Stonehaven	d					11 25		11 45	12 05	
Laurencekirk	d									
Montrose	d					11 46		12 08	12 28	
Arbroath	d					12 02		12 22	12 44	
Carnoustie	d									
Golf Street	d									
Barry Links	d									
Monifieth	d									
Balmossie	d									
Broughty Ferry	d									
Dundee	a					12 20		12 39	13 00	
	d	11 20				12 21		12 43	13 02	
Invergowrie	d									
Perth	a			11 56			12 53	13 03		
	d			11 59			12 54	13 05		
Gleneagles	d			12 15				13 20		
Dunblane 230	d			12 28				13 31		
Bridge of Allan 230	d									
Stirling 230	d		11 48	12 35	12 46			13 38		13 46
Larbert 230	d		11 57		12 55					13 55
Glasgow Queen St. 10 230 ⛴	a							14 11		
Leuchars 5	a	11 32				12 33			13 14	
St Andrews Bus Station 🚌	a	*12 55*				*12 57*			*13 37*	
St Andrews Bus Station 🚌	d	*11 15*				*12 15*			*12 55*	
Leuchars 5	d	11 33				12 34			13 17	
Cupar	d	11 40				12 41				
Springfield	d									
Ladybank	d	11 48				12 48				
Markinch	d	11 55				12 56	13 22			
Kirkcaldy 242	d	12 05				13 04	13 31		13 42	
Inverkeithing 242	d	12 21				13 20	13 47		14 00	
Haymarket 242	a	12 37	12 37	13 14	13 35	13 36	14 04		14 17	14 35
Edinburgh 10 242	a	12 42	12 42	13 20	13 40	13 42	14 09		14 23	14 41

Station		SR	SR	SR	SR	SR	GR	SR	SR	SR
		◇	◇1		◇1	◇1	R 1	◇		◇1
							E			
					trolley	trolley	restaurant trolley			trolley
Inverness	d				12 45					13 30
Carrbridge	d				13 15					
Aviemore	d				13 23					14 06
Kingussie	d				13 35					14 18
Newtonmore	d				13 40					
Dalwhinnie	d									
Blair Atholl	d				14 11					
Pitlochry	d				14 21					14 58
Dunkeld & Birnam	d				14 34					
Inverurie 240	d									
Dyce 240 ✈	d									
Aberdeen 240	a									
	d		12 47			13 31	13 47			
Portlethen	d		12 58							
Stonehaven	d		13 06			13 48	14 05			
Laurencekirk	d		13 20							
Montrose	d		13 31			14 09	14 28			
Arbroath	d		13 45			14 24	14 44			
Carnoustie	d		13 52							
Golf Street	d									
Barry Links	d									
Monifieth	d									
Balmossie	d									
Broughty Ferry	d		13 59							
Dundee	a		14 06			14 43	15 00			
	d	13 20	14 07			14 45	15 02	15 15		
Invergowrie	d									
Perth	a				14 52	15 06				15 28
	d				14 54	15 08				15 29
Gleneagles	d					15 23				
Dunblane 230	d				15 18	15 36				
Bridge of Allan 230	d									
Stirling 230	d			14 46	15 24	15 42			15 47	
Larbert 230	d			14 55	15 33				15 56	
Glasgow Queen St. 10 230 ⛴	a				15 58	16 13				
Leuchars 5	a	13 32	14 19				15 14	15 27		
St Andrews Bus Station 🚌	a	*13 55*	*14 37*				*15 37*	*15 55*		
St Andrews Bus Station 🚌	d	*13 15*	*13 55*				*14 55*	*15 15*		
Leuchars 5	d	13 33	14 20				15 16	15 28		
Cupar	d	13 40						15 35		
Springfield	d									
Ladybank	d	13 48						15 43		15 50
Markinch	d	13 55						15 50		15 58
Kirkcaldy 242	d	14 05	14 46				15 40	16 00		16 08
Inverkeithing 242	d	14 21	15 02				15 56	16 16		16 24
Haymarket 242	a	14 40	15 18	15 35			16 15	16 32	16 36	16 39
Edinburgh 10 242	a	14 45	15 23	15 40			16 22	16 38	16 41	16 44

Station		SR	SR	SR	SR	SR	SR	SR	SR	SR
		◇1		◇1	◇1	◇1	◇	◇1	◇1	◇
		trolley		trolley	trolley	trolley		trolley	trolley	
Inverness	d				15 22	16 24			15 29	
Carrbridge	d					16 58				
Aviemore	d				15 57	17 10				
Kingussie	d				16 09	17 22				
Newtonmore	d									
Dalwhinnie	d									
Blair Atholl	d					17 54				
Pitlochry	d				16 49	18 04				
Dunkeld & Birnam	d				17 01	18 18				
Inverurie 240	d								17 14	
Dyce 240 ✈	d								17 28	
Aberdeen 240	a								17 39	
	d	15 11		15 28				17 10	17 47	
Portlethen	d	15 21								
Stonehaven	d	15 30		15 44				17 26	18 04	
Laurencekirk	d			15 58					18 18	
Montrose	d	15 51		16 09				17 48	18 28	
Arbroath	d	16 05		16 23				18 01	18 43	
Carnoustie	d	16 11								
Golf Street	d									
Barry Links	d									
Monifieth	d									
Balmossie	d									
Broughty Ferry	d									
Dundee	a	16 23		16 42				18 17	19 02	
	d	16 24		16 43			17 20	18 18	19 03	19 16
Invergowrie	d									
Perth	a			17 04	17 21	18 38			19 25	
	d			17 05	17 22	18 39			19 26	
Gleneagles	d			17 20					19 42	
Dunblane 230	d			17 31		19 03				
Bridge of Allan 230	d									
Stirling 230	d		16 46	17 38		19 09			19 58	
Larbert 230	d		16 55			19 17				
Glasgow Queen St. 10 230 ⛴	a			18 12		19 41			20 32	
Leuchars 5	a	16 36					17 33	18 30		19 28
St Andrews Bus Station 🚌	a	*16 55*					*17 55*	*18 55*		*19 55*
St Andrews Bus Station 🚌	d	*16 15*					*17 15*	*18 15*		*19 15*
Leuchars 5	d	16 37					17 33	18 31		19 29
Cupar	d						17 40			19 36
Springfield	d									
Ladybank	d				17 43		17 48			19 44
Markinch	d				17 50		17 55			19 51
Kirkcaldy 242	d	17 02			18 00		18 05	18 56		20 01
Inverkeithing 242	d	17 18			18 16		18 22	19 12		20 23
Haymarket 242	a	17 34	17 35		18 31		18 39	19 27		20 48
Edinburgh 10 242	a	17 40	17 40		18 36		18 44	19 35		20 53

A To London Kings Cross. The Northern Lights
B To London Kings Cross. The Highland Chieftain
C To Reading
D trolley from Aberdeen
E To London Kings Cross

Table 229R

Sundays

8 December to 11 May

Inverurie, Dyce, Aberdeen, Dundee, Inverness and Perth - Glasgow Queen Street and Edinburgh

Network Diagram - refer to first page of Table 225

			SR	SR	SR	SR	XC	SR
			◇1	◇1	◇1	◇1	◇1	
					A			
			⚮	⚮	⚮	⚮		
Inverness		d		18 51				
Carrbridge		d		19 21				
Aviemore		d		19 30				
Kingussie		d		19 42				
Newtonmore		d		19 46				
Dalwhinnie		d		19 58				
Blair Atholl		d		20 19				
Pitlochry		d		20 29				
Dunkeld & Birnam		d		20 41				
Inverurie	240	d						
Dyce	240 ✈	d						
Aberdeen	240	a						
		d	19 07		19 36	20 07	21 28	22 27
Portlethen		d				20 17		22 37
Stonehaven		d	19 24		19 52	20 26	21 45	22 46
Laurencekirk		d				20 39		22 59
Montrose		d	19 45		20 14	20 50	22 06	23 10
Arbroath		d	19 59		20 28	21 04	22 22	23 24
Carnoustie		d	20 06					23 31
Golf Street		d						
Barry Links		d						
Monifieth		d						
Balmossie		d						
Broughty Ferry		d	20 13					23 38
Dundee		a	20 21		20 46	21 20	22 38	23 48
		d	20 22		20 50	21 21	22 39	23 49
Invergowrie		d						
Perth		a		21 00	21 10			00 12
		d		21 04	21 11			
Gleneagles		d			21 26			
Dunblane	230	d			21 38			
Bridge of Allan	230	d						
Stirling	230	d			21 43			
Larbert	230	d			21 52			
Glasgow Queen St. 10	230 ⛴	a			22 18			
Leuchars 5		a	20 35			21 34	22 51	
St Andrews Bus Station	🚌	a	*20 55*			*21 55*	*23 21*	
St Andrews Bus Station	🚌	d	*20 15*			*21 15*	*22 32*	
Leuchars 5		d	20 35			21 34	22 52	
Cupar		d				21 42	22 59	
Springfield		d						
Ladybank		d				21 49	23 06	
Markinch		d		21 33		21 57	23 14	
Kirkcaldy	242	d	21 01	21 43		22 06	23 22	
Inverkeithing	242	d	21 17	21 59		22 22	23 38	
Haymarket	242	a	21 33	22 14		22 38	23 53	
Edinburgh 10	242	a	21 38	22 19		22 43	23 58	

A ⚮ from Dundee

Table 229A - Buses for 229

Mondays to Saturdays

9 December to 17 May

229A Buses for 229 Leuchars - St Andrews Bus Station - Leuchars

		SR MX	SR	SR SO	SR SO	SR	SR SX	SR SX	SR	SR		SR SO	SR SX	SR SO	SR SX	SR	SR SX	SR	SR	SR SO		SR SX	SR SX	SR SX	SR SO
Leuchars	d	00 29		06 08			06 23			06 50		06 53			07 05	07 15				07 20		07 21			
St Andrews Bus Station	a	00 39		06 26			06 41			07 01		07 11			07 23	07 26				07 31		07 32			
	d		06 00		06 29	06 30		06 44	07 00				07 15	07 15			07 27	07 28	07 30				07 43	07 55	08 00
Leuchars	a		06 11		06 47	06 41		07 02	07 11				07 26	07 33			07 45	07 39	07 41				07 54	08 06	08 11

		SR SO	SR SX	SR SX	SR SO	SR SO		SR	SR SX	SR SX	SR SX	SR SX	SR SO	SR SO	SR SO	SR SX		SR SX	SR SO	SR	SR SX	SR SX	SR	SR SO	SR SX
Leuchars	d	07 50	07 51		08 01				08 11	08 13				08 20	08 23			08 26			08 36			08 50	08 51
St Andrews Bus Station	a	08 01	08 02		08 12				08 22	08 24				08 31	08 34			08 37			08 47			09 01	09 02
	d			08 05		08 14		08 15			08 25	08 29	08 30			08 35			08 39	08 45		08 47	08 55		
Leuchars	a			08 16		08 25		08 26			08 36	08 40	08 41			08 46			08 50	08 56		09 02	09 06		

		SR		SR	SR	SR	SR	SR	SR SX	SR	SR	SR		SR	SR	SR	SR	SR	SR	SR	SR	SR		SR	SR
Leuchars	d			09 01			09 11		09 21	09 23				09 31		09 41		09 51		10 01				10 11	
St Andrews Bus Station	a			09 12			09 22		09 32	09 34				09 42		09 52		10 02		10 12				10 22	
	d	09 05			09 15	09 17		09 25			09 35	09 39			09 45		09 55		10 05		10 15	10 17			10 25
Leuchars	a	09 16			09 26	09 32		09 36			09 46	09 50			09 56		10 06		10 16		10 26	10 32			10 36

		SR	SR	SR	SR	SR	SR	SR		SR	SR	SR	SR	SR	SR	SR	SR	SR		SR	SR	SR	SR	SR	SR
Leuchars	d	10 21	10 23			10 31		10 41			10 51		11 01			11 11		11 21		11 23			11 31		11 41
St Andrews Bus Station	a	10 32	10 34			10 42		10 52			11 02		11 12			11 22		11 32		11 34			11 42		11 52
	d			10 35	10 39		10 45			10 55		11 05		11 15	11 17		11 25				11 35	11 39		11 45	
Leuchars	a			10 46	10 50		10 56			11 06		11 16		11 26	11 32		11 36				11 46	11 50		11 56	

		SR	SR	SR		SR	SR	SR	SR	SR	SR	SR	SR	SR		SR	SR	SR	SR	SR	SR	SR	SR	SR	
Leuchars	d		11 51			12 01			12 11		12 21	12 23				12 31		12 41		12 51		13 01			
St Andrews Bus Station	a		12 02			12 12			12 22		12 32	12 34				12 42		12 52		13 02		13 12			
	d	11 55		12 05			12 15	12 17		12 25			12 35	12 39			12 45		12 55		13 05		13 15	13 17	
Leuchars	a	12 06		12 16			12 26	12 32		12 36			12 46	12 50			12 56		13 06		13 16		13 26	13 32	

		SR	SR	SR	SR	SR	SR	SR	SR	SR		SR	SR	SR	SR	SR	SR	SR	SR	SR		SR	SR	SR	SR
Leuchars	d	13 11		13 21	13 23			13 31		13 41			13 51		14 01			14 11		14 21		14 23			14 31
St Andrews Bus Station	a	13 22		13 32	13 34			13 42		13 52			14 02		14 12			14 22		14 32		14 34			14 42
	d		13 25			13 35	13 39		13 45			13 55		14 05		14 15	14 17		14 25				14 35	14 39	
Leuchars	a		13 36			13 46	13 50		13 56			14 06		14 16		14 26	14 32		14 36				14 46	14 50	

		SR	SR	SR	SR	SR		SR	SR	SR SO	SR	SR	SR	SR	SR	SR		SR	SR	SR SX	SR	SR	SR	SR	SR
Leuchars	d		14 41		14 51			15 01			15 11		15 21	15 23				15 31			15 41		15 51		16 01
St Andrews Bus Station	a		14 52		15 02			15 12			15 22		15 32	15 34				15 42			15 52		16 02		16 12
	d	14 45		14 55		15 05			15 15	15 17		15 25			15 35	15 39			15 45	15 50		15 55		16 05	
Leuchars	a	14 56		15 06		15 16			15 26	15 32		15 36			15 46	15 50			15 56	16 01		16 06		16 16	

		SR		SR SO	SR	SR	SR SX	SR	SR	SR	SR SX	SR		SR	SR	SR	SR	SR	SR	SR	SR	SR SO		SR SX	SR
Leuchars	d				16 11			16 21	16 23		16 26			16 31		16 41		16 51		17 01		17 11		17 13	
St Andrews Bus Station	a				16 22			16 32	16 34		16 37			16 42		16 52		17 02		17 12		17 22		17 24	
	d	16 15		16 17		16 25	16 27			16 35		16 39			16 45		16 55		17 10		17 17				17 25
Leuchars	a	16 26		16 32		16 36	16 42			16 46		16 50			16 56		17 06		17 21		17 32				17 36

		SR	SR SO	SR SX	SR SO	SR SO	SR	SR SX		SR SO	SR SX	SR	SR	SR SO	SR SX	SR SO	SR	SR		SR SX	SR SX	SR SO	SR SX	SR	SR
Leuchars	d		17 21	17 25	17 28	17 31		17 35		17 41	17 43			17 51	17 53	18 01				18 02	18 06	18 11		18 21	
St Andrews Bus Station	a		17 32	17 36	17 46	17 42		17 46		17 52	17 54			18 02	18 04	18 12				18 20	18 17	18 22		18 32	
	d	17 30					17 45					17 59	18 00				18 15	18 17					18 29		18 32
Leuchars	a	17 41					17 56					18 17	18 11				18 26	18 32					18 40		18 43

		SR SX	SR	SR		SR	SR	SR	SR	SR SO	SR	SR SX	SR	SR		SR	SR	SR	SR	SR	SR	SR	SR	SR	
Leuchars	d	18 24	18 35	18 40		18 50				19 01	19 05	19 09	19 20			19 26		19 50		20 03	20 07	20 20			
St Andrews Bus Station	a	18 35	18 46	18 58		19 01				19 12	19 16	19 20	19 31			19 37		20 01		20 21	20 18	20 31			
	d						19 02	19 09	19 10					19 32			19 40		20 02				20 32	20 39	
Leuchars	a						19 13	19 27	19 21					19 43			19 51		20 13				20 43	20 57	

		SR	SR	SR	SR	SR	SR	SR	SR	SR		SR	SR	SR	SR	SR	SR	SR	SR	SR		SR	SR	SR	
Leuchars	d		20 50		21 04	21 20			21 50			22 03	22 20		22 24			22 50		23 20		23 34		23 50	
St Andrews Bus Station	a		21 01		21 15	21 31			22 01			22 21	22 31		22 35			23 01		23 31		23 45		00 01	
	d	20 40		21 02			21 32	21 45		22 02				22 32		22 39	22 45		23 02				23 50		
Leuchars	a	20 51		21 13			21 43	21 56		22 13				22 43		22 57	22 56		23 13				00 06		

Table 229A - Buses for 229

Sundays

8 December to 11 May

229A Buses for 229 Leuchars - St Andrews Bus Station - Leuchars

		SR	SR	SR	SR	SR		SR	SR	SR	SR	SR	SR	SR	SR	SR		SR	SR	SR	SR	SR	SR	SR	SR
Leuchars	d	00 29		08 18					09 18		09 19		09 44	09 48				10 18			10 47	10 48		11 18	
St Andrews Bus Station	a	00 39		08 29					09 29		09 37		09 55	09 59				10 29			10 58	10 59		11 29	
	d		07 30		08 30	09 00		09 15		09 30		09 50			10 00	10 15			10 30	10 55			11 15		11 35
Leuchars	a		07 41		08 41	09 11		09 26		09 41		10 08			10 11	10 26			10 41	11 06			11 26		11 46

		SR		SR	SR	SR	SR	SR	SR	SR	SR	SR		SR	SR	SR	SR	SR	SR	SR	SR	SR		SR	SR
Leuchars	d	11 19			11 44		11 46		12 06		12 26			12 46	12 47		13 06		13 19	13 26		13 44			13 46
St Andrews Bus Station	a	11 37			11 55		11 57		12 17		12 37			12 57	12 58		13 17		13 37	13 37		13 55			13 57
	d			11 50		11 55		12 15		12 35		12 55				13 15		13 35			13 50			13 55	
Leuchars	a			12 08		12 06		12 26		12 46		13 06				13 26		13 46			14 08			14 06	

		SR	SR	SR	SR	SR	SR	SR		SR	SR	SR	SR	SR	SR	SR	SR	SR		SR	SR	SR	SR	SR	SR
Leuchars	d		14 06		14 26		14 44	14 46			15 06		15 19	15 26		15 44		15 46			16 06		16 26		16 44
St Andrews Bus Station	a		14 17		14 37		14 55	14 57			15 17		15 37	15 37		15 55		15 57			16 17		16 37		16 55
	d	14 15		14 35		14 55				15 15		15 35			15 50		15 55			16 15		16 35		16 55	
Leuchars	a	14 26		14 46		15 06				15 26		15 46			16 08		16 06			16 26		16 46		17 06	

		SR	SR	SR		SR	SR	SR	SR	SR	SR	SR	SR	SR		SR	SR	SR	SR	SR	SR	SR	SR	SR	
Leuchars	d	16 46		17 06			17 19	17 26		17 44	17 46			18 06			18 26	18 44	18 50			19 19	19 20		
St Andrews Bus Station	a	16 57		17 17			17 37	17 37		17 55	17 57			18 17			18 37	18 55	19 01			19 37	19 31		
	d		17 15			17 35			17 50			18 00	18 15			18 32				19 02	19 15			19 32	
Leuchars	a		17 26			17 46			18 08			18 11	18 26			18 43				19 13	19 26			19 43	

		SR	SR	SR	SR	SR	SR	SR	SR	SR		SR	SR	SR	SR	SR	SR	SR	SR	SR		SR	SR	SR	SR
Leuchars	d	19 44	19 50				20 20		20 44	20 50				21 20		21 44	21 49	21 50				22 20		22 44	23 20
St Andrews Bus Station	a	19 55	20 01				20 31		20 55	21 01				21 31		21 55	22 07	22 01				22 31		22 55	23 31
	d			20 02	20 15	20 20		20 32				21 02	21 15		21 32				22 10	22 15			22 32		
Leuchars	a			20 13	20 26	20 38		20 43				21 13	21 26		21 43				22 28	22 26			22 43		

Table 230

Mondays to Saturdays

9 December to 17 May

Edinburgh, Glasgow Queen Street and Falkirk Grahamston - Stirling, Alloa and Dunblane

Network Diagram - refer to first page of Table 225

Miles	Miles	Miles	Miles			SR MX A	SR MX ◇ B	SR MO ◇ B	SR MX C	SR MX A	SR	SR [1] D	SR ◇[1] E 🛒	SR	SR SO [1] F	SR SX [1] F	SR [1] D	SR SX [1] F	SR SO	SR	SR SX [1] D	SR	SR [1] 🛒
0	0	—	—	**Edinburgh** [10]	d						05 18	05 55					06 30			06 33	06 45		07 00
1¼	—	—	—	Haymarket	d						05 22	05 59					06 34			06 37	06 49		07 04
3¾	—	—	—	Edinburgh Park	d						05 27									06 43			
—	17½	—	—	Linlithgow	d						05 39	06 14					06 49			06 55	07 04		
—	22¼	—	—	Polmont [3]	d						05 44	06 20					06 56			07 01			07 22
—	—	0	0	**Glasgow Queen Street** [10] ⛴	d								05 56	06 14	06 30	06 30		06 45				06 48	07a50
—	—	3¼	3¼	Bishopbriggs	d									06 21								06 54	
—	—	6¼	6¼	Lenzie [3]	d									06 26	06 38	06a38						06 59	
—	—	11½	11½	Croy [3]	d					00 06		06a34		06 32	06a44		07a10	06a57			07a23	07 06	
—	25½	—	—	**Falkirk Grahamston** [3]	d				00 06		05 51									07 07			
—	27	—	—	Camelon [4]	d				00 09		05 54									07 10			
—	28¼	21	21	Larbert	d			00 11	00 14	00 20	06 00		06 16	06 43						07 15		07 21	
—	36½	29	29	**Stirling**	d	00 02	00 05	00 20	00 24	00a31	06 09		06 25	06 53					07 01	07 25		07 42	
—	—	—	35¾	**Alloa**	a	00 13								07 05									
—	40	32½	—	Bridge of Allan	d		00 10	00 24	00 28		06 13								07 05	07 29		07 47	
—	42	34½	—	**Dunblane**	a		00 14	00 28	00 35		06 20		06 31						07 12	07 37		07 54	

		SR [1] F 🛒	SR ◇[1] G 🛒	SR	SR [1] D 🛒	SR	SR [1] F 🛒	SR [1] D 🛒	SR ◇[1] H 🛒	SR	SR	SR [1] F 🛒	SR SX I	SR [1] D 🛒	SR [1] D 🛒	SR ◇[1] J	SR	SR [1] 🛒	SR	SR [1] F 🛒	SR ◇[1] H 🛒	SR	SR [1] 🛒
Edinburgh [10]	d			07 03	07 15			07 30		07 33				07 45	08 00		08 03	08 15				08 33	08 45
Haymarket	d			07 08	07 19			07 35		07 38				07 49	08 05		08 09	08 19				08 38	08 49
Edinburgh Park	d			07 14						07 43							08 13					08 43	
Linlithgow	d			07 26	07 34			07 50		07 55			08 01	08 06			08 25	08 35				08 55	09 05
Polmont [3]	d			07 32				07 56		08 01					08 25		08 31	08 42				09 01	09 12
Glasgow Queen Street [10] ⛴	d	07 00	07 10			07 18	07 30		07 41		07 48	08 00				08 06		09a07	08 18	08 30	08 41		09a37
Bishopbriggs	d					07 24					07 55								08 24				
Lenzie [3]	d	07a08				07 29					08 01			08a27					08 29				
Croy [3]	d				07a53	07 36	07a42	08a11			08 07	08a12			08a39				08 36	08a43			
Falkirk Grahamston [3]	d			07 39						08 08			08 12				08 38					09 08	
Camelon [4]	d			07 42						08 11			08a15				08 41					09 11	
Larbert	d			07 47		07 52				08 16	08 20						08 47		08 51			09 16	
Stirling	d		07 36	07 56		08 06			08u09	08 25	08a31					08 36	08 56		09 01		09a07	09 25	
Alloa	a					08 18													09 13				
Bridge of Allan	d			08 01						08 30						08 40	09 00					09 30	
Dunblane	a		07 42	08 08					08 15	08 37						08 44	09 07					09 37	

		SR	SR [1] F 🛒	SR ◇ J	SR	SR [1] 🛒	SR	SR [1] F 🛒	SR ◇[1] H 🛒	SR	SR [1] 🛒	SR	SR [1] F 🛒	SR ◇[1] G 🛒	SR	SR [1] 🛒	SR	SR [1] F 🛒	SR ◇[1] H 🛒	SR	SR [1] 🛒	SR	SR [1] F 🛒
Edinburgh [10]	d				09 03	09 15				09 33	09 45				10 03	10 15				10 33	10 45		
Haymarket	d				09 08	09 19				09 37	09 49				10 07	10 19				10 37	10 49		
Edinburgh Park	d				09 13					09 43					10 13					10 43			
Linlithgow	d				09 25	09 35				09 55	10 04				10 25	10 34				10 55	11 04		
Polmont [3]	d				09 31	09 41				10 00	10 10				10 31	10 40				11 01	11 10		
Glasgow Queen Street [10] ⛴	d	08 48	09 00	09 08		10a06	09 18	09 30	09 41		10a36	09 48	10 00	10 10		11a06	10 18	10 30	10 41		11a37	10 48	11 00
Bishopbriggs	d	08 54					09 24					09 54					10 24					10 54	
Lenzie [3]	d	08 59					09 29					09 59					10 29					10 59	
Croy [3]	d	09 06	09a12				09 36	09a42				10 06	10a12				10 36	10a42				11 06	11a12
Falkirk Grahamston [3]	d				09 38					10 07					10 37					11 07			
Camelon [4]	d				09 41					10 10					10 40					11 10			
Larbert	d	09 20			09 45		09 50			10 15		10 20			10 45		10 50			11 15		11 20	
Stirling	d	09 40		09 35	09 55		10 00		10a07	10 25		10a31		10 37	10 55		11 00		11a09	11 25		11 31	
Alloa	a						10 15										11 13						
Bridge of Allan	d	09 45			10 00					10 29				10 41	11 00					11 30		11 37	
Dunblane	a	09 52		09 41	10 07					10 36				10 45	11 07					11 37		11 44	

A From Glasgow Queen Street
B From Glasgow Queen Street to Perth
C From Edinburgh
D To Glasgow Queen Street
E To Dyce
F To Edinburgh
G To Inverness
H To Aberdeen
I From Kirkcaldy to Glasgow Queen Street
J To Dundee

For services between Glasgow Queen Street - Cumbernauld - Falkirk Grahamston please refer to table 224

Table 230

Edinburgh, Glasgow Queen Street and Falkirk Grahamston - Stirling, Alloa and Dunblane

Mondays to Saturdays

9 December to 17 May

Network Diagram - refer to first page of Table 225

		SR	SR 1 🛒	SR	SR 1 A 🛒	SR ◇1 B 🛒	SR	SR 1 🛒		SR	SR 1 A 🛒	SR ◇1 C 🛒	SR	SR 1 🛒	SR	SR 1 A 🛒	SR ◇1 B 🛒	SR		SR 1 🛒	SR	SR 1 A 🛒	SR	SR SO 1 🛒	SR SX 1 🛒
Edinburgh 10	d	11 03	11 15				11 33	11 45					12 03	12 15				12 33		12 45			13 03	13 15	13 15
Haymarket	d	11 07	11 19				11 37	11 51					12 07	12 19				12 37		12 49			13 08	13 19	13 20
Edinburgh Park	d	11 13					11 43						12 13					12 43					13 13		
Linlithgow	d	11 25	11 34				11 55	12 06					12 25	12 34				12 55		13 04			13 25	13 34	13 34
Polmont 3	d	11 31	11 40				12 01	12 12					12 31	12 40				13 01		13 10			13 31	13 40	13 40
Glasgow Queen Street 10 🚢	d		12a06	11 18	11 30	11 41		12a37		11 48	12 00	12 10		13a06	12 18	12 30	12 41			13a37	12 48	13 00		14a07	14a07
Bishopbriggs	d			11 24						11 54					12 24						12 54				
Lenzie 3	d			11 29						11 59					12 29						12 59				
Croy 3	d			11 36	11a42					12 06	12a12				12 36	12a42					13 06	13a12			
Falkirk Grahamston 3	d	11 37					12 07						12 37					13 07					13 37		
Camelon 4	d	11 40					12 10						12 40					13 10					13 40		
Larbert	d	11 45		11 50			12 15			12 20			12 45		12 50			13 15			13 20		13 45		
Stirling	d	11 55		12 00		12a08	12 25			12a31		12 36	12 55		13 00		13a06	13 25			13 32		13 55		
Alloa	a			12 14											13 15										
Bridge of Allan	d	12 00					12 30					12 41	13 00					13 30			13 37		14 00		
Dunblane	a	12 07					12 37					12 45	13 08					13 37			13 44		14 08		

		SR SX	SR SO	SR 1 A 🛒		SR ◇1 B 🛒	SR	SR 1 🛒	SR	SR 1 A 🛒	SR	SR 1 🛒	SR	SR 1 A 🛒		SR ◇1 B 🛒	SR	SR SO 1 🛒	SR	SR SX 1 🛒	SR 1 A 🛒	SR ◇1 C 🛒	SR	SR 1 🛒	
Edinburgh 10	d						13 33	13 45			14 03	14 15					14 33	14 45		14 45			15 03	15 15	
Haymarket	d						13 37	13 49			14 07	14 19					14 37	14 49		14 49			15 07	15 19	
Edinburgh Park	d						13 43				14 13						14 43						15 13		
Linlithgow	d						13 55	14 04			14 25	14 34					14 55	15 04		15 06			15 25	15 34	
Polmont 3	d						14 01	14 10			14 31	14 40					15 01	15 10		15 13			15 31	15 41	
Glasgow Queen Street 10 🚢	d	13 18	13 18	13 30		13 41		14a36	13 48	14 00		15a07	14 18	14 30		14 41		15a38	14 48	15a38	15 00	15 10		16a06	
Bishopbriggs	d	13 24	13 24						13 54				14 24						14 54						
Lenzie 3	d	13 29	13 29						13 59				14 29						14 59						
Croy 3	d	13 36	13 36	13a42					14 06	14a12			14 36	14a42					15 06		15a12				
Falkirk Grahamston 3	d						14 07				14 37						15 07						15 37		
Camelon 4	d						14 10				14 40						15 10						15 40		
Larbert	d	13 50	13 50				14 15		14 20		14 45		14 50				15 15		15 20				15 45		
Stirling	d	13 59	14 00			14a07	14 25		14 32		14 55		15 00			15a07	15 25		15a31			15 36	15 55		
Alloa	a	14 14	14 13										15 13												
Bridge of Allan	d						14 30		14 37		15 00						15 30					15 41	16 00		
Dunblane	a						14 37		14 44		15 07						15 37					15 45	16 07		

		SR	SR 1 A 🛒	SR	SR 1 🛒	SR	SR 1 A 🛒	SR 1 D	SR	SR 1 🛒		SR	SR 1 A 🛒	SR SX	SR SO ◇1 B 🛒	GR R 1 E 🍴🛒	SR	SR SO 1 🛒	SR SX 1 🛒	SR		SR 1 A 🛒	SR SX	SR SO ◇ F	SR SX ◇ F
Edinburgh 10	d			15 33	15 45				16 03	16 15						16 33	16 36	16 45	16 45						
Haymarket	d			15 37	15 49				16 09	16 19						16 39	16 41	16 49	16 50						
Edinburgh Park	d			15 43					16 14								16 47								
Linlithgow	d			15 55	16 04				16 26	16 34							16 59	17 06	17 06						
Polmont 3	d			16 01	16 10				16 32	16 41							17 04	17 13	17 13						
Glasgow Queen Street 10 🚢	d	15 18	15 30		16a36	15 48	16 00	16 11		17a07		16 18	16 30	16 33	16 41			17a39	17a40	16 48		17 00	17 03	17 03	17 11
Bishopbriggs	d	15 24				15 54						16 26		16 39						16 56			17 11	17 11	
Lenzie 3	d	15 29				15 59						16 31		16a44						17 01			17 15	17 15	
Croy 3	d	15 36	15a42			16 06	16a12					16 38	16a42							17 08		17a12		17 22	
Falkirk Grahamston 3	d			16 07					16 38							17 05	17 11						17a33		
Camelon 4	d			16 10					16 41								17 14								
Larbert	d	15 50		16 15		16 20			16 47			16 51					17 20			17 25				17 34	17 34
Stirling	d	16 00		16 25		16a33		16 39	16 56			17 08			17a10	17a19	17 29			17 37				17 45	17 45
Alloa	a	16 15										17 20													
Bridge of Allan	d			16 30				16 44	17 01								17 33			17 41				17 49	17 49
Dunblane	a			16 37				16 49	17 08								17 40			17 47				17 54	17 54

A To Edinburgh
B To Aberdeen
C To Inverness
D not 25 December, 26 December, 1 January, 2 January. To Arbroath
E From London Kings Cross to Inverness. The Highland Chieftain
F To Carnoustie

For services between Glasgow Queen Street - Cumbernauld - Falkirk Grahamston please refer to table 224

Table 230

Mondays to Saturdays

9 December to 17 May

Edinburgh, Glasgow Queen Street and Falkirk Grahamston - Stirling, Alloa and Dunblane

Network Diagram - refer to first page of Table 225

		SR		SR	SR	SR	SR	SR	SR	SR	SR	SR		SR	SR	SR	SR	SR	SR	SR	SR	SR		SR	SR
						SX		SX								SX	SO								
				■1			■1		◇■1		■1			■1	◇■1			■1		■1	◇■1			■1	
						A	B	C	D					B	E					B	D				
				trolley			trolley		trolley		trolley			trolley	trolley			trolley		trolley	trolley			trolley	
Edinburgh 10	d	17 03		17 15		17 26				17 33	17 45					18 03	18 03	18 15				18 33		18 45	
Haymarket	d	17 08		17 19		17 30				17 37	17 49					18 08	18 08	18 19				18 38		18 49	
Edinburgh Park	d	17 14								17 44						18 14	18 14					18 43			
Linlithgow	d	17 27		17 34						17 56	18 05					18 27	18 27	18 36				18 55		19 04	
Polmont 3	d	17 32		17 41						18 02	18 12					18 32	18 33	18 43				19 01		19 10	
Glasgow Queen Street 10	d			18a06	17 18		17 30	17 33	17 41		18a37	17 48		18 00	18 11			19a08	18 18	18 30	18 41			19a36	18 48
Bishopbriggs	d				17 25			17 39				17 55							18 25						18 54
Lenzie 3	d				17 30			17 44				18 00							18 30						19 00
Croy 3	d				17 37		17a42					18 07		18a13					18 37	18a43					19 06
Falkirk Grahamston 3	d	17 39						18a03		18 09						18 39	18 39					19 08			
Camelon 4	d	17 42								18 12						18 42	18 42					19 11			
Larbert	d	17 48			17 52	17 57				18 17		18 21			18 31	18 48	18 48		18 52			19 16			19 20
Stirling	d	17 57			18 02	18 06			18 16	18 30		18 34			18 42	18 57	18 57		19 00		19 07	19 25			19a31
Alloa	a				18 14					18 42									19 14						
Bridge of Allan	d	18 01				18 10						18 38			18 46	19 01	19 01					19 30			
Dunblane	a	18 08				18 16			18 22			18 44			18 50	19 08	19 08				19 13	19 37			

		SR	SR	SR	SR	SR	SR	SR		SR	SR	SR	SR	SR	SR	SR	SR	SR		SR	SR	SR	SR	SR	SR
				SX	SO	SX	SO	SX		SO															
		■1	◇			■1	■1				■1	◇■1			■1	■1		■1		◇■1			■1	■1	
		B	F								G	D				B		G		D			B		
		trolley										trolley													
Edinburgh 10	d			19 03	19 03	19 15	19 15				19 30		19 33		20 00			20 30			20 33			21 00	
Haymarket	d			19 07	19 07	19 19	19 20				19 34		19 37		20 04			20 34			20 37			21 04	
Edinburgh Park	d			19 13	19 13								19 43								20 43				
Linlithgow	d			19 25	19 25	19 34	19 34				19 49		19 55		20 19			20 49			20 55			21 19	
Polmont 3	d			19 31	19 31	19 40	19 40						20 01		20 25						21 01			21 25	
Glasgow Queen Street 10	d	19 00	19 09			20a07	20a07	19 18		19 18		19 41		19 48	20a51	20 00	20 18			20 41		20 48	21 00	21a51	21 18
Bishopbriggs	d							19 24		19 24				19 54			20 24					20 54			21 24
Lenzie 3	d							19 29		19 29				19 59			20 29					20 59			21 29
Croy 3	d	19a12						19 36		19 36	20a07			20 06		20a12	20 36	21a07				21 06	21a12		21 36
Falkirk Grahamston 3	d			19 37	19 37								20 07								21 07				
Camelon 4	d			19 40	19 40								20 10								21 10				
Larbert	d			19 45	19 45			19 50		19 52			20 15	20 20			20 50				21 15	21 20			21 50
Stirling	d		19 36	19 55	19 55			20 00		20 00		20a07	20 25	20 32			21 00			21 07	21 25	21a32			22 00
Alloa	a							20 13		20 13							21 13								22 13
Bridge of Allan	d		19 40	20 00	20 01								20 30	20 37							21 30				
Dunblane	a		19 44	20 08	20 08								20 38	20 44						21 13	21 37				

		SR	SR	SR		SR	SR	SR	SR	SR	SR	SR	SR	SR		SR	SR	SR	SR	SR	SR	SR			
		■1	◇■1	◇			■1	■1		■1		◇	■1	■1				■1	■1	◇					
		G	D	H			B			G		H	B	G				B	G	H					
Edinburgh 10	d	21 30		21 33				22 00		22 30	22 33			23 00		23 03			23 30		23 33				
Haymarket	d	21 34		21 37				22 04		22 34	22 37			23 04		23 07			23 34		23 37				
Edinburgh Park	d			21 43							22 43					23 13					23 43				
Linlithgow	d	21 49		21 55				22 19		22 49	22 55			23 19		23 25			23 49		23 55				
Polmont 3	d			22 01				22 25			23 01			23 24		23 31			23 54		23 59				
Glasgow Queen Street 10	d		21 41			21 48	22 00	22a51	22 18			22 48	23 00				23 18	23 30		23 36		23 48			
Bishopbriggs	d					21 54			22 24			22 54					23 24					23 54			
Lenzie 3	d					21 59			22 29			22 59					23 29					23 59			
Croy 3	d	22a07				22 06	22a12		22 36	23a07		23 06	23a12	23a38			23 36	23a42	00a10			00 06			
Falkirk Grahamston 3	d			22 07							23 07					23 37					00 06				
Camelon 4	d			22 10							23 10					23 40					00 09				
Larbert	d			22 15		22 20			22 50		23 15	23 20				23 45	23 50				00 14	00 20			
Stirling	d		22a07	22 25		22 32			23 00		23 25	23 31				23a56	00 02			00 05	00 24	00a31			
Alloa	a								23 13								00 13								
Bridge of Allan	d			22 30		22 37					23 30	23 37								00 10	00 28				
Dunblane	a			22 35		22 44					23 37	23 41								00 14	00 35				

A From Newcraighall
B To Edinburgh
C To Markinch
D To Aberdeen
E To Inverness
F To Dundee
G To Glasgow Queen Street
H To Perth

For services between Glasgow Queen Street - Cumbernauld - Falkirk Grahamston please refer to table 224

Table 230

Sundays

8 December to 11 May

Edinburgh, Glasgow Queen Street and Falkirk Grahamston - Stirling, Alloa and Dunblane

Network Diagram - refer to first page of Table 225

		SR	SR	SR	SR	SR		SR	SR	SR	SR	SR	SR	SR	SR	SR		SR	SR	SR	SR	SR	SR	SR	SR
			◇			[1]		[1]	[1]	[1]	[1]	◇[1]	[1]		[1]	[1]			[1]		[1]	[1]	◇[1]		
		A	B	C	A	D		E	E	D		F	E		D				E			D	G		
									🚲	🚲	🚲	🚲	🚲		🚲	🚲			🚲		🚲	🚲	🚲		
Edinburgh [10]	d							08 00	08 30		09 00		09 30	09 34		10 00			10 30	10 35	11 00				11 06
Haymarket	d							08 04	08 34		09 04		09 34	09 38		10 04			10 34	10 39	11 04				11 10
Edinburgh Park	d													09 43						10 44					11 15
Linlithgow	d							08 23	08 53		09 23		09 53	10 01		10 23			10 49	10 57	11 19				11 27
Polmont [3]	d							08 29			09 29			10 06		10 29				11 02	11 25				11 32
Glasgow Queen Street [10] ⛴	d					07 50				09 00	09a54	09 37			10 00	10a55		10 15			11a51	11 00	11 10	11 15	
Bishopbriggs	d																	10 21						11 21	
Lenzie [3]	d											09 46						10 27						11 27	
Croy [3]	d				00 06	08a02		08a43	09a11	09a12			10a11		10a12			10 33	11a07			11a12		11 33	
Falkirk Grahamston [3]	d			00 06										10 13						11 09					11 39
Camelon [4]	d			00 09										10 16						11 12					11 42
Larbert	d			00 14	00 20							10 01		10 22				10 45		11 18			11 30	11 45	11 50
Stirling	d	00 02	00 05	00 24	00a31							10 10		10 31				10 55		11 27			11 40	11 55	11a59
Alloa	a	00 13																11 07						12 07	
Bridge of Allan	d		00 10	00 28										10 35						11 31					
Dunblane	a		00 14	00 35								10 17		10 42						11 38			11 46		

		SR		SR	SR	SR	SR	SR	SR	SR	SR	SR		SR	SR	SR	SR	SR	SR	SR	SR	SR		SR	SR
		[1]		◇[1]		[1]	[1]			[1]		[1]		[1]			[1]	◇[1]		[1]	[1]				[1]
		E		F		D				E				D			E	F			D				E
		🚲		🚲		🚲	🚲			🚲		🚲		🚲			🚲	🚲		🚲	🚲				
Edinburgh [10]	d	11 30			11 35		12 00		12 06	12 30	12 35	13 00				13 06	13 30		13 35	14 00				14 06	14 30
Haymarket	d	11 34			11 39		12 04		12 10	12 33	12 39	13 04				13 10	13 34		13 39	14 04				14 10	14 35
Edinburgh Park	d				11 44				12 15		12 44					13 15			13 44					14 15	
Linlithgow	d	11 49			11 57		12 19		12 27	12 49	12 57	13 19				13 27	13 49		13 57	14 19				14 27	14 49
Polmont [3]	d				12 02		12 25		12 32		13 02	13 25				13 32			14 02	14 25				14 32	
Glasgow Queen Street [10] ⛴	d			11 45		12 00	12a52	12 15				13a51		13 00	13 15			13 45		14a51	14 00	14 15			
Bishopbriggs	d							12 21							13 21							14 21			
Lenzie [3]	d							12 27							13 27							14 27			
Croy [3]	d	12a07				12a12		12 33		13a07				13a12	13 33		14a07				14a12	14 33			15a06
Falkirk Grahamston [3]	d				12 09				12 39		13 09					13 39			14 09					14 39	
Camelon [4]	d				12 12				12 42		13 12					13 42			14 12					14 42	
Larbert	d				12 18			12 45	12 50		13 18				13 45	13 51			14 18			14 45		14 50	
Stirling	d			12 11	12 27			12 55	12a59		13 27				13 55	14a00		14 13	14 27			14 55		14a59	
Alloa	a							13 07							14 07							15 07			
Bridge of Allan	d				12 31						13 31								14 31						
Dunblane	a			12 17	12 38						13 38							14 19	14 38						

		SR	SR	SR	SR	SR	SR	SR		SR	SR	SR	SR	SR	SR	SR	GR	SR		SR	SR	SR	SR	SR	SR
		◇[1]		[1]	[1]			[1]		◇[1]		[1]	[1]			[1]	■ [1]			[1]	[1]			[1]	◇[1]
		H			D			E		F			D			E	I				D			E	F
		🚲		🚲				🚲		🚲		🚲	🚲			🚲	🚲			🚲	🚲				🚲
Edinburgh [10]	d		14 35	15 00			15 06	15 30			15 35	16 00			16 06	16 30	16 32	16 35		17 00			17 06	17 30	
Haymarket	d		14 39	15 04			15 10	15 34			15 39	16 04			16 10	16 34	16 37	16 39		17 04			17 10	17 34	
Edinburgh Park	d		14 44				15 15				15 44				16 15			16 44					17 15		
Linlithgow	d		14 57	15 19			15 27	15 49			15 57	16 19			16 27	16 49		16 57		17 19			17 27	17 49	
Polmont [3]	d		15 02	15 25			15 32				16 02	16 25			16 32			17 02		17 25			17 32		
Glasgow Queen Street [10] ⛴	d	14 40		15a51	15 00	15 15				15 45		16a51	16 00	16 15						17a51	17 00	17 15			17 45
Bishopbriggs	d					15 21								16 21								17 21			
Lenzie [3]	d					15 27								16 27								17 27			
Croy [3]	d				15a12	15 33		16a07					16a12	16 33		17a07					17a12	17 33		18a07	
Falkirk Grahamston [3]	d		15 09				15 39				16 09				16 39		17 04	17 09					17 39		
Camelon [4]	d		15 12				15 42				16 12				16 42			17 12					17 42		
Larbert	d	15 00	15 18			15 45	15 50				16 18			16 45	16 50			17 18				17 45	17 49		
Stirling	d	15 09	15 27			15 55	15a59			16 12	16 27			16 55	16a59		17a18	17 27				17 55	17a59		18a12
Alloa	a					16 07								17 07								18 07			
Bridge of Allan	d		15 31								16 31							17 31							
Dunblane	a	15 15	15 38							16 18	16 38							17 40							

A not 8 December. From Glasgow Queen Street
B not 8 December. From Glasgow Queen Street to Perth
C not 8 December. From Edinburgh
D To Edinburgh
E To Glasgow Queen Street
F To Aberdeen
G To Inverness
H To Elgin
I From London Kings Cross to Inverness. The Highland Chieftain

For services between Glasgow Queen Street - Cumbernauld - Falkirk Grahamston please refer to table 224

Table 230

Sundays

8 December to 11 May

Edinburgh, Glasgow Queen Street and Falkirk Grahamston - Stirling, Alloa and Dunblane

Network Diagram - refer to first page of Table 225

		SR	SR	SR	SR	SR	SR	SR	SR	SR		SR	SR	SR	SR	SR	SR	SR	SR	SR		SR	SR	SR	SR
			1	1	◇1		◇	1		1		1		1	◇1		1	1		1			1	1	
			A		B		C	D				A		D	E		A			D				A	
			bike	bike	bike			bike		bike		bike													
Edinburgh 10	d	17 35		18 00			18 06	18 30	18 35	19 00				19 30		19 35		20 00		20 30		20 35	21 00		
Haymarket	d	17 39		18 04			18 10	18 34	18 39	19 04				19 34		19 39		20 04		20 34		20 39	21 04		
Edinburgh Park	d	17 44					18 15		18 44							19 44						20 44			
Linlithgow	d	17 57		18 19			18 27	18 49	18 57	19 19				19 49		19 57		20 19		20 49		20 57	21 19		
Polmont 3	d	18 02		18 25			18 32		19 02	19 25						20 02		20 25				21 02	21 25		
Glasgow Queen Street 10 ⛴	d		18 00	18a52	18 10	18 15				19a51		19 00	19 15		19 45		20 00	20a51	20 15				21a51	21 00	21 15
Bishopbriggs	d					18 21							19 21						20 21						21 21
Lenzie 3	d					18 27							19 27						20 27						21 27
Croy 3	d		18a12			18 33		19a07				19a12	19 33	20a07			20a12		20 33	21a07				21a12	21 33
Falkirk Grahamston 3	d	18 09					18 39		19 09							20 09						21 09			
Camelon 4	d	18 12					18 42		19 12							20 12						21 12			
Larbert	d	18 18			18 30	18 45	18 50		19 18				19 45			20 18			20 45			21 18			21 45
Stirling	d	18 27			18 40	18 55	19 00		19 27				19 55		20 12	20 27			20 55			21 27			21 55
Alloa	a					19 07							20 07						21 07						22 07
Bridge of Allan	d	18 31					19 04		19 31							20 31						21 31			
Dunblane	a	18 38			18 46		19 09		19 38						20 18	20 38						21 38			

		SR	SR	SR	SR	SR		SR	SR	SR	SR	SR	SR	SR	SR
		1	◇1		1	1			1	◇	1	1	1	1	◇
		D	E		A				D	C	A	D	A	D	C
			bike												
Edinburgh 10	d	21 30		21 35		22 00			22 30	22 35		23 00		23 30	
Haymarket	d	21 34		21 39		22 04			22 34	22 39		23 04		23 34	
Edinburgh Park	d			21 44						22 44					
Linlithgow	d	21 49		21 57		22 19			22 49	22 57		23 19		23 49	
Polmont 3	d			22 02		22 25				23 02		23 25		23 55	
Glasgow Queen Street 10 ⛴	d		21 45		22 00	22a51		22 15			23 00		23 30		23 45
Bishopbriggs	d							22 21							23 50
Lenzie 3	d							22 27							23 55
Croy 3	d	22a07			22a12			22 33	23a07		23a12	23a40	23a42	00a09	23 59
Falkirk Grahamston 3	d			22 09						23 09					
Camelon 4	d			22 12						23 12					
Larbert	d			22 18				22 45		23 18					00 11
Stirling	d		22 12	22 27				22 55		23 27					00 20
Alloa	a							23 07							
Bridge of Allan	d			22 31						23 31					00 24
Dunblane	a		22 18	22 38						23 38					00 28

A To Edinburgh
B To Elgin
C To Perth
D To Glasgow Queen Street
E To Aberdeen

For services between Glasgow Queen Street - Cumbernauld - Falkirk Grahamston please refer to table 224

Table 230R

Mondays to Saturdays

9 December to 17 May

Dunblane, Alloa and Stirling - Falkirk Grahamston, Glasgow Queen Street and Edinburgh

Network Diagram - refer to first page of Table 225

Miles	Miles	Miles	Miles																						
						SR	SR	SR	SR	SR	SR	SR	SR	SR		SR	SR	SR	SR	SR	SR	SR	SR	SR	
						MO	MX	MO	MX					SX			SO	SO	SX	SX				SX	
						1	1	1	1		◇	1	1	1			1			1	1	1	◇	1	
						A	A	B	B		C	A	B	A			A			A	A	B	D	B	
																					🚲				
0	0	—	—	**Dunblane**	d					05 21	05 46							06 28	06 28				06 47		
2	2	—	—	Bridge of Allan	d					05 24	05 49							06 31	06 31				06 50		
—	—	—	0	**Alloa**	d											06 11									
5½	5½	—	6¾	**Stirling**	d					05 30	05 54					06 23		06 36	06 36				06 55		
13½	13½	—	14¾	Larbert	d					05 38	06 03					06 32		06 45	06 45				07 04		
—	15	—	—	Camelon [4]	d					05 44								06 52	06 52						
—	16½	—	—	**Falkirk Grahamston** [3]	d					05 47								06 55	06 56						
24	—	—	25¼	Croy [3]	d			00 10	00 11		06 14		06 34			06 43	06 44			06 57		07 11	07 15	07 23	
29¼	—	—	30½	Lenzie [3]	d				00 15		06 21			06 38		06 50					07 09		07 21		
32¼	—	—	33½	Bishopbriggs	d						06 25					06 54							07 26		
34½	—	—	35¾	**Glasgow Queen Street** [10] ⛴	a			00 24	00 27		06 34		06 49			07 03						07 25	07 34	07 37	
—	19½	—	—	Polmont [3]	d					05 53		06 23		06 57			06 59	07 03	07 03		07 27				
—	24¼	—	—	Linlithgow	d	00 03	00 03			06 00		06 29		07 03			07 05	07 10	07 10	07 15	07 33				
—	38	14¾	—	Edinburgh Park	d					06 13								07 23	07 23						
—	40½	17¼	—	Haymarket	d	00s19	00s20			06 21		06s45		07s20			07s20	07 29	07 29	07s32	07s50				
—	41¾	18½	—	**Edinburgh** [10] 225,242	a	00 24	00 25			06 26		06 50		07 25			07 25	07 34	07 34	07 37	07 55				

		SR	SR	SR	SR	SR	SR	SR	SR	SR		SR	SR	SR	SR	SR	SR	SR	SR	SR		SR	SR	SR	SR
		SX				SX			SX	SO			SX		SX	SO	SO	SX	SX						
			1				1	1				1		1	◇1	◇1	1	1		1				1	
			A	C			A	B	C			A		B	E	E	B	B	F	A				B	
			🚲				🚲	🚲						🚲		🚲	🚲	🚲		🚲				🚲	
Dunblane	d			07 08		07 23			07 31	07 31					07 44	07 44						07 58			08 13
Bridge of Allan	d			07 11		07 26			07 34	07 34					07 48	07 48						08 01			08 16
Alloa	d				07 12								07 39										07 57		
Stirling	d			07 17	07 23	07 31			07 39	07 39			07 49		07 53	07 53						08 07	08 11		08 23
Larbert	d			07 26	07 32	07 40			07 47	07 48			07 58		08 03	08 03						08 16	08 20		08 32
Camelon [4]	d			07 32									08 03									08 21			
Falkirk Grahamston [3]	d			07 36									08 07						08 12			08 24			
Croy [3]	d				07 43		07 43	07 53	07 59	07 59				08 11						08 12			08 32	08 40	08 43
Lenzie [3]	d	07 34			07 50				08 06	08 06					08 20	08 20	08 27	08 27	08 32				08 39		08 50
Bishopbriggs	d	07 38			07 55				08 10	08 10							08 32		08 37				08 43		08 54
Glasgow Queen Street [10] ⛴	a	07 47			08 04			08 07	08 19	08 19				08 25	08 34	08 34	08 40	08 40	08 48				08 52	08 55	09 03
Polmont [3]	d		07 39	07 44								08 10	08 14							08 27		08 32			
Linlithgow	d		07 45	07 51			08 01					08 17	08 21									08 39			
Edinburgh Park	d			08 06									08 34									08 53			
Haymarket	d		08s02	08 12		08 16	08s19					08s31	08 40							08s46		08 59			
Edinburgh [10] 225,242	a		08 07	08 19		08 22	08 25					08 36	08 44							08 51		09 04			

		SR	SR	SR	SR	SR		SR	SR	SR	SR	SR	SR	SR	SR	SR		SR	SR	SR	SR	SR	SR	SR	SR
								SX	SO				SX	SO						SX	SO	SX	SO		SX
		1	1		◇1	1		1	1	1			◇1	◇	1	1		1				◇1	◇1	1	1
		A	A		E	B		A	A	A			D	D	B	A		A				G	H	B	A
		🚲	🚲		🚲	🚲		🚲	🚲	🚲					🚲	🚲		🚲					🚲	🚲	🚲
Dunblane	d			08 28								09 03	09 07	09 07						09 28	09 28				
Bridge of Allan	d			08 31									09 11	09 11						09 31	09 31				
Alloa	d										08 36														
Stirling	d			08 37	08 44						08 53	09 09	09 15	09 15					09 23	09 36	09 36	09 43	09 43		
Larbert	d			08 46							09 02	09 18							09 32	09 45	09 45				
Camelon [4]	d			08 51								09 24								09 51	09 51				
Falkirk Grahamston [3]	d			08 54								09 27								09 54	09 54				
Croy [3]	d		08 43			09 05				09 12	09 13				09 36			09 42	09 43					10 04	
Lenzie [3]	d										09 20								09 50						
Bishopbriggs	d										09 24								09 54						
Glasgow Queen Street [10] ⛴	a				09 16	09 19					09 33		09 46	09 46	09 50				10 03			10 14	10 14	10 19	
Polmont [3]	d			09 01				09 09	09 09			09 32				09 40				10 00	10 00				10 08
Linlithgow	d	08 44		09 08				09 15	09 15			09 39				09 46				10 07	10 07				10 14
Edinburgh Park	d			09 22								09 53								10 21	10 21				
Haymarket	d	09s01	09s14	09 28				09s33	09s33	09s46		10 01				10s02		10s12		10 27	10 28				10s31
Edinburgh [10] 225,242	a	09 07	09 20	09 34				09 37	09 39	09 51		10 07				10 10		10 19		10 34	10 34				10 37

A From Glasgow Queen Street
B From Edinburgh
C From Perth
D From Dundee
E From Aberdeen
F From Kirkcaldy
G not 25 December, 26 December, 1 January, 2 January. From Inverurie
H From Inverurie

For services between Glasgow Queen Street - Cumbernauld - Falkirk Grahamston please refer to table 224

Table 230R

Mondays to Saturdays

9 December to 17 May

Dunblane, Alloa and Stirling - Falkirk Grahamston, Glasgow Queen Street and Edinburgh

Network Diagram - refer to first page of Table 225

		SR	SR	SR	SR	SR	SR	SR		GR	SR	SR	SR	SR	SR	SR	SR	SR		SR	SR	SR	SR	SR	SR
		SO																							
										R															
		1	1			1		1		1	1		◇1	1	1	1				1	1	1		◇1	
		A	A			B		A		C	A		D	B	A	A				B	A	A		E	
			🛒			🛒		🛒		🛏🛒	🛒		🛒	🛒	🛒	🛒				🛒	🛒	🛒		🛒	
Dunblane	d				09 58		10 13					10 28						10 58						11 20	11 28
Bridge of Allan	d				10 01		10 16					10 31						11 01						11 23	11 31
Alloa	d			09 41													10 36								
Stirling	d			09 53	10 06		10 23			10 32		10 36	10 43				10 53	11 06					11 23	11 29	11 36
Larbert	d			10 02	10 15		10 32					10 45					11 02	11 15					11 32		11 45
Camelon 4	d				10 21							10 51						11 21							11 51
Falkirk Grahamston 3	d				10 24					10 47		10 54						11 24							11 54
Croy 3	d		10 12	10 13		10 34	10 43				10 42			11 04		11 12	11 13			11 34		11 42	11 43		
Lenzie 3	d			10 20			10 50										11 20						11 50		
Bishopbriggs	d			10 24			10 54										11 24						11 54		
Glasgow Queen Street 10 ⛴	a			10 33		10 49	11 03						11 14	11 19			11 34			11 50			12 03	12 09	
Polmont 3	d	10 08			10 30			10 38				11 00			11 08			11 30			11 38				12 00
Linlithgow	d	10 14			10 37			10 44				11 07			11 14			11 37			11 44				12 07
Edinburgh Park	d				10 51							11 21						11 51							12 21
Haymarket	d	10s31	10s44		10 57			11s00		11 12	11s14	11 27			11s30	11s45		11 57			12s00	12s12			12 27
Edinburgh 10 225,242	a	10 37	10 50		11 04			11 07		11 17	11 21	11 34			11 35	11 51		12 07			12 07	12 19			12 34

		SR	SR	SR		SR	SR	SR	SR	SR	SR	SR	SR	SR		SR	SR	SR	SR	SR	SR	SR	SR	SR	
		◇1	1	1		1			1	1	1			◇1		1	1	1			◇1	1	1	1	
		F	B	A		A			B	A	A			D		B	A	A			G	B	A	A	
		🛒	🛒	🛒		🛒			🛒	🛒	🛒			🛒		🛒	🛒	🛒				🛒	🛒	🛒	
Dunblane	d							11 58				12 13	12 28							12 58	13 05				
Bridge of Allan	d							12 01				12 16	12 31							13 01	13 08				
Alloa	d						11 41												12 36						
Stirling	d	11 43					11 53	12 06				12 23	12 36	12 43					12 53	13 06	13 13				
Larbert	d	⌇					12 02	12 15				12 32	12 45						13 02	13 15					
Camelon 4	d	⌇						12 21					12 51							13 21					
Falkirk Grahamston 3	d	⌇						12 24					12 54							13 24					
Croy 3	d	⌇	12 04			12 12	12 13		12 34		12 42	12 43				13 04		13 12	13 13			13 34		13 42	
Lenzie 3	d	⌇					12 20					12 50							13 20						
Bishopbriggs	d	⌇					12 24					12 54							13 24						
Glasgow Queen Street 10 ⛴	a	12 15	12 20				12 34		12 49			13 03		13 14		13 19			13 33		13 47	13 51			
Polmont 3	d			12 08				12 30		12 38			13 00				13 08			13 30			13 38		
Linlithgow	d			12 14				12 37		12 44			13 07				13 14			13 37			13 44		
Edinburgh Park	d							12 51					13 21							13 51					
Haymarket	d			12s30		12s45		12 57		13s01	13s14		13 27				13s30	13s45		13 57			14s00	14s11	
Edinburgh 10 225,242	a			12 35		12 52		13 06		13 07	13 20		13 34				13 35	13 50		14 04			14 07	14 19	

		SR	SR	SR	SR	SR	SR	SR	SR	SR		SR	SR	SR	SR	SR	SR	SR	SR	SR		SR	SR	SR	SR
																				SX		SO			
				◇1	1	1	1			1		1	1		1		◇1	1	1					1	1
				D	B	A	A			B		A	A		A		D	B	A					B	A
				🛒	🛒	🛒	🛒			🛒		🛒	🛒		🛒		🛒	🛒	🛒					🛒	🛒
Dunblane	d		13 28						13 58					14 13		14 28							14 58		
Bridge of Allan	d		13 31						14 01					14 16		14 31							15 01		
Alloa	d							13 41												14 36		14 36			
Stirling	d	13 23	13 36	13 43				13 53	14 06					14 23		14 36	14 43			14 53		14 53	15 06		
Larbert	d	13 32	13 45					14 02	14 15					14 32		14 45				15 02		15 02	15 15		
Camelon 4	d		13 51						14 21							14 51							15 21		
Falkirk Grahamston 3	d		13 54						14 24							14 54							15 24		
Croy 3	d	13 43			14 04		14 12	14 13		14 34			14 42	14 43				15 04	15 12	15 13		15 13		15 34	
Lenzie 3	d	13 50						14 20						14 50						15 20		15 20			
Bishopbriggs	d	13 54						14 24						14 54						15 24		15 24			
Glasgow Queen Street 10 ⛴	a	14 03		14 14	14 19			14 33		14 49				15 03			15 14	15 21		15 33		15 34		15 51	
Polmont 3	d		14 00			14 08			14 30			14 38			15 08	15 00							15 30		15 38
Linlithgow	d		14 07			14 14			14 37			14 44			15 14	15 07							15 37		15 44
Edinburgh Park	d		14 21						14 51							15 21							15 51		
Haymarket	d		14 27			14s32	14s45		14 57			15s00	15s14		15s29	15 27			15s45				15 57		16s01
Edinburgh 10 225,242	a		14 34			14 37	14 51		15 02			15 05	15 20		15 36	15 37			15 50				16 06		16 08

A From Glasgow Queen Street
B From Edinburgh
C From Inverness to London Kings Cross. The Highland Chieftain
D From Aberdeen
E From Inverness
F not 25 December, 26 December, 1 January, 2 January. From Dyce
G From Dundee

For services between Glasgow Queen Street - Cumbernauld - Falkirk Grahamston please refer to table 224

Table 230R

Mondays to Saturdays

9 December to 17 May

Dunblane, Alloa and Stirling - Falkirk Grahamston, Glasgow Queen Street and Edinburgh

Network Diagram - refer to first page of Table 225

	SR		SR	SR	SR	SR	SR	SR	SR	SR	SR		SR	SR	SR	SR	SR	SR	SR	SR	SR		SR	SR
																	SO	SX		SX	SO			
	1				◇1	1	1	1			◇		1		1	1			1	1	1		1	
	A				B	C	A	A			D		C		A	A			C	A	A		A	
Dunblane d			15 13	15 28						15 58	16 05						16 28	16 28						
Bridge of Allan d			15 16	15 31						16 01	16 09						16 31	16 31						
Alloa d									15 41															16 34
Stirling d			15 23	15 36	15 43				15 53	16 06	16 14			16 21			16 37	16 37						16 53
Larbert d			15 32	15 45					16 02	16 15				16 30			16 45	16 45						17 02
Camelon 4 d				15 51						16 21							16 51	16 51						
Falkirk Grahamston 3 d				15 54						16 24							16 54	16 54						
Croy 3 d	15 42		15 43			16 04		16 12	16 13				16 36	16 41		16 42			17 05				17 12	17 14
Lenzie 3 d			15 50						16 20					16 48										17 20
Bishopbriggs d			15 54						16 24					16 52										17 25
Glasgow Queen Street 10 a			16 03		16 14	16 19			16 33		16 48		16 51	17 03					17 21					17 33
Polmont 3 d				16 00			16 08			16 30					16 39		17 00	17 00		17 11	17 11		17 27	
Linlithgow d				16 07			16 14			16 37					16 45		17 07	17 07		17 17	17 17			
Edinburgh Park d				16 21						16 51							17 22	17 22						
Haymarket d	16s13			16 27			16s30	16s43		16 57					17s00	17s17	17 27	17 29		17s34	17s34		17s46	
Edinburgh 10 225,242 a	16 18			16 33			16 36	16 48		17 04					17 06	17 22	17 31	17 35		17 40	17 40		17 52	

	SR	SR	SR	SR	SR	SR	SR		SR	SR	SR	SR	SR	SR	SR	SR	SR		SR	SR	SR	SR	SR	SR
																			SX	SO		SX	SO	
		1	1	1		◇1			◇1	1	1	1		1		1	1				◇1	1	1	1
		C	A	A		E			B	C	A	A		C		A	A				B	C	C	A
Dunblane d	16 58					17 21	17 28		17 37						18 11				18 28	18 28	18 38			
Bridge of Allan d	17 01					17 24	17 31								18 14				18 31	18 31				
Alloa d													17 41											
Stirling d	17 07				17 23	17 29	17 37		17 43				17 53		18 19				18 37	18 37	18 43			
Larbert d	17 16				17 32		17 46						18 02		18 28				18 46	18 46				
Camelon 4 d	17 21						17 51												18 51	18 51				
Falkirk Grahamston 3 d	17 24						17 54												18 54	18 54				
Croy 3 d		17 36		17 42	17 43					18 06		18 13	18 14	18 36	18 43		18 43					19 04	19 04	
Lenzie 3 d					17 50					18 12			18 20		18 50									
Bishopbriggs d					17 54								18 25		18 54									
Glasgow Queen Street 10 a		17 51			18 03	18 09			18 15	18 23			18 34	18 50	19 05						19 16	19 20	19 22	
Polmont 3 d	17 31			17 57			18 02				18 10					18 39			19 01	19 01				19 08
Linlithgow d	17 38		17 44	18 04			18 09				18 16					18 45			19 08	19 08				19 14
Edinburgh Park d	17 52						18 23												19 21	19 21				
Haymarket d	18 00		18s02	18s19			18 29				18s32	18s43				19s02	19s14		19 27	19 28				19s31
Edinburgh 10 225,242 a	18 06		18 08	18 25			18 34				18 38	18 49				19 07	19 20		19 33	19 33				19 39

	SR	SR	SR		SR	SR	SR	SR	SR	SR	SR	SR	SR		SR	SR	SR	SR	SR	SR	SR	SR	SR	
					SX	SO												SO	SX					
	1				1	1		1	1		◇1	1	1				◇1			1		◇1	1	
	A				C	C		A	A		B	C	A				E			A		B	C	
Dunblane d							19 13			19 28						19 58	20 05				20 28			
Bridge of Allan d							19 16			19 31						20 01	20 09				20 31			
Alloa d		18 28	18 53												19 41									
Stirling d		18 53					19 23			19 36	19 43				19 53	20 06	20 14	20 21	20 21		20 36	20 42		
Larbert d		19 02	19 15				19 32			19 45					20 02	20 15		20 30	20 30		20 45			
Camelon 4 d			19 22							19 51						20 21					20 51			
Falkirk Grahamston 3 d			19 25							19 54						20 24					20 54			
Croy 3 d	19 12	19 13			19 34	19 34	19 43					20 07	20 12		20 13			20 43	20 43				21 07	
Lenzie 3 d		19 20					19 50								20 20			20 50	20 50					
Bishopbriggs d		19 24					19 54								20 24			20 54	20 54					
Glasgow Queen Street 10 a		19 33			19 49	19 49	20 03				20 15	20 22			20 34		20 45	21 03	21 04			21 14	21 21	
Polmont 3 d			19 30					19 38	19 53	20 00						20 30				20 53	21 00			
Linlithgow d			19 37					19 44	19 58	20 07			20 29			20 37				20 59	21 07			
Edinburgh Park d			19 51							20 21						20 51					21 21			
Haymarket d	19s46		19 57					20s00	20s15	20 27			20s45			20 57				21s15	21 27			
Edinburgh 10 225,242 a	19 51		20 04					20 06	20 21	20 34			20 51			21 04				21 20	21 34			

A From Glasgow Queen Street
B From Aberdeen
C From Edinburgh
D From Dundee
E From Inverness

For services between Glasgow Queen Street - Cumbernauld - Falkirk Grahamston please refer to table 224

Table 230R

Mondays to Saturdays

9 December to 17 May

Dunblane, Alloa and Stirling - Falkirk Grahamston, Glasgow Queen Street and Edinburgh

Network Diagram - refer to first page of Table 225

	SR	SR	SR	SR	SR		SR	SR	SR	SR	SR	SR	SR	SR	SR		SR	SR	SR	SR	SR	SR	SR	SR
										SX	SO													
	1				◇1		1	1	1					◇1	1		1	1		◇1			1	1
	A				B		A	C	A					B	A		C	A		D			C	A
					🚲																			
Dunblane d			20 58	21 13								21 58								23 02	23 09			
Bridge of Allan d			21 01	21 16								22 01								23 05	23 12			
Alloa d		20 41								21 41	21 41								22 41			23 18		
Stirling d		20 53	21 06	21 23	21 49					21 53	21 53	22 06	22 23	22 48					22 53	23 09	23 17	23a27		
Larbert d		21 02	21 15	21 32						22 02	22 02	22 15	22 32						23 02		23 26			
Camelon 4 d			21 21									22 21									23 29			
Falkirk Grahamston 3 d			21 24									22 24									23 32			
Croy 3 d	21 12	21 13		21 43				22 07	22 12	22 13	22 13		22 43				23 07	23 12	23 13				23 39	23 42
Lenzie 3 d		21 20		21 50						22 20	22 20		22 50						23 20				23 44	
Bishopbriggs d		21 24		21 54						22 24	22 24		22 54						23 24				23 49	
Glasgow Queen Street 10 ⛴ a		21 33		22 04	22 20			22 23		22 33	22 34		23 03	23 19			23 22		23 33	23 43			23 58	
Polmont 3 d			21 30				21 53					22 30			22 53			23 26			23 40			23 56
Linlithgow d	21 29		21 37				21 59		22 29			22 37			22 59			23 33			23 47			00 03
Edinburgh Park d			21 51									22 51									23 59			
Haymarket d	21s45		21 57				22s15		22s46			22 57			23s15			23s49			00 06			00s20
Edinburgh 10 225,242 a	21 50		22 04				22 22		22 51			23 04			23 20			23 55			00 11			00 25

Sundays

8 December to 11 May

	SR	SR	SR	SR	SR	SR	SR	SR	SR		SR	SR	SR	SR	SR	SR	SR	SR	SR		SR	SR	SR	SR
	1	1	1	1	1	1	1				◇1	1	◇	1	1		1	◇	1		1			◇1
	E	F	A	C	A	C	A				G	A	H	C	A		A	H	C		A			B
					🚲	🚲	🚲					🚲		🚲	🚲		🚲		🚲		🚲			🚲
Dunblane d											09 33		09 43					10 38				11 01		11 34
Bridge of Allan d													09 47					10 41				11 04		
Alloa d									09 14							10 14							11 14	
Stirling d								09 05	09 25		09 39		09 51			10 25		10 46				11 10	11 25	11 43
Larbert d								09 13	09 34		09 47		10 00			10 34		10 55				11 19	11 34	
Camelon 4 d								09 19					10 05					11 00				11 24		
Falkirk Grahamston 3 d								09 22					10 08					11 03				11 27		
Croy 3 d		00 10	08 02	08 44		09 11	09 12		09 45					10 11	10 12	10 45			11 07		11 12		11 45	
Lenzie 3 d		00 15							09 52		10 01					10 52							11 52	
Bishopbriggs d									09 56							10 56							11 56	
Glasgow Queen Street 10 ⛴ a		00 27		08 58		09 25			10 07		10 14			10 28		11 07			11 21				12 05	12 14
Polmont 3 d			08 17		08 53			09 30				09 53	10 14				10 53	11 09				11 33		
Linlithgow d	00 03		08 24		08 59		09 29	09 37				09 59	10 21		10 29		10 59	11 16			11 29	11 40		
Edinburgh Park d								09 49					10 33					11 30				11 54		
Haymarket d	00s20		08 45		09s19		09s49	09 59				10s19	10 40		10s45		11s15	11 36			11s47	12 00		
Edinburgh 10 225,242 a	00 25		08 49		09 24		09 54	10 04				10 24	10 45		10 50		11 20	11 40			11 52	12 04		

	SR	SR	SR	SR	SR		SR	GR	SR	SR	SR	SR	SR	SR	SR		SR	SR	SR	SR	SR	SR	SR	SR
								R																
	1		1	1				1	1		1	1			◇1		1		1	1			1	
	A		C	A				I	A		C	A			J		A		C	A			A	
	🚲		🚲	🚲				🍴🚲	🚲		🚲	🚲			🚲				🚲	🚲			🚲	
Dunblane d					12 01			12 28					13 01		13 31						14 01			
Bridge of Allan d					12 04								13 04								14 04			
Alloa d							12 14							13 14								14 14		
Stirling d		11 48			12 10		12 25	12 35		12 46			13 10	13 25	13 38			13 46			14 10	14 25		14 46
Larbert d		11 57			12 19		12 34			12 55			13 19	13 34				13 55			14 19	14 34		14 55
Camelon 4 d		12 02			12 24					13 00			13 24					14 00			14 24			15 00
Falkirk Grahamston 3 d		12 05			12 27			12 51		13 03			13 27					14 03			14 27			15 03
Croy 3 d			12 07	12 12			12 45				13 07	13 12		13 45					14 07	14 12		14 45		
Lenzie 3 d							12 52							13 52								14 52		
Bishopbriggs d							12 56							13 56								14 56		
Glasgow Queen Street 10 ⛴ a			12 21				13 05				13 22			14 05	14 11				14 21			15 05		
Polmont 3 d	11 53	12 11			12 33				12 59	13 09			13 33				13 53	14 09			14 33		14 53	15 09
Linlithgow d	11 59	12 18		12 29	12 40				13 05	13 16		13 29	13 40				13 59	14 16		14 29	14 40		14 59	15 16
Edinburgh Park d		12 32			12 54					13 30			13 54					14 30			14 54			15 30
Haymarket d	12s15	12 38		12s45	13 00			13 15	13s19	13 36		13s47	14 00				14s17	14 36		14s47	15 00		15s15	15 36
Edinburgh 10 225,242 a	12 20	12 42		12 50	13 04			13 20	13 24	13 40		13 52	14 04				14 22	14 41		14 52	15 04		15 20	15 40

A From Glasgow Queen Street
B From Aberdeen
C From Edinburgh
D From Inverness
E not 8 December. From Glasgow Queen Street
F not 8 December. From Edinburgh
G From Dundee
H From Perth
I From Inverness to London Kings Cross. The Highland Chieftain
J From Inverurie

For services between Glasgow Queen Street - Cumbernauld - Falkirk Grahamston please refer to table 224

Table 230R

Sundays

8 December to 11 May

Dunblane, Alloa and Stirling - Falkirk Grahamston, Glasgow Queen Street and Edinburgh

Network Diagram - refer to first page of Table 225

	SR 1 A	SR 1 B	SR	SR ◇1 C	SR	SR ◇1 D	SR 1 B		SR	SR 1 A	SR 1 B	SR	SR	SR 1 B	SR	SR 1 A	SR 1 B		SR	SR	SR ◇1 D	SR 1 B	SR 1 A	SR 1 B
Dunblane d			15 01	15 18		15 36						16 01							17 01		17 31			
Bridge of Allan d			15 04									16 04							17 04					
Alloa d					15 14								16 14							17 14				
Stirling d			15 10	15 24	15 28	15 42			15 47			16 10	16 25		16 46				17 10	17 25	17 38			
Larbert d			15 19	15 33	15 37				15 56			16 19	16 34		16 55				17 19	17 34				
Camelon 4 d			15 24						16 01			16 24			17 00				17 24					
Falkirk Grahamston 3 d			15 27						16 04			16 27			17 03				17 27					
Croy 3 d	15 07	15 12			15 49					16 07	16 12		16 45			17 07	17 12			17 45			18 07	18 12
Lenzie 3 d					15 55								16 52							17 52				
Bishopbriggs d					16 00								16 56							17 56				
Glasgow Queen Street 10 a	15 22			15 58	16 08	16 13				16 22			17 05			17 22				18 05	18 12		18 22	
Polmont 3 d			15 33				15 53		16 10			16 33		16 53	17 09				17 33			17 53		
Linlithgow d		15 29	15 40				15 59		16 17		16 29	16 40		16 59	17 16		17 29		17 40			17 59		18 29
Edinburgh Park d			15 54						16 31			16 54			17 30				17 54					
Haymarket d		15s47	16 00				16s18		16 37		16s47	17 00		17s15	17 36		17s47		18 00			18s17		18s47
Edinburgh 10 225,242 a		15 52	16 04				16 24		16 41		16 52	17 04		17 20	17 40		17 52		18 04			18 22		18 52

	SR	SR	SR 1 B		SR 1 A	SR ◇1 C	SR 1 B	SR	SR	SR 1 B	SR 1 A	SR ◇1 C	SR 1 B		SR	SR	SR 1 B	SR 1 A	SR 1 B	SR	SR	SR ◇1 D	SR 1 B	
Dunblane d	18 01					19 03		19 09							20 01					21 01		21 38		
Bridge of Allan d	18 04							19 12							20 04					21 04				
Alloa d		18 14							19 14							20 14					21 14			
Stirling d	18 10	18 25				19 09		19 17	19 25			19 58			20 10	20 25				21 10	21 25	21 43		
Larbert d	18 19	18 32				19 17		19 26	19 34						20 19	20 34				21 19	21 34	21 52		
Camelon 4 d	18 24							19 31							20 24					21 24				
Falkirk Grahamston 3 d	18 27							19 34							20 27					21 27				
Croy 3 d		18 45			19 07		19 12		19 45		20 07		20 12			20 45		21 07	21 12		21 45			
Lenzie 3 d		18 52							19 52							20 52					21 52	22 05		
Bishopbriggs d		18 56							19 56							20 56					21 56			
Glasgow Queen Street 10 a		19 05			19 22	19 41			20 05		20 22	20 32				21 05		21 23			22 05	22 18		
Polmont 3 d	18 33		18 53					19 40		19 53					20 33		20 53			21 33			21 53	
Linlithgow d	18 40		18 59				19 29	19 47		19 59			20 29		20 40		20 59		21 29	21 40			21 59	
Edinburgh Park d	18 54							20 01							20 54					21 54				
Haymarket d	19 00		19s16				19s47	20 07		20s16			20s45		21 00		21s15		21s46	22 00			22s18	
Edinburgh 10 225,242 a	19 05		19 21				19 52	20 11		20 21			20 50		21 04		21 20		21 52	22 04			22 23	

	SR 1 A	SR 1 B	SR	SR 1 B	SR 1 A	SR 1 B	SR 1 A	SR 1 B
Dunblane d			22 01					
Bridge of Allan d			22 04					
Alloa d								
Stirling d			22 10					
Larbert d			22 19					
Camelon 4 d			22 24					
Falkirk Grahamston 3 d			22 27					
Croy 3 d	22 07	22 12			23 07	23 12	23 40	23 42
Lenzie 3 d								
Bishopbriggs d								
Glasgow Queen Street 10 a	22 21				23 21		23 54	
Polmont 3 d			22 33	22 53				23 56
Linlithgow d		22 29	22 40	22 59		23 29		00 03
Edinburgh Park d			22 54					
Haymarket d		22s45	23 00	23s15		23s45		00s19
Edinburgh 10 225,242 a		22 50	23 04	23 20		23 50		00 24

A From Edinburgh
B From Glasgow Queen Street
C From Inverness
D From Aberdeen

For services between Glasgow Queen Street - Cumbernauld - Falkirk Grahamston please refer to table 224

Table 232

Glasgow Queen Street - Maryhill and Annesland

Mondays to Saturdays

9 December to 17 May

Network Diagram - refer to first Page of Table 220

Miles		SR SO	SR	SR	SR	SR	SR	SR		SR		SR	SR	SR	SR		SR	SR	SR	SR	
0	**Glasgow Queen Street** 10 ⛴ d		06 26	06 56	07 26	07 56	08 26	08 56	and every 30 minutes until	10 56		11 26	11 56	12 26	12 56	and every 30 minutes until	14 56	15 26	15 56	16 26	and every 30 minutes until
2¼	Ashfield d	00 01	06 31	07 01	07 31	08 01	08 31	09 01		11 01		11 31	12 01	12 31	13 01		15 01	15 31	16 00	16 31	
3	Possilpark & Parkhouse d	00 04	06 34	07 04	07 34	08 04	08 34	09 04		11 04		11 34	12 04	12 34	13 04		15 04	15 34	16 03	16 34	
3¼	Gilshochill d	00 06	06 36	07 06	07 36	08 06	08 36	09 06		11 06		11 36	12 06	12 36	13 06		15 06	15 36	16 05	16 36	
4¼	Summerston d	00 08	06 38	07 08	07 38	08 08	08 38	09 08		11 08		11 38	12 08	12 38	13 08		15 08	15 38	16 07	16 38	
4¾	**Maryhill** d	00 10	06 40	07 10	07 40	08 10	08 40	09 10		11 10		11 40	12 10	12 40	13 10		15 10	15 40	16 09	16 40	
5½	Kelvindale d	00 12	06 42	07 12	07 42	08 12	08 42	09 12		11 12		11 42	12 12	12 42	13 12		15 12	15 42	16 12	16 42	
6¼	**Annesland** 226 a	00 15	06 45	07 15	07 46	08 15	08 46	09 15		11 15		11 47	12 15	12 46	13 15		15 15	15 46	16 16	16 45	

	SR		SR	SR		SR	SR	SR	SR	SR FO
Glasgow Queen Street 10 ⛴ d	17 56		18 26	18 56	and every 30 minutes until	21 56	22 26	22 56	23 26	23 56
Ashfield d	18 01		18 32	19 01		22 01	22 31	23 01	23 31	00 01
Possilpark & Parkhouse d	18 04		18 35	19 04		22 04	22 34	23 04	23 34	00 04
Gilshochill d	18 06		18 37	19 06		22 06	22 36	23 06	23 36	00 06
Summerston d	18 08		18 39	19 08		22 08	22 38	23 08	23 38	00 08
Maryhill d	18 10		18 41	19 10		22 10	22 40	23 10	23 40	00 10
Kelvindale d	18 12		18 43	19 12		22 12	22 42	23 12	23 42	00 12
Annesland 226 a	18 15		18 46	19 15		22 15	22 46	23 15	23 45	00 15

No Sunday Service

Table 232R

Annesland and Maryhill - Glasgow Queen Street

Mondays to Saturdays

9 December to 17 May

Network Diagram - refer to first Page of Table 220

Miles		SR	SR	SR	SR	SR SX	SR	SR	SR		SR		SR	SR	SR	SR		SR	SR	SR	SR SO
0	**Annesland** 226 d	06 21	06 51	07 21	07 51		08 22	08 51	09 21	and every 30 minutes until	10 51		11 21	11 51	12 21	12 51	and every 30 minutes until	14 51	15 21	15 51	16 21
0¾	Kelvindale d	06 23	06 53	07 23	07 53		08 24	08 53	09 23		10 53		11 23	11 53	12 23	12 53		14 53	15 23	15 53	16 23
1½	**Maryhill** d	06 25	06 55	07 25	07 55	08 19	08 26	08 55	09 25		10 55		11 25	11 55	12 25	12 55		14 55	15 25	15 55	16 25
2	Summerston d	06 27	06 57	07 27	07 57		08 28	08 57	09 27		10 57		11 27	11 57	12 27	12 57		14 57	15 27	15 57	16 27
3	Gilshochill d	06 29	06 59	07 29	07 59		08 30	08 59	09 29		10 59		11 29	11 59	12 29	12 59		14 59	15 29	15 59	16 29
3¼	Possilpark & Parkhouse d	06 31	07 01	07 31	08 01	08 23	08 32	09 01	09 31		11 01		11 31	12 01	12 31	13 01		15 01	15 31	16 01	16 31
4	Ashfield d	06 34	07 04	07 34	08 04		08 35	09 04	09 34		11 04		11 34	12 04	12 34	13 04		15 04	15 34	16 04	16 34
6¼	**Glasgow Queen Street** 10 ⛴ a	06 40	07 10	07 41	08 10	08 37	08 43	09 11	09 40		11 10		11 41	12 12	12 41	13 10		15 10	15 41	16 10	16 40

	SR SX	SR	SR	SR	SR	SR	SR	SR	SR		SR	SR	SR	SR	SR	SR
Annesland 226 d	16 21	16 51	17 21	17 51	18 21	18 51	19 21	19 51	20 21		20 51	21 21	21 51	22 21	22 51	23 21
Kelvindale d	16 23	16 53	17 23	17 53	18 23	18 53	19 23	19 53	20 23		20 53	21 23	21 53	22 23	22 53	23 23
Maryhill d	16 25	16 55	17 25	17 55	18 25	18 55	19 25	19 55	20 25		20 55	21 25	21 55	22 25	22 55	23 25
Summerston d	16 27	16 57	17 27	17 57	18 27	18 57	19 27	19 57	20 27		20 57	21 27	21 57	22 27	22 57	23 27
Gilshochill d	16 29	16 59	17 29	17 59	18 29	18 59	19 29	19 59	20 29		20 59	21 29	21 59	22 29	22 59	23 29
Possilpark & Parkhouse d	16 31	17 01	17 31	18 01	18 31	19 01	19 31	20 01	20 31		21 01	21 31	22 01	22 31	23 01	23 31
Ashfield d	16 34	17 04	17 34	18 04	18 34	19 04	19 34	20 04	20 34		21 04	21 34	22 04	22 34	23 04	23 34
Glasgow Queen Street 10 ⛴ a	16 44	17 14	17 44	18 12	18 44	19 13	19 40	20 10	20 41		21 10	21 40	22 10	22 41	23 10	23 40

No Sunday Service

Table 238

Dunbar and North Berwick - Edinburgh and Haymarket

Mondays to Fridays

9 December to 16 May

Network Diagram - refer to first page of Table 225

Miles	Miles																							
			SR	SR	XC	SR	GR	SR	SR	SR	GR		SR	GR	SR	SR	SR	XC	SR	SR	SR		XC	SR
							R				R			R										
					◇1		1				1			1				◇1					◇1	
					A	A	B				C			D				E					F	
							⊥P				⊥P			⊥P⊥o				⊥o					⊥o	
0	—	**North Berwick** d	06 07	06 47		07 17			07 56	08 43			09 26		10 26		11 26		12 26		13 26			14 26
—	0	**Dunbar** d			07 00		07 43				08 56			09 57		10 49		11 39		12 50			13 41	
4½	10¼	Drem d	06 15	06 54		07 25			08 04	08 51			09 33		10 33		11 33		12 33		13 33			14 33
9	14¾	Longniddry d	06 21	07 00		07 31			08 10	08 56			09 39		10 39		11 39		12 39		13 39			14 39
12½	18¼	Prestonpans d	06 26	07 05		07 36		08 07	08 15	09 01			09 44		10 44		11 44		12 44		13 44			14 44
14¾	20½	Wallyford d	06 29	07 08		07 40		08 10	08 19	09 04			09 47		10 47		11 47		12 47		13 47			14 47
17	22¾	Musselburgh d	06 33	07 12		07 44		08 15	08 23	09 09			09 51		10 51	11 09	11 51		12 51	13 09	13 51			14 51
22¼	28	**Edinburgh** 10 225,230,242 a	06 40	07 19	07 22	07 52	08 07	08 22	08 33	09 16	09 21		10 01	10 20	11 01	11 15	12 00	12 03	13 00	13 16	14 01		14 10	15 02
—	—	d			07 26	07 54			08 36					10 28										
23½	29¼	**Haymarket** 225,230,242 a			07 29	07 58			08 41					10 31										

	SR	SR	XC	SR	SR	SR	XC		SR	SR	SR	SR	XC	SR	SR	XC	GR		SR
																	R		
			◇1				◇1						◇1			◇1	1		
			F				G		A				H			F	I		
			⊥o				⊥o						⊥o			⊥o	⊥P⊥o		
North Berwick d		15 26		16 26		17 26			17 53	18 26	19 01	19 26		20 26	21 26				22 26
Dunbar d	15 04		15 41		17 02		17 43						19 45			21 48	22 03		
Drem d		15 33		16 33		17 33				18 33	19 09	19 33		20 33	21 33				22 33
Longniddry d		15 39		16 39		17 39				18 39	19 14	19 39		20 39	21 39				22 39
Prestonpans d		15 44		16 44		17 44				18 44	19 19	19 44		20 44	21 44				22 44
Wallyford d		15 47		16 47		17 47				18 47	19 22	19 47		20 47	21 47				22 47
Musselburgh d	15 24	15 51		16 51	17 22	17 51			18 10	18 51	19 26	19 51		20 51	21 51				22 51
Edinburgh 10 225,230,242 a	15 36	16 01	16 05	17 02	17 28	18 00	18 07		18 19	19 02	19 34	20 01	20 09	20 59	21 59	22 13	22 28		23 00
d					17 29		18 11		18 26				20 14						
Haymarket 225,230,242 a					17 32		18 14		18 29				20 16						

Saturdays

14 December to 17 May

	SR	SR	GR	SR	GR	SR	SR	GR	SR		SR	SR	SR	XC	SR	SR	SR	SR	SR		XC	SR	SR	SR
			R		R			R																
			1		1			1						◇1							◇1			
		A	B		C			D						E							F			
			⊥P⊥o		⊥P⊥o			⊥P⊥o						⊥o							⊥o			
North Berwick d	06 07	07 17		08 21		09 21	09 50		10 21		10 50		11 21		11 50	12 21	12 50		13 21			13 50	14 21	14 50
Dunbar d			07 50		08 57			09 57				11 05		11 39				13 05			13 39			
Drem d	06 15	07 25		08 27		09 27	09 57		10 27		10 57		11 27		11 57	12 27	12 57		13 27			13 57	14 27	14 57
Longniddry d	06 21	07 31		08 33		09 33	10 03		10 33		11 03		11 33		12 03	12 33	13 03		13 33			14 03	14 33	15 03
Prestonpans d	06 26	07 36		08 38		09 38	10 08		10 38		11 08		11 38		12 08	12 38	13 08		13 38			14 08	14 38	15 08
Wallyford d	06 29	07 40		08 41		09 41	10 11		10 41		11 11		11 41		12 11	12 41	13 11		13 41			14 11	14 41	15 11
Musselburgh d	06 33	07 44		08 45		09 45	10 15		10 45		11 15	11 28	11 45		12 15	12 45	13 15	13 28	13 45			14 15	14 45	15 15
Edinburgh 10 225,230,242 a	06 40	07 52	08 15	08 55	09 21	09 52	10 21	10 24	10 54		11 23	11 36	11 54	12 07	12 21	12 56	13 22	13 38	13 54		14 06	14 23	14 54	15 23
d		07 54						10 28																
Haymarket 225,230,242 a		07 58						10 31																

	SR	SR	XC	SR	SR		SR	SR	SR	XC	SR	SR	SR	SR	XC		SR	SR	XC	GR	SR
																				R	
			◇1							◇1					◇1				◇1	1	
			F							J	A				H				F	I	
			⊥o							⊥o					⊥o				⊥o	⊥P⊥o	
North Berwick d		15 21		15 50	16 21		16 50		17 21		17 50	18 21	18 50	19 21			20 21	21 21			22 21
Dunbar d	15 04		15 39					17 07		17 39					19 41				21 44	22 14	
Drem d		15 27		15 57	16 27		16 57		17 27		17 57	18 27	18 57	19 27			20 27	21 27			22 27
Longniddry d		15 33		16 03	16 33		17 03		17 33		18 03	18 33	19 03	19 33			20 33	21 33			22 33
Prestonpans d		15 38		16 08	16 38		17 08		17 38		18 08	18 38	19 08	19 38			20 38	21 38			22 38
Wallyford d		15 41		16 11	16 41		17 11		17 41		18 11	18 41	19 11	19 41			20 41	21 41			22 41
Musselburgh d	15 24	15 45		16 15	16 45		17 15	17 30	17 45		18 15	18 45	19 15	19 45			20 45	21 45			22 45
Edinburgh 10 225,230,242 a	15 37	15 54	16 04	16 23	16 56		17 24	17 37	17 57	18 03	18 23	18 56	19 23	19 54	20 05		20 54	21 54	22 08	22 38	22 54
d										18 11	18 26				20 14						
Haymarket 225,230,242 a										18 14	18 29				20 17						

A To Glasgow Central
B From Newcastle
C From Doncaster
D From Leeds to Aberdeen
E From Birmingham New Street
F From Plymouth
G From Plymouth to Aberdeen. ⊥o to Edinburgh
H From Plymouth to Dundee. ⊥o to Edinburgh
I From London Kings Cross
J From Plymouth to Aberdeen

Table 238

Sundays

8 December to 11 May

Dunbar and North Berwick - Edinburgh and Haymarket

Network Diagram - refer to first page of Table 225

		SR	GR	SR	SR	XC		GR	SR	SR	XC	SR	SR
			R					R					
			1			◇1		1			◇1		
			A			B		C			D		
			[restaurant] [trolley]			[trolley]		[restaurant] [trolley]			[trolley]		
North Berwick	d	11 20		12 20	13 20				14 20	15 20		16 20	17 20
Dunbar	d		11 33			13 33		13 54			15 40		
Drem	d	11 27		12 27	13 27				14 27	15 29		16 27	17 27
Longniddry	d	11 33		12 33	13 33				14 33	15 35		16 33	17 33
Prestonpans	d	11 38		12 38	13 38				14 38	15 40		16 38	17 38
Wallyford	d	11 41		12 41	13 41				14 41	15 43		16 41	17 41
Musselburgh	d	11 45		12 45	13 45				14 45	15 47		16 45	17 45
Edinburgh 10 225,230,242	a	11 53	11 58	12 53	13 53	13 57		14 18	14 53	15 53	16 02	16 53	17 53
	d												
Haymarket 225,230,242	a												

		XC	SR	SR		XC	SR	GR	SR	XC	XC	SR	GR
								R					R
		◇1				◇1		1		◇1	◇1		1
		E				F		G		H	I		C
		[trolley]				[trolley]		[restaurant] [trolley]		[trolley]			[restaurant] [trolley]
North Berwick	d		18 20	19 20			20 20		21 20			22 20	
Dunbar	d	17 33				19 35		20 53		21 47	21 47		23 14
Drem	d		18 27	19 27			20 27		21 27			22 27	
Longniddry	d		18 33	19 33			20 33		21 33			22 33	
Prestonpans	d		18 38	19 38			20 38		21 38			22 38	
Wallyford	d		18 41	19 41			20 41		21 41			22 41	
Musselburgh	d		18 45	19 45			20 45		21 45			22 45	
Edinburgh 10 225,230,242	a	17 57	18 53	19 53		19 57	20 53	21 16	21 53	22 12	22 12	22 53	23 39
	d	18 13						21 22					
Haymarket 225,230,242	a	18 16						21 25					

A From Leeds
B until 9 February, from 30 March. From Birmingham New Street
C From London Kings Cross
D From Bristol Temple Meads
E From Plymouth to Aberdeen. [trolley] to Edinburgh
F From Penzance
G From London Kings Cross to Glasgow Central
H until 23 March. From Exeter St Davids
I from 30 March. From Plymouth

Table 238R

Mondays to Fridays

9 December to 16 May

Haymarket and Edinburgh - North Berwick and Dunbar

Network Diagram - refer to first page of Table 225

Miles	Miles			GR	XC	SR	SR	SR	XC	SR	SR	SR	XC	SR	SR	SR	XC	SR	SR	SR	XC	SR	SR
				R 1	◇1				◇1				R ◇1				◇1				◇1		
				A	B			C	B				D				E				E		
				restaurant, trolley	trolley				trolley				trolley				trolley				trolley		
0	0	**Haymarket** 225,230,242	d		06 57			08 23	08 51				10 51										
1¼	1¼	**Edinburgh** 10 225,230,242	a		07 02			08 28	08 56				10 55										
—	—		d	05 48	07 07	07 13	08 14	08 46	09 08	09 43	10 13	10 43	11 06	11 43	12 11	12 43	13 06	13 43	14 11	14 43	15 08	15 43	16 33
6½	6½	Musselburgh	d			07 19	08 20	08 52		09 49	10 19	10 49		11 49	12 17	12 49		13 49	14 17	14 49		15 49	16 39
8¾	8¾	Wallyford	d			07 23		08 56		09 53		10 53		11 53		12 53		13 53		14 53		15 53	
11	11	Prestonpans	d			07 26		08 59		09 56		10 56		11 56		12 56		13 56		14 56		15 56	
14½	14½	Longniddry	d			07 31		09 04		10 01		11 01		12 01		13 01		14 01		15 01		16 01	
19	19	Drem	d			07 36		09 11		10 06		11 06		12 06		13 06		14 06		15 06		16 06	
—	29¼	**Dunbar**	a	06 08	07 26				09 27		10 38		11 25		12 36		13 26		14 36		15 27		16 58
23½	—	**North Berwick**	a			07 47	08 38	09 19		10 16		11 16		12 17		13 16		14 16		15 16		16 16	

		SR	XC	SR	GR	SR	XC	SR	GR	SR	SR	XC	SR	GR	SR	SR FX	SR FO	SR
			◇1		R 1		◇1		R 1			◇1		R 1				
			F	C	G		H		A			I		J				
			trolley		restaurant, trolley		trolley		restaurant, trolley					restaurant				
Haymarket 225,230,242	d			17 05	17 21	17 42	17 53			18 41		19 53		20 46				
Edinburgh 10 225,230,242	a			17 09	17 26	17 47	17 57			18 46		19 57		20 50				
	d	16 41	17 08	17 14	17 31	17 48	18 05	18 14	18 30	18 48	19 43	20 02	20 43	21 00	21 43	22 06	23 02	23 13
Musselburgh	d	16 47		17 20		17 54		18 20		18 54	19 49		20 49		21 49	22 12	23 10	23 18
Wallyford	d	16 51		17 25		17 58		18 24		18 59	19 53		20 53		21 53			23 22
Prestonpans	d	16 54		17 28		18 01		18 27		19 02	19 56		20 56		21 56			23 25
Longniddry	d	16 59		17 33		18 06		18 32		19 08	20 01		21 01		22 01			23 30
Drem	d	17 05		17 39		18 12		18 38		19 14	20 06		21 06		22 06			23 36
Dunbar	a		17 27		17 51		18 24		18 50			20 21		21 20		22 41	23 34	
North Berwick	a	17 14		17 48		18 21		18 47		19 22	20 16		21 16		22 17			23 56

Saturdays

14 December to 17 May

		GR	XC	SR	SR	XC	SR	SR	SR	SR	SR	XC	SR	SR	SR	SR	SR	XC	SR	SR	SR	SR	SR
		R 1	◇1			◇1						◇1						◇1					
		A	B		C	B						K						E					
		restaurant, trolley	trolley			trolley						trolley						trolley					
Haymarket 225,230,242	d		06 57		08 23	08 51						10 52											
Edinburgh 10 225,230,242	a		07 02		08 28	08 56						10 58											
	d	06 20	07 07	07 43	08 39	09 08	09 12	09 43	10 08	10 12	10 43	11 08	11 12	11 43	12 08	12 12	12 43	13 09	13 12	13 43	14 08	14 12	14 43
Musselburgh	d			07 49	08 48		09 18	09 48	10 15	10 18	10 48		11 18	11 48	12 15	12 18	12 48		13 18	13 48	14 15	14 18	14 48
Wallyford	d			07 53	08 52		09 22	09 52		10 22	10 52		11 22	11 52		12 22	12 52		13 22	13 52		14 22	14 52
Prestonpans	d			07 56	08 55		09 25	09 55		10 25	10 55		11 25	11 55		12 25	12 55		13 25	13 55		14 25	14 55
Longniddry	d			08 01	09 00		09 30	10 00		10 30	11 00		11 30	12 00		12 30	13 00		13 30	14 00		14 30	15 00
Drem	d			08 06	09 06		09 36	10 06		10 36	11 06		11 36	12 06		12 36	13 06		13 36	14 06		14 36	15 06
Dunbar	a	06 40	07 26			09 27			10 38			11 27			12 38			13 28			14 38		
North Berwick	a			08 16	09 16		09 45	10 16		10 45	11 16		11 45	12 16		12 45	13 16		13 46	14 16		14 45	15 16

		XC	SR	SR	SR	SR	SR	XC	SR	GR	SR	XC	SR	SR	GR	SR	SR	SR	SR	SR
		◇1						◇1		R 1		◇1			R 1					
		L						M	C	G		H			N					
		trolley						trolley		restaurant, trolley		trolley			restaurant, trolley					
Haymarket 225,230,242	d								17 05	17 21		17 53								
Edinburgh 10 225,230,242	a								17 09	17 26		17 57								
	d	15 08	15 12	15 43	16 08	16 12	16 43	17 08	17 12	17 30	17 43	18 08	18 12	18 43	19 00	19 43	20 43	21 43	22 06	23 13
Musselburgh	d		15 18	15 48	16 15	16 18	16 48		17 18		17 48		18 18	18 49		19 48	20 48	21 48	22 12	23 18
Wallyford	d		15 22	15 52		16 22	16 52		17 22		17 52		18 22	18 53		19 52	20 52	21 52		23 22
Prestonpans	d		15 25	15 55		16 25	16 55		17 25		17 55		18 25	18 56		19 55	20 55	21 55		23 25
Longniddry	d		15 30	16 00		16 30	17 00		17 30		18 00		18 30	19 00		20 00	21 00	22 00		23 30
Drem	d		15 36	16 06		16 36	17 06		17 36		18 06		18 36	19 06		20 06	21 06	22 06		23 37
Dunbar	a	15 27			16 38			17 28		17 50		18 27			19 20				22 31	
North Berwick	a		15 45	16 16		16 46	17 16		17 45		18 16		18 45	19 16		20 16	21 16	22 17		23 56

- **A** To London Kings Cross
- **B** From Glasgow Central to Plymouth. trolley from Edinburgh
- **C** From Glasgow Central
- **D** From Aberdeen to Penzance. trolley ◇ from Edinburgh R to Edinburgh
- **E** To Plymouth
- **F** To Bristol Temple Meads
- **G** From Aberdeen to London Kings Cross
- **H** From Glasgow Central to Birmingham New Street. trolley from Edinburgh
- **I** From Glasgow Central to Newcastle
- **J** From Aberdeen to Leeds
- **K** From Aberdeen to Penzance. trolley from Edinburgh
- **L** To Exeter St Davids
- **M** To Birmingham New Street
- **N** To Doncaster

Table 238R

Sundays

8 December to 11 May

Haymarket and Edinburgh - North Berwick and Dunbar

Network Diagram - refer to first page of Table 225

		SR	XC	SR	SR	XC	SR	SR	XC	XC	SR	SR	XC	GR	SR	XC	SR	GR	SR	GR	XC	SR	GR
														R				R		R			R
			◇1			◇1			◇1	◇1			◇1	1		◇1		1		1	◇1		1
			A			B			C	D			E	F		G		F		H	I		J
			[trolley]			[trolley]			[trolley]	[trolley]			[trolley]	[restaurant/trolley]		[trolley]		[restaurant/trolley]		[restaurant/trolley]			[restaurant/trolley]
Haymarket	225,230,242 d	.	.	.	.	12 49	.	.	14⌇42	14⌇42	.	.	.	.	.	17 51	.	.	.	.	19 51	.	.
Edinburgh 10	225,230,242 a	.	.	.	.	12 54	.	.	14⌇47	14⌇47	.	.	.	.	.	17 56	.	.	.	.	19 55	.	.
	d	10 33	11 05	11 33	12 33	13 08	13 33	14 33	15⌇08	15⌇08	15 33	16 33	17 08	17 30	17 33	18 08	18 33	19 00	19 33	20 00	20 15	20 33	21 00
Musselburgh	d	10 39	.	11 39	12 39	.	13 39	14 39	⌇	⌇	15 39	16 39	.	.	17 39	.	18 39	.	19 39	.	.	20 39	.
Wallyford	d	10 43	.	11 43	12 43	.	13 43	14 43	⌇	⌇	15 43	16 43	.	.	17 43	.	18 43	.	19 43	.	.	20 43	.
Prestonpans	d	10 46	.	11 46	12 46	.	13 46	14 46	⌇	⌇	15 46	16 46	.	.	17 46	.	18 46	.	19 46	.	.	20 46	.
Longniddry	d	10 51	.	11 51	12 51	.	13 51	14 51	⌇	⌇	15 51	16 51	.	.	17 51	.	18 51	.	19 51	.	.	20 51	.
Drem	d	10 56	.	11 56	12 56	.	13 56	14 56	⌇	⌇	15 56	16 56	.	.	17 56	.	18 56	.	19 56	.	.	20 56	.
Dunbar	a	.	11 24	.	.	13 27	.	.	15⌇27	15⌇27	.	.	17 27	17 50	.	18 27	.	19 20	.	20 20	20 34	.	21 20
North Berwick	a	11 06	.	12 06	13 06	.	14 06	15 06	.	.	16 06	17 06	.	.	18 06	.	19 06	.	20 06	.	.	21 06	.

		SR
Haymarket	225,230,242 d	.
Edinburgh 10	225,230,242 a	.
	d	21 33
Musselburgh	d	21 39
Wallyford	d	21 43
Prestonpans	d	21 46
Longniddry	d	21 51
Drem	d	21 56
Dunbar	a	.
North Berwick	a	22 06

A To Reading
B From Glasgow Central to Reading. [trolley] from Edinburgh
C until 23 March. From Glasgow Central to Guildford
D from 30 March. From Glasgow Central to Plymouth. [trolley] from Edinburgh
E To Birmingham New Street
F To London Kings Cross
G From Glasgow Central to Birmingham New Street. [trolley] from Edinburgh
H To Leeds
I From Glasgow Central to Newcastle
J To Newcastle

Table 239

Mondays to Saturdays

9 December to 28 March

Network Diagram - refer to first Page of Table 227

Inverness - Kyle of Lochalsh, Thurso and Wick

Miles	Miles			SR	SR	SR	SR		SR	SR	SR	SR		SR	SR	SR	SR		SR	SR	SR	SR			
				SO	SO	SX				SX	SO											FSO			
					◇	◇	◇		◇	◇	◇			◇	◇				◇	◇					
						A																			
					🛒	🛒			🛒						🛒				🛒						
—	—	Glasgow Queen Street 229	d						*07 10*	*07 10*	*07 10*	*08c41*		*10 10*	*10 10*	*10c41*	*13c41*		*13c41*		*17c41*	*19c41*			
—	—	Edinburgh 229	d						*06c33*	*06c33*	*06c33*	*08 34*		*09c35*	*09c35*	*10 36*	*13 35*		*13 35*		*17 41*	*19 44*			
—	—	Aberdeen 240	d						*08 19*	*08 19*	*08 19*			*10 13*	*10 13*	*12 00*	*13 38*		*15 27*		*18 20*	*20 12*			
0	0	**Inverness**	d		07 04	07 04	08 58		10 37	10 58	10 58	12 17		13 33	14 00	14 42	17 13		17 54		21 08	23 30			
10	10	Beauly	d		07 18	07 18	09 12		10 51	11 12	11 12	12 31		13 47	14 14	14 56	17 27		18 08		21 22	23 44			
13	13	Muir of Ord	d		07 27	07 27	09 18		10 57	11 18	11 21	12 37		13 53	14 20	15 02	17 34		18 14		21 28	23 50			
16	16	Conon Bridge	d		07 33	07 33	09 24		11 02	11 24	11 26	12 43		13 58	14 25	15 07	17 40		18 19		21 34	23 55			
18¾	18¾	Dingwall	d	00 02	07 43	07 43	09 32		11 09	11 31	11 32	12a49		14 04	14 33	15 14	17 48		18 27	18 30	21 41	00 02			
—	30½	Garve	d				09 54			11 52	11 53			14 26						18 52					
—	36	Lochluichart	d				10x01			12x00	12x01			14x33						18x59					
—	40¼	Achanalt	d				10x07			12x06	12x07			14x39						19x05					
—	46½	Achnasheen	d				10 19			12 19	12 20			14 51						19 17					
—	59¼	Achnashellach	d				10x36			12x35	12x36			15x08						19x34					
—	64½	Strathcarron	d				10 47			12 46	12 49			15 19						19 45					
—	67	Attadale	d				10x51			12x50	12x53			15x23						19x49					
—	72	Stromeferry	d				11 04			13 04	13 07			15 36						20 03					
—	75¾	Duncraig	d				11x11			13x11	13x14			15x43						20x10					
—	77	Plockton	d				11 16			13 16	13 19			15 48						20 14					
—	78½	Duirinish	d				11x18			13x18	13x21			15x50						20x16					
—	82¼	**Kyle of Lochalsh**	a				11 28			13 28	13 31			16 00						20 26					
28½	—	Alness	d	00 14	07 55	07 55			11 20						14 45	15 26	17 59		18 39		21 53	00 14			
31½	—	Invergordon	d	00 19	08 01	08 01			11 27						14 50	15a31	18 04		18 44		21 58	00 19			
40¾	—	Fearn	d	00 30	08 12	08 12			11 39						15 01		18 16		18 56		22 09	00 30			
44¼	—	Tain	d	00a36	08 18	08 18			11 45						15 07		18 23		19 02		22a15	00a36			
57¾	—	Ardgay	d		08 33	08 33			12 00						15 24		18a39		19 18						
61	—	Culrain	d		08x37	08x37			12x04						15x28				19x22						
61½	—	Invershin	d		08x38	08x38			12x05						15x29				19x23						
67	—	Lairg	d		08 55	08 55			12 18						15 43				19 37						
77	—	Rogart	d		09x08	09x08			12x31						15x55				19x54						
84½	—	Golspie	d		09 20	09 20			12 43						16 07				20 05						
87	—	Dunrobin Castle §	d																						
90½	—	Brora	d		09 30	09 30			12 54						16 18				20 15						
101½	—	Helmsdale	d		09 50	09 50			13 09						16 33				20 30						
111	—	Kildonan	d		10x01	10x01			13x21						16x44				20x41						
118¼	—	Kinbrace	d		10x11	10x11			13x30						16x54				20x51						
125¾	—	Forsinard	d		10 23	10 23			13 44						17 08				21 03						
134	—	Altnabreac	d		10x32	10x32			13x53										21x12						
143	—	Scotscalder	d		10x41	10x41			14x02						17x26				21x21						
147¼	—	Georgemas Junction	a		10 50	10 50			14 11						17 35				21 30						
—	—		d		10 52	10 52			14 13						17 37				21 32						
154	—	**Thurso**	a		11 02	11 02			14 23						17 47				21 42						
—	—		d		11 04	11 04			14 25						17 49				21 44						
160¾	—	Georgemas Junction	d		11 14	11 14			14 35						17 59				21 54						
175	—	**Wick**	a		11 32	11 32			14 52						18 16				22 11						

§ Open 30 March until 27 October

A 🛒 from Lairg

c Change at Perth for connection to Inverness

f Change at Stirling

Table 239

Mondays to Saturdays

29 March to 17 May

Network Diagram - refer to first Page of Table 227

Inverness - Kyle of Lochalsh, Thurso and Wick

		SR SO	SR SO	SR SX	SR	SR	SR SX	SR SO	SR	SR	SR	SR	SR	SR	SR	SR	SR FSO
			◇	◇	◇	◇	◇	◇		◇	◇			◇	◇		
				A													
			🛒	🛒		🛒					🛒			🛒			
Glasgow Queen Street 229	d					*07 10*	*07 10*	*07 10*	*08c41*				*13c41*	*13c41*		*17c41*	*19c41*
Edinburgh 229	d					*06c33*	*06c33*	*06c33*	*08 34*				*13 35*	*13 35*		*17 41*	*19 44*
Aberdeen 240	d					*08 19*	*08 19*	*08 19*					*13 38*	*15 27*		*18 20*	*20 12*
Inverness	d		07 04	07 04	08 58	10 37	10 58	10 58	12 17	13 33	14 00	14 42	17 13	17 54		21 08	23 30
Beauly	d		07 18	07 18	09 12	10 51	11 12	11 12	12 31	13 47	14 14	14 56	17 27	18 08		21 22	23 44
Muir of Ord	d		07 27	07 27	09 18	10 57	11 18	11 21	12 37	13 53	14 20	15 02	17 34	18 14		21 28	23 50
Conon Bridge	d		07 33	07 33	09 24	11 02	11 24	11 26	12 43	13 58	14 25	15 07	17 40	18 19		21 34	23 55
Dingwall	d	00 02	07 43	07 43	09 32	11 09	11 31	11 32	12a49	14 04	14 33	15 14	17 48	18 27	18 30	21 41	00 02
Garve	d				09 54		11 52	11 53		14 26					18 52		
Lochluichart	d				10x01		12x00	12x01		14x33					18x59		
Achanalt	d				10x07		12x06	12x07		14x39					19x05		
Achnasheen	d				10 19		12 19	12 20		14 51					19 17		
Achnashellach	d				10x36		12x35	12x36		15x08					19x34		
Strathcarron	d				10 47		12 46	12 49		15 19					19 45		
Attadale	d				10x51		12x50	12x53		15x23					19x49		
Stromeferry	d				11 04		13 04	13 07		15 36					20 03		
Duncraig	d				11x11		13x11	13x14		15x43					20x10		
Plockton	d				11 16		13 16	13 19		15 48					20 14		
Duirinish	d				11x18		13x18	13x21		15x50					20x16		
Kyle of Lochalsh	a				11 28		13 28	13 31		16 00					20 26		
Alness	d	00 14	07 55	07 55		11 20					14 45	15 26	17 59	18 39		21 53	00 14
Invergordon	d	00 19	08 01	08 01		11 27					14 50	15a31	18 04	18 44		21 58	00 19
Fearn	d	00 30	08 12	08 12		11 39					15 01		18 16	18 56		22 09	00 30
Tain	d	00a36	08 18	08 18		11 45					15 07		18 23	19 02		22a15	00a36
Ardgay	d		08 33	08 33		12 00					15 24		18a39	19 18			
Culrain	d		08x37	08x37		12x04					15x28			19x22			
Invershin	d		08x38	08x38		12x05					15x29			19x23			
Lairg	d		08 55	08 55		12 18					15 43			19 37			
Rogart	d		09x08	09x08		12x31					15x55			19x54			
Golspie	d		09 20	09 20		12 43					16 07			20 05			
Dunrobin Castle §	d		09x22	09x22		12x46					16x10						
Brora	d		09 30	09 30		12 54					16 18			20 15			
Helmsdale	d		09 50	09 50		13 09					16 33			20 30			
Kildonan	d		10x01	10x01		13x21					16x44			20x41			
Kinbrace	d		10x11	10x11		13x30					16x54			20x51			
Forsinard	d		10 23	10 23		13 44					17 08			21 03			
Altnabreac	d		10x32	10x32		13x53								21x12			
Scotscalder	d		10x41	10x41		14x02					17x26			21x21			
Georgemas Junction	a		10 50	10 50		14 11					17 35			21 30			
	d		10 52	10 52		14 13					17 37			21 32			
Thurso	a		11 02	11 02		14 23					17 47			21 42			
	d		11 04	11 04		14 25					17 49			21 44			
Georgemas Junction	d		11 14	11 14		14 35					17 59			21 54			
Wick	a		11 32	11 32		14 52					18 16			22 11			

§ Open 30 March until 27 October

A 🛒 from Lairg

c Change at Perth for connection to Inverness

f Change at Stirling

Table 239

Sundays

8 December to 11 May

Network Diagram - refer to first Page of Table 227

Inverness - Kyle of Lochalsh, Thurso and Wick

			SR		SR	SR	SR	SR		SR	SR
						◇				◇	
			A							🚲	
Glasgow Queen Street	229	d					*09c37*	*11 10*		*14c40*	*16f15*
Edinburgh	229	d					*09 33*	*10f35*		*13 56*	*16 32*
Aberdeen	240	d					*10 00*	*13 00*		*15 22*	*18 01*
Inverness		d			10 00	11 00	13 02	15 23		17 54	21 08
Beauly		d			10 14	11 14	13 16	15 37		18 08	21 22
Muir of Ord		d			10 20	11 21	13 22	15 43		18 14	21 28
Conon Bridge		d			10 26	11 27	13 27	15 48		18 20	21 34
Dingwall		d	00 02		10 33	11 34	13 33	15 54		18 27	21 41
Garve		d				11 55					
Lochluichart		d				12x03					
Achanalt		d				12x09					
Achnasheen		d				12 21					
Achnashellach		d				12x37					
Strathcarron		d				12 48					
Attadale		d				12x52					
Stromeferry		d				13 06					
Duncraig		d				13x13					
Plockton		d				13 18					
Duirinish		d				13x20					
Kyle of Lochalsh		a				13 30					
Alness		d	00 14		10 45		13 45	16 06		18 39	21 53
Invergordon		d	00 19		10 50		13 50	16a11		18 44	21 58
Fearn		d	00 30		11 01		14 01			18 56	22 09
Tain		d	00a36		11a07		14a07			19 02	22a15
Ardgay		d								19 18	
Culrain		d								19x22	
Invershin		d								19x23	
Lairg		d								19 37	
Rogart		d								19x54	
Golspie		d								20 05	
Dunrobin Castle §		d									
Brora		d								20 15	
Helmsdale		d								20 30	
Kildonan		d								20x41	
Kinbrace		d								20x51	
Forsinard		d								21 03	
Altnabreac		d								21x12	
Scotscalder		d								21x21	
Georgemas Junction		a								21 30	
		d								21 32	
Thurso		a								21 42	
		d								21 44	
Georgemas Junction		d								21 54	
Wick		a								22 11	

§ Open 30 March until 27 October

c Change at Perth for connection to Inverness

f Change at Stirling

Table 239R

Mondays to Saturdays

9 December to 28 March

Network Diagram - refer to first Page of Table 227

Wick, Thurso and Kyle of Lochalsh - Inverness

Miles	Miles			SR	SR	SR	SR	SR	SR	SR	SR	SR	SR	SR	SR	SR	SR	SR
							SX	SO										
						◇	◇	◇	◇		◇		◇	◇	◇	◇		
								A										
								⊥	⊥				⊥			⊥		
0	—	**Wick**	d				06 20	06 20	08 12				12 36			16 00		
14¼	—	Georgemas Junction	d				06 37	06 37	08 29				12 53			16 17		
21	—	**Thurso**	a				06 46	06 46	08 38				13 02			16 26		
—	—		d				06 49	06 49	08 41				13 05			16 29		
27¾	—	Georgemas Junction	a				06 59	06 59	08 50				13 14			16 38		
—	—		d				07 01	07 01	08 53				13 17			16 41		
32	—	Scotscalder	d				07x06	07x06					13x22			16x46		
41	—	Altnabreac	d				07x15	07x15					13x31			16x55		
49¼	—	Forsinard	d				07 27	07 27	09 16				13 43			17 07		
56¾	—	Kinbrace	d				07x36	07x36					13x52			17x16		
64	—	Kildonan	d				07x47	07x47					14x02			17x25		
73½	—	Helmsdale	d				08 01	08 01	09 48				14 16			17 40		
84½	—	Brora	d				08 16	08 16	10 03				14 31			17 55		
88	—	Dunrobin Castle §	d															
90½	—	Golspie	d				08 26	08 26	10 12				14 41			18 04		
98	—	Rogart	d				08x34	08x34	10x20				14x49			18x12		
108	—	Lairg	d		06 33		08 55	08 55	10 38				15 08			18 30		
113½	—	Invershin	d		06x40		09x02	09x02					15x15			18x38		
114	—	Culrain	d		06x41		09x03	09x03					15x16			18x39		
117¼	—	Ardgay	d	06 21	06 49		09 11	09 11	10 53				15 24			18 46	19 23	
130¾	—	Tain	d	06 37	07 04		09 26	09 26	11 09				15 39			19 03	19 38	22 20
134¼	—	Fearn	d	06 43	07 10		09 32	09 32					15 45			19 09	19 44	22 25
143½	—	Invergordon	d	06 55	07 22		09 44	09 44	11 26			15 39	15 57			19 20	19 55	22 37
146½	—	Alness	d	07 01	07 27		09 49	09 49	11 32			15 44	16 02			19 25	20 01	22 42
—	0	**Kyle of Lochalsh**	d			06 20					12 05			14 37	17 14			
—	3¾	Duirinish	d			06x26					12x11			14x43	17x21			
—	5¼	Plockton	d			06 32					12 16			14 49	17 25			
—	6½	Duncraig	d			06x33					12x18			14x50	17x28			
—	10¼	Stromeferry	d			06 43					12 28			15 00	17 37			
—	15¼	Attadale	d			06x54					12x38			15x11	17x48			
—	17¾	Strathcarron	d			07 01					12 46			15 20	17 54			
—	23	Achnashellach	d			07x09					12x55			15x28	18x03			
—	35¾	Achnasheen	d			07 30					13 15			15 47	18 22			
—	42	Achanalt	d			07x39					13x24			15x56	18x32			
—	46¼	Lochluichart	d			07x46					13x30			16x03	18x38			
—	51¾	Garve	d			07 56					13 41			16 15	18 53			
156¼	63½	Dingwall	d	07 13	07 42	08 19	10 04	10 04	11 47	12 54	14 04	15 56	16 14	16 36	19 16	19 39	20 15	22 55
159¼	66¼	Conon Bridge	d	07 19	07 47	08 25	10 09	10 09		13 00	14 11	16 02	16 20	16 42	19 22	19 44	20 22	23 00
162	69¼	Muir of Ord	d	07 26	07 55	08 32	10 15	10 15	11 58	13 07	14 21	16 09	16 28	16 50	19 29	19 51	20 29	23 08
164¾	72¼	Beauly	d	07 32	08 01	08 38	10 21	10 21		13 13	14 26	16 15	16 34	16 55	19 35	19 56	20 35	23 13
175	82¼	**Inverness**	a	07 46	08 15	08 52	10 35	10 35	12 15	13 27	14 40	16 29	16 48	17 09	19 57	20 10	20 49	23 27
—	—	Aberdeen 240	a		*11 25*	*11 25*	*13 13*	*13 13*	*14 55*	*16 42*	*17 45*		*19 38*	*19 38*	*23 43*	*23 43*	*23 43*	
—	—	Edinburgh 229	a	*11 17*	*12c22*	*13 23*	*14 24*	*14 24*	*16 22*		*18c26*		*21c20*	*21c20*	*00f11*	*00f11*		
—	—	Glasgow Queen Street 229	a	*11c14*	*12 09*	*13c14*	*14c14*	*14c14*	*16c14*		*18 09*		*20 45*	*20 45*	*23 43*	*23 43*		

§ Open 30 March until 27 October

A ⊥ to Lairg

c Change at Perth

f Change at Stirling

Table 239R

Mondays to Saturdays

29 March to 17 May

Network Diagram - refer to first Page of Table 227

Wick, Thurso and Kyle of Lochalsh - Inverness

		SR	SR	SR	SR SX	SR SO	SR	SR	SR	SR	SR	SR	SR	SR	SR	SR
				◇	◇	◇	◇		◇		◇	◇	◇	◇		
						A 🛒	🛒				🛒			🛒		
Wick	d				06 20	06 20	08 12				12 36			16 00		
Georgemas Junction	d				06 37	06 37	08 29				12 53			16 17		
Thurso	a				06 46	06 46	08 38				13 02			16 26		
	d				06 49	06 49	08 41				13 05			16 29		
Georgemas Junction	a				06 59	06 59	08 50				13 14			16 38		
	d				07 01	07 01	08 53				13 17			16 41		
Scotscalder	d				07x06	07x06					13x22			16x46		
Altnabreac	d				07x15	07x15					13x31			16x55		
Forsinard	d				07 27	07 27	09 16				13 43			17 07		
Kinbrace	d				07x36	07x36					13x52			17x16		
Kildonan	d				07x47	07x47					14x02			17x25		
Helmsdale	d				08 01	08 01	09 48				14 16			17 40		
Brora	d				08 16	08 16	10 03				14 31			17 55		
Dunrobin Castle §	d						10x08				14x36			18x00		
Golspie	d				08 26	08 26	10 12				14 41			18 04		
Rogart	d				08x34	08x34	10x20				14x49			18x12		
Lairg	d		06 33		08 55	08 55	10 38				15 08			18 30		
Invershin	d		06x40		09x02	09x02					15x15			18x38		
Culrain	d		06x41		09x03	09x03					15x16			18x39		
Ardgay	d	06 21	06 49		09 11	09 11	10 53				15 24			18 46	19 23	
Tain	d	06 37	07 04		09 26	09 26	11 09				15 39			19 03	19 38	22 20
Fearn	d	06 43	07 10		09 32	09 32					15 45			19 09	19 44	22 25
Invergordon	d	06 55	07 22		09 44	09 44	11 26			15 39	15 57			19 20	19 55	22 37
Alness	d	07 01	07 27		09 49	09 49	11 32			15 44	16 02			19 25	20 01	22 42
Kyle of Lochalsh	d			06 20					12 05			14 37	17 14			
Duirinish	d			06x26					12x11			14x43	17x21			
Plockton	d			06 32					12 16			14 49	17 25			
Duncraig	d			06x33					12x18			14x50	17x28			
Stromeferry	d			06 43					12 28			15 00	17 37			
Attadale	d			06x54					12x38			15x11	17x48			
Strathcarron	d			07 01					12 46			15 20	17 54			
Achnashellach	d			07x09					12x55			15x28	18x03			
Achnasheen	d			07 30					13 15			15 47	18 22			
Achanalt	d			07x39					13x24			15x56	18x32			
Lochluichart	d			07x46					13x30			16x03	18x38			
Garve	d			07 56					13 41			16 15	18 53			
Dingwall	d	07 13	07 42	08 19	10 04	10 04	11 47	12 54	14 04	15 56	16 15	16 36	19 16	19 39	20 15	22 55
Conon Bridge	d	07 19	07 47	08 25	10 09	10 09		13 00	14 11	16 02	16 21	16 42	19 22	19 44	20 22	23 00
Muir of Ord	d	07 26	07 55	08 32	10 15	10 15	11 58	13 07	14 21	16 09	16 28	16 50	19 29	19 51	20 29	23 08
Beauly	d	07 32	08 01	08 38	10 21	10 21		13 13	14 26	16 15	16 34	16 55	19 35	19 56	20 35	23 13
Inverness	a	07 46	08 15	08 52	10 35	10 35	12 15	13 27	14 40	16 29	16 48	17 09	19 57	20 10	20 49	23 27
Aberdeen 240	a		11 25	11 25	13 13	13 13	14 55	16 42	17 45		19 38	19 38	23 43	23 43	23 43	
Edinburgh 229	a	11 17	12c22	13 23	14 24	14 24	16 22		18c26		21c20	21c20	00f11	00f11		
Glasgow Queen Street 229	a	11c14	12 09	13c14	14c14	14c14	16c14		18 09		20 45	20 45	23 43	23 43		

§ Open 30 March until 27 October

A 🛒 to Lairg

c Change at Perth

f Change at Stirling

Table 239R

Sundays

8 December to 11 May

Network Diagram - refer to first Page of Table 227

Wick, Thurso and Kyle of Lochalsh - Inverness

		SR	SR	SR	SR	SR	SR	SR
				◇	◇		◇	
				A	B			
				⚮	⚮			
Wick	d			11 51	11 51			
Georgemas Junction	d			12 08	12 08			
Thurso	a			12 17	12 17			
	d			12 20	12 20			
Georgemas Junction	a			12 29	12 29			
	d			12 32	12 32			
Scotscalder	d			12x37	12x37			
Altnabreac	d			12x46	12x46			
Forsinard	d			12 58	12 58			
Kinbrace	d			13x07	13x07			
Kildonan	d			13x17	13x17			
Helmsdale	d			13 31	13 31			
Brora	d			13 46	13 46			
Dunrobin Castle §	d				13x51			
Golspie	d			13 56	13 56			
Rogart	d			14x04	14x04			
Lairg	d			14 22	14 22			
Invershin	d			14x29	14x29			
Culrain	d			14x30	14x30			
Ardgay	d			14 37	14 37			
Tain	d	11 12	14 12	14 53	14 53			22 20
Fearn	d	11 17	14 17	14 58	14 58			22 25
Invergordon	d	11 29	14 29	15 10	15 10	16 20		22 37
Alness	d	11 34	14 34	15 15	15 15	16 25		22 42
Kyle of Lochalsh	d						15 20	
Duirinish	d						15x26	
Plockton	d						15 32	
Duncraig	d						15x33	
Stromeferry	d						15 43	
Attadale	d						15x54	
Strathcarron	d						16 01	
Achnashellach	d						16x09	
Achnasheen	d						16 28	
Achanalt	d						16x37	
Lochluichart	d						16x44	
Garve	d						16 54	
Dingwall	d	11 48	14 47	15 29	15 29	16 38	17 16	22 55
Conon Bridge	d	11 53	14 51	15 35	15 35	16 42	17 22	23 00
Muir of Ord	d	12 01	14 58	15 43	15 43	16 49	17 29	23 08
Beauly	d	12 06	15 03	15 50	15 50	16 54	17 35	23 13
Inverness	a	12 20	15 17	16 04	16 04	17 08	17 49	23 27
Aberdeen 240	a	*14 46*	*17 39*			*19 28*	*23 13*	
Edinburgh 229	a	*16 44*	*18 36*	*20f11*	*20f11*	*22 19*	*22 19*	
Glasgow Queen Street 229	a	*15 58*		*19 41*	*19 41*	*22c18*	*22c18*	

§ Open 30 March until 27 October
A until 23 March
B from 30 March
c Change at Perth
f Change at Stirling

Table 239A

Scrabster - Stromness (Orkney Isles)

This ferry service is operated by Serco NorthLink ferries Ltd. Unfortunately, details of sailing times for 2014 had not been confirmed at time of print. Please telephone 0845 6000 449 or visit www.northlinkferries.co.uk for details

Customers holding Rail & Sail tickets to/from Stromness should note that a connecting taxi service between Thurso Railway Station and Scrabster is included. Taxis can be booked by calling 01847 893 434 as soon as possible after ticket purchase, but no later than Helmsdale on northbound journeys and prior to departing Stromness on southbound journeys. Staff will assist if you do not have a mobile phone

Taxis are also available for hire by other passengers. Normal fares will apply

Table 239B

Mondays to Saturdays

9 December to 3 April

Ullapool - Stornoway (Lewis), Uig (Skye), Tarbert (Harris) and Lochmaddy (North Uist)

Operated by Caledonian MacBrayne Ltd. in association with ScotRail

			MWF O		TSO	ThO		SX	TSO	MWF O		SO
Edinburgh 10	229	d						10 35	09b35	09b35		11b35
Glasgow Queen Street 10	229	d						10b41	10 10	10 10		12 10
Inverness	229	a						14c10	13 28	13 28		15c21
Inverness	239	d	08 58		08 58	08 58			13 33	13 33		
Kyle of Lochalsh	239	a	11e28		11e28	11e28			16f00	16f00		
Inverness		d						15 00				15 40
Ullapool		a						16 20				17 00
Ullapool		d						17 35				18 15
Stornoway		a						20 20				21 00
Uig		d	14 00		14 00	15 00			18 00	18 00		
Tarbert		a	15 40			16 40			19 40			
Lochmaddy		a			15 45					19 45		

Sundays

8 December to 30 March

Edinburgh 10	229	d	10k35
Glasgow Queen Street 10	229	d	11 10
Inverness	229	a	14c27
Inverness	239	d	
Kyle of Lochalsh	239	a	
Inverness		d	15 40
Ullapool		a	17 00
Ullapool		d	18 15
Stornoway		a	21 00
Uig		d	
Tarbert		a	
Lochmaddy		a	

b change at Perth

c Passengers make their own way between rail station and bus station (5 minute walk)

e Bus connection dep. Kyle of Lochalsh 1215, Uig arr. 1350

f Bus connection dep. Kyle of Lochalsh 1615, Uig arr. 1750

k Change at Stirling

For details of sailings from 4 April 2014 please telephone 08000 66 5000 or visit www.calmac.co.uk

Table 239B-R

Mondays to Saturdays

9 December to 3 April

Lochmaddy (North Uist), Tarbert (Harris), Uig (Skye), Stornoway (Lewis - Ullapool)

Operated by Caledonian MacBrayne Ltd. in association with ScotRail

					MWF O	TThS O	TSO	MWF O	ThO		SX	SO
Lochmaddy		d				07 30		11 50	12 00			
Tarbert		d			07 30		11 50					
Uig		a			09g10	09g15	13h30	13h35	13h45			
Stornoway		d	07 00								13 50	14 30
Ullapool		a	09 45								16 35	17 15
Ullapool		d	09 50								16 40	17 20
Inverness		a	11c10								18c00	18c40
Kyle of Lochalsh	239	d			12 05	12 05	17 14	17 14	17 14			
Inverness	239	a			14 40	14 40	19 57	19 57	19 57			
Inverness	229	d	12 53		14 47	14 47	20 15	20 15	20 15		18 46	20 15
Glasgow Queen Street 10	229	a	16b14		18 09	18 09	23 43	23 43	23 43		22b20	23 43
Edinburgh 10	229	a	16 22		18b26	18b26	00k11	00k11	00k11		22 19	00k11

b change at Perth

c Passengers make their own way between rail station and bus station (5 minute walk)

g Bus connection dep. Uig 0930, Kyle of Lochalsh arr. 1114

h Bus connection dep. Uig 1445, Kyle of Lochalsh arr. 1619

k Change at Stirling

No rail connected Sunday service from Lochmaddy or Tarbert to Uig or from Stornoway to Ullapool

For details of sailings from 4 April 2014 please telephone 08000 66 5000 or visit www.calmac.co.uk

Table 240

Aberdeen and Elgin - Inverness

Mondays to Saturdays

9 December to 17 May

Network Diagram - refer to first page of Table 225

Miles	Station		SR	SR	SR	SR	SR	SR	SR	SR	SR
			◇1	◇1	◇1	◇1	1	◇1	◇1	◇1	◇1
						A	B		C	D	
											Trolley
0	**Aberdeen**	d			06 14	07 15	07 48	08 19	08 52	09 58	10 13
6¼	Dyce (airport)	d			06 23	07 27	07 57	08 30	09a01	10 07	10 22
17	**Inverurie**	a			06 35	07 40	08 11	08 42		10 21	10 34
—		d			06 39	07 42		08 43			10 34
27½	Insch	d			06 51	07 54		08 56			10 47
40¾	Huntly	d			07 12	08 11		09 12			11 03
53¼	Keith	d			07 26	08 25		09 26			11 18
71¼	**Elgin**	d	06 58	07 23	07 52	08 46		09 48			11 40
83½	Forres	d	07 11	07 43	08 05	09 01		10 02			11 53
93¼	Nairn	d	07 27	07 54	08 16	09 17		10 13			12 04
108¼	**Inverness**	a	07 45	08 12	08 36	09 35		10 31			12 22

Miles	Station		SR	SR	SR	SR	SR	SR	SR	SR	SR	SR	SR	SR
									SO					
			◇1	◇1	1	◇1	◇1	◇1	◇1	1	◇1	◇1	◇1	◇1
			D				D		D	E	E	D		F
				Trolley		Trolley		Trolley					Trolley	
0	**Aberdeen**	d	11 03	12 00	12 50	13 38	14 57	15 27	15 52	16 44	17 21	17 54	18 20	19 10
6¼	Dyce (airport)	d	11 14	12 09	13 01	13 47	15 05	15 37	16 01	16a52	17 33	18 04	18 29	19 26
17	**Inverurie**	a	11 28	12 21	13 15	13 59	15 19	15 49	16 16		17 45	18 19	18 41	19 40
—		d		12 21		13 59		15 49			17 48		18 43	
27½	Insch	d		12 34		14 12		16 02			18 00		18 55	
40¾	Huntly	d		12 50		14 28		16 18			18 17		19 11	
53¼	Keith	d		13 05		14 43		16 37			18 31		19 25	
71¼	**Elgin**	d		13 29		15 08		16 59			18 55		19 47	
83½	Forres	d		13 42		15 22		17 15			19 09		20 01	
93¼	Nairn	d		13 53		15 45		17 32			19 20		20 18	
108¼	**Inverness**	a		14 13		16 03		17 48			19 39		20 36	

Station		SR	SR	SR	SR
		◇1	1	◇1	1
				D	
		Trolley			
Aberdeen	d	20 12	20 55	21 56	22 50
Dyce (airport)	d	20 21	21 05	22 05	22 59
Inverurie	a	20 33	21 19	22 17	23 13
	d	20 33		22 17	
Insch	d	20 45		22 29	
Huntly	d	21 05		22 49	
Keith	d	21 19		23 04	
Elgin	d	21 40		23 25	
Forres	d	22 04		23 38	
Nairn	d	22 15		23 49	
Inverness	a	22 33		00 07	

Sundays

8 December to 11 May

Station		SR	SR	SR	SR	SR	SR	SR	SR	SR	SR	SR
		◇1	1	1	◇1	1	◇1	1	1	◇1	1	◇1
		Trolley			Trolley		Trolley			Trolley		Trolley
Aberdeen	d	10 00	10 35	12 25	13 00	14 26	15 22	15 50	16 48	18 01	20 35	21 27
Dyce (airport)	d	10 09	10 43	12 33	13 09	14 36	15 31	15 58	16 56	18 11	20 44	21 36
Inverurie	a	10 21	10 57	12 47	13 21	14 50	15 43	16 12	17 11	18 23	20 58	21 48
	d	10 21			13 21		15 43			18 23		21 48
Insch	d	10 34			13 34		15 56			18 36		22 01
Huntly	d	10 50			13 51		16 12			18 58		22 22
Keith	d	11 08			14 06		16 34			19 13		22 36
Elgin	d	11 29			14 27		16 55			19 35		22 57
Forres	d	11 42			14 40		17 09			19 49		23 11
Nairn	d	11 53			14 51		17 30			20 00		23 22
Inverness	a	12 11			15 09		17 49			20 18		23 40

A From Dundee
B From Perth
C From Glasgow Queen Street
D From Edinburgh
E not 25 December, 26 December, 1 January, 2 January
F not 25 December, 26 December, 1 January, 2 January. From Edinburgh

Table 240R

Mondays to Saturdays

9 December to 17 May

Network Diagram - refer to first page of Table 225

Inverness and Elgin - Aberdeen

Miles			SR	SR	SR	SR	SR	SR	SR	SR	SR	SR	SR	SR	SR	SR	SR	SR	SR	SR	SR	SR	SR
				SO																			
			◇1	◇1	◇1	1	◇1	◇1	◇1	◇1	◇1	◇1	1	◇1	◇1	◇1	◇1	1	◇1	1	◇1	◇1	◇
			A	B		C	D		A		A				A		E	F			A		A
					trolley					trolley		trolley		trolley		trolley			trolley			trolley	
0	**Inverness**	d	04 53		05 54			07 09		09 00		10 57		12 46		14 27			15 29			17 15	
15	Nairn	d	05 08		06 09			07 25		09 16		11 14		13 01		14 42			15 46			17 31	
24¾	Forres	d	05 19		06 20			07 36		09 27		11 25		13 12		14 53			15 57			17 42	
37	**Elgin**	d	05 33		06 34			07 50		09 49		11 41		13 30		15 09			16 11			17 59	
55	Keith	d	05 54		06 55			08 11		10 09		12 02		13 49		15 30			16 32			18 20	
67½	Huntly	d	06 09		07 11			08 38		10 23		12 16		14 03		15 45			16 51			18 44	
80¾	Insch	d	06 25		07 27			08 57		10 48		12 35		14 19		16 03			17 06			18 59	
91¼	**Inverurie**	a	06 37		07 41			09 08		10 59		12 46		14 30		16 14			17 18			19 12	
—		d	06 38	07 13	07 43	08 16		09 10	10 38	11 00	11 33	12 47	13 33	14 31	15 24	16 17	16 38		17 18	17 51	18 42	19 12	19 45
102	Dyce ✈	d	06 50	07 26	07 59	08 29	09 08	09 23	10 50	11 13	11 45	13 02	13 48	14 43	15 38	16 30	16 53	17 05	17 34	18 05	18 55	19 27	19 56
108¼	**Aberdeen**	a	07 02	07 37	08 10	08 42	09 19	09 34	11 01	11 25	11 56	13 13	13 59	14 55	15 49	16 42	17 04	17 16	17 45	18 17	19 07	19 38	20 08

		SR	SR	SR	SR
		◇1	◇1	1	◇1
			G		
Inverness	d	18 13	20 01		21 33
Nairn	d	18 28	20 17		21 48
Forres	d	18 39	20 28		21 58
Elgin	d	18 56	20a44		22 13
Keith	d	19 18			22 34
Huntly	d	19 38			22 51
Insch	d	19 54			23 06
Inverurie	a	20 06			23 19
	d	20 06		21 24	23 19
Dyce ✈	d	20 22		21 37	23 32
Aberdeen	a	20 34		21 49	23 43

Sundays

8 December to 11 May

		SR	SR	SR	SR	SR	SR	SR	SR	SR	SR	SR	SR	SR
		◇1	◇1	1	◇1	1	1	◇1	1	◇1	◇1	1	◇1	◇1
		B						B			H			H
			trolley		trolley			trolley		trolley	trolley		trolley	trolley
Inverness	d		09 59		12 33			15 29		17 13	18 00		21 03	21 42
Nairn	d		10 14		12 48			15 44		17 29	18 15		21 18	21 57
Forres	d		10 25		12 59			15 55		17 40	18 26		21 29	22 08
Elgin	d		10 39		13 13			16 09		17 54	18a41		21 43	22a23
Keith	d		11 00		13 34			16 31		18 15			22 05	
Huntly	d		11 20		13 52			16 46		18 35			22 21	
Insch	d		11 36		14 08			17 02		18 51			22 37	
Inverurie	a		11 48		14 19			17 13		19 03			22 48	
	d	11 02	11 48	12 55	14 20	14 58	16 20	17 14	17 30	19 03		21 22	22 49	
Dyce ✈	d	11 14	12 01	13 09	14 35	15 10	16 32	17 28	17 42	19 17		21 35	23 01	
Aberdeen	a	11 25	12 12	13 20	14 46	15 21	16 43	17 39	17 53	19 28		21 47	23 13	

A To Edinburgh
B To Glasgow Queen Street
C not 25 December, 26 December, 1 January, 2 January
D not 25 December, 26 December, 1 January, 2 January. To Glasgow Queen Street
E not 25 December, 26 December, 1 January, 2 January. To Edinburgh
F not 25 December, 26 December, 1 January, 2 January. To Stonehaven
G From Kyle of Lochalsh
H From Glasgow Queen Street

Table 242

Mondays to Saturdays

9 December to 17 May

Newcraighall and Edinburgh - Dunfermline, Kirkcaldy and Glenrothes with Thornton

Network Diagram - refer to first page of Table 225

Miles	Miles			SR MX ◇ A	SR ◇1 B	SR SX	SR	SR SO ◇ C	SR SX ◇1 C	SR SO	SR SX	SR ◇ C		SR	SR SX	SR SO	SR ◇1 D	SR ◇ E	SR	SR ◇1 C	SR	SR		SR ◇1 F	SR
0	—	**Newcraighall**	d				06 02								06 57	06 59			07 26			07 56			
0¾	—	Brunstane	d				06 05								07 00	07 03			07 30			07 59			
4¾	0	**Edinburgh** 10	a				06 14								07 07	07 15			07 37			08 09			
—	—		d		05 30	06 07	06 16	06 33	06 33	06 37	06 37	07 00		07 08	07 17	07 17	07 28	07 33	07 38	08 00	08 07	08 10		08 34	08 39
6	1¼	Haymarket	d		05 34	06 11	06 20	06 37	06 37	06 41	06 41	07 04		07 13	07 21	07 21	07 32	07 38	07 42	08 04	08 11	08 15		08 38	08 42
9¼	4½	South Gyle	d			06 18	06 25			06 47	06 47			07 17	07 27	07 27			07 47		08 17	08 22			08 47
14¼	9½	Dalmeny	d			06 24	06 31			06 54	06 54			07 24	07 34	07 34			07 53			08 28			08 53
16	11¼	North Queensferry	d			06 28	06 35			06 58	06 58			07 27	07 38	07 38			07 57			08 32			08 57
18	13¼	Inverkeithing	d		05 47	06 32	06 39	06 50	06 50	07 02	07 02	07 20		07 31	07 41	07 41		07 53	08 01	08 17	08 28	08 36			09 01
—	14¾	Rosyth	d				06 42								07 45	07 45						08 39			
—	17	**Dunfermline Town**	d				06 47								07 50	07 50						08 44			
—	18½	Dunfermline Queen Margaret	d				06 51								07 54	07 54						08 48			
—	22½	Cowdenbeath	d				06 57								08 00	08 00						08 54			
—	24¾	Lochgelly	d	00 06			07 03								08 06	08 06						09 00			
—	27	Cardenden	d	00 10			07 07								08 10	08 10						09 04			
19½	—	Dalgety Bay	d			06 35				07 05	07 05			07 34					08 04		08 31				09 04
22¼	—	Aberdour	d			06 40				07 10	07 10			07 39					08 09		08 36				09 09
25	—	Burntisland	d			06 44				07 14	07 18			07 43					08 13		08 40				09 13
27½	—	Kinghorn	d			06 49				07 19	07 23			07 48					08 18		08 45				09 18
30¾	—	Kirkcaldy	d		06a03	06a56		07a06	07a06	07 24	07 29	07a36		07 53			08a03	08a09	08 23	08a33	08 50			09a07	09 23
39¾	31¾	Glenrothes With Thornton 2	a	00 16			07 16			07 35	07 41			08 06	08 19	08 19			08 35		09 01	09 13			09 36

		SR	SR ◇1 C	SR	SR	SR ◇ E	SR	SR		SR ◇1 C	SR	SR	GR R 1 G	SR	SR	VT SO ◇1 H	SR SO ◇1 C	SR SX ◇ C		SR	SR	SR ◇ E	SR	SR	SR ◇1 C
Newcraighall	d	08 35					09 20				09 47			10 17						10 47			11 17		
Brunstane	d	08 39					09 23				09 50			10 20						10 50			11 20		
Edinburgh 10	a	08 46					09 35				09 57			10 28						10 57			11 28		
	d	08 48	09 00	09 08	09 18	09 35	09 39	09 50		10 00	10 08	10 18	10 28	10 39	10 48	10ʃ52	11 00	11 00		11 08	11 18	11 35	11 39	11 48	12 00
Haymarket	d	08 52	09 04	09 12	09 23	09 40	09 44	09 54		10 04	10 15	10 23	10 33	10 42	10 52	10a56	11 04	11 04		11 12	11 23	11 40	11 42	11 52	12 04
South Gyle	d	08 57		09 17	09 27		09 50	09 57			10 20	10 27		10 47	10 57					11 17	11 27		11 47	11 57	
Dalmeny	d	09 04		09 23	09 34		09 57	10 04			10 26	10 34		10 53	11 04					11 23	11 34		11 53	12 04	
North Queensferry	d	09 07		09 27	09 38		10 00	10 07			10 30	10 38		10 57	11 07					11 27	11 38		11 57	12 07	
Inverkeithing	d	09 11	09 17	09 31	09 41	09 54	10 04	10 11		10 17	10 34	10 41	10 48	11 01	11 11		11 17	11 17		11 31	11 41	11 54	12 01	12 11	12 17
Rosyth	d	09 15			09 45			10 15				10 45			11 15						11 45			12 15	
Dunfermline Town	d	09 20			09 50			10 20				10 50			11 20						11 50			12 20	
Dunfermline Queen Margaret	d	09 23			09 54			10 23				10 54			11 23						11 54			12 23	
Cowdenbeath	d	09 30			10a03			10 30				11a03			11 30						12a03			12 30	
Lochgelly	d	09 35						10 35							11 35									12 35	
Cardenden	d	09 39						10 39							11 39									12 39	
Dalgety Bay	d			09 34			10 07				10 37			11 04						11 34			12 04		
Aberdour	d			09 39			10 12				10 42			11 09						11 39			12 09		
Burntisland	d			09 43			10 16				10 46			11 13						11 43			12 13		
Kinghorn	d			09 48			10 21				10 51			11 18						11 48			12 18		
Kirkcaldy	d		09a33	09 53		10a09	10 26			10a33	10 56		11a04	11 23			11a33	11a33		11 53		12a10	12 23		12a33
Glenrothes With Thornton 2	a	09 49		10 04			10 36	10 51			11 07			11 36	11 49					12 06			12 36	12 49	

		SR	SR	SR ◇ E		SR	SR	VT SO ◇1 H	SR ◇1 C	SR	SR	SR	SR	SR ◇1 C		SR	SR	GR R 1 I	SR ◇ E	SR SO	SR SX	SR	VT SO ◇1 H	SR ◇1 C	
Newcraighall	d	11 47				12 17				12 47		13 17				13 47				14 17	14 17				
Brunstane	d	11 50				12 20				12 50		13 20				13 50				14 20	14 20				
Edinburgh 10	a	11 57				12 28				12 57		13 28				13 57				14 29	14 29				
	d	12 08	12 18	12 35		12 39	12 48	12ʃ52	13 00	13 08	13 18	13 39	13 48	14 00		14 08	14 18	14 28	14 35	14 39	14 39	14 48	14ʃ52	15 00	
Haymarket	d	12 12	12 23	12 40		12 42	12 52	12a56	13 04	13 12	13 23	13 42	13 52	14 04		14 12	14 23	14 33	14 40	14 45	14 45	14 52	14a56	15 04	
South Gyle	d	12 17	12 27			12 47	12 57			13 17	13 27	13 47	13 57			14 17	14 27			14 50	14 50	14 57			
Dalmeny	d	12 23	12 34			12 53	13 04			13 23	13 34	13 53	14 04			14 23	14 34			14 56	14 56	15 04			
North Queensferry	d	12 27	12 38			12 57	13 07			13 27	13 38	13 57	14 07			14 27	14 38			15 00	15 00	15 07			
Inverkeithing	d	12 31	12 41	12 54		13 01	13 11		13 17	13 31	13 41	14 01	14 11	14 17		14 31	14 41	14 48	14 54	15 04	15 04	15 11		15 17	
Rosyth	d		12 45				13 15				13 45		14 15				14 45					15 15			
Dunfermline Town	d		12 50				13 20				13 50		14 20				14 50					15 20			
Dunfermline Queen Margaret	d		12 54				13 23				13 54		14 23				14 54					15 23			
Cowdenbeath	d		13a03				13 30				14a03		14 30				15a03					15 30			
Lochgelly	d						13 35						14 35									15 35			
Cardenden	d						13 39						14 39									15 39			
Dalgety Bay	d	12 34				13 04				13 34		14 04				14 34				15 07	15 07				
Aberdour	d	12 39				13 09				13 39		14 09				14 39				15 12	15 12				
Burntisland	d	12 43				13 13				13 43		14 13				14 43				15 16	15 16				
Kinghorn	d	12 48				13 18				13 48		14 18				14 48				15 20	15 21				
Kirkcaldy	d	12 53		13a10		13 23			13a33	13 53		14 23		14a33		14 53		15a03	15a10	15 25	15 26			15a33	
Glenrothes With Thornton 2	a	13 06				13 37	13 49			14 05		14 36	14 51			15 04				15 36	15 38	15 49			

A From Edinburgh to Perth
B To Aberdeen
C To Dundee
D To Inverurie
E To Perth
F To Inverness
G From Leeds to Aberdeen
H from 4 January until 8 February. To Carlisle
I From London Kings Cross to Aberdeen. The Northern Lights

Table 242

Mondays to Saturdays

9 December to 17 May

Newcraighall and Edinburgh - Dunfermline, Kirkcaldy and Glenrothes with Thornton

Network Diagram - refer to first page of Table 225

		SR	SR	SR	SR	SR		SR	SR	SR	SR	SR	SR	SR	VT	SR		SR	SR	SR	SR	SR	SR	SR	SR
								SO	SX					SO	SO	SX		SO	SX	SX	SO		SO	SX	
				◇				◇1	◇						◇1				1						◇1
				A				B	B			A			C			B	B						D
Newcraighall	d	14 47			15 17					15 47			16 17									16 47	17 08		
Brunstane	d	14 50			15 20					15 50			16 20									16 50	17 11		
Edinburgh 10	a	14 57			15 28					15 57			16 28									16 59	17 18		
	d	15 08	15 18	15 35	15 39	15 48		16 00	16 00	16 08	16 18	16 33	16 42	16 49	16ʃ52	16 53		17 00	17 00	17 08	17 08	17 11	17 18	17 18	17 41
Haymarket	d	15 12	15 23	15 40	15 45	15 52		16 04	16 04	16 12	16 23	16 37	16 46	16 54	16a56	16 57		17 04	17 04	17 12	17 12	17 16	17 23	17 23	17u46
South Gyle	d	15 17	15 27		15 50	15 57				16 17	16 27		16 51	16 59		17 02				17 18	17 17	17 23	17 31	17 31	
Dalmeny	d	15 23	15 34		15 57	16 04				16 23	16 34		16 58	17 05		17 08						17 30	17 38	17 38	
North Queensferry	d	15 27	15 38		16 00	16 07				16 27	16 38		17 02	17 09		17 12						17 33	17 42	17 42	
Inverkeithing	d	15 31	15 41	15 54	16 04	16 11		16 17	16 17	16 31	16 41	16 53	17 06	17 13		17 16		17 22	17 22	17 29	17 29	17 37	17 47	17 47	
Rosyth	d		15 45			16 15					16 45			17 17		17 20				17 33	17 33		17 50	17 52	
Dunfermline Town	d		15 50			16 20					16 50			17 22		17 25				17 37	17 38		17 55	17 57	
Dunfermline Queen Margaret	d		15 54			16 23					16 54			17 25		17 28				17 42	17 42		17 59	18 03	
Cowdenbeath	d		16a03			16 30					17a03			17a34		17a37				17 49	17 49		18 05	18 10	
Lochgelly	d					16 35														17 55	17 55		18 11	18 17	
Cardenden	d					16 39														17 58	17 58		18 15	18a23	
Dalgety Bay	d	15 34			16 07					16 34			17 09									17 40			
Aberdour	d	15 39			16 12					16 39			17 14									17 45			
Burntisland	d	15 43			16 16					16 43			17 18									17 50			
Kinghorn	d	15 48			16 21					16 48			17 23									17 55			
Kirkcaldy	d	15 53		16a10	16 26			16a33	16a33	16 53		17a08	17 28					17a37	17a37			18a02			18a14
Glenrothes With Thornton 2	a	16 06			16 37	16 49				17 05			17 39							18 13	18 08		18 24		

		SR		SR	SR	SR	XC	XC	SR	SR	SR	SR		GR	SR	SR	SR	VT	SR	SR	SR	SR		SR	SR
		SO		SX	SX	SX	SO	SX		SX	SX	SO				SX	SO	SO	SO	SX					
														R											
						◇	◇1	◇1						1	◇			◇1	◇1	◇				◇1	
						B	E	E		F				G	A			C	B	B				D	
Newcraighall	d	17 37			17 37						18 03	18 08				18 34	18 34					19 06			19 38
Brunstane	d	17 40			17 41						18 06	18 12				18 37	18 37					19 10			19 41
Edinburgh 10	a	17 47			17 48						18 13	18 19				18 50	18 48					19 17			19 49
	d	17 48		17 48	17 50	18 00	18 11	18 11	18 15		18 25	18 25		18 33	18 40	18 50	18 50	18ʃ52	19 00	19 00	19 11	19 22		19 44	19 50
Haymarket	d	17 53		17 53	17 56	18 04	18 15	18 15	18 19		18 30	18 30		18 38	18 46	18 54	18 54	18a55	19 04	19 04	19 16	19 26		19 48	19 55
South Gyle	d	17 58		17 58	18 02				18 24		18 35	18 35				18 59	18 59				19 20	19 31			19 59
Dalmeny	d	18 04		18 04	18 09				18 30	18 36	18 41	18 41				19 05	19 05				19 27	19 37			20 06
North Queensferry	d	18 08		18 08	18 12				18 34		18 45	18 45				19 09	19 09				19 30	19 41			20 09
Inverkeithing	d	18 12		18 12	18 16	18 23	18 29	18 29	18 38	18 43	18 49	18 49		18 55	19 02	19 13	19 13		19 17	19 17	19 34	19 45		20 01	20 13
Rosyth	d				18 20						18 52	18 52				19 16	19 16					19 48			20 17
Dunfermline Town	d				18 25						18 57	18 57				19 21	19 21					19 53			20 22
Dunfermline Queen Margaret	d				18 28						19 01	19 01				19 25	19 25					19 57			20 25
Cowdenbeath	d				18 35						19 07	19 07				19 31	19 31					20 03			20 32
Lochgelly	d				18 40						19 13	19 13				19 37	19 37					20 09			20 37
Cardenden	d				18 44						19 17	19 17				19 41	19 41					20 13			20 41
Dalgety Bay	d	18 15		18 15					18 41	18 46											19 37				
Aberdour	d	18 20		18 20					18 46	18 51											19 42				
Burntisland	d	18 24		18 24					18 50	18 55											19 46				
Kinghorn	d	18 29		18 29					18 55	19 00											19 51				
Kirkcaldy	d	18 34		18 34		18a39	18a43	18a46	19 00	19a04				19a11	19a19				19a33	19a33	19a59			20a17	
Glenrothes With Thornton 2	a	18 45		18 45	18 54				19 11		19 26	19 26				19 51	19 51					20 22			20 51

		SR	XC	XC	SR	SR	GR	SR		SR	SR	SR	SR	SR	SR	SR	SR	SR		SR	SR				
			SX	SO	SO	SX	SX													SO	SX				
							R																		
		◇	◇1	◇1			1	◇			◇	◇1		◇		◇	◇	◇							
		B	H	H			G	A			B	I	A	B		A	B	A							
Newcraighall	d				20 08	20 08				20 38			21 33		22 35					23 36	23 36				
Brunstane	d				20 11	20 11				20 40			21 36		22 38					23 39	23 39				
Edinburgh 10	a				20 19	20 19				20 49			21 43		22 46					23 48	23 48				
	d	20 00	20 14	20 14	20 22	20 25	20 32	20 45		20 52	21 08	21 40	21 48	22 08		22 38	23 08	23 18		23 48	23 51				
Haymarket	d	20 04	20 17	20 18	20a28	20a30	20 37	20 49		20 56	21 13	21 44	21 52	22 13		22 43	23 13	23 23		23a52	23a55				
South Gyle	d	20 09								21 01	21 18		21 57	22 18		22 48	23 18	23 27							
Dalmeny	d	20 15								21 07	21 24		22 04	22 24		22 54	23 24	23 34							
North Queensferry	d	20 19								21 11	21 28		22 07	22 28		22 58	23 28	23 38							
Inverkeithing	d	20 23	20a30	20 35			20 52	21 03		21 15	21 32		22 11	22 32		23 02	23 32	23 41							
Rosyth	d									21 18			22 15					23 45							
Dunfermline Town	d									21 23			22 20					23 50							
Dunfermline Queen Margaret	d									21 27			22 23					23 54							
Cowdenbeath	d									21 33			22 30					23 59							
Lochgelly	d									21 39			22 35					00 06							
Cardenden	d									21 43			22 39					00 10							
Dalgety Bay	d	20 26									21 35			22 35		23 05	23 35								
Aberdour	d	20 31									21 40			22 40		23 10	23 40								
Burntisland	d	20 35									21 44			22 44		23 14	23 44								
Kinghorn	d	20 40									21 49			22 49		23 19	23 49								
Kirkcaldy	d	20a44		20a50			21a08	21a18			21a53	22a12		22a54		23a23	23a53								
Glenrothes With Thornton 2	a									21 52			22 46					00 16							

A To Perth
B To Dundee
C from 4 January until 8 February. To Carlisle
D To Inverness
E From Plymouth to Aberdeen
F From Glasgow Queen Street to Markinch
G From London Kings Cross to Aberdeen
H From Plymouth to Dundee
I To Aberdeen

Table 242

Sundays

8 December to 11 May

Newcraighall and Edinburgh - Dunfermline, Kirkcaldy and Glenrothes with Thornton

Network Diagram - refer to first page of Table 225

		SR	XC	GR	SR	SR	SR	SR	SR	VT	SR	SR	SR	SR	SR	SR	VT	SR	SR	SR	SR	SR	SR
		◇ A	◇ B	[R] [1] B catering	◇[1] B	◇[1] C catering			◇[1] B catering	◇[1] D catering			◇ E			◇[1] B catering	◇[1] D catering			◇ E	◇[1] C catering		
Newcraighall	d																						
Brunstane	d																						
Edinburgh [10]	a																						
	d		08 04	09 10	09 15	09 33	09 55	10 15	10 50	10⟆51	10 55	11 15	11 34	11 55	12 15	12 40	12⟆51	12 55	13 15	13 31	13 56	14 00	14 15
Haymarket	d		08 08	09 15	09 19	09 37	09 59	10 19	10 54	10a54	10 59	11 19	11 38	11 59	12 19	12 44	12a54	12 59	13 19	13 35	14 00	14 04	14 19
South Gyle	d				09 24		10 04	10 24			11 04	11 24		12 04	12 24			13 04	13 24			14 09	14 24
Dalmeny	d				09 30		10 10	10 30			11 10	11 30		12 10	12 30			13 10	13 30			14 15	14 30
North Queensferry	d				09 34		10 14	10 34			11 14	11 34		12 14	12 34			13 14	13 34			14 19	14 34
Inverkeithing	d		08 25	09 33	09 38	09 53	10 18	10 38	11 07		11 18	11 38	11 52	12 18	12 38	12 57		13 18	13 38	13 49	14 14	14 23	14 38
Rosyth	d						10 21				11 21			12 21				13 21				14 26	
Dunfermline Town	d						10 26				11 26			12 26				13 26				14 31	
Dunfermline Queen Margaret	d						10 30				11 30			12 30				13 30				14 35	
Cowdenbeath	d						10 36				11 36			12 36				13 36				14 41	
Lochgelly	d	00⟆06					10 42				11 42			12 42				13 42				14 47	
Cardenden	d	00⟆10					10 46				11 46			12 46				13 46				14 51	
Dalgety Bay	d				09 41			10 41				11 41			12 41				13 41				14 41
Aberdour	d				09 46			10 46				11 46			12 46				13 46				14 46
Burntisland	d				09 50			10 50				11 50			12 50				13 50				14 50
Kinghorn	d				09 55			10 54				11 54			12 54				13 54				14 54
Kirkcaldy	d		08a39	09a48	10a00	10a09		10 59	11a23			11 59	12a07		12 59	13a13			13 59	14a07	14a30		14 59
Glenrothes With Thornton [2]	a	00⟆16					10 58	11 10			11 55	12 10		12 57	13 11			13 55	14 10			15 00	15 13

		GR	SR	SR	SR	SR	SR	SR	SR	SR	SR	SR	SR	SR	SR	XC	SR	GR	SR	SR	SR	SR
		[R] [1] F catering			E	◇[1] C catering		◇[1] B			◇[1] B catering		E	◇[1] G		◇[1] H		[R] [1] I catering	◇ G	◇ J		
Newcraighall	d																					
Brunstane	d																					
Edinburgh [10]	a																					
	d	14 33	14 55	15 15	15 34	15 50	15 55	16 05	16 15	16 55	17 05	17 15	17 34	17 50	17 55	18 13	18 15	18 36	18 55	19 15	19 55	20 15
Haymarket	d	14 39	14 59	15 19	15 38	15 54	15 59	16 09	16 19	16 59	17 09	17 19	17 38	17 54	17 59	18 16	18 19	18 41	18 59	19 19	19 59	20 19
South Gyle	d		15 04	15 24			16 04		16 24	17 04		17 24			18 04		18 24		19 04	19 24	20 04	20 24
Dalmeny	d		15 10	15 30			16 10		16 30	17 10		17 30			18 10		18 30		19 10	19 30	20 10	20 30
North Queensferry	d		15 14	15 34			16 14		16 34	17 14		17 34			18 14		18 34		19 14	19 34	20 14	20 34
Inverkeithing	d	14 54	15 18	15 38	15 52	16 07	16 18	16 23	16 38	17 18	17 23	17 38	17 52	18 07	18 18	18 30	18 38	18 56	19 18	19 38	20 18	20 38
Rosyth	d		15 21				16 21			17 21					18 21				19 21		20 21	
Dunfermline Town	d		15 26				16 26			17 26					18 26				19 26		20 26	
Dunfermline Queen Margaret	d		15 30				16 30			17 30					18 30				19 30		20 30	
Cowdenbeath	d		15 36				16 36			17 36					18 36				19 36		20 36	
Lochgelly	d		15 42				16 42			17 42					18 42				19 42		20 42	
Cardenden	d		15 46				16 46			17 46					18 46				19 46		20 46	
Dalgety Bay	d			15 41					16 41			17 41					18 41			19 41		20 41
Aberdour	d			15 46					16 46			17 46					18 46			19 46		20 46
Burntisland	d			15 50					16 50			17 50					18 50			19 50		20 50
Kinghorn	d			15 54					16 55			17 54					18 54			19 54		20 54
Kirkcaldy	d	15a10		15 59	16a07	16a23		16a38	16 59		17a38	17 59	18a07	18a23		18a44	18 59	19a11		19a59		20 59
Glenrothes With Thornton [2]	a		15 55	16 11			16 55		17 11	17 55		18 11			18 55		19 13		19 55		20 55	21 11

		SR	SR	SR	SR	SR
		◇[1] B			◇ E	
Newcraighall	d					
Brunstane	d					
Edinburgh [10]	a					
	d	21 00	21 15	21 55	22 25	23 36
Haymarket	d	21 05	21 19	21 59	22 29	23 40
South Gyle	d		21 24	22 04	22 34	23 45
Dalmeny	d		21 30	22 10	22 40	23 51
North Queensferry	d		21 34	22 14	22 44	23 55
Inverkeithing	d	21 19	21 38	22 18	22 48	23a58
Rosyth	d			22 21		
Dunfermline Town	d			22 26		
Dunfermline Queen Margaret	d			22 30		
Cowdenbeath	d			22 36		
Lochgelly	d			22 42		
Cardenden	d			22 46		
Dalgety Bay	d		21 41		22 51	
Aberdour	d		21 46		22 56	
Burntisland	d		21 50		23 00	
Kinghorn	d		21 54		23 05	
Kirkcaldy	d	21a34	22a02		23a09	
Glenrothes With Thornton [2]	a			22 55		

A not 8 December. From Edinburgh to Perth
B To Aberdeen
C To Inverness
D from 5 January until 9 February. To Carlisle
E To Dundee
F From London Kings Cross to Aberdeen. The Northern Lights
G To Perth
H From Plymouth to Aberdeen
I From London Kings Cross to Aberdeen
J To Dundee. Forms tight booked connection into 1T88.

Table 242R

Mondays to Saturdays

9 December to 17 May

Glenrothes with Thornton, Kirkcaldy and Dunfermline - Edinburgh and Newcraighall

Network Diagram - refer to first page of Table 225

Miles	Miles			SR	SR	SR	SR	SR	SR	SR		SR	SR	SR	SR	SR	SR	SR	XC	XC		SR	SR	SR	SR
				MX	SX	SO	SX	SO	SX	SX		SO	SX			SX	SX	SX	SO	SX		SO	SX	SO	SX
				◇					◇						◇1				◇1	◇1				◇1	◇1
				A					A	B		A		B	C		A	D	E	E				F [trolley]	F [trolley]
0	0	Glenrothes With Thornton [2]	d							06 03				06 26			06 52					07 18	07 18		
7¼	—	**Kirkcaldy**	d						05 53			06 16	06 27		06 50			07 13	07 21	07 21		07 26	07 26	07 41	07 41
10	—	Kinghorn	d						05 58			06 21	06 32		06 54			07 18				07 31	07 31		
12¾	—	Burntisland	d						06 03			06 26	06 36		06 59			07 22				07 36	07 36		
17½	—	Aberdour	d						06 08			06 31	06 41		07 04			07 27				07 40	07 40		
20¼	—	Dalgety Bay	d						06 13			06 36	06 46		07 09			07 31				07 45	07 45		
—	4¾	Cardenden	d							06 10				06 34			07 00								
—	7	Lochgelly	d							06 14				06 38			07 04								
—	9½	Cowdenbeath	d							06 20				06 44			07 10								
—	13½	Dunfermline Queen Margaret	d							06 26				06 49		07 08	07 15								
—	14¾	**Dunfermline Town**	d							06 30				06 53		07 11	07 19								
—	17	Rosyth	d							06 33				06 56		07 15	07 22								
21¾	18½	Inverkeithing	d						06 17	06 39		06 39	06 49	07 00	07 12	07 19	07 28	07 35	07 38	07 41		07 49	07 49		
23¾	20½	North Queensferry	d						06 21	06 43		06 43	06 53	07 04		07 23	07 32					07 53	07 53		
25½	22¼	Dalmeny	d	00 02					06 25	06 47		06 47	06 57	07 08	07 19		07 36	07a41				07 57	07 57		
30½	27¼	South Gyle	d	00 08					06 31	06 53		06 53	07 03	07 14	07 25	07 31	07 44					08 03	08 03		
33¾	30½	Haymarket	d	00 16	06 11	06 17	06 32	06 35	06 42	07 02		07 02	07 12	07 23	07 34	07 40	07 54		07 56	07 59		08 11	08 11	08 15	08 15
35	31¾	**Edinburgh** [10]	a	00 21	06 15	06 22	06 36	06 39	06 46	07 06		07 06	07 16	07 27	07 40	07 44	07 58		08 01	08 04		08 18	08 19	08 21	08 22
—	—		d		06 20	06 23	06 39	06 43		07 10		07 10		07 38								08 20	08 20		
39	—	Brunstane	d		06 27	06 31	06 49	06 49		07 18		07 18		07 45								08 27	08 27		
39¾	—	**Newcraighall**	a		06 31	06 34	06 52	06 53		07 22		07 22		07 49								08 31	08 31		

		SR	SR	SR	SR	SR		SR	SR	SR	SR	SR	SR	SR	SR	SR		SR	SR	SR	SR	GR	GR	SR	SR
			SX	SO	SX	SO		SX	SO	SX					SX	SO			SX	SO		SX	SO		SO
																						R	R		
						1			◇1	1					◇	◇		◇1				1	1		
		A			C	C			C	C			G		C	C		H [trolley]				I [restaurant]	I [restaurant]		
Glenrothes With Thornton [2]	d			07 37				07 46			08 08	08 21		08 40					09 08	09 08	09 21			09 38	09 51
Kirkcaldy	d	07 48			07 57	07 57			08 19	08 19		08 29	08 41		09 14	09 14		09 25			09 29	09 45	09 45		09 59
Kinghorn	d				08 01	08 01						08 34			09 18	09 18					09 34				10 04
Burntisland	d				08 06	08 06						08 39			09 23	09 23					09 39				10 09
Aberdour	d				08 11	08 11						08 43			09 28	09 28					09 43				10 13
Dalgety Bay	d				08 16	08 16						08 48			09 33	09 33					09 48				10 18
Cardenden	d		07 36	07 44				07 53			08 15			08 47					09 15	09 15				09 45	
Lochgelly	d		07 42	07 48				07 59			08 19			08 51					09 19	09 19				09 49	
Cowdenbeath	d		07 51	07 54				08 05			08 25			08 57					09 25	09 25				09 55	
Dunfermline Queen Margaret	d		07 57	08 00				08 11			08 31			09 03					09 31	09 31				10 00	
Dunfermline Town	d		08 02	08 03				08 16			08 34			09 06					09 34	09 34				10 04	
Rosyth	d		08 06	08 07				08 20			08 38			09 10					09 38	09 38				10 07	
Inverkeithing	d	08 04	08 11	08 11	08 20	08 20		08 25	08 35	08 35	08 42	08 52	08 57	09 16	09 36	09 36			09 46	09 46	09 52	10 01	10 01	10 11	10 22
North Queensferry	d			08 15				08 31			08 46	08 56		09 20							09 56			10 15	
Dalmeny	d		08 19	08 19	08 26	08 26					08 50	09 00		09 24							10 00			10 19	
South Gyle	d		08 26	08 25	08 33	08 33		08 39	08 46	08 46	08 56	09 06		09 30							10 06			10 25	10 34
Haymarket	d	08 20	08 35	08 33	08 41	08 41		08 48	08 55	08 55	09 06	09 14	09 18	09 39	09 53	09 54		09 58	10 04	10 04	10 13	10 20	10 20	10 34	10 43
Edinburgh [10]	a	08 24	08 40	08 40	08 46	08 46		08 54	09 01	09 01	09 14	09 19	09 22	09 45	09 59	09 59		10 04	10 10	10 10	10 22	10 24	10 25	10 40	10 50
	d			08 51						09 03		09 21		09 51					10 21	10 25					10 51
Brunstane	d			08 59						09 10		09 29		09 59					10 29	10 32					10 59
Newcraighall	a			09 04						09 14		09 34		10 04					10 32	10 35					11 04

		SR		XC	XC	SR	SR	SR	SR	SR	SR	SR		SR	SR	SR	SR	SR	GR	SR	SR	SR		SR	SR
		SX		SX	SO									SO	SX	SX	SO				SO	SX		SO	SX
				R															R						
				1	◇1		◇1		◇			◇1						◇	1					◇1	◇1
				J	J		C		A			C						A	K [restaurant]		L	L		C	C
Glenrothes With Thornton [2]	d	09 51						10 21		10 38	10 53					11 21	11 21			11 38	11 51	11 51			
Kirkcaldy	d	09 59		10 17	10 17		10 26	10 29	10 42		10 59	11 18				11 29	11 29	11 38	11 47		11 59	11 59		12 16	12 16
Kinghorn	d	10 04						10 34			11 04					11 34	11 34				12 04	12 04			
Burntisland	d	10 09						10 39			11 09					11 39	11 39				12 09	12 09			
Aberdour	d	10 13						10 43			11 13					11 43	11 43				12 13	12 13			
Dalgety Bay	d	10 18						10 48			11 18					11 48	11 48				12 18	12 18			
Cardenden	d									10 45										11 45					
Lochgelly	d									10 49										11 49					
Cowdenbeath	d					10 23				10 55				11 23	11 23					11 55					
Dunfermline Queen Margaret	d					10 28				11 00				11 28	11 28					12 00					
Dunfermline Town	d					10 32				11 04				11 32	11 32					12 04					
Rosyth	d					10 35				11 07				11 35	11 35					12 07					
Inverkeithing	d	10 22		10 32	10 32	10 39	10 44	10 52	10 59	11 11	11 22	11 34		11 39	11 39	11 52	11 52	11 55	12 03	12 11	12 22	12 22		12 32	12 32
North Queensferry	d					10 43		10 56		11 15	11 26			11 43	11 43					12 15	12 26	12 26			
Dalmeny	d					10 47		11 00		11 19	11 30			11 47	11 47					12 19	12 30	12 30			
South Gyle	d	10 34				10 53		11 06		11 25	11 36			11 53	11 53	12 03	12 03			12 25	12 36	12 36			
Haymarket	d	10 43		10 51	10 52	11 02	11 07	11 17	11 20	11 34	11 47	11 51		12 02	12 03	12 11	12 12	12 16	12 22	12 34	12 43	12 43		12 48	12 53
Edinburgh [10]	a	10 51		10 55	10 58	11 08	11 11	11 21	11 25	11 38	11 54	12 00		12 10	12 10	12 16	12 18	12 22	12 26	12 43	12 49	12 54		12 54	12 57
	d	10 51				11 21				11 51						12 21	12 21				12 51	12 55			
Brunstane	d	10 59				11 29				11 59						12 29	12 29				12 59	13 06			
Newcraighall	a	11 04				11 33				12 04						12 33	12 33				13 04	13 09			

A From Perth
B From Markinch
C From Dundee
D To Glasgow Queen Street
E From Dundee to Plymouth
F From Aberdeen
G From Blair Atholl
H From Inverness
I From Aberdeen to London Kings Cross
J From Aberdeen to Penzance
K From Aberdeen to London Kings Cross. The Northern Lights
L Forms tight booked connection out of 2G65.

Table 242R

Mondays to Saturdays

9 December to 17 May

Glenrothes with Thornton, Kirkcaldy and Dunfermline - Edinburgh and Newcraighall

Network Diagram - refer to first page of Table 225

		SR	SR	SR		SR	SR	SR	SR	SR	SR	SR	SR	VT		SR	SR	SR	SR	SR	SR	SR	SR	SR	
			SO	SX					SO	SX		SX	SO	SO											
						◇1			◇1	◇				◇1		◇1			◇1			◇			
						A		B	C	C				D		A		E	C			F		G	
						🛒								☕		🛒									
Glenrothes With Thornton 2	d		12 21	12 21			12 38	12 51				13 21	13 21				13 39	13 51			14 21		14 38	14 53	
Kirkcaldy	d		12 29	12 29		12 38		12 59	13 18	13 18		13 29	13 29			13 38		13 59	14 18		14 29	14 38		14 59	
Kinghorn	d		12 34	12 34				13 04				13 34	13 34					14 04			14 34			15 04	
Burntisland	d		12 39	12 39				13 09				13 39	13 39					14 09			14 39			15 09	
Aberdour	d		12 43	12 43				13 13				13 43	13 43					14 13			14 43			15 13	
Dalgety Bay	d		12 48	12 48				13 18				13 48	13 48					14 18			14 48			15 18	
Cardenden	d						12 45										13 45						14 45		
Lochgelly	d						12 49										13 49						14 49		
Cowdenbeath	d	12 23					12 55				13 23						13 55			14 23			14 55		
Dunfermline Queen Margaret	d	12 28					13 00				13 28						14 00			14 28			15 00		
Dunfermline Town	d	12 32					13 04				13 32						14 04			14 32			15 04		
Rosyth	d	12 35					13 07				13 35						14 07			14 35			15 07		
Inverkeithing	d	12 39	12 52	12 52		12 55	13 11	13 22	13 34	13 34	13 39	13 52	13 52				14 11	14 22	14 34	14 39	14 52	14 55	15 11	15 22	
North Queensferry	d	12 43	12 56	12 56			13 15	13 26			13 43	13 56	13 56				14 15	14 26		14 43	14 56		15 15	15 26	
Dalmeny	d	12 47	13 00	13 00			13 19	13 30			13 47	14 00	14 00				14 19	14 30		14 47	15 00		15 19	15 30	
South Gyle	d	12 53	13 06	13 06			13 25	13 36			13 53	14 06	14 06				14 25	14 36		14 53	15 06		15 25	15 36	
Haymarket	d	13 02	13 13	13 13		13 17	13 34	13 43	13 50	13 50	14 02	14 13	14 13	14⟆16		14 18	14 34	14 43	14 50	15 02	15 13	15 17	15 34	15 46	
Edinburgh 10	a	13 09	13 18	13 19		13 23	13 41	13 49	13 57	13 57	14 07	14 19	14 19	14⟆22		14 24	14 40	14 49	14 54	15 08	15 18	15 22	15 40	15 49	
	d		13 21	13 21				13 51				14 21	14 25					14 51			15 20			15 51	
Brunstane	d		13 29	13 29				13 59				14 29	14 33					14 59			15 29			15 59	
Newcraighall	a		13 33	13 33				14 04				14 33	14 36					15 04			15 33			16 05	

		SR	SR	SR	SR	VT	SR	SR	SR	SR		SR	SR	GR	SR	SR	SR	SR	SR	SR		VT	SR	SR	SR
						SO									SX	SO		SO	SX			SO		SO	SX
														R											
		◇1			◇1	◇1			◇1				◇	1						◇		◇1	◇		
		C			A	D		H	C				F	I			J			C		D	F		
					🛒	☕								☕🛒								☕			
Glenrothes With Thornton 2	d			15 21			15 40	15 51				16 21			16 39	16 39	16 51	17 07	17 07					17 41	17 41
Kirkcaldy	d	15 18		15 29	15 42			15 59	16 18			16 29	16 38	16 46			16 59			17 33			17 48		
Kinghorn	d			15 34				16 04				16 34					17 04			17 37					
Burntisland	d			15 39				16 09				16 39					17 09			17 42					
Aberdour	d			15 43				16 13				16 43					17 13			17 46					
Dalgety Bay	d			15 48				16 18				16 48					17 18			17 51					
Cardenden	d						15 45								16 45	16 45		17 14	17 14					17 48	17 48
Lochgelly	d						15 50								16 49	16 49		17 18	17 18					17 52	17 52
Cowdenbeath	d		15 23				15 55			16 23					16 55	16 55		17 24	17 24					17 58	17 58
Dunfermline Queen Margaret	d		15 28				16 00			16 28					17 00	17 00		17 30	17 30					18 04	18 04
Dunfermline Town	d		15 32				16 04			16 32					17 04	17 04		17 33	17 33					18 07	18 07
Rosyth	d		15 35				16 07			16 35					17 07	17 07		17 37	17 37					18 11	18 11
Inverkeithing	d	15 34	15 39	15 52	15 58		16 11	16 22	16 34	16 39		16 52	16 55	17 03	17 11	17 11	17 22	17 41	17 41	17 55			18 04	18 15	18 15
North Queensferry	d		15 43	15 56			16 15	16 26		16 43					17 15	17 15	17 26	17 45	17 45	17 59				18 19	18 19
Dalmeny	d		15 47	16 00			16 19	16 30		16 47					17 19	17 19	17 30	17 49	17 49	18 03				18 23	18 23
South Gyle	d		15 53	16 06			16 25	16 36		16 53		17 03			17 25	17 25	17 36	17 55	17 55	18 09				18 29	18 29
Haymarket	d	15 54	16 02	16 13	16 17	16⟆17	16 34	16 43	16 51	17 02		17 12	17 16	17 21	17 34	17 34	17 45	18 04	18 05	18 17		18⟆17	18 21	18 38	18 38
Edinburgh 10	a	15 58	16 10	16 19	16 22	16⟆22	16 41	16 48	16 59	17 07		17 17	17 20	17 26	17 42	17 42	17 50	18 08	18 10	18 23		18⟆24	18 26	18 42	18 43
	d			16 21				16 50				17 21			17 43	17 51		18 17	18 17					18 50	18 51
Brunstane	d			16 29				16 59				17 29			17 51	17 59		18 26	18 26					18 58	18 58
Newcraighall	a			16 33				17 04				17 34			17 55	18 03		18 31	18 31					19 02	19 02

		SR	SR	SR	SR	SR		SR	SR	SR	SR	SR	VT	SR	SR	SR		GR	SR	SR	SR	SR	SR	SR	SR
		SX	SO		SO	SX				SX			SO			SO		SX							
													R					R							
		◇	◇1					◇1			◇		1		◇	◇1		1			◇		◇	◇1	
		C	C	K				A			L		D		F	M		N			F		C	A	
								🛒					⊠			🛒		☕						🛒	
Glenrothes With Thornton 2	d				18 15	18 15			18 48	18 57		19 13		19 28					20 05			21 05			
Kirkcaldy	d	18 13	18 13		18 23	18 23		18 44		19 05	19 27			19 35	19 54	20 10		20 11		20 26	20 41		21 26	21 41	
Kinghorn	d				18 27	18 27				19 10				19 40						20 30			21 30		
Burntisland	d				18 33	18 33				19 15				19 45						20 36			21 36		
Aberdour	d				18 38	18 38				19 19				19 49						20 40			21 40		
Dalgety Bay	d				18 43	18 43				19 24				19 54						20 45			21 45		
Cardenden	d								18 55			19 20							20 12			21 12			
Lochgelly	d								18 59			19 24							20 16			21 16			
Cowdenbeath	d								19 05			19 30							20 22			21 22			
Dunfermline Queen Margaret	d								19 11			19 36							20 28			21 28			
Dunfermline Town	d								19 14			19 39							20 31			21 31			
Rosyth	d								19 18			19 43							20 34			21 34			
Inverkeithing	d	18 29	18 29		18 46	18 46		19 00	19 22	19 28	19 43	19 47		19 58		20 26		20 27	20 39	20 49	20 59	21 39	21 49		
North Queensferry	d				18 50				19 26	19 32		19 51		20 02					20 43	20 53		21 43	21 53		
Dalmeny	d				18 54	18 53			19 30	19 36		19 55		20 06					20 47	20 57		21 47	21 57		
South Gyle	d				19 00	19 12			19 36	19 42		20 01		20 12					20 53	21 03		21 53	22 03		
Haymarket	d	18 45	18 45	18 58	19 09	19 23		19 16	19 43	19 50	20 04	20 10	20⟆15	20 20	20 24	20 44		20 46	21 00	21 10	21 16	22 00	22 10	22 15	
Edinburgh 10	a	18 49	18 49	19 06	19 13	19 31		19 21	19 48	19 55	20 09	20 12	20⟆20	20 26	20 29	20 50		20 50	21 06	21 17	21 20	22 06	22 17	22 19	
	d			19 21					19 51			20 14							21 14			22 14			22 51
Brunstane	d			19 29					19 59			20 24							21 24			22 24			22 59
Newcraighall	a			19 34					20 04			20 27							21 27			22 28			23 04

A From Inverness
B Forms tight booked connection out of 2G69.
C From Dundee
D from 4 January until 8 February. From Carlisle
E Forms tight booked connection out of 2G71.
F From Perth
G Forms tight booked connection out of 2G73.
H Forms tight booked connection out of 2G75.
I From Aberdeen to London Kings Cross
J Forms tight booked connection out of 2G77.
K From Dunblane
L From Arbroath
M From Aberdeen
N From Aberdeen to Leeds

Table 242R

Mondays to Saturdays

9 December to 17 May

Glenrothes with Thornton, Kirkcaldy and Dunfermline - Edinburgh and Newcraighall

Network Diagram - refer to first page of Table 225

		SR	SR	SR	XC		XC	SR
		SO	SX		SO		SX	
				◇1	◇1		◇1	◇
				A	A		A	B
Glenrothes With Thornton 2	d	22 05	22 05					23 18
Kirkcaldy	d			22 59	23 14		23 26	
Kinghorn	d			23 04				
Burntisland	d			23 09				
Aberdour	d			23 13				
Dalgety Bay	d			23 18				
Cardenden	d	22 12	22 12					23 25
Lochgelly	d	22 16	22 16					23 29
Cowdenbeath	d	22 22	22 22					23 35
Dunfermline Queen Margaret	d	22 28	22 28					23 41
Dunfermline Town	d	22 31	22 31					23 46
Rosyth	d	22 34	22 34					23 50
Inverkeithing	d	22 39	22 39	23 22	23 31		23 42	23 54
North Queensferry	d	22 43	22 43	23 26				23 58
Dalmeny	d	22 47	22 47	23 30				00 02
South Gyle	d	22 53	22 53	23 36				00 08
Haymarket	d	23 00	23 00	23 44	23 51		23 58	00 16
Edinburgh 10	a	23 06	23 09	23 49	23 55		00 05	00 21
	d	23 15	23 15					
Brunstane	d	23 22	23 22					
Newcraighall	a	23 26	23 26					

Sundays

8 December to 11 May

		SR	SR	SR	SR	SR	SR	SR	GR	SR		SR	SR
		◇	◇	◇		◇			R 1	◇			
		C	D	B	D	B			E	D			
Glenrothes With Thornton 2	d					10 15	11 00	11 15				12 02	12 15
Kirkcaldy	d		08 07	09 25	10 07		11 08		11 41	12 05		12 08	
Kinghorn	d		08 13	09 29	10 13		11 12					12 12	
Burntisland	d		08 17	09 34	10 17		11 17					12 17	
Aberdour	d		08 22	09 39	10 22		11 22					12 22	
Dalgety Bay	d		08 27	09 44	10 27		11 27					12 27	
Cardenden	d					10 22		11 22					12 22
Lochgelly	d					10 25		11 25					12 25
Cowdenbeath	d					10 32		11 32					12 32
Dunfermline Queen Margaret	d					10 37		11 37					12 37
Dunfermline Town	d					10 41		11 41					12 41
Rosyth	d					10 44		11 44					12 44
Inverkeithing	d		08 30	09 47	10 30	10 48	11 33	11 48	11 57	12 21		12 33	12 48
North Queensferry	d		08 35	09 51	10 40	10 52	11 37	11 52				12 40	12 52
Dalmeny	d	00 02	08 42	09 58	10 44	10 54	11 41	11 54				12 45	12 54
South Gyle	d	00 08	08 48	10 04	10 50	11 00	11 47	12 00				12 51	13 00
Haymarket	d	00 16	08 57	10 13	10 59	11 09	11 56	12 09	12 16	12 37		13 00	13 09
Edinburgh 10	a	00 21	09 01	10 17	11 03	11 16	12 00	12 16	12 20	12 42		13 04	13 15
	d												
Brunstane	d												
Newcraighall	a												

		XC	SR	SR	SR	VT	GR	SR		SR	SR	SR	SR
		◇1		◇1		◇1	R 1	◇				◇1	
		F		G		H	I	D				A	
Glenrothes With Thornton 2	d		13 02		13 15					14 02	14 15		15 05
Kirkcaldy	d	13 04	13 07	13 31			13 42	14 05		14 13		14 46	15 13
Kinghorn	d		13 12							14 18			15 18
Burntisland	d		13 17							14 23			15 23
Aberdour	d		13 22							14 27			15 27
Dalgety Bay	d		13 27							14 32			15 32
Cardenden	d				13 22						14 22		
Lochgelly	d				13 25						14 25		
Cowdenbeath	d				13 32						14 32		
Dunfermline Queen Margaret	d				13 37						14 37		
Dunfermline Town	d				13 41						14 41		
Rosyth	d				13 44						14 44		
Inverkeithing	d	13 20	13 33	13 47	13 52		14 00	14 21		14 36	14 48	15 02	15 36
North Queensferry	d		13 40		13 56					14 40	14 52		15 40
Dalmeny	d		13 45		14 00					14 44	14 56		15 44
South Gyle	d		13 51		14 06					14 50	15 00		15 50
Haymarket	d	13 37	14 00	14 05	14 12	14 15	14 19	14 40		14 59	15 09	15 18	15 58
Edinburgh 10	a	13 42	14 04	14 09	14 19	14 22	14 23	14 45		15 04	15 16	15 23	16 04
	d												
Brunstane	d												
Newcraighall	a												

		SR	VT	GR	SR	SR		SR	SR	SR	SR	SR	SR
			◇1	R 1	◇	◇1				◇1			◇1
			H	I	D	G				A			G
Glenrothes With Thornton 2	d	15 15						16 02	16 15		16 58	17 15	
Kirkcaldy	d			15 40	16 00	16 08		16 13		17 02	17 07		18 00
Kinghorn	d							16 18			17 12		
Burntisland	d							16 23			17 17		
Aberdour	d							16 27			17 22		
Dalgety Bay	d							16 32			17 27		
Cardenden	d	15 22							16 22			17 22	
Lochgelly	d	15 25							16 25			17 25	
Cowdenbeath	d	15 32							16 32			17 32	
Dunfermline Queen Margaret	d	15 37							16 37			17 37	
Dunfermline Town	d	15 41							16 41			17 41	
Rosyth	d	15 44							16 44			17 44	
Inverkeithing	d	15 48		15 56	16 16	16 24		16 36	16 48	17 18	17 30	17 48	18 16
North Queensferry	d	15 52						16 40	16 52		17 34	17 52	
Dalmeny	d	15 56						16 45	16 56		17 38	17 56	
South Gyle	d	16 01						16 50	17 00		17 44	18 00	
Haymarket	d	16 12	16 15	16 17	16 33	16 40		16 59	17 11	17 34	17 53	18 12	18 32
Edinburgh 10	a	16 17	16 23	16 22	16 38	16 44		17 04	17 16	17 40	17 57	18 19	18 36
	d												
Brunstane	d												
Newcraighall	a												

		SR	SR	SR		SR	SR	SR	SR	SR	SR	SR	SR
		◇				◇1			◇	◇1			◇1
		D				A			D	A			G
Glenrothes With Thornton 2	d		18 02	18 15			18 58	19 15			20 58	21 15	
Kirkcaldy	d	18 05	18 13			18 56	19 06		20 01	21 01	21 06		21 43
Kinghorn	d		18 18				19 11		20 06		21 11		
Burntisland	d		18 23				19 16		20 10		21 16		
Aberdour	d		18 28				19 20		20 15		21 20		
Dalgety Bay	d		18 33				19 25		20 20		21 25		
Cardenden	d			18 22				19 22				21 22	
Lochgelly	d			18 25				19 25				21 25	
Cowdenbeath	d			18 32				19 32				21 32	
Dunfermline Queen Margaret	d			18 37				19 37				21 37	
Dunfermline Town	d			18 41				19 41				21 41	
Rosyth	d			18 44				19 44				21 44	
Inverkeithing	d	18 22	18 37	18 48		19 12	19 29	19 48	20 23	21 17	21 29	21 48	21 59
North Queensferry	d		18 41	18 52			19 33	19 52	20 27		21 33	21 52	
Dalmeny	d		18 45	18 56			19 37	19 56	20 31		21 37	21 56	
South Gyle	d		18 51	19 02			19 43	20 02	20 37		21 43	22 02	
Haymarket	d	18 39	19 00	19 11		19 27	19 51	20 12	20 49	21 34	21 52	22 11	22 15
Edinburgh 10	a	18 44	19 04	19 16		19 35	19 56	20 17	20 53	21 38	21 56	22 16	22 19
	d												
Brunstane	d												
Newcraighall	a												

- **A** From Aberdeen
- **B** From Perth
- **C** not 8 December. From Perth
- **D** From Dundee
- **E** From Aberdeen to London Kings Cross. The Northern Lights
- **F** From Aberdeen to Reading
- **G** From Inverness
- **H** from 5 January until 9 February. From Carlisle
- **I** From Aberdeen to London Kings Cross

Table 242R

Sundays

8 December to 11 May

Glenrothes with Thornton, Kirkcaldy and Dunfermline - Edinburgh and Newcraighall

Network Diagram - refer to first page of Table 225

		SR	SR	SR	XC
		◇1			◇1
		A			A
		⚲			
Glenrothes With Thornton 2	d			22 58	
Kirkcaldy	d	22 06	22 12	23 06	23 22
Kinghorn	d		22 16	23 11	
Burntisland	d		22 21	23 16	
Aberdour	d		22 26	23 20	
Dalgety Bay	d		22 31	23 25	
Cardenden	d				
Lochgelly	d				
Cowdenbeath	d				
Dunfermline Queen Margaret	d				
Dunfermline Town	d				
Rosyth	d				
Inverkeithing	d	22 22	22 34	23 29	23 38
North Queensferry	d		22 38	23 33	
Dalmeny	d		22 42	23 37	
South Gyle	d		22 48	23 43	
Haymarket	d	22 39	22 57	23 52	23 54
Edinburgh 10	a	22 43	23 01	23 56	23 58
	d				
Brunstane	d				
Newcraighall	a				

A From Aberdeen

Sleeper Services

Sleepers enable you to make long distance journeys while having a relaxing night's sleep. You arrive early at your destination, saving a day's travel — or the early morning dash to the airport. Five Sleeper routes link London Euston direct with over 40 stations in Scotland including most principal business and holiday locations. Direct Sleeper services also link Southwest England with London. Customers joining at the starting point of the train may occupy cabins well before departure. At terminating stations customers may vacate cabins up to approximately 0800 on trains which arrive at an earlier time.

Full details of all Sleeper services are given in Tables 400–406.

First Great Western ("Night Riviera Sleeper")

Both single and twin berth cabins are available and feature locking doors, comfortable beds with duvets, air conditioning, bedside lighting, wash basin with a shaver point and a soft hand towel.
Room service facilities, a wake up call, a light breakfast and newspaper are all complimentary.

The trains recently underwent a complete refurbishment to maximise customer comfort. Improvements include a refurbishment of seating areas and berths and the introduction of a hot breakfast offer to set our customers up for the day. All single and twin cabins are available to holders of standard class tickets and large reclining seats are provided throughout seated accommodation, again available to holders of standard class tickets. Customers in most single berths benefit from Volo TV, a new and innovative on-train entertainment service. Customers can choose from 40 different programmes including comedy, drama, documentaries, children's programmes and sport.

There are a number of inclusive Advance fares available that combine travel and accommodation on one ticket. These can be purchased until 1800 hours the day before departure. Holders of Anytime, Off-Peak and Super Off-Peak tickets may upgrade to sleeping accommodation on payment of the applicable single or twin berth supplement. The Lounge Car is provided for the use of customers travelling in Sleeper accomodation. Here you can sit back and relax with a complimentary hot drink, tempt yourself with one of our delicious hot snacks or unwind with something stronger from our well stocked bar - all served at seat by our on-board team. Customers in seated accommodation can purchase refreshments and snacks from the Express Cafe, which is situated in the Lounge Car.

Dogs and pets are not normally allowed in Sleeper cabins. There are special arrangements for guide dogs. Animals may be conveyed if properly labelled and muzzled, and in suitable containers, in the guards van.

ScotRail Caledonian Sleepers

First Class customers receive a toiletry pack and will be woken with a light breakfast accompanied by tea or coffee and a complimentary newspaper. Standard Class customers are served a light morning snack with tea or coffee. Breakfast is available for an additional small supplement and can be ordered after boarding. Customer lounges are available at the following locations - London Euston, Inverness, Carlisle (Lakes Court Hotel) and Edinburgh Waverley. At Glasgow Central customers may use the on-train Lounge Car which is available prior to departure. Full details of the Caledonian Sleeper on-train and station facilities can be found inside the Caledonian Sleeper Guide which is available from principal sleeper departure points.

There are a number of berth inclusive fares available that include travel and accommodation at one all inclusive price. First class travel is in single berth cabins while Standard Class is in twin berth cabins.

The Lounge Car offers a pleasant relaxing atmosphere in which to unwind before a night's rest. Customers can choose from a wide selection of food and drinks including sandwiches, baguettes, snacks and a well stocked bar. At busy times, use of the Lounge Car may be restricted to First Class ticket holders.

Accompanying dogs are only permitted in Sleeper Cabins providing the owner(s) has exclusive use of the cabin and pays the appropriate charge. There are special arrangements for guide dogs. Dogs and pets cannot be conveyed in the guards van. A virtual tour is available via the ScotRail website. Visit www.scotrail.co.uk for details.

Please note that as a result of on-going engineering work some sleeper services may be subject to diversion causing an extension in journey times between Scotland and London. For full details telephone National Rail Enquiries on 08457 48 49 50 (calls may be recorded).

Sleeper Reservations

To book rail tickets and reserve Sleepers, simply visit any main rail station or rail appointed travel agent. Alternatively you can book by phone using most credit/debit cards.

First Great Western Telesales (www.firstgreatwestern.co.uk)	08457 00 01 25
ScotRail Telesales (www.scotrail.co.uk)	08457 55 00 33

For further information about rail tickets or services, call National Rail Enquiries on 08457 48 49 50 (calls may be recorded for training purposes).

Sleeper Services (continued)

ScotRail Sleeper Services – The Caledonian Sleepers

Operated by ScotRail

Table 400 London and Edinburgh

		Mon-Thu	Fri	Sun	Sun
				A	B
Cabins available from		*2300*	*2245*	*2245*	*2245*
Edinburgh	d	2340	2340	2315	2321
Carstairs	d	00u16*	00u16*	23u47	-
Carlisle	d	01u40	01u40	01u12	-
Watford Junction	a	06s22	06s23	06s22	-
London Euston	a	0648	0648	0647	0706
Vacate cabins by		*0800*	*0800*	*0800*	*0800*

		Mon-Fri	Sun	Sun
			A	B
Cabins available		*2300*	*2245*	*2100*
London Euston	d	2350	2327	2145
Watford Junction	d	00u10*	23u47	23u47
Carlisle	a	05s10	05s10	-
Carstairs	a	06s19	06s19	-
Edinburgh	a	0722	0722	0550
Vacate cabins by		*0800*	*0800*	*0800*

- Train does not call at this station
✕ Restaurant Service is offered on these trains.
A From 08 December 2013 to 09 February 2014
B from 16 February to 11 May 2014
Ⓡ Reservations are compulsory on these services.
* Following morning, a - Arrival Time, d - Departure Time
Services in this table do not run on Saturday nights.
For details of overnight seated services, please refer to Table 65

Table 401 London and Glasgow

		Mon-Thu	Fri	Sun	Sun
				A	B
Cabins available from		*2200*	*2200*	*2200*	*2100*
Glasgow Central	d	2340	2340	2315	2146
Motherwell	d	0001*	0001*	2330	2207
Carstairs	d	00u16*	00u16*	23u47	2224
Carlisle	d	01u40	01u40	01u12	-
Watford Junction	a	06s22	06s23	06s22	-
London Euston	a	0648	0648	0647	0706
Vacate cabins by	a	*0800*	*0800*	*0800*	*0800*

		Mon-Thu	Fri	Sun	Sun
				A	B
Cabins available		*2300*	*2300*	*2245*	*2100*
London Euston	d	2350	2350	2327	2145
Watford Junction	d	0010*	0010*	2347	-
Carlisle	a	05s10	05s10	05s10	-
Carstairs	a	06s19	06s19*	06s19*	0700
Motherwell	a	06s54	06s54	06s54	0727
Glasgow Central	a	0718	0718	0718	0759
Vacate cabins by	a	*0800*	*0800*	*0800*	*0815*

A From 08 December 2013 to 09 February 2014
B from 16 February to 11 May 2014
✕ Restaurant Service is offered these trains.
Ⓡ Reservations are compulsory on these services.
* Following morning, a - Arrival Time, d - Departure Time
Services in this table do not run on Saturday nights.
For details of overnight seated services, please refer to Table 65

Table 402 London and Aberdeen

		Mon-Fri	Sun	Sun
			A	B
Cabins available from		*2110*	*2050*	*2050*
Aberdeen	d	2143	2143	2143
Stonehaven	d	22u01	22u01	22u01
Montrose	d	22u26	22u26	22u26
Arbroath	d	22u44	22u44	22u44
Carnoustie	d	22u53	22u53	22u53
Dundee	d	23u06	23u06	23u06
Leuchars (for St Andrews)	d	23u26	23u25	23u25
Kirkcaldy	d	23u55	23u55	23u55
Inverkeithing	d	00u13*	00u13*	00u13*
Preston	a	04s40	04s40	0440
Crewe	a	05s36	05s36	0536
London Euston	a	0747	0747	0857
Vacate cabins by		*0800*	*0900*	*0900*

		Mon-Fri	Sun	Sun
			A	B
Cabins available from		*2030*	*2000*	*1945*
London Euston	d	2116	2057	2028
Watford Junction	d	21u33	21u17	-
Crewe	d	23u53	23u33	-
Preston	d	00u52*	00u33*	-
Inverkeithing	a	04s58	04s58	04s58
Kirkcaldy	a	05s18	05s18	05s18
Leuchars (for St Andrews)	a	05s46	05s46	05s46
Dundee	a	06s08	06s08	06s08
Carnoustie	a	06s23	06s23	06s23
Arbroath	a	06s31	06s31	06s31
Montrose	a	06s48	06s48	06s48
Stonehaven	a	07s13	07s13	07s13
Aberdeen	a	0734	0734	0734
Vacate cabins by		*0800*	*0800*	*0800*

- Train does not call at this station
✕ Restaurant Service is offered on these trains.
A 08 December 2013 to 09 February 2014
B 16 February to 11 May 2014
Ⓡ Reservations are compulsory on these services.
* Following morning, a - Arrival Time, d - Departure Time
● Customers may depart from London or Watford later, and vacate cabins later, by travelling on the London Euston to Edinburgh Sleeper; then by local connecting service from Edinburgh
Services in this table do not run on Saturday nights
For details of overnight seated services, please refer to Table 65

Sleeper Services (continued)

ScotRail Sleeper Services – The Caledonian Sleepers

Operated by ScotRail

Table 403 London and Inverness

		Mon-Fri	Sun	Sun
			A	B
Cabins available from		*1945*	*1945*	*1945*
Inverness	d	2044	2026	2026
Aviemore	d	21u31	21u15	21u15
Kingussie	d	21u44	21u29	21u29
Newtonmore	d	21u50	21u35	21u35
Dalwhinnie	d	22u04	21u50	21u50
Blair Atholl	d	22u30	22u15	22u15
Pitlochry	d	22u43	22u29	22u29
Dunkeld & Birnam	d	22u58	22u43	22u43
Perth	d	23u21	23u06	23u06
Gleneagles	d	23u39	23u24	23u24
Dunblane	d	23u55	23u41	23u41
Stirling	d	00u06*	23u51	23u51
Falkirk Grahamston	d	00u23	00u08*	00u08*
Preston	a	04s40	04s40	-
Crewe	a	05s36	05s36	-
London Euston	a	0747	0747	0857
Vacate cabins by		*0800*	*0800*	*0900*

		Mon-Fri	Sun	Sun	Sun
			A	C	D
Cabins available from		*2030*	*2000*	*1945*	*1945*
London Euston	d	2116	2057	2028	2028
Watford Junction	d	21u33	21u17	-	-
Crewe	d	23u53	23u33	-	-
Preston	d	00u52*	00u33*	-	-
Stirling	a	04s55	04s55	04s55	04s59
Dunblane	a	05s04	05s04	05s04	05s08
Gleneagles	a	05s19	05s19	05s19	05s25
Perth	a	05s39	05s39	05s39	05s44
Dunkeld & Birnam	a	06s00	06s00	06s00	06s05
Pitlochry	a	06s16	06s16	06s16	06s21
Blair Atholl	a	06s28	06s28	06s28	06s32
Dalwhinnie	a	07s00	07s00	07s00	07s03
Newtonmore	a	07s12	07s12	07s12	07s15
Kingussie	a	0718	0718	0718	0720
Kingussie	d	0719	0719	0719	0721
Aviemore	a	0740	0740	0740	0740
Aviemore	d	0743	0743	0743	0741
Carrbridge	a	0753	0753	0753	0752
Carrbridge	d	0756	0756	0756	0753
Inverness	a	0836	0836	0836	0837
Vacate cabins by		*0845*	*0845*	*0845*	*0845*

- Train does not call at this station
✕ Restaurant Service is offered on these trains.
A from 08 December to 09 February C from 16 February to 23 March
B from 16 February to 11 May D from 30 March to 11 May
🅁 Reservations are compulsory on these services
* Following morning, a - Arrival Time, d - Departure Time
● Customers may depart from London or Watford later, and vacate cabins later, by travelling on the London Euston to Edinburgh Sleeper; then by local connecting service from Edinburgh.
Services in this table do not run on Saturday nights.
For details of overnight seated services, please refer to Table 65

Table 404 London and Fort William

		Mon-Fri	Sun	Sun
			A	B
Cabins available from		*1920*	*1830*	*1830*
Fort William	d	1950	1900	1900
Spean Bridge	d	2010	1920	1920
Roy Bridge	d	2017x	1927x	1927x
Tulloch	d	2031	1940	1940
Corrour	d	2052x	2001x	2001x
Rannoch	d	2106	2015	2015
Bridge of Orchy	d	2134	2047	2047
Upper Tyndrum	d	2152	2105	2105
Crianlarich	d	2205	2118	2118
Ardlui	d	2226x	2139x	2139x
Arrochar & Tarbet	d	2244	2157	2157
Garelochhead	d	2310	2223	2223
Helensburgh Upper	d	2324	2237	2237
Dumbarton Central	d	2339	2253	2253
Dalmuir	d	2351	2306	2306
Westerton	d	2359	2314	2314
Preston	a	04s40	0440	-
Crewe	a	05s36	0536	-
London Euston	a	0747	0747	0857
Vacate cabins by		*0800*	*0800*	*0900*

		Mon-Fri	Sun	Sun
			A	B
Cabins available from		*2030*	*2000*	*1945*
London Euston	d	2116	2057	2028
Watford Junction	d	21u33	21u17	-
Crewe	d	23u53	23u33	-
Preston	d	00u52*	00u33*	-
Westerton	a	0553	0553	0553
Dalmuir	a	0600	0600	0600
Dumbarton Central	a	0611	0611	0611
Helensburgh Upper	a	0626	0626	0626
Garelochhead	a	0641	0641	0641
Arrochar & Tarbet	a	0707	0707	0707
Ardlui	a	0722x	0722x	0722x
Crianlarich	a	0743	0743	0743
Upper Tyndrum	a	0756	0756	0756
Bridge of Orchy	a	0814	0814	0814
Rannoch	a	0842	0842	0842
Corrour	a	0859x	0859x	0859x
Tulloch	a	0918	0918	0918
Roy Bridge	a	0931x	0931x	0931x
Spean Bridge	a	0938	0938	0938
Fort William	a	0955	0955	0955
Vacate cabins by		*0957*	*0957*	*0957*

- Train does not call at this station
✕ Restaurant Service is offered on these trains.
A 08 December 2013 until 09 February 2014
B 16 February to 11 May 2014
x Stops on request
🅁 Reservations are compulsory on these services
* Following morning, a - Arrival Time, d - Departure Time
Services in this table do not run on Saturday nights.
For details of overnight seated services, please refer to Tables 65 and 227.

Sleeper Services (continued)

"Night Riviera" Sleeper

Operated by First Great Western

Table 406 London and Penzance

		Mon-Fri	Sun
Occupy cabins at Paddington		*2230*	*2230*
London Paddington	d	2345	2350
Reading	d	0037*	0037*
Westbury	a	0135	-
Taunton	a	0232	-
Exeter St Davids	a	0306	0305
Newton Abbot	a	0431	0455
Plymouth	a	0514	0535
Liskeard	a	0607	0652
Bodmin Parkway	a	0621	0721
Lostwithiel	a	0628	0728
Par	a	0636	0737
St Austell	a	0645	0745
Truro	a	0704	0804
Redruth	a	0718	0818
Camborne	a	0725	0826
Hayle	a	0735	0835
St Erth	a	0740	0842
Penzance	a	0753	0859
Vacate cabins at Penzance by		*on arival*	*on arival*

		Mon-Thu	FO	Sun B	Sun A
Occupy cabins at Penzance		*2115*	*2115*	*2045*	*2045*
Penzance	d	2145	2145	2115	2115
St Erth	d	2155	2155	2125	2125
Camborne	d	2207	2207	2138	2138
Redruth	d	2214	2214	2145	2145
Truro	d	2227	2227	2200	2200
St Austell	d	2245	2245	2218	2218
Par	d	2254	2254	-	-
Bodmin Parkway	d	2306	2306	2235	2235
Liskeard	d	2321	2321	2250	2250
Plymouth	d	2351	2351	2320	0150
Totnes	d	0020*	0020*	2348	0218
Newton Abbot	d	0033	0033	0001	0231
Exeter St Davids	d	0106	0106	0106	0302
Taunton	d	0142	0142	-	-
Reading	a	0400	0400	0403	0511
London Paddington	a	0523	0513	0508	0609
Vacate cabins at Paddington by		*0700*	*0700*	*0700*	*0700*

* Following morning

Train times may vary on Sundays. Please check before you travel.

A from 8 Dec to 29 Dec and from 30 Mar to 11 May

B from 16 Feb to 23 March

\- Train does not call at this station

s Stops to set down only

For details of seated services on this route, please refer to Table 135.

Passenger Representation

Passenger Focus

What is Passenger Focus?

Passenger Focus is the off cial, independent consumer organisation representing the interests of rail users nationally and bus, coach and tram users across England outside London.

With a strong emphasis on evidence-based campaigning and research, we ensure that we know what is happening on the ground. We use our knowledge to inf uence decisions on behalf of passengers and we work with the industry, other passenger groups and government to secure journey improvements.

What can Passenger Focus do for me?

We are here to put the interests of rail, bus and coach passengers f rst. We do this by:

Campaigning for improvements

- we gather research and information, like the National Passenger Survey, where 50,000 passengers give us their views about their rail journeys, so we understand the issues that matter to you
- we work with Government and the industry to ensure that the passenger voice is heard when making decisions about the future
- we focus on a number of key issues:
  - fares and tickets
  - quality and level of services
  - investment in the railway

Providing practical advice

- we provide passengers with advice on how to get the best from the network, explain their rights and help them when things go wrong
- we work with other passenger groups to support them in their work

Resolving complaints

- if you make a complaint and you are unhappy with the response we can take up your complaint with the company involved

Making a complaint

If you have a complaint or comment about any aspect of your rail service, either on the train or at the station, please contact the train company's customer service department concerned (contact details are shown on the TOC pages of this timetable).

What should you include in your complaint?

Depending on the nature of your complaint you should include:

- the reason for your complaint
- a description of the inconvenience caused
- which train and which day you travelled on, or which station you used and when
- how many people travelled with you
- your ticket(s) as evidence
- an explanation of the action you would like the company to take to rectify the problem

What next?

If you are not satisf ed with the company's response you can contact Passenger Focus or, in the London area, London TravelWatch.

How to get in touch:

Telephone:	0300 123 2350 0800 - 2000 Monday - Friday 0800 - 1600 at weekends
Address:	Passenger Focus FREEPOST (RRRE-ETTC-LEET) PO BOX 4257 MANCHESTER M60 3AR
Fax:	0161 236 1574
Email:	advice@passengerfocus.org.uk
Website:	www.passengerfocus.org.uk

London TravelWatch

London TravelWatch is the independent, statutory watchdog for transport users in and around London, including all services provided by Transport for London, and represents rail passengers in and around London. We investigate suggestions and complaints from passengers who are dissatisf ed with responses received from transport operators.

If your journey is within, or began in, London, please contact:

Telephone:	020 3176 2999 (0900-1700 Monday- Friday)
Address:	London TravelWatch Dexter House, 2 Royal Mint Court, LONDON EC3N 4QN
E-mail:	info@londontravelwatch.org.uk
Website:	www.londontravelwatch.org.uk
Twitter:	@LonTravelWatch

Compensation

Compensation may be payable under each rail company's Passenger's Charter scheme for poor performance (delays or cancellations). For daily tickets and weekly season tickets a f xed rate usually applies depending on the level of delay which you experience. Compensation is made in National Rail vouchers, as a rule, with a minimum of 20% of the fare for the affected journey leg.

Monthly or longer season tickets compensation can differ between companies. On some it is triggered if performance falls below agreed levels and is paid as discount on renewal. Others offer compensation on a journey-by journey basis like for daily tickets. Always check with the train company which issued your ticket or on which you travel for details of the relevant scheme.

81A
81A
HOLYHEAD
ANGLESEY
Valley
Rhosneigr
Ty Croes
Bodorgan
Llanfairpwll
Bangor
Llandudno
Deganwy
Llandudno Junction
Penmaenmawr
Llanfairfechan
Conwy
Colwyn Bay
Rhyl
Prestatyn
Abergele & Pensarn
Flint
Glan Conwy
Tal-y-Cafn
Dolgarrog
North Llanrwst
Llanrwst
Betws-y-Coed
Pont-y-Pant
Dolwyddelan
Roman Bridge
Blaenau Ffestiniog
Pwllheli
Abererch
Penychain
Criccieth
Porthmadog
Minffordd
Penrhyndeudraeth
Llandecwyn
Talsarnau
Tygwyn
Harlech
Llandanwg
Pensarn
Llanbedr
Dyffryn Ardudwy
Talybont
Llanaber
Barmouth
Morfa Mawddach
Fairbourne
Llwyngwril
Tonfanau
Tywyn
Aberdovey
Penhelig
Dovey Junction
Machynlleth
Caersws
Newtown
Borth
Aberystwyth
New Brighton
LIVERPOOL
West Kirby
Birkenhead
Runcorn
Warrington
Altrincham
Manchester Airport
Wilmslow
Stockport
Glossop
Chinley
Hooton
Macclesfield
Buxton
For full details see page
Hawarden
Buckley
Penyffordd
Hope
Caergwrle
Cefn-y-Bedd
Gwersyllt
Wrexham General
Wrexham Central
CHESTER
CREWE
Alsager
Congleton
Kidsgrove
Longport
Nantwich
Wrenbury
Whitchurch
STOKE-ON-TRENT
Wedgwood
Barlaston
Stone
Longton
Blythe Bridge
Uttoxeter
Norton Bridge
Tutbury & Hatton
Burton
Ruabon
Chirk
Gobowen
Prees
Wem
Yorton
STAFFORD
Rugeley Trent Valley
SHREWSBURY
Wellington
Oakengates
Telford Central
Shifnal
Hednesford
Walsall
Welshpool
WOLVERHAMPTON
Sandwell & Dudley
Stourbridge
BIRMINGHAM
Church Stretton
Craven Arms
Broome
Hopton Heath
Bucknell
Knighton
Knucklas
Llangynllo
Llanbister Road
Dolau
Pen-y-bont
Llandrindod
Builth Road
Cilmeri
Garth
Llangammarch
Llanwrtyd
Sugar Loaf
Cynghordy
Llandovery
Ludlow
For full details see page 3659
Kidderminster
Longbridge
Bromsgrove
Redditch
Droitwich Spa
WALES
ENGLAND
Leominster
WORCESTER
Stratford-upon-Avon
Malvern Link
Great Malvern
Pershore
Evesham
HEREFORD
Ledbury
Colwall
Ashchurch for Tewkesbury
CHELTENHAM SPA
GLOUCESTER
Ascott-under-Wychwood
FISHGUARD
Harbour
Fishguard & Goodwick
Clarbeston Road
Haverfordwest
Clunderwen
Whitland
Carmarthen
Johnston
Narberth
Kilgetty
Saundersfoot
Tenby
Penally
Milford Haven
Pembroke Dock
Pembroke
Lamphey
Manorbier
Ferryside
Kidwelly
Pembrey & Burry Port
Llanelli
Llanwrda
Llangadog
Llandeilo
Ffairfach
Llandybie
Ammanford
Pantyffynnon
Pontarddulais
Llangennech
Bynea
Gowerton
SWANSEA
Llansamlet
Skewen
Neath
Briton Ferry
Baglan
Port Talbot Parkway
Pyle
Caerau
Abergavenny
Merthyr Tydfil
Rhymney
Ebbw Vale Parkway
Aberdare
Treherbert
Pontypool & New Inn
Cwmbran
Maesteg
Pontypridd
Caerphilly
NEWPORT
Bridgend
CARDIFF
Penarth
Barry
Rhoose
for Cardiff International Airport
Barry Island
Lydney
Chepstow
Cam & Dursley
Yate
Stonehouse
Stroud
Kemble
Severn Beach
Bristol Parkway
BRISTOL
BATH SPA
Chippenham
Weston-super-Mare
Bristol International Airport
For full details see page 3658
Freshford
Avoncliff
Bradford-on-Avon
Melksham
Trowbridge
Pewsey
Westbury
Dilton Marsh
Warminster
Frome
Highbridge & Burnham
Minehead
Dunster
Watchet
Bishops Lydeard
Bridgwater
TAUNTON
Castle Cary
Bruton
SALISBURY
Tisbury
Gillingham
Templecombe
Sherborne
Yeovil Pen Mill
Yeovil Junction
Crewkerne
Thornford
Yetminster
Chetnole
Maiden Newton
Dorchester West
Upwey
Dorchester South
Moreton
Wool
Wareham
Holton Heath
Hamworthy
Parkstone
Branksome
BOURNEMOUTH
POOLE
WEYMOUTH
Axminster
Honiton
Feniton
Whimple
Pinhoe
Polsloe Bridge
Digby & Sowton
Topsham
Exton
Lympstone Commando
Lympstone Village
Exmouth
Tiverton Parkway
Barnstaple
Chapelton
Umberleigh
Portsmouth Arms
Kings Nympton
Eggesford
Lapford
Morchard Road
Copplestone
Yeoford
Crediton
Newton St Cyres
Okehampton
Sampford Courtenay
Bude
Holsworthy
EXETER
St Davids
Central
St James Park
St Thomas
Starcross
Dawlish Warren
Dawlish
Teignmouth
NEWTON ABBOT
Torre
Torquay
Paignton
Totnes
Ivybridge
PLYMOUTH
Gunnislake
Calstock
Bere Alston
Bere Ferrers
St Budeaux Victoria Road
St Budeaux Ferry Road
Keyham
Devonport
Dockyard
Saltash
St Germans
Menheniot
Liskeard
Coombe Junction Halt
Causeland
Sandplace
Looe
St Keyne Wishing Well Halt
Bodmin Parkway
Lostwithiel
Padstow
Wadebridge
Newquay
Quintrell Downs
St Columb Road
Roche
Bugle
Luxulyan
Eden Project
Par
St Austell
Truro
Perranwell
Penryn
Penmere
Falmouth Town
Falmouth Docks
St Ives
Carbis Bay
Lelant
Lelant Saltings
Hayle
Camborne
Redruth
PENZANCE
St Erth
Helston

Rotherham
Gainsborough Central
Gainsborough Lea Road
Market Rasen
Worksop
RETFORD
Creswell
Whitwell
Chesterfield
Shirebrook
Langwith-Whaley Thorns
Mansfield
Mansfield Woodhouse
Saxilby
LINCOLN
Hykeham
Swinderby
Collingham
Metheringham
Sutton Parkway
Kirkby-in-Ashfield
Alfreton
Newstead
Hucknall
Langley Mill
Bulwell
Belper
Duffield
Ambergate
NEWARK
North Gate
Rauceby
Ruskington
Sleaford
Ancaster
NOTTINGHAM
DERBY
Beeston
Attenborough
Spondon
Peartree
Long Eaton
East Midlands Parkway
Loughborough
Barrow-on-Soar
Willington
Sileby
Syston
Melton Mowbray
Oakham
Stamford
LEICESTER
South Wigston
Narborough
Hinckley
Nuneaton
Tamworth
GRANTHAM
Bottesford
Aslockton
Bingham
Radcliffe
Netherfield
Heckington
Swineshead
Hubberts Bridge
Boston
Thorpe Culvert
Wainfleet
Havenhouse
Skegness
Spalding
PETERBOROUGH
Corby
Oundle
Market Harborough
KETTERING
Wellingborough
RUGBY
COVENTRY
Leamington Spa
Whittlesea
March
Manea
Wisbech
KINGS LYNN
Watlington
Downham Market
Hunstanton
Sandringham
Swaffham
Dereham
Littleport
Brandon
Lakenheath
Shippea Hill
Thetford
Harling Road
Ely
Waterbeach
Sheringham
West Runton
Cromer
Roughton Road
Gunton
North Walsham
Worstead
Hoveton & Wroxham
Salhouse
NORWICH
Wymondham
Spooner Row
Attleborough
Eccles Road
Diss
Great Yarmouth
Berney Arms
Haddiscoe
Somerleyton
Oulton Broad North
Oulton Broad South
Lowestoft
Beccles
Brampton
Halesworth
Darsham
Saxmundham
Long Buckby
NORTHAMPTON
Huntingdon
St Neots
Bedford
CAMBRIDGE
Newmarket
Bury St Edmunds
Stowmarket
Westerfield
IPSWICH
Sudbury
Felixstowe
Banbury
MILTON KEYNES
Bletchley
Royston
Letchworth
Hitchin
STANSTED Airport
Buckingham
Bicester
Luton
Stevenage
Bishops Stortford
Braintree
COLCHESTER
Manningtree
HARWICH
Marks Tey
Walton-on-the-Naze
Clacton-on-Sea
Aylesbury Parkway
Aylesbury
Dunstable
Welwyn Garden City
Hertford
Harlow
Witham
Chelmsford
OXFORD
Hemel Hempstead
St Albans
Southminster
Princes Risborough
Amersham
Watford
Chinnor
High Wycombe
Shenfield
Wickford
Southend Airport
Didcot Parkway
Henley-on-Thames
Marlow
Romford
Basildon
Upminster
SOUTHEND
Shoeburyness
SWINDON
Maidenhead
Slough
Heathrow Airport
Twyford
Windsor
LONDON
Tilbury
READING
Thatcham
Theale
Aldermaston
Newbury Racecourse
Midgham
Ascot
Staines
Surbiton
Dartford
Ebbsfleet International
Sheerness-on-Sea
Chatham
Gillingham
Sittingbourne
Faversham
Herne Bay
MARGATE
RAMSGATE
Woking
East Croydon
Oxted
Maidstone
CANTERBURY
Deal
Whitchurch
Overton
Basingstoke
Aldershot
Dorking
Redhill
Sevenoaks
Guildford
Andover
Micheldever
Winchester
Shawford
Eastleigh
Chandlers Ford
Mottisfont & Dunbridge
Alton
Haslemere
GATWICK Airport
Crawley
Tonbridge
Tunbridge Wells
ASHFORD
DOVER
FOLKESTONE
CHANNEL TUNNEL
East Grinstead
Horsham
Haywards Heath
Uckfield
Rye
SOUTHAMPTON
Southampton Airport Parkway
Totton
Fareham
Havant
For full details within this box see other side of sheet
LEWES
HASTINGS
Bexhill
See page 3658
PORTSMOUTH
CHICHESTER
Littlehampton
Bognor Regis
WORTHING
Hove
BRIGHTON
Newhaven
Seaford
EASTBOURNE
For full details see pages 3654-3657
Lymington Town
Pier Head
Ryde
Esplanade
St Johns Road
Brading
Sandown
Lake
Shanklin
Ventnor
ISLE OF WIGHT

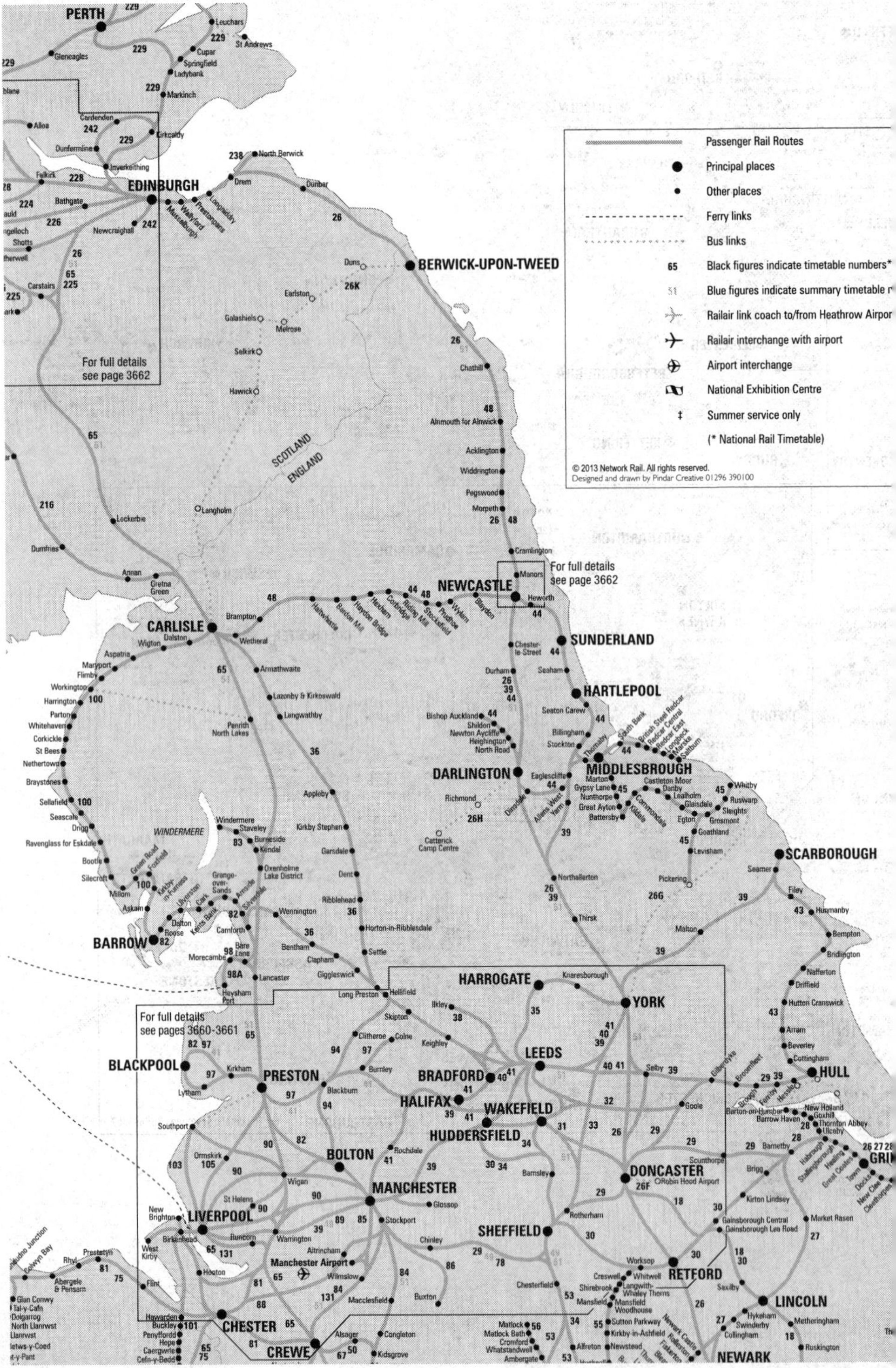

Passenger Rail Routes
Principal places
Other places
Ferry links
Bus links
Black figures indicate timetable numbers*
Railair link coach to/from Heathrow Airpor
Railair interchange with airport
Airport interchange
National Exhibition Centre
Summer service only
(* National Rail Timetable)
© 2013 Network Rail. All rights reserved.
Designed and drawn by Pindar Creative 01296 390100
PERTH
Leuchars
St Andrews
Cupar
Springfield
Ladybank
Markinch
Kirkcaldy
Gleneagles
Alloa
Cardenden
Dunfermline
Inverkeithing
Falkirk
EDINBURGH
Bathgate
Newcraighall
Shotts
Carstairs
North Berwick
Drem
Dunbar
Prestonpans
Longniddry
Wallyford
Musselburgh
For full details
see page 3662
BERWICK-UPON-TWEED
Duns
Earlston
Galashiels
Melrose
Selkirk
Hawick
Chathill
Alnmouth for Alnwick
Acklington
Widdrington
Pegswood
Morpeth
SCOTLAND
ENGLAND
Langholm
Lockerbie
Dumfries
Annan
Gretna Green
Cramlington
Manors
For full details
see page 3662
NEWCASTLE
Heworth
Brampton
Haltwhistle
Bardon Mill
Haydon Bridge
Hexham
Corbridge
Riding Mill
Stocksfield
Prudhoe
Wylam
Blaydon
CARLISLE
Wetheral
Dalston
Wigton
Aspatria
Maryport
Flimby
Workington
Harrington
Parton
Whitehaven
Corkickle
St Bees
Nethertown
Braystones
Sellafield
Seascale
Drigg
Ravenglass for Eskdale
Bootle
Silecroft
Millom
Askam
BARROW
Dalton
Roose
Ulverston
Cark
Kents Bank
Kirkby-in-Furness
Foxfield
Green Road
Grange-over-Sands
Arnside
Silverdale
Carnforth
Morecambe
Bare Lane
Lancaster
Heysham Port
WINDERMERE
Windermere
Staveley
Burneside
Kendal
Oxenholme Lake District
Armathwaite
Lazonby & Kirkoswald
Langwathby
Penrith North Lakes
Appleby
Kirkby Stephen
Garsdale
Dent
Ribblehead
Horton-in-Ribblesdale
Settle
Giggleswick
Clapham
Bentham
Wennington
Long Preston
Hellifield
SUNDERLAND
Chester-le-Street
Seaham
Durham
HARTLEPOOL
Seaton Carew
Bishop Auckland
Shildon
Newton Aycliffe
Heighington
North Road
Billingham
Stockton
Thornaby
South Bank
British Steel Redcar
Redcar Central
Redcar East
Longbeck
Marske
Saltburn
MIDDLESBROUGH
DARLINGTON
Eaglescliffe
Richmond
Catterick Camp Centre
Dinsdale
Allens West
Yarm
Marton
Gypsy Lane
Nunthorpe
Great Ayton
Battersby
Commondale
Kildale
Castleton Moor
Danby
Lealholm
Glaisdale
Egton
Grosmont
Goathland
Levisham
Pickering
Whitby
Ruswarp
Sleights
SCARBOROUGH
Seamer
Filey
Hunmanby
Bempton
Bridlington
Nafferton
Driffield
Hutton Cranswick
Arram
Beverley
Cottingham
HULL
Northallerton
Thirsk
Malton
HARROGATE
Knaresborough
YORK
Ilkley
Skipton
Keighley
LEEDS
For full details
see pages 3660-3661
BLACKPOOL
Kirkham
Lytham
PRESTON
Clitheroe
Colne
Burnley
Blackburn
BRADFORD
HALIFAX
WAKEFIELD
HUDDERSFIELD
Selby
Gilberdyke
Broomfleet
Brough
Ferriby
Hessle
Goole
Barton-on-Humber
Barrow Haven
New Holland
Goxhill
Thornton Abbey
Ulceby
Habrough
Stallingborough
Healing
Great Coates
Grimsby Town
Grimsby Docks
New Clee
Cleethorpes
Barnetby
Brigg
Kirton Lindsey
Southport
Ormskirk
BOLTON
Rochdale
Wigan
Barnsley
DONCASTER
Robin Hood Airport
Scunthorpe
St Helens
MANCHESTER
Glossop
New Brighton
LIVERPOOL
Birkenhead
West Kirby
Runcorn
Warrington
Stockport
Altrincham
Manchester Airport
Wilmslow
Chinley
SHEFFIELD
Rotherham
Gainsborough Central
Gainsborough Lea Road
Market Rasen
Worksop
RETFORD
Creswell
Whitwell
Shirebrook
Langwith-Whaley Thorns
Mansfield
Mansfield Woodhouse
Sutton Parkway
Kirkby-in-Ashfield
Newstead
Chesterfield
Saxilby
LINCOLN
Hykeham
Swinderby
Collingham
Metheringham
Ruskington
NEWARK
Newark Castle
Rolleston
Fiskerton
Alfreton
Matlock
Matlock Bath
Cromford
Whatstandwell
Ambergate
Buxton
Macclesfield
Congleton
Kidsgrove
Alsager
CREWE
CHESTER
Hawarden
Buckley
Penyffordd
Hope
Caergwrle
Cefn-y-Bedd
Hooton
Flint
Prestatyn
Rhyl
Abergele & Pensarn
Colwyn Bay
Llandudno Junction
Glan Conwy
Tal-y-Cafn
Dolgarrog
North Llanrwst
Llanrwst
Betws-y-Coed

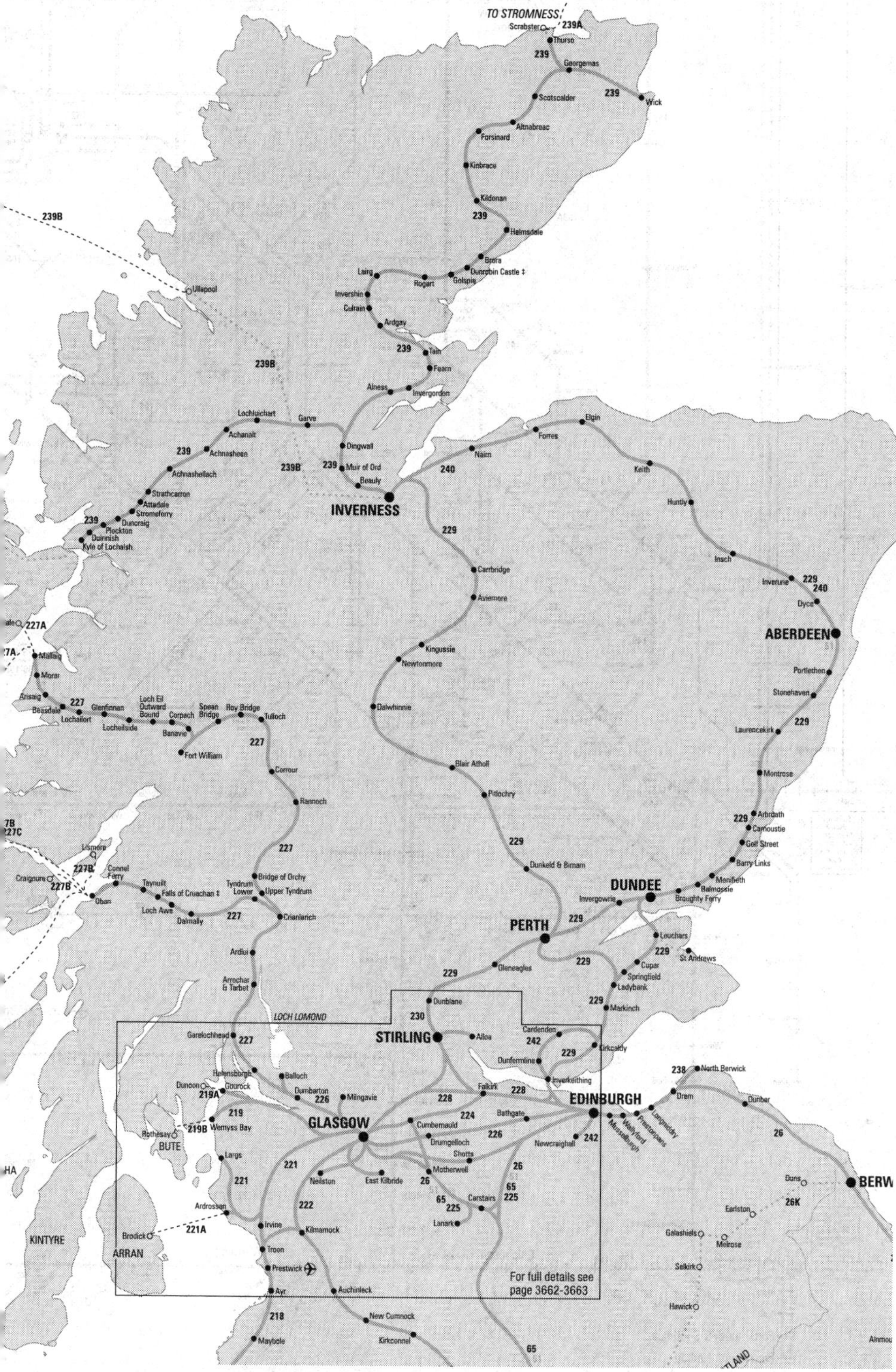
TO STROMNESS
Scrabster
239A
Thurso
239
Georgemas
Scotscalder
239
Wick
Altnabreac
Forsinard
Kinbrace
Kildonan
239
Helmsdale
Brora
Dunrobin Castle ‡
Golspie
Rogart
Lairg
Invershin
Culrain
Ardgay
239
Tain
Fearn
Alness
Invergordon
239B
Ullapool
239B
Lochluichart
Garve
Achanalt
Achnasheen
239
Dingwall
Muir of Ord
239
239B
Achnashellach
Beauly
INVERNESS
Strathcarron
Attadale
Stromeferry
Duncraig
Plockton
Duirinish
Kyle of Lochalsh
239
Nairn
240
Forres
Elgin
Keith
Huntly
Insch
Inverurie
229
240
Dyce
ABERDEEN
Portlethen
Stonehaven
229
Laurencekirk
Montrose
229
Arbroath
Carnoustie
Golf Street
Barry Links
Monifieth
Balmossie
Broughty Ferry
DUNDEE
Invergowrie
229
PERTH
Leuchars
229
St Andrews
229
Cupar
Springfield
Ladybank
229
Markinch
229
Gleneagles
229
Carrbridge
Aviemore
Kingussie
Newtonmore
Dalwhinnie
Blair Atholl
Pitlochry
229
Dunkeld & Birnam
Mallaig
Morar
Arisaig
Beasdale
227
Lochailort
Glenfinnan
Lochielside
Loch Eil Outward Bound
Corpach
Banavie
Spean Bridge
Roy Bridge
Tulloch
227
Fort William
Corrour
Rannoch
227
Bridge of Orchy
Tyndrum Lower
Upper Tyndrum
Crianlarich
227
Dalmally
Loch Awe
Falls of Cruachan ‡
Taynuilt
Connel Ferry
Oban
Lismore
227B
Craignure
227B
227A
Ardlui
Arrochar & Tarbet
LOCH LOMOND
Dunblane
230
STIRLING
Alloa
Cardenden
242
229
Kirkcaldy
Dunfermline
Inverkeithing
Garelochhead
227
Helensburgh
Balloch
Dumbarton
226
Milngavie
Dunoon
Gourock
219A
219
Wemyss Bay
219B
Rothesay
BUTE
GLASGOW
228
Falkirk
228
EDINBURGH
238
North Berwick
Drem
Dunbar
Longniddry
Prestonpans
Wallyford
Musselburgh
26
242
Newcraighall
Bathgate
224
Cumbernauld
226
Drumgelloch
Shotts
Motherwell
26
26
65
225
Carstairs
65
225
Lanark
East Kilbride
Neilston
221
Largs
221
222
Ardrossan
221A
Brodick
ARRAN
KINTYRE
Irvine
Kilmarnock
Troon
Prestwick
Ayr
Auchinleck
For full details see page 3662-3663
218
New Cumnock
Kirkconnel
Maybole
65
Duns
26K
Earlston
Galashiels
Melrose
Selkirk
Hawick

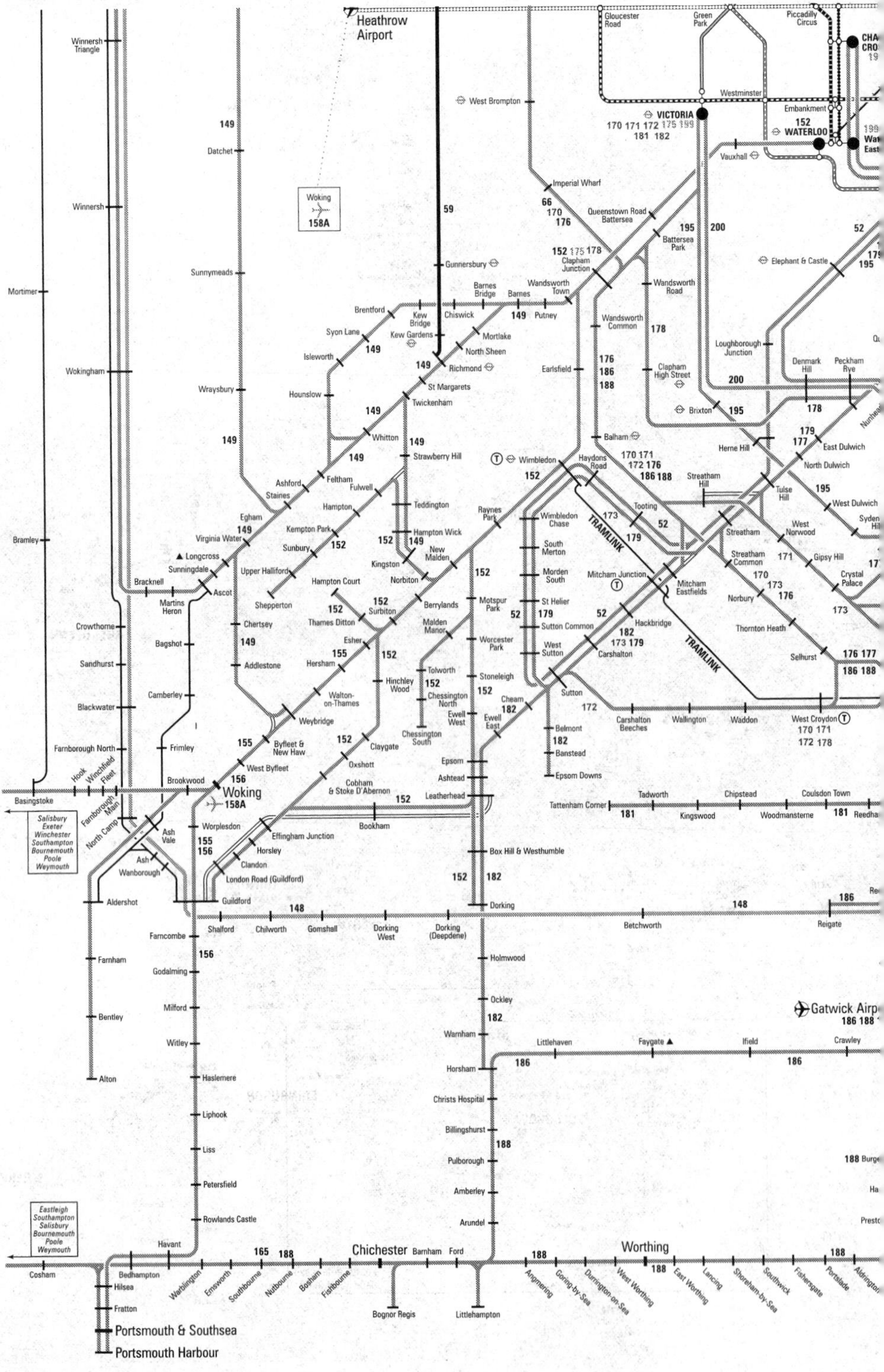
Heathrow Airport
Gloucester Road
Green Park
Piccadilly Circus
Westminster
Embankment
VICTORIA
170 171 172 175 199
181 182
152
WATERLOO
West Brompton
Vauxhall
Imperial Wharf
66
170
176
Queenstown Road Battersea
195
200
Battersea Park
152 175 178
Clapham Junction
Wandsworth Town
Wandsworth Road
Elephant & Castle
52
195
Wandsworth Common
178
Loughborough Junction
Clapham High Street
Denmark Hill
Peckham Rye
Earlsfield
176
186
188
200
Brixton
195
178
Balham
170 171
172 176
186 188
Herne Hill
179
177
East Dulwich
North Dulwich
Wimbledon
152
Haydons Road
Streatham Hill
Tulse Hill
195
West Dulwich
Tooting
173
52
179
Wimbledon Chase
TRAMLINK
Streatham
West Norwood
Streatham Common
171
Gipsy Hill
South Merton
Morden South
Mitcham Junction
Mitcham Eastfields
170
173
176
Norbury
Crystal Palace
173
St Helier
52
179
52
Hackbridge
182
173 179
Sutton Common
Carshalton
Thornton Heath
West Sutton
TRAMLINK
Selhurst
176 177
186 188
Sutton
172
Carshalton Beeches
Wallington
Waddon
West Croydon
170 171
172 178
Belmont
182
Banstead
Epsom Downs
Tattenham Corner
Tadworth
181
Kingswood
Chipstead
Woodmansterne
Coulsdon Town
181
Winnersh Triangle
Winnersh
Mortimer
Wokingham
Bramley
149
Datchet
Woking
158A
Sunnymeads
Wraysbury
149
59
Gunnersbury
Barnes Bridge
Barnes
149
Putney
Brentford
Kew Bridge
Chiswick
Syon Lane
Kew Gardens
Mortlake
149
Isleworth
North Sheen
149
Richmond
St Margarets
Hounslow
Twickenham
149
Whitton
149
149
Strawberry Hill
Ashford
Feltham
Fulwell
Staines
Hampton
Teddington
Egham
149
Kempton Park
Hampton Wick
Virginia Water
Sunbury
152
152
149
Kingston
New Malden
Raynes Park
Longcross
Sunningdale
Upper Halliford
Norbiton
152
Bracknell
Ascot
Hampton Court
Martins Heron
Shepperton
152
Surbiton
152
Berrylands
Motspur Park
Thames Ditton
Chertsey
Malden Manor
Crowthorne
Bagshot
149
Esher
Worcester Park
Sandhurst
Hersham
155
152
Tolworth
Addlestone
Hinchley Wood
152
Stoneleigh
Camberley
Chessington North
152
Blackwater
Walton-on-Thames
Ewell West
Cheam
182
Weybridge
Ewell East
Chessington South
Farnborough North
Frimley
155
Byfleet & New Haw
152
Claygate
West Byfleet
Oxshott
Epsom
Brookwood
156
Ashtead
Hook
Winchfield
Fleet
Cobham & Stoke D'Abernon
Basingstoke
Woking
158A
152
Leatherhead
Farnborough Main
Salisbury
Exeter
Winchester
Southampton
Bournemouth
Poole
Weymouth
North Camp
Ash Vale
Worplesdon
155
156
Effingham Junction
Bookham
Horsley
Box Hill & Westhumble
Ash
Clandon
Wanborough
London Road (Guildford)
152
182
Aldershot
Guildford
Dorking
148
148
186
Shalford
Chilworth
Gomshall
Dorking West
Dorking (Deepdene)
Betchworth
Reigate
Farncombe
156
Holmwood
Farnham
Godalming
Milford
Ockley
182
Bentley
Gatwick Airport
186 188
Warnham
Witley
Littlehaven
Faygate
Ifield
Crawley
186
186
Horsham
Alton
Haslemere
Christs Hospital
Liphook
Billingshurst
188
Liss
Pulborough
188
Petersfield
Amberley
Rowlands Castle
Arundel
Eastleigh
Southampton
Salisbury
Bournemouth
Poole
Weymouth
Havant
165
188
Chichester
Barnham
Ford
188
Worthing
188
188
Cosham
Bedhampton
Warblington
Emsworth
Southbourne
Nutbourne
Bosham
Fishbourne
Angmering
Goring-by-Sea
Durrington-on-Sea
West Worthing
East Worthing
Lancing
Shoreham-by-Sea
Southwick
Fishersgate
Portslade
Hilsea
Fratton
Bognor Regis
Littlehampton
Portsmouth & Southsea
Portsmouth Harbour

Continued on pages 3656-3657

London & South East

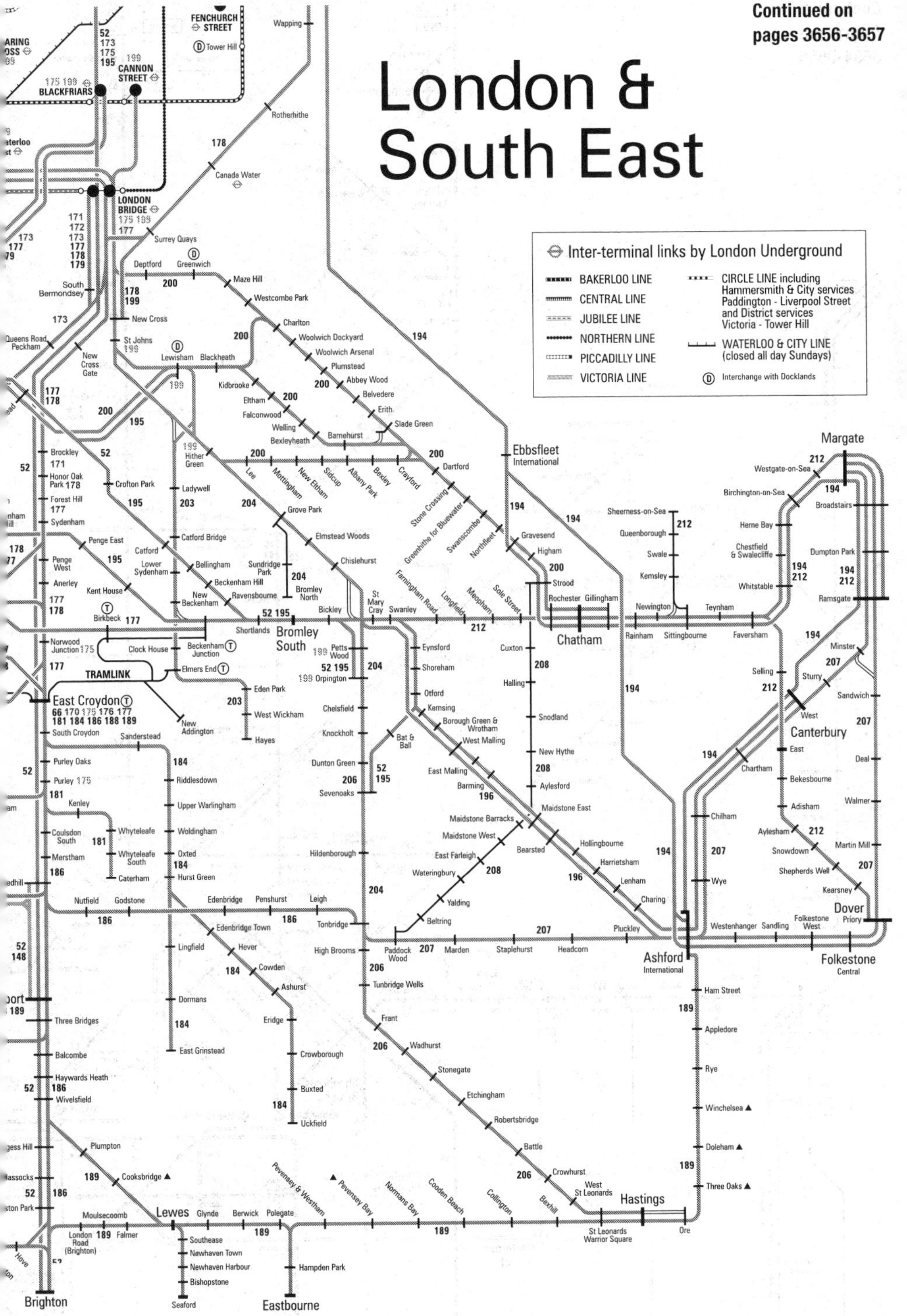

Inter-terminal links by London Underground
BAKERLOO LINE
CENTRAL LINE
JUBILEE LINE
NORTHERN LINE
PICCADILLY LINE
VICTORIA LINE
CIRCLE LINE including Hammersmith & City services Paddington - Liverpool Street and District services Victoria - Tower Hill
WATERLOO & CITY LINE (closed all day Sundays)
Interchange with Docklands
FENCHURCH STREET
Tower Hill
Wapping
CANNON STREET
BLACKFRIARS
Rotherhithe
Canada Water
LONDON BRIDGE
Surrey Quays
Greenwich
Deptford
South Bermondsey
Maze Hill
Westcombe Park
New Cross
Charlton
Queens Road Peckham
St Johns
Woolwich Dockyard
Woolwich Arsenal
New Cross Gate
Lewisham
Blackheath
Plumstead
Abbey Wood
Kidbrooke
Belvedere
Eltham
Erith
Falconwood
Slade Green
Welling
Bexleyheath
Barnehurst
Brockley
Honor Oak Park
Crofton Park
Hither Green
Lee
Mottingham
New Eltham
Sidcup
Albany Park
Bexley
Crayford
Dartford
Ebbsfleet International
Forest Hill
Ladywell
Sydenham
Grove Park
Stone Crossing
Greenhithe for Bluewater
Swanscombe
Northfleet
Gravesend
Higham
Strood
Penge East
Catford Bridge
Elmstead Woods
Catford
Penge West
Lower Sydenham
Bellingham
Sundridge Park
Chislehurst
Anerley
Kent House
Beckenham Hill
Bromley North
Ravensbourne
New Beckenham
St Mary Cray
Swanley
Farningham Road
Longfield
Meopham
Sole Street
Rochester
Gillingham
Chatham
Birkbeck
Bickley
Shortlands
Bromley South
Norwood Junction
Clock House
Beckenham Junction
Petts Wood
Orpington
Eynsford
Cuxton
Shoreham
Halling
Elmers End
TRAMLINK
Eden Park
East Croydon
Otford
Kemsing
Borough Green & Wrotham
West Malling
Snodland
New Hythe
Aylesford
Maidstone East
Maidstone Barracks
Maidstone West
East Farleigh
Wateringbury
Yalding
Beltring
Bearsted
Hollingbourne
Harrietsham
Lenham
Charing
Pluckley
West Wickham
Hayes
New Addington
Chelsfield
Knockholt
Bat & Ball
Dunton Green
Sevenoaks
East Malling
Barming
South Croydon
Sanderstead
Purley Oaks
Riddlesdown
Purley
Kenley
Upper Warlingham
Whyteleafe
Woldingham
Coulsdon South
Whyteleafe South
Oxted
Merstham
Caterham
Hurst Green
Hildenborough
Nutfield
Godstone
Edenbridge
Penshurst
Leigh
Tonbridge
Edenbridge Town
Lingfield
Hever
Cowden
Ashurst
High Brooms
Paddock Wood
Marden
Staplehurst
Headcorn
Tunbridge Wells
Dormans
Eridge
Frant
Wadhurst
Stonegate
Etchingham
Robertsbridge
Battle
Crowhurst
West St Leonards
Hastings
Ore
St Leonards Warrior Square
Bexhill
Collington
Cooden Beach
Normans Bay
Pevensey Bay
Pevensey & Westham
East Grinstead
Crowborough
Buxted
Uckfield
Three Bridges
Balcombe
Haywards Heath
Wivelsfield
Plumpton
Cooksbridge
Lewes
Moulsecoomb
London Road (Brighton)
Falmer
Glynde
Berwick
Polegate
Southease
Newhaven Town
Newhaven Harbour
Bishopstone
Seaford
Hampden Park
Eastbourne
Brighton
Hove
Margate
Westgate-on-Sea
Birchington-on-Sea
Broadstairs
Sheerness-on-Sea
Queenborough
Swale
Kemsley
Herne Bay
Chestfield & Swalecliffe
Dumpton Park
Whitstable
Ramsgate
Newington
Teynham
Rainham
Sittingbourne
Faversham
Minster
Selling
Sturry
Sandwich
Canterbury West
Canterbury East
Chartham
Deal
Bekesbourne
Walmer
Adisham
Chilham
Aylesham
Martin Mill
Snowdown
Shepherds Well
Wye
Kearsney
Dover Priory
Westenhanger
Sandling
Folkestone West
Folkestone Central
Ashford International
Ham Street
Appledore
Rye
Winchelsea
Doleham
Three Oaks

Continued from pages 3654-3655

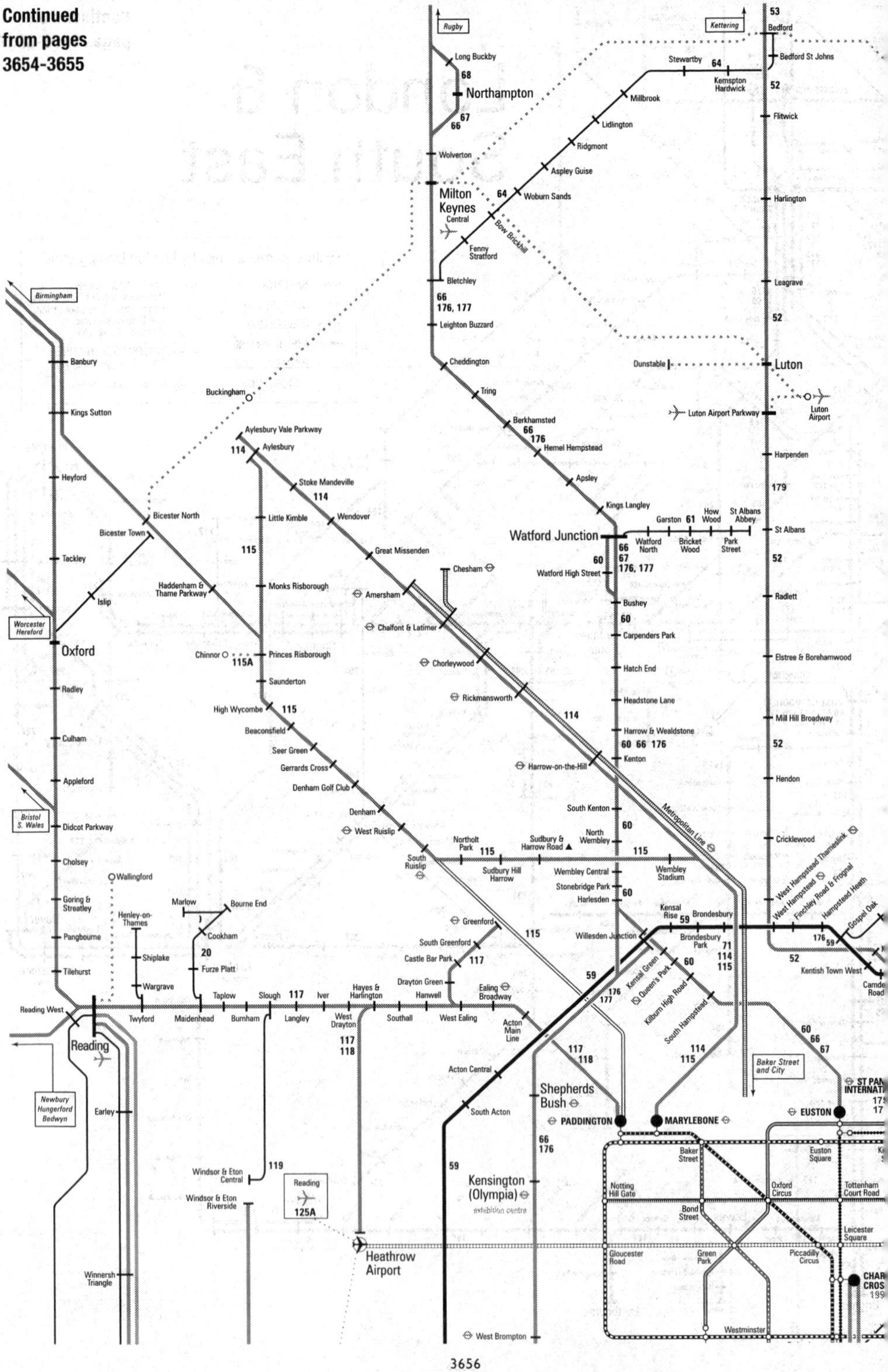

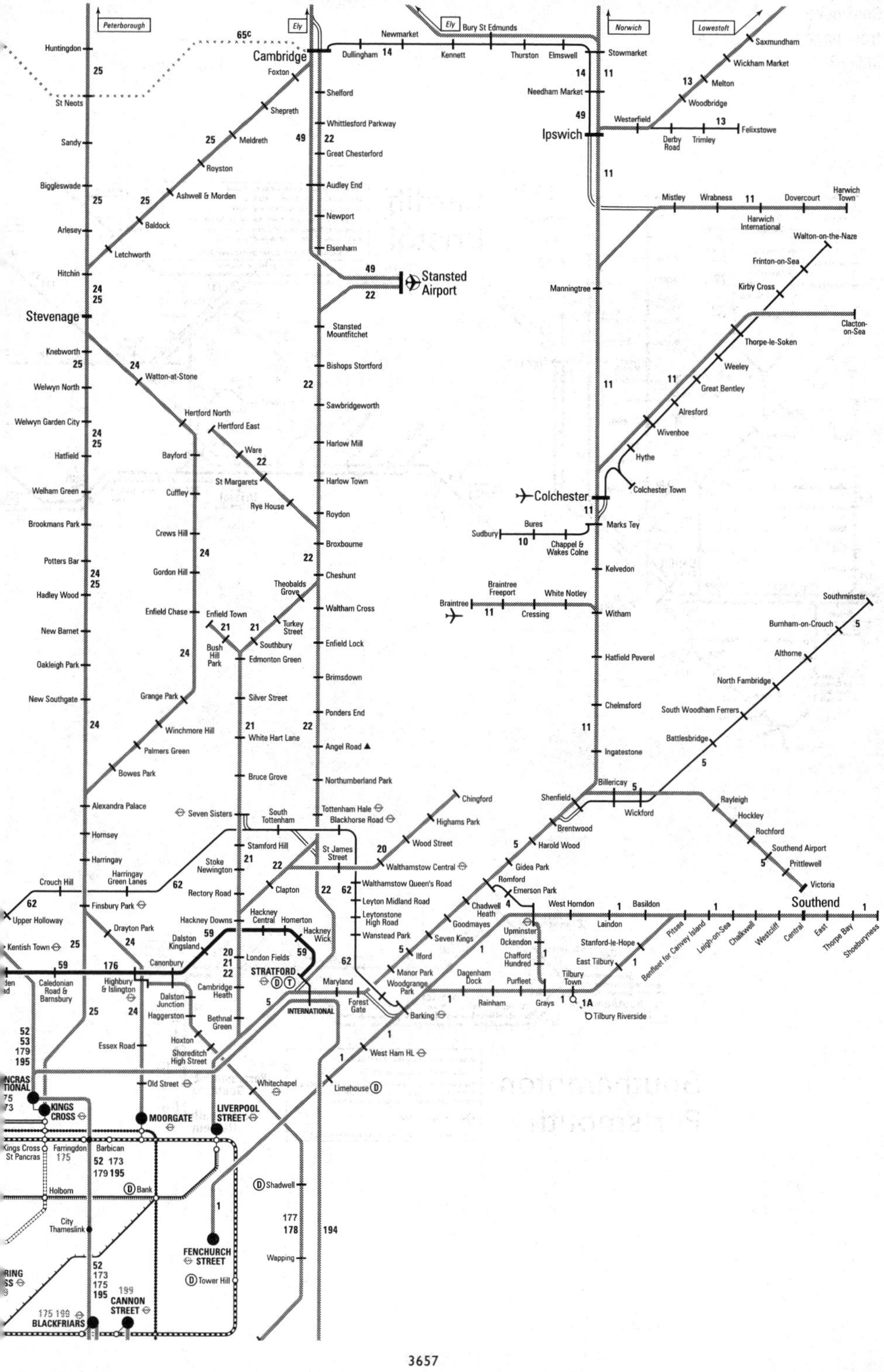

Peterborough
Ely
Ely
Norwich
Lowestoft
65C
Huntingdon
St Neots
Sandy
Biggleswade
Arlesey
Hitchin
Stevenage
Knebworth
Welwyn North
Welwyn Garden City
Hatfield
Welham Green
Brookmans Park
Potters Bar
Hadley Wood
New Barnet
Oakleigh Park
New Southgate
Alexandra Palace
Hornsey
Harringay
Finsbury Park
Drayton Park
Canonbury
Highbury & Islington
Essex Road
Old Street
MOORGATE
KINGS CROSS
Cambridge
Foxton
Shepreth
Meldreth
Royston
Ashwell & Morden
Baldock
Letchworth
Watton-at-Stone
Hertford North
Bayford
Cuffley
Crews Hill
Gordon Hill
Enfield Chase
Grange Park
Winchmore Hill
Palmers Green
Bowes Park
Hertford East
Ware
St Margarets
Rye House
Theobalds Grove
Enfield Town
Bush Hill Park
Turkey Street
Southbury
Edmonton Green
Silver Street
White Hart Lane
Bruce Grove
Seven Sisters
South Tottenham
Stamford Hill
Stoke Newington
Rectory Road
Hackney Downs
Hackney Central
Homerton
Hackney Wick
Dalston Kingsland
Dalston Junction
Haggerston
Hoxton
Shoreditch High Street
London Fields
Cambridge Heath
Bethnal Green
LIVERPOOL STREET
STRATFORD
Clapton
Crouch Hill
Harringay Green Lanes
Upper Holloway
Kentish Town
Caledonian Road & Barnsbury
Whitechapel
Shelford
Whittlesford Parkway
Great Chesterford
Audley End
Newport
Elsenham
Stansted Airport
Stansted Mountfitchet
Bishops Stortford
Sawbridgeworth
Harlow Mill
Harlow Town
Roydon
Broxbourne
Cheshunt
Waltham Cross
Enfield Lock
Brimsdown
Ponders End
Angel Road
Northumberland Park
Tottenham Hale
Blackhorse Road
St James Street
Walthamstow Central
Walthamstow Queen's Road
Leyton Midland Road
Leytonstone High Road
Wanstead Park
Chingford
Highams Park
Wood Street
Maryland
Forest Gate
INTERNATIONAL
Woodgrange Park
Barking
West Ham HL
Limehouse
Shadwell
Wapping
Newmarket
Dullingham
Kennett
Bury St Edmunds
Thurston
Elmswell
Stowmarket
Needham Market
Ipswich
Westerfield
Derby Road
Trimley
Felixstowe
Woodbridge
Melton
Wickham Market
Saxmundham
Mistley
Wrabness
Harwich International
Dovercourt
Harwich Town
Walton-on-the-Naze
Frinton-on-Sea
Kirby Cross
Clacton-on-Sea
Thorpe-le-Soken
Weeley
Great Bentley
Alresford
Wivenhoe
Hythe
Colchester Town
Manningtree
Colchester
Marks Tey
Sudbury
Bures
Chappel & Wakes Colne
Kelvedon
Braintree
Braintree Freeport
Cressing
White Notley
Witham
Hatfield Peverel
Chelmsford
Ingatestone
Shenfield
Billericay
Wickford
Brentwood
Harold Wood
Gidea Park
Romford
Emerson Park
Chadwell Heath
Goodmayes
Seven Kings
Ilford
Manor Park
Upminster
Ockendon
Chafford Hundred
Dagenham Dock
Rainham
Purfleet
Grays
Tilbury Town
Tilbury Riverside
East Tilbury
Stanford-le-Hope
West Horndon
Laindon
Basildon
Pitsea
Benfleet for Canvey Island
Leigh-on-Sea
Chalkwell
Westcliff
Southend Central
Southend East
Thorpe Bay
Shoeburyness
Southend
Rayleigh
Hockley
Rochford
Southend Airport
Prittlewell
Victoria
Battlesbridge
South Woodham Ferrers
North Fambridge
Althorne
Burnham-on-Crouch
Southminster
Kings Cross St Pancras
Farringdon
Barbican
Holborn
Bank
City Thameslink
FENCHURCH STREET
Tower Hill
CANNON STREET
BLACKFRIARS

Cardiff Bristol

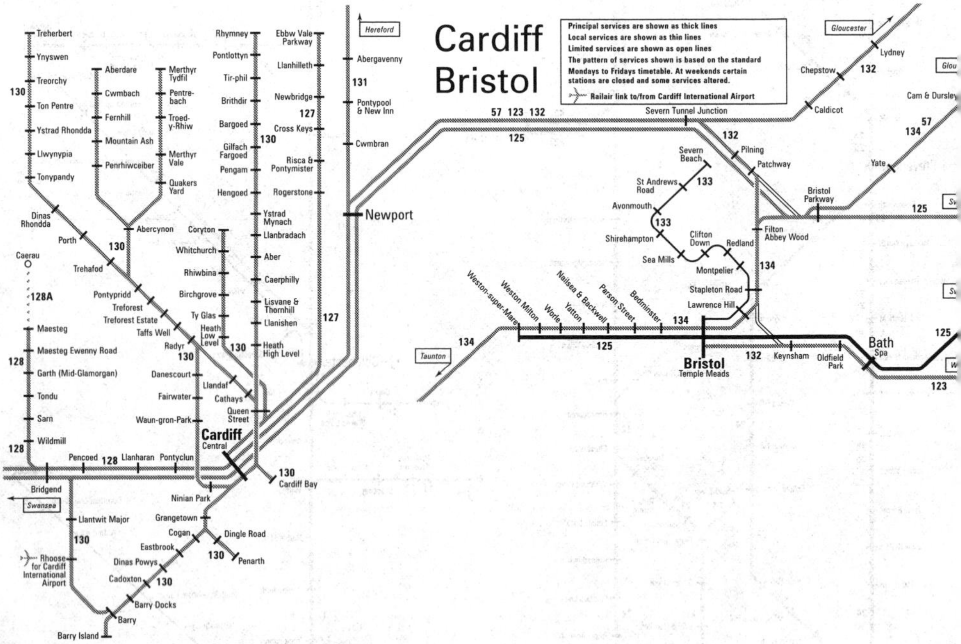
Principal services are shown as thick lines
Local services are shown as thin lines
Limited services are shown as open lines
The pattern of services shown is based on the standard Mondays to Fridays timetable. At weekends certain stations are closed and some services altered.
Railair link to/from Cardiff International Airport
Treherbert
Ynyswen
Treorchy
130
Ton Pentre
Ystrad Rhondda
Llwynypia
Tonypandy
Aberdare
Cwmbach
Fernhill
Mountain Ash
Penrhiwceiber
Merthyr Tydfil
Pentre-bach
Troed-y-Rhiw
Merthyr Vale
Quakers Yard
Rhymney
Pontlottyn
Tir-phil
Brithdir
Bargoed
Gilfach Fargoed
Pengam
Hengoed
Ebbw Vale Parkway
Llanhilleth
Newbridge
127
Cross Keys
Risca & Pontymister
Rogerstone
Hereford
Abergavenny
131
Pontypool & New Inn
Cwmbran
Newport
Dinas Rhondda
Porth
130
Abercynon
Trehafod
Caerau
128A
Pontypridd
Treforest
Treforest Estate
Taffs Well
Radyr
Maesteg
Maesteg Ewenny Road
128
Garth (Mid-Glamorgan)
Tondu
Sarn
Wildmill
128
Coryton
Whitchurch
Rhiwbina
Birchgrove
Ty Glas
Heath Low Level
130
Ystrad Mynach
Llanbradach
Aber
Caerphilly
Lisvane & Thornhill
Llanishen
Heath High Level
127
Danescourt
Llandaf
Fairwater
Cathays
Queen Street
Waun-gron-Park
Cardiff Central
Pencoed
128
Llanharan
Pontyclun
130
Cardiff Bay
Bridgend
Swansea
Ninian Park
Grangetown
Llantwit Major
130
Cogan
Dingle Road
Eastbrook
130
Penarth
Rhoose for Cardiff International Airport
Dinas Powys
Cadoxton
130
Barry Docks
Barry
Barry Island
57 123 132
125
Severn Tunnel Junction
Gloucester
Lydney
Chepstow
132
Caldicot
Glou
Cam & Dursley
57
134
132
Pilning
Patchway
Severn Beach
St Andrews Road
133
Avonmouth
133
Shirehampton
Clifton Down
Redland
Sea Mills
Montpelier
Stapleton Road
Lawrence Hill
Bristol Parkway
Yate
125
Filton Abbey Wood
134
Weston-super-Mare
Weston Milton
Worle
Yatton
Nailsea & Backwell
Parson Street
Bedminster
134
134
125
Taunton
Bristol Temple Meads
132
Keynsham
Oldfield Park
Bath Spa
125
123

Southampton Portsmouth

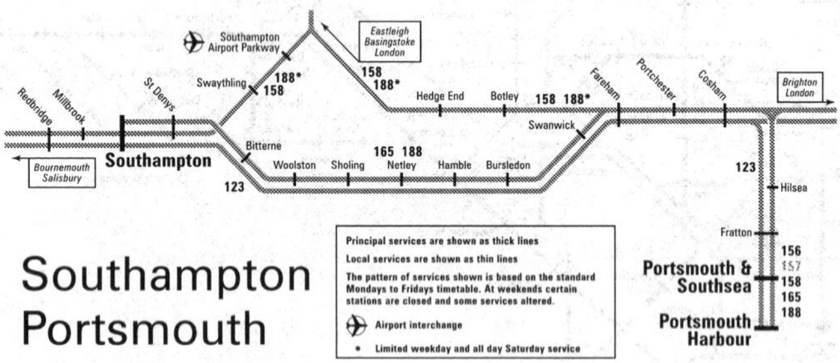
Southampton Airport Parkway
Eastleigh Basingstoke London
Swaythling
188*
158
158
188*
Redbridge
Millbrook
St Denys
Hedge End
Botley
158 188*
Fareham
Portchester
Cosham
Brighton London
Southampton
Bournemouth Salisbury
Bitterne
Swanwick
165 188
Woolston
Sholing
Netley
Hamble
Bursledon
123
123
Hilsea
Fratton
Portsmouth & Southsea
Portsmouth Harbour
156
157
158
165
188
Principal services are shown as thick lines
Local services are shown as thin lines
The pattern of services shown is based on the standard Mondays to Fridays timetable. At weekends certain stations are closed and some services altered.
Airport interchange
* Limited weekday and all day Saturday service

Birmingham
West Midlands
Principal services are shown as thick lines
Local services are shown as thin lines
Limited services are shown as open lines
The pattern of services shown is based on the standard Mondays to Fridays timetable. At weekends certain stations are closed and some services altered.
Rail-air link to/from Birmingham Airport
Tram/Metro Interchange
Shrewsbury
Stafford
Derby
Leicester
Rugby
Banbury
Evesham
Cheltenham Spa
Penkridge
Rugeley Town
Hednesford
Cannock
Landywood
Bloxwich North
Bloxwich
Walsall
Bescot Stadium
Tame Bridge
Hamstead
Perry Barr
Witton
Aston
Duddeston
Lichfield Trent Valley
Lichfield City
Shenstone
Blake Street
Butlers Lane
Four Oaks
Sutton Coldfield
Wylde Green
Chester Road
Erdington
Gravelly Hill
Tamworth
Wilnecote
Polesworth
Atherstone
Nuneaton
Bedworth
Coventry
Canley
Tile Hill
Berkswell
Hampton-in-Arden
Birmingham International for National Exhibition Centre
Coleshill Parkway
Water Orton
Adderley Park
Stechford
Lea Hall
Marston Green
Cosford
Albrighton
Codsall
Bilbrook
Wolverhampton
Coseley
Tipton
Dudley Port
Sandwell & Dudley
Smethwick Galton Bridge
METRO
The Hawthorns
Jewellery Quarter
Snow Hill
Smethwick Rolfe Street
New Street
Birmingham
Moor Street
Bordesley
Small Heath
Tyseley
Acocks Green
Olton
Solihull
Widney Manor
Dorridge
Lapworth
Hatton
Warwick Parkway
Warwick
Leamington Spa
Claverdon
Bearley
Wilmcote
Stratford-upon-Avon
Spring Road
Hall Green
Yardley Wood
Shirley
Whitlocks End
Wythall
Earlswood
The Lakes
Wood End
Danzey
Henley-in-Arden
Wootton Wawen
Langley Green
Rowley Regis
Old Hill
Cradley Heath
Lye
Stourbridge Town
Stourbridge Junction
Hagley
Blakedown
Kidderminster
Hartlebury
Droitwich Spa
Foregate Street
Worcester
Shrub Hill
Five Ways
University
Selly Oak
Bournville
Kings Norton
Northfield
Longbridge
Barnt Green
Bromsgrove
Alvechurch
Redditch
57
66
67
68
69
70
71
72
75
115
116
126

Liverpool Leeds Manchester Sheffield

Principal services are shown as thick lines
Local services are shown as thin lines
Limited services are shown as open lines
The pattern of services shown is based on the standard Mondays to Fridays timetable. At weekends certain stations are closed and some services altered.
Airport interchange
Ⓣ Tram/Metro Interchange

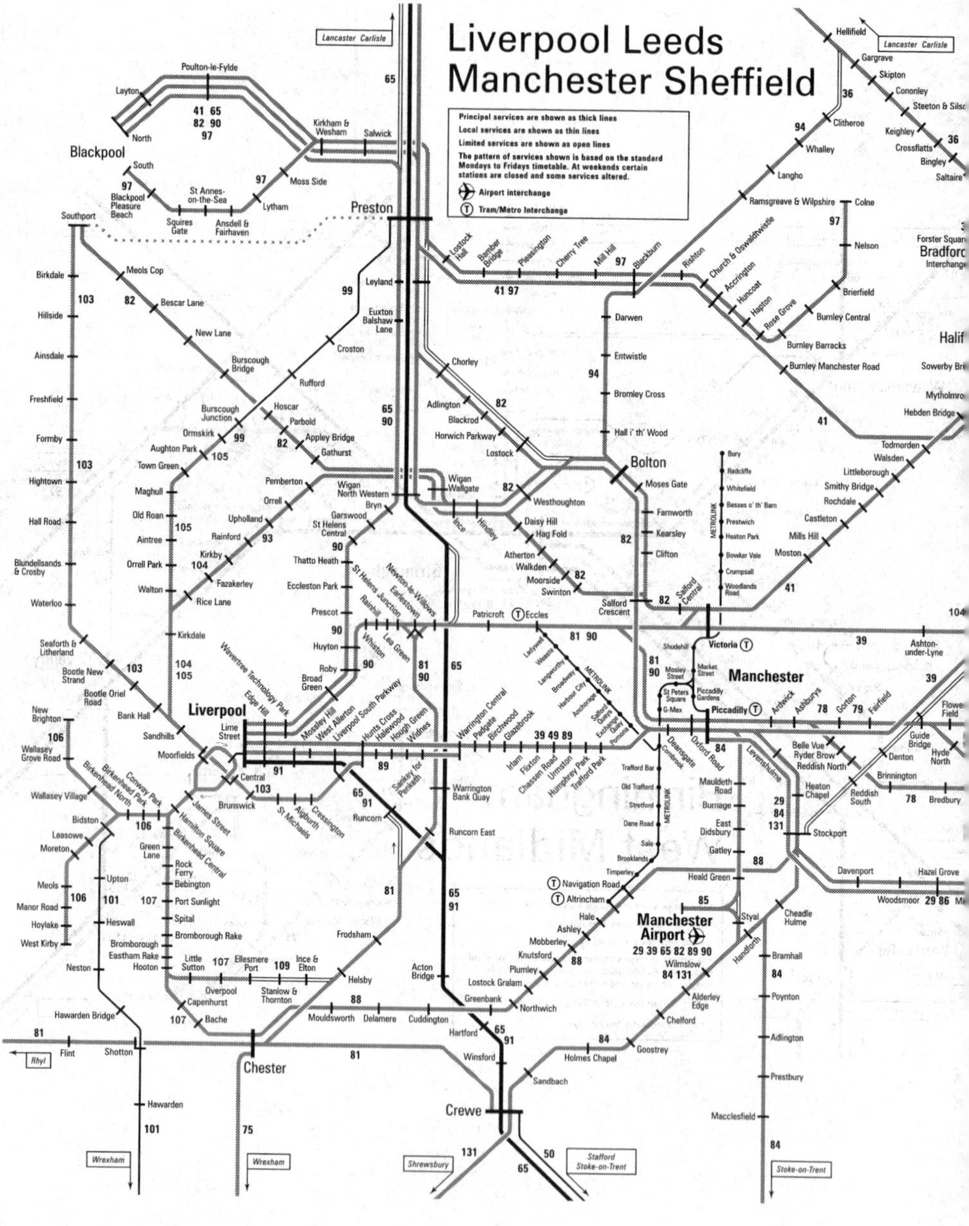

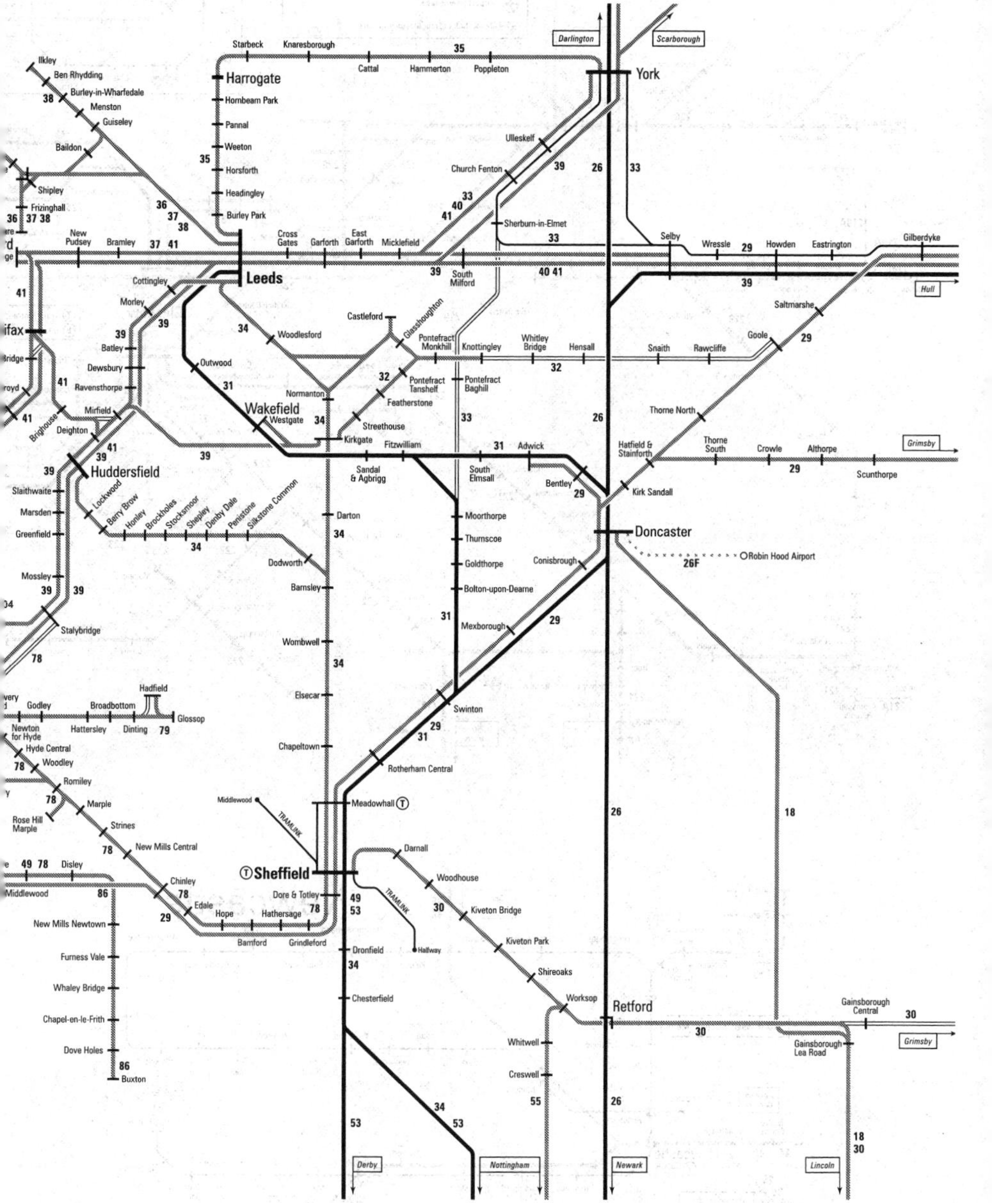

Darlington
Scarborough
York
Starbeck
Knaresborough
Cattal
Hammerton
Poppleton
35
Harrogate
Hornbeam Park
Pannal
Weeton
Horsforth
Headingley
Burley Park
Ilkley
Ben Rhydding
Burley-in-Wharfedale
Menston
Guiseley
Baildon
Shipley
Frizinghall
36 37 38
New Pudsey
Bramley
37 41
Leeds
Cross Gates
Garforth
East Garforth
Micklefield
South Milford
Ulleskelf
Church Fenton
Sherburn-in-Elmet
39
26
33
40
41
Selby
Wressle
29
Howden
Eastrington
Gilberdyke
Hull
Cottingley
Morley
Batley
Dewsbury
Ravensthorpe
Mirfield
Deighton
Brighouse
Huddersfield
Woodlesford
Outwood
Castleford
Glasshoughton
Pontefract Monkhill
Knottingley
Whitley Bridge
Hensall
Snaith
Rawcliffe
Goole
Saltmarshe
32
Normanton
Pontefract Tanshelf
Pontefract Baghill
Featherstone
Wakefield
Westgate
Streethouse
Kirkgate
Fitzwilliam
Sandal & Agbrigg
South Elmsall
Adwick
Bentley
Thorne North
Hatfield & Stainforth
Thorne South
Crowle
Althorpe
Scunthorpe
Grimsby
Kirk Sandall
Doncaster
Robin Hood Airport
26F
Slaithwaite
Marsden
Greenfield
Mossley
Stalybridge
Lockwood
Berry Brow
Honley
Brockholes
Stocksmoor
Shepley
Denby Dale
Penistone
Silkstone Common
Dodworth
Darton
Barnsley
Wombwell
Elsecar
Chapeltown
Moorthorpe
Thurnscoe
Goldthorpe
Bolton-upon-Dearne
Conisbrough
Mexborough
Swinton
Rotherham Central
Meadowhall
Middlewood
TRAMLINK
Sheffield
Darnall
Woodhouse
Kiveton Bridge
Kiveton Park
Shireoaks
Worksop
Retford
Hallway
Dore & Totley
Dronfield
Chesterfield
Hadfield
Godley
Broadbottom
Glossop
Newton for Hyde
Hattersley
Dinting
79
Hyde Central
Woodley
Romiley
Marple
Rose Hill Marple
Strines
New Mills Central
Disley
Chinley
Edale
Hope
Hathersage
Bamford
Grindleford
Middlewood
86
New Mills Newtown
Furness Vale
Whaley Bridge
Chapel-en-le-Frith
Dove Holes
Buxton
Whitwell
Creswell
55
Gainsborough Central
Gainsborough Lea Road
30
18
Derby
Nottingham
Newark
Lincoln
34
53
49
78

Glasgow Edinburgh

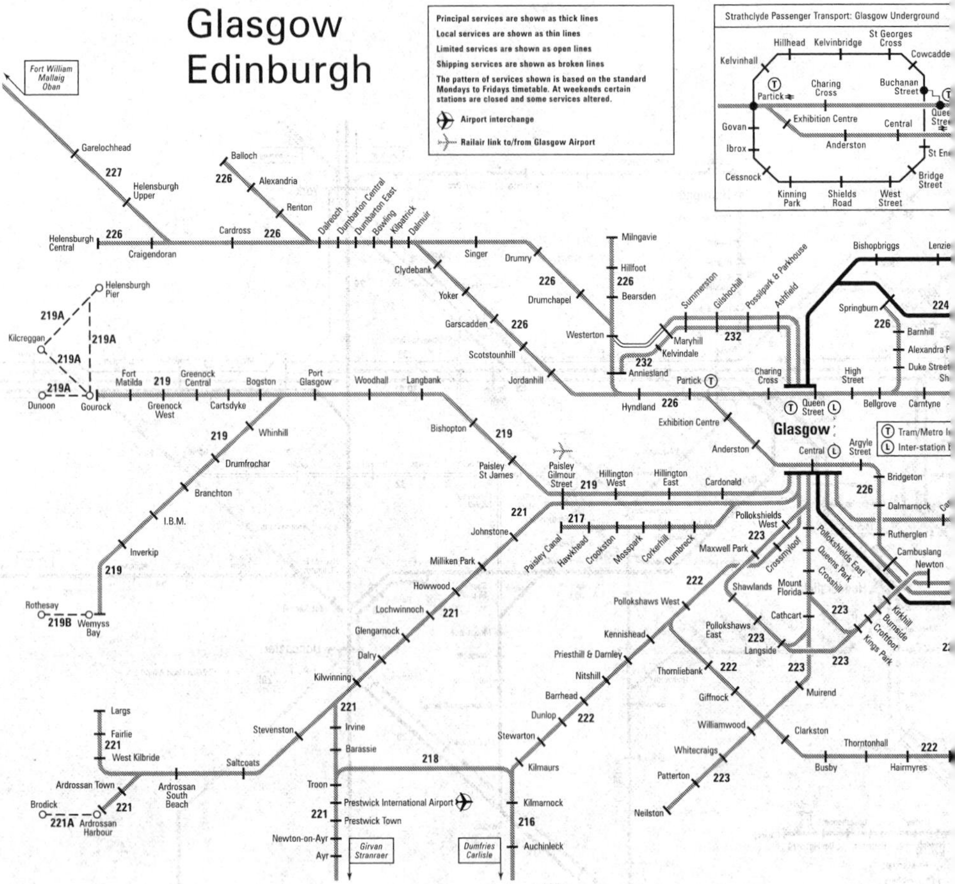

Newcastle

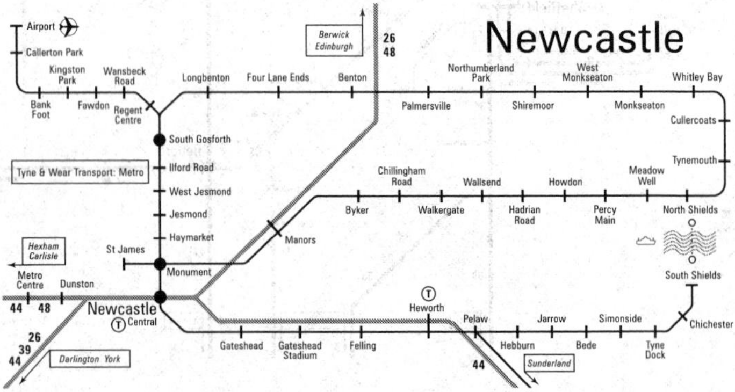

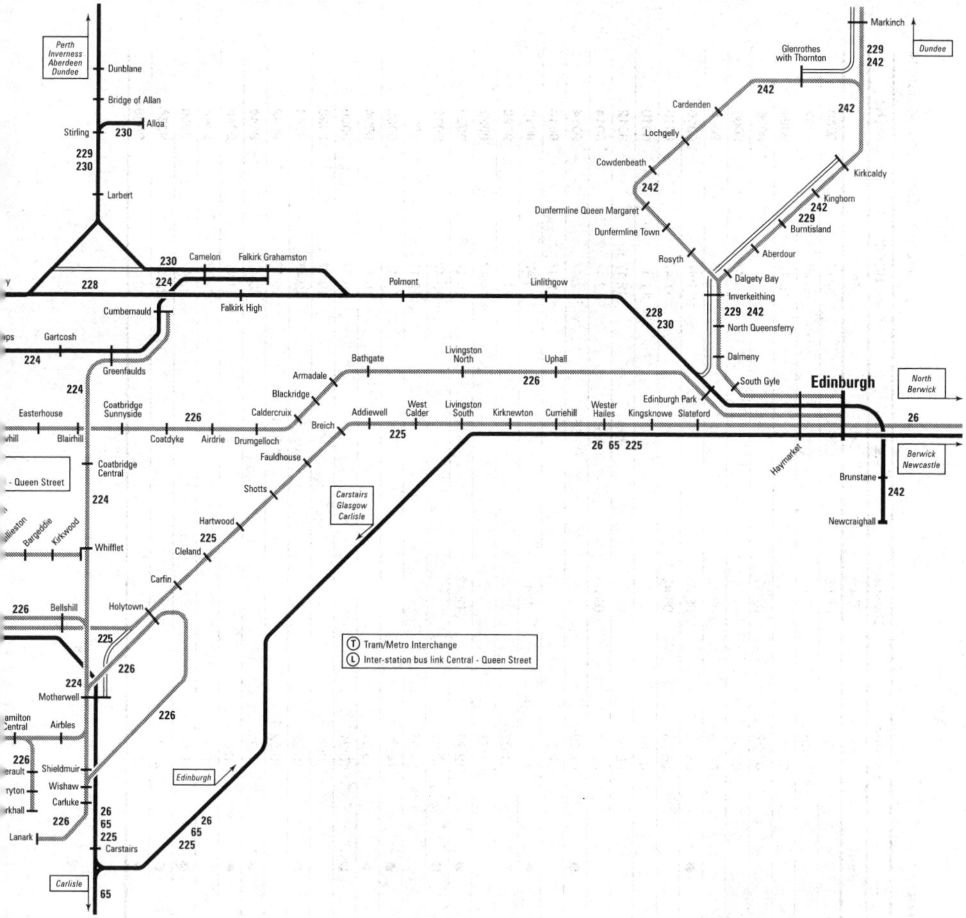
Perth
Inverness
Aberdeen
Dundee
Dunblane
Bridge of Allan
Stirling
Alloa
230
229
230
Larbert
230
Camelon
Falkirk Grahamston
228
224
Polmont
Linlithgow
Falkirk High
Cumbernauld
228
230
Gartcosh
224
Greenfaulds
224
Markinch
Dundee
Glenrothes with Thornton
229
242
242
Cardenden
242
Lochgelly
Cowdenbeath
Kirkcaldy
242
Kinghorn
Dunfermline Queen Margaret
242
229
Burntisland
Dunfermline Town
Aberdour
Rosyth
Dalgety Bay
Inverkeithing
229 242
North Queensferry
Dalmeny
South Gyle
Edinburgh
North Berwick
Bathgate
Livingston North
Uphall
Armadale
226
Blackridge
Edinburgh Park
Easterhouse
Coatbridge Sunnyside
226
Caldercruix
Addiewell
West Calder
Livingston South
Kirknewton
Curriehill
Wester Hailes
Kingsknowe
Slateford
26
Blairhill
Coatdyke
Airdrie
Drumgelloch
Breich
225
26 65 225
Haymarket
Berwick
Newcastle
Coatbridge Central
Fauldhouse
Brunstane
- Queen Street
242
224
Shotts
Carstairs
Glasgow
Carlisle
Newcraighall
Bargeddie
Kirkwood
Hartwood
Whifflet
225
Cleland
Carfin
226
Bellshill
Holytown
225
226
Tram/Metro Interchange
Inter-station bus link Central - Queen Street
224
Motherwell
226
Airbles
226
Shieldmuir
Edinburgh
Wishaw
Carluke
26
65
226
26
65
225
Lanark
225
Carstairs
Carlisle
65

Eurostar™ London St Pancras International → Paris

From 15-Dec-13 to 04-Jun-14

Notes	Mon	Tue	Wed	Thu	Fri	Sat	Sun	London Dep	Ebbsfleet Dep	Ashford Dep	Paris NORD Arr	Train No
1	●	●	●	●	●			05:40	05:58	06:24	09:17	**9080**
						●		06:18		06:55	09:47	**9002**
2	●	●	●	●	●			07:01			10:17	**9004**
						●		07:22	07:42			**9006**
	●							07:31			10:47	**9006**
2	●	●	●	●	●			07:55	08:12		11:17	**9008**
3							●	08:19	08:38		11:47	**9010**
						●		08:25	08:42		11:47	**9010**
2	●	●	●	●	●			08:31			11:47	**9010**
						●		08:54		09:25	12:17	**9012**
2	●	●	●	●	●			09:17	09:35	09:55	12:47	**9014**
3							●	09:22		09:55	12:47	**9014**
						●		09:31			12:47	**9014**
4	●	●	●	●	●		●	10:25	10:42		13:47	**9018**
						●		11:01			14:17	**9020**
2		●	●	●	●	●		11:31			14:47	**9022**
4	●	●	●	●	●	●	●	12:25	12:42		15:47	**9024**
4	●	●	●	●	●		●	13:31			16:47	**9028**
						●		14:01			17:17	**9030**
4	●	●	●	●	●		●	14:31			17:47	**9032**
3							●	15:01			18:17	**9034**
4	●	●	●	●	●	●	●	15:31			18:47	**9036**
					●			16:01			19:17	**9038**
4	●	●	●	●	●		●	16:22		16:55	19:47	**9040**
						●		16:52		17:23	20:17	**9042**
5	●	●	●	●	●	●	●	17:31			20:47	**9044**
5	●	●	●	●	●		●	18:01			21:17	**9046**
					●			18:31			21:47	**9048**
5	●	●	●	●	●	●	●	19:01			22:17	**9050**
5	●	●	●	●	●	●	●	20:01			23:17	**9054**
3							●	20:31			23:47	**9056**

Notes

1 Not running Tues 24 Dec, Wed 25 Dec, Thu 26 Dec, Tue 31 Dec, Wed 01 Jan
2 Not running Wed 25 Dec, Thu 26 Dec, Wed 01 Jan
3 Also runs Thu 26 Dec, Wed 01 Jan
4 Not running Wed 25 Dec
5 Not running Tues 24 Dec, Wed 25 Dec, Tue 31 Dec
6 Not running Tues 24 Dec, Wed 25 Dec, Thu 26 Dec, Tue 31 Dec

Eurostar™ Paris → London St Pancras International

From 15-Dec-13 to 04-Jun-14

Notes	Mon	Tue	Wed	Thu	Fri	Sat	Sun	Paris Dep	Ashford Arr	Ebbsfleet Arr	London Arr	Train No
	●							06:43			08:00	**9005**
1	●	●	●	●	●	●		07:13			08:30	**9007**
2	●	●	●	●	●			07:43			09:00	**9009**
3						●	●	08:13			09:30	**9011**
2	●	●	●	●	●			08:43			10:00	**9013**
4	●	●	●	●	●	●	●	09:13		10:18	10:39	**9015**
4	●	●	●	●	●	●	●	10:13	11:07		11:39	**9019**
4	●	●	●	●	●	●	●	11:13			12:30	**9023**
3							●	12:13			13:30	**9027**
2	●	●	●	●	●			12:43			14:00	**9029**
4	●	●	●	●	●	●	●	13:13		14:18	14:39	**9031**
						●	●	14:13			15:30	**9035**
					●			14:43			16:00	**9037**
4	●	●	●	●	●	●	●	15:13	16:07		16:39	**9039**
4	●	●	●	●	●	●	●	16:13		17:18	17:39	**9043**
3							●	16:43			18:00	**9045**
4	●	●	●	●	●	●	●	17:13			18:30	**9047**
5	●	●	●	●	●		●	18:13		19:18	19:39	**9051**
4		●	●	●	●		●	18:43			20:00	**9053**
5	●	●	●	●	●	●	●	19:13	20:07		20:39	**9055**
5	●	●	●	●	●	●	●	20:13		21:18	21:39	**9059**
3							●	20:43			22:00	**9061**
6	●	●	●	●	●		●	21:13		22:18	22:39	**9063**

Eurostar™ London St Pancras International → Paris

From 05-Jan-14 to 08-Feb-14

Notes	Mon	Tue	Wed	Thu	Fri	Sat	Sun	London	Ebbsfleet	Ashford	Paris NORD	Train No
								Dep	*Dep*	*Dep*	*Arr*	
	●	●	●	●	●			05:40	05:58	06:24	09:17	**9080**
						●		06:18		06:55	09:47	**9002**
	●	●	●	●	●			07:01			10:17	**9004**
						●		07:22	07:42			**9006**
	●							07:31			10:47	**9006**
	●	●	●	●	●			07:55	08:12		11:17	**9008**
						●		08:01			11:17	**9008**
							●	08:19	08:38		11:47	**9010**
						●		08:25	08:42		11:47	**9010**
	●				●			08:31			11:47	**9010**
	●	●	●	●	●			09:17	09:35	09:55	12:47	**9014**
						●	●	09:22		09:55	12:47	**9014**
1						●		10:01			13:17	**9016**
	●	●	●	●	●		●	10:25	10:42		13:47	**9018**
						●		11:01			14:17	**9020**
					●	●		11:31			14:47	**9022**
1						●		12:01			15:17	**9060**
	●	●	●	●	●	●	●	12:25	12:42		15:47	**9024**
	●	●	●	●	●		●	13:31			16:47	**9028**
						●		14:01			17:17	**9030**
	●	●	●	●	●		●	14:31			17:47	**9032**
							●	15:01			18:17	**9034**
	●	●	●	●	●		●	15:31			18:47	**9036**
					●			16:01			19:17	**9038**
	●	●	●	●	●		●	16:22		16:55	19:47	**9040**
						●		16:52		17:23	20:17	**9042**
	●	●	●	●	●	●	●	17:31			20:47	**9044**
	●	●	●	●	●		●	18:01			21:17	**9046**
					●			18:31			21:47	**9048**
	●	●	●	●	●	●	●	19:01			22:17	**9050**
	●	●	●	●	●	●	●	20:01			23:17	**9054**
							●	20:31			23:47	**9056**

Notes

1 Runs Sat 01 Feb only

Eurostar™ Paris → London St Pancras International

From 05-Jan-14 to 08-Feb-14

Notes	Mon	Tue	Wed	Thu	Fri	Sat	Sun	Paris Dep	Ashford Arr	Ebbsfleet Arr	London Arr	Train No
	●							06:43			08:00	**9005**
	●	●	●	●	●	●		07:13			08:30	**9007**
	●	●	●	●	●			07:43			09:00	**9009**
						●	●	08:13			09:30	**9011**
	●	●	●	●	●			08:43			10:00	**9013**
	●	●	●	●	●	●	●	09:13		10:18	10:39	**9015**
	●	●	●	●	●	●		10:13	11:07		11:39	**9019**
	●	●	●	●	●	●	●	11:13			12:30	**9023**
							●	12:13			13:30	**9027**
	●				●			12:43			14:00	**9029**
	●	●	●	●	●	●	●	13:13		14:18	14:39	**9031**
						●	●	14:13			15:30	**9035**
					●			14:43			16:00	**9037**
	●	●	●	●	●	●	●	15:13	16:07		16:39	**9039**
	●	●	●	●	●	●	●	16:13		17:18	17:39	**9043**
							●	16:43			18:00	**9045**
	●	●	●	●	●	●	●	17:13			18:30	**9047**
	●	●	●	●	●		●	18:13		19:18	19:39	**9051**
					●		●	18:43			20:00	**9053**
						●	●	19:13	20:07		20:39	**9055**
	●	●	●	●	●			19:13	20:10		20:41	**9055**
	●	●	●	●	●	●	●	20:13		21:18	21:39	**9059**
							●	20:43			22:00	**9061**
	●	●	●	●	●		●	21:13		22:18	22:39	**9063**

Eurostar™ London St Pancras International → Paris

From 09-Feb-14 to 29-Mar-14

Notes	Mon	Tue	Wed	Thu	Fri	Sat	Sun	London Dep	Ebbsfleet Dep	Ashford Dep	Paris NORD Arr	Train No
1	●	●	●	●	●			05:40	05:58	06:24	09:17	**9080**
2						●		06:18		06:55	09:47	**9002**
1	●	●	●	●	●			07:01			10:17	**9004**
2						●		07:22	07:42		10:47	**9006**
3	●							07:31			10:47	**9006**
1	●	●	●	●	●			07:55	08:12		11:17	**9008**
2						●		08:01			11:17	**9008**
							●	08:19	08:38		11:47	**9010**
2						●		08:25	08:42		11:47	**9010**
1	●	●	●	●	●			08:31			11:47	**9010**
1	●	●	●	●	●			09:17	09:35	09:55	12:47	**9014**
2, 5						●	●	09:22		09:55	12:47	**9014**
1, 5	●	●	●	●	●		●	10:25	10:42		13:47	**9018**
2						●		11:01			14:17	**9020**
4		●	●	●	●	●		11:31			14:47	**9022**
17						●		12:01			15:17	**9060**
4	●	●	●	●	●	●	●	12:25	12:42		15:47	**9024**
1, 5	●	●	●	●	●		●	13:31			16:47	**9028**
2						●		14:01			17:17	**9030**
1, 5	●	●	●	●	●		●	14:31			17:47	**9032**
5							●	15:01			18:17	**9034**
4	●	●	●	●	●		●	15:31			18:47	**9036**
14					●			16:01			19:17	**9038**
1, 5	●	●	●	●	●		●	16:22		16:55	19:47	**9040**
2						●		16:52		17:23	20:17	**9042**
4, 5	●	●	●	●	●	●	●	17:31			20:47	**9044**
1, 5	●	●	●	●	●		●	18:01			21:17	**9046**
6					●			18:31			21:47	**9048**
4, 5	●	●	●	●	●	●	●	19:01			22:17	**9050**
4, 5	●	●	●	●	●	●	●	20:01			23:17	**9054**
5							●	20:31			23:47	**9056**

Notes 1 Engineering works Tue 25 Mar, Wed 26 Mar, Thur 27 Mar, Fri 28 Mar. Additional journey time expected 2 Engineering works Sat 29 Mar. Additional journey time expected 3 Also runs Fri14 Feb, Fri 21 Feb 4 Engineering works Tue 25 Mar, Wed 26 Mar, Thur 27 Mar, Fri 28 Mar, Sat 29 Mar. Additional journey time expected 5 Ashford closed Sun 23 March 6 Engineering works Fri 28 Mar. Additional journey time expected 7 Engineering works Mon 10 Mar, Mon 17 Mar, Mon 24 March. Trains likely to leave slghtly earlier 8 Engineering works Tue 4 Mar-Sat 8 Mar, Mon 10 Mar -Sat 15 Mar, Mon 17 Mar - Sat 22 Mar, Mon 24 Mar - Sat 29 Mar. Trains likely to leave slightly earlier 9 Engineering works Tue 4 Mar-Fri 7 Mar, Mon 10 Mar -Fri 14 Mar, Mon 17 Mar - Fri 21 Mar, Mon 24 Mar - Fri 28 Mar. Trains likely to leave slightly earlier 10 Engineering works Sat 8 Mar- Sun 9 Mar, Sat 15 Mar- Sun 16 Mar, Sat 22 Mar, Sat 29 Mar. Trains likely to leave slightly earlier 11 Engineering works Tue 4 Mar-Sat 22 Mar, Mon 24 Mar - Sat 29 Mar. Trains likely to leave slightly earlier 12 Also runs Fri 14 Feb, Sat 15 Feb, Fri 21 Feb, Sat 22 Feb 13 Engineering works Fri 7 Mar, Fri 14 Mar, Fri 21 Mar, Fri 28 Mar. Trains likely to leave slghtly earlier 14 Engineering works Sun 9 Mar, Sun 16 Mar. Trains likely to leave slghtly earlier 15 Engineering works Tue 4 Mar-Fri 7 Mar, Sun 9 Mar -Fri 14 Mar, Sun 16 Mar - Fri 21 Mar, Mon 24 Mar - Fri 28 Mar. Trains likely to leave slightly earlier 16 Engineering works Tue 4 Mar-Fri 7 Mar, Sun 9 Mar, Tue 11 - Fri 14 Mar, Sun 16 Mar, - Tue 18 Mar - Fri 21 Mar, Sun 23 Mar, Tue 25 Mar - Fri 28 Mar. Trains likely to leave slightly earlier 17 Runs Sat 15 Feb and Sat 22 Feb only 18 Runs Fri 14 Feb and Fri 21 Feb only 19 Runs Sun 16 Feb and Sun 23 Feb only 20 Also runs Mon 17 Feb- Thu20 Feb

Eurostar™ Paris → London St Pancras International

From 09-Feb-14 to 29-Mar-14

Notes	Mon	Tue	Wed	Thu	Fri	Sat	Sun	Paris	Ashford	Ebbsfleet	London	Train No
								Dep	Arr	Arr	Arr	
7	●							06:43			08:00	**9005**
8	●	●	●	●	●	●		07:13			08:30	**9007**
9	●	●	●	●	●			07:43			09:00	**9009**
5, 10						●	●	08:13			09:30	**9011**
9	●	●	●	●	●			08:43			10:00	**9013**
5, 11	●	●	●	●	●	●	●	09:13		10:18	10:39	**9015**
17						●		09:43			11:00	**9017**
5, 11	●	●	●	●	●	●		10:13	11:07		11:39	**9019**
18					●			10:43			12:00	**9021**
5, 11	●	●	●	●	●	●	●	11:13			12:30	**9023**
19							●	11:43			13:00	**9025**
5, 12, 14							●	12:13			13:30	**9027**
9	●				●			12:43			14:00	**9029**
5, 11	●	●	●	●	●	●	●	13:13		14:18	14:39	**9031**
19								13:43			15:00	**9033**
5, 10						●	●	14:13			15:30	**9035**
13					●			14:43			16:00	**9037**
5, 11	●	●	●	●	●	●	●	15:13	16:07		16:39	**9039**
5, 11	●	●	●	●	●	●	●	16:13		17:18	17:39	**9043**
5, 14							●	16:43			18:00	**9045**
5, 11	●	●	●	●	●	●	●	17:13			18:30	**9047**
5, 15	●	●	●	●	●		●	18:13		19:18	19:39	**9051**
5, 16		●	●	●	●		●	18:43			20:00	**9053**
5, 10						●	●	19:13	20:07		20:39	**9055**
9	●	●	●	●	●			19:13	20:10		20:41	**9055**
5, 11	●	●	●	●	●	●	●	20:13		21:18	21:39	**9059**
5, 14							●	20:43			22:00	**9061**
5, 15	●	●	●	●	●		●	21:13		22:18	22:39	**9063**

Eurostar™ London St Pancras International → Paris

From 30-Mar-14 to 24-May-14

Notes	Mon	Tue	Wed	Thu	Fri	Sat	Sun	London Dep	Ebbsfleet Dep	Ashford Dep	Paris NORD Arr	Train No
1	●	●	●	●	●			05:40	05:58	06:24	09:17	**9080**
						●		06:18		06:55	09:47	**9002**
1	●	●	●	●	●			07:01			10:17	**9004**
						●		07:22	07:42		10:47	**9006**
1	●			●	●			07:31			10:47	**9006**
1	●	●	●	●	●			07:55	08:12		11:17	**9008**
						●		08:01			11:17	**9008**
2							●	08:19	08:38		11:47	**9010**
						●		08:25	08:42		11:47	**9010**
1	●	●	●	●	●			08:31			11:47	**9010**
1	●	●	●	●	●			09:17	09:35	09:55	12:47	**9014**
2						●	●	09:22		09:55	12:47	**9014**
3	●	●	●	●	●	●	●	10:25	10:42		13:47	**9018**
2						●	●	11:01			14:17	**9020**
	●	●	●	●	●	●	●	11:31			14:47	**9022**
4					●	●		12:01			15:17	**9060**
	●	●	●	●	●	●	●	12:25	12:42		15:47	**9024**
	●	●	●	●	●		●	13:31			16:47	**9028**
2					●	●	●	14:01			17:17	**9030**
	●	●	●	●	●		●	14:31			17:47	**9032**
2							●	15:01			18:17	**9034**
	●	●	●	●	●	●	●	15:31			18:47	**9036**
					●			16:01			19:17	**9038**
	●	●	●	●	●		●	16:22		16:55	19:47	**9040**
						●		16:52		17:23	20:17	**9042**
	●	●	●	●	●	●	●	17:31			20:47	**9044**
5	●	●	●	●	●		●	18:01			21:17	**9046**
1	●	●	●	●	●			18:31			21:47	**9048**
	●	●	●	●	●	●	●	19:01			22:17	**9050**
	●	●	●	●	●	●	●	20:01			23:17	**9054**
6							●	20:31			23:47	**9056**

Notes 1 Not running Mon 21 Apr, Mon 5 May 2 Also running Mon 21 Apr, Mon 5 May 3 Not running Sat 5 April 4 Running Fri 23 May, Sat 24 May only 5 running Fri 18 Apr 6 Also running Mon 21 Apr 7 Running Sat 24 May only 8 Also running Mon 21 Apr

Eurostar™ Paris → London St Pancras International

From 30-Mar-14 to 24-May-14

Notes	Mon	Tue	Wed	Thu	Fri	Sat	Sun	Paris Dep	Ashford Arr	Ebbsfleet Arr	London Arr	Train No
1	●							06:43			08:00	**9005**
1	●	●	●	●	●	●		07:13			08:30	**9007**
1	●	●	●	●	●			07:43			09:00	**9009**
2						●	●	08:13			09:30	**9011**
1	●	●	●	●	●			08:43			10:00	**9013**
	●	●	●	●	●	●	●	09:13		10:18	10:39	**9015**
7						●		09:43			11:00	**9017**
	●	●	●	●	●	●	●	10:13	11:07		11:39	**9019**
	●	●	●	●	●	●	●	11:13			12:30	**9023**
	●			●	●	●	●	11:43			13:00	**9025**
2					●		●	12:13			13:30	**9027**
	●	●	●	●	●			12:43			14:00	**9029**
	●	●	●	●	●	●	●	13:13		14:18	14:39	**9031**
8							●	13:43			15:00	**9033**
8						●	●	14:13			15:30	**9035**
1	●	●	●	●	●			14:43			16:00	**9037**
	●	●	●	●	●	●	●	15:13	16:07		16:39	**9039**
	●	●	●	●	●	●	●	16:13		17:18	17:39	**9043**
2							●	16:43			18:00	**9045**
	●	●	●	●	●	●	●	17:13			18:30	**9047**
	●	●	●	●	●		●	18:13		19:18	19:39	**9051**
2		●	●	●	●		●	18:43			20:00	**9053**
2						●	●	19:13	20:07		20:39	**9055**
1	●	●	●	●	●			19:13	20:10		20:41	**9055**
	●	●	●	●	●	●	●	20:13		21:18	21:39	**9059**
2							●	20:43			22:00	**9061**
	●	●	●	●	●		●	21:13		22:18	22:39	**9063**

Eurostar™ London St Pancras International → Brussels

From 15-Dec-13 to 4-Jun-14

Notes							London	Ebbsfleet	Ashford	Calais	Lille	Brussels	Train No
	Mon	Tue	Wed	Thu	Fri	Sat	Sun	Dep	Dep	Dep	Arr	Arr	Arr	
1	●	●	●	●	●			06:50	07:08	07:28	08:59	09:30	10:07	**9110**
2						●		06:57		07:28		09:26	10:11	**9110**
3	●	●	●	●	●			08:04				10:26	11:05	**9114**
3	●	●	●	●	●			08:58	09:15			11:26	12:05	**9116**
2						●	●	08:58	09:15		10:59	11:30	12:08	**9116**
3	●	●	●	●	●	●		10:58	11:15			13:26	14:05	**9126**
4	●	●	●	●	●	●	●	12:58	13:15		14:59	15:30	16:08	**9132**
5					●		●	14:04				16:26	17:05	**9136**
4	●	●	●	●	●		●	15:04				17:26	18:05	**9140**
						●		16:04				18:26	19:05	**9144**
4	●	●	●	●	●		●	17:04				19:26	20:05	**9148**
6							●	17:55		18:28		20:26	21:05	**9152**
7	●	●	●	●	●			18:04				20:26	21:05	**9152**
5						●	●	19:04			20:59	21:30	22:08	**9156**
8	●	●	●	●	●			19:34			21:29	22:00	22:38	**9158**
							●	20:04				22:26	23:05	**9162**

Notes

1 Not running Wed 25 Dec, Thu 26 Dec, Frid 27 Dec, Wed 01 Jan, Thu 02 Jan
2 Not running Sat 21 Dec, St 28 Dec
3 Not running Wed 25 Dec, Thu 26 Dec, Wed 01 Jan
4 Not running Wed 25 Dec
5 Also runs Thu 26 Dec, Wed 01 Jan
6 Also runs Thu 26 Dec, Frid 27 Dec, Wed 01 Jan
7 Not running Wed 25 Dec, Thu 26 Dec, Frid 27 Dec, Wed 01 Jan
8 Not running Tues 24 Dec, Wed 25 Dec, Thu 26 Dec, Tue 31 Dec, Wed 01 Jan
9 Also running Wed 01 Jan
10 Not running Tues 24 Dec, Wed 25 Dec, Tue 31 Dec

Eurostar™ Brussels → London St Pancras International

From 15-Dec-13 to 4-Jun-14

Notes							Brussels	Lille	Calais	Ashford	Ebbsfleet	London	Train No
	Mon	Tue	Wed	Thu	Fri	Sat	Sun	*Dep*	*Dep*	*Dep*	*Arr*	*Arr*	*Arr*	
	●							06:56	07:36				07:57	**9109**
1	●	●	●	●	●	●		07:56	08:36				08:57	**9113**
4	●	●	●	●	●	●	●	08:52	09:30	10:01			09:57	**9117**
3	●	●	●	●	●	●		10:56	11:36				11:57	**9125**
9							●	11:56	12:36				12:57	**9129**
3	●	●	●	●	●			12:52	13:30	14:01		13:45	14:03	**9133**
						●	●	14:52	15:30	16:01		15:45	16:03	**9141**
3	●	●	●	●	●			14:56	15:36			15:45	16:03	**9141**
5							●	15:56	16:36				16:57	**9145**
					●			15:56	16:36			16:45	17:03	**9145**
						●		16:56	17:36			17:48	18:09	**9149**
3	●	●	●	●	●			16:56	17:36		17:37	17:45	18:11	**9149**
3	●	●	●	●	●			17:56	18:36			18:45	19:03	**9153**
5							●	17:56	18:36		18:35		19:10	**9153**
4	●	●	●	●	●		●	18:56	19:35				19:57	**9157**
10	●	●	●	●	●		●	19:52	20:30	21:01		20:45	21:03	**9161**
2						●		19:52	20:30	21:01	20:35		21:06	**9161**

Eurostar™ London St Pancras International → Brussels

From 5-Jan-14 to 8-Feb-14

Notes								London	Ebbsfleet	Ashford	Calais	Lille	Brussels	Train No
	Mon	Tue	Wed	Thu	Fri	Sat	Sun	*Dep*	*Dep*	*Dep*	*Arr*	*Arr*	*Arr*	
	●	●	●	●	●			06:50	07:08	07:28	08:59	09:30	10:07	**9110**
						●		06:57		07:28		09:26	10:11	**9110**
	●	●	●	●	●			08:58	09:15			11:26	12:05	**9116**
						●	●	08:58	09:15		10:59	11:30	12:08	**9116**
	●	●	●	●	●	●		10:58	11:15			13:26	14:05	**9126**
	●	●	●	●	●	●	●	12:58	13:15		14:59	15:30	16:08	**9132**
							●	14:04				16:26	17:05	**9136**
	●	●	●	●	●		●	15:04				17:26	18:05	**9140**
						●		16:04				18:26	19:05	**9144**
	●	●	●	●	●		●	17:04				19:26	20:05	**9148**
							●	17:55		18:28		20:26	21:05	**9152**
					●			18:04				20:26	21:05	**9152**
						●	●	19:04			20:59	21:30	22:08	**9156**
	●	●	●	●	●			19:34			21:29	22:00	22:38	**9158**
							●	20:04				22:26	23:05	**9162**

Notes 1 Not running Wed 25 Dec, Thu 26 Dec, Frid 27 Dec, Wed 01 Jan, Thu 02 Jan 2 Not running Sat 21 Dec, St 28 Dec 3 Not running Wed 25 Dec, Thu 26 Dec, Wed 01 Jan 4 Not running Wed 25 Dec 5 Also runs Thu 26 Dec, Wed 01 Jan 6 Also runs Thu 26 Dec, Frid 27 Dec, Wed 01 Jan 7 Not running Wed 25 Dec, Thu 26 Dec, Frid 27 Dec, Wed 01 Jan 8 Not running Tues 24 Dec, Wed 25 Dec, Thu 26 Dec, Tue 31 Dec, Wed 01 Jan 9 Also running Wed 01 Jan 10 Not running Tues 24 Dec, Wed 25 Dec, Tue 31 Dec

Eurostar™ Brussels → London St Pancras International

From 5-Jan-14 to 8-Feb-14

Notes							Brussels	Lille	Calais	Ashford	Ebbsfleet	London	Train No
Mon	Tue	Wed	Thu	Fri	Sat	Sun	Dep	Dep	Dep	Arr	Arr	Arr	
●							06:56	07:36				07:57	**9109**
●	●	●	●	●	●		07:56	08:36				08:57	**9113**
●	●	●	●	●	●	●	08:52	09:30	10:01			09:57	**9117**
				●	●		10:56	11:36				11:57	**9125**
						●	11:56	12:36				12:57	**9129**
●	●	●	●	●			12:52	13:30	14:01		13:45	14:03	**9133**
					●	●	14:52	15:30	16:01		15:45	16:03	**9141**
●	●	●	●	●			14:56	15:36			15:45	16:03	**9141**
						●	15:56	16:36				16:57	**9145**
					●		16:56	17:36			17:48	18:09	**9149**
●	●	●	●	●			16:56	17:36		17:37	17:45	18:11	**9149**
●	●	●	●	●			17:56	18:36			18:45	19:03	**9153**
						●	17:56	18:36		18:35		19:10	**9153**
						●	18:56	19:35				19:57	**9157**
●	●	●	●	●		●	19:52	20:30	21:01		20:45	21:03	**9161**
					●		19:52	20:30	21:01	20:35		21:06	**9161**

Eurostar™ London St Pancras International → Brussels

From 9-Feb-14 to 29-Mar-14

Notes							London	Ebbsfleet	Ashford	Calais	Lille	Brussels	Train No
Mon	Tue	Wed	Thu	Fri	Sat	Sun	*Dep*	*Dep*	*Dep*	*Arr*	*Arr*	*Arr*	
●	●	●	●	●			06:50	07:08	07:28	08:59	09:30	10:07	**9110**
					●		06:57		07:28		09:26	10:11	**9110**
●	●	●	●	●			08:04				10:26	11:05	**9114**
●	●	●	●	●			08:58	09:15			11:26	12:05	**9116**
					●	●	08:58	09:15		10:59	11:30	12:08	**9116**
●	●	●	●	●	●		10:58	11:15			13:26	14:05	**9126**
●	●	●	●	●	●	●	12:58	13:15		14:59	15:30	16:08	**9132**
				●		●	14:04				16:26	17:05	**9136**
●	●	●	●	●		●	15:04				17:26	18:05	**9140**
					●		16:04				18:26	19:05	**9144**
●	●	●	●	●		●	17:04				19:26	20:05	**9148**
						●	17:55		18:28		20:26	21:05	**9152**
●	●	●	●	●			18:04				20:26	21:05	**9152**
					●	●	19:04			20:59	21:30	22:08	**9156**
●	●	●	●	●			19:34			21:29	22:00	22:38	**9158**
						●	20:04				22:26	23:05	**9162**

Eurostar™ Brussels → London St Pancras International

From 9-Feb-14 to 29-Mar-14

Notes	Mon	Tue	Wed	Thu	Fri	Sat	Sun	Brussels Dep	Lille Dep	Calais Dep	Ashford Arr	Ebbsfleet Arr	London Arr	Train No
	●							06:56	07:36				07:57	**9109**
	●	●	●	●	●	●		07:56	08:36				08:57	**9113**
	●	●	●	●	●	●	●	08:52	09:30	10:01			09:57	**9117**
	●	●	●	●	●	●		10:56	11:36				11:57	**9125**
							●	11:56	12:36				12:57	**9129**
	●	●	●	●	●			12:52	13:30	14:01		13:45	14:03	**9133**
						●	●	14:52	15:30	16:01		15:45	16:03	**9141**
	●	●	●	●	●			14:56	15:36			15:45	16:03	**9141**
							●	15:56	16:36				16:57	**9145**
						●		16:56	17:36			17:48	18:09	**9149**
	●	●	●	●	●			16:56	17:36		17:37		18:10	**9149**
	●	●	●	●	●			17:56	18:36			18:45	19:03	**9153**
							●	17:56	18:36		18:35		19:10	**9153**
	●	●	●	●	●		●	18:56	19:35				19:57	**9157**
	●	●	●	●	●		●	19:52	20:30	21:01		20:45	21:03	**9161**
						●		19:52	20:30	21:01	20:35		21:09	**9161**

Eurostar™ London St Pancras International → Brussels

From 9-Feb-14 to 29-May-14

Notes							London	Ebbsfleet	Ashford	Calais	Lille	Brussels	Train No
Mon	Tue	Wed	Thu	Fri	Sat	Sun	*Dep*	*Dep*	*Dep*	*Arr*	*Arr*	*Arr*	
●	●	●	●	●			06:50	07:08	07:28	08:59	09:30	10:07	**9110**
					●		06:57		07:28		09:26	10:11	**9110**
●	●	●	●	●			08:04				10:26	11:05	**9114**
●	●	●	●	●			08:58	09:15			11:26	12:05	**9116**
					●	●	08:58	09:15		10:59	11:30	12:08	**9116**
●	●	●	●	●	●		10:58	11:15			13:26	14:05	**9126**
●	●	●	●	●	●	●	12:58	13:15		14:59	15:30	16:08	**9132**
				●		●	14:04				16:26	17:05	**9136**
●	●	●	●	●		●	15:04				17:26	18:05	**9140**
					●		16:04				18:26	19:05	**9144**
●	●	●	●	●		●	17:04				19:26	20:05	**9148**
						●	17:55		18:28		20:26	21:05	**9152**
●	●	●	●	●			18:04				20:26	21:05	**9152**
					●	●	19:04			20:59	21:30	22:08	**9156**
●	●	●	●	●			19:34			21:29	22:00	22:38	**9158**
						●	20:04				22:26	23:05	**9162**

Eurostar™ Brussels → London St Pancras International

From 9-Feb-14 to 29-May-14

Notes								Brussels	Lille	Calais	Ashford	Ebbsfleet	London	Train No
	Mon	Tue	Wed	Thu	Fri	Sat	Sun	*Dep*	*Dep*	*Dep*	*Arr*	*Arr*	*Arr*	
	●							06:56	07:36				07:57	**9109**
	●	●	●	●	●	●		07:56	08:36				08:57	**9113**
	●	●	●	●	●	●	●	08:52	09:30	10:01			09:57	**9117**
	●	●	●	●	●	●		10:56	11:36				11:57	**9125**
							●	11:56	12:36				12:57	**9129**
	●	●	●	●	●			12:52	13:30	14:01		13:45	14:03	**9133**
						●	●	14:52	15:30	16:01		15:45	16:03	**9141**
	●	●	●	●	●			14:56	15:36			15:45	16:03	**9141**
							●	15:56	16:36				16:57	**9145**
						●		16:56	17:36			17:48	18:09	**9149**
	●	●	●	●	●			16:56	17:36		17:37		18:10	**9149**
	●	●	●	●	●			17:56	18:36			18:45	19:03	**9153**
							●	17:56	18:36		18:35		19:10	**9153**
	●	●	●	●	●		●	18:56	19:35				19:57	**9157**
	●	●	●	●	●		●	19:52	20:30	21:01		20:45	21:03	**9161**
						●		19:52	20:30	21:01	20:35		21:09	**9161**

Eurostar™ London St Pancras International → Brussels

From 30-Mar-14 to 24-May-14

Notes							London	Ebbsfleet	Ashford	Calais	Lille	Brussels	Train No
	Mon	Tue	Wed	Thu	Fri	Sat	Sun	Dep	Dep	Dep	Arr	Arr	Arr	
1	●	●	●	●	●			06:50	07:08	07:28	08:59	09:30	10:07	**9110**
						●		06:57		07:28		09:26	10:11	**9110**
1	●	●	●	●	●			08:04				10:26	11:05	**9114**
1	●	●	●	●	●			08:58	09:15			11:26	12:05	**9116**
						●	●	08:58	09:15		10:59	11:30	12:08	**9116**
2	●	●	●	●	●	●		10:58	11:15			13:26	14:05	**9126**
	●	●	●	●	●	●	●	12:58	13:15		14:59	15:30	16:08	**9132**
	●	●	●	●	●		●	14:04				16:26	17:05	**9136**
	●	●	●	●	●		●	15:04				17:26	18:05	**9140**
						●		16:04				18:26	19:05	**9144**
	●	●	●	●	●		●	17:04				19:26	20:05	**9148**
3							●	17:55		18:28		20:26	21:05	**9152**
1	●	●	●	●	●			18:04				20:26	21:05	**9152**
3						●	●	19:04			20:59	21:30	22:08	**9156**
1	●	●	●	●	●			19:34			21:29	22:00	22:38	**9158**
							●	20:04				22:26	23:05	**9162**

Notes 1 Not running Mon 21 Apr, Mon 5 May 2 Not running Mon 5 May 3 Also running Mon 21 Apr, Mon 5 May 4 Running Mon 21 Apr only

Eurostar™ Brussels → London St Pancras International

From 30-Mar-14 to 24-May-14

Notes								Brussels	Lille	Calais	Ashford	Ebbsfleet	London	Train No
	Mon	Tue	Wed	Thu	Fri	Sat	Sun	*Dep*	*Dep*	*Dep*	*Arr*	*Arr*	*Arr*	
1	●							06:56	07:36				07:57	**9109**
1	●	●	●	●	●	●		07:56	08:36				08:57	**9113**
	●	●	●	●	●	●	●	08:52	09:30	10:01			09:57	**9117**
1	●	●	●	●	●	●		10:56	11:36				11:57	**9125**
3							●	11:56	12:36				12:57	**9129**
1	●	●	●	●	●			12:52	13:30	14:01		13:45	14:03	**9133**
3						●	●	14:52	15:30	16:01		15:45	16:03	**9141**
1	●	●	●	●	●			14:56	15:36			15:45	16:03	**9141**
	●	●	●	●	●			15:56	16:36				16:57	**9145**
					●			16:51	17:30		17:37		18:10	**9149**
						●		16:56	17:36			17:48	18:09	**9149**
1	●	●	●	●				16:56	17:36		17:37		18:10	**9149**
1	●	●	●	●	●			17:56	18:36			18:45	19:03	**9153**
3							●	17:56	18:36		18:35		19:10	**9153**
	●	●	●	●	●		●	18:56	19:35				19:57	**9157**
	●	●	●	●	●		●	19:52	20:30	21:01		20:45	21:03	**9161**
						●		19:52	20:30	21:01	20:35		21:09	**9161**
4	●							20:56	21:35				21:57	**9165**

Eurostar™ London St Pancras International → Disneyland™ Paris Route

From 15-Dec-13 to 19-Jul-14

Notes	Mon	Tue	Wed	Thu	Fri	Sat	Sun	London	Ebbsfleet	Ashford	Lille	Marne La Vallée	Train No
								Dep	*Dep*	*Dep*	*Dep*	*Arr*	
1, 2, 3, 4	●		●	●	●		●	10:15	10:34	10:58	12:54	13:57	**9074**
5						●		10:25	10:44		12:54	13:57	**9074**

Notes

1 Does not run on Tuesdays except on 24 and 31 December, 18 February, 8 April, 15 April, 27 May
2 Does not run on Saturdays except on 21 December, 28 December, 04 January, 15 February, 22 February, 05 April, 12 April, 19 April, 03 May, 24 May, 31 May
3 Does not run Wed 25 December,
4 Ashford closed Su 23 March, Sun 27 April
5 Runs Sun 23 March, Sun 27 April
6 Also runs on the following Saturdays, 21 December, 28 December, 04 Janaury, 15 Janaury, 22 February, 5 April, 12 April, 19 April, 03 May, 24 May, 31 May
7 Also runs on the following Tuesdays, 24 Dfecember, 31 December, 18 February, 8 April, 15 April, 27 May

Eurostar™ Disneyland™ Paris Route → London St Pancras International

From 15-Dec-13 to 19-Jul-14

Notes	Mon	Tue	Wed	Thu	Fri	Sat	Sun	Marne La Vallée	Lille	Ashford	Ebbsfleet	London	Train No
								Dep	*Dep*	*Dep*	*Dep*	*Arr*	
6							●	16:54		18:09	18:26	18:46	**9057**
					●			16:54		18:10	18:30	18:45	**9057**
7	●		●	●				18:02		19:09	19:26	19:46	**9057**

Station key

London St Pancras International
Ebbsfleet Ebsfleet International, Kent
Ashford Ashford International, Kent
Calais Calais Fréthun
Lille Lille Europe
Brussels Brussels-Mid/Zuid
Paris Gare du Nord
Disneyland® Paris Marne-la-Vallée

Variations

Amended Eurostar services may run on and around Public Holidays and for engineering works. For up to date information, please refer to the Eurostar website – eurostar.com

NOTES

NOTES

NOTES

NOTES

NOTES

NOTES

NOTES

NOTES

NOTES

NOTES

NOTES

NOTES

NOTES

NOTES

NOTES

NOTES

NOTES

NOTES

NOTES

NOTES

NOTES

NOTES

NOTES

NOTES

NOTES

NOTES

NOTES

NOTES